ULRICH'S™ INTERNATIONAL PERIODICALS DIRECTORY

34th Edition

1996

Ulrich's International Periodicals Directory
is compiled by
R.R. Bowker
A Reed Reference Publishing Company
Serials Bibliography Department

Leigh C. Yuster-Freeman, Vice President, Production - Bibliographies

Editorial
Judith Salk, Publisher
Edvika Popilskis, Managing Editor
Ewa Kowalska, Dawn Lombardy, Senior Editors

Daniel Berek, Egill Halldorsson, Christopher King,
Zhaoxia Lian, Henry Wessells, Associate Editors

Mary Crouthers, O'Sheila Delgado, Editorial Assistants

Thomas J. Anerine, Jeanmarie Armas, Terence Carlson, Michael Crouthers, Mary Jo Duffy,
Karl Dusza, Katherine Eaton, Kenneth Goldstein, Qingye Guo, Michael Helme, Evelyn Irvine,
Bronislaw Jan Kowalski, Margareta Leon, Allison Lih, Beth McDonnell,
Olga Neville, Julianne Reynolds, Eline van de Poel-Becker,
Zelda Salk, and Alina Warda, Contributing Editors

Production
Doreen Gravesande, Production Director
Myriam Nunez, Managing Editor
Frank McDermott, Senior Editor

Editorial Systems Group
Gary Aiello, Director, Bibliographical and Advertising Systems
Nana Rizinashvili, and Robert Michniewicz, Senior Systems Analysts

Computer Operations Group
Nick Wikowski, Director, Network/Computer Operations
Jack Murphy, Supervisor

Reed Technology and Information Services
Donna Colahan, Account Manager

Martin Brooks, Senior Vice President-Business Manager/Bowker Bibliographic Products

Dedicated to the memory of our colleague and friend, Shirley Crawford.

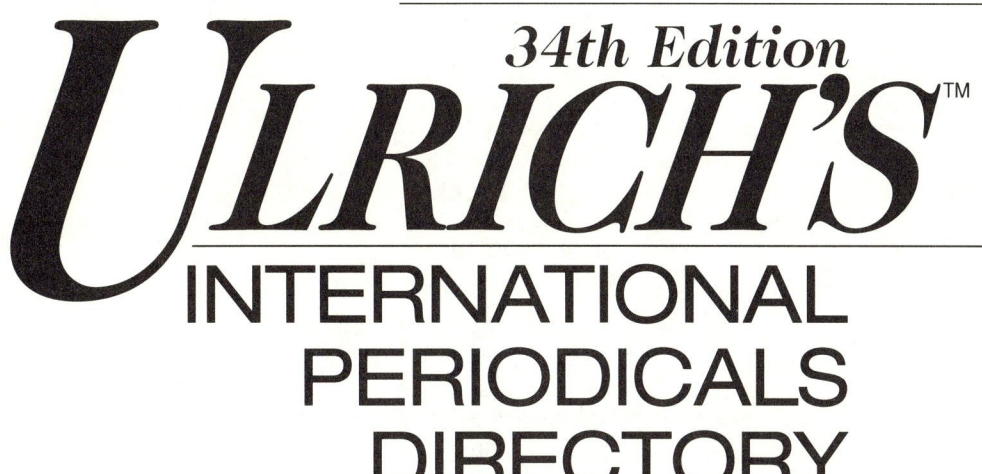

34th Edition
ULRICH'S™
INTERNATIONAL PERIODICALS DIRECTORY
1996

including
Irregular Serials & Annuals

Volume 3

Classified List of Subjects
M-Z

THE BOWKER INTERNATIONAL SERIALS DATABASE

R.R. BOWKER
A Reed Reference Publishing Company
New Providence, New Jersey

Published by R.R. Bowker
A Reed Reference Publishing Company
121 Chanlon Rd., New Providence, NJ 07974

Andrew W. Meyer, Chief Operating Officer
Peter E. Simon, Executive Vice President, Business Development and Database Publishing
Gwyn Williams, Executive Vice President, Finance and Operations
Stanley Walker, Senior Vice President, Corporate Marketing
Edward J. Roycroft, Senior Vice President, Sales

Copyright © 1995 by Reed Elsevier Inc.
All rights reserved

Ulrich's Hotline (U.S. only): 1-800-346-6049
Editorial (Canada only, call collect): 1-908-665-2875
Serials Fax (overseas users): 908-771-7725
Serials E-mail: jsalk@reedref.com
Reed Reference Publishing E-mail: info@reedref.com
Reed Reference Publishing URL: http://www.reedref.com

Ulrich's is a trademark of Reed Properties Inc., used under license

No part of this publication may be reproduced or transmitted in any form or by any means, stored in any information storage and retrieval system, without prior written permission of R.R. Bowker, 121 Chanlon Rd., New Providence, New Jersey 07974, USA.

International Standard Book Number 0-8352-3676-5
(5 Volume set)
International Standard Book Number 0-8352-3677-3
(Volume 1)
International Standard Book Number 0-8352-3678-1
(Volume 2)
International Standard Book Number 0-8352-3680-3
(Volume 3)
International Standard Book Number 0-8352-3681-1
(Volume 4)
International Standard Book Number 0-8352-3683-8
(Volume 5)
International Standard Serial Number 0000-0175

Library of Congress Catalog Card Number 32-16320

Printed and bound in the United States of America.

No payment is either solicited or accepted for the inclusion of entries in this publication. R.R. Bowker has used its best efforts in collecting and preparing material for inclusion in this publication, but does not warrant that the information herein is complete or accurate, and does not assume, and hereby disclaims any liability to any person for the loss or damage caused by errors or omissions in this publication whether such errors or omissions result from negligence, accident or any other cause.

Contents

BOWKER/ULRICH'S SERIALS LIBRARIANSHIP
    AWARD WINNERS vi
PREFACE vii
USER'S GUIDE ix
INTERNATIONAL STANDARD SERIAL NUMBER (ISSN) xviii
ABBREVIATIONS
    General Abbreviations and Special Symbols xx
    Money Symbols xxi
    Country of Publication Codes xxii
    Document Suppliers xxiv
    Micropublishers and Distributors xxv
    Reprint Services xxx
    Wire Services xxxi
    Abstracting and Indexing Services xxxii
SUBJECT GUIDE TO ABSTRACTING AND INDEXING xlv
SUBJECTS xlvi

VOLUME 1
CLASSIFIED LIST OF SERIALS/SUBJECTS A to D 1

VOLUME 2
CLASSIFIED LIST OF SERIALS/SUBJECTS E to L 2085

VOLUME 3
CLASSIFIED LIST OF SERIALS/SUBJECTS M to Z 4091

VOLUME 4
CROSS-INDEX TO SUBJECTS 6603
ISSN INDEX 6635
TITLE INDEX 7435
TITLE CHANGE INDEX 8639
CESSATIONS 8665

VOLUME 5
REFEREED 8909
SERIALS AVAILABLE ON CD-ROM 9097
PRODUCER LISTING/SERIALS ON CD-ROM 9137
SERIALS AVAILABLE ONLINE 9141
VENDOR LISTING/SERIALS ONLINE 9263
INDEX TO PUBLICATIONS OF INTERNATIONAL ORGANIZATIONS 9293
    International Organizations 9293
    International Congress Proceedings 9305
    European Communities 9309
    United Nations 9311
CONTROLLED CIRCULATION SERIALS 9319

U.S. NEWSPAPERS
USER'S GUIDE li
ABBREVIATIONS liv
DAILY NEWSPAPERS — US 9431
WEEKLY NEWSPAPERS — US 9529
TITLE INDEX 9779
DAILY NEWSPAPER INDEX 9851
WEEKLY NEWSPAPER INDEX 9869
GEOGRAPHIC INDEX 9923
CESSATIONS 9989

Bowker/Ulrich's Serials Librarianship Award

Presented by the Serials Section
Association for Library Collections and Technical Services (ALCTS)
Division of the American Library Association (ALA)

Sponsored by R.R. Bowker

This annual award is given in recognition of distinguished and ongoing contributions to serials librarianship. Qualified individuals demonstrate leadership in serials-related activities through their participation in professional associations, groups, and/or library education programs; make significant contributions to serials literature; and, in general, strive to enhance our comprehension of the serials world.

AWARD RECIPIENTS

1985	Marcia Tuttle
1986	Ruth C. Carter
1987	James P. Danky
1988	Marjorie E. Bloss
1989	John E. Merriman
1990	Jean S. Cook
1991	Deana L. Astle/Charles A. Hamaker
1992	Linda K. Bartley
1993	Ann L. Okerson
1994	Tina Feick
1995	Peter Gellatly

Preface

For 63 years, **Ulrich's International Periodicals Directory** has been the premier serials reference source. **Ulrich's**, now in its 34th edition, continues to uphold its reputation for excellence in the provision of serials bibliographic information. With the publication of this directory we, once again, provide enhancements which will improve your access to and use of the serials information contained herein.

A noteworthy change this year is probably self-evident to subscribers. The publication date of **Ulrich's** has moved from August to November. This shift in publication date is vital in that it has allowed us to provide thousands of serials price updates for 1996. We have also included, for the first time, listings for forthcoming serials. These titles have been announced for publication in 1996 and are annotated as such.

Subject access to serials listed in **Ulrich's** is critical so, with this edition, we have reorganized the directory to give prominence to an important index which had been buried at the end of the **Ulrich's** prefatory material for years—the CROSS-INDEX TO SUBJECTS. This index is now found in Volume 4 and a description of its content is found in the User's Guide, page ix. Further access to serials listed in **Ulrich's** has been provided through the addition of thousands more document type notations, as well as thousands of e-mail addresses and URLs (Uniform Resource Locators on the World Wide Web).

Our coverage of document delivery services has been expanded to include EMDOCS, the EMBASE Document Delivery Service; The Genuine Article from the Institute for Scientific Information; Haworth Document Delivery Service from Haworth Press; and the Petroleum Abstracts Document Delivery Service. Add these services to the nine already noted in **Ulrich's**, and we're flagging titles from 13 different services (see pg. xxiv). For an explanation of and contact information for these useful services, please refer to a section entitled "Document Suppliers" in the User's Guide of **Ulrich's**, pg. xiv of the prefatory material of Volumes 1-4.

Serials continue to be important as primary sources of current information and topical news in all fields of endeavor, as evidenced by the vast number of serials published and their rapid development into electronic formats. The availability of serials in electronic formats, either online or on CD-ROM, continues to grow, especially with dramatically increased use of the Internet as a publishing medium. This edition of **Ulrich's** includes 5,517 serials available exclusively online or in addition to hard copy, and 1,963 serials available on CD-ROM. These serials are indicated by a notation and a bullet (•) in the main entry.

The 34th edition of **Ulrich's** contains information on nearly 165,000 serials published throughout the world, arranged under 969 subject headings. More than 112,000 entries have been updated to reflect the most current information available and nearly 12,000 serials have been added this year, some of which have since ceased or suspended publication. Included in this edition is cessation or suspension information which has been recorded in our database during the past three years for 10,675 titles. The ceased or suspended titles are preceded by a dagger (†) in the TITLE INDEX for instant identification. Users can identify newer serials, over 2,071 of which are known to have begun publication since January 1, 1994, by looking for an upside-down solid triangle (▼) in both the CLASSIFIED LIST OF SERIALS and the TITLE INDEX. In addition, over 10,000 refereed serials notations; nearly 62,000 brief descriptions; almost 40,350 LC Classification Numbers; over 19,000 CODEN; and 3,876 vendor file names or numbers for 5,517 serials available in an online format appear in this edition.

Included in **Ulrich's** are serials which are currently available, issued more frequently than once a year and usually published at regular intervals, as well as publications issued annually or less frequently than once a year, or irregularly. Due to the vast number of serials, we have established certain criteria for inclusion, while maintaining our aim of maximum title coverage that will satisfy the widest range of use. We include all publications that meet the definition of a serial except administrative publications of governmental agencies below state level that can be easily found elsewhere, membership directories, comic books, and puzzle and game books.

This edition of **Ulrich's** is arranged within five volumes, but the organization of those volumes differs from past years, as follows: the first three volumes comprise the CLASSIFIED LIST OF SERIALS; the fourth volume contains the CROSS-INDEX TO SUBJECTS, ISSN INDEX, TITLE INDEX, TITLE CHANGE INDEX, and CESSATIONS INDEX. The fifth volume comprises the remaining indexes: REFEREED SERIALS, SERIALS AVAILABLE ON CD-ROM, PRODUCER LISTING/SERIALS ON CD-ROM, SERIALS AVAILABLE ONLINE, VENDOR LISTING/SERIALS ONLINE, INDEX TO INTERNATIONAL ORGANIZATIONS, and CONTROLLED CIRCULATION SERIALS, as well as a NEWSPAPERS section listing general-interest daily and weekly newspapers published in the United States.

International data inquiries are mailed annually to some 78,000 publishers to secure accurate and up-to-date information on current titles, new titles, title changes, and cessations. Updating of the database occurs daily using information received from publishers throughout the year and from serials research conducted in our editorial department. All post office returns are researched, and entries from publishers whose addresses cannot be verified are suspended from the file. Information about title changes, cessations, and new titles not received by the deadline for this edition will appear in **Ulrich's Update**, in the **Ulrich's Online** file available through Knight-Ridder Information, Inc. and Ovid Technologies, on **Ulrich's PLUS**™ CD-ROM, and on **Ulrich's Microfiche**.

Your purchase and use of **Ulrich's** is complemented with some additional services. **Ulrich's Update**, provided free of charge, twice a year in March and July, is a supplemental service to the annual directory. The **Ulrich's Hotline** is a toll-free number that subscribers can call to get help in solving particular serials research problems and questions. Canadian users are asked to call a special number collect, and our overseas users are asked to use a designated fax number. (Please see page iv for our mailing address, telephone/fax numbers, and e-mail address.) Finally, **The Cornerstone**, a quarterly newsletter which includes not only valuable information about serials and **Ulrich's** but also contains news about other Bowker titles and pertinent topics, is sent free of charge to subscribers of **Ulrich's**.

As we continue to research, plan, and implement enhancements to the **Ulrich's** database and our database maintenance system, we consider feedback from our users to be essential. Please contact us to let us know your thoughts. We want **Ulrich's** and its family of products to provide all necessary reference information quickly and effectively. Comments and suggestions are encouraged in order to help keep our directory of the highest quality. There is a wide variety of communication modes for you to select. You may write to us, send us a fax, call us on the telephone, or send us an e-mail. Also, be sure to visit the Reed Reference Publishing Home Page on the World Wide Web. Look for a Home Page for **Ulrich's** in the future. Please refer to page iv for all contact information.

My sincere appreciation is extended to the entire staff of **Ulrich's** for their unflagging dedication and diligent work in updating and maintaining the serials database in preparation of the 34th edition of **Ulrich's**. Many thanks to Frank Accurso and Hossam Elsherif for their technical advice and assistance as we forayed into the world of electronic data interchange. Gratitude is also extended to Donna Colahan, Account Manager at Reed Technology and Information Services for her patience in working closely with us again this year to produce this directory. Finally, I would like to thank the various information specialists, serialists, national libraries, and serials publishers throughout the world who have aided us in updating **Ulrich's**. We consider their participation and interest in the dissemination of accurate and comprehensive serials information to be of tremendous value to **Ulrich's** and its users.

Judith Salk
Publisher

User's Guide

This directory offers two primary access methods for locating periodicals: by subject in the CLASSIFIED LIST OF SERIALS (Volumes 1-3), and alphabetically in the TITLE INDEX (Volume 4). Ceased serials are listed in a separate CESSATIONS section and are also accessible by means of the TITLE INDEX. Other indexes provide listings of selected periodicals in specific categories. These indexes, in Volume 5 unless otherwise noted, are REFEREED SERIALS, CONTROLLED CIRCULATION SERIALS, SERIALS AVAILABLE ON CD-ROM, PRODUCER LISTING/SERIALS ON CD-ROM, SERIALS AVAILABLE ONLINE, VENDOR LISTING/SERIALS ONLINE, PUBLICATIONS OF INTERNATIONAL ORGANIZATIONS, ISSN INDEX (Volume 4), and TITLE CHANGE INDEX (Volume 4). See the User's Guide in Volume 5 for a content description and use instructions for the NEWSPAPERS section.

In addition, separate subheadings for "Abstracting, Bibliographies and Statistics" under major subject headings provide convenient access to these types of publications. Page references for these subheadings are given in the "Subject Guide to Abstracting and Indexing" on p. xlv. This listing provides an overview of subjects for which abstracting and indexing publications have been identified.

The "User's Guide" is separated into three divisions for ease of use: (I) Section Descriptions, (II) Full Entry Content Description, and (III) Cataloging Rules for Main Entry Title.

Section Descriptions

CLASSIFIED LIST OF SERIALS

This is the main section of the book, containing bibliographic information for currently published serials classified by subject. Entries are arranged alphabetically by title within each subject heading. Subject cross-references in the text direct the user to the location of subheadings.

Volume 1 contains subjects A-D, from "Abstracting and Indexing" through "Drug Abuse and Alcoholism." Volume 2 contains subjects E-L, "Earth Sciences" through "Lumber and Wood." Volume 3 contains subjects M-Z, from "Machine Theory" through "Zoology."

A complete listing of the "Subjects" used in the CLASSIFIED LIST OF SERIALS appears on p. xlvi. To aid international users, this list is translated into four languages. For additional guidance on the subject classification scheme, the user should also consult the CROSS-INDEX TO SUBJECTS on p. 6603, which contains additional key word references.

Each serial is listed with full bibliographic information only once. If a serial covers several subjects, title cross-references appear under the related headings, directing the user to the heading where the full entry is listed.

New serials beginning publication in 1994, 1995, or 1996 are highlighted by a ▼ in front of the title.

The "Cataloging Rules for Main Entry Title" section of this "User's Guide" explains the title cataloging rules followed in compiling **Ulrich's**.

CROSS-INDEX TO SUBJECTS

This index lists alphabetically all main subject headings in the **Ulrich's** Subject Heading File, as well as keyword references that direct users to main or subheadings where publications on those topics are likely to be found. The number following each subject term directs users to the page on which the subject begins within the CLASSIFIED LIST OF SERIALS.

A keyword may refer the user to more than one subject category. In this case, the subject references are listed in alphabetical order and are not necessarily listed in hierarchical order.

Main subject headings appear uppercased, e.g. AGRICULTURE. Subheadings contain the main subject term in uppercase and the specific subheading term in mixed case, e.g. AGRICULTURE—Agricultural Economics. The keywords, except for acronyms, are displayed entirely in mixed case.

ISSN INDEX

The ISSN INDEX lists serials in order by ISSN number. It includes all serials contained in the Bowker International

Serials Database, whether current, ceased, or inactive, to which an ISSN has been assigned in our file. A dagger symbol (†) indicates that the title is ceased. If an ISSN appears twice, it usually indicates that the serial has split into two or more parts. Titles that have changed and for which new ISSNs have been assigned will show cross-references from one ISSN to the new ISSN. If no new ISSN has been assigned, the cross-reference is from ISSN to new title. Entries for inactive titles do not appear in the book.

Italicized type indicates the page number where a complete entry can be found for active titles. Titles for which cessation was noted in the last three years have a page reference to the listing in the CESSATIONS INDEX. If no page reference appears for a ceased title, it means that the cessation was noted more than three years ago and is not listed in this edition. ISSNs of inactive titles likewise do not have page references and are not listed in this book.

A full description of the ISSN and its use is provided on p. xviii.

TITLE INDEX

The TITLE INDEX is the second major access point for serials. To locate a serial by its title, the user should be familiar with title cataloging rules as described in the "Cataloging Rules for Main Entry Titles" paragraphs of this "User's Guide."

The TITLE INDEX lists all current and ceased serials included in this directory. **Boldface** type indicates the page number where the complete entry will be found; page numbers in roman type refer to related subject categories.

For serials with identical titles published within a country, the city of publication is added in parentheses, and sometimes the year of first publication is given to further distinguish the titles.

If a serial title consists of or contains an acronym, a cross-reference is provided from the full name to the acronym form of the title.

Cross-references are provided from former titles and variant titles, and from the alternate language titles of multi-language publications. Recent title changes are noted, with a reference to the current title. The TITLE INDEX also lists the country code for all serials, along with the ISSN, if known.

The ▼ used in the "Classified List of Serials" to indicate new serials also appears in this index, preceding the title. A (†) appears preceding the title if the publication has ceased.

TITLE CHANGE INDEX

The TITLE CHANGE INDEX lists former titles alphabetically with references to new titles. Page numbers indicate where bibliographic entries are listed in the CLASSIFIED LIST OF SERIALS. This index cumulates all title changes recorded in the **Ulrich's** database since the publication of the previous, or 33rd, edition.

CESSATIONS

In this section, entries for serials for which ceassation was noted in the past three years are listed alphabetically by title. The cessation entry includes: title, Dewey Decimal Classification number, former frequency of publication, publisher name and address, country-of-publication code, and, if available, other information such as ISSN, CODEN, LC number, subtitle, corporate author, year of first issue and year ceased. Titles which were originally planned as continuing series but which have closed are included in the CESSATIONS section although back issues may still be available.

If a title has "ceased" because a new title is being used, there will not be an entry in the CESSATIONS section. Instead, the entry is maintained in the CLASSIFIED LIST OF SERIALS under the new title, with a **"Formerly"** or **"Former titles"** indication.

REFEREED SERIALS

This section is an alphabetical listing by title of all serials known to be refereed, or peer reviewed. It includes the publisher name, address, and telephone number, if known. The italicized number at the end of each entry is the page number where the full entry appears in the CLASSIFIED LIST OF SERIALS.

Omission of a title from this index does not mean that the journal is not peer-reviewed; nor does **Ulrich's** make any attempt to rate or judge the relative value of an individual journal's peer review process.

SERIALS AVAILABLE ON CD-ROM

This section is an alphabetical listing of all serials known to be available on CD-ROM, either in addition to hardcopy, or on CD-ROM only. It includes the publisher name, address, telephone and fax numbers, if known. It also includes the name of CD-ROM producers, when known. The italicized number at the end of each entry is the page number where the full entry appears in the CLASSIFIED LIST OF SERIALS.

PRODUCER LISTING/SERIALS ON CD-ROM

This section is an alphabetical listing of identified producers of serials on CD-ROM. Entries include the producer address, telephone and fax numbers, and an alphabetical listing of all serial titles known to be available.

SERIALS AVAILABLE ONLINE

If known, the serial on CD-ROM product name is listed in parentheses after the serial title. All serials listed in this index also have full bibliographic entries in the CLASSIFIED LIST OF SERIALS. Consult the TITLE INDEX or the SERIALS AVAILABLE ON CD-ROM listing for page numbers.

SERIALS AVAILABLE ONLINE

This section is an alphabetical listing of all serials known to be available online, either in addition to hardcopy, or online only. Entries include publisher name, address, telephone and fax numbers, plus names of online vendors and file names or numbers if known. The number in parentheses at the end of each entry is the page number where the full entry appears in the CLASSIFIED LIST OF SERIALS.

VENDOR LISTING/SERIALS ONLINE

This section is an alphabetical listing of identified vendors of online periodicals. Entries include addresses, telephone and fax numbers for the vendor, and an alphabetical listing of all titles known to be available, with file names or numbers, if known. All serials listed in this index also have full bibliographic entries in the CLASSIFIED LIST OF SERIALS. Consult the TITLE INDEX or the SERIALS AVAILABLE ONLINE listing for page numbers.

INDEX TO PUBLICATIONS OF INTERNATIONAL ORGANIZATIONS

Complexity of corporate author structure, as well as title page variations in multilingual texts, compound the problems in cataloging international publications. This special index is provided so that the user may have one reference point for these titles. This index consists of four sections:

International Organizations
International Congress Proceedings
European Communities
United Nations

The index contains all current titles listed in the Bowker International Serials Database. The user must consult the CLASSIFIED LIST OF SERIALS for the full bibliographic information pertaining to these titles. Page references are provided.

CONTROLLED CIRCULATION SERIALS

This section is an alphabetical listing of all serials known to have controlled circulations. It includes the publisher name and address, telephone and fax numbers, and circulation figure, if known. The italicized number at the end of each entry is a reference to the page on which the full entry appears in the CLASSIFIED LIST OF SERIALS.

Full Entry Content Description

Basic Information

The following items are mandatory for listing and appear in all entries: main entry title, frequency of publication, publisher address, country code, and Dewey Decimal Classification number.

Dewey Decimal Classification Number

The Dewey Decimal number is printed at the top left of each entry. More than one Dewey number may have been assigned if a serial covers several subjects.

LC Classification Number

The Library of Congress classification number, if known, appears directly below the Dewey Decimal number. Shelf numbers are not included.

Country Code

The Country Code is printed at the top right of each entry following the Dewey Decimal number. A complete list of country codes used will be found on p. xxii.

ISSN

The ISSN for the main entry title is printed immediately following the country code. Not all publications have been assigned an ISSN, and lack of a number does not render a publication ineligible for listing.

CODEN

The CODEN designation, if known, is printed directly below the country code and ISSN. The CODEN is an alphanumeric code, applied uniquely to a specific publication. Devised by the American Society for Testing and Materials, it is used primarily for scientific and technical titles. New CODEN are assigned by Chemical Abstracts Service.

Title Information

The main title is printed in **boldface** and upper case as the first item in the entry. Titles are catalogued according to rules described below in the "Cataloging Rules for Main Entry Title" section. For multi-language publications, the parallel language title is also printed in upper case, immediately following the main entry title, and is separated from it by a slash.

A ▼ printed before the title indicates that the title began publishing in 1994, 1995, or 1996.

An asterisk (*) printed after the title indicates that the information in the entry was not verified by the publisher for this edition.

The subtitle is printed in lower case after the title.

Variant titles or translated edition titles are given within the entry and are labeled as such.

Former titles are given at the end of the entry, along with publication dates if known. If a former title also had an ISSN, the ISSN is listed in parentheses after the former title. Many entries contain extensive former title information, providing a history of changes which may be useful for bibliographic record-keeping.

The Key Title, which is assigned at the time of ISSN assignment by the responsible center of the International Serials Data System, is given only if it is different from the main entry title.

Year First Published
The year first published is given if provided by the publisher. If information is lacking, a volume number and specific year may be provided to indicate the approximate age of the publication.

Frequency
The frequency of publication is given in abbreviated form, such as "a." for annual, "irreg." for irregular, "m." for monthly, "3/yr." for three times per year. All abbreviations used are listed in the "General Abbreviations" on p. xx.

Price
Unless otherwise indicated, the price given is the annual price for an individual subscription in the currency of the country of origin. The price in U.S. dollars may also be given in parentheses if it is provided by the publisher. No attempt is made to convert foreign currency to U.S. dollars.

SAMPLE ENTRY

(1) 930.198 490.996   **(2)** US   **(3)** ISSN 1055-7644
(4) DZ991   **(5)** CODEN: JAAPL9
(6) JOURNAL OF ANTARCTIC ARCHAEOLOGY AND PROTOLINGUISTICS;   **(7)** international communications and research.   **(8)** (Supplement avail.)   **(9)** (Text in English, French, Polynesian languages)   **(10)** 1927.   **(11)** 2/yr.   **(12)** $39 to individuals; institutions $99 (includes supplement) (effective 1996); newsstand price: $20.   **(13)** (Societe d'Archaeologie et de Linguistique Pacifiques—Society of Pacific Archaeology and Linguistics)   **(14)** W.A. Translations (Subsidiary of: Temporary Culture),   **(15)** Box 43072, Upper Montclair, NJ 07043-7072.   **(16)** TEL 908-665-2869.
(17) FAX 508-555-0010.   **(18)** TELEX 123458.   **(19)** E-mail: antarchaeol@miskaton.edu; Site addr.: http://www.miskaton.edu/.   **(20)** (Subscr. to: Department of Archaeology and Proto-Linguistics, 7 Old College Walk, Arkham, MA 01901-1011. TEL 508-555-0110. FAX 508-555-4112;
(21) Dist. in Europe by: Editions d'Erlette, Ch. de Kerangat, 56120 Plumelec, France. TEL 33-76-63-94. FAX 33-76-205).   **(22)** (Co-sponsor: Miskatonic University, Department of Archaeology and Proto-Linguistics)
(23) Eds. A.H. Whateley, J.M. Snyrnat;   **(24)** Pub. M.J. Smith.   **(25)** adv.: B&W page $400; trim 8 1/8 x 10;
(26) adv. contact: Arthur Dunwich.   **(27)** bk.rev.; abstr.; bibl.; illus.; index;
(28) circ. 500 (paid); 500 (controlled).   **(29)** (also avail. in microform from SWZ, UMI; also avail. on diskette; back issues avail.; reprint service avail. from SWZ, UMI).
(30) Indexed: Abstr. Anthropol., Br.Archaeol.Abstr.   **(31)** (1991–), Onoma (1986–), Ref.Zh.
(32) Document type: academic/scholarly publication.
(33) ● Also available online.   **(34)** Vendor(s): UTOPIA (Miskatonic).
(35) Also available on CD-ROM.   **(36)** Producer(s): TEMPCULT (Miskatonic).
(37) —BLDSC (9999.000000); CIS   **(38) CCC.**
(39) Supersedes (in 1986): Miskatonic Annals of Antarctic Archaeology and Extraterrestrial Linguistics
(40) (ISSN 0055-1298).
(41) Description: Publishes archaeological field research on prehistoric civilizations in the Pacific Islands and Antarctica, with relevant contributions discussing worldwide linguistic evidence of contacts among civilizations.
(42) *Refereed Serial*

KEY

1. Dewey Decimal Classification
2. Country Code
3. ISSN
4. LC Classification
5. CODEN
6. Main Entry Title
7. Subtitle
8. Bibliographic Note
9. Language
10. First Published
11. Frequency
12. Price
13. Corporate Author
14. Publishing Company
15. Address
16. Telephone
17. Fax
18. Telex
19. E-mail; Site Address
20. Subscription Address, Tel & Fax
21. Distributor Address, Tel & Fax
22. Co-sponsor
23. Editor
24. Publisher
25. Advertising Rate
26. Advertising Contact
27. Special Features
28. Circulation
29. Format
30. Indexed
31. Years of Coverage
32. Document Type
33. Online Availability
34. Online Vendor/File Name
35. CD-ROM Availability
36. CD-ROM Producer(s)
37. Document Suppliers
38. Copyright Clearance Center Registration Notation
39. Title Changes
40. Former ISSN
41. Brief Description
42. Refereed

Separate postage information is not given, since postal rates vary widely.

Publishing Company Information
Many serials are editorially controlled by a sponsoring organization or corporate author and published by a commercial publisher. In these instances, the commercial publishing company's name and address are given, and the name of the corporate author is given in parentheses immediately preceding. In other instances, either a sponsoring organization or a commercial publishing company has sole responsibility, and only one name is given. We avoid listing printers as publishing companies, preferring the name and address of someone with editorial responsibility. For the same reason, we avoid listing distributors as publishing companies.

If no publishing company name is given, it is assumed that the publishing company name is the same as the title.

Telephone, Fax, Telex Numbers and E-mail Addresses
Telephone, fax, telex numbers and e-mail addresses are given when provided by the publisher. U.S. and Canadian numbers are given in standard North American format. Toll-free numbers within U.S. and Canada are also included, when available. Numbers in other countries are provided in the same format as supplied by the publisher, resulting in some inconsistencies (e.g. sometimes with a country and/or city code, sometimes without). Users are advised to consult an international operator before placing calls.

In addition to providing e-mail addresses for publishers, information on publishers' URL (Universal Resource Locator) site addresses is included for the first time when known. The semi-colon separating these elements is not part of the e-mail address, nor is the final period part of the e-mail or site addresses.

Subscription or Distribution Address
A second address is given only if the address for ordering subscriptions is different from the publishing company's address. Distributors are listed only if we have been informed that a particular organization is the exclusive distributor. Additional subscription and/or distribution offices of international publishers are listed, if known. Telephone and fax numbers for subscription and/or distribution offices appear if provided by the publisher.

Editor
Only one or two names are given when known, preceded by the notation "Ed." or "Eds." Advanced degrees and titles are omitted, except for medical, military and religious titles; absence of a title does not mean that the editor has none. The abbreviation "Ed.Bd." indicates editorship by three or more persons.

Publisher
Only one or two names are given when known, preceded by the notation "Pub." or "Pubs." Advanced degrees and titles are omitted, except for medical, military and religious titles; absence of a title does not mean that the publisher has none.

If the publisher is also the editor, and no publishing company name is available, the person's name is given with the notation "Ed. & Pub."

Advertising Rates and Contact Name
When provided by the publisher, the name of the advertising contact, as well as full-page advertising rates and trim size are indicated. Most dimensions are listed in millimeters, except for U.S. publications, the dimensions of which are usually in inches.

Special Features
A listing of special features may include such items as book or other types of reviews, advertising (usually meaning commercial, not classified advertising), charts, illustrations, bibliography section, article abstracts, and an annual index to the periodical's contents.

Reprint Services
If a serial is known to be available from a reprint service, a code referring to the service appears in the entry. More than one code may be listed. For a list of reprint services and a translation of the codes, please refer to p. xxx.

Circulation
All circulation figures used are approximate. Circulation is given only if provided by the publisher. The notation "controlled" indicates that the publication is available only to the qualified persons, usually members of a particular trade or profession.

Format
Formats other than standard magazine format are noted in parentheses. Other formats may be looseleaf, duplicated (mimeographed), tabloid. If a publication is available in microform, a notation is made which includes a three-letter code for the vendor, if known. A list of names, addresses, telephone and fax numbers of micropublishers begins on p. xxv.

Abstracting and Indexing
The notation **"Indexed:"** precedes a list of abbreviations for all abstracting and indexing services known to cover the serial on a regular basis. Years of coverage immediately follow each abstracting and indexing service code, if known. The complete names of the abstracting and indexing services are listed with their abbreviations on p. xxxii. All currently published abstracting and indexing services are also listed as entries in the CLASSIFIED LIST OF SERIALS.

Document Type
Notations are included to indicate type of publication, e.g. trade publication, newsletter, or abstracting/indexing. The words "**Document type:**" appear in boldface, followed by the document type description, in entries where this information is known. More than one document type may be listed for a single publication, if applicable.

Online Availability and CD-ROM Availability
If a serial is known to be available in a full-text online format and/or on CD-ROM, a bullet symbol (●) precedes the information. Online and CD-ROM availability are noted whether they exist in addition to hardcopy or in one or both formats exclusively. Online vendors and CD-ROM producers are also listed, if known.

For a listing of serials available online, consult the SERIALS AVAILABLE ONLINE index on p. 9141. Complete names and addresses of vendors, with a listing of serials known to be available through them, are in a separate index, VENDOR LISTING/SERIALS ONLINE on p. 9263.

For a listing of serials available on CD-ROM, consult the SERIALS AVAILABLE ON CD-ROM index on p. 9097. Complete names and addresses of producers, with a list of CD-ROMs known to be available through them, are in a separate index, PRODUCER LISTING/SERIALS ON CD-ROM on p. 9137.

Document Suppliers
The **Ulrich's** database and the individual databases of the following document suppliers were matched on the presence of ISSNs. When a match was successful, the appropriate document supplier code was noted. Not all serials titles in general, or in these individual databases, have ISSNs. Therefore, the absence of one or any document supplier code in an **Ulrich's** listing does not necessarily mean the title is unavailable from one or any of these suppliers.

ADONIS™

The notation, ADONIS, appearing in a serial entry indicates the availability of that serial for document delivery through ADONIS's service, by permission from the copyright owner. Such permission is subject to change without notice.

For further information, contact: ADONIS B.V., Spuistraat 112D, 1012VA Amsterdam, The Netherlands; tel: 31-20-6262629, fax: 31-20-6261437; ADONIS USA, 238 Main St., Cambridge, MA 02142, USA; tel: 800-944-6415; fax: 617-876-7022.

British Library Document Supply Centre

The notation, BLDSC, appearing in a serial entry indicates the availability of that serial for document delivery from the British Library Document Supply Centre, by permission from the copyright owner. The BLDSC shelfmark number, a unique identifier of each serial, is preceded by an em-dash (—) which is followed by the notation "BLDSC (0000.000000)." The format of the shelfmark is four digits, a decimal point, then six digits.

For further information about BLDSC's services, contact: Customer Services, BLDSC, Boston Spa, Wetherby, LS23 7BQ, UK; tel: 44-1937-546060; fax: 44-1937-546333.

Chemical Abstracts Service

The notation, CASDDS, appearing in a serial entry indicates the availability of that serial for document delivery through Chemical Abstracts Service Document Delivery Service.

For further information, contact Chemical Abstracts Service, Document Delivery Service, P.O. Box 3012, Columbus, OH 43210, USA; tel: 800-678-4337; fax: 614-447-3648; e-mail: dds@cas.org.

Congressional Information Service, Inc.

The notation, CIS, appearing in a serial entry indicates the availability of that serial for document delivery through CIS Documents on Demand Service, by permission from the copyright owner. Such permission is subject to change without notice.

For further information, contact Congressional Information Service, Inc., 4520 East-West Hwy., Ste. 800, Bethesda, MD 20814-3389, USA; tel: 301-654-1550, 800-227-2477; fax: 301-657-3203.

EMDOCS

The notation, EMDOCS, appearing in a serial entry indicates the availability of that serial for document delivery through EMDOCS: The EMBASE Document Delivery Service, by permission from the copyright owner. Such permission is subject to change without notice.

For further information, contact EMDOCS, 469 Union Avenue, Westbury, NY 11590, USA; tel: 800-282-2720 or 516-997-0796; fax: 516-997-0890; e-mail: dds@work4u.artx.com.

Engineering Information Inc.

The notation, Ei, appearing in a serial entry indicates the availability of that serial for document delivery through EiDDS, the Ei Document Delivery Service, by permission from the copyright owner. Such permission is subject to change without notice.

For further information, contact EiDDS, One Castle Point Terrace, Hoboken, NJ 07030-5996, USA; tel: 800-221-1044 (USA & Canada), 201-216-8500; fax: 201-216-8532; e-mail: dds@einet.ei.org.

The Faxon Company, Inc.

The notation, Faxon, appearing in a serial entry indicates the availability of that serial's table of contents in Faxon Finder®, and article delivery through associated document delivery vendors, by permission from the copyright owner. Such permission is subject to change without notice. Access to Faxon Finder is offered on a subscription basis.

For further information, contact The Faxon Company, Inc., 15 Southwest Park, Westwood, MA 02090, USA; tel: 800-766-0039; fax: 800-933-6831; e-mail: finder@faxon.com.

The Genuine Article

The notation, Genuine Article, appearing in a serial entry indicates the availability of that serial for document delivery through The Institute for Scientific Information's Genuine Article, by permission from the copyright owner. Such permission is subject to change without notice.

For further information, contact The Genuine Article, 3501 Market Street, Philadelphia, PA 19104, USA; tel: 215-386-4399; fax: 215-386-4343; e-mail: tga@isinet.com.

Haworth Document Delivery Service

The notation, Haworth, appearing in a serial entry indicates the availability of that serial for document delivery through The Haworth Press's Document Delivery Service. This service is available for all Haworth journals. As the copyright holder, there will be no permission fee, but other fees are applicable.

For further information, contact Haworth Document Delivery Service, 10 Alice Street, Binghamton, NY 13904-1580, USA; tel: 800-342-9678; fax: 800-895-0582.

Petroleum Abstracts - Document Delivery Service (PADDS)

The notation, PADDS, appearing in a serial entry indicates the availability of that serial for document delivery through PADDS document delivery service, by permission from the copyright owner. Such permission is subject to change without notice.

For further information, contact Petroleum Abstracts - Document Delivery Service, University of Tulsa, McFarlin Library, 2933 E. 6th Street, Tulsa, OK 74104-3123, USA; tel: 800-247-8678; fax: 918-631-3823; e-mail: PADDS@TUred.pa.utulsa.edu.

SWETS

The notation, SWETS, appearing in a serial entry indicates the availability of that serial's table of contents in SwetScan, and document delivery through Swets, by permission from the copyright owner. Such permission is subject to change without notice.

For further information, contact Swets & Zeitlinger BV, Heereweg 347B, P.O. Box 830, 2160 SZ Lisse, The Netherlands; tel: 31-252-435111; fax: 31-252-415888; telex: 41325; www site: http://www.SWETS.nl.

UMI

The notation, UMI, appearing in a serial entry indicates the availability of that serial for document delivery through UMI InfoStore service, by permission from the copyright owner. Such permission is subject to change without notice.

For further information, contact UMI InfoStore, 500 Sansome Street, Ste. 400, San Francisco, CA 94111-3219, USA; tel: 800-248-0360 (US & Canada), 415-433-5500; fax: 415-433-0100; e-mail: orders@infostore.com.

The UnCover Company

The notation, UnCover, appearing in a serial entry indicates that the material is indexed in the UnCover database. Copies of articles are available through Uncover's document delivery service if the copyright owner has granted permission. Such permission is subject to change without notice.

For further information, contact the UnCover Co., 3801 E. Florida Ave., Ste. 200, Denver, CO 80210, USA; tel: 800-787-7979 (outside US & Canada: 303-758-3030); fax: 303-758-5946; e-mail: uncover@carl.org.

Copyright Clearance Center, Inc.
The Copyright Clearance Center, Inc. (CCC) is a not-for-profit collective licensing organization. The CCC grants permissions to institutions and individuals to photocopy works of its registered publishers upon payment of publisher set royalties. The CCC does not supply copies of registered works directly to anyone.

The boldfaced **CCC** notation appears in the entries of titles for which the CCC has been authorized by the publisher to grant photocopy permissions through its Transactional Reporting Service (TRS). Additional titles may be available for certain publishers who have authorized the CCC to grant photocopy permissions on any of their works. The same inclusive country-wide coverage is available for publishers in the following countries: Canada, the Commonwealth of Independent States, Germany, New Zealand, Norway, and Spain. To register with the CCC, please contact TRS Customer Service, 222 Rosewood Dr., Danvers, MA 01923, USA; tel: 508-750-8400; fax: 508-750-4470; www site: http://www.copyright.com/

Brief Description
A brief description of the contents and editorial focus of the publication may be provided, preceded by the word **"Description:"** at the end of the entry. These descriptions were submitted by the publisher or were written by editorial staff after examination of sample copies or publisher catalogs.

Refereed Serial
The manuscript peer review and evaluation system is utilized to protect, maintain and raise the quality of scholarly material published in serials. If a serial is known to be

refereed or juried, the notation *"Refereed Serial"* appears in italics at the end of the entry. This information is generally provided by the serial publisher.

Newspaper-Specific Data Elements

Ownership

The name of the owner(s) of a newspaper is listed, usually accompanied by the owner(s) address, and telephone and fax numbers. The owner address may differ from the newspaper location address. Owner information is preceded by the notation "Owner(s):."

Wire Services

If a newspaper is known to use one or more news or photo wire services, abbreviations or names of the services used are listed in the entry. Such information is preceded by the words "Wire Service(s):." Abbreviations for wire services used are listed on page xxxi of this volume.

Pages Per Issue; Columns Per Page

When known, the number of pages per issue (pp./issue:) and/or columns per page (cols./p.:) is/are noted.

Cataloging Rules for Main Entry Title

The majority of titles in the Bowker International Serials Database were cataloged according to *Anglo-American Cataloging Rules* prior to 1978, the date of the new edition of *Anglo-American Cataloging Rules*. The new *AACR II* reflects a trend toward the Key Title concept of cataloging as used by the International Serials Data System (ISDS) and published in its *International Standard Bibliographic Description for Serials* (1974).

Because recataloging a database the size of Bowker's was not feasible, our cataloging rules were modified but not radically changed. Cross-references are provided in the TITLE INDEX from variant forms of title, such as Key Title, to aid users searching by other methods.

Whenever possible, main entry title cataloging is done from a sample of the title page of the most recent issue, according to the following rules:

Articles at the beginning of titles are omitted, or are bypassed in filing.

Serials with distinctive titles are usually entered under title. For example:

Annual Bulletin of Historical Literature
Business Week
Milton Studies

If a title consists only of a generic term followed by the name of the issuing body, or if the name of the issuing body clarifies the content of the publication, entry is under the name of the issuing body. For example:

Newsletter of the American Theological Library Association

is entered as

American Theological Library Association. Newsletter

Economic Performance and Prospects, issued by the Private Development Corporation of the Philippines

is entered as

Private Development Corporation of the Philippines. Economic Performance and Prospects

A title which consists of a subject modified generic term followed by the name of the issuing body is considered nondistinctive and is entered under the name of the issuing body. For example:

Annual Meeting Scientific Proceedings of the American Animal Hospital Association

is entered as

American Animal Hospital Association. Annual Meeting Scientific Proceedings

Government publications with nondistinctive titles are entered under the name of the government jurisdiction of the issuing body, although distinctive titles of government organizations may be entered directly under title. For example:

Great Britain. Economic and Social Research Council. Annual Report

but

Statistical Abstract of Iceland

Titles which begin with the initials of the issuing body are entered under the initials. Cross-references from the full name are provided in the TITLE INDEX.

If a geographic name is part of the name of the issuing body, entry will be under the common form of the name of the body. For example:

University of the West Indies. Vice-Chancellor's Report

not

West Indies. University. Vice-Chancellor's Report

Note, however, that government publications retain similar cataloging as government jurisdiction.

Canada. Statistics Canada. Field Crop Reporting Series

Multilingual titles are entered under the first title given on the title page, or the first title reported by the publisher if the title page is not available. Titles in other languages are entered directly after the main entry title. Cross-references are provided in the TITLE INDEX for each language title.

FILING RULES

Due to the restrictions imposed by computer filing of titles, the following special filing rules should be noted.

Articles and prepositions within titles are alphabetized as words:

Journal of the West

precedes

Journal of Theological Studies

Hyphenated words are treated as separate words:

Pre-Text

precedes

Preaching

However, words indicating compass points (northeast, southwest, etc.) are filed as one word regardless of how printed:

Southeast Asia Builder
South-East Asia Stamp Catalogue
Southeast Dragster
South East Magazine

Titles entered under corporate author or government jurisdiction are sequenced before distinctive titles that begin with the same words:

British Columbia. Ministry of Energy, Mines and Petroleum Resources. Mineral Market Update

precedes

British Columbia Catholic

Acronyms and initials are treated as such and are listed at the beginning of each letter of the alphabet. Exceptions are the abbreviations of U.N. (United Nations), U.S. (United States), Gt. Britain (Great Britain), and St. (Saint), which are filed as words:

U R A M Newsletter
United Mutual Fund Sector
U.S. Environmental Protection Agency. Clean Water: Report to Congress

Titles in excess of 36 characters which are identical may not sort sequentially. The editors suggest that users scan the entire sequence of identical titles to locate specific entries.

Diacritical marks have been omitted. The German and Scandinavian umlaut has been replaced by the letter "e" following the vowels a, e, o, and u. In Danish, Norwegian and Swedish, the letter å is sequenced as "aa" and the letter ø as "oe."

International Standard Serial Number (ISSN)

1. What is the ISSN?

An internationally accepted, concise, unique, and unambiguous code for the identification of serial publications. One ISSN represents one serial title.

The ISSN consists of seven numbers with an eighth check digit calculated according to Modulus 11 and used to verify the number in computer processing. A hyphen is printed after the fourth digit, as a visual aid, and the acronym, ISSN, precedes the number.

2. How did the ISSN evolve as an international system?

The International Organization for Standardization Technical Committee 46 (ISO/TC 46) is the agency responsible for the development of the ISSN as an international standard. The organization responsible for the administration and coordination of ISSN assignments worldwide is the ISSN International Centre in Paris, which is supported by the French government and UNESCO.

ISSNs are assigned by over 50 national centers worldwide. The National Serials Data Program (NSDP) is the U.S. national center. The centers form a network which is coordinated by the ISSN International Centre located in Paris.

The implementation of the ISSN system started with the numbering of 70,000 titles in the serials database of R.R. Bowker (*Ulrich's International Periodicals Directory* and *Irregular Serials and Annuals*). The next serials database numbering was the *New Serials Titles 1950-70* cumulation listing 220,000 titles, cumulated, converted to magnetic tape, and published by R.R. Bowker in collaboration with the Serials Record Division of the Library of Congress. These two databases were used as the starting base for the implementation of the ISSN.

3. What types of publications are assigned ISSNs?

For assignment of an ISSN, a serial is defined as a publication in print or non-print form, issued in successive parts, usually having numerical or chronological designations, and intended to be continued indefinitely.

4. How is the ISSN used?

The ISSN is employed as a component of bar codes and as a tool for the communication of basic information about a serial title and for such processes as ordering, billing, inventory control, abstracting, and indexing. In library processes, the ISSN is used in operations such acquisitions, claiming, binding, accessioning, shelving, cooperative cataloguing, circulation, interlibrary loans, and retrieval of requests.

5. May a publication have an International Standard Book Number (ISBN) and an ISSN?

Yes! Monographic series (separate works issued indefinitely under a common title, generally in a uniform format with numeric designations) and annuals or titles planned to be issued indefinitely under the same title may be defined as serials. The ISSN is assigned to the serial title, while an ISBN is assigned to each individual title or monograph in the series.

A new ISBN is assigned to each volume or edition by the publisher, while the ISSN, which is assigned by the ISSN International Centre or national ISSN centers, remains the same for each issue. Both numbers should be printed on the copyright page or other appropriate page of each volume, with their acronyms or words preceding each number for immediate identification. With the availability of both an ISSN and ISBN, the problem of defining the overlap of serials and monographs has been resolved.

SAMPLE TITLE

Advances in the Biosciences
ISSN 0065-3446

Vol. 1 Proceedings: Berlin. Schering Symposium of Endocrinology, Berlin. Ed. by Gerhard Raspe. 1969. 40.00 (ISBN 0-08-013395-9). Pergamon.

Vol. 2 Proceedings. Schering Symposium on Biodynamics & Mechanisms of Action of Steroid Hormones, Berlin. Ed. by Gerhard Raspe. 1969. 41.25 (ISBN 0-08-006942-8). Pergamon.

Vol. 3 Proceedings. Schering Workshop on Steroid Metabolism "in Vitro Versus in Vivo," Berlin. Ed. by Gerhard Raspe. 1969. 41.25 (ISBN 0-08-017544-9). Pergamon.

Vol. 4 Proceedings. Schering Symposium on Mechanisms Involved in Conception. Berlin. Ed. by Gerhard Raspe. 1970. text ed. 41.25 (ISBN 0-08-017546-5). Pergamon.

Vol. 25 Development of Responsiveness to Steroid Hormones. Alvin M. Kaye & Myra Kaye et al. LC 79-42938. 1980. 66.00 (ISBN 0-08-024949-X). Pergamon.

6. Where should the ISSN appear on the serial?

In a prominent position on or in each issue of the serial, such as the front cover, back cover, masthead, title, or copyright pages. The international standard recommendation is that the ISSN of a periodical be printed, whenever possible, in the upper right corner of the front cover.

Promotional and descriptive materials about the serial should include the ISSN.

7. When a title changes, is a new ISSN assigned?

In most instances, a new ISSN is assigned when a title changes. However, the determination is made by the ISSN International Centre or the appropriate national ISSN centers. Publishers should report all the title changes to their respective centers.

8. How does a publisher apply for an ISSN?

The publisher should contact the appropriate national ISSN center or the ISSN International Centre. Centers require bibliographic evidence of a serial, including a copy of the title page and cover. There is no charge to publishers for the assignment of ISSNs.

For full information, publishers should contact the national library or bibliographic center in the country where they are publishing. The address of the ISSN International Centre is:

> ISSN International Centre
> 20, rue Bachaumont
> 75002 Paris
> France
> **Tel:** (33 1) 44 88 22 20
> **Fax:** (33 1) 40 26 32 43
> **Telex:** 219847F
> **E-mail:** issnic@well.com
> **www site:** http://www.well.com/user/issnic

The address for the U.S. national ISSN center is:

> National Serials Data Program (NSDP)
> Library of Congress
> Washington, DC 20540-4160
> **Tel:** 202-707-6452
> **Fax:** 202-707-6333
> **E-mail:** ISSN@loc.gov

9. What is SISAC?

SISAC stands for the Serials Industry Systems Advisory Committee. SISAC is an industry group formed to develop voluntary standardized formats for electronically transmitting serials business transaction information. SISAC provides a forum where serial (particularly journal) publishers, library system vendors, and librarians can discuss mutual concerns regarding the electronic transmission of serial information and develop cooperative solutions, in the form of standardized formats, to efficiently address these concerns.

10. What is the SISAC Symbol (SICI) and its relationship to the ISSN?

The Serial Item and Contribution Identifier (SICI) is a serial identification code which follows the ISSN and is a string of letters and/or numbers which uniquely identify a particular issue of a serial. Encoded in the SICI are chronological and enumeration data which identify serials by date and volume/issue numbers. According to SISAC, "the ANSI* standard extends the code down to the article level by adding location number and necessary title information, plus a record validation character. Code 128 is the bar code symbology selected by SISAC for displaying this number string in scannable form. When displayed in the Code 128 symbology, the SICI is called the SISAC symbol." The SICI is the ANSI standard; the SISAC symbol is the bar code.

*ANSI American National Standards Institute. Organization that coordinates the voluntary standards system in the United States. U.S. member of the International Standards Organization (ISO).

Abbreviations

General Abbreviations and Special Symbols

a.	annual	mkt.	market prices
A&I	Abstracting and Indexing	music rev.	music reviews
abstr.	abstracts	N.S.	New Series
approx.	approximately	pat.	patents
bi-m.	bimonthly (every two months)	play rev.	play reviews (theater reviews)
bi-w.	biweekly (every two weeks)	pp./issue	pages per issue
bibl.	bibliographies	Prof.	Professor
bk.rev.	book reviews	Pub.	Publisher
CCC	Copyright Clearance Center	q.	quarterly
c/o	care of	rec. rev.	record reviews
circ.	circulation	s-a.	semiannually (twice annually)
cols./p.	columns per page	s-m.	semimonthly (twice monthly)
contr.	controlled	s-w.	semiweekly (twice weekly)
cum.index	cumulative index	stat.	statistics
Cy.	county	subscr.	subscription
d.	daily	tele.rev.	television reviews
dance rev.	dance reviews	3/m.	3 times a month
Dir.	Director	3/yr.	3 times a year
dist.	distributed	tr.lit.	trade literature (manufacturers' catalogues, reader response cards)
Ed., Eds.	Editor, Editors		
Ed.Bd.	Editorial Board	tr.mk.	trade marks
film rev.	film reviews	video rev.	video reviews
fortn.	fortnightly (every two weeks)	w.	weekly
ISSN	International Standard Serial Number	*	not updated / unverified
illus.	illustrations	●	online and / or CD-ROM availability
irreg.	irregular	▼	new serial
m.	monthly	†	ceased

Money Symbols

SYMBOL	UNIT	COUNTRY
	austral	Argentina
g.$	peso	Argentina
us.$	dollar	Australia
	baht	Thailand
$	dollar	Brunei Darussalam, Belize
EF	franc	Belgium
	balboa	Panama
ol.$	peso	Bolivia
r.	birr	Ethiopia
s.	bolivar	Venezuela
TN	bonus do tesouro nacional	Brazil
TNF	bonus do tesouro nacional fiscal	Brazil
.$	cordoba; dollar	Nicaragua, Cayman Islands
an.$	dollar	Canada
FPF	franc	New Caledonia
h.$	peso	Chile
ol.	colon	Costa Rica, El Salvador
ol.$	peso	Colombia
r.$	cruzerio	Brazil
z.$	cruzado	Brazil
.	dalasi	Gambia
H., Dh.	dirham	Morocco, United Arab Emirates
KK	krone	Denmark
M.	mark	Germany
in.	dinar	Algeria, Jordan, Kuwait, Libya, Tunisia, Yugoslavia
	dollar; peso	various
r.	drachma	Greece
.	emalageni	Swaziland
As.	shilling	East Africa, Somalia, Tanzania, Uganda
C$.	dollar	Dominica, St. Lucia
CU	European currency unit	European Communities
EK	kroon	Estonia
sc.	escudo	Angola, Portugal, Mozambique
.	franc	Djibouti, France, Guadeloupe, Mali, Martinique, Monaco, Rwanda
$	dollar	Fiji
IM	markka	Finland
.	guilder; florin	Netherlands, Netherlands Antilles, Surinam
MG.	franc	Malagasy Republic
mk.	mark; markka	Finland
r.	franc	Belgium, Liechtenstein, Luxembourg, Switzerland
r.CFA	franc	African Financial Community, Benin, Burkina Faso, Burundi, Cameroon, Central African Republic, Chad, Congo, Gabon, Ivory Coast, Niger, Reunion, Senegal, Togo
t.	forint	Hungary
.	guarani	Paraguay
de.	gourde	Haiti
.$	dollar	Guyana
K$	dollar	Hong Kong
RK	kuna	Croatia
£	pound	Ireland
.D.	dinar	Iran, Iraq
RI.	riyal	Iran
S	shekel	Israel
SK	krona	Iceland
J.$	dollar	Jamaica
Jam.$	dollar	Jamaica
K.	kina; kwacha	Malawi, Papua New Guinea, Zambia

SYMBOL	UNIT	COUNTRY
Kc.	koruna	Czech Republic
Kcs.	koruny	Czechoslovakia
kip	kip	Laos
Kr.	krona; krone	Scandinavian countries
KShs.	shilling	Kenya
L.	lempira; lira	Honduras, Italy
Le.	leone	Sierra Leone
lei	lei	Rumania
Lit.	lira italiana	Italy
Ls.	lats	Latvia
Lt.	litas	Lithuania
lv.	lev	Bulgaria
M.$	dollar; ringgit	Malaysia
Mex.$	peso	Mexico
MKD	denar	Macedonia
$m.n.	moneda nacional	various
mt.	metical	Mozambique
N$	new Uruguay peso	Uruguay
NC.	cedi	Ghana
NOK	krone	Norway
NT.$	dollar	Republic of China (Taiwan)
N.Z.$	dollar	New Zealand
ORI.	riyal	Oman
P.	pula; peso	Botswana, Philippines, various
QRI.	riyal	Qatar
£	pound	Ireland, Gt. Britain, Malta
£C	pound	Cyprus
£E	pound	Egypt
£L	pound; dinar	Lebanon
£N	pound; naira	Nigeria
£S	pound	Syria
ptas.	peseta	Spain
Q.	quetzal	Guatemala
R.	rand	South Africa, Lesotho, Namibia
RD.$	peso	Dominican Republic
Rps.	rupiah	Indonesia
Rs.	riel; rial; rupee	Cambodia, India, Iran, Mauritius, Nepal, Pakistan, Seychelles, Sri Lanka
Rub.	ruble	Commonwealth of Independent States
S/	sucre; sole	Ecuador, Peru
S.	schilling	Austria
S.$	dollar	Singapore
SEK	krona	Sweden
SFr.	franc	Liechtenstein, Switzerland
SI$	dollar	Solomon Islands
SK.	koruna	Slovakia
SL.	pound	Sudan
SLT	talar	Slovenia
SRI.	riyal	Saudia Arabia
$T.	dollar	Tonga
TK.	taka	Bangladesh
TL.	pound; lira	Turkey
T.T.$	dollar	Trinidad and Tobago
tugrik	tugrik	Mongolia
UM	ouguiya	Mauritania
Urg.$	peso	Uruguay
vatu	vatu	Vanuatu
VN.$	dollar	Vietnam
Won	won (hwan)	Korea
Y	yuan	People's Republic of China
Yen	yen	Japan
YRl.	rial	Yemen
Z	zaire	Zaire
Z.$	dollar	Zimbabwe
Zl.	zloty	Poland

Country of Publication Codes

This list of countries and their codes has been taken from the list used by the Library of Congress in the MARC II format, 1992. The list used here is not the complete list of the MARC II format and is limited to countries and territories with publications listed in **Ulrich's**. The states of the United States, provinces and territories of Canada, and divisions of the United Kingdom are not listed separately.

The codes are mnemonic in most cases. Special codes not in the MARC format are used for publications of two international organizations: EI for European Communities and UN for United Nations and related organizations; and KR for Ukraine.

Country Code Sequence

Code	Country	Code	Country	Code	Country
AA	- ALBANIA	GH	- GHANA	PG	- GUINEA-BISSAU
AE	- ALGERIA	GI	- GIBRALTAR	PH	- PHILIPPINES
AF	- AFGHANISTAN	GL	- GREENLAND	PK	- PAKISTAN
AG	- ARGENTINA	GM	- GAMBIA	PL	- POLAND
AI	- ARMENIA	GO	- GABON	PN	- PANAMA
AJ	- AZERBAIJAN	GP	- GUADELOUPE	PO	- PORTUGAL
AN	- ANDORRA	GR	- GREECE	PP	- PAPUA NEW GUINEA
AO	- ANGOLA	GS	- GEORGIA	PR	- PUERTO RICO
AQ	- ANTIGUA	GT	- GUATEMALA	PY	- PARAGUAY
AS	- AMERICAN SAMOA	GU	- GUAM	QA	- QATAR
AT	- AUSTRALIA	GV	- GUINEA	RE	- REUNION
AU	- AUSTRIA	GW	- GERMANY	RH	- ZIMBABWE
AY	- ANTARCTICA	GY	- GUYANA	RM	- RUMANIA
BA	- BAHRAIN	HK	- HONG KONG	RU	- RUSSIA
BB	- BARBADOS	HO	- HONDURAS	RW	- RWANDA
BD	- BURUNDI	HT	- HAITI	SA	- SOUTH AFRICA
BE	- BELGIUM	HU	- HUNGARY	SE	- SEYCHELLES
BF	- BAHAMAS	IC	- ICELAND	SF	- SAO TOME E PRINCIPE
BG	- BANGLADESH	IE	- IRELAND	SG	- SENEGAL
BH	- BELIZE	II	- INDIA	SI	- SINGAPORE
BL	- BRAZIL	IO	- INDONESIA	SJ	- SUDAN
BM	- BERMUDA	IQ	- IRAQ	SL	- SIERRA LEONE
BN	- BOSNIA HERCEGOVINA	IR	- IRAN	SM	- SAN MARINO
BO	- BOLIVIA	IS	- ISRAEL	SO	- SOMALIA
BP	- SOLOMON ISLANDS	IT	- ITALY	SP	- SPAIN
BR	- UNION OF MYANMAR (FORMERLY BURMA)	IV	- IVORY COAST	SQ	- SWAZILAND
		JA	- JAPAN	SR	- SURINAM
BS	- BOTSWANA	JM	- JAMAICA	SU	- SAUDI ARABIA
BT	- BHUTAN	JO	- JORDAN	SW	- SWEDEN
BU	- BULGARIA	KE	- KENYA	SX	- NAMIBIA (FORMERLY SOUTH-WEST AFRICA)
BW	- BELARUS	KG	- KYRGYZSTAN		
BX	- BRUNEI DARUSSALAM	KN	- KOREA, NORTH	SY	- SYRIA
CB	- CAMBODIA	KO	- KOREA, SOUTH	SZ	- SWITZERLAND
CC	- CHINA, PEOPLE'S REPUBLIC OF	KR	- UKRAINE	TA	- TAJIKISTAN
CD	- CHAD	KU	- KUWAIT	TC	- TURKS AND CAICOS ISLANDS
CE	- SRI LANKA	KZ	- KAZAKHSTAN	TG	- TOGO
CF	- CONGO (BRAZZAVILLE)	LB	- LIBERIA	TH	- THAILAND
CH	- CHINA, REPUBLIC OF	LE	- LEBANON	TI	- TUNISIA
CI	- CROATIA	LH	- LIECHTENSTEIN	TK	- TURKMENISTAN
CJ	- CAYMAN ISLANDS	LI	- LITHUANIA	TO	- TONGA
CK	- COLOMBIA	LO	- LESOTHO	TR	- TRINIDAD & TOBAGO
CL	- CHILE	LS	- LAOS	TS	- UNITED ARAB EMIRATES
CM	- CAMEROON	LU	- LUXEMBOURG	TU	- TURKEY
CN	- CANADA	LV	- LATVIA	TV	- TUVALU
CQ	- COMOROS	LY	- LIBYA	TZ	- TANZANIA
CR	- COSTA RICA	MC	- MONACO	UA	- EGYPT (ARAB REPUBLIC OF EGYPT)
CS	- CZECHOSLOVAKIA	MF	- MAURITIUS	UG	- UGANDA
CU	- CUBA	MG	- MADAGASCAR	UI	- UNITED KINGDOM MISC. ISLANDS
CV	- CAPE VERDE	MH	- MACAO	UK	- UNITED KINGDOM
CX	- CENTRAL AFRICAN REPUBLIC	MJ	- MONTSERRAT	UN	- UNITED NATIONS
CY	- CYPRUS	MK	- OMAN	US	- UNITED STATES
DK	- DENMARK	ML	- MALI	UV	- BURKINA FASO
DM	- BENIN	MM	- MALTA	UY	- URUGUAY
DQ	- DOMINICA	MP	- MONGOLIA	UZ	- UZBEKISTAN
DR	- DOMINICAN REPUBLIC	MQ	- MARTINIQUE	VB	- BRITISH VIRGIN ISLANDS
EA	- ERITREA	MR	- MOROCCO	VC	- VATICAN CITY
EC	- ECUADOR	MU	- MAURITANIA	VE	- VENEZUELA
EG	- EQUATORIAL GUINEA	MV	- MOLDOVA	VI	- U.S. VIRGIN ISLANDS
EI	- EUROPEAN COMMUNITIES/ EUROPEAN UNION	MW	- MALAWI	VN	- VIETNAM
		MX	- MEXICO	WS	- WESTERN SAMOA
ER	- ESTONIA	MY	- MALAYSIA	XC	- MALDIVE ISLANDS
ES	- EL SALVADOR	MZ	- MOZAMBIQUE	XE	- MARSHALL ISLANDS
ET	- ETHIOPIA	NA	- NETHERLANDS ANTILLES	XI	- SAINT KITTS-NEVIS
FA	- FAEROE ISLANDS	NE	- NETHERLANDS	XK	- SAINT LUCIA
FG	- FRENCH GUIANA	NG	- NIGER	XM	- SAINT VINCENT
FI	- FINLAND	NL	- NEW CALEDONIA	XN	- MACEDONIA
FJ	- FIJI	NN	- VANUATU (NEW HEBRIDES)	XO	- SLOVAKIA
FK	- FALKLAND ISLANDS	NO	- NORWAY	XR	- CZECH REPUBLIC
FM	- FEDERATED STATES OF MICRONESIA	NP	- NEPAL	XV	- SLOVENIA
FP	- FRENCH POLYNESIA	NQ	- NICARAGUA	YE	- YEMEN, REPUBLIC OF
FR	- FRANCE	NR	- NIGERIA	YU	- YUGOSLAVIA
FT	- DJIBOUTI	NU	- NAURU	ZA	- ZAMBIA
GB	- KIRIBATI	NX	- NORFOLK ISLAND	ZR	- ZAIRE
GD	- GRENADA	NZ	- NEW ZEALAND		
GE	- GERMANY, EAST	PE	- PERU		

Country Sequence

AFGHANISTAN - AF
ALBANIA - AA
ALGERIA - AE
AMERICAN SAMOA - AS
ANDORRA - AN
ANGOLA - AO
ANTARCTICA - AY
ANTIGUA - AQ
ARGENTINA - AG
ARMENIA - AI
AUSTRALIA - AT
AUSTRIA - AU
AZERBAIJAN - AJ
BAHAMAS - BF
BAHRAIN - BA
BANGLADESH - BG
BARBADOS - BB
BELARUS - BW
BELGIUM - BE
BELIZE - BH
BENIN - DM
BERMUDA - BM
BHUTAN - BT
BOLIVIA - BO
BOSNIA HERCEGOVINA - BN
BOTSWANA - BS
BRAZIL - BL
BRITISH VIRGIN ISLANDS - VB
BRUNEI DARUSSALAM - BX
BULGARIA - BU
BURKINA FASO - UV
BURUNDI - BD
CAMBODIA - CB
CAMEROON - CM
CANADA - CN
CAPE VERDE - CV
CAYMAN ISLANDS - CJ
CENTRAL AFRICAN REPUBLIC - CX
CHAD - CD
CHILE - CL
CHINA, REPUBLIC OF - CC
CHINA, PEOPLE'S REPUBLIC OF - CH
COLOMBIA - CK
COMOROS - CQ
CONGO (BRAZZAVILLE) - CF
COSTA RICA - CR
CROATIA - CI
CUBA - CU
CYPRUS - CY
CZECH REPUBLIC - XR
CZECHOSLOVAKIA - CS
DENMARK - DK
DJIBOUTI - FT
DOMINICA - DQ
DOMINICAN REPUBLIC - DR
ECUADOR - EC
EGYPT (ARAB REPUBLIC OF EGYPT) - UA
EL SALVADOR - ES
EQUATORIAL GUINEA - EG
ERITREA - EA
ESTONIA - ER
ETHIOPIA - ET
EUROPEAN COMMUNITIES/
 EUROPEAN UNION - EI
FAEROE ISLANDS - FA
FALKLAND ISLANDS - FK
FEDERATED STATES OF MICRONESIA - FM
FIJI - FJ
FINLAND - FI
FRANCE - FR
FRENCH GUIANA - FG
FRENCH POLYNESIA - FP
GABON - GO
GAMBIA - GM

GEORGIA - GS
GERMANY - GW
GERMANY, EAST - GE
GHANA - GH
GIBRALTAR - GI
GREECE - GR
GREENLAND - GL
GRENADA - GD
GUADELOUPE - GP
GUAM - GU
GUATEMALA - GT
GUINEA - GV
GUINEA-BISSAU - PG
GUYANA - GY
HAITI - HT
HONDURAS - HO
HONG KONG - HK
HUNGARY - HU
ICELAND - IC
INDIA - II
INDONESIA - IO
IRAN - IR
IRAQ - IQ
IRELAND - IE
ISRAEL - IS
ITALY - IT
IVORY COAST - IV
JAMAICA - JM
JAPAN - JA
JORDAN - JO
KAZAKHSTAN - KZ
KENYA - KE
KIRIBATI - GB
KOREA, NORTH - KN
KOREA, SOUTH - KO
KUWAIT - KU
KYRGYZSTAN - KG
LAOS - LS
LATVIA - LV
LEBANON - LE
LESOTHO - LO
LIBERIA - LB
LIBYA - LY
LIECHTENSTEIN - LH
LITHUANIA - LI
LUXEMBOURG - LU
MACAO - MH
MACEDONIA - XN
MADAGASCAR - MG
MALAWI - MW
MALAYSIA - MY
MALDIVE ISLANDS - XC
MALI - ML
MALTA - MM
MARSHALL ISLANDS - XE
MARTINIQUE - MQ
MAURITANIA - MU
MAURITIUS - MF
MEXICO - MX
MOLDOVA - MV
MONACO - MC
MONGOLIA - MP
MONTSERRAT - MJ
MOROCCO - MR
MOZAMBIQUE - MZ
NAMIBIA (FORMERLY SOUTH-WEST AFRICA) - SX
NAURU - NU
NEPAL - NP
NETHERLANDS - NE
NETHERLANDS ANTILLES - NA
NEW CALEDONIA - NL
NEW ZEALAND - NZ
NICARAGUA - NQ
NIGER - NG

NIGERIA - NR
NORFOLK ISLAND - NX
NORWAY - NO
OMAN - MK
PAKISTAN - PK
PANAMA - PN
PAPUA NEW GUINEA - PP
PARAGUAY - PY
PERU - PE
PHILIPPINES - PH
POLAND - PL
PORTUGAL - PO
PUERTO RICO - PR
QATAR - QA
REUNION - RE
RUMANIA - RM
RUSSIA - RU
RWANDA - RW
SAINT KITTS-NEVIS - XI
SAINT LUCIA - XK
SAINT VINCENT - XM
SAN MARINO - SM
SAO TOME E PRINCIPE - SF
SAUDI ARABIA - SU
SENEGAL - SG
SEYCHELLES - SE
SIERRA LEONE - SL
SINGAPORE - SI
SLOVAKIA - XO
SLOVENIA - XV
SOLOMON ISLANDS - BP
SOMALIA - SO
SOUTH AFRICA - SA
SPAIN - SP
SRI LANKA - CE
SUDAN - SJ
SURINAM - SR
SWAZILAND - SQ
SWEDEN - SW
SWITZERLAND - SZ
SYRIA - SY
TAJIKISTAN - TA
TANZANIA - TZ
THAILAND - TH
TOGO - TG
TONGA - TO
TRINIDAD & TOBAGO - TR
TUNISIA - TI
TURKEY - TU
TURKMENISTAN - TK
TURKS AND CAICOS ISLANDS - TC
TUVALU - TV
U.S. VIRGIN ISLANDS - VI
U.S.S.R. - UR
UGANDA - UG
UKRAINE - KR
UNION OF MYANMAR (FORMERLY BURMA) - BR
UNITED ARAB EMIRATES - TS
UNITED STATES - US
UNITED NATIONS - UN
UNITED KINGDOM - UK
UNITED KINGDOM MISC. ISLANDS - UI
URUGUAY - UY
UZBEKISTAN - UZ
VANUATU (NEW HEBRIDES) - NN
VATICAN CITY - VC
VENEZUELA - VE
VIETNAM - VN
WESTERN SAMOA - WS
YEMEN, REPUBLIC OF - YE
YUGOSLAVIA - YU
ZAIRE - ZR
ZAMBIA - ZA
ZIMBABWE - RH

Document Suppliers

ADONIS	ADONIS B.V. (main office) Spuistraat 112D 1012 VA Amsterdam The Netherlands **Tel:** 31-20-6262629 **Fax:** 31-20-6261437 **ADONIS USA** 238 Main St. Cambridge, MA 02142 USA **Tel:** 800-944-6415 **Fax:** 617-876-7022	Faxon	The Faxon Company, Inc. 15 Southwest Park Westwood, MA 02090 USA **Tel:** 800-766-0039 **Fax:** 800-933-6831 **E-mail:** finder@faxon.com
		Genuine Article	The Institute for Scientific Information The Genuine Article 3501 Market St. Philadelphia, PA 19104 USA **Tel:** 215-386-4399 **Fax:** 215-386-4343 **E-mail:** tga@isinet.com
BLDSC	British Library Document Supply Centre Customer Services Boston Spa, Wetherby W. Yorkshire LS23 7BQ England **Tel:** 44-1937-546060 **Fax:** 44-1937-546333	Haworth	Haworth Press Haworth Document Delivery Service 10 Alice St. Binghamton, NY 13904-1580 USA **Tel:** 800-342-9678 **Fax:** 800-895-0582
CASDDS	Chemical Abstracts Service Document Delivery Service P.O. Box 3012 Columbus, OH 43210 USA **Tel:** 800-678-4337 **Fax:** 614-447-3648 **E-mail:** dds@cas.org	PADDS	Petroleum Abstracts - Document Delivery Service University of Tulsa, McFarlin Library 2933 E. 6th St. Tulsa, OK 74104-3123 USA **Tel:** 800-247-8678 **Fax:** 918-631-3823 **E-mail:** PADDS@TUred.pa.utulsa.edu
CIS	Congressional Information Service, Inc. CIS Documents on Demand 4520 East-West Hwy., Ste. 800 Bethesda, MD 20814-3389 USA **Tel:** 301-654-1550, 800-227-2477 **Fax:** 301-657-3203	SWETS	Swets & Zeitlinger bv Hereweg 347B P.O. Box 830 2160 SZ Lisse The Netherlands **Tel:** 31-252-435111 **Fax:** 31-252-415888 **Telex:** 41325 **www site:** http://www.SWETS.nl
Ei	Engineering Information Inc. Ei Document Delivery Service One Castle Point Terrace Hoboken, NJ 07030-5996 USA **Tel:** 800-221-1044 (USA & Canada), 201-216-8500 **Fax:** 201-216-8532 **E-mail:** dds@einet.ei.org.	UMI	UMI InfoStore 500 Sansome St., Ste. 400 San Francisco, CA 94111-3219 USA **Tel:** 800-248-0360 (USA & Canada), 415-433-5500 **Fax:** 415-433-0100 **E-mail:** orders@infostore.com
EMDOCS	EMDOCS: The EMBASE Document Delivery Service 469 Union Ave. Westbury, NY 11590 USA **Tel:** 800-282-2720, 516-997-0796 **Fax:** 516-997-0890 **E-mail:** dds@work4u.artx.com	UnCover	The UnCover Co. 3801 E. Florida Ave., Ste. 200 Denver, CO 80210 USA **Tel:** 800-787-7979, (outside US & Canada: 303-758-3030) **Fax:** 303-758-5946 **E-mail:** uncover@carl.org

Micropublishers and Distributors

ACR A.C.R.P.P.
(Association pour la Conservation et la Reproduction Photographique de la Presse)
B.P. 21
77313 Marne-La-Vallee Cedex 2
France
Tel: 1-60-17-68-10; **Fax:** 1-60-17-68-05

ADL Advanced Library Systems, Inc.
100 Brickstone Sq.
P.O. Box 246
Andover, MA 01810-0005
USA
Tel: 508-470-0610; **Fax:** 508-475-1072

AFS Fertility and Sterility
(no longer producer)
2140 11 Ave. S., Ste. 200
Birmingham, AL 35205-2800
USA
Tel: 205-933-8494; **Fax:** 205-930-9904

AGU American Geophysical Union
2000 Florida Ave., N.W.
Washington, DC 20009
USA
Tel: 202-462-6900; **Fax:** 202-328-0566

AIP American Institute of Physics
500 Sunnyside Blvd.
Woodbury, NY 11797-2999
USA
Tel: 516-576-2270; **Fax:** 516-349-9704

AIR Aircraft Technical Publishers
101 S. Hill Dr.
Brisbane, CA 94005
USA
Tel: 415-468-1705; **Fax:** 415-468-1596

AJP American Jewish Periodical Center
Hebrew Union College - Jewish Institute of Religion
3101 Clifton Ave.
Cincinnati, OH 45220
USA
Tel: 513-221-1875; **Fax:** 513-221-0519

ALP Alpha Com
Sportallee 6
22335 Hamburg
Germany
Tel: 49-40-51302-123; **Fax:** 49-40-51302111

AMP Adam Matthew Publications
8 Oxford St.
Marlborough, Wiltshire SN8 1AP
England
Tel: 44-1672-511921; **Fax:** 44-1672-511663

AMS AMS Press, Inc.
(no longer producer)
56 E. 13th St.
New York, NY 10003
USA
Tel: 212-777-4700; **Fax:** 212-995-5413

ATL American Theological Library Association, Preservation Board
820 Church St., Ste. 300
Evanston, IL 60201
USA
Tel: 708-869-7788; **Fax:** 708-869-8513

BAR Barbour Index plc
New Lodge, Drift Rd.
Windsor, Berkshire SL4 4RQ
England
Tel: 44-1344-884121; **Fax:** 44-1344-884845

BHP Brookhaven Press
P.O. Box 2287
La Crosse, WI 54602-2287
USA
Tel: 608-781-0850; **Fax:** 608-781-3883

BIO BIOSIS
2100 Arch St.
Philadelphia, PA 19103-1399
USA
Tel: 215-587-4800, 800-523-4806
Fax: 215-587-2016

BKR Bowker A&I Publishing
(See: CIS)

BLC Bloch & Company
P.O. Box 18058
Cleveland, OH 44118
USA
Tel: 216-371-0979; **Fax:** 216-371-9493

BLH Bell & Howell
(Micropublishing now operated by UMI)

MICROPUBLISHERS AND DISTRIBUTORS

BLI   **Balch Institute**
Research Library
18 S. 7th St.
Philadelphia, PA 19106
USA
Tel: 215-925-8090; **Fax:** 215-925-8195

BNB   **British Library National Bibliographic Service**
Boston Spa, Wetherby
W. Yorkshire LS23 7BQ
England
Tel: 44-1937-546585; **Fax:** 44-1937-546586

BNQ   **Bibliotheque Nationale du Quebec**
Section de la Reproduction
125, rue Sherbrooke Ouest
Montreal, PQ H2X 1X4
Canada
Tel: 514-873-1100; **Fax:** 514-873-9932

BWC   **Butterworth & Co., Ltd.**
88 Kingsway
London WC2B 6AB
England
Tel: 44-171-4056900; **Fax:** 44-171-4051332

CCM   **Core Collection Micropublishers**
Div. of Roth Publishing, Inc.
185 Great Neck Rd.
Great Neck, NY 11021
USA
Tel: 516-466-3676, 800-327-0295
Fax: 516-829-7746

CDS   **Current Digest of the Soviet Press**
3857 N. High St.
Columbus, OH 43214
USA
Tel: 614-292-4234; **Fax:** 614-267-6310

CHL   **Chadwyck-Healey Ltd.**
Cambridge Place
Cambridge CB2 1NR
England
Tel: 44-1223-311479; **Fax:** 44-1223-66440
Chadwyck-Healey Inc.
1101 King St.
Alexandria, VA 22314-2944
USA
Tel: 703-683-4890; **Fax:** 703-683-7589

CIS   **Congressional Information Service, Inc.**
4520 East-West Hwy., Ste. 800
Bethesda, MD 20814-3389
USA
Tel: 301-654-1550, 800-638-8380
Fax: 301-654-4033

CLA   **Canadian Library Association**
(no longer producer)
Microfilm Department
200 Elgin St., Ste. 602
Ottawa, ON K2P 1L5
Canada
Tel: 613-232-9625; **Fax:** 613-563-9895

CLS   **CLASS**
(Cooperative Library Agency for
Systems & Services)
1415 Koll Circle, Ste. 101
San Jose, CA 95112-4698
USA
Tel: 408-453-0444; **Fax:** 408-453-5379

CMC   **Computer Microfilm Corp.**
3900 Wheeler Ave.
Alexandria, VA 22304
USA
Tel: 703-823-0500; **Fax:** 703-823-0505

CML   **Commonwealth Microfilm Products**
202 Amber St.
Markham, ON L3R 3J8
Canada
Tel: 905-415-9498; **Fax:** 905-415-9616

EDR   **Eric Document Reproduction Service**
(See: CMC)

EEE   **Institute of Electrical and Electronics Engineers Inc.**
345 E. 47th St.
New York, NY 10017
USA
Tel: 212-705-7900; **Fax:** 212-705-7682

EMP   **Emmett Publishing, Ltd.**
W. House 21, West St.
Haslemere, Surrey GU27 2AB
England
Tel: 44-1428-654443; **Fax:** 44-1428-661582

FCM   **Fairchild Books & Visuals**
7 W. 34th St.
New York, NY 10001
USA
Tel: 212-630-3880; **Fax:** 212-630-3868

GCS   **Preston Publications**
7800 Merrimac Ave.
P.O. Box 48312
Niles, IL 60714
USA
Tel: 708-965-0566; **Fax:** 708-965-7639

GMC   **General Microfilm Co.**
(acquired by OMNISYS Corp.)

MICROPUBLISHERS AND DISTRIBUTORS

HAW   **The Haworth Press**
10 Alice St.
Binghamton, NY 13904
USA
Tel: 607-722-5857; **Fax:** 607-722-1424

HPL   **Harvester Press Microfilm Publications Ltd.**
(Now wholly owned and operated
by Primary Source Media)

IAM   **SIAM Publications**
3600 University City Science Center
Philadelphia, PA 19104-2688
USA
Tel: 215-382-9800; **Fax:** 215-386-7999

ICS   **Editions I.C.S.**
23 Ave. Villemain
75014 Paris
France
Tel: 33-1-45392244; **Fax:** 33-1-45434680

IDC   **IDC Microform Publishers bv**
P.O. Box 11205
2301 EE Leiden
The Netherlands
Tel: 31-715142700; **Fax:** 31-715131721

IFA   **International Federation of Film Archives (FIAF)**
6 Nottingham St.
London W1M 3RB
England
Tel: 44-171-2240991; **Fax:** 44-171-2241203

ILO   **ILO Publications**
49 Sheridan Ave.
Albany, NY 12210
USA
Tel: 518-436-9686; **Fax:** 518-436-7433

IMI   **Irish Microforms, Ltd.**
Unit 56
Sandyford Industrial Estate
Dublin 18
Ireland
Tel: 353-1-2893626; **Fax:** 353-1-2954270

IPC   **Institute of Paper Science & Technology, Inc.**
500 Tenth St. N.W.
Atlanta, GA 30318
USA
Tel: 404-853-9500; **Fax:** 404-853-9510

IRE   **International Research and Evaluation**
21098 IRE-Control Center
Eagan, MN 55121-0098
USA
Tel: 612-888-9635; **Fax:** 612-888-9124

ISI   **Institute for Scientific Information**
3501 Market St.
Philadelphia, PA 19104
USA
Tel: 215-386-0100
Fax: 215-386-6362, 215-386-2911

JAI   **JAI Press Inc.**
55 Old Post Rd., No. 2
P.O. Box 1678
Greenwich, CT 06836-1678
USA
Tel: 203-661-7602; **Fax:** 203-661-0792

JOH   **Johnson Reprint Microeditions**
(Out of business)

JSC   **J.S. Canner & Co.**
10 Charles St.
Needham Heights, MA 02194
USA
Tel: 617-449-9103; **Fax:** 617-449-1767

KHS   **Kansas State Historical Society Microfilm Publications**
120 W. Tenth Ave.
Topeka, KS 66612-1291
USA
Tel: 913-296-3086; **Fax:** 913-296-1005

KTO   **Kraus Microform**
(Micropublishing now operated by
Norman Ross Publishing, Inc.)

LCP   **The Library of Congress Photoduplication Service**
Washington, DC 20540-5230
USA
Tel: 202-707-5640; **Fax:** 202-707-1771

LIB   **Library Microfilms**
1115 E. Arques Ave.
Sunnyvale, CA 94086
USA
Tel: 408-736-7444; **Fax:** 408-736-4397

LOP   **Lomond Publications**
P.O. Box 88
Mt. Airy, MD 21771
USA
Tel: 301-829-1496, 800-443-6299

MCA   **Microfilming Corporation of America**
(Acquired by UMI;
operation phased out)

MCE   **Microcard Editions**
(See: CIS)

MICROPUBLISHERS AND DISTRIBUTORS

MDX   **Micromedex Inc.**
600 Grant St.
Denver, CO 80203
USA
Tel: 303-831-1400; **Fax:** 303-837-1717

MEL   **Metropolitan Library Service Agency**
(MELSA)
570 Asbury St., Ste. 201
St. Paul, MN 55104-1849
USA
Tel: 612-645-5731; **Fax:** 612-649-3169

MIM   **Elsevier Science Ltd.**
The Blvd., Langford Ln.
Kidlington, Oxford OX5 1GB
England
Tel: 44-1865-843000; **Fax:** 44-1865-843010

MIS   **Moody's Investors Service**
Sales Department
99 Church St.
New York, NY 10007
USA
Tel: 212-553-0300; **Fax:** 212-553-4700

MML   **Micromedia Limited**
20 Victoria St.
Toronto, ON M5C 2N8
Canada
Tel: 416-362-5211, 800-387-2689
Fax: 416-362-6161

MMP   **McLaren Micropublishing Ltd.**
P.O. Box 972, Sta. F
Toronto, ON M4Y 2N9
Canada
Tel: 416-960-4801; **Fax:** 416-964-3745

MUE   **University Music Editions**
Div. of High Density Systems, Inc.
P.O. Box 192, Ft. George Sta.
New York, NY 10040
USA
Tel: 212-569-5340, 5393; **Fax:** 212-569-1269

NBI   **Newsbank, Inc.**
58 Pine St.
New Canaan, CT 06840
USA
Tel: 203-966-1100, 800-243-7694
Fax: 203-966-6254

NRP   **Norman Ross Publishing, Inc.**
330 W. 58th St., Ste. 214
New York, NY 10019
USA
Tel: 212-765-8200, 800-648-8850
Fax: 212-765-2393

NTI   **National Technical Information Service**
5285 Port Royal Rd.
Springfield, VA 22161
USA
Tel: 703-487-4600; **Fax:** 703-321-8547

NYL   **New York Law Publishing Co.**
345 Park Ave., S.
New York, NY 10010
USA
Tel: 212-779-9200; **Fax:** 212-696-4287

NYT   **New York Times Information Bank**
(Operation phased out)
229 W. 43rd St.
New York, NY 10036
USA
Tel: 212-556-1234

OEC   **Organization for Economic Cooperation & Development, Publications & Information Center**
2001 L St., N.W., Ste. 650
Washington, DC 20036-4910
USA
Tel: 202-785-6323; **Fax:** 202-785-0350

OMN   **OMNISYS Corp.**
211 Second Ave.
Waltham, MA 02154
USA
Tel: 617-684-1234; **Fax:** 617-684-1245

OMP   **Oxford Microform Publication Ltd.**
(Acquired by UMI)

PMC   **Princeton Microfilm Corp.**
P.O. Box 2073
Princeton, NJ 08543
USA
Tel: 609-452-2066, 800-257-9502
Fax: 609-275-6201

PSL   **The Pretoria State Library**
P.O. Box 397
Pretoria 0001
Republic of South Africa
Tel: 27-12-218931; **Fax:** 27-12-3255984

RPI   **Primary Source Media**
12 Lunar Dr.
Woodbridge, CT 06525
USA
Tel: 203-397-2600, 800-444-0799
Fax: 203-397-3893

RRI   **Fred B. Rothman & Co.**
10368 W. Centennial Rd.
Littleton, CO 80127
USA
Tel: 303-979-5657, 800-457-1986
Fax: 303-978-1457

MICROPUBLISHERS AND DISTRIBUTORS

SAL   **South African Library**
P.O. Box 469
Capetown 8000
Republic of South Africa
Tel: 27-21-246320; **Fax:** 27-21-244848

SAS   **Society for Applied Spectroscopy**
201-B Broadway St.
Frederick, MD 21701
USA
Tel: 301-694-8122; **Fax:** 301-694-6860

SOC   **Societe Canadienne du Microfilm Inc. - Canadian Microfilming Co. Ltd.**
464 rue Saint-Jean
Montreal, PQ H2Y 2S1
Canada
Tel: 514-288-5404; **Fax:** 514-843-4690

SWZ   **Swets & Zeitlinger bv**
Backsets Department
P.O. Box 810
2160 SZ Lisse
The Netherlands
Tel: 31-252-435111; **Fax:** 31-252-415888
www site: http://www.SWETS.nl

TMI   **Tennessee Microfilms**
P.O. Box 23075
Nashville, TN 37202
USA
Tel: 615-242-3632

UMI   **University Microfilms International (A Bell & Howell Company)**
300 N. Zeeb Rd.
Ann Arbor, MI 48103
USA
Tel: 313-761-4700, 800-521-0600
Fax: 313-761-1203

UNW   **University of Wisconsin Library**
Interlibrary Loan Department
728 State St., Rm. 231
Madison, WI 53706
USA
Tel: 608-262-3193; **Fax:** 608-262-4649

UPD   **Updata Publications, Inc.**
1736 Westwood Blvd.
Los Angeles, CA 90024
USA
Tel: 310-474-5900; **Fax:** 310-474-4095

VCI   **VCH Publishers, Inc.**
303 N.W. 12th Ave.
Deerfield Beach, FL 33442-1788
USA
Tel: 305-428-5566
Fax: 305-428-8201, 800-367-8247

VFN   **Voltaire Foundation Ltd.**
99 Banbury Rd.
Oxford OX2 6JX
England
Tel: 44-1865-284600; **Fax:** 44-1865-284610

WDS   **Dawson Microfiche**
(Distributor only)
Cannon House
Parkfarm Rd.
Folkestone, Kent CT19 5EE
England
Tel: 44-1303-850101; **Fax:** 44-1303-850440

WMP   **World Microfilm Publications Ltd**
Microworld House, 2-6 Foscote Mews
London W9 2HH
England
Tel: 44-171-2662202; **Fax:** 44-171-2662314

WSH   **William S. Hein & Co., Inc.**
Hein Bldg., 1285 Main St.
Buffalo, NY 14209-1987
USA
Tel: 716-882-2600, 800-828-7571
Fax: 716-883-8100

WWS   **Williams & Wilkins**
428 E. Preston St.
Baltimore, MD 21202
USA
Tel: 410-528-8555, 800-638-6423
Fax: 410-528-8596

Reprint Services

CIS   **Congressional Information Service, Inc.**
4520 East-West Hwy., Ste. 800
Bethesda, MD 20814-3389
USA
Tel: 301-654-1550, 800-638-8380
Fax: 301-657-3203

CMC   **Computer Microfilm Corp.**
3900 Wheeler Ave.
Alexandria, VA 22304
USA
Tel: 703-823-0500
Fax: 703-823-0505

HAW   **The Haworth Press**
10 Alice St.
Binghamton, NY 13904
USA
Tel: 607-722-5857
Fax: 607-722-1424

IRC   **International Reprint Corp.**
968 Admiral Callaghan Ln., #268
Vallejo, CA 94590
USA
Tel: 707-746-0722
Fax: 707-746-1643

ISI   **Institute for Scientific Information**
3501 Market St.
Philadelphia, PA 19104
USA
Tel: 215-386-0100
Fax: 215-386-6362, 215-386-2911

JOH   **Johnson Reprint Microeditions**
(out of business)

KTO   **Kraus Microform**
(reprint service acquired by
Periodicals Service Co., PSC)

NRP   **Norman Ross Publishing, Inc.**
330 W. 58th St., Ste. 214
New York, NY 10019
USA
Tel: 212-765-8200, 800-648-8850
Fax: 212-765-2393

NTI   **National Technical Information Service**
5285 Port Royal Rd.
Springfield, VA 22161
USA
Tel: 703-487-4600
Fax: 703-321-8547

PSC   **Periodicals Service Co.**
11 Main St.
Germantown, NY 12526
USA
Tel: 518-537-4700
Fax: 518-537-5899

RPI   **Primary Source Media**
12 Lunar Dr.
Woodbridge, CT 06525
USA
Tel: 203-397-2600, 800-444-0799
Fax: 203-397-3893

RRI   **Fred B. Rothman & Co.**
10368 W. Centennial Rd.
Littleton, CO 80127
USA
Tel: 303-979-5657, 800-457-1986
Fax: 303-978-1457

SCH   **Schmidt Periodicals GmbH**
Dettendorf
D 83075 Bad Feilnbach
Germany
Tel: 49-8064221
Fax: 49-8064557

SWZ   **Swets & Zeitlinger bv**
Backsets Department
P.O. Box 810
2160 SZ Lisse
The Netherlands
Tel: 31-252-43511
Fax: 31-252-415888
Telex: 41325
www site: http://www.SWETS.nl

UMI   **University Microfilms International**
(A Bell & Howell Company)
300 N. Zeeb Rd.
Ann Arbor, MI 48103
USA
Tel: 313-761-4700, 800-521-0600
Fax: 313-761-1203

WDS   **Dawson Microfiche**
Cannon House
Parkfarm Rd.
Folkestone, Kent CT19 5EE
England
Tel: 44-1303-85010
Fax: 44-1303-850440

WSH   **William S. Hein & Co., Inc.**
Hein Bldg., 1285 Main St.
Buffalo, NY 14209-1987
USA
Tel: 716-882-2600, 800-828-7571
Fax: 716-883-8100

Wire Services

AAP	Australian Associated Press Information Services
AFP	Agence France-Press
ANP	Algemeen Nederlands Persbureau (Netherlands Press Agency)
AP	Associated Press (USA)
APP	Associated Press of Pakistan
BNS	Baltic News Service
CanP	Canadian Press
EFE	Agencia EFE (Spain)
KR	Knight-Ridder Financial News
LAT-WP	Los Angeles Times-Washington Post News Service
NPA	New Zealand Associated Press
NYT	New York Times News Service
PAP	Polska Agencja Prasowa (Polish Press Agency)
PPI	Pakistan Press International
RN	Reuters News Agency
SAPA	South African Press Association
SHNA	Scripps-Howard Newspaper Alliance - Scripps-Howard News Service
TASS	Telegrafnoe Agentstvo Suverennykh Stran (Telegraphic Agency of the Sovereign Countries)
UK News	United Kingdom News
UPI	United Press International

Abstracting and Indexing Services

This list contains the full names of all abstracting and indexing services whose abbreviations are used in entries in the CLASSIFIED LIST OF SERIALS. For all currently published abstracting and indexing services, entries containing full bibliographic information will be found in the CLASSIFIED LIST OF SERIALS. Consult the TITLE INDEX for page numbers. (Bibliographic information on titles for which cessations were noted more than three years ago are not listed in this book. To view information on such titles, one must refer to **Ulrich's PLUS**™ or **Ulrich's Online** services.)

A

A.A.P.P.Abstr.	Amino Acids, Peptides & Proteins Abstracts (Now: Cambridge Scientific Biochemistry Abstracts, Part 3: Amino Acids, Peptides & Proteins) (Ceased)
AAR	Accounting Articles
ABC	Abstracts in BioCommerce
A.B.C.Pol.Sci.	ABC Pol Sci; A Bibliography of Contents: Political Science and Government
ABI Inform.	A B I - INFORM
ABTICS	Abstracts and Book Title Index Card Services (Ceased)
A.D.& D.	Alcohol, Drugs and Driving: Abstracts and Reviews (Now: Alcohol, Drugs and Driving)
AESIS	A E S I S Quarterly (Australian Earth Sciences Information System)
A.I.Abstr.	Artificial Intelligence Abstracts (United States) (Ceased)
A.I.C.P.	Anthropological Index to Current Periodicals in the Library of the Museum of Mankind Library
A.I.D.Res.Dev. Abstr.	A.I.D. Research & Development Abstracts (Agency for International Development)
AIM	Abridged Index Medicus
A.I.P.P.	Annual Index to Poetry in Periodicals (Now: Roth's American Poetry Annual) (Ceased)
AIT Reports	A I T Reports and Publications on Renewable Energy Resources. Abstracts (Asian Institute of Technology) (Now: A I T Reports and Publications on Energy. Abstracts)
API Abstr.	A P I Abstracts: Literature (American Petroleum Institute) (Now: Literature Abstracts)
API Catal.	A P I Abstracts: Catalysts & Catalysis (Now: Literature Abstracts: Catalysts - Zeolites)
API Hlth.& Environ.	A P I Abstracts: Health & Environment (Now: Literature Abstracts: Health & Environment)
API Oil.	A P I Abstracts: Oilfield Chemicals (Now: Literature and Abstracts: Oilfield Chemicals)
API Pet.Ref.	A P I Abstracts: Petroleum Refining and Petrochemicals (Now: Literature Abstracts: Petroleum Refining and Petrochemicals)
API Pet.Subst.	A P I Abstracts: Petroleum Substitutes (Now: Literature Abstracts: Petroleum Substitutes)
API Transport.	A P I Abstracts: Transportation and Storage (Now: Literature Abstracts: Transportation and Storage)
A.S.& T.Ind.	Applied Science & Technology Index
ASCA	Automatic Subject Citation Alert (Now: Research Alert (Philadelphia))
ASEAN Manage. Abstr.	A S E A N Management Abstracts (Association of South East Asian Nations)
ASSIA	A S S I A: Applied Social Sciences Index & Abstracts
ASTIS	A S T I S Bibliography (Arctic Science & Technology Information System)
Abr.R.G.	Abridged Readers' Guide to Periodical Literature
Abstr.Anthropol.	Abstracts in Anthropology

xxxii

ABSTRACTING AND INDEXING

Abstr.Bk.Rev. Curr.Leg.Per.	Abstracts of Book Reviews in Current Legal Periodicals (Ceased)	**Adol.Ment. Hlth.Abstr.**	Adolescent Mental Health Abstracts (Ceased)
Abstr.Bulg.Sci. Med.Lit.	Abstracts of Bulgarian Scientific Medical Literature	**Agri.Eng.Abstr.**	Agricultural Engineering Abstracts
Abstr.Bull.Inst. Pap.Chem.	Institute of Paper Chemistry. Abstract Bulletin (Now: Institute of Paper Science and Technology. Abstract Bulletin)	**Agri.Ind.**	Agricultural Index (Now: Biological & Agricultural Index)
		Agrindex	Agrindex
		Agroforest.Abstr.	Agroforestry Abstracts
Abstr.Crim.& Pen.	Abstracts on Criminology and Penology (Now: Criminology, Penology & Police Science Abstracts)	**Air Un.Lib.Ind.**	Air University Library Index to Military Periodicals
		Alt.Press Ind.	Alternative Press Index
Abstr.Engl.Stud.	Abstracts of English Studies	**Amer.Bibl.Slavic & E.Ear.Stud.**	American Bibliography of Slavic and East European Studies
Abstr.Folk.Stud.	Abstracts of Folklore Studies (Ceased)		
Abstr.Health Care Manage. Stud.	Abstracts of Health Care Management Studies (Ceased)	**Amer.Hist.& Life**	America: History & Life
		Amer.Hum.Ind.	American Humanities Index
Abstr.Health Eff. Environ.Pollut.	Abstracts on Health Effects of Environmental Pollutants (Ceased)	**Amer.Stat.Ind.**	American Statistics Index
		Anal.Abstr.	Analytical Abstracts
Abstr.Hosp. Manage.Stud.	Abstracts of Hospital Management Studies (Now: Abstracts of Health Care Management Studies) (Ceased)	**Anbar**	Anbar Management Services Abstracts (Now: Management Services & Production Abstracts; Marketing & Distribution Abstracts; Personal & Training Abstracts) (Also see: Account.& Data Proc.Abstr.; also see: Computer Abstr.; also see: Top Manage.Abstr.)
Abstr.Hum.Comp. Inter.	Abstracts in Human-Computer Interaction		
Abstr.Hyg.	Abstracts on Hygiene and Communicable Diseases		
Abstr.Inter.Med.	Abstracts in Internal Medicine (Now: Abstracts in Medicine and Key Word Index) (Ceased)		
		Anim.Behav. Abstr.	Animal Behavior Abstracts
Abstr.J.Earthq. Eng.	Abstract Journal in Earthquake Engineering	**Anim.Breed. Abstr.**	Animal Breeding Abstracts
Abstr.Mil.Bibl.	Abstracts of Military Bibliography	**Anthropol.Lit.**	Anthropological Literature
Abstr.Musl.Rel.	European Muslims and Christian-Muslim Relations. Abstracts. (Ceased)	**Ap.Ind.**	Apple Index
		Apic.Abstr.	Apicultural Abstracts
Abstr.N.Amer. Geol.	Abstracts of North American Geology (Ceased)	**Appl.Ecol.Abstr.**	Applied Ecology Abstracts (Now: Ecology Abstracts)
Abstr.Pop.Cult.	Abstracts of Popular Culture (Ceased)	**Appl.Mech.Rev.**	Applied Mechanics Reviews
Abstr.Rural Dev.Trop.	Abstracts on Rural Development in the Tropics	**Aqua.Sci.& Fish.Abstr.**	Aquatic Sciences & Fisheries Abstracts (Parts 1, 2)
Abstr.Soc. Geront.	Abstracts in Social Gerontology: Current Literature on Aging	**Aquacult.Abstr.**	A S F A Aquaculture Abstracts
		Archit.Per.Ind.	Architectural Periodicals Index
Abstr.Soc.Work.	Abstracts for Social Workers (Now: Social Work Abstracts)	**Arct.Bibl.**	Arctic Bibliography (Ceased)
		Art & Archaeol. Tech.Abstr.	Art and Archaeology Technical Abstracts
Abstr.Trop.Agri.	Abstracts on Tropical Agriculture		
Acad.Ind.	Academic Index	**Art Ind.**	Art Index
Access	Access: the Supplementary Index to Periodicals	**Art.Hosp.& Tour.**	Articles in Hospitality and Tourism
Account.& Data Proc.Abstr.	Accounting & Data Processing Abstracts (Now: Accounting & Finance Abstracts) (Also see: Anbar)	**Art.Int.Abstr.**	Artificial Intelligence Abstracts (England) (Ceased)
		Artbibl.	Artbibliographies Current Titles
Account.Ind.	Accountant's Index (Now: Accounting and Tax Index)	**Artbibl.Mod.**	Artbibliographies Modern
		Arts & Hum. Cit.Ind.	Arts & Humanities Citation Index
Acid Pre.Dig.	Acid Precipitation Digest (Ceased)		
Acid Rain Abstr.	Acid Rain Abstracts (Now: Environment Abstracts)	**Ash.G.Bot.Per.**	Asher's Guide to Botanical Periodicals (Now: Guide to Botanical Periodicals) (Ceased)
Acid Rain Ind.	Acid Rain Annual Index (Now: Environment Abstracts Annual)	**Asian-Pac.Econ. Lit.**	Asian-Pacific Economic Literature
Acoust.Abstr.	Acoustics Abstracts		

Astron.& Astrophys. Abstr.	Astronomy and Astrophysics Abstracts	Bibl.Engl.Lang. & Lit.	Bibliography of English Language and Literature (Now: Annual Bibliography of English Language and Literature)
Aus.Educ.Ind.	Australian Education Index	Bibl.Ind.	Bibliographic Index
Aus.Leg.Mon. Dig.	Australian Legal Monthly Digest	Bibl.IULA	Bilbiographia I U L A (International Union of Local Authorities) (Ceased)
Aus.P.A.I.S.	Australian Public Affairs Information Service (Now: APAIS: Australian Public Affairs Information Service)	Bibl.Ling.	Linguistic Bibliography/Bibliographie Linguistique
		Bibl.Repro.	Bibliography of Reproduction (Now: Human Reproduction Update)
Aus.Rd.Ind.	Australian Road Index (Ceased)	Bibliogr.Bras. Odontol.	Bibliografia Brasileira de Odontologia
Aus.Sci.Ind.	Australian Science Index (Ceased)		
Aus.Speleo Abstr.	Australian Speleo Abstracts	Bio-Contr.News & Info.	Bio-Control News and Information
Avery Ind. Archit.Per.	Avery Index to Architectural Periodicals	Biodet.Abstr.	Biodeterioration Abstracts
		Bioeng.Abstr.	Bioengineering Abstracts
B		Biog.& Gen. Master Ind.	Biography and Genealogy Master Index
B.C.I.R.A.	B.C.I.R.A. Abstracts of International Foundry Literature (British Cast Iron Research Association) (Now: B C I R A Abstracts on International Literature on Metal Casting Production)	Biog.Ind.	Biography Index
		Biol.Abstr.	Biological Abstracts
		Biol.& Agr.Ind.	Biological & Agricultural Index
		Biol.Dig.	Biology Digest
		Biostat.	Biostatistica
BIM	Bibliography and Index of Micropaleontology	Biotech.Abstr.	Biotechnology Research Abstracts
		Biwk.Pap.Rad. Chem.& Photochem.	Biweekly List of Papers on Radiation Chemistry and Photochemistry
BMT	B M T Abstracts (British Maritime Technology)		
BNI	B N I (British Newspaper Index)		
B.P.I.	Business Periodicals Index	Bk.Rev.Dig.	Book Review Digest
BPIA	Business Publications Index and Abstracts (Ceased)	Bk.Rev.Ind.	Book Review Index
		Bk.Rev.Mo.	Book Reviews of the Month (Ceased)
B.R.I.	BioResearch Index (Now: Biological Abstracts - R R M (Reports, Reviews, Meetings))	Br.Archaeol. Abstr.	British Archaeological Abstracts (Now: British Archaeological Bibliography)
BSL Biol.	Abstracts of Bulgarian Scientific Literature. Biology (Ceased)	Br.Ceram.Abstr.	British Ceramic Abstracts (Now: World Ceramics Abstracts)
BSL Econ.	Abstracts of Bulgarian Scientific Literature. Economics and Law (Ceased)	Br.Educ.Ind.	British Education Index
		Br.Geol.Lit.	British Geological Literature
BSL Geo.	Abstracts of Bulgarian Scientific Literature. Geosciences (Ceased)	Br.Hum.Ind.	British Humanities Index
BSL Indus.	Abstracts of Bulgarian Scientific Literature. Industry, Building and Transport	Br.Rail.Bd.	British Railways Board. Monthly Review of Technical Literature (Ceased)
BSL Math.	Abstracts of Bulgarian Scientific Literature. Mathematical and Physical Sciences (Ceased)	Br.Tech.Ind.	British Technology Index (Now: Current Technology Index)
		Build.Manage. Abstr.	Building Management Abstracts (Now: Construction Information File - C I F)
Bank.Lit.Ind.	Banking Literature Index	Bull.Anal.Ent. Med.Vet.	Bulletin Analytique d'Entomologie Medicale et Veterinaire (Ceased)
Behav.Abstr.	Behavioural Abstracts (Ceased)		
Behav.Med. Abstr.	Behavioral Medicine Abstracts (Now: Annals of Behavioral Medicine)	Bull.Signal.	Bulletin Signaletique (Now: P A S C A L Explore, P A S C A L Folio, P A S C A L Thema) (Programme Applique a la Selection et la Compilation Automatique de la Literature)
Ber.Biochem. Biol.	Berichte Biochemie und Biologie (Ceased)		
Bibl Agri.	Bibliography of Agriculture		
Bibl.& Ind.Geol.	Bibliography & Index of Geology (see: GeoRef)	Bull.Thermodyn. & Thermochem.	Bulletin of Thermodynamics & Thermochemistry (Now: Bulletin of Chemical Thermodynamics) (Ceased)
Bibl.Cart.	Bibliographia Cartographica		
Bibl.Dev.Med.& Child Neur.	Bibliography of Developmental Medicine & Child Neurology. Books and Articles Received	Bus.Comput.Ind.	Business Computer Index
		Bus.Educ.Ind.	Business Education Index
		Bus.Ind.	Business Index

C

CAD CAM Abstr.	C A D - C A M Abstracts (Ceased)
CALL	C A L L (Current Awareness—Library Literature)
C.C.I.Ob.Gyn.	Combined Cumulative Index to Obstetrics and Gynecology
C.C.I.P.	Combined Cumulative Index to Pediatrics
C.C.L.P.	Contents of Current Legal Periodicals (Now: Legal Contents) (Ceased)
C.C.M.J.	Contents of Contemporary Mathematical Journals (Now: Current Mathematical Publications)
CCR	Current Christian Abstracts (Now: Current Thoughts & Trends)
CERDIC	Universite de Strasbourg. Centre de Recherche et de Documentation des Institutions Chretiennes. Bulletin du CERDIC (Ceased)
CHNI	Consumer Health & Nutrition Index
C.I.J.E.	Current Index to Journals in Education
CINAHL (also C.I.N.L.)	Cumulative Index to Nursing and Allied Health Literature
CIRF Abstr.	C I R F Abstracts (Now: T&D Abstracts) (Ceased)
C.I.S. Abstr.	C I S Abstracts (Centre International d'Information de Securite et Hygiene du Travail) (Now: Safety and Health at Work)
C.I.S. Ind.	C I S Index to Publications of the United States Congress (Congressional Information Service)
CJPI	Criminal Justice Periodical Index
C.L.I.	Current Law Index
CLOA	Current Literature on Aging (Now: Abstracts in Social Gerontology: Current Literature on Aging)
CLOSS	Current Literature on Science of Science
CMI	Canadian Magazine Index (Now: Canadian Index)
C.P.I.	Current Physics Index
C.R.E.J.	Contents of Recent Economics Journals
C.R.I.Abstr.	C R I Abstracts (Cement Research Institute of India)
C.R.I.Curr. Cont.	C R I Current Contents
CS Ind.	Canadian Statistics Index (Now: Directory of Statistics in Canada
CWHM	Current Work in the History of Medicine
Cab.Vid.Ind.	Cable-Video Index
Cadscan	Cadscan
Cal.Per.Ind.	California Periodicals Index
Cal.Tiss.Abstr.	Calcified Tissue Abstracts (Now: Calcium and Calcified Tissue Abstracts)
Can.B.P.I.	Canadian Business Periodicals Index (Now: Canadian Index)
Can.Educ.Ind.	Canadian Education Index
Can.Lit.Ind.	Canadian Literature Index (Ceased)
Can.Per.Ind.	Canadian Periodical Index
Can.Rev.Comp. Lit.	Canadian Review of Comparative Literature (Ceased)
Can.Wom.Per. Ind.	Canadian Women's Periodicals Index
Canadiana	Canadiana
Canon Law Abstr.	Canon Law Abstracts
Carcinog.Abstr.	Carcinogenesis Abstracts (Now: Cancergram)
Cath.Ind.	Catholic Periodical & Literature Index
Ceram.Abstr.	Ceramic Abstracts
Chem.Abstr.	Chemical Abstracts
Chem.Eng.Abstr.	Chemical Engineering Abstracts
Chem.Infd.	Chemischer Informationsdienst (Now: ChemInform)
Chem.Titles	Chemical Titles
Chemorec.Abstr.	Chemoreception Abstracts
Chicago Psychoanal. Lit.Ind.	Chicago Psychoanalytic Literature Index (Ceased)
Chic.Per.Ind.	Chicano Periodical Index (Now: Chicano Index)
Child.Auth.& Illus.	Children's Authors and Illustrators
Child.Bk.Rev.Ind.	Children's Book Review Index
Child Devel.Abstr.	Child Development Abstracts and Bibliography
Child.Lit.Abstr.	Children's Literature Abstracts
Chr.Per.Ind.	Christian Periodical Index
Coll.Stud.Pers. Abstr.	College Student Personnel Abstracts (Now: Higher Education Abstracts)
Commun.Abstr.	Communication Abstracts
Community Ment.Health Rev.	Community Mental Health Review (Now: Prevention in Human Services)
Compumath	Compumath Citation Index
Comput.Abstr.	Computer Abstracts (Also see: Anbar)
Comput.& Info. Sys.	Computer and Information Systems Abstracts Journal
Comput.Bus.	Computer Business
Comput.Cont.	Computer Contents (Ceased)
Comput.Dtbs.	Computer Database
Comput.Ind.	Computer Index
Comput.Indus.Up.	Computer Industry Update
Comput.Lit.Ind.	Computer Literature Index
Comput.Rev.	Computing Reviews
Concr.Abstr.	Concrete Abstracts
Consum.Ind.	Consumers Index
Cont.Pg.Educ.	Contents Pages in Education
Cont.Pg.Manage.	Contents Pages in Management
Copper Abstr.	Copper Abstracts (Now: International Copper Information Bulletin)
Corros.Abstr.	Corrosion Abstracts

Cott.& Trop.Fibr. Abstr.	Cotton and Tropical Fibres Abstracts (Now: Cotton and Tropical Fibres)	Curr.Ref. Fish Res.	Current References in Fish Research
Crim.Just.Abstr.	Criminal Justice Abstracts	Curr.Tit.Dent.	Current Titles in Dentistry
Crime Delinq. Abstr.	Crime and Delinquency Abstracts (Ceased)	Curr.Tit. Electrochem.	Current Titles in Electrochemistry
Crime Delinq.Lit.	Crime & Delinquency Literature (Now: Criminal Justice Abstracts)	Curr.Tit.Ocean	Current Titles in Ocean, Coastal, Lake & Waterway Sciences (Ceased)
Crop Physiol. Abstr.	Crop Physiology Abstracts	Cyb.Abstr.	Cybernetics Abstracts

D

Curr.Adv. Biochem.	Current Advances in Biochemistry (Now: Current Advances in Protein Biochemistry)	DAAI	Design and Applied Arts Index
Curr.Adv.Cancer. Res.	Current Advances in Cancer Research	DM&T	Defense Markets and Technology (Now: Aerospace Defense Markets and Technology) (Ceased)
Curr.Adv.Cell & Devel.Biol.	Current Advances in Cell and Developmental Biology	DNP	Digest of Neurology & Psychiatry
Curr.Adv.Clin. Chem.	Current Advances in Clinical Chemistry	DSH Abstr.	DSH Abstracts (Deafness, Speech and Hearing) (Ceased)
Curr.Adv.Ecol. Sci.	Current Advances in Ecological Sciences (Now: Current Advances in Ecological and Environmental Sciences)	Dairy Sci.Abstr.	Dairy Science Abstracts
		Data Process.Dig.	Data Processing Digest
Curr.Adv. Genetics & Molec.Biol.	Current Advances in Genetics and Molecular Biology	Deep Sea Res.& Oceanogr.Abstr.	Deep Sea Research & Oceanographic Abstracts (Now: Oceanographic Literature Review)
		Dent.Abstr.	Dental Abstracts
Curr.Adv. Immunol.	Current Advances in Immunology (Now: Current Advances in Immunology & Infectious Diseases)	Dent.Ind.	Index to Dental Literature
		Devindex	Devindex (Ceased)
		Diab.Cont.	Diabetes Contents
Curr.Adv. Microbiol.	Current Advances in Microbiology (Now: Current Advances in Applied Microbiology & Biotechnology)	Diab.Lit.Ind.	Diabetes Literature Index (Ceased)
		Diar.Dis.Res.	Journal of Diarrhoeal Diseases Research
Curr.Adv. Neurosci.	Current Advances in Neuroscience	Doc.Geogr.	Documentatio Geographica (Now: Dokumentation zur Raumentwicklung) (Ceased)
Curr.Adv. Pharmacol. & Toxicol.	Current Advances in Pharmacology & Toxicology (Now: Current Advances in Toxicology)	Documentatie- blad	Documentatieblad: The Abstracts Journal of the African Studies Centre Leiden (Now: African Studies Abstracts)
Curr.Adv.Physiol.	Current Advances in Physiology (Now: Current Advances in Endocrinology & Metabolism)	Dok.Arbeitsmed.	Dokumentation Arbeitsmedizin (Now: Arbeitsmedizin)
		Dok.Raum.	Dokumentation zur Raumentwicklung (Ceased)
Curr.Adv.Plant Sci.	Current Advances in Plant Science	Dok.Str.	Dokumentation Strasse
Curr.Aus.N.Z.Leg. Lit.Ind.	Current Australian and New Zealand Legal Literature Index (Ceased)		

E

Curr.Biotech. Abstr.	Current Biotechnology Abstracts (Now: Current Biotechnology)	E & P Hlth.	Exploration and Production Health, Safety and Environment
Curr.Bk.Rev.Cit.	Current Book Review Citations (Ceased)	EC Ind.	EC Index (European Communities)
Curr.Chem.React.	Current Chemical Reactions	E.I.	E I (Excerpta Indonesica)
Curr.Cont.	Current Contents	ELLIS	E L L I S (European Legal Literature Information Service)
Curr.Cont.Africa	Current Contents Africa (Ceased)		
Curr.Cont.M.E.	Current Contents of Periodicals on the Middle East	ERIC	Eric Clearinghouse (See: C.I.J.E.)
Curr.Dig.Sov. Press	Current Digest of the Soviet Press (Now: Current Digest of the Post-Soviet Press)	Ecol.Abstr.	Ecological Abstracts
		Econ.Abstr.	Economic Abstracts (Now: Key to Economic Science)
Curr.Ind.Stat.	Current Index to Statistics	Educ.Admin. Abstr.	Educational Administration Abstracts
Curr.Leather Lit.	Current Leather Literature (Now: Leather Science Abstracts)		
Curr.Lit.Fam. Plan.	Current Literature in Family Planning	Educ.Ind.	Education Index
Curr.Pack.Abstr.	Current Packaging Abstracts (Ceased)	Educ.Tech.Abstr.	Educational Technology Abstracts

Ekist.Ind.	Ekistic Index
Electroanal.Abstr.	Electroanalytical Abstracts (Ceased)
Electron.& Communic. Abstr.J.	Electronics and Communications Abstracts Journal
Endocrin.Ind.	Endocrinology Index (Ceased)
Energy Abstr.	Energy Abstracts
Energy Ind.	Energy Index (Now: Energy Information Abstracts Annual)
Energy Info.Abstr.	Energy Information Abstracts
Energy Res.Abstr.	Energy Research Abstracts
Energy Rev.	Energy Review (Santa Barbara) (Ceased)
Eng.Ind.	Engineering Index (Now: Engineering Index Monthly)
Eng.Mat.Abstr.	Engineered Materials Abstracts
Entomol.Abstr.	Entomology Abstracts
Environ.Abstr.	Environment Abstracts
Environ.Ind.	Environment Index (Now: Environment Abstracts Annual)
Environ.Per.Bibl.	Environmental Periodicals Bibliography
Ergon.Abstr.	Ergonomics Abstracts
Euro.LJI	European Legal Journals Index
Except.Child Educ.Abstr.	Exceptional Child Education Abstracts (Now: Exceptional Child Education Resources)
Excerp.Bot.	Excerpta Botanica (Sections A, B)
ExtraMED	ExtraMED
Excerp.Med.	Excerpta Medica

F

F.A.C.T.	Fuel Abstracts and Current Titles (Now: Fuel and Energy Abstracts)
FAMLI	F A M L I (Family Medicine Literature Index) (Ceased)
F.R.	Fanatic Reader
Fababean Abstr.	Fababean Abstracts (Ceased)
Farm & Garden Ind.	Farm & Garden Index (Ceased)
Fed Print	Fed in Print
Fert.Abstr.	Fertilizer Abstracts (Ceased)
Field Crop Abstr.	Field Crop Abstracts
Film Lit.Ind.	Film Literature Index
Fluidex	Fluidex consists of: Civil Engineering Hydraulics Abstracts (Now: Fluid Abstracts: Civil Engineering) Current Fluid Engineering Titles (Ceased) Fluid Flow Measurement Abstracts (Now: Fluid Abstracts: Process Engineering) Fluid Power Abstracts (Now: Fluid Abstracts: Process Engineering) Fluid Sealing Abstracts (Now: Fluid Abstracts: Process Engineering) Industrial Aerodynamics Abstracts (Now: Fluid Abstracts: Civil Engineering) Industrial Jetting Report (Ceased) Offshore Engineering Abstracts (Now: Fluid Abstracts: Civil Engineering) Pipelines Abstracts (Now: Fluid Abstracts: Process Engineering) Pumps & Other Fluids Machinery Abstracts (Now: Fluid Abstracts: Process Engineering) Pumps and Turbines (Ceased) River and Flood Control Abstracts (Ceased) Solid-Liquid Flow Abstracts (Now: Fluid Abstracts: Process Engineering) Tribos-Tribology Abstracts (Now: Tribology & Corrosion Abstracts) (Ceased) World Ports and Harbours Abstracts (Now: Fluid Abstracts: Civil Engineering) World Ports and Harbours News (Ceased)
Food Sci.& Tech. Abstr.	Food Science and Technology Abstracts
Foreign Leg.Per.	Index to Foreign Legal Periodicals
Forest.Abstr.	Forestry Abstracts
Forest Prod. Abstr.	Forest Products Abstracts
Foul.Prev.Res. Dig.	Fouling Prevention Research Digest (Now: Heat Transfer & Fluid Flow Service Digest)
Fuel & Energy Abstr.	Fuel & Energy Abstracts
Fut.Abstr.	Future - Abstracts
Fut.Surv.	Future Survey

G

G.Indian Per.Lit.	Guide to Indian Periodical Literature
G.Perf.Arts.	Guide to the Performing Arts (Ceased)
G.Soc.Sci.& Rel. Per.Lit.	Guide to Social Sciences and Religion in Periodical Literature
Gard.Lit.	Garden Literature
Gas Abstr.	Gas Abstracts
Gas Process.& Ppl.	Gas Processing and Pipelining
Gastroenterol. Abstr.& Cit.	Gastroenterology Abstracts & Citations (Ceased)
Gdlns.	Guidelines
Gen.Phys.Adv. Abstr.	General Physics Advance Abstracts
Gen.Sci.Ind.	General Science Index
Geneal.Per.Ind.	Genealogical Periodical Annual Index
Genet.Abstr.	Genetics Abstracts
Geo.Abstr.	Geographical Abstracts: Human Geography Geographical Abstracts: Physical Geography

Geol.Abstr.	Geological Abstracts	**IBZ**	Internationale Bibliographie der Zeitschriftenliteratur aus allen Gebieten des Wissens/International Bibliography of Periodicals from all Fields of Knowledge
Geophys.Abstr.	Geophysical Abstracts (Ceased)		
GeoRef	Bibliography and Index of Geology (Also known as GeoRef)		
Geosci.Doc.	Geoscience Documentation	**I.C.U.I.S.Abstr.**	I C U I S Abstracts Service (Institute on the Church in Urban Industrial Society) (Now: I C U I S Justice Ministries) (Ceased)
Geotech.Abstr.	Geotechnical Abstracts		
Ger.J.Psych.	German Journal of Psychology		
Graph.Arts Abstr.	Graphic Arts Abstracts (Now: G A T F World)		
		IDA	International Development Abstracts
Graph.Arts Lit. Abstr.	Graphic Arts Literature Abstracts (Now: Institute of Paper Science and Technology. Graphic Arts Bulletin)	**IIS**	Index to International Statistics
		IJCS	Index to Journals in Communication Studies
		IMFL	Inventory of Marriage and Family Literature

H

		I.M.M.Abstr.	I M M Abstracts (Institute of Mining & Metallurgy) (Now: I M M Abstracts and Index)
HMA	Healthcare Marketing Abstracts		
HR Rep.	Human Rights Internet Reporter	**I.N.E.P.**	Index to New England Periodicals
HRIS	H R I S Abstracts (Now: Highway Research Abstracts)	**INIS Atomind.**	I N I S Atomindex (International Nuclear Information System)
Helminthol.Abstr.	Helminthological Abstracts. Series A (Now: Helminthological Abstracts) Helminthological Abstracts. Series B (Now: Nematological Abstracts)	**INSPEC**	INSPEC (The Institution of Electrical Engineers): Computers & Control Abstracts (Alternative title: INSPEC, Section C. Represents: Science Abstracts. Section C) Current Papers in Computers & Control Current Papers in Electrical & Electronics Engineering Current Papers in Physics Electrical & Electronics Abstracts (Alternative title: INSPEC, Section B. Represents: Science Abstracts. Section B.) Key Abstracts - Advanced Materials Key Abstracts - Antennas & Propagation Key Abstracts - Artificial Intelligence Key Abstracts - Business Automation Key Abstracts - Computer Communication and Storage Key Abstracts - Computing in Electronics & Power Key Abstracts - Electronic Circuits Key Abstracts - Electronic Instrumentation Key Abstracts - Factory Automation Key Abstracts - High-Temperature Superconductors Key Abstracts - Human-Computer Interaction Key Abstracts - Machine Vision Key Abstracts - Measurements in Physics Key Abstracts - Microelectronics & Printed Circuits Key Abstracts - Microwave Technology Key Abstracts - Neural Networks Key Abstracts - Optoelectronics Key Abstracts - Power Systems & Applications Key Abstracts - Rotobics & Control Key Abstracts - Semiconductor Devices Key Abstracts - Software Engineering
Herb.Abstr.	Herbage Abstracts (Now: Grasslands and Forage Abstracts)		
High.Educ.Abstr.	Higher Education Abstracts		
High.Educ.Curr. Aware.Bull.	Higher Education Current Awareness Bulletin (Ceased)		
Hisp.Amer.Per. Ind.	Hispanic American Periodicals Index		
Hist.Abstr.	Historical Abstracts (Parts A, B)		
Hlth.Ind.	Health Index		
Hongkongiana	Hongkongiana		
Hort.Abstr.	Horticultural Abstracts		
Hosp.Abstr.	Hospital Abstracts (Now: Health Service Abstracts)		
Hosp.Abstr.Serv.	Hospital Abstracts Service (Ceased)		
Hosp.Lit.Ind.	Hospital Literature Index		
Hospit.Ind.	Hospitality Index		
Hum.Ind.	Humanities Index		
Human Resour. Abstr.	Human Resources Abstracts		
Hung.Build.Bull.	Hungarian Building Bulletin (Ceased)		
Hung.Lib.& Info. Sci.Abstr.	Hungarian Library and Information Science Abstracts		
Hwy.Res.Abstr.	Highway Research Abstracts (Now: Transportation Research Abstracts) (Ceased)		

I

IBM PC Ind.	IBM PC Index (Personal Computer)
IBR	I B R (International Bibliography of Book Reviews of Scholarly Literature)

ABSTRACTING AND INDEXING   xxxix

	Key Abstracts - Telecommunications Physics Abstracts (Alternative title: INSPEC, Section A. Represents: Science Abstracts. Section A)	Ind.Sci.Rev.	Index to Scientific Reviews
		Ind.Sel.Per.	Index to Selected Periodicals (Now: Index to Black Periodicals)
I.P.A.	International Pharmaceutical Abstracts	Ind.SST.	Indice Espanol de Ciencia y Tecnologia
I.R.A.	Information Resources Annual (Ceased)	Ind.U.S.Gov.Per.	Index to U.S. Government Periodicals (Now: U S Government Periodicals Index)
ISMEC	I S M E C Bulletin (Information Service in Mechanical Engineering) (Now: Mechanical Engineering Abstracts)	Ind.Vet.	Index Veterinarius
Ind.Agri.Am.Lat. Caribe	Indice Agricole de America Latina y el Caribe (Ceased)	Indian Lib.Sci. Abstr.	Indian Library Science Abstracts
Ind.Amer.Per. Verse	Index of American Periodical Verse	Indian Psychol. Abstr.	Indian Psychological Abstracts
Ind.Aric.Jew. Stud.	Index of Articles on Jewish Studies	Indian Sci.Abstr.	Indian Science Abstracts
		Indian Sci.Ind.	Indian Science Index (Ceased)
Ind.Bk.Rev.Hum.	Index to Book Reviews in the Humanities (Ceased)	Info.Media & Tech.	Information Media and Technology (Now: Information Management & Technology)
Ind.Bus.Rep.	Index to Business Reports	Inform.Sci.Abstr.	Information Science Abstracts
Ind.Can.L.P.L.	Index to Canadian Legal Periodical Literature	Inpharma	InPharma
		Instrum.Abstr.	Instrument Abstracts (Now: Metron) (Ceased)
Ind.Chem.	Index Chemicus		
Ind.Child.Mag.	Subject Index to Children's Magazines (Now: Children's Magazine Guide)	Int.Abstr.Biol.Sci.	International Abstracts of Biological Sciences (Now: Current Awareness in Biological Sciences)
Ind.Curr.Urb. Doc.	Index to Current Urban Documents	Int.Abstr.Oper. Res.	International Abstracts in Operations Research
Ind.Develop. Abstr.	Industrial Development Abstracts	Int.Aerosp.Abstr.	International Aerospace Abstracts
Ind.Free.Per.	Index to Free Periodicals	Int.Bibl.Soc.Sci.	International Bibliography of the Social Sciences: Anthropology, Political Science, Economics, Sociology (Ceased)
Ind.Heb.Per.	Index to Hebrew Periodicals		
Ind.How To Do It	Index to How to Do It Information		
Ind.Hyg.Dig.	Industrial Hygiene Digest	Int.Build.Serv. Abstr.	International Building Services Abstracts
Ind.India	Index India		
Ind.Islam.	Index Islamicus (Now: Quarterly Index Islamicus)	Int.G.Class.Stud.	International Guide to Classical Studies (Ceased)
		Int.Ind.Film Per.	International Index to Film Periodicals
Ind.Jew.Per.	Index to Jewish Periodicals	Int.Lab.Doc.	International Labor Documentation
Ind.Lit.Amer. Indian	Index to Literature on the American Indian (Ceased)	Int.Nurs.Ind.	International Nursing Index
		Int.Packag.Abstr.	International Packaging Abstracts
Ind.Lit.Dent.	Indice de la Literatura Dental Periodica en Castellano	Int.Polit.Sci.Abstr.	International Political Science Abstracts
		Int.Sci.Rev.	International Science Review Series (Ceased)
Ind.Little Mag.	Index to Little Magazines (Ceased)		
Ind.Med.	Index Medicus	Int.Z.Bibelwiss.	Internationale Zietschriften fuer Bibelwissenschaft und Grenzgebiete
Ind.Med.Esp.	Indice Medico Espanol		
Ind.N.Z.Per.	Index to New Zealand Periodicals (Now: Index New Zealand)	InterActions Bibl.	InterActions Bibliography
Ind.Per.Art.Relat. Law	Index to Periodical Articles Related to Law	Intl.Bibl.S.S.Econ.	International Bibliography of the Social Sciences: Economics
Ind.Per.Blacks	Index to Periodical Articles by and about Blacks (Now: Index to Black Periodicals)	Intl.Bibl.S.S.Pol. Sci.	International Bibliography of the Social Sciences: Political Science
Ind.Per.Lit.	Index to Indian Periodical Literature (Ceased)	Intl.Bibl.S.S. Soc.Cult.Anthro.	International Bibliography of the Social Sciences: Anthropology
Ind.Per.Negroes	Index to Periodical Articles by & about Negroes (Now: Index to Black Periodicals)	Intl.Civil Eng. Abstr.	International Civil Engineering Abstracts
		Intl.Ind.TV.	International Index to Television Periodicals
Ind.Phil.Per.	Index to Philippine Periodicals		
Ind.Rheum.	Annual Index of Rheumatology (Ceased)	Intl.Mgmt.Info.	International Management Information Business Digest (Ceased)
Ind.S.A.Per.	Index to South African Periodicals		

ABSTRACTING AND INDEXING

Intl.Polym.Sci.& Tech.	International Polymer Science and Technology
Iron & Steel Indus.Pr.	Iron and Steel Industry Profiles (Ceased)
Irr.& Drain.Abstr.	Irrigation & Drainage Abstracts

J

JAMA	JAMA: The Journal of the American Medical Association
JCT	Japan Computer Technology and Applications Abstracts (Ceased)
JTA	Japanese Technical Abstracts (Now: Japan Technology Series) (Ceased)
J.Cont.Quant.Meth.	Journal Contents in Quantitative Methods
J.Curr.Laser Abstr.	Journal of Current Laser Abstracts
J.of Abstr.Int.Educ.	Journal of Abstracts in International Education
J.of Econ.Abstr. (also: J.of Econ.Lit.)	Journal of Economic Abstracts (Now: Journal of Economic Literature)
J.of Ferroc.	Journal of Ferrocement
Jap.Per.Ind.	Japanese Periodicals Index (Humanities and Social Sciences Section; Medical Sciences and Pharmacology (Ceased); Science and Technology)
Jun.High Mag.Abstr.	Junior High Magazine Abstracts

K

Key to Econ.Sci.	Key to Economic Science (Ceased)
Key Word Ind.Wildl.Res.	Key Word Index of Wildlife Research
Kidney	Kidney (New York, 1992)

L

LAMP	L A M P (Literature Analysis of Microcomputer Publications)
LCR	Literary Criticism Register
LHTN	Library Hi Tech News
L.I.I.	Life Insurance Index (Ceased)
LISA	L I S A: Library & Information Science Abstracts
LJI	Legal Journals Index
L.R.I.	Legal Resource Index (Now: LegalTrac)
Lab.Haz.Bull.	Laboratory Hazards Bulletin
Landwirt.Zentralbl.	Landwirtschaftliches Zentralblatt (Now: Agroselekt) (Ceased)
Lang.& Lang.Behav.Abstr.	Language and Language Behaviour Abstracts (Now: Linguistics and Language Behavior Abstracts)
Lang.Teach.& Ling.Abstr.	Language Teaching and Linguistics Abstracts (Now: Language Teaching)
Law Ofc.Info.Svc.	Law Office Information Service
Lead Abstr.	Lead Abstracts (Now: Leadscan)
Left Ind.	Left Index
Leg.Cont.	Legal Contents (Ceased)
Leg.Info.Manage.Ind.	Legal Information Management Index
Leg.Per.	Index to Legal Periodicals
Lib.Lit.	Library Literature
Lib.Sci.Abstr.	Library Science Abstracts (Now: L I S A: Library & Information Science Abstracts)
Ling.Abstr.	Linguistics Abstracts
Lit.Automat.	Literature on Automation (Now: New Literature on Automation)

M

MEDOC	Medoc: Index to U.S. Government Publications in the Medical and Health Sciences
MEDSOC	Medical Socioeconomic Research Sources (Ceased)
MELSA	MELSA Messenger (Metropolitan Library Service) (Ceased)
M.L.A.	M L A Abstracts of Articles in Scholarly Journals (Ceased)
M.M.R.I.	Multi-Media Reviews Index (Now: Media Review Digest)
Mag.Ind.	Magazine Index
Maize Abstr.	Maize Abstracts
Manage.Abstr.	Management Abstracts (India) (Now: Indian Management)
Manage.Cont.	Management Contents
Mar.Aff.Bibl.	Marine Affairs Bibliography
Mar.Sci.Cont.Tab.	Marine Science Contents Tables
Mark.Res.Abstr.	Market Research Abstracts
Mass Spectr.Bull.	Mass Spectrometry Bulletin
Math.R.	Mathematical Reviews
Med.Abstr.	Medical Abstract Service (Ceased)
Med.& Surg.Dermat.	Medical & Surgical Dermatology
Med.Care Rev.	Medical Care Review
Media Rev.Dig.	Media Review Digest
Ment.Retard.Abstr.	Mental Retardation Abstracts (Now: Developmental Disabilities Abstracts) (Ceased)
Met.Abstr.	Metallurgical Abstracts (Now: Metals Abstracts)
Met.Finish.Abstr.	Metal Finishing Abstracts (Now: Surface Treatment Technology Abstracts)
Meteor.& Geoastrophys.Abstr.	Meteorological & Geoastrophysical Abstracts
Meth.Per.Ind.	Methodist Periodical Index (Now: United Methodist Periodical Index) (Ceased)
Mgmt.& Market.Abstr.	Management & Marketing Abstracts
Mich.Mag.Ind.	Michigan Magazine Index (Ceased)

ABSTRACTING AND INDEXING

Microbiol.Abstr.	Microbiological Abstracts (Sections A, B, C)	\multicolumn{2}{c	}{**P**}

Microbiol.Abstr.	Microbiological Abstracts (Sections A, B, C)
Microcomp.Ind.	Microcomputer Index
Microcomp. Indus.Up.	Microcomputer Industry Update
Mid.East: Abstr. & Ind.	Middle East: Abstracts and Index
Mineral Abstr.	Mineralogical Abstracts
Mkt.Inform. Guide	Marketing Information Guide (Ceased)
Mult.Ed.Abstr.	Multicultural Education Abstracts
Multi.Scler.Abstr.	Multiple Sclerosis Indicative Abstracts (Ceased)
Music Artic.Guide	Music Article Guide
Music Ind.	Music Index
Mycol.Abstr.	Abstracts of Mycology

N

NAA	N A A (Nordic Archaeological Abstracts)
NBA	Notiziario Bibliografico di Audiologia ORL e Foniatria
NRN	Nutrition Research Newsletter
Neurosci.Abstr.	Neurosciences Abstracts (Now: CSA Neurosciences Abstracts)
New Per.Ind.	New Periodicals Index (Ceased)
New Test.Abstr.	New Testament Abstracts
Noise Pollut. Publ.Abstr.	Noise Pollution Publications Abstracts (Ceased)
Nucl.Sci.Abstr.	Nuclear Science Abstracts (Now INIS Atomindex)
Numis.Lit.	Numismatic Literature
Nurs.Abstr.	Nursing Abstracts
Nurs.Res.Abstr.	Nursing Research Abstracts
Nutr.Abstr.	Nutrition Abstracts & Reviews (Now: Nutrition Abstracts and Reviews Series A: Human and Experimental; Nutrition Abstracts and Reviews Series B: Livestock Feeds and Feeding)

O

Ocean.Abstr.	Oceanic Abstracts
Ocean.Abstr.Bibl.	Oceanographic Abstracts and Bibliography (Now: Oceanographic Literature Review)
Ocean.Ind.	Oceanic Index (Now: Oceanic Abstracts)
Off.Tech.	Offshore Technology
Old Test.Abstr.	Old Testament Abstracts
Oncol.Abstr.	Oncology Abstracts (Ceased)
Oper.Res. Manage.Sci.	Operations Research - Management Science
Ophthal.Lit.	Ophthalmic Literature
Oral Res.Abstr.	Oral Research Abstracts (Ceased)
Ornam.Hort.	Ornamental Horticulture

P

P.A.I.S.	P A I S Bulletin (Public Affairs Information Service) (Now: P A I S International in Print)
P.A.I.S.For. Lang.Ind.	Public Affairs Information Service Foreign Language Index (Now: P A I S International in Print)
PC Abstr.	P C Abstracts (Personal Computing) (Ceased)
PCR2	P C R2 (Personal Computer Review - Squared)
PHRA	Poverty & Human Resources Abstracts (Now: Human Resources Abstracts)
P.I.R.A.	P.I.R.A. Marketing Abstracts (Packaging Industry Research Association) (Now: Management and Marketing Abstracts)
P.L.E.S.A.	Quarterly Index to Periodical Literature, Eastern and Southern Africa
P.L.I.I.	Property & Liability Insurance Index (Ceased)
P.M.I.	Photography Magazine Index (Ceased)
PMR	Popular Magazine Review (Now: Magazine Article Summaries)
P.N.I.	Pharmaceutical News Index
PROMT	Predicasts Overview of Markets and Technologies
PSI	Philanthropic Studies Index
Packag.Abstr.	Packaging Abstracts (Now: International Packaging Abstracts)
Packag.Sci.Tech.	Packaging Science and Technology Abstracts
Paper.& Bd.Abstr.	Paper and Board Abstracts
Past.Care & Couns.Abstr.	Pastoral Care & Counseling Abstracts (Now: Abstracts of Research in Pastoral Care and Counseling)
Peace Res.Abstr.	Peace Research Abstracts Journal
Peat Abstr.	Peat Abstracts
Per.Islam.	Periodica Islamica
Perf.Arts Biog. Master Ind.	Performing Arts Biography Master Index
Periodex	Periodex (Now: Point de Repere)
Pers.Lit.	Personnel Literature
Pers.Manage. Abstr.	Personnel Management Abstracts
Petrol.Abstr.	Petroleum Abstracts
Petrol.Energy B.N.I.	Petroleum - Energy Business News Index
Phil.Ind.	Philosopher's Index
Philip.Abstr.	Philippine Abstracts (Now: Philippine Science & Technology Abstracts)
Photo.Abstr.	Photographic Abstracts (Now: Imaging Abstracts)
Photo.Ind.	Photography Index
Phys.Ber.	Physikalische Berichte (Now: Physics Briefs - Physikalische Berichte) (Ceased)

Phys.Ed.Ind.	Physical Education Index	**RILA**	R I L A (International Repertory of the Literature of Art) (Now: BHA (Bibliography of the History of Art))
Pig News & Info.	Pig News and Information		
Pinpointer	Pinpointer (Ceased)		
Plant Breed. Abstr.	Plant Breeding Abstracts	**RILM**	R I L M Abstracts of Music Literature (International Repertory of Music Literature)
Plant Grow.Reg. Abstr.	Plant Growth Regulator Abstracts	**Reac.**	Reactions
Plast.Abstr.	Plastics Abstracts (Ceased)	**Ref.Pt.Food Indus.Abstr.**	Reference Point: Food Industry Abstracts
Pol.Tech.Abstr.	Polish Technical Abstracts (Now: Polish Technical and Economic Abstracts) (Ceased)	**Ref.Sour.**	Reference Sources (Ceased)
		Ref.Zh.	Referativnyi Zhurnal
Polit.Sci.Abstr.	Political Science Abstracts	**Refug.Abstr.**	Refugee Abstracts
Pollut.Abstr.	Pollution Abstracts	**Rehabil.Lit.**	Rehabilitation Literature (Ceased)
Pop.Mus.Per.Ind.	Popular Music Periodicals Index (Ceased)	**Rel.& Theol. Abstr.**	Religious & Theological Abstracts
Pop.Per.Ind.	Popular Periodical Index	**Rel.Ind.One**	Religion Index One: Periodicals
Popul.Ind.	Population Index	**Rel.Ind.Two**	Religion Index Two: Multi-Author Works
Potato Abstr.	Potato Abstracts	**Rel.Per.**	Index to Religious Periodical Literature (Now: Religion Index One: Periodicals)
Poult.Abstr.	Poultry Abstracts		
Pr.Briefs	Predi-Briefs	**Repindex**	Repindex
Print.Abstr.	Printing Abstracts	**Res.Educ.**	Research in Education (Now: Resources in Education)
Protozool.Abstr.	Protozoological Abstracts		
Psychoanal. Abstr.	Psychoanalysis Abstracts (Now: Psychoanalytic Abstracts)	**Res.High.Educ. Abstr.**	Research into Higher Education Abstracts
Psychol.Abstr.	Psychological Abstracts	**Resour.Ctr.Ind.**	Resource Center Index
Psychol.R.G.	Psychological Reader's Guide (Ceased)	**Rev.Appl. Entomol.**	Review of Applied Entomology. Series A (Now: Review of Agricultural Entomology) Review of Applied Entomology. Series B (Now: Review of Medical and Veterinary Entomology)
Psycho- pharmacol. Abstr.	Psychopharmacology Abstracts (Ceased)		
Psycscan	Psycscan: Applied Psychology		
Psycscan C.P.	Psycscan: Clinical Psychology	**Rev.Appl.Mycol.**	Review of Applied Mycology (Now: Review of Plant Pathology)
Psycscan D.P.	Psycscan: Developmental Psychology		
Pt.de Rep.	Point de Repere (Formed by the merger of Periodex and RADAR)	**Rev.Med.& Vet.Mycol.**	Review of Medical and Veterinary Mycology
Pub.Admin.Abstr.	Public Administration Abstracts and Index of Articles (Now: Documentation in Public Administration)	**Rev.Plant Path.**	Review of Plant Pathology
		Rheol.Abstr.	Rheology Abstracts
		Rice Abstr.	Rice Abstracts
		Risk Abstr.	Risk Abstracts
Q		**Robomat.**	Robomatix Reporter (Now: Robotics Abstracts) (Ceased)
Q.Abstr.	Quality Abstracts (Ceased)		
Qual.Contr. Appl.Stat.	Quality Control and Applied Statistics	**Rom.Sci.Abstr.**	Rumanian Scientific Abstracts
		Rural Devel. Abstr.	Rural Development Abstracts
R		**Rural Ext.Educ.& Tr.Abstr.**	Rural Extension, Education and Training Abstracts (Ceased)
RADAR	Repertoire Analytique d'Articles des Revues du Quebec (Now: Point de Repere)	**Rural Recreat. Tour.Abstr.**	Rural Recreation and Tourism Abstracts (Now: Leisure, Recreation and Tourism Abstracts)
RAPRA	R A P R A Abstracts (Rubber and Plastics Research Association of Great Britain)		
R.G.	Readers' Guide to Periodical Literature	**S**	
RICS	R I C S Abstracts and Reviews (Now: R I C S Library Information Service Abstracts and Reviews) (Royal Institute of Chartered Surveyors)	**S.A.Waterabstr.**	S.A. Waterabstracts (South Africa) (Ceased)
		SCIMP	S C I M P (Selective Cooperative Index of Management Periodicals) (Ceased)

ABSTRACTING AND INDEXING

SOMA	School Organization & Management Abstracts
SOPODA	Social Planning, Policy and Development Abstracts
SRI	Statistical Reference Index
SSCI	Social Science Citation Index
Saf.Sci.Abstr.	Safety Science Abstracts Journal (Now: Health and Safety Science Abstracts)
Sage Fam.Stud.Abstr.	Sage Family Studies Abstracts
Sage Pub.Admin.Abstr.	Sage Public Administration Abstracts
Sage Race Rel.Abstr.	Sage Race Relations Abstracts
Sage Urb.Stud.Abstr.	Sage Urban Studies Abstracts
Sci.Cit.Ind.	Science Citation Index
Sci.Res.Abstr.	Science Research Abstracts (Now: Solid State and Superconductivity Abstracts)
Search	Search
Seed Abstr.	Seed Abstracts
Sel.J.Water.	Selected Journals on Water (Ceased)
Sel. Water Res. Abstr.	Selected Water Resources Abstracts
Sh.& Vib.Dig.	Shock and Vibration Digest
Sinop.Odontol.	Sinopse de Odontologia (Ceased)
Small Anim.Abstr.	Small Animal Abstracts (Now: Small Animals)
So.Pac.Per.Ind.	South Pacific Periodicals Index
Soc.Sci.Ind.	Social Sciences Index
Soc.Work Res.& Abstr.	Social Work Research & Abstracts (Now: Social Work Abstracts)
Sociol.Abstr.	Sociological Abstracts
Sociol.Educ.Abstr.	Sociology of Education Abstracts
Soft.Abstr.Eng.	Software Abstracts for Engineers
Soils & Fert.	Soils & Fertilizers
Solid St.Abstr.	Solid State Abstracts (Now: Solid State and Superconductivity Abstracts)
Sorghum & Millets Abstr.	Sorghum and Millets Abstracts (Now: Sorghum and Millets)
South.Bap.Per.Ind.	Southern Baptist Periodical Index (Ceased)
Soyabean Abstr.	Soyabean Abstracts
Sp.Ed.Needs Abstr.	Special Education Needs Abstracts
Speleol.Abstr.	Speleological Abstracts
Sport Fish.Abstr.	Sport Fishery Abstracts (Now: Fisheries Review)
Sports Per.Ind.	Sports Periodicals Index (Ceased)
Sportsearch	Sportsearch
Sri Lanka Sci.Ind.	Sri Lanka Science Index
Stat.Theor.Meth.Abstr.	Statistical Theory and Method Abstracts
Stud.Wom.Abstr.	Studies on Women Abstracts
Sugar Ind.Abstr.	Sugar Industry Abstracts

T

T.C.E.A.	Theoretical Chemical Engineering Abstracts (Now: Theoretical Chemical Engineering)
TOM	T O M (Text on Microfilm)
Tech.Educ.Abstr.	Technical Education Abstracts (Now: Technical Education & Training Abstracts)
Tel.Abstr.	Telecommunications Abstracts (Ceased)
Tel.Alert	Telecommunications Alert
Telegen	Telegen Reporter (Now: Telegen Abstracts) (Ceased)
Text.Tech.Dig.	Textile Technology Digest
Therm.Abstr.	Thermal Abstracts (Now: International Building Services Abstracts)
Tob.Abstr.	Tobacco Abstracts
Top Manage.Abstr.	Top Management Abstracts (Also see: Anbar)
Tox.Abstr.	Toxicology Abstracts
Tr.& Dev.Alert	Training and Development Alert
Tr.& Indus.Ind.	Trade & Industry Index
Trans.Res.Abstr.	Transportation Research Abstracts (Ceased)
Triticale Abstr.	Triticale Abstracts (Now: Wheat, Barley and Triticale Abstracts)
Trop.Abstr.	Tropical Abstracts (Now: Abstracts on Tropical Agriculture)
Trop.Dis.Bull.	Tropical Diseases Bulletin
Trop.Oil Seeds Abstr.	Tropical Oil Seeds Abstracts (Now: Tropical Oil Seeds)

U

Urb.Aff.Abstr.	Urban Affairs Abstracts

V

Va.Hist.Abstr.	Virginia Historical Abstracts (Ceased)
Vert.File Ind.	Vertical File Index
Vet.Bull.	Veterinary Bulletin
Viol.& Abuse Abstr.	Violence & Abuse Abstracts
Virol.Abstr.	Virology Abstracts (Now: Virology and AIDS Abstracts)
Vis.Ind.	Vision Index (Ceased)
VITIS	Vitis - Viticulture and Enology Abstracts

W

W.R.C.Inf.	W.R.C. Information (Water Research Centre) (Now: Aqualine Abstracts)
Water Pollut.Abstr.	Water Pollution Abstracts (Now: Aqualine Abstracts)
Water Resour.Abstr.	Water Resources Abstracts (Now: Hydro-Abstracts)
Weed Abstr.	Weed Abstracts
Wild Life Rev.	Wildlife Review (Ceased)
Wild.Rev.	Wildlife Review (Fort Collins)

Wom.Stud.Abstr.	Women Studies Abstracts
Work Rel.Abstr.	Work Related Abstracts
World Agri.Econ. & Rural Sociol. Abstr.	World Agricultural Economics & Rural Sociology Abstracts
World Alum. Abstr.	World Aluminum Abstracts
World Bank. Abstr.	World Banking Abstracts
World Bibl.Soc. Sec.	World Bibliography of Social Security
World Fish.Abstr.	World Fisheries Abstracts (Ceased)
World Surf.Coat.	World Surface Coatings Abstracts
World Text.Abstr.	World Textile Abstracts

Y

Yrbk.Assoc.Educ. & Rehab.Blind	Association for Education and Rehabilitation of the Blind and Visually Impaired. Yearbook (Ceased)

Z

Zent.Math.	Zentralblatt fuer Mathematik und ihre Grenzgebiete
Zincscan	Zincscan
Zoo.Rec.	Zoological Record

Subject Guide to Abstracting and Indexing

The 135 subject headings listed below are major subjects which contain a sub-category headed "Abstracting, Bibliographies, Statistics." This sub-category, which follows the major subject headings in the CLASSIFIED LIST OF SERIALS, identifies publications which abstract and/or index publications in the relevant subject. Bibliographies and statistical publications pertaining to the subject are also included in this sub-category. This guide will enable users to quickly locate subject areas of interest for which abstracting and indexing publications have been identified and to build profiles by combination of relevant subject areas. Page numbers refer to the first page on which the sub-category appears.

SUBJECT CATEGORY	PAGE
Advertising and Public Relations	46
Aeronautics and Space Flight	79
Agriculture	160
Alternative Medicine	284
Animal Welfare	288
Anthropology	315
Archaeology	364
Architecture	390
Art	442
Arts and Handicrafts	450
Astronomy	467
Beauty Culture	472
Beverages	491
Biography	536
Biology	585
Birth Control	782
Building and Construction	832
Business and Economics	919
Ceramics, Glass and Pottery	1576
Chemistry	1608
Children and Youth	1685
Civil Defense	1718
Classical Studies	1728
Cleaning and Dyeing	1730
Clothing Trade	1738
Clubs	1755
Communications	1819
Computers	1895
Conservation	2030
Consumer Education and Protection	2039
Criminology and Law Enforcement	2061
Dance	2073
Drug Abuse and Alcoholism	2083
Earth Sciences	2098
Education	2256
Electronics	2398
Energy	2423
Engineering	2482
Environmental Studies	2669
Ethnic Interests	2753
Fire Prevention	2760
Fish and Fisheries	2781
Folklore	2792
Food and Food Industries	2827
Forests and Forestry	2861
Funerals	2872
Gardening and Horticulture	2898
Genealogy and Heraldry	2933
Geography	3097
Gerontology and Geriatrics	3116
Handicapped	3125
Heating, Plumbing and Refrigeration	3150
History	3178
Hobbies	3322
Home Economics	3330
Homosexuality	3340
Hospitals	3357
Hotels and Restaurants	3373
Housing and Urban Planning	3398
How-to and Do-it-Yourself	3403
Humanities: Comprehensive Works	3428
Instruments	3435
Insurance	3464
Interior Design and Decoration	3477
Jewelry, Clocks and Watches	3492
Journalism	3506
Labor Unions	3524
Law	3661
Leather and Fur Industries	3743
Leisure and Recreation	3749
Library and Information Sciences	3812
Linguistics	3895
Literary and Political Reviews	3940
Literature	4049
Machinery	4103
Mathematics	4154
Matrimony	4164
Medical Sciences	4288
Meetings and Congresses	4640
Metallurgy	4679
Meteorology	4708
Metrology and Standardization	4715
Military	4748
Mines and Mining Industry	4774
Motion Pictures	4805
Museums and Art Galleries	4825
Music	4893
Numismatics	4912
Nutrition and Dietetics	4927
Occupational Health and Safety	4941
Occupations and Careers	4956
Oriental Studies	4975
Packaging	4984
Paints and Protective Coatings	4989
Paleontology	4996
Paper and Pulp	5005
Parapsychology and Occultism	5010
Patents, Trademarks and Copyrights	5022
Petroleum and Gas	5056
Pets	5069
Pharmacy and Pharmacology	5117
Philately	5133
Philosophy	5171
Photography	5187
Physical Fitness and Hygiene	5202
Physics	5236
Plastics	5281
Political Science	5368
Population Studies	5438
Printing	5463
Psychology	5526
Public Administration	5562
Public Health and Safety	5611
Publishing and Book Trade	5640
Real Estate	5667
Religions and Theology	5730
Rubber	5837
Sciences: Comprehensive Works	5911
Shoes and Boots	5921
Social Sciences: Comprehensive Works	5963
Social Services and Welfare	6006
Sociology	6044
Sound Recording and Reproduction	6051
Sports and Games	6095
Technology: Comprehensive Works	6264
Textile Industries and Fabrics	6281
Theater	6299
Tobacco	6302
Transportation	6324
Travel and Tourism	6510
Veterinary Science	6542
Water Resources	6563
Women's Health	6566
Women's Interests	6592
Women's Studies	6600

Subjects

ENGLISH	FRENCH	GERMAN	SPANISH
Abstracting and Indexing Services	Services d'Analyse et d'Indexage	Referate- und Indexdienste	Servicios de Extractos e Indices
Advertising and Public Relations	Publicité et Relations Publiques	Reklamewesen und Public Relations	Publicidad y Relaciones Públicas
Aeronautics and Space Flight	Aéronautique et Astronautique	Luft- und Raumfahrt	Aeronáutica y Vuelo Espacial
Computer Applications	Applications des Ordinateurs	Computer Anwendung	Aplicaciones de los Ordenadores
Agriculture	Agriculture	Landwirtschaft	Agricultura
Agricultural Economics	Agriculture Économique	Agrarökonomie	Economía Agrícola
Agricultural Equipment	Outillage Agricole	Landwirtschaftsgeräte	Aparatos Agrícolas
Computer Applications	Applications des Ordinateurs	Computer Anwendung	Aplicaciones de los Ordenadores
Crop Production and Soil	Récolte et Terre	Ernte und Acker	Producción de Cosecha, Tierra
Dairying and Dairy Products	Production Laitière	Milchwirtschaft	Lechería y Productos Lácteos
Feed, Flour and Grain	Pature, Farine et Grain	Futter, Mehl und Getreide	Forraje, Granos y Harina
Poultry and Livestock	Élevage	Geflügel- und Viehwirtschaft	Ganadería
Alternative Medicine	Médecine Alternative	Alternative Heilkunde	Medicina Alternativa
Animal Welfare	Protection des Animaux	Tierschutz	Bienestar Animal
Anthropology	Anthropologie	Anthropologie	Antropología
Antiques	Antiquités	Antiquitäten	Antigüedades
Archaeology	Archeologie	Archaeologie	Arqueología
Computer Applications	Applications des Ordinateurs	Computer Anwendung	Aplicaciones de los Ordenadores
Architecture	Architecture	Architektur	Arquitectura
Computer Applications	Applications des Ordinateurs	Computer Anwendung	Aplicaciones de los Ordenadores
Art	Art	Kunst	Arte
Computer Applications	Applications des Ordinateurs	Computer Anwendung	Aplicaciones de los Ordenadores
Arts and Handicrafts	Arts et Métiers	Kunst und Handwerk	Artes y Obras de Mano
Astrology	Astrologie	Astrologie	Astrología
Astronomy	Astronomie	Astronomie	Astronomía
Computer Applications	Applications des Ordinateurs	Computer Anwendung	Aplicaciones de los Ordenadores
Beauty Culture	Soins de Beauté	Schönheitspflege	Belleza Personal
Perfumes and Cosmetics	Parfums et Cosmétiques	Kosmetik und Parfüme	Perfumes y Cosméticos
Beverages	Boissons	Getränke	Bebidas
Bibliographies	Bibliographies	Bibliographien	Bibliografías
Biography	Biographie	Biographie	Biografía
Biology	Biologie	Biologie	Biología
Bioengineering	Biogénie	Bioingenieurwesen	Bio-ingeniería
Biological Chemistry	Chimie Biologique	Biochemie	Química Biológica
Biophysics	Biophysique	Biophysik	Biofísica
Biotechnology	Biotechnologie	Biotechnologie	Biotecnología
Botany	Botanique	Botanik	Botánica
Computer Applications	Applications des Ordinatures	Computer Anwendung	Aplicaciones de los Ordenadores
Cytology and Histology	Cytologie et Histologie	Zytologie und Histologie	Citología e Histología
Entomology	Entomologie	Entomologie	Entomología
Genetics	Génétique	Genetik	Genética
Microbiology	Microbiologie	Mikrobiologie	Microbiología
Microscopy	Microscopie	Mikroskopie	Microscopia
Ornithology	Ornithologie	Ornithologie	Ornitología
Physiology	Physiologie	Physiologie	Fisiología
Zoology	Zoologie	Zoologie	Zoología
Birth Control	Limitation des Naissances	Geburtenregelung	Reglamentación del Nacimiento
Building and Construction	Bâtiment et Construction	Bauwesen	Edificios y Construcción
Carpentry and Woodwork	Charpenterie et Menuiserie	Zimmerhandwerk und Holzbau	Carpintería y Ebanistería
Hardware	Quincaillerie	Metallbaustoffe	Ferretería
Business and Economics	Affaires et Économie	Wirtschaft und Handel	Negocios y Economía
Accounting	Comptabilité	Rechnungswesen	Contabilidad
Banking and Finance	Banque et Finance	Bank- und Finanzwesen	Bancos y Finanzas

Banking and Finance-
    Computer Applications
	Banque et Finance-
	    Applications des Ordinateurs
		Bank- und Finanzwesen-
		    Computer Anwendung
			Bancos y Finanzas-
			    Aplicaciones de los Ordenadores

Chamber of Commerce
    Publications
	Publications des Chambres
	    de Commerce
		Veröffentlichungen von Handels-
		    kammern
			Publicaciones de las Cámaras de
			    Comercio

Computer Applications	Applications des Ordinateurs	Computer Anwendung	Aplicaciones de los Ordenadores
Cooperatives	Coopératives	Genossenschaften	Cooperativas
Domestic Commerce	Commerce Interieur	Binnenhandel	Comercio Interior

Economic Situation and
    Conditions
	Situations et Conditions
	    Économiques
		Wirtschaftliche Situation und
		    Verhältnisse
			Situaciones y Condiciones
			    Económicas

Economic Systems and Theories,
    Economic History
	Systèmes et Théories Économiques,
	    Histoire Économique
		Ökonomische Systeme und
		    Theorien, Wirtschafts-
		    geschichte
			Sistemas y Teorías Económicos,
			    Historia Económica

International Commerce	Commerce International	Aussenhandel	Comercio Internacional

International Development and
    Assistance
	Développement et Assistance
	    Internationaux
		Internationale Entwicklungshilfe	Desarrollo y Asistencia Inter-
			    nacionales

Investments	Investissements	Investitionen	Inversiones
Labor and Industrial Relations	Travail et Relations Industrielles	Arbeits und Industrielle Beziehungen	Trabajo y Relaciones Industriales
Macroeconomics	Macroéconomique	Makroökonomie	Macroeconomía
Management	Gestion	Betriebsführung	Gerencia
Marketing and Purchasing	Cours et Achats	Marketing und Kauf	Compra y Venta
Office Equipment and Services	Matériel et Entretien de Bureaux	Büroeinrichtung und Service	Equipo y Servicios de Oficinas
Personnel Management	Direction de Personnel	Personal Führung	Dirección de Empleados
Production of Goods and Services	Production	Produktion	Producción
Public Finance, Taxation	Finance Publique, Impots	Staatsfinanzen, Steuerwesen	Finanza Publica, Impuestos
Small Business	Petites et Moyennes Affaires	Kleinbetrieb	Negocios Pequeños

Trade and Industrial Directories	Directoires de Commerce et
	    d'Industrie
		Firmenverzeichnisse	Directorios de Comercio e
			    Industria

SUBJECTS

Ceramics, Glass and Pottery	Céramique, Verrerie et Poterie	Keramik, Glas und Töpferei	Cerámica, Vidrio y Porcelana
Chemistry	Chimie	Chemie	Química
Analytical Chemistry	Chimie Analytique	Analytische Chemie	Química Analítica
Computer Applications	Applications des Ordinateurs	Computer Anwendung	Aplicaciones de los Ordenadores
Crystallography	Cristallographie	Kristallographie	Cristalografía
Electrochemistry	Électrochimie	Elektrochemie	Electroquímica
Inorganic Chemistry	Chimie Inorganique	Anorganische Chemie	Química Inorgánica
Organic Chemistry	Chimie Organique	Organische Chemie	Química Orgánica
Physical Chemistry	Chimie Physique	Physikalische Chemie	Fisicoquímica
Children and Youth	Enfance et Adolescence	Kinder und Jugend	Niños y Jóvenes
About	Au Sujet de	Über	Acerca
For	Pour	Für	Para
Civil Defense	Defense Civile	Ziviler Bevölkerungsschutz	Defensa Civil
Classical Studies	Études Classiques	Klassische Studien	Estudios Clásicos
Cleaning and Dyeing	Nettoyage et Teinturerie	Reinigen und Färben	Limpieza y Tintura
Clothing Trade	Vêtement	Bekleidungsgewerbe	Industria de Vestidos
Fashions	Mode	Moden	Modas
Clubs	Clubs	Klubs	Clubes
College and Alumni	Université et Diplomés	Universitäten und Hochschulabsolventen	Universidades y Exalumnos
Communications	Communications	Nachrichtentechnik	Comunicaciones
Computer Applications	Applications des Ordinateurs	Computer Anwendung	Aplicaciones de los Ordenadores
Postal Affairs	Postes	Postwesen	Correo
Radio	Radio	Rundfunk	Radio
Telephone and Telegraph	Téléphone et Télégraphe	Telephon und Telegraph	Teléfono y Telégrafo
Television and Cable	Télévision	Fernsehen und Bildfrequenzkanal	Televisión y Cable
Video	Vidéo	Video	Video
Computers	Ordinateurs	Computer	Ordenadores
Artificial Intelligence	Intelligence Artificielle	Künstliche Intelligenz	Inteligencia Artificial
Automation	Automation	Automatisierung	Automación
Calculating Machines	Calculateurs	Rechenmaschine	Calculadores
Circuits	Circuits	Schaltungen	Circuitos
Computer Architecture	Architecture de la Machine	Computer Architektur	Arquitectura de los Ordenadores
Computer-Assisted Instruction	Enseignement Assisté par Ordinateur	Computerunterstützter Unterricht	Instrucción con la Ayuda de Ordenador
Computer Engineering	Technique d'Ordinateur	Computerentwicklung	Ingeniería de Ordenador
Computer Games	Jeux d'Ordinateurs	Computer Spiele	Juegos de Ordenadores
Computer Graphics	Conception Assistée par Ordinateur	Computergraphik	Diseño con la Ayuda de Ordenador
Computer Industry	Industrie d'Ordinateur	Computerbetrieb	Industria de los Ordenadores
Computer Industry Directories	Annuaire de l'Industrie Ordinateur	Computerbetriebverzeichnisse	Directorios de la Industria de los Ordenadores
Computer Industry, Vocational Guidance	Industrie d'Ordinateur, Orientation Professionnelle	Computerbetrieb Berufsberatung	Industria de los Ordenadores, Gobierno Práctico
Computer Music	Musique d'Ordinateur	Computer Musik	Música de Ordenadores
Computer Networks	Reseaux d'Ordinateurs	Rechnernetz	Red para Transmisión de Datos
Computer Programming	Programme Machine	Computerprogrammierung	Programación de Ordenadores
Computer Sales	Ventes des Ordinateurs	Computervertrieb	Ventas de Ordenadores
Computer Security	Protection des Ordinateurs	Computersicherheit	Protección de los Ordenadores
Computer Simulation	Simulation des Ordinateurs	Computersimulation	Simulación por Ordenador
Computer Systems	Systèmes des Ordinateurs	Computersystemen	Sistemas de los Ordenadores
Cybernetics	Cybernetiques	Kybernetik	Cibernética
Data Base Management	Gestion de Base de Données	Datenbankverwaltung	Datos de Comunicación
Data Communications, Data Transmission Systems	Données de Communication	Datenübertragung, Datenübertragungssystem	Gestión de Banco de Datos
Electronic Data Processing	Traitement de l'Information Électronique	Elektronische Datenverarbeitung	Proceso de Datos Electrónicos
Hardware	Materiel	Hardware	Equipo Físico
Information Science, Information Theory	Théorie de l'Information	Informationstheorie	Ciencia, Teoría de la Información
Machine Theory	Théorie de Machine	Maschinetheorie	Teoría de la Maquina
Microcomputers	Micro-Ordinateurs	Mikrocomputer	Microordenadores
Minicomputers	Mini-Ordinateurs	Minicomputer	Miniordenadores
Personal Computers	Ordinateurs Privés	Persönlichecomputer	Ordenadores Personales
Robotics	Robotique	Robotersysteme	Robótica
Software	Logiciel	Software	Soporte Lógico
Theory of Computing	Théorie de Traitement	Computertheorie	Theoria de Cálculo
Word Processing	Traitement de Textes	Textverarbeitung	Tratamiento de Textos
Conservation	Conservation	Landschaftsschutz	Conservación
Consumer Education and Protection	Protection de Consommateur	Verbraucherwirtschaftsschutz	Protección del Consumidor
Criminology and Law Enforcement	Criminologie et Police	Kriminologie und Strafvollzug	Criminologiá y Acción Policial
Computer Applications	Applications des Ordinateurs	Computer Anwendung	Aplicaciones de los Ordenadores
Security	Securité	Sicherheit	Seguridad
Dance	Danse	Tanz	Baile
Drug Abuse and Alcoholism	Toxicomanie et Alcoolisme	Rauschgiftsucht und Alkoholismus	Drogadismo y Alcoholismo
Earth Sciences	Sciences Géologiques	Wissenschaften der Erde	Ciencias Geológicas
Computer Applications	Applications des Ordinateurs	Computer Anwendung	Aplicaciones de los Ordenadores
Geology	Géologie	Geologie	Geología
Geophysics	Géophysique	Geophysik	Geofísica
Hydrology	Hydrologie	Hydrologie	Hidrología
Oceanography	Océanographie	Ozeanographie	Oceanografía
Education	Éducation	Bildungswesen	Educación
Adult Education	Enseignement des Adultes	Erwachsenenbildung	Enseñanza de Adultos
Computer Applications	Applications des Ordinateurs	Computer Anwendung	Aplicaciones de los Ordenadores
Guides to Schools and Colleges	Guides d'Écoles et Colleges	Führer zur Schulen und Universitäten	Guías de Escuelas y Colegios
Higher Education	Enseignement Supérieur	Hochschulwesen	Enseñanza Superior
International Education Programs	Programmes d'Éducation Internationale	Internazionale Erziehungsprogramme	Programas de Enseñanza Internacional
School Organization and Administration	Organisation et Administration de l'École	Organisation und Verwaltung von dem Schule	Administración y Dirección de la Escuela
Special Education and Rehabilitation	Enseignement Special et Réhabilitation	Fachunterricht und Rehabilitierung	Enseñanza Especial y Rehabilitación
Teaching Methods and Curriculum	Méthodes Pédagogiques et Programmes Scolaires	Lehrmethoden und Lehrplan	Métodos de Enseñanza y Planes de Estudios

SUBJECTS

Electronics	Électronique	Elektronik	Electrónicos
Computer Applications	Applications des Ordinateurs	Computer Anwendung	Aplicaciones de los Ordenadores
Encyclopedias and General Almanacs	Encyclopédies et Almanachs Générales	Enzyklopädien und Allgemeine Nachschlagewerke	Enciclopedias y Almanaques Generales
Energy	Énergie	Energie	Energía
Computer Applications	Applications des Ordinateurs	Computer Anwendung	Aplicaciones de los Ordenadores
Electrical Energy	Énergie Électrique	Elektrizitätsenergie	Energía Eléctrica
Geothermal Energy	Énergie Géothermique	Thermalenergie	Energía Geotérmica
Hydroelectrical Energy	Énergie Hydraulique	Hydroelektroenergie	Energía Hidroeléctrica
Nuclear Energy	Énergie Nucléaire	Kernenergie	Energía Nuclear
Solar Energy	Énergie Solaire	Sonnenenergie	Energía Solar
Wind Energy	Énergie à Vent	Windenergie	Energía de Viento
Engineering	Génie	Ingenieurwesen	Ingeniería
Chemical Engineering	Génie Chimique	Chemieingenieurwesen	Ingeniería Química
Civil Engineering	Génie Civil	Bauingenieurwesen	Ingeniería Civil
Computer Applications	Applications des Ordinateurs	Computer Anwendung	Aplicaciones de los Ordenadores
Electrical Engineering	Génie Électrique	Elektrotechnik	Ingeniería Eléctrica
Engineering Mechanics and Materials	Méchanique de Génie et Materiels	Ingenieurwesen Mechanik und Materialien	Mecanica de Ingeniería y Materiales
Hydraulic Engineering	Génie Hydraulique	Wasserbau	Ingeniería Hidráulica
Industrial Engineering	Génie Industriel	Industrieingenieurwesen	Ingeniería Industrial
Mechanical Engineering	Génie Mécanique	Maschinenbau	Ingeniería Mecánica
Environmental Studies	Science de l'Environnement	Umweltschutz	Ciencias Ecológias
Computer Applications	Applications des Ordinateurs	Computer Anwendung	Aplicaciones de los Ordenadores
Pollution	Pollution	Umweltverschmutzung	Contaminación
Toxicology and Environmental Safety	Toxicologie et Sécurité de l'Environnement	Toxokologie und Umweltsicherheit	Toxicología y Seguridad Ambiental
Waste Management	Gestion de Déchets	Abfallwirtschaft	Manejo de la Basura
Ethnic Interests	Publications de l'Orientation Ethnique	Allgemeine Völkerkunde	Publicaciones de Temas Etnicos
Fire Prevention	Précaution contre l'Incendie	Brandbekämpfung	Prevención del Fuego
Fish and Fisheries	Poisson et Pêche	Fische und Fischerei	Pesca y Pesquerías
Folklore	Folklore	Volkskunde	Folklore
Food and Food Industries	Alimentation et Industries Alimentaires	Nahrungsmittel und Lebensmittelindustrie	Alimentos e Industrias Alimenticias
Bakers and Confectioners	Boulangerie et Confiserie	Bäcker- und Konditorgewerbe	Panaderías y Dulcerías
Grocery Trade	Épicerie	Kolonialwarenhandel	Abacerías
Forest and Forestry	Forêts et Exploitation Forestiére	Forstwesen und Waldwirtschaft	Bosques y Selvicultura
Lumber and Wood	Bois	Holz	Maderas
Funerals	Funérailles	Beerdigungen	Funerales
Gardening and Horticulture	Jardinage et Horticulture	Gartenpflege und Gartenbau	Jardinería y Horticultura
Florist Trade	Commerce des Fleurs	Blumenhandel	Floristas
Genealogy and Heraldry	Généalogie et Science Héraldique	Genealogie und Wappenkunde	Genealogía y Heráldica
Computer Applications	Applications des Ordinateurs	Computer Anwendung	Aplicaciones de los Ordenadores
General Interest Periodicals (Subdivided by country)	Publications d'Intérêt Général (Selon pays)	Allgemeine Zeitschriften (nach Land)	Periódicos de Interés General (por país)
Geography	Géographie	Geographie	Geografía
Computer Applications	Applications de Ordinateurs	Computer Anwendung	Aplicaciones de los Ordenadores
Gerontology and Geriatrics	Gérontologie	Gerontologie	Gerontología y Geriátrica
Giftware and Toys	Cadeaux et Jouets	Geschenkartikel und Spielwaren	Regalos y Juguetes
Handicapped	Handicapés	Behinderung	Desventajados
Computer Applications	Applications des Ordinateurs	Computer Anwendung	Aplicaciones de los Ordenadores
Hearing Impaired	Sourds	Schwerhörigkeit	Debilitado del Oído
Physically Impaired	Handicapés Physique	Körperbehinderung	Debilitado Físicamente
Visually Impaired	Aveugles	Blindheit	Debilitado Visualmente
Heating, Plumbing, and Refrigeration	Chauffage, Plomberie et Réfrigeration	Heizung, Kühlung und Installation	Calefacción, Plomería y Refrigeración
History	Histoire	Geschichte	Historia
Computer Applications	Applications des Ordinateurs	Computer Anwendung	Aplicaciones de los Ordenadores
History of Africa	Histoire de l'Afrique	Geschichte-Afrika	Historia de Africa
History of Asia	Histoire de l'Asie	Geschichte-Asien	Historia de Asia
History of Australasia and Other Areas	Histoire de l'Australasie et Autre Pays	Geschichte-Australasien und Andere Gebieten	Historia de Australasia y Otras Areas
History of Europe	Histoire de l'Europe	Geschichte-Europa	Historia de la Europa
History of North and South America	Histoire de l'Amérique du Nord et du Sud	Geschichte-Nord- und Südamerika	Historia de la América del Norte y de la del Sur
History of Near East	Histoire du Proche-Orient	Geschichte-Nahe Osten	Historia del Cercano Oriente
Hobbies	Passe-Temps	Hobbies	Pasatiempos
Home Economics	Enseignement Ménager	Hauswirtschaft	Economía Doméstica
Homosexuality	Homosexualisme	Homosexualität	Homosexualismo
Hospitals	Hôpitaux	Krankenhäuser	Hospitales
Computer Applications	Applications des Ordinateurs	Computer Anwendung	Aplicaciones de los Ordenadores
Hotels and Restaurants	Hôtels et Restaurants	Hotels und Restaurants	Hoteles y Restaurantes
Computer Applications	Applications des Ordinateurs	Computer Anwendung	Aplicaciones de los Ordenadores
Housing and Urban Planning	Logement et Urbanisme	Wohnungswesen und Stadtplanung	Viviendas y Urbanismo
Computer Applications	Applications des Ordinateurs	Computer Anwendung	Aplicaciones de los Ordenadores
How-To and Do-It-Yourself	Bricolage	Selbstanfertigung	Cómo Hacerlo y Hágalo Si Mismo
Humanities: Comprehensive Works	Humanités: Oeuvres Compréhensives	Klassische Philologie	Humanidades: Obras Comprensivas
Computer Applications	Applications des Ordinateurs	Computer Anwendung	Aplicaciones de los Ordenadores
Instruments	Instruments	Instrumente	Instrumentos
Insurance	Assurances	Versicherungswesen	Seguros
Computer Applications	Applications des Ordinateurs	Computer Anwendung	Aplicaciones de los Ordenadores
Interior Design and Decoration	Agencements Intérieurs et Décoration	Innenarchitektur und Innenausstattung	Diseño del Interior y Ornamentación
Furniture and House Furnishings	Meubles et Articles pour la Maison	Möbel und Wohnungseinrichtung	Muebles y Articulos para el Hogar
Jewelry, Clocks and Watches	Bijouterie et Horlogerie	Schmuck und Uhren	Joyería y Relojería
Journalism	Journalisme	Journalismus	Periodismo

SUBJECTS

Labor Unions	Syndicalisme	Gewerkschaften	Sindicatos
Law	Droit	Rechtswissenschaft	Derecho
Civil Law	Droit Civil	Zivilrecht	Derecho Civil
Computer Applications	Applications des Ordinateurs	Computer Anwendung	Aplicaciones de los Ordenadores
Constitutional Law	Droit Constitutionel	Verfassungsrecht	Derecho Constitucional
Corporate Law	Droit Commercial	Handelsrecht	Derecho Corporativo
Criminal Law	Droit Pénal	Strafrecht	Derecho Criminal
Estate Planning	Succession	Mobiliarvermögensrecht	Planificación de los Bienes
Family and Matrimonial Law	Droit Familial et Matrimonial	Ehegesetz und Familienrecht	Derecho Familial y Matrimonial
International Law	Droit International	Völkerrecht	Derecho Internacional
Judicial Systems	Système Judiciaire	Gerichtswesen	Sistemas Judiciales
Legal Aid	Assistance Judiciaire	Rechtshilfe	Ayuda Legal
Maritime Law	Droit Maritime	Seerecht	Derecho Marítimo
Military Law	Droit Militaire	Kriegsrecht	Derecho Militar
Leather and Fur Industries	Maroquinerie et Pelleterie	Leder und Pelz	Pieles y Cuero
Leisure and Recreation	Loisirs et Récréation	Freizeit und Unterhaltung	Ocio y Recreo
Library and Information Science	Bibliothéconomie et Informatique	Bibliothek- und Informationswissenschaft	Bibliotecología y Ciencia de la Información
Computer Applications	Applications des Ordinateurs	Computer Anwendung	Aplicaciones de los Ordenadores
Linguistics	Lingistique	Sprachwissenschaft	Lingüística
Computer Applications	Applications des Ordinateurs	Computer Anwendung	Aplicaciones de los Ordenadores
Literary and Political Reviews	Revues Littéraires et Politiques	Literarische und Politische Zeitschriften	Revistas Literarias y Políticas
Literature	Littérature	Literatur	Literatura
Adventure and Romance	Aventure et Romance	Abenteuer und Romantik	Aventura y Romance
Mystery and Detective	Mystère et Policier	Geheimnis und Detektivroman	Misterio y Detective
Poetry	Poésie	Poesie	Poesía
Science Fiction, Fantasy, Horror	Science-Fiction, Oeuvres Fantaisiste, Oeuvre d'Epouvante	Zukunftsroman, Phantasiegebilde, Grausen	Ciencia Ficción, Fantasía, Horror
Machinery	Machines	Maschinenwesen	Maquinaria
Computer Applications	Applications des Ordinateurs	Computer Anwendung	Aplicaciones de los Ordenadores
Mathematics	Mathématiques	Mathematik	Matemática
Computer Applications	Applications des Ordinateurs	Computer Anwendung	Aplicaciones de los Ordenadores
Matrimony	Mariage	Ehestand	Matrimonio
Computer Applications	Applications des Ordinateurs	Computer Anwendung	Aplicaciones de los Ordenadores
Medical Sciences	Sciences Médicales	Medizinische Wissenschaften	Ciencias Médicas
Allergology and Immunology	Allergologie et Immunologie	Allergie und Immunologie	Alergología e Imunología
Anaesthesiology	Anesthésiologie	Anaesthesiologie	Anestesiología
Cardiovascular Diseases	Maladies Cardiovasculaires	Kreislauferkrankungen	Enfermedades Cardiovasculares
Chiropractic, Homeopathy, Osteopathy	Chiropraxie, Homéopathie, Ostéopathie	Chiropraktik, Homöopathie, Osteopathie	Quiropráctica, Homeopatía, Osteopatía
Communicable Diseases	Maladies Contagieuses	Infektiöse Krankheiten	Enfermedades Contagiosas
Computer Applications	Applications des Ordinateurs	Computer Anwendung	Aplicaciones de los Ordenadores
Dentistry	Dentisterie	Zahnmedizin	Dentistería
Dermatology and Venereology	Dermatologie et Maladies Vénériennes	Dermatologie und Geschlechtskrankheiten	Dermatología y Venereología
Endocrinology	Endocrinologie	Endokrinologie	Endocrinología
Experimental Medicine Laboratory Technique	Médecine Expérimentale, Techniques de Laboratoire	Versuchsmedizin, Laboratoriumstechnik	Medicina Experimental, Técnicas del Laboratorio
Forensic Sciences	Médecine Légale	Gerichtliche Medizin	Ciencias Forenses
Gastroenterology	Gastroentérologie	Gastroenterologie	Gastroenterología
Hematology	Hématologie	Hämatologie	Hematología
Hypnosis	Hypnose	Hypnose	Hipnotismo
Internal Medicine	Médecine Interne	Innere Medizin	Medicina Interna
Nurses and Nursing	Personnel et Soins Infirmiers	Krankenpflege	Enfermeros y Enfermería
Obstetrics and Gynecology	Obstétrique et Gynécologie	Gynäkologie und Geburtshilfe	Obstetricia y Ginecología
Oncology	Cancer	Onkologie	Oncología
Ophthalmology and Optometry	Ophtalmologie et Optométrie	Opthalmologie und Optometrie	Oftalmología y Optometría
Orthopedics and Traumatology	Orthopédie et Traumatologie	Orthopädie und Traumatologie	Ortopedia y Traumatología
Otorhinolaryngology	Otorhinolaryngologie	Otorhinolaryngologie	Otorinolaringología
Pediatrics	Pédiatrie	Pädiatrie	Pediatría
Physical Medicine and Rehabilitation	Médecine Physique et Réhabilitation	Physikalische Heilkunde und Rehabilitation	Medicina Física y Rehabilitación
Psychiatry and Neurology	Psychiatrie et Neurologie	Psychiatrie und Neurologie	Psiquiatría y Neurología
Radiology and Nuclear Medicine	Radiologie et Médecine Nucléaire	Radiologie und Nuklearmedizin	Radiología y Medicina Nuclear
Respiratory Diseases	Maladies Respiratoires	Atmungskrankheiten	Enfermedades Respiratorias
Rheumatology	Rhumatologie	Rheumatologie	Reumatología
Sports Medicine	Médecine du Sport	Sportmedizin	Medicina de Deportes
Surgery	Chirurgie	Chirurgie	Cirugía
Urology and Nephrology	Urologie et Néphrologie	Urologie und Nephrologie	Urología y Nefrología
Meetings and Congresses	Réunions et Congrès	Tagungen und Kongresse	Conferencias y Congresos
Men's Health	Santé de l'Homme	Gesundheit von Männern	Salud Masculina
Men's Interests	Publications d'Intérêt Masculin	Männer Interessen	Intereses Masculinos
Men's Studies	Études de l'Homme	Männerstudien	Estudios de los Hombres
Metallurgy	Métallurgie	Metallurgie	Metalurgia
Computer Applications	Applications des Ordinateurs	Computer Anwendung	Aplicaciones de los Ordenadores
Welding	Soudure	Schweissen	Soldadura
Meteorology	Météorologie	Meteorologie	Meteorología
Computer Applications	Applications des Ordinateurs	Computer Anwendung	Aplicaciones de los Ordenadores
Metrology and Standardization	Métrologie et Standardisation	Mass- und Gewichtskunde, Normung	Metrología y Normalización
Computer Applications	Applications des Ordinateurs	Computer Anwendung	Aplicaciones de los Ordenadores
Military	Militaires	Militärwesen	Militares
Mines and Mining Industry	Mines et Resources Minières	Bergwesen und Bergbauindustrie	Mines y Minerales
Computer Applications	Applications des Ordinateurs	Computer Anwendung	Aplicaciones de los Ordenadores
Motion Pictures	Cinéma	Film und Kino	Películas
Museums and Art Galleries	Musées et Galleries	Museen und Kunstgalerien	Museos y Galerías del Arte
Music	Musique	Musik	Música
Computer Applications	Applications des Ordinateurs	Computer Anwendung	Aplicaciones de los Ordenadores
Needlework	Travaux d'Aiguille	Näherei	Bordado
New Age	Nouvelle Ere	New Age	Nueva Epoca
Numismatics	Numismatique	Numismatik	Numismática
Nutrition and Dietetics	Nutrition et Diététique	Ernährung und Diätetik	Nutrición y Dietética
Occupational Health and Safety	Médecine du Travail et Prévention	Berufsgesundheitspflege und Sicherheit	Sanidad y Seguridad de Oficio
Occupations and Careers	Occupations et Carrières	Berufe	Empleos y Ocupaciones
Oriental Studies	Études Orientales	Orientalistik	Estudios Orientales

SUBJECTS

Packaging	Emballage	Verpackung	Empaque
Computer Applications	Applications des Ordinateurs	Computer Anwendung	Aplicaciones de los Ordenadores
Paints and Protective Coatings	Couleurs et Peintures	Farben und Beläge	Pinturas y Revestimientos Protectores
Paleontology	Paléontologie	Paleontologie	Paleontología
Computer Applications	Applications des Ordinateurs	Computer Anwendung	Aplicaciones de los Ordenadores
Paper and Pulp	Papier et Pulpe	Papier und Papierstoff	Papel y Pasta
Parapsychology and Occultism	Parapsychologie et Occultisme	Parapsychologie und Okkultismus	Parapsicología y Ocultismo
Patents, Trademarks and Copyrights	Brevets, Marques de Fabrique et Droits d'Auteur	Patente, Schutzmarken und Urheberrechte	Patentes, Marcas de Fabrica y Derechos de Autor
Petroleum and Gas	Pétrole et Gas Naturel	Petroleum und Gas	Petróleo y Gas Natural
Computer Applications	Applications des Ordinateurs	Computer Anwendung	Aplicaciones de los Ordenadores
Pets	Animaux Familiers	Haustiere	Animales Domésticos
Pharmacy and Pharmacology	Pharmacie et Pharmacologie	Pharmazie und Pharmakologie	Farmacia y Farmacología
Computer Applications	Applications des Ordinateurs	Computer Anwendung	Aplicaciones de los Ordenadores
Philately	Philatélie	Briefmarkenkunde	Filatelia
Philosophy	Philosophie	Philosophie	Filosofía
Photography	Photographie	Photographie	Fotografía
Computer Applications	Applications des Ordinateurs	Computer Anwendung	Aplicaciones de los Ordenadores
Physical Fitness and Hygiene	Santé Physique et Hygiène	Gesundheitszustand und Hygiene	Salud Física e Higiene
Physics	Physique	Physik	Física
Computer Applications	Applications des Ordinateurs	Computer Anwendung	Aplicaciones de los Ordenadores
Electricity	Électricité	Elektrizität	Electricidad
Heat	Chaleur	Wärme	Calor
Mechanics	Mécanique	Mechanik	Mecánica
Nuclear Physics	Physique Nucléaire	Kernphysik	Física Nuclear
Optics	Optique	Optik	Optica
Sound	Son	Schall	Sonido
Plastics	Plastiques	Kunststoffe	Plásticos
Computer Applications	Applications des Ordinateurs	Computer Anwendung	Aplicaciones de los Ordenadores
Political Science	Sciences Politiques	Politische Wissenschafte	Ciencias Políticas
Civil Rights	Droits Civiques	Bürgerrechte	Derechos Civiles
International Relations	Relations Internationales	Internationale Beziehungen	Relaciones Internacionales
Population Studies	Démographie	Bevölkerungswissenschaft	Demografía
Printing	Imprimerie	Druck	Imprenta
Computer Applications	Applications des Ordinateurs	Computer Anwendung	Aplicaciones de los Ordenadores
Psychology	Psychologie	Psychologie	Psicología
Public Administration	Administration Publique	Öffentliche Verwaltung	Administración Pública
Computer Applications	Applications des Ordinateurs	Computer Anwendung	Aplicaciones de los Ordenadores
Municipal Government	Gouvernement Municipal	Kommunalverwaltung	Gobierno Municipal
Public Health and Safety	Santé Publique et Prévention	Öffentliche Gesundheitspflege	Salud Pública y Seguridad
Publishing and Book Trade	Édition et Commerce du Livre	Verlagswesen und Buchhandel	Editoriales y Librería
Computer Applications	Applications des Ordinateurs	Computer Anwendung	Aplicaciones de los Ordenadores
Real Estate	Immobilièrs	Grundbesitz und Immobilien	Bienes Raíces
Computer Applications	Applications des Ordinateurs	Computer Anwendung	Aplicaciones de los Ordenadores
Religions and Theology	Religions et Théologie	Religion und Theologie	Religión y Teología
Buddhist	Bouddhisme	Buddhist	Budista
Eastern Orthodox	Églises Orthodoxes	Orthodox	Ortodoxo Oriental
Hindu	Hindou	Hindu	Hindú
Islamic	Islamique	Islamische	Islámico
Judaic	Judaïque	Jüdäistische	Judaico
Protestant	Protestant	Evangelische	Protestante
Roman Catholic	Catholique Romain	Römisch-katholische	Católico Romano
Other Denominations and Sects	Autres Sectes	Andere Bekenntnisse und Sekte	Otras Denominaciones y Sectas
Rubber	Caoutchouc	Gummi	Caucho
Computer Applications	Applications des Ordinateurs	Computer Anwendung	Aplicaciones de los Ordenadores
Sciences: Comprehensive Works	Sciences: Oeuvres Compréhensives	Wissenschaften: Umfassende Werke	Ciencias: Obras Comprensivas
Computer Applications	Applications des Ordinateurs	Computer Anwendung	Aplicaciones de los Ordenadores
Shoes and Boots	Chaussures et Bottes	Schuhe und Stiefel	Zapatos y Botas
Singles' Interests and Lifestyles	Intérêts et Style de Vie Célibataire	Ledigenstandinteressen	Intereses y Estilos de Vivir de los Solteros
Social Sciences: Comprehensive Works	Sciences Sociales: Oeuvres Compréhensives	Sozialwissenschaften: Umfassende Werke	Ciencias Sociales: Obras Comprensivas
Social Service and Welfare	Service Social et Protection Sociale	Sozialpflege und Fürsorge	Asistencia Social y Bienestar
Sociology	Sociologie	Soziologie	Sociología
Computer Applications	Applications des Ordinateurs	Computer Anwendung	Aplicaciones de los Ordenadores
Sound Recording and Reproduction	Enregistrement et Reproduction du Son	Tonaufnahme und Tonwiedergabe	Grabaciones y Reproducciones Sonoras
Computer Applications	Applications des Ordinateurs	Computer Anwendung	Aplicaciones de los Ordenadores
Sports and Games	Sports et Jeux	Sport und Spiele	Deportes y Juegos
Ball Games	Jeux de Balle	Ballspiele	Juegos de Pelota
Bicycles and Motorcycles	Bicyclettes et Motocyclettes	Fahrräder und Motorräder	Bicicletas y Motocicletas
Boats and Boating	Bateaux et Canotage	Boote und Bootfahren	Botes y Bartelaje
Horses and Horsemanship	Equitation	Pferde und Reitsport	Caballos y Equitación
Outdoor Life	Vie en Plein Air	Im Freien	Vida de Campo
Statistics	Statistique	Statistik	Estadísticas
Technology: Comprehensive Works	Technologie: Oeuvres Compréhensives	Technologie: Umfassende Werke	Tecnología: Obras Comprensivas
Textile Industries and Fabrics	Textiles	Textil	Textiles y Telas
Computer Applications	Applications des Ordinateurs	Computer Anwendung	Aplicaciones de los Ordenadores
Theater	Théâtre	Theater	Teatro
Tobacco	Tabac	Tabak	Tabaco
Transportation	Transports	Transport	Transportación
Air Transport	Transport Aérien	Luftverkehr	Transporte Aéreo
Automobiles	Automobiles	Kraftfahrzeugen	Automóviles
Computer Applications	Applications des Ordinateurs	Computer Anwendung	Aplicaciones de los Ordenadores
Railroads	Chemins de Fer	Eisenbahnen	Ferrocarriles
Roads and Traffic	Routes et Circulation	Strassen und Strassenverkehr	Caminos y Tráfico
Ships and Shipping	Navires et Transport Maritimes	Schiffe und Schiffahrt	Barcos y Embarques
Trucks and Trucking	Transports Routiers	Lastkraftwagen	Camiones
Travel and Tourism	Voyages et Tourisme	Reisen und Tourismus	Viaje y Turismo
Airline Inflight and Hotel Inroom	Revues de Vol de Lignes Aériennes et de Chambres d'Hôtels	Fluggesellschaft und Hotel Veröffentlichungen	Aerolínea en-Vuelo y Hotel en-Cuarto
Veterinary Sciences	Science Vétérinaire	Tierheilkunde	Veterinaria
Computer Applications	Applications des Ordinateurs	Computer Anwendung	Aplicaciones de los Ordenadores
Water Resources	Ressources de l'Eau	Wasserwirtschaft	Recursos de Aqua
Computer Applications	Applications des Ordinateurs	Computer Anwendung	Aplicaciones de los Ordenadores
Women's Health	Santé de la Femme	Gesundheit von Frauen	Salud Feminina
Women's Interests	Publications d'Intérêt Féminin	Fraueninteresse	Intereses Femininas
Women's Studies	Études de la Femme	Frauenstudien	Estudios de las Mujeres

Classified List of Serials Subjects M-Z

MACHINE THEORY

see Computers–Machine Theory

MACHINERY

see also Agriculture–Agricultural Equipment

621.8 GW ISSN 0340-5745
A.G.T. DOKUMENTATION. 1972. 4/yr. DM.52.20 (foreign DM.104.20). A.G.T. Verlag Thum GmbH, Postfach 109, 71601 Ludwigsburg, Germany. TEL 07141-223156. FAX 07141-223131. TELEX 7264853. Ed. Klaus-Peter Koerber. circ. 10,000. **Document type:** trade publication.
Description: All fields of drive and gear engineering, electrical engineering and electronics, CAD-CAM systems, practical hydraulics and pneumatics.

621.9 IT ISSN 0393-0483
A M U. (Annuario Italiano Macchine Utensili e Complementari) 1966. a. L.50000 (foreign L.90000). Tecniche Nuove s.p.a., Via C. Menotti, 14, 20129 Milan, Italy. TEL 02-75701. FAX 02-7610351. circ. 5,000. **Document type:** directory.
Description: Names and addresses of 1800 Italian producers together with a description of their products.

676 621.9 US
A P M A NEWSLETTER. 1979. m. membership. American Paper Machinery Association, 7297 Lee Hwy., Unit N, Falls Church, VA 22042. TEL 703-536-1748. FAX 703-841-5603. Ed. Sharri Coffin. circ. 100. (back issues avail.)
Formerly: P P M M A Newsletter.

621.92 US ISSN 0195-0932
ABRASIVE ENGINEERING SOCIETY MAGAZINE. 1963. q. $40 (foreign $65). Abrasive Engineering Society, Meadowlark Technical Services, 108 Elliot Dr., Butler, PA 16001. TEL 412-282-6210. FAX 412-282-6210. Ed. Theodore L. Giese. adv.; bk.rev.; charts; illus.; tr.lit. circ. 2,500. (back issues avail.) **Indexed:** Met.Abstr., World Alum.Abstr. **Document type:** trade publication.
Former titles: Abrasive Technology; Abrasive Methods (ISSN 0001-3285).

ADVANCED MANUFACTURING TECHNOLOGY; monthly report. see COMPUTERS — Robotics

AGRARGEWERBLICHE WIRTSCHAFT. see AGRICULTURE — Agricultural Equipment

ALAMBRE; revista tecnica international para la industria del alambre y del cable y para todos los sectores de la elaboracion de alambres metalicos. see ENGINEERING — Electrical Engineering

AMERICAN FASTENER JOURNAL. see ENGINEERING — Mechanical Engineering

AMERICAN MACHINIST. see BUSINESS AND ECONOMICS — Production Of Goods And Services

621.9 US
AMERICAN TOOL, DIE & STAMPING NEWS. 1974. bi-m. Eagle Publications, Inc., 42400 Nine Mile Rd., Ste. B, Novi, MI 48050. TEL 810-347-3490; 800-783-3491. FAX 810-347-3492. Ed. Art Brown. adv.; bk.rev. circ. 31,000. **Document type:** trade publication.
Formerly: Diemaking, Stamping and EDMing; Which was formed by the 1991 merger of: American Tool, Die and Stamping News (ISSN 0192-5709) & E D M Digest (ISSN 0199-3550)

621.9 IT
AMMONITORE. 1954. w. L.20500. Editrice Giornale L'Ammonitore s.n.c., Via Desenzano 8, Milan, Italy. TEL 2-404-02-48. TELEX 31284 LAM I. Ed. G. Tenaglia. adv. circ. 37,000.

621.9 FR
ANNUAIRE NATIONAL DES MATIERES PREMIERES DE RECUPERATION ET DU MATERIEL D'OCCASION. 1953. a. 60 F. S E P Edition, 194-196 rue Marcadet, 75018 Paris, France. adv.

ANNUARIO A N D I L (YEAR). see CERAMICS, GLASS AND POTTERY

621.9 JA
ANZEN SENTA NYUSU/JAPAN ELEVATOR SAFETY CENTRE FOUNDATION NEWS. (Text in Japanese) 1974. q. Nihon Shokoki Anzen Senta - Japan Elevator Safety Centre Foundation, 11-2, Minamiaoyama 5-chome, Minato-ku, Tokyo 107, Japan.

621.9 669 JA
AOMORI PREFECTURE TECHNICAL INFORMATION: MACHINERY AND METAL. (Text in Japanese) 1977. q. Machinery and Metallurgy Research Institute of Aomori Prefecture - Aomoriken Kikai Kinzoku Shikenjo, 7-8, Numadate 4-chome, Hachinohe-shi, Aomori-ken 031, Japan.

621.9 SI ISSN 0129-5519
ASIA PACIFIC METALWORKING EQUIPMENT NEWS. (Text in English) 1987. bi-m. S.$54 (effective 1993). Asia Pacific Technology Publications Pte. Ltd., 2 Shenton Way, 05-01-04 ICB Bldg., Singapore 0106, Singapore. TEL 65-2223422. FAX 65-2225587. Ed. C.S. Sharma. circ. 10,000. (back issues avail.)
Incorporates (1991-1993): Die and Mould Technology International (ISSN 0218-2610) & Quality Asia.

621.8 FR ISSN 0750-1269
ASSEMBLAGES; soudage, colles et adhesifs, fixations mecaniques. no.32, 1976. bi-m. (5/yr.). 300 F. (foreign 387 F.). P P I Promotion Presse Internationale, 7 ter, Cour des Petites-Ecuries, 75010 Paris, France. Ed. H. Thiron. adv. circ. 5,000.
Formerly (until 1980): Assemblages Adhesifs (ISSN 0399-7774); Which was formed by 1977 merger of: Assemblages (ISSN 0399-7766); Adhesifs (ISSN 0044-6254)

ASSOCIATED EQUIPMENT DISTRIBUTORS. RENTAL RATES COMPILATION; nationally averaged rental rates for construction equipment including complete model specifications. see BUILDING AND CONSTRUCTION

ASSOCIATION OF FRENCH MECHANICAL INDUSTRIES. BULLETIN D'INFORMATION. see METALLURGY

ASU HYVIN. see BUILDING AND CONSTRUCTION — Hardware

621.75 US ISSN 0005-1071
TJ1180.A1 CODEN: AUMAAW
AUTOMATIC MACHINING. 1939. m. $40 in US; Canada $50; elsewhere $90 (free to qualified personnel). Screw Machine Publishing Co., Inc., 1066 Gravel Rd., No. 201, Webster, NY 14580. TEL 716-787-0820. FAX 716-787-0868. Ed. Donald E. Wood; Pub. Donald E. Wood. adv.; bk.rev.; charts; illus. circ. 13,000. **Indexed:** INSPEC (1975-1985). **Document type:** trade publication. —BLDSC (1829.200000).
Description: For engineers and managers of metalworking plants. Contains articles on plant modernization, management techniques, automation applications and computer-aided design.

AUTOMOBILE & TRACTOR; ancillary & agri equipment. see AGRICULTURE — Agricultural Equipment

BAENDER, BLECHE, ROHRE; Fachzeitschrift fuer Walzwerkstechnik, Blechbearbeitung, gezogene und geschweisste Rohre. see METALLURGY

4092 MACHINERY

| 621.9 | JA | ISSN 0912-7968 |

BARUBU GIHO/VALVE TECHNICAL REVIEW. (Text in Japanese) 1986. 3/yr. Nihon Barubu Kogyokai - Japan Valve Manufacturer's Association, Kikai Shinko Kaikan, 5-8, Shinba Koen 3-chome, Minato-ku, Tokyo 103, Japan.

| 621.9 | JA | ISSN 0385-6925 |
| | | CODEN: BAREDB |

BARUKA REBYU/VALQUA REVIEW. (Text in Japanese) 1957. m. 200 Yen per no. Nippon Baruka Kogyo K.K. - Nippon Valqua Industries, Ltd., 3-1, Marunouchi 3-chome, Chiyoda-ku, Tokyo 100, Japan. Dir. Kiyoshi Yoshida. **Document type:** bulletin.
—CASDDS.

BAUSTOFF, RECYCLING UND DEPONIETECHNIK. see ENGINEERING — Engineering Mechanics And Materials

BEIJING HUAGONG XUEYUAN XUEBAO (ZIRAN KEXUE BAN)/BEIJING INSTITUTE OF CHEMICAL TECHNOLOGY. JOURNAL (NATURAL SCIENCE). see ENGINEERING — Chemical Engineering

BEIKOKU TOKKYO SHOROKU. KIKAI YOSO, KIKAI KOSAKU, ZATSUKIKAI HEN/U.S. PATENT ABSTRACTS. MACHINE ELEMENTS, MACHINE CONSTRUCTION, MISCELLANEOUS MACHINES. see PATENTS, TRADEMARKS AND COPYRIGHTS — Abstracting, Bibliographies, Statistics

BETRIEBSTECHNIK; Monatsmagazin fuer Betriebsleiter. see ENGINEERING

BLECH-ROHRE-PROFILE; internationale Fachzeitschrift fuer die Herstellung und Verarbeitung von Band, Blech, Rohren und Profilen. see METALLURGY

| 621.9 | US | ISSN 0006-5498 |

BODINE MOTORGRAM. 1916. bi-m. free. Bodine Electric Company, 2500 W. Bradley Pl., Chicago, IL 60618. TEL 312-478-3515. Ed. J.J. Kester. adv.; charts; illus. circ. 10,000.

| 621.9 | JA | ISSN 0387-0162 |
| TJ263.5 | | CODEN: BOKEA3 |

BOIRA KENKYU/JAPAN BOILER ASSOCIATION. JOURNAL. (Text in Japanese) 1937. bi-m. 500 Yen per no. Nihon Boira Kyokai - Japan Boiler Association, Minato-ku, Tokyo 108, Japan.
—CASDDS.

| 621.9 | JA |

BOIRA NENKAN/ANNUAL OF BOILERS AND PRESSURE VESSELS. (Text in Japanese) a. 6000 Yen. Nihon Boira Kyokai - Japan Boiler Association, 14-10, Mita 3-chome, Minato-ku, Tokyo 108, Japan.

| 621.9 | JA |

BOIRA NYUSU/BOILER NEWS. (Text in Japanese) 1947. m. 100 Yen per no. Nihon Boira Kyokai - Japan Boiler Association, 14-10, Mita 3-chome, Minato-ku, Tokyo 108, Japan.

| 621.9 | US |

THE BOOK, USED MACHINERY PRICING GUIDE. m., q. and a. eds. $210 for monthly ed.; quarterly ed. $30; annual ed. $170. L & M Publications, Inc., 318 Oak St., N.W., Box 3273, Gainesville, GA 30503. TEL 404-532-5610. FAX 404-532-5667. Ed. Michael Clark. adv. contact: Lin Zoller.
Former titles: Black Book Auction Report; I M N Auction Report.
Description: Pricing service for metalworking, plastic, woodworking and printing machinery.

BOUWMACHINES. see BUILDING AND CONSTRUCTION

BOVAGKRANT. see TRANSPORTATION — Automobiles

| 621 | FR | ISSN 1148-7305 |
| TJ212 | | CODEN: BEAUE3 |

BUREAUX D'ETUDES. 9/yr. 395 F. (foreign 459 F.). C E P Information Technologie, Immeuble Europais, 26 rue d'Oradour sur Glane, 75504 Paris Cedex 15, France. TEL 1-44-25-31-31. FAX 1-45-57-35-06. TELEX 270 589 F. Ed. Jean-Francois Desclaux. adv. circ. 8,000. Indexed: INSPEC (1990-).
Formerly: Bureaux d'Etudes Automatise (ISSN 0296-8517); Which was formed by the merger of: Nouvel Automatisme (ISSN 0220-8482); Bureaux d'Etudes (ISSN 0245-9981); Which was formerly (until 1983): Composants Mecaniques, Electriques et Electroniques (ISSN 0339-1558)
Description: Covers industrial design and CAD.

| 621.9 658.8 | UK | ISSN 0266-5689 |

BUSINESS RATIO REPORT: THE AGRICULTURAL EQUIPMENT INDUSTRY; an industry sector analysis. 1978. a. I C C Business Ratios Ltd., Freepost, Field House, Hampton, Mddx. TW12 1BR, England. TEL 081-783-0977. FAX 081-783-1940. charts; stat. **Document type:** trade publication.
—BLDSC (0746.294000).
Formerly (until 1984): Business Ratio Report: Agricultural Equipment Manufacturers (ISSN 0261-7315)

| 621.9 658.8 | UK | ISSN 0261-9024 |

BUSINESS RATIO REPORT: MACHINE TOOL MANUFACTURERS; an industry sector analysis. 1974. a. I C C Business Ratios Ltd., Freepost, Field House, Hampton, Mddx. TW12 1BR, England. TEL 081-783-0977. FAX 081-783-1940. charts; stat. **Document type:** trade publication.
—BLDSC (5325.850000).

| 621.86 | UK | ISSN 0261-9059 |

BUSINESS RATIO REPORT: MECHANICAL HANDLING; an industry sector analysis. 1975. a. I C C Business Ratios Ltd., Freepost, Field House, Hampton, Mddx. TW12 1BR, England. TEL 081-783-0977. FAX 081-783-1940. charts; stat. **Document type:** trade publication.
—BLDSC (5419.110000).

BUSINESS RATIO REPORT: MINING EQUIPMENT MANUFACTURERS; an industry sector analysis. see MINES AND MINING INDUSTRY

| 621.8 658.8 | UK | ISSN 0269-9680 |

BUSINESS RATIO REPORT: MOTOR BODY BUILDERS & ENGINEERS; an industry sector analysis. 1986. a. I C C Business Ratios Ltd., Freepost, Field House, Hampton, Mddx. TW12 1BR, England. TEL 081-783-0977. FAX 081-783-1940. charts; stat. **Document type:** trade publication.
—BLDSC (5972.050000).

| 621.9 658.8 | UK | ISSN 0261-9113 |

BUSINESS RATIO REPORT: MOTOR COMPONENT & ACCESSORY MANUFACTURERS; an industry sector analysis. 1973. a. I C C Business Ratios Ltd., Freepost, Field House, Hampton, Mddx. TW12 1BR, England. TEL 081-783-0977. FAX 081-783-1940. charts, stat. **Document type:** trade publication.
—BLDSC (5972.850000).

| 381.4 658.8 | UK | ISSN 0265-1041 |

BUSINESS RATIO REPORT: MOTOR GOODS DISTRIBUTORS; an industry sector analysis. 1978. a. I C C Business Ratios Ltd., Freepost, Field House, Hampton, Mddx. TW12 1BR, England. TEL 081-783-0977. FAX 081-783-1940. charts; stat. **Document type:** trade publication.
—BLDSC (5974.190000).
Formerly (until 1983): Business Ratio Report: Motor Goods Wholesalers (ISSN 0261-913X)

| 621.9 | US |

C E M A BULLETIN.* q. Conveyor Equipment Manufacturers Association, 9384D Forestwood Ln., Manassas, VA 22110-4702. TEL 301-738-2448. FAX 301-738-0076. Ed. R.J. Lloyd. **Document type:** newsletter.

| 658.7 | CN | ISSN 0008-3836 |

CANADIAN INDUSTRIAL EQUIPMENT NEWS; reader service on new, improved and redesigned industrial equipment & supplies. 1940. m. Can.$23.50 (US Can.$52, elsewhere Can.$72). Southam Magazine Group, 1450 Don Mills Rd., Don Mills, ON M3B 2X7, Canada. TEL 416-445-6641. FAX 416-442-2261. Ed. Olga Markovich. adv.; illus.; tr.lit. circ. 34,211. **Document type:** trade publication.
—CCC.
Incorporates (in May 1993): Electrical Equipment News (ISSN 0013-4333)
Description: Provides the answers to increased production, efficiency and profit by keeping readers informed of the latest technological advances in products, components and maintenance materials.

| 621.9 669 | CN | ISSN 0008-4379 |
| TJ1 | | CODEN: CMCHA3 |

CANADIAN MACHINERY & METALWORKING. 1905. 10/yr. Can.$34. Maclean Hunter Ltd., Business Publication Division, Maclean-Hunter Bldg., 777 Bay St., Toronto, ON M5W 1A7, Canada. TEL 416-596-5720. Ed. Mike Overment. adv.; bk.rev.; stat.; tr.lit. circ. 16,769. (also avail. in microfilm; back issues avail.)
—CCC.
Formerly: Canadian Machinery and Metallurgy.

CANTERAS Y EXPLOTACIONES; revista tecnica de maquinaria para canteras, minas, cementos y obras hidraulicas. see MINES AND MINING INDUSTRY

CATALOG OF U.S. VALVES. see BUSINESS AND ECONOMICS — Trade And Industrial Directories

| 621.9 669 | JA |

CHIBA KIKINSHI NYUSU. (Text in Japanese) 1969. q. Chibaken Kikai Kinzoku Shikenjo - Machinery and Metallurgy Research Institute of Chiba Prefecture, 13-1, Tendai 6-chome, Inage-ku, Chiba-shi, Chiba-ken 263, Japan.

| 621.9 669 | JA |

CHIBAKEN KIKAI KINZOKU SHIKENJO. JIGYO GAIYO/MACHINERY AND METALLURGY RESEARCH INSTITUTE OF CHIBA PREFECTURE. REPORT. (Text in Japanese) a. Chibaken Kikai Kinzoku Shikenjo, 13-1, Tendai 6-chome, Inage-ku, Chiba-shi, Chiba-ken 263, Japan.

| 621.9 | CC | ISSN 1001-2281 |

CHILUN/GEAR. (Text in Chinese) q. Jidian Bu, Zhengzhou Jixie Yanjiusuo, Zhongyuan Lu, Zhengzhou, Henan 450052, People's Republic of China. TEL 447102. Ed. Xu Hongji.

CHINA, REPUBLIC. MACHINERY AND ELECTRICAL APPARATUS INDUSTRY YEARBOOK/CHUNG HUA MIN KUO CHI CH'I YU TIEN KUNG CH'I TS'AI NIEN CHIEN. see ELECTRONICS

| 621.9 | HK | ISSN 1021-1314 |

CHINAMAC JOURNAL/JIXIE ZHIZAO; a machine building & metal working journal for P.R. China. (Text in Chinese; table of contents in Chinese, English) 1987. 4/yr. HK.$194($45) for Asia; elsewhere $46 (typically set in Jan.). (Ministry of Foreign Trade and Economic Cooperation, China National Machinery Import and Export Corporation, CC) Adsale Publishing Company, 14F Devon House, Taikoo Place, 979 King's Rd., Quarry Bay, Hong Kong. TEL 852-2811-8897. FAX 852-2516-5119. Ed. Joyce Ng. adv. circ. 22,000. (back issues avail.)
Description: Introduces to China advanced foreign technology, market trends and products in the machine building and metal-working industries.

| 681.7 | UK | ISSN 0305-7046 |

CLOTHING MACHINERY TIMES.* 1960. 5/yr. £11. Knitting and Sewing Machine Times Ltd., 15c Osborn St., London E1 6TJ, England. Ed. Wilfred Rodwell. adv.; bk.rev.; illus. circ. 3,000. **Indexed:** Text.Tech.Dig., World Text.Abstr.
Formerly: Industrial Sewing Machine Times (ISSN 0046-9254); **Incorporates:** Clothing Machinery; Equipment Review.
Description: Addresses the state of sewing machinery and allied productive equipment in the garment industry.

| 621.9 608.7 | US | ISSN 1060-538X |

COMPRESSOR NEWS AND PATENTS. 1975. m. (10/yr.). $60. Impact Publications, Box 3113, Ketchum, ID 83340-3113. TEL 208-726-2133. FAX 208-726-2115. Ed. Mary Jo Helmeke. adv.; pat.; index. (looseleaf format; back issues avail.) **Document type:** newsletter.
Formerly: Compressor News (ISSN 0884-2264)
Description: Contains new product information, current technical article titles, new books, future seminars and new patent gazette summaries concerning compressors.

| 621.9 | US |

COMPUTER LISTING SERVICE'S MACHINERY & EQUIPMENT GUIDE. 1969. m. Wineberg Publications, 7842 N. Lincoln Ave., Skokie, IL 60077. TEL 708-676-1900; 800-323-1818. FAX 708-676-0063. Ed. Daniel Laurence; Pub. Joel Wineberg. **Document type:** directory.
Formerly: Computer Listing Service's Machinery, Electrical, Industrial and Plant Equipment.

CONSTRUCTION AND AGGREGATES MACHINERY EN ESPAÑOL. see BUILDING AND CONSTRUCTION

621.9   UK   ISSN 0307-0018
CRANES TODAY. 1972. 11/yr. £60($140) (foreign £105). Wilmington Publishing, Wilmington House, Church Hill, Dartford, Kent UA2 7EF, England. TEL 0322-277788. FAX 0322-276476. (Subscr. to: Ferrari House, 258 Field End Rd., Ruislip, Middx HA4 9UX. TEL 081-868-4499) Ed. Graham Brent. adv.; bk.rev. circ. 9,049. **Indexed:** Br.Tech.Ind.
—BLDSC (3487.018300).

621.9   US   ISSN 0011-4189
                         CODEN: CTEGAP
CUTTING TOOL ENGINEERING.* 1955. 9/yr. $30. C T E Publications Inc., 400 Skokie Blvd., Ste. 395, Northbrook, IL 60062-7903. TEL 708-441-7520. FAX 708-441-8740. Ed. Don Nelson. adv.; bk.rev.; charts; illus.; tr.lit.; index. circ. 38,750. (also avail. in microform from UMI; reprint service avail. from UMI) **Indexed:** Ind.Med., ISMEC, Met.Abstr., World Alum.Abstr.
—BLDSC (3506.200000); Ei; SWETS; UMI; UnCover. **CCC.**

621.86   GW   ISSN 0723-7901
D H F - DEUTSCHE HEBE- UND FOERDERTECHNIK; Internationale Fachzeitschrift fuer Foerder-, Lager- und Transporttechnik. 1955. m. DM.108.80. A.G.T. Verlag Thum GmbH, Postfach 109, 71601 Ludwigsburg, Germany. TEL 07141-223156. FAX 07141-223131. TELEX 7264853. Ed. Hans Strothteicher. circ. 11,843. **Indexed:** C.I.S. Abstr., Excerp.Med., Fluidex, INIS Atomind. **Document type:** trade publication.
—SWETS.
Description: Presents information concerning lifting and materials-handling technology, transport rationalization, storage and transshipment technology.

621.9   GW   ISSN 0011-507X
D N Z INTERNATIONAL. (Die Naehmaschinen-Zeitung) 1879. bi-m. DM.96. Bielefelder Verlagsanstalt GmbH & Co. KG, Niederwall 53, 33602 Bielefeld, Germany. TEL 0521-595-520. adv.; bk.rev.; charts; illus.; mkt.; pat.; tr.lit.; index. circ. 5,000. **Indexed:** World Text.Abstr. **Document type:** trade publication.
Formerly: D N Z. Deutsche Naehmaschinen-Zeitung.

621.9   FR
DECOLLETAGE. 1970. 6/yr. 330 Chemin du Fresney, 74300 Cluses, France. TEL 50-98-10-89. FAX 50-71-15-16. Ed. Serge Desurmont. circ. 6,000.

DENSEI TECHNICAL JOURNAL/DENSEI. see ENGINEERING — Electrical Engineering

DESIGN NEWS; news for OEM design engineers. see TECHNOLOGY: COMPREHENSIVE WORKS

621.9   US
DESIGN NEWS O E M - SUPPLIERS SPECIAL ISSUE. 1970. a. $50. Cahners Publishing Company (Newton), Division of Reed Elsevier Inc., 275 Washington St., Newton, MA 02158-1630. TEL 617-964-3030. FAX 617-558-4470. (Subscr. to: 44 Cook St., Denver, CO 80206. TEL 800-662-7776) Ed. Lawrence D. Maloney. circ. controlled. (reprint service avail. from UMI) **Document type:** trade publication.
Former titles: Design News Electrical - Electronic Directory; Design News Electrical - Electronic Reference Edition; Incorporates: Design News Fastening Directory (ISSN 0190-2288); Which was formerly: Design News Fastening Reference Edition; Design News. Fastening (ISSN 0190-2296); Incorporates: Design News Fluid Power Directory; Which was formerly: Design News Fluid Power Reference Edition; Design News. Fluid Power (ISSN 0164-2871); Design News Annual. Fluid Power Edition; Incorporates: Design News Materials Directory; Which was formerly: Design News Materials Reference Edition; Design News. Materials (ISSN 0164-2839); Design News Annual. Materials Edition; Incorporates: Design News Power Transmission Directory; Which was formerly: Design News Power Transmission Reference Edition.

621 669   US   ISSN 1056-6090
TS229
DIE CASTING BUYERS GUIDE. 1990. a. $44.95. Die Casting Industry Publishing, 415 Bennett Rd., Elk Grove Village, IL 60007. TEL 708-364-1222. FAX 708-364-1268. adv. circ. 6,000. **Document type:** directory.
Formerly (until 1991): Die Casting Industry Blue Book.
Description: Contains alphabetical listing of machinery, equipment, products, materials, services and supplies used by die casters.

621.9   US
DOWNTIME.* 1991. bi-m. 25 Oak Forest Dr., Ronkonkoma, NY 11777-6178. Ed. John Stevens. adv. circ. 65,000.
Description: Covers new technology and information for maintenance and repair decision makers.

DRAHT; internationale Fachzeitschrift fuer die Draht- und Kabelindustrie und alle Bereiche der Drahtverarbeitung. see METALLURGY

DRVNA INDUSTRIJA. see FORESTS AND FORESTRY — Lumber And Wood

621.9   US
E D M TODAY. (Electrical Discharge Machining) 1990. bi-m. E D M Publications Inc., 230 W. Pkwy., No. 3-1, Pompton Plains, NJ 07444-1060. TEL 201-831-1334. FAX 201-831-1195. Ed. Jack Sebzda Sr. adv.; B&W page $2658; trim 8 3/8 x 10 7/8. circ. 25,132.

E P E. (European Production Engineering) see ENGINEERING — Mechanical Engineering

338.4 621.9   US   ISSN 0070-8550
HD9703.U48
ECONOMIC HANDBOOK OF THE MACHINE TOOL INDUSTRY. 1967. a. $100. N M T B A - Association for Manufacturing Technology, 7901 Westpark Dr., McLean, VA 22102. TEL 703-893-2900. FAX 703-827-5263. circ. 2,000. (also avail. in microfiche from CIS) **Indexed:** SRI.
Description: Information on the U.S. and international machine tool industries, including orders, production, consumption and trade.

ELECTRIC MACHINES AND POWER SYSTEMS. see ENGINEERING — Electrical Engineering

ELECTRONICS PRODUCTION EQUIPMENT NEWS. see ELECTRONICS

EMBALLERING. see PACKAGING

621.9   FR   ISSN 0291-8331
ENERGIE FLUIDE - L'AIR INDUSTRIEL; la pneumatique industrielle: production, traitements et applications de l'air comprime. 1972. 9/yr. 369 F. (foreign 505 F.). Editions U. Boucoiran, 7 ter, Cour des Petites-Ecuries, 75010 Paris, France. TEL 42-47-12-05. FAX 47-70-33-94. Ed. H. Thiron. abstr.; bibl.; tr.lit. circ. 5,000. (back issues avail.)
—BLDSC (3745.410000).
Formerly: Air Industriel.

ENGENHARIA AGRICOLA. see AGRICULTURE

621.9   UK
ENGINE REPAIR AND REMANUFACTURE. 1982. q. £14 (effective 1995). R G O Exhibitions and Publications Ltd., Oakapple Cottage, Furnace Ln., Broad Oak Brede, Rye, E. Sussex TN31 6ES, England. TEL 01424-882702. FAX 01424-882702. Ed. Chris Hancock. adv.: B&W page £270; color page £450; trim 212 x 150; adv. contact: Pam Bourne. bk.rev.; tr.lit.; circ. 1,400. (back issues avail.) **Document type:** trade publication.
Description: Covers all aspects of this emerging industry and discusses related environmental issues.

ENGINEERED SYSTEMS; serving the heating, ventilating, air conditioning and refrigerating engineering community. see HEATING, PLUMBING AND REFRIGERATION

621.9 330   US   ISSN 1046-6665
EQUIPMENT LEASING TODAY. 1989. m. (10/yr.). Equipment Leasing Association, 1300 N. 17th St., Ste. 1010, Arlington, VA 22209. TEL 703-527-8655. FAX 703-527-2649. adv.: B&W page $1990, color page $2490; trim 8 1/2 x 11. circ. 3,518. (also avail. in microform from UMI)
●Also available online, Vendor(s): University Microfilms International.
—UMI.
Description: Contains information on funding sources, portfolio management, sales and marketing strategy, leasing and remarketing equipment.

EQUIPMENT MANUFACTURERS INSTITUTE. FIRST OF THE WEEK NEWSLETTER. see AGRICULTURE — Agricultural Equipment

EQUIPMENT MANUFACTURERS INSTITUTE. RETAIL SALES REPORTS. see AGRICULTURE — Agricultural Equipment

EQUIPMENT MANUFACTURERS INSTITUTE. STATE OF THE INDUSTRY. see AGRICULTURE — Agricultural Equipment

621.9 658.7   US   ISSN 1057-7262
EQUIPMENT WORLD. 1972. bi-m. $58. Randall Publishing Co., Box 2029, Tuscaloosa, AL 35401. TEL 800-633-5953. adv. circ. 102,000. **Document type:** trade publication.
—UMI.
Supersedes: Contractor's Market Center (ISSN 0884-3376); Incorporates (in 1992): Equipment Management (ISSN 0733-3056); Which was formerly (until 1982): Heavy Duty Equipment Maintenance - Management (ISSN 0734-2640); (until 1979): E.M. (Heavy Duty Equipment and Maintenance).
Description: Provides information and insight needed to make business decisions when buying, renting, leasing, selling or using equipment from earthmovers to pickups.

EQUIPOS Y PRODUCTOS INDUSTRIALES. see BUSINESS AND ECONOMICS — Production Of Goods And Services

621.9   UK   ISSN 0966-002X
EUROPEAN MACHINING. q. £37 (foreign £43). Turret Group Plc., Turret House, 171 High St., Rickmansworth, Herts WD3 1SN, England. TEL 01293-777000. FAX 01293-771297. Ed. Ian Hutton. circ. 25,000. **Document type:** trade publication.

658.7   SA   ISSN 0014-6552
FACTORY EQUIPMENT & MATERIALS. Abbreviated title: F E M. (Text in English) 1968. m. R.112 (foreign R.193) (effective 1994). National Publishing (Pty) Ltd., P.O. Box 2735, Johannesburg 2000, South Africa. TEL 27-11-835-2221. FAX 27-11-835-1943. Ed. Heather Thorne. adv.: B&W page R.4315; trim 445 x 280. illus.; tr.lit. circ. 9,891. (tabloid format) **Indexed:** INIS Atomind. **Document type:** trade publication.
Formerly: Factory Equipment and Materials for Southern Africa.
Description: Products and services oriented trade journal for industrial engineers and factory management.

FACULTAD NACIONAL DE AGRONOMIA MEDELLIN. REVISTA. see AGRICULTURE

621.9   GW   ISSN 0936-8760
FERTIGUNG; Fachmagazin fuer Bearbeitung, Montage, Kontrolle. 1973. m. DM.158 (Europe DM.194; overseas DM.254). Verlag Moderne Industrie, Justus-von-Liebig-Str. 1, 86899 Landsberg, Germany. TEL 08191-125-0. FAX 08191-125-483. Ed. Helmut Augeli. adv.: B&W page DM.5670; trim 257 x 178; adv. contact: Carola Eichele. bk.rev.; illus.; index. circ. 12,350. **Document type:** trade publication.
Formerly: Moderne Fertigung (ISSN 0344-7596)

IL FILO METALLICO; rivista tecnica internazionale per l'industria del filo metallico e del cavo e per tutti i settori della lavorazione del filo metallico. see ENGINEERING — Electrical Engineering

MACHINERY

621.9 — UK
FINANCIAL SURVEY. COMPANY DATA FOR SUCCESS: AUTOMATIC VENDING. a. I C C Financial Surveys Ltd., Field House, 72 Oldfield Rd., Hampton, Mddx. TW12 2HQ, England. TEL 081-783-0977. FAX 081-783-1940. charts; stat. **Document type:** trade publication.
 Formerly (until 1991): Financial Survey Company Directory. Automatic Vending (ISSN 0952-0163)

621.9 — UK
FINANCIAL SURVEY. COMPANY DATA FOR SUCCESS: BEARING MANUFACTURERS & DISTRIBUTORS. a. I C C Financial Surveys Ltd., Field House, 72 Oldfield Rd., Hampton, Mddx. TW12 2HQ, England. TEL 081-783-0977. FAX 081-783-1940. charts; stat. **Document type:** trade publication.
 Former titles (until 1989): Financial Survey Company Directory. Bearing Manufacturers and Distributors (ISSN 0953-7686); (until 1988): Financial Survey Company Directory. Bearing Manufacturers (ISSN 0952-0007)

621.9 — US — ISSN 1062-6018
FLUID POWER SERVICE CENTER. 1991. q. Penton Publishing Co., 1100 Superior Ave., Cleveland, OH 44114. TEL 216-696-7000. FAX 216-696-1819. Ed. Tobi Goldoftas. adv. circ. 15,095.
 Description: Covers the maintenance, repair and overhaul of fluid power systems and components used on mobile and industrial machinery.

621.86 — GW — ISSN 0015-5233
FOERDERMITTEL-JOURNAL; Materialfluss, Lager, Transport und Verpackung. 1969. m. free. Europa-Fachpresse-Verlag GmbH (Subsidiary of: Sueddeutscher Verlag), Thomas-Dehler-Str. 27, 81737 Munich, Germany. TEL 089-67804-0. Ed. Peter Scherr. adv.; bk.rev.; charts. circ. 17,000. **Indexed:** INSPEC.
 —CCC.

621.86 — GW — ISSN 0015-5241
FOERDERN UND HEBEN; independent periodical for rationalisation and automation in mechanical handling and storing. (Includes special issues) (Text in German; contents page in English and German) 1951. m. DM.242 (foreign DM.282). Vereinigte Fachverlage GmbH, Lise-Meitner-Str. 2, 55129 Mainz, Germany. TEL 06131-992-01. FAX 06131-992-100. TELEX 04-187752. (Subscr. to: Postfach 2760, 55017 Mainz, Germany) Ed. Reiner Wesselowski. adv.; bk.rev.; abstr.; charts; illus.; index. circ. 12,000. **Indexed:** C.I.S. Abstr., INIS Atomind., ISMEC, Met.Abstr., World Alum.Abstr. **Document type:** trade publication.
 —CCC.

FOOD MANUFACTURE INGREDIENT AND MACHINERY SURVEY. see FOOD AND FOOD INDUSTRIES

621.9 664 — JA — ISSN 0910-6251
FOOMA/FOOD MACHINERY. (Text in Japanese) 1984. q. 500 Yen per no. Nihon Shokuhin Kikai Kogyoka - Japan Food Machinery Manufacturers' Association, 4-8, Roppongi 7-chome, Minato-ku, Tokyo 106, Japan. Ed. Tetsuo Shimaga. adv. contact: Sueichi Shimada. **Document type:** newsletter.

621.9 — HU — ISSN 0016-8572 — CODEN: GEPPAC
GEP. (Text in Hungarian; summaries and contents page in English, German, and Russian) 1949. m. $38.50. (Gepipari Tudomanyos Egyesulet - Scientific Society of Mechanical Engineering) Lapkiado Vallalat, Lenin korut 9-11, 1073 Budapest 7, Hungary. TEL 222-408. (Subscr. to: Kultura, Box 149, H-1389 Budapest, Hungary) Ed. Kornel Lehofer. adv.; bk.rev.; charts; illus. circ. 3,600. **Indexed:** Appl.Mech.Rev., Chem.Abstr., Hung.Build.Bull., INIS Atomind.
 —CASDDS.

621.9 — HU — ISSN 0016-8580 — CODEN: GEPGAJ
GEPGYARTASTECHNOLOGIA. (Text in Hungarian; summaries in English, German and Russian) 1961. m. $41.50. (Gepipari Tudomanyos Egyesulet) Lapkiado Vallalat, Lenin korut 9-11, 1073 Budapest 7, Hungary. TEL 222-408. (Subscr. to: Kultura, Box 149, H-1389 Budapest, Hungary) Ed. Geza Lang. charts; illus. **Indexed:** Appl.Mech.Rev., C.I.S. Abstr., Chem.Abstr., Fluidex, Met.Abstr., World Alum.Abstr.
 —BLDSC (4161.400000); CASDDS.

621.9 669 — JA
GIJUTSU JOHO MIE. KIKAI KINZOKU HEN/TECHNICAL INFORMATION IN MIE PREFECTURE: MACHINE AND METAL SERIES. (Text in Japanese) 1974. 3/yr. Mieken Kogyo Gijutsu Senta - Mie Industrial Research Institute, 3485, Otsuka, Takachaya Komori-cho, Tsu-shi, Mie-ken 514, Japan.

621.9 — HK — ISSN 1023-0254
GONGYE QICAI/MACHINERY & MATERIALS. (Text in Chinese) m. B & I Publication Co., Ltd., 18-F, First Pacific Bank Centre, 56 Gloucester Rd., Wanchai, Hong Kong. TEL 852-2865-2633. FAX 852-2866-1770. **Document type:** trade publication.
 Description: Covers news on manufacturing technology in the fields of metalworking, plastics processing, electronics, and packaging.

621.9 — HK — ISSN 1023-0211
GONGYE QICAI ZHONGGUOBAN/MACHINERY & MATERIALS. CHINA EDITION. bi-m. B & I Publication Co., Ltd., 18-F, First Pacific Bank Centre, 51-57 Gloucester Rd., Wanchai, Hong Kong. TEL 852-2865-2633. FAX 852-2866-1770. Ed. Alan Kwok; Pub. Henry Tang. adv. contact: Arthur Tang. **Document type:** trade publication.
 Description: Covers manufacturing technology in the fields of metalworking, plastics processing, electronics, and packaging.

665.5 — CI — ISSN 0350-350X — CODEN: GOMABN
GORIVA I MAZIVA/FUELS AND LUBRICANTS. (Text in Serbo-Croatian; summaries in English) 1962. bi-m. $40. Hrvatsko Drustvo za Goriva i Maziva, Berislaviceva 6, 41000 Zagreb, Croatia. TEL 041-442-948. Ed. Valdimir Savic. adv.; bk.rev. circ. 1,100. **Indexed:** Chem.Abstr.
 —CASDDS.
 Formerly (until 1972): Tehnika Podmazivanja i Primjena Goriva (ISSN 0497-1035)

GOVERNMENT EQUIPMENT NEWS. see BUSINESS AND ECONOMICS — Trade And Industrial Directories

621.9 — MX
GUIA DE LA INDUSTRIA: EQUIPO Y APARATOS/PLANT AND LABORATORY EQUIPMENT GUIDE; para laboratorios y plantas. (Text in English, Spanish) 1962. a. $80. Informatica Cosmos, S.A. de C.V., Calz. del Hueso 334-A1, Col. Ex-Hacienda Coapa, 14300 Mexico D.F., Mexico. TEL 525-677-48-68. FAX 525-679-35-75. (Dist. in US by: Schnell Publishing Company, Inc., 80 Broad St., 23rd Fl., New York, NY 13334. TEL 212-248-4177. FAX 212-248-4903) Ed. Raul Macazaga. adv.; B&W page $1000; trim 211 x 274; adv. contact: Mary Christen. circ. 5,000. **Document type:** directory.
 Incorporates: Guia de la Industria: Laboratorios de Especialidades y Control; **Formerly:** Equipo.
 Description: Lists 3000 suppliers of industrial plants equipment, reagents, instruments, items and laboratory services. Lists 5400 products in the country.

H O B - DIE HOLZBEARBEITUNG. see FORESTS AND FORESTRY — Lumber And Wood

HARD HAT NEWS. see BUILDING AND CONSTRUCTION

HERION - INFORMATIONEN. see ENGINEERING — Hydraulic Engineering

HIGH GEAR. see AERONAUTICS AND SPACE FLIGHT

HOLZ - KURIER; forst- und holzwirtschaftlicher Wochendienst. see FORESTS AND FORESTRY — Lumber And Wood

621.9 — US — ISSN 0744-6640 — TT205.A1
HOME SHOP MACHINIST; dedicated to precision metalworking. 1982. bi-m. $25.50. Village Press, Inc., 2779 Aero Park Dr., Traverse City, MI 49686. TEL 616-946-3712. FAX 616-946-3289. (Subscr. to: Box 1810, Traverse City, MI 49685-1810. TEL 800-447-7367) Ed. Joe D. Rice; Pub. Robert Goff. adv.; bk.rev.; illus.; stat.; index. circ. 26,357. (also avail. in microform from UMI; reprint service avail. from UMI) **Document type:** consumer publication.
 —UMI.
 Description: Features articles on metalworking projects; focuses on lathe work, drilling, milling, grinding, foundry and micromachines. Includes detailed drawings and photography.

HOSO KIKAI SHINBUN/PACKAGING MACHINERY NEWS. see PACKAGING

HUAGONG JIXIE/CHEMICAL ENGINEERING AND MACHINERY. see ENGINEERING — Chemical Engineering

I E N: INDUSTRIAL EQUIPMENT NEWS; what's new in equipment, parts, materials. see BUSINESS AND ECONOMICS — Marketing And Purchasing

621.8 — BL
I E N LATIN AMERICA - MEXICO. 1977. 6/yr. $35. T L Publicacoes Industriais Ltda., Rua Brigadeiro Tobias 356, 01032 Sao Paulo, SP, Brazil. TEL 011-2299240. FAX 011-2289373. TELEX 011-30562 TLPB. Ed. Raul Gonzalez Simon. adv.; B&W page 9435; trim 11 x 16 1/8. circ. 36,000.
 Former titles (until 1993): N E I Spanish America: Noticiario de Equipos Industriales; N E I - L A.

I H I ENGINEERING REVIEW. (Ishikawajima-Harima Heavy Industries Co., Ltd.) see TRANSPORTATION — Ships And Shipping

621.9 — SP — ISSN 0210-1777
I M H E. (Informacion de Maquinas - Herramienta Equipos y Accesorios) (Text in Spanish; summaries in English) 1974. m. (10/yr.). $170. Ediciones Tecnicas Izaro S.A., Mazustegui 21, 4a planta, 48006 Bilbao, Spain. TEL 394-415-90-22. FAX 394-416-27-43. TELEX 32333 IMHE. Ed. Ramon Urizar Arechaga. adv.; bk.rev.; bibl.; illus.; index. circ. 5,050. **Indexed:** Ind.SST. **Document type:** trade publication.

621.9 — GW — ISSN 0085-6916
I S W BERICHTE. 1972. irreg., no.87, 1992. price varies. (Universitaet Stuttgart, Institut fuer Steuerungstechnik der Werkzeugmaschinen und Fertigungseinrichtungen) Springer-Verlag, Heidelberger Platz 3, 14197 Berlin, Germany. TEL 030-8207-1. FAX 030-8214091. (Subscr. in N. America to: Springer-Verlag New York, Inc., 44 Hartz Way, Secaucus, NJ 07096-2491. TEL 201-348-4033. FAX 201-348-4505) (reprint service avail. from ISI) **Document type:** monographic series.

621.9 540 — GW — ISSN 0342-6319
I W - REPORT; Informationen fuer die technisch-industrielle Werbung und Verkaufsfoerderung. 1971. m. DM.93. Text Verlag GmbH, Postfach 106124, 2000 Hamburg, Germany. Ed. Ralph Schneider. adv.; bk.rev. circ. 3,000. (back issues avail.)
 —CCC.

621.9 669 — JA
IBARAKIKEN KOGYO GIJUTSU JOHO. KIKAI KENZOKU HEN/IBARAKI PREFECTURE INDUSTRIAL RESEARCH INFORMATION: MACHINE AND METAL SECTION. (Text in Japanese) 1976. 3/yr. Ibarakiken Kogyo Gijutsu Senta - Ibaraki Prefectural Industrial Technology Center, 3781-1, Nagaoka, Ibaraki-machi, Higashi Ibarakigun, Ibaraki-ken 311-31, Japan.

621.9 608.7 — US — ISSN 1056-1536
IMPACT PUMP NEWS AND PATENTS. 1971. m. (10/yr.). $100. Impact Publications, Box 3113, Ketchum, ID 83340-3113. TEL 208-726-2133. FAX 208-726-2115. Ed. Mary Jo Helmeke. adv. (looseleaf format; back issues avail.) **Document type:** trade publication.
 Former titles: Impact Pump Patents; Impact Pumps, Pumps-Compressors (ISSN 0883-7627)
 Description: Contains recent patent gazette summaries, new product information, current technical articles, new books and future seminars.

608.7 697 — US — ISSN 1056-1544
IMPACT VALVES NEWS AND PATENTS. 1962. 10/yr. $150. Impact Publications, Box 3113, Ketchum, ID 83340-3113. TEL 208-726-2133. FAX 208-726-2115. Ed. Mary Jo Helmeke. bk.rev.; pat. circ. 100. (back issues avail.) **Document type:** newsletter.
 Former titles: Impact Valves (ISSN 0883-7619); Valve Information Report (ISSN 0042-2436)
 Description: Contains recent patent gazette information.

IMPLEMENT & TRACTOR; the business magazine of the farm and industrial equipment industry. see AGRICULTURE — Agricultural Equipment

MACHINERY

IN-PAK; packaging and handling: from process to shelf. see PACKAGING

621.9 662 US
INDRESCO INC. MARION DIVISION. NEWS AND REVIEW. 1989. q. free. Indresco Inc., Marion Division, 617 W. Center St., Box 505, Marion, OH 43302. TEL 614-383-5211. FAX 614-382-2052. Ed. Peter Gilewicz. circ. 7,500 (controlled).
Description: Covers technical and commercial information, pertaining to the company's products and services.

INDUEQUIPO. see BUSINESS AND ECONOMICS — Production Of Goods And Services

INDUSTRIA DE BIENES DE EQUIPO. see BUSINESS AND ECONOMICS — Production Of Goods And Services

INDUSTRIA MERCATO; rivista dell'industria meccanica. see ENGINEERING — Mechanical Engineering

INDUSTRIAL EQUIPMENT NEWS. see BUSINESS AND ECONOMICS — Marketing And Purchasing

621.9 II
INDUSTRIAL EQUIPMENT NEWS. (Text in English) 1984. m. Rs.175. Sri Balaji Publishing Co. Pvt. Ltd., 22, Ida Mansion, 2nd Fl., 18, Vaju Kotak Marg., Bombay 400 001, India. TEL 2618965. Pub. S.N. Ananthakrishnan. adv.: B&W page Rs.6500, color page Rs.12000; trim 280 x 205; adv. contact: N. Mohanan. **Document type:** trade publication.

658.7 KO
INDUSTRIAL EQUIPMENT NEWS KOREA. 1986. m. Monthly Korea Co., Ltd., 113-6, Rm. 302, Dongjak-ku Sando 1 Dong, Seoul, Korea. TEL 787-22592. (U.S. addr.: Thomas International Publishing Co., One Penn Plaza, New York, NY 10119) circ. 5,446.

621.9 659.1 UK ISSN 0963-0228
INDUSTRIAL EXCHANGE & MART. 1976. w. £150. Link House Advertising Periodicals Ltd., 25 West St., Poole, Dorset BH15 1LL, England. TEL 01202-445184. FAX 01202-445189. circ. 33,640. **Document type:** trade publication.
Description: Marketplace guide to industrial and commercial plants, equipment, buildings, transport, services, and products, with a full index of classifications and announcements of auctions and sales.

621.8 380.52 UK ISSN 0954-3759
INDUSTRIAL HANDLING & STORAGE. 1979. 6/yr. £45 (foreign £60). Trinity Publishing Ltd., Times House, Station Approach, Ruislip, Middx. HA4 8NB, England. TEL 01895-677677. FAX 01895-676027. Ed. Geoff Bone. adv. circ. 20,000. **Indexed:** Account.& Data Proc.Abstr. **Document type:** trade publication. —BLDSC (4454.601500).

658 US ISSN 1047-4374
INDUSTRIAL MACHINE TRADER. w. $79. Heartland Communications, Inc., 1003 Central Ave., Fort Dodge, IA 50501. TEL 515-955-1600. **Document type:** trade publication.
Description: Keeps potential buyers and sellers current on supply and demand of machinery in the machine tool industry.

621.9 US
INDUSTRIAL MACHINERY: LATIN AMERICAN INDUSTRIAL REPORT. (Avail. for each of 22 Latin American countries) 1985. a. $435 per country report. Aquino Productions, Box 15760, Stamford, CT 06901. TEL 203-325-3138.

621.9 US
INDUSTRIAL MARKET PLACE. 1951. fortn. $160. Wineberg Publications, 7842 N. Lincoln Ave., Skokie, IL 60077. TEL 708-676-1900; 800-323-1818. FAX 708-676-0063. TELEX 327489. Ed. Daniel Laurence; Pub. Joel Wineberg. adv. contact: Adrienne Gallender. circ. 21,000. (tabloid format; back issues avail.) **Document type:** directory.
Description: Contains advertising on machinery and equipment from plants and factories nationwide.

INDUSTRIAL PRODUCTS FINDER. see BUSINESS AND ECONOMICS — Trade And Industrial Directories

621.9 GW ISSN 0172-7117
INDUSTRIEBEDARF. 1976. m. DM.60. Verlag W. Sachon, Schloss Mindelburg, 87714 Mindelheim, Germany. TEL 08261-999-0. FAX 08261-999-132. Ed. Peter Schmid. adv. contact: Holger Bernhardt. circ. 6,394. **Document type:** trade publication.

621.9 IE ISSN 0790-794X
INDUSTRY. 11/yr. 38 Grafton St., Dublin 2, Ireland. TEL 778355. FAX 797523. TELEX 91598-INDMEI-G. Ed. Tony Keegan.

621.8 GW ISSN 0170-6993
INSTANDHALTUNG; Zeitschrift fuer Wartung, Inspektion, Instandsetzung. 1972. bi-m. DM.84 (Europe DM.102; overseas DM.132). Verlag Moderne Industrie, Justus-von-Liebig-Str. 1, 86899 Landsberg, Germany. TEL 08191-125-0. FAX 08191-125-483. Ed. Uschi Winkler. adv.: B&W page DM.5470; trim 257 x 178; adv. contact: Silke Oetmanns. bk.rev.; illus. circ. 11,464. **Document type:** trade publication.
—SWETS.

INSTYTUT OBROBKI SKRAWANIEM. PRACE. MATERIALY INSTRUKTAZOWE. see ENGINEERING — Engineering Mechanics And Materials

INSTYTUT OBROBKI SKRAWANIEM. PRACE. OPRACOWANIA ANALITYCZNO-SYNTETYCZNE. see ENGINEERING — Engineering Mechanics And Materials

INSTYTUT OBROBKI SKRAWANIEM. PRACE. REFERATY. see ENGINEERING — Engineering Mechanics And Materials

INSTYTUT OBROBKI SKRAWANIEM. PRACE. ZESZYTY NAUKOWE. see ENGINEERING — Engineering Mechanics And Materials

629.1 US
INTERNATIONAL GAS TURBINE INSTITUTE TECHNOLOGY REPORT. LAND, SEA & AIR. 1978. a. free. International Gas Turbine Institute, 5801 Peachtree Dunwoody Rd., N.E., Ste. 100, Atlanta, GA 30342-1503. TEL 404-847-0072. FAX 404-847-0151. adv. contact: Scott Moore. circ. 25,000. **Document type:** academic/scholarly publication.
Formerly: International Gas Turbine and Aeroengine Technology Report.
Description: Contains information on the best industrial accomplishments and technological advances in the gas turbine and aeroengine industry. *Refereed Serial*

INTERNATIONAL JOURNAL OF ADVANCED MANUFACTURING TECHNOLOGY. see ENGINEERING — Mechanical Engineering

INTERNATIONAL JOURNAL OF APPLIED PNEUMATICS. see ENGINEERING — Mechanical Engineering

INTERNATIONAL JOURNAL OF MACHINE TOOLS & MANUFACTURE; design, research & application. see ENGINEERING — Industrial Engineering

621 US ISSN 1023-621X
▼**INTERNATIONAL JOURNAL OF ROTATING MACHINERY.** 1995. 4/yr. 91 ECU (effective 1996). Gordon and Breach Science Publishers, c/o International Publishers Distributor, 820 Town Center Dr., Langhorne, PA 19047. TEL 215-750-2642; 800-545-8398. FAX 215-750-6343. (Subscr. to: International Publishers Distributor, P.O. Box 90, Reading, Berkshire RG1 8JL, England. TEL 44-173-456-8316. FAX 44-173-456-8316) **Document type:** academic/scholarly publication.

621.9 II ISSN 0047-0996
INTERNATIONAL PRESS CUTTING SERVICE: MACHINE TOOL AND IRON STEEL INDUSTRY. 1967. w. $65. International Press Cutting Service, Box 63, Allahabad 211001, India. Ed. N. Khanna. bk.rev.; index. circ. 1,200. (processed)

INTERNATIONAL TRENDS IN MANUFACTURING TECHNOLOGY. see TECHNOLOGY: COMPREHENSIVE WORKS

658.5 IE ISSN 0047-1453
IRISH EQUIPMENT NEWS. 1969. m. free. Maxwell Publications, Kaima House, 49 Wainsfort Park, Terenure, Dublin 6, Ireland. Ed. Eugene McGee. adv. (tabloid format)

621.9 RU ISSN 0130-6782
ITOGI NAUKI I TEKHNIKI: TEKHNOLOGIYA I OBORUDOVANIE MEKHANOSBOROCHNOGO PROIZVODSTVA. irreg., vol.6, 1990. price varies. Vsesoyuznyi Institut Nauchno-Tekhnicheskoi Informatsii (VINITI), Ul. Usievicha 20-A, 125219 Moscow A-219, Russia. (Subscr. to: Mezhdunarodnaya Kniga, Moscow 121200, Russia) —BLDSC (0180.487000).

669 621.9 620 GW ISSN 0940-8789 CODEN: JJOBE3
J O T. (Journal fuer Oberflaechentechnik) 1961. m. DM.170 (effective 1996). Friedr. Vieweg und Sohn Verlagsgesellschaft mbH, Postfach 1546, 65005 Wiesbaden, Germany. TEL 0611-534389. FAX 0611-534430. Ed. Jochen Kecht. adv.; bk.rev.; bibl.; charts; illus.; mkt.; pat.; tr.lit.; index. circ. 10,200. **Indexed:** Chem.Abstr., Dok.Arbeitsmed., Excerp.Med., Met.Abstr., World Alum.Abstr., World Surf.Coat. **Document type:** trade publication.
—CASDDS; SWETS. CCC.
Formerly: Oberflaeche und J O T (ISSN 0170-4044); Which was formed by the merger of: Oberflaeche (ISSN 0029-7488); J O T (Journal fuer Oberflaechentechnik) (ISSN 0021-3756); Which supersedes: Journal fuer die Gesamte Oberflaechentechnik.

JAPANESE JOURNAL OF TRIBOLOGY. see ENGINEERING — Mechanical Engineering

621.9 720 CC ISSN 1001-554X
JIANZHU JIXIE/CONSTRUCTION MACHINERY. (Text in Chinese) 1980. m. $48 (effective 1996). (Beijing Jianzhu Jixie Zonghe Yanjiusuo - Beijing Construction Machinery Comprehensive Research Institute) Jianzhu Jixie Bianjibu, 21 Fangjia Hutong, Andingmennei, Beijing 100007, People's Republic of China. TEL 4019167. FAX 4017647. (Dist. overseas by: China International Book Trading Corp., P.O. Box 399, Beijing, P.R. China) (Co-sponsor: Zhongguo Jianshe Jixie Xiehui - China Construction Machinery Association) Ed. Zhang Shiying; Pub. Qiu Linfeng. adv. contact: Zhou Xianbiao. bk.rev. circ. 8,500.

621.9 614.85 JA
JITSUMU TENBO/SAFETY NEWS ON BOILER AND CRANE ENGINEERING. (Text in Japanese) 1967. bi-m. 500 Yen per no. Boira Kuren Anzen Kyokai - Boiler and Crane Safety Association, 1-11, Ojima 3-chome, Koto-ku, Tokyo 136, Japan.

621.9 CC ISSN 1001-0513
JIXIE KEXUE YU JISHU. (Text in Chinese) 1964. bi-m. Y1.80 per no. Jiangsu Sheng Jixie Yanjiu Shejiyuan, 445 Changhong Lu, Nanjing, Jiangsu 210012, People's Republic of China. TEL 201741. Ed. Cao Zhichao. adv.; bk.rev.

621.9 CC ISSN 1006-2343
JIXIE SHEJI YU YANJIU/MACHINE DESIGN AND RESEARCH. (Text in Chinese) 1984. q. Shanghai Jixie Gongcheng Xuehui - Shanghai Mechanical Engineering Society, Shanghai Jiaotong Daxue, 1954 Huanshan Lu, Shanghai 200030, People's Republic of China. TEL 4310310. (Co-sponsors: Shanghai Jiaotong University, Shanghai Xiechang Sewing Machine Factory) Ed. Zou Huijun. adv. circ. 1,000. **Document type:** academic/scholarly publication.
Description: Introduces new theories and methods of machine design.

612.9 CC ISSN 1000-4998
JIXIE ZHIZAO. (Text in Chinese) m. Shanghai Jidian Gongye Guanliju, 27 Huqiu Lu, Shanghai 200002, People's Republic of China. TEL 3217280. Ed. Zhu Run.

JOURNAL OF MATERIALS PROCESSING TECHNOLOGY. see ENGINEERING — Mechanical Engineering

621.9 II ISSN 0449-5721 TS191
JOURNAL OF PLANT AND MACHINERY. (Text in English) s-a. T.S.K. Rao, Ed. & Pub., 2235 Bhutgoswami Vattaram, Manojiappa St., Thanjavur 613001, India. charts; illus.

JOURNAL OF TERRAMECHANICS. see TRANSPORTATION

MACHINERY

621.9 690   JA   ISSN 0386-0388
KENKI GIHO/CONSTRUCTION MACHINERY TECHNICAL REVIEW. (Text in Japanese) 1967. a. Hokkaido Kaihatsucho Hokkaido Kaihatsukyoku, Kensetsu Kikai Kosakujo - Hokkaido Development Agency, Hokkaido Development Bureau, Construction Machinery Works, 8-chome, Higashi 2-jo, Tsukisamu, Toyohira-ku, Sapporo-shi, Hokkaido 062.

621.9 624   JA   ISSN 0385-9878
KENSETSU KIKAI/CONSTRUCTION MACHNIERY AND EQUIPMENT. (Text in Japanese) 1965. m. 1200 Yen per no. Nihon Kogyo Shuppan K.K., 3-26, Honkomagome 6-chome, Bunkyo-ku, Tokyo 113, Japan.

KENSETSU KIKAI DOKO CHOSA HOKOKU/ANNUAL REPORT OF CONSTRUCTION MACHINERY AND EQUIPMENT. see BUILDING AND CONSTRUCTION

KENSETSU KIKAIKA KENKYUJO NENPO/CONSTRUCTION METHOD AND MACHINERY RESEARCH INSTITUTE. ANNUAL REPORT. see BUILDING AND CONSTRUCTION

KENSETSU KIKAIKAI KENKYUJO SEINO SHIKEN HOKOKU/JAPANESE CONSTRUCTION METHOD AND MACHINERY RESEARCH INSTITUTE. REPORT OF PERFORMANCE TESTS. see BUILDING AND CONSTRUCTION

621.9   JA   ISSN 0285-5453
KENSETSU NO KIKAIKA/CONSTRUCTION MECHANIZATION. (Text in Japanese) 1949. m. 670 Yen per no. Nihon Kensetsu Kikaika Kyokai - Japan Construction Mechanization Association, 5-8, Shibakeon 3-chome, Minato-ku, Tokyo 105, Japan. **Indexed:** INIS Atomind.

KHIMICHESKOE I NEFTYANOE MASHINOSTROENIE/CHEMICAL AND OIL INDUSTRY. see ENGINEERING — Chemical Engineering

621.9   JA
KIKAI KOGYO KEIZAI KENKYU HOKOKUSHO/ECONOMIC RESEARCH REPORTS ON MACHINE INDUSTRY. (Text in Japanese) 10/yr. Kikai Shinko Kyokai, Keizai Kenkyujo - Japan Society for the Promotion of Machine Industry, Economic Research Institute, 5-8, Shiba Koen 3-chome, Minato-ku, Tokyo 105, Japan.

621.9   JA   ISSN 0368-5713
TJ4
KIKAI NO KENKYU/SCIENCE OF MACHINE. (Text in Japanese) 1949. m. 24500 Yen. Yokendo Co., Ltd., 30-15, Hongo 5-chome, Bunkyo-ku, Tokyo 113-91, Japan. Ed. Kiyoshi Oikawa. **Indexed:** INIS Atomind.

621.9 368   JA   ISSN 0910-2159
CODEN: KNSODW
KIKAI NO SONGAI/MACHINERY DAMAGE. (Text in Japanese) 1958. a. Nihon Kikai Hoken Renmei - Union of Machinery Insurers of Japan, 2-9, Kanda Awaji-cho, Chiyoda-ku, Tokyo 101, Japan.
—CASDDS.

621.9   JA   ISSN 0389-9500
KIKAI SHINKO/PROMOTING MACHINE INDUSTRY IN JAPAN. (Text in Japanese) 1968. m. 515 Yen per no. Kikai Shinko Kyokai - Japan Society for the Promotion of Machine Industry, 5-8, Shiba Koen 3-chome, Minato-ku, Tokyo 106, Japan.

621.9   JA
KIKAI SHINKO KAIKAN BEKKAN. SHIKEN KENKYU HOKOKUSHO/MACHINE TOOL ENGINEERING FOUNDATION. RESEARCH REPORT. (Text in Japanese) 1979. irreg. Kosaku Kikai Gijutsu Shinko Zaidan, Kikai Shinko Kaikan Bekkan, 5-22, Shiba Koen 3-chome, Minato-ku, Tokyo 105, Japan.

621.9   JA   ISSN 0385-8022
KIKAI SHINKO KYOKAI. GIJUTSU KENKYUJO. GIKEN NYUSU/JAPAN SOCIETY FOR THE PROMOTION OF MACHINE INDUSTRY. TECHNICAL NEWS. (Text in Japanese) 1976. q. Kikai Shinko Kyokai, Gijutsu Kenkyujo - Japan Society for the Promotion of Machine Industry, Technical Research Institute, 1-12, Hachinman-cho 1-chome, Higashikurume-shi, Tokyo 203, Japan.

KOMPASS PROFESSIONNEL. MACHINES - OUTILS, ROBOTIQUE, MECANIQUE GENERALE.. see BUSINESS AND ECONOMICS — Trade And Industrial Directories

621.8025489   DK   ISSN 0106-1186
KOMPASS SELECT EXPORT. MACHINE INDUSTRY. Cover title: Euro Kompass Denmark. Machinery. (Text in Danish, English, French, German and Spanish) 1980. a. DKK 300 (listed companies DKK 100). Forlaget Kompass Danmark, Oeveroedvej 5, DK-2840 Holte, Denmark. TEL 45-45-41-21-00. FAX 45-45-41-06-65. illus. **Document type:** directory.
● Also available on CD-ROM.
Formerly: Kompass Select Denmark. Machinery.

KOMPASS SELECT EXPORT. TRANSPORT EQUIPMENT. see TRANSPORTATION

621.9   FI   ISSN 0355-0729
KONEVIESTI. (Text in Finnish) 1952. fortn. FIM 235. Viestilehdet Oy, Revontulentie 8b, 02100 Espoo 10, Finland. TEL 90-131151. FAX 0-131-15209. Ed. Tarmo Luoma. adv.; circ. 53,500 (controlled). (tabloid format)
Description: Covers farm and forest mechanization, contractor and entrepreneur machinery, cattle and pig mechanization, and farm buildings.

621.9 338   SW   ISSN 0283-880X
KONJUNKTUREN VERKSTADSINDUSTRIN; en aktuell laegesbedoemning fraan Verkstadsfoereningen och Mekanfoerbundet. 1972. q. Verkstadsfoereningen, P.O. Box 5510, S-114 85 Stockholm, Sweden.

621.9   GW   ISSN 0720-5953
CODEN: KMAGGA
KONSTRUKTION; Zeitschrift fuer Konstrucktion und Entwicklung im Maschinen-, Apparate- und Geraetbau. 1949. m. DM.558($405) (effective 1996). (Verein Deutscher Ingenieure, Gesellschaft Entwicklung Konstruktion Vertrieb) Springer-Verlag, Heidelberger Platz 3, 14197 Berlin, Germany. TEL 030-8207-0. FAX 030-8214091. E-mail: orders@springer.de. (In N. America: Springer-Verlag New York, Inc., 44 Hartz Way, Secaucus, NJ 07096-2491. TEL 201-348-4033. FAX 201-348-4505) Ed. W. Beitz. adv.; bk.rev.; abstr.; bibl.; charts; illus.; pat.; index. circ. 6,000. (also avail. in microform from UMI; back issues avail.; reprint service avail. from ISI) **Indexed:** Eng.Ind, Excerp.Med., Fluidex, INIS Atomind., Sh.& Vib.Dig. **Document type:** trade publication.
—Ei; SWETS; UMI. **CCC.**
Formerly (until 1981): Konstruktion im Maschinen-, Apparate- und Geraetebau (ISSN 0023-3625)

621.9   JA
KOSAKU KIKAI/MACHINE CONSTRUCTION. (Text in Japanese) a. 3800 Yen. Taiga Shuppan Publications Co., 1-13, Kanda Awaji-cho, Chiyoda-ku, Tokyo 101, Japan.

621.9   JA   ISSN 0386-8192
KOSAKU KIKAI NYUSU/MACHINE TOOL NEWS. (Text in Japanese) 1978. bi-m. membership. Nihon Kosaku Kikai Kogyokai - Japan Machine Tool Builder's Association, 5-8, Shiba Koen 3-chome, Minato-ku, Tokyo 105, Japan.

621.   JA
KOSAKU KIKAI SETSUBITO TOKEI CHOSA HOKOKUSHO/REPORT OF SURVEY ON MACHINE TOOLS INSTALLATION. (Text in Japanese) 1952. irreg. 20000 Yen per no. Tsusho Sanggyosho, Daijin Kanbo, Chosa Tokeibu - Ministry of International Trade and Industry, Minister's Secretariat, Research and Statistics Department, 8-9, Ginza 2-chome, Chuo-ku, Tokyo 104, Japan. (Co-sponsor: Tsusan Tokei Kyokai - International Trade and Industry Statistics Association)

621.9 669   FR
LALU. 10/yr. 2 av. d'Estienne-d'Orves, 94700 Maisons Alfort, France. TEL 45-18-17-17. FAX 43-68-89-83. TELEX 233 765. Ed. M. Francois Schuster. circ. 24,000.
Description: Covers sheet metal, wire tubing, metal forming, welding, surface treatment.

621.9 918   US
LATIN AMERICAN METAL MECHANIC & ELECTRONIC INDUSTRY DIRECTORY. a. Aquino Productions, Box 15760, Stamford, CT 06901. TEL 203-325-3138. Ed. Andres C. Aquino. adv.

621.8   US   ISSN 1056-0149
TJ1350.A1
LIFT EQUIPMENT. 1988. bi-m. $24 (foreign $60). Group III Communications, 10229 E. Independence Ave., Independence, MO 64053. TEL 816-254-8735. FAX 816-254-2128. adv.; bk.rev. circ. 16,089.
Description: Reports on information about lifting personnel and materials aloft. Covers safety products and regulations, new equipment, and maintenance.

LINYE JIXIE/FORESTRY MACHINERY. see FORESTS AND FORESTRY

LOCAL AUTHORITY PLANT & VEHICLES. see PUBLIC ADMINISTRATION — Municipal Government

621.9   US
LOCATOR OF USED MACHINERY, EQUIPMENT & PLANT SERVICES. 1969. m. $38. Machinery Information Systems, Inc., 1110 Spring St., Silver Spring, MD 20910. TEL 301-585-9498. FAX 301-585-9460. TELEX 898-400. adv. contact: Bill Wood. circ. 72,500. circ. Pub. Rick Shontz. **Document type:** catalog.
Formerly: Locator (Silver Spring) (ISSN 0460-1327)
Description: Directory of used metalworking machinery and manufacturing plant supplies.

621.9   US   ISSN 0741-8760
TJ1   CODEN: LCOVAW
LOCOMOTIVE. 1867. q. free. Hartford Steam Boiler Inspection and Insurance Co., One State St., Hartford, CT 06102. TEL 203-722-1866. Ed. Nancy E. Bergeron. illus.; cum.index every 2 yrs. circ. 50,000. (also avail. in microfiche)
—Faxon; UnCover.

621.9   SZ
LOGISTIKKATALOG. 1969. a. 27 SFr. Verlag Binkert AG, CH-4335 Laufenburg, Switzerland. TEL 064-697272. FAX 064-697333. Ed. Walter Meier-Schmid. adv. contact: Ludwig Binkert. circ. 4,150. **Document type:** trade publication.
Formerly: Foerdermittelkatalog.

LOLA SAOPSTENJA/LOLA PROCEEDINGS. see ENGINEERING — Mechanical Engineering

LUBRICATING OILS DATA BOOK. see PETROLEUM AND GAS

621.9   GW
M A N ROLAND REVUE; technology and trends in sheet-fed offset. (Text in Dutch, English, Finnish, French, German, Italian, Japanese, Spanish, Swedish) 1970. s-a. free. M A N Roland Druckmaschinen Aktiengesellschaft, Muehlheimerstr. 341, 63075 Offenbach a.M., Germany. FAX 069-83051030. circ. 130,000. (back issues avail.) **Indexed:** Print.Abstr. **Document type:** trade publication.
Former titles: M A N Roland News Extra; M A N - Roland Revue; **Supersedes:** M A N Roland Nachrichten.

621.8   US
M H I NEWS. 1945. q. free to members. Material Handling Institute, 8720 Red Oak Blvd., Ste. 201, Charlotte, NC 28217-3992. TEL 704-522-8644. FAX 704-522-7826. Ed. Lisa Woodieenreich. bk.rev. circ. 1,000.
Incorporates (in 1987): Material Handling Education News.
Description: Deals with the storage, movement, control or protection of materials like cranes, storage containers, and guided vehicle systems.

621.9   US
M S C BUYER'S REFERENCE. 1990. a. M S C Industrial Supply Co., 151 Sunnyside Blvd., Plainview, NY 11803. TEL 516-349-7100. adv.: B&W page $5400, color page $6500; trim 8 1/4 x 10. circ. 179,000.
Description: Contains product information for OEM-MRO industrial buyers.

MACHINERY

621.9   IT   ISSN 0024-8959
MACCHINE; *rassegna tecnica dell'industria meccanica.* 1948. 11/yr. L.110000. (Editoriale Tecnica Macchine) E T M, S.r.l., Via Principe Eugenio 3, 20155 Milan, Italy. TEL 02-48010095. FAX 02-48010011. adv.; bk.rev.; abstr.; bibl.; charts; illus.; index. circ. 11,000.
    Description: Technical review of the mechanical engineering industry. Workshop and engineering technique, metrology, tooling, production and organization.

621.9   II   ISSN 0024-9092
MACHINE AND MACHINERY. (Text in English) 1968. m. Rs.40. L.K. Pandeya, Ed. & Pub., Block F, 105C New Alipore, Calcutta 700053, India.

621.9   II   ISSN 0541-6388
TJ1   CODEN: MBUIAR
MACHINE BUILDING INDUSTRY. (Text in English) 1962. m. Rs.30. (Indian Machine Tool Manufacturers' Association) Chary Publications, 14 Sidh Prasad, Ghatkopar Mahul Rd., Tilak Nagar, Bombay 400089, India. Ed. S.T. Chary. adv.; charts; illus. circ. 5,000.
—CASDDS.

621.9   UK
MACHINE TOOL SELECTOR. 1978. 3/yr. Nexus Media Ltd., Nexus House, Azalea Dr., Swanley, Kent BR8 8HY, England. TEL 01322-660070. FAX 01322-337633. adv.; circ. 18,634.

621.811   UK   ISSN 0939-7418
MACHINE VIBRATION. 1992. 4/yr. £150($241) (effective 1996). Springer-Verlag, Springer House, 8 Alexandra Rd., London SW19 7JZ, England. TEL 081-944-2942. FAX 081-947-4651. (U.S. subscr. to: Springer-Verlag New York, Inc., Box 2485, Secaucus, NJ 07096-2491. TEL 201-348-4033) Ed. D.G. Gorman. **Document type:** trade publication.
—BLDSC (5326.550000); SWETS. **CCC**.
    Description: Publishes experimental and analytical studies of vibration emitted from the widest range of machinery. Includes modal and finite element analysis, and applications of findings.

621   CN   ISSN 0831-8603
MACHINERY & EQUIPMENT M R O. (Maintenance Repair Overhaul) 1985. bi-m. Can.$44.94 (US Can.$68, elsewhere Can.$99). Southam Magazine Group, 1450 Don Mills Rd., Don Mills, ON M3B 2X7, Canada. TEL 416-445-6641. FAX 416-442-2077. Ed. William Roebuck. adv.; bk.rev.; circ. 25,000 (controlled). (tabloid format; back issues avail.) **Document type:** trade publication.
    Description: Directed to people responsible for mechanical and electrical maintenance, and maintenance shop operations. Focuses on mechanical power transmission, fluid power (hydraulics and pneumatics), health and safety, shop tools, electrical and electronic components.

621.9   II   ISSN 0047-5351
MACHINERY & MACHINE TOOL JOURNAL. (Text in English) 1958. m. Rs.18($3) 5-A Daryaganj, Ansari Rd., New Delhi 110002, India. Ed. R.C. Hersolay. adv.; bk.rev.; illus.; stat.; index. circ. 7,000. (tabloid format)

621.9 658.5   UK   ISSN 0024-919X
TJ1   CODEN: MPREAU
MACHINERY AND PRODUCTION ENGINEERING; a journal of production engineering and machine tools. 1912. s-m. £85 (foreign £130). Findlay Publications Ltd., Franks Hall, Franks Ln., Horton Kirby, Kent DA4 9LL, England. TEL 0322-22222. Ed. Chris Powley. adv.; bk.rev.; charts; illus.; mkt.; s-a. index. circ. 16,388. (also avail. in microform from UMI) **Indexed:** B.C.I.R.A., BMT, Br.Tech.Ind., C.I.S. Abstr., Cadscan, Eng.Ind., Fluidex, INSPEC, ISMEC, Lead Abstr., Met.Abstr., Robomat. (until 1992) World Alum.Abstr., World Text.Abstr., Zincscan. **Document type:** academic/scholarly publication.
—BLDSC (5328.200000); Ei; Faxon; SWETS; UMI; UnCover. **CCC**.
    Formerly: Machinery.

620.16   AU   ISSN 0255-3066
TJ1
MACHINERY AND STEEL. German edition: Maschinen und Stahlbau. (Text in English) 1959. 5/yr. S.330. Fachverband der Maschinen und Stahlbauindustrie Oesterreichs, Wiedner Hauptstrasse 63, 1045 Vienna 63, Austria. Ed.Bd. adv.; charts; illus.; tr.lit. **Indexed:** Met.Abstr., Sh.& Vib.Dig., World Alum.Abstr. —BLDSC (5328.250000).
    Description: Trade publication for the machinery and steel construction industry, featuring technical research and new developments. Includes industry news, and new product information.

621.9   UK   ISSN 0305-3121
MACHINERY BUYERS' GUIDE. 1926. a. £39 (foreign £48). Findlay Publications Ltd., Franks Hall, Franks Ln., Horton Kirby, Kent DA4 9LL, England. Ed. D. Butters. adv. circ. 8,000. **Indexed:** Copper Abstr. **Document type:** academic/scholarly publication.
    Formerly: Machinery's Annual Buyer's Guide (ISSN 0076-2040)

621
MACHINERY: LATIN AMERICAN INDUSTRIAL REPORT. 1985. a. $235 per country report. Aquino Productions, Box 15760, Stamford, CT 06901. TEL 203-325-3138. Ed. Andres C. Aquino.

621.9   UK   ISSN 0024-9211
MACHINERY MARKET; the commercial engineering journal. Variant title: Machinery Market and the Machinery and Engineering Materials Gazette. 1879. w. £60 (foreign £75) (effective June 1995). Machinery Market Ltd., 6 Blyth Rd., Bromley, Kent BR1 3RX, England. TEL 0181-460-4224. FAX 0181-290-1668. Ed. C. Granger. adv. contact: A.J. Stockwell. bk.rev.; abstr.; charts; illus.; mkt.; pat.; stat.; tr.mk. circ. 8,700. **Indexed:** Eng.Ind. **Document type:** trade publication.
    Incorporates: Machinery and Engineering Materials Gazette.
    Description: Lists thousands of machine tools for sale with editorial features and comment.

621.9   US   ISSN 8756-923X
MACHINERY OUTLOOK; heard in the dirt. 1984. m. $325 (foreign $375). Manfredi & Associates, 1110 Lake Cook Rd., Ste. 295, Buffalo Grove, IL 60089. TEL 708-215-2999. FAX 708-215-0455. Ed. Frank Manfredi. bk.rev. (looseleaf format; back issues avail.) **Document type:** newsletter.
    Description: Covers construction and mining machinery markets and trends.

621.9   UK
MACHINERY OUTLOOK EUROPE. 1992. m. $654. Wood Manfredi Ltd., Leafields Farm, Lower Loxley, Uttoxeter, Staffs. ST14 8SA, England. TEL 01889-500588. FAX 01889-500577. Ed. C.J. Wood. micro. (back issues avail.) **Document type:** trade publication.

621.9   US
MACHINERY TRADER. 1978. w. $59. Peed Corporation, Box 85670, Lincoln, NE 68501. TEL 402-479-2144. (tabloid format)

621.9   UK
MACHINERY WORLD. 1983. m. £45. Sheen Publishing Ltd., 50 Queens Rd., Buckhurst Hill, Essex IG9 5DD, England. TEL 0181-504-1661. FAX 0181-505-4336. TELEX 296620-SHEEN-G. Ed. Carole Titmuss. adv. contact: Jane Andrews. circ. 10,000. **Document type:** trade publication.
    Formerly: World Machinery.

621.9   FR   ISSN 0047-536X
MACHINES PRODUCTION. 1971. 24/yr. 830 F. (foreign 1100 F.). Societe Francaise d'Editions Techniques (SOFETEC), 20 rue de la Saussiere, 92100 Boulogne, France. TEL 48-25-50-30. FAX 48-25-03-13. TELEX SOFETEC 633 715 F. Ed. Michel Pech. adv. contact: Bernard Cromback. bk.rev.; illus.; index. circ. 17,500. **Indexed:** World Alum.Abstr.

621.9   US
MACHINING TECHNOLOGY. q. $60. Society of Manufacturing Engineers, One SME Dr., Box 930, Dearborn, MI 48121-0930. TEL 313-271-1500. FAX 313-271-2861. TELEX 297742 SME UR (VIA RCA). **Document type:** trade publication.

MACHINIST. see *LABOR UNIONS*

MACHINIST. see *ENGINEERING — Mechanical Engineering*

MANAGING EMPLOYEE HEALTH BENEFITS. see *INSURANCE*

MANUFACTURING ENGINEERING. see *ENGINEERING*

621.86   SP   ISSN 0025-2646
MANUTENCION Y ALMACENAJE. 1965. 11/yr. 13566 ptas. (foreign 15796 ptas.). (Federation Europeenne de la Manutention, Comite Nacional Espanol) Cetisa - Boixareu S.A., Concepcion Arenal, 5, 08027 Barcelona, Spain. Ed. Ferran Puig. adv.; bk.rev.; illus.; tr.lit.

621.9 690   SP
MAQUINARIA Y EQUIPO. 10/yr. Torpedero Tucuman 24, bajo 5, Apdo. 19130, 28016 Madrid, Spain. TEL 1-458-81-74. FAX 1-458-69-47. Ed. Antonio A. Sanchez. circ. 6,000.

621.9 669   BL   ISSN 0025-2700
TJ4
MAQUINAS & METAIS. 1964. m. $80. Aranda Editora Ltda., Rua D. Elisa no. 167, Perdizes, 01155-900 Sao Paulo, SP, Brazil. TEL 55-11-826-4511. FAX 55-11-669585. Ed. Jose Roberto Gonzalves. adv.; bk.rev.; circ. 15,000 (controlled). **Indexed:** PROMT.

621.8 669   PO
MAQUINAS E METAIS. 10/yr. Av. Antonio Augusto de Aguiar 25, 1o Esq., Lisbon, Portugal. TEL 553804. circ. 5,000.

621.9   SZ   ISSN 0025-2840
MARCHE SUISSE DES MACHINES. German edition: Schweizer Maschinenmarkt (ISSN 0036-7397) (Text in French) 1933. fortn. 93.85 SFr. (foreign 106 SFr.). Fachpresse Goldach, CH-9403 Goldach, Switzerland. TEL 071-409111. FAX 071-409511. Ed. Edouard Huguelet. adv.; abstr.; illus.; stat.; index. circ. 8,000. **Document type:** trade publication.

621.9   GW   ISSN 0340-5737
TJ3
DIE MASCHINE. Short title: D I M A. 1946. 10/yr. DM.94.50 (foreign DM.124.50). A.G.T. Verlag Thum GmbH, Postfach 109, 71601 Ludwigsburg, Germany. TEL 07141-223156. FAX 07141-223131. TELEX 7264853. Ed. L. Friedrich. circ. 10,057. **Indexed:** INIS Atomind. **Document type:** trade publication.
    Description: Construction and operation of machine tools for cutting, non-cutting, metal-removing and forming production methods.

621.9   GW   ISSN 0025-4452
MASCHINE UND WERKZEUG. 1899. 10/yr. DM.69 (foreign DM.78) (effective 1996). Resch Media Mail Verlag GmbH, Hauptstr. 40, 82229 Seefeld, Germany. TEL 08152-994-0. FAX 08152-994360. (Subscr. to: Vertriebsunion Meynen GmbH, Kaiser-Friedrich-Ring 49, 65185 Wiesbaden, Germany. TEL 0611-880432. FAX 0611-880439) adv.; bk.rev.; illus.; tr.lit.; cum.index covering 70 yrs. circ. 25,000. **Document type:** trade publication.

621.9   AU
MASCHINEN REPORT INTERNATIONAL. 1974. q. S.80. Technopress Fachzeitschriften Verlagsgesellschaft mbH, Postfach 176, A-1191 Vienna, Austria. Ed. Helmut Tober. adv.; bk.rev.; charts; illus.; tr.lit. circ. 10,000.

621.9 693.7   AU
MASCHINEN UND STAHLBAU. English edition: Machinery and Steel (ISSN 0255-3066) 1959. 5/yr. S.330. Fachverband der Maschinen und Stahlbauindustrie Oesterreichs, Wiedner Hauptstr. 63, 1045 Vienna 63, Austria. adv.; charts; illus. circ. 5,000.
    Formerly: Maschinen- und Stahlbauindustrie in Oesterreich (ISSN 0025-4460)

621.9   SZ
MASCHINENBAU. 1972. m. 58 Fr.($39) Olympia Verlag AG, Postfach, CH-8021 Zurich, Switzerland. TEL 01-242 95 45. Ed. C. Schlumpf. circ. 12,000.

MACHINERY

621.9   GW   ISSN 0025-4487
MASCHINENBAU UND FERTIGUNGSTECHNIK DER U D S S R. 1959. m. DM.375. Institut fuer Wissenschaftliche Information aus der Sowjetunion, Postfach 721, 52008 Aachen, Germany. Ed. J. Peklenik. charts; illus.; tr.lit.; index. circ. 2,000.
—CCC.

621.9   GW   ISSN 0341-5775
MASCHINENMARKT. 1895. w. DM.385. Vogel Verlag und Druck GmbH & Co. KG, Max-Planck-Str. 7-9, 97082 Wuerzburg, Germany. TEL 0931-4182145. FAX 0931-4182640. (Subscr. to: Vogel Verlag, 97064 Wuerzburg, Germany; Dist. in U.S. by: Vogel Europublishing, Inc., 19927 Villa Dr., Sonora, CA 95370. TEL 209-533-3555. FAX 209-533-9555) Ed. Helmut Groessel. adv.: B&W page DM.9342, color page DM.12242; trim 270 x 190; adv. contact: Peter Janka. bk.rev.; charts; illus.; mkt.; tr.lit.; index; circ. 49,500. **Indexed**: C.I.S. Abstr., Chem.Abstr., Excerp.Med., Fluidex, INIS Atomind., INSPEC, Key to Econ.Sci., Met.Abstr., Packag.Sci.Tech., Sh.& Vib.Dig., World Alum.Abstr. **Document type**: trade publication.
—BLDSC (5384.950000); Ei; SWETS.

621.9   JA   ISSN 0910-8106
MASHIN/MACHINE. (Text in Japanese) m. 350 Yen per no. Amada, 200, Ishida, Isehara-shi, Kanagawa-ken 259-11, Japan.

621.9   RU   ISSN 0025-4568
CODEN: MASHA7
MASHINOSTROITEL'. 1931. m. $154 (effective 1996). Izdatel'stvo Mashinostroenie, 4, Stromynsky per., 107076 Moscow, Russia. TEL 095-269-7141. FAX 095-269-4897. Ed. E.M. Korolenko. adv.: page DM.4000. bk.rev.; bibl.; charts; illus.; index. circ. 11,000. (tabloid format) **Indexed**: C.I.S. Abstr., Chem.Abstr., INIS Atomind. **Document type**: academic/scholarly publication.
—BLDSC (0103.200000); CASDDS.
Description: Acquaints readers with the advanced experience in organization of work and management along the scientific lines, economics of production, mechanization and automation of manufacturing processes and state-of-the art technology.

621.8   YU   ISSN 0461-2531
MASINSTVO. (Issued also as part of Tehnika) (Text in Serbocroatian; summaries in English, Russian) vol. 24, 1975. m. $50. Savez Inzenjera i Tehnicara Jugoslavije, Kneza Milosa 9, Box 187, 11000 Belgrade, Yugoslavia. Ed. Mirko Josifovic.

621.9 388.12   SW   ISSN 0345-7788
MASKINKONTAKT. 1966. m. SEK 985 in the Nordic countries; elsewhere SEK 2800. V MaskinKontakt AB, Datavaegen 10, S-436 32 Askim, Sweden. TEL 031-680005. FAX 46-31-68-00-09. Ed. Bjoern Johansson. adv.: B&W page SEK 11475, color page SEK 16405; trim 180 x 260. circ. 14,000. **Document type**: catalog, consumer publication, trade publication.
Description: Lists suppliers of primarily second-hand H6Vs, construction machinery, gravel machinery, forestry and lumbering machinery, cranes and lifting appliances.

621.9   DK   ISSN 0047-6102
MASKINMESTEREN. 1890. m. DKK 96. Maskinmestrenes Forening - Marine Engineer Officers' Association, Sankt Annae Plads 16, DK-1250 Copenhagen K, Denmark. adv. circ. 10,500.

621.86   US   ISSN 0025-5262
CODEN: MHENA4
MATERIAL HANDLING ENGINEERING; technical magazine for material handling, packaging and shipping specialists. 1945. 13/yr. $50 (free to qualified personnel). Penton Publishing (Subsidiary of: Pittway Company), 1100 Superior Ave., Cleveland, OH 44114-2543. TEL 216-696-7000. FAX 216-696-8765. (Subscr. to: Box 95759, Cleveland, OH 44101) Ed. Bernard Knill. adv.; charts; illus.; stat.; tr.lit.; circ. 101,447 (controlled). (also avail. in microform from UMI; reprint service avail. from UMI) **Indexed**: A.S.& T.Ind., ABI Inform., B.P.I., CAD CAM Abstr. (until 1992), Energy Info.Abstr., Eng.Ind., Ind.Sci.Rev., INSPEC, Int.Packag.Abstr., Robomat. (until 1992). **Document type**: trade publication.
●Also available online. Vendor(s): University Microfilms International.
—BLDSC (5393.280000); CIS; Ei; Faxon; Genuine Article; SWETS; UMI; UnCover. **CCC**.
Description: Offers comprehensive information on the technology and processes used in industrial material handling. Articles cover systems presently in use, new product developments, management techniques and the operations of individual companies.

621.86   US
MATERIAL HANDLING ENGINEERING HANDBOOK AND DIRECTORY. biennial. $35 (free to qualified personnel). Penton Publishing (Subsidiary of: Pittway Company), 1100 Superior Ave., Cleveland, OH 44114-2543. TEL 216-696-7000. FAX 216-696-8765. (Subscr. to: Box 95759, Cleveland, OH 44101) Ed. Bernard Knill. circ. 113,000 (controlled). (reprint service avail. from UMI) **Document type**: directory.

621.86   UK   ISSN 0025-5351
MATERIALS HANDLING NEWS. 1955. m. £65. Nexus Media Ltd., Warwick House, Azalea Dr., Swanley, Kent BR8 8HY, England. TEL 01322-660070. FAX 01322-667633. Ed. Roderick Robinson. adv.; bk.rev.; index; circ. 31,981 (controlled). (also avail. in microform from UMI; back issues avail.) **Indexed**: Account.& Data Proc.Abstr., BMT, Br.Ceram.Abstr., Br.Tech.Ind., C.I.S. Abstr., CAD CAM Abstr. (until 1992), Energy Info.Abstr., Environ.Abstr., Ergon.Abstr., Int.Packag.Abstr., ISMEC, Key to Econ.Sci., Mgmt.& Market.Abstr., Robomat. (until 1992), World Text.Abstr. **Document type**: trade publication.
—BLDSC (5395.025000); Ei; SWETS; UMI. **CCC**.
Incorporates: Mechanical Handling International; Which was formerly: Mechanical Handling (ISSN 0025-6528).
Description: Contains information on all aspects of materials handling and storage systems in manufacturing, distribution and storage industries.

MECHANICS OF STRUCTURES AND MACHINES; an international journal. see ENGINEERING — Mechanical Engineering

MECHANIK; miesiecznik naukowo-techniczny. see ENGINEERING — Mechanical Engineering

621.9   JA   ISSN 0388-7529
MEINTENANSU/MAINTENANCE. (Text in Japanese) 1980. m. 800 Yen per no. Kagaku Tosho Shuppan K.K., Gijutsu Hyoronsha, 8-8, Aisumi-cho, Shinjuku-ku, Tokyo 160, Japan.

MEKHANIZATSIYA STROITEL'STVA. see ENGINEERING — Civil Engineering

MESTNYI PROIZVODSTVENNYI OPYT V PROMYSHLENNOSTI/LOCAL LEVEL EXPERIENCE IN THE MANUFACTURING INDUSTRY; nauchno-tekhnicheskii referativnyi sbornik. see ENGINEERING — Mechanical Engineering

671   NE   ISSN 0026-0460
METAAL & KUNSTSTOF. 1963. fortn. fl.215. Misset (Subsidiary of: Reed Elsevier plc), Postbus 4, 7000 BA Doetinchem, Netherlands. TEL 31-8340-49911. FAX 31-8340-43839. TELEX 45481. Ed. Th. Evers. adv.: B&W page fl.2665; trim 215 x 285; adv. contact: Cor van Nek. bk.rev.; charts; illus.; mkt.; pat.; stat. circ. 8,090. **Indexed**: Excerp.Med., Key to Econ.Sci. **Document type**: trade publication.
—SWETS.
Description: Technical magazine for the engineering and machinery industry.

671 621.3   NE   ISSN 0167-9511
METALEKTRO PROFIEL; informatie over de metaal- en elektrotechnische industrie. 1961. 10/yr. Vereniging F M E, Postbus 190, 2700 AD Zoetermeer, Netherlands. TEL 31-79-531113. FAX 31-79-531365. Ed. J.M.G. van Woensel. adv.; charts; illus.; stat. circ. 5,000. **Indexed**: Key to Econ.Sci. **Document type**: trade publication.
Formerly (until 1981): Metalektro Visie (ISSN 0026-0738)

METALES Y METALURGIA. see METALLURGY

METALWORKING PRODUCTION & PURCHASING; Canadian publication for production, purchasing & management in metalworking. see METALLURGY

658.5   FR   ISSN 0153-9035
TS200   CODEN: TMDEDJ
METAUX DEFORMATION. Cover title: Travail des Metaux par Deformation. 1969. bi-m. 440.74 F. (foreign 690 F.) (effective 1996). Revue Francaise des Metallurgistes, 32 rue Saint-Marc, 75002 Paris, France. TEL 42-60-38-42. FAX 42-60-31-51. adv.; bk.rev. circ. 3,200.
—CASDDS.
Formerly: Formage des Materiaux (ISSN 0015-7724)

METLFAX. see METALLURGY

MINING AND ALLIED MACHINERY CORPORATION. ANNUAL REPORT. see MINES AND MINING INDUSTRY

670   US   ISSN 1076-1993
HD9703.A1
MINNESOTA PRECISION MANUFACTURING ASSOCIATION JOURNAL. 1960. bi-m. membership. Strategic Communications, 3255 Hennepin Ave. S., Ste. 75, Minneapolis, MN 55408. TEL 612-825-4559. FAX 612-825-0940. Ed. Bill MacArthur. adv. circ. 8,000. (back issues avail.) **Document type**: trade publication.
Formerly: Minnesota Tooling and Machining Association Journal (ISSN 0273-7523)
Description: Promotes the Minnesota trading area, its manufacturers, and suppliers.

621.75   US   ISSN 0026-8003
TJ1   CODEN: MMASAY
MODERN MACHINE SHOP. 1928. m. $42 (foreign $72). Gardner Publications, Inc., 6600 Clough Pike, Cincinnati, OH 45244-4090. TEL 513-231-8020. FAX 513-231-2818. Ed. Thomas L. Beard. adv. contact: Donald Kline. charts; illus.; tr.lit. circ. 106,000. (also avail. in microform from UMI; reprint service avail.) **Indexed**: A.S.& T.Ind., Bus.Ind., Chem.Abstr., Ind.Sci.Rev., INSPEC, ISMEC, Met.Abstr., Tr.& Indus.Ind., World Alum.Abstr. **Document type**: trade publication.
—BLDSC (5889.000000); Ei; Faxon; SWETS; UMI; UnCover. **CCC**.
Description: Offers comprehensive information on all aspects of the manufacturing and machining industry. Provides coverage of engineering, industrial robots, research and developments, programming, safety requirements and equipment.

621.86   US   ISSN 0026-8038
TS149   CODEN: MMHHA2
MODERN MATERIALS HANDLING. 1946. 14/yr. (includes a. Casebook Directory, a. Planning Guidebook). $80 (Canada $118; Mexico $110; elsewhere $140). Cahners Publishing Company (Newton), Division of Reed Elsevier Inc., 275 Washington St., Newton, MA 02158-1630. TEL 617-964-3030. FAX 617-558-4402. (Subscr. to: 8773 S. Ridgeline Blvd., Highlands Ranch, CO 80126. TEL 303-470-4000. FAX 303-398-7691) Ed. Raymond Kulwiec; Pub. William Sbordon. adv.; bk.rev.; charts; illus.; tr.lit.; index. circ. 100,850. (also avail. in microform) **Indexed**: A.I.Abstr. (until 1992), A.S.& T.Ind., ABI Inform., BPIA, Bus.Ind., CAD CAM Abstr. (until 1992), Comput.Lit.Ind., Energy Info.Abstr., Eng.Ind., Ind.Sci.Rev., INSPEC, Int.Packag.Abstr., Packag.Sci.Tech., PROMT, Robomat. (until 1992), Tr.& Indus.Ind. **Document type**: trade publication.
—BLDSC (5889.500000); Ei; Faxon; Genuine Article; SWETS; UMI; UnCover. **CCC**.
Description: For managers and engineers who are responsible for handling materials and managing inventories, equipment, and systems used to move, store, control and protect products throughout manufacturing, warehousing and distribution centers.

621.86 US
MODERN MATERIALS HANDLING CASEBOOK DIRECTORY.
(Suppl. to: Modern Materials Handling) a. Cahners Publishing Company (Newton), Division of Reed Elsevier Inc., 275 Washington St., Newton, MA 02158-1630. TEL 617-964-3030. FAX 617-558-4402. (Subscr. to: 8773 S. Ridgeline Blvd., Highlands Ranch, CO 80126. TEL 303-388-4511. FAX 330-398-7691) Ed. Raymond Kulwiec; Pub. William Sbordon. **Document type:** trade publication.
Description: Where-to source for equipment purchases.

621.86 US
MODERN MATERIALS HANDLING PLANNING GUIDEBOOK. (Suppl. to: Modern Materials Handling) a. Cahners Publishing Company (Newton), Division of Reed Elsevier Inc., 275 Washington St., Newton, MA 02158-1630. TEL 617-964-3030. FAX 617-558-4402. (Subscr. to: 8773 S. Ridgeline Blvd., Highlands Ranch, CO 80126. TEL 303-470-4000. FAX 303-398-7691) Ed. Raymond Kulwiec; Pub. William Sbordon. **Document type:** trade publication.
Description: How-to guide for determining plant needs and for finding new ways to increase productivity.

621.9 338 IS
MOFET.* 1977. 4/yr. free. Israel Industry Center for Research & Development, c/o Chamber of Commerce, 84 Hahashmonaim St., P.O.B. 20027, Tel Aviv 61200, Israel. FAX 972-3-236926. TELEX 341667-RMYM-IL. Ed. Y. Amitay. adv.; bk.rev. circ. 3,000.
Formerly (until 1982): Matimop.

LE MONITEUR - MATERIELS ET CHANTIERS. see *BUILDING AND CONSTRUCTION*

621.9 FR ISSN 0297-8717
MOULES, MODELES ET MAQUETTES. 1964. q. 200 F. Centre d'Etudes de la Productivite dans les Industries du Moule, Modele et Maquette, 39-41 rue Louis Blanc, 92400 Courbevoie, France. TEL 33-1-47-17-63-57. FAX 33-1-47-17-63-60. (Subscr. to: 92038 Paris la Defense Cedex, France) adv.; bk.rev.
Formerly: Moules et Modeles (ISSN 0153-9604)

621.9 SW
MOVING;* kundtidning med aktuelle information. 1974. q. Gillelije Sten och Grus, Havnen, 3250, Gilleleje, Sweden. charts; illus.

621.86 JA ISSN 0289-4351
MUJINKA GIJUTSU/DATA SYSTEMS FOR AUTOMATED PRODUCTION AND MATERIAL HANDLING. (Text in Japanese) 1960. m. 18540 Yen; newsstand price: 1500Yen. Ryutsu Kenkyusha, 13-7, Minami Ikebukuro 3-chome, Toshima-ku, Tokyo 171, Japan. Ed. Ichiro Kikuta; Pub. Tsutomu Mano. adv. contact: Hirosh Hanatani. bk.rev. circ. 23,000. **Indexed:** Comput.Lit.Ind. **Document type:** trade publication.
Formerly (until 1984): Seisan to Unpan - Modern Materials Handling (ISSN 0037-1068)

621.9 658 US
MY LITTLE SALESMAN HEAVY EQUIPMENT CATALOG. 1958. m. $18. Industrial Publishing Co., Box 70208, Eugene, OR 97401. TEL 503-342-1201. FAX 503-342-3307. Ed. Peter Powell; Pub. Richard Pierce. adv.: B&W page $895; adv. contact: Cathy Redwine. circ. 27,000. **Document type:** trade publication.
Description: Provides information to those buying or selling heavy equipment.

621.8 BL
N E I BRAZIL: NOTICIARIO DE EQUIPAMENTOS INDUSTRIAIS. 1974. m. $125. T L Publicacoes Industriais Ltda., R. Brig. Tobias, 356, 4 andar, 01032 Sao Paulo, SP, Brazil. TEL 011-2271022. FAX 011-2289373. TELEX 011-30562 TLPB. Ed. Raul Gonzalez Simon. circ. 30,000. (tabloid format; back issues avail.)
Description: Provides information about new industrial products in all industries.

621.9 NE ISSN 0027-7339
NAAIMACHINE - NIEUWS. 1944. 6/yr. fl.135. (Algemene Vereniging van Naaimachinehandelaren) Stichting Naaimachine Nieuws, Postbus 29, 2900 AA Capelle aan den Ijssel, Netherlands. TEL 31-1807-15264. FAX 31-1807-15680. Ed. G. Leenders. adv.; bk.rev.; abstr.; illus.; pat.; tr.lit.; tr.mk. circ. 1,000. **Document type:** trade publication.
Description: Trade journal for sewing machine retailers.

621.9 US
NATIONAL TOOLING AND MACHINING ASSOCIATION. BUYERS GUIDE. 1968. a. $90. National Tooling and Machining Association, 9300 Livingston Rd., Ft. Washington, MD 20744. TEL 301-248-6200. FAX 301-248-7104. Ed. Mark Jeschke. adv. circ. 10,000. **Document type:** directory.
Formerly: National Tool, Die and Precision Machining Association. Buyers Guide.
Description: Complete listings of tooling and machining capabilities of the members of the National Tooling and Machining Association, with cross-references for 95 major machining capabilities.

NEIRANJI GONGCHENG/CHINESE INTERNAL COMBUSTION ENGINE ENGINEERING. see *ENGINEERING — Engineering Mechanics And Materials*

621.9 JA ISSN 0914-5249
NEW MACHINE TOOLS/NYU MASHIN TSURU. (Text in Japanese) 1974. m. 360 Yen per no. New Machine Tool Company, 7-11, Nishigotanda 2-chome, Shinagawa-ku, Tokyo 141, Japan.

621.9 530 JA ISSN 0385-6542
T1
NEW TECHNOLOGY JAPAN. (Text in English) 1972. m. 16800 Yen($200) Japan External Trade Organization, Machinery and Technology Department, 2-5 Toranomon 2-chome, Minato-ku, Tokyo 105, Japan. TEL 03-3582-3518. FAX 03-3587-2485. TELEX J24873. (Dist. overseas by: Maruzen Co., Ltd., Export Dept., P.O. Box 5050, Tokyo International 100-31, Japan. FAX 03-3274-2270) Ed. Takehisa Okabe. circ. 2,000. (back issues avail.)
—BLDSC (6088.840400); Ei.
Formerly: Japan Industrial and Technology Bulletin.
Description: Presents new technology and developments in high-tech research.

621.9 JA
NIHON KIKAI KOGYO RENGOKAI. JIGYO HOKOKU/JAPAN MACHINERY FEDERATION. REPORT. (Text in Japanese) 1952. a. Nihon Kikai Kogyo Rengokai, 5-8, Shiba Koen 3-chome, Minato-ku, Tokyo 105, Japan.

621.9 JA
NIHON KIKO SHINBUN/JAPAN MACHINERY JOURNAL. (Text in Japanese) 1948. w. 12000 Yen. Nippon Kiko Shinbunsha, 14-15, Shiba 5-chome, Minato-ku, Tokyo 108, Japan.

621.9 JA ISSN 0912-0866
NIKKIREN GEPPO/JAPAN MACHINERY FEDERATION. MONTHLY. (Text in Japanese) 1952. m. 500 Yen per no. Nihon Kikai Kogyo Rengokai - Japan Machinery Federation, 5-8, Shiba Koen 3-chome, Minato-ku, Tokyo 105, Japan.

621.9 JA
NIPPON THOMPSON COMPANY. ANNUAL REPORT. a. Nippon Thompson Co. Ltd., 2-19-19 Takanawa, Minato-ku, Tokyo 108, Japan. TEL 03-448-5850. FAX 03-447-7637.

NORTH CAROLINA METALWORKING DIRECTORY. see *BUSINESS AND ECONOMICS — Trade And Industrial Directories*

NOTICIARIO DE TESTES E LABORATORIOS. see *INSTRUMENTS*

621.9 IT
NOTIZIARIO FERRUTENSIL. 2/yr. E.P.E. s.r.l., Via la Spezia 33, 20142 Milan, Italy. TEL 2-89-50-06-73. FAX 2-846-30-45. Ed. Vincenzo Casolaro. circ. 17,172.

621.9 IT
NOTIZIARIO INDUSTRIALE. m. (10/yr.). Editrice C E T I s.r.l., Via Console Marcello 8, 20156 Milan, Italy. TEL 2-39-214-165. FAX 2-32-54-81. Ed. Giuseppe Binetti. adv.: B&W page L.1700000, color page L.2500000; trim 185 x 265. circ. 8,011.

621.9 IT ISSN 0029-4438
NOTIZIE OLIVETTI. (Editions in English, French, German, Italian, Portuguese and Spanish) 1952. q. free. C. Olivetti & Co., S.p.A., Via G. Jervis, 77, 10015 Ivrea (Turin), Italy. TEL 125-522035. FAX 125-522916. TELEX 210030. Ed. Andrea Grammatico. circ. 40,000 (14,000 English ed.; 2,000 French ed.; 2,000 German ed.; 18,000 Italian ed.; 2,000 Portuguese ed.; 2,000 Spanish ed.). **Indexed:** C.I.S. Abstr. **Document type:** corporate report.
Formerly: Notizie di Fabbrica.
Description: Provides a view of Olivetti's corporate activities, also looks at technology and marketing.

621.9 IT
NOTIZIE OLIVETTI INTERNATIONAL EDITION. (Text in English) 1985? q? C. Olivetti & Co., S.p.A., Via G. Jervis, 77, 10015 Ivrea (Turin), Italy. TEL 125-522035. FAX 125-522916. TELEX 210030. circ. 14,000. **Document type:** corporate report.
Description: Covers general Olivetti corporate activities and marketing technology.

621.8 SP ISSN 0210-0118
NOVAMAQUINA 2000;* maquina-herramienta y produccion automatizada mecanica. 1975. m. (10/yr.). 8900 ptas.($141) (effective 1993). Pulsar, S.A., Felipe de Paz 4, 08028 Barcelona, Spain. TEL 3-425-45-44. FAX 3-425-03-68. Ed. Daniel Crespo. adv.; bk.rev.; bibl.; charts; illus. circ. 5,000. **Indexed:** Ind.SST.

OELHYDRAULIK UND PNEUMATIK; Zeitschrift fuer Fluidtechnik. see *ENGINEERING — Mechanical Engineering*

621.9 AU
OESTERREICHISCHE NAEHMASCHINEN- UND ZWEIRAD-ZEITUNG. 1964. 16/yr. S.200. (Verband des Naehmaschinen- und Fahrradhandels und Gewerbes Oesterreichs) Verlag Michael Fischer, Neulerchenfelderstr. 8, A-1160 Vienna, Austria. Ed. Michael Fischer. adv.; abstr.; bibl.; charts; illus.; stat.; tr.lit. circ. 4,000.
Formerly: Oesterreichische Naehmaschinen- und Fahrrad-Zeitung (ISSN 0029-9324)

OFF ROAD AND 4 WHEEL DRIVE. see *TRANSPORTATION — Automobiles*

OFFICIAL GUIDE: TRACTORS AND FARM EQUIPMENT. see *AGRICULTURE — Agricultural Equipment*

OFFICIAL INDUSTRIAL EQUIPMENT GUIDE. see *AGRICULTURE — Agricultural Equipment*

OUTDOOR POWER EQUIPMENT OFFICIAL GUIDE. see *AGRICULTURE — Agricultural Equipment*

621.9 621 JA ISSN 0474-9847
OYO KIKAI KOGAKU/MECHANICAL ENGINEERING APPLICATIONS. (Text in Japanese) 1960. m. 12000 Yen (foreign 26000 Yen) (effective Apr. 1989). Taiga Shuppan Publications Co., 1-13, Kanda, Awaji-cho, Chiyoda-ku, Tokyo 101, Japan. FAX 8132536448. adv. circ. 18,000. (back issues avail.) **Indexed:** JCT, JTA.

621.9 US ISSN 0475-2953
UG503
P S, THE PREVENTIVE MAINTENANCE MONTHLY. m. $19 (foreign $23.75). (U.S. Department of the Army) U.S. Government Printing Office, Washington, DC 20402. (Subscr. to: Superintendent of Documents, U.S. Government Printing Office, Box 371954, Pittsburgh, PA 15250-7954. TEL 202-512-1800. FAX 202-512-2250) illus. (back issues avail.) **Document type:** government publication.
Description: Teaches soldiers assigned to combat support units and those with organizational supply and maintenance duties how to maintain trucks and other military equipment.

PACKAGE PRINTING & CONVERTING; diemaking and diecutting, flexography, gravure and offset. see *PRINTING*

PACKAGING DIGEST MACHINERY - MATERIALS GUIDE. see *PACKAGING*

4100 MACHINERY

PLANT SERVICES. see *ENGINEERING — Mechanical Engineering*

PLANT SERVICES' HANDBOOK OF COMPUTERIZED MANAGEMENT AND PREDICTIVE MAINTENANCE. see *ENGINEERING — Mechanical Engineering*

PLANT SERVICES' LITERATURE UPDATE. see *ENGINEERING — Mechanical Engineering*

621.9 GW
POLAR EXPRESS. 1966. irreg., (approx. 2/yr.). free. Polar Mohr, Postfach 1220, 65702 Hofheim, Germany. TEL 06192-2040. FAX 06192-22193. Ed. Erhard Hennemann. adv. contact: Erhard Hennemann. circ. 125,000. (back issues avail.) **Document type:** bulletin.
Formerly (until 1992): Polar Information.

621.9 PL ISSN 0324-9646
POLITECHNIKA WROCLAWSKA. INSTYTUT KONSTRUKCJI I EKSPLOATACJI MASZYN. PRACE NAUKOWE. KONFERENCJE. 1973. irreg., no.19, 1991. price varies. Wydawnictwo Politechniki Wroclawskiej, Wybrzeze Wyspianskiego 27, 50-370 Wroclaw, Poland. FAX 22-36-64. TELEX 712559 PWRPL. (Dist. by: Ars Polona-Ruch, Krakowskie Przedmiescie 7, Warsaw, Poland) illus. **Document type:** proceedings.

620 PL ISSN 0324-962X
POLITECHNIKA WROCLAWSKA. INSTYTUT KONSTRUKCJI I EKSPLOATACJI MASZYN. PRACE NAUKOWE. MONOGRAFIE. (Text in Polish: summaries in English and Russian) 1969. irreg., no.22, 1992. price varies. Wydawnictwo Politechniki Wroclawskiej, Wybrzeze Wyspianskiego 27, 50-370 Wroclaw, Poland. FAX 22-36-64. TELEX 712559 PWRPL. (Dist. by: Ars Polona-Ruch, Krakowskie Przedmiescie 7, Warsaw, Poland) **Document type:** monographic series.
—Ei.

620 PL ISSN 0324-9638
POLITECHNIKA WROCLAWSKA. INSTYTUT KONSTRUKCJI I EKSPLOATACJI MASZYN. PRACE NAUKOWE. STUDIA I MATERIALY. (Text in Polish: summaries in English and Russian) 1970. irreg., no.25, 1989. price varies. Wydawnictwo Politechniki Wroclawskiej, Wybrzeze Wyspianskiego 27, 50-370 Wroclaw, Poland. FAX 22-36-64. TELEX 712559 PWRPL. (Dist. by: Ars Polona-Ruch, Krakowskie Przedmiescie 7, Warsaw, Poland) **Document type:** academic/scholarly publication.

621.9 PL ISSN 0239-3182
POLITECHNIKA WROCLAWSKA. INSTYTUT KONSTRUKCJI I EKSPLOATACJI MASZYN. PRACE NAUKOWE. WSPOLPRACA. (Text in Polish: summaries in English, Russian) 1979. irreg., no.4, 1991. price varies. Wydawnictwo Politechniki Wroclawskiej, Wybrzeze Wyspianskiego 27, 50-370 Wroclaw, Poland. FAX 22-36-64. TELEX 712559 PWRPL. (Dist. by: Ars Polona-Ruch, Krakowskie Przedmiescie 7, Warsaw, Poland) **Document type:** academic/scholarly publication.

621.9 KR ISSN 0372-6053
TJ241 CODEN: VKPIAS
POLITEKHNICHNYI INSTYTUT KIEV. VESTNIK. SERIYA MASHINOSTROENIYA. (Text in Russian; summaries in English) irreg. 1.21 Rub. Politekhnichnyi Instytut, Brest-Litovskii pr., 39, Kiev, Ukraine. illus.
—BLDSC (0028.438000); CASDDS.

POWDER & BULK SOLIDS YEARBOOK & DIRECTORY. see *TECHNOLOGY: COMPREHENSIVE WORKS*

POWDER HANDLING & PROCESSING. see *TECHNOLOGY: COMPREHENSIVE WORKS*

621.9 US
POWER CURBERS PROFILES. 1961. q. free. Power Curbers Inc., Box 1639, Salisbury, NC 28145-1639. TEL 704-636-5871. FAX 704-633-8140. Ed. L. Bailey. charts; illus.; stat. circ. 20,000. **Document type:** newsletter.
Formerly: News from the Gutter (ISSN 0028-9159)
Description: Covers topics relating to the use of curb-and-gutter and paving machinery, including unusual applications and features on new machinery.

POWER PRODUCTS BUSINESS. see *BUSINESS AND ECONOMICS — Production Of Goods And Services*

621.9 JA ISSN 0387-3544
PRESS WORKING/PURESU GIJUTSU. (Text in Japanese) 1963. m. 1000 Yen per no. Industrial Daily News Ltd. - Nikkan Kogyo Shinbunsha, 1-8-10 Kudan Kita, Chiyoda-ku, Tokyo 102, Japan. circ. 30,000.
Description: Specializes in the technologies for metal mold designing, manufacturing and machining in all fields of industries centering around plastic processing.

PREVISIONS GLISSANTES DETAILLEES EN PERSPECTIVES SECTORIELLES (VOL.5): CONSTRUCTION DE MACHINES. see *BUSINESS AND ECONOMICS — Economic Situation And Conditions*

PREVISIONS GLISSANTES DETAILLEES EN PERSPECTIVES SECTORIELLES (VOL.6): MACHINES - OUTILS. see *BUSINESS AND ECONOMICS — Economic Situation And Conditions*

PREVISIONS GLISSANTES DETAILLEES EN PERSPECTIVES SECTORIELLES (VOL.7): EQUIPEMENT INDUSTRIEL. see *BUSINESS AND ECONOMICS — Economic Situation And Conditions*

PREVISIONS GLISSANTES DETAILLEES EN PERSPECTIVES SECTORIELLES (VOL.8): MECANIQUE DE PRECISION. see *BUSINESS AND ECONOMICS — Economic Situation And Conditions*

621 KR ISSN 0131-2928
TJ241 CODEN: PRMSDT
PROBLEMY MASHINOSTROENIYA; respublikanskii mezhvedomstvennyi sbornik nauchnykh trudov. 1975. 2/yr. 0.82 Rub. per no. (Akademiya Nauk Ukrainy, Institut Problem Mashinostroeniya) Izdatel'stvo Naukova Dumka, c/o Yu.A. Khramov, Dir, Ul. Repina, 3, Kiev 252 601, Ukraine. (Subscr. to: Mezhdunarodnaya Kniga, Moscow, G-200, Russia) Ed. A.N. Podgornyi. illus. **Indexed:** Chem.Abstr. —CASDDS.

621.9 RU ISSN 0235-7119
TJ4 CODEN: PMNMEG
PROBLEMY MASHINOSTROENIYA I NADEZHNOSTI MASHIN. English translation: Journal of Machinery Manufacture and Reliability (US ISSN 1052-6188) 1965. bi-m. $115 (effective 1996). (Rossiiskaya Akademiya Nauk) Izdatel'stvo Nauka, Mazhdunarodnyi Otdel, Profsoyuznaya, 90, 117864 Moscow, Russia. charts; illus.; index. **Indexed:** Appl.Mech.Rev., Chem.Abstr., INIS Atomind., Met.Abstr., World Alum.Abstr. **Document type:** academic/scholarly publication.
—BLDSC (0133.409500); CASDDS.
Formerly (until 1990): Mashinovedenie (ISSN 0025-4576)

621.9 AT
PRODUCTION MACHINERY. 1948. m. Aus.$30. Reed Business Publishing Pty. Ltd. (Subsidiary of: Reed International PLC), 1-5 Railway St., Chatswood, N.S.W. 2067, Australia. TEL 02-372-5222. FAX 02-491-7399. Ed. Peter Tyldsley. adv. circ. 4,176. **Indexed:** Chem.Abstr., Eng.Ind.
Formerly: Australian Machinery and Production Engineering (ISSN 0004-9719)

605 DK ISSN 0106-0104
PRODUKTIONS NYT. 1963. 16/yr. DKK 175. Christtreu, Strandlodsvei 48, DK-2300 Copenhagen S, Denmark. TEL 45-32-84-48-48. FAX 45-31-58-20-55. Ed. B. Remby. adv.; bk.rev.; charts; illus.; circ. 24,850 (controlled).
Formerly: Vaerksteds Nyt (ISSN 0042-2126)

670.294489 DK
PRODUKTIONS NYT. LEVERANDOERREGISTER. Variant title: Produktions Nyt's Leverandoerregister. 1963. a. Christtreu Bladgruppen, Strandlodsvei 48, DK-2300 Copenhagen S, Denmark. TEL 45-32-84-48-48. FAX 45-31-58-20-55. adv. circ. 6,000.

621.9 IT
PROGETTARE. 1979. m. L.103000 (foreign L.196000). (Associazione Italiana Progettisti Industriali) Gruppo Editoriale Jackson S.p.A., Via Gorki 69, 20092 Cinisello B. (MI), Italy. TEL 39-2-66034205. FAX 39-2-66034238. Ed. Rosario Fiandaca. adv.: B&W page L.3180000, color page L.4080000; trim 181 x 270. circ. 6,563.
Description: Design of machines, equipment, devices and systems; dimensioning and application criteria for components.

621.9 IT ISSN 0392-4823
PROGETTISTA INDUSTRIALE. 1981. m. (10/yr.). L.75000 (foreign L.185000) (effective 1995). (P R O M A C) Tecniche Nuove s.p.a., Via Menotti 14, 20129 Milan, Italy. TEL 02-75701. FAX 02-7610351. TELEX 334647 TECHS I. Ed. G. Nardella. adv.: B&W page L.2470000, color page L.3260000; trim 185 x 266. circ. 6,571.
Description: Covers exhibition and congress of components, equipment and systems for the design of machines and commercial plants.

621.9 IT
PROGETTO: RIVISTA DI PROGETTAZIONE DI MACCHINE. 1979. m. (10/yr.). L.25000. ERIS S.p.A., Via E. Tellini, 14, 20155 Milan, Italy. TEL 02-33103305. FAX 02-33104245. TELEX 323314 ERIS I. adv. circ. 6,500.

621.9 US ISSN 0938-1740
PROGRESS IN MATERIALS HANDLING AND LOGISTICS. 1989. a. $79.50. Springer-Verlag, 175 Fifth Ave., New York, NY 10010. TEL 212-460-1500. FAX 212-473-6272. (Also: Berlin, Heidelberg, Tokyo and Vienna) Eds. Ira W. Pence, John A. White. **Document type:** monographic series.
Description: Provides an overview of current knowledge in the field of material handling and logistics.

621.9 790.1 US ISSN 0897-070X
PROJECTS IN METAL. 1988. bi-m. $22 (Canada $28; elsewhere $26) (effective Mar. 1995); newsstand price: $4.50 (foreign $6.50). Village Press, Inc., 2779 Aero Park Dr., Traverse City, MI 49686. TEL 616-946-3712. FAX 616-946-3289. (Subscr. to: Box 1810, Traverse City, MI 49685. TEL 800-447-7367) Ed. Joe D. Rice. Pub. Robert Goff. adv. contact: Kathy Booth. charts; illus.; video rev.; index; circ. 12,000 (paid). (also avail. in microfiche; back issues avail.) **Document type:** consumer publication.
Description: Contains material of interest to the hobby machinist, providing the reader with machining techniques and projects to build in the home machine shop.

621.9 US
PUMP USERS SYMPOSIUM. PROCEEDINGS. a. $50 (foreign $70); index $15 (foreign $20). Texas A & M University, Turbomachinery Laboratory, College Station, TX 77843-3254. TEL 409-845-7414. FAX 409-845-1835. Jean C. Bailey. **Document type:** proceedings.

621.9 US ISSN 1066-2537
TS156.A1
QUALITY IN MANUFACTURING. 1990. bi-m. $75 (Canada $95; elsewhere $125). Huebcore Communications, Inc., 29100 Aurora Rd., Solon, OH 44139. TEL 216-248-1125. FAX 216-248-0187. (Subscr. to: Box 21640, Eagan, MN 55121-0640. TEL 612-686-0303) Ed. Joseph C. Quinlan. adv. circ. 61,200.
Description: Features how-to, problem solving articles focusing on practical applications of quality technologies and processes.

REMINDER PLUS. see *ADVERTISING AND PUBLIC RELATIONS*

658.2 658.5 US ISSN 0034-4818
REPORTERO INDUSTRIAL; new equipment, machinery and techniques for industry. English edition: World Industrial Reporter (ISSN 0043-8561) (Text in Spanish) 1943. 9/yr. free. Keller International Publishing Corporation, 150 Great Neck Rd., Great Neck, NY 11021. TEL 516-829-9210. FAX 516-829-7265. TELEX 221-574 KELLE. Ed. Felicia M. Morales. adv.; charts; illus.; tr.lit.; circ. 38,428 (controlled). (tabloid format) **Document type:** trade publication.

REPRESENTATIVE. see *AGRICULTURE — Agricultural Equipment*

621.9 CU
REVISTA DE CONSTRUCCION DE MAQUINARIAS. q. $25 in N. America; S. America $26; Europe $28. (Ministerio de Educacion Superior, Departamento de Seleccion y Adquisicion) Ediciones Cubanas, Obispo No. 527, Apdo. 605, Havana, Cuba.

LA REVUE POLYTECHNIQUE. see *TECHNOLOGY: COMPREHENSIVE WORKS*

621.9   IT   ISSN 0035-6301
RIVISTA DI MECCANICA. (Text in Italian; summaries in English) 1950. fortn. L.132000 (foreign L.254000). Gruppo Editoriale Jackson S.p.A., Via Gorki 69, 20092 Cinisello B. (MI), Italy. TEL 39-2-66034205. FAX 39-2-66034238. Ed. Sergio Oltolini. adv.: B&W page L.3230000, color page L.4160000; trim 181 x 270. circ. 9,426. **Indexed:** C.I.S. Abstr., Chem.Abstr, Fluidex.
—BLDSC (7989.800000); CASDDS.
CODEN: RVMCAS

621.9   US   ISSN 1068-798X
TJ1
RUSSIAN ENGINEERING RESEARCH. English translation in part of: Stanki i Instrumenty (RU ISSN 0038-9811) Vestnik Mashinostroeniya (RU ISSN 0042-4633) 1959. m. $995 (effective 1996). (British Library, Lending Division) Allerton Press, Inc., 150 Fifth Ave., New York, NY 10011. TEL 212-924-3950. FAX 212-463-9684. Eds. D.I. Polyakov, I.A. Novosel'skii. abstr.; bibl.; charts; illus.; index. circ. 350. (back issues avail.) **Indexed:** ASCA, Chem.Abstr., Curr.Cont., Eng.Ind., Excerp.Med., Fluidex, INSPEC, ISMEC, Met.Abstr., RAPRA, Risk Abstr., Robomat. (until 1992). **Document type:** academic/scholarly publication.
—BLDSC (0420.760200); Ei; Faxon; SWETS; UnCover. **CCC.**
Formerly: Soviet Engineering Research (ISSN 0144-6622); Which was formed by the merger of: Machines and Tooling (ISSN 0024-922X); Russian Engineering Journal (ISSN 0036-0228)

621.9   US   ISSN 1068-3798
TJ163.9
RUSSIAN JOURNAL OF HEAVY MACHINERY. English translation of: Tyazheloe Mashinostroenie. 1977. m. $1005 (effective 1996). (Gosudarstvennyi Komitet Tyazhelego, Energeticheskogo i Transportnogo Mashinostroenia, RU - Ministry of Energy Machine Construction and the Scientific-Technical Society of the Machine Construction Industry) Allerton Press, Inc., 150 Fifth Ave., New York, NY 10011. TEL 212-924-3950. FAX 212-463-9684. Ed. V.A. Aleksandrov. bk.rev.; bibl.; charts; illus.; index. **Document type:** academic/scholarly publication.
—**CCC.**
Former titles (until 1992): Soviet Journal of Heavy Machinery (ISSN 1052-6196); (until 1990): Soviet Energy Technology (ISSN 0734-1024); Soviet Energy Machinery.
Description: Presents report on Russian research advances in the design, construction and operation of energy materials. Major subjects covered are materials and production systems, nuclear power station equipment, fabrication techniques and power plant systems design.

621.9   JA   ISSN 0558-4809
SANGYO KIKAI/INDUSTRIAL MACHINERY. (Text in Japanese) 1950. m. 700 Yen per no. Nihon Sangyo Kikai Kogyokai - Japan Society of Industrial Machinery Manufacturers, 5-8, Shiba Koen 3-chome, Minato-ku, Tokyo 105, Japan.

621.9   JA
SANGYO KIKAI SHINPO/INDUSTRIAL MACHINERY NEWS. (Text in Japanese) w. 62000 Yen. Jukagaku Kogyo Tsushinsha - Heavy and Chemical Industry News Agency, 2-15, Kanda Jinbo-cho, Chiyoda-ku, Tokyo 101, Japan.

SCHIFFSBETRIEBSTECHNIK FLENSBURG. see TRANSPORTATION — Ships And Shipping

SCHUETTGUT. see TECHNOLOGY: COMPREHENSIVE WORKS

621.9   SZ   ISSN 0036-7397
SCHWEIZER MASCHINENMARKT; die fuehrende polytechnische Fachzeitschrift. French edition: Marche Suisse des Machines (ISSN 0025-2840) 1900. w. 165.25 SFr. includes a buying guide: Revue (foreign 226.50 SFr.). Fachpresse Goldach, CH-9403 Goldach, Switzerland. TEL 071-409111. FAX 071-409511. Ed. Uwe Pawlowski. adv.; bk.rev.; illus. circ. 15,000. (also avail. in microform from UMI; reprint service avail. from UMI) **Indexed:** C.I.S. Abstr., Excerp.Med., Met.Abstr., World Alum.Abstr. **Document type:** trade publication.
—BLDSC (8112.320000); UMI.

SCOTTISH INDUSTRIAL HISTORY. see TECHNOLOGY: COMPREHENSIVE WORKS

621.9   GW   ISSN 0176-2656
SEKUNDAER-ROHSTOFFE; Fachzeitschrift fuer Rohstoffhandel, Wiederverwertung und Recycling-Technik. 1984. m. DM.80 (foreign DM.98). Peter Polz Verlag, Grubmuehlerfeldstr. 54, 82131 Gauting, Germany. TEL 089-8507727. adv.; bk.rev.; charts; illus. circ. 3,800. (back issues avail.)
Description: International trade with secondary materials, recycling, recycling plants and developments in machinery.

SEL'SKII MEKHANIZATOR. see AGRICULTURE — Agricultural Equipment

SEN'I KIKAI GAKKAISHI. see TEXTILE INDUSTRIES AND FABRICS

621.8 001.6   UK   ISSN 0260-2288
TA165   CODEN: SNRVDY
SENSOR REVIEW. q. £559($939) (effective 1996). M C B University Press Ltd., 60-62 Toller Ln., Bradford, W. York BD8 9BY, England. TEL 01274-499821. FAX 01274-547143. TELEX 51317-MCBUNI-G. Ed. Clive Loughlin. (reprint service avail. from SWZ) **Indexed:** A.I.Abstr. (until 1992), Abstr.Hum.Comp.Inter., B.C.I.R.A., CAD CAM Abstr. (until 1992), INSPEC, Robomat. (until 1992). **Document type:** academic/scholarly publication.
●Also available online. Vendor(s): Data-Star, Knight-Ridder, Inc.
—BLDSC (8241.782000); CASDDS; Ei; Faxon; SWETS; UMI; UnCover. **CCC.**
Description: Offers international coverage of sensor technology in advanced manufacturing processes to engineers, researchers, and managers.

621.9   CC
SHANGHAI JICHUANG/SHANGHAI MACHINE TOOL. (Text in Chinese) q. Shanghai Jichuang Yanjiusuo - Shanghai Machine Tool Research Institute, 681 Huai'an Lu, Shanghai 200041, People's Republic of China. TEL 2565880. Ed. Dong Shankang.

621.9 665.5   CC   ISSN 1001-3482
SHIYOU KUANGCHANG JIXIE/OIL FIELD EQUIPMENT. (Text in Chinese) 1972. bi-m. Y9. Ministry of Machinery Industry, Lanzhou Petroleum Machinery Research Institute, 87 Dunhuang Rd., Qilihe District, Lanzhou, Gansu Province 730050, People's Republic of China. TEL 0931-335938. FAX 0931-35223. TELEX 72010 LRMRI CN. (Co-sponsor: China Association of oil field equipment industry.) adv. **Document type:** academic/scholarly publication.
Description: Presents new developments of oil field equipments.

621.9   UK   ISSN 0143-8557
SOLIDS HANDLING; the journal of bulk materials management. 1979. bi-m. £45 (foreign £60). Trinity Publishing Ltd., Times House, Station Approach, Ruislip, Middx. HA4 8NB, England. TEL 01895-677677. FAX 01895-676027. Ed. Lena Mithani. adv. circ. 8,000. **Indexed:** Br.Ceram.Abstr., Fluidex, World Surf.Coat. **Document type:** trade publication.
—BLDSC (8327.560000).

621.9   SA   ISSN 0036-0848
SOUTH AFRICAN MACHINE TOOL REVIEW. (Text in English) 1968. m. R.120. George Warman Publications (Pty.) Ltd., P.O. Box 3847, Cape Town 8000, South Africa. TEL 27-21-245320. FAX 27-21-261332. Ed. Paddy Attwell. adv.; bk.rev.; illus. circ. 4,500. **Indexed:** Met.Abstr., World Alum.Abstr. **Document type:** trade publication.
Description: Focuses on machine tools, accessories and modern tool practice.

621.9   SA
SOUTH AFRICAN MECHANICS HANDBOOK. (Text in Afrikaans and English) a. R.1.25. Union Trades Directories (Pty) Ltd., 22-24 North Block, Mutual Sq., Davenport Rd., Box 687, Durban 4000, South Africa. adv.

SOUTHERN FARM EQUIPMENT MANUFACTURERS. NEWSLETTER. see AGRICULTURE — Agricultural Equipment

621.9   UK   ISSN 0263-5038
SPON'S PLANT AND EQUIPMENT PRICE GUIDE. 1982. a. £185($315) E. & F.N. Spon, 2-6 Boundary Row, London SE1 8HN, England. TEL 0273-6800416. FAX 0273-606588. **Document type:** directory.
Formerly: Plant and Equipment Guide.

M

STANDARDS AND TECHNOLOGY UPDATE. see ENGINEERING — Mechanical Engineering

STEAMBOATING; steamboater's handbook. see SPORTS AND GAMES — Boats And Boating

STEEL AND MATERIALS TECHNOLOGY. see METALLURGY

STORE EQUIPMENT AND DESIGN. see FOOD AND FOOD INDUSTRIES — Grocery Trade

621.9   RU   ISSN 0039-2391
STROITEL'NYE I DOROZHNYE MASHINY. 1956. m. $112 (effective 1996). Izdatel'stvo Mashinostroenie, 4, Stomynsky per., 107076 Moscow, Russia. TEL 095-269-7141. FAX 095-269-4897. (Co-sponsor: Ministerstvo Stroitel'nogo, Dorozhnogo i Kommunal'nogo Mashinostroeniya) Ed. Ya.A. Govorov. adv.: page DM.4000. bk.rev.; charts; illus.; tr.lit.; index. circ. 14,000. **Indexed:** Chem.Abstr. **Document type:** academic/scholarly publication.
Description: Carries articles about new construction, road-building and earthmoving machines.

STROJNICKY CASOPIS/MECHANICAL ENGINEERING MAGAZINE. see ENGINEERING — Mechanical Engineering

SUCCESSFUL DEALER. see TRANSPORTATION — Trucks And Trucking

621.9   JA
SUGINO NYUSU/SUGINO NEWS. (Text in Japanese) 1961. irreg. (1-2/yr.). 1000 Yen. Sugino Machine Ltd., 2410, Hongo, Uozu-shi, Toyama-ken 937, Japan. TEL 0765-24-5118. FAX 0765-24-5119. circ. 1,000. **Document type:** bulletin.
Description: Introduces technical information of the company's latest products.

SULZER TECHNICAL REVIEW. see ENGINEERING

SURFACE ENGINEERING AND APPLIED ELECTROCHEMISTRY. see ENGINEERING — Mechanical Engineering

621.9   US   ISSN 0039-615X
TJ1
SURPLUS RECORD; index of available capital equipment. 1924. m. $33. Surplus Record, Inc., 20 N. Wacker Dr., Chicago, IL 60606. TEL 312-372-9077. FAX 312-372-6537. Ed. Thomas Scanlan. adv. contact: Marjorie McFarland. bk.rev.; bibl.; illus.; stat.; circ. 70,000 (controlled). **Document type:** trade publication, catalog.
●Also available online.
Description: Lists over 35,000 items of used and surplus machine tools, chemical equipment, motors, transformers, generators, and circuit breakers. Approximately 700 dealers are listed throughout the U.S. and Canada.

621.9   SZ
SWISSMECHANIC. 1930. s-m. $8. (Schweizerischer Verband Mechanisch-Technischer Betriebe) Schelbli AG, CH-3360 Herzogenbuchsee, Switzerland. (Co-sponsor: Schweizerischer Verband Diplomierter Mechanikermeister) Ed. Hans Wittwer. adv.; bk.rev.; bibl.; charts; illus.; pat.; index. circ. 2,500.
Formerly (until 1988): Schweizerischer Mechaniker-Zeitschrift (ISSN 0036-7664)

621.46   US   ISSN 0092-1661
TK4058
SYMPOSIUM ON INCREMENTAL MOTION CONTROL SYSTEMS AND DEVICES. PROCEEDINGS. Key Title: Proceedings. Annual Symposium. Incremental Motion Control Systems and Devices. 1972. a. $95 (effective 1995). Incremental Motion Control Systems Society, Box 2772, Sta. A, Champaign, IL 61825. TEL 217-356-1523. FAX 217-356-2356. Ed. B.C. Kuo. illus. circ. 500. **Indexed:** Comput.Cont. **Document type:** proceedings.
—BLDSC (6842.290000).
Description: Provides an up-to-date review of existing technology and recent advances in systems research. Also contains exhibits with technical displays.

T T J - TIMBER TRADES JOURNAL. see FORESTS AND FORESTRY — Lumber And Wood

MACHINERY

621.9   CH
TAIWAN MACHINERY. (Text in English) 1980. 2/yr. NT.$1400($60) in Asia, Middle East, Oceania; elsewhere $70. China Economic News Service, 561 Chung Hsiao E. Rd. Sec. 4, Taipei, Taiwan 10516, Republic of China. TEL 2-642-2629. FAX 2-642-7422. TELEX 27710-CENSPC. (Subscr. to: P.O. Box 43-60, Taipei, Taiwan, R.O.C.)

621.9   CH
TARGET MACHINERY & HARDWARE. Cover title: T M H. m. $60 (foreign $70). United Pacific International Inc., P.O. Box 81-417, Taipei, Taiwan, Republic of China. TEL 02-7150751. FAX 02-7169493. TELEX 28784-UNIPAINC. adv.
  Description: Information on hardware and auto supplies, including building supplies and machinery.

TECHNISCHE REVUE. see *TECHNOLOGY: COMPREHENSIVE WORKS*

TECNICA E INDUSTRIA. see *TECHNOLOGY: COMPREHENSIVE WORKS*

TECNO 2000; revista d'innovacio a l'empresa. see *TECHNOLOGY: COMPREHENSIVE WORKS*

671.3 621   IT   ISSN 1120-9895
TECNOLOGIA DELLA DEFORMAZIONE.* 1962. bi-m. L.50000 (foreign L.75000). (Editoriale Tecnica Macchine) E T M S.r.l., Via Principe Eugenio 3, 20155 Milan, Italy. TEL 02-48010095. FAX 02-48010011. adv.; bk.rev.; charts; illus.; tr.lit.; index. circ. 5,500. **Indexed:** Met.Abstr., World Alum.Abstr.
  Formerly (until 1987): Tranciatura Stampaggio (ISSN 0041-1027)
  Description: Technical review of metal deformation.

TECNORAMA MECCANICA. see *ENGINEERING — Mechanical Engineering*

TEKHNIKA V SEL'SKOM KHOZYAISTVE. see *AGRICULTURE — Agricultural Equipment*

621.9   NZ   ISSN 0111-2767
TENDERS GAZETTE. 1964. w. Mercantile Gazette Marketing, 8 Sheffield Cres., P.O. Box 20034, Bishopdale, Christchurch, New Zealand. FAX 64-3-3584490. adv.; illus. circ. 3,000. **Document type:** newspaper.
  —CCC.
  Formerly (until 1980): New Zealand Tenders Gazette (ISSN 0028-8756)

TEXTILE MACHINERY SOCIETY OF JAPAN. JOURNAL. see *TEXTILE INDUSTRIES AND FABRICS*

621.9   US
TIMKEN MAGAZINE. (Text in English, French) 1945. 4/yr. free. Timken Co., 1835 Dueber Ave. S.W., Canton, OH 44706. TEL 216-438-3825. FAX 216-438-4118. Ed. Keith Price. illus. circ. 31,000.

671   NE   ISSN 0924-7424
TOELEVEREN & UITBESTEDEN. (Supplement to: Metaal & Kunststof (ISSN 0026-0460)) bi-m. free to qualified personnel. Misset (Subsidiary of: Reed Elsevier plc), Postbus 4, 7000 BA Doetinchem, Netherlands. TEL 31-8340-49911. FAX 31-8340-43839. TELEX 45481. Ed. Th. Evers. adv.; B&W page fl.2570; trim 215 x 285; adv. contact: Cor van Nek. circ. 7,850 (controlled). **Document type:** trade publication.
  Description: Information about all aspects of supply and subcontracting in the metal and plastics industries.

TOOLING AND MANUFACTURING ASSOCIATION. PURCHASING GUIDE. see *BUSINESS AND ECONOMICS — Production Of Goods And Services*

621.9   US   ISSN 0040-9243   CODEN: TOPRAR
TOOLING & PRODUCTION; the magazine of metalworking manufacturing. 1934. m. $90 (Canada $125; elsewhere $195). Huebcore Communications, Inc., 29100 Aurora Rd., Ste. 200, Solon, OH 44139. TEL 216-248-1125. FAX 612-686-0214. (Subscr. to: Box 21640, Eagan, MN 55121-0640. TEL 612-686-0303) Ed. Stan Modic. adv.; bk.rev.; charts; illus.; stat.; tr.lit.; index, cum.index. circ. 80,000. (also avail. in microform from UMI) **Indexed:** A.S.& T.Ind., ASCA, Bus.Ind., Eng.Ind., INSPEC, ISMEC, Met.Abstr., PROMT, Tr.& Indus.Ind., World Alum.Abstr.
  ●Also available online. Vendor(s): Knight-Ridder, Inc.
  —BLDSC (8867.000000); Ei; Faxon; Genuine Article; SWETS; UMI. **CCC.**
  Description: Emphasis on manufacturing technology for improved productivity.

621.9   UK
TOOLROOM DIRECTORY. a. Argus Business Media Ltd., International Trade Publications (Subsidiary of: Argus Press Group), Queensway House, 2 Queensway, Redhill, Surrey RH1 1QS, England. TEL 01737-768611. FAX 01737-760510. TELEX 948669 TOPJNL G. **Document type:** directory.

TORAIBOROJISUTO/JAPANESE SOCIETY OF TRIBOLOGISTS. JOURNAL. see *ENGINEERING — Mechanical Engineering*

621.8   JA   ISSN 0387-9259
TOYODA MACHINE WORKS TECHNICAL REVIEW/TOYODA KOKI GIHO. (Text in Japanese) 1960. q. Toyoda Machine Works Ltd. - Toyoda Koki K. K., 1-1 Asahimachi, Kariya-shi, Aichi-ken 448, Japan. TEL 0566-25-5272. FAX 0566-25-5489. Ed. Hiroaki Asano. bibl.; charts; illus.; pat.; cum.index. circ. 1,900.
  —BLDSC (8873.205000).
  Formerly: Toyoda Technical Review (ISSN 0041-0152)

621.9   JA   ISSN 0493-6779
TRADE TIMES.* (Text in English) 1956. m. 7200 Yen($35) Japan Machinery Exporters' Association, 5-8, Shibakoen 3-chome, Minato-ku, Tokyo 105, Japan. Ed. Fumihiro Yoshimura. adv.; illus.; pat. circ. 35,000. (also avail. in microform) **Indexed:** Met.Abstr., World Alum.Abstr.

621.9   US
TURBOMACHINERY MAINTENANCE NEWSLETTER. 1959. m. $49 membership. Turbomachinery Maintenance Institute, Inc., Box 5550, Norwalk, CT 06856-5550. TEL 203-853-6015. FAX 203-852-8175. Ed. Rena Hines. adv.; bk.rev. circ. 10,631. (also avail. in microfilm) **Document type:** newsletter.

621.9   US
TURBOMACHINERY SYMPOSIUM. PROCEEDINGS. 1972. a. $50 (foreign $70); index $15 (foreign $20). Texas A & M University, Turbomachinery Laboratory, College Station, TX 77843-3254. TEL 409-845-7417. FAX 409-845-1835. Ed. Jean C. Bailey. index. circ. 1,900. (back issues avail.) **Indexed:** Sh.& Vib.Dig. **Document type:** proceedings.

621.9   RU
TJ163.9   CODEN: EGMSAW
TYAZHELOE MASHINOSTROENIE. English translation: Russian Journal of Heavy Machinery (US ISSN 1068-3798) m. 60 Rub.($93.60) (effective 1993). (Ministry of Heavy and Transport Engineering) Izdatel'stvo Mashinostroenie, 4, Stromynsky per., 107076 Moscow, Russia. Eds. V.A. Alexandrov, V.A. Ivanova. adv.: page DM.4000. bk.rev.; bibl.; charts; illus. circ. 3,000. **Indexed:** Appl.Mech.Rev., C.I.S. Abstr., Chem.Abstr., Eng.Ind., Fluidex, INIS Atomind., Met.Abstr., World Alum.Abstr. **Document type:** academic/scholarly publication.
  —CASDDS. **CCC.**
  Formerly: Energomashinostroenie (ISSN 0131-1336)
  Description: Technical publication covering all branches of heavy engineering.

UMFORMTECHNIK. see *METALLURGY*

621.9   US   ISSN 1045-3954
USED EQUIPMENT DIRECTORY. 1949. m. $30 (foreign $100). Penton Publishing (Hasbrouck Heights) (Subsidiary of: Pittway Company), Box 823, Hasbrouck Heights, NJ 07604. TEL 800-526-6052. FAX 201-393-9553. Ed. James J. Mack. adv.; circ. 75,000 (controlled). (also avail. in microfilm; reprint service avail. from UMI) **Document type:** trade publication.
  ●Also available online.
  —CCC.
  Description: Lists over 34,000 available used machines and equipment from more than 800 dealers, with a rotational circulation list of over 150,000 plants and a monthly distribution of 75,000 users of mechanical tools, metalworking, chemical, plastic, power, electrical, and other industrial equipment.

USINE NOUVELLE; technology and economics. see *TECHNOLOGY: COMPREHENSIVE WORKS*

621.9   IT   ISSN 0392-6567   CODEN: UTEND9
UTENSIL.* 1978. 9/yr. L.75000 (foreign L.100000). E T M, S.r.l., Via Principe Eugenio 3, 20155 Milan, Italy. TEL 02-48010095. FAX 02-48010011. adv.; bk.rev.; charts; illus.; tr.lit.; index. circ. 12,000. **Indexed:** Chem.Abstr., Met.Abstr., World Alum.Abstr.
  —CASDDS.
  Description: Review of technology and marketing for the industry. Deals in the field of the tools trade, mechanical and manual operated tools, accessories, abrasives, equipment gauges and products for mechanical works.

UTENSILI E ATTREZZATURE. see *INSTRUMENTS*

621.9   MX   ISSN 1065-9862
UTILLAJE; compendio de maquinaria - tecnologia apropiada. 1993. m. Mex.$216($72) (effective 1994). Utillaje, Inc., Blvd M. Avila Camacho 1994-404, Col. San Lucas Tepetlacalco, CP 54055 Tlalnepantla E.M., Mexico. TEL 5-398-6436. FAX 5-398-7369. (And: Utillaje, Inc., 20 N. Wacker Dr., Chicago, IL 60606. TEL 312-372-9077. FAX 312-372-6537) Ed. Fabian Uribe M. adv.; B&W page $465; adv. contact: Fabian Uribe. circ. 3,000. (back issues avail.) **Document type:** trade publication, directory.
  Description: Provides classified listing of more than 10,000 pieces of available capital equipment, including machine tools, motors, processing equipment, switchgear.

620.00294489   DK   ISSN 0901-7631
V F M. Variant title: Vejviser for Maskinindustrien. 1950. a. DKK 315 (effective 1995). Industriens Forlag, Vesterbrogade 149, DK-1620 Copenhagen V, Denmark. TEL 45-33-25-01-09. FAX 45-33-25-10-88. Ed. Jan O. Teller. adv. contact: Jan Teller. circ. 5,000. **Document type:** directory.
  Formerly (until 1968): Vejviser for Maskinindustrien (ISSN 0503-7670)

621.9 330   US   ISSN 1057-2813
TS277
VALVE MAGAZINE. 1982. q. $28 (foreign $40). Valve Manufacturers Association of America, 1050 17th St., N.W., Ste. 701, Washington, DC 20036. TEL 202-331-8105. Ed. Lisa Cherubini; Pub. J. Stephen Larkin. adv. contact: Therese Draddy. stat.; tr.lit. circ. 20,000. **Document type:** trade publication.
  Description: Covers issues and applications surrounding the U.S. valve industry. Includes information on the activities of the Association.

621.9   UK
VEHICLE ELECTRICS & ELECTRONICS. 1993. q. £18 (effective 1995). R G O Exhibitions and Publications Ltd., Oakapple Cottage, Furnace Ln., Broad Oak Brede, Rye, E. Sussex TN31 6ES, England. TEL 01424-882702. FAX 01424-882702. Ed. Chris Hancock. adv.: B&W page £295, color page £495; trim 212 x 150; adv. contact: Pam Bourne. bk.rev.; tr.lit.; circ. 2,400 (controlled). (back issues avail.) **Document type:** trade publication.
  Incorporates: Fuel Injection News.
  Description: Discusses the design and maintenance of automotive electrical and electronic systems.

VEREIN DEUTSCHER INGENIEURE. INFORMATIONSDIENST. INSTANDHALTUNG. see *ENGINEERING — Abstracting, Bibliographies, Statistics*

MACHINERY — ABSTRACTING, BIBLIOGRAPHIES, STATISTICS

621.75   SW   ISSN 0042-4056
TJ4   CODEN: VSTDAL
VERKSTAEDERNA. 1905. 12/yr. SEK 475. Verkstaedernas Foerlag AB, P.O. Box 5510, S-114 85 Stockholm, Sweden. TEL 46-8-782-0800. FAX 46-8-782-0994. Ed. Stefan Hallberg. adv. contact: Lotta Stoederberg. bk.rev.; charts; illus.; tr.lit.; index. circ. 16,732. (also avail. in microfilm) **Indexed:** C.I.S. Abstr., INSPEC (1968-).
    Description: Covers methods and equipment for productive mechanical and electrotechnical workshops. Includes education, planning and logistics.

W T PRODUKTION UND MANAGEMENT; Zeitschrift fuer industrielle Fertigung. see TECHNOLOGY: COMPREHENSIVE WORKS

621   GW   ISSN 0043-2792
                          CODEN: WKUBA9
WERKSTATT UND BETRIEB; Zeitschrift fuer Maschinenbau, Konstruktion und Fertigung. 1867. 10/yr. DM.150. Carl Hanser Verlag, Kolbergerstr. 22, 81679 Munich, Germany. TEL 089-998300. FAX 089-984809. (Subscr. to: Postfach 860420, 81631 Munich, Germany) Ed. Herbert Schulz. adv.; bk.rev.; charts; illus.; mkt.; pat.; tr.lit.; index, cum.index. circ. 11,500. **Indexed:** C.I.S. Abstr., Chem.Abstr., Eng.Ind., Excerp.Med., INSPEC, Int.Aerosp.Abstr., Met.Abstr., World Alum.Abstr. **Document type:** trade publication.
—BLDSC (9296.000000); CASDDS; Ei; SWETS. CCC.

621.8   GW   ISSN 0934-0912
WERKZEUG & FORMENBAU. 1991. q. DM.84 (Europe DM.96; overseas DM.116). Verlag Moderne Industrie, Justus-von-Liebig-Str. 1, 86899 Landsberg, Germany. TEL 08191-125-0. FAX 08191-125-483. Ed. Wolfgang Klingauf. adv.: B&W page DM.5260; trim 257 x 178; adv. contact: Claus Mayer. circ. 10,500. **Document type:** trade publication.

621.9   GW   ISSN 0939-5342
WERKZEUGE. s-a. DM.48. Verlag Moderne Industrie, Justus-von-Liebig-Str. 1, 86899 Landsberg, Germany. TEL 08191-125-0. FAX 08191-125-483. Ed. Helmut Augeli. adv. contact: Carola Eichele. illus.

621.9   US
WESTERN METALWORKING DIRECTORY;* complete buying guide for all machine shop requirements. 1988. a. $55. De Roche Publications, 12 Del Italia, Irvine, CA 92714-5355. Ed. David J. De Roche. adv. circ. 22,000. (tabloid format; back issues avail.) **Document type:** directory.
    Description: Concerned with the metal working industry.

621.9   PL   ISSN 1230-4840
WIADOMOSCI TECHNICZNE. 1968. fortn. $18. (Stowarzyszenie Inzynierow i Technikow Mechanikow Polskich) Oficyna Wydawnicza SIMP Press, Ltd., Ul. Swietokrzyska 14A, 00-050 Warsaw, Poland. TEL 48-22-272604. (Dist. by: Ars Polona-Ruch, Krakowskie Przedmiescie 7, Warsaw, Poland) adv.; bk.rev.; film rev.; bibl.; illus.; pat. circ. 4,000. (tabloid format)
    Formerly (until 1993): Wiadomosci Warsztatowe (ISSN 0043-521X)

WOOD BASED PANELS INTERNATIONAL. see FORESTS AND FORESTRY — Lumber And Wood

WOOD MACHINERY MANUFACTURERS OF AMERICA. BUYER'S GUIDE AND DIRECTORY. see FORESTS AND FORESTRY — Lumber And Wood

338   US   ISSN 0043-8561
WORLD INDUSTRIAL REPORTER; new equipment, machinery and techniques for industry. Spanish edition: Reporteo Industrial (ISSN 0034-4818) (Supplements avail.: Infochem, Infomet) 1943. 9/yr. free to qualified personnel. Keller International Publishing Corporation, 150 Great Neck Rd., Great Neck, NY 11021. TEL 516-829-9210. FAX 516-829-7265. Ed. Felicia M. Morales. adv.; abstr.; charts; illus.; tr.lit.; circ. 40,093 (controlled). (tabloid format) **Document type:** trade publication.
—CCC.

621.9 614.7   JA
YUSHU KOGAI BOSHI SOCHI/SUPERIOR EQUIPMENT OF POLLUTION PREVENTION. (Text in Japanese) a. Nihon Sangyo Kikai Kogyokai - Japan Society of Industrial Machinery Manufacturers, 5-8, Shiba Koen 3-chome, Minato-ku, Tokyo 105, Japan. **Document type:** trade publication.

621.9 639.2   CC   ISSN 1001-2451
YUYE JIXIE YIQI/FISHERY MACHINERY AND INSTRUMENT. (Text in Chinese) bi-m. Y1.20 per no. Zhongguo Shuichan Kexue Yanjiuyuan - Chinese Academy of Fishery Sciences, Fishery Scientific and Technical Information Institute, 63 Chifeng Lu, Shanghai 200092, People's Republic of China. TEL 213347. Ed. Chen Sheng.
—BLDSC (3944.070000).

621 620 620   GW   ISSN 0932-0482
                         CODEN: ZZWAEM
Z W F - C I M. (Zeitschrift fuer Wirtschaftliche Fertigung und Automatisierung) 1879. 10/yr. DM.184.20. Carl Hanser Verlag, Kolbergerstr. 22, 81679 Munich, Germany. TEL 089-998300. FAX 089-984809. (Subscr. to: Postfach 860420, 81631 Munich, Germany) Ed. Guenter Spur. adv.; bibl.; charts; illus.; index. circ. 5,000. **Indexed:** Chem.Abstr., INSPEC (1976-). **Document type:** trade publication.
—CASDDS; Ei. **CCC.**
    Formerly (until 1987): Zeitschrift fuer Wirtschafliche Fertigung (ISSN 0044-3743)

621.9   CC   ISSN 1005-2402
ZHIZAO JISHU YU JICHUANG/MANUFACTURING TECHNOLOGY & MACHINE TOOL. (Text in Chinese) 1951. m. Y3.20 per no. Beijing Jichuang Yanjiusuo - Beijing Machine Tool Research Institute, J28, Guozijian St., Dongcheng, Beijing 100007, People's Republic of China. TEL 86-1-4030033. FAX 86-1-4015930. (Dist. overseas by: China International Book Trading Corp., P.O. Box 399, Beijing, P.R. China) Ed. Song Yejun. adv.
—BLDSC (5367.285500).
    Formerly (until 1994): Jichuang - Machine Tools (ISSN 1000-1271)

9N - 2N - 8N - NAA NEWSLETTER. see AGRICULTURE — Agricultural Equipment

MACHINERY — Abstracting, Bibliographies, Statistics

658.8 317   CN   ISSN 0527-6411
HF5483
CANADA. STATISTICS CANADA. VENDING MACHINE OPERATORS. (Catalogue 63-213) (Text in English and French) 1959. a. Can.$22($26) (foreign $31). Statistics Canada, Publications Sales and Services, Ottawa, Ont. K1A 0T6, Canada. TEL 613-951-7277. FAX 613-951-1584. (also avail. in microform from MML)
    Description: Presents data on sales of merchandise by vending machine operators through automatic machines, type of machine and by national and provincial location.

621.9   US
TJ1186
CUTTING TECHNOLOGY. 1984. m. $160 non-members (foreign $180); members $130 (foreign $145) (effective 1996). A S M International, Materials Information, Materials Park, OH 44073. TEL 216-338-5151. FAX 216-338-4634. TELEX 980-619. E-mail: DBarthel@po.ASM-Intl.org. (UK addr.: Institute of Materials, Materials Information, 1 Carlton House Terr., London SW1Y 5DB, England. TEL 071-839-4071) Eds. M. Stephen Chang, Michael P. Finical. **Document type:** abstracting/indexing.
    Former titles: Cutting Tool - Machining Digest (ISSN 1045-5248); Cutting Tool Technology Digest.

621.9 016   RU   ISSN 0131-7970
EKSPRESS-INFORMATSIYA. DETALI MASHIN. 1959. 24/yr. $106 (effective 1996). Vsesoyuznyi Institut Nauchno-Tekhnicheskoi Informatsii (VINITI), Baltiiskaya ul., 14, Moscow A-219, Russia. (Subscr. to: Mezhdunarodnaya Kniga, Dimitrova ul. 39, 113095 Moscow, Russia)

621.8 016   RU
EKSPRESS-INFORMATSIYA. PODVODNO-TEKHNICHESKIE, VODOLAZNYE I SUDOPOD'EMNYE RABOTY. GIDROTEKHNICHESKIE SOORUZHENIYA. 1970. 48/yr. 37.40 Rub. Vsesoyuznyi Institut Nauchno-Tekhnicheskoi Informatsii (VINITI), Baltiiskaya ul., 14, Moscow A-219, Russia. (Subscr. to: Mezhdunarodnaya Kniga, Dimitrova ul. 39, 113095 Moscow, Russia)
    Formerly: Ekspress-Informatsiya. Podvodno-Tekhnicheskie, Vodolaznye i Sudopod'emnye Raboty. (ISSN 0131-0321)

621.9   UK
EUROPEAN CUTTING TOOLS. 1993. 3/yr. £18 (overseas £24). Engineering Publicity Services, 1 Queens Dr., Newport, Shrops. TF10 7EU, England. TEL 0952-811444. Ed. Rodney Pitt. adv.: B&W page £395; color page £545. tr.lit.; circ. 2,000 (controlled). **Document type:** trade publication.
    Description: Covers tool design, material, manufacture, and performance. Also covers the cutting tool market in Europe.

621.9   GW   ISSN 0343-6411
FACHBUCHVERZEICHNIS MASCHINENBAU (YEAR). 1900. a. DM.4.30. Fr. Weidemanns Buchhandlung (H.Witt), Postfach 6406, 30064 Hannover, Germany. TEL 0511-16382-0. FAX 0511-1638266. Ed. Renate Boehm. circ. 20,000. **Document type:** trade publication.

GEPESZETI SZAKIRODALMI TAJEKOZTATO/MACHINERY ABSTRACTS. see ENGINEERING — Abstracting, Bibliographies, Statistics

GEPGYARTASTECHNOLOGIAI ES SZERSZAMGEPIPARI SZAKIRODALMI TAJEKOZTATO/MECHANICAL ENGINEERING & MACHINE TOOL ABSTRACTS. see ENGINEERING — Abstracting, Bibliographies, Statistics

621.9   JA   ISSN 0916-4014
KIKAI TOKEI GEPPO/MONTHLY REPORT OF MACHINE STATISTICS. (Text in Japanese) 1949. m. 1900 Yen per no. Tsusho Sangyosho, Daijin Kanbo, Chosa Tokeibu - Ministry of International Trade and Industry, Minister's Secretariat, Research and Statistics Department, 1-3-1 Kasumigaseki, Chiyoda-ku, Tokyo 100, Japan. (Co-sponsor: Tsusho Sangyo Chosakai - Research Institute on International Trade and Industry) circ. 1,700 (paid). **Document type:** government publication.

621.9   JA
KIKAI TOKEI NENPO/YEARBOOK OF MACHINERY STATISTICS. (Text in Japanese) 1952. a. 10300 Yen. Tsusho Sangyosho, Daijin Kanbo, Chosa Tokeibu - Ministry of International Trade and Industry, Minister's Secretariat, Research and Statistics Department, 1-3-1 Kasumikaseki, Chiyoda-ku, Tokyo 100, Japan. (Co-sponsor: Tsusho Sangyo Chosakai - Research Institute on International Trade and Industry) circ. 1,300 (paid). **Document type:** government publication.

OFF-HIGHWAY ENGINEERING. see TRANSPORTATION — Automobiles

P A S C A L. F 10: MECANIQUE, ACOUSTIQUE ET TRANSFERT DE CHALEUR. see PHYSICS — Abstracting, Bibliographies, Statistics

620 621 016   PL   ISSN 0032-3713
QA801   CODEN: PBAMA6
POLSKA BIBLIOGRAFIA ANALITYCZNA MECHANIKI/POLISH SCIENTIFIC ABSTRACTS ON MECHANICS. (Contents page and captions in English) 1953. q. (Polska Akademia Nauk, Instytut Podstawowych Problemow Techniki) Wydawnictwo Naukowe P W N, Miodowa 10, 00-251 Warsaw, Poland. TEL 48-22-312738. FAX 48-22-267163. TELEX 813763 PWN PL. Ed. M. Sokolowski. bk.rev.; abstr. circ. 350. **Indexed:** Appl.Mech.Rev., Math.R.

REFERATIVNYI ZHURNAL. GORNOE I NEFTEPROMYSLOVOE MASHINOSTROENIE. see MINES AND MINING INDUSTRY — Abstracting, Bibliographies, Statistics

REFERATIVNYI ZHURNAL. MASHINOSTROITEL'NYE MATERIALY, KONSTRUKTSII I RASCHET DETALI MASHIN. GIDROPRIVOD. see ENGINEERING — Abstracting, Bibliographies, Statistics

MACHINERY — COMPUTER APPLICATIONS

REFERATIVNYI ZHURNAL. NASOSOSTROENIE I KOMPRESSOROSTROENIE. KHOLODIL'NOE MASHINOSTROENIE. see ENGINEERING — Abstracting, Bibliographies, Statistics

385.1 016   RU   ISSN 0034-2556
REFERATIVNYI ZHURNAL. PROMYSHLENNYI TRANSPORT. 1963. m. $254 (effective 1996). Vsesoyuznyi Institut Nauchno-Tekhnicheskoi Informatsii (VINITI), Baltiiskaya ul., 14, Moscow A-219, Russia. (Subscr. to: Mezhdunarodnaya Kniga, Dimitrova ul. 39, 113095 Moscow, Russia) Document type: abstracting/indexing.

621 016   RU   ISSN 0034-2599
          CODEN: RZTMBK
REFERATIVNYI ZHURNAL. TEKHNOLOGIYA MASHINOSTROENIYA. 1956. m. $892 (effective 1996). Vsesoyuznyi Institut Nauchno-Tekhnicheskoi Informatsii (VINITI), Baltiiskaya ul., 14, Moscow A-219, Russia. (Subscr. to: Mezhdunarodnaya Kniga, Dimitrova ul. 39, 113095 Moscow, Russia) Document type: abstracting/indexing.

REFERATIVNYI ZHURNAL. TRAKTORY I SEL'SKOKHOZYAISTVENNYE MASHINY I ORUDIYA. see AGRICULTURE — Abstracting, Bibliographies, Statistics

621.9 316.8   SA
SOUTH AFRICA. CENTRAL STATISTICAL SERVICE. CENSUS OF RENTING AND LEASING OF MACHINERY AND EQUIPMENT. (Report No. 04-09-01) every 6 yrs., latest 1977. R.2.75 (foreign R.3.44). Central Statistical Service - Sentrale Statistiekdiens, Private Bag X44, Pretoria 0001, South Africa. TEL 27-12-310-8911. FAX 27-12-310-8500. (Orders to: Government Printing Works, Private Bag X85, Pretoria 0001, South Africa) Document type: government publication.

TRUCK ENGINEERING. see TRANSPORTATION — Trucks And Trucking

MACHINERY — Computer Applications

621.8   US
GUIDE TO C N C TECHNOLOGY AND MANUFACTURING SOFTWARE. (Computer Numerical Control); modern machine shop. 1970. a. $10 (effective Dec. 1990). Gardner Publications, Inc., 6600 Clough Pike, Cincinnati, OH 45244-4090. TEL 513-231-8020. FAX 513-231-2818. Ed. Thomas L. Beard. adv. contact: Donald Kline. circ. 70,000 (controlled). (also avail. in microform from UMI; back issues avail.; reprint service avail.) Document type: trade publication.
Former titles: N C - C I M Guidebook (Numerical Control - Computer Integrated Manufacturing); Modern Machine Shop N C Guidebook and Directory (ISSN 0076-9991)
Description: For numerical control (NC) equipment users and those considering other computer-aided manufacturing, programming, hardware and software.

INSIDE F M S; the comprehensive buying reference for factory automation. see COMPUTERS — Automation

629.8 003   UK   ISSN 0957-6061
TS155.6   CODEN: IMSYEY
INTEGRATED MANUFACTURING SYSTEMS. vol.3, no.1, 1985. 6/yr. £499($879) (effective 1996). M C B University Press Ltd., 62 Toller Ln., Bradford, W. Yorks BD8 9BY, England. TEL 01274-499821. FAX 01274-547143. TELEX 51317 MCBUNI G. Ed. Dr. David Bennett. adv. Indexed: A.I.Abstr. (until 1992), CAD CAM Abstr. (until 1992), INSPEC, Robomat. (until 1992).
—BLDSC (4531.816060); Faxon; SWETS; UMI. CCC.
Formerly: F M S Magazine (ISSN 0263-9777)
Description: For technologists and flexible manufacturing system professionals. Includes information on system planning, automation, design, software, technological developments and applications.

MACROECONOMICS

see Business and Economics–Macroeconomics

MANAGEMENT

see Business and Economics–Management

MARITIME LAW

see Law–Maritime Law

MARKETING AND PURCHASING

see Business and Economics–Marketing and Purchasing

MATHEMATICS

A M A T Y C REVIEW. (American Mathematical Association of Two-Year Colleges) see EDUCATION — Higher Education

510   DK   ISSN 0105-8533
AARHUS UNIVERSITET. MATEMATISK INSTITUT. DATALOGISK AFDELING. DAIMI FN. 1973. irreg. price varies. Aarhus Universitet, Matematisk Institut, Datalogisk Afdeling, Ny Munkegade, Bygning 540, DK-8000 Aarhus C, Denmark. Document type: academic/scholarly publication.

510   DK   ISSN 0106-9969
AARHUS UNIVERSITET. MATEMATISK INSTITUT. DATALOGISK AFDELING. DAIMI IR. 1973. irreg. price varies. Aarhus Universitet, Matematisk Institut, Datalogisk Afdeling, Bygn. 540, Ny Munkegade, DK-8000 Aarhus C, Denmark. Document type: academic/scholarly publication.

510   DK   ISSN 0105-8525
AARHUS UNIVERSITET. MATEMATISK INSTITUT. DATALOGISK AFDELING. DAIMI MD. 1973. irreg. price varies. Aarhus Universitet, Matematisk Institut, Datalogisk Afdeling, Ny Munkegade, DK-8000 Aarhus C, Denmark. Document type: academic/scholarly publication.

510   DK   ISSN 0105-8517
AARHUS UNIVERSITET. MATEMATISK INSTITUT. DATALOGISK AFDELING. DAIMI PB. 1972. irreg. price varies. Aarhus Universitet, Matematisk Institut, Datalogisk Afdeling, Ny Munkegade, DK-8000 Aarhus C, Denmark.

510   DK   ISSN 0106-8997
AARHUS UNIVERSITET. MATEMATISK INSTITUT. ELEMENTAERAFDELING. 1957. irreg. price varies. Aarhus Universitet, Matematisk Institut, DK-8000 Aarhus C, Denmark. illus. Document type: academic/scholarly publication.

510   DK   ISSN 0065-017X
AARHUS UNIVERSITET. MATEMATISK INSTITUT. LECTURE NOTES SERIES. 1963. irreg., no.62, 1993. price varies. Aarhus Universitet, Matematisk Institut, Ny Munkegade, DK-8000 Aarhus C, Denmark. Document type: academic/scholarly publication.

510   DK   ISSN 0106-486X
AARHUS UNIVERSITET. MATEMATISK INSTITUT. MEMOIRS. 1973. irreg., no.12, 1993. Aarhus Universitet, Matematisk Institut, Bygning 530, Ny Munkegade, DK-8000 Aarhus C, Denmark. FAX 45-86-13-17-69. Document type: academic/scholarly publication.

510   DK   ISSN 0065-0188
AARHUS UNIVERSITET. MATEMATISK INSTITUT. VARIOUS PUBLICATIONS SERIES. 1962. irreg., no.42, 1993. price varies. Aarhus Universitet, Matematisk Institut, Ny Munkegade, DK-8000 Aarhus C, Denmark.
—BLDSC (9146.650000).

510   NR   ISSN 0001-3099
QA1   CODEN: ABCSB6
ABACUS. 1960. a. NC.5. Mathematical Association of Nigeria, c/o Department of Education, University of Nigeria, Nsukka, Nigeria. Ed. R.O. Ohuche. bk.rev.

ACADEMIA DE CIENCIAS FISICAS MATEMATICAS Y NATURALES. BOLETIN. see SCIENCES: COMPREHENSIVE WORKS

ACADEMIA DE STIINTE A REPUBLICA MOLDOVA. BULETINUL. FIZICA SI TEHNICA. see PHYSICS

510   MV
          CODEN: IZFMBL
ACADEMIA DE STIINTE A REPUBLICA MOLDOVA. BULETINUL. MATEMATICA/AKADEMIYA NAUK MOLDAVSKOI RESPUBLIKI. IZVESTIYA. MATEMATIKA. 1951. 3/yr. 4.50 Rub. Academia de Stiinte a Republica Moldova, Bd. Stefan cel Mare, 1, Kishinev 27701, Moldova. TEL 7-0422-264023. Document type: academic/scholarly publication.
—BLDSC (0073.770000); CASDDS.
Formerly (until 1989): Academia de Stiinte a R.S.S. Molovesti. Buletinul. Matematika (ISSN 0236-3089); Supersedes in part (in 1968): Akademiya Nauk Moldovskoi S.S.R. Izvestiya. Seriya Fiziko-Tekhnicheskikh i Matematicheskikh Nauk (ISSN 0321-169X)

510   CH
ACADEMIA SINICA. INSTITUTE OF MATHEMATICS. BULLETIN/CHUNG YANG YEN CHIU YUAN SHU HSUEH YEN CHIU SO T'UNG PAO. 1973. q. $30. Academia Sinica, Institute of Mathematics - Chung Yang Yen Chiu Yuan Shu Hsueh Yen Chiu So, Nankang, Taipei Hsien, Taiwan 11529, Republic of China. TEL 02-7851211. FAX 02-7827432. Ed.Bd. circ. 500. Indexed: Stat.Theor.Meth.Abstr. Document type: academic/scholarly publication.

510   FR   ISSN 0764-4442
Q2   CODEN: CASMEI
ACADEMIE DES SCIENCES. COMPTES RENDUS. SERIE 1: MATHEMATIQUE. (Text and summaries in English, French) 1835. 26/yr. 4370 F. Gauthier-Villars, 15 rue Gossin, 92543 Montrouge Cedex, France. TEL 33-1-40-92-65-00. FAX 33-1-40-92-65-97. TELEX 634 916 F. (Subscr. to: Centrale des Revues, 11 rue Gossin, 92543 Montrouge Cedex, France. TEL 33-1-46-56-52-66) Eds. Paul Germain, Francois Gros. charts; illus.; s-a. index. circ. 3,200. (also avail. in microform from PMC) Indexed: Appl.Mech.Rev., Biol.Abstr., Chem.Abstr., Compumath, Curr.Cont., Deep Sea Res.& Oceanogr.Abstr., Eng.Ind., Geo.Abstr., Ind.Med., INIS Atomind., INSPEC (1984-), Int.Aerosp.Abstr., Math.R., Met.Abstr., Meteor.& Geoastrophys.Abstr., Nutr.Abstr., Zent.Math. Document type: academic/scholarly publication.
—BLDSC (3370.042000); Ei; Faxon; Genuine Article; SWETS. CCC.
Former titles (until 1984): Academie des Sciences. Comptes Rendus des Seances. Serie 1: Mathematique (ISSN 0249-6291); (until 1981): Academie des Sciences. Comptes Rendus Hebdomadaires des Seances. Series A-B: Sciences Mathematiques (ISSN 0151-0509); Formed by the merger of: Academie des Sciences. Comptes Rendus Hebdomadaires des Seances. Serie A. Sciences Mathematiques (ISSN 0302-8429); Academie des Sciences. Comptes Rendus Hebdomadaires des Seances. Serie B. Sciences Physiques (ISSN 0302-8437)
Description: Covers set theory, number theory, linear algebra, complex analysis, calculus of variations, topology, numerical analysis and more.

510 500 520   YU   ISSN 0584-9829
ACADEMIE SERBE DES SCIENCES ET DES ARTS. CLASSE DES SCIENCES MATHEMATIQUES ET NATURELLES. BULLETIN. SCIENCES MATHEMATIQUES. (Text in English, French, Russian) 1952. a. price varies. Srpska Akademija Nauka i Umetnosti - Serbian Academy of Sciences and Arts, Knez Mihailova 35, 11001 Belgrade, Serbia, Yugoslavia. FAX 38-11-182-825. TELEX 72593 SANU YU. (Dist. by: Prosveta, Terazije 16, Belgrade, Serbia, Yugoslavia) circ. 500. Indexed: Chem.Abstr., Math.R. Document type: academic/scholarly publication.
Supersedes in part: Academie Serbe des Sciences et des Arts. Classe des Sciences Mathematiques et Naturelles. Bulletin. Nouvelle Serie (ISSN 0001-4184)

ACCADEMIA DELLE SCIENZE DI TORINO. ATTI. PART 1. CLASSE DI SCIENZE FISICHE, MATEMATICHE E NATURALI. see *SCIENCES: COMPREHENSIVE WORKS*

ACCADEMIA DELLE SCIENZE DI TORINO. MEMORIE. PART 1. CLASSE DI SCIENZE FISICHE, MATEMATICHE E NATURALI. see *SCIENCES: COMPREHENSIVE WORKS*

510   IT   ISSN 1120-6330
QA1   CODEN: ADAAER
ACCADEMIA NAZIONALE DEI LINCEI. ATTI. RENDICONTI LINCEI. MATEMATICA E APPLICAZIONI. (Text in English, French, Italian; summaries in English, Italian) 1847. q. L.70000 (foreign L.90000). Accademia Nazionale dei Lincei, Via della Lungara 10, 00165 Rome, Italy. TEL 39-6-6838831. Ed. Cesare Franco Golisano. bibl.; charts; illus.; index. circ. 1,200. **Indexed:** INSPEC (1990-), Math.R. **Document type:** academic/scholarly publication.
—BLDSC (1776.014000); CASDDS; Ei; UnCover.
   Supersedes in part (in 1989): Accademia Nazionale dei Lincei. Atti. Classe di Scienze Fisiche Matematiche e Naturali. Rendiconti (ISSN 0392-7881); Which was formerly (until 1944): Reale Accademia d'Italia. Atti. Classe di Scienze Fisiche, Matematiche e Naturali. Rendiconti (ISSN 0365-5946); (until 1939): Reale Accademia dei Lincei. Atti. Classe di Scienze Fisiche, Matematiche e Naturali. Rendiconti (ISSN 0001-4435)
   Description: Includes articles by academy fellows or by scholars presented by fellows.

510 500 600   FI   ISSN 0001-5105
CODEN: AAAMA4
ACTA ACADEMIAE ABOENSIS, SERIES B: MATHEMATICA ET PHYSICA. (Text in English, German and Swedish) 1922. irreg., vol.54, 1994. price varies. Aabo Akademis Foerlag, Kaskisgatan 2 C 14, 20700 Aabo, Finland. FAX 358-21-2654865. E-mail: ghognas@abo.fi. Ed. Goeran Hoegnas. charts; index. circ. 600. **Indexed:** Abstr.Bull.Inst.Pap.Chem., Biol.Abstr., Curr.Adv.Ecol.Sci., Deep Sea Res.& Oceanogr.Abstr., Math.R. **Document type:** academic/scholarly publication, monographic series.
—CASDDS.

519   NE   ISSN 0167-8019
QA1   CODEN: AAMADV
ACTA APPLICANDAE MATHEMATICAE; an international survey journal on applying mathematics and mathematical applications. (Text and summaries in English) 1983. m. fl.1638 to institutions; $998 to institutions in U.S. (effective 1996). Kluwer Academic Publishers, Postbus 17, 3300 AA Dordrecht, Netherlands. TEL 31-78-392392. FAX 31-78-392254. TELEX 29245 KAPG NL. E-mail: SERVICES@WKAP.NL. (Dist. by: Kluwer Academic Publishers Group, P.O. Box 322, 3300 AH Dordrecht, Netherlands. TEL 31-78-392392. FAX 31-78-546474; N. America dist. addr.: Box 358, Accord Sta., Hingham, MA 02018-0358. TEL 617-871-6600. FAX 617-871-6528) Ed. Michiel Hazewinkel. adv.; bk.rev.; index. (also avail. in microform from UMI; reprint service avail. from SWZ) **Indexed:** Appl.Mech.Rev., ASCA, Compumath, Curr.Cont., Math.R., Zent.Math. **Document type:** academic/scholarly publication.
—BLDSC (0595.970000); Ei; Faxon; Genuine Article; SWETS; UMI; UnCover. **CCC.**
   Refereed Serial

510   PL   ISSN 0065-1036
QA3   CODEN: AARIA9
ACTA ARITHMETICA. (Text in English, French, German, Russian) 1936. 12/yr. (in 3 vols., 4 nos./vol.). $336. Polska Akademia Nauk, Instytut Matematyczny, Dzial Wydawnictw, Ul. Sniadeckich 8, P.O. Box 137, 00-950 Warsaw, Poland. Ed. A. Schinzel. bibl.; charts. (reprint service avail. from SWZ) **Indexed:** ASCA, Compumath, GeoRef., Math.R. **Document type:** academic/scholarly publication.
—BLDSC (0596.600000); Faxon; Genuine Article; SWETS; UnCover.
   Description: Publishes papers on number theory.
   Refereed Serial

510   II   ISSN 0970-0455
QD1   CODEN: ACIMDR
ACTA CIENCIA INDICA. MATHEMATICS. (Text in English) 1974. q. Rs.150($80) (Society for the Progress of Science) Pragati Prakashan, c/o K.K. Mittal, Business Manager, Box 62, Meerut 250001, India. adv.; bk.rev. **Indexed:** INSPEC (1984-).
—BLDSC (0611.372000).
   Supersedes in part (in 1979): Acta Ciencia Indica (ISSN 0379-5411)

510   SW   ISSN 0001-5962
QA1   CODEN: ACMAA8
ACTA MATHEMATICA. 1882. q. (2 vols/yr.). $200. Institut Mittag-Leffler - Royal Swedish Academy of Sciences, Auravaegen 17, S-182 62 Djursholm, Sweden. TEL 46-8-755-18-09. FAX 46-8-755-99-71. Ed. Lennart Carleson. index, cum.index: vols.1-100. (back issues avail.; reprint service avail. from SWZ) **Indexed:** ASCA, Compumath, Ind.Sci.Rev., Math.R., Sci.Cit.Ind.
—Faxon; Genuine Article; SWETS; UnCover.

510   NE   ISSN 0236-5294
QA1   CODEN: AMAHE9
ACTA MATHEMATICA HUNGARICA. (Text in English, French, German, Russian) 1950. 16/yr. fl.944 to institutions; $577 to institutions in U.S. (effective 1996). (Magyar Tudomanyos Akademia) Kluwer Academic Publishers, Postbus 17, 3300 AA Dordrecht, Netherlands. TEL 31-78-392392. FAX 31-78-392254. TELEX 29245 KAPG NL. E-mail: SERVICES@WKAP.NL. (Dist. by: Kluwer Academic Publishers Group, P.O. Box 322, 3300 AH Dordrecht, Netherlands. TEL 31-78-392392. FAX 31-78-546474; N. America dist. addr.: Box 358, Accord Sta., Hingham, MA 02018-0358. TEL 617-871-6600. FAX 617-871-6528) (Co-publisher: Akademiai Kiado, HU) Eds. K. Tandori, J. Szabados. bibl.; index. (also avail. in microform from UMI) **Indexed:** ASCA, Compumath, Curr.Cont., Ind.Sci.Rev., Math.R., Sci.Cit.Ind., Stat.Theor.Meth.Abstr., Zent.Math. **Document type:** academic/scholarly publication.
—BLDSC (0631.300000); Faxon; Genuine Article; SWETS; UnCover. **CCC.**
   Formerly: Academia Scientiarum Hungarica. Acta Mathematica (ISSN 0001-5954)
   Description: Covers theory of sets, mathematical logic, classical and modern analysis, algebra, number theory, geometry, topology, combinatorics, mathematical statistics, probability theory and information theory.
   Refereed Serial

510 530   NE
ACTA MATHEMATICA SCIENTIA. Chinese edition: Shuxue Wuli Xuebao (ISSN 0252-9602) (Text in English) 1981. q. 489 SFr. (effective 1996). (Academic Sinica) Baltzer Science Publishers B.V., Asterweg 1A, 1031 HL Amsterdam, Netherlands. TEL 31-20-6370061. FAX 31-20-6323651. E-mail: publish@baltzer.nl. (Subscr. in N. America to: Baltzer Science Publishers, Box 8577, Red Bank, NJ 07701-8857) (Co-publisher: Science Press, CC) Ed. Li Guoping. (back issues avail.) **Indexed:** ASCA, Compumath, Math.R. **Document type:** academic/scholarly publication.
   Refereed Serial

510   CC   ISSN 1000-9574
ACTA MATHEMATICA SINICA, NEW SERIES. Chinese edition: Shuxue Xuebao (ISSN 0583-1431) (Text in English) 1985. q. DM.430 (effective 1996). Science Press, Marketing and Sales Department, 16 Donghuangchenggen North St., Beijing 100717, People's Republic of China. TEL 4010624. FAX 4019810. (Dist. in Europe by: V S P, P.O. Box 346, 3700 AH Zeist, Netherlands. TEL 31-30-6925790. FAX 31-30-6932081; Dist. in N. America by: Science Press New York, Ltd., 84-04 58th Ave., Elmhurst, NY 11373. TEL 718-476-0238. FAX 718-476-0273) (Co-publisher: V S P) Ed. Chen Jingrun. adv. circ. 6,000. (back issues avail.) **Document type:** academic/scholarly publication.
—BLDSC (0632.010000); SWETS.
   Description: Examines all branches of pure and applied mathematics.
   Refereed Serial

510   VN   ISSN 0251-4184
ACTA MATHEMATICA VIETNAMICA. (Text mainly in English; occasionally in French, German) 1964. s-a. $40 in U.S.; Europe $35; Asia $30 (effective 1996). National Center for Scientific Research, Institute of Mathematics, P.O. Box 631, Bo Ho, 10000 Hanoi, Socialist Republic of Vietnam. FAX 84-43-43300. TELEX 411525 NCSR VT. Ed. Ngo Viet Trung. charts; illus.; stat. circ. 400. **Indexed:** Math.R. **Document type:** academic/scholarly publication.
—BLDSC (0632.100000).
   Formerly (until 1976): Acta Scientiarum Vietnamicarum.
   Description: Original papers in pure and applied mathematics.

510   CC   ISSN 0168-9673
QA1   CODEN: AASIEI
ACTA MATHEMATICAE APPLICATAE SINICA/CHINESE JOURNAL OF APPLIED MATHEMATICS. Chinese edition: Yingyong Shuxue Xuebao (ISSN 0254-3079) (Text in English) 1985. q. foreign $435 (effective 1996). (Chinese Mathematical Society) Science Press, Marketing and Sales Department, 16 Donghuangchenggen North St., Beijing 100717, People's Republic of China. (US office: Science Press New York, Ltd., 84-04 58th Ave., Elmhurst, NY 11373. TEL 718-476-0238; Exclusively dist. outside P.R.China by: Allerton Press, Inc., 150 Fifth Ave., New York, NY 10011. TEL 212-924-3950. FAX 212-463-9684) (Co-publisher: Allerton Press, Inc.) Ed. Wu Chengkang. adv.; bk.rev.; index. circ. 6,000. (back issues avail.) **Indexed:** INSPEC (1978-), Math.R. **Document type:** academic/scholarly publication.
—SWETS. **CCC.**
   Description: Covers applied mathematics research in China, including control theory and stochastic processes.
   Refereed Serial

510   UK   ISSN 0962-4929
QA297
ACTA NUMERICA. 1992. 1/yr. £36($59) (effective 1996). Cambridge University Press, Edinburgh Bldg., Shaftesbury Rd. TEL 01223-312393. FAX 01223-315052. TELEX 851817256. (N. American addr.: Cambridge University Press, Journals Dept., 40 W. 20th St., New York, NY 10011. TEL 212-924-3900. FAX 212-691-3239) Ed. A. Iserles. **Document type:** academic/scholarly publication.
—BLDSC (0641.240000); UMI. **CCC.**
   Description: Presents survey papers by researchers in numerical analysis that give overviews of recent advances and provide state-of-the-art techniques and analysis.

ACTA STEREOLOGICA. see *BIOLOGY*

510 530   XR   ISSN 0001-7140
QA1   CODEN: AUMMBZ
ACTA UNIVERSITATIS CAROLINAE: MATHEMATICA ET PHYSICA. (Text in English, French, German or Russian; summaries in Czech, English, Russian) 1959. s-a. 40 Kc.($11) (Universita Karlova, Fakulta Matematiky a Fysiky) Vydavatelstvi Karolinum, Ovocny trh 5, 116 36 Prague 1, Czech Republic. FAX 42-2-202370. (Subscr. to: Artia, Ve Smeckach 30, 111 27 Prague 1, Czech Republic) Ed. P. Simon. bibl.; charts; illus. circ. 500. **Indexed:** Astron.& Astrophys.Abstr., Math.R., Ref.Zh., Zent.Math. **Document type:** academic/scholarly publication.
—BLDSC (0584.519000).

510 370   PL   ISSN 0208-6204
ACTA UNIVERSITATIS LODZIENSIS: FOLIA MATHEMATICA. (Text in Polish; summaries in various languages) 1955-1974; N.S. 1987. irreg. Wydawnictwo Uniwersytetu Lodzkiego, Ul. Jaracza 34, Lodz, Poland. TEL 331671. (Dist. by: Ars Polona-Ruch, Krakowskie Przedmiescie 7, Warsaw, Poland) **Document type:** academic/scholarly publication.
   Supersedes in part: Uniwersytet Lodzki. Zeszyty Naukowe. Seria 2: Nauki Matematyczno-Przyrodnicze (ISSN 0076-0366)
   Description: Papers concerning various branches of theoretical mathematics mainly real functions, compound analysis, functional analysis and teaching mathematics.

510   HU   ISSN 0001-6969
ACTA UNIVERSITATIS SZEGEDIENSIS DE ATTILA JOZSEF NOMINATAE. ACTA SCIENTIARUM MATHEMATICARUM. (Text in English, French, German, Italian and Russian) 1922. a. exchange basis. Attila Jozsef University, c/o E. Szabo, Exchange Librarian, Dugonics ter 13, P.O. Box 393, Szeged H-6701, Hungary. (Subscr. to: Kultura, Box 149, H-1389 Budapest, Hungary) Ed. Laszlo Leindler. adv.; bk.rev.; index. circ. 1,000. (also avail. in microform from PMC) **Indexed:** Compumath, Curr.Cont., Math.R., Ref.Zh., Stat.Theor.Meth.Abstr., Zent.Math. **Document type:** academic/scholarly publication.
—Faxon; SWETS; UnCover.
   Description: Original papers in the field of pure mathematics.

MATHEMATICS

511.3   PL
ACTA UNIVERSITATIS WRATISLAVIENSIS. LOGIKA. (Text in Polish; summaries in English or German) 1993. irreg. price varies. (Uniwersytet Wroclawski) Wydawnictwo Uniwersytetu Wroclawskiego, Pl. Uniwersytecki 9-13, 50-137 Wroclaw, Poland. TEL 44-10-06. (Dist. by: Ksiegarnia Uniwersytetu Wroclawskiego, Pl. Uniwersytecki 9-13, 50-137 Wroclaw, Poland) Ed. Jan Zygmunt. circ. 300. **Document type:** academic/scholarly publication.

510   SI   ISSN 0218-0286
ADVANCED SERIES IN DYNAMICAL SYSTEMS. (Text in English) 1986. irreg., vol.11, 1992. price varies. World Scientific Publishing Co. Pte. Ltd., Farrer Rd., P.O. Box 128, Singapore 9128, Singapore. TEL 3825663. FAX 3825919. TELEX RS 28561 WSPC. (UK addr.: 73 Lynton Mead, Totteridge, London N20 8DH, England. TEL 44-81-4462461; US addr.: 1060 Main St., River Edge, NJ 07661. TEL 800-227-7562) **Document type:** monographic series.

ADVANCED SERIES IN MATHEMATICAL PHYSICS. see *PHYSICS*

510   US   ISSN 0884-0016
ADVANCED STUDIES IN CONTEMPORARY MATHEMATICS. 1986. irreg., vol.7, 1990. Gordon & Breach Science Publishers, c/o International Publishers Distributor, 820 Town Center Dr., Langhorne, PA 19047. TEL 215-750-2642. FAX 215-750-6343. (Subscr. to: International Publishers Distributor, P.O. Box 90, Reading, Berkshire RG1 8JL, England. TEL 44-173-456-8316) Ed. R.V. Gamkrelidze. (also avail. in microfiche; microfilm) **Document type:** monographic series.
Refereed Serial

510   JA
ADVANCED STUDIES IN PURE MATHEMATICS. (Text in English, French, German) 1983. irreg. (Mathematical Society of Japan) Kinokuniya Company Ltd., 17-7 Shinjuku 3-chome, Shinjuku-ku, Tokyo 160-91, Japan. FAX 81-3-3439-0173. Ed. Tadao Oda. **Document type:** monographic series.

510   US   ISSN 0196-8858
QA1
ADVANCES IN APPLIED MATHEMATICS. 1980. q. $228 (foreign $278) (effective 1996). Academic Press, Inc., Journal Division, 525 B St., Ste. 1900, San Diego, CA 92101-4495. TEL 619-230-1840. FAX 619-699-6800. (Subscr. to: Box 620000, Orlando, FL 32891-8340. TEL 800-543-9534) Ed. Gian-Carlo Rota. adv. (back issues avail.) **Indexed:** Compumath, Ind.Sci.Rev., Int.Aerosp.Abstr., Math.R. **Document type:** monographic series.
—BLDSC (0698.950000); Faxon; Genuine Article; SWETS; UnCover. **CCC.**
Description: Features articles on continuum mechanics, mathematical physics, statistics, mathematical biology, mathematical economics, communication theory, and computer science.
Refereed Serial

519 620.1   UK
ADVANCES IN APPLIED MATHEMATICS AND MECHANICS IN CHINA. irreg. latest vol.3. W. Snyder Associates, 5 Five Mile Rd., Oxford OX2 8HT, England. **Document type:** monographic series.

519   UK   ISSN 0001-8678
QA273   CODEN: AAPBBD
ADVANCES IN APPLIED PROBABILITY. 1969. q. £119($191.60) to institutions (effective 1996). Applied Probability Trust, School of Mathematics, University of Sheffield, Sheffield S3 7RH, England. TEL 0114-282-4269. FAX 0114-272-9782. Ed. C.C. Heyde. adv.; index, cum.index. circ. 1,100. (back issues avail.) **Indexed:** Anim.Breed.Abstr., Biol.Abstr., Biostat., Compumath, Curr.Cont., Curr.Ind.Stat., GeoRef., Ind.Sci.Rev., INSPEC (1969-), J.Cont.Quant.Meth., Math.R., Oper.Res.Manage.Sci., Qual.Contr.Appl.Stat., Ref.Zh., Sci.Cit.Ind., Stat.Theor.Meth.Abstr., Zent.Math. **Document type:** academic/scholarly publication.
—BLDSC (0699.200000); Ei; Faxon; Genuine Article; SWETS; UnCover. **CCC.**
Description: Devoted to research in applications of probability theory to the biological, physical, social, and technological sicences.

510   US   ISSN 1079-9389
▼**ADVANCES IN DIFFERENTIAL EQUATIONS.** Announced for publication in 1996. 6/yr. $590 (effective 1996). Khayyam Publishing Company, Inc., Box 429, Athens, OH 45701. TEL 614-592-6136. FAX 614-592-1252. Ed. Reza Aftabizadeh. **Document type:** academic/scholarly publication.
Description: Publishes original contributions on the mathematical aspects of differential equations and applications.
Refereed Serial

510   JA
ADVANCES IN MATHEMATICAL SCIENCES AND APPLICATIONS. (Text in English) 1992. s-a. $240 (effective 1994). (Cuba University, Faculty of Education, Department of Mathematics) Gakkotosho Co., Ltd., 1-1-14 Kitashinagawa, Shinagawa-ku, Tokyo 140, Japan. (Dist. by: Maruzen Co., Ltd., P.O. Box 5050, Tokyo International 100-31, Japan) Ed. N. Kenmochi. **Document type:** academic/scholarly publication.
Description: Covers research activities for mathematical analysis and its applications to natural sciences as well as engineering.

510   US   ISSN 0001-8708
QA1   CODEN: ADMTA4
ADVANCES IN MATHEMATICS. 1967. 16/yr. $1326 (foreign $1556) (effective 1996). Academic Press, Inc., Journal Division, 525 B St., Ste. 1900, San Diego, CA 92101-4495. TEL 619-230-1840. FAX 619-699-6800. (Subscr. to: Box 620000, Orlando, FL 32891-8340. TEL 800-543-9534) Ed. Gian-Carlo Rota. adv.; charts. (back issues avail.; reprint service avail. from SWZ) **Indexed:** Compumath, Curr.Cont., Ind.Sci.Rev., Math.R., Sci.Cit.Ind., Stat.Theor.Meth.Abstr. **Document type:** academic/scholarly publication.
—Faxon; Genuine Article; SWETS; UnCover. **CCC.**
Description: Provides research mathematicians with an effective medium for communicating important recent developments in their areas of specialization to colleagues and to scientists in related disciplines.
Refereed Serial

510   US   ISSN 0065-3217
ADVANCES IN PROBABILITY AND RELATED TOPICS. 1971. irreg. $191.60 (foreign $119) (effective 1996). Marcel Dekker, Inc., 270 Madison Ave., New York, NY 10016. TEL 212-696-9000. FAX 212-685-4540. TELEX 421419. Eds. Peter Ney, Sidney Port. **Indexed:** Math.R. **Document type:** monographic series.
—**CCC.**
Formerly: Advances in Probability.
Refereed Serial

510   US   ISSN 1051-8037
QA1
ADVANCES IN SOVIET MATHEMATICS. 1990. irreg. American Mathematical Society, Box 6248, Providence, RI 02940-6248. TEL 401-455-4000. **Document type:** monographic series.
—BLDSC (0711.458000). **CCC.**

510   SZ   ISSN 0001-9054
QA1   CODEN: AEMABN
AEQUATIONES MATHEMATICAE. (Text in English, French, German) 1968. 6/yr. 592 SFr. (foreign 610.40 SFr.). (University of Waterloo, Faculty of Mathematics, CN) Birkhaeuser Verlag, P.O. Box 133, CH-4010 Basel, Switzerland. TEL 061-2717400. FAX 061-2717666. (Dist. in N. America by: Springer-Verlag, Mercedes Distribution Center, 160 Imlay St., Brooklyn, NY 11231, USA) Ed. J. Aczel. abstr.; bibl.; charts; index. **Indexed:** Math.R., Ref.Zh. **Document type:** academic/scholarly publication.
—Faxon; SWETS; UMI; UnCover. **CCC.**

AICHI KYOIKU DAIGAKU KENKYU HOKOKU. SHIZEN KAGAKU/AICHI UNIVERSITY OF EDUCATION. NATURAL SCIENCE BULLETIN. see *SCIENCES: COMPREHENSIVE WORKS*

510   PL   ISSN 0860-2727
AKADEMIA GORNICZO-HUTNICZA IM. STANISLAWA STASZICA. ZESZYTY NAUKOWE. OPUSCULA MATHEMATICA. (Text in English; summaries in English, Polish) 1985. a. 5 Zl. Wydawnictwo A G H, Al. Mickiewicza 30, paw. A-1, 30-059 Krakow, Poland. (Dist. by: Ars Polona, Krakowskie Przedmiescie 7, 00-068 Warsaw, Poland) Ed. Z. Kleczek. illus. circ. 200. **Document type:** academic/scholarly publication.

510   PL   ISSN 0137-169X
AKADEMIA ROLNICZA, POZNAN. ROCZNIKI. ALGORYTMY BIOMETRYCZNE I STATYSTYCZNE. (Text in Polish; summaries in English) 1972. irreg. price varies. Wydawnictwo Akademii Rolniczej w Poznaniu, Ul. Witosa 45, 60-667 Poznan, Poland. TEL 48-61-487809. FAX 48-61-487802. **Indexed:** Bibl.Agri. **Document type:** academic/scholarly publication.
Description: Publications on procedures and programmes employing biometric methods, one - multidimensional methods for statistical concluding on the basis of experimental results.

510 530   GW
AKADEMIE DER WISSENSCHAFTEN IN GOETTINGEN. ABHANDLUNGEN. MATHEMATISCH-PHYSIKALISCHE KLASSE. DRITTE FOLGE. 1937. irreg. Vandenhoeck und Ruprecht, Robert-Bosch-Breite 6, 37079 Goettingen, Germany. TEL 0551-6959-0. FAX 0551-695917. (Subscr. to: 37070 Goettingen, Germany) Ed.Bd. (reprint service avail. from KTO) **Document type:** monographic series.

510   GW
AKADEMIE DER WISSENSCHAFTEN IN GOETTINGEN. ABHANDLUNGEN. MATHEMATISCH-PHYSIKALISCHE KLASSE. DRITTE FOLGE SONDERHEFTE. 1951. irreg. Vandenhoeck und Ruprecht, Robert-Bosch-Breite 6, 37079 Goettingen, Germany. TEL 0551-6959-0. FAX 0551-695917. (Subscr. to: 37070 Goettingen, Germany) Ed.Bd. (reprint service avail. from KTO) **Document type:** monographic series.

510 530   GW   ISSN 0065-5295
AS182   CODEN: NAAKA5
AKADEMIE DER WISSENSCHAFTEN IN GOETTINGEN. NACHRICHTEN 2. MATHEMATISCH-PHYSIKALISCHE KLASSE. (Text in English, German; occasionally in French) 1893. irreg. price varies. Vandenhoeck und Ruprecht, Robert-Bosch-Breite 6, 37079 Goettingen, Germany. TEL 0551-6959-0. FAX 0551-695917. (Subscr. to: 37070 Goettingen, Germany) index. (reprint service avail. from KTO) **Indexed:** GeoRef., Math.R. **Document type:** monographic series.
—BLDSC (6001.950000).

510   AI
AKADEMIYA NAUK ARMENII. IZVESTIYA. SERIYA MATEMATIKA/HAYASTANI GITUTSUNNERI AZGAIN ACADEMIAY TEGHEKAGIR MATEMATIKA. English translation: Journal of Contemporary Mathematical Analysis (US ISSN 1068-3623) (Text in Russian; summaries in Armenian) 1966. bi-m. 600 dram. Akademiya Nauk Armenii, Pr. Marshala Bagramayana, 24, 375019 Erevan, Armenia. TEL 78852-524580. FAX 78852-523640. TELEX 243344. Ed. R.V. Ambartzumian. index. **Indexed:** Math.R., World Alum.Abstr. **Document type:** academic/scholarly publication.
Formerly: Akademiya Nauk Armyanskoi S.S.R. Izvestiya. Seriya Matematika (ISSN 0002-3043)

510   AJ
     CODEN: DAZRA7
AKADEMIYA NAUK AZERBAIJANA. DOKLADY. (Text in Azerbaijani and Russian) 1945. m. Izdatel'stvo Elm, Ul. Narimanova, 37, 3700073 Baku, Azerbaijan. (Subscr. to: Mezhdunarodnaya Kniga, Moscow, G-200, Russia) Ed. G. Abdullaev. charts; illus.; index. circ. 770. **Indexed:** Biol.Abstr., Chem.Abstr., Dairy Sci.Abstr., Field Crop Abstr., GeoRef., Hort.Abstr., INIS Atomind., Math.R., Met.Abstr., Seed Abstr., Soils & Fert., Triticale Abstr., Vet.Bull., World Alum.Abstr. **Document type:** academic/scholarly publication.
—CASDDS. **CCC.**
Formerly: Akademiya Nauk Azerbaidzhanskoi S.S.R. Doklady (ISSN 0002-3078)

AKADEMIYA NAUK AZERBAIJANA. IZVESTIYA. SERIYA FIZIKO-TEKHNICHESKIKH I MATEMATICHESKIKH NAUK. see *PHYSICS*

AKADEMIYA NAUK KAZAKHSTANA. IZVESTIYA. SERIYA FIZIKO-MATEMATICHESKAYA. see *PHYSICS*

AKADEMIYA NAUK RESPUBLIKI KYRGYZSTAN. IZVESTIYA. FIZIKO-TEKHNICHESKIE I MATEMATICHESKIE NAUKI. see *PHYSICS*

MATHEMATICS

500   TA
AS581   CODEN: DANTAL
AKADEMIYA NAUK TAJIKISTANA. DOKLADY. (Text in Russian; titles of papers in English; summaries in Tadzhik) 1951. m. 30.60 Rub. Akademiya Nauk Tajikistana, Pr. Rudaki 33, 734025 Dushanbe, Tajikistan. TEL 22-50-83. Ed. K.T. Poroshin. illus.; index. circ. 700. **Indexed:** Biol.Abstr., Chem.Abstr., Cott.& Trop.Fibr.Abstr., Crop Physiol.Abstr., Field Crop Abstr., GeoRef., INIS Atomind., Math.R., Met.Abstr., Triticale Abstr., World Alum.Abstr. **Document type:** academic/scholarly publication.
—CASDDS. **CCC.**
    Formerly (until 1992): Akademiya Nauk Tadzhikskoi S.S.R. Doklady (ISSN 0002-3469)

AKADEMIYA NAUK TAJIKISTANA. IZVESTIYA. OTDELENIE FIZIKO-MATEMATICHESKIKH I GEOLOGO-KHIMICHESKIKH NAUK. see *PHYSICS*

AKADEMIYA NAUK UKRAINY. DOPOVIDI; naukovi zhurnal. see *PHYSICS*

AKADEMIYA NAUK UZBEKISTANA. IZVESTIYA. SERIYA FIZIKO-MATEMATICHESKIKH NAUK. see *PHYSICS*

AKADEMIYA NAVUK BELARUSI. VESTSI. SERIYA FIZIKA-MATEMATYCHNYKH NAVUK. see *PHYSICS*

510   JA
AKITA DAIGAKU KYOIKUGAKUBU KENKYU KIYO/AKITA UNIVERSITY. COLLEGE OF EDUCATION. MEMOIRS, NATURAL SCIENCE. (Text in English, Japanese) 1950. a. Akita University, College of Education - Akita Daigaku Kyoikugakubu, 1-1, Tegata Gakuen-machi, Akita-shi, Akita-ken 010, Japan.
—BLDSC (5581.400000).
    Former titles (until 1987): Akita University. Faculty of Education. Memoirs, Natural Science (ISSN 0365-1649); (until 1969): Akita University. Gakugei Faculty. Memoirs, Natural Science (ISSN 0365-1630)

510   SP   ISSN 0211-5239
ALEXBRA. 1967. irreg. Universidad de Santiago de Compostela, Facultad de Matematicas, Campus Universitario, 15703 Santiago de Compostela, Spain. **Document type:** academic/scholarly publication.

512 511   US   ISSN 0002-5232
QH150   CODEN: ALLOA6
ALGEBRA AND LOGIC. English translation of: Algebra i Logika (RU ISSN 0373-9252) 1968. bi-m. $995 (foreign $1165) (effective 1996). Russian Academy of Sciences, RU) Plenum Publishing Corp., Consultants Bureau, 233 Spring St., New York, NY 10013-1578. TEL 212-520-8468. FAX 212-463-0742. TELEX 23-421139. Ed. Yu.L. Ershov. (also avail. in microfilm from JSC) **Indexed:** Comput.& Info.Sys., Math.R., Zent.Math. **Document type:** academic/scholarly publication.
—Faxon; SWETS; UMI; UnCover. **CCC.**
    Refereed Serial

510   CC   ISSN 1005-3867
▼**ALGEBRA COLLOQUIUM.** (Text in English) 1994. q. $100 to individuals; institutions $160. Zhongguo Kexueyuan, Shuxue Yanjiusuo - Chinese Academy of Sciences, Institute of Mathematics, Zhongguancun, Beijing 100080, People's Republic of China. FAX 86-1-2568356. Ed. Zhexian Wan. **Document type:** academic/scholarly publication.
    Description: Publishes research articles in the field of pure and applied algebra.

510   RU   ISSN 0234-0852
ALGEBRA I ANALIZ. English translation: St. Petersburg Mathematical Journal (US ISSN 1061-0022) 1989. bi-m. $226 (effective 1996). (Rossiiskaya Akademiya Nauk, Otdelenie Matematiki) Izdatel'stvo Nauka, S.-Peterburgskoe Otdelenie, Mendeleevskaya liniya 1, 199034 St. Petersburg B-34, Russia. TEL 218-36-12. Ed. D.K. Fadeev. circ. 972.
—BLDSC (0006.315000). **CCC.**

510   US   ISSN 1041-5394
ALGEBRA, LOGIC AND APPLICATIONS. 1989. irreg., latest vol.5. Gordon & Breach Science Publishers, c/o International Publishers Distributor, 820 Town Center Dr., Langhorne, PA 19047. TEL 215-750-2642. FAX 215-750-6343. (Subscr. to: International Publihers Distributor, P.O. Box 90, Reading, Berkshire RG1 8JL, England. TEL 44-173-456-8316) Eds. R. Gobel, A. MacIntyre. (also avail. in microfilm; microfiche) **Document type:** monographic series.
—BLDSC (0787.107000).
    Refereed Serial

512   SZ   ISSN 0002-5240
QA251   CODEN: AGUVA9
ALGEBRA UNIVERSALIS. (Text in English) 1971. 8/yr. 1013 SFr. (foreign 1037 SFr.). (University of Manitoba, CN) Birkhaeuser Verlag, P.O. Box 133, CH-4010 Basel, Switzerland. TEL 061-2717400. FAX 061-2717666. (Dist. in N. America by: Springer-Verlag, Mercedes Distribution Center, 160 Imlay St., Brooklyn, NY 11231, USA) Ed. G. Graetzer. adv.; index. circ. 600. **Indexed:** Compumath, Math.R. **Document type:** academic/scholarly publication.
—Faxon; Genuine Article; SWETS; UMI; UnCover. **CCC.**

510   YU
ALGEBRAIC CONFERENCE. PROCEEDINGS. 1980. irreg. $25. Institut za Matematiku, Prirodno-Matematicki Fakultet, Ul. Dr. Ilije Duricica 4, 21000 Novi Sad, Yugoslavia. TEL 38-21-58-136. FAX 38-21-350-458. (Subscr. to: "FORUM", Izvozno Odelenje, ul. Vojvode Misica 1, 21000 Novi Sad, Yugoslavia) **Document type:** proceedings.

512 516   US   ISSN 0741-9937
QA150
ALGEBRAS, GROUPS AND GEOMETRIES. 1984. q. $150. Hadronic Press, Inc., 35246 U.S. N 131, Palm Harbor, FL 34683. **Document type:** academic/scholarly publication.
—Faxon; SWETS; UnCover.

510   US   ISSN 0937-5511
ALGORITHMS AND COMBINATORICS; study and research text. 1986. irreg., vol.8, 1989. price varies. Springer-Verlag, 175 Fifth Ave., New York, NY 10010. TEL 212-460-1500. FAX 212-473-6272. (Also: Berlin, Heidelberg, Tokyo, Vienna) (reprint service avail. from ISI) **Document type:** academic/scholarly publication.
—BLDSC (0787.339000).

510 530   HU   ISSN 0133-3399
QA1   CODEN: AMLAD8
ALKALMAZOTT MATEMATIKAI LAPOK. 1951. q. $12. (Magyar Tudomanyos Akademia, Matematikai es Fizikai Tudomanyok Osztalya) Elte T T K, Bogdanfy ut 1o-B, 1117 Budapest, Hungary. Ed. Andras Benczur. adv.; bk.rev.; index. **Indexed:** Appl.Mech.Rev., Chem.Abstr., INSPEC (1975-1991), Math.R., Stat.Theor.Meth.Abstr.
    Formerly: Magyar Tudomanyos Akademia. Matematikai es Fizikai Tudomanyok Osztalya. Kozlemenyek (ISSN 0025-035X)

510 373   GW   ISSN 0002-6395
ALPHA; Mathematik als Hobby. 1967. m. DM.70.80 (foreign DM.82.90). Reinhardt Becker Verlag, Postfach 53, 16721 Velten, Germany. TEL 03304-397430. FAX 03304-397432. Ed. Roland Becker. abstr. **Document type:** academic/scholarly publication.
—SWETS.

510 310   US   ISSN 0196-6324
T55.4   CODEN: AMMSDX
AMERICAN JOURNAL OF MATHEMATICAL AND MANAGEMENT SCIENCES. 1981. q. $274.50. American Sciences Press, Inc., 20 Cross Rd., Syracuse, NY 13224-2144. Ed. Edward J. Dudewicz. adv.; bk.rev.; charts; illus.; stat.; index. (back issues avail.) **Indexed:** Biostat., Curr.Cont., Curr.Ind.Stat., INSPEC (1986-), Int.Abstr.Oper.Res., J.Cont.Quant.Meth., Math.R., Oper.Res.Manage.Sci., Qual.Contr.Appl.Stat, Ref.Zh., Stat.Theor.Meth.Abstr., Stat.Theor.Meth.Abstr. **Document type:** academic/scholarly publication.
—BLDSC (0826.980000); Ei; Faxon; SWETS; UnCover. **CCC.**
    Description: Focuses on new work in the various areas of the mathematical and management sciences.

510   US   ISSN 0002-9327
QA1   CODEN: AJMEAN
AMERICAN JOURNAL OF MATHEMATICS. 1878. 6/yr. $59 to individuals (foreign $81.30); institutions $175 (foreign $197.30). Johns Hopkins University Press, Journals Publishing Division, 2715 N. Charles St., Baltimore, MD 21218. TEL 410-516-6987. FAX 410-516-6968. Ed. Bernard Shiffman. adv. contact: Tara Dorai-Berry. bibl.; index. circ. 1,500. (also avail. in microform from UMI,PMC; back issues avail.; reprint service avail. from KTO,UMI) **Indexed:** Compumath, Curr.Cont., Ind.Sci.Rev., Math.R., Sci.Cit.Ind., SSCI. **Document type:** academic/scholarly publication.
—Faxon; Genuine Article; SWETS; UMI; UnCover. **CCC.**
    Description: Presents pioneering work in applied and pure mathematics.

510   US   ISSN 0002-9890
QA1   CODEN: AMMYAE
AMERICAN MATHEMATICAL MONTHLY. 1894. 10/yr. $169 (effective 1996). Mathematical Association of America, 1529 Eighteenth St., N.W., Washington, DC 20036. TEL 202-387-5200. Ed. John H. Ewing. adv.; bk.rev.; index. cum.index vols. 1-80. circ. 20,000. (also avail. in microfiche from UMI; reprint service avail. from UMI) **Indexed:** Biol.Abstr., C.I.J.E., Compumath, Curr.Cont., Gen.Sci.Ind., Ind.Sci.Rev., INIS Atomind., Math.R., Sci.Cit.Ind. **Document type:** academic/scholarly publication.
—BLDSC (0842.000000); Ei; Faxon; Genuine Article; SWETS; UMI; UnCover. **CCC.**
    Description: Expository articles on all components of mathematics, pure and applied, old and new, with regular columns devoted to basic and complex problems and reviews.

510   US   ISSN 0273-0979
QA1
AMERICAN MATHEMATICAL SOCIETY. BULLETIN. NEW SERIES. 1894; N.S 1979. 4/yr. $228 (individual members $137; institutional members $182). American Mathematical Society, Box 6248, Providence, RI 02940-6248. TEL 401-455-4000. E-mail: support@e-math.ams.org. Ed. Edgar Lee Stout. bk.rev.; abstr.; cum.index vols. 71-84 (1965-1978) in 8 vols. circ. 27,000. (also avail. in microfiche from UMI; microfilm from PMC) **Indexed:** Compumath, Curr.Cont., Ind.Sci.Rev., INIS Atomind., Math.R., Sci.Cit.Ind. **Document type:** bulletin.
●Also available online.
—BLDSC (2387.000000); Faxon; Genuine Article; SWETS; UMI; UnCover. **CCC.**
    Supersedes: American Mathematical Society. Bulletin. (ISSN 0002-9904)
    Description: Contains expository articles, book reviews and research announcements.
    Refereed Serial

510   US   ISSN 0160-7642
AMERICAN MATHEMATICAL SOCIETY. C B M S REGIONAL CONFERENCE SERIES IN MATHEMATICS. (Conference Board of the Mathematical Sciences) 1970. irreg. price varies. American Mathematical Society, Box 6248, Providence, RI 02940-6248. TEL 401-455-4000. **Document type:** monographic series.
—BLDSC (7336.580000). **CCC.**

510   US   ISSN 0065-9258
AMERICAN MATHEMATICAL SOCIETY. COLLOQUIUM PUBLICATIONS. 1905. irreg. price varies. American Mathematical Society, Box 6248, Providence, RI 02940-6248. TEL 401-455-4000. index in each vol. **Indexed:** Math.R., Zent.Math. **Document type:** monographic series.
—BLDSC (3316.200000). **CCC.**
    Refereed Serial

510   US   ISSN 0894-0347
QA1
AMERICAN MATHEMATICAL SOCIETY. JOURNAL. 1988. 4/yr. $151 to non-members; individual members $91; institutional members $121. American Mathematical Society, Box 6248, Providence, RI 02940-6248. TEL 401-455-4000. circ. 1,000. **Indexed:** Math.R. **Document type:** bulletin.
—BLDSC (4688.200000); Faxon; SWETS; UnCover. **CCC.**
    Refereed Serial

MATHEMATICS

510   US   ISSN 0065-9266
QA3   CODEN: MAMCAU
AMERICAN MATHEMATICAL SOCIETY. MEMOIRS. 1950; N.S. 1975. bi-m. $353 non-members; institutional members $282. American Mathematical Society, Box 6248, Providence, RI 02940-6248. TEL 401-455-4000. circ. 1,200. **Indexed:** Compumath, Math.R., Int.Math. **Document type:** academic/scholarly publication.
—Genuine Article; SWETS. **CCC.**
    Description: Devoted to research in pure and applied mathematics.

510   US   ISSN 0002-9920
     CODEN: AMNOAN
AMERICAN MATHEMATICAL SOCIETY. NOTICES. 1953. 12/yr. $146 to non-members; individual members $88; institutional members $117. American Mathematical Society, Box 6248, Providence, RI 02940-6248. TEL 401-455-4000. Ed. James A. Voytuk. index. circ. 28,000. (also avail. in microform from UMI; reprint service avail. from UMI) **Indexed:** Comput.Rev., Math.R. **Document type:** bulletin.
—BLDSC (6170.500000); Faxon; SWETS; UMI; UnCover. **CCC.**

510   US   ISSN 0002-9939
QA1   CODEN: PAMYAR
AMERICAN MATHEMATICAL SOCIETY. PROCEEDINGS. 1950. m. $579 to non-members; individual members $347; institutional members $463. American Mathematical Society, Box 6248, Providence, RI 02940-6248. TEL 401-455-4000. Ed. Paul S. Muhly. index, cum.index every 10 yrs. circ. 1,900. (also avail. in microfiche) **Indexed:** Compumath, Curr.Cont., Math.R. **Document type:** proceedings.
—BLDSC (6627.000000); Faxon; Genuine Article; SWETS; UMI; UnCover. **CCC.**

510   US   ISSN 0082-0717
AMERICAN MATHEMATICAL SOCIETY. PROCEEDINGS OF SYMPOSIA IN PURE MATHEMATICS. 1959. irreg. price varies. American Mathematical Society, Box 6248, Providence, RI 02940-6248. TEL 401-455-4000. **Indexed:** Compumath. **Document type:** proceedings.
—BLDSC (6849.620000). **CCC.**

510   US   ISSN 0160-7634
AMERICAN MATHEMATICAL SOCIETY. SYMPOSIA IN APPLIED MATHEMATICS. PROCEEDINGS. irreg. price varies. American Mathematical Society, Box 6248, Providence, RI 02940-6248. TEL 401-455-4000. **Document type:** proceedings.
—BLDSC (6849.440000); Ei. **CCC.**
     Refereed Serial

510   US   ISSN 0002-9947
QA1   CODEN: TAMTAM
AMERICAN MATHEMATICAL SOCIETY. TRANSACTIONS. 1900. m. $938 to non-members; institutional members $750. American Mathematical Society, Box 6248, Providence, RI 02940-6248. TEL 401-455-4000. Ed. Lance W. Small. bibl.; index. circ. 1,700. (also avail. in microform from UMI,PMC) **Indexed:** Compumath, Curr.Cont., Eng.Ind., Math.R. **Document type:** academic/scholarly publication.
—BLDSC (8892.000000); Faxon; Genuine Article; SWETS; UMI; UnCover. **CCC.**
    Description: Devoted to research in pure and applied mathematics.
     Refereed Serial

510   US   ISSN 0065-9290
QA3
AMERICAN MATHEMATICAL SOCIETY. TRANSLATIONS. SERIES 2. (Supersedes Series 1) 1955. irreg. price varies. American Mathematical Society, Box 6248, Providence, RI 02940-6248. TEL 401-455-4000. Ed. Ben Silver. cum.index: 1966-1973. **Document type:** monographic series.
—BLDSC (0842.250000); SWETS. **CCC.**

510   GW   ISSN 0174-4747
ANALYSIS; international mathematical journal of analysis and its applications. (Text in English) 1981. q. DM.307 (effective 1996). R. Oldenbourg Verlag GmbH, Rosenheimerstr. 145, 81671 Munich, Germany. TEL 089-45051-0. FAX 089-45051207. (Subscr. to: Postfach 801360, 81613 Munich, Germany) Ed.Bd. adv. (back issues avail.) **Document type:** academic/scholarly publication.
—Faxon; SWETS. **CCC.**
    Description: Publication devoted to original research and survey articles in the field of classical analysis and its applications, and analytic number theories.

510   HU   ISSN 0133-3852
QA300   CODEN: ANMADK
ANALYSIS MATHEMATICA. (Text mainly in English and Russian, occasionally in French or German) 1975. q. £220($350) (effective 1996). (Magyar Tudomanyos Akademia) Akademiai Kiado, Publishing House of the Hungarian Academy of Sciences, P.O. Box 245, H-1519 Budapest, Hungary. TEL 181-2134. FAX 166-6466. TELEX 22-6228 AKNYO H. (Dist. by: Elsevier Science Ltd., Pergamon, P.O. Box 800, Kidlington, Oxford OX5 1DX, England. TEL 44-865-794141. FAX 44-865-60285; Subscr. in U.S. and Caanda to: Elsevier Science, 660 White Plains Rd., Tarrytown, NY 10591-5153. TEL 914-524-9200. FAX 914-333-2444) (Co-sponsor: Russian Academy of Sciences, RU) Eds. S.M. Nikolsky, B. Szokefalvi-Nagy. (also avail. in microform from UMI) **Indexed:** INSPEC (1977-1985), Math.R., Stat.Theor.Meth.Abstr. **Document type:** academic/scholarly publication.
—Ei; SWETS; UMI. **CCC.**
    Description: Deals with problems of classical mathematical analysis. Publishes research papers containing new essential results.

510   FI   ISSN 0066-1953
QA1   CODEN: AAFMAT
ANNALES ACADEMIAE SCIENTIARUM FENNICAE. SERIES A, I: MATHEMATICA. (Supplement avail.: Annales Academiae Scientiarum Fennicae. Series A, I: Mathematica Dissertationes) (Text in English, French, German) 1941. a. $80. Suomalainen Tiedeakatemia - Academia Scientiarum Fennica, Mariankatu 5, FIN-00170 Helsinki, Finland. (Orders to: The Bookstore Tiedekirja, Kirkkokatu 14, SF-00170 Helsinki, Finland) Ed. Olli Lehto. index, cum.index: 1941-1967 in vol. 400; 1967-1975 in vol. 600. circ. 470. (also avail. in microform; back issues avail.; reprint service avail. from UMI) **Indexed:** Bull.Signal., Compumath, INSPEC (1968-), Math.R., Ref.Zh., Sci.Cit.Ind., Zent.Math. **Document type:** academic/scholarly publication.
—BLDSC (0914.390000); Faxon; Genuine Article.
     Refereed Serial

510   FI   ISSN 0355-0087
QA1   CODEN: AAFMAT
ANNALES ACADEMIAE SCIENTIARUM FENNICAE. SERIES A, I: MATHEMATICA. DISSERTATIONES. (Supplement to: Annales Academiae Scientiarum Fennicae. Series A, I: Mathematica) (Text in English, French and German) 1975. irreg. price varies. Suomalainen Tiedeakatemia - Academia Scientiarum Fennica, Mariankatu 5, FIN-00170 Helsinki, Finland. FAX 358-0-622-1121. (Orders to: Bookstore Tiedekirja, Kirkkokatu 14, SF-00170 Helsinki, Finland) Ed. Olli Lehto. circ. 470. (also avail. in microform; back issues avail.; reprint service avail. from UMI) **Indexed:** Bull.Signal., INSPEC, Math.R., Ref.Zh., Sci.Cit.Ind., Zent.Math. **Document type:** academic/scholarly publication.
—Faxon.

510   PL   ISSN 0066-2216
QA1   CODEN: APNMA4
ANNALES POLONICI MATHEMATICI. (Text in English, Franch, German, Russian; summaries in English) 1955. 3/yr. (in 1 vol., 3 nos./vol.). $84. Polska Akademia Nauk, Instytut Matematyczny, Dzial Wydawnictw, Ul. Sniadeckich 8, P.O. Box 137, 00-950 Warsaw, Poland. Eds. J. Siciak, St. Lojasiewicz. bibl. (reprint service avail. from SWZ) **Indexed:** Math.R. **Document type:** academic/scholarly publication.
—BLDSC (0993.500000); Faxon; SWETS; UnCover.
    Description: Publishes original papers on mathematical analysis and geometry.
     Refereed Serial

510   PL   ISSN 0373-8299
QA1   CODEN: RPTPAQ
ANNALES SOCIETATIS MATHEMATICAE POLONAE. SERIES 1: COMMENTATIONES MATHEMATICAE - PRACE MATEMATYCZNE. (Text in English, French and German) 1955. a. price varies. Polskie Towarzystwo Matematyczne, Ul. Sniadeckich 8, 00-950 Warsaw, Poland. TEL 48-22-299592. (Dist. by: Ars Polona, Krakowskie Przedmiescie 7, 00-068 Warsaw, Poland. TEL 48-22-267622) Ed. J. Musielak. bibl. circ. 360. **Indexed:** Math.R. **Document type:** academic/scholarly publication.
—Faxon; SWETS; UnCover.
    Formerly: Polskie Towarzystwo Matematyczne. Roczniki. Seria 1: Prace Matematyczne (ISSN 0209-102X)

510   PL   ISSN 0137-2890
QA1
ANNALES SOCIETATIS MATHEMATICAE POLONAE. SERIES 3: APPLIED MATHEMATICS - MATEMATYKA STOSOWANA. 1973. a. price varies. Polskie Towarzystwo Matematyczne, Ul. Sniadeckich 8, 00-950 Warsaw, Poland. TEL 48-22-299592. (Dist. by: Ars Polona, Krakowskie Przedmiescie 7, 00-068 Warsaw, Poland. TEL 48-22-267622) Ed. Andrzej Kielbasinski. circ. 300. **Indexed:** Math.R. **Document type:** academic/scholarly publication.
    Formerly: Polskie Towarzystwo Matematyczne. Roczniki. Seria 3: Matematyka Stosowana.

510   PL   ISSN 0365-1029
QA1.L8   CODEN: ACAMAI
ANNALES UNIVERSITATIS MARIAE CURIE-SKLODOWSKA. SECTIO A. MATHEMATICA. (Text in English, French, German, Polish) 1946. a. price varies. Uniwersytet Marii Curie-Sklodowskiej, Wydawnictwo, Pl. M. Curie-Sklodowskiej 5, 20-031 Lublin, Poland. TEL 48-81-375304. FAX 48-81-336699. TELEX 0643223. Eds. Jan Krzyz, Adam Bielecki. circ. 650. **Indexed:** Math.R. **Document type:** academic/scholarly publication.
—BLDSC (0956.000000).

510   IT   ISSN 0003-4622
ANNALI DI MATEMATICA; pura ed applicata. (Text in English, French, German and Italian) 1850. irreg. (approx. 2-4/yr.). L.50000 per no. Zanichelli Editore S.p.A., Via Irnerio 34, 40126 Bologna, Italy. TEL 051-293-111. FAX 051-249-782. TELEX 521587 ZANED I. bibl.; charts. circ. 700. (also avail. in microform from PMC) **Indexed:** Math.R. **Document type:** academic/scholarly publication.
—SWETS; UnCover.

519.5   US   ISSN 1050-5164
QA273.A1
ANNALS OF APPLIED PROBABILITY. 1991. q. $90. Institute of Mathematical Statistics, Business Office, 3401 Investment Blvd., Ste. 7, Hayward, CA 94545-3819. TEL 510-783-8141. FAX 510-783-4131. E-mail: IMS@STAT.BERKELEY.EDU. Ed. Richard L. Tweedie. circ. 2,200 (paid). **Indexed:** Curr.Ind.Stat., Stat.Theor.Meth.Abstr. **Document type:** academic/scholarly publication.
—BLDSC (1038.190000); Faxon; SWETS; UnCover.
    Description: Publishes contributions to the theory of probability and statistics and to their applications.

510   NE   ISSN 0167-5060
ANNALS OF DISCRETE MATHEMATICS. 1977. irreg., vol.55, 1993. price varies. Elsevier Science B.V., Books Division, P.O. Box 211, 1000 AE Amsterdam, Netherlands. TEL 31-20-4853911. FAX 31-20-4853705. TELEX 18582 ESPA NL. E-mail: nlinfo-f@elsevier.nl; usinfo-f@elsevier.com; forinfo-kyf04035@niftyserve.or.jp; Site addr.: http://www.elsevier.nl/. (Subscr. in U.S. and Canada to: Elsevier Science Inc., Box 882, Madison Sq. Sta., New York, NY 10159. TEL 212-989-5800) (also avail. in microform from UMI) **Indexed:** Comput.Rev., INSPEC, Int.Abstr.Oper.Res., Math R., Zent.Math. **Document type:** monographic series.
—BLDSC (1040.355000). **CCC.**
     Refereed Serial

MATHEMATICS

516   NE   ISSN 0232-704X
ANNALS OF GLOBAL ANALYSIS AND GEOMETRY. q. fl.513 to institutions; $328 to institutions in U.S. (effective 1996). Kluwer Academic Publishers, Postbus 17, 3300 AA Dordrecht, Netherlands. TEL 31-78-392392. FAX 31-78-392254. TELEX 29245 KAPG NL. E-mail: SERVICES@WKAP.NL. (Dist. by: Kluwer Academic Publishers Group, P.O. Box 322, 3300 AH Dordrecht, Netherlands. TEL 31-78-392392. FAX 31-78-546474; N. America dist. addr.: Box 358, Accord Sta., Hingham, MA 02018-0358. TEL 617-871-6600. FAX 617-871-6528) Eds. Th. Friedrich, R. Sulanke. (also avail. in microform from UMI; reprint service avail. from SWZ) **Indexed:** Math.R., Zent.Math. **Document type:** academic/scholarly publication.
—Faxon; SWETS; UnCover. **CCC.**
Refereed Serial

510   US   ISSN 0003-486X
QA1   CODEN: ANMAAH
ANNALS OF MATHEMATICS. 1884. bi-m. $68 to individuals; institutions $200. (Princeton University) Johns Hopkins University Press, Journals Publishing Division, 2715 N. Charles St., Baltimore, MD 21218. TEL 410-516-6987. FAX 410-516-6968. (Co-sponsor: Institute for Advanced Study) Ed.Bd. adv. contact: Tara Dorai-Berry. charts; index. circ. 1,585. (also avail. in microform from UMI,PMC; reprint service avail. from KTO,UMI) **Indexed:** Compumath, Curr.Cont., Ind.Sci.Rev., Math.R. **Document type:** academic/scholarly publication.
—BLDSC (1043.000000); Faxon; SWETS; UMI; UnCover. **CCC.**

ANNALS OF MATHEMATICS AND ARTIFICIAL INTELLIGENCE. see *COMPUTERS — Artificial Intelligence*

510   US   ISSN 0066-2313
ANNALS OF MATHEMATICS STUDIES. irreg., no.124, 1990. price varies. Princeton University Press, 41 William St., Princeton, NJ 08540. TEL 609-258-4900. FAX 609-258-6305. E-mail: jhardy@pupress.princeton.edu. (reprint service avail. from KTO) **Indexed:** Compumath, Math.R. **Document type:** monographic series.

510   NE   ISSN 1021-2655
▼**ANNALS OF NUMERICAL MATHEMATICS.** (Text in English) 1994. a. 289 SFr. (effective 1996). Baltzer Science Publishers B.V., Asterweg 1A, 1031 HL Amsterdam, Netherlands. TEL 31-20-6370061. FAX 31-20-6323651. E-mail: publish@baltzer.nl. (Subscr. in N. America to: Baltzer Science Publishers, Box 8577, Red Bank, NJ 07701-8577) Ed. Claude Brezinski. **Document type:** academic/scholarly publication.
—BLDSC (1043.230000). **CCC.**
Refereed Serial

510   US   ISSN 0091-1798
HA1   CODEN: APBYAE
ANNALS OF PROBABILITY. 1973. q. $130. Institute of Mathematical Statistics, Business Office, 3401 Investment Blvd., Ste. 7, Hayward, CA 94545-3819. TEL 510-783-8141. FAX 510-783-4131. E-mail: IMS@STAT.BERKELEY.EDU. Ed. James W. Pitman. adv.; circ. 2,700 (paid). (also avail. in microfilm from UMI) **Indexed:** Biostat., Compumath, Curr.Cont., Curr.Ind.Stat., Ind.Sci.Rev., J.Cont.Quant.Meth., Math.R., Oper.Res.Manage.Sci., Qual.Contr.Appl.Stat., Sci.Cit.Ind., Stat.Theor.Meth.Abstr.
—BLDSC (1043.550000); Faxon; Genuine Article; SWETS; UMI; UnCover. **CCC.**
Refereed Serial

511.3   NE   ISSN 0168-0072
QA1   CODEN: APALD7
ANNALS OF PURE AND APPLIED LOGIC. (Text in English) 1969. 18/yr. fl.2550($1555) (effective 1996). (Association for Symbolic Logic) North-Holland (Subsidiary of: Elsevier Science B.V.), P.O. Box 211, 1000 AE Amsterdam, Netherlands. TEL 31-20-4853911. FAX 31-20-4853598. TELEX 18582 ESPA NL. (Subscr. in U.S. and Canada to: Elsevier Science Inc., Box 882, Madison Sq. Sta., New York, NY 10159. TEL 212-989-5800. FAX 212-633-3990) Ed. D.O. van Dalen. adv. circ. 700. (also avail. in microform from UMI; back issues avail.; reprint service avail. from SWZ) **Indexed:** Compumath, INSPEC (1983-), Math R., Phil.Ind. **Document type:** academic/scholarly publication.
—Faxon; Genuine Article; SWETS; UnCover. **CCC.**
Formerly (until 1983): Annals of Mathematical Logic (ISSN 0003-4843)
Description: Publishes papers and short monographs on topics of current interest in pure and applied logic.
Refereed Serial

APERIODICITY AND ORDER. see *PHYSICS*

510   US   ISSN 0003-6811
QA300   CODEN: APANCC
APPLICABLE ANALYSIS; an international journal. 1970. 16/yr. (in 4 vols., 4 nos./yr.). 313 ECU per vol. (effective 1996). Gordon and Breach Science Publishers, c/o International Publishers Distributor, 820 Town Center Dr., Langhorne, PA 19047. TEL 215-750-2642. FAX 215-750-6343. (Subscr. to: International Publishers Distributor, P.O. Box 90, Reading, Berkshire, RG1 8JL, England. TEL 44-173-456-8316) Ed. Robert P. Gilbert. adv.; index. (also avail. in microform from MIM) **Indexed:** Appl.Mech.Rev., Compumath, INSPEC (1971-), Math.R.
—BLDSC (1570.450000); Faxon; SWETS; UnCover. **CCC.**
Refereed Serial

519   US   ISSN 0862-7940
QA1   CODEN: APMTEO
APPLICATIONS OF MATHEMATICS (NEW YORK, 1956). (Text and summaries in Czech, English, French, German, Russian, Slovak) 1956. 6/yr. $515 (foreign $605) (effective 1995). (Czech Academy of Sciences, Mathematical Institute, XR) Plenum Publishing Corp., 233 Spring St., New York, NY 10013-1578. TEL 212-620-8000. FAX 212-463-0742. TELEX 23-421139. (Co-publisher: Academia, XR) Ed. Zbynek Sidak. bk.rev.; abstr.; bibl.; charts; illus.; index. circ. 1,150. **Indexed:** Appl.Mech.Rev., Comput.Rev., INSPEC (1991-), Math.R., Stat.Theor.Meth.Abstr. **Document type:** academic/scholarly publication.
—BLDSC (1571.172000); Ei; Faxon; UMI; UnCover. **CCC.**
Former titles (until 1991): Aplikace Matematiky - Applied Mathematics (ISSN 0373-6725); Aplikace Matematiky (ISSN 0003-6501)
Description: Papers dealing with the application of mathematics and computer algorithms in all branches of science, particularly in the technical sciences.

510   US   ISSN 0172-4568
CODEN: APMADY
APPLICATIONS OF MATHEMATICS (NEW YORK, 1975). 1975. irreg., vol.21, 1990. price varies. Springer-Verlag, 175 Fifth Ave., New York, NY 10010. TEL 212-460-1500. FAX 212-473-6272. (Also: Berlin, Heidelberg, Tokyo and Vienna) Eds. A.V. Balakrishnan, W. Hildenbrand. (reprint service avail. from ISI) **Indexed:** Math.R. **Document type:** monographic series.

510   US   ISSN 1063-5203
QA403   CODEN: ACOHE9
APPLIED AND COMPUTATIONAL HARMONIC ANALYSIS. 1993. q. $212 (foreign $252) (effective 1996). Academic Press, Inc., Journal Division, 525 B St., Ste. 1900, San Diego, CA 92101-4495. TEL 619-230-1840. FAX 619-699-6800. (Subscr. to: Box 620000, Orlando, FL 32891-8340. TEL 800-543-9534) Ed.Bd. Ed. INSPEC (1993-). **Document type:** academic/scholarly publication.
—BLDSC (1571.433000); Ei; SWETS. **CCC.**
Description: Presents interdisciplinary articles in all areas related to the applied and computational aspects of harmonic analysis.

519.5 330   UK   ISSN 1350-486X
HF5691
▼**APPLIED MATHEMATICAL FINANCE.** 1994. q. £55($95) to individuals; institutions in the E.U. £130 (N. America $225; elsewhere £145) (effective 1995). Chapman & Hall, Journals Department (Subsidiary of: International Thomson Publishing Group), 2-6 Boundary Row, London SE1 8HN, England. TEL 0171-865-0066. FAX 0171-522-9623. TELEX 290164 CHAPMA G. E-mail: journal@chall.mhs.compuserve.com. (Dist. by: International Thomson Publishing Services, Ltd., Cheriton House, North Way, Andover, Hants. SP10 5BE, England. TEL 01264-342713. FAX 01264-342807; N. American subscr. to: Chapman & Hall, Journals Promotion Department, One Penn Plaza, 41st Fl., New York, NY 10019. TEL 212-564-1060. FAX 212-564-1505) Ed.Bd. adv. (reprint service avail.) **Document type:** academic/scholarly publication.
—BLDSC (1573.705000). **CCC.**
Description: Encourages the confident use of applied mathematics and mathematical modeling in finance. Promotes communication among finance practitioners, academics, and applied mathematicians.
Refereed Serial

510   US   ISSN 0066-5452
QA1   CODEN: AMSCDF
APPLIED MATHEMATICAL SCIENCES. (Text in English) 1972. irreg., vol.84, 1980. price varies. Springer-Verlag, 175 Fifth Ave., New York, NY 10010. TEL 212-460-2500. FAX 212-473-6272. (Also: Berlin, Heidelberg, Tokyo and Vienna) (reprint service avail. from ISI) **Indexed:** INSPEC, Math.R. **Document type:** academic/scholarly publication.
—BLDSC (1573.720000); Ei.

510   US   ISSN 0888-479X
APPLIED MATHEMATICS. 1987. irreg. Gordon & Breach Science Publishers, c/o International Publishers Distributor, 820 Town Center Dr., Langhorne, PA 19047. TEL 215-750-2642. FAX 215-750-2642. (Subscr. to: International Publishers Distributor, P.O. Box 90, Reading, Berskshire RG1 8JL, England. TEL 44-173-456-8316) Ed. M. Blanc. (also avail. in microfilm; microfiche) **Document type:** monographic series.
Refereed Serial

519.5   US   ISSN 0096-3003
QA1   CODEN: AMHCBQ
APPLIED MATHEMATICS AND COMPUTATION. 1975. 21/yr. $1600 to institutions (effective 1996). Elsevier Science Inc., 655 Ave. of the Americas, New York, NY 10010. TEL 212-989-5800. FAX 212-633-3990. TELEX 420643 AEP UI. (Subscr. to: Box 882, Madison Sq. Sta., New York, NY 10159-0882) Eds. John L. Casti, Melvin Scott. (also avail. in microform from UMI; reprint service avail. from SWZ) **Indexed:** Appl.Mech.Rev., Biol.Abstr., CAD CAM Abstr., Compumath, Comput.Cont., Comput Dtbs., Curr.Cont., Ind.Sci.Rev., INSPEC, Math.R., Robomat., Sci.Cit.Ind. **Document type:** academic/scholarly publication.
—BLDSC (1573.731000); Ei; Faxon; Genuine Article; SWETS; UnCover. **CCC.**
Description: Addresses work at the interface between applied mathematics, numerical computation, and applications of systems-oriented ideas to the physical, biological, social, and behavioral sciences.
Refereed Serial

510 531   US   ISSN 0066-5479
APPLIED MATHEMATICS AND MECHANICS; an international series of monographs. vol.2, 1957. irreg., vol.18, 1986. Academic Press, Inc., 525 B St., Ste. 1900, San Diego, CA 92101-4495. TEL 619-231-0926. FAX 619-699-6715. (Subscr. to: Order Dept., 6277 Sea Harbor Dr., 4th Fl., Orlando, FL 32887. TEL 800-321-5068) Eds. F.N. Frenkiel, G. Temple. (reprint service avail. from ISI) **Indexed:** Appl.Mech.Rev., INSPEC, Math.R. **Document type:** monographic series.
Refereed Serial

MATHEMATICS

510 531   NE   ISSN 0253-4827
QA1   CODEN: AMMEEQ
APPLIED MATHEMATICS AND MECHANICS. Chinese edition: Yingyong Shuxue yu Lixue (ISSN 1000-0887) (Text in English) 1980. m. 853 SFr.; newsstand price: (effective 1996). Baltzer Science Publishers B.V., Asterweg 1A, 1031 HL Amsterdam, Netherlands. TEL 31-20-6370061. FAX 31-20-6323651. E-mail: publish@baltzer.nl. (U.S. subscr. to: J.C. Baltzer AG, Box 8577, Red Bank, NJ 07701-8577) Ed. Chien Wei-zang. **Indexed:** INSPEC. **Document type:** academic/scholarly publication.
—BLDSC (1573.747000); SWETS; UnCover. **CCC.**

510   US   ISSN 0095-4616
QA402.5   CODEN: AMOMBN
APPLIED MATHEMATICS AND OPTIMIZATION; an international journal. (Text mainly in English) 1974. bi-m. $397 (effective 1996). Springer-Verlag, Journals, 175 Fifth Ave., New York, NY 10010. TEL 212-460-1500. FAX 212-473-6272. (N. American subscr. to: Journal Fulfillment Services, Box 2485, Secaucus, NJ 07096-2491. TEL 800-777-4643. FAX 201-348-4505; Subscr. outside N. America to: Heidelberger Platz 3, 1000 Berlin 33, Germany. TEL 030-8207-1) Ed. G. Kallianpur. (also avail. in microform from UMI; reprint service avail. from ISI,SWZ) **Indexed:** ASCA, Compumath, Curr.Cont., Eng.Ind., Ind.Sci.Rev., INSPEC (1974-1992), Math.R., Math.R., Sci.Cit.Ind., Stat.Theor.Meth.Abstr., Zent.Math. **Document type:** academic/scholarly publication.
—BLDSC (1573.800000); Ei; Faxon; Genuine Article; SWETS; UMI; UnCover. **CCC.**
   Description: Includes contributions in both theoretical and applied aspects, as well as papers dealing with applied mathematical topics with a practical implication.
   Refereed Serial

519   UK   ISSN 0893-9659
QA1   CODEN: AMLEEL
APPLIED MATHEMATICS LETTERS; an international journal of rapid publication. 1988. bi-m. £343($546) (effective 1996). Elsevier Science Ltd., Pergamon, P.O. Box 800, Kidlington, Oxford OX5 1DX, England. TEL 44-1865-843000. FAX 44-1865-843010. E-mail: nlinfo-f@elsevier.nl; usinfo-f@elsevier.com; forinfo-kyf04035@niftyserve.or.jp; Site addr.: http://www.elsevier.nl/. (Subscr. in U.S. and Canada to: Elsevier Science, 660 White Plains Rd., Tarrytown, NY 10591-5153. TEL 914-524-9200. FAX 914-333-2444) Ed. Ervin Y. Rodin. (also avail. in microfilm from UMI; back issues avail.) **Indexed:** Biostat. **Document type:** academic/scholarly publication.
—BLDSC (1573.880000); Ei; Genuine Article; SWETS; UMI. **CCC.**
   Description: Provides a forum for short articles and research announcements.
   Refereed Serial

510   AT
APPLIED MATHEMATICS PROBLEMS. a. Aus.$39.95. Mathematical Association of South Australia, 163a Greenhill Rd., Parkside, S.A. 5063, Australia. TEL 8-3624332. FAX 8-3639002. **Document type:** academic/scholarly publication.
   Description: A collection of problems generated and implemented at senior secondary level in Australian schools.

519   UK   ISSN 8755-0024
QA274.A1   CODEN: ASMAEM
APPLIED STOCHASTIC MODELS AND DATA ANALYSIS. 1985. q. $495 (foreign $495) (effective 1996). John Wiley & Sons Ltd., Journals, Baffins Ln., Chichester, W. Sussex PO19 1UD, England. TEL 01243-779777. FAX 01243-776128. TELEX 86290 WIBOOK G. (Subscr. outside the Americas to: John Wiley & Sons Inc., 605 Third Ave., New York, NY 10158. TEL 212-850-6645. FAX 212-850-6021) Ed. J. Janssen. circ. 239. (also avail. in microform from UMI; back issues avail.; reprint service avail. from SWZ) **Indexed:** Biostat., Curr.Ind.Stat., Curr.Ind.Stat., Oper.Res.Manage.Sci., Qual.Contr.Appl.Stat., Stat.Theor.Meth.Abstr. **Document type:** academic/scholarly publication.
—BLDSC (1580.062000); Ei; Faxon; Genuine Article; SWETS; UMI. **CCC.**
   Description: Interfaces the theoretical aspects of applied probability and data analysis and their applications in the real world.
   Refereed Serial

511.4   NE   ISSN 1000-9221
APPROXIMATION THEORY AND ITS APPLICATIONS; an international mathematics journal. Short title: A T A. (Text in English) 1984. q. 299 SFr. (effective 1996). (Nanjing Daxue - Nanjing University) Baltzer Science Publishers B.V., Asterweg 1A, 1031 HL Amsterdam. TEL 31-20-6370061. FAX 31-20-6323654. E-mail: publish@baltzer.nl. (Subscr. in N America to: Baltzer Science Publishers, Box 8577, Red Bank, NY 07701-8857) (Co-publisher: Nanjing University Press, CC) (Co-sponsors: Beijing University; Huazhong University of Science and Technology) Eds. M.T. Cheng, C.K. Chui. circ. 500. (back issues avail.) **Indexed:** Math.R. **Document type:** academic/scholarly publication.
—BLDSC (1581.532000).
   Description: Focuses on approximation and expansions, Fourier and harmonic analysis, numerical approximation and applications, as well as other related areas of research.
   Refereed Serial

ARAB GULF JOURNAL OF SCIENTIFIC RESEARCH. see *SCIENCES: COMPREHENSIVE WORKS*

510 519   IT   ISSN 0003-8369
QA1
ARCHIMEDE; rivista per gli insegnanti e i cultori di matematiche pure ed applicate. 1949. q. L.31700 (foreign L.57000($44)) (effective 1994). Editoriale e Finanziaria Le Monnier, S.p.a., Via A. Meucci 2, Casella Postale 202, 50100 Florence, Italy. TEL 39-55-6813801. FAX 39-55-643983. Ed.Bd. bk.rev.; index. circ. 3,700. **Indexed:** Math.R.
—BLDSC (1597.500000).
   Description: Covers various applications and didactic problems involved with the teaching of mathematics, articles include current issues in the field of mathematics and computers.

510   SZ   ISSN 0003-889X
QA1   CODEN: ACVMAL
ARCHIV DER MATHEMATIK/ARCHIVES OF MATHEMATICS/ARCHIVES MATHEMATIQUES. (Text in English, French, German, Italian) 1948. m. 982.40 SFr. (foreign 1003.80 SFr.). Birkhaeuser Verlag, P.O. Box 133, CH-4010 Basel, Switzerland. TEL 061-2717400. FAX 061-2717666. (Dist. in N. America by: Springer-Verlag, Mercedes Distribution Center, 160 Imlay St., Brooklyn, NY 11231, USA) Ed. E. Lamprecht. adv.; charts; illus.; index. circ. 800. **Indexed:** Appl.Mech.Rev., Compumath, Curr.Cont., Ind.Sci.Rev., Math.R., Sci.Cit.Ind. **Document type:** academic/scholarly publication.
—BLDSC (1616.000000); Faxon; Genuine Article; SWETS; UMI; UnCover. **CCC.**

ARCHIVE FOR HISTORY OF EXACT SCIENCES. see *SCIENCES: COMPREHENSIVE WORKS*

511.3   GW   ISSN 0933-5846
QA9.A1   CODEN: AMLOEH
ARCHIVE FOR MATHEMATICAL LOGIC. (Text in English) 1950. 6/yr. DM.628($456) (effective 1996). Springer-Verlag, Heidelberger Platz 3, 14197 Berlin, Germany. TEL 030-8207-0. FAX 030-8214091. E-mail: orders@springer.de. (Subscr. in N. America to: Springer-Verlag New York, Inc., 44 Hartz Way, Secaucus, NJ 07096-2491. TEL 201-348-4033. FAX 201-348-4505) Ed.Bd. adv.; bibl.; charts; index. (also avail. in microform; reprint service avail. from KTO) **Indexed:** INSPEC (1988-), Math.R., Phil.Ind. **Document type:** academic/scholarly publication.
—BLDSC (1637.415000); Ei; Faxon; Genuine Article; SWETS; UMI; UnCover. **CCC.**
   Formerly (until 1987): Archiv fuer Mathematische Logik und Grundlagenforschung (ISSN 0003-9268)
   Description: Publishes research papers and occasional surveys or expositions on mathematical logic.

510 530   GW   ISSN 0003-9527
QA801.A7   CODEN: AVRMAW
ARCHIVE FOR RATIONAL MECHANICS AND ANALYSIS. (Text in English, French, German, Italian or Latin) 1957. 16/yr. (in 4 vols., 4 nos./vol.). DM.2344($1703) (effective 1996). Springer-Verlag, Heidelberger Platz 3, 14197 Berlin, Germany. TEL 030-8207-0. FAX 030-8214091. E-mail: orders@springer.de. (Subscr. in N. America to: Springer-Verlag New York, Inc., 44 Hartz Way, Secaucus, NJ 07096-2491. TEL 201-348-4033. FAX 201-348-4505) Ed. S.S. Antman. adv.; bibl.; charts; index. (also avail. in microform from UMI; reprint service avail. from ISI) **Indexed:** Appl.Mech.Rev., Chem.Abstr., Compumath, Eng.Ind., Fluidex, Ind.Sci.Rev., INIS Atomind., INSPEC (1973-), Math.R., Phys.Ber., Sci.Cit.Ind., Zent.Math. **Document type:** academic/scholarly publication.
—BLDSC (1640.650000); Ei; Faxon; Genuine Article; SWETS; UMI; UnCover. **CCC.**
   Description: Covers the discipline of mechanics as a deductive, mathematical science, and promotes pure analysis in contexts of application, especially of continuum mechanics, thermodynamics, non-linear phenomena, and dynamic systems.

510   XR   ISSN 0044-8753
QA1   CODEN: ARVMAO
ARCHIVUM MATHEMATICUM. (Text in English, French, German, Russian) 1965. q. 160 Kc. (foreign $40 to individuals; institutions $80). Masarykova Universita - Masaryk University, Janackovo Nam. 2a, 662 95 Brno, Czech Republic. TEL 42-5-41321251. FAX 42-5-41210337. Ed. Josef Janyska. circ. 500. **Indexed:** Math.R. **Document type:** academic/scholarly publication.
—BLDSC (1659.550000).

510 536   FI   ISSN 0004-1920
   CODEN: AKMDA5
ARKHIMEDES. (Text in English, Finnish, Swedish; summaries in English) 1949. q. FIM 145 (effective 1993). Suomen Fyysikkoseura - Finnish Physical Society, PL 9, SF-00014 Helsingin Yliopisto, Finland. (Co-sponsor: Finnish Mathematical Society) Ed. Risto Nieminen. adv.; bk.rev. circ. 2,000. **Indexed:** Chem.Abstr., INIS Atomind., Math.R.
—BLDSC (1672.000000); CASDDS.

510   SW   ISSN 0004-2080
QA3   CODEN: AKMTAJ
ARKIV FOER MATEMATIK. (Text in English, French and German) 1952. 2/yr. $90. Institut Mittag-Leffler - Royal Swedish Academy of Sciences, Auravaegen 17, S-182 62 Djursholm, Sweden. TEL 46-8-755-18-09. FAX 46-8-755-99-71. Ed. Lars Inge Hedberg. (back issues avail.; reprint service avail. from SWZ) **Indexed:** Compumath, INSPEC (1968-1986), Math.R.
—Faxon; Genuine Article; SWETS; UnCover.
   Supersedes in part: Arkiv foer Matematik, Astronomi och Fysik.

510   CN   ISSN 0381-7032
   CODEN: ACOMDN
ARS COMBINATORIA. 1976. 3/yr. $120. Charles Babbage Research Centre, P.O. Box 272, St. Norbert Postal Station, Winnipeg, MB R3V 1L6, Canada. TEL 204-772-2612. (Co-sponsor: University of Waterloo, Faculty of Mathematics, Department of Combinatorics and Optimization) Ed. Dr. W.L. Kocay. circ. 400. **Indexed:** Compumath, Int.Abstr.Oper.Res., Math.R. **Document type:** academic/scholarly publication.
—BLDSC (1697.360000); Faxon; Genuine Article; SWETS; UnCover. **CCC.**

ASIA - PACIFIC JOURNAL OF OPERATIONAL RESEARCH. see *COMPUTERS*

510   RU   ISSN 0320-0914
ASIMPTOTICHESKIE METODY V TEORII SISTEM. 1971. irreg. 1 Rub. Irkutskii Gosudarstvennyi Universitet im. A.A. Zhdanova, Ul. Karla Marksa, 1, Irkutsk, Russia. Ed. A.N. Panchenkov. circ. 600.

ASSISTANTSHIPS AND GRADUATE FELLOWSHIPS IN THE MATHEMATICAL SCIENCES. see *EDUCATION — Guides To Schools And Colleges*

ASSOCIATION FOR WOMEN IN MATHEMATICS. NEWSLETTER. see *WOMEN'S INTERESTS*

510　　　　　　　　FR　　ISSN 0303-1179
ASTERISQUE. (Text and summaries in English, French) 1973. irreg. (approx. 10-12/yr.) 1700 F. (effective 1995). Societe Mathematique de France, Institut Henri Poincare, 11 rue Pierre et Marie Curie, 75231 Paris Cedex 05, France. TEL 91-26-74-64. FAX 91-41-17-51. E-mail: smf@smf.univ-mrs.fr. (Subscr. to: Maison de la S.M.F., Cellule de Diffusion, B.P. 167, 12374 Marseille, France; Dist. in N. America by: American Mathematical Society, Box 6248, Providence, RI 02940.) Ed.Bd. circ. 1,300. (back issues avail.) **Indexed:** Compumath, Math.R., Zent.Math. **Document type:** academic/scholarly publication, monographic series.
—BLDSC (1747.045000); SWETS; UnCover.
  Description: Covers the spectrum of mathematics. *Refereed Serial*

510　　　　　　　　NE　　ISSN 0921-7134
　　　　　　　　　　　　　CODEN: ASANEZ
ASYMPTOTIC ANALYSIS. (Text in English, French) 1988. 8/yr. (in 2 vols.). fl.882($490) (effective 1995). I O S Press, Van Diemenstraat 94, 1013 CN Amsterdam, Netherlands. TEL 31-20-6382189. FAX 31-20-6203419. E-mail: marie-louise.kok@ios.nl. (Subscr. in U.S. and Canada to: Box 10558, Burke, VA 22009-0558. TEL 703-323-5554. FAX 703-250-4705) Ed. L.S. Frank. (back issues avail.) **Indexed:** INSPEC(1989-). **Document type:** academic/scholarly publication.
—BLDSC (1765.335800); Ei; Faxon; SWETS; UnCover. **CCC.**
  Description: Original mathematical results in the asymptotic theory of problems. *Refereed Serial*

510　　　　　　　　AT　　ISSN 0004-9727
QA1　　　　　　　　　　CODEN: ALNBAB
AUSTRALIAN MATHEMATICAL SOCIETY. BULLETIN. 1969. 6/yr. Aus.$250($192) (effective 1995). Australian Mathematical Society, c/o Dept. of Mathematics, Australian National University, A.C.T. 0200, Australia. TEL 61-6-2674268. FAX 61-6-2674263. Ed. Dr. A.S. Jones. index. (back issues avail.) **Indexed:** Appl.Mech.Rev., Biol.Abstr., Compumath, INIS Atomind., INSPEC (1972-), Math.R. **Document type:** academic/scholarly publication, bulletin.
—Faxon; Genuine Article; SWETS; UnCover. **CCC.**
  Description: Aims at quick publication of original research in all branches of mathematics.

510　　　　　　　　AT　　ISSN 0263-6115
QA1　　　　　　　　　　CODEN: JAMADS
AUSTRALIAN MATHEMATICAL SOCIETY. JOURNAL. SERIES A. PURE MATHEMATICS AND STATISTICS. 1959. 6/yr. Aus.$273($210) (effective 1995). Australian Mathematical Society, c/o Dept. of Mathematics, Australian National University, A.C.T. 0200, Australia. TEL 61-6-2674268. FAX 61-6-2674263. Ed. Dr. J.R.J. Groves. index. (also avail. in microfilm from PMC; back issues avail.) **Indexed:** Appl.Mech.Rev., Compumath, Math.R. **Document type:** academic/scholarly publication.
—BLDSC (4707.520500); Faxon; Genuine Article; SWETS. **CCC.**
  Formerly (until 1979): Australian Mathematical Society, Journal. Series A. Pure Mathematics (ISSN 0334-3316); **Supersedes (in 1975):** Australian Mathematical Society. Journal (ISSN 0004-9735)
  Description: Publication of papers on pure mathematics and statistics.

510　　　　　　　　AT　　ISSN 0334-2700
QA1　　　　　　　　　　CODEN: JAMMDU
AUSTRALIAN MATHEMATICAL SOCIETY. JOURNAL. SERIES B. APPLIED MATHEMATICS. 1975. 4/yr. Aus.$174($134) (effective 1995). Australian Mathematical Society, c/o Dept. of Mathematics, Australian National University, A.C.T. 0200, Australia. TEL 61-6-2674268. FAX 61-6-2674263. Ed. C.E.M. Pearce. stat.; index. (back issues avail.) **Indexed:** Appl.Mech.Rev., Compumath, INIS Atomind., INSPEC (1975-), Math.R. **Document type:** academic/scholarly publication.
—BLDSC (4707.521000); Faxon; Genuine Article; SWETS; UnCover. **CCC.**
  Description: Publication of papers in any field of applied mathematics and related mathematical sciences, excluding statistics.

510　　　　　　　　AT　　ISSN 0311-0729
AUSTRALIAN MATHEMATICAL SOCIETY GAZETTE. 1974. 5/yr. Aus.$48($37) (effective 1995). Australian Mathematical Society, c/o Dept. of Mathematics, Australian National University, A.C.T. 0200, Australia. TEL 61-6-2674268. FAX 61-6-2674263. Ed. Dr. T.M. Mills. **Indexed:** Math.R. **Document type:** academic/scholarly publication.
—BLDSC (1814.145000); UnCover.
  Description: Carries news items, mathematical articles of general interest and articles on tertiary mathematical teaching.

B C A M T NEWSLETTER. (B.C. Association of Mathematics Teachers) see EDUCATION — *Teaching Methods And Curriculum*

BALSKRISHNAN - NEUSTADT SERIES. see *TECHNOLOGY: COMPREHENSIVE WORKS*

510　　　　　　　　PL　　ISSN 0137-6934
　　　　　　　　　　　　　CODEN: BCPUEU
BANACH CENTER PUBLICATIONS. (Text in English, French, German, Russian) 1976. 2 vols./yr. price varies. Polska Akademia Nauk, Instytut Matematyczny - Polish Academy of Sciences, Institute of Mathematics, Dzial Wydawnictw, Ul. Sniadeckich 8, P.O. Box 137, 00-950 Warsaw, Poland. TEL 48-22-6282471. FAX 48-22-293997. Ed.Bd.
—BLDSC (1861.525000).
  Refereed Serial

510 610　　　　　　US　　ISSN 1045-5523
RA407
BASIC AND CLINICAL BIOSTATISTICS. 1990. 3/yr. Appleton & Lange (Subsidiary of: Simon & Schuster Company), 25 Van Zant St., Box 5630, Norwalk, CT 06856. TEL 203-838-4400. Ed. Beth Dawson-Saunders.
  Description: Covers the study of statistics applied to medicine, including biostatistics and quantitative methods in epidemiology.

510　　　　　　　　JA　　ISSN 0386-6319
BASIC SUGAKU. (Text in Japanese) 1969. m. Gendai Sugaku-sha, 1, Shishigatani Kita-teranomae-cho, Sakyo-ku, Kyoto-shi, Kyoto-fu 606, Japan.

BAYERISCHE AKADEMIE DER WISSENSCHAFTEN. MATHEMATISCH-NATURWISSENSCHAFTLICHE KLASSE. SITZUNGSBERICHTE. see *SCIENCES: COMPREHENSIVE WORKS*

BAYESIAN STATISTICS. see *STATISTICS*

510　　　　　　　　GW　　ISSN 0138-4821
BEITRAEGE ZUR ALGEBRA UND GEOMETRIE. 1971. irreg. DM.25. VEB Deutscher Verlag der Wissenschaften, Postfach 1216, 1080 Berlin, Germany. Ed.Bd. **Indexed:** Math.R.
—SWETS.

519　　　　　　　　UK　　ISSN 1350-7265
▼**BERNOULLI;** a journal of mathematical statistics and probability. 1995. q. £100 to institutions in the E.U. (N. America $170; elsewhere £115). (Bernoulli Society) Chapman & Hall, Journals Department (Subsidiary of: International Thomson Publishing Group), 2-6 Boundary Row, London SE1 8HN, England. TEL 0171-865-0066. FAX 0171-522-9623. TELEX 290164 CHAPMA G. E-mail: journal@chall.mhs.compuserve.com. (Subscr. to: International Thomson Publishing Services Ltd., Cheriton House, North Way, Andover, Hants. SP10 5BE, England. TEL 01264-342713. FAX 01264-342807; Subscr. in N. America to: Chapman & Hall, Journals Promotion Department, One Penn Plaza, 41st Fl., New York, NY 10119. TEL 212-564-1060. FAX 323-564-1505) Ed. Ole E. Barndorff. adv. (reprint service avail.) **Document type:** academic/scholarly publication.
—**CCC.**
  Description: Covers all aspects of mathematical statistics and probability. *Refereed Serial*

510　　　　　　　　PL　　ISSN 0519-8356
BIBLIOTEKA MATEMATYCZNA. 1953. irreg., vol.75, 1993. Wydawnictwo Naukowe P W N, Miodowa 10, 00-251 00-251 Warsaw, Poland. TEL 48-22-312738. FAX 48-22-267163. TELEX 813763 PWN PL. bibl. **Indexed:** Math.R.

BIOMATHEMATICS. see *BIOLOGY*

BIOMETRICS. see *STATISTICS*

BLACKJACK FORUM. see *SPORTS AND GAMES*

510　　　　　　　　BL
BOLETIM DE ANALISE E LOGICA MATEMATICA. 1969. irreg. Universidade Federal Fluminense, Instituto de Matematica, Niteroi, Brazil.

510　　　　　　　　IT　　ISSN 0392-4432
QA21
BOLLETTINO DI STORIA DELLE SCIENZE MATEMATICHE. 1981. s-a. L.40000. (Unione Matematica Italiana) Editrice Compositori s.r.l., Via Stalingrado 97-2, 40128 Bologna, Italy. TEL 51-327811. Ed. Enrico Giusti. **Indexed:** Math.R.

510　　　　　　　　GW　　ISSN 0524-045X
QA1
BONNER MATHEMATISCHE SCHRIFTEN. (Text in German; occasionally in English) 1957. 10/yr. DM.7.50 per no. Universitaet Bonn, Mathematisches Institut, Wegelerstr. 10, 53115 Bonn, Germany. Ed.Bd. circ. 260. **Indexed:** Math.R., Zent.Math. **Document type:** academic/scholarly publication.

BRITISH JOURNAL OF MATHEMATICAL AND STATISTICAL PSYCHOLOGY. see *PSYCHOLOGY*

510　　　　　　　　FR　　ISSN 0007-4497
　　　　　　　　　　　　　CODEN: BSMQA9
BULLETIN DES SCIENCES MATHEMATIQUES. (Text and summaries in English, French) 1870. q. 1210 F. Gauthier-Villars, 15 rue Gossin, 92543 Montrouge Cedex, France. TEL 33-1-40-92-65-00. FAX 33-1-40-92-65-97. TELEX 634 916 F. (Subscr. to: Centrale des Revues, 11 rue Gossin, 92543 Montrouge Cedex, France. TEL 33-1-76-56-52-66) Ed. P. Malliavin. adv.; bk.rev. circ. 750. (also avail. in microfilm from MIM,PMC; reprint service avail. from SWZ) **Indexed:** Compumath, Curr.Cont., Ind.Sci.Rev., Math.R., Sci.Cit.Ind., Zent.Math.
—Faxon; Genuine Article; SWETS; UnCover. **CCC.**
  Description: Covers all branches of pure mathematics.

510　　　　　　　　RM　　ISSN 0007-4691
BULLETIN MATHEMATIQUE. (Text in French, English, German, Russian) 1908. q. 100($52) Societatea de Stiinte Matematice, Str. Academiei 14, 70109 Bucharest, Rumania. (Subscr. to: ILEXIM, Str. 13 Decembrie Nr. 3, P.O. Box 136-137, Bucharest, Rumania) Ed. N. Teodorescu. bk.rev.; index. circ. 800. **Indexed:** Appl.Mech.Rev., INSPEC (1988-), Math.R.

519.5　　　　　　　JA　　ISSN 0286-522X
QA276
BULLETIN OF INFORMATICS AND CYBERNETICS. (Text and summaries in English) vol.4, 1950. a. $78. Tokei Kagaku Kenkyukai - Research Association of Statistical Sciences, c/o Kyushu University 33, 10-1, Hakozaki 6-chome, Higashi-ku, Fukuoka 812, Japan. TEL 092-641-1101. FAX 092-611-2668. E-mail: bic@rifis.kyushu-u.ac.jp. Ed. T. Yanagawa. bibl.; charts. circ. 600. **Indexed:** INSPEC (1984-), JCT, JTA, Math.R., Stat.Theor.Meth.Abstr., Zent.Math. **Document type:** academic/scholarly publication.
—BLDSC (2862.118000); SWETS; UnCover.
  Formerly (until vol.19, 1981): Bulletin of Mathematical Statistics (ISSN 0007-4993)
  Description: Offers scholarly papers on information sciences. Contains tests of statistical processes, theoretical computer science, games informatics, machine learning, logics, robotics, linguistics and mathematics.

BULLETIN OF MATHEMATICAL BIOLOGY; a journal devoted to research at the interface of theoretical and experimental biology. see *BIOLOGY*

510　　　　　　　　AG　　ISSN 0327-5647
BULLETIN OF NUMBER THEORY AND RELATED TOPICS/BOLETIN DE TEORIA DE NUMEROS Y TEMAS CONEXOS. (Text in English) 1975. a. $100. Universidad del Salvador, Vicerrectorado de Investigacion y Desarrollo, Rodriguez Pena 770, 2o piso, 1020 Buenos Aires, Argentina. TEL 54-1-42-1381. FAX 54-1-42-0631. Ed. Aldo Peretti. adv. contact: Fernando Lucero Schmidt. bk.rev. circ. 350. **Indexed:** Math.R., Ref.Zh., Zent.Math. **Document type:** bulletin.
  Description: Publishes quality research in mathematics and number theory.

MATHEMATICS

510   II   ISSN 0970-6577
QA1
BULLETIN OF PURE & APPLIED SCIENCES. SECTION E: MATHEMATICS. 1982. 2/yr. Rs.50($9) to individuals; institutions Rs.100($14). Dr. A.K. Sharma, Ed. & Pub., 140 (RPS) D.D.A. Flat, Mansarovar Park, Shahdara, New Delhi 110032, India. TEL 011-2117408. adv.; bk.rev. circ. 300. **Document type:** academic/scholarly publication.
—BLDSC (2884.508000). **CCC.**

510   BE   ISSN 1370-1444
BULLETIN OF THE BELGIAN MATHEMATICAL SOCIETY - SIMON STEVIN. (Supplement avail.) (Text in Dutch, English, French) 1994. 5/yr. 4000 BEF($130) Belgian Mathematical Society, c/o Prof. Jules Leroy, Sec., Campus Plaine, C.P. 218-01, Bd. du Triomphe, 1050 Brussels, Belgium. TEL 32-2-6505960. FAX 32-2-6505899. E-mail: leroy.ml@ulb.ac.be. Ed. Yves Felix. adv.; bk.rev.; index, cum.index: 1948-1993. circ. 700. **Indexed:** INSPEC (1968-1985), Math.R., Zent.Math. **Document type:** academic/scholarly publication.
—Faxon; SWETS; UnCover.
Formed by the merger of (1904-1993): Simon Stevin (ISSN 0037-5454) & Societe Mathematique de Belgique. Bulletin. Serie A (ISSN 0771-1204) & Societe Mathematique de Belgique. Bulletin. Serie B (ISSN 0771-1158); Which supersedes in part (1948-1977): Societe Mathematique de Belgique. Bulletin (ISSN 0373-2053)
Description: Publishes expository and research papers and book reviews in mathematics.
Refereed Serial

519   HU   ISSN 0133-3526
BULLETINS FOR APPLIED MATHEMATICS. 1977. irreg. Budapesti Muszaki Egyetem - Technical University of Budapest, 1521 Budapest, Hungary.
—BLDSC (2832.472000).

C A S M E NEWSLETTER. (Centre for the Advancement of Science & Mathematics) see *SCIENCES: COMPREHENSIVE WORKS*

519   US   ISSN 0163-9439
            CODEN: CRCMEN
C B M S - N S F REGIONAL CONFERENCE SERIES IN APPLIED MATHEMATICS. (Conference Board of the Mathematical Sciences - National Science Foundation) 1971. irreg., vol.66, Jan. 1995. price varies. Society for Industrial and Applied Mathematics, 3600 University City Science Center, Philadelphia, PA 19104-2688. TEL 215-382-9800. FAX 215-386-7999. E-mail: siam@siam.org. Ed. Tricia Manning; Pub. Vickie Kearn. **Indexed:** Appl.Mech.Rev. **Document type:** academic/scholarly publication, monographic series.
—BLDSC (3095.697100).
Formerly: Conference Board of the Mathematical Sciences. Regional Conference Series in Applied Mathematics (ISSN 0097-4455)
Refereed Serial

510   CN   ISSN 1193-9273
C M S NOTES. (Text in English and French) 1969. 9/yr. Can.$35. Canadian Mathematical Society - Societe Mathematique du Canada, 577 King Edward, P.O. Box 450, Sta. A, Ottawa, ON K1N 6N5, Canada. TEL 613-564-2223. Ed. Graham P. Wright. adv. circ. 1,100.
Formerly: Canadian Mathematical Congress. Notes, News and Comments (ISSN 0045-5164)

510   NE
C W I TRACTS. (Text in English) 1963. irreg., no.108, 1994. Stichting Mathematisch Centrum, Centrum voor Wiskunde en Informatica, P.O. Box 94079, 1090 GB Amsterdam, Netherlands. TEL 31-31-20-5924128. FAX 20-5924199. TELEX 12571 MACTR NL. Ed. M. Hazewinkel. circ. 300. **Document type:** monographic series.
Formerly (until 1984): Mathematical Centre Tracts.
Description: Contains theses and scientific research by members and non-members. Also includes CWI Conference proceedings on mathematical and computer science.

510   IT   ISSN 0008-0624
QA75.5   CODEN: CALOBK
CALCOLO. (Text in English and Italian) 1964. q. $100. (Consiglio Nazionale delle Ricerche, Istituto di Elaborazione della Informazione) Giardini Editori e Stampatori, Via S. Bibbiana, 28, 56100 Pisa, Italy. Ed. Gianfranco Capriz. adv.; charts; illus.; stat. **Indexed:** Comput.Rev., INSPEC (1973-), Math.R.
—BLDSC (2954.300000).

510   GW   ISSN 0944-2669
CALCULUS OF VARIATIONS AND PARTIAL DIFFERENTIAL EQUATIONS. (Text in English) 1993. q. DM.548($398) (effective 1996). Springer-Verlag, Heidelberger Platz 3, 14197 Berlin, Germany. TEL 030-8207-0. FAX 030-8214091. E-mail: orders@springer.de. (Subscr. in N. America to: Springer-Verlag New York, Inc., 44 Hartz Way, Secaucus, NJ 07096-2491. TEL 201-348-4033. FAX 201-348-4505) Ed. M. Giaquinta. (also avail. in microform from UMI) **Document type:** academic/scholarly publication.
—BLDSC (2954.770000); SWETS; UMI.
Description: Dedicated to the calculus of variations and its ramifications in analysis, geometry, and mathematical physics.

510   II   ISSN 0008-0659
QA1   CODEN: BCMSA5
CALCUTTA MATHEMATICAL SOCIETY. BULLETIN. (Text in English) 1908. bi-m. Rs.250($100) Calcutta Mathematical Society, AE-374, Sector-1, Salt Lake City, Calcutta 700 064, India. Ed.Bd. bibl.; index. circ. 1,000. (also avail. in microform from BHP) **Indexed:** Appl.Mech.Rev., INIS Atomind., INSPEC, Math.R., Ref.Zh.
—SWETS; UnCover.

CAMBRIDGE MONOGRAPHS ON MATHEMATICAL PHYSICS. see *PHYSICS*

CAMBRIDGE MONOGRAPHS ON MECHANICS AND APPLIED MATHEMATICS. see *PHYSICS — Mechanics*

510 530   UK   ISSN 0305-0041
Q41   CODEN: MPCPCO
CAMBRIDGE PHILOSOPHICAL SOCIETY. MATHEMATICAL PROCEEDINGS. Key Title: Mathematical Proceedings of the Cambridge Philosophical Society. 1843. bi-m. £228($424) (effective 1996). Cambridge University Press, Edinburgh Bldg., Shaftesbury Rd., Cambridge CB2 2RU, England. TEL 0223-312393. FAX 0223-315052. TELEX 851817256. (N. American addr.: Cambridge University Press, Journals Dept., 40 W. 20th St., New York, NY 10011. TEL 212-924-3900. FAX 212-691-3239) Ed. J.E. Roseblade. bibl.; charts; illus.; index, cum.index vols.1-50. (also avail. in microform from UMI,PMC; back issues avail.) **Indexed:** Appl.Mech.Rev., ASCA, Chem.Abstr., Compumath, Curr.Cont, Deep Sea Res.& Oceanogr.Abstr., Eng.Ind., GeoRef., INSPEC (1975-), Math.R., Met.Abstr., Sci.Cit.Ind., Zent.Math. **Document type:** academic/scholarly publication, proceedings.
—BLDSC (5402.576600); Faxon; Genuine Article; SWETS; UMI; UnCover. **CCC.**
Formerly: Cambridge Philosophical Society. Proceedings. Mathematical and Physical Sciences (ISSN 0008-1981)
Description: Covers the gamut of pure and applied mathematics.

510 530.15   UK   ISSN 0950-6284
CAMBRIDGE TRACTS IN MATHEMATICS. 1905. irreg., no.88, 1986. price varies. Cambridge University Press, Edinburgh Bldg., Shaftesbury Rd., Cambridge CB2 2RU, England. TEL 0223-312393. FAX 0223-315052. TELEX 851817256. (N. American addr.: Cambridge University Press, Journals Dept., 40 W. 20th St., New York, NY 10011. TEL 212-924-3900. FAX 212-691-3239) Ed.Bd. **Indexed:** Math.R. **Document type:** monographic series.
—BLDSC (3015.999500).
Formerly: Cambridge Tracts in Mathematics and Mathematical Physics (ISSN 0068-6824)

510   US   ISSN 1073-1849
QA1
CANADIAN APPLIED MATHEMATICS QUARTERLY. 1992. q. Can.$102.50($87.50) to individuals; institutions Can.$205 ($175). (Canadian Mathematical Society, CN - Societe Canadienne de Mathematiques Appliquees) Rocky Mountain Mathematics Consortium, Dept. of Mathematics, Arizona State University, Tempe, AZ 85287-1904. (In Canada subscr. to: CAMQ, AMI, University of Alberta, Edmonton, Alta. T6G 2G1, Canada) (Co-sponsor: University of Alberta, Applied Mathematics Institute) Eds. Herbert I. Freedman, T. Bryant Moodie. **Document type:** academic/scholarly publication.
Description: Publishes original research articles relating mathematics to the physical, medical, biological and engineering sciences.

510   CN   ISSN 0008-414X
QA1   CODEN: CJMAAB
CANADIAN JOURNAL OF MATHEMATICS/JOURNAL CANADIEN DE MATHEMATIQUES. (Text in English, French) 1945. bi-m. Can.$320 to non-members (foreign $320); members Can.$76 (effective 1995). Canadian Mathematical Society, 577 King Edward, Ottawa, ON K1N 6N5, Canada. TEL 613-564-2223. (Subscr. to: University of Toronto Press, 5201 Dufferin St., Downsview, ON M3H 5T8, Canada) Eds. J. Carrell, N. Ghoussoub. adv.; bibl.; index. circ. 1,400. (also avail. in microform from PMC) **Indexed:** Compumath, Curr.Cont., Ind.Sci.Rev., Math.R., Sci.Cit.Ind.
—BLDSC (3032.000000); Faxon; Genuine Article; SWETS; UMI; UnCover. **CCC.**

510   CN   ISSN 0008-4395
CANADIAN MATHEMATICAL BULLETIN/BULLETIN CANADIEN DE MATHEMATIQUES. (Text in English, French) 1958. q. Can.$160 to non-members (foreign $160); members Can.$38 (effective 1995). Canadian Mathematical Society - Societe Mathematique du Canada, 577 King Edward, Ottawa, ON K1N 6N5, Canada. TEL 613-564-2223. (Subscr. to: University of Toronto Press, 5201 Dufferin St., Downsview, ON M3H 5T8, Canada) Eds. S. Kochman, T. Salisbury. adv.; bk.rev.; charts; index. circ. 900. (also avail. in microform from UMI) **Indexed:** Compumath, Math.R. **Document type:** bulletin.
—Faxon; Genuine Article; SWETS; UMI; UnCover. **CCC.**

510   US   ISSN 0731-1036
CANADIAN MATHEMATICAL SOCIETY. CONFERENCE PROCEEDINGS. 1981. irreg. price varies. (Canadian Mathematical Society, CN) American Mathematical Society, Box 6248, Providence, RI 02940-6248. TEL 401-455-4000. **Document type:** proceedings.
—BLDSC (3409.768000). **CCC.**

CENTAURUS; international magazine of the history of mathematics, science and technology. see *SCIENCES: COMPREHENSIVE WORKS*

510   SZ
CENTRE DE RECHERCHES EN MATHEMATIQUES PURES. P 1. 1958. a. 24 SFr. Societe Mathematique Suisse - Schweizerische Mathematische Gesellschaft, Case Postale 240, CH-1211 Geneva 24, Switzerland. cum.index. **Indexed:** Math.R. **Document type:** academic/scholarly publication.
Formerly: Universite de Neuchatel. Seminaire de Geometrie. Publications. Serie 1. Courtes Publications (ISSN 0077-7641)

510   CN
CENTRE FOR RESEARCH IN ALGEBRA AND NUMBER THEORY. 1987. irreg. price varies. Carleton University, Department of Mathematics and Statistics, Ottawa, Ont. K1S 5B6, Canada. TEL 613-788-2155. FAX 613-788-3536.
Formerly (until 1991): Centre for Research in Algebra and Related Fields.

CHANTIERS DE PEDAGOGIE MATHEMATIQUE. see *EDUCATION — Teaching Methods And Curriculum*

519.2 003.7   UK   ISSN 0960-0779
Q172.5.C45   CODEN: CSFOEH
CHAOS, SOLITONS AND FRACTALS; applications in science and engineering. 1991. m. £871($1385) (effective 1996). Elsevier Science Ltd., Pergamon, P.O. Box 800, Kidlington, Oxford OX5 1DX, England. TEL 44-1865-843000. FAX 44-1865-843010. E-mail: nlinfo-f@elsevier.nl; usinfo-f@elsevier.com; forinfo-kyf04035@niftyserve.or.jp; Site addr.: http://www.elsevier.nl/. (Subscr. in U.S. and Canada to: Elsevier Science, 660 White Plains Rd., Tarrytown, NY 10591-5153. TEL 914-524-9200. FAX 914-333-2444) Ed. M. El Naschie. (also avail. in microfilm from UMI; back issues avail.) **Indexed:** Ecol.Abstr., Geo.Abstr., Geol.Abstr., INSPEC (1991-). **Document type:** academic/scholarly publication.
—BLDSC (3129.716000); CASDDS; Ei; Genuine Article; SWETS; UMI; UnCover. **CCC.**
Description: Covers bifurcation and singularity theory, deterministic chaos and fractals; stability theory, soliton and coherent phenomena; formation of pattern, evolution and complexity theory.
Refereed Serial

510   US   ISSN 0069-3286
CHICAGO LECTURES IN MATHEMATICS. 1964. irreg., latest 1984. price varies. University of Chicago Press, 5801 S. Ellis Ave., Chicago, IL 60637. TEL 312-702-7899. Ed. Irving Kaplansky. (reprint service avail. from UMI,ISI) **Indexed:** Math.R.
Refereed Serial

510   NE   ISSN 0252-9599
QA1
CHINESE ANNALS OF MATHEMATICS. SERIES B. (Text in English) 1980. q. 489 SFr. (efective 1996). Baltzer Science Publishers B.V., Asterweg 1A, 1031 HL Amsterdam, Netherlands. TEL 31-20-6370061. FAX 31-20-6323651. E-mail: publish@baltzer.nl. (U.S. subscr. to: J.C. Baltzer AG, Box 8577, Red Bank, NJ 07701-8577) (Co-publisher: Shanghai Scientific and Technological Literature Publishing House, CC) Ed. Su Buqing. (back issues avail.) **Indexed:** Curr.Cont. **Document type:** academic/scholarly publication.
—BLDSC (3180.271200); Faxon; Genuine Article; SWETS; UnCover.
Supersedes in part (in 1983): Shuxue Niankan (ISSN 0253-6137)

510   US   ISSN 0898-5111
QA1
CHINESE JOURNAL OF CONTEMPORARY MATHEMATICS. 1988. q. $450 (effective 1996). (Chinese Mathematical Society, CC) Allerton Press, Inc., 150 Fifth Ave., New York, NY 10011. TEL 212-924-3950. FAX 212-463-9684. Ed. Su Buqing. (back issues avail.) **Document type:** academic/scholarly publication.
—CCC.
Description: Covers contemporary mathematical research in China, including both pure and applied mathematics.

510   US   ISSN 0899-4358
QA297
CHINESE JOURNAL OF NUMERICAL MATHEMATICS AND APPLICATIONS. 1988. q. $450 (effective 1996). (Academia Sinica - Chinese Academy of Sciences, Computing Center, CC - Zhongguo Kexueyuan Jisuan Zhongxin) Allerton Press, Inc., 150 Fifth Ave., New York, NY 10011. TEL 212-924-3950. FAX 212-463-9684. Ed. Tang Dingyuan. (back issues avail.) **Document type:** academic/scholarly publication.
—BLDSC (3180.438600). **CCC.**
Description: Covers mathematics research in China, including numerical linear and nonlinear algebra, and analysis.

510   JA   ISSN 0287-802X
            CODEN: CSGRDU
CHOSEN SHOGAKKAI GAKUJUTSU RONBUNSHU/KOREAN SCHOLARSHIP ASSOCIATION IN JAPAN. SCIENCE REPORT. (Text and summaries in English, Japanese) 1971. a. Korean Scholarship Association in Japan - Chosen Shogakkai, 8-1, Nishi-shinjuku, 1-chome, Shinjuku-ku, Tokyo 160, Japan.
—BLDSC (2600.390000); CASDDS.

510   CC
CHUZHONGSHENG SHUXUE FUDAO/MATHEMATICS TUTORING FOR JUNIOR HIGH SCHOOL STUDENTS. (Text in Chinese) m. $50. Jiangsu Jiaoyu Chubanshe - Jiangsu Education Publishing House, 165 Zhongyang Lu, Nanjing, Jiangsu 210009, People's Republic of China. TEL 635549. Ed. Mao Yongsheng. adv. contact: Yuanyuan Qian.

510   CR
CIENCIAS MATEMATICAS. (Text in Spanish; abstracts in English, Spanish) 1990. s-a. Col.500($20) (effective 1995). Editorial de la Universidad de Costa Rica, Apdo. 75-2060, Ciudad Universitaria Rodrigo Facio, 2050 San Pedro de Montes de Oca, San Jose, Costa Rica. TEL 506-25-3133. FAX 506-24-9367. TELEX UNICORI 2544. Dir. Manuel Barahona Droguett. bibl.; charts. **Document type:** academic/scholarly publication.

510   IT   ISSN 0009-725X
QA1   CODEN: RCMMAR
CIRCOLO MATEMATICO DI PALERMO. RENDICONTI. (In 2 Series) (Text in English, French, German and Italian) 1887. q. L.100000. Circolo Matematico di Palermo, Via Archirafi 34, 90123 Palermo, Italy. bk.rev. circ. 1,000. (also avail. in microfiche from BHP) **Indexed:** Appl.Mech.Rev.; Math.R. **Document type:** proceedings.
—SWETS; UnCover.

510   CN   ISSN 0731-4043
Z696.A1
CLASS: CLASSIFICATION LITERATURE AUTOMATED SEARCH SERVICE. a. $100 (includes Journal of Classification (ISSN 0176-4268)) (effective 1996). Classification Society of North America, c/o William H.E. Day, P.O. Box 17, Port Midland, NS B0W 2V0, Canada. TEL 902-649-2996. (Subscr. in N. America to: Springer-Verlag Journals Fulfillment Services, Box 2485, Secaucus, NJ 079096-2485. TEL 800-777-4643. FAX 201-348-4505) **Document type:** bibliography.
—SWETS.
Refereed Serial

CLASSICAL AND QUANTUM GRAVITY. see *PHYSICS*

516   US
CLASSICS IN APPLIED MATHEMATICS. irreg., vol.12, May 1995. price varies. Society for Industrial and Applied Mathematics, 3600 University City Science Center, Philadelphia, PA 19104-2688. TEL 215-382-9800; 800-447-SIAM. FAX 215-386-7999. E-mail: siam@siam.org. Ed. Tricia Manning; Pub. Vickie Kearn. **Document type:** monographic series.

510   US   ISSN 0743-9199
CLASSICS OF SOVIET MATHEMATICS. irreg., latest vol.2. Gordon and Breach Science Publishers, c/o International Publishers Distributor, 820 Town Center Dr., Langhorne, PA 19047. TEL 215-750-2642. FAX 215-750-6343. (Subscr. to: International Publishers Distributor, P.O. Box 90, Reading, Berkshire RG1 8JL, England. TEL 44-173-456-8316) **Document type:** monographic series.
Refereed Serial

510   SP   ISSN 0010-0757
QD1   CODEN: COLMBA
COLLECTANEA MATHEMATICA. (Text in English, French, German, Italian, Portuguese and Spanish) 1948. q. $50 (effective 1995). Universidad de Barcelona, Barcelona, Spain. FAX 34-3-4021662. E-mail: collect@cerber.mat.ub.es. Ed. Joan Cerda. circ. 300. **Indexed:** Ind.SST, Math.R., Stat.Theor.Meth.Abstr., Zent.Math. **Document type:** academic/scholarly publication.
—BLDSC (3299.800000); UnCover. **CCC.**
Refereed Serial

510   FR   ISSN 0768-3723
COLLECTION FORMATION DES ENSEIGNANTS ET FORMATION CONTINUE. 1973. irreg. Editions Hermann, 293 rue Lecourbe, 75015 Paris, France. TEL 45-57-45-40. illus.
Formerly: Collection Formation des Enseignants.

510 378.1   US   ISSN 0746-8342
QA11.A1
COLLEGE MATHEMATICS JOURNAL. 1970. 5/yr. $97 (effective 1996). Mathematical Association of America, 1529 18th St. N.W., Washington, DC 20036. TEL 202-387-5200. Ed. Bart Braden. adv.; bk.rev.; illus. circ. 10,000. (also avail. in microfilm from UMI; reprint service avail. from UMI) **Indexed:** ASCA, C.I.J.E., Cont.Pg.Educ., Educ.Ind., Gen.Sci.Ind., Math.R. **Document type:** academic/scholarly publication.
—BLDSC (3311.172000); Faxon; SWETS; UnCover. **CCC.**
Formerly (until 1983): Two-Year College Mathematics Journal (ISSN 0049-4925)
Description: Articles on mathematics, curriculum and pedagogy, problems and solutions, classroom notes, and a special section on computers, focusing on the earlier years of college-level mathematics.
Refereed Serial

510   NE   ISSN 0139-3383
COLLOQUIA MATHEMATICA SOCIETATIS JANOS BOLYAI. 1968. irreg., vol.62, 1994. price varies. Elsevier Science B.V., Books Division, P.O. Box 211, 1000 AE Amsterdam, Netherlands. TEL 31-20-4853911. FAX 31-20-4853705. TELEX 18582 ESPA NL. E-mail: nlinfo-f@elsevier.nl; usinfo-f@elsevier.com; forinfo-kyf04035@niftyserve.or.jp; Site addr.: http://www.elsevier.nl/. (Subscr. in U.S. and Canada to: Elsevier Science Inc., Box 882, Madison Sq. Sta., New York, NY 10159. TEL 212-989-5800) (back issues avail.) **Indexed:** INSPEC. **Document type:** monographic series.
—BLDSC (3315.240000).
Refereed Serial

MATHEMATICS   4113

510   PL   ISSN 0010-1354
QA1
COLLOQUIUM MATHEMATICUM. (Text in English, French, German, Russian) 1948. 4/yr. (in 2 vols., 2 nos./vol.) $168. Polska Akademia Nauk, Instytut Matematyczny, Dzial Wydawnictw, Ul. Sniadeckich 8, P.O. Box 8, 00-950 Warsaw, Poland. TEL 48-22-6282471. FAX 48-22-293997. Ed.Bd. bibl. circ. 900. (also avail. in microform from PMC; reprint service avail. from SWZ) **Indexed:** GeoRef., Math.R. **Document type:** academic/scholarly publication.
—Faxon; SWETS; UnCover.
Description: Publishes results of original research, new proofs of important theorems and expository papers in all fields of pure mathematics.
Refereed Serial

510   HU   ISSN 0209-9683
QA164   CODEN: COMBDI
COMBINATORICA. (Text in English) 1981. 4/yr. DM.468($340) (effective 1996). (Janos Bolyai Mathematical Society) Akademiai Kiado, Publishing House of the Hungarian Academy of Sciences, P.O. Box 245, H-1519 Budapest, Hungary. TEL 181-2134. FAX 166-6466. TELEX 22-6228 AKNYO H. (Dist. outside Eastern Europe by: Springer-Verlag, Heidelberger Platz 3, 14197 Berlin, Germany. TEL 030-8207-0. FAX 030-8214091) Eds. P. Erdos, L. Lovasz. index. (back issues avail.; reprint service avail. from SWZ) **Indexed:** Compumath, Curr.Cont., INSPEC (1992-), Int.Abstr.Oper.Res., Math.R., Stat.Theor.Meth.Abstr., Zent.Math. **Document type:** academic/scholarly publication.
—BLDSC (3324.750000); Faxon; Genuine Article; SWETS; UMI; UnCover. **CCC.**
Description: Publishes research papers in a variety of areas of combinatorics and the theory of computing.

510   SZ   ISSN 0010-2571
QA1   CODEN: COMHAX
COMMENTARII MATHEMATICI HELVETICI. (Text in English, French, German and Italian) 1929. 4/yr. 313.50 SFr. (foreign 326.80 SFr.). (Schweizerischen Mathematischen Gesellschaft - Swiss Mathematical Society) Birkhaeuser Verlag, P.O. Box 133, CH-4010 Basel, Switzerland. TEL 061-2717400. FAX 061-2717666. (Dist. in N. America by: Springer-Verlag, Mercedes Distribution Center, 160 Imlay St., Brooklyn, NY 11231, USA) Ed. H. Kraft. adv.; bk.rev.; illus.; tr.lit.; index. circ. 1,000. **Indexed:** Compumath, Ind.Sci.Rev., Math.R., Sci.Cit.Ind. **Document type:** academic/scholarly publication.
—Faxon; Genuine Article; SWETS; UMI; UnCover. **CCC.**

510   JA   ISSN 0010-258X
QA1   CODEN: COMAAC
COMMENTARII MATHEMATICI UNIVERSITATIS SANCTI PAULI/RIKKYO DAIGAKU SUGAKU ZASSHI. (Text and summaries in English) 1952. s-a. $291 (effective 1995). (Rikkyo Daigaku, Rigakubu Sugaku Kyoshitsu - Rikkyo University, Faculty of Science, Department of Mathematics) Kinokuniya Shoten - Kinokuniya Co., Ltd., 17-7 Shinjuku 3-chome, Shinjuku-ku, Tokyo 163-91, Japan. (Alt. addr.: Publishing Department, 38-1 Sakuragaoka 5-chome, Setagaya-ku, Tokyo 156, Japan. TEL 03-3439-0172. FAX 03-3439-0173) index. **Indexed:** Math.R.
—Faxon; UnCover.

510   XR   ISSN 0010-2628
QA1   CODEN: CMUCAA
COMMENTATIONES MATHEMATICAE UNIVERSITATIS CAROLINAE. (Text in English) 1960. q. exchange basis. Universita Karlova, Matematicko-Fizikalni Fakulta, Sokolovska 83, 18600 Prague 8, Czech Republic. (Dist. by: Messrs. Galloway and Porter Ltd., 30 Sidney St., Cambridge CB2 3HS, England) Ed. J. Danes. abstr.; charts; index. circ. 600. (also avail. in microform from SWZ; reprint service avail. from SWZ) **Indexed:** Math.R., Ref.Zh., Zent.Math.
—Faxon; SWETS; UnCover.

COMMENTATIONES PHYSICO-MATHEMATICAE ET CHEMICO-MEDICAE. see *PHYSICS*

MATHEMATICS

510 US ISSN 0092-7872
QA150 CODEN: COALDM
COMMUNICATIONS IN ALGEBRA. 1974. 14/yr. $1675. Marcel Dekker Journals, 270 Madison Ave., New York, NY 10016. TEL 212-696-9000. FAX 212-685-4540. TELEX 421419. (Subscr. to: Box 5017, Monticello, NY 12701) Ed. Earl J. Taft. adv.; bibl.; charts; illus.; index. (also avail. in microform from RPI; reprint service avail. from SWZ) **Indexed:** Compumath, Curr.Cont., Ind.Sci.Rev., Math.R., Sci.Cit.Ind. **Document type:** academic/scholarly publication.
—BLDSC (3359.200000); Faxon; Genuine Article; SWETS; UMI; UnCover. **CCC.**
Refereed Serial

515 516 US ISSN 1019-8385
QA299.6
COMMUNICATIONS IN ANALYSIS AND GEOMETRY. 1993. a. $85 to individuals; institutions $170. International Press, Box 2872, Cambridge, MA 02238-2872. TEL 617-491-0329. FAX 617-495-2180. E-mail: julie@math.harvard.edu. Ed. Peter Li.
—BLDSC (3359.210000); SWETS.
Description: Covers classical analysis, partial differential equations, algebraic geometry, differential geometry, and topology.
Refereed Serial

COMMUNICATIONS IN MATHEMATICAL PHYSICS. see
PHYSICS

510 624 UK ISSN 1069-8299
TA335 CODEN: CANMER
COMMUNICATIONS IN NUMERICAL METHODS IN ENGINEERING. Abbreviated title: C N M E. 1985. m. $695 (foreign $695) (effective 1996). John Wiley & Sons Ltd., Journals, Baffins Ln., Chichester, W. Sussex PO19 1UD, England. TEL 01243-779777. FAX 01243-776128. TELEX 86290 WIBOOK G. (Subscr. in the Americas to: John Wiley & Sons, Inc., Journals Administration Department, 605 Third Ave., New York, NY 10158. TEL 212-850-6645. FAX 212-850-6021) Eds. Roland W. Lewis, Graham F. Carey. circ. 352. (also avail. in microform from UMI; back issues avail.; reprint service avail. from SWZ) **Indexed:** Compumath, Curr.Cont., Geo.Abstr., Geol.Abstr. **Document type:** academic/scholarly publication.
—BLDSC (3361.380000); Ei; Faxon; Genuine Article; SWETS; UMI; UnCover. **CCC.**
Formerly (until 1993): Communications in Applied Numerical Methods (ISSN 0748-8025)
Description: Contains short contributions describing important devopments in numerical methods and the applications of such techniques to the solution of practical engineering problems.
Refereed Serial

350 US ISSN 0360-5302
QA377 CODEN: CPDIDZ
COMMUNICATIONS IN PARTIAL DIFFERENTIAL EQUATIONS. 1976. 12/yr. $895. Marcel Dekker Journals, 270 Madison Ave., New York, NY 10016. TEL 212-696-9000. FAX 212-685-4540. TELEX 421419. (Subscr. to: Box 5017, Monticello, NY 12701) Eds. J. Ralston, Panagiotis Souganidis. (also avail. in microform from RPI; reprint service avail. from SWZ) **Indexed:** Compumath, INIS Atomind., Math.R. **Document type:** academic/scholarly publication.
—Faxon; Genuine Article; SWETS; UMI; UnCover. **CCC.**
Refereed Serial

COMMUNICATIONS IN STATISTICS. PART A: THEORY AND METHODS. see *STATISTICS*

COMMUNICATIONS IN STATISTICS. PART C: STOCHASTIC MODELS. see *STATISTICS*

515 519 US ISSN 1074-133X
▼**COMMUNICATIONS ON APPLIED NONLINEAR ANALYSIS;** a great American journal. 1994. q. $150. International Publications, 12046 Coed Dr., Orlando, FL 32826. TEL 407-282-5476. Ed. Ram U. Verma.
—BLDSC (3359.337500).
Description: Publishes high quality research articles in all areas of nonlinear mathematical sciences, control theory and optimization, mathematical physics, and their applications to academic fields as well as to science and industry.

510 519 US ISSN 0010-3640
QA1 CODEN: CPMAMV
COMMUNICATIONS ON PURE AND APPLIED MATHEMATICS. 1939. m. $1212 (foreign $1398) (effective 1996). (Courant Institute of Mathematical Sciences) John Wiley & Sons, Inc., Journals, 605 Third Ave., New York, NY 10158. TEL 212-850-6645. FAX 212-850-6021. TELEX 12-7063. E-mail: SUBINFO@JWILEY.COM. (Subscr. in the Americas to: John Wiley & Sons Ltd., Baffins Ln., Chishester, W. Sussex PO19 1UD, England. TEL 44-1243-779777. FAX 44-1243-776128) Ed. Natascha A. Brunswick. bibl.; illus.; index. circ. 1,400. (also avail. in microform; back issues avail.; reprint service avail. from KTO) **Indexed:** Appl.Mech.Rev., Compumath, Curr.Cont., Ind.Sci.Rev., Int.Aerosp.Abstr., Math.R., Sci.Cit.Ind. **Document type:** academic/scholarly publication.
—BLDSC (3363.000000); Faxon; Genuine Article; SWETS; UMI; UnCover. **CCC.**
Description: Examines developments in applied mathematics, mathematical physics, and mathematical analysis.
Refereed Serial

510 US ISSN 0278-1077
QA331 CODEN: CVTADV
COMPLEX VARIABLES: THEORY AND APPLICATION; an international journal. 1982. 8/yr. (in 2 vols., 4 nos./vol.). 313 ECU (effective 1996). Gordon and Breach Science Publishers, c/o International Publishers Distributor, 820 Town Center Dr., Langhorne, PA 19047. TEL 215-750-2642. FAX 215-750-6343. (Subscr. to: International Publishers Distributor, P.O. Box 90, Reading, Berkshire, RG1 8JL, England. TEL 44-173-456-8316) Eds. Robert P. Gilbert, Klaus Habetha. (also avail. in microform) **Indexed:** Math.R.
—BLDSC (3364.585000); Faxon; SWETS; UnCover. **CCC.**
Refereed Serial

510 NE ISSN 0010-437X
QA1 CODEN: CMPMAF
COMPOSITIO MATHEMATICA. (Text mainly in English) 1933. 15/yr. fl.1992.50 to institutions; $1217 to institutions in U.S. (effective 1996). Kluwer Academic Publishers, Postbus 17, 3300 AA Dordrecht, Netherlands. TEL 31-78-392392. FAX 31-78-392254. TELEX 29245 KAPG NL. E-mail: SERVICES@WKAP.NL. (Dist. by: Kluwer Academic Publishers Group, P.O. Box 322, 3300 AH Dordrecht, Netherlands. TEL 31-78-392392. FAX 31-78-546474; N. America dist. addr.: Box 358, Accord Sta., Hingham, MA 02018-0358. TEL 617-871-6600. FAX 617-871-6528) Ed. G.B.M. van der Meer. adv. (also avail. in microform from UMI; back issues avail.; reprint service avail. from KTO,SWZ) **Indexed:** ASCA, Bull.Signal., Compumath, Curr.Cont., Ind.Sci.Rev., Math.R., Sci.Cit.Ind., Zent.Math. **Document type:** academic/scholarly publication.
—Faxon; Genuine Article; SWETS; UMI; UnCover. **CCC.**
Description: Publishes papers in pure mathematics, including number theory, algebraic and analytic geometry and topology.
Refereed Serial

COMPUTATIONAL MATERIALS SCIENCE. see
ENGINEERING — Engineering Mechanics And Materials

510 530 UK ISSN 0965-5425
QA297 CODEN: CMMPA9
COMPUTATIONAL MATHEMATICS AND MATHEMATICAL PHYSICS. English translation of: Zhurnal Vychislitel'noi Matematiki i Matematicheskoi Fiziki (RU ISSN 0044-4669) 1962. m. £1140($1813) (effective 1996). (Russian Academy of Sciences, RU) Elsevier Science Ltd., Pergamon, P.O. Box 800, Kidlington, Oxford OX5 1DX, England. TEL 44-1865-843000. FAX 44-1865-843010. E-mail: nlinfo-f@elsevier.nl; usinfo-f@elsevier.com; forinfo-kyf04035@niftyserve.or.jp; Site addr.: http://www.elsevier.nl/. (Subscr. in U.S. and Canada to: Elsevier Science, 660 White Plains Rd., Tarrytown, NY 10591-5153. TEL 914-524-9200. FAX 914-333-2444) Ed. A.A. Dorodnicyn. adv.; bk.rev.; charts; illus.; index. circ. 1,000. (also avail. in microfilm from UMI; back issues avail.) **Indexed:** Appl.Mech.Rev., Compumath, Curr.Cont., INSPEC (1968-), Math.R., Stat.Theor.Meth.Abstr. **Document type:** academic/scholarly publication.
—BLDSC (0411.052000); Faxon; Genuine Article; SWETS; UMI; UnCover. **CCC.**
Formerly (until 1992): U S S R Computational Mathematics and Mathematical Physics (ISSN 0041-5553)
Description: Publishes mathematical papers from all fields of science as well as papers of a purely mathematical nature.
Refereed Serial

COMPUTATIONAL MATHEMATICS AND MODELING. see *MATHEMATICS — Computer Applications*

510 AG ISSN 0010-5147
CONCEPTOS DE MATEMATICA; revista para el maestro, el profesor y el estudiante. 1967. q. Arg.$120($6) c/o Jose Banfi, 1949 Paraguay, Buenos Aires, Argentina. adv.; bk.rev.; bibl.; charts; illus. circ. 5,000.
Supersedes: Elementos.

510 AG ISSN 0327-9170
CONGRESO DR. ANTONIO A.R. MONTEIRO. ACTA. (Text and summaries in English or Spanish) 1991. biennial. Universidad Nacional del Sur, Instituto de Matematica, Avda. Alem 1253, 8000 Bahia Blanca, Argentina. TEL 54-91-25772. FAX 54-91-27876. E-mail: inmabb@arcriba.edu.ar. **Document type:** proceedings.

510 CN ISSN 0384-9864
QA1
CONGRESSUS NUMERANTIUM; a conference journal on numerical themes. 1970. irreg. (6-7/yr.) $35 per vol. Utilitas Mathematica Publishing Inc., Box 7, University Centre, University of Manitoba, Winnipeg, MB R3T 2N2, Canada. TEL 204-474-8675. Ed. Ralph G. Stanton. circ. 400. **Indexed:** Math.R., Zent.Math. **Document type:** academic/scholarly publication.
—BLDSC (3417.547000); UnCover. **CCC.**
Incorporates (in 1971): Manitoba Conference on Numerical Mathematics and Computing. Proceedings (ISSN 0384-997X); **(in 1970):** Southeastern Conference on Combinatorics, Graph Theory and Computing Proceedings (ISSN 0316-1382)
Description: Provides up-to-date knowledge of the latest research in combinatorics and graph theory.
Refereed Serial

CONNECT (BRATTLEBORO); the newsletter of practical science and math for K-8 teachers. see
EDUCATION — Teaching Methods And Curriculum

510 US ISSN 0889-5392
QA11.A1
CONSORTIUM. 1984. q. $32 (foreign $37). Consortium for Mathematics and Its Applications, 57 Bedford St., Ste. 210, Lexington, MA 02173-4428. Ed. Margaret B. Cozzens. circ. 25,500. **Document type:** newsletter.

510 US ISSN 0176-4276
CONSTRUCTIVE APPROXIMATION; an international journal for approximations and expansions. 1985. q. $220 (effective 1996). Springer-Verlag, Journals, 175 Fifth Ave., New York, NY 10010. TEL 212-460-1500. FAX 212-473-6272. (N. American subscr. to: Journal Fulfillment Services, Box 2485, Secaucus, NJ 07096-2491. TEL 800-777-4643. FAX 201-348-4505; Elsewhere: Heidelberger Platz 3, 1000 Berlin 33, Germany. TEL 030-8207-1. FAX 030-8214091) Eds. Ronald A. DeVore, Edward B. Saff. (also avail. in microform from UMI; back issues avail.; reprint service avail. from ISI,SWZ) **Indexed**: ASCA, Compumath, Curr.Cont., Math.R., Zent.Math. **Document type**: academic/scholarly publication.
—BLDSC (3422.627500); Faxon; Genuine Article; SWETS; UnCover. **CCC**.
  Description: Covers important research in approximations and expansions
  Refereed Serial

510 US ISSN 0271-4132
CONTEMPORARY MATHEMATICS. 1980. irreg. price varies. American Mathematical Society, Box 6248, Providence, RI 02940-6248. TEL 401-455-4000. **Indexed**: INSPEC, Math.R. **Document type**: monographic series.
—BLDSC (3425.191400). **CCC**.

510 620 JA ISSN 0911-0704
QA402.3
CONTROL; theory and advanced technology. (Text and summaries in English) 1985. q. 30900 Yen($125) Mita Press, Ochanomizu Center Bldg., 8F, 2-12, Hongo-3, Bunkyo-ku, Tokyo 113, Japan. FAX 03-3818-1016. TELEX 2722813-MITA-PS-J. Eds. Y. Sunahara, D.P. Atherton. bk.rev. circ. 1,300.
—BLDSC (3463.017000); Ei; Faxon; Genuine Article; SWETS.
  Description: Deals with control systems, information sciences and related areas.

510 375 AT
CROSS SECTION. 1989. 3/yr. Aus.$22. Mathematical Association of Western Australia, P.O. Box 492, Subiaco, W.A. 6008, Australia.
  Formed by the 1989 merger of: Rhombus (ISSN 0313-4504) & Sigma (ISSN 0314-7606)

510 CN ISSN 0705-0348
CRUX MATHEMATICORUM. (Text in English, French) 1975. 10/yr. Can.$23 to members; non-members Can.$46. Canadian Mathematical Society - Societe Mathematique du Canada, 577 King Edward, Ottawa, ON K1N 6N5, Canada. TEL 613-564-2223. Ed. George Sands. bk.rev. circ. 700.
—UnCover.
  Formerly (until Mar. 1978): Eureka (ISSN 0700-558X)
  Description: Problems solving journal at the senior secondary and university undergraduate levels.

510 652.8 US ISSN 0161-1194
Z102.5 CODEN: CRYPE6
CRYPTOLOGIA; a quarterly journal devoted to all aspects of cryptology. 1977. q. $40 (foreign $44) (effective 1995). Rose-Hulman Institute of Technology, Department of Mathematics, Terre Haute, IN 47803. TEL 812-877-8412. FAX 812-877-3198. E-mail: winkel@nextwork.rose-hulman.edu. Ed. Brian J. Winkel. adv.; bk.rev.; illus.; pat.; stat. circ. 1,000. (also avail. in microform from UMI; back issues avail.) **Indexed**: Comput.Cont., INSPEC (1990-), Math.R. **Document type**: academic/scholarly publication.
—BLDSC (3490.155480); Faxon; Genuine Article; SWETS; UMI; UnCover. **CCC**.
  Description: Scholarly journal on aspects of cryptology including computer security, mathematics, codes, cryptanalysis, history, and ancient languages.

512 SP ISSN 0213-1420
CUADERNOS DE ALGEBRA. 1985-198? (no.9). irreg. price varies. Universidad de Granada, Facultad de Ciencias, Dep. de Algebra y Fundamentos, Fuentenueva, s-n, 18001 Granada, Spain. TEL 281356.

510 US ISSN 0732-4405
QA1
CURRENT TOPICS IN CHINESE SCIENCE. SECTION C: MATHEMATICS. 1982. irreg., vol.3, 1985. Gordon & Breach Science Publishers, c/o International Publishers Distributor, 820 Town Center Dr., Langhorne, PA 19047. TEL 215-750-2642. FAX 215-750-6343. (Subscr. to: International Publishers Distributor, P.O. Box 90, Reading Berkshire RG1 8JL, England. TEL 44-173-456-8316) (also avail. in microfilm) **Document type**: monographic series.
Refereed Serial

510 US ISSN 0011-4642
QA1
CZECHOSLOVAK MATHEMATICAL JOURNAL. (Text in English, French, German, Russian) 1951. q. $655 (foreign $765) (effective 1996). (Czech Academy of Sciences, Mathematical Institute, XG) Plenum Publishing Corp., 233 Spring St., New York, NY 10013-1578. TEL 212-620-8000. FAX 212-463-0742. TELEX 23-421139. (Co-publisher: Academia, XG) Ed. Miroslav Fiedler. bk.rev.; bibl.; index. circ. 1,200. (reprint service avail. from SWZ) **Indexed**: Appl.Mech.Rev., Compumath, Comput.Rev., Math.R. **Document type**: academic/scholarly publication.
—Faxon; Genuine Article; SWETS; UMI; UnCover. **CCC**.
  Formerly: Jednota Ceskoslovenskych Matematiku a Fysiku. Casopis pro Pestovani Matematiky a Fysiky.
  Description: Presents mathematical research papers, news and notices.
  Refereed Serial

519 DK ISSN 0106-6366
D C A M M REPORT. 1970. irreg. free. Danish Center for Applied Mathematics and Mechanics, Department of Solid Mechanics, Technical University of Denmark, Lyngby, Denmark. Ed. Pavli Pedersen. circ. 500. **Document type**: academic/scholarly publication.
Refereed Serial

510 DK ISSN 0106-9306
DANMARKS TEKNISKE HOEJSKOLE. MATEMATISK INSTITUT. MAT - P R. no. 2, 1984. irreg. Danmarks Tekniske Hoejskole, Matematisk Institut, 2800 Lyngby, Denmark. TEL 45-42-88-36-99. FAX 45-42-88-13-99. TELEX 37529-DTHDIA-DK. Ed. Helge Elbroend Jensen. circ. 100. **Document type**: academic/scholarly publication.
  Description: Presents old and new results from all fields of mathematics.

510 GW ISSN 0938-6572
DE GRUYTER EXPOSITIONS IN MATHEMATICS. irreg. Walter de Gruyter and Co., Genthinerstr. 13, 10785 Berlin, Germany. TEL 030-26005-0. FAX 030-26005251. (U.S. addr.: Walter de Gruyter, Inc., 200 Saw Mill River Rd., Hawthorne, NY 10532. TEL 914-747-0110) **Document type**: monographic series.
—BLDSC (3535.930400).

515 GW ISSN 0941-813X
DE GRUYTER SERIES IN NONLINEAR ANALYSIS AND APPLICATIONS. (Text in English) irreg., no.2, 1994. Walter de Gruyter und Co., Genthinerstr. 13, 10785 Berlin, Germany. TEL 030-26005-0. FAX 030-26005251. (U.S. addr.: 200 Saw Mill River Rd., Hawthorne, NY 10532. TEL 914-747-0110) Eds. J. Appell, V. Lakshmikantham. **Document type**: monographic series.
—BLDSC (3535.930450).

510 530 PL ISSN 0137-3005
DELTA; matematyczno-fizyczno-astronomiczny miesiecznik popularny. 1974. m. Uniwersytet Warszawski, Ul. Smycznkowa 5-7, 02-678 Warsaw, Poland. TEL 48-22-430243. (Dist. by: Ars Polona, Krakowskie Przedmiescie 7, 00-068 Warsaw, Poland. TEL 48-22-267622) (Co-sponsors: Polskie Towarzystwo Astronomiczne; Polskie Towarzystwo Fizyczne; Polskie Towarzystwo Matematyczne) Ed. M. Kordos. circ. 5,500.

MATHEMATICS 4115

511 005.8 NE ISSN 0925-1022
QA166.25 CODEN: DCCREC
DESIGN, CODES AND CRYPTOGRAPHY. 1991. 9/yr. fl.1150.50 to institutions; $700 to institutions in U.S. (effective 1996). Kluwer Law International (Subsidiary of: Wolters Kluwer N.V.), Postbus 85889, 2508 CN The Hague, Netherlands. TEL 31-70-3081500. FAX 31-70-3081515. E-mail: SERVICES@WKAP.NL. (Dist. by: Kluwer Academic Publishers Group, P.O. Box 322, 3300 AH Dordrecht, Netherlands. TEL 31-78-546392. FAX 31-78-546477; N. America dist. addr.: Box 358, Accord Sta., Hingham, MA 02018-0358. TEL 617-871-6600. FAX 617-871-6528) Ed. Scott A. Vanstone. (also avail. in microform from UMI; reprint service avail. from SWZ) **Indexed**: Comput.Lit.Ind., Comput.Rev., Eng.Ind., Inform.Sci.Abstr., INSPEC (1991-), Math.R., Zent.Math. **Document type**: academic/scholarly publication.
—BLDSC (3560.314000); Ei; SWETS; UMI. **CCC**.
  Description: Presents theoretical and applied papers integrating design theory, coding theory, and cryptography, with review papers reporting significant new research.
  Refereed Serial

510 GW ISSN 0012-0456
QA1 CODEN: JDMVA7
DEUTSCHE MATHEMATIKER VEREINIGUNG. JAHRESBERICHT. 1890. 4/yr. DM.128. B.G. Teubner GmbH, Postfach 801069, 70510 Stuttgart, Germany. TEL 0711-78901-0. FAX 0711-78901-10. Ed. W-D. Geyer. adv.; bk.rev.; illus.; index. circ. 3,200. (back issues avail.; reprint service avail. from SWZ,UMI) **Indexed**: Math.R. **Document type**: academic/scholarly publication.
—SWETS. **CCC**.

510 GW
DEUTSCHE MATHEMATIKER VEREINIGUNG. MITTEILUNGEN. 1890. q. Deutsche Mathematiker Vereinigung, Albertstr. 24, 79104 Freiburg, Germany. FAX 0761-272698. circ. 2,650. **Document type**: newsletter.

DEVELOPMENTS IN GEOMATHEMATICS. see *EARTH SCIENCES — Geophysics*

510 793.73 II ISSN 0300-4309
DHANDHA. (Text in Bengali) 1972. m. Rs.3($5) Mukherjee Library, 1 Gopi Mohan Dutta Lane, Calcutta 700003, India. Ed. Biswanath Bose. adv.; bibl.; illus. circ. 1,500.
  Description: Features recreational mathematics.

DIDAKTIK DER MATHEMATIK. see *EDUCATION — Teaching Methods And Curriculum*

DIDATTICA DELLE SCIENZE E INFORMATICA NELLA SCUOLA. see *EDUCATION — Teaching Methods And Curriculum*

510 US ISSN 0893-4983
DIFFERENTIAL AND INTEGRAL EQUATIONS; an international journal for theory & applications. 1988. 6/yr. $590 (effective 1996). Khayyam Publishing Company, Inc., Box 429, Athens, OH 45701. TEL 614-592-6136. FAX 614-592-1252. Ed. Reza Aftabizadeh. **Document type**: academic/scholarly publication.
—BLDSC (3584.134000); Faxon; SWETS; UnCover.
  Refereed Serial

512 US ISSN 0012-2661
QA371 CODEN: DIEQAN
DIFFERENTIAL EQUATIONS. English translation of: Differentsial'nye Uravneniya (BW ISSN 0374-0641) 1965. m. $1445 (foreign $1690) (effective 1996). (Akademiya Navuk Belarusi, BW) Plenum Publishing Corp., Consultants Bureau, 233 Spring St., New York, NY 10013-1578. TEL 212-620-8468. FAX 212-463-0742. TELEX 23-421139. Ed. V.A. Il'in. (also avail. in microfilm from JSC; back issues avail.) **Indexed**: Appl.Mech.Rev., Compumath, Comput.& Info.Sys., Zent.Math. **Document type**: academic/scholarly publication.
—BLDSC (0411.094000); Faxon; Genuine Article; SWETS; UMI; UnCover. **CCC**.
  Refereed Serial

MATHEMATICS

515   II   ISSN 0971-3514
DIFFERENTIAL EQUATIONS AND DYNAMICAL SYSTEMS; an international journal for theory and applications. (Text in English) 1993. m. Rs.1200($85) to indivuduals; foreign institutions $160. Research Square Publications, Plot No.20, H. No.13-48-1, Alakapuri, Saroornagar Post, Hyderabad 500035, India. Ed. V. Sree Hari Rao. **Document type:** academic/scholarly publication.
—BLDSC (3584.205000).

510   NE   ISSN 0926-2245
QA641   CODEN: DGAPEO
DIFFERENTIAL GEOMETRY AND ITS APPLICATIONS. (Text in English) 1991. q. fl.395($241) (effective 1996). North-Holland (Subsidiary of: Elsevier Science B.V.), P.O. Box 211, 1000 AE Amsterdam, Netherlands. TEL 31-20-4853911. FAX 31-20-4853598. TELEX 18582 ESPA NL. (Subscr. in U.S. and Canada to: Elsevier Science Inc., Box 882, Madison Sq. Sta., New York, NY 10159. TEL 212-989-5800. FAX 212-633-3990) Ed. D. Krupka. (also avail. in microform from UMI; back issues avail.) **Indexed:** INSPEC (1991-). **Document type:** academic/scholarly publication.
—BLDSC (3584.220000); Genuine Article; SWETS.
Description: Publishes original research papers and survey papers in differential geometry and in all interdisciplinary areas in mathematics which use differential geometric methods and investigate geometrical structures.
Refereed Serial

510 370   FI   ISSN 0782-6648
DIMENSIO. (Text in Finnish; summaries in English, Finnish and Swedish) 1937. 16/yr. FIM 180. Matemaattisten Aineiden Opettajien Liitto, Akavatalo, Rautatielaisenkatu 6, 00520 Helsinki 52, Finland. Ed. Kaisa-Liisa Lavonen. adv.; bk.rev.; charts; illus.; index. circ. 5,000.
Formerly: Matemaattisten Aineiden Aikakauskirja (ISSN 0025-5149)
Description: Presents study and teaching methods.

510 001.6 621.381   US   ISSN 0179-5376
QA440   CODEN: DCGEER
DISCRETE & COMPUTATIONAL GEOMETRY. 1986. 8/yr. (in 2 vols.) $278 (effective 1996). Springer-Verlag, Journals, 175 Fifth Ave., New York, NY 10010. TEL 212-460-1500. FAX 212-473-6272. (N. American subscr. to: Journal Fulfillment Services, Box 2485, Secaucus, NJ 07094-2491. TEL 800-777-4643. FAX 201-348-4505; Elsewhere: Heidelberger Platz 3, 1000 Berlin 33, Germany. TEL 030-8207-1. FAX 030-8214091) Eds. J.E. Goodman, R. Pollack. (back issues avail.; reprint service avail. from SWZ) **Indexed:** Compumath, Curr.Cont., Eng.Ind., INSPEC (1987-), Math.R., Zent.Math. **Document type:** academic/scholarly publication.
—BLDSC (3597.024000); Ei; Faxon; Genuine Article; SWETS; UMI; UnCover. **CCC.**
Description: Contains articles for mathematicians and computer scientists in the areas of combinatorial geometry, as well as the design and analysis of geometric algorithms.
Refereed Serial

510   NE   ISSN 0166-218X
QA1   CODEN: DAMADU
DISCRETE APPLIED MATHEMATICS; combinatorial operations research and computer science. (Text in English and French) 1979. 24/yr. fl.2840($1732) (effective 1996). North-Holland (Subsidiary of: Elsevier Science B.V.), P.O. Box 211, 1000 AE Amsterdam, Netherlands. TEL 31-20-4853911. FAX 31-20-4853598. TELEX 18582 ESPA NL. (Subscr. in U.S. and Canada to: Elsevier Science Inc., Box 882, Madison Sq. Sta., New York, NY 10159. TEL 212-989-5800. FAX 212-633-3990) Ed. Peter L. Hammer. abstr.; illus.; index. (also avail. in microform from UMI; back issues avail.; reprint service avail. from SWZ) **Indexed:** Compumath, Curr.Cont., Cyb.Abstr., Eng.Ind., Ind.Sci.Rev., INSPEC, Int.Abstr.Oper.Res., Math R., Sci.Cit.Ind., Stat.Theor.Meth.Abstr., Zent.Math. **Document type:** academic/scholarly publication.
—BLDSC (3597.025000); Ei; Faxon; Genuine Article; SWETS; UnCover. **CCC.**
Description: Brings together research in different areas of applied combinatorics and demonstrates the unity of the mathematical tools used in a variety of fields and applications.
Refereed Serial

510   NE   ISSN 0012-365X
QA1   CODEN: DSMHA4
DISCRETE MATHEMATICS. (Text in English) 1971. 45/yr. fl.4965($3028) (effective 1996). North-Holland (Subsidiary of: Elsevier Science B.V.), P.O. Box 211, 1000 AE Amsterdam, Netherlands. TEL 31-20-4853911. FAX 31-20-4853598. TELEX 18582 ESPA NL. (Subscr. in U.S. and Canada to: Elsevier Science Inc., Box 882, Madison Sq. Sta., New York, NY 10159. TEL 212-989-5800. FAX 212-633-3990) Ed. P.L. Hammer. adv.; bk.rev. circ. 2,000. (also avail. in microform from UMI; back issues avail.; reprint service avail. from SWZ) **Indexed:** Compumath, Comput.Rev., Curr.Cont., Cyb.Abstr., INSPEC, Int.Abstr.Oper.Res., Sci.Cit.Ind. **Document type:** academic/scholarly publication.
—BLDSC (3597.030000); Ei; Faxon; Genuine Article; SWETS; UnCover. **CCC.**
Description: Publishes research papers, notes, communications, and research problems in the field of discrete mathematics.
Refereed Serial

510   NE   ISSN 0924-9265
     CODEN: DMAPEW
DISCRETE MATHEMATICS AND APPLICATIONS. English translation of: Diskretnaya Matematika (RU ISSN 0234-0860) 1991. bi-m. DM.990 (effective 1996). (Russian Academy of Sciences, RU) V S P, P.O. Box 346, 3700 AH Zeist, Netherlands. TEL 31-30-6925790. FAX 31-30-6932081. E-mail: 100341.2372@compuserve.com. Ed. V.Y. Kozlov. bk.rev. **Document type:** academic/scholarly publication.
—BLDSC (3597.032000); Ei.
Description: Covers topics in discrete mathematics, with original articles in addition to translations.
Refereed Serial

510   RU   ISSN 0234-0860
     CODEN: DIMAEJ
DISKRETNAYA MATEMATIKA. English translation: Discrete Mathematics and Applications (NE ISSN 0924-9265) q. $106 (effective 1996). (Rossiiskaya Akademiya Nauk) Izdatel'stvo Nauka, Mezhdunarodnyi Otdel, Profsoyuznaya, 90, 117864 Moscow, Russia. Ed. V. Ya. Kozlov. **Document type:** academic/scholarly publication.
—BLDSC (0053.268700). **CCC.**

510   HU   ISSN 0070-671X
DISQUISITIONES MATHEMATICAE HUNGARICAE. (Text in English, French, German or Hungarian) 1970. irreg., vol.14, 1987. price varies. (Magyar Tudomanyos Akademia) Akademiai Kiado, Publishing House of the Hungarian Academy of Sciences, P.O. Box 245, H-1519 Budapest, Hungary. TEL 181-2134. FAX 166-6466. TELEX 22-6228 AKNYO H.

510   PL   ISSN 0012-3862
     CODEN: DSMAAH
DISSERTATIONES MATHEMATICAE/ROZPRAWY MATEMATYCZNE. (Text in English, French, German, Russian; summaries in English and Russian) 1952. irreg., vol.326, 1993. price varies. Polska Akademia Nauk, Instytut Matematyczny - Polish Academy of Sciences, Institute of Mathematics, Dzial Wydawnictw, Ul. Sniadeckich 8, P.O. Box 137, 00-950 Warsaw, Poland. TEL 48-22-6282471. FAX 48-22-293997. Eds. B. Bojarski, W. Zelazko. bibl. circ. 500. **Indexed:** Math.R. **Document type:** monographic series.
Description: Publishes research papers in any area of mathematics.
Refereed Serial

DIVREI HA-AKADEMIA HA-LEUMIT HA-YISRAELIT LEMADAIM-HA-HATIVA LE-MADAEI HA-TEVA. see *SCIENCES: COMPREHENSIVE WORKS*

510   UK   ISSN 0260-4884
THE DOZENAL JOURNAL. 1959. irreg., no.10, serial 48. £1 to non-members; free to members. Dozenal Society of Great Britain, Walnut Bank, Underhill, Moulsford, Oxon. OX10 9JH, England. TEL 01491-351448. Ed. Arthur F. Whillock. bk.rev.; index. circ. 350. (tabloid format) **Document type:** academic/scholarly publication.
Former titles (until winter 1980): Dozenal Review (ISSN 0309-8648); (until 1977): Duodecimal Review.
Description: Aimed at the study and advocacy of base twelve numeration and calculations for all social and scientific purposes with the aim of unifying the two. Reviews all methods and means for weights and measures, past, present, and future, with emphasis on the use and need of divisibility with comprehension.

510   US   ISSN 0012-7094
QA1   CODEN: DUMJAO
DUKE MATHEMATICAL JOURNAL. 1935. m. $343 to individuals (foreign $382); institutions $686 (foreign $725) (effective 1996). Duke University Press, Box 90660, Durham, NC 27708-0660. TEL 919-687-3600. FAX 919-688-4574. Ed. Morris Weisfeld. bibl.; charts; index, cum.index every 10 yrs. circ. 1,200. (also avail. in microform from MIM,UMI,KTO; reprint service avail. from ISI,UMI) **Indexed:** Compumath, Curr.Cont., Ind.Sci.Rev., Math.R., Sci.Cit.Ind. **Document type:** academic/scholarly publication.
—Faxon; Genuine Article; SWETS; UMI; UnCover. **CCC.**
Refereed Serial

513.56   US   ISSN 0046-0826
QA141
DUODECIMAL BULLETIN. 1945. 2/yr. $12. Dozenal Society of America, c/o Math Department, Nassau Community College, Garden City, NY 11530. TEL 516-669-0273. Ed. Jay Schiffman. adv. contact: Gene Zirkel. bk.rev. circ. 230. **Document type:** bulletin.
Description: Contains articles, news, and society announcements.
Refereed Serial

DYNAMATH. see *CHILDREN AND YOUTH — For*

DYNAMIC SYSTEMS AND APPLICATIONS. see *ENGINEERING*

510 500   FR   ISSN 0012-9593
     CODEN: ASENAH
ECOLE NORMALE SUPERIEURE. ANNALES SCIENTIFIQUES. (Text in English and French) 1864. 6/yr. 1410 F. Gauthier-Villars, 15 rue Gossin, 92543 Montrouge Cedex, France. TEL 33-1-40-92-65-00. FAX 33-1-40-92-65-97. TELEX 634 916 F. (Subscr. to: Centrale des Revues, 11 rue Gossin, 92543 Montrouge Cedex, France. TEL 33-1-46-56-52-66) Ed. G. Laumon. adv.; bk.rev.; charts. circ. 950. (also avail. in microform from PMC; reprint service avail. from KTO) **Indexed:** Appl.Mech.Rev., Compumath, Curr.Cont., INSPEC, Math.R., Zent.Math.
—Faxon; Genuine Article; SWETS; UnCover. **CCC.**
Description: Covers all areas of mathematics.

ECONOMIC DESIGN. see *BUSINESS AND ECONOMICS — Economic Systems And Theories, Economic History*

ECUADOR. DIRECCION DE AVIACION CIVIL. MATHEMATICS. see *TRANSPORTATION — Air Transport*

510   UK   ISSN 0013-0915
     CODEN: PEMSA3
EDINBURGH MATHEMATICAL SOCIETY. PROCEEDINGS. 1883. 3/yr. £90($180) (effective 1996). Oxford University Press, Oxford Journals, Walton St., Oxford OX2 6DP, England. TEL 01865-267907. FAX 01865-267773. TELEX 837330-OXPRES-G. E-mail: jnlorders@oup.co.uk. (U.S. subscr. to: Oxford University Press Inc., 2001 Evans Rd., Cary, NC 27513. TEL 919-677-0977. FAX 919-677-1714) Ed. John Martin. adv.; bk.rev.; index, cum.index every 20 yrs. circ. 900. (also avail. in microfiche from BHP; reprint service avail. from KTO) **Indexed:** Compumath, Curr.Cont., Math.R. **Document type:** proceedings.
—BLDSC (6693.000000); Faxon; Genuine Article; SWETS; UnCover. **CCC.**
Description: Covers a wide range of topics in both pure and applied mathematics.

MATHEMATICS

510 370 NE ISSN 0013-1954
QA1 CODEN: EDSMAN
EDUCATIONAL STUDIES IN MATHEMATICS; an international journal. (Text in English) 1968. 8/yr. fl.756 to institutions; $485 to institutions in U.S. (effective 1996). Kluwer Academic Publishers, Postbus 17, 3300 AA Dordrecht, Netherlands. TEL 31-78-392392. FAX 31-78-392254. TELEX 29245 KAPG NL. E-mail: SERVICES@WKAP.NL. (Dist. by: Kluwer Academic Publishers Group, P.O. Box 322, 3300 AH Dordrecht, Netherlands. TEL 31-78-392392. FAX 31-78-546474; N. America dist. addr.: Box 358, Accord Sta., Hingham, MA 02018-0358. TEL 617-871-6600. FAX 617-871-6528) Ed. Willibald Doerfler. adv.; bk.rev.; charts; illus.; index. (also avail. in microform from UMI; reprint service avail. from SWZ) **Indexed:** Br.Educ.Ind., C.I.J.E., Cont.Pg.Educ., Curr.Cont., Educ.Ind., Educ.Tech.Abstr., High.Educ.Curr.Aware.Bull., INSPEC, Math.R., Mult.Ed.Abstr., Ref.Zh., Res.High.Educ.Abstr., Stud.Wom.Abstr., Zent.Math. **Document type:** academic/scholarly publication.
—BLDSC (3662.523000); Faxon; SWETS; UMI; UnCover. **CCC.**
 Description: Covers didactical, methodological and pedagogical subjects relating to mathematical education.
Refereed Serial

EESTI TEADUSTE AKADEEMIA. TOIMETISED. FUUSIKA. MATEMAATIKA/ESTONIAN ACADEMY OF SCIENCES. PROCEEDINGS. PHYSICS. MATHEMATICS. see *PHYSICS*

EKONOMIKA I MATEMATICHESKIE METODY. see *BUSINESS AND ECONOMICS*

510 FR ISSN 1161-059X
QA1
ELECTRICITE DE FRANCE. DIRECTION DES ETUDES ET RECHERCHES. COLLECTION DE NOTES INTERNES. MATHEMATIQUES, INFORMATIQUE, TELECOMMUNICATIONS. (Text and summaries in English, French) 1968. irreg. 3000 F. Electricite de France (EDF), Direction des Etudes et des Recherches, 1 av. du General de Gaulle, 92141 Clamart Cedex, France. TEL 1-47-65-43-21. FAX 1-47-65-31-24. TELEX 204 347 F. Ed. Ph. Esclangon. charts; illus.; cum.index. circ. 1,000. **Indexed:** GeoRef., INIS Atomind., INSPEC, Math.R.
 Supersedes (in 1992): Electricite de France. Direction des Etudes et Recherches. Bulletin. Serie C: Mathematiques-Informatique (ISSN 0013-4511)

510 US ISSN 0896-0984
ELEMENTARY MATHEMATICIAN; a mathematics - multidisciplinary teaching unit for grades K-6. 1987. q. $16 includes membership. (Consortium for Mathematics and Its Applications) C O M A P Inc., 57 Bedford St., Ste. 210, Lexington, MA 02173. TEL 800-772-6627. FAX 617-863-1202. E-mail: info@comap.com. Ed. Larrie W. Aragon. adv. contact: Roland Cheyney. circ. 10,000. **Document type:** newsletter.
—SWETS.

510 SZ ISSN 0013-6018
QA1 CODEN: ELMMAF
ELEMENTE DER MATHEMATIK. (Text in English, French, German, Italian) 1946. 4/yr. 87.80 SFr. (foreign 98.50 SFr.). Birkhaeuser Verlag, P.O. Box 133, CH-4010 Basel, Switzerland. TEL 061-2717400. FAX 061-2717666. (Dist. in N. America by: Springer-Verlag, Mercedes Distribution Center, 160 Imlay St., Brooklyn, NY 11231, USA) Ed. U. Stammbach. adv.; bk.rev.; bibl.; charts; illus.; tr.lit.; index. **Indexed:** Math.R. **Document type:** academic/scholarly publication.
—BLDSC (3728.000000); Faxon; SWETS; UMI; UnCover. **CCC.**

510 US ISSN 0163-3287
EMPLOYMENT INFORMATION IN THE MATHEMATICAL SCIENCES. no.88, 1987. bi-m. $160 to non-members; members $96; students or unemployed $40. American Mathematical Society, Box 6248, Providence, RI 02940-6248. TEL 401-455-4000. circ. 750. **Document type:** bulletin.
● Also available online. Vendor(s): Human Resources Information Network.

ENROLLED ACTUARIES REPORT. see *INSURANCE*

510 SZ ISSN 0013-8584
QA1 CODEN: ENMAAR
ENSEIGNEMENT MATHEMATIQUE. (Text in English, French, German and Italian) 1899. q. 170 SFr. Universite de Geneve, Section de Mathematiques, 2-4, rue du Lievre, Case Postale 240, CH-1211 Geneva 24, Switzerland. Ed. Pierre Jeanquartier. adv.; bk.rev. circ. 900. (also avail. in microform from BHP,PMC; reprint service avail. from SWZ) **Indexed:** Math.R. **Document type:** academic/scholarly publication.
—BLDSC (3776.300000); Faxon; SWETS; UnCover.

510 US ISSN 0071-1136
ERGEBNISSE DER MATHEMATIK UND IHRER GRENZGEBIETE. NEUE FOLGE. (Text in German or English; occasionally French or Italian) 1955; 3rd series 1984. irreg. price varies. Springer-Verlag, 175 Fifth Ave., New York, NY 10010. TEL 212-460-1500. FAX 212-473-6272. (Also: Berlin, Heidelberg, Tokyo and Vienna) Ed. P.Z. Hilton. circ. 2,000. (reprint service avail. from ISI) **Indexed:** Math.R. **Document type:** monographic series.

515.42 UK ISSN 0143-3857
QA611.5
ERGODIC THEORY AND DYNAMICAL SYSTEMS. 1981. bi-m. £248($434) (effective 1996). (London Mathematical Society) Cambridge University Press, Edinburgh Bldg., Shaftesbury Rd., Cambridge CB2 2RU, England. TEL 01223-312393. FAX 01223-315052. TELEX 851817256. (N. American addr.: Cambridge University Press, Journals Dept., 40 W. 20th St., New York, NY 10011. TEL 212-924-3900. FAX 212-691-3239) Ed.Bd. adv.; bk.rev. circ. 558. (also avail. in microform from UMI; back issues avail.; reprint service avail. from SWZ) **Indexed:** ASCA, Compumath, Math.R. **Document type:** academic/scholarly publication.
—BLDSC (3808.330000); Faxon; Genuine Article; SWETS; UMI; UnCover. **CCC.**
 Description: Discusses applications of ergodic theory to differential geometry, statistical mechanics, number theory, and operator algebras.

ETGAR (REHOVOT). see *CHILDREN AND YOUTH — For*

510 NE ISSN 0165-0394
EUCLIDES; maandblad voor de didactiek van de wiskunde. 1925. 9/yr. fl.66. (Nederlandse Vereniging van Wiskundeleraren) WoltersgroepGroningen b.v. (Subsidiary of: Wolters Kluwer N.V.), Postbus 58, 9700 MB Groningen, Netherlands. TEL 31-50-226922. FAX 31-50-2648666. Ed. W. Kleijne. adv.; bk.rev.; index. circ. 4,000. **Indexed:** Math.R.
—SWETS.

510 530.15 UK ISSN 0071-2248
EUREKA: THE ARCHIMEDEAN'S JOURNAL. 1939. a. £2.50 to individuals (in the U.S. $5.50; elsewhere £3.50); institutions £3.50 (in the U.S. $6; elsewhere £4.50). Cambridge University, Mathematical Society, Archimedeans, c/o Arts School, Bene't St., Cambridge CB2 3PY, England. Ed. C.R. Bell. adv.: B&W page $150; adv. contact: Peter S. Mennie. bk.rev. **Indexed:** Met.Abstr. **Document type:** academic/scholarly publication.
—BLDSC (3829.000000); Faxon.
 Description: Contains articles by many leading mathematicians, as well as many easily accessible articles of a mathematical nature.

510 UK ISSN 0956-7925
EUROPEAN JOURNAL OF APPLIED MATHEMATICS. 1990. bi-m. £136($244) (effective 1996). Cambridge University Press, Edinburgh Bldg., Shaftesbury Rd., Cambridge CB2 2RU, England. TEL 01223-312393. FAX 01223-315052. TELEX 851817256. (N. American addr.: Cambridge University Press, Journals Dept., 40 W. 20th St., New York, NY 10011. TEL 212-924-3900. FAX 212-691-3239) Ed. John Ockendon. adv.: page $140; adv. contact: Nick Kelly. (back issues avail.) **Document type:** academic/scholarly publication.
—BLDSC (3829.722207); Faxon; SWETS; UMI. **CCC.**
 Description: Focuses on applied mathematics with real-world applications, as well as the development of theoretical methods.

510 UK ISSN 0195-6698
QA164 CODEN: EJOCDI
EUROPEAN JOURNAL OF COMBINATORICS/JOURNAL EUROPEEN DE COMBINATOIRE/EUROPAEISCHE ZEITSCHRIFT FUER KOMBINATORIK. 1980. 8/yr. £300 (effective 1996). Academic Press Ltd. (Subsidiary of: Harcourt Brace & Company Ltd.), 24-28 Oval Rd., London NW1 7DX, England. TEL 44-171-267-4466. FAX 44-171-482-2293. TELEX 25775 ACPRES G. (Subscr. to: Harcourt Brace & Company Ltd., Foots Cray High St., Sidcup, Kent DA14 5HP, England. TEL 44-181-300-3322. FAX 44-181-309-0807) Ed.Bd. (reprint service avail. from SWZ) **Indexed:** Compumath, Curr.Cont., INSPEC, Int.Abstr.Oper.Res., Math.R. **Document type:** academic/scholarly publication.
—BLDSC (3829.728200); Faxon; Genuine Article; SWETS; UnCover. **CCC.**
 Description: International journal of pure mathematics, specializing in theories arising from combinatorial problems.

510 US ISSN 1058-6458
QA1
EXPERIMENTAL MATHEMATICS. 1992. q. $150 (effective 1996). A.K. Peters, Ltd., 289 Linden St., Wellesley, MA 02181. TEL 617-235-2210. FAX 617-235-2404. E-mail: kpeters@harvard.edu. Ed. David B.A. Epstein. adv. **Document type:** academic/scholarly publication.
—BLDSC (3839.500000); SWETS.
 Description: Publishes experimental work intended to develop mathematical theory and insight.
Refereed Serial

510 GW ISSN 0723-0869
EXPOSITIONES MATHEMATICAE; international journal of pure and applied mathematics. (Text in English, French and German; summaries in German) 1982. q. DM.394. Bibliographisches Institut und F.A. Brockhaus AG, Postfach 100311, 68003 Mannheim, Germany. TEL 0621-3901-01. FAX 0621-3901-389. TELEX 462107. Ed. S.D. Chatterji. **Document type:** academic/scholarly publication.
—BLDSC (3843.352000); Faxon; SWETS; UnCover. **CCC.**

510 SP ISSN 0213-8743
EXTRACTA MATHEMATICAE. 1986. 3/yr. 5000 ptas. Universidad de Extremadura, Facultad de Ciencias, Departamento de Matematicas, Avda. Elvas, s-n, 06071 Badajoz, Spain.

510 II ISSN 0971-4332
FAR EAST JOURNAL OF MATHEMATICAL SCIENCES. (Text in English) 1993. s-a. Rs.500($90) University of Allahabad, Department of Mathematics and Statistics, VIJAYA NIWAS, 198, Mumfordganj, Allahabad 211 002, India. TEL 532-64078. FAX 532-623221. Ed. K.K. Azad; Pub. Dalip R. Mohun. **Document type:** academic/scholarly publication.
—BLDSC (3865.821000).

510 PL ISSN 0044-4413
QA1 CODEN: FMPMDH
FASCICULI MATHEMATICI. (Text and summaries in English, French) irreg. price varies. Politechnika Poznanska, Pl. Curie Sklodowskiej 5, Poznan, Poland. Ed. Joroslaw Werbowski. illus. circ. 180. **Indexed:** Math.R., Ref.Zh. **Document type:** academic/scholarly publication.
 Formerly: Politechnika Poznanska. Zeszyty Naukowe. Matematyka (ISSN 0079-452X)
 Description: Mathematical analysis and probability.

510 US ISSN 0015-0517
QA1 CODEN: FIBQAU
THE FIBONACCI QUARTERLY; a journal devoted to the study of integers with special properties. 1963. q. $37 to individuals; libraries $42 (effective 1995 & 1996). Fibonacci Association, c/o South Dakota State University, Computer Science Dept., Box 2201, Brookings, SD 57007-1596. TEL 605-688-5719. FAX 605-688-5878. E-mail: bergumg@mg.sdstate.edu. Ed. Gerald E. Bergum. adv. contact: ichard Vinl. bk.rev.; index; circ. 900 (paid). (also avail. in microform from UMI) **Indexed:** Compumath, Curr.Cont., Ind.Sci.Rev., Math.R., Sci.Cit.Ind. **Document type:** academic/scholarly publication.
—BLDSC (3914.700000); Faxon; Genuine Article; SWETS; UMI; UnCover.
Refereed Serial

MATHEMATICS

FINANCIAL ENGINEERING AND THE JAPANESE MARKETS. see *BUSINESS AND ECONOMICS—Banking And Finance—Computer Applications*

512   US   ISSN 1071-5797
▼**FINITE FIELDS AND THEIR APPLICATIONS.** 1995. q. $175 (foreign $210) (effective 1996). Academic Press, Inc., Journal Division, 525 B St., Ste. 1900, San Diego, CA 92101-4495. TEL 619-230-1840. FAX 619-688-6800. (Subscr. to: Box 620000, Orlando, FL 32891-8340. TEL 800-543-9534) (back issues avail.) **Document type:** academic/scholarly publication.
Refereed Serial

FIZIKO-MATEMATICHESKO SPISANIE. see *PHYSICS*

510 371.9   US   ISSN 0272-8893
QA11.A1
FOCUS ON LEARNING PROBLEMS IN MATHEMATICS. 1979. 4/yr. $30 to individuals (foreign $40); institutions $45 (foreign $55). Center for Teaching - Learning of Mathematics, Box 3149, Framingham, MA 01701. TEL 508-877-7895. FAX 508-788-3600. Ed. Mahesh Sharma. circ. 2,000. (back issues avail.) **Document type:** academic/scholarly publication.
—BLDSC (3964.216800); SWETS; UnCover. **CCC**.
Description: Covers research on issues in mathematics learning from diffrent disciplines, including mathematics, special education, psychology, and neurology.

510   XR
FOLIA FACULTATIS SCIENTIARUM NATURALIUM UNIVERSITATIS MASARYKIANAE BRUNESIS: MATHEMATICA. 1989. a. Masarykova Universita, Prirodovedecka Fakulta - Masaryk University, Faculty of Sciences, Kotlarska 2, 611 37 Bron, Czech Republic. **Document type:** academic/scholarly publication.
Formerly: Folia Facultatis Scientiarum Naturalium Universitatis Purkynianae Brunensis: Mathematica (ISSN 0862-9846)

510   JA   ISSN 0911-6036
FORMA. (Text in English) 1989. 3/yr. (Society for Science on Form, Japan - Katachi no Kagakkai) K T K Scientific Publishers - K T K Gakujutsu Tosho Shuppan, 14-17 Midorigaoka 2-chome, Meguro-ku, Tokyo 152, Japan. Ed. Ryuji Takaki. circ. 400. **Document type:** academic/scholarly publication.
Refereed Serial

510   CS
FORMATOR SYMPOSIUM ON MATHEMATICAL METHODS FOR THE ANALYSIS OF LARGE-SCALE SYSTEMS. (Text in English) ceased 1983. irreg. (Czechoslovak Academy of Sciences, Institute of Information Theory and Automation) Academia, Publishing House of the Czechoslovak Academy of Sciences, Vodickova 40, 112 29 Prague 1, Czechoslovakia. TEL 221-413.

510   GW   ISSN 0933-7741
QA1   CODEN: FOMAEF
FORUM MATHEMATICUM. (Text in English) 1989. bi-m. DM.538. Walter de Gruyter und Co., Genthiner Str. 13, 10785 Berlin, Germany. TEL 030-26005-0. FAX 030-26005-251. (U.S. subscr. to: Walter de Gruyter, 200 Saw Mill River Rd., Hawthorne, NY 10532. TEL 914-747-0110) Ed.Bd. adv.; illus.; index. (back issues avail.) **Indexed:** Math.R., Zent.Math. **Document type:** academic/scholarly publication.
—BLDSC (4024.087900); Faxon; Genuine Article; SWETS; UnCover. **CCC**.
Description: Original research articles in all fields of pure and applied mathematics, including mathematical physics.

FRANKLIN INSTITUTE. JOURNAL. see *PHYSICS*

519   US
FRONTIERS IN APPLIED MATHEMATICS. 1984. irreg., no.15, 1994. price varies. Society for Industrial and Applied Mathematics, 3600 University City Science Center, Philadelphia, PA 19104-2688. TEL 215-382-9800. FAX 215-386-7999. E-mail: pubs@siam.org. Ed. Tricia Manning; Pub. Vickie Kearn. **Document type:** academic/scholarly publication, monographic series.
Incorporates: Geometric Design Series.
Refereed Serial

519.5   NE
FRONTIERS IN PURE AND APPLIED PROBABILITY. (Text in English) 1993. irreg., vol.3, 1995. price varies. V S P, P.O. Box 346, 3700 AH Zeist, Netherlands. TEL 31-3404-25790. FAX 31-3404-32081. (Dist. in U.S. and Canada by: Books International Inc., Box 605, Herndon, VA 22070. TEL 703-435-7064. FAX 703-689-0660) (back issues avail.) **Document type:** monographic series, proceedings.

510   CC
FUJIAN ZHONGXUE SHUXUE/FUJIAN MIDDLE SCHOOL MATHEMATICS. (Text in Chinese) bi-m. Y4.15. Fujian Shifan Daxue, Shuxue Xi - Fujian Normal University, Mathematics Department, Fuzhou, Fujian 350007, People's Repubic of China. TEL 541616. (Dist. overseas by: Jiangsu Publications Import & Export Corp., 56 Gao Yun Ling, Nanjing, Jiangsu, P.R.C.) (Co-sponsor: Fujian Mathematics Association) Ed. Lin Zhangyan.
Description: Explores the teaching methods of middle school mathematics.

510   JA   ISSN 0386-6262
FUKUI-KENRITSU TANKI DAIGAKU KENKYU KIYO/FUKUI PREFECTURAL COLLEGE. BULLETIN. (Text in Japanese; summaries in English, Japanese) 1976. a. Fukui Prefectural College - Fukui-kenritsu Tanki Daigaku, 97-21-3, Obatake-cho, Fukui-shi, Fukui-ken 910, Japan.

510   JA   ISSN 0386-118X
Q4   CODEN: FDRSDG
FUKUOKA DAIGAKU RIGAKU SHUHO/FUKUOKA UNIVERSITY. CENTRAL RESEARCH INSTITUTE. SCIENCE REPORTS. (Text in English and Japanese; summaries in English) 1972. s-a. Fukuoka University, Central Research Institute - Fukuoka Daigaku Sogo Kenkyujo, 19-1, Nanakuma, 8-chome, Jonan-ku, Fukuoka-shi, Fukuoka-ken 814-80, Japan. TEL 092-871-6631.
—CASDDS.
Description: Contains original papers.

510   JA   ISSN 0287-0002
FUKUOKA DAIGAKU SOGO KENKYUJO. SHIZEN KAGAKU HEN/FUKUOKA UNIVERSITY. CENTRAL RESEARCH INSTITUTE. BULLETIN. (Text in Japanese; summaries in English) 1977. annu. Fukuoka University, Central Research Institute - Fukuoka Daigaku Sogo Kenkyujo, 19-1, Nanakuma, 8-chome, Jonan-ku, Fukuoka-shi, Fukuoka-ken 814-80, Japan. TEL 092-871-6631.

FUKUOKA KYOIKU DAIGAKU KIYO. DAI-3-BUNSATSU. SUGAKU, RIKA, GIJUTSUKA HEN/FUKUOKA UNIVERSITY OF EDUCATION. BULLETIN. PART 3: MATHEMATICS, NATURAL SCIENCES AND TECHNOLOGY. see *SCIENCES: COMPREHENSIVE WORKS*

510   AT   ISSN 0313-6825
FUNCTION. 1977. 5/yr. Aus.$17. Monash University, Department of Mathematics, Wellington Road, Clayton, Vic. 3168, Australia. TEL 61-3-9032723. FAX 61-3-9032227. TELEX MONASH AA 32691. E-mail: function@maths.monash.edu.au. Ed. R.J. Arianshod. adv.; bk.rev.; circ. 300 (paid). (back issues avail.) **Document type:** academic/scholarly publication.
Description: A journal of school mathematics.
Refereed Serial

515   US   ISSN 0016-2663
     CODEN: FAAPBZ
FUNCTIONAL ANALYSIS AND ITS APPLICATIONS. English translation of: Funktsional'nyi Analiz i Ego Prilozheniya (RU ISSN 0374-1990) 1967. q. $995 (foreign $1165) (effective 1996). (Russian Academy of Sciences, RU) Plenum Publishing Corp., Consultants Bureau, 233 Spring St., New York, NY 10013-1578. TEL 212-620-8468. FAX 212-463-0742. TELEX 23-421139. Ed. A.K. Kirillov. (also avail. in microfilm from JSC; back issues avail.) **Indexed:** Compumath, Curr.Cont., Math.R., Zent.Math. **Document type:** academic/scholarly publication.
—BLDSC (0411.763000); Faxon; Genuine Article; SWETS; UMI; UnCover. **CCC**.
Refereed Serial

510   PL   ISSN 0208-6573
QA331
FUNCTIONES ET APPROXIMATIO COMMENTARII MATHEMATICI. (Text in English) 1974. irreg., vol.22, 1993. $16. (Uniwersytet im. Adama Mickiewicza w Poznaniu, Instytut Matematyki) Adam Mickiewicz University Press, Nowowiejskiego 55, 61-734 Poznan, Poland. TEL 527-380. TELEX 413260 UAM PL. Ed.Bd. circ. 400. (also avail. in microfiche) **Indexed:** Math.R. **Document type:** academic/scholarly publication.
—BLDSC (4055.700000).
Description: Contains papers on the theory of real functions and mathematical analysis with particular emphasis on the theory of approximation.

510   PL   ISSN 0016-2736
QA1
FUNDAMENTA MATHEMATICAE. (Text in English, French, German, Russian; summaries in English) 1920. 6/yr. (in 2 vols., 3 nos./vol.). $168. Polska Akademia Nauk, Instytut Matematyczny, Dzial Wydawnictw, Ul. Sniadeckich 8, P.O. Box 137, 00-950 Warsaw, Poland. TEL 48-22-6282471. FAX 48-22-293997. Ed. R. Engelking. (also avail. in microfiche from BHP; reprint service avail. from SWZ) **Indexed:** Compumath, Math.R. **Document type:** academic/scholarly publication.
—Faxon; Genuine Article; SWETS; UnCover.
Description: Publishes original papers in set theory, topology, mathematical logic and foundations, real functions, measure and integration, abstract algebra.
Refereed Serial

510   JA   ISSN 0532-8721
QA431   CODEN: FESIAT
FUNKCIALAJ EKVACIOJ, SERIO INTERNACIA. (Text in English and French) 1958. 3/yr. Nihon Sugakkai, Kansu Hoteishiki - Mathematical Society of Japan, Division of Functional Equations, c/o Kobe Daigaku Rigakubu, Sugaku Kyoshitsu, Rokkodai-cho, Nada-ku, Kobe-shi, Hyogo-ken 657, Japan.
—BLDSC (4058.120000); UnCover.

515   RU   ISSN 0374-1990
FUNKTSIONAL'NYI ANALIZ I EGO PRILOZHENIYA. English translation: Functional Analysis and Its Applications (US ISSN 0016-2663) 1967. q. $67. (Rossiiskaya Akademiya Nauk) Izdatel'stvo Nauka, 90 Profsoyuznaya ul, 117864 Moscow, Russia. (Dist. in U.S. by: Victor Kamkin Inc., 4956 Boiling Brook Pkwy., Rockville, MD 20852. TEL 301-881-5973. FAX 301-881-1637) **Indexed:** Math.R.

510   NE   ISSN 0165-0114
QA248   CODEN: FSSYD8
FUZZY SETS AND SYSTEMS. (Text in English) 1978. 24/yr. fl.3480($2122) (effective 1996). (International Fuzzy Systems Association (IFSA)) North-Holland (Subsidiary of: Elsevier Science B.V.), P.O. Box 211, 1000 AE Amsterdam, Netherlands. TEL 31-20-4853911. FAX 31-20-4853598. TELEX 18582 ESPA NL. (Subscr. in U.S. and Canada to: Elsevier Science Inc., Box 882, Madison Sq. Sta., New York, NY 10159. TEL 212-989-5800. FAX 212-633-3990) Ed. H.J. Zimmermann. adv.; bk.rev. (also avail. in microform from UMI; back issues avail.; reprint service avail. from SWZ) **Indexed:** A.I.Abstr., Biostat., Compumath, Curr.Cont., Cyb.Abstr., INSPEC, Int.Abstr.Oper.Res., Math.R., Oper.Res.Manage.Sci., Qual.Contr.Appl.Stat., Robomat. **Document type:** academic/scholarly publication.
—BLDSC (4060.740000); Ei; Faxon; Genuine Article; SWETS; UnCover. **CCC**.
Description: Encourages communication between scientists and practitioners interested in research and applications in fuzzy sets and systems.
Refereed Serial

510 531   GW   ISSN 0936-7195
G A M M MITTEILUNGEN. 1978. s-a. DM.105 (effective 1996). (Gesellschaft fuer Angewandte Mathematik und Mechanik) Akademie Verlag GmbH, Muehlenstr. 33-34, 13187 Berlin, Germany. TEL 030-47889348. FAX 030-47889357. (U.S. subscr. to: VCH Publishers Inc., 303 N.W. 12th Ave., Deerfield Beach, FL 33442-1788) **Document type:** academic/scholarly publication.

MATHEMATICS

510 RM
GAMMA. (Text and summaries in English and Rumanian) 1978. q. 10 lei. (Number Theory Company, US) Gamma Company, Str. Harmanului Nr. 22, Sacele, Rumania. TEL 011-40-22-71032. (US addr.: Box 42561, Phoenix, AZ 85080) Eds. Mihail Bencze, Florentin Smarandache. bk.rev. circ. 1,000. (looseleaf format; back issues avail.)

510   II   ISSN 0046-5402
QA1   CODEN: GNTAAG
GANITA. (Text in English) 1950. s-a. Rs.150($25) (effective 1994). Bharata Ganita Parisad, University of Lucknow, Department of Mathematics and Astronomy, Lucknow, Uttar Pradesh, India. Ed. Dr. Sunil Datta. bk.rev. circ. 500. **Indexed:** Math.R., Zent.Math.
—UnCover.
Formerly: Benares Mathematical Society. Proceedings.

510   II   ISSN 0970-0307
QA21
GANITA BHARATI. (Text in English, German, French, Sanskrit, Hindi) 1979. q. Rs.300($60) to non-members; members Rs.60 ($30). Indian Society for History of Mathematics, c/o Dr. Man Mohan, Dept. of Math., Ramjas College, Delhi 110 007, India. Ed. R.C. Gupta. adv.; bk.rev. circ. 200. **Document type:** academic/scholarly publication, bulletin.
Description: Contains research papers, review articles and dissertation abstracts on the history of mathematics.

510   CC   ISSN 1000-081X
QA297
GAODENG XUEXIAO JISUAN SHUXUE XUEBAO. (Text in Chinese) q. Nanjing Daxue - Nanjing University, Hankou Lu, Nanjing, Jiangsu 210008, People's Republic of China. TEL 637651. Ed. He Xuechu. **Document type:** academic/scholarly publication.
—BLDSC (6184.693700).

510   CC   ISSN 1000-4424
GAOXIAO YINGYONG SHUXUE XUEBAO/APPLIED MATHEMATICS - JOURNAL OF CHINESE UNIVERSITIES. (Includes Series A and Series B) (Text in Chinese; abstracts in English) 1986. Ser. A: q.; Ser. B: s-a. $28 for Ser. A; Ser. B $9.20. Zhejiang Daxue - Zhejiang University, Zheda Lu, Hangzhou, Zhejiang 310027, People's Republic of China. TEL 0571-5172242. FAX 0571-571797. TELEX 35040 ZUFAO CN. Ed. Dong Guangchang. **Indexed:** Stat.Theor.Meth.Abstr. **Document type:** academic/scholarly publication.
Description: Publishes original papers in the field of applied mathematics.

GAUSS - GESELLSCHAFT. MITTEILUNGEN. see *ASTRONOMY*

510   RM   ISSN 1010-9943
QA1
GAZETA MATEMATICA; publicatie lunara pentu tineret. 1895. m. 24 lei($20) Societatea de Stiinte Matematice, Str. Academiei 14, 70109 Bucharest, Rumania. (Subscr. to: ILEXIM, Str. 13 Decembrie Nr. 3, P.O. Box 136-137, Bucharest, Rumania) Ed. N. Teodorescu. bk.rev.; index. **Indexed:** Math.R.
Formed by the merger of: Gazeta Matematica. Serie A (ISSN 0016-5433); Gazeta Matematica. Serie B (ISSN 0016-5441)

510   US   ISSN 1068-7122
QA1
GELFAND MATHEMATICAL SEMINARS. 1992. irreg. $59.50 (effective 1993). Birkhauser Boston, 675 Massachusetts Ave., Cambridge, MA 02139. TEL 617-876-2333; 800-777-4643. FAX 617-876-1272. Ed. Ann Kostant. adv. contact: Elizabeth Carey. **Document type:** proceedings.
Refereed Serial

516   NE   ISSN 0046-5755
QA440   CODEN: GEMDAT
GEOMETRIAE DEDICATA. (Text in English, French or German) 1972. 15/yr. fl.1962.50 to institutions; $1197 to institutions in U.S. (effective 1996). Kluwer Academic Publishers, Postbus 17, 3300 AA Dordrecht, Netherlands. TEL 31-78-392392. FAX 31-78-392254. TELEX 29245 KAPG NL. E-mail: SERVICES@WKAP.NL. (Dist. by: Kluwer Academic Publishers Group, P.O. Box 322, 3300 AH Dordrecht, Netherlands. TEL 31-78-392392. FAX 31-78-546474; N. America dist addr.: Box 358, Accord Sta., Hingham, MA 02018-0358. TEL 617-871-6600. FAX 617-871-6528) Eds. K. Strambach, F.D. Veldkamp. adv.; bk.rev. (also avail. in microform from UMI; reprint service avail. from SWZ) **Indexed:** ASCA, Compumath, Math.R., Ref.Zh. **Document type:** academic/scholarly publication.
—Faxon; Genuine Article; SWETS; UMI; UnCover. **CCC.**
Description: Publishes research articles on geometry and other disciplines of mathematics using geometrical methods.
Refereed Serial

510   SZ   ISSN 1016-443X
QA299.6
GEOMETRIC AND FUNCTIONAL ANALYSIS. (Text in English) 1991. 6/yr. 731.50 SFr. (foreign 747.40 SFr.). Birkhaeuser Verlag, P.O. Box 133, CH-4010 Basel, Switzerland. TEL 061-2717400. FAX 061-2717666. (Dist. in N. America by: Springer-Verlag, Mercedes Distribution Center, 160 Imlay St., Brooklyn, NY 11231, USA) Ed. V. Milman. **Indexed:** Curr.Cont., Math.R. **Document type:** academic/scholarly publication.
—BLDSC (4147.581000); Faxon; Genuine Article; SWETS. **CCC.**
Description: Covers geometry and analysis interactions, including elliptic operators of manifolds; global variational calculus; concentration phenomenon and geometric inequalities; and other pertinent subjects.

510   US   ISSN 1072-947X
QA1   CODEN: GMJOE5
▼**GEORGIAN MATHEMATICAL JOURNAL.** 1994. bi-m. $195 (foreign $230) (effective 1996). Plenum Publishing Corp., 233 Spring St., New York, NY 10013-1578. TEL 212-620-8000. FAX 212-463-0742. TELEX 23-421139. Ed. I. Kiguradze. adv. **Indexed:** Curr.Cont. **Document type:** academic/scholarly publication.
—BLDSC (4158.481700). **CCC.**
Description: Provides an international forum for research contributions in all areas of pure and applied mathematics.
Refereed Serial

510   UK   ISSN 0017-0895
QA1   CODEN: GLMJAS
GLASGOW MATHEMATICAL JOURNAL. (Text mainly in English; occasionally French and German) 1952. 3/yr. £74($135) (effective 1996). (Glasgow Mathematical Society) Oxford University Press, Oxford Journals, Walton St., Oxford OX2 6DP, England. TEL 01865-267907. FAX 01865-267773. TELEX 837330-OXPRES-G. E-mail: jnlorders@oup.co.uk. (U.S. subscr. to: Oxford University Press Inc., 2001 Evans Rd., Cary, NC 27513. TEL 919-677-0977. FAX 919-677-1714) Ed. S.D. Cohen. adv.; charts; illus.; index. circ. 700. **Indexed:** Compumath, Math.R. **Document type:** academic/scholarly publication.
—BLDSC (4183.700000); Faxon; Genuine Article; SWETS; UMI; UnCover. **CCC.**
Formerly: Glasgow Mathematical Association Proceedings.
Description: Original work in pure mathematics. Includes papers on applied mathematics.

510   CI   ISSN 0017-095X
QA1   CODEN: GLMAB2
GLASNIK MATEMATICKI. (Text in English, French, German, Russian and Serbocroatian) N.S. 1966. s-a. $20. Drustvo Matematicara i Fizicara SR Hrvatske, Marulicev Trg. 19, Zagreb, Croatia. Ed. Ivan Ivansic. bk.rev.; charts; illus.; index. circ. 1,000. **Indexed:** Chem.Abstr., INSPEC, Math.R., Ref.Zh., Zent.Math.
—BLDSC (4187.980000); Faxon; UnCover.
Formerly: Glasnik Matematicko-Fizicki i Astronomski.

510   US   ISSN 0072-5285
GRADUATE TEXTS IN MATHEMATICS. (Text in English) 1971. irreg, vol.111, 1986. price varies. Springer-Verlag, 175 Fifth Ave., New York, NY 10010. TEL 212-460-1500. FAX 212-473-6272. (Also: Berlin, Heidelberg, Tokyo and Vienna) Ed.Bd. (reprint service avail. from ISI) **Indexed:** Math.R. **Document type:** monographic series.
—BLDSC (4207.450000).

510   GR   ISSN 0072-7466
GREEK MATHEMATICAL SOCIETY. BULLETIN/HELLENIKE MATHEMATIKE HETAIREIA. DELTION. (Text in English; occasionally in French) 1960. a. Dr.1,500($35) Greek Mathematical Society, 34 Panepistemiou St., 106 79 Athens, Greece. TEL 30-1-3617784. FAX 30-1-3641025. Ed.Bd. circ. 1,000. **Indexed:** Math.R., Zent.Math. **Document type:** academic/scholarly publication, bulletin.

510   US
GRUNDLEHREN DER MATHEMATISCHEN WISSENSCHAFTEN. (Text in English, occasionally in French and German) 1957. irreg., vol.286, 1987. price varies. Springer-Verlag, 175 Fifth Ave., New York, NY 10010. TEL 212-460-1500. FAX 212-473-6272. (Also: Berlin, Heidelberg, Tokyo and Vienna) (reprint service avail. from ISI) **Indexed:** Math.R. **Document type:** academic/scholarly publication.
Formerly: Grundlehren der Mathematischen Wissenschaften in Einzeldarstellungen (ISSN 0072-7830)

510   TU   ISSN 1300-4263
HACETTEPE FEN VE MUHENDISLIK BILIMLERI DERGISI. SERI B: MATEMATIK VE ISTATISTIK/HACETTEPE BULLETIN OF NATURAL SCIENCES AND ENGINEERING. SERIES B: MATHEMATICS AND STATISTICS. (Text in English, Turkish) 1971. a. $10. Hacettepe Universitesi, Fen Fakultesi, 06532 Beytepe, Ankara, Turkey. TEL 90-212-2352531. Ed. Hulya Cingi. **Document type:** academic/scholarly publication.

519.5   NE
HANDBOOK OF NUMERICAL ANALYSIS. (Text in English) 1990. irreg., vol.2, 1991. price varies. Elsevier Science B.V., Books Division, P.O. Box 211, 1000 AE Amsterdam, Netherlands. TEL 31-20-4853911. FAX 31-20-4853705. TELEX 18582 ESPA NL. E-mail: nlinfo-f@elsevier.nl; usinfo-f@elsevier.com; forinfo-kyf04035@niftyserve.or.jp; Site addr.: http://www.elsevier.nl/. (Subscr. in U.S. and Canada to: Elsevier Science Inc., Box 882, Madison Sq. Sta., New York, NY 10159. TEL 212-989-5800) Eds. P.G. Ciarlet, J.L. Lions. (back issues avail.) **Document type:** monographic series.
Refereed Serial

510   II   ISSN 0073-2281
HINDU ASTRONOMICAL AND MATHEMATICAL TEXT SERIES. (In 5 volumes.) (Text in English and Sanskrit; summaries in English) 1957. irreg. $25 per vol. Bharata Ganita Parisad, University of Lucknow, Department of Mathematics and Astronomy, Lucknow, Uttar Pradesh, India. Ed. Ram Ballabh. **Indexed:** Math.R.

510   JA   ISSN 0018-2079
QA1   CODEN: HMTJAD
HIROSHIMA MATHEMATICAL JOURNAL. (Text in English) 1971. 3/yr. exchange basis only. Hiroshima Daigaku, Rigakubu, Sugaku Kyoshitsu - Hiroshima University, Faculty of Science, Department of Mathematics, Kagamiyama, Higashi-Hiroshima 724, Japan. TEL 0824-24-0710. TELEX 0824-22-7111. Ed. Yasunori Fujikoshi. circ. 700. **Indexed:** Math.R., World Alum.Abstr. **Document type:** academic/scholarly publication.
—BLDSC (4315.608000); Faxon; UnCover.
Formerly (until 1971): Hiroshima University. Journal of Science. Series A-1 Mathematics.

MATHEMATICS

510 US ISSN 0315-0860
QA21 CODEN: HIMADS
HISTORIA MATHEMATICA. 1974. q. $155 (foreign $187) (effective 1996). (International Commission on the History of Mathematics) Academic Press, Inc., Journal Division, 525 B St., Ste. 1900, San Diego, CA 92101-4495. TEL 619-230-1840. FAX 619-699-6800. (Subscr. to: Box 620000, Orlando, FL 32891-8340. TEL 800-543-9534) Eds. Eberhard Knobloch, David E. Rowe. adv.; bk.rev.; index. (back issues avail.) **Indexed:** Amer.Hist.& Life, Bull.Signal., Compumath, Hist.Abstr., Math.R., Ref.Zh., Zent.Math. **Document type:** academic/scholarly publication.
—BLDSC (4316.056000); Faxon; Genuine Article; SWETS; UnCover. **CCC.**
 Description: Concerned with the history of all aspects of the mathematical sciences in all parts of the world and all historical periods. Publishes occasional biographies of mathematicians and historians, studies of organizations and institutions, essays on historiography, and articles on the interactions among all facets of mathematical activity and other aspects of culture and society.
Refereed Serial

511 US ISSN 1069-2878
HISTORY OF LOGIC NEWSLETTER. 1992. bi-m. $15 (foreign $21) (effective 1996); newsstand price: $4. Modern Logic Publishing, 2408 1/2 W. Lincoln Way, Ames, IA 50014-7217. TEL 515-292-1819. E-mail: f1.mlp@isumvs. (Subscr. to: Order & Subscription Department, Modern Logic Publishing, 2408 1/2 W. Lincoln Way, upper Level, Ames, IA 50014-7217, USA)

510 US ISSN 0899-2428
HISTORY OF MATHEMATICS. 1988. irreg. price varies. American Mathematical Society, Box 6248, Providence, RI 02940-6248. TEL 401-455-4000. **Document type:** monographic series.
—**CCC.**

510 GW ISSN 0073-2842
HOCHSCHULBUECHER FUER MATHEMATIK. 1955. irreg. price varies. VEB Deutscher Verlag der Wissenschaften, Postfach 1216, 1080 Berlin, Germany. Ed.Bd. **Indexed:** Math.R.

510 530 JA ISSN 0367-5939
Q77 CODEN: HKDSAE
HOKKAIDO KYOIKU DAIGAKU KIYO. DAI-2-BU, A. SUGAKU, BUTSURI, KAGAKU, KOGAKU-HEN/HOKKAIDO UNIVERSITY OF EDUCATION. JOURNAL. SECTION 2 A. MATHEMATICS, PHYSICS, CHEMISTRY, ENGINEERING. (Text and summaries in English and Japanese) 1949. s-a. exchange basis. Hokkaido University of Education - Hokkaido Kyoiku Daigaku, Ainosoto 5-jou, 3-chome, Kita-ku, Sapporo-shi 002, Hokkaido, Japan. **Indexed:** Jap.Per.Ind., Math.R. **Document type:** bulletin.

510 JA ISSN 0385-4035
QA1 CODEN: HMAJDN
HOKKAIDO MATHEMATICAL JOURNAL. (Text in English, French, German) 1972. 3/yr. $222. Hokkaido Daigaku, Rigakubu Sugaku Kyoshitsu - Hokkaido University, Faculty of Science, Department of Mathematics, Nishi-8-chome, Kita-10-jo, Kita-ku, Sapporo 060, Japan. FAX 11-727-3705. TELEX 932510-HOKUSC-J. (Subscr. to: Kinokuniya Co. Ltd., 17-7 Shinjuku 3-chome, Shinjuku-ku, Tokyo 160-91, Japan) Ed. Yasunori Okabe. circ. 720. (back issues avail.) **Indexed:** Math.R. **Document type:** monographic series.
—BLDSC (4322.268000); Faxon.
 Formerly: Hokkaido University. Faculty of Science. Journal. Series 1: Mathematics (ISSN 0018-3482)

510 US ISSN 0362-1588
QA1 CODEN: HJMADZ
HOUSTON JOURNAL OF MATHEMATICS. 1975. q. $90 (foreign $95). University of Houston, Department of Mathematics, Central Campus, Houston, TX 77004-3476. TEL 713-743-3475. FAX 713-743-3505. E-mail: hjm@uh.edu. Ed. G. Auchmuty. circ. 450 (paid). **Indexed:** Compumath, INSPEC, Math.R. **Document type:** academic/scholarly publication.
—Faxon; Genuine Article; SWETS; UnCover.
 Description: Publishes mathematical research papers.
Refereed Serial

510 GW
HUMBOLDT-UNIVERSITAET ZU BERLIN. INSTITUT FUER MATHEMATIK. PREPRINT. 1980. irreg. Humboldt-Universitaet zu Berlin, Institut fuer Mathematik, 10099 Berlin, Germany. TEL 030-20932358. FAX 030-20932238. E-mail: www.mathematik.hu-berlin.de. **Document type:** academic/scholarly publication.
—BLDSC (6609.140000).
 Formerly: Humboldt-Universitaet zu Berlin. Fachbereich Mathematik. Preprint (ISSN 0863-0976)

510 GW
HUMBOLDT-UNIVERSITAET ZU BERLIN. INSTITUT FUER MATHEMATIK. SEMINARBERICHTE. 1976. irreg. Humboldt-Universitaet zu Berlin, Institut fuer Mathematik, 10099 Berlin, Germany. TEL 030-20932358. FAX 030-20932238. E-mail: www.mathematik.hu-berlin.de. **Document type:** academic/scholarly publication.
—BLDSC (8239.430730).
 Formerly: Humboldt-Universitaet zu Berlin. Fachbereich Mathematik. Seminarberichte (ISSN 0863-0968)

510 519 UK ISSN 0272-4960
QA1 CODEN: IJAMDM
I M A JOURNAL OF APPLIED MATHEMATICS. 1981. bi-m. £240($440) (effective 1996). (Institute of Mathematics and Its Applications) Oxford University Press, Oxford Journals, Walton St., Oxford OX2 6DP, England. TEL 01865-267907. FAX 01865-267773. TELEX 837330 OXPRES G. E-mail: jnlorders@oup.co.uk. (U.S. subscr. to: Oxford University Press Inc., 2001 Evans Rd., Cary, NC 27513. TEL 919-677-0977. FAX 919-677-1714) Eds. D.A. Spence, R.W. Ogden. adv.; index. circ. 1,200. (back issues avail.) **Indexed:** Appl.Mech.Rev., Chem.Abstr., Compumath, Cyb.Abstr., Excerp.Med., Fluidex, Ind.Sci.Rev., INSPEC, Int.Aerosp.Abstr., Math.R., Sci.Cit.Ind. **Document type:** academic/scholarly publication.
—BLDSC (4368.755000); Ei; Faxon; Genuine Article; SWETS; UMI; UnCover. **CCC.**
 Superseded in part (in 1981): Institute of Mathematics and its Applications. Journal (ISSN 0020-2932)
 Description: Publishes papers in all areas of the application of mathematics, including analytic and numerical treatments of both physical and nonphysical applied mathematical problems arising in industry.

510 UK ISSN 0265-0754
QA402.3
I M A JOURNAL OF MATHEMATICAL CONTROL & INFORMATION. 1984. q. £130($225) (effective 1996). (Institute of Mathematics and Its Applications) Oxford University Press, Oxford Journals, Walton St., Oxford OX2 6DP, England. TEL 01865-267907. FAX 01865-267773. TELEX 837330 OXPRES G. E-mail: jnlorders@oup.co.uk. (U.S. subscr. to: Oxford University Press Inc., 2001 Evans Rd., Cary, NC 27513. TEL 919-677-0977. FAX 919-677-1714) Ed.Bd. adv. **Indexed:** Compumath, INSPEC (1985-), Math.R. **Document type:** academic/scholarly publication.
—Ei; Genuine Article; SWETS; UMI. **CCC.**
 Description: Presents original papers in mathematical control theory, systems theory, and allied information sciences.

510 UK ISSN 0953-0061
HD30.25 CODEN: IMJIE9
I M A JOURNAL OF MATHEMATICS APPLIED IN BUSINESS AND INDUSTRY. 1986. q. £130($225) (effective 1996). (Institute of Mathematics and Its Applications) Oxford University Press, Oxford Journals, Walton St., Oxford OX2 6DP, England. TEL 01865-267907. FAX 01865-267773. TELEX 8373330 OXPRES G. E-mail: jnlorders@oup.co.uk. (U.S. subscr. to: Oxford University Press Inc., 2001 Evans Rd., Cary, NC 27513. TEL 919-677-0977. FAX 919-677-1714) Eds. S. McKee, L.C. Thomas. adv. **Indexed:** Math.R. **Document type:** academic/scholarly publication.
—BLDSC (4368.758500); Ei; SWETS; UMI. **CCC.**
 Formerly: I M A Journal of Mathematics in Management (ISSN 0268-1129)
 Description: Disseminates new mathematical theories related to any class of management problems and practical case studies involving substantial analytical argument.

510 UK ISSN 0265-0746
CODEN: IJMBEG
I M A JOURNAL OF MATHEMATICS APPLIED IN MEDICINE & BIOLOGY. 1984. q. £130($225) (effective 1996). (Institute of Mathematics and Its Applications) Oxford University Press, Oxford Journals, Walton St., Oxford OX2 6DP, England. TEL 01865-267907. FAX 01865-267773. TELEX 837330 OXPRES G. E-mail: jnlorders@oup.co.uk. (U.S. subscr. to: Oxford University Press Inc., 2001 Evans Rd., Cary, NC 27513. TEL 919-677-0977. FAX 919-677-1714) Ed. R.W. Hiorns. adv.; index. **Indexed:** Bio-Contr.News & Info., Biol.Abstr., Compumath, Curr.Cont., Excerp.Med., Math.R., Sci.Cit.Ind. **Document type:** academic/scholarly publication.
—BLDSC (4368.759000); Ei; Faxon; Genuine Article; SWETS; UMI; UnCover. **CCC.**
 Description: Covers the uses of mathematics in medical and biological research, with emphasis on the special insights and enhanced understanding that arise from these uses.

510 UK ISSN 0272-4979
QA297 CODEN: IJNADH
I M A JOURNAL OF NUMERICAL ANALYSIS. 1981. q. £160($295) (effective 1996). (Institute of Mathematics and Its Applications) Oxford University Press, Oxford Journals, Walton St., Oxford OX2 6DP, England. TEL 01865-267907. FAX 01865-267773. TELEX 837330 OXPRES G. E-mail: jnlorders@oup.co.uk. (U.S. subscr. to: Oxford University Press Inc., 2001 Evans Rd., Cary, NC 27513. TEL 919-677-0977. FAX 919-677-1714) Ed.Bd. adv.; index. circ. 800. **Indexed:** Appl.Mech.Rev., Compumath, Comput.Abstr., Curr.Cont., Fluidex, INSPEC, Int.Aerosp.Abstr., Math.R., Sci.Cit.Ind. **Document type:** academic/scholarly publication.
—BLDSC (4368.760000); Ei; Faxon; Genuine Article; SWETS; UMI; UnCover. **CCC.**
 Superseded in part (in 1981): Institute of Mathematics and its Applications. Journal (ISSN 0020-2932)
 Description: Covers theoretical and practical aspects of numerical analysis.

510 US
I M A VOLUMES IN MATHEMATICS AND ITS APPLICATIONS. 1986. irreg. price varies. Springer-Verlag, 175 Fifth Ave., New York, NY 10010. TEL 212-460-1500. FAX 212-473-6272. (Also: Berlin, Heidelberg, Tokyo and Vienna) (reprint service avail. from ISI) **Document type:** monographic series.

510 US
I M S LECTURE NOTES. MONOGRAPH SERIES. 1981. irreg. Institute of Mathematical Statistics, Business Office, 3401 Investment Blvd., Ste. 7, Hayward, CA 94545-3819. TEL 510-783-8141. FAX 510-783-4131. E-mail: IMS@STAT.BERKELEY.EDU. Ed. David Ruppert. **Document type:** monographic series.

510 AT ISSN 0311-0621
I M U CANBERRA CIRCULAR. 1972. 4/yr. free. (International Mathematical Union) B.H. Neumann, Ed. & Pub., School of Mathematical Sciences, Australian National University, A.C.T. 0200, Australia. TEL 61-6-249-4504. FAX 61-6-249-5549. TELEX AA62620. E-mail: bhn102@phys.anu.edu.au. Ed. B.H. Neumann. circ. 1,060. **Document type:** newsletter.
 Description: Covers international and Australasian mathematical meetings, deaths of mathematicians, honors awarded, and visits of mathematicians to Australia and New Zealand.

510 JA ISSN 0579-3068
IBARAKI UNIVERSITY. FACULTY OF SCIENCE. BULLETIN. SERIES A: MATHEMATICS/IBARAKI DAIGAKU RIGAKUBU KIYO. SUGAKU. (Text and summaries in English) 1968. a. exchange basis only. Ibaraki Daigaku, Rigakubu Sugaku Kyoshitsu - Ibaraki University, Faculty of Science, Department of Mathematics, 1-1, Bunkyo 2-chome, Mito-shi, Ibaraki-ken 310, Japan. FAX 29-228-8408. circ. 350. **Indexed:** Math.R. **Document type:** academic/scholarly publication.
—BLDSC (2509.030000).

MATHEMATICS

510 US ISSN 0019-2082
QA1 CODEN: IJMTAW
ILLINOIS JOURNAL OF MATHEMATICS. (Text in English, French and German) 1957. q. $108. (University of Illinois at Urbana-Champaign, Department of Mathematics) University of Illinois Press, 1325 S. Oak St., Champaign, IL 61820. TEL 217-333-0950. FAX 217-244-8082. Ed. Graham Evans. charts; illus.; stat.; index. circ. 1,100. (also avail. in microform from MIM,SWZ,UMI; reprint service avail. from SWZ,UMI) **Indexed:** Compumath, Curr.Cont., Math.R., Sci.Cit.Ind. **Document type:** academic/scholarly publication.
—Faxon; Genuine Article; SWETS; UMI; UnCover. CCC.
Refereed Serial

510 NE ISSN 0019-3577
QA1 CODEN: IMTHBJ
INDAGATIONES MATHEMATICAE. (Text in English) 1937; N.S. 1990. q. fl. 430($262) (effective 1996). (Koninklijke Nederlandse Akademie van Wetenschappen - Royal Netherlands Academy of Sciences) North-Holland (Subsidiary of: Elsevier Science B.V.), P.O. Box 211, 1000 AE Amsterdam, Netherlands. TEL 31-20-4853911. FAX 31-20-4853598. TELEX 18582 ESPA NL. (Subscr. in U.S. and Canada to: Elsevier Science Inc., Box 882, Madison Sq. Sta., New York, NY 10159. TEL 212-989-5800. FAX 212-633-3990) charts; illus.; index. circ. 1,500. (also avail. in microform from SWZ; microfilm from UMI; back issues avail.; reprint service avail. from SWZ) **Indexed:** Chem.Abstr., Compumath, Curr.Cont., Math.R. **Document type:** academic/scholarly publication.
—Faxon; Genuine Article; SWETS; UnCover. CCC. **Incorporates (in 1990):** Koninklijke Nederlandse Akademie van Wetenschappen. Series A, Mathematical Sciences. Proceedings (ISSN 0023-3358)
Refereed Serial

510 II ISSN 0970-5120
QA1
INDIAN ACADEMY OF MATHEMATICS. JOURNAL. (Text in English) 1979. s-a. $60 to individuals; institutions Rs.80($20)(effective 1991). Indian Academy of Mathematics, 46 Shankarbag, Indore 452 006, India. TEL 0731-465464. Ed. R.K. Saxena; Pub. C.L. Parihar. circ. 250. **Indexed:** Math.R., Zent.Math. **Document type:** academic/scholarly publication.
Refereed Serial

510 II ISSN 0253-4142
QA11.A1 CODEN: PIAMDO
INDIAN ACADEMY OF SCIENCES. PROCEEDINGS. MATHEMATICAL SCIENCES. (Text in English) 1934. 4/yr. Rs.75($100) (effective 1996). Indian Academy of Sciences, C.V. Raman Ave., P.O. Box 8005, Bangalore 560080, India. TEL 91-80-3342546. FAX 91-80-3346094. TELEX 0845-2178-ACAD-IN. Ed. S.G. Dani. bibl.; illus.; index. circ. 1,000. (also avail. in microfilm from UMI; reprint service avail. from ISI,UMI) **Indexed:** Compumath, Curr.Cont., INSPEC (1980-). **Document type:** academic/scholarly publication.
—CASDDS; UMI.

510 620 II ISSN 0304-9884
TA329
INDIAN JOURNAL OF ENGINEERING MATHEMATICS. (Text in English) 1968. s-a. Rs.20($5) Ram Prasad & Sons, Hospital Rd., Agra 3, India. Ed. G. Paria. adv.; bk.rev.; illus. (back issues avail.)

510 519 II ISSN 0019-5588
QA1 CODEN: IJMHAU
INDIAN JOURNAL OF PURE AND APPLIED MATHEMATICS. (Text in English) 1970. m. Rs.500 (foreign $200). Indian National Science Academy, Bahadur Shah Zafar Marg, New Delhi 110 002, India. TEL 91-11-3313153. FAX 91-11-3716648. TELEX 31-61835 INSA IN. (Dist. by: UBS Publishers' Distributors Ltd., 5 Ansari Marg, Darya Ganj, New Delhi 110 002, India) **Indexed:** Compumath, Curr.Cont., Ind.Sci.Rev., INIS Atomind., INSPEC, Math.R., Meteor.& Geoastrophys.Abstr., Sci.Cit.Ind. **Document type:** academic/scholarly publication.
—BLDSC (4420.600000); Ei; Faxon; Genuine Article; SWETS; UnCover.

510 II ISSN 0019-5839
CODEN: JIMTA2
INDIAN MATHEMATICAL SOCIETY. JOURNAL. (Text in English) 1909; N.S. 1934. a. $70. Indian Mathematical Society, Meerut University, Department of Mathematics, Meerut 250 005, India. Ed. I.B.S. Passi. bk.rev.; bibl.; pat.; tr.lit.; index. circ. 1,200. (also avail. in microform from PMC) **Indexed:** Cyb.Abstr., Math.R.
—Faxon; SWETS; UnCover.

510 620 US ISSN 0022-2518
QA1 CODEN: IUMJAB
INDIANA UNIVERSITY MATHEMATICS JOURNAL. (Text in English, French) 1952. q. $115. Indiana University, Department of Mathematics, Rawles Hall 115, Bloomington, IN 47405. TEL 812-855-2252. FAX 812-855-0046. Ed. Jiri Dadok. bibl.; charts; index. (back issues avail.) **Indexed:** Compumath, Curr.Cont., Eng.Ind., Math.R., Sci.Cit.Ind., Zent.Math. **Document type:** academic/scholarly publication.
—Faxon; Genuine Article; SWETS; UnCover. CCC. **Formerly:** Journal of Mathematics and Mechanics (ISSN 0095-9057)
Refereed Serial

510 600 US ISSN 0019-8528
TA350 CODEN: IMTHAI
INDUSTRIAL MATHEMATICS. 1950. s-a. $22 to non-members. Industrial Mathematics Society, Box 159, Roseville, MI 48066. TEL 313-771-0403. Ed. Dr. Robert Schmidt. adv.; bk.rev.; illus. circ. 400. (also avail. in microform from UMI; back issues avail.; reprint service avail. from UMI) **Indexed:** Appl.Mech.Rev., Eng.Ind., INSPEC, Math.R. **Document type:** academic/scholarly publication.
—Ei; Faxon; UMI; UnCover.

004 005.1 511 LI ISSN 0134-8639
INFORMATIKA. 1986. irreg. Akademiya Nauk Litvy, Institut Matematiki i Kibernetiki - Lithuanian Academy of Sciences, Institute of Mathematics and Information Science, Akademijos 4, 2600 Vilnius, Lithuania.
—BLDSC (4481.382000).

510.78 PL ISSN 0542-9951
INFORMATYKA. 1965. m. $61. (Polski Komitet Automatycznego Przetwarzania Informacji NOT) Wydawnictwo Czasopism i Ksiazek Technicznych SIGMA - NOT, Ul. Ratuszowa 11, P.O. Box 1004, 00-950 Warsaw, Poland. (Dist. by: SIGMA NOT Ltd., Ul. Bartycka 20, 00-716 Warsaw, Poland) (Co-sponsor: Krajowe Biuro Informatyki) Ed. Wladyslaw Klepacz. adv.; B&W page £1260. circ. 5,250. **Indexed:** Cyb.Abstr., INIS Atomind., INSPEC.
—BLDSC (4496.915000).

510 371.3 IT
INSEGNAMENTO DELLA MATEMATICA E DELLE SCIENZE INTEGRATE. (Alternating issues for primary school teachers and secondary school - college level teachers.) 1978. m. (plus q. supplement). L.50000 to individuals (foreign L.70000); institutions L.60000 (foreign L.90000) (effective 1995). (Centro Ricerche Didattiche "Ugo Morin") Giovanni Battagin Editore, Via dell'Artigianato, 2, 31020 San Zenone degli Ezzelini (TV), Italy. TEL 39-423-968234. FAX 39-423-968250. (Edit. addr.: Via S. Giacomo 4, 31010 Paderno del Grappa, Italy. TEL 39-423-930441. FAX 39-423-539098) Ed. Candido Sitia. adv. contact: G. Battagin. bk.rev.; bibl.; illus.; stat. circ. 2,500. **Document type:** academic/scholarly publication. **Description:** For elementary and secondary teachers; presents methods of improving teaching techniques in mathematics and related fields.

510 FR ISSN 0073-8301
QA1 CODEN: PMIHA6
INSTITUT DES HAUTES ETUDES SCIENTIFIQUES, PARIS. PUBLICATIONS MATHEMATIQUES. 1959. s-a. 1150 F. to individuals; institutions 1550 F. Presses Universitaires de France, Departement des Revues, 14 Avenue du Bois-de-l'Epine, B.P.90, 91003 Evry Cedex, France. TEL 1-60-77-82-05. FAX 1-60-79-20-45. TELEX PUF 600 474 F. (U.S. Subscr. to: Springer-Verlag, 175 Fifth Ave., New York, NY 10010) Ed. Jean Dieudonne. charts; illus.; index. (back issues avail.; reprint service avail. from KTO) **Indexed:** Compumath, Math.R.
—Faxon; Genuine Article; SWETS; UnCover. CCC.

510 FR ISSN 0373-0956
Q46 CODEN: AIFUA7
INSTITUT FOURIER. ANNALES. Key Title: Annales de l'Institut Fourier. (Text and summaries in English, French) 1949. 5/yr. 1100 F. (foreign 1360 F.) Association des Annales de l'Institut Fourier, B.P. 74, 38402 Saint-Martin d'Heres Cedex, France. FAX 76-51-44-78. Ed. Y. Colin de Verdiere. adv. circ. 1,000. **Indexed:** Compumath, INIS Atomind., Math.R., Zent.Math.
—BLDSC (0920.000000); Faxon; Genuine Article; SWETS; UnCover. CCC.
Formerly: Universite Scientifique et Medicale de Grenoble. Institut Fourier. Annales (ISSN 0073-8328)
Description: Covers partial differential equations, dynamical systems, foliations, harmonic analysis, algebraic geometry, theory of singularities and number theory.

510 530 FR ISSN 0294-1449
QA427
INSTITUT HENRI POINCARE. ANNALES: ANALYSE NON LINEAIRE. (Text in English) 1983. 6/yr. 1800 F. Gauthier-Villars, 15 rue Gossin, 92543 Montrouge Cedex, France. TEL 33-1-40-92-65-00. FAX 33-1-40-92-65-97. TELEX 634 916 F. (Subscr. to: Centrale des Revues, 11 rue Gossin, 92543 Montrouge Cedex, France. TEL 33-1-46-56-52-66) Ed P.L. Lions. adv.; abstr.; bibl. circ. 650. **Indexed:** Compumath, Curr.Cont., INIS Atomind., Math.R.
—Ei; Genuine Article; SWETS. CCC.
Description: Covers theoretical and numerical aspects of non-linear analysis, including applications to PDEs, mechanics, physics, economics.

INSTITUT HENRI POINCARE. ANNALES: PHYSIQUE THEORIQUE. see PHYSICS

519 FR ISSN 0246-0203
QA273.A1 CODEN: AHPBAR
INSTITUT HENRI POINCARE. ANNALES: PROBABILITES ET STATISTIQUES. (Text in English and French) 1930. q. 1230 F. (Institut Henri Poincare) Gauthier-Villars, 15 rue Gossin, 92543 Montrouge Cedex, France. TEL 33-1-40-92-65-00. FAX 33-1-40-92-65-97. TELEX 634 916 F. (Subscr. to: Centrale des Revues, 11 rue Gossin, 92543 Montrouge Cedex, France. TEL 33-1-46-56-52-66) Ed. J. Neveu. adv. circ. 800. (also avail. in microform from UMI) **Indexed:** Chem.Abstr., Compumath, Curr.Cont., Curr.Ind.Stat., INIS Atomind., INSPEC (1968-1983), Math.R., Sci.Cit.Ind., Zent.Math. **Document type:** academic/scholarly publication.
—BLDSC (0921.320270); Genuine Article; SWETS; UnCover. CCC.
Formerly (until 1983): Institut Henri Poincare. Annales. Section B: Calcul des Probabilites et Statistiques (ISSN 0020-2347); Which supersedes in part: Institut Henri Poincare. Annales (ISSN 0365-320X)
Description: Concerned with stochastic processes, mathematical statistics and contiguous domains.

510 FR
INSTITUT HENRI POINCARE. GROUPE D'ETUDE D'ANALYSE ULTRAMETRIQUE. EXPOSES. 1974. a. 60 Fr. Institut Henri Poincare, Secretariat Mathematique, 11 rue Pierre et Marie Curie, F-75231 Paris Cedex 05, France. (Subscr. to: Offilib, 48 rue Gay Lussac, F-75240 Paris Cedex 05, France) Ed. Paul Belgodere. circ. 200. (back issues avail) **Indexed:** Math.R., Ref.Zh., Zent.Math.

526 510 US
INSTITUTE OF MATHEMATICAL GEOGRAPHY. MONOGRAPH SERIES. 1986. irreg., no.18, 1994. price varies. Institute of Mathematical Geography, 2790 Briarcliff, Ann Arbor, MI 48105-1429. TEL 313-761-1231. E-mail: sarhaus@umich.edu. Ed. Sandra Lach Arlinghaus. charts; illus.; stat. (back issues avail.) **Document type:** monographic series, academic/scholarly publication.
Description: Scholarly research and conference proceedings on topics in mathematics and geography.
Refereed Serial

510 530 II
INSTITUTE OF MATHEMATICAL SCIENCES, MADRAS. REPORTS. (Text in English) 1962. irreg. $20. Institute of Mathematical Sciences, Madras 600 113, India. TEL 044-2352267. FAX 044-2351856. TELEX 041 21060 PCO IN PP WDT 20.
Formerly (until 1970): Symposia on Theoretical Physics and Mathematics (ISSN 0082-075X)

MATHEMATICS

510   US   ISSN 0146-3942
QA276.A1
INSTITUTE OF MATHEMATICAL STATISTICS. BULLETIN. 1972. 6/yr. $50. Institute of Mathematical Statistics, Business Office, 3401 Investment Blvd., Ste. 7, Hayward, CA 94545-3819. TEL 510-783-8141. FAX 510-783-4131. E-mail: IMS@STAT.BERKELEY.EDU. Ed. Susan Wilson. circ. 4,200 (paid). (also avail. in microform from UMI; reprint service avail. from UMI) **Document type:** bulletin.
—UMI.

510   UK   ISSN 0950-5628
CODEN: IMTABW
INSTITUTE OF MATHEMATICS AND ITS APPLICATIONS. BULLETIN. 1965. 8/yr. £75 to non-members (overseas £95) (effective 1996). Institute of Mathematics and Its Applications, 16 Nelson St., Southend-on-Sea, Essex SS1 1EF, England. TEL 01702-354020. FAX 01702-354111. E-mail: imacrrh@v-e.anglia.ac.uk. adv.; bk.rev. circ. 7,000. **Indexed:** Math.R. **Document type:** bulletin, academic/scholarly publication.
—BLDSC (2580.892000); SWETS; UnCover.
  Description: Contains papers of general interest to mathematicians, conference reports, forthcoming meetings.

510   UK
INSTITUTE OF MATHEMATICS AND ITS APPLICATIONS. PROCEEDINGS. bi-m. £75 (non-members). Institute of Mathematics and Its Applications, 16 Nelson St., Southend-on-Sea, Essex SS1 1EF, England. TEL 01702-354020. FAX 01702-354111. E-mail: imacrh@v-e.anglia.ac.uk.

519.5 310   NE   ISSN 0020-3157
QA276   CODEN: AISXAD
INSTITUTE OF STATISTICAL MATHEMATICS. ANNALS. Abbreviated title: A I S M. (Text and summaries in English) 1949. q. fl.746 to institutions; $478 to institutions in U.S. (effective 1996). Kluwer Academic Publishers, Postbus 17, 3300 AA Dordrecht, Netherlands. TEL 31-78-392392. FAX 31-78-392254. TELEX 29245 KAPG NL. E-mail: SERVICES@WKAP.NL. (Dist. by: Kluwer Academic Publishers Group, P.O. Box 322, 3300 AH Dordrecht, Netherlands. TEL 31-78-392392. FAX 31-78-546474; N. America dist. addr.: Box 358, Accord Sta., Hingham, MA 02018-0358. TEL 617-871-6600. FAX 617-871-6528) (Co-publisher: Kluwer Academic Publishers Tokyo, JA) Ed. H. Akaike. stat. circ. 1,500. (also avail. in microform from UMI) **Indexed:** ASCA, Bull.Signal., Compumath, Comput.Lit.Ind., Curr.Cont., Curr.Ind.Stat., J.Cont.Quant.Meth., Jap.Per.Ind., Math.R., Sci.Cit.Ind., Stat.Theor.Meth.Abstr., Zent.Math. **Document type:** academic/scholarly publication.
—Ei; Faxon; Genuine Article; SWETS; UnCover. **CCC.**
  Refereed Serial

510   AG   ISSN 0326-0690
INSTITUTO DE MATEMATICA BEPPO LEVI. CUADERNOS. 1971. irreg. exchange basis. Universidad Nacional de Rosario, Avenida Pellegrini 250, 2000 Rosario, Argentina. TEL 041-217998. TELEX 41817 CIROS AR. Ed.Bd. circ. 500. **Indexed:** Appl.Mech.Rev., Math.R., Zent.Math.

510   RM
INSTITUTUL DE SUBINGINERI ORADEA. LUCRARI STIINTIFICE: SERIA MATEMATICA. (Text in Rumanian, occasionally in English or French; summaries in English, French, German, Rumanian) 1967. a. Institutul de Subingineri Oradea, Calea Armatei Rosii Nr. 5, 3700 Oradea, Rumania.
  Formerly: Institutul Pedagogic Oradea. Lucrari Stiintifice: Seria Matematica; which continues in part (in 1973) Institutul Pedagogica Oradea. Lucrari Stiintifice: Seria Matematica, Fizica, Chimie; which superseded in part (in 1971): Institutul Pedagogica Oradea. Lucrari Stiintifice: Seria A and Seria B; which was formerly (until 1969): Institutul Pedagogica Oradea. Lucrari Stiintifice.

530 520   RM
CODEN: BMTFA3
INSTITUTUL POLITEHNIC DIN IASI. BULETINUL. SECTIA I: MATEMATICA, MECANICA, FIZICA. (Text in English, French, German, Italian, Russian, Spanish) 1946. s-a. exchange basis. Institutul Politehnic din Iasi, Bd. Copou 11, 6600 Jassy, Rumania. TEL 46577. FAX 40-81-47923. Eds. Alfred Braier, Hugo Rosman. adv.; bk.rev.; bibl. circ. 450. **Indexed:** Appl.Mech.Rev., INSPEC (1987-), Math.R., Ref.Zh.
—BLDSC (2366.102300); CASDDS.
  Former titles: Institutul Politehnic "Gheorghe Asachi" din Iasi. Buletinul. Sectia I: Mecanica Matematica, Fizica; Institutul Politehnic Iasi. Buletinul. Sectia I: Matematica, Mecanica Teoretica, Fizica (ISSN 0304-5188)

INSURANCE: MATHEMATICS & ECONOMICS. see *INSURANCE*

510   SZ   ISSN 0378-620X
QA431
INTEGRAL EQUATIONS AND OPERATOR THEORY. (Text in English) 1978. 12/yr. 896.40 SFr. (foreign 921.30 SFr.). Birkhaeuser Verlag, P.O. Box 133, CH-4010 Basel, Switzerland. TEL 061-2717400. FAX 061-2717666. (Dist. in N. America by: Springer-Verlag, Mercedes Distribution Center, 160 Imlay St., Brooklyn, NY 11231, USA) Ed. I. Gohberg. (reprint service avail. from SWZ) **Indexed:** Compumath, Math.R. **Document type:** academic/scholarly publication.
—Faxon; Genuine Article; SWETS; UMI; UnCover. **CCC.**

510   US   ISSN 1065-2469
INTEGRAL TRANSFORMS AND SPECIAL FUNCTIONS. 1993. q. 109 ECU (effective 1996). Gordon & Breach Science Publishers, c/o International Publishers Distributor, 820 Town Center Dr., Langhorne, PA 19047. TEL 215-750-2642; 800-545-8398. FAX 215-750-6343. (Subscr. to: International Publishers Distributor, P.O. Box 90, Reading, Berkshire RG1 8JL, England. TEL 44-173-456-8316) (also avail. in microfiche) **Document type:** academic/scholarly publication.

515   US
INTERNATIONAL CONFERENCE ON COMPUTING FIXED POINTS WITH APPLICATIONS. PROCEEDINGS. 1977. irreg., 1st, 1974, Clemson University (pub. 1977). Department of the Navy, Office of Naval Research, Arlington, VA 22217. TEL 202-545-6700. (Co-sponsor: U.S. Army Research Office) **Document type:** proceedings.

INTERNATIONAL JOURNAL FOR NUMERICAL METHODS IN ENGINEERING. see *ENGINEERING*

510   SI   ISSN 0218-1967
QA150   CODEN: IACOEA
INTERNATIONAL JOURNAL OF ALGEBRA AND COMPUTATION. 1991. 4/yr. $125 to individuals & institutions of developing countries; institutions of developed countries $258. World Scientific Publishing Co. Pte. Ltd., Farrer Rd., P.O. Box 128, Singapore 9128, Singapore. TEL 3825663. FAX 3825919. TELEX RS-28561-WSPC. (UK addr.: 73 Lynton Mead, Totteridge, London N20 8DH, England. TEL 44-81-4462461; US addr.: 1060 Main St., Ste. 1B, River Edge, NJ 07661. TEL 800-227-7562) Ed. J. Rhodes. **Indexed:** INSPEC (1991-). **Document type:** academic/scholarly publication.
—BLDSC (4542.005000). **CCC.**
  Description: Publishes original papers in mathematics in general, but giving a preference to those in the areas of mathematics represented by the editorial board.

510 330.1 320   GW   ISSN 0020-7276
QA269   CODEN: IJGTA2
INTERNATIONAL JOURNAL OF GAME THEORY. (Text in English) 1971. 4/yr. DM.520($377) (effective 1996). Physica-Verlag GmbH und Co., Postfach 105280, 69042 Heidelberg, Germany. TEL 06221-487492. FAX 06221-487177. (Subscr. to: Springer Verlag GmbH, Postfach 311340, 10643 Berlin, Germany. TEL 030-8207-424; Dist. in N. America by: Springer-Verlag New York Inc., 175 Fifth Ave., New York, NY 10010, U.S.A.. TEL 212-460-1500) Ed. D. Samet. adv.; bk.rev.; bibl.; charts; index. (also avail. in microform from UMI; back issues avail. from SWZ) **Indexed:** Compumath, Comput.Cont., Cyb.Abstr., INSPEC, Int.Abstr.Oper.Res., J.Cont.Quant.Meth., J.of Econ.Lit., Math.R., SSCI, Zent.Math. **Document type:** academic/scholarly publication.
—BLDSC (4542.261000); Faxon; Genuine Article; SWETS; UMI; UnCover. **CCC.**
  Description: Publishes original articles on the theory of games and its applications.

510   US   ISSN 1055-7490
INTERNATIONAL JOURNAL OF MATHEMATICAL AND STATISTICAL SCIENCES. 1992. s-a. $100 to individuals; institutions $200. Berkeley - Cambridge Press, Box 947, Carmichael, CA 95609-0947. Ed. Steve Larson. **Document type:** academic/scholarly publication.
  Description: Publishes original articles in various fields of mathematical and statistical sciences in general, and special functions, multivariate statistical analysis, and information theory.
  Refereed Serial

510 370   UK   ISSN 0020-739X
CODEN: IJMEBM
INTERNATIONAL JOURNAL OF MATHEMATICAL EDUCATION IN SCIENCE AND TECHNOLOGY. 1970. bi-m. £242($400) (effective 1996). Taylor & Francis Ltd., Rankine Rd., Basingstoke, Hants. RG24 8PR, England. TEL 44-1256-840366. FAX 44-1256-47943. TELEX 858540. E-mail: info@tandf.co.uk. (Subscr. in N. America to: Taylor & Francis Inc., 1900 Frost Rd., Ste. 101, Bristol, PA 19007-1598. TEL 800-821-8312. FAX 215-785-5515) Ed. Dennis Walker. adv.; bk.rev.; index. **Indexed:** C.I.J.E., Cont.Pg.Educ., Educ.Ind., Educ.Tech.Abstr., High.Educ.Curr.Aware.Bull., INSPEC, Intl.Civil Eng.Abstr., Math.R., Mid.East: Abstr.& Ind., Mult.Ed.Abstr., Soft.Abstr.Eng., Tech.Educ.Abstr. **Document type:** academic/scholarly publication.
—BLDSC (4542.337000); Ei; Faxon; SWETS; UnCover. **CCC.**
  Description: Provides a medium by which a wide range of experience in mathematical education can be presented, assimilated and, eventually, adapted to everyday needs in schools, colleges, polytechnics, universities, industry and commerce.
  Refereed Serial

510   SI   ISSN 0129-167X
QA1
INTERNATIONAL JOURNAL OF MATHEMATICS. (Text in English) 1990. bi-m. $195 to individuals & institutions of developing countries; institutions of developed countries $390. World Scientific Publishing Co. Pte. Ltd., Farrer Rd., P.O. Box 128, Singapore 9128, Singapore. TEL 3825663. FAX 3825919. TELEX RS-28561-WSPC. (US addr.: 1060 Main St., Ste. 1B, River Edge, NJ 07661. TEL 800-227-7562; UK addr.: 73 Lynton Mead, Totteridge, London N20 8DH, England. TEL 44-81-4462461) Eds. A. Casson, S. Kobayashi. circ. 100. **Document type:** academic/scholarly publication.
—BLDSC (4542.337500); Faxon; SWETS; UnCover. **CCC.**

510   II   ISSN 0161-1712
QA1
INTERNATIONAL JOURNAL OF MATHEMATICS AND MATHEMATICAL SCIENCES. (Text in English) 1978. q. $60. Calcutta Mathematical Society, AE-374, Sector-1, Salt Lake City, Calcutta 700 064, India. (Subscr. to: University of Central Florida, Orlando, Florida 32816, U.S.A.) circ. 200. (back issues avail.) **Indexed:** Math.R.
—Faxon; SWETS; UnCover.

INTERNATIONAL JOURNAL OF NON-LINEAR MECHANICS. see *ENGINEERING — Engineering Mechanics And Materials*

INTERNATIONAL JOURNAL OF NUMERICAL MODELLING: ELECTRONIC NETWORKS, DEVICES AND FIELDS. see ENGINEERING — Computer Applications

510   AU   ISSN 0020-7926
CODEN: IMTNA2
INTERNATIONAL MATHEMATICAL NEWS. (Text in English, French and German) 1947. 3/yr. S.300. Oesterreichische Mathematische Gesellschaft, Technische Universitaet, Wiedner Hauptstr. 8-10, A-1040 Vienna, Austria. Ed. Peter Flor. adv. contact: Inge Troch. bk.rev.; bibl. circ. 1,500. **Indexed:** Math.R. **Document type:** bulletin.
Description: News about mathematical events around the world, including reviews of mathematical books.

510   US
INTERNATIONAL MATHEMATICS RESEARCH NOTICES. irreg. (8-16/yr.). $300 to individuals (foreign $336); institutions $600 (foreign $636) (effective 1996). Duke University Press, Box 90660, Durham, NC 27708-0660. TEL 919-687-3600. FAX 919-688-4574. Ed. Morris Weisfeld.

510 530   II   ISSN 0074-705X
INTERNATIONAL MONOGRAPHS ON ADVANCED MATHEMATICS AND PHYSICS. (Text in English) 1961. irreg., latest 1989. Hindustan Publishing Corp., 4805-24, Bharat Ram Rd., Flat Nos. 1&2, 1st Fl., Daryaganj, New Delhi 110002, India. TEL 9-11-3254401. FAX 9-11-6863511. **Document type:** academic/scholarly publication, monographic series.

INTERNATIONAL SOCIETY OF PARAMETRIC ANALYSTS. CONFERENCE PROCEEDINGS. see BUSINESS AND ECONOMICS — Accounting

510   GW   ISSN 0020-9910
QA1   CODEN: INVMBH
INVENTIONES MATHEMATICAE. (Text mainly in English) 1966. 12/yr. (in 4 vols., 3 nos./vol.). DM.3712($2697) (effective 1996). Springer-Verlag, Heidelberger Platz 3, 14197 Berlin, Germany. TEL 030-8207-0. FAX 030-8214091. E-mail: orders@springer.de. (Subscr. in N. America to: Springer-Verlag New York, Inc., 44 Hartz Way, Secaucus, NJ 07096-2491. TEL 201-348-4033. FAX 201-348-4505) Ed. M. Berger. charts; illus.; stat. (also avail. in microfilm from UMI; back issues avail.; reprint service avail. from ISI) **Indexed:** Compumath, Curr.Cont., Ind.Sci.Rev., Math.R., Sci.Cit.Ind., Zent.Math. **Document type:** academic/scholarly publication.
—BLDSC (4557.660000); Faxon; Genuine Article; SWETS; UMI; UnCover. **CCC.**
Description: Forum for papers in mathematics.
Refereed Serial

519   CU   ISSN 0257-4306
T57.6.A1
INVESTIGACION OPERACIONAL. 1968. q. $29 or exchange basis. Universidad de la Habana, Departamento de Matematica Aplicada, Centro de Informacion Cientifico Tecnica, Calle L y San Lazaro, Havana 4, Cuba. TEL 537-705383. FAX 537-322757. Eds. Sira Allende, Juan Cue; Pub. Luis Chong. adv.; bk.rev.; circ. 1,200 (paid). (back issues avail.) **Indexed:** Math.R., Ref.Zh. **Document type:** academic/scholarly publication.

IOWA STATE UNIVERSITY. STATISTICAL LABORATORY. ANNUAL REPORT. see MATHEMATICS — Abstracting, Bibliographies, Statistics

511   IR   ISSN 1018-6301
IRANIAN MATHEMATICAL SOCIETY. BULLETIN/ANJOMAN-I RIYAZI-I IRAN. BULETAN-I. Key Title: Bulletin of Iranian Mathematical Society. (Text in English) 1973. s-a. $20 to non-members. Iranian Mathematical Society, P.O. Box 13145-418, Teheran, Iran. FAX 98-21-8847275. TELEX SHU 332169. E-mail: iranmath@irearn.bitnet. Ed. M. Radjabalipour. bk.rev. circ. 2,000. **Indexed:** Math.R. **Document type:** bulletin.
—BLDSC (2593.045000).
Description: Publishes research or expository articles in mathematical sciences.
Refereed Serial

510   IS   ISSN 0021-2172
QA1   CODEN: ISJMAP
ISRAEL JOURNAL OF MATHEMATICS. (Text in English) 1951. 12/yr. (in 4 vols., 3 nos./vol.). $288 (effective 1996). Magnes Press, Hebrew University, Jerusalem, P.O. Box 7695, Jerusalem 91076, Israel. TEL 972-2-660341. FAX 972-2-633370. Ed. A. Lubotzky. charts; illus.; index. circ. 950. (also avail. in microform from SWZ; reprint service avail. from SWZ) **Indexed:** Compumath, Comput.Rev., Curr.Cont., Ind.Sci.Rev., INSPEC, Math.R., Sci.Cit.Ind, Stat.Theor.Meth.Abstr. **Document type:** academic/scholarly publication.
—Faxon; Genuine Article; SWETS; UnCover.

ISSLEDOVANIA PO TEORII ALGORIFMOV I MATEMATICHESKOI LOGIKE. see PHILOSOPHY

510   RU   ISSN 0136-0949
QA21
ISTORIKO-MATEMATICHESKIE ISSLEDOVANIYA. 1948. irreg. $30 to individuals; libraries $40 (effective thru 1996). Rossiiskaya Akademiya Nauk, Institut Istorii Estestvoznaniya i Tekhniki - Russian Academy of Sciences, Institute of History of Natural Science and Technology, Staropanskii per. 1-5, 103012 Moscow, Russia. TEL 7-095-925-8107. FAX 7-095-925-9911. Ed. S.S. Dimidov. abstr.; bibl.; illus. circ. 1,500. **Indexed:** Math.R. **Document type:** academic/scholarly publication.
—BLDSC (0087.820000).
Description: Includes original articles on history of mathematics.

510   RU   ISSN 0202-7445
QA1
ITOGI NAUKI I TEKHNIKI: ALGEBRA - TOPOLOGIYA - GEOMETRIYA. irreg., vol.27, 1989. 8 Rub. Vsesoyuznyi Institut Nauchno-Tekhnicheskoi Informatsii (VINITI), Baltiiskaya ul. 14, Moscow A-219, Russia. (Subscr. to: Mezhdunarodnaya Kniga, Dimitrova ul. 39, 113095 Moscow, Russia)
—BLDSC (0006.340000).

510   RU   ISSN 0202-7453
QA300
ITOGI NAUKI I TEKHNIKI: MATEMATICHESKII ANALIZ. irreg., vol.27, 1989. 8 Rub. Vsesoyuznyi Institut Nauchno-Tekhnicheskoi Informatsii (VINITI), Baltiiskaya ul. 14, Moscow A-219, Russia. (Subscr. to: Mezhdunarodnaya Kniga, Dimitrova ul. 39, 113095 Moscow, Russia)
—BLDSC (0100.970000).

516   RU   ISSN 0202-7461
QA443
ITOGI NAUKI I TEKHNIKI: PROBLEMY GEOMETRII. irreg., vol.21, 1989. 8 Rub. Vsesoyuznyi Institut Nauchno-Tekhnicheskoi Informatsii (VINITI), Baltiiskaya ul. 14, Moscow A-219, Russia. (Subscr. to: Mezhdunarodnaya Kniga, Dimitrova 39, 113095 Moscow, Russia)
—BLDSC (0133.196500).

510   RU   ISSN 0233-6723
QA1
ITOGI NAUKI I TEKHNIKI: SOVREMENNYE PROBLEMY MATEMATIKI, FUNDAMENTAL'NYE NAPRAVLENIYA. irreg. 9.20 Rub. Vsesoyuznyi Institut Nauchno-Tekhnicheskoi Informatsii (VINITI), Ul. Usievicha 20-A, 125219 Moscow A-219, Russia. (Subscr. to: Mezhdunarodnaya Kniga, Moscow 121200, Russia)
—BLDSC (0165.589000). **CCC.**
Formerly (until 1985): Itogi Nauki i Tekhniki: Sovremennye Problemy Matematiki (ISSN 0202-747X)

510 001.53   RU   ISSN 0202-7488
QA273
ITOGI NAUKI I TEKHNIKI: TEORIYA VEROYATNOSTEJ - MATEMATICHESKAYA STATISTIKA-TEORETICHESKAYA KIBERNETIKA. (Text in Russian) 1965. irreg., vol.27, 1989. 8 Rub. Vsesoyuznyi Institut Nauchno-Tekhnicheskoi Informatsii (VINITI), Baltiiskaya ul. 14, Moscow A-219, Russia. (Subscr. to: Mezhdunarodnaya Kniga, Dimitrova ul. 39, 113095 Moscow, Russia)
—BLDSC (0178.040000).

510   RU   ISSN 0021-3446
QA1   CODEN: IVUMBY
IZVESTIYA VYSSHIKH UCHEBNYKH ZAVEDENII. SERIYA MATEMATIKA. English translation: Russian Mathematics - Iz. V U Z (US ISSN 1066-369X) 1957. m. $196 (effective 1996). Kazanskii Universitet, Ul. Lenina, 18, 420008 Kazan, Russia. Ed. A.P. Norden. charts; illus. circ. 2,000. **Indexed:** Compumath, INSPEC, Math.R.
—BLDSC (0077.530000); Genuine Article. **CCC.**

510   JA   ISSN 0386-2194
QA1   CODEN: PJAADT
JAPAN ACADEMY. PROCEEDINGS. SERIES A: MATHEMATICAL SCIENCES/NIPPON GAKUSHIIN KIYO A. (Text in English, French, German) 1945. 10/yr. $165 includes series B. Nippon Gakushiin - Japan Academy, 7-32 Ueno Koen, Taito-ku, Tokyo 110, Japan. (Subscr. to: Maruzen Co., Ltd., 3-10 Nihonbashi 2-chome, Chuo-ku, Tokyo 103, Japan; Dist. overseas by: Import and Export Dept., Box 5050, Tokyo International, Tokyo 100-31, Japan) Ed.Bd. bibl.; charts; illus.; index, cum.index. (also avail. in microform from PMC) **Indexed:** Anim.Breed.Abstr., Biol.Abstr., Chem.Abstr., Compumath, Curr.Cont., Field Crop Abstr., Herb.Abstr., INSPEC, Math.R., Met.Abstr., Sci.Cit.Ind., World Alum.Abstr. **Document type:** academic/scholarly publication, proceedings.
—BLDSC (6742.050000); Faxon; SWETS; UnCover.
Supersedes in part and continues numbering of (vol.53): Japan Academy. Proceedings (ISSN 0021-4280)

510   JA   ISSN 0916-7005
QA1
JAPAN JOURNAL OF INDUSTRIAL AND APPLIED MATHEMATICS. (Text and summaries in English) 1984. 3/yr. $436 (effective 1995). Kinokuniya Shoten - Kinokuniya Co., Ltd., 17-7, Shinjuku 3-chome, Shinjuku-ku, Tokyo 163-91, Japan. (Alt. addr.: Publishing Department, 38-1 Sakuragaoka 5-chome, Setagaya-ku, Tokyo 156, Japan. TEL 03-3439-0172. FAX 03-3439-0173) Ed.Bd.
—BLDSC (4648.328000); Faxon.
Formerly (until 1991): Japan Journal of Applied Mathematics (ISSN 0910-2043)

510   US   ISSN 1058-7349
QA402   CODEN: JJFSE9
JAPANESE JOURNAL OF FUZZY THEORY AND SYSTEMS. 1989. bi-m. $760 (effective 1996). Allerton Press, Inc., 150 Fifth Ave., New York, NY 10011. TEL 212-924-3950. FAX 212-463-9684. Ed. Misaharu Mizumoto. **Indexed:** INSPEC (1992-). **Document type:** academic/scholarly publication.
—BLDSC (4651.965000). **CCC.**
Description: Covers fuzzy set theory and its manifold operations.

510   JA   ISSN 0289-2316
QA1   CODEN: JJMAAK
JAPANESE JOURNAL OF MATHEMATICS. (Text in English) 1924; N.S. 1975. s-a. $303 (effective 1995). (Nihon Sugakkai - Mathematical Society of Japan) Kinokuniya Shoten - Kinokuniya Co., Ltd., 17-7, Shinjuku 3-chome, Shinjuku-ku, Tokyo 163-91, Japan. TEL 03-3439-0172. FAX 03-3439-0173. **Indexed:** Math.R. **Document type:** academic/scholarly publication.
—SWETS.

510   CC   ISSN 0254-7791
QA297
JISUAN SHUXUE/MATHEMATICA NUMERICA SINICA. English edition: Journal of Computational Mathematics (ISSN 0254-9409) (Text in Chinese) 1964. q. $71.60. (Chinese Academy of Sciences, Computer Centre) Science Press, Marketing and Sales Department, 16 Donghuangchenggen North St., Beijing 100717, People's Republic of China. TEL 4010642. FAX 4019810. adv. circ. 11,000. **Indexed:** INSPEC (1981-). **Document type:** academic/scholarly publication.
—BLDSC (5399.870000).
Description: Contains original research papers on computational mathematics, such as numerical linear and non-linear algebra, numerical optimization and approximations, computational geometry, statistics and probability, Monte Carlo methods, numerical methods for ordinary, integral, and partial differential equations, and computational math problems in science and engineering.
Refereed Serial

MATHEMATICS

510   JA   ISSN 0914-3378
JOCHI DAIGAKU SUGAKU KOKYUROKU/SOPHIA KOKYUROKU IN MATHEMATICS. (Text in Japanese) 1977. a. Sophia University, Department of Mathematics - Jochi Daigaku Sugaku Kyoshitsu, 7-1, Kioi-cho, Chiyoda-ku, Tokyo 102, Japan.

510   IS   ISSN 0021-7670
QA1   CODEN: JOAMAV
JOURNAL D'ANALYSE MATHEMATIQUE. (Text in English) 1951. 3/yr. $210 (effective 1996). Magnes Press, Hebrew University, Jerusalem, P.O. Box 7695, Jerusalem, Israel. TEL 972-2-660341. FAX 972-2-633370. Ed. L. Zalcman. bibl.; charts. circ. 750. (also avail. in microfilm from PMC; reprint service avail. from SWZ) **Indexed:** Compumath, Curr.Cont., Ind.Sci.Rev., Math.R., Sci.Cit.Ind. **Document type:** academic/scholarly publication.
—Faxon; SWETS; UnCover.

510 519   FR   ISSN 0021-7824
QA1   CODEN: JMPAAM
JOURNAL DE MATHEMATIQUES PURES ET APPLIQUEES. (Text in English, French) 1836. 6/yr. 1650 F. Gauthier-Villars, 15 rue Gossin, 92543 Montrouge Cedex, France. TEL 33-1-40-92-65-00. FAX 33-1-40-92-65-97. TELEX 634 916 F. (Subscr. to: Centrale des Revues, 11 rue Gossin, 92543 Montrouge Cedex, France. TEL 33-1-46-56-52-66) Ed. J.L. Lions. adv.; bk.rev. circ. 1,000. (also avail. in microfilm from UMI,PMC; reprint service avail. from KTO,UMI) **Indexed:** Appl.Mech.Rev., Compumath, Curr.Cont., Ind.Sci.Rev., INIS Atomind., Math.R., Sci.Cit.Ind., Zent.Math.
—Faxon; Genuine Article; SWETS; UnCover. **CCC**.
Description: Covers all branches of pure mathematics.

510.07 378   US   ISSN 0021-8251
QA11.A1   CODEN: JRMEDN
JOURNAL FOR RESEARCH IN MATHEMATICS EDUCATION. 1970. 5/yr. $45. National Council of Teachers of Mathematics, 1906 Association Dr., Reston, VA 22091. TEL 703-620-9840. FAX 703-476-2970. E-mail: nctmath@tmn.com. Ed. Framk K. Lester, Jr. adv.; index every 2 yrs. circ. 11,000. (also avail. in microform from UMI; reprint service avail. from UMI) **Indexed:** C.I.J.E., Cont.Pg.Educ., Educ.Ind., Psychol.Abstr. (1971-), Tech.Educ.Abstr. **Document type:** academic/scholarly publication, abstracting/indexing.
—BLDSC (5052.015000); Ei; Faxon; Genuine Article; SWETS; UMI; UnCover.
Description: Research reports and reviews on the teaching and learning of mathematics at all levels. Includes annual annotated index of mathematics education research articles from 60 journals.
Refereed Serial

510   GW   ISSN 0075-4102
QA1   CODEN: JRMAA8
JOURNAL FUER DIE REINE UND ANGEWANDTE MATHEMATIK. (Text in English, German, and French) 1826. m. DM3298. Walter de Gruyter und Co., Genthiner Str. 13, 10785 Berlin, Germany. TEL 030-26005-0. FAX 030-26005251. TELEX 184027. (U.S. addr.: Walter de Gruyter, Inc., 200 Saw Mill River Rd., Hawthorne, NY 10532. TEL 914-747-0110) Ed.Bd. adv. (also avail. in microform from UMI,PMC; reprint service avail. from UMI) **Indexed:** Compumath, Math.R., Sci.Cit.Ind. **Document type:** academic/scholarly publication.
—BLDSC (5049.000000); Faxon; Genuine Article; SWETS; UMI; UnCover. **CCC**.

510 370   GW   ISSN 0173-5322
JOURNAL FUER MATHEMATIK-DIDAKTIK; Zeitschrift der Gesellschaft fuer Didaktik der Mathematik. 1980. q. DM.52. Verlag Ferdinand Schoeningh GmbH, Postfach 2540, 33055 Paderborn, Germany. TEL 05251-127665. FAX 05251-127860. Ed. Werner Blum. adv. circ. 700. (back issues avail.) **Indexed:** Tech.Educ.Abstr. **Document type:** academic/scholarly publication.
—BLDSC (5013.830000). **CCC**.

512   US   ISSN 0021-8693
   CODEN: JALGA4
JOURNAL OF ALGEBRA. 1964. 24/yr. $2300 (foreign $2663) (effective 1996). Academic Press, Inc., Journal Division, 525 B St., Ste. 1900, San Diego, CA 92101-4495. TEL 619-230-1840. FAX 619-699-6800. (Subscr. to: Box 620000, Orlando, FL 32891-8340. TEL 800-543-9534) Ed. Walter Feit. adv.; bibl.; index. (back issues avail.; reprint service avail. from SWZ) **Indexed:** Compumath, Curr.Cont., Ind.Sci.Rev., Math.R., Sci.Cit.Ind. **Document type:** academic/scholarly publication.
—BLDSC (4926.750000); Faxon; Genuine Article; SWETS; UnCover. **CCC**.
Description: Presents articles concerning original research in the field of algebra.
Refereed Serial

512   US   ISSN 0925-9899
QA164   CODEN: JAOME7
JOURNAL OF ALGEBRAIC COMBINATORICS; an international journal. 1992. q. fl.468 to institutions; $300 to institutions in U.S. (effective 1996). Kluwer Academic Publishers Boston, Box 358, Accord Sta., Hingham, MA 02018-0358. TEL 617-871-6600. FAX 617-871-6528. TELEX 200190. (Dist. outside N. America by: Kluwer Academic Publishers Group, P.O. Box 322, 3300 AH Dordrecht, Netherlands. TEL 31-78-392392. FAX 31-78-546474) Ed.Bd. (also avail. in microform from UMI; back issues avail.; reprint service avail. from SWZ) **Indexed:** ASCA, Compumath, Comput.Lit.Ind., Comput.Rev., Eng.Ind., Inform.Sci.Abstr., INSPEC (1992-), Math.R., Zent.Math. **Document type:** academic/scholarly publication.
—BLDSC (4926.770000); Ei; Genuine Article; UMI. **CCC**.
Description: Provides a forum for theoretical and applied papers examining the interaction between algebra and combinatorics.
Refereed Serial

510   US   ISSN 1056-3911
JOURNAL OF ALGEBRAIC GEOMETRY. 1991. q. $188 to non-members; individual members $120. American Mathematical Society, Box 6248, Providence, RI 02940-6248. TEL 401-455-4000. Ed. Stephen S.-T. Yau. **Document type:** academic/scholarly publication.
—BLDSC (4926.780000); Faxon; SWETS; UnCover.
Description: Provides a forum for work in algebraic geometry, the study of singularities, and related fields.

519.5   UK   ISSN 0883-7252
HB139   CODEN: JAECET
JOURNAL OF APPLIED ECONOMETRICS. 1986. bi-m. $495 (foreign $495) (effective 1996). John Wiley & Sons Ltd., Journals, Baffins Ln., Chichester, W. Sussex PO19 1UD, England. TEL 01243-779777. FAX 01243-775612. TELEX 86290 WIBOOK G. (Subscr. in the Americas to: John Wiley & Sons, Inc., 605 Third Ave., New York, NY 10158. TEL 212-850-6645. FAX 212-850-6021) Ed. M. Hashem Pesaran. circ. 1,253. (also avail. in microform from UMI; back issues avail.; reprint service avail. from SWZ) **Indexed:** Curr.Cont., Curr.Ind.Stat., J.of Econ.Lit., Oper.Res.Manage.Sci., Qual.Contr.Appl.Stat., Stat.Theor.Meth.Abstr. **Document type:** academic/scholarly publication.
—BLDSC (4942.520000); Faxon; Genuine Article; SWETS; UMI; UnCover. **CCC**.
Description: Articles dealing with the application of econometric techniques to a wide variety of problems in economics and related subjects; covering topics in measurement, estimation, testing, forecasting, and policy analysis.

JOURNAL OF APPLIED MATHEMATICS AND MECHANICS. see ENGINEERING — Engineering Mechanics And Materials

511.3   FR   ISSN 1166-3081
JOURNAL OF APPLIED NON-CLASSICAL LOGICS. 1991. 2/yr. 530 F. (foreign 630 F.). Editions Hermes, 14 rue Lantiez, 75017 Paris, France. TEL 42-29-44-66. FAX 42-29-15-56. Ed. Luis Farinas des Cerro.
—BLDSC (4943.400000).

519   UK   ISSN 0021-9002
QA276   CODEN: JPRBAM
JOURNAL OF APPLIED PROBABILITY. 1964. q. £119($191.60) (foreign £119) (effective 1996). Applied Probability Trust, School of Mathematics, University of Sheffield, Sheffield S3 7RH, England. TEL 0114-282-4269. FAX 0114-272-9782. Ed. C.C. Heyde. adv.; stat.; charts; index; cum.index. circ. 1,500. (back issues avail.) **Indexed:** Anim.Breed.Abstr., Biol.Abstr., Biostat., Compumath, Comput.Abstr., Curr.Cont., Curr.Ind.Stat., Cyb.Abstr., Field Crop Abstr., Ind.Sci.Rev., INIS Atomind., INSPEC, J.Cont.Quant.Meth., Math.R., Oper.Res.Manage.Sci., Qual.Contr.Appl.Stat., Ref.Zh., Sci.Cit.Ind., Stat.Theor.Meth.Abstr., Zent.Math. **Document type:** academic/scholarly publication.
—BLDSC (4946.700000); Ei; Faxon; Genuine Article; SWETS; UnCover. **CCC**.
Description: Devoted to research in applications of probability theory to the biological, physical, social and technological sciences. Contains research papers and short communications.

519.5   US   ISSN 1067-5817
QA276.A1
JOURNAL OF APPLIED STATISTICAL SCIENCE. 1993. q. $115 (effective 1996). Nova Science Publishers, Inc., 6080 Jericho Tpke., Ste. 207, Commack, NY 11725-2808. TEL 516-499-3103. FAX 516-499-3146. E-mail: novasci1@aol.com. Eds. M. Ahsanullah, M. Atiquallah. **Document type:** academic/scholarly publication.
Description: Contributed to the advancement of statistical science, including those on theory oriented to real-life problems, comparison of existing methods.

JOURNAL OF APPLIED STATISTICS. see STATISTICS

510   US   ISSN 0021-9045
QA221   CODEN: JAXTAZ
JOURNAL OF APPROXIMATION THEORY. (Text and summaries in English and German) 1968. m. $858 (foreign $987) (effective 1996). Academic Press, Inc., Journal Division, 525 B St., Ste. 1900, San Diego, CA 92101-4495. TEL 619-230-1840. FAX 619-699-6800. (Subscr. to: Box 620000, Orlando, FL 32891-8340. TEL 800-543-9534) Eds. Paul Nevai, Allan Pinkus. adv.; charts; stat. (back issues avail.; reprint service avail. from SWZ) **Indexed:** Compumath, Curr.Cont., Ind.Sci.Rev., INSPEC, Math.R., Sci.Cit.Ind. **Document type:** academic/scholarly publication.
—Faxon; Genuine Article; SWETS; UnCover. **CCC**.
Description: Devoted to new advances in pure and applied approximation theory and related areas.
Refereed Serial

510   US   ISSN 0176-4268
BD241
JOURNAL OF CLASSIFICATION. 1984. s-a. $131 (includes Class: Classification Literature Automated Search Service (ISSN 0731-4043)) (effective 1996). (Classification Society of North America) Springer-Verlag, Journals, 175 Fifth Ave., New York, NY 10010. TEL 212-460-1500. FAX 212-473-6272. (N. American subscr. to: Journal Fulfillment Services, Box 2485, Secaucus, NJ 07096-2491. TEL 800-777-4643. FAX 201-348-4505; Elsewhere: Heidelberger Platz 3, 1000 Berlin 33, Germany. TEL 030-8207-1. FAX 030-8214091) Ed. Phipps Arabie. (also avail. in microform from UMI; reprint service avail. from SWZ) **Indexed:** ASCA, ASCA, Biol.Abstr., Biostat., Compumath, Curr.Cont., Curr.Cont., Curr.Ind.Stat., J.Cont.Quant.Meth., LISA, Math.R., Psychol.Abstr. (1984-), Stat.Theor.Meth.Abstr., Zent.Math.
—BLDSC (4958.369550); Faxon; Genuine Article; SWETS; UnCover. **CCC**.
Description: Covers a wide range of topics in the field of classification.
Refereed Serial

MATHEMATICS

510   US   ISSN 1063-8539
QA166.25   CODEN: JDESEU
JOURNAL OF COMBINATORIAL DESIGNS. 1993. bi-m. $270 (foreign $363) (effective 1996). John Wiley & Sons, Inc., Journals, 605 Third Ave., New York, NY 10158. TEL 212-850-6645. FAX 212-850-6021. TELEX 12-7068. E-mail: SUBINFO@JWILEY.COM. (Subscr. outside the Americas to: John Wiley & Sons Ltd., Baffins Ln., Chichester, W. Sussex PO19 1UD, England. TEL 44-1243-779777. FAX 44-1243-776128) Ed. Charles Colbourn. (also avail. in microform from UMI; back issues avail.) **Indexed:** Stat.Theor.Meth.Abstr. **Document type:** academic/scholarly publication.
—BLDSC (4960.280000); UnCover.
Refereed Serial

510 001.539   CN   ISSN 0835-3026
QA164   CODEN: JJCCEE
JOURNAL OF COMBINATORIAL MATHEMATICS AND COMBINATORIAL COMPUTING. 1987. 3/yr. $120. Charles Babbage Research Centre, Box 272, St. Norbert Postal Sta., Winnipeg, MB R3V 1L6, Canada. TEL 204-772-2612. Ed. W.L. Kocay. circ. 200. (back issues avail.) **Indexed:** INSPEC (1990-). **Document type:** academic/scholarly publication.
—BLDSC (4960.300000); Faxon; UnCover.
Refereed Serial

510   US   ISSN 0097-3165
QA164   CODEN: JCBTA7
JOURNAL OF COMBINATORIAL THEORY. SERIES A. 1966. 8/yr. $797 (foreign $960) (effective 1996). Academic Press, Inc., Journal Division, 525 B St., Ste. 1900, San Diego, CA 92101-4495. TEL 619-230-1840. FAX 619-699-6800. (Subscr. to: Box 620000, Orlando, FL 32891-8340. TEL 800-543-9534) Eds. Basil Gordon, Bruce Rothschild. adv.; charts; illus.; index. (back issues avail.) **Indexed:** Compumath, Curr.Cont., Excerp.Med., Ind.Sci.Rev., INSPEC, Int.Abstr.Oper.Res., Math.R., Sci.Cit.Ind. **Document type:** academic/scholarly publication.
—BLDSC (4960.510000); Faxon; Genuine Article; SWETS. **CCC.**
Supersedes in part: Journal of Combinatorial Theory (ISSN 0021-9800)
Description: Publishes original mathematical research concerned with theoretical and physical aspects of the study of finite and discrete structures in all branches of science. Series A is primarily concerned with structure, design, and applications of combinatorics.
Refereed Serial

510   US   ISSN 0095-8956
QA166   CODEN: JCBTB8
JOURNAL OF COMBINATORIAL THEORY. SERIES B. 1966. bi-m. $564 (foreign $667) (effective 1996). Academic Press, Inc., Journal Division, 525 B St., Ste. 1900, San Diego, CA 92101-4490. TEL 619-230-1840. FAX 619-699-6800. (Subscr. to: Box 620000, Orlando, FL 32891-8340. TEL 800-543-9534) Eds. Adrian Bondy, U.S.R. Murty. adv.; charts; illus.; index. (back issues avail.) **Indexed:** Compumath, Curr.Cont., Ind.Sci.Rev., INSPEC, Math.R., Sci.Cit.Ind. **Document type:** academic/scholarly publication.
—BLDSC (4960.520000); Faxon; Genuine Article; SWETS; UnCover. **CCC.**
Supersedes in part: Journal of Combinatorial Theory (ISSN 0021-9800)
Description: Publishes original mathematical research dealing with theoretical and physical aspects of the study of finite and discrete structures in all branches of science. Series B is primarily concerned with graph theory and matroid theory.
Refereed Serial

519.5   NE   ISSN 0377-0427
QA1   CODEN: JCAMDI
JOURNAL OF COMPUTATIONAL AND APPLIED MATHEMATICS. (Text in English) 1975. 22/yr. fl. 3696($2254) (effective 1996). (Computational and Applied Mathematics Group) North-Holland (Subsidiary of: Elsevier Science B.V.), P.O. Box 211, 1000 AE Amsterdam, Netherlands. TEL 31-20-4853911. FAX 31-20-4853598. TELEX 18582 ESPA NL. (Subscr. in U.S. and Canada to: Elsevier Science Inc., Box 882, Madison Sq. Sta., New York, NY 10159. TEL 212-989-5800. FAX 212-633-3990) Ed.Bd. bk.rev.; bibl.; charts; index. (back issues avail.; reprint service avail. from SWZ) **Indexed:** Appl.Mech Rev., BMT, Compumath, Comput.Abstr., Cyb.Abstr., INSPEC, Int.Abstr.Oper.Res., Int.Aerosp.Abstr., Math.R. **Document type:** academic/scholarly publication.
—BLDSC (4963.450000); Ei; Faxon; Genuine Article; SWETS; UnCover. **CCC.**
Description: Publishes original papers describing new computational techniques for solving scientific problems.
Refereed Serial

510 310   US   ISSN 1061-8600
QA276.4
JOURNAL OF COMPUTATIONAL AND GRAPHICAL STATISTICS. 1992. q. $50. American Statistical Association, 1429 Duke St., Alexandria, VA 22314-3402. TEL 703-684-1221. FAX 703-684-2037. Ed. William Eddy. **Indexed:** Curr.Ind.Stat., Stat.Theor.Meth.Abstr. **Document type:** academic/scholarly publication.
—BLDSC (4963.451000); SWETS; UnCover. **CCC.**

510   CC   ISSN 0254-9409
   CODEN: JCMMEB
JOURNAL OF COMPUTATIONAL MATHEMATICS. Chinese edition: Jisuan Shuxue (ISSN 0254-7791) (Text in English) 1983. q. DM.460 (effective 1996). Science Press, Marketing and Sales Department, 16 Donghuangchenggen North St., Beijing 100717, People's Republic of China. TEL 4010642. FAX 4019810. (Dist. outside China by: V S P, P.O. Box 346, 3700 AH Zeist, Netherlands. TEL 31-30-6925790. FAX 31-30-6932081) Ed. Feng Kang. (back issues avail.) **Indexed:** INSPEC (1987-). **Document type:** academic/scholarly publication.
—BLDSC (4963.480000); Faxon; SWETS; UnCover.
Description: Presents numerical methods, analysis and applications from all branches of computational mathematics, including optimization, computational statistics, and problems in diverse fields of science and engineering.
Refereed Serial

510   US   ISSN 1068-3623
QA297
JOURNAL OF CONTEMPORARY MATHEMATICAL ANALYSIS. English translation of: Akademiya Nauk Armenii. Izvestiya. Seriya Matematika. 1979. bi-m. $870 (effective 1996). (Armenian Academy of Sciences, AI) Allerton Press, Inc., 150 Fifth Ave., New York, NY 10011. TEL 212-924-3950. FAX 212-463-9684. Ed. Rouben Ambartsumian. **Indexed:** Math.R. **Document type:** academic/scholarly publication.
—BLDSC (0414.240000); Faxon; SWETS. **CCC.**
Formerly: Soviet Journal of Contemporary Mathematical Analysis (ISSN 0735-2719)

652   US   ISSN 0933-2790
Z102.5   CODEN: JOCREQ
JOURNAL OF CRYPTOLOGY. 1989. q. $145 (effective 1996). (International Association for Cryptologic Research) Springer-Verlag, Journals, 175 Fifth Ave., New York, NY 10010. TEL 212-460-1500. FAX 212-474-6272. (N. American subscr. to: Journals Fulfillment Services, Box 2485, Secaucus, NJ 07096-2491. TEL 800-777-4643. FAX 201-348-4505; Elsewhere: Springer-Verlag, Heidelberger Platz 3, 1000 Berlin 33, Germany. TEL 030-8207-1. FAX 030-8214091) Ed. G. Brassard. (also avail. in microform from UMI; reprint service avail.) **Indexed:** INSPEC (1988-). **Document type:** academic/scholarly publication.
—BLDSC (4965.720000); Ei; Genuine Article; SWETS; UMI; UnCover. **CCC.**
Description: Publishes original research in cryptology, cryptography, cryptanalysis and related fields, including theoretical studies, applications and standards issues.
Refereed Serial

510   US   ISSN 1023-6198
▼**JOURNAL OF DIFFERENCE EQUATIONS AND APPLICATIONS.** 1994. 4/yr. 78 ECU (effective 1996). Gordon & Breach Science Publishers, c/o International Publishers Distributor, 820 Town Center Dr., Langhorne, PA 19047. TEL 215-750-2642; 800-545-8398. FAX 215-750-6343. (Subscr. to: International Publishers Distributor, P.O. Box 90, Reading, Berkshire RG1 8JL, England. TEL 44-173-456-8316) (back issues avail.) **Document type:** academic/scholarly publication.

510   US   ISSN 0022-0396
QA371   CODEN: JDEQAK
JOURNAL OF DIFFERENTIAL EQUATIONS. 1965. 18/yr. $1680 (foreign $1938) (effective 1996). Academic Press, Inc., Journal Division, 525 B St., Ste. 1900, San Diego, CA 92101-4495. TEL 619-230-1840. FAX 619-699-6800. (Subscr. to: Box 620000, Orlando, FL 32891-8340. TEL 800-543-9534) Ed. Jack K. Hale. adv.; charts. (back issues avail.) **Indexed:** Appl.Mech.Rev., Compumath, Curr.Cont., Ind.Sci.Rev., INSPEC, Math.R., Sci.Cit.Ind. **Document type:** academic/scholarly publication.
—BLDSC (4969.500000); Faxon; Genuine Article; SWETS; UnCover. **CCC.**
Description: Covers the theory and application of differential equations.
Refereed Serial

516   US   ISSN 0022-040X
QA641   CODEN: JDGEAS
JOURNAL OF DIFFERENTIAL GEOMETRY. 1967. 6/yr. $190 to non-members; members $48. Lehigh University, Box F 13, Bethlehem, PA 18015. TEL 215-865-1522. Ed. C.C. Hsiung. bk.rev. circ. 950. (also avail. in microform from PMC; back issues avail.) **Indexed:** Compumath, Math.R. **Document type:** academic/scholarly publication.
—Faxon; Genuine Article; SWETS; UnCover.

JOURNAL OF DYNAMICAL AND CONTROL SYSTEMS. see ENGINEERING — Industrial Engineering

510   US   ISSN 1040-7294
QA370   CODEN: JDDEEH
JOURNAL OF DYNAMICS AND DIFFERENTIAL EQUATIONS. 1989. q. $225 (foreign $265) (effective 1996). Plenum Publishing Corp., 233 Spring St., New York, NY 10013-1578. TEL 212-620-8000. FAX 212-463-0742. TELEX 23-421139. Ed. George R. Sell. adv. (also avail. in microform from JSC; back issues avail.) **Indexed:** INSPEC (1991-). **Document type:** academic/scholarly publication.
—BLDSC (4970.650000); Faxon; SWETS; UMI; UnCover. **CCC.**
Description: Original papers covering topics including attractors, bifurcation theory, dichotomies, ergodic theory, finite and infinite dimensional systems.
Refereed Serial

JOURNAL OF ECONOMETRICS. see BUSINESS AND ECONOMICS — Economic Systems And Theories, Economic History

JOURNAL OF EMPIRICAL FINANCE. see BUSINESS AND ECONOMICS — Banking And Finance

JOURNAL OF ENGINEERING MATHEMATICS. see ENGINEERING

515   US   ISSN 0022-1236
QA320   CODEN: JFUAAW
JOURNAL OF FUNCTIONAL ANALYSIS. (Text in English, French) 1967. 16/yr. $1498 (foreign $1736)(effective 1996). Academic Press, Inc., Journal Division, 525 B St., Ste. 1900, San Diego, CA 92101-4495. TEL 619-230-1840. FAX 619-699-6800. (Subscr. to: Box 620000, Orlando, FL 32891-8340. TEL 800-543-9534) Ed. Irving Segal. (back issues avail.; reprint service avail. from SWZ) **Indexed:** Compumath, Curr.Cont., Ind.Sci.Rev., INSPEC, Math.R., Sci.Cit.Ind., Stat.Theor.Meth.Abstr. **Document type:** academic/scholarly publication.
—Faxon; Genuine Article; SWETS; UnCover. **CCC.**
Description: Presents original research papers in all scientific disciplines in which functional analysis plays a role.
Refereed Serial

MATHEMATICS

511   US   ISSN 1066-8950
QA248
JOURNAL OF FUZZY MATHEMATICS. 1993. 3/yr. $120 to individuals (foreign $133); institutions $358 (foreign $398) (effective 1996). International Fuzzy Mathematics Institute, Box 639, San Gabriel, CA 91778. TEL 818-458-1829. FAX 818-282-7775. Ed. Hu Cheng-ming. Document type: academic/scholarly publication.
—BLDSC (4986.920000).
    Description: Encourages the development of theory and application in the fuzzy realm.

510   US   ISSN 1050-6926
QA299.6   CODEN: JGANEG
JOURNAL OF GEOMETRIC ANALYSIS. bi-m. $99.95 to individuals; institutions $225. American Mathematical Society, Box 6248, Providence, RI 02940-6248. TEL 401-455-4000; 800-321-4267. FAX 401-331-3848. **Document type:** academic/scholarly publication.
—BLDSC (4994.400000); Ei; Genuine Article; SWETS; UnCover. **CCC.**
    Description: Provides a forum for mathematical work that exhibits an interface among classical analytic methods, geometry, and partial differential equations.

516   SZ   ISSN 0047-2468
QA443
JOURNAL OF GEOMETRY. (Text in English and German) 1971. 6/yr. 416.40 SFr. (foreign 430.50 SFr.). Birkhaeuser Verlag, P.O. Box 133, CH-4010 Basel, Switzerland. TEL 061-2717400. FAX 061-2717666. (Dist. in N. America by: Springer-Verlag, Mercedes Distribution Center, 160 Imlay St., Brooklyn, NY 11231, USA) Ed. H.-J. Kroll. abstr.; index. circ. 1,000. (reprint service avail. from SWZ) **Indexed:** Math.R. Document type: academic/scholarly publication.
—Faxon; SWETS; UMI; UnCover. **CCC.**

510 536   NE   ISSN 0393-0440
                                 CODEN: JGPHE5
JOURNAL OF GEOMETRY AND PHYSICS. (Text in English) 1984-1987; resumed vol.8, 1991. m. fl.1122($684) (effective 1996). North-Holland (Subsidiary of: Elsevier Science B.V.), P.O. Box 211, 1000 AE Amsterdam, Netherlands. TEL 31-20-4853911. FAX 31-20-4853598. TELEX 18582 ESPA NL. (Subscr. in U.S. and Canada to: Elsevier Science Inc., Box 882, Madison Sq. Sta., New York, NY 10159. TEL 212-989-5800. FAX 212-633-3990) Ed. Marco Modugno. (also avail. in microform from UMI; back issues avail.) **Indexed:** INSPEC (1992-). Document type: academic/scholarly publication.
—BLDSC (4994.700000); Faxon; Genuine Article; SWETS; UnCover. **CCC.**
    Description: Designed to promote interaction between geometry and physics. Includes articles on mathematical physics, pure geometry and physics.
Refereed Serial

511.5   US   ISSN 0364-9024
QA166   CODEN: JGTHDO
JOURNAL OF GRAPH THEORY. 1976. m. $792 (foreign $978) (effective 1996). John Wiley & Sons, Inc., Journals, 605 Third Ave., New York, NY 10158. TEL 212-850-6645. FAX 212-850-6021. TELEX 12-7063. E-mail: SUBINFO@JWILEY.COM. (Subscr. outside the Americas to: John Wiley & Sons Ltd., Baffins Ln., Chichester, W. Sussex PO19 1UD, England. TEL 44-1243-779777. FAX 44-1243-776128) Eds. Fan Chung, Carsten Thomassen. adv.; index. circ. 700. (also avail. in microform from UMI; back issues avail.) **Indexed:** Compumath, Curr.Cont., Ind.Sci.Rev., INSPEC, Int.Abstr.Oper.Res., Math.R., Sci.Cit.Ind. **Document type:** academic/scholarly publication.
—BLDSC (4996.450000); Faxon; Genuine Article; SWETS; UMI; UnCover. **CCC.**
    Description: Covers a variety of topics in graph structures, as well as graph algorithms, with theoretical emphasis. Also covers related areas in combinatorics and other math sciences.
Refereed Serial

003 519   II   ISSN 0252-2667
QA75.5   CODEN: JIOSDC
JOURNAL OF INFORMATION & OPTIMIZATION SCIENCES. (Text in English) 1980. 3/yr. Rs.450($90) (effective 1995 & 1996). Analytic Publishing Co., F-23 Model Town, Delhi-110009, India. TEL 7129726. Ed. Bal Kishan Dass. bk.rev.; circ. 330 (paid). (back issues avail.) **Indexed:** Biostat., INSPEC (1980-), Int.Abstr.Oper.Res., Math.R., Oper.Res.Manage.Sci., Qual.Contr.Appl.Stat., Zent.Math. Document type: academic/scholarly publication.
—BLDSC (5006.745000); Ei; Faxon; UnCover. **CCC.**
    Description: Devoted to advances in information sciences, optimization sciences, and related aspects as discrete math., computer science and statistics.
Refereed Serial

510 620   US   ISSN 1064-1246
TJ217.5.   CODEN: JIFSE2
JOURNAL OF INTELLIGENT AND FUZZY SYSTEMS. 1993. q. $336 (foreign $398) (effective 1996). John Wiley & Sons, Inc., Journals, 605 Third Ave., New York, NY 10158. TEL 212-850-6645. FAX 212-850-6021. TELEX 12-7068. E-mail: SUBINFO@JWILEY.COM. (Subscr. outside the Americas to: John Wiley & Sons Ltd., Baffins Ln., Chichester, W. Sussex PO19 1UD, England. TEL 44-1243-779777. FAX 44-1243-776128) Eds. Mohammad Jamshidi, Timothy Ross. (also avail. in microform from UMI; back issues avail.) **Document type:** academic/scholarly publication.
—BLDSC (5007.538480); SWETS.
    Description: Focuses on current and potential applications, case studies, and education in intelligent or fuzzy systems for engineering and related technical fields.
Refereed Serial

510   NE   ISSN 0928-0219
                                 CODEN: JIVPE5
JOURNAL OF INVERSE AND ILL-POSED PROBLEMS. (Text in English) 1993. bi-m. DM.790 (effective 1996). V S P, P.O. Box 346, 3700 AH Zeist, Netherlands. TEL 31-30-6925790. FAX 31-30-6932081. E-mail: 100341.2372@compuserve.com. Ed. M.M. Lavrent'ev. (back issues avail.) **Document type:** academic/scholarly publication.
—BLDSC (5007.900000); Ei.
    Description: Publishes original articles on the theory and application of inverse and ill-posed problems.
Refereed Serial

510   SI   ISSN 0218-2165
QA612.2
JOURNAL OF KNOT THEORY AND ITS RAMIFICATIONS. (Text in English) 1992. q. $240 to institutions of developed countries; individuals and developing countries $120. World Scientific Publishing Co. Pte. Ltd., Farrer Rd., P.O. Box 128, Singapore 9128, Singapore. TEL 3826553. FAX 3825919. TELEX RS 28561 WSPC. (U.K. addr.: 73 Lynton Mead, Totteridge, London N20 8DH, England. TEL 44-181-4462461; U.S. addr.: 1060 Main St., Ste. 1B, River Edge, NJ 07661. TEL 800-227-7562) **Document type:** academic/scholarly publication.
—BLDSC (5009.855000); SWETS; UnCover.
    Description: Provides a forum for new developments in knot theory, particularly developments that create connections between knot theory and other aspects of mathematics and natural sciences.

515   US   ISSN 0022-247X
QA1   CODEN: JMANAK
JOURNAL OF MATHEMATICAL ANALYSIS AND APPLICATIONS. 1960. 24/yr. $2498 (foreign $2900) (effective 1996). Academic Press, Inc., Journal Division, 525 B St., Ste. 1900, San Diego, CA 92101-4495. TEL 619-230-1840. FAX 619-699-6800. (Subscr. to: Box 620000, Orlando, FL 32891-8340. TEL 800-543-9534) Eds. William F. Ames, George Leitmann. adv.; charts; index. (back issues avail.) **Indexed:** Appl.Mech.Rev., Compumath, Curr.Cont., Eng.Ind., Ind.Sci.Rev., INIS Atomind., INSPEC, Int.Abstr.Oper.Res., Math.R., Risk Abstr., Sci.Cit.Ind. Document type: academic/scholarly publication.
—BLDSC (5012.350000); Ei; Faxon; Genuine Article; SWETS; UnCover. **CCC.**
    Description: Presents mathematical papers that treat classical analysis and its numerous applications.
Refereed Serial

510 530   II   ISSN 0047-2557
QC20   CODEN: JMPSB9
JOURNAL OF MATHEMATICAL AND PHYSICAL SCIENCES. (Text in English) 1967. bi-m. Rs.200($50) to individuals; institutions Rs.500($90). Indian Institute of Technology, Madras, Central Library, IIT, Madras 600 036, India. TEL 044-235-1365. FAX 044-2350509. TELEX 041-8926 IITM IN. E-mail: Lib@iitm.ernet.in. Ed. G. Subramanian. (back issues avail.) **Indexed:** Appl.Mech.Rev., Curr.Cont., INIS Atomind., INSPEC, Int.Aerosp.Abstr., Math.R., Zent.Math.
—Faxon; UnCover.

510   US   ISSN 0732-3123
QA11.A1
JOURNAL OF MATHEMATICAL BEHAVIOR. 1984. q. $50 to individuals; institutions $140. Ablex Publishing Corporation, 355 Chestnut St., Norwood, NJ 07648. TEL 201-767-8450. FAX 201-767-6717. TELEX 135-393. Ed. Robert B. Davis. index. circ. 400. **Indexed:** Psychol.Abstr. (1971-).
—BLDSC (5012.372000); Faxon; SWETS; UnCover. **CCC.**
Refereed Serial

JOURNAL OF MATHEMATICAL BIOLOGY. see *BIOLOGY*

519   NE   ISSN 0259-9791
QD39.3.M3   CODEN: JMCHEG
JOURNAL OF MATHEMATICAL CHEMISTRY. (Text in English) 1987. 8/yr. (in 2 vols., 4 nos./vol.). 996 SFr. (effective 1996). Baltzer Science Publishers B.V., Asterweg 1A, 1031 HL Amsterdam, Netherlands. TEL 31-20-6370061. FAX 31-20-6323651. E-mail: publish@baltzer.nl. (Subscr in N. America to: Baltzer Science Publishers, Box 8577, Red Bank, NJ 07701-8577) Ed. P.G. Mezey. adv. **Document type:** academic/scholarly publication.
—BLDSC (5012.376000); CASDDS; Faxon; Genuine Article; SWETS. **CCC.**
    Description: Special attention is given to topics such as the topology of chemical knots, theory of chemical clusters, study of chirality, chemical kinetics and mathematical analysis of polymer structure.

JOURNAL OF MATHEMATICAL ECONOMICS. see *BUSINESS AND ECONOMICS — Economic Systems And Theories, Economic History*

JOURNAL OF MATHEMATICAL IMAGING AND VISION. see *MATHEMATICS — Computer Applications*

JOURNAL OF MATHEMATICAL PHYSICS. see *PHYSICS*

JOURNAL OF MATHEMATICAL PSYCHOLOGY. see *PSYCHOLOGY*

510   JA   ISSN 1340-5705
QA1
JOURNAL OF MATHEMATICAL SCIENCES. (Text in English, French, German) 1925. 3/yr. price varies. University of Tokyo, Department of Mathematical Sciences, 3-1, Hongo 7-chome, Bunkyo-ku, Tokyo 113, Japan. TEL 03-3816-1303. (Subscr. to: Maruzen Co., Ltd., 3-10, Nihonbashi 2-chome, Chuo-ku, Tokyo 103, Japan; Overseas subscr. to: International Division, P.O. Box 5050, Tokyo International, Tokyo 100-31, Japan) Ed. Yukio Matsumoto. illus. circ. 850. **Indexed:** Chem.Abstr., INSPEC (1968-), JCT, JTA, Math.R. Document type: academic/scholarly publication.
—BLDSC (5012.445000); UnCover.
    Supersedes (in 1994): University of Tokyo. Faculty of Science. Journal. Section 1A: Mathematics - Tokyo Daigaku Rigakubu Kiyo, Dai-1-rui A, Sugaku (ISSN 0040-8980); Supersedes in part: University of Tokyo. Faculty of Science. Journal. Section 1: Mathematics, Astronomy, Physics, Chemistry.

510   US   ISSN 1072-3374
QA1   CODEN: JMTSEW
JOURNAL OF MATHEMATICAL SCIENCES. 1973. 30/yr. $3445 (foreign $4030) (effective 1996). (Russian Academy of Sciences, Mathematical Institute - V.A. Steklova, RU) Plenum Publishing Corp., Consultants Bureau, 233 Spring St., New York, NY 10013-1578. TEL 212-620-8468. FAX 212-463-0742. TELEX 23-421139. (also avail. in microfilm from JSC; back issues avail.) **Indexed:** Comput.& Info.Sys., INIS Atomind., Math.R., Zent.Math. **Document type:** academic/scholarly publication.
—Faxon; SWETS; UMI; UnCover. **CCC.**
Formerly (until 1994): Journal of Soviet Mathematics (ISSN 0090-4104); Which was formed by the merger of: Progress in Mathematics (ISSN 0079-6433); Seminars in Mathematics (ISSN 0080-8873)
Description: English translation from several Russian mathematical journals.
Refereed Serial

JOURNAL OF MATHEMATICAL SOCIOLOGY. see *SOCIOLOGY*

510   JA   ISSN 0075-4293
QA1   CODEN: JMTUBZ
JOURNAL OF MATHEMATICS. (Text in English) 1967. a. exchange basis. Tokushima Daigaku, Sogo Kagakubu - Tokushima University, Faculty of Integrated Arts and Sciences, 1-1, Minami-Josanjima-cho, Tokushima-shi, Toshima-ken 770, Japan. **Indexed:** Math.R.
—BLDSC (5012.490000); UnCover.

519.53   US   ISSN 0047-259X
QA278   CODEN: JMVAAI
JOURNAL OF MULTIVARIATE ANALYSIS; an international journal. (Text in English, French, German) 1971. 8/yr. $693 (foreign $827) (effective 1996). Academic Press, Inc., Journal Division, 525 B St., Ste. 1900, San Diego, CA 92101-4495. TEL 619-230-1840. FAX 619-699-6800. (Subscr. to: Box 620000, Orlando, FL 32891-8340. TEL 800-543-9534) Ed. Barry Arnold. adv. (back issues avail.; reprint service avail. from SWZ) **Indexed:** Compumath, Curr.Cont., Curr.Ind.Stat., Eng.Ind., Ind.Sci.Rev., INSPEC, J.Cont.Quant.Meth., Math.R., Stat.Theor.Meth.Abstr. **Document type:** academic/scholarly publication.
—BLDSC (5021.080000); Ei; Faxon; Genuine Article; SWETS; UnCover. **CCC.**
Description: Presents articles on fundamental theoretical aspects of multivariate analysis as well as on other aspects concerned with applications of new theoretical methods.
Refereed Serial

516   UK   ISSN 0963-2654
JOURNAL OF NATURAL GEOMETRY. 1992. q. £100 (Europe £120; elsewhere £140). University of London, Mathematical Research Unit, Birbeck College, 7-15 Gresse St., London W1P 1PA, England. TEL 0171-580-7710. FAX 0171-631-6270. E-mail: c.sharma@mru.bbk.ac.uk. Ed. Chandra Shekhar Sharma. adv. **Document type:** academic/scholarly publication.
—BLDSC (5021.197000).
Description: Dedicated to bringing unity through simplicity in the mathematics of natural structures.
Refereed Serial

JOURNAL OF NATURAL SCIENCES AND MATHEMATICS. see *SCIENCES: COMPREHENSIVE WORKS*

510   US   ISSN 0022-314X
QA241   CODEN: JNUTA9
JOURNAL OF NUMBER THEORY. 1969. m. $943 (foreign $1118) (effective 1996). Academic Press, Inc., Journal Division, 525 B St., Ste. 1900, San Diego, CA 92101-4495. TEL 619-230-1840. FAX 619-699-6800. (Subscr. to: Box 620000, Orlando, FL 32891-8340. TEL 800-543-9534) Ed. Alan C. Woods. adv. (back issues avail.) **Indexed:** Compumath, Curr.Cont., Ind.Sci.Rev., INSPEC, Math.R. **Document type:** academic/scholarly publication.
—Faxon; Genuine Article; SWETS; UnCover. **CCC.**
Description: Features selected research articles that represent the broad spectrum of interest in contemporary number theory and allied areas.
Refereed Serial

510   RM   ISSN 0379-4024
JOURNAL OF OPERATOR THEORY. (Text in English, French, German or Russian) 1983. 4/yr. $80. (Increst, Department of Mathematics) Editura Academiei Romane, Calea Victoriei 125, 79717 Bucharest, Rumania. (Dist. by: Rompresfilatelia, Calea Grivitei 64-66, P.O. Box 12-201, 78104 Bucharest, Rumania) Ed.Bd. **Indexed:** Compumath, Math.R.
—Faxon; SWETS; UnCover.

519   US   ISSN 0022-3239
QA402.5   CODEN: JOTABN
JOURNAL OF OPTIMIZATION THEORY AND APPLICATIONS. m. $995 (foreign $1165) (effective 1996). Plenum Publishing Corp., 233 Spring St., New York, NY 10013-1578. TEL 212-620-8000. FAX 212-463-0742. TELEX 23-421139. Ed. Angelo Miele. adv.; bibl.; charts; illus. (also avail. in microfilm from JSC; back issues avail.) **Indexed:** Appl.Mech.Rev., Compumath, Comput.Cont., Curr.Cont., Cyb.Abstr., Ind.Sci.Rev., INIS Atomind., INSPEC, Int.Aerosp.Abstr., Math.R., Sci.Cit.Ind., Zent.Math. **Document type:** academic/scholarly publication.
—BLDSC (5026.370000); Ei; Faxon; Genuine Article; SWETS; UMI; UnCover. **CCC.**
Refereed Serial

JOURNAL OF PARAMETRICS. see *BUSINESS AND ECONOMICS — Accounting*

510   CC   ISSN 1000-940X
QA370   CODEN: JPDEEX
JOURNAL OF PARTIAL DIFFERENTIAL EQUATIONS. 1988. 4/yr. $160. (Zhengzhou University, Institute of Mathematics, CC) International Academic Publishers (IAP), 137 Chaonei Dajie, Beijing 100010, People's Republic of China. TEL 86-1-4035533. FAX 86-1-5063101. TELEX 22313 CPC CN. Ed. Jiang Lishang. circ. 110. (back issues avail.) **Document type:** academic/scholarly publication.
—BLDSC (5029.280000); Faxon. **CCC.**

JOURNAL OF PUBLIC ECONOMICS. see *BUSINESS AND ECONOMICS — Economic Systems And Theories, Economic History*

512 519   NE   ISSN 0022-4049
QA150   CODEN: JPAAA2
JOURNAL OF PURE AND APPLIED ALGEBRA. 1971. 24/yr. fl.3040($1854) (effective 1996). North-Holland (Subsidiary of: Elsevier Science B.V.), P.O. Box 211, 1000 AE Amsterdam, Netherlands. TEL 31-20-4853911. FAX 31-20-4853598. TELEX 18582 ESPA NL. (Subscr. in U.S. and Canada to: Elsevier Science Inc., Box 882, Madison Sq. Sta., New York, NY 10159. TEL 212-989-5800. FAX 212-633-3990) Ed.Bd. cum.index: vols. 1-10, 1977. (also avail. in microfilm from UMI; back issues avail.; reprint service avail. from SWZ) **Indexed:** Compumath, Curr.Cont., Ind.Sci.Rev., Math.R., Zent.Math. **Document type:** academic/scholarly publication.
—BLDSC (5043.675000); Faxon; Genuine Article; SWETS; UnCover. **CCC.**
Description: Publishes papers in algebra of general mathematical interest.
Refereed Serial

510   US   ISSN 0022-412X
QA95   CODEN: JRMAB9
JOURNAL OF RECREATIONAL MATHEMATICS. 1968. q. $88 (effective 1996). Baywood Publishing Co., Inc., 26 Austin Ave., Box 337, Amityville, NY 11701. TEL 516-691-1270. FAX 516-691-1770. Ed. Joseph S. Madachy. bk.rev.; charts; illus. (back issues avail.) **Indexed:** Gen.Sci.Ind., Math.R. **Document type:** academic/scholarly publication.
—BLDSC (5048.180000); Faxon; SWETS; UnCover.
Description: Contains thought-provoking, stimulating, wit-sharpening games, puzzles, and articles.

JOURNAL OF REGIONAL CRITICISM. see *ART*

JOURNAL OF SCIENCE AND MATHEMATICS EDUCATION IN SOUTHEAST ASIA. see *EDUCATION — Teaching Methods And Curriculum*

JOURNAL OF STATISTICAL PLANNING AND INFERENCE. see *STATISTICS*

JOURNAL OF STRUCTURAL LEARNING. see *PSYCHOLOGY*

JOURNAL OF SYMBOLIC LOGIC. see *PHILOSOPHY*

510   US   ISSN 0894-9840
QA273.A1   CODEN: JTPREO
JOURNAL OF THEORETICAL PROBABILITY. 1988. q. $295 (foreign $345) (effective 1996). Plenum Publishing Corp., 233 Spring St., New York, NY 10013-1578. TEL 212-620-8000. FAX 212-463-0742. TELEX 23-421139. Ed. A. Mukherjea. adv. (also avail. in microfilm from JSC; back issues avail.) **Indexed:** Stat.Theor.Meth.Abstr. **Document type:** academic/scholarly publication.
—BLDSC (5069.075700); Faxon; SWETS; UMI; UnCover. **CCC.**
Refereed Serial

510 378   US   ISSN 0022-5339
QA1
JOURNAL OF UNDERGRADUATE MATHEMATICS. 1969. s-a. $3 to individuals; libraries $6. Guilford College, Department of Mathematics, Greensboro, NC 27410. Ed. J. R. Boyd. index. **Document type:** academic/scholarly publication.
—Faxon; SWETS; UnCover.
Refereed Serial

510   FI   ISSN 0075-4641
JYVASKYLAN YLIOPISTO. MATEMATIIKAN LAITOS. REPORT. 1967. irreg. exchange basis only. University of Jyvaskyla, Department of Mathematics - Jyvaskylan Yliopisto, P.O. Box 35, FIN-40351 Jyvaskyla, Finland. FAX 358-41-602701. Ed. Pertti Mattila. **Indexed:** Math.R., Zent.Math. **Document type:** academic/scholarly publication.
—BLDSC (7620.992000).
Description: Publication including studies in the whole field of mathematics. Each issue devoted to one single topic.

510   NE   ISSN 0920-3036
QA612.33   CODEN: KTHEEO
K - THEORY; interdisciplinary journal for the development, application and influence of K-theory in the mathematical sciences. (Text in English) 1987. bi-m. fl.651 to institutions; $418 to institutions in U.S. (effective 1996). Kluwer Academic Publishers, Postbus 17, 3300 AA Dordrecht, Netherlands. TEL 31-78-392392. FAX 31-78-392254. TELEX 29245 KAPG NL. E-mail: SERVICES@WKAP.NL. (Dist. by: Kluwer Academic Publishing Group, P.O. Box 322, 3300 AH Dordrecht, Netherlands. TEL 31-78-392392. FAX 31-78-546474; N. America dist. addr.: Box 358, Accord Sta., Hinhgam, MA 02018-0358. TEL 617-871-6600. FAX 617-871-6528) Ed. A. Bak. (also avail. in microform from UMI; back issues avail.; reprint service avail. from SWZ) **Indexed:** Math.R., Zent.Math. **Document type:** academic/scholarly publication.
—BLDSC (5079.080000); Faxon; SWETS; UMI; UnCover. **CCC.**
Refereed Serial

KAGOSHIMA DAIGAKU RIGAKUBU KIYO. SUGAKU, BUTSURIGAKU, KAGAKU/KAGOSHIMA UNIVERSITY. FACULTY OF SCIENCE. REPORTS. MATHEMATICS, PHYSICS, CHEMISTRY. see *SCIENCES: COMPREHENSIVE WORKS*

510   JA
KEIO UNIVERSITY. FACULTY OF SCIENCE AND TECHNOLOGY. DEPARTMENT OF MATHEMATICS. RESEARCH REPORT. (Text and summaries in English) irreg. Keio Gijuku Daigaku, Rikogakubu, Suri Kagakka - Keio University, Faculty of Science and Technology, Department of Mathematics, 14-1, Hiyoshi 3-chome, Kohoku-ku, Yokohama-shi, Kanagawa-ken 223, Japan. **Document type:** academic/scholarly publication.

KEIRYO KOKUGO GAKKAI/MATHEMATICAL LINGUISTICS. see *LINGUISTICS*

KEISANKI TOKEIGAKU/BULLETIN OF THE COMPUTATIONAL STATISTICS OF JAPAN. see *STATISTICS*

510   KR
KHAR'KOVSKII GOSUDARSTVENNYI UNIVERSITET. MATEMATIKA I MEKHANIKA. (Subseries of: Khar'kovskii Gosudarstvennyi Universitet. Vestnik) 1965. irreg. 1 Rub. per issue. Izdatel'stvo Vysshaya Shkola, Khar'kovskoe Otdelenie, Universitetskaya 16, 310003 Kharkov, Ukraine. Ed. I. Tarapov. circ. 500.

MATHEMATICS

510   NE   ISSN 0927-4529
KLUWER TEXTS IN THE MATHEMATICAL SCIENCES. 1986. irreg., latest 1992. price varies. Kluwer Academic Publishers, Postbus 17, 3300 AA Dordrecht, Netherlands. TEL 31-78-392392. FAX 31-78-392254. TELEX 29245 KAPG NL. (Dist. by: Kluwer Academic Publishers Group, P.O. Box 322, 3300 AH Dordrecht, Netherlands. TEL 31-78-392392. FAX 31-78-546474; N. America dist. addr.: Box 358, Accord Sta., Hingham, MA 02018-0358. TEL 617-871-6600. FAX 617-871-6528) (back issues avail.) **Indexed:** INSPEC. **Document type:** monographic series.
—BLDSC (5099.740000).
Formerly (until 1992): Reidel Texts in the Mathematical Sciences (ISSN 0921-9315)
Refereed Serial

510   JA   ISSN 0289-9051
QA1
KOBE JOURNAL OF MATHEMATICS. (Text in English) 1984. s-a. exchange basis. Kobe University, Association for Mathematical Science, 2-1, Tsurukabuto 1-chome, Nada-ku, Kobe-shi, Hyogo-ken 657, Japan. TEL 078-881-1212. FAX 078-803-0830. Ed. Yuzuru Kakuda. **Document type:** academic/scholarly publication.
—BLDSC (5100.579700).

510   JA   ISSN 0389-0252
QA1
KOCHI UNIVERSITY. FACULTY OF SCIENCE. MEMOIRS. SERIES A, MATHEMATICS/KOCHI DAIGAKU RIGAKUBU KIYO. SUGAKU. (Text in English) 1980. a. Kochi University, Faculty of Science - Kochi Daigaku Rigakubu, 5-1, Akebono-cho 2-chome, Kochi-shi, Kochi-ken 780, Japan. Ed. Jun-iti Umehara. **Document type:** academic/scholarly publication.
—BLDSC (5597.830000); UnCover.

510   JA   ISSN 0386-5991
QA1
KODAI MATHEMATICAL JOURNAL. (Text mainly in English, occasionally in German and French) 1949. 3/yr. 25000 Yen($303) (effective 1995). Tokyo Kogyo Daigaku, Rigakubu Sugaku Kyoshitsu - Tokyo Institute of Technology, Faculty of Science, Department of Mathematics, 12-1 Ookayama 2-chome, Meguro-ku, Tokyo 152, Japan. TEL 81-3-5734-2220. FAX 81-3-5734-2738. (Subscr. to: Kinokuniya Company Ltd., Shinjuku 3-chome, Shinjuku-ku, Tokyo 163-91, Japan) Ed.Bd. circ. 520. **Indexed:** Math.R. **Document type:** academic/scholarly publication.
—Faxon; UnCover.
Formerly (until 1978): Kodai Mathematical Seminar Reports (ISSN 0023-2599)

530 510   DK   ISSN 0023-3323
AS281   CODEN: KDVSAK
KONGELIGE DANSKE VIDENSKABERNES SELSKAB. MATEMATISK - FYSISKE MEDDELELSER. (Text in English, French, German) 1919. irreg., vol.44, no.2, 1995. price varies. Kongelige Danske Videnskabernes Selskab - Royal Danish Academy of Sciences and Letters, H.C. Andersens 35, DK-1553 Copenhagen V, Denmark. TEL 45-33-12-85-70. FAX 45-33-12-93-87. (Dist. by: Munksgaard Export and Subscription Service, P.O. Box 2148, Noerre Soegade 35, DK-1060 Copenhagen K, Denmark) bibl.; charts; illus.; index. **Indexed:** Chem.Abstr., INSPEC (1975-), Math.R., Met.Abstr. **Document type:** monographic series.
—BLDSC (5392.000000); CASDDS. **CCC.**

510 373   HU   ISSN 1215-9247
KOZEPISKOLAI MATEMATIKAI ES FIZIKAI LAPOK. 1947. 10/yr. Bolyai Janos Matematikai Tarsulat, Fo u. 68, II emelet 243, 1027 Budapest, Hungary. TEL 201-8682. Ed. Lugosi Erzsebet. **Document type:** academic/scholarly publication.
—BLDSC (5115.350000).
Formerly (until 1991): Kozepiskolai Matematikai Lapok (ISSN 0133-1833); Supersedes (1925-1939): Kozepiskolai Matematikai es Fizikai Lapok (ISSN 0200-9188); (1894-1914): Kozepiskolai Matematikai Lapok (ISSN 0200-917X)

510   UZ
KRAEVYE ZADACHI DLYA DIFFERENTSIAL'NYKH URAVNENII. 1971. irreg. 1.10 Rub. Akademiya Nauk Uzbekistana, Institut Matematiki im. V.I. Romanoskogo, Ul. Ul. Khodzhaeva 33, Akademgorodok, 700143 Tashkent, Uzbekistan.

510 530 540   JA   ISSN 0914-675X
QA1   CODEN: KJMAEZ
KUMAMOTO JOURNAL OF MATHEMATICS. (Text in English) a. Kumamoto Daigaku, Rigakubu Sugaku Kyoshitsu - Kumamoto University, Faculty of Science, Department of Mathematics, 39-1, Kurokami 2-chome, Kumamoto-shi, Kumamoto-ken 860, Japan. FAX 096-345-4196. Ed. Mitsuhiko Kohno. charts; stat. **Indexed:** GeoRef., INSPEC (1988-), JTA, Math.R. **Document type:** academic/scholarly publication.
—BLDSC (5121.685000).
Formerly: Kumamoto Journal of Science. Mathematics (ISSN 0385-6763); Supersedes in part: Kumamoto Journal of Science. Series A: Mathematics, Physics and Chemistry (ISSN 0023-5318)

KVANT. see *SCIENCES: COMPREHENSIVE WORKS*

510 500   JA   ISSN 0023-6101
CODEN: KKDSAD
KYOTO KYOIKU DAIGAKU KIYO. B. SHIZEN KAGAKU/KYOTO UNIVERSITY OF EDUCATION. BULLETIN. SERIES B: MATHEMATICS AND NATURAL SCIENCE. (Text in English, Japanese) 1951. s-a. exchange basis. Kyoto University of Education - Kyoto Kyoiku Daigaku, 1 Fukakusa Fujinomori-cho, Fushimi-ku, Kyoto 612, Japan. Ed.Bd. bibl.; charts. circ. 700. **Indexed:** Biol.Abstr., Chem.Abstr., INIS Atomind., Math.R. **Document type:** academic/scholarly publication.
—CASDDS; UnCover.
Formerly: Kyoto Gakugei University. Bulletin. Series B: Mathematics and Natural Science.

510   JA   ISSN 0023-608X
QA1   CODEN: JMKYAZ
KYOTO UNIVERSITY. JOURNAL OF MATHEMATICS/KYOTO DAIGAKU RIGAKUBU SUGAKU KIYO. (Text in European languages) 1961. 4/yr. price varies. Kyoto University, Department of Mathematics - Kyoto Daigaku Rigakubu Sugaku Kyoshitsu, Oiwake-cho, Kitashirakawa, Sakyo-ku, Kyoto-shi, Kyoto-fu 606, Japan. (Dist. by: Kinokuniya Bookstore Co. Ltd, 3-17-7 Shinjuku, Shinjuku-ku, Tokyo 160, Japan) circ. 900. **Indexed:** Compumath, Math.R., Sci.Cit.Ind. **Document type:** academic/scholarly publication.
—BLDSC (5012.460000); Faxon; SWETS; UnCover.

510   JA   ISSN 0287-9980
KYUSHU DAIGAKU KYOYOBU SUGAKU ZASSHI/KYUSHU UNIVERSITY. COLLEGE OF GENERAL EDUCATION. MATHEMATICAL REPORTS. (Text and summaries in English) a. Kyushu University, College of General Education, Department of Mathematics - Kyushu Daigaku Kyoyobu Sugaku Kyoshitsu, 2-1, Ropponmatsu 4-chome, Chuo-ku, Fukuoka-shi, Fukuoka-ken 810, Japan. TEL 092-731-8745. FAX 092-771-4161.

510 500   JA   ISSN 0454-8221
Q4   CODEN: BKTMAA
KYUSHU INSTITUTE OF TECHNOLOGY. BULLETIN: MATHEMATICS, NATURAL SCIENCE/KYUSHU KOGYO DAIGAKU KENKYU HOKOKU: SHIZEN KAGAKU. (Text in European languages) 1955. a. exchange basis. Kyushu Institute of Technology - Kyushu Kogyo Daigaku, Tobata, Kitakyushu 804, Japan. **Indexed:** INSPEC (1968-), Math.R.
—BLDSC (2601.530000); UnCover.

511   JA   ISSN 0373-6385
QA1   CODEN: MFKAAF
KYUSHU UNIVERSITY. FACULTY OF SCIENCE. MEMOIRS. SERIES A: MATHEMATICS/KYUSHU DAIGAKU RIGAKUBU KIYO A. SUGAKU. (Text in English, French, German) 1940. s-a. exchange basis. Kyushu University, Faculty of Science, Department of Mathematics - Kyushu Daigaku Rigakubu Sugaku Kyoshitsu, 10-1, Hakozaki 6-chome, Higashi-ku, Fukuoka-shi, Fukuoka-ken 812, Japan. circ. 700. **Indexed:** Deep Sea Res.& Oceanogr.Abstr., INSPEC, JCT, JTA, Met.Abstr.
—UnCover.

510 574   US   ISSN 0341-633X
CODEN: LNBMAH
LECTURE NOTES IN BIOMATHEMATICS. 1974. irreg. price varies. Springer-Verlag, 175 Fifth Ave., New York, NY 10010. TEL 212-460-1500. FAX 212-473-6272. (Also: Berlin, Heidelberg, Tokyo and Vienna) Ed. S. Levin. (reprint service avail. from ISI) **Indexed:** Biol.Abstr., Chem.Abstr, INSPEC. **Document type:** monographic series.
—CASDDS. **CCC.**

003 330   US   ISSN 0075-8442
LECTURE NOTES IN ECONOMICS AND MATHEMATICAL SYSTEMS; operations research, computer science, social science. 1968. irreg. price varies. Springer-Verlag, 175 Fifth Ave., New York, NY 10010. TEL 212-460-1500. FAX 212-473-6272. (Also: Berlin, Heidelberg, Tokyo and Vienna) Eds. M. Beckmann, W. Krelle. cum.index nos. 1-170. (reprint service avail. from ISI) **Indexed:** Compumath, Cyb.Abstr., INSPEC, SSCI. **Document type:** monographic series.
—BLDSC (5180.195000); Genuine Article.
Formerly (until 1971): Lecture Notes in Operations Research and Mathematical Systems; Which supersedes (1967-1968): Lecture Notes in Operations Research and Mathematical Economics; Lecture Notes in Operations Research and Mathematical Systems.

510   GW
LECTURE NOTES IN LOGIC. (Text in English) 1993. irreg. DM.44. Springer-Verlag, Heidelberger Platz 3, 14197 Berlin, Germany. TEL 030-8207-1. FAX 030-8214091. (Subscr. in N. America to: Springer-Verlag New York, Inc., 44 Hartz Way, Secaucus, NJ 07096-2491. TEL 201-348-4033. FAX 201-348-4505) Ed. T. Slaman. **Document type:** monographic series.

510   US   ISSN 0075-8434
QA3   CODEN: LNMAA2
LECTURE NOTES IN MATHEMATICS. (Text in English; occasionally in German and French) 1964. irreg. price varies. Springer-Verlag, 175 Fifth Ave., New York, NY 10010. TEL 212-460-1500. FAX 212-473-6272. (Also: Berlin, Heidelberg, Tokyo and Vienna) Eds. A. Dold, B. Eckmann. (reprint service avail. from ISI) **Indexed:** Compumath, INSPEC, Math.R. **Document type:** monographic series.
—BLDSC (5180.200000); Ei; Faxon; Genuine Article. **CCC.**

510   CN
LECTURE NOTES IN MATHEMATICS. 1972. irreg. price varies. Carleton University, Department of Mathematics and Statistics, Ottawa, Ont. K1S 5B6, Canada. TEL 613-788-2155. FAX 613-788-3536. **Indexed:** Math.R.
—BLDSC (3053.416400).
Former titles (until 1992): Carleton-Ottawa Mathematical Lecture Note Series (ISSN 0827-3669); (until 1985): Carleton Lecture Note Series (ISSN 0318-6288)

510   US   ISSN 0075-8469
LECTURE NOTES IN PURE AND APPLIED MATHEMATICS. 1971. irreg., vol.169, 1995. price varies. Marcel Dekker, Inc., 270 Madison Ave., New York, NY 10016. TEL 212-696-9000. FAX 212-685-4540. TELEX 421419. Ed.Bd.
—BLDSC (5180.370000); Ei.

510   US   ISSN 0075-8485
LECTURES IN APPLIED MATHEMATICS. 1959. irreg. price varies. American Mathematical Society, Box 6248, Providence, RI 02940-6248. TEL 401-455-4000. **Indexed:** Biol.Abstr., Math.R., Zent.Math. **Document type:** monographic series.
—BLDSC (5179.870000). **CCC.**

510 570   US   ISSN 0075-8523
CODEN: LMLSAA
LECTURES ON MATHEMATICS IN THE LIFE SCIENCES. 1968. irreg. price varies. American Mathematical Society, Box 6248, Providence, RI 02940-6248. TEL 401-455-4000. **Indexed:** Biol.Abstr., Chem.Abstr., Math.R., Zent.Math. **Document type:** monographic series.
—BLDSC (5179.980000); CASDDS. **CCC.**

510 370   GW
LEHRBUECHER UND MONOGRAPHIEN ZUR DIDAKTIK DER MATHEMATIK. 1985. irreg., vol.28, 1995. DM.48. Bibliographisches Institut und F.A. Brockhaus AG, Postfach 100311, 68003 Mannheim, Germany. TEL 0621-3901-01. FAX 0621-3901-389. Eds. N. Knoche, H. Scheid. **Document type:** monographic series.

510   IT
LETTERA PRISTEM. 1990. q. L.30000 (effective 1995). P.RI.ST.E.M. Centro Eleusi, Via Gobbi 5, 20136 Milan, Italy. TEL 39-2-58365113. FAX 39-2-58365112. Ed. Simonetta Di Sieno. adv.; bk.rev. circ. 3,000. **Document type:** newsletter.
Description: Contains notices of mathematics and the history of mathematics

LETTERS IN MATHEMATICAL PHYSICS; a journal for the rapid dissemination of short contributions in the field of mathematical physics. see PHYSICS

LEUVEN NOTES IN MATHEMATICAL AND THEORETICAL PHYSICS. SERIES A, MATHEMATICAL PHYSICS. see PHYSICS

510 US ISSN 0278-5307
QA1
LIBERTAS MATHEMATICA. (Text in English, French, German) 1981. a. $30 to individuals; institutions $60 (effective thru 1996). (American Romanian Academy of Arts and Sciences) A R A Publications (Arlington), Department of Mathematics, University of Texas, Box 19408, Arlington, TX 76019. TEL 817-794-5765. FAX 817-794-5802. E-mail: conrdun@utarlg.uta.edu. Ed. Constantin Corduneanu. bibl.; illus.; stat. circ. 250. (back issues avail.) **Document type:** academic/scholarly publication.
—BLDSC (5186.762500).
Refereed Serial

510 LI ISSN 0132-2818
QA1
LIETUVOS MATEMATIKOS RINKINYS/LITOVSKII MATEMATICHESKII SBORNIK. English translation: Lithuanian Mathematical Journal (US ISSN 0363-1672) (Text in Russian; summaries in English and Lithuanian) 1961. q. 15 Lt. per issue. Lietuvos Mokīsu Akademija, Matematikos if Informatikos Institutas - Lithuanian Academy of Sciences, Institute of Mathematics and Information Science, c/o Prof. E. Geciauskas, Akademijos 4, 2600 Vilnius, Lithuania. TEL 45-85-25. TELEX 261240 TLG SU. (Subscr. to: Lietuvos Postas, Laisvis pr. 58, 2600 Vilnius, Lithuania. TEL 228028) Ed. P. Kubilius. circ. 1,050. **Indexed:** M.L.A. **Document type:** academic/scholarly publication.
Description: Articles on probability theory and mathematical statistics, differential equations and theory of functions.

LIFETIME DATA ANALYSIS; an international journal devoted to the methods and applications of reliability and survival analysis. see INSURANCE

512 US ISSN 0024-3795
QA251 CODEN: LAAPAW
LINEAR ALGEBRA AND ITS APPLICATIONS. 1968. 54/yr. $2298 to institutions (effective 1996). Elsevier Science Inc., 655 Ave. of the Americas, New York, NY 10010. TEL 212-989-5800. FAX 212-633-3990. TELEX 420663 AEP UI. (Subscr. to: Box 882, Madison Sq. Sta., New York, NY 10159-0882) Eds. Richard Brualdi, Hans Schneider. adv.; bk.rev.; charts; illus.; index. (also avail. in microform from UMI; reprint service avail. from SWZ) **Indexed:** Compumath, Curr.Cont., Eng.Ind., Ind.Sci.Rev., INIS Atomind., INSPEC, Int.Aerosp.Abstr., Math.R., Ref.Zh. **Document type:** academic/scholarly publication.
—BLDSC (5221.110000); Ei; Faxon; Genuine Article; SWETS; UnCover. **CCC**.
Description: Provides information on the analytic, algebraic, combinatorial, and numerical aspects of linear algebra and matrix theory.
Refereed Serial

510 US ISSN 0308-1087
QA184 CODEN: LNMLAZ
LINEAR AND MULTILINEAR ALGEBRA. 12/yr. (in 3 vols., 4 nos./vol.). 313 ECU per vol. (effective 1996). Gordon and Breach Science Publishers, c/o International Publishers Distributor, 820 Town Center Dr., Langhorne, PA 19047. TEL 215-750-2642. FAX 215-750-6343. (Subscr. to: International Publishers Distributor, PO Box 90, Reading, Berkshire RG1 8JL, England. TEL 44-173-456-8316) Ed. William E. Watkins. adv.; bk.rev. (also avail. in microform) **Indexed:** Int.Abstr.Oper.Res., Math.R. **Document type:** academic/scholarly publication.
—Faxon; SWETS; UnCover. **CCC**.
Refereed Serial

510 US ISSN 0363-1672
QA1 CODEN: LMJTD6
LITHUANIAN MATHEMATICAL JOURNAL. English translation of: Litovskii Matematicheskii Sbornik (LI ISSN 0132-2818) 1973. q. $885 (foreign $1035) (effective 1996). Plenum Publishing Corp., Consultants Bureau, 233 Spring St., New York, NY 10013-1578. TEL 212-620-8468. FAX 212-463-0742. TELEX 23-421139. Ed. J. Kubilius. (also avail. in microfilm from JSC; back issues avail.) **Indexed:** Math.R. **Document type:** academic/scholarly publication.
—BLDSC (0415.590000); Faxon; SWETS; UMI. **CCC**.
Former titles: Lithuanian Mathematical Transactions (ISSN 0148-8279); Academy of Sciences of the Lithuanian S.S.R. Mathematical Transactions (ISSN 0094-1719)
Refereed Serial

510 UK ISSN 0024-6093
QA1 CODEN: LMSBBT
LONDON MATHEMATICAL SOCIETY. BULLETIN. 1969. bi-m. £149.75($291) (effective 1996). London Mathematical Society, Burlington House, Piccadilly, London W1V 0NL, England. TEL 0171-437-5377. FAX 0171-439-4629. (Subscr. to: Cambridge University Press, Edinburgh Bldg., Shaftesbury Rd., Cambridge CB2 2RU, England. TEL 01223-312393. FAX 01223-315052; N. American addr.: Cambridge University Press, Journals Dept., 40 W. 20th St., New York, NY 10011-4211. TEL 212-924-3900. FAX 212-691-3239) Eds. R.J. Archbold, J.R. Hubbuck. bk.rev.; bibl.; index. circ. 2,060. (also avail. in microform from UMI) **Indexed:** Compumath, Curr.Cont., Math.R., Sci.Cit.Ind., Zent.Math. **Document type:** academic/scholarly publication.
—Faxon; Genuine Article; SWETS; UMI; UnCover.
Refereed Serial

510 UK ISSN 0024-6107
QA1 CODEN: JLMSAK
LONDON MATHEMATICAL SOCIETY. JOURNAL. Key Title: Journal of the London Mathematical Society. 1926. bi-m. £314($610) (effective 1996). Cambridge University Press, Edinburgh House, Shaftesbury Rd., Cambridge CB2 2RU, England. TEL 01223-312393. FAX 01223-315052. TELEX 851817256. (N. American addr.: Cambridge University Press, Journals Dept., 40 W. 20th St., New York, NY 10011. TEL 212-924-3900. FAX 212-691-3239) Eds. P.J. Bushell, R.A. Fenn. adv. (also avail. in microfilm from PMC; back issues avail.) **Indexed:** Compumath. **Document type:** academic/scholarly publication.
—BLDSC (4818.000000); Faxon; Genuine Article; SWETS; UMI; UnCover.
Description: Covers number theory, algebra, analysis, differential equations, geometry and topology.

510 UK ISSN 0076-0552
CLASSED SEPARATELY
LONDON MATHEMATICAL SOCIETY. LECTURE NOTE SERIES. 1971. irreg., no.175, 1992. price varies. Cambridge University Press, Edinburgh Bldg., Shaftesbury Rd., Cambridge CB2 2RU, England. TEL 01223-312393. FAX 01223-315052. TELEX 851817256. (N. American addr.: Cambridge University Press, Journals Dept., 40 W. 20th St., New York, NY 10011. TEL 212-924-3900. FAX 212-691-3239) Ed. J.W.S. Cassels. index. **Indexed:** Math.R. **Document type:** monographic series.
—BLDSC (5293.900000).

510 US
LONDON MATHEMATICAL SOCIETY. MONOGRAPHS. 1970. irreg., latest 1985. Academic Press, Inc., 525 B St., Ste. 1900, San Diego, CA 92101-4495. TEL 619-231-0926. FAX 619-699-6715. (Subscr. to: Order Dept., 6277 Sea Harbor Dr., 4th Fl., Orlando, FL 32887. TEL 800-321-5068) Eds. P.M. Cohn, Barry E. Johnson. (reprint service avail. from ISI) **Indexed:** Math.R. **Document type:** monographic series.
Supersedes (1970-1985): L M S Monographs (ISSN 0076-0560)
Refereed Serial

510 UK ISSN 0024-6115
QA1 CODEN: PLMTAL
LONDON MATHEMATICAL SOCIETY. PROCEEDINGS. 1865. bi-m. £348($682) (effective 1996). Oxford University Press, Oxford Journals, Walton St., Oxford OX2 6DP, England. TEL 01865-267907. FAX 01865-267773. TELEX 837330-OXPRES-G. E-mail: jnlorders@oup.co.uk. (U.S. subscr. to: Oxford University Press Inc., 2001 Evans Rd., Cary, NC 27513. TEL 919-677-0977. FAX 919-677-1714) Ed. S. Brenner, C. Wall. adv.; bibl. circ. 1,400. (also avail. in microform from UMI,PMC) **Indexed:** Appl.Mech.Rev., Compumath, Curr.Cont., Math.R., Sci.Cit.Ind., Stat.Theor.Meth.Abstr. **Document type:** proceedings.
—BLDSC (6751.000000); Faxon; Genuine Article; SWETS; UMI; UnCover. **CCC**.
Description: Presents research papers in the fields of real and complex analysis, differential equations and related areas, topology, geometry, logic, probability and statistics, algebra, number theory, and combination theory.

510 UK
LONDON MATHEMATICAL SOCIETY NEWSLETTER. 1973. 11/yr. membership. London Mathematical Society, Burlington House, Picadily, London W1V 0NL, England. TEL 0171-437-5377. FAX 0171-439-4629. Ed. S.M. Oakes. adv.: B&W page £140; trim 190 x 120; adv. contact: S.M. Oakes. circ. 2,200. (back issues avail.) **Document type:** newsletter.

510 370 US ISSN 0731-2040
QA1
M A A FOCUS. 1981. bi-m. membership only. Mathematical Association of America, 1529 18th St., N.W., Washington, DC 20036. TEL 202-387-5200. Ed. Peter Renz. circ. 26,000. **Document type:** newsletter.

510 530 US ISSN 0275-7265
M M I PRESS POLYMER MONOGRAPH SERIES. irreg., latest vol.3. price varies. Harwood Academic Publishers, c/o International Publishers Distributor, 820 Town Center Dr., Langhorne, PA 19047. TEL 215-750-2642. FAX 215-750-6343. (Subscr. to: International Publishers Distributor, PO Box 90, Reading, Berkshire, RG1 8JL, England. TEL 44-173-456-8316) Ed. R. Breitmaier. (also avail. in microform) **Document type:** monographic series.
—BLDSC (5879.793200).

510 530 US ISSN 0195-3966
CODEN: MPSSDC
M M I PRESS SYMPOSIUM SERIES. 1980. irreg., latest vol.5. price varies. Harwood Academic Publishers, c/o International Publishers Distributor, 820 Town Center Dr., Langhorne, PA 19047. TEL 215-750-2642. FAX 215-750-6343. (Subscr. to: International Publishers Distributor, PO Box 90, Reading, Berkshire, RG1 8JL, England. TEL 44-173-456-8316) Ed. H.G. Elias. (also avail. in microform) **Indexed:** Chem.Abstr., INSPEC. **Document type:** monographic series.
—CASDDS. **CCC**.

510 US
M S U MATHEMATICS NEWSLETTER. 1958. 3/yr. $5. Montana State University, Mathematical Sciences Department, Bozeman, MT 59717. TEL 406-994-3601. Ed. Joe Gore. bk.rev.; circ. controlled. (processed) **Document type:** newsletter.
Formerly (until 1978): M S U Mathematics Letter (ISSN 0024-8479)

AL-MAJALLAH AL-IHSA'IYYAH AL-MISRIYYAH/EGYPTIAN STATISTICAL JOURNAL. see STATISTICS

MAKEDONSKA AKADEMIJA NA NAUKITE I UMETNOSTITE. ODDELENIE ZA MATEMATICKI I TEHNICKI NAUKI. PRILOZI/MACEDONIAN ACADEMY OF SCIENCES AND ARTS. SECTION OF MATHEMATICAL AND TECHNICAL SCIENCES. CONTRIBUTIONS. see SCIENCES: COMPREHENSIVE WORKS

510 MY ISSN 0126-6705
QA1
MALAYSIAN MATHEMATICAL SOCIETY. BULLETIN. (Text in English) 1970. 2/yr. $50. Malaysian Mathematical Society, c/o Department of Mathematics, University of Malaya, 59100 Kuala Lumpur, Malaysia. Ed. Chin Seong Tah. adv. circ. 500. **Indexed:** Math.R. **Document type:** bulletin.
—UnCover.

MATHEMATICS

510   GW   ISSN 0025-2611
QA1   CODEN: MSMHB2
MANUSCRIPTA MATHEMATICA. (Text in English) 1969. 12/yr. (in 3 vols., 4 nos./vol.). DM.1626($1181) (effective 1996). Springer-Verlag, Heidelberger Platz 3, 14197 Berlin, Germany. TEL 030-8207-0. FAX 030-8214091. E-mail: orders@springer.de. (Subscr. in N. America to: Springer-Verlag New York, Inc., 44 Hartz Way, Secaucus, NJ 07096-2491. TEL 201-348-4033. FAX 201-348-4505) Ed.Bd. adv.; bibl.; illus. (also avail. in microform from UMI; back issues avail.; reprint service avail. from ISI) **Indexed:** Compumath, Curr.Cont., Ind.Sci.Rev., Math R., Zent.Math. **Document type:** academic/scholarly publication.
—BLDSC (5368.300000); Faxon; Genuine Article; SWETS; UMI; UnCover. **CCC.**
Description: Provides a forum for the rapid publication of advances in mathematical research.

510   XR
MASARYK UNIVERSITY. FACULTY OF SCIENCES. SCRIPTA MATHEMATICS/SCRIPTA FACULTATIS SCIENTIARUM NATURALIUM UNIVERSITATIS MASARYKIANAE BRUNENSIS. MATHEMATICA. (Text in English, French, German and Russian) 1971. a. Masarykova Universita, Prirodovedecka Fakulta - Masaryk University, Faculty of Sciences, Kotlarska 2, 611 37 Brno, Czech Republic. **Indexed:** Math.R. **Document type:** academic/scholarly publication.
Formerly: Scripta Facultatis Scientiarum Naturalium Universitatis Purkynianae Brunensis: Mathematica (ISSN 0231-6021)

MATCH; communications in mathematical chemistry. see **CHEMISTRY**

MATEKON; translations of Russian and East European mathematical economics. see **BUSINESS AND ECONOMICS**

510   IT   ISSN 1120-9968
MATEMATICA E LA SUA DIDATTICA. 1987. 3/yr. L.40000 (effective 1995). Pitagora Scolastica, Via del Legatore 3, 40138 Bologna, Italy. FAX 39-51-535301. Dir. Bruno D'Amore. circ. 1,000. **Document type:** academic/scholarly publication.
Description: For the dissemination of ideas. Contributions from different aspects of mathematics, its history, fundamentals and didactic principals with no specific reference to any school level.
Refereed Serial

510 530   KR   ISSN 0130-9382
QC19.2
MATEMATICHESKAYA FIZIKA I FUNKTSIONAL'NYI ANALIZ. (Text in Russian; summaries in English) 1969. irreg. 1 Rub. (Akademiya Nauk Ukrainy, Fiziko-Tekhnicheskii Institut Nizkikh Temperatur) Vidavnitstvo Naukova Dumka, Vul. Tereshchenkivska 3, 252601 Kiev, Ukraine.

510   KR   ISSN 0233-7568
QC19.2
MATEMATICHESKAYA FIZIKA I NELINEINAYA MEKHANIKA; respublikanskiy mezhvedomstvennyi sbornik nauchnykh trudov. 1964. s-a. (Akademiya Nauk Ukrainy, Institut Matematiki) Vidavnitstvo Naukova Dumka, Vul. Tereshchenkivska 3, 252601 Kiev, Ukraine. TEL 044-224-4068. FAX 044-224-7060. (Dist. by: Mezhdunarodnaya Kniga, B. Yakimanka 39, 117049 Moscow, Russia) Ed. Yu.A. Mitropol'skii. **Indexed:** INSPEC, Int.Aerosp.Abstr., Math.R. **Document type:** academic/scholarly publication.
—BLDSC (0100.515000).
Formerly (until 1984): Matematicheskaya Fizika (ISSN 0542-9986)

510   KR   ISSN 0130-9420
QC19.2   CODEN: MMFPDJ
MATEMATICHESKIE METODY I FIZIKO-MEKHANICHESKIE POLYA; respublikanskii mezhvedomstvennyi sbornik nauchnykh trudov. (Text in Russian, Ukrainian) 1975. s-a. $80 (effective 1996). (Natsional'naya Akademiya Nauk Ukrainy, Institut Prikladnykh Problem Mekhaniki i Matematiki im. Y.S. Podstrigacha) Vidavnitstvo Naukova Dumka, Vul. Tereshchenkivska 3, 252601 Kiev, Ukraine. (Dist. by: Mezhdunarodnaya Kniga, B. Yakimanka 39, 117049 Moscow, Russia) Ed. H.S. Kit. **Indexed:** Math.R. **Document type:** academic/scholarly publication.
—BLDSC (0100.830000); CASDDS.

510   RU   ISSN 0025-567X
QA1
MATEMATICHESKIE ZAMETKI. English translation: Russian Academy of Sciences. Mathematical Notes (US ISSN 1067-9073) 1967. m. $179. (Rossiiskaya Akademiya Nauk) Izdatel'stvo Nauka, Mezhdunarodnyi Otdel, Profsoyuznaya, 90, 117864 Moscow, Russia. (Dist. in U.S. by: Victor Kamkin Inc., 4956 Boiling Brook Pkwy, Rockville, MD 20852. TEL 301-881-5973) Ed. V.P. Maslov. bk.rev.; tr.lit. circ. 380,000. (also avail. in microfiche from BHP) **Indexed:** INIS Atomind. **Document type:** academic/scholarly publication.

510   RU   ISSN 0368-8666
QA1   CODEN: MATSAB
MATEMATICHESKII SBORNIK. English translation: Russian Academy of Sciences. Sbornik. Mathematics (US ISSN 1064-5616) 1866. m. 66 Rub. (Rossiiskaya Akademiya Nauk, Institut Matematiki) Izdatel'stvo Nauka, Mezhdunarodnyi Otdel, Profsoyuznaya, 90, 117864 Moscow, Russia. (Co-sponsor: Moskovskoe Matematicheskoe Obshchestvo) Ed. A.A. Gonchar. bibl.; illus.; index. circ. 2,285. (reprint service avail. from KTO) **Indexed:** Chem.Abstr., INIS Atomind., Math.R. **Document type:** academic/scholarly publication.
—BLDSC (0101.000000).

510   YU   ISSN 0025-5165
QA1   CODEN: MVNSAQ
MATEMATICKI VESNIK. (Text in Serbo-Croatian and international languages) vol.14, 1977. q. 7000 din.($20) Drustvo Matematicara S R Srbije, Knez Mihailova 35-IV, Belgrade, Yugoslavia. (Co-sponsor: Drustvo Matematicara, Fizicara i Astronoma Yugoslavie) Ed. Dusan Adnadjevic. bk.rev. circ. 600. **Indexed:** Appl.Mech.Rev., Math.R., Ref.Zh.
—BLDSC (0101.040000); UnCover.
Formerly: Vesnik Drustva Matematicara i Fizicara SR Srbije.

MATEMATIKA, FYZIKA, INFORMATIKA. see **EDUCATION**

510 370   RU   ISSN 0130-9358
QA1
MATEMATIKA V SHKOLE. 1934. bi-m. $59 (effective 1996). Izdatel'stvo Pedagogika, Smolensky per. 4, 100034 Moscow, Russia. TEL 095-246-5969. (Dist. in U.S. by: Victor Kamkin Inc., 4956 Boiling Brook Pkwy, Rockville, MD 20852. TEL 301-881-5973) Ed. R.S. Cherkasov. bk.rev.; tr.lit. circ. 430,000.
—BLDSC (0100.400000).

510   HU   ISSN 0025-519X
QA1   CODEN: MTLPAR
MATEMATIKAI LAPOK/MATHEMATICAL PAPERS. (Text in Hungarian; summaries in English and Russian) 1892. q. $24.50. Bolyai Janos Matematikai Tarsulat, Fo u. 68, 1027 Budapest, Hungary. Ed. A. Csaszar. adv.; bk.rev.; charts; index. **Indexed:** INSPEC, Math.R.

510   PL   ISSN 0551-6625
QA1
MATEMATYKA (POZNAN). 1963. irreg., no.13, 1992. price varies. Uniwarsytet im. Adama Mickiwicza w Poznaniu, Wydzial Matematyki i Informatyki, Nowowiejskiego 55, 61-734 Poznan, Poland. TEL 527-380. FAX 61-52625. circ. 270. **Document type:** academic/scholarly publication.
Formerly: Uniwersytet im. Adama Mickiewicza w Poznaniu. Wydzial Matematyki, Fizyki i Chemii. Prace. Seria Matematyka (ISSN 1230-0055)
Description: Each volume contains current research results of one author in the field of mathematics, their Ph.D. works and other monographs.

510   PL   ISSN 0137-8848
QA1
MATEMATYKA (WROCLAW). 1948. bi-m. $12. (Ministerstwo Edukacji Narodowej) Wydawnictwa Szkolne i Pedagogiczne (Wroclaw), Ul. Dawida 1a, 50-527 Wroclaw, Poland. TEL 48-71-677028. (Dist. by: Ars Polona- Ruch, Krakowskie Przedmiescie 7, Warsaw, Poland) Ed. Agnieszka Wojciechowska. circ. 10,300.
—BLDSC (5392.270000).
Description: Publishes articles dealing with teaching mathematics, descriptions of lessons, discusses new lesson techniques, and presents other research useful for mathematics teachers.

510   AT
MATH MATH WORLD. 1976. 4/yr. Aus.$10. Mathematical Association of Western Australia, P.O. Box 492, Subiaco, W.A. 6008, Australia.
Formerly: It's a Math Math World (ISSN 0159-9976)

510 371.9   US   ISSN 0272-8885
MATH NOTEBOOK. 1979. 5/yr. $18 to individuals (foreign $23); institutions $25 (foreign $30). Center for Teaching - Learning of Mathematics, Box 3149, Framingham, MA 01701. TEL 508-877-7895. FAX 508-788-3600. Ed. Mahesh Sharma. circ. 2,000. (back issues avail.) **Document type:** academic/scholarly publication.
—CCC.
Description: Addresses mathematics learning problems, diagnosis, remediation and techniques for improving mathematics instruction.

301.412   US
MATH SCIENCE NETWORK BROADCAST.* 1978. q. $25 membership. Math Science Network, Mills College Math Science, Oakland, CA 94613. bk.rev.
Description: Encourages the participation and advancement of women in the fields of mathematics, science, and technology.

510   UK
▼**MATHEMATECH;** the global review of mathematics and its applications. 1994. q. £120($175) Parrish Platt International, Great Percy House, 26 Great Percy St., London WC1X 9QP, England. TEL 0171-278-3650. FAX 0171-278-3659. (Subscr. in U.S. (east of Mississippi) to: Box 2852, Des Plaines, IL 60017-2852; Subscr. in U.S. (west of Mississippi) to: Box 390547, Mountain View, CA 94039-0547) Ed. John Piper; Pub. Clifford Parrish. circ. 27,000. **Document type:** academic/scholarly publication.

510   RM   ISSN 0025-5505
QA1   CODEN: MTHCA2
MATHEMATICA; revue d'analyse numerique et de theorie de l'approximation. (Text in English, French, German, Italian and Russian) 1929. s-a. 40 lei($50) (Academia Romana) Editura Academiei Romane, Calea Victoriei nr.125, sectorul 1, R-79717 Bucharest, Rumania. (Dist. by: Rompresfilatelia, Calea Grivitei 64-66, P.O. Box 12-201, 78104 Bucharest, Rumania) Ed. E. Popoviciu. abstr.; charts; illus.; index. **Indexed:** Appl.Mech.Rev., Math.R.
—SWETS.

510   XR   ISSN 0862-7959
QA1   CODEN: MABOEF
MATHEMATICA BOHEMICA. (Text, contents page and summaries in Czech, English, French, German, Russian, Slovak) 1872. q. DM.218. Ceska Akademie Ved, Matematicky Ustav, Zitna 25, 115 67 Prague 1, Czech Republic. TEL 22-66-01. (Dist. in Western countries by: Kubon & Sagner, P.O. Box 34 01 08, 8000 Munich, Germany) Ed. S. Schwabik. bk.rev.; index. circ. 800. **Indexed:** Comput.Rev., Math.R. **Document type:** academic/scholarly publication.
—Faxon; UnCover.
Formerly (until 1991): Casopis pro Pestovani Matematiky (ISSN 0528-2195)
Description: Presents mathematical research and expository papers, news and notices, and problems.

510   GW   ISSN 0172-8407
MATHEMATICA DIDACTICA. 1978. 2/yr. Verlag Franzbecker KG, Postfach 100420, 31104 Hildesheim, Germany. TEL 05064-9397-0. FAX 05064-939766. Ed.Bd. adv.; bk.rev. circ. 350. **Document type:** academic/scholarly publication.
—BLDSC (5399.580000). **CCC.**
Formerly (until 1979): Mathematica Didact (ISSN 0170-1541)

510 370   US
QA20.C65
MATHEMATICA IN EDUCATION AND RESEARCH. 1992. q. $60 (electronic version $30) (effective 1996). Telos: The Electronic Library of Science (Subsidiary of: Springer-Verlag New York), 3600 Pruneridge Ave., Ste. 200, Santa Clara, CA 95051. TEL 408-249-9314. FAX 408-777-4643. E-mail: MathInEd@telospub.com. (Subscr. to: Springer-Verlag New York, Inc, 44 Hartz Way, Secaucus, NJ 07096-2491. TEL 800-777-4643) Ed. Paul R. Wellin; Pub. Allan M. Wylde. bk.rev.; illus. (also avail. in diskette format; reprint service avail.) **Document type:** academic/scholarly publication.
●Also available online.
—BLDSC (5399.620000). **CCC.**
   Formerly (until 1995): Mathematica in Education (ISSN 1065-2965)
   Description: Discusses methods for allowing computers to solve, visualize, and harness the power of mathematics in an educational context.

510   JA   ISSN 0025-5513
QA1   CODEN: MAJAA9
MATHEMATICA JAPONICA. (Text in English and European languages) 1948. bi-m. $330. Nihon Suri Kagaku Kyokai - Japanese Association of Mathematical Sciences, Shin Sakai-Higashi Bldg., 2-1-18 Minami-Hanadaguchi, Sakai-shi, Osaka-fu 590, Japan. FAX 0722-22-7987. (Co-sponsors: Osaka Joshi Daigaku; Osaka Kyoiku Daigaku; Osaka Furitsu; Osaka-kenritsu Daigaku) Ed.Bd. bibl.; charts; index. circ. 850. **Indexed:** Math.R. **Document type:** academic/scholarly publication.
—BLDSC (5399.800000); Faxon; SWETS; UnCover.

510   DK   ISSN 0025-5521
QA1   CODEN: MTSCAN
MATHEMATICA SCANDINAVICA. (Text in English, French and German) 1953. 4/yr. (in 2 vols., 2 nos./vol.). DKK 1070 (typically set in Sep.). (Mathematical Societies in Scandinavia) Mathematica Scandinavica, Aarhus University, Bldg.530, DK-8000 Aarhus C, Denmark. TEL 45-89-42-34-37.
FAX 45-86-13-17-69. E-mail: mscand@mi.aau.dk. Ed. Joergen Vesterstroem. circ. 1,000. (back issues avail.) **Indexed:** Compumath, Ind.Sci.Rev., Math.R. **Document type:** academic/scholarly publication.
—BLDSC (5400.000000); Faxon; SWETS; UnCover.

510   XO   ISSN 0139-9918
QA1   CODEN: MASLDM
MATHEMATICA SLOVACA. (Text in English, French, German, Russian; summaries in English, Russian) 1951. q. $25. Slovenska Akademia Vied, Matematicky Ustav, Stefaníkova 49, 814 73 Bratislava, Slovakia. (Dist. by: Slovart, Gottwaldovo nam. 6, 817 64 Bratislava, Slovakia) Ed. Stefan Schwarz. bibl.; charts; illus.; index. circ. 1,000. **Indexed:** INSPEC, Math.R. **Document type:** academic/scholarly publication.
—SWETS; UnCover.
   Former titles (until 1976): Matematicky Casopis (ISSN 0025-5173); Matematicko-Fyzikalny Casopis.
   Description: Publishes original scientific papers of Czechoslovak as well as foreign authors on various mathematical disciplines. The contributions are mainly from algebra, theory of numbers, graphs, differential equations, real functions, functional analysis, harmonic analysis and mathematical statistics.

510   AG   ISSN 0025-553X
QA1   CODEN: MANOA3
MATHEMATICAE NOTAE. (Text in English, French, German, Italian and Spanish) 1941. a. exchange basis. (Instituto de Matematica Beppo Levi) Universidad Nacional de Rosario, Avenida Pellegrini 250, 2000 Rosario, Argentina. TEL 041-217998. TELEX 41817 CIROS AG. Ed.Bd. bk.rev. circ. 500. **Indexed:** Appl.Mech.Rev.; Math.R, Zent.Math.

510   UK   ISSN 0895-7177
QA401   CODEN: MCMOEG
MATHEMATICAL AND COMPUTER MODELLING; an international journal. 1980. 24/yr. £1100($1749) (effective 1996). (International Association for Mathematical and Computer Modelling) Elsevier Science Ltd., Pergamon, P.O. Box 800, Kidlington, Oxford OX5 1DX, England. TEL 44-1865-843000. FAX 44-1865-843010.
E-mail: nlinfo-f@elsevier.nl; usinfo-f@elsevier.com; forinfo-kyf04035@niftyserve.or.jp; Site addr.: http://www.elsevier.nl/. (Subscr. in U.S. and Canada to: Elsevier Science, 660 White Plains Rd., Tarrytown, NY 10591-5153. TEL 914-524-9200. FAX 914-333-2444) Ed. Ervin Y. Rodin. (also avail. in microfilm from UMI) **Indexed:** Abstr.Bull.Inst.Pap.Chem., Biostat., Compumath, Comput.Abstr., Curr.Adv.Ecol.Sci., Curr.Cont., Cyb.Abstr., Excerp.Med., Fluidex, INSPEC, Irr.& Drain.Abstr., Math.R., Oper.Res.Manage.Sci., Qual.Contr.Appl.Stat., Robomat., Soils & Fert. **Document type:** academic/scholarly publication.
—BLDSC (5401.350000); Ei; Faxon; Genuine Article; SWETS; UMI; UnCover. **CCC.**
   Formerly: Mathematical Modelling (ISSN 0270-0255)
   Description: Publishes papers on the utilization of mathematical modelling as a theoretical or practical working tool.
   Refereed Serial

510 530   UA   ISSN 1110-0613
MATHEMATICAL AND PHYSICAL SOCIETY OF EGYPT. PROCEEDINGS. (Text in English; summaries in Arabic and English) 1937. s.a. $57 (effective 1996). (Mathematical and Physical Society of Egypt, Research Department) National Information and Documentation Centre (NIDOC), Tahrir St., Dokki, Awqaf P.O., Cairo, Egypt. TEL 20-2-701696. Ed. M. El-Nady. charts; illus. circ. 1,000. (reprint service avail. from IRC) **Document type:** proceedings.
—BLDSC (6755.900000).

510   II   ISSN 0025-5556
QA11.A1
MATHEMATICAL ASSOCIATION OF INDIA. BULLETIN. (Text in English) 1969. q. Rs.40($8) per no. Mathematical Association of India, Indian Institute of Technology Kanpur, Mathematics Department, Kanpur, India. Ed. Prof. J. N. Kapur. adv.; bk.rev. circ. 500. **Indexed:** Math.R.

510 576   US   ISSN 0025-5564
QH324   CODEN: MABIAR
MATHEMATICAL BIOSCIENCES; an international journal. 1967. 16/yr. $1558 to institutions (effective 1996). Elsevier Science Inc., 655 Ave. of the Americas, New York, NY 10010. TEL 212-989-5800. FAX 212-633-3990. TELEX 420643 AEP UI. (Subscr. to: Box 882, Madison Sq. Sta., New York, NY 10159-0882) Ed. John A. Jacquez. adv.; bk.rev.; abstr.; bibl.; charts; illus.; index. circ. 1,000. (also avail. in microform from UMI) **Indexed:** Appl.Mech.Rev., Biol.Abstr., Biostat., Chem.Abstr., Compumath, Comput.Abstr., Curr.Adv.Ecol.Sci., Curr.Cont., Deep Sea Res.& Oceanogr.Abstr., Ecol.Abstr., Eng.Ind., Excerp.Med., Helminthol.Abstr., Ind.Med. (1992-), Ind.Sci.Rev., Ind.Vet., INIS Atomind., INSPEC, Math.R., Risk Abstr., Sport Fish.Abstr., Wild.Rev., Zoo.Rec. **Document type:** academic/scholarly publication.
—BLDSC (5401.700000); CASDDS; Ei; EMDOCS; Faxon; Genuine Article; SWETS; UnCover. **CCC.**
   Description: Publishes research and expository papers on the formulation, analysis and solution of mathematical models in the biosciences.
   Refereed Serial

MATHEMATICAL CHEMISTRY. see *CHEMISTRY*

MATHEMATICAL COGNITION. see *PSYCHOLOGY*

510   US   ISSN 0885-9418
MATHEMATICAL CONCEPTS AND METHODS IN SCIENCE AND ENGINEERING. 1976. irreg., vol.44, 1994. Plenum Publishing Corp., 233 Spring St., New York, NY 10013-1578. TEL 212-620-8000.
FAX 212-463-0742. TELEX 23-421139. Ed. Angelo Miele. (back issues avail.) **Indexed:** INSPEC. **Document type:** monographic series.
—BLDSC (5401.930000).
   Refereed Serial

510 370   KO   ISSN 1225-1380
MATHEMATICAL EDUCATION. (Text and summaries in English and Korean) 1962. s-a. 2500 Won($4) Korea Society of Mathematical Education, c/o College of Education, Seoul National University, Seoul, South Korea. Ed. Han Shick Park. adv.; bk.rev.; abstr.; bibl.; charts; illus.; stat. circ. 500. (back issues avail.)

510 370   II   ISSN 0970-5759
MATHEMATICAL EDUCATION. (Text in English) 1984. q. Rs.100($40) (University Grants Commission) New Age International Pvt. Ltd., Journals Division, 4835-24 Ansari Rd., Daryaganj, New Delhi 110 002, India. TEL 91-11-3267996.
FAX 91-11-3267437. TELEX 031-66507-WELIN. circ. 1,000. **Document type:** academic/scholarly publication.
—BLDSC (5401.952500).

519 628.5   NE   ISSN 0169-121X
MATHEMATICAL ENGINEERING IN INDUSTRY. (Text in English) q. DM.330 (effective 1996). V S P, P.O. Box 346, 3700 AH Zeist, Netherlands. TEL 31-30-6925790. FAX 31-30-6932081. E-mail: 100341.2372@compuserve.com. Ed. F.A. Goldsworthy. (back issues avail.) **Document type:** academic/scholarly publication.
—BLDSC (5401.960000); Ei; UnCover.
   Description: Academic and practical papers covering new mathematical applications in industry.
   Refereed Serial

MATHEMATICAL FINANCE; an international journal of mathematics, statistics and financial economics. see *BUSINESS AND ECONOMICS — Banking And Finance*

510   UK   ISSN 0025-5572
QA1   CODEN: MAGAAS
MATHEMATICAL GAZETTE. 1894. 3/yr. £36 (foreign £40). Mathematical Association, 259 London Rd., Leicester LE2 3BE, England. TEL 0116-270-3877. FAX 0116-244-8508. Ed. S. Abbott. adv.; bk.rev.; charts; index. circ. 5,000. (also avail. in microform; reprint service avail. from UMI) **Indexed:** Ind.Sci.Rev., Math.R. **Document type:** academic/scholarly publication.
—BLDSC (5402.000000); Faxon; SWETS; UMI; UnCover.

510   US   ISSN 0343-6993
QA1   CODEN: MAINDC
THE MATHEMATICAL INTELLIGENCER. 1978. q. $45 (effective 1996). Springer-Verlag, Journals, 175 Fifth Ave., New York, NY 10010.
TEL 212-460-1500. FAX 212-473-6272. E-mail: bbrash@springer-ny.com. (N. American subscr. to: Journal Fulfillment Services, Box 2485, Secaucus, NJ 07096-2491. TEL 800-777-4643. FAX 201-348-4505; Elsewhere: Heidelberger Platz 3, 1000 Berlin 33, Germany. TEL 030-8207-1. FAX 030-821-4091) Ed. Chandler Davis. adv.; bk.rev.; charts; illus.; index. (also avail. in microform from UMI; back issues avail.; reprint service avail. from ISI,SWZ) **Indexed:** Curr.Cont., Gen.Sci.Ind., Ind.Sci.Rev., Math.R., Phys.Ber., Zent.Math. **Document type:** academic/scholarly publication.
—BLDSC (5402.250000); Faxon; Genuine Article; SWETS; UMI; UnCover. **CCC.**
   Description: Informs and entertains an international readership of professional mathematicians, especially those stimulated by discussion of developments in specialties other than their own.
   Refereed Serial

510   JA   ISSN 0030-1566
QA1   CODEN: MJOKAP
MATHEMATICAL JOURNAL OF OKAYAMA UNIVERSITY. (Text in English, French, German) 1952. s-a. exchange basis. Okayama Daigaku, Rigakubu Sugaku Kyoshitsu - Okayama University, Faculty of Science, Department of Mathematics, 3-1-1 Tsushima-Naka, Okayama-shi, Okayama-ken 700, Japan. Ed.Bd. charts; index. circ. 700. **Indexed:** Bull.Signal., Math.R., Zent.Math.
—BLDSC (5402.300000); UnCover.

510   US   ISSN 0025-5580
MATHEMATICAL LOG. 1957. 4/yr. $3 (foreign $5.50). Mu Alpha Theta, 601 Elm St., Rm. 423, Norman, OK 73019. TEL 405-325-4489. Ed. Thomas Butts. bk.rev.; charts; illus.; circ. 25,000 (controlled).

MATHEMATICS

511.3 519   GW   ISSN 0942-5616
QA1   CODEN: MLQUEF
MATHEMATICAL LOGIC QUARTERLY. (Text in English, French, German) 1955. q. DM.366 (foreign DM.370). (Humboldt-Universitaet zu Berlin, Institut fuer Mathematische Logik) Huethig GmbH, Postfach 102869, 69018 Heidelberg, Germany. TEL 06221-489261. FAX 06221-489205. Ed. G. Asser. adv.: B&W page DM.650; trim 167 x 240; adv. contact: Micheline Cohen. bk.rev.; charts; illus.; index. circ. 500. **Indexed:** Compumath, INSPEC, Math.R. **Document type:** academic/scholarly publication.
—BLDSC (5402.430000); Faxon; Genuine Article; UnCover.
Formerly: Zeitschrift fuer Mathematische Logik und Grundlagen der Mathematik (ISSN 0044-3050)
Description: Covers the entire field of mathematical logic and related areas by means of original publications.

510   UK   ISSN 0170-4214
QA1   CODEN: MMSCDB
MATHEMATICAL METHODS IN THE APPLIED SCIENCES. (Text in English) 1979. 18/yr. $1295 (foreign $1295) (effective 1996). John Wiley & Sons Ltd., Journals, Baffins Ln., Chichester, W. Sussex PO19 1UD, England. TEL 01243-779777. FAX 01243-776128. (Subscr. in the Americas to: John Wiley & Sons, Inc., 605 Third Ave., New York, NY 10158. TEL 212-850-6645. FAX 212-850-6021) Eds. S.B. Brosowski, G.F. Roach. adv.; bk.rev. circ. 271. (also avail. in microform from UMI; back issues avail.; reprint service avail. from SWZ) **Indexed:** Appl.Mech.Rev., Compumath, Curr.Cont., Eng.Ind., Int.Aerosp.Abstr., Math.R. **Document type:** academic/scholarly publication.
—BLDSC (5402.530000); Ei; Faxon; Genuine Article; SWETS; UMI; UnCover. **CCC.**
Description: Covers mathematical methods that could be necessary for the further understanding and eventual solution of problems in the applied sciences.
Refereed Serial

510   US   ISSN 1066-5307
QA276.A1
MATHEMATICAL METHODS OF STATISTICS. 1992. q. $285 (effective 1996). Allerton Press, Inc., 150 Fifth Ave., New York, NY 10011. TEL 212-924-3950. FAX 212-463-9684. Ed. Dmitry Chibisov. **Document type:** academic/scholarly publication.
—BLDSC (5402.543000); SWETS. **CCC.**
Description: Devoted to the mathematical foundations of the statistical theory and provides an outlet for research papers in advanced statistical methodology and for studies where such methodology is effectively used or which stimulate its further development.

510   SI   ISSN 0218-2025
QA401   CODEN: MMMSEU
MATHEMATICAL MODELS AND METHODS IN APPLIED SCIENCES. (Text in English) 1991. bi-m. $308 to institutions of developed countries; individuals & developing countries $148. World Scientific Publishing Co. Pte. Ltd., Farrer Rd., P.O. Box 128, Singapore 9128, Singapore. TEL 3825663. FAX 3825919. TELEX RS 28561 WSPC. (UK addr.: 73 Lynton Mead, Totteridge, London N20 8DH, England. TEL 44-81-4462461; US addr.: 1060 Main St., River Edge, NJ 07661. TEL 800-227-7562) Eds. Nicola Bellomo, Franco Brezzi. **Indexed:** INSPEC (1991-). **Document type:** academic/scholarly publication.
—BLDSC (5402.549000); Genuine Article. **CCC.**
Description: Provides a medium of exchange for scientists engaged in applied sciences where there exists a nontrivial interplay among mathematics, mathematical modelling of real systems, and mathematical and computer methods oriented toward the qualitative and quantitative analysis of real physical systems.

510   US
MATHEMATICAL NOTES (PRINCETON). 1966. irreg., no.39, 1991. price varies. Princeton University Press, 41 William St., Princeton, NJ 08540. TEL 609-258-4900. FAX 609-258-6305. E-mail: jhardy@pupress.princeton.edu. Co-publisher: University of Tokyo Press) (also avail. in microfilm from JSC; reprint service avail. from UMI) **Indexed:** Compumath, Math.R. **Document type:** monographic series.

519 530.15   NE   ISSN 0165-2419
CODEN: MPAMD6
MATHEMATICAL PHYSICS AND APPLIED MATHEMATICS. 1976. irreg., vol.11, 1993. price varies. Kluwer Academic Publishers, Postbus 17, 3300 AA Dordrecht, Netherlands. TEL 31-78-392392. FAX 31-78-392254. TELEX 29245 KAPG NL. (Dist. by: Kluwer Academic Publishers Group, P.O. Box 322, 3300 AH Dordrecht, Netherlands. TEL 31-78-392392. FAX 31-78-546474; N. America dist. addr.: Box 358, Accord Sta., Hingham, MA 02018-0358. TEL 617-871-6600. FAX 617-871-6528) Eds. M. Flato, R. Raczka. **Indexed:** INSPEC, Math.R. **Document type:** monographic series.
—BLDSC (5402.576400); CASDDS.
Refereed Serial

MATHEMATICAL PHYSICS REVIEWS. see *PHYSICS*

MATHEMATICAL PHYSICS STUDIES. see *PHYSICS*

510 370   UK   ISSN 0025-5602
MATHEMATICAL PIE. 1951. 3/yr. £1.80 (foreign £2.90). Mathematical Association, 259 London Rd., Leicester LE2 3BF, England. TEL 0116-270-3877. FAX 0116-244-8508. Ed. G. Fowler. bibl.; charts; illus. circ. 12,000. **Document type:** academic/scholarly publication.
Description: For pupils in the 10-15 age range and their teachers.

MATHEMATICAL POPULATION STUDIES; an international journal of mathematical demography. see *POPULATION STUDIES*

510   CN
MATHEMATICAL PREPRINTS. (Text in English and French) 1971. irreg. price varies. Carleton University, Department of Mathematics and Statistics, Ottawa, Ont. K1S 5B6, Canada. TEL 613-788-2155. FAX 613-788-3536. **Indexed:** Math.R.
Formerly (until 1991): Carleton Mathematical Series (ISSN 0069-0600)

510   US   ISSN 0275-7214
MATHEMATICAL REPORTS. a. 112 ECU (effective 1993). Harwood Academic Publishers, c/o International Publishers Distributor, 820 Town Center Dr., Langhorne, PA 19047. TEL 215-750-2642. FAX 215-750-6343. (Subscr. to: International Publishers Distributor, PO Box 90, Reading, Berkshire, RG1 8JL England. TEL 44-173-456-8316) adv. (also avail. in microform) **Indexed:** Math.R. (1983-1988). **Document type:** academic/scholarly publication.
—**CCC.**
Refereed Serial

510 531   GW
MATHEMATICAL RESEARCH. 1972. irreg., vol.82, 1994. price varies. Akademie Verlag GmbH, Muehlenstr. 33-34, 13187 Berlin, Germany. TEL 030-47889348. FAX 030-47889357. Ed.Bd. **Indexed:** INSPEC, Math.R. **Document type:** monographic series.
—BLDSC (5402.650000).
Former titles: Mathematische Forschung; Mathematische Forschung. Schriftenreihe (ISSN 0138-3019); Zentralinstitut fuer Mathematik und Mechanik. Schriftenreihe.

510   US   ISSN 1073-2780
▼**MATHEMATICAL RESEARCH LETTERS.** 1994. bi-m. $85 to individuals; institutions $130. International Press, Box 2872, Cambridge, MA 02238-2872. TEL 617-491-0329. FAX 617-491-0329. E-mail: mrl@ucsd.edu. Eds. Linda P. Rothschild, M. Salah Baouendi.
—BLDSC (5402.660000).
Description: Dedicated to rapid publication of research announcements, complete papers and expository papers.

510   US   ISSN 0940-4740
MATHEMATICAL SCIENCES RESEARCH INSTITUTE PUBLICATIONS. 1984. irreg. price varies. Springer-Verlag, 175 Fifth Ave., New York, NY 10010. TEL 212-460-1500. FAX 212-473-6272. (Also: Berlin, Heidelberg, Tokyo, Vienna) (reprint service avail. from ISI) **Document type:** monographic series.

510   UK   ISSN 0312-3685
QA1
THE MATHEMATICAL SCIENTIST. 1976. s-a. £10($15.70) (effective 1996). Applied Probability Trust, School of Mathematics, University of Sheffield, Sheffield S3 7RH, England. TEL 0114-282-4269. FAX 0114-272-9782. Ed. J. Gani. circ. 750. (back issues avail.) **Indexed:** Curr.Cont., Curr.Ind.Stat., J.Cont.Quant.Meth., Math.R., Oper.Res.Manage.Sci., Qual.Contr.Appl.Stat., Zent.Math. **Document type:** academic/scholarly publication.
—BLDSC (5403.350000); Faxon; SWETS; UnCover.
Description: Publishes papers on a variety of topics for the general information and enjoyment of mathematicians, statisticians, and computer scientists.

510 300   NE   ISSN 0165-4896
CODEN: MSOSDD
MATHEMATICAL SOCIAL SCIENCES. (Text in English) 1980. bi-m. fl.890($543) (effective 1996). North-Holland (Subsidiary of: Elsevier Science B.V.), P.O. Box 211, 1000 AE Amsterdam, Netherlands. TEL 31-20-4853911. FAX 31-20-4853598. TELEX 18582 ESPA NL. (Subscr. in U.S. and Canada to: Elsevier Science Inc., Box 882, Madison Sq. Sta., New York, NY 10159. TEL 212-989-5800. FAX 212-633-3990) Ed. Ki Hang Kim. adv.; bk.rev. (also avail. in microform from UMI; back issues avail.) **Indexed:** Compumath, Curr.Cont., Cyb.Abstr., INSPEC (1980-), J.Cont.Quant.Meth., J.of Econ.Lit., Lang.& Lang.Behav.Abstr., Math.R., Sage Fam.Stud.Abstr., Sociol.Abstr., SSCI. **Document type:** academic/scholarly publication.
—BLDSC (5403.400000); Faxon; Genuine Article; SWETS; UnCover. **CCC.**
Description: Publishes original research, as well as survey papers, short notes, news items, a calendar of meetings which are of broad interest in the mathematical social sciences.
Refereed Serial

510   JA   ISSN 0025-5645
QA1   CODEN: NISUBC
MATHEMATICAL SOCIETY OF JAPAN. JOURNAL. (Text in European languages) 1885. q. 5000 Yen per no. Nihon Sugakkai - Mathematical Society of Japan, 25-9-203, Hongo 4-chome, Bunkyo-ku, Tokyo 113, Japan. TEL 03-3816-5961. FAX 03-3816-5940. (also avail. in microform from PMC) **Indexed:** Compumath, Curr.Cont., Jap.Per.Ind., Math.R., Sci.Cit.Ind.
—Faxon; SWETS; UnCover.

510   JA   ISSN 0549-4540
MATHEMATICAL SOCIETY OF JAPAN. PUBLICATIONS. (Text in English and European languages) 1959. irreg. Nihon Sugakkai - Mathematical Society of Japan, 25-9-203, Hongo 4-chome, Bunkyo-ku, Tokyo 113, Japan. TEL 03-3816-5961. FAX 03-3816-5940.

510   UK   ISSN 0025-5653
QA1   CODEN: MSPEB8
MATHEMATICAL SPECTRUM. 1968. 3/yr. £8.50($14) (effective Sep. 1995). Applied Probability Trust, School of Mathematics, University of Sheffield, Sheffield S3 7RH, England. TEL 0114-282-4269. FAX 0114-272-9782. Ed. D.W. Sharpe. adv.; bk.rev.; software rev. circ. 2,000. (back issues avail.) **Indexed:** Cont.Pg.Educ., Fluidex, INSPEC, Math.R., Oper.Res.Manage.Sci., Qual.Contr.Appl.Stat., Ref.Zh. **Document type:** academic/scholarly publication.
—BLDSC (5403.500000); Faxon; SWETS; UnCover.
Description: Covers all branches of mathematics for students. Contains computer column, letters, problems, and solutions.

510   US   ISSN 0885-4653
MATHEMATICAL SURVEYS & MONOGRAPHS. 1943. irreg. price varies. American Mathematical Society, Box 6248, Providence, RI 02940-6248. TEL 401-455-4000. (Street addr.: 201 Charles St., Providence, RI 02904) **Indexed:** Math.R., Zent.Math. **Document type:** monographic series.
—BLDSC (5404.050000). **CCC.**
Formerly (until 1981): Mathematical Surveys (ISSN 0076-5376)
Description: Covers current topics in mathematical research.

MATHEMATICAL SYSTEMS IN ECONOMICS. see *BUSINESS AND ECONOMICS — Economic Systems And Theories, Economic History*

MATHEMATICS

510   US   ISSN 0025-5661
QA1   CODEN: MASTBA
MATHEMATICAL SYSTEMS THEORY; an international journal on mathematical computing theory. 1966. q. $221 (effective 1996). Springer-Verlag, Journals, 175 Fifth Ave., New York, NY 10010. TEL 212-460-1500. FAX 212-473-6272. (N. American subscr. to: Journal Fulfillment Services, Box 2485, Secaucus, NJ 07096-2491. TEL 800-777-4643. FAX 201-348-4505; Elsewhere: Heidelberger Platz 3, 1000 Berlin 33, Germany. TEL 030-8207-1. FAX 030-821-4091) Ed. Arnold L. Rosenberg. adv. (also avail. in microform from UMI; reprint service avail. from ISI,SWZ) **Indexed:** Compumath, Curr.Cont., Ind.Sci.Rev., INSPEC, Math.R., Zent.Math. **Document type:** academic/scholarly publication.
—BLDSC (5404.200000); Faxon; Genuine Article; SWETS; UMI; UnCover. **CCC.**
     Description: Devoted to current research in the theories of both discrete and continuous systems.
     Refereed Serial

510   GW
MATHEMATICAL TOPICS. 1993. irreg., vol.7, 1995. price varies. Akademie Verlag GmbH, Muehlenstr. 33-34, 13187 Berlin, Germany. TEL 030-47889348. FAX 030-47889357. Ed. Karl-Heinz Elster. **Document type:** monographic series.

MATHEMATICS AND COMPUTER EDUCATION. see *MATHEMATICS — Computer Applications*

510   US   ISSN 0543-0941
MATHEMATICS AND ITS APPLICATIONS. 1962. irreg., vol.16, 1988. price varies. Gordon & Breach Science Publishers, c/o International Publishers Distributor, 820 Town Center Dr., Langhorne, PA 19047. TEL 215-750-2642. FAX 215-750-6343. (Subscr. to: International Publishers Distributor, P.O. Box 90, Reading, Berkshire RG1 8JL, England. TEL 44-173-456-8316) Eds. Jacob T. Schwartz, Maurice Levy. (also avail. in microform) **Indexed:** Math.R. **Document type:** monographic series.
—BLDSC (5405.150000).
     Formerly (until 1971): Notes on Mathematics and Its Applications.
     Refereed Serial

510   NE   ISSN 0921-3791
     CODEN: MTAPB7
MATHEMATICS AND ITS APPLICATIONS. 1977. irreg., vol.305, 1994. Kluwer Academic Publishers, Postbus 17, 3300 AA Dordrecht, Netherlands. TEL 31-78-392392. FAX 31-78-392254. TELEX 29245 KAPG NL. (Dist. by Kluwer Academic Publishers Group, P.O. Box 322, 3300 AH Dordrecht, Netherlands. TEL 31-78-392392. FAX 31-78-546474; N. America dist. addr.: Box 358, Accord Sta., Hingham, MA 02018-0358. TEL 617-871-6600. FAX 617-871-6528) Ed. M. Hazewinkel. **Indexed:** INSPEC, Math.R. **Document type:** monographic series.
—BLDSC (5405.130000).
     Refereed Serial

519   NE   ISSN 0924-5952
MATHEMATICS AND ITS APPLICATIONS: CHINESE SERIES. (Text in English) 1989. irreg., vol.5, 1993. price varies. Kluwer Academic Publishers, Postbus 17, 3300 AA Dordrecht, Netherlands. TEL 31-78-392392. FAX 31-78-392254. TELEX 29245 KAPG NL. (Dist. by: Kluwer Academic Publishers Group, P.O. Box 322, 3300 AH Dordrecht, Netherlands. TEL 31-78-392392. FAX 31-78-546474; N. America dist. addr.: Box 358, Accord Sta., Hingham, MA 02018-0358. TEL 617-871-6700. FAX 617-871-6528) Ed. M. Hazewinkel. **Document type:** monographic series.
     Refereed Serial

510   NE   ISSN 0169-507X
MATHEMATICS AND ITS APPLICATIONS: EAST EUROPEAN SERIES. 1982. irreg., vol.60, 1993. price varies. Kluwer Academic Publishers, Postbus 17, 3300 AA Dordrecht, Netherlands. TEL 31-78-392392. FAX 31-78-392254. TELEX 29245 KAPG NL. (Dist. by: Kluwer Academic Publishers Group, P.O. Box 322, 3300 AH Dordrecht, Netherlands. TEL 31-78-392392. FAX 31-78-546474; N. America dist. addr.: Box 358, Accord Sta., Hingham, MA 02018-0358. TEL 617-871-6600. FAX 617-871-6528) Ed. M. Hazewinkel. **Indexed:** Math.R. **Document type:** monographic series.
     Refereed Serial

510   NE   ISSN 0924-4913
MATHEMATICS AND ITS APPLICATIONS: JAPANESE SERIES. 1983. irreg. price varies. Kluwer Academic Publishers, Postbus 17, 3300 AA Dordrecht, Netherlands. TEL 31-78-392392. FAX 31-78-392254. TELEX 29245 KAPG NL. (Dist. by: Kluwer Academic Publishers Group, P.O. Box 322, 3300 AH Dordrecht, Netherlands. TEL 31-78-392392. FAX 31-78-546474; N. America dist. addr.: Box 358, Accord Sta., Hingham, MA 02018-0358. TEL 617-871-6600. FAX 617-871-6528) Ed. M. Hazewinkel. **Document type:** monographic series.
     Refereed Serial

510   NE   ISSN 0169-6378
MATHEMATICS AND ITS APPLICATIONS: SOVIET SERIES. 1984. irreg., vol.88, 1993. price varies. Kluwer Academic Publishers, Postbus 17, 3300 AA Dordrecht, Netherlands. TEL 31-78-392392. FAX 31-78-392254. TELEX 29245 KAPG NL. (Dist. by: Kluwer Academic Publishers Group, P.O. Box 322, 3300 AH Dordrecht, Netherlands. TEL 31-78-392392. FAX 31-78-546474; N. America dist. addr.: Box 358, Accord Sta., Hingham, MA 02018-0358. TEL 617-871-6600. FAX 617-871-6528) Ed. M. Hazewinkel. **Indexed:** INSPEC, Math.R. **Document type:** monographic series.
     Refereed Serial

MATHEMATICS AND MECHANICS OF SOLIDS. see *PHYSICS*

510 370   II   ISSN 0047-6269
QA1
THE MATHEMATICS EDUCATION. (Text in English) 1967. q. Rs.400 (effective 1994). Nirala Nagar, Siwan, Bihar, India. Ed. J.B. Prasad. adv. contact: Indu Mani Prasad. bk.rev.; bibl.; charts; index. circ. 900. **Indexed:** Math.R. **Document type:** academic/scholarly publication.
—BLDSC (5405.900000); UnCover.
     Description: Presents research and teaching methods in pure and applied mathematics.

MATHEMATICS EDUCATION LIBRARY. see *EDUCATION*

MATHEMATICS EDUCATION RESEARCH JOURNAL. see *EDUCATION — Teaching Methods And Curriculum*

MATHEMATICS FOR THE FUTURE (YEAR); first degree courses in mathematics and related subjects. see *EDUCATION — Guides To Schools And Colleges*

510   UK   ISSN 0305-7259
MATHEMATICS IN SCHOOL. 1972. 5/yr. £40 (Europe £41; elsewhere £50). (Mathematical Association) Pitman Publishing, 128 Long Acre, London WC2E 9AN, England. TEL 0171-379-7383. FAX 0171-240-5771. Ed. J. Bradshaw. adv.; bk.rev.; charts; illus.; stat.; index. circ. 9,000. (also avail. in microfilm; back issues avail.; reprint service avail. from UMI) **Indexed:** C.I.J.E., Cont.Pg.Educ., SOMA, Tech.Educ.Abstr. **Document type:** academic/scholarly publication.
—BLDSC (5406.500000); SWETS; UnCover. **CCC.**
     Description: Provides a topical forum for those concerned with the teaching of mathematics to children from ages 7-16.
     Refereed Serial

510 620   US   ISSN 0076-5392
MATHEMATICS IN SCIENCE AND ENGINEERING; series of monographs and textbooks. 1961. irreg., vol.184, 1990. Academic Press, Inc., 525 B St., Ste. 1900, San Diego, CA 92101-4495. TEL 619-231-0926. FAX 619-699-6715. (Subscr. to: Order Dept., 6277 Sea Harbor Dr., 4th Fl., Orlando, FL 32887. TEL 800-321-5068) Ed. William F. Ames. (reprint service avail. from ISI) **Indexed:** Math.R. **Document type:** monographic series.
—BLDSC (5406.600000); Faxon; UnCover.
     Refereed Serial

510   US   ISSN 0025-570X
     CODEN: MAMGA8
MATHEMATICS MAGAZINE. 1926. bi-m. (Sep.-June). $89 (effective 1996). Mathematical Association of America, 1529 Eighteenth St., N.W., Washington, DC 20036. TEL 202-387-5200. Ed. Martha J. Siegel. adv.; bk.rev.; index, cum.index: vols.1-50. circ. 14,000. (also avail. in microfiche from UMI; reprint service avail. from UMI) **Indexed:** Gen.Sci.Ind., Ind.Sci.Rev., Math.R. **Document type:** academic/scholarly publication, newsletter.
—BLDSC (5406.000000); Faxon; SWETS; UMI; UnCover. **CCC.**
     Incorporates (in 1976): Delta (Washington) (ISSN 0011-801X)
     Description: Articles, mathematical problems, and book reviews of interest to undergraduate students and faculty, focusing on the history and contemporary application of mathematics.

510   II
MATHEMATICS NEWSLETTER. (Text in English) 1971. every 6 weeks. Rs.2. Mathematical Society, Central College, Bangalore 1, India. Ed. F.J. Noronha. adv.; charts.

510   US   ISSN 0025-5718
QA47   CODEN: MCMPAF
MATHEMATICS OF COMPUTATION. 1943. 4/yr. $262 to non-members; individual members $157; institutional members $210. American Mathematical Society, Box 6248, Providence, RI 02940-6248. TEL 401-455-4000. (Street addr.: 201 Charles St., Providence, RI 02901-9930) Ed. Walter Gautschi. adv.; bk.rev.; abstr.; cum.index: vols.1-23. circ. 2,200. (also avail. in microfilm from UMI,PMC; microfiche) **Indexed:** A.S.& T.Ind., Abstr.Bull.Inst.Pap.Chem., Appl.Mech.Rev., Compumath, Curr.Cont., Cyb.Abstr., Ind.Sci.Rev., INIS Atomind., INSPEC, Int.Aerosp.Abstr., Math.R. **Document type:** academic/scholarly publication.
—BLDSC (5405.800000); Ei; Faxon; Genuine Article; SWETS; UMI; UnCover. **CCC.**
     Description: Covers all aspects of numerical mathematics, tables and technical notes.
     Refereed Serial

MATHEMATICS OF CONTROL, SIGNALS AND SYSTEMS. see *ENGINEERING — Industrial Engineering*

MATHEMATICS OF OPERATIONS RESEARCH. see *COMPUTERS*

510 370   II   ISSN 0025-5742
QA1   CODEN: MTHSBH
MATHEMATICS STUDENT. 1933. q. $60. Indian Mathematical Society, Meerut University, Department of Mathematics, Meerut 250 005, India. Ed. A.M. Vaidya. bk.rev. circ. 1,200. **Indexed:** Math.R.
—BLDSC (5407.000000); Faxon; SWETS.
     Description: Presents study and teaching methods and research papers.

510 370   US   ISSN 0025-5769
QA1
MATHEMATICS TEACHER. 1908. m. (Sep.-May). $45 to individuals; institutions $50. National Council of Teachers of Mathematics, 1906 Association Dr., Reston, VA 22091. TEL 703-620-9840. FAX 703-476-2970. E-mail: nctmath@tmn.com. Ed. Harry B. Tunis; Pub. James D. Gates. adv.; bk.rev.; bibl.; illus.; index, cum.index: 1908-1965, 1966-1975, 1976-1985. circ. 58,000. (also avail. in microform from UMI; reprint service avail. from UMI) **Indexed:** Biog.Ind., C.I.J.E., Cont.Pg.Educ., Educ.Ind., Except.Child.Educ.Abstr., LAMP, Math.R., Media Rev.Dig., Yrbk.Assoc.Educ.& Rehab.Blind.
—BLDSC (5407.200000); Faxon; SWETS; UMI; UnCover.
     Description: Articles and features on the improvement of mathematics instruction in junior and senior high schools, two-year colleges, and teacher education colleges.
     Refereed Serial

MATHEMATICS

510.78 370   UK   ISSN 0025-5785
MATHEMATICS TEACHING. 1956. q. £42 to individual members; institutional members £60 (effective 1996) (includes Micromath). Association of Teachers of Mathematics, 7 Shaftesbury St., Derby DE3 8YB, England. TEL 01332-46599. FAX 01332-204257. Eds. B. & D. Ball. adv.; bk.rev.; circ. 3,800 (controlled). (tabloid format; also avail. in microfilm from UMI; reprint service avail. from UMI) **Indexed:** C.I.J.E., Cont.Pg.Educ., Educ.Ind., High.Educ.Curr.Aware.Bull., Res.High.Educ.Abstr., Tech.Educ.Abstr. **Document type:** trade publication.
—BLDSC (5407.500000); SWETS; UMI; UnCover. CCC.
Description: Presents study and teaching methods.

510 370   US   ISSN 1072-0839
QA13
▼**MATHEMATICS TEACHING IN THE MIDDLE SCHOOL.** 1994. 5/yr. (during school year). $45 to individuals; institutions $50; students $22.50. National Council of Teachers of Mathematics, 1906 Association Dr., Reston, VA 22091-1593. TEL 703-620-9840. FAX 703-476-2970. E-mail: nctmath@tmn.com. Ed. Harry B. Tunis; Pub. James D. Gates. adv. circ. 26,000. **Indexed:** C.I.J.E., Cont.Pg.Educ. **Document type:** academic/scholarly publication.
—UMI.
Description: Publishes articles, teaching ideas and features on the improvement of mathematics instruction in junior high and middle schools.
Refereed Serial

510   II
MATHEMATICS TODAY. m. H-2A, Green Park Extension, New Delhi 110 016, India. TEL 664119.
Description: Devoted to mathematics education in India.

510   GW   ISSN 0543-100X
MATHEMATIK FUER NATURWISSENSCHAFT UND TECHNIK. 1957. irreg. price varies. VEB Deutscher Verlag der Wissenschaften, Postfach 1216, 1080 Berlin, Germany. Eds. H. Heinrich, H. Schubert.

371 510   GW   ISSN 0465-3750
MATHEMATIK IN DER SCHULE. 1963. 11/yr. DM.60.50. Paedagogischer Zeitschriftenverlag, Postfach 269, 10107 Berlin, Germany. TEL 030-20343431. FAX 030-20343432. bk.rev.; bibl.; index. circ. 7,600. **Document type:** academic/scholarly publication.
—SWETS.

MATHEMATIK LEHREN. see *EDUCATION — Teaching Methods And Curriculum*

510 519   UK   ISSN 0025-5793
QA1   CODEN: MTKAAB
MATHEMATIKA; a journal of pure and applied mathematics. 1954. s-a. £52. (University College London, Department of Mathematics) J.W. Arrowsmith Ltd., 71 Winterstoke Rd., Bristol BS3 2NT, England. TEL 0117-9667545. FAX 0117-9637829. Ed.Bd. bk.rev.; bibl.; charts; index. circ. 750. **Indexed:** Appl.Mech.Rev., Compumath, Curr.Cont., Ind.Sci.Rev., Math.R., Zent.Math. **Document type:** academic/scholarly publication.
—BLDSC (5408.000000); Faxon; Genuine Article; SWETS; UnCover.

510 371   GW   ISSN 0025-5807
DER MATHEMATIKUNTERRICHT; Beitraege zu seiner wissenschaftlichen und methodischen Gestaltung. 1955. 6/yr. DM.124.80 (foreign DM.132). Erhard Friedrich Verlag GmbH, Im Brande 17, 30926 Seelze, Germany. TEL 0511-40004-0. FAX 0511-4000444. (Subscr. to: Postfach 100150, 30917 Seelze, Germany) Ed.Bd. index, cum.index. circ. 5,100. **Indexed:** Math.R. **Document type:** academic/scholarly publication.
—BLDSC (5408.070000); SWETS. CCC.

510   GW   ISSN 0025-5831
QA1   CODEN: MAANA3
MATHEMATISCHE ANNALEN. (Text in English) 1868. 12/yr. (in 3 vols., 4 nos./vol.). DM.3432($2494) (effective 1996). Springer-Verlag, Heidelberger Platz 3, 14197 Berlin, Germany. TEL 030-8207-0. FAX 030-8214091. E-mail: orders@springer.de. (Subscr. in N. America to: Springer-Verlag New York, Inc., 44 Hartz Way, Secaucus, NJ 07096-2491. TEL 201-348-4033. FAX 201-348-4505) Ed. H. Bauer. adv.; charts; illus. (also avail. in microform from UMI,PMC; back issues avail.; reprint service avail. from ISI) **Indexed:** Compumath, Curr.Cont., Ind.Sci.Rev., Math.R., Zent.Math. **Document type:** academic/scholarly publication.
—BLDSC (5410.000000); Faxon; Genuine Article; SWETS; UMI; UnCover. CCC.
Description: Covers mathematics, especially complex analysis, algebraic geometry, algebraic number theory, modular forms, differential geometry, and functional analysis.

510   GW   ISSN 0340-4358
CODEN: MNGBAK
MATHEMATISCHE GESELLSCHAFT IN HAMBURG. MITTEILUNGEN. 1881. s-a. DM.48. Mathematische Gesellschaft in Hamburg, Bundesstr. 55, 20146 Hamburg, Germany. TEL 040-41235124. FAX 040-41235117. Ed. Gerhard Opfer. adv.; index. circ. 800. (back issues avail.) **Document type:** academic/scholarly publication.
—CCC.

510   GW   ISSN 0076-5422
MATHEMATISCHE LEHRBUECHER UND MONOGRAPHIEN. ABTEILUNG 1: MATHEMATISCHE LEHRBUECHER. 1951. irreg., vol.39, 1991. price varies. Akademie Verlag GmbH, Muehlenstr. 33-34, 13187 Berlin, Germany. TEL 030-47889348. FAX 030-47889357. **Document type:** monographic series.

510   GW   ISSN 0076-5430
MATHEMATISCHE LEHRBUECHER UND MONOGRAPHIEN. ABTEILUNG 2: MATHEMATISCHE MONOGRAPHIEN. 1952. irreg., vol.84, 1991. price varies. Akademie Verlag GmbH, Muehlenstr. 33-34, 13187 Berlin, Germany. TEL 030-47889348. FAX 030-47889357. **Document type:** monographic series.
—BLDSC (5410.300000).

510   GW   ISSN 0543-1042
MATHEMATISCHE MONOGRAPHIEN. 1958. irreg. price varies. VEB Deutscher Verlag der Wissenschaften, Postfach 1216, 1080 Berlin, Germany. Eds. W. Groebner, H. Reichardt. **Document type:** monographic series.

510   GW   ISSN 0025-584X
QA1   CODEN: MTMNAQ
MATHEMATISCHE NACHRICHTEN. (Text in English, French, German; summaries in English) 1948. 6/yr. DM.298 to individuals; institutions DM.1948 (effective 1996). Akademie Verlag GmbH, Muehlenstr. 33-34, 13187 Berlin, Germany. TEL 030-47889348. FAX 030-47889357. Ed. R. Mennicken. adv.; charts; illus. (reprint service avail. from SWZ) **Indexed:** Compumath, Curr.Cont., Ind.Sci.Rev., Math.R., Stat.Theor.Meth.Abstr. **Document type:** academic/scholarly publication.
—Faxon; Genuine Article; SWETS; UnCover.

510   GW   ISSN 0076-5449
MATHEMATISCHE SCHUELERBUECHEREI. 1956. irreg. price varies. VEB Deutscher Verlag der Wissenschaften, Postfach 1216, 1080 Berlin, Germany. **Indexed:** Math.R.

510 530   GW   ISSN 0720-728X
MATHEMATISCHE SEMESTERBERICHTE; zur Foerderung der Mathematik in Unterricht und Kultur. 1932. 2/yr. DM.92($66) (effective 1996). Springer-Verlag, Heidelberger Platz 3, 14197 Berlin, Germany. TEL 030-8207-0. FAX 030-8214091. E-mail: orders@springer.de. (U.S. subscr. to: Springer-Verlag New York, Inc., 44 Hartz Way, Secaucus, NJ 07096-2491. TEL 201-348-4033. FAX 201-348-4505) Ed. N. Knoche. adv.; bk.rev.; charts; illus.; index. circ. 580. **Indexed:** Math.R. **Document type:** academic/scholarly publication.
—BLDSC (5410.720000); Faxon; SWETS; UMI. CCC.
Formerly: Mathematisch-Physikalische Semesterberichte (ISSN 0340-4897)

510 500 370   GW   ISSN 0025-5866
CODEN: MNWUAL
DER MATHEMATISCHE UND NATURWISSENSCHAFTLICHE UNTERRICHT. 1948. 8/yr. DM.82. Ferd. Duemmlers Verlag, Kaiserstr. 31-37, 53113 Bonn, Germany. TEL 0228-223031. FAX 0228-213040. (Subscr. to: Postfach 1480, 53004 Bonn, Germany) Ed. Helmut Schmidt. adv.; bk.rev.; illus.; index. circ. 8,000. **Indexed:** Chem.Abstr., Excerp.Med., Math.R. **Document type:** academic/scholarly publication.
—BLDSC (5410.800000); CASDDS; SWETS. CCC.

510   GW   ISSN 0025-5874
QA1   CODEN: MAZEAX
MATHEMATISCHE ZEITSCHRIFT. (Text in English) 1918. 12/yr. (in 3 vols., 4 nos./vol.). DM.3084($2241) (effective 1996). Springer-Verlag, Heidelberger Platz 3, 14197 Berlin, Germany. TEL 030-8207-0. FAX 030-8214091. E-mail: orders@springer.de. (Subscr. in N. America to: Springer-Verlag New York, Inc., 44 Hartz Way, Secaucus, NJ 07096-2491. TEL 201-348-4033. FAX 201-348-4505) Ed.Bd. adv.; bibl.; index. (also avail. in microform from UMI,PMC; back issues avail.; reprint service avail. from ISI) **Indexed:** Chem.Abstr., Compumath, Curr.Cont., Ind.Sci.Rev., Math.R., Zent.Math. **Document type:** academic/scholarly publication.
—Faxon; Genuine Article; SWETS; UMI; UnCover. CCC.
Description: Covers a variety of topics in modern mathematics, from algebra to analysis and applied disciplines.

510   GW   ISSN 0373-8221
QA1   CODEN: MMUGAU
MATHEMATISCHEN SEMINAR GIESSEN. MITTEILUNGEN. (Text in English and German) 1921. 6/yr. DM.100. Mathematischen Seminar Giessen, Arndtstr. 2, 35392 Giessen, Germany. Eds. Dieter Gaier, F. Timmesfeld. (back issues avail.) **Document type:** academic/scholarly publication.
—BLDSC (5878.360000); UnCover.

510   MX   ISSN 0185-6200
QA21   CODEN: MATHEG
MATHESIS; filosofia e historia de las ciencias matematicas. (Text in Spanish; abstracts in English, Spanish) 1985. q. Mex.$60($30) to individuals; institutions $60 (effective 1996). Universidad Nacional Autonoma de Mexico, Departamento de Matematicas, Ciudad Universitaria, Cubiculo No. 016, 04510 Mexico DF, Mexico. TEL 525-622-48-58. FAX 525-622-48-59. E-mail: mathesis@servidor.unam.mx. Ed. Alejandro R. Garciadiego. bk.rev.; adv.; bibl.; illus.; cum.index: 1985-1992, 1985-1994. circ. 1,000. **Indexed:** Amer.Hist.& Life (1993-), Hist.Abstr. (1993-), Phil.Ind. **Document type:** academic/scholarly publication.
Description: Covers all periods and subjects in the history and philosophy of the mathematical sciences. Provides a forum for original research.
Refereed Serial

MECHANICS. see *PHYSICS — Mechanics*

510   NE
MECHANICS AND MATHEMATICAL METHODS - SERIES OF HANDBOOKS. Series A: Computational Methods in Mechanics (ISSN 0169-300X); Series B: Thermal Stresses (ISSN 0921-9749); Series C: Acoustic, Electronic and Elastic Wave Scattering (ISSN 0921-9331) (Text in English) 1983. irreg., vol.C1, 1991. price varies. Elsevier Science B.V., Books Division, P.O. Box 211, 1000 AE Amsterdam, Netherlands. TEL 31-20-4853911. FAX 31-20-4853705. TELEX 18582 ESPA NL. E-mail: nlinfo-f@elsevier.nl; usinfo-f@elsevier.com; forinfo-kyf04035@niftyserve.or.jp; Site addr.: http://www.elsevier.nl/. (Subscr. in U.S. and Canada to: Elsevier Science Inc., Box 882, Madison Sq. Sta., New York, NY 10159. TEL 212-989-5800) Ed. J.D. Achenbach. **Indexed:** INSPEC. **Document type:** monographic series.
Refereed Serial

510   MY   ISSN 0126-9003
MENEMUI MATEMATIK. (Text in English, Malay) 1979. 3/yr. $50. Malaysian Mathematical Society, c/o Department of Mathematics, University of Malaya, 59100 Kuala Lumpur, Malaysia. Ed. Ng Boon Yian.

510 530　　　　GW　ISSN 0170-9321
METHODEN UND VERFAHREN DER MATHEMATISCHEN PHYSIK. 1969. irreg., no.40, 1995. price varies. (Bibliographies Institut) Peter Lang GmbH Europaeischer Verlag der Wissenschaften, Eschborner Landstr. 42-50, 60489 Frankfurt a.M., Germany. TEL 069-7807050. FAX 069-785893. Eds. Bruno Brosowski, Erich Martensen.

515　　　　US　ISSN 1073-2772
▼**METHODS AND APPLICATIONS OF ANALYSIS.** 1994. q. $100 to individuals; institutions $200. International Press, Box 2872, Cambridge, MA 02238-2872. TEL 617-491-0329. FAX 617-491-0329. E-mail: IP@math.harvard.edu. Eds. Robert M. Miura, Roderick S.C. Wong. **Document type:** academic/scholarly publication.
—BLDSC (5746.610000).
　Description: Publishes mathematical papers treating that part of analysis that has direct or potential applications to the biological and physical sciences and engineering.

METRIKA; international journal for theoretical and applied statistics. see *STATISTICS*

510　　　　US　ISSN 0026-2285
QA1
MICHIGAN MATHEMATICAL JOURNAL. (Text in English, French) 1952. 3/yr. $50 to individuals; institutions $90 (typically set in Jan.). University of Michigan, Department of Mathematics, Ann Arbor, MI 48109-1003. TEL 313-763-2150. FAX 313-764-2495. Ed. M.S. Ramanujan. index; circ. 1,200 (paid). **Indexed:** Compumath, Curr.Cont., Ind.Sci.Rev., Math.R. **Document type:** academic/scholarly publication.
—Faxon; SWETS; UnCover.

510.78 370　　　　UK　ISSN 0267-5501
MICROMATH. 1985. 3/yr. £42 to individual members; institutional members £60 (effective 1996) (includes Mathematics Teaching). Association of Teachers of Mathematics, 7 Shaftesbury St., Derby DE23 8YB, England. TEL 01332-46599. FAX 01332-204357. Eds. Janet Ainley, Ronnie Goldstein. adv.; bk.rev. circ. 6,000. (also avail. in microform; reprint service avail. from SWZ) **Indexed:** Cont.Pg.Educ., Tech.Educ.Abstr. **Document type:** trade publication.
—BLDSC (5759.190000); SWETS; UMI; UnCover. **CCC.**

511　　　　US　ISSN 1047-5982
MODERN LOGIC; international journal of the history of mathematical logic, set theory, and foundation of mathematics. (Text in English, French, German, Russian, Spanish) 1990. q. $110 (effective 1996). Modern Logic Publishing, 2408 1/2 W. Lincoln Way, Ames, IA 50014-7217. TEL 515-292-1819. E-mail: f1.mlp@isumvs. (Subscr. to: Order & Subscription Department, Modern Logic Publishing, 2408 1/2 W. Lincoln Way, Upper Level, Ames, IA 50014-7217, USA) Ed. Irving H. Anellis. bk.rev. circ. 120.
Document type: academic/scholarly publication.
—BLDSC (5888.500000).
　Description: Publishes expository surveys and historical studies of 19th- and 20th-century mathematical logic, set theory, and foundation of mathematics.
Refereed Serial

510　　　　AU　ISSN 0026-9255
　　　　　　CODEN: MNMTA2
MONATSHEFTE FUER MATHEMATIK. (Text in English and German) 1890. 8/yr. (in 2 vols., 4 nos./vol.). DM.880($639) (effective 1996). Springer-Verlag, Sachsenplatz 4-6, Postfach 89, A-1201 Vienna, Austria. TEL 0222-3302415. FAX 0222-3302426. (N. American subscr. to: Journal Fulfillment Services, Box 2485, Secaucus, NJ 07096-2491. TEL 800-777-4643. FAX 201-348-4505; Elsewhere: Heidelberger Platz 3, 1000 Berlin 33, Germany. TEL 030-8207-1. FAX 030-821-4091) Ed. S. Graber. adv.; bk.rev.; charts; illus.; index. (also avail. in microform from UMI; reprint service avail. from ISI) **Indexed:** ASCA, Compumath, Curr.Cont., Ind.Sci.Rev., Math.R., Zent.Math. **Document type:** academic/scholarly publication.
—Faxon; Genuine Article; SWETS; UMI; UnCover. **CCC.**
　Description: Devoted to research in pure mathematics in its broadest significance.

510　　　　BL　ISSN 0100-0934
MONOGRAFIAS DE MATEMATICA. 1969. irreg., no.53, 1992. $15. Instituto de Matematica Pura e Aplicada, Estrada Dona Castorna, 110 Jardim Botanico, CEP 22460-320 Rio de Janeiro RJ, Brazil. TEL 55-21-2949032. FAX 55-21-5124115. TELEX 21-21145 IAMP. E-mail: impa@impa.br. Ed. Jacob Palis. circ. 600. **Indexed:** Math.R. **Document type:** monographic series, academic/scholarly publication.

510　　　　RM
MONOGRAFII MATEMATICE. 1973. irreg. 120 lei($5) Universitatea din Timisoara, Facultatea de Matematica, Bd. Vasile Pirvan Nr. 4, Timisoara, Rumania. Ed. Dumitru Gaspar. circ. 150. **Indexed:** Math.R. **Document type:** monographic series.

510　　　　US
MONOGRAPHS IN CONTEMPORARY MATHEMATICS. (Text in English) irreg., latest 1994. price varies. Plenum Publishing Corp., Consultants Bureau, 233 Spring St., New York, NY 10012-1578. TEL 212-620-8000. FAX 212-463-0742. Ed. Revaz Gamkrelidze. (back issues avail.) **Document type:** monographic series.
　Formerly (until 1994): Contemporary Soviet Mathematics.
　Description: Publishes the latest developments in Russian mathematical research.
Refereed Serial

510　　　　US
MONOGRAPHS ON NUMERICAL ANALYSIS. irreg. price varies. Oxford University Press, 200 Madison Ave., New York, NY 10016. TEL 212-679-7300. Eds. J. Walsh, L. Fox. **Indexed:** Math.R. **Document type:** monographic series.
Refereed Serial

510.8　　　　US　ISSN 0077-1554
QA1　　　　　CODEN: TMMSD4
MOSCOW MATHEMATICAL SOCIETY. TRANSACTIONS. English translation of: Moskovskoe Matematicheskoe Obshchestvo. Trudy (RU ISSN 0134-8663) 1978. a. $253 to non-members; institutional members $202. American Mathematical Society, Box 6248, Providence, RI 02940-6248. TEL 401-455-4000. (Street addr.: 201 Charles St., Providence, RI 02904) (Co-sponsor: London Mathematical Society) Ed. Ben Silver. circ. 600. **Indexed:** Math.R. **Document type:** academic/scholarly publication.
—BLDSC (0427.800000); SWETS. **CCC.**

510　　　　US　ISSN 0027-1322
　　　　　　CODEN: MUMBA
MOSCOW UNIVERSITY MATHEMATICS BULLETIN. English translation of: Moskovskii Universitet. Vestnik. Seriya 1: Matematika i Mekhanika (RU ISSN 0579-9368) 1966. bi-m. $875 (effective 1996). (Moskovskii Universitet, RU) Allerton Press, Inc., 150 Fifth Ave., New York, NY 10011. TEL 212-924-3950. FAX 212-463-9684. Ed. O.B. Lupanov. bk.rev.; abstr.; bibl.; charts; illus.; index. **Indexed:** Appl.Mech.Rev., Math.R. **Document type:** academic/scholarly publication.
—BLDSC (0416.239000); Faxon; SWETS; UnCover. **CCC.**

510 531　　　　RU　ISSN 0579-9368
QA1　　　　　CODEN: VMMMA5
MOSKOVSKII UNIVERSITET. VESTNIK. SERIYA 1: MATEMATIKA I MEKHANIKA. English translations of: Moskovskii Universitet Mathematics Bulletin (ISSN 0027-1322); Moscow University Mechanics Bulletin (US ISSN 0027-1330) (Text in Russian; contents page in English) bi-m. $85 (effective 1996). Moskovskii Universitet, Ul. Gertsena 5-7, 103009 Moscow, Russia. bk.rev.; bibl.; index. **Indexed:** Int.Aerosp.Abstr., Math.R.
—**CCC.**

510　　　　RU　ISSN 0134-8663
MOSKOVSKOE MATEMATICHESKOE OBSHCHESTVO. TRUDY. English translation: Moscow Mathematical Society. Transactions (US ISSN 0077-1554) 1952. irreg. 2.90 Rub. per no. Moskovskii Universitet, Moskovskoe Matematicheskoe Obshchestvo, Universitetskii Prospekt, 13, Moscow V-234, Russia. Ed. O. Oleinik. bibl.; illus. circ. 1,270. **Indexed:** Int.Aerosp.Abstr., Math.R. **Document type:** academic/scholarly publication.
—BLDSC (0330.600000).

510 500　　　　NE　ISSN 0258-2023
　　　　　　CODEN: NSCSDW
N A T O ADVANCED SCIENCE INSTITUTES SERIES C: MATHEMATICAL AND PHYSICAL SCIENCES. (Text in English) irreg., vol.411, 1993. price varies. (North Atlantic Treaty Organization, Scientific Affairs Division, BE) Kluwer Academic Publishers, Postbus 17, 3300 AA Dordrecht, Netherlands. TEL 31-78-392392. FAX 31-78-392254. TELEX 29245 KAPG NL. (Dist. by: Kluwer Academic Publishing Group, P.O. Box 322, 3300 AH Dordrecht, Netherlands. TEL 31-78-392392. FAX 31-78-546474; N. America dist. addr.: Box 358, Accord Sta., Hingham, MA 02018-0358. TEL 617-871-6600. FAX 617-871-6528) **Indexed:** GeoRef., INSPEC, Meteor.& Geoastrophys.Abstr., Phys.Ber. **Document type:** monographic series.
　●Also available online. Vendor(s): European Space Agency (File no.128).
—BLDSC (6033.648730); CASDDS; SWETS. **CCC.**
　Formerly (until 1983): N A T O Advanced Study Institutes Series. Series C: Mathematical and Physical Sciences (ISSN 0377-2071)
Refereed Serial

N C T M NEWS BULLETIN. (National Council of Teachers of Mathematics) see *EDUCATION — Teaching Methods And Curriculum*

510　　　　JA　ISSN 0027-7630
QA1　　　　　CODEN: NGMJA2
NAGOYA MATHEMATICAL JOURNAL/NAGOYA SUGAKU ZASSHI. (Text in English, French, German) 1950. q. $339 (effective 1994). Nagoya Daigaku Rigakubu, Sugaku Kyoshitsu - Nagoya University, School of Science, Department of Mathematics, Chikusa-ku, Nagoya 464-01, Japan. TEL 52-781-4437. (Subscr. to: Kinokuniya Shoten - Kinokuniya Co., Ltd., 17-7, Shinjuku 3-chome, Shinjuku-ku, Tokyo 160, Japan; Subscr. in US to: Kinokuniya Book Stores of America Co., Ltd., West Bldg., Japanese Cultural and Trade Center, 1581 Webster St., San Francisco, CA 94115) Ed. Y. Shikata. charts; index, cum.index: vols.1-40, 41-70, also vols.1-100 in 1985, vols.101-110 in 1988, vols.111-120 in 1990, vols.121-130 in 1993; circ. 1,250 (controlled). **Indexed:** Compumath, Curr.Cont., Ind.Sci.Rev., Math.R., Sci.Cit.Ind. **Document type:** academic/scholarly publication.
—Faxon; Genuine Article; SWETS; UnCover.
　Description: Publishes research papers on mathematics.

510　　　　JA　ISSN 0288-500X
NANZAN UNIVERSITY. NANZAN ACADEMIC SOCIETY. BULLETIN. (Text and summaries in English, Japanese) 1983. irreg. Nanzan University, Nanzan Academic Society - Nanzan Daigaku Nanzan Gakkai, 18, Yamazato-cho, Showa-ku, Nagoya-shi, Aichi-ken 466, Japan.

510　　　　IR　ISSN 1015-2857
NASHR-I RIYAZY/MATHEMATICS JOURNAL. (Text in Persian) 1988. 2/yr. IRI.2700 (Middle East £12; Europe £13; elsewhere £14). Markaz-i Nashr-i Danishgahi - Iran University Press, 85 Park Ave., Dr. Bihishti Ave., P.O. Box 15875-4748, Tehran, Iran. TEL 98-21-8713232. FAX 98-21-8861749. TELEX 213636-8-D5300. Ed. S. Shahshahani. circ. 3,000. **Document type:** academic/scholarly publication.
　Description: Publishes advances in mathematics and its applications, as well as studies of cultural, historical and philosophical aspects.

510 370　　　　US
NATIONAL COUNCIL OF TEACHERS OF MATHEMATICS. PROFESSIONAL REFERENCE SERIES. 1980. irreg. National Council of Teachers of Mathematics, 1906 Association Dr., Reston, VA 22091. TEL 703-620-9840. FAX 703-476-2970. E-mail: nctmath@tmn.com. (reprint service avail. from UMI) **Document type:** monographic series.
　Description: Scholarly monographs on topics of interest to mathematics teachers and educators.

MATHEMATICS

510 370 US ISSN 0077-4103
QA1
NATIONAL COUNCIL OF TEACHERS OF MATHEMATICS. YEARBOOK. 1926. a. $20. National Council of Teachers of Mathematics, 1906 Association Dr., Reston, VA 22091. TEL 703-620-9840. FAX 703-476-2970. E-mail: nctmath@tmn.com. circ. controlled. (also avail. in microform from UMI; back issues avail.; reprint service avail. from UMI) Indexed: Educ.Ind. **Document type:** academic/scholarly publication.
—BLDSC (9391.000000); UMI.
Description: Scholarly papers of interest to mathematics teachers and educators.

NATIONAL INSTITUTE OF STANDARDS AND TECHNOLOGY. JOURNAL OF RESEARCH. see *METROLOGY AND STANDARDIZATION*

510 KR
NELINEINYE GRANICHNYE ZADACHI; respublikanskii mezhvedomstvennyi sbornik nauchnykh trudov. 1989. a. (Akademiya Nauk Ukrainy, Institut Prikladnoi Matematiki i Mekhaniki) Vidavnitstvo Naukova Dumka, Vul. Tereshchenkivska 3, 252601 Kiev, Ukraine. TEL 044-224-4069. FAX 044-224-7060. (Dist. by: Mezhdunarodnaya Kniga, B. Yakimanka 39, 117049 Moscow, Russia) Ed. I.V. Skripnik.

NEW PARADIGMS NEWSLETTER. see *SCIENCES: COMPREHENSIVE WORKS*

519 NE ISSN 0928-1614
NEW TRENDS IN PROBABILITY AND STATISTICS. (Text in English) 1991. irreg., vol.2, 1992. price varies. V S P, P.O. Box 346, 3700 AH Zeist, Netherlands. TEL 31-3404-25790. FAX 31-3404-32081. (Dist. in U.S. and Canada by: Books International Inc., Box 605, Herndon, VA 22070. TEL 703-435-7064. FAX 703-689-0660) (back issues avail.) **Document type:** monographic series.

510 NZ ISSN 1171-6096
QA1 CODEN: MTHCB3
NEW ZEALAND JOURNAL OF MATHEMATICS. 1969. s-a. NZ.$25 to individuals; institutions NZ.$50. University of Auckland, Department of Mathematics, Private Bag 92019, Auckland, New Zealand. FAX 64-9-3737457. E-mail: nzjmath@mat.aukuni.ac.nz. (Co-sponsor: New Zealand Mathematical Society) Ed. J.CC. Butcher. bibl.; charts; cum.index: vols.1-10. circ. 300. Indexed: Math.R. **Document type:** academic/scholarly publication.
—BLDSC (6094.560000).
Formerly (until vol.20, 1991): Mathematical Chronicle (ISSN 0581-1155)
Description: Publishes research papers and expository or survey articles in pure and applied mathematics.

510 NE ISSN 0028-9825
QA1
NIEUW ARCHIEF VOOR WISKUNDE. (Text in English; occasionally in Dutch, French, German) 1875. 3/yr. fl.97.50 (foreign fl.117.50). Stichting Mathematisch Centrum, Kruislaan 413, 1098 SJ Amsterdam, Netherlands. TEL 31-20-592-9333. FAX 31-20-592-4199. TELEX 12571 MATCTR NL. (Subscr. to: Stichting Mathematisch Centrum, Postbus 4079, 1009 AB Amsterdam, Netherlands) (Co-sponsor: Wiskundig Genootschap) Eds. M. Hazewinkel, H. Bart. adv.; bk.rev.; index. circ. 2,000. Indexed: Math.R., Ref.Zh., Zent.Math. **Document type:** academic/scholarly publication.
—BLDSC (6111.000000); SWETS; UnCover.

511 JA
NIHONKAI MATHEMATICAL JOURNAL. (Text in English) 1964. s-a. exchange basis. Niigata Daigaku, Rigakubu - Niigata University, Faculty of Science, c/o Dept. of mathematics, 8050, Igarashi 2, Niigata, 951-21, Japan. Ed. Tsuyoshi Watabe. Indexed: Math.R.
Formerly (until 1990): Niigata University. Faculty of Science. Science Reports. Series A: Mathematics - Niigata Daigaku Rigakubu Kenkyu Hokoku. A-rui, Sugaku (ISSN 0369-576X)
Refereed Serial

510 500 SZ ISSN 1021-9722
▼**NO D E A - NONLINEAR DIFFERENTIAL EQUATIONS AND APPLICATIONS.** (Text in English) 1994. q. 306.20 SFr. (foreign 318.40 SFr.). Birkhaeuser Verlag, P.O. Box 133, CH-4010 Basel, Switzerland. TEL 061-2717400. FAX 061-2717666. (Dist. in N. America by: Springer-Verlag, Mercedes Distribution Center, 160 Imlay St., Brooklyn, NY 11231, USA) Ed. L. Salvadori. **Document type:** academic/scholarly publication.
—BLDSC (6115.155350).

519.5 NE
▼**NONCONVEX OPTIMIZATION AND ITS APPLICATIONS.** (Text in English) 1994. irreg., vol.2, 1995. price varies. Kluwer Academic Publishers, Postbus 17, 3300 AA Dordrecht, Netherlands. TEL 31-78-392392. FAX 31-78-392254. TELEX 29245 KAPG NL. (Dist. by: Kluwer Academic Publishers Group, P.O. Box 322, 3300 AH Dordrecht, Netherlands. TEL 31-78-392392. FAX 31-78-546474; N. America dist. addr.: Box 358, Accord Sta., Hingham, MA 02018-0358. TEL 617-871-6600. FAX 617-871-6528) Eds. Panos Pardalos, Reiner Horst. **Document type:** monographic series.

510 UK
NONLINEAR SCIENCE: THEORY AND APPLICATIONS. 1985. irreg. price varies. John Wiley & Sons Ltd., Journals, Baffins Lane, Chichester, W. Sussex PO19 1UD, England. TEL 01243-779777. FAX 01243-776128. TELEX 96290 WIBOOK G. Ed. A.V. Holden. **Document type:** academic/scholarly publication.

519 US ISSN 0938-9008
QA427 CODEN: NSTOE4
NONLINEAR SCIENCE TODAY. (Print edition ceased with 1994 publication of vol.4, no.4) 1991. q. free. Springer-Verlag, Journals, 175 Fifth Ave., New York, NY 10010. TEL 212-460-1500. FAX 212-473-6272. E-mail: em-helpdesk@sprint-ny.com; Site addr.: http://www.springer-ny.com/nst. (N. American subscr. to: Box 2485, Secaucus, NJ 07096-2491. TEL 800-777-4643. FAX 201-348-4505; Elsewhere: Heidelberger Platz 3, 1000 Berlin 33, Germany. TEL 030-8207-1. FAX 030-821-4091) Eds. P. Holmes, R. Behringer. (also avail. in microform from UMI; back issues avail.; reprint service avail.) **Document type:** academic/scholarly publication, newsletter.
●Also available online.
—BLDSC (6117.318000); Genuine Article; SWETS; UnCover. **CCC.**
Description: Informal organ of communication on interdisciplinary issues, problems and methods, including professional news, calendars of meetings and workshops, and discussion of controversies.

519.5 NE ISSN 0925-6660
NONLINEAR TOPICS IN THE MATHEMATICAL SCIENCES. (Text in English) 1990. irreg. price varies. Kluwer Academic Publishers, Postbus 17, 3300 AA Dordrecht, Netherlands. TEL 31-78-392392. FAX 31-78-392254. TELEX 29245 KAPG NL. (Dist. by: Kluwer Academic Publishers Group, P.O. Box 322, 3300 AH Dordrecht, Netherlands. TEL 31-78-392392. FAX 31-78-546474; N. America dist. addr.: Box 358, Accord Sta., Hingham, MA 02018-0358. TEL 617-871-6600. FAX 617-871-6528) **Document type:** monographic series.
—BLDSC (6117.319000).

510 GW ISSN 0942-5608
▼**NONLINEAR WORLD.** 1994. 4/yr. DM.368. (International Federation of Nonlinear Analysts) Walter de Gruyter und Co., Genthiner Str. 13, 10785 Berlin, Germany. TEL 030-26005-0. FAX 030-26005251. TELEX 184027. (U.S. addr.: Walter de Gruyter, Inc., 200 Saw Mill River Rd., Hawthorne, NY 10532. TEL 914-747-0110. FAX 914-747-1326) Eds. V. Lakshmikantham, T. Hallam. adv. contact: Elvira Schmiel. circ. 500. **Document type:** academic/scholarly publication.
—BLDSC (6117.320100).

510 530 UK ISSN 0951-7715
QA427 CODEN: NONLE5
NONLINEARITY. 1988. bi-m. £420($840) (effective 1996). (London Mathematical Society) I O P Publishing Ltd., Techno House, Redcliffe Way, Bristol, Avon BS1 6NX, England. TEL 0117-929-7481. FAX 0117-929-4318. TELEX 449149 INSTP G. (U.S. addr.: American Institute of Physics, Subscr. Serv., 500 Sunnyside Blvd., Woodbury, NY 11797-2999. TEL 516-576-2200) (Co-sponsor: Institute of Physics) Eds. R. Mackay, I Procaccio. index. circ. 699. (also avail. in microform from AIP; microfiche from AIP; back issues avail.) **Indexed:** Abstr.Hum.Comp.Inter., INSPEC (1988-). **Document type:** academic/scholarly publication.
—BLDSC (6117.320500); Faxon; Genuine Article; SWETS; UnCover. **CCC.**
Description: Publishes papers on a wide range of nonlinear mathematics, mathematical and experimental physics and other areas in the sciences where nonlinear phenomena are of fundamental importance.

510 NO ISSN 0801-3500
QA1
NORMAT. (Nordisk Matematisk Tidsskrift) (Text in Scandinavian languages; summaries in English) 1953. q. NOK 380 in Nordic countries; elsewhere $74 (effective 1996). Scandinavian University Press, P.O. Box 2959 Toeyen, N-0608 Oslo, Norway. TEL 47-22-57-54-00. FAX 47-22-57-53-53. (U.S. addr.: Scandinavian University Press, 200 Meacham Ave., Elmont, NY 11003. TEL 516-352-7300) Ed. Jon Reed. bibl.; index. circ. 1,500. **Indexed:** Math.R.
Supersedes (1953-1979): Nordisk Matematisk Tidskrift (ISSN 0029-1412)
Description: Focuses on mathematics, also covering educational aspects.

510 NE ISSN 0924-6509
NORTH-HOLLAND MATHEMATICAL LIBRARY. 1971. irreg., vol.51, 1993. price varies. Elsevier Science B.V., Books Division, P.O. Box 211, 1000 AE Amsterdam, Netherlands. TEL 31-20-4853911. FAX 31-20-4853705. TELEX 18582 ESPA NL. E-mail: nlinfo-f@elsevier.nl; usinfo-f@elsevier.com; forinfo-kyf04035@niftyserve.or.jp; Site addr.: http://www.elsevier.nl/. (Subscr. in U..S and Canada to: Elsevier Science Inc., Box 882, Madison Sq. Sta., New York, NY 10159. TEL 212-989-5800) **Indexed:** INSPEC. **Document type:** monographic series.
—BLDSC (6150.005000).
Refereed Serial

510 NE ISSN 0304-0208
CODEN: NMSTD5
NORTH-HOLLAND MATHEMATICS STUDIES. 1970. irreg., vol.180, 1994. price varies. Elsevier Science B.V., Books Division, P.O. Box 211, 1000 AE Amsterdam, Netherlands. TEL 31-20-4853911. FAX 31-20-4853705. TELEX 18582 ESPA NL. E-mail: nlinfo-f@elsevier.nl; usinfo-f@elsevier.com; forinfo-kyf04035@niftyserve.or.jp; Site addr.: http://www.elsevier.nl/. (Subscr. in U.S. and Canada to: Elsevier Science Inc., Box 882, Madison Sq. Sta., New York, NY 10159. TEL 212-989-5800) **Indexed:** INSPEC. **Document type:** monographic series.
—BLDSC (6150.006000).
Refereed Serial

620 510 NE ISSN 0167-5931
NORTH-HOLLAND SERIES IN APPLIED MATHEMATICS AND MECHANICS. 1967. irreg., vol.37, 1993. price varies. Elsevier Science B.V., Books Division, P.O. Box 211, 1000 AE Amsterdam, Netherlands. TEL 31-20-4853911. FAX 31-20-4853705. TELEX 18582 ESPA NL. E-mail: nlinfo-f@elsevier.nl; usinfo-f@elsevier.com; forinfo-kyf04035@niftyserve.or.jp; Site addr.: http://www.elsevier.nl/. (Subscr. in U.S. and Canada to: Elsevier Science Inc., Box 882, Madison Sq. Sta., New York, NY 10159. TEL 212-989-5800) Ed.Bd. **Indexed:** INSPEC, Math.R. **Document type:** monographic series.
—BLDSC (6150.010000).
Supersedes: Applied Mathematics and Mechanics (ISSN 0066-5460)
Refereed Serial

MATHEMATICS

519.5   NE   ISSN 0168-1974
CODEN: NHSPDQ
NORTH-HOLLAND SERIES IN STATISTICS AND PROBABILITY. (Text in English) 1982. irreg., vol.7, 1993. price varies. Elsevier Science B.V., Books Division, P.O. Box 211, 1000 AE Amsterdam, Netherlands. TEL 31-20-4853911. FAX 31-20-4853705. E-mail: nlinfo-f@elsevier.nl; usinfo-f@elsevier.com; forinfo-kyf04035@niftyserve.or.jp; Site addr.: http://www.elsevier.nl/. (Subscr. in U.S. and Canada to: Elsevier Science Inc., Box 882, Madison Sq. Sta., New York, NY 10159-0882. TEL 212-989-5800. FAX 212-633-3680) **Indexed:** INSPEC. **Document type:** monographic series.
Refereed Serial

510   AG   ISSN 0078-2009
NOTAS DE ALGEBRA Y ANALISIS. (Text in English, French and Spanish) 1966. irreg., no.17, 1991. price varies. Universidad Nacional del Sur, Instituto de Matematica, Avda. Alem 1253, 8000 Bahia Blanca, Argentina. TEL 54-91-25772. FAX 54-91-27876. E-mail: inmabb@arcriba.edu.ar. circ. 1,000. **Indexed:** Math.R., Zent.Math.

510   AG   ISSN 0325-8963
NOTAS DE GEOMETRIA Y TOPOLOGIA. 1980. irreg. Universidad Nacional del Sur, Instituto de Matematica, Avda. Alem 1253, 8000 Bahia Blanca, Argentina. TEL 54-91-25772. FAX 54-91-27876. E-mail: inmabb@arcriba.edu.ar. circ. 750.

510   AG   ISSN 0078-2017
NOTAS DE LOGICA MATEMATICA. (Text in English, French, Portuguese, Spanish) 1963. irreg., no.38, 1994. price varies. Universidad Nacional del Sur, Instituto de Matematica, Avda. Alem 1253, 8000 Bahia Blanca, Argentina. TEL 54-91-25772. FAX 54-91-27876. E-mail: inmabb@arcriba.edu.ar. abstr.; charts; stat. circ. 1,000. **Indexed:** Math.R., Zent.Math.
Description: Covers research in the mathematical sciences.

510   AG   ISSN 0326-1336
NOTAS DE MATEMATICA DISCRETA. 1982. irreg., vol.2, 1994. Universidad Nacional del Sur, Instituto de Matematica, Avda. Alem 1253, 8000 Bahia Blanca, Argentina. TEL 54-91-25772. FAX 54-91-27876. E-mail: inmabb@arcriba.edu.ar. charts; illus. **Indexed:** Math.R.

510   BL   ISSN 0085-5413
NOTAS E COMUNICACOES DE MATEMATICA. (Text in English, French, Portuguese, Spanish) 1965. irreg., vol. 148, 1987. price varies. Universidade Federal de Pernambuco, Departamento de Matematica, Cidade Universitaria, 50.739 Recife, PE, Brazil. FAX 005508127711833. Ed. Sostenes Lins. circ. 125.

510   CL   ISSN 0716-131X
NOTAS MATEMATICAS. English edition: Mathematical Notes. 1972. a. free. Universidad Catolica de Chile, Instituto de Matematicas, Casilla 114-D, Santiago, Chile. (Subscr. to: Instituto de Matematica, Vicuna Mackenna 4860, Santiago, Chile) Ed. Alvaro Cofre. circ. 200.

510   AT   ISSN 0818-304X
NOTES ON PURE MATHEMATICS. 1974. irreg., no.13, 1986. price varies. Australian National University, Department of Mathematics, I A S, G.P.O Box 4, Canberra, A.C.T. 2601, Australia. FAX 61-62-490759. Ed. M.F. Newman. circ. 200. **Document type:** academic/scholarly publication.

511.3 160   US   ISSN 0029-4527
BC1   CODEN: NDJFAM
NOTRE DAME JOURNAL OF FORMAL LOGIC. 1960. q. $25 to individuals; institutions $45. University of Notre Dame, Box 5, Notre Dame, IN 46556. TEL 219-631-6157. FAX 219-631-8609. Ed.Bd. adv.; bk.rev.; index, cum.index. circ. 825. (back issues avail.) **Indexed:** INSPEC, Math.R., Phil.Ind.
—BLDSC (6175.400000); Faxon; SWETS; UnCover.
Description: Focuses on philosophical and mathematical logic.

510   US
QA150
NOVA JOURNAL OF MATHEMATICS, GAME THEORY AND ALGEBRA. 1992. q. $350 (effective 1996). Nova Science Publishers, Inc., 6080 Jericho Tpke., Ste. 207, Commack, NY 11725-2808. TEL 516-499-3103. FAX 516-499-3146. E-mail: novasci1@aol.com. **Document type:** academic/scholarly publication.
Formerly: Nova Journal of Algebra and Geometry (ISSN 1060-9881); Incorporates: Siberian Journal of Computer Mathematics (ISSN 1062-7944)
Description: Devoted to new advances in pure and applied mathematics.

510   US
QA297
NOVA JOURNAL OF THEORETICAL PHYSICS. 1992. q. $325 (effective 1996). Nova Science Publishers, Inc., 6080 Jericho Tpke., Ste. 207, Commack, NY 11725-2808. TEL 516-499-3103. FAX 516-499-3146. E-mail: novasci1@aol.com. Ed. A.V. Andreev. **Document type:** academic/scholarly publication.
Formerly: Journal of Quantum Nonlinear Phenomena (ISSN 1062-8053)
Description: Covers new theoretical and mathematical methods in quantum nonlinear dynamics; nonclassical states in optics; mesoscopy; quantum chaos; and correlative and fluctuative effects in quantum statistics and quantum optics.

510   US
NUMBERS YOU NEED. 1992. quinquennial. $29.95. Gale Research Inc., 835 Penobscot Bldg., Detroit, MI 48266. TEL 313-961-2242. FAX 313-961-6083.
Description: Provides answers and explanations to numerical problems in everyday life.

510   NE   ISSN 1017-1398
QA297   CODEN: NUALEG
NUMERICAL ALGORITHMS. 1991. 8/yr. (in 2 vols., 4 nos./vol.). 682 SFr. (effective 1996). Baltzer Science Publishers B.V., Asterweg 1A, 1031 HL Amsterdam, Netherlands. TEL 31-20-6370061. FAX 31-20-6323651. E-mail: publish@baltzer.nl. (Subscr. in N. America to: Baltzer Science Publishers, Box 8577, Red Bank, NJ 07701-8577) Ed. Claude Brezinski. **Indexed:** INSPEC (1991-). **Document type:** academic/scholarly publication.
—BLDSC (6184.671000); SWETS. CCC.

510   US   ISSN 0163-0563
QA320   CODEN: NFAODL
NUMERICAL FUNCTIONAL ANALYSIS AND OPTIMIZATION; an international journal for rapid publication. 1979. 10/yr. $312.50 to individuals; institutions $625. Marcel Dekker Journals, 270 Madison Ave., New York, NY 10016. TEL 212-696-9000. FAX 212-685-4540. TELEX 421419 MARDEEK. (Subscr. to: Box 5017, Monticello, NY 12701) Ed. M. Z. Nashed. (also avail. in microform from RPI) **Indexed:** Compumath, Curr.Cont., INSPEC, Math.R.
—BLDSC (6184.692000); Ei; Faxon; Genuine Article; SWETS; UMI; UnCover. CCC.
Refereed Serial

512   UK   ISSN 1070-5325
CODEN: NLAAEM
▼**NUMERICAL LINEAR ALGEBRA;** with applications. 1994. bi-m. $315 (foreign $315) (effective 1996). John Wiley & Sons Ltd., Journals, Baffins Ln., Chichester, W. Sussex PO19 1UD, England. TEL 01243-779777. FAX 01243-776128. TELEX 86290 WIBOOK G. (Subscr. in the Americas to: John Wiley & Sons, Inc., 605 Third Ave., New York, NY 10158. TEL 212-850-6645. FAX 212-850-6021) Ed. Owe Axelsson. (also avail. in microform from UMI; back issues avail.) **Document type:** academic/scholarly publication.
—BLDSC (6184.692750).
Refereed Serial

510   US   ISSN 0749-159X
QA377   CODEN: NMPDEB
NUMERICAL METHODS FOR PARTIAL DIFFERENTIAL EQUATIONS: AN INTERNATIONAL JOURNAL. 1985. bi-m. $660 (foreign $753) (effective 1996). John Wiley & Sons, Inc., Journals, 605 Third Ave., New York, NY 10158. TEL 212-850-6645. FAX 212-850-6021. TELEX 12-7063. E-mail: SUBINFO@JWILEY.COM. (Subscr. outside the Americas to: John Wiley & Sons Ltd., Baffins Ln., Chichester, W. Sussex PO19 1UD, England. TEL 44-1243-779777. FAX 44-1243-776128) Ed. George F. Pinder. (also avail. in microform from UMI; back issues avail.) **Indexed:** Appl.Mech.Rev. **Document type:** academic/scholarly publication.
—BLDSC (6184.696600); Ei; Faxon; SWETS; UMI; UnCover. CCC.
Description: Focuses on technique rather than application. Topics include applied numerical analysis, computational methods.
Refereed Serial

NUMERISCHE MATHEMATIK. see *MATHEMATICS — Computer Applications*

500 510   US   ISSN 0379-0207
AS142   CODEN: AMNDBP
OESTERREICHISCHE AKADEMIE DER WISSENSCHAFTEN, VIENNA. MATHEMATISCH - NATURWISSENSCHAFTLICHE KLASSE. DENKSCHRIFTEN. (Text in German) irreg. price varies. Springer-Verlag, 175 Fifth Ave., New York, NY 10010. TEL 212-460-1500. FAX 212-473-6272. (Also: Berlin, Heidelberg, Tokyo and Vienna) (reprint service avail. from ISI) **Indexed:** Biol.Abstr., Math.R. **Document type:** monographic series.
—CCC.
Formerly: Oesterreichische Akademie der Wissenschaften, Vienna. Mathematisch - Naturwissenschaftliche Klasse. Anzeiger (ISSN 0065-535X)

510   GW   ISSN 0942-0363
OHIO STATE UNIVERSITY MATHEMATICAL RESEARCH INSTITUTE PUBLICATIONS. (Text in English) irreg., no. 2, 1992. (Ohio State University, International Mathematical Research Institute) Walter de Gruyter und Co., Genthiner Str. 13, 10785 Berlin, Germany. TEL 030-26005-0. FAX 030-26005-251. (U.S. addr.: Walter de Gruyter, Inc., 200 Saw Mill River Rd., Hawthorne, NY 10532. TEL 914-747-0110) Ed.Bd. **Document type:** academic/scholarly publication.
—BLDSC (6247.423000).

510   UK   ISSN 0261-1023
OKIKIOLU SCIENTIFIC AND INDUSTRIAL ORGANIZATION. BULLETIN OF MATHEMATICS. 1981. q. £24. Okikiolu Scientific and Industrial Co., 377 Edgware Rd., London W2 1BT, England. Ed. Dr. G.O. Okikiolu. **Indexed:** Zent.Math. **Document type:** academic/scholarly publication.
—CCC.
Description: Scholarly research papers on new results of research in mathematics.

510   CN   ISSN 0030-3011
ONTARIO MATHEMATICS GAZETTE. 1962. 4/yr. Can.$40. Ontario Association for Mathematics Education, University of Guelph, Guelph, ON N1G 3A6, Canada. TEL 519-824-4120. FAX 519-837-0221. E-mail: jweiner@msnet.mathstat.uogeulph.ca. Ed. Jack Weiner. adv. contact: Dean Murray. bk.rev.; charts. circ. 1,700. **Document type:** academic/scholarly publication.
Refereed Serial

OPERATIONS RESEARCH. see *COMPUTERS*

519   RU   ISSN 0134-3998
QA402.5
OPTIMIZATSIYA.* 1975. irreg. (5-6/yr.). Rossiiskaya Akademiya Nauk, Sibirskoe Otdelenie, Institute Matematiki, Universitetskii pr. 4, 630090 Novosibirsk, Russia. Ed. L.V. Vantorovich. **Indexed:** Math.R.
—BLDSC (0128.035000).

MATHEMATICS

510 NE ISSN 0167-8094
QA171.48 CODEN: ORDER5
ORDER; a journal on the theory of ordered sets. 1984. q. fl.456 to institutions; $292 to institutions in U.S. (effective 1996). Kluwer Academic Publishers, Postbus 17, 3300 AA Dordrecht, Netherlands. TEL 31-78-392392. FAX 31-78-392254. TELEX 29245 KAPG NL. E-mail: SERVICES@WKAP.NL. (Dist. by: Kluwer Academic Publishers Group, P.O. Box 322, 3300 AH Dordrecht, Netherlands. TEL 31-78-392392. FAX 31-78-546474; N. America dist. addr.: Box 358, Accord Sta., Hingham, MA 02018-0358. TEL 617-871-6600. FAX 617-871-6528) Ed. Ivan Rival. adv.; bk.rev.; charts; index. (also avail. in microform from UMI; reprint service avail. from SWZ) **Indexed:** ASCA, Bull.Signal., Compumath, Math.R., Zent.Math. **Document type:** academic/scholarly publication.
—BLDSC (6278.859000); Faxon; Genuine Article; SWETS; UMI; UnCover. **CCC**.
 Description: Discusses the theory of order and its applications, especially in operations research and computer science.
 Refereed Serial

510 US ISSN 0078-6330
ORGANIZATION OF AMERICAN STATES. DEPARTMENT OF SCIENTIFIC AFFAIRS. SERIE DE MATEMATICA: MONOGRAFIAS. no.2, 1965. irreg., no.22, 1979. $3.50 per no. Organization of American States, Department of Publications, 1889 F St., N.W., Washington, DC 20006. TEL 703-941-1617. **Document type:** monographic series.

510 JA ISSN 0030-6126
QA1 CODEN: OJMAA7
OSAKA JOURNAL OF MATHEMATICS. (Text in English, French, German) 1964. 4/yr. $257. Osaka Daigaku, Rigakubu Sugaku Kyoshitsu - Osaka University, Faculty of Science, Department of Mathematics, 1-1 Machikaneyama-cho, Toyonaka-shi, Osaka-fu 560, Japan. FAX 06-845-1163. (Subscr. to: Kinokuniya Co. Ltd., 17-7 Shinjuku 3-chome, Shinjuku-ku, Tokyo 160-91, Japan) (Co-sponsor: Osaka-shiritsu Daigaku Sugaku Kyoshitsu - Osaka City University, Department of Mathematics) Ed. Mitsuro Ikawa. cum.index: vols.1-15. (reprint service avail.) **Indexed:** Compumath, Math.R., Sci.Cit.Ind. **Document type:** academic/scholarly publication.
—Faxon; SWETS; UnCover.
 Formed by the merger of (1949-1963): Osaka Mathematical Journal; (1950-1963): Journal of Mathematics.

510 530 XR
CODEN: SPPFDO
OSTRAVSKE UNIVERSITY. PRIRODOVEDECKA FAKULTA. SBORNIK PRACI. RADA A: MATEMATIKA, FYZIKA. (Text in Czech; summaries in English, German, Russian) 1971. irreg. Ostravske University, Prirodovedecka Fakulta, Ostrava, Czech Republic. (Subscr.to: c/o Dr. Lubojacza, Dekanat P F Ostrava, Dvorakova c.7, 701 03 Ostrava 1, Czech Republic). illus.
—CASDDS.
 Former titles (until 1992): Pedagogicka Fakulta v Ostrave. Sbornik Praci. Rada A: Matemetika, Fyzika (ISSN 0862-4046); (until 1986): Pedagogicka Fakulta v Ostave. Sbornik Praci. Rada A (ISSN 0139-6498)

519.5 US ISSN 0953-3044
CODEN: OAMSE2
OXFORD APPLIED MATHEMATICS AND COMPUTING SERIES. 1974. irreg. price varies. Oxford University Press, 200 Madison Ave., New York, NY 10016. TEL 212-679-7300. **Indexed:** INSPEC. **Document type:** monographic series.

510 US ISSN 0964-9174
OXFORD MATHEMATICAL MONOGRAPHS. 1979. irreg. price varies. Oxford University Press, 200 Madison Ave., New York, NY 10016. TEL 212-679-7300. **Indexed:** Math.R. **Document type:** monographic series.
 Refereed Serial

OXFORD STATISTICAL SCIENCE SERIES. see *STATISTICS*

OYO TOKEIGAKU/JAPANESE JOURNAL OF APPLIED STATISTICS. see *STATISTICS*

510 US ISSN 0030-8730
QA1 CODEN: PJMAAI
PACIFIC JOURNAL OF MATHEMATICS. 1951. m. (5 vols./yr.). $215. International Press, Pacific Journal of Mathematics, Mathematics Department, University of California, Los Angeles, CA 90095-1555. FAX 310-206-6673. Ed. Sun Yung A. Chang. bibl.; charts; index. circ. 1,600. (back issues avail.; reprint service avail. from KTO) **Indexed:** Compumath, Curr.Cont., Math.R., Zent.Math. **Document type:** academic/scholarly publication.
—BLDSC (6330.000000); Faxon; Genuine Article; SWETS; UnCover.
 Refereed Serial

PARAMETRIC WORLD. see *BUSINESS AND ECONOMICS* — Accounting

510 RU ISSN 1054-6618
TA1650 CODEN: PIANES
PATTERN RECOGNITION AND IMAGE ANALYSIS; advances in mathematical theory and applications. (English translation of Russian title) 1991. 4/yr. $325 in U.S. & Canada (elsewhere $365) (effective 1995). Interperiodica, Ul. Profsoyuznaya 90, Moscow 117864, Russia. TEL 7-095-3360066. FAX 7-095-3360666. (Subscr. to: Interperiodica, Box 1831, Birmingham, AL 35201-1831. TEL 205-995-1567. FAX 205-995-1588) Ed. Yuri Zhuravlev. **Document type:** academic/scholarly publication.
—BLDSC (0416.679700).
 Refereed Serial

510 US ISSN 0031-4870
QA1
THE PENTAGON; a mathematics magazine for students. 1940. s-a. $5 (foreign $7). Kappa Mu Epsilon, c/o Larry Scott, Bus. Manager, Div. of Mathematics & Computer Science, Emporia State University, Emporia, KS 66801. TEL 316-341-5638. E-mail: dawsonbr@esjvm1.emporia.edu. Ed. C. Bryan Dawson. adv.; bk.rev.; index. circ. 3,000. (also avail. in microform from UMI; back issues avail.; reprint service avail. from UMI) **Document type:** academic/scholarly publication.
—UMI; UnCover.
 Refereed Serial

510 NE ISSN 0031-5303
QA1 CODEN: PMHGAW
PERIODICA MATHEMATICA HUNGARICA. (Text in English, French, German; summaries in English) 1970. bi-m. fl.671 to institutions; $431 to institutions in U.S. (effective 1996). (Janos Bolyai Mathematical Society, HU) Kluwer Academic Publishers, Postbus 17, 3300 AA Dordrecht, Netherlands. TEL 31-78-392392. FAX 31-78-392254. TELEX 29245 KAPG NL. E-mail: SERVICES@WKAP.NL. (Dist. by: Kluwer Academic Publishers Group, P.O. Box 322, 3300 AH Dordrecht, Netherlands. TEL 31-78-392392. FAX 31-78-546474; N. America dist. addr.: Box 358, Accord Sta., Hingham, MA 02018-0358. TEL 617-871-6600. FAX 617-871-6528) (Co-publisher: Akademiai Kiado, HU) Ed. I. Ratko. adv.; bk.rev. (also avail. in microform from UMI; back issues avail.) **Indexed:** INSPEC, Math.R., Zent.Math. **Document type:** academic/scholarly publication.
—Faxon; SWETS; UnCover. **CCC**.
 Description: Publishes research articles in any area of pure and applied mathematics, including algebra, geometry, analysis and other topics.
 Refereed Serial

510 US ISSN 0172-6641
CODEN: SSIMDV
PERSPECTIVES IN MATHEMATICAL LOGIC. 1975. irreg. price varies. Springer-Verlag, 175 Fifth Ave., New York, NY 10010. TEL 212-460-1500. FAX 212-473-6272. (reprint service avail. from ISI) **Indexed:** Math.R. **Document type:** academic/scholarly publication.

510 US ISSN 1040-4368
PERSPECTIVES IN MATHEMATICS. 1986. irreg., vol.13, 1990. Academic Press, Inc., 525 B St., Ste. 1900, San Diego, CA 92101-4495. TEL 619-231-6616. FAX 619-699-6715. (Subscr. to: Order Dept., 6277 Sea Harbor Dr., 4th Fl., Orlando, FL 32887. TEL 800-321-5068) Eds. John Coates, Sigurdur Helhason. (back issues avail.)
—BLDSC (6428.144330).
 Refereed Serial

PHILOSOPHIA MATHEMATICA; philosophy of mathematics, its learning, and its application. see *PHILOSOPHY*

510 US ISSN 0031-952X
QA1 CODEN: PMEJBR
PI MU EPSILON JOURNAL. 1949. s-a. $12 for 2 yrs. to non-members; members $8. Pi Mu Epsilon, c/o Matehmatics Dept., DePauw University, Greencastle, IN 46135. TEL 317-658-4488. E-mail: dudley@depauw.edu. Ed. Underwood Dudley. adv.; bk.rev.; charts; illus.; cum.index every 5 yrs.; circ. 4,000 (paid). (also avail. in microform from UMI; back issues avail.; reprint service avail. from UMI) **Indexed:** Math.R. **Document type:** academic/scholarly publication.
—BLDSC (6498.000000); Faxon; UMI; UnCover.
 Description: Research and expository articles, problems and solutions, chapter reports and news items submitted by members.
 Refereed Serial

510 520 530 PL ISSN 0239-7269
QA1 CODEN: BAPMAN
POLISH ACADEMY OF SCIENCES. BULLETIN. MATHEMATICAL SCIENCES. (Text in English, French, German and Russian) 1953. q. $100. Polska Akademia Nauk, Centrum Upowszechniania Nauki, Palac Kultury i Nauki, Pietro XXIII, pok.23-10, 00-901 Warsaw, Poland. (Dist. by: Ars Polona, Krakowskie Przedmiescie 7, 00-068 Warsaw, Poland) Ed. A. Lasota. adv. contact: Ewa Bartkowiak. bibl.; charts; illus. circ. 520. (also avail. in microform from UMI; reprint service avail. from UMI) **Indexed:** Chem.Abstr., INSPEC, Math.R., Met.Abstr., Phys.Ber., Stat.Theor.Meth.Abstr. **Document type:** monographic series, bulletin.
—SWETS; UnCover.
 Formerly (until 1983): Academie Polonaise des Sciences. Bulletin. Serie des Sciences Mathematiques, Astronomiques et Physiques (ISSN 0001-4117).

510 PL ISSN 0072-0372
POLITECHNIKA GDANSKA. ZESZYTY NAUKOWE. MATEMATYKA. (Text in Polish and English; summaries in Russian and one West-European language) 1963. irreg. price varies. Politechnika Gdanska, Ul. G. Narutowicza 11-12, 80-952 Gdansk 6, Poland. (Dist. by: Osrodek Rozpowszechniania Wydawnictw Naukowych PAN, Palac Kultury i Nauki, 00-901 Warsaw, Poland) bibl.; charts; illus. **Document type:** academic/scholarly publication.

510 PL ISSN 0137-2572
POLITECHNIKA LODZKA. ZESZYTY NAUKOWE. MATEMATYKA. (Text in various languages; summaries in Polish and Russian) 1972. irreg. price varies. Wydawnictwo Politechniki Lodzkiej, Ul. Leslaw Gajek, 93-005 Lodz, Poland. (Dist. by: Ars Polona-Ruch, Krakowskie Przedmiescie 7, Warsaw, Poland) Ed. Janusz Matkowski. circ. 166. **Indexed:** Math.R. **Document type:** academic/scholarly publication.
—BLDSC (9512.320000).
 Description: Focuses on applied mathematics.

510 PL ISSN 0239-488X
POLITECHNIKA POZNANSKA. ZESZYTY NAUKOWE. GEOMETRIA. (Text in English, French) irreg. price varies. Politechnika Poznanska, Pl. Curie-Sklodowskiej 5, Poznan, Poland. Ed. Eugeniusz Korczak. **Document type:** academic/scholarly publication.
—BLDSC (9512.322950).
 Formerly: Politechnika Poznanska. Zeszyty Naukowe. Geometria Wykreslna.
 Description: Papers dealing with foundations of geometry, geometry of incidence, non-Euclidean geometries and geometrical transformations.

510 530 PL ISSN 0072-470X
QA1 CODEN: PSMFBT
POLITECHNIKA SLASKA. ZESZYTY NAUKOWE. MATEMATYKA - FIZYKA. (Text in Polish; summaries in English, German, Russian) 1961. irreg. price varies. Politechnika Slaska, Katowicka 7, 44-100 Gliwice, Poland. FAX 371655. TELEX 036304. (Dist. by: Ars Polona, Krakowskie Przedmiescie 7, 00-068 Warsaw, Poland) Ed. Boguslaw Nosowicz. circ. 205. **Indexed:** Chem.Abstr., Math.R.
—BLDSC (9512.328000); CASDDS.

510   PL   ISSN 0137-6268
POLITECHNIKA WROCLAWSKA. INSTYTUT MATEMATYKI. PRACE NAUKOWE. KONFERENCJE. 1977. irreg., no.2, 1986. price varies. Wydawnictwo Politechniki Wroclawskiej, Wybrzeze Wyspianskiego 27, 50-370 Wroclaw, Poland. FAX 22-36-64. TELEX 712559 PWRPL. **Document type:** proceedings.

510   PL   ISSN 0324-9603
TJ260.A1   **CODEN:** PNMMEI
POLITECHNIKA WROCLAWSKA. INSTYTUT MATEMATYKI. PRACE NAUKOWE. MONOGRAFIE. (Text in Polish; summaries in English and Russian) 1974. irreg., no.7, 1992. price varies. Wydawnictwo Politechniki Wroclawskiej, Wybrzeze Wyspianskiego 27, 50-370 Wroclaw, Poland. FAX 22-36-64. TELEX 712559 PWRPL. (Dist. by: Ars Polona-Ruch, Krakowskie Przedmiescie 7, Warsaw, Poland) circ. 475. **Indexed:** Math.R. **Document type:** monographic series.
—BLDSC (6590.505000).

510 530   PL   ISSN 0324-9611
TJ260.A1
POLITECHNIKA WROCLAWSKA. INSTYTUT MATEMATYKI. PRACE NAUKOWE. STUDIA I MATERIALY. (Former Name of Institute: Instytut Matematyki i Fizyki Teoretycznej) (Text in Polish; summaries in English and Russian) 1970. irreg., no.15, 1980. price varies. Wydawnictwo Politechniki Wroclawskiej, Wybrzeze Wyspianskiego 27, 50-370 Wroclaw, Poland. FAX 22-36-64. TELEX 712559 PWRPL. (Dist. by: Ars Polona-Ruch, Krakowskie Przedmiescie 7, Warsaw, Poland) **Indexed:** Math.R. **Document type:** academic/scholarly publication.

510   PL   ISSN 0373-8302
QA1   **CODEN:** RPTWAD
POLSKIE TOWARZYSTWO MATEMATYCZNE. ROCZNIKI. SERIA 2: WIADOMOSCI MATEMATYCZNE. 1955. a. price varies. Polskie Towarzystwo Matematyczne, Ul. Sniadeckich 8, 00-950 Warsaw, Poland. TEL 48-22-299592. (Dist. by: Ars Polona, Krakowskie Przedmiescie 7, 00-068 Warsaw, Poland. TEL 48-22-267622) Ed. Roman Duda. bk.rev.; bibl.; index. circ. 2,000.

510   PL   ISSN 0208-8916
QA11.A1
POLSKIE TOWARZYSTWO MATEMATYCZNE. ROCZNIKI. SERIA 5: DYDAKTYKA MATEMATYKI. 1982. a. price varies. Polskie Towarzystwo Matematyczne, Ul. Sniadeckich 8, 00-950 Warsaw, Poland. TEL 48-22-299592. (Dist. by: Ars Polona, Krakowskie Przedmiescie 7, 00-068 Warsaw, Poland. TEL 48-22-267622) Ed. Stefan Turnau. circ. 400. **Document type:** academic/scholarly publication.

510   PO   ISSN 0032-5155
QA1   **CODEN:** POMAAJ
PORTUGALIAE MATHEMATICA. (Text in English, French and Portuguese) 1937. q. $126 in Europe; elsewhere $135 (effective 1996) (or exchange basis). Sociedade Portuguesa de Matematica, Avenida da Republica 37-4o, 1000 Lisbon, Portugal. TEL 351-1-7939785. FAX 351-1-7952349. Ed. A. Pereira Gomes. index. circ. 400. **Indexed:** Math.R. **Document type:** academic/scholarly publication.
—BLDSC (6557.000000); Faxon; SWETS; UnCover.
Description: Publishes original research papers in all fields of pure and applied mathematics.

519.2   NE   ISSN 0926-2601
QA404.7   **CODEN:** POANE2
POTENTIAL ANALYSIS; an international journal devoted to the interactions between potential theory, probability theory, geometry and functional analysis. (Text in English) 1992. bi-m. fl.630 to institutions; $404 to institutions in U.S. (effective 1996). Kluwer Academic Publishers, Postbus 17, 3300 AA Dordrecht, Netherlands. TEL 31-78-392392. FAX 31-78-392254. TELEX 29245 KAPG NL. E-mail: SERVICES@WKAP.NL. (Dist. by: Kluwer Academic Publishers Group, P.O. Box 322, 3300 AH Dordrecht, Netherlands. TEL 31-78-392392. FAX 31-78-546474; N. America dist. addr.: Box 358, Accord Sta., Hingham, MA 02018-0358. TEL 617-871-6600. FAX 617-871-6528) Ed. D. Feyel. (also avail. in microform from UMI; back issues avail.; reprint service avail. from SWZ) **Indexed:** ASCA, Compumath, Curr.Cont., Math.R., Stat.Theor.Meth.Abstr., Zent.Math. **Document type:** academic/scholarly publication.
—BLDSC (6565.515000); Genuine Article; UMI.
Description: Publishes original papers describing applications of potential theory.
Refereed Serial

POZNANSKIE TOWARZYSTWO PRZYJACIOL NAUK. KOMISJA MATEMATYCZNO-PRZYRODNICZA. PRACE. see *PHYSICS*

510   GW   ISSN 0032-7042
QA1
PRAXIS DER MATHEMATIK. 1959. bi-m. DM.96 (foreign DM.105). Aulis-Verlag Deubner und Co. KG, Antwerpener Str. 6-12, 50672 Cologne, Germany. TEL 0221-951454-0. FAX 0221-518443. Ed.Bd. adv.; bk.rev.; bibl.; charts; illus. (reprint service avail. from KTO) **Indexed:** Math.R. **Document type:** academic/scholarly publication.
—BLDSC (6603.172000); SWETS. **CCC.**

510 600   RU   ISSN 0032-8235
QA801   **CODEN:** PMAMAF
PRIKLADNAYA MATEMATIKA I MEKHANIKA. English translation: Journal of Applied Mathematics and Mechanics (RU ISSN 0021-8928) (Text in English, French or German) 1933. bi-m. $211 (effective 1996). (Rossiiskaya Akademiya Nauk) Izdatel'stvo Nauka, Mezhdunarodnyi Otdel, Profsoyuznaya, 90, 117864 Moscow, Russia. Ed. V.V. Rumyancev. bibl.; charts; index. circ. 3,015. (reprint service avail. from KTO) **Indexed:** Appl.Mech.Rev., Eng.Ind., Geotech.Abstr., INSPEC, Int.Aerosp.Abstr., Math.R. **Document type:** academic/scholarly publication.
—BLDSC (0132.000000); CASDDS. **CCC.**

510   PP
PRIME. s-a. K.3 par no. Mathematics and Statistics Department, Private Mail Bag, Lae, Papua New Guinea. Ed. G.R. Baird.

510   US   ISSN 1051-1970
QA11.A1
PRIMUS; problems, resources, and issues in mathematics undergraduate studies. 1991. q. $40 (foreign $44) (effective 1995). Rose-Hulman Institute of Technology, Department of Mathematics, Terre Haute, IN 47803. TEL 812-877-8412. FAX 812-877-3198. E-mail: winkel@nextwork.rose-hulman.edu. Ed. Brian J. Winkel. **Indexed:** Tech.Educ.Abstr. **Document type:** academic/scholarly publication.
—BLDSC (6612.930850); UMI. **CCC.**
Description: Provides a forum for discussion of all aspects of collegiate mathematics education.
Refereed Serial

510   US   ISSN 0079-5194
PRINCETON MATHEMATICAL SERIES. 1946. irreg., no.39, 1990. price varies. Princeton University Press, 41 William St., Princeton, NJ 08540. TEL 609-258-4900. FAX 609-258-6305. E-mail: jhardy@pupress.princeton.edu. (back issues avail.; reprint service avail. from UMI) **Document type:** monographic series.
Refereed Serial

510   PE   ISSN 1012-3938
PRO MATHEMATICA. 1989. s-a. $16. Pontificia Universidad Catolica del Peru, Departamento de Ciencias, Fondo Editorial, Apdo. 1761, Lima 100, Peru. TEL 626390. FAX 5114-611785. Ed. Alejandro Ortiz.

519.5   PL   ISSN 0208-4147
QA273.A1
PROBABILITY AND MATHEMATICAL STATISTICS. (Text in English or French; abstracts in English) 1980. s-a. $42. (Uniwersytet Wroclawski - University of Wroclaw) Wydawnictwo Uniwersytetu Wroclawskiego, Pl. Uniwersytecki 9-13, 50-137 Wroclaw, Poland. TEL 48 71 21-15-00. (Dist. by: Ksiegarnia Uniwersytetu Wroclawskiego, Pl. Uniwersytecki 9-13, 50-137 Wroclaw, Poland) (Co-sponsor: Technical University of Wroclaw) Ed. Kazimierz Urbanik. circ. 1,000. **Indexed:** Math.R., Stat.Theor.Meth.Abstr. **Document type:** academic/scholarly publication.
—BLDSC (6617.220000); SWETS; UnCover.

519   US   ISSN 0079-5607
PROBABILITY AND MATHEMATICAL STATISTICS; a series of monographs and textbooks. 1967. irreg., latest 1988. Academic Press, Inc., 525 B St., Ste. 1900, San Diego, CA 92101-4495. TEL 619-231-0926. FAX 619-699-6715. (Subscr. to: Order Dept., 6277 Sea Harbor Dr., 4th Fl., Orlando, FL 32887. TEL 800-321-5068) Eds. Z.W. Birnbaum, E. Lukacs. **Indexed:** Math.R. **Document type:** monographic series.
Refereed Serial

519   US
PROBABILITY: PURE AND APPLIED. 1984. irreg., vol.9, 1991. price varies. Marcel Dekker, Inc., 270 Madison Ave., New York, NY 10016. TEL 212-696-9000. FAX 212-685-4540. TELEX 421419. Ed. Marcel Neuts.

510   GW   ISSN 0178-8051
QA273   **CODEN:** PTRFEU
PROBABILITY THEORY AND RELATED FIELDS. (Text in English) 1962. 12/yr. (in 3 vols., 4 nos./vol.) DM.2814($2045) (effective 1996). Springer-Verlag, Heidelberger Platz 3, 14197 Berlin, Germany. TEL 030-8207-0. FAX 030-8214091. E-mail: orders@springer.de. (Subscr. in N. America to: Springer-Verlag New York, Inc., 44 Hartz Way, Secaucus, NJ 07096-2491. TEL 201-348-4033. FAX 201-348-4505) Ed. O. Kallenberg. adv.; charts; illus. (also avail. in microform from UMI; back issues avail.; reprint service avail. from ISI) **Indexed:** Compumath, Curr.Cont., Curr.Ind.Stat., Math.R., Stat.Theor.Meth.Abstr., Zent.Math. **Document type:** academic/scholarly publication.
—BLDSC (6617.223500); Ei; Faxon; Genuine Article; SWETS; UMI; UnCover. **CCC.**
Superseded: Zeitschrift fuer Wahrscheinlichkeitstheorie und Verwandte Gebiete (ISSN 0044-3719)
Description: Publishes research papers in probability theory on an advanced level, as well as other fields including optimization theory, statistical mechanics, ergodic theory, and measure theory or analytical number theory.

510   US   ISSN 0941-3502
PROBLEM BOOKS IN MATHEMATICS. 1981. irreg. price varies. Springer-Verlag, 175 Fifth Ave., New York, NY 10010. TEL 212-460-1500. FAX 212-473-6272. (Also: Berlin, Heidelberg, Tokyo and Vienna) Ed. P. Halmos. **Document type:** monographic series.

510   RU
PROBLEMY ISTORII MATEMATIKI I MEKHANIKI. 1972. irreg. 1 Rub. Moskovskii Universitet, Ul. Gertsena 5-7, 103009 Moscow, Russia. illus.

PROGRESS IN BIOCHEMISTRY, BIOTECHNOLOGY, AND NONLINEAR BIOLOGY. see *BIOLOGY — Biophysics*

510   SZ
PROGRESS IN MATHEMATICS. (Text in English) 1979. irreg., no.118, 1994. 78 SFr. Birkhaeuser Verlag, P.O. Box 133, CH-4010 Basel, Switzerland. TEL 061-2717400. FAX 061-2717666. (Subscr. in N. America to: Birkhaeuser, 333 Meadowlands Pkwy., Secaucus, NJ 07094-2491) Eds. Joseph Oesterle, Alan Weinstein. **Document type:** monographic series.

519.5   NE
PROGRESS IN PURE AND APPLIED DISCRETE MATHEMATICS. (Text in English) 1993. irreg. price varies. V S P, P.O. Box 346, 3700 AH Zeist, Netherlands. TEL 31-3404-25790. FAX 31-3404-32081. (Dist. in U.S. and Canada by: Books International Inc., Box 605, Herndon, VA 22070. TEL 703-435-7064. FAX 703-689-0660) **Document type:** monographic series.

510   CL   ISSN 0716-0917
PROYECCIONES; revista de matematica. (Text in English, French, Spanish) 1982. s-a. $60 per no. or exchange basis. Universidad Catolica del Norte, Departamento de Matematicas, Avda. Angamos 0610, Casilla 1280, Antofagasta, Chile. TEL 241148. FAX 241724. TELEX 225097 UNORTE CL. Ed. Ricardo L. Soto Montero. circ. 500. **Description:** Publishes papers from all areas of mathematics.

MATHEMATICS

510 — **QA1** — SP — ISSN 0214-1493
PUBLICACIONS MATEMATIQUES. (Text mainly in English, occasionally in French, Spanish; abstracts in English) 1976. s-a. $40 to individuals; institutions $80 (effective 1996). Universitat Autonoma de Barcelona, Departamento de Matematicas, Apartat Postal 53, 08193 Bellterra (Barcelona), Spain. TEL 34-3-5811304. FAX 34-3-5812790. E-mail: imrev@cc.uab.es. Ed. Joan Verdera. **Document type:** academic/scholarly publication.
Former titles (until 1988): Universitat Autonoma de Barcelona. Publicacions. Seccio de Matematiques (ISSN 0210-2978); (until 1981): Universitat Autonoma de Barcelona. Seccio de Matematiques. Publicacions (ISSN 0210-4555)
Description: Publishes quality research papers in all fields of mathematics.
Refereed Serial

510 — **QA1** — HU — ISSN 0033-3883 — CODEN: PUMAAR
PUBLICATIONES MATHEMATICAE. (Text in English and French) 1949. s-a. $25. Kossuth Lajos Tudomanyegyetem, Matematikai Intezet, Egyetem Ter 1, Debrecen 4010, Hungary. (Subscr. to: Kultura, PO Box 149, H-1389 Budapest, Hungary) bk.rev.; index. circ. 600. (back issues avail.) **Indexed:** Compumath, Math.R.
—Genuine Article; SWETS; UnCover.

510 — YU — ISSN 0350-1302
PUBLICATIONS DE L'INSTITUT MATHEMATIQUE. (Text in English, French, German, Russian) 1932. s-a. $100. Matematicki Institut, Knez Mihailova 35, p.p. 367, 11001 Belgrade, Yugoslavia. TEL 011-630-170. FAX 011-186-105. TELEX 72593 SANU YU. (Subscr. to: Kubon & Sagner, Buchexport-Import GMBH, Hesstr. 39-41, Posfach 34 01 08, D-3000 Munich 34, Germany) Ed. Slobodan Aljancic. circ. 600. (back issues avail.) **Indexed:** Math.R., Zent.Math.
—UnCover.

510 — **QA1** — PK — ISSN 1016-2526
PUNJAB UNIVERSITY JOURNAL OF MATHEMATICS. (Text in English) 1967. a. $15 (effective 1994). University of the Punjab, Department of Mathematics, New Campus, Lahore 54590, Pakistan. TEL 7864184. Ed. Abdul Majeed. circ. 500. **Indexed:** Math.R. **Document type:** academic/scholarly publication.
—BLDSC (7160.330000).
Formerly: University of the Punjab. Department of Mathematics. Journal.

510 — **QA3** — US — ISSN 0079-8169
PURE AND APPLIED MATHEMATICS; a series of monographs and textbooks. 1949. irreg., vol.137, 1989. Academic Press, Inc., 525 B St., Ste. 1900, San Diego, CA 92101-4495. TEL 619-231-0926. FAX 619-699-6715. (Subscr. to: Order Dept., 6277 Sea Harbor Dr., 4th Fl., Orlando, FL 32887. TEL 800-321-5068) Ed.Bd. (reprint service avail. from ISI) **Indexed:** Math.R. **Document type:** monographic series.
—BLDSC (7161.450000).
Refereed Serial

510 — US
PURE AND APPLIED MATHEMATICS: A WILEY INTERSCIENCE SERIES OF TEXTS, MONOGRAPHS AND TRACTS. 1948. irreg., latest 1990. price varies. John Wiley & Sons, Inc., Wiley Interscience Journals, 605 Third Ave., New York, NY 10158-0012. TEL 212-850-6418. Ed. L. Bers. **Indexed:** Math.R. **Document type:** monographic series.
Formed by the merger of: Interscience Tracts in Pure and Applied Mathematics (ISSN 0074-994X); Pure and Applied Mathematics; a Series of Texts and Monographs (ISSN 0079-8185)
Refereed Serial

510 — US — ISSN 0079-8177
PURE AND APPLIED MATHEMATICS SERIES. 1970. irreg., vol.190, 1995. price varies. Marcel Dekker, Inc., 270 Madison Ave., New York, NY 10016. TEL 212-696-9000. FAX 212-685-4540. TELEX 421419. Ed. S. Kobayashi. **Document type:** monographic series.
—BLDSC (7161.452000).
Refereed Serial

510.5 001.6 — **621.381** — II — ISSN 0379-3168
PURE AND APPLIED MATHEMATIKA SCIENCES. (Text in English) 1974. s-a. Rs.250($150) Mathematika Sciences Society of India, M.S. College, Department of Mathematics, P.O. Box 65, Saharanpur, India. TEL 25407. Ed. P.L. Maggu. adv.; bk.rev.; illus. (back issues avail.) **Indexed:** Math.R., Zent.Math.
—BLDSC (7161.458000); Faxon.
Formerly: Mathematika Sciences.

510 — HU — ISSN 0866-4943
QA150
PURE MATHEMATICS AND APPLICATIONS. 1990. q. $100. Budapest University of Economics, Department of Mathematics, P.O. Box 489, 1828 Budapest, Hungary. TEL 361-117-4505. E-mail: kmsz014@ursus.bke.hu. (Co-sponsor: University of Siena, Department of Mathematics (IT)) Ed. Peter Tallos. bk.rev. **Document type:** academic/scholarly publication.
Description: Publishes original research works, surveys, historical and biographical articles in all fields of pure and applied mathematics.

510 — UK — ISSN 0260-0781
QARCH. 1980. irreg. £1($1.50) Cambridge University, Mathematical Society, Archimedeans, c/o The Arts School, Bene't St., Cambridge CB2 3PY, England. Ed. M.R. Walters, W.V.N. de Silva. charts. circ. 1,000. (back issues avail.) **Document type:** academic/scholarly publication.
Description: Contains solved and unsolved mathematical problems of interest to professional mathematicians or those who enjoy puzzles.

QINGBAO KEXUE/INFORMATION SCIENCE. see COMPUTERS — *Information Science And Information Theory*

QUANTUM (NEW YORK); the magazine of math and science. see SCIENCES: COMPREHENSIVE WORKS

510 — **QA1** — UK — ISSN 0033-5606 — CODEN: QJMAAT
QUARTERLY JOURNAL OF MATHEMATICS. (Oxford Second Series) 1950. q. £99($175) (effective 1996). Oxford University Press, Oxford Journals, Walton St., Oxford OX2 6DP, England. TEL 01865-267907. FAX 01865-267773. TELEX 837330-OXPRES-G. E-mail: jnlorders@oup.co.uk. (U.S. subscr. to: Oxford University Press Inc., 2001 Evans Rd., Cary, NC 27513. TEL 919-677-0977. FAX 919-677-1714) Ed.Bd. adv.; bibl.; index. circ. 1,000. (also avail. in microform from UMI) **Indexed:** Compumath, Curr.Cont., Math.R., Sci.Cit.Ind., Stat.Theor.Meth.Abstr. **Document type:** academic/scholarly publication.
—BLDSC (7192.000000); Faxon; Genuine Article; SWETS; UMI; UnCover. **CCC.**
Description: Addresses original contributions to pure mathematics as well as the main branches of algebra, analysis, combinatorics and topology.

510 620.1 — **QA1** — UK — ISSN 0033-5614 — CODEN: QJMMAV
QUARTERLY JOURNAL OF MECHANICS AND APPLIED MATHEMATICS. 1948. q. £135($240) (effective 1996). Oxford University Press, Oxford Journals, Walton St., Oxford OX2 6DP, England. TEL 01865-267907. FAX 01865-267773. TELEX 837330-OXPRES-G. E-mail: jnlorders@oup.co.uk. (U.S. subscr. to: Oxford University Press Inc., 2001 Evans Rd., Cary, NC 27513. TEL 919-677-0977. FAX 919-677-1714) Ed.Bd. adv.; bibl.; index. circ. 900. (also avail. in microform from UMI) **Indexed:** Appl.Mech.Rev., Br.Ceram.Abstr., Chem.Abstr., Compumath, Curr.Cont., Deep Sea Res.& Oceanogr.Abstr., Eng.Ind., Fluidex, Geo.Abstr., INSPEC (1971-), Int.Aerosp.Abstr., Math.R., Met.Abstr., Sci.Cit.Ind., Sh.& Vib.Dig. **Document type:** academic/scholarly publication.
—BLDSC (7193.000000); Ei; Faxon; Genuine Article; SWETS; UMI; UnCover. **CCC.**
Description: Addresses original articles in the general field of mechanics, particularly theoretical mechanics, classical electromagnetism, nonlinear dynamics and combined fields such as magnetohydro-numerical methods.

519 — **QA1** — US — ISSN 0033-569X — CODEN: QAMAAY
QUARTERLY OF APPLIED MATHEMATICS. 1943. q. $80. American Mathematical Society, Box 6248, Providence, RI 02940. TEL 401-455-4177. Ed. Walter F. Freiberger. adv.; bk.rev.; index. circ. 1,600. (also avail. in microform from UMI; reprint service avail. from UMI) **Indexed:** Appl.Mech.Rev., Biol.Abstr., Chem.Abstr., Compumath, Curr.Cont., Eng.Ind., INSPEC, Int.Aerosp.Abstr., Math.R., Petrol.Abstr. **Document type:** academic/scholarly publication.
—BLDSC (7170.000000); Ei; Faxon; Genuine Article; SWETS; UMI; UnCover. **CCC.**
Refereed Serial

510 — CN — ISSN 0079-8797
QUEEN'S PAPERS IN PURE AND APPLIED MATHEMATICS. (Text in English and French) 1966. irreg. price varies. Queen's University, Department of Mathematics and Statistics, Kingston, Ont. K7L 3N6, Canada. TEL 613-545-2390. Ed. Grace Orzech. **Indexed:** Math.R.
Formerly: Queen's University at Kingston. Department of Mathematics. Research Report.

510 — **QA1** — FR — ISSN 0764-583X — CODEN: RMMAEV
R A I R O - M 2 A N MATHEMATICAL MODELLING AND NUMERICAL ANALYSIS. (Revue Francaise d'Automatique d'Informatique et de Recherche Operationelle) 1966. 7/yr. 2550 F. (Association Francaise des Sciences et Technologies de l'Information et des Systemes) Dunod, 15 rue Gossin, 92543 Montrouge Cedex, France. TEL 33-1-40-92-65-00. FAX 33-1-40-92-65-97. TELEX 634 916 F. (Subscr. to: Centrale des Revues, 11 rue Gossin, 92543 Montrouge Cedex, France. TEL 33-1-46-56-52-66) Ed. R. Temam. adv.; bibl.; charts. circ. 1,150. (also avail. in microfilm from UMI) **Indexed:** Compumath, Curr.Cont., INSPEC (1985-), Math.R.
—BLDSC (5402.548000); Genuine Article; SWETS; UnCover. **CCC.**
Formerly (1977-1985): R A I R O Analyse Numerique - Numerical Analysis (ISSN 0399-0516)
Description: Presents original research and survey papers of high scientific level in numerical analysis and mathematical modelling.

R E C S A M NEWS. (Regional Centre for Education in Science and Mathematics) see EDUCATION — *Teaching Methods And Curriculum*

510 — **QA1** — II — ISSN 0079-9602
RANCHI UNIVERSITY MATHEMATICAL JOURNAL. (Text in English) 1970. a. Rs.40($10) Ranchi University, Department of Mathematics, Ranchi 834008, Bihar, India. TEL 22914. Ed. R.C. Choudhary. circ. 150. **Indexed:** Math.R. (until 19??).

510 — **QA614.8** — US — ISSN 1061-835X — CODEN: RCDYEM
RANDOM AND COMPUTATIONAL DYNAMICS. 1992. 4/yr. $125 to individuals; institutions $250. Marcel Dekker, Inc., 270 Madison Ave., New York, NY 10016. TEL 212-696-9000. FAX 212-685-4540. TELEX 421419. (Subscr. to: Box 5017, Monticello, NY 12701) Eds. Leonid A. Bunimovich, S. Chow. adv.; bibl.; charts; illus. (also avail. in microform from RPI) **Indexed:** INSPEC (1992-). **Document type:** academic/scholarly publication.
—BLDSC (7254.410970); Ei; SWETS; UMI.

RANDOM MATERIALS AND PROCESSES. see PHYSICS

510 — NE — ISSN 0926-6364
RANDOM OPERATORS AND STOCHASTIC EQUATIONS. (Text in English) 1992. q. DM.670 (effective 1996). V S P, P.O. Box 346, 3700 AH Zeist, Netherlands. TEL 31-30-6925790. FAX 31-30-6932081. E-mail: 100341.2372@compuserve.com. Eds. V. Girko, A. Skorokhod. **Document type:** academic/scholarly publication.
—BLDSC (7254.411920).

510　　　　　　　　US　　ISSN 1042-9832
QA166
RANDOM STRUCTURES & ALGORITHMS. 1990. 8/yr. $392 (foreign $516) (effective 1996). John Wiley & Sons, Inc., Journals, 605 Third Ave., New York, NY 10158. TEL 212-850-6645. FAX 212-850-6021. TELEX 12-7063. E-mail: SUBINFO@JWILEY.COM. (Subscr. outside the Americas to: John Wiley & Sons Ltd., Baffins Ln., Chichester, W. Sussex PO19 1UD, England. TEL 44-1243-779777. FAX 44-1243-776128) Ed. Michal Karonski. (also avail. in microform from UMI; back issues avail.) **Indexed:** Stat.Theor.Meth.Abstr. **Document type:** academic/scholarly publication. —BLDSC (7254.411950); Faxon; Genuine Article; SWETS; UMI. **CCC.**
　　Description: Covers the latest research on discrete random structures and the applications of probablistic techniques to problem solving in various areas of mathematics, computer science, and operations research.
　　Refereed Serial

510　　　　　　　　SP　　ISSN 0211-1721
Q65　　　　　　　　　　CODEN: MACFAN
REAL ACADEMIA DE CIENCIAS EXACTAS, FISICAS Y NATURALES. MEMORIA. SERIE DE CIENCIAS EXACTAS. 1930. irreg. price varies. Real Academia de Ciencias Exactas, Fisicas y Naturales, Valverde 22, 28004 Madrid, Spain.

510　　　　　　　　US　　ISSN 0147-1937
QA331.5
REAL ANALYSIS EXCHANGE. (Text in English; occasionally in French or German) 1976. s-a. $47 (effective 1996). Michigan State University, Department of Mathematics, East Lansing, MI 48824-1027. TEL 517-353-8489. FAX 517-432-1562. E-mail: weil@math.msu.edu. Ed. Clifford E. Weil. circ. 425. (back issues avail.) **Indexed:** Math.R. **Document type:** academic/scholarly publication. —BLDSC (7303.245000); SWETS; UnCover.
　　Description: Contains surveys, research articles, inroads and queries concerning this branch of mathematics.

510　　　　　　　　FR　　ISSN 0246-9367
RECHERCHES EN DIDACTIQUE DES MATHEMATIQUES. (Text in English and French; summaries in English and Spanish) 3/yr. 290 F. to individuals (foreign 310 F.); institutions 395 F. (foreign 420 F.). Pensee Sauvage Editions, B.P. 141, 38002 Grenoble Cedex, France. TEL 76-87-13-03. FAX 76-46-27-25.

519　　　　　　　　IT　　ISSN 0034-4427
　　　　　　　　　　　　CODEN: RNMTAN
RENDICONTI DI MATEMATICA; e delle sue applicazioni. (Text in English, French, Italian; summaries in English and Italian) 1913. q. DM.260 (effective 1993). (Istituto Matematico G. Castlenuovo) Edizioni Scientifiche Inglesi Americane, E S I A Books and Journals, Via Palestro, 30, 00185 Rome, Italy. TEL 396-4441220. FAX 396-4747743. (Co-sponsors: Istituto di Alta Matematica; Istituto Mathematica Applicata) Ed. G. Roghi. index. circ. 1,000. **Indexed:** Appl.Mech.Rev., Math.R. —SWETS; UnCover.

511.3　　　　　　　　PL　　ISSN 0137-2904
QA9.A1　　　　　　　　　CODEN: RMLODX
REPORTS ON MATHEMATICAL LOGIC. (Text in English; summaries in Polish) 1973. irreg., no.24, 1991. price varies. Uniwersytet Jagiellonski, Ul. Golebia 24, 31-007 Krakow, Poland. (Dist. by: Ars Polona, Krakowskie Przedmiescie 7, 00-068 Warsaw, Poland) (Co-sponsor: Uniwersytet Slaski w Katowicach) Ed. W.A. Pogorzelski. circ. 700. **Indexed:** Math.R., Phil.Ind., Ref.Zh.
　　Formerly: Uniwersytet Jagiellonski, Krakow. Zeszyty Naukowe. Prace z Logiki (ISSN 0083-4432)

510　　　　　　　　JA　　ISSN 0034-5318
　　　　　　　　　　　　CODEN: KRMPBV
RESEARCH INSTITUTE FOR MATHEMATICAL SCIENCES. PUBLICATIONS/KYOTO DAIGAKU SURI KAISEKI KENKYUJO KIYO. (Text in English and European languages) 1965. bi-m. 36000 Yen($436) Kyoto University, Research Institute for Mathematical Sciences - Kyoto Daigaku Suri Kaiseki Kenkyujo, Kita-Shirakawa Oiwake-cho, Sakyo-ku, Kyoto-shi, Kyoto-fu 606-01, Japan. TEL 075-753-7210. FAX 075-753-7272. E-mail: rims@kurim.s.kyoto-u.ac.jp. (Dist. by: Kinokuniya Company Ltd., 17-7, Shinjuku 3-chome, Shinjuku-ku, Tokyo 163-91, Japan) Ed. Huzihiro Araki. circ. 1,100. **Indexed:** Compumath, JTA, Math.R., Sci.Cit.Ind. **Document type:** academic/scholarly publication.
—BLDSC (7107.919000); Genuine Article; UnCover.
　　Formerly (until vol.4, 1969): Kyoto University. Research Institute for Mathematical Sciences. Publications: Series A (ISSN 0454-7845)

516　　　　　　　　JA
RESEARCH NOTES AND MEMORANDA OF APPLIED GEOMETRY FOR PREVENIENT NATURAL PHILOSOPHY. (Text in English; summaries in English and Japanese) 1973. m. 4000 Yen. Post-R A A G Library, 1570 Yotsukaido, Yotsukaido-shi, Chiba-ken 284, Japan. TEL 043-422-2839. Ed. Kazuo Kondo. **Document type:** academic/scholarly publication.

510　　　　　　　　US
RESEARCH NOTES IN MATHEMATICS. 1975. irreg., no.269, 1993. John Wiley & Sons, Inc., Journals, 605 Third Ave., New York, NY 10158-0012. TEL 212-850-6000. FAX 212-850-6088. TELEX 12-7063. **Indexed:** Math.R.
　　Refereed Serial

RESEARCH REPORTS ON INFORMATION SCIENCES. SERIES A, MATHEMATICAL SCIENCE. see COMPUTERS — *Information Science And Information Theory*

510　　　　　　　　SZ　　ISSN 0378-6218
QA1
RESULTS IN MATHEMATICS/RESULTATE DER MATHEMATIK. (Text in English and German) 1978. 8/yr. 672.80 SFr. (foreign 693 SFr.). Birkhaeuser Verlag, P.O. Box 133, CH-4010 Basel, Switzerland. TEL 061-2717400. FAX 061-2717666. (Dist. in N. America by: Springer-Verlag, Mercedes Distribution Center, 160 Imlay St., Brooklyn, NY 11231, USA) Ed. H.-J. Arnold. **Indexed:** Math.R. **Document type:** academic/scholarly publication.
—BLDSC (7782.500000); Faxon; SWETS; UMI; UnCover. **CCC.**

REVIEWS IN MATHEMATICAL PHYSICS; a journal for survey and expository articles in the field of mathematical physics. see *PHYSICS*

510　　　　　　　　CK　　ISSN 0034-7426
QA1　　　　　　　　　　CODEN: RCMABQ
REVISTA COLOMBIANA DE MATEMATICAS. (Text in English, French, Portuguese and Spanish) 1952. q. $22. Sociedad Colombiana de Matematicas, Apdo. Aereo No. 25-21, Bogota, Colombia. FAX 2686465. Ed. Xavier Caicedo. bk.rev.; bibl.; index. circ. 800. **Indexed:** Math.R. **Document type:** academic/scholarly publication.
—BLDSC (7851.402000).
　　Formerly: Revista de Matematicas Elementales.
　　Refereed Serial

510　　　　　　　　CU　　ISSN 0256-5374
REVISTA CUBANA DE CIENCIAS MATEMATICAS. (Text in Spanish; summaries in English, Spanish) 1980. 3/yr. C.$4.50($18) Universidad de La Habana, Direccion de Informacion Cientifica y Tecnica, Havana 4, Cuba. (Dist. by: Ediciones Cubanas, Obispo 527, Apdo. 605, Havana, Cuba) (back issues avail.)

510　　　　　　　　BL　　ISSN 0102-0811
　　　　　　　　　　　　CODEN: RMAEDG
REVISTA DE MATEMATICA E ESTATISTICA. (Text in Portuguese; abstracts in English and Portuguese) 1983. a. $30 or exchange basis. Universidade Estadual Paulista, Av. Vicente Ferreira 1278, Caixa Posta 603, 17515-901 Marilia SP, Brazil. TEL 0144-33-1844. FAX 0144-22-2504. TELEX 111 9016 UJME BR. abstr.; bibl.; charts; stat. **Indexed:** Math.R. **Document type:** academic/scholarly publication.
　　Description: Cover original articles and research in the field of mathematics and statistics.

510　　　　　　　　CK　　ISSN 0120-419X
REVISTA INTEGRACION; temas de matematicas. (Text mainly in Spanish, occasionally in English, French; summaries in English and Spanish) 1980. s-a. Col.$6000($8) for 2 yrs. or exchange basis. Universidad Industrial de Santander, Apdo. Aereo 678, Bucaramanga, Santander, Colombia. FAX 5776-351946. adv.; bk.rev.; bibl.; charts; illus.; stat. **Document type:** academic/scholarly publication.

510　　　　　　　　SP　　ISSN 0213-2230
QA1
REVISTA MATEMATICA IBEROAMERICANA. 1985. 3/yr. 20000 ptas. in Europe; elsewhere $180 (effective 1995). Real Sociedad Matematica Espanola, c/o Departamento de Matematicas, Universidad Autonoma de Madrid, 28049 Madrid, Spain. TEL 34-1-397-4930. FAX 34-1-397-4889. E-mail: RM1@CCUAM3.SDI.UAM.ES. Eds. J.L. Fernandez, A. Cordoba. bk.rev.; illus.; index. **Indexed:** Math.R. **Document type:** academic/scholarly publication.
—BLDSC (7864.020000); SWETS. **CCC.**
　　Supersedes (1919-1982): Revista Matematica Hispano-Americana (ISSN 0373-0999)
　　Refereed Serial

510 574　　　　　　　FR　　ISSN 0035-1024
QH323.5　　　　　　　　　CODEN: RBIMBZ
REVUE DE BIO-MATHEMATIQUE/BIOMATHEMATICS. (Text in English and French) 1962. q. 180 F. (International Society of Mathematical Biology) Editions Europeennes, 11 bis Ave. de la Providence, 92160 Antony, France. Ed. Francis Collot. adv.; bk.rev. circ. 1,000. **Indexed:** Biol.Abstr., Chem.Abstr., Math.R. **Document type:** newspaper, proceedings. —CASDDS.
　　Refereed Serial

510　　　　　　　　FR　　ISSN 0035-1504
QA1
REVUE DE MATHEMATIQUES SPECIALES. 1890. 10/yr. 610 F. Librairie Vuibert, 63 bd. Saint-Germain, 75005 Paris, France. TEL 44-41-73-41. FAX 43-25-75-86. Ed. Marc Jammet. adv.; bk.rev.; index. circ. 3,000. **Document type:** academic/scholarly publication.
—Faxon.
　　Description: General survey of the entrance examination to the French "Grandes Ecoles": Ecole Polytechnique, Ecole Normale Superieure.
　　Refereed Serial

510　　　　　　　　RM　　ISSN 0035-3965
QA1　　　　　　　　　　CODEN: RRMPB6
REVUE ROUMAINE DE MATHEMATIQUES PURES ET APPLIQUEES. (Text in English, French, German, Russian and Spanish) 1956. 10/yr. 400 lei($110) (Academia Romana) Editura Academiei Romane, Calea Victoriei 125, 79717 Bucharest, Rumania. (Dist. by: Rompresfilatelia, Calea Grivitei 64-66, P.O. Box 12-201, 78104 Bucharest, Rumania) adv.; bk.rev.; abstr.; bibl.; charts; index. **Indexed:** Appl.Mech.Rev., Biostat., Chem.Abstr., Compumath, Int.Aerosp.Abstr., Math.R., Oper.Res.Manage.Sci., Qual.Contr.Appl.Stat.
—SWETS; UnCover.

510　　　　　　　　IT　　ISSN 0035-5038
　　　　　　　　　　　　CODEN: RCMTAE
RICERCHE DI MATEMATICA. 1952. s-a. L.60000 per vol. Universita degli Studi di Napoli, Istituto di Matematica, Via Mezzocannone 8, Naples, Italy. (Orders to: Libreria Liguori, Via Mezzocannone 23, 80134 Naples, Italy) Ed. Prof. Carlo Miranda. charts. circ. 750. **Indexed:** Curr.Cont., Math.R. —BLDSC (7965.495000); SWETS; UnCover.

MATHEMATICS

510 US ISSN 0272-4332
T174.5 CODEN: RIANDF
RISK ANALYSIS. 1980. bi-m. $395 (foreign $460) (effective 1996). (Society for Risk Analysis) Plenum Publishing Corp., 233 Spring St., New York, NY 10013-1578. TEL 212-620-8000. FAX 212-463-0742. TELEX 23-421139. Ed. Curtis C. Travis. adv.; bk.rev.; illus.; index. (also avail. in microfilm from JSC; back issues avail.) **Indexed:** Curr.Cont., Dok.Arbeitsmed., Ecol.Abstr., Energy Ind., Energy Info.Abstr., Eng.Ind., Environ.Abstr., Geo.Abstr., IDA, INSPEC, Psychol.Abstr. (1985-), Ref.Zh., Risk Abstr., W.R.C.Inf. **Document type:** academic/scholarly publication.
—BLDSC (7972.583000); Ei; Faxon; Genuine Article; SWETS; UMI; UnCover. **CCC.**
Refereed Serial

510 IT
RIVISTA DI MATEMATICA PER LE SCIENZE ECONOMICHE E SOCIALI. (Text and summaries in English and Italian) 1978. s-a. L.100000. Associazione per la Matematica Applicata alle Scienze Economiche e Sociali, Via Sarfatti 25, 20136 Milan, Italy. TEL 39-2-58365116. FAX 39-2-58365130. Ed. Piera Mazzoleni. adv.; bk.rev. circ. 2,000. (back issues avail.) **Indexed:** Int.Polit.Sci.Abstr., Math.R. **Document type:** academic/scholarly publication.

510 IT ISSN 1121-7111
RIVISTA DI MATEMATICA PURA ED APPLICATA. (Text in English, French, German, Italian) s-a. L.150000. Aviani Editore, Via A. Diaz 27, 33019 Tricesimo UD, Italy. TEL 39-432-46478. FAX 39-432-43420.
—BLDSC (7989.470000).
Description: Publishes original research works containing significant results in the field of pure and applied mathematics.

510 US ISSN 0035-7596
QA1 CODEN: RMJMAE
ROCKY MOUNTAIN JOURNAL OF MATHEMATICS. 1971. q. $175 to individuals; institutions $350. Rocky Mountain Mathematics Consortium, Arizona State University, Department of Mathematics, Tempe, AZ 85287. TEL 602-965-3788. Ed. Andrew Bremner. index. circ. 600. (back issues avail.) **Indexed:** Compumath, INSPEC, Math.R.
—BLDSC (8002.630000); Faxon; Genuine Article; SWETS; UnCover.
Refereed Serial

510 RU
ROSSIISKAYA AKADEMIYA NAUK. IZVESTIYA. SERIYA MATEMATICHESKAYA. English translation: Russian Academy of Science. Izvestiya. Mathematics (US ISSN 1064-5632) 1937. bi-m. Rossiiskaya Akademiya Nauk, Otdelenie Matematiki, Ul. Vavilova, d.42, 117966 Moscow, Russia. TEL 7-95-1353250. (Subscr. to: Mezhdunarodnaya Kniga, B. Yakimanka 39, 114079 Moscow, Russia) Ed. V.S. Vladimirov. bibl.; index, cum.index: vol.1-20 (in 2 vols.). circ. 2,135. **Indexed:** Comput.Rev., INIS Atomind., Math.R.
—SWETS.
Formerly: Akademiya Nauk S.S.S.R. Izvestiya. Seriya Matematicheskaya (ISSN 0373-2436)

500 IE ISSN 0035-8975
CODEN: PRIAAK
ROYAL IRISH ACADEMY. PROCEEDINGS. SECTION A: MATHEMATICAL AND PHYSICAL SCIENCES. 1836. 2/yr. price varies. Royal Irish Academy, 19 Dawson St., Dublin 2, Ireland. TEL 01-762570. FAX 01-762346. Ed. B. Young. index, cum.index. circ. 500. (also avail. in microfilm from PMC) **Indexed:** Art & Archaeol.Tech.Abstr., Chem.Abstr., Curr.Cont., Field Crop Abstr., GeoRef., Herb.Abstr., Ind.Vet., INSPEC (1968-), Intl.Civil Eng.Abstr., Math.R, Phys.Ber., RILA, Soft.Abstr.Eng., Vet.Bull., Zent.Math. **Document type:** proceedings.
—BLDSC (6799.050000); UnCover.
Formerly: Royal Irish Academy. Proceedings. Section A: Mathematical, Astronomical and Physical Science.

510 UK ISSN 0308-2105
Q41
ROYAL SOCIETY OF EDINBURGH. PROCEEDINGS. SECTION A (MATHEMATICS). 1832. 6/yr. £198. Royal Society of Edinburgh, 22 George St., Edinburgh EH2 2PQ, Scotland. TEL 0131-225-6057. FAX 0131-220-6889. E-mail: rse@festival.ed.ac.uk. Ed. J. Carr. circ. 1,000. (also avail. in microfiche from BHP,PMC) **Indexed:** Appl.Mech.Rev., Biol.Abstr., Chem.Abstr., Compumath, Curr.Cont., Eng.Ind., INSPEC, Math.R., Met.Abstr., Nucl.Sci.Abstr. **Document type:** academic/scholarly publication.
—BLDSC (6803.000000); Faxon; SWETS; UnCover.
Formerly: Royal Society of Edinburgh. Proceedings. Section A. Mathematical and Physical Sciences (ISSN 0080-4541)
Description: Publishes papers of international standard across the whole spectrum of mathematics.
Refereed Serial

ROYAL SOCIETY OF LONDON. PHILOSOPHICAL TRANSACTIONS. SERIES A. PHYSICAL SCIENCES AND ENGINEERING. see *PHYSICS*

500 510 UK ISSN 0962-8444
QA1 CODEN: PRLAAZ
ROYAL SOCIETY OF LONDON. PROCEEDINGS. SERIES A. MATHEMATICAL AND PHYSICAL SCIENCES. 1832. m. £375 in Europe; U.S. and Canada £401. Royal Society of London, 6 Carlton Terrace, London SW1Y 5AG, England. TEL 0171-839-5561. FAX 0171-976-1837. Ed. D.G. Crighton. circ. 1,457. (also avail. in microform from PMC; reprint service avail. from ISI) **Indexed:** Appl.Mech.Rev., Br.Archaeol.Abstr., Chem.Abstr., Curr.Cont., Deep Sea Res.& Oceanogr.Abstr., Eng.Ind., Excerp.Med., Fluidex, Forest Prod.Abstr., Geo.Abstr., Geol.Abstr., GeoRef, INSPEC, Mass Spectr.Bull., Math.R., Met.Abstr., Petrol.Abstr. **Document type:** academic/scholarly publication.
—BLDSC (6804.500000); Ei; Faxon; Genuine Article; SWETS.
Description: Contains original papers on any aspect of mathematical and physical sciences, including chemistry and engineering, at postgraduate level and above.
Refereed Serial

ROYAL STATISTICAL SOCIETY. JOURNAL. SERIES A: STATISTICS IN SOCIETY. see *STATISTICS*

510 UK ISSN 1064-5632
QA1
RUSSIAN ACADEMY OF SCIENCE. IZVESTIYA. MATHEMATICS. English translation of: Rossiiskaya Akademiya Nauk. Izvestiya. Seriya Matematicheskaya. 1967. bi-m. $880 (effective 1996). (Russian Academy of Sciences, RU) Turpin Distribution Services Limited, Blackhorse Rd., Letchworth, Hertfordshire SG6 1HN, England. TEL 44-1462-672555. FAX 44-1462-480947. Ed. Lev J. Leifman. index. circ. 700. (also avail. in microfiche; microfilm) **Indexed:** Compumath, Curr.Cont., Ind.Sci.Rev., Math.R. **Document type:** academic/scholarly publication.
—BLDSC (0420.751500); Faxon; Genuine Article; SWETS; UMI; UnCover. **CCC.**
Formerly (until 1992): Mathematics of the U S S R - Izvestiya (ISSN 0025-5726)
Refereed Serial

510 RU ISSN 1064-5624
QA1
RUSSIAN ACADEMY OF SCIENCES. DOKLADY. MATHEMATICS. English translation in part of: Rossiiskaya Akademiya Nauk. Doklady. 1960. bi-m. $903 in U.S. and Canada (elsewhere $915). (Rossiiskaya Akademiya Nauk) Interperiodica, Ul. Profsoyuznaya 90, Moscow 117864, Russia. TEL 7-095-3360066. FAX 7-095-3360666. (Subscr. to: Interperiodica, Box 1831, Birmingham, Al 35201-1831. TEL 205-9995-1567. FAX 205-995-1588) Ed. Lev J. Leifman. adv.; bibl.; index. circ. 1,000. (also avail. in microfiche) **Indexed:** INSPEC, Math.R. **Document type:** academic/scholarly publication.
—BLDSC (0420.751000); Faxon; SWETS; UMI; UnCover. **CCC.**
Formerly (until 1992): Soviet Mathematics - Doklady (ISSN 0197-6788)

510 US ISSN 1067-9073
QA1
RUSSIAN ACADEMY OF SCIENCES. MATHEMATICAL NOTES. Key Title: Mathematical Notes (Rossiiskaya Akamediya Nauk). English translation of: Matematicheskie Zametki (RU ISSN 0025-567X) 1950. m. (2 vols./yr.) $1295 (foreign $1515) (effective 1995). (Rossiiskaya Akademiya Nauk, RU) Plenum Publishing Corp., Consultants Bureau, 233 Spring St., New York, NY 10013-1578. TEL 212-620-8468. FAX 212-463-0742. TELEX 23-421139. Ed. V.P. Maslov. charts; illus. (back issues avail.) **Indexed:** Appl.Mech.Rev., Comput.& Info.Sys., Curr.Cont., Ind.Sci.Rev., Math.R., Phys.Ber., Zent.Math. **Document type:** academic/scholarly publication.
—BLDSC (0415.814900); Faxon; Genuine Article; SWETS; UMI; UnCover. **CCC.**
Formerly (until 1992): Academy of Sciences of the U S S R. Mathematical Notes (ISSN 0001-4346)
Refereed Serial

510 UK ISSN 1064-5616
QA1
RUSSIAN ACADEMY OF SCIENCES. SBORNIK. MATHEMATICS. English translation of: Matematicheskii Sbornik (RU ISSN 0368-8666) 1967. bi-m. $1120 (effective 1996). (Russian Academy of Sciences, Institute of Mathematics, RU) Turpin Distribution Services Limited, Blackhorse Rd., Letchworth, Hertfordshire SG6 1HN, England. TEL 44-1462-672555. FAX 44-1462-480947. Ed. Lev J. Leifman. index. circ. 700. (also avail. in microfiche) **Indexed:** Compumath, Curr.Cont., Ind.Sci.Rev., Math.R. **Document type:** academic/scholarly publication.
—BLDSC (0420.789500); Faxon; Genuine Article; SWETS; UMI; UnCover. **CCC.**
Formerly (until 1992): Mathematics of the U S S R - Sbornik (ISSN 0025-5734)

RUSSIAN JOURNAL OF MATHEMATICAL PHYSICS. see *PHYSICS*

510 NE ISSN 0927-6467
QA297 CODEN: RJNMEH
RUSSIAN JOURNAL OF NUMERICAL ANALYSIS AND MATHEMATICAL MODELLING. (Text in English) 1986. bi-m. DM.1040 (effective 1996). V S P, P.O. Box 346, 3700 AH Zeist, Netherlands. TEL 31-30-6925790. FAX 31-30-6932081. E-mail: 100341.2372@compuserve.com. Ed. G.I. Marchuk. adv. (back issues avail.) **Document type:** academic/scholarly publication.
—BLDSC (8052.715000); Ei; SWETS; UnCover.
Formerly (until vol.7, 1992): Soviet Journal of Numerical Analysis and Mathematical Modelling (ISSN 0169-2895)
Description: Provides English translations of Russian research on theoretical aspects of numerical analysis as well as application of mathematical methods to simulation and modelling.
Refereed Serial

510 UK ISSN 0036-0279
QA1
RUSSIAN MATHEMATICAL SURVEYS. English translation of: Uspekhi Matematicheskikh Nauk (RU ISSN 0042-1316) vol.15, 1960. bi-m. £326 (effective 1995). (Russian Academy of Science, RU) British Library, Subscr. to: Turpin Distribution Services Ltd., Blackhorse Rd., Letchworth, Herts. SG6 1HW, England. TEL 01937-846000. FAX 01937-546333. TELEX 557381. (Subscr. to: Turpin Distribution Services Ltd., Blackhorse Rd., Letchworth, Herts. SG6 1HN, England. TEL 01462-672555. FAX 01462-480947) (Co-sponsor: London Mathematical Society) bibl.; index. (also avail. in microform) **Indexed:** Compumath, Math.R. **Document type:** academic/scholarly publication.
—BLDSC (0420.766000); Faxon; Genuine Article; SWETS; UnCover.

510 US ISSN 1066-369X
QA1
RUSSIAN MATHEMATICS - IZ. V U Z. English translation of: Izvestiya Vysshikh Uchebnykh Zavedenii. Seriya Matematika (UR ISSN 0021-3446) 1974. m. $1025 (effective 1996). (Ministerstvo Visshego i Srednego Spetsialnogo Obrazovaniya, RU) Allerton Press, Inc., 150 Fifth Ave., New York, NY 10011. TEL 212-924-3950. FAX 212-463-9684. Ed. Ya.I. Zabotin. charts; index. **Indexed:** Math.R. **Document type:** academic/scholarly publication.
—BLDSC (0420.766500); Faxon; SWETS; UnCover. **CCC.**
Formerly: Soviet Mathematics - Iz. V U Z (ISSN 0197-7156)

519 US ISSN 0080-5084
CODEN: SAMPBY
S I A M - A M S PROCEEDINGS. 1969. irreg. price varies. (Society for Industrial and Applied Mathematics) American Mathematical Society, Box 6248, Providence, RI 02940-6248. TEL 401-455-4000. (Street addr.: 201 Charles St., Providence, RI 02904) Ed.Bd. index in each vol. **Indexed:** Math.R., Zent.Math. **Document type:** proceedings.
—CCC.
Formerly: American Mathematical Society. Proceedings of Symposia in Applied Mathematics.
Refereed Serial

519 US ISSN 0036-1399
QA1 CODEN: SMJMAP
S I A M JOURNAL ON APPLIED MATHEMATICS. 1953. bi-m. $262 to non-members (overseas $368); members $58 (overseas $63) (effective 1995). Society for Industrial and Applied Mathematics, Attn: M. Lafferty, 3600 University City Science Center, Philadelphia, PA 19104-2688. TEL 215-382-9800. FAX 215-386-7999. E-mail: PUB@SIAM.ORG. Ed. James P. Keener. adv.; index. circ. 2,350. (also avail. in microform from IAM; back issues avail.) **Indexed:** A.S.& T.Ind., Abstr.Bull.Inst.Pap.Chem., Appl.Mech.Rev., ASCA, Biostat., Chem.Abstr., Compumath, Comput.Cont., Comput.Rev., Cyb.Abstr., Deep Sea Res.& Oceanogr.Abstr., Eng.Ind., INSPEC, Int.Abstr.Oper.Res., Int.Aerosp.Abstr., Math.R., Oper.Res.Manage.Sci., Qual.Contr.Appl.Stat., Sh.& Vib.Dig. **Document type:** academic/scholarly publication.
—BLDSC (8271.350000); Ei; Faxon; Genuine Article; SWETS; UnCover. **CCC.**
Formerly: Society for Industrial and Applied Mathematics. Journal.
Description: Contains research articles in mathematical methods and their applications in the physical, engineering, biological, and medical sciences.
Refereed Serial

S I A M JOURNAL ON COMPUTING. (Society for Industrial and Applied Mathematics) see MATHEMATICS — Computer Applications

519 600 US ISSN 0363-0129
QA402.3 CODEN: SJCODC
S I A M JOURNAL ON CONTROL AND OPTIMIZATION. 1963. bi-m. $313 to non-members (overseas $360); members $58 (overseas $63) (effective 1995). Society for Industrial and Applied Mathematics, Attn: M. Lafferty, 3600 University City Science Center, Philadelphia, PA 19104-2688. TEL 215-382-9800. FAX 215-386-7999. TELEX 446-715. E-mail: PUB@SIAM.ORG. Ed. John Lagrese. adv.; index. circ. 1,766. (also avail. in microform from IAM; back issues avail.) **Indexed:** A.S.& T.Ind., Appl.Mech.Rev., ASCA, Compumath, Comput.Cont., Comput.Rev., Cyb.Abstr., INSPEC (1968-), Int.Abstr.Oper.Res., Int.Aerosp.Abstr., Math.R. **Document type:** academic/scholarly publication.
—BLDSC (8271.355200); Ei; Faxon; Genuine Article; SWETS. **CCC.**
Formerly (until 1976): S I A M Journal on Control (ISSN 0036-1402)
Description: Publishes research articles in the mathematical theory of control and its applications and the associated areas of systems theory and optimization, the theories of games and differential games, and the topics in mathematical analysis, algebra, differential geometry, probability, statistics, and stochastics that apply to control, systems theory, and optimization.
Refereed Serial

519 US ISSN 0895-4801
QA76.9.M35 CODEN: SJDMEC
S I A M JOURNAL ON DISCRETE MATHEMATICS. 1980. q. $238 to non-members (overseas $272); members $48 (overseas $51) (effective 1995). Society for Industrial and Applied Mathematics, Attn: P. Clifford, 3600 University City Science Center, Philadelphia, PA 19104-2688. TEL 215-382-9800. FAX 215-386-7998. E-mail: PUB@SIAM.ORG. Ed. Clyde Monma. adv.; index. circ. 1,059. (also avail. in microform from IAM; back issues avail.) **Indexed:** Biostat., Compumath, Int.Abstr.Oper.Res., Math.R., Oper.Res.Manage.Sci., Qual.Contr.Appl.Stat. **Document type:** academic/scholarly publication.
—BLDSC (8271.355400); Ei; Faxon; Genuine Article; SWETS; UnCover. **CCC.**
Supersedes in part (in 1987): S I A M Journal on Algebraic and Discrete Methods (ISSN 0196-5212)
Description: Publishes research articles on a broad range of topics from pure and applied mathematics including combinatorics and graph theory, discrete optimization and operations research, theoretical computer science, coding and communication theory, and game theory and mathematical modeling.
Refereed Serial

519 US ISSN 0036-1410
QA300 CODEN: SJMAAH
S I A M JOURNAL ON MATHEMATICAL ANALYSIS. 1970. bi-m. $372 to non-members (overseas $422); members $58 (overseas $63) (effective 1995). Society for Industrial and Applied Mathematics, Attn: M. Lafferty, 3600 University City Science Center, Philadelphia, PA 19104-2688. TEL 215-382-9800. FAX 215-386-7999. E-mail: PUB@SIAM.ORG. Ed. D. Benedetto. adv.; index. circ. 1,340. (also avail. in microform from IAM; back issues avail.) **Indexed:** Appl.Mech.Rev., ASCA, Compumath, Comput.Rev., INSPEC, Int.Aerosp.Abstr., Math.R. **Document type:** academic/scholarly publication.
—BLDSC (8271.356000); Ei; Faxon; Genuine Article; SWETS; UnCover. **CCC.**
Description: Focuses on those parts of classical and modern analysis that have direct or potential application to the natural sciences and engineering. Papers fall into two broad categories, the first being those that analyze interesting problems associated with realistic mathematical models for natural phenomena. The second category includes those papers which contribute in a substantial way to the general, analytical information and techniques likely to bear upon such models.
Refereed Serial

519 US ISSN 0895-4798
QA188 CODEN: SJMAEL
S I A M JOURNAL ON MATRIX ANALYSIS AND APPLICATIONS. 1980. q. $254 to non-members (overseas $288); members $48 (overseas $51) (effective 1995). Society for Industrial and Applied Mathematics, Attn: M. Lafferty, 3600 University City Science Center, Philadelphia, PA 19104-2688. TEL 215-382-9800. FAX 215-386-7999. E-mail: PUB@SIAM.ORG. Ed. Gene Golub. adv.; index. circ. 1,236. (also avail. in microfilm from IAM) **Indexed:** INSPEC (1988-). **Document type:** academic/scholarly publication.
—BLDSC (8271.356300); Ei; Faxon; Genuine Article; SWETS; UnCover. **CCC.**
Supersedes in part (in 1987): S I A M Journal on Algebraic and Discrete Methods (ISSN 0196-5212)
Description: Contains research articles on numerical linear algebra as well as the application of matrix analysis to areas such as Markov chains, networks, signal processing, systems and control theory, mathematical programming, economic and biological modeling, and statistics and operations research.
Refereed Serial

MATHEMATICS 4143

519 600 US ISSN 0036-1429
CODEN: SJNAAM
S I A M JOURNAL ON NUMERICAL ANALYSIS. 1964. bi-m. $272 to non-members (overseas $318); members $58 (overseas $63) (effective 1995). Society for Industrial and Applied Mathematics, Attn.: M. Lafferty, 3600 University City Science Center, Philadelphia, PA 19104-2688. TEL 215-382-9800. FAX 215-386-7999. E-mail: PUB@SIAM.ORG. Ed. M.L. Luskin. adv.; charts; index. circ. 2,272. (also avail. in microform from IAM; back issues avail.) **Indexed:** A.S.& T.Ind., Appl.Mech.Rev., ASCA, Compumath, Comput.Abstr., Comput.Rev., INSPEC (1968-), Math.R. **Document type:** academic/scholarly publication.
—BLDSC (8271.357000); Ei; Faxon; Genuine Article; SWETS. **CCC.**
Description: Publishes research articles on the development and analysis of numerical methods including their convergence, stability, and error analysis, as well as related results in functional analysis and approximation theory. Computational experiments and new types of numerical applications are also included.
Refereed Serial

519 600 US ISSN 1052-6234
QA402.5 CODEN: SJOPE8
S I A M JOURNAL ON OPTIMIZATION. 1991. q. $216 to non-members (overseas $246); members $48 (overseas $51) (effective 1995). Society for Industrial and Applied Mathematics, Attn: M. Lafferty, 3600 University City Science Center, Philadelphia, PA 19104. TEL 215-382-9800. FAX 215-386-7999. E-mail: PUB@SIAM.ORG. Ed. John E. Dennis, Jr. adv.; index. circ. 905. (also avail. in microform from IAM) **Document type:** academic/scholarly publication.
—BLDSC (8271.357100); Faxon; SWETS; UnCover. **CCC.**
Description: Publishes research and expository articles on the application of mathematics to the problems of computer science and the nonnumerical aspects of computing.
Refereed Serial

519 US ISSN 1064-8275
QA297 CODEN: SJOCE3
S I A M JOURNAL ON SCIENTIFIC COMPUTING. 1980. bi-m. $260 to non-members; members $54 (effective 1995). Society for Industrial and Applied Mathematics, Attn: M. Lafferty, 3600 University City Science Center, Philadelphia, PA 19104-2688. TEL 215-382-9800. FAX 215-386-7999. E-mail: PUB@SIAM.ORG. Ed. J.M. Hyman. charts; illus.; stat.; index. circ. 1,777. (also avail. in microform from IAM; back issues avail.) **Indexed:** ASCA, Biostat., Compumath, Comput.Abstr., Cyb.Abstr., INSPEC, Int.Aerosp.Abstr., J.Cont.Quant.Meth., Math.R., Oper.Res.Manage.Sci., Qual.Contr.Appl.Stat. **Document type:** academic/scholarly publication.
—BLDSC (8271.357500); Ei; Faxon; Genuine Article; SWETS; UnCover. **CCC.**
Formerly (until 1993): S I A M Journal on Scientific and Statistical Computing (ISSN 0196-5204)
Description: Contains research articles on numerical methods and techniques for scientific computation.
Refereed Serial

519 US
S I A M MISCELLANEOUS TITLES IN APPLIED MATHEMATICS. irreg., no. 47, Spring 1995. price varies. Society for Industrial and Applied Mathematics, 3600 University City Science Center, Philadelphia, PA 19104. TEL 215-382-9800. FAX 215-386-7999. E-mail: siam@siam.org. Ed. Tricia Manning; Pub. Vickie Kearn. **Document type:** monographic series.

519 US
S I A M NEWS. 1968. bi-m. $18. Society for Industrial and Applied Mathematics, Attn: M. Lafferty, 3600 University City Science Center, Philadelphia, PA 19104-2688. TEL 215-382-9800. FAX 215-386-7999. E-mail: PUB@SIAM.ORG. Ed. I.E. Block. adv. circ. 11,910. **Indexed:** Math.R. **Document type:** academic/scholarly publication.
Formerly: S I A M Newsletter (ISSN 0036-1437)
Refereed Serial

MATHEMATICS

519 US
S I A M PROCEEDINGS IN APPLIED MATHEMATICS. irreg., no.78, Jun. 1995. price varies. Society for Industrial and Applied Mathematics, 3600 University City Science Center, Philadelphia, PA 19104-2688. TEL 215-382-9800; 800-447-SIAM. FAX 215-386-7999. E-mail: siam@siam.org. Ed. Tricia Manning; Pub. Vickie Kearn. **Document type:** proceedings.

519 US
S I A M REPORTS. irreg., Nov. 1993. price varies. Society for Industrial and Applied Mathematics, 3600 University Science Center, Philadelphia, PA 19104-2688. TEL 215-382-9800. FAX 213-386-9800. E-mail: PUBS@SIAM.ORG. **Document type:** monographic series.
Refereed Serial

519 US ISSN 0036-1445
QA1 CODEN: SIREAD
S I A M REVIEW. 1959. q. $158 to non-members (overseas $186) (effective 1995). Society for Industrial and Applied Mathematics, Attn: M. Lafferty, 3600 University City Science Center, Philadelphia, PA 19104-2688. TEL 215-382-9800. FAX 215-386-7999. Ed. Richard Sincovec. adv.; bk.rev.; index. circ. 10,530. (also avail. in microform from IAM; back issues avail.) **Indexed:** A.S.& T.Ind., Appl.Mech.Rev., ASCA, Biostat., Compumath, Comput.Rev., Deep Sea Res.& Oceanogr.Abstr., INSPEC (1968-), Int.Abstr.Oper.Res., Math.R., Oper.Res.Manage.Sci., Qual.Contr.Appl.Stat., Risk Abstr. **Document type:** academic/scholarly publication.
—BLDSC (8271.360000); Ei; Faxon; Genuine Article; SWETS; UnCover. **CCC.**
Description: Publishes primarily expository and survey papers as well as occasional essays on topics of interest to applied mathematicians. Other features are classroom notes, problems and solutions.
Refereed Serial

510 CN ISSN 0316-5779
S M T S JOURNAL - NEWSLETTER. 3/yr. Can.$25 for 2 yrs. (Saskatchewan Mathematics Teachers' Society) Saskatchewan Teachers' Federation, Box 1108, Saskatoon, SK S7K 3N3, Canada. Ed. Don Kapoor. **Document type:** newsletter.

S S M A CLASSROOM ACTIVITIES MONOGRAPH SERIES. (School Science and Mathematics Association) see EDUCATION — Teaching Methods And Curriculum

S S M A TOPICS FOR TEACHERS MONOGRAPH SERIES. (School Science and Mathematics Association) see EDUCATION — Teaching Methods And Curriculum

S S M ARRT. (School Science and Mathematics Association) see EDUCATION — Teaching Methods And Curriculum

510 JA ISSN 0916-5746
QA1
S U T JOURNAL OF MATHEMATICS. (Text and summaries in English) 1965. s-a. free. Science University of Tokyo - Tokyo Rika Daigaku, 1-3, Kagurazaka, Shinjuku-ku, Tokyo 162, Japan. Ed. Toshihiko Yamada. **Document type:** academic/scholarly publication.
—BLDSC (8553.388000).
Formerly: T R U Mathematics (ISSN 0496-6597)

SACHUNTERRICHT UND MATHEMATIK IN DER PRIMARSTUFE. see EDUCATION — Teaching Methods And Curriculum

SAECHSISCHE AKADEMIE DER WISSENSCHAFTEN, LEIPZIG. MATHEMATISCH-NATURWISSENSCHAFTLICHE KLASSE. ABHANDLUNGEN. see SCIENCES: COMPREHENSIVE WORKS

SAECHSISCHE AKADEMIE DER WISSENSCHAFTEN, LEIPZIG. MATHEMATISCH-NATURWISSENSCHAFTLICHE KLASSE. SITZUNGSBERICHTE. see SCIENCES: COMPREHENSIVE WORKS

SAGA DAIGAKU RIKOGAKUBU SHUHO/SAGA UNIVERSITY. FACULTY OF SCIENCE AND ENGINEERING. REPORTS. see ENGINEERING

SAINS MALAYSIANA: JERNAL SAINS ALAM SEMULA; jadi. see SCIENCES: COMPREHENSIVE WORKS

510 US ISSN 1061-0022
QA150
ST. PETERSBURG MATHEMATICAL JOURNAL. English translation of: Algebra i Analiz (RU ISSN 0234-0852) 1990. bi-m. $935 to non-members; institutional members $748. (Russian Academy of Sciences, Institut of Mathematics, RU) American Mathematical Society, Box 6248, Providence, RI 02940-6248. TEL 401-455-4000. (Subscr. to: Box 6248, Providence, RI 02940-6248) Ed. A.N. Andrianov. bk.rev. **Document type:** academic/scholarly publication.
—BLDSC (0425.843000); SWETS; UnCover.
Formerly (until 1992): Leningrad Mathematical Journal (ISSN 1048-9924)

510 US ISSN 1063-4541
QA1
ST. PETERSBURG UNIVERSITY. VESTNIK: MATHEMATICS. English translation of the mathematics section of: Sankt-Peterburgskii Universitet. Vestnik. Seriya: Matematika, Makhanika i Astronomiya. 1984. q. $715 (effective 1996). (St. Petersburg University, RU) Allerton Press, Inc., 150 Fifth Ave., New York, NY 10011. TEL 212-924-3950. FAX 212-463-9684. Ed. S.P. Merkure'v. (also avail. in microfiche from IDC) **Indexed:** Chem.Abstr., Math.R. **Document type:** academic/scholarly publication.
—BLDSC (0429.580000); SWETS; UnCover. **CCC.**
Formerly: Leningrad University. Vestnik: Mathematics (ISSN 0146-924X)

510 530 540 JA ISSN 0289-0739
QA1
SAITAMA MATHEMATICAL JOURNAL. (Text in English) 1952. a. exchange basis. Saitama Daigaku, Rigakubu, Sugaku Kyoshitsu - Saitama University, Faculty of Science, Department of Mathematics, 255, Shimo-Okubo, Urawa-shi, Saitama-ken 338, Japan. FAX 048-858-3699. Ed. Tsutomu Sakurai. circ. 500. **Indexed:** INSPEC, Math.R. **Document type:** academic/scholarly publication.
—BLDSC (8070.438000).
Former titles (until 1983): Saitama University. Science Reports. Series A: Mathematics; Saitama University. Science Reports. Series A: Mathematics, Physics and Chemistry (ISSN 0558-2431)
Description: Publishes original papers in pure and applied mathematics.

510 520 RU
AS262 CODEN: VMMAA3
SANKT-PETERBURGSKII UNIVERSITET. VESTNIK. SERIYA: MATEMATIKA, MEKHANIKA I ASTRONOMIYA. Partial English translations: St. Petersburg University Mechanics Bulletin; St. Petersburg University. Vestnik: Mathematics. (Text in Russian; contents page and summaries in English) 1946. q. 18.60 Rub. Sankt-Peterburgskii Universitet, Universitetskaya Nab., 7-9, St. Petersburg V-164, Russia. (Subscr. to: Mezhdunarodnaya Kniga, Moscow, G-200, Russia) Ed. S.P. Merkur'ev. abstr.; illus.; index. circ. 1,300. **Indexed:** Chem.Abstr., Int.Aerosp.Abstr., Math.R. **Document type:** academic/scholarly publication.
—CASDDS; UMI.
Formerly (until 1992): Leningradskii Universitet. Vestnik. Seriya: Matematika, Mekhanika i Astronomiya (ISSN 0024-0850)

510 US ISSN 0198-8379
SCHOLASTIC MATH. 1980. 10/yr. $6.95. Scholastic Inc., 555 Broadway, New York, NY 10012-3999. TEL 212-343-6100. Ed. Tracy Randinelli. circ. 311,000. (also avail. in microform from UMI; reprint service avail. from UMI) **Document type:** trade publication.
—UMI.
Description: Contains activities and features focusing on consumer math, math on the job, computation to problem-solving practice.

SCHOOL SCIENCE AND MATHEMATICS; journal for all science and mathematical teachers. see EDUCATION

SCIEN TECH/SAGA DAIGAKU RIKOGAKUBU KOHO. see ENGINEERING

510 CL ISSN 0716-8446
SCIENTIA, SERIES A: MATHEMATICAL SCIENCES. (Subseries of: Scientia (ISSN 0036-8679)) (Text in English or Spanish) 1988. a. $20. Universidad Tecnica Federico Santa Maria, Casilla 110-V, Valparaiso, Chile. TEL 0056-32-626364. FAX 0056-32-660504. TELEX 330622 UTFSM CK. E-mail: scientia@utfsm.bitnet. Ed. Luis Salinas C. **Indexed:** Math.R.
—BLDSC (8173.600000).
Description: Publishes original research papers from all areas of pure and applied mathematics. Survey articles of particularly high standard may also be considered.
Refereed Serial

510 530 IT ISSN 0391-173X
QA1 CODEN: PSNAAI
SCUOLA NORMALE SUPERIORE DI PISA. ANNALI. CLASSE DI SCIENZE. (Text in English, French, German, Italian) 1871; N.S. 1973. q. L.180000($180) Scuola Normale Superiore di Pisa, Piazza dei Cavalieri 7, 56136 Pisa, Italy. TEL 050-509111. FAX 050-563513. TELEX 590548 SNSP I. Ed. Edoardo Vesentini. index, cum.index. circ. 1,300. (also avail. in microfilm from BHP) **Indexed:** Appl.Mech.Rev., INIS Atomind., Math.R.
—Faxon; SWETS; UnCover.
Formerly: Scuola Normale Superiore di Pisa. Annali. Scienze, Fisiche e Matematiche (ISSN 0036-9918)

SEIKEN N S T SHINPOJUMU KOEN RONBUNSHU. see COMPUTERS — Computer Simulation

510 SZ ISSN 1022-1824
QA1
SELECTA MATHEMATICA. (Text in English) 1981. 4/yr. 723.60 SFr. (foreign 737.80 SFr.). Birkhaeuser Verlag, P.O. Box 133, CH-4010 Basel, Switzerland. TEL 061-2717400. FAX 061-2717666. (Dist. in N. America by: Springer-Verlag, Mercedes Distribution Center, 160 Imlay St., Brooklyn, NY 11231, USA) Ed. I.M. Gelfand. index. circ. 800. (back issues avail.) **Indexed:** INSPEC, Math.R. **Document type:** academic/scholarly publication.
—BLDSC (8231.595000); Faxon; SWETS; UMI; UnCover. **CCC.**
Formerly (until 1993): Selecta Mathematica Sovietica (ISSN 0272-9903)

519.5 US ISSN 0094-8837
QA276.25
SELECTED TABLES IN MATHEMATICAL STATISTICS. 1970. irreg. price varies. American Mathematical Society, Box 6248, Providence, RI 02940-6248. TEL 401-455-4000. (Street addr.: 201 Charles St., Providence, RI 02904) **Document type:** monographic series.
—**CCC.**
Refereed Serial

510 519 US ISSN 0065-9274
QA273 CODEN: SMSRB
SELECTED TRANSLATIONS IN MATHEMATICAL STATISTICS AND PROBABILITY. 1961. irreg. price varies. (Institute of Mathematical Statistics) American Mathematical Society, Box 6248, Providence, RI 02940-6248. TEL 401-455-4000. (Street addr.: 201 Charles St., Providence, RI 02904) Ed. Ben Silver. cum.index: 1966-1973. **Document type:** monographic series.
—**CCC.**

MATHEMATICS

510 US ISSN 0037-1912
QA171 CODEN: SMGFAN
SEMIGROUP FORUM. 1970. bi-m. $281 (effective 1996). Springer-Verlag, Journals, 175 Fifth Ave., New York, NY 10010. TEL 212-460-1500. FAX 212-473-6272. (N. American subscr. to: Journal Fulfillment Services, Box 2485, Secaucus, NJ 07096-2491. TEL 800-777-4643. FAX 201-348-4505; Elsewhere: Heidelberger Platz 3, 1000 Berlin 33, Germany. TEL 030-8207-1. FAX 030-821-4091) Ed.Bd. bk.rev. (also avail. in microform from UMI; reprint service avail. from ISI) Indexed: ASCA, ASCA, Compumath, Curr.Cont., Math.R., Zent.Math. **Document type:** academic/scholarly publication.
—Faxon; Genuine Article; SWETS; UMI; UnCover. **CCC.**
 Description: Encompasses algebraic, topological, partially ordered, and transformation semigroups, semigroups of measures, harmonic analysis of semigroups, semigroups of operators, and applications of semigroup theory to other topics such as ring theory, category theory, automata, and logic.
 Refereed Serial

510 RM ISSN 0255-8718
SEMINAR ARGHIRIADE. (Text in English, French, Rumanian, Russian) 1974. irreg. 50 lei($2) Universitatea din Timisoara, Facultatea de Matematica, Bd. Vasile Pirvan Nr. 4, Timisoara, Rumania. Ed. Achim Dragomir. circ. 250. **Indexed:** Math.R., Zent.Math. **Document type:** monographic series.

510 JA
SEMINAR ON MATHEMATICAL SCIENCES. (Text in Japanese) 1980. irreg. Keio Gijuku Daigaku, Rikogakubu, Suri Kagakka - Keio University, Faculty of Science and Technology, Department of Mathematics, 14-1, Hiyoshi 3-chome, Kohoku-ku, Yokohama-shi, Kanagawa-ken 223, Japan.

510 SP ISSN 1130-1376
SEMINARIO DE ANALISIS NUMERICO. 1984. a. free. Escuela Tecnica Superior de Ingenieros de Minas, Rios Rodas 21, 28003 Madrid, Spain.

510 RM ISSN 0255-8874
SEMINARUL OF ECUATII FUNCTIONALE/SEMINAR OF DIFFERENTIAL EQUATIONS. (Text in English, French) 1969. irreg. 200 lei. Universitatea de Vest din Timisoara, Facultatea de Matematica, Bd. Vasile Parvan, no.4, Timisoara, Rumania. TEL 40-56-190333. Ed. Mircea Reghis. **Document type:** proceedings.
—BLDSC (8239.490200).
 Description: Publishes orignal and expository papers presented during the scientific seminars.

510 BU ISSN 0204-4110
QA1 CODEN: SERDDJ
SERDIKA; BULGARSKO MATEMATICHESKO SPISANIE/SERDICA; BULGARICAE MATHEMATICAE PUBLICATIONES. (Text in English, German, Russian) 1975. q. 2.70 lv. per no. (Bulgarska Akademiia na Naukite) Publishing House of the Bulgarian Academy of Sciences, Acad. G. Bonchev St., Bldg. 6, 1113 Sofia, Bulgaria. (Dist. by: Hemus, 6, Rouski Blvd., 1000 Sofia, Bulgaria) Ed. L. Iliev. charts. (reprint service avail. from IRC) **Indexed:** Math.R.
—BLDSC (0164.087800).

510 530
SERIE DI MATEMATICA E FISICA. TESTI. 1974. irreg., no.11, 1988. price varies. Liguori Editore s.r.l., Via Mezzocannone 19, 80134 Naples, Italy. TEL 081-5527139. Ed. G. Vidossich. **Document type:** monographic series.
 Formerly: Serie di Matematica e Fisica (ISSN 0391-3252)

510 SI ISSN 0218-0189
SERIES IN PURE MATHEMATICS. (Text in English) 1984. irreg., vol.19, 1993. price varies. World Scientific Publishing Co. Pte. Ltd., Farrer Rd., P.O. Box 128, Singapore 9128, Singapore. TEL 3825663. FAX 3825919. TELEX RS 28561 WSPC. (UK addr.: 73 Lynton Mead, Totteridge, London N20 8DH, England. TEL 44-81-4462461; US addr.: 1060 Main St., River Edge, NJ 07661. TEL 800-227-7562) Ed. C.C. Hsiung. **Document type:** monographic series.
—BLDSC (8250.200300).

510 SI
SERIES IN REAL ANALYSIS. (Text in English) 1988. irreg., vol.3, 1992. price varies. World Scientific Publishing Co. Pte. Ltd., Farrer Rd., P.O. Box 128, Singapore 9128, Singapore. TEL 3825663. FAX 3825919. TELEX RS 28561 WSPC. (UK addr.: 73 Lynton Mead, Totteridge, London N20 8DH, England. TEL 44-81-4462461; US addr.: 1060 Main St., River Edge, NJ 07661. TEL 800-227-7562) **Document type:** monographic series.

510 SI
SERIES ON ADVANCES IN MATHEMATICS FOR APPLIED SCIENCES. (Text in English) 1990. irreg., vol.12, 1992. price varies. World Scientific Publishing Co. Pte. Ltd., Farrer Rd., P.O. Box 128, Singapore 9128, Singapore. TEL 3825663. FAX 3825919. TELEX RS 28561 WSPC. (UK addr.: 73 Lynton Mead, Totteridge, London N20 8DH, England. TEL 44-81-4462461; US addr.: 1060 Main St., River Edge, NJ 07661. TEL 800-227-7562) Ed. N. Bellomo. **Document type:** monographic series.

510 SI
SERIES ON APPLIED MATHEMATICS. (Text in English) irreg., vol.2, 1993. price varies. World Scientific Publishing Co. Pte. Ltd., Farrer Rd., P.O. Box 128, Singapore 9128, Singapore. TEL 3825663. FAX 3825919. (UK addr.: 73 Lynton Mead, Totteridge, London N20 8DH, England. TEL 44-81-4462461; US addr.: 1060 Main St., Ste. 1B, River Edge, NJ 07661. TEL 800-227-7562)

510 SI
SERIES ON KNOTS AND EVERYTHING. (Text in English) 1991. irreg. price varies. World Scientific Publishing Co. Pte. Ltd., Farrer Rd., P.O. Box 128, Singapore 9128, Singapore. TEL 3825663. FAX 3825919. TELEX RS 28561 WSPC. (UK addr.: 73 Lynton Mead, Totteridge, London N20 8DH, England. TEL 44-81-4462461; US addr.: 1060 Main St., River Edge, NJ 07661. TEL 800-227-7562) Ed. L.H. Kauffman. **Document type:** monographic series.

510 SI
SERIES ON SOVIET AND EAST EUROPEAN MATHEMATICS. (Text in English) 1991. irreg., vol.12, 1992. price varies. World Scientific Publishing Co. Pte. Ltd., Farrer Rd., P.O. Box 128, Singapore 9128, Singapore. TEL 3825663. FAX 3825919. TELEX RS 28561 WSPC. (UK addr.: 73 Lynton Mead, Totteridge, London N20 8DH, England. TEL 44-81-4462461; US addr.: 1060 Main St., River Edge, NJ 07661. TEL 800-227-7562) **Document type:** monographic series.

515 NE ISSN 0927-6947
QA611.3 CODEN: SVANEG
SET-VALUED ANALYSIS; an international journal devoted to the theory of multifunctions and its applications. (Text in English) 1993. q. fl.414 to institutions; $265 to institutions in U.S. (effective 1996). Kluwer Academic Publishers, Postbus 17, 3300 AA Dordrecht, Netherlands. TEL 31-78-392392. FAX 31-78-392254. TELEX 29245 KAPG NL. E-mail: SERVICES@WKAP.NL. (Dist. by: Kluwer Academic Publishers Group, P.O. Box 322, 3300 AH Dordrecht, Netherlands. TEL 31-78-392392. FAX 31-78-546474; N. America dist. addr.: Box 358, Accord Sta., Hingham, MA 02018-0358. TEL 617-871-6600. FAX 617-871-6528) Ed. Biagio Ricceri. (back issues avail.; reprint service avail. from SWZ) **Indexed:** Math.R., Zent.Math. **Document type:** academic/scholarly publication.
—BLDSC (8253.352700). **CCC.**
 Description: Publishes studies of mathematical analysis involving multifunctions or set-valued maps and topics related to them.
 Refereed Serial

510 RU ISSN 0321-3005
QE1 CODEN: ISTVAY
SEVERO-KAVKAZSKII NAUCHNYI TSENTR VYSSHEI SHKOLY. ESTESTVENNYE NAUKI. IZVESTIYA/NORTH-CAUCASUS SCIENTIFIC CENTER OF HIGH SCHOOL. NATURAL SCIENCES. NEWS. 4/yr. 7.20 Rub. Rostovski Universitet, Ul. Pushkinskaia 160, 344 700 Rostov-na-Donu, Russia. TEL 8-863-536411. TELEX 123520 NAUKA.
—CASDDS.

510 370 CC
SHANGHAI ZHONGXUE SHUXUE/SHANGHAI SECONDARY SCHOOL MATHEMATICS. (Text in Chinese) bi-m. Shanghai Shifan Daxue, Shuxue Xi - Shanghai Normal University, Mathematics Department, 10 Guilin Lu, Shanghai 4362223, People's Republic of China. Ed. Ying Zhiyi.

SHINSHU UNIVERSITY. FACULTY OF TEXTILE SCIENCE AND TECHNOLOGY. JOURNAL. SERIES F: PHYSICS AND MATHEMATICS. see *PHYSICS*

510 CC ISSN 1000-0984
SHUXUE DE SHIJIAN YU RENSHI/MATHEMATICS IN PRACTICE AND COGNITION. (Text in Chinese) 1984. q. $52.80. (Chinese Academy of Sciences, Institute of Systems Science) Science Press, Marketing and Sales Department, 16 Donghuangchenggen North St., Beijing 100717, People's Republic of China. TEL 4010642. FAX 4019810. adv.; bk.rev. circ. 16,000. **Indexed:** Math.R. **Document type:** academic/scholarly publication.
 Description: Carries articles on results attained in the application of theories and methods of mathematics. Includes efficient mathematical methods, lectures, academic developments, history of mathematics, practical mathematic questions to be solved, and news.
 Refereed Serial

SHUXUE JIAOXUE/MATHEMATICS TEACHING. see *EDUCATION — Teaching Methods And Curriculum*

510 CC ISSN 1001-8875
SHUXUE JIAOXUE TONGXUN/MATHEMATICS TEACHING BULLETIN. (Text in Chinese) 1979. bi-m. Xinan Shifan Daxue, Shuxue Xi - Southwest Normal University, Mathematics Department, 1, Tiansheng Lu, Beipei, Chongqing, Sichuan 630715, People's Republic of China. TEL 630715. Ed. Zhou Zhongqun.

510 CC ISSN 1000-8314
SHUXUE NIANKAN (A JI)/CHINESE ANNALS OF MATHEMATICS. SERIES A. (Text in Chinese) 1980. bi-m. Fudan Daxue Shuxue Yanjiusuo, c/o Fudan University, 220 Handan Rd., Shanghai 200433, People's Republic of China. **Document type:** academic/scholarly publication.
—BLDSC (3180.271100).
 Supersedes in part (in 1983): Shuxue Niankan (ISSN 0253-6137)

510 CC ISSN 0488-7395
SHUXUE TONGXUN/MATHEMATICS BULLETIN. (Text in Chinese) m. Wuhan Shi Shuxue Xuehui, Huazhong Shifan Daxue, Guizishan, Wuchang-qu, Wuhan, Hubei 430070, People's Republic of China. TEL 715601. Ed. Li Xiumu.

510 530 CC ISSN 0252-9602
SHUXUE WULI XUEBAO. English edition: Acta Mathematica Scientia. (Text in Chinese) 1981. q. $82.80. Science Press, Marketing and Sales Department, 16 Donghuangchenggen North St., Beijing 100717, People's Republic of China. TEL 4010642. FAX 4019810. adv. circ. 6,000. (reprint service avail. from KTO) **Indexed:** ASCA, Compumath, Math.R. **Document type:** academic/scholarly publication.
—Genuine Article; UnCover.
 Description: Aims to present important new achievements in the mathematical sciences. Publishes original expository papers in areas bordering on both mathematics and the physical sciences.

510 CC ISSN 0583-1431
SHUXUE XUEBAO. English edition: Acta Mathematica Sinica, New Series (ISSN 1000-9574) (Text in Chinese; summaries in English) 1936. bi-m. $117.60. (Chinese Academy of Science, Institute of Mathematics) Science Press, Marketing and Sales Department, 16 Donghuangchenggen North St., Beijing 100717, People's Republic of China. TEL 4010642. FAX 4019810. adv.; bibl.; index. circ. 24,000. (reprint service avail. from KTO) **Indexed:** INSPEC (1985-), Math.R. **Document type:** academic/scholarly publication.
—BLDSC (0632.000000).
 Description: Contains original papers on pure mathematics.
 Refereed Serial

MATHEMATICS

SHUXUE YILIN. (Text in Chinese) 1982. q. $30 to individuals; institutions $40. Zhongguo Kexueyuan, Shuxue Yanjiusuo - Chinese Academy of Sciences, Institute of Mathematics, Zhongguancun, Beijing 100080, People's Republic of China. TEL 283376. FAX 86-1-2568356. Ed. Tian Fangzeng. circ. 550.
510   CC   ISSN 1003-3092
Document type: academic/scholarly publication.
Description: Introduces latest advances in mathematics, and discusses academic affairs in mathematics, mathematical education and mathematical philosophy.

SHUZHI JISUAN YU JISUANJI YINGYONG/JOURNAL ON NUMERICAL METHODS AND COMPUTER APPLICATIONS. see *SCIENCES: COMPREHENSIVE WORKS — Computer Applications*

510   US   ISSN 1055-1344
QA1
SIBERIAN ADVANCES IN MATHEMATICS. 1991. q. $465 (effective 199). (Russian Academy of Sciences, Institute of Mathematics, Siberian Branch, RU) Allerton Press, Inc., 150 Fifth Ave., New York, NY 10011. TEL 212-924-3950. FAX 212-463-9684. Ed. A.A. Borovkov. **Document type:** academic/scholarly publication.
—BLDSC (0420.807500). **CCC.**
Description: Covers both pure and applied mathematics, reflecting achievements of mathematicians in the eastern part of Russia.

510   US   ISSN 0037-4466
QA1   CODEN: SMTJAW
SIBERIAN MATHEMATICAL JOURNAL. English translation of: Sibirskii Matematicheskii Zhurnal (RU ISSN 0037-4474) 1966. bi-m. $1560 (foreign $1825) (effective 1996). (Russian Academy of Sciences, Siberian Division, RU) Plenum Publishing Corp., Consultants Bureau, 233 Spring St., New York, NY 10013-1578. TEL 212-620-8468. FAX 212-463-0742. TELEX 23-421139. Ed. M.M. Lavrent'ev. (also avail. in microfilm from JSC; back issues avail.) **Indexed:** Compumath, Comput.& Info.Sys., Curr.Cont., Math.R., Zent.Math. **Document type:** academic/scholarly publication.
—BLDSC (0420.810000); Faxon; Genuine Article; SWETS; UMI; UnCover. **CCC.**
Refereed Serial

510   RU   ISSN 0037-4474
SIBIRSKII MATEMATICHESKII ZHURNAL. English translation: Siberian Mathematical Journal (US ISSN 0037-4466) 1960. bi-m. $242 (effective 1996). Rossiiskaya Akademiya Nauk, Sibirskoe Otdelenie, Morkoy pr. 2, 630090 Novosibirsk, Russia. TEL 3832-350570. FAX 3832-356092. Ed. A.I. Mal'tzev. index. (tabloid format)
—BLDSC (0164.120000).

510   US   ISSN 1053-4792
QA246
SMARANDACHE FUNCTION JOURNAL. 1990. a. $9.99. Number Theory Publishing Company, Box 10163, Glendale, AZ 85318-0163. Eds. V. Seleacu, C. Dumitrescu; Pub. R. Muller. bk.rev. circ. 1,000. **Indexed:** Math.R., Ref.Zh., Zent.Math. **Document type:** academic/scholarly publication.
Description: Publishes solved and unsolved problems, notes and articles of research about the Smarandache Function in number theory, i.e., S(n) is the smallest integer m such that m! is divisible by n.

510   MX   ISSN 1405-213X
QA1   CODEN: BSMXAU
SOCIEDAD MATEMATICA MEXICANA. BOLETIN. (Text in English, French and Spanish) 1944. 2/yr. Mex.$280($50) (effective 1995). Sociedad Matematica Mexicana, Apdo. Postal 14-170, 07000 Mexico, D.F., Mexico. TEL 525-747-7103. FAX 525-747-7104. E-mail: bsmm@math.cinvestav.mx. Eds. Monica Clapp, Enrique Ramirez de Arellano. circ. 900 (controlled). (reprint service avail. from ISI) **Indexed:** Math.R. **Document type:** academic/scholarly publication.
Description: Presents original papers on mathematics.
Refereed Serial

510   US   ISSN 0100-3569
QA1   CODEN: BSBMDD
SOCIEDADE BRASILEIRA DE MATEMATICA. BOLETIM, NOVA SERIE/BRAZILIAN MATHEMATICAL SOCIETY. BULLETIN, NEW SERIES. (Text in English, French, Portuguese) 1970; N.S. 1989. s-a. $96 (effective 1996). (Sociedade Brasileira de Matematica, BL - Brazilian Mathematical Society) Springer-Verlag, 175 Fifth Ave., New York, NY 10010. TEL 212-460-1500. FAX 212-473-6272. (Subscr. in N. America to: Journal Fulfillment Services, Box 2485, Secaucus, NJ 07096. TEL 800-777-4643. FAX 201-348-4505; Subscr. outside N. America to: Springer-Verlag, Heidelberger Platz 3, 14197 Berlin, Germany. TEL 030-8207-0. FAX 030-821-7448) Ed.Bd. bk.rev.; illus. circ. 2,000. **Indexed:** Zent.Math. **Document type:** academic/scholarly publication.
—SWETS.
Description: Publishes high-class papers on various topics in mathematics.
Refereed Serial

510   BL   ISSN 0037-8712
SOCIEDADE PARANAENSE DE MATEMATICA. BOLETIM. 1958. 2/yr. $40. Sociedade Paranaense de Matematica, Caixa Postal 1261, 80001 Curitiba, Parana, Brazil. FAX 55-41-2674236. (Subscr. to: Editora UFPR, Trav. Alfredo Bufrem, 140, 3a andar, 80020 Curitiba PR, Brazil) Ed. Jair M. Abe. adv.; bk.rev.; charts; illus. circ. 600. **Indexed:** Math.R., Zent.Math. **Document type:** bulletin.

510   FR   ISSN 0037-9484
QA1   CODEN: BSMFAA
SOCIETE MATHEMATIQUE DE FRANCE. BULLETIN. (Supplement avail.: Societe Mathematique de France. Memoire (ISSN 0249-633X)) (Text in English, French; summaries in English) 1873. q. 910 F. to non-members (outside Europe 960 F.); members 480 (outside Europe 530 F.) (effective 1995). Societe Mathematique de France, Institut Henri Poincare, 11 rue Pierre et Marie Curie, 75231 Paris Cedex 05, France. TEL 91-26-74-64. FAX 91-41-17-51. E-mail: smf@smf.univ-mrs.fr. (Subscr. to: Maison de la S.M.F., Cellule de Diffusion, B.P. 13274 Marseille Cedex 09, France) (Co-sponsor: Centre National de la Recherche Scientifique) Ed.Bd. (also avail. in microfilm from BHP) **Document type:** academic/scholarly publication.
—BLDSC (2745.400000); Faxon; Genuine Article; SWETS; UnCover. **CCC.**

510   FR   ISSN 0249-633X
SOCIETE MATHEMATIQUE DE FRANCE. MEMOIRE. (Supplement to: Societe Mathematique de France. Bulletin (ISSN 0037-9484)) 1964. irreg. Societe Mathematique de France, Institut Henri Poincare, 11 rue Pierre et Marie Curie, 75231 Paris Cedex 05, France. TEL 91-26-74-64. FAX 91-41-17-51. E-mail: smf@smf.univ-mrs.fr. (Subscr. to: Maison de la S.M.F., Cellule de Diffusion, B.P. 13274 Marseille Cedex 09, France) (Co-sponsor: Centre National de la Recherche Scientifique) (back issues avail.) **Document type:** monographic series.
—BLDSC (5569.465000); SWETS.
Formerly (until 1980): Societe Mathematique de France. Bulletin. Memoire (ISSN 0583-8665)

SOCIETE NATIONALE DES SCIENCES NATURELLES ET MATHEMATIQUES DE CHERBOURG. MEMOIRES. see *SCIENCES: COMPREHENSIVE WORKS*

510   BU   ISSN 0081-1858
QA1   CODEN: GSUMDR
SOFIISKI UNIVERSITET. FAKULTET PO MATEMATIKA I MEKHANIKA. GODISHNIK/UNIVERSITE DE SOFIA. FACULTE DES MATHEMATIQUES ET DE MECANIQUE. ANNUAIRE. (Text in Bulgarian and English) irreg. vol.67, 1972/73. price varies. Publishing House of the Bulgarian Academy of Sciences, Acad. G. Bonchev St., Bldg. 6, 1113 Sofia, Bulgaria. Ed. M. Pecheva. circ. 550. (reprint service avail. from IRC) **Indexed:** Chem.Abstr., Math.R.
—CASDDS.

526 510   US   ISSN 1059-5325
SOLSTICE: AN ELECTRONIC JOURNAL OF GEOGRAPHY AND MATHEMATICS. 1990. 2/yr. $15.95 for print edition (effective 1992). Institute of Mathematical Geography, 2790 Briarcliff, Ann Arbor, MI 48105-1429. TEL 313-761-1231. E-mail: solstice@um.cc.umich.edu. Ed. Sandra Lach Arlinghaus. charts; illus.; stat. (back issues avail.) **Document type:** academic/scholarly publication.
●Also available online.
Description: Publishes papers discussing the interactions between geography and mathematics, in which elements of one discipline shed light on the other. Disseminates original scientific research in electronic format.
Refereed Serial

510 500   CH   ISSN 0250-3255
QA1
SOOCHOW JOURNAL OF MATHEMATICS. Key Title: Dongwu Shuli Xuebao. 1975. q. $25 per no. Soochow University, Wai Shuang Hsi, Shih Lin, Taipei, Taiwan, Republic of China. FAX 886-02-8812317. (reprint service avail.) **Indexed:** Math.R. **Document type:** academic/scholarly publication.
—BLDSC (8328.016000).
Former titles: Soochow Journal of Mathematical and Natural Sciences; (until 1978): Soochow Journal of Mathematics.

510   US   ISSN 0172-6315
SOURCES IN THE HISTORY OF MATHEMATICS AND PHYSICAL SCIENCES. 1976. irreg. price varies. Springer-Verlag, 175 Fifth Ave., New York, NY 10010. TEL 212-460-1500. FAX 212-473-6272. (Also: Berlin, Heidelberg, Tokyo and Vienna) (reprint service avail. from ISI) **Document type:** academic/scholarly publication.

SOUTH AFRICAN STATISTICAL JOURNAL/SUID-AFRIKAANSE STATISTIESE TYDSKRIF. see *STATISTICS*

510   SI   ISSN 0218-0006
SOUTHEAST ASIAN BULLETIN OF MATHEMATICS. 1977. s-a. $40. (Southeast Asian Mathematical Society) World Scientific Publishing Co. Pte. Ltd., Farrer Rd., P.O. Box 128, Singapore 9128, Singapore. TEL 3825663. FAX 3825919. TELEX RS-28561-WSPC. (US addr.: 1060 Main St., River Edge, NJ 07661. TEL 800-227-7562; UK addr.: 73 Lynton Mead, Totteridge, London N20 8DH, England. TEL 44-81-4462461) Eds. R.F. Turner-Smith, P.Y. Lee. bk.rev. circ. 150. **Indexed:** Math.R.
—SWETS. **CCC.**

510 370   BS   ISSN 1022-4572
▼**SOUTHERN AFRICA JOURNAL OF MATHEMATICS AND SCIENCE.** (Text in English) 1994. s-a. $40 to individuals; institutions $50. University of Botswana, Department of Mathematics and Science Education, Private Bag 0022, Gaborone, Botswana. TEL 267-351151. FAX 267-256591. TELEX 2429 BD. Ed. M.B. Ogunniyi. bk.rev. **Document type:** academic/scholarly publication.
Description: Disseminates research findings of high quality in mathematics, science, and technological education to an international readership.

SPECTRUM; natural science journal for teachers and lecturers. see *SCIENCES: COMPREHENSIVE WORKS*

510   US   ISSN 0179-3632
SPRINGER SERIES IN COMPUTATIONAL MATHEMATICS. 1983. irreg. price varies. Springer-Verlag, 175 Fifth Ave., New York, NY 10010. TEL 212-460-1500. FAX 212-473-6272. (Also: Berlin, Heidelberg, Tokyo and Vienna) (reprint service avail. from ISI) **Document type:** monographic series.
—BLDSC (8424.755800).

SPRINGER SERIES IN OPERATIONS RESEARCH. see *COMPUTERS*

510   US   ISSN 0939-1169
SPRINGER SERIES IN SOVIET MATHEMATICS. 1983. irreg. price varies. Springer-Verlag, 175 Fifth Ave., New York, NY 10010. TEL 212-460-1500. FAX 212-473-6272. (Also: Berlin, Heidelberg, Tokyo and Vienna) (reprint service avail. from ISI) **Document type:** monographic series.

510 530　　　　GW　　ISSN 0081-4113
STAATLICHE MATHEMATISCH-PHYSIKALISCHE SALONS, DRESDEN. VEROEFFENTLICHUNGEN. 1960. irreg. price varies. VEB Deutscher Verlag der Wissenschaften, Postfach 1216, 1080 Berlin, Germany. Ed. H. Groetzsch.

STATISTICA NEERLANDICA. see *STATISTICS*

STATISTICAL METHODS IN MEDICAL RESEARCH. see *STATISTICS*

STATISTICAL SCIENCE; a review journal. see *STATISTICS*

STATISTICS; a journal of theoretical and applied statistics. see *STATISTICS*

510　　　　GW　　ISSN 0721-2631
STATISTICS AND DECISIONS; an international mathematical journal for stochastic methods and models. (Text in English) 1982. q. DM.307 (effective 1996). R. Oldenbourg Verlag GmbH, Rosenheimerstr. 145, 81671 Munich, Germany. TEL 089-45051-0. FAX 089-45051207. (Subscr. to: Postfach 801360, 81613 Munich, Germany) Ed.Bd. adv. **Indexed**: Curr.Ind.Stat., Math.R., Stat.Theor.Meth.Abstr. **Document type**: academic/scholarly publication.
—Faxon; SWETS. **CCC**.
Description: Covers classical and multiple statistical decision procedures, asymptotic and nonparametric statistical procedures, including sequential analysis, abstract and applied statistical inference for stochastic processes.

STATISTICS & PROBABILITY LETTERS. see *STATISTICS*

510　　　　RU　　ISSN 0081-5438
QA1
STEKLOV INSTITUTE OF MATHEMATICS. PROCEEDINGS. Russian edition: Matematicheskii Institut im. V.A. Steklova. Trudy (ISSN 0371-9685) (Text in English) 1967. q. $667 in U.S. and Canada (elsewhere $675). Interperiodica, Ul. Profsoyuznaya 90, Moscow 117864. TEL 7-095-3360066. FAX 7-095-3360666. (Subscr. to: Interperiodica, Box 1831, Birmingham, AL 35201-1831. TEL 205-995-1567. FAX 205-995-1588) Ed. Ben Silver. circ. 550. **Indexed**: Math.R. **Document type**: proceedings.
—SWETS; UnCover. **CCC**.

510　　　　US　　ISSN 0736-2994
QA274.2　　　　CODEN: SAAPDA
STOCHASTIC ANALYSIS AND APPLICATIONS. 1983. 5/yr. $297.50 to individuals; institutions $595. Marcel Dekker Journals, 270 Madison Ave., New York, NY 10016. TEL 212-696-9000. FAX 212-685-4540. TELEX 421419 MARDEEK. (Subscr. to: Box 5017, Monticello, NY 12701) Eds. V. Lakshmikantham, G.S. Ladde. charts; stat.; index. (also avail. in microform from RPI) **Indexed**: ASCA, Compumath, Curr.Ind.Stat., Math.R., Stat.Theor.Meth.Abstr. **Document type**: academic/scholarly publication.
—BLDSC (8465.250000); Faxon; Genuine Article; SWETS; UMI; UnCover. **CCC**.
Refereed Serial

STOCHASTIC HYDROLOGY AND HYDRAULICS. see *ENGINEERING — Hydraulic Engineering*

519　　　　US　　ISSN 1063-2409
QA402.5
STOCHASTIC OPTIMIZATION AND DESIGN. 1993. irreg. price varies. Nova Science Publishers, Inc., 6080 Jericho Tpke., Ste. 207, Commack, NY 11725-2808. TEL 516-499-3103. Ed. Sergey Ermakov. **Document type**: monographic series.
Description: Deals with all theoretical and applied aspects of stochastic optimization.

519　　　　NE　　ISSN 0304-4149
QA274.A1　　　　CODEN: STOPB7
STOCHASTIC PROCESSES AND THEIR APPLICATIONS. 1973. m. fl.2478($1511) (effective 1996). (Bernoulli Society for Mathematical Statistics and Probability) North-Holland (Subsidiary of: Elsevier Science B.V.), P.O. Box 211, 1000 AE Amsterdam, Netherlands. TEL 31-20-4853911. FAX 31-20-4853598. TELEX 18582 ESPA NL. (Subscr. in U.S. and Canada to: Elsevier Science Inc., Box 882, Madison Sq. Sta., New York, NY 10159. TEL 212-989-5800. FAX 212-633-3990) Ed. P. Jagers. (also avail. in microform from UMI; back issues avail.; reprint service avail. from SWZ) **Indexed**: ASCA, Biostat., Compumath, Curr.Ind.Stat., Cyb.Abstr., INSPEC, Int.Abstr.Oper.Res., J.Cont.Quant.Meth., Math.R., Oper.Res.Manage.Sci., Qual.Contr.Appl.Stat., Stat.Theor.Meth.Abstr., Zent.Math. **Document type**: academic/scholarly publication.
—BLDSC (8465.300000); Ei; Faxon; Genuine Article; SWETS; UnCover. **CCC**.
Description: Publishes papers on the theory and applications of stochastic processes.
Refereed Serial

510　　　　US　　ISSN 1045-1129
QA274.A1　　　　CODEN: SSTREY
STOCHASTICS AND STOCHASTICS REPORTS. (Text in English; occasionally in French and German) 1978. 16/yr. (in 4 vols., 4 nos./vol.). 389 ECU per vol. (effective 1996). Gordon and Breach Science Publishers, c/o International Publishers Distributor, 820 Town Center Dr., Langhorne, PA 19047. TEL 215-750-2642. FAX 215-750-6343. (Subscr. to: International Publishers Distributor, P.O. Box 90, Reading, Berkshire RG1 8JL, England. TEL 44-173-456-8316) Ed. Mark H.A. Davis. adv.; index. (also avail. in microform) **Indexed**: Curr.Ind.Stat., INSPEC, Math.R., Stat.Theor.Meth.Abstr.
—BLDSC (8465.331000); Faxon; SWETS; UnCover. **CCC**.
Formerly: Stochastics (ISSN 0090-9491)
Refereed Serial

510　　　　US　　ISSN 0275-5785
STOCHASTICS MONOGRAPHS. 1985. irreg., latest vol.8. Gordon & Breach Science Publishers, c/o International Publishers Distributor, 820 Town Center Dr., Langhorne, PA 19047. TEL 215-750-2642. FAX 215-750-6343. (Subscr. to: International Publishers Distributor, P.O. Box 90, Reading, Berkshire RG1 8JL, England. TEL 44-173-456-8316) Ed. M. Davis. (also avail. in microform) **Document type**: monographic series.
—BLDSC (8465.333000).
Refereed Serial

STRATEGIES. see *EDUCATION — Teaching Methods And Curriculum*

510　　　　CN　　ISSN 0085-6800
STUDENT MATHEMATICS. 1970. a. Can.$0.20. c/o S.K. Harburn, Ed., Faculty of Education, Rm. 373, University of Toronto, 371 Bloor St. West, Toronto, Ont. M5S 2R7, Canada. TEL 416-978-2011. bk.rev. circ. 3,000.

STUDIA LOGICA; an international journal for symbolic logic. see *PHILOSOPHY*

510　　　　PL　　ISSN 0039-3223
QA1　　　　CODEN: SMATAZ
STUDIA MATHEMATICA. (Text in English, French, German, Russian; summaries in English) 1929. irreg., approx. 3-4/vols./yr., 3 nos./vol. $84 per vol. Polska Akademia Nauk, Instytut Matematyczny, Dzial Wydawnictw, Ul. Sniadeckich 8, P.O. Box 137, 00-950 Warsaw, Poland. TEL 48-22-6282471. FAX 48-22-293997. Ed.Bd. bibl.; index. circ. 1,100. (reprint service avail. from SWZ) **Indexed**: ASCA, Compumath, Math.R. **Document type**: academic/scholarly publication.
—BLDSC (8483.000000); Faxon; Genuine Article; SWETS; UnCover.
Description: Publishes original papers mainly in functional analysis, abstract methods of mathematical analysis and probabiliby theory.

510　　　　HU　　ISSN 0081-6906
　　　　　　CODEN: SSMHAX
STUDIA SCIENTIARUM MATHEMATICARUM HUNGARICA. (Text mainly in English, occasionally in French, German, Russian) 1971. q. $88 (effective 1992). (Magyar Tudomanyos Akademia) Akademiai Kiado, Publishing House of the Hungarian Academy of Sciences, P.O. Box 245, H-1519 Budapest, Hungary. TEL 181-2134. FAX 166-6466. TELEX 22-6228 AKNYO H. Ed. Andras Hajnal. **Indexed**: Math.R.
—SWETS; UnCover. **CCC**.
Description: Publishes original research papers on mathematics and its diverse fields of application in science, technology, economics, etc. Includes theory of probability, statistics, numerical and graphic methods, and differential equation.

510　　　　RM
STUDIA UNIVERSITATIS "BABES-BOLYAI". MATHEMATICA. (Text in English, French, German, Rumanian) 1958. q. exchange basis. Universitatea "Babes-Bolyai", Biblioteca Centrala Universitara, Str. Clinicilor Nr. 2, Cluj-Napoca 3400, Rumania. TEL 36-64-197092. FAX 36-64-197633. Ed. I. Haiduc. charts; illus. **Indexed**: Math.R. **Document type**: academic/scholarly publication.
Formerly: Studia Universitatis "Babes-Bolyai". Series Mathematica - Physica (ISSN 0039-3436)

510 378　　　　GW
STUDIENFUEHRER MATHEMATIK. 1973. a. free. Technical University Berlin, Department of Mathematics, Strasse des 17.Juni 135, 10623 Berlin, Germany. FAX 030-31421110. illus. circ. 400.

519　　　　US　　ISSN 0022-2526
QA1　　　　CODEN: SAPMB6
STUDIES IN APPLIED MATHEMATICS (CAMBRIDGE). 1922. 8/yr (in 2 vols.). $370 (foreign $415) (effective 1995). (Massachusetts Institute of Technology, Applied Mathematics Group) Blackwell Publishers, 238 Main St., Cambridge, MA 02142. TEL 617-547-7110. Ed. David Benney. charts. (also avail. in microform from UMI; back issues avail.) **Indexed**: A.S.& T.Ind., Appl.Mech.Rev., Compumath, Curr.Cont., Deep Sea Res.& Oceanogr.Abstr., Eng.Ind., INSPEC, Math.R., Sci.Cit.Ind. **Document type**: academic/scholarly publication.
—BLDSC (8489.480000); Faxon; Genuine Article; SWETS; UnCover. **CCC**.
Formerly: Journal of Mathematics and Physics.
Description: Reports results involving core concepts: propagation, equilibrium, stability, and optimization, as well as discrete and random processes.
Refereed Serial

519　　　　US
STUDIES IN APPLIED MATHEMATICS (PHILADELPHIA). irreg., vol.15, 1994. price varies. Society for Industrial and Applied Mathematics, 3600 University City Science Center, Philadelphia, PA 19104-2688. TEL 215-382-9800; 800-447-SIAM. FAX 215-386-7999. E-mail: siam@siam.org. Ed. Tricia Manning; Pub. Vickie Kearn. **Document type**: monographic series.

519.4　　　　NE
STUDIES IN COMPUTATIONAL MATHEMATICS. (Text in English) 1988. irreg., vol.4, 1992. price varies. Elsevier Science B.V., Books Division, P.O. Box 211, 1000 AE Amsterdam, Netherlands. TEL 31-20-4853911. FAX 31-20-4853705. TELEX 18582 ESPA NL. E-mail: nlinfo-f@elsevier.nl; usinfo-f@elsevier.com; forinfo-kyf04035@niftyserve.or.jp; Site addr.: http://www.elsevier.nl/. (Subscr. in U.S. and Canada to: Elsevier Science Inc., Box 882, Madison Sq. Sta., New York, NY 10159. TEL 212-989-5800) Eds. C. Brezinski, L. Wuytack. (back issues avail.) **Document type**: monographic series.
Refereed Serial

511.3 160　　　　US
STUDIES IN LOGIC AND COMPUTATION. irreg., vol.2, 1993. price varies. Oxford University Press, 200 Madison Ave., New York, NY 10016. TEL 212-679-7300. Ed. D.M. Gabbay. (back issues avail.) **Document type**: monographic series.
Refereed Serial

MATHEMATICS

511 NE ISSN 0049-237X
STUDIES IN LOGIC AND THE FOUNDATIONS OF MATHEMATICS. Proceedings subseries: Logic, Methodology and Philosophy of Science. 1954. irreg., vol.134, 1995. price varies. Elsevier Science B.V., Books Division, P.O. Box 211, 1000 AE Amsterdam, Netherlands. TEL 31-20-4853911. FAX 31-20-4853705. TELEX 18582 ESPA NL. E-mail: nlinfo-f@elsevier.nl; usinfo-f@elsevier.com; forinfo-kyf4035@niftyserve.or.jp; Site addr.: http://www.elsevier.nl/. (Subscr. in U.S. and Canada to: Elsevier Science Inc., Box 882, Madison Sq. Sta., New York, NY 10159. TEL 212-989-5800) Ed.Bd. **Indexed:** INSPEC. **Document type:** monographic series, proceedings.
—*Refereed Serial*

STUDIES IN MATHEMATICAL AND MANAGERIAL ECONOMICS. see *BUSINESS AND ECONOMICS — Management*

STUDIES IN MATHEMATICAL PHYSICS. see *PHYSICS*

510 US ISSN 0081-8208
STUDIES IN MATHEMATICS (WASHINGTON). Variant title: M A A Studies in Mathematics. 1962. irreg., no.26, 1987. Mathematical Association of America, 1529 Eighteenth St., N.W., Washington, DC 20036. TEL 202-387-5200. Ed. C.W. Curtis. (reprint service avail. from UMI) **Document type:** academic/scholarly publication.
—*Refereed Serial*

510 NE ISSN 0168-2024
CODEN: SMIADL
STUDIES IN MATHEMATICS AND ITS APPLICATIONS. 1975. irreg., vol.26, 1992. price varies. Elsevier Science B.V., Books Division, P.O. Box 211, Amsterdam, Netherlands. TEL 31-20-4853911. FAX 31-20-4853705. TELEX 18582 ESPA NL. E-mail: nlinfo-f@elsevier.nl; usinfo-f@elsevier.com; forinfo-kyf4035@niftyserve.or.jp; Site addr.: http://www.elsevier.nl/. (Subscr. in U.S. and Canada to: Elsevier Science Inc., Box 882, Madison Sq. Sta., new Yrok, NY 10159. TEL 212-989-5800) Ed.Bd. bibl. **Indexed:** INSPEC, Math.R. **Document type:** monographic series.
—BLDSC (8491.090000).
—*Refereed Serial*

511.3 NE
STUDIES IN PROOF THEORY. (Text in English) 1990. irreg., vol.3, 1992. price varies. Elsevier Science B.V., Books Division, P.O. Box 211, 1000 AE Amsterdam, Netherlands. TEL 31-20-4853911. FAX 31-20-4853705. TELEX 18582 ESPA NL. E-mail: nlinfo-f@elsevier.nl; usinfo-f@elsevier.com; forinfo-kyf4035@niftyserve.or.jp; Site addr.: http://www.elsevier.nl/. (Subscr. in U.S. and Canada to: Elsevier Science Inc., Box 882, Madison Sq. Sta., New York, NY 10159. TEL 212-989-5800) Ed.Bd. (back issues avail.) **Document type:** monographic series.
—*Refereed Serial*

STUDIES IN STATISTICAL MECHANICS. see *PHYSICS — Mechanics*

510 US ISSN 1040-6441
STUDIES IN THE DEVELOPMENT OF MODERN MATHEMATICS. irreg., latest vol.2. price varies. Gordon and Breach Science Publishers, c/o International Publishing Distributor, 820 Town Center Dr., Langhorne, PA 19047. TEL 215-750-2643. FAX 215-750-6343. (Subscr. to: International Publishing Distributor, P.O. Box 90, Reading, Berkshire RG1 8JL, England. TEL 44-173-456-8316) Ed. Yu. I. Manin. **Document type:** monographic series.
—BLDSC (8490.391000).
—*Refereed Serial*

510.1 NE ISSN 0928-2017
STUDIES IN THE HISTORY AND PHILOSOPHY OF MATHEMATICS. (Text in English) 1990. irreg., vol.3, 1991. price varies. Elsevier Science B.V., Books Division, P.O. Box 211, 1000 AE Amsterdam, Netherlands. TEL 31-20-4853911. FAX 31-20-4853705. TELEX 18582 ESPA NL. E-mail: nlinfo-f@elsevier.nl; usinfo-f@elsevier.com; forinfo-kyf4035@niftyserve.or.jp; Site addr.: http://www.elsevier.nl/. (Subscr. in U.S. and Canada to: Elsevier Science Inc., Box 882, Madison Sq. Sta., New York, NY 10159. TEL 212-989-5800) Ed.Bd. (back issues avail.) **Document type:** monographic series.
—BLDSC (8490.651700).
—*Refereed Serial*

510 RM ISSN 0039-4068
QA1
STUDII SI CERCETARI MATEMATICE. (Text in Rumanian; summaries in English, French, German or Spanish) 1950. 6/yr. 180 lei($72) (Academia Romana) Editura Academiei Romane, Calea Victoriei 125, 79717 Bucharest, Rumania. (Dist. by: Rompresfilatelia, Calea Grivitei 64-66, P.O. Box 12-201, 78104 Bucharest, Rumania) adv.; bk.rev.; abstr.; charts; index. **Indexed:** Appl.Mech.Rev., Math.R.
—BLDSC (8497.500000); UnCover.

510 JA ISSN 0039-470X
CODEN: SUGKAQ
SUGAKU/MATHEMATICS. English translation: Sugaku Expositions (US ISSN 0898-9583) (Text in Japanese) 1947. q. 3500 Yen. (Nihon Sugakkai - Mathematical Society of Japan) Iwanami Shoten Publishers, 5-5, Hitotsubashi 2-chome, Chiyoda-ku, Tokyo 101-02, Japan. FAX 03-3239-9618. (Dist. overseas by: Japan Publications Trading Co., Ltd., Box 5030, Tokyo International, Tokyo 100-31, Japan; Or: 1255 Howard St., San Francisco, CA 94103) Ed.Bd. bk.rev. **Indexed:** Jap.Per.Ind., Math.R.

510 US ISSN 0898-9583
QA1
SUGAKU EXPOSITIONS. English translation of: Sugaku (JA ISSN 0039-470X) 1988. s-a. $105 to non-members; individual members $63; institutional members $84. (Mathematical Society of Japan, JA) American Mathematical Society, Box 6248, Providence, RI 02904-6248. TEL 401-455-4000. (Street addr.: 201 Charles St., Providence, RI 02904) circ. 950. **Indexed:** Math.R. **Document type:** academic/scholarly publication.
—BLDSC (8509.910000); SWETS; UnCover.

510 JA ISSN 0912-7569
SUGAKU OCHIKOBORE TSUSHIN. (Text in Japanese) 1986. s-a. (Sugaku Ochikobore Semina - Enjoy Mathematics Seminar) Saientsutosha - Scientist Inc., 3-2, Kanda Surugadai, Chiyoda-ku, Tokyo 101, Japan.

510 JA ISSN 0386-4960
SUGAKU SEMINA/SUGAKU SEMINAR. (Text in Japanese) 1962. s-a. Nippon Hyoronsha Co., Ltd., 10-10, Minami-Otsuka 3-chome, Toshima-ku, Tokyo 170, Japan.

510.92 JA ISSN 0386-9555
QA27.J3
SUGAKUSHI KENKYU/JOURNAL OF THE HISTORY OF MATHEMATICS, JAPAN. (Text in Japanese) 1962. q. Nihon Sugakushi Gakkai - History of Mathematics Society of Japan, Fuji Tanki Daigaku, 7-7, Shimo-Ochiai 1-chome, Shinjuku-ku, Tokyo 161, Japan. **Indexed:** Jap.Per.Ind.

510 II ISSN 0971-6475
SUGANITAM. (Text in English or Gujarati) 1963. bi-m. Rs.25($6) Suganitam Trust, Department of Mathematics, Gujarat University, Ahmedabad 380009, India. Ed. A.M. Vaidya. adv.; bk.rev.; illus. circ. 1,500. **Document type:** academic/scholarly publication.

510 JA
SUGEI PAZURU. (Text in Japanese) 1964. bi-m. Sugei Pazuru Aikokai, c/o Mr. Akio Suzuki, 9-1, Tsutsui 2-chome, Higashi-ku, Nagoya-shi, Aichi-ken 461, Japan.
Description: Contains mathematical puzzles.

SUHAK KWA MULLI. see *PHYSICS*

510 JA ISSN 0386-2240
Q172 CODEN: SUKADJ
SURI KAGAKU/MATHEMATICAL SCIENCES. (Text in Japanese) 1963. m. 10800 Yen. Saiensu-sha Co., Ltd., 1-3-25, Sendagaya, Shibuga-ku, Tokyo 151, Japan. TEL 03-5474-8500. FAX 03-5474-8900. Ed. K. Hirase. adv.; bk.rev. circ. 14,000. **Indexed:** Chem.Abstr., Jap.Per.Ind. **Document type:** academic/scholarly publication.
—BLDSC (5403.200000); CASDDS.
Description: Informs students of the current researches on mathematical sciences.

510 JA
SURI KAISEKI KENKYUJO DAYORI. (Text in Japanese) s-a. Kyoto University, Research Institute for Mathematical Sciences - Kyoto Daigaku Suri Kaiseki Kenkyujo, Oiwake-cho, Kita-Shirakawa, Sakyo-ku, Kyoto-shi, Kyoto-fu 606-01, Japan. Ed. Huzihiro Araki. **Document type:** academic/scholarly publication.
Description: Contains news of the Institute.

510 001.642 JA
SURI KEIKAKU SHINPOJUMU RONBUNSHU/MATHEMATICAL PROGRAMMING SYMPOSIUM, JAPAN. PROCEEDINGS. (Text in English and Japanese; summaries in English) 1980. a. Suri Keikaku Shinpojumu Iinkai - Committee of Mathematical Programming Symposium, Japan, c/o Mr. Masao Iri, Tokyo Daigaku Kogakubu Keisu Kogakka, 3-1, Hongo 7-chome, Bunkyo-ku, Tokyo 113, Japan.

519 US
▼**SURVEYS IN APPLIED MATHEMATICS.** 1995. irreg. price varies. Plenum Publishing Corp., 233 Spring St., New York, NY 10013-1578. TEL 212-620-8035. FAX 212-463-0742. TELEX 23-421139. Ed.Bd. **Document type:** monographic series.
Description: Covers current research developments in all major areas of applied mathematics.

510 AU ISSN 0938-1953
SURVEYS ON MATHEMATICS FOR INDUSTRY. 1991. q. DM.284($206) (effective 1996). Springer-Verlag, Sachsenplatz 4-6, Postfach 89, A-1201 Vienna, Austria. TEL 0222-3302415. FAX 0222-3302426. (Subscr. in N. America to: Springer-Verlag New York, Inc., 44 Hartz Way, Secaucus, NJ 07096-2491. TEL 201-348-4033. FAX 201-348-4505) Ed.Bd. (also avail. in microform from UMI) **Indexed:** INSPEC (1991-). **Document type:** academic/scholarly publication.
—BLDSC (8550.545000); UMI. **CCC**.

512.92 JA ISSN 0288-4046
SUSHIKI SHORI TSUSHIN/COMMUNICATIONS FOR SYMBOLIC AND ALGEBRAIC MANIPULATION. (Text in English and Japanese) 1983. 3/yr. Saientsutosha - Scientist Inc., 3-2, Kanda Surugadai, Chiyoda-ku, Tokyo 101, Japan.

510 US ISSN 0082-0725
SYMPOSIA MATHEMATICA. (Contributions in English, French, German and Italian) 1969. irreg., vol.33, 1993. (Istituto Nazionale di Alta Matematica Francesco Severi) Academic Press, Inc., 525 B St., Ste. 1900, San Diego, CA 92101-4495. TEL 619-231-0926. FAX 619-699-6715. (Subscr. to: Order Dept., 6277 Sea Harbor Dr., 4th Fl., Orlando, FL 32887. TEL 800-321-5068) (reprint service avail. from ISI) **Indexed:** Math.R, Zent.Math.
—*Refereed Serial*

515.74 JA
SYMPOSIUM ON APPLIED FUNCTIONAL ANALYSIS. PROCEEDINGS. (Text in English) 1978. a. Society of Applied Functional Analysis - Oyo Kansu Kaisekigaku Kenkyukai, c/o Mr. Hisaharu Umegaki, Tokyo Kogyo Daigaku Rigakubu, 12-1, Ookayama 2-chome, Meguro-ku, Tokyo 152, Japan.
Formerly: Seminar on Applied Functional Analysis.

SYMPOSIUM ON COMPUTER ARITHMETIC. PROCEEDINGS. see *COMPUTERS — Cybernetics*

512.4 JA
SYMPOSIUM ON RING THEORY. PROCEEDINGS. (Text in English) 1968. a. Okayama Daigaku - Okayama University, 1-1, Tsushima Naka 1-chome, Okayama-shi, Okayama-ken 700, Japan. **Document type:** proceedings.

510 US ISSN 0232-9298
QA402 CODEN: SAMSEC
SYSTEMS ANALYSIS MODELLING SIMULATION; journal of mathematical modelling and simulation in systems analysis. (Text in English) 1984. 12/yr. (in 3 vols., 4 nos./vol.). 131 ECU per vol. (effective 1996). Gordon and Breach Science Publishers, c/o International Publishers Distributor, 820 Town Center Dr., Langhorne, PA 19047. TEL 215-750-2642. FAX 215-750-6343. (Subscr. to: Internation al Publishers Distributor, P.O. Box 90, Reading, Berkshire RG1 8JL, England. TEL 44-173-456-8316) Ed. Achim Sydow. bk.rev.; illus.; index. **Indexed:** Compumath, Comput.Abstr., Cyb.Abstr. **Document type:** academic/scholarly publication.
—BLDSC (8589.287500); Faxon; SWETS; UnCover. **CCC.**

SYSTEMS SCIENCE. see *ENGINEERING*

510 001.6 CC ISSN 1000-9590
Q295 CODEN: SMASE2
SYSTEMS SCIENCE AND MATHEMATICAL SCIENCES. Chinese edition: Xitong Kexue yu Shuxue (ISSN 1000-0577) 1988. q. foreign $410 (effective 1996). (Chinese Academy of Sciences, Institute of Systems Science) Science Press, Marketing and Sales Department, 16 Donghuangchenggen North St., Beijing 100717, People's Republic of China. (Exclusively dist. outside P.R.China by: Allerton Press, Inc., 150 Fifth Ave., New York, NY 10011. TEL 212-924-3950. FAX 212-463-9684) (Co-publisher: Allerton Press, Inc.) Ed. Chen Hanfu. adv. circ. 6,000. (back issues avail.) **Document type:** academic/scholarly publication.
—BLDSC (8589.432000). **CCC.**
Description: Presents original papers in mathematics from mainland China, including systems theory, system modeling, and system control.
Refereed Serial

510 620 PL ISSN 0860-6706
SZCZECINSKIE ROCZNIKI NAUKOWE, NAUKI MATEMATYCZNE I TECHNICZNE. 1987. a. price varies. (Szczecinskie Towarzystwo Naukowe - Szczecin Scientific Society) Ossolineum, Publishing House of the Polish Academy of Sciences, Rynek 9, 50-106 Wroclaw, Poland. TEL 48-71-386-25. FAX 48-71-448-103. TELEX 0712771 OSS PL.

510 SP
QA329
T O P. (Text in English) 1950. a. 12000 ptas. Sociedad de Estadistica e Investigacion Operativa, Hortaleza, 104, 2o Izda., 28004 Madrid, Spain. TEL 34-1-3082474. **Indexed:** Ind.SST, Math.R.
Formerly (until 1992): Trabajos de Investigacion Operativa (ISSN 0213-8204); Supersedes in part (in 1986): Trabajos de Estadistica e Investigacion Operativa (ISSN 0041-0241); Which was formerly (until 1963): Trabajos de Estadistica (ISSN 0210-5675).

510 CH ISSN 0049-2930
TAMKANG JOURNAL OF MATHEMATICS. (Text in English) 1970. q. $50. (Tamkang University, Graduate School of Mathematics) Tamkang University Press, Tamsui, Taipei Hsien 25137, Taiwan, Republic of China. TEL 886-2-621-5656. FAX 886-2-620-2613. E-mail: bsm01@twntku10. Ed. Thakyin Hu. circ. 300 (controlled). **Indexed:** Math.R., Zent.Math. **Document type:** academic/scholarly publication.
—BLDSC (8601.610000); UnCover.
Description: Covers pure and applied mathematics. *Refereed Serial*

510 375 TZ ISSN 0856-065X
TANZANIAN MATHEMATICAL BULLETIN. (Text in English and Swahili) 1966. s-a. Sh.500($15) Mathematical Association of Tanzania - Chama Cha Hisabati Tanzania, P.O. Box 35062, Dar es Salaam, Tanzania. TEL 255-51-49192. Ed. M.J. OReilly. bk.rev.; index. circ. 700. (looseleaf format) **Document type:** bulletin.
Formerly (until 1970): Mathematical Association of Tanzania. Bulletin (ISSN 0047-6250)
Description: Covers all mathematics topics relevant to primary, secondary and university education.

510 GS ISSN 0320-9512
QA1
TBILISSKII UNIVERSITET. INSTITUT PRIKLADNOI MATEMATIKI. SEMINAR. DOKLADI. (Text in Russian; summaries in English and Georgian) 1969. irreg., no.21, 1990. price varies. Tbilisskii Universitet, Institut Prikladnoi Matematiki - University of Tbilisi, Institute of Applied Mathematics, University St. 2, 380043 Tbilisi, Georgia. Ed. D. Gordeziani. circ. 300.
Formerly: Tbilisskii Universitet. Institut Prikladnoi Matematiki. Seminar. Annotatsii Dokladov (ISSN 0082-2191)

513 370 US ISSN 1073-5836
TEACHING CHILDREN MATHEMATICS. 1954; N.S. 1994. m. (Sep.-May). $45 to individuals; institutions $50 (effective 1994). National Council of Teachers of Mathematics, 1906 Association Dr., Reston, VA 22091-1593. TEL 703-620-9840. FAX 703-476-2970. E-mail: nctmath@tmn.com. Ed. Harry B. Tunis. adv.; bk.rev.; bibl.; illus.; index, cum.index: 1954-1973; 1974-1983. circ. 57,400. (also avail. in microform from UMI; reprint service avail. from UMI) **Indexed:** Acad.Ind., Biog.Ind., C.I.J.E., Cont.Pg.Educ., Educ.Ind., Except.Child.Educ.Abstr., Jun.High.Mag.Abstr., LAMP, Media Rev.Dig.
—BLDSC (8614.055500); Faxon; SWETS; UMI; UnCover.
Formerly (until May 1994): Arithmetic Teacher (ISSN 0004-136X)
Description: Articles, teaching ideas, and features of interest to teachers of mathematics in kindergarten through the middle grades.
Refereed Serial

510 375 UK ISSN 0268-3679
TEACHING MATHEMATICS AND ITS APPLICATIONS. 1982. q. £45($80) (effective 1996). Oxford University Press, Oxford Journals, Walton St., Oxford OX2 6DP, England. TEL 01865-267907. FAX 01865-267773. TELEX 837330-OXPRES-G. E-mail: jnlorders@oup.co.uk. (U.S. subscr. to: Oxford University Press Inc., 2001 Evans Rd., Cary, NC 27513. TEL 919-677-0977. FAX 919-677-1714) Ed.Bd. adv.; bk.rev. circ. 700. **Document type:** academic/scholarly publication.
—BLDSC (8614.289000); Ei; SWETS; UMI. **CCC.**
Description: Provides teaching aids for mathematics teachers in secondary and tertiary education.

TECHNICAL UNIVERSITY OF DENMARK. INSTITUTE OF MATHEMATICAL STATISTICS AND OPERATIONS RESEARCH. TECHNICAL REPORT. see *STATISTICS*

510 NE
TECHNISCHE UNIVERSITEIT EINDHOVEN. FACULTEIT DER WISKUNDE EN INFORMATICA. E U T REPORTS - W S K. 1968. irreg. free. Technische Universiteit Eindhoven, Faculteit der Wiskunden Informatica - Eindhoven University of Technology, Department of Mathematics and Computing Science, Postbus 513, 5600 MB Eindhoven, Netherlands. Ed. J. Boersma. circ. 100. **Indexed:** Math.R., Ref.Zh., Zent.Math. **Document type:** academic/scholarly publication.
Former titles: Technische Hogeschool Eindhoven. Onderafdeling der Wiskunde en Informatica. E U T Reports - W S K; Technische Hogeschool Eindhoven. Onderafdeling der Wiskunde. E U T Reports - W S K; Technische Hogeschool Eindhoven. Onderafdeling der Wiskunde. T H Report W S K.
Refereed Serial

510 530 DK ISSN 0106-6242
TEKSTER FRA I M F U F A. 1978. irreg. Roskilde Universitetscenter, Institut for Studiet af Matematik og Fysik samt deres Funktioner i Undervisning Forskning og Anvendelse, P.O. Box 260, DK-4000 Roskilde, Denmark. TEL 45-46-75-77-11. illus.

510 600 JA ISSN 0040-3504
QA1 CODEN: TNSRAZ
TENSOR. (Text in English, French, German and Italian) 1938. 3/yr. $750. Tensor Society - Tenzoru Gakkai, Kawaguchi Sutikenkyujo - Kawaguchi Institute of Mathematical Sciences, 7-15, Matsu-ga-oka 2-chome, Chigasaki-shi, Kanagawa-ken 253, Japan. (Dist. by: Intercontinental Marketing Corp., I.P.O. Box 5056, Tokyo 100-30, Japan. TEL 81-3-3661-7458. FAX 81-3-3667-9646) Ed. M. Kawaguchi. illus.; index; circ. 600 (controlled). **Indexed:** INIS Atomind., Math.R. **Document type:** academic/scholarly publication.
—Faxon; SWETS; UnCover.

510 KR ISSN 0321-4427
QA331
TEORIYA FUNKTSII, FUNKTSIONAL'NYI ANALIZ I IKH PRILOZHENIYA. 1965. s-a. 1.40 Rub. per issue. (Khar'kovskii Gosudarstvennyi Universitet) Izdatel'stvo Vysshaya Shkola, Khar'kovskoe Otdelenie, Ul. Universitetskaya 16, 310003 Kharkov, Ukraine. Ed. V. Marchenko. abstr.; charts. **Indexed:** Math.R.
—BLDSC (0178.500000).
Description: Presents articles on the theory of function of many complex variables.

510 RU
TEORIYA FUNKTSII KOMPLEKSNOGO PEREMENNOGO I KRAEVYE ZADACHI. 1972. irreg. 0.80 Rub. Chuvashskii Gosudarstvennyi Universitet, Moskovskii prospekt, 15, Cheboksary, Chuvash A.R., Russia.

510 KR ISSN 0321-3900
QA274.A1
TEORIYA SLUCHAINYKH PROTSESSOV; respublikanskii mezhvedomstvennyi sbornik nauchnykh trudov. (Text in Russian) 1973. a. (Akademiya Nauk Ukrainy, Institut Prikladnoi Matematiki i Mekhaniki) Vidavnitstvo Naukova Dumka, Vul. Tereshchenivska 3, 252601 Kiev, Ukraine. TEL 044-224-4068. FAX 044-224-7060. (Dist. by: Mezhdunarodnaya Kniga, B. Yakimanka 39, 117049 Moscow, Russia) Ed. Yu.N. Lin'kov. circ. 1,400.
—BLDSC (0178.420000).

510 RU ISSN 0040-361X
QA273 CODEN: TVPRA8
TEORIYA VEROYATNOSTEI I EE PRIMENENIYA. English translation: Theory of Probability and Its Applications (US ISSN 0040-585X) (Text in Russian; summaries in English) 1956. q. $32.40. (Rossiiskaya Akademiya Nauk, Institut Matematiki) Izdatel'stvo Nauka, Mezhdunarodnyi Otdel, Profsoyuznaya, 90, 117864 Moscow, Russia. Ed. V. Statulyavichus. bk.rev.; charts; index. circ. 2,515. **Indexed:** Chem.Abstr., INSPEC, Math.R. **Document type:** academic/scholarly publication.
—BLDSC (0178.000000).

510 GW ISSN 0233-0962
TEUBNER-ARCHIV ZUR MATHEMATIK. 1984. 2/yr. B.G. Teubner Verlagsgesellschaft mbH, Johannisgasse 16, 04103 Leipzig, Germany. TEL 216860. **Document type:** academic/scholarly publication.

510 GW ISSN 0138-502X
TEUBNER-TEXTE ZUR MATHEMATIK. (Text in English, German) 1976. 2/yr. B.G. Teubner Verlagsgesellschaft mbH, Johannisgasse 16, 04103 Leipzig, Germany. TEL 216860. Ed.Bd. **Document type:** academic/scholarly publication.

THEORETICAL AND MATHEMATICAL PHYSICS. see *PHYSICS*

THEORY AND APPLICATIONS OF TRANSPORT IN POROUS MEDIA. see *PHYSICS*

519.5 NE ISSN 0921-3392
THEORY AND DECISION LIBRARY. SERIES B: MATHEMATICAL AND STATISTICAL METHODS. (Text in English) 1973; N.S. 1984. irreg., vol.25, 1993. price varies. Kluwer Academic Publishers, Postbus 17, 3300 AA Dordrecht, Netherlands. TEL 31-78-392392. FAX 31-78-392254. TELEX 29245 KAPG NL. (Dist. by: Kluwer Academic Publishers Group, P.O. Box 322, 3300 AH Dordrecht, Netherlands. TEL 31-78-392392. FAX 31-78-546474; N. America dist. addr.: Box 358, Accord Sta., Hingham, MA 02018-0358. TEL 617-871-6600) Ed. H.J. Skala. (back issues avail.) **Indexed:** Int.Polit.Sci.Abstr., Psychol.Abstr. **Document type:** monographic series.
—BLDSC (8814.628040).
Supersedes in part (in 1984): Theory and Decision Library (ISSN 0921-3376)
Refereed Serial

MATHEMATICS 4149

M

MATHEMATICS

519   US   ISSN 0040-585X
QA273   CODEN: TPRBAU
THEORY OF PROBABILITY AND ITS APPLICATIONS.
English translation of: Teoriya Veroyatnostei i ee Primeneniya (RU ISSN 0040-361X) 1956. q. $374 to non-members (overseas $420); members $99 (overseas $102) (effective 1995). (Russian Academy of Sciences, Institute of Mathematics, RU) Society for Industrial and Applied Mathematics, Attn: M. Lafferty, 3600 University City Science Center, Philadelphia, PA 19104-2688. TEL 215-382-9800. FAX 215-386-7999. E-mail: PUB@SIAM.ORG. Ed. Natasha Brunswick. adv. circ. 960. (also avail. in microform from IAM; back issues avail.) **Indexed:** Appl.Mech.Rev., ASCA, Compumath, Comput.Rev., Curr.Cont., Curr.Ind.Stat., INSPEC, Math.R., Stat.Theor.Meth.Abstr. **Document type:** academic/scholarly publication.
—BLDSC (0427.000000); Faxon; Genuine Article; SWETS; UnCover. **CCC.**
   Description: Contains papers on the theory and application of probability, statistics, and stochastic processes.
   Refereed Serial

510   US   ISSN 0094-9000
QA273.A1   CODEN: TPMSCO
THEORY OF PROBABILITY AND MATHEMATICAL STATISTICS. English translation of: Teoriya Veroyatnostei i Matematicheskaya Statistika. 1970. 2/yr. $359 to non-members; institutional members $287. (Kievskii Universitet, UR) American Mathematical Society, Box 6248, Providence, RI 02940-6248. TEL 401-455-4000. (Street addr.: 201 Charles St., Providence, RI 02904) Ed. Ben Silver. charts; stat. circ. 250. **Indexed:** Curr.Ind.Stat., J.Cont.Quant.Meth., Math.R. **Document type:** academic/scholarly publication.
—Faxon; SWETS; UnCover. **CCC.**

510   UK   ISSN 0953-0738
THETA. 1987. s-a. £6. Crewe & Alsager College of Higher Education, Faculty of M M U, Crewe, Cheshire CW1 1DU, England. TEL 0270-500661. FAX 0270-583433. Ed.Bd. adv.; bk.rev. circ. 1,500. **Document type:** academic/scholarly publication.
   Description: Covers general mathematics for all who teach, learn, practice and enjoy it.

510 370   JA   ISSN 0913-221X
TOHOKU - HOKURIKU SUGAKU KYOIKU KISOTEKI KENKYU HOKOKU. (Text and summaries in Japanese) 1973. s-a. Tohoku - Hokuriku Sugaku Kyoiku Kisoteki Kenkyukai - Study Group on the Mathematics Education in Tohoku-Hokuriku District, c/o Iwate Daigaku Kyoikugakubu, Saeki Kenkyushitsu, 18-33, Ueda 3-chome, Morioka-shi, Iwate-ken 020, Japan.
   Description: Reports on mathematics education in the district.

510   JA   ISSN 0040-8735
QA1   CODEN: TOMJAM
TOHOKU MATHEMATICAL JOURNAL/TOHOKU SUGAKU ZASSHI. (Text in English, French, German) 1911. q. $250 or exchange basis. Tohoku Daigaku, Suugaku Kyoushitsu - Tohoku University, Mathematical Institute, Aramaki aza Aoba, Aoba-ku, Sendai-shi, Miyagi-ken 980-77, Japan. FAX 022-263-6793. (Subscr. to: Maruzen Co., Ltd., P.O. Box 5050, Tokyo International, Tokyo 100-31, Japan) Ed. Tadao Oda. circ. 1,000. (also avail. in microfiche from BHP) **Indexed:** ASCA, Compumath, JCT, JTA, Math.R., Sci.Cit.Ind., Zent.Math. **Document type:** academic/scholarly publication.
—BLDSC (8862.300000); Faxon; Genuine Article; SWETS; UnCover.
   Refereed Serial

TOKEI. see *STATISTICS*

510 310   JA
TOKEI SURI KENKYUZYO KENKYU RIPOTO/INSTITUTE OF STATISTICAL MATHEMATICS. RESEARCH REPORT. GENERAL SERIES. (Text in Japanese) 1955. irreg. free. Tokei Suri Kenkyujo - Institute of Statistical Mathematics, 4-6-7, Minami-Azabu, Minato-ku, Tokyo 106, Japan. TEL 03-3446-1501. FAX 03-3446-1695. Ed. Noboru Ohsumi. **Document type:** monographic series.

510   JA   ISSN 0387-3870
TOKYO JOURNAL OF MATHEMATICS. (Text and summaries in English) 1978. 2/yr. $291 (effective 1995). (Sophia University, Department of Mathematics - Jochi Daigaku Sugaku Kyoshitsu) Kinokuniya Shoten - Kinokuniya Co., Ltd., Publishing Dept., 38-1 Sakuragaoka 5-chome, Setagaya-ku, Tokyo 156, Japan. TEL 03-3439-0172. FAX 03-3439-0173. circ. 120. **Document type:** academic/scholarly publication.
—BLDSC (8863.390000); Faxon; UnCover.

511   NE   ISSN 0927-5819
TOPICS IN DISCRETE MATHEMATICS. (Text in English) 1992. irreg., vol.8, 1993. price varies. Elsevier Science B.V., Books Division, P.O. Box 211, 1000 AE Amsterdam, Netherlands. TEL 31-20-4853911. FAX 31-20-4853705. TELEX 18582 ESPA NL. E-mail: nlinfo-f@elsevier.nl; usinfo-f@elsevier.com; forinfo-kyf04035@niftyserve.or.jp; Site addr.: http://www.elsevier.nl/. (Subscr. in U.S. and Canada to: Elsevier Science Inc., Box 882, Madison Sq. Sta., New York, NY 10159. TEL 212-989-5800) Ed. P.L. Hammer. (back issues avail.) **Document type:** monographic series.
   Refereed Serial

514   PL   ISSN 1230-3429
QA321.5
TOPOLOGICAL METHODS IN NONLINEAR ANALYSIS. 1993. q. $100 to individuals; institutions, libraries $200. Juliusz Schauder Center for Nonlinear Studies, Uniwersytet Mikolaja Kopernika, Ul. Chopina 12-18, 87-100 Torun, Poland. E-mail: tmna@ipxl.mat.torun.edu.pl. (Subscr. to: American Mathematical Society, Box 6248, Providence, RI 02940. TEL 401-455-8070) Ed.Bd. (back issues avail.)
—BLDSC (8867.550000); SWETS.

250   UK   ISSN 0040-9383
QA611   CODEN: TPLGAF
TOPOLOGY; an international journal of mathematics. (Text in English, French, German or Italian) 1962. q. £563($896) (effective 1996). Elsevier Science Ltd., Pergamon, P.O. Box 800, Kidlington, Oxford OX5 1DX, England. TEL 44-1865-843000. FAX 44-1865-843010. E-mail: nlinfo-f@elsevier.nl; usinfo-f@elsevier.com; forinfo-kyf04035@niftyserve.or.jp; Site addr.: http://www.elsevier.nl/. (Subscr. in U.S. and Canada to: Elsevier Science, 660 White Plains Rd., Tarrytown, NY 10591-5153. TEL 914-524-9200. FAX 914-333-2444) Ed.Bd. adv.; bk.rev.; charts; illus.; index. circ. 1,500. (also avail. in microfilm from UMI) **Indexed:** ASCA, Compumath, Curr.Cont., Math.R. **Document type:** academic/scholarly publication.
—BLDSC (8867.700000); Faxon; Genuine Article; SWETS; UMI; UnCover. **CCC.**
   Description: Publishes mathematical papers with a special emphasis on subjects pertaining to topology and geometry.
   Refereed Serial

514   NE   ISSN 0166-8641
QA611.A1   CODEN: TIAPD9
TOPOLOGY AND ITS APPLICATIONS; a journal devoted to general, geometric, set-theoretic and algebraic topology. (Text in English) 1971. 21/yr. fl.2695($1643) (effective 1996). North-Holland (Subsidiary of: Elsevier Science B.V.), P.O. Box 211, 1000 AE Amsterdam, Netherlands. TEL 31-20-4853911. FAX 31-20-4853598. TELEX 18582 ESPA NL. (Subscr. in U.S. and Canada to: Elsevier Science Inc., Box 882, Madison Sq. Sta., New York, NY 10159. TEL 212-989-5800. FAX 212-633-3990) Eds. Richard B. Sher, Jerry E. Vaughan. adv.; index. circ. 700. (also avail. in microform from UMI; back issues avail.; reprint service avail. from SWZ) **Indexed:** ASCA, Compumath, Math.R. **Document type:** academic/scholarly publication.
—Faxon; Genuine Article; SWETS; UnCover. **CCC.**
   Formerly: General Topology and Its Applications (ISSN 0016-660X)
   Refereed Serial

510   US   ISSN 0146-4124
QA611.A1
TOPOLOGY PROCEEDINGS. 1976. a. $80 (foreign $85). Auburn University, Mathematics Department, Auburn, AL 36830. TEL 205-844-6566. FAX 205-887-3799. Ed.Bd. circ. 300 (paid). **Indexed:** Math.R. **Document type:** proceedings.
—BLDSC (8867.720000); UnCover.
   Refereed Serial

510   JA   ISSN 0916-6009
QA1   CODEN: MJTUEG
TOYAMA UNIVERSITY. MATHEMATICS JOURNAL. (Text in English) 1978. a. Toyama University, Department of Mathematics, 3190, Gofuku, Toyama 930, Japan. **Indexed:** INSPEC (1990-).
—BLDSC (5405.951000).
   Formerly (until 1990): Toyama University. Mathematics Reports (ISSN 0386-832X)

TRAITEMENT DU SIGNAL; signal, image, parole. see *PHYSICS*

510 620   US
TRANSLATION SERIES IN MATHEMATICS AND ENGINEERING. 1984. irreg. price varies. Springer-Verlag, 175 Fifth Ave., New York, NY 10010. TEL 212-460-1500. FAX 212-473-6272. (Also: Berlin, Heidelberg, Tokyo, Vienna) (reprint service avail. from ISI) **Document type:** monographic series.

510   US   ISSN 0065-9282
TRANSLATIONS OF MATHEMATICAL MONOGRAPHS. (Chiefly from Russian sources) 1962. irreg. price varies. American Mathematical Society, Box 6248, Providence, RI 02940-6248. TEL 401-455-4000. (Street addr.: 201 Charles St., Providence, RI 02904) Ed. Ben Silver. circ. 400. **Indexed:** Math.R. **Document type:** monographic series.
—BLDSC (9024.895000). **CCC.**
   Description: Contains works of advanced mathematical research and exposition.

510   FR
TRAVAUX EN COURS. 1983. irreg. Editions Hermann, 293 rue Lecourbe, 75015 Paris, France. TEL 45-57-45-40. FAX 40-60-12-93. TELEX 200595.

510   JA   ISSN 0387-4982
QA1
TSUKUBA JOURNAL OF MATHEMATICS. (Text and summaries in English) 1930. s-a. 28000 Yen($339) (typically set in Sep.; effective 1993). Tsukuba Daigaku, Sugakukei - University of Tsukuba, Institute of Mathematics, 1-1, Tennodai 1-chome, Tsukuba-shi, Ibaraki-ken 305, Japan. TEL 0298-53-4384. FAX 0298-53-6501. (Subscr. to: Kinokuniya Co., Ltd., 17-7 Shinjuku 3-Chome, Shinjuku-ku, Tokyo 163091, Japan) Ed. M. Takeuchi. **Document type:** academic/scholarly publication.
—BLDSC (9067.785000); UnCover.

510   TU   ISSN 1300-0284
TURKISH JOURNAL OF MATHEMATICS. (Text in English, summaries in English, Turkish) 1976. 3/yr. $80 (effective 1995 & 1996). Scientific and Technical Research Council of Turkey - TUBITAK - Turkiye Bilimsel ve Teknik Arastirma Kurumu, Ataturk Bulvari, No. 221, Kavaklidere, 06100 Ankara, Turkey. TEL 90-312-4685300. FAX 90-312-4271336. TELEX 43186 BTAK TR. Ed. Tosun Terzioglu. **Indexed:** INSPEC (1984-1985), Math.R. **Document type:** academic/scholarly publication.
   Former titles (until 1994): Doga Turkish Journal of Mathematics (ISSN 1010-7622); Supersedes in part (in 1986): Doga Bilim Dergisi. Serie A: Basic Sciences.
   Refereed Serial

510 371.3   US   ISSN 0197-3622
QA11.A1
U M A P JOURNAL. (Undergraduate Mathematics Applications Project); the journal of undergraduate mathematics and its applications. 1980. q. $64 to individuals (foreign $74); libraries $120 (foreign $132); institutions $155 (foreign $167) (includes UMAP Modules: Tools for Teaching). Consortium for Mathematics and Its Applications, 57 Bedford St., Ste. 210, Lexington, MA 02173-4428. TEL 617-862-7878. FAX 617-863-1202. TELEX 9102504757. Ed. P.J. Campbell. adv.; bk.rev. circ. 1,500. **Indexed:** Educ.Ind. **Document type:** academic/scholarly publication.
—Faxon; SWETS; UnCover.

510 US ISSN 0041-5995
QA1 CODEN: UKMJB6
UKRAINIAN MATHEMATICAL JOURNAL. English translation of: Ukrainskii Matematicheskii Zhurnal (KR ISSN 0041-6053) 1967. m. $1445 (foreign $1690) (effective 1996). (Ukrainian Academy of Sciences, Mathematical Institute, KR) Plenum Publishing Corp, Consultants Bureau, 233 Spring St., New York, NY 10013-1578. TEL 212-620-8468. FAX 212-463-0742. TELEX 23-421139. Ed. Yu.A. Mitropol'skii. (also avail. in microfilm from JSC; back issues avail.) **Indexed:** Comput.& Info.Sys., Math.R., Zent.Math. **Document type:** academic/scholarly publication.
—BLDSC (0428.950000); Faxon; SWETS; UMI; UnCover. **CCC.**
Refereed Serial

510 KR ISSN 0041-6053
QA1 CODEN: UMZHAA
UKRAINSKII MATEMATICHESKII ZHURNAL/UKRAINS'KYI MATEMATYCHNYI ZHURNAL; nauchnyi zhurnal. English translation: Ukrainian Mathematical Journal (US ISSN 0041-5995) (Text in Russian) 1949. m. (effective 1996). (Akademiya Nauk Ukrainy, Institut Matematiki) Vidavnitstvo Naukova Dumka, Vul. Tereshchenkivska 3, 252601 Kiev, Ukraine. TEL 044-224-4068. FAX 044-224-7060. (Dist. in U.S. by: Victor Kamkin Inc., 4956 Boiling Brook Pkwy., Rockville, MD 20852. TEL 301-881-5973. FAX 301-881-1637) Ed. Yu.A. Mitropol'skii. index. circ. 1,352. **Indexed:** Chem.Abstr., Math.R.

510 US ISSN 1071-7021
▼**ULAM QUARTERLY.** AMSTEX format (ISSN 1068-6010); Postscript format (ISSN 1068-6002) 1994. 4/yr. Gordon and Breach Science Publishers, c/o International Publishers Distributor, 820 Town Center Dr., Langhorne, PA 19047. TEL 215-750-2642; 800-545-8398. FAX 215-750-6343. (Subscr. to: International Publishers Distributor, P.o. Box 90, Reading, Berkshire RG1 8JL, England. TEL 44-173-456-8316. FAX 44-173-46-8316) (back issues avail.) **Document type:** academic/scholarly publication.
●Also available online.
Description: Publishes original research and articles covering a broad range of topics in pure and applied mathematics.
Refereed Serial

510 US ISSN 0172-6056
UNDERGRADUATE TEXTS IN MATHEMATICS. 1974. irreg. price varies. Springer-Verlag, 175 Fifth Ave., New York, NY 10010. TEL 212-460-1500. FAX 212-473-6272. (Also: Berlin, Heidelberg, Tokyo and Vienna) (reprint service avail. from ISI) **Document type:** monographic series.

510 AG ISSN 0041-6932
QA1 CODEN: RMAFAG
UNION MATEMATICA ARGENTINA. REVISTA. (Text in English and Spanish) 1936. 2/yr. $40 (effective 1996). Union Matematica Argentina, Ciudad Universitaria, 5000 Cordoba, Argentina. TEL 54-51-690068. FAX 54-51-690307. E-mail: revuma@criba.edu.ar. Ed. Luiz Monteiro. bk.rev.; bibl.; index. circ. 2,000. **Indexed:** Math.R., Zent.Math. **Document type:** academic/scholarly publication.
—BLDSC (7834.900000).
Formerly: Union Matematica Argentina y Asociacion Fisica Argentina Revista.
Description: Original papers in pure and applied mathematics.
Refereed Serial

519.5 JA ISSN 0034-4842
HA1 CODEN: RARJAT
UNION OF JAPANESE SCIENTISTS AND ENGINEERS. REPORTS OF STATISTICAL APPLICATION RESEARCH. (Text in English) 1951. q. 8700 Yen($103) Union of Japanese Scientists and Engineers, 5-10-11, Sendagaya, Shibuya-ku, Tokyo 151, Japan. (Dist. by: Intercontinental Marketing Corp., I.P.O. Box 5056, Tokyo 100-31, Japan. TEL 81-3-3661-7458. FAX 81-3-3667-9646) Ed. T. Okuno. adv.; index. circ. 1,000. **Indexed:** Chem.Abstr., JTA, Math.R. **Document type:** academic/scholarly publication.

510 IT ISSN 0041-7084
QA1 CODEN: BLUMAM
UNIONE MATEMATICA ITALIANA. BOLLETTINO. (In 4 sections; supplements avail.) (Text in French, Italian and Spanish) 1922. bi-m. L.220000 (foreign L.270000) (effective 1994). Zanichelli Editore S.p.A., Via Irnerio 34, 40126 Bologna, Italy. TEL 39-51-293111. FAX 39-51-249782. Ed. Prof. Giovanni Ricci. bk.rev.; index. **Indexed:** Appl.Mech.Rev., Compumath, Math.R.
—SWETS.

510 SP ISSN 0214-3577
QA1
UNIVERSIDAD COMPLUTENSE DE MADRID. REVISTA MATEMATICA. 1988. 2/yr. 6000 ptas. (effective 1995-96). Universidad Complutense de Madrid, Facultad de Matematicas, Ciudad Universitaria, 28040 Madrid, Spain. TEL 34-1-3944482. FAX 34-1-3944607. TELEX UCMAT 41802. E-mail: revista@MATSS2.MAT.VCM.ES. Ed. E. Outerelo. circ. controlled. **Document type:** academic/scholarly publication.
Refereed Serial

510
UNIVERSIDAD DE CANTABRIA. DEPARTAMENT DE MATEMATICAS, ESTADISTICA Y COMPUTACION. PUBLICACION. SERIE COMPUTACION. 1989. irreg. free. Universidad de Cantabria, Servicio de Publicaciones, Avda. de los Castros, s-n, 39005 Santander, Spain.

510 SP
UNIVERSIDAD DE CANTABRIA. DEPARTAMENTO DE MATEMATICAS, ESTADISTICA Y COMPUTUTACION. PUBLICACION. 1989. irreg. free. Universidad de Cantabria, Servicio de Publicaciones, Avda. de los Castors, s-n, 39005 Santander, Spain.

510 UY ISSN 0255-9188
UNIVERSIDAD DE LA REPUBLICA. FACULTAD DE HUMANIDADES Y CIENCIAS. REVISTA. SERIE CIENCIAS EXACTAS. 1980. irreg. exchange basis. Universidad de la Republica, Facultad de Humanidades y Ciencias, Seccion Revista, Tristan Narvaja 1674, Montevideo, Uruguay. Dir. Beatriz Martinez Osorio.
Supersedes in part: Universidad de la Republica. Facultad de Humanidades y Ciencias. Revista.

510 MX ISSN 0185-0644
UNIVERSIDAD NACIONAL AUTONOMA DE MEXICO. INSTITUTO DE MATEMATICAS. ANALES. 1950. a. $15 per no. Universidad Nacional Autonoma de Mexico, Instituto de Matematicas, Area de la Investigacion Cientifica, Circuito Exterior, Ciudad Universitaria, 04510 Mexico, DF, Mexico. TEL 548-20-07. FAX 548-94-99. bk.rev.; cum.index: vols.1-26 (1961-1986). circ. 500. **Indexed:** Math.R.

510 MX ISSN 0187-4780
UNIVERSIDAD NACIONAL AUTONOMA DE MEXICO. INSTITUTO DE MATEMATICAS. MONOGRAFIAS. 1975. irreg., no.23, 1991. $15 per vol. Universidad Nacional Autonoma de Mexico, Instituto de Matematicas, Area de la Investigacion Cientifica, Circuito Exterior, Ciudad Universitaria, 04510 Mexico, DF, Mexico. TEL 548-20-07. FAX 548-94-99. **Indexed:** Math.R. **Document type:** monographic series.

510 BL ISSN 0103-1015
UNIVERSIDADE FEDERAL DO RIO DE JANEIRO. INSTITUTO DE MATEMATICA. ESTUDOS E COMUNICACOES. (Text in English, French, Portuguese, Spanish; summaries in English) 1983. irreg., no.47, 1993. $3 to institutions; free to individuals. Universidade Federal do Rio de Janeiro, Instituto de Matematica, C.P. 68530, 21944 Rio de Janeiro, RJ, Brazil. circ. controlled.
Description: Articles in mathematics, statistics and computer science.

510 BL ISSN 0103-491X
UNIVERSIDADE FEDERAL DO RIO DE JANEIRO. INSTITUTO DE MATEMATICA. TEXTOS DE METODOS MATEMATICOS. (Text in language of author) 1972. irreg., no.28, 1992. $5 institutions; free to individuals. Universidade Federal do Rio de Janeiro, Instituto de Matematica, C.P. 68530, 21944 Rio de Janeiro, RJ, Brazil. **Document type:** monographic series.
Formerly: Universidade Federal do Rio de Janeiro. Instituto de Matematica. Notas de Matematica Fisica.
Description: Expository monographs dedicated to graduate students in mathematics.

510 530 IT ISSN 0041-8986
CODEN: ASMMAK
UNIVERSITA DEGLI STUDI DI MODENA. SEMINARIO MATEMATICO E FISICO. ATTI. Variant title: Universita di Modena. Seminario Matematico e Fisico. Atti. (Text and summaries in English and Italian) 1947. s-a. exchange basis only. Universita degli Studi di Modena, Seminario Matematico e Fisico, Via Campi 213-b, 41100 Modena, Italy. FAX 39-59-370513. Dir. Calogero Vinti. bk.rev.; bibl.; charts. circ. 450. **Indexed:** Appl.Mech.Rev., INSPEC (1969-), Math.R. **Document type:** academic/scholarly publication.
—BLDSC (1786.370000).
Description: Presents original papers in mathematics and physics.

510 IT ISSN 0035-6298
UNIVERSITA DEGLI STUDI DI PARMA. RIVISTA DI MATEMATICA. (Text in English, French, German, Italian and Spanish) 1950. a. L.115000($100) Universita degli Studi di Parma, Rivista di Matematica, Via Universita 12, 43100 Parma, Italy. (Subscr. to: Via D'Azeglio 85, 43100 Parma, Italy. TEL 39-521-902320. FAX 39-521-902353) Ed. G.B. Rizza. bk.rev.; bibl.; charts; index. circ. 500. **Indexed:** Appl.Mech.Rev., Math.R. **Document type:** academic/scholarly publication.
—BLDSC (7989.400000).

510 IT ISSN 0049-4704
QA1 CODEN: RIMTDP
UNIVERSITA DEGLI STUDI DI TRIESTE. ISTITUTO DI MATEMATICA. RENDICONTI. (Text in English, French, German, Italian; summaries in English and Italian) 1969. a. exchange basis. Universita degli Studi di Trieste, Dipartimento di Scienze Matematiche, Piazzale Europa 1, 34100 Trieste, Italy. TEL 39-40-6763727. FAX 39-40-6763256. E-mail: celada@univ.triest.it. Ed. Graziano Gentili. index. circ. 300. **Indexed:** Math.R., Ref.Zh., Zent.Math.
—BLDSC (7358.950000).
Description: Publishes original papers by Italian and foreign authors concerning all branches of mathematics.

510 IT ISSN 0041-8994
QA1
UNIVERSITA DI PADOVA. SEMINARIO MATEMATICO. RENDICONTI. (Text in English, French, German, Italian or Spanish) 1929. 2/yr. L.180000 (foreign L.230000) (effective 1995). Casa Editrice Dott. Antonio Milani, Via Jappelli 5-6, 35121 Padua, Italy. TEL 049-656677. FAX 049-8752900. Ed. Francesco Baldassarri. circ. 500. **Indexed:** Appl.Mech.Rev. **Document type:** academic/scholarly publication.
—SWETS; UnCover.
Description: Presents original works in all fields of mathematics.

510 IT ISSN 0373-1243
UNIVERSITA E POLITECNICO DI TORINO. SEMINARIO MATEMATICO. RENDICONTI. q. L.143000 (Europe L.180000; elsewhere L.270000) (effective 1993). Rosenberg & Sellier, Via Andrea Doria, 14, 10123 Turin, Italy. TEL 39-11-8127820. FAX 39-11-8127744.

510 GW ISSN 0025-5858
QA1 CODEN: AMHAAJ
UNIVERSITAET HAMBURG. MATHEMATISCHES SEMINAR. ABHANDLUNGEN. 1922. a. Vandenhoeck und Ruprecht, Robert-Bosch-Breite 6, 37079 Goettingen, Germany. TEL 0551-6959-26. FAX 0551-695917. (Subscr. to: 37070 Goettingen, Germany) Eds. R. Ansorge, O. Riemenschneider. adv.; tr.lit. circ. 410. **Indexed:** Compumath, Math.R. **Document type:** academic/scholarly publication.
—Genuine Article; SWETS; UnCover. **CCC.**

510 AU
UNIVERSITAET INNSBRUCK. MATHEMATISCHE STUDIEN. (Subseries of: Universitaet Innsbruck. Veroeffentlichungen) 1974. irreg. price varies. Oesterreichische Kommissionsbuchhandlung, Maximilian Str. 17, A-6020 Innsbruck, Austria. Ed. Roman Liedl.

MATHEMATICS

510 RM ISSN 0041-9109
QA1 CODEN: AUZMAV
UNIVERSITATEA "AL. I. CUZA" DIN IASI. ANALELE STIINTIFICE. SECTIUNEA 1A: MATEMATICA. (Text in English, French, German, Italian, Russian, Spanish) 1900; N.S. 1955. 4/yr. 40 lei. Universitatea "Al. I. Cuza" din Iasi, Calea M. Eminescu 11, Jassy, Rumania. (Subscr. to: ILEXIM, Str. 13 Decembrie Nr. 3, P.O. Box 136-137, Bucharest, Rumania) Eds. Adolf Haimovici, D. Iesan. bk.rev.; abstr.; charts; illus. circ. 500. (also avail. in microfilm; back issues avail.) **Indexed:** Bull.Signal., Chem.Abstr., Math.R., Ref.Zh.
—BLDSC (0869.600000).
Description: Papers in all fields of pure and applied mathematics, and informatics.

510 530 RM ISSN 0253-1860
QA1 CODEN: ACSFDM
UNIVERSITATEA DIN CRAIOVA. ANALE. SERIA: MATEMATICA, FIZICA-CHIMIE. (Text in English, French and German) a. Universitatea din Craiova, Str. A.I. Cuza Nr. 13, Craiova, Rumania.
—CASDDS.

510 RM
UNIVERSITATEA DIN TIMISOARA. ANALELE: STIINTE MATEMATICE. (Text and summaries in English, French, Rumanian and Russian) 1963. 3/yr. 200 lei($8) per no. Universitatea din Timisoara, Facultatea de Metamatica, Bd. Vasile Pirvan Nr. 4, Timisoara, Rumania. Ed. Dr. Papuc I. Dan. bk.rev.; index. circ. 400. **Indexed:** Math.R., Ref.Zh., Zent.Math.

514 516 RM
UNIVERSITATEA DIN TIMISOARA. FACULTATEA DE MATEMATICA. LUCRARILE SEMINARULUI DE GEOMETRIE SI TOPOLOGIE. (Text in English, French, German and Rumanian) 1972. irreg. 50 lei($2) Universitatea din Timisoara, Facultatea de Matematica, Bd. Vasile Pirvan Nr.4, Timisoara, Rumania. Ed. Dan I. Papuc. circ. 250.
Formerly: Universitatea din Timisoara. Facultatea de Stiinte ale Naturii. Lucrarile Seminarului de Geometrie si Topologie.

510 RM
UNIVERSITATEA DIN TIMISOARA. FACULTATEA DE MATEMATICA. SEMINARUL DE MECANICA. (Text in English, French) 1987. irreg. 50 lei($2) Universitatea din Timisoara, Facultatea de Matematica, Bd. Vasile Parvan Nr. 4, Timisoara, Rumania. Ed. V. Obadeanu. circ. 250.
Formerly: Universitatea din Timisoara. Facultatea de Stiinte ale Naturii. Seminarul de Mecanica.

510 RM ISSN 0255-8904
UNIVERSITATEA DIN TIMISOARA. FACULTATEA DE MATEMATICA. SEMINARUL DE OPERATORI LINIARI SI ANALIZA ARMONICA. Key Title: Seminarul de Operatori.Liniari si Analiza Armonica. (Text in English) 1978. irreg. 200 lei. Universitatea de Vest din Timisoara, Facultatea de Matematica, Bd. Vasile Parvan no.4, Timisoara, Rumania. TEL 40-56-190333. Ed. Dumitru Gaspar. **Document type:** proceedings.
—BLDSC (8239.494000).

510 RM
UNIVERSITATEA DIN TIMISOARA. FACULTATEA DE MATEMATICA. SEMINARUL DE TEORIA STRUCTURILOR. (Text in English, French, German, and Rumanian) 1971. irreg. 50 lei($2) Universitatea din Timisoara, Facultatea de Matematica, Bd. Vasile Pirvan Nr. 4, Timisoara, Rumania. Ed. Constantin Popa. circ. 250.
Formerly: Universitatea din Timisoara. Facultatea de Stiinte ale Naturii. Seminarul de Teoria Structurilor.

510 RM ISSN 0255-8920
UNIVERSITATEA DIN TIMISOARA. FACULTATEA DE STIINTE ALE NATURII. SEMINARUL DE TEORIA PROBABILITATILOR SI APLICATII. (Text in English, French, German, Rumanian) 1973. irreg. 50 lei($2) Universitatea din Timisoara, Facultatea de Matematica, Bd. Vasile Pirvan Nr.4, Timisoara, Rumania. Ed. Gh. Constantin. circ. 250.
—BLDSC (8239.495300).
Former titles: Universitatea din Timisoara. Facultatea de Stiinte ale Naturii. Seminarul de Teoria Probabilitatilor si Aplicatii; (until 1980, no.51): Universitatea din Timisoara. Facultatea de Stiinte ale Naturii. Seminarul de Teoria Functiilor si Matematici Aplicate. A: Spatii Metrice Probabiliste.

510 RM ISSN 0255-8890
UNIVERSITATEA DIN TIMISOARA. SECTIA MATEMATICA INFORMATICA. SEMINARUL DE INFORMATICA SI ANALIZA NUMERICA. (Text in English, French, German, Rumanian) 1975. irreg. 20 lei. Universitatea din Timisoara, Sectia Matematica Informatica, Bd. Vasile Pirvan Nr.4, Timisoara, Rumania. Ed. S. Maruster. circ. 250.
Formerly (until 1981): Universitatea din Timisoara. Facultatea de Stiinte ale Naturii. Seminarul de Teoria Functiilor si Matematici Aplicate. B: Analiza Numerica.

510 530 RM
UNIVERSITATEA POLITEHNICA BUCURESTI. BULETIN STIINTIFIC. MATEMATICA APLICATA SI FISICA/POLYTECHNICAL UNIVERSITY OF BUCHAREST. SCIENTIFIC BULLETIN. APPLIED MATHEMATICS AND PHYSICS. (Text in English, French, or German) 1993. q. $100. Universitatea Politehnica Bucuresti, Biblioteca Centrala, Splaiul Independentei 313, 77206 Bucharest 16, Rumania. FAX 40-1-3120188. **Document type:** academic/scholarly publication.
Supersedes (1929-1940): Buletinul de Mathematique et de Physique Pures et Appliquees.

510 530 570 RM ISSN 1220-9414
UNIVERSITATEA TRANSILVANIA DIN BRASOV. BULETINUL. SERIA C. MATEMATICA, FIZICA, CHIMIE/TRANSYLVANIA UNIVERSITY OF BRASOV. BULLETIN. SERIES C. MATHEMATICS, PHYSICS, CHEMISTRY. (Text in English, French and German) 1956. a. price varies. Universitatea Transilvania din Brasov - Transylvania University of Brasov, Bd. Eroilor, Nr. 29, 2200 Brasov, Rumania. TEL 40-921-41580. bibl.; charts; stat. **Indexed:** Chem.Abstr., Math.R.
—BLDSC (2782.304000).
Former titles (until 1990): Universitatea din Brasov. Buletinul. Seria C. Matematica, Fizica, Chimie; Universitatea din Brasov. Buletinul. Seria C. Stiinte ale Naturri si Pedagogie; Universitatea din Brasov. Buletinul. Seria C. Matematica, Fizica, Chimie.

510 BE
UNIVERSITE CATHOLIQUE DE LOUVAIN. INSTITUT DE MATHEMATIQUE. RAPPORT DE MATHEMATIQUE.. (Text and summaries in French, English) 1978. irreg., latest no.201. price varies. Universite Catholique de Louvain, Institut de Mathematique Pure et Appliquee, Chemin du Cyclotron, 2, 1348 Louvain-la-Neuve, Belgium. bibl.; charts.
Formerly: Universite Catholique de Louvain. Institut de Mathematique Pure et Appliquee. Rapport.

510 FR ISSN 0076-1656
UNIVERSITE CLAUDE BERNARD. DEPARTEMENT DE MATHEMATIQUES. PUBLICATIONS. 1964. q. 80 F. Universite de Lyon I, Departement de Mathematiques, 43, Boulevard du 11 November 1918, 69622 Villeurbanne, France. **Indexed:** Compumath, Math.R.

510 AE ISSN 0002-5321
UNIVERSITE D'ALGER. PUBLICATIONS SCIENTIFIQUES. SERIE A: MATHEMATIQUES.* 1954. s-a. 15 fr.per no. Universite.d'Alger, 2 rue Didouche-Mourad, Algiers, Algeria. **Indexed:** Math.R.

510 FR ISSN 0069-472X
UNIVERSITE DE CLERMONT-FERRAND II. ANNALES SCIENTIFIQUES. SERIE MATHEMATIQUES. 1962. irreg., latest no.95, 1991. price varies. Universite de Clermont-Ferrand II, Departement de Mathematiques, 63177 Aubiere, France. circ. 250. (back issues avail.)

510 FR ISSN 0246-1501
UNIVERSITE DE CLERMONT-FERRAND II. ANNALES SCIENTIFIQUES. SERIE PROBABILITES ET APPLICATIONS. irreg. price varies. Universite de Clermont-Ferrand II, Departement de Mathematiques, 63177 Aubiere, France.

UNIVERSITE DE MADAGASCAR. ETABLISSEMENT D'ENSEIGNEMENT SUPERIEUR DES SCIENCES. ANNALES: SERIE SCIENCES DE LA NATURE ET MATHEMATIQUES. see *SCIENCES: COMPREHENSIVE WORKS*

510 FR ISSN 0240-2963
Q46 CODEN: AFSMDU
UNIVERSITE PAUL SABATIER. FACULTE DES SCIENCES. ANNALES; mathematiques. (Text in English and French) 1887. q. 700 F. (foreign 900 F.) Universite Paul Sabatier, 118 route de Narbonne, 31062 Toulouse cedex, France. Ed. Paul Sabatier. adv. (also avail. in microfilm from BHP) **Indexed:** INSPEC, Math.R., Zent.Math.
—BLDSC (0915.736000); UnCover.
Formerly: Universite de Toulouse. Faculte des Sciences. Annales (ISSN 0240-2955)

510 530 US ISSN 0172-5939
UNIVERSITEXTS. 1973. irreg. price varies. Springer-Verlag, 175 Fifth Ave., New York, NY 10010. TEL 212-460-1500. FAX 212-473-6272. (reprint service avail. from ISI) **Document type:** monographic series.

510 US ISSN 0886-2176
UNIVERSITY OF ARKANSAS. LECTURE NOTES IN THE MATHEMATICAL SCIENCES. irreg., vol.13, 1992. John Wiley & Sons, Inc., 605 Third Ave., New York, NY 10158. TEL 212-850-6000. FAX 212-850-6088. TELEX 12-7063. bibl.; index. **Indexed:** Math.R. **Document type:** monographic series.
—BLDSC (9104.020000).
Refereed Serial

510 NZ ISSN 0110-4152
UNIVERSITY OF AUCKLAND. DEPARTMENT OF MATHEMATICS AND STATISTICS. REPORT SERIES. 1971. irreg., no.314, 1995. free to individuals or on exchange. University of Auckland, Department of Mathematics & Statistics, Private Bag 92019, Auckland, New Zealand. FAX 64-9-3737457. circ. 175.

510 NO ISSN 0084-778X
UNIVERSITY OF BERGEN. DEPARTMENT OF APPLIED MATHEMATICS. REPORT. (Text in English) 1964. irreg. exchange basis. University of Bergen, Department of Applied Mathematics, Allegate 55, N-5007 Bergen, Norway. TEL 47-55-21-28-38. FAX 47-55-31-00-25. circ. 100. (processed) **Document type:** academic/scholarly publication.
—BLDSC (7620.854000).

510 NO ISSN 0333-1865
UNIVERSITY OF BERGEN. DEPARTMENT OF MATHEMATICS. STATISTICAL REPORT. (Text in English) 1981. irreg., vol.24, 1994. exchange basis. University of Bergen, Department of Mathematics, Allegtate 55, N-5007 Bergen, Norway. TEL 47-55-21-28-38. FAX 47-55-31-00-25. adv. contact: Ann-Elizabeth Engelsen. **Document type:** academic/scholarly publication.
—BLDSC (7620.854300).

510 NO ISSN 0332-5407
UNIVERSITY OF BERGEN. DEPARTMENT OF PURE MATHEMATICS. REPORT. (Text in various languages) 1974. irreg. exchange basis. University of Bergen, Department of Pure Mathematics, Allegate 55, N-5007 Bergen, Norway. TEL 47-55-21-28-36. FAX 47-55-31-00-25. Ed. Alf Oeien.
—BLDSC (9104.170000).

510 UK
UNIVERSITY OF BRADFORD. DEPARTMENT OF MATHEMATICS. REPORT. irreg. University of Bradford, Department of Mathematics, Richmond Rd., Bradford, W. Yorks BD7 1DP, England. **Document type:** academic/scholarly publication.

510 CN
UNIVERSITY OF CALGARY. DEPARTMENT OF MATHEMATICS AND STATISTICS. RESEARCH PAPERS. 1966. irreg. free. University of Calgary, Department of Mathematics and Statistics, Calgary, AB T2N 1N4, Canada. TEL 403-220-7456. FAX 403-282-5150. Ed. P. Zvengrowski. circ. 40. **Document type:** academic/scholarly publication.
Formerly: University of Calgary. Department of Mathematics and Computing Science. Research Papers (ISSN 0575-206X)

519.5 DK ISSN 0909-2080
UNIVERSITY OF COPENHAGEN. INSTITUTE OF MATHEMATICAL STATISTICS. ANNUAL REPORT. (Text in English) a. free. Koebenhavns Universitet, Institut for Matematisk Statistik, 5, Universitetsparken, DK-2100 Copenhagen OE, Denmark.

MATHEMATICS 4153

510   US   ISSN 0076-5341
UNIVERSITY OF NOTRE DAME. DEPARTMENT OF MATHEMATICS. MATHEMATICAL LECTURES. 1941. irreg., vol.11, 1989. price varies. University of Notre Dame Press, Notre Dame, IN 46556. TEL 219-631-6346. FAX 219-631-8148. (Orders to: 11030 S. Langley Ave. Chicago, IL 60628. TEL 800-621-2736. FAX 800-621-8476; Overseas orders to: Eurospan University Press Group, Order Dept., 3 Henrietta St., London WC2E 8LU, England) **Document type:** academic/scholarly publication.

510 375   AT   ISSN 1036-0697
UNIVERSITY OF TECHNOLOGY, SYDNEY. FACULTY OF MATHEMATICAL & COMPUTING SCIENCES HANDBOOK. 1990. a. Aus.$5 (foreign $10). University of Technology, Sydney, P.O. Box 123, City Campus, Broadway, N.S.W. 2007, Australia. TEL 02-330-1990. FAX 02-330-1551.

510   JA   ISSN 0286-9640
Q4   CODEN: BCSRDZ
UNIVERSITY OF THE RYUKYUS. COLLEGE OF SCIENCE. BULLETIN/RYUKYU DAIGAKU RIGAKUBU KIYO. (Text in English, Japanese; summaries in English) 1957. irreg. University of the Ryukyus, College of Science - Ryukyu Daigaku Rigakubu, 1 Senbaru, Nishihara-cho, Nakagami-gun, Okinawa-ken 903-01, Japan. **Indexed:** INSPEC (1980-).
—BLDSC (2448.730000); CASDDS.

510   YU   ISSN 0352-0900
QA1
UNIVERZITET U NOVOM SADU. PRIRODNO-MATEMATICKI FAKULTET. ZBORNIK RADOVA. SERIJA ZA MATEMATIKU. (Text in English, French, German and Russian) 1971. 2/yr. $60. Institut za Matematiku, Prirodno-Matematicki Fakultet - Institute of Mathematics, Dr. Ilije Djuricica 4, 21000 Novi Sad, Yugoslavia. TEL 38-21-58-136. FAX 38-21-350-458. (Subscr. to: "FORUM", Izvozno Odelenje, 21000 Novi Sad, ul. Vojvode Misica 1, Yugoslavia) Ed. Olga Hadzic. circ. 650. **Indexed:** Math.R., Nutr.Abstr., Ref.Zh.

510   PL   ISSN 0072-0402
UNIWERSYTET GDANSKI. WYDZIAL MATEMATYKI, FIZYKI I CHEMII, ZESZYTY NAUKOWE. MATEMATYKA. (Text in Polish; summaries in English) 1972. irreg., latest no.7. price varies. Uniwersytet Gdanski, Wydzial Matematyki, Fizyki i Chemii, c/o Biblioteka Glowna, Ul. Armii Krajowej 110, 81-824 Sopot, Poland. TEL 51-0061. TELEX 051 2247 BMOR PL. (Dist. by: Ars Polona-Ruch, Krakowskie Przedmiescie 7, 00-680 Warsaw, Poland) illus. circ. 250. **Document type:** academic/scholarly publication.
Description: Covers operational calculus, topology, real functions, geometry, differential equations, mathematical foundation of computer science, didactics of mathematics, set theory, and probability calculus.

510   PL   ISSN 0860-0120
QA1
UNIWERSYTET JAGIELLONSKI. ZESZYTY NAUKOWE. ACTA MATEMATICA. (Text in Polish; summaries in French, English, Russian) no.5, 1959. irreg. price varies. Uniwersytet Jagiellonski, Ul. Golebia 24, 31-007 Krakow, Poland. TEL 48-12-221033. FAX 48-12-226306. (Dist. by: Ars Polona, Krakowskie Przedmiescie 7, 00-068 Warsaw, Poland) **Indexed:** Math.R.
Formerly (until 1984): Uniwersytet Jagiellonski. Zeszyty Naukowe. Prace Matematyczne (ISSN 0083-4386); Which superseded in part: Seria Nauk Matematyczno-Przyrodniczych. Matematyka, Fizyka, Chemia.

510   PL   ISSN 0860-2107
QA1
UNIWERSYTET SLASKI W KATOWICACH. PRACE NAUKOWE. ANNALES MATHEMATICAE SILESIANAE. (Text in English) 1969. irreg. price varies. Wydawnictwo Uniwersytetu Slaskiego, Ul. Bankowa 12B, 40-007 Katowice, Poland. TEL 48-32-596-915. FAX 48-32-599-605. TELEX 0315584 USKPL. (Dist. by: CHZ Ars Polona, P.O. Box 1001, 00-950 Warsaw, Poland) **Document type:** academic/scholarly publication.
Formerly (until 1985): Uniwersytet Slaski w Katowicach. Prace Matematyczne (ISSN 0208-5410)
Description: Covers all aspects of pure and applied mathematics in general, in particular: algebra and theory of numbers, differential equations and dynamical systems, functional and real analysis, functional equations, geometry, topology.

510   RU   ISSN 0042-1316
QA1   CODEN: UMANA5
USPEKHI MATEMATICHESKIKH NAUK. English translation: Russian Mathematical Surveys (UK ISSN 0036-0279) 1936. bi-m. 47.40 Rub. (Rossiiskaya Akademiya Nauk) Izdatel'stvo Nauka, Mezhdunarodnyi Otdel, Profsoyuznaya, 90, 117864 Moscow, Russia. (Dist. by: Mezhdunarodnaya Kniga, ul. Dimitrova D.39, 113095 Moscow, Russia) (Co-sponsor: Moskovskoe Matematicheskoe Obshchestvo) Ed. S.P. Novikov. bk.rev.; bibl.; charts. circ. 3,120. (also avail. in microfiche from BHP; reprint service avail. from KTO) **Indexed:** Chem.Abstr., INSPEC, Math.R. **Document type:** academic/scholarly publication.
—BLDSC (0385.900000). **CCC**.

510   CN   ISSN 0382-0718
VECTOR. 1968. irreg. Can.$45 to non-members; members Can.$30; students Can.$15. (B.C. Association of Mathematics Teachers) B.C. Teachers' Federation, 100-550 W. 6th Ave., Vancouver, BC V5Z 4P2, Canada. TEL 604-871-1848. FAX 604-871-2291. illus. circ. 650. **Indexed:** Can.Educ.Ind.
Formerly: British Columbia Association of Mathematics Teachers. Newsletter (ISSN 0382-0726)

510 372   AT   ISSN 0157-759X
VINCULUM. 1963. 4/yr. membership (foreign Aus.$68). Mathematical Association of Victoria, 61 Blyth St., Brunswick, Vic. 3056, Australia. TEL 61-3-380-2399. FAX 61-3-840-8243. Ed. John Gough. adv.; bk.rev. circ. 1,200. **Indexed:** Aus.Educ.Ind. **Document type:** academic/scholarly publication.
—BLDSC (9236.852600).

510   JA   ISSN 0913-0195
WASEDA DAIGAKU KYOIKUGAKUBU GAKUJUTSU KENKYU. SUGAKU HEN/WASEDA UNIVERSITY. SCHOOL OF EDUCATION. SCIENTIFIC RESEARCHES: MATHEMATICS. (Text in English and Japanese) 1952. a. Waseda Daigaku, Kyoikugakubu - Waseda University, School of Education, Shinjuku-ku, Tokyo 169-50, Japan. TEL 03-3203-4141. FAX 03-3208-1032. **Indexed:** Jap.Per.Ind.

510   US   ISSN 0043-082X
WASHINGTON STATE UNIVERSITY. MATHEMATICS NOTES. 1958. irreg. free. Washington State University, Department of Pure and Applied Mathematics, Pullman, WA 99164-3113. TEL 509-335-8518. Ed. Jack Robertson. bk.rev. circ. 1,400. **Document type:** newsletter.

WHICH DEGREE. SCIENCES, MEDICINE, MATHEMATICS. see *SCIENCES: COMPREHENSIVE WORKS*

510 305.4   US
WOMEN AND MATHEMATICS EDUCATION NEWSLETTER. 1979. 3/yr. $10. Mount Holyoke College, Women & Mathematics Education - Summer Math, 302 Shattuck Hall, South Hadley, MA 01075. TEL 413-538-2608. Ed. Pam Cemen. bk.rev. circ. 400. (back issues avail.) **Document type:** newsletter.

510   US   ISSN 0512-2740
QA30
WORLD DIRECTORY OF MATHEMATICIANS. 1958. quadrennial, 9th ed., 1990. $40. (International Mathematical Union) American Mathematical Society, Box 6248, Providence, RI 02940-6248. TEL 401-455-4000. (Street addr.: 201 Charles St., Providence, RI 02904) Ed. G.D. Mostow. circ. 2,000. **Document type:** directory.
Description: Contains names and addresses of about 40,000 mathematicians from 83 countries.

510   SI
WORLD SCIENTIFIC SERIES IN APPLICABLE ANALYSIS. (Text in English) irreg., vol.2, 1993. price varies. World Scientific Publishing Co. Pte. Ltd., Farrer Rd., P.O. Box 128, Singapore 9128, Singapore. TEL 3825663. FAX 3825919. (UK addr.: 73 Lynton Mead, Totteridge, London N20 8DH, England. TEL 44-81-4462461)

510   SI
WORLD SCIENTIFIC SERIES IN APPROXIMATIONS AND DECOMPOSITIONS. (Text in English) irreg., no.3, 1993. World Scientific Publishing Co. Pte. Ltd., Farrer Rd., P.O. Box 552, Singapore 9128, Singapore. TEL 3825663. FAX 3825919. TELEX RS 28561 WSPC. (UK addr.: 73 Lynton Mead, Totteridge, London N20 8DH, England. TEL 44-81-4462461; US addr.: Ste. 1B, 1060 Main St., River Edge, NJ 07661. TEL 800-2277562)

510   SI
WORLD SCIENTIFIC SERIES ON NONLINEAR SCIENCE. irreg., vol.12, 1993. price varies. World Scientific Publishing Co. Pte. Ltd., Farrer Rd., P.O. Box 128, Singapore 9128, Singapore. TEL 3825663. FAX 3825663. TELEX RS-28561-WSPC. (U.S. Addr.: Ste. 1B, 1060 Main St., River Edge, NJ 07661. TEL 800-227-7562; U.K. addr.: 73 Lynton Mead, Totteridge, London N20 8DH, England. TEL 44-81-446-2461) **Document type:** monographic series.

510   PL   ISSN 0239-7978
AS142.K66
WYZSZA SZKOLA PEDAGOGICZNA IM. KOMISJI EDUKACJI NARODOWEJ W KRAKOWIE. ROCZNIK NAUKOWO-DYDAKTYCZNY. PRACE MATEMATYCZNE. 1954. irreg., no.12, 1987. price varies. Wydawnictwo Naukowe W S P, Ul. Karmelicka 41, 31-128 Krakow, Poland. TEL 33-78-20. (Co-sponsor: Ministerstwo Edukacji Narodowej)

510   PL
WYZSZA SZKOLA PEDAGOGICZNA IM. KOMISJI EDUKACJI NARODOWEJ W KRAKOWIE. ROCZNIK NAUKOWO-DYDAKTYCZNY. PRACE Z DYDAKTYKI MATEMATYKI. 1974. irreg., no.3, 1986. price varies. Wydawnictwo Naukowe W S P, Ul. Karmelicka 41, 31-128 Krakow, Poland. TEL 33-78-20. (Co-sponsor: Ministerstwo Edukacji Narodowej)

730   PL   ISSN 0860-6994
WYZSZA SZKOLA PEDAGOGICZNA IM. KOMISJI EDUKACJI NARODOWEJ W KRAKOWIE. ROCZNIK NAUKOWO-DYDAKTYCZNY. PRACE Z RACHUNKU PRAWDOPODOBIENSTWA I JEGO DYDAKTYKI. 1987. irreg. price varies. Wydawnictwo Naukowe W S P, Ul. Karmelicka 41, 31-129 Krakow, Poland. TEL 33-78-20. (Co-sponsor: Ministerstwo Edukacji Narodowej)

510   PL   ISSN 0078-5431
WYZSZA SZKOLA PEDAGOGICZNA, OPOLE. ZESZYTY NAUKOWE. SERIA A. MATEMATYKA. (Text in Polish; summaries in English) 1961. irreg., vol.28, 1991. available on exchange. Wyzsza Szkola Pedagogiczna, Opole, Oleska 48, 45-951 Opole, Poland. TEL 48-77-383-87. (Dist. by: Ars Polona-Ruch, Krakowskie Przedmiescie 7, Warsaw, Poland) Ed. Krystyna Pirog-Rzepecka. **Indexed:** Math.R. **Document type:** academic/scholarly publication.
—BLDSC (9512.478980).

510 371.3   CC
XIAOXUE SHUXUE JIAOSHI/ARITHMETIC TEACHER. (Text in Chinese) bi-m. (foreign Y220). Shanghai Jiaoyu Chubanshe - Shanghai Educational Publishing House, 123 Yongfu Rd., Shanghai 200031, People's Republic of China. TEL 4377165. (Dist. in US by: China Books & Periodicals, Inc., 2929 24th St., San Francisco, CA 94110. TEL 415-282-2994) Ed. Chen He. circ. 120,000. **Document type:** trade publication.
Description: For elementary school arithmetic teachers.

XITONG KEXUE YU SHUXUE. see *COMPUTERS — Computer Systems*

519   CC   ISSN 1001-9847
YINGYONG SHUXUE/MATHEMATICA APPLICATA. (Text in Chinese) 1988. q. Y8. Huazhong Ligong Daxue, Shuxue Xi - Central-China University of Science and Technology, Department of Mathematics, Yujiashan, Wuchang-qu, Wuhan, Hubei 430074, People's Republic of China. TEL 027-7801152. FAX 027-7801737. Ed. Chen Qingyi.
—BLDSC (5399.532000).

MATHEMATICS — ABSTRACTING, BIBLIOGRAPHIES, STATISTICS

510   CC   ISSN 0254-3079
QA1   CODEN: YYSPDS
YINGYONG SHUXUE XUEBAO. English edition: Acta Mathematicae Applicatae Sinica (ISSN 0168-9673) (Text in Chinese; summaries in English) 1976. q. $83.20. (Chinese Mathematics Society) Science Press, Marketing and Sales Department, 16 Donghuangchenggen North St., Beijing 100717, People's Republic of China. TEL 4010642. FAX 4019810. adv. circ. 11,000. **Document type:** academic/scholarly publication.
—BLDSC (0632.200000).
    Description: Covers mathematics research in China and abroad, including control theory and stochastic processes.
Refereed Serial

510 531   CC   ISSN 1000-0887
TA349   CODEN: YSHLEM
YINGYONG SHUXUE YU LIXUE. English edition: Applied Mathematics and Mechanics (ISSN 0253-4827) (Text in Chinese; abstracts in Chinese, English) 1980. m. Chongqing Jiaotong Xueyuan, 205 Changjing Er Lu, Chongqing, Sichuan 630050, People's Republic of China. TEL 0811-8813708. (Dist. overseas by: China International Book Trading Corp., 35 Chegongzhuang Xilu, P.O. Box 399, Beijing 100044, P.R. China) Ed. Qian Weichang. **Document type:** academic/scholarly publication.
    Description: Publishes original academic papers in the fields of mechanics and applied mathematics.
Refereed Serial

510   JA   ISSN 0044-0523
QA1
YOKOHAMA MATHEMATICAL JOURNAL. (Text and summaries in English) 1953. s-a. exchange basis. Yokohama City University, 22-2 Seto, Kanazawa-ku, Yokohama 236, Japan. TEL 045-787-2311. FAX 045-787-2202. (Co-sponsor: Yakohama National University) Ed. Shigeo Ichiraku. **Indexed:** Math.R., Zent.Math. **Document type:** academic/scholarly publication.
—BLDSC (9419.000000); UnCover.

YUGOSLAV JOURNAL OF OPERATIONS RESEARCH; an international journal dealing with theoretical and computational aspects of operations research, systems science, and management science. see COMPUTERS

Z O R - METHODS AND MODELS OF OPERATIONS RESEARCH. see COMPUTERS

519   PL   ISSN 0044-1899
QA1   CODEN: ZAMTAK
ZASTOSOWANIA MATEMATYKI/APPLICATIONES MATHEMATICAE. (Text and summaries in English) 1954. 4/yr. (in 1 vol., 4 nos./vol.) $60. Polska Akademia Nauk, Instytut Matematyczny, Dzial Wydawnictw, Ul. Sniadeckich 8, P.O. Box 137, 00-950 Warsaw, Poland. TEL 48-22-6282471. FAX 48-22-293997. Eds. R. Zielinski, T. Kucharczyk. bibl.; charts; illus.; index. circ. 540. **Indexed:** Appl.Mech.Rev., Math.R., Ref.Zh. **Document type:** academic/scholarly publication.
—BLDSC (1570.776000); UnCover.
    Description: Publishes original papers in different branches of applications of mathematics.
Refereed Serial

ZAVODSKAYA LABORATORIYA; zhurnal po analiticheskoi khimii, fizicheskim, matematicheskim i mekhanicheskim metodam issledovaniya materialov. see CHEMISTRY — Analytical Chemistry

519 620   GW   ISSN 0044-2267
TA3   CODEN: ZAMMAX
ZEITSCHRIFT FUER ANGEWANDTE MATHEMATIK UND MECHANIK; applied mathematics and mechanics. Abbreviated title: Z A M M. (Text in English and German) 1921. 14/yr. DM.345 to individuals; institutions DM.1798 (effective 1996). Akademie Verlag GmbH, Muehlenstr. 33-34, 13187 Berlin, Germany. TEL 030-47889348. FAX 030-47889357. Ed. G. Schmidt. adv.; charts; illus.; index. (also avail. in microform from PMC) **Indexed:** Appl.Mech.Rev., Chem.Abstr., Compumath, Curr.Cont., Eng.Ind., INSPEC, Int.Aerosp.Abstr., Math.R., Met.Abstr., Sh.& Vib.Dig. **Document type:** academic/scholarly publication.
—BLDSC (9449.000000); Ei; Faxon; Genuine Article; SWETS; UnCover. **CCC.**

519 530   SZ   ISSN 0044-2275
QA1   CODEN: ZAMPDB
ZEITSCHRIFT FUER ANGEWANDTE MATHEMATIK UND PHYSIK/JOURNAL OF APPLIED MATHEMATICS AND PHYSICS/JOURNAL DES MATHEMATIQUES ET DE PHYSIQUE APPLIQUEES. (Text and summaries in English, French, German) 1950. bi-m. 905.60 SFr. (foreign 921.40 SFr.). Birkhaeuser Verlag, P.O. Box 133, CH-4010 Basel, Switzerland. TEL 061-2717400. FAX 061-2717666. (Dist. in N. America by: Springer-Verlag, Mercedes Distribution Center, 160 Imlay St., Brooklyn, NY 11231, USA) Ed. U. Kirchgraber. adv./ bk.rev.; bibl.; charts; illus.; index. circ. 1,000. **Indexed:** Appl.Mech.Rev., Chem.Abstr., Compumath, Curr.Cont., Deep Sea Res.& Oceanogr.Abstr., Eng.Ind., INSPEC, Int.Aerosp.Abstr., Math.R., Met.Abstr., Phys.Ber. **Document type:** academic/scholarly publication.
—BLDSC (9449.050000); CASDDS; Faxon; Genuine Article; SWETS; UMI; UnCover. **CCC.**

510 371   GW   ISSN 0044-4103
ZENTRALBLATT FUER DIDAKTIK DER MATHEMATIK. 1969. bi-m. DM.290. Fachinformationszentrum Karlsruhe, Gesellschaft fuer wissenschaftlich-technische Information mbH, 76344 Eggenstein-Leopoldshafen, Germany. TEL 07247-808-333. FAX 07247-808-135. TELEX 724710-FIZKA. (Co-sponsor: Zentrum fuer Didaktik der Mathematik) Ed. Gerhard Koenig. bk.rev.; abstr.; bibl.; index. cum.index. circ. 660. **Document type:** academic/scholarly publication.
● Also available online. Vendor(s): STN International.
—BLDSC (9504.800000); SWETS.

ZHONGXUESHENG SHU-LI-HUA (GAOZHONG BAN). see EDUCATION — Teaching Methods And Curriculum

510 028.5   CC
ZHONGXUESHENG SHUXUE/MATHEMATICS FOR MIDDLE SCHOOL STUDENTS. (Text in Chinese) m. Zhongguo Shuxuehui, Puji Gongzuo Weiyuanhui - Chinese Mathematics Association, Popularization Commission, Fuwai Huayuancun, Capital Normal University, Mathematics Dept., Beijing 100037, People's Republic of China. TEL 841-4411. Ed. Mei Xiangming. **Document type:** academic/scholarly publication.

510 530   RU   ISSN 0044-4669
QA297   CODEN: ZVMFAN
ZHURNAL VYCHISLITEL'NOI MATEMATIKI I MATEMATICHESKOI FIZIKI. English translation: Computational Mathematics and Mathematical Physics (UK ISSN 0965-5425) 1961. m. $288 (effective 1996). (Rossiiskaya Akademiya Nauk) Izdatel'stvo Nauka, Mezhdunarodnyi Otdel, Profsoyuznaya, 90, 117864 Moscow, Russia. TEL 135-2489. Ed. A.A. Dorodnitzyn. adv.; bk.rev.; charts; illus.; index. circ. 2,100. **Indexed:** Appl.Mech.Rev., Chem.Abstr., INSPEC, Int.Aerosp.Abstr., Math.R. **Document type:** academic/scholarly publication.
—BLDSC (0060.700000). **CCC.**

ZUGAKU KENKYU/JOURNAL OF GRAPHIC SCIENCE OF JAPAN. see ART

MATHEMATICS — Abstracting, Bibliographies, Statistics

510   GW   ISSN 0933-9663
ABSTRACTS AND REVIEWS FROM ZENTRALBLATT FUER MATHEMATIK. (Text in English, French, German) 1981. m. DM.168($135) Fachinformationszentrum Karlsruhe, Gesellschaft fuer wissenschaftlich-technische Information mbH, 76344 Eggenstein-Leopoldshafen, Germany. TEL 07247-808333. FAX 07247-808666. (U.S. subscr. to: Scientific Information Service Inc., 7 Woodland Avenue, Larchmont, NY 10538) bk.rev. circ. 300. (looseleaf format) **Document type:** abstracting/indexing.
● Also available online.
—BLDSC (0553.842010).

016.510   US   ISSN 0192-5857
QA1
AMERICAN MATHEMATICAL SOCIETY. ABSTRACTS OF PAPERS PRESENTED. 1979. 6/yr. $71 to non-members. American Mathematical Society, Box 16248, Providence, RI 02940-6248. TEL 401-455-4000. circ. 4,400. **Indexed:** Math.R. **Document type:** abstracting/indexing.
—UMI. **CCC.**
Refereed Serial

BIOSTATISTICA. see BIOLOGY — Abstracting, Bibliographies, Statistics

510   GW   ISSN 0938-3174
COMPACTMATH - COMPACT MATHEMATICS LIBRARY. s-a. DM.7900 (effective 1996). Springer-Verlag, Heidelberger Platz 3, 14197 Berlin, Germany. TEL 030-8207-0. FAX 030-8214091. E-mail: orders@springer.de; blange@springer-ny.com. (Subscr. in N. America to: Springer-Verlag, Electronic Media Dept., 175 Fifth Ave., New York, NY 10010. TEL 212-460-1682. FAX 201-348-4505) **Document type:** abstracting/indexing.
● Available only on CD-ROM.
    Description: Cumulative CD-ROM edition of Zentralblatt fuer Mathematik - Mathematics Abstracts.

510   US   ISSN 0730-6199
Z6653
COMPUMATH CITATION INDEX. Short title: C M C I. (Includes: Source Index, Research Front Speciality Index, Citation Index, Permuterm Subject Index, and Corporate Index) 3/yr. $1955. Institute for Scientific Information, 3501 Market St., Philadelphia, PA 19104. TEL 215-386-0100. FAX 215-386-2991. (And: Brunel Science Park, Brunel University, Uxbridge UB8 3PQ, England) cum.index: 1976-80. (also avail. in magnetic tape) **Document type:** abstracting/indexing.
● Also available online. Vendor(s): Ovid Technologies.
    Description: A multidisciplinary index to the journal literature of computer science, mathematics, applications and chemistry and engineering, plus other related disciplines such as mathematical physics and econometrics.

016 311   US   ISSN 0364-1228
QA276.A1
CURRENT INDEX TO STATISTICS; applications-methods-theory. 1976. a. $50. American Statistical Association, 1429 Duke St., Alexandria, VA 22314-3402. TEL 703-684-1221. FAX 703-684-2037. (Co-sponsor: Institute of Mathematical Statistics) index. circ. 2,000. **Indexed:** Stat.Theor.Meth.Abstr.
● Also available online. Vendor(s): Ovid Technologies (MATH), Knight-Ridder, Inc., European Space Agency.
—**CCC.**

510 016   US   ISSN 0361-4794
Z6653   CODEN: CUMPBW
CURRENT MATHEMATICAL PUBLICATIONS. 1969. 17/yr. $377 to non-members; individual members $226; institutional members $302; reviewer $144. American Mathematical Society, Box 6248, Providence, RI 02940-6248. TEL 401-455-4000. (Street addr.: 201 Charles St., Providence, RI 02904) Ed. Robert G. Bartle. abstr. circ. 1,600. **Indexed:** Math.R. **Document type:** bibliography.
● Also available online. Vendor(s): Ovid Technologies, Knight-Ridder, Inc., European Space Agency. Also available on CD-ROM. Producer(s): SilverPlatter Information, Inc. (MathDisc).
—**CCC.**
    Formed by the 1975 merger of: American Mathematical Society. New Publications (ISSN 0002-9912); Contents of Contemporary Mathematical Journals (ISSN 0010-759X)

510   GW   ISSN 0343-639X
FACHBUCHVERZEICHNIS MATHEMATIK - PHYSIK (YEAR). 1900. a. DM.7.50. Fr. Weidemanns Buchhandlung (H.Witt), Postfach 6406, 30064 Hannover, Germany. TEL 0511-16382-0. FAX 0511-1638266. Ed. Renate Boehm. circ. 20,000. **Document type:** academic/scholarly publication.

510 016   US   ISSN 0019-3917
Z6653
INDEX OF MATHEMATICAL PAPERS. Variant title: Mathematical Reviews Annual Index. (Special issue of Mathematical Reviews (ISSN 0025-5629)) 1971. a. price varies. American Mathematical Society, Box 6248, Providence, RI 02940-6248. TEL 401-455-4000. (Street addr.: 201 Charles St., Providence, RI 02904) circ. 3,500. **Document type:** abstracting/indexing.

MATHEMATICS — ABSTRACTING, BIBLIOGRAPHIES, STATISTICS

510 US
IOWA STATE UNIVERSITY. STATISTICAL LABORATORY. ANNUAL REPORT. 1945. a. free. Iowa State University of Science and Technology, Statistical Laboratory, 102 Snedecor Hall, Ames, IA 50011. TEL 515-294-3440. FAX 515-294-4040. Ed. Jauvanta M. Walker. bk.rev.; abstr.; bibl.; illus. circ. 2,100. (back issues avail.) **Indexed:** Biol.Abstr. **Document type:** academic/scholarly publication.

JOURNAL FOR RESEARCH IN MATHEMATICS EDUCATION. see *MATHEMATICS*

512 016 RU
KOL'TSA;* bibliografiya. irreg. Rossiiskaya Akademiya Nauk, Sibirskoe Otdelenie, Institut Matematiki, Universitetskii pr. 4, 630090 Novosibirsk, Russia.

510 016 US ISSN 0025-5629
QA1 CODEN: MAREAR
MATHEMATICAL REVIEWS; a reviewing journal covering the world literature of mathematical research. (Text in English, French, German and Italian) 1940. m. $4594 (institutional members $3674). American Mathematical Society, Box 6248, Providence, RI 02940-6248. TEL 401-455-4000. (Street addr.: 201 Charles St., Providence, RI 02904) Ed. Robert G. Bartle. bk.rev.; index. circ. 2,400. (also avail. in microfiche) **Indexed:** Appl.Mech.Rev., Math.R. **Document type:** academic/scholarly publication.
●Also available online. Vendor(s): Ovid Technologies (MATH), Knight-Ridder, Inc., European Space Agency (File no.80/MATHSCI).
Also available on CD-ROM. Producer(s): SilverPlatter Information, Inc. (MathDisc).
—BLDSC (5403.000000); UMI. **CCC.**
Refereed Serial

510 US
N T I S ALERTS: MATHEMATICAL SCIENCES. w. $140 (outside N. America $195). U.S. National Technical Information Service, 5285 Port Royal Rd., Springfield, VA 22161. TEL 703-487-4650. FAX 703-321-8547. TELEX 64617. bibl. **Document type:** abstracting/indexing, government publication.

NIHON KODO KEIRYO GAKKAI TAIKAI HAPPYO RONBUN SHOROKUSHU. see *PSYCHOLOGY — Abstracting, Bibliographies, Statistics*

510 JA
NIHON SUGAKKAI KOEN ABUSUTORAKUTO. DAISU BUNKAKAI. (Text in Japanese) 2/yr. Nihon Sugakkai - Mathematical Society of Japan, 25-9-203, Hongo 4-chome, Bunkyo-ku, Tokyo 113, Japan. abstr.
Description: Contains abstracts of speeches from the society's conference on algebra.

510 JA
NIHON SUGAKKAI KOEN ABUSUTORAKUTO. JITSUKANSURON BUNKAKAI. (Text in Japanese) 2/yr. Nihon Sugakkai - Mathematical Society of Japan, 25-9-203, Hor.go 4-chome, Bunkyo-ku, Tokyo 113, Japan. abstr.
Description: Contains abstracts of speeches from the society's conference on real variable functions.

510 JA
NIHON SUGAKKAI KOEN ABUSUTORAKUTO. KANSU HOTEISHIKIRON BUNKAKAI. (Text in Japanese) 2/yr. Nihon Sugakkai - Mathematical Society of Japan, 25-9-203, Hongo 4-chome, Bunkyo-ku, Tokyo 113, Japan. abstr.
Description: Contains abstracts of speeches from the society's conference on functional equations.

510 JA
NIHON SUGAKKAI KOEN ABUSUTORAKUTO. KANSU KAISEKIGAKU BUNKAKAI. (Text in Japanese) 2/yr. Nihon Sugakkai - Mathematical Society of Japan, 25-9-203, Hongo 4-chome, Bunkyo-ku, Tokyo 113, Japan. abstr.
Description: Contains abstracts of speeches from the society's conference on functional analysis.

510 JA
NIHON SUGAKKAI KOEN ABUSUTORAKUTO. KANSURON. (Text in Japanese) 2/yr. Nihon Sugakkai - Mathematical Society of Japan, 25-9-203, Hongo 4-chome, Bunkyo-ku, Tokyo 113, Japan. abstr.
Description: Contains abstracts of speeches from the society's conference on the theory of functions.

510 JA
NIHON SUGAKKAI KOEN ABUSUTORAKUTO. KIKAGAKU BUNKAKAI. (Text in Japanese) 2/yr. Nihon Sugakkai - Mathematical Society of Japan, 25-9-203, Hongo 4-chome, Bunkyo-ku, Tokyo 113, Japan. abstr.
Description: Contains abstracts of speeches from the society's conference on geometry.

510 JA
NIHON SUGAKKAI KOEN ABUSUTORAKUTO. OYO SUGAKU BUNKAKAI. (Text in Japanese) 2/yr. Nihon Sugakkai - Mathematical Society of Japan, 25-9-203, Hongo 4-chome, Bunkyo-ku, Tokyo 113, Japan. abstr.
Description: Contains abstracts of speeches from the society's conference on applied mathematics.

510 JA
NIHON SUGAKKAI KOEN ABUSUTORAKUTO. SUGAKU KISORON BUNKAKAI. (Text in Japanese) 2/yr. Nihon Sugakkai - Mathematical Society of Japan, 25-9-203, Hongo 4-chome, Bunkyo-ku, Tokyo 113, Japan. abstr.
Description: Contains abstracts of speeches from the society's conference on basic mathematical theory.

510 310 JA
NIHON SUGAKKAI KOEN ABUSUTORAKUTO. TOKEI SUGAKU BUNKAKAI. (Text in Japanese) 2/yr. Nihon Sugakkai - Mathematical Society of Japan, 25-9-203, Hongo 4-chome, Bunkyo-ku, Tokyo 113, Japan. abstr.
Description: Contains abstracts of speeches from the society's conference on mathematical statistics.

510 JA
NIHON SUGAKKAI KOEN ABUSUTORAKUTO. TOPOROJI BUNKAKAI. (Text in Japanese) 2/yr. Nihon Sugakkai - Mathematical Society of Japan, 25-9-203, Hongo 4-chome, Bunkyo-ku, Tokyo 113, Japan. abstr.
Description: Contains abstracts of speeches from the society's conference on topology.

510 US
OPTIMIZATION; a journal of mathematical programming and operations research. (Text in English, French, German, Russian) 1970. 12/yr. (in 3 vols., 4 nos./vol.). 116 ECU per vol. (effective 1996). (Technische Hochschule Ilmenau, Sektion Mathematik, Rechentechnik und Oekenomische Kybernetik, SW) Gordon and Breach Science Publishers, c/o International Publishers Distributor, 820 Town Center Dr., Langhorne, PA 19047. TEL 215-750-2642. FAX 215-750-6343. (Subscr. to: International Publishers Distributor, P.O. Box 90, Reading, Berkshire RG1 8JL, England. TEL 44-173-456-8316) Ed. Karl-Heinz Elster. illus.; index. **Indexed:** INSPEC (1992-), Int.Abstr.Oper.Res., J.Cont.Quant.Meth., Math.R. **Document type:** academic/scholarly publication.
—BLDSC (6275.100000); SWETS. **CCC.**
Formerly: Series Optimization (ISSN 0233-1934); Which superseded in part (from 1977): Mathematische Operationsforschung und Statistik (ISSN 0047-6277)

510 016 RU ISSN 0034-2467
QA1
REFERATIVNYI ZHURNAL. MATEMATIKA. 1953. m. $1134 (effective 1996). Vsesoyuznyi Institut Nauchno-Tekhnicheskoi Informatsii (VINITI), Baltiiskaya ul., 14, Moscow A-219, Russia. (Subscr. to: Mezhdunarodnaya Kniga, Dimitrova ul. 39, 113095 Moscow, Russia) Ed. R.V. Gamkrelidze. circ. 2,296. (also avail. in microfiche from BHP,PMC) **Document type:** academic/scholarly publication.
—BLDSC (0145.000000).

S S O R YOKOSHU/PROCEEDINGS OF S S O R. (Summer Symposium of Operation Research) see *COMPUTERS — Abstracting, Bibliographies, Statistics*

SEIKEN N S T SHINPOJUMU KOEN KOGAISHU. see *COMPUTERS — Abstracting, Bibliographies, Statistics*

513.028 JA
SHUZAN KENKYU RONBUN SHIRYO MOKUROKUSHU. (Text in Japanese) 1963. 4/yr. Zenkoku Shuzan Kyoiku Renmei, 28, Higashi-Hieijo-cho, Nishi-9-jo, Minami-ku, Kyoto-shi, Kyoto-fu 601, Japan. bibl.; abstr.
Description: Bibliography of papers about calculation on abacus.

519.5 016 NE ISSN 0039-0518
HA1
STATISTICAL THEORY AND METHOD ABSTRACTS. 1959. 4/yr. $191.82. International Statistical Institute, Prinses Beatrixlaan 428, Postbus 950, 2270 AZ Voorburg, Netherlands. TEL 31-70-3375737. FAX 31-70-3860025. Eds. C. van Eeden, J.L. Mynheer. adv.; index. circ. 1,400. (reprint service avail. from KTO) **Indexed:** Hort.Abstr., Math.R. **Document type:** abstracting/indexing.
Formerly: International Journal of Abstracts.
Description: Provides international coverage of published articles on mathematical statistics and probability; contains almost 4,000 abstracts.

510 JA ISSN 0912-6112
TOKEI SURI/INSTITUTE OF STATISTICAL MATHEMATICS. PROCEEDINGS. (Text in Japanese; summaries in English) 1953. s-a. free. Institute of Statistical Mathematics, 4-6-7 Minami-Azabu, Minato-ku, Tokyo 106, Japan. TEL 03-3446-1501. FAX 03-3446-1695. Ed. T. Komazawa. stat. circ. 800. (back issues avail.) **Indexed:** Curr.Ind.Stat., Stat.Theor.Meth.Abstr. **Document type:** academic/scholarly publication, government publication.
—BLDSC (6718.000000).

510 310 BL ISSN 0102-6631
UNIVERSIDADE FEDERAL DO RIO DE JANEIRO. INSTITUTO DE MATEMATICA. MEMORIAS DE MATEMATICA. (Text in English, French, Portuguese, Spanish; summaries in English) 1971. irreg., no.148, 1987. $4 to institutions; free to individuals. Universidade Federal do Rio de Janeiro, Instituto de Matematica, C.P. 68530, 21944 Rio de Janeiro, RJ, Brazil. Ed.Bd. circ. controlled.
Description: Original articles accepted for publication in journals or proceedings of scientific meetings.

310 FR ISSN 0041-9184
UNIVERSITE DE PARIS VI (PIERRE ET MARIE CURIE). INSTITUT DE STATISTIQUE. PUBLICATIONS. 1952. 3/yr. 300 F. (foreign 350 F.). Universite de Paris VI (Pierre et Marie Curie), Institut de Statistique, 4, Place Jussieu, 75230 Paris Cedex 05, France. Ed. Denis Bosq. charts; stat. circ. 650. **Indexed:** Math.R.
Refereed Serial

510 016 GW ISSN 0044-4235
QA1
ZENTRALBLATT FUER MATHEMATIK UND IHRE GRENZGEBIETE/MATHEMATICS ABSTRACTS. (Text in English, German) 1931. 30/yr. DM.7900($5741) (effective 1996). (Fachinformationszentrum Karlsruhe, Abteilung Berlin) Springer-Verlag, Heidelberger Platz 3, 14197 Berlin, Germany. TEL 030-8207-0. FAX 030-8214091. E-mail: orders@springer.de. (Subscr. in N. America to: Springer-Verlag New York, Inc., 44 Hartz Way, Secaucus, NJ 07096-2491. TEL 201-348-4033. FAX 201-348-4505) (Co-sponsor: Heidelberger Akademie der Wissenschaften) Ed. B. Wegner. s-a. index, cum.index every 2 yrs. (also avail. in microform from UMI,PMC; reprint service avail. from ISI) **Indexed:** Appl.Mech.Rev., Math.R. **Document type:** abstracting/indexing.
●Also available online. Vendor(s): STN International (MATH).
Also available on CD-ROM.
—UMI. **CCC.**
Description: Publishes more than 50,000 abstracts, reports and reviews of mathematical research works, providing timely, worldwide coverage in all related disciplines.

510 CC ISSN 1001-1919
ZHONGGUO SHUXUE WENZHAI/CHINESE MATHEMATICS ABSTRACTS. (Text in Chinese, English) 1987. bi-m. $90. Zhongguo Kexueyuan, Wenxian Qingbao Zhongxin - Chinese Academy of Sciences, Documentation Information Center, 8 Kexueyuan Nanlu, Zhongguancun, Beijing 100080, People's Republic of China. TEL 2562784. FAX 2566846. Ed. Shen Xinyao. circ. 2,500. **Document type:** abstracting/indexing.

MATHEMATICS — Computer Applications

510   US
A C M COLLECTED ALGORITHM SUPPLEMENT. q. $75 to non-members. Association for Computing Machinery, 1515 Broadway, 17th Fl., New York, NY 10036-5701. TEL 212-869-7440. FAX 212-944-1318. TELEX 421686. (also avail. in diskette format)
 Description: Offers code listings for all algorithms printed in ACM journals.

A C M TRANSACTIONS ON MATHEMATICAL SOFTWARE. see COMPUTERS — Software

510   FR   ISSN 0989-6074
A M S E CONCEPTS. (Text mainly in English) 1988. q. membership. (Association for the Advancement of Modelling and Simulation Techniques in Enterprises) A M S E Press, 16 av. de Grange Blanche, 69160 Tassin-la-Demi-Lune, France. TEL 78-34-54-17. FAX 78-34-54-17. TELEX 389 595. **Document type:** academic/scholarly publication.
 —BLDSC (5883.534162); Ei.

510   FR
A M S E NEWS. (Text mainly in English) q. membership. (International Association for the Advancement of Modelling and Simulation Techniques in Enterprises) A M S E Press, 16 av. de Grange Blanche, 69160 Tassin-la-Demi-Lune, France. TEL 78-34-36-04. FAX 78-34-54-17. TELEX 389 595. Ed. G. Mesnard.

510   FR   ISSN 0761-2532
                               CODEN: AMTREW
A M S E TRANSACTIONS. (Text mainly in English) 1987. q. membership. (Association for the Advancement of Modelling and Simulation Techniques in Enterprises) A M S E Press, 16 av. de Grange Blanche, 69160 Tassin-la-Demi-Lune, France. TEL 78-34-36-04. FAX 78-34-54-17. TELEX 389 595. **Indexed:** Eng.Ind., INPSEC (1987-). **Document type:** academic/scholarly publication.
 —Ei.

ACTA POLYTECHNICA SCANDINAVICA. MATHEMATICS AND COMPUTING IN ENGINEERING SERIES. see COMPUTERS

ADVANCES IN COMPUTATIONAL ECONOMICS. see BUSINESS AND ECONOMICS — Computer Applications

519   NE   ISSN 1019-7168
                               CODEN: ACMHEX
ADVANCES IN COMPUTATIONAL MATHEMATICS. (Text in English) 1993. 4/yr. 299 SFr. (effective 1996). Baltzer Science Publishers B.V., Asterweg 13, 1031 HL Amsterdam, Netherlands. TEL 31-20-6370061. FAX 31-20-6323651. E-mail: publish@baltzer.nl. (Subscr. in N. America to: Box 8577, Red Bank, NJ 07701-8577) Eds. Charles A. Micchelli, John C. Mason. **Document type:** academic/scholarly publication.
 —BLDSC (0704.104000). **CCC.**
 Description: Interdisciplinary journal emphasizing innovation, application and practicality in computational mathematics theory and practice. Includes discussions of software used.
 Refereed Serial

510 332.1   US   ISSN 1048-4760
HG4001
ADVANCES IN MATHEMATICAL PROGRAMMING AND FINANCIAL PLANNING; a research annual. 1987. a. $63.50 to institutions. J A I Press Inc., 55 Old Post Rd., No. 2, P.O. Box 1678, Greenwich, CT 06836-1678. FAX 203-661-0792. (Addr. in the U.K. and rest of Europe: J A I Press Ltd., The Courtyard, 28 High St., Hampton Hill, Mddx. TW12 1PD, England. TEL 44-81-943-9296. FAX 44-81-943-9317) Ed. Kenneth D. Lawrence.

510   FR
ADVANCES IN MODELLING & ANALYSIS. A: GENERAL MATHEMATICAL & COMPUTER TOOLS. (Text mainly in English) irreg. 95 F.($19) per no. (International Association for the Advancement of Modelling and Simulation Techniques in Enterprises) A M S E Press, 16 av. de Grange Blanche, 69160 Tassin-la-Demi-Lune, France. TEL 78-34-36-04. FAX 78-34-54-17. TELEX 389 595. Ed. G. Mesnard. (back issues avail.)
 Description: Centers on the methodological aspects of mathematical problems and tools, general mathematical modelling, general computer tools.
 Refereed Serial

510   FR   ISSN 1240-4543
ADVANCES IN MODELLING & ANALYSIS. B: SIGNALS, INFORMATION, DATA, PATTERNS. (Text in English) 1984. q. (International Association for the Advancement of Modelling and Simulation Techniques in Enterprises) A M S E Press, 16 av. de Grange Blanche, 69160 Tassin-la-Demi-Lune, France. TEL 78-34-36-04. FAX 78-34-54-17. TELEX 389 595. Ed. G. Mesnard. **Indexed:** INSPEC (1992-).
 —BLDSC (0709.433500); Ei.
 Formerly (until 1992): A M S E Review (ISSN 0761-2486)
 Description: Looks at methodological aspects of signals, information, patterns, data acquisition, transmission, processing and classification.

510   FR   ISSN 1240-4535
ADVANCES IN MODELLING & ANALYSIS. C: SYSTEMS ANALYSIS, CONTROL & DESIGN. 1984. irreg. (International Association for the Advancement of Modelling and Simulation Techniques in Enterprises) A M S E Press, 16 av. de Grange Blanche, 69160 Tassin-la-Demi-Lune, France. TEL 78-34-36-04. Ed. G. Mesnard. **Indexed:** INSPEC (1992-).
 —BLDSC (0709.433800); Ei. **CCC.**
 Formerly (until 1992): Advances in Modelling and Simulation (ISSN 0761-2494)
 Description: Centers on the methodological aspects of systems analysis, control and design, simulation and CAD.

510   US
ADVANCES IN THE THEORY OF COMPUTATION AND COMPUTATIONAL MATHEMATICS. 1992. irreg. price varies. Ablex Publishing Corporation, 355 Chestnut St., Norwood, NJ 07648. TEL 201-767-8450. FAX 201-767-6717. TELEX 135-393. Ed. Lee Keener. **Document type:** academic/scholarly publication.

ANNALS OF MATHEMATICS AND ARTIFICIAL INTELLIGENCE. see COMPUTERS — Artificial Intelligence

510   GW   ISSN 0938-1279
                               CODEN: AAECEW
APPLICABLE ALGEBRA IN ENGINEERING, COMMUNICATION AND COMPUTING. (Text in English) 1990. 6/yr. DM.398($289) (effective 1996). Springer-Verlag, Heidelberger Platz 3, 14197 Berlin, Germany. TEL 030-8207-0. FAX 030-8214091. E-mail: orders@springer.de. (Subscr. in N. America to: Springer-Verlag New York, Inc., 44 Hartz Way, Secaucus, NJ 07096-2491. TEL 201-348-4033) Ed. J. Calmet. **Indexed:** INSPEC (1990-). **Document type:** academic/scholarly publication.
 —BLDSC (1570.445000); Ei; Genuine Article; SWETS; UMI. **CCC.**
 Description: Publishes mathematically rigorous, original research papers reporting on algebraic methods and techniques relevant to all domains concerned with computers, intelligent systems and communications.

519   NE   ISSN 0927-2852
QA169   CODEN: ACASE6
APPLIED CATEGORICAL STRUCTURES; a journal devoted to applications of categorical methods in algebra, analysis, order, topology and computer science. (Text in English) 1993. q. fl.411 to institutions; $263 to institutions in U.S. (effective 1996). Kluwer Academic Publishers, P.O. Box 17, 3300 AA Dordrecht, Netherlands. TEL 31-78-392392. FAX 31-78-392254. TELEX 29245 KAPG NL. E-mail: SERVICES@WKAP.NL. (Dist. by: Kluwer Academic Publishers Group, P.O. Box 322, 3300 AH Dordrecht, Netherlands. TEL 31-78-392392. FAX 31-78-546474; N. American dist. addr.: Box 358, Accord Sta., Hingham, MA 02018-0358. TEL 617-871-6600. FAX 617-871-6528) Ed. R. Lowen. (reprint service avail. from SWZ) **Indexed:** INSPEC (1993-), Math.R., Zent.Math. **Document type:** academic/scholarly publication.
 —BLDSC (1571.921900); Ei.
 Description: Publishes research, techniques and applications relating to categorical methods in mathematics and computer science.
 Refereed Serial

519.5 006   US   ISSN 0307-904X
QA1   CODEN: AMMODL
APPLIED MATHEMATICAL MODELLING; simulation & computation for engineering & environmental systems. 1976. m. $755 to institutions (effective 1996). Butterworth - Heinemann, Part of the Reed Elsevier group, 313 Washington St., Newton, MA 02158. TEL 617-928-2500; 800-366-2665. FAX 617-928-2610. (Subscr. to: Elsevier Science Inc., Box 882, Madison Sq. Sta., New York, NY 10159-0882. TEL 212-989-5800. FAX 212-633-3990) Ed. Mark Cross. adv.; bk.rev.; abstr.; bibl.; charts; illus.; stat.; index. (also avail. in microform from UMI; back issues avail.) **Indexed:** Abstr.J.Earthq.Eng., Appl.Mech.Rev., BMT, Br.Tech.Ind., CAD CAM Abstr., CLOSS, Compumath, Comput.Abstr., Curr.Cont., Energy Ind., Energy Info.Abstr., Eng.Ind., Environ.Abstr., Excerp.Med., Fluidex, Geo.Abstr., Geol.Abstr., GeoRef., INSPEC, Intl.Civil Eng.Abstr., Math.R., Risk Abstr., Sel.Water Res.Abstr., Soft.Abstr.Eng. **Document type:** academic/scholarly publication.
 —BLDSC (1573.715000); CIS; Ei; Faxon; Genuine Article; SWETS; UMI; UnCover. **CCC.**
 Description: Research on all aspects of mathematical modelling pertinent to practical systems analysis.
 Refereed Serial

APPLIED MATHEMATICS AND COMPUTATION. see MATHEMATICS

519   NE   ISSN 0168-9274
QA297
APPLIED NUMERICAL MATHEMATICS. (Text in English) 1985. m. fl.1815($1107) (effective 1996). (International Association for Mathematics and Computers in Simulation) North-Holland (Subsidiary of: Elsevier Science B.V.), P.O. Box 211, 1000 AE Amsterdam, Netherlands. TEL 31-20-4853911. FAX 31-20-4853598. TELEX 18582 ESPA NL. (Subscr. in U.S. and Canada to: Elsevier Science Inc., Box 882, Madison Sq. Sta., New York, NY 10159. TEL 212-989-5800. FAX 212-633-3990) Eds. R. Vichnevetsky, J.E. Flaherty. (also avail. in microform from UMI; back issues avail.; reprint service avail. from SWZ) **Indexed:** Appl.Mech.Rev., Compumath, Comput.Abstr., INSPEC (1985-). **Document type:** academic/scholarly publication.
 —BLDSC (1576.234000); Ei; Faxon; Genuine Article; SWETS; UnCover. **CCC.**
 Description: Devoted to contemporary problems in numerical computing.
 Refereed Serial

610   NE   ISSN 0169-4669
C W I MONOGRAPHS. (Text in English) 1984. irreg., no.7, 1988. (Stichting Mathematisch Centrum, Centrum voor Wiskunde en Informatica) Elsevier Science B.V., Books Division, P.O. 211, 1000 AE Amsterdam, Netherlands. TEL 31-20-4853911. (Subscr. in U.S. and Canada to: Elsevier Science Publishing Co., Inc., Box 882, Madison Sq. Sta., New York, NY 10159. TEL 212-989-5800) Ed.Bd. **Indexed:** INSPEC. **Document type:** monographic series.
 Description: Covers mathematics and computer science.
 Refereed Serial

MATHEMATICS — COMPUTER APPLICATIONS

610   NE
C W I PUBLICATIONS. (Text in Dutch, English) 1981. irreg. price varies. Stichting Mathematisch Centrum, Centrum voor Wiskunde en Informatica, P.O. Box 94079, 1090 GB Amsterdam, Netherlands. TEL 31-20-5924128. FAX 31-20-5924199. TELEX 12571 MACTR NL. Ed.Bd. **Document type:** academic/scholarly publication.
   Description: Disseminates research and theories on mathematics and computer science.

510   NE
C W I SYLLABI. (Text in English) 1969. irreg., no.38, 1994. price varies. Stichting Mathematisch Centrum, Centrum voor Wiskunde en Informatica, P.O. Box 94079, 1090 GB Amsterdam, Netherlands. TEL 31-20-5924128. FAX 31-20-5924199. TELEX 12571 MACTR NL. Ed.Bd. **Document type:** academic/scholarly publication.
   Formerly (until 1984): Mathematical Centre Syllabi.
   Description: Details seminar reports, course manuals, and lecture notes revisions on mathematics and computer science.

510 004   NE   ISSN 0169-0388
CENTRUM VOOR WISKUNDE EN INFORMATICA. DEPARTMENT OF NUMERICAL MATHEMATICS. REPORT. (Text in English) 1973. irreg. Stichting Mathematisch Centrum, Centrum voor Wiskunde en Informatica, Department of Numerical Mathematics, P.O. Box 94079, 1090 GB Amsterdam, Netherlands. TEL 31-20-5924128. FAX 31-20-5924199. abstr. **Document type:** academic/scholarly publication.
   Formerly (until 1984): Stichting Mathematisch Centrum. Afdeling Numerieke Wiskunde. Rapport (ISSN 0376-4036)

CHANCE; new directions for statistics and computers. see *STATISTICS*

CHAOS, SOLITONS AND FRACTALS; applications in science and engineering. see *MATHEMATICS*

510   UK   ISSN 0963-5483
QA164
COMBINATORICS, PROBABILITY & COMPUTING. 1992. q. £104($190) (effective 1996). Cambridge University Press, Edinburgh Bldg., Shaftesbury Rd., Cambridge CB2 2RU, England. TEL 01223-312393. FAX 01223-315052. TELEX 851817256. (N. American addr.: Cambridge University Press, Journals Dept., 40 W. 20th St., New York, NY 10011. TEL 212-924-3900. FAX 212-691-3239) Ed. Bela Bollobas. adv. (back issues avail.) **Document type:** academic/scholarly publication.
—BLDSC (3324.770000); UMI. **CCC.**
   Description: Encompasses combinatorics in a broad sense, including classical and algebraic graph theory, extremal set theory, matriod theory and other theories.

COMMUNICATIONS IN STATISTICS. PART B: SIMULATION AND COMPUTATION. see *STATISTICS*

510 620   UK   ISSN 0332-1649
TK1.A1   CODEN: CODUDU
COMPEL; the international journal for computation and mathematics in electrical and electronic engineering. 1982. q. $210. James & James (Science Publishers) Ltd., Waterside House, 47 Kentish Town Rd., London NW1 8NZ, England. TEL 0171-284-3833. FAX 0171-284-3737. (Dist. by: Taylor & Francis Ltd., Rankine Rd., Basingstoke, Hants. RG24 OPR, England. TEL 01256-840366; N. America addr.: Taylor & Francis, 1900 Frost Rd., Ste. 101, Bristol, PA 19007-1598. TEL 215-785-5800) Ed. J. Sykulski; Pub. Edward Milford. adv. contact: Paul Diamond. bk.rev. **Indexed:** Compumath, INSPEC (1982-1989). **Document type:** academic/scholarly publication.
—BLDSC (3363.924000); Ei; Faxon; SWETS; UMI; UnCover.

COMPSTAT SYMPOSIUM. PROCEEDINGS. (Computational Statistics) see *STATISTICS*

510 003   US   ISSN 1381-298X
▼**COMPUTATIONAL & MATHEMATICAL ORGANIZATION THEORY.** 1995. q. fl.478 to institutions; $306 to institutions in U.S. (effective 1996). Kluwer Academic Publishers Boston, Box 358, Accord Sta., Hingham, MA 02018-0358. TEL 617-871-6600. FAX 617-871-6528. (Dist. outside N. America by: Kluwer Academic Publishers Group, P.O. Box 322, 3300 AH Dordrecht, Netherlands. TEL 31-78-392392. FAX 31-78-546474) Eds. Kathleen M. Carley, William A. Wallace. (back issues avail.) **Document type:** academic/scholarly publication.
Refereed Serial

510   SZ   ISSN 1016-3328
QA267   CODEN: CPTCEU
COMPUTATIONAL COMPLEXITY. (Text in English) 1991. 4/yr. 415.50 SFr. (foreign 428.40 SFr.). Birkhaeuser Verlag, P.O. Box 133, CH-4010 Basel, Switzerland. TEL 061-2717400. FAX 061-2717666. (Dist. in N. America by: Springer-Verlag, Mercedes Distribution Center, 160 Imlay St., Brooklyn, NY 11231, USA) Ed. J. von zur Gathen. **Indexed:** Comput.Rev., Curr.Cont., INSPEC (1991-), Math.R. **Document type:** academic/scholarly publication.
—BLDSC (3390.580000). **CCC.**
   Description: Interface between mathematics and theoretical computer science.

510 004   NE   ISSN 0925-7721
QA448.D38   CODEN: CGOME6
COMPUTATIONAL GEOMETRY; theory and applications. (Text in English) 1991. bi-m. fl.385($235) (effective 1996). North-Holland (Subsidiary of: Elsevier Science B.V.), P.O. Box 211, 1000 AE Amsterdam, Netherlands. TEL 31-20-4853911. FAX 31-20-4853598. TELEX 18582 ESPA NL. (Subscr. in U.S. and Canada to: Elsevier Science Inc., Box 882, Madison Sq. Sta., New York, NY 10159. TEL 212-989-5800. FAX 212-633-3990) Eds. Joerg-Ruediger Sack, Jorge Urrutia. (also avail. in microform from UMI; back issues avail.) **Indexed:** Geo.Abstr., INSPEC (1991-), Math.R. **Document type:** academic/scholarly publication.
—BLDSC (3390.592000); Ei; Genuine Article; SWETS. **CCC.**
   Description: Publishes fundamental research in all areas of computational geometry, and disseminates information on the applications, techniques and uses of computational geometry.
Refereed Serial

510   US   ISSN 1046-283X
QA76.95   CODEN: CMMOEA
COMPUTATIONAL MATHEMATICS AND MODELING. 1991. q. $525 (foreign $615) (effective 1996). Plenum Publishing Corp., Consultants Bureau, 233 Spring St., New York, NY 10013. TEL 212-620-8000. FAX 212-463-0742. TELEX 23-421139. Ed.Bd. (also avail. in microform from JSC; back issues avail.) **Indexed:** INSPEC (1990-). **Document type:** academic/scholarly publication.
—BLDSC (0411.054000); Faxon; UnCover. **CCC.**
   Description: Contains current Russian mathematical articles in translation covering discrete mathematics, numerical analysis, and computational number theory.
Refereed Serial

621   GW   ISSN 0178-7675
COMPUTATIONAL MECHANICS; solids, fluids, fracture, transport phenomena, multi-body dynamics and variational methods. (Text in English) 1986. 12/yr. (in 2 vols., 6 nos./vol.) DM.1996($1450) (effective 1996). Springer-Verlag, Heidelberger Platz 3, 14197 Berlin, Germany. TEL 030-8207-0. FAX 030-8214091. E-mail: orders@springer.de. (Subscr. in N. America to: Springer-Verlag New York, Inc., 44 Hartz Way, Secaucus, NJ 07096-2491. TEL 201-348-4033. FAX 201-348-4505) Eds. S.N. Atluri, G. Yagawa. **Indexed:** Cyb.Abstr. **Document type:** academic/scholarly publication.
—BLDSC (3390.615300); Ei; Faxon; Genuine Article; SWETS; UMI; UnCover. **CCC.**
   Description: Reports on theoretical and computational methods, and their rational application in solid and structural mechanics, fluid mechanics and engineering, fracture mechanics, transport phenomena, heat transfer, and inelastic and finite deformation response.

531   SZ   ISSN 0927-7951
TA349
COMPUTATIONAL MECHANICS ADVANCES. (Text in English) 1993. q. 470 SFr.($385) (effective 1996). (International Association for Computational Mechanics) Elsevier Science S.A., P.O. Box 564, CH-1001 Lausanne 1, Switzerland. TEL 41-21-3207381. FAX 41-21-3235444. TELEX 450260-ELSA-CH. (Subscr. in U.S. and Canada to: Elsevier Science Inc., Box 882, Madison Sq. Sta., New York, NY 10159. TEL 212-989-5800. FAX 212-633-3990) Ed. J. Tinsley Oden. (also avail. in microform from UMI) **Document type:** academic/scholarly publication, monographic series.
—BLDSC (3390.615350); Ei; SWETS. **CCC.**
   Description: Publishes review papers concerned with applications of computers to problems of applied mechanics and engineering.
Refereed Serial

COMPUTATIONAL MECHANICS AND PHYSICS OF FRACTURE. see *ENGINEERING — Computer Applications*

519.3   US   ISSN 0926-6003
QA402.5
COMPUTATIONAL OPTIMIZATION AND APPLICATIONS; an international journal. 1992. bi-m. fl.697 to institutions; $447 to institutions in U.S. (effective 1996). Kluwer Academic Publishers Boston, Box 358, Accord Sta., Hingham, MA 02018-0358. TEL 617-871-6600. FAX 617-871-6528. TELEX 200190. (Dist. outside N. America by: Kluwer Academic Publishers Group, P.O. Box 322, 3300 AH Dordrecht, Netherlands. TEL 31-78-392392. FAX 31-78-546474) Ed. William W. Hager. (also avail. in microform from UMI; reprint service avail. from SWZ) **Indexed:** Appl.Mech.Rev., Comput.Lit.Ind., Comput.Rev., Eng.Ind., Inform.Sci.Abstr., INSPEC (1992-), Math.R., Zent.Math. **Document type:** academic/scholarly publication.
—BLDSC (3390.620500); Ei; UMI; UnCover. **CCC.**
   Description: Research in the analysis and development of computational algorithms for optimization, covering both general principles and specific applications.
Refereed Serial

COMPUTATIONAL STATISTICS. see *STATISTICS*

519.5   NE   ISSN 0167-9473
QA276.A1   CODEN: CSDADW
COMPUTATIONAL STATISTICS AND DATA ANALYSIS. (Text in English) 1983. m. fl.1750($1067) (effective 1996). North-Holland (Subsidiary of: Elsevier Science B.V.), P.O. Box 211, 1000 AE Amsterdam, Netherlands. TEL 31-20-4853911. FAX 31-20-4853598. TELEX 18582 ESPA NL. (Subscr. in U.S. and Canada to: Elsevier Science Inc., Box 882, Madison Sq. Sta., New York, NY 10159. TEL 212-989-5800. FAX 212-633-3990) Eds. S.P. Azen, P. Naeve. adv.; bk.rev. circ. 1,000. (also avail. in microform from UMI; back issues avail.; reprint service avail. from SWZ) **Indexed:** Biostat., Compumath, Comput.Cont., Curr.Ind.Stat., Geo.Abstr., INSPEC (1983-), J.Cont.Quant.Meth., Math.R., Oper.Res.Manage.Sci., Qual.Contr.Appl.Stat., Stat.Theor.Meth.Abstr. **Document type:** academic/scholarly publication.
—BLDSC (3390.625000); Ei; Faxon; Genuine Article; SWETS; UnCover. **CCC.**
   Incorporates (in 1991): Statistical Software Newsletter (ISSN 0173-5896)
   Description: For statisticians, software managers and consultants in computer centers, and researchers in the social, engineering, natural, physical and medical sciences. Covers topics such as pattern recognition, algorithms, graphical presentations and computer-assisted analyzers.
Refereed Serial

COMPUTER SCIENCE AND SCIENTIFIC COMPUTING. see *COMPUTERS*

COMPUTERS & GEOSCIENCES; an international journal. see *EARTH SCIENCES — Computer Applications*

MATHEMATICS — COMPUTER APPLICATIONS

510   UK   ISSN 0898-1221
QA76   CODEN: CMAPDK
COMPUTERS & MATHEMATICS WITH APPLICATIONS. 1975. 24/yr. £1314($2090) (effective 1996). Elsevier Science Ltd., Pergamon, P.O. Box 800, Kidlington, Oxford OX5 1DX, England. TEL 44-1865-843000. FAX 44-1865-843010. E-mail: nlinfo-f@elsevier.nl; usinfo-f@elsevier.com; forinfo-kyf04035@niftyserve.or.jp; Site addr.: http://www.elsevier.nl/. (Subscr. in U.S. and Canada to: Elsevier Science, 660 White Plains Rd., Tarrytown, NY 10591-5153. TEL 914-524-9200. FAX 914-333-2444) Ed. Ervin Y. Rodin. adv.; bk.rev.; charts; illus.; index. circ. 1,125. (also avail. in microfilm from UMI) **Indexed:** Appl.Mech.Rev., Biostat., Compumath, Comput.Abstr., Comput.Cont., Comput.Rev., Curr.Cont., Fluidex, Ind.Sci.Rev., INSPEC, Int.Abstr.Oper.Res., Intl.Civil Eng.Abstr., Math.R., Sci.Cit.Ind., Soft.Abstr.Eng. **Document type:** academic/scholarly publication.
—BLDSC (3394.730000); Ei; Faxon; Genuine Article; SWETS; UMI; UnCover. **CCC.**
   Formed by the 1987 merger of: Computers and Mathematics with Applications. Part A (ISSN 0886-9553); Computers and Mathematics with Applications. Part B (ISSN 0886-9561); Which superseded (in 1986): Computers and Mathematics with Applications (ISSN 0097-4943)
   Description: Covers computers in mathematical research, mathematical models of computer systems and interactive applications.
   Refereed Serial

COMPUTERS IN EDUCATION: ENGINEERING, SCIENCE, AND MATHEMATICS. see *EDUCATION — Computer Applications*

DEVELOPMENTS IN ENVIRONMENTAL MODELLING. see *ENVIRONMENTAL STUDIES — Computer Applications*

519   NE   ISSN 0928-0200
                   CODEN: EJNMEA
EAST-WEST JOURNAL OF NUMERICAL MATHEMATICS. (Text in English) 1993. 4/yr. DM.410 (effective 1996). V S P, P.O. Box 346, 3700 AH Zeist, Netherlands. TEL 31-30-6925790. FAX 31-30-6932081. E-mail: 100341.2372@compuserve.com. Ed. Yu.A. Kuznetsov. (back issues avail.) **Document type:** academic/scholarly publication.
—BLDSC (3646.560800); Ei.
   Description: Promotes the exchange of ideas and results in numerical mathematics between scientists in Eastern Europe and Western countries.
   Refereed Serial

ENERGY: PHYSICAL PROCESSES AND MATHEMATICAL MODELLING. see *ENERGY*

510.28   SI   ISSN 0218-348X
QA614.86   CODEN: FRACEG
FRACTALS; an interdisciplinary journal on the complex geometry of nature. 1993. q. $116 for developing countries; developed countries $260. World Scientific Publishing Co. Pte. Ltd., Farrer Rd., P.O. Box 128, Singapore 9128, Singapore. TEL 3825663. FAX 3825919. TELEX RS-28561-WSPC. (UK addr.: 73 Lynton Mead, Totteridge, London N20 8DH, England. TEL 44-81-4462461; US addr.: 1060 Main St., Ste. 1B, River Edge, NJ 07661. TEL 800-227-7562) Ed. T. Vicsik. **Indexed:** INSPEC (1993-). **Document type:** academic/scholarly publication.
—BLDSC (4030.655000). **CCC.**

510   NE   ISSN 0169-2968
QA267   CODEN: FUMAAJ
FUNDAMENTA INFORMATICAE. (Text in English) 1977. 8/yr. (in 2 vols.) fl.942($523) (effective 1995). (Polskie Towarzystwo Matematyczne, PL - Polish Mathematical Society) I O S Press, Van Diemenstraat 94, 1013 CN Amsterdam, Netherlands. TEL 31-20-6382189. FAX 31-20-6203419. E-mail: marie-louise.kok@ios.nl. (In N. America: Box 10558, Burke, VA 22009-0558. TEL 703-323-5554. FAX 703-250-4705) (Co-sponsor: European Association of Theoretical Computer Science) Ed.Bd. **Indexed:** INSPEC (1978-). **Document type:** academic/scholarly publication.
—BLDSC (4055.987000); Ei; Faxon. **CCC.**
   Formerly (until 1986): Annales Societatis Mathematicae Polonae. Seria 4. Fundamenta Informaticae (ISSN 0324-8429)
   Description: Publishes original papers on topics including solutions by mathematical methods of problems in computer science, and mathematical problems inspired by computer science with special preference given to logical systems and methods of computer science, and algebraical models and methods of computer science.
   Refereed Serial

GAMES AND ECONOMIC BEHAVIOR. see *PSYCHOLOGY*

510   GW   ISSN 0911-0119
                   CODEN: GRCOE5
GRAPHS AND COMBINATORICS. (Text in English) 1985. 4/yr. DM.518($376) (effective 1996). Springer-Verlag, Heidelberger Platz 3, 14197 Berlin, Germany. TEL 030-8207-0. FAX 030-8214091. E-mail: orders@springer.de. (Subscr. in Japan to: Springer-Verlag Tokyo, 37-3 Hongo 3-chome, Bunkyo-ku, Tokyo 113, Japan. TEL 03-38120331; Subscr. in N. America to: Springer-Verlag New York, Inc., 44 Hartz Way, Secaucus, NJ 07096-2491. TEL 201-348-4033. FAX 201-348-4505) (Co-publisher: Springer-Verlag Tokyo) Ed. Hoon Heng Teh. (also avail. in microform from UMI; back issues avail.; reprint service avail. from ISI) **Indexed:** Compumath, INSPEC, Math.R., Zent.Math. **Document type:** academic/scholarly publication.
—Faxon; Genuine Article; SWETS; UMI; UnCover. **CCC.**
   Description: Devoted to research concerning combinatorial mathematics in the form of research papers, survey articles, short communications, research problems and announcements.

INTERNATIONAL JOURNAL OF ALGEBRA AND COMPUTATION. see *MATHEMATICS*

510   SI   ISSN 0218-1959
QA448.D38   CODEN: IJCAEV
INTERNATIONAL JOURNAL OF COMPUTATIONAL GEOMETRY AND APPLICATIONS. 1991. q. $120 to individuals & institutions of developing countries; institutions of developed countries $242. World Scientific Publishing Co. Pte. Ltd., Farrer Rd., P.O. Box 128, Singapore 9128, Singapore. TEL 3825633. FAX 3825919. TELEX RS-28561-WSPC. (US addr.: 1060 Main St., Ste. 1B, River Edge, NJ 07661. TEL 800-227-7562; UK addr.: 73 Lynton Mead, Totteridge, London N20 8DH, England. TEL 44-81-4462461) Ed. D.T. Lee. **Indexed:** INSPEC (1991-). **Document type:** academic/scholarly publication.
—BLDSC (4542.173710); SWETS.
   Description: Covers the design and analysis of algorithms, and its applications to various fields including computer-aided geometry design, computer graphics, constructive solid geometry, operations research, pattern recognition, robotics, solid modelling, and others.

510   US   ISSN 0020-7160
QA76   CODEN: IJCMAT
INTERNATIONAL JOURNAL OF COMPUTER MATHEMATICS. 1964. 16/yr. (in 4 vols., 4 nos./vol.). 402 ECU per vol. (effective 1996). Gordon and Breach Science Publishers, c/o International Publishers Distributor, 820 Town Center Dr., Langhorne, PA 19047. TEL 215-750-2642. FAX 215-750-6343. (Subscr. to: International Publishers Distributors, P.O. Box 90, Reading, Berkshire RG1 8JL, England. TEL 44-173-456-8316) Ed. David J. Evans. adv.; abstr.; charts; illus.; index. (also avail. in microform) **Indexed:** Appl.Mech.Rev., CAD CAM Abstr., Compumath, Comput.Rev., Curr.Cont., Cyb.Abstr., Eng.Ind., Ind.Sci.Rev., INIS Atomind., INSPEC, Math.R., Sci.Cit.Ind.
—BLDSC (4542.175000); Faxon; SWETS; UnCover. **CCC.**
   Description: Research papers on the theory and development of programming languages and their translators.
   Refereed Serial

510   NE   ISSN 1382-3892
▼**INTERNATIONAL JOURNAL OF COMPUTERS FOR MATHEMATICAL LEARNING.** (Text in English) Announced for publication in 1996. 3/yr. fl.292 to institutions; $188 to institutions in U.S. (effective 1996). Kluwer Academic Publishers, Postbus 17, 3300 AA Dordrecht, Netherlands. TEL 31-78-392392. FAX 31-78-392254. E-mail: SERVICES@WKAP.NL. (Dist. by: Kluwer Academic Publishers Group, P.O. Box 322, 3300 AH Dordrecht, Netherlands. TEL 31-78-392392. FAX 31-78-546474; N. America dist. addr.: Box 358, Accord Sta., Hingham, MA 02018-0358. TEL 617-871-6600. FAX 617-871-6528) **Document type:** academic/scholarly publication.
   Refereed Serial

510 620 621.381   UK   ISSN 0266-5611
QA1   CODEN: INPEEY
INVERSE PROBLEMS; inverse problems, inverse methods and computerized inversion of data. 1985. bi-m. £475($979) (effective 1996). (Institute of Physics) I O P Publishing Ltd., Techno House, Redcliffe Way, Bristol, Avon BS1 6NX, England. TEL 0117-929-7481. FAX 0117-929-4318. TELEX 449149 INSTP G. (U.S. subscr. to: American Institute of Physics, Member and Subscription Services, 500 Sunnyside Blvd., Woodbury, NY 11797-2900. TEL 516-349-7800) Ed. M. Bertero. circ. 430. (also avail. in microfiche; microfilm from PMC; back issues avail.) **Indexed:** Compumath, Curr.Cont., Deep Sea Res.& Oceanogr.Abstr., INSPEC (1985-). **Document type:** academic/scholarly publication.
—BLDSC (4557.703170); Ei; Faxon; Genuine Article; SWETS; UnCover. **CCC.**
   Description: Aims to combine theoretical, experimental and mathematical papers on inverse problems with numerical and practical approaches to their solution.

INVERSE PROBLEMS IN ENGINEERING. see *ENGINEERING*

JAPANESE SOCIETY OF COMPUTATIONAL STATISTICS. JOURNAL. see *STATISTICS*

JOURNAL OF ALGEBRAIC COMBINATORICS; an international journal. see *MATHEMATICS*

510   US   ISSN 0196-6774
QA76.6   CODEN: JOALDV
JOURNAL OF ALGORITHMS. 1980. bi-m. $312 (foreign $368) (effective 1996). Academic Press, Inc., Journal Division, 525 B St., Ste. 1900, San Diego, CA 92101-4495. TEL 619-230-1840. FAX 619-699-6800. (Subscr. to: Box 620000, Orlando, FL 32891-8340. TEL 800-543-9534) Ed.Bd. adv. (back issues avail.; reprint service avail. from SWZ) **Indexed:** Compumath, Comput.Cont., INSPEC, Int.Abstr.Oper.Res., Math.R. **Document type:** academic/scholarly publication.
—BLDSC (4926.800000); Ei; Faxon; Genuine Article; SWETS; UnCover. **CCC.**
   Description: Presents papers on algorithms that are inherently discrete and finite and that have some definite mathematical content in a natural way, either in their objective or in their analysis.
   Refereed Serial

MATHEMATICS — COMPUTER APPLICATIONS

510   US   ISSN 0885-064X
QA267   CODEN: JOCOEH
JOURNAL OF COMPLEXITY. 1985. q. $201 (foreign $236) (effective 1996). Academic Press, Inc., Journal Division, 525 B St., Ste. 1900, San Diego, CA 92101-4495. TEL 619-230-1840. FAX 619-699-6800. (Subscr. to: Box 620000, Orlando, FL 32891-8340. TEL 800-543-9534) Ed. Joseph F. Traub. (back issues avail.) **Indexed:** INSPEC (1985-). **Document type:** academic/scholarly publication.
—BLDSC (4963.393000); Ei; Faxon; SWETS; UnCover. **CCC.**
Description: Publishes original research papers that contain mathematical results on complexity as broadly received.
Refereed Serial

510 500 371.3 500   US   ISSN 0731-9258
QA20.C65   CODEN: JCMTDV
JOURNAL OF COMPUTERS IN MATHEMATICS AND SCIENCE TEACHING. Variant title: J C M S T. 1981. q. $65 to individuals (foreign $80); institutions $83 (foreign $103). Association for the Advancement of Computing in Education, Box 2966, Charlottesville, VA 22902-2966. TEL 804-973-3987. Ed. Dan Shepardson. adv.; bk.rev. circ. 3,500. (also avail. in microfiche; back issues avail.) **Indexed:** C.I.J.E., Comput.Dtbs., Cont.Pg.Educ., Educ.Ind., Educ.Tech.Abstr., ERIC, INSPEC, Microcomp.Ind., Tech.Educ.Abstr. **Document type:** academic/scholarly publication.
—BLDSC (4963.760000); Ei; Faxon; SWETS; UMI; UnCover. **CCC.**
Description: For mathematics and science teachers of all levels. Articles cover various aspects of computer literacy, ideas and experiences of instruction with computers and the characteristics of mathematics-science teachers and students using computers.
Refereed Serial

JOURNAL OF HEURISTICS. see *PHILOSOPHY*

510   US   ISSN 0924-9907
TA1637   CODEN: JMIVEK
JOURNAL OF MATHEMATICAL IMAGING AND VISION. 1991. q. fl.533 to institutions; $341 to institutions in U.S. (effective 1996). Kluwer Academic Publishers Boston, Box 358, Accord Sta., Hingham, MA 02018-0358. TEL 617-871-6600. FAX 617-871-6528. TELEX 200190. (Dist. outside N. America by: Kluwer Academic Publishers Group, P.O. Box 322, 3300 AH Dordrecht, Netherlands. TEL 31-78-392392. FAX 31-78-546474) Ed. Gerhard X. Ritter. (also avail. in microform from UMI; back issues avail.; reprint service avail. from SWZ) **Indexed:** INSPEC (1992-). **Document type:** academic/scholarly publication.
—BLDSC (5012.385000); Ei; UMI. **CCC.**
Description: Covers all aspects of mathematical imaging, including theoretical research papers and medical, industrial, military, and geophysical applications.
Refereed Serial

510   US   ISSN 1052-0600
QA402.3   CODEN: JMCOE3
JOURNAL OF MATHEMATICAL SYSTEMS, ESTIMATION AND CONTROL. 1991. 4/yr. $265 (foreign $288). Birkhaeuser, 675 Massachusetts Ave., Cambridge, MA 02139-3309. FAX 201-348-4505. (Dist. by: Springer-Verlag New York, Inc., Journal Fulfillment Services, Box 2485, Secaucus, NJ 07096-2491. TEL 201-348-4033) Ed. Clyde F. Martin. adv. contact: Robert Vrooman. **Document type:** academic/scholarly publication.
—BLDSC (5012.452000); Ei; UMI.
Description: For researchers in numeric analysis, the computer sciences, or the natural sciences; presents new methods in numerical linear algebra.

JOURNAL OF STATISTICAL COMPUTATION AND SIMULATION. see *COMPUTERS — Computer Simulation*

510   UK   ISSN 0747-7171
QA76.95
JOURNAL OF SYMBOLIC COMPUTATION. 1985. m. £350 (effective 1996). Academic Press Ltd. (Subsidiary of: Harcourt Brace & Company Ltd.), 24-28 Oval Rd., London NW1 7DX, England. TEL 44-171-267-4466. FAX 44-171-482-2293. TELEX 25775 ACPRES G. (Subscr. to: Harcourt Brace & Company Ltd., Foots Cray High St., Sidcup, Kent DA14 5HP, England. TEL 44-181-300-3322. FAX 44-181-309-0807) Ed. B. Buchberger. index. (reprint service avail. from SWZ) **Indexed:** Compumath, Comput.Abstr., INSPEC (1986-). **Document type:** academic/scholarly publication.
—BLDSC (5067.900000); Ei; Faxon; Genuine Article; SWETS; UnCover. **CCC.**
Description: Directed to mathematicians and computer scientists who have a particular interest in symbolic computation.

519   BL   ISSN 0101-8205
QA297   CODEN: MACOEK
MATEMATICA APLICADA E COMPUTACIONAL/COMPUTATIONAL AND APPLIED MATHEMATICS. (Text in English, Portuguese) 1982. 3/yr. $85 to individuals; institutions $125 (effective 1995). Sociedade Brasileira de Matematica Aplicada e Computacional, Rua Lauro Muller, 455 Botafogo CEP, 22290 Rio de Janeiro RJ, Brazil. TEL 55-21-541-2132. (Dist. by: Birkhauser Boston, 675 Massachusetts Ave., Cambridge, MA 02139-3309. TEL 617-876-2333. FAX 617-876-1272) Ed.Bd. circ. 700 (controlled). **Indexed:** Compumath, Curr.Cont., INSPEC (1984-), Math.R., Zent.Math. **Document type:** academic/scholarly publication.
—Genuine Article; UMI.
Description: Articles on all areas of applied mathematics using a computational approach. Includes special issues on high performance scientific computing.
Refereed Serial

510   US   ISSN 1047-5974
QA76.95
MATHEMATICA JOURNAL. 1990. q. $55. Miller Freeman, Inc. (Subsidiary of: United Newspapers), 600 Harrison St., San Francisco, CA 94107. TEL 415-905-2298. FAX 415-905-2233. Ed. Alan Zeichick. adv.: B&W page $1020, color page $1770; trim 8 x 10 7/8. circ. 6,500.
—BLDSC (5399.810000); Faxon; SWETS; UnCover. **CCC.**

MATHEMATICAL AND COMPUTER MODELLING; an international journal. see *MATHEMATICS*

510   RU   ISSN 1054-6634
MATHEMATICAL MODELING. (English translation of Russian title) 1991. m. $130 to individuals (outside N. America $160); institutions $330 (outside N. America $350). (Russian Academy of Sciences, Department of Information, Computer Technology and Automation, RU) Interperiodica, Ul. Profsoyuznaya 90, Moscow 117864, Russian. TEL 7-095-3360066. FAX 7-095-3360666. (Dist. in US by: Interperiodica Publishing, Box 1831, Birmingham, AL 35201-1831. TEL 205-995-1567. FAX 205-995-1588) Ed. A.A. Samarskii.

519   US   ISSN 1061-7590
QA401   CODEN: MMCEE6
MATHEMATICAL MODELING AND COMPUTATIONAL EXPERIMENT. Short title: M M C E. 1993. q. $340 (foreign $395) (effective 1996). John Wiley & Sons, Inc., Journals, 605 Third Ave., New York, NY 10158. TEL 212-850-6645. FAX 212-850-6021. TELEX 12-7063. E-mail: SUBINFO@JWILEY.COM. (Subscr. outside the Americas to: John Wiley & Sons Ltd., Baffins Ln., Chichester, W. Sussex PO19 1UD, England. TEL 44-1243-779777. FAX 44-1243-776128) (also avail. in microform from UMI; back issues avail.) **Document type:** academic/scholarly publication.
—BLDSC (5402.544700).
Refereed Serial

MATHEMATICAL MODELLING OF SYSTEMS; methods, tools and applications in engineering and related sciences. see *ENGINEERING — Computer Applications*

510   NE   ISSN 0025-5610
QA264   CODEN: MHPGA4
MATHEMATICAL PROGRAMMING. (In 2 series: A and B) 1971. m. fl.1400($854) (effective 1996). (Mathematical Programming Society) North-Holland (Subsidiary of: Elsevier Science B.V.), P.O. Box 211, 1000 AE Amsterdam, Netherlands. TEL 31-20-4853911. FAX 31-20-4853598. TELEX 18582 ESPA NL. (Subscr. in U.S. and Canada to: Elsevier Science Inc., Box 882, Madison Sq. Sta., New York, NY 10159. TEL 212-989-5800. FAX 212-633-3990) Eds. R. Bixby, W.R. Pulleyblank. cum.index: 1976-1981. (also avail. in microform from UMI; back issues avail.; reprint service avail. from SWZ) **Indexed:** Compumath, Comput.Rev., Curr.Cont., Cyb.Abstr., Ind.Sci.Rev., INSPEC, Int.Abstr.Oper.Res., J.Cont.Quant.Meth., Math.R., Oper.Res.Manage.Sci., Qual.Contr.Appl.Stat. **Document type:** academic/scholarly publication.
—BLDSC (5402.577000); Ei; Faxon; Genuine Article; SWETS; UnCover. **CCC.**
Description: Publishes original articles dealing with every aspect of mathematical programming.
Refereed Serial

570   UK   ISSN 0960-1295
QA76.9.M35   CODEN: MCSCEA
MATHEMATICAL STRUCTURES IN COMPUTER SCIENCE. 1991. bi-m. £144($248) (effective 1996). Cambridge University Press, The Edinburgh Bldg., Shaftesbury Rd., Cambridge CB2 2RU, England. TEL 01223-312393. FAX 01223-315052. TELEX 851817256. (N. American addr.: Cambridge University Press, Journals Dept., 40 W. 20th St., New York, NY 10011. TEL 212-924-3900. FAX 212-691-3239) Ed. G. Longo. adv. (back issues avail.) **Indexed:** INSPEC (1993-). **Document type:** academic/scholarly publication.
—BLDSC (5403.620000); SWETS; UMI. **CCC.**
Description: Covers theoretical computer science, focusing on the application of ideas from the structural side of mathematics and mathematical logic to computer science.

510   US   ISSN 0730-8639
QA13   CODEN: MCEDDA
MATHEMATICS AND COMPUTER EDUCATION. 1967. 3/yr. $27 to individuals (foreign $33); institutions $62 (foreign $75). M A T Y C Journal, Inc., Box 158, Old Bethpage, NY 11804. TEL 516-822-5475. Ed. George M. Miller. adv.; bk.rev.; illus. circ. 1,400. (also avail. in microfilm from UMI; reprint service avail. from UMI) **Indexed:** C.I.J.E., Comput.& Info. Sys., Comput.Lit.Ind., Comput.Rev., Cont.Pg.Educ., Educ.Tech.Abstr., INSPEC, Math R., Tech.Educ.Abstr. **Document type:** academic/scholarly publication.
—BLDSC (5405.175000); Faxon; UMI; UnCover. Formerly (until 1982): M A T Y C Journal (ISSN 0092-1424)
Description: For college and high school educators. Articles cover computers in education, mathematics, mathematical applications, remedial instruction and teaching ideas and methods.
Refereed Serial

MATHEMATICS AND COMPUTERS IN SIMULATION. see *COMPUTERS — Computer Simulation*

510.28   SP   ISSN 1134-5632
▼**MATHWARE AND SOFT COMPUTING.** (Text in English) 1994. s-a. plus one monograph. 5000 ptas. (foreign $50) (effective 1994). Universitat Politecnica de Catalunya, E T S d'Arquitecture de Barcelona, Seccio de Matematiques i Informacion, Diagonal 649, 08028 Barcelona, Spain. FAX 34-3-4016367. E-mail: mathware@ea.upc.es. Ed. Joan Jacas. circ. 500. **Document type:** academic/scholarly publication.
Description: Includes theoretical contributions that use mathematical tools and models that could be relevant in applications for cognitive sciences, pure or applied logic, and artificial intelligence.
Refereed Serial

510 620   CN   ISSN 0849-8180
MICRO CONTROL JOURNAL. 1989. 6/yr. Can.$17.50($17.50) Micro Control Journal, 27 Penrith Crescent, London, Ont. N6G 4M8, Canada. TEL 519-434-6904. FAX 519-668-1450. Ed. S. Gupta. adv.; bk.rev. circ. 5,000. (back issues avail.)
Description: Covers applications of computers to real time control systems, data acquisitions, sensors and motor controls.

MATHEMATICS — COMPUTER APPLICATIONS

510 FR
MODELLING, MEASUREMENT AND CONTROL. (In 4 series: Series A (ISSN 0761-2508); Series B (ISSN 0761-2516); Series C (ISSN 0761-2524); Series D (ISSN 0989-6074)) (Text mainly in English) irreg. 95 F.($19) per no. (International Association for the Advancement of Modelling and Simulation Techniques in Enterprises) A M S E Press, 16 av. de Grange Blanche, 69160 Tassin-la-Demi-Lune, France. TEL 78-34-36-04. FAX 78-34-54-17. TELEX 389 595. Ed. G. Mesnard. (back issues avail.) **Indexed:** INSPEC (1992-). **Document type:** academic/scholarly publication.
Description: Provides examples of signals, data and systems problems in all areas of activity.
Refereed Serial

510 NE ISSN 0929-9629
▼**MONTE CARLO METHODS AND APPLICATIONS.** (Text in English) 1995. q. DM.410 (effective 1996). V S P, P.O. Box 346, 3700 AH Zeist, Netherlands. TEL 31-30-6925790. FAX 31-30-6932081. E-mail: 100341.2732@compuserve.com. Ed. K.K. Sabelfeld. (back issues avail.) **Document type:** academic/scholarly publication.
—BLDSC (5928.190500).
Description: Publishes original papers on topics in the theory of Monte Carlo methods, including integration using ergodicity, simulation of random variables, stochastic processes and fields, and applications in such disciplines as aerosol science, chemical kinetics and combustion, and statistical simulation of turbulence.
Refereed Serial

MULTIDIMENSIONAL SYSTEMS AND SIGNAL PROCESSING; an international journal. see COMPUTERS — Computer Systems

NATURAL HAZARDS. see EARTH SCIENCES

510 US ISSN 0028-3045
CODEN: NTWKAA
NETWORKS; an international journal. 1970. 8/yr. $696 (foreign $820) (effective 1996). John Wiley & Sons Inc., Journals, 605 Third Ave., New York, NY 10158. TEL 212-850-6645. FAX 212-850-6021. TELEX 12-7063. E-mail: SUBINFO@JWILEY.COM. (Subscr. outside the Americas to: John Wiley & Sons Ltd., Baffins Ln., Chichester, W. Sussex PO19 1UD, England. TEL 44-1243-779777. FAX 44-1243-776128) Ed. F.T. Boesch. adv.; bk.rev.; charts; illus.; index. circ. 950. (also avail. in microform from UMI; back issues avail.; reprint service avail. from UMI) **Indexed:** Commun.Abstr., Compumath, Comput.Abstr., Comput.Cont., Curr.Cont., Cyb.Abstr., Eng.Ind., INSPEC, Int.Abstr.Oper.Res., J.Cont.Quant.Meth., Math.R., Tel.Abstr. **Document type:** academic/scholarly publication.
—BLDSC (6077.205000); Faxon; Genuine Article; SWETS; UMI; UnCover. **CCC.**
Description: Presents applications and theory for innovations in design and use of computer networks, telecommunications, transportation systems, power grids, distributions systems and other networks.
Refereed Serial

NEURAL, PARALLEL & SCIENTIFIC COMPUTATIONS. see COMPUTERS

510 GW ISSN 0029-599X
QA76.5 CODEN: NUMMA7
NUMERISCHE MATHEMATIK. Electronic edition (ISSN 0945-3245) (Text mainly in English; occasionally French and German) 1959. 12/yr. (in 3 vols., 4 nos./vol.). DM.4100($2979) (effective 1996). Springer-Verlag, Heidelberger Platz 3, 14197 Berlin, Germany. TEL 030-8207-0. FAX 030-8214091. E-mail: orders@springer.de; Site addr.: http://www.springer-ny.com. (Subscr. in N. America to: Springer-Verlag New York, Inc., 44 Hartz Way, Secaucus, NJ 07096-2491. TEL 201-348-4033. FAX 201-348-4505) Ed. P.G. Ciarlet. adv. (also avail. in microform from UMI; back issues avail.; reprint service avail. from ISI) **Indexed:** Appl.Mech.Rev., Compumath, Comput.Abstr., Curr.Cont., Ind.Sci.Rev., INSPEC, Math.R., Zent.Math. **Document type:** academic/scholarly publication.
●Also available online.
—BLDSC (6184.700000); Ei; Faxon; Genuine Article; SWETS; UMI; UnCover. **CCC.**
Description: Aids international dissemination of contributions on mathematical topics arising in contemporary numerical computation, including optimization of parallel computers.

510 US ISSN 1055-6788
QA402.5 CODEN: OMSOE2
OPTIMIZATION METHODS AND SOFTWARE. 1993. q. 121 ECU (effective 1996). Gordon & Breach Science Publishers, c/o International Publishers Distributor, 820 Town Center Dr., Langhorne, PA 19047. TEL 215-750-2642. FAX 215-750-6343. (Subscr. to: International Publishers Distributor, P.O. Box 90, Reading, Berkshire RG1 8JL, England. TEL 44-173-456-8316) (also avail. in microform) —**CCC.**
Description: Presents the latest developments in the theory and realization of optimization methods, with emphasis on the interface between software development and algorithm design.

PRAGUE CONFERENCE ON INFORMATION THEORY, STATISTICAL DECISION FUNCTIONS, RANDOM PROCESSES. TRANSACTIONS. see COMPUTERS — Information Science And Information Theory

PRINCIPLES OF COMPUTER SCIENCE SERIES. see ENGINEERING — Computer Applications

ROYAL STATISTICAL SOCIETY. JOURNAL. SERIES C: APPLIED STATISTICS. see STATISTICS

519 621.381 US ISSN 0097-5397
QA76 CODEN: SMJCAT
S I A M JOURNAL ON COMPUTING. 1972. bi-m. $248 to non-members (overseas $282); members $58 (overseas $63) (effective 1995). Society for Industrial and Applied Mathematics, Attn: M. Lafferty, 3600 University City Science Center, Philadelphia, PA 19104-2688. TEL 215-382-9800. FAX 215-386-7999. E-mail: PUB@SIAM.ORG. Ed. Zvi Galil. adv. circ. 1,841. (also avail. in microform from IAM; back issues avail.) **Indexed:** A.S.& T.Ind., Appl.Mech.Rev., ASCA, Compumath, Comput.Abstr., Comput.Rev., Cyb.Abstr., INSPEC (1972-), Math.R. **Document type:** academic/scholarly publication.
—BLDSC (8271.353000); Ei; Faxon; Genuine Article; SWETS; UnCover.
Description: Aimed at mathematicians, scientific and computer professionals and members of the society. Publishes research articles in the application of mathematics to the problems of computer science and the nonnumerical aspects of computing.
Refereed Serial

S I A M JOURNAL ON DISCRETE MATHEMATICS. (Society for Industrial and Applied Mathematics) see MATHEMATICS

510 US ISSN 0163-5778
QA297 CODEN: SNEWD6
S I G N U M NEWSLETTER. 1965. q. $23. Association for Computing Machinery, Special Interest Group on Numerical Mathematics, 1515 Broadway, 17th Fl., New York, NY 10036. TEL 212-869-7440. Ed. P.W. Gafney. charts; stat.; circ. 1,800 (controlled). (back issues avail.) **Indexed:** INSPEC. **Document type:** newsletter.
—Faxon; SWETS; UnCover.

510 US ISSN 0163-5824
QA155.7.E4 CODEN: SIGSBZ
S I G S A M BULLETIN. q. $25 (students $6). Association for Computing Machinery, Special Interest Group on Symbolic and Algebraic Manipulation, 1515 Broadway, 17th Fl., New York, NY 10036. TEL 212-869-7440. Ed. Robert Grossman. **Indexed:** INSPEC.
—Faxon; SWETS; UnCover.

SHUZHI JISUAN YU JISUANJI YINGYONG/JOURNAL ON NUMERICAL METHODS AND COMPUTER APPLICATIONS. see SCIENCES: COMPREHENSIVE WORKS — Computer Applications

510 NE ISSN 0169-1015
BF469 CODEN: SPVIEU
SPATIAL VISION. (Text in English) 1985. q. DM.290 (effective 1996). V S P, P.O. Box 346, 3700 AH Zeist, Netherlands. TEL 31-30-6925790. FAX 31-30-6932081. E-mail: 100341.2372@compuserve.com. Eds. D.H. Foster, A. Reeves. adv. (back issues avail.) **Indexed:** Abstr.Hum.Comp.Inter., INSPEC (1988-), Psychol.Abstr. (1987-). **Document type:** academic/scholarly publication.
—BLDSC (8361.785700); Ei; Faxon; SWETS; UnCover.
Description: International psychophysical, perceptual and cognitive research on the visual processing of spatial information.
Refereed Serial

STATISTICS; a journal of theoretical and applied statistics. see STATISTICS

STOCHASTIC OPTIMIZATION AND DESIGN. see MATHEMATICS

519 NE ISSN 0928-3986
STUDIES IN PROBABILITY, OPTIMIZATION AND STATISTICS. (Text in English) 1992. irreg., vol.2, 1992. price varies. I O S Press, Van Diemenstraat 94, 1013 CN Amsterdam, Netherlands. TEL 31-20-6382189. FAX 31-20-6203419. E-mail: marie-louise.kok@ios.nl. (In N. America: Box 10558, Burke, VA 22090-0558. TEL 703-323-5554. FAX 703-250-4705) (back issues avail.) **Document type:** monographic series.

510.25 AU
TEXTS AND MONOGRAPHS IN SYMBOLIC COMPUTATION. 1993. irreg. S.415. Springer-Verlag, Sachsenplatz 4-6, Postfach 89, A-1201 Vienna, Austria. TEL 0222-3302415. FAX 0222-3302426. (Subscr. in N. America to: Springer-Verlag New York, Inc., 44 Hartz Way, Secaucus, NJ 07096-2491. TEL 201-348-4033. FAX 201-348-4505) Eds. B. Buchberger, G. Collins. **Document type:** monographic series.

TEXTS ON COMPUTATIONAL MECHANICS. see ENGINEERING — Mechanical Engineering

519.3 519.7 003 NE ISSN 0924-6126
THEORY AND DECISION LIBRARY. SERIES C: GAME THEORY, MATHEMATICAL PROGRAMMING AND OPERATIONS RESEARCH. (Text in English) 1973; N.S. 1988. irreg., vol.10, 1993. price varies. Kluwer Academic Publishers, Postbus 17, 3300 AA Dordrecht, Netherlands. TEL 31-78-392392. FAX 31-78-392254. TELEX 29245 KAPG NL. (Dist. by: Kluwer Academic Publishers Group, P.O. Box 322, 3300 AH Dordrecht, Netherlands. TEL 31-78-392392. FAX 31-78-546474; N. America dist. addr.: Box 358, Accord Sta., Hingham, MA 02018-0358. TEL 617-871-6600. FAX 617-871-6528) Ed. S.H. Tijs. (back issues avail.) **Indexed:** Int.Polit.Sci.Abstr. **Document type:** monographic series.
—BLDSC (8814.628060).
Supersedes in part (in 1988): Theory and Decision Library (ISSN 0921-3376)
Refereed Serial

510 US ISSN 0275-5815
TOPICS IN COMPUTER MATHEMATICS. 1983. irreg., latest vol.5. Gordon & Breach Science Publishers, c/o International Publishers Distributor, 820 Town Center Dr., Langhorne, PA 19047. TEL 215-750-2642. FAX 215-750-6343. (Subscr. to: International Publishers Distributor, P.O. Box 90, Reading Berkshire RG1 8 JL, England. TEL 44-173-456-8316) Ed. D.J. Evans. (also avail. in microform) **Document type:** monographic series.
Refereed Serial

TOPICS IN DISCRETE MATHEMATICS. see MATHEMATICS

510 001.6 CN ISSN 0315-3681
CODEN: UTMADA
UTILITAS MATHEMATICA; international journal of discrete and combinatorial mathematics and statistical design. 1972. s-a. $80. Utilitas Mathematica Publishing Inc., Box, 7, University Centre, University of Manitoba, Winnipeg, MB R3T 2N2, Canada. Ed. Ralph G. Stanton. circ. 350. (back issues avail.) **Indexed:** Appl.Mech.Rev., Compumath, Comput.Rev., Math.R., Stat.Theor.Meth.Abstr., Zent.Math. **Document type:** academic/scholarly publication.
—BLDSC (9135.377000); Faxon; Genuine Article; UnCover. **CCC.**

ZASTOSOWANIA MATEMATYKI/APPLICATIONES MATHEMATICAE. see MATHEMATICS

ZENTRALBLATT FUER DIDAKTIK DER MATHEMATIK. see MATHEMATICS

MATRIMONY

Includes: divorce.

see also Home Economics

305.412 338 US ISSN 1053-9107
A B C DIALOGUE. 1981. bi-m. $24 membership. Association of Bridal Consultants, 200 Chestnutland Rd., New Milford, CT 06776-2521. TEL 203-355-0464. FAX 203-354-1404. Ed. Gerard J. Monaghan. adv.; bk.rev.; circ. 1,700 (controlled). **Document type**: newsletter.
    Description: Information related to weddings and wedding business, especially consultants.

306.8 US ISSN 0272-7897
HQ536
ANNUAL EDITIONS: MARRIAGE AND FAMILY. 1974. a. $12.95. Dushkin Publishing Group, Sluice Dock, Guilford, CT 06437-9989. TEL 203-453-4351. FAX 203-453-6000. Ed. Kathleen Gilbert; Pub. Ian Nielsen. illus. **Document type**: academic/scholarly publication.
    Formerly: Annual Editions: Readings in Marriage and Family (ISSN 0095-6155)
    Refereed Serial

306.8 052 UK ISSN 1351-900X
▼**BLISS**. 1994. q. £16 (U.S. £51); newsstand price: £2.95. Leith Publishing Co. Ltd., Admiral House, 30 Maritime St., Edinburgh EH6 6SE, Scotland. TEL 0131-555-6511. FAX 0131-555-6587. Eds. Cheryll Barnet, Liz Coggins; Pub. Samantha Blake. adv.: color page £1695; trim 297 x 233; adv. contact: Julia Christ. bk.rev.; circ. 60,000 (paid). (back issues avail.) **Document type**: consumer publication.

051 US
BLUSHING BRIDE. 1989. q. $3 per no. Baker - Brown Enterprise, Inc., 11402 Merrick Blvd., Jamaica, NY 11434-1335. TEL 718-739-1296. circ. 10,000.
    Description: Bridal magazine for blacks. Covers wedding planning.

306.8 GW ISSN 0947-5982
BRAEUTE HEUTE. 2/yr. DM.6.80 per issue. Ivy Stoll Verlag, Ridlerstr. 36, 80339 Munich, Germany. TEL 089-509545. FAX 089-503189. Ed. Ivy Stoll. circ. 70,000. (back issues avail.) **Document type**: consumer publication.

BRIDAL APPAREL NEWS. see CLOTHING TRADE — Fashions

306.8 658 UK
BRIDAL BUYER. 9/yr. £20 (foreign £25); newsstand price: £2.50. Ras Publishing Ltd., The Old Town Hall, Lewisham Rd., Slaitwaite, Huddersfield, Yorks. HD7 5AL, England. TEL 01484-846069. FAX 01484-846232. Ed. Anita Saunders; Pub. Colette Mahon. adv. contact: Anne Jones. (tabloid format; back issues avail.) **Document type**: trade publication.
    Description: Contains trade news, trend reports, and feature articles of interest to bridal buyers, retailers, manufacturers, agents, and designers.

745.5 US
BRIDAL CRAFTS. 1991. a. $3.95. Clapper Communications Companies, 2400 E. Devon Ave., Ste. 375, Des Plaines, IL 60018-4618. TEL 708-635-5800. FAX 708-635-6311. Ed. Julie Stephani. adv. circ. 40,000. **Document type**: consumer publication.
    Description: Aimed at women who wish to customize their wedding through hand-made items.

301.42 US ISSN 0882-7451
BRIDAL GUIDE; the how to for "I do". 1982. bi-m. $18.95. Globe Communications Corp. (New York), 441 Lexington Ave., New York, NY 10017. TEL 212-949-4040; 800-472-7744. FAX 212-286-0072. Ed. Stephanie Wood. adv. circ. 250,000.

301.412 US
BRIDAL TRENDS. m. Meridian Publishing, Inc., Box 10010, Ogden, UT 84409. TEL 801-394-9446. Ed. Marjorie Rice.
    Formerly: Bridal Fair.

305 US
BRIDE AND GROOM. 1981. s-a. Chevalier Associates, Inc., 2 Westborough Business Park, Westborough, MA 01581-3911. TEL 508-366-1476; 800-276-7068. FAX 508-366-1480. Ed. Germaire A. Chevalier; Pub. Richard E. Chevarier. adv.: B&W page $960, color page $1500; trim 8 3/8 x 11. circ. 20,000.
    Description: For the central New England bride, groom and wedding party.

306.8 AT ISSN 1033-7075
BRIDE TO BE. 1967. q. Aus.$7.50. Reed Business Publishing Pty. Ltd. (Subsidiary of: Reed International PLC), Level 12, 105 Railway St., Chatswood, N.S.W. 2067, Australia. TEL 61-2-372-5222. FAX 61-2-412-3572. (Dist. by: Gordon & Gotch, 68-72 Kingsgrove St., Belmore, N.S.W. 2192, Australia. TEL 61-2-789-6444) Ed. Gina Leros. circ. 40,000. **Document type**: consumer publication.
    Description: Covers fashion, beauty, homewares, flowers, jewellery, honeymoon.

640 UK ISSN 0006-9787
BRIDES & SETTING UP HOME. 1955. bi-m. £19.50 (foreign £24.00). Conde Nast Publications Ltd., Vogue House, Hanover Sq., London W1R 0AD, England. TEL 0171-499-9080. FAX 0171-492-1345. (Subscr. to: Quadrant Subscription Services, Oakfield House, Perrymount Rd., Haywards Heath, W. Sussex RH16 3DH, England) Ed. Sandra Boler; Pub. Helen Fifield. adv.; bk.rev.; illus. circ. 63,161. **Document type**: consumer publication.

051 US ISSN 1059-7476
BRIDE'S & YOUR NEW HOME. 1934. bi-m. $18. Conde Nast Publications Inc., Bride's & Your New Home Magazine, 2 Grand Central Tower, 140 E. 45th St., 39th Fl., NY 10017. TEL 212-880-8800. FAX 212-880-8331. E-mail: Letters@brides.com. (Subscr. to: Box 2886, Boulder, CO 80322) Ed. Millie Martini Bratten; Pub. Roger Antin. adv. contact: Kit Logan. bk.rev.; bibl.; charts; illus.; stat. circ. 327,595. (also avail. in microform from UMI; reprint service avail. from UMI) **Indexed**: PMR. **Document type**: consumer publication.
    —UMI; UnCover.
    Former titles (until Nov. 1991): Bride's (ISSN 0161-1992); Bride's Magazine (ISSN 0006-9795)
    Description: Features articles on all aspects of planning a wedding, honeymoon travel, and advice for new homeowners.

306.8 UK ISSN 0957-3933
BRIDES OF BERKSHIRE. (Part of the Brides of Britain Series) 1988. s-a. Brides of Britain Magazines Ltd., Highfield House, 2 Highfield Ave., Newbury, Berks. RG14 5DS, England. TEL 0635-38888. FAX 0635-528638. **Document type**: consumer publication.

306.8 UK ISSN 0957-7432
BRIDES OF BRISTOL, BATH & AVON. (Part of the Brides of Britain Series) 1988? s-a. Brides of Britain Magazines Ltd., Highfield House, Highfield Ave., Newbury, Berks. RG14 5DS, England. TEL 0635-38888. FAX 0635-528638. **Document type**: consumer publication.

306.8 UK
BRIDES OF BRITAIN SERIES. 1988. s-a. £1.50. Brides of Britain Magazines Ltd., Highfield House, 2 Highfield Ave., Newbury, Berks. RG14 5DS, England. TEL 0635-38888. FAX 0635-528638. Ed. Alison Moore. circ. 8,000.
    Description: Regional bridal magazine for many areas of Britain.

306.8 UK ISSN 0957-3941
BRIDES OF DEVON & CORNWALL. (Part of the Brides of Britain Series) 1989. s-a. Brides of Britain Magazines Ltd., Highfield House, 2 Highfield Ave., Newbury, Berks. RG14 5DS, England. TEL 0635-38888. FAX 0635-528638. **Document type**: consumer publication.

306.8 UK ISSN 0957-7270
BRIDES OF EAST ANGLIA. (Part of the Brides of Britain Series) 1989. s-a. Brides of Britain Magazines Ltd., Highfield House, 2 Highfield Ave., Newbury, Berks. RG14 5DS, England. TEL 0635-38888. FAX 0635-528638. **Document type**: consumer publication.

306.8 UK ISSN 0957-395X
BRIDES OF HERTS, BUCKS & BEDS. (Part of the Brides of Britain Series) 1989. s-a. Brides of Britain Magazines Ltd., Highfield House, 2 Highfield Ave., Newbury, Berks. RG14 5DS, England. TEL 0635-38888. FAX 0635-528638. **Document type**: consumer publication.

306.8 UK ISSN 0957-7440
BRIDES OF NORTH EAST ENGLAND. (Part of the Brides of Britain Series) 1989? s-a. Brides of Britain Magazines Ltd., Highfield House, 2 Highfield Ave., Newbury, Berks. RG14 5DS, England. TEL 0635-38888. FAX 0635-528638. **Document type**: consumer publication.

306.8 UK ISSN 0957-7289
BRIDES OF SCOTLAND. (Part of the Brides of Britain Series) 1989? s-a. Brides of Britain Magazines Ltd., Highfield House, 2 Highfield Ave., Newbury, Berks. RG14 5DS, England. TEL 0635-38888. FAX 0635-528638. **Document type**: consumer publication.

306.8 UK ISSN 0957-3968
BRIDES OF SOMERSET. (Part of the Brides of Britain Series) 1989. s-a. Brides of Britain Magazines Ltd., Highfield House, 2 Highfield Ave., Newbury, Berks. RG14 5DS, England. TEL 0635-38888. FAX 0635-528638. **Document type**: consumer publication.

051 US ISSN 1061-2491
BRIDES TODAY. 1991. q. $3.95 per no. H & S Publications, 3400 Dundee Rd., Northbrook, IL 60062. TEL 708-498-0618. Ed. Andrew Sawyer. adv.: B&W page $3000, color page $4600. circ. 100,000.
    Description: For African-American brides and grooms; planning guide for brides, grooms and their families.

392.5 US
C O F O MEMO. 3/yr. $12. Consortium of Family Organizations, c/o FSA Office on Governmental Affairs, 1319 F St., N.W., Ste. 606, Washington, DC 20004. TEL 202-347-1124.
    Description: Addresses current legislation and programs that affect families.

391 US
CHICAGOLAND WEDDING GUIDE. 1983. s-a. P B Communications, Inc., 874 Green Bay Rd., Winnetka, IL 60093. TEL 708-441-7892. Ed. Asher J. Birnbaum. adv. circ. 60,000. **Document type**: consumer publication.
    Description: Guide to weddings and special events.

301.412 US
▼**CINCINNATI WEDDING**. 1994. 2/yr. $12.95. Marblehead Publications Inc., Box 868, Cincinnati, OH 45201-0868. TEL 513-421-9922. Ed. Doug Wolske. adv. contact: Leigh Ann Hieronymus. circ. 12,000. **Document type**: consumer publication.

306.8 AT
COLLECTIONS INCLUDING VEILS AND HEADPIECES. 1988. a. Reed Business Publishing Pty. Ltd. (Subsidiary of: Reed International PLC), Level 12, 1-5 Railway St., Chatswood, N.S.W. 2067, Australia. TEL 61-2-372-5222. FAX 61-2-412-3572. (Dist. by: Gordon & Gotch, 68-72 Kingsgrove St., Belmore, N.S.W. 2192, Australia. TEL 61-2-789-6444) Ed. Gina Leros. circ. 20,000. **Document type**: consumer publication.
    Formerly: Bride to Be's Bridal Collection (ISSN 1035-249X)
    Description: Presents bridal fashion, shoes, veils and headpieces.

301.412 US
COLUMBUS BRIDE. 1985. 2/yr. $12.95. Marblehead Publications Inc., 580 S. High St., Ste. 160, Columbus, OH 43215. TEL 614-228-1607. Ed. Doug Wolske. adv. contact: Leigh Ann Hieronymus. circ. 15,000. **Document type**: consumer publication.
    Formerly: Columbus Bride and Groom (ISSN 1073-8282)

DIVORCE LITIGATION. see LAW — Family And Matrimonial Law

MATRIMONY

659.152   IT
DOMINA SPOSA. 1988. s-a. L.10000 per no. Domina s.r.l., Via Cavour 2, 22012 Cernobbio (CO), Italy. TEL 39-31-513434. FAX 39-31-340753. Ed. Stefania Bosco Di Camastra. adv.: B&W page L.5050000, color page L.6550000; adv. contact: Damiana Domieli. circ. 74,000. **Document type:** consumer publication.

306.8   IT
DUE - SPOSA. 1989. s-a. newsstand price: L.9000. Northia s.r.l., Piazzale Ponte Ticino 7, 27100 Pavia, Italy. TEL 39-382-303997. FAX 39-382-530188. Ed. Laura Meriggi. adv.: color page L.3000000; trim 210 x 290; adv. contact: Giorgio Nisi. circ. 78,178.
   Formerly (until 1994): Due - Matrimonio e Idee.

305   US
ELEGANT BRIDE. 1988. bi-m. $30. Pace Communications Inc., 1301 Carolina St., Greensboro, NC 27401. TEL 910-378-6065. FAX 910-275-2864. Ed. Jaclyn Barrett Hirschhaut; Pub. Bonnie McElveen-Hunter. adv. contact: Edward Calfo. circ. 119,358. **Document type:** consumer publication.
   Formerly: Southern Bride.
   Description: National bridal magazine featuring photography of bridal gowns, wedding traditions, home furnishings and honeymoon travel.

392.5   US
F S A WASHINGTON MEMO. (Former name of issuing body: Consortium of Family Organizations) m. free. Family Service America, Inc., Office of Public Policy, 1319 F St., N.W., Ste. 204, Washington, DC 20004-1180. TEL 202-347-1124. (And: Family Service America, Inc., 11700 W. Lake Park Dr., Milwaukee, WI 53224) Ed. Ronald H. Field. **Document type:** newsletter.
   Formerly: C O F O Washington Memo.

THE FAMILY JOURNAL; counseling and therapy for couples and families. see PSYCHOLOGY

FAMILY THERAPY NEWS. see PSYCHOLOGY

659.152 640   US   ISSN 1064-8089
FOR THE BRIDE BY DEMETRIOS. (Editions in English, German, Italian, Spanish) 1991. q. $4.95 per no. D J E Publications, c/o Patricia Daly, Adv. Dir., 222 W. 37th St., 5th Fl., New York, NY 10018. TEL 212-967-0750; 212-947-7024. Ed. Eileen Drenick. adv.: B&W page $8000, color page $10000. circ. 152,000. (back issues avail.) **Document type:** consumer publication.
   Description: Emphasizes fashion, tabletop, home furnishings, health and beauty, nutrition, travel and money matters.

FULL-TIME DADS; the magazine for caring fathers. see MEN'S INTERESTS

301.412   US
GREATER CINCINNATI - NORTHERN KENTUCKY BRIDE & GROOM MAGAZINE. s.a. C O N A Publishing Corp., 7320 S. Timberlanne Dr., Cincinnati, OH 45243-1844. TEL 513-651-2662. Ed. Ted Deutsch III. adv. circ. 20,000.

HEADPIECE. see CLOTHING TRADE

HISTORY OF THE FAMILY; an international quarterly. see SOCIAL SCIENCES: COMPREHENSIVE WORKS

053.1   GW   ISSN 0720-7301
HOCHZEIT; die Zeitschrift fuer Brautpaare. 1966. 6/yr. DM.78 (foreign DM.108). Terra Verlag GmbH, Postfach 102144, 78421 Konstanz, Germany. TEL 07531-8122-0. FAX 07531-812299. Ed. Christel Poensgen. adv.; bk.rev. circ. 72,000. **Document type:** consumer publication.
   Description: Information on wedding clothes, fashion accessories, ceramics, glass and pottery, wedding gifts, furnishings.

306.8   US
HOMESTEAD HOTLINE. 1979. q. $25. 720 Morrow Ave., Clayton, NJ 08312. TEL 609-881-0319. Manny /Castlewitz, Ed. & Pub. adv. circ. 6,000. **Document type:** consumer publication.

640   US   ISSN 1003-2991
HUNYIN YU JIATING/MARRIAGE & FAMILY. (Text in Chinese) 1985. m. $41.30. China Books & Periodicals, Inc., 2929 24th St., San Francisco, CA 94110. TEL 415-282-2994. FAX 415-282-0994.

I T MAGAZINE. (Irish Tatler) see GENERAL INTEREST PERIODICALS — Ireland

659.152   IT
IDEE SPOSABELLA. s.a. Casa Editrice Moda Italiana S.p.A., Viale Umbria 52, 20135 Milan, Italy. TEL 39-2-5517303. FAX 39-2-5458285. Ed. Rita Rabassi. adv.: B&W page L.4700000, color page L.8000000; adv. contact: Daniela Trevisan. circ. 130,000. **Document type:** consumer publication.

301.428   US   ISSN 1050-2556
K10   CODEN: JDREEJ
JOURNAL OF DIVORCE & REMARRIAGE; clinical studies and research in family therapy, family mediation, family studies and family law. 1977. q. (in 2 vols.). $500 (foreign $700) (effective Mar. 1995). Haworth Press, Inc., 10 Alice St., Binghamton, NY 13904. TEL 607-722-5857; 800-342-9678. FAX 607-722-1424. Ed. Craig A. Everett. adv.; bk.rev. circ. 511. (also avail. in microfiche from UMI; reprint service avail. from HAW,WSH) **Indexed:** Adol.Ment.Hlth.Abstr., Bull.Signal., C.I.J.E., Chicago Psychoanal.Lit.Ind., Curr.Cont., Human Resour.Abstr., IMFL, Mult.Ed.Abstr., Past.Care & Couns.Abstr., Psychol.Abstr. (1977-), Sage Fam.Stud.Abstr., Soc.Sci.Ind. (1994-), Soc.Work Res.& Abstr., SSCI, Stud.Wom.Abstr.
   —BLDSC (4969.910000); Faxon; Genuine Article; Haworth; SWETS; UnCover.
   Formerly (until 1990): Journal of Divorce (ISSN 0147-4022)
   Description: Presents current interdisciplinary findings on all aspects of divorce, from clinical practice, to theory, to research.
   Refereed Serial

301.4157 155.3   AT   ISSN 1322-9400
HQ1
JOURNAL OF FAMILY STUDIES. 1980. 3/yr. Aus.$30 to individuals; institutions and libraries Aus.$35; foreign Aus.$35. La Trobe University Press, Bundoora, ic. 3085, Australia. TEL 61-3-94791460. FAX 61-3-94702011. Ed. Cynthia Schultz. adv.; bk.rev.; index. circ. 900. (back issues avail.) **Indexed:** Psychol.Abstr. (1983-), Sage Fam.Stud.Abstr.
   —BLDSC (1810.220000); UnCover.
   Former titles (until 1995): Australian Journal of Marriage and Family (ISSN 1034-652X); (until vol.10, 1989): Australian Journal of Sex, Marriage and Family (ISSN 0159-1487)
   Description: For accademics, researchers, administrators, educators and clinicians in the helping professions.
   Refereed Serial

JOURNAL OF MARITAL AND FAMILY THERAPY. see PSYCHOLOGY

JOURNAL OF MARRIAGE AND THE FAMILY. see SOCIOLOGY

306.8   UK
KEY NOTE MARKET REVIEW: U K WEDDING MARKET. Variant title: U K Wedding Market. irregg £375. Key Note Publications Ltd., Field House, 72 Oldfield Rd., Hampton, Middlesex TW12 2HQ, England. TEL 0181-783-0755. FAX 0181-783-1720. **Document type:** trade publication.
   ●Also available online.
   Also available on CD-ROM.

640   CN
LIFESTYLES (YEAR). 1973. bi-m. Can.$18. A.T.E. Publishing Co. Ltd., Box 1000, 155 E. Beaver Creek Rd., Unit 25, Downsview, ON L4B 2N1, Canada. TEL 905-881-3070. Ed. Gabriel Erem. adv.; illus.
   Formerly: Bride and Groom Magazine.

306.8 340   US
LIVE & LOVE. 1975. m. $22. Luna Ventures, Box 398, Suisun, CA 94585. Ed. Daun. **Document type:** newsletter.
   Former titles: Poly (ISSN 1042-7791); Intentional Families.
   Description: Covers line marriage, polygamy and other alternate lifestyles, with articles on law and living arrangements.

LOVING MORE. see SOCIOLOGY

306.8   CN   ISSN 0840-805X
MARIAGE QUEBEC. 1989. 2/yr. Can.$3.95 per no. 740 Notre Dame W., Ste. 780, Montreal, PQ H3C 3X6, Canada. TEL 514-392-9030. FAX 514-392-0328. Ed. Janine Saine; Pub. Suzanne Hurst. adv. contact: Suzanne Hurst. bk.rev. circ. 25,000. **Document type:** consumer publication.
   Description: A fashion, beauty, lifestyle and travel guide for the bride-to-be, the engaged couple, their bridal party and entourage.

640   FR   ISSN 0025-2980
MARIAGES. 1960. q. $25. Editions Rusconi, 8 rue Halevy, 75009 Paris, France. Eds. Piere Louchel, Andre Thiebaut. adv.; illus. circ. 40,000.

MARRIAGE & FAMILY REVIEW. see SOCIOLOGY

306.8   US   ISSN 1063-1054
MARRIAGE MAGAZINE. 1972. 9/yr. $19.95 (foreign $24.95). International Marriage Encounter, Inc., 955 Lake Dr., St. Paul, MN 55120. TEL 612-454-6434. FAX 612-452-0466. Ed. Kyrsta Eryn Kavenaugh. adv.: B&W page $480. bk.rev.; film rev.; music rev.; circ. 11,000 (paid). (back issues avail.) **Document type:** consumer publication.
   Formerly: Marriage Encounter (ISSN 0734-0052)
   Description: Celebrates the potential of marriage by focusing on topics such as communication, intimacy, leisure and play, romance, sexuality, conflict, self-esteem and spirituality in effort to create healthy, intimate, committed marriages.

301.412   US   ISSN 0897-5469
MARRIAGE PARTNERSHIP. q. $19.95. Christianity Today, Inc., 465 Gundersen Dr., Carol Stream, IL 60188. TEL 708-260-6200. FAX 708-260-0114. E-mail: mpedit@aol.com. (Subscr. to: CDS, Box 11618, Des Moines, IA 50340. TEL 800-627-4942) Ed. Ron Lee. circ. 65,000. **Document type:** consumer publication.
   —UMI.
   Formerly: Partnership (ISSN 0747-9190)
   Description: Offers practical help in building a healthy marriage.

306.8 646   AT   ISSN 0729-5081
MODE BRIDES. 1955. q. Aus.$30. A C P Publishing Pty. Ltd., 54-58 Park St., Sydney, N.S.W. 2000, Australia. TEL 02-282-8717. FAX 02-267-4912. Ed. Catherine Sanders; Pub. Richard Walsh. adv. contact: Patricia Connolly. illus. circ. 29,434. **Document type:** consumer publication.
   Formerly: Australian Bride Magazine (ISSN 0004-8771)

306.8   US   ISSN 0026-7546
HQ1
MODERN BRIDE; a complete guide for the bride to be. 1949. 6/yr. $17.97 (Canada $25.97; elsewhere $42.97). Cahners Publishing Company (New York), Consumer Division, Division of Reed Elsevier Inc., 249 W. 17th St., New York, NY 10011. TEL 212-337-7000. FAX 212-337-7129. (Dist. by: Neodata Services, Box 2606, Boulder, CO 80322-2606. TEL 303-447-9330) Ed. Cele Lalli. adv.: B&W page $25600, color page $33080; adv. contact: Leland Hoch. illus.; tr.lit. circ. 322,000. (also avail. in microform from UMI) **Indexed:** Mag.Ind., PMR. **Document type:** consumer publication.
   ●Also available online. Vendor(s): Knight-Ridder, Inc..
   —UMI; UnCover. **CCC.**
   Description: Complete bridal guide to wedding planning; the honeymoon; the first apartment. Covers fashion, home furnishings.

MOTHER-TO-MOTHER. see CHILDREN AND YOUTH — About

NATIONAL COUNCIL ON FAMILY RELATIONS. REPORT. see SOCIOLOGY

306.8   US   ISSN 0744-6861
NEW ENGLAND BRIDE. 1972. m. $24. New England Publishing Group, 215 Newbury St., Peabody, MA 01960. TEL 508-535-4186. Ed. Lisa Amore. adv.; bk.rev. circ. 15,300. **Document type:** consumer publication.
   —CCC.
   Description: Complete guide to help newly engaged men and women plan their weddings. Includes honeymoon travel, table top purchases, invitations and bridal fashions.

MATRIMONY 4163

301.412   US
NEW JERSEY BRIDE. 1988. s-a. $3.95 per no. Tomlinson Enterprises, 55 Park Place, Box 920, Morristown, NJ 07960-0920. TEL 201-539-8230. FAX 201-538-2953. Ed. Barbara Landy. adv. contact: Dorothy McCarthy. circ. 40,000.
Description: Provides information about getting married in New Jersey.

306.8   US
NOVIA LINDA. (Text in English, Spanish) 1992. bi-m. $2.50 per no. Victor Diaz Publishing, 3523 S. Halstead, Chicago, IL 60609. TEL 312-523-8636. Ed. Art Diaz. adv.: B&W page $1200, color page $3900; trim 8 1/2 x 10 3/4. circ. 10,000. **Document type:** consumer publication.

301.412   US   ISSN 1073-3035
REVISTA PARA NOVIAS. (Text in English, Spanish) 1992. q. $14.95. White Lace, Inc., Box 630518, North Miami, FL 33163. TEL 305-944-9444. FAX 305-949-0544. adv.: B&W page $4115, color page $6096; trim 8 1/8 x 10 7/8. circ. 100,000. **Document type:** consumer publication.
Description: Bilingual wedding guide for Hispanic couples with information about planning, budgeting, fashion, beauty, etiquette, ceremonies, receptions, honeymoons, and the new home.

392.5   US
▼**SAVOIR AFFAIRES**; the ultimate wedding magazine. 1994. s-a. $2.95 per issue. Hansen Lithography, 557 Fischer Blvd., Toms River, NJ 08753. TEL 908-270-1188. Ed. Kim Chandlee McCabe; Pub. Robert W. Hansen. **Document type:** consumer publication.
Description: For brides-to-be in Monmouth and Ocean Counties, New Jersey.

SINGLE AGAIN. see *SINGLES' INTERESTS AND LIFESTYLES*

SOUTH AFRICA. CENTRAL STATISTICAL SERVICE. REPORT ON MARRIAGES AND DIVORCES - WHITES, COLOUREDS AND ASIANS - SOUTH AFRICA. see *POPULATION STUDIES — Abstracting, Bibliographies, Statistics*

640   SA   ISSN 1011-1611
SOUTH AFRICAN BRIDE TO BE: FIRST HOME. (Text in English) s-a. R.3 per no. Cotswold Publications, 208 Gale St., P.O. Box 1925, Durban 4000, South Africa. TEL 031-3055974. FAX 031-3015926. Ed. Sue Miles. adv.

306.8   US
SOUTH FLORIDA BRIDE. 1993. 2/yr. Florida Media Affiliates, Inc. (Subsidiary of: Micromedia Affiliates), Box 019068, Miami, FL 33101-9068. TEL 305-445-4500. FAX 305-445-4600. **Document type:** consumer publication.

640   IT   ISSN 0038-8319
SPOSA. 1962. s-a. L.28000($28) Edizioni Moderne Internazionali, Via Burlamacchi, 11, 20135 Milan, Italy. TEL 39-2-55189297. FAX 39-2-5465954. Ed. A. Maria Pietraccini. adv.: B&W page L.3000000. circ. 110,000.

395   CN
SPOSA MAGAZINE; the bilingual wedding planner. 1989. s-a. Can.$15. Word - Picture Advertising, Inc., 77 Mowat Ave., Ste. 410, Toronto, ON M6K 3E3, Canada. TEL 416-534-1851. FAX 416-534-0262. Ed. Ross Skoggard; Pub. Gulshan Sippy. adv.: color page Can.$4750; adv. contact: Gulshan Sippy. circ. 32,000.
Former titles (until 1994): Wedding Planner Sposa (ISSN 1191-8683); (until 1992): Sposa 2000 (ISSN 1193-1582)
Description: Contains a 10 chapter wedding planner plus changing editorial features on fashion, beauty, relationships, travel and home decor.

659.152   IT   ISSN 0394-3682
SPOSABELLA. 1973. s-a. L.24000 (Europe L.65000; elsewhere L.85000). Casa Editrice Moda Italiana S.p.A., Viale Umbria 52, 20135 Milan, Italy. TEL 39-2-5517303. FAX 39-2-5458285. TELEX 332082 MODAIT I. Ed. Rita Rabassi. adv.: B&W page L.5300000, color page L.9000000; adv. contact: Cristina Grubas. circ. 130,000.

646.3   AT   ISSN 1031-9115
STUDIO FOR BRIDES. s-a. Aus.$84. Studio Magazines Pty. Ltd., Level 3, 101-111 William St., Sydney, N.S.W. 2011, Australia. TEL 02-360-1422. FAX 02-360-9723. **Document type:** consumer publication.

640   CN   ISSN 0226-1758
TODAY'S BRIDE. 1979. s-a. Family Communications, Inc., 37 Hanna Ave., Toronto, ON M6K 3E3, Canada. circ. 100,000. **Document type:** consumer publication.

301.412   US
TODAY'S MARRIAGE.* q. $1.95 per no. Dell Magazines, 1540 Broadway, New York, NY 10036. TEL 212-354-6500. FAX 212-782-8338.

TOUCHPOINT; network for the nonmonogamous. see *SINGLES' INTERESTS AND LIFESTYLES*

305.412 640   UK
ULSTER BRIDE. 1970. s-a. £1.50 per no. Ulster Journals Ltd., 39 Boucher Rd., Belfast BT12 6UT, N. Ireland. Ed. P. Rainey. adv.; illus. **Document type:** consumer publication.

U.S. NATIONAL CENTER FOR HEALTH STATISTICS. VITAL AND HEALTH STATISTICS. SERIES 21. DATA ON NATALITY, MARRIAGE, AND DIVORCE. see *PUBLIC HEALTH AND SAFETY — Abstracting, Bibliographies, Statistics*

UTAH MARRIAGE AND DIVORCE ANNUAL REPORT. see *POPULATION STUDIES — Abstracting, Bibliographies, Statistics*

306.8   IT
▼**VILLE E CASTELLI SPOSI.** 1994. a. L.10000. Convegni s.r.l., Viale Lombardia 20, 20131 Milan, Italy. TEL 39-2-70600058. FAX 39-2-70601411. Ed. Vittore Castellazzi. adv.: color page L.7500000. **Document type:** consumer publication.

055.1 659.152   IT   ISSN 1120-7809
VOGUE SPOSA. 1981. q. L.35200 (foreign L.64600). Edizioni Conde Nast S.p.A., Piazza Castello 27, 20121 Milan, Italy. TEL 39-2-85611. FAX 39-2-8055716. Ed. I. Monti. adv.: page L.9500000. circ. 35,914. **Document type:** consumer publication.

306.8   US
VOWS;* the bridal and wedding business journal. 1989. bi-m. $25 (foreign $55). Grimes and Associates, 1911 11th St., Ste. 209, Boulder, CO 80302-5122. TEL 714-546-4271. FAX 714-546-4738. adv.: B&W page $1658, color page $2450; trim 8 3/8 x 10 7/8. circ. 13,000. **Document type:** trade publication.
Description: Focuses on new products, retail opportunities, customer service, store operation and consulting.

640   UK   ISSN 0955-6311
WEDDING AND HOME. 1975. bi-m. £19. I P C Magazines, Southbank Publishing Group (Subsidiary of: Reed Elsevier group), King's Reach Tower, Stamford St., London SE1 9LS, England. TEL 071-261-5000. FAX 0444-440619. TELEX 892084 REEDBP G. (Dist. by: Quadrant Subscription Services, Oakfield House, Perrymount Rd., Haywards Heath, W. Sussex RH16 3DH, England. TEL 0444-440421) Ed. Debbie Djordjevic. adv. contact: Rosemary Archer. bk.rev. circ. 44,798. **Document type:** consumer publication.
Formerly (until 1984): Wedding Day and First Home (ISSN 0307-6474)

306.8   CN   ISSN 0829-5654
WEDDING BELLS MAGAZINE. (Text in English, French) 1985. q. Can.$15. 120 Front St. E., Ste. 200, Toronto, ON M5A 4L9, Canada. TEL 416-869-8479. FAX 416-862-2184. Ed. Crys Stewart; Pub. Diane Hall. adv. contact: Diane Hall. circ. 107,000. **Document type:** consumer publication.
Description: A complete wedding planning source for the bride and groom.

306.8   AT
THE WEDDING BOOK. a. Aus.$12. Reed Business Publishing Pty. Ltd. (Subsidiary of: Reed International PLC), Level 12, 1-5 Railway St., Chatswood, N.S.W. 2067, Australia. TEL 61-2-372-5222. FAX 61-2-412-3572. (Dist. by: Gordon & Gotch 68-72 Kingsgrove St., Belmore, N.S.W. 2192, Australia. TEL 61-2-789-6444) Ed. Gina Leros. circ. 15,000. **Document type:** consumer publication.
Formerly: Bride to Be's Wedding Book.
Description: Provides general information about planning a wedding, etiquette, etc.

392.5   US
WEDDING DAY MAGAZINE. 1986. q. Worldwide Group, 100 Crescent Rd., Ste. 1A, Needham, MA 02194. TEL 617-455-1480. FAX 17-455-8408. Ed. Patricia Fiore. adv.: B&W page $1000, color page $1200; trim 8 1/8 x 10 7/8. circ. 15,000. **Document type:** consumer publication.

745.92   AT   ISSN 1035-2481
WEDDING FLOWERS. Cover title: Bride to Be's Wedding Flowers. 1988. a. Reed Business Publishing Pty. Ltd. (Subsidiary of: Reed International PLC), Level 12, 1-5 Railway St., Chatswood, N.S.W. 2067, Australia. TEL 61-2-372-5222. FAX 61-2-412-3572. (Dist. by: Gordon & Gotch, 68-72 Kingsgrove St., Belmore, N.S.W. 2192, Australia. TEL 61-2-789-6444) Ed. Gina Leros. circ. 30,000. **Document type:** consumer publication.
Description: Includes bouquets, headpieces, corsages.

306.8   US   ISSN 1067-0041
WEDDING GOWN GUIDE. 1993. a. newsstand price: $3.95. Cahners Publishing Company (New York), Consumer Division, Division of Reed Elsevier Inc., 249 W. 17th St., New York, NY 10011. TEL 212-337-7000. FAX 212-337-7049. Ed. Cele Lalli. adv. contact: Linda Platzner. circ. 10,000 (paid). (back issues avail.) **Document type:** consumer publication.
Description: Focuses exclusively on the bride's complete wedding look. Covers everything she needs to know about selecting her dress, headpiece, accessories, hairstyle and makeup.

306.8   CN
WEDDING PAGES. 1989. a. Wedding Pages Inc., 1962 Yonge St., Ste. 205, Toronto, Ont. M4S 1Z4, Canada. TEL 416-322-5590. FAX 416-481-6055. adv. circ. 5,000. **Document type:** consumer publication.

306.8   AT   ISSN 1035-2503
WEDDING PLANNER. Key Title: Bride to Be's Wedding Planner. 1988. a. Reed Business Publishing Pty. Ltd. (Subsidiary of: Reed International PLC), Level 12, 1-5 Railway St., Chatswood, N.S.W. 2067, Australia. TEL 61-2-372-5222. FAX 61-2-412-3572. (Dist. by: Gordon & Gotch, 68-72- Kingsbrove St., Belmore, N.S.W. 2192, Australia. TEL 61-2-789-6444) Ed. Gina Leros. circ. 15,000. **Document type:** consumer publication.
Description: Covers planning reception, seating arrangements, ceremonies.

306.8 646
WEDDINGS. 1990. a. Butterick Co., Inc., 161 Ave. of the Americas, New York, NY 10011. TEL 212-620-2500. Ed. Norah O'Hara. adv. contact: Herman Fine.

306.8   US
WOMAN'S DAY BEAUTIFUL BRIDES. a. $3.95. Hachette Magazines, Inc., Woman's Day Special Publications, 1633 Broadway, 45th Fl., New York, NY 10019. TEL 212-767-6000. **Document type:** consumer publication.

306.8   UK   ISSN 0267-2391
YOU AND YOUR WEDDING. (Supplement avail.: Homebuying and Homemaker (ISSN 0267-2456)) 1985. q. newsstand price: £3.95. Aim Publications Ltd., Silver House, 21-35 Beak St., London W1R 3LD, England. TEL 0171-437-0796. FAX 0171-437-8787. **Document type:** consumer publication.

306.8   UK
YOU AND YOUR WEDDING DRESSES. q. newsstand price: £2.95. Aim Publications Ltd., Silver House, 31-35 Beak St., London W1R 3LD, England. TEL 0171-437-0796. FAX 0171-437-8787. **Document type:** consumer publication.

MATRIMONY — Abstracting, Bibliographies, Statistics

306.8 016   US   ISSN 0094-7814
Z7164.M2
INVENTORY OF MARRIAGE AND FAMILY LITERATURE. 1974. a. $134.95 (effective 1993). National Council on Family Relations, 3989 Central Ave., N.E., Ste. 550, Minneapolis, MN 55421-3921. TEL 612-781-9331. FAX 612-781-9331. Ed. John Touliatos. (back issues avail.) **Document type:** abstracting/indexing.
● Also available online. Vendor(s): Knight-Ridder, Inc., Ovid Technologies.
—BLDSC (4557.690000).
Formerly: International Bibliography of Research in Marriage and the Family (ISSN 0095-4551)
Description: Indexes current literature on topics relating to marriage and the family.

312   KU
KUWAIT. CENTRAL STATISTICAL OFFICE. VITAL STATISTICS - MARRIAGE AND DIVORCE/KUWAIT. AL-IDARAH AL-MARKAZIYYAH LIL-IHSA'. AL-IHSA'AT AL-HAYAWIYYAH - AL-ZAWAJ WAL-TALAQ. (Text in Arabic, English) 1967. a. latest 1989. Central Statistical Office - Al-Idarah al-Markaziyyah lil-Ihsa', P.O. Box 26188, Safat 13122, Kuwait. TEL 965-2428200. FAX 965-2430464. TELEX 22468 TAKHTET KT. **Document type:** government publication.

306.8   IT
MATRIMONI, SEPARAZIONI E DIVORZI. 1988. a. L.18000 (effective 1993). Istituto Nazionale di Statistica, Via Cesare Balbo 16, 00100 Rome, Italy. FAX 06-46735198. **Document type:** government publication.
Supersedes in part: Statistiche Demografiche. Tomo 2. Parte Seconda.

315.61 306.89021   TU   ISSN 1300-1183
TURKEY. DEVLET ISTATISTIK ENSTITUSU. BOSANMA ISTATISTIKLERI/TURKEY. STATE INSTITUTE OF STATISTICS. DIVORCE STATISTICS. Key Title: Bosanma Istatistikleri. (Text in English, Turkish) 1960. a., latest 1990. $25. Devlet Istatistik Enstitusu - State Institute of Statistics, Necatibey Caddesi No. 114, 06100 Ankara, Turkey. TEL 90-312-4185027. FAX 90-312-4170432. **Document type:** government publication.

315.61 306.81021   TU   ISSN 1300-1086
TURKEY. DEVLET ISTATISTIK ENSTITUSU. EVLENME ISTATISTIKLERI/TURKEY. STATE INSTITUTE OF STATISTICS. MARRIAGE STATISTICS. Key Title: Evlenme Istatistikleri. (Text in English, Turkish) 1960. a., latest 1991. $25. Devlet Istatistik Enstitusu - State Institute of Statistics, Necatibey Caddesi No. 114, 06100 Ankara, Turkey. TEL 90-312-4185027. FAX 90-312-4170432. circ. 850. **Document type:** government publication.

MECHANICAL ENGINEERING

see Engineering–Mechanical Engineering

MECHANICS

see Physics–Mechanics

MEDICAL SCIENCES

see also Medical Sciences–Allergology and Immunology; Medical Sciences–Anaesthesiology; Medical Sciences–Cardiovascular Diseases; Medical Sciences–Chiropractic, Homeopathy, Osteopathy; Medical Sciences–Communicable Diseases; Medical Sciences–Computer Applications; Medical Sciences–Dentistry; Medical Sciences–Dermatology and Venereology; Medical Sciences–Endocrinology; Medical Sciences–Experimental Medicine, Laboratory Technique; Medical Sciences–Forensic Sciences; Medical Sciences–Gastroenterology; Medical Sciences–Hematology; Medical Sciences–Hypnosis; Medical Sciences–Internal Medicine; Medical Sciences–Nurses and Nursing; Medical Sciences–Obstetrics and Gynecology; Medical Sciences–Oncology; Medical Sciences–Ophthalmology and Optometry; Medical Sciences–Orthopedics and Traumatology; Medical Sciences–Otorhinolaryngology; Medical Sciences–Pediatrics; Medical Sciences–Physical Medicine and Rehabilitation; Medical Sciences–Psychiatry and Neurology; Medical Sciences–Radiology and Nuclear Medicine; Medical Sciences–Respiratory Diseases; Medical Sciences–Rheumatology; Medical Sciences–Sports Medicine; Medical Sciences–Surgery; Medical Sciences–Urology and Nephrology; Alternative Medicine; Drug Abuse and Alcoholism; Gerontology and Geriatrics; Hospitals; Men's Health; Nutrition and Dietetics; Pharmacy and Pharmacology; Physical Fitness and Hygiene; Women's Health

617   CN   ISSN 0743-4618
                         CODEN: AAACEC
A A C: AUGMENTATIVE AND ALTERNATIVE COMMUNICATION. q. $80 to individuals (outside US & Canada $100); institutions $125 (outside US & Canada $145) (effective 1996). (International Society for Augmentative and Alternative Communication) Decker Periodicals, P.O. Box 620, LCD 1, Hamilton, ON L8N 3K7, Canada. TEL 416-522-7017; 800-568-7281. FAX 416-522-7839. E-mail: decker@io.org. (US addr.: Box 785, Lewiston, NY 14092-0785) Ed. Lyle L. Lloyd. adv. circ. 1,600. (also avail. in microform from PMC; back issues avail.) **Indexed:** Ling.Abstr.; Psychol.Abstr. (1985-). **Document type:** academic/scholarly publication.
—BLDSC (1791.440000); Ei; UnCover. **CCC.**
Description: Articles on systems and devices for speech- and language-impaired individuals for speech-language specialists, special educators, rehabilitation engineers.

610.73 362.1   US   ISSN 1046-7467
A A C N CLINICAL ISSUES; advanced practice in acute and critical care. 1990. q. $62 to individuals (foreign $60); institutions $125 (foreign $135) (effective 1996). (American Association of Critical Care Nurses) Lippincott - Raven Publishers, 227 E. Washington Sq., Philadelphia, PA 19106. TEL 215-238-4200. Ed. Mary Lou Noll.
Refereed Serial

A A M C CURRICULUM DIRECTORY. (Association of American Medical Colleges) see EDUCATION — Teaching Methods And Curriculum

A A M C DIRECTORY OF AMERICAN MEDICAL EDUCATION. (Association of American Medical Colleges) see EDUCATION — School Organization And Administration

610.28   US   ISSN 0146-146X
A A M I ANNUAL MEETING. PROCEEDINGS. 1974. a. $49 to non-members; members $25. Association for the Advancement of Medical Instrumentation, c/o Elizabeth Tilly, 3330 Washington Blvd., Ste. 400, Arlington, VA 22201-4598. TEL 703-525-4890. FAX 703-276-0793.
Description: Papers presented at the association's annual meeting.

610   US   ISSN 0894-0509
A A P A NEWS. 1979. m. $75. American Academy of Physician Assistants, 950 N. Washington St., Alexandria, VA 22314. TEL 703-836-2272. FAX 703-684-1924. Ed. Dale Smith. adv. contact: Greg Thomas. circ. 20,000 (controlled). **Document type:** newsletter.
Description: Keeps physician assistants current on academy, legislative, educational and professional issues affecting their practice.

610   US   ISSN 8750-9687
A A P S NEWS. 1943. m. $250 membership. Association of American Physicians & Surgeons, Inc., 1601 N. Tucson Blvd., Ste. 9, Tucson, AZ 85716-3405. TEL 602-327-4885. FAX 602-290-9674. Ed. Dr. Jane M. Orient. cum.index: 1987-1992. circ. 3,000. (back issues avail.)
Formerly: A A P S News Letter (ISSN 0001-0170)
Description: Covers socio-economic aspects of medical practice.

610   UK
A B H I DIRECTORY. (Text in English; summaries in French, German and Spanish) 1965. a. (Association of British Health-Care Industries) Kogan Page Ltd., 120 Pentonville Rd., London N1 9JN, England. TEL 0171-278-0433. FAX 0171-837-6348. TELEX 263088 KOGAN G. Ed. J.W. Christopher. circ. 500. **Document type:** directory.
Description: Guide to health-care equipment, services and supplies.

610   US
A B M S RECORD. 1981. 8/yr. American Board of Medical Specialties, 1007 Church St., Ste. 404, Evanston, IL 60201-5913. TEL 708-491-9091. FAX 708-328-3596. Ed. Dr. J. Lee Dockery. circ. 1,200. (looseleaf format)
Description: Covers graduate medical education, specialty certification, evaluation of physician performance, and legislation.

610.7   CN   ISSN 0836-3463
A C M C FORUM. (Text in English and French) 1968. 4/yr. Can.$30 (Can.$35 in U.S.; Can.$40 elsewhere) (effective 1996). Association of Canadian Medical Colleges, 774 Echo Dr., Ottawa, Ont. K1S 5P2, Canada. TEL 613-730-0687. FAX 613-730-1196. Ed. Dr. David Hawkins. adv.: B&W page Can.$350; trim 8 1/2 x 11. bk.rev. circ. 1,200. (processed) **Document type:** newsletter.
Formerly: (until vol.7, no.2, 1974): A C M C Newsletter (ISSN 0001-0774)
Description: Deals primarily with medical education in Canada. Reports on major activities in Canadian medical schools, such as appointments and promotions, and publishes any other news of interest to medical educators.

A C P JOURNAL CLUB. (American College of Physicians) see MEDICAL SCIENCES — Abstracting, Bibliographies, Statistics

610 614.44   US   ISSN 1044-4211
A C P M NEWS.* 1957. q. $25. American College of Preventive Medicine, 1660 L St., N.W., Ste. 206, Washington, DC 20036-5603. TEL 202-789-0003. FAX 202-289-8274. Ed. Emily Slough. adv.; bk.rev.; charts. circ. 2,000. (also avail. in microform from UMI) **Document type:** newsletter.
Former titles: Preventive Medicine Newsletter (ISSN 0199-2481); American College of Preventive Medicine Newsletter (ISSN 0002-8029)

MEDICAL SCIENCES 4165

610 US
A F I P ATLAS OF RADIOLOGIC-PATHOLOGIC CORRELATION. a. $50 (foreign $60). (Armed Forces Institute of Pathology) Hanley & Belfus, Inc., 210 S. 13th St., Philadelphia, PA 19107. TEL 215-546-7293. FAX 215-790-9330. Ed. Dr. Alan J. Davidson.
Refereed Serial

610 500 600 FR ISSN 0397-829X
A F P SCIENCES; bulletin information scientifique, technique, medicale. 1976. w. 7560 F. (foreign 8244 F.) (effective 1996). Agence France-Presse, 13 Place de la Bourse, B.P. 20, 75061 Paris Cedex 2, France. TEL 40-41-46-46. TELEX 210064 AFPA.

610 658 CN
A H R A RECORD. bi-m. membership. Alberta Health Records Association, Box 1752, Edmonton, AB T5J 2P1, Canada. circ. 600. **Document type**: newsletter.

610 616 AT ISSN 1038-4766
A I M S NEWSLETTER. 1971. 6/yr. Aus.$15 to non-members. Australian Institute of Medical Scientists, P.O. Box 450, Toowong, Qld. 4066, Australia. TEL 61-7-371-3370. FAX 61-7-870-4857. Ed. Brendon Walker. adv. contact: Brendon Walker. **Document type**: newsletter.
Former titles: A I M L S Newsletter; A I M T Newsletter (ISSN 0311-1253)
Description: Discusses interests, legislation and meetings pertaining to medical laboratory science. Continuing education material and details are included.

610 AT ISSN 0813-6394
A M A VICTORIA BRANCH NEWS. m. Aus.$20. Australian Medical Association, Victoria Branch, 293 Royal Parade, Parkville, Vic. 3052, Australia. FAX 03-347-9871. adv.; illus.; circ. controlled.
—CCC.
Formerly: Australian Medical Association. Victoria Branch. Monthly Paper.

610 US
A M I NEWS. 1958. bi-m. $25 (foreign $30). Association of Medical Illustrators, 1819 Peachtree St. N.E., Ste. 712, Atlanta, GA 30309-1851. TEL 404-350-7900. FAX 404-351-3348. Ed. Linda Warren. adv. contact: Vernon Lomax. bk.rev.; illus. circ. 950. **Indexed**: Ind.Med. **Document type**: newsletter.
Formerly: A M I Newsletter (ISSN 0001-1916)

070.5 US
A M P A NEWSLETTER. q. $50 to non-members; free to members. American Medical Publishers' Association, 14 Fort Hill Rd., Huntington, NY 11743. TEL 516-423-0075. Ed. Jill Rudansky. circ. 450. (back issues avail.) **Document type**: newsletter.
Description: Provides information on health science publishing industry.

610 US
A M P R A REVIEW. 1984. q. $75 to non-members. American Medical Peer Review Association, 1140 Connecticut Ave., N.W., Ste. 1050, Washington, DC 20036. TEL 202-331-5790. FAX 202-933-2047. circ. 900. (looseleaf format; back issues avail.)

610 US ISSN 0746-9217
A M T EVENTS. 1939. 6/yr. $35 (foreign $45). American Medical Technologists, 710 Higgins Rd., Park Ridge, IL 60068-5765. TEL 708-823-5169. FAX 708-823-0458. Ed. Eleanore Bors. adv. contact: Charles Healy. bk.rev. circ. 21,700. (microfilm; back issues avail.)
—UMI.
Description: Technical and industry news for clinical laboratory and allied health professionals.

610 301.16 US ISSN 0194-004X
A M W A FREELANCE DIRECTORY. 1975. biennial. American Medical Writers Association, 9650 Rockville Pike, Bethesda, MD 20814. TEL 301-493-0003. circ. 4,500. **Document type**: directory.
Description: Lists freelance writers specializing in any medical or health care topic.

610 301.16 US
A M W A JOURNAL. 1972. q. $35. American Medical Writers Association, 9650 Rockville Pike, Bethesda, MD 20814. TEL 301-493-0003. adv.; bk.rev. circ. 3,500. **Document type**: bulletin.
—BLDSC (4689.103000).
Formerly: Medical Communications (ISSN 0090-046X); Which supersedes: American Medical Writers Association. Bulletin (ISSN 0002-9971)

A N A D: WORKING TOGETHER. (National Association of Anorexia Nervosa and Associated Disorders) see *PSYCHOLOGY*

A N R E D ALERT. (Anorexia Nervosa & Related Eating Disorders, Inc.) see *PSYCHOLOGY*

A P M I S. see *BIOLOGY*

A P M I S SUPPLEMENTUM. see *BIOLOGY*

610 US ISSN 1058-2916
RD130 CODEN: AJOUET
A S A I O JOURNAL. 1955. q. $180 to individuals (foreign $280); institutions $250 (foreign $370) (effective 1996). (American Society for Artificial Internal Organs, Inc.) Lippincott - Raven Publishers, 227 E. Washington Sq., Philadelphia, PA 19106. TEL 215-238-4282. Ed. Dr. Eli A. Friedman. adv. contact: Kathleen Phelan. charts; illus.; index. (also avail. in microform; reprint service avail. from UMI) **Indexed**: Chem.Abstr., Excerp.Med. (1993-), INIS Atomind., Kidney.
—BLDSC (1738.840500); CASDDS; Ei; Faxon; Genuine Article; SWETS; UMI; UnCover. **CCC**.
Formerly (until 1992): A S A I O Transactions (ISSN 0889-7190); Which was formed by the 1986 merger of: American Society for Artificial Internal Organs. Transactions (ISSN 0066-0078); (1978-1985): A S A I O Journal (ISSN 0162-1432)

A S H A. (American Speech - Language - Hearing Association) see *HANDICAPPED — Hearing Impaired*

A U L INSIGHTS. (Americans United for Life) see *LAW*

A U L STUDIES IN LAW, MEDICINE & SOCIETY. (Americans United for Life) see *LAW*

610 AT ISSN 0310-8341
ABORIGINAL MEDICAL SERVICE. NEWSLETTER. 1973. irreg. donation. Aboriginal Medical Service, P.O. Box 1174, Strawberry Hills, N.S.W. 2012, Australia. TEL 699-2493. FAX 319-3345. **Document type**: newsletter.

610 CL ISSN 0716-2588
ACADEMIA CHILENA DE MEDICINA. BOLETIN ANUAL. 1967. a. $25. Academia Chilena de Medicina, Clasificador 1349, Santiago 1, Chile. Eds. Dr. Amador Neghme, Dr. Alberto Donoso. index. circ. 1,000. (back issues avail.) **Indexed**: Ind.Med.
Formerly: Academia de Medicina. Boletin.

610 BL ISSN 0001-3838
ACADEMIA NACIONAL DE MEDICINA. BOLETIM. (Text in Portuguese; summaries in English) 1831. m. Academia Nacional de Medicina, Caixa Postal 459, Rio de Janeiro, Brazil. charts; bibl.; illus. **Indexed**: Biol.Abstr., Chem.Abstr., Helminthol.Abstr.
Formerly: Academia Nacional de Medicina Revista.

610 MX
ACADEMIA NACIONAL DE MEDICINA. BOLETIN. 1993. q. Academia Nacional de Medicina, Unidad de Congresos del Centro Medico Nacional, Siglo XXI, Bloque B, Av. Cuauhtemoc Num. 330, 06725 Mexico D.F., Mexico. TEL 52-5782044. FAX 52-5784271. Ed. Dr. Pelayo Vilar Puig. **Document type**: bulletin.
Description: Presents activities of the organization.

610 PL ISSN 0303-4135
CODEN: AAMGBD
ACADEMIAE MEDICAE GEDANENSIS. ANNALES. Key Title: Annales Academiae Medicae Gedanensis. (Text in English, Polish; summaries in English) 1971. a. 60000 Zl.($20) Academia Medyczna w Gdansku, Ul. Marii Sklodowskiej-Curie 3a, 80-210 Gdansk, Poland. FAX 58-316-115. Ed. Stefan Raszeja. index. circ. 300. (back issues avail.) **Indexed**: Biol.Abstr., Ind.Med. **Document type**: academic/scholarly publication.
—BLDSC (0914.263000); CASDDS.
Description: Details medical research and includes historical aspects.

ACADEMIC EMERGENCY MEDICINE. see *MEDICAL SCIENCES — Orthopedics And Traumatology*

610.7 US ISSN 1040-2446
R11 CODEN: ACMEEO
ACADEMIC MEDICINE. 1926. m. $70 in US, Canada, Latin America (elsewhere $85); students in US, Canada $35 (elsewhere $45). Association of American Medical Colleges, 2450 N St., Washington, DC 20037-1126. TEL 202-828-0416. FAX 202-828-1123. Ed. Addeane S. Caelleigh. adv.; bk.rev.; bibl.; illus.; stat.; index. circ. 5,800. (also avail. in microform from PMC,UMI; microfiche from CIS; reprint service avail. from UMI) **Indexed**: Abstr.Health Care Manage.Stud., AIM, Behav.Med.Abstr., Biol.Abstr., C.I.J.E., Chem.Abstr., CINAHL, Cont.Pg.Educ., Crim.Just.Abstr., Curr.Cont., Curr.Lit.Fam.Plan., Educ.Tech.Abstr., Excerp.Med., FAMLI, Hosp.Lit.Ind., Ind.Med., Ind.Sci.Rev., Int.Nurs.Ind., Med.Care Rev., Mult.Ed.Abstr., Psychol.Abstr. (1967-), Res.High.Educ.Abstr., Sci.Cit.Ind., SRI, Stud.Wom.Abstr., Tech.Educ.Abstr., Trop.Dis.Bull. **Document type**: academic/scholarly publication.
—BLDSC (0570.513500); Faxon; Genuine Article; SWETS; UMI; UnCover.
Former titles (until 1988): Journal of Medical Education (ISSN 0022-2577); (until 1951): Medical Education.
Description: Serves as an international forum for the exchange of ideas and informaton on policy issues, and research concerning academic medicine, including strenghtening the quality of medical education and training, enhacing the search for biomedical knowledge, advancing research in health services, and integrating education and reserach into the provision of effective health care.
Refereed Serial

610 FR ISSN 0001-4079
CODEN: BANMAC
ACADEMIE NATIONALE DE MEDECINE. BULLETIN. 1836. 9/yr. 650 F. (foreign 700 F) (effective 1995). Academie Nationale de Medecine, 16 rue Bonaparte, 75006 Paris Cedex 06, France. TEL 43-26-96-80. FAX 40-46-87-55. Ed. R. Bastin. bk.rev.; charts. circ. 1,300. **Indexed**: Abstr.Hyg., B.R.I., Biol.Abstr., Bull.Signal., C.I.S. Abstr., Chem.Abstr., Curr.Adv.Ecol.Sci., Curr.Cont., Excerp.Med., Helminthol.Abstr., Ind.Med., Ind.Vet., Nutr.Abstr., Pig News & Info., Trop.Dis.Bull., Vet.Bull. **Document type**: bulletin.
—BLDSC (2367.300000); CASDDS; Faxon; Genuine Article; SWETS. **CCC**.
Formerly: Academie de Medicine. Memoirs.

610 BE ISSN 0377-8231
R41 CODEN: BMABDZ
ACADEMIE ROYALE DE MEDECINE DE BELGIQUE. BULLETIN ET MEMOIRES. 1841. m. 3000 BEF. Academie Royale de Medecine de Belgique, Palais des Academies, Rue Ducale 1, B-1000 Brussels, Belgium. **Indexed**: Biol.Abstr., Chem.Abstr., Dent.Ind., Excerp.Med., Ind.Med., INIS Atomind. **Document type**: bulletin.
—BLDSC (2853.600500); CASDDS.
Formed by the merger of: Academie Royale de Medecine de Belgique. Memoires. (ISSN 0065-0595); Academie Royale de Medecine de Belgique. Bulletin (ISSN 0001-4168)

610 SI ISSN 0304-4602
CODEN: AAMSCG
ACADEMY OF MEDICINE, SINGAPORE. ANNALS. 1972. bi-m. S.$90($50) Academy of Medicine, Singapore, 16 College Road, 01-01 College of Medicine Bldg., Singapore 0316, Singapore. TEL 2245166. FAX 2255155. TELEX RS 40173 ACAMED. Ed. Dr. Lee Seng Teik. adv.; bk.rev.; bibl.; charts; illus. circ. 1,600. **Indexed**: Dent.Ind., Excerp.Med., ExtraMED, Ind.Med.
●Also available online. Vendor(s): National Library of Medicine.
Also available on CD-ROM.
—BLDSC (1018.300000); Faxon; SWETS.
Description: Published to help young writers improve in medical and scientific writing.

610 CN ISSN 0001-4311
ACADEMY OF MEDICINE, TORONTO. BULLETIN. 1927. m. Can.$12.50. Academy of Medicine, Toronto, P.O. Box 509, Sta. A, 704 Spadina Rd., Toronto, ON M5S 2T1, Canada. TEL 416-922-1134. Ed. Dr. Ted Mullens. adv.; bk.rev.; charts; index. circ. 2,700. **Document type**: bulletin.

MEDICAL SCIENCES

610   IT   ISSN 0394-8811
ACCADEMIA DELLA SCIENZE MEDICHE. ATTI. (Text in Italian; summaries in English, French) 1889. a. Accademia della Scienze Mediche, Via L. Giuffre 5, 90127 Palermo, Italy. TEL 091-217938. Ed. Giuseppe di Gesu.
   Formerly (1890-1946): Reale Accademia delle Scienze Mediche. Atti (ISSN 0394-9613)

610   IT   ISSN 0390-7783
ACCADEMIA DELLE SCIENZE DI SIENA DETTA DE FISIOCRITICI. 1760; currently series 15. a. L.25000. Accademia delle Scienze di Siena Detta de Fisiocritici, Piazza S. Agostino 5, 53100 Siena, Italy. **Indexed:** Biol.Abstr.
   —CASDDS.
   Formerly: Accademia dei Fisiocritici, Siena. Sezione Medico-Fisica (ISSN 0065-0722)

610   IT   ISSN 0001-4427
                      CODEN: AAMLAR
ACCADEMIA MEDICA LOMBARDA. ATTI. (Issued in 2 vols.) 1862. a. L.50000 (foreign L.100000). Accademia Medica Lombarda, Policlinico Pad. Beretta Est., Via F. Sforza 35, 20122 Milan, Italy. Ed. Emilio Trabucchi. bibl.; illus.; index, cum.index. circ. 500. **Indexed:** Biol.Abstr., Chem.Abstr., Excerp.Med., Ind.Med., INIS Atomind. **Document type:** proceedings.

610   IT   ISSN 0366-1954
                      CODEN: BOMFAG
ACCADEMIA MEDICA PISTOIESE "FILIPPO PACINI". BOLLETTINO. 1928. a. L.5000($20) Accademia Medica Pistoiese "Filippo Pacini", Via della Rosa, Pistoia, Italy. Ed. Collatino Cantieri. adv.

610   AT   ISSN 0817-1351
ACCESS (TOORAK). 1976. q. Aus.$60 to non-members. Victorian Medical Postgraduate Foundation Inc., P.O. Box 27, Parkville, Vic. 3052, Australia. TEL 61-3-93479633. FAX 61-3-93474547. adv. circ. 600.
   Description: Diary of postgraduate medical events in Australia and overseas.

610   CN   ISSN 0845-5260
ACCESS (TORONTO). (Text in English and French) bi-m. membership. Canadian Rehabilitation Council, 45 Sheppard Ave. E., Ste. 801, Willowdale, ON M2N 5W9, Canada. TEL 416-250-7490. FAX 416-229-1371. circ. 800.

610   FR
ACOPSIS.* 1972. bi-m. 35 F. I R F A, 42 rue Boileau, 75106 Paris, France. Ed. Francois Anger. adv. circ. 15,000. (also avail. in microfilm)

611 574.87   SZ   ISSN 0001-5180
QL801   CODEN: ACATA5
ACTA ANATOMICA; international journal of anatomy, embryology and cell biology. (Text in English) 1945. m. (in 3 vols.). 1261.80 SFr.($970.20) to individuals; institutions 2103 SFr.($1617) (effective 1996). S. Karger AG, Allschwilerstr. 10, P.O. Box, CH-4009 Basel, Switzerland. TEL 061-3061111. FAX 061-3061234. E-mail: karger@Karger.ch. Eds. H. Denker, A.W. English. adv.; abstr.; illus.; index. circ. 1,200. (also avail. in microform from PMC,RPI; reprint service avail. from ISI) **Indexed:** Abstr.Anthropol., Anim.Breed.Abstr., ASCA, Biol.Abstr., Chem.Abstr., Curr.Adv.Ecol.Sci., Curr.Cont., Dairy Sci.Abstr., Dent.Ind., Excerp.Med., Ind.Med., Ind.Sci.Rev., Ind.Vet., Pig News & Info., Poult.Abstr., Sci.Cit.Ind., Small Anim.Abstr., Sport Fish.Abstr., Vet.Bull., Wild.Rev., Zoo.Rec. **Document type:** academic/scholarly publication.
   —BLDSC (0594.000000); CASDDS; Faxon; Genuine Article; SWETS; UnCover. **CCC.**
   Refereed Serial

ACTA ANATOMICA NIPPONICA/KAIBOGAKU ZASSHI. see *BIOLOGY*

ACTA BIOLOGICA ET MEDICA. see *BIOLOGY*

610   BE
ACTA BIOMEDICA LOVANIENSIA. 1988. irreg. (8-10/yr.), vol.107, 1995. price varies. Leuven University Press, Krakenstraat 3, B-3000 Leuven, Belgium. TEL 32-16-324175. FAX 32-16-323782. **Document type:** academic/scholarly publication, monographic series.
   Description: Research monographs on topics in the bio-medical sciences.

ACTA BIOQUIMICA CLINICA LATINOAMERICANA. see *BIOLOGY — Biological Chemistry*

610   BE   ISSN 0001-5512
                      CODEN: ACCBAT
ACTA CLINICA BELGICA. 1945. bi-m. 1700 BEF (foreign 2300 BEF) (effective 1996). Jardin Martin V, 69, B.P. 41-4375, 1200 Brussels, Belgium. TEL 32-2-7641869. FAX 32-2-7642836. Ed. C. van Ypersele de Strihou. adv.; bk.rev.; index. circ. 1,300. (reprint service avail. from ISI) **Indexed:** ASCA, Biol.Abstr., Biotech.Abstr., Chem.Abstr., Curr.Adv.Cancer Res., Curr.Adv.Ecol.Sci., Curr.Cont., Excerp.Med., Helminthol.Abstr., Ind.Med., Ind.Sci.Rev., Nutr.Abstr., Sci.Cit.Ind. **Document type:** academic/scholarly publication.
   —BLDSC (0611.650000); CASDDS; Faxon; Genuine Article; SWETS.

610   CI   ISSN 0353-9466
                      CODEN: ABSJAO
ACTA CLINICA CROATICA. (Includes two monographic supplements per volume) (Text in Croatian; summaries in English) 1962. q. $20. Klinicka Bolnica "Sestre Milosrdnice", Vinogradska 29, 41000 Zagreb, Croatia. TEL 041-575-045. Ed. V. Hudolin. adv.; bk.rev.; bibl.; illus. circ. 1,000. **Indexed:** Biol.Abstr., Excerp.Med. (1993-).
   —BLDSC (0611.650200).
   Former titles (until 1991): Anali Klinicke Bolnice "Dr. M. Stojanovic" (ISSN 0301-2255); Anali Bolnice "Dr. M. Stojanovic".

610   CI   ISSN 0065-1206
                      CODEN: AFMFBB
ACTA FACULTATIS MEDICAE FLUMINENSIS. (Text in Croatian or English) 1963. s-a. 100 HRK to individuals; institutions 3000 HRK (foreign $50). Sveuciliste u Rijeci, Medicinski Fakultet, Brace Branchetta 20-22, 51000 Rijeka, Croatia. TEL 051-513-222. FAX 051-514-915. (Co-sponsor: Republicka Zajednica za Znanstveni Rad) Ed. Juraj Sepcic. adv.; bk.rev. circ. 700. (reprint service avail.) **Indexed:** Biol.Abstr., Chem.Abstr., Excerp.Med. (1988-), Ref.Zh. **Document type:** academic/scholarly publication.
   —BLDSC (0580.750000); EMDOCS.
   Description: Publishes leading articles, original scientific and professional papers, preliminary communications, review articles, reports on scientific meetings and congresses, and other contributions.

610   XR   ISSN 0521-2561
                      CODEN: AMUBAJ
ACTA FACULTATIS MEDICAE UNIVERSITATIS BRUNENSIS. (Text and summaries in Czech, English, Russian) 1958. irreg. price varies. Masarykova Universita, Lekarska Fakulta - Masaryk University, Medical Faculty, Komenskeho nam.2, 66243 Brno, Czech Republic. Ed. M. Dokladal. bk.rev. circ. 800. **Indexed:** Apic.Abstr., Biol.Abstr., Excerp.Med.
   —CASDDS.

575.1   IT   ISSN 0001-5660
                      CODEN: AGMGAK
ACTA GENETICAE MEDICAE ET GEMELLOLOGIAE: TWIN RESEARCH; international quarterly of twin research. 1952. q. $300 (effective 1993-95). Gregor Mendel Institute for Medical Genetics and Twin Studies, Piazza Galeno 5, 00162 Rome, Italy. TEL 396-8552055. FAX 396-8555179. Ed. Luigi Gedda. adv.; bk.rev.; abstr.; bibl.; charts; illus.; index. (also avail. in microfilm; reprint service avail. from ISI) **Indexed:** A.I.C.P., Abstr.Anthropol., ASCA, Biol.Abstr., Curr.Adv.Ecol.Sci., Curr.Cont., Dairy Sci.Abstr., Dent.Ind., Excerp.Med, Helminthol.Abstr., Ind.Med., Ind.Sci.Rev., INIS Atomind., Psychol.Abstr. (1976-), Sci.Cit.Ind.
   —BLDSC (0618.000000); Faxon; Genuine Article; SWETS; UnCover.
   Formerly (until 1978): Acta Geneticae Medicae et Gemellologiae.

574   GW   ISSN 0065-1281
                      CODEN: AHISA9
ACTA HISTOCHEMICA; international journal of structural biochemistry. (Text in English, French, German; summaries in English) 1954. 4/yr. DM.506 (foreign DM.514). Gustav Fischer Verlag Jena, Villengang 2, 07745 Jena, Germany. TEL 03641-626444. FAX 03641-6266500. (Subscr. to: Postfach 100537, 07705 Jena, Germany) Ed. R. Grossrau. bk.rev.; bibl.; charts; illus.; index. (also avail. in microform from PMC,SWZ; reprint service avail. from ISI) **Indexed:** ASCA, Biol.Abstr., Chem.Abstr., Curr.Adv.Ecol.Sci., Curr.Cont., Dairy Sci.Abstr., Dent.Ind., Excerp.Med, Helminthol.Abstr., Ind.Med., Ind.Sci.Rev., Ind.Vet., INIS Atomind., Nutr.Abstr., Ref.Zh., Sci.Cit.Ind., Sport Fish.Abstr., Vet.Bull., Wild.Rev., Zoo.Rec. **Document type:** academic/scholarly publication.
   —BLDSC (0624.000000); CASDDS; Ei; EMDOCS; Faxon; Genuine Article; SWETS; UnCover. **CCC.**

ACTA HISTORICA LEOPOLDINA. see *SCIENCES: COMPREHENSIVE WORKS*

ACTA HISTORICA SCIENTIARUM NATURALIUM ET MEDICINALIUM. see *SCIENCES: COMPREHENSIVE WORKS*

610   MX   ISSN 0001-5997
R21   CODEN: ACMDBI
ACTA MEDICA. (Text in Spanish; summaries in English, Spanish) 1965. q. Mex.$500($20) Instituto Politecnico Nacional, Escuela Superior de Medicina, Prolongacion de Diaz Miron y Plan de San Luis, 2 piso, C.P. 11340, Apdos. Postales 42-161 y 42-200 (Z.P.), Mexico 17, D.F., Mexico. Ed. Carlos de la Vega Lezama. adv.; bk.rev.; bibl.; charts; illus. **Indexed:** Biol.Abstr.
   —BLDSC (0632.640000); CASDDS; Faxon.

610   CU   ISSN 0864-3210
ACTA MEDICA. (Text in Spanish; summaries in English, Spanish) 1987. 3/yr. $28 in S. America; N. America $30; elsewhere $34. Ministerio de Salud Publica, Centro Nacional de Informacion de Ciencias Medicas, Calle E No. 452, e-19 y 21, Plaza de la Revolucion, Apdo. 6520, Havana, Cuba. TEL 809-32-5338. (Dist. by: Ediciones Cubanas, Obispo No. 527, Apdo. 605, Havana, Cuba) (Co-sponsor: Hospital Clinico-Quirurgico Hermanos Ameijeiras) Ed. Maura Diaz. circ. 1,500. **Document type:** government publication.
   Description: Covers clinical and preventive medicine.

610   GW   ISSN 0303-8173
                      CODEN: AMAUBB
ACTA MEDICA AUSTRIACA. (Text in German or English; summaries in English) 1920. 5/yr. DM.210($156) in Europe; rest of world DM.228($169) (effective 1996). (Oesterreichische und Wiener Gesellschaft fuer Innere Medizin) Blackwell Wissenschaft, Kurfuerstendamm 57, 10707 Berlin, Germany. TEL 030-327906-0. FAX 030-32790610. (Co-sponsors: Oesterreichische Gesellschaft fuer Innere Medizin; Oesterreichische Nuklearmedizinische Gesellschaft; Austro-Transplant) Ed.Bd. adv.; bk.rev.; illus.; stat.; index. circ. 1,500. (reprint service avail. from ISI) **Indexed:** ASCA, Biol.Abstr., Chem.Abstr., Dent.Ind., Dok.Arbeitsmed., Excerp.Med., Ind.Med., Ind.Sci.Rev., INIS Atomind., Nutr.Abstr., Sci.Cit.Ind. **Document type:** academic/scholarly publication.
   —BLDSC (0633.100000); ADONIS; CASDDS; Faxon; Genuine Article; SWETS; UMI. **CCC.**
   Formerly: Wiener Zeitschrift fuer Innere Medizin und ihre Grenzgebiete. (ISSN 0043-5376)

610   GW   ISSN 0946-3445
▼**ACTA MEDICA BALTICA.** (Text and summaries in English) 1994. 2/yr. DM.60($45) Pabst Science Publishers, Am Eichengrund 28, 49525 Lengerich, Germany. TEL 05484-308. FAX 05484-550. Ed. Regina Svirska. adv.; bk.rev. **Document type:** academic/scholarly publication.

610   CR   ISSN 0001-6012
                      CODEN: ATCTAW
ACTA MEDICA COSTARRICENSE. (Text in Spanish; summaries in English) 1957. 3/yr. Cr.$25. Colegio de Medicos y Cirujanos, Apdo. 548-1000, San Jose, Costa Rica. Ed.Bd. adv.; abstr.; charts; illus.; index. circ. 2,000. **Indexed:** Biol.Abstr., Chem.Abstr., Excerp.Med., Trop.Dis.Bull.
   —CASDDS.

616.07	CI	ISSN 1330-0164
		CODEN: AMCREF

ACTA MEDICA CROATICA. (Text in English, French, German and Serbo-Croatian; summaries in English and Serbo-Croatian) 1946. 5/yr. $150. Hrvatska Akademija Medicinskih Znanosti - Croatian Academy of Medical Sciences, Subiceva 29, 41000 Zagreb, Croatia. TEL 38-41-419446. Ed. Stojan Knezevic. adv.; index. circ. 800. **Indexed:** Biol.Abstr., Chem.Abstr., Dent.Ind., Excerp.Med., Ind.Med., INIS Atomind. **Document type:** academic/scholarly publication.
—BLDSC (0633.600000); CASDDS.
  Former titles (until 1991): Acta Medica Yugoslavica (ISSN 0375-8338) & Acta Medica Yugoslavica (English Edition) (ISSN 0375-8346)

610	DR	ISSN 0379-4857
		CODEN: AMDOEB

ACTA MEDICA DOMINICANA. 1979. bi-m. RD.$80($20) Jose Contreras no. 8, Santo Domingo, Dominican Republic. TEL 809-688-4010. Eds. Julio M. Rodriguez, Mariano Defillo. adv.; bk.rev.; bibl.; charts; illus.

610 574	JA	ISSN 0567-7734
		CODEN: AMBNAS

ACTA MEDICA ET BIOLOGICA/IGAKU SEIBUTSUGAKU KENKYU KIYO. (Text in English and European languages) 1953. q. 10000 Yen or exchange basis. Niigata Daigaku, Igakubu - Niigata University, School of Medicine, Ichiban-cho, Asahimachi-dori, Niigata 951, Japan. Ed. Tsuneo Fujita. circ. 100 (paid); 600 (controlled). **Indexed:** Biol.Abstr., Chem.Abstr., Excerp.Med., INIS Atomind., Nutr.Abstr. **Document type:** academic/scholarly publication.
—BLDSC (0634.000000); CASDDS; UnCover.

610	HU	ISSN 0236-5286
		CODEN: AMEHDS

ACTA MEDICA HUNGARICA. (Text in English) 1950. q. $72 (effective 1992). (Magyar Tudomanyos Akademia), Akademiai Kiado, Publishing House of the Hungarian Academy of Sciences, P.O. Box 245, H-1519 Budapest, Hungary. TEL 181-2134. FAX 166-6466. TELEX 22-6228 AKNYO H. Ed. Ervin Stark. adv.; bk.rev.; bibl.; charts; illus.; index. **Indexed:** ASCA, Biol.Abstr., Chem.Abstr., Curr.Adv.Ecol.Sci., Curr.Cont., Excerp.Med., Helminthol.Abstr., Ind.Med., INIS Atomind.
—BLDSC (0635.000000); CASDDS; Genuine Article. **CCC.**
  Formerly (until 1982): Academiae Scientiarum Hungaricae. Acta Medica (ISSN 0001-5989)
  Description: Publishes original research papers in clinical experimental medicine, covering primarily fundamental and applied pathophysiology.

610	IR	ISSN 0044-6025
		CODEN: AMEIAS

ACTA MEDICA IRANICA. (Text in English, French or German; summaries in English and French) 1960. q. IRI.2000($20) Tehran University of Medical Sciences, Faculty of Medicine, Poursina St., Tehran 14174, Iran. TEL 98-21-6112743. FAX 98-21-6404377. Ed. Dr. Parviz Jabalameli. charts; illus.; index. circ. 2,000. **Indexed:** Abstr.Hyg., Biol.Abstr., Chem.Abstr., Excerp.Med., Nutr.Abstr., Rev.Med.& Vet.Mycol., Trop.Dis.Bull. **Document type:** academic/scholarly publication.
—BLDSC (0635.080000); CASDDS.
  Description: Publishes original research papers, case reports, review articles on all aspects of the medical sciences.
  Refereed Serial

610	JA	ISSN 0386-6092
		CODEN: AMKUDT

ACTA MEDICA KINKI UNIVERSITY. (Text and summaries in English) 1976. s-a. 2000 Yen($30) Kinki University Medical Association - Kinki Daigaku Igakkai, 2-377, Ohno-Higashi, Osaka-Sayama, Osaka 589, Japan. TEL 0723-66-0221. FAX 0723-66-0206. Ed. Osamu Matsuo. bk.rev.; index. circ. 1,300. (back issues avail.) **Indexed:** Chem.Abstr., Excerp.Med. **Document type:** academic/scholarly publication.
—BLDSC (0632.684000); CASDDS.
  Description: Covers original articles, reviews and case reports of inventive work on medical services.

610	LI	ISSN 1392-0138

▼**ACTA MEDICA LITUANICA.** 1994. q. (Lietuvos Mokslu Akademija) Leidykla Academia, A. Gostauto 12, 2600 Vilnius, Lithuania. Ed. A. Matulis. circ. 400.
—BLDSC (0635.120000).

610	YU	ISSN 0365-4478
		CODEN: AMMNCH

ACTA MEDICA MEDIANAE. 1962. 8/yr. 40 din. Srpsko Lekarsko Drustvo, Podruznica u Nisu, 18000 Nis, Yugoslavia. Ed. Radoslav Zivic. adv.; bk.rev. circ. 700. **Indexed:** Biol.Abstr., Chem.Abstr.
—CASDDS.

610	IT	ISSN 0393-6384

ACTA MEDICA MEDITERRANEA. (Text in English, French and Italian) 1960. 3/yr. L.40000($40) Carbone Editore, Via G. Daita, 29, 90139 Palmero, Italy. TEL 091-321273. FAX 091-321782. abstr.; bibl.; illus.; stat.; index. circ. 3,000.
  Formerly: Archivio Siciliano di Medicina e Chirurgia (Sezione Medica).
  Description: Clinical cases are reviewed and discussed.

610	JA	ISSN 0001-6055

ACTA MEDICA NAGASAKIENSIA. (Text in English) 1939. q. exchange basis. Nagasaki Daigaku, Igakubu - Nagasaki University, School of Medicine, 12-4 Sakamoto-machi, Nagasaki-shi, Nagasaki-ken 852, Japan. Dir. Kuniaki Hayashi. charts; illus.; index. circ. 370. **Indexed:** Abstr.Hyg., Biol.Abstr., Chem.Abstr., Excerp.Med., Ind.Med., INIS Atomind., Trop.Dis.Bull. **Document type:** academic/scholarly publication.
—BLDSC (0635.150000).

610	JA	ISSN 0386-300X
		CODEN: AMOKAG

ACTA MEDICA OKAYAMA. (Text in English and European languages) 1928. bi-m. free or exchange basis. Okayama Daigaku, Igakubu - Okayama University, School of Medicine, 2-5-1 Shikata-cho, Okayama-shi, Okayama-ken 700, Japan. TEL 086-223-7151. FAX 086-225-6295. Ed. Tadaatsu Akagi. adv. contact: Takao Tsuji. bk.rev.; bibl.; charts; illus.; index, cum.index; circ. 600 (controlled). (back issues avail.; reprint service avail. from ISI) **Indexed:** ASCA, Biol.Abstr., C.I.S.Abstr., Chem.Abstr., Curr.Adv.Cancer Res., Curr.Adv.Cell & Devel.Biol., Curr.Adv.Ecol.Sci., Curr.Cont., Dairy Sci.Abstr., Dent.Ind., Excerp.Med., Helminthol.Abstr., Ind.Med., Ind.Sci.Rev., Ind.Vet., INIS Atomind., Nutr.Abstr., Sci.Cit.Ind., Small Anim.Abstr., Vet.Bull. **Document type:** academic/scholarly publication.
—BLDSC (0635.155000); CASDDS; Faxon; Genuine Article; UnCover.
  Formerly: Acta Medicinae Okayama (ISSN 0001-6152)
  Description: Publishes papers from all areas of basic and clinical medicine.

610	PE	ISSN 1018-8800

ACTA MEDICA PERUANA. (Text in Spanish; summaries in English) 1972. q. S.250($6) Colegio Medico del Peru, Malecon Armendarir 791, Miraflores, Lima, Peru. Ed. Dr. Fausto Garmendia. adv.; abstr.; charts; illus.; index. circ. 10,000. **Indexed:** Biol.Abstr., Curr.Cont.

610	PH	ISSN 0001-6071

ACTA MEDICA PHILIPPINA. 1938. q. P.120($40) University of the Philippines, College of Medicine, P.O. Box 593, Manila, Philippines. (Co-sponsor: College of Public Health) Ed. Dr. Romeo R. Gutierrez. adv.; bk.rev.; abstr.; charts; illus.; index. circ. 2,000. **Indexed:** Abstr.Hyg., Biol.Abstr., Chem.Abstr., Excerp.Med., Ind.Med., Ind.Phil.Per., INIS Atomind. **Document type:** academic/scholarly publication.
—Faxon.
  Incorporates: University of the Philippines. College of Medicine. Proceedings.

610	IT	ISSN 0001-6098
		CODEN: AMROBA

ACTA MEDICA ROMANA. (Text in English) 1963. q. L.175000 (foreign L.245000($185)) (effective 1996). (Universita Cattolica del Sacro Cuore, Facolta di Medicina e Chirurgia) Vita e Pensiero, Largo Gemelli 1, 20123 Milan, Italy. TEL 39-2-72342310. FAX 39-2-72342260. TELEX 321033 UCATMI 1. Ed. Luigi Ortona. adv.; bk.rev.; abstr.; bibl.; charts; illus.; stat.; index. circ. 550. **Indexed:** Biol.Abstr., Chem.Abstr., Excerp.Med (1994-). **Document type:** academic/scholarly publication.
—BLDSC (0635.250000); CASDDS.
  Description: Publishes original research in psychology, biology, medicine and surgery.

MEDICAL SCIENCES 4167

574.4	HU	ISSN 0236-5391
QP1		CODEN: AMHUDE

ACTA MORPHOLOGICA HUNGARICA. (Text in English) 1951. q. $88 (effective 1992). (Magyar Tudomanyos Akademia) Akademiai Kiado, Publishing House of the Hungarian Academy of Sciences, P.O. Box 245, H-1519 Budapest, Hungary. TEL 181-2134. FAX 166-6466. TELEX 22-6228 AKNYO H. Ed. Karoly Lapis. adv.; bk.rev.; charts; illus.; index. **Indexed:** Abstr.Bulg.Sci.Med.Lit., ASCA, Biol.Abstr., Chem.Abstr., Curr.Adv.Ecol.Sci., Curr.Cont., Excerp.Med., Helminthol.Abstr., Ind.Med., INIS Atomind., Sci.Cit.Ind., Vet.Bull.
—CASDDS; Faxon. **CCC.**
  Formerly (until 1982): Academiae Scientiarum Hungaricae. Acta Morphologica (ISSN 0001-6217)
  Description: Promotes an integrated approach to experimental medical subjects.

ACTA PHYSIOLOGICA PHARMACOLOGICA ET THERAPEUTICA LATINOAMERICANA; fisiologia, farmacologia, bioquimica y ciencias afines. see BIOLOGY — Physiology

ACTA PHYSIOLOGICA SCANDINAVICA. see BIOLOGY — Physiology

ACTA PHYSIOLOGICA SCANDINAVICA. SUPPLEMENTUM. see BIOLOGY — Physiology

ACTA REGIAE SOCIETATIS SCIENTARIUM ET LITTERARUM GOTHOBURGENSIS. BIOMEDICA. see BIOLOGY

ACTA STEREOLOGICA. see BIOLOGY

610 340	IT	ISSN 1121-2098
		CODEN: ATLMEQ

ACTA TECNOLOGIAE ET LEGIS MEDICAMENTI. 1990. 4/yr. L.50000 (foreign L.10000) (effective 1994). C E M Casa Editoriale Maccari, Via Trento 53, 43100 Parma, Italy. FAX 39-521-771268. circ. 1,000. **Indexed:** Excerp.Med. (1995-). **Document type:** academic/scholarly publication.
—BLDSC (0664.450000); CASDDS.

ACTA TROPICA; journal of biomedical sciences. see MEDICAL SCIENCES — Communicable Diseases

610	XR	ISSN 0001-7116
		CODEN: AUNCA9

ACTA UNIVERSITATIS CAROLINAE: MEDICA. (Text in English) 8/yr. $66. (Universita Karlova, Fakulta Vseobecneho Lekarstvi) Vydavatelstvi Karolinum, Ovocny trh 5, 116 36 Prague 1, Czech Republic. (Dist. by: Artia, Ve Smeckach 30, 111 27 Prague 1, Czech Republic) **Indexed:** Biol.Abstr., C.I.S. Abstr., Chem.Abstr., Dent.Ind., Diar.Dis.Res., Excerp.Med., Ind.Med. **Document type:** academic/scholarly publication.
—CASDDS.
  Description: Summarizes results in studies of anatomy.

610	FI	ISSN 0355-3221
		CODEN: AUODDK

ACTA UNIVERSITATIS OULUENSIS. SERIES D. MEDICA. (Text in English) 1972. irreg. price varies. University of Oulu, Publications Committee, P.O. Box 191, FIN-90101 Oulu, Finland. FAX 358-81-5375153. Ed. Seppo Lakovaara. cum.index. circ. 400. **Indexed:** Biol.Abstr., Curr.Adv.Cell & Devel.Biol., Curr.Adv.Ecol.Sci., Curr.Adv.Genetics & Molec.Biol., Psychol.Abstr. **Document type:** academic/scholarly publication, monographic series, proceedings.
—BLDSC (0585.290000).

610	XR	ISSN 0301-2514
		CODEN: AUPMAF

ACTA UNIVERSITATIS PALACKIANAE OLOMUCENSIS. FACULTATIS MEDICAE. (Text in English) 1955. q. 460 Kc.($70) Universita Palackeho, Olomouc, Lekarska Fakulta - Palacky University, Medical Faculty, Olomouc, Hnevotinska 3, 775 15 Olomouc, Czech Republic. TEL 42-68-5412551. FAX 42-68-541-3541. E-mail: VILIM@RISC.UPOL.CZ. Ed. Dr. Vilim Simanek. bk.rev.; charts; illus. circ. 400. **Indexed:** Biol.Abstr., C.I.S. Abstr., Chem.Abstr., Dent.Ind., Excerp.Med., Helminthol.Abstr., Ind.Med., INIS Atomind. **Document type:** academic/scholarly publication.
—BLDSC (0585.450000); CASDDS.
  Formerly: Acta Universitatis Palackianae, Facultatis Medicae (ISSN 0001-7167)
  Refereed Serial

MEDICAL SCIENCES

ACTA UNIVERSITATIS UPSALIENSIS. see *SCIENCES: COMPREHENSIVE WORKS*

610   **PO**
ACTUALIDADES MEDICAS. 104/yr. Rua Tristo Vaz 15-2o D., Lisbon, Portugal.

ACUPUNCTURE AND ELECTRO-THERAPEUTICS RESEARCH; the international journal. see *ALTERNATIVE MEDICINE*

ACUTE TOXICITY DATA. see *PHARMACY AND PHARMACOLOGY*

636.089 610   **AT**   **ISSN 0065-1907**
ADELAIDE. INSTITUTE OF MEDICAL AND VETERINARY SCIENCE. ANNUAL REPORT OF THE COUNCIL. 1937. a. free. Institute of Medical and Veterinary Science, Frome Rd., Adelaide, S.A., Australia. TEL 08-228-7317. FAX 08-2287538. Ed. Dr. R.J. Kimber. circ. 500.

610 069   **SA**   **ISSN 0379-6531**
ADLER MUSEUM BULLETIN. 1975. 3/yr. R.34.20 to individuals; libraries & academic institutions R.57; overseas R.66($20) (effective 1995). Adler Museum of the History of Medicine, P.O. Box 1038, Johannesburg 2001, South Africa. TEL 27-11-4899482. FAX 27-11-4899001. Eds. D.G Moyes, A. Dubb. bk.rev. circ. 1,000. (back issues avail.) **Document type:** academic/scholarly publication, newsletter.
—BLDSC (0681.740000).
Description: Covers topics relating to the history of medicine.

614.58   **US**   **ISSN 0894-587X**
RA790.A1   **CODEN: APMHEM**
ADMINISTRATION AND POLICY IN MENTAL HEALTH. 1972. bi-m. $295 (foreign $345) (effective 1996). Human Sciences Press, Inc. (Subsidiary of: Plenum Publishing Corp.), 233 Spring St., New York, NY 10013-1578. TEL 212-620-8000. FAX 212-463-0742. TELEX 23-421139. Ed. Saul Feldman. adv.; bk.rev.; abstr.; bibl. (reprint service avail. from ISI,UMI) **Indexed:** Abstr.Health Care Manage.Stud., Abstr.Soc.Work., C.I.J.E., Curr.Cont., Educ.Admin.Abstr., Excerp.Med., Hosp.Lit.Ind., PSI, Psychol.Abstr. (1973-), Sage Pub.Admin.Abstr., Soc.Work Res.& Abstr., SSCI. **Document type:** academic/scholarly publication.
—BLDSC (0681.956200); Faxon; Genuine Article; UMI; UnCover. **CCC.**
Formerly (until 1988): Administration in Mental Health (ISSN 0090-1180)
Description: Seeks to improve effectiveness of mental health and related human service programs.
Refereed Serial

610   **US**   **ISSN 0044-6335**
ADOLESCENT MEDICINE (WASHINGTON); report for the health professionals with teenage patients. 1969. m. $69 (foreign $75). Nathaniel Polster, Ed. & Pub., 821 Delaware Ave., S.W., Washington, DC 20024. TEL 202-488-7533. bk.rev./ stat. **Document type:** newsletter.

610   **US**   **ISSN 1050-7299**
ADULT'S HEALTH ADVISER. 1987. q. Whittle Communications L.P., 333 Main Ave., Knoxville, TN 37902. TEL 615-595-5300. Ed. Margot Leske. **Document type:** trade publication.
Formerly (until 1990): Healthwatch (ISSN 1047-3742)
Description: Provides medical information designed to enhance the well-being of adult patients and to support and reaffirm an internist's own advice.

610   **US**
ADVANCE FOR DIRECTORS IN REHABILITATION. 1992. bi-m. Merion Publications, 650 Park Ave., Box 61556, King of Prussia, PA 19406. TEL 610-265-7812. FAX 610-265-8971. E-mail: blammey@merion.com. Ed. Maria Wolf. adv.; B&W page $1764; trim 8 1/2 x 11. circ. 25,000. **Document type:** trade publication.

651 026   **US**   **ISSN 1061-3269**
ADVANCE FOR HEALTH INFORMATION PROFESSIONALS. 1991. bi-w. Merion Publications, 650 Park Ave. W., Box 61556, King of Prussia, PA 19406. TEL 610-265-7812. FAX 610-265-8971. E-mail: blammey@lmerion.com. Ed. Lisa A. Algeo. adv.: B&W page $1260, color page $1760; trim 10 x 13 1/4. circ. 44,583. **Document type:** trade publication.
Formerly (until 1992): Advance for Medical Record Professionals (ISSN 1061-3188)

615 613.62   **US**
ADVANCE FOR OCCUPATIONAL THERAPISTS. 1985. w. Merion Publications, 650 Park Ave., Box 61556, PA 19406. TEL 610-265-7812. FAX 610-265-8971. E-mail: blammey@merion.com. Ed. E.J. Brown. adv.: B&W page $1764, color page $2380; trim 10 x 13 1/4. circ. 53,548. **Document type:** trade publication.

610   **US**   **ISSN 0741-9783**
RC49   **CODEN: AJMHEE**
ADVANCES (KALAMAZOO); the journal of mind-body health. 1983. q. $49 to individuals (Canada & Mexico $54; elsewhere $56); institutions $79 (Canada & Mexico $84; elsewhere $86) (effective 1996). Fetzer Institute, 9292 West KL Ave., Kalamazoo, MI 49009-9398. TEL 616-375-2000; 800-875-2997. FAX 616-372-2163. (Subscr. to: Subscr. Dept. AVN, Box 3000, Denville, NJ 07834. TEL 800-875-2997) Ed. Harris Dienstfrey. bk.rev.; abstr.; bibl.; charts. circ. 6,300. (back issues avail.) **Indexed:** Psychol.Abstr. (1983-). **Document type:** academic/scholarly publication.
—BLDSC (0697.060000); Genuine Article; UnCover. **CCC.**
Description: Examines developments in the study and understanding of mind-body health. Encourages discussions and exchanges among researchers and healthcare professionals.

610   **US**   **ISSN 1072-4109**
▼**ADVANCES IN ANATOMIC PATHOLOGY.** 1994. bi-m. $95 to individuals (foreign $100); institutions $118 (foreign $137) (effective 1996). Lippincott - Raven Publishers, 227 E. Washington Sq., Philadelphia, PA 19106. TEL 215-238-4200. Eds. Dr. John K.C. Chan, Dr. John G. Batsakis. (back issues avail.) **Document type:** academic/scholarly publication.
—BLDSC (0698.790000). **CCC.**
Description: Provides specific coverage of the most recent key developments in anatomic and surgical pathology.
Refereed Serial

612.015 574.192   **UK**   **ISSN 0065-2571**
QP601.A1   **CODEN: AEZRA2**
ADVANCES IN ENZYME REGULATION. 1963. a. £310($493) (effective 1996). Elsevier Science Ltd., Pergamon, P.O. Box 800, Kidlington, Oxford OX5 1DX, England. TEL 44-1865-843000. FAX 44-1865-843010. E-mail: nlinfo-f@elsevier.nl; usinfo-f@elsevier.com; forinfo-kyf04035@niftyserve.or.jp; Site addr.: http://www.elsevier.nl/. (Subscr. in U.S. and Canada to: Elsevier Science, 660 White Plains Rd., Tarrytown, NY 10591-5153. TEL 914-524-9200. FAX 914-333-2444) Ed. George Weber. adv. (also avail. in microform from UMI) **Indexed:** Biol.Abstr., Chem.Abstr., Curr.Adv.Ecol.Sci., Curr.Cont., Ind.Med., Ind.Sci.Rev., Sci.Cit.Ind. **Document type:** academic/scholarly publication, proceedings.
—BLDSC (0705.950000); CASDDS; Faxon; Genuine Article; SWETS; UMI; UnCover. **CCC.**
Description: Evaluates topics including metabolic regulation, inborn errors of metabolism, metabolic diseases, diabetes, and cancer in the light of new research results.
Refereed Serial

ADVANCES IN EXPERIMENTAL MEDICINE AND BIOLOGY. see *BIOLOGY*

610   **US**   **ISSN 1054-1888**
RA410.A1
ADVANCES IN HEALTH ECONOMICS AND HEALTH SERVICES RESEARCH. SUPPLEMENT. 1990. irreg. J A I Press Inc., 55 Old Post Rd., No. 2, Box 1678, Greenwich, CT 06836-1678. TEL 203-661-7602.

610   **US**   **ISSN 0197-8322**
           CODEN: ADIRDF
ADVANCES IN INFLAMMATION RESEARCH. 1979. irreg., latest vol.12. price varies. Raven Press (Subsidiary of: Wolters Kluwer N.V.), 1185 Ave. of the Americas, New York, NY 10036. TEL 212-930-9500. FAX 212-869-3495. Ed. Gerald Weissmann. (reprint service avail. from UMI) **Indexed:** Biol.Abstr., Chem.Abstr., Curr.Adv.Ecol.Sci., Curr.Cont. **Document type:** monographic series.
—BLDSC (0709.130000); CASDDS. **CCC.**
Refereed Serial

ADVANCES IN MEDICAL SOCIAL SCIENCE; health and illness as view by anthropology, geography, history, psychology and sociology. see *SOCIAL SCIENCES: COMPREHENSIVE WORKS*

ADVANCES IN MEDICAL SOCIOLOGY. see *SOCIOLOGY*

615   **US**   **ISSN 1067-5698**
RS400   **CODEN: ADCHEO**
ADVANCES IN MEDICINAL CHEMISTRY. 1992. a. J A I Press Inc., 55 Old Post Rd., No. 2, Greenwich, CT 06836. TEL 203-661-7602. FAX 203-661-0792. Eds. Bruce Maryanoff, Cynthia Maryanoff.
—CASDDS.

ADVANCES IN PAIN RESEARCH AND THERAPY. see *MEDICAL SCIENCES — Psychiatry And Neurology*

616.07   **US**   **ISSN 1057-1256**
RB1
ADVANCES IN PATHOLOGY AND LABORATORY MEDICINE. 1988. a. $79.95 (residents $40) (effective 1996). Mosby - Year Book, Inc. (Chicago) (Subsidiary of: Times Mirror Company), 200 N. LaSalle St., Chicago, IL 60601-1080. TEL 312-726-9733. FAX 312-726-6075. TELEX 206155. (Subscr. to: 11830 Westline Industrial Dr., St. Louis, MO 63146. TEL 800-325-4177) Ed. Dr. Ronald S. Weinstein.
—BLDSC (0709.588200); Faxon.
Formerly: Advances in Pathology (ISSN 0889-3969)
Description: Presents a collection of original, fully referenced clinical reviews and articles in pathology.

610   **UK**   **ISSN 0269-0071**
           CODEN: APIREW
ADVANCES IN PINEAL RESEARCH. 1986. irreg. John Libbey & Company Ltd., 13 Smiths Yard, Summerley St., London SW18 4HR, England. TEL 0181-947-2777. FAX 0181-947-2664. E-mail: libbey@earlsfield.win-uk.net. **Document type:** monographic series.
—BLDSC (0710.070000); CASDDS; Faxon.

610   **BE**   **ISSN 0775-051X**
QP609.P56   **CODEN: APPHE3**
ADVANCES IN PROTEIN PHOSPHATASES. 1985. irreg., vol.8, 1994. price varies. Leuven University Press, Krakenstraat 3, B-3000 Leuven, Belgium. TEL 32-16-324175. FAX 32-16-323782. Ed. W. Merlevede. **Document type:** academic/scholarly publication, monographic series.
—BLDSC (0711.015000); CASDDS; Faxon.

615.1 610   **UK**   **ISSN 0044-6394**
           CODEN: ADRBBA
ADVERSE DRUG REACTION BULLETIN. (Editions in English, Italian) 1966. bi-m. £15 to institutions in the E.U. (N. America $30; elsewhere £18) (effective 1995). Chapman & Hall, Journals Department (Subsidiary of: International Thomson Publishing Group), 2-6 Boundary Row, London SE1 8HN, England. TEL 0171-865-0066. FAX 0171-522-9623. TELEX 290164 CHAPMA G. E-mail: journal@chall.mhs.compuserve.com. (Subscr. to: International Thomson Publishing Services Ltd., Cheriton House, North Way, Andover, Hants. SP10 5BE, England. TEL 01264-342713. FAX 01264-342807; N. American subscr. to: Chapman & Hall, Journals Promotion Department, One Penn Plaza, 41st Fl., New York, NY 10119. TEL 212-564-1060. FAX 212-564-1505) Ed. D. Davies. index. circ. 30,000. (looseleaf format; also avail. in microfilm from UMI; back issues avail.; reprint service avail.) **Indexed:** Biol.Abstr., Curr.Adv.Ecol.Sci., Excerp.Med., I.P.A., Ind.Med. **Document type:** academic/scholarly publication.
—BLDSC (0712.232000); EMDOCS; UMI.
Description: Provides comprehensive coverage on adverse drug reactions.
Refereed Serial

MEDICAL SCIENCES

610 011 GW ISSN 0175-5811
AERZTE ZEITUNG; die Tagesinformation fuer den Arzt. 1982. d. (Mon.-Fri.). DM.149.80. Aerzte Zeitung Verlagsgesellschaft mbH, Am Forsthaus Gravenbruch 5, 63263 Neu-Isenburg, Germany. TEL 06102-5060. FAX 06102-58740. E-mail: compuserve@100316,453. Ed. Hagen Rudolph; Pub. Gerald Kosaris. adv. contact: Ute Krille. bk.rev.; circ. 50,000. **Document type:** newspaper.
—CCC.

610 GW ISSN 0720-3489
AERZTEBLATT BADEN-WUERTTEMBERG. 1945. m. DM.185.40 (foreign DM.216) (effective 1995). (Landesaerztekammer Baden-Wuerttemberg) Verlagsgemeinschaft Gentner Verlag - Strobel Verlag, Forststr. 131, 70193 Stuttgart, Germany. TEL 0711-63672-0. FAX 0711-6367211. Ed. Juergen Dreher. adv. contact: G. Keuchen. bk.rev.; illus.; index. circ. 42,300. (back issues avail.) **Indexed:** Chem.Abstr. **Document type:** academic/scholarly publication.

610 GW ISSN 0939-3323
AERZTEBLATT MECKLENBURG-VORPOMMERN. 1990. m. DM.78 (students DM.58.50). Deutscher Aerzte-Verlag GmbH, Postfach 400265, 50832 Cologne, Germany. TEL 02234-7011-0. FAX 02234-7011444. circ. 6,900. **Document type:** trade publication.

610 GW ISSN 0001-9488
AERZTEBLATT RHEINLAND-PFALZ. 1948. m. DM.150. (Landesaerztekammer Rheinland-Pfalz) Verlag Kirchheim und Co. GmbH, Kaiserstr. 41, 55116 Mainz, Germany. TEL 06131-96070-0. FAX 06131-9607070. Ed. Prof. Dr. W. Ohler. adv. contact: Andreas Goerner. bk.rev.; abstr.; illus.; index, cum.index. circ. 15,600. **Document type:** academic/scholarly publication.
—CCC.
Description: Publication for physicians and specialists. Covers various medical issues, public health, medical research and news from local medical institutions.

610 GW ISSN 0938-8478
AERZTEBLATT SACHSEN. 1989. m. DM.157.80 (foreign DM.186) (effective 1995). (Saechsische Landesaerztekammer) Verlagsgemeinschaft Gentner Verlag - Strobel Verlag, Forststr. 131, 70193 Stuttgart, Germany. TEL 0711-63672-0. FAX 0711-6367211. Ed. Juergen Dreher. adv. contact: G. Keuchen. **Document type:** academic/scholarly publication.

610 GW
AERZTEBLATT SACHSEN-ANHALT. 1990. m. DM.72. H. Block und Druckhaus GmbH, Grosse-Diesdorfer-Str. 64, 39110 Magdeburg, Germany. TEL 0391-5616009. circ. 7,800. **Document type:** newsletter.
Formerly: Offizielles Aerzteblatt fuer Sachsen-Anhalt (ISSN 0938-9261)

610 GW ISSN 0863-5412
AERZTEBLATT THUERINGEN. 1990. m. DM.50 (foreign DM.68). Gustav Fischer Verlag Jena, Villengang 2, 07745 Jena, Germany. TEL 03641-626444. FAX 02641-626500. (Subscr. to: Postfach 100537, 07705 Jena, Germany) Ed. E. Beleites. adv.; bk.rev.; bibl.; charts; illus.; index. **Document type:** academic/scholarly publication.

616.98 GW ISSN 0930-6900
AERZTEBUCH; Fachaddressbuch des gesamten Gesundheitswesens Deutschland. (Text in German; summaries in English, French, German and Italian) 1977. a. DM.135. Aerztebuch Verlag GmbH, Postfach 360129, 10971 Berlin, Germany. TEL 030-6123049. circ. 8,500.

AERZTEZEITSCHRIFT FUER NATURHEILVERFAHREN. see ALTERNATIVE MEDICINE

616.1 GW ISSN 0001-9534
AERZTLICHE PRAXIS. 1948. 2/w. DM.126. Reed Elsevier Deutschland GmbH (Subsidiary of: Reed Elsevier group), Hans-Cornelius-Str. 4, 82166 Graefelfing, Germany. TEL 089-8917-0. FAX 089-853799. Ed. Burkhard Bierschenck; Pub. Wolfram Haase. adv. contact: Norbert Palm. bk.rev.; abstr.; bibl.; charts; illus.; stat.; index. **Indexed:** C.I.S. Abstr., INIS Atomind. **Document type:** newspaper.
—SWETS; UMI. CCC.

610 GW ISSN 0723-8010
AERZTLICHES MITTEILUNGSBLATT SCHWABEN.* 1980. bi-m. DM.36. c/o Rita Botzenhart, Frohsinnstr. 2, 86150 Augsburg, Germany. Ed. Dr. Klaus Hellmann. circ. 5,500. **Document type:** academic/scholarly publication.

610 910.202 GW ISSN 0946-2945
AERZTLICHES REISE & MEDIZIN JOURNAL. 1977. m. DM.90. Otto Hoffmanns Verlag GmbH, Possartstr. 9, 81679 Munich, Germany. TEL 089-41940440. FAX 089-41940449. Eds. Konrad Zweyer, Jan Murken; Pub. Konrad Zweyer. adv. contact: Ria Lorsbach. circ. 54,000. **Document type:** trade publication.

610 UK ISSN 0141-9536
AFRICA HEALTH. 1978. bi-m. £40($95) (overseas £60) (effective 1995). F S G Communications Ltd., Vine House, Fair Green, Reach, Cambridge CB5 0JD, England. TEL 01638-743633. FAX 01638-743998. Ed. Paul Chinnock; Pub. Bryan Pearson. adv. contact: Mark Temple-Smith. bk.rev.; circ. 5,000 (controlled). **Indexed:** ASSIA, Trop.Dis.Bull. **Document type:** academic/scholarly publication.
—BLDSC (0732.157700).
Description: Contains review articles, news, and letters for physicians working in Africa.

610 UK ISSN 0951-8266
AFRICA HEALTH MARKETLETTER. 10/yr. £225($375) (effective 1995). F S G Communications Ltd., Vine House, Fair Green, Reach, Cambridge CB5 0JD, England. TEL 01638-743633. FAX 01638-743998. Ed. Paul Chinnock; Pub. Bryan Pearson. adv. contact: Mark Temple-Smith. **Document type:** newsletter.
Description: Publishes news stories of interest to persons doing business in Africa's health care sector.

610 KE
AFRICA MEDICINE AND HEALTH. (Text in English) 1978. m. Oryx Publications Ltd., P.O. Box 40106, Nairobi, Kenya. adv.; illus. circ. 5,000.

610 KE ISSN 1022-9272
▼**AFRICAN JOURNAL OF HEALTH SCIENCES**. 1994. q. $30 to individuals (foreign $35); institutions $45 (foreign $50). (Kenya Medical Research Institute (KEMRI)) African Forum for Health Sciences, P.O. Box 54840, Nairobi, Kenya. TEL 254-2-722541. FAX 254-2-720030. Ed. Dr. Davy Koech. adv. contact: Lawrence Gikaru. bk.rev. circ. 1,000. **Document type:** academic/scholarly publication.
—BLDSC (0732.522500).
Description: Provides a forum to communicate research results and policy issues in the health sciences and related disciplines.
Refereed Serial

610 KE
AFRICAN JOURNAL OF MEDICAL PRACTICE. bi-m. KShs.1000 to individuals (rest of Africa $50; elsewhere $70); institutions KShs.1200 (rest of Africa $60; elsewhere $80) (effective 1995). (African Academy of Sciences) Academy Science Publishers, P.O. Box 14798, Nairobi, Kenya. TEL 254-2-884401. FAX 254-2-884406. TELEX 25446 AFACS. E-mail: aas@arcc.kaact.kenya-net.org. Ed. Dr. Tom Mboya. adv.: B&W page KShs.30000 ($500); color page $1500; adv. contact: Serah W. Mwanycky. **Document type:** academic/scholarly publication.
Description: Seeks to promote continued medical education and research in Africa by providing a forum for medical practitioners in the private and primary health care sectors.

610 NR ISSN 0309-3913
CODEN: AJMSDC
AFRICAN JOURNAL OF MEDICINE & MEDICAL SCIENCES. 1970. q. £N64($100) to individuals; institutions N£128 ($150) (effective 1995). (Postgraduate Institute for Medical Research and Training) Spectrum Books Ltd., College of Medicine, University College Hospital, Ibadan, Oyo State, Nigeria. TEL 234-22-400010. TELEX 31520 TEACHOS NG. Ed. B.O. Onadeko. adv. contact: A.O. Fadare. bk.rev. circ. 490. (back issues avail.; reprint service avail. from ISI) **Indexed:** Abstr.Hyg., Biol.Abstr., Chem.Abstr., Curr.Adv.Ecol.Sci., Curr.Cont., Excerp.Med., Helminthol.Abstr., Ind.Med., Trop.Dis.Bull. **Document type:** academic/scholarly publication.
—BLDSC (0732.530000); CASDDS; Faxon; UMI. CCC.
Formerly: African Journal of Medical Sciences (ISSN 0002-0028)
Description: Disemminates information about topics and issues in the medical sciences in Africa and throughout the world and provides an international forum to review international conferences in the medical sciences held in Africa.
Refereed Serial

610 FR ISSN 0299-3007
AFRIQUE MEDECINE ET SANTE. 1986. m. 300 F. S A P E F, 11 rue de Teheran, 75008 Paris, France. Ed. Michel de Breteuil. adv.; bk.rev. circ. 7,750.

610 SG ISSN 0002-0516
AFRIQUE MEDICALE. (Text in French) 1958. 11/yr. 250 F. (foreign 300 F.). B.P. 1826, Dakar, Senegal. TEL 23-48-80. FAX 22-56-30. TELEX 1300 ATT AFRICA. Ed. P. Correa. adv.; charts; illus. circ. 7,500. **Indexed:** Abstr.Hyg., Biol.Abstr., ExtraMED, Nutr.Abstr., Rev.Med.& Vet.Mycol., Trop.Dis.Bull.
●Also available on CD-ROM.

610 KE ISSN 0378-4851
AFYA. 1966. q. KShs.75 (Africa $10; Europe and Asia $13; America $15). African Medical and Research Foundation, P.O. Box 30125, Nairobi, Kenya. TEL 501301. FAX 506112. TELEX 23254. Ed. N.O. Bwibo. bk.rev. circ. 7,000.
Description: Contains information for and about medical and health workers.

610 IT ISSN 0392-3002
AGGIORNAMENTO MEDICO; rivista mensile di cultura e pratica medica. 1982. m. (10/yr.). L.60000 (foreign $60). Editrice Kurtis s.r.l., Via L. Zoja, 30, 20153 Milan, Italy. TEL 39-2-48202740. FAX 39-2-48201219. Ed.Bd. adv.: B&W page L.6350000, color page L.11150000; trim 210 x 280. charts; stat. circ. 80,000.
Description: Presents research papers and articles on a wide variety of topics in modern medicine.

612 615 FR ISSN 0002-1148
BF575.A3 CODEN: AGSOA6
AGRESSOLOGIE; revue internationale de physiobiologie et de pharmacologie appliquees aux effets de l'agression. (Text in English, French, German, Russian, Spanish) 1959. 10/yr. (Hopital Lariboisiere, Departement d'Anesthesie Reanimation) Societe de Presse Medicale, 14 rue Drouot, 75009 Paris, France. TEL 33-1-48249693. FAX 47-70-02-73. TELEX 660 484 F OSTRAPE. Ed. Dr. Bernard Weber. adv.; bk.rev.; charts; illus.; index. circ. 5,000. (also avail. in microform from UMI) **Indexed:** Biol.Abstr., Biotech.Abstr., Chem.Abstr., Excerp.Med. (until 1992; 1995-), Ind.Med., Nutr.Abstr. **Document type:** academic/scholarly publication.
—BLDSC (0738.750000); CASDDS; SWETS; UMI. CCC.
Description: Studies anaesthesia, transfusion, nutrition, emergency cardiology, toxicology.

AGRI DERGISI; turk algoloji (agri) derneginin yayin organdir. see MEDICAL SCIENCES — Psychiatry And Neurology

MEDICAL SCIENCES

610   IR
AHWAZ UNIVERSITY OF MEDICAL SCIENCES. SCIENTIFIC MEDICAL JOURNAL/MAJALLEH ELMI PESESHKI DANESHGAHE ELOME PEZESHKI AHWAZ. (Text in Persian; summaries in English) 1971. s-a. free. Ahwaz University of Medical Sciences, P.O. Box 189, Ahwaz, Iran. TEL 98-61-32036. FAX 98-61-61544. Ed. Dr. S. Zahedi. circ. 1,000. **Indexed:** ExtraMED. **Document type:** academic/scholarly publication.
●Also available on CD-ROM.
Description: Publishes original clinical research papers, review articles, case reports and contributions on all subjects relevant to medicine.

610   JA
AICHI IHO/AICHI MEDICAL REPORT. (Text in Japanese) 1956. 3/m. 3600 Yen. Aichi Ihosha, Aichiken Ishikai, 14-28, Sakae 4-chome, Naka-ku, Nagoya-shi, Aichi-ken 460, Japan.

610   JA   ISSN 0286-9187
AICHI IKA DAIGAKU KISO KAGAKKA KIYO/AICHI MEDICAL UNIVERSITY. BULLETIN OF THE LIBERAL ARTS AND SCIENCE COURSE. (Text in English, Japanese; summaries in English) 1974. a. Aichi Ika Daigaku - Aichi Medical University, 21, Yazakokarimata, Nagakutecho, Aichi-gun, Aichiken 480-11, Japan.

610   JA   ISSN 0301-0902   CODEN: AIDZAC
AICHI MEDICAL UNIVERSITY ASSOCIATION. JOURNAL/AICHI IKA DAIGAKU IGAKKAI ZASSHI. (Text in English and Japanese; summaries in English) 1973. q. 3000 Yen. Aichi Medical University Association, 21, Yazakokarimata, Nagakutecho, Aichi-gun, Aichi-ken 480-11, Japan. Ed. Kazumi Takeya. circ. 1,700. **Indexed:** Chem.Abstr., Excerp.Med., INIS Atomind. **Document type:** academic/scholarly publication.
—CASDDS.

610   JA
AIJINKAI IGAKU KENKYUSHI/AIJINKAI MEDICAL JOURNAL. (Text in Japanese) 3/yr. Aijinkai, 4-12, Toganocho, Kita-ku, Osaka 530, Japan.

610   JA   ISSN 0386-4502
AIMIKKU/I M I C. (Text in Japanese) 1978. q. Kokusai Igaku Joho Senta - International Medical Information Center, 2-14 Sumiyoshicho, Shinjuku-ku, Tokyo 162, Japan.

610   UA   ISSN 0002-2144   CODEN: AIMJA9
AIN SHAMS MEDICAL JOURNAL. 1949. bi-m. Ain Shams University, University Hospital, Abbassia, Cairo, Egypt. (Co-sponsor: Ain Shams Clinical and Scientific Society) Ed. Ahmed Ghareeb. adv.; bk.rev.; abstr.; charts; illus.; stat. circ. 2,000. **Indexed:** Biol.Abstr., C.I.S. Abstr., Chem.Abstr., Excerp.Med., Helminthol.Abstr., Trop.Dis.Bull.
—CASDDS.

616.98   US   ISSN 1067-991X
AIR MEDICAL JOURNAL. 1986. bi-m. $30. J E M S Communications, 1947 Camino Vida Roble, Ste.200, Box 2789, Carlsbad, CA 92008. TEL 619-431-9797. FAX 619-431-8176. Ed. L.M. Gilbert. adv.; bk.rev.; illus. circ. 10,000.
—BLDSC (0776.349990).
Formerly (until 1993): Journal of Air Medical Transport (ISSN 1046-9095); Formed by the 1989 merger of: AeroMedical Journal (ISSN 0894-8321); Hospital Aviation Journal (ISSN 0740-8315)
Description: News and continuing educational material for professionals involved in emergency air care services.

610   JA   ISSN 0917-9267
AIRAGUN ISHIKAI IGAKKAISHI/AIRA COUNTY MEDICAL ASSOCIATION. JOURNAL. (Text in Japanese) 1988. a. Airagun Ishikai - Aira County Medical Association, 124-1, Uchiyamada, Hayatocho, Aira-gun, Kagoshima-ken 899-51, Japan.

610   PL   ISSN 0067-6489   CODEN: RJMBA9
AKADEMIA MEDYCZNA W BIALYMSTOKU. ROCZNIKI/ANNALES ACADEMIAE MEDICAE BIALOSTOCENSIS. (Supplement avail.: Bibliografia Publikacji Naukowych Pracownikow Naukowych Akademii Medycznej w Bialymstoku (ISSN 0301-1941)) (Text and summaries in English, Polish) 1955. a. $20 per vol. Akademia Medyczna w Bialymstoku, Ul. Kilinskiego 1, 15-230 Bialystok, Poland. TEL 48-85-424781. FAX 48-85-424907. TELEX 2200 AMPL. Ed. Jan Olbrmoski. (back issues avail.) **Indexed:** Ind.Med. **Document type:** academic/scholarly publication.
—CASDDS.

610   IR
AKHBAR-E PEZESHKI. w. Dr. T. Foruzin, Ed. & Pub., 86 Ghaem Magham Farahani Ave., Teheran, Iran.

610   JA   ISSN 0386-6106   CODEN: AKIGDV
AKITA IGAKU/AKITA JOURNAL OF MEDICINE. (Text in English, Japanese; summaries in English) 1974. q. 10000 Yen. Akita Daigaku, Igakubu - Akita University, School of Medicine, 1-1, Hondo 1-chome, Akita-shi, Akita-ken 010, Japan. Ed. Kentaro Yoshimura. adv. contact: Chiyoshi Nagasawa. circ. 800. **Indexed:** Chem.Abstr., INIS Atomind. **Document type:** academic/scholarly publication.
—BLDSC (0785.589810); CASDDS.
Refereed Serial

610   JA   ISSN 0002-368X
AKITA JOURNAL OF RURAL MEDICINE/AKITAKEN NOSON IGAKKAI ZASSHI. 1954. a. Akita Association of Rural Medicine - Akitaken Noson Igakkai, 64-2, Inokawara, Yabase, Akita-shi, Akita-ken 010, Japan. Ed. Dr. Masakazu Tatsumi. adv.; abstr.; charts; illus.; stat.; cum.index.
—BLDSC (0785.590000).

610   JA   ISSN 0286-7656   CODEN: AKISAU
AKITAKEN ISHIKAI ZASSHI/AKITA MEDICAL JOURNAL. (Text in Japanese) 1949. s-a. Akitaken Ishikai - Akita Medical Association, 6-6, Kubotamachi, Senshu, Akita-shi, Akita-ken 010, Japan. **Indexed:** Chem.Abstr., INIS Atomind.
—CASDDS.

AKTUELLE ERNAEHRUNGSMEDIZIN; Klinik und Praxis. see *NUTRITION AND DIETETICS*

AKUPUNKTUR: THEORIE UND PRAXIS. see *ALTERNATIVE MEDICINE*

615.89   GW   ISSN 0172-9322
DER AKUPUNKTURARZT - AURIKULOTHERAPEUT. 1980. q. DM.92 (students DM.69). (Deutsche Akademie fuer Akupunktur und Aurikulo-Medizin) M M V Medizin Verlag, Neumarkter Str. 18, 81673 Munich, Germany. TEL 089-43189648. FAX 089-43189633. Ed. Dr. F.R. Bahr. adv.; bk.rev. (back issues avail.) **Document type:** academic/scholarly publication.
—CCC.

610   US
ALABAMA EPIC. 1981. q. American College of Emergency Physicians, Alabama Chapter, Box 210727, Montgomery, AL 36121-0727. Ed. Kathryn Lauder. circ. 250.
Description: Covers emergency medicine.

610   US   ISSN 0738-4947
ALABAMA MEDICINE. 1931. m. $30. Medical Association of the State of Alabama, 19 S. Jackson St., Montgomery, AL 36104. TEL 205-263-6441. Ed. Dr. Claude R. Brown, Jr. adv.; bk.rev.; bibl.; illus.; index. circ. 4,600. **Indexed:** Chem.Abstr., Excerp.Med., Ind.Med., INIS Atomind, Rev.Med.& Vet.Mycol.
—BLDSC (0786.522920); Faxon.
Formerly: Medical Association of the State of Alabama. Journal (ISSN 0025-7044)

610   US   ISSN 0002-4414
ALAMEDA-CONTRA COSTA MEDICAL ASSOCIATION. BULLETIN. 1945. m. membership. Alameda-Contra Costa Medical Association, 6230 Claremont Ave., Oakland, CA 94618. TEL 510-654-5383. FAX 510-654-8959. Ed. Dr. James Richardson. adv. circ. 2,950. **Document type:** bulletin.

610   US   ISSN 0002-4538
ALASKA MEDICINE. 1959. q. $30. Alaska State Medical Association, American Society for Circumpolar Health, 4107 Laurel St., Anchorage, AK 99508. TEL 907-562-2662. FAX 907-561-2063. Ed. Donald Rogers. adv. contact: Verna Paluba. bk.rev.; index. circ. 1,400. (reprint service avail. from UMI) **Document type:** academic/scholarly publication.
—BLDSC (0786.528000); Faxon; UMI.
Refereed Serial

610   UA   ISSN 0516-5849
ALEXANDRIA MEDICAL JOURNAL. (Text in Arabic, English, French) 1955. q. Alexandria Medical Association, 4 G. Carducci St., Alexandria, Egypt. Ed. Amin Rida. circ. 1,500. **Indexed:** Biol.Abstr., C.I.S. Abstr., Excerp.Med., Nutr.Abstr.

574.1 612   DK   ISSN 0105-3639   CODEN: ABSYB2
ALFRED BENZON SYMPOSIUM. PROCEEDINGS. 1969. irreg. price varies. Munksgaard International Publishers Ltd., Book Division, 35 Noerre Soegade, P.O. Box 2148, DK-1016 Copenhagen K, Denmark. TEL 45-33-1270-30. FAX 45-33-12-93-87. **Indexed:** Biol.Abstr., Chem.Abstr.
—BLDSC (0786.991000); CASDDS. **CCC**.

610   AE
ALGERIE MEDICALE. 1964. 2/yr. Union Medicale Algerienne, 3 bd. Zirout Youcef, Algiers, Algeria. adv. circ. 3,000. **Indexed:** Biol.Abstr.

610   US   ISSN 0098-3772
ALLEGHENY COUNTY MEDICAL SOCIETY. BULLETIN. 1911. s-m. (except July and Aug.) $35 to profit organizations; non-profit organizations $25. Allegheny County Medical Society, 713 Ridge Ave., Pittsburgh, PA 15212. TEL 412-321-5030. FAX 412-321-5323. Ed. Dr. Jack E. Wilberger. adv.; bk.rev.; charts; illus.; index. circ. 3,700 (controlled). (back issues avail.) **Document type:** trade publication, bulletin.

616.07   GW   ISSN 0172-7249
DER ALLGEMEINARZT. q. DM.84.60 (students DM.51.30). (Fachverbandes Deutscher Allgemeinarzte e.V.) Verlag Kirchheim und Co. GmbH, Kaiserstr. 41, 55116 Mainz, Germany. TEL 06131-96070-0. FAX 06131-9607070. Ed.Bd. adv. contact: Andreas Goerner. charts; illus. **Document type:** academic/scholarly publication.
—CCC.

ALLIANCE (CHARLESTON). see *COLLEGE AND ALUMNI*

ALLIED HEALTH EDUCATION DIRECTORY. see *EDUCATION — Guides To Schools And Colleges*

610 371.42   US
ALLIED HEALTH GRADUATE. 1991. a. Peterson's - C O G Publishing, 16030 Ventura Blvd., Ste. 560, Encino, CA 91436. TEL 818-789-5293. FAX 818-789-5488. Ed. Al Austin. adv.: B&W page $4150; trim 8 x 10 3/4. circ. 30,000.
Description: Focuses on the many career opportunities and employment challenges available in this field.

610   SY
AL-MAJALLA AL-TOUBIYA AL-ARABIYA. m. Arab Medical Commission, Al-Jala St., Damascus, Syria. Ed. Adnan Takriti.

610   UA
AL-MAJALLAH AL-TIBBIYYAH AL-MISRIYYAH AL-JADIDAH/NEW EGYPTIAN JOURNAL OF MEDICINE.* vol.2, 1988. q. Egyptian Junior Medical Doctors Association, Medical Information and Publishing Center, c/o Egyptian Medical Association, 42 Sharia Kasr El-Aini, Cairo, Egypt. **Indexed:** ExtraMED. **Document type:** academic/scholarly publication.
●Also available on CD-ROM.

613   US   ISSN 0893-5025
ALTERNATIVES (INGRAM). Variant title: Alternatives for the Health Conscious Individual. 1985. m. $69. Mountain Home Publishing, Box 829, Ingram, TX 78025. TEL 210-367-4492. Ed. Dr. David Williams; Pub. Brenda Lyman. circ. 200,000. (also avail. in audio cassette; back issues avail.) **Document type:** newsletter.
Description: Emphasizes natural therapies and self-help techniques to obtain optimal health without the use of drugs or surgery.

MEDICAL SCIENCES 4171

610 US
ALTSCHUL SYMPOSIA SERIES. 1991. irreg., vol.2, 1993. price varies. (Altschul Symposium) Plenum Publishing Corp., 233 Spring St., New York, NY 10012-1578. TEL 212-620-8000. FAX 212-463-0742. Eds. Sergey Fedoroff, Gary Burkholder. (back issues avail.) **Document type:** proceedings.

ALZHEIMER'S ASSOCIATION NEWSLETTER. see *GERONTOLOGY AND GERIATRICS*

610 362.7 UK ISSN 1355-5626
▼**AMBULATORY CHILD HEALTH.** 1995. q. £90 (U.S. & Canada $135). Radcliffe Medical Press Ltd., 18 Marcham Rd., Abingdon, Oxon OX14 1AA, England. TEL 01235-528820. FAX 01235-528830. Eds. Rashmin Tamhne, Frances Glascoe. adv.; bk.rev.; circ. 1,000 (paid). **Document type:** academic/scholarly publication.
Description: Aims to encourage innovation in the early detection of clinical, developmental and social problems, and to promote multidisciplinary teamwork at clinic, organization and community levels.

610 US ISSN 0893-7400
AMERICAN ACADEMY OF PHYSICIAN ASSISTANTS. JOURNAL. 1988. 10/yr. $42 to individuals (foreign $57); institutions $62 (foreign $77). Medical Economics Publishing Co., Inc., Five Paragon Dr., Montvale, NJ 07645. TEL 201-358-7200. FAX 201-573-1045. Ed. Leslie A. Kole. adv.; bk.rev.; abstr.; charts; illus. circ. 25,782. (also avail. in microform from UMI; back issues avail.) **Document type:** academic/scholarly publication.
—BLDSC (4683.732500); UMI. **CCC.**
Description: Focuses on the clinical conditions seen in the primary care and specialty settings where physician assistants practice.
Refereed Serial

651.5 370 US ISSN 0745-2624
AMERICAN ASSOCIATION FOR MEDICAL TRANSCRIPTION. JOURNAL. 1985. bi-m. $150. American Association for Medical Transcription, Box 576187, Modesto, CA 95357. TEL 209-551-0883. FAX 209-551-9317. Ed. Claudia Tessier. adv.: B&W page $750; trim 8 1/2 x 11; adv. contact: Lori Smith. index. circ. 11,200. **Document type:** trade publication.
Description: Features medical and non-medical educational articles for the medical transcriptionist as well as medical word lists, updates on medical terminology and discoveries, technology, professional opportunities, and information about products.

610 US ISSN 8756-6095
AMERICAN ASSOCIATION OF BLOOD BANKS. NEWS BRIEFS. 1981. 11/yr. membership only. American Association of Blood Banks, 8101 Glenbrook Rd., Bethesda, MD 20814. TEL 301-907-6977. FAX 301-907-6895. Ed. Elizabeth A. Smith. circ. 12,000. **Document type:** newsletter.

610 US ISSN 0270-2673
AMERICAN ASSOCIATION OF TISSUE BANKS NEWSLETTER. 1976. q. membership. American Association of Tissue Banks, 1350 Beverly Rd., Ste. 220A, McLean, VA 22101. TEL 703-827-9582. FAX 703-356-2198. Ed. J. Mowe. circ. 1,000 (controlled). **Document type:** newsletter.

AMERICAN BLOOD RESOURCES ASSOCIATION. JOURNAL. see *BIOLOGY*

610 US ISSN 0893-8652
CODEN: JABPEJ
AMERICAN BOARD OF FAMILY PRACTICE. JOURNAL. Key Title: Journal of the American Board of Family Practice. Abbreviated title: J A B F P. 1988. bi-m. $58 (effective 1995). American Board of Family Practice, 2228 Young Dr., Lexington, KY 40505. TEL 606-269-5626. FAX 606-266-9699. TELEX 5106017779 NEJM BOS. Ed. Dr. John Geyman. adv.; bk.rev.; abstr.; bibl.; charts; illus.; index. circ. 50,223. (also avail. in microfiche; microfilm; back issues avail.) **Indexed:** FAMLI.
●Also available online.
Also available on CD-ROM.
—BLDSC (4683.950000); SWETS; UMI; UnCover. **CCC.**
Description: Covers clinical studies that have relevance for improved patient care in family medicine.
Refereed Serial

610 US ISSN 0272-9741
R729.5.S6
AMERICAN BOARD OF MEDICAL SPECIALTIES. ANNUAL REPORT & REFERENCE HANDBOOK. 1970. a. $3. American Board of Medical Specialties, 1007 Church St., Ste. 404, Evanston, IL 60201-5913. TEL 708-491-9091. FAX 708-328-3596. Ed. Dr. J. Lee Dockery. circ. 6,000.
Formerly: American Board of Medical Specialties. Annual Report (ISSN 0146-5872)

610 US
AMERICAN BOARD OF PRACTICE. JOURNAL. 6/yr. Massachusetts Medical Society, 1440 Main St., Waltham, MA 02154. TEL 617-893-3800. FAX 617-893-0413. Ed. John Geyman. circ. 39,000. **Document type:** bulletin.

616.98 US ISSN 0065-7778
CODEN: TACCAN
AMERICAN CLINICAL AND CLIMATOLOGICAL ASSOCIATION. TRANSACTIONS. 1881. a. $35 to members. (American Clinical and Climatological Association) Noverly Press, 1314 Guilford Ave., Baltimore, MD 21202-3995. TEL 507-284-3320. FAX 507-284-2053. (And: Lynwood H. Smith, M.D., Sec.-Treas., Mayo Clinic, 1601 Guggenheim, 200 First St., S.W., Rochester, MN 55905; Mary Allen, M.D., 1 Country Club Ln., Pelham Manor, NY 10803. TEL 914-738-0211) circ. 500. **Indexed:** Biol.Abstr., Excerp.Med., Ind.Med. **Document type:** academic/scholarly publication.
—BLDSC (8886.300000); CASDDS.

610 370.196 US
AMERICAN COLLEGE OF INTERNATIONAL PHYSICIANS. ANNUAL PROGRAM AND REPORT. a. American College of International Physicians, 711 Second St., N.E., Ste. 200, Washington, DC 20002. TEL 202-544-7498. FAX 202-546-7105. **Document type:** newsletter.

610 US
AMERICAN COLLEGE OF MEDICAL QUALITY FOCUS. 1973. m. $70 to libraries; others $75. American College of Medical Quality, 9005 Congressional Ct., Potomac, MD 20854-4608. TEL 301-365-3570. FAX 301-365-3202. Ed. Ralph H. Rosenblum. adv.; bk.rev. circ. 2,200. (tabloid format; back issues avail.) **Document type:** newsletter.
Former titles (until 1993): American College of Medical Quality Newsletter; American College of Utilization Review Physicians Newsletter.
Description: Covers quality assurance, utilization review, risk management, cost containment, seminar announcements, and news briefs.

610 US ISSN 1053-0967
R15
AMERICAN COLLEGE OF PHYSICIANS. MEMBERSHIP DIRECTORY. 1929. irreg., latest 1989. American College of Physicians, Independence Mall W., Sixth St. at Race, Philadelphia, PA 19106-1572. TEL 215-351-2400. **Document type:** directory.
Formerly (until 1980): American College of Physicians. Directory (ISSN 0197-5455)

610 US ISSN 0279-9529
AMERICAN COLLEGE OF PHYSICIANS OBSERVER. 1981. m. $18. American College of Physicians, Independence Mall W., Sixth St. at Race, Philadelphia, PA 19106-1572. TEL 215-351-2400. Ed. Robert Spanier. adv.; index. circ. 67,468 (controlled). (tabloid format) **Document type:** bulletin.
—**CCC.**

AMERICAN COLLEGE OF TOXICOLOGY. JOURNAL. see *ENVIRONMENTAL STUDIES — Toxicology And Environmental Safety*

610 US ISSN 0002-838X
R11
AMERICAN FAMILY PHYSICIAN. 1950. 16/yr. $72 (foreign $99) to individuals; institutions $88 (foreign $120); students, residents $45 (foreign $75). American Academy of Family Physicians, 8880 Ward Pkwy., Kansas City, MO 64114. TEL 816-333-9700. FAX 816-333-0303. Ed. Sharon Morey. bk.rev.; charts; illus.; mkt.; pat.; tr.lit.; s-a. index, cum.index; circ. 150,000 (controlled). (also avail. in microfilm from UMI,PMC; reprint service avail. from UMI) **Indexed:** A.D.& D., Adol.Ment.Hlth.Abstr., AIM, Bus.Ind., C.I.S.Abstr., Chem.Abstr., CINAHL, Curr.Cont., Dent.Ind., Dok.Arbeitsmed., Excerp.Med., FAMLI, Gen.Sci.Ind., Helminthol.Abstr., Hlth.Ind., Ind.Med., Ind.Sci.Rev., Med.Care Rev., NRN, Nutr.Abstr., Protozool.Abstr., Rev.Med.& Vet.Mycol., Sci.Cit.Ind., Tr.& Indus.Ind.
●Also available online. Vendor(s): Lexis-Nexis, Ovid Technologies.
Also available on CD-ROM.
—BLDSC (0814.700000); Faxon; Genuine Article; SWETS; UMI; UnCover.
Formerly (until 1970): G P (ISSN 0016-3600)
Description: Provides continuing medical education for doctors involved with primary care.
Refereed Serial

614.8 340 US ISSN 1063-2026
AMERICAN GROUP PRACTICE ASSOCIATION. EXECUTIVE NEWS SERVICE. 1980. 22/yr. membership. American Group Practice Association, 1422 Duke St., Alexandria, VA 22314. TEL 703-838-0033. FAX 703-548-1890. Ed. Brent Miller. circ. 2,200. (looseleaf format; back issues avail.) **Document type:** newsletter.
Description: Current federal legislation and regulations and health law affecting physicians, hospitals and clinics with emphasis on Medicare reimbursement, health politics, and quality of care.

610 US ISSN 0098-2377
RA977
AMERICAN GROUP PRACTICE ASSOCIATION DIRECTORY. 1952. a. $125. American Group Practice Association, 1422 Duke St., Alexandria, VA 22314. TEL 703-838-0033. FAX 703-548-1890. adv. circ. 2,500. **Document type:** directory.
Formerly: American Association of Medical Clinics. Directory (ISSN 0569-2679)

610 US ISSN 1060-5487
RA976 CODEN: JAHIES
AMERICAN HEALTH INFORMATION MANAGEMENT ASSOCIATION. JOURNAL. 1929. m. $72. American Health Information Management Association, 919 N. Michigan Ave., Ste. 1400, Chicago, IL 60611-1601. TEL 312-787-2672. Ed. Mary Campbell. adv.; bk.rev.; charts; illus.; stat.; index. circ. 34,000. **Indexed:** Abstr.Health Care Manage.Stud., CINAHL, Curr.Cont., Excerp.Med., Hosp.Lit.Ind.
—BLDSC (4682.200000); Genuine Article; SWETS.
Former titles (until 1990): American Medical Record Association. Journal (ISSN 0273-9976); (until 1980): Medical Record News (ISSN 0025-7486)

613.081 618.082 US ISSN 1047-2517
AMERICAN INSTITUTE OF STRESS. NEWSLETTER. 1985. m. $35 (foreign $45). American Institute of Stress, 124 Park Ave., Yonkers, NY 10703. TEL 914-963-1200. FAX 914-965-6267. Ed. Dr. Paul J. Rosch. bk.rev. circ. 2,000. (back issues avail.; reprint service avail.) **Document type:** academic/scholarly publication, newsletter.
Description: Covers all stress related subjects - stress and cancer, cardiovascular, GI, and skin disease, job stress, stress reduction techniques, psychological stress, stress of retirement, post traumatic stress disorder, and stress assessment and measurement.

AMERICAN INTERNATIONAL JOURNAL OF ARTS, SCIENCES, ENGINEERING AND MEDICINE. see *ART*

AMERICAN JOURNAL OF ACUPUNCTURE. see *ALTERNATIVE MEDICINE*

MEDICAL SCIENCES

615.89 US ISSN 0192-415X
R601 CODEN: AJCMBA
AMERICAN JOURNAL OF CHINESE MEDICINE. 1973. 3/yr. (in 4 vols.). $75. Institute for Advanced Research in Asian Science and Medicine, Box 67336, Chestnut Hill, MA 02167-0003. TEL 617-739-1182. FAX 617-739-1183. Ed. Dr. John J. Kao. bk.rev. (also avail. in microfilm from UMI) **Indexed:** Biol.Abstr., Curr.Adv.Ecol.Sci., Curr.Cont., Excerp.Med., Helminthol.Abstr., Ind.Med., Med.Care Rev., Psychol.Abstr. **Document type:** academic/scholarly publication.
—BLDSC (0822.700000); CASDDS; Genuine Article; SWETS; UMI; Uncover.
   Former titles (until 1978): Comparative Medicine East and West (ISSN 0147-2917); (until 1977): American Journal of Chinese Medicine (ISSN 0090-2942)
   Description: Covers basic science and clinical research in indigenous medical techniques and therapeutic procedures, medicinal plants, and traditional medicine.

AMERICAN JOURNAL OF CLINICAL NUTRITION; a journal reporting the practical application of our world-wide knowledge of nutrition. see NUTRITION AND DIETETICS

616.07 574.2 US ISSN 0002-9173
RB1 CODEN: AJCPAI
AMERICAN JOURNAL OF CLINICAL PATHOLOGY. (Supplement avail.: Pathology Patterns (ISSN 1050-9194)) 1931. m. $180 to individuals (foreign $265; institutions $290 (foreign $355) (effective 1996). (American Society of Clinical Pathologists) Lippincott - Raven Publishers, 227 E. Washington Sq., Philadelphia, PA 19106. TEL 215-238-4200. Ed. Dr. Mark R. Wick; Pub. Marcia E. Serepy. adv. contact: Jennifer Bass. illus.; index, cum.index. circ. 15,323. (also avail. in microform from UMI) **Indexed:** AIM, Biol.Abstr., Biotech.Abstr., C.I.S.Abstr., Chem.Abstr., Curr.Adv.Cancer Res., Curr.Adv.Ecol.Sci., Curr.Adv.Genetics & Molec.Biol., Curr.Cont., Dairy Sci.Abstr., Dent.Ind., Diar.Dis.Res., Dok.Arbeitsmed., Excerp.Med., Hosp.Lit.Ind., Ind.Med., Ind.Sci.Rev., Ind.Vet., INIS Atomind., Lead Abstr., Med.& Surg.Dermat., Protozool.Abstr., Rev.Med.& Vet.Mycol., Sci.Cit.Ind., SSCI, Zincscan. **Document type:** academic/scholarly publication.
—BLDSC (0824.000000); CASDDS; Faxon; Genuine Article; SWETS; UMI; Uncover. **CCC.**
   Description: Helps pathologists and other clinical laboratory scientists keep their professional knowledge current. Publishes original investigations and observation in clinical pathology, the articles cover a broad spectrum of subspecialty topics.
   Refereed Serial

616.5 US ISSN 0193-1091
RL95 CODEN: AJODDB
AMERICAN JOURNAL OF DERMATOPATHOLOGY. 1979. bi-m. $167 to individuals (foreign $203); institutions $270 (effective 1996). (International Society of Dermatopathology) Lippincott - Raven Press, 227 E. Washington Sq., Philadelphia, PA 19106. TEL 215-238-4200. Ed. Clifton R. White, Jr. adv. contact: Phyllis Noyes. bk.rev.; abstr.; charts; illus.; index. circ. 2,500. (also avail. in microform; back issues avail.; reprint service avail. from UMI) **Indexed:** Curr.Adv.Cancer Res., Curr.Cont., Dent.Ind., Excerp.Med., Ind.Med., Ind.Sci.Rev., Ind.Vet., Med.& Surg.Dermat., Rev.Med.& Vet.Mycol., Sci.Cit.Ind., Small Anim.Abstr. **Document type:** academic/scholarly publication.
—BLDSC (0824.240000); CASDDS; Faxon; Genuine Article; SWETS; UMI; Uncover. **CCC.**
   Refereed Serial

610 US ISSN 0002-9262
CODEN: AJEPAS
AMERICAN JOURNAL OF EPIDEMIOLOGY. 1921. s-m. (2 vols./yr.). $250 (foreign $258); newsstand price: $15. (Society for Epidemiologic Research) Johns Hopkins University, School of Hygiene and Public Health, 2007 E. Monument St., Baltimore, MD 21205. TEL 410-955-3441. FAX 410-955-0344. Ed. Moyes Szklo. adv.; illus.; index, cum.index. circ. 6,200. (also avail. in microform; microfilm from WWS) **Indexed:** Abstr.Health Care Manage.Stud., Abstr.Hyg., Behav.Med.Abstr., Bibl.Dev.Med.& Child Neur., Biol.Abstr., Biol.Dig., Biostat., C.I.S.Abstr., Chem.Abstr., CINAHL, Curr.Adv.Cancer Res., Curr.Adv.Ecol.Sci., Curr.Cont., Dairy Sci.Abstr., Diab.Cont., Diar.Dis.Res., Dok.Arbeitsmed., Excerp.Med., Helminthol.Abstr., IDA, Ind.Med., Ind.Sci.Rev., Ind.Vet., INIS Atomind., Lab.Haz.Bull., Med.& Surg.Dermat., NRN, Nutr.Abstr., Poult.Abstr., Protozool.Abstr., Rev.Appl.Entomol., Rev.Plant Path, Risk Abstr., Sci.Cit.Ind., Sel.Water Res.Abstr., Small Anim.Abstr., So.Pac.Per.Ind., Sport Fish.Abstr., SSCI, Trop.Dis.Bull., Vet.Bull., W.R.C.Inf., Wild.Rev., Zoo.Rec. **Document type:** academic/scholarly publication.
—BLDSC (0824.600000); Faxon; Genuine Article; SWETS; Uncover. **CCC.**
   Former titles: American Journal of Hygiene; Journal of Hygiene (ISSN 0096-5294)
   Refereed Serial

AMERICAN JOURNAL OF HYPERTENSION. see MEDICAL SCIENCES — Cardiovascular Diseases

AMERICAN JOURNAL OF LAW & MEDICINE. see LAW

AMERICAN JOURNAL OF MEDICAL GENETICS. see BIOLOGY — Genetics

AMERICAN JOURNAL OF MEDICAL GENETICS. SUPPLEMENT. see BIOLOGY — Genetics

610 US ISSN 0002-9343
RC60 CODEN: AJMEAZ
THE AMERICAN JOURNAL OF MEDICINE. 1946. m. $215 to institutions outside the Americas; $125 to institutions in U.S (effective 1996). Excerpta Medica, Inc. (Subsidiary of: Reed Elsevier Medical group), 105 Raider Blvd., Belle Mead, NJ 08502. TEL 908-874-8550. FAX 908-874-8419. (Subscr. to: Box 3085, Princeton, NJ 08543-3085) Eds. J. Claud Bennett, Monica Schmidt. adv.; bibl.; illus.; index. circ. 53,751. (also avail. in microform; back issues avail.) **Indexed:** Abstr.Hyg., Abstr.Inter.Med., AIM, Behav.Med.Abstr., Biol.Abstr., Biol.Dig., Biostat., Biotech.Abstr., C.I.S.Abstr., Chem.Abstr., CINAHL, Curr.Adv.Biochem., Curr.Adv.Cancer Res., Curr.Adv.Cell & Devel.Biol., Curr.Adv.Ecol.Sci., Curr.Adv.Genetics & Molec.Biol., Curr.Cont., Dairy Sci.Abstr., Dent.Ind., Diab.Cont., Diar.Dis.Res., Dok.Arbeitsmed., Excerp.Med., Helminthol.Abstr., I.P.A., Ind.Med., Ind.Sci.Rev., INIS Atomind., Kidney, Lead Abstr., Med.& Surg.Dermat., Nutr.Abstr., Protozool.Abstr., Rev.Plant Path., Risk Abstr., Sci.Cit.Ind., Telegen, Trop.Dis.Bull. **Document type:** academic/scholarly publication.
●Also available online. Vendor(s): Ovid Technologies, Lexis-Nexis.
—BLDSC (0828.100000); ADONIS; CASDDS; Faxon; Genuine Article; SWETS; UMI; Uncover. **CCC.**
   Description: Contains the original output of clinical investigators worldwide. Includes case reports and clinical-pathologic conferences, symposia, and essays and editorials on medicine, science, and society.
   Refereed Serial

AMERICAN JOURNAL OF OCCUPATIONAL THERAPY. see OCCUPATIONAL HEALTH AND SAFETY

610 US ISSN 1059-1494
RB127
AMERICAN JOURNAL OF PAIN MANAGEMENT. 1991. q. $65. (American Academy of Pain Management) A J P M Inc., c/o University of the Pacific, School of Pharmacy, CA 95211. TEL 209-946-2300. E-mail: RSupernaw@uop.edu. Ed. Robert B. Supernaw. adv.; bk.rev.; circ. 6,300 (paid). **Document type:** academic/scholarly publication.

616.07 US ISSN 0002-9440
RB1 CODEN: AJPAA4
AMERICAN JOURNAL OF PATHOLOGY. 1901. m. $160 to individuals (foreign $225); institutions $230 (foreign $295). American Society for Investigative Pathology, 9650 Rockville Pike, Bethesda, MD 20814. TEL 301-530-7130. FAX 301-571-0108. (Subscr. to: Fulco, Box 3000, Denville, NJ 07843. TEL 800-875-2997. FAX 201-627-5872) Ed. Nelson Fausto. adv. contact: Priscilla Smith. illus. circ. 5,000. (also avail. in microform from UMI,PMC) **Indexed:** AIM, Biol.Abstr., Biol.Dig., Biotech.Abstr., Chem.Abstr., Curr.Adv.Cancer Res., Curr.Adv.Cell & Devel.Biol., Curr.Adv.Ecol.Sci., Curr.Adv.Genetics & Molec.Biol., Curr.Cont., Diar.Dis.Res., Dok.Arbeitsmed., Excerp.Med., Helminthol.Abstr., Ind.Med., Ind.Sci.Rev., Ind.Vet., INIS Atomind., Kidney, Maize Abstr., Med.& Surg.Dermat., Poult.Abstr., Protozool.Abstr., Sci.Cit.Ind., Sport Fish.Abstr., SSCI, Vet.Bull., Wild.Rev., Zoo.Rec. **Document type:** academic/scholarly publication.
—BLDSC (0829.600000); CASDDS; Faxon; Genuine Article; SWETS; UMI; Uncover. **CCC.**
   Formerly: Journal of Medical Research (ISSN 0097-3599)
   Description: Publishes research papers on the cellular and molecular mechanisms of disease, without preference for specific method of analysis.
   Refereed Serial

AMERICAN JOURNAL OF PHYSIOLOGY. see BIOLOGY — Physiology

610 614.8 US ISSN 0749-3797
RA421 CODEN: AJPMEA
AMERICAN JOURNAL OF PREVENTIVE MEDICINE. 1984. bi-m. £125($190) (effective 1996). (American College of Preventive Medicine) Oxford University Press, Journals, 2001 Evans Rd., Cary, NC 27513. TEL 919-677-0977; 800-852-7323. FAX 919-677-1714. E-mail: jnlorders@oup-usa.org. (Subscr. outside N. America to: Oxford University Press, Journals, Walton St., Oxford OX2 6DP, England. TEL 44-1865-56767. FAX 44-1865-267773) (Co-sponsor: Association of Teachers of Preventive Medicine) Eds. Dr. Kevin Patrick, Dr. F. Douglas Scutchfield. adv.; bk.rev.; charts; illus. circ. 2,700. (back issues avail.) **Indexed:** Abstr.Health Care Manage.Stud., Curr.Cont., Excerp.Med., Ind.Med., Med.& Surg.Dermat., NRN, Psychol.Abstr. (1989-). **Document type:** academic/scholarly publication.
—BLDSC (0834.370000); CASDDS; Faxon; Genuine Article; SWETS; UMI; Uncover. **CCC.**
   Description: Original articles and correspondence on all aspects of practice, teaching, and research in preventive medicine.
   Refereed Serial

616.07 US ISSN 0147-5185
RD57 CODEN: AJSPDX
AMERICAN JOURNAL OF SURGICAL PATHOLOGY. 1977. m. $190 to individuals (foreign $275); institutions $350 (foreign $425) (effective 1996). (Arthur Purdy Stout Society of Surgical Pathologists) Lippincott - Raven Publishers, 227 E. Washington Sq., Philadelphia, PA 19106. TEL 215-238-4200. Ed. Dr. Stephen S. Sternberg. adv. contact: Phyllis Noyes. bk.rev.; charts; illus.; stat.; index. circ. 8,000. (also avail. in microform; back issues avail.) **Indexed:** Biol.Abstr., Curr.Adv.Cancer Res., Curr.Adv.Ecol.Sci., Curr.Cont., Dent.Ind., Excerp.Med., Ind.Med., Ind.Sci.Rev., INIS Atomind., Kidney, Med.& Surg.Dermat., Protozool.Abstr., Rev.Med.& Vet.Mycol., Sci.Cit.Ind. **Document type:** academic/scholarly publication.
—BLDSC (0838.520000); Faxon; Genuine Article; SWETS; UMI; Uncover. **CCC.**
   Description: Covers diagnostic and prognostic technical advances.
   Refereed Serial

MEDICAL SCIENCES 4173

610 US ISSN 0002-9629
R11 CODEN: AJMSA9
AMERICAN JOURNAL OF THE MEDICAL SCIENCES.
1820. m. $145 to individuals (foreign $205); institutions $275 (foreign $320) (effective 1996). Lippincott - Raven Publishers, 227 E. Washington Sq., Philadelphia, PA 19106. TEL 215-238-4200. Ed. Dr. Manuel Martinez-Maldonado. bibl.; illus.; s-a. index. circ. 2,391. (also avail. in microform from UMI,PMC) **Indexed:** Abstr.Hyg., AIM, Biol.Abstr., Chem.Abstr., Curr.Adv.Ecol.Sci., Dent.Ind., Excerp.Med., Helminthol.Abstr., I.P.A., Ind.Med., Ind.Sci.Rev., Ind.Vet., INIS Atomind., Kidney, Med.& Surg.Dermat., NRN, Nutr.Abstr., Sci.Cit.Ind., Small Anim.Abstr., Vet.Bull.
—BLDSC (0828.000000); CASDDS; Faxon; Genuine Article; SWETS; UMI; UnCover. **CCC.**
Refereed Serial

615.5 UK ISSN 1075-2765
▼**AMERICAN JOURNAL OF THERAPEUTICS.** 1994. m. £75($110) to individuals; institutions in the E.U. £125 (N. America $150; elsewhere £140) (effective 1995). Chapman & Hall, Journals Department (Subsidiary of: International Thompson Publishing Group), 2-6 Boundary Row, London SE1 8HN, England. TEL 0171-856-0066. FAX 0171-522-9623. TELEX 290164 CHAPMA G. E-mail: journal@chall.mhs.compuserve.com. (Subscr. to: International Thomson Publishing Services Ltd., Cheriton House, North Way, Andover, Hants. SP10 5BE, England. TEL 01264-342713. FAX 01264-342807; Subscr. in N. America to: Chapman & Hall, Journals Promotion Department, One Penn Plaza, 41st Fl., New York, NY 10119. TEL 212-564-1060. FAX 212-564-1505) Ed. John C. Somberg. adv. (reprint service avail.) **Document type:** academic/scholarly publication.
—BLDSC (0838.780000).
Description: Assesses pharmacological developments in various medical specialties.
Refereed Serial

615.8 US
AMERICAN JOURNAL OF THERAPY. 1974. m. $28. McMahon Publishing Co., 83 Peaceable St., West Redding, CT 06896. TEL 203-544-9343. (Subscr. to: 121 S. Gertrude Ave., Paramus, NJ 07652) Ed. Jack Phillips. (back issues avail.)
Refereed Serial

610 US
AMERICAN MEDICAL ASSOCIATION. COUNCIL ON ETHICAL AND JUDICIAL AFFAIRS. CURRENT OPINIONS WITH ANNOTATIONS. 1981. irreg. $35.95 to non-members; members $14.95. American Medical Association, Council on Ethical and Judicial Affairs, 515 N. State St., Chicago, IL 60610. TEL 800-621-8335. Ed. David Orentlicher. adv. contact: R.L. Schmidt. circ. 20,000 (paid). **Document type:** academic/scholarly publication.
Former titles (until 1994): American Medical Association. Council on Ethical and Judicial Affairs. Current Opinions; American Medical Association. Judicial Council. Current Opinions.
Description: Addresses social policy issues, practice matters, professional rights and responsibilities, and other topics important to the practice of medicine.

610 US
R712.A1
AMERICAN MEDICAL DIRECTORY. 1906. biennial, 34th ed., 1994. $545 for 4 vols. American Medical Association, 515 N. State St., Chicago, IL 60610. TEL 312-464-5000; 800-262-2350. FAX 312-464-5834. **Document type:** directory.
Former titles: American Medical Directory of Physicians; American Medical Directory (ISSN 0065-9339)

610 US ISSN 0001-1843
AMERICAN MEDICAL NEWS. 1958. w. $99. American Medical Association, 515 N. State St., Chicago, IL 60610. TEL 312-464-5000; 800-262-2360. FAX 312-464-4184. Ed. Barbara Bolsen. adv.; bk.rev.; charts; illus.; s-a. index. circ. 366,000. (also avail. in microform from UMI; microfiche) **Indexed:** Bus.Ind., Chic.Per.Ind., Hlth.Ind., Hosp.Lit.Ind., Med.Care Rev., MEDSOC, Tr.& Indus.Ind. **Document type:** academic/scholarly publication.
—Faxon; UMI. **CCC.**
Formerly: A M A News.

610 US ISSN 0098-8421
R15
AMERICAN MEDICAL WOMEN'S ASSOCIATION. JOURNAL.
Key Title: Journal of the American Medical Women's Association. 1915. bi-m. $50 (foreign $55). American Medical Women's Association, Inc., 801 N. Fairfax St., Ste. 400, Alexandria, VA 22314. TEL 212-387-3864. FAX 212-387-3897. Ed. Wendy Chavkin. adv. contact: Jane Williamson. bk.rev.; bibl.; illus.; index; circ. 11,000 (paid). (also avail. in microform from UMI; reprint service avail. from UMI) **Indexed:** Biol.Abstr., Ind.Med., Mult.Ed.Abstr., Stud.Wom.Abstr. **Document type:** academic/scholarly publication.
—BLDSC (4689.100000); Faxon; UMI; UnCover. **CCC.**
Formerly: Woman Physician (ISSN 0002-7103)
Refereed Serial

AMERICAN REHABILITATION. see *SOCIAL SERVICES AND WELFARE*

610 US ISSN 1045-9901
RC875
AMERICAN SOCIETY OF ANDROLOGY. MEETING PROGRAM AND ABSTRACTS. a. $225 to institutions (foreign $245) with Journal of Andrology (effective 1994). American Society of Andrology, c/o Denise Lecy, Guggenheim 1711, Mayo Clinic, 200 First St., S.W., Rochester, MN 55905. Eds. Donald Tindall, Ronald Lewis. **Document type:** proceedings.

610 US
AMP. 1920. m. $25. National Amputation Foundation, 73 Church St., Malverne, NY 11565. TEL 516-887-3600. FAX 516-887-3667. Ed. Sol Kaminsky. adv.; bk.rev. circ. 2,500. **Document type:** newsletter.

616 TU ISSN 0255-6553
ANADOLU KLINIGI. 1933. q. Turkish Medical Society - Turk Tip Dernigi, Valikonagi Caddesi 10, Harbiye, Istanbul.

ANAEROBE. see *BIOLOGY — Microbiology*

610 SP
ANALES CUIDADOS INTENSIVOS. 6/yr. Nunez de Balboa 120 2o, 28006 Madrid, Spain.

610 SP ISSN 0003-2530
ANALES DEL INSTITUTO CORACHAN.* vol.23, 1971. q. free. Instituto Corachan, Buigas 19, Barcelona, Spain. adv.; bk.rev.; charts; illus.; stat. **Indexed:** Chem.Abstr., Excerp.Med.
—**CCC.**

610 AT ISSN 1033-8810
ANALGESIC GUIDELINES. 1988. irreg., approx. biennial. Aus.$18. Victorian Medical Postgraduate Foundation Inc., Therapeutics Committee, Chelsea House, Level 3, 55 Flemingron Rd., N. Melbourne, Vic. 3051, Australia. TEL 03-329-1566. FAX 03-326-5632. circ. 8,000. **Document type:** academic/scholarly publication.
Description: Covers clinical aspects of the management of pain for doctors, nurses and pharmacists.

610 SP ISSN 0212-4572
ANALISIS CLINICOS. (Supplement avail.: Actualidades en el Laboratorio Clinico (ISSN 0212-4564)) 1975. 8/yr. 9900 ptas.($109) (effective 1995). (Asociacion Espanola de Farmaceuticos Analistas) Editorial Garsi, S.A., Juan Bravo 46, 28006 Madrid, Spain. TEL 34-1-4021212. FAX 34-1-4020954. Ed. J.M. Guardiola Vicente. circ. 3,500.

THE ANATOMICAL RECORD. see *BIOLOGY*

ANATOMICAL SOCIETY OF INDIA. JOURNAL. see *BIOLOGY*

ANATOMIESE VERENIGING VAN SUIDER-AFRIKA. KONGRESVERRIGTINGE/ANATOMICAL SOCIETY OF SOUTHERN AFRICA. PROCEEDINGS OF ANNUAL CONGRESS. see *BIOLOGY — Physiology*

574.4 611 GW ISSN 0066-1562
QL801 CODEN: VHAGAS
ANATOMISCHE GESELLSCHAFT. VERHANDLUNGEN. (Supplement to: Annals of Anatomy) 1887. a. price varies. Gustav Fischer Verlag Jena, Villengang 2, 07745 Jena, Germany. TEL 03641-626444. FAX 03641-626500. (Subscr. to: Postfach 100537, 07705 Jena, Germany) (reprint service avail. from ISI) **Indexed:** Biol.Abstr., Chem.Abstr., Excerp.Med., Ind.Med. **Document type:** proceedings.
—CASDDS.

ANATOMY AND EMBRYOLOGY. see *BIOLOGY — Physiology*

610 IT
ANCH'IO. 1978. m. free. Associazione Laziale Motulesi (A.L.M.), Via Laurentina 5, 00142 Rome, Italy. TEL 5406705. Ed. Carmello Pelle. illus.
Description: Covers news and events for and about the handicapped.

ANCIENT SCIENCE OF LIFE. see *ALTERNATIVE MEDICINE*

610 GW ISSN 0303-4569
CODEN: ANDRDQ
ANDROLOGIA. (Text and summaries in English or German) 1969. bi-m. DM.363($269) to individuals in Europe (rest of world DM.392($290)); institutions in Europe DM.441($327) (rest of world DM.470($348)) (effective 1996). (Deutsche Gesellschaft fuer Andrologie) Blackwell Wissenschaft, Kurfuerstendamm 57, 10707 Berlin, Germany. TEL 030-32790624. FAX 030-32790610. Eds. W.B. Schill, G. Aumueller. adv.; B&W page DM.1800; trim 240 x 170. index. circ. 1,200. (reprint service avail. from UMI) **Indexed:** Anim.Breed.Abstr., Biol.Abstr., Biotech.Abstr., Chem.Abstr., Curr.Adv.Cell & Devel.Biol., Curr.Adv.Ecol.Sci., Curr.Adv.Genetics & Molec.Biol., Curr.Cont., Dok.Arbeitsmed., Excerp.Med., Ind.Med., Ind.Sci.Rev., Nutr.Abstr., Pig News & Info., Sci.Cit.Ind., Small Anim.Abstr. **Document type:** academic/scholarly publication.
—BLDSC (0900.443000); ADONIS; CASDDS; Faxon; Genuine Article; SWETS; UMI; UnCover. **CCC.**
Formerly: Andrologie.
Description: Provides an international forum for original papers on the current clinical, morphological, biochemical, and experimental status of organic male infertility and sexual disorder in men.

612 FR ISSN 1166-2654
CODEN: AROLEO
ANDROLOGIE. 1987. 3/yr. Societe d'Andrologie de Langue Francaise, 49 rue de la Bassee, 59000 Lille, France. **Indexed:** Excerp.Med. (1994-).
Formerly (until 1991): Societe d'Andrologie de Langue Francaise. Bulletin (ISSN 1154-3418)

610 CC ISSN 1000-1492
ANHUI YIKE DAXUE XUEBAO/ANHUI UNIVERSITY OF MEDICAL SCIENCES. JOURNAL. (Text in Chinese) q. Anhui Yike Daxue - Anhui University of Medical Sciences, Meishan Lu, Hefei, Anhui 230032, People's Republic of China. TEL 336600. Ed. Gong Xiyu. **Document type:** academic/scholarly publication.

610 CC ISSN 1000-0399
ANHUI YIXUE/ANHUI MEDICAL SCIENCES. (Text in Chinese) bi-m. Anhui Yixue Qingbao Yanjiusuo - Anhui Institute of Medical Information, 1 Yonghong Lu, Hefei, Anhui 230061, People's Republic of China. TEL 277688. Ed. Lu Yayi.

610 CC ISSN 1000-2219
ANHUI ZHONGYI XUEYUAN XUEBAO/ANHUI INSTITUTE OF TRADITIONAL CHINESE MEDICINE. JOURNAL. (Text in Chinese) q. Anhui Zhongyi Xueyuan - Anhui Institute of Traditional Chinese Medicine, Meishan Lu, Hefei, Anhui 230038, People's Republic of China. TEL 331006. Ed. Liu Zhongben. **Document type:** academic/scholarly publication.

610 TU ISSN 0365-8104
CODEN: AUTFAE
ANKARA UNIVERSITESI. TIP FAKULTESI. MECMUASI.* (Supplement avail. (ISSN 0365-2238)) (Text in Turkish; summaries in English) q. free. Ankara Universitesi, Tip Fakultesi - Ankara University, Faculty of Medicine, Tandogan, Ankara, Turkey. FAX 4-2236370. circ. 1,000. **Indexed:** Biol.Abstr., Chem.Abstr., Helminthol.Abstr., Nutr.Abstr.
—CASDDS.

MEDICAL SCIENCES

610 **PL** ISSN 0066-1945
CODEN: RPMKAA
ANNALES ACADEMIAE MEDICAE STETINENSIS/ROCZNIKI POMORSKIEJ AKADEMII MEDYCZNEJ W SZCZECINIE. (Supplements avail.) 1951. a. price varies. Pomorska Akademia Medyczna w Szczecinie, Ul. Rybacka 1, 70-204 Szczecin, Poland. TEL 802-41. (Dist. by: Ars Polona-Ruch, Krakowskie Przedmiescie 7, 00-068 Warsaw, Poland) **Indexed:** Dent.Ind., Excerp.Med. (until 1995), Ind.Med.
—BLDSC (8008.260000); CASDDS; EMDOCS.

610 **BE** ISSN 0003-3863
ANNALES COLLEGII MEDICI ANTVERPIENSIS. 1946. m. (10/yr.). 350 Fr. Koninklijke Geneeskundige Kring van Antwerpen, Louizastraat 8, 2000 Antwerp, Belgium. adv.; bk.rev. circ. 1,000.

ANNALES DE BIOLOGIE CLINIQUE. see *BIOLOGY*

ANNALES DE PATHOLOGIE. see *BIOLOGY*

610 **FR** ISSN 0221-3796
CODEN: AMNADI
ANNALES MEDICALES DE NANCY ET DE L'EST. 1879. bi-m. 350 F. Societe de Medecine de Nancy, Centre Hospitalier Regional Universitaire de Nancy, 29 av. de Lattre de Tassigny, 54037 Nancy Cedex, France. TEL 33-83-57-61-61. FAX 83-85-26-22. Ed. A. Larcan. adv.; abstr. circ. 4,905. **Indexed:** Biol.Abstr., Bull.Signal., C.I.S. Abstr., Chem.Abstr., Excerp.Med., Rev.Plant Path. **Document type:** academic/scholarly publication.
—BLDSC (0982.600000); CASDDS; Faxon.
Former titles (until 1978): Annales Medicales de Nancy (ISSN 0003-4460); (until 1962): Revue Medicale de Nancy (ISSN 0370-6354)

ANNALES MEDICO-PSYCHOLOGIQUES. see *PSYCHOLOGY*

610 **PL** ISSN 0066-2240
B6 CODEN: AUMKAS
ANNALES UNIVERSITATIS MARIAE CURIE-SKLODOWSKA. SECTIO D. MEDICINA. (Text in English or Polish; summaries and table of contents in English) 1946. a. price varies. Uniwersytet Marii Curie-Sklodowskiej, Wydawnictwo, Pl. M. Curie-Sklodowskiej 5, 20-031 Lublin, Poland. TEL 48-81-375304. FAX 48-81-336699. TELEX 0643223. Ed. Stanislaw Bryc. circ. 600. **Indexed:** Biol.Abstr., Chem.Abstr., Curr.Adv.Ecol.Sci., Excerp.Med., Field Crop Abstr., Herb.Abstr., Ind.Med., Ind.Vet., INIS Atomind., Rev.Appl.Entomol., Vet.Bull. **Document type:** academic/scholarly publication.
—BLDSC (0958.995000); CASDDS.

610 **GW** ISSN 0173-6973
CODEN: AUSSEI
ANNALES UNIVERSITATIS SARAVIENSIS. MEDICINAE. 1953-1976; resumed 1980. 2/yr. DM.35. (Universitaet des Saarlandes, Medizinische Fakultaet) Verlag Ermer KG, Postfach 1155, 66424 Homburg-Saar, Germany. TEL 06841-78186. FAX 06841-72257. Ed. E. Wenzel. adv.; bk.rev.; bibl.; charts; illus.; index. circ. 8,000. (reprint service avail. from IRC) **Indexed:** Biol.Abstr., C.I.S. Abstr., Chem.Abstr., Excerp.Med., Ind.Med.
—BLDSC (0962.989000); CASDDS. **CCC.**
Formerly: Annales Universitatis Saraviensis. Reihe: Medizin (ISSN 0003-4533)

616.98 **IT** ISSN 0003-4630
CODEN: AMDNA4
ANNALI DI MEDICINA NAVALE. (Text in Italian; summaries in English and Italian) 1895. 3/m. L.20000. Ministero Difensa - Marina, Lungo Tevere delle Navi, 00196 Rome, Italy. bk.rev. circ. 500. **Indexed:** Abstr.Hyg., Biol.Abstr., C.I.S. Abstr., Chem.Abstr., Excerp.Med., Helminthol.Abstr., Ind.Med., INIS Atomind., Trop.Dis.Bull.
—CASDDS.
Description: Features items on military medicine.

574.4 611 **GW** ISSN 0940-9602
QL801 CODEN: ANANAU
ANNALS OF ANATOMY; Zentralblatt fuer die gesamte wissenschaftliche Anatomie. (Text in English, French and German; summaries in English) 1886. 6/yr. DM.660 (foreign DM.672). Gustav Fischer Verlag Jena, Villengang 2, 07745 Jena, Germany. TEL 03641-626444. FAX 03641-626500. (Subscr. to: Postfach 100537, 07705 Jena, Germany) Ed. W. Kuehnel. adv.; bk.rev.; bibl.; charts; illus.; index, cum.index: vols.1-100. (also avail. in microfilm from PMC; reprint service avail. from ISI) **Indexed:** Biol.Abstr., Chem.Abstr., Curr.Adv.Cell & Devel.Biol., Curr.Adv.Ecol.Sci., Curr.Cont., Dairy Sci.Abstr., Dent.Ind., Excerp.Med., Ind.Med., Ind.Sci.Rev., Ind.Vet., INIS Atomind., Ref.Zh., Sci.Cit.Ind., Vet.Bull. **Document type:** academic/scholarly publication.
—BLDSC (1036.200000); CASDDS; Faxon; Genuine Article; SWETS. **CCC.**
Formerly: Anatomischer Anzeiger (ISSN 0003-2786)

616.07 **US** ISSN 0883-6612
R726.5 CODEN: ABMEEH
ANNALS OF BEHAVIORAL MEDICINE. 1979. q. $135 (foreign $160) (effective 1995). Society of Behavioral Medicine, 103 S. Adams St., Rockville, MD 20850. TEL 301-251-2790. FAX 301-279-6749. Ed. Dennis C. Turk. adv.; bk.rev. circ. 3,000. (also avail. in microfilm from WWS,PMC; back issues avail.) **Indexed:** Behav.Abstr., Behav.Med.Abstr., Biol.Abstr., Excerp.Med., Psychol.Abstr. (1979-), Soc.Work Res.& Abstr., Sociol.Abstr. **Document type:** academic/scholarly publication.
—BLDSC (1038.700000); Faxon; UnCover.
Incorporates (in 1991): Behavioral Medicine Abstracts (ISSN 0197-7717); **Formerly:** Behavioral Medicine Update.
Description: Covers behavioral advances across the spectrum of health care disciplines.

610.28 **US** ISSN 0090-6964
R856.A1 CODEN: ABMECF
ANNALS OF BIOMEDICAL ENGINEERING. 1979. bi-m. $450 (foreign $480) (effective 1996). (Biomedical Engineering Society) Blackwell Science Inc., 238 Main St., Cambridge, MA 02142. TEL 617-876-7022; 800-759-6102. FAX 617-492-5263. Ed. Dr. Hun H. Sun. adv.; index. circ. 2,200. (also avail. in microfilm from UMI) **Indexed:** Appl.Mech.Rev., Bioeng.Abstr., Biol.Abstr., Chem.Abstr., Curr.Adv.Ecol.Sci., Curr.Cont., Eng.Ind., Excerp.Med., Ind.Med., Ind.Sci.Rev., Ind.Vet., INIS Atomind., INSPEC (1974-), Sci.Cit.Ind. **Document type:** academic/scholarly publication.
—BLDSC (1039.400000); CASDDS; Ei; EMDOCS; Faxon; Genuine Article; SWETS; UMI; UnCover. **CCC.**
Incorporates: Journal of Bioengineering (ISSN 0145-3068)
Description: Comprised of scholarly articles on areas such as bioelectric phenomena and quantative electrophysiology, biomaterial and biomechanics, biochemical transducers and information systems theory applications.
Refereed Serial

ANNALS OF EMERGENCY MEDICINE. see *MEDICAL SCIENCES — Orthopedics And Traumatology*

ANNALS OF EPIDEMIOLOGY. see *PUBLIC HEALTH AND SAFETY*

ANNALS OF HEALTH LAW. see *LAW*

610 **TU** ISSN 1300-0683
ANNALS OF MEDICAL SCIENCES. (Text in English) 1992. 3/yr. Cukurova Universitesi, Tip Fakultesi, Yayin ve Dokumentasyon Kurulu, Balcali, 01330 Adana, Turkey. **Indexed:** Excerp.Med. (1994-).

ANNALS OF MEDICINE. see *MEDICAL SCIENCES — Experimental Medicine, Laboratory Technique*

610 **SU** ISSN 0256-4947
CODEN: ANSMEJ
ANNALS OF SAUDI MEDICINE. (Text in English; summaries in Arabic) 1981. bi-m. SRI.25 per issue (free to qualified personnel). King Faisal Specialist Hospital and Research Centre, P.O. Box 3354, Riyadh 11211, Saudi Arabia. TEL 966-1-4647272. FAX 966-1-4427237. (Co-sponsors: King Saud University College of Medicine; King Khalid University Hospital) Ed. Dr. Mohammed Akhtar. adv.: B&W page $1120, color page $1860; trim 290 x 220. bk.rev.; abstr.; circ. 19,500 (controlled). (back issues avail.) **Indexed:** Abstr.Hyg., Curr.Adv.Ecol.Sci., Curr.Cont., Diar.Dis.Res., Excerp.Med., Int.Abstr.Biol.Sci., Protozool.Abstr., Rev.Med.& Vet.Mycol. **Document type:** academic/scholarly publication.
—BLDSC (1043.925000); Faxon; Genuine Article.
Formerly: King Faisal Specialist Hospital Medical Journal (ISSN 0253-4770)
Description: A multidisciplinary medical journal dealing with aspects of clinical, academic, investigative medicine and research.
Refereed Serial

ANNUAIRE MEDICAL DE L'HOSPITALISATION FRANCAISE.. see *HOSPITALS*

610 **FR**
ANNUAIRE MEDICAL DU DR. PORCHERON ET PROF. G. BELTRAMI. 1912. a. 120 F. SO-GE-CO-PRO S.A.R.L, 20-26 rue Caisserie, 13235 Marseille Cedex 1, France. adv.

ANNUAL BOOK OF A S T M STANDARDS. VOLUME 13.01. MEDICAL DEVICES. see *ENGINEERING — Engineering Mechanics And Materials*

ANNUAL EDITIONS: HUMAN DEVELOPMENT. see *BIOLOGY — Physiology*

610 **US** ISSN 0066-4219
CODEN: ARMCAH
ANNUAL REVIEW OF MEDICINE: SELECTED TOPICS IN THE CLINICAL SCIENCES. 1950. a. $47 (foreign $52) (effective Jan. 1995). Annual Reviews Inc., 4139 El Camino Way, Box 10139, Palo Alto, CA 94303-0139. TEL 415-493-4400; 800-523-8635. TELEX 910-290-0275. E-mail: annrevu@class.org. Ed. C.H. Coggins. bibl.; index, cum.index (also avail. in microfilm from UMI; back issues avail.; reprint service avail.) **Indexed:** Biol.Abstr., Chem.Abstr., Curr.Adv.Cancer Res., Curr.Adv.Ecol.Sci., Curr.Cont., Dent.Ind., Diar.Dis.Res., Excerp.Med., Helminthol.Abstr., Ind.Med., Ind.Sci.Rev., Ind.Vet., M.M.R.I, Nutr.Abstr., Protozool.Abstr., Psychol.Abstr. (1969-), Sci.Cit.Ind., Vet.Bull. **Document type:** academic/scholarly publication.
—BLDSC (1522.700000); ADONIS; CASDDS; EMDOCS; Faxon; Genuine Article; SWETS; UMI; UnCover. **CCC.**
Description: Original critical reviews of the significant primary literature and current developments in medicine.

ANNUAL REVIEW OF SEX RESEARCH. see *PSYCHOLOGY*

610 **IT** ISSN 0365-4621
CODEN: AMSNAB
ANTHOLOGIA MEDICA SANTORIANA. 1959. a. price varies. Giardini Editori e Stampatori, Via Santa Bibbiana 28, 56100 Pisa, Italy. TEL 050 502531. Ed. Marcello Comel.
—CASDDS.
Formed by the merger of: Anthological de Medicina Externa; Archivium de Dermatologia Experimentale et Functionale (ISSN 0365-1622); Which was formerly (until 1954): Archivi di Dermatologia Sperimentale e Funzionale (ISSN 0392-9256)

610 **AT** ISSN 0729-218X
ANTIBIOTIC GUIDELINES. 1978. biennial. Aus.$18($10) Victorian Medical Postgraduate Foundation Inc., Therapeutics Committee, Chelsea House, Level 3, 55 Flemington Rd., N. Melbourne, Vic. 3051, Australia. TEL 03-329-1566. FAX 03-326-5632. (Co-sponsor: Victorian Drug Usage Advisory Committee) bk.rev. circ. 25,000. **Document type:** academic/scholarly publication.
—CCC.
Description: Disease-oriented guide to therapeutic use of anti-microbial agents for doctors, nurses and pharmacists.

MEDICAL SCIENCES 4175

610   CK   ISSN 0044-8389
ANTIOQUIA MEDICA. (Text in Spanish; summaries in English, Spanish) 1950. 10/yr. Col.$100($7.50) Universidad de Antioquia, Facultad de Medicina-Academia de Medicina, Apdo. Aereo 52278, Medellin, Colombia. Ed. Jose Luis Ramirez Castro. bk.rev.; abstr.; index. circ. 1,200. (looseleaf format) **Indexed:** Biol.Abstr., Chem.Abstr., Excerp.Med., Ind.Vet., Rev.Plant Path., Trop.Dis.Bull., Vet.Bull.

610   IT   ISSN 0393-0726
ANTOLOGIA MEDICA ITALIANA; mensile di medicina, chirurgia e branche affini. (Text in Italian; summaries in English) 1984. m. L.20000. Casa Editrice L'Antologia, Via G. Tropeano 48, 80131 Naples, Italy. TEL 39-81-7701302. **Document type:** academic/scholarly publication.

610   CL
ANUARIO ENFERMEDADES DE NOTIFICACION OBLIGATORIA. 1947. a. $5. Ministerio de Salud, Departamento de Control y Evaluacion, Santiago, Chile.

610   JA   ISSN 0918-1369
AOMORI ROSAI BYOIN ISHI/AOMORI ROSAI MEDICAL JOURNAL. (Text in Japanese) 1991. s-a. Rodo Fukushi Jigyodan, Aomori Rosai Byoin - Labor Welfare Corp., Aomori Rosai Hospital, 1, Minamigaoka, Shiroganecho, Hachinohe-shi, Aomori-ken 031, Japan.

610   JA   ISSN 0914-7500
AOMORI SHIMIN BYOIN ISHI/AOMORI CITY HOSPITAL MEDICAL JOURNAL. (Text in Japanese) 1987. s-a. Aomori Shimin Byoin - Aomori City Hospital, 14-20, Katsuta 1-chome, Aomori-shi, Aomori-ken 030, Japan.

610   JA   ISSN 0914-6873
AOMORIKEN ISHIKAIHO/AOMORI MEDICAL ASSOCIATION. JOURNAL. (Text in Japanese) 1960. m. 300 Yen per no. Aomoriken Ishikai - Aomori Medical Association, 8-21, Shinmachi 2-chome, Aomori-shi, Aomori-ken 030, Japan.

610 658   JA   ISSN 0913-4581
AOMORIKEN JICHITAI IGAKKAISHI/AOMORI MUNICIPAL HOSPITAL ESTABLISHMENT ASSOCIATION. JOURNAL. (Text in Japanese) a. Aomoriken Jichitai Byoin Kaisetsusha Kyogikai - Aomori Municipal Hospital Establishment Association, Kokuhoren, 4-1, Shinmachi 2-chome, Aomori-shi, Aomori-ken 030, Japan.

610   JA   ISSN 0916-0450
AOMORIKEN NOSON IGAKKAI ZASSHI/AOMORI SOCIETY OF RURAL MEDICINE. JOURNAL. (Text in Japanese) 1975. irreg. membership. Aomoriken Noson Igakkai - Aomori Society of Rural Medicine, Aomoriken Nogyo Kyodo Kumiai Chuokai, 87-11 Maeda, Ono, Aomori-shi, Aomori-ken 030, Japan. TEL 81-177-29-8765. FAX 81-177-62-1085.

APPLIED CARDIOPULMONARY PATHOPHYSIOLOGY; the interface between laboratory and clinical practice. see BIOLOGY — Physiology

610   US   ISSN 1064-8542
                                   CODEN: ACLTEU
APPLIED CLINICAL TRIALS; the global magazine of applied clinical science. 1991. m. Advanstar Communications, Inc. (Eugene), 859 Wilamette St., Box 10460, Eugene, OR 97401-6806. TEL 503-343-1200. FAX 503-3434-3514. (U.S. subscr. to: 1 E. First St., Duluth, MN 55082. TEL 800-346-0085; Addr. in the U.K.: Advanstar House, Park West, Sealand Rd., Chester CH1 4RN, England. TEL 44-244-378888. FAX 44-244-370011) Ed. Jennifer Lindsey; Pub. Ralph Vitaro. adv.: B&W page £1460; color page £2275; adv. contact: Wayne K. Blow. circ. 10,000. (back issues avail.; reprint service avail.) **Document type:** academic/scholarly publication, trade publication.
—BLDSC (1571.936450); SWETS. **CCC.**
Description: For clinical research professionals in the United States, Western Europe, and Japan. Offers practical, hands-on information that helps clinical research scientists develop, execute, and file new drug applications and expedite drug approval.

610   US   ISSN 1062-3345
                                   CODEN: APIMEH
APPLIED IMMUNOHISTOCHEMISTRY. 1993. q. $106 to individuals (foreign $119); institutions $129 (foreign $139) (effective 1996). (Society for Applied Immunohistochemistry) Lippincott - Raven Press, 227 E. Washington Sq., Philadelphia, PA 19106. TEL 215-238-4200. Ed. Hector Battifora. adv. contact: Phyllis Noyes. bk.rev.// illus.; index. circ. 1,000. (also avail. in microform from UMI; back issues avail.) **Indexed:** Excerp.Med. (1995-).
Document type: academic/scholarly publication.
—BLDSC (1573.130000); CASDDS; Genuine Article; SWETS; UMI. **CCC.**
Description: Original articles on the diagnostic and prognostic applications of immunohistochemistry to human disease.

610   SJ   ISSN 0254-9492
ARAB MEDICAL BULLETIN. (Text in Arabic or English) 1979. m. $200 to individuals; institutions SL.100. P.O. Box 1882, Khartoum, Sudan. Ed. T.A. Rahman. adv.; bk.rev. circ. 1,500. **Indexed:** Abstr.Hyg., Excerp.Med.
Formerly: Sudan Medical Bulletin.

610   GW   ISSN 0723-5100
ARAB MEDICO; alam al tubb wa al-saydazah. (Text in Arabic) 1983. bi-m. DM.58($39) Beta Verlag GmbH, Postfach 140121, 53056 Bonn, Germany. TEL 0228-25206-1. FAX 0228-252067. TELEX 869536-BETA-D. Ed. Taleb Ulama. adv.; charts; illus. circ. 15,900. (back issues avail.) **Indexed:** ExtraMED.
Document type: academic/scholarly publication.
●Also available on CD-ROM.

610   GW   ISSN 0174-268X
ARBEITEN ZUR GESCHICHTE DER MEDIZIN IN GIESSEN. 1979. irreg., vol.17, 1993. DM.80. Wilhelm Schmitz Verlag, Staufenbergerweg 22, 35457 Lollar, Germany. TEL 06406-2324. **Document type:** monographic series.

ARBEITSMEDIZIN, SOZIALMEDIZIN, UMWELTMEDIZIN; Zeitschrift fuer Praxis, Klinik, Forschung, Begutachtung. see PUBLIC HEALTH AND SAFETY

ARBEITSMEDIZIN, SOZIALMEDIZIN, UMWELTMEDIZIN. SUPPLEMENT. see PUBLIC HEALTH AND SAFETY

615.8   SW   ISSN 0345-0988
ARBETSTERAPEUTEN; facklig yrkes- och idetidskrift. 1949. 16/yr. SEK 400 (effective 1995). Foerbundet Sveriges Arbetsterapeuter (FSA) - Swedish Association of Occupational Therapists, P.O. Box 760, S-131 24 Nacka, Sweden. TEL 46-8-466-24-49. FAX 46-8-466-24-24. Ed. Inga-Britt Lindstroem. adv.: B&W page SEK 17600, color page SEK 25500. bk.rev. circ. 8,000. **Document type:** trade publication.

610   SP   ISSN 0211-2027
ARCANO. 1978. 6/yr. M. Pedrayes 2, 6o, 33004 Oviedo, Spain. TEL 85-23-65-10. Ed. B. Lozano Llamazares.

ARCHIVES D'ANATOMIE, D'HISTOLOGIE ET D'EMBRYOLOGIE; normales et experimentales. see BIOLOGY

616.07   FR   ISSN 0395-501X
                                   CODEN: AACPDQ
ARCHIVES D'ANATOMIE ET DE CYTOLOGIE PATHOLOGIQUES. 1953. 6/yr. 1220 F. to individuals (foreign 1530 F.); students 610 F. (foreign 765 F.). (Semaine des Hopitaux) Expansion Scientifique, 15 rue Saint-Benoit, 75278 Paris Cedex 06, France. TEL 40-62-64-00. FAX 45-55-69-20. **Indexed:** Biol.Abstr., C.I.S. Abstr., Chem.Abstr., Curr.Cont., Dent.Ind., Excerp.Med., Helminthol.Abstr., Ind.Med.
—BLDSC (1630.970000); Faxon; SWETS. **CCC.**
Formerly: Archives d'Anatomie Pathologique (ISSN 0003-9608)

610   US   ISSN 0148-5016
QP253   CODEN: ARANDR
ARCHIVES OF ANDROLOGY; an international journal. 1978. bi-m. £294($485) (effective 1996). Taylor & Francis Inc., 1900 Frost Rd., Ste. 101, Bristol, PA 19007-1598. TEL 215-785-5800; 800-821-8312. FAX 215-785-5515. (Subscr. in Europe to: Taylor & Francis Ltd., Rankine Rd., Basingstoke, Hants. RG24 8PR, England. TEL 44-1256-840366. FAX 44-1256-479438) Ed. E.S.E. Hafez. bk.rev. (back issues avail.; reprint service avail. from UMI) **Indexed:** Anim.Breed.Abstr., Biol.Abstr., Chem.Abstr., Curr.Adv.Ecol.Sci., Curr.Cont., Excerp.Med., Ind.Med., Ind.Sci.Rev., Pig News & Info., Sci.Cit.Ind. **Document type:** academic/scholarly publication.
—BLDSC (1631.220000); ADONIS; CASDDS; Faxon; Genuine Article; SWETS; UnCover. **CCC.**
Description: Covers reproduction, fertility and regulation, and infertility in the human and animal male.
Refereed Serial

614.7 016   US   ISSN 0003-9896
RC963   CODEN: AEHLAU
ARCHIVES OF ENVIRONMENTAL HEALTH. 1950. bi-m. $112. (Helen Dwight Reid Educational Foundation) Heldref Publications, 1319 Eighteenth St., N.W., Washington, DC 20036-1802. TEL 202-296-6267. FAX 202-296-5149. Ed. Patricia McCready. adv. contact: Raymond Rallo. bk.rev.; charts; illus.; index. circ. 2,000. (also avail. in microform; reprint service avail.) **Indexed:** A.S.& T.Ind., Abstr.Hyg., Acid Pre.Dig., AIM, API Abstr., API Catal., API Hlth.& Environ., API Oil., API Pet.Ref., API Pet.Subst., API Transport, Biodet.Abstr., Biol.Abstr., Biotech.Abstr., Br.Ceram.Abstr., C.I.S.Abstr., Cadscan, Chem.Abstr., Curr.Adv.Cancer Res., Curr.Adv.Ecol.Sci., Curr.Cont., Dairy Sci.Abstr., Dent.Ind., Diar.Dis.Res., Energy Info.Abstr., Energy Rev., Environ.Abstr., Environ.Ind., Environ.Per.Bibl. (1972-), Environ.Per.Bibl., Excerp.Med., Fuel & Energy Abstr., G.Soc.Sci.& Rel.Per.Lit., Gas Abstr., Helminthol.Abstr., Hosp.Lit.Ind., Ind.Hyg.Dig., Ind.Med., Ind.Sci.Rev., Ind.Vet., INIS Atomind., Intl.Polym.Sci.& Tech., Lab.Haz.Bull., Lead Abstr., Med.& Surg.Dermat., NRN, Nutr.Abstr., Pollut.Abstr., RAPRA, Repindex, Rev.Plant Path., Risk Abstr., Sci.Cit.Ind., Sel.Water Res.Abstr., Small Anim.Abstr., Vet.Bull., W.R.C.Inf., Zincscan. **Document type:** academic/scholarly publication.
●Also available on CD-ROM. Producer(s): University Microfilms International.
—BLDSC (1634.250000); CASDDS; Faxon; Genuine Article; SWETS; UMI; UnCover. **CCC.**
Refereed Serial

610   US   ISSN 1063-3987
ARCHIVES OF FAMILY MEDICINE. 1992. m. $95 (foreign $130). American Medical Association, 515 N. State St., Chicago, IL 60610. TEL 312-464-5000; 800-262-2350. FAX 312-464-4184. Ed. Dr. Marjorie Bowman. adv. (also avail. in microform from UMI) **Indexed:** Ind.Med. (1993-). **Document type:** academic/scholarly publication.
—BLDSC (1634.278100); SWETS; UMI; UnCover. **CCC.**
Description: Provides clinically practical information for family and general physicians.
Refereed Serial

ARCHIVES OF HISTOLOGY AND CYTOLOGY/SOSHIKI SAIBOGAKU KIROKU. see BIOLOGY — Cytology And Histology

616.98   IT   ISSN 0003-9934
ARCHIVES OF MEDICAL HYDROLOGY. (Text in English, French, German, Italian) 1928. irreg. (3-4/yr.). $5. International Society of Medical Hydrology and Climatology, Via Rovereto 11, 00198 Rome, Italy. bibl. circ. 550. **Indexed:** Chem.Abstr.
Description: Covers climatological medicine.

M

MEDICAL SCIENCES

610   MX   ISSN 0188-4409
CODEN: AEDEER
ARCHIVES OF MEDICAL RESEARCH. (Supplements avail.) (Text in English) 1970. q. $25. Instituto Mexicano del Seguro Social, Oficina de Bibliotecas y Divulgacion, P.O. Box 73-032, 06720 Mexico D.F., Mexico. TEL 5-7611503. Ed. Luis Benitez-Bribiesca. circ. 5,000. (also avail. in microform from UMI) **Indexed:** Abstr.Hyg., Biol.Abstr., Chem.Abstr., Curr.Cont., Excerp.Med., Helminthol.Abstr., Ind.Med., Ind.Sci.Rev., Nutr.Abstr., Sci.Cit.Ind., Trop.Dis.Bull. **Document type:** academic/scholarly publication.
—CASDDS; UMI.
  Formerly (until 1991): Archivos de Investigacion Medica (ISSN 0066-6769)
  Refereed Serial

610   FR   ISSN 0750-6244
ARCHIVES OF OTOLARYNGOLOGY/JOURNAL D'O.R.L. 1981. 4/yr. 230 F. (foreign 400 F.). Publications Medicales Internationales, 24 bis bd. Verd de Saint-Julien, 92190 Meudon, France. Ed. Michelle Deker.

616.07   US   ISSN 0363-0153
RB1   CODEN: ARPAAQ
ARCHIVES OF PATHOLOGY & LABORATORY MEDICINE. 1926. m. $135 (foreign $185). College of American Pathologists, 325 Waukegan Rd., Northfield, IL 60093-2750. TEL 708-446-8800. FAX 708-446-3563. Ed. Dr. William W. McLendon. adv.; bk.rev.; charts; illus.; index. circ. 15,500. (also avail. in microform from UMI,PMC) **Indexed:** Abstr.Hyg., AIM, Biol.Abstr., C.I.S. Abstr., Chem.Abstr., CINAHL, Curr.Adv.Cancer Res., Curr.Adv.Ecol.Sci., Curr.Adv.Genetics & Molec.Biol., Curr.Cont., Dent.Ind., Dok.Arbeitsmed., Excerp.Med., Helminthol.Abstr., Ind.Med., Ind.Sci.Rev., Ind.Vet., INIS Atomind., Med.& Surg.Dermat., Nutr.Abstr., Protozool.Abstr., Rev.Med.& Vet.Mycol., Rev.Plant Path., Sci.Cit.Ind., Trop.Dis.Bull., Vet.Bull. **Document type:** academic/scholarly publication.
● Also available online. Vendor(s): Lexis-Nexis.
—BLDSC (1638.610000); CASDDS; Faxon; Genuine Article; SWETS; UMI; UnCover. **CCC.**
  Formerly: Archives of Pathology (ISSN 0003-9985)
  Refereed Serial

610   US   ISSN 0004-0002
HQ1   CODEN: ASXBA8
ARCHIVES OF SEXUAL BEHAVIOR. 1971. bi-m. $435 (foreign $510) (effective 1996). Plenum Publishing Corp., 233 Spring St., New York, NY 10013-1578. TEL 212-620-8000. FAX 212-463-0742. TELEX 23-421139. Ed. Dr. Richard Green. adv.; bk.rev. (back issues avail.) **Indexed:** Abstr.Crim.& Pen., Adol.Ment.Hlth.Abstr., Behav.Med.Abstr., Biol.Abstr., Chem.Abstr., Curr.Adv.Ecol.Sci., Curr.Cont., Curr.Lit.Fam.Plan., Excerp.Med., IMFL, Ind.Med., Mid.East: Abstr.& Ind., Mult.Ed.Abstr., Psychol.Abstr. (1971-), Ref.Zh., SSCI, Stud.Wom.Abstr. **Document type:** academic/scholarly publication.
—BLDSC (1643.128000); CASDDS; Faxon; Genuine Article; SWETS; UMI; UnCover. **CCC.**
  Refereed Serial

ARCHIVIO ITALIANO DI ANATOMIA E DI EMBRIOLOGIA/ITALIAN JOURNAL OF ANATOMY AND EMBRYOLOGY. see *BIOLOGY*

610   BO   ISSN 0004-0525
ARCHIVOS BOLIVIANOS DE MEDICINA. 1943. 3/yr. free. Universidad Mayor, Real y Pontificia de San Francisco Xavier de Chuquisaca, Facultad de Ciencias de la Salud, Calle Colon No. 235, Casilla Coreo 460, Sucre, Bolivia. Eds. Antonio Dubravcic L., Alberto Aquirre. adv.; bk.rev.; bibl.; charts; illus. circ. 650.

ARCHIVOS DE BIOLOGIA ANDINA. see *BIOLOGY*

616 574.29   PL   ISSN 0004-069X
CODEN: AITEAT
ARCHIVUM IMMUNOLOGIAE ET THERAPIAE EXPERIMENTALIS. (Text in English) 1953. bi-m. $87. (Polska Akademia Nauk, Instytut Immunologii i Terapii Doswiadczalnej) Ossolineum, Publishing House of the Polish Academy of Sciences, Rynek 9, 50-106 Wroclaw, Poland. TEL 48-71-386-25. FAX 48-71-448-103. TELEX 0712771 OSS PL. Ed. Janna d. Inglot. charts; illus.; index. circ. 790. (also avail. in microfilm from PMC; reprint service avail. from ISI, UMI) **Indexed:** Abstr.Hyg., C.I.S. Abstr., Chem.Abstr., Curr.Adv.Cell & Devel.Biol., Curr.Adv.Ecol.Sci., Curr.Adv.Genetics & Molec.Biol., Curr.Cont., Dent.Ind., Excerp.Med., Helminthol.Abstr., Ind.Med., Ind.Sci.Rev., Ind.Vet., INIS Atomind., Sci.Cit.Ind, Trop.Dis.Bull. **Document type:** academic/scholarly publication.
—BLDSC (1659.500000); CASDDS; Faxon; Genuine Article; SWETS; UMI.
  Description: Publishes papers containing original results of scientific research and experiments that make a contribution to immunology or experimental therapy.

610   PL   ISSN 0860-1844
R131
ARCHIWUM HISTORII I FILOZOFII MEDYCYNY. (Text in Polish; summaries in English and Russian) 1924. q. $32. Polskie Towarzystwo Historii Medycyny - Polish Society of History of Medicine, c/o Glowna Biblioteka Lekarska, Ul. Chocimska 22, 00-791 Warsaw, Poland. (Dist. by: Ars Polona-Ruch, Krakowskie Przedmiescie 7, 00-068 Warsaw, Poland) Ed. Andrzej Srodka. bk.rev.; index. circ. 860. (reprint service avail. from UMI) **Indexed:** Amer.Hist.& Life, Biol.Abstr., Hist.Abstr., Ind.Med.
—BLDSC (1661.045000); UMI.
  Formerly (until 1985): Archiwum Historii Medycyny (ISSN 0004-0762)
  Description: Provides papers to Polish scholars in medicine, medical societies, evolution of medical research and results.

610 001.3   IT
L'ARCO DI GIANO; revista di medical humanities. 1993. 3/yr. L.69000 (foreign L.90000) (effective 1993). (Istituto per l'Analisi dello Stato Sociale) Franco Angeli Editore, Viale Monza 106, 20127 Milan, Italy. TEL 02-2827651. Ed. Sandro Spinsanti.

610 236   FI   ISSN 0782-226X
RC955   CODEN: AMRSEP
ARCTIC MEDICAL RESEARCH. 1972. q. $70. Nordic Council for Arctic Medical Research, Aapistie 1, SF-90220 Oulu, Finland. FAX 358-81-537-6203. (Co-sponsor: International Union for Circumpolar Health) Ed. Dr. Mikal Knip. bk.rev.; circ. 1,500 (controlled). (back issues avail.) **Document type:** academic/scholarly publication.
—BLDSC (1663.152000); UnCover.

610   IT   ISSN 1120-8643
ARGOMENTI DI CHEMIOANTIBIOTICOTERAPIA. 1991. q. L.8400($60) (effective 1994). Masson S.p.A., Divisione Periodici, Via Statuto 2-4, 20121 Milan, Italy. TEL 02-6367-1. FAX 02-6367-211. Ed. Franco Fraschini. adv.: B&W page L.3750000, color page L.6100000. circ. 12,000.

ARIZONA POISON CONTROL SYSTEM NEWSLETTER. see *PHARMACY AND PHARMACOLOGY*

ARKANSAS. DIVISION OF REHABILITATION SERVICES. ANNUAL REPORT. see *EDUCATION — Special Education And Rehabilitation*

610   US   ISSN 0004-1858
CODEN: JAMSAB
ARKANSAS MEDICAL SOCIETY. JOURNAL. 1890. m. $30 (foreign $40). Arkansas Medical Society, Box 5776, Little Rock, AR 72215-5776. TEL 501-224-8967. FAX 501-224-6489. Ed. Tina G. Wade. adv.; bk.rev.; abstr.; bibl.; charts; illus.; stat.; index. circ. 3,400. **Indexed:** Chem.Abstr., Dent.Ind., Ind.Med., INIS Atomind., Nutr.Abstr. **Document type:** trade publication.
—BLDSC (4700.850000); CASDDS; Faxon; SWETS.

616.07   RU   ISSN 0004-1955
CODEN: ARPTAF
ARKHIV PATOLOGII/ARCHIVES OF PATHOLOGY. (Text in Russian; summaries in English) 1935. bi-m. $146 (effective 1996). (Rossiiskaya Akademiya Meditsinskikh Nauk) Izdatel'stvo Meditsina, Petroverigskii pereulok 6-8, 101000 Moscow, Russia. (Dist. by: Mezhdunarodnaya Kniga, B. Yakimanka 39, 117049 Moscow, Russia. TEL 7-095-2384600. FAX 7-095-2384634) (Co-sponsors: Nauchnoe Obshchestvo Patologanatomov; Moskovskaya Meditsinskaya Akademiya im. I.I. Sechenova) Ed. A.V. Smol'iyannikov. bk.rev.; index. **Indexed:** Biol.Abstr., Biotech.Abstr., Chem.Abstr., Dent.Ind., Excerp.Med., Helminthol.Abstr., Ind.Med., Ind.Vet., INIS Atomind., Nutr.Abstr., Protozool.Abstr., Rev.Med.& Vet.Mycol., Vet.Bull. **Document type:** academic/scholarly publication.
—BLDSC (0009.800000); CASDDS; Genuine Article. **CCC.**
  Description: Deals with original investigation on pressing problems of general pathology and pathologic anatomy, performed with the help of the newest research methods and describing major provisions of the theory and practice of different human diseases, as well as problems of experimental, comparative and geographic pathology.

ARMY MEDICAL SERVICES MAGAZINE. see *MILITARY*

AROGYA; a journal of health sciences. see *PHYSICAL FITNESS AND HYGIENE*

616.07   PO   ISSN 0004-2714
CODEN: APALA4
ARQUIVO DE PATOLOGIA. vol.43, 1971. 3/yr. Esc.150. Instituto Portugues de Oncologia de Francisco Gentil, Palhava, Lisbon, Portugal. circ. 800. **Indexed:** Biol.Abstr., Chem.Abstr., Excerp.Med., Ind.Med.

610   BL   ISSN 0365-0723
ARQUIVOS BRASILEIROS DE MEDICINA. (Text in Portuguese; summaries in English and Portuguese) 1911. m. Cr.$37($100) (effective 1995). Editora Cientifica Nacional Ltda., Rua da Gloria, 366 3o andar, 20241-180 Rio de Janeiro, RJ, Brazil. TEL 55-21-2215235. FAX 55-21-2521691. Ed. Antonio Alves do Couto. adv. contact: Maria Louiza Carvalho Donedo. bk.rev.; index, cum.index. circ. 10,000. **Indexed:** Biol.Abstr., Excerp.Med., Ind.Med. **Document type:** academic/scholarly publication.
—BLDSC (1695.220000); UMI.

610   BL   ISSN 0004-2773
ARQUIVOS CATARINENSES DE MEDICINA. (Text in Portuguese; summaries in English) 1967. q. Cr.$40.000($40) (Associacao Catarinense de Medicina) Artes Graficas Ltda., Rua Jeronimo Coelho 359, Andar 4, 88000 Florianopolis SC, Brazil. Ed. Mario Jose da Conceicao. adv.; bk.rev.; bibl.; charts; index. circ. 5,000. (back issues avail.) **Indexed:** Biol.Abstr., Ind.Med.

610   PO   ISSN 0871-3413
ARQUIVOS DE MEDICINA; revista de ciencia e arte medicas. (Text in English and Portuguese) 1987. bi-m. Esc.5000 to doctors; students Esc.2500; foreign Esc.10000 (effective 1996). A E F M U P, Alameda Prof. Hernani Montiero, Piso 1, Apdo. 4514, 4008 Porto Codex, Portugal. TEL 351-2-524901. FAX 351-2-5509096. (Co-sponsors: Hospital de Sao Joao, Faculdade de Medicina do Porto, Sociedade Portugesa de Engenharia Biomedica) Dir. Levi Guerra. adv.: B&W page Esc.60000; adv. contact: Luisa Botelho. circ. 7,500. **Indexed:** Excerp.Med. **Document type:** academic/scholarly publication.
—BLDSC (1695.590000).

616.07   PO   ISSN 0066-7854
ARQUIVOS DE PATOLOGIA GERAL E ANATOMIA PATOLOGICA. (Text in Portuguese; summaries in English and French) 1913. a. exchange basis. Universidade de Coimbra, Instituto de Anatomia Patologica, Faculdade de Medicina, 3049 Coimbra Codex, Portugal. Ed. Renato Trincao. bk.rev. circ. 400. **Indexed:** Biol.Abstr., Excerp.Med.

ARQUIVOS DOS HOSPITAIS E DA FACULDADE DE CIENCIAS MEDICAS DA SANTA CASA DE SAO PAULO. see *HOSPITALS*

MEDICAL SCIENCES   4177

610   SZ   ISSN 0004-2897
ARS MEDICI; Schweizer Zeitschrift fuer Allgemeinmedizin. 1910. 19./yr. 70 SFr. (West Europe 135 SFr.; elsewhere 185 SFr.). S A E M Verlag AG, Rosenbergstr. 115, CH-8212 Neuhausen, Switzerland. TEL 053-227822. FAX 053-227823. Ed. Dr. Richard Altorfer. adv.; bk.rev.; index. circ. 8,500. **Indexed:** Biol.Abstr., Excerp.Med. **Document type:** academic/scholarly publication.
—BLDSC (1697.636000); SWETS.

610   GW   ISSN 0933-7946
ARTHROSKOPIE. 6/yr. DM.298($216) (effective 1996). Springer-Verlag, Heidelberger Platz 3, 14197 Berlin, Germany. TEL 030-8207-0. FAX 030-8214091. E-mail: orders@springer.de. (Subscr. in N. America to: Springer-Verlag New York, Inc., 44 Hartz Way, Secaucus, NJ 07096-2491. TEL 201-348-4033. FAX 201-348-4505) **Document type:** academic/scholarly publication.
—UMI.

617.95   NE   ISSN 0924-3054
                     CODEN: AORTE8
ARTIFICIAL ORGANS TODAY. (Text in English) 1991. q. DM.420 (effective 1996). (Japan Society for Artificial Organs, JA) V S P, P.O. Box 346, 3700 AH Zeist, Netherlands. TEL 31-30-6925790. FAX 31-30-6932081. E-mail: 100341.2372@compuserve.com. Ed. T. Agishi. **Document type:** academic/scholarly publication.
—BLDSC (1735.053000); CASDDS.
Description: Covers international research and practical information on artificial organs.
Refereed Serial

610   NE   ISSN 0928-611X
ARTS ASSISTENT. 1990. q. (Landelijke Vereniging van Assistent-Geneeskundigen) Misset (Subsidiary of: Reed Elsevier plc), Postbus 4, 7000 BA Doetinchem, Netherlands. TEL 31-8340-49371. FAX 31-8340-63638. (Editorial addr.: Postbus 1110, 3600 BC Maarssen, Netherlands. TEL 31-3465-58260. FAX 31-3465-58255) adv.; B&W page fl.3330, color page fl.5150; trim 210 x 280; adv. contact: Cor van Nek. circ. 5,000. **Document type:** trade publication.

619   JA   ISSN 0913-7343
ARUMEIDA IHO/OITA CITY MEDICAL ASSOCIATION. JOURNAL. (Text in Japanese) 1975. 3/yr. Oitashi Ishikai - Oita City Medical Association, 1315, Miyazaki, Oita-shi, Oita-ken 870-11, Japan.

ARUT PERUM JOTHI. see *RELIGIONS AND THEOLOGY — Hindu*

614   AU   ISSN 0004-4180
ARZT IN NIEDEROESTERREICH. 1965. m. $1. Ueberparteilicher Aerzteverband Niederoesterreichs, Klostergasse 6-8, A-3100 St. Poelten, Austria. Ed. Dr. Erich Klier. adv.; bk.rev.; abstr.; film rev.; illus.; stat. circ. 3,000.

610 338.3   GW   ISSN 0341-4434
ARZT UND AUTO; der kraftfahrende Arzt. 1924. m. DM.30. K V D A Verlag, Johanna-Melber-Weg 8, 60599 Frankfurt a.M., Germany. TEL 069-622007. FAX 069-622496. Ed. Dr. E. Wernicke. adv.; bk.rev. circ. 10,000. **Document type:** academic/scholarly publication.
—CCC.
Formerly (until 1971): Kraftfahrende Arzt.

610   GW   ISSN 0341-9754
ARZT UND KRANKENHAUS. 1976. m. DM.48. (Verband der Leitenden Krankenhausaerzte Deutschlands) Hansische Verlagskontor H. Scheffler, 23547 Luebeck, Germany. Ed. K. Jeute. illus. circ. 8,000. **Document type:** trade publication.
—BLDSC (1738.160000).

610   AU
ARZT UND PRAXIS; der praktische Arzt - der Facharzt in der Praxis. 1946. 21/yr. S.400 (foreign S.600). Medizinische Fachzeitschriften GmbH, A-2464 Goettlesbrunn 124, Austria. TEL 02162-8735. FAX 02162-887354. Eds. H. Schiel, O. Hartl. adv.; bk.rev. circ. 11,000. (tabloid format) **Indexed:** Biol.Abstr. **Document type:** academic/scholarly publication.
Formerly (until 1995): Praktische Arzt (ISSN 0048-5128)

610   SZ   ISSN 1016-8400
ARZT UND PRAXIS; Magazin fuer Praxismanagement. 1989. 4/yr. 48 SFr. (West Europe 65 SFr.; elsewhere 76 SFr.). S A E M Verlag AG, Rosenbergstr. 115, CH-8212 Neuhausen, Switzerland. TEL 053-227822. FAX 053-227823. Ed. Christine Kaiser. **Document type:** academic/scholarly publication.

610 340   GW
ARZTHAFTUNGSRECHT. 1987. irreg. DM.128. Luchterhand Verlag, Heddesdorferstr. 31, 56564 Neuwied, Germany. TEL 02631-801210. FAX 02631-801210. Ed. Klaus Kuntz. (looseleaf format) **Document type:** bulletin.

610 340   GW   ISSN 0343-5733
ARZTRECHT; Kompendium des Gesamten Rechtes der Medizin. 1965. m. DM.60. Verlag fuer Arztrecht, Schinnrainstr. 15, 76227 Karlshue, Germany. TEL 0721-402904. Ed. Dr. Manfred Andreas. adv.; bk.rev.; circ. controlled.
Description: Examines the role of the law in medical practice.

610   JA   ISSN 0285-9017
ASAHI CHUO BYOIN IHO/ASAHI GENERAL HOSPITAL. MEDICAL JOURNAL. (Text in English, Japanese) 1979. s-a. Asahi Chuo Byoin - Asahi General Hospital, I 1326, Asahi-shi, Chiba-ken 289-25, Japan.

610   JA   ISSN 0913-4603
ASAHIGAWASO KENKYU NENPO/ASAHIGAWASO INSTITUTE OF MEDICAL WELFARE. ANNUAL REPORT. (Text in Japanese) 1968. a. Asahigawaso - Asahigawaso Institute of Medical Welfare, Chisaki, Gion, Okayama-shi, Okayama-ken 703, Japan.

610   JA   ISSN 0918-7022
ASAHIKAWA IKA DAIGAKU NENPO/ASAHIKAWA MEDICAL COLLEGE. ANNUAL REPORT. (Text in Japanese) 1988. a. Asahikawa Ika Daigaku - Asahikawa Medical College, 5 Go, Nishikagura 4 Sen, Asahikawa-shi, Hokkaido 078, Japan.

610   JA   ISSN 0913-4417
ASAHIKAWA SEKIJUJI BYOIN IGAKU ZASSHI/ASAHIKAWA RED CROSS HOSPITAL. MEDICAL JOURNAL. (Text in Japanese) 1987. a. Asahikawa Sekijuji Byoin - Asahikawa Red Cross Hospital, 1, Akebono 1-jo, Asahikawa-shi, Hokkaido 070, Japan.

610   JA   ISSN 0287-024X
ASAHIKAWA SHIRITSU BYOIN ISHI/ASAHIKAWA CITY HOSPITAL. JOURNAL. (Text in Japanese) 1968. a. Asahikawa Shiritsu Byoin - Asahikawa City Hospital, 1-65, Kinseicho 1-chome, Asahikawa-shi, Hokkaido 070, Japan.

610 572   SP   ISSN 0210-4466
R131.A1
ASCLEPIO; archivo iberoamericano de historia de la medicina. 1949. s-a. 3300 ptas. (foreign 4950 ptas.). Consejo Superior de Investigaciones Cientificas (C.S.I.C.), Centro de Estudios Historicos, Departamento de Historia de la Medicina, Vitruvio, 8, 28006 Madrid, Spain. Ed. Pedro Lain Entralgo. bk.rev.; bibl.; cum.index: 1949-1973. (reprint service avail. from SCH) **Indexed:** A.I.C.P., Ind.Med.Esp.
—BLDSC (1739.250000).
Description: Contains original studies and researches in the fields of medical history, science, and medical anthropolgy.

610   US   ISSN 1062-0281
ASEPSIS; the infection prevention forum. 1975. q. free to qualified personnel. (Johnson & Johnson Medical, Inc.) Ad-Com Inc. Publishing, 2003 E. Lamar Blvd., Arlington, TX 76006. TEL 800-486-8247. FAX 817-261-1399. Ed. Barbara Gruendemann; Pub. Bill Pierce. adv. contact: Teri Scholtheis. circ. 30,000 (controlled). **Indexed:** CINAHL, Hosp.Lit.Ind. **Document type:** trade publication.

610   HK   ISSN 1011-596X
ASIAN HOSPITAL; Asia's forum for hospital professionals. (Text in English) 1987. bi-m. HK.$350 (Asia $45; elsewhere $60). Health Asia Communications, Ltd., G.P.O. Box 1099, Hong Kong. TEL 852-2869-4933. FAX 852-2525-6086. Dir. Laura Tse; Pub. John R. Longbotham. adv.: B&W page $3800, color page $5060; 285 x 210. circ. 38,361 (controlled).
Description: Covers management, financing, information systems, technology, trends and issues critical to the healthcare industry.

610   JA   ISSN 0004-461X
                     CODEN: ASMJAB
ASIAN MEDICAL JOURNAL. (Text in English) 1958. m. 7200 Yen. Japan Medical Association - Nihon Ishi Kai, 28-16, Hongo 2-chome, Bunkyo-ku, Tokyo 113, Japan. (U.S. subscr. to: Maruzen Company, Ltd., 1251 Ave. of the Americas, New York, NY 10020) Ed. Yuichiro Goto. adv.; index, cum.index vols.1-9. circ. 6,000. **Indexed:** Abstr.Hyg., Biol.Abstr., C.I.S.Abstr., Chem.Abstr., Diar.Dis.Res., Excerp.Med., Ind.Med., Ind.Vet., NRN, Rev.Med.& Vet.Mycol., Rev.Plant Path., Small Anim.Abstr. **Document type:** academic/scholarly publication.
—BLDSC (1742.700000); CASDDS; Faxon; UMI.

610   HK   ISSN 0250-3328
ASIAN MEDICAL NEWS. (Text and summaries in English) 1979. m. HK.$250($65) MediMedia Asia Ltd., 8F Pacific Plaza, 410 Des Voeux Rd. W., Hong Kong. TEL 852-2559-5888. FAX 852-2559-6910. TELEX HX-63267. Ed. Joanne McManus. adv.; bk.rev.; index. circ. 34,635. **Document type:** newspaper.
—BLDSC (1742.700200).

610   PR   ISSN 0004-4849
ASOCIACION MEDICA DE PUERTO RICO. BOLETIN. (Text in English and Spanish) 1903. m. $40. Asociacion Medica de Puerto Rico, Avenida Fernandez Juncos, No. 1305, Apdo. de Correo 9387, Santurce, PR 00908. Ed.Bd. adv.; bk.rev.; bibl.; illus.; index. circ. 3,500. **Indexed:** Abstr.Hyg., Bio-Contr.News & Info., Biol.Abstr., Chem.Abstr., CINAHL, Dent.Ind., Ind.Med., Nutr.Abstr., Sel.Water Res.Abstr., Trop.Dis.Bull.
—BLDSC (2160.850000); Faxon.

610.7   MX   ISSN 0004-4857
ASOCIACION MEXICANA DE FACULTADES Y ESCUELAS DE MEDICINA. BOLETIN. 1962. irreg. free. Asociacion Mexicana de Facultades y Escuelas de Medicina, Queretaro No. 147, Oficinas 501 y 502, Apdo. Postal 12927, 06760 Mexico, D.F., Mexico. Ed. Dr. Manuel Loria-Mendez. bibl.; charts; illus.; index. circ. 750.

610   MX   ISSN 0004-489X
ASOCIACION PARA EVITAR LA CEGUERA EN MEXICO. ARCHIVOS. 1956. q. free. Asociacion para Evitar la Ceguera en Mexico, Vicente Garcia Torres 46, Coyoacan 21, 04330 Mexico D.F, Mexico. Ed. Dr. Teodulo M. Agundis. adv.; bibl.; charts; illus.

610 378   US
ASSEMBLY ON EDUCATION NETWORK. 1985. q. $15. American Health Information Management Association, 919 N. Michigan Ave., Ste. 1400, Chicago, IL 60611-1601. TEL 312-787-2672. Ed. Betty Bowman. circ. 750. (back issues avail.)
Formerly: Medical Record Educator.
Description: Focuses on academic issues and research related to medical record education. Articles cover field research, grants and funding, recruitment and retention, creative classroom and teaching methods, joint ventures and international news.

610   IS   ISSN 0334-3871
ASSIA. (Text in Hebrew) 1970. irreg. (4 nos./vol.). $25 per vol. Shaare Zedek Medical Center, Falk Schlesinger Institute for Medical Halachic Research, P.O. Box 3235, Jerusalem 91031, Israel. TEL 972-2-555266. FAX 972-2-555342. Ed. Rabbi Dr. Mordechai Halperin. circ. 1,000. **Indexed:** Ind.Heb.Per.

174.2 296.3   IS   ISSN 0793-2952
ASSIA - JEWISH MEDICAL ETHICS. (Text in English) 1988. irreg. (2 nos./vol.). $25 per vol. Shaare Zadek Medical Center, Falk Schlesinger Institute for Medical Halachic Research, P.O. Box 3235, Jerusalem 91031, Israel. TEL 972-2-555266. FAX 972-2-555342. Ed. Rabbi Dr. Mordechai Halperin. adv. circ. 500. **Document type:** academic/scholarly publication.

MEDICAL SCIENCES

610   US
ASSISTED REPRODUCTIVE TECHNOLOGY - ANDROLOGY; international journal. Abbreviated title: A R T A. 1990. q. $180 to individuals (foreign $190); institutions $200 (foreign $210) (effective 1996). Reproductive Health Center, 78 Surfsong Rd., Kiawah Island, SC 29455. TEL 803-768-5556. FAX 803-768-6494. **Document type:** academic/scholarly publication.
Refereed Serial

ASSISTIVE TECHNOLOGY. see *EDUCATION — Special Education And Rehabilitation*

610   BL
ASSOCIACAO MEDICA BRASILEIRA. BOLETIM. 1962. m. Associacao Medica Brasileira, Sao Carlos Pinhal 324, Sao Paulo, SP, Brazil. TEL 55-11-289-3511. FAX 55-11-2896002. Ed. Virginio Sanches; Pub. Carlos Correa. adv. circ. 45,000. **Indexed:** Soils & Fert. **Document type:** newspaper.

610   BL ISSN 0004-5233
ASSOCIACAO MEDICA BRASILEIRA. JORNAL.* w. Cr.$5.($5.) Associacao Medica Brasileira, Rua Sao Carlos do Pinhal 324, CEP 01333 Sao Paulo, Brazil. Ed. Dr. Pedro Kassab. adv.; bk.rev.; charts; illus. circ. 30,000.

610   BL ISSN 0004-5241
ASSOCIACAO MEDICA BRASILEIRA. REVISTA. (Text in Portuguese; summaries in English and French) 1954. m. Associacao Medica Brasileira, Sao Carlos Pinhal 324, CEP 01333 Sao Paulo, SP, Brazil. Ed. Abrao Rapoport. adv.; bk.rev.; abstr.; charts; illus.; index. circ. 40,000. **Indexed:** Biol.Abstr., Chem.Abstr., Excerp.Med., Ind.Med.

610   BL ISSN 0004-525X
CODEN: RAMMDG
ASSOCIACAO MEDICA DE MINAS GERAIS. REVISTA. (Text in Portuguese; summaries in English) 1949. q. Cr.$400($30) (Associacao Medica de Minas Gerais) Edicao & Mercado, Av. Men de Sa, 801 St. Efigenia, 30000 Belo Horizonte Minas Gerais, Brazil. Dir. Jose Netto. adv.; bk.rev.; bibl.; charts; illus.; stat; index. circ. 5,000. (also avail. in microfilm) **Indexed:** Biol.Abstr., Nutr.Abstr.

611 574.4 FR ISSN 0066-8915
ASSOCIATION DES ANATOMISTES. BULLETIN. 1899. q. 680 F. (foreign 800 F.). Association des Anatomistes, Faculte Medecine, B.P. 184, 54505 Vandoeuvre les Nancy Cedex, France. TEL 83-59-28-33. FAX 83-44-60-65. Ed. Georges Grignon. adv. circ. 1,100. **Indexed:** Biol.Abstr., Bull.Signal., Dent.Ind., Excerp.Med., Ind.Med. **Document type:** bulletin.
Formerly: Association des Anatomistes. Comptes Rendus.

610   CN ISSN 0004-539X
ASSOCIATION DES MEDECINS DE LANGUE FRANCAISE DU CANADA. BULLETIN. 1967. m. membership. Association des Medecins de Langue Francaise du Canada, 8355 boul. St-Laurent, Montreal, PQ H2P 2Z6, Canada. TEL 514-388-2228. bk.rev.; illus. circ. 13,446. (looseleaf format; reprint service avail. from UMI) **Document type:** bulletin.

ASSOCIATION FOR PSYCHOANALYTIC MEDICINE. BULLETIN. see *PSYCHOLOGY*

610 338.476 UK ISSN 1351-5969
▼**ASSOCIATION FOR QUALITY IN HEALTHCARE. JOURNAL.** Key Title: Journal of the Association for Quality in Healthcare. Abbreviated title: J A Q H. 1994. q.? £35 to non-member individuals; institutions £55 (foreign £65). Association for Quality in Healthcare, 9 Chesil St., Winchester, Hants. SO23 8HU, England. Ed. Nancy Dixon. adv. **Document type:** academic/scholarly publication.
—BLDSC (4705.221300).
Description: Aims to improve the quality of healthcare services by disseminating information about ideas, practical approaches and techniques, experiences, innovations, research findings, and events.
Refereed Serial

388.3 610 US ISSN 0892-6484
ASSOCIATION FOR THE ADVANCEMENT OF AUTOMOTIVE MEDICINE. PROCEEDINGS.* 1959. a. $40 to US and Canada; Europe $50; others $55. Association for the Advancement of Automotive Medicine, c/o Associated Life Ins., 222 Merchandise Mart Plaza, Ste. 1450, Chicago, IL 60654-1203. TEL 312-390-8927. circ. 1,000. (also avail. in microform) **Indexed:** Psychol.Abstr. **Document type:** proceedings.
—BLDSC (1082.217000).
Formerly (until 1987): American Association for Automotive Medicine. Proceedings (ISSN 0401-6351)

610   US
ASSOCIATION OF AMERICAN INDIAN PHYSICIANS NEWSLETTER.* q. Association of American Indian Physicians, 1235 Sovereign Row, No. C-7, Oklahoma City, OK 73108-1833.

610   US ISSN 1081-650X
R15 CODEN: TAAPAI
ASSOCIATION OF AMERICAN PHYSICIANS. TRANSACTIONS. 1886. bi-m. $170 (foreign $200) (effective 1996). Blackwell Science Inc., 238 Main St., Cambridge, MA 02142. TEL 617-876-7022; 800-759-6102. FAX 617-492-5263. circ. 1,000. (also avail. in microfilm from BHP) **Indexed:** Chem.Abstr., Excerp.Med., Ind.Med. **Document type:** academic/scholarly publication.
—BLDSC (8902.700000); CASDDS; Faxon.
Formerly: Association of American Physicians. Transactions (ISSN 0066-9458)

616.04 US
ASSOCIATION OF BIRTH DEFECT CHILDREN NEWSLETTER. 1980. q. free to members. Association of Birth Defect Children, 827 Irma Ave., Orlando, FL 32803-3806. TEL 407-245-7035; 800-435-7352. Ed. Betty Mekdeci. bk.rev. circ. 10,000. (back issues avail.) **Document type:** newsletter.
Description: Provides information about birth defects to parents and professionals.

ASSOCIATION OF LIFE INSURANCE MEDICAL DIRECTORS OF AMERICA. TRANSACTIONS. see *INSURANCE*

610   II ISSN 0004-5772
CODEN: JPHIAR
ASSOCIATION OF PHYSICIANS OF INDIA. JOURNAL. vol.28, 1980. m. Rs.450. Association of Physicians of India, Laud Mansion, 3rd Fl., 21 M. Karve Rd., Bombay 400 004, India. Ed. Dr. V.R. Joshi. adv.; bk.rev. circ. 5,500. **Indexed:** Chem.Abstr., Dent.Ind., Ind.Med., Nutr.Abstr., Trop.Dis.Bull.
—BLDSC (4705.120000); CASDDS; Faxon; UnCover.

610   MX ISSN 0185-6235
ATENCION MEDICA. 1970. m. Mex.$180($60) Intersistemas, S.A. de C.V., Fernando Alencastre No. 110 Lomas de Virreyes, 11000 Mexico D.F., Mexico. TEL 525-540-0798. FAX 525-540-3764. Ed. Pedro Vera-Cervera. adv. contact: Miguel Alberto Gonzalez. circ. 15,500. **Document type:** academic/scholarly publication.

610   SP ISSN 0212-6567
CODEN: ATEPEY
ATENCION PRIMARIA.* 12/yr. Haymarket, S.A., Travesera Gracia 17-21, 5o 2o, 08022 Barcelona, Spain. TEL 3-237-22-66. FAX 3-237-66-88. Ed. Dr. J.F. Cano Perez. **Indexed:** FAMLI (1991-1992).
—BLDSC (1765.858500).

610   BO
ATENEO DE MEDICINA. 6/yr. Casilla 549, La Paz, Bolivia. adv.

610 574 IT ISSN 0004-6531
ATENEO PARMENSE. ACTA BIO-MEDICA. (Text and summaries in English and Italian) 1929. bi-m. L.25000 (foreign L.50000) (effective 1994). (Societa di Medicina e Scienze Naturali di Parma) Ateneo Parmense, Via Gramsci 14, 43100 Parma, Italy. TEL 39-521-983364. Ed. Fulvio Allegra; Pub. Paolo Bobbio. bk.rev.; bibl.; charts; illus.; stat.; index, cum.index. circ. 550. **Indexed:** Biol.Abstr., Chem.Abstr., Excerp.Med., Ind.Med., INIS Atomind., Nutr.Abstr. **Document type:** academic/scholarly publication, proceedings.
—BLDSC (0603.000000).
Description: Research papers covering a variety of medical topics.

610   US
ATLANTA HEALTHSCOPE 2000. 1992. q. $7.50. 3254 Colquill Trail, Ste. 200, Kenneshaw, GA 30145. TEL 404-919-7022. FAX 404-422-1382. Ed. Mary N. Miltiades; Pub. Mary N. Miltiades. adv.: B&W page $1949, color page $2498; trim 8 3/8 x 10 7/8. **Document type:** consumer publication.

610 309 IO
ATMA JAYA RESEARCH CENTRE. SOCIO-MEDICAL RESEARCH REPORT/PUSAT PENELITIAN ATMA JAYA. PENELITIAN TENTANG KEBUTUHAN KESEHATAN MASYARAKAT DAN SISTEM PELEYANAN KESEHATAN DI KECAMATAN PENJARINGAN. 1978. irreg. Atma Jaya Research Centre - Pusat Penelitian Atma Jaya, Jalan Jenderal Sudirman 51, P.O. Box 2639, Jakarta 10001, Indonesia. Ed. Paul W. Kartono. **Indexed:** Abstr.Rural Dev.Trop. **Document type:** monographic series.

610   JA ISSN 0915-6003
ATSUGI BYOIN ISHI/ATSUGI MEDICAL JOURNAL. (Text in Japanese) 1981. a. Kanagawa Kenritsu Atsugi Byoin - Kanagawa Prefectural Atsugi Hospital, 16-36, Mizuhiki 1-chome, Atsugi-shi, Kanagawa-ken 243, Japan.

610   US ISSN 0271-1362
AUDIO-DIGEST FAMILY PRACTICE. 1953. w. & s-m. $336 w. edition; s-m. edition $168. Audio-Digest Foundation (Subsidiary of: California Medical Association), 1577 E. Chevy Chase Dr., Glendale, CA 91206. TEL 213-245-8505. FAX 818-240-7379. (audio cassette)
—UnCover.
Formerly: Audio-Digest General Practice (ISSN 0571-8619)
Refereed Serial

AUDIOLOGISCH AKUSTIK/AUDIOLOGICAL ACOUSTICS. see *PHYSICS — Sound*

AUSTRALIA. DEPARTMENT OF HEALTH. OPERATIONS OF THE REGISTERED HEALTH INSURANCE ORGANIZATIONS. ANNUAL REPORT. see *INSURANCE*

610   AT ISSN 0004-8291
CODEN: ANZJB8
AUSTRALIAN AND NEW ZEALAND JOURNAL OF MEDICINE. 1952. bi-m. Aus.$170 (effective 1993). (Royal Australasian College of Physicians) Adis International Pty. Ltd., 9 Rodborough Rd., Frenchs Forest, N.S.W. 2089, Australia. TEL 61-2-9759100. FAX 61-2-9759199. Ed. Graham MacDonald. adv.; bk.rev.; charts; illus.; index. circ. 6,500. (also avail. in microform from PMC) **Indexed:** Abstr.Hyg., Biol.Abstr., Biotech.Abstr., Chem.Abstr., Curr.Adv.Ecol.Sci., Curr.Cont., Dairy Sci.Abstr., Dok.Arbeitsmed., Excerp.Med., Helminthol.Abstr., I.P.A., Ind.Med., Ind.Sci.Rev., INIS Atomind., Med.& Surg.Dermat., NRN, Nutr.Abstr., Protozool.Abstr., Rev.Plant Path., Sci.Cit.Ind., Trop.Dis.Bull. **Document type:** academic/scholarly publication.
●Also available online.
—BLDSC (1796.888000); CASDDS; Faxon; Genuine Article; SWETS; UMI; UnCover. **CCC.**
Formerly: Australasian Annals of Medicine.

610   AT ISSN 1039-7116
AUSTRALIAN DOCTOR. 1984. w. Aus.$175. Reed Business Publishing Pty. Ltd. (Subsidiary of: Reed International PLC), 1-5 Railway St., Chatswood, N.S.W. 2067, Australia. TEL 02-372-5222. FAX 02-419-7633. Ed. Kathryn Ryan. circ. 20,000. (tabloid format; back issues avail.)
Former titles (until 1993): Australian Dr Weekly (ISSN 1033-9221); (until 1987): Australian Dr (ISSN 0814-6012)
Description: Examines the clinical, socio-economic and leisure aspects of the medical professional.

610   AT ISSN 0300-8495
CODEN: AFPHCX
AUSTRALIAN FAMILY PHYSICIAN. 1956. m. Aus.$126 (foreign Aus.$169). Royal Australian College of General Practitioners, 1 Palmerston Crescent, S. Melbourne, Vic. 3205, Australia. TEL 61-3-2141414. FAX 61-3-2141401. Ed. John Burke. adv.: B&W page Aus.$2348, color page Aus.$2905; trim 275 x 205; adv. contact: Anoni J. Graham. bk.rev.; abstr.; charts; illus.; index. circ. 22,000. (tabloid format; back issues avail.) **Indexed:** Curr.Adv.Cancer Res., Curr.Adv.Ecol.Sci., Dent.Ind., Dok.Arbeitsmed., Excerp.Med., FAMLI, Ind.Med.
—BLDSC (1798.922000); SWETS; UnCover. **CCC.**
Formerly: Annals of General Practice (ISSN 0003-4789)

MEDICAL SCIENCES 4179

610 616   AT   ISSN 1038-1643
CODEN: AUJMEN
AUSTRALIAN JOURNAL OF MEDICAL SCIENCE. 4/yr. Aus.$50 to non-members (foreign Aus.$65). Australian Institute of Medical Scientists, P.O. Box 450, Toowong, Qld. 4066, Australia. TEL 67-371-3370. FAX 61-7-870-4857. Ed. Trevor Forster, Keith Harrison. **Indexed:** Chem.Abstr., Excerp.Med., INIS Atomind.
—BLDSC (1810.270000); CASDDS; UnCover.
Former titles: Australian Journal of Laboratory Science (ISSN 0158-4960); (until 1980): Australia Journal of Medical Technology (ISSN 0312-956X); Medical Technology in Australia.
Description: Scientific and technological papers relating to clinical laboratory practice.

AUSTRALIAN JOURNAL OF PSYCHOTHERAPY. see *PSYCHOLOGY*

174.2 614   AT
AUSTRALIAN MEDICINE. 1989. s-m. Aus.$180 (foreign Aus.$270) (effective 1995). Australian Medical Association, Level 4, 42 Macquarie St., Barton, A.C.T., Australia. TEL 61-6-270-5400. FAX 61-6-270-5499. Ed. Bill Norman. adv. contact: Vivienne Kacsof. bk.rev. circ. 20,500. (back issues avail.) **Document type:** newspaper.
Description: Provides information relating to health care politics, medical ethics and legal news.

AUSTRALIAN OCCUPATIONAL THERAPY JOURNAL. see *MEDICAL SCIENCES — Physical Medicine And Rehabilitation*

610   AT   ISSN 0817-3834
AUSTRALIAN PRIVATE DOCTOR. 1968. bi-m. Aus.$60 (typically set Jan.). Private Doctors of Australia Ltd., 194 Derby St., Penrith, N.S.W. 2750, Australia. TEL 61-47-322977. FAX 61-47-323762. Ed. Ian Tait. adv. contact: Ron Hill. bk.rev.; illus.; circ. 2,500 (controlled). (also avail. in microform; back issues avail.) **Document type:** trade publication.
—UMI.
Formerly (until 1985): Australian G P (ISSN 0045-0499)

AUTONOMIC NERVOUS SYSTEM. see *BIOLOGY — Physiology*

610   DK
AUTORISEREDE LAEGER I DANMARK. 1982. irreg. DKK 80. Sundhedsstyrelsen, Amaliegade 13, 1012 Copenhagen K, Denmark. (Subscr. to: Statens Informationtjeneste, P.O. Box 1103, Copenhagen K, Denmark) circ. 900.
Former titles (until 1992): Autoriserede Laeger, Tandlaeger, Dyrlaeger i Danmark (ISSN 0108-4739); Fortegnelse over Autoriserede Laeger, Tandlaeger, Dyrlaeger i Danmark (ISSN 0106-7354)

610   US
AVENUES (SONORA). 1980. 2/yr. $7.50 donation. National Support Group for Arthrogryposis Multiplex Congenita, Box 5192, Sonora, CA 95370. TEL 209-928-3688. Ed. Mary Anne Schmidt. circ. 1,000. (looseleaf format; back issues avail.) **Document type:** newsletter.
Description: Publishes research articles, reviews and family experiences to enable families to network on a national and international level.

616.98   RU   ISSN 0233-528X
RC1050   CODEN: AEKME
AVIAKOSMICHESKAYA I EKOLOGICHESKAYA MEDITSINA/AEROSPACE AND ENVIRONMENTAL MEDICINE. (Text in Russian; summaries in English) 1967. bi-m. $48. Institut Mediko-biologicheskikh Problem, Khoroshevskoe shosse, d. 76a, 123007 Moscow, Russia. TEL 095-5718272. (Subscr. to: Mezhdunarodnaya Kniga, B. Yakimanka 39, 117049 Moscow, Russia) Ed. A.I. Grigor'ev. bk.rev.; abstr.; bibl.; charts; illus.; index. **Indexed:** Biol.Abstr., Chem.Abstr., Curr.Adv.Ecol.Sci., Curr.Cont., Dairy Sci.Abstr., Dent.Ind., Dok.Arbeitsmed., Excerp.Med., Field Crop Abstr., Ind.Med., Ind.Sci.Rev., INIS Atomind., Nutr.Abstr., Psychol.Abstr. (1982-), Triticale Abstr. **Document type:** academic/scholarly publication.
—BLDSC (0000.230000); CASDDS; Genuine Article. **CCC.**
Former titles (until 1992): Kosmicheskaya Biologiya i Aviakosmicheskaya Meditsina (ISSN 0321-5040); Kosmicheskaya Biologiya i Meditsina (ISSN 0023-4192)
Description: Articles both of scientific and applied character on a wide range of problems in the field of aerospace medicine and biology. Includes physiology and hygiene of flight, psychophysiological peculiarities of flight activity, psychological screening and medical examination for flight fitness.

AVIATION MEDICAL EDUCATION SERIES. see *AERONAUTICS AND SPACE FLIGHT*

610 629.132   II   ISSN 0250-5045
AVIATION MEDICINE. (Text in English) 1951. s-a. Rs.100. Aero Medical Society of India, Medical Directorate, Air Headquarters, R.K. Puram West, Block 6, New Delhi 110 006, India. TEL 60661. Ed. Ari Cude Pe Chatterje. adv.; bk.rev.; index. circ. 700.

616.98   US   ISSN 0095-6562
RC1050   CODEN: ASEMCG
AVIATION, SPACE, AND ENVIRONMENTAL MEDICINE. 1930. m. $125 (foreign $135). Aerospace Medical Association, 320 S. Henry St., Alexandria, VA 22314-3579. TEL 703-739-2240. Ed. Dr. David R. Jones. adv.; bk.rev.; index. circ. 5,000. (also avail. in microfiche from UMI) **Indexed:** Air Un.Lib.Ind., Biol.Abstr., C.I.S.Abstr., Chem.Abstr., CINAHL, Curr.Adv.Ecol.Sci., Curr.Cont., Dent.Ind., Ergon.Abstr., Excerp.Med., Ind.Med., Ind.Sci.Rev., INIS Atomind., Noise Pollut.Publ.Abstr., Nutr.Abstr., Psychol.Abstr. (1950-), Psycscan, Risk Abstr., Sci.Cit.Ind. **Document type:** academic/scholarly publication.
—BLDSC (1838.640000); CASDDS; EMDOCS; Faxon; Genuine Article; SWETS; UMI; UnCover. **CCC.**
Formerly (until 1975): Aerospace Medicine (ISSN 0001-9402)
Refereed Serial

610   IT   ISSN 0392-6877
L'AVVENIRE MEDICO. a. price varies. Giardini Editori e Stampatori, Via Santa Bibbiana 28, 56100 Pisa, Italy. TEL 050 502531.

610   JA
AWAJI ISHIKAI NYUSU/AWAJI MEDICAL ASSOCIATION NEWS. (Text in Japanese) 1982. q. Awaji Ishikai - Awaji Medical Association, 1-12, Sakaemachi 1-chome, Sumoto-shi, Hyogo-ken 656, Japan.

610   II   ISSN 0005-2469
R606
AYU. (Text in English, Gujarati, Hindi and Sanskrit) 1964. m. Rs.15. Gujarat Ayurved University, Institute of Post Graduate Teaching and Research, Jamnagar, P.O. Box 511, Gujarat, India. Ed.Bd. adv.; bk.rev.; bibl.; charts. circ. 225.

610   II   ISSN 0005-2493
AYURVEDA DOOT. (Text in English, Hindi) 1969. w. Rs.10.50. Rajasthan Ayurvedic Research Laboratories, Ayurveddoot Karyalaya 4, Dhamani Market, Sawai Mansingh Highway, Jaipur 3, India. Ed. Dhan Kumar Jain.

610   AJ   ISSN 0005-2523
CODEN: AZMZA6
AZERBAIDZHANSKII MEDITSINSKII ZHURNAL/AZERBAIDZHAN TIBB ZHURNALY. (Text in Azerbaijani and Russian) 1928. m. 21 Rub. (Ministerstvo Zdravookhranieniya Azerbaijana) Izdatel'stvo Elm, Ul. Narimonova, 37, 370073 Baku, Azerbaijan. (Dist. by: Mezhdunarodnaya Kniga, Moscow, G-200, Russia) **Indexed:** Biol.Abstr., Chem.Abstr.
—CASDDS. **CCC.**

616.39 575.1   NE   ISSN 0925-4439
CODEN: BBADEX
B B A - MOLECULAR BASIS OF DISEASE. (Section of: Biochimica et Biophysica Acta (ISSN 0006-3002)) 9/yr. fl.1383($843) (effective 1996). Elsevier Science B.V., P.O. Box 211, 1000 AE Amsterdam, Netherlands. TEL 31-20-4853911. FAX 31-20-4853598. TELEX 18582 ESPA NL. E-mail: nlinfo-f@elsevier.nl; usinfo-f@elsevier.nl; usinfo-f@elsevier.com; forinfo-kyf04035@niftyserve.or.jp; Site addr.: http://www.elsevier.nl/. (Subscr. in U.S. and Canada to: Elsevier Science Inc., Box 882, Madison Sq. Sta., New York, NY 10159. TEL 212-989-5800. FAX 212-633-3990) Ed.Bd. (also avail. in microfilm from UMI) **Indexed:** Excerp.Med. **Document type:** academic/scholarly publication.
—ADONIS; Faxon; Genuine Article; SWETS; UnCover. **CCC.**
Description: Focuses on a fundamental biochemical and genetic approach to understanding dysfunction in human disease states and their models.
Refereed Serial

M

610 320   UK   ISSN 0306-5472
B M A NEWS REVIEW. (In 2 editions: General Practitioner & Hospital) 1966. m. £45($71.55) British Medical Association, B.M.A. House, Tavistock Sq., London WC1H 9JP, England. TEL 0171-387-4499. FAX 0171-383-6566. (U.S. subscr. to: Box 560-B, Kennebunkport, ME 04046) Ed. Mark Jessop. circ. 95,000 (controlled). **Indexed:** Curr.Adv.Ecol.Sci.
—BLDSC (2116.035000).
Description: Directed to doctors from all parts of the profession with news and information about a wide range of topics. Includes features on other socio-health-related subjects.
Refereed Serial

B M E: BIO MEDICAL ENGINEERING. see *BIOLOGY — Bioengineering*

610   US
B M E S BULLETIN. 1976. q. $25. Biomedical Engineering Society, Box 2399, Culver City, CA 90231. TEL 310-618-9322. Eds. Jerry Collins, Rita M. Schaffer. adv. circ. 2,000. **Document type:** newsletter.

MEDICAL SCIENCES

610 UK ISSN 0959-535X
R31 CODEN: BMJOAE
B M J. (British Medical Journal) Clinical Research edition (ISSN 0959-8138); International edition (ISSN 0959-8146); General Practice edition (ISSN 0959-8154); South African edition (ISSN 1019-8350); Hungarian edition (ISSN 1216-7495) (Supplement avail.: Student B M J (ISSN 0966-6494). Local editions also avail.: Bulgarian, Dutch, Greek, Hungarian, Indian, Mexican, Middle Eastern, Pakistani, Polish, Portuguese, Rumanian, South African, Spanish) 1840. w. £90 to individuals (International edition $137 to individuals; institutions £190 ($275); Clinical Research edition $377). (British Medical Association) B M J Publishing Group, B.M.A. House, Tavistock Sq., London WC1H 9JR, England. TEL 0171-383-6270. FAX 0171-383-6402. (N. American subscr. to: Box 480, Franklin, MA 02038. TEL 800-2-FON-BMJ. FAX 800-2-FAX-BMJ) Ed. Richard Smith. adv. contact: Muriel Bankhead. bk.rev.; abstr.; bibl.; charts; illus.; index. (also avail. in microform from UMI,PMC; reprint service avail. from UMI) **Indexed:** Abstr.Crim.& Pen., Abstr.Health Care Manage.Stud., Abstr.Hyg., Abstr.Inter.Med., AIM, Anal.Abstr., ASSIA, Behav.Med.Abstr., Bibl.Dev.Med.& Child Neur., Biol.Abstr., Biotech.Abstr., C.I.S. Abstr., Cadscan, Chem.Abstr., CINAHL, Curr.Adv.Cancer Res., Curr.Adv.Ecol.Sci., Curr.Adv.Genetics & Molec.Biol., Curr.Cont., Curr.Lit.Fam.Plan., Dairy Sci.Abstr., Dent.Ind., Diab.Cont., Diar.Dis.Res., Dok.Arbeitsmed., Excerp.Med., FAMLI, Food Sci.& Tech.Abstr., Helminthol.Abstr., High.Educ.Curr.Aware.Bull., HRIS, I.P.A., Ind.Hyg.Dig., Ind.Med., Ind.Sci.Rev., Ind.Vet., INIS Atomind., Kidney, Lab.Haz.Bull., Lead Abstr., Med.& Surg.Dermat., Med.Care Rev., Mult.Ed.Abstr., NRN, Nutr.Abstr., Popul.Ind., Potato Abstr., Protozool.Abstr., Res.High.Educ.Abstr., Rev.Appl.Entomol., Rev.Med.& Vet.Mycol., Rev.Plant Path., Risk Abstr., Sci.Cit.Ind., Sp.Ed.Needs Abstr., Stud.Wom.Abstr., Trop.Dis.Bull., Vet.Bull., W.R.C.Inf., Zincscan. **Document type:** academic/scholarly publication.
●Also available online. Vendor(s): Ovid Technologies, University Microfilms International.
Also available on CD-ROM.
—BLDSC (2330.000000); CASDDS; UnCover. **CCC.**
Formerly (until 1980): British Medical Journal (ISSN 0007-1447)
Description: Covers all branches of medicine for the professional and lay person.
Refereed Serial

610 SA ISSN 1019-8350
B M J. Key Title: B M J. British Medical Journal (South African Edition). (Text in English) 1992. m. George Warman Publications (Pty.) Ltd., P.O. Box 3487, Cape Town 8000, South Africa. TEL 27-21-245320. FAX 27-21-261332.

B N A'S HEALTH LAW REPORTER; a weekly review of legislative, regulatory, and legal developments. see *LAW*

610 340 US ISSN 1049-7986
B N A'S MEDICARE REPORT. 1990. w. $688 (effective July 1995). The Bureau of National Affairs, Inc., 1231 25th St., N.W., Washington, DC 20037. TEL 202-452-4200. FAX 202-822-8092. TELEX 285656 BNAI WSH. (Subscr. to: 9435 Key West Ave., Rockville, MD 20850. TEL 800-372-1033) Ed. Mary Davis. (back issues avail.)
●Also available online. Vendor(s): Human Resources Information Network (File DD).
—CCC.
Description: Notification service covering legislative, regulatory, and legal developments affecting or pertaining to the Medicare program.

610 BA ISSN 1012-7666
CODEN: BMBUEU
BAHRAIN MEDICAL BULLETIN. (Text in English) 1979. 3/yr. P.O. Box 32159, Manama, Bahrain. TEL 973-279472. Ed. Jaffar al-Ibriq. circ. 1,750. **Indexed:** Excerp.Med. (until 1992), ExtraMED. **Document type:** bulletin.
●Also available on CD-ROM.

610 BA ISSN 1015-6321
CODEN: JBSOE
BAHRAIN MEDICAL SOCIETY. JOURNAL. Key Title: Journal of the Bahrain Medical Society. 1979. 3/yr. Bahrain Medical Society, P.O. Box 26136, Manama, Bahrain. TEL 973-742666. Ed. Dr. Ali M. Matar. **Indexed:** Excerp.Med., ExtraMED. **Document type:** academic/scholarly publication.
●Also available on CD-ROM.
—BLDSC (4707.637800).

614.88 UK
BAILLIERE'S HANDBOOK OF FIRST AID. 1958. irreg., vol.7, 1985. £8.95 (effective 1994). Bailliere Tindall - W.B. Saunders Co. Ltd. (Subsidiary of: Harcourt Brace & Company Ltd.), 24-28 Oval Rd., London NW1 7DX, England. TEL 0171-267-4466. FAX 0171-482-2293. TELEX 25775 ACPRES G. (Subscr. to: Harcourt Brace & Company Ltd., Journals Subscription Deparment, Foots Cray High St., Sidcup, Kent DA14 5HP, England. TEL 0181-300-3322. FAX 0181-309-0807; Subscr. in N. America to: W.B. Saunders Co., Journal Subscription Fulfillment, 6277 Sea Harbor Dr., 4th Fl., Orlando, FL 32887-4800. TEL 800-874-6418) (back issues avail.) **Document type:** academic/scholarly publication.
Refereed Serial

610 JA ISSN 0917-4915
BAIOMEDIKARU/JAPANESE BIOMEDICAL FORUM. JOURNAL. (Text in Japanese; summaries in English, Japanese) 1991. a. 2000 Yen. Baiomedikaru Foramu - Biomedical Forum, Tokyo Keisatsu Byoin ICU, 10-41, Fujimi 2-chome, Chiyoda-ku, Tokyo 102, Japan.

610 CC ISSN 0253-3707
CODEN: PEIPDB
BAIQIUEN YIKE DAXUE XUEBAO/NORMAN BETHUNE UNIVERSITY OF MEDICAL SCIENCES. JOURNAL. (Text in mainly in Chinese, sometimes in English) 1959. bi-m. $24. Baiqiuen Yike Daxue, Xuebao Bianjibu - Norman Bethune University of Medical Sciences, Journal Editorial Department, 86, Xinmin Dajie, Changchun, Jilin 130021, People's Republic of China. TEL 86-431-5645911.
FAX 86-431-644739. (Dist. overseas by: China International Book Trading Corp., P.O. Box 399, Beijing, P.R. China) Ed. Li Guangsheng. circ. 2,500 (paid); 1,000 (controlled). **Document type:** academic/scholarly publication.
—BLDSC (4833.735000); CASDDS.
Description: Contains scientific, clinical and experimental research papers, case reports, and new developments in medical technology and drugs.

610 JA ISSN 0910-5816
BAISHO IGAKU/JOURNAL OF COMPENSATION MEDICINE. (Text in Japanese) 1985. s-a. 1600 Yen per no. (Nihon Baisho Igakkai - Japanese Society of Compensation Medicine) Maruzen Co., Ltd., 3-10, Nihonbashi 2-chome, Chuo-ku, Tokyo 103, Japan.

615.8 PL ISSN 0005-4402
CODEN: BAPOBT
BALNEOLOGIA POLSKA. (Text in Polish; summaries in English, Polish) 1950. q. $20 per no. Polskie Towarzystwo Balneoklimatologii, Bioklimatologii i Medycyny Fizykalnej, Ul. Mickiewicza 16, 87-720 Ciechocinek, Poland. TEL 48-54-837200. Ed. Szymon Kubiak. adv.; bk.rev.; illus.; index; circ. 700 (controlled). **Indexed:** Biol.Abstr. **Document type:** bulletin.
—BLDSC (1861.300000); CASDDS.
Formerly: Wiadomosci Uzdrowiskowe.

BANBU/BAMBOO. see *SOCIAL SERVICES AND WELFARE*

610 BG ISSN 0301-035X
BANGLADESH MEDICAL JOURNAL. Short title: B.M.J. (Text in English) 1972. q. $20. Bangladesh Medical Association, B.M.A. House, 15-2 Topkhana Rd., Dhaka 2, Bangladesh. Ed. Nazrul Islam. adv.; bk.rev.; bibl.; charts; illus. circ. 6,000. **Indexed:** Abstr.Hyg., Diar.Dis.Res., Excerp.Med., Trop.Dis.Bull.
Supersedes: East Pakistan Medical Journal (ISSN 0424-1401)

610 BG ISSN 0377-9238
CODEN: BMRBDI
BANGLADESH MEDICAL RESEARCH COUNCIL BULLETIN. (Text in English) 1976. 3/yr. Tk.300($30) Bangladesh Medical Research Council, Mokakhali, Dhaka 1212, Bangladesh. Ed. S.M. Keramat Ali. adv.; index. circ. 1,000. (reprint service avail. from IRC) **Indexed:** Abstr.Hyg., Diar.Dis.Res., Excerp.Med. (until 1993), ExtraMED, Ind.Med., Nutr.Abstr., Trop.Dis.Bull. **Document type:** bulletin.
●Also available on CD-ROM.
—BLDSC (1861.717000).

BARCLAYS HEALTH LAW BULLETIN (CALIFORNIA EDITION). see *LAW*

BASIC AND CLINICAL BIOSTATISTICS. see *MATHEMATICS*

610 574 SZ
R131.A1
BASLER VEROEFFENTLICHUNGEN ZUR GESCHICHTE DER MEDIZIN UND DER BIOLOGIE. NEUE FOLGE. 1953. irreg., no.6, 1994. price varies. Schwabe und Co. AG, Steinentorstr. 13, CH-4010 Basel, Switzerland. TEL 061-2725523. FAX 061-2725573. Ed. Ulrich Troehler. index. **Document type:** academic/scholarly publication.
—CCC.
Formerly: Basler Veroeffentlichungen zur Geschichte der Medizin und der Biologie (ISSN 0067-4524)

610 US ISSN 0067-4672
CODEN: BAYSAH
BAYER-SYMPOSIEN. (Text in English) 1969. irreg., vol.9, 1985. price varies. (Bayer AG, GW) Springer-Verlag, 175 Fifth Ave., New York, NY 10010. TEL 212-460-1500. FAX 212-473-6272. (Also: Berlin, Heidelberg, Tokyo and Vienna) (reprint service avail. from ISI) **Indexed:** Biol.Abstr. **Document type:** monographic series.
—CASDDS.

610 GW ISSN 0176-4993
DER BAYERISCHE INTERNIST; Zeitschrift fuer Klinik und Praxis. 1980. bi-m. DM.48. (Vereinigung der Bayerischen Internisten e.V.) Juergen Hartmann Verlag GmbH, Seefeld 18, 91093 Hessdorf-Klebheim, Germany. TEL 09135-7123-0. FAX 09135-712340. Eds. J. Hartmann, H. Holzgartner. adv. contact: E. Michel. bk.rev.; index; circ. 13,000 (paid). (back issues avail.) **Document type:** academic/scholarly publication.
Refereed Serial

610 GW ISSN 0005-7126
BAYERISCHES AERZTEBLATT. 1946. m. DM.5 per no. Bayerische Landesaerztekammer, Muehlbaurstr. 16, 81677 Munich, Germany. TEL 089-4147-1. FAX 089-4147202. (Co-sponsor: Kassenaerztliche Vereinigung Bayerns) Ed.Bd. adv.; bk.rev.; bibl.; charts; illus.; stat. circ. 47,000. **Document type:** trade publication.
—CCC.

610 US
BAYLOR MEDICINE. 1970. 11/yr. free to qualified personnel. Baylor College of Medicine, Office of Publications, One Baylor Plaza, Houston, TX 77030. TEL 713-798-4726. FAX 713-798-3348. Ed. B.J. Almond. circ. 23,100. **Document type:** newspaper.
Description: For the college's friends and supporters, board, alumni, faculty, students, housestaff, and staff.

BAYLOR PROGRESS. see *HOSPITALS*

BEHAVIOR GENETICS; an international journal devoted to research in the inheritance of behavior in animals and man. see *BIOLOGY — Genetics*

610   CC   ISSN 1000-1530
    CODEN: BYDXEV
BEIJING YIKE DAXUE XUEBAO/BEIJING UNIVERSITY OF MEDICAL SCIENCES. JOURNAL. (Text in Chinese or English) 1959. bi-m. Beijing Yike Daxue - Beijing Medical University, Xueyuan Lu, Beijing 100083, People's Republic of China. TEL 861-2091551. FAX 861-2015681. (Subscr. to: China International Book Trading Corp., P.O. Box 399, Beijing, P.R. China) Ed. Feng Chuanhan. **Document type:** academic/scholarly publication.
—CASDDS.
  Description: Covers clinical medicine, oral medicine, surgery, pharmacology and pharmacy, and public health.
  Refereed Serial

630   CC   ISSN 0253-9713
    CODEN: PCIHD7
BEIJING YIXUE/BEIJING MEDICAL JOURNAL. (Text in Chinese) 1965. bi-m. Y2.30 per no. Zhonghua Yixuehui, Beijing Fenhui - Chinese Association of Medicine, Beijing Branch, 7-A Dongdan Santiao, Beijing 100005, People's Republic of China. TEL 551589. (Dist. overseas by: China International Book Trading Corp., P.O. Box 399, Beijing, P.R. China) Ed. Gao Shouzheng. circ. 8,000. **Document type:** academic/scholarly publication.
—CASDDS.
  Description: Contains research papers on clinical experiences, and pharmaceutical studies.

BEIJING ZHONGYI/BEIJING TRADITIONAL CHINESE MEDICINE. see *ALTERNATIVE MEDICINE*

613.7   CC   ISSN 0258-8811
BEIJING ZHONGYI XUEYUAN XUEBAO/BEIJING INSTITUTE OF TRADITIONAL CHINESE MEDICINE. JOURNAL. (Text in Chinese) bi-m. Beijing Zhongyi Xueyuan - Beijing Institute of Traditional Chinese Medicine, Hepingjie Beikou, Beijing 100029, People's Republic of China. TEL 4212731. Ed. Liu Duzhou.

610   US   ISSN 1064-1424
BEING WELL. 1989. q. $55 membership. Society for Professional Well-Being, 21 W. Colony Pl., Ste. 150, Durham, NC 27705-5596. TEL 919-419-0011. Ed. Dr. Marjorie Harrison. bk.rev. circ. 600. (back issues avail.) **Document type:** bulletin, newsletter.
  Formerly: Professional Well-Being.
  Description: Covers professional practice from internship through active retirement. Members share useful reprinted articles and information from other publications. Contains membership activities and calendar of events.

610   SZ
    CODEN: BEINEM
BEITRAEGE ZUR INFUSIONSTHERAPIE UND TRANSFUSIONSMEDIZIN/CONTRIBUTIONS TO INFUSION THERAPY AND TRANSFUSION MEDICINE. (Text in English, German) 1978. irreg. price varies. S. Karger AG, Allschwilerstr. 10, P.O. Box, CH-4009 Basel, Switzerland. TEL 061-3061111. FAX 061-3061234. E-mail: Karger@Karger.ch. Ed.Bd. (back issues avail.) **Indexed:** Biol.Abstr., Chem.Abstr., Curr.Cont., Ind.Med. **Document type:** academic/scholarly publication.
—CASDDS.
  Former titles: Beitraege zu Infusionstherapie (ISSN 1011-6974); Beitraege zu Infusionstherapie und Klin. Ernaehrung (ISSN 0378-8679)
  Refereed Serial

616.02   SZ   ISSN 0254-8275
BEITRAEGE ZUR INTENSIV- UND NOTFALLMEDIZIN. (Text in German) 1983. irreg. price varies. S. Karger AG, Allschwilerstr. 10, P.O. Box, CH-4009 Basel, Switzerland. TEL 061-3061111. FAX 061-3061234. E-mail: Karger@Karger.ch. Ed. G. Kalff. **Document type:** academic/scholarly publication.
—BLDSC (1884.403300). **CCC.**
  Refereed Serial

610   GW
BEITRAEGE ZUR NATIONALSOZIALISTISCHEN GESUNDHEITS- UND SOZIALPOLITIK. 1985. s-a. price varies. Rotbuch Verlag, Potsdammerstr. 98, 1000 Berlin 30, Germany. TEL 030-261196. FAX 030-2626182. bk.rev. circ. 2,500. (back issues avail.)

BEITRAEGE ZUR PSYCHOLOGIE UND SOZIOLOGIE DES KRANKEN MENSCHEN. see *PSYCHOLOGY*

610   II   ISSN 0005-8793
BENGAL MEDICAL JOURNAL. (Text in English) 1962. m. Rs.12. Indian Medical Association, Bengal State Branch, 67 Dharmatola St., Calcutta 13, India. Ed. Dr. Amiya Kumar Bose. circ. 5,500.

BERICHTE NATURWISSENSCHAFTLICH - MEDIZINISCHEN VEREINS IN INNSBRUCK. see *BIOLOGY*

610   MY   ISSN 0126-7140
BERITA M M A/M M A NEWSLETTER. (Text in English) 1969. m. free. Malaysian Medical Association, 4th Fl., MMA House, 124 Jalan Pahang, 53000 Kuala Lumpur, Malaysia. TEL 03-4420617. FAX 03-4418187. **Document type:** newsletter.

610   GW
BERLINER AERZTE. 1964. m. DM.84. (Aerztekammer Berlin) Quintessenz Verlags GmbH, Ifenpfad 2-4, 12107 Berlin, Germany. TEL 030-74006-46. FAX 030-7415080. illus. circ. 18,500. **Document type:** academic/scholarly publication.
—CCC.
  Formerly: Berliner Aerztekammer (ISSN 0568-0743)

610   GW   ISSN 0172-8490
BERLINER AERZTEBLATT. 1887. s-m. DM.120. CB Verlag Carl Boldt, Baseler Str. 80, 12205 Berlin, Germany. TEL 030-8337087. FAX 030-8339125. Ed. Peter Gesellius. adv.; bk.rev.; index, cum.index; circ. 18,500 (controlled). (back issues avail.) **Document type:** academic/scholarly publication.
—CCC.

610   JA   ISSN 0915-129X
BESSATSU MEDIKARU HYUMANITI/SUPPLEMENT MEDICAL HUMANITY. (Supplement to: Medikaru Hyumaniti (ISSN 0911-7075)) (Text in Japanese) 1988. irreg. 2500 Yen per no. Sokyusha, 10-14-403, Otsuka 1-chome, Bunkyo-ku, Tokyo 112, Japan. Ed. Kiyoshi Nojima.

610   US   ISSN 1072-7884
R712.A1
THE BEST DOCTORS IN AMERICA. 1992. biennial. $95. Woodward - White, Inc., 129 First Ave., Aiken, SC 29801. TEL 803-648-0300. FAX 803-641-1709. Eds. Steven Naifeh, Gregory White Smith. **Document type:** directory.
  Description: Lists approximately 7,200 of the best physicians in the U.S., as determined through a national poll of their peers. Lists hospital or university affiliations.

BIBLIOTEK FOR LAEGER. see *LIBRARY AND INFORMATION SCIENCES*

BIBLIOTHECA MEDICA CANADIANA. see *LIBRARY AND INFORMATION SCIENCES*

610   NE   ISSN 0168-9428
BIJBLIJVEN (HOUTEN). 1985. m. Bohn Stafleu van Loghum B.V. (Subsidiary of: Wolters Kluwer N.V.), Postbus 246, 3990 GA Houten, Netherlands. TEL 31-3403-95711. FAX 31-3403-50903. adv.
—SWETS.

610 574   II
BIO MED. (Text in English) 1993. bi-m. $40. Industrial Publications (Subsidiary of: Exihibition and Communication Enterprises Pvt. Ltd.), 206-210 Balaram Bldg., 2nd Fl., Bandra Kurla Commercial Complex, Bandra (E), Bombay 400 051, India. TEL 91-22-6442291. FAX 91-22-6402117. Ed. Dr. Padam Singhvi. adv.: B&W page Rs.7500, color page Rs.10000. index. circ. 5,000. (also avail. in microfilm; reprint service avail.) **Document type:** trade publication.
  Description: Covers the new development of medical world as well as the medical equipment industry.

BIO-MEDICAL MATERIALS AND ENGINEERING; an international journal. see *BIOLOGY — Bioengineering*

BIO-NYT/BIO-NEWS; biologi, medicin, natur, miljoe. see *BIOLOGY*

BIO-TECHNOLOGY; the international monthly for industrial biology. see *BIOLOGY — Biotechnology*

BIOCHEMICAL AND MOLECULAR MEDICINE; an international journal. see *BIOLOGY — Biological Chemistry*

BIOCHEMISTRY OF DISEASE. see *BIOLOGY — Biological Chemistry*

BIOETHICS. see *PHILOSOPHY*

BIOETHICS YEARBOOK. see *RELIGIONS AND THEOLOGY*

615   US
BIOFEEDBACK CLINICIANS. Variant title: A A B C Newsletter. 1976. q. $16. American Association of Biofeedback Clinicians, 2424 Dempster Ave., Des Plaines, IL 60016. TEL 312-827-0440. Eds. Joseph Sargent, Charles Sheridan. adv. **Indexed:** Excerp.Med., Psychol.Abstr.
  Formerly: American Association of Biofeedback Clinicians. News.

BIOLOGICAL RHYTHMS. see *BIOLOGY — Physiology*

BIOLOGICAL THERAPIES IN DENTISTRY. see *MEDICAL SCIENCES — Dentistry*

610.28   UK   ISSN 0142-9612
R857.M3   CODEN: BIMADU
BIOMATERIALS. 1980. 24/yr. £900($1431) (effective 1996). Butterworth - Heinemann, Part of the Reed Elsevier group, Linacre House, Jordan Hill, Oxford OX2 8DP, England. TEL 01865-310366. FAX 01865-310898. TELEX 83111 BHPOXF G. (Subscr. to: Elsevier Science Ltd., P.O. Box 800, Kidlington, Oxford OX5 1DX, England. TEL 01865-843000. FAX 01865-843010; Subscr. in U.S. and Canada to: Elsevier Science, 660 White Plains Rd., Tarrytown, NY 10591-5153. TEL 914-524-9200. FAX 914-333-2444) Ed.Bd. adv.; bk.rev.; charts; illus.; index. (also avail. in microform from UMI; back issues avail.) **Indexed:** Biol.Abstr., Br.Tech.Ind., Chem.Abstr., Curr.Adv.Ecol.Sci., Curr.Cont., Curr.Leather Lit., Curr.Tit.Dent., Dent.Ind., Excerp.Med., Ind.Med., Ind.Sci.Rev., INSPEC (1980-), Intl.Polym.Sci.& Tech., RAPRA, Telegen. **Document type:** academic/scholarly publication.
—BLDSC (2087.715000); CASDDS; Ei; Faxon; Genuine Article; SWETS; UMI; UnCover. **CCC.**
  Description: Focuses on the structure, properties, interactions, functions and applications of biomaterials. For biomaterials and materials scientists, clinicians, biochemists and pharmacologists.
  Refereed Serial

614.49 615.9   CC   ISSN 0895-3988
RA565.A1   CODEN: BESCE5
BIOMEDICAL AND ENVIRONMENTAL SCIENCES. (Text in English) 1988. q. $188. Zhongguo Yufang Kexue Yanjiuyuan - Chinese Academy of Preventive Medicine, 10 Tian Tan Xi Li, Beijing 100050, People's Republic of China. TEL 4377008. TELEX 181726. (Dist. overseas by: Academic Press, Inc., Journal Division, 1250 Sixth Ave., San Diego, CA 92101. TEL 619-230-1840) Eds. Frederick Coulston, Chen Chunming. (back issues avail.) **Indexed:** Apic.Abstr. **Document type:** academic/scholarly publication.
● Available only on CD-ROM. Producer(s): SilverPlatter Information, Inc..
—BLDSC (2087.753700); Faxon; Genuine Article; UnCover. **CCC.**
  Description: Provides a forum for the publication of preventive medicine. Covers toxicology, hygiene, environment, health, and health promotion.
  Refereed Serial

610   EI   ISSN 0778-4910
BIOMEDICAL & HEALTH RESEARCH. Variant title: Newsletter Biomedical & Health Research. 1990. 3/yr. free. Commission of the European Communities, Medical Research Division, DG-XII-E-4, 200, rue de la Loi, B-1049 Brussels, Belgium. TEL 295-74-07. FAX 295-53-65. TELEX COMEU B 21877. Ed. Manuel Hallen. bk.rev. **Document type:** newsletter.
—BLDSC (2087.753800).

MEDICAL SCIENCES

610.28 NE ISSN 0929-6743
BIOMEDICAL AND HEALTH RESEARCH SERIES. (Text in English) 1993. irreg., vol.6, 1994. price varies. (Commission of the European Union, Directorate - General XII, Science, Research and Development, EI) I O S Press, Van Diemenstraat 94, 1013 CN Amsterdam, Netherlands. TEL 31-20-6382189. FAX 31-20-6203419. E-mail: marie-louise.kok@ios.nl. (In N. America: Box 10558, Burke, VA 22009-0558. TEL 703-323-5554. FAX 703-250-4705) Document type: monographic series, proceedings.
  Description: Publishes results of the Biomedical & Health Research Programme.

610.28 US ISSN 0006-3398
R856 CODEN: BIOEAF
BIOMEDICAL ENGINEERING. English translation of: Meditsinskaya Tekhnika (RU ISSN 0025-8075) 1967. bi-m. $1025 (foreign $1200) (effective 1996). (Ministerstvo Zdravookhraneniya, RU) Plenum Publishing Corp, Consultants Bureau, 233 Spring St., New York, NY 10013-1578. TEL 212-620-8468. FAX 212-463-0742. TELEX 23-421139. Ed. V.A. Viktorov. (also avail. in microfilm from JSC; back issues avail.) Indexed: Appl.Mech.Rev., Biol.Abstr., Eng.Ind., Excerp.Med., Ind.Med., INIS Atomind. Document type: academic/scholarly publication.
  —BLDSC (0406.050000); Faxon; SWETS; UMI; UnCover. **CCC.**
  Refereed Serial

BIOMEDICAL ENGINEERING AND INSTRUMENTATION SERIES. see *BIOLOGY — Bioengineering*

174.2 US ISSN 0742-1796
R724
BIOMEDICAL ETHICS REVIEWS. 1983. a. Humana Press Inc., 999 Riverview Dr., Ste. 208, Totowa, NJ 07512. TEL 201-256-1699. FAX 201-256-8341. Eds. James M. Humber, Robert F. Almeder. Document type: academic/scholarly publication.
  —BLDSC (2087.816000).
  Description: Dedicated to controversial topics in bioethics such as physician-assisted death, and the allocation of health care resources.

610 JA ISSN 0915-9274
BIOMEDICAL FUZZY SYSTEMS BULLETIN. (Text in English, Japanese) 1990. a. Biomedical Fuzzy Systems Association - Baiomedikaru Faji Shisutemu Kenkyukai, 820-1, Yokota, Iizuka-shi, Fukuoka-ken 820, Japan.

610.28 US ISSN 0899-8205
R856.A1 CODEN: BITYE2
BIOMEDICAL INSTRUMENTATION & TECHNOLOGY. 1967. bi-m. $72 to individuals (foreign $82); institutions $96 (foreign $106). (Association for the Advancement of Medical Instrumentation) Hanley & Belfus, Inc., 210 S. 13th St., Philadelphia, PA 19107. TEL 215-546-7293. FAX 215-790-9330. (Alt. addr.: 3330 Washington Blvd., Ste. 400, Arlington, VA 22201-4598) Ed. Michael Kallock. adv. contact: Diane R. Sherel. bk.rev.; charts; illus.; index. circ. 6,000. (also avail. in microfilm from WWS; back issues avail.) Indexed: Abstr.Health Care Manage.Stud., Bioeng.Abstr., Biol.Abstr., CINAHL, Curr.Adv.Ecol.Sci., Curr.Cont., Excerp.Med., Ind.Med., INIS Atomind., INSPEC (1989-), Ref.Zh., Sci.Cit.Ind.
  —BLDSC (2087.830500); Ei; Faxon; Genuine Article; SWETS; UnCover. **CCC.**
  Former titles (until 1989): Medical Instrumentation (ISSN 0090-6689); Biomedical Technology Today; Incorporating: Clinical Engineering; Which was formerly: Medical Instrumentation Journal; Association for the Advancement of Medical Instrumentation. Journal (JAAMI) (ISSN 0004-5446)
  Description: Covers the development, use and maintenance of medical instrumentation, including testing, evaluation, and purchasing.
  Refereed Serial

BIOMEDICAL LETTERS; a prestige international biomedical journal for the rapid publication of biomedical communications. see *BIOLOGY — Cytology And Histology*

BIOMEDICAL MARKET NEWSLETTER. see *BUSINESS AND ECONOMICS — Marketing And Purchasing*

610.28 UK ISSN 0955-7717
CODEN: BMATEM
BIOMEDICAL MATERIALS; an international newsletter. 1975. m. £298($474) (effective 1996). Elsevier Science Ltd., P.O. Box 800, Kidlington, Oxford OX5 1DX, England. TEL 44-1865-843000. FAX 44-1865-843010. E-mail: nlinfo-f@elsevier.nl; usinfo-f@elsevier.com; forinfo-kyf04035@niftyserve.or.jp; Site addr.: http://www.elsevier.nl/. (Subscr. in U.S. and Canada to: Elsevier Science, 660 White Plains Rd., Tarrytown, NY 10591-5153. TEL 914-524-9200. FAX 914-333-2444) Eds. P. Read, Richard Juniper. bk.rev.; charts; stat. (also avail. in microform from UMI; back issues avail.) Indexed: Intl.Polym.Sci.& Tech., RAPRA. Document type: newsletter.
  ●Also available online. Vendor(s): Data-Star, Knight-Ridder, Inc..
  —BLDSC (2087.838000). **CCC.**
  Formerly (until 1988): Biomedical Polymers (ISSN 0267-5439)
  Description: Provides coverage of design, production and research management in the fibre and polymer industries, and in related research departments and institutes. Also provides a survey for senior general management, serving to highlight new trends and possibilities, market gaps and business opportunities.

610 574 JA ISSN 0918-6514
BIOMEDICAL PERSPECTIVES. (Text in Japanese) 1992. 3/yr. 1900 Yen per no. Medikaru Rebyusha - Medical Review Co., Ltd., 7-3, Hiranomachi 1-chome, Chuo-ku, Osaka 541, Japan.

681.761 610.28 US ISSN 0192-1266
BIOMEDICAL PRODUCTS. 1976. m. $36 (Canada $38.52; elsewhere $50.40) (effective 1996). Gordon Publications, Inc., Part of Cahners Publishing Company, Division of Reed Elsevier Inc., 301 Gibraltar Dr., Box 650, Morris Plains, NJ 07950-0650. TEL 201-292-5100. FAX 201-898-9281. Ed. Steve Ernst. adv. circ. 75,000. (tabloid format) Indexed: Curr.Pack.Abstr.
  —**CCC.**
  Description: Reaches directors, principle investigators, biochemists, chemists, medical researchers, microbiologists, professors and medical school teachers in the life science-biotech research laboratories of universities, medical institutions, pharmaceutical companies, industry, and biotechnology and research centers.

610.2 US
BIOMEDICAL SAFETY & STANDARDS NEWSLETTER. 1971. s-m. (m. in Jan. & Aug.). $248 (foreign $280). Quest Publishing Co., Inc., A Division of Raven Press Ltd. (Subsidiary of: Wolters Kluwer N.V.), 1351 Titan Way, Brea, CA 92621-3787. TEL 714-738-6400. FAX 714-525-6258. (Subscr. to: Raven Press, 1185 Ave. of the Americas, New York, NY 10036. TEL 212-930-9500. FAX 212-869-3495) Ed. Gregg Nilswonger; Pub. Mary Waltham. bk.rev.; index. (looseleaf format; back issues avail.) Document type: newsletter.
  —SWETS. **CCC.**
  Formerly: Newsletter of Biomedical Safety and Standards (ISSN 0048-0282)
  Description: Covers medical device safety and standards, hazards, recalls, legal actions, legislation and regulations, BMET and CE activities and meetings.

610 UK ISSN 0955-9701
R31 CODEN: BSCHE4
BIOMEDICAL SCIENCE. 1990. m. £190. Pion Ltd., 207 Brondesbury Park, London NW2 5JN, England. TEL 0181-459-0066. FAX 0181-451-6454. (Co-sponsors: Academy of Sciences of Russia) Eds. Rem Petrov, Bernard Donovan. Document type: academic/scholarly publication.
  —CASDDS.
  Refereed Serial

610.28 US ISSN 0067-8856
R856 CODEN: BMSIA7
BIOMEDICAL SCIENCES INSTRUMENTATION. 1963. a. $40 to non-members; members $32. Instrument Society of America, 67 Alexander Dr., Box 12277, Research Triangle Park, NC 27709. TEL 919-549-8411. FAX 919-549-9288. TELEX 802540 ISA DURM. (also avail. in microform from UMI; reprint service avail. from ISI,UMI) Indexed: Appl.Mech.Rev., Biol.Abstr., Chem.Abstr., Dent.Ind., Eng.Ind., Excerp.Med., Ind.Med. Document type: proceedings.
  —BLDSC (2087.880000); CASDDS; Ei; EMDOCS; Faxon. **CCC.**
  Refereed Serial

610 US ISSN 0147-2682
CODEN: BTISE6
BIOMEDICAL TECHNOLOGY INFORMATION SERVICE. 1974. s-m. (m. in Jan. & Aug.). $271 (foreign $315). Quest Publishing Co., Inc., A Division of Raven Press Ltd. (Subsidiary of: Wolters Kluwer N.V.), 1351 Titan Way, Brea, CA 92621. TEL 714-738-6400. FAX 714-525-6258. (Subscr. to: Raven Press, 1185 Ave. of the Americas, New York, NY 10036. TEL 212-930-9500. FAX 212-869-3495) Ed. Gregg Nilswonger; Pub. Mary Waltham. bk.rev.; index. (looseleaf format; back issues avail.) Document type: newsletter.
  —SWETS; UMI. **CCC.**
  Formed by the merger of: Advanced Biomedical Technology (ISSN 0094-0100); Biomedical Inventions Reporter (ISSN 0094-0119); Government Documents Review (ISSN 0094-0127); Health Care Statistics Report (ISSN 0094-0135)
  Description: Covers advances in medical device technology and biomedical engineering, including latest biomedical inventions and federal regulations.

610 US ISSN 1073-1210
R855
BIOMEDICAL TECHNOLOGY MANAGEMENT. (Former name of issuing body: Satellite Publishing Company) 1986. bi-m. free to qualified personnel; others $29 (foreign $50-$85). Second Source Publications, Inc, 10 Risho Ave., East Providence, RI 02914-1215. TEL 401-434-1050. FAX 401-434-1090. Pub. Jack Spears. circ. 12,500 (controlled). Document type: trade publication.
  —Genuine Article.
  Formerly (until 1994): Second Source Biomedical (ISSN 1053-6868); Which supersedes in part (in 1990): Second Source (ISSN 0892-3426)
  Description: Provides health care professionals with the latest news and information for the cost-effective management of biomedical equipment and technology.

610.285 615 FR ISSN 0753-3322
CODEN: BIPHEX
BIOMEDICINE AND PHARMACOTHERAPY. (Text and summaries in English, French) 1956. 10/yr. 1895 F. in France; foreign 2370 F.($463) (effective 1996). Editions Scientifiques Elsevier, 141 rue de Javel, 75747 Paris, France. TEL 33-1-45589063. (Subscr. in U.S. and Canada to: Elsevier Science Inc., Box 882, Madison Sq. Sta., New York, NY 10159. TEL 212-989-5800) Ed. G. Mathe. adv.; bk.rev.; bibl.; illus.; index. circ. 2,000. (also avail. in microform from UMI; reprint service avail. from ISI) Indexed: Biol.Abstr., Chem.Abstr., Dairy Sci.Abstr., Excerp.Med., Helminthol.Abstr., Ind.Med., Ind.Vet., INIS Atomind., Vet.Bull. Document type: academic/scholarly publication.
  —BLDSC (2087.883300); ADONIS; CASDDS; Faxon; Genuine Article; SWETS; UMI; UnCover. **CCC.**
  Former titles: Biomedicine (ISSN 0300-0893); Revue Europeenne d'Etudes Cliniques et Biologiques (ISSN 0035-3019)
  Description: Discusses medical ailments with an emphasis on how they relate to pharmacological drugs and subsequent treatments.
  Refereed Serial

MEDICAL SCIENCES 4183

610.28   GW   ISSN 0013-5585
R856.A1   CODEN: BMZTA7
BIOMEDIZINISCHE TECHNIK/BIOMEDICAL ENGINEERING. 1955. m. (10/yr.) DM.510. (Deutsche Gesellschaft fuer Biomedizinische Technik - German Association on Bio-Medical Engineering) Fachverlag Schiele und Schoen GmbH, Markgrafenstr. 11, 10969 Berlin, Germany. TEL 030-253752-0. FAX 030-2517248. Eds. M. Schaldach, U. Boenick. adv.; bk.rev.; abstr.; bibl.; charts. circ. 1,500. Indexed: Biol.Abstr., C.I.S. Abstr., Chem.Abstr., Curr.Adv.Ecol.Sci., Excerp.Med., Helminthol.Abstr., Ind.Med., Ind.Sci.Rev., INIS Atomind., INSPEC (1971-), Sci.Cit.Ind., Vet.Bull. Document type: academic/scholarly publication.
—BLDSC (2087.890000); CASDDS; Ei; Faxon; Genuine Article; SWETS. **CCC.**
Formerly: Elektromedizin.

610   GW   ISSN 0933-2871
BIOMEDIZINSCHE FORSCHUNG - INFORMATIONEN.* 1987. s-a. DM.34. Gesellschaft zur Foerderung Biomedizinischer Forschung, Medizinische Hochschule, Konstanty-Gutschw-Str. 8, 30625 Hannover, Germany. circ. 1,500. Document type: academic/scholarly publication.

BIOORGANIC & MEDICINAL CHEMISTRY. see CHEMISTRY — Organic Chemistry

BIOORGANIC & MEDICINAL CHEMISTRY LETTERS; for rapid dissemination of preliminary communications on all aspects of bioorganic chemistry, medicinal chemistry and related disciplines. see CHEMISTRY — Organic Chemistry

616   US   ISSN 0895-2140
CODEN: BINSEM
BIOPSY INTERPRETATION SERIES. irreg., latest 1995. price varies. Raven Press, 1185 Ave. of the Americas, New York, NY 10036. TEL 212-930-9500. FAX 212-869-3495. Ed. Steven L. Silverberg. (reprint service avail. from UMI) Indexed: Curr.Cont. Document type: monographic series.
Refereed Serial

BIOPSYCHE; rivista di scienze antropologiche. see PSYCHOLOGY

BIOTECHNOLOGY ADVANCES; research reviews and patent abstracts. see BIOLOGY — Biotechnology

BIOTECHNOLOGY AND GENETIC ENGINEERING REVIEWS. see BIOLOGY — Biotechnology

BIOTHERAPY; an international journal on biological agents. see BIOLOGY — Biotechnology

BIOTHERAPY. see BIOLOGY — Biotechnology

BIRMINGHAM HEALTHCARE REVIEW & FORECAST ANNUAL. see HOSPITALS

616.043   US   ISSN 1048-051X
BIRTH DEFECTS INSTITUTE SYMPOSIA. 1971. irreg. Academic Press, Inc., 525 B St., Ste. 1900, San Diego, CA 92101-4495. TEL 619-231-0926. FAX 619-699-6715. (Subscr. to: Order Dept., 6277 Sea Harbor Dr., 4th Fl., Orlando, FL 32887. TEL 800-321-5068) Ed. Ian H. Porter. (reprint service avail. from ISI)
Refereed Serial

BISHVILEI HAREFUAH. see RELIGIONS AND THEOLOGY — Judaic

610   UK
BLACK'S MEDICAL DICTIONARY. 1906. irreg. (every 2-3 yrs.) £19.99 (effective 1996). A & C Black (Publishers) Ltd., Howard Rd., Eaton Socon, Huntingdon, Cambs. PE19 3EZ, England. TEL 01480-212666. FAX 01480-405014. Ed. Dr. G. Macpherson. Document type: academic/scholarly publication.
Description: Comprehensive medical dictionary for lay people and specialists.

610   US   ISSN 0747-2420
BLOOD BANK WEEK. 1984. w. $128 to non-members (foreign $150); members $98 (foreign $130). American Association of Blood Banks, 8101 Glenbrook Rd., Bethesda, MD 20814. TEL 301-907-6977. FAX 301-907-6895. Ed. Eileen Church. circ. 1,400. (back issues avail.) Document type: newsletter.

610   JA   ISSN 0386-8133
CODEN: BIDKDF
BOEI IKA DAIGAKKO SHINGAKU KATEI KENKYU KIYO/NATIONAL DEFENSE MEDICAL COLLEGE. BULLETIN OF LIBERAL ARTS AND SCIENCES. (Text in English, Japanese) 1978. a. Boeicho, Boei Ika Daigakko - Defense Agency, National Defense Medical College, 3-2, Namiki, Tokorozawa-shi, Saitama-ken 359, Japan.
—BLDSC (2865.890000); CASDDS.

610   JA   ISSN 0385-1796
CODEN: BIDZDQ
BOEI IKA DAIGAKKO ZASSHI/NATIONAL DEFENSE MEDICAL COLLEGE. JOURNAL. (Text in English, Japanese) 1976. q. Boeicho, Boei Ika Daigakko - Defense Agency, National Defense Medical College, 3-2, Namiki, Tokorozawa-shi, Saitama-ken 359, Japan. Indexed: Biol.Abstr., Chem.Abstr., Excerp.Med., INIS Atomind. Document type: academic/scholarly publication.
—BLDSC (4830.160000); CASDDS.

BOLETIN DE BIOTECNOLOGIA. see BIOLOGY — Biotechnology

610 574   MX   ISSN 0067-9666
R21   CODEN: BEMBA2
BOLETIN DE ESTUDIOS MEDICOS Y BIOLOGICOS. (Text in English) 2/yr. $50. Universidad Nacional Autonoma de Mexico, Instituto de Investigaciones Biomedicas, Ciudad Universitaria, Coyoacan, 04510 Mexico, D.F., Mexico. Ed. Dr. Alfonso Escobar. bk.rev. Indexed: Biol.Abstr., Excerp.Med., Ind.Med.
—BLDSC (2203.870000); CASDDS.

610   CU
BOLETIN DE MEDICIANA TRADICIONAL GRUPO "JUAN TOMAS ROIG". a. Academia de Ciencias, Instituto de Documentacion e Informacion Cientifico-Tecnica (I D I C T), Capitolio Nacional, Prado y San Jose, La Habana 2, Havana, Cuba.

610   IT   ISSN 0007-5787
BOLLETTINO DELLE SCIENZE MEDICHE. 1823. 4/yr. L.20000. Societa Medica Chirurgica di Bologna-Archiginnasio, Piazza Galvani, 1, 40100 Bologna, Italy. Ed. Michele Fiorentino. adv.; bk.rev. Indexed: Biol.Abstr., Chem.Abstr.

BOLLETTINO DI MICROBIOLOGIA ED INDAGINI DI LABORATORIO. see BIOLOGY — Microbiology

610   II   ISSN 0524-0182
BOMBAY HOSPITAL JOURNAL. (Text in English) 1959. q. Rs.100. Bombay Hospital Institute of Medical Sciences, 16th Floor, 12 Marine Lines, Bombay 400 020, India. Ed. Dr. O.P. Kapoor. adv.; bk.rev.; charts; illus.; index. circ. 5,000. Indexed: Biol.Abstr., Indian Sci.Abstr., INIS Atomind.
—BLDSC (2245.800000).

THE BONE AND MINERAL RESEARCH ANNUAL. see MEDICAL SCIENCES — Orthopedics And Traumatology

610   GW   ISSN 0935-8013
BONNER AERZTLICHE NACHRICHTEN. 1967-1984; resumed 198? q. DM.12. (Bonner Aerzte-Verein e.V.) Asgard-Verlag Dr. Werner Hippe KG, Postfach 1465, 5205 St. Augustin, Germany. TEL 02241-3164-0. adv.; bk.rev.; illus. circ. 3,800.
—**CCC.**

610   US   ISSN 0894-4024
RA1190
BOSTON BULLETIN ON CHEMICALS AND DISEASE; objective reports on the health effects of chemicals. 1985. q. $20 to individuals; students $15; non-profit libraries $30; corporations $50. ChemoPathology ResourCenter, Inc., 30 Worthington St., Boston, MA 02120-1605. TEL 617-731-1350. FAX 617-732-4434. Ed. S. Szabo. bk.rev. circ. 2,000. (back issues avail.)
Description: Contains summaries, mini-reviews, and brief news items about how chemicals effect our health.

610 340   US
BRANDEIS UNIVERSITY. INSTITUTE FOR HEALTH POLICY. RESEARCH NEWS. 1986. s-a. Brandeis University, Institute for Health Policy, 415 South St., Box 9110, Waltham, MA 02254-9110. TEL 617-736-3910. FAX 617-736-3905. Dir. Stanley S. Wallack. circ. 1,000. (back issues avail.) Document type: newsletter.
Description: Includes public policy articles on long-term care, substance abuse, medicare, county health policy, state policy, and home health care.

610   GW   ISSN 0939-3471
BRANDENBURGISCHES AERZTEBLATT. 1990. m. DM.78 (students DM.58.50). Deutscher Aerzte-Verlag GmbH, Postfach 400265, 50832 Cologne, Germany. TEL 02234-7011-0. FAX 02234-7011444. circ. 7,600. Document type: trade publication.

610   BL   ISSN 0006-9205
BRASIL-MEDICO;* revista de medicina e cirurgia. (Text in English, French, Portuguese or Spanish) 1887. bi-m. Policlinica Geral do Rio de Janeiro, Av. Nilo Pecanha 38, Rio de Janeiro, Brazil. adv.; bk.rev.; abstr.; bibl.; illus.; index. Indexed: Biol.Abstr., Chem.Abstr.

610   BL   ISSN 0524-2053
BRASILIA MEDICA. 1968. s-a. Cz.$1000($30) Associacao Medica de Brasilia, EQS 713-913, Modulo E, 70930 Brasilia, D.F., Brazil. TEL 061-245-1408. FAX 061-245-2501. Ed. Dr. Luiz Fernando G. Salinas. adv.; bk.rev. circ. 5,000. Indexed: Ind.Med. Document type: academic/scholarly publication.
●Also available on CD-ROM.

610   XO   ISSN 0006-9248
CODEN: BLLIAX
BRATISLAVSKE LEKARSKE LISTY. (Text in Slovak; summaries in Russian and Slovak) 1921. m. $55. Slovenska Akademia Vied, Ustav Molekularnej Fyziologie a Genetiky, Stefanikova 3, 811 06 Bratislava, Slovakia. (Dist. by: Slovart, Nam. Slobody 6, 817 64 Bratislava, Slovakia) Ed. Dr. Jozef Pogady. bk.rev.; charts; illus.; s-a. index, cum.index: 1921-1950, 1951-1955. Indexed: Biol.Abstr., C.I.S. Abstr., Chem.Abstr., Dent.Ind., Dok.Arbeitsmed., Excerp.Med., Ind.Med., INIS Atomind., Protozool.Abstr.
—BLDSC (2275.500000); CASDDS.
Description: Presents original works written by domestic and foreign authors covering experimental and clinical medicine, public health, therapy and practical spheres as well as reviews and studies of history.

610   US   ISSN 0888-6008
RC280.B8
BREAST DISEASE; an international journal. 1987. bi-m. $340 to institutions (effective 1996). Elsevier Science Inc., 655 Ave. of the Americas, New York, NY 10010. TEL 212-989-5800. FAX 212-633-3990. TELEX 420643 AEP UI. (Subscr. to: Box 882, Madison Sq. Sta., New York, NY 10159-0882) Ed. Dr. Douglas J. Marchant. Indexed: Excerp.Med. Document type: academic/scholarly publication.
—BLDSC (2277.494070), Faxon; SWETS. **CCC.**
Description: Provides information on all aspects of human breast disease - benign and malignant - to help improve the health care and management of patients.
Refereed Serial

BREAST IMPLANT LITIGATION REPORTER. see LAW

610   GW   ISSN 0340-5362
BREMER AERZTEBLATT. 1948. m. DM.60. (Aerztekammer Bremen) Carl Ed. Schuenemann KG, Postfach 106067, 28060 Bremen, Germany. TEL 0421-36903-72. FAX 0421-36903-34. Ed. W. Arens. circ. 4,000. Indexed: Excerp.Med. Document type: academic/scholarly publication.
—**CCC.**

BRIEFINGS ON J C A H O; alternative perspectives on accreditation. see HOSPITALS

BRIEFINGS ON LONG-TERM CARE REGULATIONS. see HOSPITALS

MEDICAL SCIENCES

610 658 US ISSN 1076-6006
BRIEFINGS ON PRACTICE MANAGEMENT. m. $97. Opus Communications, Box 1168, Marblehead, MA 01945. TEL 617-639-1872. FAX 617-639-2982. (looseleaf format) **Document type:** newsletter.
  Description: Provides information on effective medical practice management, including compliance and regulations, reimbursement, money management, and related issues such as managed care.

610 US ISSN 1076-5999
▼**BRIEFINGS ON SUBACUTE CARE.** 1994. m. $296. Opus Communications, Box 1168, Marblehead, MA 01945. TEL 617-639-1872. FAX 617-639-2982. (looseleaf format) **Document type:** newsletter.
  Description: Provides news, analysis and advice to develop and operate a subacute care unit.

BRITISH ACUPUNCTURE ASSOCIATION. NEWSLETTER. see *ALTERNATIVE MEDICINE*

610 CN ISSN 0715-5379
BRITISH COLUMBIA MEDICAL ASSOCIATION. NEWS. 1972. bi-m. membership. British Columbia Medical Association, 115-1665 West Broadway, Vancouver, BC V6J 5A4, Canada. TEL 604-736-5551. FAX 604-733-7317. Ed. Dr. Robert Young. adv. contact: Ian Jamieson. **Document type:** newspaper.
—CCC.

610 CN ISSN 0007-0556
BRITISH COLUMBIA MEDICAL JOURNAL. 1959. m. Can.$50 (foreign $65). British Columbia Medical Association, 115-1665 West Broadway, Vancouver, BC V6J 5A4, Canada. TEL 604-736-5551. FAX 604-733-7317. Ed. Dr. James A. Wilson. adv.; bk.rev.; charts; illus.; stat.; index. circ. 7,800. (back issues avail.) **Indexed:** Med.Care Rev. **Document type:** academic/scholarly publication.
—BLDSC (2297.100000). **CCC.**
Refereed Serial

BRITISH JOURNAL OF ACUPUNCTURE. see *ALTERNATIVE MEDICINE*

610 UK ISSN 0007-0947
R11 CODEN: BJCPAT
BRITISH JOURNAL OF CLINICAL PRACTICE. (Supplements avail.) 1947. 8/yr. £56 (foreign £64). Medicom (UK) Ltd., The Quadrant, 118 London Rd., Kingston-upon-Thames KT2 6QJ, England. TEL 0181-541-5666. FAX 0181-541-4746. Ed. Graham Jackson; Pub. Michael Young. adv.; bk.rev.; bibl.; illus.; index. circ. 2,500. **Indexed:** Abstr.Hyg., Biotech.Abstr., Chem.Abstr., Curr.Adv.Ecol.Sci., Curr.Cont., Excerp.Med., Helminthol.Abstr., I.P.A., Ind.Med., Ind.Sci.Rev., NRN, Nutr.Abstr., Rev.Med.& Vet.Mycol., Sci.Cit.Ind., Sp.Ed.Needs Abstr., Trop.Dis.Bull. **Document type:** academic/scholarly publication.
●Also available online.
—BLDSC (2307.200000); Faxon; SWETS; UnCover.
  Description: Publishes original papers, reviews, features, case reports and meeting reports.
Refereed Serial

610 UK ISSN 0262-8767
BRITISH JOURNAL OF CLINICAL PRACTICE. SYMPOSIUM SUPPLEMENT. (Supplement to: British Journal of Clinical Practice (ISSN 0007-0947)) 1945. irreg., no.75, 1994. £16. Medicom (UK) Ltd., The Quadrant, 118 London Rd., Kingston-upon-Thames, Surrey KT2 6QJ, England. TEL 0181-541-5666. FAX 0181-541-4746. Ed. Graham Jackson. circ. 2,500 (paid). **Document type:** monographic series.
—BLDSC (2307.211000); UnCover.
Refereed Serial

610 UK ISSN 0961-1053
CODEN: BJCRE5
BRITISH JOURNAL OF CLINICAL RESEARCH. (Supplement avail.) 1990. s-m. £95 (outside Europe £125) (effective 1995). Brookwood Medical Publications, Orchard House, Brookwood, Surrey GU24 0AT, England. TEL 01483-797915. FAX 01483-797915. **Indexed:** Excerp.Med. (1993-). **Document type:** academic/scholarly publication.
—BLDSC (2307.235000). **CCC.**
  Description: Covers research on new drugs, devices and other products, clinical trials phases I to IV, including papers showing negative results, clinical pharmacology, preclinical studies, drug metabolism.
Refereed Serial

610 UK ISSN 0960-1643
CODEN: BJGPEJ
BRITISH JOURNAL OF GENERAL PRACTICE. 1958. m. £110. Royal College of General Practitioners, 14 Princes Gate, London SW7 1PU, England. (Subscr. to: Bailey Management Services, 127 Sandgate Rd., Folkestone, Kent CT20 2BL, England) Ed. Dr. A.F. Wright. adv.; bk.rev.; charts; illus.; stat.; index. circ. 17,000. (back issues avail.) **Indexed:** Abstr.Hyg., CINAHL, Curr.Adv.Ecol.Sci., Diab.Cont., Dok.Arbeitsmed., FAMLI, Geo.Abstr., Helminthol.Abstr., Ind.Med., Med.Care Rev., Nutr.Abstr., Protozool.Abstr., Trop.Dis.Bull. **Document type:** academic/scholarly publication.
—BLDSC (2308.360000); Faxon; Genuine Article; SWETS; UnCover.
  Formerly: Royal College of General Practitioners. Journal (ISSN 0035-8797)

BRITISH JOURNAL OF HEALTH PSYCHOLOGY. see *PSYCHOLOGY*

610 UK ISSN 0007-1064
CODEN: BJHMAB
BRITISH JOURNAL OF HOSPITAL MEDICINE. Spanish edition (ISSN 0210-0258) 1966. fortn. £74 (overseas £120). Mark Allen Publishing Ltd., Croxted Mews, 288 Croxted Rd., London SE24 9BY, England. TEL 0181-671-7521. FAX 0181-671-1722. Ed. Jack Tinker; Pub. Mark Allen. adv. contact: Ian White. bk.rev.; bibl.; charts; illus.; stat.; index. (processed; also avail. in microform from UMI; reprint service avail. from UMI) **Indexed:** Abstr.Hyg., Biol.Abstr., Chem.Abstr., Curr.Adv.Cancer Res., Curr.Adv.Ecol.Sci., Curr.Cont., Dent.Ind., Excerp.Med., Helminthol.Abstr., Ind.Med., Ind.Sci.Rev., Ind.Vet., INSPEC (1981-1984), Nutr.Abstr., Pig News & Info., Trop.Dis.Bull., Vet.Bull. **Document type:** academic/scholarly publication.
—BLDSC (2309.500000); CASDDS; Genuine Article; SWETS; UMI; UnCover.
  Formerly: Hospital Medicine.

614.88 UK ISSN 0961-7930
CODEN: BJICEO
BRITISH JOURNAL OF INTENSIVE CARE. 1991. 10/yr. £60 to individuals (rest of Europe £90; elsewhere £108); institutions £84 (rest of Europe £114; elsewhere £132) (effective 1994). Greycoat Publishing, 1 Harley St., London W1N 1DA, England. TEL 0171-637-1828. FAX 0171-631-3020. Ed. Dr. Michael Rennie. adv. contact: Ashley Wallis. bk.rev.; circ. 275 (paid); 13,956 (controlled). **Indexed:** Excerp.Med. (1992-). **Document type:** academic/scholarly publication.
—BLDSC (2311.047000).
  Description: Provides a forum for specialists in critical care, including intensivists, anesthesiologists, nurses, neonatologists, cardiologists, general surgeons, hematologists, and pharmacists.

610 657.832 UK ISSN 0962-1423
BRITISH JOURNAL OF MEDICAL ECONOMICS. 1991. s-m. £95 (outside Europe £125) (effective 1995). Brookwood Medical Publications, Orchard House, Brookwood, Surrey GU24 0AT, England. TEL 01483-797975. FAX 01483-797915. **Indexed:** Excerp.Med. (1993-). **Document type:** academic/scholarly publication.
—BLDSC (2311.370000). **CCC.**
  Description: Publishes papers on cost-effectiveness evaluations and aspects of health economics.
Refereed Serial

615.85 UK ISSN 0308-0226
BRITISH JOURNAL OF OCCUPATIONAL THERAPY. 1937. m. £46. College of Occupational Therapists Ltd., 6-8 Marshalsea Rd., Southwark, London SE1 1HL, England. TEL 071-357-6480. FAX 071-378-8095. Ed.Bd. adv.; bk.rev.; charts; illus.; index. circ. 13,500. **Indexed:** Abstr.Health Care Manage.Stud., ASSIA, CINAHL, Curr.Adv.Ecol.Sci., Psychol.Abstr., Rehabil.Lit. **Document type:** academic/scholarly publication.
—BLDSC (2312.700000); SWETS; UnCover.

610 UK ISSN 0301-5572
CODEN: BJMEDF
BRITISH JOURNAL OF SEXUAL MEDICINE. Abbreviated title: B J S M. 1974. bi-m. £45 (overseas £51) (effective 1995). Hayward Medical Communications Ltd., 44 Earlham St., Covent Garden, London WC2H 9LA, England. TEL 44-171-240-4493. FAX 44-171-240-4479. (Subscr. to: Essex House, Cromwell Park, Chipping Norton, Oxon. OX7 5SR, England. TEL 44-1608-645564. FAX 44-1608-645545) Ed. Dr. Paul Wooley. adv.; bk.rev. circ. 22,000. **Indexed:** Biol.Abstr., Curr.Adv.Cancer Res., Curr.Adv.Ecol.Sci., Excerp.Med. (until 1993). **Document type:** academic/scholarly publication.
—BLDSC (2324.600000); SWETS; UnCover.

BRITISH JOURNAL OF SPECIAL EDUCATION. see *EDUCATION — Special Education And Rehabilitation*

610 UK ISSN 0007-1420
R31 CODEN: BMBUAQ
BRITISH MEDICAL BULLETIN. 1943. q. £134($222) (effective 1995). (British Council, Medical Department) Churchill Livingstone Journals (Subsidiary of: Pearson Professional), Robert Stevenson House, 1-3 Baxter's Pl., Leith Walk, Edinburgh EH1 3AF, Scotland. TEL 0131-556-2424. FAX 0131-459-1177. (Subscr. to: Pearson Professional Ltd., P.O. Box 77, Fourth Ave., Harlow, Essex CM19 5AA, England. TEL 01279-623760; U.S. subscr. to: Churchill Livingstone, 650 Ave. of the Americas, New York, NY 10011. TEL 212-206-5000) Ed. Dr. Gill Haddock. adv. contact: David Dunnachie. charts; illus.; index. circ. 2,900. (also avail. in microform from UMI; reprint service avail. from UMI) **Indexed:** Abstr.Hyg., Anim.Breed.Abstr., Bibl.Dev.Med.& Child Neur., Biol.Abstr., Biotech.Abstr., C.I.S. Abstr., Chem.Abstr., Curr.Adv.Ecol.Sci., Curr.Cont., Dairy Sci.Abstr., Diar.Dis.Res., Excerp.Med., Helminthol.Abstr., I.P.A., Ind.Med., Ind.Sci.Rev., Ind.Vet., Nutr.Abstr., Rev.Plant Path., Sci.Cit.Ind., Vet.Bull. **Document type:** academic/scholarly publication.
●Also available online.
—BLDSC (2329.000000); ADONIS; CASDDS; Faxon; Genuine Article; SWETS; UnCover. **CCC.**

610 SP ISSN 0213-3954
BRITISH MEDICAL JOURNAL (EDICION ESPANOLA). 1986. bi-m. 6000 ptas.($65) (effective 1995). Editorial Garsi, S.A., Juan Bravo 46, 28006 Madrid, Spain. TEL 34-1-4021212. FAX 34-1-4020954. Ed. Joan Rodes. adv.; bk.rev.; index. circ. 15,000. (back issues avail.; reprint service avail.)

610 US
BRONX MEDICINE. vol.45, 1967. 4/yr. $10. Bronx County Medical Society, 2600 Netherland Ave., Bronx, NY 10463. TEL 718-548-4401. FAX 718-549-6681. Ed. Dr. John P. Albanese. adv.; illus. circ. 1,800. **Indexed:** Med.Care Rev.
  Formerly: Bronx County Medical Society. Bulletin (ISSN 0007-2257)

610 SW ISSN 0345-1208
BUKPRESSEN. 1967. bi-m. SEK 10 (effective 1991). Medicinska Foereningen i Stockholm, P.O. Box 60421, S-104 01 Stockholm, Sweden.

410 AA
BULETINI I SHKENCAVE MJEKESORE/BULLETIN DES SCIENCES MEDICALES. (Text in Albanian; summaries in French) s-a. $3.85. Enver Hoxha Universitet, Tirana, Albania. Ed. Ylvi Vehbiu. **Indexed:** Chem.Abstr.

610 BU ISSN 0861-9883
BULGARSKA MEDICINA/BULGARIAN MEDICINE. 1993. irreg. Academy of Medicine, 1 G. Sofiiski Boul., Sofia 1431, Bulgaria. **Indexed:** Excerp.Med. (1994-). **Document type:** academic/scholarly publication.
—BLDSC (0018.630555).

610 JA ISSN 0007-4705
BULLETIN MEDICAL FRANCO-JAPONAIS/NICHI-FUTSU IGAKU. (Text in French and Japanese) 1954. q. 800 Yen. Societe Franco-Japonaise de Medecine - Nichi-Futsu Igakkai, 2-3 Kanda Surugadai, Chiyoda-ku, Tokyo 101, Japan. Ed. Tatsuo Kobayashi. adv.; bk.rev.; charts; illus. circ. 250. (also avail. in microform)

BULLETIN OF EXPERIMENTAL BIOLOGY AND MEDICINE. see *BIOLOGY*

610   US   ISSN 0007-5140
R11
BULLETIN OF THE HISTORY OF MEDICINE. 1933. q. $32 to individuals (foreign $42.70); institutions $61.50 (foreign $72.20). (American Association for the History of Medicine) Johns Hopkins University Press, Journals Publishing Division, 2715 N. Charles St., Baltimore, MD 21218. TEL 410-516-6987. FAX 410-516-6968. (Co-sponsor: Johns Hopkins Institute of the History of Medicine) Eds. Gert H. Brieger, Jerome J. Bylebyl. adv. contact: Tara Dorai-Berry. bk.rev.; bibl.; illus.; index, cum.index vols.1-56. circ. 2,400. (also avail. in microform from UMI,PMC; micropaque; back issues avail.; reprint service avail. from UMI) **Indexed:** Amer.Bibl.Slavic & E.Eur.Stud., Amer.Hist.& Life, Arts & Hum.Cit.Ind., Biol.Abstr., Chem.Abstr., Curr.Cont., Excerp.Med., Hist.Abstr., Ind.Med., Sci.Cit.Ind., SSCI, Trop.Dis.Bull. —BLDSC (2856.000000); Faxon; Genuine Article; SWETS; UMI; UnCover. **CCC.**
   Description: Presents articles that analyze advances in medical science, examine changes in clinical practices, and explore how the response of societies to health care needs have varied with times and cultures.

610   US
BULLETIN OF THE MEDICAL SOCIETY OF THE COUNTY OF QUEENS AND THE ACADEMY OF MEDICINE OF QUEENS. 1925. 10/yr. $10. Medical Society of the County of Queens, 112-25 Queens Blvd., Forest Hills, NY 11375. FAX 718-268-6918. (Co-sponsor: Academy of Medicine of Queens County) Ed. Dr. Lorraine Maria Giordano. adv.; illus.; tr.lit. circ. 2,000.

BUNDESARBEITSGEMEINSCHAFT HILFE FUER BEHINDERTE. BERICHTE. JAHRESSPIEGEL. see *EDUCATION — Special Education And Rehabilitation*

610   BR   ISSN 0007-6295
BURMA MEDICAL JOURNAL.* vol.12, 1964. q. Burma Medical Association, 249 Theinbyu Rd., Yangon, Union of Myanmar. **Indexed:** Chem.Abstr.

610.2 658.8   UK   ISSN 0261-9075
BUSINESS RATIO REPORT: MEDICAL EQUIPMENT MANUFACTURERS; an industry sector analysis. 1978. a. I C C Business Ratios Ltd., Freepost, Field House, Hampton, Mddx. TW12 1BR, England. TEL 081-783-0977. FAX 081-783-1940. charts; stat. **Document type:** trade publication.
—BLDSC (5527.365000).

610   JA
BYOIN SHINBUN/HOSPITAL NEWS. (Text in Japanese) w. 1300 Yen per mo. Byoin Shinbunsha, 4-1, Hirakawacho 2-chome, Chiyoda-ku, Tokyo 102, Japan.

BYOTAI SEIRI TO SHINDAN CHIRYO/SANWA KAGAKU CO. MEDICAL REPORT. see *BIOLOGY — Physiology*

BYULLETEN' EKSPERIMENTAL'NOI BIOLOGII I MEDITSINY. see *BIOLOGY*

610   US   ISSN 0891-1525
C A P TODAY; pathology-laboratory medicine-laboratory management. 1987. m. $40 (N. America $60; foreign $95) (free to qualified personnel). College of American Pathologists, 325 Waukegan Rd., Northfield, IL 60093-2750. TEL 708-446-8800. FAX 708-446-3563. Ed. Sherrie Rice. adv. contact: Bob McGonnagle. circ. 48,000. (tabloid format) **Document type:** trade publication.
—BLDSC (3050.624000).

C A S NYT. (Centrale Afdeling for Sygehushygiejne) see *HOSPITALS*

266   GW
C B M FREUNDESBRIEF. 1961. bi-m. free. Christoffel-Blindenmission e.V., Nibelungenstr. 124, 64625 Bensheim. TEL 06251-131-0. FAX 06251-131122. (U.S. subscr. to: Christian Blind Mission International Inc., 450 E. Park Ave., Greenville, SC 29601. TEL 803-239-0065. FAX 803-239-0069) circ. 110,000. **Document type:** bulletin.

C H A C INFO/INFO A C C S. (Catholic Health Association of Canada) see *HOSPITALS*

C H A C REVIEW. (Catholic Health Association of Canada) see *HOSPITALS*

610 029   CN
C H R A PROGRESS NOTES. 1949. 4/yr. Can.$60. Canadian College of Health Record Administrators, Canadian Health Record Association, 1090 Don Mills Rd., N. York, ON M3C 3R6, Canada. TEL 416-447-4900. FAX 416-447-4598. Ed. Diana Kellington. adv. contact: Diana Kellington. bk.rev.; charts; illus. circ. 3,200. **Indexed:** Hosp.Lit.Ind. **Document type:** newsletter.
   Former titles: C C H R A - C H R A Progress Notes; (until 1984): C C H R A - C H R A Bulletin; (until 1979): Canadian Health Record Association. Bulletin (ISSN 0227-3748); C A M R L Recorder; Canadian Association of Medical Record Librarians. Bulletin (ISSN 0045-4397)

614.88 384.5   IT
C I R M. (Text in English) 1935. q. free. Centro Internazionale Radio-Medico, Via Architettura 41, 00144 Rome, Italy. TEL 39-6-5923331. FAX 39-6-5923333. TELEX 612068 CIRM I. Ed. Dr. Antonio Dauri. bk.rev.; charts; illus. circ. 5,000. **Document type:** bulletin.
   Description: Publishes scientific papers on seamen pathophysiology. Covers news, activities and services of the medical center.
   Refereed Serial

610   US
C I R NEWS. 1971. q. $12 to individuals; institutions $24. Committee of Interns and Residents, 386 Park Ave. S., New York, NY 10016. TEL 212-725-5500. Ed. Mark Levy. adv.; bk.rev. circ. 15,000. (tabloid format; back issues avail.) **Document type:** bulletin.
   Former titles: C I R Bulletin; Committee of Interns and Residents Bulletin (ISSN 0090-1660)

610   CN   ISSN 0820-3946
      CODEN: CMAJAX
C M A J/J A M C. (JOURNAL DE L'ASSOCIATION MEDICALE CANADIENNE). (Canadian Medical Association Journal) (Text in English, French) 1911. s-m. Can.$90($115) (effective 1996). Canadian Medical Association, 1867 Alta Vista Dr., Box 8650, Ottawa, ON K1G 0G8, Canada. TEL 613-731-9331. FAX 613-523-0937. (Subscr. to: Information Technology, CMA, PO Box 8650, Ottawa, ON K1G 0G8, Canada) Ed. Dr. Bruce P. Squires. adv.: B&W page Can. $2575, color page Can. $4360; trim 8 1/2 X 10 7/8. bibl.; charts; illus.; index. circ. 57,000. (also avail. in microform from UMI; reprint service avail. from UMI) **Indexed:** Abstr.Health Care Manage.Stud., Abstr.Hyg., AIM, Bibl.Dev.Med.& Child Neur., Biol.Abstr., Biol.Dig., Biotech.Abstr., C.I.S. Abstr., Can.B.P.I., Can.Per.Ind., CINAHL, Curr.Adv.Biochem., Curr.Adv.Ecol.Sci., Curr.Adv.Genetics & Molec.Biol., Curr.Cont., Dairy Sci.Abstr., Dent.Ind., Diar.Dis.Res., Dok.Arbeitsmed., Excerp.Med., FAMLI, Helminthol.Abstr., I.P.A., Ind.Med., Ind.Sci.Rev., INIS Atomind., Lab.Haz.Bull., Med.& Surg.Dermat., Med.Care Rev., NRN, Nutr.Abstr., Protozool.Abstr., Rev.Med.& Vet.Mycol., Rev.Plant Path., Risk Abstr., Sci.Cit.Ind., Sportsearch, Trop.Dis.Bull., 010437177r. **Document type:** academic/scholarly publication.
•Also available online. Vendor(s): Ovid Technologies. Also available on CD-ROM.
   —BLDSC (3038.000000); ADONIS; CASDDS; Faxon; Genuine Article; SWETS; UMI; UnCover. **CCC.**
   Formerly (until 1985): Canadian Medical Association Journal (ISSN 0008-4409)
   Description: Includes notices of upcoming conferences, summaries of C.M.A. policies and news and features of interest to members of the Association and others in the health care professions.
   Refereed Serial

610.28   CN   ISSN 0830-8845
C M B E S - S C G B NEWSLETTER. 1966. 4/yr. Canadian Medical and Biological Engineering Society Inc. - Societe Canadienne de Genie Biomedical, Rm. 393, Bldg. M-55, National Research Council, Ottawa, ON K1A 0R8, Canada. TEL 613-993-1686. FAX 613-954-2216. TELEX 053 3145 NRCADMINOTT. Ed. Brian Graham. circ. controlled. **Document type:** newsletter.
   Formerly (until 1984): Canadian Medical and Biological Engineering Society. Newsletter (ISSN 0384-1820)

MEDICAL SCIENCES   4185

610   SA   ISSN 1016-6742
C M E; South Africa's continuing medical education monthly - Suid Afrika se maandblad van voortgesette mediese onderrig. (Text in Afrikaans, English) 1983. m. R.205 (foreign R.320($95)) (effective 1995). (Medical Association of South Africa - Mediese Vereniging van Suid-Afrika) M A S A Publications, Private Bag X1, Pinelands 7430, South Africa. TEL 27-21-531-3081. FAX 27-21-531-4126. Ed. Dr. F.N. Sanders. adv.; bk.rev.; index. circ. 14,600. (also avail. in microfiche; back issues avail.) **Indexed:** Ind.S.A.Per. **Document type:** trade publication.
—UMI.
   Formerly (until 1989): S.A. Journal of Continuing Medical Education (ISSN 0256-2170)

610 378   CN
C M E - CONTINUING MEDICAL EDUCATION. m. S T A Communications Inc., 955 St. John's Blvd., Ste. 306, Pointe Claire, Que. H9R 5K3, Canada. TEL 514-695-7623. FAX 514-695-8554. Ed. Paul Brand. circ. 30,082.

610   US   ISSN 0276-8283
RB115
C P T. (Physicians' Current Procedural Terminology) 1966. a. $44.95 to non-members (floppy disk $175); members $34.95 (floppy disk $140). American Medical Association, 515 N. State St., Chicago, IL 60610. TEL 312-464-5000; 800-262-2350. FAX 312-464-4184. (also avail. in microfiche) **Document type:** academic/scholarly publication.
   Formerly (1st & 2nd eds.): Current Procedural Terminology (ISSN 0065-9312)

610   FR   ISSN 0007-9480
CADUCEE. 1961. 13/yr. 170 F. B.C. Savy, 18 av. de la Marne, 92600 Asnieres, France. TEL 47-93-05-88. FAX 47-93-68-95. adv.; abstr.; bibl.; illus.; stat.; index. circ. 13,000.
—CCC.

CADUCEUS; a humanities journal for medicine and the health sciences. see *MUSEUMS AND ART GALLERIES*

610   FR   ISSN 1157-5999
      CODEN: SMOFEX
CAHIERS D'ETUDES ET DE RECHERCHES FRANCOPHONES SANTE. Key Title: Sante (Montrouge). Variant title: Cahiers Sante. 1990. 6/yr. 400 F. to individuals; institutions 680 F.; students 260 F. (effective 1995). John Libbey Eurotext, 127 av de la Republique, 92120 Montrouge, France. TEL 1-46-73-06-60. FAX 1-40-84-09-99. (Subscr. to: A T E I, 23-25 rue Fernand Combette, 93100 Montreuil sous Bois, France. TEL 48-59-58-11. FAX 48-59-57-99) Ed. Dominique Richard-Lenoble. **Indexed:** Excerp.Med. (1994-), Ind.Med. (1994-).
—BLDSC (2952.195550).
   Description: Aims to establish the medical research of the francophone world and expose the research of developing countries.

610.28   FR   ISSN 0575-0563
CAHIERS DE BIOTHERAPIE. 1964. q. 450 F. (foreign 500 F.). (Societe Medicale de Biotherapie) Editions Similia, 71 rue Beaubourg, 75003 Paris, France. TEL 42-71-68-66. adv.; bk.rev. circ. 6,000.
—CCC.

610   FR
CAHIERS DE GEOGRAPHIE DE LA SANTE/JOURNAL OF GEOGRAPHY OF HEALTH. Short title: GEOS. irreg. Universite de Montpellier (Universite Paul Valery), B.P. 5043, 34032 Montpellier Cedex 1, France. TEL 67-14-20-00.
   Description: Covers the research done at the university level by geographers, either in the form of excerpts, digests or research positions. Covers the geographical study of illness, health care and health care services.

610   FR   ISSN 0007-9936
CAHIERS DE MEDECINE INTERPROFESSIONNELLE. 1961. q. 261 F. (Association Interprofessionnelle des Centres Medicaux et Sociaux de la Region Parisienne) Editions Docis, 31 rue Mederic, 75832 Paris Cedex 17, France. Ed.Bd. bk.rev. circ. 1,250. **Indexed:** C.I.S. Abstr.
—BLDSC (2949.740000).

MEDICAL SCIENCES

612 FR ISSN 0336-5913
CAHIERS DE SEXOLOGIE CLINIQUE.* 1975. bi-m. 300 F. (students 200 F.). Nouvelles Editions Medicales Francaises, P.B. 451, 95005 Clergy Pontoise Cedex, France. **Indexed:** Biol.Abstr.

610 SZ ISSN 0409-8757
CAHIERS MEDICO-SOCIAUX. 1956. 4/yr. 67 SFr. to individuals; institutions 113 SFr. Editions Medecine et Hygiene, Case Postale 456, CH-1211 Geneva 4, Switzerland. TEL 022-3469355. FAX 022-3475610. Ed. O. Jeanneret. **Document type:** academic/scholarly publication.
—BLDSC (2949.784000). **CCC.**

610 II ISSN 0008-0667
R97 CODEN: CMJRAY
CALCUTTA MEDICAL JOURNAL. (Text in English) 1906. m. Rs.12($4.) Calcutta Medical Club, 91-B Chittaranjan Ave., Calcutta 12, India. Ed. K.K. Sen-Gupta. adv.; bk.rev.; abstr.; charts; illus. **Indexed:** Biol.Abstr., Chem.Abstr., Excerp.Med., Helminthol.Abstr., Ind.Med., Nutr.Abstr.
—BLDSC (2954.950000); CASDDS.

610 IT ISSN 0394-3291
CALEIDOSCOPIO. English edition: Kaleidoscope. 1983. irreg. Medical Systems S.p.A., Via Rio Torbido 40, 16165 Genova, Italy. TEL 010-83401. FAX 010-804661. Ed. Sergio Rassu.

610 IT ISSN 1120-6756
CALEIDOSCOPIO LETTERARIO. 1990. q. Medical Systems S.p.A., Via Rio Torbido 40, 16165 Genova, Italy. TEL 010-83401. FAX 010-804661. Ed. Sergio Rassu.

CALENDAR OF CONGRESSES OF MEDICAL SCIENCES.
see *MEETINGS AND CONGRESSES*

610 US ISSN 0410-2894
CALIFORNIA FAMILY PHYSICIAN. 1950. bi-m. $35. California Academy of Family Physicians, 114 Sansome St., Ste. 1305, San Francisco, CA 94104-3824. FAX 415-394-9119. Ed. Sheri L. Cardo. adv.; circ. 6,900 (controlled).
Formerly: California G P.
Description: Covers socioeconomic issues of relevance to family physicians.

616.98 338.476 US ISSN 8750-1813
CALIFORNIA PHYSICIAN. 1984. m. $35 to non-members. California Medical Association, 221 Main St., San Francisco, CA 94105. TEL 415-882-5118. FAX 415-882-5116. (Subscr. to: Box 7690, San Francisco, CA 94120-7690) Ed.Bd. circ. 33,000. (back issues avail.) **Document type:** trade publication.
—CCC.
Description: Non-clinical medical publication. Covers economic, legal, social and political issues affecting medical practice in California.

610 UK ISSN 0952-1119
CAMBRIDGE MEDICINE. 1981. 2/yr. £4.50. Cambridge Clinical School, Cambridge Medical Committee, Cambridge, England. Ed. M. Goodman. adv.; bk.rev. circ. 1,000.

610 UK ISSN 0963-1801
R724
CAMBRIDGE QUARTERLY OF HEALTHCARE ETHICS; the international journal for healthcare ethics and ethics committees. 1992. q. £59($99) (effective 1996). Cambridge University Press, Edinburgh Bldg., Shaftesbury Rd., Cambridge CB2 2RU, England. TEL 01223-312393. FAX 01223-315052. TELEX 851817256. (N. American addr.: Cambridge University Press, Journals Dept., 40 W. 20th St., New York, NY 10011. TEL 212-924-3900. FAX 212-691-3239) Ed.Bd. adv.; bk.rev. (back issues avail.) **Indexed:** Ind.Med. (1993-). **Document type:** academic/scholarly publication.
—BLDSC (3015.976000); UMI; UnCover. **CCC.**
Description: Provides an international forum for the wide range of issues faced by members of health care ethics committees. Devoted to the practical application of bioethics in the delivery of health care.

CAMBRIDGE UNIVERSITY MEDICAL LIBRARY BULLETIN.
see *LIBRARY AND INFORMATION SCIENCES*

610 CN ISSN 0008-2791
CODEN: CAMHA3
CANADA'S MENTAL HEALTH. French edition: Sante Mentale au Canada (ISSN 0707-2910) (Supplements avail.) (Editions in English, French) 1953. q. Can.$26.75 to individuals (foreign $32.50) institutions Can.$37.45 (foreign $45.50). Department of National Health and Welfare, Health Services & Promotion Branch, Ottawa, ON K1A 1B4, Canada. TEL 613-954-8644. FAX 613-957-1406. (Dist. by: Canada Communication Group - Publishing, Ottawa, ON K1A 0S9, Canada) Ed. Thomas Lips. bk.rev.; abstr.; bibl.; index. circ. 4,000. (also avail. in microfilm from CML) **Indexed:** Abstr.Hosp.Manage.Stud., ASSIA, Can.B,P.I., Can.Educ.Ind., Can.Per.Ind., Chicago Psychoanal.Lit.Ind., CMI, Except.Child.Educ.Abstr., Hosp.Lit.Ind., Mid.East: Abstr.& Ind., P.A.I.S., Psychol.Abstr. (1965-), Pt.de Rep., Rehabil.Lit., Sage Fam.Stud.Abstr., Soc.Work Res.& Abstr. **Document type:** academic/scholarly publication, government publication.
—Faxon; UnCover.

CANADIAN ASSOCIATION OF ANATOMISTS. BULLETIN.
see *BIOLOGY*

610 CN
CANADIAN ASSOCIATION OF CRITICAL CARE NURSES. OFFICIAL JOURNAL.* q. Can.$60 to non-members. Pappin Communications, The Victoria Centre, 84 Isabella St., Pembroke, ON K8A 5S5, Canada. TEL 613-735-0952. FAX 613-735-7983. (Subscr. to: CACCN, P.O. Box 22006, London, ON N6C 4N0, Canada. TEL 519-649-5284) Ed. Francis Loos. adv.
Description: Represents nurses in clinical practice, education, research and administration within adult, neonatal and pediatric critical care in Canada.

616.07 CN ISSN 0703-8372
CANADIAN ASSOCIATION OF PATHOLOGISTS. NEWSLETTER. (Text in English, French) 1969. bi-m. membership. Canadian Association of Pathologists, Office of the Secretariat, Box 1570, 190 Railway, Kingston, ON K7L 5C8, Canada. TEL 613-531-8889. FAX 613-531-0626. E-mail: cap@limestone.kosone.com. Ed. Gregory Flynn. bk.rev. circ. 1,000. **Document type:** newsletter.

610 CN ISSN 0823-2105
R461
CANADIAN BULLETIN OF MEDICAL HISTORY/BULLETIN CANADIEN D'HISTOIRE DE LA MEDECINE. (Text and summaries in English, French) 1984. 2/yr. Can.$40. (Canadian Society for the History of Medicine - Societe Canadienne d'Histoire de la Medecine) Wilfrid Laurier University Press, Waterloo, ON N2L 3C5, Canada. TEL 519-884-0710. FAX 519-725-1399. E-mail: mach1.wlu.ca. Ed. Jim Connor. bk.rev. (back issues avail.) **Indexed:** Amer.Hist.& Life, Hist.Abstr. (1990-). **Document type:** academic/scholarly publication.
—BLDSC (3017.900000).
Description: Presents articles, notes, review articles and book reviews.
Refereed Serial

610 CN ISSN 0826-6778
CANADIAN CRITICAL CARE NURSING JOURNAL. 1984. 4/yr. Can.$15($20) Health Media Inc., 14453 29A Ave., White Rock, B.C. V4A 9K8, Canada. TEL 604-535-7933. Ed. Agnes Forster. adv. circ. 3,000. **Indexed:** CINAHL.

CANADIAN DIRECTORY OF HEALTH CARE CONFERENCES/REPERTOIRE CANADIEN DES CONFERENCES DE SOINS DE SANTE. see *MEETINGS AND CONGRESSES*

610 CN ISSN 0008-350X
CANADIAN FAMILY PHYSICIAN/MEDECIN DE FAMILLE CANADIEN. 1954. m. Can.$78.65 (US Can.$84; outside N. America Can.$115). College of Family Physicians of Canada, 2630 Skymark Ave., Mississauga, ON L4W 5A4, Canada. TEL 905-629-0900. FAX 905-629-0893. Ed. Tony Dixon. adv. contact: Gloria C. Bowes. bk.rev.; abstr.; bibl.; charts; illus.; stat.; index. circ. 30,000. **Indexed:** CMI, Curr.Cont., Excerp.Med., FAMLI (1980-1992), Helminthol.Abstr., Ind.Med. (1992-), Protozool.Abstr.
—BLDSC (3022.100000); Faxon; Genuine Article; SWETS. **CCC.**
Formerly: College of General Practice Journal.
Description: Aimed at practicing, teaching and research for family physicians and general practitioners.
Refereed Serial

368.382 CN
CANADIAN HEALTH CARE MANAGEMENT. 1986. 12/yr. Can.$349. M P L Communications Inc., 700-133 Richmond St. W., Toronto, ON M5H 3M8, Canada. TEL 416-869-1177. FAX 416-869-0456. Ed. John Hobel. circ. 500. **Document type:** newsletter.
Description: Provides current, need-to-know information for health care administrators, senior personnel.

610 CN ISSN 0839-1866
CANADIAN JOURNAL OF DIAGNOSIS. 1984. m. $9.50. S T A Communications Inc., 955 boul. St. Jean, Ste. 306, Pointe-Claire, Que. H9R 5K3, Canada. TEL 514-695-7623. FAX 514-695-8554. Ed. Paul F. Brand. adv. circ. 33,849.
—BLDSC (3031.137000).
Formerly: (until 1987): Diagnosis (ISSN 0825-4656)

CANADIAN JOURNAL OF VETERINARY RESEARCH/REVUE CANADIENNE DE RECHERCHE VETERINAIRE. see *VETERINARY SCIENCE*

610 CN ISSN 0068-9203
CANADIAN MEDICAL DIRECTORY. 1955. a. Can.$108.83($169) Southam Information and Technology Group, 1450 Don Mills Rd., Don Mills, ON M3B 2X7, Canada. TEL 416-445-6641. FAX 416-442-2261. Ed. Rolande Doyle. **Document type:** directory.
Description: Lists doctors both alphabetically and geographically within Canada. Includes addresses, telephone numbers, certifications and specializations.

615.8 CN ISSN 0824-2917
CANADIAN PHYSIOTHERAPY ASSOCIATION. SPORTS PHYSIOTHERAPY DIVISION. NEWSLETTER. bi-m. Canadian Physiotherapy Association, Sports Physiotherapy Division - Association Canadienne de Physiotherapie, 890 Yonge St., 9th Fl., Toronto, ON M4W 3P4, Canada. TEL 416-924-5312. FAX 416-924-7335. **Indexed:** Sportsearch (1981-).

616.04 CN ISSN 0226-2347
CANDID FACTS/A PROPOS. (Text in English and French) 1960. q. free. Canadian Cystic Fibrosis Foundation, 2221 Yonge St., Ste 601, Toronto, ON M4S 2B4, Canada. TEL 416-485-9149. FAX 416-485-0960. Ed. Deborah Blackstone. circ. 6,000. **Document type:** newsletter.

610 SA
THE CAPE DOCTOR. (Text in Afrikaans; English) 1959. 4/yr. membership. Medical Association of South Africa, Cape Western Branch, Private Bag X1, Pinelands 7430, South Africa. TEL 27-21-5313081. FAX 27-21-5314126. illus. **Document type:** newsletter.
Former titles (until vol.33, no.1, 1993): M A S A News - Cape Western Branch; (until vol.21, no.1, 1981): Medical Association of South Africa. Cape Western Branch. Newsletter.

610 IT ISSN 0576-7202
CARDARELLI; medicina - chirugia - specialita. q. free to members. Scuola Medica Ospedaliera, Casella Postale 1102, 80100 Naples, Italy. Ed. R. Sessa. adv.
—BLDSC (3051.017500).
Description: Publishes original works on clinical and experimental subjects.

MEDICAL SCIENCES

610 US ISSN 1053-5500
CASE MANAGEMENT ADVISOR. 1990. m. $189. American Health Consultants, Inc., Six Piedmont Center, Ste. 400, Atlanta, GA 30305. TEL 800-688-2321. FAX 800-284-3291. Ed. Miriam Romain. circ. 1,850. **Indexed:** CINAHL. **Document type:** newsletter.
—BLDSC (3058.137200). **CCC.**

651.5 368.382 US ISSN 1061-9259
THE CASE MANAGER. 1990. bi-m. $40 to individuals (Canada $62.06; elsewhere $58); institutions $42 (Canada $64.20; elsewhere $60) (effective 1996). (Individual Case Management Association) Mosby - Year Book, Inc. (Subsidiary of: Times Mirror Company), 11830 Westline Industrial Dr., St. Louis, MO 63146-3318. TEL 314-872-8370; 800-325-4177. FAX 314-432-1380. TELEX 44-2402. E-mail: terry.vanschaik@mosby.com. Ed. Tom Strickland. adv.: B&W page $1700, color page $2100; trim 8 1/8 x 10 7/8; adv. contact: Donna Ricko. bk.rev. circ. 20,000.
—**CCC.**
Description: Provides education, marketing and networking support to medical case managers who coordinate and manage services involving large or serious claims in the health and compensation industry.

610 XR ISSN 0008-7335
CODEN: CLCEAL
CASOPIS LEKARU CESKYCH. (Text mainly in Czech or Slovak; summaries in English, French, German, Russian) 1862. 52/yr. $114.70. (Ceska Lekarska Spolecnost J.E. Purkyne - Czech Medical Society) Nakladateske Stredisko C L S J.E. Purkyne, Sokolska 31, 120 26 Prague 2, Czech Republic. FAX 42-0-202788. (Subscr. to: Artia, Ve Smeckach 30, 111 27 Prague 1, Czech Republic) Ed. Michaela Malinova. adv.; bk.rev.; bibl.; charts; illus.; index. **Indexed:** Abstr.Hyg., Biol.Abstr., C.I.S. Abstr., Chem.Abstr., Curr.Adv.Ecol.Sci., Dent.Ind., Excerp.Med., Ind.Med., INIS Atomind., Nutr.Abstr., Trop.Dis.Bull.
—BLDSC (3061.400000); CASDDS; Genuine Article. **CCC.**

610 SP
CATALOGO DE TRABAJOS DE INVESTIGACION EN SALUD. 1990. a. (Osasunketa eta Kontsumo Saila - Departamento de Sanidad y Consumo) Eusko Jaurlaritzaren Argitalpen-Zerbitzu Nagusia - Servicio Central de Publicaciones del Gobierno Vasco, Duque de Wellington 2, 01011 Vitoria-Gasteiz, Spain. circ. 2,000.

610 US
CATALYST (CHARLESTON). w. free to the University community. Medical University of South Carolina, Public Relations Department, 171 Ashley Ave., Charleston, SC 29425. TEL 803-792-3621. Ed. Dick Peterson. adv. circ. 7,500. (tabloid format) **Document type:** newspaper.
Description: Provides news of current issues, research projects and other items of interest to faculty, staff, students and patients of the Medical University.

610 200 UK ISSN 0008-8226
CATHOLIC MEDICAL QUARTERLY. 1923. q. $30. Guild of Catholic Doctors, Ed. Dr. Peter Doherty, 60 Grove End Rd., London NW8 9NH, England. TEL 0171-266-4246. FAX 0171-266-4813. adv.; bk.rev.; bibl.; index. circ. 2,000. **Document type:** directory.
Description: Consists of information about bio-ethics, the Guild's activities and letters.

610 KO
CATHOLIC UNIVERSITY MEDICAL COLLEGE JOURNAL.* (Text in English or Korean; summaries in English) 1957. q. free. Catholic University, Graduate School, c/o Catholic Medical College, 505 Banpo-dong, Kangnam-gu, Seoul 135, S. Korea. TEL 02-593-5141. FAX 02-532-3112. Ed. Dr. Yong Whee Bahk. circ. 1,000 (controlled). **Indexed:** Biol.Abstr., Chem.Abstr.
Formerly: Catholic Medical College Journal.

CELL BIOCHEMISTRY AND FUNCTION. see *BIOLOGY — Biological Chemistry*

CELL CALCIUM (EDINBURGH). see *BIOLOGY — Cytology And Histology*

CELL CALCIUM (SHEFFIELD). see *BIOLOGY — Biological Chemistry*

CELL MEMBRANES. see *BIOLOGY — Cytology And Histology*

CELL NUCLEUS. see *BIOLOGY — Cytology And Histology*

CELL VISION; journal of analytical morphology. see *BIOLOGY*

610.28 US ISSN 1051-6794
R857.M3 CODEN: CEMAEE
CELLS AND MATERIALS. 1991. q. $75 (foreign $90). Scanning Microscopy International, Inc., 1034 Alabam Dr., Elk Grove Village, IL 60007-2920. TEL 708-529-6677. FAX 708-980-6698. Ed. Dr. A. Jay Wasserman. **Indexed:** Excerp.Med. (1995-). **Document type:** academic/scholarly publication.
—BLDSC (3097.913000); CASDDS; Ei; Genuine Article; SWETS; UnCover. **CCC.**
Description: The scope of topics covered includes cardiovascular, ocular, and orthopedic prostheses, drug delivery systems, and related topics. Emphasis is on morphological aspects of replaceable tissues, and their subsequent fortification or substitution by a biomaterial.
Refereed Serial

CELLULAR SIGNALLING. see *BIOLOGY — Cytology And Histology*

616 JA ISSN 0078-6632
CENTER FOR ADULT DISEASES, OSAKA. ANNUAL REPORT. (Text in English) 1961. a. free. Center for Adult Diseases, Osaka, 1-3-3 Nakamichi, Higashinari-ku, Osaka 537, Japan. Ed. Dr. Nobuyuki Senda. **Indexed:** Biol.Abstr., Excerp.Med.

610 US
CENTERSCOPE. 3/yr. Boston University, School of Medicine, Office of Publication Services, 80 E. Concord St., Boston, MA 02118. Ed. Owen McNamara. circ. 13,000.
Description: Informs alumni and friends of research and events at the School of Medicine.

610 RH ISSN 0008-9176
CODEN: CAJMA3
CENTRAL AFRICAN JOURNAL OF MEDICINE. 1955. m. $40. (University of Zimbabwe, Faculty of Medicine) Central African Journal of Medicine Co., P.O. Box A195, Avondale, Harare, Zimbabwe. TEL 263-4-791631. Ed. H.M. Chinyanga. adv.; bk.rev.; charts; illus.; index. circ. 1,500. (reprint service avail. from ISI) **Indexed:** Abstr.Hyg., Biol.Abstr., Chem.Abstr., Curr.Adv.Ecol.Sci., Curr.Cont., Dairy Sci.Abstr., Dent.Ind., Diar.Dis.Res., Excerp.Med., ExtraMED, Helminthol.Abstr., Ind.Med., Ind.S.A.Per., NRN, Nutr.Abstr., Protozool.Abstr., Rev.Appl.Entomol., Rev.Med.& Vet.Mycol., Rev.Plant Path., Trop.Dis.Bull. **Document type:** academic/scholarly publication.
●Also available on CD-ROM.
—BLDSC (3105.800000); Faxon; Genuine Article; SWETS; UnCover.

610 US ISSN 0008-946X
CENTRAL NEW YORK ACADEMY OF MEDICINE. BULLETIN. 1936. bi-m. $4. Central New York Academy of Medicine, 210 Clinton Rd., New Hartford, NY 13413. TEL 315-735-2204. (Co-sponsors: Medical Societies of the Counties of Oneida, Herkimer, Madison and Chenango) Ed. Dr. Edwin P. Russell, Jr. adv.; charts; illus.; stat. circ. 2,475.

610 MG
CENTRE D'INFORMATION ET DE DOCUMENTATION SCIENTIFIQUE ET TECHNIQUE. RECHERCHES POUR LE DEVELOPPEMENT. SERIE MEDECINE. (Text in French, summaries in English, French) 2/yr. 60 F.($10) Centre d'Information et de Documentation Scientifique et Technique, B.P. 6224, Antananarivo 101, Madagascar. TEL 33288.

CENTRE FOR MEDICINES RESEARCH WORKSHOP. see *PHARMACY AND PHARMACOLOGY*

610 FR ISSN 0338-7070
CENTRE LYONNAIS D'ACUPUNCTURE DE SAINT-LUC. BULLETIN DE LIAISON. 1975. 2/yr. Hopital St. Luc, 20 Quai Claude-Bernard, 69007 Lyon, France. Ed. Dr. Castro. (processed)

CEREBRAL CORTEX. see *MEDICAL SCIENCES — Psychiatry And Neurology*

610 TU ISSN 0376-7833
CODEN: CTFDDO
CERRAHPASA MEDICAL FACULTY. JOURNAL/CERRAHPASA TIP FAKULTESI DERGISI. (Text in Turkish; summaries in English) 1971? q. University of Istanbul, Cerrahpasa Medical Faculty, Cerrahpasa Tip Fakultesi, Aksaray, 34303 Istanbul, Turkey. TEL 90-1-588-4800. Ed. Vural Solok. abstr.; bibl.; charts; illus.; index. **Indexed:** Excerp.Med. **Document type:** academic/scholarly publication.
Description: Contains research studies of the Cerrahpasa Medical Faculty.

616.07 574.2 XR ISSN 1210-7875
CESKO-SLOVENSKA PATOLOGIE A SOUNDI LEKARSTVI. (Text in Czech; summaries in English and Russian) 1965. 4/yr. $31.20. (Ceska Lekarska Spolecnost J.E. Purkyne - Czech Medical Society) Nakladatelske Stredisko C L S J.E. Purkyne, Sokolska 31, 120 26 Prague 2, Czech Republic. FAX 42-2-202788. (Dist. by: Artia, Ve Smeckach 30, 111 27 Prague 1, Czech Republic) Ed. Dr. B. Bednar. bk.rev.; index. circ. 1,000. **Indexed:** Biol.Abstr., Chem.Abstr., Curr.Adv.Ecol.Sci., Excerp.Med., Ind.Med., INIS Atomind.
—BLDSC (3122.475000). **CCC.**
Formerly (until 1993): Ceskoslovenska Patologie (ISSN 0009-0611)

CESKOSLOVENSKA FYZIOLOGIE/CZECHOSLOVAK PHYSIOLOGY. see *BIOLOGY — Physiology*

610 CE ISSN 0011-2232
CEYLON JOURNAL OF MEDICAL SCIENCE. (Text in English) 1949. 2/yr. $5 per no. University of Colombo, Faculty of Medicine, Kynsey Rd., Colombo 8, Sri Lanka. TEL 01-698449. FAX 01-698449. (Subscr. to: The Librarian, University of Colombo, Colombo 3, Sri Lanka) Ed. T.W. Wikramanayake. bk.rev.; charts; illus. circ. 700. (back issues avail.) **Indexed:** Biol.Abstr., Chem.Abstr., Helminthol.Abstr., Ind.Med., Rev.Appl.Entomol., Sri Lanka Sci.Ind., Trop.Dis.Bull. **Document type:** academic/scholarly publication.
—BLDSC (3125.000000).
Description: Covers all branches of medical, dental, and veterinary sciences.
Refereed Serial

610 CE ISSN 0009-0875
CEYLON MEDICAL JOURNAL. (Text in English) 1887. q. $60. Sri Lanka Medical Association, Wijerama House, 6 Wijerama Mawatha, Colombo 7, Sri Lanka. TEL 941-693324. FAX 941-698032. Eds. Dr. C.G. Uragoda, C. Goonaratna. adv.: page $100. bk.rev.; charts; illus. circ. 1,500. **Indexed:** Abstr.Hyg., Biol.Abstr., Chem.Abstr., Diar.Dis.Res., Excerp.Med., ExtraMED, Helminthol.Abstr., Ind.Med., Nutr.Abstr., Sri Lanka Sci.Ind., Trop.Dis.Bull. **Document type:** academic/scholarly publication.
●Also available on CD-ROM.
—BLDSC (3128.200000); Faxon; SWETS; UnCover. *Refereed Serial*

610 658 US
CHANGING MEDICAL MARKETS; the international monthly newsletter for executives in the healthcare and biotechnology industries. 1978. m. $195. Theta Corporation, Theta Bldg., Middlefield, CT 06455. TEL 203-349-1054. FAX 203-349-1227. Ed. Phyllis Klaben. circ. controlled. (back issues avail.) **Document type:** newsletter.
Description: Comprehensive coverage of corporate activities, new products and services, emerging opportunities around the world, technology assessment, the impact of legislation and news from healthcare associations.

610 US
CHECK SAMPLE. (Subject areas offered include: Anatomic Pathology, Cytopathology, Forensic Pathology, Chemistry, Hematopathology, Immunopathology, Microbiology, and Transfusion Medicine) 1949. bi-w. $2077 for complete series; price varies for individual subject area. American Society of Clinical Pathologists, 2100 W. Harrison St., Chicago, IL 60612. TEL 312-738-4890. FAX 312-738-1619. Ed. Raymond Gambino. circ. 2,000.
Formerly (until 1958): Institute for Clinical Science. Proficiency Test Service. Report (ISSN 0073-8638)
Description: Each series consists of exercises which present patient cases for diagnosis or other laboratory study supplemented with kodachromes or specimen analytic materials.

MEDICAL SCIENCES

610   IT
CHECK-UP INCONTRI. 11/yr. Viale Molise 54, 20137 Milan, Italy. TEL 2-540-87-58. FAX 2-55-10140. Ed. Dr. A. Lanzalaco. circ. 136,000.

610   TH   ISSN 0125-5983
CODEN: CMMBB2
CHIANG MAI MEDICAL BULLETIN. (Text in English and Thai) 1961. q. B.80($40) to individuals; institutions $100. Chiang Mai University, Faculty of Medicine, 110 Intavaroros Street, Chiang Mai 50002, Thailand. TEL 52-221122. FAX 53-217144. Ed. Dr. Watana Navacharoen. adv.; bk.rev.; abstr.; charts; illus.; stat.; circ. 1,000 (controlled). **Indexed:** Chem.Abstr., Diar.Dis.Res.

610   JA   ISSN 0303-5476
CODEN: CIZAAZ
CHIBA IGAKU ZASSHI/CHIBA MEDICAL JOURNAL. (Text in Japanese; summaries in English) 1923. bi-m. 4000 Yen($29) Chiba Igakkai - Chiba Medical Society, c/o Chiba Daigaku Igakubu, 8-1 Inohana 1-chome, Chuo-ku, Chiba-shi 260, Japan. TEL 043-222-7171. FAX 043-222-7853. Ed. Yoshio Nakajima. adv.; bk.rev. circ. 3,200. **Indexed:** Biol.Abstr., Chem.Abstr., Excerp.Med., INIS Atomind. **Document type:** academic/scholarly publication.
—CASDDS.
  Formerly: Chiba Medical Society. Journal (ISSN 0009-3459)
  Description: Presents review articles, original papers, case reports, and news of the society.

610   JA   ISSN 0910-7436
CHIBAKEN ISHIKAI ZASSHI/CHIBA MEDICAL ASSOCIATION. JOURNAL. (Text in Japanese) 1949. m. 400 Yen per no. Chibaken Ishikai, 5-25, Chibako, Chuo-ku, Chiba-shi, Chiba-ken 260, Japan.

CHICAGO HISTORY OF SCIENCE AND MEDICINE. see *HISTORY*

610   US   ISSN 0009-3637
CHICAGO MEDICINE. 1902. s-m. $30 to non-members; members $15. Chicago Medical Society, 515 N. Dearborn, Chicago, IL 60610. TEL 312-670-2550. FAX 312-670-3646. Ed. Gary Baldnin. adv.: B&W page $500; adv. contact: Liz Sidney. bk.rev.; charts; illus.; index. circ. 11,000. **Indexed:** Med.Care Rev.
  Description: Provides a forum for the discussion of medical, ethical, legal, socioeconomic, and other concerns affecting physicians in Chicago and Cook County.

610   JA   ISSN 0911-5528
CHIGASAKI MEDICUS. (Text in English, Japanese) 1985. a. Chigasaki Tokushukai Sogo Byoin - Chigasaki Tokushukai Medical Center, 14-1 Saiwaicho, Chigasaki-shi, Kanagawa-ken 253, Japan.

610   JA   ISSN 0289-9752
CHIIKI IRYO/MEDICAL TREATMENT IN LOCAL DISTRICT. (Annual supplement avail.: Chiiki Iryo. Zokango (ISSN 0289-9752)) (Text in Japanese) 1961. q. Zenkoku Kokumin Kenko Hoken Shinryo Shisetsu Kyogikai - Japan National Health Insurance Clinics & Hospitals Association, Daiyamondo Puraza, 25, Ichibancho, Chiyoda-ku, Tokyo 102, Japan.

610   II
CHIKITSAK BARTA. (Supplements avail.) (Text in Bengali) 1973. fortn. Rs.10($3) Amal Ghosh-hajra, Ed. & Pub., 240 Diamond Harbour Rd., Behala, Calcutta 700060, West Bengal, India. adv.; bk.rev.; abstr.; bibl.; stat.; index. circ. 15,000.

610   II   ISSN 0009-3858
CHIKITSAK SAMAJ. (Supplements avail.) (Text in several languages) 1969. m. Rs.15. Amal Ghosh-hajra, Ed. & Pub., 240 Diamond Harbour Rd., Behala, Calcutta 700060, West Bengal, India. adv.; bk.rev.; abstr.; bibl.; film rev.; play rev.; stat.; index. circ. 5,500.

610   JA   ISSN 0289-9590
CHIKURIN/HIGASHI HIROSHIMA MEDICAL ASSOCIATION. JOURNAL. (Text in Japanese) a. Higashihiroshima Chiku Ishikai - Higashi Hiroshima Medical Association, 6-29, Saijo Kamiichimachi, Higashihiroshima-shi, Hiroshima-ken 724, Japan.

610   US   ISSN 0069-3685
CHINA MEDICAL BOARD OF NEW YORK. ANNUAL REPORT. 1951. a. membership. China Medical Board of New York, 750 Third Ave., New York, NY 10003. TEL 212-682-8000. FAX 212-9949-8726. circ. 300.

610   SI   ISSN 0218-6241
CHINA MEDICAL FOCUS. (Text in English) m. $240. T W L Publishing (Singapore) Pte. Ltd., 25 Genting Rd., No. 07-01, Soon Seng Bldg., Singapore 1334, Singapore. (Co-sponsors: China Information Centre (Singapore) Pte. Ltd.; Beijing Medical University) Pub. Tang Kin Eng.
—BLDSC (3180.199000).

610 615   CC
CHINA PHARMACEUTICAL AND MEDICAL INSTRUMENTS. (Text in Chinese, English) q. $55.20 (effective 1994). State Pharmaceutical Administration of China, China Pharmaceutical and Medical Instruments Editorial Office, No. 841 Sichuan Beilu, Shanghai 200085, People's Republic of China. TEL 3069602. (Dist. by: China National Publications Import & Export Corporation (CNPIEC), Export Department, 16 Gongti E. Rd., Chaoyang District, P.O. Box 88, Beijing 100020, P.R.C.. TEL 01-506-6688) Ed. Shi Huan.
  Description: Covers Chinese medicine, pharmaceuticals, medical apparatuses and instruments, pharmaceutical production machinery and packaging.

CHINESE JOURNAL OF PHYSIOLOGY/CHUNG-KUO SHENG LI HSUEH TSA CHIH. see *BIOLOGY — Physiology*

610   CC   ISSN 0366-6999
CODEN: CMJODS
CHINESE MEDICAL JOURNAL/ZHONGHUA YIXUE ZAZHI YINGWEN BAN. Chinese edition: Zhonghua Yixue Zazhi (ISSN 0376-2491) (Text in English) 1887-1966; resumed 1975. 12/yr. £110($181) (effective 1994). Chinese Medical Association - Zhonghua Yixuehui, 42 Dongsi Xidajie, Beijing 100710, People's Republic of China. TEL 5133311. (Dist. outside China by: T W L Publishing Pte. Ltd., Block 1004, No. 03-77, Aljunied Ave. 5, Singapore 1438, Singapore) Ed. Feng Chuan-han. abstr.; bibl.; charts; illus. circ. 5,000. (also avail. in microfilm from UMI; back issues avail.) **Indexed:** Abstr.Hyg., Biol.Abstr., Chem.Abstr., Curr.Adv.Ecol.Sci., Curr.Cont., Dairy Sci.Abstr., Dent.Abstr., Dent.Ind., Diar.Dis.Res., Excerp.Med. (1983-), Helminthol.Abstr., I.P.A., Ind.Med., Ind.Sci.Rev., Med.Care Rev., Nutr.Abstr., Protozool.Abstr., Rehabil.Lit., Rev.Med.& Vet.Mycol., Rev.Plant Path., Sci.Cit.Ind., Trop.Dis.Bull. **Document type:** academic/scholarly publication.
●Also available online.
—BLDSC (3180.390000); CASDDS; Genuine Article; SWETS; UMI; UnCover.
  Formerly (until 1932): China Missionary Medical Journal.
  Description: Introduces advances and research results in China's medical sciences and technology, serving primarily senior medical clinicians and research personnel of high academic level.
Refereed Serial

610   CH   ISSN 0578-1337
R97.7.C5   CODEN: CIHCDM
CHINESE MEDICAL JOURNAL (TAIPEI). 1915. m. $55 (other Asian countries $80; elsewhere $90) (effective 1996). Chinese Medical Association - Taipei, P.O. Box 3043, 201 Shih-pai Rd., Sec. 2, Taipei, Taiwan 112, Republic of China. TEL 886-2-871-2121. FAX 886-2-87410977. Ed. Mau-Song Chang; Pub. Fang-Ku Peng. adv. **Indexed:** Excerp.Med. **Document type:** academic/scholarly publication.
—BLDSC (3181.010000).

610   CC   ISSN 1001-9294
CODEN: CMSJEP
CHINESE MEDICAL SCIENCES JOURNAL. (Text in English) 1986. q. Y20 (foreign £90 ($150)) (effective 1996). Chinese Academy of Medical Sciences (CAMS) - Zhongguo Yixue Kexueyuan, 9 Dong Dan San Tiao, Beijing 100730, People's Republic of China. TEL 5133074. FAX 5124876. TELEX 222689-CAMS-CN. (Subscr. to: Taylor & Francis Ltd., Rankine Rd., Basingstoke, Hants. RG24 0PR, England. TEL 44-1256-840366. FAX 44-1256-479438) Ed. Ba Denian. adv.; bk.rev.; bibl.; charts; index. circ. 1,500. (back issues avail.) **Indexed:** Excerp.Med., Ind.Med. **Document type:** academic/scholarly publication.
—BLDSC (3181.012000); CASDDS; Faxon.
  Formerly (until 1991): Chinese Academy of Medical Sciences and Peking Union Medical College. Proceedings - Zhongguo Yixue Kexueyuan, Zhongguo Xiehe Yike Daxue Xuebao (ISSN 0258-8757)
  Description: Presents recent advances in medical research. Includes information on clinical medicine, pharmacology, as well as traditional Chinese medicine.
Refereed Serial

610   CC   ISSN 1000-7911
CHONGQING YIYAO/CHONGQING MEDICINE. (Text in Chinese) bi-m. (Chongqingshi Weishengju - Chongqing Public Health Bureau) Chongqing Yiyao Bianjibu, 44 Qingnian Lu, Chongqing, Sichuan 630010, People's Republic of China.

174.2 241.642   NE   ISSN 1380-3603
▼**CHRISTIAN BIOETHICS;** non-ecumenical studies in medical morality. (Text and summaries in English) 1995. 3/yr. fl.107($59) to individuals; institutions fl.250($137). Swets & Zeitlinger bv, P.O. Box 825, 2160 SZ Lisse, Netherlands. TEL 31-2521-35111. FAX 31-2521-15888. TELEX 41325 SZLIS NL. E-mail: orders@swets.nl. (Dist. in N. America by: Swets & Zeitlinger, 440 Creamery Way, Ste. A, Exton, PA 19341. TEL 610-524-5355) Ed.Bd. adv.; bk.rev.; index; circ. 500 (paid). (also avail. in microfilm from SWZ; back issues avail.) **Document type:** academic/scholarly publication.
—BLDSC (3181.779645).
  Description: Explores the commitments of the Christian faith with regard to the meaning of human life, sexuality, suffering, illness and death within the context of medicine and healthcare.
Refereed Serial

610   US
CHRISTIAN MEDICAL & DENTAL SOCIETY JOURNAL. 1949. 6/yr. $25 to non-members. Christian Medical & Dental Society, 501 Fifth St., King Bldg., 3rd Fl., Bristol, TN 37620. TEL 615-844-1000. FAX 615-844-1005. Ed. David B. Biebel. adv.; bk.rev. circ. 12,000. **Indexed:** Chr.Per.Ind. **Document type:** academic/scholarly publication.
—UMI.
  Incorporates (in 1993): C M D S; Formerly: Christian Medical Society Journal (ISSN 0009-546X)
  Description: Aims to motivate and equip doctors to practice faith in Jesus Christ in their personal and professional lives.
Refereed Serial

610   II   ISSN 0009-5443
CHRISTIAN MEDICAL ASSOCIATION OF INDIA. JOURNAL.* (Text in English) 1925. m. Rs.20($7) E.L. Press, c/o I. M. A., Indraprstha Marg., New Delhi 110 002, India. Ed. Dr. Samuel Joseph. adv.; bk.rev.; abstr.; charts; illus.; index. circ. 1,500. **Indexed:** Biol.Abstr.

610   II   ISSN 0009-5451
CHRISTIAN MEDICAL COLLEGE VELLORE ALUMNI JOURNAL. (Text in English) 1967. q. Rs.40 per no. to non-members; members Rs.25($6). Christian Medical College, Alumni Association, Vellore 632 002, Tamil Nadu, India. TEL 22603. TELEX 405-202 CMCH IN. Ed. Dr. Thomas Sen Bhanu. adv.; bk.rev.; abstr.; bibl.; charts; illus.; circ. 2,000 (controlled). **Document type:** academic/scholarly publication.
  Description: Provides updated material of scientific interest to doctors.

MEDICAL SCIENCES

610 US
CHRONIC PAIN LETTER; an information source for the sufferer. 1984. bi-m. $20 to individuals; institutions and professionals $35. Robert J. Fabian Memorial Foundation, Box 1303 Old Chelsea Station, New York, NY 10011-1303. TEL 718-797-0015. FAX 212-614-9266. Ed. Alice Delury. **Document type:** newsletter.
  Description: Contains current information on the management of chronic pain for the sufferer and the professional.

CHRONOBIOLOGY INTERNATIONAL; a journal of basic and applied biological rhythm research. see *BIOLOGY*

610 JA ISSN 0913-8684
CHUBU BYOIN IGAKU ZASSHI/OKINAWA CHUBU HOSPITAL BULLETIN. (Text in English, Japanese; summaries in Japanese) 1975. a. Chubu Byoin, Igaku Zasshi Henshu Iinkai - Okinawa Chubu Hospital, Editorial Committee, Okinawa Kenritsu Chubu Byoin, 208-3, Miyazato, Gushikawa-shi, Okinawa-ken 904-22, Japan. (Co-sponsor: Hawai Daigaku Jimusho - University of Hawaii Postgraduate Medical Education Program)

CHUI RINSHO/CLINICAL JOURNAL OF TRADITIONAL CHINESE MEDICINE. see *ALTERNATIVE MEDICINE*

610 US ISSN 0084-8786
CIBA COLLECTION OF MEDICAL ILLUSTRATIONS. 1953. irreg., vol.8, Pt.3, 1993. price varies. Ciba Geigy Corporation, Medical Education & Publications Division, 556 Morris Ave., Summit, NJ 07901. TEL 908-277-4785. TELEX 131411. Ed. Gina Dingle. illus. (also avail. on slides) **Indexed:** 908-277-4478.
  Description: Dr. Frank Netter's illustrated anatomical atlases for each body system.

610 SP ISSN 0212-6052
CIENCIA MEDICA; para la practica diaria. 1983. 11/yr. 7500 ptas.($100) (Europe $80). Alpe Editores, S.A., Pedro Rico, 27, 28029 Madrid, Spain. TEL 34-1-7338811. FAX 34-1-3159652. Ed. Dr. J. Abascal Morte; Pub. A. Alvarez. adv.: color page 160000 ptas.; 210 x 280; adv. contact: C. Alvarez. circ. 8,000 (controlled).

610 US ISSN 0163-0075
CINCINNATI MEDICINE. 1921. m. $25 to members; non-members $35 (effective thru 1996). Academy of Medicine of Cincinnati, 320 Broadway, Cincinnati, OH 45202. TEL 513-421-7010. FAX 513-721-4378. Ed. Rhonda Rice Tepe. adv. contact: Kimberly Weaver. bk.rev.; bibl.; illus.; index, cum.index. circ. 3,000. (tabloid format) **Indexed:** Chem.Abstr., Ind.Med. **Document type:** newspaper, trade publication.
  Supersedes (in 1978): Cincinnati Journal of Medicine (ISSN 0009-6873)

610 US
THE CIVIL ABOLITIONIST. 1986. q. $5 (effective 1995 & 1996). Coalition to Protect Animals in Parks & Refuges, Box 26, Swain, NY 14884. TEL 607-545-6213. Ed. Bina Robinson. bk.rev. circ. 2,600. **Document type:** bulletin.
  Former titles: Civitas Abolitionist; (until vol.3, no.3, 1988): Civitas.
  Description: Aims to promote better human health care (as opposed to sickness care), by abolishing the practice of vivisection, i.e. animal experimentation.

610 629.1 US
CIVIL AVIATION MEDICAL ASSOCIATION. BULLETIN. 1955. q. $15. Civil Aviation Medical Association, Box 23864, Oklahoma City, OK 73123-2864. TEL 405-840-0199. FAX 405-848-1053. Ed. Dr. Robert L. Wick, Jr. circ. 2,000. (looseleaf format; reprint service avail.) **Document type:** bulletin.

610 US ISSN 0891-1150
R11 CODEN: CCJMEL
CLEVELAND CLINIC JOURNAL OF MEDICINE. 1931. 6/yr. $45 (effective 1996). Cleveland Clinic Educational Foundation, 9500 Euclid Ave., Cleveland, OH 44195-5058. TEL 216-444-2662. FAX 216-444-9385. Ed. Herbert P. Wiedemann; Pub. Linda K. Hengstler. adv. contact: Bruce Marich. bk.rev.; bibl.; charts; illus.; index. circ. 54,000. (also avail. in microfilm from UMI) **Indexed:** Biol.Abstr., Curr.Adv.Cancer Res., Curr.Adv.Genetics & Molec.Biol., Curr.Cont., Dok.Arbeitsmed., Excerp.Med., Ind.Med., Ind.Sci.Rev., INIS Atomind., Sci.Cit.Ind. **Document type:** academic/scholarly publication.
  —BLDSC (3278.649800); Faxon; Genuine Article; SWETS; UMI; UnCover. **CCC.**
  Formerly (until 1987): Cleveland Clinic Quarterly (ISSN 0009-8787)
  Description: Original contributions, case reports, and timely reviews on subjects of interest to physicians in clinical practice.
  Refereed Serial

610 US
CLEVELAND PHYSICIAN. 1920. m. $24. (Academy of Medicine of Cleveland) Academy Graphic Communication, 1000 Brookpark, Cleveland, OH 44109. Ed. George Reitz. adv.; bk.rev.; illus. circ. 4,800. **Document type:** bulletin.
  Formerly: Academy of Medicine of Cleveland. Bulletin (ISSN 0001-4281)

610.28 UK ISSN 0144-7777
CODEN: CLNCD5
CLINICA; world medical device & diagnostic news. 1980. w. £420 (foreign $750). P J B Publications Ltd., 18-20 Hill Rise, Richmond, Surrey TW10 6UA, England. TEL 0181-948-3262. FAX 0181-948-5598. TELEX 8951042. Ed. Jeanette Marchant. adv. contact: Robin Baker. bk.rev. circ. 2,000. **Indexed:** ABC, PROMT, Psychol.Abstr. **Document type:** newsletter.
  ●Also available online. Vendor(s): Ovid Technologies (PHIN,PHIC,PHID), Data-Star, Knight-Ridder, Inc..
  —BLDSC (3286.170000); SWETS. **CCC.**
  Description: News for the medical device and diagnostic industry.

615.19 NE ISSN 0009-8981
RB1 CODEN: CCATAR
CLINICA CHIMICA ACTA; international journal of clinical chemistry and medical biochemistry. (Text in English) 1956. 22/yr. fl.5060($3085) (effective 1996). Elsevier Science B.V., P.O. Box 211, 1000 AE Amsterdam, Netherlands. TEL 31-20-4853911. FAX 31-20-4853598. TELEX 18582 ESPA NL. E-mail: nlinfo-f@elsevier.nl; usinfo-f@elsevier.com; forinfo-kyf04035@niftyserve.or.jp; Site addr.: http://www.elsevier.nl/. (Subscr. in U.S. and Canada to: Elsevier Science Inc., Box 882, Madison Sq. Sta., New York, NY 10159-0882. TEL 212-989-5800. FAX 212-633-3990) Ed.Bd. adv.; charts; illus.; index. (also avail. in microform from UMI; reprint service avail. from ISI) **Indexed:** Anal.Abstr., Biol.Abstr., Biotech.Abstr., Chem.Abstr., Curr.Adv.Biochem., Curr.Adv.Cancer Res., Curr.Adv.Ecol.Sci., Curr.Adv.Genetics & Molec.Biol., Curr.Chem.React., Curr.Cont., Dairy Sci.Abstr., Dent.Ind., Excerp.Med., Helminthol.Abstr., Ind.Chem., Ind.Med., Ind.Sci.Rev., Ind.Vet., INIS Atomind., Int.Abstr.Biol.Sci., Mass Spectr.Bull., Nutr.Abstr., Potato Abstr., Sci.Cit.Ind., Triticale Abstr., Vet.Bull., Weed Abstr. **Document type:** academic/scholarly publication.
  —BLDSC (3286.200000); ADONIS; CASDDS; Faxon; Genuine Article; SWETS; UnCover. **CCC.**
  Description: Publishes information leading to a better understanding of biological mechanisms of human diseases, their diagnosis and treatment.
  Refereed Serial

610 IT ISSN 0393-7585
CLINICA MEDICA DEL NORD AMERICA. bi-m. L.180000($180) Piccin Editore, Via Altinate 107, 35100 Padua, Italy. TEL 049-655566. FAX 049-8750693. (reprint service avail. from UMI)

610 SP ISSN 0301-0392
CLINICA; PORTAVOZ DEL INTERNADO. 1989. a. 400 ptas. Universidad de Valladolid, Secretariado de Publicaciones, Facultad de Medicina, C. Juan Mambrilla, 14, 47003 Valladolid, Spain. TEL 983-423000. FAX 34-83-290300. TELEX 26357. **Document type:** academic/scholarly publication.

610 SP ISSN 0210-7945
CLINICA RURAL. 24/yr. Ronda de San Pedro 22, 08010 Barcelona, Spain. TEL 3-301-24-33. circ. 17,000.

615.5 IT ISSN 0009-9074
CODEN: CLTEA4
CLINICA TERAPEUTICA. (Text in Italian; summaries in English, Italian) 1951. s-m. L.100000 (foreign L.200000). Societa Editrice Universo, Via G.B. Morgagni 1, 00161 Rome, Italy. Ed. Prof. Michele De Martiis. adv.; bk.rev.; abstr.; bibl.; index. circ. 10,000. (tabloid format; back issues avail.) **Indexed:** Biol.Abstr., Biotech.Abstr., Chem.Abstr., Excerp.Med., Ind.Med., Nutr.Abstr.
  —BLDSC (3286.237000); CASDDS; SWETS.

CLINICAL AND BIOCHEMICAL ANALYSIS. see *BIOLOGY — Biological Chemistry*

610 CN ISSN 0147-958X
CODEN: CNVMDL
CLINICAL AND INVESTIGATIVE MEDICINE/MEDECINE CLINIQUE ET EXPERIMENTALE. 1978. 6/yr. Can.$65 to individuals; institutions Can.$150. Canadian Society for Clinical Investigation, Montreal General Hospital, 1650 Cedar Ave., Montreal, PQ H3G 1A4, Canada. TEL 514-933-9770. Ed. C. Goresky. adv. contact: Jayne Lamb. abstr.; bibl.; charts; illus.; stat.; index. circ. 1,384. (also avail. in microform from MIM,UMI; back issues avail.) **Indexed:** Biol.Abstr., Chem.Abstr., Curr.Adv.Cancer Res., Curr.Adv.Ecol.Sci., Curr.Cont., Dairy Sci.Abstr., Dok.Arbeitsmed., Excerp.Med., Helminthol.Abstr., Ind.Med., Kidney, Nutr.Abstr., Rev.Med.& Vet.Mycol., Risk Abstr. **Document type:** academic/scholarly publication.
  —BLDSC (3286.253000); CASDDS; Faxon; Genuine Article; SWETS; UnCover. **CCC.**

610.28 NE ISSN 0927-5487
CLINICAL ASPECTS OF BIOMEDICINE. (Text in English) 1991. irreg., vol.2, 1993. Elsevier Science B.V., Books Division, P.O. Box 211, 1000 AE Amsterdam, Netherlands. TEL 31-20-4853911. FAX 31-20-4853705. TELEX 18582 ESPA NL. E-mail: nlinfo-f@elsevier.nl; usinfo-f@elsevier.com; forinfo-kyf04035@niftyserve.or.jp; Site addr.: http://www.elsevier.nl/. (Susbcr. in U.S. and Canada to: Elsevier Science Inc., Box 882, Madison Sq. Sta., New York, NY 10159. TEL 212-989-5800) (back issues avail.) **Document type:** monographic series.
  —BLDSC (3286.259600).
  Refereed Serial

610 UK ISSN 0959-9851
CODEN: CAURE9
CLINICAL AUTONOMIC RESEARCH. 1991. bi-m. £210($355) to institutions (effective 1995). (Clinical Autonomic Research Society) Rapid Communications of Oxford Ltd., The Old Malthouse, Paradise St., Oxford OX1 1LD, England. TEL 01865-790447. FAX 01865-244012. E-mail: rapidcom@vax.oxford.ac.uk. Ed. Christopher Mathias. adv. contact: Julie Gribben. (reprint service avail.) **Indexed:** Excerp.Med. (1993-), Ind.Med. (1992-). **Document type:** academic/scholarly publication.
  ●Also available on CD-ROM.
  —BLDSC (3286.259900); ADONIS; Genuine Article. **CCC.**
  Description: Aims to draw together and disseminate research work from the various disciplines and specialities dealing with clinical problems resulting from autonomic dysfunction.

CLINICAL BIOCHEMISTRY. see *BIOLOGY — Biological Chemistry*

610 US ISSN 0191-7870
CLINICAL BIOMECHANICS. 1971. irreg. Clinical Biomechanics Corp., Box 35185, Los Angeles, CA 90035.

MEDICAL SCIENCES

615.19 US ISSN 0009-9147
RB1 CODEN: CLCHAU
CLINICAL CHEMISTRY; clinical chemistry reference edition (the institutional edition). 1955. m. $130 to individuals (Canada & Mexico $150; elsewhere $170); institutions $260 (Canada & Mexico $280; elsewhere $300). American Association for Clinical Chemistry, Inc., 2101 L St. N.W., Ste. 202, Washington, DC 20037-1526. TEL 800-892-1400; 800-892-1400. FAX 202-887-5093. Ed. David E. Bruns. adv.; bk.rev.; abstr.; bibl.; charts; illus.; index, cum.index. circ. 15,000. (also avail. in microfiche; microfilm; back issues avail.; reprint service avail.) **Indexed:** Anal.Abstr., Biodet.Abstr., Biol.Abstr., C.I.S. Abstr., Chem.Abstr., Curr.Adv.Cancer Res., Curr.Adv.Ecol.Sci., Curr.Cont., Dairy Sci.Abstr., Dent.Ind., Diar.Dis.Res., Excerp.Med., Ind.Med., Ind.Sci.Rev., Ind.Vet., INIS Atomind., Mass Spectr.Bull., Nutr.Abstr., Rev.Med.& Vet.Mycol., Sci.Cit.Ind., So.Pac.Per.Ind., Vet.Bull. **Document type:** academic/scholarly publication.
—BLDSC (3286.268000); ADONIS; CASDDS; Faxon; Genuine Article; SWETS; UMI; UnCover. **CCC.**
Description: Covers analytical and biochemical techniques, instrumentation, statistical analysis of data, clinical investigations in which clinical chemistry has played a major role, and a variety of in vivo and in vitro studies of human disease.
Refereed Serial

610 011 UK ISSN 0958-3513
CLINICAL CONGRESS NEWS. 1989. irreg. Cambridge Medical Publications Ltd., Wicker House, High St., Worthing, W. Sussex BN11 1DJ, England. TEL 01903-205884. FAX 01903-234862. TELEX 878372 PPSLTD G. circ. (controlled). **Document type:** proceedings.
Description: Provides rapid reports of specific medical meetings and symposia.

610.28 US
CLINICAL ENGINEERING SERIES. 1972. irreg., vol.5, 1981. Academic Press, Inc., 525 B St., Ste. 1900, San Diego, CA 92101-4495. TEL 619-231-0926. FAX 619-699-6715. (Subscr. to: Order Dept., 6277 Sea Harbor Dr., 4th Fl., Orlando, FL 32887. TEL 800-321-5068) Ed. Cesar A. Caceres. (reprint service avail. from ISI)
Description: Details research in the biomedical fields.
Refereed Serial

610 US
CLINICAL LABORATORY NEWS. 1978. m. $30 (foreign $65); free to qualified personnel. American Association for Clinical Chemistry, Inc., 2101 L St. N.W., Ste. 202, Washington, DC 20037-1526. TEL 800-892-1400. FAX 202-887-5093. Ed. Nancy Sasavage. adv.; bk.rev. circ. 30,000. **Indexed:** Chem.Abstr.
—UMI. **CCC.**
Formerly: Clinical Chemistry News (ISSN 0161-9640)
Description: Contains top news stories on technology and regulatory issues.

610.28 UK ISSN 0267-6605
CODEN: CLNME2
CLINICAL MATERIALS. 1986. m. (in 3 vols., 4 nos./vol.). £455($678) (effective 1995). Elsevier Science Ltd., P.O. Box 800, Kidlington, Oxford OX5 1DX, England. TEL 44-1865-843000. FAX 44-1865-843010. E-mail: nlinfo-f@elsevier.nl; usinfo-f@elsevier.com; forinfo-kyf04035@niftyserve.or.jp; Site addr.: http://www.elsevier.nl/. (Subscr. in U.S. and Canada to: Elsevier Science, 660 White Plains Rd., Tarrytown, NY 10591-5153. TEL 914-524-9200. FAX 914-333-2444) Ed.Bd. adv. (also avail. in microform from UMI) **Indexed:** Biol.Abstr., Excerp.Med., Intl.Polym.Sci.& Tech., Met.Abstr., RAPRA. **Document type:** academic/scholarly publication.
—BLDSC (3286.299000); CASDDS; Ei; Genuine Article; SWETS. **CCC.**
Incorporates (in 1991): Critical Reviews in Biocompatibility (ISSN 0748-5204)
Description: Publishes research papers and state of the art reviews focusing on the development and application of materials, particularly biomaterials, for use in the clinical medical environment.
Refereed Serial

174.2 614.1 NE ISSN 0926-969X
CLINICAL MEDICAL ETHICS. (Text in English) 1991. irreg., vol.4, 1993. price varies. Kluwer Academic Publishers, Postbus 17, 3300 AA Dordrecht, Netherlands. TEL 31-78-392392. FAX 31-78-392254. TELEX 29245 KAPG NL. (Dist. by: Kluwer Academic Publishers Group, P.O. Box 322, 3300 AH Dordrecht, Netherlands. TEL 31-78-392392. FAX 31-78-546474; N. America dist. addr.: Box 358, Accord Sta., Hingham, MA 02018-0358. TEL 617-871-6600. FAX 617-871-6528) Eds. H. Tristam Engelhardt Jr., Stuart F. Spicker. (back issues avail.) **Document type:** monographic series.
—BLDSC (3286.300000).
Description: In-depth examination of issues at the forefront of the medical ethics debate.
Refereed Serial

616.01 FR ISSN 1198-743X
▼**CLINICAL MICROBIOLOGY AND INFECTION.** 1995. q. 622 F.($115) to individuals; institutions 810 F.($150). (European Society of Clinical Microbiology and Infectious Diseases) Decker Europe, 67 rue St. Jacques, 75005 Paris, France.
TEL 33-1-43251178. FAX 33-1-43251254.
Document type: academic/scholarly publication.

610 576 US ISSN 0196-4399
CODEN: CMNEEJ
CLINICAL MICROBIOLOGY NEWSLETTER. 1979. 24/yr. $199 to institutions in U.S.; $270 to institutions outside the Americas (effective 1996). Elsevier Science Inc., 655 Ave. of the Americas, New York, NY 10010. TEL 212-989-5800.
FAX 212-633-3990. TELEX 420643 AEP UI. (Subscr. to: Box 882, Madison Sq. Sta., New York, NY 10159-0882) Ed.Bd. (also avail. in microform from UMI) **Indexed:** Abstr.Hyg., Diar.Dis.Res., Excerp.Med., Rev.Med.& Vet.Mycol., Trop.Dis.Bull. **Document type:** newsletter.
—BLDSC (3286.305600); SWETS; UnCover. **CCC.**
Description: For clinical microbiologists, clinical pathologists, laboratory technologists and technicians.

612 UK ISSN 0144-5979
RB113 CODEN: CLPHDU
CLINICAL PHYSIOLOGY. 1981. bi-m. £60 to individuals in Europe; elsewhere £66($106); institutions in Europe £265; elsewhere £291($468) (effective 1996). (Scandinavian Society of Clinical Physiology) Blackwell Science Ltd., Osney Mead, Oxford OX2 OEL, England. TEL 01865-206206.
FAX 01865-206219. TELEX 83355 MEDBOK G. Ed. J. Bulow. adv.; charts; illus.; index. circ. 300. (back issues avail.) **Indexed:** ASCA, Biol.Abstr., Chem.Abstr., Curr.Adv.Biochem., Curr.Adv.Ecol.Sci., Curr.Cont., Excerp.Med., Ind.Med., Ind.Sci.Rev., Sci.Cit.Ind. **Document type:** academic/scholarly publication.
—BLDSC (3286.332500); CASDDS; Faxon; Genuine Article; SWETS; UMI; UnCover. **CCC.**
Refereed Serial

610 574 UK ISSN 0143-5221
CODEN: CSCIAE
CLINICAL SCIENCE. 1909. m. £238($430) Portland Press Ltd., 59 Portland Place, London W1N 3AJ, England. TEL 0171-580-5530.
FAX 0171-323-1136. E-mail: sales@portlandpress.co.uk. (Subscr. to: Commerce Way, P.O. Box 32, Colchester, Essex CO2 8HP, England. TEL 01206-796351. FAX 01206-799331) (Co-sponsor: Medical Research Society) Ed. A.M. Heagerty. adv. contact: Adam Marshall. bibl.; illus.; index. (also avail. in microform from PMC; back issues avail.) **Indexed:** Biol.Abstr., Biotech.Abstr., Chem.Abstr., Curr.Adv.Ecol.Sci., Curr.Cont., Dairy Sci.Abstr., Dent.Ind., Diar.Dis.Res., Excerp.Med., Helminthol.Abstr., Ind.Med., Ind.Sci.Rev., INIS Atomind., Kidney, NRN, Sci.Cit.Ind., Trop.Dis.Bull. **Document type:** academic/scholarly publication.
—BLDSC (3286.375000); ADONIS; CASDDS; Faxon; Genuine Article; SWETS; UnCover. **CCC.**
Formerly: Heart.
Description: Studies of clinical science with emphasis on biochemical, physiological and metabolic approaches.
Refereed Serial

610 US ISSN 0009-9295
R11
CLINICAL SYMPOSIA. 1948. 4/yr. $15. Ciba Geigy Corporation, Medical Education & Publications Division, 556 Morris Ave., Summit, NJ 07901. TEL 908-277-4478. FAX 908-277-4478. Ed. Maria Erdelyi-Brown; Pub. Richard Klein. adv.; charts; illus.; circ. 9,000 (paid); 161,600 (controlled). **Indexed:** Biol.Abstr., C.I.N.L., Ind.Med. **Document type:** monographic series.
—BLDSC (3286.399000); UnCover.
Formerly (1950-1956): Ciba Clinical Symposia.

610 US ISSN 0149-2918
RM260 CODEN: CLTHDG
CLINICAL THERAPEUTICS; the international journal of drug therapy. 1978. bi-m. $109 to institutions outside the Americas; $90 to institutions in U.S (effective 1996). Excerpta Medica, Inc., Core Publishing Division (Subsidiary of: Reed Elsevier Medical group), 105 Raider Blvd., Belle Mead, NJ 08502-1510. TEL 908-874-8550.
FAX 908-874-5633. (Subscr. to: Box 3085, Princeton, NJ 08543-3085) Ed. Dr. Arthur Krosnick; Pub. Stan Heimberger. charts; illus.; index. circ. 3,500. **Indexed:** Biol.Abstr., Chem.Abstr., Curr.Adv.Cancer Res., Excerp.Med., Helminthol.Abstr., I.P.A., Ind.Med., Med.& Surg.Dermat., Nutr.Abstr.
—BLDSC (3286.399450); ADONIS; CASDDS; Faxon; Genuine Article; SWETS; UnCover. **CCC.**
Description: Publishes review articles and results of original clinical and pharmacoeconomic research in the broad field of medical and pharmaceutical therapy and related areas.
Refereed Serial

610 616.9 US
CLINICAL TOPICS IN INFECTIOUS DISEASE. 1986. irreg. price varies. Springer-Verlag, 175 Fifth Ave., New York, NY 10010. TEL 212-460-1500.
FAX 212-473-6272. (Also: Berlin, Heidelberg, Tokyo and Vienna) (reprint service avail. from ISI) **Document type:** monographic series.

615 US
CLINICAL TRIALS MONITOR. 1992. 12/yr. $1137 (foreign $1199) (effective 1995). C T B International Publishing Inc., Box 218, Maplewood, NJ 07040-0218. TEL 201-379-7749.
FAX 201-379-1158. Ed. Christopher Brogna; Pub. Oykwe Brogna. index. (back issues avail.) **Document type:** newsletter.
—CCC.
Formerly (until Oct. 1993): Clinical Trials (ISSN 1061-608X)
Description: Intelligence service that tracks clinical trials of human pharmaceuticals, in vivo imaging agents and extracorporeal therapies from beginning to end.

610 SP
CLINICAS DE MEDICINA DE URGENCIAS DE NORTEAMERICA. 4/yr. 13992 ptas. (effective 1990). Interamericana de Espana, S.A., Division de Ciencias de la Salud de McGraw-Hill, Manuel Ferrero, 13, 28036 Madrid, Spain. TEL 315-0340. FAX 733-6627.

610 SP
CLINICAS MEDICAS DE NORTEAMERICA. Spanish translation of: Medical Clinics of North America. 1959. 6/yr. 18126 ptas.($133) (effective 1990). Interamericana de Espana, S.A., Division de Ciencias de la Salud de McGraw-Hill, Calle Manuel Ferrero, 13, 28036 Madrid, Spain. TEL 315-0340. FAX 733-6627. charts; illus.; cum.index.

610 II ISSN 0009-9341
CODEN: CLCNBF
CLINICIAN; monthly journal of medical science and news. (Text in English) 1936. m. $6. Cosme Matias Menezes Pvt. Ltd., Rua de Ourem, P.O. Box 12, Panjim-Goa, India. Ed.Bd. adv.; bk.rev. circ. 5,000. **Indexed:** Chem.Abstr., Curr.Cont., Excerp.Med., Helminthol.Abstr.
—CASDDS.

MEDICAL SCIENCES 4191

610 658 UK ISSN 0965-5751
THE CLINICIAN IN MANAGEMENT. 1992. bi-m. £35($57) to non-member individuals; institutions £71 ($114); members £21.60 (effective 1995). (British Association of Medical Managers) Churchill Livingstone Journals (Subsidiary of: Pearson Professional), Robert Stevenson House, 1-3 Baxter's Pl., Leith Walk, Edinburgh EH1 3AF, Scotland. TEL 0131-556-2424. FAX 0131-459-1177. (Subscr to: Pearson Professional Ltd., P.O. Box 77, Fourth Ave., Harlow, Essex CM19 5AA, England. TEL 01279-623760; U.S. subscr. to: Churchill Livingstone, 650 Ave. of the Americas, New York, NY 10011. TEL 212-206-5000) Ed. Dr. Jenny Simpson. adv. contact: David Dunnachie. bk.rev. circ. 600. **Document type:** newsletter.
—BLDSC (3286.512300).
Description: Offers timely advice to physicians becoming involved in management.

610 US ISSN 1052-0627
CLINICIAN REVIEWS; a journal for physician assistants and nurse practitioners reporting on the latest advances in medicine. 1990. 10/yr. $45 (foreign $70). Clinicians Publishing Group, 4 Brighton Rd., Clifton, NJ 07012. TEL 201-916-1000. FAX 201-916-0021. (Co-publisher: Williams & Wilkins) Ed. Bob DeDonato; Pub. David Mittman. adv.: B&W page $2260, color page $3135; trim 8 1/2 x 10 7/8; adv. contact: Brian Blitz. circ. 500 (paid); 52,000 (controlled). **Document type:** trade publication.
—CCC.
Description: Reports from medical literature and major medical meetings. Also includes review articles of contemporary topics.
Refereed Serial

616.07 CN ISSN 0832-9184
CLINICIEN. 1986. 12/yr. S T A Communications Inc., 955 Boul. St. Jean, Ste. 306, Pointe-Claire, Que. H9R 5K3, Canada. TEL 514-695-7623. FAX 514-695-8554. Ed. Paul Brand. adv. circ. 14,494.

610 FR ISSN 0009-935X
CLINIQUE; * revue du medecin praticien. 1906. m. 100 F. (Societe Medicale des Praticiens) Editions de Medecine Pratique, 4, rue Louis-Armand, 92600 Asnieres, France. bibl.; index. **Indexed:** Ind.Med.
—CCC.

610 NE ISSN 0045-7183
CLIO MEDICA. Variant series title: Wellcome Institute Series in the History of Medicine. (Text in English, French and German) 1966. irreg., vol.25, 1994. price varies. Editions Rodopi B.V., Keizersgracht 302-304, 1016 EX Amsterdam, Netherlands. TEL 31-20-6227507. FAX 31-20-6380948. E-mail: F.van.der.Zee@Rodopi.nl. (In N. America: 233 Peachtree St. N.E., Ste. 404, Atlanta GA 30303-1504. TEL 800-225-3998. FAX 404-522-7116) Eds. W. Bynum, Roy Porter. adv.; bk.rev.; illus.; index. circ. 550. **Indexed:** Amer.Hist.& Life, Biol.Abstr., Hist.Abstr., Ind.Med. **Document type:** academic/scholarly publication.
—BLDSC (3286.650000); SWETS.
Description: Explores all aspects of the history of medicine, including ethical, social and cultural topics.

610 SP
CO M B REVISTA. 12/yr. Colegio Medico de Barcelona, Passeig de la Bonanova 47, 08017 Barcelona, Spain. TEL 3-418-88-88.

610 SP
COLECCION CIENCIAS MEDICAS DE BOLSILLO. 1977. irreg., no.17, 1984. price varies. (Universidad de Navarra, Facultad de Medicina) Ediciones Universidad de Navarra, S.A., Apdo. 396, 31080 Pamplona, Spain. TEL 94 825 6250.

610 SP
COLECCION LIBROS DE MEDICINA. 1974. irreg., no.24, 1989. price varies. (Universidad de Navarra, Facultad de Medicina) Ediciones Universidad de Navarra, S.A., Apdo. 396, 31080 Pamplona, Spain. TEL 94 825 6250.
Formerly: Coleccion Medicina.

610 ES ISSN 0010-0641
COLEGIO MEDICO DE EL SALVADOR. ARCHIVAS. (Text in Spanish; summaries in English) 1947. q. $3.50. Colegio Medico de El Salvador, Final Pasaje 10, Col. Miramonte, San Salvador, El Salvador. Ed. Dr. Ramon Lucio Fernandez. adv.; bibl.; charts; illus.; index. **Indexed:** Biol.Abstr., Ind.Med.

610 SA
COLIMPEX MEDICAL EXECUPAD. (Text in Afrikaans and English) a. free to qualified personnel. Colimpex Africa (Pty) Ltd., P.O. Box 5838, Johannesburg 2000, South Africa. adv.

610 CN
COLLEGE DES MEDECINS DU QUEBEC. ANNUAIRE MEDICAL. a. Can.$58. College des Medecins du Quebec, 2170 boul. Rene-Levesque Ouest, Montreal, PQ H3H 2T8, Canada. TEL 514-933-4441. FAX 514-933-3112. **Document type:** directory.
Formerly: Corporation Professionnelle des Medecins du Quebec. Annuaire Medical (ISSN 0315-226X)
Description: List of physicians appearing on the roll of the Corporation Professionnelle des Medecins du Quebec.

610 CN
COLLEGE DES MEDECINS DU QUEBEC. BULLETIN. 1961. 6/yr. free. College des Medecins du Quebec, 2170 boul. Rene-Levesque Ouest, Montreal, PQ H3H 2T8, Canada. TEL 514-933-4441. FAX 514-933-3112. Ed. Danielle Lapointe. circ. 20,500. **Indexed:** Pt.de Rep. **Document type:** bulletin.
Former titles: Corporation Professionnelle des Medecins du Quebec. Bulletin (ISSN 0315-2979); College des Medecins et Chirurgiens de la Province de Quebec. Bulletin (ISSN 0069-5599)

610 SA ISSN 0375-3220
COLLEGE OF MEDICINE OF SOUTH AFRICA. TRANSACTIONS. (Text and summaries in Afrikaans, English) 1957. s-a. R.15. College of Medicine of South Africa, 17 Milner Rd., Rondebosch, Cape Town 7700, South Africa. TEL 27-21-689-9533. FAX 27-21-685-3766. Ed. P.J. Commerford. adv.; bk.rev.; charts; illus. circ. 5,000. **Indexed:** Biol.Abstr., Ind.S.A.Per. **Document type:** academic/scholarly publication.
—BLDSC (8912.800000).
Formerly: College of Physicians, Surgeons and Gynecologists of South Africa. Transactions (ISSN 0010-1095)

610 CN
COLLEGE OF PHYSICIANS AND SURGEONS OF BRITISH COLUMBIA. ANNUAL REPORT. a. membership. College of Physicians and Surgeons of British Columbia, 1807 W. 10th Ave., Vancouver, B.C. V6J 2A9, Canada. TEL 604-736-5551. **Document type:** directory.

610 CN ISSN 0069-5726
COLLEGE OF PHYSICIANS AND SURGEONS OF BRITISH COLUMBIA. MEDICAL DIRECTORY. a. Can.$48. College of Physicians and Surgeons of British Columbia, 1807 W. 10th Ave., Vancouver, B.C. V6J 2A9, Canada. TEL 604-733-7758. **Document type:** directory.

610 US ISSN 0010-1087
R15 CODEN: TSCPAI
COLLEGE OF PHYSICIANS OF PHILADELPHIA. TRANSACTIONS & STUDIES. 1793. a. $15. College of Physicians of Philadelphia, 19 S. 22nd St., Philadelphia, PA 19103. TEL 215-563-3737. FAX 215-561-6477. circ. 2,300. (also avail. in microfilm from BHP) **Indexed:** Biol.Abstr., Chem.Abstr., Ind.Med. **Document type:** academic/scholarly publication.
—BLDSC (9020.210000); Faxon; UnCover.

610 CK ISSN 0120-8322
COLOMBIA MEDICA. * 1970. 4/yr. Col.$8000($15) Corporacion Editora Medica del Valle, Calle 4B, No 36-00, Cali, Valle Valle, Colombia. TEL 581939. (Co-sponsors: Academia de Medicina del Valle del Cauca; Asociacion Colombiana de Medicina Interna; Sociedad Colombiana de Epidemiologia) Ed. Dr. Francisco Falabella. adv.; bk.rev.; illus.; stat. circ. 2,000. (also avail. in microform from UMI) **Indexed:** Chem.Abstr.
Formerly (until 1980): Acta Medica del Valle (ISSN 0044-6017)
Description: Original research papers and articles in all areas of medicine.

610 US ISSN 0199-7343
R11
COLORADO MEDICINE. 1903. m. $30. Colorado Medical Society, 7800 E. Dorado Pl., Englewood, CO 80111. TEL 303-779-5455. FAX 303-771-8657. (Subscr. to: Box 17550, Denver, CO 80217-0550) Ed. William Pierson; Pub. Sandra Maloney. adv. contact: Michael Thompson. bk.rev.; charts; illus.; tr.lit.; index, cum.index. circ. 5,000. (also avail. in microform from UMI; reprint service avail. from UMI) **Indexed:** Biol.Abstr., C.I.S. Abstr., Chem.Abstr., Curr.Cont., Dent.Ind., Excerp.Med., Ind.Med., Med.Care Rev. **Document type:** trade publication.
—BLDSC (3321.630000); Faxon; UMI; UnCover.
Supersedes in part: Rocky Mountain Medical Journal (ISSN 0035-760X); Formed by the merger of: Colorado Medicine; Utah State Medical Journal.
Refereed Serial

COMMENTATIONES PHYSICO-MATHEMATICAE ET CHEMICO-MEDICAE. see PHYSICS

COMMENTS ON TOXICOLOGY. see ENVIRONMENTAL STUDIES — Toxicology And Environmental Safety

COMMUNITY HEALTH FUNDING REPORT. see PUBLIC ADMINISTRATION

360 UK ISSN 1358-0981
COMMUNITY NURSE. 1977. m. £18.50 to individuals; institutions £37. Macmillan Magazines Ltd., 4 Little Essex St., London WC2R 3LF, England. TEL 0171-836-6633. Ed. Pat Anderson. adv. contact: Charlotte Havard. circ. 17,500 (controlled). **Indexed:** CINAHL. **Document type:** bulletin.
—BLDSC (3363.646515); UnCover. **CCC.**
Formerly (until 1995): Community Outlook (ISSN 1351-1416)

610 US ISSN 1041-116X
COMPARATIVE PATHOLOGY BULLETIN. 1969. q. $15. Registry of Comparative Pathology, Washington, DC 20306-6000. TEL 202-576-2452. FAX 202-576-9161. Ed. Linda Johnson. circ. 1,000. **Document type:** academic/scholarly publication, bulletin.
—BLDSC (3363.793000).
Description: Discusses animal models of human disease; news and devleopments in clinical and comparative pathology.

610 US ISSN 1061-5903
COMPARATIVE STUDIES OF HEALTH SYSTEMS & MEDICAL CARE. 1978. irreg., vol.37, 1993. price varies. University of California Press, 2120 Berkeley Way, Berkeley, CA 94720. TEL 510-642-4247. FAX 510-643-7127. (Orders to: California-Princeton Fulfillment Services, 1445 Lower Ferry Rd., Ewing, NJ 08618. TEL 800-777-4726. FAX 800-999-1958) Ed. John M. Janzen. (back issues avail.) **Document type:** monographic series.
Description: Discusses the past and present Western and Eastern practice of medicine, as well as sociopolitical, ethical, philosophical, and ecological issues.
Refereed Serial

COMPENSATION IN MEDICAL EQUIPMENT MANUFACTURING. see BUSINESS AND ECONOMICS — Labor And Industrial Relations

COMPETITIVE HEALTHCARE MARKET REPORTER. see BUSINESS AND ECONOMICS — Marketing And Purchasing

610 US
▼**COMPETITIVE INSIGHT.** 1994. m. $675. Medical Data International, 2 Park Plaza, Ste. 750, Irvine, CA 92714. TEL 714-251-2780. FAX 714-251-2781. Ed. Joseph A. Miccio. **Document type:** newsletter.

MEDICAL SCIENCES

615 US ISSN 0098-8243
COMPREHENSIVE THERAPY. 1975. m. $159 (foreign $189) (effective 1995). American Society of Contemporary Medicine and Surgery, 4711 W. Golf Rd., Ste. 408, Skokie, IL 60076. TEL 708-568-1500; 800-621-4002. FAX 708-568-1527. Eds. Randall T. Bellows, David A. Bellows. bk.rev.; circ. 1,400 (paid). **Indexed:** Biol.Abstr., CINAHL, Dent.Ind., Excerp.Med. (until 1990; 1995-), Ind.Med., INIS Atomind., Lang.& Lang.Behav.Abstr., NRN. **Document type:** academic/scholarly publication.
—BLDSC (3366.390700); EMDOCS; Faxon; SWETS; UnCover.
  Description: Each issue focues on a single subject such as endocrinology, neuropsychiatry, pediatrics, cancer and cardiovascular disease.
  Refereed Serial

615.8 FR ISSN 0293-9908
CODEN: CRTCD9
COMPTES RENDUS DE THERAPEUTIQUE ET DE PHARMACOLOGIE CLINIQUE. 1982. m. (11/yr.). 200 F. (students 130 F. foreign 360 F.). D & D Medical, 6 rue Emile Verhaeren, B.P. 4 92210 Saint-Cloud, France. TEL 1-47-71-27-18. FAX 1-46-02-72-55. Ed. Serge Dard. adv.; bk.rev. circ. 3,500. **Indexed:** Chem.Abstr., Excerp.Med.
—CASDDS. **CCC.**

COMPUTERS IN BIOLOGY AND MEDICINE; an international journal. see *BIOLOGY — Computer Applications*

COMUNICACIONES BIOLOGICAS. see *BIOLOGY*

610 US
CONCERN (ANAHEIM). 1984. 4/yr. $15 to non-members (foreign $25). Society of Critical Care Medicine, 8101 E. Kaiser Blvd., Anaheim, CA 92808-2214. TEL 714-282-6000. FAX 714-282-6050. Ed. Deborah Kincade-Branch. adv. circ. 6,000. (back issues avail.)
  Description: Non-scientific articles and activities of the Society's members.

610 FR ISSN 0010-5309
CODEN: COMEAO
CONCOURS MEDICAL. 1879. 40/yr. 640 F. 37 rue de Bellefond, 75441 Paris Cedex 09, France. TEL 45-96-32-00. FAX 40-16-80-83. Ed. Dr. Francois Mignon. adv.; bk.rev.; bibl.; charts; illus.; index. circ. 70,000. **Indexed:** Biol.Abstr., C.I.S. Abstr., Chem.Abstr., Excerp.Med. (until 1993), Ind.Med., INIS Atomind.
—BLDSC (3399.480000); SWETS. **CCC.**

616.043 JA ISSN 0914-3505
CODEN: CGANE7
CONGENITAL ANOMALIES. (Text in English) 1960. q. 8000 Yen($80) (effective 1995). Nihon Senten Ijo Gakkai - Japanese Teratology Society, Kinki University School of Medicine, Osaka-Sayama-shi, Osaka 589, Japan. TEL 0723-66-0221. FAX 0723-66-0206. Ed. Mineo Yasuda. adv. contact: Fukuda Shouten. bk.rev.; abstr.; bibl.; charts; illus.; index. circ. 1,700. (processed) **Indexed:** Biol.Abstr., Chem.Abstr., Excerp.Med. **Document type:** academic/scholarly publication.
—BLDSC (3410.683000); CASDDS.
  Former titles (until 1987): Senten Ijo (ISSN 0037-2285); (until 1963): Nihon Senten Ijo Gakkai Kaiho.
  Description: Reports studies in all areas of abnormal development and related fields.
  Refereed Serial

610 US ISSN 0010-6178
CONNECTICUT MEDICINE. 1936. m. $25 (foreign $40). Connecticut State Medical Society, 160 St. Ronan St., New Haven, CT 06511. TEL 203-865-0587. FAX 203-865-4997. Ed. Dr. Robert U. Massey. adv.; bk.rev.; bibl.; illus.; index. circ. 6,500. **Indexed:** Biol.Abstr., C.I.S.Abstr., Chem.Abstr., CINAHL, Curr.Cont., Dent.Ind., Excerp.Med., Ind.Med., INIS Atomind., Med.Care Rev. **Document type:** directory, newsletter.
—BLDSC (3417.655000); Faxon; SWETS; UnCover.
  Formerly (1940-1958): Connecticut State Medical Journal (ISSN 0096-0179)

CONNECTIONS (LARGO). see *HOSPITALS*

610 JA ISSN 0916-572X
CODEN: COTIE7
CONNECTIVE TISSUE. (Text in English, Japanese; summaries in English) 1969. q. Nihon Ketsugo Soshiki Gakkai - Japanese Society for Connective Tissue Research, Tokyo Ika Daigaku Byorigaku Kyoshitsu, 1-1, Shinjuku 6-chome, Shinjukuku, Tokyo 160, Japan. **Indexed:** Chem.Abstr., Excerp.Med. **Document type:** academic/scholarly publication.
—BLDSC (3417.663800); CASDDS.

610 US ISSN 0010-7069
R11
CONSULTANT (GREENWICH). 1961. 12/yr. $70. Cliggott Publishing Co., 55 Holly Hill Ln., Box 4010, Greenwich, CT 06830. TEL 203-661-0600. Ed. Charles F. Williams; Pub. Kenneth A. Sylvia. adv. contact: David S. March. charts; illus. circ. 129,800. (also avail. in microform from UMI; reprint service avail. from UMI) **Indexed:** C.I.N.L., Hlth.Ind., Tr.& Indus.Ind. **Document type:** academic/scholarly publication.
—BLDSC (3423.760000); Faxon; UMI; UnCover. **CCC.**
  Description: Practical clinical information on diagnosis and therapy.
  Refereed Serial

615.8 FR ISSN 0751-7718
CONSULTATION. 1983. m. (11/yr.). 200 F. (students 130 F.; foreign 360 F.). D & D Medical, 6 rue Emile Verhaeren, B.P. 4 92210 Saint-Cloud, France. TEL 1-47-71-27-18. FAX 1-46-02-72-55. Ed. S. Dard. adv. circ. 33,500.
—**CCC.**

610 JO ISSN 0254-7147
CONSULTING MEDICAL LABORATORIES. BULLETIN. (Text in English) 1983. q. $25. Consulting Medical Laboratories, P.O. Box 35198, Amman, Jordan. FAX 962-6-644414. TELEX 21207 JOR HTL JO. Ed. Yahia F. Dajani. circ. 2,000. (back issues avail.) **Document type:** bulletin.

CONTACT. see *RELIGIONS AND THEOLOGY*

610 CN
CONTACT (OTTAWA, 1974). (Text in English, French) 1974. 4/yr. Canadian College of Health Service Executives, 350 Sparks St., Ste. 402, Ottawa, ON K1R 7S8, Canada. TEL 613-235-7218. FAX 613-235-5451. Ed. Danielle Sarazin. adv.: B&W page Can.$1100; trim 8 1/2 x 11. circ. 3,500.

610 US ISSN 0886-8220
CONTRIBUTIONS IN MEDICAL STUDIES. 1978. irreg., no.36, 1992. price varies. Greenwood Press, Inc. (Subsidiary of: Greenwood Publishing Group Inc.), 88 Post Rd. W., Box 5007, Westport, CT 06881-5007. TEL 203-226-3571. FAX 203-222-1502. Ed. John Burnham.
—BLDSC (3459.900000).
  Formerly: Contributions in Medical History (ISSN 0147-1058)

612 SZ ISSN 0301-4193
CODEN: CHDEDZ
CONTRIBUTIONS TO HUMAN DEVELOPMENT. (Text in English) 1962. irreg. (approx. 1/yr.). price varies. S. Karger AG, Allschwilerstr. 10, CH-4009 Basel, Switzerland. TEL 061-3061111. FAX 061-3061234. E-mail: Karger@Karger.ch. Ed. D. Kuhn. (reprint service avail. from ISI) **Indexed:** Biol.Abstr., Chem.Abstr., Curr.Cont., Ind.Med., Psychol.Abstr. **Document type:** academic/scholarly publication.
—BLDSC (3458.630000). **CCC.**
  Formerly: Bibliotheca Vita Humana.
  Refereed Serial

610 365 US
CORHEALTH. 1975. bi-m. $45. American Correctional Health Services Association, Box 2307, Dayton, OH 45401-2307. TEL 513-223-9630. FAX 513-223-6307. Ed. H.A. Rosefield. adv.; bk.rev. circ. 1,700.
  Description: Covers health care in correctional institutions.

610 378 US
CORNELL UNIVERSITY MEDICAL COLLEGE ALUMNI MAGAZINE. vol.41, 1978. q. free. Cornell University Medical College, 1300 York Ave., New York, NY 10021. TEL 212-746-6546. Eds. C. Richard Minick, Thomas McGovern. adv.; bk.rev.; illus. circ. 9,000. **Document type:** bulletin.
  Former titles (until 1993): Cornell University Medical College Alumni Quarterly (ISSN 0010-8898); Cornell University Medical College Alumni Bulletin.

610 US
CORNHUSKER FAMILY PHYSICIAN. q. $5. Nebraska Academy of Family Physicians, 7101 Newport Ave., No. 201, Omaha, NE 68152-2158. TEL 402-572-3530. FAX 402-572-3532. Ed. Dr. David H. Filipi. adv.; circ. 3,000 (controlled). **Document type:** trade publication.

610 GW ISSN 0070-0347
R126.A1
CORPUS MEDICORUM GRAECORUM. 1958. irreg., vol.11, 1992. price varies. Akademie Verlag GmbH, Muehlenstr. 33-34, 13187 Berlin, Germany. TEL 030-47889348. FAX 030-47889357. (Co-sponsors: Koenigliche Daenische Akademie; Saechsische Akademie der Wissenschaften, Leipzig) **Document type:** monographic series.

610 US
CORRECTIONAL HEALTH CARE MANAGEMENT. 1993. m. $189. American Health Consultants, Inc., Six Piedmont Center, Ste. 400, Atlanta, GA 30305. TEL 404-262-7436; 800-688-2421. FAX 800-284-3291. Ed. Gilbert Kulers. circ. 405. **Document type:** newsletter.
  Description: Practical management and clinical information for correctional health care administrators.

610 IT
CORRIERE MEDICO. 104/yr. R C S Editoriale Quotidiani S.p.A., Via Solferino 28, 20121 Milan, Italy. TEL 2-63-39. circ. 75,000.

610 US ISSN 1048-5791
CORTLANDT FORUM. m. $60. Cortlandt Group, Inc., 500 Executive Blvd., Ste. 302, Ossining, NY 10562. TEL 914-762-0647. FAX 914-762-8820.

610 668.5 US
COSMETIC SCIENCE AND TECHNOLOGY SERIES. 1984. irreg., vol.13, 1994. price varies. Marcel Dekker, Inc., 270 Madison Ave., New York, NY 10016. TEL 212-696-9000. FAX 212-685-4540. TELEX 421419. Ed. Eric Jungerman.
  Refereed Serial

338.4 610.6 US ISSN 1064-4571
R729.5.G6
COST SURVEY. Cover title: Cost Survey Report. 1970. a. $210. Medical Group Management Association, 104 Inverness Terrace E., Enlgewood, CO 80112. TEL 303-799-1111. Ed.Bd. charts; stat. circ. 10,000. (back issues avail.) **Indexed:** SRI.

610 SZ
COURRIER DU MEDECIN VAUDOIS. 10/yr. Route d'Oron 1, Case Postale 76, CH-1010 Lausanne 10, Switzerland. TEL 021-6529932. FAX 021-6523221. circ. 2,500. **Document type:** academic/scholarly publication.

616 US ISSN 0886-9634
CODEN: CRANEG
CRANIO: JOURNAL OF CRANIOMANDIBULAR PRACTICE. 1982. q. $65 to individuals (foreign $88); institutions $97 (foreign $117). Chroma Inc., Box 8887, Chatanooga, TN 37414. TEL 800-624-4141. FAX 615-490-0791. Dr. Riley H. Lunn. adv. contact: Janice McKinney. bk.rev. circ. 4,500. (also avail. in microform from PMC) **Indexed:** Curr.Tit.Dent., Dent.Abstr., Dent.Ind., Excerp.Med. **Document type:** academic/scholarly publication.
—BLDSC (3487.046400); Faxon; Genuine Article; SWETS; UnCover.
  Formerly (until 1985): Journal of Craniomandibular Practice (ISSN 0734-5410)
  Description: Discusses diagnosis and treatment of craniomandibular disorders for dentists, physicians and physical therapists.
  Refereed Serial

MEDICAL SCIENCES

610 US ISSN 1067-9502
CRITICAL CARE ALERT. 1993. m. $158. American Health Consultants, Inc., Six Piedmont Center, Ste. 400, Atlanta, GA 30305. TEL 404-262-7436; 800-688-2421. FAX 800-284-3291. Ed. Dr. David Pierson. circ. 720. **Document type:** newsletter.

610 US ISSN 0749-0704
RC86 CODEN: CCCLEH
CRITICAL CARE CLINICS. 1985. q. $120 (foreign $145) (effective 1996). W.B. Saunders Co. (Subsidiary of: Harcourt Brace & Company), Curtis Center, 3rd Fl., Independence Sq. W., Philadelphia, PA 19106-3399. TEL 215-238-7800. FAX 215-238-6445. (Subscr. to: Periodicals Fulfillment, W.B. Saunders Co., 6277 Sea Harbor Dr., 4th Fl., Orlando, FL 32891-4800. TEL 800-654-2452. FAX 800-874-6418) Ed. Helaine Barron. circ. 3,650. (also avail. in microfilm; back issues avail.) **Indexed:** CINAHL, Excerp.Med. **Document type:** academic/scholarly publication.
—BLDSC (3487.450700); Faxon; Genuine Article; SWETS; UMI; UnCover. **CCC.**

610 US ISSN 1070-4523
CRITICAL CARE MANAGEMENT. 1993. m. $219. American Health Consultants, Inc., Six Piedmont Center, Ste. 400, Atlanta, GA 30305. TEL 404-262-7436; 800-688-2421. FAX 800-284-3291. Ed. Kent Anderson. circ. 170. **Document type:** newsletter.

610 US ISSN 0090-3493
RC86 CODEN: CCMDC7
CRITICAL CARE MEDICINE. 1973. m. $109 to individuals; institutions $169 (effective 1995). (Society of Critical Care Medicine) Williams & Wilkins, 428 E. Preston St., Baltimore, MD 21202. TEL 410-528-4000; 800-638-6423. FAX 410-528-4312. Ed. Dr. Bart Chernow. illus. circ. 11,000. (also avail. in microfilm from WWS) **Indexed:** Abstr.Health Care Manage.Stud., AIM, CINAHL, Curr.Adv.Ecol.Sci., Curr.Cont., Excerp.Med., Ind.Med., Ind.Sci.Rev., INIS Atomind., Kidney, Sci.Cit.Ind. **Document type:** academic/scholarly publication.
—BLDSC (3487.451000); EMDOCS; Faxon; Genuine Article; SWETS; UnCover. **CCC.**
Description: Provides mulitdisciplinary coverage of all aspects of acute and emergency care for hospital-based specialists, including anaesthesiologists and critical-care nurses.
Refereed Serial

CRITICAL REVIEWS IN BIOMEDICAL ENGINEERING. see BIOLOGY — Bioengineering

616.07 610.28 US ISSN 1040-8363
RB37 CODEN: CRCLBH
CRITICAL REVIEWS IN CLINICAL LABORATORY SCIENCES. 1970. q. $90 to individuals; institutions $420. C R C Press, Inc., 2000 Corporate Blvd., N.W., Boca Raton, FL 33431. TEL 407-994-0555; 800-272-7737. FAX 407-998-9784. TELEX 568689-CRC PRESS. Eds. Drs. John Batsakis, John Savory. bibl.; charts; illus. circ. 530. (back issues avail.) **Indexed:** Biol.Abstr., Chem.Abstr., Curr.Cont., Dent.Ind., Helminthol.Abstr., Ind.Med., Ind.Sci.Rev., INIS Atomind., Nutr.Abstr., Sci.Cit.Ind. **Document type:** academic/scholarly publication.
—BLDSC (3487.473000); ADONIS; CASDDS; Faxon; Genuine Article; SWETS; UnCover. **CCC.**
Formerly: C R C Critical Reviews in Clinical Laboratory Sciences (ISSN 0590-8191)
Description: Provides critical evaluations of new concepts, methods, and data in the biomedical fields.
Refereed Serial

610 GW ISSN 0353-9504
CODEN: CMEJE
CROATIAN MEDICAL JOURNAL. (Text and summaries in English) 1953-1976 (vol.24); resumed, vol.25, 1984. 4/yr. DM.120($80) (Sveuciliste u Zagrebu, Medicinski Fakultet, Cl - University of Zagreb, Medical School) Pabst Science Publishers, Am Eichengrund 28, 49525 Lengerich, Germany. TEL 05484-308. FAX 05484-550. Eds. Ana Marusic, Matko Marusic. adv.; bk.rev.; charts; illus.; index. **Indexed:** Biol.Abstr., Chem.Abstr., Excerp.Med., ExtraMED, Ind.Med. **Document type:** academic/scholarly publication.
●Also available on CD-ROM.
—BLDSC (3487.498200). **CCC.**
Formerly (until 1992): Sveuciliste u Zagrebu. Medicinski Fakultet. Radovi (ISSN 0033-8575)

610 EC
CUADERNOS DE SALUD COLECTIVA. 1990. q. $10. Centro de Estudios y Asesoria en Salud, Calle Roca 549, Dpto. 602, Quito, Ecuador. TEL 593-2-506175. FAX 593-2-566714. (Co-sponsor: Panamerican Health Organization) Ed. Dr. Jose Yepez. bk.rev.; bibl.; illus.

610 500 SP ISSN 0011-2577
CUADERNOS VALENCIANOS DE HISTORIA DE LA MEDICINA Y DE LA CIENCIA. (Text in Spanish and classical languages) 1962. irreg. (2-3/yr.). price varies. Universidad de Valencia, C.S.I.C., Instituto de Estudios Documentales e Historicos sobre la Ciencia, Avda. Blasco Ibanez 17, Valencia 10, Spain. FAX 96-331-39-75. Dir. Jose Maria Lopez Pinero. charts; illus. circ. 500. (reprint service avail.) **Document type:** monographic series.
—CCC.

CULTURE, ILLNESS AND HEALING; studies in comparative cross-cultural research. see ANTHROPOLOGY

CULTURE, MEDICINE AND PSYCHIATRY; an international journal of comparative cross-cultural research. see ANTHROPOLOGY

616.97 US ISSN 0160-1660
CUMITECHS. (Cumulative Techniques and Procedures in Clinical Microbiology) 1974. irreg. (2-3/yr.). $12 to non-members; members $$9. American Society for Microbiology, 1325 Massachusetts Ave., N.W., Washington, DC 20005. TEL 703-787-3305. Ed. Steven C. Specter. **Indexed:** Diar.Dis.Res.
—CCC.

610 IT ISSN 0391-8904
CUORE E VASI. 10/yr. L.25000($25) C I C Edizioni Internazionali s.r.l., Via L. Spallanzani, 11, 00161 Rome, Italy. TEL 06-8412673. FAX 06-44242033. TELEX 622099 CIC.

CURRENT ADVANCES IN CLINICAL CHEMISTRY. see CHEMISTRY — Abstracting, Bibliographies, Statistics

610 574 UK
CURRENT AWARENESS. S D I SERVICE. (Text in English, French, German and Italian) 1963. w. £20. Scientific Documentation Centre Ltd., Halbeath House, Dunfermline, Fife KY12 0TZ, Scotland. TEL 01383-723535. FAX 01383-723535.
Formerly (until 1967): Spectra Index and S D C Bulletin.

616.4 NE ISSN 0168-6917
CODEN: CCPSEZ
CURRENT CLINICAL PRACTICE. 1982. irreg., vol.65, 1993. price varies. Elsevier Science B.V., Books Division, P.O. Box 211, 1000 AE Amsterdam, Netherlands. TEL 31-20-4853911. FAX 31-20-4853705. TELEX 18582 ESPA NL. E-mail: nlinfo-f@elsevier.nl; usinfo-f@elsevier.com; forinfo-kyf04035@niftyserve.or.jp; Site addr.: http://www.elsevier.nl/. (Subscr. in U.S. and Canada to: Elsevier Science Inc., Box 882, Madison Sq. Sta., New York, NY 10159. TEL 212-989-5800) (back issues avail.) **Document type:** monographic series.
—BLDSC (3496.055700); CASDDS. **CCC.**
Refereed Serial

610 US ISSN 0092-8682
RC71
CURRENT MEDICAL DIAGNOSIS AND TREATMENT. 1962. a. price varies. Appleton & Lange (Subsidiary of: Simon & Schuster Company), 25 Van Zant St., Box 5630, Norwalk, CT 06856. TEL 203-838-4400. Ed.Bd.
—BLDSC (3500.220000). **CCC.**
Formerly: Current Diagnosis and Treatment.

610 II ISSN 0011-3700
CODEN: CMDPAW
CURRENT MEDICAL PRACTICE. 1956. m. Rps.50($15) Current Technical Literature Co. Pvt. Ltd., Malhotra House, P.O. Box 1374, Bombay 1, India. Ed. B.S. Singhal. adv.; bk.rev.; abstr.; illus. circ. 2,500. (also avail. in microform from UMI; reprint service avail. from UMI) **Indexed:** Biol.Abstr., Chem.Abstr.
—BLDSC (3500.280000); CASDDS; UMI.

610 615 UK ISSN 0300-7995
CODEN: CMROCX
CURRENT MEDICAL RESEARCH AND OPINION. (Supplement avail. (ISSN 0141-9951)) 1972. irreg. $60. Clayton-Wray Publications Ltd., 1A High St., Alton, Hants GU34 1BA, England. TEL 0420-87293. Ed. N.B. Clayton. index. circ. 6,000. (also avail. in microform from UMI; back issues avail.; reprint service avail. from UMI) **Indexed:** Abstr.Hyg., Biotech.Abstr., Chem.Abstr., Curr.Adv.Ecol.Sci., Curr.Cont., Excerp.Med., Helminthol.Abstr., Ind.Med., Ind.Sci.Rev., NRN, Nutr.Abstr., Rev.Med.& Vet.Mycol., Rev.Plant Path., Sci.Cit.Ind., Trop.Dis.Bull.
—BLDSC (3500.301000); CASDDS; Genuine Article; SWETS; UMI; UnCover.

CURRENT MEDICINAL CHEMISTRY. see CHEMISTRY

610 UK ISSN 0953-9352
CURRENT MEDICINE. 1988. a. Royal College of Physicians of Edinburgh, 9 Queen St., Edinburgh EH2 1JQ, Scotland. TEL 0131-225-7324. FAX 0131-220-3939. **Document type:** academic/scholarly publication.

610 US ISSN 0011-393X
CODEN: CTCEA9
CURRENT THERAPEUTIC RESEARCH; clinical and experimental. 1960. m. $136 to institutions outside the Americas; $120 to institutions in U.S (effective 1996). Excerpta Medica, Inc., Core Publishing Division (Subsidiary of: Reed Elsevier Medical group), 105 Raider Blvd., Belle Mead, NJ 08502-1510. TEL 908-874-8550. FAX 908-874-5611. (Subscr. to: Box 3085, Princeton, NJ 08543-3085) Ed. Charles R. Ream; Pub. Stan Heimberger. circ. 1,500. **Indexed:** Biotech.Abstr., Chem.Abstr., Curr.Adv.Ecol.Sci., Curr.Cont., Dairy Sci.Abstr., Excerp.Med., Helminthol.Abstr., I.P.A., Ind.Sci.Rev., Int.Nurs.Ind., Nutr.Abstr., Psychol.Abstr. (1964-), Rev.Med.& Vet.Mycol., Rev.Plant Path., Sci.Cit.Ind., Sugar Ind.Abstr.
—BLDSC (3504.600000); ADONIS; CASDDS; Faxon; Genuine Article; SWETS; UnCover. **CCC.**
Description: Publishes results of original research in the broad field of medical and pharmaceutical therapy and related areas.
Refereed Serial

610 US ISSN 0732-4448
R97 CODEN: CGMSDD
CURRENT TOPICS IN CHINESE SCIENCE. SECTION G: MEDICAL SCIENCE. 1982. irreg., vol.3, 1984. Gordon & Breach Science Publishers, c/o International Publishers Distributor, 820 Town Center Dr., Langhorne, PA 19047. TEL 215-750-2642. FAX 215-750-6343. (Subscr. to: International Science Publishers, P.O. Box 90, Reading, Berkshire RG1 8JL, England. TEL 44-173-456-8316) (also avail. in microfilm; microfiche) **Document type:** monographic series.
Refereed Serial

616.07 574.2 US ISSN 0070-2188
CODEN: CTPHBG
CURRENT TOPICS IN PATHOLOGY. irreg. price varies. Springer-Verlag, 175 Fifth Ave., New York, NY 10010. TEL 212-460-1500. FAX 212-473-6272. (Also: Berlin, Heidelberg, Tokyo and Vienna) (also avail. in microform from PMC; reprint service avail. from ISI) **Indexed:** Biol.Abstr., Chem.Abstr., Ind.Med., Ind.Vet., Vet.Bull. **Document type:** monographic series.
—BLDSC (3504.895000); CASDDS; Faxon; SWETS. **CCC.**
Formerly: Ergebnisse der Allgemeinen Pathologie und Pathologischen Anatomie.

615.9 IT ISSN 1122-3804
CODEN: CTOTEG
CURRENTS IN TOXICOLOGY AND THERAPY. 1993. 3/yr. L.50000 (foreign L.100000) (effective 1994). C E M Casa Editoriale Maccari, Via Trento 53, 43100 Parma, Italy. TEL 39-521-771268. circ. 1,200. **Indexed:** Excerp.Med. (1994-).
—CASDDS.

610 IE
CYSTIC FIBROSIS NEWS. 1979. m. Cystic Fibrosis Association of Ireland, Dublin, Ireland. **Indexed:** Curr.Adv.Ecol.Sci.

MEDICAL SCIENCES

616.37   DK   ISSN 0901-4500
CYSTISK FIBROSE. 1980. 4/yr. free. Landsforeningen til Bekaempelse af Cystisk Fibrose - Danish Cystic Fibrosis Association, Hyrdebakken 246, DK-8800 Viborg, Denmark. TEL 45-86-67-44-22. FAX 45-86-67-66-66. adv.; illus. circ. 1,300.
    Formerly (until 1985): Hej (ISSN 0108-5409)

CYTOBIOS; a prestige international biomedical research journal of cell biology. see BIOLOGY — Cytology And Histology

CYTOGENETICS AND CELL GENETICS. see BIOLOGY — Genetics

CYTOKINES. see BIOLOGY — Microbiology

610   GW
D G F MITTEILUNGSBLATT. q. Deutsche Gesellschaft fuer Fachkrankenpflege e.V., Langenbeckstr. 1, 55131 Mainz, Germany. TEL 173237.

610   DK   ISSN 0108-7320
D I M S BULLETIN. 1981. 3/yr. free. Dansk Idraetsmedicinsk Selskab, Idraettens Hus, Broendby Stadion, DK-2605 Broendby, Denmark. Ed. Jens H. Kristensen. adv.; bk.rev.

610   SZ
D JOURNAL. (Diabetes) 1974. 6/yr. 30 SFr. (foreign 36 SFr.). Schweizerische Diabetes Gesellschaft, Postfach 610, CH-8025 Zurich, Switzerland. TEL 01-2616650. FAX 01-2625745. adv.: B&W page 1510 SFr., color page 3230 SFr.; trim 195 x 260. bk.rev. circ. 19,000. **Document type:** academic/scholarly publication.

D R G HANDBOOK; comparative clinical and financial standards. (Diagnosis Related Group) see HOSPITALS

D W D NEWSLETTER. (Dying with Dignity) see LAW

610   SG   ISSN 0850-797X
DAKAR MEDICAL. 1956. s-a. 20000 Fr.CFA. Societe Medicale d'Afrique Noire de Langue Francaise - Medical Society of the French Speaking Zone of Black Africa, B.P. 450, Dakar, Senegal. Ed. Mansour Ndiaye. adv.; bk.rev.; illus. circ. 1,300. **Indexed:** Abstr.Hyg., Biol.Abstr., Dent.Ind., Excerp.Med., ExtraMED, Helminthol.Abstr., Ind.Med., Rev.Plant Path., Trop.Dis.Bull. **Document type:** bulletin.
●Also available on CD-ROM.
—UnCover.
    Former titles (until 1980): Societe Medicale d'Afrique Noire de Langue Francaise. Bulletin (ISSN 0049-1101); (until 1959): A.O.F. Bulletin Medical.

610   CC   ISSN 1000-5676
DALIAN YIXUEYUAN XUEBAO/DALIAN MEDICAL COLLEGE. JOURNAL OF MEDICINE. (Text in Chinese) 1960. q. $20. Dalian Yixueyuan - Dalian Medical College, 465 Zhongshan Lu, Dalian, Liaoning 116023, People's Republic of China. TEL 24-0411-491802. Ed. Jin Yongxi. **Document type:** academic/scholarly publication.

610   UA
DALIL AL-AHRAM AL-TIBBI/AL-AHRAM MEDICAL GUIDE. 1989. a. Mu'assasat al-Ahram, Sharia al-Galaa, Cairo, Egypt. TEL 02-758333. FAX 02-745888. TELEX 92001.

610   US   ISSN 0011-586X
DALLAS MEDICAL JOURNAL. 1914. m. $36 membership. Dallas County Medical Society, Box 4680, Sta. A, Dallas, TX 75208. TEL 214-948-3622. FAX 214-946-5805. Ed. Amy VanVleck. adv. circ. 4,000. **Indexed:** Ind.Med. **Document type:** academic/scholarly publication.

DANCE AUSTRALIA. see DANCE

610   IR
DANESHKADE PEZESHKI. 1947. 10/yr. Teheran Medical Sciences University, Faculty of Medicine, Enghelab Ave., Teheran 14-714, Iran. TEL 021-6112743. Ed. Hassan Arefi. adv. circ. 1,500.

610   DK   ISSN 0907-8916
                       CODEN: DMBUAE
DANISH MEDICAL BULLETIN. 1954. irreg. (6-8/yr.). DKK 250 (free to medical institutions on request). Almindelige Danske Laegeforening - Danish Medical Association, Trondhjemsgade 9, DK-2100 Copenhagen, Denmark. TEL 31-385500. (Subscr. to: Laegeforeningens Forlag, Esplanaden 8 A, DK-1263 Copenhagen K, Denmark) Eds. John Christiansen, Erik Juhl. adv.; charts; illus. circ. 5,300. (also avail. in microform from UMI,PMC; reprint service avail. from UMI) **Indexed:** Abstr.Hyg., Biol.Abstr., Chem.Abstr., Curr.Adv.Cancer Res., Curr.Adv.Ecol.Sci., Curr.Adv.Genetics & Molec.Biol., Curr.Cont., Dairy Sci.Abstr., Diar.Dis.Res., Excerp.Med., Ind.Med., Ind.Sci.Rev., Med.& Surg.Dermat., NRN, Nutr.Abstr., Rehabil.Lit., Risk Abstr., Sci.Cit.Ind., Trop.Dis.Bull. **Document type:** bulletin.
—BLDSC (3519.400000); CASDDS; Faxon; Genuine Article; SWETS; UMI; UnCover.
    Former titles (until 1992): D M B (Danish Medical Bulletin) (ISSN 0011-6092); (until 1975): Danish Medical Bulletin (ISSN 0901-6929)

610   DK   ISSN 0084-9588
R539
DANSK MEDICINHISTORISK AARBOG/YEARBOOK OF DANISH MEDICAL HISTORY. (Text in Danish; summaries in English) 1972. a. DKK 130. Medical History Societies in Denmark, H.P. Hanssensgade 42, DK-6200 Aabenraa, Denmark. Ed. Tage Grodum. adv. circ. 900. **Indexed:** NAA.

610   TZ   ISSN 0856-0099
DAR ES SALAAM MEDICAL JOURNAL. 1969. s-a. University of Dar es Salaam, Faculty of Medicine, Nuhimbili Medical Centre, P.O. Box 65007, Dar es Salaam, Tanzania. (Co-sponsor: Association of Dar es Salaam Medical Students) Ed. Ernest Komba. adv.; bk.rev.; bibl.; illus. **Indexed:** Biol.Abstr. **Document type:** academic/scholarly publication.

610 378   US
DARTMOUTH MEDICINE. 1976. q. free to qualified personnel. Dartmouth Medical School, Hanover, NH 03756. TEL 603-650-4058. FAX 603-650-4041. E-mail: DartMed@Dartmorth.edu. Ed. Dana Cook Grossman. adv.; bk.rev.; charts; illus. circ. 22,000. (back issues avail.)
    Formerly: Dartmouth Medical School Alumni Magazine.

610   US   ISSN 0742-7484
DATA CENTRUM. 1984. m. $32 (free to qualified personnel). Whitmore Jenson Publishers, 100 Greene St., New York, NY 10012-3813. TEL 212-586-4287. Ed. Stu Chapman. adv. circ. 127,500.

610   LH   ISSN 0011-7005
DATENJOURNAL. (Text and summaries in English and German) 1969. q. 80 Fr. (International Society for Prospective Medicine) Mecudo Aktiengesellschaft, Vaduz, Liechtenstein. (Subscr. to: Dr. Josef Schmid, Walfischgasse 10, 1010 Vienna, Austria) adv.; abstr.; bibl.; charts; illus.; stat. circ. 2,000. (tabloid format; also avail. in cards) **Indexed:** Biol.Abstr.
    Description: Features latest in medical electronics.

610   CC   ISSN 1000-8470
RC81.A1
DAZHONG YIXUE/POPULAR MEDICINE. (Text in Chinese) 1948. m. $1 per no. Shanghai Scientific and Technical Publishers, Journal Department, 450 Ruijin 2 Lu, Shanghai 200020, People's Republic of China. (Dist. outside China by: China International Book Trading Corp., P.O. Box 399, Beijing, P.R.C.)

610   BE   ISSN 0931-8305
DE NATURA RERUM; international medical review for documentation and information. (Text in English, French, German, Italian and Spanish) q. DM.74 to individuals; students DM.52. (C.E.I.A. Benelux) Editions Haug International, Chaussee de Ninove 1072, 1080 Brussels, Belgium. Ed. Dr. Eric Reymond. **Document type:** academic/scholarly publication.

610   US
DEAR DOCTOR; written by health-care professionals for your family's well-being. 1989. bi-m. $27 (foreign $30). Dear Doctor, Inc., Rt. 6, Box 81, Brewster, NY 10509. TEL 914-279-7510. Ed. Marion Roach.

610 016   GW   ISSN 0178-3351
DEGUO YIXUE/DEUTSCHE MEDIZIN; an international journal. (Text in Chinese) q. DM.98($71) (effective 1996). Heidelberger Platz 3, 14197 berlin, Germany. TEL 030-8207-1. FAX 030-8214091. (Subscr. in N. America to: Springer-Verlag New York, Inc., 44 Hartz Way, Secaucus, NJ 07096-2491. TEL 201-348-4033. FAX 201-348-4505) Ed. Dr. Quiu Fazu. **Document type:** academic/scholarly publication.
—CCC.
    Description: Selected articles from German medical periodicals.

610   US   ISSN 0011-7781
DELAWARE MEDICAL JOURNAL. 1929. m. $25 (foreign $35). Medical Society of Delaware, 1925 Lovering Ave., Wilmington, DE 19806-2147. TEL 302-658-7596. FAX 302-658-9669. Eds. Dr. E. Wayne Martz, Heidi Norman. adv.; bk.rev.; bibl.; illus.; index. circ. 1,600. (also avail. in microfilm from UMI; reprint service avail. from UMI) **Indexed:** Chem.Abstr., Curr.Cont., Ind.Med., INIS Atomind. **Document type:** academic/scholarly publication.
—BLDSC (3547.500000); Faxon; SWETS; UMI.
    Refereed Serial

610   II   ISSN 0011-7854
DELHI MEDICAL JOURNAL. (Text in English) vol.4, 1969. s-a. Rs.4. Delhi Medical Association, House Daryaganj, Delhi 6, India. Ed. Dr. Kili Tuli. adv.; abstr.; charts.

DEMETER KONGRESS KALENDER MEDIZIN. see MEETINGS AND CONGRESSES

610.711489   DK   ISSN 0108-9781
DENMARK. SUNDHEDSSTYRELSEN. KURSUSOVERSIGT; specialistnaevnets udvalg for den teoretiske videreuddanelse. 1982. a. DKK 45. Sundhedsstyrelsen, P.O. Box 2020, DK-1012 Copenhagen K, Denmark. (Orders to: Danske Boghandleres Kommissionsanstalt, Siljangade 6, 2300 Copenhagen S, Denmark)

610   US   ISSN 0098-471X
DETROIT MEDICAL NEWS. w. $40 (effective Jan. 1991). Wayne County Medical Society, 1010 Antietam, Detroit, MI 48207-2899. TEL 313-567-1640. Ed. Dr. Susan Adelman. adv. circ. 4,500. **Document type:** newsletter.

610   GW   ISSN 0027-7460
DEUTSCHE GESELLSCHAFT FUER GESCHICHTE DER MEDIZIN, NATURWISSENSCHAFT UND TECHNIK. NACHRICHTENBLATT. 1951. 3/yr. DM.50 membership. Deutsche Gesellschaft fuer Geschichte der Medizin, Naturwissenschaft und Technik e.V., Bundesstr. 55, 20146 Hamburg, Germany. Ed. Dr. Monika Renneberg. adv. contact: Christoph Meinel. circ. 720. **Document type:** newsletter.
—CCC.

616.02   US   ISSN 0070-4067
                       CODEN: VDGIA2
DEUTSCHE GESELLSCHAFT FUER INNERE MEDIZIN. VERHANDLUNGEN. 44th congress, 1932. irreg., 90th congress, 1984. price varies. Springer-Verlag, 175 Fifth Ave., New York, NY 10010. TEL 212-460-1500. FAX 212-473-6272. (Also: Berlin, Heidelberg, Tokyo and Vienna) Ed. B. Schlegel. (also avail. in microfiche from BHP; reprint service avail. from ISI) **Indexed:** Biol.Abstr., Excerp.Med. (until 1995). **Document type:** monographic series.
—CASDDS; EMDOCS. CCC.

616.07 574.2   GW   ISSN 0070-4113
                       CODEN: VDGPAN
DEUTSCHE GESELLSCHAFT FUER PATHOLOGIE. VERHANDLUNGEN. a. price varies. Gustav Fischer Verlag, Wollgrasweg 49, 70599 Stuttgart, Germany. TEL 0711-458030. FAX 0711-4580334. TELEX 7111-488-FIBUCH. (Subscr. to: Postfach 720143, 70577 Stuttgart, Germany; U.S. address: VCN Publishers Inc., 303 N.W. 12th Ave., Deerfield Beach, FL 33442-1788) **Indexed:** Biol.Abstr., Chem.Abstr., Ind.Med. **Document type:** academic/scholarly publication.
—BLDSC (9163.310000); CASDDS; Faxon; SWETS; UMI. CCC.

MEDICAL SCIENCES

610   GW
DEUTSCHE GESELLSCHAFT FUER UNFALLCHIRURGIE. MITTEILUNGEN. 1978. s-a. DM.42. Demeter Verlag GmbH und Co. KG, Bussardstr. 5, 82166 Graefelfing, Germany. TEL 089-85463-0. FAX 089-8543347. Ed. Dr. Probst. **Document type:** academic/scholarly publication.
Formerly: Deutsche Gesellschaft fuer Unfallheilkunde. Mitteilungen und Nachrichten (ISSN 0177-3747)

610   GW   ISSN 0012-0472
                    CODEN: DMWOAX
DEUTSCHE MEDIZINISCHE WOCHENSCHRIFT/GERMAN MEDICAL WEEKLY. (Editions in German, Japanese; summaries in English, German) 1875. w. DM.270 (students DM.92). Georg Thieme Verlag, Ruedigerstr. 14, 70469 Stuttgart, Germany. TEL 0711-8931-0. FAX 0711-8931298. (Subscr. to: Postfach 104853, 70042 Stuttgart, Germany) Ed.Bd. adv.; bk.rev.; abstr.; bibl.; illus.; stat.; index. circ. 43,000. (also avail. in microform from UMI,PMC; reprint service avail. from UMI) **Indexed:** Abstr.Hyg., Biol.Abstr., Biotech.Abstr., C.I.S. Abstr., Chem.Abstr., Curr.Adv.Ecol.Sci., Curr.Adv.Genetics & Molec.Biol., Curr.Cont., Dairy Sci.Abstr., Dent.Ind., Excerp.Med., Forest Prod.Abstr., Helminthol.Abstr., Ind.Med., Ind.Sci.Rev., INIS Atomind., Med.& Surg.Dermat., Nutr.Abstr., Protozool.Abstr., Rev.Med.& Vet.Mycol., Rev.Plant Path., Risk Abstr., Sci.Cit.Ind., Small Anim.Abstr., Trop.Dis.Bull. **Document type:** academic/scholarly publication.
—BLDSC (3573.000000); ADONIS; CASDDS; Genuine Article; SWETS; UMI. **CCC.**

615.89   GW   ISSN 0415-6412
DEUTSCHE ZEITSCHRIFT FUER AKUPUNKTUR; Zeitschrift fuer die wissenschaftliche Erforschung und praktische Anwendung der Akupunktur in Klinik und Praxis. (Text in German; summaries in English) bi-m. DM.106 (students DM.86). (Oesterreichische Gesellschaft fuer Akupunktur und Auriculotherapie) Karl F. Haug Verlag GmbH, Fritz-Frey-Str. 21, 69121 Heidelberg, Germany. TEL 06221-4062-0. FAX 06221-400727. TELEX 461683-HVVFMD. (Subscr. to: Postfach 102840, 69018 Heidelberg, Germany) Ed. Johannes Bischko. adv. contact: J. Schulz. **Indexed:** Excerp.Med. **Document type:** academic/scholarly publication.
—BLDSC (3575.720000). **CCC.**

610   GW   ISSN 0940-4783
DEUTSCHER FORSCHUNGSDIENST. BERICHTE AUS DER WISSENSCHAFT - AUSWAHL MEDIZIN. m. DM.78. Deutscher Forschungsdienst, Ahrstr. 45, 53175 Bonn, Germany. TEL 0228-302210. FAX 0228-302270. **Document type:** academic/scholarly publication.

610   GW   ISSN 0012-1207
DEUTSCHES AERZTEBLATT; aerztliche Mitteilungen. 1903. w. DM.538.20 (students DM.134.50). (Bundesaerztekammer) Deutscher Aerzte-Verlag GmbH, Postfach 400265, 50832 Cologne, Germany. TEL 02234-7011-0. FAX 02234-7011444. (Co-sponsor: Kassenaerztliche Bundesvereinigung) Ed. Norbert Jachertz. adv.; bk.rev. circ. 295,120. **Indexed:** Excerp.Med., INIS Atomind. **Document type:** academic/scholarly publication.
—BLDSC (3576.285000). **CCC.**

DEVELOPMENT (CAMBRIDGE). see *BIOLOGY*

DEVELOPMENTAL AND COMPARATIVE IMMUNOLOGY; ontogeny - phylogeny - aging. see *MEDICAL SCIENCES — Allergology And Immunology*

DEVELOPMENTAL BRAIN DYSFUNCTION. see *MEDICAL SCIENCES — Psychiatry And Neurology*

DEVELOPMENTAL DYNAMICS. see *BIOLOGY*

DEVELOPMENTS IN BIOTHERAPY. see *BIOLOGY — Biotechnology*

610   FR   ISSN 0396-8014
DEVELOPPEMENT ET SANTE. 1975. 6/yr. 200 F. John Libbey Eurotext, 127 av de la Republique, 92120 Montrouge, France. TEL 1-46-73-06-60. FAX 1-40-84-09-99. (Subscr. to: A T E I, 23-25 rue Fernand Combette, 93100 Montreuil sous Bois, France. TEL 48-59-58-11. FAX 48-59-57-99) Ed. Bernard Lagardere. **Document type:** academic/scholarly publication.
Description: Pedagogical information for caregivers in developing, tropical areas.

610   SZ   ISSN 1015-8154
DEVENIR. 1989. q. 80 SFr. to individuals; institutions 120 SFr. Editions Medecine et Hygiene, Case Postale 456, CH-1211 Geneva 4, Switzerland. TEL 022-3469355. FAX 022-3475610. **Document type:** academic/scholarly publication.

610   US   ISSN 0098-7573
DEVICES & DIAGNOSTICS LETTER. 1974. w. $667. Washington Business Information, Inc., c/o Karen Harrington, 1117 N. 19th St., Ste. 200, Arlington, VA 22209. TEL 703-247-3434. FAX 703-247-3421. bk.rev. (looseleaf format) **Document type:** newsletter.
●Also available online. **Vendor(s):** Ovid Technologies (DIOG), Data-Star, Knight-Ridder, Inc.
—CCC.
Description: For business leaders concerned with government regulation of medical devices and in vitro diagnostics. Covers compliance and inspection programs, defect reporting, labeling, and testing rules.

610   AG   ISSN 0012-1762
DIA MEDICO.* (Supplements avail.) 1928. m. Tucuman 1452, 1050 Buenos Aires, Argentina. Ed.Bd. adv.; bk.rev.; charts; illus.; index. circ. 8,000. **Indexed:** Biol.Abstr., Ind.Med.

610   US
DIAGNOSTIC IMAGING SCAN. 1987. s-m. $597. Miller Freeman, Inc. (Subsidiary of: United Newspapers), 600 Harrison St., San Francisco, CA 94107. TEL 415-905-2200. FAX 415-905-5232. TELEX 278273. Ed. Roger Lindahl.

610   US   ISSN 1052-9551
                    CODEN: DMPAES
DIAGNOSTIC MOLECULAR PATHOLOGY. (Supplement to: American Journal of Surgical Pathology (ISSN 0147-5185)) 1992. q. $88 to individuals; institutions $110 (effective 1995). Lippincott - Raven Press, 227 E. Washington Sq., Philadelphia, PA 19106. TEL 215-238-4200. Eds. Ronald A. DeLellis, Hubert J. Wolfe. adv. contact: Phyllis Noyes. bk.rev.; charts; illus. (reprint service avail. from UMI) **Indexed:** Excerp.Med. (1993-), Ind.Med. (1993-). **Document type:** academic/scholarly publication.
—BLDSC (3579.662500); Faxon; Genuine Article; SWETS; UMI; UnCover. **CCC.**
Description: Publishes contributions on molecular probes for diagnosis, such as tumor suppressor genes, oncogenes, the polymerase chain reaction, and in situ hybridization.
Refereed Serial

610   FR   ISSN 0336-3449
DIAGNOSTICS.* 1965. 22/yr. 140 F. Office Universitaire de Presse, 15 rue Tiphaine, 75015 Paris, France. adv.; circ. 22,500 (controlled).

DIAGNOSTICS INTELLIGENCE. see *PHARMACY AND PHARMACOLOGY*

616.075   PL   ISSN 0012-1932
                    CODEN: DLJNAQ
DIAGNOSTYKA LABORATORYJNA. 1964. bi-m. $96. Polskie Towarzystwo Diagnostyki Laboratoryjnej, Ul. Kopernika 15, 31-501 Krakow, Poland. TEL 21-39-76. (Dist. by: Ars Polona-Ruch, Krakowskie Przedmiescie 7, Warsaw, Poland) Ed. Dr. Stefan Angielski. adv.; bk.rev. circ. 1,450. **Indexed:** Biol.Abstr., Chem.Abstr., Excerp.Med., INIS Atomind.
—CASDDS.
Description: Examines clinical chemistry, cytomorphology, parasitology and serology.

DIARIO DE CONGRESOS MEDICOS. see *MEETINGS AND CONGRESSES*

DICTIONNAIRE PERMANENT: BIOETHIQUE ET BIOTECHNOLOGIES. see *BIOLOGY — Biotechnology*

DIMENSIONE SALUTE. see *PHYSICAL FITNESS AND HYGIENE*

610   US   ISSN 0891-947X
R835
DIRECTORY OF AUDIO-VISUAL PROGRAMS FOR THE HEALTH SCIENCES AND RELATED FIELDS.* 1987. a. $35. Med-Av Publishing Co. Inc., 32 Bellport Pl., Garfield, NJ 07026-1421. TEL 201-423-3330. Ed. Charles M. Murtaugh. circ. 1,000. (back issues avail.) **Document type:** directory.

614.88 616.02   UK
DIRECTORY OF EMERGENCY AND SPECIAL CARE UNITS (YEAR). a. £45. C M A Medical Data Ltd., Cambridge Research Laboratories, 181A Huntingdon Rd., Cambridge CB3 0DJ, England. TEL 01223-277709. FAX 01223-276444. **Document type:** directory.
Description: Contains detailed information on emergency and special care units and services throughout the British Isles.

DIRECTORY OF MEDICAL AND HEALTH CARE LIBRARIES IN THE UNITED KINGDOM AND REPUBLIC OF IRELAND. see *LIBRARY AND INFORMATION SCIENCES*

610 378.0025   US   ISSN 0160-6468
R735.A1
DIRECTORY OF MEDICAL SCHOOLS WORLDWIDE. irreg., 6th ed. 1994. $59.95. U S Directory Service, A Reed Reference Publishing Company, Part of the Reed Elsevier group, 121 Chanlon Rd., New Providence, NJ 07974. TEL 800-521-8110. FAX 908-665-6688. TELEX 138 755. (Subscr. to: Order Dept., Box 31, New Providence, NJ 07974-9903) **Document type:** directory.
Description: Comprehensive listing of 1,200 medical schools from over 100 countries. Detailed introduction provides facts and information on admissions, statistics, language and curricula.

616.07 574.2   US   ISSN 0070-6086
DIRECTORY OF PATHOLOGY TRAINING PROGRAMS (YEAR). 1968. a. $25. Intersociety Committee on Pathology Information, 4733 Bethesda Ave., Ste. 700, Bethesda, MD 20814. TEL 301-656-2944. FAX 301-656-3179. Ed. Eileen Lavine. circ. 2,500. **Document type:** directory.
Description: Describes residency programs and post-graduate subspecialty fellowships in anatomic and clinical pathology in the U.S. and Canada, and post-sophomore fellowships.

DIRECTORY OF PERSECUTED SCIENTISTS, ENGINEERS AND HEALTH PROFESSIONALS. see *POLITICAL SCIENCE — Civil Rights*

610 658   US
DIRECTORY OF THE JAPANESE HEALTHCARE INDUSTRY. a (with q. updates). 80000 Yen($450) Japan Publications Inc., 41 Sutter St., Ste. 1112, San Francisco, CA 94104. TEL 415-772-5555. FAX 415-772-5659. **Document type:** directory.
Description: Over 1600 corporate profiles of private, public, and foreign-capital firms from every segment of the Japanese healthcare industry detailing financial performance, marketing and business development.

613.7   US
DIRECTORY OF U.S. INTERNATIONAL HEALTH ORGANIZATIONS. 1980. irreg., latest 1995. $60 to non-members; members $30. National Council for International Health, 1701 K St., N.W., Ste. 600, Washington, DC 20006. TEL 202-833-5900. FAX 202-833-0075. E-mail: NCIH@acces.dogex.net. Ed. Elizabeth Tuico. adv.; bk.rev. circ. 1,000. **Document type:** directory.
Formerly: Directory of U.S. Based Agencies Involved in International Health Assistance.
Description: Provides a comprehensive list of all major U.S. organizations supporting international health.

610   US   ISSN 0011-5029
R11
DISEASE-A-MONTH. 1954. m. $70 to individuals (foreign $79); institutions $100 (foreign $109); students $45 (foreign $54) (effective Jan. 1994). Mosby - Year Book, Inc. (Subsidiary of: Times Mirror Company), 11830 Westline Industrial Dr., St. Louis, MO 63146. TEL 314-872-8370; 800-325-4177. FAX 314-432-1380. Ed. Dr. Roger C. Bone. charts; illus.; stat.; cum.index. circ. 4,606. (also avail. in microform from UMI; back issues avail.; reprint service avail. from UMI) **Indexed:** AIM, Curr.Cont., Excerp.Med., Ind.Med., NRN.
—BLDSC (3598.100000); Genuine Article; SWETS; UMI; UnCover. **CCC.**
Description: For the general internist. Each issue is a single topic discussion that focuses on the integrated management of a particular disease.

MEDICAL SCIENCES

610 615 UK
DISPENSING DOCTORS' ASSOCIATION. JOURNAL. 1984. q. £12 to non-members. (Dispensing Doctors' Association) Medical and Scientific Publishing, Ottinge House, The Close, Saltwood, Kent CT21 4RA, England. TEL 01303-262272. FAX 01303-262269. (Subscr. to: The Spinney, Welford, Northampton NN6 6HG, England. TEL 01858-575557. FAX 01858-575166) Ed. Dr. David Roberts. adv. contact: Iain McGhie. bk.rev.; film rev.; bibl.; charts; illus.; tr.lit. circ. 4,400. (back issues avail.) **Document type:** trade publication.
  Description: Aims to maintain and improve the service dispensing doctors provide.

610 SW ISSN 0283-9830
DISTRIKTLAEKAREN. 1983. m. SEK 360 membership (effective 1991). (Svenska Distriktlaekarfoereningen SDF) Sveriges Laekarfoerbund, P.O. Box 5610, S-114 86 Stockholm, Sweden. **Document type:** trade publication.
  Formerly (until 1987): D L F Informerar.

610 JA ISSN 0288-559X
 CODEN: DITEDV
DITERUMAN/DETAILMAN INFORMATION. (Text in Japanese) 1975. m. 2900 Yen per no. Mikushu - Medical Information Express, 28-2, Kanda Ogawamachi 3-chome, Chiyoda-ku, Tokyo 101, Japan.
 —CASDDS.

DIVERSION (NEW YORK); for physicians at leisure. see LEISURE AND RECREATION

610 JA ISSN 0287-2153
DOAI IGAKU ZASSHI/FRATERNITY MEMORIAL HOSPITAL. MEDICAL JOURNAL. (Text in Japanese) 1959. biennial. Dokai Kinen Byoin - Fraternity Memorial Hospital, 1-11, Yokoami 2-chome, Sumida-ku, Tokyo 130, Japan. Ed. Yasuhiro Saito. **Document type:** academic/scholarly publication.

613 UA ISSN 0012-4435
AD-DOCTOR; health education magazine. (Text in Arabic) 1947. m. £E1($4) 8 Sharia Hoda Shaarawy, Cairo, Egypt. Ed. Dr. Ahmad M. Kamal. bibl.; index, cum.index. circ. 30,000.

610 UK ISSN 0046-0451
DOCTOR. 1971. w. £80 (free to qualified personnel). Reed Healthcare Publishing (Subsidiary of: Reed Elsevier group), Quadrant House, The Quadrant, Sutton, Surrey SM2 5AS, England. TEL 081-652-8740. FAX 081-652-8701. Ed. Helena Sturidge. adv.; bk.rev.; abstr.; charts; illus. circ. 36,000. (tabloid format; also avail. in microfilm from UMI) **Document type:** trade publication.
 —BLDSC (3606.400000); UMI. **CCC.**
  Description: Provides general practitioners with latest news on medicine, political subjects, clinical developments and innovations.

610 JA
DOCTOR. (Text in Japanese) 1966. w. 7300 Yen. Yakuji Nyususha, 5-5, Doshomachi 1-chome, Chuo-ku, Osaka 541, Japan. stat.

610 IT ISSN 1120-592X
DOCTOR. 1983. s-m. L' Ariete Edizioni, Via Stephensen 33, 20157 Milan, Italy. TEL 02-332141. FAX 2-39002607. Ed. Dario Passoni. adv.: B&W page L.8700000, color page L.12500000; trim 185 x 246. circ. 77,093.

362.1 174.1 US
DOCTOR - PATIENT STUDIES. 1989. q. free. University of Chicago, Center for Clinical Medical Ethics, MC 6098, 5811 S. Maryland, Chicago, IL 60637. TEL 312-702-3742. FAX 312-702-0090. Ed. James J. Hughes. bk.rev.; circ. 600 (controlled). (back issues avail.) **Document type:** abstracting/indexing, bibliography, newsletter.
  Description: Describes the activities at the center and provides an abstract service for selected scholars on research concerning the doctor - patient relationship and clinical ethics.

US
DOCTORS FOR DISASTER PREPAREDNESS NEWSLETTER. Short title: D D P. 1984. bi-m. $10. Doctors for Disaster Preparedness, Box 272, 2509 N. Campbell, Tucson, AZ 85719. TEL 904-964-5397. Ed. Jane Orient. adv. circ. 1,000. (back issues avail.)
  Formerly: Triage!

610 US ISSN 0733-2262
THE DOCTOR'S OFFICE. 1982. m. $98. Wentworth Worldwide Media, 1861 Colonial Village Ln., Box 10488, Lancaster, PA 17605-0488. TEL 717-393-1000; 800-331-5196. FAX 717-393-2732. Ed. Ann Mead Ash. circ. 50,000 (paid). (back issues avail.) **Indexed:** Hlth.Ind. **Document type:** newsletter.
  Description: Provides information to clarify insurance regulations, collections techniques, marketing ideas and other practice management techniques, as well as dealing with managed care.

DOCTOR'S REVIEW; leisure-time journal for physicians. see TRAVEL AND TOURISM

610 US
DOCTOR'S SHOPPER. 1983. q. $5 per no. Marketing Communications, Inc., 1086 Remsen Ave., Brooklyn, NY 11236. TEL 718-257-8484. FAX 718-257-8845. Ed. Ralph Selitzek. adv.; bk.rev.; illus.; pat.; stat.; tr.lit.; circ. 208,000 (controlled).

DOCTOR'S TAX REPORT. see BUSINESS AND ECONOMICS — Public Finance, Taxation

610 NR ISSN 0046-0508
DOKITA. 1960. s-a. £N2.40($5) to individuals; $3 to students. (University of Ibadan Medical Students' Association, Dept. of Medicine) Ibadan University Press, University of Ibadan, Ibadan, Nigeria. Ed. A. Ibe Otuka. adv.; bk.rev.; charts; illus. circ. 1,000. (looseleaf format) **Indexed:** Biol.Abstr.

610 JA ISSN 0385-5023
 CODEN: DJMSDB
DOKKYO JOURNAL OF MEDICAL SCIENCES. Japanese edition: Dokkyo Igakkai Zasshi (ISSN 0911-5900) (Text in English) 1974. s-a. 5000 Yen (effective till 1994). Dokkyo University School of Medicine, Dokkyo Medical Society - Dokkyo Daigaku Igakubu Dokkyo Igakkai, Mibu, Tochigi 321-02, Japan. TEL 282-86-1111. FAX 282-86-5678. TELEX 3562118. Ed. Shigeru Matsuzaki. adv.: page 50000 Yen. bk.rev. circ. 1,300. **Indexed:** Biol.Abstr., Chem.Abstr., Excerp.Med., Ind.Med., INIS Atomind. **Document type:** academic/scholarly publication.
 —BLDSC (3614.950000); CASDDS.

610 SW ISSN 1100-9861
DOKTORAND; en handledning foer dig som taenker doktorera. 1988. biennial. SEK 20 (effective 1990). S A C O, P.O. Box 2206, S-103 15 Stockholm, Sweden.

610 JA ISSN 0389-7303
DOKUTA SARON/DOCTOR SALON. (Text in Japanese) 1957. m. 300 Yen per no. Kyorin Medikaru Sapurai - Kyorin Medical Supply, 8-16, Sarugakucho 2-chome, Chiyoda-ku, Tokyo 101, Japan.

610 SP ISSN 0214-1485
 CODEN: DOINEC
DOLOR E INFLAMACION; farmacoterapia, investigacion y clinica medica. 6/yr. 4000 ptas. (Liga Reumatologica Espanola) Saned, S.A., Paseo de la Habana 202-bis, 28036 Madrid, Spain. TEL 1-359-40-92. Ed. A. Sanchez del Rio. circ. 3,000. **Indexed:** Excerp.Med.
 —BLDSC (3616.614000).

610 JA ISSN 0288-1829
DONAN IGAKKAISHI/MEDICAL ASSOCIATION OF SOUTH HOKKAIDO. JOURNAL. (Text in Japanese) 1957. a. Donan Igakkai, 33-19, Motomachi, Hakodate-shi, Hokkaido 040, Japan. Ed.Bd. circ. 850.
 —BLDSC (4824.160000).

610 US
DORLAND'S MEDICAL DIRECTORY. EASTERN PENNSYLVANIA AND SOUTHERN NEW JERSEY EDITION. 1952. a. $70.85. Legal Communications, Ltd., 1617 JFK Blvd., Ste. 1245, Philadelphia, PA 19103. TEL 215-563-9000. FAX 215-563-4911. Ed. Debra Silverman Shain. adv. circ. 6,500.
  Former titles: Dorland's Medical Directory. Delaware Valley Edition; Dorland's Medical Directory. Philadelphia Metropolitan Area.
  Description: Listings of physicians, health care organizations, hospitals and specialists in the greater Philadelphia metropolitan area.

610 SZ ISSN 1011-288X
DOULEUR ET ANALGESIE. q. 73 SFr. to individuals; institutions 123 SFr. Editions Medecine et Hygiene, Case Postale 456, CH-1211 Geneva 4, Switzerland. TEL 022-3469355. FAX 022-3475610. **Document type:** academic/scholarly publication.
 —BLDSC (3619.931800).

610 US
DR. ALEXANDER GRANT'S HEALTH GAZETTE; a monthly digest of medical facts and news. 1978. m. (10/yr.) $24.95 (effective Jan. 1995). Alexander Grant and Associates, Inc., Box 1786, Indianapolis, IN 46206. FAX 317-253-8582. Ed. Dr. Alexander Grant. cum.index. circ. 40,000. (looseleaf format; back issues avail.) **Document type:** newsletter.
  Formerly: Healthwise (ISSN 0740-1086)

610 615.19 GW ISSN 0173-430X
DR. MED. MABUSE. 1976. 6/yr. DM.48 (foreign DM.54). Mabuse Verlag GmbH, Kasselerstr. 1A, 60486 Frankfurt a.M., Germany. TEL 069-705053. FAX 069-704152. Ed. Dr. Hermann Loeffler. adv.; bk.rev. circ. 15,000. (back issues avail.) **Document type:** trade publication.
  Description: Publication for those working in the health field. Features a broad variety of health and medical issues worldwide. Includes readers' letters, list of events and positions available.

610 US
DRUG ENFORCEMENT ADMINISTRATION REGISTRATION FILE - ACTIVE. Short title: D E A Registration File - Active. q. $3760 in U.S., Canada, Mexico; elsewhere $7520. (Department of Treasury, Drug Enforcement Administration) U.S. National Technical Information Service, 5825 Port Royal Rd., Springfield, VA 22161. TEL 703-487-4630. (magnetic tape)
  Description: Lists all those registered under the Controlled Substance Act who are doing business registered in their own name rather than that of a business name.

612.39 615 US ISSN 0360-2532
 CODEN: DMTRAR
DRUG METABOLISM REVIEWS. 1972. 4/yr. $52 (effective 1996). Marcel Dekker Journals, 270 Madison Ave., New York, NY 10016. TEL 212-696-9000. FAX 212-685-4540. TELEX 421419. (Subscr. to: Box 5017, Monticello, NY 12701) Ed. Frederick J. DiCarlo. (also avail. in microform from RPI) **Indexed:** Abstr.Inter.Med., Biol.Abstr., Biotech.Abstr., Chem.Abstr., Curr.Adv.Biochem., Curr.Adv.Ecol.Sci., Curr.Cont., Dairy Sci.Abstr., Excerp.Med., I.P.A., Ind.Med., Ind.Sci.Rev., Ind.Vet., Pig News & Info., Poult.Abstr., Sci.Cit.Ind., Vet.Bull. **Document type:** academic/scholarly publication.
 —BLDSC (3629.330000); ADONIS; CASDDS; Faxon; Genuine Article; SWETS; UMI; UnCover. **CCC.**
 Refereed Serial

610 FI ISSN 0012-7183
 CODEN: DUODAG
DUODECIM; laaketieteellinen aikakauskirja. 1885. s-m. FIM 650. Finnish Medical Society Duodecim, Kalevankatu 11 A, 00100 Helsinki, Finland. TEL 90-611050. FAX 90-611185. Ed. Hannu Jalanko. adv.; bk.rev.; film rev.; bibl.; charts; illus.; index, cum.index. circ. 18,000. **Indexed:** Biol.Abstr., Chem.Abstr., Curr.Adv.Ecol.Sci., Dent.Ind., Excerp.Med., Ind.Med., INIS Atomind. **Document type:** bulletin.
 —BLDSC (3631.195000); CASDDS.

610 SP ISSN 0211-9536
R131.A1
DYNAMIS; acta hispanica ad medicinae scientiarumque historiam illustrandam. 1981. a. 3000 ptas. (effective 1995). Universidad de Granada, Departamento de Historia de la Medicina, Servicio de Publicaciones, Antiguo Colegio Maximo, Campus de Cartuja, 18071 Granada, Spain. TEL 34-58-243930. FAX 34-58-242827. Ed. Esteban Rodriguez. bk.rev. circ. 150. **Indexed:** Amer.Hist.& Life, Bull.Signal., Hist.Abstr., Ind.Med.Esp.
 —BLDSC (3637.146000).

MEDICAL SCIENCES

611 US ISSN 0179-051X
CODEN: DYSPE2
DYSPHAGIA; an international multidisciplinary journal devoted to swallowing and its disorders. 1986. q. $180 (effective 1996). Springer-Verlag, Journals, 175 Fifth Ave., New York, NY 10010. TEL 212-460-1500. FAX 212-473-6272. (N. American subscr. to: Journal Fulfillment Services, Box 2491, Secaucus, NJ 07096-2491. TEL 800-777-4643. FAX 201-348-4505; Elsewhere: Heidelberger Platz 3, 1000 Berlin 33, Germany. TEL 030-8207-1. FAX 030-8214091) Ed. Bronwyn Jones. (also avail. in microform from UMI; reprint service avail.) **Indexed:** Excerp.Med.
—BLDSC (3637.270000); Faxon; SWETS; UMI. CCC.
Description: Surveys all aspects of normal ingestion involving the mouth, pharynx, and esophagus; covers material related to dysphagia, its diagnosis, and its clinical treatment.
Refereed Serial

610 US
DYSTONIA DIALOGUE. 1976. q. free. Dystonia Medical Research Foundation, 1 E Wacker Dr., Ste. 2430, Chicago, IL 60601-2001. TEL 312-755-0198. FAX 312-803-0138. E-mail: dystfndt@aol.com. Ed. Kimberly Kuman. circ. 21,000. **Document type:** newsletter.
Description: Helps to build awareness of dystonia in the medical and lay community.

610.09 509 NE ISSN 1383-7427
▼**EARLY SCIENCE AND MEDICINE**; a journal for the study of science, medicine and technology in the pre-modern period. (Text in English) Announced for publication in 1996. 3/yr. fl.90($58) to individuals; institutions fl.180 ($116) (effective 1996). E.J. Brill, Postbus 9000, 2300 PA Leiden, Netherlands. TEL 31-71-5353500. FAX 31-71-5317532. TELEX 39692 BRILL NL. E-mail: ejborders@ejbrill.com. (In N. America: E.J. Brill, 24 Hudson St., Kinderhook, NY 12106. TEL 800-962-4406. FAX 518-758-1959) Ed. H. Thijssen. bk.rev. **Document type:** academic/scholarly publication.
Description: Publishes studies dealing with the content and influence of science, medicine and technology from the earliest times through the end of the seventeenth century.
Refereed Serial

610 KE ISSN 0012-835X
R98 CODEN: EAMJAV
EAST AFRICAN MEDICAL JOURNAL. 1923. m. KShs.24750($375) (effective 1994-1995). Kenya Medical Association House, Chyulu Rd., P.O. Box 41632, Nairobi, Kenya. TEL 254-2-724711. FAX 254-2-724617. Ed. W. Lore. adv. contact: Silvanus Oriedi. bk.rev.; index; circ. 4,500 (paid). (reprint service avail. from IRC) **Indexed:** Abstr.Hyg., Biodet.Abstr., BIol.Abstr., Chem.Abstr., Curr.Cont., Dent.Ind., Diar.Dis.Res., Dok.Arbeitsmed., Excerp.Med. (1993-), ExtraMED, Geo.Abstr., Helminthol.Abstr., HRIS, IDA, Ind.Med., Ind.Sci.Rev., Ind.Vet., Med.Abstr., NRN, Nutr.Abstr., Protozool.Abstr., Rev.Appl.Entomol., Rev.Plant Path., Sci.Cit.Ind., Sp.Ed.Needs Abstr., Trop.Dis.Bull., Vet.Bull. **Document type:** academic/scholarly publication.
●Also available on CD-ROM.
—BLDSC (3645.000000); CASDDS; Genuine Article; SWETS.
Refereed Serial

610 RM ISSN 1220-8795
EAST EUROPEAN MEDICAL JOURNAL. Issued with: East European Medical Journal Supplement (ISSN 1220-8787) (Rumanian supplement avail.: East European Medical Journal; Supliment in Limba Romana) (Text in English) 1992. q. (s-a., plus s-a. supplement). 15000 lei($15) (foreign $30) to individuals; institutions 20000 lei($20) (foreign $40) (effective 1992). Edit Dan Publishing Co., P.O. Box 209, 600 Iasi 1, Rumania. TEL 40-98-135778. FAX 40-98-117607. Ed. Dr. Traian Mihaescu. adv.: B&W page $700, color page $1700; adv. contact: Alina Gramescu. bk.rev.; abstr. circ. 2,000. **Indexed:** Ind.Med.
Description: Dedicated to specific health care problems in East Europe and Eurasia.
Refereed Serial

610 US ISSN 1050-6675
EAST TEXAS MEDICINE.* 1989. bi-m. $20. 10702 Hancock Dr., Tyler, TX 75707-9426. TEL 214-592-8533. FAX 903-593-0494. Ed. Dr. Gary D. Boyd. adv. circ. 5,000.
Description: Forum for physicians in the East Texas area. Presents doctors' case studies and research.

610 UK ISSN 0260-3934
EDINBURGH MEDICINE. 1980. q. £10 (foreign $15). Hermiston Publications Ltd., 2 Hill Sq., Edinburgh EH8 9DR, Scotland. TEL 0131-668-3753. Ed. Dr. Ian H. McKee. adv.; bk.rev.; illus. circ. 4,000. **Document type:** academic/scholarly publication.

610 JA ISSN 0915-9061
EDOGAWA/EDOGAWA CITY MEDICAL ASSOCIATION. JOURNAL. (Text in Japanese) 1965. bi-m. Edogawaku Ishikai - Edogawa City Medical Association, 24-14, Chuo 4-chome, Edogawa-ku, Tokyo 132, Japan.

610 JA ISSN 0915-8693
EDOGAWA IGAKKAISHI/EDOGAWA CITY MEDICAL ASSOCIATION. PROCEEDINGS. (Text in Japanese) 1983. a. Edogawaku Ishikai, 24-14, Chuo 4-chome, Edogawa-ku, Tokyo 132, Japan. **Document type:** proceedings.

610 PO ISSN 0871-7958
EDUCACAO MEDICA. (Text in English and Portuguese) 1989. 3/yr. free. A E F M U P, Alameda Prof. H. Monteiro, Piso 1, Apdo. 4014, 4008 Porto Codex, Portugal. TEL 351-2-524901. FAX 351-2-5509096. (Co-sponsors: Hospital de S. Joao, Faculdade de Medicina do Porto) Ed. Pinto Machado. adv.: B&W page Esc.40000; adv. contact: Luisa Botelho. circ. 1,250. **Document type:** academic/scholarly publication.

610 CK
EDUCACION CONTINUA EN SALUD (YEAR) TEMAS ESCOGIDOS.* 1989. a. Bs.6000($15) Corporacion Editora Medica del Valle, Calle 4B No. 36-00, Cali, Valle Valle, Colombia. TEL 581939.
Description: Provides updated topics on themes of importance and of interest to general practitioners.

EDUCACION MEDICA Y SALUD. see EDUCATION — Guides To Schools And Colleges

EDUCATION AND HEALTH. see EDUCATION — School Organization And Administration

610 378 UK
EDUCATION FOR GENERAL PRACTICE. 1990. 4/yr. £65. Radcliffe Medical Press Ltd., 18 Marcham Rd., Abingdon, Oxon OX14 1AA, England. TEL 01235-528820. FAX 01235-528830. Ed. Declan Dwyer. adv. contact: Andrew Bax. bk.rev. circ. 1,500. (back issues avail.) **Document type:** academic/scholarly publication.
Formerly (until 1993): Postgraduate Education for General Practice (ISSN 0959-4299)
Description: Postgraduate education in family practice, general practice for trainers and all others interested.

352.3 US ISSN 0145-2037
RA396.A3
EDUCATIONAL COMMISSION FOR FOREIGN MEDICAL GRADUATES. ANNUAL REPORT. 1958. a. free. Educational Commission for Foreign Medical Graduates, 3624 Market St., 4th Fl., Philadelphia, PA 19104-2685. TEL 215-386-5900. FAX 215-387-9963. Ed.Bd. circ. 5,000.
Formerly: Educational Council for Foreign Medical Graduates. Annual Report (ISSN 0422-6690)
Description: Provides information on programs of international medical education, including entry of foreign graduates of medical schools into graduate medical education in the United States, and research and development programs.

610 UK ISSN 0965-0288
EFFECTIVE HEALTH CARE. 1992. irreg., no.9, 1995. £3 (foreign £4). University of Leeds, Nuffield Institute for Health, 71-75 Clarendon Rd., Leeds LS2 9LP, England. TEL 01532-334868. FAX 01532-460899. circ. 30,000. **Document type:** academic/scholarly publication.
—BLDSC (3664.020355).

610 UA ISSN 0013-2411
CODEN: JEMAAJ
EGYPTIAN MEDICAL ASSOCIATION. JOURNAL. (Text in Arabic and English) 1917. m. membership. Egyptian Medical Association, Dar El-Hekma, 42 Kasr-El Aini St., Cairo, Egypt. Ed. Prof. Dr. M. Ibrahim. adv.; bk.rev.; charts; illus.; index. **Indexed:** Biol.Abstr., C.I.S. Abstr., Chem.Abstr., Excerp.Med. (until 19??), Helminthol.Abstr., Ind.Med. (until 19??), Nutr.Abstr., Rev.Plant Path., Trop.Dis.Bull., Zoo.Rec. **Document type:** academic/scholarly publication.
—BLDSC (4735.800000); CASDDS; UnCover.

610 JA ISSN 0286-3677
EHIME IGAKU/EHIME MEDICAL JOURNAL. (Text in Japanese; summaries in English) 1982. q. 1000 Yen per no. Ehime Igakkai - Ehime Medical Association, Ehimeken Ishikai, 5-3, Sanbancho 4-chome, Matsuyama-shi, Ehime-ken 790, Japan. **Indexed:** INIS Atomind.

610 JA ISSN 0289-5463
EHIME KENRITSU BYOIN GAKKAI KAISHI/EHIME JOURNAL OF MEDICINE. (Text in Japanese; summaries in English) 1961. 2/yr. (Ehime Kenritsu Byoin - Ehime Prefectural Hospital) Ehimeken Koei Kigyo Kanrikyoku - Ehime Prefectural Government, Public Enterprise Administration Division, 4-2 Ichibancho 4-chome, Matsuyama-shi, Ehime-ken 790, Japan.
—BLDSC (3664.705800).

610 JA ISSN 0915-3012
EHIME KENRITSU IRYO GIJUTSU TANKI DAIGAKU KIYO/EHIME COLLEGE OF HEALTH SCIENCES. BULLETIN. (Text in English, Japanese; summaries in Japanese) 1988. a. Ehime Kenritsu Iryo Gijutsu Tanki Daigaku, 543, Takaoda, Tobecho, Iyo-gun, Ehime-ken 791-21, Japan. **Document type:** bulletin.

610 JA
EHIMEKEN ISHIKAIHO/MEDICAL ASSOCIATION OF EHIME. JOURNAL. (Text in Japanese) 1953. m. Ehimeken Ishikai, 5-3, Sanbancho 4-chome, Matsuyama-shi, Ehime-ken 790, Japan.

THE EINSTEIN QUARTERLY; journal of biology and medicine. see BIOLOGY

610 IS ISSN 0334-3928
EITANIM; monthly of health issues. (Text in Hebrew) 1948. m. IS.35($17.50) Merkaz Kupat Holim, P.O. Box 16250, Tel Aviv 62098, Israel. FAX 03-433500. Ed. David Taggar. adv.; bk.rev.; index. circ. 20,000. **Indexed:** Ind.Heb.Per.

EIZO JOHO MEDIKARU/IMAGE TECHNOLOGY & INFORMATION DISPLAY, MEDICAL. see PHYSICS

610 US ISSN 0070-959X
ELDRIDGE REEVES JOHNSON FOUNDATION FOR MEDICAL PHYSICS. COLLOQUIUM. PROCEEDINGS. 1963. irreg., 5th 1969. price varies. University of Pennsylvania, Eldridge Reeves Johnson Foundation for Medical Physics, D501 Richards Bldg., 37th & Hamilton Walk, Philadelphia, PA 19104-6089. TEL 215-898-4342. FAX 216-898-0465. **Document type:** proceedings.

615.845 GW ISSN 0340-5389
ELECTROMEDICA (DEUTSCHE AUSGABE). English edition (ISSN 0013-4724) 1932. s-a. DM.29($22) (effective 1996). Siemens Verlag AG, Postfach 3240, 91050 Erlangen, Germany. (Subscr. to: V C H Publishers, Postfach 101161, 69451 Weinheim, Germany. TEL 06201-606147. FAX 06201-606117; US addr.: V C H Publishers Inc., 220 E. 23rd St., New York, NY 10010-4606. TEL 212-683-8333) **Indexed:** Excerp.Med., INIS Atomind., INSPEC. **Document type:** trade publication.
—CCC.
Formerly: Siemens Electromedica (ISSN 0037-4660)
Description: Covers medical electronics.

MEDICAL SCIENCES

616.8 612   BE   ISSN 0301-150X
RC77.5   CODEN: EMCNA9
ELECTROMYOGRAPHY AND CLINICAL NEUROPHYSIOLOGY. (Text in English) 1961. 8/yr. $100. Editions Nauwelaerts S.A., Rue de l'Eglise St. Suplice 19, B-1320 Beauvechain, Belgium. TEL 32-10-866737. FAX 32-2-7514708. Eds. N. Rosselle, W. T. Liberson. abstr.; bibl.; charts; illus.; index. **Indexed:** Biol.Abstr., Excerp.Med., Ind.Med., INSPEC. **Document type:** academic/scholarly publication.
—BLDSC (3699.720000); Faxon; SWETS; UnCover.
    Formerly: Electromyography (ISSN 0013-4732)

610   US   ISSN 1044-9167
EMERGENCY DEPARTMENT MANAGEMENT. 1989. m. $249. American Health Consultants, Inc., Six Piedmont Center, Ste. 400, Atlanta, GA 30305. TEL 404-262-7436; 800-688-2421. FAX 800-284-3291. Ed. David Reynolds. circ. 1,170. **Document type:** newsletter.
    Incorporates (in 1991): Reports in Emergency Nursing.

EMERGENCY LEGAL BRIEFINGS. see *LAW*

610 340   US   ISSN 0884-4836
EMERGENCY MEDICAL TECHNICIAN LEGAL BULLETIN. 1977. q. $15. Med-Law Publishers, Inc., Box 293, Westville, NJ 08093. Ed. Dr. James E. George. index. (back issues avail.) **Indexed:** CINAHL. **Document type:** newsletter, bulletin.

610   US   ISSN 1054-0725
EMERGENCY MEDICINE NEWS; the news magazine for the emergency care professional. 1979. m. $94 to individuals (foreign $122); institutions $130 (foreign $173) (effective 1966); newsstand price: $16. Lippincott - Raven Publishers, 227 E. Washington Sq., Philadelphia, PA 19106. TEL 215-238-4200. (Subscr. to: 12107 Insurance Way, Hagerstown, MD 21740) Ed. Lisa Hoffman. adv. contact: Barbara Nakahara. circ. 23,000. circ. Pub. Michael Randers-Pehrson. (tabloid format) —UMI. **CCC.**
    Former titles: Emergency Medicine and Ambulatory Care News; (until Aug. 1986): Emergency Department News.
    Description: Disseminates information in all areas of emergency medicine, as well as emergency departments and ambulatory care centers.

610   US   ISSN 0746-2506
EMERGENCY MEDICINE REPORTS; the practical journal for primary care physicians. 1980. fortn. $219. American Health Consultants, Inc., Six Piedmont Center, Ste. 400, Atlanta, GA 30305. TEL 404-262-7436; 800-688-2421. FAX 404-262-7837. Ed. Dr. Phil Fontanarosa. circ. 6,250. **Document type:** newsletter.
●Also available online. Vendor(s): Ovid Technologies.
—BLDSC (3733.190700). **CCC.**
    Incorporates (1983-1990): Advanced Clinical Updates; Which was formerly (until 1985): Family Medicine Reports; Formerly (until 1983): E R Reports (Emergency Room) (ISSN 0732-9628)

610 340   US
EMERGENCY MEDICINE REPORTS LEGAL BRIEFINGS. m. $130. American Health Consultants, Inc., Six Piedmont Center, Ste. 400, 3525 Piedmont Rd., N.E., Atlanta, GA 30305. TEL 404-262-7436. FAX 800-284-3291. (Subscr. to: Box 740056, Atlanta, GA 30374-9822. TEL 800-688-2421) Ed. Deborah Lydon. circ. 900.

610 340   US   ISSN 0098-1524
EMERGENCY PHYSICIAN LEGAL BULLETIN. Abbreviated title: E P L B. 1975. q. $25. Med-Law Publishers, Inc., Box 293, Westville, NJ 08093. TEL 609-848-3817. FAX 609-848-1431. Ed. Dr. James E. George. index. (back issues avail.) **Document type:** newsletter, bulletin.

610   TS   ISSN 0250-6882
                           CODEN: EMEJD
EMIRATES MEDICAL JOURNAL. (Text in English) 1981. 3/yr. $50. Emirates Medical Association, P.O. Box 6600, Dubai, United Arab Emirates. TEL 971-4-377377. FAX 971-4-344082. Ed. Dr. Yousef Mohamed Abdulrazzaq. adv.; bk.rev. circ. 2,000. **Indexed:** Excerp.Med., ExtraMED. **Document type:** academic/scholarly publication.
●Also available on CD-ROM.
    Refereed Serial

ENTWICKLUNGSLAENDER-STUDIEN; Bibliographie entwicklungslaenderbezogener Forschungsarbeiten. see *BUSINESS AND ECONOMICS — Abstracting, Bibliographies, Statistics*

614   US   ISSN 0196-0598
ENVIRONMENTAL HEALTH LETTER; policy, technology, research. 1962. fortn. $299 (effective Sep. 1992). Business Publishers, Inc., 951 Pershing Dr., Silver Spring, MD 20910-4464. TEL 301-587-6300. FAX 301-585-9075. Ed. Kathleen Hart. (looseleaf format) **Document type:** newsletter.
●Also available online. Vendor(s): NewsNet.
—**CCC.**

ENVIRONMENTAL MANAGEMENT & HEALTH. see *ENVIRONMENTAL STUDIES*

610   JA   ISSN 0287-0517
RA565.A1   CODEN: ENMEE9
ENVIRONMENTAL MEDICINE. (Text in English) 1951. s-a. free. Nagoya Daigaku, Kankyo Igaku Kenkyujo - Nagoya University, Research Institute of Environmental Medicine, Furo-cho, Chikusa-ku, Nagoya 464-01, Japan. TEL 81-52-789-3873. FAX 81-52-789-3887. Ed. Hideki Yamamura. circ. 400. **Indexed:** Biol.Abstr., Chem.Abstr., Excerp.Med., INIS Atomind. **Document type:** academic/scholarly publication.
—BLDSC (3791.522500); CASDDS.
    Formerly (until vol.25, 1980): Nagoya University. Research Institute of Environmental Medicine. Annual Report (ISSN 0469-4759)
    Refereed Serial

610   IT   ISSN 1120-9763
EPIDEMIOLOGIA E PREVENZIONE. 1977. q. L.49000 (foreign L.59000). Nuova Italia Scientifica, Via Sardegna 50, 00187 Rome, Italy. TEL 06-4742176. Ed. Giuseepe Lojacono.
—BLDSC (3793.536000).

614.4   US   ISSN 0193-936X
RA648.5   CODEN: EPIRD7
EPIDEMIOLOGIC REVIEWS. 1979. s-a. $20 price varies. Johns Hopkins University, School of Hygiene & Public Health, 2007 E. Monument St., Baltimore, MD 21205. TEL 301-955-3441. Ed. Haroutune K. Armenian. (also avail. in microfilm from WWS) **Indexed:** Abstr.Hyg., Biol.Dig., Biostat., Curr.Adv.Ecol.Sci., Diar.Dis.Res., Excerp.Med., Helminthol.Abstr., Ind.Med., Ind.Sci.Rev., Ind.Vet., Sci.Cit.Ind, Trop.Dis.Bull., Vet.Bull.
—BLDSC (3793.540000); Faxon; Genuine Article; SWETS; UnCover. **CCC.**

610 614   CE
EPIDEMIOLOGICAL BULLETIN. (Text in English) 1960. q. free. Department of Health, Epidemiological Unit, N.T.I. Building, 385 Dean's Road, Colombo 10, Sri Lanka. Ed. Charles A.L. Forbes. circ. 750. **Indexed:** Ind.Vet., Trop.Dis.Bull., Vet.Bull.

610   US   ISSN 0744-0898
                           CODEN: EPMOEJ
EPIDEMIOLOGY MONITOR. 1980. m. $35 (students $30; institutions $55). 2560 Whisper Wind Ct., Roswell, GA 30076. TEL 404-594-1613. FAX 404-594-0997. Ed. Roger H. Bernier. circ. 1,900. (tabloid format; back issues avail.)
—SWETS.
    Description: Covers preventive medicine, public health and epidemiology.

610   US
EPISOURCE; a guide to resources in epidemiology. 1991. irreg., 1st ed. 1991. $89.95. 2560 Whisper Wind Ct., Roswell, GA 30076. TEL 404-594-1613. FAX 404-594-0997.

610 681   SP
EQUIPOS MEDICOS. 6/yr. Comercio 4 bajo C 1a Esc., 28007 Madrid, Spain. TEL 1-433-45-23. Ed. A.M. Blanco Sanchez.

610   CU
EQUIPOS Y PRODUCTOS. BIOMEDICINA. m. Academia de Ciencias, Instituto de Documentacion e Informacion Cientifico-Tecnica (I D I C T), Capitolio Nacional, Prado y San Jose, Havana 2, Havana, Cuba.

610   JA   ISSN 0913-3887
EREKUTORONIKUSU NO RINSHO/ELECTRONICS IN MEDICAL CLINICS. (Text in Japanese) 1971. irreg. 300 Yen per no. Medikaru Erekutoro Taimusu - Medical Electro Times Co., Ltd., 35-8, Hongo 2-chome, Bunkyo-ku, Tokyo 113, Japan.

610   GW   ISSN 0014-0082
                           CODEN: ERFAAK
ERFAHRUNGSHEILKUNDE/ACTA MEDICA EMPIRICA; Zeitschrift fuer die aerztliche Praxis. (Text in German; summaries in English) 1951. m. DM.196 (students DM.98). (Gesellschaft der Aerzte fuer Erfahrungsheilkunde e.V.) Karl F. Haug Verlag GmbH, Fritz-Frey-Str. 21, 69121 Heidelberg, Germany. TEL 06221-4062-0. FAX 06221-400727. TELEX 461683-HVVFMD. (Subscr. to: Postfach 102840, 69018 Heidelberg, Germany) Ed. Dr. Gyoergy Irmey. adv. contact: J. Schulz. bk.rev.; abstr.; charts; illus. circ. 7,500. **Indexed:** Chem.Abstr., Dok.Arbeitsmed. **Document type:** academic/scholarly publication.
—BLDSC (3801.500000); CASDDS. **CCC.**

610   GW   ISSN 0936-9228
ERGEBNISSE DER DIAGNOSTIK, THERAPIE UND NACHSORGE. 1989. irreg., vol.2, 1991. DM.58. W. Zuckschwerdt Verlag GmbH, Industriestr. 17, 82110 Germering, Germany. TEL 089-894349-0. FAX 089-89434950. Ed. H. Sauer. **Document type:** academic/scholarly publication.

615.851   DK   ISSN 0105-8282
ERGOTERAPEUTEN. 1972. 22/yr. DKK 500 (effective Jan. 1995). Ergoterapeutforeningen - Danish Organisation of Occupational Therapists, Noerre Voldgade 90, DK-1358 Copenhagen K, Denmark. TEL 45-33-13-82-11. FAX 45-33-14-34-37. Ed. Esther Boserup. adv.: B&W page DKK 2900, color page DKK 9700; trim 217 x 151. bk.rev. circ. 5,100. **Document type:** academic/scholarly publication.
    Formerly (until 1939): Tidsskrift for Ergoterapeuter.
    Description: News on occupational therapy.

ESCALPELO. see *COLLEGE AND ALUMNI*

611   US
ESO MONOGRAPHS. 1986. irreg. price varies. Springer-Verlag, 175 Fifth Ave., New York, NY 10010. TEL 212-460-1500. FAX 212-473-6272. (Also: Berlin, Heidelberg, Tokyo and Vienna) (reprint service avail. from ISI) **Document type:** monographic series.

ESSENTIALS OF MANAGED HEALTH CARE. see *INSURANCE*

610   US   ISSN 0014-0937
ESSEX COUNTY MEDICAL SOCIETY. BULLETIN. vol.314, 1970. 9/yr. membership only. Essex County Medical Society, 80 Pompton Ave., Verona, NJ 07044. TEL 201-239-9392. Ed. Enio Callouri, M.D. adv.; illus. **Document type:** bulletin.

610 574   MX   ISSN 0020-3858
ESTUDIOS MEDICOS Y BIOLOGICOS. BOLETIN. (Text in English) 1942. q. free to qualified personnel. Universidad Nacional Autonoma de Mexico, Instituto de Investigaciones Biomedicas, Del. Coyoacan, Circuito Interior, Ciudad Universitaria, 04510 Mexico D.F., Mexico. Ed. Dr. Alfonso Escobar. bk.rev.; charts; illus.; index. circ. 1,800. **Indexed:** Biol.Abstr., Chem.Abstr., Ind.Med., INIS Atomind.
    Formerly: Instituto de Estudios Medicos y Biologicos. Boletin.

610   UK   ISSN 0266-688X
ETHICS AND MEDICINE. 3/yr. £10.50 (foreign £11). The Paternoster Press, P.O. Box 300, Kingstown Broadway, Carlisle, Cumbria CA3 0QS, England. TEL 0228-512512. FAX 0228-514949. (Dist. in U.S. & Canada by: Paternoster Press, P.O. Box 11127, Birmingham, AL 35201-1127) Ed. Nigel de S. Cameron. **Indexed:** Rel.& Theol.Abstr. (1985-). **Document type:** academic/scholarly publication.
—BLDSC (3814.657000).
    Description: Presents an international Christian perspective on bioethics.

ETHICS AND MEDICS. see *PHILOSOPHY*

ETHIK IN DER MEDIZIN. see *PHILOSOPHY*

610 ET ISSN 0014-1755
CODEN: EMDJA2
ETHIOPIAN MEDICAL JOURNAL. 1962. 4/yr.
Eth.$36($40) Ethiopian Medical Association, P.O.
Box 3472, Addis Ababa, Ethiopia. TEL 158174. Ed.
Abrehet Habtemariam. adv.; bk.rev.; illus. circ. 500.
Indexed: Abstr.Hyg., Biol.Abstr., Curr.Adv.Ecol.Sci.,
Curr.Adv.Genetics & Molec.Biol., Curr.Cont., Dairy
Sci.Abstr., Dent.Ind., Excerpt.Med., ExtraMED,
Helminthol.Abstr., Ind.Med., MEDSOC, Nutr.Abstr.,
Protozool.Abstr., Sci.Cit.Ind., Triticale Abstr.,
Trop.Dis.Bull., Zoo.Rec. **Document type:**
academic/scholarly publication.
●Also available on CD-ROM.
—BLDSC (3814.800000); Faxon; Genuine Article.

610 US ISSN 1049-510X
RA652 CODEN: ETDIEI
ETHNICITY & DISEASE. 1991. q. $40 to individuals
(foreign $48); institutions $90 (foreign $98).
(Loyola University, Department of Preventive
Medicine and Epidemiology) International Society on
Hypertension in Blacks, 69 Butler St. S.E., Atlanta,
GA 30303. FAX 708-216-4117. Ed. Richard S.
Cooper. adv.; bk.rev. **Indexed:** Ind.Med. (1992-).
Document type: academic/scholarly publication.
—BLDSC (3814.840500); UnCover.
Description: Covers population differences in
disease patterns and provides a comprehensive
source of information on causal relationships in the
etiology of common illnesses through the study of
ethnic patterns of disease.
Refereed Serial

**EURO COURSES. HEALTH PHYSICS AND RADIATION
PROTECTION.** see ENERGY — Nuclear Energy

612 SP
CODEN: AANOA7
EUROPEAN JOURNAL OF ANATOMY. (Text in Spanish;
summaries in English) 1952. 2/yr. $100.
Universidad de Zaragoza, Ciudad Universitaria, C.
Domingo Miral s-n, 50009 Zaragoza, Spain.
TEL 34-76-352745. adv.; bk.rev. **Indexed:**
Chem.Abstr., Excerpt.Med. **Document type:**
academic/scholarly publication.
—BLDSC (0887.900000); CASDDS. **CCC.**
Formerly: Anales de Anatomia (ISSN 0569-9894)

**EUROPEAN JOURNAL OF APPLIED PHYSIOLOGY AND
OCCUPATIONAL PHYSIOLOGY.** see BIOLOGY —
Physiology

EUROPEAN JOURNAL OF BIOCHEMISTRY. see
BIOLOGY — Biological Chemistry

EUROPEAN JOURNAL OF BIOCHEMISTRY (C D - R O M).
see BIOLOGY — Biological Chemistry

610 UK ISSN 0014-2972
R850.A1 CODEN: EJCIB8
EUROPEAN JOURNAL OF CLINICAL INVESTIGATION.
(Supplement avail. (ISSN 0960-135X)) 1971. bi-m.
£325 in Europe; elsewhere £359($578) (effective
1996). (European Society for Clinical Investigation)
Blackwell Science Ltd., Osney Mead, Oxford OX2
OEL, England. TEL 01865-206206.
FAX 01865-206219. TELEX 83355 MEDBOK G.
Ed.Bd. adv.; abstr.; bibl.; charts; illus.; index. circ.
1,770. (also avail. in microform from UMI; back
issues avail.: reprint service avail. from ISI) **Indexed:**
ASCA, Biol.Abstr., Biotech.Abstr., Chem.Abstr.,
Curr.Adv.Biochem., Curr.Adv.Ecol.Sci., Curr.Cont.,
Dairy Sci.Abstr., Excerpt.Med., Helminthol.Abstr.,
Ind.Med., Ind.Sci.Rev., INIS Atomind., Kidney, NRN,
Nutr.Abstr., Sci.Cit.Ind, Soyabean Abstr., Telegen.
Document type: academic/scholarly publication.
—BLDSC (3829.727100); ADONIS; CASDDS;
Faxon; Genuine Article; SWETS; UMI; UnCover. **CCC.**
Refereed Serial

610 UK ISSN 0960-135X
**EUROPEAN JOURNAL OF CLINICAL INVESTIGATION.
SUPPLEMENT.** 1990. a. (European Society for
Clinical Investigation) Blackwell Science Ltd., Osney
Mead, Oxford OX2 OEL, England.
TEL 01865-240201. FAX 01865-721205. TELEX
83355 MEDBOK G. **Indexed:** Excerpt.Med. (1993-).
Document type: academic/scholarly publication.
—ADONIS. **CCC.**

610 UK ISSN 0961-3692
EUROPEAN JOURNAL OF CLINICAL RESEARCH.
(Supplement avail.) 1991. s-m. £95 (outside £125)
(effective 1995). Brookwood Medical Publications,
Orchard House, Brookwood, Surrey GU24 OAT,
England. TEL 01483-797975.
FAX 01483-797915. **Indexed:** Excerpt.Med. (1993-).
Document type: academic/scholarly publication.
—BLDSC (3829.728120).
Description: Covers clinical and medical research
on drugs, devices and other products.
Refereed Serial

610 614 NE ISSN 0393-2990
CODEN: EJEPE8
EUROPEAN JOURNAL OF EPIDEMIOLOGY. (Text in
English) 1985. bi-m. fl.556 to institutions; $357 to
institutions in U.S. (effective 1996). Kluwer
Academic Publishers, Postbus 17, 3300 AA
Dordrecht, Netherlands. TEL 31-78-392392.
FAX 31-78-392254. E-mail: SERVICES@WKAP.NL.
(Dist. by: Kluwer Academic Publishers Group, P.O.
Box 322, 3300 AH Dordrecht, Netherlands. TEL
31-78-392392. FAX 31-78-546474; N. America
dist. addr.: Box 358, Accord Sta., Hingham, MA
02018-0358. TEL 617-871-6600. FAX
617-871-6528) Ed. Claude Hannoun. bk.rev.; index.
Indexed: Chem.Abstr., Curr.Cont., Excerpt.Med.,
Ind.Med., Int.Abstr.Biol.Sci., Protozool.Abstr.,
Rev.Med.& Vet.Mycol. **Document type:**
academic/scholarly publication.
—BLDSC (3829.728900); CASDDS; Faxon; Genuine
Article; UnCover. **CCC.**
Description: Forum on the epidemiology of
communicable and non-communicable diseases and
their control.
Refereed Serial

610 NE ISSN 1381-4788
▼**THE EUROPEAN JOURNAL OF GENERAL PRACTICE.**
(Text in English) 1995. q. fl.125($72) to
individuals; institutions fl.200(115). Mediselect B.V.,
Postbus 28091, 3828 ZH Hoogland, Netherlands.
TEL 31-33-808020. FAX 31-33-805881. Ed. Dr. F.
Sips; Pub. J. Blom. **Document type:** trade publication.
—BLDSC (3829.729430).
Description: Covers general medicine, family
practice and related developments in Europe.
Refereed Serial

340 610 NE ISSN 0929-0273
K5 CODEN: EJHLEB
▼**EUROPEAN JOURNAL OF HEALTH LAW.** (Text in
English) 1994. q. fl.324 to institutions; $207 to
institutions in U.S. (effective 1996). Kluwer Law
International (Subsidiary of: Wolters Kluwer N.V.),
Postbus 85889, 2508 CN The Hague, Netherlands.
TEL 31-70-3081500. FAX 31-70-3081515. E-mail:
SERVICES@WKAP.NL. (Dist. by: Kluwer Academic
Publishers Group, P.O. Box 322, 3300 AH
Dordrecht, Netherlands. TEL 31-78-546392. FAX
31-78-546477; N. America dist. addr.: Box 358,
Accord Sta., Hingham, MA 02018-0358. TEL
617-871-6600. FAX 617-871-6528) Eds. J.K.M
Gevers, H.D.C. Roscam Abbing. abstr. (reprint
service avail. from WSH) **Document type:**
academic/scholarly publication.
—BLDSC (3829.729850). **CCC.**
Description: Discusses the evolution of health law
in Europe on a national and international level.
Refereed Serial

EUROPEAN JOURNAL OF HISTOCHEMISTRY. see
BIOLOGY — Biological Chemistry

610 NE ISSN 0924-3860
QL799 CODEN: EJMOEB
EUROPEAN JOURNAL OF MORPHOLOGY. (Text in
English, French and German) 1956. 4/yr. $231.
Swets & Zeitlinger bv, Heereweg 347, 2161 CA
Lisse, Netherlands. TEL 31-2521-35111.
FAX 31-2521-15888. TELEX 41325. (Dist. in N.
America by: Swets & Zeitlinger, 440 Creamery Way,
Ste. A, Exton, PA 19341. TEL 800-447-9387. FAX
610-524-5366) Ed. Dr. J. Drukker. adv.; bk.rev.;
bibl.; charts; index. circ. 600. (reprint service avail.
from SWZ) **Indexed:** Anim.Breed.Abstr., ASCA,
Biol.Abstr., Chem.Abstr., Curr.Adv.Ecol.Sci.,
Curr.Cont., Dent.Ind., Excerpt.Med., Helminthol.Abstr.,
Ind.Med., Ind.Sci.Rev., Sci.Cit.Ind, Vet.Bull. **Document
type:** academic/scholarly publication.
—BLDSC (3829.731660); CASDDS; Faxon; Genuine
Article; SWETS; UnCover. **CCC.**
Formerly: Acta Morphologica
Neerlando-Scandinavica (ISSN 0001-6225)

MEDICAL SCIENCES 4199

610 GW ISSN 0939-6365
CODEN: EJPAE
EUROPEAN JOURNAL OF PAIN. q. DM.108 (students
DM.85). Verlag fuer Medizin Dr. Ewald Fischer
GmbH, Fritz-Frey-Str. 21, 69121 Heidelberg,
Germany. TEL 06221-4062-0. Ed. Dr. W. Nix. adv.
Indexed: Excerpt.Med. **Document type:**
academic/scholarly publication.
—BLDSC (3829.733380). **CCC.**
Formerly (until 1990): Schmerz (Heidelberg) (ISSN
0174-4895)

610.5 179 UK ISSN 0963-6056
EUROPEAN MEDICAL JOURNAL. 1991. q. £10 (foreign
£15). European Medical Journal, P.O. Box 30,
Barnstaple, Devon EX32 9YU, England. Ed. Dr.
Vernon Coleman. **Document type:** academic/scholarly
publication.

EUROPEAN NEWSLETTER ON QUALITY ASSURANCE. see
HOSPITALS

610 US ISSN 0163-2787
RA399.A1
EVALUATION AND THE HEALTH PROFESSIONS. 1978. q.
$59 to individuals; institutions $180 (effective Sep.
1995). Sage Publications, Inc., 2455 Teller Rd.,
Thousand Oaks, CA 91320. TEL 805-499-0721.
FAX 805-499-0871. E-mail: libraries@sagepub.com.
(Overseas subscr. to: Sage Publications Ltd., 6
Bonhill St., London EC2A 4PU, England; Sage
Publications India Pvt. Ltd., P.O. Box 4215, New
Delhi 110 048, India) Ed. R. Barker Bausell. adv.;
bk.rev.; bibl.; charts; stat.; index. circ. 1,100. (back
issues avail.; reprint service avail.) **Indexed:**
Abstr.Health Care Manage.Stud., Biostat., C.I.J.E.,
CINAHL, Excerpt.Med., Med.Care Rev., Mid.East:
Abstr.& Ind., Psychol.Abstr. (1984-), Risk Abstr.,
Sage Pub.Admin.Abstr., Viol.& Abuse Abstr.
Document type: academic/scholarly publication.
—BLDSC (3830.564000); Faxon; Genuine Article;
SWETS; UMI; UnCover. **CCC.**
Description: Provides a forum for all health care
professionals interested or engaged in the study,
design, and control of the physical environment and
its interaction with human behavioral systems.

610 US ISSN 1068-4557
RA413.5.U5
EXECUTIVE MANAGED CARE DIRECTORY. 1991. a. $65.
Medicom International, Inc., 66 Palmer Ave., Ste. 49,
Bronxville, NY 10708. TEL 914-337-7878.
FAX 914-337-5023. Pub. Raymond Hargreaves.
adv.: B&W page $3922, color page $5391. circ.
21,050. **Document type:** directory.
Description: Provides comprehensive reference
information on managed care suppliers and plans.

616.07 US ISSN 0014-4800
RB1 CODEN: EXMPA6
EXPERIMENTAL AND MOLECULAR PATHOLOGY. 1962.
bi-m. $533 (foreign $624) (effective 1996).
Academic Press, Inc., Journal Division, 525 B St.,
Ste. 1900, San Diego, CA 92101-4495.
TEL 619-230-1840. FAX 619-699-6800. (Subscr.
to: Box 620000, Orlando, FL 32891-8340. TEL
800-543-9534) Eds. Frederick Coulston, Wilbur A.
Thomas. adv.; bibl.; charts; illus.; index. (back issues
avail.) **Indexed:** Biol.Abstr., Chem.Abstr.,
Curr.Adv.Cancer Res., Dairy Sci.Abstr., Dent.Ind.,
Excerpt.Med., Helminthol.Abstr., Ind.Med.,
Ind.Sci.Rev., Ind.Vet., INIS Atomind., Nutr.Abstr.,
Rev.Med.& Vet.Mycol., Sci.Cit.Ind, Vet.Bull., Weed
Abstr. **Document type:** academic/scholarly
publication.
—BLDSC (3838.700000); ADONIS; CASDDS;
Faxon; Genuine Article; SWETS; UnCover. **CCC.**
Description: Presents articles on disease processes
in relation to structural and biochemical alterations
in mammalian tissues and fluids and on the
application of the newer techniques of analytical
chemistry, histochemistry, pharmacology, toxicology,
and electronic microscopy to problems of pathology
in humans and animals.
Refereed Serial

MEDICAL SCIENCES

619 GW ISSN 0940-2993
CODEN: ETPAEK
EXPERIMENTAL AND TOXICOLOGIC PATHOLOGY. (Text in English) 1967. 6/yr. DM.660($384) (foreign DM.672). Gustav Fischer Verlag Jena, Villengang 2, 07745 Jena, Germany. TEL 03641-626444. FAX 03641-626500. (Subscr. to: Postfach 100537, 07705 Jena, Germany) Ed. F. Bolck. adv.; bk.rev.; bibl.; charts; illus.; index. (reprint service avail. from ISI) **Indexed:** Biol.Abstr., Chem.Abstr., Curr.Adv.Cancer Res., Curr.Adv.Cell & Devel.Biol., Curr.Adv.Ecol.Sci., Curr.Cont., Dairy Sci.Abstr., Dent.Ind., Excerp.Med., Helminthol.Abstr., Ind.Med., Ind.Sci.Rev., INIS Atomind., Nutr.Abstr., Rev.Med.& Vet.Mycol., Sci.Cit.Ind. **Document type:** academic/scholarly publication.
—BLDSC (3838.720000); CASDDS; Faxon; Genuine Article; SWETS. **CCC.**
Former titles: Experimental Pathology (ISSN 0232-1513); Experimentelle Pathologie (ISSN 0014-4908)

EXPERIMENTAL CELL RESEARCH. see BIOLOGY — Cytology And Histology

EXPERIMENTAL PHYSIOLOGY. see BIOLOGY — Physiology

EXPERT OPINION ON THERAPEUTIC PATENTS; authoritative analysis of patenting trends. see PATENTS, TRADEMARKS AND COPYRIGHTS

EXTRAMED. see MEDICAL SCIENCES — Abstracting, Bibliographies, Statistics

610 JA ISSN 0915-2687
EZAI KENKYUJO NENPO/EISAI RESEARCH LABORATORIES. ANNUAL REPORT. (Text in English, Japanese) a. Ezai K.K. - Eisai Co., Ltd., 6-10, Koishikawa 4-chome, Bunkyo-ku, Tokyo 112, Japan.

610 SP ISSN 0210-8852
F A C: REVISTA PRACTICA DE MEDICINA. 1969. irreg. (4-5/yr.). free to qualified personnel. Laboratorio Alonga, S.A., Avda. Aragon, 18, 28027 Madrid, Spain. Ed. Francisco Llagostera Campillo. adv.; bk.rev. circ. 30,000.
—CCC.
Formerly: F A C: Revista Practica del Estudiante de Medicina.

610 US
F M A TODAY (JACKSONVILLE). 1985. bi-m. $15.90 (effective June 1992). Florida Medical Association, 760 Riverside Ave., Jacksonville, FL 32204. TEL 940-356-1571. FAX 904-353-1247. (Subscr. to: Box 2411, Jacksonville, FL 32203) Ed. Dr. R.G. Lacsamana. adv.; tr.lit. circ. 18,000. (tabloid format) **Document type:** newspaper.
Description: Covers association news, members' achievements, upcoming and past meetings, health issues, and health-related legislation.

610 US
F P REPORTER. (Family Physicians) 1974. m. membership. American Academy of Family Physicians, 8880 Ward Pkwy., Kansas City, MO 64114. TEL 816-333-9700. FAX 816-333-3344. Ed. Paula Binder. circ. 80,000. (tabloid format) **Document type:** newspaper.
Formerly (until 1995): A A F P Reporter (ISSN 0896-6877)
Description: News and features covering information specific to family physicians. Covers all medical-socioeconomic matters affecting family medicine.

610 US ISSN 0888-5656
RA396.A3
F S M B HANDBOOK. a. $15 to non-members. Federation of State Medical Boards, 400 Fuller Wiser Rd., Ste. 300, Euless, TX 76039-3855. TEL 817-868-4000. FAX 817-868-4099. Ed. Linda Chandler. circ. 1,000. **Document type:** directory.
—CCC.
Description: Covers 3 areas: history, goals and services; a directory; and articles of incorporation and bylaws.

610 US ISSN 1062-5380
F S M B NEWSLINE. 1981. m. $35. Federation of State Medical Boards, 400 Fuller Wiser Rd., Ste. 300, Euless, TX 76039-3855. TEL 817-868-4000. FAX 817-868-4099. Ed. Linda Chandler. circ. 2,000. **Document type:** newsletter.
—CCC.
Formerly (until 1991): F S M B Newsletter (ISSN 0888-5664)
Description: Focuses on current issues of interest to medical licensing and disciplinary authorities.

610 US ISSN 0163-0512
FACETS (CHICAGO). 1939. 6/yr. $7 to non-members; members $3.50. American Medical Association, 515 N. State St., Chicago, IL 60610. TEL 312-464-5000; 800-262-2350. FAX 312-464-4184. Ed. Kathleen T. Jordan. adv.; bk.rev.; abstr.; charts; illus.; stat. circ. 90,000. **Document type:** bulletin.
—CCC.
Former titles (until 1978): M D'S Wife (ISSN 0024-807X); (until 1965): American Medical Association Auxiliary. Bulletin (ISSN 0098-3748)

362 FR ISSN 0014-6951
FAIRE FACE. 1933. m. (11/yr.). 110 F. (typically set in Jan.). Association des Paralyses de France, 17 bd. Auguste Blanqui, 75013 Paris, France. TEL 40-78-69-00. FAX 45-89-40-57. Ed. Jean-Marie Creff. adv.; bk.rev.; illus. circ. 50,000. **Document type:** newspaper.
Description: Features rehabilitation techniques.

610 NE ISSN 0161-5580
CODEN: FASYDI
FALK SYMPOSIUM. (Text in English) irreg., vol.69, 1993. price varies. Kluwer Academic Publishers, Postbus 17, 3300 AA Dordrecht, Netherlands. TEL 31-78-392392. FAX 31-78-392254. TELEX 29245 KAPG NL. (Dist. by: Kluwer Academic Publishers Group, P.O. Box 322, 3300 AH Dordrecht, Netherlands. TEL 31-78-392392. FAX 31-78-546474; N. America dist. addr.: Box 358, Accord Sta., Hingham, MA 02018-0358. TEL 617-871-6600. FAX 617-871-6528) **Document type:** proceedings.
—BLDSC (3865.524000); CASDDS. **CCC.**
Refereed Serial

610 US ISSN 1050-463X
FAMILY HEALTH ADVISER. q. Whittle Communications L.P., 333 Main Ave., Knoxville, TN 37902. TEL 615-595-5300. Ed. Margot Leake.
Description: Helps family members to better understand how the family unit influences health (emotionally and physically) and provides a wide spectrum of health information and medical news that speaks to all age groups, sexes, and health interests.

610 370 US ISSN 0742-3225
FAMILY MEDICINE. 1968. 10/yr. $75 to individuals (overseas $90); institutions $100 (overseas $115). Society of Teachers of Family Medicine, Box 8729, 8880 Ward Pkwy., Kansas City, MO 64114. TEL 816-333-9700; 800-274-2237. FAX 816-333-3884. (Co-sponsor: North American Primary Care Research Group) Ed. Dr. Barry Weiss. adv.: B&W page $745; color page $1870; trim 8 3/8 x 10 7/8; adv. contact: Stacy Brundgardt. bk.rev.; bibl.; charts; illus.; cum.index (1981-1986). circ. 4,500. **Indexed:** Behav.Med.Abstr., Excerp.Med., FAMLI, Ind.Med. **Document type:** academic/scholarly publication.
—BLDSC (3865.567450); Faxon; SWETS; UnCover.
Former titles: Family Medicine Teacher; Family Medicine Times.
Description: Presents research studies and teaching methods for family physicians, family medicine educators, researchers, residents, and students.

610 US ISSN 0014-732X
FAMILY PHYSICIAN. 1951. bi-m. $30 to members (foreign $48); non-members $5 per no. Illinois Academy of Family Physicians, 1101 Perimeter Dr., Ste. 730, Schaumburg, IL 60173. TEL 708-240-5522. FAX 708-240-5887. Ed. Christine H. Emerson. adv. circ. 5,000. (tabloid format) **Indexed:** Biol.Abstr.
Description: Includes news of academy programs and articles about issues related to the practice of family medicine in Illinois.

610 UK ISSN 0263-2136
FAMILY PRACTICE. 1984. bi-m. £110($190) (effective 1996). Oxford University Press, Oxford Journals, Walton St., Oxford OX2 6DP, England. TEL 01865-267907. FAX 01865-267773. TELEX 837330-OXPRES-G. E-mail: jnlorders@oup.co.uk. (U.S. subscr. to: Oxford University Press Inc., 2001 Evans Rd., Cary, NC 27513. TEL 919-677-0977. FAX 919-677-1714) Ed. R.H. Jones. adv.; bk.rev. circ. 800. (also avail. in microform) **Indexed:** Curr.Cont., Excerp.Med. **Document type:** academic/scholarly publication.
—BLDSC (3865.574700); Genuine Article; SWETS; UMI; UnCover. **CCC.**
Description: Intends to serve as a means of broadening the international base of family medicine in general practice. Covers health care delivery, epidemiology, public health and medical sociology.

610 CN
FAMILY PRACTICE. 1989. 32/yr. Can.$48.15 (foreign Can.$69.55). Thomson Healthcare Communications, 1120 Birchmount Rd., Ste. 200, Scarborough, ON M1K 5G4, Canada. TEL 416-750-8900. FAX 416-751-8126. Ed. John Shaughnessy; Pub. Frank B. Lederer. adv.; bk.rev. circ. 24,000. (tabloid format) **Indexed:** Psychol.Abstr. (1991-).

610 658 US ISSN 1069-5648
R728
FAMILY PRACTICE MANAGEMENT. 1993. 10/yr. $47 to individuals. American Academy of Family Physicians, 8880 Ward Pkwy., Kansas City, MO 64114. TEL 816-333-9700. FAX 816-333-0303. Ed. Bob Edsall. adv.: B&W page $4250. circ. 90,000.
—BLDSC (3865.574725).
Description: Advises on practive management and coping with changes in reimbursement systems and increases in government regulations.

610 US ISSN 0300-7073
FAMILY PRACTICE NEWS. 1971. s-m. $96. International Medical News Group, 12230 Wilkins Ave., Rockville, MD 20852. TEL 301-816-8700. Ed. Mary Jo M. Dales. circ. 72,000. (tabloid format; also avail. in microform from UMI) **Document type:** newspaper.
—UMI.

610 US ISSN 0163-6642
R11
FAMILY PRACTICE RECERTIFICATION. 1979. m. $60 free to qualified personnel. (Medical Recertification Associates) M R A Publications, Inc., 3 Greenwich Office Park, Greenwich, CT 06831-5154. TEL 203-629-3550. FAX 203-629-2536. Eds. Diann Peterson, Paul Dishart. adv.: B&W page $3740, color page $4280; trim 8 1/8 x 11. bk.rev.; index. circ. 84,479. **Indexed:** FAMLI. **Document type:** trade publication.
—BLDSC (3865.574750).
Description: Directed towards physicians associated with family medicine; includes articles on new developments in medicine, clinical issues and family practice skills.
Refereed Serial

610 US ISSN 1063-8555
FAMILY PRACTICE RESIDENT. 1992. bi-m. $44. Slack, Inc., 6900 Grove Rd., Thorofare, NJ 08086. TEL 609-848-1000. FAX 609-853-5991. adv.: B&W page $1700, color page $2800; trim 8 1/8 x 10 7/8. circ. 10,708.

610 US
FAMILY PRACTICE TODAY. 1993. bi-m. Dowden Publishing Company, 110 Summit Ave., Montvale, NJ 07645. TEL 201-391-9100. FAX 201-391-2778. adv.: color page $6200; trim 7 x 10. circ. 77,950. **Document type:** trade publication.

MEDICAL SCIENCES 4201

610 US ISSN 0736-1718
R729.5.G4
FAMILY SYSTEMS MEDICINE. 1983. q. $35 to individuals (foreign $41); institutions $70 (foreign $76). Box 6542, Syracuse, NY 13217. FAX 201-236-0954. (And: 70 W. Allendale Ave., Ste. D, Allendale, NJ 07401. TEL 201-236-8381) Ed. Donald Bloch. adv.; bk.rev. circ. 1,500. (also avail. in microfilm; reprint service avail. from SWZ) Indexed: CINAHL, Excerp.Med., FAMLI, Lang.& Lang.Behav.Abstr., Psychol.Abstr., Sociol.Abstr. (1983-). **Document type:** academic/scholarly publication.
—BLDSC (3865.576300); Faxon; SWETS; UMI; UnCover.
Description: Publishes clinical, research and teaching materials relating to interface between family medicine, healthcare and family therapy.

610 US ISSN 1066-3517
FANLIGHT NEWS. 1985-1991 (vol.7 no.1); resumed 1992 (vol.8 no.1). s-a. free. Fanlight Productions, 47 Halifax St., Boston, MA 02130. TEL 617-524-0980; 800-937-4113. FAX 617-524-8838. Ed. Ben Achtenberg. bk.rev.; film rev. circ. 15,000. **Document type:** newsletter.
Description: Describes new media resources and general information of interest to healthcare and social services professionals, educators, librarians and administrators.

610 350 US ISSN 1047-8892
RA395.A3
FAULKNER AND GRAY'S MEDICINE AND HEALTH. Short title: Medicine and Health. 1946. w. $495 (includes Medical Health Perspectives) (effective 1995). Faulkner & Gray, Healthcare Information Center (Subsidiary of: Thomson Publishing Group), 1133 15th St., N.W., Ste. 450, Washington, DC 20005. TEL 202-828-4150. FAX 202-828-2352. Ed. Janet Firshein. index.
●Also available online. Vendor(s): NewsNet (HH21).
Former titles (until Sep. 1989): McGraw-Hill's Washington Report on Medicine and Health (ISSN 1047-8922); (until 1986): Washington Report on Medicine and Health (ISSN 0043-0730); (until 1968): Washington Report on the Medical Sciences (ISSN 1047-8876)
Description: Covers current developments in the health care industry, including legislative matters, with in-depth coverage of selected specific topics.

610 VE ISSN 0533-0327
FEDERACION PANAMERICANA DE ASOCIACIONES DE FACULTADES DE MEDICINA. BOLETIN. 1963. bi-m. free. (Federacion Panamericana de Asociaciones de Facultades de Medicina - Panamerican Federation of Associations of Medical Schools) Editorial Fepafem, Apdo. 60411, Caracas 1060-A, Venezuela. FAX 58-2-934275. Ed. Dr. Roberto Rondon Morales. bk.rev.; bibl. circ. 2,000. Indexed: FAMLI.

FEDERAL HEALTH MONITOR. see *PUBLIC HEALTH AND SAFETY*

610 US ISSN 1078-4497
FEDERAL PRACTITIONER; for the health care professionals of the VA, DoD and PHS. 1984. m. $131 to institutions outside the Americas; $74 to institutions in U.S (effective 1996). Excerpta Medica, Inc. (Subsidiary of: Reed Elsevier Medical group), 105 Raider Blvd., Belle Meade, NJ 08502. TEL 908-874-8550. FAX 908-874-8419. (Subscr. to: Box 3085, Princeton, NJ 08543-3085) Ed. Annette M. Skiendziel; Pub. James F. Breuning. adv.; index. circ. 25,854. (also avail. in microform from UMI; back issues avail.) **Document type:** trade publication.
—BLDSC (3901.930500). **CCC.**
Formerly (until vol.11, no.10, 1994): V A Practitioner (ISSN 0883-5721)
Description: An independent journal geared to the needs of the health care professional working in the Federal health care system.

610 CN ISSN 0843-0780
FEDERATION DES MEDECINS RESIDENTS DU QUEBEC. BULLETIN. 1977. 5/yr. Can.$5 to non-members. Federation des Medecins Residents du Quebec, 445 Sherbrooke West, Montreal, PQ H3A 1B6, Canada. TEL 514-282-0256. FAX 514-282-0471. Ed. Geamn Gouin. adv. contact: Patrick Labelle. circ. 2,000. **Document type:** bulletin.
Formerly: Federation des Medecins Residents et Internes du Quebec. Bulletin (ISSN 0821-2406)

610 US ISSN 0888-5648
RA396.A3
FEDERATION EXCHANGE. biennial. $60 for 3 section set. Federation of State Medical Boards, 400 Fuller Wiser Rd., Ste. 300, Euless, TX 76039-3855. TEL 817-868-4000. FAX 817-868-4099.
—**CCC.**
Description: Contains information on examination and licensing requirements in all US jurisdictions, and on medical board structure and disciplinary function.

610.7 US ISSN 0014-9306
FEDERATION OF STATE MEDICAL BOARDS OF THE UNITED STATES. FEDERATION BULLETIN; the journal of medical licensure and discipline. 1913. q. $35 (effective 1995). Federation of State Medical Boards, 400 Fuller Wiser Rd., Ste. 300, Euless, TX 76039-3855. TEL 817-868-4000. FAX 817-868-4099. Ed. Linda Chandler. bk.rev.; charts; index. circ. 4,000. (also avail. in microform from UMI; reprint service avail. from UMI) Indexed: Ind.Med.
—UMI; UnCover. **CCC.**
Description: Presents study and teaching methods.

610.6 060 IT
FEDERAZIONE DELLE SOCIETA MEDICO-SCIENTIFICHE ITALIANE. CONGRESSI (YEAR). (Text in English, Italian) 1978. a. free. Centro Trasfusionale e di Immunologia dei Trapianti, Ospedale Policlinico, Via Francesco Sforza 35, 20122 Milan, Italy. TEL 39-2-55181346. FAX 39-2-5458129. adv.; charts; illus. circ. 8,000. **Document type:** directory.
Former titles: Federazione delle Societa Medico-Scientifiche Italiane. Bollettino Congressi (Year) & Comitato per la Collaborazione tra Societa Medico-Scientifiche Italiane. Federazione delle Societa Medico-Scientifiche Italiane. Bollettino Congressi (Year); C C S S
Description: Lists international medical and scientific conferences.

610 IT ISSN 0014-9500
FEDERAZIONE MEDICA. 1921. m. (11/yr.). free. Federazione Nazionale degli Ordini dei Medici, Via Candido Viberti 7, 10141 Turin, Italy. TEL 11-338-507. FAX 11-38-52-750. Ed.Bd. adv.; bk.rev.; charts; illus.; bibl.; index. circ. 288,000. Indexed: C.I.S. Abstr.

610 IT ISSN 0014-9659
CODEN: FGTOAW
FEGATO. vol.24, 1978. 3/yr. L.5000. Societa Terme di Chianciano, S.p.A., 5302 Chianciano Terme, Italy. Ed. Piero Valori. bk.rev. Indexed: Chem.Abstr., Excerp.Med.
—BLDSC (3902.600000); CASDDS.

610 UK ISSN 0305-9324
FELLOWSHIP FOR FREEDOM IN MEDICINE. NEWSLETTER. 1948. s-a. £2 to non-members. Fellowship for Freedom in Medicine, Stockbury House, Church St., Storrington, Sussex RH20 4LD, England. Ed.Bd. **Document type:** newsletter.
Formerly (until 1973): Fellowship for Freedom in Medicine. Bulletin (ISSN 0014-9829)

610 NE ISSN 0167-7004
CODEN: FFOSDF
FERNSTROM FOUNDATION SERIES. 1982. irreg., vol.15, 1991. price varies. Elsevier Science B.V., Books Division, P.O. Box 211, 1000 AE Amsterdam, Netherlands. TEL 31-20-4853911. FAX 31-20-4853705. TELEX 18582 ESPA NL. E-mail: nlinfo-f@elsevier.nl; usinfo-f@elsevier.com; forinfo-kyf04035@niftyserve.or.jp; Site addr.: http://www.elsevier.nl/. (Subscr. in U.S. and Canada to: Elsevier Science Inc., Box 882, Madison Sq. Sta., New York, NY 10159. TEL 212-989-5800) Ed.Bd. (back issues avail.) Indexed: Excerp.Med. **Document type:** monographic series.
—CASDDS. **CCC.**
Refereed Serial

610 GW
▼**FIBRIN SEALING IN SURGICAL AND NONSURGICAL FIELDS.** 1994. irreg. DM.88. Springer-Verlag, Heidelberger Platz 3, 14197 Berlin, Germany. TEL 030-8207-1. FAX 030-8214091. Eds. G. Schlag, H. Redl. **Document type:** monographic series.

610 US
FIBROMYALGIA NETWORK NEWSLETTER. 1988. m. $19 (Canada $21; elsewhere $25) (effective 1995). Fibromyalgia Network, Box 31750, Tucson, AZ 85751-1750. TEL 520-290-5508; 800-853-2929. FAX 520-290-5550. Ed. Kristin Thorson. bk.rev. circ. 20,000. **Document type:** newsletter.
Description: Provides information for patients and physicians on Fibromyalgia Syndrome (FMS), a major disabling, chronic condition characterized by multiple areas of pain plus disrupted sleep.

611 US ISSN 1121-0419
FIDIA RESEARCH SERIES. 1986. irreg. price varies. Springer-Verlag, 175 Fifth Ave., New York, NY 10010. TEL 212-460-1500. FAX 212-473-6272. (Also: Berlin, Heidelberg, Tokyo and Vienna) (reprint service avail. from ISI) **Document type:** monographic series.

610 FJ ISSN 0301-1089
FIJI MEDICAL JOURNAL. 1960. m. F.$10. Fiji Medical Association, Box 1116, Suva, Fiji. Ed. Dr. K.D. Sharma. adv.; bk.rev. circ. 1,000. Indexed: So.Pac.Per.Ind.
—BLDSC (3925.557000).

FINLAND. KANSANELAKELAITOS. JULKAISUJA. SARJA AL. see *INSURANCE*

FINLAND. KANSANELAKELAITOS. JULKAISUJA. SARJA ML. see *INSURANCE*

610 617.6 FI
FINLAND. LAAKINTOHALLITUS. LAAKARIT - LAKKARE. (Text in Finnish and Swedish) 1976. a. FIM 195. National Institute of Health Research, P.O. Box 220, FI-00531 Helsinki, Finland. TEL 358-0-39672308. FAX 358-0-39672450. **Document type:** directory.
Formerly: Finland. Laakintohallitus. Laakarit, Hammaslaakarit - Laekare, Tandlaekare (ISSN 0430-5299)

FINLAND. TILASTOKESKUS. KUOLEMANSYYT/FINLAND. STATISTIKCENTRALEN. DOEDSORSAKER/FINLAND. CENTRAL STATISTICAL OFFICE. CAUSES OF DEATH IN FINLAND. see *BUSINESS AND ECONOMICS — Abstracting, Bibliographies, Statistics*

610 FI ISSN 0015-2501
FINSKA LAEKARESAELLSKAPET. HANDLINGAR. (Text in Swedish; summaries in English) 1841. 2/yr. FIM 80 membership only. Finska Laekaresaellskapet - Medical Society of Finland, P.O. Box 316, FIN-00171 Helsinki 17, Finland. TEL 358-0-665576. FAX 358-0-1356463. Ed. Svante Stenman. adv.; charts; illus. circ. 2,000. Indexed: Biol.Abstr., Chem.Abstr., Curr.Adv.Ecol.Sci., Excerp.Med. **Document type:** trade publication.
—BLDSC (4259.000000).
Description: Covers basic, experimental and clinical medical sciences. Includes original articles, association news, obituaries.

614.88 US
FIRST AIDER. 4/yr. $5. Cramer Products, Inc., Box 1001, Gardner, KS 66030. TEL 913-884-7511; 800-345-2231. Ed. Mary Horvatin. Indexed: Sportsearch (1979-). **Document type:** newsletter.

FISIOPATOLOGIA DELLA RIPRODUZIONE. see *BIOLOGY*

610 UK ISSN 0962-130X
THE FITZHUGH DIRECTORY OF INDEPENDENT HEALTHCARE. FINANCIAL INFORMATION. ACUTE SECTOR. 1986. a. £220. Health Care Information Services (Subsidiary of: W A F Health Care Consultant Ltd.), 12 Riverview Grove, London W4 3QJ, England. TEL 0181-995-1752. FAX 0181-742-2418. **Document type:** directory.
Formerly (until 1990): Fitzhugh Directory of Independent Hospitals and Provident Associations.
Description: Surveys the financial dynamics of this growing market.

MEDICAL SCIENCES

610 658   UK   ISSN 0959-6305
THE FITZHUGH DIRECTORY OF LONG TERM CARE. FINANCIAL INFORMATION. 1989. a. £220. (Ashbourne Homes) Health Care Information Services (Subsidiary of: W A F Health Care Consultant Ltd.), 12 Riverview Grove, London W4 3QJ, England. TEL 0181-995-1752. FAX 0181-742-2418. (Co-sponsor: Independent British Hospitals) Ed. William Fitzhugh. charts; stat. **Document type:** directory.
—BLDSC (3948.415500).
    Description: Gives business and financial profiles of long-term care institutions.

FIZIOLOGICHESKII ZHURNAL (KIEV); nauchno-teoreticheskii zhurnal. see *BIOLOGY — Physiology*

FIZIOLOGICHESKII ZHURNAL IM. SECHENOVA/SECHENOV PHYSIOLOGICAL JOURNAL. see *BIOLOGY — Physiology*

FLORIDA BAR. HEALTH LAW SECTION. NEWSLETTER. see *LAW*

610   US   ISSN 0015-4067
FLORIDA FAMILY PHYSICIAN. 1953. q. membership. (Florida Academy of Family Physicians) Journalistic, Inc., 4905 Pine Cone Dr., Durham, NC 27707. TEL 919-489-1916. FAX 919-489-4767. (Subscr. to: Florida Academy of Family Physicians, 1627 Rogero Rd., Jacksonville, FL 32211. TEL 904-743-6304) Ed. Dr. R. Edward Dodge. adv. contact: Jon Morton. charts; illus. circ. 18,000. **Document type:** academic/scholarly publication.
—BLDSC (3956.005000).
    Formerly: Florida Academy of General Practice Journal.
    Refereed Serial

FLORIDA HEALTHTRAC. see *LAW*

610   US   ISSN 0015-4148
                                   CODEN: JFMAAQ
FLORIDA MEDICAL ASSOCIATION. JOURNAL. 1914. m. $30 (foreign $35). Florida Medical Association, Inc., Box 2411, Jacksonville, FL 32203. TEL 904-356-1571; 800-940-9451. FAX 904-353-1247. Ed. Dr. Jacques R. Caldwell. adv. contact: Joy Freiha. bk.rev.; bibl.; charts; illus.; stat.; index. circ. 17,000. (also avail. in microform from UMI; reprint service avail. from UMI) **Indexed:** Chem.Abstr., Curr.Cont., Dent.Ind., Excerp.Med., Helminthol.Abstr., Ind.Med., INIS Atomind., Nutr.Abstr. **Document type:** trade publication.
—BLDSC (4754.200000); Faxon; SWETS; UMI; UnCover.
    Refereed Serial

616.9   US   ISSN 0015-4857
FLYING PHYSICIAN. 1955. q. $30 (foreign $60). Flying Physician Association, Box 677427, Orlando, FL 32867-7427. TEL 816-763-9336. Ed. Dr. George M. Gumbert, Jr. adv.; bk.rev.; illus. circ. 5,000.
    Description: Discusses aerospace medicine.

610   US
FOCUS (NEW YORK, 1978). 1978. m. during academic year. free. State University of New York, Health Science Center at Brooklyn, 450 Clarkson Ave., Brooklyn, NY 11203. Ed. M. Ellen Griffin. circ. controlled.
    Incorporates: State University of New York. Downstate Medical Center. Faculty Briefs (ISSN 0039-0208); Former titles: Downstate Medical Center; Downstate Examiner; Supersedes (1969-1978): What's News.

610   GW   ISSN 0940-9998
FOCUS M U L; Zeitschrift fuer Wissenschaft, Forschung und Lehre an der medizinischen Universitaet zu Luebeck. q. DM.74. (Medizinischen Universitaet zu Luebeck) Hansisches Verlagskontor H. Scheffler, 23547 Luebeck, Germany. TEL 0451-1605-0. Eds. H.F. Piper, R. Labahn. adv. contact: Christiane Kermel. circ. 5,000. **Document type:** academic/scholarly publication.
—BLDSC (3964.203570).

FOCUS ON BRITISH BIOLOGICAL AND MEDICAL SCIENCES RESEARCH. see *BIOLOGY*

610   DK   ISSN 0107-3362
FODPLEJEREN. 1976. q. Sammenslutningen af Danske Fodplejere, c/o Hartvig Pedersen, Tegelvaerksvej 20, Brundby, 8791 Tranebjerg, Denmark.
    Formerly: Fodspecialisten (ISSN 0107-4148)

610   BL   ISSN 0015-5454
FOLHA MEDICA. (Text in Portuguese; summaries in English and Portuguese) 1920. m. $180. Cidade - Editora Cientifica Ltda., Rua Mexico 90-2 Andar, 20031 Rio de Janeiro RJ, Brazil. TEL 021-240-4578. Ed. Fernando Moyses. adv.; bk.rev.; abstr.; bibl.; charts; illus.; index. circ. 15,000. **Indexed:** Biol.Abstr., Chem.Abstr., Excerp.Med., Ind.Med., INIS Atomind.
—BLDSC (3965.400000); Faxon.

610   BN   ISSN 0352-9657
FOLIA ANATOMICA IUGOSLAVICA. (Text in Serbo-Croatian; summaries in English) 1972. a. $14. Savez Drustava Anatoma Jugoslavije, Mose Pijade 6, 71000 Sarajevo, Bosnia Hercegovina. Ed. M. Scepovic. bk.rev. circ. 600. **Indexed:** Excerp.Med. (until 1992).
—BLDSC (3966.100000).

610   PL   ISSN 0015-5616
                           CODEN: FMCRAW
FOLIA MEDICA CRACOVIENSIA. (Text in Polish; summaries in English and Russian) 1959. 4/yr. price varies. (Polska Akademia Nauk, Oddzial w Krakowie) Ossolineum, Publishing House of the Polish Academy of Sciences, Ryne 9, 50-106 Wroclaw, Poland. TEL 48-71-386-25. FAX 48-71-448-103. TELEX 0712771 OSS PL. Ed. Dr. Zdzislaw Mach. bibl.; charts; illus.; index. **Indexed:** Biol.Abstr., Chem.Abstr, Excerp.Med. (until 1993), Ind.Med. **Document type:** academic/scholarly publication.
—BLDSC (3971.405000); CASDDS.
    Description: Presents both clinical and experimental research and discusses the mechanisms of pathogenesis of various diseases.

FOOD, DRUG, COSMETIC, AND MEDICAL DEVICE LAW DIGEST. see *LAW*

610   US   ISSN 1049-6742
FOR THE RECORD (VALLEY FORGE). 1989. w. $13 to qualified persons; non-qualified $52. Great Valley Publishing, Box 2224, Valley Forge, PA 19482. TEL 610-917-9300; 800-278-4400. FAX 610-917-9186. Ed. Leah Rapposelli. adv.; bk.rev.; charts; illus.; circ. (controlled).
    Description: Publishes items of general interest to medical record professionals, including legislation, software, and management issues.

610   HK   ISSN 0929-6646
                           CODEN: JFASEO
FORMOSAN MEDICAL ASSOCIATION. JOURNAL. (Includes q. supplement) (Text in English) 1907. m. $60 (foreign $90). (Formosan Medical Association, CH) Excerpta Medica Asia Ltd., Eight Commercial Tower, 19th Fl., 8 Sun Yip St., Chai Wan, Hong Kong. TEL 852-9651300. (Subscr. to: Formosan Medical Association, No. 1, Chang-Te St., Taipei 10016, Taiwan, Republic of China. TEL 02-3810367. FAX 02-3896716) Ed. Dr. Tsu-pei Hung. adv.; charts; illus. circ. 5,400. (reprint service avail. from IRC) **Indexed:** Abstr.Hyg., Biol.Abstr., Chem.Abstr., Dent.Ind., Excerp.Med., Helminthol.Abstr., Ind.Med., Trop.Dis.Bull. **Document type:** academic/scholarly publication.
—BLDSC (4754.900000); CASDDS; Genuine Article; SWETS; UnCover.
    Former titles (until Nov. 1993): Taiwan I Hsueh Hui Tsa Chih (ISSN 0371-7682); (until 1946): Taiwan Igakkai Zasshi - Medical Association of Taiwan. Journal (ISSN 0372-3321)
    Description: Covers basic, experimental, and clinical medical sciences. Includes original articles, case reports, brief communications, review articles, association news, announcements of meetings, etc. Supplement issues include programs and abstracts of meetings.

610   SZ   ISSN 1021-7096
▼**FORSCHENDE KOMPLEMENTAERMEDIZIN.** (Text in English, German) 1994. bi-m. 69.500 SFr.($53.50) to individuals; institutions 139 SFr.($107) (effective 1996). S. Karger AG, Allschwilerstr. 10, CH-4009 Basel, Switzerland. TEL 061-3061111. FAX 061-3061234. Ed.Bd. adv. contact: Christiane Opitz. circ. 5,000. **Document type:** academic/scholarly publication.
—BLDSC (4008.991100).

FORSKNING I GROENLAND-TUSAAT. see *EARTH SCIENCES*

610   GW   ISSN 0170-3331
FORTSCHRITT UND FORTBILDUNG IN DER MEDIZIN. a. Deutscher Aerzte-Verlag GmbH, Postfach 400265, 50832 Cologne, Germany. TEL 02234-70110. FAX 02234-7011444. **Document type:** trade publication.
—BLDSC (4018.610000).

610   GW   ISSN 0015-8178
                           CODEN: FMDZAR
FORTSCHRITTE DER MEDIZIN; Internationale Zeitschrift fuer die gesamte Heilkunde. (Supplement avail. (ISSN 0932-5611)) (Text in German, summaries in English) 1882. 3/m. DM.212($154) (effective 1996). Urban und Vogel, Lindwurmstr. 95, 80337 Munich, Germany. TEL 089-53292-0. FAX 089-53292-100. (Subscr. to: Postfach 152209, 80052 Munich, Germany) adv.; bk.rev.; abstr.; bibl.; charts; illus.; stat.; index; circ. 47,000 (controlled). **Indexed:** Biol.Abstr., Chem.Abstr., Curr.Adv.Cancer Res., Curr.Adv.Ecol.Sci., Curr.Cont., Dent.Ind., Excerp.Med., Helminthol.Abstr., Ind.Med., INIS Atomind., Nutr.Abstr. **Document type:** academic/scholarly publication.
—BLDSC (4021.950000); CASDDS; Faxon; Genuine Article; SWETS. **CCC.**
    Description: Publication for physicians, covering all fields of medicine. Features current research and technology, news, and reports of events.

610   GW   ISSN 0932-5611
                           CODEN: FMSUE
FORTSCHRITTE DER MEDIZIN. SUPPLEMENT. (Text in German, summaries in English) irreg. Urban und Vogel, Lindwurmstr. 95, 80337 Munich, Germany. TEL 089-53292-0. FAX 089-53292-100. (Subscr. to: Postfach 152209, 80052 Munich, Germany) **Indexed:** Excerp.Med. **Document type:** monographic series.
—BLDSC (4021.951100).

610   GW   ISSN 0930-925X
FORTSCHRITTE IN DER ARTHROSKOPIE. 1985. irreg., vol.8, 1992. price varies. Ferdinand Enke Verlag, Postfach 300366, 70443 Stuttgart, Germany. TEL 0711-135798-0. FAX 0711-135798-30. TELEX 07252275-GTV-D. Eds. H. Hofer, W. Glinz. (reprint service avail. from IRC) **Document type:** monographic series.

610   SP   ISSN 0212-9965
FORUM. 1982. 24/yr. free. Ediciones Mayo, S.A., Muntaner 374, 4o, 08006 Barcelona, Spain. TEL 34-3-2090255. FAX 34-3-2020643. Ed. J.M. Ferrando. adv. circ. 10,000. **Document type:** academic/scholarly publication.

610   GW   ISSN 0015-850X
FORUM DES PRAKTISCHEN ARZTES. 1962. m. DM.40. (Vereinigung der Praktischen Aerzte Bayerns e.V.) Verlag A. Fruehmorgen, Schwindstr. 5, 80798 Munich, Germany. Ed. A. Fruhmorgen. adv.; bk.rev.; illus. circ. 20,000. (tabloid format)
—**CCC.**

610   AU
FORUM DR. MED. (Text in German; summaries in English, German) 1976. 18/yr. S.540. Medizinische Fachzeitschriften GmbH, A-2464 Goettlesbrunn 124, Austria. TEL 02162-8735. FAX 02162-87354. Ed. Gerhard Fillitz. adv.: B&W page S.29000, color page S.36800; trim 185 x 263; adv. contact: Evelyne Bures. circ. 28,500. **Document type:** academic/scholarly publication.

610   GW   ISSN 0932-0547
FORUM LOGOPAEDIE. 1987. q. DM.72. (Deutscher Bundesverband fuer Logopaedie e.V.) Schulz - Kirchner Verlag GmbH, Itzbachweg 2, 65510 Idstein, Germany. TEL 06126-9320-0. FAX 06126-52179. Ed. Dietlinde Schrey-Dern. adv.: page DM.1380; trim 180 x 266; adv. contact: Doris Zimmerman. bk.rev.; index. circ. 5,600. **Document type:** academic/scholarly publication.

610   IT   ISSN 0015-9271
                           CODEN: FRACAC
FRACASTORO. 1907. 3/yr. L.10000 per no. Istituti Ospitalieri Verona, Via Bassini 1, Verona, Italy. FAX 45-8301200. Ed. G. Mastella. adv.; bk.rev. circ. 4,000. **Indexed:** Biol.Abstr., Chem.Abstr., Curr.Adv.Ecol.Sci., Excerp.Med. (until 1993), Ind.Med.
—BLDSC (4030.600000).

MEDICAL SCIENCES

610   FR   ISSN 0763-7098
FRANCE. INSTITUT NATIONAL DE LA SANTE ET DE LA RECHERCHE MEDICALE. COLLOQUES. (Text mainly in English) 1971. irreg. price varies. Institut National de la Sante et de la Recherche Medicale, 101 rue de Tolbiac, 75654 Paris Cedex 13, France. TEL 44-23-60-00. FAX 44-23-60-99. **Document type:** proceedings, academic/scholarly publication.

362   SZ
FREUNDE DER MILCHSUPPE.* 1953. 6/yr. Verein Freunde der Milchsuppe, Postfach 205, CH-4025 Basel, Switzerland. Ed. Christiane Muschter. adv.; illus.
     Formerly (until 1979): Milchsuppe (ISSN 0026-377X)

610   IT   ISSN 0016-1535
IL FRIULI MEDICO; alpe-adria journal of medicine. (Text in English or Italian; summaries in English and Italian) 1946. q. L.75000 (foreign L.85000). (Consorzio per la Costituzione e lo Sviluppo degli Insegnamenti Universitari di Udine) Tipografia Editorice A. Pellegrini, Via della Vigna 24-A, 33100 Udine, Italy. TEL 39-432-559400. FAX 39-432-559420. Ed. Carlos Alberto Beltrami. adv.: page L.1500000. bk.rev.; bibl.; charts; illus.; stat.; index, cum.index. circ. 1,500. **Indexed:** Biol.Abstr., Chem.Abstr., Excerp.Med., Ind.Med. **Document type:** academic/scholarly publication, proceedings.
     —BLDSC (4040.200000).
     Description: Features research papers on a wide variety of topics in medicine. Includes much research carried out in northeastern Italy.
     Refereed Serial

610   IT   ISSN 0390-9166
FRONTE SANITARIO; quindicinale dei medici italiani. 1944. 11/yr. L.30000. Via Galata 20-5, 16121 Genoa, Italy. TEL 020-294500. Ed. Gianfranco de Ferrari. adv.: B&W page L.3200000. circ. 12,000.

616.072   US   ISSN 1066-8322
                            CODEN: FHREE3
FRONTIERS IN HEADACHE RESEARCH. 1991. irreg., vol.5, 1995. price varies. Raven Press (Subsidiary of: Wolters Kluwer N.V.), 1185 Ave. of the Americas, New York, NY 10036. TEL 212-930-9500. FAX 212-869-3495. (reprint service avail. from UMI) **Document type:** monographic series.
     —BLDSC (4042.022800); CASDDS.
     Refereed Serial

FRONTIERS OF HEALTH SERVICES MANAGEMENT. see *HOSPITALS*

FRONTIERS OF MEDICAL AND BIOLOGICAL ENGINEERING. see *BIOLOGY — Bioengineering*

610   JA   ISSN 0288-2744
FUJI MEDIKARU FORAMU/FUJI MEDICAL FORUM. (Text in Japanese) 1955. q. 100 Yen per no. Fuji Medikaru Shisutemu K.K. - Fuji Medical System Co., Ltd., 13-8, Ginza 7-chome, Chuo-ku, Tokyo 104, Japan.

FUJIAN YIYAO ZAZHI/FUJIAN MEDICAL AND PHARMACOLOGICAL JOURNAL. see *PHARMACY AND PHARMACOLOGY*

610   CC   ISSN 1004-5627
FUJIAN ZHONGYI XUEYUAN XUEBAO/FUJIAN COLLEGE OF TRADITIONAL CHINESE MEDICINE. JOURNAL. (Text in Chinese) 1991. q. Y1.50 per no. Fujian Zongyi Xueyuan, 282 Wusi Lu, Fuzhou, Fujian 350003, People's Republic of China. TEL 0591-7841296. FAX 0591-7842524. (Dist. overseas by: China International Book Trading Corp., Chegongzhuang Xilu 34, P.O. Box 399, Beijing, P. R. China) Ed. Du Jian. adv.; bk.rev. circ. 16,000. **Document type:** academic/scholarly publication.
     Description: Aims to popularize traditional Chinese medicine. Carries papers, articles that reflect the new developments in Chinese medical science.

610   JA   ISSN 0288-5441
                            CODEN: FGIGDO
FUJITA GAKUEN IGAKKAISHI/FUJITA MEDICAL SOCIETY. BULLETIN. (Text in Japanese) 1977. s-a. Fujita Gakuen Igakkai, Fujita Hoken Eisei Daigaku, 1-98 Dengakugakubo, Kutsukakecho, Toyoake-shi, Aichi-ken 470-11, Japan. **Indexed:** Chem.Abstr.
     —BLDSC (2523.100800); CASDDS.

610   JA   ISSN 0915-423X
FUKUI IKA DAIGAKU KENKYU KATSUDO ICHIRAN/FUKUI MEDICAL SCHOOL. LIST OF RESEARCH ACTIVITIES. (Text in English, Japanese) 1989. a. Fukui Ika Daigaku, 23-3, Shimoaizuki, Matsuokacho, Yoshida-gun, Fukui-ken 910-11, Japan.

610   JA   ISSN 0016-254X
                            CODEN: FKIZA4
FUKUOKA ACTA MEDICA/FUKUOKA IGAKU ZASSHI. (Text in Japanese; summaries in English) 1907. m. 3000 Yen($6.70) Fukuoka Medical Society - Fukuoka Igakkai, c/o Kyushu Daigaku Igakubu, Maidashi 3-1-1, Higashi-ku, Fukuoka 812, Japan. FAX 092-631-2794. Ed. Naohide Inoue. adv.; charts; mkt.; index. circ. 1,200. **Indexed:** Biol.Abstr., Chem.Abstr., Curr.Adv.Cancer Res., Curr.Adv.Ecol.Sci., Dent.Ind., Excerp.Med., Ind.Med., INIS Atomind.
     —BLDSC (4054.896200); CASDDS.

610   JA   ISSN 0385-9347
                            CODEN: FIKIDK
FUKUOKA DAIGAKU IGAKU KIYO/FUKUOKA UNIVERSITY. MEDICAL BULLETIN. (Text in English, Japanese) 1974. q. Fukuoka Daigaku, Sogo Kenkyujo - Fukuoka University, Central Research Institute, 19-1, Nanakuma 8-chome, Jonan-ku, Fukuoka-shi, Fukuoka-ken 814-80, Japan. TEL 092-871-6631. **Indexed:** INIS Atomind.

610   JA   ISSN 0285-3418
FUKUOKAKEN IHO/FUKUOKA MEDICAL ASSOCIATION. JOURNAL. (Text in Japanese; summaries in English) 1948. m. 2400 Yen. Fukuokaken Ishikai, 9-30, Hakataeki Minami 2-chome, Hakata-ku, Fukuoka-shi, Fukuoka-ken 812, Japan.

610   JA   ISSN 0917-9011
FUKUROI SHIRITSU FUKUROI SHIMIN BYOIN KENKYUSHI/FUKUROI MUNICIPAL HOSPITAL. JOURNAL. (Text in English, Japanese) 1992. a. Fukuroi Shiritsu Fukuroi Shimin Byoin, 2515-1 Kuno, Fukuro-shi, Shizuoka-ken 437, Japan.

610   JA   ISSN 0016-2590
                            CODEN: FJMSAU
FUKUSHIMA JOURNAL OF MEDICAL SCIENCE. (Text in English) 1954. s-a. membership. Fukushima Society of Medical Science, Fukushima Medical College Library, 1, Hikariga-oka, Fukushima 960-12, Japan. FAX 81-245-48-2535. Ed. Teizo Fujita. charts; illus.; index. circ. 1,600. **Indexed:** Abstr.Hyg., Biol.Abstr., Chem.Abstr., Curr.Adv.Ecol.Sci., Excerp.Med., Ind.Med., INIS Atomind., Nutr.Abstr., Trop.Dis.Bull. **Document type:** academic/scholarly publication.
     —BLDSC (4055.000000); CASDDS; UnCover.

610   JA   ISSN 0913-2864
FUKUSHIMA KENRITSU BYOIN IGAKU KENKYUSHI/FUKUSHIMA MEDICAL BULLETIN. (Text in Japanese) 1985. a. Fukushima Kenritsu Byoin - Fukushima Prefectural Hospital, 3, Haraguchi, Iizakamachi, Fukushima-shi, Fukushima-ken 960-02, Japan.

610   JA   ISSN 0016-2582
                            CODEN: FSIZAQ
FUKUSHIMA MEDICAL JOURNAL/FUKUSHIMA IGAKU ZASSHI. (Text in Japanese; summaries in English) 1951. q. membership. Fukushima Society of Medical Science, Fukushima Medical College Library, 1, Hikariga-oka, Fukushima 960-12, Japan. FAX 81-245-48-2535. Ed. Yukihiko Kayama. charts; illus.; index. circ. 1,330. **Indexed:** Biol.Abstr., Chem.Abstr., Excerp.Med., INIS Atomind. **Document type:** academic/scholarly publication.
     —BLDSC (4055.200000); CASDDS.

610   JA   ISSN 0911-9426
FUKUSHIMAKEN NOSON IGAKKAI ZASSHI/FUKUSHIMA JOURNAL OF RURAL MEDICINE.* (Text in Japanese) a. Fukushimaken Noson Igakkai - Fukushima Rural Medical Association, c/o Japan Medical Association, Bunkyo-ku, Tokyo 113, Japan.

610   JA   ISSN 0917-1835
FUKUYAMA IGAKU/FUKUYAMA MEDICAL ASSOCIATION. JOURNAL. (Text in Japanese; summaries in English, Japanese) 1991. a. Fukuyamashi Ishikai, Fukuyamashi Ishi Kaikan, 11-25 Miyoshicho 2-chome, Fukuyama-shi, Hiroshima-ken 720, Japan.

FUNDAMENTAL AND APPLIED TOXICOLOGY. see *ENVIRONMENTAL STUDIES — Toxicology And Environmental Safety*

610   JA
FURI RAJIKARU NO RINSHO/FREE RADICALS IN CLINICAL MEDICINE. (Text in Japanese) 1987. a. 5150 Yen. Nihon Igakukan, 9-6-505, Otsuka 3-chome, Bunkyo-ku, Tokyo 112, Japan. TEL 81-3942-7631. FAX 03-3942-2086. Ed. Toshiaki Kikuzawa. **Document type:** academic/scholarly publication.

610   GW   ISSN 0179-6372
FUTURA. (Text in English and German) 1986. q. (Boehringer Ingelheim Fonds, Stiftung fuer Medizinische Grundlagenforschung) Hippokrates Verlag GmbH, Postfach 300504, 70445 Stuttgart, Germany. TEL 0711-89310. FAX 0711-8931453. circ. 2,200. **Document type:** academic/scholarly publication.

610   DK   ISSN 0904-6895
FYNSKE LAEGER. 1981. bi-m. DKK 150. Laegekredsforeningen for Fyns Amt, Skt. Anne Plads 2, 5 sal, DK-5000 Odense C, Denmark. TEL 45-66-13-32-11. Ed. Erik Himmelstrup. adv.; bk.rev.; illus. circ. 1,900. **Document type:** trade publication.
     Formerly (until 1981): Laegekredsforeningen Fyns Amt (ISSN 0109-5439)

610   UK
G P. 1963. w. £104 (free to full-time general practitioners). Haymarket Medical Ltd., 30 Lancaster Gate, London W2 3LP, England. TEL 0171-413-4095. (Subscr. to: Galleon, P.O. Box 219, Woking, Surrey GU21 1ZW, England. TEL 01483-733800) Ed. Dr. Farine Clarke. adv. contact: Richard Court. circ. 41,561. **Document type:** trade publication.
     ●Also available online. Vendor(s): Data-Star (GPGP).
     —CCC.
     Formerly (until 1994): General Practitioner (ISSN 0046-5607)

610   NZ   ISSN 1171-347X
G P WEEKLY. Variant title: General Practitioners Weekly. 1984. fortn. NZ.$75 (effective 1994). Adis International Limited, Private Bag 65901, Mairangi Bay, Auckland 1010, New Zealand. TEL 09-479-8100. FAX 09-479-8066. Ed. Lyndsey Swan. adv. contact: James White. bk.rev. circ. 3,900. (tabloid format; back issues avail.) **Document type:** newspaper.
     —CCC.
     Former titles (until Dec. 1991): New Zealand General Practice (ISSN 0114-2550); (until 1988): Journal of General Practice (ISSN 0112-2541)
     Description: For general practitioners covering health news and issues, medicopolitical comment and life-style pages.

610   CK   ISSN 0121-6309
GACETA MEDICA. 1991. q. Asociacion Colombiana de Facultades de Medicina, Av. 68 No. 40-21 Sur, Bogota, Colombia. TEL 571-2303573. TELEX 045703 TPTAR CO. Ed. Dr. Cesar A. Salcedo C. circ. 12,000 (controlled). (tabloid format) **Document type:** newspaper, trade publication.

610   SP   ISSN 0304-4858
                            CODEN: GCMBA9
GACETA MEDICA DE BILBAO. (Text in Spanish; summaries in English and Spanish) 1895. q. 1000 ptas.($30) Academia de Ciencias Medicas de Bilbao, Lersundi 9, 1o, 48009 Bilbao, Spain. TEL 4-423-37-68. Ed. Angel Arrien Echevarri. adv. circ. 5,000. (back issues avail.) **Indexed:** Excerp.Med., Ind.Med.Esp.
     —CCC.

610   VE   ISSN 0367-4762
GACETA MEDICA DE CARACAS. 1893. q. free. Academia Nacional de Medicina, Apdo. Postal 804, Caracas 1010-A, Venezuela. (Co-sponsor: Congreso Venezolano de Ciencias Medicas) Ed. Dr. Oscar Aguero. bk.rev.; bibl.; illus. circ. 1,000. **Indexed:** Abstr.Hyg., Chem.Abstr., Excerp.Med., Trop.Dis.Bull.
     —UMI.

MEDICAL SCIENCES

610   MX   ISSN 0016-3813
R21   CODEN: GMMEAK
GACETA MEDICA DE MEXICO. (Text in Spanish; summaries in English) 1864. bi-m. $100 to individuals; institutions $150 (effective 1995). Academia Nacional de Medicina, Unidad de Congresos, Bloque B, Centro Medico Nacional, Av. Cuauhtemoc 330, 06725 Mexico D.F., Mexico. TEL 525-5782044. FAX 525-5784271. (Co-sponsor: Instituto Mexicano del Seguro Social) Eds. Dr. Luis Benitez, Dr. Fabio Salamanca. bk.rev.; bibl.; illus.; index. circ. 40,000. (also avail. in microform from UMI; reprint service avail. from UMI) **Indexed:** Biol.Abstr., Chem.Abstr., Ind.Med., Ind.Vet., Rev.Med.& Vet.Mycol., Small Anim.Abstr., Soils & Fert., Trop.Dis.Bull. **Document type:** academic/scholarly publication.
—BLDSC (4066.080000); CASDDS; Faxon; UMI.

GACETA SANITARIA. see *PUBLIC HEALTH AND SAFETY*

613.7   NE   ISSN 0966-6362
QP310.W3
GAIT AND POSTURE. 1993. q. fl.370($226) (effective 1996). Elsevier Science B.V., P.O. Box 211, 1000 AE Amsterdam, Netherlands. TEL 31-20-4853911. FAX 31-20-4853598.
E-mail: nlinfo-f@elsevier.nl; usinfo-f@elsevier.com; forinfo-kyf04035@niftyserve.or.jp; Site addr.: http://www.elsevier.nl/. (Subscr. in U.S. and Canada to: Elsevier Science, Box 882, Madison Sq. Sta., New York, NY 10159-0882. TEL 212-989-5800. FAX 212-633-3390) (also avail. in microform from UMI; back issues avail.) **Document type:** academic/scholarly publication.
—BLDSC (4066.386100); Genuine Article; SWETS; UMI.
Refereed Serial

610   SP   ISSN 0304-4866
GALICIA CLINICA. 6/yr. Juana de Vega 13, 2o, 15004 La Coruna, Spain. TEL 81-22-25-96. Ed. Luis G. Moyano. circ. 33,000.
—BLDSC (4067.400000).

362   US   ISSN 1077-9965
GATHERED VIEW. 1975. bi-m. $21 to individuals; families $26; professionals $31. Prader-Willi Syndrome Association, 2510 S. Brentwood Blvd., Ste. 220, St. Louis, MO 63144-2326. TEL 800-926-4797. FAX 314-962-7869. Ed. Linda Keder, Lota Mitchell. bk.rev. circ. 1,800. (back issues avail.)
Description: Intended to educate anyone interested in caring for persons with Prader-Willi syndrome.

610   US
GAUCHER'S DISEASE NEWSLETTER.* bi-m. $35. National Gaucher Foundation, 11140 Rockville Pike, No. 350, Rockville, MD 20852-3106. TEL 800-925-8885. Ed. Karen A. Cohen. circ. 2,500. (back issues avail.) **Document type:** newsletter.

610   US
GAZETTE INTERNATIONAL NETWORKING INSTITUTE. PROCEEDINGS. irreg., 3rd, 1985. $8 (foreign $9.35). Gazette International Networking Institute, 5100 Oakland Ave., Ste. 206, St. Louis, MO 63110-1406. TEL 314-534-0475. FAX 314-534-5070. Eds. Gini Laurie, Judith Raymond. **Document type:** proceedings.

610   FR   ISSN 0016-5557
CODEN: GAMFA7
GAZETTE MEDICALE DE FRANCE. (Text in English and French) 1892. w. 100 F. 123 rue de Tocqueville, 75017 Paris, France. Ed. D. Testard. adv.; bk.rev.; abstr.; bibl.; charts; illus.; index. circ. 45,000. (also avail. in microform from UMI; back issues avail.; reprint service avail.from UMI) **Indexed:** Biol.Abstr., C.I.S. Abstr., Curr.Adv.Cancer Res., Curr.Adv.Ecol.Sci., Curr.Cont., Excerp.Med., Helminthol.Abstr., Ind.Med., Nutr.Abstr.
—CASDDS; UMI. **CCC.**
Formerly: Gazette Medicale de France et Science Medicale Pratique.

610   MG
GAZETY MEDIKALY. 1965. m. Lot 12 B, Ampahibe, 101 Antananarivo, Madagascar. TEL 27898. Ed. Paul Ratsimiseta. circ. 2,000. **Document type:** newspaper.

610   TU   ISSN 1300-056X
GAZI MEDICAL JOURNAL. (Text in English) 1990. 4/yr. Gazi Universitesi, Tip Fakultesi Dekanligi - Gazi University, Faculty of Medicine, Dean's Office, Besevler, 06510 Ankara, Turkey. TEL 90-312-2141000. FAX 90-312-2124647. Ed. Dr. Mehmet Ali Gurer. abstr.; bibl.; illus. **Indexed:** Excerp.Med. **Document type:** academic/scholarly publication.
—BLDSC (4094.655900).
Description: Publishes original articles on clinical or experimental investigations and case histories reporting unusual clinical syndromes or diseases.
Refereed Serial

610   TU
CODEN: GTDEE
GAZI TIP DERGISI. 4/yr. Gazi Universitesi, Tip Fakultesi Dekanligi - Gazi University, Medical Faculty, Dean's Office, Besevler, 06510 Ankara, Turkey. **Indexed:** Excerp.Med. (1992-).
Refereed Serial

610   IT   ISSN 0393-3660
CODEN: GMIMES
GAZZETTA MEDICA ITALIANA ARCHIVIO PER LE SCIENZE MEDICHE. bi-m. $95 to individuals; institutions $145 (effective 1995). Edizioni Minerva Medica, Corso Bramante 83-85, Turin 10126, Italy. TEL 39-11-678282. FAX 39-11-3121736. Ed. M.L. Benzo; Pub. Alberto Oliaro. adv.: B&W page $1100, color page $1900; trim 190 x 270; adv. contact: F. Filippo. circ. 3,000 (paid). **Indexed:** Biol.Abstr., C.I.S. Abstr., Chem.Abstr., Excerp.Med., Ind.Med., INIS Atomind. **Document type:** academic/scholarly publication.
—BLDSC (4095.153000); CASDDS; Faxon; UMI.
Formed by the merger of: Archivio per le Scienze Mediche (ISSN 0004-0312) & Gazzetta Medica Italiana - Aggiornamenti Clinicoterapeutici (ISSN 0392-159X); Which was formed by the 1983 merger of: Gazzetta Medica Italiana (ISSN 0016-5670); Aggiornamenti Clinicoterapeutici (ISSN 0002-0907)
Description: Cover clinical and experimental medicine and surgery.

610   JA   ISSN 0914-4277
GEKKAN CHIIKI IGAKU/MONTHLY COMMUNITY MEDICINE. (Text in Japanese) 1987. m. 600 Yen. Chiiki Iryo Shinko Kyokai - Japan Association for Development of Community Medicine, 6-3, Hirakawacho 2-chome, Chiyoda-ku, Tokyo 100, Japan. TEL 81-3-3221-7279. FAX 81-3-3221-7289. Ed. Ken-ichi Fujimoto. adv. contact: Katsutoshi Ikematsu. circ. 2,500.
Description: Contains scholarly papers, reviews, proceedings of meetings, and activity reports concerning community medicine.
Refereed Serial

610   JA   ISSN 0385-8588
GEKKAN HOKEN SHINRYO/MONTHLY REVIEW OF INSURANCE TREATMENT. (Text in Japanese) 1946. m. 2000 Yen. Igaku Tsushinsha, 9-4, Uchikanda 1-chome, Chiyoda-ku, Tokyo 101, Japan.
Formerly (until 1971): Shukan Igaku Tsushin.

610   JA   ISSN 0917-1061
GEKKAN IGAKU JOHO/CLIPPING MONTHLY REPORT. (Text in Japanese) 1989. m. 2000 Yen. Koseisha Infomeshon Sabisu - Koseisha Information Service, 2-7, Dojima 3-chome, Kita-ku, Osaka 530, Japan.

610   JA   ISSN 0913-9443
GEKKAN IRYO JOHO/MEDICAL NEWS OF THE MONTH. (Text in Japanese) 1987. m. 2700 Yen. Nihon Shuppan Koho Senta - Nihon Publishing Center, 10-3, Taito 1-chome, Taito-ku, Tokyo 110, Japan.

610   JA
GEKKAN MEDIKARU & FAIN/MONTHLY MEDICAL & FINE. (Text in Japanese) 1977. m. 60800 Yen. Gendai Shuppan Co., Ltd., 30-13, Hatchobori 2-chome, Chuo-ku, Tokyo 104, Japan.

610   JA   ISSN 0917-7507
GEKKAN SEKUSHUARU SAIENSU/SEXUAL SCIENCE. (Text in Japanese) 1991. m. 1200 Yen per no. Nihon Akuseru Shupuringa Shuppan K.K., Japan Publishing Inc. - Axel Springer, Japan Publishing Inc., 2-1, Niban-cho, Chiyoda-ku, Tokyo 102, Japan.

610   JA   ISSN 0910-7991
GEKKAN SHIN IRYO/NEW MEDICAL TREATMENT. (Text in Japanese) 1974. m. 1500 Yen. Emu I Shinko Kyokai - Association of Promotion for Medical Engineering, 13-15, Ginza 7-chome, Chuo-ku, Tokyo 104, Japan.

610   JA   ISSN 0386-1791
GEKKAN SOSHIKI BAIYO/TISSUE CULTURE. (Text in Japanese) 1975. m. 2200 Yen. Nyu Saiensusha - New Science Co., 1-5-12 Akasaka, Minato-ku, Tokyo 107, Japan. Dir. Hisako Fukuda. bk.rev. circ. 6,000 (paid). **Document type:** academic/scholarly publication.
Description: Covers the latest development in the study of tissue culture, including reports on techniques, equipments, mediums, base medicines, cells and microscopes.

610   JA   ISSN 0433-3047
CODEN: GEIGAI
GENDAI IGAKU/CURRENT MEDICINE. (Text in Japanese) 1950. 3/yr. Aichiken Ishikai - Aichi Medical Association, 14-28, Sakae 4-chome, Naka-ku, Nagoya-shi, Aichi-ken 460, Japan. **Indexed:** Chem.Abstr., INIS Atomind.
—BLDSC (3500.310000).

610   JA   ISSN 0533-7259
GENDAI IRYO/MODERN MEDICAL TREATMENT.* (Text in Japanese) 1969. m. 2700 Yen. Gendai Iryosha, 7-501 Kanda-Nishiki-cho 2-chome, Chiyoda-ku, Tokyo 101, Japan. **Indexed:** INIS Atomind.
—BLDSC (4096.399550).

610   JA
GENDAI IRYOGAKU/MODERN MEDICAL INTELLIGENCE. (Text in Japanese) 1985. bi-m. 2400 Yen per no. Gendai Shuppan Co., Ltd., 30-13, Hatchobori 2-chome, Chuo-ku, Tokyo 104, Japan.

616.042   UK   ISSN 0969-7128
▼**GENE THERAPY (BASINGSTOKE).** 1994. bi-m. Macmillan Press Ltd., Houndmills, Basingstoke, Hants RG21 2XS, England. TEL 44-1256-817245. FAX 44-1256-28339. **Indexed:** Excerp.Med. (1995-). **Document type:** academic/scholarly publication.
—BLDSC (4096.402720).

610   SA   ISSN 0016-643X
CODEN: GENEB4
GENEESKUNDE. (Text in Afrikaans) 1957. 10/yr. R.68.40. P.O. Box 546, Groenkloof 0027, South Africa. TEL 27-12-466541. FAX 27-12-467387. Ed. O.B.W. Greeff. adv. contact: Baltus Bierman. bk.rev.; charts; illus.; index. circ. 4,000. **Indexed:** Chem.Abstr., Ind.S.A.Per., INIS Atomind. **Document type:** academic/scholarly publication.
—CASDDS.
Description: Contains scientific articles written by South African doctors for South Africa.

GENEESKUNDE EN SPORT. see *MEDICAL SCIENCES — Sports Medicine*

610   NE   ISSN 0302-864X
R713.49
GENEESKUNDIG ADRESBOEK NEDERLAND. a. fl.231. Nijgh Periodieken B.V., Postbus 122, 3100 AC Schiedam, Netherlands. TEL 31-10-4274100. FAX 31-10-4739911. adv.: B&W page fl.3530, color page fl.5720; trim 148 x 210; adv. contact: Bert Niewold. circ. 11,500. **Document type:** directory.
Supersedes in part: Geneeskundig Jaarboekje.

610   NE   ISSN 0302-6752
R101
GENEESKUNDIG JAARBOEK MEDICIJNEN. a. fl.57.50. Nijgh Periodieken B.V., Postbus 122, 3100 AC Schiedam, Netherlands. TEL 31-10-4274100. FAX 31-10-4739911. adv.: B&W page fl.2793, color page fl.4983; trim 100 x 150; adv. contact: Bert Niewold. circ. 9,250. **Document type:** directory.
Supersedes in part: Geneeskundig Jaarboekje.

MEDICAL SCIENCES

616.07 574.2   GW   ISSN 0947-823X
RB1   CODEN: ZEPAEA
GENERAL AND DIAGNOSTIC PATHOLOGY. (Text and summaries in English and German) 1890. 6/yr. DM.380 (foreign DM.392). Gustav Fischer Verlag Jena, Villengang 2, 07745 Jena, Germany. TEL 03641-626444. FAX 03641-626500. (Subscr. to: Postfach 100537, 07705 Jena, Germany) Ed. A. Roessner. adv.; bk.rev.; abstr.; bibl.; charts; illus.; index, cum.index: vols.1-20. (also avail. in microfiche from BHP; reprint service avail. from ISI) **Indexed:** Biol.Abstr., Chem.Abstr., Dent.Ind., Excerp.Med., Ind.Med., Ind.Vet., Ref.Zh., Vet.Bull. **Document type:** academic/scholarly publication.
—BLDSC (9511.510000); SWETS. **CCC.**
Former titles: Zentralblatt fuer Pathologie (ISSN 0863-4106); Zentralblatt fuer Allgemeine Pathologie und Pathologische Anatomie (ISSN 0044-4030)
Description: Devoted to the publication of articles from the entire spectrum of morphologic research which extend the recognition and knowledge of human diseases.

610   UK
GENERAL MEDICAL COUNCIL. ANNUAL REPORT. 1859. a. General Medical Council, 44 Hallam St., London W1N 6AE, England. TEL 0171-580 7642. FAX 0171-436-1384. **Document type:** corporate report.

610   UK   ISSN 0072-0763
GENERAL MEDICAL COUNCIL. MEDICAL REGISTER. 1859. a. £90. General Medical Council, 44 Hallam St., London W1N 6AE, England. TEL 0171-580-7642. FAX 0171-436-1384.

610.6   UK
GENERAL MEDICAL COUNCIL. MINUTES. 1858. a. price varies. General Medical Council, 44 Hallam St., London W1N 6AE, England. TEL 0171-580-7642. FAX 0171-436-1384.

610   FR   ISSN 0183-4568
GENERALISTE. 1975. 89/yr. 185 F. (effective 1995). Editions du Medecin Generaliste, 11 bd. de Sebastopol, 75001 Paris, France. TEL 44-82-33-33. FAX 42-21-05-98. Ed. Edouard Bourreau. adv.; bk.rev. circ. 60,000. **Document type:** newspaper.
—BLDSC (5487.605000). **CCC.**

630   US
GENESEE COUNTY MEDICAL SOCIETY BULLETIN. 1927. m. $60. Genesee County Medical Society, 806 Tuuri Place, Flint, MI 48503. TEL 810-238-3781. FAX 810-238-3792. Ed. Dr. Willys F. Mueller, Jr; Pub. Peter Levine. adv. contact: Evelyn Lukes. circ. 610. (back issues avail.) **Document type:** trade publication.
Description: Contains information and articles of interest to the members.

616.07   US   ISSN 1061-2289
GENESIS REPORT - DX; business implications of technology innovation in diagnostic medicine. 1991. bi-m. $837 (foreign $890) (effective Jun. 1995). Genesis Group Associates, Inc., 29 Park St., Montclair, NJ 07042. TEL 201-509-7740. FAX 201-509-7745. Ed. Robert E. Hannan. **Document type:** newsletter.

610   US
▼**GENESIS REPORT - M CX;** managed care strategic briefing. 1994. 10/yr. $995 (foreign $1040) (effective Jan. 1996). Genesis Group Associates, Inc., 29 Park St., Montclair, NJ 07042. TEL 201-509-7735. FAX 201-509-7745. Ed. Robert E. Hannan. **Document type:** newsletter.

610   FR   ISSN 0016-6839
GENIE MEDICAL; symbiose medico-artistique. 1949. m. 25 F. E.S.T.E.C., 127 bd. Saint Michel, 75005 Paris, France. Ed. Dr. H. Drouin. adv.; bk.rev.; film rev.; illus.; tr.lit. circ. 23,500.

610   US   ISSN 0016-8106
R11   CODEN: GTMBAQ
GEORGETOWN MEDICAL BULLETIN. q. $6. 3900 Reservoir Rd., N.W., Washington, DC 20007. Ed. Karen Jones. bk.rev. circ. 10,000. **Indexed:** Biol.Abstr., Chem.Abstr.

610   US
GERSON HEALING NEWSLETTER. 1984. q. $25 (foreign $30). Gerson Institute, Box 430, Bonita, CA 91908. TEL 619-472-7450. FAX 619-267-6441. E-mail: gersoninst@aol.com. Ed. Howard Straus. adv. contact: Sandy Butler. bk.rev. circ. 3,000. (back issues avail.) **Document type:** newsletter.
Formerly: Healing Newsletter.
Description: Covers alternative medicine, nutritional immunology, disease prevention, and health policy reform.

610.9   NE   ISSN 0929-6824
GESCHIEDENIS DER GENEESKUNDE. 1993. bi-m. fl.97.50. Mediselect B.V., Postbus 28091, 3828 ZH Hoogland, Netherlands. TEL 31-33-808020. FAX 31-33-805881. Eds. Dr. H. Beukers, Dr. R. Van Mee; Pub. J. Blom. circ. 2,000 (paid). **Document type:** academic/scholarly publication.
Description: Covers the history of medicine, pharmacy and related disciplines.

610   SZ   ISSN 0016-9161
GESNERUS; Swiss journal of the history of medicine and sciences. (Text in English, French, German and Italian) 1943. 3/yr. 95 SFr. (Schweizerische Gesellschaft fuer Geschichte der Medizin und der Naturwissenschaft) Schwabe und Co. AG, Farnsburgerstr. 8, CH-4132 Muttenz, Switzerland. Ed. Dr. Marcel Bickel. adv.: B&W page 625 SFr.; trim 117 x 170. bk.rev.; illus.; index, cum.index. circ. 650. **Indexed:** Biol.Abstr., Chem.Abstr., Excerp.Med., Ind.Med. **Document type:** academic/scholarly publication.
—BLDSC (4163.000000); Faxon; SWETS. **CCC.**

610   AU
GESUNDES TIROL. 1991. 2/yr. (Aerztekammer fuer Tirol) Ablinger und Garber, Johannesfeldstr. 2, A-6111 Volders, Austria. TEL 05224-57367. FAX 05224-5736717. circ. 80,000. **Document type:** newsletter.

GEZONDHEIDSZORG, BELEID EN ORGANIZATIE. see HOSPITALS

610   GH   ISSN 0855-0328
GHANA MEDICAL JOURNAL. 1962. q. $50. Ghana Medical Association, P.O. Box 1596, Accra, Ghana. TEL 233-665401. Ed. J.H. Addy. adv. contact: Dr. Mercy Newman. bk.rev.; abstr.; bibl.; charts; illus.; stat. circ. 1,000. (reprint service avail. from IRC) **Indexed:** Biol.Abstr., Curr.Cont., Excerp.Med., Ind.Med., INIS Atomind., Nutr.Abstr. **Document type:** academic/scholarly publication.

610   JA   ISSN 0072-4521
                    CODEN: GDIKAN
GIFU DAIGAKU IGAKUBU KIYO. Varient title: Acta Scholae Medicinalis Universitatis in Gifu. (Text English, Japanese; summaries in English) 1953. bi-m. Gifu Daigaku, Igakubu - Gifu University, School of Medicine, 40 Tsukasa-cho, Gifu-shi, Gifu-ken 500, Japan. Ed.Bd. circ. 370. **Indexed:** Biol.Abstr., Chem.Abstr., Dairy Sci.Abstr., Excerp.Med., INIS Atomind.
—BLDSC (0582.720000); CASDDS.
Formerly (until 1967): Gifu Ika Daigaku Kiyo - Acta Scholae Medicinalis in Gifu (ISSN 0376-0340)

610   JA   ISSN 0912-0513
GIFU IRYO GIJUTSU TANKI DAIGAKU KIYO/GIFU COLLEGE OF MEDICAL TECHNOLOGY. BULLETIN. (Text in English, Japanese; summaries in English) 1985. a. Gifu Iryo Gijutsu Tanki Daigaku, 795-1, Nagamine, Hiraga, Seki-shi, Gifu-ken 501-32, Japan.

610   JA   ISSN 0914-9538
GIFUKEN ISHIKAI IGAKU ZASSHI/GIFU MEDICAL ASSOCIATION. JOURNAL. (Text in Japanese) 1988. a. Gifuken Ishikai, 30-1, Yabuta 10-chome, Gifu-shi, Gifu-ken 500, Japan.

GIFUKEN KOSEIREN IGAKU ZASSHI/GIFU WELFARE FEDERATION. JOURNAL. see SOCIAL SERVICES AND WELFARE

610   JA   ISSN 0385-6259
GINKYO GAKUEN KIYO/GINKYO COLLEGE OF MEDICAL SCIENCE. BULLETIN. (Text in English, Japanese) 1976. a. Ginkyo Gakuen Tanki Daigaku - Ginkyo College of Medical Science, 819, Okubo, Shimizucho, Kumamoto-shi, Kumamoto-ken 860, Japan.

610   IT   ISSN 0391-8866
GIORNALE DEI CONGRESSI MEDICI. (Text in English, French, German, Italian and Spanish) bi-m. L.50000($50) C I C Edizioni Internazionali s.r.l., Via L. Spallanzani, 11, 00161 Rome, Italy. TEL 06-8412673. FAX 06-44242033. TELEX 622-099-CIC I.

610   IT   ISSN 0393-8492
GIORNALE DEL MEDICO; bisettimanale di informazione per il medico pratico. 1985. s-w. (60/yr.). L.17000 (effective 1994). Masson S.p.A., Divisione Periodici, Via Statuto 4, 20121 Milan, Italy. TEL 02-6367-1. FAX 02-6367-211. Ed. Carlo Grassi. adv.: B&W page L.14100000, color page L.18400000; trim 266 x 390. circ. 60,000. (tabloid format)

616.07   IT   ISSN 1120-8392
                    CODEN: GCMTEX
GIORNALE DI CLINICA MEDICA & BASI RAZIONALI DELLA TERAPIA. Short title: G e B. (Text in Italian; summaries in English, French, German) 1991. s-m. L.98000($125) Piccin Editore, Via Altinate 107, 35100 Padua, Italy. TEL 049-655566. FAX 049-8750693. Ed. Prof. Luciano Campanacci. adv.: B&W page L.6000000, color page L.9900000; trim 175 x 251. bk.rev.; charts; illus.; index. circ. 64,300. **Indexed:** Biol.Abstr., Chem.Abstr., Excerp.Med., Ind.Med.
—CASDDS.
Formed by the merger of (1920-1991): Giornale di Clinica Medica (ISSN 0017-0275); (1971-1991): Basi Razionali della Terapia (ISSN 0393-7569)

616.98   IT   ISSN 0017-0364
                    CODEN: GMMIAW
GIORNALE DI MEDICINA MILITARE. 1851. bi-m. L.60000($75) (effective 1995). Direzione Generale della Sanita Militare, Via S. Stefano Rotondo, n.4, 00184 Rome, Italy. TEL 39-4735-7939. Ed. Domenico Mario Monaco. adv.; bk.rev.; abstr.; illus.; index. circ. 3,000. **Indexed:** C.I.S. Abstr., Chem.Abstr., Excerp.Med., Ind.Med. **Document type:** academic/scholarly publication.
●Also available online.
—CASDDS.

612.6   IT
▼**GIORNALE ITALIANO DI ANDROLOGIA.** 1994. q. L.86000 (foreign $100) (effective 1995). Pacini Editore s.r.l., Via A. Gherardesca 1, 56121 Ospedaletto (Pisa), Italy. TEL 39-50-982439. FAX 39-50-983906. Ed. F. Menchini-Fabris.

GIORNALE ITALIANO DI CHIMICA CLINICA. see BIOLOGY — Biological Chemistry

616.07   IT   ISSN 0393-5957
GIORNALE ITALIANO DI RICERCHE CLINICHE E TERAPEUTICHE. (Text and summaries in English, Italian) 1979. bi-m. L.25000. E S I Stampa Medica s.r.l., Casella Postale 42, Lgo. Volontari del Sangue 10, 22097 S. Donato, Milan, Italy. TEL 39-2-5274241. FAX 39-2-55600670. TELEX 324894. adv. contact: Ornella Galbiati. bk.rev. circ. 25,000. (back issues avail.)
—BLDSC (4178.244000).
Description: Covers clinical medicine.

610   PL   ISSN 0373-174X
GLOWNA BIBLIOTEKA LEKARSKA. BIULETYN. 1952. s-a. 30000 Zl.($30) Glowna Biblioteka Lekarska - Central Medical Library, Ul. Chocimska 22, 00-791 Warsaw, Poland. TEL 48-22-497404. FAX 48-22-497802. TELEX 814820. (Dist. by: Ars Polona - Ruch, Krakowskie Przedmiescie 7, 00-068 Warsaw, Poland) Ed. Janusz Kapuscik. adv.; bk.rev.; bibl.; index. circ. 625. **Indexed:** Excerp.Med. **Document type:** bulletin.
—BLDSC (2098.700000).

GOLD INSTITUTE. INTERNATIONAL CONFERENCE ON GOLD & SILVER IN MEDICINE. PROCEEDINGS. see MINES AND MINING INDUSTRY

610   GW   ISSN 0942-3842
GOLDENE GESUNDHEIT. 1976. m. Bastei Verlag Gustav H. Luebbe GmbH und Co., Scheidtbachstr. 23-31, 51469 Bergisch Gladbach, Germany. TEL 02202-121-0. FAX 02202-121875. Ed. Udo Beling; Pub. Gustav Luebbe. adv. contact: Frank Mueller. circ. 111,039. **Document type:** consumer publication.

GOLFER'S COMPANION. see SPORTS AND GAMES — Ball Games

MEDICAL SCIENCES

610   CC   ISSN 1001-814X
GONGQI YIKAN/ENTERPRISE MEDICAL JOURNAL. (Text in Chinese) q. Harbin Gongchang Qiye Yiyuan Guanli Weiyuanhui - Harbin Enterprise-owned Hospital Management Committee, 34, Siwu Daojie, Daoli-qu, Harbin, Heilongjiang 150010, People's Republic of China. TEL 413165. Ed. Mu Rui.

610   GW   ISSN 0177-3941
GOURMED; magazine for doctors. 1984. m. DM.53.50. Medizinische Praxis-Verlagsgesellschaft mbH, Basler Str. 19, 79189 Bad Krozingen, Germany. TEL 07633-14081. Ed. Christa von Luebke. circ. 50,000. **Document type:** trade publication.

610.6   CE
GOVERNMENT MEDICAL OFFICERS' ASSOCIATION. NEWSLETTER. q. Government Medical Officers' Association, 6 Wijerama Mawatha, Colombo 7, Sri Lanka. **Document type:** government publication, trade publication, newsletter.

GRADUATE MEDICAL EDUCATION DIRECTORY (YEARS). see *EDUCATION — Higher Education*

GREAT BRITAIN. GENERAL REGISTER OFFICE. STUDIES ON MEDICAL AND POPULATION SUBJECTS. see *POPULATION STUDIES*

610   UK   ISSN 0141-2256
GREAT BRITAIN. MEDICAL RESEARCH COUNCIL. ANNUAL REPORT (YEAR). a. £10. Medical Research Council, 20 Park Crescent, London W1N 4AL, England. TEL 071-636-5422. FAX 071-436-6179. TELEX 24897. **Document type:** corporate report.
—BLDSC (1340.190000).
Formerly (until 1965): Great Britain. Medical Research Council. Report (ISSN 0072-6567)

610   UK   ISSN 0309-0132
R854.G7
GREAT BRITAIN. MEDICAL RESEARCH COUNCIL. HANDBOOK (YEAR). a. £10. Medical Research Council, 20 Park Crescent, London W1N 4AL, England. TEL 071-636-5422. FAX 071-436-6179. TELEX 24897. **Document type:** corporate report.
—BLDSC (4247.500000).

610   US   ISSN 0894-508X
GREATER KANSAS CITY MEDICAL BULLETIN. 1907. m. $7 to non-members; members $5. Metropolitan Medical Society of Greater Kansas City, Metropolitan Medical Society, 3036 Gillham Rd., Kansas City, MO 64108. TEL 816-531-8432. Ed. Dr. John H. Renner. adv.; bk.rev. circ. 3,100.

362 610   US   ISSN 0199-5103
GROUP PRACTICE JOURNAL. 1951. bi-m. $65. American Group Practice Association, 1422 Duke St., Alexandria, VA 22314-3430. TEL 703-838-0033. FAX 703-548-1890. Ed. Laura Johnson. adv.; bk.rev.; index. circ. 47,000. (back issues avail.) **Indexed:** Abstr.Health Care Manage.Stud., Excerp.Med., Hosp.Lit.Ind., Med.Care Rev., MEDSOC. **Document type:** trade publication.
—BLDSC (4220.182100); Faxon; UnCover.
Formerly: Group Practice (ISSN 0017-4726)
Description: Concentrates on the socio-economic, political, business, and legal aspects of medical care by group practice, HMOs, PPOs, and managed care.

610   BE   ISSN 0771-0313
GROUPE D'ETUDE POUR UNE REFORME DE LA MEDICINE. CAHIER. Key Title: Cahiers du G.E.R.M. (Text in French) 1951. q. Groupe d'Etudes pour une Reforme de la Medicine asbl, 29, rue du Gouvernement Provisoire, 1000 Brussels, Belgium. TEL 32-2-2196766. Dir. Thierry Poucet. **Document type:** newsletter.
—BLDSC (2948.970600).
Formerly (until 1981): Groupe d'Etude pour une Reforme de la Medicine. Lettre d'Information (ISSN 0771-0267)

612.6   US   ISSN 1041-1232
QH511.A1   CODEN: GDAGE9
GROWTH, DEVELOPMENT & AGING. 1937. q. $90 to non-members (foreign $110); members $40 (foreign $50) (effective 1995 & 1996). Growth Publishing Co., Inc., Box 42, Bar Harbor, ME 04609-0042. TEL 207-288-3533. FAX 207-288-5079. Ed. Dr. D.E. Harrison. adv. contact: Patricia Harrison. bk.rev.; bibl.; charts; illus.; index. circ. 750. (also avail. in microform from UMI,PMC; reprint service avail. from UMI,ISI) **Indexed:** Abstr.Anthropol., Anim.Breed.Abstr., Biol.Abstr., Biol.& Agr.Ind., Chem.Abstr., Curr.Adv.Ecol.Sci., Curr.Cont., Dairy Sci.Abstr., Dent.Ind., Excerp.Med., Ind.Med., Ind.Sci.Rev., Ind.Vet., INIS Atomind., Mid.East: Abstr.& Ind., Nutr.Abstr., Sci.Cit.Ind., Vet.Bull., W.R.C.Inf. **Document type:** academic/scholarly publication.
—BLDSC (4223.032500); CASDDS; Faxon; Genuine Article; SWETS; UMI; UnCover.
Formerly (until 1987): Growth (ISSN 0017-4793)
Description: Devoted to problems of normal and abnormal growth patterns; relationship among growth, development and aging; and mathematical models related to these areas.
Refereed Serial

610   CC   ISSN 1001-9448
CODEN: GUYIEG
GUANGDONG YIXUE/GUANGDONG MEDICAL JOURNAL. (Text in Chinese) 1963. bi-m. Y1.60 per no. (effective 1994). Guangdong Yixue Qingbao Yanjiusuo - Guangdong Medical Information Institute, No. 2, Jinbuli, Huifu Xilu, Guangzhou, Guangdong 510180, People's Republic of China. TEL 884610. Ed. Zhu Fumin. adv. contact: Su Huanqun. **Indexed:** Chem.Abstr.
—BLDSC (4223.858170); CASDDS.
Description: General medical science periodical reflecting the latest progress in medical sciences, technology and practices.

610   CC
GUANGXI YIXUE/GUANGXI MEDICAL JOURNAL. (Text in Chinese) 1975. bi-m. $10.80. Guangxi Yixue Qinbaosuo - Guangxi Institute of Medical Science Information, 20 Gucheng Lu, Nanning, Guangxi 530022, People's Republic of China. TEL 86-771-5864744. Ed. Yu Zhifang. **Document type:** academic/scholarly publication.

GUANGXI ZHONGYI YAO/GUANGXI TRADITIONAL CHINESE MEDICINE. see *ALTERNATIVE MEDICINE*

610   CC   ISSN 1000-5056
GUANGZHOU ZHONGYI XUEYUAN XUEBAO/GUANGZHOU COLLEGE OF TRADITIONAL CHINESE MEDICINE. JOURNAL. (Text in Chinese) 1986. q. Y1.20 per no. Guangzhou Zhongyi Xueyuan - Guangzhou College of Traditional Chinese Medicine, Sanyuanli, Guangzhou, Guangdong 510407, People's Republic of China. TEL 6661233. FAX 6664735. Ed. Ou Ming. **Document type:** academic/scholarly publication.

610   SP
GUIA DE CONGRESOS MEDICOS JANO. 1987. 3/yr. 2500 ptas. Ediciones Doyma S.A., Travesera de Gracia, 17-21, 08021 Barcelona, Spain. TEL 34-1-200-07-11. FAX 34-1-209-11-36. TELEX 51964 INK E. Ed. C. Ribera Banus. adv.: page 380000 ptas.; trim 230 x 295; adv. contact: Cristina Garrote. circ. 20,000.
Former titles: Congresos Medicos Jano (ISSN 0214-4689); (until 1988): Guia de Congresos Medicos Jano (ISSN 0213-8077)
Description: Offers information on congresses, courses, reunions, symposiums, and round tables at national and international levels.

610   FR   ISSN 0992-3993
GUIDE ROSENWALD: ANNUAIRE MEDICAL. 1887. a. 1180 F.($200) (typically set in Dec.). I C Publications, 10 rue Vineuse, 75116 Paris, France. TEL 44-30-81-00. FAX 44-30-81-11. adv. circ. 10,000.
Formerly: Guide Rosenwald: Annuaire Medical et Pharmaceutique (ISSN 0072-8209)

610   JA
GUIDE TO MEDICAL DEVICE REGISTRATION IN JAPAN. (Editions in English, Japanese) irreg., latest 5th ed. 17000 Yen($210) Yakuji Nippo, Ltd., 1 Kanda Izumicho, Chiyoda-ku, Tokyo 101, Japan. TEL 81-3-3862-2141. FAX 81-3-5821-8757. **Document type:** government publication.
Description: Covers the Japanese medical device regulation systems.

610   US   ISSN 0888-6768
RA396.A3
GUIDE TO THE ESSENTIALS OF A MODERN MEDICAL PRACTICE ACT. triennial. $10. Federation of State Medical Boards, 400 Fuller Wiser Rd., Ste. 300, Euless, TX 76039-3855. TEL 817-868-4006. FAX 817-868-4099. Ed. Linda Chandler.
—CCC.
Description: Contains basic recommendations for use in the development, evaluation, or revision of state statutes governing the practice of medicine.

GUIDE TO THE MANAGED CARE INDUSTRY. see *INSURANCE*

GUIDELINES FOR HEALTH SUPERVISION II. see *HOSPITALS*

610   TU   ISSN 1300-0543
CODEN: GATBD
GULHANE ASKERI TIP AKADEMISI BULTEN/GULHANE MILITARY MEDICAL ACADEMY. BULLETIN. 1956. s-a. $70 (effective 1996). Gulhane Askeri Tip Akademisi - Gulhane Military Medical Academy, 06018 Etlik - Ankara, Turkey. TEL 90-312-3212353. FAX 90-312-3234923. Ed. A. Onder Berk. adv.; bk.rev. **Indexed:** Excerp.Med. **Document type:** bulletin.
Description: Publishes review articles, original research, case reports and letters on topics relating to meidcal science.
Refereed Serial

610   JA   ISSN 0389-7540
GUNMA DAIGAKU IRYO GIJUTSU TANKI DAIGAKUBU KIYO/GUNMA UNIVERSITY. COLLEGE OF MEDICAL CARE AND TECHNOLOGY. ANNUAL REPORTS. (Text in English, Japanese; summaries in English) 1980. a. Gunma Daigaku, Iryo Gijutsu Tanki Daigakubu, 39-15, Showamachi 3-chome, Maebashi-shi, Gunma-ken 371, Japan.

610   JA   ISSN 0285-0656
GUNMA IGAKU/GUNMA MEDICAL ASSOCIATION. JOURNAL. (Text in Japanese) 1953. a. Gunmaken Ishikai - Gunma Medical Association, 7-4, Chiyodamachi 1-chome, Maebashi-shi, Gunma-ken 371, Japan.

610   JA   ISSN 0386-0760
CODEN: GRMSBU
GUNMA REPORTS ON MEDICAL SCIENCES/GUNMA REPOTO. (Text in English and European languages) 1952. s-a. Gunma University, School of Medicine - Gunma Daigaku Igakubu, 39-22 Showa-machi, Maebashi, Gunma-ken 371, Japan. Ed.Bd. illus. circ. 700. **Indexed:** Biol.Abstr., Chem.Abstr.
Supersedes (in Jan. 1970): Gunma Journal of Medical Sciences (ISSN 0017-565X)

612.015   CC
GUOWAI YIXUE (LINCHUANG SHENGWU HUAXUE YU JIANYAN FENCE)/FOREIGN MEDICAL SCIENCES (CLINICAL BIOCHEMISTRY AND INSPECTION). (Text in Chinese) bi-m. Chongqing Yixue Qingbao Yanjiusuo - Chongqing Medical Science Information Research Institute, 44 Qingnian Lu, Chongqing, Sichuan 630010, People's Republic of China. TEL 41978.

610   US   ISSN 0882-696X
GUTHRIE JOURNAL. vol.40, 1970. q. free. Donald Guthrie Foundation for Medical Research, Sayre, PA 18840. TEL 717-888-6666. Ed. Ralph D. Zehr. adv. contact: Jean Antes. bk.rev.; charts; illus.; index. circ. 6,400. **Indexed:** C.I.S.Abstr., Chem.Abstr, Excerp.Med. **Document type:** academic/scholarly publication.
—BLDSC (4232.650000); UnCover.
Former titles (until vol.55, 1985): Guthrie Bulletin (ISSN 0735-4592); Guthrie Clinic Bulletin (ISSN 0017-5838)

H C E A EXHIBITORS ADVISORY COUNCIL'S ACTION MEMO. (Healthcare Convention & Exhibitors Association) see *MEETINGS AND CONGRESSES*

H C E A HANDBOOK; a directory of healthcare meetings and conventions. (Healthcare Convention & Exhibitors Association) see *MEETINGS AND CONGRESSES*

MEDICAL SCIENCES

338.025　　　US　ISSN 1045-6058
HD9994.U5
H I D A MANUFACTURERS DIRECTORY. a. $80. (Health Industry Distributors Association) Medical Economics Publishing Co., Inc., Five Paragon Dr., Montvale, NJ 07645. TEL 201-358-7200. FAX 201-573-8979. (also avail. in microform from UMI) **Document type:** directory, trade publication.
—UMI.
 Formerly (until 1989): Directory of Health Care Manufacturers, Products and Supplies (ISSN 0888-2797)
 Description: Lists over 9,000 medical products distributed through medical products distributors. Contains a company name section, a product index section and a trade name section.

H L A B C FORUM. (Health Libraries Association of British Columbia) see *LIBRARY AND INFORMATION SCIENCES — Computer Applications*

H M O MAGAZINE. (Health Maintenance Organization) see *INSURANCE*

610　　　US　ISSN 0891-6624
H M O PRACTICE. 1987. q. $150. H M O Group, 900 Guaranty Bldg., Buffalo, NY 14202. TEL 716-857-6361. FAX 908-220-0298. E-mail: 6988148@mcimail.com. Ed. Dr. Leonard A. Katz. adv.; bk.rev. circ. 11,000. (also avail. in microform from UMI) **Indexed:** Hosp.Lit.Ind. **Document type:** academic/scholarly publication.
—BLDSC (4319.370000); UMI.
 Description: Focuses on issues of concern to physicians and clinical health professionals practicing in group-staff model HMOs. Provides information, opinion and scholarly discussion on topics such as health services research, clinical and program innovations, health policy and resource management including new technologies.

610　　　TU　ISSN 0259-2282
　　　　　　CODEN: HMJOEG
HACETTEPE MEDICAL JOURNAL/HACETTEPE TIP DERGISI. (Editions in English, Turkish) 1968. q. $30. (University of Hacettepe, Faculty of Medicine - Hacettepe Universitesi, Tip Fakultesi) Hacettepe University Press, Hacettepe 06100, Ankara, Turkey. TELEX 42-237 HKT TR. Ed. Dr. Dogan Taner. adv.; bibl.; charts; illus.; index. circ. 980. **Indexed:** Biol.Abstr., Excerp.Med.
—BLDSC (4237.437570).
 Formerly (until 1983): Hacettepe Bulletin of Medicine-Surgery - Hacettepe Tip Cerrahi Bulteni (ISSN 0017-6451)
 Description: Contains papers on original research, case reports, reviews, short communications for practical applications, letters, editorials, and announcements concerning the medical sciences.

610 658　　　JA　ISSN 0389-5122
HACHINOHE SHIRITSU SHIMIN BYOIN ISHI/HACHINOHE CITY HOSPITAL. MEDICAL JOURNAL. (Text in Japanese) 1976. 2/yr. Hachinohe Shiritsu Shimin Byoin, Nakazuka, Hachinohe-shi, Aomori-ken 031, Japan.

HADASHOT KUPOT HOLIM. see *INSURANCE*

610　　　CC
HAINAN YIXUE/HAINAN MEDICAL SCIENCE. (Text in Chinese) q. Hainan Sheng Yixuehui - Hainan Medical Society, No. 42, Haifu Dadao, Haikou, Hainan 570003, People's Republic of China. TEL 32513. Ed. Zheng Jianchao.

610　　　JA　ISSN 0910-0725
HAKODATE IGAKUSHI/HOKODATE MEDICAL JOURNAL. (Text in Japanese) 1977. a. Shiritsu Hokodate Byoin - Hakodate Municipal Hospital, 2-23, Yayoicho, Hakodate-shi, Hokkaido 040, Japan.

610　　　GW
HAMBURG-MANNHEIMER-STIFTUNG FUER INFORMATIONSMEDIZIN. SCHRIFTENREIHE. 1985. irreg., vol.5, 1991. price varies. (Hamburg-Mannheimer Stiftung fuer Informationsmedizin) Ferdinand Enke Verlag, Postfach 300366, 70443 Stuttgart, Germany. TEL 0711-135798-0. FAX 0711-135798-30. TELEX 07252275-GTV-D. (reprint service avail. from IRC) **Document type:** monographic series.

610　　　GW　ISSN 0017-6915
HAMBURGER AERZTEBLATT. 1947. m. DM.115. Hamburger Aerzteverlag GmbH, Humboldtstr. 58, 22083 Hamburg, Germany. TEL 040-22802307. FAX 040-2277381. Ed. Dr. Ulrich Lamparter. adv. contact: Donald Horn. bk.rev.; charts; illus.; stat.; tr.lit.; index. circ. 10,800. **Document type:** academic/scholarly publication.
—BLDSC (4241.250000).

610　　　PK　ISSN 0250-7188
HAMDARD MEDICUS; journal of science and medicine. (Text in English) 1957. q. Rs.200($28) Hamdard Foundation, Nazimabad No. 3, Karachi 74600, Pakistan. TEL 92-21-6616001. FAX 92-21-6641766. TELEX 24529 HAMD PK. Ed. Hakim Mohammed Said. adv.; bk.rev.; charts. circ. 2,000. (back issues avail.) **Indexed:** Abstr.Hyg., Biol.Abstr., Curr.Adv.Ecol.Sci., ExtraMED, Per.Islam. (1991-), Trop.Dis.Bull. **Document type:** academic/scholarly publication.
● Also available on CD-ROM.
 Former titles: Hamdard; Hamdard Medical Digest (ISSN 0017-7024)

610　　　US
HAMPDEN HIPPOCRAT. 1942. bi-m. membership. Hampden District Medical Society, 1111 Elm St., Ste. 22, W. Springfield, MA 01089-1540. TEL 413-736-0661. Ed. Brigid K. Glackin. adv. circ. 1,800. **Document type:** academic/scholarly publication.

616.1　　　NE　ISSN 0924-6541
　　　　　　CODEN: HAHYEK
HANDBOOK OF HYPERTENSION. (Text in English) 1983. irreg., vol.16, 1994. price varies. Elsevier Science B.V., Books Division, P.O. Box 211, 1000 AE Amsterdam, Netherlands. TEL 31-20-4853911. FAX 31-20-4853705. TELEX 18582 ESPA NL. E-mail: nlinfo-f@elsevier.nl; usinfo-f@elsevier.com; forinfo-kyf04035@niftyserve.or.jp; Site addr.: http://www.elsevier.nl/. (Subscr. in U.S. and Canada to: Elsevier Science Inc., Box 882, Madison Sq. Sta., New York, NY 10159. TEL 212-989-5800) Eds. W.H. Birkenhaeger, J.L. Reid. (back issues avail.) **Document type:** monographic series.
—BLDSC (4250.528000); CASDDS.
 Refereed Serial

610　　　NE　ISSN 0167-5567
RB131
HANDBOOK OF INFLAMMATION. 1979. irreg., vol.6, 1989. Elsevier Science B.V., Books Division, P.O. Box 211, 1000 AE Amsterdam, Netherlands. TEL 31-20-4853911. FAX 31-20-4853705. TELEX 18582 ESPA NL. E-mail: nlinfo-f@elsevier.nl; usinfo-f@elsevier.com; forinfo-kyf04035@niftyserve.or.jp; Site addr.: http://www.elsevier.nl/. (Subscr. in U.S. and Canada to: Elsevier Science Inc., Box 882, Madison Sq. Sta., New York, NY 10159. TEL 212-989-5800) Ed.Bd. **Document type:** monographic series.
 Refereed Serial

HANDBOOK OF MEDICAL EDUCATION. see *EDUCATION — Guides To Schools And Colleges*

616.02　　　US　ISSN 0072-9841
HANDBOOK OF MEDICAL TREATMENT.* 1949. biennial. $7.50. Jones Medical Publications, 355 Los Cerros Dr., Greenbrae, CA 94904. Ed. Milton J. Chatton.

610 615.9　　　US
HANDBOOK OF NATURAL TOXINS. 1983. irreg., vol.8, 1995. Marcel Dekker, Inc., 270 Madison Ave., New York, NY 10016. TEL 212-696-9000. FAX 212-685-4540. TELEX 421419.
 Refereed Serial

610　　　UK
HANDBOOK OF PRACTICE MANAGEMENT. 1992. q. £50 (effective 1995). Churchill Livingstone Journals (Subsidiary of: Pearson Professional), Robert Stevenson House, 1-3 Baxter's Pl., Leith Walk, Edinburgh EH1 3AF, Scotland. TEL 0131-556-2424. FAX 0131-459-1177. (Subscr. to: Pearson Professional Ltd., P.O. Box 77, Fourth Ave., Harlow, Essex CM19 5AA, England. TEL 01279-623760; U.S. subscr. to: Churchill Livingstone, 650 Ave. of the Americas, New York, NY 10011. TEL 212-206-5000) Ed. Dr. J. Hasler. adv. contact: David Dunnachie. **Document type:** academic/scholarly publication.
 Description: Provides updates to help practice managers and partners cope with the demands of general practice.

612　　　US　ISSN 0072-9906
HANDBOOK OF SENSORY PHYSIOLOGY. (Supplement avail.: Foundations of Sensory Science) 1971. irreg., vol.9, 1984. price varies. Springer-Verlag, 175 Fifth Ave., New York, NY 10010. TEL 212-460-1500. FAX 212-473-6272. (Also: Berlin, Heidelberg, Tokyo, Vienna) (reprint service avail. from ISI) **Document type:** academic/scholarly publication.

610　　　US
HANDBOOK OF THE SPINAL CORD. 1983. irreg., vol.5, 1986. Marcel Dekker, Inc., 270 Madison Ave., New York, NY 10016. TEL 212-696-9000. FAX 212-685-4540. TELEX 421419.
 Refereed Serial

610　　　GW
HANDBUCH FUER DAS GESUNDHEITSWESEN IN SCHLESWIG-HOLSTEIN. 1948. a. DM.48. Boettcher und Buelter, Justus-von-Liebig-Str. 2-4, 24537 Neumuenster, Germany. TEL 04321-90720. FAX 04321-907220. adv. circ. 5,000. **Document type:** directory.
 Description: Listing of doctors, dentists, hospitals, etc. in Schleswig-Holstein.

610.73　　　AU　ISSN 0073-0181
R500
HANDBUCH FUER DIE SANITAETSBERUFE OESTERREICH. 1950. a. S.890. Verlag Dieter Goeschl GmbH, Hernalser Hauptstr. 213, A-1170 Vienna, Austria. TEL 01-4864240. FAX 01-4854902. Ed. K.H. Kux. adv.; index. circ. 8,000. **Document type:** trade publication.

362　　　NE　ISSN 1380-6661
HANDICAP & BELEID; tijdschrift voor beleidmakers en dienstverleners. 1954. 6/yr. fl.69. Uitgeverij De Tijdstroom b.v., Postbus 19135, 3501 DC Utrecht, Netherlands. TEL 31-30-586900. FAX 31-30-586950. Ed. P.C. van der Krogt; Pub. A. de Sitter. adv.; bk.rev.; illus. circ. 1,500. **Document type:** trade publication.
 Former titles (until 1993): Hefaistos (ISSN 0928-6659); Formed by the 1992 merger of: Brandpunt (ISSN 0166-3453) & Handicap Magazine (ISSN 0920-4202); Which was formed by the 1986 merger of: Grip (ISSN 0920-4261); And: R - Maandblad voor Revalidatie (ISSN 0165-1382); Which was formerly titled (until 1977): Revalidatie (ISSN 0304-503X); (until 1971): Tijdschrift voor Revalidatie (ISSN 0040-7593).

610　　　GW　ISSN 0944-7369
HARTMANNBUND MAGAZIN. 1951. 12/yr. DM.48. Hartmannbund - Verband der Aerzte Deutschlands e.V., Godesberger Allee 54, 53175 Bonn, Germany. TEL 0228-8104-0. Ed. Uwe Hasenbeck. adv.; bk.rev. circ. 50,000. **Indexed:** Excerp.Med. **Document type:** trade publication.
—CCC.
 Formerly: Deutsche Arzt (ISSN 0011-9873)
 Description: Contains news and information of interest to all German physicians. Features new medical research, public health issues, political and economical issues. Includes readers' comments.

HARVARD MEDICAL ALUMNI BULLETIN. see *COLLEGE AND ALUMNI*

610　　　US　ISSN 0073-0874
R111.H33　　　CODEN: HALEAA
HARVEY LECTURES. 1953. irreg., vol.79, 1985. Academic Press, Inc., 525 B St., Ste. 1900, San Diego, CA 92101-4495. TEL 619-231-0926. FAX 619-699-6715. (Subscr. to: Order Dept., 6277 Sea Harbor Dr., 4th Fl., Orlando, FL 32887. TEL 800-321-5068) cum.index: series 1-50 in series 50 (1956). (reprint service avail. from ISI) **Indexed:** Biol.Abstr., Chem.Abstr., Curr.Adv.Ecol.Sci., Ind.Med., Ind.Sci.Rev., Sci.Cit.Ind.
—BLDSC (4271.000000); CASDDS; UnCover.
 Refereed Serial

MEDICAL SCIENCES

610 100 US ISSN 0093-0334
R724 CODEN: HSCRAS
HASTINGS CENTER REPORT. Key Title: Report - Hastings Center. 1971. bi-m. $55 to individuals; libraries and institutions $70; students and senior citizens $42. Hastings Center, 255 Elm Rd., Briarcliff Manor, NY 10510. TEL 914-762-8500. FAX 914-762-2124. Ed. Bette Crigger. bk.rev.; bibl.; index. circ. 11,700. (also avail. in microfilm from UMI; reprint service avail. from UMI) **Indexed:** Acad.Ind., Biol.Abstr., CINAHL, Curr.Cont., Curr.Lit.Fam.Plan., Fut.Surv., Gen.Sci.Ind., Hlth.Ind., IMFL, Ind.Med., Med.Care Rev., P.A.I.S., Per.Islam. (1991-), Phil.Ind., Rel.Ind.One, Soc.Sci.Ind., Soc.Work Res.& Abstr., SSCI. **Document type:** academic/scholarly publication.
●Also available online. Vendor(s): University Microfilms International.
—BLDSC (4273.019000); Faxon; Genuine Article; SWETS; UMI; UnCover.
Formerly: Hastings Center Studies (ISSN 0093-3252)

610 GW
HAUSARZT BAYERN. 1990. m. DM.30. Berliner Medizinische Verlagsanstalt GmbH, Clausewitzstr. 4, 10629 Berlin, Germany. TEL 030-8823569. FAX 030-8812225. Ed. Hans Kapp. adv. circ. 6,000. **Document type:** academic/scholarly publication.
—CCC.
Formerly (until 1992): InVitro Diagnostika Nachrichten (ISSN 0938-0922)

610 GW ISSN 0934-3164
HAUSARZT HESSEN. 1978. bi-m. DM.30. (Berufsverband der Praktischen Aerzte) Berliner Medizinische Verlagsanstalt GmbH, Clausewitzstr. 4, 10629 Berlin, Germany. TEL 030-8823569. FAX 030-8812225. Ed. Hans Folesky. adv.; bk.rev. circ. 5,000. (back issues avail.; reprint service avail. from UMI) **Document type:** trade publication.

610 GW
HAUSARZT NORDRHEIN. bi-m. DM.30. Berliner Medizinische Verlagsanstalt GmbH, Clausewitzstr. 4, 10629 Berlin, Germany. TEL 030-8823569. FAX 030-8812225. adv.; bk.rev. circ. 4,000. **Document type:** trade publication.

610 GW
HAUSARZT PRAXIS SACHSEN. 1993. bi-m. DM.18. Berliner Medizinische Verlagsanstalt GmbH, Clausewitzstr. 4, 10629 Berlin, Germany. TEL 030-8823569. FAX 030-8812225. Ed. Dr. Ditmar Sturm. adv.; bk.rev. circ. 4,000. **Document type:** trade publication.

610 GW
HAUSARZT THUERINGEN. 1989. bi-m. DM.30. (Landesverband Thueringen in B P A) Berliner Medizinische Verlagsanstalt GmbH, Clausewitzstr. 4, 10629 Berlin, Germany. TEL 030-8823569. FAX 030-8812225. Ed. Dr. Sighardt Freier. adv.; bk.rev. circ. 2,800. **Document type:** trade publication.

610 US ISSN 0017-8594
CODEN: HWMJAE
HAWAII MEDICAL JOURNAL. 1941. m. $25. Hawaii Medical Association, 1360 S. Beretania St., 2nd Fl., Honolulu, HI 96814. TEL 808-536-7702. FAX 808-528-2376. Ed. Norman Goldstein. adv. contact: Jan Estidko. bk.rev.; charts; illus.; index. circ. 1,800. (also avail. in microform from UMI; back issues avail. from ISI,UMI) **Indexed:** Abstr.Hyg., Biol.Abstr., Chem.Abstr., Curr.Adv.Cancer Res., Curr.Adv.Ecol.Sci., Curr.Cont., Excerp.Med., Ind.Med., Soc.Work Res.& Abstr., Trop.Dis.Bull. **Document type:** academic/scholarly publication.
—BLDSC (4273.903000); Faxon; UMI; UnCover.
Refereed Serial

HAWAII'S NATIONAL GAY COMMUNITY NEWS; Hawaii and Western States. see HOMOSEXUALITY

610 AI
HAYASTANI BZHSHKAGITUTYUN/MEDITSINSKAYA NAUK ARMENII/ARMENIAN MEDICAL JOURNAL. (Text in Armenian, English, Russian) 1952. 4/yr. 400 dram. Akademiya Nauk Armenii, Pr. Marshala Bagramayana, 24, 375019 Erevan, Armenia. TEL 78852-524580. TELEX 243344. **Indexed:** Biol.Abstr., Chem.Abstr., Ind.Med., Ind.Vet., Vet.Bull. **Document type:** academic/scholarly publication.
—CASDDS.
Formerly: Eksperimental ev Klinikakam Bzhshkut'yun (ISSN 0514-7484)

610 CN
HEAD TO TOE. 1983. q. free. British Columbia Medical Association, 115-1665 W. Broadway, Vancouver, BC V6J 5A4, Canada. TEL 604-736-5551. FAX 604-733-7317. Ed. Avrill Peters. circ. 25,000. (back issues avail.) **Document type:** newsletter.

610 US ISSN 1059-7565
RC392 CODEN: HQUAEN
HEADACHE QUARTERLY; current treatment and research. 1990. q. $51.50 to individuals (foreign $96); institutions $77.25 (foreign $122). International Universities Press, Inc., 59 Boston Post Rd., Box 1524, Madison, CT 06443-1524. TEL 203-245-4000. FAX 203-245-0775. (Co-sponsors: Diamond Headache Foundation, Inpatient Headache Unit of Weiss Memorial Hospital) Ed. Dr. Seymour Diamond. adv.; bk.rev.; abstr.; charts. **Indexed:** Psychol.Abstr. (1990-). **Document type:** academic/scholarly publication.
—BLDSC (4274.643000); SWETS.
Description: Reports on current research, futuristic therapies and headache theories. Covers histamines, serotonin, prostaglandins, radiological and diagnostic advances and behavioral medicine.
Refereed Serial

610 US
HEADLINES.* 1990. q. $18. J R Publishing, Inc. (Boston), 87 Larch Row, Wenham, MA 01984-1621. TEL 617-426-5959. FAX 617-350-7811. Ed. Beverly Lucas. adv. contact: Randi Kashnig. circ. 135,000 (controlled). **Document type:** academic/scholarly publication.
Description: Studies the many facets of neurologic injury and presents new research.

610 US ISSN 0272-9954
RA773
HEALTH (BOCA RATON). (Subseries of: S I R S Social Issues (ISSN 0740-3127)) 0974. a. price varies. Social Issues Resources Series, Box 2348, Boca Raton, FL 33427-2348. TEL 407-994-0079; 800-232-7477. FAX 407-994-4704. (looseleaf format; also avail. in microfiche; back issues avail.)
Description: Reprints articles that examine problems and challenges to health care.

HEALTH ACTION. see HOSPITALS

610 US ISSN 1075-024X
RA410.56
HEALTH ALLIANCE ALERT. 1986. bi-w. $450 (effective 1995). Faulkner & Gray, Healthcare Information Center (Subsidiary of: Thomson Publishing Group), 1133 15th St., N.W., Ste. 450, Washington, DC 20005. TEL 202-828-4150. FAX 202-828-2352. Ed. John Reichard. **Document type:** trade publication.
●Also available online. Vendor(s): Knight-Ridder, Inc., NewsNet (HH23).
Former titles (until 1994): Health Business (ISSN 1062-6107) & MacGraw-Hill's Health Business (ISSN 0888-9805)
Description: Covers financial and economic aspects of the US health care industry.

HEALTH & HEALING. see PHYSICAL FITNESS AND HYGIENE

HEALTH & MEDICAL YEAR BOOK. see PHYSICAL FITNESS AND HYGIENE

HEALTH & PLACE; an international journal. see GEOGRAPHY

610 362 UK ISSN 0374-8014
RA421 CODEN: HBHSA5
HEALTH BULLETIN. 1941. bi-m. £6. Scottish Office, Home and Health Department, St. Andrew's House, Edinburgh EH1 3DG, Scotland. FAX 0131-244-2835. TELEX 72202. Ed. Dr. Patrick Brooks. bk.rev.; bibl.; index. circ. 15,200. (back issues avail.) **Indexed:** Abstr.Health Care Manage.Stud., Abstr.Hyg., ASSIA, Biol.Abstr., CINAHL, Curr.Adv.Ecol.Sci., Dent.Ind., Excerp.Med., Ind.Med., Med. Care Rev, Nutr.Abstr., Trop.Dis.Bull. **Document type:** bulletin, government publication.
—BLDSC (4274.935400).

610 UK ISSN 1065-3058
RA394 CODEN: HCAVEO
▼**HEALTH CARE ANALYSIS.** 1994. q. $215 (foreign $215) (effective 1996). John Wiley & Sons Ltd., Journals, Baffins Ln., Chichester, W. Sussex PO19 1UD, England. TEL 01243-779777. FAX 01243-776128. TELEX 86290 WIBOOK G. (Subscr. outside the Americas to: John Wiley & Sons, Inc., 605 Third Ave., New York, NY 10158. TEL 212-850-6645. FAX 212-850-6021) Ed. David Seedhouse. (also avail. in microform from UMI; back issues avail.) **Document type:** academic/scholarly publication.
—BLDSC (4274.937800). CCC.
Refereed Serial

362.1 US ISSN 0195-8631
RA410.53
HEALTH CARE FINANCING REVIEW. (Annual supplement avail. (ISSN 1057-9389)) 1979. q. $29 (foreign $36.25) (effective 1995). U.S. Health Care Financing Administration, Department of Health and Human Services, Oak Meadows Bldg., Rm. 1A9, 6325 Security Blvd., Baltimore, MD 21207. TEL 410-966-6572. FAX 410-966-6511. (Subscr. to: Superintendent of Documents, U.S. Government Printing Office, Box 371954, Pittsburgh, PA 15250-7954. TEL 202-512-1800. FAX 202-512-2250; Or: National Technical Information Service, 5285 Port Royal Blvd., Springfield, VA 22161. TEL 703-487-4650. FAX 703-321-8547; Alt. addr.: Hubert H. Humphrey Bldg., 200 Independence Ave., S.W., Rm. 314G, Washington, DC 20201. TEL 202-245-6726) Ed. Linda F. Wolf. bk.rev.; charts; stat. (also avail. in microform from UMI; microfiche from CIS; back issues avail.; reprint service avail. from CIS) **Indexed:** ABI Inform, Abstr.Health Care Manage.Stud., Amer.Stat.Ind. (1979-), CLOA, Excerp.Med., Hosp.Lit.Ind., Ind.U.S.Gov.Per., Med.Care Rev, MEDOC, PROMT, Soc.Work Res.& Abstr., World Bibl.Soc.Sec. **Document type:** government publication.
●Also available online. Vendor(s): University Microfilms International.
—BLDSC (4274.941800); Faxon; SWETS; UMI; UnCover.
Description: Includes statistics and projections on health expenditures, research articles on health care financing and delivery, policy and legislation affecting the Medicare and Medicaid programs.

HEALTH CARE IN LATER LIFE. see GERONTOLOGY AND GERIATRICS

HEALTH CARE LAW NEWSLETTER. see LAW

HEALTH CARE LAWYER. see LAW

HEALTH CAREER POST. see HOSPITALS

610 US ISSN 0046-7022
R856.A1
HEALTH DEVICES. (Includes: Health Devices Alerts; Health Technology Management; Computer Services and Technical Assistance) 1971. m. $2495. (Emergency Care Research Institute) E C R I, 5200 Butler Pike, Plymouth Meeting, PA 19462. TEL 610-825-6000. FAX 610-834-1275. Ed. Pamela Bond. bk.rev.; illus.; index. (back issues avail.) **Document type:** directory.
—BLDSC (4274.963000). CCC.
Description: Contains evaluation and ratings of medical devices used by hospitals. Reports on hazardous devices, access to ECRI's online computer network, technical assistance, help with SMDA, and other device-related information.
Refereed Serial

610 US ISSN 8756-8713
HEALTH DEVICES INSPECTION & PREVENTIVE MAINTENANCE SYSTEM. 1990. a. $695 (Health Devices System members $495). (Emergency Care Research Institute) E C R I, 5200 Butler Pike, Plymouth Meeting, PA 19462. TEL 610-825-6000. FAX 610-834-1275. Ed. Susan Bastnagel.
—CCC.
Description: Includes complete inspection and preventive maintenance forms, how-to's and background information.
Refereed Serial

MEDICAL SCIENCES

681 US ISSN 0278-3452
R856.48
HEALTH DEVICES SOURCEBOOK. 1979. a. $265 (foreign $285). (Emergency Care Research Institute) E C R I, 5200 Butler Pike, Plymouth Meeting, PA 19462. TEL 610-825-6000. FAX 610-834-1275. Ed. Dorothy Wood. **Document type:** directory.
●Also available online. Vendor(s): Knight-Ridder, Inc. (File no.188).
—CCC.
Description: Directory of medical device manufacturers and their product lines. Includes service firms which lease or repair equipment, and which buy and sell used equipment.
Refereed Serial

610 US ISSN 1047-3920
HEALTH DIGEST. q. Whittle Communications L.P., 333 Main Ave., Knoxville, TN 37902. TEL 615-595-5300. Ed. Ron King.
Description: Presents factual information about gastroenterology procedures and medications, tips on relieving common symptoms and discomforts, and advice for reducing stress that may complicate an ailment.

338.476 UK ISSN 1057-9230
RA410.A1 CODEN: HEECEZ
HEALTH ECONOMICS. 1992. bi-m. $275 (foreign $275) (effective 1996). John Wiley & Sons Ltd., Journals, Baffins Ln., Chichester, W. Sussex PO19 1UD, England. TEL 01243-779777. FAX 01243-776128. TELEX 86290 WIBOOK G. (Subscr. in the Americas to: John Wiley & Sons, Inc., 605 Third Ave., New York, NY 10158. TEL 212-850-6645. FAX 212-850-6021) Eds. Alan Maynard, John Hutton. circ. 595. (also avail. in microform from UMI; back issues avail.) **Indexed:** Ind.Med. (1993-). **Document type:** academic/scholarly publication.
—BLDSC (4274.966900); Genuine Article; SWETS; UMI. **CCC.**
Description: Contains articles on all aspects of health economics: theoretical contributions, empirical studies, economic evaluations and analyses of health policy from the economic perspective.
Refereed Serial

610 614 CN
HEALTH ECONOMICS. 1993. bi-m. Can.$55 (foreign Can.$75). Thomson Healthcare Communications, 1120 Birchmount Rd., Ste. 200, Scarborough, ON M1K 5G4, Canada. TEL 416-750-8900. FAX 416-751-8126. adv.: B&W page Can.$2850, color page Can.$3245; trim 8 1/8 x 10 3/4; adv. contact: Suzanne Stone. circ. 10,305.

610 US ISSN 0195-8402
RA440.A1 CODEN: HEQUDC
HEALTH EDUCATION QUARTERLY. 1957-1978; resumed 1980. q. $78 to individuals; institutions $288 (effective Sep. 1995). (Society for Public Health Education) Sage Publications, Inc., 2455 Teller Rd., Thousand Oaks, CA 91320. TEL 805-499-0721. FAX 805-499-0871. E-mail: libraries@sagepub.com. (Subscr. outside the Americas to: Sage Publications Ltd., 6 Bonhill St., London EC2A 4PU, Engand; Sage Publications India Pvt. Ltd., P.O. Box 4125, New Delhi 110 048, England) Ed. Noreen M. Clark. adv. circ. 2,200. (also avail. in microform from UMI; back issues avail.; reprint service avail. from UMI) **Indexed:** CINAHL, Cont.Pg.Educ., Excerp.Med., NRN, Phys.Ed.Ind., Psychol.Abstr. (1970-), Risk Abstr., Soc.Work Res.& Abstr., Sociol.Abstr. **Document type:** academic/scholarly publication.
—BLDSC (4275.011400); Faxon; Genuine Article; SWETS; UMI; UnCover. **CCC.**
Supersedes (in 1980): Health Education Monographs (ISSN 0073-1455)
Description: Discusses the promotion of public health by elevating the quality of health education, improving medical practice, and stimulating research.
Refereed Serial

HEALTH EDUCATION RESEARCH; theory and practice. see *SOCIAL SERVICES AND WELFARE*

610 US ISSN 0742-8081
HEALTH EXCHANGE. 1984. q. Medical Group Management Association, 104 Inverness Terrace E., Englewood, CO 80112. TEL 303-799-1111. Ed. Marilee Aust. circ. 100,000. (back issues avail.)
Description: Covers health maintenance and wellness topics used as a marketing tool by group practices. Geared toward the education of patients.

610 US
HEALTH HOTLINES. a. U.S. National Library of Medicine, 8600 Rockville Pike, Bethesda, MD 20894. (Subscr. to: Superintendent of Documents, U.S. Government Printing Office, Box 371954, Pittsburgh, PA 15250-7954. TEL 202-783-3238. FAX 202-512-2233) **Document type:** directory, government publication.
Description: Lists toll-free phone numbers of public and private organizations that provide health information on specific diseases and conditions.

610 US ISSN 0892-7731
HEALTH INDUSTRY BUYERS GUIDE.* 1940. a. $105. S - N Publications, Inc., Box 908, Spring House, PA 19477-0903. TEL 708-426-6100. FAX 708-426-6416. Ed. Mike Kennedy. adv. circ. 4,000. (also avail. in microform from UMI)
—UMI.
Formerly: Surgical Trade Buyers Guide (ISSN 0081-9654)

610 US ISSN 0745-4678
CODEN: HITOD3
HEALTH INDUSTRY TODAY; the market letter for health care industry vendors. 1938. m. $277 to individuals (foreign $295) (effective Aug. 1994). Business Word Inc., 5350 S. Roslyn St., Ste. 400, Englewood, CO 80111-2145. TEL 303-290-8500. FAX 303-290-9025. Ed. Curt Werner. adv.; bk.rev.; illus.; stat.; index. circ. 750. (also avail. in microform from UMI; reprint service avail. from UMI) **Indexed:** PROMT. **Document type:** trade publication.
●Also available online. Vendor(s): University Microfilms International.
—BLDSC (4275.016700); UMI. **CCC.**
Formerly (until 1982): Surgical Business (ISSN 0039-6095)

HEALTH INFORMATION AND LIBRARIES; international journal for medical, health and welfare librarians and information officers. see *LIBRARY AND INFORMATION SCIENCES*

610 KE
HEALTH INFORMATION SYSTEM. 1977. q. Ministry of Health, Division of Health Information System, P.O. Box 20781, Nairobi, Kenya. TEL 501341.

610 658 US ISSN 1051-9394
KF3580.H4
HEALTH LABOR RELATIONS ALERT.* 1981. m. $119. National Health Publishing, 428 E. Preston St., Baltimore, MD 21202-3923. TEL 301-363-6400. circ. 175.
Incorporates (in Jan. 1990): Director of Nursing Labor Alert (ISSN 0272-636X)
Description: Information on effective management of labor.

HEALTH LAW BULLETIN. see *PUBLIC HEALTH AND SAFETY*

HEALTH LAW NEWS. see *LAW*

HEALTH LAW REVIEW. see *LAW*

HEALTH LAW WEEK. see *LAW*

HEALTH LAWYER. see *LAW*

HEALTH LAWYERS NEWS REPORT. see *LAW*

614 US
KF3821.A15
HEALTH LEGISLATION. 1975. w. (50/yr.). $595 (effective 1995). Faulkner & Gray, Healthcare Information Center (Subsidiary of: Thomson Publishing Group), 1133 15th St., N.W., Ste. 450, Washington, DC 20005. TEL 202-828-4150. FAX 202-828-2352. Ed. Craig Havighurst. index. (looseleaf format; back issues avail.) **Indexed:** Med.Care Rev.
●Also available online. Vendor(s): NewsNet (HH22).
Former titles (until Sep. 1992): Health Legislation and Regulation (ISSN 0899-8965); (until 1986): Washington Report on Health Legislation and Regulation (ISSN 0740-7793); (until 1983): Washington Report on Health Legislation (ISSN 0098-2512)
Description: Covers health care related legislative issues at the federal and congressional level.

610 650 US ISSN 0882-598X
RA421
HEALTH LETTER (WASHINGTON). 1985. m. $18. Public Citizen Health Research Group, 2000 P St. N.W., Washington, DC 20036. TEL 202-872-0320. FAX 202-785-3584. Ed. Sidney M. Wolfe. bk.rev. circ. 35,000. (also avail. in microform from UMI)
—UMI.
Description: Information on common health problems as well as information pried from tightly sealed government and industry files.

HEALTH LIBRARIES REVIEW. see *LIBRARY AND INFORMATION SCIENCES*

610 020 614.8
640.73 US
HEALTH LITERATURE REPORTS. 1983. m. $280. H L R Publications, Box 50536, Indianapolis, IN 46250. TEL 317-253-0966. adv.; bk.rev.; bibl. circ. 350. (back issues avail.).
Formerly: Health Literature Review (ISSN 0740-7262)

HEALTH MATRIX: JOURNAL OF LAW-MEDICINE. see *LAW*

610 UK ISSN 0954-903X
HEALTH MATTERS. 1988. q. £19 to individuals (foreign £24); institutions £29 (foreign 34) (effective 1995-1996). Health Matters Publications Ltd., P.O. Box 459, Sheffield S11 8GJ, England. TEL 0114-266-6171. Ed. James F. Munro. adv. contact: James F. Munro. bk.rev.; circ. 1,500 (paid). (back issues avail.)
Description: Covers health policy, environmental issues, the NHS, and related topics.

610 CN ISSN 0821-3925
HEALTH NEWS (TORONTO). French edition: Action Sante (ISSN 1180-1050) 1983. bi-m. Can.$22.95($26.95) (University of Toronto, Faculty of Medicine) Hilborn: The Newsletter Group Inc., 205 - 109 Vanderhoof Ave., Toronto, ON M4G 2H7, Canada. TEL 416-696-8818. FAX 416-424-3016. Ed. Dr. June V. Engel. illus. circ. 24,000. (looseleaf format; also avail. in microform from UMI; back issues avail.) **Indexed:** Can.B.P.I., Can.Per.Ind. **Document type:** newsletter.
●Also available online. Vendor(s): Information Access Co.
—BLDSC (4275.055100); UMI.
Description: General health publication dealing with wellness, fitness, good eating habits, diseases, psychosocial topics.
Refereed Serial

610 US ISSN 1042-2781
HEALTH NEWS DAILY. 1989. d. $1250 (effective Jan. 1995). F-D-C Reports, Inc., 5550 Friendship Blvd., Ste. One, Chevy Chase, MD 20815. TEL 301-657-9830. FAX 301-656-3094. Ed. John Zakotnik. (looseleaf format; back issues avail.; reprint service avail.) **Document type:** trade publication.
●Also available online. Vendor(s): Ovid Technologies (HNDY), Data-Star (HNDO), Knight-Ridder, Inc. (File no.43), NewsNet (HH01).
—CCC.
Description: Information service for executives and decision-makers in the health industries. Coverage includes healthcare reform, pharmaceuticals, medical devices and diagnostics, biomedical research, federal health policy, Medicare-Medicaid, and cost containment.

MEDICAL SCIENCES

610 614   US   ISSN 0277-8653
R711
HEALTH ORGANIZATIONS OF THE U.S., CANADA AND THE WORLD; a directory of voluntary associations, professional societies and other groups concerned with health and related fields. 1961. irreg., 5th ed., 1981. $90. Gale Research Inc., 835 Penobscot Bldg., Detroit, MI 48226. TEL 313-961-2242. FAX 313-961-6083. TELEX 810-221-7086. Eds. Paul Wasserman, Marek Kaszubski.
   Formerly (until 1977): Health Organizations of the United States, Canada and Internationally (ISSN 0440-5609)
   Description: Directory of volunteer and professional health organizations worldwide.

HEALTH - P A C BULLETIN. (Health Policy Advisory Center) see *PUBLIC HEALTH AND SAFETY*

610 658   US
HEALTH PAGES. 1993. m. 135 Fifth Ave., 7th Fl., New York, NY 10010. TEL 212-505-0103. Ed. Martin Schneider. adv.: B&W page $2500. circ. 90,000.
   Document type: consumer publication.

610   CN   ISSN 0837-7251
HEALTH PERSONNEL IN CANADA/PERSONNEL DE LA SANTE AU CANADA. (Text in English and French) 1969. a. free. Department of National Health, Health Information Division, Jeanne Mance Bldg., Ottawa, ON K1A 0K9, Canada. TEL 613-957-1372. FAX 613-952-0271. stat. circ. 1,200. (also avail. in diskette format) **Document type:** government publication.
   Formerly (until 1988): Canada Health Manpower Inventory (ISSN 0381-2561)
   Description: Provides year-end statistics for 31 occupational groups of health care practitioners over an 11-year period.

610   US   ISSN 0017-9078
QH505.A1   CODEN: HLTPAO
HEALTH PHYSICS; the radiation protection journal. 1958. m. (2 vols./yr.). $169 to individuals; institutions $633 (effective 1995). (Health Physics Society) Williams & Wilkins, 428 E. Preston St., Baltimore, MD 21202. TEL 410-528-4000; 800-638-6423. FAX 410-528-4312. Ed. Kenneth L. Miller. adv.; charts; illus.; stat.; index. circ. 8,938. (also avail. in microfilm from MIM,UMI; reprint service avail. from UMI; back issues avail.) **Indexed:** Abstr.Health Care Manage.Stud., Abstr.Hyg., Apic.Abstr., Appl.Mech.Rev., Biol.Abstr., C.I.S. Abstr., Chem.Abstr., Curr.Adv.Ecol.Sci., Curr.Cont., Dairy Sci.Abstr., Deep Sea Res.& Oceanogr.Abstr., Dent.Ind., Dok.Arbeitsmed., Energy Info.Abstr., Energy Rev., Environ.Abstr., Environ.Per.Bibl. (1972-), Excerp.Med., Food Sci.& Tech.Abstr., Ind.Med., Ind.Vet., INIS Atomind., INSPEC, Int.Aerosp.Abstr., Nutr.Abstr., Ocean.Abstr., Pollut.Abstr., Poult.Abstr., Risk Abstr., Sci.Cit.Ind., Sel.Water Res.Abstr., So.Pac.Per.Ind., Soils & Fert., Vet.Bull., W.R.C.Inf. **Document type:** academic/scholarly publication.
—BLDSC (4275.100000); ADONIS; CASDDS; Faxon; Genuine Article; SWETS; UnCover. **CCC.**
   Description: Reports on theoretical and applied disciplines of radiation protection.
   Refereed Serial

HEALTH PHYSICS SOCIETY. NEWSLETTER. see *MEDICAL SCIENCES — Radiology And Nuclear Medicine*

610   US   ISSN 0162-3605
    CODEN: DRRSAL
HEALTH POLICY & BIOMEDICAL RESEARCH: THE BLUE SHEET. 1957. w. $420 (foreign $495) (effective 1995). F-D-C Reports, Inc., 5550 Friendship Blvd., Ste. One, Chevy Chase, MD 20815. TEL 301-657-9830. FAX 301-656-3094. Ed. John Parker. (looseleaf format; back issues avail.; reprint service avail.) **Indexed:** P.N.I., Rehabil.Lit. **Document type:** trade publication.
● Also available online. Vendor(s): Ovid Technologies (FDCR), Data-Star (FDCR), Lexis-Nexis.
—Faxon. **CCC.**
   Formerly: Drug Research Reports: The Blue Sheet (ISSN 0012-6608)
   Description: Covers developments among the major governmental, academic and private biomedical research institutions.

HEALTH POLICY MONOGRAPHS. see *PUBLIC HEALTH AND SAFETY*

610   UK   ISSN 1351-4679
HEALTH PRACTICE MANAGEMENT HANDBOOK (YEAR). a. £22.50. Kogan Page Ltd., 120 Pentonville Rd., London N1 9JN, England. TEL 0171-278-0433. FAX 0171-837-6348. TELEX 263088-KOGAN-G. Ed. David Loshak. **Document type:** directory.

HEALTH PSYCHOLOGY. see *PSYCHOLOGY*

610.6   UK   ISSN 0951-4848
RA440.6   CODEN: HSRMEO
HEALTH SERVICES MANAGEMENT RESEARCH. 1988. 4/yr. £58 (foreign £64). (University of Birmingham, Health Services Management Centre) Longman Group UK Ltd., Westgate House, 6th Fl., The High, Harlow, Essex CM20 1YR, England. TEL 0279-442601. FAX 0279-444501. (Subscr. to: Journals Dept., Fourth Ave., Harlow, Essex CM19 5AA, England. TEL 0279-623924) Ed. Peter Spurgeon. adv.; bk.rev.; index. circ. 700. (also avail. in microfilm; microfiche) **Indexed:** Diar.Dis.Res. **Document type:** academic/scholarly publication.
—BLDSC (4275.108200); Faxon; SWETS; UMI. **CCC.**
   Description: Current research and its implications for management.
   Refereed Serial

HEALTH SERVICES RESEARCH. see *HOSPITALS*

610 600   US
HEALTH TECHNOLOGY MANAGEMENT. a. $360. (Emergency Care Research Institute) E C R I, 5200 Butler Pike, Plymouth Meeting, PA 19462. TEL 610-825-6000. FAX 610-834-1275. Ed. Michael Argentieri. (looseleaf format)
   Description: Reference material for handling technology related issues including planning, legal & regulatory responsibilities and procedures, plus special reports.
   Refereed Serial

610   US   ISSN 1041-6072
HEALTH TECHNOLOGY TRENDS; for health care executives. 1989. m. $275. (Emergency Care Research Institute) E C R I, 5200 Butler Pike, Plymouth Meeting, PA 19462. TEL 610-825-6000. FAX 610-834-1275. Ed. Cynthia Wallace.
—**CCC.**
   Description: Covers economic, legal, and product news related to health care technology for executives.
   Refereed Serial

610 614   UK   ISSN 0017-9132
RA485   CODEN: HETBAT
HEALTH TRENDS. 1969. q. £11.90 (effective 1994). (Departments of Health and Social Security) H.M.S.O., 51 Nine Elms Ln., London SW8 5DP, England. TEL 0171-873-0011. FAX 0171-873-8463. (Subscr. to: H.M.S.O. Publications Centre, P.O. Box 276, London SW8 5DT, England. TEL 0171-873-9090. FAX 0171-873-8200) Ed. Valerie M. Willcocks. **Indexed:** Abstr.Health Care Manage.Stud., Abstr.Hyg., ASSIA, Biol.Abstr., Curr.Adv.Ecol.Sci., Excerp.Med., Trop.Dis.Bull. **Document type:** government publication.
—BLDSC (4275.240000); SWETS.

610   US
HEALTHBEAT. 1989. q. free. Write Ideas, Box 157, Waldwick, NJ 07463. TEL 201-447-0306. Ed. Suzanne Ordas-Curry. adv. contact: Suzanne Ordas-Curry. circ. 7,500. **Document type:** newsletter.
   Description: Covers various aspects of preventative health, pediatrics, geriatrics, and women's health.

HEALTHCARE CAREER DIRECTORY. see *OCCUPATIONS AND CAREERS*

610 658.8   US   ISSN 0894-9980
HEALTHCARE COMMUNITY RELATIONS & MARKETING LETTER. 1987. 12/yr. $197. Health Resources Publishing, 3100 Hwy. 138, Wall Township, NJ 07719-1442. TEL 908-681-1133. FAX 908-681-0490. Ed. Edward Miles; Pub. Robert K. Jenkins. adv. contact: Marcia Balkin. index. (tabloid format; back issues avail.) **Document type:** newsletter.
—**CCC.**
   Description: Helps professional managers stay atop the latest innovations and keep pace with the changes in the healthcare field.

610 371.42   US
HEALTHCARE EMPLOYMENT JOURNAL; serving healthcare professionals. 1991. m. $21. Employment Journals of America, 1614 Lancaster Ave., Reynoldsburg, OH 43068. TEL 614-861-4600. FAX 614-861-5558. Ed. Susan Erwin. adv.: B&W page $4100; trim 11 1/2 x 13 3/4. circ. 65,000.
   Formerly (until 1993): Employment Journal of Ohio.
   Description: Focuses on employment opportunities for healthcare professionals.

610
HEALTHCARE ENVIRONMENTAL MANAGEMENT SYSTEM. a. (plus m. updates). $695 (C H E M members $495). (Emergency Care Research Institute) E C R I, 5200 Butler Pike, Plymouth Meeting, PA 19462. TEL 610-825-6000. FAX 610-834-1275. (Co-sponsor: C H E M - Center for Healthcare Environmental Management) Ed. Marge deMarteleire.
   Description: Provides articles on management plans, compliance directions for environmental and occupational health and safety.
   Refereed Serial

610 658   US
HEALTHCARE FINANCIAL RELATIONSHIPS. 1992. fortn. $287. Atlantic Information Services, Inc., 1050 17th St., N.W., Ste. 480, Washington, DC 20036-5500. TEL 202-775-9008. FAX 202-331-9542.
   Description: Healthcare financial compliance related to safe harbor, joint ventures, self-referrals, physician recruitment, fraud and abuse, antitrust and tax.

658   US   ISSN 1050-575X
HEALTHCARE HAZARDOUS MATERIALS MANAGEMENT. 1987. m. $225 (includes membership to CHEM. (Emergency Care Research Institute) E C R I, 5200 Butler Pike, Plymouth Meeting, PA 19462. TEL 610-834-1275. FAX 610-834-1275. (Co-sponsor: C H E M - Center for Healthcare Environment Management) Ed. Paul Segal. **Document type:** newsletter.
—**CCC.**
   Formerly: Hospital Hazardous Materials Management (ISSN 0895-7169)
   Description: Highlights current information for hazardous materials, and environmental and occupational health safety.
   Refereed Serial

610   CN   ISSN 0840-4704
    CODEN: HMFOEU
HEALTHCARE MANAGEMENT FORUM. 1988. q. Canadian College of Health Service Executives, 350 Sparks St., Ottawa, ON K1R 7S8, Canada. TEL 613-235-7218. **Indexed:** Excerp.Med. (until 1993).
—BLDSC (4275.247880); Faxon.

610 375   US   ISSN 1073-4937
HEALTHCARE MEDIA LOCATOR. 1992. a. $145 (effective 1996). Olympic Media Information, Box 190, West Park, NY 12493. TEL 914-384-6563. E-mail: medprofile@aol.com. (diskette format) **Document type:** abstracting/indexing, directory.
   Description: Provides information on rental and purchase of healthcare films and videos, with a complete supplier directory.

610 659.1   US   ISSN 1072-3684
HEALTHCARE P R & MARKETING NEWS. 1992. bi-w. $397 (foreign $430) (effective 1994). Phillips Business Information, Inc., 1201 Seven Locks Rd., Potomac, MD 20854. TEL 301-424-3338. FAX 301-309-3847. E-mail: pbi@phillips.com. Ed. Tom Moore. (back issues avail.) **Document type:** newsletter.
—**CCC.**

610.6   US
HEALTHCARE RESOURCE AND REFERENCE GUIDE. irreg. $49.95 to non-members; members $39.95. American Medical Association, 515 N. State St., Chicago, IL 60610. TEL 312-464-5000. FAX 312-464-4184.

MEDICAL SCIENCES 4211

610 US ISSN 1044-4076
RA399.A3
HEALTHCARE STANDARDS DIRECTORY. (Supplement avail.: Healthcare Standards Update (ISSN 1048-8103)) 1989. a. $285. (Emergency Care Research Institute) E C R I, 5200 Butler Pike, Plymouth Meeting, PA 19462. TEL 610-825-6000. FAX 610-834-1275. Ed. Marybeth Paul. **Document type:** directory.
—CCC.
Description: Covers published standards, clinical practice guidelines and regulations for the delivery of healthcare services.

HEALTHCARE SYSTEM REFORM ALERT. see *INSURANCE*

610 330 US ISSN 1049-4499
HEALTHCARE TECHNOLOGY & BUSINESS OPPORTUNITIES.* 1980. m. $295. Biomedical Business International (Subsidiary of: Macmillan Inc.), 2 Park Plz, Ste. 900, Irvine, CA 92714-8519. TEL 714-755-5757. FAX 714-755-5724. (back issues avail.) **Document type:** newsletter.
●Also available online. Vendor(s): Knight-Ridder, Inc.
—CCC.
Formerly: Medical Product Development.
Description: Includes listing of technologies available for license and transfer, business opportunities, US, Japanese and European patent activity, and resources.

610 US ISSN 1074-9810
▼**HEALTHCARE TECHNOLOGY MANAGEMENT INTERNATIONAL.** 1994. q. $50 (free to qualified overseas personnel). Second Source Publications, Inc., 10 Risho Ave., East Providence, RI 02914-1215. TEL 401-434-1050. FAX 401-434-1090. Pub. Jack Spears. **Document type:** trade publication.
Description: Provides health care professionals with cost-effective solutions for the service, support, and management of medical equipment.

HEALTHCARE TRENDS AND TRANSITION. see *OCCUPATIONS AND CAREERS*

HEALTHCARE 1500. see *PUBLIC HEALTH AND SAFETY*

614 US ISSN 0738-811X
HEALTHFACTS. 1976. m. $21 (Canada and Mexico $24; Asia and Europe $33). Center for Medical Consumers, 237 Thompson St., New York, NY 10012. TEL 212-674-7105. FAX 212-674-7100. Ed. Maryann Napoli. bk.rev.; index, cum.index, circ. 12,000. (back issues avail.) **Indexed:** CHNI, Hlth.Ind. **Document type:** trade publication.
—BLDSC (4275.247975).
Description: Designed for informed medical decision-making.

610 617.6
HEALTHSTATE. 1982. q. University of Medicine and Dentistry of New Jersey, 30 Bergen St., ADMC 121, Newark, NJ 07107-3000. Ed. Eve Jacobs. adv. circ. 48,000. **Document type:** newsletter.

610 CC ISSN 1000-1581
CODEN: HYXUEI
HEBEI YIXUE YUAN XUEBAO/HEBEI ACADEMY OF MEDICAL SCIENCES. JOURNAL. (Text in Chinese) bi-m. Hebei Yixue Yuan - Hebei Academy of Medical Sciences, 5 Chang'an Xilu, Shijiazhuang, Hebei 050017, People's Republic of China. TEL 44121. Ed. Wu Shenchun.
—CASDDS.

HEBEI ZHONGYI/HEBEI TRADITIONAL MEDICINE. see *ALTERNATIVE MEDICINE*

613 GW ISSN 0017-9604
HEILBERUFE; Fortbildung fuer Pflege- und Assistenzberufe in stationaeren und ambulanten Bereich. 1949. m. DM.80($58) (effective 1996). Urban und Vogel, Lindwurmstr. 95, 80337 Munich, Germany. TEL 089-53292-0. FAX 089-53292100. adv.; bk.rev.; charts; illus.; index. circ. 25,000. **Indexed:** Excerp.Med. **Document type:** academic/scholarly publication.
—CCC.

610 CC ISSN 1000-9906
R97.7.C5
HEILONGJIANG ZHONGYIYAO/HEILONGJIANG TRADITIONAL CHINESE MEDICAL SCIENCE. (Text in Chinese) bi-m. Heilongjiang Zhongyi Yanjiuyuan - Heilongjiang Institute of Traditional Chinese Medicine, 72, Sanfu Jie, Xiangfang-qu, Harbin, Heilongjiang 150036, People's Republic of China. TEL 53086. Ed. Zhang Qi.

610 II ISSN 0017-9922
HELAN MEDICAL MAGAZINE. (Text in Tamil) 1960. m. Rs.6. Thilaga Medical Publications, 28 Melaponnagaram, 8th St., Madurai 10, India. Ed. Dr. N. Thankaraj. adv.; pat. circ. 1,000.

610 NE ISSN 0925-0018
HELEN DOWLING INSTITUTE FOR BIOPSYCHOSOCIAL MEDICINE. PUBLICATION. (Text in English) 1990. irreg., vol.6, 1993. price varies. Swets & Zeitlinger bv, Heereweg 347, 2161 CA Lisse, Netherlands. TEL 31-2521-35111. FAX 31-2521-15888. TELEX 41325 SZLIS NL. (Dist. in N. America by: Swets & Zeitlinger, 440 Creamery Way, Ste. A, Exton PA 19341. TEL 800-447-9387. FAX 610-524-5366) (back issues avail.) **Document type:** monographic series, proceedings.
—BLDSC (7072.250000).
Description: Publishes proceedings of symposia and seminars, and original contributions in the field of biopsychosocial medicine, including investigation of the physical, psychological and social determinants of the healing process.
Refereed Serial

HELICOBACTER. see *BIOLOGY — Microbiology*

HELLENIKE MIKROBIOLOGIKE KAI HYGIENOLOGIKE HETAIREIA. DELTION/ACTA MICROBIOLOGICA HELLENICA. see *BIOLOGY — Microbiology*

610 FI ISSN 0437-2468
HELSINGIN LAAKARILEHTI. 1954. 9/yr. FIM 160. Helsingin Laakariyhdistys ry - Helsinki Medical Society, Museokatu 13 A 2, FIN-00100 Helsinki 10, Finland. TEL 358-0-490403. FAX 358-0-408170. Ed. Dr. Matti Romo. adv. contact: T. Tennila. bk.rev. circ. 14,400. **Document type:** bulletin, corporate report.
Description: Explores doctors' jobs, relations with the government, free time, education and pensions.

616.85 362.2 340 US ISSN 1074-1593
R726
HEMLOCK TIMELINES. 1980. bi-m. $35. Hemlock Society U S A, Box 11830, Eugene, OR 97440. TEL 503-342-5748. FAX 503-345-2751. Ed. Kris Larson. circ. 40,000. (also avail. in looseleaf format; back issues avail.) **Document type:** newsletter.
Formerly (until 1994): Hemlock Quarterly (ISSN 0742-5376)

610 US ISSN 0883-2285
HEMOCHROMATOSIS AWARENESS; a quarterly update on hereditary and acquired iron-overload. 1982. q. $25. Hemochromatosis Foundation, Inc., Box 8569, Albany, NY 12208. TEL 518-489-0972. Ed. Tim Casey. bk.rev.; tr.lit. circ. 1,500. (looseleaf format)
Description: Discusses all aspects of heriditary hemochromatosis, a disorder of iron metabolism, in which dietary iron absorption exceeds body needs. Reviews relevent literature and relevant public policy and food regulatory issues.

HENRY FORD HOSPITAL MEDICAL JOURNAL. see *HOSPITALS*

610 JA
HERUSU SAIENSU SENTA NENPO/HEALTH SCIENCE CENTER. ANNUAL REPORT. (Text in Japanese) 1977. a. Herusu Saiensu Senta, Kitasato Daigaku Byoin, 15-1, Kitazato 1-chome, Sagamihara-shi, Kanagawa-ken 228, Japan.

616.07 GW ISSN 0171-9661
HESSISCHES AERZTEBLATT. m. DM.150. Verlag Kirchheim und Co. GmbH, Kaiserstr. 41, 55116 Mainz, Germany. TEL 06131-96070-0. FAX 06131-9607070. Ed.Bd. adv.; charts; illus. **Document type:** academic/scholarly publication.

616.07 615.8 IT ISSN 1120-7000
HIP INTERNATIONAL; the journal of clinical and experimental research on hip pathology and therapy. 1991. q. L.140000($140) (effective 1994). Wichtig Editore s.r.l., Via Friuli, 72-74, 20135 Milan, Italy. TEL 02-5452306. FAX 02-5451843.
—CCC.

610 US ISSN 1050-9631
QP383.25 CODEN: HIPPEL
THE HIPPOCAMPUS. 1991. bi-m. $396 (foreign $489) (effective 1996). John Wiley & Sons, Inc., Journals, 605 Third Ave., New York, NY 10158. TEL 212-850-6645. FAX 202-850-6021. TELEX 12-7063. E-mail: SUBINFO@JWILEY.DOC. (Subscr. outside the Americas to: John Wiley & Sons Ltd., Baffins Ln., Chichester, W. Sussex, PO19 1UD, England. TEL 44-1243-779777. FAX 44-1243-776128) Eds. Dr. David Amaral, Dr. Menno Witter. (also avail. in microform from UMI; back issues avail. **Indexed:** Excerp.Med. (1993-), Ind.Med. (1993-). **Document type:** academic/scholarly publication.
—BLDSC (4315.255000); CASDDS; Genuine Article; SWETS; UMI. **CCC.**
Refereed Serial

610 US ISSN 0892-2977
RA773
HIPPOCRATES. 1987. 10/yr. free to qualified personnel. Heath Publishing Group (Subsidiary of: Time Publishing Ventures, Inc.), 301 Howard St., 18th Fl., San Francisco, CA 94105-2252. TEL 415-512-9100. Ed. Eric W. Schrier. adv.; circ. controlled. **Indexed:** Hlth.Ind.
●Also available online.
—UMI; UnCover.
Description: For medical professionals.

610 616.1 JA ISSN 0910-0377
HIROSAKI DAIGAKU IGAKUBU EISEIGAKU KYOSHITSU GYOSEKISHU. (Text in Japanese; summaries in English) 1954. irreg. Hirosaki Daigaku, Igakubu - Hirosaki University, School of Medicine, 5 Zaifu-cho, Hirosaki-shi, Aomori-ken 036, Japan. Ed. Naosuke Sasaki. circ. 90.

610 JA ISSN 0385-793X
HIROSAKI DAIGAKU IRYO GIJUTSU TANKI DAIGAKUBU KIYO/HIROSAKI UNIVERSITY. SCHOOL OF ALLIED MEDICAL SCIENCES. BULLETIN. (Text in English, Japanese) 1976. a. Hirosaki Dagaku, Iryo Gijutsu Tanki Daigakubu, 66-1, Honcho, Hirosaki-shi, Aomori-ken 036, Japan. **Document type:** bulletin.

610 574 JA ISSN 0439-1721
CODEN: HIRIA6
HIROSAKI IGAKU/HIROSAKI MEDICAL JOURNAL. (Text in English, Japanese; summaries in English) 1950. q. Hirosaki Daigaku, Igakubu - Hirosaki University, School of Medicine, 5 Zaifu-cho, Hirosaki-shi, Aomori-ken 036, Japan. circ. 400. **Indexed:** Biol.Abstr., Chem.Abstr., Excerp.Med., INIS Atomind.
—BLDSC (4315.570000); CASDDS.

610 JA ISSN 0912-5930
HIROSAKISHI ISHIKAIHO/HIROSAKI CITY MEDICAL ASSOCIATION. JOURNAL. (Text in Japanese) 1966. bi-m. Hirosakishi Ishikai, 7-1, Noda 2-chome, Hirosaki-shi, Amomori-ken 036, Japan.

610 JA ISSN 0018-2087
CODEN: HDIZAB
HIROSHIMA DAIGAKU IGAKU ZASSHI. English edition: Hiroshima University. Medical Journal. (Text in Japanese; summaries in English) 1952. bi-m. 5000 Yen. Hiroshima University, School of Medicine - Hiroshima Daigaku Igakubu, 1-2-3 Kasumi, Hiroshima 734, Japan. Ed. Yoshiyasu Matsuo. bibl.; charts; illus.; index. circ. 450. **Indexed:** Biol.Abstr., Chem.Abstr., INIS Atomind.
—BLDSC (5527.820000); CASDDS.
Former titles (until 1962): Gencho Hiroshma Igaku (ISSN 0375-8982); (until 1956): Hiroshima Igaku, Gencho Go.

610 JA ISSN 0387-6454
CODEN: HBISDD
HIROSHIMA KENRITSU BYOIN ISHI/HIROSHIMA PREFECTURAL HOSPITAL. MEDICAL JOURNAL. (Text in English, Japanese) 1969. a. Hiroshima Kenritsu Byoin, 5-54, Ujina Kanda 1-chome, Hiroshima-shi, Hiroshima-ken 734, Japan.
—CASDDS.

MEDICAL SCIENCES

610   JA   ISSN 0367-5904
CODEN: HIRGAY
HIROSHIMA MEDICAL ASSOCIATION. JOURNAL/HIROSHIMA IGAKU. (Text in Japanese) 1896. m. 1700 Yen($13) (effective 1992). Hiroshima Medical Association - Hiroshima Igakkai, 1-1-1 Kannonhon-machi, Nishi-ku, Hiroshima 733, Japan. TEL 082-232-7211. FAX 082-293-3363. Ed. Dr. Teruaki Fukuhara. adv.; bibl.; charts; illus.; index; circ. 5,800 (controlled). **Indexed:** C.I.S. Abstr., Chem.Abstr., INIS Atomind.
—BLDSC (4758.300000); CASDDS.
Formerly (until 1948): Geibi-Iji.

HIROSHIMA SHUDO DAIGAKU RINSHO SHINRIGAKU KENKYU/HIROSHIMA SHUDO UNIVERSITY. BULLETIN OF CLINICAL PSYCHOLOGY. see *PSYCHOLOGY*

610   JA
CODEN: HIJMAC
HIROSHIMA UNIVERSITY. MEDICAL JOURNAL. Japanese edition: Hiroshima Daigaku Igaku Zasshi (ISSN 0018-2087) (Text in English) 1951. q. $20. Hiroshima University, School of Medicine - Hiroshima Daigaku Igakubu, 1-2-3 Kasumi, Hiroshima 734, Japan. Ed. Yoshiyasu Matsuo. bibl.; charts; illus.; index. circ. 600. (also avail. in microform from UMI; reprint service avail. from UMI) **Indexed:** Biol.Abstr., Chem.Abstr., Curr.Adv.Ecol.Sci., Curr.Cont., Dairy Sci.Abstr., Dent.Ind., Excerp.Med., Helminthol.Abstr., Ind.Med., Ind.Sci.Rev., INIS Atomind., Sci.Cit.Ind.
—BLDSC (4315.600000); CASDDS; UMI; UnCover.
Formerly: Hiroshima Journal of Medical Sciences (ISSN 0018-2052)

610   JA
HIROSHIMASHI ISHIKAI DAYORI/HIROSHIMA CITY MEDICAL ASSOCIATION. JOURNAL. (Text in Japanese) m. Hiroshimashi Ishikai, 1-1, Kan'onhonmachi 1-chome, Nishi-ku, Hiroshima-shi, Hiroshima-ken 733, Japan.

610   JA
HIROSHIMASHI ISHIKAI RINSHO KENSA SENTA DAYORI/HIROSHIMA CITY MEDICAL ASSOCIATION. MEDICAL LABORATORY CENTER. NEWS. (Text in Japanese) 1970. m. Hiroshimashi Ishikai, Rinsho Kensa Senta, 8-6, Sendamachi 3-chome, Naka-ku, Hiroshima-shi, Hiroshima-ken 730, Japan.

610   SP   ISSN 0018-2125
HISPALIS MEDICA; revista sevillana de medicina y cirugia. 1944. m. $50. Miguel y Rafael Rios Mozo, Eds. & Pubs., Gravina 29, 41001 Seville, Spain. TEL 54-422-17-51. adv.; bk.rev.; abstr.; bibl.; illus.; index, cum.index. circ. 1,000. **Indexed:** Chem.Abstr., Dent.Ind., Ind.Med.Esp., Nutr.Abstr.
—CCC.

610   JA   ISSN 0286-0171
HITACHI IGAKKAISHI/HITACHI MEDICAL JOURNAL. (Text in Japanese) 1962. s-a. Hitachi Igakkai - Hitachi Medical Association, Hitachi Sogo Byoin, 1-1, Jonancho 2-chome, Hitachi-shi, Ibaraki-ken 317, Japan.

610   JA
HITO TO IRYO/HUMAN BEING AND MEDICAL CARE. (Text in Japanese) bi-m. Jitchi Ika no Tameno Kai - Medical Practitioner's Society, Kyowa Kikaku, 2-20, Shinbashi, Minato-ku, Tokyo 105, Japan.

HOITOTIEDE. see *MEDICAL SCIENCES — Nurses And Nursing*

610   JA
HOKEN SANGYO JIHO/MEDICAL INSTRUMENT NEWS. (Text in Japanese) 1956. 3/m. 6000 Yen. Hoken Sangyo Jihosha, 14-5, Minamiikebukuro 3-chome, Toshima-ku, Tokyo 171, Japan.

610   JA   ISSN 0915-2083
HOKKAIDO DAIGAKU IRYO GIJUTSU TANKI DAIGAKUBU KIYO/HOKKAIDO UNIVERSITY. COLLEGE OF MEDICAL TECHNOLOGY. ANNUAL REPORTS. (Text in English, Japanese) 1988. a. Hokkaido Daigaku, Iryo Gijutsu Tanki Daigakubu, Nishi 5-chome, Kita 12-jo, Kita-ku, Sapporo-shi, Hokkaido 060, Japan.

610   JA   ISSN 0913-0217
HOKKAIDO IHO/HOKKAIDO MEDICAL ASSOCIATION. NEWS. (Text in Japanese) s-m. 250 Yen per no. Hokkaido Ishikai, Ishi Kaikan, Nishi 6-chome, Odori, Chuo-ku, Sapporo-shi, Hokkaido 060, Japan.

610   JA   ISSN 0367-6102
CODEN: HOIZAK
HOKKAIDO JOURNAL OF MEDICAL SCIENCE/HOKKAIDO IGAKU ZASSHI. (Text in English, Japanese) 1923. bi-m. 6000 Yen per no. Hokkaido Medical Society - Hokkaido Igakkai, Hokkaido Daigaku Igakubu, Nishi 7-chome, Kita 15-jo, Kita-ku, Sapporo-shi, Hokkaido 060, Japan. TEL 011-706-5073. FAX 011-706-7866. Ed. Masamichi Kato. adv. circ. 1,200. (back issues avail.) **Indexed:** Biol.Abstr., Chem.Abstr., Ind.Med., INIS Atomind. **Document type:** academic/scholarly publication.
—BLDSC (4322.261000).

610   JA   ISSN 0285-0664
HOKKAIDO KINROSHA IRYO KYOKAI IGAKU ZASSHI/HOKKAIDO ASSOCIATION OF MEDICAL SERVICE FOR WORKERS. MEDICAL JOURNAL. (Text in Japanese) 1973. s-a. Hokkaido Kinrosha Iryo Kyokai, 5, 3-chome Kikusui 3-jo, Shiraishi-ku, Sapporo-shi, Hokkaido 003, Japan.

610   JA
HOKKAIDO NOSON IGAKKAI ZASSHI/HOKKAIDO ASSOCIATION OF RURAL MEDICINE. JOURNAL. (Text in Japanese) s-a. Hokkaido Noson Igakkai, Hokkaido Nosangyoson Kenko Kanri Senta, Nishi 7-chome, Kita 4-jo, Chuo-ku, Sapporo-shi, Hokkaido 060, Japan.

610   JA
HOKKAIDO PURAIMARI KEA KENKYUKAI KAIHO/HOKKAIDO JOURNAL OF PRIMARY CARE. (Text in English, Japanese) 1985. a. Hokkaido Puraimari Kea Kenkyukai - Hokkaido Association of Primary Care, Hokkaido Ishikai, Nishi 6-chome, Odori, Chuo-ku, Sapporo-shi, Hokkaido 060, Japan.

610   JA   ISSN 0389-3928
HOKURIKU ISHI/HOKURIKU MEDICAL HISTORY. (Text in Japanese) 1979. a. Hokuriku Ishigaku Dokokai - Hokuriku Medical History Society, Fukuiken Ishikaikan, 4-10, Daiganji 3-chome, Fukui-shi, Fukui-ken 910, Japan.

HOLISTIC MEDICINE. see *ALTERNATIVE MEDICINE*

HOMBRE Y TRABAJO; boletin de medicina, seguridad e higiene. see *PUBLIC HEALTH AND SAFETY*

HOME HEALTH BUSINESS REPORT; news trends & strategies for the home healthcare executive. see *BUSINESS AND ECONOMICS — Management*

610   US   ISSN 1070-2431
HOME HEALTH PRODUCTS. 1992. bi-m. Stevens Publishing Corporation, 3630 J.H. Kultgen Frwy., Waco, TX 76706. TEL 817-776-9000. FAX 817-776-9018. Ed. Sharon Johnson; Pub. Marc Sheiner. adv.: B&W page $4180, color page $4955; trim 10 7/8 x 15 7/8; adv. contact: Michael Bracken. circ. 15,375. (tabloid format; also avail. in tabloid format) **Document type:** trade publication.
Description: Provides information on new products released by manufacturers; analyses of market trends; coverage of manufacturers' research and development initiatives.

610.73   US   ISSN 0884-741X
CODEN: HHNUEJ
HOME HEALTHCARE NURSE. 1983. bi-m. $34 to individuals (foreign $65); institutions $95 (foreign $120) (effective 1996); newsstand price: $11. Lippincott - Raven Publishers, 227 E. Washington Sq., Philadelphia, PA 19106. (Subscr. to: 12107 Insurance Way, Hagerstown, MD 21740. TEL 800-777-2295) Ed. Joan E. Caserta; Pub. Lisa R. Marshall. adv. contact: Kathleen M. Phelan. bk.rev.; illus.; stat.; tr.lit. circ. 8,791. (also avail. in microfilm from UMI; back issues avail.; reprint service avail. from UMI) **Indexed:** CINAHL, Int.Nurs.Ind., Nurs.Abstr.
—BLDSC (4326.054000); Faxon; SWETS; UMI; UnCover. **CCC.**
Incorporates (1979-1983): Nephrology Nurse (ISSN 0164-4386)

610   US
HOME INFUSION THERAPY MANAGEMENT. 1993. m. $229. American Health Consultants, Inc., Six Piedmont Center, Ste. 400, Atlanta, GA 30305. TEL 404-262-7436; 800-688-2421. FAX 800-284-3291. Ed. Kathy Cline. **Document type:** newsletter.

610   HK   ISSN 1024-2708
HONG KONG MEDICAL JOURNAL. (Text in English) 1948. q. $300 to non-members. Hong Kong Medical Association, Duke of Windsor Bldg., 15 Hennessy Rd., 5th Fl., Hong Kong. TEL 852-527-8285. FAX 852-865-0943. (Co-sponsor: Hong Kong Academy of Medicine) Ed. Joseph Lee. adv. circ. 6,000. (back issues avail.) **Indexed:** Excerpt.Med., ExtraMED. **Document type:** academic/scholarly publication.
●Also available on CD-ROM.
—BLDSC (4758.568000).
Former titles (until Mar. 1995): Hong Kong Medical Association. Journal (ISSN 1010-8424); (until 1985): Hong Kong Medical Association. Bulletin.
Refereed Serial

HOSPICE TODAY. see *SOCIAL SERVICES AND WELFARE*

610   PO   ISSN 0046-8037
HOSPITAIS CIVIS DE LISBOA. BOLETIM CLINICO. vol.35, 1974. 4/yr. Esc.150. Livraria Sa da Costa Editora, Praca Luis de Camoes, 22-4, 1294 Lisbon, Portugal. TEL 3607215. TELEX 15574 SACOST. Ed. Dr. Fernando Nogueira. bibl.; charts; illus.

658   US   ISSN 0018-5485
EL HOSPITAL (CINCINNATI). (Includes Buyer's Guide) (Text in Spanish) 1944. bi-m. free to qualified personnel. Salud Publications International Inc., 2724 Erie Ave., Ste. B, Cincinnati, OH 45208-2125. TEL 513-533-5470. FAX 513-533-5474. Ed. Gregory Loomis; Pub. Gregory Loomis. adv.: B&W page $2500, color page $3700. bk.rev.; film rev.; charts; illus.; stat.; tr.lit.; index, cum.index; circ. 14,850 (controlled). (back issues avail.) **Document type:** trade publication.
Description: Reports on latest developments in medical technology, equipment and supplies.
Refereed Serial

610   UK   ISSN 0262-3145
HOSPITAL DOCTOR. 1967. w. £70. Reed Healthcare Publishing (Subsidiary of: Reed Elsevier group), Quadrant House, The Quadrant, Sutton, Surrey SM2 5AS, England. TEL 081-652-8745. FAX 081-652-8701. Ed. Jane King. adv.; bk.rev. circ. 34,000. (tabloid format) **Document type:** trade publication.
—BLDSC (4333.148000).
Incorporated (in Apr. 1981): On Call.

610 618.92   CN   ISSN 0082-5034
HOSPITAL FOR SICK CHILDREN, TORONTO. RESEARCH INSTITUTE. ANNUAL REPORT. (Text in English) 1969. a. Hospital for Sick Children, 555 University Ave., Toronto, ON M5G 1X8, Canada. TEL 416-597-1500. Ed. Dr. A. Rothstein. circ. 500.

HOSPITAL INFECTION CONTROL. see *HOSPITALS*

610   UA   ISSN 0046-8010
HOSPITAL MEDICAL PRACTICE. (Text in Arabic and English) 1971. q. ££1($3.) Scientific Society of the Medical Care Organization, 375 Ramses St., Abbassieh, Cairo, Egypt. Ed. Mohammed Sadek Sabbour. adv.; bk.rev.; abstr.; bibl.; charts; illus.; pat.; index. circ. 5,000.

610   US   ISSN 0441-2745
R11
HOSPITAL MEDICINE; for primary care physicians. 1965. m. $126 to institutions outside the Americas; $84 to institutions in U.S (effective 1996). Excerpta Medica, Inc. (Subsidiary of: Reed Elsevier Medical group), 105 Raider Blvd., Belle Mead, NJ 08502. TEL 908-874-8550. FAX 908-874-8419. (Subscr. to: Box 3085, Princeton, NJ 08543-3085) Ed. Marian Moss Berger. adv.; charts; illus.; index; circ. 34,000 (controlled). **Indexed:** CINAHL. **Document type:** trade publication.
—BLDSC (4333.205800); Faxon; SWETS; UMI; UnCover. **CCC.**
Description: For primary care physicians who are office and hospital based. Editorial covers cardiovascular, GI, respiratory, arthritis and all other areas of medical interest to the primary care physician.
Refereed Serial

HOSPITAL PAYMENT AND INFORMATION MANAGEMENT. see *HOSPITALS*

MEDICAL SCIENCES

610 US ISSN 0888-241X
CODEN: HOPYA
HOSPITAL PHYSICIAN: INTERNAL AND FAMILY MEDICINE EDITION. 1957. m. $65 (Canada $85, elsewhere $150); students $50 (effective 1995). (Association for Hospital Medical Education) Turner White Communications, Inc., 125 Strafford Ave., Ste. 220, Wayne, PA 19087-3391. TEL 610-975-4541. FAX 610-975-4564. Ed. Julie Kostecky. adv.: B&W page $4330; adv. contact: Judith Webber. charts; illus. circ. 90,000 (controlled). (also avail. in microform from UMI; reprint service avail. from UMI) Indexed: Med.Care Rev. **Document type:** trade publication.
—UMI.
Former titles (until 1985): Hospital Physician: Resident - Staff Edition (ISSN 8750-7560); Hospital Physician (ISSN 0018-5795); (until 1965): R I S S - National Magazine for Residents, Interns, and Senior Students (ISSN 0485-8182)
Description: Covers issues concerning or of interest to residents and staff physicians, including epidemiology, diagnosis, and treatment; new prescription drugs; and clinical outcomes.
Refereed Serial

610 US ISSN 8750-2836
R11 CODEN: HOPRBW
HOSPITAL PRACTICE. 1966. m. $54 (Canada $58; elsewhere $68) (free to qualified physicians). McGraw-Hill, Inc., 4530 W. 77th St., Minneapolis, MN 55434. TEL 612-835-3222. FAX 612-835-3460. Ed. Dr. Lee Powers. adv. contact: Debora Higgins. bk.rev.; charts; illus.; index. circ. 120,766. (also avail. in microfilm from UMI; reprint service avail. from UMI) Indexed: AIM, Biol.Abstr., C.I.N.L., Curr.Adv.Cancer Res., Curr.Adv.Ecol.Sci., Curr.Cont., Curr.Lit.Fam.Plan., Dent.Ind., Excerp.Med., Hosp.Lit.Ind., I.P.A., Ind.Med., Ind.Sci.Rev., INIS Atomind., Med.Care Rev., Nutr.Abstr., Sci.Cit.Ind.
●Also available online.
—BLDSC (4333.208300); Faxon; Genuine Article; SWETS; UMI; UnCover. **CCC.**
Incorporates: Clinical Experience.
Description: Review articles with information on problem areas in medicine and clinical research.
Refereed Serial

HOSPITAL UPDATE; the journal of continuing education for hospital doctors. see HOSPITALS

610 SA ISSN 1018-1458
HOSPITAL UPDATE (SOUTH AFRICAN EDITION). UK edition: Hospital Update (ISSN 0305-4136) (Text in English) 1990. m. R.90. George Warman Publications (Pty.) Ltd., P.O. Box 3847, Cape Town 8000, South Africa. TEL 27-21-245320. FAX 27-21-261332. Ed. Diana Procter. circ. 5,500. **Document type:** academic/scholarly publication.

610 VE ISSN 0018-5884
HOSPITAL VARGAS. ARCHIVOS.* vol.9, 1967. q. Hospital Vargas, Caracas, Venezuela. Ed.Bd. illus. Indexed: Abstr.Hyg., Biol.Abstr., Chem.Abstr, Trop.Dis.Bull.

610 US ISSN 1060-7838
RA971.32
HOSPITAL'S MEDICARE POLICY & PAYMENT REPORT. 1989. m. $379 (includes Physician's Coding Strategist). American Health Consultants, Inc., Six Piedmont Center, Ste. 400, Atlanta, GA 30305. TEL 404-262-7436; 800-688-2421. FAX 800-284-3291. Ed. Reba Griffith. circ. 1,060. **Document type:** newsletter.
Formerly (until 1992): Physician's Payment Update; **Incorporates (in 1992):** Ophthalmology Alert; **Formerly (until 1991):** Physician's Payment Advisory.

610 612 AT
HOWARD FLOREY INSTITUTE OF EXPERIMENTAL PHYSIOLOGY & MEDICINE. ANNUAL REPORT. 1974. a. Howard Florey Institute of Experimental Physiology & Medicine, Parkville, Vic., Australia. FAX 03-348-1707. illus. circ. 3,000. **Document type:** academic/scholarly publication.
Formerly: Howard Florey Institute of Experimental Physiology and Medicine. Annual Report and Notice of Meeting (ISSN 0314-6162)

610 CC ISSN 0257-7712
CODEN: HYDXET
HUAXI YIKE DAXUE XUEBAO/WEST CHINA UNIVERSITY OF MEDICAL SCIENCES. JOURNAL. (Text in Chinese; summaries, table of contents in English) 1959. q. Y8 (foreign Y80 or $16). Huaxi Yike Daxue - West China University of Medical Sciences, Renmin Nanlu Sec. 3, No. 17, Chengdu, Sichuan 610044, People's Republic of China. FAX 583252. TELEX 60251-WCUMS-CN. (Dist. overseas by: China International Book Trading Corporation, P.O. Box 2820, Beijing 100044, P.R.C.) Ed. Yang Guanghua. abstr.; bibl.; charts; illus.; stat.; index. circ. 2,500. (back issues avail.) Indexed: Biol.Abstr., Chem.Abstr., Excerp.Med., Ind.Med.
—BLDSC (4915.650000); CASDDS.
Formerly (until 1985): Sichuan Yixueyuan Xuebao - Acta Academiae Medicinae Sichuan (ISSN 0253-4290)

610 CC ISSN 1002-0179
HUAXI YIXUE/WEST CHINA MEDICAL JOURNAL. (Text in Chinese; summaries in Chinese and English) 1986. q. Y14.40 (foreign $20). Huaxi Yike Daxue, Fushu Diyi Yiyuan - West China University of Medical Sciences, 1st University Hospital, No. 37, Guoxue Xiang, Chengdu, Sichuan 610041, People's Republic of China. TEL 86-28-551255. FAX 86-28-582944. Ed. Tang Xiaoda. adv. contact: Huasong Rao. abstr.; bibl.; charts; illus.; stat.; index. circ. 5,000. (also avail. in microfilm; microfiche; back issues avail.) **Document type:** academic/scholarly publication.
Description: Contains two sections: medicine and surgery.

610 US
HUDSON MONITOR. 1993. 10/yr. Cortlandt Group, Inc., 500 Executive Blvd., Ossining, NY 10562. TEL 914-762-0647. FAX 914-762-8820. Ed. Ruth Cohen. adv.: B&W page $5000, color page $6240; trim 8 x 10 3/4. circ. 120,000.

610 GW ISSN 0179-7581
HUFELAND - JOURNAL; Zeitschrift fuer Hufelandgesellschaft fuer Gesamtmedizin. 1986-1987; resumed 1991. q. DM.70 (students DM.52). Karl F. Haug Verlag GmbH, Fritz-Frey-Str. 21, 69121 Heidelberg, Germany. TEL 06221-4062-0. FAX 06221-400727. TELEX 461683-HVVFM-D. (Subscr. to: Postfach 102840, 69018 Heidelberg, Germany) Ed. Dr. Franz Schmid. **Document type:** academic/scholarly publication.

610 NE ISSN 0018-7070
HUISARTS EN WETENSCHAP. (Text in Dutch; summaries in Dutch, English) 1950. m. fl.157.50 (students fl.89.75) (effective 1995). (Nederlands Huisartsengenootschap) Bohn Stafleu van Loghum B.V. (Subsidiary of: Wolters Kluwer N.V.), Postbus 246, 3990 GA Houten, Netherlands. TEL 31-3403-95711. FAX 31-3403-50903. Ed. F.J. Meyman. adv.; bk.rev. circ. 5,075. Indexed: Excerp.Med., FAMLI.
—BLDSC (4335.850000); SWETS.
Refereed Serial

HUMAN FACTORS & AVIATION MEDICINE. see AERONAUTICS AND SPACE FLIGHT

615.8 NE ISSN 0167-9457
QP303 CODEN: HMSCDO
HUMAN MOVEMENT SCIENCE; journal devoted to pure and applied research on human movement. (Text in English) 1982. bi-m. fl.721($440) (effective 1996). North-Holland (Subsidiary of: Elsevier Science B.V.), P.O. Box 211, 1000 AE Amsterdam, Netherlands. TEL 31-20-4853911. FAX 31-20-4853598. TELEX 18582 ESPA NL. (Subscr. in U.S. and Canada to: Elsevier Science Inc., Box 882, Madison Sq. Sta., New York, NY 10159. TEL 212-989-5800. FAX 212-633-3990) Ed. H.T.A. Whitting. bk.rev. (back issues avail.) Indexed: Psychol.Abstr. (1990-), Sportsearch (1987-). **Document type:** academic/scholarly publication.
—BLDSC (4336.210000); Faxon; Genuine Article; SWETS; UnCover. **CCC.**
Description: Consists of empirical reports, overviews, methodologies as well as announcements of seminars, conferences and research programs relevant to the study of human movement.
Refereed Serial

616.07 US ISSN 0046-8177
CODEN: HPCQA4
HUMAN PATHOLOGY. 1970. m. $185 (foreign $241) (effective 1996). W.B. Saunders Co. (Subsidiary of: Harcourt Brace & Company), Curtis Center, 3rd Fl., Independence Sq. W., Philadelphia, PA 19106-3399. TEL 215-238-7800. FAX 215-238-6445. (Subscr. to: Periodicals Fulfillment, W.B. Saunders Co., 6277 Sea Harbor Dr., 4th Fl., Orlando, FL 32891-4800. TEL 800-654-2452. FAX 800-874-6418) Ed. Dr. Fred Gorstein; Pub. Joan W. Blumberg. adv.: B&W page $950, color page $1825; 7 x 10; adv. contact: Steve Gray. bk.rev. circ. 7,484. (also avail. in microform from MIM,UMI; reprint service avail. from ISI,UMI) Indexed: Biol.Abstr., Chem.Abstr., Curr.Adv.Cancer Res., Curr.Adv.Ecol.Sci., Curr.Cont., Excerp.Med., Helminthol.Abstr., Ind.Med., Ind.Sci.Rev., INIS Atomind., Med.& Surg.Dermat., Rev.Plant Path., Sci.Cit.Ind. **Document type:** academic/scholarly publication.
—BLDSC (4336.260000); CASDDS; EMDOCS; Faxon; Genuine Article; SWETS; UMI; UnCover. **CCC.**
Description: Contains original contributions, news items, case studies, and special notices in the field of human pathology.
Refereed Serial

610 CN ISSN 0828-7090
HUMANE MEDICINE; a journal of the art of healing. 1985. q. Can.$52 (foreign $62). Canadian Medical Association, P.O. Box 8650, Ottawa, ON K1G 0G8, Canada. TEL 613-731-9331. FAX 613-523-0937. Eds. Dr. D.G. Oreopoulos, Dr. J.O. Godden. adv. circ. 45,000. (also avail. in microfilm from UMI; reprint service avail. from UMI) Indexed: CINAHL, Curr.Cont. **Document type:** academic/scholarly publication.
—BLDSC (4336.472600); Genuine Article; UMI; UnCover. **CCC.**
Description: Provides an international forum for the discussion of critical ethical and philosophical issues that concern those dedicated to promoting compassionate health care.
Refereed Serial

610 100 GW ISSN 0938-9717
HUMANES LEBEN - HUMANES STERBEN. (Text in German; summaries in English, German) 1981. 3/yr. DM.27.60 (foreign DM.29.70). Gesellschaft fuer Humanes Sterben e.V., Postfach 110529, 86030 Augsburg, Germany. TEL 0821-502350. FAX 0821-5023555. bk.rev.; charts; stat.; circ. 40,000. (back issues avail.) **Document type:** newsletter.
Description: Essays concerning all aspects of dying with dignity.

610 GW
CODEN: HYGMED
HYGIENE & MEDIZIN - INFECTION CONTROL AND HEALTHCARE; international journal for applied hygiene and preventive medicine in hospital and general practice. (Text in English, German) 1976. m. DM.133 (foreign DM.147). M H P Verlag GmbH, Ostring 13, 65205 Wiesbaden, Germany. TEL 06122-770931. FAX 06122-76331. Ed. Dr. H.-P. Werner. adv.: B&W page DM.3450; adv. contact: M. Szuppauehl. bk.rev. circ. 4,977. (reprint service avail from IRC) Indexed: Excerp.Med. **Document type:** academic/scholarly publication.
—BLDSC (4352.267000).
Formerly: Hygiene und Medizin (ISSN 0172-3790)
Description: Information on all areas of applied hygiene and preventive medicine, especially infection control, nosocomial infections, epidemiology and hospital hygiene.
Refereed Serial

610 JA ISSN 0385-7638
CODEN: HIDZDO
HYOGO IKA DAIGAKU IGAKKAI ZASSHI. (Text in Japanese; summaries in English) 1976. 3/yr. 2000 Yen. Hyogo Ika Daigaku Igakkai - Medical Society of Hyogo College of Medicine, 1-1 Mukogawa-cho, Nishinomiya-shi, Hyogo 663, Japan. TEL 0798-45-6289. FAX 0798-48-8045. Ed. Toshihide Tamura. circ. 1,400. (back issues avail.) Indexed: Chem.Abstr., Excerp.Med., INIS Atomind. **Document type:** academic/scholarly publication.
—BLDSC (0635.020000); CASDDS.
Description: Publishes both experimental and theoretical papers in the field of medical sciences.

MEDICAL SCIENCES

610 JA ISSN 0910-8238
HYOGOKEN ISHIKAI IGAKU ZASSHI/HYOGO MEDICAL ASSOCIATION. JOURNAL. (Text in Japanese) q. Hyogoken Ishikai, 1-30 Nakayamate Dori 6-chome, Chuo-ku, Kobe-shi, Hyogo-ken 661, Japan.

610 JA ISSN 0388-7561
HYOGOKEN ISHIKAIHO/HYOGO MEDICAL ASSOCIATION. MONTHLY REPORT. (Text in Japanese) 1948. m. Hyogoken Ishikai, 1-30, Nakayamate Dori 6-chome, Chuo-ku, Kobe-shi, Hyogo-ken 650, Japan.

610 AT ISSN 0819-9558
I A A H NEWSLETTER. 1987. q. $25. International Association for Adolescent Health, Center for Adolescent Health, William Buckland House, 2 Gatehouse St., Parkville, Vic. 3052, Australia. TEL 03-345-5890. FAX 03-345-6502. Ed. John Court. adv.; bk.rev. circ. 450. **Document type:** newsletter.
Description: Contains reports and discussion of all topics relevant to adolescent health, health education and medical care.

I A L NEWS. (International Association of Laryngectomees) see *EDUCATION — Special Education And Rehabilitation*

I C H P E R CONGRESS PROCEEDINGS. (International Council on Health, Physical Education and Recreation) see *PHYSICAL FITNESS AND HYGIENE*

610 II ISSN 0377-4910
I C M R BULLETIN. (Text in English) 1971. m. Indian Council of Medical Research, Division of Publication & Information, P.O. Box 4911, Ansari Nagar, New Delhi 110 029, India. TEL 91-11-6963980. FAX 91-11-6868662. TELEX 031-73067. E-mail: icmrhqd@ren.nic.in. Ed. Dr. N. Medappa. abstr.; index; circ. 7,200 (controlled). (back issues avail.). **Document type:** bulletin.
Description: Offers medical research articles, seminar and training program calendars.

I E E E ENGINEERING IN MEDICINE AND BIOLOGY MAGAZINE. see *BIOLOGY — Bioengineering*

I E E E TRANSACTIONS ON BIOMEDICAL ENGINEERING. see *BIOLOGY — Bioengineering*

I E H REPORT. (Institute for Environment and Health) see *ENVIRONMENTAL STUDIES*

I F M B E NEWS. (M) (International Federation for Medical and Biological Engineering) see *BIOLOGY — Bioengineering*

I M A JOURNAL OF MATHEMATICS APPLIED IN MEDICINE & BIOLOGY. (Institute of Mathematics and Its Applications) see *MATHEMATICS*

616.02 FR ISSN 0378-0546
CODEN: INSSDM
I N S E R M SYMPOSIA. 1975. irreg. price varies. Institut National de la Sante et de la Recherche Medicale, 101 rue de Tolbiac, 75654 Paris Cedex 13, France. TEL 44-23-60-00. FAX 44-23-60-99. Indexed: Biol.Abstr., Chem.Abstr. (1975-1985), Dairy Sci.Abstr. **Document type:** proceedings.
—CASDDS.

610 US ISSN 1016-2216
I S S X NEWSLETTER. 1981. q. $45 membership. International Society for the Study of Xenobiotics, 9650 Rockville Pike, Bethesda, MD 20814. TEL 301-983-2434. FAX 301-983-5357. Ed. Stanley Howell. adv. contact: Nancy Holahan. bk.rev. circ. 2,000. **Document type:** newsletter.
Description: Contains news and views about xenobiotic research and development from around the world.

610 US ISSN 1061-3439
QP529
I S S X PROCEEDINGS. 1992. s-a. $25 per no. International Society for the Study of Xenobiotics, 9650 Rockville Pike, Bethesda, MD 20814. TEL 301-983-2434. FAX 301-983-5357. circ. 2,300. **Document type:** proceedings.

610 US ISSN 1066-534X
I V U N NEWS. 1987. s-a. $8 to individuals (foreign $10); health professionals and institutions $20 (foreign $22). (International Ventilator Users Network) Gazette International Networking Institute, 5100 Oakland Ave., Ste. 206, St. Louis, MO 63110-1406. TEL 314-534-0475. Eds. Judith Raymond Fischer, Joan Headley. circ. 2,500. (back issues avail.) **Document type:** newsletter.
Description: Shares information of ventilator users and health care professionals experienced in home mechanical ventilation. Discusses topics such as equipment, breathing techniques, travel and family life.

IAN RAMSEY CENTRE. PUBLICATIONS. see *PHILOSOPHY*

610 GR ISSN 0303-4925
IATRIKA CHRONIKA/MEDICAL ANNALS. (Text in English) 1961. m. Dr.12000. Aspasias St. 77, Cholargos, 155 61 Cholargos, Greece. TEL 30-1-6546-645. FAX 30-1-6546-477. Ed. Tzigounis Basilios; Pub. E.M. Moraitou-Sideridi. adv. contact: Sideridis Demetrious. circ. 9,000. (also avail. in diskette format) **Document type:** trade publication.

610 GR ISSN 0019-0942
IATRIKA PEPRAGMENA. (Text in Greek; summaries in English and French) 1964. s-a. free. Army Pension Share Hospital, Athens, Greece. abstr.; bibl.; charts; illus.; stat. circ. 900.

610 GR ISSN 0019-0950
IATRIKI. (Text in Greek; summaries in English) 1962. m. Dr.5000. (Society for Medical Studies) Beta Medical Arts, 5 Sisini St., 115 28 Athens, Greece. Ed. Dr. Nicholas P. Zissis. adv.; bk.rev.; abstr.; bibl.; stat.; index. cum.index. circ. 6,000. (back issues avail.)

610.6 US
IATROFON;* the voice of Iatros. 1981. q. $5 free to qualified personnel. Iatros, 101 Hillside Dr., W., Oelwein, IA 50662-2640. TEL 319-283-3491. FAX 319-283-4985. Ed. Dr. Robert S. Jaggard. circ. 1,000. **Document type:** newsletter.
Description: Newsletter for private and independent doctors.

610 DK ISSN 0905-717X
CODEN: ITRNEB
IATROGENICS. ceased after one issue, 1991. irreg. (International Society for the Prevention of Iatrogenic Complaints) Munksgaard International Publishers Ltd., 35 Snorre Sogade, P.O. Box 2148, DK-1016 Copenhagen, Denmark. TEL 33-127030. FAX 33-129387. Indexed: Excerp.Med. (1992-). **Document type:** academic/scholarly publication.
—CCC.

610 NG
IBADAN TROPICAL MEDICINE SERIES. irreg. (University of Ibadan) Ibadan University Press, Ibadan, Oyo State, Nigeria. TEL 234-22-400550. TELEX UNIVPRESS IBADAN NG. (Dist. outside Africa by: African Books Collective Ltd., The Jam Factory, 27 Park End St., Oxford OX1 1HU, England. TEL 01865-726686. FAX 44-1865-793298) **Document type:** monographic series.

610 JA ISSN 0912-9952
IBARAKI KENRITSU BYOIN IGAKU ZASSHI/IBARAKI PREFECTURAL HOSPITAL. MEDICAL JOURNAL. (Text in Japanese) 1983. q. Ibaraki Kenritsu Chuo Byoin - Ibaraki Prefectural Central Hospital, 6528, Koibuchi, Tomobemachi, Nishiibaraki-gun, Ibaraki-ken 309-17, Japan.

610 JA ISSN 0914-4501
IBARAKIKEN ISHIKAIHO/IBARAKI MEDICAL ASSOCIATION. JOURNAL. (Text in Japanese) m. 200 Yen per no. Ibarakiken Ishikai, 489, Kasaharacho, Mito-shi, Ibaraki-ken 310, Japan.

610 JA ISSN 0912-117X
IBARAKIKEN KYUKYU IGAKKAI ZASSHI/IBARAKI JOURNAL OF ACUTE MEDICINE. (Text in Japanese) a. Ibarakiken Ishikai, Kyukyu Iryo Kyokai - Ibaraki Medical Association, Emergency Medical Department, 489, Kasaharacho, Mito-shi, Ibaraki-ken 310, Japan.

610 JA ISSN 0915-1982
IBARAKIKEN NOSON IGAKKAI ZASSHI/IBARAKI SOCIETY OF RURAL MEDICINE. JOURNAL. (Text in Japanese) 1988. a. Ibarakiken Noson Igakkai, Ibarakiken Kosei Nogyo Kyodo Kumiai Rengokai, 1-4, Baiko 1-chome, Mito-shi, Ibaraki-ken 310, Japan.

610 360 US
ICARUS FILE. 1980. q. $4 (foreign $10). Phoenix Society, Inc., 11 Rust Hill Rd., Levittown, PA 19056. TEL 215-946-2876. FAX 215-946-4788. Ed. Alan Jeffry Breslau. adv.: bk.rev. circ. 7,500. (back issues avail.) **Document type:** newsletter.
Description: For burn survivors, their families and professionals in fields related to burn injuries. Features news regarding prevention, treatment and rehabilitation, personal stories, listing of area coordinators, and resource materials available.

IDO NO NIPPON/JOURNAL OF JAPANESE ACUPUNCTURE & MOXIBUSTION. see *ALTERNATIVE MEDICINE*

610 JA ISSN 0387-0006
IGAKU CHUO ZASSHI/JAPANA CENTRA REVUO MEDICINA. (Text in Japanese) 1903. m. 322596 Yen. Igaku Chuo Zasshi Kankokai - Japan Medical Abstracts Society, 5-18, Takaido Higashi 2-chome, Suginami-ku, Tokyo 168, Japan. Ed. Tsneki Sinohane. **Document type:** abstracting/indexing.
●Also available online.
Also available on CD-ROM.

610 JA ISSN 0019-1574
IGAKU HYORON/JAPANA MEDICINA REVUO. (Text in Japanese) 1950. s-a. 1350 Yen. Shin Nihon Ishi Kyokai - New Japanese Doctors' Association, Hidaka Bldg., 1-10-2 Nishi-Ikebukuro, Toshima-ku, Tokyo 171, Japan. Ed. Sadatoshi Yoshida. circ. 1,200.

610 JA ISSN 0076-597X
CODEN: IGKEAO
IGAKU KENKYU/ACTA MEDICA. (Text in English, Japanese) 1927. irreg. Daido Gakkan Shuppanbu, c/o Kyushu Daigaku Igakubu Hoigaku Kyoshitsu, 1-1, Maidashi 3-chome, Higashi-ku, Fukuoka-shi, Fukuoka-ken 812, Japan. Indexed: Chem.Abstr., Excerp.Med., Ind.Med., INIS Atomind.
—BLDSC (0632.630000); CASDDS.

610 JA ISSN 0386-9644
IGAKU KYOIKU/MEDICAL EDUCATION. (Text in Japanese; summaries in English) 1970. bi-m. 1600 Yen. Nihon Igaku Kyoiku Gakkai - Japan Society for Medical Education, 11-7, Hongo 2-chome, Bunkyo-ku, Tokyo 113, Japan. TEL 03-3816-5311. FAX 03-3816-5314. Ed. Takashi Yamada. adv. contact: Hideo Ito. bk.rev. **Document type:** academic/scholarly publication.
Description: Publishes origianl reports on current medical education.

610 JA ISSN 0039-2359
CODEN: IGAYAY
IGAKU NO AYUMI/JOURNAL OF CLINICAL AND EXPERIMENTAL MEDICINE. (Text in English, Japanese) 1946. w. 57767 Yen. Ishiyaku Shuppan K.K. - Ishiyaku Publishers, Inc., 7-10 Honkomagome 1-chome, Bunkyo-ku, Tokyo 113, Japan. TEL 81-3-5395-7622. FAX 81-3-5395-7624. E-mail: KYB01177@miftyserve.or.jp. Ed. Hiroshi Miura. adv. contact: Isao Kaito. bk.rev.; charts; illus.; index every 3 mos.; circ. 8,800 (paid). Indexed: C.I.S.Abstr., Chem.Abstr., INIS Atomind., Jap.Per.Ind. **Document type:** consumer publication.
—BLDSC (4363.381000); CASDDS.

610 JA ISSN 0019-1582
IGAKU TO FUKUIN/MEDICINE AND GOSPEL. (Text in Japanese) 1949. m. 400 Yen($4) Japan Christian Medical Association - Nihon Kirisutosha Ika Renmei, 2-3-18-23, Nishi-Waseda, Shinjuku-ku, Tokyo 169, Japan. FAX 03-3232-6922. Ed. Dr. Kiyosumi Nakamura. bk.rev. circ. 1,200.

610 JA ISSN 0287-5950
IGAKU TO KIKAI/MEDICINE AND INSTRUMENTS. (Text in Japanese) 1955. m. 360 Yen per no. Igaku Janarusha - Medical Journal Co., 12-3, Minamisenba 1-chome, Chuo-ku, Osaka 542, Japan. Ed. Kosaku Maeda; Pub. Jaka Akagi. adv. contact: Ichihiko Akagi.

MEDICAL SCIENCES 4215

**610 574 JA ISSN 0019-1604
CODEN: IGSBAL
IGAKU TO SEIBUTSUGAKU/MEDICINE AND BIOLOGY.**
(Text in Japanese) 1942. m. 12000 Yen. Ogata Institute for Medical and Chemical Research, 2-10-14 Higashi-Kanda, Chiyoda-ku, Tokyo 101, Japan. FAX 03-3865-7510. Ed. Kan Suzuki. adv.; abstr.; charts; illus.; index. circ. 1,200. **Indexed:** C.I.S. Abstr., Chem.Abstr., Dairy Sci.Abstr., Food Sci.& Tech.Abstr., Ind.Med., INIS Atomind.
—BLDSC (5534.005000); CASDDS.

IGAKU TOSHOKAN/JAPAN MEDICAL LIBRARY ASSOCIATION. JOURNAL. see *LIBRARY AND INFORMATION SCIENCES*

**610 JA ISSN 0019-1612
IGAKUSHI KENKYU/STUDIUM HISTORIAE MEDICAE.**
(Text in Japanese) 1961. a. 1500 Yen. Igakushi Kenkyukai - Collegium ad Studium Historiae Medicae, Osaka Daigaku Igakubu Kankyo Igaku Kyoshitsu, 2-2 Yamadaoka, Suita-shi, Osaka 565, Japan. Ed. Hiroshi Maruyama. adv.; bk.rev.; abstr.; bibl.; illus.; cum.index: 1961-1968. circ. 700. **Indexed:** Curr.Cont., Jap.Per.Ind.

**610 IT ISSN 0391-8068
IGEA MEDICA.** 1978. q. L.15000. Casa Editrice Menna, Via C.so Vittorio Emanuele 123, 83100 Avellino, Italy. Ed. Luigi Tulimiero. adv. circ. 3,000.

**610 JA
IHO HANAMAKI/HANAMAKI CITY MEDICAL ASSOCIATION. NEWS.** (Text in Japanese) 1980. m. Hanamakishi Ishikai, Hanamaki Shoko Kaigisho Kaikan, 10-27, Kajomachi, Hanamaki-shi, Iwate-ken 025, Japan.

**610 GW
IHR ARZT AN SIE.** 1970. m. DM.120. Verlag A. Fruehmorgen, Schwindstr. 5, 80798 Munich, Germany. TEL 089-526083. Ed. A. Fruehmorgen. circ. 10,000.
Description: Magazine for medical waiting rooms.

**610 JA ISSN 0285-0729
IJI KENKYU/MEDICAL JOURNAL.** Variant title: Gekkan Iji Kenkyu. (Text in Japanese) 1972. m. 6000 Yen. (Nihon Iryo Kyoiku Zaidan - Japan Foundation for Medical Education) Tokyo Marunouchi Shuppan, 2-2, Kanda Nishikicho, Chiyoda-ku, Tokyo 101, Japan.

**610 JA ISSN 0912-6597
IJIGAKU KENKYU/JOURNAL OF INTERDISCIPLINARY HUMANISTIC MEDICAL RESEARCH.** (Text in Japanese) 1986. a. Iwate Ika Daigaku, Ijigaku Kenkyukai - Iwate Medical University, Society for Interdisciplinary Humanistic Medical Research, 16-1, Honcho Dori 3-chome, Morioka-shi, Iwate-ken 020, Japan.

**610 JA ISSN 0385-440X
IKA KIKAIGAKU/JAPANESE JOURNAL OF MEDICAL INSTRUMENTATION.** (Text in Japanese; summaries in English) 1923. m. 500 Yen per no. Nihon Ika Kikai Gakkai - Medical Instruments Society of Japan, 39-15, Hongo 3-chome, Bunkyo-ku, Tokyo 113, Japan.
—BLDSC (4656.217000).

**610 JA ISSN 0914-5117
CODEN: IOKHEP
IKAGAKU OYO KENKYU ZAIDAN KENKYU HOKOKU/SUZUKEN MEMORIAL FOUNDATION. RESEARCH PAPERS.** (Text in English, Japanese; summaries in English) 1982. a. Ikagaku Oyo Kenkyu Zaidan, Suzuken Honsha, 8, Higashikatahamachi, Higashi-ku, Nagoya-shi, Aichi-ken 461, Japan. TEL 052-961-2331. **Indexed:** Chem.Abstr.
—BLDSC (7754.420000).

**610 JA ISSN 0019-1728
IKAI JIHO.** 1957. 3/m. 10 Yen($1.66) Kanehara & Co., Ltd., 2-31-14 Yushima, Bunkyo-ku, Tokyo 113, Japan. Ed. Hideo Kanehara. adv.; bk.rev. circ. 100,000.

IKAKIKAI GAKU ZASSHI/JOURNAL OF MEDICAL INSTRUMENTS. see *INSTRUMENTS*

**610 US ISSN 1044-6400
CODEN: IMJOAN
ILLINOIS MEDICINE.** 1899. bi-w. $12 to non-members; foreign $19. Illinois State Medical Society, 20 N. Michigan Ave., Ste. 700, Chicago, IL 60602. TEL 312-782-1654. FAX 312-782-2023. Ed. Lynn Koslowsky. adv.; charts; illus. circ. 19,500. (also avail. in microfilm from UMI) **Indexed:** Biol.Abstr., Excerp.Med., Helminthol.Abstr., HRIS, Ind.Med., INIS Atomind., Lang.& Lang.Behav.Abstr., Med.Care Rev., Rehabil.Lit. **Document type:** newspaper.
—UMI.
Formerly (until no.6, vol.174, 1988): Illinois Medical Journal (ISSN 0019-2120)
Description: Covers health care issues and professional concerns including health care legislation, medical professional liability, malpractice news and information and regulatory agency and peer review organization updates.

ILLUSTRERAD VETENSKAP. see *SCIENCES: COMPREHENSIVE WORKS*

**611 574.4 SZ
CODEN: BIANA6
IMAGING AND CLINICAL ANATOMY.** (Text in English) 1961. irreg. price varies. S. Karger AG, Allschwilerstr. 10, P.O. Box, CH-4009 Basel, Switzerland. TEL 061-3061111. FAX 061-3061234. E-mail: Karger@Karger.ch. Ed. A.W. English. (reprint service avail. from ISI, back issues avail.) **Indexed:** Biol.Abstr., Chem.Abstr., Curr.Cont., Ind.Med. **Document type:** academic/scholarly publication.
—CASDDS. **CCC.**
Former titles: Imaging and Surgical Anatomy; Bibliotheca Anatomica (ISSN 0067-7833); Incorporates: European Conference on Microcirculation. Proceedings.
Refereed Serial

**610 378 US
IMPACT (OMAHA).** 1983. q. University of Nebraska Medical Center, 600 S. 42nd St., Omaha, NE 68198-5230. TEL 402-559-4353. FAX 402-559-4103. Ed. Barbara Newcomer-Jaeger. circ. 9,000.
Description: Covers issues associated with education, research, and medical care at the center.

**610 FR ISSN 0758-4237
IMPACT INTERNAT.** m. Edinter, 20 bd. du Parc, 92521 Neuilly Cedex, France. TEL 46-41-33-00. FAX 46-41-02-00. Ed. Dr. Yves Degueurence. circ. 22,000.

IMPACT MEDECIN. see *BUSINESS AND ECONOMICS — Management*

**330 610 US ISSN 0733-1398
IN VIVO;** the business and medicine report. 1983. m. (11/yr.). $595 (foreign $670) (typically set in Jan.). Windhover Information, Inc., 50 Washington St., 5th Fl., South Norwalk, CT 06864. TEL 203-838-4401. FAX 203-838-3214. (Subscr. to: Box 360 South Norwalk, CT 06856-0360) Eds. Roger Longman, David Cassak. adv. (back issues avail.) **Document type:** newsletter.
●Also available online. Vendor(s): Information Access Co.
—BLDSC (4372.510000); SWETS. **CCC.**
Description: Reports about the medical industry and its effect on business. Features range from industry trends and new products to controversial issues in the medical field as they relate to business.

**610 II
INDIAN INSTITUTE OF HISTORY OF MEDICINE. BULLETIN (MADRAS).** (Text in English) 1956. s-a. Rs.8. Indian Institute of the History of Medicine, 497 Poonamalee, Madras 7, India. Ed. Dr. K. Bhasker Rao. adv.; bk.rev.; bibl.; illus.; cum.index every 10 yrs. circ. 500.
Formerly: Indian Journal of the History of Medicine (ISSN 0019-5677)

**610 II ISSN 0970-6666
INDIAN JOURNAL OF AEROSPACE MEDICINE.** (Text in English) 1954. s-a. Rs.200 (foreign Rs.25). Indian Society of Aerospace Medicine, Directorate General of Medical Services, Air Headquarters, Rk Puram West, New Delhi 110 066, India. TEL 3010231-1176. Ed. Surjit Singh. bk.rev. circ. 800. **Document type:** academic/scholarly publication.
Formerly: Journal of Aeromedical Society of India.
Description: Includes original articles, topical reviews and other scientific information in the field of aerospace medicine and allied sciences.

**613.62 II ISSN 0019-5278
CODEN: IJIDAW
INDIAN JOURNAL OF INDUSTRIAL MEDICINE.** Variant title: Indian Association of Occupational Medicine. Journal. (Text in English) 1949. q. Rs.20($5.) Indian Association of Occupational Health, 82-B Shakespeare Sarani, Calcutta 700017, India. Ed. Dr. B.B. Chatterjee. bk.rev.; abstr.; bibl.; charts; illus.; stat.; index, cum.index. circ. 1,000. **Indexed:** Biol.Abstr., C.I.S. Abstr.

INDIAN JOURNAL OF MEDICAL PHOTOGRAPHY. see *PHOTOGRAPHY*

**616.9 II ISSN 0970-955X
R97
INDIAN JOURNAL OF MEDICAL RESEARCH. SECTION A: INFECTIOUS DISEASES.** (Text in English) 1913. bi-m. Rs.1500($90) Indian Council of Medical Research, Division of Publication & Information, P.O. Box 4911, Ansari Nagar, New Delhi 110 029, India. TEL 91-11-6963980. FAX 91-11-6868662. TELEX 031-73067. E-mail: icmehad@ren.nic.in. Ed. Dr. N. Medappa. adv.; bk.rev.; bibl.; charts; illus.; index; circ. 700 (controlled). (reprint service avail. from ISI, UMI) **Indexed:** Abstr.Hyg., Agri.Eng.Abstr., Anim.Breed.Abstr., Bio-Contr.News & Info., Biol.Abstr., Chem.Abstr., Curr.Adv.Cancer Res., Curr.Adv.Ecol.Sci., Curr.Adv.Genetics & Molec.Biol., Curr.Cont., Dairy Sci.Abstr., Dent.Ind., Diar.Dis.Res, Dok.Arbeitsmed., Excerp.Med., ExtraMED, Helminthol.Abstr., Ind.Med., Ind.Sci.Rev., Ind.Vet., INIS Atomind., Nutr.Abstr., Pig News & Info., Potato Abstr., Poult.Abstr., Protozool.Abstr., Rev.Appl.Entomol., Rev.Med.& Vet.Mycol., Rev.Plant Path., Rice Abstr., Sci.Cit.Ind., Trop.Dis.Bull., Vet.Bull. **Document type:** academic/scholarly publication.
●Also available on CD-ROM.
—BLDSC (4416.500000); CASDDS; EMDOCS; Faxon; Genuine Article; SWETS; UMI; UnCover.
Supersedes in part (in 1989): Indian Journal of Medical Research (ISSN 0019-5340)
Refereed Serial

**616 II ISSN 0970-9568
INDIAN JOURNAL OF MEDICAL RESEARCH. SECTION B: BIOMEDICAL RESEARCH OTHER THAN INFECTIOUS DISEASES.** (Text in English) 1913. bi-m. Rs.1500($90) Indian Council of Medical Research, Division of Publication & Information, Box 4911, Ansari Nagar, New Delhi 110 029, India. TEL 91-11-6963980. FAX 91-11-6868662. E-mail: icmehad@ren.nic.in. Ed. Dr. N. Medappa. **Indexed:** Excerp.Med. **Document type:** academic/scholarly publication.
—EMDOCS; Genuine Article.
Supersedes in part (in 1989): Indian Journal of Medical Research (ISSN 0019-5340)

**610 II ISSN 0367-9012
INDIAN JOURNAL OF MEDICAL RESEARCH. SUPPLEMENT.** (Text in English) 1922. irreg. Rs.1500($90) (subscr. includes Journal). Indian Council of Medical Research, Division of Publication & Information, P.O. Box 4911, Ansari Nagar, New Delhi 110029, India. TEL 91-11-6963980. FAX 91-11-6868662. TELEX 031-73067. E-mail: icmrhqd@ren.nic.in. Ed. Dr. N. Medappa. bk.rev.; bibl.; charts. circ. 700. (reprint service avail. from ISI, UMI) **Indexed:** Biol.Abstr., Chem.Abstr., Curr.Cont., Ind.Med., Nutr.Abstr., Sci.Cit.Ind., Trop.Dis.Bull. **Document type:** academic/scholarly publication.
Description: Features orginal communications on a specific topic of biomedical research.

MEDICAL SCIENCES

610 — II — ISSN 0019-5359 — CODEN: INJMAO
INDIAN JOURNAL OF MEDICAL SCIENCES. (Text in English) 1947. m. Rs.250 (foreign Rs.750). Indian Journal of Medical Sciences Trust, c/o J.C. Patel, Back Bay View, New Queen's Rd., Bombay 4, India. Ed. Dr. J.C. Patel. adv.; bk.rev.; abstr.; charts; illus.; index. circ. 3,000. (reprint service avail. from IRC) **Indexed:** Abstr.Hyg., Biol.Abstr., Chem.Abstr., Curr.Adv.Cancer Res., Curr.Adv.Ecol.Sci., Excerp.Med., Ind.Med., INIS Atomind., NRN, Nutr.Abstr., Rev.Plant Path., Trop.Dis.Bull. **Document type:** academic/scholarly publication.
—BLDSC (4416.550000); CASDDS; EMDOCS; Faxon; SWETS; UnCover.
Incorporates: Medical Bulletin.

616.07 576 — II — ISSN 0377-4929 — CODEN: IJPMDT
INDIAN JOURNAL OF PATHOLOGY & MICROBIOLOGY. (Text in English) 1958. q. Rs.700 (foreign Rs.1500). Indian Association of Pathologists and Microbiologists, Department of Laboratory Medicine, Safdarjung Hospital, New Delhi 110029, India. TEL 011-668433. (Subscr. to: Ila M. Vora, Treasurer, Dept. of Pathology, T.N. Medical College and BYL Nair Hospital, Dr. A.L. Nair Rd., Bombay 400008, India) Ed. V.H. Talib. adv.: page Rs.7000. bk.rev.; abstr.; bibl.; charts; illus.; index. circ. 3,000. (reprint service avail. from IRC) **Indexed:** Biol.Abstr., Chem.Abstr., Curr.Adv.Ecol.Sci., Dent.Ind., Diar.Dis.Res., Excerp.Med., ExtraMED, Ind.Med., Ind.Vet., Nutr.Abstr., Rev.Med.& Vet.Mycol., Rev.Plant Path., Vet.Bull. **Document type:** academic/scholarly publication.
●Also available on CD-ROM.
—BLDSC (4417.950000); Faxon; SWETS; UnCover.
Formerly: Indian Journal of Pathology and Bacteriology (ISSN 0019-5448)

INDIAN JOURNAL OF VETERINARY ANATOMY. see *VETERINARY SCIENCE*

610 — II — ISSN 0019-5847 — CODEN: JIMAAD
INDIAN MEDICAL ASSOCIATION. JOURNAL. (Text in English) 1931. m. Rs.455($60) Indian Medical Association, I.M.A House, 53 Creek Row, Calcutta 700 014, India. TEL 26-3598. adv.: B&W page Rs.6250; 220 x 260. bk.rev.; abstr.; charts; illus. circ. 4,055. (reprint service avail. from UMI) **Indexed:** Abstr.Hyg., Biol.Abstr., Chem.Abstr., Dent.Ind., Diar.Dis.Res., Excerp.Med., Helminthol.Abstr., Ind.Med., Nutr.Abstr., Rev.Plant Path., Trop.Dis.Bull.
—BLDSC (4767.400000); CASDDS; EMDOCS; Faxon; SWETS; UMI; UnCover.

INDIAN MEDICAL GAZETTE. see *MEDICAL SCIENCES — Surgery*

610 — II — ISSN 0019-6169
THE INDIAN PRACTITIONER; a monthly journal of medicine, surgery & public health. (Text in English) 1947. m. Rs.200($30) Indian Practitioner Group, 101, Lawrence Apartments-2, 1st Floor, Vidyanagari Marg, Opp. Lakhbir Petrol Pump, Kalina, Santa Cruz (E), Bombay 400 098, India. TEL 6116170. Ed. V. Godinho. adv.; bk.rev. circ. 43,967. (reprint service avail. from IRC) **Indexed:** Biol.Abstr., Chem.Abstr., Dent.Ind., Ind.Med.
—Faxon.

610 — US — ISSN 0746-8288
R15
INDIANA MEDICINE. 1908. bi-m. $15 to individuals (foreign $18); medical libraries $14 (foreign $16); medical students $8. Indiana State Medical Association, 322 Canal Walk, Indianapolis, IN 46202-3252. TEL 317-261-2060. FAX 317-261-2076. Ed. Tina Sims. adv.; abstr.; charts; illus.; index. circ. 7,000. (also avail. in microform from UMI; reprint service avail. from UMI) **Indexed:** Biol.Abstr., Chem.Abstr., Excerp.Med., Hosp.Lit.Ind., Ind.Med., INIS Atomind.
—BLDSC (4431.769300); Faxon; SWETS; UMI.
Formerly (until 1984): Indiana State Medical Association. Journal (ISSN 0019-6770)
Description: Publishes socioeconomic, practice management, legal, legislative, ethical and financial issues affecting medicine.

INDUSTRIAL HEALTH FOUNDATION. MEDICAL SERIES. BULLETINS. see *OCCUPATIONAL HEALTH AND SAFETY*

610 — US — ISSN 0073-5639
INFACT MEDICAL SCHOOL INFORMATION SYSTEM. 1967. 3/yr. $210 (Canada $220) (effective Dec. 1993). Dataflow Systems Inc., 7758 Wisconsin Ave., Bethesda, MD 20814. TEL 301-654-9133. Ed. J.B. Malcom. index. circ. 100. (microfiche; back issues avail.)
Description: Indexed collection of current U.S. and Canadian medical school catalogs on microfiche.

610 — GW — ISSN 0300-8126 — CODEN: IFTNAL
INFECTION; journal of infectious disease - clinical study and treatment. (Text in English and German) 1973. 6/yr. DM.240. (Deutsche Gesellschaft fuer Infektiologie) M M V Medizin Verlag, Neumarkter Str. 18, 81673 Munich, Germany. TEL 089-43189-0. FAX 089-43189633. Ed. W. Marget. adv.; bk.rev. circ. 3,000. **Indexed:** Abstr.Hyg., Biol.Abstr., Biotech.Abstr., Chem.Abstr., Curr.Adv.Ecol.Sci., Curr.Cont., Dent.Ind., Excerp.Med., Helminthol.Abstr., Ind.Med., Ind.Sci.Rev., Ind.Vet., INIS Atomind., Med.& Surg.Dermat., Rev.Med.& Vet.Mycol., Sci.Cit.Ind., Trop.Dis.Bull., Vet.Bull. **Document type:** academic/scholarly publication.
—BLDSC (4478.710000); ADONIS; CASDDS; Faxon; Genuine Article; SWETS; UnCover. **CCC**.

INFECTION CONTROL YEARBOOK. see *MEDICAL SCIENCES — Nurses And Nursing*

INFECTIOUS DISEASE NEWS. see *MEDICAL SCIENCES — Communicable Diseases*

610 — US — ISSN 1056-9103 — CODEN: IDCPEY
INFECTIOUS DISEASES IN CLINICAL PRACTICE. 1991. bi-m. $87 to individuals; institutions $135 (effective 1995). Williams & Wilkins, 428 E. Preston St., Baltimore, MD 21202-3993. TEL 410-528-4000; 800-638-6423. FAX 410-528-4312. Ed. Sherwood Gorbach. adv.: B&W page $650, color page $1400; trim 8 1/8 x 10 7/8; adv. contact: Donald Pfarr. circ. 6,900. **Indexed:** Excerp.Med. (1994-). **Document type:** academic/scholarly publication.
—BLDSC (4478.727950); Genuine Article; SWETS. **CCC**.
Description: For physicians who treat patients with infectious diseases.

INFECTIOUS WASTES NEWS. see *ENVIRONMENTAL STUDIES — Waste Management*

610 — FR — ISSN 0981-0560
INFIRMIERE MAGAZINE; revue d'enseignement technique et de developpement professionnel. 1923. 11/yr. 580 F. to individuals; institutions 685 F. Editions Lamarre-Poinat, 47 rue St. Andre des Arts, 75006 Paris, France. FAX 46-34-75-01. Ed. Thierry Verret. adv.; illus. circ. 70,000. **Indexed:** Int.Nurs.Ind. **CCC**.
Formerly: Infirmiere Francaise (ISSN 0019-9613)

610 — SP — ISSN 1132-6263 — CODEN: IFLAE
INFLAMACION. 1990. 6/yr. Accion Medica S.A., C. Llodio, Edificio A1, P4A y B, 28034 Madrid, Spain. TEL 01-3581191. **Indexed:** Excerp.Med. (1994-). **Document type:** academic/scholarly publication.

610 — US — ISSN 0360-3997
RB131 — CODEN: INFLD4
INFLAMMATION. 1975. bi-m. $355 (foreign $415) (effective 1996). Plenum Publishing Corp., 233 Spring St., New York, NY 10013-1578. TEL 212-620-8000. FAX 212-463-0742. TELEX 23-421139. Ed. Gerald Weissmann. adv.; illus. (also avail. in microfilm from JSC; back issues avail.) **Indexed:** Biol.Abstr., Biotech.Abstr., Chem.Abstr., Curr.Adv.Biochem., Curr.Adv.Ecol.Sci., Curr.Cont., Excerp.Med., Ind.Med., Ind.Sci.Rev., Ind.Vet., INIS Atomind., Ref.Zh., Rev.Med.& Vet.Mycol., Vet.Bull. **Document type:** academic/scholarly publication.
—BLDSC (4478.845000); ADONIS; CASDDS; Faxon; Genuine Article; SWETS; UMI; UnCover. **CCC**
Refereed Serial

INFLAMMOPHARMACOLOGY; an international interdisciplinary journal publishing original articles and topical reviews on inflammation and pharmacology. see *PHARMACY AND PHARMACOLOGY*

INFOCARE; information strategies for healthcare networks. see *INSURANCE*

610 574 — GW — ISSN 0943-5581
INFORMATIK, BIOMETRIE UND EPIDEMIOLOGIE. (Text in English or German) 1970. q. DM.330 (foreign DM.334). Gustav Fischer Verlag, Wollgrasweg 49, 70599 Stuttgart, Germany. TEL 0711-4580330. FAX 0711-4580334. TELEX 7111488-FIBUCH. (Subscr. to: Postfach 720143, 70577 Stuttgart, Germany; U.S. addr.: VCH Publishers, Inc., 303 N.W. 12th Ave., Deerfield Beach, FL 33442-1788) Ed.Bd. circ. 1,000. **Indexed:** Biol.Abstr., Comput.Rev., Forest.Abstr., VITIS. **Document type:** academic/scholarly publication.
—BLDSC (4481.361500); SWETS; UMI. **CCC**.
Former titles (until 1993): Biometrie und Informatik (ISSN 0934-9235); E D V in Medizin und Biologie - E D V in Medicine and Biology (ISSN 0300-8282)

610 — UK
INFORMATION SOURCES IN THE MEDICAL SCIENCES. irreg., 4th edition, 1994. £58($100) Bowker - Saur Ltd., A part of Reed Reference Publishing, Maypole House, Maypole Rd., E. Grinstead, W. Sussex RH19 1HH, England. FAX 44-1342-330100. (Subscr. to: c/o Butterworths Service Co., Borough Green, Sevenoaks, Kent TN15 8PH, England. TEL 44-1732-884567) Eds. Leslie Morton, Shane Godbolt. **Document type:** directory.
Description: Identifies and reviews a wide range of literature covering both preclinical and clinical medicine. Coverage ranges from anatomy and physiology to public health.

610.6 — SP — ISSN 0210-5365
INFORMATIVO MEDICO. no.131, 1974. m. Colegios Medicos de Espana, Consejo General, Villanueva 11, Madrid 1, Spain. adv.; bk.rev. circ. 108,000.
Formerly: Colegios Medicos de Espana. Consejo General. Boletin Informativo.

610 — SZ — ISSN 0253-1089
INFORMIERTE ARZT. 1980. 12/yr. 75 SFr. I M P Kommunikation AG, Urs-Graf-Str. 8, CH-4020 Basel, Switzerland. TEL 061-3125566. FAX 061-3125560. Ed. Renate Bonifer. adv. contact: Hans Stegemann. circ. 10,500. **Document type:** academic/scholarly publication.

610 — SP
INFORUN 5. 12/yr. Pasaje de la Virgen de la Alegria 14, 28027 Madrid, Spain. TEL 1-405-15-95. FAX 1-403-49-07. Ed. Miguel A. Barroso. circ. 46,320.

INNOVATIONS (YEAR). see *HOSPITALS*

614 362 — US — ISSN 0046-9580
RA410.A1 — CODEN: INQYA
INQUIRY (ROCHESTER); the journal of health care organization, provision and financing. 1963. q. $70 (effective 1996). Blue Cross and Blue Shield Association, Box 25399, Rochester, NY 14625. TEL 716-264-9122. (Subscr. to: Box 527, Glenview, IL 60025) Ed. Jack Hadley. bk.rev.; charts; index, cum.index: 1963-1973, 1974-1978. circ. 2,500. (tabloid format; also avail. in microform from UMI; back issues avail.; reprint service avail. from UMI) **Indexed:** Abstr.Health Care Manage.Stud., Abstr.Hyg., Acad.Ind., B.P.I., BPIA, Bus.Ind., Curr.Cont., Excerp.Med., Hosp.Abstr., Hosp.Lit.Ind., Ind.Med., J.of Econ.Lit., Med.Care Rev., Mid.East: Abstr.& Ind., P.A.I.S., PHRA, Soc.Sci.Ind., SSCI, Tr.& Indus.Ind., Trop.Dis.Bull. **Document type:** academic/scholarly publication.
—BLDSC (4516.100000); EMDOCS; Faxon; Genuine Article; SWETS; UMI; UnCover. **CCC**.
Refereed Serial

610 — JA — ISSN 0288-7908
INSATSUKYOKU IHO/JAPAN. MINISTRY OF FINANCE. PRINTING BUREAU. MEDICAL JOURNAL. (Text in English, Japanese; summaries in English) 1955. s-a. Insatsukyoku Igakkai - Ministry of Finance, Medical Association of the Printing Bureau, Okurasho Insatsukyoku Tokyo Byoin, 3-6, Nishigahara 2-chome, Kita-ku, Tokyo 114, Japan.

INSIGHT (ATLANTA). see *MEETINGS AND CONGRESSES*

MEDICAL SCIENCES 4217

610   **FR**   **ISSN 0020-2142**
INSTANTANES MEDICAUX. At head of title: E M C Encyclopedie Medico Chirurgicale. 1949. m. (Encyclopedie Medico Chirurgicale) Editions Techniques, 123 rue d'Alesia, 75014 Paris, France. TEL 45-39-22-91. FAX 45428155. TELEX EDITEC 270737 F. Ed.Bd. adv.; bk.rev.; charts; pat. circ. 68,800. **Indexed:** C.I.S. Abstr., INIS Atomind.
—CCC.

362   **CN**
INSTITUT DE READAPTATION DE MONTREAL. BULLETIN. (Text in English, French) 1967. 4/yr. free. Institut de Readaptation de Montreal, Communications Branch, 6300 Ave. Darlington, Montreal, Que. H3S 2J4, Canada. TEL 514-340-2085. FAX 514-340-2149. Ed. Solange-Marie Gagnon. adv.; bk.rev.; illus. circ. 7,000.
Formerly: Rehabilitation Institute of Montreal. Bulletin (ISSN 0316-4454)

INSTITUT NATIONAL DE LA SANTE ET DE LA RECHERCHE MEDICALE. ACTUALITES. see *PUBLIC HEALTH AND SAFETY*

610   **CX**
INSTITUT PASTEUR DE BANGUI. RAPPORT BISANNUEL. 1961. a. $25. Institut Pasteur de Bangui, B.P. 923, Bangui, Central African Republic. FAX 236-610109. TELEX 5312 RC. adv. circ. 200. **Indexed:** Biol.Abstr.
Formerly (until 1984): Institut Pasteur de Bangui. Rapport Annuel.

610 574   **TI**   **ISSN 0020-2509**
                            CODEN: APTUAO
INSTITUT PASTEUR DE TUNIS. ARCHIVES. 1906. q. $25 (effective 1994). Institut Pasteur de Tunis, 13 Place Pasteur, B.P. 74, 1002 Tunis Belvedere, Tunisia. TEL 216-1-283022. FAX 216-1-791833. TELEX 14391 PAS TU. Ed. Koussay Dellagi. adv.; bk.rev. circ. 700. **Indexed:** Abstr.Hyg., Bio-Contr.News & Info., Biol.Abstr., Cott.& Trop.Fibr.Abstr., Curr.Adv.Ecol.Sci., Excerp.Med., ExtraMED, Helminthol.Abstr., Ind.Med., Ind.Vet., Protozool.Abstr., Rev.Appl.Entomol., Rev.Med.& Vet.Mycol., Small Anim.Abstr., Trop.Dis.Bull., Vet.Bull. **Document type:** academic/scholarly publication.
● Also available on CD-ROM.
—CASDDS.
Description: Publishes research in biology and medicine.

610   **UK**
INSTITUTE OF HEALTH RECORD INFORMATION & MANAGEMENT. JOURNAL. 1948. q. £18 to non-members; free with membership. Institute of Health Record Information & Management, c/o Publications Manager, 93 Moss Bank, Winsford, Ches. CW7 2EW, England. adv.: page £200. bk.rev.; charts; illus.; stat.; index. cum.index: 1965-1972. circ. 1,500. **Indexed:** Excerp.Med., Hosp.Lit.Ind. **Document type:** academic/scholarly publication, newsletter.
Former titles: Journal of Health Information & Medical Records Officers; A M R O; Medical Record (ISSN 0025-7478)
Description: Contains articles and papers relevent to healh records, informatics, and computing. Reports changes in government policy affecting members and includes member communications.

610   **MK**
INSTITUTE OF HEALTH SCIENCES. QUARTERLY MEDICAL NEWS BULLETIN. q. Ministry of Health, Institute of Health Sciences, P.O. Box 6720, Ruwi, Muscat, Sultanate of Oman. TEL 560066. TELEX 5465.

610   **NP**   **ISSN 0259-0972**
                            CODEN: JIMEET
INSTITUTE OF MEDICINE. JOURNAL. (Text in English) 1979. q. $12 per no. Institute of Medicine, P.O. Box 2533, Kathmandu, Nepal. Ed. Hemang Dixit. adv.; bk.rev.; charts; illus. circ. 500. **Indexed:** Abstr.Hyg., Diar.Dis.Res., Excerp.Med., Protozool.Abstr.
—BLDSC (4776.980000).

610   **US**   **ISSN 0091-746X**
                            CODEN: PMICAP
INSTITUTE OF MEDICINE OF CHICAGO. PROCEEDINGS. 1916. 2/yr. $25. Institute of Medicine of Chicago, 332 S. Michigan Ave., Chicago, IL 60604-4022. TEL 312-663-0040. FAX 312-663-9058. Ed. Margaret Hastings. adv. contact: David Cugell. bk.rev. circ. 4,000. **Indexed:** Biol.Abstr. **Document type:** proceedings, academic/scholarly publication.
Refereed Serial

610   **BG**   **ISSN 1017-9216**
NOT IN LC   **CODEN: JIPREF**
INSTITUTE OF POSTGRADUATE MEDICINE AND RESEARCH. JOURNAL. (Text in English) 1986. s-a. Tk.30 (foreign $10). Institute of Postgraduate Medicine and Research, Dhaka 1000, Bangladesh. Ed. T.A. Chowdhury. **Indexed:** Excerp.Med.
—BLDSC (4786.020000).
Description: Publishes original articles, reviews, practical procedures, case reports on the latest developments in the field of medicine.

INSTITUTION OF MECHANICAL ENGINEERS. PROCEEDINGS. PART H: JOURNAL OF ENGINEERING IN MEDICINE. see *BIOLOGY — Bioengineering*

610   **BO**
INSTITUTO MEDICO "SUCRE". REVISTA. 1905. a. free. Instituto Medico "Sucre", Calle San Alberto No. 30, Casilla Correo 82, Sucre, Bolivia. TEL 591-64-21956. FAX 591-64-25559. Ed. Dr. Antonio Dubravcic-Luksic. adv. contact: Gonzalo Virreira-Reyes. bk.rev.
Description: Information on all aspects of health and medicine in Bolivia.

INSTITUTO OSWALDO CRUZ, RIO DE JANEIRO. MEMORIAS. see *BIOLOGY*

610   **GW**   **ISSN 0942-6035**
INTENSIV; Fachzeitschrift fuer Intensivpflege und Anaesthesie. 1993. q. DM.98. Georg Thieme Verlag, Ruedigerstr. 14, 70469 Stuttgart, Germany. TEL 0711-8931443. FAX 0711-8931258. Ed. Angelika Stockinger. adv.: B&W page DM.1700; trim 250 x 175; adv. contact: Paul Berger. bk.rev.; index; circ. 3,000 (paid). (also avail. in diskette format; back issues avail.) **Document type:** academic/scholarly publication.
—BLDSC (4531.832400).
Refereed Serial

610   **GW**   **ISSN 0947-5362**
                            CODEN: NTNSDQ
INTENSIV- UND NOTFALLBEHANDLUNG. 1976. q. DM.96($74) Dustri-Verlag Dr. Karl Feistle, Bahnhofstr. 9, 82041 Deisenhofen, Germany. TEL 089-613861-0. FAX 089-613-5412. Ed. Dr. B. Landauer. **Indexed:** Biol.Abstr., Curr.Adv.Ecol.Sci., Curr.Cont., Excerp.Med. **Document type:** academic/scholarly publication.
—CCC.
Formerly: Intensivbehandlung (ISSN 0341-3063)

610   **UK**   **ISSN 0265-5241**
INTENSIVE & CRITICAL CARE DIGEST. q. King & Wirth Publishing Co. Ltd., Hillside, Arnolds Ln., Hinxworth, Baldock, Hertfordshire SG7 5HR, England. TEL 046274-2580. FAX 046274-2986. Ed. Dr. Simon Bursztein. adv. contact: Philip King. **Document type:** academic/scholarly publication.
Description: Articles about state-of-the-art intensive and critical care medicine.

614.88   **UK**   **ISSN 0967-5728**
INTENSIVE CARE BRITAIN (YEAR). 1992. a. £35 to individuals in the U.K. (rest of Europe £60; elsewhere £75); institutions £50 (rest of Europe £75; elsewhere £90). Greycoat Publishing, 1 Harley St., London W1N 1DA, England. TEL 0171-637-1828. FAX 0171-631-3020. Ed. Michael Rennie; Pub. Ashley Wallis. **Document type:** trade publication.
—BLDSC (4531.836500).

610   **GW**   **ISSN 0342-4642**
                            CODEN: ICMED9
INTENSIVE CARE MEDICINE. (Text in English) 1974. 12/yr. DM.748($543) (effective 1996). (European Society of Intensive Care Medicine) Springer-Verlag, Heidelberger Platz 3, 14197 Berlin, Germany. TEL 030-8207-0. FAX 030-8214091. E-mail: orders@springer.de. (Subscr. in N. America to: Springer-Verlag New York, Inc., 44 Hartz Way, Secaucus, NJ 07096-2491. TEL 201-348-4033. FAX 201-348-4505) Ed. F. Lemaire. (also avail. in microform from UMI; back issues avail.; reprint service avail. from ISI) **Indexed:** Curr.Cont., Excerp.Med., Ind.Med., Ind.Sci.Rev., INIS Atomind., Sci.Cit.Ind., Sugar Ind.Abstr. **Document type:** academic/scholarly publication.
—BLDSC (4531.837000); CASDDS; Faxon; Genuine Article; SWETS; UMI; UnCover. **CCC**.
Formerly: European Journal of Intensive Care Medicine.
Description: Provides information for those concerned with pre-clinical subjects and medical sciences basic to intensive care, critical care, internal medicine, bioengineering, surgery and anaesthesiology.

610 542   **UK**   **ISSN 0266-7037**
INTENSIVE CARE WORLD. 1984. q. $60. King & Wirth Publishing Co. Ltd., Hillside, Arnolds Ln., Hinxworth, Baldock, Herts SG7 5HR, England. TEL 046274-2580. FAX 046274-2986. Ed. Geoffrey Dobb. adv. contact: Philip King. bk.rev.; abstr.; bibl.; illus. circ. 26,889. **Indexed:** Curr.Adv.Ecol.Sci. **Document type:** academic/scholarly publication.
Description: Articles about state-of-the-art intensive and critical care medicine.

610   **GW**   **ISSN 0175-3851**
                            CODEN: INNOEK
INTENSIVMEDIZIN UND NOTFALLMEDIZIN. (Text in German; summaries in English) 1961. 8/yr. DM.448($325) (effective 1996)). Dr. Dietrich Steinkopff Verlag, Saalbaustr. 12, 64283 Darmstadt, Germany. TEL 06151-1745-0. FAX 06151-174510. (Subscr. to: Postfach 111442, 64229 Darmstadt, Germany) Ed.Bd. adv.; bk.rev. circ. 2,500. (also avail. in microform from UMI) **Indexed:** Biol.Abstr., Curr.Cont., Excerp.Med. **Document type:** academic/scholarly publication.
—BLDSC (4531.845000); CASDDS; UMI. **CCC**.
Former titles: Intensivmedizin (ISSN 0303-6251); Wiederbelebung-Organersatz-Intensivmedizin (ISSN 0043-5252)

610   **NG**   **ISSN 0534-4735**
INTER-AFRICAN CONFERENCE ON MEDICAL CO-OPERATION. MEETING.* Title varies slightly; some issues called reports. irreg. 1955 3rd. (Commission for Technical Co-Operation in Africa South of the Sahara) Maison de l'Afrique, B.P. 878, Niamey, Niger.

610   **SP**
INTERCON. Spanish edition of: Vademecum. 1967. a. 6000 ptas. (foreign $60). Editores Medicos, S.A., C. Gabriela Mistral 2, 28035 Madrid, Spain. TEL 34-1-3860033. FAX 34-1-3739907. circ. 40,000.

INTERFACE (CHICAGO, 1978). see *LIBRARY AND INFORMATION SCIENCES*

INTERFACES: LINGUISTICS, PSYCHOLOGY AND HEALTH THERAPEUTICS; an international journal of research, notes and commentary. see *LINGUISTICS*

610   **SZ**   **ISSN 0026-9212**
INTERKANTONALE KONTROLLSTELLE FUER HEILMITTEL. MONATSBERICHT/OFFICE INTERCANTONAL DE CONTROLE DE MEDICAMENTS. BULLETIN MENSUEL/UFFICIO INTERCANTONALE DI CONTROLLO DEI MEDICAMENTI. BOLLETTINO MENSILE. (Text in French, German, Italian) 1947. m. 110 SFr. (foreign 130 SFr.). Interkantonale Kontrollstelle fuer Heilmittel, Erlachstr. 8, CH-3000 Bern 9, Switzerland. FAX 031-240654. adv.; index. circ. 3,000. **Document type:** bulletin.

INTERNATIONAL ACADEMY OF LEGAL MEDICINE AND OF SOCIAL MEDICINE. (CONGRESS REPORTS). see *MEDICAL SCIENCES — Forensic Sciences*

MEDICAL SCIENCES

611 574.4 RU ISSN 0074-1353
INTERNATIONAL ANATOMICAL CONGRESS. PROCEEDINGS. (Text in English, French and German) 1905. quinquennial, 1970, 9th, Leningrad. International Anatomical Congress, c/o Prof. Dr. Shdanow, Karl Marx Prospekt 18, Moscow K-9, Russia. TEL 203-74-09.

610 FR ISSN 0074-1760
INTERNATIONAL ASSOCIATION OF THALASSOTHERAPY. CONGRESS REPORTS. (Proceedings published by organizing committee) 1954. triennial; 1975, 16th, Opatija, Yugoslavia. International Association of Thalasso-Therapy, c/o Professeur D. Leroy, 6, rue Lafayette, 35000 Rennes, France. **Document type:** corporate report.
Description: Covers marine medicine.

610 UK
INTERNATIONAL BACK PAIN NEWS. 1986. 3/yr. £30. (International Back Pain Society) Congress Team International (U.K.) Ltd., 15 Bedford Rd., Northwood, Middlesex HA6 2BA, England. TEL 081 206 0426. FAX 081-206-0427.

610 UK ISSN 0962-4570
INTERNATIONAL CLINICAL PRACTICE SERIES. irreg. Wells Medical Ltd., Chapel Place, Royal Tunbridge Wells, Kent TN1 1BP, England.
TEL 01892-511600. FAX 01892-511400.
Document type: monographic series.
—BLDSC (4538.673700).

610 341 NE
INTERNATIONAL ENCYCLOPAEDIA OF LAWS. MEDICAL LAW. (Text in English) 1993. base vol. (plus irreg. updates). fl.225($122) (effective 1994). Kluwer Law International (Subsidiary of: Wolters Kluwer N.V.), Postbus 85889, 2508 CN The Hague, Netherlands. TEL 31-70-3081500.
FAX 31-70-3081515. (Dist. by: Libresso Distribution Centre, P.O. Box 23, 7400 GA Deventer, Netherlands. TEL 31-5700-33155. FAX 31-5700-33834; In N. America: Kluwer Law International, 675 Massachusetts Ave., Cambridge, MA 02139. TEL 617-354-0140. FAX 617-354-8595) Ed. Herman Nys. (looseleaf format) **Document type:** monographic series.
Description: Covers national and international law relating to the practice of medicine, including discussion of: international and regional bodies such as WHO; the European Code of Medical Ethics; and the law relating to the medical profession, the physician-patient relationship, euthanasia and abortion, and laws and regulation governing health care systems in individual countries.

610 NE ISSN 0074-6037
INTERNATIONAL FEDERATION OF MEDICAL STUDENTS' ASSOCIATIONS. MINUTES AND REPORTS OF THE GENERAL ASSEMBLY. 1951. a. International Federation of Medical Students' Associations, c/o Mrs. M. Hilhorst, Meibergdreef 15, 1105 AZ Amsterdam, Netherlands. FAX 31-20-6972316. circ. 150.

610 US
INTERNATIONAL FEDERATION OF MEDICAL STUDENTS' ASSOCIATIONS. NEWSLETTER. bi-m. International Federation of Medical Students' Associations, c/o Mrs. M. Hilhorst, Meibergdreef 15, 1105 AZ Amsterdam, Netherlands. FAX 31-20-6972316. **Document type:** newsletter.

610 BE
INTERNATIONAL HOSPITAL EQUIPMENT. 1975. 9/yr. $95 (free to qualified personnel). Pan European Publishing Co. (Subsidiary of: Reed Elsevier plc), Rue Verte 216, B-1210 Brussels, Belgium.
TEL 32-2-2402611. FAX 32-2-2427111. TELEX 25828. Ed. Y. Cordonnier. adv.; illus.; circ. 30,010 (controlled). (tabloid format) **Indexed:** Key to Econ.Sci. **Document type:** trade publication.
Description: Reports on hospital products and equipment in the diagnostic, therapeutic and patient handling fields from manufacturers worldwide.

610 UK ISSN 1353-4505
RA399.A1
INTERNATIONAL JOURNAL FOR QUALITY IN HEALTH CARE. 1989. bi-m. £250($398) (effective 1996). (International Society for Quality in Health Care) Elsevier Science Ltd., Pergamon, P.O. Box 800, Kidlington, Oxford OX5 1DX, England.
TEL 44-1865-843000. FAX 44-1865-843010.
E-mail: nlinfo-f@elsevier.nl; usinfo-f@elsevier.com; forinfo-kyf04035@niftyserve.or.jp; Site addr.: http://www.elsevier.nl/. (Subscr. in U.S. and Canada to: Elsevier Science, 660 White Plains Rd., Tarrytown, NY 10591-5153. TEL 914-524-9200. FAX 914-333-2444) Ed. Peter Reizenstein. (also avail. in microfilm from UMI; back issues avail.) **Document type:** academic/scholarly publication.
—BLDSC (4542.510500); SWETS; UMI; UnCover. CCC.
Formerly (until 1994): Quality Assurance in Health Care (ISSN 1040-6166)
Description: Seeks to make more widely available the results of quality assessment studies and quality assurance activities.
Refereed Serial

610 619 IT ISSN 0391-3988
RD130 Db .I576 CODEN: IJAODS
INTERNATIONAL JOURNAL OF ARTIFICIAL ORGANS. 1978. m. L.340000($300) (effective 1994). Wichtig Editore s.r.l., Via Friuli, 72-74, 20135 Milan, Italy. TEL 02-5452306. FAX 02-5451843. Ed. Diego Brancaccio. adv.; bk.rev. circ. 2,000. **Indexed:** Chem.Abstr. Curr.Cont., Excerp.Med., Ind.Med., Ind.Sci.Rev., Kidney, Protozool.Abstr., Rev.Med.& Vet.Mycol., Sci.Cit.Ind.
—BLDSC (4542.105000); CASDDS; Faxon; Genuine Article; SWETS; UnCover. CCC.
Incorporates: Life Support Systems (ISSN 0261-989X)
Description: Provides the most current information available on clinical and experimental developments in the field of artificial organs. Automated therapeutic aids and devices are covered in occasional articles.

610 700 US ISSN 1057-4263
R702.5
INTERNATIONAL JOURNAL OF ARTS MEDICINE. Abbreviated title: I J A M. 1991. s-a. $20 (foreign $25). (International Arts Medicine Association) I J A M, M M B Music, Inc., Contemporary Arts Bldg., 3526 Washington Ave., St. Louis, MO 63103-1019. TEL 314-531-9635. FAX 314-531-8384.
(Co-sponsors: International Society for Music in Medicine) Ed. Rosalie Rebollo Pratt; Pub. Norman A. Goldberg. adv. contact: Marcia Lee Goldberg. bk.rev.; charts; illus. circ. 1,000. (back issues avail.) **Document type:** academic/scholarly publication.
—BLDSC (4542.105500).
Description: Offers a theoretical, clinical, and philosophical exploration of how creative arts aid in healing. Covers international conferences, presents current research, and contains reviews of media resources and interviews.
Refereed Serial

INTERNATIONAL JOURNAL OF BIOMETEOROLOGY. see *METEOROLOGY*

INTERNATIONAL JOURNAL OF CLINICAL ACUPUNCTURE. see *ALTERNATIVE MEDICINE*

610 GW ISSN 0940-5437
CODEN: ICLREA
INTERNATIONAL JOURNAL OF CLINICAL AND LABORATORY RESEARCH; an international multidisciplinary journal devoted to research pertinent to human biology and disease. (Text in English) 1975. 4/yr. DM.386($280) (effective 1996). Springer-Verlag, Heidelberger Platz 3, 14197 Berlin, Germany. TEL 030-8207-0.
FAX 030-8214091. E-mail: orders@springer.de. (Subscr. in N. America to: Springer-Verlag New York, Inc., 44 Hartz Way, Secaucus, NJ 07096-2491. TEL 201-348-4033. FAX 201-348-4505) Ed. F. Dammacco. adv.; bk.rev.; abstr.; bibl.; illus.; index. circ. 6,000. (also avail. in microfilm from UMI; reprint service avail. from UMI) **Indexed:** Biol.Abstr., Bull.Signal., Chem.Abstr., Curr.Adv.Ecol.Sci., Curr.Cont., Dent.Ind., Excerp.Med., Ind.Med., Ref.Zh. **Document type:** academic/scholarly publication.
—BLDSC (4542.170100); CASDDS; Faxon; Genuine Article; SWETS; UMI. CCC.
Former titles (until 1991): Research in Clinic and Laboratory; Ricerca in Clinica e in Laboratorio (ISSN 0390-5748)

614.4 UK ISSN 0300-5771
RA651 CODEN: IJEPBF
INTERNATIONAL JOURNAL OF EPIDEMIOLOGY. 1972. bi-m. £170($315) (effective 1996). (International Epidemiological Association) Oxford University Press, Oxford Journals, Walton St., Oxford OX2 6DP, England. TEL 01865-267907.
FAX 01865-267773. TELEX 837330-OXPRES-G.
E-mail: jnlorders@oup.co.uk. (U.S. subscr. to: Oxford University Press, Inc., 2001 Evans Rd., Cary, NC 27513. TEL 919-677-0977. FAX 919-677-1714) Ed. P.O.D. Pharoah. adv.; bk.rev.; illus.; index. circ. 3,300. (also avail. in microform from UMI; reprint service avail. from UMI) **Indexed:** Abstr.Hyg., Bibl.Dev.Med.& Child Neur., Biol.Abstr., C.I.S. Abstr., Curr.Adv.Cancer Res., Curr.Adv.Ecol.Sci., Curr.Cont., Dairy Sci.Abstr., Dent.Ind., Diar.Dis.Res., Excerp.Med., Geo.Abstr., Helminthol.Abstr., IDA, Ind.Med., Ind.Sci.Rev., Ind.Vet., INIS Atomind., Lab.Haz.Bull., NRN, Nutr.Abstr., Protozool.Abstr., Risk Abstr., Sci.Cit.Ind., Sel.Water Res.Abstr., Small Anim.Abstr., SSCI, Trop.Dis.Bull., Vet.Bull., W.R.C.Inf. **Document type:** academic/scholarly publication.
—BLDSC (4542.244000); Faxon; Genuine Article; SWETS; UMI; UnCover. CCC.
Description: Epidemiology of infectious and non-infectious diseases. Includes research results, new methods, statistical or otherwise, for the analysis of data used by those who practice social and preventive medicine.

616.07 UK ISSN 0959-9673
RB1 CODEN: IJEPEI
INTERNATIONAL JOURNAL OF EXPERIMENTAL PATHOLOGY. 1920. bi-m. £195.50 in Europe; elsewhere £214($345) (effective 1996). Blackwell Science Ltd., Osney Mead, Oxford OX2 0EL, England. TEL 44-1865-206206.
FAX 44-1865-721205. TELEX 83355 MEDBOK G.
Ed. D. Katz. adv.; abstr.; bibl.; illus.; index. circ. 800. (also avail. in microform from UMI; reprint service avail. from UMI) **Indexed:** Abstr.Hyg., Biol.Abstr., Biotech.Abstr., Chem.Abstr., Curr.Adv.Cancer Res., Curr.Adv.Ecol.Sci., Curr.Cont., Dairy Sci.Abstr., Dent.Ind., Excerp.Med., Helminthol.Abstr., Ind.Med., Ind.Sci.Rev., Ind.Vet., Lab.Haz.Bull., Nutr.Abstr., Protozool.Abstr., Rev.Plant Path., Sci.Cit.Ind, Trop.Dis.Bull., Vet.Bull. **Document type:** academic/scholarly publication.
—BLDSC (4542.244820); ADONIS; CASDDS; Faxon; Genuine Article; SWETS; UMI; UnCover. CCC.
Formerly: British Journal of Experimental Pathology (ISSN 0007-1021)
Refereed Serial

612.6 574.16 US ISSN 1069-3130
QP251 CODEN: IFMEEV
INTERNATIONAL JOURNAL OF FERTILITY AND MENOPAUSAL STUDIES. 1955. bi-m. $55 (foreign $65) (effective 1995); newsstand price: $15. (U S International Foundation for Studies in Reproduction, Inc.) M S P (Medical Science Publishing) International, Inc., 405 Main St., Port Washington, NY 11050. TEL 516-944-7340.
FAX 516-944-8663. (Co-sponsors: Scandinavian Association for Studies in Fertility; Fallopius International Society; International Society of Reproductive Medicine; World Menopause Foundation) Ed. Kathleen M. Yasas; Pub. Michael L. Fried. adv.; bibl.; charts; illus.; index. circ. 25,000. (reprint service avail.) **Indexed:** Anim.Breed.Abstr., Biol.Abstr., Biotech.Abstr., Chem.Abstr., Curr.Adv.Ecol.Sci., Curr.Cont., Curr.Lit.Fam.Plan., Dairy Sci.Abstr., Dent.Ind., Excerp.Med., Helminthol.Abstr., Ind.Med., Ind.Sci.Rev., Ind.Vet., Sci.Cit.Ind., Vet.Bull. **Document type:** academic/scholarly publication.
—BLDSC (4542.250020); CASDDS; EMDOCS; Faxon; SWETS; UnCover.
Formerly: International Journal of Fertility (ISSN 0020-725X)
Description: Scholarly articles on medical treatments, surgery, and pathology pertaining to human reproduction.

INTERNATIONAL JOURNAL OF GYNECOLOGICAL PATHOLOGY. see *MEDICAL SCIENCES — Obstetrics And Gynecology*

MEDICAL SCIENCES 4219

610 UK ISSN 0952-6862
INTERNATIONAL JOURNAL OF HEALTH CARE QUALITY ASSURANCE. 7/yr. £679($1129) (effective 1996). M C B University Press Ltd., 60-62 Toller Ln., Bradford, W. Yorks BD8 9BY, England. TEL 01274-499821. FAX 01274-547143. TELEX 51317-MCBUNI-G. (N. American subscr. to: M C B University Press Limited, Box 1943, Birmingham, AL 35202) Ed. Robin Gourlay. (reprint service avail. from SWZ) **Indexed:** Anbar. **Document type:** academic/scholarly publication.
—BLDSC (4542.275000); SWETS; UMI. **CCC.**
Incorporates: Health Care Management (ISSN 0269-2104)
Description: Theory and practice of quality assurance: measuring quality and customer satisfaction, alternative methodologies for implementing programs.

INTERNATIONAL JOURNAL OF HEALTH PLANNING AND MANAGEMENT. see *SOCIAL SERVICES AND WELFARE*

610 NE ISSN 0924-2287
CODEN: IJHSE8
INTERNATIONAL JOURNAL OF HEALTH SCIENCES. (Text in English) 1990. q. fl.165. (Northern Centre for Health Care Research and Education) Van Gorcum en Co. B.V., P.O. Box 43, 9400 AA Assen, Netherlands. TEL 31-5920-46846. FAX 31-5920-72064. Ed. W.J.A. vanden Heuvel. adv.; bk.rev. circ. 1,200. **Document type:** academic/scholarly publication.
—BLDSC (4542.277900); SWETS.

614.88 UK ISSN 1350-2794
▼**INTERNATIONAL JOURNAL OF INTENSIVE CARE.** 1994. bi-m. £50 to individuals (overseas £68); institutions £62 (overseas £80). Greycoat Publishing, 1 Harley St., London W1N 1DA, England. TEL 0171-637-1828. FAX 0171-637-3020. adv.; bk.rev.; circ. 27 (paid); 25,221 (controlled). **Document type:** academic/scholarly publication.
—BLDSC (4542.310900).
Description: Embraces original research on all aspects of intensive care therapy from countries around the world.

610 US
RA1190
INTERNATIONAL JOURNAL OF MEDICAL AND BIOLOGICAL FRONTIERS. 1992. q. $385 (effective 1996). Nova Science Publishers, Inc., 6080 Jericho Tpke., Ste. 207, Commack, NY 11725-2808. TEL 516-499-3103. E-mail: novasci1@aol.com. **Document type:** academic/scholarly publication.
—CASDDS.
Formed by the merger of: International Journal of Medicine and Biology & Journal of Microbiology; **Incorporates:** Current Toxicology (ISSN 1069-4587) & International Journal of Radiation Hygiene (ISSN 1066-7016)

610 SZ ISSN 0167-6865
QP106.6 CODEN: IMCEDT
INTERNATIONAL JOURNAL OF MICROCIRCULATION: CLINICAL & EXPERIMENTAL. 1982. 6/yr. 321 SFr.($247.20) to individuals; institutions 535 SFr.($412) (effective 1996). (European Society for Microcirculation) S. Karger AG, Altschwilerstr. 10, P.O. Box, CH-4009 Basel, Switzerland. TEL 061-3061111. FAX 061-3061234. Eds. B. Farrell, K. Messmer. adv.; bk.rev. (back issues avail.; reprint service avail. from SWZ,UMI) **Indexed:** Chem.Abstr., Curr.Adv.Ecol.Sci., Curr.Cont., Excerp.Med., Ind.Sci.Rev., Sci.Cit.Ind. **Document type:** academic/scholarly publication.
—BLDSC (4542.354000); CASDDS; Faxon; Genuine Article; SWETS; UMI; UnCover. **CCC.**
Description: Publishes papers describing theoretical, experimental and clinical work which focus on the terminal blood vessels, the blood circulating through them, and related tissues and lymphatic fluids.
Refereed Serial

INTERNATIONAL JOURNAL OF ORIENTAL MEDICINE/GUOJI HANFANG YIYAO ZAZHI. see *ALTERNATIVE MEDICINE*

INTERNATIONAL JOURNAL OF PEPTIDE & PROTEIN RESEARCH. see *BIOLOGY — Biological Chemistry*

610 617.6 150 US ISSN 0884-8297
615.19 CODEN: IJPOEY
INTERNATIONAL JOURNAL OF PSYCHOSOMATICS. 1954. q. $40 foreign $60. International Psychosomatics Institute, Box 1296, Philadelphia, PA 19105. TEL 215-565-1964. Ed. Dr. Arnold H. Gessel. adv.; bk.rev.; abstr.; bibl.; charts; illus.; index. circ. 1,000. (also avail. in microform from UMI) **Indexed:** Behav.Med.Abstr., Biol.Abstr., Dent.Ind., Excerp.Med., Ind.Med., Psychol.Abstr. **Document type:** academic/scholarly publication.
—BLDSC (4542.506700); Faxon; UMI; UnCover.
Formerly (until 1984): American Society of Psychosomatic Dentistry and Medicine. Journal (ISSN 0003-1194)

610 NE ISSN 0924-6479
CODEN: IJMDEM
INTERNATIONAL JOURNAL OF RISK AND SAFETY IN MEDICINE; side effects of drugs - devices - surgery - prevention - liability. 1990. bi-m. fl.1058($645) (effective 1996). Elsevier Science B.V., P.O. Box 211, 1000 AE Amsterdam, Netherlands. TEL 31-20-4853911. FAX 31-20-4853598. TELEX 18582 ESPA NL. E-mail: nlinfo-f@elsevier.nl; usinfo-f@elsevier.com; forinfo-kyf04035@niftyserve.or.jp; Site addr.: http://www.elsevier.nl/. (Subscr. in U.S. and Canada to: Elsevier Science Inc., Box 882, Madison Sq. Sta., New York, NY 10159. TEL 212-989-5800. FAX 212-633-3990) Ed. M.N.G. Dukes. bk.rev. (also avail. in microform from UMI; back issues avail.) **Indexed:** Excerp.Med. (1992-). **Document type:** academic/scholarly publication.
—BLDSC (4542.538200); SWETS. **CCC.**
Description: Covers medical science, pharmacology, public health and safety.
Refereed Serial

610 US ISSN 1072-5245
RA785 CODEN: ISMAE8
▼**INTERNATIONAL JOURNAL OF STRESS MANAGEMENT.** 1994. q. $95 (foreign $110) (effective 1996). (International Stress Management Association) Human Sciences Press, Inc. (Subsidiary of: Plenum Publishing Corp.), 233 Spring St., New York, NY 10013. TEL 212-620-8000. FAX 212-463-0742. TELEX 12-421139. Ed. F.J. McGuigan. adv.; B&W page $400. bk.rev. **Document type:** academic/scholarly publication.
—BLDSC (4542.681480).
Description: Aims to advance the study of stress management by encouraging sound research and practice. Covers the fields of psychology, psychiatry, psychophysiology, education, medicine, dentistry, physical and speech therapy and business.
Refereed Serial

610 US ISSN 1045-3121
INTERNATIONAL MED-TECH DIRECTORY; the international financial guide to over 800 publicly traded healthcare companies. 1982-199?. resumed 1993. a. $295 (effective 1993). Westergaard Publishing Corporation, c/o Pamela McLernon, 560 W. 43rd St., New York, NY 10036. FAX 212-947-6643. Ed. Emile Westergaard. **Document type:** directory.
Description: Compiles information on public health care firms.

610 JA
▼**INTERNATIONAL MEDICAL JOURNAL.** (Text in English) 1994. q. Japan International Cultural Exchange Foundation, 2-15-5-207 Shoto, Shibuya-ku, Tokyo 150, Japan. TEL 81-3-3467-7316. FAX 81-3-3467-7317. Ed. Tsutomu Sakuta. circ. 5,000.
Description: Publishes significant clinical studies, conceptual contributions and reviews on contemporary issues.

610 JA ISSN 0535-1405
INTERNATIONAL MEDICAL NEWS. (Text in English, Japanese) 1952. m. exchange basis. International Medical Society of Japan - Nihon Kokusai Igaku Kyokai, 4-12, Kamium 1-chome, Setagaya-ku, Tokyo 154, Japan.

610 RU ISSN 0869-6683
INTERNATIONAL MEDICAL REVIEWS/MEZHDUNARODNYE MEDITSINSKIE OBZORY. (Text in Russian; summaries in English) 12/yr. Avalanche Publishers Ltd., Izmailovsky pr. 14, St. Petersburg 198052, Russia. TEL 7-812-1126510. FAX 7-812-3118549. Ed. Vladimir L. Larin. adv. contact: Lyudimila V. Vltchek. **Indexed:** Excerp.Med. (1994-).
—BLDSC (0107.822300).
Description: Covers Russian medical affairs.

610 615 JA
INTERNATIONAL MOCHIDA MEMORIAL SYMPOSIUM. (Text in English) 1988. biennial. Mochida Memorial Foundation for Medical and Pharmaceutical Research - Mochida Kinen Igaku Yakugaku Shinko Zaidan, 1-7, Yotsuya, Shinjuku-ku, Tokyo 160, Japan. **Document type:** proceedings.

610 BE
INTERNATIONAL ORGANIZATION FOR COOPERATION IN HEALTH CARE. GENERAL ASSEMBLY. REPORT. 1979. a. free. Medicus Mundi International, Rue du Marteau 19, 1040 Brussels, Belgium. TEL 32-2-2199588. **Document type:** academic/scholarly publication, newsletter.
Supersedes: International Organization for Medical Cooperation. General Assembly. Report (ISSN 0579-3912)

362 US ISSN 0020-8477
CODEN: IRERB
INTERNATIONAL REHABILITATION REVIEW. 1949. 3/yr. $30. Rehabilitation International, 25 E. 21st St., 4th Fl., New York, NY 10010. TEL 212-420-1500. FAX 212-505-0871. TELEX 446412. Ed. Barbara Duncan. adv.; bk.rev.; film rev.; play rev.; illus. circ. 20,000. (tabloid format; back issues avail.) **Indexed:** CINAHL, Except.Child.Educ.Abstr., Excerp.Med., Rehabil.Lit., Soc.Work Res.& Abstr. **Document type:** newspaper.
—BLDSC (4545.797000); UMI.
Formerly: Rehabilitation International Newsletter.
Description: Issues and developments in disability prevention and rehabilitation worldwide.

616.07 US ISSN 0074-7718
RB6 CODEN: IRXPAT
INTERNATIONAL REVIEW OF EXPERIMENTAL PATHOLOGY. 1962. irreg., vol.34, 1993. Academic Press, Inc., 525 B St., Ste. 1900, San Diego, CA 92101-4495. TEL 619-231-0926. FAX 619-699-6715. (Subscr. to: Order Dept., 6277 Sea Harbor Dr., 4th Fl., Orlando, FL 32887. TEL 800-321-5068) Ed. G.W. Richter. index. (reprint service avail. from ISI) **Indexed:** Abstr.Hyg., Biol.Abstr., Chem.Abstr., Curr.Adv.Cell & Devel.Biol., Excerp.Med., Ind.Med., Ind.Sci.Rev., Ind.Vet., Sci.Cit.Ind., Trop.Dis.Bull., Vet.Bull.
—BLDSC (4547.150000); CASDDS; Faxon; SWETS; UnCover. **CCC.**
Refereed Serial

INTERNATIONAL SOCIETY ON OPTICS WITHIN LIFE SCIENCES. SERIES (PROCEEDINGS). see *BIOLOGY*

610 JA
INTERNATIONAL SYMPOSIUM ON QUALITY CONTROL. (Text in English) 1974. every 4 yrs. Ekuseputa Medica K.K. - Excerpta Medica Ltd., Tokyo, 15-23, Nishiazabu 4-chome, Minato-ku, Toyo 106, Japan.

610 US ISSN 1045-0572
RA783.5
INTERNATIONAL TRAVEL HEALTH GUIDE. 1989. a. Travel Medicine, Inc., 351 Pleasant St., Ste. 312, Northampton, MA 01060.

574 610 VE ISSN 0535-5133
CODEN: ICLIAD
INVESTIGACION CLINICA. (Supplements avail.) (Text and summaries in English and Spanish) 1960. q. $50 (effective 1995). Universidad del Zulia, Instituto de Investigaciones Clinicas, Facultad de Medicina, Apdo. Postal 1151, Maracaibo, Venezuela. TEL 5861-523844. FAX 58-61-916053. Ed. Dra. Elena Ryder. bibl.; charts. circ. 2,000. **Indexed:** Abstr.Hyg., Biol.Abstr., Chem.Abstr., Curr.Cont., Excerp.Med., Helminthol.Abstr., Nutr.Abstr., Rev.Med.& Vet.Mycol., Sugar Ind.Abstr., Trop.Dis.Bull. **Document type:** academic/scholarly publication.
—BLDSC (4557.720000); CASDDS; Genuine Article.

MEDICAL SCIENCES

610   MX   ISSN 0185-2108
CODEN: IMEID
INVESTIGACION MEDICA INTERNACIONAL. 1974. bi-m. Investigacion Medica Internacional S.A., Matias Romero 116, Col. del Valle, 03100 Mexico D.F., Mexico. TEL 5592755. **Indexed:** Excerp.Med. **Document type:** academic/scholarly publication.

610   US   ISSN 0746-8709
R15
IOWA MEDICINE. 1910. m. $25. Iowa Medical Society, 1001 Grand Ave., W. Des Moines, IA 50265. TEL 515-223-1401. FAX 515-223-8420. Ed. Christine McMahon. adv. contact: Jane I. Nieland. charts; illus.; index. circ. 4,750. (back issues avail.) **Indexed:** Biol.Abstr., Chem.Abstr., Ind.Med., INIS Atomind., Med.Care Rev.
—BLDSC (4566.400000); Faxon.
Formerly (until 1984): Iowa Medical Society. Journal (ISSN 0021-0587)
Description: Scientific and socioeconomic medical journal.

610   IR   ISSN 0253-0716
CODEN: IJMSDW
IRANIAN JOURNAL OF MEDICAL SCIENCES. (Text and summaries in English) 1970. 4/yr. $80. Shiraz University of Medical Sciences, Nemazee Hospital, Shiraz 71934, Iran. FAX 98-71-661001. Ed. Dr. Karim Vessal. adv.; bk.rev.; charts; illus.; stat. circ. 3,000. (reprint service avail. from IRC) **Indexed:** Biol.Abstr., Biotech.Abstr., Chem.Abstr., Chem.Abstr., Curr.Cont., Excerp.Med., Helminthol.Abstr., Ind.Med., Nutr.Abstr., Trop.Dis.Bull. **Document type:** academic/scholarly publication.
—BLDSC (4567.528900); CASDDS.
Formerly (until 1979): Pahlavi Medical Journal (ISSN 0030-9427)
Description: Publishes original clinical and research experiences of Iranian physicians on prevalent diseases in the region, and analysis of various regional parameters which may modulate the incidence, course and management of diseases and relevant medical problems.

610   IQ   ISSN 0021-0927
IRAQI MEDICAL PROFESSIONS' ASSOCIATION. JOURNAL.* (Text in Arabic and English) vol.13, 1965. 3/yr. Iraqi Medical Professions' Association, Republican Hospital, Baghdad, Iraq. Ed. Dr. F.H. Ghali. adv.; charts; illus.; stat. **Indexed:** Biol.Abstr., Ind.Med.

610   JA
IRI SANGYO SHINBUN/MEDICAL AND PHYSICAL INSTRUMENTS NEWSPAPER. (Text in Japanese) 1975. s-m. 5000 Yen. Iri Sangyo Shinbunsha, 22-9-401, Sakuragawa 3-chome, Itabashi-ku, Tokyo 174, Japan. **Document type:** newspaper.

610   IE   ISSN 0374-8405
CODEN: IPSJB7
IRISH COLLEGES OF PHYSICIANS AND SURGEONS. JOURNAL. 1971. q. I£57 (Europe I£63; elsewhere I£70). Royal College of Surgeons in Ireland, Mercer Library, Mercer St. Lower, Dublin 2, Ireland. TEL 0353-1-4780674. FAX 0353-1-4780934. Ed. Austin Leahy; Pub. Beatrice Doran. adv.; bk.rev.; charts; illus.; index. circ. 3,500. **Indexed:** Biol.Abstr., Curr.Adv.Ecol.Sci., Curr.Cont., INIS Atomind. **Document type:** academic/scholarly publication.
—BLDSC (4802.780000); Faxon.
Supersedes: Royal College of Surgeons in Ireland. Journal (ISSN 0035-8827)

610   IE   ISSN 0790-9314
IRISH DOCTOR. (Text in English, Irish; summaries in English) 1989. m. I£25 (U.K. and N. Ireland £28; elsewhere £40). Medical Press Ltd., Tara House, Tara St., Dublin 2, Ireland. TEL 01-6713500. FAX 01-6713074. Ed. Dr. Bridget Maher; Pub. Maria Farren. adv.: color page I£950; adv. contact: Michael Quigley. bk.rev. circ. 5,838. (back issues avail.) **Document type:** trade publication.
—BLDSC (4571.286000).
Description: Concerns post-graduate medical practice for general practitioners and non-consultant hospital doctors.

610   IE   ISSN 0021-1265
CODEN: IJMSAT
IRISH JOURNAL OF MEDICAL SCIENCES. 1832. m. I£60 (foreign I£100). Royal Academy of Medicine in Ireland, 6 Kildare St., Dublin 2, Ireland. TEL 01-6767650. FAX 01-6611684. Ed. Thomas F. Gorey. adv.: page I£1000; adv. contact: Daniela Korcel. bk.rev. circ. 2,000. (also avail. in microfilm; reprint service avail. from UMI) **Indexed:** Biol.Abstr., Chem.Abstr., Curr.Adv.Cancer Res., Dent.Ind., Excerp.Med., Helminthol.Abstr., Ind.Med., Ind.Sci.Rev., INIS Atomind., NRN, Nutr.Abstr., Rev.Plant Path., Sci.Cit.Ind. **Document type:** academic/scholarly publication.
—BLDSC (4572.000000); CASDDS; EMDOCS; Faxon; Genuine Article; SWETS; UnCover.

610   IE   ISSN 0332-3102
CODEN: IMDJBD
IRISH MEDICAL JOURNAL. 1937-1987 (Dec.); resumed 1988 (Sep.). bi-m. I£80 ireland and Europe; elsewhere £95. Irish Medical Organization, 10 Fitzwilliam Pl., Dublin 2, Ireland. TEL 01-6767273. FAX 01-6622818. Ed. John Murphy. adv. contact: Caroline Leacy. bk.rev.; charts; illus.; s-a. index. circ. 5,861. **Indexed:** Biol.Abstr., Chem.Abstr., Curr.Cont., Dent.Ind., Dok.Arbeitsmed., Excerp.Med., Helminthol.Abstr., Ind.Med., INIS Atomind., NRN, Nutr.Abstr. **Document type:** academic/scholarly publication.
—BLDSC (4572.910000); CASDDS; Faxon; Genuine Article; SWETS; UnCover.
Former titles: Irish Medical Organization; Irish Medical Association. Journal (ISSN 0021-129X)
Description: Forum for all aspects of Irish medicine.

610   IE   ISSN 0790-2905
IRISH MEDICAL NEWS. 1974. w. £50 to non-members. Winstone Publishing, 10 Fitzwilliam Place, Dublin 2, Ireland. TEL 01-767273. FAX 01-612758. Ed. John Gibbons. adv.; bk.rev. circ. 5,000.
Formerly (until 1984): I M J Appointments.

610   UK   ISSN 0047-147X
IRISH MEDICAL TIMES. 1967. w. £45. Medical Publications Ltd., 30 Lancaster Gate, London W2 3LP, England. (Subscr. to: 12-14 Ansdell St., London W8 5TR, England) Ed. Dr. John F. O'Connell. adv.; bk.rev.; circ. controlled. (tabloid format; also avail. in microfilm from UMI; reprint service avail. from UMI)
—BLDSC (4572.950000); UMI. **CCC**.

610   JA   ISSN 0910-6030
IRYO (YEAR). 1985. m. 14400 Yen. Medical Friend Co. Ltd. - Mejikaru Furendo Sha, 2-4, 3-chome, Kudan-Kita, Chiyoda-ku, Tokyo 102, Japan. FAX 03-3261-6602. Ed. Kazuhazu Ogura. adv.; bk.rev. circ. 30,000. (back issues avail.) **Indexed:** Excerp.Med.
Description: Analyzes and discusses health service trends.

610   JA
IRYO FUKUSHI GIJUTSU/MEDICAL AND WELFARE TECHNOLOGY. (Text in Japanese) 1980. q. Gijutsu Kenkyu Kumiai Iryo Fukushi Kiki Kenkyujo - Technology Research Association of Medical and Welfare Apparatus, 5-8, Shiba Koen 3-chome, Minato-ku, Tokyo 105, Japan.

IRYO JIKO JOHO SENTA. SENTA NYUSU/MEDICAL MALPRACTICE INFORMATION CENTER IN JAPAN. NEWSLETTER. see *LAW — Civil Law*

610   JA
IRYO JOHO SHISUTEMU KENKYU KAIHATSU HOKOKUSHO/REPORT OF RESEARCH AND DEVELOPMENT OF MEDICAL INFORMATION SYSTEM. (Text in Japanese) a. Iryo Joho Shisutemu Kaihatsu Senta - Medical Information System Development Center, 3-4, Akasaka 2-chome, Minato-ku, Tokyo 107, Japan.

610   JA   ISSN 0289-8055
IRYO JOHOGAKU/JAPAN JOURNAL OF MEDICAL INFORMATICS. (Text in Japanese; summaries in English, Japanese) 1980. q. 2500 Yen. Nihon Iryo Joho Gakkai - Japan Association for Medical Informatics, Iryo Joho Shisutemu Kaihatsu Senta, Randikku Akasaka, 3-4, Akasaka 2-chome, Minato-ku, Tokyo 107, Japan. **Indexed:** Excerp.Med.

610 360   JA   ISSN 0287-1521
IRYO TO FUKUSHI/JAPANESE JOURNAL OF MEDICAL SOCIAL WORK. (Text in Japanese) 1965. a. 1000 Yen. Nihon Iryo Shakai Jigyo Kyokai - Medical Social Worker Society, Zenkoku Shinshin Shogaiji Fukushi Zaidan Biru, 2-8, Nishiwaseda 2-chome, Shinjuku-ku, Tokyo 162, Japan.

610   JA   ISSN 0916-9202
IRYO TO SHAKAI/MEDICAL SERVICE AND SOCIETY. (Text in Japanese) 1991. a. 2000 Yen. Iryo Kagaku Kenkyujo - Health Care Science Institute, 6-10, Koishikawa 4-chome, Bunkyo-ku, Tokyo 112, Japan.

610   JA
IRYO TO SHISETSU/MEDICAL SERVICE AND FACILITY. (Text in Japanese) 1971. q. 1000 Yen. Iryo Taimususha - Medical Times, 11-2, Kanda Ogawamachi 3-chome, Chiyoda-ku, Tokyo 101, Japan.

610 617.6 615   JA   ISSN 0911-8470
ISHI SHIKAISHI YAKUZAISHI CHOSA/SURVEY ON PHYSICIANS, DENTISTS AND PHARMACEUTISTS. (Text in Japanese) 1955. biennial. Koseisho, Daijin Kanbo, Tokei Johobu - Ministry of Health and Welfare, Minister's Secretariat, Statistics and Information Department, 7-3, Ichigaya Honmuracho, Shinjuku-ku, Tokyo 162, Japan.

610   JA   ISSN 0287-1777
ISHIKAWA KENRITSU CHUO BYOIN IGAKUSHI/ISHIKAWA PREFECTURAL CENTRAL HOSPITAL. MEDICAL JOURNAL. (Text in English, Japanese) 1978. a. Ishikawa Kenritsu Chuo Byoin, Nu 153, Minamishinpomachi, Kanazawa-shi, Ishikawa-ken 920-02, Japan.

ISLAMIC ACADEMY OF SCIENCES. JOURNAL. see *SCIENCES: COMPREHENSIVE WORKS*

610   SU   ISSN 0950-4567
ISLAMIC WORLD MEDICAL JOURNAL. (Text in English) 1984. bi-m. Islamic Press Agency, P.O. Box 4288, Jeddah, Saudi Arabia.

ISOTOPE NEWS. see *BIOLOGY — Biological Chemistry*

610   IS   ISSN 0021-2180
R97   CODEN: IJMDAI
ISRAEL JOURNAL OF MEDICAL SCIENCES. (Text in English) 1965. m. $200 to institutions (effective 1996). Israel Journal of Medical Sciences, 2 Etzel St., French Hill, Jerusalem 97853, Israel. TEL 972-2-817727. FAX 972-2-815722. Ed. Dr. Moshe Prywes. adv. contact: Shulamit L. Noy. bk.rev.; bibl.; charts; illus.; index. circ. 5,000. (also avail. in microform from UMI; reprint service avail. from UMI) **Indexed:** Abstr.Hyg., Biol.Abstr., Biotech.Abstr., Chem.Abstr., Curr.Adv.Cancer Res., Curr.Cont., Dairy Sci.Abstr., Dent.Ind., Dok.Arbeitsmed., Excerp.Med., Helminthol.Abstr., Ind.Med., Ind.Sci.Rev., Ind.Vet., INIS Atomind., Int.Abstr.Biol.Sci, Int.Nurs.Ind., Med.& Surg.Dermat., NRN, Nutr.Abstr., Pig News & Info., Poult.Abstr., Rev.Med.& Vet.Mycol., Rev.Plant Path., Sci.Cit.Ind., Small Anim.Abstr., Soyabean Abstr., Vet.Bull. **Document type:** academic/scholarly publication.
—BLDSC (4583.812000); CASDDS; Ei; EMDOCS; Faxon; Genuine Article; SWETS; UMI; UnCover. **CCC**.
Incorporates: Israel Journal of Experimental Medicine; Israel Medical Journal.
Description: Publishes original papers on basic medical sciences, clinical medicine, epidemiology, public health, and relevant topics in biology, and reports on medical news and scientific meetings in Israel for an international audience.
Refereed Serial

610   IS
ISRAEL MEDICAL ASSOCIATION. QUARTERLY MEDICAL REVIEW. (Editions in English, French, Spanish) q. membership. Fraser, 17 Bugrashov St., Tel Aviv, Israel. Ed. Yehuda Shoefeld. adv.; illus.
Formerly: Israel Medical Association. Quarterly Review. (ISSN 0021-2253)

ISSUES: A CRITICAL EXAMINATION OF CONTEMPORARY ETHICAL ISSUES IN HEALTH CARE. see *PHILOSOPHY*

ISSUES IN BIOMEDICINE. see *BIOLOGY*

ISSUES IN LAW AND MEDICINE. see *HANDICAPPED*

MEDICAL SCIENCES

610 TU ISSN 0374-1656
R97.7.T8 CODEN: TFMEAC
ISTANBUL MEDICAL FACULTY. MEDICAL BULLETIN/ISTANBUL TIP FAKULTESI. MECMUASI. Cover title: Istanbul Universitesi. Istanbul Tip Fakultesi. Mecmuasi. (Text in English; summaries in English, French, German) 1919; N.S. 1938. biennial. free. Istanbul University, Istanbul Medical Faculty - Istanbul Universitesi, Istanbul Tip Fakultesi, Dekanligi Capa, 34390 Istanbul, Turkey. TEL 90-1-5243031. FAX 90-1-5326066. illus. circ. 1,000. **Indexed:** Biol.Abstr., Chem.Abstr., Excerp.Med. (1992-), Ind.Med., Nutr.Abstr.
Formerly: Istanbul Universitesi. Tip Fakultesi. Tip Fakultesi Mecmuasi (ISSN 0047-1623)

610 IT ISSN 0021-2431
RC306 CODEN: AICFAF
ISTITUTO CARLO FORLANINI. ANNALI. 1937-1969; resumed. q. $90 (effective 1994). Edizioni Luigi Pozzi s.r.l., Via Panama, 68, 00198 Rome, Italy. TEL 39-6-8553548. FAX 39-6-8554105. bk.rev.; bibl.; charts; illus.; index. **Indexed:** Chem.Abstr., Ind.Med.

ISTITUTO SUPERIORE DI SANITA. ANNALI. see *PUBLIC HEALTH AND SAFETY*

612.39 574.133 IT ISSN 1121-1709
CODEN: IMEME
ITALIAN JOURNAL OF MINERAL & ELECTROLYTE METABOLISM. (Text in English) 1987. q. $110 to individuals; institutions $150 (effective 1995). (Italian Society of Mineral Metabolism) Edizioni Minerva Medica, Corso Bramante 83-85, 10126 Turin, Italy. TEL 39-11-678282. FAX 39-11-3121736. Ed. Giorgio Coen; Pub. Alberto Oliaro. adv.: B&W page $1100, color page $1900; trim 215 x 280; adv. contact: F. Filippo. circ. 2,000 (paid). **Indexed:** Chem.Abstr., Excerp.Med. (1994-). **Document type:** academic/scholarly publication.
—BLDSC (4588.340640); CASDDS.
Formerly (until 1990): Giornale Italiano di Metabolismo Minerale ed Elettrolitico (ISSN 0394-1566)
Description: Deals with mineral and electrolyte metabolism and with calcified tissue.
Refereed Serial

610 JA ISSN 0536-0307
ITAN/JAPAN SOCIETY OF MEDICAL HISTORY. KANSAI BRANCH. JOURNAL. (Text in Japanese) 1038. irreg. Nihon Ishi Gakkai, Kansai Shibu, c/o Mr. Yoji Nagatoya, 1-12-308, Shinkanaokacho 3-chome, Sakai-shi, Osaka 591, Japan. **Indexed:** Jap.Per.Ind.

610 JA ISSN 0021-3284
CODEN: IIZAAX
IWATE IGAKU ZASSHI/IWATE MEDICAL ASSOCIATION. JOURNAL. (Text in Japanese; abstracts in English) 1945. bi-m. 5000 Yen. Iwate Igakkai - Iwate Medical Association, c/o Iwate Medical University, 19-1 Uchimaru, Morioka-shi, Iwate-ken 020, Japan. TEL 0196-51-5111. FAX 0196-25-0547. Ed. Takeshi Kashimoto. adv.; abstr.; bibl.; charts; illus.; index. circ. 1,400. **Indexed:** Biol.Abstr., Chem.Abstr., Excerp.Med., INIS Atomind. **Document type:** academic/scholarly publication.
—BLDSC (4803.200000); CASDDS.
Description: Publishes original medical research reports.

610 JA
IWATE IHO/IWATE MEDICAL SOCIETY. NEWS. (Text in Japanese) m. 500 Yen per no. Iwateken Ishikai, 8-20, Saien 2-chome, Morioka-shi, Iwate-ken 020, Japan.

610 JA ISSN 0385-9320
IWATE KENRITSU BYOIN IGAKKAI ZASSHI/IWATE PREFECTURAL HOSPITAL. MEDICAL JOURNAL. (Text in Japanese) 1961. s-a. Iwate Kenritsu Byoin Igakkai, Iwate Kenritsu Chuo Byoin, 4-1 Ueda 1-chome, Morioka-shi, Iwate-ken 020, Japan. **Indexed:** INIS Atomind.

610 JA ISSN 0917-1177
IWATE KENRITSU MIYAKO BYOIN IGAKU ZASSHI/IWATE PREFECTURAL MIYAKO HOSPITAL. MEDICAL JOURNAL. (Text in English, Japanese) 1990. a. Iwate Kenritsu Miyako Byoin, 1-6, Sakaecho, Miyako-shi, Iwate-ken 027, Japan.

610 JA ISSN 0287-0894
CODEN: IYKEDH
IYAKUHIN KENKYU/STUDY OF MEDICAL SUPPLIES. (Text in English, Japanese; summaries in English) 1970. bi-m. Nihon Koteisho Kyokai - Society of Japanese Pharmacopoeia, 12-15, Shibuya 2-chome, Shibuya-ku, Tokyo 150, Japan.
—BLDSC (4589.220000); CASDDS.

615.845 610.28 JA ISSN 0021-3292
CODEN: IYSEAKI
IYO DENSHI TO SEITAI KOGAKU/JAPANESE JOURNAL OF MEDICAL ELECTRONICS AND BIOLOGICAL ENGINEERING. (Text in Japanese; summaries in English) 1963. bi-m. 7200 Yen. (Japan Society of Medical Electronics and Biological Engineering - Nihon M-E Gakkai) Gakkaishi Kanko Senta - Center for Academic Publications, Japan, 4-16, Yayoi 2-chome, Bunkyo-ku, Tokyo 113, Japan. Ed. Dr. Nozomu Hoshimiya. adv. contact: Hideki Murata. bk.rev.; bibl.; charts; illus.; stat.; index. **Indexed:** Biol.Abstr., Chem.Abstr., Dent.Ind., Eng.Ind., Excerp.Med., Ind.Med., INSPEC (1971-), Jap.Per.Ind., JCT, JTA. **Document type:** academic/scholarly publication.
—CASDDS; EMDOCS.
Refereed Serial

610 JA
IYO KIKI/MEDICAL APPLIANCE. (Text in Japanese) 1974. m. Nihon Iyo Kiki Kogyokai - Japan Association of Medical Equipment Industries, 39-15, Hongo 3-chome, Bunkyo-ku, Tokyo 116, Japan.

IYO KOGAKU KENKYU SHISETSU HOKOKU/TOKYO WOMEN'S MEDICAL COLLEGE. INSTITUTE OF BIOMEDICAL ENGINEERING. REPORTS. see *BIOLOGY — Bioengineering*

610 JA ISSN 0911-0852
IZAI TO MEKKIN/STUDIES ON MEDICAL IMPLEMENTS AND THEIR DISINFECTION. (Text in Japanese) 1978. 3/yr. Chuzai Gyomu Kenkyukai - Research Group of Central Sterile Supply Department, c/o Ms. Kazue Hayashi, Kokuritsu Chiba Byoin, 1-2, Tsubakimori 4-chome, Chuo-ku, Chiba 260, Japan.

610 US ISSN 0210-9913
J A M A EN COLOMBIA.* (Journal of the American Medical Association) 1977. m. 1800 ptas.($42) American Medical Association, 515 N. State St., Chicago, IL 60610. Ed. Dr. Cesar A. Pantoja. circ. 7,500.
—CCC.

610 US ISSN 0211-4445
J A M A EN ESPANOL.* (Journal of the American Medical Association) 1975. m. 1800 ptas.($23) American Medical Association, 515 N. State St., Chicago, IL 60610. Ed. Dr. J. Ferre Fuentes. adv.; charts; illus.; stat.; index; circ. 35,000 (controlled). **Indexed:** Dok.Arbeitsmed., Nutr.Abstr.
—CCC.

610 US ISSN 0210-9921
J A M A EN VENEZUELA.* (Journal of the American Medical Association) 1977. m. Bol.$130($30) American Medical Association, 515 N. State St., Chicago, IL 60610. Ed. Dr Francisco Kerdel. adv.; charts; illus.; stat.; index. circ. 7,000.
—CCC.

610 FR ISSN 0221-7678
J A M A - FRANCE. (Journal of the American Medical Association) 1980. s-m. 270 F.($30) to individuals (foreign 480 F.); students 210 F. (foreign 370 F.). Publications Medicales Internationales, 24 bis bd. Verd de Saint-Julien, 92190 Meudon, France. Ed. Jean Pascal Huve. adv. circ. 32,000.
—CCC.

610 US ISSN 0098-7484
R15 CODEN: JAMAAP
J A M A: THE JOURNAL OF THE AMERICAN MEDICAL ASSOCIATION. Chinese translation: Meiguo Yixuehui Zazhi (Zhongwen Ban) (CC ISSN 1000-842X) 1848. w. (2 vols./yr.). $120 (foreign $160). American Medical Association, 515 N. State St., Chicago, IL 60610. TEL 312-464-5000; 800-262-2350. FAX 312-464-4184. Ed. Dr. George D. Lundberg. adv.: B&W page $7098. bk.rev.; abstr.; bibl.; charts; illus.; s-a. index. circ. 372,000. (also avail. in microform from UMI,PMC; reprint service avail. from UMI) **Indexed:** Abstr.Anthropol., Abstr.Crim.& Pen., Abstr.Health Care Manage.Stud., Abstr.Hyg., Acad.Ind., Adol.Ment.Hlth.Abstr., AIM, Behav.Med.Abstr., Bibl.Dev.Med.& Child Neur., Biol.Abstr., Biostat., Biotech.Abstr., C.I.S. Abstr., CAD CAM Abstr., Chem.Abstr., CINAHL, Curr.Adv.Cancer Res., Curr.Cont., Dairy Sci.Abstr., Deep Sea Res.& Oceanogr.Abstr., Dent.Abstr., Dent.Ind., Diab.Cont., Diar.Dis.Res., Environ.Abstr., Excerp.Med., FAMLI, Food Sci.& Tech.Abstr., Gen.Sci.Ind., Helminthol.Abstr., Hlth.Ind., I.P.A., Ind.Hyg.Dig., Ind.Med., Ind.Vet., INIS Atomind., Int.Nurs.Ind., Kidney, Lab.Haz.Bull., Mag.Ind., Med.& Surg.Dermat., Med.Care Rev., NRN, Nutr.Abstr., Protozool.Abstr., Psychol.Abstr. (1994-), Rev.Appl.Entomol., Rev.Med.& Vet.Mycol., Rev.Plant Path., Risk Abstr., Sci.Cit.Ind., Small Anim.Abstr., Telegen, Tr.& Indus.Ind., Trop.Dis.Bull., Vet.Bull. **Document type:** academic/scholarly publication.
●Also available online. Vendor(s): Lexis-Nexis, Ovid Technologies (JWAT).
—BLDSC (4689.000000); CASDDS; CIS; EMDOCS; Faxon; Genuine Article; SWETS; UMI; UnCover. **CCC.**
Former titles (until 1960): American Medical Association. Journal (ISSN 0002-9955); (until 1883): American Medical Association. Transactions (ISSN 1050-2793)
Description: Keeps physicians abreast of current events, current therapies and research-in-progress. Covers virtually every specialty and aspects of medicine.
Refereed Serial

610 IT ISSN 0393-554X
J A M A: THE JOURNAL OF THE AMERICAN MEDICAL ASSOCIATION (ITALIAN EDITION). 1989. m. (10/yr.). L.50000. E S I Stampa Medica s.r.l., Casella Postale 42, Lgo. Volontari del Sangue 10, 20097 S. Donato, Milan, Italy. TEL 02-5274241. FAX 02-55600670. TELEX 324894. Ed. Diego Onestinghel. adv.: B&W page L.11000000, color page L.14500000; trim 175 x 237; adv. contact: Ornella Galbiati. bk.rev. circ. 56,000.

610 FR ISSN 0299-3953
J A M I F. (Journal Association des Medecins Israelites de France) 1952. 10/yr. 100 F.($75) (effective Jan. 1990). Association des Medecins Israelites de France, 11 ave. de la Republique, 94260 Fresnes, France. Ed. Dr. D. Bellaiche. adv.; bk.rev.; abstr.; film rev.; play rev.; circ. 8,500 (controlled).
Former titles: Association des Medecins Israelites de France. Revue Medicale (ISSN 0298-2900); A M I F (ISSN 0400-132X)

610 530 JA
J A M P NEWS. (Text in Japanese) 1985. s-a. Japanese Association of Medical Physics - Nihon Igaku Butsuri Gakkai, Hoshasen Igaku Sogo Kenkyujo Butsuri Kenkyubu, 9-1, Anagawa 4-chome, Inage-ku, Chiba 263, Japan.

616.89 JA
J A S C T NEWSLETTER. (Text in Japanese) 1982. q. membership. Japanese Association of Sex Counselors and Therapists - Nihon Sei Kagakkai, c/o Hase Kurinikku, Shin'aoyama biru Nishikan, 3F, 1-1, Minamiaoyama 1-chome, Minato-ku, Tokyo 107, Japan. Ed. Takao Osada. **Document type:** newsletter.

610 US ISSN 0197-2510
J E M S. (Journal of Emergency Medical Services) 1980. m. $21.97. Jems Publishing Co., Inc., Box 2789, Carlsbad, CA 92018. TEL 619-431-9797. FAX 619-431-8176. Ed. Keith Griffiths. adv.; bk.rev.; charts; illus.; stat. circ. 22,385. (also avail. in microform; back issues avail.) **Indexed:** CINAHL.
—BLDSC (4663.525000); Faxon; SWETS; UnCover.

J O P S O M. (Journal of Preventive and Social Medicine) see *PUBLIC HEALTH AND SAFETY*

JACKSON LABORATORY SCIENTIFIC REPORT. see *BIOLOGY — Genetics*

MEDICAL SCIENCES

610   US
JACKSONVILLE MEDICINE; the journal of the Duval County Medical Society. m. $25. Duval County Medical Society, 515 Lomax St., Jacksonville, FL 32204. TEL 904-355-6561. FAX 904-353-5848. Ed. Dr. James P. Bolling. adv.: page $440 per issue; trim 7 1/4 x 9 1/2; adv. contact: Marigrace Doran. circ. 1,800 (controlled). (back issues avail.) **Document type:** academic/scholarly publication.
     Formerly: Jacksonville Medicine Bulletin.
     Refereed Serial

610   CE   ISSN 0379-3877
JAFFNA MEDICAL JOURNAL. (Text in English) 1953. s-a. Rs.1000($20) Jaffna Medical Association, General Hospital, Jaffna, Sri Lanka. TEL 222661. Ed. Dr. N. Sivarajah. adv.; bk.rev. circ. 700. **Indexed:** Sri Lanka Sci.Ind. **Document type:** academic/scholarly publication.

610 614.8   GW
JAHRBUCH KRITISCHE MEDIZIN. 1976. a. DM.34 to individuals. Argument-Verlag GmbH, Rentzelstr. 1, 20146 Hamburg, Germany. TEL 040-456018. FAX 040-445189. circ. 2,000. **Document type:** academic/scholarly publication.
     Formerly: Kritische Medizin im Argument (ISSN 0341-0943)
     Description: Discusses economic and world politics, peace research, feminism, critical studies of medicine and psychology, international socialism, Marxism, culture, racism, and literary studies.

610   SP   ISSN 0210-220X
JANO "MEDICINA Y HUMANIDADES". 1971. w. (45/yr.). 8400 ptas.($87) (free to qualified personnel). Ediciones Doyma S.A., Travesera de Gracia 17-21, 08021 Barcelona, Spain. TEL 34-1-200-07-11. FAX 34-1-209-11-36. TELEX 51964 INK-E. Ed. Celia Ribera Banus. adv.: page 470000 ptas.; trim 230 x 295; adv. contact: Cristina Garrote. circ. 40,000. (reprint service avail. from UMI)
     —CCC.
     Description: Covers topics in clinical medicine, diagnosis and treatment, to support the continuing education of postgraduates. Includes cultural topics in history, the arts, literature, music, films and theater.

610   JA   ISSN 0021-4493
     CODEN: NIZABL
JAPAN MEDICAL ASSOCIATION. JOURNAL/NIHON ISHIKAI ZASSHI. (Text in Japanese) 1921. s-m. 12000 Yen. Japan Medical Association - Nihon Ishi Kai, 28-16, Hongo 2-chome, Bunkyo-ku, Tokyo 113, Japan. FAX 03-3946-6295. Ed. Yuichiro Goto. adv.; bk.rev.; bibl.; charts; illus. circ. 120,000. **Indexed:** C.I.S.Abstr. **Document type:** academic/scholarly publication.
     —CASDDS.

610.28   JA
JAPAN MEDICAL INSTRUMENT CATALOG. (Text in English and Spanish) 1957. irreg., latest 9th ed. $160. Japan Medical Products International Trade Association (JAMPITA), Ninjin Bldg., 7-1 Nihonbashi-Honcho 4-chome, Chuo-ku, Tokyo 103, Japan. TEL 81-3-3241-2106. FAX 81-3-3241-2109. Ed. Kuniichiro Ohno. **Document type:** catalog.
     Description: Introduces medical and dental devices in Japan.

610   JA   ISSN 0385-9215
JAPAN MEDICAL JOURNAL. (Text in Japanese) 1921. w. 30500 Yen. Nihon Iji Shimposha, 2-9 Kanda Surugadai, Chiyoda-ku, Tokyo 101, Japan. FAX 03-3292-1550. Ed. Shinji Umezawa. circ. 45,000. (back issues avail.)
     Description: Published mainly for family physicians.

610   JA   ISSN 0021-4515
JAPAN MEDICAL NEWS. (Text in English) 1959. bi-m. free. Japan Medical Products International Trade Association (JAMPITA), Ninjin Bldg., 7-1 Nihonbashi-Honcho 4-chome, Chuo-ku, Tokyo 103, Japan. TEL 81-3-3241-2106. FAX 81-3-3241-2109. Ed. Kuniichiro Ohno. adv.; bk.rev.; abstr.; charts; illus. circ. 2,500. (tabloid format) **Document type:** newspaper.
     —BLDSC (4648.360000).
     Description: Introduces medical products manufactured in Japan, including related information for both the industry and government administration.

610 658   US   ISSN 0914-0255
     CODEN: JMEREM
JAPAN MEDICAL REVIEW; a monthly report on the Japanese healthcare industry. 1986. m. 80000 Yen($450) Japan Publications, Inc., 41 Sutter St., Ste. 1112, San Francisco, CA 94104. TEL 415-772-5555. FAX 415-772-5659. Ed. S. Nakamura. s-a. index. (back issues avail.) **Document type:** newsletter.
     Description: Authoritative business report of the Japanese healthcare industry for international healthcare executives. Contains latest Ministry of Health regulations, policies, research and development licenses, manufacturer and distributor profiles, research and development breakthroughs, company profiles and competitive activity.

610 615.329   JA   ISSN 0368-2781
     CODEN: JJANAX
JAPANESE JOURNAL OF ANTIBIOTICS. (Text in Japanese; summaries in English) 1948. m. $130 (effective 1995). Japan Antibiotics Research Association - Nihon Koseibusshitsu Gakujutsu Kyogikai, 2-20-8 Kamiosaki, Shinagawa-ku, Tokyo 141, Japan. TEL 03-3491-0181. FAX 03-3491-0179. Ed. Kihachiro Shimizu. adv.; bibl.; charts; index. circ. 1,500. (also avail. in microform from UMI; back issues avail.; reprint service avail. from UMI) **Indexed:** Biotech.Abstr., Chem.Abstr., Curr.Chem.React., Curr.Cont., Dent.Ind., Excerp.Med., Ind.Chem., Ind.Med., Mass Spectr.Bull. **Document type:** academic/scholarly publication.
     —BLDSC (4650.845000); CASDDS; Genuine Article; UMI.
     Formerly: Journal of Antibiotics. Series B.

610   JA   ISSN 0047-1852
JAPANESE JOURNAL OF CLINICAL MEDICINE/NIPPON RINSHO. (Text in Japanese) 1943. m. 30000 Yen (effective 1995); newsstand price: 2500Yen. Nippon Rinsho Co., Inc., 2-3-8 Dosho-machi, Chuo-ku, Osaka 541, Japan. Ed. Tokio Jomei; Pub. Akio Nishimura. adv. contact: Uzo Koizumi. illus. circ. 8,000. **Indexed:** Curr.Cont., Ind.Med. **Document type:** academic/scholarly publication.
     —BLDSC (4651.375000); EMDOCS.

616.07   JA   ISSN 0047-1860
     CODEN: RBYOAI
JAPANESE JOURNAL OF CLINICAL PATHOLOGY/RINSHO BYORI. (Text in Japanese) 1953. m. $41.60. Japan Society of Clinical Pathology - Nippon Rinsho Byori Gakkai, c/o Rinsho Byori Kanko-kai, 18-8, Koishikawa 5-chome, Bunkyo-ku, Tokyo 112, Japan. Ed. Dr. Shiro Hino. adv.; bk.rev.; illus. circ. 6,000. **Indexed:** Chem.Abstr., Dent.Ind., Ind.Med., INIS Atomind.
     —BLDSC (4651.400000); CASDDS.

610 574   JA   ISSN 0021-5112
R97   CODEN: JJMCAQ
JAPANESE JOURNAL OF MEDICAL SCIENCE AND BIOLOGY. (Text in English) 1948. bi-m. $100. National Institute of Health, 23-1, Toyama 1-chome, Shinjuku-ku, Tokyo 162, Japan. Ed. Tatsuo Miyamura; Pub. Shudo Yamazaki. bk.rev.; charts; illus. circ. 1,100. (also avail. in microform from PMC) **Indexed:** Abstr.Hyg., Apic.Abstr., Biol.Abstr., Chem.Abstr., Curr.Cont., Dairy Sci.Abstr., Dent.Ind., Diar.Dis.Res., Excerp.Med., Helminthol.Abstr., Ind.Med., Ind.Sci.Rev., Ind.Vet., INIS Atomind., NRN, Nutr.Abstr., Protozool.Abstr., Sci.Cit.Ind., Trop.Dis.Bull., Vet.Bull. **Document type:** academic/scholarly publication.
     —BLDSC (4656.320000); CASDDS; EMDOCS; Faxon; Genuine Article; SWETS; UnCover.
     Description: Publishes full and short communications, reviews, epidemiological reports and reports dealing with fundamental aspects of medical science and biology.

JAPANESE JOURNAL OF PHYSIOLOGY. see *BIOLOGY — Physiology*

610 574   JA
JAPANESE MATRIX (COLLAGEN) CLUB. PROCEEDINGS OF THE ANNUAL MEETING. (Text in Japanese; summaries in English) 1959. a. 3000 Yen($15) Japanese Matrix (Collagen) Club, c/o Tokyo Medical and Dental University, Department of Tissue Physiology, Kanda Surugadai 2-3-10, Chiyoda-ku, Tokyo 101, Japan. TEL 81-3-5280-8056. FAX 81-3-5280-8055. Ed. Yutaka Nagai. adv. circ. 300. (back issues avail.) **Document type:** proceedings.
     Formerly: Japanese Collagen Club. Proceedings of the Annual Meeting.
     Description: Investigates the structure, function and metabolism of extracellular matrix macromolecules, especially collagen.

610   JA   ISSN 0536-3489
JAPANESE MEDICAL RESEARCHERS DIRECTORY. (Text in English and Japanese) 1959. a. 33000 Yen. Igaku-Shoin Ltd., 5-24-3 Hongo, Bunkyo-ku, Tokyo 113-91, Japan. TEL 03-3817-5721. Ed. Hiromasa Kita. circ. 4,000. **Indexed:** Biol.Abstr.

610   II   ISSN 0379-1653
JASLOK HOSPITAL & RESEARCH CENTRE. BULLETIN. (Text in English) 1976. q. Rs.25. Jaslok Hospital & Research Centre, 15 Dr. G. Deshmukh Marg, Bombay 400026, India. TEL 4933333. FAX 4950508. TELEX 011-75743-JASH-IN. Ed. S. Sadikot. adv.: B&W page Rs.6000; trim 21 x 15. bk.rev. circ. 1,500. **Document type:** bulletin.

610   II
JEEVAK. (Text in English, Hindi, and Sanskrit) q. Rs.41. Jeevak Anshathlya, Sahitya Marg, Barnalla, India. adv.; bk.rev.; abstr.; tr.lit.; index. circ. 1,500. (also avail. in record; microform)

610   US   ISSN 0021-5821
JEFFERSON MEDICAL COLLEGE ALUMNI BULLETIN. vol.19, 1970. q. free to alumni. Jefferson Medical College, Alumni Association - M 41, 1020 Locust St., Philadelphia, PA 19107-6799. TEL 215-298-7750. Ed. Mary B. Monteith. circ. 13,000. **Document type:** bulletin.

610   CC   ISSN 1001-7321
JIAMUSI YIXUEYUAN XUEBAO/JIAMUSI MEDICAL INSTITUTE. JOURNAL. (Text in Chinese) q. Jiamusi Yixueyuan, Xuebao Bianjibu, Jiamusi, Heilongjiang 154002, People's Republic of China. TEL 32949. Ed. Liu Fangzhen.

JIANGSU ZHONGYI/JIANGSU TRADITIONAL CHINESE MEDICINE. see *ALTERNATIVE MEDICINE*

JIANKANG BAO/HEALTH NEWS. see *PHYSICAL FITNESS AND HYGIENE*

610   CC   ISSN 1001-6325
JICHU YIXUE YU LINCHUANG/BASIC MEDICAL SCIENCE AND CLINICS. (Text in Chinese) 1990. bi-m. Zhongguo Yixue Kexueyuan, Jichu Yixue Yanjiusuo - Chinese Academy of Medical Sciences, Institute of Basic Medical Science, 5 Dongdan Santiao, Beijing 100730, People's Republic of China. TEL 5127733. Ed. Cheng Mengqin.

610   JA   ISSN 0021-6968
     CODEN: JMEJAS
JIKEIKAI MEDICAL JOURNAL. (Text in English) 1954. q. exchange basis. Jikei University School of Medicine - Tokyo Jikeikai Ika Daigaku, 3-25-8 Nishi Shinbashi, Minato-ku, Tokyo 105, Japan. Ed. Kenji Sakurai. charts; illus.; stat.; index. circ. 1,000. **Indexed:** Abstr.Hyg., Biol.Abstr., Chem.Abstr., Excerp.Med., INIS Atomind., Trop.Dis.Bull.
     —BLDSC (4669.000000); CASDDS; EMDOCS; Faxon; UnCover. **CCC.**

JILIN ZHONGYIYAO/JILIN TRADITIONAL CHINESE MEDICINE. see *ALTERNATIVE MEDICINE*

610 616.6   JA   ISSN 0385-2156
JIN TO TOSEKI/KIDNEY AND DIALYSIS. 1976. m. 35600 Yen($272) (effective 1994). Tokyo Igakusha Ltd., 35-4, Hongo 3-chome, Bunkyo-ku, Tokyo 113, Japan. Ed.Bd. circ. 6,000.
     —BLDSC (5094.210000).

JINAN DAXUE XUEBAO/JINAN UNIVERSITY. JOURNAL. see *SCIENCES: COMPREHENSIVE WORKS*

MEDICAL SCIENCES

610　　　　JA　　ISSN 0300-0818
　　　　　　　　CODEN: JNZKA7
JINKO ZOKI/JAPANESE JOURNAL OF ARTIFICIAL ORGANS. (Text in Japanese) 1964. bi-m. 1500 Yen per no. Nihon Jinko Zoki Gakkai - Japanese Society for Artificial Organs and Tissues, Nihon Gakkai Jimu Senta, 16-9, Honkomagome 5-chome, Bunkyo-ku, Tokyo 113, Japan. **Indexed:** Biol.Abstr., Excerp.Med., INIS Atomind.
—BLDSC (4650.920000); CASDDS.

610　　　　JO　　ISSN 0446-9283
　　　　　　　　CODEN: JOMJAE
JORDAN MEDICAL JOURNAL/AL-MAJALLAH AL-TIBBIYYAH AL-URDANIYYAH. (Text and summaries in Arabic and English) 1965. s-a. $20. Jordan Medical Association, P.O. Box 915, Amman, Jordan. (Co-sponsor: Royal Jordanian Medical Services) Ed. Mahmoud M. Abu-Khalaf. adv. circ. 4,000. **Indexed:** Abstr.Hyg., Biol.Abstr., Diar.Dis.Res., Excerp.Med., ExtraMED, Nutr.Abstr., Trop.Dis.Bull. **Document type:** academic/scholarly publication.
●Also available on CD-ROM.
—BLDSC (4673.670000).
　　Description: Contains original papers, reviews, case reports, and brief communications.

610　　　　BL　　ISSN 0047-2077
　　　　　　　　CODEN: JBRMAP
JORNAL BRASILEIRO DE MEDICINA. Cover title: J B M. (Text in Portuguese; summaries in English) 1959. m. Editora de Publicacoes Cientificas Ltda., Rua Major Suckow, 30 a 36, P.O. Box 20.911, Rio de Janeiro, RJ, Brazil. TEL 021-201-3722. FAX 021-261-3749. Ed. Ismar C. de Silveira. adv.; bk.rev.; abstr.; bibl.; charts; illus.; cum.index. circ. 30,000. **Indexed:** Biol.Abstr., Chem.Abstr.
—BLDSC (4663.438000).

610　　　　PO　　ISSN 0871-8822
　　　　　　　　CODEN: JCMEE
JORNAL DAS CIENCIAS MEDICAS. 1834. m. Esc.3500. (Sociedade das Ciencias Medicas de Lisboa) Edicoes Recipe, Calcada do Monte 23 r-c, 1100 Lisbon, Portugal. TEL 1-874847. **Indexed:** Excerp.Med.
—BLDSC (4674.685300).
　　Formerly (until 1988): Sociedade das Ciencias Medicas de Lisboa. Jornal.

610　　　　PO
JORNAL POLICLINICO. 11/yr. Rua Tristo Vaz 15-2o D., 1400 Lisbon, Portugal. TEL 3011989. FAX 3015539. Ed. Jose Reis, Jr. circ. 12,500.

610 640.73 336　　FR　　ISSN 0294-0736
JOURNAL D'ECONOMIE MEDICALE. (Text in French; summaries in English) 1982. 8/yr. 780 F. to individuals (foreign 941 F.); institutions 887 F. (foreign 1051 F.) (effective 1995). (Association Lyonnaise de Medecine Legale) Editions E S K A, 27 rue Dunois, 75013 Paris, France. TEL 44-06-80-42. FAX 44-24-06-94. Ed. Dr. C. Colin. adv.; bk.rev.; index. circ. 3,183. (back issues avail.) **Indexed:** Excerp.Med., World Bibl.Soc.Sec. **Document type:** academic/scholarly publication.
—BLDSC (4973.095500). **CCC.**
　　Formerly (until 1983): Bulletin d'Economie Medicale (ISSN 0769-9654)
　　Description: Provides a link among economists, physicians, and hospital managers by discussing issues of medical and economic importance, such as Social Security and other forms of public health care financing.

610　　　　FR　　ISSN 0021-7883
　　　　　　　　CODEN: JMLYA6
JOURNAL DE MEDECINE DE LYON;* organe de professeurs, agreges, medecins des hopitaux et medecins practiciens de Lyon. (Text in French; summaries in English) 1920. m. 95 F. 109-113 rue du 1er Mars 1943, 69100 Villeurbaine, France. TEL 7-2330499. Ed.Bd. adv.; bk.rev.; illus.; index. **Indexed:** Biol.Abstr., Chem.Abstr., Excerp.Med. (until 1993), Ind.Med., Nutr.Abstr.
—BLDSC (5017.015000); CASDDS.

610　　　　FR　　ISSN 0021-7905
　　　　　　　　CODEN: JMSTBR
JOURNAL DE MEDECINE DE STRASBOURG. 1970. 5/yr. 390 F. to individuals (foreign 555 F.); students 195 F. (foreign 330 F.). (Faculte de Medecine et de la Communaute Medicale d'Alsace et de Moselle) Expansion Scientifique, 31 bd. de la Tour Maubourg, 75007 Paris, France. TEL 40-62-64-00. FAX 45-55-69-20. Ed. Dr. Paul Rohmer. adv.; bk.rev. circ. 6,500. (also avail. in microform) **Indexed:** Biol.Abstr., Chem.Abstr., Curr.Cont., Excerp.Med., Helminthol.Abstr., Nutr.Abstr.
—BLDSC (5017.040000); CASDDS; EMDOCS. **CCC.**

618.92　　　　FR　　ISSN 0987-7983
JOURNAL DE PEDIATRIE ET DE PUERICULTURE. 1972; N.S. 1988. 8/yr. 495 F. in France; foreign 555 F.($108) (effective 1996). Editions Scientifiques Elsevier, 141 rue de Javel, 75747 Paris, France. TEL 33-1-45589063. (Subscr. in U.S. and Canada to: Elsevier Science Inc., Box 882, Madison Sq. Sta., New York, NY 10159-0882. TEL 212-989-5800. FAX 212-633-3990) Ed. C. Turberg Romain. (also avail. in microfilm from UMI) **Document type:** academic/scholarly publication.
—BLDSC (5030.310000).
　　Formerly (until 1988): Jonctions (ISSN 0300-0478)
　　Refereed Serial

610　　　　FR　　ISSN 0762-6398
JOURNAL DU JEUNE PRATICIEN. 42/yr. Editions Vaucouleurs, 20 rue Thiers, 92100 Boulogne, France. TEL 49-10-90-09. FAX 46-20-03-42. Ed. Dr. Armand Prudent. adv. contact: Soezic Mellet. circ. 22,000.

610　　　　US　　ISSN 1074-5807
R693
JOURNAL FOR MINORITY MEDICAL STUDENTS. 1972. q. $10. Spectrum Unlimited, 4203 Canal St., New Orleans, LA 70019. TEL 504-488-5100. FAX 504-488-7072. Ed. Laura Scholes; Pub. Bill Bowers. adv. contact: Bill Bowers. charts; illus.; stat. circ. 10,000. (back issues avail.) **Document type:** academic/scholarly publication.
　　Former titles (until 1993): Student National Medical Association. Journal (ISSN 1044-1654); (until 1989): Black Bag (ISSN 0196-1594)
　　Description: Discusses social legal, financial, and academic issues.

JOURNAL INTERNATIONAL DE BIOETHIQUE/INTERNATIONAL JOURNAL OF BIOETHICS. see *PHILOSOPHY*

610　　　　FR　　ISSN 0241-0109
JOURNAL INTERNATIONAL DE MEDECINE.* 1979. 28/yr. 180 F. Societe d'Edition et de Presse Internationale Medicale, 25 bis, av. Pierre-Grenier, 92100 Boulogne, France. TEL 49-10-06-06. Ed. J. Haroche. adv. circ. 35,000.
—BLDSC (5007.673800).

610　　　　US　　ISSN 1054-139X
RJ550　　　　　CODEN: JADHE5
JOURNAL OF ADOLESCENT HEALTH. 1980. m. $420 to institutions (effective 1996). (Society for Adolescent Medicine) Elsevier Science Inc., 655 Ave. of the Americas, New York, NY 10010. TEL 212-989-5800. FAX 212-633-3990. TELEX 420643 AEP UI. (Subscr. to: Box 882, Madison Sq. Sta., New York, NY 10159-0882) Ed. H. Verdain Barnes. (also avail. in microform from UMI) **Indexed:** Adol.Ment.Hlth.Abstr., ASSIA, Behav.Med.Abstr., Biol.Abstr., CINAHL, Curr.Cont., Curr.Lit.Fam.Plan., Energy Info.Abstr., Energy Info.Abstr., Excerp.Med., Ind.Med., NRN, Psychol.Abstr. (1980-), Risk Abstr., Soc.Sci.Ind., SSCI. **Document type:** academic/scholarly publication.
—BLDSC (4918.942800); Faxon; Genuine Article; SWETS; UnCover. **CCC.**
　　Formerly (until 1991): Journal of Adolescent Health Care (ISSN 0197-0070)
　　Refereed Serial

610　　　　US　　ISSN 0894-5888
　　　　　　　　CODEN: JAMEE7
JOURNAL OF ADVANCEMENT IN MEDICINE. 1988. q. $245 (foreign $285) (effective 1996). (American College of Advancement in Medicine) Human Sciences Press, Inc. (Subsidiary of: Plenum Publishing Corp.), 233 Spring St., New York, NY 10013-1578. TEL 212-620-8000. FAX 212-807-1047. TELEX 12-421139. Ed. Derrick Lonsdale. adv. contact: Robin Green. bk.rev. (reprint service avail. from UMI) **Document type:** academic/scholarly publication.
—BLDSC (4918.947950); UMI. **CCC.**
　　Description: Presents information about innovative, emerging, and nontraditional advances in preventive medicine, nutrition, risk factors, and modification of harmful life-style.
　　Refereed Serial

610　　　　UK
JOURNAL OF ADVANCES IN HEALTH CARE. 1992. q. Quay Publishing Ltd., Nereus House, New Quay Rd., Lancaster LA1 5SA, England. Eds. Annie Anderson, Linda McKie. **Document type:** trade publication.
　　Formerly (until 1993): Journal of Advances in Health and Nursing Care (ISSN 0960-9857)

JOURNAL OF AGROMEDICINE. see *OCCUPATIONAL HEALTH AND SAFETY*

610　　　　US　　ISSN 1055-324X
RA395.A3
JOURNAL OF AMERICAN HEALTH POLICY. 1991. bi-m. $129.95. Faulkner & Gray, Healthcare Information Center (Subsidiary of: Thomson Publishing Group), 1133 15th St., N.W., Ste. 450, Washington, DC 20005. TEL 202-828-4148. FAX 202-828-2352. Ed. Cathy Tokarski; Pub. Luci S. Koizumi. adv.
—BLDSC (4927.270000); UMI.
　　Description: Provides the latest information on all aspects of health policy developments and debate. Contains articles, analyses, investigative reports, interviews, and up-to-date data on federal, regional, and state health policy issues and trends.

612　　　　II　　ISSN 0970-1842
　　　　　　　　CODEN: JAS
JOURNAL OF ANATOMICAL SCIENCES. (Text in English) 1979. s-a. $60. Anatomical Society of India, Uttar Pradesh Chapter, c/o Dept. of Anatomy, G.S.V.M. Medical College, Kanpur 208 002, India. TEL 0512-214667. Ed. Vinod Kumar. circ. 500. **Indexed:** Excerp.Med. (1994-). **Document type:** academic/scholarly publication.

JOURNAL OF ANATOMY. see *BIOLOGY*

616.6　　　　US　　ISSN 0196-3635
QP253　　　　　CODEN: JOAND3
JOURNAL OF ANDROLOGY. 1980. bi-m. $237 (foreign $258) (effective 1996). American Society of Andrology, c/o Dept. of Urology Research, Guggenheim 1711, Mayo Clinic, 200 First St., S.W., Rochester, MN 55905. TEL 507-284-2421. FAX 507-284-2384. E-mail: ASA@Mayo.Edu. (Subscr. to: Journal of Andrology, c/o Allen Press, Inc., Box 1897, Lawrence, KS 66044-8897. TEL 913-843-1221) Eds. Drs. Donald Tindall, Ronald Lewis. adv.: B&W page $475; color page $755. illus.; index. circ. 1,300. (also avail. in microform from UMI) **Indexed:** Anim.Breed.Abstr., Biol.Abstr., Chem.Abstr., Curr.Adv.Cell & Devel.Biol., Curr.Cont., Excerp.Med., Ind.Med., Ind.Sci.Rev., Sci.Cit.Ind., SSCI. **Document type:** academic/scholarly publication.
—BLDSC (4935.340000); CASDDS; Faxon; Genuine Article; SWETS; UMI; UnCover. **CCC.**
　　Description: Publishes significant new findings of basic and clinical research on human and animal male reproductive tracts.
　　Refereed Serial

MEDICAL SCIENCES

615.329 JA ISSN 0021-8820
CODEN: JANTAJ
JOURNAL OF ANTIBIOTICS; an international journal devoted to research on bioactive microbial products. (Text in English) 1947. m. $300. Japan Antibiotics Research Association - Nihon Koseibusshitsu Gakujutsu Kyogikai, 2-20-8 Kamiosaki, Shinagawa-ku, Tokyo 141, Japan. TEL 03-3491-0181. FAX 03-3491-0179. Ed. Morimasa Yagisawa. adv.; bibl.; charts; index. circ. 2,000. (also avail. in microform from UMI,PMC; reprint service avail. from UMI) **Indexed:** Biol.Abstr., Biotech.Abstr., Chem.Abstr., Curr.Adv.Genetics & Molec.Biol., Curr.Biotech.Abstr., Curr.Cont., Excerp.Med., Helminthol.Abstr., Ind.Chem., Ind.Med., Ind.Sci.Rev., Rev.Med. & Vet.Mycol., Rev.Plant Path., Sci.Cit.Ind. **Document type:** academic/scholarly publication.
—BLDSC (4937.900000); CASDDS; EMDOCS; Faxon; Genuine Article; SWETS; UMI; UnCover.
Formerly: Journal of Antibiotics. Series A.

610 JA
JOURNAL OF APPLIED MEDICINE/OYO IGAKU. (Text in English, Japanese and European languages) 1960. q. membership. Society of Applied Medicine - Nihon Oyo Igakkai, 108 Shimogamo Miyazakai-cho, Sakyo-ku, Kyoto 606, Japan. abstr. **Indexed:** Chem.Abstr.

610 II ISSN 0377-0400
CODEN: JAMED6
JOURNAL OF APPLIED MEDICINE. (Text in English) 1975. m. Rs.144. Living Media India Pvt. Ltd., F-14/15 Connaught Place, New Delhi 110 001, India. TEL 3313076. FAX 91-11-3712998. TELEX 031-62634 INTO IN. Ed. G.S. Sainani. adv.; bk.rev.; bibl.; illus.
—CASDDS; Faxon.

JOURNAL OF APPLIED PHYSIOLOGY. see *BIOLOGY — Physiology*

610 375 UK ISSN 0140-511X
CODEN: JAUMD2
JOURNAL OF AUDIOVISUAL MEDIA IN MEDICINE. 1951. q. £125($199) (effective 1996). (Institute of Medical & Biological Illustration) Butterworth - Heinemann, Part of the Reed Elsevier group, Linacre House, Jordan Hill, Oxford OX2 8DP, England. TEL 01865-310366. FAX 01865-310898. TELEX 83111 BHPOXF G. (Subscr. to: Elsevier Science Ltd., P.O. Box 800, Kidlington, Oxford OX5 1DX, England. TEL 44-1865-843000. FAX 44-1865-843010; Subscr. in U.S. and Canada to: Elsevier Science, 660 White Plains Rd., Tarrytown, NY 10591-5153. TEL 914-524-9200. FAX 914-333-2444) Ed. K.P. Duguid. adv.; bk.rev.; film rev.; abstr.; charts; illus.; index. (also avail. in microform from UMI; reprint service avail.; back issues avail.) **Indexed:** Abstr.Hyg., Art & Archaeol.Tech.Abstr., Biol.Abstr., Chem.Abstr., Curr.Cont., Dent.Ind., Educ.Tech.Abstr., Geo.Abstr., Ind.Med., Ind.Vet., Res.High.Educ.Abstr., Sci.Cit.Ind., Trop.Dis.Bull., Vet.Bull. **Document type:** academic/scholarly publication.
—BLDSC (4949.350000); Faxon; SWETS; UMI. CCC.
Formerly: Medical and Biological Illustration (ISSN 0025-6978)
Description: Presents information and ideas on the development, implementation and use of audiovisual media for education, recording and research purposes in all areas of the health sciences.
Refereed Serial

174.2 220 US ISSN 1050-3404
JOURNAL OF BIBLICAL ETHICS IN MEDICINE. 1987. q. $18. Biblical Medical Ethics, Inc., Box 13231, Florence, SC 29504. TEL 803-665-6853. (And: 720 S. McQueen St., Florence, SC 29501) Ed. Hilton P. Terrel. bk.rev.; cum.index: 1987-1991. circ. 1,500. (back issues avail.; reprint service avail.) **Document type:** academic/scholarly publication.
Description: Focuses on medical-ethical issues from a conservative evangelical worldview.
Refereed Serial

610.78 US ISSN 0094-2499
R118
THE JOURNAL OF BIOCOMMUNICATION. 1974. 4/yr. $33 to individuals; institutions $40; students $27. Journal of Biocommunication, Inc., c/o Eastern Business Service, One Wedgewood Dr., Ste. 28, Jewett City, CT 06351. TEL 203-376-8150. FAX 203-376-6621. (Co-sponsors: Association of Biomedical Communications Directors; Association of Medical Illustrators; Health Sciences Communications Association) bk.rev.; film rev.; illus. circ. 2,000. (also avail. in microform from UMI; back issues avail.; reprint service avail. from UMI) **Indexed:** B.R.I., Biol.Abstr., C.I.J.E., Dent.Abstr., Hosp.Lit.Ind., Ind.Med., Mid.East: Abstr.& Ind.
—BLDSC (4952.300000); Faxon; UMI; UnCover.
Supersedes: Medical Art (ISSN 0076-5902); Which was formerly (1953-1964): Association of Medical Illustrators. Journal (ISSN 0098-8456); Graphics.

610.28 US ISSN 0148-0731
R856.A1 CODEN: JBENDY
JOURNAL OF BIOMECHANICAL ENGINEERING. 1977. q. $100 (members $29). American Society of Mechanical Engineers, 22 Law Dr., Fairfield, NJ 07007-2300. TEL 800-843-2763. Ed. R. Skalak. (also avail. in microform from UMI; reprint service avail. from UMI) **Indexed:** A.S.& T.Ind., Appl.Mech.Rev., Bioeng.Abstr., Biotech.Abstr., CAD CAM Abstr., Chem.Abstr., Chem.Eng.Abstr., Curr.Cont., Excerp.Med., Fluidex, Ind.Med., INSPEC, Sci.Cit.Ind., T.C.E.A. **Document type:** academic/scholarly publication.
—BLDSC (8896.700000); CASDDS; Ei; Faxon; Genuine Article; SWETS; UMI; UnCover. CCC.
Refereed Serial

610.28 UK ISSN 0021-9290
QP303 CODEN: JBMCBS
JOURNAL OF BIOMECHANICS. 1968. m. £775($1233) (effective 1996). (American Society of Biomechanics) Elsevier Science Ltd., Pergamon, P.O. Box 800, Kidlington, Oxford OX5 1DX, England. TEL 44-1865-843000. FAX 44-1865-843010. E-mail: nlinfo-f@elsevier.nl; usinfo-f@elsevier.com; forinfo-kyf04035@niftyserve.or.jp; Site addr.: http://www.elsevier.nl/. (Subscr. in U.S. and Canada to: Elsevier Science, 660 White Plains Rd., Tarrytown, NY 10591-5153. TEL 914-524-9200. FAX 914-333-2444) (Co-sponsor: European Society of Biomechanics) Eds. Richard A. Brand, Rik Huiskes. adv.; bk.rev.; charts; illus.; stat.; index. circ. 1,600. (also avail. in microfilm from UMI; back issues avail.; reprint service avail. from UMI) **Indexed:** Appl.Mech.Rev., Bioeng.Abstr., Biol.Abstr., Curr.Cont., Dent.Ind., Eng.Ind., Excerp.Med., Ind.Med., Ind.Sci.Rev., INIS Atomind., INSPEC, Int.Aerosp.Abstr., Sci.Cit.Ind. **Document type:** academic/scholarly publication.
—BLDSC (4953.600000); Ei; EMDOCS; Faxon; Genuine Article; SWETS; UMI; UnCover. CCC.
Description: Publishes original research concerning the application of mechanics to medical and biological problems.
Refereed Serial

JOURNAL OF BIOMEDICAL MATERIALS RESEARCH. see *BIOLOGY — Biotechnology*

610 574 SZ ISSN 1021-7770
CODEN: JBCIEA
▼**JOURNAL OF BIOMEDICAL SCIENCE.** (Text in English) 1994. 4/yr. 192 SFr.($147.50) to individuals; institutions 384 SFr.($295) (effective 1996). S. Karger AG, Allschwilerstr. 10, P.O. Box, CH-4009 Basel, Switzerland. TEL 061-3061111. FAX 061-3061234. E-mail: Karger@Karger.ch. Ed. C.C. Chang. (also avail. in microform from UMI) **Indexed:** Excerp.Med. (1995-). **Document type:** academic/scholarly publication.
—BLDSC (4953.769000); CASDDS.
Description: Provides a forum devoted to the promotion of basic medical science and its significance for human welfare.
Refereed Serial

JOURNAL OF BIOTECHNOLOGY IN HEALTHCARE. see *BIOLOGY — Biotechnology*

614.88 US ISSN 0273-8481
CODEN: JBCRD2
JOURNAL OF BURN CARE AND REHABILITATION. 1980. bi-m. $66 to individuals (Canada $85.60; elsewhere $80); institutions $103 (Canada $125.19; elsewhere $117); students, residents $29 (Canada $46.01; elsewhere $43) (effective 1996); newsstand price: 12. (American Burn Association) Mosby - Year Book, Inc. (Subsidiary of: Times Mirror Company), 11830 Westline Industrial Dr., St. Louis, MO 63146-3318. TEL 314-872-8370; 800-325-4177. FAX 314-432-1380. TELEX 44-2402. Ed. Dr. Charles R. Baxter. adv.; B&W page $1240, color page $2140; trim 8 1/4 x 11. bk.rev.; index. circ. 3,761. (also avail. in microform from UMI; back issues avail.) **Indexed:** Chem.Abstr., CINAHL, Excerp.Med.
—BLDSC (4954.640000); CASDDS; Faxon; SWETS; UMI; UnCover. CCC.
Refereed Serial

610 362 US ISSN 1061-3706
HV43 CODEN: JCMNEE
JOURNAL OF CASE MANAGEMENT. 1992. q. $39 to individuals (foreign $44); institutions $78 (foreign $87) (effective 1996). (Case Management Institute) Springer Publishing Company, 536 Broadway, New York, NY 10012-3955. TEL 212-431-4370. FAX 212-941-7842. Ed. Joan Quinn. bk.rev. **Indexed:** Excerp.Med. (1993-). **Document type:** trade publication, academic/scholarly publication.
—BLDSC (4954.885800).
Description: Serves as a key forum for professional discussion of the complex issues that have revolutionized the approach to community-based care in the U.S., providing both philosophical and practical perspectives.
Refereed Serial

JOURNAL OF CELLULAR PHYSIOLOGY. see *BIOLOGY — Physiology*

JOURNAL OF CHINESE MEDICINE. see *ALTERNATIVE MEDICINE*

610 US ISSN 1057-3321
▼**JOURNAL OF CHRONIC FATIGUE SYNDROME;** multidisciplinary innovations in research, theory & clinical practice. 1995. q. $75 (foreign $105) (effective 1996). Haworth Press, Inc., 10 Alice St., Binghamton, NY 13904. TEL 800-342-9678. FAX 607-722-1424. Eds. Nancy Klimas, Roberto Patarca; Pub. Bill Cohen. adv.; page $300. bk.rev. (also avail. in microfiche) **Indexed:** Abstr.Anthropol., Dent.Abstr., DNP, Human Resour.Abstr., IMFL, Past.Care & Couns.Abstr., Sociol.Abstr. **Document type:** academic/scholarly publication.
—BLDSC (4958.362000); Haworth.
Description: Covers all aspects of chronic fatigue syndromes and what are considered to be related immune deficiency disorders (CFIDS).
Refereed Serial

JOURNAL OF CLINICAL ENGINEERING. see *BIOLOGY — Bioengineering*

MEDICAL SCIENCES 4225

616.9 614.4 UK ISSN 0895-4356
RB156 CODEN: JCEPEE
JOURNAL OF CLINICAL EPIDEMIOLOGY; including pharmacoepidemiology reports; devoted to the problems and management of chronic illness in all age groups. 1955. m. $998 to institutions (effective 1996). Elsevier Science Ltd., Pergamon, P.O. Box 800, Kidlington, Oxford OX5 1DX, England. TEL 44-1865-843000. FAX 44-1865-843010. E-mail: nlinfo-f@elsevier.nl; usinfo-f@elsevier.com; forinfo-kyf04035@niftyserve.or.jp; Site addr/: http://www.elsevier.nl/. (Subscr. in U.S. and Canada to: Elsevier Science, 660 White Plains Rd., Tarrytown, NY 10591-5153. TEL 914-524-9200. FAX 914-333-2444) Eds. Alvan R. Feinstein, Walter O. Spitzer. adv.; bk.rev.; bibl.; charts; illus.; index. circ. 2,200. (also avail. in microfilm from UMI; reprint service avail. from UMI) **Indexed:** Abstr.Health Care Manage.Stud., Abstr.Hyg., Behav.Med.Abstr., Biol.Abstr., C.I.S. Abstr., Chem.Abstr., CINAHL, Curr.Cont., Dent.Ind., Diar.Dis.Res., Dok.Arbeitsmed., Excerp.Med., Helminthol.Abstr., Hosp.Lit.Ind., I.P.A., Ind.Med., Ind.Sci.Rev., INIS Atomind., Int.Nurs.Ind., Med.Care Rev., NRN, Nutr.Abstr., Psychol.Abstr., Risk Abstr., Sci.Cit.Ind., Trop.Dis.Bull. **Document type:** academic/scholarly publication.
●Also available online.
—BLDSC (4958.435000); CASDDS; Faxon; Genuine Article; SWETS; UMI; UnCover. **CCC**.
Formerly: Journal of Chronic Diseases (ISSN 0021-9681)
Refereed Serial

610 340 US ISSN 1046-7890
R724 CODEN: JCLEEG
JOURNAL OF CLINICAL ETHICS. 1990. q. $59 to individuals; institutions $115. The Journal of Clinical Ethics, Inc., 107 E. Church St., Frederick, MD 21701. TEL 301-694-8531. Ed. Dr. Edmund G. Howe; Pub. N. Quist. bk.rev. (also avail. in microfilm; back issues avail.; reprint service avail. from WSH) **Indexed:** Ind.Med. **Document type:** academic/scholarly publication.
—BLDSC (4958.440000); Genuine Article; SWETS; UnCover.
Description: Addresses the complex ethical, legal, and social issues in clinical medicine, biomedicine, ethics consultation, and direct patient care.
Refereed Serial

610 US ISSN 0021-9738
R11 CODEN: JCINAO
JOURNAL OF CLINICAL INVESTIGATION. 1924. m. $275 (effective 1994). (American Society for Clinical Investigation) Rockefeller University Press, 222 E. 70th St., New York, NY 10021. TEL 212-327-8572. FAX 212-327-7944. (Subscr. to: Box 5108, GPO, New York, NY 10087-5108) Ed. Ajit Varki. adv.; bibl.; charts; illus.; index. circ. 6,237. (also avail. in microform from UMI,PMC; reprint service avail. from ISI, UMI) **Indexed:** Abstr.Hyg., AIM, Biol.Abstr., Biotech.Abstr., C.I.S. Abstr., Chem.Abstr., Curr.Adv.Biochem., Curr.Adv.Cancer Res., Curr.Adv.Cell & Devel.Biol., Curr.Adv.Genetics & Molec.Biol., Curr.Cont., Dairy Sci.Abstr., Diab.Cont., Diar.Dis.Res., Excerp.Med., Food Sci.& Tech.Abstr., Helminthol.Abstr., Ind.Med., Ind.Sci.Rev., Ind.Vet., INIS Atomind., Kidney, Med.& Surg.Dermat., NRN, Nutr.Abstr., Protozool.Abstr., Rev.Med.& Vet.Mycol., Rev.Plant Path., Sci.Cit.Ind., Small Anim.Abstr., Soyabean Abstr., Trop.Dis.Bull., Vet.Bull. **Document type:** academic/scholarly publication.
●Also available online. Vendor(s): Ovid Technologies.
—BLDSC (4958.500000); CASDDS; EMDOCS; Faxon; Genuine Article; SWETS; UMI; UnCover. **CCC**.
Description: Provides a forum for research that links basic science to clinical practice. Includes brief summaries of emerging avenues of investigation.
Refereed Serial

616.07 US ISSN 0748-1977
CODEN: JCMOEH
JOURNAL OF CLINICAL MONITORING. 1985. bi-m. $150 for individuals (foreign $213); institutions $253 (foreign $323); resident $105 (foreign $130) (effective Oct. 1994). (Society for Technology in Anesthesia) Little, Brown and Company, Medical Journals, 34 Beacon St., Boston, MA 02108. TEL 617-859-5500. FAX 617-859-0629. Ed.Bd. adv.: B&W page $660; trim 8 1/8 x 10 7/8. bk.rev.; abstr.; charts; illus.; stat.; index. circ. 1,312. (also avail. in microform from UMI; back issues avail.; reprint service avail. from UMI) **Indexed:** Curr.Cont., Excerp.Med., Ind.Med.
—BLDSC (4958.572000); Ei; Faxon; Genuine Article; SWETS; UMI; UnCover. **CCC**.
Description: Contains original articles on the latest monitoring techniques, research findings, new developments, updates on monitoring equipment, analyses of monitoring procedures, case reports and clinical controversies.
Refereed Serial

616.07 UK ISSN 0021-9746
CODEN: JCPAAK
JOURNAL OF CLINICAL PATHOLOGY. (Bimonthly supplement avail.: Clinical - Molecular Pathology) 1947. m. £265($418) (Association of Clinical Pathologists) B M J Publishing Group, B.M.A. House, Tavistock Sq., London WC1H 9JR, England. TEL 0171-383-6270. FAX 0171-383-6402. (N. American subscr. to: Box 480, Franklin, MA 02038. TEL 800-2-FON-BMJ. FAX 800-2-FAX-BMJ) Ed. D. Lowe. adv. contact: Sheila Rowe. bk.rev.; abstr.; charts; illus.; index. (also avail. in microform from UMI; reprint service avail. from UMI) **Indexed:** Abstr.Hyg., AIM, Biol.Abstr., Biotech.Abstr., C.I.S. Abstr., Chem.Abstr., CINAHL, Curr.Adv.Biochem., Curr.Adv.Cancer Res., Curr.Adv.Genetics & Molec.Biol., Curr.Cont., Dent.Ind., Diar.Dis.Res., Dok.Arbeitsmed., Excerp.Med., Helminthol.Abstr., Ind.Med., Ind.Sci.Rev., INIS Atomind., Lab.Haz.Bull., Med.& Surg.Dermat., Nutr.Abstr., Protozool.Abstr., Rev.Med.& Vet.Mycol., Rev.Plant Path., Sci.Cit.Ind., Vet.Bull., W.R.C.Inf. **Document type:** academic/scholarly publication.
●Also available online. Vendor(s): Ovid Technologies.
—BLDSC (4958.650000); ADONIS; CASDDS; EMDOCS; Faxon; Genuine Article; SWETS; UMI; UnCover. **CCC**.
Description: Core publication for professionals in all disciplines of clinical pathology.
Refereed Serial

610 US ISSN 0898-7386
JOURNAL OF CLINICAL PRACTICE IN SEXUALITY. 1985. m. Gordon L. Deal, Inc., 3 Bunker Hill Run, E. Brunswick, NJ 08816. Ed. Dr. Alan J. Wabrek.
—BLDSC (4958.687000).

JOURNAL OF CLINICAL PSYCHOLOGY IN MEDICAL SETTINGS. see *PSYCHOLOGY*

610 614 US ISSN 0094-5145
RA421 CODEN: JCMHB
JOURNAL OF COMMUNITY HEALTH; the publication for health promotion and disease prevention. 1975. bi-m. $285 (foreign $335) (effective 1996). Human Sciences Press, Inc. (Subsidiary of: Plenum Publishing Corp.), 233 Spring St., New York, NY 10013-1578. TEL 212-620-8000. FAX 212-463-0742. TELEX 23-421139. Ed. Pascal J. Imperato. adv.; bk.rev.; index. (also avail. in microform from UMI; reprint service avail. from ISI,UMI) **Indexed:** Abstr.Crim.& Pen., Abstr.Health Care Manage.Stud., Abstr.Hyg., Acad.Ind., Adol.Ment.Hlth.Abstr., C.I.J.E., CINAHL, Community Ment.Health Rev., Except.Child.Educ.Abstr., Excerp.Med., FAMLI, Gen.Sci.Ind., Hlth.Ind., Hosp.Lit.Ind., Human Resour.Abstr., Ind.Med., INIS Atomind., Lang.& Lang.Behav.Abstr., Med.Care Rev., Nurs.Abstr., Nutr.Abstr., Saf.Sci.Abstr., Sage Urb.Stud.Abstr., Sel.Water Res.Abstr., Soc.Work Res.& Abstr., Sociol.Abstr., Trop.Dis.Bull. **Document type:** academic/scholarly publication.
—BLDSC (4961.720000); EMDOCS; Faxon; SWETS; UMI; UnCover. **CCC**.
Description: Covers new community health information, including the areas of preventive medicine, new forms of health manpower, analysis of environmental factors, delivery of health care services, and the study of health maintenance and health insurance programs.
Refereed Serial

610 340 US ISSN 0882-1046
K10 CODEN: JCLPEF
JOURNAL OF CONTEMPORARY HEALTH LAW AND POLICY. 1985. a. $15 (foreign $17). Catholic University of America, Columbus School of Law, Washington, DC 20064. TEL 202-319-5732. FAX 202-315-9313. Ed.Bd. (also avail. in microform from WSH; reprint service avail. from WSH) **Indexed:** C.L.I., Leg.Per. **Document type:** academic/scholarly publication.
—BLDSC (4965.228500); Faxon; UnCover.
Refereed Serial

610.07 CN ISSN 0894-1912
R845 CODEN: JCHPET
JOURNAL OF CONTINUING EDUCATION IN THE HEALTH PROFESSIONS. 1981. q. $42 to individuals (outside US & Canada $65); institutions $75 (outside US & Canada $95) (effective 1996). Decker Periodicals, P.O. Box 620, LCD 1, Hamilton, ON L8N 3K7, Canada. TEL 905-522-7017. FAX 905-522-7839. E-mail: decker@io.org. (U.S. addr.: Box 785, Lewiston, NY 14092-0785) (Co-sponsors: Alliance for Continuing Medical Education; Society of Medical College Directors of Continuing Medical Education) Ed. Dr. William C. Felch. adv.; bk.rev.; index; circ. 2,100 (paid). (also avail. in microfilm; back issues avail.) **Indexed:** Abstr.Health Care Manage.Stud., C.I.J.E., CINAHL, Curr.Cont. **Document type:** academic/scholarly publication.
—BLDSC (4965.245800); Faxon; UMI. **CCC**.
Formerly (until 1987): Mobius (ISSN 0272-3425)
Description: Covers development, conduct and evaluation of continuing health education programs.
Refereed Serial

610 US
JOURNAL OF CONTINUING MEDICAL EDUCATION INTERNATIONAL. 1975. q. $50. Association for International Medical Study, Inc., 1040 E. McDonald St., Lakeland, FL 33801. Ed. Dr. Ben H. McConnell. adv.; charts; illus.; stat. circ. 500,000.

610 US ISSN 1040-0257
JOURNAL OF CRITICAL ILLNESS. 1986. m. $70. Cliggott Publishing Co., 55 Holly Hill Lane, Box 4010, Greenwich, CT 06830. TEL 203-661-0600. Ed. Ellen M. Rosen; Pub. Dominic Baron. adv. contact: Orsa Britton. circ. 83,600. (reprint service avail.) **Document type:** academic/scholarly publication.
—BLDSC (4965.635000). **CCC**.
Description: Presents practical information on clinical management of critically ill patients. Includes original review articles and instructions on specific procedures used.
Refereed Serial

JOURNAL OF CYTOLOGY AND GENETICS. see *BIOLOGY — Genetics*

JOURNAL OF DEVELOPMENTAL PHYSIOLOGY. see *MEDICAL SCIENCES — Obstetrics And Gynecology*

JOURNAL OF ELECTRON MICROSCOPY. see *BIOLOGY — Microscopy*

MEDICAL SCIENCES

614.44 UK ISSN 0143-005X
CODEN: JECHDR
JOURNAL OF EPIDEMIOLOGY & COMMUNITY HEALTH.
1947. bi-m. £116($183) B M J Publishing Group, B.M.A. House, Tavistock Sq., London WC1H 9JR, England. TEL 0171-383-6270. FAX 0171-383-6402. (N. American subscr. to: Box 480, Franklin, MA 02038. TEL 800-2-FON-BMJ. FAX 800-2-FAX-BMJ) Ed. S. Donnan. adv. contact: Sheila Rowe. bk.rev.; bibl.; charts; illus.; index. (also avail. in microform from UMI; reprint service avail. from UMI) **Indexed:** Abstr.Hyg., Behav.Med.Abstr., Bibl.Dev.Med.& Child Neur., Biol.Abstr., Biostat., C.I.S. Abstr., Chem.Abstr., Curr.Adv.Cancer Res., Curr.Lit.Fam.Plan., Dairy Sci.Abstr., Dent.Ind., Dok.Arbeitsmed., Excerp.Med., Geo.Abstr., Helminthol.Abstr., Hosp.Lit.Ind., IDA, Ind.Med., Ind.Sci.Rev., INIS Atomind., Lab.Haz.Bull., Nutr.Abstr., Psychol.Abstr. (1972-), Risk Abstr., Sci.Cit.Ind., SSCI, Stud.Wom.Abstr., Trop.Dis.Bull. **Document type:** academic/scholarly publication.
—BLDSC (4979.475000); Faxon; Genuine Article; SWETS; UMI; UnCover. **CCC.**
Former titles (in 1979): Epidemiology and Community Health (ISSN 0142-467X); (in 1978): Journal of Epidemiology and Community Medicine (ISSN 0141-7681); (until Dec. 1977): British Journal of Preventive and Social Medicine (ISSN 0007-1242)
Description: Presents original work in the field of epidemiology and community health that relates to a total defined population, numerically rated.
Refereed Serial

610 UK ISSN 1356-1294
▼**JOURNAL OF EVALUATION IN CLINICAL PRACTICE.**
1995. q. £143 in Europe; elsewhere £157($253) (effective 1996). Blackwell Science Ltd., Osney Mead, Oxford OX2 0EL, England. TEL 44-1865-206206. FAX 44-1865-206219. Ed. Andrew Miles. (back issues avail.) **Document type:** academic/scholarly publication.

JOURNAL OF EXPOSURE ANALYSIS AND ENVIRONMENTAL EPIDEMIOLOGY. see *ENVIRONMENTAL STUDIES*

610 US ISSN 0022-1058
QP110.A7 CODEN: JEXCBD
JOURNAL OF EXTRA-CORPOREAL TECHNOLOGY. 1968. q. $40 (foreign $55). American Society of Extra-Corporeal Technology, Inc., 11480 Sunset Hills Rd., Ste. 210E, Reston, VA 22090. TEL 703-435-8556. FAX 703-435-0056. Ed. Phyllis Palmer Stark. bk.rev. circ. 2,800. (back issues avail.) **Indexed:** CINAHL, Excerp.Med.
Document type: trade publication.
—BLDSC (4983.300000); EMDOCS; Faxon; SWETS; UnCover.

610 US ISSN 0094-3509
R11
JOURNAL OF FAMILY PRACTICE. 1974. m. $80 to individuals (foreign $100); institutions $135 foreign $175); students $65 (foreign $80). Appleton & Lange, Journal Division (Subsidiary of: Simon & Schuster Company), 25 Van Zant St., Box 5630, Norwalk, CT 06855. TEL 203-838-4400. (Subscr. to: Appleton & Lange, Box 118, Pearle River, NY 10965-9850) Ed. Dr. Paul M. Fischer. adv.: B&W $3574; adv. contact: Nancy Graves. bk.rev.; charts; illus.; stat.; s-a. index. circ. 76,000. (also avail. in microform from UMI; back issues avail.; reprint service avail.) **Indexed:** Abstr.Health Care Manage.Stud., Adol.Ment.Hlth.Abstr., AIM, Biol.Abstr., CINAHL, Curr.Adv.Cancer Res., Curr.Cont., Dent.Ind., Dok.Arbeitsmed., Excerp.Med., FAMLI, Helminthol.Abstr., HRIS, I.P.A., Ind.Med., Ind.Sci.Rev., Ind.Vet., INIS Atomind., Med.Care Rev., Nutr.Abstr., Psychol.Abstr. (1974-), Sci.Cit.Ind., Small Anim.Abstr. **Document type:** academic/scholarly publication.
●Also available online.
—BLDSC (4983.730000); EMDOCS; Faxon; Genuine Article; SWETS; UMI; UnCover. **CCC.**
Description: Contains original research articles, clinical reviews, case reports, editorials, and technology reviews that have clinical applications in family medicine.
Refereed Serial

614 US
▼**JOURNAL OF GENDER, CULTURE AND HEALTH.**
Announced for publication in 1996. q. $110 (foreign $130) (effective 1996). Plenum Publishing Corp., 233 Spring St., New York, NY 10013-1578. TEL 212-620-8000. FAX 212-463-0742. TELEX 23-421139. **Document type:** academic/scholarly publication.
Refereed Serial

610 II ISSN 0970-566X
JOURNAL OF GENERAL MEDICINE; a quarterly for the family physician. (Supplement avail.: The Indian Practitioner) 1988. q. Rs.120($35) Indian Practitioner Group, 101, Lawrence Apartments-2, 1st Fl., Vidyanagari Marg, Opp. Lakhbir Petrol Pump, Kalina, Santa Cruz (E), Bombay 400 098, India. TEL 273809. Ed. Joan Godinho. adv.; abstr.; bibl.; charts; illus.; stat. circ. 33,413. (reprint service avail. from IRC)
—BLDSC (4987.950000).

JOURNAL OF GENERAL PHYSIOLOGY. see *BIOLOGY — Physiology*

JOURNAL OF HEALTH & HEALING. see *PHYSICAL FITNESS AND HYGIENE*

610 340 US ISSN 1046-4360
KF3825.A59
JOURNAL OF HEALTH AND HOSPITAL LAW. bi-m. $135. American Academy of Hospital Attorneys, One North Franklin, Chicago, IL 60606. TEL 312-422-3700. FAX 312-422-4574. (Subscr. to: DePaul University College of Law, 25 E. Jackson Blvd., Chicago, IL 60604-2287. TEL 312-362-5634) index. circ. 3,000. (back issues avail.)
Formerly: Hospital Law.
Description: News for physicians, attorneys, hospitals on long and short-term care facilities and current court decisions.

610 362.5 US ISSN 1049-2089
RA418.5.P6 CODEN: JHCUEK
JOURNAL OF HEALTH CARE FOR THE POOR AND UNDERSERVED. 1990. q. $47 to individuals; institutions $99 (effective Sep. 1995). (Meharry Medical College, Institute on Health Care for the Poor and Underserved) Sage Publications, Inc., 2455 Teller Rd., Thousand Oaks, CA 91320. (Subscr. to: Sage Publications, Inc., Box 5084, Thousand Oaks, CA 91359; Overseas subscr. to: Sage Publications Ltd., 6 Bonhill St., London EC2A 4PU, England; Sage Publications India Pvt. Ltd., Box 5215, New Delhi 110 048, India) Ed. Kirk A. Johnson. bk.rev.; illus.; illus. circ. 2,000. (also avail. in microfiche from UMI; back issues avail.; reprint service avail.) **Indexed:** CINAHL, Hosp.Lit.Ind., Ind.Med., Past.Care & Couns.Abstr., Psychol.Abstr. (1990-), Soc.Work Res.& Abstr., Sociol.Abstr. **Document type:** academic/scholarly publication.
—BLDSC (4996.739000); UMI; UnCover. **CCC.**
Description: Focuses on the health of underserved communities. Explores health problems of the poor, elderly, rural and inner-city residents, and the uninsured and underinsured. Also addresses issues on accessibility and quality of health care among this population.
Refereed Serial

320 340 US ISSN 0361-6878
RA395.A3 CODEN: JHPLDN
JOURNAL OF HEALTH POLITICS, POLICY AND LAW.
1976. q. $48 to individuals (foreign $60); institutions $105 (foreign $117) (effective 1996). (Duke University, Department of Health Administration) Duke University Press, Box 90660, Durham, NC 27708-0660. TEL 919-687-3600. FAX 919-687-4574. Ed. Mark A. Peterson. adv.; bk.rev. circ. 2,400. (also avail. in microfilm from UMI,WSH,PMC; microfiche from WSH; back issues avail.; reprint service avail. from WSH) **Indexed:** ABI Inform., Abstr.Bk.Rev.Curr.Leg.Per., Abstr.Health Care Manage.Stud., Abstr.Hyg., Adol.Ment.Hlth.Abstr., Biol.Abstr., C.L.I., CINAHL, Curr.Cont., Dent.Ind., Excerp.Med., Fut.Surv., Hlth.Ind., Hosp.Abstr., Hosp.Lit.Ind., Ind.Med., Int.Polit.Sci.Abstr., L.R.I., Lang.& Lang.Behav.Abstr., Leg.Per., Med.Care Rev., P.A.I.S., Polit.Sci.Abstr., PSI, Risk Abstr., Sage Pub.Admin.Abstr., Sociol.Abstr., SSCI, Trop.Dis.Bull. **Document type:** academic/scholarly publication.
—BLDSC (4996.870000); Faxon; Genuine Article; SWETS; UMI; UnCover. **CCC.**
Refereed Serial

JOURNAL OF HEALTH PSYCHOLOGY; an interdisciplinary, international journal. see *PSYCHOLOGY*

JOURNAL OF HERBS, SPICES & MEDICINAL PLANTS. see *GARDENING AND HORTICULTURE*

JOURNAL OF HUMAN ERGOLOGY. see *BUSINESS AND ECONOMICS — Labor And Industrial Relations*

JOURNAL OF HUMAN MOVEMENT STUDIES. see *PSYCHOLOGY*

JOURNAL OF INSURANCE MEDICINE. see *INSURANCE*

610 US ISSN 0885-0666
JOURNAL OF INTENSIVE CARE MEDICINE. 1986. bi-m. $155 (foreign $185) (effective 1996). Blackwell Science Inc., 238 Main St., Cambridge, MA 02142-1413. TEL 617-876-7022. FAX 617-492-5263. Eds. Drs. Richard S. Irwin, James M. Rippe. bk.rev.; charts; illus.; index. circ. 1,300. (back issues avail.) **Document type:** academic/scholarly publication.
—BLDSC (5007.539000); SWETS; UMI; UnCover. **CCC.**
Refereed Serial

610 UK ISSN 0300-0605
CODEN: JIMRBV
JOURNAL OF INTERNATIONAL MEDICAL RESEARCH.
(Supplements avail.) 1972. bi-m. £60 (overseas $110). Cambridge Medical Publications Ltd., Wicker House, High St., Worthing, W. Sussex BN11 1DJ, England. TEL 01903-205884. FAX 01903-234862. TELEX 878372 PPSLTD G. Ed.Bd. bk.rev. circ. 2,500. (also avail. in microfiche from UMI) **Indexed:** Abstr.Hyg., Biol.Abstr., Biotech.Abstr., Chem.Abstr., Curr.Adv.Ecol.Sci., Curr.Cont., Dent.Ind., Diar.Dis.Res, Excerp.Med., Helminthol.Abstr., HRIS, Ind.Med., Int.Sci.Rev., Nutr.Abstr., Rev.Plant Path., Sci.Cit.Ind., Trop.Dis.Bull. **Document type:** academic/scholarly publication.
—BLDSC (5007.674000); CASDDS; Faxon; Genuine Article; SWETS; UMI; UnCover. **CCC.**
Description: Presents original papers and reviews in clinical and medical research. Topics include animal and clinical pharmacology, pharmacokinetics and drug metabolism, toxicology, teratology, and clinical trials.
Refereed Serial

613 UK
JOURNAL OF INTERPROFESSIONAL CARE. 1984. 3/yr. £44 to individuals; institutions £148 (effective 1996). (British Holistic Medical Association) Carfax Publishing Co., P.O. Box 25, Abingdon, Oxon. OX14 3UE, England. TEL 01235-555335. FAX 01235-553559. (Subscr. in N. America to: Carfax Publishing Co., 875-81 Massachusetts Ave., Cambridge, MA 02139) (Co-sponsor: Marylebone Centre Trust) Ed. Dr. Patrick Pietroni. **Indexed:** Curr.Adv.Ecol.Sci., Curr.Cont., Excerp.Med. **Document type:** academic/scholarly publication.
—UMI. **CCC.**
Former titles (until 1990): Holistic Medicine (ISSN 0884-3988); (until 1984): British Journal of Holistic Medicine (ISSN 0266-1330)
Description: Covers issues in personal care within the community, in primary health, hospital and other institutional settings.
Refereed Serial

610 II ISSN 0022-2054
JOURNAL OF J.J. GROUP OF HOSPITALS AND GRANT MEDICAL COLLEGE. (Text in English) 1956. a. Rs.40. Research Society, Grant Medical College and J.J. Group of Hospitals, 2nd Fl., Front Wing, Skin & S.T.D. Bldg., J.J. Hospital Campus, Byculla, Bombay 400 008, India. TEL 22-376-7949. Ed. Dr. H.B. Chandalia. adv.; bk.rev.; abstr.; bibl.; charts; illus.; index. circ. 600. **Indexed:** Chem.Abstr., Ind.Med., Nutr.Abstr.

JOURNAL OF LAW AND HEALTH. see *LAW*

JOURNAL OF LAW & MEDICINE. see *LAW*

THE JOURNAL OF LAW, MEDICINE & ETHICS. see *LAW*

JOURNAL OF LEARNING DISABILITIES. see *EDUCATION — Special Education And Rehabilitation*

MEDICAL SCIENCES 4227

610 340   US   ISSN 0194-7648
K10
THE JOURNAL OF LEGAL MEDICINE. 1979. q. £88($145) (effective 1996). (American College of Legal Medicine) Taylor & Francis Inc., 1900 Frost Rd., Ste. 101, Bristol, PA 19007-1598. TEL 215-785-5800; 800-821-8312. FAX 215-785-5515. (Subscr. to: Taylor & Francis Ltd., Rankine Rd., Basingstoke, Hants. RG24 8PR, England. TEL 44-1256-840366. FAX 44-1256-479438) Ed. Theodore R. Leblang. bk.rev. (also avail. in microform from UMI,WSH; back issues avail.; reprint service avail. from WSH) **Indexed:** Abstr.Bk.Rev.Curr.Leg.Per., C.L.I., Excerp.Med., Hlth.Ind., Ind.Med., L.R.I., Leg.Cont., Leg.Per., Psychol.Abstr. (1991-), Risk Abstr., SSCI. **Document type:** academic/scholarly publication.
—BLDSC (5010.270300); ADONIS; Faxon; Genuine Article; SWETS; UnCover. **CCC.**
Description: Publishes articles, comments, and essays on topics of interest in legal medicine: health law and policy, professional liability, hospital law, food and drug law, medicolegal research and education, and the history of legal medicine.
Refereed Serial

616.026   US   ISSN 0741-5400
QP185   CODEN: JLBIE7
JOURNAL OF LEUKOCYTE BIOLOGY. 1967. m. (2 vols./yr.) to individuals (N. America $125; elsewhere $153); institutions $696 (N. America $716; elsewhere $744); members $80 (outside N. America $125). (Society for Leukocyte Biology) Federation of American Societies for Experimental Biology, 9650 Rockville Pike, Bethesda, MD 20814. TEL 301-530-7000. FAX 301-571-1855. Ed. Carleton C. Stewart. adv.; charts; illus.; index. (back issues avail.) **Indexed:** ASCA, Biol.Abstr., Chem.Abstr., Curr.Adv.Cancer Res., Curr.Adv.Cell & Devel.Biol., Curr.Adv.Ecol.Sci., Curr.Cont., Dairy Sci.Abstr., Dent.Ind., Excerp.Med., Ind.Med., Ind.Sci.Rev., Ind.Vet., INIS Atomind., Int.Aerosp.Abstr., Pig News & Info., Rev.Med.& Vet.Mycol., Sci.Cit.Ind, Small Anim.Abstr., Vet.Bull. **Document type:** academic/scholarly publication.
●Also available online.
—BLDSC (5010.305000); CASDDS; Faxon; Genuine Article; SWETS; UnCover. **CCC.**
Formerly (until 1984): R E S. Reticuloendothelial Society. Journal (ISSN 0033-6890)
Description: Presents manuscripts of original investigations on the origins, developmental biology, and functions of granulocytes, lymphocytes, and monuclear phagocytes.

JOURNAL OF LIPID MEDIATORS AND CELL SIGNALING. see *BIOLOGY — Biological Chemistry*

658 610   US   ISSN 1050-6934
   CODEN: JLEIEM
JOURNAL OF LONG-TERM EFFECTS OF MEDICAL IMPLANTS. q. $84 to individuals; institutions $229 (effective 1996). Begell House Inc., 79 Madison Ave., Ste. 1201, New York, NY 10016-7892. TEL 212-725-1999. FAX 212-213-8368. E-mail: 74353.2052@compuserve.com. Ed. Stephen D. Bruck. **Indexed:** Excerp.Med. (1993-). **Document type:** academic/scholarly publication.
—BLDSC (5010.560500); CASDDS; Ei; Faxon; Genuine Article. **CCC.**
Description: Aims to better understand the mechanism of failure of pre-clinically tested medical implants during long-term in vivo service life both in appropriate animal models and in humans, and establishing an effective linkage between pre-clinical and clinical studies.

610   UK   ISSN 0268-9235
JOURNAL OF MANAGEMENT IN MEDICINE. 1986. 6/yr. £459($749) (effective 1996). M C B University Press Ltd., 60-62 Toller Ln., Bradford, W. Yorks BD8 9BY, England. TEL 01274-499821. FAX 01274-547143. TELEX 51317-MCBUNI-G. Ed. Dr. Frada Eskin. adv.; bk.rev. (reprint service avail. from SWZ) **Indexed:** Diar.Dis.Res. **Document type:** academic/scholarly publication.
—BLDSC (5011.370000); SWETS; UMI.

JOURNAL OF MATERIALS SCIENCE: MATERIALS IN MEDICINE. see *ENGINEERING — Engineering Mechanics And Materials*

JOURNAL OF MEDICAL AND PHARMACEUTICAL MARKETING. see *BUSINESS AND ECONOMICS — Marketing And Purchasing*

JOURNAL OF MEDICAL BIOGRAPHY. see *BIOGRAPHY*

610.28   UK   ISSN 0309-1902
R856.A1   CODEN: JMTEDN
JOURNAL OF MEDICAL ENGINEERING & TECHNOLOGY. 1965. bi-m. £130($215) (effective 1996). Taylor & Francis Ltd., Rankine Rd., Basingstoke, Hants. RG24 8PR, England. TEL 44-1256-840366. FAX 44-1256-479438. TELEX 858540. E-mail: info@tandf.co.uk. (Subscr. in N. America to: Taylor & Francis Inc., 1900 Frost Rd., Ste. 101, Bristol, PA 19007-1598. TEL 800-821-8312. FAX 215-785-5515) Ed. R.E. Trotman. adv.; bk.rev.; abstr.; illus.; pat.; tr.lit.; tr.mkt.; index. **Indexed:** Agri.Eng.Abstr., Appl.Mech.Rev., Biol.Abstr., Br.Tech.Ind., Chem.Abstr., Curr.Adv.Ecol.Sci., Curr.Cont., Eng.Ind., Ergon.Abstr., Excerp.Med., Ind.Med., Ind.Sci.Rev., Ind.Vet., INSPEC, Vet.Bull. **Document type:** academic/scholarly publication.
—BLDSC (5017.057000); ADONIS; Ei; Faxon; Genuine Article; SWETS; UnCover. **CCC.**
Formerly: Biomedical Engineering (ISSN 0006-2898)
Description: Provides information on the application of engineering and technology in medical research and clinical medicine. Articles from around the world cover treatment techniques, instrument design and development, and evaluation of equipment.
Refereed Serial

610 174.2   UK   ISSN 0306-6800
   CODEN: JMETDR
JOURNAL OF MEDICAL ETHICS. 1975. bi-m. £100($158) (Institute of Medical Ethics) B M J Publishing Group, B.M.A. House, Tavistock Sq., London WC1H 9JR, England. TEL 0171-383-6270. FAX 0171-383-6402. (N.American subscr. to: Box 480, Franklin, MA 02038. TEL 800-2-FON-BMJ. FAX 800-2-FAX-BMJ) Ed. R. Gillon. bk.rev.; index. **Indexed:** Biol.Abstr., CERDIC, CINAHL, Curr.Adv.Ecol.Sci., Curr.Cont., Excerp.Med., Ind.Med., Phil.Ind., SSCI. **Document type:** academic/scholarly publication.
●Also available online. Vendor(s): University Microfilms International.
—BLDSC (5017.062000); Faxon; Genuine Article; SWETS.
Description: Presents interdisciplinary articles on ethical aspects of health care.
Refereed Serial

JOURNAL OF MEDICAL GENETICS. see *BIOLOGY — Genetics*

100 174   US   ISSN 1041-3545
R724   CODEN: JMHBEN
JOURNAL OF MEDICAL HUMANITIES. 1976. q. $195 (foreign $230) (effective 1996). Human Sciences Press, Inc. (Subsidiary of: Plenum Publishing Corp.), 233 Spring St., New York, NY 10013-1578. TEL 212-620-8000. FAX 212-463-0742. TELEX 23-421139. Ed. Charles Perakis. adv. circ. 400. (also avail. in microform from UMI; reprint service avail. from ISI,UMI) **Indexed:** Curr.Adv.Ecol.Sci., Phil.Ind., Psychol.Abstr. **Document type:** academic/scholarly publication.
—BLDSC (5017.070500); Faxon; UMI; UnCover. **CCC.**
Former titles (until 1991): Journal of Medical Humanities and Bioethics (ISSN 0882-6498); (until vol.6, 1985): Journal of Bioethics (ISSN 0278-9523); (until 1982): Bioethics Quarterly (ISSN 0163-9803); Bioethics Northwest (ISSN 0362-0824)
Description: Highlights the relationship between medicine and art, ethics, history, literature, philosophy, sociology, economics, and jurisprudence.
Refereed Serial

616.01   UK   ISSN 0022-2615
QR46   CODEN: JMMIAV
JOURNAL OF MEDICAL MICROBIOLOGY. 1968. m. £269($458) to institutions (effective 1995). (Pathological Society of Great Britain and Ireland) Churchill Livingstone Journals (Subsidiary of: Pearson Professional), Robert Stevenson House, 1-3 Baxter's Pl., Leith Walk, Edinburgh EH1 3AF, Scotland. TEL 0131-556-2424. FAX 0131-459-1177. (Subscr. to: Pearson Professional Ltd., P.O. Box 77, Fourth Ave., Harlow, Essex CM19 5AA, England. TEL 01279-623760; U.S. subscr. to: Churchill Livingstone, 650 Ave. of the Americas, New York, NY 10011. TEL 212-206-5000) Ed. B.I. Duerden. adv. contact: David Dunnachie. bk.rev.; illus.; index. circ. 1,400. (also avail. in microform from UMI; back issues avail.) **Indexed:** Abstr.Hyg., Biol.Abstr., Biotech.Abstr., Chem.Abstr., Curr.Adv.Ecol.Sci., Curr.Adv.Genetics & Molec.Biol., Curr.Cont., Dairy Sci.Abstr., Diar.Dis.Res., Excerp.Med., Helminthol.Abstr., Ind.Med., Ind.Sci.Rev., Ind.Vet., INIS Atomind., Nutr.Abstr., Pig News & Info., Poult.Abstr., Protozool.Abstr., Rev.Med.& Vet.Mycol., Rev.Plant Path., Vet.Bull. **Document type:** academic/scholarly publication.
—BLDSC (5017.079000); ADONIS; CASDDS; EMDOCS; Faxon; Genuine Article; SWETS; UnCover. **CCC.**

610   US   ISSN 8755-0229
JOURNAL OF MEDICAL PRACTICE MANAGEMENT. 1985. q. $99 to individuals; institutions $110 (effective 1995). Williams & Wilkins, 428 E. Preston St., Baltimore, MD 21202. TEL 410-528-4000; 800-638-6423. FAX 410-528-4312. Ed. Dr. Marcel Frenkel. circ. 2,500. (also avail. in microform from WWS) **Document type:** academic/scholarly publication.
—BLDSC (5017.081500). **CCC.**
Description: Offers perspectives on legislation, litigation, office management and other issues that affect the medical practice of office-based physicians and health care professionals.

616.01   US   ISSN 0146-6615
RC114.5   CODEN: JMVIDB
JOURNAL OF MEDICAL VIROLOGY. 1977. m. $1488 (foreign $1674) (effective 1996). John Wiley & Sons, Inc., Journals, 605 Third Ave., New York, NY 10158. TEL 212-850-6645. FAX 212-850-6021. TELEX 12-7063. E-mail: SUBINFO@JWILEY.COM. (Subscr. outside the Americas to: John Wiley & Sons Ld., Baffins Ln., Chichester, W. Sussex PO19 1UD, England. TEL 44-1243-779777. FAX 44-1243-776128) Ed. Arie J. Zuckerman. charts; illus. (back issues avail.; reprint service avail. from ISI) **Indexed:** Abstr.Hyg., Biol.Abstr., Chem.Abstr., Curr.Adv.Ecol.Sci., Curr.Adv.Genetics & Molec.Biol., Curr.Cont., Dairy Sci.Abstr., Dent.Ind., Excerp.Med., Ind.Med., Ind.Sci.Rev., Ind.Vet., INIS Atomind., Med.& Surg.Dermat., Sci.Cit.Ind., Trop.Dis.Bull., Vet.Bull. **Document type:** academic/scholarly publication.
●Also available online.
—BLDSC (5017.095000); ADONIS; CASDDS; Faxon; Genuine Article; SWETS; UnCover. **CCC.**
Description: Covers the structure and composition of viruses, epidemiology, humoral and cell-mediated immune responses, and clinical features of infection.
Refereed Serial

610   US   ISSN 0025-7850
R11   CODEN: JNMDBO
JOURNAL OF MEDICINE; clinical, experimental, molecular. 1970. bi-m. $140 (foreign $175). P J D Publications Ltd., Box 966, Westbury, NY 11590. TEL 516-626-0650. FAX 516-626-5546. Ed. Dr. Julian L. Ambrus; Pub. Barbara Sankar. adv.; bk.rev.; charts; illus.; stat.; index. (reprint service avail.) **Indexed:** Biol.Abstr., Biotech.Abstr., C.I.S. Abstr., Chem.Abstr., CINAHL, Curr.Adv.Ecol.Sci., Curr.Cont., Curr.Lit.Fam.Plan., Excerp.Med., Helminthol.Abstr., Ind.Med., INIS Atomind., L.R.I., Nutr.Abstr., Rev.Med.& Vet.Mycol., Sci.Cit.Ind. **Document type:** academic/scholarly publication.
—BLDSC (5017.300000); CASDDS; EMDOCS; Faxon; Genuine Article; SWETS; UnCover. **CCC.**
Description: Articles on all areas of medicine and medical science.
Refereed Serial

MEDICAL SCIENCES

610 174.24   NE   ISSN 0360-5310
R723   CODEN: JMPHDC
THE JOURNAL OF MEDICINE AND PHILOSOPHY; a forum for bioethics and philosophy of medicine. (Text in English) 1976. bi-m. fl.427 to institutions; $247 to institutions in U.S. (effective 1996). (Baylor College of Medicine, Center for Ethics, Medicine, and Public Issues, US) Kluwer Academic Publishers, Postbus 17, 3300 AA Dordrecht, Netherlands. TEL 31-78-392392. FAX 31-78-392254. TELEX 29245 KAPG NL. E-mail: SERVICES@WKAP.NL. (Dist. by: Kluwer Academic Publishers Group, P.O. Box 322, 3300 AH Dordrecht, Netherlands. TEL 31-78-392392. FAX 31-78-546474; N. America dist. addr.: Box 358, Accord Sta., Hingham, MA 02018-0358. TEL 617-871-6600. FAX 617-871-6528) (Co-sponsors: Society for Health and Human Values, US; Association for Philosophical and Ethical Research in Medicine, JA; European Society for Philosophy of Medicine and Health Care) Ed. H. Tristram Engelhardt, Jr. adv.; bk.rev.; bibl.; index. (also avail. in microform from UMI; reprint service avail. from SWZ) **Indexed:** Abstr.Crim.& Pen., ASCA, Biol.Abstr., Curr.Cont., Dent.Ind., Excerp.Med., G.Soc.Sci.& Rel.Per.Lit., Hum.Ind., IBR, IBZ, Ind.Med., Lang.& Lang.Behav.Abstr., Phil.Ind., Sociol.Abstr., SSCI. **Document type:** academic/scholarly publication.
—BLDSC (5017.385000); Faxon; Genuine Article; SWETS; UMI. **CCC.**
   Refereed Serial

JOURNAL OF MICROENCAPSULATION. see *PHARMACY AND PHARMACOLOGY*

610   GW   ISSN 0946-2716
CODEN: JMLME8
JOURNAL OF MOLECULAR MEDICINE. (Text in English) 1922. 12/yr. DM.528($383) (effective 1996). (Gesellschaft Deutscher Naturforscher und Aerzte) Springer-Verlag, Heidelberger Platz 3, 14197 Berlin, Germany. TEL 030-8207-0. FAX 030-8214091. E-mail: orders@springer.de. (U.S. subscr. to: Springer-Verlag New York, Inc., 44 Hartz Way, Secaucus, NJ 07096-2491. TEL 201-348-4033. FAX 201-348-4505) Ed. N. Zoellner. adv.; bibl.; charts; illus.; index. (also avail. in microform from UMI,PMC; back issues avail.; reprint service avail. from ISI) **Indexed:** Biol.Abstr., Biotech.Abstr., Chem.Abstr., Curr.Adv.Cancer Res., Curr.Adv.Ecol.Sci., Curr.Cont., Dairy Sci.Abstr., Dent.Ind., Excerp.Med., Helminthol.Abstr., Ind.Med., Ind.Sci.Rev., INIS Atomind., Med.& Surg.Dermat., Nutr.Abstr., Protozool.Abstr., Rev.Med.& Vet.Mycol., Risk Abstr., Sci.Cit.Ind., Trop.Oil Seeds Abstr. **Document type:** academic/scholarly publication.
—BLDSC (5020.716000); ADONIS; CASDDS; Faxon; Genuine Article; SWETS; UMI; UnCover. **CCC.**
   Former titles: Clinical Investigator (ISSN 0941-0198); (until 1993): Clinical Investigation; (until 1991): Klinische Wochenschrift (ISSN 0023-2173)
   Description: Publishes original papers and reviews in all fields of clinical research, with emphasis on molecular medicine, clinical pharmacology, and case reports.

JOURNAL OF MORPHOLOGY. see *BIOLOGY*

612   UK   ISSN 0142-4319
CODEN: JMRMD3
JOURNAL OF MUSCLE RESEARCH AND CELL MOTILITY. 1980. bi-m. £70($120) to individuals; institutions in the E.U. £335 (N. America $335; elsewhere £360) (effective 1995). Chapman & Hall, Journals Department (Subsidiary of: International Thomson Publishing Group), 2-6 Boundary Row, London SE1 8HN, England. TEL 0171-865-0066. FAX 0171-522-9623. TELEX 290164 CHAPMA G. E-mail: journal@chall.mhs.compuserve.com. (Dist. by: International Thomson Publishing Services Ltd., Cheriton House, North Way, Andover, Hants, SP10 5BE, England. TEL 01264-342713. FAX 01264-342807; N. American subscr. to: Chapman & Hall, One Penn Plaza, 41st Fl., New York, NY 10119) Ed.Bd. adv.; bk.rev.; bibl.; illus.; index. (reprint service avail. from ISI, UMI) **Indexed:** Biol.Abstr., Chem.Abstr., Chem.Abstr., Curr.Adv.Ecol.Sci., Dent.Ind., Excerp.Med., Ind.Med., Ind.Sci.Rev. **Document type:** academic/scholarly publication.
—BLDSC (5021.120000); ADONIS; CASDDS; Faxon; Genuine Article; SWETS; UMI; UnCover. **CCC.**
   Description: Presents original research papers on any aspect of muscle, contractive mechanisms, and cell motility.
   Refereed Serial

610   US   ISSN 1043-609X
R850.A1   CODEN: JNREEL
JOURNAL OF N I H RESEARCH. (National Institutes of Health) 1989. m. $129 (foreign $144) (effective 1996). William M. Miller, 1444 I St., NW, Ste. 1000, Washington, DC 20005. TEL 202-785-5333. FAX 202-872-7738. Ed. Dr. Deborah Barnes. adv.: B&W page $3525; trim 8 1/9 x 10 7/8. circ. 1,975 (paid); 29,730 (controlled). (also avail. in microform from UMI) **Document type:** trade publication.
—BLDSC (5022.817000); Faxon; SWETS; UMI; UnCover. **CCC.**
   Description: Covers life science, research, and lab techniques.

610   US   ISSN 1076-2752
RC963   CODEN: JOEMFM
JOURNAL OF OCCUPATIONAL AND ENVIRONMENTAL MEDICINE. 1959. m. $114 to individuals; institutions $149 (effective 1995). (American College of Occupational and Environmental Medicine) Williams & Wilkins, 428 E. Preston St., Baltimore, MD 21202. TEL 410-528-4000; 800-638-6423. FAX 410-528-4312. Ed. Paul W. Brandt-Rauf. adv.; bk.rev.; abstr.; bibl.; charts; index, cum.index. circ. 9,566. (also avail. in microfiche from UMI,WWS; reprint service avail. from UMI) **Indexed:** Abstr.Hyg., Biol.Abstr., Bus.Ind., C.I.S. Abstr., Cadscan, Chem.Abstr., CINAHL, Curr.Cont., Dent.Ind., Environ.Per.Bibl. (1990-), Ergon.Abstr., Excerp.Med., Helminthol.Abstr., Hlth.Ind., Ind.Hyg.Dig., Ind.Med., Ind.Sci.Rev., Ind.Vet., INIS Atomind., Intl.Polym.Sci.& Tech., Lab.Haz.Bull., Lead Abstr., Med.& Surg.Dermat., Noise Pollut.Publ.Abstr., RAPRA, Sci.Cit.Ind., Stud.Wom.Abstr., Tr.& Indus.Ind., Trop.Dis.Bull., World Surf.Coat., Zincscan. **Document type:** academic/scholarly publication.
—BLDSC (5026.081000); CASDDS; EMDOCS; Faxon; Genuine Article; SWETS; UMI; UnCover. **CCC.**
   Former titles: Journal of Environmental Medicine (ISSN 0096-1736); J O M: Journal of Occupational Medicine (ISSN 0022-3212); (until 1968): Journal of Occupational Medicine.
   Description: Contains original articles on occupational medical practice, including epidemiology, toxicology, health screening, ergonomics, assessment, rehabilitation, health education, and administration.
   Refereed Serial

610 642   CN   ISSN 0825-8597
JOURNAL OF PALLIATIVE CARE. 1985. q. Can.$70($110) (foreign $120) (effective 1996). Center for Bioethics, Clinical Research Institute of Montreal, 110 Pine Ave. W., Montreal, PQ H2W 1R7, Canada. TEL 514-987-5619. FAX 514-987-5695. Ed. Dr. David J. Roy. adv.; bk.rev. circ. 1,000. (also avail. in microform from MML; back issues avail.) **Indexed:** Can.B.P.I., Can.Per.Ind., CINAHL, Ind.Med., PSI, Psychol.Abstr. (1985-).
—BLDSC (5028.260000); Faxon; UMI; UnCover. **CCC.**
   Description: Publishes up-to-date scientific research in the field of palliative-hospice care, combining scientific validation with humanistic concerns.

616.07   UK   ISSN 0022-3417
CODEN: JPTLAS
JOURNAL OF PATHOLOGY. 1892. m. $615 (foreign $615) (effective 1996). (Pathological Society of Great Britain and Ireland) John Wiley & Sons Ltd., Journals, Baffins Ln., Chichester, W. Sussex PO19 1UD, England. TEL 01243-779777. FAX 01243-776128. TELEX 86290 WIBOOK G. (Subscr. in the Americas to: John Wiley & Sons, Inc., 605 Third Ave., New York, NY 10158. TEL 212-850-6645. FAX 212-850-6021) Ed. D.H. Weight. adv.; bk.rev.; bibl.; charts; illus.; cum.index: vols.1-90. (also avail. in microform from PMC,UMI; back issues avail.) **Indexed:** Abstr.Hyg., Biol.Abstr., C.I.S. Abstr., Chem.Abstr., Curr.Adv.Cancer Res., Curr.Adv.Cell & Devel.Biol., Curr.Adv.Ecol.Sci., Curr.Adv.Genetics & Molec.Biol., Curr.Cont., Dairy Sci.Abstr., Dent.Ind., Diar.Dis.Res., Excerp.Med., Ind.Med., Ind.Sci.Rev., Ind.Vet., Kidney, Med.& Surg.Dermat., Nutr.Abstr., Pig News & Info., Rev.Med.& Vet.Mycol., Rev.Plant Path., Sci.Cit.Ind., Trop.Dis.Bull., Vet.Bull. **Document type:** academic/scholarly publication.
—BLDSC (5029.900000); ADONIS; CASDDS; EMDOCS; Faxon; Genuine Article; SWETS; UMI; UnCover. **CCC.**
   Incorporates (in Jan. 1984): Diagnostic Histopathology (ISSN 0272-7749); Which was formerly: Investigative and Cell Pathology (ISSN 0146-7611)
   Description: Covers the field of experimental pathology, relevent to the understanding of human disease, and includes papers on the use of techniques such as immunology and molecular biology to elucidate disease mechanisms.

JOURNAL OF PHARMACEUTICAL AND MEDICAL SCIENCES. see *PHARMACY AND PHARMACOLOGY*

JOURNAL OF PHYSIOLOGY. see *BIOLOGY — Physiology*

JOURNAL OF PHYSIOLOGY (PARIS); an integrative neuroscience journal. see *BIOLOGY — Physiology*

610   II   ISSN 0022-3859
CODEN: JPMDA3
JOURNAL OF POSTGRADUATE MEDICINE. (Text in English) 1955. q. Rs.80($50) Seth G.S. Medical College and K.E.M. Hospital, Staff Society, Dept. of Nephrology, Bombay 400012, India. TEL 4132118. Ed. A.F. Almeida. adv.; bk.rev.; charts; illus.; stat.; index. circ. 1,000. **Indexed:** Biol.Abstr., Chem.Abstr., Dent.Ind., ExtraMED, Ind.Med., Nutr.Abstr. **Document type:** academic/scholarly publication.
●Also available on CD-ROM.
—BLDSC (5041.150000); CASDDS; Faxon; SWETS; UnCover.

JOURNAL OF PRODUCTS AND TOXICS LIABILITY. see *LAW*

616.07   AT   ISSN 1320-5455
CODEN: JQCPE
JOURNAL OF QUALITY IN CLINICAL PRACTICE. 1979. q. Aus.$210($210) (effective 1996). Blackwell Science Pty Ltd, P.O. Box 378, Carlton, Vic. 3053, Australia. TEL 61-3-93470300. FAX 61-3-93493016. Ed. John Duggan. adv.: B&W page $720, color page $1510. bk.rev.; illus.; index. circ. 900. (back issues avail.) **Indexed:** Excerp.Med. (1994-), Ind.Med. **Document type:** academic/scholarly publication.
—BLDSC (5043.684700); UMI; UnCover. **CCC.**
   Formerly: Australian Clinical Review (ISSN 0726-3139)
   Description: Reference data designed to keep health professionals informed about quality assurance developments in Australia and abroad.

610   US
QH603.C43   CODEN: JRERDM
JOURNAL OF RECEPTOR AND SIGNAL TRANSACTION RESEARCH. 1980. 8/yr. $297.50 to individuals; institutions $595. Marcel Dekker Journals, 270 Madison Ave., New York, NY 10016. TEL 212-696-9000. FAX 212-685-4540. TELEX 421419 MARDEEK. (Subscr. to: Box 5017, Monticello, NY 12701) Eds. Ross B. Mikkelsen, Vladimir K. Pliska. (also avail. in microform from RPI) **Indexed:** Biol.Abstr., Chem.Abstr., Curr.Adv.Ecol.Sci., Curr.Cont., Dairy Sci.Abstr., Excerp.Med., Ind.Med., Ind.Sci.Rev., Protozool.Abstr. **Document type:** academic/scholarly publication.
—CASDDS; Genuine Article; SWETS; UMI; UnCover. **CCC.**
   Formerly (until 1995): Journal of Receptor Research (ISSN 0197-5110)
   Refereed Serial

JOURNAL OF RELIGION AND HEALTH. see *RELIGIONS AND THEOLOGY*

JOURNAL OF REPRODUCTION AND FERTILITY (INDIA). see *BIOLOGY*

616.07   US   ISSN 0890-765X
RA771.A1
JOURNAL OF RURAL HEALTH. 1985. q. $90 to institutions. (University of North Carolina) National Rural Health Association, 1 W. Armour Blvd., Ste. 301, Kansas City, MO 64111. TEL 816-756-3140. FAX 816-756-3144. Ed. Thomas Ricketts. adv. contact: Stephen Levine. bk.rev.; abstr.; charts; illus.; stat.; index. circ. 2,200. (back issues avail.) **Indexed:** Ind.Med. **Document type:** academic/scholarly publication.
—BLDSC (5052.128850); Faxon; UnCover.
Description: Advances professional practice, research, theory development and public policy relating to rural health.
Refereed Serial

JOURNAL OF SCIENTIFIC RESEARCH IN PLANTS & MEDICINES. see *PHARMACY AND PHARMACOLOGY*

JOURNAL OF SEX RESEARCH. see *PSYCHOLOGY*

610   150   UK   ISSN 0962-1105
QP425   CODEN: JSRSEU
JOURNAL OF SLEEP RESEARCH. (Supplement avail. (ISSN 0966-6826)) 1992. q. £119 (outside Europe £131($208)) (effective 1996). (European Sleep Research Society) Blackwell Science Ltd., Osney Mead, Oxford OX2 0EL, England. TEL 01865-240201. FAX 01865-721205. TELEX 83355 MEDBOK G. Ed. J.A. Horne. adv.; bibl.; illus.; index. circ. 700. (also avail. in microform from UMI; back issues avail.) **Indexed:** Excerp.Med. (1993-). **Document type:** academic/scholarly publication.
—BLDSC (5064.680000); ADONIS; Genuine Article; SWETS; UMI. **CCC.**
Refereed Serial

610   UK   ISSN 0966-6826
JOURNAL OF SLEEP RESEARCH. SUPPLEMENT. 1992. irreg. Blackwell Science Ltd., Osney Mead, Oxford OX2 0EL, England. TEL 01865-240201. FAX 01865-721205. TELEX 83355 MEDBOK G. **Indexed:** Excerp.Med. (1993-). **Document type:** academic/scholarly publication.
—ADONIS.

610   UK   ISSN 0959-2431
    CODEN: JSRDEJ
JOURNAL OF SMOKING-RELATED DISORDERS. 1991. 3/yr. £77. Gardiner - Caldwell Communications Ltd., Old Ribbon Mill, Pitt St., Macclesfield, Ches. SK11 7PT, England. TEL 01625-618507. FAX 01625-614161. Ed. David Caldwell. **Indexed:** Excerp.Med. (1993-). **Document type:** academic/scholarly publication.
—BLDSC (5064.711000).

610   JA   ISSN 0916-8737
    CODEN: JSMRE2
JOURNAL OF SMOOTH MUSCLE RESEARCH/NIHON HEIKATSUKIN GAKKAI KIKANSHI. (Text in English) 1965. q. (Nihon Heikatsukin Gakkai - Japanese Society of Smooth Muscle Research) Journal of Smooth Muscle Research, 5 Zaifucho, Hirosaki-shi, Aomori 036, Japan. TEL 03-3272-7981. FAX 03-3273-2445. Ed.Bd. adv.; bk.rev.; abstr.; charts; illus.; index. circ. 950. **Indexed:** Biol.Abstr., Excerp.Med., Ind.Med.
—BLDSC (5064.711500); CASDDS.
Formerly (until 1991): Nihon Heikatsukin Gakkai Zasshi - Japanese Journal of Smooth Muscle Research (ISSN 0374-3527)

616   US   ISSN 1052-3057
RC388.5
JOURNAL OF STROKE AND CEREBROVASCULAR DISEASES. 1991. q. $80 to individuals in U.S. & Canada (elsewhere $100); institutions $115 in U.S. & Canada (elsewhere $135). National Stroke Association, 8480 E. Orchard Rd., Ste. 1000, Englewood, CO 80111-5015. TEL 303-771-1700. adv.: B&W page $595, color page $1320; trim 8 1/4 x 11. bk.rev. circ. 4,000.
—BLDSC (5066.873900).
Description: Contains original articles, review articles and other features relating to comprehensive diagnosis and management of cerebrovascular disease.

617.07   UK   ISSN 1078-9553
▼**JOURNAL OF SURGICAL PATHOLOGY.** 1995. q. £55($95) to individuals; institutions £130 (N. America $175) (effective 1995). Chapman & Hall, Journals Department (Subsidiary of: International Thomson Publishing Group), 2-6 Boundary Row, London SE1 8HN, England. TEL 0171-522-9623. FAX 0171-856-0066. TELEX 290164 CHAPMA G. E-mail: journal@chall.mhs.compuserve.com. (Subscr. to: International Thomson Publishing Services Ltd., Cheriton House, North Way, Andover, Hants. SP10 5BE, England. TEL 01264-342713. FAX 01264-342807; N. American subscr. to: Chapman & Hall, Journals Promotion Department, One Penn Plaza, 41st Fl., New York, NY 10119. TEL 212-564-1060. FAX 212-564-1505) Eds. Michael J. Warhol, Geraldine S. Pinkus. (reprint service avail.) **Document type:** academic/scholarly publication.
Description: Covers developments in all the disciplines relevant to surgical pathology.
Refereed Serial

362 649.8   UK   ISSN 1357-633X
▼**JOURNAL OF TELEMEDICINE AND TELECARE.** 1995. q. £72 to individuals; institutions £98. Royal Society of Medicine Press Ltd., 1 Wimpole St., London W1M 8AE, England. TEL 0171-290-2928. FAX 0171-290-2929. Ed. Richard Wootton. **Document type:** academic/scholarly publication.
—BLDSC (5069.027000).

610   SZ
JOURNAL OF THE AMERICAN MEDICAL ASSOCIATION. SWISS EDITION. m. Keller und Co. AG, Baselstr. 11, CH-6002 Luzern, Switzerland. TEL 041-281111. FAX 041-222253. TELEX 868910. Ed. Carl Herzog. circ. 6,000.

610   US   ISSN 0022-5045
R131.A1   CODEN: JHMAA6
JOURNAL OF THE HISTORY OF MEDICINE AND ALLIED SCIENCES. 1946. q. $45 to individuals; institutions $65. Journal of the History of Medicine and Allied Sciences, Inc., 333 Cedar St., New Haven, CT 06510. TEL 203-785-4341. (Subscr. to: 1017 Turnpike St., Canton, MA 02021) Ed. Dr. Stanley W. Jackson. adv. contact: Maria K. Modlin. bk.rev.; charts; illus.; cum.index: vols.1-30 (1946-1975). circ. 1,500. (also avail. in microform from UMI,PMC; reprint service avail. from UMI) **Indexed:** Amer.Hist.& Life, Bibl.Engl.Lang.& Lit., Biol.Abstr., Chem.Abstr., Curr.Adv.Ecol.Sci., Curr.Cont., Dent.Ind., Excerp.Med., Hist.Abstr., Ind.Med., Ind.Sci.Rev., Mid.East: Abstr.& Ind., Sci.Cit.Ind., SSCI. **Document type:** academic/scholarly publication.
—BLDSC (5001.000000); Faxon; Genuine Article; SWETS; UMI; UnCover.

610   II   ISSN 0022-507X
JOURNAL OF THE INDIAN MEDICAL PROFESSION. (Text in English) 1954. m. Rs.15($4.50) United Asia Publications Pvt. Ltd., 12 Rampart Row, Bombay 1, India. Ed. Dr. R.M. Rajpal. adv.; charts; illus. (tabloid format) **Indexed:** Chem.Abstr., Ind.Med.

610   IO   ISSN 0126-1312
JOURNAL OF THE MEDICAL SCIENCES/BERKALA ILMU KEDOKTERAN. (Text and summaries in English and Indonesian) 1969. q. Rps.8000($20) Gadjah Mada University, College of Medicine, Department of Physical Anthropology - Universitas Gadjah Mada, Fakultas Kedokteran, Sekip, Yogyakarta, Indonesia. Ed. Teuku Jacob. adv.; bk.rev.; charts; illus.; stat. circ. 1,200. **Indexed:** Chem.Abstr.
—CCC.
Formerly: Gadjah Mada Journal of the Medical Sciences.

610   JA   ISSN 0022-5207
JOURNAL OF THERAPY/CHIRYO. (Text in Japanese) 1920. m. Nanzando Co., Ltd., 4-1-11 Yushima, Bunkyo-ku, Tokyo 113, Japan. Ed. Masatsugu Suzuki. adv. **Indexed:** Chem.Abstr., INIS Atomind., Jap.Per.Ind.
Formed by the merger of: Chiryo Oyobi Shono; Naika Oyobi Shonika.

JOURNAL OF TOXICOLOGIC PATHOLOGY. see *ENVIRONMENTAL STUDIES — Toxicology And Environmental Safety*

610   CN   ISSN 1195-1982
▼**JOURNAL OF TRAVEL MEDICINE.** 1994. q. $58 to individuals (outside US & Canada $75); institutions $75 (outside US & Canada $95) (effective 1996). (International Society of Travel Medicine) Decker Periodicals, P.O. Box 620, LCD 1, Hamilton, ON L8N 3K7, Canada. TEL 905-522-7017; 800-568-7281. FAX 905-522-7839. E-mail: decker@io.org. (U.S. addr.: Box 785, Lewiston, NY 14092-0785) (Co-sponsor: Asia Pacific Travel Health Association) Ed. Dr. Charles D. Ericsson. adv. contact: John Birkby. (also avail. in microfilm from UMI) **Document type:** trade publication.
—BLDSC (5070.547000).

JOURNAL OF VESTIBULAR RESEARCH: EQUILIBRIUM AND ORIENTATION. see *BIOLOGY — Physiology*

610   US   ISSN 0896-7210
JOURNAL WATCH. 1987. s-m. $89 (Canada $98; elsewhere $105) (effective 1996). Massachusetts Medical Society, 1440 Main St., Waltham, MA 02154. TEL 617-843-6356. FAX 617-893-8103. Ed. Dr. Allan S. Brett. **Document type:** abstracting/indexing.
—SWETS.

JOURNALS OF GERONTOLOGY. SERIES A: BIOLOGICAL SCIENCES & MEDICAL SCIENCES. see *GERONTOLOGY AND GERIATRICS*

JUNDI SHAPUR UNIVERSITY. FACULTY OF MEDICINE. LIBRARY BULLETIN/DANESHGAH-E JONDISHAPUR. DANESHKADE-YE PEZESAKI. BULTAN-E KETABKHANEH. see *LIBRARY AND INFORMATION SCIENCES*

610   JA   ISSN 0022-6769
    CODEN: JUIZAG
JUNTENDO MEDICAL JOURNAL/JUNTENDO IGAKU. (Text in Japanese) 1887. q. 5000 Yen (effective 1996). Juntendo Medical Society - Juntendo Igakkai, 2-1-1 Hongo, Bunkyo-ku, Tokyo 113, Japan. FAX 3814-9100. Ed. Inaba Yutaka. adv.; abstr.; index; circ. 3,500 (controlled). **Indexed:** Chem.Abstr., INIS Atomind. **Document type:** academic/scholarly publication.
—CASDDS.
Refereed Serial

610   MY   ISSN 0127-1075
JURNAL PERUBATAN U K M. (Text in English and Malay) 1979. s-a. $15 per no. Penerbit Universiti Kebangsaan Malaysia, 43600 UKM Bangi, Selangor, Malaysia.
—BLDSC (5075.601500).

610   JA   ISSN 0022-7226
    CODEN: JUZIAG
JUZEN IGAKKAI ZASSHI/JUZEN MEDICAL SOCIETY. JOURNAL. (Text in English and Japanese) 1896. 6/yr. 3000 Yen($20) Kanazawa Daigaku Igakubu, Juzen Igakkai - Kanazawa University, School of Medicine, Juzen Medical Society, 13-1 Takara-machi, Kanazawa-shi, Ishikawa-ken 920, Japan. adv.; abstr.; bibl.; illus. **Indexed:** Biol.Abstr., C.I.S.Abstr., Chem.Abstr., INIS Atomind.
—BLDSC (4810.100000); CASDDS.

616   US   ISSN 0090-5089
K A F P JOURNAL. 1956. q. membership. Kentucky Academy of Family Physicians, Medical Arts Bldg., Ste. 3323, 1169 Eastern Pkwy., Louisville, KY 40217. TEL 502-451-0370. FAX 502-451-5914. Eds. Drs. Walter Zukof, James E. Redmon, Jr. adv. contact: Margaret Roberts. circ. 2,000. **Document type:** academic/scholarly publication.
Formerly: K A G P Journal (ISSN 0022-7250)
Description: Articles and essays focusing on the practical issues that affect the health and welfare of families, and on conferences, activities, and issues relevant to contemporary family physicians.

610   US   ISSN 0886-4772
K C M S BULLETIN. 1921. 6/yr. $15 to non-members; members $2.50. Medical Society County of Kings, Inc., 1313 Bedford Ave., Brooklyn, NY 11216. TEL 718-467-9000. FAX 718-778-0380. (Co-publisher: Academy of Medicine of Brooklyn) Ed. Randall D. Bloomfield. adv.; bk.rev.; charts; tr.lit.; index; circ. 2,800. (back issues avail.)
Formerly: Medical Society of the County of Kings and Academy of Medicine of Brooklyn. Bulletin (ISSN 0025-7532).

MEDICAL SCIENCES

610   JA   ISSN 0368-5063
CODEN: KDIZAA
KAGOSHIMA DAIGAKU IGAKU ZASSHI/MEDICAL JOURNAL OF KAGOSHIMA UNIVERSITY. 1945. q. Kagoshima Daigaku, Igakubu - Kagoshima University, Faculty of Medicine, 8-35-1, Sakuragaoka, Kagoshima 890, Japan. TEL 81-922-75-5188. FAX 81-992-75-1124. **Indexed:** INIS Atomind. **Document type:** academic/scholarly publication.
—BLDSC (5527.830000).

610   JA   ISSN 0913-5073
KAGOSHIMA KYUKYU IGAKKAISHI/KAGOSHIMA ASSOCIATION FOR ACUTE MEDICINE. JOURNAL. (Text in Japanese) 1978. irreg. Kagoshima Kyukyu Igakkai, 8-1, Chuocho, Kagoshima-shi, Kagoshima-ken 890, Japan.

610.6   JA
KANAGAWA MEDICAL PREFECTURE ASSOCIATION. JOURNAL. 1973. s-a? Kanagawa Medical Prefecture Association - Kanagawa Igakki Zasshi, 4-104 Nishi-ku, Yokohama City, Japan. Ed. Kinzo Kiyokawa. **Formerly:** Kanagawa Medical Association. Journal.

KANAGAWA RINSHO SHINRIGAKU KENKYU/KANAGAWA CLINICAL PSYCHOLOGY. see *PSYCHOLOGY*

610   JA   ISSN 0917-4796
KANAZAWA DAIGAKU IRYO GIJUTSU TANKI DAIGAKUBU SAGYO RYOHOGAKKA SOTSUGYO KENKYU RONBUNSHU/KANAZAWA UNIVERSITY. SCHOOL OF ALLIED MEDICAL PROFESSIONS. DEPARTMENT OF OCCUPATIONAL THERAPY. COLLECTION OF PAPERS. (Text in Japanese) 1982. a. free. Kanazawa Daigaku, Iryo Gijutsu Tanki Daigakubu, Sagyo Ryohogakka, 11-80, Kodatsuno 5-chome, Kanazawa-shi, Ishikawa-ken 920, Japan. TEL 0762-22-2211. FAX 0762-34-4375. Ed. Nobuyasu Kobayashi. circ. 250. **Document type:** academic/scholarly publication.
Description: Collection of graduate thesis of the Department of Occupational Therapy.
Refereed Serial

610.7   JA
CODEN: KIDZAK
KANSAI MEDICAL UNIVERSITY. JOURNAL/KANSAI IKA DAIGAKU. ZASSHI. (Text and summaries in English, German and Japanese) 1948. q. 1000 Yen($2.80) Kansai Medical University, 1 Fumizono-cho, Moriguchi 570, Japan. adv.; abstr.; bibl.; charts; illus.; index. **Indexed:** Biol.Abstr., Chem.Abstr., Excerp.Med., INIS Atomind.
—CASDDS; EMDOCS.
Formerly: Kansai Medical School. Journal (ISSN 0022-8400)

610   US   ISSN 8755-0059
R15   CODEN: KAMEEI
KANSAS MEDICINE. 1901. m. $45 (foreign $50) (effective 1993). Kansas Medical Society, 623 S.W. 10th Ave., Topeka, KS 66612. TEL 913-235-2383. Ed. Dr. David E. Gray. adv.; bk.rev.; software rev.; bibl.; charts; illus.; tr.lit.; index. circ. 3,600. (also avail. in microform from UMI; reprint service avail. from UMI) **Indexed:** Dent.Ind., Hosp.Lit.Ind., Ind.Med., INIS Atomind.
—BLDSC (5085.647000); Faxon; UMI.
Formerly (until 1984): Kansas Medical Society. Journal (ISSN 0022-8699)

610   CH   ISSN 0257-5655
CODEN: KHHCE2
KAOHSIUNG JOURNAL OF MEDICAL SCIENCES. Key Title: Gaoxiong Yixue Kexue Zazhi. (Text in Chinese and English) 1985. m. $60. Kaohsiung Medical College, 100 Shih-Chuan 1st Rd., Kaohsiung 80708, Taiwan, Republic of China. TEL 07-3121101. FAX 07-3210564. Ed. Eng-Rin Chen. adv.; charts; illus.; index. circ. 1,500. (back issues avail.) **Indexed:** Chem.Abstr., Excerp.Med., Nutr.Abstr., Soyabean Abstr.
—BLDSC (5085.674500); CASDDS.
Description: Scientific papers in all fields of medicine; review articles, and case reports.

610   II   ISSN 0377-9378
KARNATAKA MEDICAL JOURNAL. (Text in English) 1939. q. Rs.75 to individuals; institutions Rs.100. Indian Medical Association, Karnataka State Branch, IMA House, Alur Venkata Rao Rd., Bangalore 560018, India. Ed. D. Somasekharaiah. adv.; bk.rev. circ. 5,000. **Indexed:** Biol.Abstr.
—BLDSC (5086.250000).
Formerly (until 1974): Mysore Medical Association. Journal.

610   US   ISSN 1040-3353
CODEN: KINSEJ
KAROLINSKA INSTITUTE NOBEL CONFERENCE SERIES. 1980. irreg., latest 1990. price varies. Raven Press (Subsidiary of: Wolters Kluwer N.V.), 1185 Ave. of the Americas, New York, NY 10036. TEL 212-930-9500. FAX 212-869-3495. (reprint service avail. from UMI) **Document type:** proceedings, monographic series.
Refereed Serial

610   VE   ISSN 0075-5222
KASMERA. (Text in Spanish; abstracts in English) 1962. a. exchange basis. Universidad del Zulia, Departamento de Microbiologia y Patologia Tropical, Apdo. 526, 4011 Maracaibo, Venezuela. Ed. Dr. Ricardo Soto Urribarri. bibl.; charts; illus.; stat. circ. 1,000. (also avail. in microform) **Indexed:** Abstr.Hyg., Biol.Abstr., Trop.Dis.Bull.
Description: Publishes research by the Faculty of Medicine in areas of bacteriology, immunology, parasitology and other topics.

610   GW
KATHOLISCHER BERUFSVERBAND FUER PFLEGEBERUFE. MITTEILUNGSBLATT. bi-m. Katholischer Berufsverband fuer Pflegeberufe e.V., Kaiserstr. 42, 55116 Mainz, Germany. TEL 06131-232340.

610   JA   ISSN 0386-5924
CODEN: KAIGD3
KAWASAKI IGAKKAI SHI. (Text in Japanese; summaries in English and Japanese) 1975. q. 10000 Yen. Kawasaki Medical Society, 577 Matsushima, Kurashiki-shi, Okayama 701-01, Japan. FAX 086-462-1199. Ed.Bd. bk.rev.; illus. circ. 1,050. **Indexed:** INIS Atomind.
—BLDSC (5088.096000); CASDDS.

610   JA   ISSN 0385-0234
CODEN: KAMJDW
KAWASAKI MEDICAL JOURNAL. (Text in English; summaries in Japanese) 1975. q. 20000 Yen. Kawasaki Medical Society, 577 Matsushima, Kurashiki-shi, Okayama 701-01, Japan. FAX 086-462-1199. Eds. Yoshihito Yawata, Fumihiko Kajiya. bk.rev.; illus. circ. 800. **Indexed:** Abstr.Hyg., Biol.Abstr., Chem.Abstr., Excerp.Med., INIS Atomind., Trop.Dis.Bull.
—BLDSC (5088.097000); CASDDS.

610   JA   ISSN 0022-9717
CODEN: KJMEA9
KEIO JOURNAL OF MEDICINE. (Text in English) 1952. q. $90. Keio Gijuku Daigaku, Igakubu - Keio University, School of Medicine, 35 Shinano-machi, Shinjuku-ku, Tokyo 160, Japan. TEL 81-3-3353-1211. FAX 81-3-5379-6059. Ed. Toyomi Fujino. circ. 1,400. **Indexed:** Abstr.Hyg., Biol.Abstr., Chem.Abstr., Diar.Dis.Res., Excerp.Med., Ind.Med., Nutr.Abstr., Trop.Dis.Bull. **Document type:** academic/scholarly publication.
—BLDSC (5089.000000); CASDDS; EMDOCS; Faxon; UnCover.
Refereed Serial

KEIRAKU SHINRYO. see *ALTERNATIVE MEDICINE*

170 610   US
KENNEDY INSTITUTE OF ETHICS. SCOPE NOTE. 1982. q. $5 (in U.S., Canada and Mexico; elsewhere $8). Kennedy Institute of Ethics, National Reference Center for Bioethics Literature, Georgetown University, Washington, DC 20057-1065. TEL 202-687-3885. FAX 202-687-6770. Ed. Doris Goldstein. circ. 2,000. **Indexed:** Vert.File.Ind. **Document type:** monographic series.
Formerly: Kennedy Institute of Bioethics. Scope Note.
Description: Presents current viewpoints related to specific topics in biomedical ethics. Intended specifically for scholars, journalists, medical and legal practitioners, students and interested laypersons.

174.2   US   ISSN 1054-6863
QH332   CODEN: KIEJEF
KENNEDY INSTITUTE OF ETHICS JOURNAL. 1991. q. $50 to individuals; institutions $73; students $25. (Kennedy Institute of Ethics) Johns Hopkins University Press, Journals Publishing Division, 2715 N. Charles St., Baltimore, MD 21218. TEL 410-516-6987. FAX 410-516-6968. Eds. Robert M. Veatch, Carol Mason Spicer. adv. contact: Tara Dorai-Berry. circ. 1,900. (reprint service avail. from WSH) **Document type:** academic/scholarly publication.
—BLDSC (5089.517000); UnCover. **CCC.**

616   US   ISSN 0023-0294
CODEN: JKMAB5
KENTUCKY MEDICAL ASSOCIATION. JOURNAL. 1903. m. $25 (foreign $30). Kentucky Medical Association, 301 N. Hurstbourne Pkwy., Ste. 200, Louisville, KY 40222-8512. TEL 502-426-6200. FAX 502-426-6877. Ed. Dr. A. Evan Overstreet. adv. contact: Sue Tharp. bk.rev.; bibl.; illus.; index. circ. 5,600. (also avail. in microform from UMI; reprint service avail. from UMI) **Indexed:** Biol.Abstr., Chem.Abstr., Curr.Cont., Excerp.Med., Helminthol.Abstr., Ind.Med., Rev.Plant Path. **Document type:** academic/scholarly publication.
—BLDSC (4810.740000); EMDOCS; Faxon; SWETS; UMI.
Refereed Serial

610   KE
KENYA. MINISTRY OF HEALTH. ANNUAL REPORT. a. Ministry of Health, P.O. Box 52, Homa Bay, Kenya.

610   KE   ISSN 0076-5988
KENYA MEDICAL RESEARCH INSTITUTE. ANNUAL REPORT. 1966. a. free. Kenya Medical Research Institute, P.O. Box 54840, Nairobi, Kenya. **Indexed:** Biol.Abstr. **Document type:** corporate report, academic/scholarly publication.

610   II   ISSN 0301-4827
KERALA MEDICAL JOURNAL. (Text in English) 1959. m. membership. Indian Medical Association, Kerala State Branch, Cochin 682 016, India. Ed. I.S. Menon. adv.; bk.rev.; film rev.; bibl.; charts; illus. circ. 4,500.

610   UK   ISSN 1356-6113
▼**KEY NOTE MARKET REVIEW: U K HEALTHCARE.** Variant title: U K Healthcare. 1994. irreg. £375. Key Note Publications Ltd., Field House, 72 Oldfield Rd., Hampton, Middlesex TW12 2HQ, England. TEL 0181-783-0755. FAX 0181-783-1720. **Document type:** trade publication.
●Also available online.
Also available on CD-ROM.

610   UK   ISSN 0961-1665
KEY NOTE REPORT: MEDICAL EQUIPMENT. Variant title: Medical Equipment. irreg. £185. Key Note Publications Ltd., Field House, 72 Oldfield Rd., Hampton, Middlesex TW12 2HQ, England. TEL 0181-783-0755. FAX 0181-783-1720. **Document type:** trade publication.
●Also available online.
Also available on CD-ROM.

610   UK   ISSN 0950-3196
KEY NOTE REPORT: PRIVATE HEALTHCARE. Variant title: Private Healthcare. irreg. £185. Key Note Publications Ltd., Field House, 72 Oldfield Rd., Hampton, Middlesex TW12 2HQ, England. TEL 0181-783-0755. FAX 0181-783-1720. **Document type:** trade publication.
●Also available online.
Also available on CD-ROM.
—BLDSC (6617.063710).

610   SU   ISSN 0254-413X
CODEN: KAMJEX
KING ABDULAZIZ MEDICAL JOURNAL. (Text in English) 1981. q. King Abdul Aziz University, College of Medicine and Allied Sciences, P.O. Box 1540, Jeddah 21441, Saudi Arabia. **Indexed:** Chem.Abstr., ExtraMED. **Document type:** academic/scholarly publication.
●Also available on CD-ROM.
—CASDDS.

610 US
KING COUNTY MEDICAL SOCIETY. BULLETIN. 1916. m. $17.30 in Washington state; elsewhere $21.62. (King County Medical Society) Journal and Bulletin Agency, Box 10249, Bainbridge Island, WA 98110. TEL 206-682-7813. adv.: B&W page $350; trim 9 3/4 x 7 1/2. circ. 4,400.

610 UK ISSN 0085-2546
KING'S GAZETTE; the journal of King's College Hospital. 1921. s-a. £2.75. Kings College Hospital Medical School, Denmark Hill, London SE5 8RX, England. Ed. Sarah Hawxwell. adv.; bk.rev.; illus. circ. 1,500.

612.76 CN ISSN 0823-0536
KINNECTION. 1983. bi-m. membership. Ontario Association of Applied Kinesiology, 6519 B Mississauga Rd., Mississauga, ON L5N 1A6, Canada. TEL 905-567-7194. FAX 905-567-7191. Ed. Rick Roach. adv.: page Can.$200; adv. contact: Leslie Wright. bk.rev. circ. 400. (looseleaf format; also avail. in diskette format) Document type: newsletter.
Description: Contains information on legislation, association business, continuing education opportunities, employment opportunities and new advances in the science of kinesiology.

610 JA ISSN 0913-6452
KINSEI KAGAKU/KINSEI SCIENCE - A SCIENTIFIC APPROACH TO POSTURES. (Text in Japanese; summaries in English, German) 1986. a. Shisei Hoken Igakkai - Medical Association of Posture and Health, 4-22, Ohashi 2-chome, Meguro-ku, Tokyo 153, Japan.

610 JA ISSN 0023-1908
CODEN: KKAIA2
KITAKANTO MEDICAL JOURNAL/KITAKANTO IGAKU. (Text in Japanese; summaries in English) 1951. bi-m. 4500 Yen. Kitakanto Medical Society - Kitakanto Igakkai, c/o Gumma Daigaku Igakubu, 3-39-22 Showa-machi, Maebashi-shi 371, Japan. TEL 0272-31-7221. Ed. Katsuhiro Shibata. abstr.; charts; illus. Indexed: Biol.Abstr., Chem.Abstr., Excerp.Med., INIS Atomind.
—BLDSC (5098.100000); CASDDS; EMDOCS.

610 JA ISSN 0023-1916
CODEN: KBYKAV
KITANO HOSPITAL JOURNAL OF MEDICINE. (Text in Japanese and European languages; summaries and table of contents in English) 1955. q. Tazuke Kofukai Foundation, Medical Research Institute, 13-3 Kamiyama-cho, Kita-ku, Osaka 530, Japan. Ed. Haruhiko Kikuchi. charts; illus.; stat. circ. 500. Indexed: Biol.Abstr., Excerp.Med. Document type: academic/scholarly publication.
—BLDSC (5098.150000); CASDDS.

610 JA ISSN 0385-2024
KITASATO INSTITUTE. ANNUAL REPORT. (Text in English, Japanese) 1964. a. Kitasato Institute - Kitasato Kenkyujo, 9-1, Shirokane 5-chome, Minato-ku, Tokyo 108, Japan.
—BLDSC (1318.680000).

610 RU ISSN 0023-2149
R91 CODEN: KLMIAZ
KLINICHESKAYA MEDITSINA/CLINICAL MEDICINE. (Text in Russian; summaries in English) 1920. bi-m. $104 (effective 1996). (Ministerstvo Zdravookhraneniya) Izdatel'stvo Meditsina, Petroverigskii pereulok 6-8, 101838 Moscow, Russia. (Dist. by: Mezhdunarodnaya Kniga, B. Yakimanka 39, 117049 Moscow, Russia. TEL 7-095-2384600. FAX 7-095-2384634) Ed. F.I. Komarov. bk.rev.; adv. Indexed: Biol.Abstr., Biotech.Abstr., Chem.Abstr., Curr.Cont., Dent.Ind., Excerp.Med., Helminthol.Abstr., Ind.Med., Ind.Sci.Rev., INIS Atomind., Nutr.Abstr., Rev.Med.& Vet.Mycol.
—BLDSC (0089.240000); CASDDS; EMDOCS. Genuine Article. CCC.
Description: Discusses principal issues of clinical medicine, dealing mainly with matters of diagnosis, pathogenesis, prophylaxis, treatment and clinical course. Includes original essays on the scientific developments of Soviet medicine and surveys of modern theoretical medicine abroad.

610 TU ISSN 1300-0675
KLINIK GELISIM; journal of Istanbul chamber of medicine. 1987. q. (Istanbul Tabip Odasi - Istanbul Chamber of Medicine) Tanim Ltd., Macka Cad. Ralli Apt.59-3, Tesvikiye, 80200 Istanbul, Turkey. TEL 90-1-231549. Indexed: Excerp.Med. (1993-).

610 GW ISSN 0341-2350
KLINIKARZT; Medizin im Krankenhaus. 1972. m. DM.96 (effective 1996). Perimed - Spitta Medizinische Verlagsgesellschaft mbH, Ammonitenstr. 1, 72336 Balingen, Germany. TEL 07433-952-0. FAX 07433-952185. adv.; bk.rev.; index. circ. 24,000. Document type: academic/scholarly publication.
—BLDSC (5099.284900). CCC.

610 GW ISSN 0176-1765
KLINISCHE UND EXPERIMENTELLE NOTFALLMEDIZIN. 1984. irreg., vol.13, 1991. DM.39. W. Zuckschwerdt Verlag GmbH, Industriestr. 17, 82110 Germering, Germany. TEL 089-894349-0. FAX 089-89434950. Ed.Bd. Document type: academic/scholarly publication.

616.3 GW
KLOPFZEICHEN; eine Informationszeitschrift rund um CF. 1981. s-a. free. Cystic Fibrosis Selbsthilfe Bundesverband e.V., Meyerholz 3, 28832 Achim, Germany. TEL 04202-82280. Ed. Eva Bode; Pub. Hermann Prietzsch. adv.; bk.rev. circ. 6,500. Document type: bulletin.

610 JA ISSN 0075-6431
CODEN: KDIKAX
KOBE DAIGAKU IGAKUBU KIYO/KOBE UNIVERSITY. MEDICAL JOURNAL. (Table of contents and summaries in English) 1949. a. free. (Kobe Daigaku Igakkai - Kobe University Medical Society) Kobe Daigaku, Igakubu, 5-1, Kusunoki-cho 7-chome, Chuo-ku, Kobe 650, Japan. TEL 81-78-341-7451. FAX 81-78-382-2080. Ed. Masato Kasuga. Indexed: Biol.Abstr., Excerp.Med., Ind.Med., INIS Atomind. Document type: academic/scholarly publication.
—BLDSC (5527.840000); EMDOCS.
Formerly (until 1968): Kobe Ika Daigaku. Kiyo.

610 JA ISSN 0023-2513
CODEN: KJMDA6
KOBE JOURNAL OF MEDICAL SCIENCES. (Text and summaries in English, French, German) 1951. bi-m. 6000 Yen. Kobe Daigaku, Igakubu - Kobe University, School of Medicine, 5-1, Kusunoki-cho 7-chome, Chuo-ku, Kobe-shi, Hyogo-ken 650, Japan. TEL 81-78-341-7451. Ed. Takeo Matsumura. abstr.; charts; illus.; index. circ. 650. (back issues avail.) Indexed: Abstr.Hyg., Biol.Abstr., Chem.Abstr., Excerp.Med., Ind.Med., INIS Atomind., Trop.Dis.Bull. Document type: academic/scholarly publication.
—BLDSC (5100.580000); CASDDS; EMDOCS; Faxon; UnCover.

610 JA ISSN 0911-9531
KOBE UNIVERSITY. BULLETIN OF ALLIED MEDICAL SCIENCES. (Text in English) 1985. a. Kobe University, School of Allied Medical Sciences - Kobe Daigaku Iryo Gijutsu Tanki Daigakubu, 10-2, Tomogaoka 7-chome, Suma-ku, Kobe-shi, Hyogo-ken 654, Japan.

610 JA ISSN 0914-4250
KOCHI IRYO GAKUIN DOSOKAISHI/KOCHI SCHOOL OF ALLIED HEALTH AND MEDICAL PROFESSIONS. ALUMNI ASSOCIATION JOURNAL. (Text in Japanese) 1983. irreg. Kochi Iryo Gakuin Dosokai, 6012-1, Higashinamimatsu, Nagahama, Kochi-shi, Kochi-ken 781-02, Japan.

610 DK ISSN 0105-4139
KOEBENHAVNS UNIVERSITET. INSTITUT FOR SOCIAL MEDICIN. PUBLIKATIONER. no.13, 1981. irreg. price varies. Foreningen af Danske Laegestuderendes Forlag, Prinsesse Charlottesgade 29, st.tv., 2200 Copenhagen N, Denmark. TEL 31-356287. FAX 35-366229. TELEX 16698 UNBOG. illus. circ. 500.

616.98 JA ISSN 0023-2858
KOKU IGAKU JIKKENTAI HOKOKU/JAPAN AIR SELF DEFENSE FORCE. AEROMEDICAL LABORATORY. REPORTS. (Text in Japanese; summaries in English) 1958. q. exchange basis. Japan Air Self Defense Force, Aeromedical Laboratory - Kokujieitai Koku Igaku Jikkentai, 2-10, Sakae-cho 1-chome, Tachikawa-shi, Tokyo, Japan. TEL 0245-24-4131. Ed.Bd. bibl.; charts; illus. circ. 500. Indexed: Biol.Abstr., INIS Atomind., Int.Aerosp.Abstr., Psychol.Abstr. (1969-).
—BLDSC (7368.740000).
Description: Presents the results of research and usability tests for pilots' personnel equipments.
Refereed Serial

610 JA
KOKU KAIBO KENKYU/JOURNAL OF ORAL ANATOMY. (Text in Japanese; summaries in English) irreg. Tokyo Dental College, Department of Anatomy, 2-2, Masago 1-chome, Mihama-ku, Chiba-shi, Chiba-ken 261, Japan. Document type: academic/scholarly publication.

KOKUTETSU CHUO HOKEN KANRIJOHO; health control. see PUBLIC HEALTH AND SAFETY

610 HU ISSN 0075-6792
CODEN: KSTUAJ
KORANYI SANDOR TARSASAG. TUDOMANYOS ULESEK. 1961. irreg. price varies. Akademiai Kiado, Publishing House of the Hungarian Academy of Sciences, P.O. Box 245, H-1519 Budapest, Hungary. TEL 181-2134. FAX 166-6466. TELEX 22-6228 AKNYO H.
—CASDDS.

610 KO ISSN 0023-4028
R97.7.K6 CODEN: THUHA7
KOREAN MEDICAL ASSOCIATION. JOURNAL.* Key Title: Taehan Uihak Hyophoe Chi. (Text in Korean; summaries in English) 1908. m. free. Korean Medical Association, Box 2062, Seoul, S. Korea. Ed. Dr. Hee Young Lee. adv.; abstr.; charts; illus.; stat.; index. Indexed: Diar.Dis.Res., Excerp.Med., Ind.Med., INIS Atomind.
—BLDSC (4812.340000); CASDDS; EMDOCS.

610.9 IS ISSN 0023-4109
KOROTH; a bulletin devoted to the history of medicine and science. (Text in English, Hebrew) 1952. a., vol.11, 1995. $25. (Israel Institute of the History of Medicine) Magnes Press, Hebrew University, Jerusalem, P.O. Box 7697, Jerusalem, Israel. TEL 972-2-660341. FAX 972-2-633370. Ed. Samuel Kottek. adv.; bk.rev.; abstr.; bibl.; illus.; index. circ. 250. Indexed: Amer.Hist.& Life, Hist.Abstr., Ind.Heb.Per. Document type: academic/scholarly publication.
Formerly: Jerusalem Historical Medical Publications (ISSN 0449-4881)

610 IT ISSN 0393-2095
KOS. 1983. bi-m. L.60000. Europa Scienze Umane Editrice s.r.l., Via Olgettina 60, 20132 Milan, Italy. TEL 39-2-26410150. Ed. Luigi Maria Verze. adv.: page L.7000000. circ. 15,000.

610 JA ISSN 0300-919X
CODEN: KUIZAR
KUMAMOTO IGAKKAI ZASSHI/KUMAMOTO MEDICAL SOCIETY. JOURNAL. (Text in Japanese; summaries in English) 1925. m. Kumamoto Igakkai - Kumamoto Medical Society, c/o Kumamoto Daigaku Igakubu, 2-1, Honjo 2-chome, Kumamoto-shi, Kumamoto-ken 860, Japan. Ed. Katsuhide Nishi. Indexed: INIS Atomind.

610 JA ISSN 0023-5326
CODEN: KUMJAX
KUMAMOTO MEDICAL JOURNAL. (Text in English) 1938-1942; resumed 1951. q. free. (Ministry of Education, Science and Culture) Kumamoto Daigaku Igakubu, 2-1 Honjo 2-chome, Kumamoto-shi, Kumamoto-ken 860, Japan. TEL 096-373-5009. FAX 096-372-6140. Ed. Yasuharu Nishimura. abstr.; charts; illus.; index. circ. 450. Indexed: Biol.Abstr., Chem.Abstr., Excerp.Med., Ind.Med., INIS Atomind., Nutr.Abstr. Document type: academic/scholarly publication.
—BLDSC (5122.000000); CASDDS; EMDOCS.
Description: Contains original papers from the medical school.

610 JA ISSN 0389-7451
KURINIKKU MAGAJIN/CLINIC MAGAZINE. (Text in Japanese) 1974. m. 1130 Yen. 3-15, Nihonbashi Honcho 2-chome, Chuo-ku, Tokyo 103, Japan.

610 JA ISSN 0387-1541
KURINISHIAN/CLINICIAN. (Text in Japanese) 1953. m. 300 Yen per no. Ezai K.K. - Eisai Co., Ltd., 6-10 Koishikawa 4-chome, Bunkyo-ku, Tokyo 112, Japan.

MEDICAL SCIENCES

610   JA   ISSN 0368-5810
CODEN: KIZAAL
KURUME MEDICAL ASSOCIATION. JOURNAL/KURUME IGAKKAI ZASSHI. (Text in Japanese; summaries in European languages) 1936. m. Kurume Medical Association - Kurume Igakkai, c/o Kurume University School of Medicine, 67 Asahi-machi, Kurume 830, Japan. **Indexed:** Biol.Abstr., C.I.S. Abstr., INIS Atomind.
—BLDSC (4812.700000).

610   JA   ISSN 0023-5679
CODEN: KRMJAC
KURUME MEDICAL JOURNAL. (Text in English) 1954. q. exchange basis. Kurume University School of Medicine - Kurume Daigaku Igakubu, 67 Asahi-machi, Kurume 830, Japan. TEL 942-35-3311. FAX 942-32-1665. Ed. Takashi Akasu. adv.; charts; illus. circ. 550. **Indexed:** Abstr.Hyg., Biol.Abstr., Chem.Abstr., Excerp.Med., Ind.Med., INIS Atomind., Nutr.Abstr., Trop.Dis.Bull. **Document type:** academic/scholarly publication.
—BLDSC (5131.420000); CASDDS; EMDOCS; Faxon; UnCover.

610   JA   ISSN 0915-5015
KUTSU NO IGAKU/MEDICAL FOOTWEAR. (Text in Japanese) 1987. a. 5100 Yen. Nihon Kutsu Igakkai - Japanese Society for Study of Medical Footwear, Jonan Byoin, 19-8, Shimomeguro 3-chome, Meguro-ku, Tokyo 153, Japan.

610   KU   ISSN 0023-5776
CODEN: KMAJAG
KUWAIT MEDICAL ASSOCIATION. JOURNAL. (Text in English) 1967. q. Kuwait Medical Association, P.O. Box 1303, Kuwait. adv.; bk.rev.; abstr.; bibl.; charts; illus.; index. circ. 4,000. **Indexed:** Abstr.Hyg., Biol.Abstr., Curr.Adv.Ecol.Sci., Curr.Cont., Excerp.Med. (until 1992), Helminthol.Abstr., Nutr.Abstr., Rev.Plant Path., Trop.Dis.Bull.
—BLDSC (4812.800000); CASDDS.
Description: Collection of review articles, original articles, case reports in all areas within the medical sciences as well as general information concerning the Association.

610 618.97   JA   ISSN 0368-5829
CODEN: KIZSB8
KYORIN IGAKKAI ZASSHI/KYORIN MEDICAL SOCIETY. JOURNAL. (Text in Japanese; summaries in English) 1970. q. 5000 Yen. Kyorin Medical Society, Kyorin University, 20-2, 6-chome, Shinkawa, Mitaka-shi, Tokyo 181, Japan. FAX 0422-40-7281. Ed. Nobuo Watanabe. adv.; index. circ. 1,800. (back issues avail.) **Indexed:** Chem.Abstr., INIS Atomind. **Document type:** academic/scholarly publication.
—CASDDS.
Refereed Serial

KYOTO DAIGAKU. REICHORUI KENKYUJO NENPO/KYOTO UNIVERSITY. PRIMATE RESEARCH INSTITUTE. ANNUAL REPORT. see *ANTHROPOLOGY*

610   JA
KYOTO DAIGAKU IGAKUBU. KAIBOGAKU DAI 2 KOZA. RONBUNSHU/KYOTO UNIVERSITY. FACULTY OF MEDICINE, SECOND DEPARTMENT OF ANATOMY. PROCEEDINGS. (Text in Japanese; summaries in English) irreg. Kyoto Daigaku Igakubu, Kaibogaku Dai 2 Koza, Yoshida Konoe-cho, Sakyo-ku, Kyoto-shi, Kyoto 606, Japan. **Document type:** academic/scholarly publication, proceedings.

610   JA   ISSN 0023-6012
CODEN: KFIZAO
KYOTO PREFECTURAL UNIVERSITY OF MEDICINE. MEDICAL SOCIETY. JOURNAL/KYOTO-FURITSU IKA DAIGAKU ZASSHI. (Text in Japanese and English; summaries in English) 1927. m. 6000 Yen($50) (effective 1993). Kyoto Prefectural University of Medicine, Kyoto Foundations for the Promotion of Medical Science - Kyoto-furitsu Ika Daigaku, Hirokoji, Kawara-machi, Kamigyo-ku, Kyoto 602, Japan. TEL 81-75-212-5466. FAX 81-75-212-5467. E-mail: morimoto@phys.kpu.m.ac.jp. Ed. Taketoshi Morimoto. adv.; abstr.; index. circ. 1,400. **Indexed:** Biol.Abstr., Chem.Abstr., INIS Atomind. **Document type:** academic/scholarly publication.
—BLDSC (4812.857000); CASDDS.
Refereed Serial

610   JA   ISSN 0385-8162
KYUKYU IGAKU/JAPANESE JOURNAL OF ACUTE MEDICINE. (Text in Japanese) 1977. m. 1800 Yen per no. Herusu Shuppan, 2-3, Nakano 2-chome, Nakano-ku, Tokyo 164, Japan. **Indexed:** INIS Atomind., Jap.Per.Ind.
—BLDSC (4650.778600).

610   JA   ISSN 0913-9958
KYUMEI KYUKYU IRYO KENKYUKAI ZASSHI/JAPANESE ASSOCIATION FOR CRITICAL CARE MEDICINE. JOURNAL. (Text in Japanese) 1987. a. 2500 Yen. Kyumei Kyukyu Iryo Kenkyukai, Nihon Ika Daigaku Kyukyu Igaku Kyoshitsu, 1-5, Sendagi 1-chome, Bunkyo-ku, Tokyo 113, Japan.

610   US   ISSN 0162-7163
L A C M A PHYSICIAN. 1871. 20/yr. $30 to non-members; members $15. Los Angeles County Medical Association, Box 3465, Los Angeles, CA 90051-1465. TEL 213-483-1581. FAX 213-484-1699. Ed. Janice M. Nagano. adv. contact: Chele Graham. bk.rev. circ. 10,500. (processed) **Indexed:** CINAHL. **Document type:** trade publication.
Formerly: Los Angeles County Medical Association. Bulletin (ISSN 0047-5076)
Description: Informs on pertinent trends in the world of medicine, from a socioeconomic and political standpoint. Covers state laws and regulations, trends affecting physicians, and societal events which impact upon physicians.

610   US   ISSN 0742-3896
CODEN: LMSED6
L E R S MONOGRAPH SERIES. 1983. irreg., latest vol.8. price varies. (Laboratoires d'Etudes et de Recherches Synthelabo, FR) Raven Press (Subsidiary of: Wolters Kluwer N.V.), 1185 Ave. of the Americas, New York, NY 10036. TEL 212-930-9500. FAX 212-869-3495. (reprint service avail. from UMI) **Document type:** monographic series.
—CASDDS.
Refereed Serial

610.9489   DK   ISSN 0105-1830
LAEGEFORENINGENS VEJVISER. 1965. a. DKK 320. (Almindelige Danske Laegeforening) Laegeforeningens Forlag, Esplanaden 8A, DK-1263 Copenhagen K, Denmark. TEL 45-31-38-55-00. FAX 45-33-15-28-58.
Former titles (until 1976): Vejviser (ISSN 0105-0427); (until 1973): Laegeforeningens Vejviser (ISSN 0458-6158)

610   DK   ISSN 0902-1787
LAEGEMAGASINET. (Supplement avail.: Dit Laegemagasin (ISSN 0904-2369)) 1987. a. DKK 360. Forlaget Jan Vaboe A-S, Emiliekildevej 35, DK-2930 Klampenborg, Denmark. TEL 45-39-90-80-00. FAX 45-39-90-82-80. Ed. Jannie P. Helle. adv. contact: Kirsten Waaben. circ. 5,200.
Formerly: Laegen.

610   SW   ISSN 0023-7205
LAEKARTIDNINGEN. (Text in Swedish; summaries in English) 1904. w. SEK 844 (effective 1994). Sveriges Laekarfoerbund - Swedish Medical Association, P.O. Box 5603, S-114 86 Stockholm, Sweden. FAX 08-207435. Ed. Bosse Tolander. adv.; bk.rev.; bibl.; charts; illus.; index. circ. 30,000. **Indexed:** C.I.S. Abstr., Chem.Abstr., Dok.Arbeitsmed., Ind.Med, INIS Atomind., Protozool.Abstr., Rev.Med.& Vet.Mycol.
—BLDSC (5143.920000); SWETS.
Former titles (until 1965): Svenska Laekartidningen; (until 1965): Almaenna Svenska Laekartidningen.

610   IC   ISSN 0023-7213
LAEKNABLADID/ICELANDIC MEDICAL JOURNAL. 1915. m. $95. Icelandic Medical Association, Hlidasmari 8, 200 Kopavogur, Iceland. TEL 354-764-4104. FAX 354-764-4106. Eds. Vilhjalmur Rafnsson. adv. contact: Margret Adalsteinsdottir. circ. 1,600.
—BLDSC (5143.650000).

610   UK   ISSN 0140-6736
R31   CODEN: LANCAO
THE LANCET. North American edition (ISSN 0099-5355) (Translations avail. in Spanish, Italian) 1823. w. £90($112) to individuals (outside Europe £110); institutions 145 (outside Europe £155); students and interns £75 (outside Europe £85) (effective 1995). The Lancet Ltd. (Subsidiary of: Reed Elsevier group), 42 Bedford Sq., London WC1B 3SL, England. TEL 0171-436-4981. FAX 0171-436-7570. Ed. Robin Fox; Pub. David Gilbertson. adv.: B&W page £1800; trim 7 x 10. bk.rev.; abstr.; s-a. index. circ. 50,000. (also avail. in microform from UMI; microfiche from IDC; back issues avail.) **Indexed:** Abstr.Crim.& Pen., Abstr.Health Care Manage.Stud., Abstr.Hyg., Acad.Ind., AIM, Apic.Abstr., ASSIA, Bibl.Dev.Med.& Child Neur., Biol.Abstr., Biol.Dig., Biotech.Abstr., C.I.S. Abstr., CAD CAM Abstr., Cadscan, Chem.Abstr., Curr.Adv.Cancer Res., Curr.Adv.Ecol.Sci., Curr.Adv.Genetics & Molec.Biol., Curr.Cont., Curr.Lit.Fam.Plan., Curr.Tit.Dent., Dairy Sci.Abstr., Deep Sea Res.& Oceanogr.Abstr., Dent.Ind., Diab.Cont., Diar.Dis.Res., Dok.Arbeitsmed., Environ.Abstr., Excerp.Med., FAMLI, Food Sci.& Tech.Abstr., Geo.Abstr., Helminthol.Abstr., High.Educ.Curr.Aware.Bull., Hlth.Ind., Hosp.Lit.Ind., I.P.A., Ind.Hyg.Dig., Ind.Med., Ind.Sci.Rev., Ind.Vet., INIS Atomind., Int.Nurs.Ind., Kidney, Lab.Haz.Bull., Lead Abstr., Med.& Surg.Dermat., Med.Care Rev., Nutr.Abstr., Popul.Ind., Protozool.Abstr., Res.High.Educ.Abstr., Rev.Appl.Entomol., Rev.Med.& Vet.Mycol., Rev.Plant Path., Risk Abstr., Small Anim.Abstr., Stud.Wom.Abstr., Telegen, Trop.Dis.Bull., Vet.Bull., W.R.C.Inf., Zincscan. **Document type:** academic/scholarly publication.
●Also available online. Vendor(s): Ovid Technologies, University Microfilms International.
Also available on CD-ROM.
—BLDSC (5146.000000); ADONIS; CASDDS; Genuine Article; SWETS; UMI. **CCC.**
Description: International journal of medical science and practice.
Refereed Serial

610   SP   ISSN 0212-0151
THE LANCET (EDICION ESPANOLA). Spanish translation of: The Lancet (UK ISSN 0140-6736) 1982. m. (2 vols./yr.) 7200 ptas.($68) Ediciones Doyma, S.A., Travesera de Gracia, 17-21, 08021 Barcelona, Spain. TEL 34-1-200-07-11. FAX 34-1-209-11-36. TELEX 51694 INK-E. Dir. M. Foz i Sala. adv.: page 280000 ptas.; trim 210 x 280; adv. contact: Anna Pahissa. circ. 8,000. (reprint service avail. from UMI)
—SWETS.
Description: Publishes clinical observations, physiopathological interpretations, descriptions of new syndromes, diagnostic methodology, and other developments in the medical sciences.

610   IT   ISSN 0393-0637
THE LANCET (EDIZIONE ITALIANA). Italian translation of: The Lancet (UK ISSN 0140-6736) 1984. m. (10/yr.). L.85000 (effective 1994). Masson S.p.A., Divisione Periodici, Via Statuto 2-4, 20121 Milan, Italy. TEL 02-6367-1. FAX 02-6367211. Ed. Carlo Zanussi. adv.: B&W page L.7500000, color page L.9650000. circ. 18,000. **Document type:** academic/scholarly publication.

610   US   ISSN 0099-5355
R31
THE LANCET (NORTH AMERICAN EDITION). British edition (ISSN 0140-6736) 1966. w. $112 to individuals; institutions $207 (effective 1995). The Lancet Ltd. (Subsidiary of: Reed Elsevier plc), 655 Ave. of the Americas, New York, NY 10011. TEL 212-633-3800; 800-462-6198. FAX 212-633-3850. Ed. Dr. Richard Horton. adv. contact: Louise Young. index. circ. 18,000. (also avail. in microfilm from UMI) **Indexed:** CINAHL. **Document type:** academic/scholarly publication.
●Also available on CD-ROM.
—Faxon; UnCover. **CCC.**
Description: Covers major developments in general medicine and clinical research worldwide.
Refereed Serial

610   DK   ISSN 0900-0380
LANDSFORENINGEN AF KRONISK SYGE. MEDLEMSBLAD.* 1939. q. Landsforeningen af Kronisk Syge, Odinsgade 46/st tv, 7100 Vejle, Denmark. Ed. Johs Nielsen. illus.
Formerly (until 1983): Kronisk Syges Blad (ISSN 0903-0360)

LANGUAGE AND SPEECH. see *LINGUISTICS*

610 300   IT   ISSN 0393-7445
LANTERNINO; trimestrale di storia della medicina e studi sociali. 1978. q. free. Dr. Claudio Bevilacqua, Ed. & Pub., Via Rossetti 25, 34100 Trieste, Italy. TEL 39-40-360332. bibl. circ. 2,000.

610   JA   ISSN 0898-5901
CODEN: LATHE7
LASER THERAPY; an international journal of low level laser therapy and photobioactivation. 1989. q. $200 (effective 1996). International Laser Therapy Association, c/o 14-18 Iwaicho, Tochigi City, Tochigi 328, Japan. TEL 81-282-24-0313. FAX 81-282-22-5019. Eds. O. Kemmotsu, C. Enwemeka. bk.rev. (reprint service avail. from SWZ) **Indexed:** INSPEC (1989-). **Document type:** academic/scholarly publication.
—BLDSC (5156.651000); UMI. **CCC.**
   Description: Links an international outlook in the field of laser therapy with academic contents; contains clinical and basic scientific studies in the use of low level laser therapy.
Refereed Serial

610 535.58   UK   ISSN 0268-8921
CODEN: LMSCEZ
LASERS IN MEDICAL SCIENCE. 1986. q. £70 in Europe (rest of world $128) to individuals; institutions £99 in Europe (rest of world $178). (European Laser Association) W.B. Saunders Ltd. (Subsidiary of: Harcourt Brace & Company Ltd.), 24-28 Oval Rd., London NW1 7DX, England. TEL 0171-267-4466. FAX 0171-482-2293. TELEX 25775-ACPRES-G. (Subscr. to: Harcourt Brace & Company Ltd., Foots Cray High St., Sidcup, Kent DA14 5HP, England. TEL 0181-300-3322. FAX 0181-309-0807; US, Canadian, and Mexican subscr. to: W.B. /Saunders Co., Journal Subscription Fulfillment, 6277 Sea Harbor Dr., 4th Fl., Orlando, FL 32887-4800. TEL 800-654-2452. FAX 800-874-6418) Ed.Bd. (back issues avail.) **Indexed:** Curr.Adv.Ecol.Sci., Med.& Surg.Dermat. **Document type:** academic/scholarly publication.
—BLDSC (5156.680800); Ei; Faxon; Genuine Article; SWETS; UnCover. **CCC.**
   Description: Brings together the work of clinicians and basic scientists in the field of the medical applications of lasers.

174.24 179.7   CN   ISSN 1198-3922
LAST RIGHTS. q. Right to Die Society of Canada, Box 39018, Victoria, BC V8V 4X8, Canada. TEL 604-380-1112. FAX 604-386-3800. E-mail: rights@islandnet.com. Ed. John Hofsess.
   Description: Specializes in international coverage of right to die issues and original research in methods of self-deliverance.

610 658   US   ISSN 1067-716X
THE LATEST WORD. 1993. bi-m. $42 (foreign $58) (effective 1996). W.B. Saunders Co. (Subsidiary of: Harcourt Brace & Company), Curtis Center, 3rd Fl., Independence Sq. W., Philadelphia, PA 19106-3399. TEL 215-238-7800. FAX 215-238-6445. (Subscr. to: Periodicals Fulfillment, W.B. Saunders Co., 6277 Sea Harbor Dr., 4th Fl., Orlando, FL 32891-4800. TEL 800-654-2452. FAX 800-874-6418) Eds. Ellen Drake, Susan Dooley. adv. **Document type:** newsletter.
—UMI. **CCC.**
   Description: Ensures that medical transcriptionists and medical records administrators and technicians keep abreast of advances in medicine and new terminology.

610   IT
LEADERSHIP MEDICA; mensile di medicina, economia, attualita e cultura per opinion leaders. (Text in English; summaries in Italian) 1985. m. $186. Ce.S.I.L. srl, Via Olmetto 5, 20123 Milan, Italy. TEL 02-878397. FAX 02-866576. Dir. Genina Jacobone. adv. contact: Marcella Caradonna. circ. 85,000.
Refereed Serial

610   LE   ISSN 0023-9852
R97.5.F8   CODEN: LMJJA7
LEBANESE MEDICAL JOURNAL/JOURNAL MEDICAL LIBANAIS. (Text in English and French) 1948. 4/yr. Order of Physicians in Lebanon, P.O. Box 640, Beirut, Lebanon. Ed. Dr. Adel E. Barbari. adv.; bk.rev.; abstr.; bibl.; charts; illus.; index. circ. 3,500. **Indexed:** Biol.Abstr., Chem.Abstr., Curr.Cont., Excerp.Med., Ind.Med.
   Description: Publishes original articles and research, news from the Order of Physicians, and contributions on the history of medicine in Lebanon.

610   US   ISSN 0172-7788
LECTURE NOTES IN MEDICAL INFORMATICS. 1978. irreg. price varies. Springer-Verlag, 175 Fifth Ave., New York, NY 10010. TEL 212-460-1500. FAX 212-473-6272. (Also: Berlin, Heidelberg, Tokyo and Vienna) Eds. D.A.B. Lindberg, P.L. Reichertz. (reprint service avail. from ISI) **Indexed:** Cyb.Abstr. **Document type:** monographic series.
—Faxon.

610.7   SA   ISSN 0377-9696
CODEN: LECHAC
THE LEECH. (Text in English) 1929. 3/yr. R.15 (foreign R.45). University of the Witwatersrand Medical School, 7 York Rd., Parktown 2193, South Africa. TEL 27-11-6472451. FAX 27-11-6434318. Ed. Manfred Spanger. adv.; bk.rev. circ. 7,000. **Document type:** academic/scholarly publication.
—BLDSC (5181.200000); CASDDS.
   Supersedes: Auricle (ISSN 0004-8070)
   Description: Contains research articles, drug reviews, conference information, coverage of changing trends in health care, and departmental news for students and graduates of the University of the Witwatersrand Medical School.
Refereed Serial

610   XO   ISSN 0075-8736
LEKARSKE PRACE. (Text mainly in Slovak; occasionally in English, German or Russian; summaries in one or two of the other languuages) 1961. irreg. (approx. s-a.); vol.10, no.2, 1973. (Slovenska Akademia Vied) Veda, Publishing House of the Slovak Academy of Sciences, Klemensova 19, 814 30 Bratislava, Slovakia. (Dist. by: Slovart, Nam. Slobody 6, 817 64 Bratislava, Slovakia) **Indexed:** Biol.Abstr., Ind.Med.
—BLDSC (5182.315000).

610 615.19   XO   ISSN 0457-4214
CODEN: LEOBAK
LEKARSKY OBZOR. (Text in Czech or Slovak; summaries in English, German, Russian) m. $78. Institut pre Dalsie Vzelavanie Pracovnikov v Zdravotnictve - Institute of Further Education of Physicians and Pharmaceutists in Bratislava, Limbova 12, 833 03 Bratislava, Slovakia. (reprint service avail. from IRC) **Indexed:** C.I.S. Abstr., Chem.Abstr., INIS Atomind.
—BLDSC (5182.330000); CASDDS.

610   PL   ISSN 0867-8235
LEKARZ KOLEJOWY. 1965. s-a. $2. Centrum Naukowe Medycyny Kolejowej, Ul. Grojecka 17a, P.O. Box 214, 00-973 Warsaw, Poland. Ed. Jacek A. Piatkiewicz. charts; illus. circ. 1,000. **Indexed:** C.I.S. Abstr. **Document type:** academic/scholarly publication.
   Formerly (until 1989): Medycyna Komunikacyjna (ISSN 0025-861X)
   Description: Original papers on medicine of transport, reviews in occupational medicine, conferences and symposia reports, organizational topics in railway health service.

616.98   PL   ISSN 0024-0745
CODEN: LEKWAT
LEKARZ WOJSKOWY. m. $8.40. Szefostwo Sluzby Zdrowia SG WP, Al. Niepodleglosci 243 A, 00-909 Warsaw 60, Poland. TEL 48-2-6844750. Ed. Piotr Kobylecki. **Indexed:** Excerp.Med., INIS Atomind.
—BLDSC (5182.380000); CASDDS.

610   FR   ISSN 0398-1436
LETTRE DU MEDECIN. 1976. w. Espace No. 1, 13 rue Chanzy, 75011 Paris, France. TEL 43-70-97-20. Ed. Joel Haroche. circ. 10,000.

610   FR   ISSN 0153-4742
LETTRE MEDICALE. 1975. 10/yr. $31. Lettre Medicale, 27, rue du Fg, St. Jacques, 75674 Paris Cedex 14, France. TEL 42341684. Ed. M. Detilleux. circ. 3,000.

MEDICAL SCIENCES   4233

LIAONING ZHONGYI ZAZHI/LIAONING JOURNAL OF TRADITIONAL CHINESE MEDICINE. see *ALTERNATIVE MEDICINE*

610   AU
LIEFERKATALOG FUER KRANKENHAUS, ARZT, APOTHEKE UND LABOR; Lieferfirmen- und Bezugsquellennachweis. 1974. a. S.240. Verlag Dieter Goeschl GmbH, Hernalser Hauptstr. 213, A-1170 Vienna, Austria. TEL 01-4864240. FAX 01-4854902. adv. circ. 15,000. **Document type:** catalog.

610   CI   ISSN 0024-3477
CODEN: LIVJA5
LIJECNICKI VJESNIK. (Text in Croatian; contents page and summaries in English) 1878. m. $120. Zbor Lijecnika Hrvatske - Medical Association of Croatia, Subiceva 9, 41000 Zagreb, Croatia. TEL 041-440-621. Ed. Ivan Bakran. adv.; bk.rev.; abstr.; bibl.; charts; illus.; index; circ. 7,400 (controlled). **Indexed:** Biol.Abstr., C.I.S. Abstr., Chem.Abstr., Dent.Ind., Excerp.Med., Ind.Med.
—BLDSC (5215.800000); CASDDS; EMDOCS.

610   KR   ISSN 1019-5297
R91   CODEN: LISPEC
LIKARSKA SPRAVA/VRACHEBNOE DELO. (Text in Russian, Ukrainian) 1918. m. Vydavnytstvo Zdorovya, Ul. Chkalova 65, 252054 Kiev, Ukraine. TEL 044-216-89-08. adv.; bk.rev.; circ. 5,000 (paid). **Indexed:** Biol.Abstr., Chem.Abstr., Dent.Ind., Excerp.Med., Ind.Med.
—CASDDS; EMDOCS; Genuine Article. **CCC.**
   Formerly (until 1991): Vrachebnoe Delo (ISSN 0049-6804)
   Description: Publishes articles relating to the different fields of medicine.

610   FR   ISSN 0981-1095
CODEN: LIMEEH
LILLE MEDICAL. (Summaries in English, French) vol.11, 1966. 10/yr. 375 Fr. (Facultes de Medecine de Lille) Medi-Presse, 1 Place de Verdun, 59045 Lille Cedex, France. adv.; abstr.; charts; illus.; stat.; tr.lit. **Indexed:** Biol.Abstr., C.I.S. Abstr., Chem.Abstr., Curr.Cont., Dent.Ind., Dok.Arbeitsmed., Excerp.Med., Helminthol.Abstr., Ind.Med., Nutr.Abstr.
—CASDDS.
   Former titles: L A R C Medical; Lille Medical (ISSN 0024-3507); Echo Medical du Nord.

610   US   ISSN 0024-3639
R15
LINACRE QUARTERLY. 1932. q. $24. National Federation of Catholic Physicians Guilds, 850 Elm Grove Rd., Elm Grove, WI 53122. TEL 414-784-3435. FAX 414-782-8788. Ed. Dr. John P. Mullooly. adv.; bk.rev.; abstr.; bibl.; index. circ. 11,150. (also avail. in microfilm from UMI; back issues avail.) **Indexed:** Cath.Ind., CERDIC.
—BLDSC (5220.170000); UMI.
   Description: Journal of the philosophy and ethics of medical practice.

610   CC
LINCHUANG HUICUI/CLINICAL FOCUS; daneike. (Text in Chinese) m. Y14.40. Hebei Yixue Yuan - Hebei Academy of Medical Sciences, 5 Chang'an Xilu, Shijiazhuang, Hebei 050017, People's Republic of China. TEL 44121. Ed. Du Benfa.

610   CC   ISSN 1001-7399
LINCHUANG YU SHIYAN BINGLIXUE ZAZHI/JOURNAL OF CLINICAL AND EXPERIMENTAL PATHOLOGY. (Text in Chinese) q. Anhui Yike Daxue - Anhui University of Medical Sciences, Meishan Lu, Hefei, Anhui 230032, People's Republic of China. TEL 336600. Ed. Zheng Guohao.

LITERATURE & MEDICINE. see *LITERATURE*

LONG TERM CARE - DIRECTORY OF MAJOR PROVIDERS. see *BUSINESS AND ECONOMICS — Trade And Industrial Directories*

LONGITUDINAL RESEARCH IN THE BEHAVIORAL, SOCIAL AND MEDICAL SCIENCES. see *SOCIAL SCIENCES: COMPREHENSIVE WORKS*

MEDICAL SCIENCES

610 US
LOOSE CONNECTIONS. 1986. q. $20 includes membership. Ehlers-Danlos National Foundation, Box 1212, Southgate, MI 48195. TEL 313-282-0180. FAX 313-282-2793. Ed. Gerald J. Rogowski. adv.; bk.rev. circ. 3,000. **Document type:** newsletter.
   Description: Provides emotional support and information to those who suffer from Ehlers Danlos Syndrome, and serves as communication link with the medical community.

610 US ISSN 0024-6921
CODEN: JLSMAW
LOUISIANA STATE MEDICAL SOCIETY. JOURNAL. 1844. m. $18 (foreign $21). Journal of the Louisiana State Medical Society, Inc., 3501 N. Causeway Blvd., Ste. 800, Metairie, LA 70002-3625. TEL 504-832-9815. FAX 504-833-7685. Ed. Conway S. Magee. adv. contact: Anne Gooch. bk.rev.; bibl.; illus.; index. circ. 6,300. (also avail. in microform from UMI; reprint service avail. from UMI) **Indexed:** Biol.Abstr., C.I.S. Abstr., Chem.Abstr., Dent.Ind., Ind.Med., INIS Atomind., Rev.Med.& Vet.Mycol. **Document type:** trade publication.
   —BLDSC (4818.700000); Faxon; SWETS; UMI; UnCover.
   Refereed Serial

610 BE ISSN 0024-6956
CODEN: LOMEAL
LOUVAIN MEDICAL. (Text in French; summaries in English and French) 1966. m. (except July-Aug. combined). 2000 Fr.($14) 52, Ave. E. Mounier, B-1200 Brussels, Belgium. adv.; bk.rev.; abstr.; index. circ. 3,000. (back issues avail.) **Indexed:** Biol.Abstr., Chem.Abstr., Curr.Adv.Ecol.Sci., Curr.Cont., Excerp.Med., Helminthol.Abstr., Nutr.Abstr.
   —BLDSC (5296.350000); CASDDS; EMDOCS; UMI.
   Formerly: Revue Medicale de Louvain et Recipe.

610 US ISSN 1068-6991
▼**LOWER EXTREMITY.** 1994. 4/yr. $79 to individuals; institutions $119. Churchill Livingstone Inc., 650 Ave. of the Americas, New York, NY 10011. TEL 212-206-5040; 800-553-5426. FAX 212-727-7808. **Indexed:** Excerp.Med. (1995-). **Document type:** academic/scholarly publication.
   —BLDSC (5298.572000). CCC.
   Refereed Serial

610 US
LYCOMING MEDICINE. 1910. m. $20. Lycoming County Medical Society, 777 Rural Ave., Williamsport, PA 17701-3198. TEL 717-321-2171. Ed. Dr. Judith A. Gouldin. adv.; bk.rev. circ. 325.

610 FR ISSN 0766-5466
LYON MEDITERRANEE MEDICAL - MEDECINE DU SUD EST. m. 240 F. to individuals (foreign 330 F.); students 210 F. (foreign 300 F.). Galliena Promotions, 58 A, Rue du Dessous des Berges, 75013 Paris, France. TEL 45-84-97-66. FAX 45-84-92-56.
   —BLDSC (5311.980000).
   Formerly: Lyon Mediterranee Medical (ISSN 0399-032X)

LYSOSOMES IN BIOLOGY AND PATHOLOGY. see *BIOLOGY*

M A P NEWS. (Medical Aid for Palestine) see *SOCIAL SERVICES AND WELFARE*

610 BU ISSN 0324-119X
RM1
M B I. (Medico-Biologic Information) (Editions in English and Russian) 1967. bi-m. free. Pharmachim, 16, Iliensko Chaussee, 1220 Sofia, Bulgaria. Ed. A. Damyanov. adv.; illus. circ. 2,000 (English ed.). **Indexed:** Biol.Abstr., Curr.Adv.Ecol.Sci., Excerp.Med. (until 1993).

610 US ISSN 0047-6471
M C G TODAY.* 1970. q. free to alumni and donors. Medical College of Georgia Foundation, Inc., Alumni Center, 919 15th St., Augusta, GA 30912. TEL 404-721-4421. Ed. Christine Deriso. circ. 15,000.

610 MX ISSN 0024-8002
M D EN ESPANOL. (Medical Doctor) 1963. m. Mex.$250 (foreign $190) (effective 1995). Mundo Medico, S.A., Ejercity Nacional 381, 11520 Mexico DF, Mexico. TEL 525-559-27-55. FAX 525-559-28-21. Ed. Joaquin Armando Chacon. adv. contact: Oscar Bagnarelli. circ. 18,000.

610 US
▼**M D I JOURNAL.** 1995. m. $200. Medical Data International, 2 Park Plaza, Ste. 750, Irvine, CA 92714. TEL 714-251-2780. FAX 714-251-2781. Ed. Minda Sandler. **Document type:** newsletter.

610 640.73 US ISSN 0890-7587
M D R WATCH. (Medical Device Reporting); an independent guide to medical device reporting. 1986. m. $597. Washington Business Information, Inc., c/o Karen Harrington, 1117 N. 19th St., Ste. 200, Arlington, VA 22209. TEL 703-247-3434. FAX 703-247-3427. Ed. Sean Oberle. charts; stat. (back issues avail.) **Document type:** newsletter.
   —CCC.
   Description: Monitors compliance with the FDA's MDR regulation with charts by manufacturer, product, and company. Includes current and year-to-date figures.

610 JA ISSN 0025-8830
M E J. (Medical Equipment Journal of Japan); monthly information on medical, surgical & dental instruments. (Text in English) 1957. m. $117. Genyosha Publications Inc., 18-2, Shibuya 3-chome, Shibuya-ku, Tokyo 150, Japan. TEL 03-3407-7521. FAX 03-3407-7902. (Dist. by: Intercontinental Marketing Corp., I.P.O. Box 5056, Tokyo 100-31, Japan. TEL 81-3-3667-9646) Ed. Masami Eda. adv. circ. 6,984. (tabloid format) **Indexed:** JTA.

610 US
M F M C REVIEW. 1985. q. Mississippi Foundation for Medical Care, 735 Riverside Dr., Box 4665, Jackson, MS 39296-4665. TEL 601-354-0304. FAX 601-948-8917. Ed. Carole Kelly. circ. 5,000. **Document type:** newsletter.

M G Z. (Maatschappelijke Gezondheidszorg) see *MEDICAL SCIENCES — Nurses And Nursing*

M H H - INFO. (Medizinische Hochschule Hannover) see *COLLEGE AND ALUMNI*

M H L A NEWS. (Manitoba Health Libraries Association) see *LIBRARY AND INFORMATION SCIENCES*

M I M S. (Monthly Index of Medical Specialties) see *PHARMACY AND PHARMACOLOGY*

610 SA
M I M S COMPANION. 1981. irreg. M I M S, Division of Times Media Limited, P.O. Box 2059, Pretoria 0001, South Africa. TEL 27-12-3485010. FAX 27-12-477716. Ed. R. van Rooyen. adv.; circ. 3,000 (paid).
   Formerly: M I M S Medical Memory Aids.
   Description: Examines symptoms, clinical signs, investigations, pathology, treatments and syndromes for medical professions.

610 AT
M I M S COMPANION. biennial. Aus.$35. M I M S Australia, 48 Albany St., Crows Nest, N.S.W. 2065, Australia.
   Description: Guide to symptoms, clinical signs, investigations, pathology, diagnosis, treatment and prognosis.

610 IE ISSN 0300-8223
M I M S IRELAND. 1960. m. $150. Medical Publications (Ireland) Ltd., 15 Harcourt St., Dublin 2, Ireland. TEL 4757461. FAX 757467. (Subscr. to: 12-14 Ansdell St., London W8 5TR, England) Ed. Dr. J.F. O'Connell. adv. contact: Juliette Browne. circ. 3,460. **Document type:** academic/scholarly publication.
   Refereed Serial

610 US ISSN 0543-2774
M L A DIRECTORY (YEAR). 1959. a. $150. Medical Library Association, Six N. Michigan Ave., Ste. 300, Chicago, IL 60602-4805. TEL 312-419-9094. FAX 312-419-8950. adv.; B&W page $1174; adv. contact: Barbara Redmond. circ. 4,200. **Document type:** directory.

610 026 US ISSN 0541-5489
Z675.M4
M L A NEWS (CHICAGO). 1961. 10/yr. $48.50 (foreign $61.50). Medical Library Association, Six N. Michigan Ave., Ste. 300, Chicago, IL 60602-4805. TEL 312-419-9094. FAX 312-419-8950. Ed. Jean Demas. adv.; B&W page $1077. circ. 5,050. (reprint service avail. from UMI, ISI) **Document type:** newsletter.
   —BLDSC (5879.715400); Genuine Article; SWETS.

610 US
M M NEWS. 6/yr. $15. New York County Medical Society, 15 E. 26th St., New York, NY 10010. FAX 212-684-4741. Ed. Cheryl Malone. adv. circ. 6,200. (looseleaf format) **Document type:** newsletter.
   Formerly: New York County Medical Society Newsletter.

610 SA ISSN 1017-611X
M R C NEWS/M N R NUUS. (Text in Afrikaans, English) 1972. bi-m. free. Medical Research Council, P.O. Box 19070, Tygerberg 7505, South Africa. TEL 27-21-938-0293. FAX 27-21-938-0395. Ed. Leverne Gething. circ. 1,400. **Document type:** newsletter.

610 UK ISSN 0143-0130
M R C NEWS. q. free. Medical Research Council, 20 Park Crescent, London W1N 4AL, England. TEL 0171-636-5422. FAX 0171-436-6179. Ed. Susanna Lithiby. **Document type:** bulletin.
   —BLDSC (5980.749000).

610 CN
▼**M S N S NEWS.** 1994. m. Can.$20. (Medical Society of Nova Scotia) Keith Health Care Communications, 1382 Hurontario St., Mississauga, ON L5G 3H4, Canada. TEL 905-278-6700. FAX 905-278-4850. Ed. Donna Christopher. adv.; B&W page Can.$703, color page Can.$1338; trim 8 3/4 x 11 1/4; adv. contact: Camille Sobrian. **Document type:** newsletter.

616.8 CN ISSN 0707-0934
M S ONTARIO. 1977. q. Can.$10 membership. Multiple Sclerosis Society of Canada, Ontario Division, 250 Bloor St. E., Ste. 820, Toronto, ON M4W 3P9, Canada. TEL 416-922-6065. FAX 416-922-7538. Ed. Deanna Groetzinger. adv.; bk.rev. circ. 12,000. **Document type:** newsletter.

618 GW ISSN 0930-4622
CODEN: MTAAEX
M T A - FACHZEITSCHRIFT FUER TECHNISCHE ASSISTENTEN DER MEDIZIN. (Medizinisch-Technische Assistenten); Monatszeitschrift fuer MTA's, Labormediziner, Fachleute Radio-Diagnostik, Lehrer und Studenten. (Includes supplement: Gelernt-Vergessen) m. DM.123.60 (students DM.92.40). Umschau Zeitschriftenverlag Breidenstein GmbH, Stuttgarter Str. 18-24, 60329 Frankfurt a.M., Germany. TEL 069-2600-0. FAX 069-2600-619. Ed. Ruth Nitz. adv.: B&W page DM.4950, color page DM.8664; trim 176 x 257; adv. contact: Barbara Eckert. circ. 27,044. **Document type:** academic/scholarly publication.
   —BLDSC (5980.874600); CASDDS. CCC.
   Formerly: M T A - Journal (ISSN 0171-8037)

610 GW ISSN 0935-137X
M T DIALOG. (Medizin-Technischer) 1975. m. DM.256. M T D Verlag GmbH und Co., Wangenerstr. 12, 88279 Amtzell, Germany. TEL 07520-958-0. FAX 07520-95899. Ed. Rolf Schmid. adv. contact: Christl Morgen. **Document type:** trade publication.

610 DK ISSN 0373-2746
MAANEDSSKRIFT FOR PRAKTISK LAEGEGERNING. 1922. m. Kr.150. (Koebenhavn Praktiserende Laeger) Laegeforeningens Forlag, P.O. Box 93, DK-1003 Copenhagen K, Denmark. Ed. Dr. Flemming Holberg. adv. **Indexed:** Chem.Abstr.

610 IS
MABAT LAMERPAOT. 1987. q. Association of Kupat Cholim Doctors, 6 Tel Hai St., Tel Aviv, Israel. TEL 03-280118. Ed. Dr. Dor Michael.

610 GW ISSN 0720-597X
MADE IN EUROPE - MEDICAL EQUIPMENT AND SUPPLY GUIDE. (Text in English) 1981. a. DM.75($50) Made in Europe Marketing Organization GmbH, Hahnstr. 70, 60528 Frankfurt a.M., Germany. TEL 069-6680380. FAX 069-66803838. Ed. Franziska Bastanier; Pub. Martin Romer. adv. contact: Franziska Bastanier. index. circ. 20,000. (back issues avail.) **Document type:** catalog.

MAGNESIUM BULLETIN. see *CHEMISTRY — Analytical Chemistry*

612 FR
▼**LA MAIN.** Announced for publication in 1996. q. 565 F. to individuals (foreign 750 F.($152)); institutions 980 F. (foreign 1200 F.($243)) (effective 1996). Arnette Blackwell, 1 rue de Lille, 75007 Paris, France. TEL 33-1-44-86-07-70. FAX 33-1-44-86-07-66.

MEDICAL SCIENCES 4235

610   IO   ISSN 0377-1121
MAJALAH KEDOKTERAN INDONESIA; the journal of the Indonesian Medical Association. (Text in English) 1950. m. Rps.35000($17.75) (effective Jan. 1992). Indonesian Medical Association, Yayasan penerbitan IDI, Jl. Dr. Samratulangi No. 29, Jakarta 10350, Indonesia. TEL 62-021-337910. Ed. Chicf Tjokronegoro. adv. circ. 18,000. (back issues avail.)

610   IO   ISSN 0303-7932
R97.7.I5
MAJALAH KEDOKTERAN SURABAYA. (Text in Indonesian; summaries in English) 1964. q. Rps.1000. Airlangga University, School of Medicine, Jalan Dharmahusada No. 47, Surabaya, Indonesia. Ed. Soedarso Djojonegoro. adv.; bk.rev. circ. 4,000.
  Former titles: Madjalah Kedokteran Surabaja (ISSN 0024-9564); Madjalah Research Kedokteran, Surabaja.

MAKEDONSKA AKADEMIJA NA NAUKITE I UMETNOSTITE. ODDELENIE ZA BIOLOSKI I MEDICINSKI NAUKI. PRILOZI/MACEDONIAN ACADEMY OF SCIENCES AND ARTS. SECTION OF BIOLOGICAL AND MEDICAL SCIENCES. CONTRIBUTIONS. see *BIOLOGY*

610   UG   ISSN 0025-1119
MAKERERE MEDICAL JOURNAL. Abbreviated title: M M J. 1957. s-a. $6.25. Makerere University Medical Students' Association (MUMSA), P.O. Box 7072, Kampala, Uganda. adv.: page $85. bk.rev.; bibl.; charts; illus. circ. 600. **Indexed:** Biol.Abstr., Chem.Abstr., ExtraMED, Trop.Dis.Bull. **Document type:** academic/scholarly publication, proceedings.
  ●Also available on CD-ROM.
  Description: Publishes the research of Makerere University medical students and contains news of the medical school.

610   UG
MAKERERE MEDICAL NEWSLETTER. 1993. m. $5.60. Makerere University Students Association (MUMSA), P.O. Box 7072, Kampala, Uganda. TEL 256-41-531350. (Co-sponsor: World Health Organization) Ed. Haumba Samson Malwa. adv.: page $50. circ. 1,000. **Document type:** consumer publication.
  Description: Informs the public about health matters with the aim to improve health and hygiene and to prevent disease.

174.2   US   ISSN 1082-1015
R724
MAKING THE ROUNDS IN HEALTH, FAITH AND ETHICS. 1995. bi-w. $29.95. Park Ridge Center, 211 E. Ontario St., Ste. 800, Chicago, IL 60611-3219. TEL 312-266-2222. FAX 312-266-6086. Ed. Martin E. Marty; Pub. Laurence J. O'Connell. bk.rev.; index; circ. 2,000 (paid). (also avail. in microform from UMI) **Indexed:** Chr.Per.Ind. (1995-), CINAHL, Hosp.Lit.Ind. (1995-), Past.Care & Couns.Abstr. (1995-), Rel.Ind.One (1995-).
  ●Also available online.
  —BLDSC (8216.150250); UMI.
  Supersedes (1986-1995): Second Opinion (Chicago) (ISSN 0890-1570)
  Description: Provides in-depth coverage of current issues such as abortion, AIDS, euthanasia, organ transplantation, genetic research and new reproductive technologies, by and for people working at the interchange of health, faith, and ethics.

616.07   MY   ISSN 0126-8635
MALAYSIAN JOURNAL OF PATHOLOGY. 1978. s-a. $30 per no. Malaysian Society of Pathologists, Department of Pathology, c/o University of Malaysia, Faculty of Medicine, 59100 Kuala Lumpur, Malaysia. FAX 603-7573661. TELEX UNIMAL-MA-39845. Ed. L.M. Looi. adv.; bk.rev. circ. 500. **Indexed:** Ind.Med. **Document type:** academic/scholarly publication.
  —BLDSC (5356.068500).
  Description: Publishes results of study and research in pathology, especially those relating to human disease occuring in Malaysia.

658   610   US   ISSN 1062-3388
MANAGED CARE; a guide for physicians. 1992. m. $78. Stezzi Communications, Inc., 301 Oxford Valley Rd., Ste. 603B, Yardley, PA 19067. TEL 215-321-6663. FAX 215-321-6670. E-mail: 75407.3364@compuserve.com. Ed. Patrick Mullen; Pub. Timothy Search. adv.: B&W page $3950; adv. contact: Timothy Stezzi. circ. 76,000 (controlled). **Document type:** trade publication.
  Description: Advises physicians in managed care on the conduct of their careers. Informs them of their rapidly changing options and opportunities.

610   330   US   ISSN 1073-1520
▼**MANAGED CARE MEDICINE.** 1994. bi-m. $95. (National Association of Managed Care Physicians) Health Care Communications, Inc., 1 Bridge Plaza, Ste. 350, Fort Lee, NJ 07024. TEL 201-947-5545. FAX 201-947-8406. Ed. R.S. Venable. adv.: B&W page $2925; adv. contact: Bradley Kalish. circ. 25,000. (back issues avail.) **Document type:** trade publication.
  Description: Focuses on the business side of medicine.

MANAGED CARE QUARTERLY. see *HOSPITALS*

658   US   ISSN 1056-7461
MANAGED CARE WEEK. 1991. w. (45/yr.). $325. Atlantic Information Services, Inc., 1050 17th St., N.W., Ste. 480, Washington, DC 20036-5500. TEL 202-775-9008. FAX 202-331-9542.
  —CCC.
  Description: Current news of business affairs and compliance strategies of HMOs, PPOs and other managed care plans and the role of managed care in health care financing reforms.

610   US
MANAGED HEALTHCARE NEWS. 1986. m. $85 to institutions (foreign $100) (effective 1996). Excerpta medica, Inc., Knolls Group, 201 Littleton Rd., Ste. 100, Morris Plains, NJ 07950-2932. TEL 201-285-0855. FAX 201-285-1472. (Subscr. to: Box 3000, Denville, NJ 07834) Ed. Donald Pizzi. adv. contact: Robert Raisman. bk.rev. circ. 68,456. (tabloid format) **Document type:** newspaper, trade publication.
  Former titles (until Oct. 1995): Group Practice Managed Healthcare News; Group Practice News.
  Description: Provides useful information for physicians, administrators, pharmacists, and key HMO/PPO professionals in group practice or managed healthcare settings.

610   658   US   ISSN 0196-9455
MANAGEMENT UPDATE (DENVER). Variant title: M G M Update. 1961. m. membership. Medical Group Management Association, 104 Inverness Terrace E., Englewood, CO 80112. TEL 303-799-1111. Ed. Brenda Hull. adv. contact: Eileen Barker. circ. 18,500 (controlled). (tabloid format) **Document type:** newspaper.
  Description: Covers the latest in medical practice management trends and issues.

MANAGING AUDIT IN GENERAL PRACTICE. see *BUSINESS AND ECONOMICS — Accounting*

610   JA   ISSN 0913-2899
MANIPYURESHON/JAPANESE JOURNAL OF MANIPULATIVE THERAPEUTICS. (Text in Japanese) 1986. q. 2500 Yen per no. Enterprise Co., Ltd., 1-3, Honkomagome 2-chome, Bunkyo-ku, Tokyo 113, Japan.

MANUAL OF BIOLOGICAL MARKERS OF DISEASE. see *BIOLOGY — Physiology*

610   DK   ISSN 0107-9190
MANUEL MEDICIN. 1981. q. free. (Dansk Selskab for Manuel Medicin) Dagl. Service Afdeling, Aarhus Amtssygehus, DK-8000 Aarhus C, Denmark. FAX 66-13-28-54. Ed. Dr. Johannes Fossgreen. adv.; bk.rev. circ. 950.

MARKETER'S GUIDEPOST. see *BUSINESS AND ECONOMICS — Marketing And Purchasing*

610   US   ISSN 0886-0572
R11   CODEN: MMJRA8
MARYLAND MEDICAL JOURNAL. 1952. m. $45 to non-members (foreign $57) (typically set in June). Medical and Chirurgical Faculty of Maryland, 1211 Cathedral St, Baltimore, MD 21201. TEL 410-539-0872. FAX 410-547-0915. Ed. Dr. John W. Buckley. adv. contact: Rluth M Seaby. bk.rev.; bibl.; charts; illus.; index; circ. 7,500 (controlled). (also avail. in microform from UMI; reprint service avail. from ISI) **Indexed:** Biol.Abstr., Chem.Abstr., CINAHL, Curr.Cont., Excerp.Med. (until 1995), Ind.Med., INIS Atomind., Med.Care Rev. **Document type:** academic/scholarly publication.
  —BLDSC (5383.517000); EMDOCS; Faxon; SWETS; UnCover.
  Formerly (until 1985): Maryland State Medical Journal (ISSN 0025-4363)
  Description: Contains original research, case studies and articles related to clinical medicine; information on medical practice and the art of medicine; legislative updates on medicine-related topics; and member information.

610   PL   ISSN 0025-5246
                         CODEN: MMDPA6
MATERIA MEDICA POLONA; the Polish journal of medicine and pharmacy. (Text in English, French) 1969. q. $60. Centrum Medyczne Ksztalcenia Podyplomowego, Ul. Marymoncka 99, 01-813 Warsaw, Poland. TELEX 813567 AGPOL PL. Ed. Edward Ruzyllo. adv.; bk.rev.; index. circ. 3,000. **Indexed:** Abstr.Hyg., Biol.Abstr., Dent.Ind., Excerp.Med., Ind.Med., Nutr.Abstr., Trop.Dis.Bull.
  —BLDSC (5392.600000); CASDDS; EMDOCS; Faxon.

610   GW   ISSN 0945-053X
QP552.C6   CODEN: MTBOEC
MATRIX - BIOLOGY; clinical and experimental. (Text in English) irreg. DM.796 (foreign DM.814). Gustav Fischer Verlag, Wollgrasweg 49, 70599 Stuttgart, Germany. TEL 0711-458030. FAX 0711-4580334. TELEX 7111488-FIBUCH. (Subscr. to: Postfach 720143, 70577 Stuttgart, Germany; U.S. addr.: VCH Publishers, Inc., 303 N.W. 12th Ave., Deerfield Beach, FL 33442-1788) Ed. Karl Piez. **Indexed:** Biol.Abstr., Chem.Abstr., Curr.Adv.Ecol.Sci., Curr.Cont., Curr.Leather Lit., Dent.Ind., Excerp.Med., Ind.Med., Ind.Sci.Rev., Sci.Cit.Ind. **Document type:** academic/scholarly publication.
  —BLDSC (5412.050000); CASDDS; Faxon; Genuine Article; SWETS; UMI; UnCover. **CCC**.
  Former titles (until 1993): Matrix (ISSN 0934-8832); (until 1988): Collagen and Related Research (ISSN 0174-173X)

610   US
MAUDSLEY MONOGRAPHS. irreg. price varies. Oxford University Press, 200 Madison Ave, New York, NY 10016. TEL 212-679-7300. Ed.Bd. **Document type:** monographic series.

610   US
MAYO ALUMNI. 1965. q. free to qualified personnel. Mayo Foundation, Mayo Clinic, Rochester, MN 55905. Ed. Rosemary Cashman. circ. 14,000 (controlled).
  Formerly (until 1992): Mayo Alumnus.
  Description: Directed to the physicians, scientists and medical educators who trained at Mayo.

362.1   **613**   **610.69**   US   ISSN 0741-6245
                         CODEN: MCHLEG
MAYO CLINIC HEALTH LETTER; reliable information for a healthier life. 1983. m. $24. (Mayo Foundation for Medical Education and Research) Mayo Medical Ventures, 200 First St., S.W., Rochester, MN 55905. TEL 507-284-0773. FAX 507-284-5410. (Box 53886, Boulder, CO 80323-3886. TEL 800-333-9038) Ed. N. Nicole Spelhaug. index,cum.index. circ. 400,000. (looseleaf format) **Indexed:** CINAHL, Hlth.Ind. **Document type:** newsletter.
  —BLDSC (5413.347000); UnCover.
  Description: Presents timely facts and findings on a broad variety of health issues.

MEDICAL SCIENCES

610   **US**   ISSN 0025-6196
CODEN: MACPAJ
MAYO CLINIC PROCEEDINGS. 1926. m. $72 (effective 1996). (Mayo Clinic) Mayo Foundation for Medical Education and Research, Rochester, MN 55905. TEL 507-284-2154. FAX 507-284-0252. Ed. Dr. Udaya B.S. Prakash. adv. contact: Anthony M. DiBiase. bk.rev.; abstr.; charts; illus.; index; circ. 95,000 (controlled). (also avail. in microform from PMC) **Indexed:** Abstr.Hyg., AIM, Biol.Abstr., Chem.Abstr., Child Devel.Abstr., CINAHL, Curr.Adv.Biochem., Curr.Adv.Cancer Res., Curr.Adv.Ecol.Sci., Curr.Cont., Diar.Dis.Res., Excerp.Med., Helminthol.Abstr., Ind.Hyg.Dig., Ind.Med., Ind.Sci.Rev., INIS Atomind., Kidney, Med.& Surg.Dermat., Nutr.Abstr., Rehabil.Lit., Rev.Plant Path., Risk Abstr., Sci.Cit.Ind., Trop.Dis.Bull. **Document type:** academic/scholarly publication, proceedings.
●Also available on CD-ROM.
—BLDSC (5413.350000); CASDDS; EMDOCS; Faxon; Genuine Article; SWETS; UMI; UnCover. **CCC.**
Description: Articles on the results of medical research and technology, including abstracts, editorials, subject reviews, case reports and announcements for the medical community.
Refereed Serial

610   **US**   ISSN 0882-6617
MAYO CLINICAL UPDATE. 1985. q. free to qualified personnel. Mayo Foundation, Mayo Clinic, 200 First St. S.W., Rochester, MN 55905. **Document type:** newsletter.
Description: Information for physicians.

MEALEY'S LITIGATION REPORT: BREAST IMPLANTS. see *LAW — Civil Law*

610   **US**
MECKLENBURG COUNTY MEDICAL SOCIETY. BULLETIN. 1970. m. $25. Tri Mark, 1112 Harding Pl., Ste. 200, Charlotte, NC 28204-2825. Ed. J. Carole Carney. adv. contact: Leslie Shinn. circ. 1,400. (back issues avail.) **Document type:** trade publication, bulletin.
Description: Updates area physicians on health care and medical practice issues.

610   **IE**
MED. 12/yr. 1 Pembroke Pl., Ballsbridge, Dublin 4, Ireland. TEL 682750. FAX 685184.

610   **GW**   ISSN 0937-7093
MED ORGANICA. 4/yr. DM.38. Schmidt-Roemhild Verlag, Mengstr. 16, 23552 Luebeck, Germany. TEL 0451-1605-0. FAX 0451-1605253. **Document type:** academic/scholarly publication.

MEDDELELSER OM GROENLAND, MAN & SOCIETY. see *ANTHROPOLOGY*

610   **FR**   ISSN 0399-385X
MEDECIN DE FRANCE. 1929. 44/yr. 60 bd. de la Tour-Maurbourg, 75007 Paris, France. TEL 45-55-20-20. FAX 45-51-82-13. Ed. Dr. Jacques Beaupere. circ. 35,799.

610   **FR**   ISSN 0397-9172
MEDECIN DE RESERVE. 1960. 6/yr. Union Nationale de Reserve, 65-67 av. des Champs-Elysees, 75008 Paris, France. TEL 45-63-21-45. Ed. Jean de Kearney. circ. 2,600.

610   **FR**   ISSN 0768-9942
MEDECIN DU MIDI. 1982. 22/yr. Sorems, 25 rue Roquelaine, 31000 Toulouse, France. TEL 61-62-00-68. FAX 61-62-06-82. Ed. Dr. H.-J. Bussiere. circ. 6,000.
Formerly (until 1983): Medecin (ISSN 0758-2188)

610   **CN**   ISSN 0025-6692
MEDECIN DU QUEBEC. (Text in French, summaries in English) 1965. m. Can.$75 (effective 1995). Federation des Medecins Omnipraticiens du Quebec - Federation of General Practitioners of Quebec, 1440 W. St. Catherine St., Ste. 1100, Montreal, PQ H3G 1R8, Canada. TEL 514-878-1911. FAX 514-878-4455. Ed. Dr. Georges Boileau. adv.; bk.rev.; bibl.; index; circ. 19,300 (controlled). (back issues avail.) **Indexed:** Anim.Breed.Abstr., Pt.de Rep. (1983-).

616.98   **FR**   ISSN 0294-0817
RC1050 CODEN: MSMHD4
MEDECINE AERONAUTIQUE ET SPATIALE. (Summaries in English, French) 1962. 4/yr. $30 (foreign 450 F.). I.M.A.S.S.A., 26 bd Victor, 00460 Armees, France. TEL 1-45-52-67-91. FAX 1-45-52-65-90. Ed. J.R. Galle-Tessonneau. adv.; bk.rev.; abstr.; bibl.; charts; illus.; index. **Indexed:** Chem.Abstr., Excerp.Med. **Document type:** academic/scholarly publication.
—CASDDS.
Former titles: Medecine Aeronautique et Spatiale - Medecine Subaquatique et Hyperbare (ISSN 0399-6417); (until 1976): Revue de Medecine Aeronautique et Spatiale (ISSN 0035-1520); (until 1965): Revue de Medecine Aeronautique.

610   **SG**   ISSN 0047-6404
MEDECINE D'AFRIQUE NOIRE. 1952. m. P.O. Box 1281, Dakar, Senegal. TEL 221-217176. Ed. Emile Lalanne. circ. 8,250. **Indexed:** Abstr.Hyg., Biol.Abstr., Excerp.Med., Helminthol.Abstr., Protozool.Abstr., Trop.Dis.Bull.
—EMDOCS; UMI.

610   **FR**   ISSN 0543-2243
MEDECINE DE L'HOMME. 1968. 6/yr. 350 F. Centre Catholique des Medecins Francais, 5 ave. de l'Observatoire, 75006 Paris, France. TEL 46-34-39-15. FAX 43-54-10-07. Ed. Claude Laroche. adv.; bk.rev. circ. 4,376.

616.98   **FR**   ISSN 0300-4937
CODEN: MDARC4
MEDECINE ET ARMEES. 1973. 8/yr. 240 F. (foreign 310 F.) (effective 1996). Association pour le Developpement et la Diffusion de l'Information Militaire, 6 rue Saint Charles, 75015 Paris, France. TEL 45-77-03-76. adv.; bk.rev.; charts; illus.; index. circ. 6,000. **Indexed:** Biol.Abstr., C.I.S. Abstr., Chem.Abstr., Curr.Cont., Excerp.Med., Helminthol.Abstr., Ind.Med., Nutr.Abstr.
—BLDSC (5487.727000); CASDDS; Genuine Article.
Supersedes: Revue des Corps de Sante des Armees (ISSN 0035-1954)
Description: Looks at medical sciences from a military point of view.

610 613   **SZ**   ISSN 0025-6749
CODEN: MEHGAB
MEDECINE ET HYGIENE. (Text in French) 1943. w. 85 SFr. (foreign 165 SFr.). Editions Medecine et Hygiene, Case Postale 456, CH-1211 Geneva 4, Switzerland. TEL 022-3469355. FAX 022-3475610. Ed. Dr. Bertrand Kiefer. adv.; bk.rev.; bibl.; charts; illus.; index. circ. 7,500. (reprint service avail. from UMI) **Indexed:** Biol.Abstr., C.I.S. Abstr., Chem.Abstr., Dent.Ind., Excerp.Med. **Document type:** academic/scholarly publication.
—BLDSC (5487.730000); CASDDS; EMDOCS; Genuine Article; SWETS; UMI. **CCC.**

MEDECINE ET NUTRITION. see *NUTRITION AND DIETETICS*

610   **FR**   ISSN 0767-0974
CODEN: MSMSE4
MEDECINE SCIENCES. 1985. 10/yr. 460 F. to individuals; institutions 1030 F.; students 285 F. (effective 1995). John Libbey Eurotext, 127 av de la Republique, 92120 Montrouge, France. TEL 1-46-73-06-60. FAX 1-40-84-09-99. (Subscr. to: A T E I, 23-25 rue Fernand Combette, 93100 Montreuil sous Bois, France. TEL 48-59-58-11. FAX 48-59-57-99) Ed. Axel Khan. **Indexed:** Med.& Surg.Dermat. **Document type:** academic/scholarly publication.
—BLDSC (5980.840100); Genuine Article; SWETS.
Description: Studies the biology of today and the medicine of tomorrow.

610   **FR**
▼**MEDECINE THERAPEUTIQUE.** 1995. 10/yr. 550 F. (EU & Switzerland 650 F.; elsewhere 700 F.). John Libbey Eurotext, 127 av. de la Republique, 92120 Montrouge, France. TEL 33-1-46730660. FAX 33-1-40840999. (Subscr. to: A T E I, 23-25 rue Fernand-Combette, 93100 Montreuil, France. TEL 33-1-48595811. FAX 33-1-48595799) Eds. Pierre Bougneres, Christian Boitard. adv.; illus. **Document type:** academic/scholarly publication.
Description: Covers all aspects of modern medicine. Serves as a link between basic research and medical practice.
Refereed Serial

610   **FR**
MEDECINS DES HOPITAUX PUBLICS.* bi-m. Union Nationale des Syndicats de Medecins des Hopitaux Publics, 15 rue Beaugrenelle, 75015 Paris, France. TEL 40-59-48-27. Ed. Jean Cordebar. adv.

610   **FR**   ISSN 0183-5734
MEDECINS DU VAL-DE-MARNE. 1977. 4/yr. 4 rue Octave de-Mesnil, 94000 Creteil, France. TEL 42-07-78-66. Ed. Dr. Vergeylen. circ. 4,500.

610   **UK**   ISSN 0144-4271
MEDECONOMICS. 1980. m. £64. Haymarket Medical Ltd., 30 Lancaster Gate, London W2 3LP, England. TEL 0171-413-4402. (Subscr. to: Galleon, P.O. Box 219, Woking, Surrey GU21 1ZW, England. TEL 01483-733800) Ed. Ann Warburton. adv. contact: James Ranft. circ. 41,807. **Document type:** trade publication.
●Also available online. Vendor(s): Data-Star.
—BLDSC (5488.060000). **CCC.**

610   **US**   ISSN 0740-1892
RA440.55
MEDIA PROFILES: HEALTH SCIENCES EDITION. 1974. q. $145 (effective 1996). Olympic Media Information, Box 190, West Park, NY 12493. TEL 914-384-6563. E-mail: medprofile@aol.com. Ed. Walt Carroll. film rev.; abstr.; index, cum.index every 2 yrs. circ. 1,000. (looseleaf format; back issues avail.) **Indexed:** Media Rev.Dig.
Formerly: Hospital - Health Care Training Media Profiles (ISSN 0095-0580)
Description: Reference resource of films, videos and media based courses of interest to libraries and learning resource centers serving healthcare professionals who teach medical and nursing students and patients.

610   **UK**   ISSN 0962-9351
CODEN: MNFLEF
MEDIATORS OF INFLAMMATION. 1992. bi-m. £260($445) to institutions (effective 1995). Rapid Communications of Oxford Ltd., The Old Malthouse, Paradise St., Oxford OX1 1LD, England. TEL 01865-790447. FAX 01865-244012. E-mail: rapidcom@vax.oxford.ac.uk. Ed. Ivan Bonta. (reprint service avail.) **Indexed:** Excerp.Med. (1993-). **Document type:** academic/scholarly publication.
●Also available on CD-ROM.
—BLDSC (5525.385100); ADONIS; CASDDS; Genuine Article. **CCC.**
Description: Promotes the rapid publication of original and fundamental research articles on all aspects of cellular mediators.

610   **CI**   ISSN 0351-0093
CODEN: MEJAD6
MEDICA JADERTINA. 1969. 4/yr. Medical Center Zadar, Scientific Unit, Boze Pericica 5, 57000 Zadar, Croatia. **Indexed:** Excerp.Med. **Document type:** academic/scholarly publication.

MEDICAID FRAUD REPORT. see *LAW*

MEDICAID RECIPIENT CHARACTERISTICS AND UNITS OF SELECTED MEDICAL SERVICES. see *SOCIAL SERVICES AND WELFARE*

610 614   **US**
MEDICAL ADMINISTRATION EXECUTIVE. bi-m. $60. American Academy of Medical Administrators, 30555 Southfield Rd., Ste. 150, Southfield, MI 48076. TEL 313-540-4310. FAX 313-645-0590. Ed. Thomas R. O'Donovan. adv.; bk.rev. circ. 3,000.
Formerly: A A M A Executive (ISSN 0065-6879)

MEDICAL & BIOLOGICAL ENGINEERING & COMPUTING. see *BIOLOGY — Bioengineering*

610   **BS**
MEDICAL AND DENTAL ASSOCIATION OF BOTSWANA. JOURNAL. (Text in English) 1971. q. $11. Medical and Dental Association of Botswana, P.O. Box 798, Gaborone, Botswana. adv.; charts. circ. 200. (back issues avail.) **Indexed:** Ind.S.A.Per.

MEDICAL SCIENCES

610 US ISSN 0363-0366
R5
MEDICAL AND HEALTH ANNUAL. 1976. a. $33.95 (effective 1995). Encyclopaedia Britannica, Inc., 310 S. Michigan Ave., Chicago, IL 60604. TEL 312-347-7000. FAX 312-347-7914. Ed. Ellen Bernstein. index.
—BLDSC (5525.954000).
Description: For lay readers, covers broad areas of medicine and health including in-depth articles. Reviews important developments in the medical specialties.

MEDICAL AND HEALTHCARE MARKETPLACE GUIDE. see BUSINESS AND ECONOMICS — Trade And Industrial Directories

MEDICAL AND NUTRITIONAL RESEARCH COMMUNICATIONS. see NUTRITION AND DIETETICS

MEDICAL ANTHROPOLOGY; cross-cultural studies in health and illness. see ANTHROPOLOGY

MEDICAL ANTHROPOLOGY QUARTERLY; international journal for the cultural and social analysis of health. see ANTHROPOLOGY

610 US ISSN 0025-7028
R15
MEDICAL ASSOCIATION OF GEORGIA. JOURNAL. 1911. m. $40 in Georgia; other states $60. Medical Association of Georgia, 938 Peachtree St., N.E., Atlanta, GA 30309. TEL 404-876-7535. FAX 404-874-8651. Ed. Dr. Miguel A. Faria, Jr. adv.; bk.rev.; bibl.; charts; illus.; index. circ. 10,000. (also avail. in microform) **Indexed:** Chem.Abstr., Dent.Ind., Ind.Med., INIS Atomind.
—BLDSC (4824.130000); Faxon; UMI; UnCover.

610 TH ISSN 0125-2208
CODEN: JMTHBU
MEDICAL ASSOCIATION OF THAILAND. JOURNAL. Key Title: Chot Mai Het Thang Phaet. (Supplement avail. (ISSN 0025-7036) (Text in English; summaries in Thai) 1917. m. $40. Medical Association of Thailand, 67-9 Soi Soonvichai, New Pechburi Rd., Bangkok 10, Thailand. TEL 66-2-314-4333. FAX 66-2-314-4333. Ed. Dr. Prasert Thongcharoen. adv.; abstr.; charts; illus.; index. circ. 3,500. **Indexed:** Abstr.Hyg., Biol.Abstr., Chem.Abstr., Curr.Adv.Ecol.Sci., Curr.Cont., Dairy Sci.Abstr., Diar.Dis.Res., Excerp.Med., Helminthol.Abstr., Ind.Med., Maize Abstr., Protozool.Abstr., Rev.Med.& Vet.Mycol., Rev.Plant Path., Seed Abstr., Soyabean Abstr., Trop.Dis.Bull. **Document type:** academic/scholarly publication.
—BLDSC (4824.200000); CASDDS; SWETS.

610 TH ISSN 0025-7036
CODEN: JMTHBU
MEDICAL ASSOCIATION OF THAILAND. JOURNAL. SUPPLEMENT. 1918. m. Medical Association of Thailand, 67-9 Soi Soonvichai, New Pechburi Rd., Bangkok 10, Thailand. TEL 66-2-314-4333. FAX 66-2-314-4333. **Document type:** academic/scholarly publication.
—Faxon.

MEDICAL AUDIT NEWS. see BUSINESS AND ECONOMICS — Accounting

MEDICAL BENEFITS. see INSURANCE — Abstracting, Bibliographies, Statistics

610 US
MEDICAL BULLETIN OF NORTHERN VIRGINIA. 10/yr. $20 (effective Jan. 1994). 3720 Jocelyn St., N.W. Ate. 300, Washington, DC 20015. TEL 202-363-6631. FAX 202-364-8876. Ed. Kathleen M. Healy. adv.; bk.rev. circ. 2,200. (back issues avail.) **Document type:** newspaper.

MEDICAL BUSINESS REVIEW; medical business analysis for the doctor-executive. see BUSINESS AND ECONOMICS — Management

610 614 US ISSN 0025-7079
RA1 CODEN: MDLCBD
MEDICAL CARE. 1963. m. $155 to individuals (foreign $199); institutions $270 (foreign $315) (effective 1996); newsstand price: $28. (American Public Health Association, Medical Care Section) Lippincott - Raven Publishers, 227 E. Washington Sq., Philadelphia, PA 19106. TEL 215-238-4200. Ed. Dr. Duncan Neuhauser. index. circ. 2,303. (also avail. in microform from UMI) **Indexed:** Abstr.Health Care Manage.Stud., CINAHL, Curr.Cont., Dent.Ind., Dok.Arbeitsmed., Excerp.Med., FAMLI, Hosp.Lit.Ind., Ind.Med., Ind.Sci.Rev., Int.Nurs.Ind., Psychol.Abstr. (1986-), Risk Abstr., Sci.Cit.Ind., SSCI.
—BLDSC (5526.900000); Faxon; Genuine Article; SWETS; UMI; UnCover. **CCC**.
Refereed Serial

610 US ISSN 1068-1779
MEDICAL CARE INTERNATIONAL. (Text in English; summaries in French, German, Italian, Spanish) 1991. bi-m. $95. Globetech Publishing, 30 Cannon Rd., Wilton, CT 06897. TEL 203-762-3432. FAX 203-762-8640. Ed. Dr. Daniel H. Adler; Pub. Marc Gueron. adv. contact: Patricia Walsh. circ. 30,000 (controlled). **Document type:** trade publication.

610 US ISSN 1066-825X
MEDICAL CARE PRODUCTS. 1982. 8/yr. $24 (Canada $25; Mexico $24; elsewhere $34) (effective 1996). Gordon Publications, Inc., Part of Cahners Publishing Company, Division of Reed Elsevier Inc., 301 Gibraltar Dr., Box 650, Morris Plains, NJ 07950-0650. TEL 201-292-5100. FAX 201-898-9281. circ. 87,500. (tabloid format)
—**CCC**.
Description: Serves nursing supervisors, medical department heads, purchasing and materials managment directors, and phsucian administrators responsible for patient care in hospitals, nursing homes and medical clinics.

610 371.42 AT ISSN 0812-7077
MEDICAL CAREERS IN AUSTRALIA. 1984. irreg., 3rd ed., 1992. Aus.$15. Victorian Medical Postgraduate Foundation Inc., P.O. Box 27, Parkville, Vic. 3052, Australia. TEL 61-3-93479633. FAX 61-3-93474547. Ed. Dr. P. Philips. circ. 5,000. **Description:** Career advice in medicine for undergraduates and recent graduates.

610 UK ISSN 0025-7095
MEDICAL CENTRE JOURNAL. 1967. 3/yr. free. (Bedfordshire District Health Authority) Luton & Dunstable Hospital, Medical Centre, Luton, Bedfordshire, England. Ed. D.I.M. Siegler. circ. 600.

610 SA ISSN 0025-7117
MEDICAL CHRONICLE. 1964. m. Newspaper Representations (S.A.) (Pty.), Box 549, Johannesburg, South Africa. Eds. L.P. Thomas, B.S. Unterhalter. adv.; bk.rev.; film rev.; illus.; tr.lit. circ. 13,695. (tabloid format)

MEDICAL CLIENT NEWSLETTER. see BUSINESS AND ECONOMICS — Accounting

610 US ISSN 0025-7125
RC60 CODEN: MCNAA9
MEDICAL CLINICS OF NORTH AMERICA. 1916. bi-m. $110 (foreign $137) (effective 1996). W.B. Saunders Co. (Subsidiary of: Harcourt Brace & Company), Curtis Center, 3rd Fl., Independence Sq. W., Philadelphia, PA 19106-3399. TEL 215-238-7800. FAX 215-238-6445. (Subscr. to: Periodicals Fulfillment, W.B. Saunders Co., 6277 Sea Harbor Dr., 4th Fl., Orlando, FL 32891-4800. TEL 800-654-2452. FAX 800-874-6418) Ed. Naina Chohan. bibl.; charts; illus.; index, cum.index. (also avail. in microform from UMI,PMC; reprint service avail. from UMI,ISI) **Indexed:** AIM, Biol.Abstr., Biotech.Abstr., Chem.Abstr., CINAHL, Curr.Adv.Ecol.Sci., Curr.Cont., Dairy Sci.Abstr., Diar.Dis.Res., Excerp.Med., Helminthol.Abstr., I.P.A., Ind.Med., Ind.Sci.Rev., INIS Atomind., Int.Nurs.Ind., Nutr.Abstr., Risk Abstr., Sugar Ind.Abstr. **Document type:** academic/scholarly publication.
—BLDSC (5527.000000); CASDDS; EMDOCS; Faxon; Genuine Article; SWETS; UMI; UnCover. **CCC**.
Formerly: Medical Clinics.

610 II ISSN 0025-7133
MEDICAL COLLEGE AND HOSPITAL, CALCUTTA. BULLETIN. (Text in English) 1967. Rs.12. Medical College and Hospital, Department of Medicine, 88 College St., Calcutta 12, India. Ed. Dr. Nalini Ranjan Konar. adv.; charts; illus. circ. 600.

610 JA ISSN 0465-4978
MEDICAL CORNER. (Text in Japanese) 1967. bi-m. Meiji Seika Kaisha, Ltd., 4-16, Kyobashi 2-chome, Chuo-ku, Tokyo 104, Japan.

610 US ISSN 0272-989X
CODEN: MDMADE
MEDICAL DECISION MAKING; an international journal. 1980. q. $88 to individuals (foreign $98); institutions $98 (foreign $112). (Society for Medical Decision Making, Inc.) Hanley & Belfus, Inc., 210 S. 13th St., Philadelphia, PA 19107. TEL 215-546-7293. FAX 215-790-9330. Ed. Artnurs Elstein. illus.; charts; stat.; index. circ. 1,600. (back issues avail.) **Indexed:** Abstr.Health Care Manage.Stud., Abstr.Hyg., Excerp.Med., Ind.Med., Ind.Sci.Rev.
—BLDSC (5527.053500); Faxon; Genuine Article; SWETS; UnCover. **CCC**.
Description: Concerned with the quantitative science of decision-making in medicine.
Refereed Serial

MEDICAL DEVICE COMPANIES ANALYSIS. see INSTRUMENTS

610 UK ISSN 1048-6690
MEDICAL DEVICE TECHNOLOGY. 1990. 10/yr. free to qualified persons in Europe (non-qualified persons in Europe £60; others £85) (effective 1996). Advanstar Communications, Advanstar House, Park West, Sealand Rd., Chester CH1 4RN, England. TEL 01244-378888. FAX 01244-370512. Ed. Annie Ellerton; Pub. Fran Waldie. adv.: B&W page £4980; color page £6495; adv. contact: Celia Smith. tr.lit. circ. 20,000. (back issues avail.; reprint service avail.) **Indexed:** Intl.Polym.Sci.& Tech., RAPRA. **Document type:** trade publication.
—BLDSC (5527.055420); Genuine Article. **CCC**.
Description: Gives the latest news and views on medical device technology for research and development and for QA-QC professionals in manufacturing.

615 US ISSN 0163-2426
CODEN: MDDIDR
MEDICAL DEVICES, DIAGNOSTICS & INSTRUMENTATION REPORTS: THE GRAY SHEET. Short title: M D D I Reports. 1975. w. $630 (foreign $675) (effective Jan. 1994). F-D-C Reports, Inc., 5550 Friendship Blvd., Ste. One, Chevy Chase, MD 20815. TEL 301-657-9830. FAX 301-656-3094. Ed. Janet Coleman. adv.: B&W page $1400; adv. contact: Richard Messmer. (looseleaf format; back issues avail.; reprint service avail.) **Document type:** trade publication.
• Also available online. Vendor(s): Ovid Technologies (FDCR), Data-Star (FDCR), Knight-Ridder, Inc. (File no.187), Lexis-Nexis.
—BLDSC (5413.519050). **CCC**.
Description: Provides coverage of the medical devices, diagnostics and instrumentation industries. Includes regulatory agency and congressional activities, industry developments, investor and financial news.

610 US
MEDICAL DEVICES REPORTER. 1976. m. $580. Commerce Clearing House, Inc., 4025 W. Peterson Ave., Chicago, IL 60646. TEL 312-583-8500. Ed. D. Newquist.

610 JA ISSN 0543-2618
MEDICAL DIGEST. (Text in Japanese) 1952. bi-m. 300 Yen per no. Daiichi Seiyaku Co., Ltd., 14-10, Nihonbashi 3-chome, Chuo-ku, Tokyo 103, Japan.

610 UK ISSN 0305-3342
MEDICAL DIRECTORY; an alphabetical listing of medical practitioners registered in Britain. a. £149. Longman Group UK Ltd., Westgate House, 6th Fl., The High, Harlow, Essex CM20 1YR, England. TEL 0279-442601. FAX 0279-444501. adv.: B&W page £395; 203 x 121. **Document type:** directory.
—BLDSC (5527.070000).

MEDICAL SCIENCES

610   US   ISSN 0273-0561
MEDICAL DIRECTORY OF NEW YORK STATE. 1950. biennial. $115. Medical Society of the State of New York, 420 Lakeville Rd., Lake Success, NY 11042. Ed. Joan Rosenberg. **Document type:** directory.

610   US   ISSN 0025-7206
R723.5
MEDICAL ECONOMICS. 1923. fortn. $99 (foreign $159). Medical Economics Publishing Co., Inc., Five Paragon Dr., Montvale, NJ 07645. TEL 201-358-7200. FAX 201-573-1045. Ed. Stephen K. Murata. adv.: B&W page $6670, color page $9225. charts; illus.; stat.; index. circ. 152,818. (also avail. in microform from RPI,UMI) **Indexed:** Abstr.Health Care Manage.Stud., Account.Ind. (1974-), BPIA, Bus.Ind., CINAHL, Curr.Lit.Fam.Plan., Hlth.Ind., Med.Care Rev., P.A.I.S., Tr.& Indus.Ind. **Document type:** trade publication.
●Also available online. Vendor(s): Knight-Ridder, Inc.
—BLDSC (5527.160000); Faxon; UMI; UnCover. **CCC.**
Description: Publishes original articles designed to help the private practice physician with practice management, professional and patient relations, health insurance issues, relevant legislation, and personal and financial affairs.

610.7 378   UK   ISSN 0308-0110
R735.A1
MEDICAL EDUCATION. 1966. bi-m. £149 in Europe; elsewhere £164($264) (effective 1996). (Association for the Study of Medical Education) Blackwell Science Ltd., Osney Mead, Oxford OX2 0EL, England. TEL 44-1865-206206. FAX 44-1865-721205. TELEX 83355 MEDBOK G. Ed. H.J. Walton. adv.; bk.rev.; bibl.; index. circ. 1,450. (also avail. in microform from UMI; back issues avail.; reprint service avail. from ISI) **Indexed:** Abstr.Health Care Manage.Stud., Abstr.Hyg., ASCA, Biol.Abstr., CINAHL, Cont.Pg.Educ., Curr.Adv.Ecol.Sci., Curr.Cont., Dent.Ind., Educ.Tech.Abstr., Excerp.Med., FAMLI, High Educ.Curr.Aware.Bull., Ind.Med., Ind.Sci.Rev., Mid.East: Abstr.& Ind., Mult.Ed.Abstr., Psychol.Abstr. (1986-), Res.High.Educ.Abstr., Sci.Cit.Ind., Sociol.Educ.Abstr., Tech.Educ.Abstr, Trop.Dis.Bull. **Document type:** academic/scholarly publication.
—ADONIS; Faxon; Genuine Article; SWETS; UMI; UnCover. **CCC.**
Formerly: British Journal of Medical Education (ISSN 0007-1110)
Description: Covers medical school issues pertaining to students and instructors alike.
Refereed Serial

615.845   US   ISSN 0149-9734
R856.A1
MEDICAL ELECTRONICS. 1970. bi-m. $22. Measurements & Data Corp., 2994 W. Liberty Ave., Pittsburgh, PA 15216. TEL 412-343-9666. Ed. Harish Saluja. adv.; charts; illus.; tr.lit. circ. 75,000. (also avail. in microform from UMI; reprint service avail. from UMI) **Indexed:** Biol.Abstr., Comput.Lit.Ind.
—BLDSC (5527.196000); Faxon; UMI; UnCover.
Incorporates: American Journal of Electromedicine (ISSN 0894-8291); Former titles: Medical Electronics and Data (ISSN 0098-3446); M E D (ISSN 0024-810X)
Description: Covers medical electronics.

615.845   US   ISSN 0361-4174
                       CODEN: MEEQA
MEDICAL ELECTRONICS AND EQUIPMENT NEWS. 1961. 6/yr. $40 (foreign $60) (free to qualified personnel). Reilly Publishing Co., 532 Busse Hwy., Park Ridge, IL 60068. TEL 312-693-3773. FAX 708-696-0946. Ed. Paula Ficara. adv.; bk.rev.; abstr.; charts; illus.; stat.; tr.lit. circ. 45,000. (tabloid format) **Indexed:** Excerp.Med.
—SWETS; UMI.
Formerly: Medical Electronics News (ISSN 0025-7230)
Description: Covers medical electronics.

610.28   UK   ISSN 1350-4533
                       CODEN: MEPHEO
MEDICAL ENGINEERING AND PHYSICS. 1979. 8/yr. £410($652) (effective 1996). (Biological Engineering Society) Butterworth - Heinemann, Part of the Reed Elsevier group, Linacre House, Jordan Hill, Oxford OX2 8DP, England. TEL 0865-310366. FAX 0865-310898. TELEX 83111 BHPOXF G. (Subscr. to: Elsevier Science Ltd., P.O. Box 800, Kidlington, Oxford OX5 1DX, England. TEL 44-865-843000. FAX 44-865-843010; Subscr. in U.S. and Canada to: Elsevier Science, 660 White Plains Rd., Tarrytown, NY 10591-5153. TEL 914-524-9200. FAX 914-333-2444) Ed. G.H. Byford. adv.; bk.rev.; abstr.; illus.; index. (also avail. in microform from UMI; back issues avail.) **Indexed:** Bioeng.Abstr., Biol.Abstr., Chem.Abstr., Curr.Cont., Cyb.Abstr., Dent.Ind., Excerp.Med., Ind.Med., Ind.Sci.Rev., INSPEC, Sci.Cit.Ind. **Document type:** academic/scholarly publication.
—BLDSC (5527.323000); ADONIS; CASDDS; Ei; Faxon; Genuine Article; SWETS; UMI; UnCover. **CCC.**
Formerly (until 1994): Journal of Biomedical Engineering (ISSN 0141-5425)
Description: Provides a forum in which developments in health care can be described and analyzed critically. Covers advances in instrumentation, solutions to particular patient problems, biomedical computing, clinical engineering, biological systems, and function replacement.
Refereed Serial

MEDICAL EQUIPMENT DESIGNER. see *INSTRUMENTS*

174.2   US   ISSN 0886-0653
MEDICAL ETHICS ADVISOR. 1985. m. $249. American Health Consultants, Inc., Six Piedmont Center, Ste. 400, Atlanta, GA 30305. TEL 404-262-7436; 800-688-2421. FAX 800-284-3291. Ed. Ann Carns. circ. 1,095. (reprint service avail.) **Document type:** newsletter.
—**CCC.**

610   II
MEDICAL EXPRESS; newspaper of the medical profession. (Text in English) 1974. fortn. Rs.12($6) Amal Ghosh-Hajra, Ed. & Pub., 240 Diamond Harbour Rd., Behala, Calcutta 700060, West Bengal, India. adv.; bk.rev.; abstr.; bibl.; index. circ. 10,500. **Document type:** newspaper.

610 011   UK   ISSN 0956-8298
MEDICAL EXPRESS REPORTS. 1989. irreg. Cambridge Medical Publications Ltd., Wicker House, High St., Worthing, W. Sussex BN11 1DJ, England. TEL 01903-205884. FAX 01903-234862. TELEX 878372 PPSLTD G. circ. (controlled). **Document type:** proceedings.
Description: Provides fast coverage of specific medical meetings.

610 011   UK   ISSN 0958-3505
MEDICAL FORUM REPORTER. 1989. irreg. Cambridge Medical Publications Ltd., Wicker House, High St., Worthing, W. Sussex BN11 1DJ, England. TEL 01903-205884. FAX 01903-234862. TELEX 0878372 PPSLTD G. circ. (controlled). **Document type:** proceedings.
Description: Provides close reporting of symposia and specific congress and conference sessions.

610   PK
MEDICAL GAZETTE. (Text in English) vol.2, 1971. s-m. Rs.200. Pakistan Medical Association, P.M.A. House, Aga Khan III Rd., Karachi 74400, Pakistan. TEL 92-21-7214632. FAX 92-21-7226443. circ. 12,000.

610   US   ISSN 0277-805X
                       CODEN: MGRODY
MEDICAL GRAND ROUNDS. 1982. w. $150 (effective 1996). University of Texas, Southwestern Medical Center, 5323 Harry Hines Blvd., Dallas, TX 75235-9030. TEL 214-648-2635. FAX 214-648-9100. Ed. Patrick Wong. adv.; bibl.; illus. (back issues avail.) **Indexed:** Excerp.Med. **Document type:** academic/scholarly publication.
—**CCC.**
Refereed Serial

610   US   ISSN 1040-2330
R729.5.G6
MEDICAL GROUP MANAGEMENT ASSOCIATION. DIRECTORY. 1961. a. $300. Medical Group Management Association, 104 Inverness Terrace E., Englewood, CO 80112. TEL 303-799-1111. Ed. Dennis Barnhardt. circ. 18,500. **Document type:** directory.
Formerly: Medical Group Management Association. International Directory (ISSN 0094-9604)

658   US   ISSN 0025-7257
R729.5.G6
MEDICAL GROUP MANAGEMENT JOURNAL. 1953. bi-m. $46.50. Medical Group Management Association, 104 Inverness Terrace E., Englewood, CO 80112. TEL 303-799-1111. Ed. Dr. Fred E. Graham II. adv.; charts; illus.; stat.; index. circ. 27,000. (also avail. in microform from UMI) **Indexed:** Abstr.Health Care Manage.Stud., Hosp.Lit.Ind, Med.Care Rev.
—Genuine Article; UMI; UnCover.

MEDICAL, HEALTH AND WELFARE LIBRARIES GROUP. NEWSLETTER. see *LIBRARY AND INFORMATION SCIENCES*

610   US   ISSN 0891-799X
THE MEDICAL HERALD. 1991. m. $18. Medical Herald Publishing Co., Inc., 211 E. 43rd St., Ste. 908, New York, NY 10017. TEL 212-983-3525. FAX 212-922-9211. Ed. Hugh W. Wyatt. adv.: B&W page $3440, color page $4600; trim 8 3/16 x 11 1/2. circ. 50,000. **Document type:** newspaper.
Description: Reports on subjects of concern to attending physicians who practice in the urban centers of America, including the impact of the current fiscal crisis on health care, AIDS, hypertension, cancer and other diseases.

610   UK   ISSN 0025-7273
R131.A1   CODEN: MDHIAA
MEDICAL HISTORY; devoted to the history and bibliography of medicine and the related sciences. 1957. q. £69. (Wellcome Institute for the History of Medicine) Professional & Scientific Publications, BMA House, Tavistock Sq., London WC1H 9JR, England. TEL 0171-383-6640. FAX 0171-383-6662. Eds. W.F. Bynum, V. Nutton. adv.; bk.rev.; bibl.; illus.; index. circ. 1,000. **Indexed:** Abstr.Hyg., Amer.Hist.& Life, Biol.Abstr., Br.Archaeol.Abstr., Curr.Adv.Ecol.Sci., Curr.Cont., Dairy Sci.Abstr., Excerp.Med., Hist.Abstr., Ind.Med., Ind.Sci.Rev., Ind.Vet., Nutr.Abstr., Trop.Dis.Bull., Vet.Bull. **Document type:** academic/scholarly publication.
—BLDSC (5527.500000); Faxon; SWETS; UMI; UnCover.
Refereed Serial

MEDICAL HUMANITIES REVIEW. see *HUMANITIES: COMPREHENSIVE WORKS*

610   UK   ISSN 0306-9877
R5   CODEN: MEHYDY
MEDICAL HYPOTHESES. 1975. m. £421($676) (effective 1995). Churchill Livingstone Journals (Subsidiary of: Pearson Professional), Robert Stevenson House, 1-3 Baxter's Pl., Leith Walk, Edinburgh EH1 3AF, Scotland. TEL 0131-556-2424. FAX 0131-459-1177. (Subscr. to: Pearson Professional Ltd., P.O. Box 77, Fourth Ave., Harlow, Essex CM19 5AA, England. TEL 01279-623760; U.S. subscr. to: Churchill Livingstone, 650 Ave. of the Americas, New York, NY 10011. TEL 212-206-5000) Ed. Dr. David F. Horrobin. adv. contact: David Dunnachie. bk.rev. circ. 300. (also avail. in microform from UMI; back issues avail.) **Indexed:** Anim.Breed.Abstr., Biol.Abstr., C.I.S. Abstr., Chem.Abstr., Curr.Adv.Cancer Res., Curr.Adv.Cell & Devel.Biol., Curr.Adv.Ecol.Sci., Curr.Adv.Genetics & Molec.Biol., Curr.Cont., Dairy Sci.Abstr., Dok.Arbeitsmed., Excerp.Med., Helminthol.Abstr., Ind.Med., Ind.Sci.Rev., Ind.Vet., Nutr.Abstr., Protozool.Abstr., Psychol.Abstr., Small Anim.Abstr., Vet.Bull., Weed Abstr. **Document type:** academic/scholarly publication.
—BLDSC (5527.530000); ADONIS; CASDDS; Faxon; Genuine Article; SWETS; UnCover. **CCC.**

MEDICAL SCIENCES 4239

610 US ISSN 1073-1202
MEDICAL IMAGING (PORTSMOUTH). 1986. m. free to qualified personnel; others $49 (foreign $75-$125). Second Source Publications, Inc., 10 Risho Ave., East Profidence, RI 02914-1215. TEL 401-434-1050. FAX 401-434-1090. Pub. Jack Spears. circ. 17,000 (controlled). **Document type:** trade publication.
Formerly (until 1994): Second Source Imaging (ISSN 1053-6876); Which supersedes in part (in 1990): Second Source (ISSN 0892-3426)
Description: Provides health care professionals with the latest business news and information for the cost-effective management of medical imaging equipment and technology.

610 AT
MEDICAL IMAGING AND MONITORING. q. Aus.$20. Reed Business Publishing Pty. Ltd. (Subsidiary of: Reed International PLC), 1-5 Railway St., Chatswood, N.S.W. 2067, Australia. TEL 02-372-5222. FAX 02-419-3799. Ed. L. Lange. adv.; illus. circ. 3,024. (tabloid format)
Former titles: Imaging and Monitoring News & Medical Electronics News.

610 US ISSN 1060-5193
MEDICAL INDUSTRY EXECUTIVE.* 1992. 6/yr. $55 (foreign $95). Medical Industry Publications, Inc., 1130 Hightower Trail, Atlanta, GA 30350-2910. TEL 404-998-9797. FAX 404-594-6998. Ed. Elizabeth R. Porter. adv.; B&W page $26500. circ. 20,235. **Document type:** trade publication.
Description: Focuses on reports and analyses of market trends, business, issues, regulatory requirements, product development and technology research for executives in the medical equipment, device and supply manufacturing industry.

610 US ISSN 0896-4831
MEDICAL INTERFACE. 1988. m. $68 to individuals (foreign $90); institutions $90 (foreign $110). Medicom International, Inc., 66 Palmer Ave., Ste. 49, Bronxville, NY 10708. TEL 914-337-7878. FAX 914-337-5023. Ed. Stanton R. Mehr; Pub. Raymond Hargreaves. adv.; B&W page $3402, color page $4844; trim 8 1/8 x 10 7/8; adv. contact: Laura Jeanne Czuba. circ. 27,194. **Document type:** trade publication.
—BLDSC (5527.586500).
Description: Open forum for the managed health-care industry.

616.98 II ISSN 0377-1237
MEDICAL JOURNAL ARMED FORCES, INDIA. (Text in English) 1945. q. Rs.200($60) (effective Jan. 1990). Armed Forces Medical College, Pune 411 040, Maharashtra, India. TEL 673290. Ed. Col. VC. Ohri. adv.: page Rs.5000. bk.rev.; charts; illus.; stat. circ. 5,000. **Indexed:** Biol.Abstr., Excerp.Med. (until 19??), ExtraMED, Trop.Dis.Bull. **Document type:** academic/scholarly publication.
●Also available on CD-ROM.
—BLDSC (5528.900000).
Formerly (until 1974): Armed Forces Medical Journal, India (ISSN 0004-2218)

610 AT ISSN 0025-729X
CODEN: MJAUAJ
MEDICAL JOURNAL OF AUSTRALIA. 1914. s-m. Aus.$225 (foreign Aus.$325). (Australian Medical Association) Australasian Medical Publishing Co., Private Bag 901, N Sydney, N.S.W. 2059, Australia. TEL 61-2-954-8666. FAX 61-2-956-7644. E-mail: ampco@magna.com.au. Ed. Martin Van Der Weyden. adv.: B&W page Aus.$1475, color page Aus.$2310. bk.rev.; abstr.; bibl.; illus.; s-a. index. circ. 23,000. (also avail. in microform from UMI,PMC; reprint service avail. from UMI) **Indexed:** A.D.& D., Abstr.Hyg., Aus.P.A.I.S., Aus.Rd.Ind., Bibl.Dev.Med.& Child Neur., Biol.Abstr., Biotech.Abstr., C.I.S. Abstr., Chem.Abstr., CINAHL, Curr.Adv.Cancer Res., Curr.Adv.Ecol.Sci., Curr.Cont., Dent.Ind., Diar.Dis.Res., Dok.Arbeitsmed., Excerp.Med., Helminthol.Abstr., HRIS, I.P.A., Ind.Med., Ind.Sci.Rev., Ind.Vet., INIS Atomind., Int.Nurs.Ind., Kidney, Lab.Haz.Bull., Med.& Surg.Dermat., Med.Care Rev., Nutr.Abstr., Protozool.Abstr., Rev.Plant Path., Risk Abstr., Trop.Dis.Bull.
●Also available online.
—BLDSC (5529.000000); CASDDS; EMDOCS; Faxon; Genuine Article; SWETS; UMI; UnCover. **CCC**.
Refereed Serial

610 MY ISSN 0300-5283
CODEN: MJMLAI
MEDICAL JOURNAL OF MALAYSIA. q. M.$280. Malaysian Medical Association, 124 Jalan Pahang, 53000 Kuala Lumpur, Malaysia. TEL 03-4420617. FAX 03-4418187. Ed. Prof. Victor Lim. adv.; bk.rev.; charts; illus.; stat. **Indexed:** Abstr.Hyg., Biol.Abstr., Chem.Abstr., CINAHL, Dent.Ind., Excerp.Med., Helminthol.Abstr., Ind.Med., Nutr.Abstr., Protozool.Abstr., Rev.Appl.Entomol., Rev.Med.& Vet.Mycol., Soyabean Abstr., Trop.Dis.Bull.
—BLDSC (5529.151000); CASDDS; SWETS; UnCover.
Formerly: Medical Journal of Malaya (ISSN 0025-7303)

610 IR ISSN 1016-1430
MEDICAL JOURNAL OF THE ISLAMIC REPUBLIC OF IRAN. (Text in English) 1987. q. $50 to individuals; institutions $80; students $20. National Center for Scientific Research, 1188 Enghelab Ave., P.O. Box 13145-554, Tehran 13158, Iran. TEL 98-21-6462778. FAX 98-21-6467928. Ed. Dr. N. Simforoosh. adv. contact: A.A. Pourfathollah. **Indexed:** ExtraMED, Per.Islam. **Document type:** academic/scholarly publication.
●Also available on CD-ROM.
Description: Publishes original articles in clincal science and basic science in medicine, case reports, review articles, and articles on medicine in Islamic culture.

610 ZA ISSN 0047-651X
CODEN: MJZAAG
MEDICAL JOURNAL OF ZAMBIA.* 1967. bi-m. Zambia Medical Association, P.O. Box 717, Ndola, Zambia. Ed. M.N. Lowenthal. adv.; bk.rev.; index. circ. 1,700. **Indexed:** Abstr.Hyg., Biol.Abstr., Curr.Cont., Excerp.Med., Helminthol.Abstr., Ind.Med., Ind.Vet., Nutr.Abstr., Protozool.Abstr., Trop.Dis.Bull, Vet.Bull.

MEDICAL LASER REPORT. see *PHYSICS* — Optics

MEDICAL LAW INTERNATIONAL. see *LAW*

342.441 610 UK ISSN 0957-9346
MEDICAL LAW REPORTS. 1989. 10/yr. (with a. cumulation). £165($255) includes cumulation (effective 1996). Oxford University Press, Oxford Journals, Walton St., Oxford OX2 6DP, England. TEL 44-1865-56767. FAX 44-1865-56646. (Subscr. in U.S. & Canada to: Oxford University Press Inc., 2001 Evans Rd., Cary, NC 27513. TEL 919-677-0977. FAX 919-677-1714) **Document type:** academic/scholarly publication.

MEDICAL LAW REVIEW. see *LAW*

610 026 US ISSN 0025-7338
CODEN: BMLAAG
MEDICAL LIBRARY ASSOCIATION. BULLETIN. 1911. q. $150 (foreign $174). Medical Library Association, 6 N. Michigan Ave., Ste. 300, Chicago, IL 60602-4805. TEL 312-419-9094. FAX 312-419-8905. Ed. Naomi C. Broering. adv.: B&W page $799. bk.rev.; bibl.; index, cum.index. circ. 5,685. (also avail. in microform from UMI; reprint service avail. from UMI,ISI,KTO) **Indexed:** Abstr.Health Care Manage.Stud., Abstr.Hyg., Biol.Abstr., C.I.N.L., Curr.Adv.Ecol.Sci., Dent.Ind., Excerp.Med., Hosp.Lit.Ind., I.P.A., Ind.Med., INSPEC (1982-), Int.Nurs.Ind., LHTN, Lib.Lit., LISA, Nutr.Abstr., Sci.Cit.Ind., SSCI, Telegen, Trop.Dis.Bull. **Document type:** academic/scholarly publication, trade publication.
—BLDSC (2612.090000); CASDDS; EMDOCS; Faxon; Genuine Article; SWETS; UMI; UnCover.
Description: Contains features and articles of interest to information management professionals, particularly those in the health information field.
Refereed Serial

MEDICAL MALPRACTICE: HANDLING EMERGENCY CASES. see *LAW* — Civil Law

MEDICAL MALPRACTICE: HANDLING INTERNAL MEDICINE CASES. see *LAW* — Civil Law

MEDICAL MALPRACTICE LAW & STRATEGY. see *LAW* — Civil Law

MEDICAL MALPRACTICE REPORTS. see *LAW* — Civil Law

MEDICAL MALPRACTICE VERDICTS, SETTLEMENTS & EXPERTS. see *LAW* — Civil Law

610 AT
MEDICAL MARKET PLACE. 1974-199? 3/yr. free. Permail Pty. Ltd., P.O. Box 56, Artarmon, N.S.W. 2064, Australia. adv. circ. 36,950.

610 US ISSN 1077-3436
MEDICAL MATERIALS UPDATE. 1993. m. $325. Business Communications Co., Inc. (Norwalk), 25 Van Zant St., Ste. 13, Norwalk, CT 06855. TEL 203-853-4266. FAX 203-853-0348. Ed. Melvin Schlechter. **Document type:** newsletter.

MEDICAL MICROBIOLOGY LETTERS. see *BIOLOGY* — Microbiology

610 UK ISSN 1350-6897
MEDICAL MONITOR WEEKLY. 1987. w. £50. Medicom (UK) Ltd., The Quadrant, 118 London Rd., Kingston-upon-Thames, Surrey KT2 6QJ, England. TEL 0181-541-5666. FAX 0181-541-4746. Ed. Corinne Short; Pub. Stephen Townsend. **Document type:** trade publication.
—BLDSC (5908.966900).
Formerly (until 1993): Medical Monitor (ISSN 0953-1408)

610 US ISSN 0025-7397
MEDICAL - MORAL NEWSLETTER. 1964. 10/yr. $25. Ayd Medical Communications, 1130 E. Cold Spring Ln., Baltimore, MD 21239. TEL 410-433-9220. FAX 410-532-5419. Ed. Dr. Frank J. Ayd, Jr. bk.rev. circ. 1,000. **Document type:** newsletter.
Formerly: Medical Newsletter for Religious.
Description: Discusses medical ethics.

MEDICAL NEWS REPORT. see *BUSINESS AND ECONOMICS* — Marketing And Purchasing

MEDICAL OFFICE MANAGER; the newsletter for physician office administrators. see *BUSINESS AND ECONOMICS* — Management

610 368.382 US ISSN 0895-4313
MEDICAL OFFICE REPORT. 1988. m. $156 (typically set in Jan.). Washington G - 2 Reports, 1111 14th St. N.W., Ste. 500, Washington, DC 20005. TEL 202-789-1034; 800-LAB-REGS. FAX 202-289-4062. Ed. D.J. Curren; Pub. Dennis W. Weissman. charts; stat.; circ. 16,000 (paid). (looseleaf format; back issues avail.)
Description: Offers the latest Medicare reimbursement and policy information for the office physician.

610 US ISSN 1067-4195
MEDICAL OUTCOMES AND GUIDELINES ALERT. 1993. s-m. $395 (effectve 1995). Faulkner & Gray, Healthcare Information Center (Subsidiary of: Thomson Publishing Group), 1133 15th St., N.W., Ste. 450, Washington, DC 20005. TEL 202-828-4148. FAX 202-828-2352. Ed. David Strickland.
●Also available online. Vendor(s): Knight-Ridder, Inc., NewsNet.
Description: Covers medical outcomes research and clinical guidelines development.

530 610 US ISSN 0094-2405
R895.A1 CODEN: MPHYA6
MEDICAL PHYSICS. 1970. m. $430 (foreign $470) (effective 1996). (American Association of Physicists in Medicine) American Institute of Physics, One Physics Ellipse, College Park, MD 20740-3843. TEL 301-209-3000. Ed. J.S. Laughlin. adv.; bk.rev.; abstr.; cum.index: vols. 1-10, 1985; vols. 11-20, 1994. (also avail. in microform from AIP; microfiche from AIP; back issues avail.) **Indexed:** Abstr.Health Care Manage.Stud., Appl.Mech.Rev., Biol.Abstr., C.P.I., Chem.Abstr., Curr.Cont., Dent.Ind., Excerp.Med., Gen.Phys.Adv.Abstr., Ind.Med., Ind.Sci.Rev., INIS Atomind., INSPEC, Phys.Ber. **Document type:** academic/scholarly publication.
—BLDSC (5531.130000); CASDDS; EMDOCS; Faxon; Genuine Article; SWETS; UnCover. **CCC**.
Formerly: A.A.P.M. Quarterly Bulletin (ISSN 0001-0162)
Refereed Serial

610 530 US ISSN 0076-5953
MEDICAL PHYSICS SERIES. 1969. irreg., vol.8, 1985. Academic Press, Inc., 525 B St., Ste. 1900, San Diego, CA 92101-4495. TEL 619-231-0926. FAX 619-699-6715. (Subscr. to: Order Dept., 6277 Sea Harbor Dr., 4th Fl., Orlando, FL 32887. TEL 800-321-5068) Ed. P.N.T. Wells. (reprint service avail. from ISI)
Refereed Serial

MEDICAL SCIENCES

610 681 US
▼**MEDICAL PLASTICS AND BIOMATERIALS**. 1994. q. $55 (free to qualified readers). Canon Communications, Inc., 3340 Ocean Park Blvd., Ste. 1000, Santa Monica, CA 90405-3216. TEL 310-392-5509. FAX 310-392-5509. Ed. Jon Katz; Pub. William Cobert. adv.: B&W page $1995; adv. contact: Mary Pat Kuppig. circ. 5,000. **Document type:** trade publication.
  Description: Provides in-depth technical information on the full range of plastics and biomaterials and related equipment used in manufacturing and packaging of medical products.

610 CN ISSN 0025-7435
MEDICAL POST. 1965. fortn. Can.$41. Maclean-Hunter Ltd., Business Publication Division, Maclean-Hunter Bldg., 777 Bay St., Toronto, ON M5W 1A7, Canada. TEL 416-596-5770. TELEX 062-19547. Ed. Derek Cassels. adv.; bk.rev.; abstr.; charts; illus. circ. 37,000. (tabloid format) **Indexed:** Can.B.P.I.
—BLDSC (5531.150000). **CCC.**
  Description: Covers clinical, political and social news for physicians.

610 JA ISSN 0910-1551
MEDICAL PRACTICE. Variant title: M.P. Medical Practice. (Text in Japanese) 1984. m. 2000 Yen per no. Bunkodo Co., Ltd., 2-7, Hongo 7-chome, Bunkyo-ku, Tokyo 113, Japan.

610 SZ ISSN 1011-7571
MEDICAL PRINCIPLES AND PRACTICE. 1989. q. 177 SFr.($13620) to individuals; institutions 295 SFr.($227) (effective 1996). Kuwait University, Health Science Center, KU) S. Karger AG, Allschwilerstr. 10, P.O. Box, CH-4009 Basel, Switzerland. TEL 061-3061111. FAX 061-3061234. E-mail: Karger@Karger.ch. Ed. B. Al-Nakib. (also avail. in microform from UMI) **Indexed:** Excerp.Med. (until 1993). **Document type:** academic/scholarly publication.
—BLDSC (5531.260000). **CCC.**
  Description: Concentrates on the recent advances made in basic medical sciences, clinical practice and associated disciplines within human medicine.
  Refereed Serial

610 780 US ISSN 0885-1158
CODEN: MPPAEC
MEDICAL PROBLEMS OF PERFORMING ARTISTS. 1986. q. $48 to individuals (foreign $58); institutions $58 (foreign $68). Hanley & Belfus, Inc., 210 S. 13th St., Philadelphia, PA 19107. TEL 215-546-7293. FAX 215-790-9330. Ed. Alice Brand Frohnmayer. adv.; bk.rev.; index. circ. 1,000. (back issues avail.)
—BLDSC (5531.280000); Faxon; Genuine Article; SWETS; UnCover. **CCC.**
  Description: Concerned with medical and surgical problems deriving from artistic performance in dance, music and theater.
  Refereed Serial

610 380.1 JA
MEDICAL PRODUCTS OF JAPAN; medical equipment directory. (Text in English) no.15, 1993. a. $125. Genyosha Publications, Inc., 8-7 Shibuya 2-chome, Shibuya-ku, Tokyo 105, Japan. TEL 03-3407-7521. FAX 03-3407-7902. adv. circ. 7,500. **Document type:** directory.
  Description: Covers more than 2,300 products from some 400 companies, ranging from small diagnostic tools to large systems like computer tomography unit.

610 681 US ISSN 0279-4802
MEDICAL PRODUCTS SALES. 1970. m. $49.95 (Canada $55.95; elsewhere $69.95). (Health Industry Distributors Association) McKnight Medical Communications Co. (Subsidiary of: Medical Economics Publishing Co., Inc.), Two Northfield Plaza, Ste. 300, Northfield, IL 60093. TEL 708-441-3700. Ed. Bill Briggs. adv. contact: Deborah Tobiaski. bk.rev.; illus. circ. 24,035. (back issues avail.)
—UMI. **CCC.**
  Formerly (until 1981): Medical Products Salesman (ISSN 0192-432X)

MEDICAL PROGRESS THROUGH TECHNOLOGY; signal processing - imaging systems - assist systems - implants - sensors and instrumentation - computers. see *BIOLOGY — Biotechnology*

610 UK ISSN 0076-5961
MEDICAL PROTECTION SOCIETY. ANNUAL REPORT. 1892. a. membership. Medical Protection Society Ltd., 50 Hallam St., London W1N 6DE, England. TEL 071-637-0541. FAX 071-636-0690. TELEX 8952848 MEDPRO G. Ed. Lynne Richmond. adv. contact: Steven Grundy. circ. 135,000 (controlled). **Document type:** corporate report.

610 MW ISSN 1017-2920
MEDICAL QUARTERLY. (Text in English) 1980. q. (Medical Association of Malawi) Centraf Associates Ltd., P.O. Box 30462, Chichiri, Blantyre 3, Malawi. **Indexed:** Rural Devel.Abstr., Rural Ext.Educ.& Tr.Abstr.

MEDICAL RECORD RISKS: CLAIMS & LITIGATION. see *INSURANCE*

MEDICAL RECORDS BRIEFING. see *HOSPITALS*

610 CN
MEDICAL REFORM. 1979. bi-m. $25. Medical Reform Group, P.O. Box 158, Sta. D, Toronto, ON M6P 3J8, Canada. TEL 416-588-9167. Ed. Dr. Haresh Kirpolomi. adv.; bk.rev. circ. 300. (back issues avail.) **Document type:** newsletter.
  Description: Covers the social, economic and political dimensions of health care provision.

610 UK
MEDICAL RESEARCH CENTRES; a world directory of organizations and programmes. irreg., 10th ed., 1993. £295. Longman Group UK Ltd., Westgate House, 6th Fl., The High, Harlow, Essex CM20 1YR, England. TEL 0279-442601. FAX 0279-444501. (Dist. in U.S. and Canada by: Gale Research Inc., 835 Penobscot Bldg., Detroit, MI 48226) **Document type:** directory.
  Formerly: Medical Research Index (ISSN 0076-6003)

610 GH
MEDICAL RESEARCH CENTRES IN GHANA: CURRENT RESEARCH PROJECTS. 1973. irreg. free. Council for Scientific and Industrial Research, PO Box M32, Accra, Ghana. Ed. D.K. Opare-Sem. (back issues avail.)

610 CN ISSN 0047-6560
MEDICAL RESEARCH COUNCIL NEWSLETTER/CONSEIL DE RECHERCHES MEDICALES. ACTUALITES. (Text in English and French) 1970. q. free. Medical Research Council of Canada, 1600 Scott St., Tower B, Ottawa, ON K1A 0W9, Canada. TEL 613-954-1806. FAX 613-954-6653. circ. 4,500 (controlled). **Document type:** newsletter.

610 CN ISSN 0839-8283
MEDICAL RESEARCH COUNCIL OF CANADA. GRANTS AND AWARDS GUIDE/GUIDE DE SUBVENTIONS ET BOURSES. Key Title: University - Industry Grants and Awards Guide. (Text and summaries in English and French) 1988. a. Medical Research Council of Canada, 1600 Scott St., Tower B, Ottawa, ON K1A 0W9, Canada. TEL 613-954-1806. FAX 613-954-6653. charts. circ. 7,400. **Document type:** bulletin.

610 CN ISSN 0384-2029
R854.C2
MEDICAL RESEARCH COUNCIL OF CANADA. REPORT OF THE PRESIDENT. (Text in English, French) 1960. a. free. Medical Research Council of Canada, 1600 Scott St., Tower B, Ottawa, ON K1A 0W9, Canada. TEL 613-954-1806. FAX 613-954-6653. charts; illus.; stat.; index; circ. 2,300 (controlled). **Document type:** corporate report.

MEDICAL RESEARCH FUNDING BULLETIN. see *SOCIAL SERVICES AND WELFARE*

MEDICAL SCHOOL ADMISSION REQUIREMENTS, UNITED STATES AND CANADA. see *EDUCATION — Higher Education*

610 US ISSN 0885-1557
MEDICAL SCIENCE. (Subseries of: S I R S Science (ISSN 0885-1530)) 1985. a. $80. Social Issues Resources Series, Box 2348, Boca Raton, FL 33427-2348. TEL 407-994-0079; 800-232-7477. FAX 407-994-4704. (looseleaf format; also avail. in microfiche)
  Description: Reprints articles that cover developments in the medical sciences.

610 JA ISSN 0019-1590
MEDICAL SCIENCE AND MEDICAL CARE/GEKKAN IGAKU TO IRYO. (Text in Japanese) 1969. m. 600 Yen. Nippon Medical Association - Nippon Igaku Kyokai, 7-2-8 Hongo, Bunkyo-ku, Tokyo 113, Japan. Ed. Tomoyuki Horikoshi; Pub. Takeshi Oda.

610 UK ISSN 0269-8951
CODEN: MSCREJ
MEDICAL SCIENCE RESEARCH; rapid publication of concise reports in medical science. m. £130($220) (effective 1996). Chapman & Hall, Journals Department (Subsidiary of: International Thomson Publishing Group), 2-6 Boundary Row, London SE1 8HN, England. TEL 0171-856-0066. FAX 0171-522-9623. (Subscr. to: International Thomson Publishing Services Ltd., Cheriton House, North Way, Andover, Hants. SP10 5BE, England. TEL 01264-342713. FAX 01264-342807; Subscr. in N. America to: Chapman & Hall, Journals Promotion Dept., 1 Penn Plaza, 41st Fl., New York, NY 10119. TEL 212-564-1060. FAX 212-564-1505) Ed. Bernard Dixon. adv.; bk.rev.; abstr. (reprint service avail.) **Indexed:** Anim.Breed.Abstr., Biol.Abstr., Curr.Adv.Cancer Res., Curr.Cont., Dairy Sci.Abstr., Excerp.Med., Ind.Vet., Pig News & Info., Poult.Abstr., Psychol.Abstr., Rev.Med.& Vet.Mycol., Vet.Bull. **Document type:** academic/scholarly publication.
●Also available online. Vendor(s): DIMDI, Data-Star, Ovid Technologies.
—BLDSC (5531.892000); ADONIS; CASDDS; Faxon; Genuine Article; SWETS; UnCover. **CCC.**
  Formed by the 1986 merger of: I R C S Medical Science: Anatomy and Human Biology (ISSN 0305-6686); I R C S Medical Science: Biochemistry (ISSN 0305-6708); I R C S Medical Science: Biomedical Technology (ISSN 0305-6716); I R C S Medical Science: Cancer (ISSN 0305-6724); I R C S Medical Science: Cardiovascular System (ISSN 0305-6732); I R C S Medical Science: Cell and Molecular Biology; Which incorporates: I R C S Medical Science: Cell and Membrane Biology (ISSN 0305-6740) and I R C S Medical Science: Key Reports in Cell and Molecular Biology (ISSN 0142-484X); I R C S Medical Science: Clinical Biochemistry (ISSN 0309-1481); I R C S Medical Science: Clinical Medicine and Surgery.
  Refereed Serial

610 NE ISSN 0928-9550
CODEN: MSSYEI
MEDICAL SCIENCE SYMPOSIA SERIES. (Text in English) 1992. irreg., vol.3, 1993. price varies. Kluwer Academic Publishers, Postbus 17, 3300 AA Dordrecht, Netherlands. TEL 31-78-392392. FAX 31-78-392254. (Dist. by: Kluwer Academic Publishers Group, P.O. Box 322, 3300 AH Dordrecht, Netherlands. TEL 31-78-392392. FAX 31-78-546474; N. America dist. addr.: Box 358, Accord Sta., Hingham, MA 02018-0358. TEL 617-871-6600. FAX 617-871-6528) (back issues avail.) **Document type:** proceedings.
—BLDSC (5531.892380); CASDDS.

MEDICAL SCIENCES BULLETIN; focus on clinical pharmacology: theory and practice. see *PHARMACY AND PHARMACOLOGY*

MEDICAL SCIENCES INTERNATIONAL WHO'S WHO. see *BIOGRAPHY*

616.98 US ISSN 0041-7491
RC1050
MEDICAL SERVICE DIGEST. Variant title: U.S. Air Force Medical Service Digest. 1950. q. $5 (foreign $6.25). U.S. Air Force, Office of the Surgeon General, HQ USAF-SGI, Bldg. 5681-Bolling AFB, Washington, DC 20332-6188. TEL 202-767-5046. FAX 202-767-1456. (Subscr. to: Superintendent of Documents, U.S. Government Printing Office, Box 371954, Pittsburgh, PA 15250-7954. TEL 202-783-3238. FAX 202-512-2233) Ed. Elizabeth Taber. circ. 8,000. (back issues avail.) **Document type:** government publication.
  Description: Presents information about the people, programs and activities of the Air Force Medical Service.

610 UK ISSN 0076-6011
MEDICAL SOCIETY OF LONDON. TRANSACTIONS. 1773. a. £15. Medical Society of London, 11 Chandos St., Cavendish Sq., London W1N OEB, England. TEL 0171-580-1043. FAX 0171-580-5793. Ed. P.S. London. bk.rev.; circ. 550. **Indexed:** Excerp.Med., Ind.Med. **Document type:** proceedings.
—BLDSC (8982.500000).

MEDICAL SCIENCES

610   US
MEDICAL SOCIETY OF MILWAUKEE COUNTY. MEMBERSHIP NEWSLETTER. 1975. m. Medical Society of Milwaukee County, 1126 S. 70th St., Ste. S-507, Milwaukee, WI 53214. TEL 414-475-4750. FAX 414-475-4799. Ed. Frank Bialek. adv. circ. 2,400. (tabloid format) **Document type:** newsletter.

610   US   ISSN 1076-6022
MEDICAL STAFF BRIEFING; the newsletter for volunteer/elected medical staff leaders. (Includes supplement: M S B Credentialing) 1991. m. $247 (effective 1995). Opus Communications, Box 1168, Marblehead, MA 01945. TEL 617-639-1872. FAX 617-639-2982. Ed. Cathy A. Rossi. bk.rev.; index. circ. 1,500. (looseleaf format; back issues avail.) **Document type:** newsletter.
   Description: Covers issues affecting medical staff administration, staff relations, and physician-patient relations.

MEDICAL STAFF LAW MANUAL. see *LAW — Civil Law*

610   US   ISSN 0565-811X
Z695.1.M48   CODEN: MSHEE5
MEDICAL SUBJECT HEADINGS (BLACK BOOK). (Also issued as Part 2 of Jan. Index Medicus) 1960. a. $43 (foreign $53.75). U.S. National Library of Medicine, 8600 Rockville Pike, Bethesda, MD 20894. (Orders to: Superintendent of Documents, U.S. Government Printing Office, Box 371954, Pittsburgh, PA 15250-7954. TEL 202-512-1800. FAX 202-512-2250; Or: Bernan, 4611-F Assembly Dr., Lanham, MD 20706. TEL 301-459-7666. FAX 301-459-0056) circ. 8,000. **Document type:** directory, government publication.
—CASDDS.
   Description: Provides an alphabetized and categorized list of all the subject descriptors used to analyze the biomedical literature in the National Library of Medicine.

610   UK   ISSN 0142-159X
MEDICAL TEACHER. 1979. q. £74 to individuals; institutions £198 (effective 1996). Carfax Publishing Co., P.O. Box 25, Abingdon, Oxon. OX14 3UE, England. TEL 01235-555335. FAX 01235-553559. (Subscr. in N. America to: Carfax Publishing Co., 875-81 Massachusetts Ave., Cambridge, MA 02139) Ed. R.M. Harden. adv.; bk.rev.; charts; cum.index. (also avail. in microfiche; back issues avail.) **Indexed:** Curr.Adv.Ecol.Sci., Educ.Tech.Abstr., Tech.Educ.Abstr. **Document type:** academic/scholarly publication.
—BLDSC (5531.965000); Genuine Article; SWETS; UMI; UnCover. **CCC.**
   Description: Examines pedagogy and its relevance to the study and teaching medicine.
Refereed Serial

MEDICAL TECHNOLOGY STOCK LETTER. see *BUSINESS AND ECONOMICS — Investments*

610 677   UK   ISSN 0266-2078
MEDICAL TEXTILES; an international newsletter. 1984. m. £298($474) (effective 1996). Elsevier Science Ltd., P.O. Box 800, Kidlington, Oxford OX5 1DX, England. TEL 44-1865-843000. FAX 44-1865-843010. E-mail: nlinfo-f@elsevier.nl; usinfo-f@elsevier.com; forinfo-kyf04035@niftyserve.or.jp; Site addr.: http://www.elsevier.nl/. (Subscr. in U.S. and Canada to: Elsevier Science, 660 White Plains Rd., Tarrytown, NY 10591-5153. TEL 914-524-9200. FAX 914-333-2444) (Co-publisher: British Textile Technology Group) Eds. Peter Lennon-Kerr, Edward Love. bk.rev.; charts; stat. (back issues avail.) **Document type:** newsletter.
●Also available online. Vendor(s): Data-Star, Knight-Ridder, Inc.
—BLDSC (5532.028700). **CCC.**
   Description: Provides coverage of design, production and research management in the fiber and polymer industries and in related research departments and institutes. Also provides a survey of this whole area for senior general management, serving to highlight new trends and possibilities, market gaps and business opportunities.

MEDICAL TRIAL TECHNIQUE QUARTERLY. see *LAW — Civil Law*

610   US   ISSN 0279-9340
R5
MEDICAL TRIBUNE.* 1960. 26/yr. $75 (free to qualified personnel) (typically set in Oct.). Medical Tribune, Inc., 100 Ave. of the Americas, 9th Fl., New York, NY 10013-1606. TEL 212-674-8500. FAX 212-529-8490. Ed. David Bronstein. adv.; bk.rev.; charts; illus.; stat.; circ. 130,000 (controlled). **Indexed:** Curr.Lit.Fam.Plan. **Document type:** trade publication.
—BLDSC (5532.050000); Genuine Article; UMI. **CCC.**
   Former titles (until vol.21, 1980): Medical Tribune and Medical News (ISSN 0098-6240); (until vol.3, 1963): Medical Tribune (ISSN 0025-7605)

610   IT   ISSN 0392-7199
MEDICAL TRIBUNE. 1982. w. (42/yr.). L.35000. E S I Stampa Medica s.r.l., Casella Postale 42, Lgo. Volontari del Sangue 10, 20097 S. Donato, Milan, Italy. TEL 39-2-5274241. FAX 39-2-55600670. TELEX 3248944. Ed. Diego Onestinghel. adv.: B&W page L.14500000, color page L.17500000; trim 268 x 364; adv. contact: Ornella Galbiati. bk.rev. circ. 56,000.

610   SZ   ISSN 0170-1894
MEDICAL TRIBUNE. 46/yr. Baeumleingasse 22, Postfach 1711, CH-4001 Basel, Switzerland. TEL 061-2718333. FAX 061-2718358. Ed. Klaus Nuernberger. circ. 10,000.

MEDICAL UPDATE FOR PSYCHIATRISTS. see *MEDICAL SCIENCES — Psychiatry And Neurology*

610   US
RA972
MEDICAL UTILIZATION MANAGEMENT. 1973. bi-w. $395 (effective 1995). Faulkner & Gray, Healthcare Information Center (Subsidiary of: Thomson Publishing Group), 1133 15th St., N.W., Ste. 450, Washington, DC 20005. TEL 202-828-4150. FAX 202-828-2352. Ed. Spencer Vibbert. (looseleaf format; back issues avail.; reprint service avail.)
●Also available online. Vendor(s): Knight-Ridder, Inc., NewsNet.
   Former titles (until 1994): Medical Utilization Review; MacGraw-Hill's Medical Utilization Review (ISSN 0734-1970); (until 1982): P S R O Letter (Professional Standards Review Organizations) (ISSN 0149-5844)
   Description: Covers operational, financial, governmental and legal issues of the utilization review industry.

610   IT
MEDICAL VIDEO FLASH. 1976. 8/yr. Editoriale Dumas S.p.A., Via Grandi 5-7, 20089 Rozzano (Mi), Italy. Ed. Gianni Mazzocchi. adv. circ. 108,000.

MEDICAL WASTE NEWS. see *ENVIRONMENTAL STUDIES — Waste Management*

610   US   ISSN 0025-763X
R11   CODEN: MDWNA
MEDICAL WORLD NEWS;* the newsmagazine of medicine. 1936. m. $75 (free to qualified physicians). Medical Tribune, Inc., 100 Ave. of the Americas, 9th Fl., New York, NY 10013-1606. TEL 212-674-8500. FAX 212-529-8490. TELEX 278273. Ed. Nicholas K. Zittell. adv.; bk.rev.; charts; illus. circ. 130,000. (also avail. in microform from UMI) **Indexed:** Biol.Abstr., Biol.Dig., CINAHL, Curr.Lit.Fam.Plan., Hlth.Ind., I.P.A., PROMT. **Document type:** trade publication.
—Faxon; Genuine Article; UMI; UnCover. **CCC.**

MEDICARE ADVISOR. see *INSURANCE*

MEDICARE COMPLIANCE ALERT. see *INSURANCE*

MEDICARE MANAGER. see *INSURANCE*

MEDICARE REVIEW. see *INSURANCE*

610   AG   ISSN 0025-7680
R21   CODEN: MEDCAD
MEDICINA; Buenos Aires. (Text in English; summaries in English, Spanish) 1939. bi-m. Arg.$60 (Latin America $70; elsewhere $90) (effective 1995). (Instituto de Investigaciones Medicas) Fundacion Revista Medicina, Donato Alvarez 3150, 1427 Buenos Aires, Argentina. TEL 541-523-6619. (Co-sponsor: Sociedad Argentina de Investigacion Clinica) Dir. Dr. A.P. Barousse. adv.; bk.rev.; abstr.; bibl.; illus.; stat.; index. circ. 5,000. (also avail. in microfilm from UMI) **Indexed:** Abstr.Hyg., Biol.Abstr., Chem.Abstr., Curr.Cont., Dent.Ind., Excerp.Med., Helminthol.Abstr., Ind.Med., INIS Atomind., Nutr.Abstr., Protozool.Abstr., Rev.Med.& Vet.Mycol., Sci.Cit.Ind., Trop.Dis.Bull.
—BLDSC (5532.390000); CASDDS; EMDOCS; Faxon; Genuine Article; SWETS; UMI.
   Description: Original papers in clinical research.
Refereed Serial

610   CI   ISSN 0025-7729
MEDICINA. (Supplement avail.: Acta Facultatis Medicae Fluminensis) (Text in Croatian; summaries in English) 1964. q. $30. Hrvatski Lijecnicki Zbor, Podruznica Rijeka, Borisa Kidrica 40-II, 51000 Rijeka, Croatia. TEL 051-34-542. Ed. Mladen Persic. adv.; bk.rev. circ. 2,000. **Indexed:** Abstr.Hyg., Biol.Abstr., Biol.Abstr., Chem.Abstr., Excerp.Med., Ref.Zh., Trop.Dis.Bull.
   Description: Publishes original scientific papers, professional papers on all aspects of medicine.

610   BL   ISSN 0076-6046
MEDICINA. (Text in Portuguese; summaries in English and Portuguese) 1961. q. Cr.$40($50) (effective 1995). Universidade de Sao Paulo, Faculdade de Medicina de Ribeirao Preto, Hospital das Clinicas, Campus Universitario, Av. Bandeirantes, 3900, 14049 Ribeirao Preto, SP, Brazil. FAX 016-6331144. TELEX 016-583. Ed. Dr. Julio C. Voltarelli. adv. contact: Gilberto Guedes de Padua. bk.rev.; bibl.; charts; illus. circ. 2,000. **Indexed:** Biol.Abstr., Curr.Adv.Genetics & Molec.Biol., Excerp.Med. (1992-), Ind.Med. **Document type:** academic/scholarly publication.
—EMDOCS.
Refereed Serial

610   SP   ISSN 0025-7753
   CODEN: MCLBA2
MEDICINA CLINICA. (Text in Spanish; summaries in English) 1943. w. (40/yr.). 7800 ptas.($90) Ediciones Doyma, S.A., Travesera de Gracia 17-21, 08021 Barcelona, Spain. TEL 34-1-200-07-11. FAX 34-1-209-11-36. TELEX 51694 INK-E. (Co-sponsors: Hospitales y Sociedades Medicas de Barcelona) Ed. C. Rozman Borstnar. adv.: page 240000 ptas.; trim 210 x 280; adv. contact: Enric Brotons. bk.rev.; abstr.; charts; illus. circ. 8,500. (reprint service avail. from UMI) **Indexed:** Biol.Abstr., Chem.Abstr., Curr.Cont., Dent.Ind., Dok.Arbeitsmed., Excerp.Med., Helminthol.Abstr., Ind.Med., Ind.Med.Esp., Ind.Vet., Nutr.Abstr., Protozool.Abstr., Rev.Med.& Vet.Mycol.
—BLDSC (5532.600000); CASDDS; EMDOCS; Genuine Article; SWETS; UMI. **CCC.**
   Description: Contains works of original research and articles for the continuing education of practicing professionals in clinical medicine.

610   YU   ISSN 0025-7796
MEDICINA DANAS; casopis za strucno usavrsavanje lekara. 1965. 6/yr. 30 din.($16.70) Institut za Strucno Usavrsavanje i Specijalizaciju Zdravstvenih Radnika Srbije, Nusiceva 25-I, Belgrade, Yugoslavia. Ed. Ljubisa Sablic. circ. 5,000.

610   SP   ISSN 0210-9433
MEDICINA INTEGRAL; medicina preventiva y asistencial en el medio rural. 1980. bi-w. 6050 ptas. Ediciones Idepsa, Travesera de Gracia, 17-21, 08021 Barcelona, Spain. FAX 563-23-93. Dir. J.M. Sanchez Tapias. adv. circ. 20,000. **Indexed:** Ind.Med.Esp.
—BLDSC (5533.300000).

610   SP   ISSN 0210-5691
   CODEN: MDINE
MEDICINA INTENSIVA. (Text in Spanish; summaries in English) m. 6500 ptas.($75) (Sociedad Espanola de Medicina Intensiva y Unidades Coronarias) Ediciones Idepsa, S.A., Principe de Vergara, 112, 28002 Madrid, Spain. TEL 34-1-5637306. Dir. Dr. J. Ibanez Juve. circ. 4,683. **Indexed:** Excerp.Med., Ind.Med.Esp.
—BLDSC (5533.420000). **CCC.**
   Description: Covers intensive care medicine.

MEDICAL SCIENCES

610 IT ISSN 0394-2627
MEDICINA MODERNA OGGI/MODERN MEDICINE TODAY. (Text in English, Italian) 1985. s-a. L.10000($6) Amorosino Editore Roma, Via Francesco Salata, 18, 00177 Rome, Italy. TEL 06-274040.

610 RM
MEDICINA MUNCII SI MEDICINA SOCIALA. vol.38, 1990. bi-m. Uniunea Societatilor de Stiinte Medicale din Romania, Str. Progresului 8-10, Bucharest, Sector 1, Rumania. TEL 13-89-73. (Subscr. to: Rompresfilatelia, P.O. Box 12-201, Bucharest, Rumania)

610 IT ISSN 1121-5518
MEDICINA NATURALE. 1991. bi-m. L.50000 (foreign L.120000) (effective 1995). Tecniche Nuove s.p.a., Via C. Menotti, 14, 20129 Milan, Italy. TEL 02-75701. FAX 02-7610351. adv.: B&W page L.2820000, color page L.3810000; trim 184 x 250. circ. 12,866.

610 IT ISSN 0394-9001
R5 CODEN: MDSCAD
MEDICINA NEI SECOLI: ARTE E SCIENZA; rivista storico medica. (Text in English or Italian) 1964; N.S. 1989. 3/yr. L.40000($40) Universita degli Studi di Roma, Dipartimento di Medicina Sperimentale, Medicina Nei Secoli, Viale Regina Elena, 324, 00161 Rome, Italy. TEL 4461974. FAX 4454820. bk.rev. circ. 500. (also avail. in microfiche) **Indexed:** Biol.Abstr., Ind.Med.
—BLDSC (5533.665000); CASDDS.
Formerly: Medicina nei Secoli (ISSN 0025-7877); **Supersedes:** Pagine di Storia della Medicina (ISSN 0030-9400)

610 IT ISSN 0392-4548
MEDICINA OGGI; periodico di attualita in medicina e chirurgia. (Supplement avail.) (Text in Italian; summaries in English) 1980. q. L.55000($95) (effective 1995). Casa Editrice Idelson, Via A. DeGasperi, 55, 80133 Naples, Italy. TEL 39-81-5524733. FAX 39-81-5518295. Ed. Lucio Zarrilli. bibl. (back issues avail.) **Indexed:** Excerp.Med.
Description: Includes a wide variety of topics in medicine, current trends in surgery, and extensive research.

610 IT ISSN 0391-7231
MEDICINA OSPEDALIERA ROMANA. (Text in Italian; summaries in English and Italian) 1980. q. L.20000($13) (Societa di Medicina Ospedaliera) Edizioni Medicina Ospedaliera Romana, Via Marco Papio 47, 00175 Rome, Italy. Ed. Salvatore Pasquale. adv.; bk.rev. circ. 500. (back issues avail.)

616.988 IT ISSN 0580-9320
CODEN: MTCLD7
MEDICINA TERMALE E CLIMATOLOGIA. (Includes: Osservatorio Lariano di Climatologia Applicata. Bolletino and Societa Italiana per le Scienze Ambientali. Notiziario). (Text in Italian; summaries in English) 1969. q. L.1500. (Universita degli Studi di Milano, Centro di Ricerche di Bioclimatologia Medica) Edizioni Libreria dello Studente di F. Lucisano, Viale Romagna 37, 20133 Milan, Italy. Ed. R. Gualtierotti. adv.; bk.rev.
—CASDDS.
Description: Covers climatological medicine.

610 917.106 US
MEDICINA Y CULTURA.* (Editions avail. for U.S. and Puerto Rico) (Text in Spanish) 1992. m. Mundo Medico USA, Inc., 100 Melrose Ave., Ste. 104, Greenwich, CT 06830. TEL 201-236-0026. FAX 201-236-0031. adv.: B&W page $2880, color page $4470; trim 8 1/4 x 10 5/8. circ. 32,000.
Document type: consumer publication.

610 540 US ISSN 1054-2523
RS400 CODEN: MCREEB
MEDICINAL CHEMISTRY RESEARCH; an international journal for rapid communications on design and mechanisms of action of biologically active agents. 1991. a. (9 nos./vol.). $80 to individuals; institutions $294 (foreign $334). Birkhaeuser, 675 Massachusetts Ave., Cambridge, MA 02139-3309. FAX 201-348-4505. (Dist. by: Springer-Verlag New York, Inc., Journal Fulfillment Services, Box 2485, Secaucus, NJ 07096-2491. TEL 201-348-4033) Ed. Richard Glennon. **Document type:** academic/scholarly publication.
—BLDSC (5533.983000); ADONIS; CASDDS; Genuine Article; SWETS; UMI. **CCC.**
Description: Includes papers on novel experimental achievements in the many facets of drug design, drug discovery, and the elucidation of mechanisms of action of biologically active compounds.
Refereed Serial

610 US
MEDICINAL RESEARCH SERIES. 1967. irreg., vol.12, 1989. price varies. Marcel Dekker, Inc., 270 Madison Ave., New York, NY 10016. TEL 212-696-9000. FAX 212-658-4540. TELEX 421419. Ed. Gary Grunewald. **Indexed:** Biol.Abstr. **Document type:** monographic series.
Formerly: Medicinal Research: A Series of Monographs (ISSN 0076-6062)
Refereed Serial

610 SP
MEDICINE. 24/yr. Principe de Vergara 112, 28002 Madrid, Spain. TEL 1-563-73-06. FAX 1-563-23-93. Ed. A. Garcia de la Fuente.

610 US ISSN 0025-7974
R11 CODEN: MEDIAV
MEDICINE (BALTIMORE); analytical reviews of general medicine, neurology, psychiatry, dermatology and pediatrics. 1922. bi-m. $75 to individuals; institutions $140 (effective 1995). Williams & Wilkins, 428 E. Preston St., Baltimore, MD 21202. TEL 410-528-4000; 800-638-6423. FAX 410-528-4312. TELEX 87669. Ed. Dr. Victor A. McKusick. adv.; bibl.; charts; illus. circ. 4,100. (also avail. in microfilm from WWS) **Indexed:** AIM, Biol.Abstr., Chem.Abstr., Curr.Adv.Ecol.Sci., Curr.Adv.Genetics & Molec.Biol., Dairy Sci.Abstr., Diar.Dis.Res., Excerp.Med., Helminthol.Abstr., Ind.Med., Ind.Sci.Rev., INIS Atomind., Kidney, Med.& Surg.Dermat., Nutr.Abstr., Rev.Med.& Vet.Mycol., Rev.Plant Path. **Document type:** academic/scholarly publication.
—BLDSC (5534.000000); EMDOCS; Faxon; Genuine Article; SWETS; UnCover. **CCC.**
Refereed Serial

610 UK ISSN 1350-4002
▼**MEDICINE & GLOBAL SURVIVAL.** 1994. q. £80($120) B M J Publishing Group, B.M.A. House, Tavistock Sq., London WC1H 9JR, England. TEL 0171-383-6270. FAX 0171-383-6402. (N. American subscr. to: Box 480, Franklin, MA 02038. TEL 800-2-FON-BMJ. FAX 800-2-FAX-BMJ) Ed. J. Leaning. adv. contact: Sheila Rowe. **Document type:** academic/scholarly publication.
—BLDSC (5312.991000). **CCC.**
Formerly (until 1991): P S R Quarterly (ISSN 1051-2438)
Description: Contains an international analysis of major issues relating to war, civil conflict, disaster, the environment, public health and development, and human rights.

MEDICINE AND LAW; an international journal. see *LAW*

610 UK ISSN 0748-8009
RC970 CODEN: MEWAE4
MEDICINE AND WAR. 1965. q. £30($45) to individuals; institutions £85 ($120) (effective 1996). Frank Cass, Newbury House, 890-900 Eastern Ave., Newbury Park, Ilford, Essex IG2 7HH, England. TEL 44-181-599-8866. FAX 44-181-599-0984. E-mail: 100067,1576@compuserve.com. Eds. Douglas Holdstock, Nevin Hughes Jones. adv.: B&W page £195 ($275); adv. contact: Anne Kidson. bk.rev.; stat.; index, cum.index: 1965-1969. (tabloid format; also avail. in microfilm from UMI; back issues avail.) **Indexed:** Curr.Adv.Ecol.Sci., Curr.Cont., P.A.I.S., Peace Res.Abstr. **Document type:** academic/scholarly publication.
—BLDSC (5534.008500); Faxon; UMI; UnCover. **CCC.**
Former titles (until 1985): Medical Association for Prevention of War. Journal (ISSN 0265-2196); (until Autumn 1982): Medical Association for Prevention of War. Proceedings (ISSN 0025-701X)
Description: Intended for medical health care professionals and peace researchers regarding the causes and effects of wars and other forms of social violence.
Refereed Serial

610 UK ISSN 0140-9158
MEDICINE DIGEST. (Editions for: Caribbean, Middle East, English-speaking Africa, French-speaking Africa, South East Asia) (Editions in English and French) 1974. m. $48 (Anglophone Africa $48; Caribbean $25; Middle East $78) (effective 1995). Medicine Digest Ltd., 11-12 Bouverie St., London EC4Y 8DP, England. TEL 0171-353-0585. FAX 0171-353-0614. Ed. Dr. Hugh de Glanville; Pub. David Bromilow. adv. contact: Joy del Rosario. bk.rev. circ. 88,785. (reprint service avail. from IRC) **Indexed:** Abstr.Hyg., Diar.Dis.Res., Trop.Dis.Bull. **Document type:** abstracting/indexing.

610 UK ISSN 0144-0438
MEDICINE INTERNATIONAL (MIDDLE EASTERN EDITION). 1980. m. £54. The Medicine Group (Journals) Ltd., Publishing House, 62 Stert St., Abingdon, Oxon OX14 3UQ, England. TEL 01235-555770. FAX 01235-554691. Ed. Jill McFarland; Pub. Simon Campbell-Smith. adv. contact: Christian Benzing. charts; illus.; circ. 20,000 (controlled). **Document type:** academic/scholarly publication.
—SWETS.
Description: Covers all aspects of medicine.

610 UK ISSN 0144-0411
MEDICINE INTERNATIONAL (QUARTERLY EDITION). 1981; N.S. 1984; N.S. 1988. q. The Medicine Group (Journals) Ltd., Publishing House, 62 Stert St., Abingdon, Oxon OX14 3UQ, England. TEL 01235-555770. FAX 01235-554691. Ed.Bd. adv.; illus. **Document type:** academic/scholarly publication.
Description: Covers all aspects of medicine.

610 SA ISSN 0260-2334
MEDICINE INTERNATIONAL (SOUTHERN AFRICAN EDITION). m. R.96.63 (effective 1992). Medicine Group (S A) (Pty) Ltd., P.O. Box 51930, Randburg 2125, South Africa. TEL 011-789-4010. FAX 011-789-4028. adv. circ. 5,500.
Formerly (until 1981): Medicine S.A.

610 CN ISSN 0225-3895
MEDICINE NORTH AMERICA. 1980. m. Can.$48($52) Parkhurst Publishing, 400 McGill St., Montreal, PQ H2Y 2G1, Canada. TEL 514-397-9393. Ed. Dr. Ian Hart; Pub. David Elkins. adv.; charts; illus.; index, cum.index: circ. 34,000. (back issues avail.) **Indexed:** FAMLI. **Document type:** academic/scholarly publication.
—BLDSC (5534.091000).

610 US
MEDICINE NORTHWEST. 1984. s-a. University of Washington, School of Medicine, Mail Stop SC-60, Seattle, WA 98195. TEL 206-685-0381. Ed. Leila Gray; Pub. Dr. Philip J. Fialkow. circ. 17,000 (controlled). (back issues avail.)
Description: Informs consituents of the University of Washington School of Medicine about its activities in education, instruction, patient care, and community service.

MEDICINE ON THE MIDWAY. see *COLLEGE AND ALUMNI*

MEDICAL SCIENCES   4243

**610   UK   ISSN 1357-3039
MEDICINE - UK EDITION.** 1981; N.S. 1984; N.S. 1988. m. £64 (foreign £72). The Medicine Group (Journals) Ltd., Publishing House, 62 Stert St., Abingdon OX14 3UQ, England. TEL 01235-555770. FAX 01235-554691. adv. contact: Christian Benzing. charts; illus.; stat. circ. 250,000. Indexed: Curr.Adv.Ecol.Sci., Diar.Dis.Res., Helminthol.Abstr. **Document type:** academic/scholarly publication.
—BLDSC (5533.998000).
Formerly (until 1995): Medicine International (UK Edition) (ISSN 0144-0403)
Description: Covers all aspects of medicine.

**610   DK   ISSN 0461-6308
MEDICINSK AARBOG.** (Text in Danish, Norwegian, Swedish) 1957. a. price varies. Munksgaard International Publishers Ltd., Book Division, 35 Noerre Soegade, P.O. Box 2148, DK-1016 Copenhagen K, Denmark. TEL 45-33-12-70-30. FAX 45-33-12-93-87. illus.

**610   XN   ISSN 0065-1214
                                      CODEN: GZMSAH
MEDICINSKA MISLA/ACTA FACULTATIS MEDICINAE SKOPIENSIS;** godisen zbornik na medicinskiot fakultet vo Skopje. (Text in Macedonian or English) 1954. s-a. $30 to institutions. Univerzitet vo Skoplje, Medicinski Fakultet, Central Library, Vodnjanska bb, 91000 Skopje, Macedonia. Ed. Avram Sadikario. **Indexed:** Biol.Abstr., Ind.Med.
—BLDSC (4197.700000); CASDDS. **CCC**.

**610   YU   ISSN 0025-8091
MEDICINSKI GLASNIK.** vol.20, 1966. m. 50 din.($5.75) Savez Lekarskih Drustava SFR Jugoslavije, Zeleni Venac 1-I, Belgrade, Yugoslavia. Ed. Lazar Stanojevic. **Indexed:** Biol.Abstr., C.I.S. Abstr., Dent.Ind., Ind.Med.

**610   YU   ISSN 0369-1527
                                      CODEN: MPODAC
MEDICINSKI PODMLADAK.** (Text in Serbo-Croatian; summaries in English) 1948. q. 1000 din.($26) Medicinski Podmladak, Dr. Subotica 8, 11000 Belgrade, Yugoslavia. Ed. Snezana D. Andrejevic. bk.rev. circ. 1,000. (back issues avail.)
—BLDSC (5534.167000); CASDDS.

**610   YU   ISSN 0025-8105
                                      CODEN: MEPEAB
MEDICINSKI PREGLED.** (Text in Serbian; abstracts in English) 1948. bi-m. $60. Drustvo Lekara Vojvodine - Serbian Medical Society of Vojvodina, Vase Stajica 9, Novi Sad, Vojvodina, Yugoslavia. TEL 021-28767. Ed. Vojislav Nikolic. adv.; bk.rev. circ. 1,500. **Indexed:** Biol.Abstr., Chem.Abstr., Dent.Ind., Ind.Med., Nutr.Abstr.
—BLDSC (0106.400000).
Description: Covers clinical medicine of all specialities.

**610   XV   ISSN 0025-8121
                                      CODEN: MRAZAM
MEDICINSKI RAZGLEDI.** (Text in Slovenian; summaries and contents page in English) 1961. q. 500 SLT to individuals; institutions 1000 SLT; students 350 SLT. Univerza v Ljubljani, Medicinska Fakulteta, Klub Studentov, Korytkova 2, 61105 Ljubljana, Slovenia. TEL 442-356. (Co-sponsor: Raziskovalna Skupnost Slovenije) Ed. Igor Cabrian. adv.; bk.rev.; index. circ. 3,200. **Indexed:** Biol.Abstr., Chem.Abstr., Nutr.Abstr.
—CASDDS.
Description: Medical practice, research and review articles.

**610   SW   ISSN 1104-2370
MEDICINSKT FORUM;** tidskrift foer allmaenmedicin. 1993. 10/yr. (free to qualified personnel). Astra - Draco - Tica, P.O. Box 2, S-221 00 Lund, Sweden.

**610   IT   ISSN 0025-8148
MEDICO D'ITALIA.** 1964. d. free. Federazione Nazionale degli Ordini dei Medici, Piazza Cola di Rienzo 80-A, 00192 Rome, Italy. TEL 06-3222455. FAX 06-3223814. Ed. Dr. Andrea Sermonti. adv.; bk.rev.; charts; illus.; stat. circ. 313,000. (tabloid format)

**610   IT   ISSN 0390-0347
MEDICO E PAZIENTE.** 1975. s-m. (18/yr.). Edifarm S.p.A., Viale Sabotino 19-2, 20135 Milan, Italy. adv.; B&W page L.8400000, color page L.13500000; trim 185 x 250. circ. 75,000.

**616.07   US   ISSN 0278-9779
MEDICO INTERAMERICANO.*** 1981. m. $25. Interamerican College of Physicians and Surgeons, 50 Galesi Dr., Wayne, NJ 07470. Ed. Charles H. Messina. adv. circ. 32,500.

MEDICO-LEGAL ADVISOR. see *LAW — Civil Law*

MEDICO-LEGAL SOCIETY OF VICTORIA. PROCEEDINGS. see *LAW — Civil Law*

MEDICO-LEGAL WATCH. see *LAW — Civil Law*

**610 658   IT
MEDICO OSPEDALIERO.** 10/yr. Via Camindella 21, 20123 Milan, Italy. TEL 2-870946. Ed. Umberto Marini. circ. 30,000.

**610   SP
EL MEDICO, PROFESION Y HUMANIDADES.** w. Saned, S.A., Paseo de la Habana 202-bis, 28036 Madrid, Spain. TEL 1-3594902. Dir. Fernando Gimenez. circ. 50,000.

MEDICOLEGAL LIBRARY. see *LAW — International Law*

**610   KE   ISSN 0253-0961
MEDICOM;** African journal of hospital medicine. 1979. bi-m. EAs.200($12.50) Update Publishers Ltd., Box 73824, Nairobi, Kenya. Ed. Dr. Peter A. Odhiambo. adv.; bk.rev. circ. 1,000. (back issues avail.)

MEDIGRAM. see *ADVERTISING AND PUBLIC RELATIONS*

**610 615.329 614.8   GW   ISSN 0171-3876
MEDIKAMENT & MEINUNG;** Zeitschrift fuer Arzneimittel- und Gesundheitswesen. 1978. m. free. Bundesverband der Pharmazeutischen Industrie, Karlstr. 21, 60329 Frankfurt a.M., Germany. FAX 069-237813. Ed. Thomas Postina. adv. contact: Kerstin Kilian. bk.rev. circ. 36,000. (back issues avail.) **Document type:** bulletin.

**610   JA   ISSN 0911-7075
MEDIKARU HYUMANITI/MEDICAL HUMANITY.** (Supplement avail.: Bessatsu Medikaru Hyumaniti (ISSN 0915-129X)) (Text in Japanese) 1985. q. 1602 Yen per no. Sokyusha, 10-14-403, Otsuka 1-chome, Bunkyo-ku, Tokyo 112, Japan. Ed.Kiyoshi Nojima.

**610   SP   ISSN 1130-2690
MEDIKUAREN BERRIA.** 1990. 6/yr. Colegio de Medicos de Vizcaya, Puente de Deusto 7, 3o Dpto. 5, 48014 Bilbao, Spain. TEL 4-447-84-14. Ed. Aintzane Olabarrieta. circ. 33,000.

MEDINDEX. see *INSTRUMENTS*

MEDIPHARM. see *PHARMACY AND PHARMACOLOGY*

**610   NR   ISSN 0794-3733
                                      CODEN: MEMJEF
MEDIPHARM MEDICAL JOURNAL.** (Text in English) q. $50 to individuals; institutions $60. Literamed Nigeria Ltd., Plot 45, Alausa, Oregun Village, P.M.B. 21068, Ikeja, Lagos, Nigeria. Ed. Oladapo A. Ashiru. adv. circ. 2,000.
—CASDDS.

**610   SZ   ISSN 0237-4021
MEDIPRESS.** (Text in English, Polish) 1985. q. Clyancourt Corporation AG, Postfach 5016, CH-6305 Zug, Switzerland. TEL 042-413044. FAX 042-417844. Ed. R.G. Coenen. circ. 10,000. **Document type:** abstracting/indexing.

**610   CN   ISSN 1188-0333
MEDISCAN.** 1980. 3/yr. (Canadian Federation of Medical Students) Canadian Medical Association, 1867 Alta Vista Dr., Ottawa, ON K1G 3Y6, Canada. TEL 613-731-9331. FAX 613-523-0937. Ed. Debbie A. Rupert. adv.; B&W page Can.$1100, color page Can.$2000; trim 8 1/2 x 11. circ. 5,500.

**610   NE   ISSN 0025-8245
MEDISCH CONTACT.** (Includes m. supplement: Geneesmiddelenbulletin (ISSN 0304-4629)) 1945. w. membership. (Koninklijke Nederlandse Maatschappij tot Bevordering der Geneeskunst - Royal Dutch Society for the Advancement of Medicine) Misset (Subsidiary of: Reed Elsevier plc), Postbus 4, 7000 BA Doetinchem, Netherlands. TEL 31-8340-49371. FAX 31-8340-63638. (Editorial addr.: Lomanlaan 103, 3526 XD Utrecht, Netherlands. TEL 31-30-823384) Ed. Dr. C. Spreeuwenberg. adv.: B&W page fl.3745, color page fl.7575; trim 210 x 297; adv. contact: Cor van Nek. illus. circ. 28,178. **Indexed:** Abstr.Crim.& Pen., Excerp.Med., Key to Econ.Sci. **Document type:** trade publication.
—BLDSC (5534.400000); SWETS.

**610   UK   ISSN 0261-7099
MEDISCOPE;** manchester medical gazette. 1898. 3/yr. £5 to individuals (foreign £7); libraries £5.50 (foreign £9). University of Manchester, Medical School, Manchester M13 9PT, England. TEL 0161-275-5532. Ed. Russell Young. adv. contact: Aafia Chadhury. bk.rev.; charts; illus. circ. 2,000. **Indexed:** Ind.Med. **Document type:** trade publication.
Formerly: Manchester Medical Gazette (ISSN 0025-2018)

**610 658   UK   ISSN 1352-1179
MEDISTAT.** 1987. m. £625($930) M D I S Publications Ltd., MDIS House, City Fields Business Park, City Fields Way, Chichester, W. Sussex PO20 6FS, England. TEL 01243-533322. FAX 01243-532124. Ed. Ian Taylor. adv.: page £250; trim 240 x 170; adv. contact: Helena Mancey. circ. 500. (looseleaf format; also avail. in diskette format; back issues avail.) **Document type:** newsletter.
—CCC.
Description: Market analysis and product news for manufacturers of medical equipment and supplies.

**610   IT   ISSN 1120-5962
MEDITIME.*** 1987. w. L' Ariete Edizioni, Via Stephenson 33, 20154 Milan, Italy. TEL 02-330241. FAX 02-39216592. adv.: B&W page L.11000000, color page L.14500000; trim 265 x 380. circ. 76,557.

**610   RU   ISSN 0025-8318
MEDITSINSKAYA GAZETA.** 1938. s-w. $69. (Medical Workers' Union) Meditsinskaya Gazeta, Sukarevskaya pl. 1-2, 129010 Moscow, Russia. TEL 095-208-8695. (Dist. in U.S. by: Victor Kamkin Inc., 4956 Boiling Brook Pkwy, Rockville, MD 20852. TEL 301-881-5973) Ed. K.V. Sheglov. index. circ. 1,430,000. (also avail. in microform from UMI) **Indexed:** Biol.Abstr., Curr.Dig.Sov.Press.

**610   RU   ISSN 0025-8075
                                      CODEN: MEDTBV
MEDITSINSKAYA TEKHNIKA/MEDICAL ENGINEERING.** English translation: Biomedical Engineering (US ISSN 0006-3398) 1967. bi-m. $63. (Mezhdunarodnoe Nauchno-technicheskoe Obshchestvo Priborostroitelei i Metrologov) Izdatel'stvo Meditsina, Petroverigskii pereulok 6-8, 101000 Moscow, Russia. (Dist. by: Mezhdunarodnaya Kniga, B. Yakimanka 39, 117049 Moscow, Russia. TEL 7-095-2384600. FAX 7-095-2384634) Ed. V.A. Viktorov. adv.; bk.rev. circ. 5,000. **Indexed:** Biol.Abstr., Chem.Abstr., Dent.Ind., Ind.Med., INIS Atomind., INSPEC.
—BLDSC (0106.100000); CASDDS. **CCC**.
Description: Deals with theoretical and practical problems of the development of medical engineering and its application in public health practice.

**610   UZ   ISSN 0025-830X
                                      CODEN: MZUZA8
MEDITSINSKII ZHURNAL UZBEKISTANA.** 1948. m. $9.20. Izdatel'stvo Meditsina, Otdelenie v Uzbekistane, Ul. Navoi, 30, Tashkent, Uzbekistan. Ed. K.C. Zaupoe. **Indexed:** Biol.Abstr., Chem.Abstr., Nutr.Abstr.
—BLDSC (0106.500000); CASDDS. **CCC**.

MEDICAL SCIENCES

610   GW   ISSN 0939-351X
MEDIZIN, GESELLSCHAFT UND GESCHICHTE. (Text in English, German) 1985. a. DM.48 (students DM.38.40). (Institut fuer Geschichte der Medizin der Robert Bosch Stiftung) Franz Steiner Verlag Wiesbaden GmbH, Birkenwaldstr. 44, 70191 Stuttgart, Germany. TEL 0711-25820. FAX 0711-2582390. (Subscr. to: Postfach 101061, 70009 Stuttgart, Germany) Ed. Robert Juette. **Document type:** academic/scholarly publication.
   Formerly: Institut fuer Geschichte der Medizin der Robert Bosch Stiftung. Jahrbuch.

610   GW   ISSN 0941-5033
MEDIZIN, GESELLSCHAFT UND GESCHICHTE. BEIHEFTE. 1992. irreg., vol.6, 1995. Franz Steiner Verlag Wiesbaden GmbH, Birkenwaldstr. 44, 70191 Stuttgart, Germany. TEL 0711-2582-0. FAX 0711-2582390. (Subscr. to: Postfach 101061, 70009 Stuttgart, Germany) Ed. Robert Juette. **Document type:** academic/scholarly publication.

MEDIZIN IN RECHT UND ETHIK. see *LAW — Civil Law*

610   AU
MEDIZIN POPULAER. bi-m. free. Oesterreichische Aerztekammer, Pressestelle und Verlag, Weihburggasse 10-12, A-1011 Vienna, Austria. TEL 01-5124486. FAX 01-513192524. adv. **Document type:** bulletin.

610 600   GW
MEDIZIN, TECHNIK UND GESELLSCHAFT. 1993. irreg. Peter Lang GmbH Europaeischer Verlag der Wissenschaften, Eschborner Landstr. 42-50, 60489 Frankfurt a.M., Germany. TEL 069-7807050. FAX 069-785893. Ed. Kurt Bayertz. **Document type:** monographic series.

610   GW   ISSN 0025-8431
R131.A1   CODEN: MEDJE4
MEDIZINHISTORISCHES JOURNAL. (Text in English, French and German) 1966. 4/yr. DM.146 (foreign DM.154). (Akademie der Wissenschaften und der Literatur, Mainz, Kommission fuer Geschichte der Medizin und der Naturwissenschaften) Gustav Fischer Verlag, Wollgrasweg 49, 70599 Stuttgart, Germany. TEL 0711-458030. FAX 0711-4580334. TELEX 7111488-FIBUCH. (Subscr. to: Postfach 720143, 70577 Stuttgart, Germany; U.S. address: VCH Publishers, Inc., 303 N.W. 12th Ave., Deerfield Beach, FL 33442-1788) Ed.Bd. adv.; bk.rev.; index. circ. 1,000. **Indexed:** Biol.Abstr., Chem.Abstr. **Document type:** academic/scholarly publication.
—SWETS. **CCC**.

610   US   ISSN 0342-4103
MEDIZINISCHE INFORMATIK UND STATISTIK. (Text in German) 1976. irreg. price varies. Springer-Verlag, 175 Fifth Ave., New York, NY 10010. TEL 212-460-1500. FAX 212-473-6272. (Also: Berlin, Heidelberg, Tokyo and Vienna) Ed.Bd. (reprint service avail. from ISI) **Document type:** academic/scholarly publication.

610   GW   ISSN 0723-5003
CODEN: MEKLA7
MEDIZINISCHE KLINIK. 1906. m. DM.216($156) (effective 1996). (Deutsche Gesellschaft fuer Innere Medizin) Urban und Vogel, Lindwurmstr. 95, 80337 Munich, Germany. TEL 089-53292-0. FAX 089-53292-100. (Subscr. to: Postfach 152209, 80052 Munich, Germany) circ. 10,000 (controlled). **Indexed:** Biol.Abstr., Biotech.Abstr., C.I.S. Abstr., Chem.Abstr., Curr.Cont., Excerp.Med., Helminthol.Abstr., Ind.Med., Ind.Sci.Rev., INIS Atomind., Nutr.Abstr. **Document type:** academic/scholarly publication.
—BLDSC (5535.080000); CASDDS; Faxon; Genuine Article; SWETS; UMI. **CCC**.

MEDIZINISCHE KONGRESSE; national - international. see *MEETINGS AND CONGRESSES*

610   US   ISSN 0076-6151
MEDIZINISCHE LAENDERKUNDE. GEOMEDICAL MONOGRAPH SERIES. Short title: Geomedical Monograph Series. (Text in German) 1967. irreg. price varies. Springer-Verlag, 175 Fifth Ave., New York, NY 10010. TEL 212-460-1500. FAX 212-473-6272. (Also: Berlin, Heidelberg, Tokyo and Vienna) (reprint service avail. from ISI) **Document type:** monographic series.

610   GW   ISSN 0342-9601
CODEN: MMPHDB
MEDIZINISCHE MONATSSCHRIFT FUER PHARMAZEUTEN. 1947. m. DM.149.40 (DM.77.40 to students and subscribers to Deutsche Apotheker Zeitung and Oesterreichische Apotheker Zeitung). Deutscher Apotheker Verlag, Postfach 101061, 70009 Stuttgart, Germany. TEL 0711-2582-0. FAX 0711-2582290. (Co-publisher: Wissenschaftliche Verlagsgesellschaft mbH) Ed. Susanne Heinzl. adv.; bk.rev.; illus.; tr.lit. circ. 12,000. **Indexed:** Biol.Abstr., Biotech.Abstr., Chem.Abstr., Excerp.Med., Ind.Med. **Document type:** trade publication.
—BLDSC (5535.108000); CASDDS; Faxon; SWETS. **CCC**.
   Formerly: Medizinische Monatsschrift (ISSN 0025-8474)

610   GW   ISSN 0025-8490
DER MEDIZINISCHE SACHVERSTAENDIGE. 1904. bi-m. DM.215.70 (foreign DM.250.80) (effective 1995). Verlagsgemeinschaft Gentner Verlag - Strobel Verlag, Forststr. 131, 70193 Stuttgart, Germany. TEL 0711-63672-0. FAX 0711-6367211. Ed. Winfried Hackhausen. adv. contact: G. Keuchen. bk.rev.; abstr.; charts; illus.; index. circ. 1,450. **Indexed:** C.I.S. Abstr., Chem.Abstr. **Document type:** academic/scholarly publication.
—**CCC**.

610   GW   ISSN 0025-8512
CODEN: MEWEAC
DIE MEDIZINISCHE WELT. (Supplements avail.: Die Internistische Welt (ISSN 0344-4201); Natur- und Ganzheitsmedizin (ISSN 0934-7909) 1950. m. DM.275($1226.50) F.K. Schattauer Verlagsgesellschaft mbH, Lenzhalde 3, 70192 Stuttgart, Germany. TEL 0711-22987-0. FAX 0711-22987-50. adv.; bk.rev.; bibl.; charts; illus.; index. circ. 4,300. (also avail. in microform from PMC) **Indexed:** Biol.Abstr., Biotech.Abstr., C.I.S. Abstr., Chem.Abstr., Curr.Adv.Ecol.Sci., Curr.Cont., Dent.Ind., Excerp.Med., Helminthol.Abstr., Ind.Med., INIS Atomind., Nutr.Abstr. **Document type:** academic/scholarly publication.
—BLDSC (5535.200000); CASDDS; EMDOCS; Genuine Article; SWETS. **CCC**.

610   GW   ISSN 0944-6885
▼**MEDIZINPRODUKTE JOURNAL.** 1994. q. DM.39. Wissenschaftliche Verlagsgesellschaft mbH, Postfach 101061, 70009 Stuttgart, Germany. TEL 0711-2582-0. FAX 0711-2582290. Ed. S. Imhoff-Hasse. **Document type:** trade publication.
—SWETS.

MEDIZINSOZIOLOGIE. see *SOCIAL SCIENCES: COMPREHENSIVE WORKS*

610   GW   ISSN 0344-9416
CODEN: MDZNDG
MEDIZINTECHNIK. 1880. bi-m. DM.122.70 (foreign DM.134.70). Verlag T Ue V Rheinland GmbH, Viktoriastr. 26, 51149 Cologne, Germany. TEL 02203-170902. FAX 02203-15411. Ed. R.D. Boeckmann. adv.; bk.rev.; rec.rev.; charts; illus.; pat.; index. circ. 3,200. **Indexed:** Chem.Abstr., Excerp.Med., INIS Atomind. **Document type:** academic/scholarly publication.
—CASDDS. **CCC**.
   Formerly: Medizinische Technik (ISSN 0025-8504)

610   SZ
MEDKALENDER. (Text in German) 1878. a. 60 SFr. Schwabe und Co. AG, Steinentorstr. 13, CH-4010 Basel, Switzerland. TEL 061-2725523. FAX 061-2725573. adv.; index. circ. 6,000. **Document type:** trade publication.
—**CCC**.
   Former titles: Schweizerischer Medizinalkalender; Schweizerischer Medizinalkalender und Arzneimittelueberischt; Schweizerischer Medizinalkalender (ISSN 0251-1762)
   Description: Provides information for medical doctors and pharmacists on drugs and preparations with notes on pharmacology and dosages, as well as information on emergency treatment of poisoning.

610   US
MEDPRO MONTH. 1990. m. $775. Medical Data International, 2 Park Plaza, Ste. 750, Irvine, CA 92714. TEL 714-251-2780. FAX 714-251-2781. Ed. Pieter Walter. circ. 700 (paid). **Document type:** newsletter.
   Description: Provides an insight into how the healthcare marketplace is unfolding, identifying markets at risk, as well as those with opportunities for growth.

MEDYCYNA DOSWIADCZALNA I MIKROBIOLOGIA. see *BIOLOGY — Microbiology*

610 613.62   PL   ISSN 0465-5893
CODEN: MEPAAX
MEDYCYNA PRACY. (Text in Polish; summaries in English) 1950. bi-m. $90. Instytut Medycyny Pracy im. Jerzego Nofera - Nofer's Institute of Occupational Medicine, Ul. Sw. Teresy 8, P.O. Box 199, 90-950 Lodz, Poland. TEL 48-42-552505. FAX 48-42-348331. Ed. Janusz Indulski. adv. contact: Teresa Starzynska. index. **Indexed:** Abstr.Hyg., Biol.Abstr., C.I.S. Abstr., Chem.Abstr., Dent.Ind., Excerp.Med., Fuel & Energy Abstr., Ind.Med., INIS Atomind., Psychol.Abstr. (1990-), Trop.Dis.Bull. **Document type:** academic/scholarly publication.
—BLDSC (5536.020000); CASDDS.
   Description: Explores occupational hygiene, pathologies, epidemiology, physiology and psychology of health care organizations.

610   PL   ISSN 0025-8636
MEDYCYNA WIEJSKA/RURAL MEDICINE. (Text in English, Polish) 1953. q. $60. Instytut Medycyny Wsi, Ul. Jaczewskiego 2, 20-950 Lublin, Poland. TEL 48-81-778027. FAX 48-81-778646. (Dist. by: Ars Polona - Ruch, Krakowskie Przedmiescie 7, 00-068 Warsaw, Poland) Ed. Maciej Latalski. adv.; bk.rev.; index. circ. 1,000. (reprint service avail.; back issues avail.) **Indexed:** Apic.Abstr., C.I.S. Abstr.
   Description: For the rural physicians from the village health centers and the physicians employed in regional outpatient clinics in the towns. Contains publications concerning the evaluation of the living and working environment in rural areas.

610   PL   ISSN 1230-4565
MEDYCYNA 2000. Variant title: Medycyna Dwa Tysiace. 1990. m. Fundacja Rowoju Nauki Polskiej, Ul. Lubomelska 12, 01-805 Warsaw, Poland. TEL 48-22-341147. FAX 48-22-332674. TELEX 812745 DORHA PL. Ed. Malgorzata Godziembia-Maliszewska. circ. 5,000.

610   PL   ISSN 0867-3055
MEDYK/PHYSICIAN. 1953. m. 18 Zl. (effective 1995). Medyk Ltd. Co., Foksal 11, Warsaw, Poland. TEL 48-22-263250. (Dist. by: Ruch S.A., ul. Towarowa 28, 00-958 Warsaw, Poland) Ed. Andrzej Doroba. adv.: B&W page DM.320, color page DM.512; trim 250 x 350). adv. contact: Marlena Drozdz. bk.rev. circ. 25,000.
   Formerly: Nowy Medyk (ISSN 0137-7175)

MEIKAI UNIVERSITY SCHOOL OF DENTISTRY. JOURNAL. see *MEDICAL SCIENCES — Dentistry*

610   JA   ISSN 0287-9085
MEJIKARU NYUSU/MEDICAL NEWS. (Text in Japanese) 1960. bi-m. 100 Yen per no. (Kyowa Kikaku Tsushin) Dainippon Seiyaku K.K. - Dainippon Pharmaceutical Co., Ltd., 3-25, Doshomachi, Higashi-ku, Osaka 541, Japan.

MEMBRANE PROTEINS. see *BIOLOGY — Biological Chemistry*

616.988   NE
MEMISA MEDISCH. 1934. bi-m. free to qualified personnel. Memisa, Eendrachtsweg 48, 3012 LD Rotterdam, Netherlands. FAX 31-10-4047319. TELEX 24541 MEMIS NL. bk.rev.; abstr.; charts; illus.; index; circ. 5,000 (controlled). (tabloid format)
   Formerly: Memisa Nieuws (ISSN 0025-9063)
   Description: Covers tropical medicine.

610   US
MENDOCINO MEDICINE & GAZETTEER. q. Mendocino Academy of Science, Box 165, Mendocino, CA 95460. Dir. Dr. Richard White.

MEDICAL SCIENCES

610 US ISSN 0076-6526
RC55
MERCK MANUAL: A HANDBOOK OF DIAGNOSIS AND THERAPY. 1899. irreg., 16th ed., 1992. $26. Merck Publishing Co., Attn. Merck Publishing, Box 2000, Rg 7-220, Rahway, NJ 07065. TEL 908-594-4600. Ed. Dr. Robert Berkow.

MERIDIANS; redefining health. see *ALTERNATIVE MEDICINE*

610 299.93 GW ISSN 0935-798X
DER MERKURSTAB. 1950. bi-m. DM.135. Gesellschaft Anthroposophischer Aerzte in Deutschland, Postfach 750221, 70602 Stuttgart, Germany. TEL 0711-471501. FAX 0711-4780186. bk.rev. **Document type:** academic/scholarly publication.

610 US ISSN 0885-7490
RC394.M48 CODEN: MBDIEE
METABOLIC BRAIN DISEASE. 1986. q. $375 (foreign $440) (effective 1996). Plenum Publishing Corp., 233 Spring St., New York, NY 10013-1578. TEL 212-620-8000. FAX 212-463-0742. TELEX 23-421139. Ed. Roger F. Butterworth. adv.; bk.rev.; charts; illus. (also avail. in microfilm from JSC; back issues avail.) **Indexed:** Curr.Adv.Biochem., Curr.Adv.Cell & Devel.Biol., Curr.Cont. **Document type:** academic/scholarly publication.
—BLDSC (5683.266500); CASDDS; Faxon; Genuine Article; SWETS; UMI; UnCover. **CCC.**
Refereed Serial

610 029 GW ISSN 0026-1270
R51 CODEN: MIMCAI
METHODS OF INFORMATION IN MEDICINE; journal of methodology in medical research, information and documentation. 1962. 5/yr. DM.271($193.30) to individuals; institutions DM.366($255.30). F.K. Schattauer Verlagsgesellschaft mbH, Lenzhalde 3, Postfach 104545, 70192 Stuttgart, Germany. TEL 0711-22987-0. FAX 0711-22987-50. Ed. J.H. van Bemmel. adv.; bibl.; charts; illus.; index. circ. 1,300. **Indexed:** Abstr.Health Care Manage.Stud., Biol.Abstr., Curr.Cont., Cyb.Abstr., Excerp.Med., Ind.Med., Ind.Sci.Rev., INSPEC, Telegen.
—BLDSC (5748.100000); EMDOCS; Faxon; Genuine Article; SWETS; UMI; UnCover. **CCC.**
Description: Covers methodology of medical research, documentation, information science and medical informatics.

610 SP
METODOS TERAPEUTICOS DE ACTUALIDAD. 12/yr. Provenza 385-387, 08025 Barcelona, Spain. TEL 3-459-22-20. FAX 3-258-15-35. Ed. Dr. F. Prandi.

MEYLER'S SIDE EFFECTS OF DRUGS; the encyclopedia of adverse reactions. see *PHARMACY AND PHARMACOLOGY*

610 US ISSN 0026-2293
R15
MICHIGAN MEDICINE. (Includes Medigram) 1902. m. $100; newsstand price: $5. Michigan State Medical Society, P.O. Box 950, East Lansing, MI 48826-0950. TEL 517-337-1351. FAX 517-337-2490. Ed. Betty Jeanne McNerney. adv.; illus.; index. circ. 11,000. (also avail. in microfilm from UMI; reprint service avail. from UMI) **Indexed:** C.I.S. Abstr., CINAHL, Ind.Med., Med. Care Rev., Mich.Mag.Ind.
—BLDSC (5755.400000); UMI.
Formerly (until 1964): Michigan State Medical Society. Journal (ISSN 0098-7522); **Incorporates:** Michigan State Medical Society. Transactions.
Description: Dedicated to providing information for Michigan physicians about actions of the Michigan State Medical Society. Covers contemporary issues, with special emphasis on socio-economics legislation and news about medicine.

MICROBIAL DRUG RESISTANCE: MECHANISM, EPIDEMIOLOGY, AND DISEASE. see *BIOLOGY — Microbiology*

MICROBIOLOGIA MEDICA. see *BIOLOGY — Microbiology*

MICROBIOS; a prestige international biomedical research journal of chemical and general microbiology. see *BIOLOGY — Microbiology*

610 576 UK ISSN 1350-4916
▼**MICROCIRCULATION (LONDON).** 1994. q. $130 to institutions in the E.U. (N. America $205; elsewhere £145) (effective 1995). Chapman & Hall (Subsidiary of: International Thomson Publishing Group), 2-6 Boundary Row, London SE1 8HN, England. TEL 0171-865-0066. FAX 0171-865-9623. TELEX 290164 CHAPMA G. E-mail: journal@chall.mhs.compuserve.com. (Dist. by: International Thomson Publishing Services Ltd., Cheriton House, North Way, Andover, Hants. SP10 5BE, England. TEL 01264-342713. FAX 01264-342807; N. American subscr. to: Chapman & Hall, Journals Promotion Department, One Penn Plaza, 41st Fl., New York, NY 10119. TEL 212-564-1060. FAX 212-564-1505) Ed. Mary E. Gerritsen. (reprint service avail.) **Document type:** academic/scholarly publication.
—CCC.
Description: Covers applications of the methods of physiology, biophysics, bioengineering, genetics, cell biology, biochemistry, and molecular biology to microcirculation.
Refereed Serial

MICROCIRCULATION REVIEWS. see *BIOLOGY — Physiology*

610 026 US
MIDDLE ATLANTIC PERSPECTIVE. 1983. bi-m. free to qualified personnel. Middle Atlantic Region, N N - L M, New York Academy of Medicine, 1216 Fifth Ave., New York, NY 10029. TEL 212-876-8763. FAX 212-534-7042. Dir. Arthur Downing. charts; stat.; circ. 2,100 (controlled). **Document type:** newsletter.
Supersedes in part (in 1991): Greater Northeastern Regional Medical Library Program Newsletter; **Formerly (until 1983):** New York and New Jersey Regional Medical Library News.
Description: News items, information, and announcements pertaining to the Network of Libraries of Medicine serving New York, New Jersey, Pennsylvania and Delaware.

610 JA ISSN 0026-3532
CODEN: MMJJAI
MIE MEDICAL JOURNAL. (Text in European languages) 1950. 3/yr. free. Mie Daigaku, Igakubu - Mie University, School of Medicine, 2-174 Edobashi, Tsu-shi, Mie-ken 514, Japan. Ed. Toshio Tanaka. charts; illus.; stat.; index. circ. 850. **Indexed:** Abstr.Hyg., Biol.Abstr., Chem.Abstr., Dent.Abstr., Dent.Ind., Excerp.Med., Ind.Med., Nutr.Abstr., Rev.Appl.Entomol., Trop.Dis.Bull.
—BLDSC (5761.450000); CASDDS; EMDOCS; UnCover.
Description: Multidisciplinary papers on medicine.

610 IS ISSN 0026-363X
MIKHTAV LEHAVER. 1940. m. Israel Medical Association, 39 Shaul Hamelech Blvd., Tel Aviv, Israel. TEL 972-3-6969639. FAX 972-3-6956103. Ed. Dr. M. Zangen. adv.; charts; illus.
Description: Contains organization news.

MIKROBIOLOGI-NYT. see *VETERINARY SCIENCE*

616.98 US ISSN 0026-4075
RD1 CODEN: MMEDA9
MILITARY MEDICINE. 1891. m. $45 (foreign $50). Association of Military Surgeons of the U S, 9320 Old Georgetown Rd., Bethesda, MD 20814. TEL 301-897-8800. FAX 301-530-5446. Ed. Dr. John C. Duffy. adv.; bk.rev.; bibl.; charts; illus.; stat.; index, cum.index. circ. 16,755. (also avail. in microfilm; back issues avail.; reprint service avail. from UMI) **Indexed:** Abstr.Health Care Manage.Stud., Abstr.Hyg., Biol.Abstr., C.I.S. Abstr., Chem.Abstr., CINAHL, Curr.Cont., Dent.Ind., Excerp.Med., Helminthol.Abstr., Hosp.Lit.Ind., Ind.Med., Ind.Vet., Nutr.Abstr., Protozool.Abstr., Psychol.Abstr. (1955-), Small Anim.Abstr., Trop.Dis.Bull., Vet.Bull. **Document type:** newsletter, trade publication.
—BLDSC (5768.150000); CASDDS; EMDOCS; Faxon; Genuine Article; SWETS; UMI; UnCover. **CCC.**
Description: Supports knowledge concerning medical activities of the Federal Medical Services, including developments in medical technology, education, management and research.
Refereed Serial

MIND: THE MEETINGS INDEX. see *TECHNOLOGY: COMPREHENSIVE WORKS*

612.39 574.133 SZ ISSN 0378-0392
CODEN: MELMDI
MINERAL AND ELECTROLYTE METABOLISM. (Text in English) 1978. bi-m. 224.35 SFr.($172.55) to individuals; institutions 641 SFr.($493) (effective 1996). S. Karger AG, Allschwilerstr. 10, P.O. Box, CH-4009 Basel, Switzerland. TEL 061-3061111. FAX 061-3061234. E-mail: Karger@Karger.ch. Ed. S.G. Massry. adv.; illus.; index. circ. 850. (also avail. in microform from UMI; back issues avail.) **Indexed:** Chem.Abstr., Curr.Adv.Cell & Devel.Biol., Curr.Adv.Ecol.Sci., Curr.Cont., Dent.Ind., Excerp.Med., Ind.Med. **Document type:** academic/scholarly publication.
—BLDSC (5776.710000); CASDDS; Faxon; Genuine Article; SWETS; UnCover. **CCC.**
Refereed Serial

MINERVA AEROSPAZIALE; a journal on aerospace culture, law and medicine. see *AERONAUTICS AND SPACE FLIGHT*

615.8 UK ISSN 0961-625X
CODEN: MITREY
MINIMALLY INVASIVE THERAPY. (Supplement avail. (ISSN 0967-9766)) 1992. bi-m. £210 in Europe; elsewhere £231($372) (effective 1996). Blackwell Science Ltd., Osney Mead, Oxford OX2 0EL, England. TEL 01865-240201. FAX 01865-721205. TELEX 83355 MEDBOK G. Ed. J. Wickham. adv.; bibl.; illus.; index. circ. 750. (also avail. in microform from UMI; back issues avail.) **Indexed:** Excerp.Med. (1993-). **Document type:** academic/scholarly publication.
—BLDSC (5797.713000); ADONIS; Genuine Article; UMI. **CCC.**
Refereed Serial

615.8 UK ISSN 0967-9766
MINIMALLY INVASIVE THERAPY. SUPPLEMENT. irreg. Blackwell Science Ltd., Osney Mead, Oxford OX2 0EL, England. TEL 01865-240201. FAX 01865-721205. TELEX 83355 MEDBOK G. **Indexed:** Excerp.Med. (1993-). **Document type:** academic/scholarly publication.
—ADONIS.

610.5 US ISSN 0026-556X
R15 CODEN: MIMDAL
MINNESOTA MEDICINE. 1918. m. $36 (foreign $60). Minnesota Medical Association, 3433 Broadway St., N.E., Ste. 300, Minneapolis, MN 55413-1761. TEL 612-378-1875. FAX 612-378-3875. Ed. Dr. Charles R. Meyer. adv. contact: Sherry Makela. bk.rev.; abstr.; bibl.; charts; illus.; index. circ. 10,000 (controlled). (also avail. in microform from UMI; reprint service avail. from UMI) **Indexed:** Biol.Abstr., Chem.Abstr., Curr.Adv.Cancer Res., Curr.Cont., Dent.Ind., Excerp.Med., Helminthol.Abstr., Hosp.Lit.Ind., Ind.Med.
●Also available online.
—BLDSC (5810.400000); Faxon; Genuine Article; SWETS; UMI; UnCover. **CCC.**
Description: Covers clinical, ethical, legal, socioeconomic, and other issues relating to how medicine is practiced in Minnesota.

378 US ISSN 0085-3488
R745
MINORITY STUDENT OPPORTUNITIES IN UNITED STATES MEDICAL SCHOOLS. 1970. biennial. $7.50. Association of American Medical Colleges, 2450 N St., Washington, DC 20037-1126. TEL 202-828-0572. FAX 202-828-1123. (reprint service avail. from UMI)
Description: Provides infomation to underrepresented minorities - black Americans, American Indians, Mexican Americans - Chicanos, and mainland Puerto Ricans - applying to medical school. Contains descriptive entries of US medical schools with information on recruitment programs, admission policies and procedures, academic support programs, and financial aid for underrepresented minority students.

MIRKACHTON. see *PHARMACY AND PHARMACOLOGY*

MISSISSIPPI ACADEMY OF SCIENCE. JOURNAL. see *SCIENCES: COMPREHENSIVE WORKS*

MEDICAL SCIENCES

610 US ISSN 0026-6396 CODEN: MSMJB8
MISSISSIPPI STATE MEDICAL ASSOCIATION. JOURNAL. 1960. m. $35 (foreign $45). Mississippi State Medical Association, 735 Riverside Dr., Box 5229, Jackson, MS 39296-5229. TEL 601-354-5433. Ed. Ginger Cocke. adv.; bk.rev.; charts; illus.; stat.; tr.lit.; index. circ. 2,900. (also avail. in microform from UMI; reprint service avail. from UMI) **Indexed:** Ind.Med., INIS Atomind. **Document type:** academic/scholarly publication.
—BLDSC (4828.210000); Faxon; UMI; UnCover.
Refereed Serial

610 US ISSN 0026-6620
MISSOURI MEDICINE. 1904. m. $60. Missouri State Medical Association, Box 1028, 113 Madison St., Jefferson City, MO 65102. TEL 314-636-5151. FAX 314-636-8552. Ed. Dr. J. Regan Thomas. adv.; bk.rev.; charts; illus.; index. circ. 7,000. (also avail. in microfilm) **Indexed:** Biol.Abstr., Chem.Abstr., Curr.Cont., Dent.Ind., Excerp.Med., Helminthol.Abstr., Ind.Med. **Document type:** directory.
—BLDSC (5829.080000); EMDOCS; Faxon; UMI; UnCover.
Description: Prints scientific articles, editorials on medical issues. Includes medical school news, classifieds, and information on new members, deaths, continuing medical education courses, and practice management.

610 360 GW
MITEINANDER. 1977. 3/yr. Deutsches Aussaetzigen Hilfswerk e.V., Postfach 110462, 8700 Wuerzburg 11, Germany. TEL 0931-50784. FAX 0931-51358. TELEX 68583-DAHW-D. Ed. Peter Schweiger. bk.rev. circ. 80,000. (back issues avail.)
Description: Leprosy aid and health problems in developing countries.

MITOCHONDRIA. see *BIOLOGY — Cytology And Histology*

610 AU
MITTEILUNGEN DER AERZTEKAMMER FUER WIEN - WIENER ARZT. 1948. m. S.407. Aerztekammer fuer Wien, Weihburggasse 10-12, A-1010 Vienna, Austria. TEL 01-51501223. FAX 01-51501289. Ed. Dr. Guenther Knogler. adv.: page S.13350; trim 186 x 256; adv. contact: Nina Chalupsky. bk.rev.; circ. 12,000. (back issues avail.) **Document type:** newsletter.
Former titles (until 1992): Ae K W M (Aerztekammer fuer Wien Mitteilungen) (ISSN 0377-9874); (until 1975): Aerztekammer fuer Wien. Mitteilungen (ISSN 0377-9866); (until 1967): Aerztekammer fuer Wien. Mitteilungsblatt (ISSN 0377-9858); (until 1956): Aerztekammer fuer Wien. Mitteilungen.

610 US ISSN 0888-6792
MODEL FOR THE PREPARATION OF A GUIDEBOOK ON MEDICAL DISCIPLINE. triennial. $8. Federation of State Medical Boards, 400 Fuller Wiser Rd., Ste. 300, Euless, TX 76039-3855. TEL 817-868-4006. FAX 817-868-4099. Ed. Dale G. Breaden.
—CCC.
Description: Detailed example booklet to help state medical boards to develop guidebooks.

610 US ISSN 0026-8070
R11
MODERN MEDICINE. 1932. m. $50. Advanstar Communications, Inc., 7500 Old Oak Blvd., Cleveland, OH 44130. TEL 216-826-2839. FAX 216-891-2726. (Subscr. to: 131 W. First St., Duluth, MN 55802. TEL 800-346-0085) Ed. Martin M. Stevenson. adv.; abstr.; illus. circ. 121,500. (also avail. in microform from UMI) **Indexed:** Chem.Abstr., Curr.Lit.Fam.Plan., Med. Care Rev., Nutr.Abstr. **Document type:** trade publication.
—BLDSC (5889.810000); SWETS; UMI; UnCover. CCC.
Incorporates: Quarterly Journal of Geriatrics.
Description: Professional journal on diagnosis and therapy, clinical techniques, highlights from medical meetings.
Refereed Serial

610 AT ISSN 1030-3782
MODERN MEDICINE OF AUSTRALIA. 1957. m. Modern Medicine of Australia Pty. Ltd., 3-15 Grosvenor St., Neutral Bay, N.S.W. 2089, Australia. TEL 61-2-908-2155. FAX 61-2-908-1961. Ed. Dr. John Ellard. adv. contact: Judith Briggs. bk.rev.; illus. circ. 21,099. **Indexed:** Curr.Adv.Ecol.Sci., Excerp.Med., Helminthol.Abstr., Nutr.Abstr.
—BLDSC (5889.880000); UnCover.
Former titles: Modern Medicine (ISSN 0312-875X); Modern Medicine of Australia (ISSN 0026-8089)

610 SA ISSN 0259-9333
MODERN MEDICINE OF SOUTH AFRICA. 1976. 12/yr. R.184.68 (foreign R.265.68) (effective 1994). National Publishing (Pty) Ltd., P.O. Box 2271, Clareinch 7740, South Africa. TEL 27-21-611140. FAX 27-21-611389. Ed. Dr Issy Levy. adv.; abstr.; illus.; index. circ. 9,101. **Document type:** trade publication.

616.07 574.2 US ISSN 0893-3952
RB37.A1 CODEN: MODPEO
MODERN PATHOLOGY. 1988. 9/yr. $139 to individuals; institutions $227 (effective 1995). (U S and Canadian Academy of Pathology) Williams & Wilkins, 428 E. Preston St., Baltimore, MD 21202. TEL 410-528-4000; 800-638-6423. FAX 410-528-4312. TELEX 87669. Ed. Dr. Stacey E. Mills. adv.; bk.rev.; index, cum.index. circ. 5,702. (also avail. in microfilm from WWS; back issues avail.) **Indexed:** Excerp.Med. (1995-), Kidney, Med.& Surg.Dermat. **Document type:** academic/scholarly publication.
—BLDSC (5890.767000); Faxon; Genuine Article; SWETS; UnCover. CCC.
Description: Provides a forum for the presentation of advances in the understanding of pathological processes. It is practice-oriented and concentrates on diagnostic human pathology.
Refereed Serial

MODERNE GERIATRIE/GERIATRIE MODERNE. see *GERONTOLOGY AND GERIATRICS*

610 US
CODEN: MOANE
MOLECULAR ANDROLOGY; an international journal. 4/yr. $180 to individuals (foreign $190); institutions $200 (foreign $210) (effective 1996). Reproductive Health Center, 78 Surfsong Rd., Kiawah, SC 29455. TEL 803-768-5556. FAX 803-768-6494. **Indexed:** Excerp.Med. **Document type:** academic/scholarly publication.

610 UK ISSN 0098-2997
RB112 CODEN: MAMED5
MOLECULAR ASPECTS OF MEDICINE; an interdisciplinary review journal. 1975. bi-m. £365($581) (effective 1996). Elsevier Science Ltd., Pergamon, P.O. Box 800, Kidlington, Oxford OX5 1DX, England. TEL 44-1865-843000. FAX 44-1865-843010. E-mail: nlinfo-f@elsevier.nl; usinfo-f@elsevier.com; forinfo-kyf04035@niftyserve.or.jp; Site addr.: http://www.elsevier.nl/. (Subscr. in U.S. and Canada to: Elsevier Science, 660 White Plains Rd., Tarrytown, NY 10591-5153. TEL 914-524-9200. FAX 914-333-2444) Ed.Bd. adv.; bk.rev.; illus.; stat.; index. (also avail. in microform from UMI) **Indexed:** Biol.Abstr., Chem.Abstr., Curr.Adv.Biochem., Curr.Adv.Cell & Devel.Biol., Curr.Adv.Ecol.Sci., Curr.Cont., Excerp.Med., Ind.Med., Ind.Sci.Rev. **Document type:** academic/scholarly publication.
—BLDSC (5900.768000); CASDDS; EMDOCS; Faxon; Genuine Article; SWETS; UMI; UnCover. CCC.
Description: Integrates molecular biochemistry and clinical medicine, focusing on the application of molecular insights to medical problems.
Refereed Serial

MOLECULAR BIOTECHNOLOGY. see *BIOLOGY — Biotechnology*

MOLECULAR GENETIC MEDICINE. see *BIOLOGY — Genetics*

616.4 US ISSN 1076-1551
▼**MOLECULAR MEDICINE.** 1995. bi-m. $175 (foriegn $215) (effective 1996). Blackwell Science Inc., 238 Main St., Cambridge, MA 02142. TEL 617-876-7022; 800-759-6102. FAX 617-492-5263. (back issues avail.) **Document type:** academic/scholarly publication.

616.4 UK ISSN 1357-4310
▼**MOLECULAR MEDICINE TODAY.** 1995. m. £386 to institutions; $614 to institutions (effective 1996). Elsevier Science Ltd., Oxford Fulfilment Centre, P.O. Box 800, Kidlington, Oxford OX5 1DK, England. TEL 44-1865-843000. FAX 44-1865-843010. E-mail: nlinfo-f@elsevier.nl; usinfo-f@elsevier.com; forinfo-kyf04035@niftyserve.or.jp; Site addr.: http://www.elsevier.nl/. (Subscr. in U.S. and Canada to: Elsevier Science, 660 White Plains Rd., Tarrytown, NY 10591-5153. TEL 914-524-9200. FAX 914-333-2444) adv. (also avail. in microform from UMI; back issues avail.) **Document type:** academic/scholarly publication.

MONASH BIOETHICS REVIEW. see *PHILOSOPHY*

630 MP
MONGOLYN ANAGAAKH UKHAAN/MONGOLIAN MEDICAL SCIENCES. (Text in Mongolian; summaries in English) 1970. q. 200 tugrik. Ministry of Health, Ulan Bator, Mongolia. TEL 976-1-321307. FAX 976-1-321278. TELEX 247 MINHE MH. (Co-sponsor: Scientific Society of Physicians) Ed. P. Nymadawa. circ. 3,000. **Document type:** academic/scholarly publication, government publication.

MONITOR (WASHINGTON, 1970). see *INSURANCE*

610 SP
MONOGRAFIAS DE SALUD RURAL. 15/yr. Antonio Lopez Aguado 4, 28029 Madrid, Spain. TEL 1-314-43-38. FAX 1-314-44-99. Ed. Dolores de la Pena.

610 574.87 SZ ISSN 0077-0809
MONOGRAPHS IN CLINICAL CYTOLOGY. (Text in English) 1965. irreg. (approx. 1/yr.). price varies. S. Karger AG, Allschwilerstr. 10, P.O. Box, CH-4009 Basel, Switzerland. TEL 061-3061111. FAX 061-3061234. E-mail: Karger@Karger.ch. Ed. G.L. Wied. **Indexed:** Biol.Abstr., Chem.Abstr., Curr.Cont., Ind.Med. **Document type:** monographic series.
—BLDSC (5915.410000). CCC.
Description: Instructive texts that guide the introduction of improved diagnostic techniques and procedures.
Refereed Serial

610 US ISSN 0883-0266
MONTHLY PRESCRIBING REFERENCE. 1985. m. $78 to individuals; institutions $100. Prescribing Reference, Inc., 53 Park Pl., Ste. 1010, New York, NY 10007. TEL 212-766-7200. FAX 212-732-2360. Ed. Ellen K. Weil. adv. circ. 114,000. **Document type:** monographic series.
—UMI.
Description: Provides up-to-date information to prescribing physicians including the latest Federal Drug Administration drug approvals.

MORFOLOGIYA. see *BIOLOGY*

MORTALITY. see *PUBLIC HEALTH AND SAFETY*

610 IQ ISSN 0027-1446
CODEN: ACMMBB
MOSUL UNIVERSITY. COLLEGE OF MEDICINE. ANNALS. Cover title: Annals of the College of Medicine, Mosul. (Text in Arabic and English) 1966. s-a. $4. Mosul University, College of Medicine, Mosul, Iraq. Ed.Bd. adv.; bk.rev.; charts; illus.; index. circ. 2,000. (reprint service avail. from IRC) **Indexed:** Chem.Abstr., Excerp.Med.
—CASDDS.
Description: Review articles, papers on laboratory and clinical research. preliminary communications and clinical case reports.

610 SW ISSN 0347-0989
MOTPOL; tidskrift foer sjukvaardsdebatt. 1922. irreg.(2-4/yr.). SEK 125 in Sweden; other Nordic countries SEK 155; elsewhere SEK 165. Foereningen Motpol, c/o PROGEK, P.O. Box 31003, S-400 32 Goeteborg, Sweden. adv.; bk.rev. circ. 3,000.
Former titles (until vol.5, 1976): M F T. Medicinska Foereningarnas Tidskrift; (until vol.7, 1969): M F T. Medicinska Foereningens Tidskrift; (until 1966): Medicinska Foereningens Tidskrift (ISSN 0025-8059)

MEDICAL SCIENCES 4247

362 610   US   ISSN 0027-2507
R11   CODEN: MSJMAZ
MOUNT SINAI JOURNAL OF MEDICINE. 1934. bi-m. $75 to individuals (foreign $85); all libraries $85 (effective 1995). Mount Sinai Hospital, Committee on Medical Education and Publications, 50 E. 98th St., New York, NY 10029. TEL 212-241-6108. FAX 212-722-6386. Ed. Dr. Sherman Kupfer. adv.: B&W page $700, color page $1800; adv. contact: Dr. Julius Wolf. bk.rev.; index; circ. 2,000 (paid). (also avail. in microform from UMI) **Indexed:** Biol.Abstr., Chem.Abstr., Curr.Cont., Curr.Lit.Fam.Plan., Dent.Ind., Excerp.Med., Helminthol.Abstr., Ind.Med., Ind.Sci.Rev., Int.Nurs.Ind., Nutr.Abstr., Rev.Med.& Vet.Mycol. **Document type:** academic/scholarly publication.
●Also available online. Vendor(s): Knight-Ridder, Inc.
—BLDSC (5978.750000); CASDDS; EMDOCS; Faxon; Genuine Article; SWETS; UMI; UnCover.
Formerly (until 1970): Mount Sinai Hospital. Journal.
Refereed Serial

610   IT   ISSN 0393-9405
MOVIMENTO. 1985. 3/yr. $60. Edizioni Luigi Pozzi s.r.l., Via Panama, 68, 00198 Rome, Italy. TEL 39-6-8553548. FAX 39-6-8554105. **Indexed:** Psychol.Abstr.

610   CC   ISSN 1001-7550
MUDANJIANG YIXUEYUAN XUEBAO/MUDANJIANG MEDICAL INSTITUTE. JOURNAL. (Text in Chinese) q. Mudanjiang Yixueyuan, Xuebao Bianjibu, Tongxiang Lu, Aimin-qu, Mudanjiang, Heilongjiang 157011, People's Republic of China. TEL 26156.

610   GW   ISSN 0341-3098
CODEN: MMMWD7
MUENCHENER MEDIZINISCHE WOCHENSCHRIFT. Key Title: M M W. (Text in German; summaries in English and German) 1853. w. DM.144. M M V Medizin Verlag, Neumarkter Str. 18, 81673 Munich, Germany. TEL 089-43189647. FAX 089-43189633. Ed. Dr. H.-S. Fuessl. adv.; bk.rev.; bibl.; illus.; index. circ. 55,000. (also avail. in microform from PMC; back issues avail.) **Indexed:** Biol.Abstr., Biotech.Abstr., C.I.S. Abstr., Chem.Abstr., Curr.Cont., Helminthol.Abstr., Ind.Med., Nutr.Abstr., Protozool.Abstr., Rev.Plant Path., Trop.Dis.Bull. **Document type:** academic/scholarly publication.
—BLDSC (5983.720000); CASDDS; Faxon; Genuine Article; SWETS. **CCC.**

610   MX   ISSN 0185-2302
MUNDO MEDICO. 1973. m. Mex.$250 (foreign $190) (effective 1995). Mundo Medico, S.A., Ejercito Nacional 381, 11520 Mexico DF, Mexico. TEL 525-5451798. FAX 525-2036418. Ed. Beatriz Elizalde. adv. contact: Oscar Bagnarelli. bk.rev. circ. 15,000.

610   US   ISSN 0148-639X
RC925.A1   CODEN: MUNEDE
MUSCLE & NERVE. 1979. m. $756 (foreign $942) (effective 1996). John Wiley & Sons, Inc., Journals, 605 Third Ave., New York, NY 10158. TEL 212-850-6645. FAX 212-850-6021. TELEX 12-7063. E-mail: SUBINFO@JWILEY.COM. (Subscr. outside the Americas to: John Wiley & Sons Ltd., Baffins Ln., Chichester, W. Sussex PO19 1UD, England. TEL 44-1243-779777. FAX 44-1243-776128) Ed. Jun Kimura. adv. circ. 3,500. (also avail. in microform from UMI; back issues avail.) **Indexed:** Bibl.Dev.Med.& Child Neur., Biol.Abstr., Chem.Abstr., Curr.Adv.Biochem., Curr.Adv.Ecol.Sci., Curr.Adv.Genetics & Molec.Biol., Dent.Ind., Excerp.Med., Ind.Med., Ind.Sci.Rev., Poult.Abstr., Risk Abstr. **Document type:** academic/scholarly publication.
—BLDSC (5986.493000); CASDDS; Faxon; Genuine Article; SWETS; UMI; UnCover. **CCC.**
Description: Covers muscle, the peripheral motor and sensory neurons, and the neuromuscular junction in both health and disease.
Refereed Serial

610 616.891   GW   ISSN 0933-6885
MUSIK-, TANZ- UND KUNSTTHERAPIE. (Text in German; summaries in English and German) 1988. q. DM.92. Hogrefe Verlag fuer Psychologie, Rohnsweg 25, 37085 Goettingen, Germany. TEL 0551-496090. FAX 0551-4960988. Ed. Karl Hoermann. adv.; bk.rev.; abstr.; bibl.; illus. circ. 1,600. **Document type:** academic/scholarly publication.

610   JA   ISSN 0454-7586
CODEN: KYIHAZ
MUTUAL AID ASSOCIATION. MEDICAL JOURNAL.* (Text and summaries in English and Japanese) 1951. q. Kokka Komuin Kyosai Kumiai Rengokai, Toranomon Hospital, 2-2-2, Minato-ku, Tokyo 105, Japan. Ed. Kinori Kosaka. index. circ. 1,550. (back issues avail.) **Indexed:** INIS Atomind.
—CASDDS.

MYAKKANGAKU/JAPANESE COLLEGE OF ANGIOLOGY. JOURNAL. see *MEDICAL SCIENCES — Cardiovascular Diseases*

610   GW   ISSN 0933-7407
QR145   CODEN: MYCSEU
MYCOSES. (Supplement avail. (ISSN 0943-7312)) (Text in English; summaries in English, German) 1957. 6/yr. DM.288($213) to individuals in Europe (rest of world DM.326($241)); institutions in Europe DM.448($332) (rest of world DM.486($360)) (effective 1996). (Deutschsprachige Mykologische Gesellschaft e.V.) Blackwell Wissenschaft, Kurfuerstendamm 57, 10707 Berlin, Germany. TEL 030-32790624. FAX 030-32790610. Ed. J. Mueller. adv.: B&W page DM.1800, color DM.3270; trim 240 x 170. bk.rev.; charts; illus.; tr.lit.; index. circ. 1,200. **Indexed:** Biol.Abstr., Biotech.Abstr., Chem.Abstr., Curr.Adv.Ecol.Sci., Curr.Cont., Excerp.Med., Hort.Abstr., Ind.Med., Ind.Sci.Rev., Ind.Vet., Med.& Surg.Dermat., Poult.Abstr., Rev.Med.& Vet.Mycol., Rev.Plant Path., Rice Abstr., Soils & Fert., Vet.Bull. **Document type:** academic/scholarly publication.
—BLDSC (5995.753000); ADONIS; CASDDS; Faxon; Genuine Article; SWETS; UMI; UnCover. **CCC.**
Formerly (until 1987): Mykosen (ISSN 0027-5557)
Description: Provides an international forum for papers on the pathogenesis, diagnosis, therapy, prophylaxis, and epidemiology of fungal infectious diseases in humans and animals.

610   GW   ISSN 0943-7312
CODEN: MYSUE
MYCOSES. SUPPLEMENT. (Supplement to Mycoses (ISSN 0933-7407)) 1988. irreg. Blackwell Wissenschafts-Verlag GmbH, Kurfuerstendamm 57, 10707 Berlin, Germany. TEL 030-32790624. FAX 030-32790610. **Indexed:** Excerp.Med. (1994-). **Document type:** academic/scholarly publication, monographic series.
—ADONIS.

610   US
N A A C L S NEWS. 1970. 3/yr. $15 (includes Agency's Annual Report). National Accrediting Agency for Clinical Laboratory Sciences, 8410 W. Bryn Mawr, Ste. 670, Chicago, IL 60631. TEL 312-714-8880. FAX 312-714-8886. Ed. Megan M. Hennessy-Eggert. adv. circ. 2,000. (back issues avail.) **Document type:** newsletter.
Description: Current industry news in allied health education and accreditation, NAACLS news of interest to clinical laboratory officials in the U.S.

610   US
N A E M T NEWS. 1980. m. $25. National Association of Emergency Medical Technicians, 102 W. Leake St., Clinton, MS 39056-4252. TEL 601-924-7744; 800-346-2368. FAX 601-924-7325. Ed. Greg Connel. adv. circ. 6,000. **Document type:** newsletter.
Formerly: N A E M T Newsletter.

610.6   US
N A H C REPORT. 1983. w. $325. National Association for Home Care, 519 C St., N.E., Washington, DC 20002-5809. TEL 202-547-7424. FAX 202-547-3540. adv. circ. 3,300. **Document type:** newsletter.
Description: Covers legislative, regulatory, operational, and financial developments affecting the home care industry.

N A R I STETHOSCOPE. (National Association of Residents and Interns) see *BUSINESS AND ECONOMICS — Investments*

610   US   ISSN 1057-9400
N C R R REPORTER. 1977. m. $9. U.S. National Institutes of Health, National Center for Research Resources, Westwood Bldg., Rm. 10A15, 5333 Westbard Ave., Bethesda, MD 20892. TEL 301-594-7938. (Subscr. to: Superintendent of Documents, U.S. Government Printing Office, Box 371954, Pittsburgh, PA 15250-7954. TEL 202-783-3238. FAX 202-512-2250; Alt. addr.: Research Resources Information Center, 1601 Research Blvd., Rockville, MD 20850. TEL 301-251-4970. FAX 301-251-4981) Ed. Ole Henriksen. index. circ. 13,500. (back issues avail.) **Indexed:** Ind.U.S.Gov.Per., MEDOC. **Document type:** government publication, academic/scholarly publication.
Formerly: Research Resources Reporter (ISSN 0160-807X)
Description: Describes current biomedical research studies.

610   FR   ISSN 0301-6374
N G M. (Nouveau Genie Medical) 1974. bi-m. 25 F. E S T E C, 127 bd. St-Michel, 75005 Paris, France. Ed. Christian Damois. adv.; bk.rev. circ. 15,250.

610.6   US   ISSN 1057-5871
RA11
N I H RECORD. fortn. National Institutes of Health, Bldg. 31, Rm. 2B03, Bethesda, MD 20892. TEL 301-496-2125. Ed. Richard McManus. circ. 16,000.

610   US
N T S A NEWSLETTER. 1975. q. $20 membership includes: Tuberous Sclerosis Resources. National Tuberous Sclerosis Association, 8000 Corporate Dr., Ste. 120, Landover, MD 20785-2239. TEL 800-225-6872. FAX 301-459-0394. Ed. Vicky H. Whittemore. bk.rev. circ. 6,500. (looseleaf format; back issues avail.) **Document type:** newsletter.
Description: Includes current research developments, fund raising efforts and other Association news.

610   NZ   ISSN 0110-022X
CODEN: NZFPDJ
N Z FAMILY PHYSICIAN. 1974. q. NZ.$48 (foreign NZ.$60) (effective Sep. 1991). Royal New Zealand College of General Practitioners, c/o Dr. T. Turnbull, Ed., 62 Park Rd., Katikati, New Zealand. TEL 64-7-54904112. FAX 64-7-5491222. adv.; bk.rev. circ. 3,000. **Document type:** academic/scholarly publication.
—BLDSC (6091.400000); CASDDS. **CCC.**
Description: Contains original papers, news, academic commentary and College reports of interest to NZ and international general practitioners, trainees and students.
Refereed Serial

NAGANOKEN SAGYO RYOHOSHIKAI GAKUJUTSUSHI/NAGANO ASSOCIATION OF OCCUPATIONAL THERAPISTS. JOURNAL. see *OCCUPATIONAL HEALTH AND SAFETY*

610   II   ISSN 0027-7576
NAGARJUN. (Text and summaries in English) 1957. m. Rs.150. O.N. Pandeya, 105-C Block F, New Alipore, Calcutta 700053, India. Ed. L.K. Pandeya.
Description: Covers medicine and health.

610   JA   ISSN 0369-3228
CODEN: NAGZAC
NAGASAKI IGAKKAI ZASSHI/NAGASAKI MEDICAL JOURNAL. (Text in Japanese; summaries in English) 1923. q. 2000 Yen($20) (Nagasaki Medical Association) Fujiki Publishing Co., 5-13 Yorozuya-machi, Nagasaki 850, Japan. TEL 0978-47-2111. FAX 0958-47-5054. (Subscr. to: Nagasaki University School of Medicine, Department of Pathology, 12-4 Sakamoto-machi, Nagasaki 852, Japan) Ed. Takayoshi Ikeda. adv.; index. circ. 900. **Indexed:** Biol.Abstr. **Document type:** academic/scholarly publication.
—CASDDS.
Description: Contains papers on the specific diseases of the district and abstracts of local scientific meetings.

MEDICAL SCIENCES

610 JA ISSN 0027-7622
R97 CODEN: NJMSAG
NAGOYA JOURNAL OF MEDICAL SCIENCE. (Text in European languages) 1923. q. Nagoya Daigaku, Igakubu - Nagoya University, School of Medicine, 65 Tsuruma-cho, Showa-ku, Nagoya 466, Japan. FAX 052-741-1654. Ed.Bd. circ. 750. **Indexed:** Abstr.Hyg., Biol.Abstr., Chem.Abstr., Curr.Adv.Ecol.Sci., Excerp.Med., Ind.Med., Nutr.Abstr., Trop.Dis.Bull.
—BLDSC (6014.000000); CASDDS; Faxon; UnCover.

610 JA ISSN 0027-7649
CODEN: NMJOAA
NAGOYA MEDICAL JOURNAL. (Text in European languages) 1953. q. free (effective 1994-96). Nagoya-shiritsu Daigaku, Igakubu - Nagoya City University, Medical School, Kawasumi 1, Mizuho-cho, Mizuho-ku, Nagoya 467, Japan. FAX 052-851-4166. Ed. Tadaaki Eimoto. bk.rev.; bibl.; charts; illus.; index. circ. 800. **Indexed:** Abstr.Hyg., Biol.Abstr., C.I.S.Abstr., Chem.Abstr., Curr.Adv.Ecol.Sci., Excerp.Med., Ind.Med., Rev.Appl.Entomol., Rev.Med.& Vet.Mycol., Trop.Dis.Bull. **Document type:** academic/scholarly publication.
—BLDSC (6015.050000); CASDDS; UnCover.
Description: Presents original articles and reviews in all branches of the medical sciences.
Refereed Serial

610 JA ISSN 0027-7606
CODEN: NASDA6
NAGOYA SHIRITSU DAIGAKU IGAKKAI ZASSHI/NAGOYA CITY UNIVERSITY. MEDICAL ASSOCIATION. JOURNAL. (Text in Japanese) 1950. q. 4000 Yen membership (effective Jan. 1995). Nagoya-shiritsu Daigaku, Igakubu - Nagoya City University, Medical Association, 1 Kawasumi, Mizuho-cho, Mizuho-ku, Nagoya-shi, Aichi-ken 467, Japan. TEL 81-52-853-8084. FAX 81-52-842-0863. Eds. Nobu Matsui, Kazuyori Yamada. adv. contact: Akira Masaoka. charts; illus.; index. circ. 1,200. **Indexed:** Chem.Abstr., Excerp.Med. **Document type:** academic/scholarly publication.
—CASDDS; EMDOCS.
Description: Publishes review articles, original papers and case reports.
Refereed Serial

610 CC ISSN 1001-7275
CODEN: NTYXET
NANJING TIEDAO YIXUEYUAN XUEBAO/NANJING RAILWAY MEDICAL COLLEGE. JOURNAL. (Text in Chinese; abstracts in English) 1960-1963; resumed 1982. q. $60. Nanjing Tiedao Yixueyuan - Nanjing Railway Medical College, 87 Dingjiaqiao, Nanjing, Jiangsu 210009, People's Republic of China. TEL 301509. FAX 3317073. Ed. Liu Yongyan. adv.: page $2000. circ. 1,000. **Document type:** proceedings.
Description: Publishes articles on experimental research of modern medical sciences, traditional Chinese medicine, preventive medicine and clinical experiences.
Refereed Serial

610 CC ISSN 1000-5331
CODEN: NAYXEW
NANJING YIXUEYUAN XUEBAO/NANJING INSTITUTE OF MEDICAL SCIENCES. JOURNAL. (Text in Chinese) q. Nanjing Yixueyuan - Nanjing Institute of Medical Sciences, 140 Hanzhong Lu, Nanjing, Jiangsu 210029, People's Republic of China. TEL 649141. Ed. Wang Jingliang.
—BLDSC (0579.715000); CASDDS.

610 CC ISSN 1000-5005
NANJING ZHONGYI XUEBAO XUEBAO/NANJING INSTITUTE OF TRADITIONAL CHINESE MEDICINE. JOURNAL. (Text in Chinese) q. Nanjing Zhongyi Xueyuan - Nanjing Institute of Traditional Chinese Medicine, 282 Hanzhong Lu, Nanjing, Jiangsu 210029, People's Republic of China. TEL 649121. Ed. Zhou Zhongying.

610 CC ISSN 1000-2057
NANTONG YIXUEYUAN XUEBAO/NANTONG INSTITUTE OF MEDICAL SCIENCES. JOURNAL. (Text in Chinese) q. Nantong Yixueyuan - Nantong Institute of Medical Sciences, 19 Qixiu Lu, Nantong, Jiangsu 216001, People's Republic of China. TEL 517191. Ed. Meng Xianyong.

610 JA ISSN 0469-5550
CODEN: NAIZAM
NARA IGAKU ZASSHI/NARA MEDICAL ASSOCIATION. JOURNAL. (Text in Japanese and European languages) 1950. bi-m. 3000 Yen (effective 1994). Nara Igakkai - Nara Medical Association, Nara Medical University, Kashihara 634, Nara, Japan. TEL 07442-2-3051. Ed. Dr. Yasunori Enoki. index; circ. 1,000 (controlled). **Indexed:** Biol.Abstr., C.I.S.Abstr., Chem.Abstr., Excerp.Med., Ind.Med., Nutr.Abstr. **Document type:** academic/scholarly publication.
—BLDSC (4828.700000); CASDDS.

NASE LIECIVE RASTLINY. see *BIOLOGY — Botany*

610 II
NATIONAL ACADEMY OF INDIAN MEDICINE. ANNALS. (Text in English) s-a. Rs.100($100) National Academy of Indian Medicine, Department of Shalya-Shalakya, Institute of Medical Sciences, Banaras Hindu University, Varanasi 221 005, India.

610 II ISSN 0379-038X
CODEN: ANAIDI
NATIONAL ACADEMY OF MEDICAL SCIENCES. ANNALS. (Text and summaries in English) 1965. q. Rs.50($10) National Academy of Medical Sciences, Nams House, Ansari Nagar, Mahatma Gandhi Marg, New Delhi 110 029, India. Ed. Dr. Somnath Roy. adv.; bk.rev.; charts. circ. 755. **Indexed:** Biol.Abstr., Chem.Abstr., Curr.Cont., Excerp.Med., Nutr.Abstr.
—CASDDS.
Formerly: Indian Academy of Medical Sciences. Annals (ISSN 0019-4263)
Description: Technical articles on many aspects of medical science; news of the Academy.

612 US
NATIONAL COMMITTEE ON THE TREATMENT OF INTRACTABLE PAIN. NEWSLETTER.* 1978. 2/yr. donation. National Committee on the Treatment of Intractable Pain, c/o Carol Rilley, 5500 Beech Ave., Bethesda, MD 20814. Ed. Jeffrey Finn. circ. 6,500.

NATIONAL COMP AND HEALTH BULLETIN. see *INSURANCE*

362.175 UK ISSN 1351-9441
NATIONAL COUNCIL FOR HOSPICE AND SPECIALIST PALLIATIVE CARE SERVICES. OCCASIONAL PAPER. 1992. irreg., no.7, 1995. price varies. National Council for Hospice and Specialist Palliative Care Services, 59 Bryanston St., London W1A 2AZ, England. TEL 0171-611-1153. FAX 0171-724-4341. Ed. Jean Gaffin. **Document type:** monographic series.
—BLDSC (6218.560000).

616.98 JA ISSN 0006-5528
CODEN: BOEIAJ
NATIONAL DEFENSE MEDICAL JOURNAL/BOEI EISEI. (Text in Japanese; summaries in English) 1954. m. 5000 Yen. National Defense Medical Society - Boei Eisei Kyokai, c/o Boei-cho, Eisei-kyoku, Eisei-ka, 9-7-45 Akasaka, Minato-ku, Tokyo 107, Japan. Ed. Dr. Hiroshi Kobayashi. adv.; bk.rev. circ. 3,200. **Indexed:** Chem.Abstr., INIS Atomind.
—BLDSC (6021.872000); CASDDS.

NATIONAL DIRECTORY OF H M OS. see *INSURANCE*

174.2 US
NATIONAL FEDERATION OF CATHOLIC PHYSICIANS' GUILDS. NEWSLETTER. q. National Federation of Catholic Physicians Guilds, 850 Elm Grove Rd., Elm Grove, WI 53122. TEL 414-784-3435. **Document type:** newsletter.

610 US ISSN 1071-1201
R853.R46
NATIONAL GUIDE TO FUNDING IN HEALTH. 1990. biennial. $145. Foundation Center, 79 Fifth Ave., New York, NY 10003. TEL 212-620-4230. FAX 212-807-3677. Ed. James Danmgartner. **Document type:** directory.
Description: Contains facts on over 3400 foundations and corporate direct-giving programs interested in funding health and health-related organization, programs and services.

NATIONAL INSTITUTE OF POLAR RESEARCH. MEMOIRS. SERIES E: BIOLOGY AND MEDICAL SCIENCE. see *BIOLOGY*

NATIONAL INTELLIGENCE REPORT; the biweekly on Medicare policy for laboratories, blood banks & physician services. see *PUBLIC ADMINISTRATION*

NATIONAL LIBRARY OF MEDICINE NEWS. see *LIBRARY AND INFORMATION SCIENCES*

610 617.6 US ISSN 0027-9676
NATIONAL MEDICAL AND DENTAL ASSOCIATION. BULLETIN. (Text mainly in English; occasionally in Polish) 1926. a. $15. (National Medical and Dental Association of America) Polstar Publishing Corp., c/o Raymond S. Dziejma, Ed., 72-41 Grand Ave., Maspeth, NY 11378. TEL 718-478-3333. adv.; bk.rev.; illus. circ. 3,000. **Document type:** bulletin.

610 US ISSN 0027-9684
R15 CODEN: JNMAAE
NATIONAL MEDICAL ASSOCIATION. JOURNAL. 1908. m. $78 to individuals (effective 1994). Slack, Inc., 6900 Grove Rd., Thorofare, NJ 08086. TEL 609-848-1000. FAX 609-853-5991. (Alt. addr.: National Medical Association, 1012 Tenth St., N.W., Washington, DC 20001. TEL 202-347-1895) Ed. Dr. Calvin C. Sampson. adv. contact: Susan Walker. bk.rev.; abstr.; bibl.; charts; illus.; stat.; index. circ. 26,800. (back issues avail.) **Indexed:** Biol.Abstr., Chem.Abstr., Chic.Per.Ind., Curr.Adv.Cancer Res., Curr.Cont., Dent.Ind., Excerp.Med., Hosp.Lit.Ind., I.P.A., Ind.Med., INIS Atomind., Int.Nurs.Ind., Med. Care Rev., Nutr.Abstr., Psychol.Abstr. (1977-). **Document type:** academic/scholarly publication.
●Also available online.
—BLDSC (4831.114000); CASDDS; Faxon; Genuine Article; SWETS; UMI; UnCover.
Description: Covers all fields of medical research and practice, with emphasis on topics vital to African-American physicians and medical professionals serving the African-American population.
Refereed Serial

610 US
NATIONAL MEDICAL FELLOWSHIPS NEWSLETTER. 3/yr. free. National Medical Fellowships Inc., 254 W. 31st St., 7th Fl., New York, NY 10001-2813. Ed. Paul E. Cothran. circ. 11,000. **Document type:** newsletter.

610 II ISSN 0970-258X
R97 CODEN: NMJIEU
NATIONAL MEDICAL JOURNAL OF INDIA. 1988. 6/yr. Rs.250 to individuals; institutions Rs.500 (UK £50; N. America $80). All India Institute of Medical Sciences, New Delhi 110 029, India. TEL 91-11-6863002. FAX 91-11-6862663. TELEX 31-73042 AIIMS IN. E-mail: nundy@w.pro.nic.in. Ed. Samiran Nundy. adv.; bk.rev.; index. circ. 3,500. **Indexed:** Excerp.Med., ExtraMED, Ind.Med. (1992-), Trop.Dis.Bull. **Document type:** academic/scholarly publication.
●Also available on CD-ROM.
—BLDSC (6027.090000); UMI. **CCC.**
Description: Provides a forum for Indian doctors in India or abroad. Publishes original and review articles relevant to clinical practice. Also encourages discussion of social and political problems.
Refereed Serial

610 CH ISSN 0028-0275
NATIONAL TAIWAN UNIVERSITY. COLLEGE OF MEDICINE. MEMOIRS. Key Title: Guoli Taiwan Daxue Yixueyuan Yanjiu Lunwen Zhaiyaoji. 1947. a. National Taiwan University, College of Medicine, No. 1 Jen-Ai Rd. Sec. 1, Taipei, Taiwan, Republic of China. TEL 02-3970800. Ed. Wen-Pin Chen. bibl.; charts; illus.; stat. circ. 1,500. **Indexed:** Abstr.Hyg., Anim.Breed.Abstr., Biol.Abstr., Trop.Dis.Bull. **Document type:** academic/scholarly publication.
Description: Contains orignial articles and reviews published by the faculties.
Refereed Serial

610 GW ISSN 0934-7909
NATUR- UND GANZHEITSMEDIZIN; Forschung Wissenschaft Praxis. (Supplement to: Die Medizinische Welt (ISSN 0025-8512)) 1989. 4/yr. F.K. Schattauer Verlagsgesellschaft mbH, Lenzhalde 3, 70192 Stuttgart, Germany. TEL 0711-22987-0. FAX 0711-22987-50. Ed. Rosemarie Zundler. **Document type:** academic/scholarly publication.
—BLDSC (6033.863000); SWETS. **CCC.**

MEDICAL SCIENCES

610 GW ISSN 0931-1513
NATURAMED; die Aerztzeitschrift. 1986. 11/yr. DM.78. (Naturamed Verlagsgesellschaft mbH) Verlag Kirchheim und Co. GmbH, Kaiserstr. 41, 55116 Mainz, Germany. TEL 06131-96070-0. FAX 06131-9607070. adv.; bk.rev.; illus.; charts. (back issues avail.) **Document type:** academic/scholarly publication.
—BLDSC (6036.580000).
   Description: New therapies for general practitioners.

610 UK ISSN 1078-8956
RB113 CODEN: NAMEFI
▼**NATURE MEDICINE**. 1995. m. to individuals (outside Europe £125); institutions £350 (outside Europe £400). Macmillan Magazines Ltd. (Subsidiary of: Macmillan Publishers Ltd.), Porters South, Crinan St., London N1 9SQ, England. TEL 0171-843-4962. FAX 0171-843-4998. (Subscr. in US to: Nature, 65 Bleecker St., New York, NY 10012. TEL 212-477-9600; Subscr. to: Brunel Rd., Houndmills, Basingstoke, Hants RG21 2BR, England. TEL 01256-29242. FAX 01256-812358) Ed. Barbara J. Culliton. adv.: B&W page £1700, color page £2200; adv. contact: Errol Lawrence. bk.rev.; illus. circ. 10,000. **Indexed:** Excerp.Med. (1995-). **Document type:** academic/scholarly publication.
—BLDSC (6047.030000); CASDDS; SWETS. **CCC**.
   Description: Publishes papers at the cutting edge of biomedical research, and provides the proper clinical context. Also reports on biomedical news and related issues of interest to scientists, researchers and academic clinicians.
   Refereed Serial

NATURHEILPRAXIS; Fachzeitschrift fuer Naturheilkunde, Erfahrungsheilkunde und biologische Heilverfahren. see *ALTERNATIVE MEDICINE*

610 YU ISSN 0352-5856
NAUCNI PODMLADAK. SVESKA ZA MEDICINKS NAUKE; strucni casopis studenata Univerziteta u Nisu. (Text in Serbo-Croatian; summaries in English) 1969. q. 4000 din.($5) Univerzitet u Nisu, Trg bratislava i Jedinstva 2, 1800 Nis, Serbia, Yugoslavia. Ed. Milorad Pavlovic. adv. circ. 1,300.
   Former titles (until 1984): Naucni Podmladak. Medicinska Sveska (ISSN 0352-1613); (until 1982): Naucni Podmladak. Medicinske Nauke (ISSN 0350-6576); Supersedes in part (in 1971): Naucni Podmladak: Tehnicka Nauke. Drustvene Nauki.

NAUKOVE TOVARYSTVO IMENI SHEVCHENKA. PROCEEDINGS OF THE SECTION OF CHEMISTRY, BIOLOGY AND MEDICINE. see *CHEMISTRY*

616.98 US ISSN 0895-8211
R11
NAVY MEDICINE. 1943. bi-m. $11 (foreign $13.75). U.S. Navy, Bureau of Medicine and Surgery, Washington, DC 20372. TEL 202-653-1297. FAX 202-653-1280. (Subscr. to: Superintendent of Documents, U.S. Government Printing Office, Box 371954, Pittsburgh, PA 15250-7954. TEL 202-512-1800. FAX 202-512-2250) Ed. Jan Kenneth Herman. bk.rev.; s-a. index. circ. 175,000. (also avail. in microfiche; back issues avail.) **Indexed:** Curr.Cont., Dent.Abstr., Dent.Ind., Ind.U.S.Gov.Per., MEDOC. **Document type:** trade publication, government publication.
—BLDSC (6067.592000); Faxon; UMI; UnCover.
   Former titles (until Mar. 1987): U.S. Navy Medicine (ISSN 0364-6807) & U.S. Navy Medical Newsletter (ISSN 0041-7998); B U Med Newsletter.
   Description: Contains professional informaiton on medicine, dentistry, and the allied health sciences primarily for U.S. Navy Medical Department personnel.

610 US ISSN 0091-6730
CODEN: NBMJAZ
NEBRASKA MEDICAL JOURNAL. 1916. m. $23 (foreign $25) (effective 1994). Nebraska Medical Association, 233 S. 13th St., Ste. 1512, Lincoln, NE 68508-2091. TEL 402-474-4472. FAX 402-474-2198. Ed. Dr. Benjamin Gelber. adv.; bk.rev.; illus. circ. 2,000. (also avail. in microform from UMI; reprint service avail. from UMI) **Indexed:** Biol.Abstr., Chem.Abstr., Dent.Ind., Ind.Med.
—BLDSC (6068.280000); SWETS; UMI; UnCover.
   Formerly: Nebraska State Medical Journal.

610 NE ISSN 0028-2103
NEDERLANDS MILITAIR GENEESKUNDIG TIJDSCHRIFT. (Text in Dutch, summaries in English) 1948. bi-m. fl.23.50. Ministerie van Defensie, Militair Geneeskundig Comite, Postbus 20701, 2500 ES The Hague, Netherlands. TEL 31-70-3187159. Ed. Kol. G.D.J. de Lange. adv.; bk.rev.; bibl.; charts; illus.; index. circ. 9,000. **Indexed:** Chem.Abstr., Excerp.Med.

NEDERLANDS TIJDSCHRIFT VOOR FARMACOTHERAPIE. see *PHARMACY AND PHARMACOLOGY*

610 NE ISSN 0028-2162
CODEN: NETJAN
NEDERLANDS TIJDSCHRIFT VOOR GENEESKUNDE. 1856. w. fl.224 to individuals; students fl.99.50 (effective 1994). Bohn Stafleu Van Loghum B.V. (Subsidiary of: Wolters Kluwer N.V.), Postbus 246, 3990 GA Houten, Netherlands. TEL 31-3403-95711. FAX 31-3403-50903. Ed.Bd. adv.; bk.rev.; abstr.; bibl.; charts; illus.; index. circ. 30,000. (also avail. in microform from PMC) **Indexed:** Abstr.Crim.& Pen., Abstr.Hyg., Biol.Abstr., Biotech.Abstr., Chem.Abstr., Dairy Sci.Abstr., Dent.Ind., Excerp.Med., Ind.Med., Nutr.Abstr., Ornam.Hort., Potato Abstr., Protozool.Abstr., Rev.Med.& Vet.Mycol., Sugar Ind.Abstr., Trop.Dis.Bull.
—BLDSC (6071.850000); CASDDS; EMDOCS; Genuine Article; SWETS.

610 NE ISSN 0926-7522
NEDERLANDS TIJDSCHRIFT VOOR HEELKUNDE. 1992. bi-m. (Nederlandse Vereniging voor Heelkunde) Mediselect B.V., Postbus 28091, 3828 ZH Hoogland, Netherlands. TEL 31-33-808020. FAX 31-33-805881. (Co-sponsor: Vereniging voor Assistent-Geneeskundigen in de Heelkunde) Pub. J. Blom. adv. **Document type:** trade publication.

NEDERLANDS TIJDSCHRIFT VOOR MEDISCHE MICROBIOLOGIE. see *BIOLOGY — Microbiology*

610 CC
NEI JING. (Text in Chinese) q. Zhonghua Yixuehui, Nanjing Fenhui - Chinese Society of Medical Sciences, Nanjing Chapter, 291 Zhongshan Lu, Nanjing, Jiangsu 210008, People's Republic of China. TEL 303848.

610 NP ISSN 0028-2715
NEPAL MEDICAL ASSOCIATION. JOURNAL. Running title: J N M A. (Text in English) 1963. q. $24. Nepal Medical Association, Siddhi Sadan, Exhibition Road, G.P.O. Box 189, Kathmandu, Nepal. Ed. Neelam Adhikari. adv.; bk.rev.; abstr.; charts; illus.; index. circ. 1,250. **Indexed:** Diar.Dis.Res., Trop.Dis.Bull.
—BLDSC (4831.750000).

NETHERLANDS JOURNAL OF MEDICINE. see *MEDICAL SCIENCES — Internal Medicine*

NETWORK (DENVILLE). see *CONSUMER EDUCATION AND PROTECTION*

610 GW ISSN 0300-8371
NEUE MUENCHNER BEITRAEGE ZUR GESCHICHTE DER MEDIZIN UND NATURWISSENSCHAFTEN. MEDIZINHISTORISCHE SERIE. 1970. irreg., vol.8, 1978. price varies. (Werner Fritsch Verlag) Theodor Ackermann, Ludwigstr. 7, 80539 Munich, Germany. TEL 284787. Eds. Heinz Goerke, Joern Wolf. index. **Indexed:** Ind.Med.

610 US
NEVADA STATE MEDICAL ASSOCIATION. BULLETIN. 1973. bi-m. $30. Nevada State Medical Association, 3660 Baker Ln., Reno, NV 89509. Ed.Bd. adv. circ. 1,250. **Document type:** bulletin.

610 CN ISSN 0836-2688
NEW BRUNSWICK MEDICAL SOCIETY. NEWSLETTER. m. membership. New Brunswick Medical Society, 176 York St., Fredericton, NB E3B 3N8, Canada. TEL 506-458-8860. circ. 800. **Document type:** newsletter.

610.73 301 AT ISSN 0313-2153
NEW DOCTOR. 1976. q. Aus.$27. Doctors' Reform Society, P.O. Box 14, 4 Goulburn St., Sydney, N.S.W. 2000, Australia. FAX 02-267-4393. Ed. Greg Heron. adv.; bk.rev. circ. 2,000. (back issues avail.) **Indexed:** Aus.P.A.I.S. **Document type:** academic/scholarly publication.
—BLDSC (6083.498000); UnCover.
   Description: Concerns with the wider sociological, political and environmental issues of health care provision and medical practice in modern society.

610 US ISSN 0028-4793
R11 CODEN: NEJMAG
NEW ENGLAND JOURNAL OF MEDICINE. 1812. w. $109. Massachusetts Medical Society, 1440 Main St., Waltham, MA 02154. TEL 617-893-3800. FAX 617-893-8103. (Subscr. to: Box 1940, Waltham, MA 02254) Ed. Jerome Kassirer. adv.: B&W page $4530, color page $6345. bk.rev.; bibl.; charts; illus.; stat.; s-a. index. circ. 168,000. (also avail. in microform from UMI; PMC; reprint service avail.) **Indexed:** Abstr.Crim.& Pen., Abstr.Health Care Manage.Stud., Abstr.Hyg., Abstr.Soc.Geront., Acad.Ind., AIM, Behav.Med.Abstr., Bibl.Dev.Med.& Child Neur., Biol.Abstr., Biol.Dig., Biotech.Abstr., C.I.S.Abstr., Cadscan, Chem.Abstr., CINAHL, Crim.Just.Abstr., Curr.Adv.Cancer Res., Curr.Adv.Ecol.Sci., Curr.Cont., Curr.Lit.Fam.Plan, Dairy Sci.Abstr., Deep Sea Res.& Oceanogr.Abstr., Dent.Abstr., Diab.Cont., Diar.Dis.Res., Environ.Abstr., Environ.Ind., Excerp.Med., FAMLI, Food Sci.& Tech.Abstr., Fut.Surv., Gen.Sci.Ind., Helminthol.Abstr., Hlth.Ind., Hosp.Lit.Ind., I.P.A., Ind.Hyg.Dig., Ind.Med., Ind.Sci.Rev., Ind.Vet., Int.Nurs.Ind., Kidney, Lang.& Lang.Behav.Abstr., Lead Abstr., Mag.Ind., Med.& Surg.Dermat., Med.Care Rev., Nurs.Abstr., Nutr.Abstr., Protozool.Abstr., Psychol.Abstr. (1928-), Rehabil.Lit., Rev.Plant Path., Risk Abstr., Sci.Cit.Ind., Soc.Work Res.& Abstr., Telegen, Tr.& Indus.Ind., Trop.Dis.Bull., Vet.Bull., W.R.C.Inf., Yrbk.Assoc.Educ.& Rehab.Blind, Zincscan. **Document type:** trade publication.
● Also available online. Vendor(s): Ovid Technologies (NEJM).
Also available on CD-ROM.
—BLDSC (6084.000000); CASDDS; CIS; EMDOCS; Faxon; Genuine Article; SWETS; UMI; UnCover. **CCC**.
   Description: Presents original articles and interpretive reviews of a variety of developments in the major aspects of medicine, its science, its art and practice and its position in today's society.
   Refereed Serial

610 US
NEW ENGLAND JOURNAL OF MEDICINE (INTERNATIONAL EDITION). w. Massachusetts Medical Society, 1440 Main St., Waltham, MA 02154. TEL 617-893-3800. Ed. Dr. Jerome Kassirer. adv. circ. 55,588. **Indexed:** Diar.Dis.Res. **Document type:** trade publication.
   Description: Presents original articles and reviews of new developments in science, art, medical practices; including its positition in today's socio-political structure.

616 US
NEW HORIZONS IN THERAPEUTICS: SMITH, KLINE & FRENCH LABORATORIES RESEARCH SYMPOSIA SERIES. 1984. irreg., latest 1994. price varies. Plenum Publishing Corp., 233 Spring St., New York, NY 10013-1578. TEL 212-620-8000. FAX 212-463-0742. TELEX 23-421139. Eds. George Poste, Stanley T. Crooke. **Document type:** proceedings.
   Formerly: New Horizons in Therapeutics.
   Refereed Serial

610 US ISSN 0885-842X
R15
NEW JERSEY MEDICINE. 1904. m. $35. Medical Society of New Jersey, 2 Princess Rd., Trenton, NJ 08648. TEL 609-896-1766. Ed. Dr. Howard D. Slobodien. adv.; bk.rev.; abstr.; bibl.; charts; illus.; index. circ. 10,400. (also avail. in microfilm from UMI) **Indexed:** Excerp.Med., Ind.Med., INIS Atomind.
—BLDSC (6084.310900); Faxon; SWETS; UMI.
   Formerly (until 1985): Medical Society of New Jersey. Journal (ISSN 0025-7524)
   Description: Publishes scientific and N.J. legislative articles as well as health care system news.

MEDICAL SCIENCES

617.8 US ISSN 0028-5935
NEW JERSEY SPEECH AND HEARING ASSOCIATION. JOURNAL.* 1963. s-a. $10. New Jersey Speech and Hearing Association, c/o Auriemma, 6 Crest Ln., Warren, NJ 07059-5110. adv.; bk.rev.; circ. 1,100 (controlled).

610 US ISSN 0028-6451
NEW PHYSICIAN.* 1952. m. (9/yr.). $22 to non-members. American Medical Student Association, 1902 Association Dr., Reston, VA 22091-1502. TEL 703-620-6600. FAX 703-620-5873. Ed. Laura Milani. adv.; bk.rev. circ. 30,000. (also avail. in microform from UMI; reprint service avail. from UMI) **Indexed:** Biol.Abstr., Hosp.Lit.Ind., I.P.A., Med. Care Rev., Phys.Ber. **Document type:** trade publication.
—BLDSC (6084.980000); Faxon; UMI; UnCover.

610 US ISSN 1040-9904
NEW PRACTICE PLANNING. 1987. bi-m. $30. Health Care Publications & Research, Inc., 17 Larchdell Way, Mountain Lakes, NJ 07046. TEL 201-316-6873. Ed. Melvin J. Silverberg. adv.: B&W page $3605; trim 11 x 14 1/4; adv. contact: Gail D. Aherne. circ. 37,300. **Document type:** trade publication.
Description: Provides useful practice management and planning information for post-resident practice.

610 681 UK ISSN 1350-2220
NEW WORLD HEALTH (YEAR). a. Sterling Publications Ltd. (Subsidiary of: Sterling Publishing Group Plc.), P.O. Box 839, London W2 2YW, England. TEL 071-915-9660. Ed. Leslie Paine. **Document type:** bulletin.
—BLDSC (6089.220400).

610.6 US
NEW YORK ACADEMY OF MEDICINE. ANNUAL REPORT. a. New York Academy of Medicine, 2 E. 103rd St., New York, NY 10029. TEL 212-876-8200. FAX 212-876-6620. **Document type:** corporate report.

610 US ISSN 0028-7091
R15 CODEN: BNYMAM
NEW YORK ACADEMY OF MEDICINE. BULLETIN. 1925. 2/yr. $35 (foreign $40). New York Academy of Medicine, 2 E. 103rd St., New York, NY 10029. TEL 212-876-8200. FAX 212-876-6620. Ed. Dr. William D. Sharpe. bk.rev.; charts; illus.; stat.; index. circ. 3,500. (also avail. in microform from UMI,PMC; back issues avail.; reprint service avail. from UMI) **Indexed:** Abstr.Health Care Manage.Stud., Abstr.Hyg., Biol.Abstr., Biotech.Abstr., Chem.Abstr., CINAHL, Curr.Adv.Ecol.Sci., Curr.Cont., Dairy Sci.Abstr., Excerp.Med., Helminthol.Abstr., Hosp.Lit.Ind., Ind.Med., INIS Atomind., Int.Nurs.Ind., NRN, Numis.Lit., Nutr.Abstr., Sci.Cit.Ind., Trop.Dis.Bull. **Document type:** bulletin.
—BLDSC (2650.000000); CASDDS; EMDOCS; Faxon; Genuine Article; SWETS; UMI; UnCover.

610 US ISSN 0898-6401
NEW YORK DOCTOR; the newsmagazine for New York physicians. 1988. 12/yr. $65 (free to qualified personnel). Chase Communications, Ltd., 25-35 Beechwood Ave., Box 9001, Mt. Vernon, NY 10552-9001. TEL 914-699-2020. FAX 914-664-1503. Ed. S. Acunto. adv.; circ. 15,000 (controlled).
Description: Covers hospital politics, malpractice cases, medical ethics, insurance, legislation, regulation and commercial real estate.

610 US ISSN 1074-0996
RA421
▼**NEW YORK HEALTH SCIENCES JOURNAL.** 1994. q. $120 (foreign $150) (effective 1996). New York Medical College, Graduate School of Health Sciences, Valhalla, NY 10595.
—BLDSC (6089.302000).
Description: Provides insight into timely issues, provokes discussion and reflection, and poses solutions that are bothe theoretical and practical.

610 US
NEW YORK STATE MEDICAL NEWS. q. Schueler Communications, Inc., 208 N. Townsend St., Syracuse, NY 13203-2339. TEL 315-472-6948. FAX 315-422-0040. Ed. Laurie E. Crossman; Pub. Gary W. Schueler. adv. contact: Laurie E. Crossman. circ. 42,000. **Document type:** newspaper, trade publication.

610.28 US
NEW YORK UNIVERSITY BIOMEDICAL ENGINEERING SERIES. 1987. irreg. price varies. New York University Press, 70 Washington Square S., New York, NY 10012. TEL 212-998-2575; 800-996-3833. FAX 212-995-3833. TELEX 235128 NYU UR. Ed. Walter Welkowitz. **Document type:** monographic series.

610 NZ ISSN 0028-8446
CODEN: NZMJAX
NEW ZEALAND MEDICAL JOURNAL. 1887. s-m. $135. (New Zealand Medical Association) Southern Colour Print, P.O. Box 920, Dunedin, New Zealand. TEL 03-455-0554. FAX 03-455-0303. Ed. R.G. Robinson. adv.; bk.rev.; charts; illus.; index, cum.index; circ. 5,000 (paid). (also avail. in microform from UMI; reprint service avail. from UMI) **Indexed:** Abstr.Hyg., Bibl.Dev.Med.& Child Neur., Biol.Abstr., Biotech.Abstr., C.I.S. Abstr., Chem.Abstr., CINAHL, Curr.Adv.Cancer Res., Curr.Adv.Ecol.Sci., Curr.Cont., Dairy Sci.Abstr., Dent.Ind., Excerp.Med., Helminthol.Abstr., HRIS, Ind.Med., Ind.Sci.Rev., Ind.Vet., Nutr.Abstr., Pig News & Info., Rev.Med.& Vet.Mycol., Rev.Plant Path., Sel.Water Res.Abstr., So.Pac.Per.Ind., Trop.Dis.Bull., Vet.Bull. **Document type:** academic/scholarly publication.
—BLDSC (6096.100000); CASDDS; EMDOCS; Faxon; Genuine Article; SWETS; UnCover. CCC.

610 CN ISSN 0078-0316
NEWFOUNDLAND MEDICAL DIRECTORY. 1961. a. (plus q. updates). Can.$15 (free to qualified personnel). Newfoundland Medical Board, Registrar, 15 Rowan St., St. John's, NF A1B 2X2, Canada. TEL 709-726-8546. circ. 2,000. **Document type:** directory.

610 US
NEWS CAPSULE. vol.37, no.9, 1990. 6/yr. $12 to non-members. Fairfield County Medical Association, 2285 Reservoir Ave., Trumbull, CT 06611-4743. TEL 203-372-4543. FAX 203-372-5293. Ed. Mark S. Thompson. adv.: B&W page $250; adv. contact: Mary Beth Henry. circ. 2,000. **Document type:** newsletter.
Description: Contains capsulized information for practicing physicians.

610 US ISSN 0028-9264
NEWS OF NEW YORK. 1945. m. $36. Medical Society of the State of New York, 420 Lakeville Rd., P.O. Box 5404, Lake Success, NY 11042. TEL 516-488-6100. FAX 516-328-1982. Ed. Charlotte K. Petersen. charts; illus. circ. 29,000. **Document type:** trade publication.
Formerly: Medical Society of the State of New York. News Letter.
Description: Focuses on regulatory, legislative and economic issues that have immediate impact on the daily practice of New York physicians.

610 JA ISSN 0029-0424
CODEN: NICHAS
NICHIDAI IGAKU ZASSHI/NIHON UNIVERSITY. JOURNAL OF MEDICINE. (Supplements avail.) (Text in Japanese; summaries in English) 1937. m. 5000 Yen. Nihon Daigaku Igakkai - Nihon University Medical Association, 30 Oyaguchi Kami-cho, Itabashi-ku, Tokyo 173, Japan. (Co-sponsor: Nihon University School of Medicine) Ed. Dr. Yukiyasu Sezai. adv.; bk.rev.; illus.; index. circ. 500. (reprint service avail. from IRC) **Indexed:** Biol.Abstr., C.I.S. Abstr., Chem.Abstr., Excerp.Med.
—CASDDS.

610 GW ISSN 0468-1746
DER NIEDERGELASSENE ARZT. 1952. m. DM.102. N A V - Verband der Niedergelassenen Aertze Deutschlands e.V., Belfortstrasse 9V, 50668 Cologne, Germany. TEL 0221-727072. FAX 0221-7391239. adv.; bk.rev. circ. 50,000.
—CCC.

610 GW ISSN 0028-9795
NIEDERSAECHSISCHES AERZTEBLATT. 1927. s-m. DM.192. (Aerztekammer Niedersachsen) Hannoversche Verlagsunion GmbH, Berliner Allee 20, 30175 Hannover, Germany. TEL 0511-3802282. adv.; bk.rev.; abstr.; stat.; index. circ. 25,766. **Document type:** newsletter.
—CCC.

610 NE ISSN 0168-9827
NIEUWE NEDERLANDSE BIJDRAGEN TOT DE GESCHIEDENIS DER GENEESKUNDE EN DER NATUURWETENSCHAPPEN. (Text in Dutch, English, French and German) 1978. irreg. price varies. Erasmus Publishing B.V., Mathenesserlaan 332, 3021 HZ Rotterdam, Netherlands. TEL 31-10-4777277. FAX 31-10-4779580. Ed.Bd. circ. 508. **Document type:** monographic series.
Formerly (until 1979): Nieuwe Nederlandse Bijdragen tot de Geschiedenis der Geneeskunde (ISSN 0167-4404)

610 NR ISSN 0300-1652
CODEN: NGMDAI
NIGERIAN MEDICAL JOURNAL. 1964. q. $275 (typically set in Jan.). Nigerian Medical Association, P.O. Box 1108, Lagos, Nigeria. TEL 234-1-801500. FAX 231-1-837630. TELEX 002763NG. Ed. A.E. Ohwovoriole. adv.; bk.rev. circ. 4,500. **Indexed:** Biol.Abstr., ExtraMED, Helminthol.Abstr., Ind.Med., Nutr.Abstr., Trop.Dis.Bull. **Document type:** academic/scholarly publication.
●Also available on CD-ROM.
Formerly: Nigerian Medical Association. Journal.

615.8 JA ISSN 0029-0343
NIHON ONSEN KIKO BUTSURI IGAKKAI ZASSHI/JAPANESE ASSOCIATION OF PHYSICAL MEDICINE, BALNEOLOGY, AND CLIMATOLOGY. JOURNAL. (Text in Japanese; summaries in English) 1935. s-a. 2000 Yen($7.60) Nihon Onsen Kiko Butsuri Igakkai - Japanese Association of Physical Medicine, Balneology, and Climatology, c/o Japan Health and Research Institute, 1-5-20 Ishizuka Yaesu Bldg., Yaesu, Chuo-ku, Tokyo, Japan. FAX 03-274-5833. Ed. Terumasa Miyamoto. adv.; bk.rev.; bibl.; charts; illus.; index, cum.index. circ. 1,300. **Indexed:** Excerp.Med.
—BLDSC (4809.050000); EMDOCS.
Description: Includes physiotherapy techniques.

NIHON SEIRIGAKU ZASSHI/PHYSIOLOGICAL SOCIETY OF JAPAN. JOURNAL. see BIOLOGY — Physiology

NIHON SHIKKAN MODERU DOBUTSU KENKYUKAI KIROKU/JAPANESE ASSOCIATION OF ANIMAL MODELS FOR HUMAN DISEASES. PROCEEDINGS. see BIOLOGY — Physiology

NIHON TAISHITSUGAKU ZASSHI/JAPANESE JOURNAL OF CONSTITUTIONAL MEDICINE. see BIOLOGY — Physiology

610 JA ISSN 0911-2588
CODEN: NTKKEM
NIHON TEITAION KENKYUKAI KAISHI/JAPANESE SOCIETY OF HYPOTHERMIA. JOURNAL. (Text in Japanese; summaries in English) 1981. a. Nihon Teitaion Kenkyukai, Kokuritsu Shoni Byoin Shinzo Kekkan Geka, 35-31, Taishido 3-chome, Setagaya-ku, Tokyo 154, Japan. **Indexed:** Chem.Abstr.
—CASDDS.

610 JA ISSN 0029-0440
CODEN: NIGZAY
NIIGATA IGAKKAI ZASSHI/NIIGATA MEDICAL JOURNAL. (Text in Japanese) 1887. m. 6500 Yen. Niigata Igakkai - Niigata Medical Society, c/o Niigata Daigaku Igakubu, Asahi-machi 1, Niigata 951, Japan. Ed. H. Yamanouchi. adv.; bibl.; charts; illus.; mkt.; stat.; index. circ. 1,000. (also avail. in microform; reprint service avail. from IRC) **Indexed:** C.I.S.Abstr., Chem.Abstr. **Document type:** academic/scholarly publication.
—BLDSC (6113.170000); CASDDS.

610 JA
NIIGATAKEN KANKYO HOKENBU KETSUEKI JIGYO NO GENKYO. 1865. a. free. Niigataken Kankyo Hokenbu - Niigata Prefectural Government, Health and Environment Department, 4-1, Shinkocho, Niigata-shi, Niigata-ken 950, Japan.

NIKKEI HEALTH BUSINESS. see HOSPITALS

NIKKEI HEALTHCARE. see HOSPITALS

MEDICAL SCIENCES 4251

610   JA   ISSN 0385-1699
NIKKEI MEDICAL/NIKKEI MEDIKARU. (Text in Japanese) 1972. 15/yr. 19000 Yen (6000 Yen for doctors). Nikkei Business Publications, Inc. (Subsidiary of: Nihon Keizai Shimbun, Inc.), 2-7-6 Hirakawa-cho, Chiyoda-ku, Tokyo 102, Japan. TEL 03-5210-8502. FAX 03-5210-8119. (Subscr. to: Nikkei Business Pub. Inc., Reader Service Center, P.O. Box 20, Kasai Post Office, Tokyo 134, Japan) Ed. Hitoshi Sawai; Pub. Hitoshi Sawai. adv. contact: Akio Ishizeki. circ. 104,000 (controlled). **Indexed:** JTA. **Document type:** trade publication.
    Description: Contains specialized reports for clinicians, offering insight into both clinical and economic aspects of medicine.

610   JA   ISSN 0048-0444
CODEN: NIDZAJ
NIPPON MEDICAL SCHOOL. JOURNAL/NIPPON IKA DAIGAKU ZASSHI. (Text in English and Japanese) 1927. 6/yr. $60. Nippon Medical School, Medical Association - Nippon Ika Daigaku Igakkai, 1-1-5 Sendagi, Bunkyo-ku, Tokyo 113, Japan. FAX 03-3822-8575. TELEX 03-3822-2131-314. Ed. Kozo Yokomuro. adv.; bk.rev.; circ. 2,600 (controlled). **Indexed:** Biol.Abstr., C.I.S. Abstr., Chem.Abstr., Dent.Ind., Excerp.Med., Ind.Med. **Document type:** academic/scholarly publication.
● Also available online. Vendor(s): JICST.
—BLDSC (4833.600000); CASDDS; EMDOCS.
    Description: Covers developments in medical science from the association.

610   IT
NO.ME. NOTIZIARIO MEDICO PER LO SPECIALISTA. w. Piccin Editore, Via Altinate 107, 35121 Padua, Italy. TEL 049-655566. FAX 049-98750692. TELEX 432074 PICCIN I. adv.: B&W page L.3500000, color page L.4500000; trim 175 x 250. circ. 5,000.

610   DK   ISSN 0029-1420
NORDISK MEDICIN. (Text in Danish, Norwegian and Swedish; summaries in English) 1929. 10/yr. DKK 260. (Den Almindelige Danske Laegeforening - Danish Medical Association) Laegeforeningens Forlag, Esplanaden 8A, DK-1263 Copenhagen K, Denmark. TEL 31-38-55-00. FAX 33-15-28-58. adv.; bk.rev.; index. circ. 60,000. **Indexed:** Abstr.Hyg., Biol.Abstr., C.I.S. Abstr., Chem.Abstr., Dent.Ind., Ind.Med., Nutr.Abstr., Trop.Dis.Bull.
—BLDSC (6122.500000); Faxon; SWETS.

610   SW   ISSN 0303-6480
R538.5
NORDISK MEDICINHISTORISK AARSBOK. (Supplement avail.) (Text in Swedish; summaries in English) 1953. a. SEK 120 (incl. supplement). Medicinhistoriska Museet - Museum of Medical History, Aasoegatan 146, 116 32 Stockholm, Sweden. TEL 08-6-642-41-66. FAX 08-644-02-86. Ed. Goeran Lundh. adv. circ. 1,000. **Indexed:** Amer.Hist.& Life, Hist.Abstr. **Document type:** academic/scholarly publication.
    Former titles (until 1968): Medicinhistorisk Aarsbok; (until 1958): Aarsskrift - Foereningen Medicinhistoriska Museets Vaenner (ISSN 0346-8704)

612.6   DK   ISSN 0108-271X
NORDISK SEXOLOGI. (Text in Danish, Norwegian or Swedish; abstracts in English) 1983. 4/yr. DKK 370 (students DKK 280; foreign DKK 296). Dansk Psykologisk Forlag, Hans Knudsens Plads 1A, 2100 Copenhagen Oe, Denmark. TEL 45-31-18-27-57. FAX 45-31-18-57-58. Ed. Henning Bech. adv.; bk.rev.; abstr.; charts; illus. circ. 900. **Indexed:** Psychol.Abstr. (1986-).
—BLDSC (6122.785000).

616.026   GW   ISSN 0029-1609
NORDWESTDEUTSCHE GESELLSCHAFT FUER INNERE MEDIZIN. KONGRESSBERICHT. 1953. s-a. DM.10($6) Hansisches Verlagskontor H. Scheffler, 23547 Luebeck, Germany. Ed. Dr. A. Doenhardt. adv.; illus. circ. 1,800. **Document type:** academic/scholarly publication.
—CCC.
    Description: Covers internal medicine.

610   NO   ISSN 0029-2001
CODEN: TNLAAH
NORSKE LAEGEFORENING. TIDSSKRIFT/NORWEGIAN MEDICAL ASSOCIATION. JOURNAL; tidsskrift for praktisk medisin. (Supplements avail.) (Text in Norwegian; summaries in English) 1881. 3/m. NOK 720. Norske Laegeforening - Norwegian Medical Association, Fjellveien 5, N-1324 Lysaker, Norway. TEL 02-124600. FAX 02-124800. Ed. Magne Nylenna. adv.; bk.rev.; abstr.; charts; illus.; index, cum.index. circ. 15,200. **Indexed:** Biol.Abstr., Chem.Abstr., Excerp.Med., Ind.Med., Protozool.Abstr., Rev.Med.& Vet.Mycol.
—BLDSC (8822.350000); EMDOCS; Faxon; Genuine Article; SWETS. **CCC**.

610   US   ISSN 0029-2559
R11
NORTH CAROLINA MEDICAL JOURNAL. 1940. m. $17. North Carolina Medical Society, Box 3910, DUMC, Durham, NC 27710. TEL 919-286-6410. FAX 919-286-9219. Ed. Dr. Francis A. Neelon. adv.; bk.rev.; illus.; index. circ. 9,200. (also avail. in microfilm from UMI) **Indexed:** C.I.S. Abstr., Chem.Abstr., CINAHL, Curr.Cont., Dent.Ind., Excerp.Med., Helminthol.Abstr., Ind.Med., Rev.Med.& Vet.Mycol. **Document type:** academic/scholarly publication.
—BLDSC (6149.080000); Faxon; SWETS; UMI.

610   II
NORTH EASTERN DOCTORS CALLING.* 1984. bi-m. Rs.35 to individuals (foreign Rs.80); institutions Rs.60 (foreign Rs.130). Indian Medical Association, I.M.A. House, Indraprastha Marg, New Delhi 110 002, India. Ed.Bd. adv.; bk.rev.; abstr.; bibl.; charts; stat.
    Description: Examines current professional, academic and related trends of interest to those in medical professions.
    Refereed Serial

610   US   ISSN 0029-3334
NORTHWEST COMMUNITY HOSPITAL MEDICAL BULLETIN;* practice of medicine in a community hospital. 1964. 3/yr. $3. Northwest Community Hospital, 800 W. Central, Arlington Heights, IL 60005. TEL 708-259-1000. bk.rev.; charts; illus. circ. 2,000. **Document type:** bulletin.

610 370   US
NORTHWESTERN UNIVERSITY MEDICAL CENTER MAGAZINE.* 1963. 3/yr. free. Northwestern University Alumni Association, Medical Division, 303 E. Chicago Ave., Ward-Bldg. 1004, Chicago, IL 60611. TEL 312-503-8012. FAX 312-503-0146. bk.rev.; illus.; stat. circ. 7,000.
    Formerly: Northwestern University Medical School Magazine (ISSN 0029-358X)
    Description: Presents study and teaching methods.

610   GW   ISSN 0177-2309
DER NOTARZT; notfallmedizinische Informationen. 1985. bi-m. DM.99. Georg Thieme Verlag, Ruedigerstr. 14, 70469 Stuttgart, Germany. TEL 0711-8931-0. FAX 0711-8931298. (Subscr. to: Postfach 104853, 70042 Stuttgart, Germany) Ed. P. Sefrin. circ. 8,600. **Document type:** academic/scholarly publication.
—BLDSC (6152.910000).

610   SP   ISSN 0029-4225
NOTICIAS MEDICAS; el periodico de la medicina espanola. 1967. w. 9000 ptas.($120) (supplement $60). Editores Medicos, S.A., C. Gabriela Mistral 2, 28035 Madrid, Spain. TEL 34-1-3860033. FAX 34-1-3739907. Ed. Adolfo Berzosa Blanco. adv.; bk.rev.; charts; illus. circ. 50,000. **Document type:** newspaper.
—CCC.

610   PO   ISSN 0870-2055
NOTICIAS MEDICAS. 1971. s-w. free to qualified personnel. Citecnica - Publicacoes Tecnicas e Cientificas Lda., Rua Tristao Vaz, 15-2o Dt., 1400 Lisbon, Portugal. TEL 3011989. FAX 3016636. Ed. Jose Reis, Jr. adv. circ. 29,000. (tabloid format; back issues avail.)

610   IT
NOTIZIARIO MEDICO E BIBLIOGRAFICO. 52/yr. Piccin Editore, Via Altinate 107, 35121 Padua, Italy. TEL 49-655-566. FAX 49-87-50-693.

610   FR   ISSN 0292-384X
NOUVEAU CENTRE DE SANTE. vol.21, 1977. 10/yr. 275 F. (foreign 350 F.). Union des Syndicats de Medecins de Centres de Sante, Centre de Sante, 23 rue de Leningrad, 75008 Paris, France. TEL 45-22-21-40.
    Formerly: Revue de Medecine Moderne (ISSN 0035-1539)

610   SZ   ISSN 0254-8712
B785.P24
NOVA ACTA PARACELSICA. a. (Schweizerische Paracelsus Gesellschaft) Peter Lang AG, Jupiterstr. 15, CH-3000 Bern 15, Switzerland. TEL 031-9411122. FAX 031-9411131. Ed. Alois Haas. **Document type:** academic/scholarly publication.

610   CN   ISSN 0838-2638
CODEN: NOMBAY
NOVA SCOTIA MEDICAL JOURNAL. 1922. bi-m. $25. Medical Society of Nova Scotia, City of Lakes Business Park, 5 Spectacle Lakes Dr., Dartmouth, NS B3B 1X7, Canada. TEL 902-468-1866. FAX 902-468-6578. Ed. Dr. John F. O'Connor. adv.; bk.rev.; charts; illus.; index. circ. 2,025. **Indexed:** Chem.Abstr., Excerp.Med., Ind.Med. **Document type:** academic/scholarly publication.
—CASDDS.
    Formerly (until 1988): Nova Scotia Medical Bulletin (ISSN 0029-5094)

NOVOSTI FARMATSII I MEDITSINY/NEWS IN PHARMACOLOGY AND MEDICINE. see PHARMACY AND PHARMACOLOGY

610   US
NUCLEUS SCIENCE JOURNAL. 1957. a. $10. 3409 Shelbourne Rd., Baltimore, MD 21208. TEL 410-764-6132. (Co-sponsor: Queens College, Flushing NY) Ed. Dr. Mark A. Young. adv.; bk.rev.; bibl.; charts; illus.; stat.; index. circ. 7,000. (back issues avail.)

610 574   JA   ISSN 0469-2071
NUKADA INSTITUTE FOR MEDICAL AND BIOLOGICAL RESEARCH. REPORTS. (Text in English) irreg. exchange basis. Nukada Institute for Medical and Biological Research - Nukada Igaku Seibutsugaku Kenkyujo, 5-18 Inage-cho, Chiba-shi 280, Japan.

610   IT   ISSN 0394-8889
NUOVI ARGOMENTI DI MEDICINA. 12/yr. Via Napo Torriani 30, 20124 Milan, Italy. TEL 2-66-94-767. Ed. Enrico Bollero. circ. 42,000.

NURSING RESEARCH ABSTRACTS. see MEDICAL SCIENCES — Abstracting, Bibliographies, Statistics

NUTRITION & THE M.D.; a continuing education service for physicians and nutritionists. see NUTRITION AND DIETETICS

610 613.2   CN
NUTRITION REVIEW. a. M P I Medical Publishing Inc., 14 Ronan Ave., Toronto, Ont. M4N 2X9, Canada. TEL 416-481-6384.

610   CM   ISSN 0255-5352
O C E A C BULLETIN DE LIAISON ET DE DOCUMENTATION. q. 7500 Fr.CFA. Organisation de Coordination pour la Lutte Contre les Endemies en Afrique Centrale, BP 288, Yaounde, Cameroun. FAX 237-23-00-61. TELEX 8411KN. Ed. Henri Gelas. adv.; bk.rev. **Indexed:** Excerp.Med.

610   US
O H S U VIEWS. 1979. 3/yr. $25. Oregon Health Sciences University, 3181 S.W. Sam Jackson Park Rd., Portland, OR 97201. TEL 503-494-8231. FAX 503-494-8246. E-mail: levinm@ohsu.edu. Ed. Marlys Levin Pierson. charts; illus.; stat. circ. 35,000. **Document type:** academic/scholarly publication.
    Formerly (until Nov. 1988): Oregon Health Sciences University News.

610   US
OAK RIDGE ASSOCIATED UNIVERSITIES. MEDICAL SCIENCES DIVISION. RESEARCH REPORT. 1951. a. free. Oak Ridge Associated Universities, Inc., Office of Information Services, Box 117, Oak Ridge, TN 37831-0117. TEL 615-576-3146. Ed. Fred L. Snyder. circ. 2,500. (also avail. in microform from NTI; reprint service avail. from NTI)
    Formerly: Oak Ridge Institute for Nuclear Studies. Medical Division. Research Report (ISSN 0078-2890)

MEDICAL SCIENCES

610 UK ISSN 0955-6389
OBESITY IN EUROPE. 1989. irreg. John Libbey & Company Ltd., 13 Smiths Yard, Summerley St., London SW18 4HR, England. TEL 0181-947-2777. FAX 0181-947-2664.
E-mail: libbey@earlsfield.win-uk.net. **Document type:** monographic series.
—BLDSC (6196.952000).

616.3 US ISSN 1071-7323
RC628 CODEN: OBREFR
OBESITY RESEARCH. (Supplement avail.) 1993. 6/yr. (plus irreg. supplements). $105 to individuals (outside N. America $130); institutions $180 (outside N. America $200) (effective 1995). North American Association for the Study of Obesity, c/o Pennington Biomedical Research Center, 6400 Perkins Rd., Baton Rouge, LA 70808.
TEL 504-765-0934. Ed. Dr. George A. Bray. bibl. **Document type:** academic/scholarly publication.
—BLDSC (6196.952500); CASDDS.
Description: Publishes original scientific research and review articles in clinical and basic research related to obesity.
Refereed Serial

574.2 616 BU ISSN 0324-1998
CODEN: OSPADK
OBSTA I SRAVNITELNA PATOLOGIIA. (Text in various languages) 1976. s-a. price varies. (Bulgarska Akademiia na Naukite) Publishing House of the Bulgarian Academy of Sciences, Acad. G. Bonchev St., Bldg. 6, 1113 Sofia, Bulgaria. circ. 500. (reprint service avail. from IRC) **Indexed:**
Abstr.Bulg.Sci.Med.Lit., Biol.Abstr., BSL Biol., Chem.Abstr., Excerp.Med., Ind.Vet., Poult.Abstr., Vet.Bull.
—BLDSC (0126.705200); CASDDS.

610 UK
OBSTETRIC ULTRASOUND. 1993. irreg. Oxford University Press, Oxford Journals, Walton St., Oxford OX2 6DP, England. TEL 01865-267907.
FAX 01865-267773. E-mail: jnlorders@oup.co.uk. (US subscr. to: Oxford University Press Inc., 2001 Evans Rd., Cary, NC 27512. TEL 919-677-0977. FAX 919-677-1714) Eds. James Neilson, S.E. Chambers. **Document type:** monographic series.

OCCUPATIONAL MEDICINE. see *OCCUPATIONAL HEALTH AND SAFETY*

OCCUPATIONAL MEDICINE (NORWALK). see *OCCUPATIONAL HEALTH AND SAFETY*

610 US
OCCUPATIONAL THERAPY FORUM. w. (50/yr.). Forum Publishing, Inc., 251 W. Dekalb Pike, Ste. A-115, King of Prussia, PA 19406. TEL 215-337-0381. FAX 215-337-3979. adv. circ. 38,233.
Description: Covers new methodology, equipment, research trends and practical and philosophical aspects of the profession.

615.8 US ISSN 0738-0577
CODEN: OTHCES
OCCUPATIONAL THERAPY IN HEALTH CARE; a journal of contemporary practice. 1984. q. $105 (foreign $147) (effective 1996). Haworth Press, Inc., 10 Alice St., Binghamton, NY 13904.
TEL 607-722-5857; 800-342-9678.
FAX 607-722-1424. TELEX 4932599. Ed. Susan Heling Kaplan. adv.; bk.rev. circ. 383. (also avail. in microfiche from UMI; reprint service avail. from HAW) **Indexed:** Arts & Hum.Cit.Ind., CINAHL, CLOA, Curr.Cont., Except.Child Educ.Abstr., Excerp.Med., Hosp.Abstr., Soc.Work Res.& Abstr., Viol.& Abuse Abstr.
—BLDSC (6231.254000); Haworth; SWETS; UnCover.
Description: Provides answers to clinical questions of current concern to occupational therapy practitioners.
Refereed Serial

OCCUPATIONAL THERAPY IN MENTAL HEALTH; a journal of psychosocial practice and research. see *MEDICAL SCIENCES — Psychiatry And Neurology*

610 US ISSN 0276-1599
RM735.A1 CODEN: OTJRDE
OCCUPATIONAL THERAPY JOURNAL OF RESEARCH. Abbreviated title: O T J R. 1981. bi-m. $80 to non-members; members $55. (American Occupational Therapy Foundation, Inc.) Slack, Inc., 6900 Grove Rd., Thorofare, NJ 08086-9447.
TEL 609-848-1000. FAX 609-853-5991. Ed. Dr. Kenneth J. Ottenbacher. adv.; bk.rev.; abstr.; charts; bibl.; illus.; index. circ. 900. (back issues avail.) **Indexed:** CIJE, CINAHL, Excerp.Med., Psychol.Abstr. (1981-), SSCI.
—BLDSC (6231.255000); Genuine Article; SWETS; UnCover.
Refereed Serial

610 AU ISSN 0029-8786
OESTERREICHISCHE AERZTEZEITUNG. 1945. s-m. S.810. Oesterreichische Aerztekammer, Pressestelle und Verlag, Weihburggasse 10-12, A-1011 Vienna, Austria. TEL 01-5124486. FAX 01-513192524. Ed. Martin Stickler. adv.; B&W page S.29900, color page S.41200; trim 171 x 260; adv. contact: Burghilde Hunger. bk.rev.; illus.; index. circ. 34,000. **Indexed:** C.I.S. Abstr., Excerp.Med. **Document type:** bulletin.
—BLDSC (6304.400000); EMDOCS.
Description: Covers politics, laws and regulations, medical news, economics, educational material in all fields of medicine, and culture. Includes announcements of events, foreign news, reports and letters.

610 AU ISSN 0029-8875
DER OESTERREICHISCHE ARZT. 1950. 8/yr. S.200. (Vereinigung Oesterreichischer Aerzte) Steiger-Werbung Verlags- und Werbegesellschaft mbH, Hermanngasse 25, A-1070 Vienna, Austria. Ed. Franz-Josef Feichtenberger. adv.; bk.rev. circ. 20,000.

610 US ISSN 0000-1406
R712.A1
OFFICIAL A B M S DIRECTORY OF BOARD CERTIFIED MEDICAL SPECIALISTS. 1940. a., 27th ed., 1995. $425 for 4-vol. set. Marquis Who's Who, A Reed Reference Publishing company, 121 Chanlon Rd., New Providence, NJ 07974. TEL 908-464-6800. FAX 908-665-6688. TELEX 138 755. (Subscr. to: Order Dept., Box 31, New Providence, NJ 07974-9903. TEL 800-621-9669) Ed. Roy Crego. (also avail. in magnetic tape) **Document type:** directory.
●Also available on CD-ROM. Producer(s): Bowker - Reed Reference Electronic Publishing.
—CCC.
Incorporates (in 1992): Directory of Medical Specialists (ISSN 0070-5829); (1987-1992): A B M S Compendium of Certified Medical Specialists (ISSN 0884-1543)
Description: Presents current professional and biographical information on more than 447,000 practicing specialists, as well as profiles of nearly 35,000 newly board-certified physicians.

610 US ISSN 0000-1430
RC86
OFFICIAL AMERICAN BOARD OF MEDICAL SPECIALTIES (A B M S) DIRECTORY OF BOARD CERTIFIED EMERGENCY PHYSICIANS. 1983. biennial. $99.95. Marquis Who's Who, A Reed Reference Publishing company, 121 Chanlon Rd., New Providence, NJ 07974. TEL 908-464-6800. FAX 908-665-2898. (Subscr. to: Order Dept., Box 31, New Providence, NJ 07974-9903. TEL 800-521-8110) Ed. Roy Crego. **Document type:** directory.
Formerly: A B M S Directory of Certified Emergency Physicians (ISSN 0742-0366)
Description: Biographical sketches of U.S. medical specialists sorted alphabetically with a geographical index.

610 US ISSN 0000-1554
R712.A1
OFFICIAL AMERICAN BOARD OF MEDICAL SPECIALTIES (A B M S) DIRECTORY OF BOARD CERTIFIED FAMILY PHYSICIANS. 1985. biennial. $99.95. Marquis Who's Who, A Reed Reference Publishing Company, 121 Chanlon Rd., New Providence, NJ 07974.
TEL 908-464-6800. FAX 908-665-2898. (Subscr. to: Order Dept., Box 31, New Providence, NJ 07974-9903. TEL 800-521-8110) Ed. Roy Crego. **Document type:** directory.
Formerly: A B M S Directory of Certified Family Physicians (ISSN 0884-643X)
Description: Biographical sketches of U.S. certified medical specialists sorted geographically with an alphabetical index.

OFFICIAL AMERICAN BOARD OF MEDICAL SPECIALTIES (A B M S) DIRECTORY OF BOARD CERTIFIED MEDICAL GENETICISTS. see *BIOLOGY — Genetics*

610 US ISSN 0000-1643
RA423.5
OFFICIAL AMERICAN BOARD OF MEDICAL SPECIALTIES (A B M S) DIRECTORY OF BOARD CERTIFIED PREVENTIVE MEDICINE SPECIALISTS. 1985. biennial. $59.95. Marquis Who's Who, A Reed Reference Publishing company, 121 Chanlon Rd., New Providence, NJ 07974. TEL 908-464-6800.
FAX 908-665-2898. (Subscr. to: Order Dept., Box 31, New Providence, NJ 07974-9903. TEL 800-521-8110) Ed. Roy Crego. **Document type:** directory.
Formerly: A B M S Directory of Certified Preventive Medicine Specialists (ISSN 0883-2978)
Description: Biographical sketches of U.S. certified medical specialists sorted alphabetically with a geographical index.

610 617 US ISSN 0000-1481
RD10.U6
OFFICIAL AMERICAN BOARD OF MEDICAL SPECIALTIES (A B M S) DIRECTORY OF BOARD CERTIFIED THORACIC SURGEONS. 1983. biennial. $99.95. Marquis Who's Who, A Reed Reference Publishing company, 121 Chanlon Rd., New Providence, NJ 07974. TEL 908-464-6800. FAX 908-665-2898. (Subscr. to: Order Dept., Box 31, New Providence, NJ 07974-9903. TEL 800-521-8110) Ed. Roy Crego. **Document type:** directory.
Formerly (until 1992): A B M S Directory of Certified Thoracic Surgeons (ISSN 0884-1462)
Description: Biographical sketches of U.S. certified medical specialists sorted alphabetically with a geographical index.

610 US
THE OHIO FAMILY PHYSICIAN. 1955. m. $2. Ohio Academy of Family Physicians, 4075 N. High St., Columbus, OH 43214. TEL 614-267-7867. Ed. Dr. Edward T. Bope. adv.; B&W page $373; 7 1/2 x 9 5/8. circ. 4,000 (controlled). **Document type:** trade publication.
Formerly: Ohio Family Physician News (ISSN 0030-0888)

OHIO HEALTH LAW UPDATE. see *LAW*

610 US ISSN 0892-2454
CODEN: OHMEE
OHIO MEDICINE. 1905. m. $35 to non-members (effective 1995). Ohio State Medical Association, 1500 Lakeshore Dr., Columbus, OH 43204-3824. TEL 614-486-2401. FAX 614-486-3130. Ed. Karen Edwards. adv. contact: George Quigley. bk.rev.; bibl.; illus.; index. circ. 12,000. (tabloid format) **Indexed:** Biol.Abstr., Dent.Ind., Excerp.Med. (until 1993), Ind.Med. (until 1992). **Document type:** newspaper.
—BLDSC (6247.117000); Faxon; SWETS.
Formerly: Ohio State Medical Journal (ISSN 0030-1124)
Description: Covers legislative, legal and reimbursement issues for Ohio physicians, with association news and reports on Ohio trends in science and medical education.

610 US ISSN 0030-1132
OHIO STATE UNIVERSITY. COLLEGE OF MEDICINE. JOURNAL. 1947. q. Ohio State University, College of Medicine, 941 Chatham Ln., Columbus, OH 43221. TEL 614-459-3909. FAX 614-293-3666. Ed. Dr. Ernest W. Johnson. bk.rev.; bibl.; charts; illus.; stat.; circ. 13,700 (controlled).

OKAJIMA'S FOLIA ANATOMICA JAPONICA/OKAJIMA FORIA ANATOMIKA YAPONIKA. see *BIOLOGY*

MEDICAL SCIENCES

610   JA   ISSN 0030-1558
CODEN: OIZAAV
OKAYAMA IGAKKAI ZASSHI/MEDICAL ASSOCIATION OF OKAYAMA. JOURNAL. (Text in Japanese; summaries in English) vol.87, 1975. m. Okayama Igakkai - Medical Association of Okayama, c/o Okayama University Medical School, 5-1 Shikata-cho 2-chome, Okayama 700, Japan. Ed. Isamu Nisida. adv.; abstr.; charts; illus.; stat.; index. circ. 500. **Indexed:** Biol.Abstr., C.I.S. Abstr., Chem.Abstr.
—BLDSC (6252.830000).

610   JA   ISSN 0917-2424
OKAYAMA KOTSUSOSHOSHO KANFARENSU KIROKUSHU/OSTEOPOROSIS. (Text in Japanese) 1989. a. Okayama Kotsusoshosho Kanfarensu - Okayama Conference on Osteoporosis, c/o Okayama Daigaku Igakubu Seikei Gekagaku Kyoshitsu, 5-1, Shikatacho 2-chome, Okayama-shi, Okayama-ken 700, Japan.

610   US
OKLAHOMA MEDICAL RESEARCH FOUNDATION. FINDINGS. Cover title: O M R F Findings. 1991. 3/yr. donation. Oklahoma Medical Research Foundation, 825 N.E. 13th St., Oklahoma City, OK 73104. TEL 405-271-8537. Ed. Shari Hawkins. illus. **Document type:** newsletter.
Description: Publishes news of research projects, activities and programs sponsored by the foundation.

610   US   ISSN 0030-1876
OKLAHOMA STATE MEDICAL ASSOCIATION. JOURNAL. 1908. m. $30. Oklahoma State Medical Association, 601 N.W. Expressway, Oklahoma City, OK 73118. TEL 405-843-9571. Ed. Dr. Ray V. McIntyre. adv.; bk.rev.; abstr.; bibl.; illus.; stat.; index. circ. 4,400. (also avail. in microfilm from UMI) **Indexed:** Biol.Abstr., Chem.Abstr., Dent.Ind., Ind.Med, INIS Atomind., Nutr.Abstr.
—BLDSC (4835.300000); Faxon; UMI; UnCover.

615.5   IT   ISSN 0030-2260
CODEN: OMDTA6
OMNIA MEDICA ET THERAPEUTICA.* 1949. q. L.3500. Edizioni Omnia Medica, Via S. Michele degli Scalzi 63, I-56100 Pisa, Italy. bk.rev.; abstr.; bibl.; illus.; index. **Indexed:** Biol.Abstr., Chem.Abstr., Excerp.Med., Ind.Med.
—CASDDS.

610   CN   ISSN 1195-0242
OMNIPRACTICIEN. 1993. 24/yr. Can.$48.50 (US Can.$60, elsewhere Can.$75). Thomson Healthcare Communications, 1120 Birchmount Rd., Ste. 200, Scarborough, ON M1K 5G4, Canada. TEL 416-750-8900. FAX 416-751-8126. Ed. Lyse Savard. circ. 10,500.

ON THE BEAM. see *HANDICAPPED — Visually Impaired*

610   NE   ISSN 0920-8100
ONDERWIJS EN GEZONDHEIDSZORG. 1977. 10/yr. fl.87.75. (Vereniging van Opleidingsinstituten voor Verplegende en Verzorgende Beroepen) Bohn Stafleu Van Loghum B.V., Postbus 246, 3990 GA Houten, Netherlands. TEL 31-3403-95711. FAX 31-3403-50903. adv. circ. 1,285. **Document type:** trade publication.
—SWETS.

362   US   ISSN 0258-610X
ONE-IN-TEN. (Text in Arabic, English, French, Spanish) 1980. q. free. Rehabilitation International, 25 E. 21st St., New York, NY 10010. TEL 212-420-1500. FAX 212-505-0871. TELEX 446412. (Co-sponsor: U N I C E F) Ed. Susan Hammerman. circ. 10,000. **Document type:** newsletter.
Description: Covers childhood disabilities, their prevention and rehabilitation.

610   UK   ISSN 1059-2725
CODEN: OJCTEI
THE ONLINE JOURNAL OF CURRENT CLINICAL TRIALS. 1992. irreg. £80($120) to individuals; institutions £130 (in N. America $195) (effective 1995) (includes print cumulation). Chapman & Hall, Journals Department (Subsidiary of: International Thomson Publishing Group), 2-6 Boundary Row, London SE1 8HN, England. TEL 212-564-1060. FAX 212-564-1505. TELEX 290164 CHAPMA G. E-mail: journal@chall.mhs.compuserve.com. (Subscr. to: International Thomson Publishing Services Ltd., Cheriton House, North Way, Andover, Hants. SP10 5BE, England. TEL 01264-342713. FAX 01264-342807; Subscr. in N. America to: Chapman & Hall, Journals Promotion Department, One Penn Plaza, 41st Fl., New York, NY 10119. TEL 212-564-1060. FAX 212-564-1505) Ed.Bd. abstr.; charts; illus. (also avail. in microfiche; back issues avail.) **Indexed:** Ind.Med. (1994-). **Document type:** academic/scholarly publication.
●Available only online. Vendor(s): OCLC.
—BLDSC (6260.762538).
Description: Publishes studies of current therapies, procedures, and developments relevant to patient care in oncology, infectious disease, cardiology, pediatrics, gynecology, dermatology, psychology, and surgery.
Refereed Serial

ONLINE MEDICAL DATABASES. see *LIBRARY AND INFORMATION SCIENCES — Computer Applications*

610   CN   ISSN 0030-302X
ONTARIO MEDICAL REVIEW. 1922. m. Can.$50 to non-members (in U.S. Can.$57; elsewhere Can.$74) (effective 1995). Ontario Medical Association, 525 University Ave., Ste. 300, Toronto, ON M5G 2K7, Canada. TEL 416-599-2580. FAX 416-599-9309. Ed. R.D. Fletcher. adv. contact: Trish Sullivan. bibl.; charts; illus.; index. circ. 26,000. (back issues avail.) **Indexed:** Chem.Abstr. **Document type:** trade publication.
—BLDSC (6262.050000).
Description: For all Ontario licensed physicians, interns and residents and OMA member medical students, as well as physicians residing outside Ontario who are members of OMA.

610   CN   ISSN 0712-6689
ONTARIO MEDICINE. 24/yr. Can.$49. Maclean-Hunter Ltd., Maclean-Hunter Bldg., 777 Bay St., Toronto, ON M5W 1A7, Canada.

610   SZ
OPTIMA. (Text in French, German) 1974. m. Editions Optima SA, Av. de Chillon 90, CH-1820 Montreux, Switzerland. TEL 021-9635161. FAX 021-9631874. Ed. Gerard Geiger. adv. contact: Serge Ducret. **Document type:** bulletin.

610   PO   ISSN 0030-4506
ORDEM DOS MEDICOS. BOLETIM. m. free to qualified personnel. Medical Association of Portugal, Ave. de Liberdade 65, Lisbon, Portugal.

610   IT
ORDINE DEI MEDICI E DEGLI ODONTOIATRI DELLA PROVINCIA DI VENEZIA. NOTIZIARIO. 1957. bi-m. free to members. Ordine dei Medici, S. Polo 625, 30125 Venice, Italy. TEL 522-9081. FAX 528-96-81. Ed. Giuliano Bruscagnin. adv. circ. 3,500.
Formerly: Ordine dei Medici della Provincia di Venezia. Notiziario.

610   FR   ISSN 0030-4565
ORDRE NATIONAL DES MEDECINS. BULLETIN. 1941. 11/yr. 147 F. (foreign 221 F.) (effective 1996). Masson - Periodiques, Villa Laromiguiere, 75005 Paris, France. TEL 1-40-46-62-00. FAX 1-40-46-62-01. Ed. O. Dubois. circ. 70,000. (reprint service avail. from ISI) **Document type:** bulletin.
—CCC.
Description: Presents the activity of the national council, and the regional and departmental councils. Deals with the professional organization of medicine.

610   US
ORGANIZATION OF TEACHERS OF ORAL DIAGNOSIS. NEWSLETTER. Also known as: Organization of Teachers of Oral Diagnosis. News. 1963. q. membership. (Organization of Teachers of Oral Diagnosis) University of Texas Dental School, 7703 Floyd Curl Dr., San Antonio, TX 78284. TEL 512-567-3333. Ed. James A. Cottone. bk.rev.; illus. circ. 150. (looseleaf format) **Document type:** newsletter.

ORIENTAL MEDICINE. see *ALTERNATIVE MEDICINE*

610   IT   ISSN 0394-2678
ORIS MEDICINA; monthly of cultural, scientific and technical information. (Text in English, Italian) 1987. 11/yr. L.135000 in Europe; American L.180000. Diade s.r.l., Via Ausonio 5, 20123 Milan, Italy. TEL 39-2-8372407. FAX 39-2-58100311. Ed. Franco Marelli Coppola. adv. contact: Paola Pirogalli. bk.rev. circ. 23,000.
Description: Publishes original articles, research results and clinical experiments from Italian university professors, researchers and hospital specialists.
Refereed Serial

616 619   US   ISSN 0887-0306
ORPHAN DISEASE UPDATE. 1983. 3/yr. $25. National Organization for Rare Disorders, Inc., Box 8923, New Fairfield, CT 06812. TEL 203-746-6518. FAX 203-746-6481. Ed. Abbey S. Meyers. bk.rev.; charts; illus. circ. 80,000. (tabloid format; back issues avail.) **Document type:** consumer publication, newsletter.
●Also available online. Vendor(s): CompuServe, Inc. (GO NORD).
Description: Information on orphan drugs and diseases. Covers medical advances, biomedical research, patient coping strategies, and legislative issues related to the field.

610   HU   ISSN 0030-6002
R96.H8   CODEN: ORHEAG
ORVOSI HETILAP. (Text in Hungarian; summaries in English) 1857. w. 4700 Ft.($130) (Markusovszky Lajos Foundation) Springer Hungarica Kiado Ltd., Wesselenyi u. 28, 1410 Budapest 7, Hungary. TEL 25-15-892. FAX 25-15-973. (Subscr. to: Kultura, Box 149, 1389 Budapest, Hungary) Ed. Dr. Janos Feher. adv.; bk.rev.; illus.; index. circ. 10,000. **Indexed:** Biol.Abstr., Chem.Abstr., Dent.Ind., Dok.Arbeitsmed., Excerp.Med., Ind.Med., Nutr.Abstr., Protozool.Abstr., Sugar Ind.Abstr.
—BLDSC (6296.500000); CASDDS.

610.7   HU   ISSN 0030-6037
R91   CODEN: ORVOAE
ORVOSKEPZES. (Text in Hungarian; summaries in English and Russian) 1911. 6/yr. Szabolcs u 33-35, 1389 Budapest, Hungary. TEL 1-1208588. (Subscr. to: Kultura, Box 149, H-1389 Budapest, Hungary) Ed. Dr. Frigyes Kulka. adv.; index. circ. 3,200. **Indexed:** Biol.Abstr., Excerp.Med.
—BLDSC (6296.520000); EMDOCS.
Description: Covers medical training.

610   HU   ISSN 0010-3551
ORVOSTORTENETI KOZLEMENYEK/COMMUNICATIONS DE HISTORIA ARTIS MEDICINAE. (Text occasionally in English, French, German) 1955. q. $20. Semmelweis Orvostorteneti Muzeum, Konyvtar es Leveltar, Torok u. 12, 1023 Budapest, Hungary. TEL 36-1-2125421. FAX 36-1-1753936. (Co-sponsor: Magyar Orvostortenelmi Tarsasag) Ed. Dr. Maria Vida. adv.; bk.rev.; cum.index. circ. 1,000. **Indexed:** Numis.Lit. **Document type:** academic/scholarly publication.

610   JA   ISSN 0386-4103
CODEN: OIGZDE
OSAKA CITY MEDICAL JOURNAL. (Text in European languages) 1951. 2/yr. 7000 Yen($35) Osaka City Medical Center - Osaka-shi Igakkai, 1-4-54 Asahi-machi, Abeno-ku, Osaka 545, Japan. Ed. Shushi Matsuura. charts; illus.; stat. circ. 1,200. (back issues avail.) **Indexed:** Biol.Abstr., C.I.S. Abstr., Chem.Abstr., Diar.Dis.Res., Excerp.Med., Ind.Med., Nutr.Abstr.
—BLDSC (4838.000000); CASDDS.

MEDICAL SCIENCES

610   JA   ISSN 0387-446X
OSAKA DAIGAKU IRYO GIJUTSU TANKI DAIGAKUBU KENKYU KIYO. SHIZEN KAGAKU IRYO KAGAKU HEN/OSAKA UNIVERSITY. COLLEGE OF BIO-MEDICAL TECHNOLOGY AND NURSING. STUDIES IN NATURAL SCIENCE AND HEALTH TECHNOLOGY. (Text in Japanese; summaries in English and Japanese) 1968. a. Osaka Daigaku, Iryo Gijutsu Tanki Daigakubu - Osaka University. College of Bio-Medical Technology and Nursing, 1-1 Machikaneyama-cho, Toyonaka-shi, Osaka-fu 560, Japan.

610   JA   ISSN 0916-2844
                           CODEN: BOMCEB
OSAKA MEDICAL COLLEGE. BULLETIN. (Text in English) 1954. a. free to medical institutions; exchange basis. Osaka Medical College - Osaka Ika Daigaku, 2-7 Daigaku-machi, Takatsuki-shi, Osaka 569, Japan. Ed. Hideo Matsumoto. charts; illus.; index. **Indexed:** Biol.Abstr., Excerp.Med., Ind.Med. (until 1992), INIS Atomind. **Document type:** bulletin.
—CASDDS.
    Formerly (until 1988): Osaka Medical School. Bulletin (ISSN 0030-6142)

610   JA   ISSN 0030-6118
                           CODEN: OIDZAU
OSAKA MEDICAL COLLEGE. JOURNAL/OSAKA IKA DAIGAKU ZASSHI. (Text in Japanese; summaries in English) 1932. q. 1000 Yen. Osaka Medical College - Osaka Ika Daigaku, 2-7 Daigaku-machi, Takatsuki, Osaka 569, Japan. Ed. Hiroaki Takahashi. bk.rev. **Indexed:** Biol.Abstr., Chem.Abstr.
—BLDSC (4839.200000); CASDDS.

OSLER LIBRARY NEWSLETTER. see *LIBRARY AND INFORMATION SCIENCES*

OSPEDALE AL MARE. ARCHIVIO. see *HOSPITALS*

610   IT   ISSN 0369-7843
                           CODEN: OSMAA
L'OSPEDALE MAGGIORE. 1906. q. L.73000($99) (effective 1994). Masson S.p.A., Divisione Periodici, Via Statuto 2-4, 20121 Milan, Italy. TEL 02-6367-1. FAX 02-6367211. Ed. Elio E. Polli. adv.: B&W page L.2750000, color page L.4200000. circ. 5,000. **Indexed:** Excerp.Med. (1995-).

610   UK   ISSN 0937-941X
                           CODEN: OSINEP
OSTEOPOROSIS INTERNATIONAL. 1990. 6/yr. £185($297) (effective 1996). (European Foundation for Osteoporosis) Springer-Verlag, Springer House, 8 Alexandra Rd., London SW19 7JZ, England. TEL 081-944-2942. FAX 081-947-4651. (Co-sponsor: National Osteoporosis Foundation, US) Eds. Robert Lindsay, Pierre J. Meunier. (also avail. in microfilm from UMI) **Indexed:** Excerp.Med. (1992-), Ind.Med. (1992-). **Document type:** academic/scholarly publication.
—BLDSC (6303.873500); Genuine Article; SWETS. **CCC.**

616.7   US
OSTEOPOROSIS REPORT. 1985. q. $10 to individuals; institutions $95. National Osteoporosis Foundation, 1150 17th St., N.W., Ste. 500, Washington, DC 20036. TEL 202-223-2226. FAX 202-223-2237. Ed. Laurie Gibson Linberg. circ. 10,000.
    Description: Covers clinical updates, reports on activities, programs, and consumer information.

610   UK   ISSN 0962-7022
OSTEOPOROSIS REVIEW. 1991. 3/yr. £10. (National Osteoporosis Society) Macmillan Magazines Ltd., 4 Little Essex St., London WC2R 3LF, England. TEL 0171-836-6633. FAX 0171-379-4204. Ed. Anthony Woolf; Pub. Jane Jones. **Document type:** academic/scholarly publication.
—BLDSC (6303.873900).

610   US   ISSN 0030-6517
OSTOMY QUARTERLY. 1963. q. $25. United Ostomy Association, Inc., 36 Executive Park, Ste. 120, Irvine, CA 92714-6744. TEL 714-660-8624. FAX 714-660-9262. Ed. Nelson Carnicelli. adv.; bk.rev.; index. circ. 48,000. (also avail. in microfilm from UMI) **Indexed:** Hlth.Ind., Rehabil.Lit.
—BLDSC (6312.375000); Faxon; UMI.

610   FR   ISSN 0048-2366
OUEST MEDICAL. 1948. 20/yr. 50 F. (students 25F). Expansion Scientifique, 15 rue Saint Benoit, 75278 Paris Cedex 06, France. Ed.Bd. adv.; bk.rev.; illus. circ. 8,500. (also avail. in microform) **Indexed:** Biol.Abstr., C.I.S. Abstr., Chem.Abstr., Curr.Cont., Excerp.Med., Nutr.Abstr.
—BLDSC (6314.230000). **CCC.**

610 620   US   ISSN 0957-5766
OXFORD MEDICAL ENGINEERING SERIES. 1979. irreg. price varies. Oxford University Press, 200 Madison Ave., New York, NY 10016. TEL 212-679-7300. **Document type:** monographic series.
—BLDSC (6321.006800).

610   UK   ISSN 0030-7661
OXFORD MEDICAL SCHOOL GAZETTE. 1949. 3/yr. £6. University of Oxford Medical School, John Radcliffe Hospital, Headington, Oxford OX3 9DU, England. TEL 01865-221689. FAX 01865-750750. E-mail: whyte@vax.ox.ac.uk. Ed. Sean Whyte. adv. contact: Oliver Howes. bk.rev.; charts; illus.; stat. circ 1,000. **Document type:** academic/scholarly publication.

610 575   US   ISSN 1352-240X
OXFORD MONOGRAPHS ON MEDICAL GENETICS. 1966. irreg. price varies. Oxford University Press, 200 Madison Ave., New York, NY 10016. TEL 212-679-7300. Ed.Bd. **Document type:** monographic series.
    Refereed Serial

P A CAREER. (Physician Assistants) see *OCCUPATIONS AND CAREERS*

610   US
P & S JOURNAL. (Physicians and Surgeons) 1955. 3/yr. free to qualified personnel. Columbia University, College of Physicians and Surgeons, 630 W. 168 St., New York, NY 10032. TEL 212-305-3877. FAX 212-928-5799. E-mail: enochsb@cuadmin.cis.columbia.edu. Site addr.: http://cpmcnet.columbia.edu/. Ed. Dr. Donald F. Tapley. bk.rev.; illus. circ. 16,000. (also avail. in microfilm from UMI; reprint service avail. from UMI) **Document type:** academic/scholarly publication.
●Also available online.
    Formerly (until 1981): P and S Quarterly (ISSN 0030-7831)

P B S BULLETIN. (Philippine Biochemical Society) see *BIOLOGY — Biological Chemistry*

P H R RECORD. (Physicians for Human Rights) see *POLITICAL SCIENCE — International Relations*

610   GW   ISSN 0722-477X
P M D - PRAXIS MEDIZINISCHER DOKUMENTATION. 1980. q. DM.40. P W D Presseverlag GmbH, Goethestr. 21, 80336 Munich, Germany. TEL 089-591964. FAX 089-553079. Ed. Ulli Hoffmann. adv.: page DM.1798; adv. contact: Doris Tegethoff. bk.rev. circ. 2,000. (back issues avail.) **Document type:** academic/scholarly publication.
    Description: Contains articles about medical documentation and record keeping. Also includes health care information, association news and reports, international news, events, and positions available.

P P O LETTER. (Preferred Provider Organizations) see *BUSINESS AND ECONOMICS*

616.02   US   ISSN 0938-9016
RB127   CODEN: PADIE6
PAIN DIGEST. 1991. q. $175 (effective 1996). Springer-Verlag, Journals, 175 Fifth Ave., New York, NY 10010. TEL 212-460-1575. FAX 212-473-6272. (N. American subscr. to: Journal Fulfillment Servies, Box 2485, Secaucus, NJ 07096-2491. TEL 800-777-4643. FAX 201-348-4505; Elsewhere: Springer-Verlag, Heidelberger Platz 3, 1000 Berlin 33, Germany. TEL 030-8207-1. FAX 030-821-4091) Ed. P. Prithvi Raj. (also avail. in microform from UMI; back issues avail.; reprint service avail. from UMI) **Indexed:** Excerp.Med. (1994-). **Document type:** academic/scholarly publication.
—BLDSC (6333.799000); UMI. **CCC.**
    Description: Contains up-to-date knowledge of the research, evaluation methods, and techniques of pain management.
    Refereed Serial

610   NE   ISSN 0921-3287
PAIN RESEARCH AND CLINICAL MANAGEMENT. Represents: World Congress of Pain. Proceedings. (Text in English) 1987. irreg., vol.9, 1993. price varies. Elsevier Science B.V., Books Division, P.O. Box 211, 1000 AE Amsterdam, Netherlands. TEL 31-20-4853911. FAX 31-20-4853705. TELEX 18582 ESPA NL.
E-mail: nlinfo-f@elsevier.nl; usinfo-f@elsevier.com; forinfo-kyf04035@niftyserve.or.jp; Site addr.: http://www.elsevier.nl/. (Subscr. in U.S. and Canada to: Elsevier Science Inc., Box 882, Madison Sq. Sta., New York, NY 10159. TEL 212-989-5800) (back issues avail.) **Document type:** monographic series, proceedings.
—BLDSC (6333.810000); Faxon.
    Refereed Serial

610   UK   ISSN 0968-1302
▼**PAIN REVIEWS.** 1994. q. £44($95) to individuals; institutions £70 ($135) (effective 1996). Arnold (Subsidiary of: Hodder Headline plc.), 338 Euston Rd., London NW1 3BH, England. TEL 0171-873-6000. FAX 0171-873-6325. (Subscr. to: Turpin Distribution Services Ltd., Blackhorse Rd., Letchworth, Herts. SG6 1HN, England. TEL 01462-672555. FAX 01462-480947) **Indexed:** Excerp.Med. (1995-). **Document type:** academic/scholarly publication.
—BLDSC (6333.830000).

610   US
PAIN SERIES. 1968. irreg. price varies. F.A. Davis Company, 1915 Arch St., Philadelphia, PA 19103. TEL 800-523-4049. Ed. Rene Cailliet. **Document type:** monographic series.

610   UK
PAIN SOCIETY OF GREAT BRITAIN AND IRELAND. JOURNAL. 1987. s-a. £35. Pain Society of Great Britain and Ireland, 9 Bedford Square, London WC1B 3RA, England. Ed. Robert Johnson. adv.; bk.rev. circ. 700. (back issues avail.)
    Formerly: Intractable Pain Society of Great Britain and Ireland. Journal.

610   PK   ISSN 0030-9842
PAKISTAN JOURNAL OF MEDICAL RESEARCH. (Text in English) 1961. q. $75. Pakistan Medical Research Council, Shahrah-e-Jumhuriat G-5-2, P.O. Box 2598, Islamabad, Pakistan. TEL 92-51-217416. FAX 92-51-216774. Ed. Dr. N. Rehan. adv.; bk.rev.; charts; illus.; stat.; index. circ. 1,000. (also avail. in microfilm from UMI; reprint service avail. from UMI) **Indexed:** Abstr.Hyg., Biol.Abstr., Nutr.Abstr. **Document type:** academic/scholarly publication.
    Description: Publishes results of clinical and biomedical research.

612   PK
PAKISTAN JOURNAL OF PATHOLOGY. (Text in English) 1990. 2/yr. Pakistan Association of Pathologists, P.O. Box 260, Rawalpindi, Pakistan. Ed. Syed Azhar Ahmed. **Document type:** academic/scholarly publication.

610   PK   ISSN 0030-9982
                           CODEN: JJPAD4
PAKISTAN MEDICAL ASSOCIATION. JOURNAL. Abbreviated title: J P M A. (Text in English) 1950. m. Rs.200($75) Pakistan Medical Association, P.M.A. House, Aga Khan III Rd., Karachi 74400, Pakistan. TEL 92-21-7214632. FAX 92-21-7226443. Ed. Dr. S.J. Zuberi. adv.; bk.rev.; charts; illus.; stat. circ. 6,000. (also avail. in microform from UMI; reprint service avail. from UMI) **Indexed:** Abstr.Hyg., Diar.Dis.Res., Excerp.Med., ExtraMED, Ind.Med., Rev.Med.& Vet.Mycol., Trop.Dis.Bull. **Document type:** academic/scholarly publication.
●Also available on CD-ROM.
—BLDSC (4839.497000); CASDDS; EMDOCS; Faxon; SWETS; UMI.

MEDICAL SCIENCES 4255

610   UK   ISSN 0269-2163
CODEN: PAMDE2
PALLIATIVE MEDICINE. 1987. q. £75($135) to individuals; institutions £163 ($293) (effective 1996). Arnold (Subsidiary of: Hodder Headline plc.), 338 Euston Rd., London NW1 3BH, England. TEL 0171-873-6000. FAX 0171-873-6325. (Subscr. to: Turpin Distribution Services Ltd., Blackhorse Rd., Letchworth, Herts. SG6 1HN, England. TEL 01462-672555. FAX 01462-480947) adv.; bk.rev. **Indexed:** Excerp.Med. (1993-), IMFL, Ind.Med. (1993-). **Document type:** academic/scholarly publication.
—BLDSC (6345.562060); SWETS; UnCover. **CCC.**
Description: Dedicated to improving knowledge and clinical practice in the care of patients with advanced diseases.

610   IT   ISSN 1120-303X
PANDORA; giornale di ricerca clinica e diagnostica. 1989. 3/yr. Medical Systems S.p.A., Via Rio Torbido 40, 16165 Genova, Italy. TEL 010-83401. FAX 010-804661.

610   IT
CODEN: PMMDAE
PANMINERVA MEDICA. (Text in English) 1959. q. $90 to individuals; institutions $140 (effective 1995). (Associazione Medica Italiana) Edizioni Minerva Medica, Corso Bramante 83-85, 10126 Turin, Italy. TEL 39-11-678282. FAX 39-11-3121736. (Co-sponsor: Europa Medica) Ed. M.L. Benzo; Pub. Alberto Oliaro. adv.: B&W page $1100, color page $1900; trim 215 x 280; adv. contact: F. Filippo. bk.rev.; abstr.; bibl.; charts; illus.; circ. 5,000 (paid). (also avail. in microfilm from UMI) **Indexed:** Biol.Abstr., Chem.Abstr., Curr.Cont., Dent.Ind., Helminthol.Abstr., Ind.Med., Nutr.Abstr., Sci.Cit.Ind. **Document type:** academic/scholarly publication.
—BLDSC (6357.380000); CASDDS; Genuine Article; SWETS; UMI.
Formerly: Panminerva Medica - Europa Medica; Formed by the merger of: Panminerva Medica (ISSN 0031-0808); Europa Medica (ISSN 0014-2557)
Description: Covers clinical and experimental medicine and surgery.
Refereed Serial

610   FR   ISSN 0339-073X
PANORAMA DU MEDECIN. 1975. 260/yr. 37 av. des Champs Elysees, 75008 Paris, France. TEL 49-53-68-00. FAX 42-25-40-06. TELEX 290 275 LES ECHO. Ed. Yannick Guiheneuf. circ. 57,000.

610   MX
PANORAMA MEDICO. 1971. m. free to doctors in Mexico. Dr. Javier Aranda Apellaniz, Ed. & Pub., Avda. Coyocan 1025, Edificio A no. 2, Condominio Jardin del Valle, Mexico 12, D.F., Mexico. adv. circ. 15,000.

615.89   GW   ISSN 0937-2512
PANTA. q. DM.46 (students DM.30). (Internationale Medizinische Gesellschaft fuer Elektroakupunktur) Karl F. Haug Verlag GmbH, Fritz-Frey-Str. 21, 69121 Heidelberg, Germany. TEL 06221-4062-0. FAX 06221-400727. TELEX 461683-HVVFM-D. (Subscr. to: Postfach 102840, 69018 Heidelberg, Germany) Ed. Dr. G. Hanzl. **Document type:** academic/scholarly publication.

610   NE   ISSN 0168-6771
DE PAPIEREN VISITE. 1984. bi-w. Reed HealthCare (Subsidiary of: Reed Elsevier plc), P.O. Box 1126, 1000 BC Amsterdam, Netherlands. TEL 31-20-5153350. Ed. G.S.P. Reehuis. adv. contact: G.J.M. van den Akker. circ. 9,300. **Document type:** trade publication.
Description: For general practitioners, pharmacists and nursing home physicians.

610   PP   ISSN 0256-2901
CODEN: MSPREG
PAPUA NEW GUINEA INSTITUTE OF MEDICAL RESEARCH. MONOGRAPH SERIES. 1970. irreg. price varies. Papua New Guinea Institute of Medical Research, P.O. Box 60, Goroka, Papua New Guinea. TEL 675-721469. FAX 675-721998. Ed. Dr. M.P. Alpers. bibl.; charts; illus. circ. 1,000. **Document type:** monographic series.
Description: A series of monographs on topics related to health and medical science in Papua New Guinea and elsewhere.

610   PP   ISSN 0031-1480
CODEN: PGMJBP
PAPUA NEW GUINEA MEDICAL JOURNAL. 1955. q. $60. Medical Society of Papua New Guinea, P.O. Box 60, Goroka, EHP, Papua New Guinea. TEL 675-721469. FAX 675-721998. Ed. M. Alpers. adv.; bk.rev.; abstr.; bibl.; charts; illus.; index every 3 yrs. circ. 500. (also avail. in microfilm from UMI; back issues avail.; reprint service avail. from UMI) **Indexed:** Abstr.Hyg., Biol.Abstr., Curr.Cont., Helminthol.Abstr., Ind.Med., Ind.Vet., Nutr.Abstr., Protozool.Abstr., Rev.Appl.Entomol., Rev.Med.& Vet.Mycol., Rural Devel.Abstr., Rural Ext.Educ.& Tr.Abstr., Trop.Dis.Bull., Vet.Bull. **Document type:** academic/scholarly publication.
—BLDSC (6404.514000); Faxon; Genuine Article; SWETS; UMI; UnCover.

610   US   ISSN 1050-7302
PARENT'S HEALTH ADVISER. 1985. m. Whittle Communications L.P., 333 Main Ave., Knoxville, TN 37902. TEL 615-595-5300. Ed. Margot Leske.
Formerly (until 1990): Parenting Adviser (ISSN 1047-3769)
Description: Serves as a guide to parents by offering practical, comprehensive health care information about children.

610   US
PARK-NICOLLET MEDICAL FOUNDATION BULLETIN. 1956. q. free to qualified personnel. (Park Nicollet Medical Foundation) Park Nicollet Medical Center, 5000 W. 39th St, Minneapolis, MN 55416. TEL 612-927-3123. Ed. R.C. Woellner. charts; illus.; cum.index. circ. 9,000. **Indexed:** Ind.Med. **Document type:** academic/scholarly publication, bulletin.
Formerly: St. Louis Park Medical Center. Bulletin (ISSN 0036-2980)
Description: Articles on diseases and treatment for physicians in primary care.

610   IT   ISSN 0031-2312
PARMAMEDICA;* bollettino dell'ordine dei medici. vol.15, 1967. m. L.2000 (free to qualified personnel). Ordine dei Medici della Provincia di Parma, Borgo al Collegio Maria Luigia 17, Parma, Italy. Ed. Carlo Molinari. adv.

PART B NEWS. see *INSURANCE*

362.175 658   UK   ISSN 1352-7746
▼**PARTNERS IN PALLIATIVE CARE.** 1994. q. The Old Ribbon Mill, Pitt St., Macclesfield, Ches. SK11 7PT, England. TEL 01625-618507. FAX 01625-614161. Ed. C.M. Riggs. **Document type:** trade publication.
—BLDSC (6407.743500).

616.07 576 574.8   SZ   ISSN 1015-2008
RB125   CODEN: PATHEF
PATHOBIOLOGY; journal of immunopathology, molecular and cellular biology. (Text in English) 1938. bi-m. 190.25 SFr.($146.25) to individuals; institutions 761 SFr.($585) (effective 1996). S. Karger AG, Allschwilerstr. 10, P.O. Box, CH-4009 Basel, Switzerland. TEL 061-3061111. FAX 061-3061234. E-mail: Karger@Karger.ch. Ed. J.M. Cruse. adv.; bibl.; charts; illus.; index. cum.index. circ. 1,050. (also avail. in microform from RPI; back issues avail.) **Indexed:** Abstr.Hyg., ASCA, Biol.Abstr., Biotech.Abstr., C.I.S. Abstr., Chem.Abstr., Curr.Adv.Cancer Res., Curr.Adv.Cell & Devel.Biol., Curr.Adv.Ecol.Sci., Curr.Cont., Dairy Sci.Abstr., Dent.Ind., Excerp.Med., Helminthol.Abstr., Ind.Med., Ind.Sci.Rev., Ind.Vet., Nutr.Abstr., Rev.Plant Path., Sci.Cit.Ind., Trop.Dis.Bull., Vet.Bull. **Document type:** academic/scholarly publication.
—BLDSC (6412.738000); CASDDS; Faxon; Genuine Article; SWETS; UnCover. **CCC.**
Formed by the merger of: Experimental Cell Biology (ISSN 0304-3568); Pathology and Immunopathology Research (ISSN 0257-2761); Experimental Cell Biology; Which was formerly: Pathologia et Microbiologia; Schweizerische Zeitschrift fuer Allgemeine Pathologie und Bakteriologie (ISSN 0031-2959); Pathology and Immunopathology Research; Which was formerly: Survey and Synthesis of Pathology Research (ISSN 0253-438X)
Refereed Serial

616.07   GW   ISSN 0172-8113
DER PATHOLOGE; pathologie und klinik. 1979. 6/yr. DM.380($276) (effective 1996). (Deutsche Gesellschaft fuer Pathologie) Springer-Verlag, Heidelberger Platz 3, 14197 Berlin, Germany. TEL 030-8207-0. FAX 030-8214091. E-mail: orders@springer.de. (Subscr. in N. America to: Springer-Verlag New York, Inc., 44 Hartz Way, Secaucus, NJ 07096-2491. TEL 201-348-4033. FAX 201-348-4505) (Co-sponsors: Internationalen Akademie fuer Pathologie; Oesterreichische Gesellschaft fuer Pathologie) Ed. V. Becker. (also avail. in microform from UMI; reprint service avail. from ISI) **Indexed:** Curr.Adv.Cell & Devel.Biol., Curr.Adv.Ecol.Sci., Curr.Cont., Excerp.Med., Ind.Med. **Document type:** academic/scholarly publication.
—BLDSC (6412.747000); Faxon; Genuine Article; SWETS; UMI. **CCC.**

616.07   IT   ISSN 0031-2983
CODEN: PATHAB
PATHOLOGICA. (Text in English, French, Italian; summaries in English and Italian) 1908. bi-m. L.50000. E.O. Ospedali Galliera, Cappuccine 14, I-16128 Genoa, Italy. Eds. Pier Augusto Gemignani, Marco Canepa. adv.; bk.rev.; index. circ. 850. (back issues avail.) **Indexed:** Biol.Abstr., Excerp.Med., Ind.Med.
—BLDSC (6412.780000); EMDOCS; Faxon; SWETS.

616.07 574.2   FR   ISSN 0031-3009
CODEN: PTBIAN
PATHOLOGIE BIOLOGIE. 1953. 10/yr. 1230 F. to individuals (foreign 1620 F.); students 615 F. (foreign 870 F.). (Semaine des Hopitaux) Expansion Scientifique, 31 bd. de la Tour Maubourg, 75007 Paris, France. TEL 40-62-64-00. FAX 45-55-69-20. Ed. M. Boiron. adv. **Indexed:** Biol.Abstr., Chem.Abstr., Curr.Adv.Ecol.Sci., Curr.Cont., Dairy Sci.Abstr., Excerp.Med., Helminthol.Abstr., Ind.Med., Ind.Vet., Nutr.Abstr., Protozool.Abstr., Rev.Plant Path., Risk Abstr., Vet.Bull.
—CASDDS.

616.07 574.2   AT   ISSN 0031-3025
CODEN: PTLGAX
PATHOLOGY. 1969. q. Aus.$90. (Royal College of Pathologists of Australasia) Modern Medicine Australia Pty. Ltd., Ste. 33, 15 Grosvenor St., Neutral Bay, N.S.W. 2089, Australia. TEL 02-331-1431. Ed. B.A. Warren. adv.; bk.rev.; charts; illus.; index. circ. 1,800. **Indexed:** Abstr.Hyg., Biol.Abstr., Chem.Abstr., Curr.Adv.Ecol.Sci., Curr.Cont., Dairy Sci.Abstr., Excerp.Med., Helminthol.Abstr., Ind.Med., Ind.Vet., Med.& Surg.Dermat., Nutr.Abstr., Rev.Plant Path., Risk Abstr., So.Pac.Per.Ind., Trop.Dis.Bull., Vet.Bull.
—BLDSC (6412.810000); CASDDS; EMDOCS; Faxon; Genuine Article; SWETS; UMI; UnCover. **CCC.**

610   US   ISSN 1041-3480
PATHOLOGY; state of the art reviews. s-a. $70 (foreign $80). Hanley & Belfus, Inc., 210 S. 13th St., Philadelphia, PA 19107. TEL 215-546-7293. FAX 215-790-9330.
—BLDSC (6412.809000). **CCC.**
Refereed Serial

616.07 574.2   US   ISSN 0079-0184
RB1   CODEN: PATABP
PATHOLOGY ANNUAL. 1966. s-a. price varies. Appleton & Lange (Subsidiary of: Simon & Schuster Company), 25 Van Zant St., Box 5630, Norwalk, CT 06856. TEL 203-838-4400. Eds. Dr. Peter Rosen, Dr. Robert E. Fechner. bibl.; charts; illus. **Indexed:** Biol.Abstr., Curr.Adv.Ecol.Sci., Excerp.Med., Ind.Med., Ind.Sci.Rev.
—BLDSC (6412.820000); CASDDS; Faxon; SWETS; UnCover. **CCC.**
Description: Original articles written by an international contingent of scientists for practicing pathologists.
Refereed Serial

MEDICAL SCIENCES

616.07 574.2   AT   ISSN 1320-5463
CODEN: PITEES
PATHOLOGY INTERNATIONAL. (Text in English) 1950. m. Aus.$528($375) (36000 Yen) (effective 1996). (Japanese Society of Pathology, JA - Nihon Byori Gakkai) Blackwell Science Pty Ltd, P.O. Box 378, Carlton, Vic. 3053, Australia. TEL 61-3-347-0300. FAX 61-3-347-5001. Ed. Yukio Shimosato. adv.: B&W page $720, color page $1510; trim 275 x 210. bk.rev.; charts; illus. circ. 4,200. (reprint service avail. from ISI) Indexed: ASCA, Biol.Abstr., Chem.Abstr., Curr.Adv.Cell & Devel.Biol., Curr.Adv.Ecol.Sci., Curr.Adv.Genetics & Molec.Biol., Curr.Cont., Excerp.Med., Helminthol.Abstr., Ind.Med., Ind.Sci.Rev., INIS Atomind., Rev.Med.& Vet.Mycol., Sci.Cit.Ind. Document type: academic/scholarly publication.
—BLDSC (6412.823000); ADONIS; CASDDS; Faxon; Genuine Article; SWETS; UMI; UnCover. **CCC**.
Formerly: Acta Pathologica Japonica (ISSN 0001-6632)
Description: Presents original papers on human and experimental pathology.

616.07 574.2   US   ISSN 1050-9194
PATHOLOGY PATTERNS. (Supplement to: American Journal of Clinical Pathology (ISSN 0002-9173)) s-a. (American Society of Clinical Pathologists) J.B. Lippincott Co., E. Washington Sq., Philadelphia, PA 19106. TEL 800-777-2295. Ed. Dr. William T. Lockard, Jr.
Description: Provides commentaries on current developments in the field of pathology and laboratory medicine.

616.07   GW   ISSN 0344-0338
CODEN: PARPDS
PATHOLOGY, RESEARCH AND PRACTICE. (Text in English, German and French) 1886. m. DM.1362 (foreign DM.1383). (European Society of Pathology) Gustav Fischer Verlag, Wollgrasweg 49, 70599 Stuttgart, Germany. TEL 0711-458030. FAX 0711-4580334. TELEX 7111488-FIBUCH. (Subscr. to: Postfach 720143, 70577 Stuttgart, Germany; US addr.: VCH Publishers, Inc., 303 N.W. 12th Ave., Deerfield Beach, FL 33442-1788) Ed. H.E. Schaefer. adv.; bk.rev. Indexed: Biol.Abstr., Chem.Abstr., Curr.Adv.Cancer Res., Curr.Adv.Cell & Devel.Biol., Curr.Adv.Ecol.Sci., Curr.Cont., Dent.Ind., Dok.Arbeitsmed., Helminthol.Abstr., Ind.Med., Ind.Vet., Nutr.Abstr, Rev.Med.& Vet.Mycol., Vet.Bull. Document type: academic/scholarly publication.
—BLDSC (6412.827000); CASDDS; Faxon; Genuine Article; SWETS; UMI; UnCover. **CCC**.
Former titles: Pathology and Practice; Beitraege zur Pathologie (ISSN 0005-8165)

PATHOPHYSIOLOGY. see *BIOLOGY — Physiology*

610   SA   ISSN 1022-2170
PATHWAYS TO HEALTH. (Text in English) 1993. bi-m. R.28. F A S Publications, P.O. Box 31516, Braamfontein 2017, South Africa. Document type: consumer publication.

610   US   ISSN 0031-305X
R11
PATIENT CARE. 1967. 20/yr. $82 (foreign $118). Medical Economics Publishing Co., Inc., Five Paragon Dr., Montvale, NJ 07645. TEL 201-358-7200. FAX 201-573-4625. Ed. Jeff Forster. adv.; charts; illus.; cum.index. circ. 117,707. (also avail. in microform from RPI,UMI; reprint service avail. from RPI) Indexed: Bus.Ind., C.I.N.L., FAMLI, Hlth.Ind., Tr.& Indus.Ind. Document type: trade publication.
●Also available online. Vendor(s): University Microfilms International.
—BLDSC (6412.861200); Faxon; Genuine Article; SWETS; UMI; UnCover. **CCC**.
Description: Focuses on the diagnosis and treatment of problems encountered by the office-based, primary care physician.

610   SZ
PATIENT CARE. 10/yr. Villa Unterhasli, CH-6005 Luzern, Switzerland. TEL 041-441165. FAX 041-441218. circ. 3,000.

610   CN   ISSN 0845-065X
PATIENT CARE. 1990. 9/yr. Can.$48 (foreign Can.$63). Thomson Healthcare Communications, 1120 Birchmount Rd., Ste.200, Scarborough, ON M1K 5G4, Canada. TEL 416-750-8900. FAX 416-751-8126. Ed. Vil Meere. adv.: B&W & color; B&W page Can.$1550; trim 8 1/8 x 10 3/4. circ. 25,546.

610.6   US   ISSN 1069-6520
PATIENT OUTCOMES; in managed care. 1993. 10/yr. $75 to individuals; institutions $125 (effective 1995). Williams & Wilkins, 428 E. Preston St., Baltimore, MD 21202. TEL 410-528-4000; 800-638-6423. FAX 410-528-4312. TELEX 87669. Ed. Ann Pongracz. adv. contact: Roland Reve. abstr.; circ. 55,000 (controlled). (back issues avail.) Indexed: Excerp.Med. (1995-). Document type: academic/scholarly publication.
—BLDSC (6412.867300).
Formerly: Patient Outcomes in Managed Care Settings.
Description: Provides clinically oriented guidelines for screening, diagnosing, and managing diseases encountered in primary-care settings. Presents original, abstracted and reprinted research on patient outcomes, including psychosocial outcome measures.

610   UK
PATIENT VOICE. q. £18. Patients Association, 8 Guilford St., London WC1N 1DT, England. TEL 0171-242-3460. FAX 0171-242-3461. Ed. Mike Hyde. adv. contact: Simon Merricks. bk.rev. circ. 1,200. Document type: newsletter.

610   II   ISSN 0031-3084
CODEN: PAJMAA
PATNA JOURNAL OF MEDICINE. (Text in English) 1925. m. Rs.215. Indian Medical Association, Bihar State Branch, Medical Association Bldg., Patna 800004, India. TEL 655542. (Co-sponsor: Patna Medical Association) Ed. Dr. I.B. Sinha. adv.; bk.rev.; charts; illus.; stat.; index. circ. 8,500. (also avail. in microform; reprint service avail. from IRC) Indexed: Biol.Abstr. Document type: academic/scholarly publication.
Description: Aims to promote and advance medical and allied sciences, and the improvement of public health and medical education in Bihar and India.

616.07 574.2   SP   ISSN 0031-3106
PATOLOGIA. (Text in Spanish; summaries in English) 1968. q. 600 ptas.($2.0) Sociedad Espanola de Anatomia Patologica, Dept. de Anatomia Patologica, Fac. de Medicina, Universidad de Malaga, 29071 Malaga, Spain. TEL 52-39-47-00. Dir. A. Anaya. adv.; bk.rev.; bibl.; charts; illus.; stat.; index. circ. 6,000. (also avail. in microfilm from UMI; reprint service avail. from UMI) Indexed: Chem.Abstr., Helminthol.Abstr., Ind.Med.Esp., Nutr.Abstr.

PATOLOGIA. see *BIOLOGY*

616.07 574.2   RU   ISSN 0031-2991
RB1   CODEN: PAFEAY
PATOLOGICHESKAYA FIZIOLOGIYA I EKSPERIMENTAL'NAYA TERAPIYA/PATHOLOGICAL PHYSIOLOGY AND EXPERIMENTAL THERAPY. (Text in Russian; summaries in English) 1957. q. $96 (effective 1996). (Rossiiskaya Akademiya Meditsinskikh Nauk) Izdatel'stvo Meditsina, Petroverigskii pereulok 6-8, 101000 Moscow, Russia. TEL 7-095-9248785. FAX 7-095-9286003. (Dist. by: Mezhdunarodnaya Kniga, B. Yakimanka 39, 117049 Moscow, Russia. TEL 7-095-2384600. FAX 7-095-2384634; Dist. in U.S. by: Victor Kamkin Inc., 4956 Boiling Brook Pkwy., Rockville, MD 20852) (Co-sponsor: Vsesoyuznoe Nauchnoe Obshchestvo Patofiziologov) Ed. B.B. Moroz. bk.rev.; illus.; index. Indexed: Apic.Abstr.; Biol.Abstr., Biotech.Abstr., Chem.Abstr, Dent.Ind., Excerp.Med., Ind.Med., Int.Aerosp.Abstr., Nutr.Abstr.
—BLDSC (0129.200000); CASDDS; EMDOCS. **CCC**.
Description: Publishes materials on pressing problems of modern theoretical medicine - the etiology, pathogenesis of disease processes and individual nosological forms of the disease.

610   US   ISSN 0031-4595
R11   CODEN: PNMDAL
PENNSYLVANIA MEDICINE. 1897. m. $35. Pennsylvania Medical Society, Box 8820, Harrisburg, PA 17105-8820. TEL 717-558-7750. FAX 717-558-7740. Ed Elaine S. Herrmann. adv.; abstr.; bibl.; illus. circ. 20,000. (also avail. in microfilm) Indexed: Biol.Abstr., C.I.S. Abstr., Chem.Abstr., CINAHL, Curr.Cont., Excerp.Med., Helminthol.Abstr., Ind.Med., Med. Care Rev. Document type: trade publication.
—BLDSC (6421.745000); Faxon.
Formerly: Pennsylvania Medical Journal.
Description: Covers issues related to the practice of medicine, including public health topics, government regulations and policies, medical economics, and other concerns.

615.53   US   ISSN 0479-9534
PENNSYLVANIA OSTEOPATHIC MEDICAL ASSOCIATION. JOURNAL. Key Title: Journal of the Pennsylvania Osteopathic Medical Association. 1945. 5/yr. membership only. Pennsylvania Osteopathic Medical Association, 1330 Eisenhower Blvd., Harrisburg, PA 17111. TEL 717-939-9318. FAX 717-939-7255. Ed. Dr. Leonard H. Finkelstein. adv.; circ. 3,200 (controlled). Document type: academic/scholarly publication.
Description: Publishes articles on topics relating to the practice of osteopathic medicine.

PEOPLE PLANT CONNECTION. see *PUBLIC HEALTH AND SAFETY*

PEOPLE'S MEDICAL SOCIETY NEWSLETTER. see *CONSUMER EDUCATION AND PROTECTION*

618   US   ISSN 0747-3079
RD598.35.A77
PERFUSION LIFE. 1973. m. (11/yr.). $35 (foreign $60). American Society of Extra-Corporeal Technology, Inc., 11480 Sunset Hills Rd., Ste. 210E, Reston, VA 22090. TEL 703-435-8556. Ed. Ron Richards. circ. 2,400. Document type: trade publication.

PERIODICUM BIOLOGORUM. see *BIOLOGY*

610 616.6   CN   ISSN 0896-8608
PERITONEAL DIALYSIS INTERNATIONAL. 1980. q. $65 to nurses; physicians $110; institutions $160. (International Society for Peritoneal Dialysis) Multimed, Inc., 1120 Finch Ave., W., Ste. 601, Downsview, ON M3J 3H7, Canada. TEL 416-650-0610. FAX 416-650-0639. Ed. Dimitrios Oreopoulos. index. (also avail. in microform from UMI; back issues avail.) Indexed: Curr.Cont., Excerp.Med., Kidney. Document type: academic/scholarly publication.
—BLDSC (6426.459000); Faxon; Genuine Article; SWETS. **CCC**.
Formerly: Peritoneal Dialysis Bulletin.

PERMANENT HEALTH INSURANCE; the city financial review. see *INSURANCE*

PERSONAL AND MEDICAL INJURIES LAW LETTER. see *LAW*

610   US   ISSN 1061-4125
RC81.A1
PERSONAL HEALTH REPORTER. a. $95. Gale Research Inc., 835 Penobscot Bldg., Detroit, MI 48266. TEL 313-961-2242. FAX 313-961-6083. Eds. Alan Rees, Charlene Willey. Document type: trade publication.
Description: Provides excerpts of significant articles concerning physical and mental health.

MEDICAL SCIENCES 4257

610 570   US   ISSN 0031-5982
QH301   CODEN: PBMEA8
PERSPECTIVES IN BIOLOGY AND MEDICINE. 1957. q. $35 to individuals; institutions $60; students $15. University of Chicago Press, Journals Division, 5720 S. Woodlawn Ave., Chicago, IL 60637. TEL 312-753-3347. FAX 312-753-0811. TELEX 25-4603. (Subscr. to: Box 37005, Chicago, IL 60637) Ed. Richard L. Landau. adv.; bk.rev.; bibl.; index. circ. 2,900. (also avail. in microform from UMI; reprint service avail. from UMI,ISI) **Indexed:** Biol.Abstr., Biol.& Agr.Ind., Biol.Dig., Chem.Abstr., Curr.Adv.Cancer Res., Curr.Adv.Ecol.Sci., Curr.Cont., Deep Sea Res.& Oceanogr.Abstr., Dent.Abstr., Dent.Ind., Excerp.Med., Helminthol.Abstr., Ind.Med., Ind.Vet., Lang.& Lang.Behav.Abstr., Psychol.Abstr., Sci.Cit.Ind., Small Anim.Abstr., Sport Fish.Abstr., Vet.Bull., Wild.Rev., Zoo.Rec. **Document type:** academic/scholarly publication.
—BLDSC (6428.138200); CASDDS; EMDOCS; Faxon; Genuine Article; SWETS; UMI; UnCover. **CCC.**
    Refereed Serial

PERSPECTIVES IN DRUG DISCOVERY AND DESIGN. see *PHARMACY AND PHARMACOLOGY*

PERSPECTIVES IN PEDIATRIC PATHOLOGY. see *MEDICAL SCIENCES — Pediatrics*

610.09 300   NE
PERSPECTIVES ON CULTURE AND MEDICINE. (Text in English) irreg. price varies. Kluwer Academic Publishers, Postbus 17, 3300 AA Dordrecht, Netherlands. TEL 31-78-392392. FAX 31-78-392254. TELEX 29245 KAPG NL. (Dist. by: Kluwer Academic Publishers Group, P.O. Box 322, 3300 AH Dordrecht, Netherlands. TEL 31-78-392392. FAX 31-78-546474; N. America dist. addr.: Box 358, Accord Sta., Hingham, MA 02018-0358. TEL 617-871-6600. FAX 617-871-6528) **Document type:** monographic series.

610 614.8   PE   ISSN 1018-6212
PERU. POLICIA NACIONAL. REVISTA DE LA SANIDAD. Key Title: Revista de la Sanidad Policia Nacional del Peru. (Text in Spanish; abstracts in English, Spanish) 1940. s-a. $60. Ministerio del Interior, Direccion de Sanidad de las Fuerzas Policiales, Casilla 1683, Lima 100, Peru. (Subscr. to: Ave. Arequipa 4849, Miraflores Lima 18, Peru) Ed. Oscar Guillermo Quiroz Jara. adv.; bk.rev.; abstr.; bibl.; illus.; index. circ. 3,000. **Indexed:** Chem.Abstr, Excerp.Med.
    Former titles (until 1988): Peru. Fuerzas Policiales. Revista de la Sanidad (ISSN 0254-3435); Peru. Direccion de Sanidad. Revista de la Sanidad; Instituto de Investigaciones Medicas de la Fuerza Armada y Fuerzas Policiales del Peru; Revista de la Sanidad de las Fuerzas Policiales del Peru; Revista de la Sanidad de Policia (ISSN 0034-8430)

610   BL   ISSN 0048-3567
PESQUISA MEDICA. (Text in Portuguese; summaries in English) 1965. s-a. Cr.$20000($25) Fundacao Faculdade Federal de Ciencias Medicas de Porto Alegre, Centro Academico XXII de Marco, Rua Sarmento Leite, 245, 90050-170 Porto Alegre RS, Brazil. TEL 0512-24-8822. FAX 0512-26-7913. Ed. Miriam C. Oliveira. adv.; bibl.; illus.; index; circ. 1,000 (controlled). **Indexed:** Biol.Abstr., Chem.Abstr. **Document type:** academic/scholarly publication.

PETERSON'S JOB OPPORTUNITIES IN HEALTH CARE. see *OCCUPATIONS AND CAREERS*

612   GW   ISSN 0031-6768
QP1   CODEN: PFLABK
PFLUEGERS ARCHIV/EUROPEAN JOURNAL OF PHYSIOLOGY. (Text mainly in English; occasionally in French, German) 1868. 12/yr. (in 2 vols., 6 nos./vol.). DM.2998($2178) (effective 1996). Springer-Verlag, Heidelberger Platz 3, 14197 Berlin, Germany. TEL 030-8207-0. FAX 030-8214091. E-mail: orders@springer.de. (Subscr. in N. America to: Springer-Verlag New York, Inc., 44 Hartz Way, Secaucus, NJ 07096-2491. TEL 201-348-4033. FAX 201-348-4505) Ed. K. Thurau. adv.; charts; illus. (also avail. in microform from UMI,BHP,PMC; back issues avail.; reprint service avail. from ISI) **Indexed:** Biol.Abstr., C.I.S. Abstr., Chem.Abstr., Curr.Adv.Ecol.Sci., Curr.Cont., Dairy Sci.Abstr., Excerp.Med., Ind.Med., Ind.Vet., Nutr.Abstr., Phys.Ber., Sport Fish.Abstr., Vet.Bull., Wild.Rev., Zoo.Rec. **Document type:** academic/scholarly publication.
—BLDSC (6440.999000); ADONIS; CASDDS; EMDOCS; Faxon; Genuine Article; SWETS; UMI; UnCover. **CCC.**
    Formerly: Pfluegers Archiv fuer die Gesamte Physiologie des Menschen und der Tiere.
    Description: Covers original research on the most current developments in areas of specialization, in interdisciplinary work, and in the physiological sciences as a whole.

PHARMACEUTICAL MEDICINE (LONDON). see *PHARMACY AND PHARMACOLOGY*

610 615   UK   ISSN 0142-1581
PHARMACEUTICAL MEDICINE (WORTHING); symposium proceedings. 1979. irreg. Cambridge Medical Publications Ltd., Wicker House, High St., Worthing, W. Sussex BN11 1DJ, England. TEL 01903-205884. FAX 01903-234862. TELEX 878372 PPSLTD G. circ. (controlled). **Indexed:** Curr.Adv.Ecol.Sci. **Document type:** proceedings.

610   UK   ISSN 0308-051X
    CODEN: PHARDW
PHARMATHERAPEUTICA. (Text and summaries in various languages) 1976. irreg. $60. Clayton-Wray Publications Ltd., 1A High St., Alton, Hants. GU34 1BA, England. Ed. Nigel Clayton. circ. 5,500. **Indexed:** Abstr.Hyg., Biol.Abstr, Biotech.Abstr., Chem.Abstr., Curr.Adv.Ecol.Sci., Curr.Cont., Dent.Ind., Excerp.Med., Helminthol.Abstr., Ind.Med., Nutr.Abstr.
—CASDDS.

610   US   ISSN 0031-7179
LJ105.A6
PHAROS (MENLO PARK). 1938. q. free to members. Alpha Omega Alpha Honor Medical Society, 525 Middlefield Rd., Ste. 130, Menlo Park, CA 94025. TEL 415-329-0291. FAX 415-329-1618. Ed. Dr. Robert J. Glaser. bk.rev.; bibl.; charts. circ. 70,000. **Indexed:** Ind.Med., RILA. **Document type:** academic/scholarly publication.
—BLDSC (6449.120000); UnCover.
    Refereed Serial

610   US   ISSN 0031-7306
    CODEN: PHMEBH
PHILADELPHIA MEDICINE. 1906. m. $15. Philadelphia County Medical Society, 2100 Spring Garden St., Philadelphia, PA 19130. TEL 215-563-5343. FAX 215-563-3627. Ed. Dr. William Weiss. adv. contact: Anne Hlwyiak. circ. 4,300 (controlled). **Document type:** academic/scholarly publication.

610   PH   ISSN 0031-7748
    CODEN: JPMEA6
PHILIPPINE MEDICAL ASSOCIATION. JOURNAL. 1928. q. $20. P M A Press, P M A House, North Ave., Diliman, Quezon City, Philippines. Ed. Conrado Dayrit. adv.; bk.rev.; charts; illus.; stat.; index. circ. 13,000. **Indexed:** Biol.Abstr., C.I.S. Abstr., Chem.Abstr., Diar.Dis.Res., INIS Atomind., Trop.Dis.Bull.
—CASDDS.

PHILOSOPHY AND MEDICINE. see *PHILOSOPHY*

616.20   GW   ISSN 0939-978X
    CODEN: PHLBE
PHLEBOLOGIE. 1972. 6/yr. DM.179($144) to individuals; institutions DM.220($171). (German and Swiss Society of Phlebology) F.K. Schattauer Verlagsgesellschaft mbH, Lenzhalde 3, 70192 Stuttgart, Germany. TEL 0711-22987-0. FAX 0711-2298750. (Co-sponsor: Berufsverband der Phlebologen e.V.) adv.; bk.rev. circ. 2,200. **Indexed:** Excerp.Med. **Document type:** academic/scholarly publication.
—BLDSC (6465.100100). **CCC.**
    Formerly (until 1991): Phlebologie und Proktologie (ISSN 0340-305X)

610 530   IT   ISSN 1120-1797
PHYSICA MEDICA. 1985. q. L.264000 (effective 1994). (Associazione Italiana di Fisica Biomedica) Giardini Editori e Stampatori, Via delle Sorgenti 23, 56010 Agnano (PI), Italy. TEL 39-50-934242. FAX 39-50-934200. TELEX 522027. E-mail: physmed@ferrara.infn.it. (Ed. addr.: Univ. di Ferrara, Dipt. di Fisica, Via Paradiso 12, 44100 Ferrara, Italy. TEL 39-532-781822. FAX 39-532-781810) Ed. Alberto Del Guerra. adv.; bk.rev. circ. 700. **Indexed:** INSPEC (1991-).
—BLDSC (6475.070000); Genuine Article.
    Incorporates: Fisica in Medicina.
    Description: Research and reviews in medical physics and biomedical engineering.

610   US   ISSN 8750-7544
R697.P45
PHYSICIAN ASSISTANT. 1976. m. $89 to institutions outside the Americas; $68 to institutions in U.S (effective 1996). Excerpta Medica, Inc., Core Publishing Division (Subsidiary of: Reed Elsevier Medical group), 105 Raider Blvd., Belle Mead, NJ 08052. TEL 908-874-8550. FAX 908-874-0707. (Subscr. to: Box 3085, Princeton, NJ 08543-3085) illus. circ. 18,000. (also avail. in microfilm from UMI; reprint service avail. from UMI) **Indexed:** CINAHL.
—BLDSC (6476.361500); UMI; UnCover. **CCC.**
    Former titles (1979-1982): Physician Assistant - Health Practitioner (ISSN 0197-713X); (1978-1979): Health Practitioner, Physician Assistant (ISSN 0192-7310); Which was formed by the merger of: Physician Assistant; (1977-1978): Health Practitioner (ISSN 0149-6549)

610   US   ISSN 1051-600X
R847.5
PHYSICIAN ASSISTANT PROGRAMS DIRECTORY. 1975. a. $25. Association of Physician Assistant Programs, 950 N. Washington St., Alexandria, VA 22314-1534. TEL 703-836-2272. FAX 703-684-1924. Ed.Bd. circ. 15,000. **Document type:** directory.
    Former titles (until 1989): Physician Assistant Programs, A National Directory; National Health Practitioner Program Profile (ISSN 0277-3376); National New Health Practitioner Program Profile (ISSN 0145-3793)
    Description: Contains summary charts detailing the PA program and postgraduate PA program entrance requirements, fees, deadlines, program length, and credentials awarded.

PHYSICIAN EXECUTIVE; journal of management. see *HOSPITALS*

610   US   ISSN 1055-1603
RA972
PHYSICIAN MANAGER. 1990. m. $231. Atlantic Information Services, Inc., 1050 17th St., N.W., Ste. 480, Washington, DC 20036. TEL 202-775-9008. FAX 202-331-9542. Ed. Michael Carbine.
—**CCC.**
    Description: News, advice and practical management tips for the physician executive.

610   US   ISSN 1068-5278
PHYSICIAN RELATIONS ADVISOR. 1992. m. $199. American Health Consultants, Inc., Six Piedmont Center, Ste. 400, Atlanta, GA 30305. TEL 404-262-7436; 800-688-2421. FAX 800-284-3291. Ed. Joy Daughtery. circ. 960. **Document type:** newsletter.

MEDICAL SCIENCES

610 US ISSN 0093-4461
RS75 CODEN: PDPSBC
PHYSICIANS' DESK REFERENCE. 1947. a. $64.95. Medical Economics Publishing Co., Inc., Five Paragon Dr., Montvale, NJ 07645. TEL 201-357-7200. FAX 201-573-1045. (Subscr. to: P D R, Box 10689, Des Moines, IA 50336) circ. 485,000 (controlled).
●Also available online.
Also available on CD-ROM.
—CASDDS. **CCC.**
 Formerly: Physicians' Desk Reference to Pharmaceutical Specialties and Biologicals (ISSN 0093-447X)
 Description: Contains prescription drug information.

610 US ISSN 1044-1395
RM671.A1
PHYSICIANS' DESK REFERENCE FOR NONPRESCRIPTION DRUGS. 1980. a. $41.95. Medical Economics Publishing Co., Inc., Five Paragon Dr., Montvale, NJ 07645. TEL 201-358-7200. FAX 201-573-1045. (Subscr. to: P D R, Box 10689, Des Moines, IA 50336) circ. 315,000 (controlled).
●Also available online.
Also available on CD-ROM.
 Description: Covers over-the-counter drugs.

610 US
PHYSICIANS FORUM BULLETIN. 1985. 3/yr. $75. Physicians Forum, 1507 53rd St., Ste. 155, Chicago, IL 60615. TEL 312-922-1968. FAX 312-633-6442. Ed. Barbara Linn. (back issues avail.) **Document type:** newsletter.

610 615 US
PHYSICIANS' GENRX; * the official drug reference of FDA prescribing information and therapeutic equivalents. 1991. a. $77. Data Pharmaceutica, Inc., 1111 E. Putnam Ave., Ste. 303, Riverside, CT 06878-1335. TEL 212-751-8033; 800-626-3516. FAX 212-751-8033. (Subscr. to: Box 1336, Smithtown, NY 11787) Ed. Jonathan A. Epner. circ. 20,000. **Document type:** directory.
●Also available on CD-ROM.
 Formerly (until 1992): Physicians' Generix (ISSN 1064-7783)
 Description: Drug reference manual, containing prescribing information and prices for all drugs, both branded and generic.

610 US ISSN 0079-192X
RC55
PHYSICIAN'S HANDBOOK. 1941. irreg., 21st ed., 1985. Appleton & Lange (Subsidiary of: Simon & Schuster Company), 25 Van Zant St., Box 5630, Norwalk, CT 06856. TEL 203-838-4400.
 Description: Essential medical facts include diagnostic tests, patient examination, laboratory tests, emergency medical examination, drugs and hormones.

PHYSICIANS LIFESTYLE MAGAZINE. see *GENERAL INTEREST PERIODICALS — United States*

610 US
PHYSICIAN'S MANAGED CARE REPORT. 1993. m. $249. American Health Consultants, Inc., Six Piedmont Center, Ste. 400, Atlanta, GA 30305. TEL 404-262-7436; 800-688-2421. FAX 800-284-3291. Ed. Allyson Harris. **Document type:** newsletter.

610 US ISSN 0031-9066
R728
PHYSICIAN'S MANAGEMENT; the doctor's business journal. 1961. m. $50. Advanstar Communications, Inc., 7500 Old Oak Blvd., Cleveland, OH 44130. TEL 216-826-2839. FAX 216-891-2726. (Subscr. to: 131 W. First St., Duluth, MN 55802. TEL 800-346-0085) Ed. Bob Feigenbaum. adv.; illus.; stat.; index. circ. 120,000. (also avail. in microform from UMI) **Indexed:** Account.Ind. (1987-). **Document type:** trade publication.
—Faxon; UMI. **CCC.**
 Description: Covers management techniques and economic factors affecting the doctor's practice.

610 658 CN ISSN 0705-6311
PHYSICIAN'S MANAGEMENT MANUALS. 1976. m. Can.$81. Maclean-Hunter Ltd., Business Publication Division, Maclean-Hunter Bldg., 777 Bay St., Toronto, ON M5W 1A7, Canada. TEL 416-596-5724. Ed. Will Koteff. adv. circ. 41,500. **Indexed:** Can.B.P.I.
—**CCC.**
 Description: Information for Canadian doctors on practice management and investment.

610 US ISSN 1042-2625
PHYSICIANS MARKETING & MANAGEMENT. m. $179. American Health Consultants, Inc., Six Piedmont Center, Ste. 400, Atlanta, GA 30305. TEL 404-262-7436; 800-688-2421. FAX 800-284-3291. Ed. Joy Daughtery. charts; illus.; tr.lit.; index. circ. 1,230. (back issues avail.) **Document type:** newsletter.
 Incorporates (1986-1992): Practice Personnel Bulletin (ISSN 0888-9066); **Formerly:** Physician's Marketing.
 Description: Covers all aspects of private practice management, including personnel, capital and risk management, and how-to marketing methods.

610 US ISSN 1079-6312
PHYSICIAN'S NEWS DIGEST (DELAWARE VALLEY EDITION); a local forum for physicians to receive information and exchange views. 1987. m. $35. Physician's News Digest, Inc., 230 Windsor Ave., Narbeth, PA 19072. TEL 610-668-1040. FAX 610-668-9177. E-mail: 71740,2504@compuserve.com. Ed. Jeffrey Barg; Pub. Jeffrey Barg. adv. circ. 13,000. (tabloid format)
 Description: Provides news and information on issues of interest to physicians.

610 US
PHYSICIAN'S PATIENT NEWSLETTER. 1983. q. $495 per quarter for 1000 copies. Doctor's Press, Box 10488, Lancaster, PA 17605-0488. TEL 717-393-1000. Ed. Kim Conlin; Pub. Cincy A. Young. adv. contact: Rem Jackson. index. **Document type:** newsletter.
 Description: For family practice physicians and general practitioners to use to market their practice by providing health information.

610 US ISSN 1050-8791
PHYSICIAN'S PAYMENT UPDATE. 1989. m. $239. American Health Consultants, Inc., Six Piedmont Center, Ste. 400, Atlanta, GA 30305. TEL 404-262-7436; 800-688-2421. FAX 800-284-3291. Ed. Reba Griffith. circ. 2,220. **Document type:** newsletter.

PHYSICIANS' TRAVEL & MEETING GUIDE. see *TRAVEL AND TOURISM*

610 US ISSN 1047-3793
PHYSICIAN'S WEEKLY. 48/yr. Whittle Communications L.P., 333 Main Ave., Knoxville, TN 37902. TEL 615-595-5300. Ed. Mark Blume.
 Description: Offers highlights and analyses of medical news about a wide range of specialties.

574.191 610 UK ISSN 0031-9155
QH505 CODEN: PHMBA7
PHYSICS IN MEDICINE AND BIOLOGY. (Text in English; abstracts in English, French, German) 1956. m. £575($1080) (effective 1996). (Institute of Physics) I O P Publishing Ltd., Techno House, Redcliffe Way, Bristol, Avon BS1 6NX, England. TEL 0117-929-7481. FAX 0117-929-4318. TELEX 449149 INSTP G. (U.S. subscr. to: American Institute of Physics, Member and Subscriber Services, 500 Sunnyside Blvd., Woodbury, NY 11797-2900. TEL 516-349-7800) (Co-sponsors: Hospital Physicists Association, U.K.; International Organization for Medical Physics; European Federation of Organizations for Medical Physics) Ed. B.L. Diffey. adv.; bk.rev.; bibl.; charts; illus.; index. circ. 769. (also avail. in microfilm from AIP; microfiche from AIP; back issues avail.; reprint service avail. from IRC) **Indexed:** Biol.Abstr., Chem.Abstr., Curr.Adv.Ecol.Sci., Curr.Cont., Dairy Sci.Abstr., Dok.Arbeitsmed., Excerp.Med., Ind.Med., INSPEC, Nutr.Abstr. **Document type:** academic/scholarly publication.
—BLDSC (6478.800000); CASDDS; Ei; EMDOCS; Faxon; Genuine Article; SWETS; UnCover. **CCC.**
 Description: Covers the use of physical agents such as ionizing and non-ionizing radiation, electromagnetic fields and ultrasound in diagnosis, therapy and radiobiology; corresponding physical methods of dosimetry; associated hazards and protection requirements.

615.8 GW ISSN 0940-6689
CODEN: PMRKEU
PHYSIKALISCHE MEDIZIN REHABILITATIONSMEDIZIN KURORTMEDIZIN. (Text in German; summaries in English, German and Russian) 1949. 6/yr. DM.132. Georg Thieme Verlag, Ruedigerstr. 14, 70469 Stuttgart, Germany. TEL 0711-8931-0. FAX 0711-8931298. (Subscr. to: Postfach 104853, 70042 Stuttgart, Germany) Eds. R. Callies, E. Senn. adv.; bk.rev.; abstr.; charts; illus. circ. 2,750. **Indexed:** Biol.Abstr., Chem.Abstr., Excerp.Med., Ind.Med. **Document type:** academic/scholarly publication.
—BLDSC (6482.280000); Genuine Article.
 Former titles (until 1991): Zeitschrift fuer Physiotherapie (ISSN 0003-9357); Archiv fuer Physikalische Therapie, Balneologie und Klimatologie.

615.8 CN ISSN 0706-4284
PHYSIO-QUEBEC. 1975. q. Can.$27($38.95) Corporation Professionnelle des Physiotherapeutes du Quebec, 1100 Beaumont, No. 530, Mount-Royal, PQ H3P 3E5, Canada. FAX 514-737-6431. Ed. Johanne Sabourin. adv.; bk.rev. circ. 3,250.

610 530 UK ISSN 0967-3334
CODEN: PMEAE3
PHYSIOLOGICAL MEASUREMENT. 1980. q. £163($295) (effective 1996). (Institute of Physical Sciences in Medicine) I O P Publishing Ltd., Techno House, Redcliffe Way, Bristol, Avon BS1 6NX, England. TEL 0117-929-7481. FAX 0117-929-4318. (U.S. subscr. to: American Institute of Physics, Member and Subscriber Services, 500 Sunnyside Blvd., Woodbury, NY 11797-2900. TEL 516-349-7800) (Co-sponsors: Hospital Physicists' Association; European Federation of Organizations for Medical Physics; German Society for Medical Physics) Ed. D.H. Evans. adv.; bk.rev.; bibl.; illus.; charts; index. circ. 214. (also avail. in microfiche; microfilm from AIP; back issues avail.; reprint service avail.) **Indexed:** Biol.Abstr., Curr.Adv.Ecol.Sci., Curr.Cont., Dent.Ind., Excerp.Med., Ind.Med., Ind.Sci.Rev., INSPEC, Sci.Cit.Ind.
—BLDSC (6484.760000); Ei; Faxon; Genuine Article; SWETS; UnCover. **CCC.**
 Formerly: Clinical Physics and Physiological Measurement (ISSN 0143-0815)
 Description: Covers the applications of physics and physical measurement to clinical practice and investigation.

PHYSIOLOGICAL RESEARCH. see *BIOLOGY — Physiology*

PHYSIOLOGICAL REVIEWS. see *BIOLOGY — Physiology*

PHYSIOLOGIST. see *BIOLOGY — Physiology*

612 574.1   CN   ISSN 0822-9058
PHYSIOLOGY CANADA. (Text in English and French) 1969. 3/yr. Can.$11.50 (foreign $16). Canadian Physiological Society, Department of Physiology, University of Western Ontario, London, ON N6A 5C1, Canada. TEL 519-661-3480. FAX 519-661-3827. Ed. D.L. Jones. adv.; bk.rev. circ. 700. **Indexed:** Biol.Abstr.

610   GW   ISSN 0944-7113
RM666.H33   CODEN: PYTOEY
▼**PHYTOMEDICINE.** 1994. irreg. DM.382 (foreign DM.390). Gustav Fischer Verlag, Wollgrasweg 49, 70599 Stuttgart, Germany. TEL 0711-458030. FAX 0711-4580334. TELEX 7111488-FIBUCH. (N. American subscr. to: VCH Publishers Inc., 303 N.W. 12th Ave., Deerfield Beach, FL 33442-1788) Eds. N.R. Farnsworth, H. Wagner. **Document type:** academic/scholarly publication.
—BLDSC (6491.500000); CASDDS.
Description: Publishes results of research on phytotherapy, phytopharmacology and phytotoxicology obtained with plant extracts as well as isolated compunds from these extracts.

PHYTOTHERAPY RESEARCH; an international journal devoted to medical and scientific research on plants and plant products. see *BIOLOGY — Botany*

610   IT
PIEMONTE MEDICO. 1953. m. free. Federazione Regionale Ordini dei Medici Chirurghi e degli Odontoiatri, Via Caboto 35, 10129 Turin, Italy. Ed. Luigi Triberti. adv. circ. 20,150.
Formerly: Ordine dei Medici. Bollettino (ISSN 0471-7708)

PILLS-A-GO-GO; journal of pills. see *PHARMACY AND PHARMACOLOGY*

PITTSBURGH SERIES IN PHILOSOPHY & HISTORY OF SCIENCE. see *PHILOSOPHY*

610   LE   ISSN 0032-0404
PJICHK.* (Text in Armenian) 1956. m. £L12.($5.) Atlas Publishing Co., Spears St., Beirut, Lebanon. Eds. Dr. V. Sahakian, Dr. A. Kazandian.

610   BE   ISSN 0774-7950
PLACE DE LA SANTE. 1986. m. 29, rue du Gouvernement Provisioire, 1000 Brussels, Belgium. Dir. Christine Peers.

610.69   CN
PLACE OF GRADUATION; a status report on the place of graduation for selected health personnel in the province of British Columbia. 1975. biennial. free. University of British Columbia, Centre for Health Services and Policy Research, No. 429 - 2194 Health Sciences Mall, Vancouver, BC V6T 1Z3, Canada. TEL 604-822-4810. FAX 604-822-5690. circ. 200 (controlled). **Document type:** bulletin.
Formerly: Place of Graduation for Selected Health Occupations.
Description: Provides an analysis by province or country of graduation for each of the groups represented.

610   FR   ISSN 1165-0788
PODOLOGUE. 1971. bi-m. 1000 F. to non-members; students 200 F. (Federation Nationale des Podologues) Mallet Conseil, 163 rue St. Honore, 75001 Paris, France. Ed. L. Olie. adv.; B&W page 3640 F., color page 6540 F.; trim 210 x 270.
Former titles (until 1992): Revue de Podologie (ISSN 0300-1296); (until 1971): Revue de Podologue (ISSN 0246-1722); Which was formed by merger of (1970-1971): Revue du Practicien en Podologie (ISSN 0300-130X); (1952-1971): Revue de Podologie (ISSN 0484-8594)

610   IT   ISSN 0048-4717
POLICLINICO. SEZIONE MEDICA. 1893. q. $170 (includes Policlinico. Sezione Pratica). Edizioni Luigi Pozzi s.r.l., Via Panama 68, 00198 Rome, Italy. TEL 39-6-8553548. FAX 39-6-8554105. Ed.Bd. adv.; illus. circ. 1,900. **Indexed:** Chem.Abstr., Excerp.Med., Ind.Med.
—BLDSC (6543.302000); EMDOCS.

610   IT   ISSN 0032-2644
POLICLINICO. SEZIONE PRATICA. (Text in Italian; summaries in English and Italian) 1893. m. $170 (includes Policlinico. Sezione Medica). Edizioni Luigi Pozzi s.r.l., Via Panama 68, 00198 Rome, Italy. TEL 39-6-8553548. FAX 39-6-8554105. adv.; bk.rev.; charts; illus.; stat.; index. circ. 11,500. **Indexed:** Chem.Abstr., Dent.Ind., Excerp.Med.
Description: Covers internal medicine.

POLIMERY W MEDYCYNIE. see *CHEMISTRY — Organic Chemistry*

610   US   ISSN 1066-5331
POLIO NETWORK NEWS. q. $12 to individuals (foreign $16); health professionals and institutions $20 (foreign $24). (International Polio Network) Gazette International Networking Institute, 5100 Oakland Ave., Ste. 206, St. Louis, MO 63110-1406. TEL 314-534-0475. Ed. Joan Headley. circ. 6,000. **Document type:** newsletter.
Description: Serves as a communications network for polio survivors, support groups and health professionals. Highlights the late effects of polio (post-polio syndrome) - cause, treatment, and current research.

610 327   UK   ISSN 0730-9384
JA80
POLITICS AND THE LIFE SCIENCES. 1982. s-a. £47($82) to institutions (effective 1996). (Association for Politics and the Life Sciences) Beech Tree Publishing, 10 Watford Close, Guildford, Surrey GU1 2EP, England. TEL 01483-67497. FAX 01483-67497. (Subscr. to: Turpin Distribution Services Ltd., Blackhorse Rd., Letchworth, Herts. SG6 1HN, England. TEL 01462-672555. FAX 01462-480947) (Co-sponsor: Northern Illinois University) Ed. Garry Johnson. adv.; bk.rev.; bibl.; charts; illus.; circ. 750 (paid). (back issues avail.) **Indexed:** A.B.C.Pol.Sci., Biol.Abstr., Biol.Dig., CLOSS, Curr.Cont., Int.Polit.Sci.Abstr., Soc.Sci.Ind. (1994-), SSCI. **Document type:** academic/scholarly publication.
—BLDSC (6543.941850); Faxon; Genuine Article; UnCover. **CCC.**
Description: Provides a forum for scholars interested in both the methods and the findings of research in the life sciences that relates to the study of politics and public policy.
Refereed Serial

610   PL   ISSN 0032-3756
                         CODEN: POLEAQ
POLSKI TYGODNIK LEKARSKI. (Text in Polish; summaries in English) 1946. w. $320 (effective 1993). Fundacja Lekarzy Polskich - Pro Medica, Ul. Miodowa 1, 00-080 Warsaw, Poland. TEL 48-22-261517. FAX 48-22-260982. Ed. Jan Taton. adv.; bk.rev.; abstr.; charts; illus.; s-a. index. circ. 9,200. **Indexed:** Biol.Abstr., C.I.S. Abstr., Chem.Abstr., Dent.Ind., Dok.Arbeitsmed., Excerp.Med. (until 1993), Ind.Med., Nutr.Abstr., Protozool.Abstr., Rev.Plant Path. **Document type:** academic/scholarly publication.
—BLDSC (6545.950000); CASDDS.
Description: Presents papers, editorials and case reports on radiodiagnosis, nuclear medicine, medical disciplines, social hygiene, deontology and ethics.

610   IT   ISSN 0392-9264
IL POLSO; medicina attualita. 1969. 18/yr. L.38000($58) (effective 1994). Masson S.p.A., Divisione Periodici, Via Statuto 4, 20121 Milan, Italy. TEL 02-63671. FAX 02-6570984. Ed. Gabriele Bianchi Porro. adv.: B&W page L.8450000, color page L.12750000; trim 210 x 285. circ. 70,000. **Document type:** academic/scholarly publication.
—BLDSC (6547.300000).

610   BL   ISSN 0103-2690
PONTIFICIA UNIVERSIDADE CATOLICA DO RIO GRANDE DO SUL. REVISTA DE MEDICINA. 1988. 4/yr. Cr.$15($19) Editora da P U C R S, Caixa Postal 12001, 90620 Porto Alegre RS, Brazil. Ed. Leonel Lerner. circ. 3,000.

610   US
POST-POLIO DIRECTORY. a. $4 to individuals (foreign $5); health professionals and institutions $8 (foreign $9). (International Polio Network) Gazette International Networking Institute, 5100 Oakland Ave., St. Louis, MO 63110-1406. TEL 314-534-0475. **Document type:** directory.
Description: Lists self-identified clinics, health professionals, and support groups knowledgeable about the late effects of polio.

MEDICAL SCIENCES 4259

610   PL   ISSN 0032-5449
                         CODEN: PHMDAD
POSTEPY HIGIENY I MEDYCYNY DOSWIADCZALNEJ. (Text in Polish; summaries in English and Russian) 1949. bi-m. $72. (Polska Akademia Nauk, Instytut Immunologii i Terapii Doswiadczalnej - Polish Academy of Science, Institute of Immunology and Experimental Therapy) Ossolineum, Publishing House of the Polish Academy of Sciences, 9 Rynek, 50-106 Wroclaw, Poland. TEL 48-71-386-25. FAX 48-71-448-103. TELEX 0712771 OSS PL. Ed. M. Mordarski. charts; illus.; index. circ. 980. (reprint service avail. from ISI) **Indexed:** Abstr.Hyg., Biol.Abstr., Chem.Abstr., Curr.Adv.Ecol.Sci., Ind.Med., Nutr.Abstr., Rev.Plant Path., Trop.Dis.Bull. **Document type:** academic/scholarly publication.
—CASDDS.
Description: Reports of experimental medical research, proceedings of scientific conferences on immunology and experimental medicine.

610 378   PL   ISSN 0860-6196
POSTEPY NAUK MEDYCZNYCH. 1988. 6/yr. Centrum Medyczne Ksztalcenia Podyplomowego - Medical Center of Postgraduate Education, Ul. Marymoncka 99, 01-813 Warsaw, Poland. TEL 48-22-346847. FAX 48-22-340470. TELEX 816826. Ed. Ryszard Brzozowski.

610   UK   ISSN 0142-7946
POSTGRADUATE DOCTOR: AFRICA; the journal of prevention, diagnosis and treatment. 1979; suspended 1992-1993. q. £20 to individuals (worldwide); institutions £30 (worldwide) (effective 1996). Barker Publications Ltd., Barker House, 539 London Rd., Isleworth, Mddx. TW7 4DA, England. TEL 44-181-847-1774. FAX 44-181-568-2766. TELEX 24667 IMPEMP G. Ed. Dr. David Harvey; Pub. Peter H. Barker. adv.; bk.rev.; charts; illus.; index; circ. 11,300 (controlled). (back issues avail.) **Indexed:** Abstr.Hyg., Nutr.Abstr., Trop.Dis.Bull. **Document type:** academic/scholarly publication.
—BLDSC (6563.851800). **CCC.**
Description: Contains specially commissioned review articles on general medicine at the postgraduate levels for physicians practicing in Africa.

610   UK   ISSN 0267-0275
POSTGRADUATE DOCTOR: CARIBBEAN; the journal of prevention, diagnosis and treatment. 1985. bi-m. £20 (outside Europe £27); institutions £30 (outside Europe £40) (effective 1996). Barker Publications Ltd., Barker House, 539 London Rd., Isleworth, Mddx. TW7 4DA, England. TEL 44-181-874-1774. FAX 44-181-568-2766. TELEX 24667 IPEMP G. Ed. Dr. David Harvey; Pub. Peter H. Barker. adv.; bk.rev.; charts; illus.; index; circ. 3,000 (controlled). (back issues avail.) **Indexed:** Nutr.Abstr. **Document type:** academic/scholarly publication.
—**CCC.**
Description: Contains specially commissioned reveiw articles of general medicine at the postgraduate level for practicing physicians throughout the English-speaking Caribbean.

610   UK   ISSN 0140-7724
POSTGRADUATE DOCTOR: MIDDLE EAST; the journal of prevention, diagnosis & treatment. 1978. m. £48 to individuals (outside Europe £64); institutions £62 (outside Europe £80) (effective 1996). Barker Publications Ltd., Barker House, 539 London Rd., Isleworth, Mddx. TW7 4DA, England. TEL 44-181-847-1774. FAX 44-181-568-2766. TELEX 24667 IMPEMP G. Ed. Dr. David Harvey; Pub. Peter H. Barker. adv.; bk.rev.; charts; illus.; circ. 19,300 (controlled). (back issues avail.) **Indexed:** Abstr.Hyg., Nutr.Abstr., Trop.Dis.Bull. **Document type:** academic/scholarly publication.
—BLDSC (6563.852000). **CCC.**
Description: Contains specially commissioned graduate-level review clinical articles aimed at practicing physicians in the Middle East.

MEDICAL SCIENCES

610   II   ISSN 0302-2404
CODEN: BPIRD8
POSTGRADUATE INSTITUTE OF MEDICAL EDUCATION AND RESEARCH, CHANDIGARH. BULLETIN. (Text in English) 1967. q. Rs.50($25) to individuals; libraries Rs.100. Postgraduate Institute of Medical Education and Research, Chandigarh, Chandigarh 160012, India. TEL 45157. TELEX 395-315 PGI IN. Ed. N.K. Gangauly. adv.; bk.rev.; bibl.; illus. circ. 550. **Indexed:** Abstr.Hyg., Biol.Abstr., Chem.Abstr., Excerp.Med, Ind.Sci.Rev., INIS Atomind., Trop.Dis.Bull. **Document type:** bulletin.
—CASDDS.
   Description: Contains articles contributed by faculty and students of the Institute. Includes editorial and research articles, case reports, and a Clinico-Pathological Conference report.

610   UK   ISSN 0032-5473
CODEN: PGMJAO
POSTGRADUATE MEDICAL JOURNAL. (Supplement avail. (ISSN 0951-4341)) 1924. m. £135($213) (Fellowship of Postgraduate Medicine) B M J Publishing Group, B.M.A. House, Tavistock Sq., London WC1H 9JR, England. TEL 0256-29242. FAX 0256-28339. Ed. C. Hind. adv.; bk.rev.; bibl.; charts; illus.; stat.; index. circ. 2,000. (also avail. in microfilm from SWZ; microfilm from UMI; back issues avail.; reprint service avail. from ISI) **Indexed:** Abstr.Health Care Manage.Stud., Abstr.Hyg., ASCA, Biol.Abstr., Biotech.Abstr., Chem.Abstr., CINAHL, Curr.Adv.Cancer Res., Curr.Adv.Ecol.Sci., Curr.Cont., Dent.Ind., Excerp.Med., Food Sci.& Tech.Abstr., Helminthol.Abstr., I.P.A., Ind.Med., Nutr.Abstr., Sci.Cit.Ind., Trop.Dis.Bull. **Document type:** academic/scholarly publication.
●Also available online.
—BLDSC (6563.860000); CASDDS; EMDOCS; Faxon; Genuine Article; SWETS; UMI; UnCover. **CCC.**
   Former titles (until 1925): Fellowship of Medicine and Post-graduate Medical Association. Bulletin (ISSN 0951-4341); (until 1919): Fellowship of Medicine. Emergency Post-graduate Scheme. Weekly Programme.
   Description: Contains current clinical research and practice, surveys and case reports.

610   US   ISSN 0032-5481
R11   CODEN: POMDAS
POSTGRADUATE MEDICINE; the journal of applied medicine for physicians providing primary care. 1947. 112/yr. $63 (Canada $63; elsewhere $130). McGraw-Hill, Inc., 1221 Ave. of the Americas, New York, NY 10020. TEL 212-512-2000. (Subscr. to: 4530 W. 77th St., Minneapolis, MN 55435) Ed. Glen C. Griffin. adv.; bk.rev.; charts; illus.; s-a. index. circ. 125,889. (also avail. in microfilm from UMI,PMC; reprint service avail. from UMI) **Indexed:** AIM, Biol.Abstr., C.I.S.Abstr., Chem.Abstr., CINAHL, Curr.Adv.Cancer Res., Curr.Adv.Ecol.Sci., Curr.Cont., Dent.Ind., Diar.Dis.Res., Excerp.Med., FAMLI, Helminthol.Abstr., Ind.Med., Int.Nurs.Ind., Med.& Surg.Dermat., Nutr.Abstr.
●Also available online. Vendor(s): Knight-Ridder, Inc. (PGM), Dow Jones News Retrieval (PGM), NewsNet (ME06).
—BLDSC (6563.900000); EMDOCS; Faxon; Genuine Article; SWETS; UMI; UnCover. **CCC.**
   Description: Presents original clinical articles stressing the diagnosis and treatment of problems encountered in general medical practice.
   Refereed Serial

610   PL   ISSN 0137-5350
CODEN: POMDDV
POZNANSKIE ROCZNIKI MEDYCZNE. 1964. a. (Akademia Medyczna im. Karola Marcinkowskiego w Poznaniu) Wydawnictwo Naukowe P W N, Ul. Miodowa 10, 00-251 Warsaw, Poland. (Co-sponsors: Poznanskie Towarzystwo Przyjaciol Nauk; Polska Akadmia Nauk, Oddzial w Poznaniu) **Document type:** academic/scholarly publication.
—BLDSC (6579.132000); CASDDS.
   Formerly (until 1977): Roczniki Akademii Medycznej w Poznaniu (ISSN 0137-5369)

613.62 616.9803   XR   ISSN 0032-6291
CODEN: PRLFAG
PRACOVNI LEKARSTVI. (Text in Czech or Slovak; summaries in English and Russian) 1948. 10/yr. $55.50. (Ceska Lekarska Spolecnost J.E Purkyne - Czech Medical Society) Nakladatelske Stredisko C L S J.E. Purkyne, Sokolska 31, 120 26 Prague 2, Czech Republic. (Dist. by: Artia, Ve Smeckach 30, 111 27 Prague 1, Czech Republic) (Co-sponsor: Ceska Spolecnost pro Pracovni Lekarstvi) Ed. Dr. A. Zeleny. adv.; bk.rev.; abstr.; index. circ. 1,200. **Indexed:** Abstr.Hyg., C.I.S. Abstr., Chem.Abstr., Ergon.Abstr., Excerp.Med., Ind.Med., Trop.Dis.Bull.
—BLDSC (6593.500000); CASDDS; EMDOCS. **CCC.**
   Description: Covers industrial medicine.

A PRACTICAL GUIDE TO PREVENTING LEGAL MALPRACTICE. see *LAW*

610   DK   ISSN 0109-2235
PRACTICUS. 1977. bi-m. free. (Dansk Selskab for Almen Medecin) Tidsskrift for Praktisk Laegegerning, Stockholmsgade 55, DK-2100 Copenhagen Oe, Denmark. TEL 35-43-36-73. FAX 35-43-36-73. illus.
   Formerly (until 1984): D S A M Orientering (ISSN 0108-0717)

610   UK   ISSN 0032-6518
THE PRACTITIONER. 1868. 12/yr. $134. Miller Freeman Professional Ltd., Miller Freeman House, 30 Calderwood St., London SE18 6QH, England. TEL 0181-855-7777. FAX 0181-854-9716. Ed. Gavin Atkin. adv. contact: Peter Higgins. bk.rev.; illus.; pat.; index. circ. 39,975. (also avail. in microform from UMI,PMC; back issues avail.; reprint service avail. from UMI) **Indexed:** Abstr.Health Care Manage.Stud., Biol.Abstr., Biotech.Abstr., Chem.Abstr., CINAHL, Curr.Adv.Cancer Res., Curr.Adv.Ecol.Sci., Dent.Ind., Dok.Arbeitsmed., Excerp.Med. (until 1993), Helminthol.Abstr., Ind.Med., Int.Nurs.Ind., Nutr.Abstr., Rev.Plant Path., Trop.Dis.Bull. **Document type:** trade publication.
—BLDSC (6598.000000); Faxon; SWETS; UnCover.

DER PRAEPARATOR. see *CONSERVATION*

610   GW
PRAEVENTION UND REHABILITATION. 1989. q. DM.96($74) Dustri-Verlag Dr. Karl Feistle, Bahnhofstr. 9, 82041 Deisenhofen, Germany. TEL 089-613861-0. FAX 089-6135412. Ed. J. Lecheler. **Indexed:** Excerp.Med. (1993-). **Document type:** academic/scholarly publication.

610   CN   ISSN 1195-8693
PRAIRIE MEDICAL JOURNAL. 1929. 4/yr. Can.$49. (University of Manitoba, Department of Continuing Medical Education) Pulsus Group Inc., 2902 S. Sheridan Way, Oakville, ON L6J 7L6, Canada. TEL 905-829-4770. FAX 905-829-4799. Ed. Ian Carr; Pub. Robert B. Kalina. adv.; bk.rev. circ. 15,000. (back issues avail.) **Document type:** trade publication.
—BLDSC (6598.550980).
   Former titles: Manitoba Medicine (ISSN 0832-6096); (until 1987): University of Manitoba. Medical Journal (ISSN 0076-4108)
   Description: A forum for medical, scientific or historical articles, particularly those of relevance to the Prairie provinces, for postgraduate educational material and for news.

610   XR   ISSN 0032-6739
CODEN: PRLEAD
PRAKTICKY LEKAR. (Text in Czech or Slovak) 1920. 2/yr. (plus q. supplements). $65.50. (Ceska Lekarska Spolecnost J.E. Purkyne - Czech Medical Society) Nakladatelske Stredisko C L S J.E. Purkyne, Sokolska 31, 120 26 Prague 2, Czech Republic. FAX 42-0-2-202788. (Dist. by: Artia, Ve Smeckach 30, 111 27 Prague 1, Czech Republic) Ed. Dr. J. Strejcek. adv.; bk.rev.; abstr.; bibl.; illus.; stat.; index, cum.index. circ. 9,000. **Indexed:** Biol.Abstr., C.I.S. Abstr., Chem.Abstr.
—BLDSC (6598.700000); CASDDS. **CCC.**

610   NE   ISSN 0169-1910
PRAKTIJKMANAGEMENT. (Supplement to: Tijdschrift voor Huisartsgeneeskunde (ISSN 0928-4672)) 1985. m. Mediselect B.V., Postbus 28091, 3828 ZH Hoogland, Netherlands. TEL 31-33-808020. FAX 31-33-805881. Pub. J. Blom. adv. **Document type:** trade publication.

610   GW
PRAXIS - DEPESCHE. 1987. bi-m. DM.39 (foreign DM.61). Gesellschaft fuer Medizinische Information, Baumkirchnerstr. 53a, 81673 Munich, Germany. TEL 089-4361066. FAX 089-43670977. Ed. H. Spude. adv. circ. 50,000. **Document type:** academic/scholarly publication.

610   GW   ISSN 0941-1046
CODEN: PMMEE
PRAXISMAGAZIN MED. m. DM.204($148) (effective 1996). Springer-Verlag, Heidelberger Platz 3, 14197 Berlin, Germany. TEL 030-8207-0. FAX 030-8214091. E-mail: orders@springer.de. (Subscr. in N. America to: Springer-Verlag New York, Inc., 44 Hartz Way, Secaucus, NJ 07096-2491. TEL 201-348-4033. FAX 201-348-4505) **Indexed:** Excerp.Med. (1993-). **Document type:** academic/scholarly publication.
—BLDSC (6603.171955); ADONIS. **CCC.**

614.8   US   ISSN 1049-023X
PREHOSPITAL AND DISASTER MEDICINE; an international journal. (Text in English) 1981. q. $48 to individuals (foreign $68); institutions $78 (foreign $98). (World Association for Disaster and Emergency Medicine) Jems Publishing Co., Inc., Box 2789, Carlsbad, CA 92018. TEL 619-431-9797. FAX 619-431-8176. (Co-sponsors: National Association of Emergency Medical Service Physicians; National Association of State Emergency Medical Services Directors) Ed. Dr. Marvin L. Birnbaum. adv.; bk.rev.; abstr.; bibl.; stat.
—BLDSC (6605.910000).
   Former titles (until 1989): Journal of Prehospital Medicine; (until 1987): World Association for Emergency and Disaster Medicine. Journal (ISSN 0882-7397)
   Description: Establishes, maintains, and promulgates the sciences associated with the delivery of emergency services to one or multiple victims of sudden illness or injury through the stimulation and dissemination of quality research in the areas of prehospital emergency medical care and disaster medicine.
   Refereed Serial

610   BO
PRENSA MEDICA. 6/yr. Casilla 891, La Paz, Bolivia. Ed. Dr. Santiago Medeiros. adv.

610   VE
PRENSA MEDICA. 1975. m. Editorial TERSEG C.A., Edif. San Jose 1o, Avda. Prinicipal Mariperez, Caracas, Venezuela. circ. 8,000.

610   AG   ISSN 0032-745X
CODEN: PMARAU
PRENSA MEDICA ARGENTINA. (Text in Spanish; summaries in English) 1914. m. (10/yr.). $120 (effective 1995). Prensa Medica Argentina s.r.l., Junin 845, 1113 Buenos Aires, Argentina. TEL 54-1-961-9793. FAX 54-1-961-9494. Ed. Dr. Pablo A. Lopez. adv.; B&W page $5000, color page $800; 200 x 280. bk.rev.; charts; illus.; index. circ. 8,000. (also avail. in microform from UMI; back issues avail.; reprint service avail. from UMI) **Indexed:** Biol.Abstr., Curr.Cont., Excerp.Med., Helminthol.Abstr., Nutr.Abstr.
—BLDSC (6607.700000); CASDDS; EMDOCS; Genuine Article; UMI.

PRESCRIRE INTERNATIONAL. see *PHARMACY AND PHARMACOLOGY*

MEDICAL SCIENCES

610   FR   ISSN 0755-4982
                                 CODEN: PRMEEM
LA PRESSE MEDICALE. (Text in English, French) 1893. w. 1194 F. (foreign 1635 F.) (effective 1996). Masson - Periodiques, Villa Laromiguiere, 75005 Paris, France. TEL 40-46-62-00. FAX 40-46-62-01. Eds. Drs. Ph. Letonturier, J.C. Patel. adv. contact: M.J. Leroy. bk.rev.; abstr.; illus. circ. 16,000. (also avail. in microform from UMI,PMC; microfiche from BHP; reprint service avail. from ISI) **Indexed:** Biol.Abstr., Biotech.Abstr., C.I.S. Abstr., Chem.Abstr., Curr.Adv.Cancer Res., Curr.Adv.Ecol.Sci., Curr.Cont., Dairy Sci.Abstr., Dent.Ind., Dok.Arbeitsmed., Excerp.Med., Helminthol.Abstr., Ind.Med., Ind.Sci.Rev., Med.& Surg.Dermat., Nutr.Abstr., Protozool.Abstr., Rev.Med.& Vet.Mycol., Rev.Plant Path., Risk Abstr. **Document type:** academic/scholarly publication.
—BLDSC (6612.500000); CASDDS; Faxon; Genuine Article; SWETS; UMI. **CCC.**
     Former titles (until 1982): Nouvelle Presse Medicale (ISSN 0301-1518); (until 1972): Presse Medicale (ISSN 0032-7867)
     Description: Publishes leading work in all the clinical specialties of medicine. Includes editorials, original articles, authoritative reviews, and correspondence.
     Refereed Serial

610   IT   ISSN 0393-0653
LA PRESSE MEDICALE: EDIZIONE ITALIANA. 1984. m. (10/yr.). L.7000. Masson S.p.A., Divisione Periodici, Via Statuto 2-4, 20121 Milan, Italy. TEL 02-6367-1. FAX 02-6367211. Ed. Claudio Ortolani. adv.; B&W page L.3800000, color page L.5500000; trim 210 x 270. circ. 15,000. **Indexed:** Dairy Sci.Abstr. **Document type:** academic/scholarly publication.

615.8   FR   ISSN 0032-7875
                                CODEN: PTCLA3
PRESSE THERMALE ET CLIMATIQUE. 1864. 4/yr. 275 F. to individuals (foreign 350 F.); students 140 F. (foreign 215 F.). (Societe Francaise d'Hydrologie) Expansion Scientifique, 31 bd. de la Tour Maubourg, 75007 Paris, France. TEL 40-62-64-00. FAX 45-55-69-20. Eds. J. Cottet, R. Flurin. adv.; bk.rev. circ. 2,000. (also avail. in microform) **Indexed:** Biol.Abstr., Chem.Abstr., Dent.Ind., Excerp.Med.
—CASDDS. **CCC.**

610   US   ISSN 0889-0242
PRESSURE (BETHESDA). 1972. bi-m. $25. Undersea and Hyperbaric Medical Society, Inc., 10531 Metropolitan Ave., Kensington, MD 20895. TEL 301-942-2980. FAX 301-942-7804. Ed. R.W. Hamilton, Jr. bk.rev.; abstr.; bibl. circ. 3,000. **Document type:** academic/scholarly publication.
     Formerly: Hyperbaric Medicine Newsletter (ISSN 0018-831X)

610   SP
PREVENCION. 3/yr. Commission for Congenital Metabolic Diseases, Avda. del Jordan, Edif. B-2, 08035 Barcelona, Spain. TEL 3-212-43-97. Ed. Maruja Fernandez. circ. 5,202.

610   US
PREVENTION'S MEDICAL CARE YEARBOOK. a. $19.95. Rodale Press, Inc., Prevention Magazine, 33 E. Minor St., Emmaus, PA 18098. TEL 610-967-5171. FAX 610-967-3044. Ed. Mark Bricklin.
     Formerly: Medical Care Yearbook.

614 610   US   ISSN 0091-7435
RA421   CODEN: PVTMA3
PREVENTIVE MEDICINE; an international journal devoted to practice and theory. 1972. bi-m. $293 (foreign $348) (effective 1996). (American Society of Preventive Oncology) Academic Press, Inc., Journal Division, 525 B St., Ste. 1900, San Diego, CA 92101-4495. TEL 619-230-1840. FAX 619-699-6800. (Subscr. to: Box 620000, Orlando, FL 32891-8340. TEL 800-543-9534) Ed. Ernst L. Wynder. index. (back issues avail.) **Indexed:** Abstr.Hyg., Biol.Abstr., C.I.S. Abstr., Chem.Abstr., Curr.Adv.Cancer Res., Curr.Adv.Ecol.Sci., Curr.Cont., Dent.Ind., Excerp.Med., Helminthol.Abstr., Ind.Med., Nutr.Abstr., Psychol.Abstr. (1993-), Trop.Dis.Bull. **Document type:** academic/scholarly publication.
—BLDSC (6612.790000); CASDDS; EMDOCS; Faxon; Genuine Article; SWETS; UnCover. **CCC.**
     Refereed Serial

PREVISIONS GLISSANTES DETAILLEES EN PERSPECTIVES SECTORIELLES (VOL.38): PHARMACIE - SANTE. see *BUSINESS AND ECONOMICS — Economic Situation And Conditions*

610   US   ISSN 0095-4543
R11
PRIMARY CARE; clinics in office practice. 1974. q. $100 (foreign $117) (effective 1996). W.B. Saunders Co. (Subsidiary of: Harcourt Brace & Company), Curtis Center, 3rd Fl., Independence Sq. W., Philadelphia, PA 19106-3399. TEL 215-238-7800. FAX 215-238-6445. (Subscr. to: Periodicals Fulfillment, W.B. Saunders Co., 6277 Sea Harbor Dr., 4th Fl., Orlando, FL 32891-4800. TEL 800-654-2452. FAX 800-874-6418) Ed. Melissa Mitchell. (also avail. in microform from MIM,UMI; reprint service avail. from ISI,UMI) **Indexed:** CINAHL, Curr.Cont., Dent.Ind., Excerp.Med., FAMLI, Ind.Med. **Document type:** academic/scholarly publication.
—BLDSC (6612.908000); EMDOCS; Faxon; Genuine Article; SWETS; UMI; UnCover. **CCC.**
     Description: Contains articles to help primary-care physicians in their practices.

610   JA   ISSN 0914-8426
PRIMARY CARE. (Text in Japanese; summaries in English and Japanese) 1977. q. 6000 Yen($48) (effective 1995). (Japanese Medical Society of Primary Care) Kyowakikakutsusin Ltd., 2-20, Shimbashiekimae Bldg., Shinbashi, Minatoku, Tokyo 105, Japan. FAX 03-3575-4748. Ed. Dr. Katsumi Iijima. adv.; bk.rev.; index. circ. 2,500. (back issues avail.)
     Formerly (until vol.11, no.1): Japanese Journal of Primary Care (ISSN 0387-3501)

362.068   UK   ISSN 0969-4978
PRIMARY CARE MANAGEMENT. 1991. m. £58 to individuals (outside Europe £60 ($91)); institutions £108 (outside Europe £110 ($172)) (effective 1995). Churchill Livingstone Journals (Subsidiary of: Pearson Professional), Robert Stevenson House, 1-3 Baxter's Pl., Leith Walk, Edinburgh EH1 3AF, Scotland. TEL 0131-556-2424. FAX 0131-459-1177. (Subscr. to: Pearson Professional Ltd., P.O. Box 77, Fourth Ave., Harlow, Essex CM19 5AA, England. TEL 01279-623760; U.S. subscr. to: Churchill Livingstone, 650 Ave. of the Americas, New York, NY 10011. TEL 212-206-5000) Eds. G. Meads. adv. contact: David Dunnachie. circ. 2,850. **Document type:** newsletter.
—BLDSC (6612.908300). **CCC.**
     Formerly (until Mar. 1993): Primary Health Care Management (ISSN 0960-250X)
     Description: Explores a range of policy and practical issues affecting primary care from various organizational and professional perspectives.

610   US   ISSN 1079-9273
PRIMARY CARE MEDICINE BULLETIN. 1988. s-m. $50 to individuals (foreign $128); institutions $101 (foreign $128) (effective 1996); newsstand price: $7. Lippincott - Raven Publishers, 227 E. Washington Sq., Philadelphia, PA 19106. TEL 215-238-4200. (Subscr. to: 12107 Insurance Way, Hagerstown, MD 21740)
—UMI. **CCC.**
     Formerly: Ambulatory Medicine Letter (ISSN 0897-554X)
     Description: Devoted exclusively to summarizing and interpreting the latest advances in outpatient medicine.

PRIMARY CARE MEDICINE DRUG ALERTS. see *PHARMACY AND PHARMACOLOGY*

362.4 616   US   ISSN 1081-0722
▼**PRIMARY CARE WEEKLY.** 1994. w. $469 to individuals (Canada $489; elsewhere $509); institutions $499 (Canada $519; elsewhere $539) (effective Jul. 1995). Manisses Communications Group, Inc., Box 9758, Providence, RI 02940-6370. TEL 401-831-6020. FAX 401-861-6370. Eds. Gary A. Enos, Alexandra Zaleski.
     Description: Contains news, analysis and interpretation for decision makers in one of the fastest growing sectors of health care.

610   US   ISSN 0032-891X
R11
PRIVATE PRACTICE.* 1969. m. $18. Congress of County Medical Societies (CCMS) Publishing Co., Box 1485, Shawnee, OK 74802-1485. Ed. Karen Murphy. adv.; bk.rev.; index. circ. 190,000. (also avail. in microform from UMI; reprint service avail. from UMI)
—UMI.

610   AU   ISSN 0944-6125
▼**PRO MED;** das Praxismagazin fuer Aerztliche Fortbildung. 1995. m. DM.140($101) (effective 1996). Springer-Verlag, Sachsenplatz 4-6, Postfach 89, A-1201 Vienna, Austria. TEL 0222-3302415. FAX 0222-3302426. **Document type:** academic/scholarly publication.

368 610   US   ISSN 1078-456X
▼**PROACTIVE RISK MANAGEMENT.** 1994. m. $160 (foreign $180) (effective 1995). Quest Publishing Co., Inc., A Division of Raven Press Ltd. (Subsidiary of: Wolters Kluwer N.V.), 1351 Titan Way, Brea, CA 92621. TEL 714-738-6400. FAX 714-525-6258. (Subscr. to: Raven Press, 1185 Ave. of the Americas, New York, NY 10036. TEL 212-930-9500. FAX 212-869-3495) Pub. Mary Waltham. circ. 149 (paid). **Document type:** newsletter.
—**CCC.**
     Description: Dedicated to proactive healthcare risk management by improving safety, training and quality programs and policies.

615.5   GW
PROBATUM EST; Informationen fuer den Arzt. 1950. 10/yr. Wissenschaft und Werbung, Freiburger Str. 23, 90443 Nuernberg, Germany. Ed. Rolf Nipken. adv.; pat.; index; circ. controlled.
     Former titles: Probatum Est Therapeutica Nova; Therapeutica Nova (ISSN 0049-3716)

610.69   CN
PRODUCTION; a status report on the production of health personnel in the province of British Columbia. 1975. biennial. free. University of British Columbia, Centre for Health Services and Policy Research, No. 429 - 2194 Health Sciences Mall, Vancouver, BC V6T 1Z3, Canada. TEL 604-822-4810. FAX 604-822-5690. circ. 300 (controlled). **Document type:** bulletin.
     Description: Offers a status report on the current and projected number of entrants into and graduates from health education programs in B.C.

610   SP   ISSN 0212-8837
PROFESION MEDICA. s-m. Saned, S.A., Paseo de la Habana 202-bis, 28036 Madrid, Spain. TEL 1-3594092. Ed. A. Martinez Magro. adv.; bk.rev.; illus. circ. 35,000.

PROFESSIONAL LIABILITY NEWSLETTER. see *LAW*

610   FR   ISSN 0339-3666
PROFILS MEDICO-SOCIAUX. 1972. 45/yr. 170 F. Union Nationale pour l'Avenir de la Medecine, 18 av. de la Marne, 92600 Asnieres, France. TEL 47-93-05-88. FAX 47-93-68-95. Ed. Alexandre Savy. adv.; bk.rev. circ. 60,000.

PROGRESS & CARE; at the Medical Center Hospital. see *HOSPITALS*

PROGRESS IN BIOMEDICAL ENGINEERING. see *BIOLOGY — Bioengineering*

610   US   ISSN 0361-7742
                             CODEN: PCBRD2
PROGRESS IN CLINICAL AND BIOLOGICAL RESEARCH. 1975. irreg., vol.373, 1992. price varies. John Wiley & Sons, Inc., Journals, 605 Third Ave., New York, NY 10158. TEL 212-475-7700. (reprint service avail. from ISI) **Indexed:** Biol.Abstr., Chem.Abstr., Chic.Per.Ind., Dent.Ind., Dok.Arbeitsmed., Excerp.Med., Ind.Med., Ind.Vet., Vet.Bull.
—BLDSC (6867.400000); CASDDS; Faxon; SWETS; UnCover. **CCC.**
     Refereed Serial

PROGRESS IN MEDICINAL CHEMISTRY. see *CHEMISTRY*

MEDICAL SCIENCES

613   UK   ISSN 0962-7936
CODEN: POBREJ
PROGRESS IN OBESITY RESEARCH (YEAR). 1977. irreg. price varies. John Libbey & Company Ltd., 13 Smiths Yard, Summerley St., London SW18 4HR, England. TEL 0181-947-2777. FAX 0181-947-2664. E-mail: libbey@earlsfield.win-uk.net. Ed.Bd. illus. **Indexed:** Chem.Abstr. **Document type:** academic/scholarly publication.
—BLDSC (6871.240000); CASDDS.
  Formerly (until 1990): Recent Advances in Obesity Research (ISSN 0306-7548)
  Refereed Serial

612   US   ISSN 0721-9156
QP431   CODEN: PSPYDZ
PROGRESS IN SENSORY PHYSIOLOGY. 1981. irreg. price varies. Springer-Verlag, 175 Fifth Ave., New York, NY 10010. TEL 212-460-1500. FAX 212-473-6272. (Also: Berlin, Heidelberg, Tokyo and Vienna) (reprint service avail. from ISI) **Document type:** monographic series.
—BLDSC (6924.552000); CASDDS; Faxon. **CCC.**

617.07   US   ISSN 0271-2350
RD57
PROGRESS IN SURGICAL PATHOLOGY. 1980. irreg., vol.13, 1993. $135 to individuals; institutions $175 (effective 1996). Field & Wood, Medical Periodicals, Inc., Box 975, Blue Bell, PA 19422. TEL 610-828-4010. FAX 215-482-0226. Ed.Bd. **Document type:** academic/scholarly publication.
  Refereed Serial

616.07   IT   ISSN 0393-7658
PROGRESSI CLINICI: MEDICINA. 1985. bi-m. L.180000($180) Piccin Editore, Via Altinate 107, 35100 Padua, Italy. TEL 049-655566. FAX 049-8750693. circ. 3,000.

610   IT   ISSN 0370-1514
CODEN: PRMOAE
IL PROGRESSO MEDICO. (Text in Italian; summaries in English) 1944. bi-m. L.150000 (effective 1994). Lombardo Editore, Via Verona, 22, 00161 Rome, Italy. TEL 39-6-44290974. FAX 39-6-44238543. Ed. M. Condorelli. adv. contact: Giorgio Lombardo. index. (also avail. in microform) **Indexed:** Excerp.Med. **Document type:** academic/scholarly publication.
—BLDSC (6924.672000); Faxon.
  Description: Covers internal medicine and surgery.

610   FR   ISSN 0033-1392
PROPOS UTILES AUX MEDECINS. 1950. 50/yr. 490 F. 6 rue Montalivet, 75008 Paris, France. TEL 42-65-84-33. FAX 42-68-05-86. TELEX 290 144. Ed. Roland Lesage. adv.; index. circ. 11,000.

616.99   US   ISSN 0270-4137
RC899   CODEN: PRSTDS
THE PROSTATE. 1980. m. $852 (foreign $1038) (effective 1996). John Wiley & Sons, Inc., Journals, 605 Third Ave., New York, NY 10158. TEL 212-850-6645. FAX 212-850-6021. TELEX 12-7063. E-mail: SUBINFO@JWILEY.COM. (Subscr. outside the Americas to: John Wiley & Sons, Ltd., 605 Third Ave., New York, NY 10158. TEL 44-1243-779777. FAX 44-1243-776128) Eds. Avery A. Sandberg, Gerald P. Murphy. adv.; bibl.; charts; illus.; index. (also avail. in microform from UMI; back issues avail.) **Indexed:** Biol.Abstr., Chem.Abstr., Curr.Cont., Excerp.Med., Ind.Med. **Document type:** academic/scholarly publication.
●Also available online.
—BLDSC (6935.194000); CASDDS; Faxon; Genuine Article; SWETS; UnCover. **CCC.**
  Description: Serves as an international medium presenting comprehensive coverage of clinical, anatomic, embryologic, physiologic, endocrinologic, and biochemical studies.
  Refereed Serial

PROTECTIVE APPAREL CONFERENCE PAPERS. see *TEXTILE INDUSTRIES AND FABRICS*

610   PL   ISSN 0033-2240
CODEN: PRLKAV
PRZEGLAD LEKARSKI. (Text in Polish; summaries in English and Russian) 1862. m. $180. Fundacja Lekarzy Polskich - Pro Medica, Ul. Miodowa 1, 00-080 Warsaw, Poland. (Dist. by: Ars Polona-Ruch, Krakowskie Przedmiescie 7, 00-068 Warsaw, Poland) Ed. Dr. Jan Sznajd. index. **Indexed:** Abstr.Hyg., Biol.Abstr., C.I.S. Abstr., Chem.Abstr., Dok.Arbeitsmed., Excerp.Med. (until 1993), Ind.Med., Trop.Dis.Bull. **Document type:** academic/scholarly publication.
—BLDSC (6942.800000); CASDDS.

610   UK   ISSN 0033-2585
PSIONIC MEDICINE. 1969. s-a. £9.50($20) Psionic Medical Society, Hindhead, Surrey, England. FAX 01507-328942. Ed. Dr. Peter Mansfield. bk.rev.; bibl.; circ. 100 (controlled). (tabloid format) **Document type:** newsletter.
  Description: Techniques for diagnosing the cause of disease dynamically.
  Refereed Serial

PSYCHOLOGIA A PATOPSYCHOLOGIA DIETATA. see *PSYCHOLOGY*

PSYCHOLOGY, HEALTH & MEDICINE. see *PSYCHOLOGY*

152 612   UK   ISSN 0048-5772
QP351   CODEN: PSPHAF
PSYCHOPHYSIOLOGY; an international journal. 1964. bi-m. £66($105) (effective 1996). (Society for Psychophysiological Research) Cambridge University Press, Edinburgh Bldg., Shaftesbury Rd., Cambridge CB2 2RU, England. TEL 01223-312393. FAX 01223-315052. TELEX 851817256. (N. American addr.: Cambridge University Press, Journals Dept., 40 W. 20th St., New York, NY 10011. TEL 212-924-3900. FAX 212-691-3239) Ed. John T. Cacippo. adv.; bk.rev.; abstr.; charts; illus.; index. circ. 2,400. (also avail. in microfilm from UMI; back issues avail.; reprint service avail. from UMI) **Indexed:** Behav.Med.Abstr., Bibl.Dev.Med.& Child Neur., Biol.Abstr., Curr.Adv.Ecol.Sci., Curr.Cont., Excerp.Med., Ind.Med., Psychol.Abstr. (1964-). **Document type:** academic/scholarly publication.
—BLDSC (6946.552000); EMDOCS; Faxon; SWETS; UMI; UnCover. **CCC.**
  Formerly: Psychophysiology Newsletter.
  Description: Concerns the relationships between human autonomic and central nervous system behavior on the one hand and cognitive performance, personality and emotions on the other. Studies effects of stress, individual differences, aging, anxiety, and psychosomatic and psychiatric disease.
  Refereed Serial

614 610   UK   ISSN 0033-3506
CODEN: PUHEAE
PUBLIC HEALTH. 1888. BI-M. £130 to E.C.; elsewhere £140($210). (Society of Public Health) Stockton Press, Houndmills, Basingstoke, Hampshire RG2 2XS, England. TEL 01256-817245. FAX 01256-28339. Ed. M.W. Beaver; Pub. Marija Vukovojac. adv. contact: Michael Rowley. bk.rev.; charts; illus.; stat.; index. circ. 1,500. **Indexed:** Abstr.Hyg., ASSIA, Biol.Abstr., C.I.S. Abstr., Chem.Abstr., Curr.Adv.Cancer Res., Curr.Adv.Ecol.Sci., Curr.Cont., Dent.Ind., Diar.Dis.Res., Excerp.Med., Helminthol.Abstr., IMFL, Ind.Med., Ind.Vet., Nutr.Abstr., SSCI, Trop.Dis.Bull., Vet.Bull. **Document type:** academic/scholarly publication.
—BLDSC (6963.850000); EMDOCS; Genuine Article; SWETS; UMI; UnCover. **CCC.**
  Description: Covers all aspects of community health and medicine, including preventive medicine and epidemiology.

PUBLIKATIONEN ZU WISSENSCHAFTLICHEN FILMEN. SEKTION MEDIZIN. see *MOTION PICTURES*

610 360   PR
PUERTO RICO. DEPARTMENT OF HEALTH. INFORME DE RECURSOS HUMANOS DE LA SALUD. (Text in Spanish) 1979. triennial. free. Department of Health, Auxiliary Secretariat of Planning, Evaluation and Statistics, Division of Statistics, Box 70184, San Juan, PR 00936. TEL 809-274-7875. FAX 809-274-7877. circ. 900. **Document type:** government publication.
  Formerly: Puerto Rico. Department of Health. Informe del Registro de Professionales de la Salud.

610 574   PR   ISSN 0738-0658
CODEN: PRHJDB
PUERTO RICO HEALTH SCIENCES JOURNAL. (Text in English, Spanish) 1982. 4/yr. $35 to individuals; institutions $45 (effective 1996). University of Puerto Rico, Office of the Dean for Academic Affairs, Medical Sciences Campus, Box 365067, San Juan, PR 00936-5067. TEL 809-758-2525. FAX 809-764-2470. Ed. Dr. Rafael Villavicencio. bk.rev.; index. circ. 600. (back issues avail.) **Indexed:** Chem.Abstr., Ind.Med. **Document type:** academic/scholarly publication.
●Also available on CD-ROM.
—BLDSC (7156.225000); CASDDS.
  Description: Covers medical, dental, pharmaceutical and biosocial sciences. Discusses historical, philosophical and ethical matters of health sciences.

610   UK   ISSN 0048-6000
PULSE. 1959. w. $196. Miller Freeman Professional Ltd., Miller Freeman House, 30 Calderwood St., London SE18 6QH, England. TEL 0181-855-7777. FAX 0181-854-9716. Ed. Howard Griffiths. adv. contact: Fergus Wilson. bk.rev.; illus. circ. 40,956. (tabloid format) **Document type:** trade publication.
—BLDSC (7160.070000).

610   II   ISSN 0033-4340
PUNJAB MEDICAL JOURNAL. (Text in English) 1951. m. Rs.10.($4) 590, Sector 10, Punchkula 134 109, India. Ed. Dr. R. R. Laroia. adv.; bk.rev.; abstr.; charts; illus.; index. **Indexed:** Biol.Abstr., Chem.Abstr., Excerp.Med., Nucl.Sci.Abstr.

610   SP
PUNTEX MEDICO. 2/yr. C. Mare de Deu del Coll 14, 08023 Barcelona, Spain. TEL 3-237-71-24. FAX 3-217-57-83. TELEX 97131 GPMM E. Ed. Ramon Marti. circ. 85,000.

610   US   ISSN 0899-6784
Q M P CLINICAL SERIES. (Consists of 4 subseries, Perspectives in: Colon & Rectal Surgery; Neurological Surgery; Plastic Surgery; Vascular Surgery) 8/yr. price varies. Quality Medical Publishing, Inc., 11970 Borman Dr., Ste. 222, St. Louis, MO 63146. TEL 314-878-7808; 800-348-7808. FAX 314-878-9937. (back issues avail.) **Document type:** monographic series.

610   US
Q: THE PHYSICIANS GUIDE TO QUALITY. 1991. bi-m. Target Marketing, Inc., 5 Victory Ln., Ste. 101, Liberty, MO 64068. TEL 816-781-7557. FAX 816-781-3298. Ed. Norman Aronson. adv.; B&W or color page $4990; trim 7 7/8 x 10 3/4. circ. 66,000.

610   QA   ISSN 0253-8253
QATAR MEDICAL JOURNAL. (Text in English) 1980. a. Ministry of Public Health, P.O. Box 42, Doha, Qatar.

610   CC   ISSN 1001-4047
QINGDAO YIXUEYUAN XUEBAO/QINGDAO MEDICAL INSTITUTE. JOURNAL. (Text in Chinese) m. Qingdao Yixueyuan, No. 10, Huangtai Lu, Qingdao, Shandong 266012, People's Republic of China. TEL 228106. Ed. Li Juesheng.

QUADERNI DI ANATOMIA PRATICA. see *BIOLOGY*

610 617   IT   ISSN 0393-5930
CODEN: QMCHE
QUADERNI DI MEDICINA E CHIRURGIA. 1985. 4/yr. Comitato Progetto Cultura Medica Q M C, Via M. Stanzione 18, 80129 Naples, Italy. TEL 39-81-5565285. **Indexed:** Excerp.Med. (1994-). **Document type:** academic/scholarly publication.

610   IT   ISSN 1122-2654
QUADERNI INTERNAZIONALI DI STORIA DELLA MEDICINA E DELLA SANITA. 1992. s-a. C I S O Toscano, Istituto di Patologia Speciale Medica, Ospedale S. Maria della Scala, Piazza Duomo 2, 53100 Siena, Italy. TEL 0577-43247. Ed. Francesca Vannozzi. **Document type:** academic/scholarly publication.
—BLDSC (7166.361000).

MEDICAL SCIENCES

610 US ISSN 1049-7323
RA440.85 CODEN: QHREEM
QUALITATIVE HEALTH RESEARCH. 1991. q. $56 to individuals; institutions $148 (effective Sep. 1995). Sage Publications, Inc., 2455 Teller Rd., Thousand Oaks, CA 91320. TEL 805-499-0721. FAX 805-499-0871. E-mail: libraries@sagepub.com. (Overseas subscr. to: Sage Publications, Ltd., 6 Bonhill St., London EC2A 4PU, England; Sage Publications India Pvt. Ltd., P.O. Box 4215, New Delhi 110 048, India) Ed. Janice M. Morse. adv.; bk.rev. circ. 1,250. (back issues avail.; reprint service avail.) **Indexed:** CINAHL, Psychol.Abstr. (1991-), Viol.& Abuse Abstr. **Document type:** academic/scholarly publication.
—BLDSC (7168.124200); Faxon; SWETS. **CCC.**
Description: Provides an interdisciplinary forum that will enhance health care and further the development and understanding of qualitative research methods in health care settings.

610 UK ISSN 0963-8172
QUALITY IN HEALTH CARE. 1992. q. £97($158) B M J Publishing Group, B.M.A. House, Tavistock Sq., London WC1H 9JR, England. TEL 0171-383-6270. FAX 0171-383-6402. (N. American subscr. to: Box 408, Franklin, MA 02038. TEL 800-2-FON-BMJ. FAX 800-2-FAX-BMJ) Ed. F. Moss. adv. contact: Sheila Rowe. bk.rev.; illus.; stat. (back issues avail.)
—BLDSC (7168.152260); SWETS.
Description: Presents information relevant to any aspect of health care that identifies problems in practice quality or health care delivery, suggests indications for practice change, or helps define standards and outcome of care.
Refereed Serial

QUALITY MANAGEMENT IN HEALTH CARE; an information service. see *HOSPITALS*

610 150 FR ISSN 1161-6407
QUALITY OF LIFE NEWS LETTER. (Text in English) 1991. q. M A P I Research Institute, 27 rue de la Villette, 69003 Lyon, France. TEL 33-72-136667. FAX 33-72136668. E-mail: 100070.2212@compuserve.com. Dir. Bernard Jambon. **Document type:** newsletter.
—BLDSC (7168.152460).
Description: Provides a basis for communication among those involved in health-related quality-of-life issues including epidemiologists, psychologists, economists, pharmaceutical industry managers, regulatory authorities, insurance companies and physicians.

610 UK ISSN 0962-9343
CODEN: QLREEG
QUALITY OF LIFE RESEARCH. 1992. bi-m. £265($450) to institutions (effective 1995). Rapid Communications of Oxford Ltd., The Old Malthouse, Paradise St., Oxford OX1 1LD, England. TEL 01865-790447. FAX 01865-244012. E-mail: rapidcom@vax.oxford.ac.uk. Ed. Maurice Staquet. adv. contact: Julie Gribben. (reprint service avail.) **Indexed:** Excerp.Med. (1993-), Ind.Med. (1993-), Psychol.Abstr. (1992-). **Document type:** academic/scholarly publication.
●Also available on CD-ROM.
—BLDSC (7168.152470); ADONIS; Genuine Article. **CCC.**
Description: Aimed specifically at researchers involved with any aspect of quality of life research in theory, methodology and clinical practice.

610 US
QUALITY RESOURCE. 1983. bi-m. membership only. American Health Information Management Association, Quality Assurance Section, 919 N. Michigan Ave., Ste. 1400, Chicago, IL 60611-1601. TEL 312-787-2672. Ed. Patrice Spath. bk.rev.; index. circ. 3,000. (tabloid format; back issues avail.) **Document type:** newsletter.
Formerly (until Jan. 1993): Q A Section Connection (ISSN 1040-2950)
Description: Devoted to articles helpful to quality management professionals working in inpatient and outpatient health care facilities.

610 US ISSN 1072-9607
QUALITY SOURCE. 1991. q. membership. (Baxter International Inc.) American Group Practice Association, 1422 Duke St., Alexandria, VA 22314. TEL 703-838-0033. FAX 703-548-1890. (Co-sponsor: Ernest & Young) Ed. Julie Sanderson-Austin. circ. controlled. **Document type:** newsletter.
Description: Focuses on outcomes measurement and research, practice guidelines, quality improvement strategies, and other state-of-the-art quality strategies.

610 UK ISSN 0033-5622
R31 CODEN: QJMEA7
QUARTERLY JOURNAL OF MEDICINE. Cover title: Q J M. 1907. m. £155($270) (effective 1996). (Association of Physicians of Great Britain and Ireland) Oxford University Press, Oxford Journals, Walton St., Oxford OX2 6DP, England. TEL 01865-267907. FAX 01865-267773. TELEX 837330-OXPRES-G. E-mail: jnlorders@oup.co.uk. (U.S. subscr. to: Oxford University Press Inc., 2001 Evans Rd., Cary, NC 27513. TEL 919-677-0977. FAX 919-677-1714) Ed. J.M. Hopkin. adv.; bibl.; charts; illus.; cum.index every 20 vols. circ. 2,300. (also avail. in microform from UMI,PMC; back issues avail.) **Indexed:** Abstr.Hyg., Adol.Ment.Hlth.Abstr., Biol.Abstr., Chem.Abstr., Curr.Adv.Ecol.Sci., Curr.Cont., Dairy Sci.Abstr., Diab.Cont., Excerp.Med., I.P.A., Ind.Med., Med.& Surg.Dermat., Nutr.Abstr., Protozool.Abstr., Sci.Cit.Ind., Trop.Dis.Bull. **Document type:** academic/scholarly publication.
●Also available online. Vendor(s): Ovid Technologies.
—CASDDS; Faxon; Genuine Article; SWETS; UMI; UnCover. **CCC.**
Description: Covers the whole field of medicine with emphasis on internal medicine.

610 II ISSN 0481-2158
QUARTERLY MEDICAL REVIEW. (Text in English) 1949. q. free to qualified personnel. Raptakos, Brett & Co., Ltd, Dr. Annie Besant Rd., Worli, Bombay 400025, India. Ed. Dr. G.B. Ramasarma. adv. circ. 70,000. **Indexed:** Ind.Med.

610 UK ISSN 0033-6033
QUEENS MEDICAL MAGAZINE. vol.62, 1970. 3/yr. £10. (Birmingham Medical Society) Birmingham Medical and Dental Schools, Birmingham 15, England. Ed. Clive Meanwell. adv.; bk.rev.; charts; illus.; stat.; tr.lit. circ. 5,000.

610 CN ISSN 0079-8789
QUEEN'S MEDICAL REVIEW. 1951. a. Aesculapian Society, Queen's University, Kingston, Ont., Canada. TEL 613-545-2542. Ed.Bd. adv. circ. 1,000.

QUINTESSENCE. see *ALTERNATIVE MEDICINE*

610 AG ISSN 0325-2345
QUIRON. (Text in Spanish; summaries in English and French) 1970. q. $25 (foreign $45). (Fundacion Dr. Jose Maria Mainetti para el Progreso de la Medicina) Editorial Quiron, Calle 508 entre 16 y 18, 1897 M. B. Gonnet, Buenos Aires, Argentina. TEL 021-71-2616. FAX 54-71-2222. Ed. Dr. Alberto Mainetti. adv.; bk.rev.; charts; bibl.; illus. circ. 3,000. (reprint service avail. from IRC) **Indexed:** Ind.Med. **Document type:** academic/scholarly publication.

610 FR
QUOTIDIEN DU MEDECIN. 220/yr. Societe d'Editions Scientifiques & Culturelles, 140 rue Jules-Guesde, 92593 Levallois Cedex, France. TEL 47307500. FAX 47307575. Ed. Richard Liscia. circ. 82,500.

610 AT
R.A.C.G.P. TRAINING PROGRAM VICTORIA NEWSLETTER. 1977. m. Royal Australian College of General Practitioners, Trawalla, 22 Lascelles Ave., Toorak, Vic. 3142, Australia. TEL 61-3-2141414. FAX 61-3-2141401. Ed. Dr. Ken Mulligan. adv.; bk.rev. circ. 2,800. **Document type:** newsletter.
Formerly: Family Medicine Programme. R.A.C.G.P. Victoria Newsletter.

R & D INNOVATOR; researcher's monthly tool for invention and discovery. see *TECHNOLOGY: COMPREHENSIVE WORKS*

R B M - REVUE EUROPEENNE DE TECHNOLOGIE BIOMEDICALE. see *BIOLOGY — Biotechnology*

R V S FEE SCHEDULE. (Relative Value Scale) see *INSURANCE*

362.3 NE ISSN 0166-4298
RAAKPUNT. 1957. 8/yr. fl.25($15) Vereniging van Ouders en Verwanten van Mensen met een Verstandelijke Handicap V O G G, Postbus 85274, 3508 AG Utrecht, Netherlands. TEL 31-30-363744. FAX 31-30-313054. Ed. S.T. Overbeek. adv.; bk.rev.; illus. circ. 18,000. (processed) **Document type:** newspaper.
Formerly: Zorgenkind (ISSN 0044-5339)
Description: Contains news and information for parents and relatives of persons with mental disabilities.

RADIOISOTOPES. see *BIOLOGY — Biological Chemistry*

610 UK
RADIONIC JOURNAL; an approach to health and harmony. 1954. 2/yr. membership only. Radionic Association Ltd., Baerlein House, Goose Green, Deddington, Banbury, Oxon OX15 0SZ, England. TEL 01869-38852. Ed. Linda Everitt. adv.; bk.rev. circ. 500. **Document type:** newsletter.
Former titles (until 1994): Radionic Quarterly (ISSN 0481-6722); *Formerly (until 1957):* Radionic Therapy.
Description: Discusses distant healing practice using instruments and radiesthesia.

616.6 IT ISSN 0033-992X
RASSEGNA DI UROLOGIA E NEFROLOGIA. (Text in Italian; summaries in English) 1963. q. L.30000 (foreign L.60000) (effective 1994). C E M Casa Editrice Maccari, Via Trento, 53, 43100 Parma, Italy. FAX 039-521-771268. Ed.Bd. adv.; bk.rev. circ. 1,000. **Indexed:** Excerp.Med.
—UMI.

610 IT ISSN 0033-9695
RASSEGNA INTERNAZIONALE DI CLINICA E TERAPIA. 1920. bi-m. L.25000($30) Bruno Buonomo La Rossa, Ed. & Pub., Pallonetto S. Chiara 8, 80134 Naples, Italy. TEL 081-5520424. adv.; bk.rev.; abstr.; bibl.; charts; illus.; index. circ. 15,000. (also avail. in microform from UMI; reprint service avail. from UMI) **Indexed:** Biol.Abstr., Chem.Abstr., Excerp.Med., Ind.Med.
—BLDSC (7294.240000); EMDOCS; Faxon; UMI.

610 GW ISSN 0722-7949
RAUM UND ZEIT; die Neue Dimension der Wissenschaft. 1981. bi-m. DM.84 (foreign DM.92). Ehlers Verlag GmbH, Muehlweg 2B, 82054 Sauerlach, Germany. TEL 08104-2269. FAX 08104-2127. Ed. Hans-Joachim Ehlers. adv. contact: Birgitt Schmied. bk.rev. circ. 20,000. (back issues avail.) **Document type:** consumer publication.

610 PK ISSN 0303-5212
CODEN: RMEJEI
RAWAL MEDICAL JOURNAL. (Text in English) 1976. q. Rs.60($60) Pakistan Medical Association, Rawalpindi-Islamabad Branch, Rawalpindi, Pakistan. adv.; bk.rev. circ. 1,500. **Indexed:** ExtraMED. **Document type:** academic/scholarly publication.
●Also available on CD-ROM.

REACHING OUT. see *HANDICAPPED*

610 SP ISSN 0034-0634
REAL ACADEMIA NACIONAL DE MEDICINA. ANALES. 1879. q. 7200 ptas.($60) Real Academia Nacional de Medicina, Prof. Dr. D. Valentin Matilla y Gomez, C. Arrieta 12, 28013 Madrid, Spain. TEL 34-1-5470320. FAX 34-1-5470318. illus. circ. 600. **Indexed:** Biol.Abstr., Chem.Abstr., Ind.Med. **Document type:** academic/scholarly publication.
—BLDSC (0882.150000); Faxon.

610 FR ISSN 0765-5290
CODEN: RMDUA8
REANIMATION, SOINS INTENSIFS, MEDECINE D'URGENCE. 1968. 6/yr. 1035 F. to individuals (foreign 1340 F.); students 205 F. (foreign 265 F.). (Societe de Reanimation de Langue Francaise) Expansion Scientifique, 31 bd. de la Tour Maubourg, 75007 Paris, France. TEL 40-62-64-00. FAX 45-55-69-20. Ed. C. Chopin. circ. 3,000.
—BLDSC (7303.555000); CASDDS. **CCC.**
Formerly: Reanimation et Medecine d'Urgence (ISSN 0246-1234)

MEDICAL SCIENCES

610   UK   ISSN 0952-1089
RECENT ADVANCES IN CRITICAL CARE MEDICINE. 1977. irreg. Churchill Livingstone Medical Journals, Robert Stevenson House, 1-3 Baxter's Pl., Leith Walk, Edinburgh EH1 3AF, Scotland. TEL 0131-556-2424. FAX 0131-459-1177. **Document type:** academic/scholarly publication, monographic series.
—BLDSC (7303.814300).
Formerly (until 1983): Recent Advances in Intensive Therapy (ISSN 0143-344X)

610   IT   ISSN 0034-1193
                      CODEN: RPMDAN
RECENTI PROGRESSI IN MEDICINA. (Text and summaries in English or Italian) 1946. m. (11/yr.). L.379500($230) (effective 1996). Pensiero Scientifico Editore s.r.l., Via Bradano 3-C, 00199 Rome, Italy. TEL 06-86207158. FAX 06-86207160. Ed. Lorenzo Bonomo. adv.; bk.rev.; abstr.; bibl.; illus.; index. circ. 2,000. **Indexed:** Biol.Abstr., Chem.Abstr., Dent.Ind., Dok.Arbeitsmed., Excerp.Med., Ind.Med. **Document type:** academic/scholarly publication.
—BLDSC (7305.100000); CASDDS; EMDOCS; Faxon; SWETS.

RECEPTOR. see *BIOLOGY — Biological Chemistry*

RECHT DER MEDIZIN. see *LAW*

RECHTSMEDIZIN. see *MEDICAL SCIENCES — Forensic Sciences*

RECHTSMEDIZINISCHE FORSCHUNGSERGEBNISSE. see *LAW*

610   IS   ISSN 0017-7768
                      CODEN: HAREA6
HA-REFUAH. (Text in Hebrew; summaries in English) 1930. fortn. $300. Israel Medical Association, 39 Shaul Hamelech Blvd., Tel Aviv, Israel. TEL 972-3-6969639. FAX 972-3-6956103. Ed. Y. Rotem. adv.; bk.rev.; abstr.; bibl.; charts; illus.; stat.; index. **Indexed:** Biol.Abstr., Chem.Abstr., Curr.Cont., Dent.Ind., Excerp.Med., Ind.Med., INIS Atomind., Psychol.Abstr.
—BLDSC (4264.000000); CASDDS; SWETS.

REGAN REPORT ON MEDICAL LAW. see *LAW*

610   SA
REGISTER OF MEDICAL PRACTITIONERS, INTERNS AND DENTISTS FOR THE REPUBLIC OF SOUTH AFRICA. (Text and summaries in Afrikaans, English) a. (with m. supplements). R.60 (plus R.15 for m. supplements). South African Medical & Dental Council, P.O. Box 205, Pretoria 0001, South Africa. TEL 27-12-286680. FAX 27-12-285120. **Document type:** directory.

615.8   US   ISSN 0899-6237
REHAB MANAGEMENT. 1988. bi-m. $5 per no. Curant Communications, Inc., 4676 Admiralty Way, Ste. 202, Marina Del Rey, CA 90292-6603. TEL 213-479-1769. FAX 213-301-3329. Ed. Tony Ramos. adv. circ. 20,000.
—BLDSC (7350.045000).
Description: Directed toward physical therapists, directors and managers of rehabilitation hospitals, and occupational therapists. Features the business aspects of rehabilitation, plus case histories.

615   XO   ISSN 0375-0922
REHABILITACIA/REHABILITATION. (Supplements avail.) (Text in Czech or Slovak; summaries in English, French, German, Russian) 1967. 8/yr. $36. (Institut pre Dalsie Vzdelavanie Lekarov a Farmaceutov - Institute of Further Education of Physicians and Pharmaceutists) F. Liecreh, Cervenova 34, 811 03 Bratislava, Slovakia. (Dist. by: Slovart, Gottwaldovo nam. 48, 805 32 Bratislava, Slovakia) Ed. Dr. Miroslav Palat. bk.rev.; film rev.; bibl.; charts; illus.; index. circ. 2,500. (tabloid format; back issues avail.) **Indexed:** Biol.Abstr., Excerp.Med.
—BLDSC (7350.050000).

362   GW   ISSN 0034-3536
DIE REHABILITATION. (Text in German; summaries in English, German) 1961. q. DM.148. (Deutsche Vereinigung fuer die Rehabilitation Behinderter) Georg Thieme Verlag, Ruedigerstr. 14, 70469 Stuttgart, Germany. TEL 0711-8931-0. FAX 0711-8931298. (Subscr. to: Postfach 104853, 70042 Stuttgart, Germany) Ed.Bd. adv.; bk.rev.; bibl.; charts; illus.; stat.; index. circ. 1,800. (also avail. in microform from UMI; reprint service avail. from UMI) **Indexed:** Curr.Cont., Excerp.Med., Ind.Med. **Document type:** academic/scholarly publication.
—BLDSC (7350.210000); EMDOCS; Faxon; SWETS; UMI. **CCC.**

REHABILITATION DIGEST. see *EDUCATION — Special Education And Rehabilitation*

362   US   ISSN 0172-6412
REHABILITATION UND PRAEVENTION. 1977. irreg. price varies. Springer-Verlag, 175 Fifth Ave., New York, NY 10010. TEL 212-460-1500. FAX 212-473-6272. (Also: Berlin, Heidelberg, Tokyo and Vienna) (reprint service avail. from ISI)

610 338   US   ISSN 1065-7681
RELATIVE VALUES FOR PHYSICIANS. 1984. q. $239. McGraw-Hill Inc., 1221 Avenue of the Americas, New York, NY 10020. TEL 212-512-2995. FAX 212-512-4138. Ed.Bd. (also avail. in magnetic tape; diskette format)
Description: Fee scheduling system for physicians, medical groups and insurers to determine physicians charges and reimbursement.

RELAX; the travel magazine for practicing physicians. see *TRAVEL AND TOURISM*

612.015   IT   ISSN 0048-7198
RELAZIONI CLINICO SCIENTIFICHE. * (Text in Italian; summaries in English) 1948. bi-m. free to medical doctors. Istituto Ganassini di Ricerche Biochimiche, Via Gaggia 16, Milan, Italy. adv.; bk.rev.; abstr.; bibl.; illus.; index, cum.index. circ. 13,000. **Indexed:** Chem.Abstr.

REMEDIA. see *BIBLIOGRAPHIES*

610   AT   ISSN 0816-990X
RENAL EDUCATOR. * 1978. q. Aus.$40. Renal Society of Australasia, 8 Bell Ave., W. Ryde, N.S.W. 2114, Australia. TEL 02-569-5876. Ed. Kim Grimley. adv.; bk.rev. circ. 1,000.
—BLDSC (7356.869000); UnCover.
Formerly (until 1985): Dialysis.

610   NE
REPERTORIUM. 1967. a. fl.89.50. Dutch Association of the Innovative Pharmaceutical Industry (NEFARMA), Postbus 9193, 3506 GD Utrecht, Netherlands. FAX 31-30-614554. (Dist. by: S D U, Postbus 30446, 2500 GK the Hague, Netherlands. TEL 31-70-3429700) (Co-sponsor: Dutch Association of the Pharmaceutical Industry of Proprietary medicines (NEPROFARM)) Ed.Bd. adv.; abstr.; cum.index. circ. 44,000.
● Also available on CD-ROM.
Former titles: Repertorium Farmaceutische Specialites Periodiek Overzicht voor Artsen; Repertorium Verpakte Geneesmiddelen Periodiek Overzicht voor Artsen (ISSN 0034-463X)

610 020   US
REPORT ON HEALTHCARE INFORMATION MANAGEMENT. m. $335. Capitol Publications Inc., 1101 King St., Ste. 444, Alexandria, VA 22314. TEL 703-683-4100. FAX 703-739-6501. Ed. Pam Vaupel; Pub. Cindy Carter. **Document type:** newsletter.
Description: Keeps executives on top of what's working in information systems and what's in store. Reports on standards for claims submission and EDI and what those developments mean.

610   AG
REPORTERO MEDICO. m. Editorial Artes y Ciencias, Santa Fe 2436, segundo, Buenos Aires, Argentina. Ed. Dr. Rufino J. Flores Belaunde. adv.

610 574   CH   ISSN 0255-6596
Q72.5   CODEN: PNBSEF
REPUBLIC OF CHINA. NATIONAL SCIENCE COUNCIL. PROCEEDINGS. PART B: LIFE SCIENCES. (Text in English) 1984. q. NT.$240($16) National Science Council, Rm. 1701, 106 Ho-ping E. Rd. Sec.2, Taipei 106, Taiwan, Republic of China. TEL 2-737-7594. FAX 2-737-7248. Ed. Jung-Yaw Lin. circ. 2,600. (also avail. in microfiche) **Indexed:** Anim.Breed.Abstr., Field Crop Abstr., Plant Grow.Reg.Abstr., Rev.Med.& Vet.Mycol., Sport Fish.Abstr., Wild.Rev., Zoo.Rec. **Document type:** academic/scholarly publication.
—BLDSC (6769.884600); CASDDS; UnCover.
Description: Publishes research papers in biology, agriculture and medical sciences.
Refereed Serial

610   IT   ISSN 0014-8784
RES MEDICAE. 1935. bi-m. L.6000. (Ordine Ospedaliero di S. Giovanni di Dio) Fatebenefratelli, Via S. Vittore 12, 20123 Milan, Italy. adv.; bk.rev.; bibl.; charts; illus.; stat.; index. circ. 6,000.

614.88   US   ISSN 1041-0651
RESCUE (CARLSBAD); magazine of rescue professionals. 1988. bi-m. $14.95. Jems Publishing Co., Inc., Box 2789, Carlsbad, CA 92018. TEL 619-431-9797. FAX 619-431-8176. Ed. Jeff Berend. adv.; bk.rev. circ. 25,000. (also avail. in microfiche)

RESEARCH AND CLINICAL CENTER FOR CHILD DEVELOPMENT. ANNUAL REPORT. see *CHILDREN AND YOUTH — About*

610   UK   ISSN 0143-3083
                      CODEN: RCLFD4
RESEARCH AND CLINICAL FORUMS. 1979. irreg. Wells Medical Ltd., Chapel Pl., Tunbridge Wells, Kent TN1 1BP, England. TEL 44-1892-511600. FAX 44-1892-511400. circ. 50,000. **Indexed:** Chem.Abstr., Curr.Adv.Ecol.Sci. **Document type:** proceedings.
—BLDSC (7714.445000); CASDDS; Faxon. **CCC.**
Description: Presents materials discussed at medico-scientific and medico-therapeutic congresses and symposia.

616.07 615   US   ISSN 1078-0297
                      CODEN: RCMPE6
RESEARCH COMMUNICATIONS IN MOLECULAR PATHOLOGY AND PHARMACOLOGY. 1970. m. $240 (foreign $280). P J D Publications Ltd., Box 966, Westbury, NY 11590. TEL 516-626-0650. Ed. D.B. Sankar; Pub. Barbara Sankar. adv.; bk.rev.; abstr.; charts; illus.; index. circ. 1,000. (also avail. in microform from PMC; reprint service avail. from ISI) **Indexed:** Biol.Abstr., Biotech.Abstr., Chem.Abstr., Curr.Adv.Biochem., Curr.Adv.Ecol.Sci., Curr.Cont., Dairy Sci.Abstr., Dent.Ind., Excerp.Med., Ind.Med., Ind.Vet., Nutr.Abstr., Poult.Abstr., Rev.Plant Path., Vet.Bull. **Document type:** academic/scholarly publication.
—BLDSC (7736.540000); CASDDS; EMDOCS; Faxon; Genuine Article; SWETS; UnCover. **CCC.**
Formerly (until 1994): Research Communications in Chemical Pathology and Pharmacology (ISSN 0034-5164)
Description: Articles on all areas of pathology, pharmacology, toxicology in their basic and clinical aspects.
Refereed Serial

614.8   US   ISSN 0275-4959
RA418
RESEARCH IN THE SOCIOLOGY OF HEALTH CARE; a research annual. 1980. irreg. vol.12, 1995. J A I Press Inc., 55 Old Post Rd., No. 2, Box 1678, Greenwich, CT 06836-1678. TEL 203-661-7602. Ed. Jennie Kronenfeld. **Indexed:** Lang.& Lang.Behav.Abstr., Sociol.Abstr. (1980-). **Document type:** academic/scholarly publication.
—BLDSC (7770.720000); Faxon. **CCC.**

MEDICAL SCIENCES 4265

612 NE ISSN 0378-6129
CODEN: RMTPD8
RESEARCH MONOGRAPHS IN CELL AND TISSUE PHYSIOLOGY. (Text in English) 1976. irreg., vol.17, 1991. price varies. Elsevier Science B.V., Books Division, P.O. Box 211, 1000 AE Amsterdam, Netherlands. TEL 31-20-4853911. FAX 31-20-4853705. TELEX 18582 ESPA NL. E-mail: nlinfo-f@elsevier.nl; usinfo-f@elsevier.com; forinfo-kyf04035@niftyserve.or.jp; Site addr.: http://www.elsevier.nl/. (Subscr. in U.S. and Canada to: Elsevier Science Inc., Box 882, Madison Sq. Sta., New York, NY 10159. TEL 212-989-5800) Ed. J.T. Dingle. **Document type:** monographic series.
—BLDSC (7743.355000); CASDDS. **CCC.**
Refereed Serial

RESIDENT AND STAFF PHYSICIAN. see *HOSPITALS*

RESPIRATION PHYSIOLOGY. see *BIOLOGY — Physiology*

614.88 GW ISSN 0178-2525
RETTUNGSDIENST; Zeitschrift fuer praeklinische Notfallmedizin. (Text in German; summaries in English) 1978. m. DM.79. Stumpf und Kossendey Verlags GmbH, Postfach 1361, 26183 Edewecht, Germany. TEL 04405-9181-0. FAX 04405-918133. Ed. D. Jahlstrom. adv. contact: L. Kossendey. circ. 20,000. **Document type:** academic/scholarly publication.
—SWETS.

REVIEWS IN MEDICAL MICROBIOLOGY. see *BIOLOGY — Microbiology*

610 BL ISSN 0102-2105
CODEN: RAMRAS
REVISTA A M R I G S. (Text in Portuguese; summaries in English, Portuguese) 1957. q. Cr.$600($20) Associacao Medica do Rio Grande do Sul, Av. Ipiranga, 5311, 90620 Porto Alegre, Brazil. adv.; bk.rev.; illus. circ. 7,000. **Indexed:** Biol.Abstr., Excerp.Med., Ind.Med.
Formerly (until 1975): Associacao Medica do Rio Grande do Sul. Revista (ISSN 0004-5268)

610 BL ISSN 0100-3232
CODEN: CLTRDC
REVISTA BRASILEIRA DE CLINICA E TERAPEUTICA. Short title: C T. (Includes: Booklet of Abstracts) (Text in Portuguese; summaries in English and Portuguese) m. Cr.$290000 (effective Nov. 1992). Moreira Jr. Editora Ltda., Rua Henrique Martins, 493, 04504 Sao Paulo SP, Brazil. TEL 011-884-9911. FAX 011-884-9993. Eds. Dr. Jose Rubens Barbosa Cortez, Dr. Jose Abu Assali. adv.; bk.rev.; abstr.; bibl.; charts; illus.; index. circ. 30,000. (back issues avail.) **Indexed:** Abstr.Hyg., Biol.Abstr., Chem.Abstr., Excerp.Med., Ind.Med.
—BLDSC (7844.157000).
Description: Presents results of medical research.

610 BL ISSN 0034-7264
CODEN: RBMEAU
REVISTA BRASILEIRA DE MEDICINA. Short title: R B M. (Table of contents and summaries in English and Portuguese) 1943. m. Cr.$296000($250) (effective Nov. 1992). Moreira Jr. Editora Ltda., Rua Henrique Martins, 493, 04504 Sao Paulo, Brazil. TEL 011-884-9911. FAX 011-884-9993. Dir. Dr. Joaquim Prado P. de Moraes. adv.; bk.rev.; abstr.; bibl.; charts; illus.; stat.; index. circ. 30,000. (back issues avail.) **Indexed:** Abstr.Hyg., Biol.Abstr., Chem.Abstr., Curr.Cont., Excerp.Med., Helminthol.Abstr., Microbiol.Abstr., Trop.Dis.Bull.
—BLDSC (7845.275000); CASDDS; EMDOCS; Genuine Article.
Description: Presents studies in all fields of medicine.

616.07 BL ISSN 0034-7302
CODEN: RBPTBN
REVISTA BRASILEIRA DE PATOLOGIA CLINICA. (Text in Portuguese; abstracts in English) 1950. q. r.$20 (foreign $60) (effective 1994). Sociedade Brasileira de Patologia Clinica - Brazilian Clinical Pathology Society, Rua Sampaio Viana, 92, 20261-040 Rio de Janeiro, RJ, Brazil. TEL 55-21-2933848. FAX 55-21-2932041. (Co-sponsor: Associacao Latino-Americana de Patologia Clinica - Latin-American Clinical Pathology Association) Ed. J. Alfred Sturm. adv.: B&W page $430, color page $640; 210 x 280; adv. contact: Cristina Morgado. bk.rev.; abstr.; bibl.; charts; illus.; stat.; index. circ. 3,000. (tabloid format; back issues avail.; reprint service avail. from IRC) **Indexed:** Biol.Abstr., Chem.Abstr., Ind.Med.
●Also available on CD-ROM.
—CASDDS.
Description: Contains original review and update papers in laboratory medicine.

610 574 BL ISSN 0100-879X
CODEN: BJMRDK
REVISTA BRASILEIRA DE PESQUISAS MEDICAS E BIOLOGICAS/BRAZILIAN JOURNAL OF MEDICAL AND BIOLOGICAL RESEARCH. (Text in English) 1968. m. $25 (in U.S. $80). c/o Eduardo Moacy Krieger, Faculdade de Medicina de Ribeirao Preto, Campus de Ribeirao Preto, 14049-900 Ribeirao Preto SP, Brazil. TEL 016-633-3825. TELEX 0166-354. Ed.Bd. adv.; bk.rev.; bibl.; charts; illus. circ. 5,000. (also avail. in microform from UMI; reprint service avail. from UMI, ISI) **Indexed:** Abstr.Hyg., Biol.Abstr., Chem.Abstr., Curr.Adv.Biochem., Curr.Adv.Cancer Res., Curr.Adv.Cell & Devel.Biol., Curr.Adv.Ecol.Sci., Curr.Adv.Genetics & Molec.Biol., Curr.Cont., Dairy Sci.Abstr., Dent.Ind., Excerp.Med., Helminthol.Abstr., Ind.Med., Ind.Sci.Rev., Ind.Vet., Kidney, Nutr.Abstr., Protozool.Abstr., Rev.Med.& Vet.Mycol., Sci.Cit.Ind., Trop.Dis.Bull., Vet.Bull.
—BLDSC (2277.419500); CASDDS; EMDOCS; Faxon; Genuine Article. **CCC.**

610 SP ISSN 0014-2565
CODEN: RCESA5
REVISTA CLINICA ESPANOLA. (Text in Spanish; summaries in English) 1940. 16/yr. 7000 ptas.($80) Editorial Idepsa, S.A., Principe de Vergara 112, 1.o F, 28002 Madrid, Spain. TEL 34-1-5637306. Ed. E. Bouza Santiago. adv.; bk.rev.; illus. circ. 7,514. **Indexed:** Biol.Abstr., Chem.Abstr., Curr.Cont., Dent.Ind., Excerp.Med., Helminthol.Abstr., Ind.Med., Ind.Med.Esp., Nutr.Abstr., Rev.Plant Path.
—BLDSC (7851.170000); CASDDS; Faxon; Genuine Article; SWETS. **CCC.**
Incorporates: Europa Medica (ISSN 0375-8869)

610 CR ISSN 0253-2948
CODEN: RCCMEF
REVISTA COSTARRICENSE DE CIENCIAS MEDICAS. (Text in Spanish; abstracts in English) 1979. 4/yr. $15 free to qualified personnel. Caja Costarricense de Seguro Social, Apdo. 10105, San Jose, Costa Rica. FAX 506-2338359. Ed. Jessie M. Orlich; Pub. Gerardo Campos. adv.; bk.rev. circ. 2,000. **Indexed:** Biol.Abstr., Excerp.Med., Ind.Med. **Document type:** academic/scholarly publication.
●Also available on CD-ROM.
—BLDSC (7852.070000).

610 378 CU ISSN 0864-2141
REVISTA CUBANA DE EDUCACION MEDICA SUPERIOR. (Text in Spanish; summaries in English and Spanish) 1987. s-a. $30 in S. America; N. America $32; elsewhere $34. Ministerio de Salud Publica, Centro Nacional de Informacion de Ciencias Medicas, Calle E No. 452, e-19 y 21, Plaza de la Revolucion, Apdo. 6520, Havana, Cuba. TEL 809-32-5338. (Dist. by: Ediciones Cubanas, Obispo No. 526, Apdo. 605, Havana, Cuba) (Co-sponsor: Sociedad Cubana de Educacion Medica Superior) Ed. Maria Julia Zamorano. circ. 1,000.
Description: Covers pedagogical science and its applications in medicine.

REVISTA CUBANA DE INVESTIGACIONES BIOMEDICAS. see *BIOLOGY*

610 CU ISSN 0034-7523
CODEN: RCBMA6
REVISTA CUBANA DE MEDICINA. (Text in Spanish; summaries in English, Spanish) 1962. 3/yr. $34 in S. America; N. America $36; elsewhere $38. Ministerio de Salud Publica, Centro Nacional de Informacion de Ciencias Medicas, Calle E No. 452, e-19 y 21, Plaza de la Revolucion, Apdo. 6520, Havana, Cuba. TEL 809-32-5338. (Dist. by: Ediciones Cubanas, Obispo No. 527, Apdo. 605, Havana, Cuba) Ed. Milagros de los Reyes. bibl.; charts; illus.; index. circ. 2,300. **Indexed:** Abstr.Hyg., Bio-Contr.News & Info., Biol.Abstr., Chem.Abstr., Curr.Adv.Ecol.Sci., Excerp.Med., Trop.Dis.Bull.
—BLDSC (7852.120000); CASDDS; EMDOCS.

610 CU ISSN 0864-2125
REVISTA CUBANA DE MEDICINA GENERAL INTEGRAL. (Text in Spanish; summaries in English, Spanish) 1985. 4/yr. $36 in S. America; N. America $38; elsewhere $44. Ministerio de Salud Publica, Centro Nacional de Informacion de Ciencias Medicas, Calle E No. 452, e-19 y 21, Plaza de la Revolucion, Apdo. 6520, Havana, Cuba. TEL 809-32-5338. (Dist. by: Ediciones Cubanas, Obispo No. 527, Apdo. 605, Havana, Cuba) Ed. Elibel Atala. abstr.; charts; illus.; index. circ. 17,500.
●Also available online.
Description: Covers preventive medicine, primary health care, diabetes mellitus, community medicine, emergency medical service, and the family physician.

616.98 CU ISSN 0138-6557
REVISTA CUBANA DE MEDICINA MILITAR. 2/yr. $3. Ministerio de Salud Publica, Centro Nacional de Informacion de Ciencias Medicas, Calle E no. 452, e 19 y 21, Plaza de la Revolucion, Apdo. 6520, Havana, Cuba. TEL 809-32-5338. (Co-sponsor: Cuba, Ministerio de las Fuerzas Armada Revolucionarias, Seccion de Servicios Medicos de la Jefatura de Retaguardia) Ed. Milagros de los Reyes. circ. 1,000.

610 SP
REVISTA DE BIOMECANICA. s-a. 4000 ptas.($50) (effective 1995). Editorial Garsi, S.A., Juan Bravo 46, 28006 Madrid, Spain. TEL 34-1-4021212. FAX 34-1-4020954.

REVISTA DE CHIRURGIE, ONCOLOGIE, RADIOLOGIE, O.R.L., OFTALMOLOGIE, STOMATOLOGIE. ONCOLOGIE. see *MEDICAL SCIENCES — Oncology*

610 BL ISSN 0101-322X
CODEN: RCBIDV
REVISTA DE CIENCIAS BIOMEDICAS. (Text in Portuguese; summaries in English and Portuguese) 1980. a. $30 or exchange basis. Universidade Estadual Paulista, Av. Vicente Ferreira 1278, Caixa Postal 603, 17515-901 Marilia SP, Brazil. TEL 0144-33-1844. FAX 0144-22-2504. TELEX 111-9016-UJME BR. abstr.; bibl.; charts; illus.; stat. **Indexed:** Biol.Abstr., Bull.Signal., Chem.Abstr., Excerp.Med. (1994-), Ind.Med., Ind.Vet., Protozool.Abstr. **Document type:** academic/scholarly publication.
—BLDSC (7851.031000); CASDDS; EMDOCS.
Description: Presents biomedical research results.

REVISTA DE IGIENA, BACTERIOLOGIE, VIRUSOLOGIE, PARAZITOLOGIE, PNEUMOFTIZIOLOGIE. IGIENA. see *PHYSICAL FITNESS AND HYGIENE*

610 MX ISSN 0034-8376
CODEN: RICLAG
REVISTA DE INVESTIGACION CLINICA. (Text and summaries in English and Spanish) 1948. bi-m. Mex.$75($30) (effective 1995). Instituto Nacional de la Nutricion "Salvador Zubiran", Av. San Fernando y Viaducto Tlalpan, Mexico 22, D.F., Mexico. TEL 915-573-1200. FAX 915-655-1076. Eds. Ruben Lisker, Alvar Loria. adv.; bk.rev.; bibl.; charts; illus.; stat.; index. circ. 1,800. **Indexed:** Biol.Abstr., Chem.Abstr., Curr.Cont., Excerp.Med., Helminthol.Abstr., Ind.Med., Nutr.Abstr. **Document type:** academic/scholarly publication.
●Also available on CD-ROM.
—BLDSC (7862.010000); CASDDS; EMDOCS; Faxon; Genuine Article.

REVISTA DE LA MEDICINA TRADICIONAL CHINA. see *ALTERNATIVE MEDICINE*

MEDICAL SCIENCES

610   BL   ISSN 0034-8554
REVISTA DE MEDICINA. (Text in Portuguese; summaries in English) 1916. q. free. Universidade de Sao Paulo, Faculdade de Medicina, Centro Academico "Oswaldo Cruz", Av. Dr. Arnaldo 455, Sao Paulo CEP 01246, Brazil. Ed. Sylvia Massue Iriya. adv.; bk.rev.; bibl.; charts; illus.; tr.lit.; tr.mk.; index. circ. 2,000. (processed; also avail. in microform from UMI; reprint service avail. from UMI) **Indexed:** Biol.Abstr., Excerp.Med., Ind.Med., Trop.Dis.Bull.

610   SP   ISSN 0556-6177
REVISTA DE MEDICINA. (Text in Spanish; summaries in English and Spanish) 1957. 4/yr. free. (Universidad de Navarra, Facultad de Medicina) Servicio de Publicaciones de la Universidad de Navarra, S.A., Apdo. 177, 31080 Pamplona, Spain. TEL 48-25-27-00. FAX 48-17-55-00. Eds. Diego Martinez Caro, Eduardo Alegria. adv.; bk.rev.; bibl.; charts; illus.; stat. circ. 12,000. (back issues avail.) **Indexed:** Biol.Abstr., Chem.Abstr., Excerp.Med., Ind.Med., Psychol.Abstr.
—CCC.

610 355   RM   ISSN 1221-7018
REVISTA DE MEDICINA MILITARA. q.? Calea Plevnei 134, 77103 Bucharest, Rumania.
     Formerly (until 1989): Revista Sanitara Militara (ISSN 1221-700X)

610   RM   ISSN 1221-2229
                      CODEN: REMTAS
REVISTA DE MEDICINA SI FARMACIE/ORVOSI ES GYOGYSZERESZETI SZEMLE. (Text in English, French, German, Hungarian, Rumanian; abstracts in English) 1955. s-a. 1000 lei($20) Universitatea de Medicina si Farmacie din Targu Mures, Str. Gh. Marinescu Nr. 38, 4300 Targu-Mures, Rumania. TEL 40-65-113127. FAX 40-65-130804. (Subscr. to: Rodipet S.A., Piata Presei Libere Nr.1, 71341 Bucharest, Rumania) Ed. Ion Pascu. bk.rev.; abstr.; bibl.; charts; illus. circ. 500. (also avail. in microfilm from UMI; reprint service avail. from UMI) **Indexed:** Chem.Abstr., Excerp.Med. **Document type:** academic/scholarly publication.
—CASDDS.
     Formerly (until 1991): Revista Medicala - Medical Review (ISSN 0034-995X)
     Description: For medical and pharmaceutical practitioners and researchers.

610 574   EC   ISSN 0034-9313
                      CODEN: REMBA8
REVISTA ECUATORIANA DE MEDICINA Y CIENCIAS BIOLOGICAS. (Text in Spanish; summaries in English) 1963. q. $20. Casa de la Cultura Ecuatoriana, Avda. 6 de Diciembre 332, Casilla 67, Quito, Ecuador. Ed. Dr. Plutarco Naranjo. adv.; bk.rev.; charts; illus.; index. circ. 2,500. **Indexed:** Biol.Abstr., C.I.S. Abstr., Chem.Abstr.

REVISTA ESPANOLA DE FISIOLOGIA. see *BIOLOGY — Physiology*

610   BL   ISSN 0034-9585
REVISTA GOIANA DE MEDICINA. (Text in Portuguese; table of contents and summaries in English and Portuguese) 1955. q. Cr.$150000($100) to non-members. (Associacao Medica de Goias) Imprensa da Universidade Federal de Goias, Av. Portugal, Esq. Av. Mutirao Sector Bueno, Caixa Postal 254, 74000 - Goiania, Goias, Brazil. TEL 251-1422. (Co-sponsor: Faculdade de Medicina da Universidade Federal de Goias) Ed. Joffre M. DeRezende. adv.; bk.rev.; abstr.; bibl.; charts; illus.; cum.index. circ. 3,000. (also avail. in microform from UMI; reprint service avail. from UMI) **Indexed:** Abstr.Hyg., Chem.Abstr., Excerp.Med., Helminthol.Abstr., Ind.Med., Protozool.Abstr., Trop.Dis.Bull. **Document type:** academic/scholarly publication.
—BLDSC (7858.270000); UMI.
     Description: Original papers and research in all branches of medicine, with emphasis on surgery.

REVISTA IBEROAMERICANA DE MICOLOGIA. see *BIOLOGY — Botany*

616   MX   ISSN 1405-101X
REVISTA IBEROLATINOAMERICANA DE CUIDADOS INTENSIVOS. (Text in Spanish; summaries in English, Portuguese, Spanish) 1992. bi-m. $55. Obsidiana Editores, S.A., Czda. de Tlalpan 2365, Col. Ciudad Jardin, 04370 Mexico DF, Mexico. TEL 6899133. FAX 6896545. Eds. Dr. Jose Benitez, Dr. Jose Elizalde; Pub. Jorge Godoy. **Document type:** academic/scholarly publication.
     Description: Contains original articles, research reports, review articles, clinical cases and notices, related to critical medicine.

610   BO   ISSN 0482-6760
REVISTA MEDICA (LA PAZ). 1977. q. Caja Nacional de Seguridad Social, La Paz, Bolivia. illus.

616.98 358.4   BL   ISSN 0370-6141
                      CODEN: RMABE8
REVISTA MEDICA DA AERONAUTICA DO BRASIL. 1951? s-a. Diretoria de Saude da Aeronautica, Av. Churchill 157-5oA, 20020 Castelo, RJ, Brazil. TEL 061-248-3040. charts; illus.; stat. **Indexed:** Excerp.Med., Ind.Med.

610   CL   ISSN 0034-9887
                      CODEN: RMCHAW
REVISTA MEDICA DE CHILE. 1872. m. $200 (effective 1996). Sociedad Medica de Santiago, Clasificador 168, Correo 55, Santiago 9, Chile. TEL 56-2-2748985. FAX 56-2-3413068. Ed. Dr. Alejandro Goic G. adv.; bk.rev.; abstr.; bibl.; charts; illus.; stat.; index. circ. 2,000. **Indexed:** Abstr.Hyg., Biol.Abstr., Chem.Abstr., Curr.Cont., Dent.Ind., Helminthol.Abstr., Ind.Med., Ind.Vet., Nutr.Abstr., Protozool.Abstr., Rev.Plant Path., Trop.Dis.Bull., Vet.Bull.
—BLDSC (7864.250000); CASDDS; Genuine Article; SWETS.

610   CR
REVISTA MEDICA DE COSTA RICA Y CENTROAMERICA. 1933. q. $16 in Central America; elsewhere $20 (or exchange basis). Dr. Manuel Zeledon, Ed. & Pub., Apdo. 978, 1000 San Jose, Costa Rica. TEL 506-255-29-69. adv.; bk.rev.; charts; illus. circ. 4,000. (reprint service avail. from UMI) **Indexed:** Biol.Abstr., Excerp.Med. (until 1993). **Document type:** academic/scholarly publication.
     Formerly (until 1994): Revista Medica de Costa Rica (ISSN 0034-9909)

610   CL   ISSN 0034-9917
REVISTA MEDICA DE VALPARAISO. (Text in Spanish; summaries in English) 1948. q. $15. Sociedad Medica de Valparaiso, Av. Brazil 1689, Valparaiso, Chile. Ed. Dr. Antonio Barbera. adv.; bibl.; charts; illus. circ. 1,000. **Indexed:** Chem.Abstr.

610   MX   ISSN 0034-9925
REVISTA MEDICA DEL HOSPITAL GENERAL DE MEXICO S.S.A. 1938. m. Mex.$1400($26) Sociedad Medica del Hospital General de Mexico, S.S.A., Dr. Balmis 148, Auditorio Abraham Ayala Gonzalez, Mexico, D.F. 06726, Mexico. Ed. Dr. Patricia Alonso de Ruiz. adv.; bk.rev.; illus. circ. 3,000. **Indexed:** Chem.Abstr., Excerp.Med., Ind.Med.

610   PY   ISSN 0034-9933
REVISTA MEDICA DEL PARAGUAY. (Text in Spanish; summaries in Spanish and English) 1955. q. 500 g.($5) Sociedad de Pediatria y Puericultura del Paraguay, 25 de Mayo y Tacuai, Asuncion, Paraguay. adv.; bibl.; charts; illus.; stat.; index. circ. 800. (tabloid format) **Indexed:** Biol.Abstr.

610   BL   ISSN 0100-0195
REVISTA MEDICA DO ESTADO DO RIO DE JANEIRO. (Text in English, French and Portuguese) 1941; N.S. 1977. 3/yr. free. Secretaria de Estado de Saude, Centro de Informacao Cientifica para a Saude, Secao de Editoracao, Rua Moncorvo Filho, 100-2 Andar, Rio de Janeiro CEP 20211, Brazil. Ed. Henrique Antunes Franco. bk.rev.; abstr.; adv.; index. circ. 3,000. **Indexed:** Biol.Abstr., Chem.Abstr., Excerp.Med.
     Formerly (until vol.42, no.2, 1975): Revista Medica do Estado da Guanabara (ISSN 0034-9941)

610 617   RM   ISSN 0048-7848
REVISTA MEDICO-CHIRURGICALA. (Text mainly in Rumanian, occasionally in English, French, German; summaries in English) 1887. q. 4000 lei($20) Societatea de Medici si Naturalisti din Iasi - Society of Physicians and Natural Scientists, Bd. Independentei 16, P.O. Box 25, 6600 Iasi, Rumania. TEL 98-142980. Ed. Gr. Scripcaru. adv.; bk.rev.; illus. circ. 1,500. (also avail. in microform from UMI) **Indexed:** Biol.Abstr., Bull.Signal., Chem.Abstr., Dent.Ind., Excerp.Med., Ind.Med., Ref.Zh.
—BLDSC (7865.300000); EMDOCS; UMI.

REVISTA MEXICANA DE MICOLOGIA. see *BIOLOGY — Botany*

610   AA   ISSN 0255-6790
                      CODEN: REMJE2
REVISTA MJEKESORE. bi-m. Ministria e Shendetesise - Ministry of Health, Tirana, Albania. TELEX 4205.
—CASDDS.

610   BL   ISSN 0035-0362
REVISTA PAULISTA DE MEDICINA. (Text in English) 1932. bi-m. $70. Associacao Paulista de Medicina, Av. Brigadeiro Luiz Antonio, 278, andar 8, 01318 Sao Paulo SP, Brazil. FAX 011-366773. TELEX 7136. adv.; bibl.; charts; illus. circ. 2,500. **Indexed:** Biol.Abstr., Chem.Abstr., Dent.Ind., Excerp.Med., Ind.Med.
—BLDSC (7869.570000); EMDOCS.

616.98   PO   ISSN 0482-7171
                      CODEN: RPMMAG
REVISTA PORTUGUESA DE MEDICINA MILITAR; orgao dos servicos de saude do exercito, marinha e forca aerea. (Text in English, French, Portuguese) 1953. q. Esc.2.200($40) Escola do Servico de Saude Militar, Rua Infantaria, 16, n. 30, 1200 Lisbon, Portugal. TEL 3887869. FAX 3874991. Ed. Carlos Manuel Vieira Reis. adv.; index. circ. 2,000. (back issues avail.) **Document type:** government publication.
—CASDDS.

610 614.86   FR
REVUE AUTOMOBILE MEDICALE. 6/yr. Automobile - Club Medical de France, 74 av. Kleber, 75116 Paris, France. TEL 47-04-31-30. FAX 47-55-43-97. Ed. Bruno Soubizan. circ. 17,201.

610   FR   ISSN 0035-2330
REVUE D'HISTOIRE DE LA MEDECINE HEBRAIQUE.* (Text in French, Hebrew) 1948. q. 75 F.($12) Societe d'Histoire de la Medecine Hebraique, 177 bd. Malesherbes, 75017 Paris, France. Ed. Isidore Simon. adv.; bk.rev.; bibl.; illus.; index, cum.index. circ. 1,000.

610   FR   ISSN 1247-0163
REVUE DE MEDECINE DE TOURS ET DU CENTRE-OUEST. 1960. 8/yr. 260 F. (foreign 270 F.)(effective 1993). Editions La Simarre, Z.I. No. 2 - rue Joseph-Cugnot, 37300 Joue-les-Tours, France. TEL 47-53-53-66. FAX 47-67-45-05.
     Former titles (until 1984): Revue de Medicine de Tours (ISSN 0557-7721); (until 1967): Revue Medicale de Tours (ISSN 0484-8926)

610 615   FR   ISSN 1240-9782
REVUE DE MEDECINES ET PHARMACOPEES AFRICAINES. 1987. s-a. 100 F. (foreign 150 F.). Agence de Cooperation Culturelle et Technique, 38 rue du Bois Gramond, 33320 Eysines, France. TEL 56-28-38-67. FAX 56-16-06-66. (Co-sponsor: Groupe de Recherche et d'Information sur la Pharmacopee et l'Environnement Tropical) Ed.Bd.
—BLDSC (7932.010000).
     Formerly (until 1992): Medecine Traditionnelle et Pharmacopee (ISSN 1015-0382)

610   FR
REVUE DE PHYTOTHERAPY PRATIQUE. q. (foreign 300 F.). (Institut National de Phytotherapie) Groupe des Revue Associes, 25, rue Dagorno, 75012 Paris, France. FAX 43-47-30-80. (Co-Sponsor: College Francais des Medecines de Terrain et Science Appliquees) adv.
     Formerly: Phytotherapy (ISSN 0292-9406)

MEDICAL SCIENCES 4267

610 FR ISSN 0035-2640
REVUE DU PRATICIEN. 1951. 20/yr. 850 F. (foreign 1050 F.). Editions J.B. Baillere, 37 av. des Champs-Elysees, 75008 Paris, France. TEL 49-53-69-00. FAX 49-53-01-65. Ed. Pierre Louis Fagniez. adv. contact: Marianne Bouilloux-Lafont. bk.rev.; charts; illus.; pat.; index. circ. 59,000. **Indexed:** Biol.Abstr., C.I.S. Abstr., Curr.Cont., Dent.Ind., Dok.Arbeitsmed., Excerp.Med., Helminthol.Abstr., Ind.Med., Nutr.Abstr.
—BLDSC (7942.600000); EMDOCS; Genuine Article; SWETS. **CCC.**

610 551.46 FR ISSN 0035-3493
RA600 CODEN: RVOMAY
REVUE INTERNATIONALE D'OCEANOGRAPHIE MEDICALE. (Text in English, French) 1966. q. 443.10 F. (Institut National de la Sante et de la Recherche Medicale) Centre d'Etudes et de Recherches de Biologie et d'Oceanographie Medicale (C.E.R.B.O.M.), Parc de la Cote, 1 av. Jean-Lorrain, 06300 Nice, France. TEL 93-89-72-49. FAX 93-26-62-27. Ed.Bd. adv.; bk.rev. circ. 2,000. **Indexed:** Aqua.Sci.& Fish.Abstr., Biol.Abstr., Bull.Signal., Chem.Abstr., Curr.Adv.Ecol.Sci., Curr.Cont., Deep Sea Res.& Oceanogr.Abstr., Excerp.Med., Geo.Abstr., Helminthol.Abstr., Ocean.Abstr., Pollut.Abstr., W.R.C.Inf., Water Pollut.Abstr. **Document type:** academic/scholarly publication.
—BLDSC (7925.117000); CASDDS.
Description: Specializes itself in the presentation of scientific work and research with a special orientation towards a number of themes that define the links existing between man and the sea.

610 BE ISSN 0035-3639
CODEN: RMBRDQ
REVUE MEDICALE DE BRUXELLES. 1944. 6/yr. 2000 BEF. Association des Medecins Anciens Etudiants de l'Universite Libre de Bruxelles (A.M.U.B.), Route de Lennik 808, Bte. 612, 1070 Brussels, Belgium. TEL 32-2-555-6062. FAX 32-2-555-6117. Ed. Michel Vanhaeverbeek. adv.; bk.rev.; abstr.; bibl.; charts; illus.; stat.; tr.lit.; circ. 3,000 (controlled). **Indexed:** Biol.Abstr., C.I.S. Abstr., Dent.Ind., Excerp.Med., Ind.Med. **Document type:** academic/scholarly publication.
—BLDSC (7932.037000); EMDOCS; Faxon.
Refereed Serial

610 SZ ISSN 0035-3655
CODEN: RMSRA6
REVUE MEDICALE DE LA SUISSE ROMANDE. 1880. m. 95 SFr. Societe Medicale de la Suisse Romande, 2 Bellefontaine, CH-1003 Lausanne, Switzerland. FAX 021-3239737. Ed. E.C. Bonard. adv.; bk.rev.; charts; illus.; stat.; index. circ. 5,100. **Indexed:** Biol.Abstr., C.I.S. Abstr., Chem.Abstr., Dent.Ind., Excerp.Med., Ind.Med. **Document type:** academic/scholarly publication.
—BLDSC (7932.300000); EMDOCS; Faxon; SWETS.

610 BE ISSN 0035-3663
REVUE MEDICALE DE LIEGE; journal du praticien. (Text in French) 1946. m. 2000 BEF (foreign 2800 BEF). (Universite de Liege) Institut de Medecine, 13 rue Alex Bouvy, 4020 Liege, Belgium. TEL 32-41-437572. FAX 32-41-437572. Ed. H. Kulbertus. adv.; bk.rev.; abstr.; bibl.; charts; illus.; index. circ. 3,000. (also avail. in microform from UMI; reprint service avail. from UMI) **Indexed:** Biol.Abstr., C.I.S. Abstr., Chem.Abstr., Dent.Ind., Excerp.Med., Ind.Med., Ind.Vet., Protozool.Abstr.
—BLDSC (7932.080000); EMDOCS.
Description: Technical journal of interest to physicians; covers all aspects of the medical profession.
Refereed Serial

610 614 RW ISSN 0557-8590
REVUE MEDICALE RWANDAISE. 1968. q. Ministere de la Sante Publique, B.P. 84, Kigali, Rwanda. Ed. Dr. Butera. adv.

REVUE ROUMAINE DE PHYSIOLOGIE/ROMANIAN JOURNAL OF PHYSIOLOGY. see BIOLOGY — Physiology

610 GW ISSN 0035-4481
RHEINISCHES AERZTEBLATT. 1946. s-m. DM.180. (Aerztekammer Nordrhein) W W F Verlags GmbH, Gutenbergstr. 7, 48268 Greven, Germany. TEL 02571-55051. (Co-sponsor: Kassenaerztliche Vereinigung Nordrhein) Ed.Bd. adv.; illus. circ. 36,516. **Document type:** newsletter.
—**CCC.**

610 GW ISSN 0720-390X
RHEUMA; Therapeutische Richtlinien-Diagnosehilfen. bi-m. DM.95 (students DM.80). Verlag fuer Medizin Dr. Ewald Fischer GmbH, Fritz-Frey-Str. 21, 69121 Heidelberg, Germany. TEL 06221-4062-0. Eds. Dr. Otto Bergsmann, Dr. Matthias Heinitz. **Document type:** academic/scholarly publication.
—**CCC.**

610 US ISSN 1061-222X
CODEN: RIMEEF
RHODE ISLAND MEDICINE. 1878. m. $40 (foreign $50). Rhode Island Medical Society, 106 Francis St., Providence, RI 02903. TEL 401-331-3207. Ed. Dr. Stanley M. Aronson. adv.; bk.rev.; bibl.; illus.; index. circ. 1,700. (also avail. in microform from UMI; reprint service avail. from UMI) **Indexed:** A.D.& D., Apic.Abstr., Chem.Abstr., CINAHL, Curr.Cont., Dent.Ind., Excerp.Med., Helminthol.Abstr., Ind.Med. **Document type:** academic/scholarly publication.
—BLDSC (7960.801000); Faxon; UMI; UnCover.
Former titles (until 1992): Rhode Island Medical Journal (ISSN 0363-7913); (until 1976): R.I. Medical Journal (ISSN 0360-067X); (until 1974): Rhode Island Medical Journal (ISSN 0035-4627); (until 1917): Providence Medical Journal (ISSN 0898-1361); (until 1900): Rhode Island Medical Society. Transactions (ISSN 0898-137X)

610 615 IT ISSN 0035-5259
CODEN: RIMEAB
LA RIFORMA MEDICA; rivista quadrimestrale di farmacologia e terapia. (Text in Italian; summaries in English, Italian) 1885. 3/yr. $90 to individuals; institutions $140 (effective 1995). Edizioni Minerva Medica, Corso Bramante 83-85, 10126 Turin, Italy. TEL 39-11-378282. FAX 39-11-3121736. Ed. F. Rossi; Pub. Alberto Oliaro. adv.: B&W page $1100, color page $1900; trim 190 x 270; adv. contact: F. Filippo. bk.rev.; charts; illus.; stat.; index; circ. 3,000 (paid). **Indexed:** Biol.Abstr., C.I.S. Abstr., Chem.Abstr., Dent.Ind., Excerp.Med., Ind.Med. **Document type:** academic/scholarly publication.
—BLDSC (7970.600000); CASDDS; EMDOCS; Faxon.
Description: Covers pharmacology and therapy.

610 JA ISSN 0915-700X
RIGAKU SHINRYO/JOURNAL OF PHYSICAL MEDICINE. (Text in Japanese) 1990. a. 2000 Yen. Nihon Rigaku Shinryo Igakkai - Japanese Society for Physical Medicine, Nihon Daigaku Igakubu Seikei Gekagaky Kyoshitsu, 30-1, Oyaguchi Kamicho, Itabashi-ku, Tokyo 173, Japan.

610 JA
RINSHO KENSA NO SHINPO TO TOMONI. (Text in Japanese) 1980. 4/yr. Kokusai Shiyaku K.K. - International Reagents Corp., 1-30, Hamabe Dori 2-chome, Chuo-ku, Kobe-shi, Hyogo-ken 651, Japan.

610 JA ISSN 0389-1887
CODEN: METCDS
RINSHO KENSAGAKU ZASSHI/MEDICAL TECHNOLOGY. (Text in Japanese) 1973. m. 650 Yen per no. Ishiyaku Publishers, Inc., 7-10 Honkomagome 1-chome, Bunkyo-ku, Tokyo 113, Japan. Ed. Hiroshi Miura. circ. 14,500. **Indexed:** Chem.Abstr.
—CASDDS.

610 JA
RINSHO TAION/CLINICAL THERMOMETRY. (Text in Japanese; summaries in English) 1980. s-a. Rinsho Taion Kenkyukai - Japan Clinical Thermometry Association, Tokyo Ika Shika Daigaku Iyo Kizai Kenkyujo Keisoku Bumon, 3-10, Kanda Surugadai 2-chome, Chiyoda-ku, Tokyo 101, Japan.

610 IT ISSN 0392-4858
RIVISTA DEL MEDICO PRATICO. 1981. w. (44/yr.). L.46000($100) (effective 1994). (Associazione del Medico Practico) Masson S.p.A., Divisione Periodici, Via Statuto 2-4, 20121 Milan, Italy. TEL 02-6367-1. FAX 02-6367211. Ed. Carlo Grassi. adv.: B&W page L.9700000, color page L.14700000; trim 210 x 285. circ. 75,000. **Document type:** academic/scholarly publication.

616.992 616.07
574.2 IT ISSN 0048-8364
RIVISTA DI ANATOMIA PATOLOGICA E DI ONCOLOGIA. 1948. 3/yr. L.90000($125) (Universita degli Studi di Messina, Istituto di Anatomia e Istologia Patologica) Piccin Editore, Via Altinate 107, 35100 Padua, Italy. TEL 049-655566. FAX 049-8750693. illus. (reprint service avail. from UMI) **Indexed:** Biol.Abstr., Excerp.Med. (until 1993), Ind.Med.
—BLDSC (7980.800000).

616.98 IT ISSN 0035-631X
CODEN: RMDSA2
RIVISTA DI MEDICINA AERONAUTICA E SPAZIALE. 1938. q. L.30000 (foreign L.45000). Corps Sanitario Aeronautico, Via P. Gobetti 2, Rome, Italy. FAX 06-49865611. Ed. L. Spuri. adv.; bk.rev.; abstr.; bibl.; charts; illus.; stat.; index. circ. 1,300. **Indexed:** Biol.Abstr., C.I.S. Abstr., Chem.Abstr., Excerp.Med., Ind.Med.
—CASDDS.
Description: Covers aerospace medicine.

610 616 IT
RIVISTA DI MEDICINA E CHIRURGIA. 1979. q. Giardini Editori e Stampatori, Via Santa Bibbiana 28, 56100 Pisa, Italy. TEL 050 502531. Ed.Bd.

616.07 IT ISSN 0035-6417
RIVISTA DI PATOLOGIA E CLINICA. (Text in Italian; summaries in English and Italian) 1946. bi-m. L.60000 (foreign L.120000) (effective 1994). Casa Editrice Maccari, Via Trento 53, 43100 Parma, Italy. FAX 039-521-771268. adv.; charts; illus.; stat.; index. circ. 1,800. **Indexed:** Chem.Abstr., Excerp.Med.
—BLDSC (7992.325000); UMI.

616.07 IT ISSN 0394-4549
CODEN: RPSCEK
RIVISTA DI PATOLOGIA E SPERIMENTAZIONE CLINICA. 1960. q. L.80000($120) Piccin Editore, Via Altinate 107, 35100 Padua, Italy. TEL 049-655566. FAX 049-8750693. Ed. Prof. Giovanni Lanza. adv.; charts; illus. (reprint service avail. from UMI) **Indexed:** Biol.Abstr., Excerp.Med.
—BLDSC (7992.340000).
Formerly (until 1986): Rivista di Patologia Clinica e Sperimentale (ISSN 0035-6409)

155.3 610 IT ISSN 0392-1670
RIVISTA DI SESSUOLOGIA. (Text in Italian; summaries in English and Italian) 1960. q. L.55000 (foreign L.80000) (effective 1994). (Centro Italiano di Sessuologia) Cooperativa Libraria Universitaria Editrice Bologna, Via Marsala 24, 40126 Bologna, Italy. TEL 051-220736. FAX 051-237758. Ed. R. Forleo. adv.; bk.rev.; bibl.; charts; illus.; index. circ. 1,000. **Indexed:** Excerp.Med.
—**CCC.**
Formerly: Sessuologia (ISSN 0037-2838)

610 IT ISSN 0393-1129
RIVISTA ITALIANA DI AGOPUNTURA.* 1973. 3/yr. L.9000. Societa Italiana di Agopuntura, Via Diaz 5, 21047 Saronno, Italy. Ed. Dr. U. Lanza. adv.; bk.rev.; bibl.; charts; illus. circ. 1,000.

610 574 IT ISSN 0393-1137
RIVISTA ITALIANA DI BIOLOGIA E MEDICINA. q. $90 to individuals; institutions $140 (effective 1995). Edizioni Minerva Medica, Corso Bramante 83-85, 10126 Turin, Italy. TEL 39-11-678282. FAX 39-11-3121736. Ed. P.A. Vertova; Pub. Alberto Oliaro. circ. 5,000. **Indexed:** Excerp.Med. **Document type:** academic/scholarly publication.
—BLDSC (7987.291500).
Description: Devoted to the biological and medical aspects of man.

610 IT ISSN 0394-9109
RIVISTA ITALIANA DI COLON-PROCTOLOGIA.* q. L.90000 includes supplement. Promo Leader Service s.r.l., Borgo Pinti, 68, 50121 Florence, Italy.
—BLDSC (7987.293300).

610 IT
RIVISTA ITALIANA DI MEDICINA SOCIALE E PREVENTIVA. 1951. s-a. L.40000 (foreign L.80000) (effective 1994). C E M Casa Editoriale Maccari, Via Trento 53, 43100 Parma, Italy. FAX 039-521-771268. Ed. C. Palenzona. adv.; bk.rev.; charts; illus.; index. circ. 500.
—UMI.
Formerly: Rivista Italiana di Medicina Sociale (ISSN 0025-7915)

MEDICAL SCIENCES

610   IT   ISSN 0394-9982
RIZA PSICOSOMATICA. 1980. m. L.78000. Edizioni Riza, Via Luigi Anelli 1, 20122 Milan, Italy. TEL 39-2-58301022. FAX 39-2-58318162. Ed. Dr. Raffaele Morelli. adv.: B&W page L.3700000, color page L.6600000. circ. 57,500.

610 613   US   ISSN 0091-3472
RA440.6
ROBERT WOOD JOHNSON FOUNDATION. ANNUAL REPORT. Key Title: Annual Report - Robert Wood Johnson Foundation. 1971. a. free. Robert Wood Johnson Foundation, Box 2316, Princeton, NJ 08543-2316. TEL 609-452-8701. Ed. F. Karel. illus. circ. 30,000. **Indexed:** Med.Care Rev. **Document type:** corporate report.

610   UK   ISSN 0305-0688
ROCK CARLING FELLOWSHIP. 1971. a. Nuffield Provincial Hospitals Trust, 59 New Cavendish St., London W1M 7RD, England. Ed.Bd. **Document type:** bulletin.
—BLDSC (8001.450000).

610   US
ROCKEFELLER UNIVERSITY, NEW YORK. SCIENTIFIC AND EDUCATIONAL PROGRAMS. 1979. a. free. Rockefeller University Press, 222 E. 70th St., New York, NY 10021. TEL 212-327-8568. FAX 212-327-7944. circ. 9,000. (reprint service avail. from ISI,UMI).
Supersedes (1955-1979): Rockefeller University, New York. Annual Report (ISSN 0080-3405)

610   IS   ISSN 0374-776X
ROFEH HA-MISHPACHA/FAMILY PHYSICIAN. (Text in Hebrew; summaries in English) 1969. 3/yr. free. Kupat Holim Health Insurance Institution, 101 Arlosoroff St., P.O. Box 16250, Tel Aviv, Israel. TEL 972-3-6923388. Ed. Max R. Polliack. bk.rev. circ. 4,500. **Indexed:** Abstr.Hyg., Biol.Abstr., C.I.S. Abstr., Excerp.Med., FAMLI, Ind.Heb.Per. **Document type:** academic/scholarly publication.
—BLDSC (3865.568000).

610.69   CN   ISSN 0707-3542
ROLLCALL; a status report of selected health personnel in the province of British Columbia. 1974. biennial. free. University of British Columbia, Centre for Health Services and Policy Research, No. 429-2194 Health Sciences Mall, Vancouver, BC V6T 1Z3, Canada. TEL 604-822-4810. FAX 604-822-5690. illus. circ. 250. **Document type:** bulletin.
Description: Describes the distribution of health personnel in British Columbia by health region.

ROMANIAN JOURNAL OF MORPHOLOGY AND EMBRYOLOGY/REVUE ROUMAINE DE MORPHOLOGIE ET EMBRYOLOGIE. see BIOLOGY

610   RU   ISSN 0869-6047
CODEN: VAMEE3
ROSSIISKAYA AKADEMIYA MEDITSINSKIKH NAUK. VESTNIK/ACADEMY OF MEDICAL SCIENCES OF RUSSIA. ANNALS. (Text in Russian; summaries in English) 1946. m. $206 (effective 1996). Izdatel'stvo Meditsina, Petroverigskii pereulok 6-8, 101000 Moscow, Russia. Ed. N.P. Bochkov. bk.rev.; charts; illus.; index. **Indexed:** Biol.Abstr., Chem.Abstr., Dent.Ind., Ind.Med. **Document type:** academic/scholarly publication.
—BLDSC (0032.753000); CASDDS; Genuine Article. **CCC.**
Formerly: Akademiya Meditsinskikh Nauk S.S.S.R. Vestnik (ISSN 0002-3027)
Description: Publishes original scientific papers and review articles on the important problems of medical science and public health practice.

616.98   UK   ISSN 0035-8665
UH201   CODEN: JRAMAI
ROYAL ARMY MEDICAL CORPS. JOURNAL. 1903. 3/yr. £12. Royal Army Medical Corps, RAMC RHQ, Keogh Barracks, Ash Vale Aldershot, Hants GU12 5RQ, England. TEL 01252-340250. FAX 01252-340224. Ed. Col. G.O. Hopkins. adv.; bk.rev.; charts; illus.; index. circ. 1,500. **Indexed:** Abstr.Hyg., Biol.Abstr., Chem.Abstr., Curr.Adv.Ecol.Sci., Ergon.Abstr., Excerp.Med., Helminthol.Abstr., Ind.Med., Trop.Dis.Bull. **Document type:** bulletin.
—BLDSC (4853.000000); Faxon.

610   UK
ROYAL COLLEGE OF GENERAL PRACTITIONERS. OCCASIONAL PAPERS. 1976. irreg., no.70, 1995. Royal College of General Practitioners, 9 Marlborough Rd., Exeter EX2 4TJ, England. TEL 01392-57938. FAX 01392-413449. (Subscr. to: RCGP Sales, 14 Princes Gate, Hyde Park, London SW7 1PU, England. TEL 0171-823-9698. FAX 0171-225-3047) Ed. Dr. Patricia Greenhalgh. adv.; bk.rev. circ. 1,500. **Indexed:** Excerp.Med., Ind.Med. **Document type:** academic/scholarly publication, monographic series.

ROYAL COLLEGE OF GENERAL PRACTITIONERS. OFFICIAL REFERENCE BOOK. see COLLEGE AND ALUMNI

610   UK
▼**ROYAL COLLEGE OF GENERAL PRACTITIONERS. PRACTICE ORGANISATION SERIES.** 1995. irreg. £16.50. Royal College of General Practitioners, 9 Marlborough Rd., Exeter EX2 4TJ, England. TEL 01392-57938. FAX 01392-413449. (Subscr. to: RCGP Sales, 14 Princes Gate, Hyde Park, London SW7 1PU, England. TEL 0171-823-9698. FAX 0171-225-3047) Ed. Dr. Bruce Lervy. **Document type:** monographic series.

616.07 574.2   AT   ISSN 1036-157X
ROYAL COLLEGE OF PATHOLOGISTS OF AUSTRALASIA. BROADSHEETS. 1967. irreg. price varies (free to members). Royal College of Pathologists of Australasia, Durham Hall, 207 Albion St., Surry Hills, N.S.W. 2010, Australia. TEL 61-2-332-4266. FAX 61-2-331-1431. Ed. V. Stoermer. circ. 2,500. **Document type:** monographic series.
Formerly: Royal College of Pathologists of Australia. Broadsheets.
Description: Provides updates in all disciplines of pathology, with emphasis on advances in laboratory medicine; diagnosis and monitoring of common and important disorders, laboratory methods, application and interpretation of diagnostic tests.

610   CN   ISSN 0035-8800
R15
ROYAL COLLEGE OF PHYSICIANS AND SURGEONS OF CANADA. ANNALS/COLLEGE ROYAL DES MEDECINS ET CHIRURGIENS DU CANADA. ANNALES. (Text in English, French) 1968. 8/yr. Can.$40 (Can.$50 in U.S; elsewhere Can.$60) (effective Jan. 1996). Royal College of Physicians & Surgeons of Canada - College Royal des Medecins et Chirurgiens du Canada, 774 Echo Dr., Ottawa, ON K1S 5N8, Canada. TEL 613-730-6200. FAX 613-730-8830. Ed. John Last. adv. contact: Lynne Quon-Mak. bk.rev.; bibl.; charts; illus.; stat.; index. circ. 28,000. (back issues avail.) **Indexed:** Biol.Abstr., Curr.Cont., Excerp.Med. **Document type:** academic/scholarly publication.
—BLDSC (1031.530000); EMDOCS.
Description: Covers continuing medical education, medical history, biomedical ethics, internal medicine and surgery.
Refereed Serial

610   UK   ISSN 0953-0932
ROYAL COLLEGE OF PHYSICIANS OF EDINBURGH. PROCEEDINGS. 1910. 4/yr. £20. Royal College of Physicians of Edinburgh, 9 Queen St., Edinburgh EH2 1JQ, Scotland. TEL 0131-225-7324. FAX 0131-220-3939. Ed. W. Sircus. adv.; circ. 6,100. **Document type:** proceedings.
Former titles: Royal College of Physicians of Edinburgh. Directory; Royal College of Physicians of Edinburgh. Yearbook and Calendar.
Description: Editorials on topical medical issues, basic science and current practice of medicine, medical philosophy, history and ethics, and Royal College affairs.
Refereed Serial

610   UK   ISSN 0035-8819
R31   CODEN: RCPJAX
ROYAL COLLEGE OF PHYSICIANS OF LONDON. JOURNAL. 1966. bi-m. £52 (foreign £80). Royal College of Physicians, 11 St. Andrews Pl., Regents Park, London NW1 4LE, England. TEL 0171-935-1174. FAX 0171-487-5218. Ed. Dr. David Kerr. adv.; bk.rev.; charts; illus.; index. circ. 7,000. (back issues avail.) **Indexed:** Abstr.Health Care Manage.Stud., Abstr.Hyg., Biol.Abstr., C.I.S. Abstr., CINAHL, Curr.Adv.Cancer Res., Curr.Adv.Ecol.Sci., Curr.Cont., Diab.Cont., Dok.Arbeitsmed., Excerp.Med., Helminthol.Abstr., Ind.Med., Kidney, Nutr.Abstr., Trop.Dis.Bull. **Document type:** academic/scholarly publication.
—BLDSC (4856.150000); EMDOCS; Faxon; Genuine Article; SWETS; UnCover.
Refereed Serial

616.98   UK   ISSN 0035-9033
CODEN: JRNMAF
ROYAL NAVAL MEDICAL SERVICE. JOURNAL. 1915. 3/yr. £15. Institute of Naval Medicine, Alverstoke, Gosport, Hants. PO12 2DL, England. TEL 01705-768110. FAX 01705-768106. Ed.Bd. adv.; bk.rev.; bibl.; illus.; index. circ. 1,000. (also avail. in microform from UMI; reprint service avail. from UMI) **Indexed:** Abstr.Hyg., Biol.Abstr., C.I.S. Abstr., Curr.Adv.Ecol.Sci., Excerp.Med., Ind.Med., Trop.Dis.Bull. **Document type:** academic/scholarly publication.
—BLDSC (4862.150000); EMDOCS; Faxon; UMI; UnCover.
Refereed Serial

ROYAL NETHERLANDS ACADEMY OF SCIENCES. PROCEEDINGS; biological, chemical, geological, physical and medical sciences. see SCIENCES: COMPREHENSIVE WORKS

610   UK   ISSN 0144-8676
R35
ROYAL SOCIETY OF MEDICINE. ANNUAL REPORT OF THE COUNCIL. (Previously issued in the Society's Calendar) 1959. a. free. Royal Society of Medicine Press Ltd., 1 Wimpole St., London W1M 8AE, England. TEL 0171-290-2900. FAX 0171-290-2929. circ. 17,500. (reprint service avail. from ISI,UMI) **Document type:** proceedings.
—BLDSC (1423.500000).

610   UK   ISSN 0142-2367
CODEN: RMISDU
ROYAL SOCIETY OF MEDICINE. INTERNATIONAL CONGRESS AND SYMPOSIUM SERIES. 1978. irreg., vol.178, 1991. Royal Society of Medicine Press Ltd., 1 Wimpole St., London W1M 8AE, England. TEL 0171-290-2900. FAX 0171-290-2929. Ed. Lord Walton. **Document type:** monographic series.
—BLDSC (4538.996000); CASDDS; Faxon; Genuine Article. **CCC.**

610   UK   ISSN 0141-0768
R35   CODEN: JRSMD9
ROYAL SOCIETY OF MEDICINE. JOURNAL. 1907. m. £98 (foreign £106). Royal Society of Medicine Press Ltd., 1 Wimpole St., London W1M 8AE, England. TEL 0171-290-2900. FAX 0171-290-2929. Ed. J.D. Swales. adv.; bk.rev.; bibl.; charts; illus.; index. circ. 18,000. (also avail. in microform from UMI; reprint service avail. from ISI,UMI) **Indexed:** Abstr.Hyg., Anim.Breed.Abstr., Apic.Abstr., Biol.Abstr., Biotech.Abstr., C.I.S. Abstr., Chem.Abstr., CINAHL, Curr.Adv.Cancer Res., Curr.Adv.Ecol.Sci., Curr.Cont., Curr.Tit.Dent., Dairy Sci.Abstr., Dent.Abstr., Dent.Ind., Diar.Dis.Res., Ergon.Abstr., Excerp.Med., Helminthol.Abstr., Hort.Abstr., I.P.A., Ind.Med., Ind.Vet., INIS Atomind., Int.Nurs.Ind., Lab.Haz.Bull., Med.& Surg.Dermat., Nutr.Abstr., Res.High.Educ.Abstr., Rev.Med.& Vet.Mycol., Risk Abstr., Trop.Dis.Bull., Vet.Bull. **Document type:** academic/scholarly publication.
●Also available online.
—BLDSC (4864.550000); ADONIS; CASDDS; Faxon; Genuine Article; SWETS; UMI; UnCover. **CCC.**
Formerly (until vol.70, 1978): Royal Society of Medicine. Proceedings (ISSN 0035-9157)
Description: Publishes clinical research and reviews across the range of specialties for general medicine.
Refereed Serial

MEDICAL SCIENCES 4269

610   UK   ISSN 0267-5331
CODEN: JRMSEW
ROYAL SOCIETY OF MEDICINE. JOURNAL. SUPPLEMENT. 1982. irreg. Royal Society of Medicine Press Ltd., 1 Wimpole St., London W1M 8AE, England. TEL 0171-290-2900. FAX 0171-290-2929. **Document type:** monographic series.
—BLDSC (4864.560000); ADONIS; SWETS.

610   UK   ISSN 0268-3091
ROYAL SOCIETY OF MEDICINE. ROUND TABLE SERIES. 1980. irreg. Royal Society of Medicine Press Ltd., 1 Wimpole St., London W1M 8AE, England. TEL 0171-290-2900. FAX 0171-290-2929. **Document type:** monographic series.
—BLDSC (8025.870000).
Formerly: Royal Society of Medicine. Forum Series (ISSN 0144-5618)

RURAL HEALTH F Y I. see *PUBLIC HEALTH AND SAFETY*

610   US
RYPINS' MEDICAL BOARDS REVIEW: CLINICAL SCIENCES. 1933. a. J.B. Lippincott Co., E. Washington Sq., Philadelphia, PA 19106. TEL 215-238-4200. Ed. Edward D. Frohlich. index.
Former titles (until 1987): Rypins' Medical Licensure Examinations; (until 1939): Medical State Board Examinations.

610   SZ
S A B INFORMATION. 5/yr. Holenackerstr. 85C, CH-3027 Bern, Switzerland. TEL 031-550949. Ed. Werner Thuerig. circ. 1,500.

S I R S SCIENCE. see *SCIENCES: COMPREHENSIVE WORKS*

610   PH
S L U JOURNAL OF MEDICINE. (Text in English) 1979. q. free. Saint Louis University, P.O. Box 71, Baguio City 2600, Philippines. TEL 442-3043. Ed. Robert Legaspi. circ. 500.

610   AT   ISSN 0813-1988
S P U M S JOURNAL. 1972. q. Aus.$80. South Pacific Underwater Medicine Society Incorporated, c/o Australian and New Zealand College of Anaesthetists, 630 St. Kilda Rd., Melbourne, Vic. 3004, Australia. TEL 61-3-819-4898. FAX 61-3-819-5298. Ed. John Knight. adv.; bk.rev. circ. 1,400. (back issues avail.) **Document type:** academic/scholarly publication.
—BLDSC (8425.050700); UnCover.

610   US
S T F M MESSENGER. 1968. bi-m. membership. Society of Teachers of Family Medicine, Box 8729, 8880 Ward Pkwy., Kansas City, MO 64114. TEL 816-333-9700. Ed. Stacy Brungardt. adv. contact: Stacy Brungardt. circ. 3,600. **Document type:** newsletter.
Formerly: S T F M Newsletter.
Description: Contains news of concern to family medicine educators, society meetings and organizational information.

616.8   GW   ISSN 0946-0020
S T K. 1985. q. DM.60($43) (effective 1996). (Schmerztherapeutisches Kolloquium e.V.) Urban und Vogel, Lindwurmstr. 95, 80337 Munich, Germany. TEL 089-53292-0. (Subscr. in N. America to: Springer-Verlag New York, Inc., 44 Hartz Way, Secaucus, NJ 07096-2491. TEL 201-348-4033. FAX 201-348-4505)
Former titles: Schmerztherapeutisches Kolloquium (ISSN 0931-5888); (until 1986): Kolloquium Schmerz-Therapie (ISSN 0177-9060)

610   GW   ISSN 0340-644X
SAARLAENDISCHES AERZTEBLATT. 1947. m. DM.90 (students DM.67.50). (Aerztekammer Saarland) W W F Verlags GmbH, Gutenbergstr. 7, 48268 Greven, Germany. TEL 02571-55051. adv. circ. 5,900. **Document type:** newsletter.
—BLDSC (8062.200000). **CCC.**

SAINT GEORGE'S HOSPITAL GAZETTE. see *HOSPITALS*

610   UK
ST. GEORGE'S HOSPITAL MEDICAL SCHOOL. REPORT. irreg. no.6, 1993. St. George's Hospital Medical School, Cranmer Terrace, London SW17 0RE, England. TEL 0181-672-9944. **Document type:** monographic series.

610 362.1   US
ST. JOHN HOSPITAL AND MEDICAL CENTER. MEDICAL BULLETIN. 1979. a. St. John Hospital and Medical Center, 22101 Moross Rd., Detroit, MI 48236-2172. TEL 313-343-3400. Ed. Marilyn T. Wayland. charts; illus. circ. 800. **Document type:** bulletin.

610   II   ISSN 0970-4221
ST. JOHN'S JOURNAL OF MEDICINE. (Text in English) 1988. q. Rs.100($20) St. John's Medical College, Alumni Association, (Subsidiary of: Catholic Bishop's Conference of India Society for Medical Education), c/o Dr. S.V. Srikishna, Gen. Sec., Robert Koch Bhavan, 1st Fl., St. John's Medical College, Bangalore 560 034, India. TEL 565435. Ed. Dr. Ashley D'Cruz. adv.; bibl.; charts; illus. circ. 1,500. (back issues avail.)
Refereed Serial

610   US   ISSN 0892-1334
ST. LOUIS METROPOLITAN MEDICINE. 1979. m. $50. St. Louis Metropolitan Medical Society, 3839 Lindell Blvd., St. Louis, MO 63108. TEL 314-371-5225. FAX 314-533-8601. Ed. Martin M. Pomphrey. adv. contact: Terry Watson. bk.rev.; index. circ. 3,100. (back issues avail.) **Document type:** trade publication.

610   UK   ISSN 0036-312X
ST. MARY'S HOSPITAL GAZETTE. 1890. 8/yr. £2($2.40) St. Mary's Hospital Medical School Students' Union, Paddington, London WC2, England. adv.; bk.rev.; bibl.; charts; illus.; stat.; index. circ. 1,500.

616.98   VE   ISSN 0036-3642
SALUS MILITIAE. 1965. s-a. free. Hospital Central de las Fuerzas Armadas, San Martin, Caracas-1060, Venezuela. (Subscr. to: Apdo. Postal 16.297, Caracas, Venezuela) Ed. Luis Martinez Iturriza. abstr.; bibl.; charts; illus.; circ. 1,000 (controlled).

610   SZ
SAMARITER. 26/yr. Schweizerischer Samariterbund, Postfach, CH-4601 Olten, Switzerland. TEL 062-261818. FAX 062-262141. Ed. Eugen Kiener. circ. 30,639.

610   BE   ISSN 0775-7905
SAMSOM ARTSENPRAKTIJK. (Supplement avail.) (Text in Flemish) 1986. s-m. 3286 BEF. C E D Samsom (Subsidiary of: Wolters Samsom Belgie n.v.), Kouterveld 14, B-1831 Diegem, Belgium. TEL 32-2-7231111. index.
Description: Provides fiscal and administrative advice for doctors in regards to their practices.

610   US   ISSN 0036-4061
SAN DIEGO PHYSICIAN. 1915. m. $25. San Diego County Medical Society, 3702 Ruffin Rd., Box 23581, San Diego, CA 92193. TEL 619-565-8888. FAX 619-569-1334. Ed. Kevin P. Glynn. adv. contact: Katrina Strathmann. bk.rev.; charts; illus.; tr.lit. circ. 3,200. **Document type:** trade publication.
Formerly: San Diego County Medical Society. Bulletin.

610   US   ISSN 0361-705X
SAN FRANCISCO MEDICINE. 1928. 10/yr. $33 (effective 1995). San Francisco Medical Society, 1409 Satter St., San Francisco, CA 94109. TEL 415-561-0861. FAX 415-561-0833. Ed. Toni J. Brayer. adv.; bk.rev. circ. 3,200. **Document type:** trade publication.
Formerly: San Francisco Medical Society. Bulletin (ISSN 0036-4142)
Description: Contains material of interest to physicians residing and practicing in San Francisco County, CA.

610   PH   ISSN 0115-1126
SANTO TOMAS JOURNAL OF MEDICINE. (Includes supplement: Medical Gazette) (Text in English) 1955. bi-m. P.400 (students P.200; foreign $50). (University of Santo Tomas, Faculty of Medicine and Surgery) Santo Tomas University Press, Rm. 207, St. Martin de Porres Bldg., Espana St., Manila 1008, Philippines. TEL 02-731-3101. FAX 632-731-3126. Ed. Benjamin G. Co. adv.; bk.rev.; abstr. circ. 3,500. **Indexed:** Biol.Abstr., Chem.Abstr., Excerp.Med. (until 19??), ExtraMED. **Document type:** academic/scholarly publication.
●Also available on CD-ROM.

610   JA   ISSN 0036-472X
CODEN: SIZSAR
SAPPORO IGAKU ZASSHI/SAPPORO MEDICAL JOURNAL. (Text in English, Japanese; contents page and summaries in English) 1950. bi-m. exchange basis. Sapporo Ika Daigaku - Sapporo Medical College, Nishi-17-chome, Minami-1-jo, Chuo-ku, Sapporo-shi, Hokkaido 060, Japan. Ed.Bd. bibl.; charts; illus.; stat.; index. circ. 500. **Indexed:** Biol.Abstr., C.I.S. Abstr., Chem.Abstr., Curr.Adv.Ecol.Sci., Excerp.Med.
—BLDSC (8075.800000); CASDDS; EMDOCS.

610   CN   ISSN 1182-0063
SASKATCHEWAN MEDICAL JOURNAL. 1970. 4/yr. Can.$25. University of Saskatchewan, Division of Continuing Medical Education, Saskatoon, SK S7N 0W0, Canada. TEL 306-966-7787. FAX 306-966-7673. (Co-sponsor: Saskatchewan Medical Association) Eds. Mona Chappell, Dr. Murray Flotre. adv. circ. 1,900. (back issues avail.) **Document type:** academic/scholarly publication.
Formerly: C M E News (ISSN 0701-4880)
Refereed Serial

610   SU   ISSN 0379-5284
CODEN: SAMJDI
SAUDI MEDICAL JOURNAL. (Text in English; summaries in Arabic, English) 1979. bi-m. £30. Saudi Arabian Armed Forces Ministry of Defence and Aviation, Medical Services Department, P.O. Box 7897, Riyadh 11159, Saudi Arabia. TEL 966-1-4777714. FAX 966-1-4788033. TELEX 401645 RKHPA SJ. Ed. Dr. Saleh al-Deeb. adv.; bibl.; charts; illus. circ. 24,000. (also avail. in microform from UMI; back issues avail.) **Indexed:** Curr.Cont., Diar.Dis.Res., Excerp.Med., ExtraMED. **Document type:** academic/scholarly publication.
●Also available on CD-ROM.
—BLDSC (8076.975000); Genuine Article; UMI. **CCC.**
Description: Covers a broad range of medical problems with emphasis on Saudi Arabia and the Middle East.
Refereed Serial

SAVING HEALTH. see *RELIGIONS AND THEOLOGY — Protestant*

610   BU   ISSN 0562-7192
CODEN: SUMEA4
SAVREMENNA MEDICINA. (Text in Bulgarian; summaries in English and Russian) 1950. bi-m. 390 lv.($130) Tsentar za Informatsiia po Medicina, 1, Sv. Georgi Sofiiski St., 1431 Sofia, Bulgaria. TEL 359 2-522342. Ed. M. Miltchev. circ. 500. **Indexed:** Abstr.Bulg.Sci.Med.Lit., BSL Biol., Chem.Abstr. **Document type:** academic/scholarly publication.
—CASDDS.

610   XR   ISSN 0036-5327
CODEN: SBLEA2
SBORNIK LEKARSKY. (Text in Czech; summaries in English and Russian) 1898. m. 43.20 Kc.($28.60) (Universita Karlova, Fakulta Vseobecneho Lekarstvi) Vydavatelstvi Karolinum, Ovocny trh 5, 116 36 Prague 1, Czech Republic. TEL 29 62 63. (Dist. by: Artia, Ve Smeckach 30, 111 27 Prague 1, Czech Republic) Ed. F. Macholda. bibl.; charts; illus.; index. **Indexed:** ASCA, Biol.Abstr., Chem.Abstr., Curr.Adv.Ecol.Sci., Curr.Cont., Dent.Ind., Excerp.Med. (until 1993), Helminthol.Abstr., Ind.Med., Nutr.Abstr.
—CASDDS.

610   NO   ISSN 0283-9318
CODEN: SJSCEN
SCANDINAVIAN JOURNAL OF CARING SCIENCES. (Text in English) 1987. q. NOK 810 in Nordic countries; elsewhere $139 (effective 1996). (Nordic College of Caring Sciences) Scandinavian University Press, P.O. Box 2959 Toyen, N-0608 Oslo, Norway. TEL 47-22-57-54-00. FAX 47-22-57-53-53. (U.S. addr.: Scandinavian University Press, 200 Meacham Ave., Elmont, NY 11003. TEL 516-352-7300) Ed. Anna-Christina Ek. **Indexed:** CINAHL, Excerp.Med. (until 1993; 1994-), Psychol.Abstr. (1990-). **Document type:** academic/scholarly publication.
—BLDSC (8087.495000); Genuine Article; SWETS.
Description: Strives to communicate scientific knowledge and research findings to diferent groups within the health field such as nurses, occupational therapists, physiotherapists, physicians, social workers and others with an interest in patient care.

SCANDINAVIAN JOURNAL OF CLINICAL & LABORATORY INVESTIGATION. see *MEDICAL SCIENCES — Experimental Medicine, Laboratory Technique*

MEDICAL SCIENCES

SCANDINAVIAN JOURNAL OF CLINICAL AND LABORATORY INVESTIGATION. SUPPLEMENT. see MEDICAL SCIENCES — Experimental Medicine, Laboratory Technique

613.62 615.85   NO   ISSN 1103-8128
▼SCANDINAVIAN JOURNAL OF OCCUPATIONAL THERAPY. (Text in English) 1994. s-a. NOK 595 in Nordic countries; elsewhere $102 (effective 1996). Scandinavian University Press, P.O. Box 2959 Toeyen, N-0608 Oslo, Norway. TEL 47-22-57-54-00. FAX 47-22-57-53-53. (U.S. addr.: Scandinavian University Press, 200 Meecham Ave., Elmont, Ny 11003. TEL 516-352-7300) Ed. Birgitta Lundgren-Lindquist.
—BLDSC (8087.517650).
  Description: Publishes original articles from all branches of occupational therapy
  Refereed Serial

610   NO   ISSN 0281-3432
CODEN: SJPCD7
SCANDINAVIAN JOURNAL OF PRIMARY HEALTH CARE. (Supplement avail. (ISSN 0284-6020)) (Text in English) 1983. q. NOK 920 in Nordic countries; elsewhere NOK $152 (effective 1996). Scandinavian University Press, P.O. Box 2959 Toeyen, N-0608 Oslo, Norway. TEL 47-22-57-54-00. FAX 47-22-57-53-53. (U.S. addr.: Scandinavian University Press, 200 Meacham Ave., Elmont, NY 11003. TEL 516-352-7300) Ed. Christian F. Borchgrevinck. adv.; bk.rev. circ. 6,500. **Indexed**: Biol.Abstr., Excerp.Med., FAMLI, IMFL, Ind.Med. **Document type**: academic/scholarly publication.
—BLDSC (8087.519500); SWETS. **CCC**.

610   NO   ISSN 0284-6020
SCANDINAVIAN JOURNAL OF PRIMARY HEALTH CARE. SUPPLEMENT. (Text in English) 1988. irreg. Scandinavian University Press, P.O. Box 2959 - Toeyen, N-0608 Oslo, Norway. TEL 47-22-575400. FAX 47-22-575353. (U.S. addr.: Scandinavian University Press, 200 Meacham Ave., Elmont, NY 11003. TEL 516-352-7300) **Indexed**: Excerp.Med. (1995-), Ind.Med. **Document type**: academic/scholarly publication.

362   NO   ISSN 0036-5505
CODEN: SJRMAA
SCANDINAVIAN JOURNAL OF REHABILITATION MEDICINE. (Supplements avail.) (Text in English) 1969. q. NOK 780 in Nordic countries; elsewhere $135 (incl. supplements) (effective 1996). Scandinavian University Press, P.O. Box 2959 Toeyen, N-0608 Oslo, Norway. TEL 47-22-57-54-00. FAX 47-22-57-53-53. (U.S. addr.: Scandinavian University Press, 200 Meacham Ave., Elmont, NY 11003. TEL 516-352-7377) Ed. Dr. Olle Hoeok. adv.; bk.rev.; charts; illus. circ. 1,200. **Indexed**: Bibl.Dev.Med.& Child Neur., Biol.Abstr., CINAHL, Curr.Cont., Ergon.Abstr., Except.Child.Educ.Abstr., Excerp.Med., Ind.Med., Psychol.Abstr., Sportsearch.
—BLDSC (8087.530000); EMDOCS; Faxon; Genuine Article; SWETS; UnCover.
  Description: Publishes articles concerned with medical, psychological, social, economic and technological aspects of rehabilitation.

610 360   NO   ISSN 0300-8037
CODEN: SJSMAF
SCANDINAVIAN JOURNAL OF SOCIAL MEDICINE. (Supplement avail. (ISSN 0301-7311)) (Text in English) 1973. 4/yr. NOK 910 in Nordic countries; elsewhere $155 (effective 1996). (Nordisk Socialmedicinsk Foerening - Scandinavian Association for Social Medicine) Scandinavian University Press, P.O. Box 2959 Toeyen, N-0608 Oslo, Norway. TEL 47-22-57-54-00. FAX 47-522-57-53-53. (U.S. addr.: Scandinavian University Press, 200 Meacham Ave., Elmont, NY 11003. TEL 516-352-7300) Ed.Bd. adv.; charts. circ. 900. **Indexed**: Abstr.Hyg., ASCA, Biol.Abstr., C.I.S. Abstr., CINAHL, Curr.Cont., Dent.Ind., Excerp.Med., Ind.Med., Risk Abstr., SSCI, Trop.Dis.Bull. **Document type**: academic/scholarly publication.
—BLDSC (8087.548000); Faxon; Genuine Article; UnCover.
  Formerly: Acta Socio-Medica Scandinavica (ISSN 0044-6141)

362.1 368.4   NO   ISSN 0301-7311
CODEN: SJSSD2
SCANDINAVIAN JOURNAL OF SOCIAL MEDICINE. SUPPLEMENT. (Text in English) 1973. irreg. (Nordisk Socialmedicinsk Foerening - Scandinavian Association for Social Medicine) Scandinavian University Press, P.O. Box 2959 Toeyen, N-0608 Oslo, Norway. TEL 47-22-57-53-53. (US addr.: Scandinavian University Press, 200 Meacham Ave., Elmont, NY 11003. TEL 516-352-7300) **Indexed**: Excerp.Med., Ind.Med. **Document type**: academic/scholarly publication.
—BLDSC (8087.548300); SWETS.

616.98   GW   ISSN 0080-679X
SCHIFFAHRTSMEDIZINISCHES INSTITUT DER MARINE, KIEL. VEROEFFENTLICHUNGEN. 1969. irreg. free. Schiffahrtsmedizinisches Institut der Marine, Kopperpahler Allee 120, 24119 Kiel-Kronshagen, Germany. Ed. B. Greiner. adv.; bk.rev. circ. 2,000. **Document type**: proceedings.

610   GW   ISSN 0341-8707
SCHLESWIG-HOLSTEINISCHES AERZTEBLATT. 1947. m. DM.90. Quintessenz Verlags GmbH, Ifenpfad 2-4, 12107 Berlin, Germany. TEL 030-74006027. FAX 030-7415080. adv. circ. 11,767. **Document type**: newsletter.
—CCC.

610   GW   ISSN 0932-433X
CODEN: SCMZA
DER SCHMERZ (BERLIN); Konzepte, Klinik und Forschung. 6/yr. DM.238($172) (effective 1996). Springer-Verlag, Heidelberger Platz 3, 14197 Berlin, Germany. TEL 030-8207-0. FAX 030-8214091. E-mail: orders@springer.de. (Subscr. in N. America to: Springer-Verlag New York, Inc., 44 Hartz Way, Secaucus, NJ 07096-2491. TEL 201-348-4033. FAX 201-348-4505) **Indexed**: Excerp.Med. (1995-). **Document type**: academic/scholarly publication.
—BLDSC (8090.965000); UMI. **CCC**.

SCHOOL SCIENCE REVIEW. see *SCIENCES: COMPREHENSIVE WORKS*

610   SZ   ISSN 0036-7486
SCHWEIZERISCHE AERZTEZEITUNG/BULLETIN DES MEDECINS SUISSES/BOLLETTINO DEI MEDICI SVIZZERI. (Text in French, German and Italian) 1919. w. 227 SFr. (foreign 349 SFr.). (Schweizerische Aerzteorganisation - Federation of Swiss Physicians) Verlag Hans Huber, Laenggasstr. 76, CH-3000 Bern 9, Switzerland. TEL 031-3004500. FAX 031-3004590. adv.; bk.rev.; bibl.; charts; stat.; index. circ. 25,300. **Indexed**: Biol.Abstr., C.I.S. Abstr. **Document type**: newspaper.
—CCC.

610   SZ   ISSN 0036-7672
CODEN: SMWOAS
SCHWEIZERISCHE MEDIZINISCHE WOCHENSCHRIFT. (Text in French and German; summaries in original languages and English) 1871. w. 150 SFr. (students 45 SFr.) (effective 1995). Schwabe und Co. AG, Steinentorstr. 13, CH-4010 Basel, Switzerland. TEL 061-2725523. FAX 061-2725573. Ed.Bd. adv.; bk.rev.; abstr.; bibl.; charts; illus.; index. circ. 5,500. (also avail. in microform from PMC; back issues avail.) **Indexed**: Abstr.Hyg., ASCA, Biol.Abstr., Biotech.Abstr., C.I.S. Abstr., Chem.Abstr., Curr.Adv.Ecol.Sci., Curr.Cont., Dairy Sci.Abstr., Dent.Ind., Excerp.Med., Helminthol.Abstr., Ind.Med., Nutr.Abstr., Protozool.Abstr., Rev.Med.& Vet.Mycol., Risk Abstr., Sci.Cit.Ind., Trop.Dis.Bull. **Document type**: academic/scholarly publication.
—BLDSC (8118.570000); CASDDS; EMDOCS; Faxon; Genuine Article; SWETS; UMI; UnCover. **CCC**.
  Description: Publishes original research across many medical disciplines; includes continuing education courses for the Swiss Society of Internal Medicine.

610   SZ   ISSN 0250-5525
CODEN: SMWSD9
SCHWEIZERISCHE MEDIZINISCHE WOCHENSCHRIFT (SUPPLEMENTUM). (Text in French, German; summaries in English) 1975. irreg., no.64, 1994. 4.60 SFr. Schwabe und Co. AG, Steinentorstr. 13, CH-4010 Basel, Switzerland. TEL 061-2725523. FAX 061-2725573. adv. circ. 4,500. (back issues avail.) **Indexed**: Ind.Med. **Document type**: academic/scholarly publication.
—BLDSC (8118.571000); CASDDS; UMI.

610   SZ   ISSN 1013-2058
CODEN: SRMPDJ
SCHWEIZERISCHE RUNDSCHAU FUER MEDIZIN PRAXIS/REVUE SUISSE DE MEDECINE. (Text in French and German; summaries in English, French and German) 1911. w. 186 SFr. (foreign 249 SFr.). Hallwag AG, Nordring 4, CH-3001 Bern, Switzerland. TEL 031-3323131. FAX 031-3314133. TELEX 912661-CH. adv.; bk.rev.; abstr.; bibl.; illus. circ. 3,513. **Indexed**: Biotech.Abstr., C.I.S. Abstr., Curr.Cont., Dent.Ind., Excerp.Med., Ind.Med. **Document type**: academic/scholarly publication.
—Faxon.

616.98   SZ   ISSN 0377-8347
SCHWEIZERISCHE ZEITSCHRIFT FUER MILITAER- UND KATASTROPHENMEDIZIN/REVUE SUISSE DE MEDECINE MILITAIRE ET DE CATASTROPHES. (Text in French, German and Italian) q. 60 SFr. (foreign 80 SFr.). (Schweizerische Gesellschaft der Offiziere der Sanitatstruppen) Editions Medecine et Hygiene, Case Postale 456, CH-1211 Geneva 4, Switzerland. TEL 022-3469355. FAX 022-3475610. Ed.Bd. adv.; bk.rev.; charts. circ. 3,200. **Indexed**: Excerp.Med. **Document type**: academic/scholarly publication.
—UMI.
  Former titles: Schweizerische Zeitschrift fuer Militaermedizin (ISSN 0036-8024); Vierteljahrsschrift fuer Schweizerische Sanitats-Offiziere.

610   SZ   ISSN 0080-7400
SCHWEIZERISCHES MEDIZINISCHES JAHRBUCH. (Text in French and German) 1968. a. 135 SFr. (Schweizerische Aerzteorganisation - Federation of Swiss Physicians) Schwabe und Co. AG, Steinentorstr. 13, CH-4010 Basel, Switzerland. TEL 061-2725523. FAX 061-2725573. adv.; index. circ. 5,000. **Document type**: directory.
—CCC.
  Description: Comprised of, in part, a directory of personnel and institutions.

SCIENCE AS CULTURE. see *SCIENCES: COMPREHENSIVE WORKS*

610   FR   ISSN 0048-9727
SCIENCES MEDICALES. revue des universites nouvelles. vol.3, 1972. 6/yr. 205 F. "R" Rhumatologie, 15 rue Turgot, 78100 St. Germain en Laye, France. (also avail. in microform from UMI; reprint service avail. from UMI) **Indexed**: Chem.Abstr., Excerp.Med.

SCIENCES ORGONOMIQUES; revue des lois de la vie. see *BIOLOGY*

610   US   ISSN 0194-9063
SCIENTIFIC AMERICAN MEDICINE. 1978. base vol. (plus m. updates). $299 to individuals; institutions $359. Scientific American, Inc., 415 Madison Ave., New York, NY 10017. TEL 212-754-0550. Eds. Daniel Federman, David C. Dale. adv. circ. 30,000. (looseleaf format) **Document type**: academic/scholarly publication.
●Also available online. Vendor(s): Ovid Technologies (SAMM).
  Description: Current medical information for physicians, with reports on the latest developments in medicine.
  Refereed Serial

610   UK   ISSN 0036-9330
CODEN: SMDJAK
SCOTTISH MEDICAL JOURNAL. 1956. bi-m. £49($98) Hermiston Publications Ltd., 2 Hill Sq., Edinburgh EH8 9DR, Scotland. TEL 0131-668-3753. Ed. Dr. C.D. Forbes. adv.; bk.rev. (also avail. in microform from PMC; back issues avail.) **Indexed**: Abstr.Hyg., ASCA, ASSIA, Biol.Abstr., Biotech.Abstr., Chem.Abstr, Curr.Adv.Ecol.Sci., Curr.Cont., Excerp.Med., Helminthol.Abstr., Ind.Med., Nutr.Abstr., Potato Abstr., Trop.Dis.Bull. **Document type**: academic/scholarly publication.
—BLDSC (8210.900000); CASDDS; EMDOCS; Faxon; Genuine Article; SWETS; UnCover. **CCC**.
  Description: Papers on original investigations in all branches of medicine. Publishes review articles and clinical memoranda, as well as papers on historical subjects of medical interest.

MEDICAL SCIENCES

610   UK   ISSN 0261-3921
SCOTTISH MEDICINE. 1981-1989; resumed 1991. bi-m. free. Hermiston Publications Ltd., 2 Hill Sq., Edinburgh EH8 9DR, Scotland. TEL 0131-668-3753. adv.; bk.rev.; illus.; circ. 5,000 (controlled). **Document type:** academic/scholarly publication.
—BLDSC (8210.925000).

610   US   ISSN 1049-5614
SCRIPPS CLINIC PERSONAL HEALTH LETTER. 1990. m. $29. Phillips Publishing, Inc., Consumer Publishing, 7811 Montrose Rd., Potomac, MD 20854. TEL 301-340-2100. FAX 301-309-3847. Ed. Dr. Donald J. Dalessio.
—CCC.
Description: Promotes good health and ways to overcome and solve medical problems.

610   US
SCRIPPS RESEARCH INSTITUTE. SCIENTIFIC REPORT. 1974. a. free. Scripps Research Institute, 10666 N. Torrey Pines Rd., La Jolla, CA 92037. TEL 619-455-8263. FAX 619-554-6357. Ed. Dennis Blakeslee. circ. 5,000 (controlled).
Former titles (until 1990): Research Institute of Scripps Clinic. Scientific Report; Scripps Clinic and Research Foundation. Research Institute. Scientific Report; (until 1977): Scripps Clinic and Research Foundation. Scientific Report (ISSN 0361-3054)

610   XR   ISSN 0036-9721
                   CODEN: SCMEBF
SCRIPTA MEDICA. (Text mainly in English, occasionally in German or Russian; summaries in Czech, English, Russian) 1922. 8/yr. 80 Kc. or exchange basis. Masarykova Universita, Lekarska Fakulta - Masaryk University, Medical Faculty, Komenskeho nam. 2, 662430 Brno, Czech Republic. Ed. Dr. Milan Dokladal. bk.rev.; charts; illus.; index. circ. 900. **Indexed:** Biol.Abstr., C.I.S. Abstr., Chem.Abstr., Excerp.Med., Ind.Med., Nutr.Abstr.
—CASDDS.
Description: Examines scientific research in medical fields.

610   GW   ISSN 0940-9270
SEIBT MEDIZINISCHE TECHNIK. (Text in English, French, German, Spanish) 1955. a. DM.32. Seibt Verlag GmbH, Leopoldstr. 208, 80804 Munich, Germany. TEL 089-360903-0. FAX 089-364317. circ. 8,000. **Document type:** directory.
● Also available online. Vendor(s): GBI.
Also available on CD-ROM.

618.1   FR   ISSN 1163-1961
                   CODEN: SENSE
LE SEIN. 1991. q. 596 F. (foreign 781 F.) (effective 1996). (French Society of Mastology and Breast Imagery) Masson - Periodiques, Villa Laromiguiere, 75005 Paris, France. TEL 1-40-46-62-00. FAX 1-40-46-62-01. Ed. J-L. Lamarque. adv.; bk.rev.; abstr.; illus. circ. 2,000. **Indexed:** Excerp.Med. (1994-). **Document type:** academic/scholarly publication.
—BLDSC (8219.751500).
Description: Includes 3 sections: original articles, post-graduate teaching and updates, and radio-clinical case reports.

610   GW
SELECTA - MEDIZIN AKTUELL; Magazin fuer den Vertragsarzt. 1959. 10/yr. DM.102 (students DM.63). Selecta Verlagsgesellschaft mbH, Postfach 4240, 65032 Wiesbaden, Germany. TEL 0611-1705-0. FAX 0611-1705379. Ed. Dr. Henning Grosse-Nordhaus, Dr. Alexander Kretzschmar. adv. contact: Sabine Kirchner. bk.rev.; circ. controlled. **Document type:** trade publication.
—CCC.
Formed by the merger of: Medizin Aktuell (ISSN 0323-5386) & Selecta (ISSN 0582-4877); Which incorporated: Praxis-Kurier (ISSN 0030-8056)

610   FR   ISSN 0037-1777
                   CODEN: SHPAAI
LA SEMAINE DES HOPITAUX. Key Title: Semaine des Hopitaux de Paris. 1925. bi-m. 350 F. to individuals (foreign 580 F.); institutions 1670 F. (foreign 2140 F.). (Semaine des Hopitaux) Expansion Scientifique, 31 bd. de la Tour Maubourg, 75007 Paris, France. TEL 40-62-64-00. FAX 45-55-69-20. adv. circ. 16,808. **Indexed:** ASCA, Biol.Abstr., Biotech.Abstr., C.I.S. Abstr., Chem.Abstr., Curr.Adv.Cancer Res., Curr.Cont., Dent.Ind., Dok.Arbeitsmed., Excerp.Med., Helminthol.Abstr., Nutr.Abstr., Protozool.Abstr., Rev.Med.& Vet.Mycol.
—BLDSC (8237.500000); CASDDS; EMDOCS; Faxon; Genuine Article; SWETS.

610   AG   ISSN 0370-9590
                   CODEN: SEMEAS
SEMANA MEDICA. 1894. m. Arenales 3574, 1425 Buenos Aires, Argentina. TEL 824-5673. Ed. Dr. Eduardo F. Mele. circ. 7,000.

610   SP   ISSN 0214-1450
                   CODEN: SEMRE3
SEMER. 20/yr. Saned, S.A., Paseo de la Habana 202-bis, 28036 Madrid, Spain. TEL 1-3594092. Ed. Rafael Tagua. circ. 20,000.

610 616.07   US   ISSN 0740-2570
SEMINARS IN DIAGNOSTIC PATHOLOGY. 1983. q. $169 (foreign $198) (effective 1996). W.B. Saunders Co. (Subsidiary of: Harcourt Brace & Company), Curtis Center, 3rd Fl., Independence Sq. W., Philadelphia, PA 19106-3399. TEL 215-238-7800. FAX 215-238-6445. (Subscr. to: Periodicals Fulfillment, W.B. Saunders Co., 6277 Sea Harbor Dr., 4th Fl., Orlando, FL 32891-4800. TEL 800-654-2452. FAX 800-874-6418) Ed. Dr. Daniel J. Santa Cruz; Pub. Joan W. Blumberg. adv.: B&W page $580, color page $1380; 7 x 10; adv. contact: Steve Gray. abstr.; bibl.; charts; illus.; index. circ. 3,003. **Indexed:** Curr.Cont. **Document type:** academic/scholarly publication.
● Also available online.
—BLDSC (8239.448900); Faxon; Genuine Article; SWETS; UMI; UnCover. **CCC.**
Description: Serves as a forum for the dissemination of information in the field; most issues cover a single topic from various viewpoints.

610   TU   ISSN 1016-5134
                   CODEN: SENDE
SENDROM. 1988. m. Logos Yayincilik Ticaret A.S., Yildiz Posta Cad., Sinan Apt. No. 36 D 66-67, Gayrettepe 80280 - Istanbul, Turkey. TEL 90-212-2880541. FAX 90-212-2116185. Ed. Dr. Aydemir Yalman. adv. contact: Ipek Karisman. **Indexed:** Excerp.Med. (1993-). **Document type:** academic/scholarly publication.
—BLDSC (8241.212000).

610   KO   ISSN 0582-6802
R97.7.K68   CODEN: SUICAC
SEOUL JOURNAL OF MEDICINE/SEOUL UIDAE HAKSULJI. Key Title: Sehur Ruidaihagsurji. (Text in English; summaries in Korean) 1960. q. $20. Seoul National University, College of Medicine, 28 Yongon-dong, Chongno-gu, Seoul 110-799, S. Korea. TEL 82-2-745-2430. FAX 82-2-764-8340. Ed. Soon-Hyung Lee. bk.rev.; circ. 1,500 (controlled). (tabloid format) **Indexed:** Abstr.Hyg., Biol.Abstr., Excerp.Med., Helminthol.Abstr., Nutr.Abstr., Trop.Dis.Bull. **Document type:** academic/scholarly publication.
—BLDSC (8241.810000); CASDDS.

610 615   KO
SEOUL NATIONAL UNIVERSITY. FACULTY PAPERS..* (Text in English; summaries in Korean) 1972. a. Seoul National University, San 56-1, Sinlim-dong, Kwanak-ku, Seoul 151-742, S. Korea. Ed. Byong Seol Seo. **Document type:** academic/scholarly publication.

610   YU   ISSN 0370-8179
SERBIAN ARCHIVES OF GENERAL MEDICINE. (Text in Serbo-Croatian; summaries in English, French and German) 1872. m. 400 din. Serbian Medical Association, Ulica Narodnog Fronta No. 1-3, P.O. Box 838, 11112 Belgrade, Yugoslavia. (Co-sponsor: Serbian Science and Culture Council) Ed. Dr. Ratibor Micic. adv.; bk.rev. circ. 3,000.
—BLDSC (0166.680000).

610   IT
SERENO SYMPOSIA REVIEW. irreg., no.15, 1988. Ares - Serono Symposia, Via Ravenna 8, Rome, Italy.

610   US   ISSN 0730-9627
                   CODEN: PCCRD7
SERONO CLINICAL COLLOQUIA ON REPRODUCTION SERIES. 1980. irreg., vol.3, 1983. Academic Press, Inc., 525 B St., Ste. 1900, San Diego, CA 92101-4495. TEL 619-231-0962. FAX 619-699-6715. (Subscr. to: Order Dept., 6277 Sea Harbor Dr., 4th Fl., Orlando, FL 32887. TEL 800-321-5068) **Document type:** monographic series.
—CASDDS.

610   US
SERONO FOUNDATION SYMPOSIA. 1973. irreg., vol.51, 1983. Academic Press, Inc., 525 B St., Ste. 1900, San Diego, CA 92101-4495. TEL 619-231-0926. FAX 619-699-6715. (Subscr. to: Order Dept., 6277 Sea Harbor Dr., 4th Fl., Orlando, FL 32887. TEL 800-321-5068) (reprint service avail. from ISI) **Indexed:** Chem.Abstr.

SEXUAL ABUSE; a journal of research and treatment. see *PSYCHOLOGY*

SEXUAL AND MARITAL THERAPY. see *PSYCHOLOGY*

610 362.4   US   ISSN 0146-1044
HQ30.5   CODEN: SDISDC
SEXUALITY AND DISABILITY; a journal devoted to the psychological and medical aspects of sexuality in rehabilitation and community settings. 1978. q. $185 (foreign $215) (effective 1996). Human Sciences Press, Inc. (Subsidiary of: Plenum Publishing Corp.), 233 Spring St., New York, NY 10013-1578. TEL 212-620-8000. FAX 212-463-0742. TELEX 12-421139. Ed. Stanley Ducharme. adv. (also avail. in microform from UMI; reprint service avail. from ISI,UMI) **Indexed:** ASCA, Biol.Abstr., CINAHL, Curr.Cont., Curr.Lit.Fam.Plan., Excerp.Med., IMFL, Past.Care & Couns.Abstr., Psychol.Abstr. (1978-), Rehabil.Lit., Sociol.Abstr., SSCI, Stud.Wom.Abstr. **Document type:** academic/scholarly publication.
—BLDSC (8254.485200); Faxon; SWETS; UMI; UnCover. **CCC.**
Description: Provides a forum for clinical and research developments in the area of sexuality as it relates to a wide range of physical and mental illnesses and disabling conditions.
Refereed Serial

610   GW   ISSN 0341-4884
SEXUALMEDIZIN. Austrian edition: Sexualmedizin (Ausgabe Oesterreich) (ISSN 0344-0346) 1972. m. Medical Tribune Verlagsgesellschaft mbH, Rheinstr. 19, 65185 Wiesbaden, Germany. TEL 0611-1705-0. FAX 0611-300365. TELEX 4186160-MTWI-D. adv. circ. 40,000. **Document type:** academic/scholarly publication.
—BLDSC (8254.489000).

610   SZ   ISSN 0170-1908
SEXUALMEDIZIN. 1978. m. 90 SFr. Medical Tribune AG, Baeumleingasse 22, CH-4001 Basel, Switzerland. TEL 061-2718333. FAX 061-2718358. Ed. Dr. Alexander Schulz. adv. contact: Ingeborg Schmidt. bk.rev. circ. 5,000. **Document type:** academic/scholarly publication.

610   GW   ISSN 0944-7105
▼**SEXUOLOGIE.** 1994. irreg. DM.146 (foreign DM.150). (Akademie fuer Sexualmedizin) Gustav Fischer Verlag, Wollgrasweg 49, 70599 Stuttgart, Germany. TEL 0711-458030. FAX 0711-4580334. TELEX 7111488-FIBUCH. Ed.Bd. **Document type:** academic/scholarly publication.
—BLDSC (8254.489300).

610   CC   ISSN 1002-168X
SHAANXI ZHONGYI XUEYUAN XUEBAO/SHAANXI INSTITUTE OF TRADITIONAL CHINESE MEDICINE. JOURNAL. (Text in Chinese) 1978? q. Y3. Shaanxi Zhongyi Xueyuan - Shaanxi Institute of Traditional Chinese Medicine, Xianyang, Shaanxi 712083, People's Republic of China. **Document type:** academic/scholarly publication.
Description: Presents theoretical research, emphasizing clinical applications. Also covers clinical medicine, pharmacy, experimental research, and education.

SHAFTESBURY PEOPLE. see *SOCIAL SERVICES AND WELFARE*

MEDICAL SCIENCES

610   CC   ISSN 1000-0496
                    CODEN: SYXBEE
SHANDONG YIKE DAXUE XUEBAO/SHANDONG UNIVERSITY OF MEDICAL SCIENCES. JOURNAL. (Text in Chinese, abstracts in Chinese, English) 1956. q. Shandong Yike Daxue, Xuebao Bianjibu, No. 44, Wenhua Xilu, Jinan, Shandong 250012, People's Republic of China. TEL 0531-2952424. FAX 0531-2953813. TELEX 390007 MED JN CN. (Dist. overseas by: China International Book Trading Corp., P.O. Box 399, Beijing, P.R. China) Ed. Xi Yaosheng. abstr.; index. circ. 8,000. **Document type:** academic/scholarly publication.
—BLDSC (0579.722600); CASDDS.
Description: Presents research reports on clinical medicine, preventive medicine, and traditional Chinese and Western medicine.

610   615   CC   ISSN 1002-266X
SHANDONG YIYAO/SHANDONG MEDICAL JOURNAL. (Text in Chinese) 1957. m. Y2 per no. Shandong Sheng Weisheng Ting - Shandong Public Health Bureau, No. 1, Qingnian Donglu, Jinan, Shandong 250011, People's Republic of China. TEL 2956921. FAX 2950172. Ed. Xu Jia'an. adv.; bk.rev. circ. 6,800. **Document type:** academic/scholarly publication.
Formerly: Shandong Medical Periodical.
Description: Covers the latest developments in medical research, and serves as a forum to exchange information and ideas.

610   CC   ISSN 0257-8131
                    CODEN: SYDXEE
SHANGHAI YIKE DAXUE XUEBAO/SHANGHAI UNIVERSITY OF MEDICAL SCIENCES. JOURNAL. (Text in Chinese; abstracts in English) 1956. bi-m. $13.32. (Shanghai Yike Daxue - Shanghai University of Medical Sciences) Shanghai Scientific and Technical Publishers, Journal Department, 450 Ruijin 2 Lu, Shanghai 200020, People's Republic of China. Ed. Wu Jue. **Document type:** academic/scholarly publication.
—BLDSC (0579.722700); CASDDS.
Description: Covers original contributions in experimental, clinical studies in general medicine, public health, pharmacy and the related fields.

610   CC   ISSN 0253-9934
R97.7.C5   CODEN: SIHSD8
SHANGHAI YIXUE/SHANGHAI MEDICAL JOURNAL. (Text in Chinese; abstracts in Chinese, English) m. $16.44. Zhonghua Yixuehui, Shanghai Fenhui - Chinese Medical Association, Shanghai Branch, 1623 Beijing Xilu, Shanghai 200040, People's Republic of China. TEL 2531885. Ed. Wu Mengchao. circ. 5,000.
—BLDSC (8254.589900); CASDDS.

SHANGHAI ZHONGYIYAO ZAZHI/SHANGHAI JOURNAL OF TRADITIONAL CHINESE MEDICINE/REVUE DE MEDECINE TRADITIONNELLE CHINOISE/REVISTA DE MEDICINA TRADICIONAL CHINA DE SHANGHAI. see *ALTERNATIVE MEDICINE*

SHANXI ZHONGYI/SHANXI TRADITIONAL MEDICINE. see *ALTERNATIVE MEDICINE*

SHENGLI KEXUE JINZHAN/PROGRESS IN PHYSIOLOGICAL SCIENCES. see *BIOLOGY — Physiology*

610.28   CC   ISSN 1001-5515
SHENGWU YIXUE GONGCHENGXUE ZAZHI/JOURNAL FOR BIOMEDICAL ENGINEERING. (Text in Chinese, English) 1984. q. $80. Sichuan Society for Biomedical Engineering, Chengdu Kexue Jishu Daxue, Chengdu, Sichuan 610065, People's Republic of China. TEL 581554. (Dist. outside China by: Guoji Shudian - China Interanational Book Trading Corp., P.O. Box 399, Beijing, P.R.C. TEL 8414284) (Co-sponsors: West China University of Medical Sciences; Chengdu University of Science and Technology; Sichuan Biomedical Engineering Research and Development Center) Ed. Le Yilun. **Document type:** academic/scholarly publication.
Description: Interdisciplinary journal that covers original research papers, review articles, and brief notes on biomaterials, artificial organs, biomechanics and computer applications to medical systems.

SHEPARD'S - MCGRAW-HILL. MEDICAL MALPRACTICE SERIES. see *LAW — Civil Law*

SHEPARD'S MEDICAL MALPRACTICE CITATIONS. see *LAW — Civil Law*

610   JA   ISSN 0037-3699
                    CODEN: SKIZAB
SHIKOKU IGAKU ZASSHI/SHIKOKU ACTA MEDICA. (Text in Japanese; summaries in English) 1950. bi-m. 3000 Yen exchange basis. Tokushima Igakkai - Tokushima Medical Association, c/o Tokushima Daigaku Igakubu, Kuramoto-cho 3-chome, Tokushima-shi, Tokushima-ken 770, Japan. FAX 0886-33-0771. Ed. Kazunori Ishimura. adv.; tr.lit.; index. circ. 800. **Indexed:** Abstr.Hyg., Biol.Abstr., Chem.Abstr., Excerp.Med., Nutr.Abstr., Trop.Dis.Bull.
—BLDSC (8256.600000); CASDDS; EMDOCS.

500   JA   ISSN 0387-9097
SHIMANE IKA DAIGAKU KIYO/SHIMANE MEDICAL UNIVERSITY. BULLETIN. (Text mainly in Japanese; abstracts, contents page and some articles in English) 1978. a. Shimane Ika Daigaku - Shimane Medical University, 89-1 En'ya-cho, Izumo-shi, Shimane-ken 693, Japan. FAX 0583-21-1731. Ed.Bd. **Document type:** academic/scholarly publication.
Description: Contains research articles on medicine, as well as articles on anthropology, computers, linguistics, history, and translations of literature.

610   JA   ISSN 0386-5959
                    CODEN: SJSCDM
SHIMANE JOURNAL OF MEDICAL SCIENCE; an official journal of Shimane Medical University. (Text and summaries in English) 1977. a. Shimane Ika Daigaku - Shimane Medical University, 89-1 En'ya-cho, Izumo-shi, Shimane-ken 693, Japan. Ed. Yuzuru Kato. charts; illus. (back issues avail.) **Indexed:** Biol.Abstr., Chem.Abstr. **Document type:** academic/scholarly publication.
—BLDSC (8256.716000); CASDDS.
Description: Publishes scientific studies done by the faculty and co-workers of Shimane Medical University.

610   JA   ISSN 0037-3826
                    CODEN: SIZAA7
SHINSHU MEDICAL JOURNAL/SHINSHU IGAKU ZASSHI. (Text in Japanese; abstracts in English) 1952. 6/yr. 9000 Yen($90) Shinshu University, School of Medicine, 3-1-1 Asahi-machi, Matsumoto, Nagano 390, Japan. FAX 81-263-33-5701. Ed. K. Uemura. adv.; charts; illus. circ. 2,000. **Indexed:** Biol.Abstr., Chem.Abstr., Excerp.Med., Ind.Med. **Document type:** academic/scholarly publication.
—BLDSC (8256.870000); CASDDS; EMDOCS.

610.73   JA   ISSN 0385-1982
SHINSHU UNIVERSITY. SCHOOL OF ALLIED MEDICAL SCIENCES. TREATISES AND STUDIES. (Text in Japanese; summaries in English) 1975. a. free. Shinshu Daigaku, Iryo Gijutsu Tanki Daigakubu, 3-1-1, Asahi, Matsumoto-shi 390, Japan. Ed.Bd. circ. 450. (back issues avail.) **Document type:** academic/scholarly publication.

630   CC
SHIYONG ZHONGXIYI JIEHE ZAZHI. (Text in Chinese) m. Changzhi Yixueyuan - Changzhi Medical Institute, 46, Yan'an Lu, Changzhi, Shanxi 046000, People's Republic of China. TEL 33322. Ed. Wong Weiliang.
Description: Discusses the combined application of traditional Chinese medicine and Western medicine.

610   JA   ISSN 0388-9734
                    CODEN: SHIGE5
SHOJINKAI IGAKUSHI/MATSUSHITA MEDICAL JOURNAL. (Text in Japanese) 1980. a. Shohjinkai Medical Society, 2-35, Sotojima-cho, Moriguchi-shi, Osaka, Japan. TEL 06-992-5131.
—BLDSC (5413.255700); CASDDS.

SHONI NO HOKEN/OSAKA CHILDREN'S MEDICAL CENTER. JOURNAL. see *CHILDREN AND YOUTH — About*

630   CC   ISSN 1000-0305
SHOUDU YIXUEYUAN XUEBAO/CAPITAL INSTITUTE OF MEDICINE. JOURNAL. (Text in Chinese) 1980. q. Y14($10) Shoudu Yixueyuan, You'anmenwai, Beijing 100054, People's Republic of China. TEL 861-3291133. FAX 861-3291972. Ed. Xu Qunyuan. **Document type:** academic/scholarly publication.
Refereed Serial

610   JA
SHUKAN IGAKKAI SHINBUN/NEW MEDICAL WORLD WEEKLY. (Text in Japanese) 1950. w. 5000 Yen. Igaku-Shoin Ltd., 5-24-3 Hongo, Bunkyo-ku, Tokyo 113-91, Japan. TEL 03-817-5694. circ. 50,000.

SICHUAN ZHONGYI/SICHUAN JOURNAL OF TRADITIONAL CHINESE MEDICINE. see *ALTERNATIVE MEDICINE*

SIDE EFFECTS OF DRUGS ANNUAL; a yearly critical survey of the world's literature on adverse reactions to drugs. see *PHARMACY AND PHARMACOLOGY*

610   617.6   SL   ISSN 0253-8482
SIERRA LEONE MEDICAL AND DENTAL ASSOCIATION. JOURNAL. 1973. a. Le.17. Sierra Leone Medical and Dental Association, Box 850, Freetown, Sierra Leone. TEL 225539. Ed. Dr. E.C. Gooding. adv.; bk.rev. circ. 200. **Indexed:** Abstr.Hyg., Trop.Dis.Bull. **Document type:** academic/scholarly publication.
Formerly (until vol.3, no.1): Sierra Leone Medical and Dental Association. Bulletin.
Description: Publishes articles on disease patterns in the country and in the West African subregion.

610   SP   ISSN 0214-3011
SIETE DIAS MEDICOS. 1988. 44/yr. 5000 ptas. (Europe 9900 ptas.; elsewhere 10500 ptas.) (effective 1995). Ediciones Mayo, S.A., Muntaner 374 4a, 08006 Barcelona, Spain. TEL 34-3-2090255. FAX 34-3-2020643. Ed. Josep M. Ferrando. adv.; bk.rev.; circ. 30,000 (controlled). **Document type:** academic/scholarly publication.
Description: Covers medical topics and literature. Addressed to general practitioners and specialists.

SIGNAL TRANSDUCTION & CYCLIC NUCLEOTIDES. see *BIOLOGY — Biological Chemistry*

610   SI   ISSN 0037-5675
                    CODEN: SIMJA3
SINGAPORE MEDICAL JOURNAL. (Text in English) 1960. bi-m. S.$240. Singapore Medical Association, Level 2, Alumni Medical Centre, 2 College Rd., Singapore 0316, Singapore. TEL 2231264. FAX 2247827. Ed. Chee Yam Cheng. adv.; bk.rev. circ. 4,000. **Indexed:** Abstr.Hyg., Biol.Abstr., Biol.Abstr., Chem.Abstr., CINAHL, Dent.Ind., Diar.Dis.Res., Excerp.Med., ExtraMED, Helminthol.Abstr., Ind.Med., Ind.Vet., Pig News & Info., Protozool.Abstr., Rev.Appl.Entomol., Rev.Med.& Vet.Mycol., Trop.Dis.Bull., Vet.Bull. **Document type:** academic/scholarly publication.
●Also available on CD-ROM.
—BLDSC (8285.480000); EMDOCS; Faxon; SWETS.

615.8   SW   ISSN 0037-6019
SJUKGYMNASTEN. 1943. 11/yr. SEK 430. Legitimerade Sjukgymnasters Riksfoerbund, P.O. Box 3196, S-103 63 Stockholm, Sweden. TEL 08-241490. FAX 08-217931. Ed. Lena Lindstroem. adv.; bk.rev.; illus.; index. circ. 9,973. (also avail. in audio cassette)
—BLDSC (8294.830300).
Formerly (until 1957): Tidskrift i Sjukgymnastik.

SMITH MEDICAL FUNDING REPORT; the quarterly guide to research - project grant opportunities for hospitals & medical centers. see *SOCIAL SERVICES AND WELFARE*

SNAKEROOT EXTRACT. see *HISTORY*

615.89   UK   ISSN 0951-631X
R131.A1
SOCIAL HISTORY OF MEDICINE ANNUAL. 1970. 3/yr. £54($99) (effective 1996). (Society for the Social History of Medicine) Oxford University Press, Oxford Journals, Walton St., Oxford OX2 6DP, England. TEL 01865-267907. FAX 01865-267773. TELEX 837330-OXPRES-G. E-mail: jnlorders@oup.co.uk. (U.S. subscr. to: Oxford University Press Inc., 2001 Evans Rd., Cary, NC 27513. TEL 919-677-0977. FAX 919-677-1714) Ed. P. Weindlins. adv. contact: Jane Parker. bk.rev.; abstr.; bibl.; cum.index: 1970-1977. circ. 1,000. (back issues avail.) **Document type:** academic/scholarly publication.
—BLDSC (8318.099000); Faxon; Genuine Article; SWETS; UMI; UnCover.
Formerly (until 1987): Society for the Social History of Medicine. Bulletin (ISSN 0307-6792)
Description: Covers all aspects of health, illness and medical treatment, as well as biological aspects of normal life.

SOCIAL RESPONSIBILITY: BUSINESS, JOURNALISM, LAW, MEDICINE. see *PHILOSOPHY*

MEDICAL SCIENCES

610 301   UK   ISSN 0277-9536
RA418   CODEN: SSMDEP
SOCIAL SCIENCE & MEDICINE. 1978. 24/yr. £1345($2139) (effective 1996). Elsevier Science Ltd., Pergamon, P.O. Box 800, Kidlington, Oxford OX5 1DX, England. TEL 44-1865-843000. FAX 44-1865-843010. (Subscr. in U.S. and Canada to: Elsevier Science, 660 White Plains Rd., Tarrytown, NY 10591-5153. TEL 914-524-9200. FAX 914-333-2444) Ed. P.J.M. McEwan. adv.; bk.rev.; index. circ. 1,400. (also avail. in microfilm from UMI; back issues avail.) **Indexed:** Abstr.Anthropol., Abstr.Health Care Manage.Stud., Abstr.Hyg., Abstr.Rural Dev.Trop., Adol.Ment.Hlth.Abstr., ASCA, ASSIA, Behav.Abstr., Bibl.Dev.Med.& Child Neur., Biol.Abstr., Chic.Per.Ind., CINAHL, Curr.Adv.Ecol.Sci., Curr.Cont., Curr.Lit.Fam.Plan., Dairy Sci.Abstr., Dent.Ind., Diar.Dis.Res., E.I., Excerp.Med., FAMLI, Geo.Abstr., IDA, Ind.Med., Int.Nurs.Ind., Lang.& Lang.Behav.Abstr., Med.Care Rev., Mid.East: Abstr.& Ind., Mult.Ed.Abstr., Nutr.Abstr., Popul.Ind., Protozool.Abstr., Psychol.Abstr. (1969-), Res.High.Educ.Abstr., Rice Abstr., Risk Abstr., Rural Devel.Abstr., Rural Ext.Educ.& Tr.Abstr., Soc.Sci.Ind., SSCI, Stud.Wom.Abstr., Tech.Educ.Abstr., Trop.Dis.Bull., World Agri.Econ.& Rural Sociol.Abstr. **Document type:** academic/scholarly publication.
●Also available online.
—BLDSC (8318.157000); Faxon; Genuine Article; SWETS; UMI; UnCover. **CCC.**
Formed by the merger of: Social Science and Medicine. Part A: Medical Sociology (ISSN 0271-7123); Social Science and Medicine. Part B: Medical Anthropology (ISSN 0160-7987); Social Science and Medicine. Part C: Medical Economics (ISSN 0160-7995); Social Science and Medicine. Part D: Medical Geography (ISSN 0160-8002); Social Science and Medicine. Part E: Medical Psychology (ISSN 0271-5384); Social Science and Medicine. Part F: Medical Ethics (ISSN 0271-5392); Which were formerly (until 1980): Ethics in Science and Medicine (ISSN 0306-4581); (until 1976): Science, Medicine and Man (ISSN 0300-9955).
Description: Provides an international forum among social scientists, medical researchers and practitioners, and health administrators and planners.
Refereed Serial

610   SW   ISSN 0037-833X
SOCIALMEDICINSK TIDSKRIFT. 1924. m. (10/yr.). SEK 260 (effective 1995). Slaattervaegen 38, S-178 37 Ekeroe, Sweden. TEL 46-8-560-346-60. FAX 46-8-560-301-21. Ed. Dr. Claes-Goeran Westrin. adv. contact: Ann Appelgren. bk.rev.; abstr.; charts; illus.; index. circ. 4,500. **Indexed:** C.I.S. Abstr., Excerp.Med., Ind.Med. **Document type:** academic/scholarly publication, consumer publication.
—Faxon.

610   SP   ISSN 0213-3601
SOCIEDAD DE ESTUDIOS VASCOS. CUADERNOS DE SECCION. CIENCIAS MEDICAS. 1984. irreg. Eusko Ikaskuntza, Legazpi, 10-1, 20004 Donostia-San Sebastian, Spain. TEL 425111.

610   SP   ISSN 0583-7480
SOCIEDAD ESPANOLA DE HISTORIA DE LA MEDICINA. BOLETIN. vol.14, 1974. a. Sociedad Espanola de Historia de la Medicina, Duque de Medinaceli 4, Madrid-14, Spain. bibl.

616.07   FR   ISSN 0037-9085
CODEN: BSPEAM
SOCIETE DE PATHOLOGIE EXOTIQUE ET DE SES FILIALES. BULLETIN. (Text in French; summaries in English) 1908. 5/yr. 630 F. (foreign 812 F.) (effective 1996). Masson - Periodiques, Villa Laromiguiere, 75005 Paris, France. TEL 1-40-46-62-00. FAX 1-40-46-62-01. Ed. A. Dodin. adv.; bk.rev.; bibl.; charts; illus.; maps; index. circ. 1,350. (also avail. in microform from PMC; reprint service avail. from ISI) **Indexed:** Abstr.Hyg., Biol.Abstr., Chem.Abstr., Curr.Adv.Ecol.Sci., Excerp.Med., Helminthol.Abstr., Ind.Med., Ind.Vet., Nutr.Abstr., Protozool.Abstr., Rev.Appl.Entomol., Rev.Med.& Vet.Mycol., Rev.Plant Path., So.Pac.Per.Ind., Trop.Dis.Bull., Vet.Bull. **Document type:** academic/scholarly publication.
—BLDSC (2747.370000); CASDDS; Genuine Article; SWETS. **CCC.**
Description: Publishes original articles and monographs on epidemiology, trpoical and exotic medicine, human and veterinary parasitology and immunology. Includes minutes of the society's meetings.

610   LU   ISSN 0037-9247
CODEN: BMGLAO
SOCIETE DES SCIENCES MEDICALES DU GRAND-DUCHE DE LUXEMBOURG. BULLETIN. (Text in English, French, German) 1863. 2/yr. free to institutions. Societe des Sciences Medicales du Grand-Duche de Luxembourg, 72 rue de Schoenfels, L-8151 Bridel, Luxembourg. TEL 352-339608. adv.; bk.rev.; bibl.; charts; illus. circ. 1,200. **Indexed:** Biol.Abstr., Chem.Abstr., Dent.Ind., Excerp.Med., Ind.Med. **Document type:** bulletin.
—BLDSC (2752.700000); CASDDS; EMDOCS.
Description: Collection of research papers covering a variety of topics in medicine.

610   MG
SOCIETE DU CORPS MEDICAL MALAGACHE. BULLETIN. (Text in Malagasy) m. Imprimerie Volamahitsy, 101 Antananarivo, Madagascar. Ed. Dr. Rakotomalala.

SOCIETY FOR ENVIRONMENTAL THERAPY. NEWSLETTER. see *NUTRITION AND DIETETICS*

THE SOCIETY NEWSLETTER. see *PSYCHOLOGY*

615.8 371.9   JA   ISSN 0386-9822
SOGO REHABILITATION. (Text in Japanese) 1973. m. 20640 Yen($159) Igaku-Shoin Ltd., 5-24-3 Hongo, Bunkyo-ku, Tokyo 113-91, Japan. TEL 03-817-5704. Ed.Bd. circ. 6,000.
Description: Studies rehabilitation medicine and related medical fields.

610   US
SONOMA COUNTY PHYSICIAN. 1984. bi-m. $18. Sonoma County Medical Association, 3033 Cleveland Ave., Santa Rosa, CA 95403. TEL 707-525-4325. FAX 707-544-0312. Ed. Steve Osborn. adv. contact: Susan Gumucio. circ. 1,000. **Document type:** academic/scholarly publication, bulletin.
Description: Provides a forum for physicians; topics include managed care, preventive medicine, and at-risk behavior.
Refereed Serial

SOURCEBOOK ON ASBESTOS DISEASES. see *LAW*

SOURCEBOOK ON ASBESTOS DISEASES CASE LAW QUARTERLY. see *LAW*

610   SA
SOUTH AFRICAN FAMILY PRACTICE. 1980. m. R.120 (foreign R.175). South African Academy of Family Practice - Primary Care - Suid-Afrikaanse Akademie van Huisartspraktyk - Primere Sorg, P.O. Box 3172, Cramerview 2060, South Africa. TEL 27-11-4635252. FAX 27-11-4635256. Ed. Sam Fehrsen. abstr. **Document type:** academic/scholarly publication.
Formerly (until Apr. 1994): S A Family Practice - S A Huisartspraktyk.
Description: Publishes original research contributions from family practitioners and primary health care workers, as well as news of issues, meetings and forthcoming events of interest to members.
Refereed Serial

610 574   SA
SOUTH AFRICAN INSTITUTE FOR MEDICAL RESEARCH. PUBLICATION. (Text in English) 1917. irreg. South African Institute for Medical Research, P.O. Box 1038, Johannesburg 2000, South Africa. FAX 011-725-2319. TELEX 4-22211. circ. 150. (back issues avail.)

615.8   SA   ISSN 0038-2337
SOUTH AFRICAN JOURNAL OF OCCUPATIONAL THERAPY. (Text in English) 1949. 2/yr. R.30 (foreign R.60) (effective 1995). South African Association of Occupational Therapists, P.O. Box 145, Rondebosch 7700, South Africa. TEL 27-2241-42244. FAX 27-2241-42244. TELEX 95-527943 SA. Ed. Valerie Claxton. adv.; bk.rev.; abstr.; bibl.; charts; illus.; pat.; stat.; circ. 900 (controlled). **Indexed:** Ind.S.A.Per. **Document type:** academic/scholarly publication.
—BLDSC (8339.305000).

610 360   SA
SOUTH AFRICAN MEDICAL AND DENTAL COUNCIL. REGISTER OF SUPPLEMENTARY HEALTH SERVICES PROFESSIONS. a. (with m. supplements). R.90 (plus R.6 for supplements). South African Medical and Dental Council, P.O. Box 205, Pretoria 0001, South Africa. TEL 27-12-286680. FAX 27-12-285120. **Document type:** directory.
Description: Provides names and addresses of all supplementary health services personnel registered with the council.

610   SA   ISSN 0256-9574
R98   CODEN: SAMJAF
SOUTH AFRICAN MEDICAL JOURNAL/SUID-AFRIKAANSE MEDIESE TYDSKRIF. Key Title: S A M J. (Text in Afrikaans, English) 1884. m. R.205 (foreign R.320($95)) (effective 1995). (Medical Association of South Africa - Mediese Vereniging van Suid-Afrika) M A S A Publications, Private Bag X1, Pinelands 7430, South Africa. TEL 27-21-531-3081. FAX 27-21-531-4126. Ed. D.J. Ncayiyana. adv.; bk.rev.; bibl.; illus.; index. circ. 20,000. **Indexed:** Abstr.Hyg., ASCA, Bibl.Dev.Med.& Child Neur., Biol.Abstr., Biotech.Abstr., C.I.S. Abstr., Chem.Abstr., CINAHL, Curr.Adv.Cancer Res., Curr.Adv.Ecol.Sci., Curr.Cont., Dairy Sci.Abstr., Dent.Ind., Diar.Dis.Res., Dok.Arbeitsmed., Excerp.Med., Food Sci.& Tech.Abstr., Helminthol.Abstr., Ind.Med., Ind.S.A.Per., Ind.Vet., Med.& Surg.Dermat., Nutr.Abstr., Protozool.Abstr., Rev.Med.& Vet.Mycol., Rev.Plant Path., Trop.Dis.Bull., Vet.Bull., W.R.C.Inf., World Agri.Econ.& Rural Sociol.Abstr., Zoo.Rec. **Document type:** academic/scholarly publication.
—BLDSC (8341.700000); CASDDS; EMDOCS; Faxon; Genuine Article; SWETS; UMI; UnCover.
Formerly (until 1985): South African Medical Journal (ISSN 0038-2469); Incorporates (as special issue, from vol.11, 1973): South African Journal of Obstetrics and Gynecology (ISSN 0038-2329)

610   SA   ISSN 0081-248X
R854.S6
SOUTH AFRICAN MEDICAL RESEARCH COUNCIL. ANNUAL REPORT. Key Title: Annual Report of the South African Medical Research Council. 1969. a. free. Medical Research Council, P.O. Box 19070, Tygerberg 7505, South Africa. TEL 27-21-938-0205. FAX 27-21-938-0395. Eds. Leverne Gething, Michelle Galloway. **Document type:** corporate report.
Supersedes in part (in 1989): South African Medical Research Council. Research Report (ISSN 1015-2377); Which supersedes (in 1985): South African Institute for Medical Research. Annual Report (ISSN 0375-1880)
Description: Summarizes the research activities of the council during the preceding year, lists current research programs and units, and provides financial statements.

SOUTH AFRICAN SOCIETY OF PATHOLOGISTS. CONGRESS BROCHURE. see *MEETINGS AND CONGRESSES*

MEDICAL SCIENCES

610 — US — ISSN 0038-3139 — CODEN: JSCMAZ
SOUTH CAROLINA MEDICAL ASSOCIATION. JOURNAL. 1905. m. $25 to non-members; members $15. South Carolina Medical Association, Box 11188, Columbia, SC 29211. TEL 803-798-6207. FAX 803-772-6783. Ed. Dr. Charles S. Bryan. adv.; bk.rev.; charts; illus.; index; circ. 4,500 (controlled). (also avail. in microform from UMI; reprint service avail. from UMI) **Indexed:** Biol.Abstr., Chem.Abstr., Ind.Med., INIS Atomind. **Document type:** academic/scholarly publication.
—BLDSC (4902.110000); Faxon; SWETS; UMI; UnCover.
Refereed Serial

610 — US — ISSN 0038-3317 — CODEN: SDMEAL
SOUTH DAKOTA JOURNAL OF MEDICINE. 1946. m. $15 (foreign $18). South Dakota State Medical Association, 1323 S. Minnesota Ave., Sioux Falls, SD 57105. TEL 605-336-1965. FAX 605-336-0270. Eds. Drs. Jerome Freeman, John Barlow. adv.; bk.rev.; abstr.; illus.; index; circ. 1,400 (controlled). **Indexed:** Biol.Abstr., Chem.Abstr., Ind.Med. **Document type:** academic/scholarly publication.
—BLDSC (8350.900000); Faxon.
Refereed Serial

610 — US — ISSN 0038-4348
R11 — CODEN: SMJOAV
SOUTHERN MEDICAL JOURNAL. 1908. m. $70 (foreign $95) (effective 1996). Southern Medical Association, 35 Lakeshore Dr., Box 190088, Birmingham, AL 35219-0088. TEL 205-945-1840. FAX 205-945-1548. Ed. Dr. Graham Smith, Jr Pub. William J. Ranieri. adv. contact: Wency Ried. bibl.; charts; illus.; index. circ. 31,000. (also avail. in microform from UMI; back issues avail; reprint service avail.) **Indexed:** Adol.Ment.Hlth.Abstr., AIM, ASCA, Biol.Abstr., Biotech.Abstr., C.I.S. Abstr., Chem.Abstr., CINAHL, Curr.Adv.Cancer Res., Curr.Cont., Curr.Lit.Fam.Plan., Dent.Ind., Dok.Arbeitsmed., Excerp.Med., Helminthol.Abstr., Hosp.Lit.Ind., HRIS, Ind.Med., Med.& Surg.Dermat., Nutr.Abstr., Protozool.Abstr., Rehabil.Lit., Rev.Med.& Vet.Mycol., Rev.Plant Path., Trop.Dis.Bull. **Document type:** academic/scholarly publication.
—BLDSC (8354.400000); CASDDS; EMDOCS; Faxon; SWETS; UMI; UnCover.
Description: Geared toward practicing physicians and surgeons. Presents original articles and papers in clinical medicine.
Refereed Serial

614.44 — SZ — ISSN 0303-8408 — CODEN: SZPMAA
SOZIAL- UND PRAEVENTIVMEDIZIN/MEDECINE SOCIALE ET PREVENTIVE. (Text and summaries in English, French and German) 1955. bi-m. 239.80 SFr. (foreign 251.30 SFr.). (Schweizerische Gesellschaft fuer Sozial und Praeventivmedizin - Swiss Society of Social and Preventive Medicine) Birkhaeuser Verlag, P.O. Box 133, CH-4010 Basel, Switzerland. TEL 061-2717400. FAX 061-2717666. (Dist. in N. America by: Springer-Verlag, Mercedes Distribution Center, 160 Imlay St., Brooklyn, NY 11231, USA) Ed. R. Steffen. adv.; bk.rev.; abstr.; bibl.; charts; illus.; index. **Indexed:** Abstr.Hyg., ASCA, Biol.Abstr., C.I.S. Abstr., Chem.Abstr., Excerp.Med., Helminthol.Abstr., Ind.Med., Trop.Dis.Bull. **Document type:** academic/scholarly publication.
—BLDSC (8361.009000); CASDDS; Genuine Article; SWETS.
Formerly: Zeitschrift fuer Praeventivmedizin (ISSN 0044-3379)

610 — SZ
SOZIALE MEDIZIN. 1974. 6/yr. 63 SFr. (foreign 70 SFr.). Schweizerische Gesellschaft fuer ein Soziales Gesundheitswesen, Postfach, CH-4007 Basel, Switzerland. TEL 061-6911332. Ed. Ruedi Spoendlin. adv. contact: Fritz Wilechi. bk.rev. circ. 3,200. **Document type:** bulletin.

610 — PK — ISSN 1017-4699 — CODEN: SPCAE
SPECIALIST; Pakistan's journal of medical sciences. (Text in English) 1984. q. Rs.250($35) Doctor Publications, P.O. Box 8766, Raja Ghazanfar Ali Rd., Saddar, Karachi, Pakistan. TEL 92-21-5688791. FAX 92-21-5689860. Ed. M. Jalisi. adv. contact: Shaukat Ali Juwaid. bk.rev. circ. 2,000. **Indexed:** Excerp.Med. (1992-), ExtraMED. **Document type:** academic/scholarly publication.
● Also available on CD-ROM.
—BLDSC (8404.772500).
Description: Publishes original research articles, case reports of interesting and rare diseases, and review articles.
Refereed Serial

616.07 — US — ISSN 0081-3699
SPEZIELLE PATHOLOGISCHE ANATOMIE. 1966. irreg. price varies. Springer-Verlag, 175 Fifth Ave., New York, NY 10010. TEL 212-460-1500. FAX 212-473-6272. (Also: Berlin, Heidelberg, Tokyo and Vienna) (reprint service avail. from ISI) **Document type:** academic/scholarly publication.

610 — UK — ISSN 0038-741X
SPHINCTER. (Supplement avail.: Sphincter Minimi) 1937. 2/yr. £0.50. University of Liverpool, Medical School, Royal Liverpool Hospital, Box 147, Liverpool L69 3BX, England. Ed. Callum Pearce. adv.; bk.rev.; circ. 900 (controlled).

616.04 — US — ISSN 0160-9475
SPINA BIFIDA THERAPY.* 1978. q. Eterna International, Inc., Box 6558, Flushing, NY 11365-6558. Ed. Stephen B. Parrish. bk.rev. **Indexed:** Psychol.Abstr.

610 — GW — ISSN 0932-0555
SPORTVERLETZUNG - SPORTSCHADEN. 1987. q. DM.148. Georg Thieme Verlag, Ruedigerstr. 14, 70469 Stuttgart, Germany. TEL 0711-8931-0. FAX 0711-8931298. (Subscr. to: Postfach 104853, 70042 Stuttgart, Germany) Ed.Bd. circ. 1,500. **Document type:** academic/scholarly publication.
—BLDSC (8419.860600); SWETS.

610 — SZ
SPRECHSTUNDE. 6/yr. Alpenblickstr. 15, CH-8630 Rueti, Switzerland. TEL 055-321934. Ed. Augie Hagmann. circ. 142,000.

SPRINGER SERIES ON MEDICAL EDUCATION. see EDUCATION — Higher Education

610 — YU — ISSN 0081-3966 — CODEN: SUGMAW
SRPSKA AKADEMIJA NAUKA I UMETNOSTI. ODELJENJE MEDICINSKIH NAUKA. GLAS. (Text in Serbo-Croatian; summaries in English, French, German or Russian) 1949. N.S. irreg. price varies. Srpska Akademija Nauka i Umetnosti, Knez Mihailova 35, 11001 Belgrade, Serbia, Yugoslavia. (Dist. by: Prosveta, Terazije 16, Belgrade, Serbia, Yugoslavia) circ. 1,000. **Indexed:** Excerp.Med., Ind.Med.
—BLDSC (0050.130000).

610 — YU — ISSN 0081-4016
SRPSKA AKADEMIJA NAUKA I UMETNOSTI. ODELJENJE MEDICINSKIH NAUKA. POSEBNA IZDANJA. (Text in Serbo-Croatian; summaries in English, French, German or Russian) 1950. irreg. price varies. Srpska Akademija Nauka i Umetnosti, Knez Mihailova 35, 11001 Belgrade, Serbia, Yugoslavia. FAX 38-11-182-825. TELEX 72593 SANU YU. (Dist. by: Prosveta, Terazije 16, Belgrade, Serbia, Yugoslavia) circ. 1,000. **Indexed:** Chem.Abstr., Excerp.Med., Ind.Med.

610 — YU — ISSN 0049-0210
SRPSKI ARHIV ZA CELOKUPNO LEKARSTVO/SERBIAN ARCHIVES OF ENTIRE MEDICINE. (Text in Serbo-Croatian, written in Cyrillic alphabet; title and some summaries in English, French, German) 1872. m. 2000 din. Srpsko Lekarsko Drustvo, Dzordza Vasingtona 19, Belgrade, Yugoslavia. Ed. Vladimir Slavkovic. illus. **Indexed:** Biol.Abstr., Dent.Ind., Excerp.Med., Ind.Med., Nutr.Abstr.

614 — IT — ISSN 0038-9323
STAMPA MEDICA. 1960. s-m. (21/yr.). L.35000. E S I Stampa Medica s.r.l., Casella Postale 42, Lgo. Volontari del Sangue 10, 20097 S. Donato, Milan, Italy. TEL 39-2-5274241. FAX 39-2-55600670. TELEX 324894. Ed. Diego Onestinghel. adv.: B&W page L.12100000, color page L.15000000; trim 171 x 235; adv. contact: Ornella Galbiati. bk.rev. circ. 69,000.

STATE HEALTH NOTES. see PUBLIC HEALTH AND SAFETY

STATISTICAL METHODS IN MEDICAL RESEARCH. see STATISTICS

STEROIDS. see BIOLOGY — Biological Chemistry

610 — CN — ISSN 1199-1747
STITCHES; the journal of medical humour. 1990. 10/yr. Can.$38 (in the U.S. $40; elsewhere $60) (effective 1995). Stitches Publishing Inc., 16787 Warden Ave., R.R. 3, Newmarket, ON L3Y 4W1, Canada. TEL 905-853-1884. FAX 905-853-6565. Ed. Simon Hally; Pub. John Cocker. adv. contact: Don Kirkpatrick. bk.rev.; illus.; circ. 42,000 (controlled). (back issues avail.) **Document type:** trade publication.
Formerly (until 1993): Punch Digest for Canadian Doctors (ISSN 1182-5405)
Description: A humor and life-style magazine for physicians.

610 — US
STRAUB FOUNDATION. PROCEEDINGS. 1952. s-a. free to physicians and librarians. Straub Foundation, 1100 Ward Ave., Ste. 1010, Honolulu, HI 96814. TEL 808-524-6755. FAX 808-531-0123. Ed. Dr. Bo Eklof. adv.; bk.rev.; charts; illus.; index. circ. 2,500. (also avail. in microfiche; reprint service avail. from UMI) **Document type:** proceedings, academic/scholarly publication.
Former titles (until 1995): Straub Pacific Health Foundation Proceedings; (until 1988): Straub Proceedings (ISSN 0741-8930); (until 1982): Straub Clinic Proceedings (ISSN 0039-2251); (until 1982): Straub Clinic Staff Meetings. Proceedings (ISSN 0093-3538)

STRITCH M.D.. see COLLEGE AND ALUMNI

323.4 — US
STROKE CLUB INTERNATIONAL BULLETIN. 1971. a. Stroke Clubs International, 805 12th St., Galveston, TX 77550. TEL 409-762-1022. Ed. John Ellis Williamson. bibl. circ. 45,000. **Document type:** bulletin.
Description: Contains information about the rights of citizens who have suffered from strokes.

610 — DK — ISSN 0039-2634
STUD. MED. 1936. irreg. (2-4/yr.). DKK 100. Danish Medical Students Association, Blegdamsvej 3, DK-2200 Copenhagen N, Denmark. Ed. Niels Saxtrup. bk.rev.; illus.; pat.; circ. 5,000 (controlled). **Description:** Written by and for medical students in Denmark on all kinds of medical subjects. Includes short stories and poetry.

610 — UK — ISSN 0966-6494
STUDENT B M J. (British Medical Journal) (Supplement to: B M J (ISSN 0959-535X) 1992. m. £34($62) to individuals; institutions £58 ($91). B M J Publishing Group, B.M.A. House, Tavistock Sq., London WC1H 9HR, England. TEL 0171-383-4499. FAX 0171-383-6661. (N. American subscr. to: Box 408, Franklin, MA 02038. TEL 800-2-FON-BMJ. FAX 800-2-FAX-BMJ) Ed. Luisa Dillner. **Document type:** academic/scholarly publication.
—BLDSC (8479.729500).

610 — SA
▼**STUDENT B M J (SOUTH AFRICAN EDITION).** (British Medical Journal) (Text in English) 1994. bi-m. George Warman Publications (Pty.) Ltd., P.O. Box 3847, Cape Town 8000, South Africa. TEL 27-21-245320. FAX 27-21-261332. adv.; illus. **Document type:** academic/scholarly publication.

MEDICAL SCIENCES 4275

610   IT   ISSN 0371-3172
CODEN: SSSEAK
STUDI SASSARESI. (Text in Italian; summaries in English) 1932. q. L.40000. Societa Sassarese di Scienze Mediche e Naturali, Vale Mancini 1, Piazza Universita, 07100 Sassari, Italy. (Subscr. to: Institute of Human Physiology, Via Muroni 23A, 07100 Sassari, Italy) Ed. Pierangelo Catalano. adv.; index. circ. 1,000. (back issues avail.) **Indexed:** Biol.Abstr., Excerp.Med., Food Sci.& Tech.Abstr. —CASDDS.

610   PL   ISSN 0860-9594
STUDIA SOCIETATIS SCIENTIARUM TORUNENSIS. SECTIO H. MEDICINA. 1989. irreg., vol.1, no.2, 1991. price varies. Towarzystwo Naukowe w Toruniu, Ul. Wysoka 16, 87-100 Torun, Poland. TEL 48-56-23941. TELEX 552388 FSBH PL. Ed. Lech Bieganowski. circ. 220. **Document type:** monographic series.
—BLDSC (8482.100000).

610   GW   ISSN 0081-7333
CODEN: SMNJA2
STUDIEN ZUR MEDIZINGESCHICHTE DES NEUNZEHNTEN JAHRUNDERTS. 1963. irreg. Vandenhoeck und Ruprecht, Robert-Bosch-Breite 6, 37079 Goettingen, Germany. TEL 0551-6959-0. FAX 0551-695917. (Subscr. to: 37070 Goettingen, Germany) **Document type:** monographic series.
Description: Studies medical history of the nineteenth century.

610.09   NE   ISSN 0925-1421
STUDIES IN ANCIENT MEDICINE. 1990. irreg., vol.12, 1995. price varies. E.J. Brill, P.O. Box 9000, 2300 PA Leiden, Netherlands. TEL 31-71-5353500. FAX 31-71-5317532. TELEX 39296 BRILL NL. (In N. America: E.J. Brill, 24 Hudson St., Kinderhook, NY 12106. TEL 800-962-4406. FAX 518-758-1959) Ed. John Scarborough. (back issues avail.) **Document type:** monographic series.
Description: Scholarly monographs on historical texts and their authors, materia medica, and related topics in ancient medicine.
Refereed Serial

610.28   NE   ISSN 0926-9630
STUDIES IN HEALTH TECHNOLOGY AND INFORMATICS. (Text in English) 1992. irreg., vol.18, 1995. price varies. I O S Press, Van Diemenstraat 94, 1013 CN Amsterdam, Netherlands. TEL 31-20-6382189. FAX 31-20-6203419. E-mail: marie-louise.kok@ios.nl. (In N. America: Box 10558, Burke, VA 22009-0558. TEL 703-323-5554. FAX 703-250-4705) Ed.Bd. (back issues avail.) **Document type:** monographic series, proceedings.
—BLDSC (8490.628200).
Description: Publishes papers and studies dealing with the impact of technological developments and information sciences on health care and health policy, particularly in Europe.

610   II   ISSN 0970-5562
STUDIES IN HISTORY OF MEDICINE AND SCIENCE. (Text in English) 1977. q. Rs.100($25) Jamia Hamdard, Department of History of Medicine and Science - Hamdard University, Hamdard Nagar, New Delhi 110 062, India. Ed. Hakim Abdul Hameed. bk.rev. circ. 600.
—BLDSC (8490.673300).
Formerly (until 1984): Studies in History of Medicine (ISSN 0379-3915)

610 614   UK   ISSN 0473-8837
STUDIES ON CURRENT HEALTH PROBLEMS. 1962. irreg. price varies. (Association of the British Pharmaceutical Industry) Office of Health Economics, 12 Whitehall, London SW1A 2DY, England. FAX 071-976-1962. Ed.Bd. charts. circ. 15,000.
—BLDSC (8490.320000).

610   US   ISSN 1060-4351
STURZA'S MEDICAL INVESTMENT LETTER. 1991. irreg. (45-50/yr.). $295. Taurus Littrow Publishing, Inc., 424 W. End Ave., 7th Fl., New York, NY 10024. TEL 212-873-7200. FAX 212-873-7799. Ed. Evan Sturza. index, cum.index. (back issues avail.; also avail. by fax) **Document type:** newsletter.
Description: Assess the most promising stocks and emerging medical technologies in the healthcare industry.

610   SJ   ISSN 0491-4481
SUDAN MEDICAL JOURNAL. (Text in English) vol.12, 1974. q. $10. (Sudan Medical Association) Khartoum University Press, P.O. Box 321, Khartoum, Sudan. Ed. D.M.Y. Sukkar. adv.; charts; illus.; index. circ. 2,000. **Indexed:** C.I.S. Abstr., ExtraMED. **Document type:** academic/scholarly publication.
●Also available on CD-ROM.

610   II   ISSN 0971-0272
SUDHANIDHI. (Text in Hindi) 1973. m. Rs.35. Dhanvantari Karyalaya, Aligarha, India. Ed. Sri Raghivir Prasad Trivedi. adv.; bk.rev. circ. 12,000.

610 500   GW   ISSN 0039-4564
Q3   CODEN: SZWBAC
SUDHOFFS ARCHIV; Zeitschrift fuer Wissenschaftsgeschichte. (Text in English, French, German) 1908. s-a. DM.148 (supplements individually priced). Franz Steiner Verlag Wiesbaden GmbH, Birkenwaldstr. 44, 70191 Stuttgart, Germany. TEL 0711-2582-0. FAX 0711-2582390. (Subscr. to: Postfach 101061, 70009 Stuttgart, Germany) Ed.Bd. adv.; bk.rev.; bibl.; illus.; index. circ. 500. (back issues avail.) **Indexed:** Amer.Hist.& Life, Chem.Abstr., Excerp.Med., Hist.Abstr., Ind.Med., Math.R. **Document type:** academic/scholarly publication.
—BLDSC (8509.150000); SWETS. **CCC**.
Formerly: Sudhoffs Archiv fuer Geschichte der Medizin und der Naturwissenschaften.

610 500   GW   ISSN 0341-0773
SUDHOFFS ARCHIV. BEIHEFTE. irreg., vol.35, 1995. price varies. Franz Steiner Verlag Wiesbaden GmbH, Birkenwaldstr. 44, 70191 Stuttgart, Germany. TEL 0711-2582-0. FAX 0711-2582390. (Subscr. to: Postfach 101061, 70009 Stuttgart, Germany) Ed.Bd. **Indexed:** GeoRef., Ind.Med. **Document type:** monographic series.

610   FI   ISSN 0039-5560
SUOMEN LAAKARILEHTI/FINLANDS LAEKARTIDNING/FINNISH MEDICAL JOURNAL. 1946. 32/yr. FIM 675 (outside Scandinavia FIM 830). Suomen Laakariliitto - Finnish Medical Association, Makelankatu 2, 00500 Helsinki, Finland. TEL 358-90-393-0795. Ed. Taito Pekkarinen. adv.; bk.rev.; bibl.; illus.; index; circ. 21,500 (controlled). **Indexed:** Biol.Abstr., Ind.Med.
—BLDSC (8543.700000).
Description: Covers general medical topics relating to diagnostics, treatment and rehabilitation, pharmaceutical advances, research results and more. The emphasis is on practical applications for physicians.
Refereed Serial

617.07   US   ISSN 0899-8175
CODEN: SUPAFC
SURGICAL PATHOLOGY. 1988. q. $115 to individuals; institutions $150 (effective 1996). Field & Wood, Medical Periodicals, Inc., Box 975, Blue Bell, PA 19422. TEL 610-828-4010. FAX 215-482-0226. Eds. Drs. Cecilia Fenoglio-Preiser, Virginia LiVolsi. **Document type:** academic/scholarly publication.
—BLDSC (8548.243000); SWETS.
Incorporates (in 1994): Digestive Disease Pathology (ISSN 0896-0062)
Refereed Serial

610   US   ISSN 1062-4732
SURGICAL PRODUCTS. 1980. 9/yr. $18 (Canada $19.26; Mexico $18; elsewhere $26) (effective 1996). Gordon Publications, Inc., Part of Cahners Publishing Company, Division of Reed Elsevier Inc., 301 Gibraltar Dr., Box 650, Morris Plains, NJ 07950-0650. TEL 201-292-5100. FAX 201-898-9281. adv. circ. 76,000. (tabloid format)
—CCC.
Formerly: Surgical Product News (ISSN 0279-4829)
Description: Focuses on hospitals, surgicenters and emergicenters engaged in surgical procedures.

610   CC   ISSN 1000-5749
SUZHOU YIXUEYUAN XUEBAO/SUZHOU INSTITUTE OF MEDICAL SCIENCES. JOURNAL. (Text in Chinese) q. Suzhou Yixueyuan - Suzhou Institute of Medical Sciences, 48 Renmin Lu, Suzhou, Jiangsu 215007, People's Republic of China. TEL 225696. Ed. Du Ziwei. **Document type:** academic/scholarly publication.

610   SW   ISSN 0284-5342
SVENSK MEDICIN. 1988. irreg. (approx. 8/yr.). SEK 600. Sjukvaardens och Socialvaardens Planerings och Rationaliseringsinstitut (SPRI), Box 70487, S-107 26 Stockholm, Sweden. TEL 08-7024600. FAX 08-7024799. (Co-sponsor: Svenska Laekaresaellskapet)

610   SW   ISSN 0349-1722
R85
SVENSKA LAEKARESAELLSKAPETS HANDLINGAR. 1812-1834; resumed 1837-1902; resumed 1907. 5/yr. Svenska Laekaresaellskapet, P.O. Box 738, S-101 35 Stockholm, Sweden. TEL 46-8-24-33-50. FAX 46-8-24-43-48. E-mail: sls@swedemedsoc.se. adv. **Document type:** academic/scholarly publication.
—BLDSC (8565.000000).
Former titles (until 1980): Hygiea; (until 1975): Svenska Laekaresaellskapets Handlingar; (until 1902): Svenska Laekaresaellskapets Nya Handlingar; (until 1834): Svenska Laekaresaellskapets Handlingar.

610   SW   ISSN 0346-6000
SWEDEN. SOCIALSTYRELSEN. FOERFATTNINGSSAMLING: MEDICAL. Variant title: S O S F S (M). irreg. (approx. 30/yr.). SEK 418. Socialstyrelsen - National Board of Health and Welfare, S-106 30 Stockholm, Sweden. FAX 48-8-783-30-06. TELEX 16773 NBHWS. (Subscr. to: Fritzes Subscription Department, S-106 47 Stockholm, Sweden. TEL 46-8-690-90-90. FAX 46-8-205021) Ed. Gunnar Fahlberg. index. circ. 8,000. (looseleaf format) **Document type:** directory.
●Also available online.
Supersedes in part (1883-1976): Sweden. Medicinalvaesendet. Foerfattningssamling (ISSN 0346-5837)
Description: Directory and general advice on medical welfare.

610   SW   ISSN 0345-0171
SWEDEN. SOCIALSTYRELSEN. LEGITIMERADE LAEKARE/SWEDEN. NATIONAL BOARD OF HEALTH AND WELFARE. AUTHORIZED PHYSICIANS. 1971. a. SEK 500. Fritzes AB, S-106 47 Stockholm, Sweden. TEL 46-8-690-9100. FAX 46-18-69-62-19. index. circ. 10,000. **Document type:** government publication, directory.

610   SZ
SWISS MEDICAL DIGEST. (Text in English, German) 8/yr. Luzerner Tagblatt, Baselstr. 11, CH-6005 Luzern, Switzerland. TEL 041-281111. FAX 041-222253. TELEX 868910. Ed. H.P. Mueller.

SWITZERLAND. BUNDESAMT FUER SOZIALVERSICHERUNG. SPEZIALITAETENLISTE - LISTE DES SPECIALITES - ELENCO DELLE SPECIALITA. see PHARMACY AND PHARMACOLOGY

616.089   NE   ISSN 0167-6407
CODEN: SFOMD4
SYMPOSIA FOUNDATION MERIEUX. Running title: Transplantation and Clinical Immunology (ISSN 0168-7085) 1979. irreg., vol.19, 1992. price varies. Elsevier Science B.V., Books Division, P.O. Box 211, 1000 AE Amsterdam, Netherlands. TEL 31-20-4853911. FAX 31-20-4853705. TELEX 18582 ESPA NL. E-mail: nlinfo@elsevier.nl; usinfo-f@elsevier.com; forinfo-kyf04035@niftyserve.or.jp; Site addr.: http://www.elsevier.nl/. (Subscr. in U.S. and Canada to: Elsevier Science Inc., Box 882, Madison Sq. Sta., New York, NY 10159. TEL 212-989-5800) Ed. J.L. Touraine. (back issues avail.) **Document type:** monographic series, proceedings.
—BLDSC (8583.760000); CASDDS. **CCC**.
Refereed Serial

610   GW
SYMPOSIUM MEDICAL. irreg. DM.25. (Aerztliche Fortbildungskongresse) Berliner Medizinische Verlagsanstalt GmbH, Clausewitzstr. 4, 10629 Berlin, Germany. TEL 030-8823569. FAX 030-8812225. Ed. Elke Klug. circ. 5,000. **Document type:** trade publication.
—CCC.
Formerly: Med - Report (ISSN 0934-3148)

610   BE
SYNDIKALE KAMER. 1963. s-a. membership. Sindikale Kamer der Geneesheren der Provincies Oost & West Vlaanderen, 2 Henri Beyaertstraet, B-8500 Kortrijk, Belgium. Ed. L. van Steenberge. bk.rev. circ. 5,100.

ULRICH'S INTERNATIONAL PERIODICALS DIRECTORY 1996

MEDICAL SCIENCES

610   370.196   CN   ISSN 0838-0368
SYNERGY/SYNERGIE. (Text in English, French) q. free. Canadian Society for International Health, 170 Laurier Ave. W., Ste. 902, Ottawa, ON K1P 5V5, Canada.
Description: Addresses international health issues, reports on Canadian projects, events and publications of the field and contains career ads.

610   FR   ISSN 0399-2160
SYNTHESE MEDICALE; le journal du dialogue entre practiciens. w. 100 F. Editions Techniques et Medicales, 18 rue des Huissiers, 92200 Neuilly, France. TEL 47-47-74-74. FAX 47-47-71-03. Ed. Vincent Heugas. adv.; charts; illus. circ. 55,000.

610   FR   ISSN 0993-3557
SYNTHESE MEDICALE GESTION. 10/yr. 150 F. Editions Techniques et Medicales, 18 rue des Huissiers, 92200 Neuilly-sur-Seine, France. TEL 47-47-74-74. FAX 47-47-71-03. Ed. Guy-Vincent Heugas. adv.
Description: Covers the business end of running a medical practice.

610   PL   ISSN 0082-125X
                          CODEN: SZTNBY
SZCZECINSKIE TOWARZYSTWO NAUKOWE. WYDZIAL NAUK LEKARSKICH. PRACE. (Text in Polish; summaries in English, Polish and Russian) 1959. irreg. price varies. Szczecinskie Towarzystwo Naukowe, Wydzial Nauk Lekarskich, Ul. Wojska Polskiego 96, 70-481 Szczecin, Poland. TEL 23-18-62. (Dist. by: Ars Polona-Ruch, Krakowskie Przedmiescie 7, 00-068 Warsaw, Poland)
—BLDSC (8589.940000); CASDDS.

610   IT
T C. (Terapia del Comportamento) 1984. q. L.50000. Bulzoni Editore, Via dei Liburni n.14, 00185 Rome, Italy. TEL 06-4455207. FAX 06-4450355. Ed. Paolo Meazzini.

610   US   ISSN 0885-9191
T M J UPDATE: A CURRENT REVIEW OF TEMPOROMANDIBULAR JOINT DEVELOPMENTS. 1983. bi-m. $69 (Canada & Mexico $79; elsewhere $84). Anadem Publishing, Inc., 3620 N. High St., Columbus, OH 43214. TEL 614-262-2539. index. (looseleaf format) *Document type:* newsletter.
Description: Summarizes medical and dental journal articles about TMJ disorders and craniofacial pain.

610   AT
T S TODAY. 1982. 3/yr. Aus.$20 (membership). Australasian Tuberous Sclerosis Society Inc., 22 Mason St., Thirroul, N.S.W. 2515, Australia. TEL 61-42-673992. Eds. Lynn McKinnon, Beth Wilson. circ. 380. (back issues avail.) *Document type:* newsletter.
Formerly: Lynn's Letter.
Description: Covers tuberous sclerosis and related subjects.

610   GW   ISSN 0256-6869
T W SCHWEIZ. 1985. m. 76 SFr. Verlag G. Braun GmbH, Karl-Friedrich-Str. 14-18, 76133 Karlsruhe, Germany. TEL 0721-165-392. FAX 0721-165191. *Document type:* trade publication.
—BLDSC (8814.761000).

610   UA
TABIBAK AL-KHASS. 1969. m. £60. Dar Al-Hilal, 16 Sharia Muhammad Ezz el-Arab, Cairo, Egypt. TEL 02-27954. TELEX 92703. Ed. Abdel Rahman Nour El Dine. adv.; bk.rev. circ. 133,000.

610   LE
TABIBOK/YOUR DOCTOR. (Text in Arabic) 1956. m. $55. Scientific Publications Ltd., P.O. Box 90434, Beirut, Lebanon. FAX 963-11-3711316. TELEX 411513 MEDEQ SY. Ed. Sami Kabbani. adv.; bk.rev. circ. 85,221. (back issues avail.)
Description: Provides up-to-date medical and health information and advice for a general audience.

610   IR
TABRIZ UNIVERSITY OF MEDICAL SCIENCES. MEDICAL JOURNAL. (Text in English, Farsi, French) 1960. q. Rs.200. Tabriz University of Medical Sciences, Faculty of Medicine, Tabriz, Iran. TEL 041-30081. FAX 041-34013. TELEX 412045. Ed. Dr. M. Chakoshian. adv.; abstr.; bibl.; charts; illus.; stat. circ. 1,000. (looseleaf format) *Document type:* academic/scholarly publication.
Former titles: University of Azarabadegan. Faculty of Medicine. Journal - Daneshkaden Pezeshki Azarabadegan. Majallah; Daneshkaden Pezeshki Tabriz. Majalleh.

610   GW   ISSN 0494-464X
TAEGLICHE PRAXIS; Zeitschrift fuer den praktisch taetigen Arzt. 4/yr. DM.228. Hans Marseille Verlag GmbH, Buerkleinstr. 12, 80538 Munich, Germany. TEL 089-227988. FAX 089-2904643. Eds. H. Feiereis, R. Saller. *Document type:* academic/scholarly publication.
—BLDSC (8598.402500); Genuine Article; SWETS. CCC.

610   100   US
TAKING SIDES: CLASHING VIEWS ON CONTROVERSIAL BIOETHICAL ISSUES. irreg., 4th ed., 1991. $13.95. Dushkin Publishing Group, Sluice Dock, Guilford, CT 06437-9989. TEL 203-453-4351. FAX 203-453-6000. Ed. Carol Levine; Pub. Mimi Egan. illus. *Document type:* academic/scholarly publication.

610   UK
TALKING MEDICINE. (Includes audio cassette) 1990. bi-m. £85 to individuals; institutions £115 ($220) (effective 1995). John Wiley & Sons Ltd., Wiley Professional Language Training, Baffins Ln., Chichester, W. Sussex PO19 1UD, England. TEL 01243-779777. FAX 01243-776128. TELEX 86290 WIBOOK G. Ed. Richard Edelstein. *Document type:* academic/scholarly publication.
Formerly (until 1995): English Audio Reviews (ISSN 1141-5134)

610   NE   ISSN 0924-610X
THE TARDIEU SERIES. (Text in English) 1978. irreg. price varies. Kluwer Academic Publishers, Postbus 17, 3300 AA Dordrecht, Netherlands. TEL 31-78-392392. FAX 31-78-392254. TELEX 29245 KAPG NL. (Dist. by: Kluwer Academic Publishers Group, P.O. Box 322, 3300 AH Dordrecht, Netherlands. TEL 31-78-392392. FAX 31-78-546474; N. America dist. addr.: Box 358, Accord Sta., Hingham, MA 02018-0358. TEL 617-871-6600. FAX 617-871-6528) *Document type:* monographic series.

610   US   ISSN 1046-1906
                          CODEN: TDTSEB
TARGETED DIAGNOSIS AND THERAPY. 1988. irreg., vol.7, 1992. price varies. Marcel Dekker, Inc., 270 Madison Ave., New York, NY 10016. TEL 212-696-9000. FAX 212-685-4540. TELEX 421419. *Document type:* monographic series.
—BLDSC (8606.254200); CASDDS.

610   US
TASK FORCE QUARTERLY.* 1990. q. $16 to non-members; institutions $20; members $8. American Medical Student Association, 1902 Associaiton Dr., Reston, VA 22091-1502. TEL 703-620-6600. FAX 703-620-5873. Ed. Nancy B. Busse. circ. 3,500.
Description: Written primarily by medical students for medical students to inform about activities of the task forces and opportunities for involvement in projects, as well as to provide information about each task force's area of interest.

610   US   ISSN 1040-1334
TEACHING AND LEARNING IN MEDICINE; an international journal. 1989. q. $39 to individuals (foreign $64); institutions $195 (foreign $220). Lawrence Erlbaum Associates, Inc., 10 Industrial Dr., Mahwah, NJ 07430-2262. TEL 201-236-9500. FAX 201-236-0072. Ed. Terrill A. Mast. adv.: page $325; 7 x 10. bk.rev. Indexed: Behav.Med.Abstr., Mult.Ed.Abstr., Psychol.Abstr. (1989-), Tech.Educ.Abstr. *Document type:* academic/scholarly publication.
—BLDSC (8614.004000); SWETS.
Description: Addresses practical issues in the conduct of medical education, providing the analysis and empirical research needed to facilitate decision-making about the education of medical professionals.
Refereed Serial

362   JA   ISSN 0040-0734
TEASHI NO FUJIYUUNA KODOMOTACHI/CRIPPLED CHILDREN. (Text in Japanese) 1958. m. 720 Yen. Japanese Society for Disabled Children - Nihon Shitai Fujiyuuji Kyokai, 1-7, 1-chome, Komone, Itabashi-ku, Tokyo 173, Japan. circ. 6,000.
Description: Focuses on rehabilitation practices.

610   US
TECH SAMPLE. (Subject areas offered include: Chemistry, Hematology, Immunohematology, Microbiology, Education and Management, Histotechnology, Cytotechnology and Generalist) 1979. w. $450 for complete series; price varies for individual subject. American Society of Clinical Pathologists, 2100 W. Harrison St., Chicago, IL 60612. TEL 312-738-4890. FAX 312-738-1619. Ed. Dr. Deanna Klosinski. circ. 4,000. *Document type:* academic/scholarly publication.
Description: Each series consists of exercises which present patient or laboratory-related problems for workup.

610   NE   ISSN 0169-622X
TECHNIEK IN DE GEZONDHEIDSZORG; beheer en toepassing. 1985. m. fl.99 (foreign fl.240). Keesing Noordervliet B.V., De Molen 82-86, 3995 AX Houten, Netherlands. TEL 31-3403-58585. FAX 31-3403-58500. Ed. M.A. Romijn. adv. contact: P. Holst. index. circ. 1,759. (back issues avail.) *Document type:* trade publication.
—SWETS.
Description: Covers issues relating to technology in health care.

TECHNOLOGIE & SANTE. see *TECHNOLOGY: COMPREHENSIVE WORKS*

610.285   NE   ISSN 0928-7329
TECHNOLOGY AND HEALTH CARE. 1993. q. fl.514($313) (effective 1996). (European Society for Engineering and Medicine) Elsevier Science B.V., P.O. Box 211, 1000 AE Amsterdam, Netherlands. TEL 31-20-4853911. FAX 31-20-4853598. TELEX 18582 ESPA NL. E-mail: nlinfo-f@elsevier.nl; usinfo-f@elsevier.com; forinfo-kyf04035@niftyserve.or.jp; Site addr.: http://www.elseveir.nl/. (Subscr. in U.S. and Canada to: Elsevier Science Inc., Box 882, Madison Sq. Sta., New York, NY 10159-0882. TEL 212-989-5800. FAX 212-633-3990) Ed. P.F. Niederer. (also avail. in microfilm from UMI; back issues avail.) Indexed: Excerp.Med. (1994-), INSPEC (1993-). *Document type:* academic/scholarly publication.
—BLDSC (8758.625000); Genuine Article. CCC.
Description: Serves as a forum for discussion of current research in biomedical engineering, advances in diagnostics, therapeutic procedures and devices, including artificial organs and implants, and for the review of major social, policy or ethical issues relating to new applications of technology in medicine.
Refereed Serial

610   US
TECHNOLOGY IN HEALTH CARE NEWSLETTER SERIES. m. (Emergency Care Research Institute) E C R I, 5200 Butler Pike, Plymouth Meeting, PA 19462. TEL 610-825-6000. FAX 610-834-1275.

MEDICAL SCIENCES 4277

610 615.9 UK
TECHNOMARK REGISTER. CONTRACT RESEARCH ORGANISATIONS. 1988. irreg. £225. Technomark Consulting Services Ltd., King House, 5-11 Westbourne Grove, London W2 4UA, England. TEL 071-229-9239. FAX 071-792-2587. Ed. R.G. Hughes. circ. 250. (looseleaf format) **Document type:** directory.
Description: Listing of Contract Research Organizations in U.K. with details of expertise.

610 JA ISSN 0285-4473
TEION IGAKU/LOW TEMPERATURE MEDICINE. (Text in English, Japanese; summaries in English) 1976. q. 2000 Yen per no. Nihon Teion Igaku Kenkyukai - Japan Society for Low Temperature Medicine, Teion Iryo Kenkyu Shisetsu, 2-2 Jonai, Chuo-ku, Fukuoka-shi, Fukuoka-ken 810, Japan. **Indexed:** INIS Atomind.

610 PO
TEMPO MEDICINA. 1982. 48/yr. Esc.3000. Impremedica, Quinta do Pinheiro, Lote 5, Cavela, 1675 Pontinha, Portugal. TEL 351-1-4783075. FAX 351-1-4783081. Ed. Jose Antunes. adv. contact: Joao Barroca. circ. 15,000 (paid). (also avail. in diskette format) **Document type:** newspaper.

610 IT ISSN 0492-6749
HC391
TEMPO MEDICO. 1959. w. L.30000. Parpinelli Tre srl, Via Lanino 5, 20144 Milan, Italy. TEL 39-2-427047. FAX 39-2-48951591. Ed. Roberto Satolli. adv.: B&W page L.13600000, color page L.16300000; trim 262 x 384; adv. contact: Elisabetta Cozzi. bk.rev. circ. 40,000. **Document type:** newspaper.

TENNESSEE HEALTH LAW UPDATE. see *LAW*

610 US ISSN 0040-3318
TENNESSEE MEDICAL ASSOCIATION. JOURNAL. 1902. m. $20. Tennessee Medical Association, Box 120909, 2301 21st Ave. S., Nashville, TN 37212-0909. TEL 615-385-2100. FAX 615-383-5918. Ed. Dr. John B. Thomison. adv. contact: Jean Wishnick. bk.rev.; abstr.; bibl.; illus.; index. circ. 6,400. **Indexed:** Dent.Ind., Excerp.Med., Ind.Med., INIS Atomind. **Document type:** trade publication, academic/scholarly publication.
—BLDSC (4907.200000); UnCover.
Formerly: Tennessee State Medical Association Journal.

TENNESSEE MEDICO-LEGAL REPORTER. see *LAW*

610 RU ISSN 0040-3660
CODEN: TEARAI
TERAPEVTICHESKII ARKHIV/THERAPEUTIC ARCHIVES. (Text in Russian; summaries in English) 1923. m. $120 (effective 1996). (Nauchnoe Obshchestvo Terapevtov) Izdatel'stvo Meditsina, Petroverigskii pereulok 6-8, 101000 Moscow, Russia. TEL 7-095-1209081. FAX 7-095-2384634. (Co-sponsor: Ministerstvo Zdravookhraneniya) Ed. E.I. Chazov. bk.rev. **Indexed:** ASCA, Biol.Abstr., Biotech.Abstr., Chem.Abstr., Dent.Ind., Excerp.Med., Helminthol.Abstr., Ind.Med., Nutr.Abstr., Protozool.Abstr., Sugar Ind.Abstr.
—BLDSC (0180.000000); CASDDS; EMDOCS; Genuine Article; SWETS. **CCC.**
Description: Presents clinical and clinico-experimental studies, as well as reviews and articles on all pressing problems concerning the diseases of the internal organs.

610 PL ISSN 1230-3917
TERAPIA. 1993. m. free. Warsaw Voice S.A., Ksiecia Janusza 64, 01-452 Warsaw, Poland. TEL 48-22-366377. FAX 48-22-371995. adv.: page 3125 Zl.; 180 x 261. illus. **Document type:** newspaper.
Description: Addressed to the medical community in Poland.

TERAPIA FAMILIARE. see *PSYCHOLOGY*

610 IT ISSN 0040-3695
CODEN: TPMDAB
TERAPIA MODERNA. English edition: Modern Treatment. (Text in Italian; summaries in English) 1965. q. L.330000($200) (effective 1996). Pensiero Scientifico Editore s.r.l., Via Bradano 3-C, 00199 Rome, Italy. TEL 06-86207158. FAX 06-86207160. adv.; bibl.; illus.; index, cum.index: 1965-1968. circ. 1,000. **Indexed:** Excerp.Med. (until 1993). **Document type:** academic/scholarly publication.
—CASDDS.

570 US ISSN 0270-3211
CODEN: TCMUD8
TERATOGENESIS, CARCINOGENESIS, AND MUTAGENESIS. 1980. bi-m. $510 (foreign $603) (effective 1996). John Wiley & Sons, Inc., Journals, 605 Third Ave., New York, NY 10158. TEL 212-850-6645. FAX 212-850-6021. TELEX 12-7063. E-mail: SUBINFO@JWILEY.DOC. (Subscr. outside the Americas to: John Wiley & Sons Ltd., Baffins Ln., Chichester, W. Sussex PO19 1UD, England. TEL 44-1243-779777. FAX 44-1243-776128) Ed. Philippe Shubick. (also avail. in microform from UMI; back issues avail.) **Indexed:** ASCA, Biol.Abstr., Biotech.Abstr., C.I.S. Abstr., Chem.Abstr., Curr.Adv.Ecol.Sci., Curr.Cont., Dent.Ind., Dok.Arbeitsmed., Excerp.Med., Ind.Med., Lab.Haz.Bull., Rev.Med.& Vet.Mycol., Risk Abstr. **Document type:** academic/scholarly publication.
●Also available online.
—BLDSC (8792.130000); ADONIS; CASDDS; Faxon; Genuine Article; SWETS; UnCover. **CCC.**
Description: Contains reports of original research and methods concerned with the detection, classification, and evaluation of risks associated with exposure to environmentally induced agents. Serves as a forum for comments on controversial issues in biological risk assessment.
Refereed Serial

TERATOLOGY; the international journal of abnormal development. see *BIOLOGY*

TEXAS HEALTH LAW REPORTER. see *LAW*

610 US ISSN 1069-1308
TEXAS M.D. 1991. q. $20. Republic of Texas Publishing Co., Box 1836, Helotes, TX 78023. TEL 210-670-1836. Ed. Paul Carr. adv. circ. 10,000.
Formerly (until vol.3, no.2, 1993): San Antonio M.D. (ISSN 1068-6169)
Description: Physician written, physician oriented medical magazine.

610 US ISSN 0040-4470
R11 CODEN: TXMDAX
TEXAS MEDICINE. 1905. m. $40 to non-members; members $20. Texas Medical Association, 401 W. 15th St., Austin, TX 78701. TEL 512-370-1300. FAX 512-370-1362. Ed. Jean Pietrobono. adv. contact: Laurie Reece. charts; illus.; index; circ. 31,000 (paid). (also avail. in microform from UMI) **Indexed:** ASCA, Biol.Abstr., C.I.S. Abstr., Chem.Abstr., CINAHL, Curr.Adv.Cancer Res., Curr.Cont., Dent.Ind., Dok.Arbeitsmed., Excerp.Med., Helminthol.Abstr., Ind.Med., Med.Care Rev., Nutr.Abstr., Rehabil.Lit. **Document type:** trade publication, academic/scholarly publication.
—BLDSC (8799.550000); EMDOCS; Faxon; SWETS.
Formerly: Texas State Journal of Medicine.

THEOLOGY AND MEDICINE. see *RELIGIONS AND THEOLOGY*

610 100 NE ISSN 0167-9902
R723 CODEN: THMEDT
THEORETICAL MEDICINE; an international journal for the philosophy and methodology of medical research and practice. (Text in English) 1980. q. fl.418 to institutions; $268 to institutions in U.S. (effective 1996). Kluwer Academic Publishers, Postbus 17, 3300 AA Dordrecht, Netherlands. TEL 31-78-392392. FAX 31-78-392254. TELEX 29245 KAPG NL. E-mail: SERVICES@WKAP.NL. (Dist. by: Kluwer Academic Publishers Group, P.O. Box 322, 3300 AH Dordrecht, Netherlands. TEL 31-78-392392. FAX 31-78-546474; N. America dist. addr.: Box 358, Accord Sta., Hingham, MA 02018-0358. TEL 617-871-6600. FAX 617-871-6528) Ed. David Thomasma. adv.; bk.rev.; index. (also avail. in microform from UMI; reprint service avail. from SWZ) **Indexed:** Curr.Cont., Excerp.Med., IBZ, Ind.Med., INIS Atomind., Phil.Ind., Ref.Zh., SSCI. **Document type:** academic/scholarly publication.
—BLDSC (8814.561500); Faxon; Genuine Article; SWETS; UMI; UnCover. **CCC.**
Former titles: Metamedicine (ISSN 0166-2031); Metamed (ISSN 0342-6866)
Description: Provides a forum for interdisciplinary studies in the philosophy and methodology of medical practice and research, including such issues as clinical judgement and decision making, knowledge acquisition and theory formation in medicine.
Refereed Serial

610 FR ISSN 0396-7107
THERAPEUTIQUES NATURELLES; revue francaise de vulgarisation. 1975. bi-m. 140 F. (Groupement National pour l'Organisation des Medecines Alternatives) Presses de la Vallee, 7 rue Larreyleue, 31000 Toulouse, France. Dir. J.M. Girardin. adv.; bk.rev.
Formerly: Groupement National pour l'Organisation de la Medecine Auxiliaire. Bulletin de Liaison (ISSN 0396-7115)

610 FR ISSN 0040-5957
CODEN: THERAP
THERAPIE. (Text in French; summaries in English, French) 1866. 6/yr. (Societe Francaise de Therapeutique et de Pharmacodynamie) John Libbey Eurotext, 127 av. de la Republique, 92120 Montrouge, France. TEL 33-1-46730660. adv.; bk.rev.; bibl.; charts; illus. (also avail. in microform from PMC) **Indexed:** ASCA, Biol.Abstr., Biotech.Abstr., Chem.Abstr., Curr.Adv.Ecol.Sci., Curr.Cont., Dairy Sci.Abstr., Dent.Ind., Excerp.Med., Helminthol.Abstr., Ind.Med., Protozool.Abstr. **Document type:** academic/scholarly publication.
—BLDSC (8814.750000); CASDDS; EMDOCS; Faxon; Genuine Article; SWETS; UMI. **CCC.**
Supersedes (in 1946): Societe de Therapeutique. Bulletins et Memoires (ISSN 1153-3668)

610 GW ISSN 0040-5973
CODEN: THEWA6
THERAPIEWOCHE. (Text in English) 1950. 36/yr. DM.129 (foreign DM.154). Verlag G. Braun GmbH, Karl-Friedrich-Str. 14-18, 76133 Karlsruhe, Germany. TEL 0721-165392. FAX 0721-165191. Ed. R.G. Sommer. adv.; bk.rev.; film rev.; abstr.; charts; illus.; index. circ. 40,000. **Indexed:** Biol.Abstr., Biotech.Abstr., Chem.Abstr., Excerp.Med., Ind.Med. **Document type:** trade publication.
—BLDSC (8814.760000); CASDDS; EMDOCS; Genuine Article; SWETS. **CCC.**

610 658 US
THETA MARKET RESEARCH REPORTS. 1970. irreg., no.420, May 1994. $195. Theta Corporation, c/o Phyllis Klaben, Theta Bldg., Middlefield, CT 06455. TEL 203-349-1054. FAX 203-349-1227. Ed.Bd.
Description: Provides comprehensive coverage of new market research in health care.

MEDICAL SCIENCES

610 UK ISSN 0040-6376
CODEN: THORA7
THORAX. 1946. m. £185($309) (British Thoracic Society) B M J Publishing Group, B.M.A. House, Tavistock Sq., London WC1H 9JR, England. TEL 0171-383-6270. FAX 0171-383-6402. (N. American subscr. to: Box 408, Franklin, MA 02038. TEL 800-2-FON-BMJ. FAX 800-2-FAX-BMJ) Ed. S. Spiro. adv. contact: Sheila Rowe. bk.rev.; charts; illus.; index. (also avail. in microform from UMI; reprint service avail. from UMI) **Indexed:** Abstr.Hyg., ASCA, Biol.Abstr., C.I.S. Abstr., Chem.Abstr., Curr.Adv.Cancer Res., Curr.Adv.Ecol.Sci., Curr.Cont., Dent.Ind., Dok.Arbeitsmed., Excerp.Med., Helminthol.Abstr., Ind.Med., Ind.Vet., Lab.Haz.Bull., Rev.Plant Path., Trop.Dis.Bull. **Document type:** academic/scholarly publication.
●Also available online. Vendor(s): Ovid Technologies.
—BLDSC (8820.250000); ADONIS; CASDDS; EMDOCS; Faxon; Genuine Article; SWETS; UMI; UnCover. **CCC.**
Description: Covers respiratory medicine with clinical and experimental research articles from various disciplines, including pathology, immunology and surgery. Tracks recent developments in basic biomedical sciences including cellular biochemistry and molecular biology.
Refereed Serial

THYROID HORMONES. see *MEDICAL SCIENCES — Endocrinology*

610 II ISSN 0970-1257
TIBETAN MEDICINE. 1980. irreg. $3 per no. Library of Tibetan Works and Archives, Dharamshala 176 215, India. TELEX TF 22467. (back issues avail.) **Document type:** monographic series.
—BLDSC (8820.644000).
Description: Provides an international forum for the study of Tibetan medicine.

TIDSKRIFT FOER YNGRE LAEKARE. see *BUSINESS AND ECONOMICS — Labor And Industrial Relations*

610 CC ISSN 1001-0912
TIEDAO YIXUE/RAILWAY MEDICAL JOURNAL. (Text in Chinese; abstracts in English) 1964-1966; resumed 1976. bi-m. $60. Nanjing Tiedao Yixueyuan - Nanjing Railway Medical College, 87 Dingjiaqiao, Nanjing, Jiangsu 210009, People's Republic of China. TEL 3301508. FAX 3317073. Ed. Sun Zaiyang. adv.: page $2000. bk.rev. circ. 2,000. **Document type:** academic/scholarly publication.
Description: Publishes articles on clinical experiences, traditional Chinese medicine and herbs, hygiene and nursing.
Refereed Serial

610 SP ISSN 0210-9999
TIEMPOS MEDICOS. 1973. 13/yr. 9000 ptas. (foreign $120). Editores Medicos, S.A., C. Gabriela Mistral 2, 28035 Madrid, Spain. TEL 34-1-3860033. FAX 34-1-3739907. Ed. Dr. A. Chicharro Papiri. adv. contact: Raquel Moran. bk.rev.; illus.; index, cum.index. circ. 35,000. (back issues avail.) **Document type:** academic/scholarly publication.

610 360 NE ISSN 0925-6881
TIJDSCHRIFT GEZONDHEIDSBEVORDERING. 1989. q. fl.75. (Nederlandse Vereniging voor Gezondheidsbevordering Voorlichting en Opvoeding) Van Gorcum en Co. B.V., P.O. Box 43, 6400 AA Assen, Netherlands. TEL 31-5920-46846. FAX 31-5920-72064. **Document type:** academic/scholarly publication.
—SWETS.

610 368 NE ISSN 0929-600X
TIJDSCHRIFT VOOR BEDRIJFS- EN VERZEKERINGSGENEESKUNDE. Short title: T B V. 1963. 6/yr. (Stichting tot Bevordering der Bedrijfs- en Verzekeringsgeneeskunde) Bohn Stafleu van Loghum B.V. (Subsidiary of: Wolters Kluwer B.V.), Postbus 246, 3990 GA Houten, Netherlands. TEL 31-3403-95711. FAX 31-3403-50903. Ed. N.H.Th. Croon. adv.; bk.rev. circ. 4,000. **Document type:** trade publication.
—SWETS.
Former titles (until 1993): Tijdschrift voor Verzekeringsgeneeskunde (ISSN 0169-0698); (until 1985): Arts en Sociale Verzekering (ISSN 0004-3974)

610 BE ISSN 0005-8440
TIJDSCHRIFT VOOR GENEESKUNDE. Variant title: Belgisch Tijdschrift voor Geneeskunde. (Text in Dutch) 1945. s-m. 1450 BEF. Tijdschrift voor Geneeskunde A.S.B.L., De Pintelaan 185, B-9000 Ghent, Belgium. TEL 32-9-2403330. FAX 32-9-2403390. Eds. I. Leusen, J. Lauwereyns. adv.; bk.rev.; abstr.; illus.; index; circ. 9,000. (paid). **Indexed:** Biotech.Abstr., Chem.Abstr., Excerp.Med., Ind.Med. **Document type:** academic/scholarly publication.
Refereed Serial

610 174 NE ISSN 0925-2819
TIJDSCHRIFT VOOR GENEESKUNDE EN ETHIEK. 1991. q. fl.50. (Stichting Geneeskunde en Ethiek) Van Gorcum en Co. B.V., P.O. Box 43, 6400 AA Assen, Netherlands. TEL 31-5920-46846. FAX 31-5920-72064. **Document type:** academic/scholarly publication.
—SWETS.
Description: Publishes original scholarship on topics relating to medical ethics.

610 614.8 NE ISSN 0167-8647
TIJDSCHRIFT VOOR GEZONDHEID EN POLITIEK. 1983. q. fl.75. Van Gorcum en Co. B.V., P.O. Box 43, 9400 AA Aasen, Netherlands. TEL 31-5920-46864. FAX 31-5920-72064. Ed. M. Bots. adv.; bk.rev. circ. 1,500.
—SWETS.
Description: Covers health and politics.

TIJDSCHRIFT VOOR GEZONDHEIDSRECHT. see *PUBLIC HEALTH AND SAFETY*

610 NE ISSN 0928-4672
TIJDSCHRIFT VOOR HUISARTSGENEESKUNDE. (Supplement avail.: Praktijkmanagement (ISSN 0169-1910)) 1984. s-m. Mediselect B.V., Postbus 28091, 3828 ZH Hoogland, Netherlands. TEL 31-33-808020. FAX 31-33-805881. Pub. J. Blom. adv. **Document type:** trade publication.
—SWETS.
Formerly (until 1992): Practitioner (ISSN 0168-3047)

TIJDSCHRIFT VOOR INTEGRALE GENEESKUNDE. see *ALTERNATIVE MEDICINE*

610 NE ISSN 0920-0517
TIJDSCHRIFT VOOR SOCIALE GEZONDHEIDSZORG; gezondheid & samenleving. Short title: T S G. (Text mainly in Dutch, occasionally in English; summaries in Dutch, English) 1923. 8/yr. fl.132.40 to individuals; institutions fl.210.85 (includes European Journal of Public Health) (effective 1996). (Vereniging voor Volksgezondheid en Wetenschap) Stichting Journals for Public Health and Science, Admiraal Helfrichlaan 1, 3527 KV Utrecht, Netherlands. TEL 31-30-913252. FAX 31-30-913242. (Editorial addr.: c/o Katholieke Universiteit Nijmegen, Postbus 91010, 6500 HB Nijmegen, Netherlands. TEL 31-80-613116. FAX 31-80-541790) Ed. Dr. J.W.J. van der Gulden. adv.: B&W page fl.1923; adv. contact: Mrs. D. Davidse. bk.rev.; abstr.; bibl.; charts; circ. 2,000 (paid). **Indexed:** Chem.Abstr., Ergon.Abstr., Excerp.Med., HRIS, World Bibl.Soc.Sec. **Document type:** academic/scholarly publication.
—SWETS; UMI.
Formerly (until 1983): Tijdschrift voor Sociale Geneeskunde (ISSN 0040-7607)
Refereed Serial

610 574 DK ISSN 0001-2815
QR180 CODEN: TSANA2
TISSUE ANTIGENS. (Text in English) 1971. 12/yr. DKK 2200 (effective 1996). Munksgaard International Publishers Ltd., 35 Noerre Soegade, P.O. Box 2148, DK-1016 Copenhagen K, Denmark. TEL 33-127030. FAX 33-129387. Ed. Bo Dupont. adv.; illus. circ. 900. (reprint service avail. from SWZ) **Indexed:** Abstr.Hyg., Anim.Breed.Abstr., ASCA, Biol.Abstr., Chem.Abstr., Curr.Adv.Cancer Res., Curr.Adv.Ecol.Sci., Curr.Cont., Excerp.Med., Helminthol.Abstr., Ind.Med., Ind.Vet., Protozool.Abstr., So.Pac.Per.Ind., Trop.Dis.Bull., Vet.Bull.
—BLDSC (8858.690000); CASDDS; Faxon; Genuine Article; SWETS; UnCover. **CCC.**
Refereed Serial

TOBACCO CONTROL; an international journal. see *TOBACCO*

610 US
TODAY IN MEDICINE. 10/yr. Data Centrum Communications, Inc., 110 Greene St., New York, NY 10012. TEL 212-226-5252. Ed. Heidi Greene.

610 US
TODAY'S HEALTH CARE. (Published in several regional editions) m. Transcontinental Publishing Inc., Box 45454, Phoenix, AZ 85016. TEL 602-331-8900. FAX 602-331-8448. Pub. Philip T. Zeni, Sr. adv.; circ. controlled. (reprint service avail.) **Document type:** trade publication.
Description: Contains articles and features of interest to regional medical professionals and key decision-makers in health care.

610 UY
TODOVIDA. 1991. q. 4000 N$ per no. Bartolome Mitre, 1488, Ap. 105, Montevideo, Uruguay. TEL 953794. Eds. Selma Varsi, Mara de Oliveira. **Document type:** consumer publication.

610 JA ISSN 0040-8670
CODEN: TOIZAG
TOHO UNIVERSITY MEDICAL SOCIETY. JOURNAL/TOHO IGAKKAI ZASSHI. (Text in English, Japanese, and European Languages) 1954. bi-m. 6000 Yen. Toho University Medical Society - Toho Daigaku Igakkai, c/o Library, School of Medicine, 5-21-16 Omori Nishi, Ota-ku, Tokyo 143, Japan. FAX 764-1642. Ed. Setsuo Takeuchi. adv.; bk.rev.; illus.; stat. circ. 1,200. (processed) **Indexed:** Biol.Abstr., Chem.Abstr., Excerp.Med.
●Also available online.
—BLDSC (4824.300000); EMDOCS.

610 JA ISSN 0040-8700
CODEN: THIZAZ
TOHOKU MEDICAL JOURNAL/TOHOKU IGAKU ZASSHI. (Text in Japanese; summaries in English and Japanese) 1916. s-a. 3000 Yen. Tohoku Medical Society - Tohoku Igakkai, 2-1 Seiryo-machi, Sendai 980, Japan. Ed.Bd. adv.; bibl.; charts; illus.; mkt.; index, cum.index. circ. 1,200. **Indexed:** Biol.Abstr., Chem.Abstr., Curr.Cont., Excerp.Med., Ind.Med.

610 JA ISSN 0371-2761
CODEN: SRTCAC
TOHOKU UNIVERSITY. SCIENCE REPORTS OF THE RESEARCH INSTITUTES. SERIES C: MEDICINE/TOHOKU DAIGAKU KENKYUJO HOKOKU, C-SHU, IGAKU. 1949. 4/yr. exchange basis. Tohoku Daigaku, Kenkyujo Rengokai - Tohoku University, Association of the Research Institutes, 4-1 Seiryo-machi, Aoba-ku, Sendai-shi, Miyagi-ken 980, Japan. FAX 022-264-7984. (also avail. in microform from PMC) **Indexed:** Biol.Abstr., Chem.Abstr., Excerp.Med., Ind.Med.
—CASDDS.

610 JA ISSN 0385-0005
CODEN: TJEMDR
TOKAI JOURNAL OF EXPERIMENTAL AND CLINICAL MEDICINE. (Text and summaries in English) 1976. bi-m. 3000 Yen($15) (Tokai Daigaku, Igakubu - Tokai University, School of Medicine) Tokai Daigaku Shuppansha - Tokai University Press (Kanagawa), Boseidai, Isehara, Kanagawa 259-11, Japan. FAX 0463-91-3328. TELEX 3882-413. Ed. Makoto Sakai. circ. 1,700. (back issues avail.) **Indexed:** Dairy Sci.Abstr. **Document type:** bulletin.
●Also available on CD-ROM.
—BLDSC (8862.705000); CASDDS; Faxon; UnCover.

610 JA ISSN 0040-9022
CODEN: TJIZAF
TOKYO JOSHI IKA DAIGAKU ZASSHI/TOKYO WOMEN'S MEDICAL COLLEGE. JOURNAL. (Text in Japanese; summaries in English) 1931. m. 6000 Yen($50) Tokyo Joshi Ika Daigaku Gakkai - Society of Tokyo Women's Medical College, c/o Library, 8-1 Kawada-cho, Shinjuku-ku, Tokyo 162, Japan. TELEX 2322317-TWMLIB-J. Ed. Toshio Tsushima. adv. contact: Takako Itoh. index; circ. 1,750 (controlled). **Indexed:** C.I.S.Abstr., Chem.Abstr., Excerp.Med. **Document type:** academic/scholarly publication.
—BLDSC (4909.050000); EMDOCS.
Refereed Serial

MEDICAL SCIENCES

610.28   JA   ISSN 0082-4739
CODEN: IKKHBS
TOKYO MEDICAL AND DENTAL UNIVERSITY. INSTITUTE FOR MEDICAL AND DENTAL ENGINEERING. REPORTS/IYO KIZAI KENKYUJO HOKOKU. (Text in Japanese; table of contents and summaries in English) 1967. a. free. Tokyo Medical and Dental University, Institute for Medical and Dental Engineering - Tokyo Ika Shika Daigaku Iyo Kizai Kenkyujo, 3-10 Surugadai 2-chome, Kanda, Chiyoda-ku, Tokyo 101, Japan. TEL 03-5280-8000. FAX 03-5280-8005. Ed. Yoji Imai. **Indexed:** Dent.Ind. **Document type:** academic/scholarly publication.
—BLDSC (7520.950000).

610   JA   ISSN 0040-8956
TOKYO MEDICAL ASSOCIATION. JOURNAL/TOKYOTO ISHIKAI ZASSHI. (Text in Japanese) 1947. m. Tokyo Medical Association - Tokyoto Ishikai, 2-5 Kanda Surugadai, Chiyoda-ku, Tokyo 101, Japan. adv.; bk.rev.

610   JA   ISSN 0040-8905
CODEN: TIDZAH
TOKYO MEDICAL COLLEGE. JOURNAL/TOKYO IKA DAIGAKU ZASSHI. (Text in English and Japanese; summaries in English) 1938. bi-m. 3000 Yen. Medical Society of Tokyo Medical College - Tokyo Ikadaigaku Igakukai, 1-1, Shinjuku 6-chome, Shinjuku-ku, Tokyo 160, Japan. Ed. Yuichi Otaka. adv.; index. circ. 1,400. **Indexed:** Biol.Abstr., C.I.S. Abstr., Chem.Abstr., Excerp.Med., Ind.Med.
—BLDSC (4908.950000); CASDDS; EMDOCS.

610   JA   ISSN 0082-4771
CODEN: TRENAF
TOKYO-TORITSU EISEI KENKYUJO KENKYU NENPO/TOKYO METROPOLITAN RESEARCH LABORATORY OF PUBLIC HEALTH. ANNUAL REPORT. (Text in Japanese; summaries occasionally in English) 1949. a. exchange basis. Tokyo-toritsu Eisei Kenkyujo - Tokyo Metropolitan Research Laboratory of Public Health, 24-1 Hyakunin-cho 3-chome, Shinjuku-ku, Tokyo 160, Japan. circ. 600. **Indexed:** Biodet.Abstr., Dairy Sci.Abstr., Food Sci.& Tech.Abstr., Rice Abstr.
—BLDSC (1471.740000); CASDDS.

610   US
TOLEDO MEDICINE. 1916. q. $15 (effective 1994). Academy of Medicine of Toledo and Lucas County, 4428 Secor Rd., Toledo, OH 43623. TEL 419-473-3200. FAX 419-475-6744. Ed. Gerald Marsa. adv. contact: Janice Schutt. illus.; circ. 1,500 (controlled). **Document type:** bulletin.
Formerly (until 1987): Academy of Medicine of Toledo and Lucas County. Bulletin (ISSN 0001-4303)

610   CC   ISSN 0257-716X
CODEN: JTMUEI
TONGJI MEDICAL UNIVERSITY. JOURNAL. Chinese edition: Tongji Yike Daxue Xuebao (ISSN 0258-2090) (Text in English and German) 1981. q. $36 (effective 1996). Tongji Medical University - Tongji Yike Daxue, c/o Prof. Liu Xunfang, Wuhan, Hubei 430030, People's Republic of China. TEL 01-506-6688. FAX 01-506-3101. TELEX 22313 CPC CN. (Dist. by: China National Publications Import & Export Corporation (CNPIEC), Export Department, P.O. Box 88, 16 Gongti E. Rd., Chaoyang District, Beijing 100020, P.R.C. TEL 01-506-6688) Ed. Qiu Fazu. circ. 1,000. **Indexed:** Chem.Abstr., ExtraMED, Ind.Med., Math.R. **Document type:** academic/scholarly publication.
●Also available on CD-ROM.
—BLDSC (4909.158000); CASDDS; Faxon. **CCC**.
Incorporates (in 1985): Acta Academiae Medicinae Wuhan (ISSN 0253-3316); Which was formerly: Wuhan Yixueyuan Xuebao (ISSN 0510-9752)
Description: Comprehensive journal of medical science. Includes basic and clinical medicine, public health, and forensic medicine.
Refereed Serial

610   GW   ISSN 0931-9522
TOP MEDIZIN; Internistische Wochenzeitschrift. 1987. w. DM.199.50. P M I Verlagsgruppe GmbH, August-Schanz-Str. 21, 60433 Frankfurt a.M., Germany. TEL 069-54800000. FAX 069-54800077. Ed. Peter Hoffmann. adv.; bk.rev. circ. 16,000. (tabloid format; back issues avail.) **Document type:** academic/scholarly publication.

610   US   ISSN 0164-2340
TOPICS IN EMERGENCY MEDICINE. 1979. q. $81 (foreign $97). Aspen Publishers, Inc., 200 Orchard Ridge Dr., Gaithersburg, MD 20878. TEL 301-417-7500. FAX 301-417-7550. **Indexed:** CINAHL, Excerp.Med.
—BLDSC (8867.437400); Faxon; SWETS; UMI; UnCover. **CCC**.

610   US   ISSN 0882-5645
TOPICS IN PAIN MANAGEMENT; current concepts and treatment strategies. 1985. m. $95 to individuals; institutions $120 (effective 1995). Williams & Wilkins, 428 East Preston St., Baltimore, MD 21202. TEL 410-528-4000; 800-638-6423. FAX 410-528-4312. TELEX 87699. Ed. Dr. Joel R. Saper. circ. 5,500. **Document type:** academic/scholarly publication.
—CCC.
Description: Contains reviews and abstracts from the international literature available on pain disorders and management.

610   FR   ISSN 0295-6292
TOUT PREVOIR - REVUE DE L'A G M F. 1858. 10/yr. 30 bd. Pasteur, 75740 Paris, France. TEL 45-67-55-06. FAX 43-06-30-66. TELEX 201 449 F MEDITEL. Ed. Odile Lucien Brun. circ. 65,000. **Document type:** bulletin.
—CCC.
Former titles (until 1979): A G M F. Bulletin (ISSN 0150-5203); (1948-1977): Generale des Medicins de France. Bulletin (ISSN 0004-5519)

TOXICOLOGIC PATHOLOGY. see *ENVIRONMENTAL STUDIES — Toxicology And Environmental Safety*

TOXICOLOGY IN VITRO. see *ENVIRONMENTAL STUDIES — Toxicology And Environmental Safety*

TOXICON; an international journal specialising in toxins. see *PHARMACY AND PHARMACOLOGY*

610   GW   ISSN 0946-2104
CODEN: TEMDE6
TRACE ELEMENTS AND ELECTROLYTES. (Text in English) 1984. q. DM.168($98) Dustri-Verlag Dr. Karl Feistle, Bahnhofstr. 9, 82041 Deisenhofen, Germany. TEL 089-613861-0. FAX 089-613-5412. Ed. Dr. K.H. Rahn. bk.rev. **Indexed:** Curr.Adv.Ecol.Sci. **Document type:** academic/scholarly publication.
—BLDSC (8876.873000); CASDDS; Faxon; Genuine Article. **CCC**.
Formerly (until 1994): Trace Elements in Medicine (ISSN 0174-7371)
Description: Covers developments in trace elements; intended for clinicians, as well as theoretical scientists (biologists, pharmacologists, physiologists).

TRACTRIX; yearbook for the history of science, medicine, technology, and mathematics. see *SCIENCES: COMPREHENSIVE WORKS*

610   II   ISSN 0970-5031
TRADITIONAL MEDICAL SYSTEMS. 1979. q. Rs.410($45) K.K. Roy (Private) Ltd., 55 Gariahat Rd., P.O. Box 10210, Calcutta 700 019, India. Ed. Dr. K.K. Roy. adv.; abstr.; bibl.; index. circ. 2,100.

615.65   US   ISSN 0041-1132
RC633.A1   CODEN: TRANAT
TRANSFUSION. 1961. 11/yr. $135 to individuals (foreign $170); institutions $195 (foreign $335). American Association of Blood Banks, 8101 Glenbrook Rd., Bethesda, MD 20814. TEL 301-907-6977. FAX 301-907-6895. Ed. Dr. Jeffrey McCullough. adv.; illus.; index. circ. 13,300. (also avail. in microform from UMI) **Indexed:** Biol.Abstr., Chem.Abstr., Curr.Adv.Cell & Devel.Biol., Curr.Adv.Ecol.Sci., Curr.Cont., Dent.Ind., Excerp.Med., Helminthol.Abstr., Hosp.Lit.Ind., Ind.Med., Protozool.Abstr., Rev.Med.& Vet.Mycol., Sci.Cit.Ind., SSCI. **Document type:** academic/scholarly publication.
—BLDSC (9020.704000); CASDDS; EMDOCS; Faxon; SWETS; UMI; UnCover.
Supersedes (1947-1960): American Association of Blood Banks. Bulletin (ISSN 0360-9197)

610   US   ISSN 1079-2473
▼**TRANSITIONS MAGAZINE.** 1994. bi-m. $99. International Subacute Healthcare Association, 4040 W. 70th St., Minneapolis, MN 55435. TEL 612-926-1773. FAX 612-926-1624. Ed. Janine Tobeck. adv. (back issues avail.) **Document type:** trade publication.
Description: Fosters professional dialogue about the emerging subacute care industry. Aims to educate and report on specific trends and issues affecting this growing healthcare niche.

610   GW   ISSN 0934-0874
RD120.7
TRANSPLANT INTERNATIONAL. (Text in English) 1989. 6/yr. DM.798($579) (effective 1996). (European Society of Organ Transplantation) Springer-Verlag, Heidelberger Platz 3, 14197 Berlin, Germany. TEL 030-8207-0. FAX 030-8214091. E-mail: orders@springer.de. (Subscr. in N. America to: Springer-Verlag New York, Inc., 44 Hartz Way, Secaucus, NJ 07096-2491. TEL 201-348-4033. FAX 201-348-4505) Ed. G. Kootstra. **Indexed:** Kidney. **Document type:** academic/scholarly publication.
—BLDSC (9024.989000); Faxon; Genuine Article; SWETS; UMI; UnCover. **CCC**.
Description: Serves as a forum in the field of transplantation.

TRANSPLANTOLOGY; journal of cell and organ transplantation. see *MEDICAL SCIENCES — Surgery*

TRAUMA & EMERGENCY MEDICINE. see *MEDICAL SCIENCES — Orthopedics And Traumatology*

610   US
TRAVEL MEDICINE ADVISOR. 1991. bi-m. $248. American Health Consultants, Inc., Six Piedmont Center, Ste. 400, Atlanta, GA 30305. TEL 404-262-7436; 800-688-2421. FAX 800-284-3291. Ed. Dr. Elaine Long. circ. 800. **Document type:** newsletter.

610 616.98   UK   ISSN 0267-3606
TRAVEL MEDICINE INTERNATIONAL. 1983. bi-m. £120 (foreign £145). Mark Allen Publishing Ltd., Croxted Mews, 288 Croxted Rd., London SE24 9BY, England. TEL 0181-671-7521. FAX 0181-671-1722. Ed. Dr. Hugh L'Etang; Pub. Mark Allen. **Indexed:** Abstr.Hyg. **Document type:** academic/scholarly publication.
—BLDSC (9045.452700).
Formerly (until 1984): Travel and Traffic Medicine International (ISSN 0263-8657)

TRAVELING HEALTHY. see *TRAVEL AND TOURISM*

610 900   US
TREASURES. 1980. 3/yr. free. University of Alabama at Birmingham, Reynolds Historical Library, 1700 University Blvd., Birmingham, AL 35294. TEL 205-934-4475. FAX 205-975-8476. Ed. M.G. McGuinn. illus. circ. 2,000. (looseleaf format; back issues avail.) **Document type:** newsletter.
Description: Disseminates news and information about the collection of rare books, manuscripts, letters, and papers concerning the history of medicine.

610   US
TREATMENT IN CLINICAL MEDICINE. 1984. irreg. price varies. Springer-Verlag, 175 Fifth Ave., New York, NY 10010. TEL 212-460-1500. FAX 212-473-6272. (Also: Berlin, Heidelberg, Tokyo and Vienna) (reprint service avail. from ISI) **Document type:** monographic series.

TRENDS IN GENETICS; DNA, differentiation and development. see *BIOLOGY — Genetics*

TRENDS IN GENETICS (REFERENCE EDITION). see *BIOLOGY — Genetics*

MEDICAL SCIENCES

362.1 344.73 174.2   US   ISSN 1062-5364
K24
TRENDS IN HEALTH CARE, LAW & ETHICS; a journal of contemporary issues in health care. 1985. q. $40 to individuals; institutions $50 (Canada and Mexico $58; elsewhere $68) (effective 1995-1996). University of Medicine and Dentistry of New Jersey, Robert Wood Johnson Medical School, Box 896, Piscataway, NJ 08855-0896. TEL 908-235-4549. FAX 908-235-4569. E-mail: Trends@umdnj.edu. Ed. Russell L. McIntyre; Pub. Russell L. McIntyre. adv.; bk.rev. circ. 2,700. **Document type:** academic/scholarly publication.
—BLDSC (9049.620000); UnCover.
   Description: Discusses important medical legal and ethical issues.

TRIBUNA BIOLOGICA E MEDICA. see *BIOLOGY*

610   SP   ISSN 0212-7512
TRIBUNA MEDICA. 1964. w. 7200 ptas.($80) (effective 1995). Editorial Garsi, S.A, Juan Bravo 46, 28006 Madrid, Spain. TEL 34-1-4021212. FAX 34-1-4020954. Ed. Jose Maria Garcia. adv.; bk.rev.; index. circ. 35,000. (tabloid format; back issues avail.)
—CCC.

610   CK   ISSN 0120-2529
TRIBUNA MEDICA. (Editions avail. for: Mexico, Central America, Colombia, Venezuela, Ecuador, Peru) 1961. 24/yr. Ediciones Lerner Ltda., Calle 8A No.68A-41, Bogota, Colombia. TEL 261-5047. FAX 262-4459. Ed. Salomon Lerner. adv. circ. 50,000.
—BLDSC (9050.245000).

610   MX
TRIBUNA MEDICA. 1966. 24/yr. Jose Maria Rico 121, Desp. 604, Colonia del Valle 03100, Mexico 12, DF, Mexico. Ed. Ricardo Blaksley. circ. 20,000.

610   PE
TRIBUNA MEDICA. 1964. 24/yr. Ave. Angamos Oeste 371, Apto. 405, Miraflores, Lima, Peru. Ed. Jose Alva Neira. adv. circ. 6,000.

610   VE
TRIBUNA MEDICA. 1963. 14/yr. $75. Tribuna Medica Venezolana C.A., Av. Principal los Ruices, Ofc. 319, Apartado 51064, Caracas, 10A, Venezuela. FAX 354456. TELEX 27326 TRIME VC. adv. circ. 9,000.

610   CK
TRIBUNA MEDICA FOR CENTRAL AMERICA, PANAMA AND THE DOMINICAN REPUBLIC. 1969. 24/yr. Ediciones Lerner, Calle 8A, No. 68 a41, Bogota, Colombia. FAX 2624864. Ed. Eduardo Chegwin. adv. circ. 10,000.

610 340   US   ISSN 1066-3681
TRINGA PRESS MONOGRAPH SERIES. 1992. irreg. $5 per no. Tringa Press, Box 8181, St. Paul, MN 55108. TEL 612-222-7476. FAX 612-699-0666. Ed. Debora Slee. index. (looseleaf format; back issues avail.) **Document type:** academic/scholarly publication, monographic series.

610   US
TUBEROUS SCLEROSIS RESOURCES; for scientists, physicians and other health professionals. s-a. $25 membership includes N T S A Newsletter. National Tuberous Sclerosis Association, 8000 Corporate Center Dr., Ste. 120, Landover, MD 20785-2239. TEL 800-225-6872. FAX 301-459-0394.
   Description: News for the medical community.

610   US
TUFTS MEDICINE. 1941. 3/yr. Tufts University, School of Medicine, 203 Harrison Ave., Boston, MA 02111. TEL 617-956-5705. FAX 617-350-8075. Ed. Marjorie H. Dwyer. circ. 10,000. (back issues avail.) **Document type:** bulletin.
   Formerly: Tufts Medical Alumni Bulletin.

610   US
TULANE MEDICINE. 1969. q. free. Tulane University, Office of University Publications, 300 Hebert Hall, New Orleans, LA 70118-5698. TEL 504-865-5714. FAX 504-865-5621. E-mail: medlet@mailhost.tcs.tulane.edu. Ed. Anne Yeoman. adv.; bk.rev.; abstr.; charts; AC. circ. 18,500.
   Formerly: Tulane Medicine: Faculty and Alumni (ISSN 0041-400X); Which superseded: Tulane University Medical Faculty. Bulletin.

610.6   US
TULSA MEDICINE.* 1935. m. $10. Tulsa County Medical Society, 2021 S. Lewis, No. 560, Tulsa, OK 74104-5758. Ed. Jack Spears. adv. circ. 1,100.
   Formerly (until Oct. 1977): Tulsa County Medical Society. Bulletin.

610   TI   ISSN 0041-4131
LA TUNISIE MEDICALE. (Text in French; summaries in Arabic, English, French) 1911. 12/yr. 25 din.($40) Societe Tunisienne des Sciences Medicales, 16 Rue Touraine, 1002 Tunis - Belvedere, Tunisia. TEL 790-924. (Co-sponsor: Conseil de l'Ordre des Medecins) Ed. A. Chabbou. adv.; bk.rev.; charts; index. circ. 2,500. **Indexed:** Abstr.Hyg., Biol.Abstr., Chem.Abstr., Excerp.Med., ExtraMED, Ind.Med., P.A.I.S.For.Lang.Ind., Trop.Dis.Bull. **Document type:** academic/scholarly publication.
●Also available on CD-ROM.
—BLDSC (9071.150000); EMDOCS.
   Formed by the merger of: Revue Tunisienne des Sciences Medicales; Bulletin de l'Hopital Sadiki.
   Description: Scientific journal featuring original papers and clinical cases in the medical sciences as well as updating reviews and state of the art discussions of medical questions.
Refereed Serial

610   TU   ISSN 0377-2497
TURK TIP DERNEGI DERGISI. (Text in Turkish; summaries and table of contents in English) 1935. m. Turkish Medical Society - Turk Tip Dernegi, Valikonagi Caddesi 10, Harbiye, Istanbul, Turkey. Dir. Dr. Kazim Ismail Gurkan. adv.; abstr.; bibl.; charts; stat. **Document type:** academic/scholarly publication.
   Former titles (until 1973): Turk Tip Cemiyeti Mecmuasi (ISSN 0494-2736); **Supersedes (1965-1973):** Turkish Medical Association. Journal (ISSN 0041-431X)

610 574   TU   ISSN 1016-3611
TURKISH JOURNAL OF MEDICAL & BIOLOGICAL RESEARCH. (Text in English) 1990. q. Istanbul University, Beyazit, Istanbul, Turkey. **Document type:** academic/scholarly publication.

610   TU   ISSN 1300-0144
   CODEN: TJMEEA
TURKISH JOURNAL OF MEDICAL SCIENCES. (Text and summaries in English) 1976. m. $300 (effective 1995 & 1996). Scientific and Technical Research Council of Turkey - TUBITAK - Turkiye Bilimsel ve Teknik Arastirma Kurumk, Ataturk Bulvari, No. 221, Kavaklidere, 06100 Ankara, Turkey. TEL 90-312-4685300. FAX 90-312-4271336. TELEX 43186 BTAK TR. Ed. Sinasi Ozsoylu. **Indexed:** Biol.Abstr., Chem.Abstr., Excerp.Med. **Document type:** academic/scholarly publication.
—BLDSC (9072.469000); CASDDS.
   Former titles (until 1994): Doga Turkish Journal of Medical Sciences; (until 1988): Doga Turkish Journal of Medicine and Pharmacy (ISSN 1010-7584); Incorporates: Doga Turk Eczacilik Dergisi; Supersedes: Doga Bilim Dergisi. Series C: Medicine.
Refereed Serial

610   FI   ISSN 0355-9483
   CODEN: TYJMDL
TURUN YLIOPISTO. JULKAISUJA. SARJA D. MEDICA - ODONTOLOGICA. (Latin title: Annales Universitatis Turkuensis) (Text in English) 1972. irreg. price varies. Turun Yliopisto - University of Turku, SF-20500 Turku 50, Finland. FAX 358-21-6335050. TELEX 62123 TYK SF. **Indexed:** Chem.Abstr.
—BLDSC (0963.354000); CASDDS.
   Description: Studies medicine and dentistry.

U A P D REPORT. (Union of American Physicians and Dentists) see *LABOR UNIONS*

610   US   ISSN 0082-7134
   CODEN: UCMSAA
U C L A FORUM IN MEDICAL SCIENCES. 1962. irreg., vol.28, 1988. (University of California at Los Angeles) Academic Press, Inc., 525 B St., Ste. 1900, San Diego, CA 92101-4495. TEL 619-231-0926. FAX 619-699-6715. (Subscr. to: Order Dept., 6277 Sea Harbor Dr., 4th Fl., Orlando, FL 32887. TEL 800-321-5068) (reprint service avail. from ISI) **Indexed:** Biol.Abstr., Chem.Abstr., Ind.Med. **Document type:** academic/scholarly publication.
—CASDDS.
Refereed Serial

610   US
U C S F MAGAZINE. 1978. s-a. free. University of California at San Francisco, Public Affairs, 3333 California St., Ste. 103, San Francisco, CA 94143. TEL 415-476-8299. FAX 415-476-3541. (Co-sponsors: U C S F Schools of Dentistry, Medicine, Nursing and Pharmacy) Ed. Jeff Miller. circ. 46,000. (back issues avail.) **Document type:** consumer publication.
   Description: Showcases people, programs, scientific and medical achievements, and outreach efforts that distinguish U.C.S.F.

610   UK
U M D S ANNUAL REPORT. a. United Medical and Dental Schools, Lambeth Palace Rd., London SE1 7EH, England. TEL 071-928-9292. **Document type:** corporate report.

610   US   ISSN 0191-6246
U S MEDICINE; an independent national newspaper for physicians. 1964. m. $125. U S Medicine, Inc., 1155 21st St., N.W., Washington, DC 20036. TEL 202-463-6000. Ed. Nancy Tomich; Pub. Nancy Tomich. adv. contact: Ann Finch. bk.rev.; charts; illus. circ. 31,000. **Document type:** newspaper.
   Description: Serves the field of medicine for civilian, V.A. and military and hospital professionals on the federal, state, and local levels as well as medical schools and managed-care organizations.

362 614   BE   ISSN 0777-9364
U Z MAGAZINE. (Universitaire Ziekenhuis) (Text in Dutch) 1985. q. free. U Z Gasthuisberg Organisatie-en Personeelsontwikkeling, Herestraat 49, 3000 Leuven, Belgium. TEL 32-16-344198. FAX 32-16-345500. Ed. Roland Vermeylen. adv. circ. 5,500. (back issues avail.)
   Description: News and information for patients, visitors and families.

610   DK   ISSN 0041-5782
   CODEN: UGLAAD
UGESKRIFT FOR LAEGER. (Text in Danish; summaries in English) 1839. w. DKK 1.420($116) Almindelige Danske Laegeforening - Danish Medical Association, Trondhjemsgade 9, DK-2100 Copenhagen, Denmark. TEL 31 38 55 00. FAX 31-15-28-58. (Subscr. to: Laegeforeningens Forlag, Esplanaden 8 A, DK-1263 Copenhagen K, Denmark) Eds. Povl Riis, Bente Hjelmar. adv.; bk.rev.; abstr.; bibl.; charts; illus.; stat.; index, cum.index. circ. 20,000. **Indexed:** Biol.Abstr., C.I.S. Abstr., Chem.Abstr., Dairy Sci.Abstr., Dent.Ind., Dok.Arbeitsmed., Excerp.Med., Ind.Med., Nutr.Abstr., Protozool.Abstr., Rev.Med.& Vet.Mycol., Trop.Oil Seeds Abstr.
—BLDSC (9080.000000); CASDDS; EMDOCS; Genuine Article; SWETS.

610   US   ISSN 0041-607X
UKRAINIAN MEDICAL ASSOCIATION OF NORTH AMERICA. JOURNAL. (Text in Ukrainian) vol.17, 1970. m. $20. Ukrainian Medical Association of North America, 2 E. 79th St., New York, NY 10027. TEL 212-535-8659. Ed. Dr. Paul J. Dzul. adv.; bk.rev. circ. 1,000.

610   UK   ISSN 0041-6193
ULSTER MEDICAL JOURNAL. 1932. s-a. £30. Ulster Medical Society, c/o Queens University Medical Library, Institute of Clinical Science, Grosvenor Rd., Belfast BT12 6BA, Northern Ireland. TEL 0232-322043. FAX 0232-247068. TELEX 747578-QUBMED-G. Ed. Dr. D.R. Hadden. adv.; bk.rev.; bibl.; illus.; index. circ. 1,060. (also avail. in microfilm from UMI; reprint service avail. from IRC,UMI) **Indexed:** Abstr.Hyg., Chem.Abstr., Curr.Adv.Ecol.Sci., Curr.Cont, Excerp.Med., Helminthol.Abstr., Ind.Med., Sci.Cit.Ind., Trop.Dis.Bull. **Document type:** academic/scholarly publication.
●Also available on CD-ROM. Producer(s): SilverPlatter Information, Inc. (MEDLINE).
—BLDSC (9082.745000); EMDOCS; Faxon; Genuine Article; UMI; UnCover.
Refereed Serial

MEDICAL SCIENCES

610 GW ISSN 0172-4614
ULTRASCHALL IN DER MEDIZIN. 1980. bi-m. DM.228. (Deutsche Gesellschaft fuer Ultraschall in der Medizin) Georg Thieme Verlag, Ruedigerstr. 14, 70469 Stuttgart, Germany. TEL 0711-8931-0. FAX 0711-89312988. (Subscr. to: Postfach 104853, 70042 Stuttgart, Germany) Ed.Bd. adv.; bk.rev.; abstr.; bibl.; charts; illus. circ. 3,200. (reprint service avail. from UMI) **Indexed:** Curr.Cont., Excerp.Med., Ind.Med. **Document type:** academic/scholarly publication.
—BLDSC (9082.786000); Faxon; Genuine Article; UMI. **CCC.**

610 GW ISSN 0930-8040
ULTRASCHALL IN KLINIK UND PRAXIS. 4/yr. DM.245($178) (effective 1996). Springer-Verlag, Heidelberger Platz 3, 14197 Berlin, Germany. TEL 030-8207-0. FAX 030-8214091. E-mail: orders@springer.de. (Subscr. in N. America to: Springer-Verlag New York, Inc., 44 Hartz Way, Secaucus, NJ 07096-2491. TEL 201-348-4033. FAX 201-348-4505) Ed.Bd. **Document type:** academic/scholarly publication.
—BLDSC (9082.785700); UMI. **CCC.**

ULTRASOUND IN MEDICINE & BIOLOGY. see BIOLOGY

616 US ISSN 1066-2936
RC1000 CODEN: UHMEE7
UNDERSEA & HYPERBARIC MEDICINE. 1974. q. $85. Undersea and Hyperbaric Medical Society, Inc., 10531 Metropolitan Ave., Kensington, MD 20895. TEL 301-942-2980. FAX 301-942-7804. Ed. H. Van Liew. bk.rev.; index. circ. 2,000. **Indexed:** Biol.Abstr., Chem.Abstr., Curr.Adv.Ecol.Sci., Curr.Cont., Deep Sea Res.& Oceanogr.Abstr., Dent.Ind., Excerp.Med., Ind.Med., Ocean.Abstr., Pollut.Abstr., Psychol.Abstr. **Document type:** academic/scholarly publication.
—BLDSC (9088.570000); CASDDS; Faxon; Genuine Article; SWETS; UMI; UnCover.
Formed by the 1993 merger of: Undersea Biomedical Research (ISSN 0093-5387) & Journal of Hyperbaric Medicine (ISSN 0884-1225); Which supersedes (1980-1985): Hyperbaric Oxygen Review (ISSN 0195-9263)
Refereed Serial

UNDO SHOGAI/MOVEMENT DISORDER AND DISABILITY. see HANDICAPPED

610 US
UNIFORMED SERVICES ACADEMY OF FAMILY PHYSICIANS NEWSLETTER.* q. membership. Uniformed Services Academy of Family Physicians, 4211 Dover Rd., Richmond, VA 23221-3267. TEL 804-794-2106. Ed. Dr. R. Dean Kirkham. adv. circ. 2,600.

610 RM ISSN 0041-6940
UNION MEDICALE BALKANIQUE. ARCHIVES. (Text in French; summaries in English) 1963. bi-m. $80. Union Medicale Balkanique, Str. Gabriel Peri Nr. 1, Bucharest, Rumania. (Subscr. to: ILEXIM, Str. 13 Decembrie Nr. 3, P.O. Box 136-137, Bucharest, Rumania) Ed. Prof. Popescu Buzeu. bk.rev.; abstr.; bibl.; charts; illus.; index; circ. 2,000 (controlled). **Indexed:** Biol.Abstr., Ind.Med., Nutr.Abstr.

610 CN ISSN 0041-6959
CODEN: UMCAAA
UNION MEDICALE DU CANADA. (Text in French; summaries in English and French) 1872. m. Can.$75($90) Association des Medecins de Langue Francaise du Canada, 8355 boul. St-Laurent, Montreal, PQ H2P 2Z6, Canada. TEL 514-388-2228. Ed. Dr. Henri Menard. adv.; bk.rev.; abstr.; bibl.; charts; illus.; index. circ. 13,446. (reprint service avail. from UMI) **Indexed:** Biol.Abstr., Chem.Abstr., Curr.Adv.Genetics & Molec.Biol., Curr.Cont., Dent.Ind., Dok.Arbeitsmed., Excerp.Med., Helminthol.Abstr., Ind.Med., Nutr.Abstr., Pt.de Rep. (1983-).
—BLDSC (9090.750000); CASDDS; Faxon; Genuine Article; UMI.

610 371.42 US ISSN 1059-6100
UNIQUE OPPORTUNITIES. 1991. bi-m. $30. U O, Inc., 455 S. Fourth Ave., Ste. 817, Louisville, KY 40202. TEL 502-589-8250. FAX 502-587-0848. E-mail: unop@aol.com. Ed. Mollie Vento Hudson. adv.: B&W page $3995, color page $4850; trim 8 1/8 x 10 7/8; adv. contact: Mel Weinberger. circ. 80,000. **Document type:** trade publication.
Description: Aimed at physicians interested in their first or next career opportunity. Offers physicians useful information and first-hand experiences to guide them in making informed decisions about their careers.

616.98 TS
UNITED ARAB EMIRATES. AL-QIYADAH AL-AAMAH LIL-QUWWAT AL-MUSALLIHAH. MAJALLAH AL-TIBBIYYAH/UNITED ARAB EMIRATES. GENERAL COMMAND FOR THE ARMED FORCES. MEDICAL JOURNAL. (Text in Arabic) 1989. q. exchange basis. General Command for the Armed Forces, Medical Services Administration - Al-Qiyadah al-Aamah lil-Quwwat al-Musallihah, Mudiriyyah al-Khidamat al-Tibbiyyah, P.O. Box 4224, Abu Dhabi, United Arab Emirates. TEL 447999. Ed. Muhammad Farid. circ. 1,000.
Description: Discusses topics in military medicine and medical concerns of the armed forces.

610 US
U.S. DEPARTMENT OF VETERANS AFFAIRS. SUMMARY OF MEDICAL PROGRAMS. s-a. free. U.S. Department of Veterans Affairs, 810 Vermont Ave., N.W. (008C2), Washington, DC 20420. TEL 202-273-5121. FAX 202-273-5121. (also avail. in diskette format) **Indexed:** Amer.Stat.Ind. (1975-). **Document type:** government publication.
Formerly: U.S. Veterans Administration. Summary of Medical Programs.

U.S. LIBRARY OF CONGRESS. NATIONAL LIBRARY SERVICE FOR THE BLIND AND PHYSICALLY HANDICAPPED. NEWS. see HANDICAPPED — Visually Impaired

610 US
U.S. OFFICE OF TECHNOLOGY ASSESSMENT. REPORTS. HEALTH PROGRAM. irreg. price varies. U.S. Office of Technology Assessment, Publication Distribution, U.S. Congress, 600 Pennsylvania Ave., S.E., Washington, DC 20510-8025. TEL 202-224-8713. FAX 202-228-6098. E-mail: PUBREQUEST@OTA.GOV. (Dist. by: Superintendent of Documents, U.S. Government Printing Office, Box 371954, Pittsburgh, PA 15250-7954. TEL 202-783-3238. FAX 202-512-2250; And: National Technical Information Service, 5285 Port Royal Rd., Springfield, VA 22161. TEL 703-487-4650. FAX 703-321-8547) (also avail. in microfiche from CIS; reprint service avail. from CIS; back issues avail.) **Document type:** monographic series, government publication.
Description: Reports provide information on clinical and laboratory technologies in medical research; economic issues on communicable diseases are also covered.

U.S. SURGEON GENERAL. REPORT. see DRUG ABUSE AND ALCOHOLISM

610 EC ISSN 0041-8412
UNIVERSIDAD DE GUAYAQUIL. FACULTAD DE CIENCIAS MEDICAS. REVISTA.* s-a. free. Universidad de Guayaquil, PO Box 3637, Guayaquil, Ecuador. Ed. Dr. Carlos Palan. charts; illus. circ. 700.

610 SP ISSN 0210-5527
UNIVERSIDAD DE OVIEDO. FACULTAD DE MEDICINA. ARCHIVOS. 1976. a. price varies. Universidad de Oviedo, Facultad de Medicina, Servicio de Publicaciones, C. Arguelles 19, 33003 Oviedo, Spain. TEL 34-85-210160. FAX 34-85-218352. Ed. Bernardo Marin Fernandez. abstr.; illus. circ. 500. **Document type:** academic/scholarly publication.

610 SP
CODEN: AUHMDC
UNIVERSIDAD DE SEVILLA. SERIE: MEDICINA. 1949. irreg., latest no.49. Universidad de Sevilla, Servicio de Publicaciones, Valparaiso 5, 41013 Seville, Spain. TEL 954-231958. FAX 954-232245. charts; illus.
—CASDDS.
Former titles: Universidad Hispalense. Anales. Serie: Medicina (ISSN 0586-9919); (Until 1967): Universidad Hispalense. Anales. Facultad de Medicina (ISSN 0210-7651)

UNIVERSIDAD INDUSTRIAL DE SANTANDER. REVISTA - INVESTIGACIONES. see ENGINEERING

610 CK ISSN 0121-0807
CODEN: RUIMDY
UNIVERSIDAD INDUSTRIAL DE SANTANDER. REVISTA - SALUD. (Text in Spanish; summaries in English, French, German and Spanish) 1959. s-a. Col.$6000($8) for 2 yrs. or exchange basis. Universidad Industrial de Santander, Facultad de Salud, Adpo. Aereo 678, Bucaramanga, Santander, Colombia. FAX 5776-351946. adv.; bk.rev.; bibl.; charts; illus.; stat; cum.index: 1969-1987. (back issues avail.) **Document type:** academic/scholarly publication.
Formerly: Universidad Industrial de Santander. Revista - Medicina (ISSN 0120-0909); Which superseded in part (in 1969): Universidad Industrial de Santander. Revista (ISSN 0041-8587)
Description: Covers research and current issues on various topics in medical science and health.

610 CK ISSN 0120-0011
UNIVERSIDAD NACIONAL DE COLOMBIA. FACULTAD DE MEDICINA. REVISTA. 1932. q. exchange basis. Universidad Nacional de Colombia, Facultad de Medicina, Aereo No. 14490, Bogota D.E., Colombia. Dir. Milton Arguello Jimenex. adv.; illus. circ. 5,000. **Indexed:** Biol.Abstr.

610 AG ISSN 0014-6722
UNIVERSIDAD NACIONAL DE CORDOBA. FACULTAD DE CIENCIAS MEDICAS. REVISTA. (Text in Spanish; summaries in English, French, German or Italian) 1943. q. $5. Universidad Nacional de Cordoba, Facultad de Ciencias Medicas, Ciudad Universitaria, Estafeta 32, 5000 Cordoba, Argentina. Ed. E.E. Tello. abstr.; charts; illus.; index. **Indexed:** Abstr.Hyg., Biol.Abstr., Dent.Ind., Excerp.Med., Ind.Med., Trop.Dis.Bull.
—BLDSC (7811.645000).

610 BL ISSN 0041-8781
CODEN: RHCFAP
UNIVERSIDADE DE SAO PAULO. HOSPITAL DAS CLINICAS. REVISTA. (Text in English, Portuguese) 1946. bi-m. $35. Universidade de Sao Paulo, Faculdade de Medicina, Caixa Postal 8091, Sao Paulo, Brazil. Ed. Ruy G. Bevilacqua. adv.; charts; illus.; index. cum.index. circ. 10,000. **Indexed:** Abstr.Hyg., Excerp.Med., Ind.Med., Nutr.Abstr., Protozool.Abstr., Trop.Dis.Bull.
—BLDSC (7815.850000); CASDDS; Faxon.

610 BL ISSN 0100-1302
CODEN: RMUCD8
UNIVERSIDADE FEDERAL DO CEARA. CENTRO DE CIENCIAS DA SAUDE. REVISTA DE MEDICINA/FEDERAL UNIVERSITY OF CEARA. SCHOOL OF MEDICINE. JOURNAL OF MEDICINE. (Text in English or Portuguese; summaries in English and Portuguese) 1961. s-a. free. Universidade Federal do Ceara, Centro de Ciencias da Saude, Rua Alexandre Barauna 949, Caixa Postal 3170, 60430 Fortaleza, Ceara, Brazil. TEL 085-243-9002. FAX 085-243-90-10. Ed. Maria Guimaraes Ferreira. adv.; play rev.; charts; illus.; stat.; circ. 2,000 (controlled). (tabloid format) **Indexed:** Excerp.Med.
—BLDSC (7864.440000); CASDDS.
Formerly (until 1973): Universidade Federal do Ceara. Faculdade de Medicina. Revista (ISSN 0041-8889)

610 XR ISSN 0049-5514
R95.P7 CODEN: SVLKAO
UNIVERSITA KARLOVA. FAKULTA VSEOBECNEHO LEKARSTVI. SBORNIK VEDECKYCH PRACI. (Text in English; summaries in Czech, English) 1958. 4/yr. Universita Karlova, Lekarska Fakulta, Simkova 870, 500 38 Hradec Kralove, Czech Republic. illus. **Indexed:** Ind.Med. **Document type:** academic/scholarly publication.
—BLDSC (8087.390000); CASDDS; EMDOCS.

610 XR ISSN 0049-5522
CODEN: SVKSA9
UNIVERSITA KARLOVA. LEKARSKA FAKULTA. SBORNIK VEDECKYCH PRACI: SUPPLEMENTUM. (Text in Czech; summaries in Czech, English) 1958. a. Universita Karlova, Lekarska Fakulta, Simkova 870, 500 83 Hradec Kralove, Czech Republic. illus. **Indexed:** Ind.Med. **Document type:** academic/scholarly publication.

MEDICAL SCIENCES

610 AU ISSN 0579-7772
UNIVERSITAET INNSBRUCK. MEDIZINISCHE FAKULTAET. ARBEITEN. 1970. irregr. price varies. Oesterreichische Kommissionsbuchhandlung, Maximilianstrasse 17, A-6020 Innsbruck, Austria. Ed. Hans Schroecksnadel.

610 CK ISSN 0041-9095
CODEN: UNMEBC
UNIVERSITAS MEDICA. (Text in Spanish; summaries in English and Spanish) 1951. q. Col.$10000($30) (students Col.$6000) (effective Mar. 1993). Pontificia Universidad Javeriana, Facultad de Medicina, Carrera 7a. N. 40-62 Piso 5, Hospital San Ignacio, Bogota, Colombia. TEL 57-1-2882166. FAX 57-1-2889273. Ed. Dr. Saul Rujeles. adv.; bk.rev.; abstr.; bibl.; charts; illus.; stat.; index. circ. 3,000. **Indexed:** Chem.Abstr., Excerp.Med. **Document type:** academic/scholarly publication.
—BLDSC (9101.390000); CASDDS.
Description: Covers articles written on research done in medicine.

610 UA ISSN 1010-6324
CODEN: BAFMD9
UNIVERSITY OF ALEXANDRIA. FACULTY OF MEDICINE. BULLETIN. (Text in English) 1965. q. £E50. University of Alexandria, Faculty of Medicine, 22 Sharia al-Gaish, Al-Shatby, Alexandria, Egypt. Ed. Nahmoud Naim. bibl.; illus. **Indexed:** Biol.Abstr., Chem.Abstr., ExtraMED, Soils & Fert. **Document type:** bulletin.
●Also available on CD-ROM.
—CASDDS.

610 IQ ISSN 0041-9419
CODEN: JFAQAE
UNIVERSITY OF BAGHDAD. FACULTY OF MEDICINE. JOURNAL. 1936. 4/yr. University of Baghdad, Medical College, Baghdad, Iraq. Ed. Dr. Fakhri al-Hadthy. adv.; bk.rev.; charts. circ. 1,500. **Indexed:** Biol.Abstr., Chem.Abstr., Helminthol.Abstr., Nutr.Abstr., Protozool.Abstr., Trop.Dis.Bull. **Document type:** academic/scholarly publication.
—CASDDS.

610 UA ISSN 0045-3803
CODEN: MJCUDW
UNIVERSITY OF CAIRO. FACULTY OF MEDICINE. MEDICAL JOURNAL. (Supplement avail.) (Text in English) 1932. q. £E8($40) University of Cairo, Faculty of Medicine, Clinical Society Office, Manyal University Hospital, Kasr El-Aini Post, Cairo, Egypt. TEL 726-0595. Eds. Khairy A. Samrah, Mahmoud Khairy. adv.; bk.rev.; abstr.; index. circ. 400. (back issues avail.) **Document type:** academic/scholarly publication.
—BLDSC (5527.600000); CASDDS.
Formerly: University of Cairo. Faculty of Medicine. Gazette; **Incorporates:** Kasr El-Aini Clinical Society. Faculty of Medicine. Gazette.
Description: Presents original papers and research activities of medical school personnel. Features review articles, abstracts from current literature and historical notes.
Refereed Serial

610 II ISSN 0008-0705
CODEN: BUYMA3
UNIVERSITY OF CALCUTTA. UNIVERSITY COLLEGE OF MEDICINE. BULLETIN. 1963. s-a. free. Calcutta University Press, Sri Sibendra Nath Kanjilal, 48 Hazra Rd., Calcutta 19, India. Ed. S.N. Sen. bibl.; charts; illus. **Indexed:** Biol.Abstr., Chem.Abstr., Excerp.Med.

UNIVERSITY OF CALIFORNIA. LAWRENCE BERKELEY LABORATORY. BIOLOGY AND MEDICINE DIVISION. ANNUAL REPORT. see *BIOLOGY — Biological Chemistry*

610 IR
UNIVERSITY OF FERDOWSI. FACULTY OF MEDICINE. LETTERS/DANESHGAH-E FERDOWSI. DANESHKADE-YE PAZESHKI. NAMEH. (Text in Persian) 1956. bi-m. Rs.200. University of Ferdowsi, Faculty of Medicine, Ta'lifat Va Entesharat, Mashhad, Iran. Ed. Manuchehr Radpur.

610 LB
UNIVERSITY OF LIBERIA. A.M. DOGLIOTTI COLLEGE OF MEDICINE. ANNUAL REPORT OF THE DEAN.* a. University of Liberia, A.M. Dogliotti College of Medicine, Monrovia, Liberia.

610 010.7 UK ISSN 0076-0854
UNIVERSITY OF LONDON. ROYAL POSTGRADUATE MEDICAL SCHOOL. ANNUAL REPORT. 1936. a. free. University of London, Royal Postgraduate Medical School, Hammersmith Hospital, Du Cane Rd., London W12 0NN, England. TEL 0181-740-3201. FAX 0181-740-3203. Ed. J.M. Budd. circ. 1,000 (controlled). **Document type:** corporate report.

610 AT ISSN 0312-6137
R831.N46
UNIVERSITY OF NEW SOUTH WALES. FACULTY HANDBOOKS: MEDICINE. a. Aus.$4. University of New South Wales, Sydney, N.S.W. 2052, Australia. TEL 61-2-385-2840. FAX 61-2-662-2163.

UNIVERSITY OF OCCUPATIONAL AND ENVIRONMENTAL HEALTH. JOURNAL. see *OCCUPATIONAL HEALTH AND SAFETY*

610 NZ ISSN 0301-6331
CODEN: PUOMA
UNIVERSITY OF OTAGO MEDICAL SCHOOL. PROCEEDINGS. 1922. 3/yr. NZ.$38 (effective 1995 & 1996). Otago Medical School Research Society, P.O. Box 913, Dunedin, New Zealand. TEL 64-3-4797570. FAX 64-3-4790401. **Indexed:** Excerp.Med. **Document type:** academic/scholarly publication, proceedings.
—BLDSC (6830.400000).
Refereed Serial

UNIVERSITY OF SOUTH FLORIDA. INTERNATIONAL BIOMEDICAL SYMPOSIA SERIES. see *BIOLOGY*

UNIVERSITY OF TEHERAN. FACULTY OF MEDICINE. LIBRARY BULLETIN/DANESHGAH-E TEHRAN. DANESHKADE-YE PEZESHKI. NASHRIYE-YE KETABKHANEH. see *LIBRARY AND INFORMATION SCIENCES*

610 CN ISSN 0833-2207
UNIVERSITY OF TORONTO MEDICAL JOURNAL. 1923. 3/yr. $25. University of Toronto, Medical Society, Medical Sciences Bldg., Toronto, ON M5S 1A8, Canada. TEL 416-978-8730. Eds. Joan Saary, Chris Bouliasbrook. adv.; bk.rev.; charts; illus. circ. 2,000. (also avail. in microform from MML) **Indexed:** Biol.Abstr., Excerp.Med. **Document type:** academic/scholarly publication.
Refereed Serial

610 CN ISSN 0042-0336
UNIVERSITY OF WESTERN ONTARIO MEDICAL JOURNAL; an interdisciplinary medical sciences publication. 1930. 3/yr. $15. University of Western Ontario, Faculty of Medicine, Health Sciences Centre, London, Ont. N6A 5C1, Canada. TEL 519-885-1211. adv.; bk.rev.; bibl.; charts; illus.; stat. circ. 2,100. **Indexed:** Biol.Abstr., Chem.Abstr.

610.7 UK ISSN 0301-5718
UPDATE; the journal of postgraduate medical education. 1968. s-m. £86 (free to qualified personnel). Reed Healthcare Publishing (Subsidiary of: Reed Elsevier group), Quadrant House, The Quadrant, Sutton, Surrey SM2 5AS, England. TEL 0181-652-8878. FAX 0181-652-8946. Ed. Andrew Baxter. adv.; bk.rev.; charts; illus.; stat.; index. circ. 36,000. **Indexed:** Excerp.Med., FAMLI, Helminthol.Abstr., L.R.I., Rehabil.Lit. **Document type:** trade publication.
—BLDSC (9121.900000); SWETS. **CCC.**
Description: Covers the spectrum of medicine addressing the postgraduate needs of the general practitioner.

610 SA ISSN 0258-929X
UPDATE; the journal of continuing education for general practitioners. UK edition: Update (ISSN 0301-5718) (Text in English) 1986. m. R.140. George Warman Publications (Pty.) Ltd., P.O. Box 3847, Cape Town 8000, South Africa, South Africa. TEL 021-245320. FAX 021-261332. Ed. Diana Procter. adv.; bk.rev.; illus.; index; circ. 8,400 (controlled). (back issues avail.)
Description: Publishes clinical articles on developments in all medical specializations of interest to the general practitioner.
Refereed Serial

610 US ISSN 0933-6788
UPDATE IN INTENSIVE CARE AND EMERGENCY MEDICINE. 1986. irregr. price varies. Springer-Verlag, 175 Fifth Ave., New York, NY 10010. TEL 212-460-1500. FAX 212-473-6272. (Also: Berlin, Heidelberg, Tokyo and Vienna) (reprint service avail. from ISI) **Document type:** monographic series.
—BLDSC (9121.954900).

610 UK
UPDATE POSTGRADUATE CENTRE SERIES. 1970. irreg. Reed Elsevier Medical Publishers, Reed Healthcare Communications (Subsidiary of: Reed Elsevier group), Quadrant House, The Quadrant, Sutton, Surrey SM2 5AS, England. TEL 0181-652-8439. FAX 0181-652-8946. Ed. Catherine Richards. adv. circ. 11,500. (back issues avail.; reprint service avail.) **Document type:** monographic series.
Description: Comprises booklets written for U.K. general practitioners.

610 NO ISSN 0300-9734
CODEN: UJMSAP
UPSALA JOURNAL OF MEDICAL SCIENCES. (Supplement avail. (ISSN 0300-9726)) (Text in English) 1865. 3/yr. NOK 400 in Nordic countries; elsewhere $70 (incl. supplements) (effective 1996). (Uppsala Laekarefoerening - Uppsala Medical Society) Scandinavian University Press, P.O. Box 2959 Toeyen, N-0608 Oslo, Norway. TEL 47-22-57-54-00. FAX 47-22-57-53-53. (U.S. addr.: Scandinavian University Press, 200 Meacham Ave., Elmont, NY 11003. TEL 516-352-7377) Ed. Gunnar Ronquist. charts; illus.; index. circ. 1,350. **Indexed:** Biol.Abstr., Chem.Abstr., Curr.Adv.Biochem., Curr.Adv.Ecol.Sci., Curr.Cont., Excerp.Med., Helminthol.Abstr., Ind.Med., Nutr.Abstr., Sci.Cit.Ind. **Document type:** academic/scholarly publication.
—BLDSC (9122.700000); CASDDS; Faxon; Genuine Article; SWETS; UnCover.
Former titles (until 1972): Acta Societatis Medicorum Upsaliensis (ISSN 0001-6985); (until 1950): Upsala Laekarefoerenings Foerhandlingar.
Description: Publishes clinical and experimental original works in the international medical field.

610 NO ISSN 0300-9726
CODEN: UJMSBQ
UPSALA JOURNAL OF MEDICAL SCIENCES. SUPPLEMENT. (Text in English) irreg. (Uppsala Laekarefoerening - Uppsala Medical Society) Scandinavian University Press, P.O. Box 2959 Toeyen, N-0608 Oslo, Norway. TEL 47-22-57-54-00. FAX 47-22-57-53-53. (US addr: Scandinavian University Press, 200 Meacham Ave., Elmont, NY 11003. TEL 516-352-7377) **Indexed:** Ind.Med. **Document type:** academic/scholarly publication.
—BLDSC (9122.710000); CASDDS; SWETS.
Formerly (until 1972): Acta Societatis Medicorum Upsaliensis. Supplementum.

URBANISATION AND HEALTH NEWSLETTER. see *PUBLIC HEALTH AND SAFETY*

610 FR ISSN 0923-2524
CODEN: URGME3
URGENCES MEDICALES. (Text in French; summaries in English, French) 1982. bi-m. 1035 F. in France; foreign 1155 F.($226) (effective 1996). (French Societe de Medecine de Catastrophe) Editions Scientifiques Elsevier, 141 rue de Javel, 75747 Paris, France. TEL 33-1-45589063. (Subscr. in U.S. and Canada to: Elsevier Science Inc., Box 882, Madison Sq. Sta., New York, NY 10159. TEL 212-989-5800) Ed. P. Huguenard. adv. circ. 3,000. (also avail. in microform from UMI) **Indexed:** Curr.Cont., Excerp.Med. **Document type:** academic/scholarly publication.
—BLDSC (9124.170000). **CCC.**
Formerly: Convergences Medicales.
Description: Provides a forum for communication and exchange between all disciplines connected with emergency and natural disaster medicine: anesthesiology, pathophysiology of aggression and pharmacology.

V A MEDICAL CENTER DIRECTORY. see *HOSPITALS*

610 SW ISSN 0347-0911
VAARDFACKET. 1977. s-m. (22/yr.) SEK 460 (effective 1990). Svenska Haelso- och Sjukvaardens Tjaenstemannafoerbund, P.O. Box 3260, 103 65 Stockholm, Sweden. adv. circ. 74,959.

MEDICAL SCIENCES

610   VE
VENEZUELA. HOSPITAL CENTRAL DE LA FUERZAS ARMADAS. BOLETIN MEDICO. 1970. q. free. Hospital Central de las Fuerzas Armadas, San Martin, Caracas, Venezuela. Ed. Dr. Leandro Potenza. abstr.; bibl.; illus. circ. 1,500. **Document type:** bulletin, government publication.

610   GW   ISSN 0174-738X
                              CODEN: VERDEJ
VERDAUUNGSKRANKHEITEN; gastroenterologische Zeitschrift fuer Klinik und Praxis. 1983. bi-m. DM.116($89) Dustri-Verlag Dr. Karl Feistle, Bahnhofstr. 9, 82041 Deisenhofen, Germany. TEL 089-613861-0. FAX 089-613-5412. Ed. Dr. O. Leiss. adv. **Document type:** academic/scholarly publication.
—BLDSC (9155.828000); CASDDS. **CCC.**

610   US
VERMONT STATE MEDICAL SOCIETY. REPORTER. 1949. m. $35. Vermont State Medical Society, Box 1457, Montpelier, VT 05602. TEL 802-223-7898. Ed. Karen N. Meyer. adv. circ. 1,100. (back issues avail.) **Document type:** newsletter.
   Formerly: Vermont State Medical Society. Newsletter.
   Description: Provides non-technical information of interest to practicing Vermont physicians.

610   GW   ISSN 0340-241X
                              CODEN: VEPADX
VEROEFFENTLICHUNGEN AUS DER PATHOLOGIE. irreg. price varies. Gustav Fischer Verlag, Wollgrasweg 49, 70599 Stuttgart, Germany. TEL 0711-458030. FAX 0711-4580334. TELEX 7111-488-FIBUCH. (Subscr. to: Postfach 720143, 70577 Stuttgart, Germany) **Indexed:** Dent.Ind., Ind.Med. **Document type:** monographic series.
—BLDSC (6872.420000); UMI. **CCC.**

610   GW   ISSN 0933-4548
                              CODEN: VERSEU
VERSICHERUNGSMEDIZIN; Prognose Therapie Begutachtung. 1949. bi-m. DM.22.43. (Verband der Lebensversicherungsunternehmen e.V.) Verlag Versicherungswirtschaft e.V., Klosestr. 20-24, 76137 Karlsruhe, Germany. TEL 0721-3509-0. FAX 0721-31833. Ed. Othard Raestrup. adv.; bk.rev.; abstr.; charts; tr.lit.; index. circ. 16,000. **Indexed:** Biol.Abstr., Excerp.Med., Ind.Med. **Document type:** academic/scholarly publication.
—BLDSC (9195.570000). **CCC.**
   Formerly: Lebensversicherungsmedizin (ISSN 0024-0044)

610   RM
VIATA MEDICALA - PENTRU MEDICI. (Text in Rumanian; summaries in French, German, Russian) 1954. m. $25. Uniunea Societatilor de Stiinte Medicale din Republica Socialista Rumania, Str. Progresului No. 8, Bucharest, Rumania. (Subscr. to: ILEXIM, Str. 13 Decembrie Nr. 3, P.O. Box 136-137, Bucharest, Rumania) Ed.Bd. adv.; bk.rev.; abstr. **Indexed:** Biol.Abstr., C.I.S. Abstr., Chem.Abstr., Ind.Med.
   Formerly: Viata Medicala - Pentru Cadre Superioare.

610   SP   ISSN 0213-5744
VIDEO - MEDICINA PRIMARIA. 1986. q. 16000 ptas. to individuals; institutions 20000 ptas. (foreign $400). Video Medica, S.L., Badal 102 Bis. Loc. 1, 08014 Barcelona, Spain. TEL 34-3-4319666. FAX 34-3-4219942. Dir. A. Ferrer Rodriguez. adv. contact: Angela Ferrer Rodriguez. circ. 20,000. (video cassette; plus text) **Document type:** trade publication.

VIRCHOWS ARCHIV. see *BIOLOGY*

610   US
VIRGINIA MASON CLINIC BULLETIN. 1922. s-a. free to hospitals, libraries, and physicians. Virginia Mason Clinic, 1100 Ninth Ave., Box 900, Seattle, WA 98111. TEL 206-223-6985. Ed. Dr. D.G. Fryer. charts, illus, stat.; index. circ. 5,000. **Document type:** bulletin.
   Formerly (until 1987): Mason Clinic. Bulletin (ISSN 0025-4657)

610   US   ISSN 1052-4231
VIRGINIA MEDICAL QUARTERLY. 1874. q. $24 (foreign $30). Medical Society of Virginia, 4205 Dover Rd., Richmond, VA 23221. TEL 804-353-2721. FAX 804-355-6189. Ed. Edwin L. Kendig, Jr., M.D. adv.; bk.rev.; abstr.; charts; illus.; stat.; tr.lit.; index. circ. 7,200. (also avail. in microfiche) **Indexed:** Ind.Med.
—BLDSC (9240.020000); Faxon; UMI; UnCover.
   Formerly (until July 1990): Virginia Medical.

VITA OSPEDALIERA. see *HOSPITALS*

VITAL SIGNS (CAMBRIDGE). see *PUBLIC HEALTH AND SAFETY*

610   US
VITAL SIGNS (FRESNO). 1949. m. $24. Fresno-Madera Medical Society, 3425 N. First St., Box 31, Fresno, CA 93707. TEL 209-224-4224.
FAX 209-224-0276. Ed. Dr. John Bonner. adv.; illus. circ. 1,300. **Document type:** newsletter.
   Formerly: Fresno County Medical Society. Bulletin (ISSN 0016-1160)

VITAMINS AND HORMONES: ADVANCES IN RESEARCH AND APPLICATIONS. see *PHARMACY AND PHARMACOLOGY*

610   RU
VITAS. 1991. irreg., (1-2/m.). 0.50 Rub. per issue. Assotsiatsiya "Vitas", Ul. Pravdy 9, k.20, 630090 Novosibirsk, Russia. (Co-sponsor: Assotsiatsiya Transaktnogo Analiza) circ. 100,000. **Document type:** newspaper.

616.026   XR   ISSN 0042-773X
                              CODEN: VNLEAH
VNITRNI LEKARSTVI. (Text in Czech; summaries in Czech, English and Russian) 1955. 12/yr. $83.80. (Ceska Lekarska Spolecnost J.E. Purkyne - Czech Medical Society) Nakladatelske Stredisko C L S J.E. Purkyne, Sokolska 31, 120 26 Prague 2, Czech Republic. FAX 42-0-2-202788. (Dist. by: Artia, Ve Smeckach 30, 111 27 Prague 1, Czech Republic) Ed. Dr. Mrkos. adv.; bk.rev.; charts; illus.; stat.; index. **Indexed:** C.I.S. Abstr., Chem.Abstr., Excerp.Med., Ind.Med., Nutr.Abstr.
—BLDSC (9250.300000); CASDDS; EMDOCS. **CCC.**
   Description: Covers internal medicine.

616.98   RU   ISSN 0026-9050
                              CODEN: VMEZA4
VOENNO-MEDITSINSKII ZHURNAL. 1823. m. $76 (effective 1996). Voenizdat, Ul. Zorge 1, 103160 Moscow, K-160, Russia. TEL 095-195-4595. **Indexed:** Biol.Abstr., Chem.Abstr., Dent.Ind., Ind.Med., Int.Aerosp.Abstr.
—BLDSC (0041.450000); CASDDS.
   Description: Covers issues pertinent to military medicine.

362.4   UK   ISSN 0966-789X
QP306
VOICE. 1992. s-a. £38($110) to individuals; institutions £59 (effective 1996). (British Voice Association) Whurr Publishers Ltd., 19b Compton Terrace, London N1 2UN, England.
TEL 0171-359-5979. FAX 0171-226-5290. (Subscr. to: Turpin Distribution Services Ltd., Blackhorse Rd., Letchworth, Herts. SG6 1HN, England. TEL 01462-672555. FAX 01462-480947; Subscr. in N. America to: Whurr Publishers Ltd., Box 1897, Lawrence, KS 66044-8897, USA. TEL 913-843-1221) adv.: page £150; adv. contact: Sarah Vicary. **Document type:** academic/scholarly publication.
—BLDSC (9251.420430); UnCover.
   Description: Promotes and encourages research in all areas of voice disorder.

616.98   XR   ISSN 0372-7025
VOJENSKE ZDRAVOTNICKE LISTY. (Text in Czech; summaries in English, Russian) 1925. bi-m. 12 Kc. Vojenska Lekarska Akademie J.E. Purkyne, 502 60 Hradec Kralove, Czech Republic. (Co-sponsor: Ministerstvo Narodni Obrany) Ed. Jaroslav Paces. bk.rev.; abstr.; index. (also avail. in microfiche; back issues avail.)
—BLDSC (9251.640000).
   Description: Essays on military science, medical sciences, veterinary sciences and pharmacology.

616.98   YU   ISSN 0042-8450
VOJNOSANITETSKI PREGLED/MILITARY MEDICAL AND PHARMACEUTICAL REVIEW; casopis lekara i farmaceuta jugoslovenske narodne armije. (Text in Serbo-Croatian; summaries in English, Russian) 1944. bi-m. 5000 din.($60) Savezni Sekretarijat za Narodnu Odbranu, Sanitetska Uprava, P.O. Box 1003, 11000 Belgrade, Serbia, Yugoslavia.
FAX 669-689. Ed. Cedomir Markovic. adv.; bk.rev.; abstr.; charts; illus.; stat.; index. circ. 2,000. **Indexed:** Biol.Abstr., C.I.S. Abstr., Chem.Abstr., Dent.Ind., Ergon.Abstr., Excerp.Med., I.P.A., Ind.Med., Psychol.Abstr., Ref.Zh.
—BLDSC (9251.652000); EMDOCS.

610   FR   ISSN 1241-9648
VOUS ET VOTRE SANTE. 1963. bi-m. 350 F. Vous sarl, 4 rue Marivaux, 75002 Paris, France.
FAX 34-69-99-94. Ed. Pierre Andrillon. bk.rev. circ. 20,000. **Document type:** consumer publication.
   Former titles: Vous (ISSN 1143-4686) & Actualite de la Medecine Officielle et Medecine Naturelle (ISSN 0044-6149)

610   NE   ISSN 0924-3186
                              CODEN: VOHOE
VOX HOSPITII. 1977. q. (Nederlandse Vereniging van Verpleeghuis Artsen) Reed HealthCare (Subsidiary of: Reed Elsevier plc), P.O. Box 1126, 1000 BC Amsterdam, Netherlands. TEL 31-20-5153350. FAX 31-20-5153354. Ed. Mrs. M.A.P. Verhoeven-Reynders. adv. contact: G.J.M. van den Akker. circ. 1,000. **Indexed:** Excerp.Med. (1994-).
—SWETS.
   Description: For nursing home physicians.
   Refereed Serial

610   UN   ISSN 0512-3054
RA8   CODEN: WHOTAC
W H O TECHNICAL REPORT SERIES. Spanish edition: Organizacion Mundial de la Salud. Serie de Informes Tecnicos (ISSN 0509-2507); French edition: Organisation Mondiale de la Sante. Serie de Rapports Techniques (ISSN 0373-3998); Russian edition: Vsemirnaja Organizacija Zdravoohranenija. Serija Tehniceskih Dokladov (ISSN 0250-8737); Arabic edition: Munazzamat al-Sihhah al-'Alamiyyah. Silsilat al-Taqarir al-Fanniyyah (ISSN 0251-0111) 1950. irreg., (approx. 15/yr.), latest no.849. $106. World Health Organization, Distribution and Sales, CH-1211 Geneva 27, Switzerland.
TEL 41-22-791-2476. FAX 41-22-791-4857. TELEX 27821-OMS. **Indexed:** Abstr.Hyg., Abstr.Rural Dev.Trop., Biol.Abstr., Dent.Ind., Diar.Dis.Res., Excerp.Med., Food Sci.& Tech.Abstr., I.P.A., Ind.Med., Ind.Vet., Med.Care Rev., Nutr.Abstr., Rural Ext.Educ.& Tr.Abstr., Rural Recreat.Tour.Abstr., Sport Fish.Abstr., Trop.Dis.Bull., Vet.Bull., Wild.Rev., World Agri.Econ.& Rural Sociol.Abstr., Zoo.Rec. **Document type:** monographic series.
—BLDSC (8725.000000); Genuine Article; UnCover.
   Description: Summarizes current technical knowledge on a given disease, health risk, medical technology or research approach.

610 574   JA   ISSN 0511-084X
                              CODEN: WKMRAH
WAKAYAMA MEDICAL REPORTS. (Text in English, French or German) 1953. q. exchange basis. Wakayama Medical College, Library - Wakayama-kenritsu Ika Daigaku Toshokan, Wakayama 640, Japan.
FAX 0734-26-8333. TELEX 5542-488. Ed. Akira Ooshima. bibl.; charts; illus.; index. circ. 800. **Indexed:** Abstr.Hyg., Biol.Abstr., C.I.S. Abstr., Chem.Abstr., Excerp.Med., Nutr.Abstr., Trop.Dis.Bull.
—BLDSC (9261.400000); CASDDS.

610 574   JA   ISSN 0043-0013
                              CODEN: WKMIAO
WAKAYAMA MEDICINE/WAKAYAMA IGAKU. (Text in Japanese; summaries in English, French and German) 1950. q. 2000 Yen($20) Wakayama Medical Society - Wakayama Igakkai, c/o Wakayama Medical College, 9 Kyuban-cho, Wakayama 640, Japan. Ed. Hirotoshi Iwata. charts; illus.; stat. circ. 1,200. **Indexed:** Biol.Abstr., Chem.Abstr., Excerp.Med., Jap.Per.Ind., Nutr.Abstr.
—BLDSC (4912.600000); CASDDS; EMDOCS.

WARY CANARY; a news network for allergics, "sensitive birds," & environmental health advocates. see *ENVIRONMENTAL STUDIES*

MEDICAL SCIENCES

610   US   ISSN 0164-1514
WASHINGTON HEALTH RECORD. 1979. w. $195 (effective 1995). Faulkner & Gray, Healthcare Information Center (Subsidiary of: Thomson Publishing Group), 1133 15th St., N.W., Ste. 450, Washington, DC 20005. TEL 202-828-4150. FAX 202-828-2352. Ed. Anika Trahan. (looseleaf format)
● Also available online. Vendor(s): Knight-Ridder, Inc., NewsNet (HH25).

THE WATERMARK. see *LIBRARY AND INFORMATION SCIENCES*

616.98   GW   ISSN 0043-2148
WEHRMEDIZIN UND WEHRPHARMAZIE. 1963. q. DM.44. Beta Verlag GmbH, Postfach 140121, 53056 Bonn, Germany. TEL 0228-91937-0. FAX 0228-252067. TELEX 8869536-BETA-D. Ed. Dr. Hannes Sautter. circ. 7,900. (back issues avail.) **Document type:** academic/scholarly publication.
Formerly (until 1968): Wehrmedizin (ISSN 0343-155X)
Description: For doctors, pharmacists and scientists in the medical corps of Germany.

610   GW   ISSN 0043-2156
CODEN: WEMOBZ
WEHRMEDIZINISCHE MONATSSCHRIFT; Organ des Sanitaets- und Gesundheitswesen der Bundeswehr. (Text in German; summaries in English, German) 1956. 8/yr. DM.52. (Bundesministerium der Verteidigung) Beta Verlag GmbH, Postfach 140121, 53056 Bonn, Germany. TEL 0228-91937-0. FAX 0228-252067. (Co-sponsor: Deutsche Gesellschaft fuer Wehrmedizin und Wehrpharmazie) Ed. Karl-Wilhelm Wedel. adv.; bk.rev.; abstr.; charts; illus.; stat.; cum.index. circ. 5,300. **Indexed:** Biol.Abstr., Chem.Abstr. **Document type:** trade publication.
—BLDSC (9288.120000); CASDDS. **CCC.**
Formerly: Wehrmedizinische Mitteilungen.

630   CC
WEISHENG DULIXUE ZAZHI. (Text in Chinese) q. Zhonghua Yufang Yixuehui - China Preventive Medical Society, 16, Hepingli Zhongjie, Beijing 100013, People's Republic of China. TEL 4218457. Ed. Liu Shijie.

610   CC
WEIZHONGBING JIJIU YIXUE. (Text in Chinese) q. Tianjin Shi Jijiu Yixue Yanjiusuo, 162, Munan Dao, Tianjin 300050, People's Republic of China. TEL 306917. Ed. Wang Jinda.

615.89   UK   ISSN 0143-7984
WELLCOME UNIT FOR THE HISTORY OF MEDICINE. RESEARCH PUBLICATIONS. 1979. irreg., latest issue 11, 1992. price varies. Wellcome Unit for the History of Medicine, University of Oxford, 45-47 Banbury Rd., Oxford OX2 6PE, England. TEL 0865-274060. FAX 0865-274605. bibl. circ. 200. (back issues avail.) **Document type:** bibliography.
—BLDSC (7759.155300).
Description: Contains bibliographical, documentary and research aids for the social history of medicine and health from the year 1500 to the present.

610   CN   ISSN 1194-4781
WELLNESS M D; the health promotion and disease prevention magazine. 1991. 6/yr. Can.$45. Wellness Publishing Company Inc., 344 Edgeley Blvd., Unit 17, Concord, ON L4K 4B7, Canada. TEL 905-738-9086. FAX 905-738-4994. Ed. Gordon Bagley; Pub. Frederick W. Conlin. adv.: B&W page Can.$2238, color page Can.$3724; trim 8 1/8 x 10 7/8. circ. 38,700.
Description: Reaches doctors personally and professionally with topical, thought-provoking, scientific information dealing with elements that affect an individual's state of wellness.

610   UK
WELSH MEDICAL GAZETTE. 1970. q. free to qualified personnel. Welsh Medical Press Ltd., 23 Blenheim Rd., Cardiff, Wales. Eds. Drs. Eric Payne, Bernard Knight. adv.; bk.rev.; illus. circ. 5,000.

610   CC   ISSN 1000-2138
WENZHOU YIXUEYUAN XUEBAO/WENZHOU INSTITUTE OF MEDICAL SCIENCES. JOURNAL. (Text in Chinese) q. Wenzhou Yixueyuan - Wenzhou Institute of Medical Sciences, Wenzhou, Zhejiang 325003, People's Republic of China. TEL 34941. **Document type:** academic/scholarly publication.

610   JM   ISSN 0043-3144
CODEN: WIMJAD
WEST INDIAN MEDICAL JOURNAL. (Supplement avail.) 1951. q. J.$500 (foreign $60). University of the West Indies, Faculty of Medical Sciences, Mona Campus, Kingston 7, Jamaica, W.I. TEL 809-927-1214. FAX 809-927-2556. Ed. Dr. Vasil Persaud. adv.: B&W page $225; color page $390; adv. contact: Bridget Williams. bk.rev.; bibl.; charts; illus. circ. 2,000. (also avail. in microform; reprint service avail. from IRC,ISI,UMI) **Indexed:** Abstr.Hyg., Biol.Abstr., Chem.Abstr., Curr.Cont., Dent.Ind., Diar.Dis.Res., Excerp.Med., Helminthol.Abstr., I.P.A., Ind.Med., Ind.Vet., Nutr.Abstr., Rev.Med.& Vet.Mycol., Trop.Dis.Bull. **Document type:** academic/scholarly publication.
—BLDSC (9299.100000); CASDDS; EMDOCS; Faxon; Genuine Article; SWETS; UMI; UnCover.
Description: Addresses areas of medical research of the greatest potential benefit to the people of the Commonwealth Caribbean. Contains articles covering those relevant medical topics.
Refereed Serial

610   US   ISSN 0043-3284
WEST VIRGINIA MEDICAL JOURNAL. 1906. m. $45 (foreign $80). West Virginia State Medical Association, 4307 MacCorkle Ave., Box 4106, Charleston, WV 25364. TEL 304-925-0342. FAX 304-925-0345. Ed. Dr. Stephen D. Ward. adv. contact: Michelle Ellison. bk.rev.; bibl.; illus.; index. circ. 2,900. (also avail. in microform from UMI) **Indexed:** Biol.Abstr., Chem.Abstr., Curr.Cont., Dent.Ind., Excerp.Med., Helminthol.Abstr., Ind.Med., Med.Care Rev., Nutr.Abstr., Rev.Med.& Vet.Mycol. **Document type:** academic/scholarly publication.
—BLDSC (9300.050000); Faxon; SWETS; UMI.
Refereed Serial

610   US
WESTCHESTER BULLETIN. vol.42, 1974. 10/yr. $2. Westchester Academy of Medicine, Purchase, NY 10577. TEL 914-948-4100. adv.; bk.rev. circ. 2,000.

610   US   ISSN 0093-0415
R15   CODEN: WJMDA2
WESTERN JOURNAL OF MEDICINE. 1902. m. $40 (foreign $70) (effective 1996). California Medical Association, Box 7690, 221 Main St., San Francisco, CA 94105. TEL 415-882-5179. FAX 415-882-5116. (Co-sponsors: Medical Associations of Arizona, California, Idaho, Nevada State, New Mexico, Utah State, Washington State, and Wyoming) Ed. Dr. Linda Hawes Clever. adv. contact: J. Crook. index. circ. 46,000. (also avail. in microfilm from UMI; reprint service avail. from UMI) **Indexed:** Abstr.Health Care Manage.Stud., AIM, Biol.Abstr., C.I.S.Abstr., Chem.Abstr., CINAHL, Curr.Adv.Cancer Res., Curr.Adv.Ecol.Sci., Curr.Cont., Dairy Sci.Abstr., Dent.Ind., Dok.Arbeitsmed., Excerp.Med., Helminthol.Abstr., Hlth.Ind., Hosp.Lit.Ind., Ind.Med., Ind.Vet., Med.& Surg.Dermat., Med.Care Rev., Nutr.Abstr., Protozool.Abstr., Rev.Med.& Vet.Mycol., Small Anim.Abstr. **Document type:** academic/scholarly publication.
—BLDSC (9300.830000); CASDDS; EMDOCS; Faxon; Genuine Article; SWETS; UMI; UnCover. **CCC.**
Incorporates (1944-1985): Arizona Medicine (ISSN 0004-1556); Former titles (1946-1973): California Medicine (ISSN 0008-1264); (1924-1946): California and Western Medicine (ISSN 0093-4038)
Refereed Serial

WHICH DEGREE. SCIENCES, MEDICINE, MATHEMATICS. see *SCIENCES: COMPREHENSIVE WORKS*

WHICH? WAY TO HEALTH. see *PHYSICAL FITNESS AND HYGIENE*

610   PL   ISSN 0043-5147
CODEN: WILEAR
WIADOMOSCI LEKARSKIE. (Text in Polish; summaries in English and Russian) 1948. bi-w. $216. Fundacja Lekarzy Polskich - Pro Medica, Ul. Miodowa 1, 00-080 Warsaw, Poland. Ed. Dr. Jan Dzieniszewski. **Indexed:** Biol.Abstr., Chem.Abstr., Dent.Ind., Dok.Arbeitsmed., Excerp.Med., Ind.Med., Protozool.Abstr. **Document type:** academic/scholarly publication.
—BLDSC (9313.800000); CASDDS.
Description: Explores clinical medicine and post-graduate education of physicians.

610   GW   ISSN 0179-3004
WIE GEHT'S HEUTE?; Ratschlaege und Informationen aus Ihrem Sanitaetsfachgeschaeft. 1985. 3/yr. DM.0.98. M T D Verlag GmbH und Co., Wangenerstr. 12, 88279 Amtzell, Germany. TEL 07520-958-0. FAX 07520-95899. Eds. Klaus Witzer, Wolf-Dieter Seitz. adv. contact: Christl Morgen. (back issues avail.) **Document type:** consumer publication.

610   AU   ISSN 0043-5325
CODEN: WKWOAO
WIENER KLINISCHE WOCHENSCHRIFT. (Supplement avail. (ISSN 0300-5178)) 1887. 24/yr. DM.355($257) (effective 1996). Springer-Verlag, Sachsenplatz 4-6, A-1201 Vienna, Austria. TEL 0222-3302415. FAX 0222-3302426. (N. American subscr. to: Journal Fulfillment Services, Box 2485, Secaucus, NJ 07096-2491. TEL 800-777-4643. FAX 201-348-4505) Eds. O. Kraupp, E. Deutsch. adv.; bk.rev.; charts; illus.; index. (also avail. in microform from UMI; reprint service avail. from ISI) **Indexed:** Biol.Abstr., Biotech.Abstr., C.I.S. Abstr., Chem.Abstr., Curr.Adv.Biochem., Curr.Adv.Cell & Devel.Biol., Curr.Cont., Dairy Sci.Abstr., Dent.Ind., Excerp.Med., Helminthol.Abstr., Ind.Med., Kidney, Nutr.Abstr., Soyabean Abstr. **Document type:** academic/scholarly publication.
—BLDSC (9315.900000); CASDDS; EMDOCS; Faxon; Genuine Article; SWETS; UMI. **CCC.**

610   AU   ISSN 0300-5178
CODEN: WKWSA2
WIENER KLINISCHE WOCHENSCHRIFT. SUPPLEMENTUM. 1972. irreg. Springer-Verlag, Sachsenplatz 4-6, A-1201 Vienna, Austria. TEL 0222-3302415. FAX 0222-3302426. (N. American subscr. to: Springer-Verlag New York, Inc., Box 2485, Secaucus, NJ 07096-2491. TEL 800-777-4643) **Indexed:** Ind.Med. **Document type:** academic/scholarly publication.
—BLDSC (9315.901000); CASDDS; SWETS; UMI.

610   GW   ISSN 0043-5341
CODEN: WMWOA4
WIENER MEDIZINISCHE WOCHENSCHRIFT. (Text in German; summaries in English) 1851. 24/yr. DM.327($242) in Europe; rest of world DM.415($307) (effective 1996). Blackwell Wissenschaft, Kurfuerstendamm 57, 10707 Berlin, Germany. TEL 030-32790476. FAX 030-32790610. Ed.Bd. adv.; bk.rev.; abstr.; bibl.; illus.; index. circ. 4,150. (also avail. in microform from PMC; reprint service avail. from ISI) **Indexed:** Biol.Abstr., Biotech.Abstr., Chem.Abstr., Curr.Cont., Excerp.Med., Helminthol.Abstr., Ind.Med., Nutr.Abstr. **Document type:** academic/scholarly publication.
—BLDSC (9315.925000); ADONIS; CASDDS; EMDOCS; Faxon; Genuine Article; SWETS; UMI. **CCC.**

610   US   ISSN 1073-502X
WILDERNESS MEDICINE LETTER. 1984. q. $30. Wilderness Medical Society, Box 2463, Indianapolis, IN 46206-2463. TEL 317-631-1745. FAX 317-269-8150. Ed. Christine O'Conner Brokau. adv. contact: Rian Simkins. bk.rev. circ. 2,500. (looseleaf format; back issues avail.) **Document type:** newsletter.
Formerly: Wilderness Medicine.
Description: Covers research on human activities in wilderness environments.

610   US   ISSN 1059-6518
WILDERNESS MEDICINE NEWSLETTER. 1988. bi-m. $24 (effective 1995-1996). Wilderness Medicine Institute, Box 3150, Conway, NH 03818. TEL 603-447-2310. FAX 603-447-6711. Ed. Holly A. Weber. bk.rev. **Document type:** newsletter.
Description: Publishes articles written from a variety of perspectives for layperson's practicing teaching in the wilderness medicine arena. Includes regular guest columns by authors considered to be the founders of this branch of medicine.
Refereed Serial

610 636.089   US   ISSN 0736-6094
Z6674
WILDLIFE DISEASE REVIEW. 1983. m. $225 (foreign $255). PO. Box 1522, Ft. Collins, CO 80522. TEL 303-484-6267. FAX 303-482-6184. TELEX 820567. Ed. B. Zimmerman. index. circ. 150.

MEDICAL SCIENCES

610   US
WINDOW (NEW YORK). 1981. q. free. New York Hospital - Cornell Medical Center, Office of Public Affairs, 525 E. 68th St., New York, NY 10021. TEL 212-821-0560. Ed. Felicia E. Narvaez. circ. 16,000. (tabloid format) **Document type:** newspaper.

610   US   ISSN 0043-6542
R11
WISCONSIN MEDICAL JOURNAL. 1903. m. $35 (foreign $40) (effective 1995). State Medical Society of Wisconsin, 330 E. Lakeside St., Box 1109, Madison, WI 53701. TEL 608-257-6781. FAX 608-283-5401. Ed. Russel K. King; Pub. Jame Paxton. adv. contact: Lynne Bjorgo. bk.rev.; bibl.; illus.; index. circ. 7,000. **Indexed:** Biol.Abstr., Chem.Abstr., CINAHL, Curr.Cont., Dent.Ind., Excerp.Med., Helminthol.Abstr., Ind.Med., Nutr.Abstr., Rehabil.Lit. **Document type:** academic/scholarly publication.
—BLDSC (9325.800000); EMDOCS; Faxon; SWETS; UnCover.
Refereed Serial

WOHNUNG & GESUNDHEIT; Fachzeitschrift fuer oekologisches Bauen & Leben. see *ARCHITECTURE*

610   US   ISSN 1055-6370
WORCESTER MEDICINE. 1937. bi-m. $10. (Worcester District Medical Society) Cotton Communications, 321 Main St., Worcester, MA 01608. TEL 508-755-4500. FAX 508-799-0256. Ed. J. Paul Lock. adv.; bk.rev. circ. 2,100.
Formerly: Worcester Medical News (ISSN 0043-7905)

WORKERS' COMP MANAGED CARE. see *INSURANCE*

WORLD BOOK HEALTH AND MEDICAL ANNUAL. see *ENCYCLOPEDIAS AND GENERAL ALMANACS*

610   UN   ISSN 0251-2432
RA441   CODEN: WHFODN
WORLD HEALTH FORUM. Italian edition: Foro Mondiale della Sanita (ISSN 0256-1638); Spanish edition: Foro Mundial de la Salud (ISSN 0257-3024); French edition: Forum Mondial de la Sante (ISSN 0251-8716); Chinese edition: Shijie Weisheng Lutan (ISSN 0257-3016); Russian edition: Vsemirnyi Forum Zdravoohraneniya (ISSN 0207-7809) Arabic edition: Minbar al-Sihhah al-'Alami (UN ISSN 0257-3008) 1980. q. 75 SFr.($60) World Health Organization, Distribution and Sales, CH-1211 Geneva 27, Switzerland. TEL 41-22-791-2476. FAX 41-22-791-4857. TELEX 27821-OMS. (also avail. in microfiche from CIS) **Indexed:** Abstr.Hyg., Abstr.Rural Dev.Trop., Adol.Ment.Hlth.Abstr., ASSIA, Biol.Abstr., Curr.Adv.Ecol.Sci., Diar.Dis.Res., Environ.Abstr., Environ.Per.Bibl., Excerp.Med., Geo.Abstr., Helminthol.Abstr., IDA, IIS, Ind.Hyg.Dig., Med.Care Rev., Protozool.Abstr., Repindex, Rural Devel.Abstr., Rural Ext.Educ.& Tr.Abstr., Rural Recreat.Tour.Abstr., Sage Pub.Admin.Abstr., Soc.Work Res.& Rural Sociol.Abstr., World Bibl.Soc.Sec.
—BLDSC (9356.040200); Faxon; Genuine Article; SWETS; UMI; UnCover.
Description: Contains practical information on public health policy and practice.

610   UN   ISSN 0042-9686
R5   CODEN: BWHOA6
WORLD HEALTH ORGANIZATION. BULLETIN. Arabic edition: Munazzamat al-Sihhiyyah al-'Alamiyyah. Nashrah (ISSN 0257-599X); Chinese edition: Shijie Weisheng Zuzhi Tongbao. Xuanyi (ISSN 0258-0640); Russian edition: Vsemirnaya Organizatsiya Zdravookhraneniya. Byulleten' (ISSN 0250-8699) (Supplements avail.) (Text in English, French) 1947. bi-m. 176 SFr.($141) World Health Organization, Distribution and Sales, CH-1211 Geneva 27, Switzerland. TEL 41-22-791-2476. FAX 41-22-791-4857. TELEX 27821-OMS. Ed. A. Hussein. bibl.; charts; illus.; index. circ. 5,500. (also avail. in microform from PMC,CIS; back issues avail.) **Indexed:** Abstr.Hyg., Adol.Ment.Hlth.Abstr., ASSIA, Bio-Contr.News & Info., Biol.Abstr., Biotech.Abstr., Curr.Adv.Ecol.Sci., Curr.Cont., Dairy Sci.Abstr., Dent.Abstr., Dent.Ind., Diar.Dis.Res., Environ.Per.Bibl., Excerp.Med., Helminthol.Abstr., IIS, Ind.Med., Ind.Vet., INIS Atomind., Med.& Surg.Dermat., NRN, Nutr.Abstr., Ocean.Abstr., Pollut.Abstr., Poult.Abstr., Protozool.Abstr., Psychol.Abstr, Repindex, Rev.Appl.Entomol., Rev.Plant Path., Sci.Cit.Ind., Sel.Water Res.Abstr., Sport Fish.Abstr., Trop.Dis.Bull., Vet.Bull., Weed Abstr., Wild.Rev., Zoo.Rec. **Document type:** academic/scholarly publication.
—BLDSC (2819.000000); EMDOCS; Faxon; Genuine Article; SWETS; UMI; UnCover.
Formerly (until 1948): League of Nations. Health Organization. Bulletin (ISSN 0368-7961)
Description: Presents original research findings selected on the basis of their immediate or potential relevance to problems of human health.

610 658.8   UK
WORLD HEALTHCARE MARKETING DIRECTORY. irreg., latest 1993. £255($510) (effective 1996). Euromonitor, 60-61 Britton St., London EC1M 5NA, England. TEL 0171-251-8024. FAX 0171-608-3149. (Addr. in N. America: Euromonitor International, 122 S. Michigan Ave., Ste. 1200, Chicago, IL 60603. TEL 312-922-1115. FAX 312-922-1157) **Document type:** directory.
Description: Contains detailed information on every aspect of the health care industry. Profiles 34 of the world's leading pharmaceutical companies and more than 3,000 worldwide health care organizations.

610   GW   ISSN 0049-8122
R5
WORLD MEDICAL JOURNAL. 1954. bi-m. DM.42 (students DM.31,50). (World Medical Association) Deutscher Aerzte-Verlag GmbH, Postfach 400265, 50832 Cologne, Germany. TEL 02234-7011-0. FAX 0221-7011-444. Ed. Iran M. Gillibrand. adv.; bk.rev.; abstr.; bibl.; charts; illus.; index. circ. 3,800. (tabloid format) **Indexed:** Biol.Abstr., Hosp.Lit.Ind., Med. Care Rev. **Document type:** trade publication.
—BLDSC (9356.650000); UMI; UnCover.

WORLD MEETINGS: MEDICINE. see *MEETINGS AND CONGRESSES*

610   US   ISSN 0742-535X
WORLD RIGHT-TO-DIE NEWSLETTER. 1979. s-a. free. World Federation of Right-to-Die Societies, Box 162, Francestown, NH 03043. TEL 603-547-3474. E-mail: dhumphry@efn.org. Ed. Luis H. Gallop; Pub. Derek Humphry. bk.rev. circ. 300. (also avail. in looseleaf format) **Document type:** newsletter.
Description: Features news of the society, such as meetings and conferences dealing with euthanasia and its growing support.

610   US
WYOMING PHYSICIANS NEWSLETTER. 1962. bi-w. $24 to non-members. Wyoming State Medical Society, Box 4009, Cheyenne, WY 82001. TEL 307-635-3955. FAX 307-632-1793. Ed. Wendy P. Curran. adv. 550. (looseleaf format) **Document type:** newsletter.
Former titles: Medical Wire; Pulse (ISSN 0043-9797)

610   CC   ISSN 0253-9802
R97.7.C5   CODEN: XINYD9
XIN YIXUE/NEW MEDICAL SCIENCE. (Text in Chinese) m. Zhongshan Yike Daxue - Sun Yat-sen Medical University, 74 Zhongshan Erlu, Guangzhou, Guangdong 510089, People's Republic of China. TEL 778223.
—BLDSC (6082.608000); CASDDS.

XINZHONGYI/NEW JOURNAL OF TRADITIONAL CHINESE MEDICINE. see *ALTERNATIVE MEDICINE*

610   CC   ISSN 1000-2065
XUZHOU YIXUEYUAN XUEBAO/XUZHOU INSTITUTE OF MEDICAL SCIENCES. JOURNAL. (Text in Chinese) q. Xuzhou Yixueyuan - Xuzhou Institute of Medical Sciences, 84 Huihai Xilu, Xuzhou, Jiangsu 221002, People's Republic of China. TEL 34650. Ed. Wang Pingyu. **Document type:** academic/scholarly publication.

610   JA   ISSN 0916-1139
     CODEN: YADOEL
YAKUBUTSU DOTAI/XENOBIOTIC METABOLISM. (Text in Japanese) 1986. bi-m. Japanese Society for the Study of Xenobiotics, 35, Shinano-machi, Shinjuku-ku, Tokyo, Japan.
—BLDSC (9367.019500); CASDDS. **CCC.**

610 574   US   ISSN 0044-0086
R11   CODEN: YJBMAU
YALE JOURNAL OF BIOLOGY AND MEDICINE. 1928. bi-m. $45 to individuals; institutions $95. Yale Journal of Biology and Medicine, Inc., 333 Cedar St., New Haven, CT 06510. TEL 203-785-4251. FAX 203-785-6309. Ed. William C. Summers. adv.; bk.rev.; bibl.; charts; illus.; index. circ. 500. (also avail. in microform from UMI,PMC; reprint service avail. from KTO) **Indexed:** Biol.Abstr., Biol.Dig., Chem.Abstr., Curr.Adv.Ecol.Sci., Curr.Cont., Deep Sea Res.& Oceanogr.Abstr., Excerp.Med., Helminthol.Abstr., Ind.Med., Int.Aerosp.Abstr., JAMA, Med.& Surg.Dermat., Nutr.Abstr., Risk Abstr., Sport Fish.Abstr., Vet.Bull., Wild.Rev., Zoo.Rec. **Document type:** academic/scholarly publication.
—BLDSC (9370.000000); CASDDS; EMDOCS; Faxon; Genuine Article; SWETS; UMI; UnCover. **CCC.**
Description: Original contributions and review articles in all fields of medicine and related sciences.
Refereed Serial

610   JA   ISSN 0513-1812
     CODEN: BYMSAN
YAMAGUCHI UNIVERSITY. SCHOOL OF MEDICINE. BULLETIN/YAMAGUCHI DAIGAKU IGAKUBU KIYO. Key Title: Bulletin of the Yamaguchi Medical School. (Text in English or German; summaries in English) 1953. 4/yr. exchange basis. Yamaguchi Daigaku, Igakubu - Yamaguchi University, School of Medicine, Kogushi, Ube-shi 755, Japan. Ed.Bd. circ. controlled. **Indexed:** Abstr.Hyg., Biol.Abstr., Chem.Abstr., Excerp.Med., INIS Atomind., Trop.Dis.Bull.
—BLDSC (2822.000000); CASDDS.

YAMAGUCHIKEN EISEI KOGAI KENKYU SENTA GYOSEKI HOKOKU. see *PUBLIC HEALTH AND SAFETY*

610   US   ISSN 0734-3299
YEAR BOOK OF CRITICAL CARE MEDICINE. 1983. a. $72.95 (residents $35) (effective 1996). Mosby - Year Book, Inc., Continuity Division, 200 N. LaSalle, Chicago, IL 60601. TEL 312-726-9733. Ed. Dr. C. Parsillo. illus. (reprint service avail.)
●Also available on CD-ROM. Producer(s): SilverPlatter Information, Inc. (ClinMED-CD).
—BLDSC (9411.624360).

610   US   ISSN 0147-1996
R101
YEAR BOOK OF FAMILY PRACTICE. 1977. a. $59.95 (residents $35) (effective 1996). Mosby - Year Book, Inc., Continuity Division, 200 N. LaSalle, Chicago, IL 60601. TEL 312-726-9733. FAX 312-726-6075. TELEX 206155. Ed. Dr. Alfred O. Berg. illus. (reprint service avail.)
●Also available online. Vendor(s): Ovid Technologies.

616.025   GW   ISSN 0942-5381
YEARBOOK OF INTENSIVE CARE AND EMERGENCY MEDICINE. (Text in English) 1992. a. Springer-Verlag, Heidelberger Platz 3, 14197 Berlin, Germany. TEL 030-8207-1. FAX 030-8214091. (Subscr. in N. America to: Box 2485, Secaucus, NJ 01096-2491. TEL 800-777-4643. FAX 201-348-4505) Ed. Jean-Louis Vincent. **Document type:** bulletin.

610   US   ISSN 0084-3873
R101
YEAR BOOK OF MEDICINE. 1933. a. $66.95 (residents $35) (effective 1996). Mosby - Year Book, Inc., Continuity Division, 200 N. LaSalle, Chicago, IL 60601. TEL 312-726-9733. FAX 312-726-6075. TELEX 206155. Ed. Dr. R. Epstein. (reprint service avail.) **Indexed:** Curr.Adv.Ecol.Sci., Diar.Dis.Res.
●Also available online. Vendor(s): Ovid Technologies.
—BLDSC (9414.570000); SWETS.

MEDICAL SCIENCES

616.9803 US ISSN 0899-8035
RC963.A1
YEAR BOOK OF OCCUPATIONAL AND ENVIRONMENTAL MEDICINE. 1991. a. $69.95 (residents $35) (effective 1996). Mosby - Year Book, Inc. (Chicago) (Subsidiary of: Times Mirror Company), 200 N. LaSalle St., Chicago, IL 60601-1080. TEL 312-726-9733. FAX 312-726-6075. TELEX 206155. Ed. Dr. Edward A. Emmett. illus.
●Also available online. Vendor(s): Ovid Technologies.
—BLDSC (9414.655000). **CCC.**

612.8 616 US
▼**YEAR BOOK OF PAIN.** 1994. a. $61.95 (residents $35) (effective 1996). Mosby - Year Book, Inc. (Chicago) (Subsidiary of: Times Mirror Company), 200 N. LaSalle St., Chicago, IL 60601-1080. TEL 312-726-9733. FAX 312-726-6075. TELEX 206155. Ed. Gerald Gebhart.

616.07 US
YEAR BOOK OF PATHOLOGY AND LABORATORY MEDICINE. 1940. a. $72.95 (residents $35) (effective 1996). Mosby - Year Book, Inc., Continuity Division, 200 N. LaSalle, Chicago, IL 60601. TEL 312-726-9733. FAX 312-726-6075. TELEX 206155. Ed. Dr. J. Mills. illus. (reprint service avail.) **Indexed:** Curr.Adv.Ecol.Sci.
●Also available online. Vendor(s): Ovid Technologies.
—BLDSC (9414.700000).
Former titles: Year Book of Pathology and Clinical Pathology (ISSN 0084-3946); (until 1942): Year Book of Pathology and Immunology (ISSN 0891-3617)

610 CC ISSN 1002-0756
YICHUAN YU JIBING/HEREDITY AND DISEASE. (Text in Chinese) q. Huaxi Yike Daxue - West China University of Medical Sciences, 17, Renmin Nanlu 3 Duan, Chengdu, Sichuan 610041, People's Republic of China. TEL 581130. Ed. Liu Zudong.

610 CC ISSN 1001-7585
YIXUE LILUN YU SHIJIAN/MEDICAL THEORY AND PRACTICE. (Text in Chinese) 1988. m. $2.50 per no. (effective 1996). Hebei Langfang Diqu Yixue Qingbaozhan, P.O. Box 62, Langfang, Hebei 102800, People's Republic of China. TEL 0316-2013206. Ed. Zhong Yuhua. circ. 5,500. **Description:** Covers the latest development in medical science.

610 JA ISSN 0285-0877
YOBO IGAKU/HEALTH SERVICES JOURNAL. 1967. m. 3708 Yen (effective Jan. 1991). Japan Association of Health Services, c/o Hokenkaikan, 1-2 Sadohara-Cho, Ichigaya, Shinjuku-ku, Tokyo 162, Japan. TEL 03-3268-1800. FAX 03-3266-8767. Ed. Wataru Kunii. adv. circ. 6,000. (back issues avail.)

610 JA ISSN 0044-0531
CODEN: YMBUA7
YOKOHAMA MEDICAL BULLETIN. (Text in English, French, German) 1950. 3/yr. exchange basis. Yokohama-shiritsu Daigaku, Igakubu - Yokohama City University, School of Medicine, 3-9 Fukuura, Kanazawa-ku, Yokohama 236, Japan. FAX 45-787-2560. Ed.Bd. bk.rev.; bibl.; charts; illus. circ. 1,000. **Indexed:** Biol.Abstr., C.I.S. Abstr., Chem.Abstr., Excerp.Med., Helminthol.Abstr., Ind.Vet., Nutr.Abstr., Vet.Bull.
—BLDSC (9420.000000); CASDDS; EMDOCS; UnCover.

610 574 614.8 JA ISSN 0372-7726
CODEN: YKIGAK
YOKOHAMA MEDICAL JOURNAL. (Text in Japanese; summaries in English, French, German) 1948. bi-m. exchange basis. Yokohama-shiritsu Daigaku, Igakubu - Yokohama City University, School of Medicine, 3-9 Fukuura, Kanazawa-ku, Yokohama 236, Japan. FAX 45-787-2560. Ed.Bd. index. circ. 2,600. **Indexed:** Biol.Abstr., Rev.Med.& Vet.Mycol.
—BLDSC (9420.100000); CASDDS.

610 JA ISSN 0513-5710
CODEN: YOAMAQ
YONAGO ACTA MEDICA. (Text in English and European languages) 1954. 3/yr. exchange basis. Tottori Daigaku, Igakubu - Tottori University, Faculty of Medicine, 86 Nishi-machi, Yonago 683, Japan. TEL 0859-34-8053. Ed. Kenzo Takeshita. circ. 700. **Indexed:** Biol.Abstr., Chem.Abstr., Curr.Cont., Dairy Sci.Abstr., Excerp.Med., Helminthol.Abstr., Ind.Med., Nutr.Abstr., Rev.Med.& Vet.Mycol. **Document type:** bulletin.
—BLDSC (9421.000000); CASDDS.

610 JA ISSN 0044-0558
CODEN: YOIZA3
YONAGO MEDICAL ASSOCIATION. JOURNAL/YONAGO IGAKU ZASSHI. (Text in Japanese; summaries in English and European languages) 1948. bi-m. 2000 Yen. Yonago Medical Association - Yonago Igakkai, Tottori University School of Medicine, 86 Nishi-machi, Yonago 683, Japan. Ed. Kazumitsu Hirai. adv.; bk.rev.; index. circ. 980. **Indexed:** Chem.Abstr. **Document type:** academic/scholarly publication.
—BLDSC (4917.730000); CASDDS.

610 KO ISSN 0372-7858
R97.7.K6 CODEN: YUNMAV
YONSEI JOURNAL OF MEDICAL SCIENCE. (Text in Korean; summaries in English) 1968. s-a. exchange basis. Yonsei University, College of Medicine, C.P.O. Box 8044, Seoul, S. Korea. TEL 392-0161. abstr.; bibl.; charts; illus.; stat. (tabloid format) **Indexed:** Biol.Abstr., Chem.Abstr.
—CASDDS.

610 KO ISSN 0513-5796
CODEN: YOMJA9
YONSEI MEDICAL JOURNAL. (Text in English) 1960. q. exchange basis. Yonsei University, College of Medicine, C.P.O. Box 8044, Seoul, S. Korea. Ed. Tchan Kyu Park. abstr.; charts; illus.; stat. (tabloid format) **Indexed:** Biol.Abstr., Chem.Abstr., Excerp.Med., Ind.Med. **Document type:** academic/scholarly publication.
—BLDSC (9421.100000); CASDDS.

YOUR PRIVATE HEALTH OPTION. see BUSINESS AND ECONOMICS — Investments

YUNNAN ZHONGYI ZAZHI/YUNNAN JOURNAL OF TRADITIONAL CHINESE MEDICINE. see ALTERNATIVE MEDICINE

610 GW ISSN 0341-9835
Z F A MIT KARTEI DER PRAKTISCHEN MEDIZIN. (Zeitschrift fuer Allgemeinmedizin) 1924. fortn. DM.174. (Vereinigung der Hochschullehrer und Lehrbeauftragten fuer Allgemeinmedizin) Hippokrates Verlag GmbH, Postfach 300504, 70445 Stuttgart, Germany. TEL 0711-8931-0. FAX 0711-8931453. Ed.Bd. adv.; bk.rev.; bibl.; charts; illus.; index. circ. 45,000. **Indexed:** Dent.Ind., Excerp.Med., Ind.Med., Nutr.Abstr. **Document type:** academic/scholarly publication.
—BLDSC (9446.870000); Faxon; UMI. **CCC.**
Former titles: Z F A; Landarzt (ISSN 0023-7728)

610 XV
ZDRAVNISKI VESTNIK. (Text in Slovenian; summaries in English) 1929. m. 6000 din.($110) Slovensko Zdravnisko Drustvo, Komenskega 4, P.O. Box 26, 61001 Ljubljana, Slovenia. TEL 061-317-868. (Co-sponsors: Raziskovalna Skupnost Slovenije, Zdravstvena Skupnost Slovenije) Eds. Joze Drinovec, Martin Janko. adv.; bk.rev. circ. 4,100. **Indexed:** Biol.Abstr., Curr.Cont., Excerp.Med.
—Genuine Article.
Formerly: Zdravstveni Vestnik (ISSN 0350-0063)

610 GW ISSN 0044-2178
ZEITSCHRIFT FUER AERZTLICHE FORTBILDUNG. 1904. 8/yr. DM.138 (foreign DM.152). Gustav Fischer Verlag Jena, Villengang 2, 07745 Jena, Germany. TEL 03641-626444. FAX 03641-626500. (Subscr. to: Postfach 100537, 07705 Jena, Germany) Ed. G. Ollenschlager. adv.; bk.rev.; abstr.; bibl.; charts; illus.; index. (reprint service avail. from ISI) **Indexed:** Biol.Abstr., C.I.S. Abstr., Chem.Abstr., Dent.Ind., Excerp.Med., Ind.Med., Ref.Zh. **Document type:** academic/scholarly publication.
—BLDSC (9452.800000); EMDOCS; Faxon; SWETS. **CCC.**

610 170 GW ISSN 0944-7652
ZEITSCHRIFT FUER MEDIZINISCHE ETHIK. 1955. q. DM.79. Schwaben Verlag AG, Senefelderstr. 12, 73760 Ostfildern, Germany. TEL 0711-4406160. FAX 0711-4406177. Ed. Martin Guenther. adv.; bk.rev. **Document type:** academic/scholarly publication.
Formerly (until 1992): Arzt und Christ (ISSN 0403-3884)

ZEITSCHRIFT FUER NATURHEILKUNDE. see ALTERNATIVE MEDICINE

610 155.3 GW ISSN 0932-8114
HQ21
ZEITSCHRIFT FUER SEXUALFORSCHUNG. 1988. q. DM.98. (Deutsche Gesellschaft fuer Sexualforschung) Ferdinand Enke Verlag, Postfach 300366, 70443 Stuttgart, Germany. TEL 0711-135798-0. FAX 0711-135798-30. TELEX 07252275-GTV-D. Ed.Bd. (reprint service avail. from IRC) **Indexed:** Psychol.Abstr. (1988-). **Document type:** academic/scholarly publication.
—BLDSC (9486.322000).

610 GW ISSN 0942-6086
ZENTRALSTERILISATION - CENTRAL SERVICE; international journal of processing and sterile supply. (Text in English, German) 1993. bi-m. DM.81.60 (foreign DM.94.50). (European Society for Hospital Sterile Supply) M H P Verlag GmbH, Ostring 13, 65205 Wiesbaden, Germany. TEL 06122-770931. FAX 06122-76331. Ed. Dr. P. Heeg. adv.: B&W page DM.3070; adv. contact: W. Bockemuehl. circ. 4,000. **Document type:** academic/scholarly publication.
Refereed Serial

610 CC ISSN 1000-1743
CODEN: ZYDXDM
ZHEJIANG YIKE DAXUE XUEBAO/ZHEJIANG MEDICAL UNIVERSITY. JOURNAL. (Text in Chinese; summaries in English) 1958. bi-m. $12. Zhejiang Yike Daxue, Xuebao Bianji Shi, 157 Yan'an Rd., Hangzhou, Zhejiang 310006, People's Republic of China. TEL 0571-7022700. FAX 0571-7071571. Ed. Zheng Shu. adv.: B&W page $295; adv. contact: Zhang Lianrong. bibl.; illus. circ. 5,000. **Document type:** academic/scholarly publication.
—CASDDS.
Description: Covers clinical medicine, preventive medicine, biomedical science and pharmacy.

615.89 615.328 CC
ZHEJIANG ZHONGYI XUEYUAN XUEBAO/ZHEJIANG TRADITIONAL CHINESE MEDICAL COLLEGE. JOURNAL. (Text in Chinese) bi-m. $1.30 per no. Zhejiang Zhongyi Xueyuan - Zhejiang Traditional Chinese Medical College, Zhejiang, People's Republic of China. (Dist. by: Guoji Shudian (China Publications Centre), Chegongzhuang Xilu 21, P.O. Box 339, Beijing, P.R.C.)

ZHEJIANG ZHONGYI ZAZHI/ZHEJIANG JOURNAL OF TRADITIONAL CHINESE MEDICINE. see ALTERNATIVE MEDICINE

610 CC ISSN 1000-6486
ZHIYE YIXUE/OCCUPATIONAL MEDICINE. (Text in Chinese) 1978. bi-m. $20. Huanan Qu Laodong Weisheng Zhiyebing Fangzhi Zhongxin - South China Centre of Occupational Health, No. 78, Yile Rd., Guangzhou, Guangdong 510260, People's Republic of China. TEL 86-20-4448002. Ed. Tan Bingde; Pub. He Yiping. adv. contact: Chen Zhong-yi.

ZHONG CAO YAO/CHINESE HERBAL MEDICINE. see PHARMACY AND PHARMACOLOGY

615.89 CC ISSN 0254-9034
R97.7.C5
ZHONG-XIYI JIEHE ZAZHI/CHINESE JOURNAL OF INTEGRATED TRADITIONAL AND WESTERN MEDICINE. (Text in Chinese) bi-m. $1.20 per no. (Zhongyi Yanjiuyuan, Zhongguo Zhong-Xiyi Jiehe Yanjiuhui - Academy of Traditional Chinese Medicine, Chinese Association of the Integration of Traditional and Western Medicine) Guoji Shudian, Qikan Bu - China International Book Trading Corp., Chegongzhuang Xilu 21, P.O. Box 399, Beijing 100044, People's Republic of China. **Indexed:** Dent.Ind., Ind.Med.
—BLDSC (3180.358000).

MEDICAL SCIENCES

610 CC ISSN 1000-4718
CODEN: ZBSZEB
ZHONGGUO BINGLI SHENGLI ZAZHI/CHINESE JOURNAL OF PATHOPHYSIOLOGY. (Text in Chinese or English) 1985. bi-m. $18. Zhongguo Bingli Shengli Xuehui - Chinese Pathophysiological Society, Jinan University, Shipai, Guangzhou, Guangdong 510632, People's Republic of China. TEL 5516511. FAX 5516941. Ed. Li Chujie. adv. contact: Cao Yi. **Indexed:** Apic.Abstr. **Document type:** academic/scholarly publication.
—CASDDS.
Description: Publishes research papers, short communications, reviews and experimental techniques in the field of clinical and experimental pathophysiology.
Refereed Serial

610 CC ISSN 1001-568X
ZHONGGUO CHUJI WEISHENG BAOJIAN/CHINESE PRIMARY HEALTH CARE. (Text in Chinese) m. Heilongjiang Sheng Weishengting - Heilongjiang Provincial Bureau of Health, 27, Xiangshun Jie, Xiangfang-qu, Harbin, Heilongjiang 150036, People's Republic of China. TEL 54637. Ed. Li Yihe.

610 CC ISSN 1001-1889
ZHONGGUO DIFANGBING FANGZHI ZAZHI/CHINESE JOURNAL OF CONTROL OF ENDEMIC DISEASES. (Text in Chinese) 1987. bi-m. Y16.80 (effective 1996). Institute for Endemic Disease Control and Research, 23 Chongqing Jie, Jilin 132001, People's Republic of China. TEL 456645. FAX 453670. (Dist. overseas by: China International Book Trading Corp., P.O. Box 399, Beijing, P.R. China) Ed. Gao Shufen. adv. contact: Xie Jiliang. circ. 4,000 (paid).
Document type: academic/scholarly publication.
Description: Focuses on seven endemic diseases - Keshan disease, keshin-beck disease, iodine deficiency disorders, plague, brucellosis, endemic fluorosis and arsenic poisoning.

610 CC
ZHONGGUO JIJIU YIXUE/CHINESE FIRST AID MEDICAL SCIENCE. (Text in Chinese) bi-m. Heilongjiang Sheng Keji Qingbaosuo - Heilongjiang Institute of Science and Technology Information, 30, Yinhang Jie, Nangang-qu, Harbin, Heilongjiang 150001, People's Republic of China. TEL 33977. Ed. Pei Lizhong.

610 CC ISSN 1001-1242
ZHONGGUO KANGFU YIXUE ZAZHI/CHINESE JOURNAL OF REHABILITATION MEDICINE. (Text in Chinese) 1986. bi-m. $19.80. Zhongguo Kangfu Yixuehui - Chinese Association of Rehabilitation Medicine, Zhongri Youhao Yiyuan, Yinghuayuan East St., Beijing 100029, People's Republic of China. TEL 010-422-1122. FAX 010-421-7749. Ed. Wang Shuangjuan.
Description: Publishes original articles that deal with fundamental and clinical research in the fields of physical therapy, occupational therapy, speech therapy, rehabilitation engineering, and rehabilitation medicine and education.

610 CC ISSN 1000-629X
ZHONGGUO MAFENG ZAZHI/CHINESE JOURNAL OF LEPROSY. (Text in Chinese) 1985. q. $16. Zhongguo Mafeng Fangzhi Xiehui - China Leprosy Association, 87 Hengfu Rd., Guangzhou, Guangdong 510095, People's Republic of China. TEL 020-3348354. Ed. Zhao Xiding. adv. contact: Ma Xuefen. bk.rev. circ. 3,000. **Document type:** academic/scholarly publication.

630 CC
ZHONGGUO NONGCUN YIXUE/MEDICAL SCIENCE IN RURAL CHINA. (Text in Chinese) m. $2.50. Renmin Weisheng Chubanshe, 10 Tiantan Xili, Beijing 100050, People's Republic of China. TEL 7015802. Ed. Li Fang. adv. contact: Xia Zemin. circ. 150,000. **Document type:** academic/scholarly publication.

610.285 CC ISSN 0258-8021
R856.A1 CODEN: ZSYXEI
ZHONGGUO SHENGWU YIXUE GONGCHENG XUEBAO/CHINESE JOURNAL OF BIOMEDICAL ENGINEERING. (Text in Chinese, English) 1982. q. $24 (foreign $30.70). Chinese Society of Biomedical Engineering, 9 Dond Dan San Tiao, Beijing 100730, People's Republic of China. TEL 86-1-5295930. FAX 81-1-5124876. (Co-sponsor: Chinese Academy of Medical Sciences) Ed. Ba Denian. adv. contact: Zhao Guanglu. **Indexed:** Excerp.Med., INSPEC (1985-). **Document type:** academic/scholarly publication.
—BLDSC (3180.296500); CASDDS.
Description: Covers biomechanics, artificial organs, biomedical materials, biocybernetics, and mass transfers.

610 CC
RD1
ZHONGGUO WEISHENG NIANJIAN/YEAR BOOK: HEALTH CARE IN CHINA. (Text in Chinese, English) 1983. a. $47. Renmin Weisheng Chubanshe, 10 Tiantan Xili, Beijing 100050, People's Republic of China. circ. 5,000.
Formerly: Zhongguo Waike Nianjian (ISSN 1002-0136)

630 CC
ZHONGGUO XIANGCUN YISHENG/CHINESE RURAL DOCTORS. (Text in Chinese) m. Jilin Kexue Jishu Chubanshe - Jilin Science and Technology Publishers, 102, Stalin Street, Changchun, Jilin 130021, People's Republic of China. TEL 884778. Ed. Shan Shujian.

610 CC ISSN 1001-7658
ZHONGGUO XIAODUXUE ZAZHI/CHINESE JOURNAL OF DISINFECTION. (Text in Chinese) 1984. q. $5.48 (foreign $18.17)(typically set in Oct.). Zhonghua Yufang Yixuehui (Fengtai) - China Preventive Medical Society (Fengtai), A-23 Qilizhuang Lu, Fengtai, Beijing 100071, People's Republic of China. TEL 6888229. FAX 861-8213044. (Dist. outside China by: Guoji Shudian - China International Book Trading Corp., P.O. Box 399, Beijing, P.R.C.) Ed. Liu Yujing. adv.; bk.rev. circ. 6,000.
Formerly (until 1990): Disinfection and Sterilization.
Description: Reports research achievements in area of disinfection sterilization in China, including mechanism of germicidal action, experimental techniques, administration and monitoring.
Refereed Serial

610 CC ISSN 1000-503X
CODEN: CIHPDR
ZHONGGUO YIXUE KEXUEYUAN XUEBAO/ACTA ACADEMIAE MEDICINAE SINICA. (Text in Chinese) bi-m. $4.30 per no. Chinese Academy of Medical Sciences (CAMS) - Zhongguo Yixue Kexueyuan, 9 Dong Dan San Tiao, Beijing 100730, People's Republic of China. TEL 5133074. (Dist. by: China International Book Trading Corp., Chegongzhuang Xilu 21, P.O. Box 399, Beijing, P.R.C.) Ed. Bao Denian. **Indexed:** ExtraMED, Helminthol.Abstr. **Document type:** academic/scholarly publication.
●Also available on CD-ROM.
—BLDSC (0579.723200); CASDDS.
Refereed Serial

ZHONGGUO ZHENJIU/CHINESE ACUPUNCTURE AND MOXIBUSTION. see *ALTERNATIVE MEDICINE*

610 CC ISSN 1000-6680
ZHONGHUA CHUANRANBING ZAZHI/CHINESE JOURNAL OF INFECTIOUS DISEASES. (Text in Chinese; abstracts in Chinese, English) q. $5.48. Zhonghua Yixuehui, Shanghai Fenhui - Chinese Medical Association, Shanghai Branch, 1623 Beijing Xilu, Shanghai 200040, People's Republic of China. TEL 2531885. Ed. Xianghui. circ. 15,000. **Indexed:** ExtraMED. **Document type:** academic/scholarly publication.
●Also available on CD-ROM.

610 CC
ZHONGHUA LIUXINGBINGXUE ZAZHI/CHINESE JOURNAL OF EPIDEMIOLOGY. (Text in Chinese) bi-m. Zhonghua Yufang Yixuehui - China Preventive Medical Society, 16, Hepingli Zhongjie, Beijing 100013, People's Republic of China. TEL 4218457. Ed. He Guanqing. **Indexed:** Diar.Dis.Res., ExtraMED. **Document type:** academic/scholarly publication.
●Also available on CD-ROM.

610 CC
ZHONGHUA YISHI ZAZHI/CHINESE JOURNAL OF MEDICAL HISTORY. (Text in Chinese) q. $3 per no. Guoji Shudian, Qikan Bu - China International Book Trading Corp., Chegongzhuang Xilu 21, P.O. Box 399, Beijing 100044, People's Republic of China. **Indexed:** ExtraMED. **Document type:** academic/scholarly publication.
●Also available on CD-ROM.

610 CC
ZHONGHUA YUFANG YIXUE ZAZHI/CHINESE JOURNAL OF PREVENTIVE MEDICINE. (Text in Chinese) bi-m. $3 per no. Zhonghua Yufang Yixuehui - China Preventive Medical Society, 16, Hepingli Zhongjie, Beijing 100013, People's Republic of China. **Indexed:** Chem.Abstr., ExtraMED, Ind.Med., Rev.Med.& Vet.Mycol. **Document type:** academic/scholarly publication.
●Also available on CD-ROM.

630 CC ISSN 1001-0025
ZHONGRI YOUHAO YIYUAN XUEBAO/SINO-JAPANESE FRIENDSHIP HOSPITAL JOURNAL. (Text in Chinese) q. Zhongri Youhao Yiyuan, Hepingjie Beikou, Beijing 100029, People's Republic of China. TEL 4221122. Ed. Bian Zhiqiang.

610 CC ISSN 1000-257X
ZHONGSHAN YIKE DAXUE XUEBAO/SUN YAT-SEN UNIVERSITY OF MEDICAL SCIENCES. ACADEMIC JOURNAL. (Text in Chinese) 1980. q. Y2.50 per no. Zhongshan Yike Daxue - Sun Yat-Sen University of Medical Sciences, Editorial Board of Acad. J. SUMS, 74 Zhongshan Erlu, Guangzhou, Guangdong Province 510089, People's Republic of China. Ed. Peng Wenwei.
—BLDSC (0570.512500).
Formerly (until 1983): Zhongshan Yixueyuan Xuebao (ISSN 0254-1440)

ZHONGYAO TONGBAO/CHINESE MEDICINE BULLETIN. see *PHARMACY AND PHARMACOLOGY*

610 CC ISSN 1001-6910
ZHONGYI YANJIU/TRADITIONAL CHINESE MEDICINAL RESEARCH. (Text in Chinese, table of contents in English) q. Y3.20. Zhongyi Yanjiu Bianjibu, 7 Chengbei Lu, Zhengzhou, Henan 450004, People's Republic of China. TEL 22705. (Dist. overseas by: China International Book Trading Corporation - Guoji Shudian, P.O. Box 399, Beijing, P.R.C.)

ZHONGYI ZAZHI/JOURNAL OF TRADITIONAL CHINESE MEDICINE. see *ALTERNATIVE MEDICINE*

613 CI ISSN 0350-7335
ZIVOT I ZDRAVIJE; obitelski casopis za proucavanje i promicanje prirodnih zdravstvenih nacela. (Editions in Croatian and Serbian) 1972. q. $4 per issue. Centar za Proucavanje Prirodnih Zdravstvenih Nacela, Maksimirska 9, 41000 Zagreb, Croatia. TEL 041 217-264. Ed. Slavko Cop. circ. 15,500 (6,500 Croatian ed.; 9,000 Serbian ed.) (back issues avail.)

610 PL ISSN 0084-5825
QL55 CODEN: ZWLAAA
ZWIERZETA LABORATORYJNE. (Text in Polish; summaries in English) 1963. irreg., vol.29-30, 1994. price varies. (Polska Akademia Nauk, Instytut Immunologii i Terapii Doswiadczalnej im. Ludwika Hirszfelda - Polish Academy of Sciences, L. Hirszfeld Institute of Immunology and Experimental Therapy) Wydawnictwo Naukowe P W N, Ul. Miodowa 10, 00-251 Warsaw, Poland. TEL 374022. Ed. Czeslaw Radzikowski. abstr.; charts; illus. **Indexed:** Anim.Breed.Abstr., Biol.Abstr., Chem.Abstr., Curr.Adv.Ecol.Sci., Helminthol.Abstr., Vet.Bull. **Document type:** monographic series.
—BLDSC (9538.770000); CASDDS.
Description: Covers laboratory animal science: biology, genetics, nutrition, breeding, immunogenetics, environmental and health control.

ZWISCHENSCHRITTE; Beitraege zu einer morphologischen Psychologie. see *PSYCHOLOGY*

MEDICAL SCIENCES — ABSTRACTING, BIBLIOGRAPHIES, STATISTICS

610   CU   ISSN 0257-7402
16 DE ABRIL; organo científico estudiantil de las ciencias medicas de Cuba. 1961. q. $15 in America; Europe $25; elsewhere $30. Ministerio de Salud Publica, Instituto Superior de Ciencias Medicas de la Habana, Calle G s-n, e. 25 y 27, Plaza de la Revolucion, 10400 Vedado, Havana, Cuba. TEL 308942. FAX 537-333063. E-mail: 16-abril@infomed.sld.cu. (Dist. by: Centro Nacional de Informacion de Ciencias Medicas, Calle G No. 110 e. M y N, 10400 Vedado Havana, Cuba) Ed. Abel Garcia Valdes. bk.rev.; charts; illus. circ. 5,000. **Document type:** academic/scholarly publication.
  Description: Original papers, research reports, reviews, notes and other medical articles.
  Refereed Serial

MEDICAL SCIENCES — Abstracting, Bibliographies, Statistics

016 610.73   US   ISSN 1055-8349
A A C N NURSING SCAN IN CRITICAL CARE. 1991. bi-m. $45 to individuals (foreign $60); institutions $68 (foreign $83). (American Association of Critical Care Nurses) Nursecom Inc., 1211 Locust St., Philadelphia, PA 19107. TEL 215-545-7222. FAX 215-545-8107. Ed. Gayle Whitman; Pub. Margo C. Neal. circ. 5,800. **Indexed:** CINAHL. **Document type:** abstracting/indexing, bibliography.
—BLDSC (0537.137900).
  Description: Abstracts articles from multidisciplinary literature that address topics in critical care nursing, with commentary on applications to nursing practice.
  Refereed Serial

A A C O M ANNUAL STATISTICAL REPORT. (American Association of Colleges of Osteopathic Medicine) see EDUCATION — Abstracting, Bibliographies, Statistics

616.1   US   ISSN 1062-1458
                           CODEN: ACJREE
A C C CURRENT JOURNAL REVIEW. 1993. bi-m. $155 to institutions (effective 1996). (American College of Cardiology) Elsevier Science Inc., 655 Ave. of the Americas, New York, NY 10010. TEL 212-633-3950. FAX 212-633-3990. (Subscr. to: Box 882, Madison Sq. Sta., New York, NY 10159-0882) Ed. S.B. Knoebel. **Indexed:** Excerp.Med. (1995-). **Document type:** abstracting/indexing.
—CCC.
  Refereed Serial

618   US   ISSN 0897-1471
A C O G CURRENT JOURNAL REVIEW. 1988. bi-m. $140 to institutions (effective 1996). (American College of Obstetricians and Gynecologists) Elsevier Science Inc., 655 Ave. of the Americas, New York, NY 10010. TEL 212-989-5800. FAX 212-633-3990. TELEX 420643 AEP UI. (Subscr. to: Box 882, Madison Sq. Sta., New York, NY 10159-0882) Ed. Dr. Albert B. Gerbie. (also avail. in microform from UMI) **Document type:** abstracting/indexing.
—CCC.
  Description: Designed to keep the reader up-to-date on issues in obstetrics and gynecology. Includes current abstracts of 28 medical journals published worldwide.
  Refereed Serial

616.005   US   ISSN 1056-8751
R11   CODEN: AJCLEA
A C P JOURNAL CLUB. (Supplement to: Annals of Internal Medicine (ISSN 0003-4819)) 1991. bi-m. $50 (effective 1995). American College of Physicians, Independence Mall W., Sixth St. at Race, Philadelphia, PA 19106-1572. TEL 215-351-2400. Ed. Dr. Frank Davidoff. **Indexed:** Ind.Med. (1994-). **Document type:** abstracting/indexing.
—BLDSC (0578.698300).
  Description: Current awareness publication providing abstracts of current medical research of high scientific merit for clinical practice. Includes commentary and clinical applications.

610.73 016   US   ISSN 1072-5067
A O N E'S LEADERSHIP PROSPECTIVES. 1986. bi-m. $45 to individuals (foreign $60); institutions $68 (foreign $83) (effective 1996). (American Organization of Nurse Executives) Nursecom Inc., 1211 Locust St., Philadelphia, PA 19107. TEL 215-545-7222. FAX 215-545-8107. Ed. Joan Trofino; Pub. Margo C. Neal. circ. 2,400. (also avail. in microform from UMI) **Document type:** academic/scholarly publication, abstracting/indexing.
—BLDSC (1567.712500); UMI.
  Formerly (until Nov. 1993): Nursing Scan in Administration (ISSN 0888-6288)
  Description: Contains abstracts from mulitdisciplinary literature on topics relating to administration, with commentary on applications to nursing practice.
  Refereed Serial

610.16   US   ISSN 0001-3331
                         CODEN: AIXMA
ABRIDGED INDEX MEDICUS. Abbreviated title: A I M. (Annual cumulation avail.: Cumulated Abridged Index Medicus (ISSN 0090-1377)) 1970. m. $55 (foreign $68.75) (effective 1995). U.S. National Library of Medicine, 8600 Rockville Pike, Bethesda, MD 20894. (Subscr. to: Superintendent of Documents, U.S. Government Printing Office, Box 371954, Pittsburgh, PA 15250-7954. TEL 202-512-1800. FAX 202-512-2250) cum.index. circ. 4,700. (also avail. in microform from UMI; back issues avail.) **Indexed:** MEDOC. **Document type:** abstracting/indexing, government publication.
—UMI.
  Description: Indexes articles from 118 English-language medical journals, arranged by subject and author.

616.07 619 574.8   UK   ISSN 0268-4993
ABSTRACTS: CELLULAR PATHOLOGY. 1979. q. £15 to individuals (overseas £25); institutions £45 (overseas £52) (effective 1994). Charnlind Ltd., P.O. Box 29, Woking, Surrey GU21 1AE, England. Ed. S. Jones. adv.; bk.rev. circ. 3,000. **Document type:** abstracting/indexing.
  Formerly (until 1986): Abstracts: Histopathology, Cytopathology (ISSN 0143-800X)

610 016   BU   ISSN 0001-3536
ABSTRACTS OF BULGARIAN SCIENTIFIC MEDICAL LITERATURE. (Text in English) 1958. q. 120 lv. Higher Medical Institute, Central Medical Library, Central Medical Library, 1, Sveti Georgi Sofijski St., 1431 Sofia, Bulgaria. TEL 359-523171. Ed. V. Trenkova. index. circ. 200. **Indexed:** Chem.Abstr. **Document type:** abstracting/indexing.
●Also available online.
—BLDSC (0554.565600).
  Description: Presents abstracts from Bulgarian medical periodicals.

610 011   US
ABSTRACTS OF CLINICAL CARE GUIDELINES. 1989. 10/yr. $95. Joint Commission on Accreditation of Healthcare Organization, 1 Renaissance Blvd., Oakbrook Terrace, IL 60181. TEL 708-916-5800. (Subscr. to: Mosby Yearbook Inc., 11830 Westline Industrial, St. Louis, MO 63146. TEL 800-453-4351) (also avail. in microform from UMI)

616.98   UK   ISSN 0260-5511
RA421
ABSTRACTS ON HYGIENE AND COMMUNICABLE DISEASES. 1926. m. £235($425) (effective 1996). CAB International, Wallingford, Oxon. OX10 8DE, England. TEL 01491-832111. FAX 01491-833508. TELEX 847964 COMAGG G. E-mail: cabi@cabi.org. adv.; bk.rev.; index. circ. 450. (also avail. in diskette format; microform from UMI; reprint service avail. from IRC) **Indexed:** Biol.Abstr., C.I.S. Abstr., Ergon.Abstr., Ind.Vet., Nutr.Abstr., Rev.Appl.Entomol., Rev.Plant Path., Vet.Bull., World Text.Abstr. **Document type:** abstracting/indexing.
●Also available online. Vendor(s): DIMDI.
—BLDSC (0564.407000); UMI.
  Former titles: Abstracts on Hygiene (ISSN 0001-3692); Bulletin of Hygiene.

ADVANCES IN ORTHOPAEDIC SURGERY. see MEDICAL SCIENCES — Orthopedics And Traumatology

610 629.13   US   ISSN 0001-9410
Z6664.3
AEROSPACE MEDICINE AND BIOLOGY; a continuing bibliography. 1964. m. $16.50. U.S. National Aeronautics and Space Administration, Center for AeroSpace Information, N A S A Access Help Desk, 800 Elkridge Landing Rd., Linthicum Heights, MD 21090-2934. TEL 301-621-0390. FAX 301-621-0134. E-mail: help@sti.nasa.gov. (Compiled by: U.S. Library of Congress and American Institute of Aeronautics and Astronautics) index. (back issues avail.) **Indexed:** Noise Pollut.Publ.Abstr. **Document type:** bibliography.
  Formerly: Aerospace References in Medicine and Biology.
  Description: Abstracts medical and biological research. Articles cover the biological, physiological, and environmental effects to which humans are subjected to during and following space flight.

616.9   US   ISSN 1350-2840
AIDS (YEAR); a year in review. (Supplement to: AIDS) 1988. a. $74.95 to individuals. Current Science, 400 Market St., Ste. 700, Philadelphia, PA 19106. TEL 215-574-2210; 800-552-5866. FAX 215-574-2270. (And: Current Science Ltd., 34-42 Cleveland St., London W1P 6LB, England. TEL 0171-323-0323. FAX 0171-636-6911) Ed.Bd. adv.; bibl.; illus. **Indexed:** Psychol.Abstr. **Document type:** academic/scholarly publication.
—ADONIS.
  Description: Reviews all major developments during the preceding year. Topics include virology; epidemiology; vaccines and immunology; clinical treatment; social, cultural and political aspects; and global statistics.

616.9   UK
AIDS ABSTRACTS; international literature on acquired immunodeficiency syndrome and related retroviruses. 1985. m. £88 to individuals; institutions £190 (effective 1996). (University of Leeds, Oncology Information Service) Carfax Publishing Co., P.O. Box 25, Abingdon, Oxon. OX14 3UE, England. TEL 01235-555335. FAX 01235-553559. (Subscr. in N. America to: Carfax Publishing Co., 875-81 Massachusetts Ave., Cambridge, MA 02139) Ed. Arthur W. Boylston. adv. circ. 1,000. (back issues avail.) **Document type:** abstracting/indexing.
—UMI. **CCC.**
  Formerly (until 1993): AIDS Information (ISSN 0953-1580)
  Description: Provides full details of recently published papers on all aspects of AIDS and related animal and human retroviruses.

616.9   US   ISSN 1074-2891
▼**AIDS & T B WEEKLY ABSTRACTS FROM CONFERENCE PROCEEDINGS.** 1994. w. $995. Charles W. Henderson, Ed. & Pub., Box 5528, Atlanta, GA 31107-0528. TEL 404-377-8895. FAX 404-378-5411. TELEX 78-2661. (Subscr. to: Box 830409, Birmingham, AL 35283-0409. TEL 800-633-4931. FAX 205-995-1588) index. (looseleaf format) **Document type:** abstracting/indexing.
—UMI. **CCC.**
  Description: Features reports on AIDS and tuberculosis research prior to their publication in journals.

616.9   US   ISSN 1074-2883
▼**AIDS & T B WEEKLY ARTICLE SUMMARIES.** 1994. w. $995. Charles W. Henderson, Ed. & Pub., Box 5528, Atlanta, GA 31107-0528. TEL 404-377-8895. FAX 404-378-5411. TELEX 78-2661. (Subscr. to: Box 830409, Birmingham, AL 35283-0409. TEL 800-633-4931. FAX 205-995-1588) index. (looseleaf format) **Document type:** abstracting/indexing.
—UMI. **CCC.**
  Description: Features summaries of recent AIDS and tuberculosis journal articles published worldwide. Indexed by author, key word and institution.

MEDICAL SCIENCES — ABSTRACTING, BIBLIOGRAPHIES, STATISTICS   4289

610 616.9   US   ISSN 1052-0287
Z6664.A27
AIDS BIBLIOGRAPHY (BETHESDA). 1988. m. $84 (foreign $105) (effective 1995). U.S. National Library of Medicine, 8600 Rockville Pike, Bethesda, MD 20894. TEL 202-483-3238. (Subscr. to: Superintendent of Documents, U.S. Government Printing Office, Box 371954, Pittsburgh, PA 15250-7954. TEL 202-512-1800. FAX 202-512-2250) (back issues avail.) **Document type:** bibliography, government publication.
Description: Lists current articles and audiovisual materials on acquired immunodeficiency syndrome.

AMERICAN PSYCHIATRIC ASSOCIATION. SCIENTIFIC PROCEEDINGS IN SUMMARY FORM. see *MEDICAL SCIENCES — Psychiatry And Neurology*

610 013   PL   ISSN 0066-1937
ANNALES ACADEMIAE MEDICAE CRACOVIENSIS. (Text in English, Polish and Russian) 1955. a. price varies. Akademia Medyczna im. Mikolaja Kopernika w Krakowie - Nicholas Copernicus Medical Academy in Cracow, Ul. Sw. Anny 12, 31-008 Krakow, Poland. TEL 48-12-22-07-11. (Dist. by: Ars Polona-Ruch, Krakowskie Przedmiescie 7, Warsaw, Poland) Ed. Dr. Mieczyslaw Goldsztajn. circ. 1,000.
Formerly: Akademia Medyczna w Krakowie. Dzialalnosc Naukowa.

616.1   US   ISSN 0952-0562
ANNUAL OF CARDIAC SURGERY. 1987. a. $144.95. Current Science, 400 Market St., Ste. 700, Philadelphia, PA 19106. TEL 312-733-2980; 800-892-7456. FAX 312-733-3107. (And: Current Science Ltd., 34-43 Cleveland St., London W1P 6LB, England. TEL 0171-323-0323. FAX 0171-636-3911) Ed. Magdi Yacoub. bibl.; illus. circ. 3,000. **Document type:** academic/scholarly publication.
—BLDSC (1077.965000).
Description: For cardiac surgeons, cardiologists and researchers involved with coronary artery disease. Reviews the year's research papers and presents invited reviews in featured such areas as pediatric and fetal cardiac surgery.

616.3   US   ISSN 0952-6293
ANNUAL OF GASTROINTESTINAL ENDOSCOPY. (Supplement avail.: Slide Atlas of Gastrointestinal Endoscopy (Year)) 1988. a. $119.95. Current Science, 400 Market St., Ste. 700, Philadelphia, PA 19106. TEL 312-733-2980; 800-892-7456. FAX 312-733-3107. (And: Current Science Ltd., 34-42 Crescent St., London W1P 6LB, England. TEL 0171-323-0323. FAX 0171-636-6911) Ed.Bd. bibl.; illus. **Document type:** academic/scholarly publication.
—BLDSC (1085.673500).
Description: For physicians, endoscopists, surgeons, radiologists and others interested in gastroenterology and gastrointestinal imaging or therapy.

617.6   US
ANNUAL REPORT ON ALLIED DENTAL HEALTH EDUCATION. 1967. a. $20 to non-members; members $10. American Dental Association, 211 E. Chicago Ave., Chicago, IL 60611. TEL 312-440-2674. FAX 312-440-3538. (also avail. in microfiche from CIS) **Indexed:** SRI. **Document type:** academic/scholarly publication.
Formerly: Annual Report on Dental Auxillary Education (ISSN 0084-6554)

617.6   US   ISSN 0147-0256
ANNUAL REPORT ON DENTAL EDUCATION. 1967. a. $20 to non-members; members $10. American Dental Association, 211 E. Chicago Ave., Chicago, IL 60611. TEL 312-440-2674. FAX 312-440-3538. (also avail. in microfiche from CIS) **Indexed:** SRI. **Document type:** academic/scholarly publication.
Formerly: Dental Students' Register (ISSN 0065-8049)

610   US   ISSN 8756-4734
ASTHMA UPDATE; a newsletter for people with asthma. 1985. q. $12. 123 Monticello Ave., Annapolis, MD 21401. TEL 410-267-8329. FAX 410-267-0309. Ed. David Jamison. (back issues avail.) **Document type:** abstracting/indexing, newsletter.
Description: Contains annotated abstracts from current medical journals.

616.4 615   UK   ISSN 0268-1641
ATRIAL NATRIURETIC FACTORS. 1986. s-m. (diskette m.). £105 (diskette £115; both £175) (effective 1995). S U B I S, Mansion House, 19 Kingfield Rd., Sheffield S11 9AS, England. TEL 0114-2554433. FAX 0114-2554626. E-mail: admin@sheffac.demon.co.uk. (also avail. in diskette format) **Document type:** abstracting/indexing.
—CCC.
Description: Current awareness service for researchers in clinical and life sciences. Covers atrial natriuretic factors: peptides, cardionatrin, atriopeptin, and cardiac endocrinology.

618.92 310   AT
AUSTRALIA. BUREAU OF STATISTICS. CHILDREN'S HEALTH SCREENING. 1979. irreg., latest 1995. Aus.$16. Australian Bureau of Statistics, P.O. Box 10, Belconnen, A.C.T. 2616, Australia. **Document type:** government publication.
Formerly: Sight, Hearing and Dental Health (Persons Aged 2 to 14 Years).
Description: Contains information about health screening practices. Topics include: testing of sight and hearing; visits to dental professionals and visits to baby health clinics.

616.097 618.92   AT
310
AUSTRALIA. BUREAU OF STATISTICS. CHILDREN'S IMMUNISATION. 1983. irreg., latest 1995. Aus.$16. Australian Bureau of Statistics, P.O. Box 10, Belconnen, A.C.T. 2616, Australia. **Document type:** government publication.
Description: Contains statistics on coverage and practice regarding the immunization of children against selected preventable diseases.

610   SP
BASQUE REGION. OSASUN SAILEKO. AURREKONTUA/BASQUE REGION. DEPARTAMENTO DE SANIDAD. PRESUPUESTO. a. Eusko Jaurlaritzaren Argitalpen-Zerbitzu Nagusia - Servicio Central de Publicaciones del Gobierno Vasco, C. Duque de Wellington 2, 01011 Vitoria-Gasteiz, Spain. circ. 1,000.

618   BH
BELIZE FAMILY HEALTH SURVEY. 1991. irreg. $10. Ministry of Finance, Central Statistical Office, Belmopan, Belize. TEL 08-22207. FAX 08-23206. **Document type:** government publication.
Description: Provides information on fertility, infant morality, family planning and the use of maternal and child health services in Belize.

618 016   GW   ISSN 0722-9852
BERICHTE GYNAEKOLOGIE - GEBURTSHILFE/GYNECOLOGY - OBSTETRICS. (Text in English, German) 1923. 26/yr. (in 2 vols, 13 nos./vol.). DM.5612($4078) (effective 1996). Springer-Verlag, Heidelberger Platz 3, 14197 Berlin, Germany. TEL 030-8207-0. FAX 030-8214091. E-mail: orders@springer.de. (Subscr. in N. America to: Springer-Verlag New York, Inc., 44 Hartz Way, Secaucus, NJ 07096-2491. TEL 201-348-4033. FAX 201-348-4505) Ed.Bd. (also avail. in microform from UMI; reprint service avail. from ISI) **Document type:** abstracting/indexing.
—BLDSC (1936.037000). UMI. **CCC.**
Formerly (until 1982): Berichte Gynaekologie und Geburtshilfe Sowie Deren Grenzgebiete (ISSN 0005-9064)
Description: Abstracts articles in gynecology-obstetrics.

616.07 016   GW   ISSN 0722-9674
BERICHTE PATHOLOGIE/TRENDS IN PATHOLOGY. (Text in English, German) 1948. 26/yr. (in 2 vols./vol.). DM.3670($2667) (effective 1996). Springer-Verlag, Heidelberger Platz 3, 14197 Berlin, Germany. TEL 030-8207-0. FAX 030-8214091. E-mail: orders@springer.de. (Subscr. in N. America to: Springer-Verlag New York, Inc., 44 Hartz Way, Secaucus, NJ 07096-2491. TEL 201-348-4033. FAX 201-348-4505) Eds. A. Bohle, W. Doerr. (also avail. in microform from UMI; back issues avail.; reprint service avail. from ISI) **Document type:** abstracting/indexing.
—UMI. **CCC.**
Former titles: Pathologie; Berichte ueber die Allgemeine und Spezielle Pathologie (ISSN 0005-9056)
Description: Abstracts articles in pathology.

617.643   BL   ISSN 0100-6266
RKZ6668
BIBLIOGRAFIA BRASILEIRA DE ODONTOLOGIA. 1966. a. $30 to individuals; free to institutions. Universidade de Sao Paulo, Faculdade de Odontologia, Servico de Documentacao Odontologica, Av. Prof. Lineu Prestes, 2227, Caixa Postal 8216, 05508-900 Sao Paulo SP, Brazil. TEL 55-11-818-7861. FAX 55-11-818-7413. circ. 350. **Document type:** bibliography.
●Also available online.
Also available on CD-ROM.
Description: Covers Brazilian literature in the area of dentistry.

610 015   PL   ISSN 0301-1941
BIBLIOGRAFIA PUBLIKACJI NAUKOWYCH PRACOWNIKOW AKADEMII MEDYCZNEJ W BIALYMSTOKU/BIBLIOGRAPHY OF THE SCIENTIFIC PUBLICATIONS OF THE STAFF OF MEDICAL SCHOOL IN BIALYSTOK. (Supplement to: Akademia Medyczna w Bialymstoku. Roczniki (ISSN 0067-6489)) (Text in English, Polish) 1966. biennial. 730000($20) per vol. Akademia Medyczna w Bialymstoku, Ul. Kilinskiego 1, 15-230 Bialystok, Poland. TEL 48-85-420161. FAX 48-85-424907. TELEX 2200 AM PL. Ed. Jan Olbromski. (back issues avail.) **Document type:** academic/scholarly publication, bibliography.

610 016   CI   ISSN 0067-6799
BIBLIOGRAFIJA MEDICINSKE PERIODIKE JUGOSLAVIJE/INDEX MEDICUS IUGOSLAVICUS. (Text in Serbo-Croatian; summaries in English, French, German and Russian) 1966. a. $10. Opca Bolnica "Dr. Josip Kajfes", Miskine 64, Zagreb, Croatia.

610 016   XR   ISSN 0067-6802
BIBLIOGRAPHIA MEDICA CECHOSLOVACA. 1969. m. 840 Kc. Narodni Lekarska Knihovna, Sokolska 31, 121 32 Prague 2, Czech Republic. TEL 2491-5774. FAX 2491-4625. Ed. M. Votipkova. index. circ. 110. (also avail. in diskette format) **Document type:** bibliography.
●Also available online.
—BLDSC (1963.400000).
Formerly (until 1973): Annual of Czechoslovak Medical Literature. Bibliographia Medica Cechoslovaca (ISSN 0303-4119); Formed by the merger of (1956-1969): Annual of Czechoslovak Medical Literature (ISSN 0517-9424) and (1949-1969): Bibliographia Medica Cechoslovaca (ISSN 0862-3201).

610 011   US   ISSN 0896-6591
BIBLIOGRAPHIES AND INDEXES IN MEDICAL STUDIES. 1988. irreg. price varies. Greenwood Press, Inc. (Subsidiary of: Greenwood Publishing Group Inc.), 88 Post Rd. W., Box 5007, Westport, CT 06881-5007. TEL 203-226-3571. FAX 203-222-1502.

610 016   US   ISSN 0363-0161
Z6675.E8
BIBLIOGRAPHY OF BIOETHICS. 1975. a. price varies. Kennedy Institute of Ethics, National Reference Center for Bioethics Literature, Georgetown University, Washington, DC 20057-1065. TEL 202-687-6738. FAX 202-687-6770. Eds. LeRoy Walters, Tamar Joy Kahn. circ. 1,500. **Indexed:** CERDIC. **Document type:** bibliography.
●Also available online. Vendor(s): Data-Star, National Library of Medicine, Telesystemes - Questel (BIOETHICS).

610 016   US   ISSN 0067-7280
Z6660
BIBLIOGRAPHY OF THE HISTORY OF MEDICINE. 1965. quinquennial, latest 1991. $55 (foreign $68.75). U.S. National Library of Medicine, 8600 Rockville Pike, Bethesda, MD 20894. (Orders to: Superintendent of Documents, U.S. Government Printing Office, Box 371954, Pittsburgh, PA 15250-7954. TEL 202-512-1800. FAX 202-512-2250; Or: Bernan, 4611-F Assembly Dr., Lanham, MD 20706. TEL 301-459-7666. FAX 301-459-0056) **Document type:** bibliography, government publication.
●Also available online. Vendor(s): National Library of Medicine.
Description: Bibliographic listing of citations dealing with the history of medicine and its related sciences and professions.

MEDICAL SCIENCES — ABSTRACTING, BIBLIOGRAPHIES, STATISTICS

610 174.2 US ISSN 0886-8913
BIOETHICS LITERATURE REVIEW. m. $49 to individuals; institutions $69. University Publishing Group, Inc., 107 E. Church St., Frederick, MD 21701. TEL 800-654-8188. **Document type:** newsletter.
Description: Covers recent literature in bioethics and related subject areas; reviews 500 health, medical, and major law journals each month.

610 US
BIOMEDICAL ENGINEERING CITATION INDEX. bi-m. $1950. Institute for Scientific Information, 3501 Market St., Philadelphia, PA 19104. TEL 215-386-0100. FAX 215-386-2991. (U.K. Addr.: Brunel Science Park, Brunel University, Uxbridge UB6 3PQ, England) (also avail. in magnetic tape) **Document type:** abstracting/indexing.
● Also available on CD-ROM.
Description: Provides bibliographic data, cited references, related records and English-language author abstracts from international scholarly research journals and conference proceedings.

616.15 UK ISSN 0266-6294
BLOOD COAGULATION FACTORS; current awareness service for researchers in life sciences. 1985. s-m. (diskette). £120 (diskette £115; both £175) (effective 1995). S U B I S, Mansion House, 19 Kingfield Rd., Sheffield S11 9AS, England. TEL 0114-2554433. FAX 0114-2554626. E-mail: admin@sheffac.demon.co.uk. (also avail. in diskette format) **Document type:** abstracting/indexing.
—CCC.
Description: Covers fibrinogen, thrombin, plasminogen activators and other coagulation factors.

616.15 617 UK ISSN 0261-4596
BLOOD TRANSFUSION. m. £80 (effective 1995). S U B I S, Mansion House, 19 Kingfield Rd., Sheffield S11 9AS, England. TEL 0114-2554433. FAX 0114-2554626. E-mail: admin@sheffac.demon.co.uk. (looseleaf format; back issues avail.) **Document type:** abstracting/indexing.
—CCC.
Description: Current awareness service for researchers in clinical and life sciences.

330.9 614 BS ISSN 1013-5723
BOTSWANA. CENTRAL STATISTICS OFFICE. HEALTH STATISTICS REPORT. a. P.5. Central Statistics Office, Private Bag 0024, Gaborone, Botswana. TEL 267-352200. (Orders to: Government Printer, P.O. Box 87, Gaborone, Botswana) Ed. G.M. Chaumbira; Pub. J.G. Segwe. **Document type:** government publication.

610 US ISSN 1043-321X
BREAST DISEASES. 1990. q. $75 to individuals (foreign $89); institutions $112.50 (foreign $126.50); students $47.25 (foreign $61.25). Mosby - Year Book, Inc. (Subsidiary of: Times Mirror Company), 11830 Westline Industrial Dr., St. Louis, MO 63146. TEL 314-872-8370; 800-325-4177. FAX 314-432-1380. TELEX 44-2402. (also avail. in microfilm from UMI; reprint service avail. from UMI)
—CCC.
Description: Provides an interdisciplinary perspective on advances in prevention, diagnosis, and management of breast diseases. Each issue includes more than 40 abstracts selected from 700 different journals worldwide.

649 016 US ISSN 0896-4572
BREASTFEEDING ABSTRACTS. 1981. q. $12.50. La Leche League International, Inc., 9616 Minneapolis Ave., Box 1209, Franklin Park, IL 60131. TEL 708-455-7730. FAX 708-455-0125. Ed. Cindy Smith. bk.rev. circ. 2,000. **Document type:** abstracting/indexing.
—BLDSC (2277.494250).
Description: Abstracts medical journal articles related to breastfeeding.

610 GW
BUECHER FUER DAS STUDIUM - MEDIZIN. a. Dr. Lothar Rossipaul Verlagsgesellschaft mbH, Menzingerstr. 37, 80638 Munich, Germany. TEL 089-179106-0. FAX 089-179106-22. Ed. Rainer Rossipaul. circ. 25,000. **Document type:** bibliography.
Description: Bibliography of available medical books for students.

C A S BIOTECH UPDATES. ANTIBODY CONJUGATES. see CHEMISTRY — Abstracting, Bibliographies, Statistics

616.7 US ISSN 1040-7111
CODEN: CAISEK
C A SELECTS. AIDS AND RELATED IMMUNODEFICIENCIES. 1989. s-w. $220 to non-members; members $65 (effective 1996). Chemical Abstracts Service (Subsidiary of: American Chemical Society), 2540 Olentangy River Rd., Box 3012, Columbus, OH 43210-0012. TEL 614-447-3600. FAX 614-447-3713. TELEX 6842086. **Document type:** abstracting/indexing.
Description: Covers etiology, pathophysiology, clinical manifestations, diagnosis, and therapy of AIDS and other immunodeficiencies.

616.97 US ISSN 1047-8191
CODEN: CSAGE2
C A SELECTS. ALLERGY AND ANTIALLERGIC AGENTS. 1981. s-w. $220 to non-members; members $65 (effective 1996). Chemical Abstracts Service (Subsidiary of: American Chemical Society), 2540 Olentangy River Rd., Box 3012, Columbus, OH 43210-0012. TEL 614-447-3600. FAX 614-447-3713. TELEX 6842086. (reprint service avail.) **Document type:** abstracting/indexing.
Formerly (until 1989): BIOSIS CAS Selects: Allergy and Antiallergy (ISSN 0276-3095)
Description: Covers the pathogenesis, diagnosis, and biochemistry of various allergic conditions, including asthma, dermatitis, and allergies of food, drugs, and environmental agents.

616.8 US ISSN 1047-8183
CODEN: CSDDE8
C A SELECTS. ALZHEIMER'S DISEASE & RELATED MEMORY DYSFUNCTIONS. 1986. s-w. $220 to non-members; members $65 (effective 1996). Chemical Abstracts Service (Subsidiary of: American Chemical Society), 2540 Olentangy River Rd., Box 3012, Columbus, OH 43210-0012. TEL 614-447-3600. FAX 614-447-3713. TELEX 6842086. **Document type:** abstracting/indexing.
Formerly (until 1989): BIOSIS CAS Selects: Alzheimer's Disease and Senile Dementias.
Description: Covers Alzheimer's Disease and related dementias; includes pathogenesis, diagnosis, and biochemistry of the disease as well as studies on drugs that control such dementias.

616.7 US ISSN 0148-2394
CODEN: CSARDY
C A SELECTS. ANTI-INFLAMMATORY AGENTS AND ARTHRITIS. s-w. $220 to non-members; members $65 (effective 1996). Chemical Abstracts Service (Subsidiary of: American Chemical Society), 2540 Olentangy River Rd., Box 3012, Columbus, OH 43210-0012. TEL 614-447-3600. FAX 614-447-3713. TELEX 6842086. **Document type:** abstracting/indexing.
Description: Covers biochemistry of arthritis and rheumatism; effects and mechanism of action of inflammation inhibitors; and synthesis and structure-activity relationships of drugs with potential anti-inflammatory activity.

616.1 US ISSN 1051-3892
CODEN: CANTEE
C A SELECTS. ANTIARRHYTHMICS. 1990. s-w. $220 to non-members; members $65 (effective 1996). Chemical Abstracts Service (Subsidiary of: American Chemical Society), 2540 Olentangy River Rd., Box 3012, Columbus, OH 43210-0012. TEL 614-447-3600. FAX 614-447-3713. TELEX 6842086. **Document type:** abstracting/indexing.
Description: Covers established and developmental drugs that ameliorate disorders of normal heart rhythms.

610 US ISSN 1047-8175
CODEN: CSALEH
C A SELECTS. ANTICONVULSANTS & ANTIEPILEPTICS. 1986. s-w. $220 to non-members; members $65 (effective 1996). Chemical Abstracts Service (Subsidiary of: American Chemical Society), 2540 Olentangy River Rd., Box 3012, Columbus, OH 43210-0012. TEL 614-447-3600. FAX 614-447-3713. TELEX 6842086. **Document type:** abstracting/indexing.
Formerly (until 1989): BIOSIS CAS Selects: Anticonvulsants.
Description: Covers the anticonvulsant and antiepileptic activities of both established and developmental drugs. Includes synthesis, mechanism(s) of action, formulation, and structure-activity relationships.

610 US ISSN 0148-2386
CODEN: CSAADH
C A SELECTS. ANTITUMOR AGENTS. s-w. $220 to non-members; members $65 (effective 1996). Chemical Abstracts Service (Subsidiary of: American Chemical Society), 2540 Olentangy River Rd., Box 3012, Columbus, OH 43210-0012. TEL 614-447-3600. FAX 614-447-3713. TELEX 6842086. **Document type:** abstracting/indexing.
Description: Covers cytotoxic agents, antimetabolites, alkylating agents, neoplasm inhibitors; effect and mechanism of action; synthesis and structure-activity relationships of drugs with potential antitumor activity; and pharmacology of most common antitumor agents.

616.1 US ISSN 0148-2378
CODEN: CASDDO
C A SELECTS. ATHEROSCLEROSIS & HEART DISEASE. s-w. $220 to non-members; members $65 (effective 1996). Chemical Abstracts Service (Subsidiary of: American Chemical Society), 2540 Olentangy River Rd., Box 3012, Columbus, OH 43210-0012. TEL 614-447-3600. FAX 614-447-3713. TELEX 6842086. **Document type:** abstracting/indexing.
Description: Covers atherosclerosis, arteriosclerosis, heart disease, hypertension, hypotension, embolic and thrombotic disorders, shock, pharmacology and treatment of cardiovascular disease.

616.8 US ISSN 0162-7716
CODEN: CBASDK
C A SELECTS. BIOGENIC AMINES & THE NERVOUS SYSTEM. s-w. $220 to non-members; members $65 (effective 1996). Chemical Abstracts Service (Subsidiary of: American Chemical Society), 2540 Olentangy River Rd., Box 3012, Columbus, OH 43210-0012. TEL 614-447-3600. FAX 614-447-3713. TELEX 6842086. **Document type:** abstracting/indexing.
Description: Covers biogenic amines in the nervous system and neurotransmission.

616.15 US ISSN 0162-7732
CODEN: CBCODI
C A SELECTS. BLOOD COAGULATION. s-w. $220 to non-members; members $65 (effective 1996). Chemical Abstracts Service (Subsidiary of: American Chemical Society), 2540 Olentangy River Rd., Box 3012, Columbus, OH 43210-0012. TEL 614-447-3600. FAX 614-447-3713. TELEX 6842086. **Document type:** abstracting/indexing.
Description: Covers blood-coagulation factors, vitamin K, anticoagulants; blood preservation and preservatives; and blood platelet biochemistry.

616.99 US ISSN 0148-2408
CODEN: CSCTDG
C A SELECTS. CARCINOGENS, MUTAGENS & TERATOGENS. s-w. $220 to non-members; members $65 (effective 1996). Chemical Abstracts Service (Subsidiary of: American Chemical Society), 2540 Olentangy River Rd., Box 3012, Columbus, OH 43210. TEL 614-447-3600. FAX 614-447-3713. TELEX 6842086. **Document type:** abstracting/indexing.
Description: Covers biological response to carcinogens, mutagens, and teratogens; mechanism of action and structural requirements for activity; detection and quantification in feed and food material; occupational exposure and resulting health hazard and safety requirements.

C A SELECTS. DRUG INTERACTIONS. see PHARMACY AND PHARMACOLOGY — Abstracting, Bibliographies, Statistics

C A SELECTS. FORENSIC CHEMISTRY. see CHEMISTRY — Abstracting, Bibliographies, Statistics

610 612.015 US ISSN 1051-3922
CODEN: CAHAET
C A SELECTS. HYPERTENSION & ANTIHYPERTENSIVES. 1990. s-w. $220 to non-members; members $65 (effective 1996). Chemical Abstracts Service, 2540 Olentangy River Rd., Box 3012, Columbus, OH 43210-0012. TEL 614-447-3600. FAX 614-447-3713. TELEX 6842086. **Document type:** abstracting/indexing.
Description: Covers etiology, pathophysiology, clinical manifestations, and diagnosis of hypertension.

MEDICAL SCIENCES — ABSTRACTING, BIBLIOGRAPHIES, STATISTICS 4291

616.97 US ISSN 1048-874X CODEN: CSIMEQ
C A SELECTS. IMMUNOCHEMICAL METHODS. 1981. s-w. $220 to non-members; members $65 (effective 1996). Chemical Abstracts Service (Subsidiary of: American Chemical Society), 2540 Olentangy River Rd., Box 3012, Columbus, OH 43210-0012. TEL 614-447-3600. FAX 614-447-3713. TELEX 6842086. (reprint service avail.) **Document type:** abstracting/indexing.
Formerly (until 1989): BIOSIS CAS Selects: Immunochemical Methods (ISSN 0276-3168)
Description: Covers use of antigen-antibody reactions in the detection, determination, and separation of sample components.

610 011 US ISSN 1047-8094 CODEN: CMOAEC
C A SELECTS. MONOCLONAL ANTIBODIES. 1984. s-w. $220 to non-members; members $65 (effective 1996). Chemical Abstracts Service (Subsidiary of: American Chemical Society), 2540 Olentangy River Rd., Box 3012, Columbus, OH 43210-0012. TEL 614-447-3600. FAX 614-447-3713. TELEX 6842086. **Document type:** abstracting/indexing.
Formerly (until 1989): BIOSIS CAS Selects: Monoclonal Antibodies.
Description: Covers the preparation, characterization, and use of monoclonal antibodies and monoclonal antibody conjugates. Includes pathophysiology and hybridoma technology.

616.19 011 US ISSN 1047-8116 CODEN: CSNCEL
C A SELECTS. NUTRITIONAL ASPECTS OF CANCER. 1985. s-w. $220 to non-members; members $65 (effective 1996). Chemical Abstracts Service (Subsidiary of: American Chemical Society), 2540 Olentangy River Rd., Box 3012, Columbus, OH 43210-0012. TEL 614-447-3600. FAX 614-447-3713. TELEX 6842086. **Document type:** abstracting/indexing.
Formerly: BIOSIS CAS Selects: Cancer and Nutrition.
Description: Covers all aspects of cancer and nutrition; includes the role of nutrition in the development and control of neoplastic diseases.

610 011 US ISSN 1047-8132 CODEN: CSOLEJ
C A SELECTS. OSTEOPOROSIS & RELATED BONE LOSS. 1989. s-w. $220 to non-members; members $65 (effective 1996). Chemical Abstracts Service (Subsidiary of: American Chemical Society), 2540 Olentangy River Rd., Box 3012, Columbus, OH 43210-0012. TEL 614-447-3600. FAX 614-447-3713. TELEX 6842086. **Document type:** abstracting/indexing.
Formerly (until 1989): BIOSIS CAS Selects: Osteoporosis.
Description: Covers osteoporosis and related bone losses; includes the etiology, diagnosis, pathophysiology, biochemistry, and pharmacology of osteoporosis.

616.07 US ISSN 1047-8159 CODEN: CSUIE6
C A SELECTS. ULCER INHIBITORS. 1986. s-w. $220 to non-members; members $65 (effective 1996). Chemical Abstracts Service (Subsidiary of: American Chemical Society), 2540 Olentangy River Rd., Box 3012, Columbus, OH 43210-0012. TEL 614-447-3600. FAX 614-447-3713. TELEX 6842086. **Document type:** abstracting/indexing.
Formerly: BIOSIS CAS Selects: Antiulcer Agents.
Description: Covers the digestive-tract antiulcer inhibitors of both established and developmental drugs; includes synthesis, mechanic(s) of action, formulation, and structure-activity relationship.

616.9 US
C D C HIV-AIDS SURVEILLANCE REPORTS. 1988. q. free. U.S. Centers for Disease Control, OD-OPS-MASO, 1-B49, Mailstop A-22, Atlanta, GA 30333. TEL 404-639-3311. **Document type:** government publication.
Description: Provides official analysis of AIDS statistics.

616.8 011 US ISSN 0141-7711
QP351
C S A NEUROSCIENCES ABSTRACTS. 1982. m. $740 (foreign $815). Cambridge Scientific Abstracts, 7200 Wisconsin Ave., 6th Fl., Bethesda, MD 20814. TEL 301-961-6750. FAX 301-961-6720. E-mail: market@csa.com. Pub. Ted Caris. abstr.; index. (also avail. in magnetic tape; back issues avail.) **Document type:** abstracting/indexing.
●Also available online. Vendor(s): Knight-Ridder, Inc. (File no.76/LIFE SCIENCES COLLECTION), STN International.
Also available on CD-ROM. Producer(s): SilverPlatter Information, Inc.
Incorporates: Endocrinology Abstracts (ISSN 0749-8020)
Description: Covers all aspects of vertebrate and invertebrate neuroscience, with special coverage of neuroimaging, dementia, pain, drug addiction, and memory.

016 610 CN ISSN 0707-7629
Z6660
CANADIAN LOCATIONS OF JOURNALS INDEXED FOR MEDLINE/DEPOTS CANADIENS DES REVUES INDEXEES POUR MEDLINE. 1970. a. Can.$75. (National Research Council of Canada) Canada Institute for Scientific and Technical Information, Cataloguing Section, Ottawa, ON K1A 0S2, Canada. TEL 613-993-3449. circ. 300.
Formerly: Canadian Locations of Journals Indexed in Index Medicus (ISSN 0316-3938)

610.73 CN ISSN 0710-2437
CANADIAN NURSES ASSOCIATION. HELEN K. MUSSALLEM LIBRARY. PERIODICAL HOLDINGS. (Text in English, French) a. Can.$10. Canadian Nurses Association, Helen K. Mussallem Library - Association des Infirmieres et Infirmiers du Canada, 50 Driveway, Ottawa, ON K2P 1E2, Canada. TEL 613-627-2133. FAX 613-237-3520. (reprint service avail. from UMI) **Document type:** bibliography, catalog.
Formerly (until 1981): Canadian Nurses Association. Library. Periodical Holdings (ISSN 0383-0101)
Description: Provides a complete catalogue of the library periodicals, listed alphabetically. Includes titles, publishers and the extent of the holdings.

619.99 UK
CANCER TOPICS ABSTRACTS SERVICE; news on advances in clinical and experimental oncology. 1981. q. free. (Lederle Laboratories) Eurocommunica Publications, 4 Bersted Mews, Bersted St., Bognor Regis, W. Sussex PO22 9RR, England. TEL 01243-823180. FAX 01243-823180. Ed. Rod Robinson. adv. **Document type:** academic/scholarly publication, abstracting/indexing.
Description: Highlights recently published papers about important developments in experiemental and clinical oncology.
Refereed Serial

011 616.99 649 US
CANDLELIGHTERS CHILDHOOD CANCER FOUNDATION BIBLIOGRAPHY AND RESOURCE GUIDE. 1976. a. $5 (Canada and Mexico $8; elsewhere $11). Candlelighters Childhood Cancer Foundation, 7910 Woodmont Ave., Ste. 460, Bethesda, MD 20814. TEL 301-657-8410. bk.rev. circ. 4,000. **Document type:** bibliography.
Former titles: Candlelighters Childhood Cancer Foundation Annotated Bibliography and Resource Guide; Candlelighters Foundation Bibliography and Resource Guide.

610.73 US ISSN 1066-4815
CAPSULES & COMMENTS IN CRITICAL CARE NURSING. 1993. q. $34.95. Mosby - Year Book, Inc. (Chicago) (Subsidiary of: Times Mirror Company), 200 N. LaSalle St., Chicago, IL 60601-1080. TEL 312-726-9733. FAX 312-726-6075. TELEX 206155. Ed. Cathie Guzzetta.
Description: Features abstracts of full-length journal articles pertinent to the field of critical care nursing.

610.73 US ISSN 1068-6088
CAPSULES & COMMENTS IN NURSING MANAGEMENT AND LEADERSHIP. 1993. q. $49.95. Mosby - Year Book, Inc. (Chicago) (Subsidiary of: Times Mirror Company), 200 N. LaSalle St., Chicago, IL 60601-1080. TEL 312-726-9733. FAX 312-726-6075. TELEX 206155. Ed. Connie Curran.
Description: Features abstracts of full-length journal articles pertinent to the field of nursing management and leadership.

610.73 616.99 US ISSN 1066-4114
CAPSULES & COMMENTS IN ONCOLOGY NURSING. 1993. q. $39.95. Mosby - Year Book, Inc. (Chicago) (Subsidiary of: Times Mirror Company), 200 N. LaSalle St., Chicago, IL 60601-1080. TEL 312-726-9733. FAX 312-726-6075. TELEX 206155. Ed. Christine Miakowski.
Description: Features abstracts of full-length journal articles pertinent to the field of oncology nursing.

610.73 US
▼**CAPSULES & COMMENTS IN PSYCHIATRIC NURSING.** 1994. q. $34.95 (effective 1996). Mosby - Year Book, Inc. (Chicago) (Subsidiary of: Times Mirror Company), 200 N. LaSalle St., Chicago, IL 60601-1080. TEL 312-726-9733. FAX 312-726-6075. TELEX 106155. Eds. Holly Skodol Wilson, Carol Ren Kneisl.
Description: Features abstracts of full-length journal articles pertinent to the field of psychiatric nursing.

616.1 016 IT ISSN 0008-6320
CARDIOLOGIA NEL MONDO; recensioni di riviste di cardiologia di tutto il mondo. 1950. m. L.50000($70) C N M s.r.l., Via Cimabue 28, 20032 Cormano (MI), Italy. TEL 615-29-88. FAX 615-53-239. TELEX 323126 FARSIM I. Dir. Prof. G. Marchetti. adv. circ. 10,000.

016.6161 US ISSN 1079-7564
▼**CARDIOLOGY JOURNAL CLUB JOURNAL.** 1995. bi-m. $80 to individuals (foreign $85); institutions $110 (foreign $115) (effective 1996). Lippincott - Raven Publishers, 227 E. Washington Sq., Philadelphia, PA 19106. TEL 215-238-4200. Ed. Dr. Shahbudin Rahimtoola. **Document type:** abstracting/indexing.
Description: Presents structured abstracts of key articles from world literature, with expert commentary.

616 CC ISSN 1000-9086
CHINA MEDICAL ABSTRACTS (INTERNAL MEDICINE). Chinese edition: Zhongguo Yixue Wenzhai (Neike Xue) (ISSN 1001-4136) (Text in English) 1985. q. $60. Nanjin Tiedao Yixueyuan - Nanjing Railway Medical College, 87 Dingjiaqiao, Nanjing, Jiangsu 210009, People's Republic of China. TEL 3301509. FAX 3317073. Ed. Sun Zaiyang. adv.: page $2000. circ. 1,000. **Document type:** abstracting/indexing.
Description: Abstracts of experimental research of modern medical sciences, traditional Chinese medicine, preventive medicine and clinical experiences.

617 016 GW ISSN 0009-4722
DER CHIRURG; Zeitschrift fuer alle Gebiete der operativen Medizin. 1928. 12/yr. DM.498($361) (effective 1996). (Berufsverbandes der Deutschen Chirurgen e.V.) Springer-Verlag, Heidelberger Platz 3, 14197 Berlin, Germany. TEL 030-8207-0. FAX 030-8214091. E-mail: orders@springer.de. (Subscr. in N. America to: Springer-Verlag New York, Inc., 44 Hartz Way, Secaucus, NJ 07096-2491. TEL 201-348-4033. FAX 201-348-4505) Ed.Bd. adv.; bk.rev.; abstr.; bibl.; charts; illus.; index. (also avail. in microform from UMI; back issues avail.; reprint service avail. from ISI) **Indexed:** Biol.Abstr., Biotech.Abstr., Chem.Abstr., Curr.Adv.Cancer Res., Curr.Cont., Dok.Arbeitsmed., Excerp.Med., Helminthol.Abstr., Ind.Med., Ind.Sci.Rev., INIS Atomind., Nutr.Abstr., Sci.Cit.Ind. **Document type:** academic/scholarly publication.
—BLDSC (3181.150000); Faxon; Genuine Article; SWETS; UMI. **CCC.**

617.3 JA
CHUBU NIHON SEIKEI GEKA SAIGAI GEKA GAKKAI SHOROKU/CENTRAL JAPAN ORTHOPAEDIC AND TRAUMATIC SURGERY SOCIETY. ABSTRACTS. (Text in Japanese) s-a. Chubu Nihon Seikei Geka Saigai Geka Gakkai, Imadegawa Sagaru, Kamigyo-ku, Kyoto 602, Japan. **Document type:** abstracting/indexing.

M

ULRICH'S INTERNATIONAL PERIODICALS DIRECTORY 1996

MEDICAL SCIENCES — ABSTRACTING, BIBLIOGRAPHIES, STATISTICS

610 011 US ISSN 1043-3031
CODEN: CCTFEG
CLINICAL ABSTRACTS - CURRENT THERAPEUTIC FINDINGS. Short title: C A - C T F. vol.9, no.11, 1990. m. $36 to individuals (foreign $51); institutions $56 (foreign $71); students $15 (foreign $30) (effective 1995). Harvey Whitney Books Company, Box 42696, Cincinnati, OH 45242. TEL 513-793-3555. FAX 513-793-3600. Ed.Bd. **Document type:** academic/scholarly publication.

616.1 US ISSN 0958-1650
CLINICIAN'S MANUAL ON HYPERLIPIDEMIA (YEAR). 1991. a. $15.95. Current Science, 400 Market St., Ste. 700, Philadelphia, PA 19106. TEL 215-574-2210; 800-552-5866. FAX 215-574-3533. (And: Current Science Ltd., 34-42 Cleveland St., London W1P 6LB, England. TEL 0171-323-0323. FAX 0171-636-6911) Ed. A.M. Gotto. illus. **Document type:** academic/scholarly publication.
Description: For the general practitioner. Focuses on hyperlipidemia, including diagnostic, treatment and screening concerns.

616.1 US ISSN 0952-6307
CLINICIAN'S MANUAL ON HYPERTENSION (YEAR). 1990. a. $15.95. Current Science, 400 Market St., Ste. 700, Philadelphia, PA 19106. TEL 215-574-2210; 800-552-5866. FAX 215-574-3533. (And: Current Science Ltd., 34-42 Cleveland St., London W1P 6LB, England. TEL 0171-323-0323. FAX 0171-636-6911) Ed.Bd. illus. **Document type:** academic/scholarly publication.
Description: For the general practitioner. Focuses on all aspects of hypertension treatment in a concise, easy-to-read format.

618 US ISSN 0884-8092
COMBINED CUMULATIVE INDEX TO OBSTETRICS AND GYNECOLOGY. 1984. a. $145. Numarc Book Corporation, 60 Alcona Ave., Buffalo, NY 14226. TEL 716-834-1390. FAX 716-834-1382. Ed. Carl W. Hepp. circ. 2,000. (back issues avail.) **Document type:** abstracting/indexing.
Description: Original author and subject index to 7 obstetrical and gynecological journals.

618 Z6671.5 US ISSN 0190-4981
COMBINED CUMULATIVE INDEX TO PEDIATRICS. 1979. a. $137.50. Numarc Book Corporation, 60 Alcona Ave., Buffalo, NY 14226. TEL 716-834-1390. FAX 716-834-1382. Ed. Carl W. Hepp. circ. 2,000. (back issues avail.) **Document type:** abstracting/indexing.
Description: Original author and subject index to 17 pediatric journals.

615.89 616.891 641.1 UK ISSN 0950-6667
COMPLEMENTARY MEDICINE INDEX. m. £53 (outside Europe £69) (effective 1995). British Library, Medical Information Centre, Boston Spa, Wetherby, W. Yorks. LS23 7BQ, England. TEL 01937-546039. FAX 01937-546458. E-mail: maggie.taylor@bl.uk. Pub. Maggie Taylor. **Document type:** abstracting/indexing.
●Also available online.
—BLDSC (3364.203720).
Description: Lists current index of literature for alternative medicine.

618.92 US ISSN 0178-5192
COMPREHENSIVE MANUALS IN PEDIATRICS. 1982. irreg. price varies. Springer-Verlag, 175 Fifth Ave., New York, NY 10010. TEL 212-460-1500. FAX 212-473-6272. (Also: Berlin, Heidelberg, Tokyo and Vienna) Eds. M. Katz, E.R. Stiehm. **Document type:** monographic series.

610 011 US ISSN 1040-4074
COMPREHENSIVE MEDLINE. (Subscription Option A: current & 2 yr. backfile; Option B: current & 5 yr. backfile; Option C: current & 9 yr. backfile; Option D: full file from 1966 to present) 1987. m. $1095 for Option A; Option B $1495; Option C $2195; Option D $2795. (U.S. National Library of Medicine) EBSCO Publishing (Subsidiary of: EBSCO Industries, Inc.), 83 Pine St., Peabody, MA 01960-7250. TEL 508-535-8500; 800-221-1826. FAX 508-535-8545. (Co-sponsor: U.S. Department of Health & Human Services)
●Available only on CD-ROM.
Description: Includes material on all titles in Index Medicus, International Nursing Index and Index to Dental Literature.

617.75 US ISSN 0885-9264
CONTACT LENS UPDATE. 1982. bi-m. $69 (Canada & Mexico $79; elsewhere $84). Anadem Publishing, Inc., 3620 N. High St., Columbus, OH 43214. TEL 614-262-2539. index. (looseleaf format) **Document type:** newsletter.
Description: Summarizes medical and optometry journal articles about specialty contact lens practice.

617.7 US
CONTACTO. 1955. 3/yr. $85. National Eye Research Foundation, 910 Skokie Blvd., Ste. 207A, Northbrook, IL 60062. TEL 718-564-4652; 800-621-2258. FAX 708-564-0807. Ed. Pamela Baker. adv.; bk.rev.; charts; illus.; index. circ. 500.
Indexed: Excerp.Med.
Former titles: Contacto: Mini-Abstracts; Contacto (ISSN 0045-8317)
Description: Scientific clinical journal.

616.12 016 NE ISSN 0165-9405
CODEN: CJCADW
CORE JOURNALS IN CARDIOLOGY. (Text in English) 1980. 11/yr. fl.600($366) (effective 1996). Excerpta Medica (Subsidiary of: Elsevier Science B.V.), P.O. Box 548, 1000 AM Amsterdam, Netherlands. TEL 31-20-4853911. FAX 31-20-4853598. TELEX 18582 ESPA NL. (Subscr. to: Excerpta Medica Core Journals, P.O. Box 85, Limerick, Ireland. TEL 353-61-471944. FAX 353-61-472144; Subscr. in U.S. and Canada to: Elsevier Science Inc., Box 882, Madison Sq. Sta., New York, NY 10159. TEL 212-989-5800. FAX 212-633-3990) Ed.Bd. **Document type:** abstracting/indexing.
—BLDSC (3470.620000). CCC.
Description: Abstracts of relevant articles in cardiology from the principal medical journals.
Refereed Serial

016 616.8 NE ISSN 0165-1056
CORE JOURNALS IN CLINICAL NEUROLOGY. 1978. 11/yr. fl.600($366) (effective 1996). Excerpta Medica (Subsidiary of: Elsevier Science B.V.), P.O. Box 548, 1000 AM Amsterdam, Netherlands. TEL 31-20-4853911. FAX 31-20-4853598. TELEX 18582 ESPA NL. (Subscr. to: Excerpta Medica Core Journals, P.O. Box 85, Limerick, Ireland. TEL 353-61-471944. FAX 353-61-472-144; Subscr. in U.S. and Canada to: Elsevier Science Inc., Box 882, Madison Sq. Sta., New York, NY 10159. TEL 212-989-5800. FAX 212-633-3990) **Document type:** abstracting/indexing.
—CCC.
Description: Current awareness service reporting relevant developments in clinical neurology from the principal medical journals.
Refereed Serial

616.5 016 NE ISSN 0167-5796
CORE JOURNALS IN DERMATOLOGY. (Text in English) 1982. 11/yr. fl.600($366) (effective 1996). Excerpta Medica (Subsidiary of: Elsevier Science B.V.), P.O. Box 548, 1000 AM Amsterdam, Netherlands. TEL 31-20-4853911. FAX 31-20-4853598. TELEX 18582 ESPA NL. (Subscr. to: Excerpta Medica Core Journals, P.O. Box 85, Limerick, Ireland. TEL 353-61-471944. FAX 353-61-472144; Subscr. in U.S. and Canada to: Elsevier Science Inc., Box 882, Madison Sq. Sta., New York, NY 10159. TEL 212-989-5800. FAX 212-633-3990) Ed.Bd. **Document type:** abstracting/indexing.
—CCC.
Description: Current awareness service reporting important developments in dermatology from the principal medical journals.
Refereed Serial

616.3 016 NE ISSN 0165-8719
CODEN: CJGADI
CORE JOURNALS IN GASTROENTEROLOGY. (Text in English) 1980. 11/yr. fl.600($366) (effective 1996). Excerpta Medica (Subsidiary of: Elsevier Science B.V.), P.O. Box 548, 1000 AM Amsterdam, Netherlands. TEL 31-20-4853911. FAX 31-20-4853598. TELEX 18582 ESPA NL. (Subscr. to: Excerpta Medica Core Journals, P.O. Box 85, Limerick, Ireland. TEL 353-61-471944. FAX 353-61-472144; Subscr. in U.S. and Canada to: Elsevier Science Inc., Box 882, Madison Sq. Sta., New York, NY 10159. TEL 212-989-5800. FAX 212-633-3990) Ed.Bd. **Document type:** abstracting/indexing.
—CCC.
Description: Current awareness service providing abstracts of recent papers in gastroenterology from the principal medical journals.
Refereed Serial

618 016 NE ISSN 0376-5059
CODEN: CJOGD8
CORE JOURNALS IN OBSTETRICS - GYNECOLOGY. 1977. 11/yr. fl.600($366) (effective 1996). Excerpta Medica (Subsidiary of: Elsevier Science B.V.), P.O. Box 548, 1000 AM Amsterdam, Netherlands. TEL 31-20-4853911. FAX 31-20-4853598. TELEX 18582 ESPA NL. (Subscr. to: Excerpta Medica Core Journals, P.O. Box 85, Limerick, Ireland. TEL 353-61-471944. FAX 353-61-472144; Subscr. in U.S. and Canada to: Elsevier Science Inc., Box 882, Madison Sq. Sta., New York, NY 10159. TEL 212-989-5800. FAX 212-633-3990) **Document type:** abstracting/indexing.
—CCC.
Description: Current awareness service providing abstracts of recent articles relevant to obstetrics and gynecology from the principal medical journals.
Refereed Serial

016 617.7 NE ISSN 0165-1005
CORE JOURNALS IN OPHTHALMOLOGY. 1978. 11/yr. fl.600($366) (effective 1996). Excerpta Medica (Subsidiary of: Elsevier Science B.V.), P.O. Box 548, 1000 AM Amsterdam, Netherlands. TEL 31-20-4853911. FAX 31-20-4853598. TELEX 18582 ESPA NL. (Subscr. to: Excerpta Medica Core Journals, P.O. Box 85, Limerick, Ireland. TEL 353-61-471944. FAX 353-61-472144; Subscr. in U.S. and Canada to: Elsevier Science Inc., Box 882, Madison Sq. Sta., New York, NY 10159. TEL 212-989-5800. FAX 212-633-3990) **Document type:** abstracting/indexing.
—CCC.
Description: Current awareness service providing abstracts of recent papers in ophthalmology from the principal medical journals.
Refereed Serial

618.92 016 NE ISSN 0376-5040
CODEN: CJPED7
CORE JOURNALS IN PEDIATRICS. 1978. 11/yr. fl.600($366) (effective 1996). Excerpta Medica (Subsidiary of: Elsevier Science B.V.), P.O. Box 548, 1000 AM Amsterdam, Netherlands. TEL 31-20-4853911. FAX 31-20-4853598. TELEX 18582 ESPA NL. (Subscr. to: Excerpta Medica Core Journals, P.O. Box 85, Limerick, Ireland. TEL 353-61-471944. FAX 353-61-472144; Subscr. in U.S. and Canada to: Elsevier Science Inc. Box 882, Madison Sq. Sta., New York, NY 10159. TEL 212-989-5800. FAX 212-933-3990) **Document type:** abstracting/indexing.
—CCC.
Description: Current awareness service providing abstracts of current papers from the principal medical journals on topics pertaining to pediatrics.
Refereed Serial

610 011 US ISSN 1040-4066
CORE MEDLINE. 1989. q. $795. (U.S. National Library of Medicine) EBSCO Publishing, 83 Pine St., Peabody, MA 01960. TEL 800-221-1826. FAX 508-535-8545.
Description: Includes abstracts and indexing for over 560 journals encompassing all titles in the Abridged Index Medicus and all Medline titles from the three Brandon and Hill lists. Clinically oriented and contains most of English-language nursing and psychology titles.

MEDICAL SCIENCES — ABSTRACTING, BIBLIOGRAPHIES, STATISTICS

616.1 US ISSN 0954-6928
RC685.C6 CODEN: CADIEX
CORONARY ARTERY DISEASE. 1990. m. $144.95 to individuals; institutions $295; residents $99.95. Current Science, 400 Market St., Ste. 700, Philadelphia, PA 19106. TEL 215-574-2210; 800-552-5866. FAX 215-574-3533. (And: Current Science Ltd., 34-42 Cleveland St., London W1P 5LB, England. TEL 0171-323-0323. FAX 0171-636-6911) Ed. Dr. Burton E. Sobel. adv.; bibl.; illus. circ. 1,897. (also avail. in diskette format) **Indexed:** Excerp.Med., Ind.Med. (1993-). **Document type:** academic/scholarly publication.
—BLDSC (3472.049000); ADONIS; Genuine Article; SWETS. CCC.
Description: Presents original research and clinical investigations in the expanding field of coronary artery research; includes reviews with annotated references. Each issue features a bibliography of the current world literature published during the previous year.

610.16 US ISSN 0090-1377
Z6660
CUMULATED ABRIDGED INDEX MEDICUS. a. $93 (foreign $111.60). U.S. National Library of Medicine, 8600 Rockville Pike, Bethesda, MD 20894. (Orders to: Superintendent of Documents, U.S. Government Printing Office, Box 371954, Pittsburgh, PA 15250-7954. TEL 202-512-1800. FAX 202-512-2250; Or: Bernan, 4611-F Assembly Dr., Lanham, MD 20706. TEL 301-459-7666. FAX 301-459-0056) circ. 1,500. **Document type:** abstracting/indexing, government publication.
Description: Cumulative list of citations during the preceding year of articles from 118 English-language medical journals by subject and author.

610 016 US ISSN 0090-1423
Z6660
CUMULATED INDEX MEDICUS. (Cumulates citations appearing in Index Medicus (ISSN 0019-3879) during the previous year.) a. (in 16 vols.). $397 (foreign $496.25). U.S. National Library of Medicine, 8600 Rockville Pike, Bethesda, MD 20894. (Orders to: Superintendent of Documents, U.S. Government Printing Office, Box 371954, Pittsburgh, PA 15250-7954. TEL 202-512-1800. FAX 202-512-2250; Or: Bernan, 4611-F Assembly Dr., Lanham, MD 20706. TEL 301-459-7666. FAX 301-459-0056) circ. 5,000. (also avail. in microfilm from UMI,PMC; microfiche; reprint service avail. from UMI) **Indexed:** MEDOC. **Document type:** abstracting/indexing, bibliography, government publication.
—BLDSC (4382.502000); UMI.
Supersedes: Quarterly Cumulated Index Medicus.
Description: Compiles and indexes articles from 3,000 of the world's foremost biomedical journals.

610.73 016 US ISSN 0146-5554
Z6675.N7
CUMULATIVE INDEX TO NURSING & ALLIED HEALTH LITERATURE. Short title: C I N A H L. 1961. bi-m. (plus a. cumulation). $315. (C I N A H L) C I N H A L Information Systems, 1509 Wilson Terr., Box 871, Glendale, CA 91209-0871. TEL 818-409-8005; 800-959-7167. FAX 818-546-5679. Ed. Sarah Marcarian. adv.; cum.index: 1956 to date. circ. 4,000. (also avail. in microform from UMI; magnetic tape; reprint service avail. from UMI) **Document type:** abstracting/indexing.
●Also available online. Vendor(s): Ovid Technologies (NAHL).
Also available on CD-ROM. Producer(s): C I N A H L, SilverPlatter Information, Inc.
—BLDSC (3492.190000); UMI.
Incorporates: Nursing and Allied Health Index (ISSN 0744-8732); Which was formerly (1956-1976): Nursing Literature Index; (until 1977): Cumulative Index to Nursing Literature (ISSN 0011-3018); Incorporates: C I N A H L'S List of Subject Headings; Which was formerly (until 1977): Cumulative Index to Nursing Literature, Nursing Subject Headings (ISSN 0070-1793)
Description: Contains more than 200,000 citations from 1983 to present with abstracts to articles published in nearly 700 nursing and allied health journals. Also covers relevant materials from biomedicine, management, behavioral sciences, health sciences librarianship, education and consumer health and 17 allied health disciplines.

616.994 UK ISSN 0895-9803
Z6664.C2
CURRENT ADVANCES IN CANCER RESEARCH. 1988. m. £661($1051) (effective 1996). Elsevier Science Ltd., Pergamon, P.O. Box 800, Kidlington, Oxford OX5 1DX, England. TEL 44-1865-843000. FAX 44-1865-843010.
E-mail: nlinfo-f@elsevier.nl; usinfo-f@elsevier.com; forinfo-kyf04035@niftyserve.or.jp; Site addr.: http://www.elsevier.nl/. (Subscr. in U.S. and Canada to: Elsevier Science, 660 White Plains Rd., Tarrytown, NY 10591-5153. TEL 914-524-9200. FAX 914-333-2444) (also avail. in microfilm from UMI; back issues avail.) **Document type:** abstracting/indexing.
●Also available online. Vendor(s): Ovid Technologies (CABS).
—BLDSC (3494.061500); UMI.
Description: Provides a current awareness service in the sphere of cancer research. Lists titles of cancer research papers published throughout the world and classified into 38 main areas, with a comprehensive list of review articles.

612 UK ISSN 0964-8720
QP1
CURRENT ADVANCES IN ENDOCRINOLOGY & METABOLISM. 1984. m. £562($894) (effective 1996). Elsevier Science Ltd., Pergamon, P.O. Box 800, Kidlington, Oxford OX5 1DX, England. TEL 44-1865-843000. FAX 44-1865-843010. E-mail: nlinfo-f@elsevier.nl; usinfo-f@elsevier.com; forinfo-kyf04035@niftyserve.or.jp; Site addr.: http://www.elsevier.nl/. (Subscr. in U.S. and Canada to: Elsevier Science, 660 White Plains Rd., Tarrytown, NY 10591-5153. TEL 914-524-9200. FAX 914-333-2444) adv. (also avail. in microfilm from UMI) **Indexed:** Curr.Cont. **Document type:** abstracting/indexing.
●Also available online. Vendor(s): Ovid Technologies (CABS).
—BLDSC (3494.063700); UMI.
Formerly (until 1992): Current Advances in Physiology (ISSN 0741-1693)
Description: Provides current awareness service in the fields of endocrinology and metabolic studies. Gives listings of titles of these papers published throughout the world classified into 149 main areas and provides a comprehensive listing of review articles.

616.97 UK ISSN 0964-8747
Z6663.I4
CURRENT ADVANCES IN IMMUNOLOGY & INFECTIOUS DISEASES. 1984. m. £740($1177) (effective 1996). Elsevier Science Ltd., Pergamon, P.O. Box 800, Kidlington, Oxford OX5 1DX, England. TEL 44-1865-843000. FAX 44-1865-843010.
E-mail: nlinfo-f@elsevier.nl; usinfo-f@elsevier.com; forinfo-kyf04035@niftyserve.or.jp; Site addr.: http://www.elsevier.nl/. (Subscr. in U.S. and Canada to: Elsevier Science, 660 White Plains Rd., Tarrytown, NY 10591-5153. FAX 914-333-2444) Ed. H. Smith. adv. (also avail. in diskette format; microfilm from UMI) **Indexed:** Curr.Cont. **Document type:** abstracting/indexing.
●Also available online. Vendor(s): Ovid Technologies (CABS).
—BLDSC (3494.064220); UMI.
Formerly (until 1992): Current Advances in Immunology (ISSN 0741-1650)
Description: Provides a current awareness service in the sphere of immunology and infectious diseases. Gives listings of titles of immunological papers published throughout the world classified into 271 main areas and provides a comprehensive listing of review articles.

616.8 UK ISSN 0741-1677
QP351
CURRENT ADVANCES IN NEUROSCIENCE. 1984. m. £794($1263) (effective 1996). Elsevier Science Ltd., Pergamon, P.O. Box 800, Kidlington, Oxford OX5 1DX, England. TEL 44-1865-843000. FAX 44-1865-843010.
E-mail: nlinfo-f@elsevier.nl; usinfo-f@elsevier.com; forinfo-kyf04035@niftyserve.or.jp; Site addr.: http://www.elsevier.nl/. (Subscr. in U.S. and Canada to: Elsevier Science, 660 White Plains Rd., Tarrytown, NY 10591-5153. TEL 914-524-9200. FAX 914-333-2444) adv. (also avail. in diskette format; microfilm from UMI) **Indexed:** Curr.Cont. **Document type:** abstracting/indexing.
●Also available online. Vendor(s): Ovid Technologies (CABS).
—BLDSC (3494.064340); UMI.
Description: Provides a current awareness service in the sphere of neuroscience. Gives listings of titles of neuroscientific papers published throughout the world classified into 28 main areas and provides a comprehensive listing of review articles.

616.9 UK ISSN 0952-8075
CURRENT AIDS LITERATURE. 1986. m. £295($530) (effective 1996). CAB International, Wallingford, Oxon. OX10 8DE, England. TEL 01491-832111. FAX 01491-833508. TELEX 847964 COMAGG G. Ed. D.W. Fitzsimons. adv.; bk.rev.; illus. circ. 250. **Document type:** abstracting/indexing.
—BLDSC (3494.125000).
Formerly (until 1988): AIDS and Retroviruses Update (ISSN 0269-7688)
Description: Features information on every paper published on AIDS in the previous month in 1,400 journals. Includes brief summaries of every paper, commentary, literature overview, correspondence, addresses of authors, statistical data, and a cumulative author index.

617.7 US ISSN 0090-1164
CURRENT CITATIONS ON STRABISMUS, AMBLYOPIA, AND OTHER DISEASES OF OCULAR MOTILITY. 1970. q. $10 to non-members. Wills Eye Hospital, Walnut St. & Ninth St., Philadelphia, PA 19107. TEL 215-928-3003. FAX 215-592-0685. Ed. Dr. R.D. Reinecke. circ. 600. (processed) **Document type:** bibliography.

610 016 US ISSN 0891-3358
CODEN: CCCMEK
CURRENT CONTENTS: CLINICAL MEDICINE. Short title: C C: C M. (Includes Author Index and Address Directory, Current Book Contents and Title Word Index) 1973. w. $442. Institute for Scientific Information, 3501 Market St., Philadelphia, PA 19104. TEL 215-386-0100. FAX 215-386-2991. (And: Brunel Science Park, Brunel University, Uxbridge UB8 3PQ, England) (also avail. in magnetic tape; diskette format) **Indexed:** Compumath, Curr.Lit.Fam.Plan., Ind.Sci.Rev., Sci.Cit.Ind. **Document type:** academic/scholarly publication, bibliography.
●Also available online. Vendor(s): Knight-Ridder, Inc. (File no.440), Ovid Technologies (CTOC,CBIB,CLIN). Also available on CD-ROM.
—BLDSC (3496.162000); CASDDS.
Formerly: Current Contents: Clinical Pratice (ISSN 0091-1704)
Description: Tables of contents of the world's most important publications covering clinical medicine.

CURRENT CONTENTS: LIFE SCIENCES. see *BIOLOGY — Abstracting, Bibliographies, Statistics*

616.6 US
CURRENT LITERATURE IN NEPHROLOGY, HYPERTENSION AND TRANSPLANTATION. 1982. m. $52 (foreign $64). Current Literature Publications, Inc., 1513 E St., Bellingham, WA 98225. TEL 206-676-2298. FAX 206-676-8814. Ed. Dr. Jon C. Ransom. adv.; index. circ. 1,400.
Formerly: Current Literature in Nephrology (ISSN 0743-8036)
Description: Bibliography of clinical nephrology.

MEDICAL SCIENCES — ABSTRACTING, BIBLIOGRAPHIES, STATISTICS

617.96 US ISSN 0952-7907
CODEN: COAEE2
CURRENT OPINION IN ANAESTHESIOLOGY. 1988. bi-m. $169.95 to individuals; institutions $345.50; residents $55. Current Science, 400 Market St., Ste. 700, Philadelphia, PA 19106. TEL 215-574-2210; 800-552-5866. FAX 215-574-3533. (And: Current Science Ltd., 34-42 Cleveland St., London W1P 6LB, England. TEL 0171-323-0323. FAX 0171-536-6911) Eds. C. Prys-Roberts, J.F.B. Ebuyck. adv.; bibl.; illus. circ. 3,970. (also avail. in diskette format) **Indexed:** CINAHL, Excerp.Med. (1994-). **Document type:** academic/scholarly publication.
●Also available online. Vendor(s): OCLC.
Also available on CD-ROM.
—BLDSC (3500.772000); ADONIS; SWETS. **CCC.**
Description: Directed toward researchers and practicing anesthesiologists. Presents review articles followed by annotated bibliographies of references consulted. Includes a bibliography of the current world literature published during the previous year.

616.2 US ISSN 0268-4705
CODEN: COPCE3
CURRENT OPINION IN CARDIOLOGY. 1986. bi-m. $134.95 to individuals; institutions $269.95; residents $55. Current Science, 400 Market St. Ste. 700, Philadelphia, PA 19106. TEL 215-574-2210; 800-552-5866. FAX 215-574-3533. (And: Current Science Ltd., 34-42 Cleveland St., London W1P 6LB, England. TEL 0171-323-0323. FAX 0171-636-6911) Ed. Eric J. Topol. adv.; bibl.; illus. circ. 5,122. (also avail. in diskette format) **Indexed:** Excerp.Med., Ind.Med. (1993-). **Document type:** academic/scholarly publication.
●Also available online. Vendor(s): OCLC.
Also available on CD-ROM.
—BLDSC (3500.773000); ADONIS; Faxon; Genuine Article; SWETS; UnCover. **CCC.**
Description: Directed toward clinicians and surgeons in cardiology. Presents review articles followed by annotated bibliographies of references consulted. Includes a bibliography of the current world literature published during the previous year.

617.6 US ISSN 1065-6278
CURRENT OPINION IN COSMETIC DENTISTRY. 1991. a. $79.95 to individuals; institutions $159.95; residents $33. Current Science, 400 Market St., Ste. 700, Philadelphia, PA 19106. TEL 312-733-2980; 800-892-7456. FAX 312-733-3107. (And: Current Science Ltd., 34-42 Cleveland St., London W1P 6LB, England. TEL 0171-323-0323. FAX 0171-636-6911) Ed. J. Golub-Evans. adv.: B&W page $580; color page $1980; trim 8 1/2 x 11. illus. circ. 765. **Document type:** academic/scholarly publication.
●Also available on CD-ROM.
—BLDSC (3500.773600); ADONIS; Genuine Article. **CCC.**
Supersedes in part (in 1993): Current Opinion in Dentistry (ISSN 1046-0764)
Description: Directed toward dentists in clinical and office environments. Presents comprehensive review articles, reporting on new developments in this specialty. Each article contains annotated references and a reference to the current literature available on the subject.

616.3 US ISSN 0267-1379
CODEN: COGAEK
CURRENT OPINION IN GASTROENTEROLOGY. 1985. bi-m. $134.95 to individuals; institutions $269.95; residents $55. Current Science, 400 Market St., Ste. 700, Philadelphia, PA 19106. TEL 215-574-2210; 800-552-5866. FAX 215-574-3533. (And: Current Science, Ltd., 34-42 Cleveland St., London W1P 6LB, England. TEL 0171-323-0323. FAX 0171-580-1938) Ed. T. Yamada. adv.; bibl.; illus. circ. 4,900. (also avail. in diskette format) **Indexed:** Curr.Adv.Cancer Res., Diar.Dis.Res., Excerp.Med. **Document type:** academic/scholarly publication.
●Also available online. Vendor(s): OCLC.
Also available on CD-ROM.
—BLDSC (3500.775000); ADONIS; Faxon; Genuine Article; SWETS; UnCover. **CCC.**
Description: Directed toward clinicians, surgeons and endoscopists. Presents review articles followed by annotated bibliographies of references consulted. A bibliography of the current world literature published during the previous year.

616.97 US ISSN 0952-7915
CODEN: COPIEL
CURRENT OPINION IN IMMUNOLOGY. 1988. bi-m. $159 to individuals; institutions $475 (effective 1996). Current Biology Ltd., 400 Market St., Ste. 700, Philadelphia, PA 19106. TEL 800-552-5866. FAX 215-574-2270. (And: Current Biology Ltd., 34-42 Cleveland St., London W1P 6LB, England. TEL 0171-323-0323. FAX 0171-636-6911) Eds. F.W. Alt, P. Marrack. adv.; bibl.; illus. circ. 3,000. (also avail. in diskette format) **Indexed:** Curr.Cont., Excerp.Med., Ind.Med. **Document type:** academic/scholarly publication.
●Also available online. Vendor(s): OCLC.
Also available on CD-ROM.
—BLDSC (3500.775300); ADONIS; CASDDS; Faxon; Genuine Article; SWETS; UnCover. **CCC.**
Description: Directed toward researchers, educators, and students in immunology. Presents review articles followed by annotated bibliographies of references consulted. Includes a bibliography of the current world literature published during the previous year.

616.9 US ISSN 0951-7375
RC109 CODEN: COIDE5
CURRENT OPINION IN INFECTIOUS DISEASES. 1988. bi-m. $134.95 to individuals; institutions $269.95; residents $55. Current Science, 400 Market St., Ste. 700, Philadelphia, PA 19106. TEL 215-574-2210; 800-552-5866. FAX 215-574-3533. (And: Current Science Ltd., 34-42 Cleveland St., London W1P 6LB, England. TEL 0171-323-0323. FAX 0171-636-6911) Eds. R.G. Finch, V.T. Andriole. adv.; bibl.; illus. circ. 3,716. (also avail. in diskette format) **Indexed:** CINAHL, Diar.Dis.Res., Excerp.Med. **Document type:** academic/scholarly publication.
●Also available online. Vendor(s): OCLC.
Also available on CD-ROM.
—BLDSC (3500.775500); ADONIS; Faxon; Genuine Article; SWETS. **CCC.**
Description: Directed toward clinicians and researchers in infectious diseases, both general and specialized. Presents review articles followed by annotated bibliographies of references consulted. Includes a bibliography of the current world literature published during the previous year.

616.1 US ISSN 0957-9672
QP751 CODEN: COPLEU
CURRENT OPINION IN LIPIDOLOGY. 1990. bi-m. $169.95 to individuals; institutions $345.50; residents $55. Current Science, 400 Market St., Ste. 700, Philadelphia, PA 19106. TEL 215-574-2210; 800-552-5866. FAX 215-574-3533. (And: Current Science Ltd., 34-42 Cleveland St., London W1P 6LB, England. TEL 0171-323-0323. FAX 0171-636-6911) Ed. Dr. S.M. Grundy. adv.; bibl.; illus. circ. 2,954. (also avail. in diskette format) **Indexed:** Excerp.Med., Ind.Med. (1994-). **Document type:** academic/scholarly publication.
●Also available online. Vendor(s): OCLC.
Also available on CD-ROM.
—BLDSC (3500.775800); ADONIS; CASDDS; Genuine Article; SWETS. **CCC.**
Description: Directed toward cardiologists involved with lipids in research and clinical practice. Presents reviews and updates on the latest developments in all areas of lipidology. Each issue features a bibliography of the current world literature published during the previous year.

610 616.6 US ISSN 1062-4821
CURRENT OPINION IN NEPHROLOGY & HYPERTENSION. 1992. bi-m. $169.95 to individuals; institutions $345.50; residents $55. Current Science, 400 Market St., Ste. 700, Philadelphia, PA 19106. TEL 215-574-3533; 800-552-5866. FAX 215-574-2270. (And: Current Science Ltd., 34-42 Cleveland St., London W1P 6LB, England. TEL 0171-323-0323. FAX 0171-636-6911) Ed. Barry M. Bonner. adv.; bibl.; illus. circ. 3,670. (also avail. in diskette format) **Indexed:** Excerp.Med. (1995-), Ind.Med. (1994-). **Document type:** academic/scholarly publication.
●Also available online. Vendor(s): OCLC.
Also available on CD-ROM.
—BLDSC (3500.775830); ADONIS. **CCC.**
Description: Presents review articles directed toward clinicians and practicing kidney and hypertension specialists.

616.8 US ISSN 1350-7540
CODEN: CONEEX
CURRENT OPINION IN NEUROLOGY. 1988. bi-m. $169.95 to individuals; institutions $345.50; residents $55. Current Science, 400 Market St., Ste. 700, Philadelphia, PA 19106. TEL 215-574-2210; 800-552-5866. FAX 215-574-3533. (And: Current Science Ltd., 34-42 Cleveland St., London W1P 6LB, England. TEL 0171-323-0323. FAX 0171-636-6911) Ed. R.T. Johnson. adv.; bibl.; illus. circ. 4,220. (also avail. in diskette format) **Indexed:** Excerp.Med., Ind.Med. (1992-). **Document type:** academic/scholarly publication.
●Also available online. Vendor(s): OCLC.
Also available on CD-ROM.
—BLDSC (3500.775870); ADONIS; Genuine Article; SWETS; UnCover. **CCC.**
Formerly: Current Opinion in Neurology and Neurosurgery (ISSN 0951-7383)
Description: Directed toward clinicians, surgeons and researchers in the field. Presents review articles followed by annotated bibliographies of references consulted. Includes a bibliography of the current world literature published during the previous year.

618 011 US ISSN 1040-872X
RG1 CODEN: COOGEA
CURRENT OPINION IN OBSTETRICS & GYNECOLOGY. 1989. bi-m. $134.95 to individuals; institutions $269.95; residents $55. Current Science, 400 Market St., Ste. 700, Philadelphia, PA 19106. TEL 800-552-5866. FAX 215-574-2270. (And: Current Science Ltd., 34-42 Cleveland St., London W1P 6LB, England. TEL 0171-323-0323. FAX 0171-636-6911) Eds. S. Campbell, A. DeCherney. adv.; bibl.; illus. circ. 3,381. (also avail. in diskette format) **Indexed:** CINAHL, Excerp.Med., Ind.Med. **Document type:** academic/scholarly publication.
●Also available online. Vendor(s): OCLC.
Also available on CD-ROM.
—BLDSC (3500.776200); ADONIS; Genuine Article; SWETS. **CCC.**
Description: Directed toward researchers and practicing obstetricians and gynecologists. Presents review articles followed by annotated bibliographies of references consulted. A bibliography of the current world literature published during the previous year is available.

616.99 016 US ISSN 1040-8746
RC254.A1 CODEN: CUOOE8
CURRENT OPINION IN ONCOLOGY. 1989. bi-m. $169.95 to individuals; institutions $345.50; residents $55. Current Science, 400 Market St., Ste. 700, Philadelphia, PA 19106. TEL 800-552-5866. FAX 215-574-2270. (And: Current Science Ltd., 34-42 Cleveland St., London W1P 5FB, England. TEL 0171-323-0323. FAX 0171-636-6911) Ed. Martin P. Abeloff. bibl.; illus. circ. 4,844. (also avail. in diskette format) **Indexed:** Excerp.Med., Ind.Med. **Document type:** academic/scholarly publication.
●Also available online. Vendor(s): OCLC.
Also available on CD-ROM.
—BLDSC (3500.776400); ADONIS; SWETS; UnCover. **CCC.**
Description: Directed toward researchers and practicing oncologists. Presents review articles followed by annotated bibliographies of references consulted. A bibliography of the current world literature published during the previous year available.

617.7 016 US ISSN 1040-8738
CODEN: COOTEF
CURRENT OPINION IN OPHTHALMOLOGY. (Supplement avail.: Slide Atlas of Current Ophthalmology (Year)) 1990. bi-m. $224.95 to individuals; institutions $449.95; residents $99.95. Current Science, 400 Market St., Ste. 700, Philadelphia, PA 19106. TEL 215-574-2210; 800-552-5866. FAX 215-574-2270. (And: Current Science Ltd., 34-42 Cleveland St., London W1P 6LB, England. TEL 0171-323-0323. FAX 0171-636-6911) Ed. George W. Weinstein. adv.; bibl.; illus. circ. 2,078. (also avail. in diskette format) **Indexed:** Excerp.Med. **Document type:** academic/scholarly publication.
●Also available online. Vendor(s): OCLC.
Also available on CD-ROM.
—BLDSC (3500.776500); ADONIS; Genuine Article; SWETS; UnCover. **CCC.**
Description: Directed toward researchers and practicing ophthalmologists. Presents review articles followed by annotated bibliographies of references consulted. A bibliography of the current world literature published during the previous year is available.

MEDICAL SCIENCES — ABSTRACTING, BIBLIOGRAPHIES, STATISTICS

617.3 016   US   ISSN 1041-9918
CURRENT OPINION IN ORTHOPEDICS. (Supplement avail.: Slide Atlas of Current Orthopaedics (Year) 1989. bi-m. $224.95 to individuals; institutions $449.95; residents $99.95. Current Science, 400 Market St., Ste. 700, Philadelphia, PA 19106. TEL 215-571-2210; 800-552-5866. FAX 215-574-3533. (And: Current Science Ltd., 34-42 Cleveland St., London W1P 6LB, England. TEL 0171-323-0323. FAX 0171-636-6911) Eds. J.H. Herndon, William R.J. Rennie. adv.; bibl.; illus. circ. 2,438. (also avail. in diskette format) **Indexed:** CINAHL, Excerp.Med., Ind.Med. (1995-). **Document type:** academic/scholarly publication.
●Also available online. Vendor(s): OCLC.
Also available on CD-ROM.
—BLDSC (3500.776600); ADONIS. **CCC.**
Description: Directed toward researchers and practicing orthopedists. Presents review articles followed by annotated bibliographies of references consulted. A bibliography of the current world literature published during the previous year is available.

618.92 016   US   ISSN 1040-8703
RJ1   CODEN: COPEE9
CURRENT OPINION IN PEDIATRICS. 1989. bi-m. $119.95 to individuals; institutions $239.95; residents $55. Current Science, 400 Market St., Ste. 700, Philadelphia, PA 19106. TEL 215-574-2210; 800-552-5866. FAX 215-574-3533. (And: Current Science Ltd., 34-42 Cleveland St., London W1P 6LB, England. TEL 0171-323-0323. FAX 0171-636-6911) Eds. David G. Nathan, F.A. Oski. adv.; bibl.; illus. circ. 3,300. (also avail. in diskette format) **Indexed:** Excerp.Med., Ind.Med. (1993-). **Document type:** academic/scholarly publication.
●Also available online. Vendor(s): OCLC.
Also available on CD-ROM.
—BLDSC (3500.776800); ADONIS; SWETS. **CCC.**
Description: Directed toward researchers and practicing pediatricians. Presents review articles followed by annotated bibliographies of references consulted. A bibliography of the current world literature published during the previous year is available.

617.6   US   ISSN 1065-626X
CURRENT OPINION IN PERIODONTOLOGY. 1991. a. $79.95 to individuals; institutions $159.95; residents $33. Current Science, 400 Market St., Ste. 700, Philadelphia, PA 19106. TEL 215-574-2285; 800-552-5866. FAX 215-574-2270. (And: Current Science Ltd., 34-42 Cleveland St., London W1P 6LB, England. TEL 0171-323-0323. FAX 0171-636-6911) illus. circ. 2,400. **Document type:** academic/scholarly publication.
●Also available online. Vendor(s): OCLC.
Also available on CD-ROM.
—BLDSC (3500.776900); Genuine Article. **CCC.**
Incorporates (1991-1995): Current Opinion in Orthodontics and Pedodontics; Supersedes in part (in 1993): Current Opinion in Dentistry (ISSN 1046-0764)
Description: Directed toward dentists in clinical and office environments. Presents comprehensive review articles, reporting on new developments in this specialty. Each article contains annotated references and a reference to the current literature available on the subject.

616.8   US   ISSN 0951-7367
                 CODEN: COPPE8
CURRENT OPINION IN PSYCHIATRY. 1988. bi-m. $119.95 to individuals; institutions $239.95; residents $55. Current Science, 400 Market St., Ste. 700, Philadelphia, PA 19106. TEL 215-574-2210; 800-552-5866. FAX 215-574-2270. (And: Current Science Ltd., 34-42 Cleveland St., London W1P 6LB, England. TEL 0171-323-0323. FAX 0171-636-6911) Eds. H.G. Morgan, D.J. Kuper. adv.; bibl.; illus. circ. 4,328. (also avail. in diskette format) **Indexed:** CINAHL, Excerp.Med. **Document type:** academic/scholarly publication.
●Also available online. Vendor(s): OCLC.
Also available on CD-ROM.
—BLDSC (3500.777000); ADONIS; SWETS. **CCC.**
Description: Directed toward practicing psychiatrists and researchers. Presents review articles followed by annotated bibliographies of references consulted. A bibliography of the current world literature published during the previous year is available.

616.7 016   US   ISSN 1040-8711
RC925.A1   CODEN: CORHES
CURRENT OPINION IN RHEUMATOLOGY. 1989. bi-m. $134.95 to individuals; institutions $269.95; residents $55. Current Science, 400 Market St., Ste. 700, Philadelphia, PA 19106. TEL 800-552-5866. FAX 215-574-2270. (And: Current Science Ltd., 34-42 Cleveland St., London W1P 6LB, England. TEL 0171-323-0323. FAX 0171-636-6911) Ed. G.G. HundercCarty. adv.; bibl.; illus. circ. 4,171. (also avail. in diskette format) **Indexed:** CINAHL, Excerp.Med., Ind.Med. **Document type:** academic/scholarly publication.
●Also available online. Vendor(s): OCLC.
Also available on CD-ROM.
—BLDSC (3500.778000); ADONIS; SWETS; UnCover. **CCC.**
Description: Directed toward researchers and practicing rheumatologists. Presents review articles followed by annotated bibliographies of references consulted. A bibliography of the current world literature published during the previous year is available.

610 616.1   US   ISSN 0963-0643
                 CODEN: CUOUEQ
CURRENT OPINION IN UROLOGY. 1992. bi-m. $169.95 to individuals; institutions $345.50; residents $55. Current Science, 400 Market St., Ste. 700, Philadelphia, PA 19106. TEL 215-574-2210; 800-552-5866. FAX 215-574-2270. (And: Current Science Ltd., 34-42 Cleveland St., London W1P 6LB, England. TEL 0171-232-0323. FAX 0171-636-6911) Eds. Geoffrey D. Chisholm, David F. Paulson. adv.; bibl.; illus. circ. 3,165. (also avail. in diskette format) **Indexed:** Excerp.Med. (1993-). **Document type:** academic/scholarly publication.
●Also available online. Vendor(s): OCLC.
Also available on CD-ROM.
—BLDSC (3500.779500); ADONIS. **CCC.**
Description: Presents review articles directed toward clinicians and practicing urologists.

016.6176   DK   ISSN 0903-3483
CURRENT TITLES IN DENTISTRY. (Text in English, German, French) m. DKK 300($60) in Nordic countries; Europe DKK 450; elsewhere DKK 520. Royal Dental College Library, 9 Vennelyst Boulevard, DK-8000 Aarhus C, Denmark. TEL 45-86-12-01-13. FAX 45-86-13-16-65. Ed. Preben Junker Jacobsen. circ. 400. **Document type:** abstracting/indexing.
—**CCC.**
Description: Lists all major national and international journals in dentistry and related fields throughout the world.

610 016   UK   ISSN 0011-3999
CURRENT WORK IN THE HISTORY OF MEDICINE; an international bibliography. 1954. q. £21 to individuals; institutions £31.35. (Wellcome Institute for the History of Medicine) Professional & Scientific Publications, BMA House, Tavistock Sq., London WC1H 9JR, England. TEL 0171-383-6640. FAX 0171-383-6662. bibl. circ. 750. **Indexed:** A.I.C.P. **Document type:** bibliography.
—BLDSC (3505.000000).
Description: Covers the history of medicine.

DEMOGRAPHIC AND HEALTH SURVEY (YEAR). see POPULATION STUDIES — Abstracting, Bibliographies, Statistics

617.6 016   US   ISSN 0011-8486
RK1
DENTAL ABSTRACTS. 1955. bi-m. $44 to individuals (foreign $59); institutions $82.50 (foreign $97.50). (American Dental Association) Mosby - Year Book, Inc. (Subsidiary of: Times Mirror Company), 11830 Westline Industrial Dr., St. Louis, MO 63146. TEL 314-872-8370; 800-325-4177. FAX 314-432-1380. TELEX 44-2402. Ed. Lawrence H. Meskin. adv.; bk.rev.; abstr.; charts; illus.; stat.; index. circ. 8,000. (also avail. in microform from UMI; reprint service avail. from UMI) **Indexed:** Biol.Abstr.
—BLDSC (3553.240000); UMI.
Description: Presents articles from more than 100 dental and medical journals.

616.4   UK   ISSN 0951-8487
DIABETES CONTENTS. 1987. q. £14 (rest of Europe £16; elsewhere £20). British Diabetic Association, 10 Queen Anne St., London W1M 0BD, England. TEL 0171-323-1531. FAX 0171-637-3644. Ed. Katy Griggs. circ. 500. **Document type:** abstracting/indexing.
Description: Reproduces the contents pages of all the leading English-language diabetes journals and carries citations of papers from leading non-diabetes journals in which papers on diabetes appear frequently.

616.46 612   UK   ISSN 0263-7294
DIABETES MELLITUS. s-m. (diskette m.). £105 (diskette £115; both £175) (effective 1995). S U B I S, Mansion House, 19 Kingfield Rd., Sheffield S11 9AS, England. TEL 0114-2554433. FAX 0114-2554626. E-mail: admin@sheffac.demon.co.uk. (also avail. in diskette format; looseleaf format; back issues avail.)
Document type: abstracting/indexing.
—**CCC.**
Description: Current awareness service for researchers in clinical and life sciences.

610 616.3   FR   ISSN 1011-8594
DIARRHOEAL DISEASES/MALADIES DIARRHEIQUES. (Text in English, French) 1982. 2/yr. 240 F. for 2 yrs. Centre International de l'Enfance - International Children's Center, Chateau de Longchamp, Bois de Boulogne, 75016 Paris, France. TEL 1-45-20-79-92. FAX 1-45-25-73-67. **Document type:** abstracting/indexing.
Description: Abstracts on epidemiology, etiology, immunology and physiopathology, planification and evaluation of programs for combating diarrhoeal diseases, prevention and treatment, research and oral rehydration.

616.8 016   US   ISSN 0012-2769
DIGEST OF NEUROLOGY & PSYCHIATRY. 1932. q. $25 (foreign $30). Institute of Living, 400 Washington St., Hartford, CT 06106. TEL 203-241-6824. Ed. Dr. Harold I. Schwartz. bk.rev.; abstr.; index. circ. 2,000. (also avail. in microfilm from UMI; reprint service avail. from UMI) **Indexed:** Rehabil.Lit.
—BLDSC (3588.150000); UMI.

DIRECTORY OF BIOMEDICAL AND HEALTH CARE GRANTS. see EDUCATION — Abstracting, Bibliographies, Statistics

610 016   UK   ISSN 1352-321X
DIRECTORY OF EUROPEAN MEDICAL ORGANISATIONS. 1993. irreg. £90($180) C.B.D. Research Ltd., 15 Wickham Rd., Beckenham, Kent BR3 2JS, England. TEL 0181-650-7745. FAX 0181-650-0768. (Dist. in the U.S. by: Gale Research Co., Penobscot Bldg., Detroit, MI 48226) **Document type:** directory.
Description: Lists 4,000 national medical organizations based in all countries of Europe.

610 620   US   ISSN 1060-1759
DIRECTORY OF PUBLISHED PROCEEDINGS. SERIES M - L S: MEDICAL, LIFE SCIENCES. 1991. a. $120. InterDok Corp., 173 Halstead Ave., Box 326, Harrison, NY 10528. TEL 914-835-3506. FAX 914-835-6757. bibl.; index, cum.index. **Document type:** directory.
Description: Index of conferences and the published proceedings in the fields of medicine and life sciences.

614 016   GW
DOKUMENTATION PUBLIC HEALTH, OEFFENTLICHES GESUNDHEITSWESEN, GESUNDHEITSWISSENSCHAFT. (Abstracts and summaries in English and German) 1969. 4/yr. DM.66. Landesinstitut fuer den Oeffentlichen Gesundheitsdienst Nordrhein-Westfalen, Westerfeldstr. 35-37, 33611 Bielefeld, Germany. TEL 0521-8007269. FAX 0521-8007200. (Subscr. to: Postfach 201012, 33548 Bielefeld, Germany) Ed. Dr. Wolfgang Gerdel. bk.rev.; abstr.; cum.index. circ. 620. **Document type:** abstracting/indexing.
Former titles: Dokumentation Sozialmedizin, Oeffentlicher Gesundheitsdienst, Gesundheitserziehung (ISSN 0932-5387); (until 1984): Dokumentation Sozialmedizin, Oeffentlicher Gesundheitsdienst, Arbeitsmedizin (ISSN 0012-513X); Which incorporates: Dokumentation Oeffentliches Gesundheitswesen, Sozialhygiene-Sozialmedizin.

MEDICAL SCIENCES — ABSTRACTING, BIBLIOGRAPHIES, STATISTICS

610 US ISSN 1074-9632
R11
DOODY'S HEALTH SCIENCES BOOK REVIEW ANNUAL.
Variant title: Doody's Annual. 1993. a. $295. Doody Publishing, Inc., 1145 Westgate, Ste. 200, Oak Park, IL 60301. TEL 708-386-9500; 800-219-9500. FAX 708-386-9500.
—CCC.

610 US ISSN 1071-7560
R11
DOODY'S HEALTH SCIENCES BOOK REVIEW JOURNAL.
1993. bi-m. $195. Doody Publishing, Inc., 1145 Westgate, Ste. 200, Oak Park, IL 60301. TEL 708-386-9500; 800-219-9500. FAX 708-386-9500. **Document type:** bibliography, abstracting/indexing.
—CCC.
Description: Aimed at health sciences librarians. Provides timely, independent reviews of newly published health sciences books. Includes complete bibliographic information.

616.8 UK ISSN 1351-5276
▼**EATING DISORDERS.** 1994. m. £75. S U B I S, Mansion House, 19 Kingfield Rd., Sheffield S11 9AS, England. TEL 0114-2554433. FAX 0114-2554626. E-mail: admin@sheffac.demon.co.uk. **Document type:** abstracting/indexing.
Description: Current awareness service for researchers in clinical and life sciences.

016.61 NE ISSN 0929-3302
EMBASE LIST OF JOURNALS INDEXED (YEAR). (Text in English) 1964. a. Excerpta Medica (Subsidiary of: Elsevier Science B.V.), P.O. Box 548, 1000 AM Amsterdam, Netherlands. TEL 31-20-4853911. FAX 31-20-4853598. TELEX 18582 ESPA NL. (Subscr. in U.S. and Canada to: Elsevier Science Inc., Box 882, Madison Sq. Sta., New York, NY 10159. TEL 212-633-3971. FAX 212-633-3975) index. (back issues avail.) **Document type:** abstracting/indexing, bibliography.
—BLDSC (3733.004500).
Former titles (until 1993): List of Journals Abstracted (ISSN 0923-5582); Excerpta Medica Foundation. List of Journals Abstracted (ISSN 0167-613X); Excerpta Medica. List of Journals Abstracted (ISSN 0531-5123)
Description: Lists approximately 3,500 biomedical journals screened for items for inclusion in EMBASE and the other Excerpta Medica services. Each entry includes full journal title, EMBASE abbreviation, ISSN and CODEN, publisher's name, address and telephone and indicates subject classification list, title changes, new titles screened, and discontinued titles.

619 574.28 US ISSN 1078-7712
ENTREZ DOCUMENT RETRIEVAL SYSTEM. (Not avail. in printed format) bi-m. $106 (Canada $136.22; Mexico $138.80; S. America $141.68; Europe $155.36; Middle East and Africa $137.36; Asia and Australia $168.20) (effective 1996). U.S. National Center for Biotechnology Information, National Library of Medicine, Bldg. 38A, Rm. 8N-803, 8600 Rockville Pike, Bethesda, MD 20894. TEL 301-496-2475. FAX 301-480-9241. E-mail: info@ucbi.nlm.nih.gov; Site addr.: http://www.ncbi.nlm.nih.gov. (Subscr. to: Superintendent of Documents, U.S. Government Printing Office, Box 371954, Pittsburgh, PA 15250-7954. TEL 202-512-1800. FAX 202-512-2250) **Document type:** abstracting/indexing, government publication.
●Also available online.
Also available on CD-ROM.
Formed by the merger of (1992-1995): Entrez: Sequences (ISSN 1065-707X); (1992-1995): Entrez: References (ISSN 1072-3072); Incorporates (in 1995): N C B I - Sequences (ISSN 1080-7438)
Description: Cites and abstracts papers with molecular sequence data from MEDLINE, as well as nucleotide sequences from GenBank, EMBL, DDBJ, and dbEST and protein sequences from PIR, Swiss-Prot, PDB, and PRF. DNA, protein, and bibliographic records are linked.

610 UK ISSN 0142-808X
ERYTHROCYTES. 1979. s-m. (diskette m.). £110 (diskette £115; both £175) (effective 1995). S U B I S, Mansion House, 19 Kingfield Rd., Sheffield S11 9AS, England. TEL 0114-2554433. FAX 0114-2554626. E-mail: admin@sheffac.demon.co.uk. bk.rev. (also avail. in diskette format) **Document type:** abstracting/indexing.
Description: Covers red blood cell function, structure, haemoglobin and parasitology.

610 BL ISSN 0101-3033
RA984.B8
ESTATISTICAS DA SAUDE: ASSISTENCIA MEDICO-SANITARIA. 1976. a. $70. Fundacao Instituto Brasileiro de Geografia e Estatistica, Centro de Documentacao e Disseminacao de Informacoes, Rua General Canabarro 666, 2o andar, Maracana 20271-201 Rio de Janeiro, Brazil. TEL 55-21-2645424. FAX 55-21-2289575. **Document type:** government publication.

616.99 310 GR ISSN 0302-9697
RC279.G75
ETESIA STATISTIKE. EREVNA TOU KARKINOU/ANNUAL STATISTICAL SURVEY OF CANCER. 1967. biennial. $5. National Statistical Service of Greece, Statistical Information and Publications Division - Ethniki Statistiki Yperesia tes Ellados, 14-16 Lykourgou, 101 66 Athens, Greece. TEL 30-1-3244-748. FAX 30-1-3222-205. TELEX 216734 ESYE GR. circ. 1,000. (back issues avail.) **Document type:** government publication.

016.6161 UK ISSN 0421-7527
EUROPEAN CONGRESS OF CARDIOLOGY. ABSTRACTS OF PAPERS. (Supplement to: European Heart Journal (ISSN 0195-668X)) (Text in English) 1952. a. (European Society of Cardiology) Academic Press Ltd. (Subsidiary of: Harcourt Brace & Company Ltd.), 24-28 Oval Rd., London NW1 7DX, England. TEL 44-171-267-4466. FAX 44-171-482-2293. TELEX 25775 ACPRES G. (Subscr. to: Harcourt Brace & Company Ltd., Foots Cray High St., Sidcup, Kent DA14 5HP, England. TEL 44-181-300-3322) **Document type:** abstracting/indexing.

616.3 US ISSN 0954-691X
CODEN: EJGHES
EUROPEAN JOURNAL OF GASTROENTEROLOGY AND HEPATOLOGY. 1989. m. $144.95 to individuals; institutions $295; residents $99.95. Current Science, 400 Market St., Ste. 700, Philadelphia, PA 19106. TEL 215-574-2210; 800-552-5866. FAX 215-574-3533. (And: Current Science Ltd., 34-42 Cleveland St., London W1P 6LB, England. TEL 0171-323-0323. FAX 0171-636-6911) Ed. J.J. Misiewicz. adv.; bibl.; illus. circ. 2,347. (also avail. in diskette format) **Indexed:** Diar.Dis.Res., Excerp.Med. **Document type:** academic/scholarly publication.
●Also available on CD-ROM.
—BLDSC (3829.729400); ADONIS; Faxon; Genuine Article; SWETS. CCC.
Description: Directed toward practicing gastroenterologists, hepatologists and researchers. Presents review articles followed by annotated bibliographies of references consulted. Includes a bibliography of the current world literature published during the previous year.

610 016 NE ISSN 0921-822X
EXCERPTA MEDICA ABSTRACT JOURNALS. (Consists of 41 Sections) 1947. 756/yr. (in 91 vols., 6-10 nos./vol.). fl.55950($29447) includes s-a. cumulation for CD-ROM (Section 38: Adverse Reactions Titles not included) (effective 1995). Excerpta Medica (Subsidiary of: Elsevier Science B.V.), P.O. Box 548, 1000 AM Amsterdam, Netherlands. TEL 31-20-4853911. FAX 31-20-4853598. TELEX 18582 ESPA NL. (Dist. by: Elsevier Science Ireland Ltd., P.O. Box 85, Limerick, Ireland. TEL 353-61-471944. FAX 353-61-472144; Subscr. in U.S. and Canada to: Elsevier Science Inc., Box 882, Madison Sq. Sta., New York, NY 10159. TEL 212-989-5800. FAX 212-633-3975) Ed.Bd. index, cum.index. (back issues avail.) **Document type:** abstracting/indexing.
●Also available online. Vendor(s): Ovid Technologies, DIMDI, Data-Star, Knight-Ridder, Inc., JICST.
Also available on CD-ROM. Producer(s): SilverPlatter Information, Inc. (Excerpta Medica Library Service).
Description: Comprehensive medical abstract service providing relevant abstracts and bibliographic data from more than 3,500 international biomedical journals covered by the EMBASE Excerpta Medica Database.

574.92 016 NE ISSN 0014-4053
CODEN: AAEHA9
EXCERPTA MEDICA. SECTION 1: ANATOMY, ANTHROPOLOGY, EMBRYOLOGY & HISTOLOGY. 1947. m. fl.1950($1189) (effective 1996). Excerpta Medica (Subsidiary of: Elsevier Science B.V.), P.O. Box 548, 1000 AM Amsterdam, Netherlands. TEL 31-20-4853911. FAX 31-20-4853598. TELEX 18582 ESPA NL. (Dist. by: Elsevier Science Ireland Ltd., P.O. Box 85, Limerick, Ireland. TEL 353-61-471944. FAX 353-61-472144; Subscr. in U.S. and Canada to: Elsevier Science Inc., Box 882, Madison Sq. Sta., New York, NY 10159. TEL 212-989-5800. FAX 212-633-3990) adv.; index, cum.index. **Indexed:** A.I.C.P., Chem.Abstr., Lab.Haz.Bull. **Document type:** abstracting/indexing.
●Also available online. Vendor(s): Ovid Technologies, DIMDI, Data-Star, Knight-Ridder, Inc., JICST.
Also available on CD-ROM. Producer(s): SilverPlatter Information, Inc.
—BLDSC (3835.812000). CCC.

612 016 NE ISSN 0367-1089
CODEN: PHSGA
EXCERPTA MEDICA. SECTION 2: PHYSIOLOGY. 1948. 30/yr. fl.3600($2195) (effective 1996). Excerpta Medica (Subsidiary of: Elsevier Science B.V.), P.O. Box 548, 1000 AM Amsterdam, Netherlands. TEL 31-20-4853911. FAX 31-20-4853598. TELEX 18582 ESPA NL. (Dist. by: Elsevier Science Ireland Ltd., P.O. Box 85, Limerick, Ireland. TEL 353-61-471944. FAX 353-61-472144; Subscr. in U.S. and Canada to: Elsevier Science Inc., Box 882, Madison Sq. Sta., New York, NY 10159. TEL 212-989-5800. FAX 212-633-3990) adv.; charts; index, cum.index. **Indexed:** Chem.Abstr. **Document type:** abstracting/indexing.
●Also available online. Vendor(s): Ovid Technologies, DIMDI, Data-Star, Knight-Ridder, Inc., JICST.
Also available on CD-ROM. Producer(s): SilverPlatter Information, Inc.
—BLDSC (3835.870000). CCC.
Supersedes in part (in 1964): Excerpta Medica. Section 2: Physiology, Biochemistry and Pharmacology (ISSN 0014-4061)

616.4 016 NE ISSN 0014-407X
CODEN: EEXCA
EXCERPTA MEDICA. SECTION 3: ENDOCRINOLOGY. 1947. 24/yr. fl.2875($1753) (effective 1996). Excerpta Medica (Subsidiary of: Elsevier Science B.V.), P.O. Box 548, 1000 BM Amsterdam, Netherlands. TEL 31-20-4853911. FAX 31-20-4853598. TELEX 18582 ESPA NL. (Dist. by: Elsevier Science Ireland Ltd., P.O. Box 85, Limerick, Ireland. TEL 353-61-471944. FAX 353-61-472144; Subscr. in U.S. and Canada to: Elsevier Science Inc., Box 882, Madison Sq. Sta., New York, NY 10159. TEL 212-989-5800. FAX 212-633-3990) adv.; charts; index, cum.index. **Indexed:** Chem.Abstr. **Document type:** abstracting/indexing.
●Also available online. Vendor(s): Ovid Technologies, DIMDI, Data-Star, Knight-Ridder, Inc., JICST.
Also available on CD-ROM. Producer(s): SilverPlatter Information, Inc.
—BLDSC (3835.830000). CCC.

MEDICAL SCIENCES — ABSTRACTING, BIBLIOGRAPHIES, STATISTICS

576 016 NE ISSN 0927-2771
EXCERPTA MEDICA. SECTION 4: MICROBIOLOGY: BACTERIOLOGY, MYCOLOGY, PARASITOLOGY AND VIROLOGY. 1948. 32/yr. fl.4625($2820) (effective 1996). Excerpta Medica (Subsidiary of: Elsevier Science B.V.), P.O. Box 548, 1000 AM Amsterdam, Netherlands. TEL 31-20-4853911. FAX 31-20-4853598. TELEX 18582 ESPA NL. (Dist. by: Elsevier Science Ireland Ltd., P.O. Box 85, Limerick, Ireland. TEL 353-61-471944. FAX 353-61-472144; Subscr. in U.S. and Canada to: Elsevier Science Inc., Box 882, Madison Sq. Sta., New York, NY 10159. TEL 212-989-5800. FAX 212-633-3990) Ed.Bd. adv.; index, cum.index. **Indexed:** Chem.Abstr. **Document type:** abstracting/indexing.
●Also available online. Vendor(s): Ovid Technologies, DIMDI, Data-Star, Knight-Ridder, Inc., JICST.
Also available on CD-ROM. Producer(s): SilverPlatter Information, Inc.
—BLDSC (3835.850800).
 Incorporates (1971-1991): Excerpta Medica. Section 47: Virology (ISSN 0304-4084); Former titles (until 1992): Excerpta Medica. Section 4: Microbiology: Bacteriology, Mycology and Parasitology; Excerpta Medica. Section 4: Microbiology: Bacteriology, Virology, Mycology and Parasitology (ISSN 0014-4088)
 Description: Covers general aspects of infectious diseases, diagnosis, treatment, epidemiology and prevention of diseases. Includes bacteriology, parasitology, mycology, algae and sexually transmitted diseases.

616.07 016 574.2 NE ISSN 0014-4096
RB1 CODEN: GPPABB
EXCERPTA MEDICA. SECTION 5: GENERAL PATHOLOGY AND PATHOLOGICAL ANATOMY. 1948. 24/yr. fl.3700($2256) (effective 1996). Excerpta Medica (Subsidiary of: Elsevier Science B.V.), P.O. Box 548, 1000 AM Amsterdam, Netherlands. TEL 31-20-4853911. FAX 31-20-4853598. TELEX 18582 ESPA NL. (Dist. by: Elsevier Science Ireland Ltd., P.O. Box 85, Limerick, Ireland. TEL 353-61-471944. FAX 353-61-472144; Subscr. in U.S. and Canada to: Elsevier Science Inc., Box 882, Madison Sq. Sta., New York, NY 10159. TEL 212-989-5800. FAX 212-633-3990) adv.; index, cum.index. **Indexed:** Chem.Abstr. **Document type:** abstracting/indexing.
●Also available online. Vendor(s): Ovid Technologies, DIMDI, Data-Star, Knight-Ridder, Inc., JICST.
Also available on CD-ROM. Producer(s): SilverPlatter Information, Inc.
—BLDSC (3835.832000). **CCC.**

616.026 016 NE ISSN 0014-410X
CODEN: IMDCBQ
EXCERPTA MEDICA. SECTION 6: INTERNAL MEDICINE. 1947. 24/yr. fl.2850($1738) (effective 1996). Excerpta Medica (Subsidiary of: Elsevier Science B.V.), P.O. Box 548, 1000 AM Amsterdam, Netherlands. TEL 31-20-4853911. FAX 31-20-4853598. TELEX 18582 ESPA NL. (Dist. by: Elsevier Science Ireland Ltd., P.O. Box 85, Limerick, Ireland. TEL 353-61-471944. FAX 353-61-472144; Subscr. in U.S. and Canada to: Elsevier Science Inc., Box 882, Madison Sq. Sta., New York, NY 10159. TEL 212-989-5800. FAX 212-633-3990) Ed.Bd. adv.; index, cum.index. **Indexed:** Chem.Abstr. **Document type:** abstracting/indexing.
●Also available online. Vendor(s): Ovid Technologies, DIMDI, Data-Star, Knight-Ridder, Inc., JICST.
Also available on CD-ROM. Producer(s): SilverPlatter Information, Inc.
—BLDSC (3835.844000). **CCC.**

618.92 016 NE ISSN 0373-6512
CODEN: PPSUDH
EXCERPTA MEDICA. SECTION 7: PEDIATRICS AND PEDIATRIC SURGERY. 1947. 18/yr. fl.2949($1798) (effective 1996). Excerpta Medica (Subsidiary of: Elsevier Science B.V.), P.O. Box 548, 1000 AM Amsterdam, Netherlands. TEL 31-20-4853911. FAX 31-20-4853598. TELEX 18582 ESPA NL. (Dist. by: Elsevier Science Ireland Ltd., P.O. Box 85, Limerick, Ireland. TEL 353-61-471944. FAX 353-61-472144; Subscr. in the U.S. and Canada to: Elsevier Science Inc., Box 882, Madison Sq. Sta., New York, NY 10159. TEL 212-989-5800. FAX 212-633-3990) adv.; index, cum.index. **Document type:** abstracting/indexing.
●Also available online. Vendor(s): Ovid Technologies, DIMDI, Data-Star, Knight-Ridder, Inc., JICST.
Also available on CD-ROM. Producer(s): SilverPlatter Information, Inc.
—BLDSC (3835.866500). **CCC.**
 Formerly: Excerpta Medica. Section 7: Pediatrics (ISSN 0014-4118)
 Description: Covers all aspects of development and organic disease in neonates, children and adolescents, including surgery.

616.8 016 NE ISSN 0014-4126
CODEN: NLNSB2
EXCERPTA MEDICA. SECTION 8: NEUROLOGY AND NEUROSURGERY. 1948. 32/yr. fl.3875($2363) (effective 1996). Excerpta Medica (Subsidiary of: Elsevier Science B.V.), P.O. Box 548, 1000 AM Amsterdam, Netherlands. TEL 31-20-4853911. FAX 31-20-4853598. TELEX 18582 ESPA NL. (Dist. by: Elsevier Science Ireland Ltd., P.O. Box 85, Limerick, Ireland. TEL 353-61-471944. FAX 353-61-472144; Subscr. in U.S. and Canada to: Elsevier Science Inc., Box 882, Madison Sq. Sta., New York, NY 10159. TEL 212-989-5800. FAX 212-633-3990) Ed.Bd. adv.; index, cum.index. **Document type:** abstracting/indexing.
●Also available online. Vendor(s): Ovid Technologies, DIMDI, Data-Star, Knight-Ridder, Inc., JICST.
Also available on CD-ROM. Producer(s): SilverPlatter Information, Inc.
—BLDSC (3835.854000). **CCC.**
 Description: Covers clinical neurology and neurosurgery, including epilepsy and neuromuscular disorders.

617 016 NE ISSN 0014-4134
CODEN: EMSGAY
EXCERPTA MEDICA. SECTION 9: SURGERY. 1947. 20/yr. fl.2870($1750) (effective 1996). Excerpta Medica (Subsidiary of: Elsevier Science B.V.), P.O. Box 548, 1000 AM Amsterdam, Netherlands. TEL 31-20-4853911. FAX 31-20-4853598. TELEX 18582 ESPA NL. (Dist. by: Elsevier Science Ireland Ltd., P.O. Box 85, Limerick, Ireland. TEL 353-61-471944. FAX 353-61-472144; Subscr. in U.S. and Canada to: Elsevier Science Inc., Box 882, Madison Sq. Sta., New York, NY 10159. TEL 212-989-5800. FAX 212-633-3990) Ed.Bd. adv.; index, cum.index. **Indexed:** Chem.Abstr. **Document type:** abstracting/indexing.
●Also available online. Vendor(s): Ovid Technologies, DIMDI, Data-Star, Knight-Ridder, Inc., JICST.
Also available on CD-ROM. Producer(s): SilverPlatter Information, Inc.
—BLDSC (3835.881000). **CCC.**
 Description: Covers general, abdominal, thoracic and peripheral vascular surgery, cosmetic, plastic and reconstructive surgery, microsurgery, pre- and post-operative care and surgical aspects of intensive care medicine.

618 016 NE ISSN 0014-4142
CODEN: EMOGAE
EXCERPTA MEDICA. SECTION 10: OBSTETRICS AND GYNECOLOGY. 1948. 20/yr. fl.2775($1692) (effective 1996). Excerpta Medica (Subsidiary of: Elsevier Science B.V.), P.O. Box 548, 1000 AM Amsterdam, Netherlands. TEL 31-20-4853911. FAX 31-20-4853598. TELEX 18582 ESPA NL. (Dist. by: Elsevier Science Ireland Ltd., P.O. Box 85, Limerick, Ireland. TEL 353-61-471944. FAX 353-61-472144; Subscr. in U.S. and Canada to: Elsevier Science Inc., Box 882, Madison Sq. Sta., New York, NY 10159. TEL 212-989-5800. FAX 212-633-3990) Ed.Bd. adv.; index, cum.index. **Indexed:** Chem.Abstr. **Document type:** abstracting/indexing.
●Also available online. Vendor(s): Ovid Technologies, DIMDI, Data-Star, Knight-Ridder, Inc., JICST.
Also available on CD-ROM. Producer(s): SilverPlatter Information, Inc.
—BLDSC (3835.858000). **CCC.**
 Description: Covers human obstetrics and gynecology, including female infertility, fetal monitoring, anticonception in women, and neonatal care of normal children.

616.21 016 NE ISSN 0014-4150
RF1 CODEN: ORLGA8
EXCERPTA MEDICA. SECTION 11: OTORHINOLARYNGOLOGY. 1948. m. fl.1870($1140) (effective 1996). Excerpta Medica (Subsidiary of: Elsevier Science B.V.), P.O. Box 548, 1000 AM Amsterdam, Netherlands. TEL 31-20-4853911. FAX 31-20-4853598. TELEX 18582 ESPA NL. (Dist. by: Elsevier Science Ireland Ltd., P.O. Box 85, Limerick, Ireland. TEL 353-61-471944. FAX 353-61-472144; Subscr. in U.S. and Canada to: Elsevier Science Inc., Box 882, Madison Sq. Sta., New York, NY 10159. TEL 212-989-5800. FAX 212-633-3990) adv.; index, cum.index. **Indexed:** Chem.Abstr. **Document type:** abstracting/indexing.
●Also available online. Vendor(s): Ovid Technologies, DIMDI, Data-Star, Knight-Ridder, Inc., JICST.
Also available on CD-ROM. Producer(s): SilverPlatter Information, Inc.
—BLDSC (3835.864000). **CCC.**
 Description: Covers all aspects of diseases of the ear, nose, and throat, and includes phonetics and speech disorders, craniofacial disorders, vestibular disorders, surgery, stomatology and audiology.

617.7 016 NE ISSN 0014-4169
CODEN: OPHYAS
EXCERPTA MEDICA. SECTION 12: OPHTHALMOLOGY. 1947. m. fl.1870($1140) (effective 1996). Excerpta Medica (Subsidiary of: Elsevier Science B.V.), P.O. Box 548, 1000 AM Amsterdam, Netherlands. TEL 31-20-4853911. FAX 31-20-4853598. TELEX 18582 ESPA NL. (Dist. by: Elsevier Science Ireland Ltd., P.O. Box 85, Limerick, Ireland. TEL 353-61-471944. FAX 353-61-472144; Subscr. in U.S. and Canada to: Elsevier Science Inc., Box 882, Madison Sq. Sta., New York, NY 10159. TEL 212-989-5800. FAX 212-633-3990) adv.; index, cum.index. **Indexed:** Chem.Abstr. **Document type:** abstracting/indexing.
●Also available online. Vendor(s): Ovid Technologies, DIMDI, Data-Star, Knight-Ridder, Inc., JICST.
Also available on CD-ROM. Producer(s): SilverPlatter Information, Inc.
—BLDSC (3835.860000). **CCC.**
 Description: Covers both surgical and non-surgical aspects of eye disease and vision disorders and includes articles on the anatomy, physiology and biochemistry of the eye, orbit and visual system.

MEDICAL SCIENCES — ABSTRACTING, BIBLIOGRAPHIES, STATISTICS

616.5 016 NE ISSN 0014-4177
CODEN: DVENB4
EXCERPTA MEDICA. SECTION 13: DERMATOLOGY AND VENEREOLOGY. 1947. m. fl.2260($1378) (effective 1996). Excerpta Medica (Subsidiary of: Elsevier Science B.V.), P.O. Box 548, 1000 AM Amsterdam, Netherlands. TEL 31-20-4853911. FAX 31-20-4853598. TELEX 18582 ESPA NL. (Dist. by: Elsevier Science Ireland Ltd., P.O. Box 85, Limerick, Ireland. TEL 353-61-471944. FAX 353-61-472144; Subscr. in U.S. and Canada to: Elsevier Science Inc., Box 882, Madison Sq. Sta., New York, NY 10159. TEL 212-989-5800. FAX 212-633-3990) adv.; index, cum.index. **Indexed:** Chem.Abstr. **Document type:** abstracting/indexing.
●Also available online. Vendor(s): Ovid Technologies, DIMDI, Data-Star, Knight-Ridder, Inc., JICST. Also available on CD-ROM. Producer(s): SilverPlatter Information, Inc.
—BLDSC (3835.826000). **CCC.**
 Description: Covers all aspects of skin and venereal diseases, and includes microbiology, sexually transmitted diseases, immunology, allergy and skin toxicology, skin physiology and biochemistry.

616.994 016 NE ISSN 0014-4207
CODEN: CEXCA3
EXCERPTA MEDICA. SECTION 16: CANCER. 1953. 32/yr. fl.3880($2366) (effective 1996). Excerpta Medica (Subsidiary of: Elsevier Science B.V.), P.O. Box 548, 1000 AM Amsterdam, Netherlands. TEL 31-20-4853911. FAX 31-20-4853598. TELEX 18582 ESPA NL. (Dist. by: Elsevier Science Ireland Ltd., P.O. Box 85, Limerick, Ireland. TEL 353-61-471944. FAX 353-61-472144; Subscr. in U.S. and Canada to: Elsevier Science Inc., Box 882, Madison Sq. Sta., New York, NY 10159. TEL 212-989-5800. FAX 212-633-3990) adv.; index, cum.index. **Indexed:** Chem.Abstr. **Document type:** abstracting/indexing.
●Also available online. Vendor(s): Ovid Technologies, DIMDI, Data-Star, Knight-Ridder, Inc., JICST. Also available on CD-ROM. Producer(s): SilverPlatter Information, Inc.
—BLDSC (3835.820000). **CCC.**
 Description: Covers both experimental and clinical aspects of malignant neoplastic disease, including research in cancer immunology, oncogenes, viral and chemical carcinogenesis, and cancer chemotherapeutic agents.

574 016 616 NE ISSN 0014-4258
CODEN: DBITA
EXCERPTA MEDICA. SECTION 21: DEVELOPMENTAL BIOLOGY AND TERATOLOGY. 1961. m. fl.2325($1418) (effective 1996). Excerpta Medica (Subsidiary of: Elsevier Science B.V.), P.O. Box 548, 1000 AM Amsterdam, Netherlands. TEL 31-20-4853911. FAX 31-20-4853598. TELEX 18582 ESPA NL. (Dist. by: Elsevier Science Ireland Ltd., P.O. Box 85, Limerick, Ireland. TEL 353-61-471944. FAX 353-61-472144; Subscr. in U.S. and Canada to: Elsevier Science Inc., Box 882, Madison Sq. Sta., New York, NY 10159. TEL 212-989-5800. FAX 212-633-3990) adv.; index, cum.index. **Document type:** abstracting/indexing.
●Also available online. Vendor(s): Ovid Technologies, DIMDI, Data-Star, Knight-Ridder, Inc., JICST. Also available on CD-ROM. Producer(s): SilverPlatter Information, Inc.
—BLDSC (3835.828000). **CCC.**
 Description: Covers both experimental and clinical aspects of embryology and fetal, neonatal development.

EXCERPTA MEDICA. SECTION 17: PUBLIC HEALTH, SOCIAL MEDICINE & EPIDEMIOLOGY. see *PUBLIC HEALTH AND SAFETY — Abstracting, Bibliographies, Statistics*

EXCERPTA MEDICA. SECTION 22: HUMAN GENETICS. see *BIOLOGY — Abstracting, Bibliographies, Statistics*

615.842 016 NE ISSN 0014-4185
CODEN: RDGYA6
EXCERPTA MEDICA. SECTION 14: RADIOLOGY. 1947. 20/yr. fl.2856($1742) (effective 1996). Excerpta Medica (Subsidiary of: Elsevier Science B.V.), P.O. Box 548, 1000 AM Amsterdam, Netherlands. TEL 31-20-4853911. FAX 31-20-4853598. TELEX 18582 ESPA NL. (Dist. by: Elsevier Science Ireland Ltd., P.O. Box 85, Limerick, Ireland. TEL 353-61-471944. FAX 353-61-472144; Subscr. in U.S. and Canada to: Elsevier Science Inc., Box 882, Madison Sq. Sta., New York, NY 10159. TEL 212-989-5800. FAX 212-633-3990) adv.; index, cum.index. **Indexed:** Chem.Abstr. **Document type:** abstracting/indexing.
●Also available online. Vendor(s): Ovid Technologies, DIMDI, Data-Star, Knight-Ridder, Inc., JICST. Also available on CD-ROM. Producer(s): SilverPlatter Information, Inc.
—BLDSC (3835.878000). **CCC.**
 Description: Covers articles on radiodiagnosis, radiotherapy and radiobiology, including ultrasound diagnosis, thermography, adverse reactions to radiotherapy, as well as techniques and apparatus.

616.1 016 NE ISSN 0014-4223
CODEN: CDCSA
EXCERPTA MEDICA. SECTION 18: CARDIOVASCULAR DISEASES AND CARDIOVASCULAR SURGERY. 1957. 24/yr. fl.3030($1848) (effective 1996). Excerpta Medica (Subsidiary of: Elsevier Science B.V.), P.O. Box 548, 1000 AM Amsterdam, Netherlands. TEL 31-20-4853911. FAX 31-20-4853598. TELEX 18582 ESPA NL. (Dist. by: Elsevier Science Ireland Ltd., P.O. Box 85, Limerick, Ireland. TEL 353-61-471944. FAX 353-61-472144; Subscr. in U.S. and Canada to: Elsevier Science Inc., Box 882, Madison Sq. Sta., New York, NY 10159. TEL 212-989-5800. FAX 212-633-3990) adv.; index, cum.index. **Document type:** abstracting/indexing.
●Also available online. Vendor(s): Ovid Technologies, DIMDI, Data-Star, Knight-Ridder, Inc., JICST. Also available on CD-ROM. Producer(s): SilverPlatter Information, Inc.
—BLDSC (3835.822000). **CCC.**
 Description: Covers both surgical and non-surgical aspects of cardiovascular disease, including cardiovascular aspects of hypertension.

615.842 016 NE ISSN 0014-4274
CODEN: NUMEAH
EXCERPTA MEDICA. SECTION 23: NUCLEAR MEDICINE. 1964. m. fl.2000($1220) (effective 1996). Excerpta Medica (Subsidiary of: Elsevier Science B.V.), P.O. Box 548, 1000 AM Amsterdam, Netherlands. TEL 31-20-4853911. FAX 31-20-4853598. TELEX 18582 ESPA NL. (Dist. by: Elsevier Science Ireland Ltd., P.O. Box 85, Limerick, Ireland. TEL 353-61-471944. FAX 353-61-472144; Subscr. in U.S. and Canada to: Elsevier Science Inc., Box 882, Madison Sq. Sta., New York, NY 10159. TEL 212-989-5800. FAX 212-633-3990) adv.; index, cum.index. **Indexed:** Chem.Abstr. **Document type:** abstracting/indexing.
●Also available online. Vendor(s): Ovid Technologies, DIMDI, Data-Star, Knight-Ridder, Inc., JICST. Also available on CD-ROM. Producer(s): SilverPlatter Information, Inc.
—BLDSC (3835.856000). **CCC.**
 Description: Covers the diagnostic and therapeutic applications of radioisotopes in biomedicine, including the radiobiology of isotopes, aspects of radiohygiene, new labelling techniques and tracer applications.

616.2 016 NE ISSN 0014-4193
RC306 CODEN: CDTSA
EXCERPTA MEDICA. SECTION 15: CHEST DISEASES, THORACIC SURGERY AND TUBERCULOSIS. 1948. 16/yr. fl.1990($1214) (effective 1996). Excerpta Medica (Subsidiary of: Elsevier Science B.V.), P.O. Box 548, 1000 AM Amsterdam, Netherlands. TEL 31-20-4853911. FAX 31-20-4853598. TELEX 18582 ESPA NL. (Dist. by: Elsevier Science Ireland Ltd., P.O. Box 85, Limerick, Ireland. TEL 353-61-471944. FAX 353-61-472144; Subscr. in U.S. and Canada to: Elsevier Science Inc., Box 882, Madison Sq. Sta., New York, NY 10159. TEL 212-989-5800. FAX 212-633-3990) adv.; index, cum.index. **Indexed:** Chem.Abstr. **Document type:** abstracting/indexing.
●Also available online. Vendor(s): Ovid Technologies, DIMDI, Data-Star, Knight-Ridder, Inc., JICST. Also available on CD-ROM. Producer(s): SilverPlatter Information, Inc.
—BLDSC (3835.824000). **CCC.**
 Description: Covers all aspects of lung and respiratory tract diseases, thoracic surgery and tuberculosis, including respiratory infections, mediastical and pleural diseases, chronic chest diseases, allergy and bronchial asthma, and neoplastic disease.

612 016 NE ISSN 0014-4231
CODEN: RHPMA
EXCERPTA MEDICA. SECTION 19: REHABILITATION AND PHYSICAL MEDICINE. 1958. 8/yr. fl.1215($741) (effective 1996). Excerpta Medica (Subsidiary of: Elsevier Science B.V.), P.O. Box 548, 1000 AM Amsterdam, Netherlands. TEL 31-20-4853911. FAX 31-20-4853598. TELEX 18582 ESPA NL. (Dist. by: Elsevier Science Ireland Ltd., P.O. Box 85, Limerick, Ireland. TEL 353-61-471944. FAX 353-61-472144; Subscr. in U.S. and Canada to: Elsevier Science Inc., Box 882, Madison Sq. Sta., New York, NY 10159. TEL 212-989-5800. FAX 212-633-3990) adv.; index, cum.index. **Document type:** abstracting/indexing.
●Also available online. Vendor(s): Ovid Technologies, DIMDI, Data-Star, Knight-Ridder, Inc., JICST. Also available on CD-ROM. Producer(s): SilverPlatter Information, Inc.
—BLDSC (3835.879000). **CCC.**
 Description: Covers all aspects of the rehabilitation of somatic and mental disorders using physiotherapy and other therapeutic techniques.

617.96 016 NE ISSN 0014-4282
CODEN: ATSYA
EXCERPTA MEDICA. SECTION 24: ANESTHESIOLOGY. 1966. 10/yr. fl.1530($933) (effective 1996). Excerpta Medica (Subsidiary of: Elsevier Science B.V.), P.O. Box 548, 1000 AM Amsterdam, Netherlands. TEL 31-20-4853911. FAX 31-20-4853598. TELEX 18582 ESPA NL. (Dist. by: Elsevier Science Ireland Ltd., P.O. Box 85, Limerick, Ireland. TEL 353-61-471944. FAX 353-61-472144; Subscr. in U.S. and Canada to: Elsevier Science Inc., Box 882, Madison Sq. Sta., New York, NY 10159. TEL 212-989-5800. FAX 212-633-3990) adv.; index, cum.index. **Document type:** abstracting/indexing.
●Also available online. Vendor(s): Ovid Technologies, DIMDI, Data-Star, Knight-Ridder, Inc., JICST. Also available on CD-ROM. Producer(s): SilverPlatter Information, Inc.
—BLDSC (3835.814000). **CCC.**
 Description: Covers both clinical and experimental aspects of anesthesiology, and includes resuscitation and intensive care medicine, pharmacology of anesthetic agents, spinal, epidural and caudal anesthesia, and acupuncture used as an anaesthetic procedure.

EXCERPTA MEDICA. SECTION 20: GERONTOLOGY AND GERIATRICS. see *GERONTOLOGY AND GERIATRICS — Abstracting, Bibliographies, Statistics*

MEDICAL SCIENCES — ABSTRACTING, BIBLIOGRAPHIES, STATISTICS

616.15 016 NE ISSN 0014-4290
CODEN: HEMYA
EXCERPTA MEDICA. SECTION 25: HEMATOLOGY. 1967. 24/yr. fl.2900($1768) (effective 1996). Excerpta Medica (Subsidiary of: Elsevier Science B.V.), P.O. Box 548, 1000 AM Amsterdam, Netherlands. TEL 31-20-4853911. FAX 31-20-4853598. TELEX 18582 ESPA NL. (Dist. by: Elsevier Science Ireland Ltd., P.O Box 85, Limerick, Ireland. TEL 353-61-471944. FAX 353-61-472144; Subscr. in U.S. and Canada to: Elsevier Science Inc., Box 882, Madison Sq. Sta., New York, NY 10159. TEL 212-989-5800. FAX 212-633-3990) Ed.Bd. adv.; index, cum.index. **Document type:** abstracting/indexing.
●Also available online. Vendor(s): Ovid Technologies, DIMDI, Data-Star, Knight-Ridder, Inc., JICST.
Also available on CD-ROM. Producer(s): SilverPlatter Information, Inc.
—BLDSC (3835.836000). **CCC.**
  Description: Covers all aspects of blood cell biology and disorders of the blood, its cells and the lymphatic tissues.

615.37 016 NE ISSN 0014-4304
CODEN: ISTNB
EXCERPTA MEDICA. SECTION 26: IMMUNOLOGY, SEROLOGY AND TRANSPLANTATION. 1967. 32/yr. fl.3600($2195) (effective 1996). Excerpta Medica (Subsidiary of: Elsevier Science B.V.), P.O. Box 548, 1000 AM Amsterdam, Netherlands. TEL 31-20-4853911. FAX 31-20-4853598. TELEX 18582 ESPA NL. (Dist. by: Elsevier Science Ireland Ltd., P.O. Box 85, Limerick, Ireland. TEL 353-61-471944. FAX 353-61-472144; Subscr. in U.S. and Canada to: Elsevier Science Inc., Box 882, Madison Sq. Sta., New York, NY 10159. TEL 212-989-5800. FAX 212-633-3990) adv.; index, cum.index. **Document type:** abstracting/indexing.
●Also available online. Vendor(s): Ovid Technologies, DIMDI, Data-Star, Knight-Ridder, Inc., JICST.
Also available on CD-ROM. Producer(s): SilverPlatter Information, Inc.
—BLDSC (3835.842000). **CCC.**
  Description: Covers both clinical and experimental immunology and includes humoral immunity and associated factors.

610.28 016 NE ISSN 0014-4312
CODEN: BBMIA
EXCERPTA MEDICA. SECTION 27: BIOPHYSICS, BIO-ENGINEERING AND MEDICAL INSTRUMENTATION. 1967. 16/yr. fl.2600($1585) (effective 1996). Excerpta Medica (Subsidiary of: Elsevier Science B.V.), P.O. Box 548, 1000 AM Amsterdam, Netherlands. TEL 31-20-4853911. FAX 31-20-4853598. TELEX 18582 ESPA NL. (Dist. by: Elsevier Science Ireland Ltd., P.O. Box 85, Limerick, Ireland. TEL 353-61-471944. FAX 353-61-472144; Subscr. in U.S. and Canada to: Elsevier Science Inc., Box 882, Madison Sq. Sta., New York, NY 10159. TEL 212-989-5800. FAX 212-633-3990) adv.; index, cum.index. **Document type:** abstracting/indexing.
●Also available online. Vendor(s): Ovid Technologies, DIMDI, Data-Star, Knight-Ridder, Inc., JICST.
Also available on CD-ROM. Producer(s): SilverPlatter Information, Inc.
—BLDSC (3835.818000). **CCC.**
  Description: Covers the application of biophysical principles to the development of instrumentation, the use of automation in biomedicine, biomechanics and bioengineering.

616.6 016 NE ISSN 0014-4320
CODEN: URNLA
EXCERPTA MEDICA. SECTION 28: UROLOGY AND NEPHROLOGY. 1967. 16/yr. fl.2490($1518) (effective 1996). Excerpta Medica (Subsidiary of: Elsevier Science B.V.), P.O. Box 548, 1000 AM Amsterdam, Netherlands. TEL 31-20-4853911. FAX 31-20-4853598. TELEX 18582 ESPA NL. (Dist. by: Elsevier Science Ireland Ltd., P.O. Box 85, Limerick, Ireland. TEL 353-61-471944. FAX 353-61-472144; Subscr. in U.S. and Canada to: Elsevier Science Inc., Box 882, Madison Sq. Sta., New York, NY 10159. TEL 212-989-5800. FAX 212-633-3990) Ed.Bd. adv.; index, cum.index. **Document type:** abstracting/indexing.
●Also available online. Vendor(s): Ovid Technologies, DIMDI, Data-Star, Knight-Ridder, Inc., JICST.
Also available on CD-ROM. Producer(s): SilverPlatter Information, Inc.
—BLDSC (3835.883000). **CCC.**
  Description: Covers both clinical and experimental aspects of nephrological and urological disorders in either sex, kidney transplantation and dialysis, and the male reproductive system, including male fertility and the prostate.

574.192 016 NE ISSN 0927-278X
EXCERPTA MEDICA. SECTION 29: CLINICAL AND EXPERIMENTAL BIOCHEMISTRY. 1948. 40/yr. fl.3800($2317) (effective 1996). Excerpta Medica (Subsidiary of: Elsevier Science B.V.), P.O. Box 548, 1000 AM Amsterdam, Netherlands. TEL 31-20-4853911. FAX 31-20-4853598. TELEX 18582 ESPA NL. (Dist. by: Elsevier Science Ireland Ltd., P.O. Box 85, Limerick, Ireland. TEL 353-61-471944. FAX 353-61-472144; Subscr. in U.S. and Canada to: Elsevier Science Inc., Box 882, Madison Sq. Sta., New York, NY 10159. TEL 212-989-5800. FAX 212-633-3990) adv.; bk.rev.; charts; index, cum.index. **Indexed:** Chem.Abstr. **Document type:** abstracting/indexing.
●Also available online. Vendor(s): Ovid Technologies, DIMDI, Data-Star, Knight-Ridder, Inc., JICST.
Also available on CD-ROM. Producer(s): SilverPlatter Information, Inc.
—BLDSC (3835.824200). **CCC.**
  Former titles (until 1992): Excerpta Medica. Section 29. Clinical Biochemistry (ISSN 0300-5372); Excerpta Medica. Section 29: Biochemistry (ISSN 0014-4339); Which supersedes in part (in 1964): Excerpta Medica. Section 2: Physiology, Biochemistry and Pharmacology (ISSN 0014-4061)
  Description: Covers both clinical chemistry and general biochemistry and includes analytical methods, chemical function tests, enzyme assay, enzyme mode of action studies, biochemical roles in disease, metabolic biochemistry, nutritional analysis and molecular transport.

EXCERPTA MEDICA. SECTION 30: CLINICAL AND EXPERIMENTAL PHARMACOLOGY. see *PHARMACY AND PHARMACOLOGY — Abstracting, Bibliographies, Statistics*

616.742 016 NE ISSN 0014-4355
RC933.A1 CODEN: EXARB
EXCERPTA MEDICA. SECTION 31: ARTHRITIS AND RHEUMATISM. 1965. 8/yr. fl.1225($747) (effective 1996). Excerpta Medica (Subsidiary of: Elsevier Science B.V.), P.O. Box 548, 1000 AM Amsterdam, Netherlands. TEL 31-20-4853911. FAX 31-20-4853598. TELEX 18582 ESPA NL. (Dist. by: Elsevier Science Ireland Ltd., P.O. Box 85, Limerick, Ireland. TEL 353-61-471944. FAX 353-61-472144; Subscr. in U.S. and Canada to: Elsevier Science Inc., Box 882, Madison Sq. Sta., New York, NY 10159. TEL 212-989-5800. FAX 212-633-3990) adv.; index, cum.index. **Document type:** abstracting/indexing.
●Also available online. Vendor(s): Ovid Technologies, DIMDI, Data-Star, Knight-Ridder, Inc., JICST.
Also available on CD-ROM. Producer(s): SilverPlatter Information, Inc.
—BLDSC (3835.815000). **CCC.**
  Description: Covers both clinical and experimental aspects of arthritis, rheumatism, bone and joint pathology, and includes spine disorders, connective tissue disorders and rheumatic fever.

616.89 016 NE ISSN 0014-4363
CODEN: PSCYA
EXCERPTA MEDICA. SECTION 32: PSYCHIATRY. 1948. 20/yr. fl.2770($1689) (effective 1996). Excerpta Medica (Subsidiary of: Elsevier Science B.V.), P.O. Box 548, 1000 AM Amsterdam, Netherlands. TEL 31-20-4853911. FAX 31-20-4853598. TELEX 18582 ESPA NL. (Dist. by: Elsevier Science Ireland Ltd., P.O. Box 85, Limerick, Ireland. TEL 353-61-471944. FAX 353-61-472144; Subscr. in U.S. and Canada to: Elsevier Science Inc., Box 882, Madison Sq. Sta., New York, NY 10159. TEL 212-989-5800. FAX 212-633-3990) adv.; index, cum.index. **Document type:** abstracting/indexing.
●Also available online. Vendor(s): Ovid Technologies, DIMDI, Data-Star, Knight-Ridder, Inc., JICST.
Also available on CD-ROM. Producer(s): SilverPlatter Information, Inc.
—BLDSC (3835.874000). **CCC.**
  Description: Covers all aspects of medical psychology and psychiatry, including the psychological aspects of addiction, alcoholism, sexual behavior and suicide.

617.3 016 NE ISSN 0014-4371
RD701 CODEN: OSUGA
EXCERPTA MEDICA. SECTION 33: ORTHOPEDIC SURGERY. 1956. 10/yr. fl.1700($1037) (effective 1996). Excerpta Medica (Subsidiary of: Elsevier Science B.V.), P.O. Box 548, 1000 AM Amsterdam, Netherlands. TEL 31-20-4853911. FAX 31-20-4853598. TELEX 18582 ESPA NL. (Dist. by: Elsevier Science Ireland Ltd., P.O. Box 85, Limerick, Ireland. TEL 353-61-471944. FAX 353-61-472144; Subscr. in U.S. and Canada to: Elsevier Science Inc., Box 882, Madison Sq. Sta., New York, NY 10159. TEL 212-989-5800. FAX 212-633-3990) adv.; index, cum.index. **Document type:** abstracting/indexing.
●Also available online. Vendor(s): Ovid Technologies, DIMDI, Data-Star, Knight-Ridder, Inc., JICST.
Also available on CD-ROM. Producer(s): SilverPlatter Information, Inc.
—BLDSC (3835.862000). **CCC.**
  Description: Covers the general, diagnostic and surgical aspects of orthopedics, and includes surgical aspects of other bone diseases, bone tumors, trauma of the musculoskeletal system and biomechanics of the musculoskeletal system.

613.62 016 NE ISSN 0014-4398
RC963 CODEN: EMOHA
EXCERPTA MEDICA. SECTION 35: OCCUPATIONAL HEALTH AND INDUSTRIAL MEDICINE. 1971. m. fl.2200($1342) (effective 1996). Excerpta Medica (Subsidiary of: Elsevier Science B.V.), P.O. Box 548, 1000 AM Amsterdam, Netherlands. TEL 31-20-4853911. FAX 31-20-4853598. TELEX 18582 ESPA NL. (Dist. by: Elsevier Science Ireland Ltd., P.O. Box 85, Limerick, Ireland. TEL 353-61-471944. FAX 353-61-472144; Subscr. in U.S. and Canada to: Elsevier Science Inc., Box 882, Madison Sq. Sta., New York, NY 10159. TEL 212-989-5800. FAX 212-633-3990) adv.; index, cum.index. **Indexed:** Ergon.Abstr. **Document type:** abstracting/indexing.
●Also available online. Vendor(s): Ovid Technologies, DIMDI, Data-Star, Knight-Ridder, Inc., JICST.
Also available on CD-ROM. Producer(s): SilverPlatter Information, Inc.
—BLDSC (3835.859000). **CCC.**
  Description: Covers the health aspects of work and the working environment, and includes ergonomics, sports medicine, the influence of life style and psychosocial aspects.

EXCERPTA MEDICA. SECTION 36: HEALTH POLICY, ECONOMICS AND MANAGEMENT. see *HOSPITALS — Abstracting, Bibliographies, Statistics*

MEDICAL SCIENCES — ABSTRACTING, BIBLIOGRAPHIES, STATISTICS

610 016   NE   ISSN 0001-8848
CODEN: ADRTA
EXCERPTA MEDICA. SECTION 38: ADVERSE REACTIONS TITLES. 1966. m. fl.13000($7927) (effective 1996). Excerpta Medica (Subsidiary of: Elsevier Science B.V.), P.O. Box 548, 1000 AM Amsterdam, Netherlands. TEL 31-20-4853911. FAX 31-20-4853598. TELEX 18582 ESPA NL. (Dist. by: Elsevier Science Ireland Ltd., P.O. Box 85, Limerick, Ireland. TEL 353-61-471944. FAX 353-61-472144; Subscr. in U.S. and Canada to: Elsevier Science Inc., Box 882, Madison Sq. Sta., New York, NY 10159. TEL 212-989-5800. FAX 212-633-3990) adv.; index, cum.index. **Document type:** abstracting/indexing.
●Also available online. Vendor(s): Ovid Technologies, DIMDI, Data-Star, Knight-Ridder, Inc., JICST. Also available on CD-ROM. Producer(s): SilverPlatter Information, Inc.
—BLDSC (3835.805000). **CCC.**

EXCERPTA MEDICA. SECTION 40: DRUG DEPENDENCE, ALCOHOL ABUSE AND ALCOHOLISM. see *DRUG ABUSE AND ALCOHOLISM — Abstracting, Bibliographies, Statistics*

EXCERPTA MEDICA. SECTION 46: ENVIRONMENTAL HEALTH AND POLLUTION CONTROL. see *ENVIRONMENTAL STUDIES — Abstracting, Bibliographies, Statistics*

616.3 016   NE   ISSN 0031-3580
CODEN: EMGSA
EXCERPTA MEDICA. SECTION 48: GASTROENTEROLOGY. 1971. 16/yr. fl.2050($1250) (effective 1996). Excerpta Medica (Subsidiary of: Elsevier Science B.V.), P.O. Box 548, 1000 AM Amsterdam, Netherlands. TEL 31-20-4853911. FAX 31-20-4853598. TELEX 18582 ESPA NL. (Dist. by: Elsevier Science Ireland Ltd., P.O. 85, Limerick, Ireland. TEL 353-61-471944. FAX 353-61-472144; Subscr. in U.S. and Canada to: Elsevier Science Inc., Box 882, Madison Sq. Sta., New York, NY 10159. TEL 212-989-5800. FAX 212-633-3990) adv.; bk.rev.; index, cum.index. **Document type:** abstracting/indexing.
●Also available online. Vendor(s): Ovid Technologies, DIMDI, Data-Star, Knight-Ridder, Inc., JICST.
Also available on CD-ROM. Producer(s): SilverPlatter Information, Inc.
—BLDSC (3835.831000). **CCC.**
Description: Covers all aspects of digestive system disease and includes disorders of the mouth and pharynx, the hepatobiliary system, the exocrine pancreas, the peritoneum, mesentery and omentum.

614 363.2 016   NE   ISSN 0303-8459
RA1001   CODEN: FSABD
EXCERPTA MEDICA. SECTION 49: FORENSIC SCIENCE ABSTRACTS. 1975. bi-m. fl.1300($793) (effective 1996). Excerpta Medica (Subsidiary of: Elsevier Science B.V.), P.O. Box 548, 1000 AM Amsterdam, Netherlands. TEL 31-20-4853911. FAX 31-20-4853598. TELEX 18582 ESPA NL. (Dist. by: Elsevier Science Ireland Ltd., P.O. Box 85, Limerick, Ireland. TEL 353-61-471944. FAX 353-61-472144; Subscr. in U.S. and Canada to: Elsevier Science Inc., Box 882, Madison Sq. Sta., New York, NY 10159. TEL 212-989-5800. FAX 212-633-3990) adv.; index, cum.index. **Document type:** abstracting/indexing.
●Also available online. Vendor(s): Ovid Technologies, DIMDI, Data-Star, Knight-Ridder, Inc., JICST.
Also available on CD-ROM. Producer(s): SilverPlatter Information, Inc.
—BLDSC (3835.830700). **CCC.**
Formerly: Excerpta Medica. Section 49: Forensic Science.
Description: Covers all aspects of biomedicine and science of relevance to criminal investigation or coroners.

616.853 016   NE   ISSN 0031-0743
RA1001   CODEN: EMEPAP
EXCERPTA MEDICA. SECTION 50: EPILEPSY ABSTRACTS. 1968. bi-m. fl.1030($628) (effective 1996). Excerpta Medica (Subsidiary of: Elsevier Science B.V.), P.O. Box 548, 1000 AM Amsterdam, Netherlands. TEL 31-20-4853911. FAX 31-20-4853598. TELEX 18582 ESPA NL. (Dist. by: Elsevier Science Ireland Ltd., P.O. Box 85, Limerick, Ireland. TEL 353-61-471944. FAX 353-61-472144; Subscr. in U.S. and Canada to: Elsevier Science Inc., Box 882, Madison Sq. Sta., New York, NY 10159. TEL 212-989-5800. FAX 212-633-3990) adv.; bk.rev.; index, cum.index. **Document type:** abstracting/indexing.
●Also available online. Vendor(s): Ovid Technologies, DIMDI, Data-Star, Knight-Ridder, Inc., JICST.
Also available on CD-ROM. Producer(s): SilverPlatter Information, Inc.
—BLDSC (3835.830500). **CCC.**
Formerly: Excerpta Medica. Section 50: Epilepsy.
Description: Covers both clinical and experimental aspects of epilepsy and brain seizures, and includes psychosocial aspects of epilepsy and electoencephalography (EEG).

EXCERPTA MEDICA. SECTION 52: TOXICOLOGY. see *ENVIRONMENTAL STUDIES — Abstracting, Bibliographies, Statistics*

616.5 617   GW   ISSN 0342-2828
EXTRACTA DERMATOLOGICA; weltweit Auserlesen. 1977. bi-m. DM.45. Media-Derm, Postfach 100745, 20005 Hamburg, Germany. Ed. Volker Misgeld. adv.; bk.rev.; bibl.; charts; illus. circ. 3,000. (back issues avail.)

617.3   GW   ISSN 0344-5046
EXTRACTA ORTHOPAEDICA; Weltweit Auserlesen. 1978. bi-m. DM.99. Selecta Verlagsgesellschaft mbH, Postfach 4240, 65032 Wiesbaden, Germany. TEL 0611-17050. FAX 0611-1705379. Ed. Dr. Wolfgang Dorn. adv.; bk.rev. circ. 3,200. (back issues avail.) **Document type:** academic/scholarly publication.

016.61 610   UK
▼**EXTRAMED.** 1994. m. £1000($1500) (World Health Organization, ExtraMED Consortium) Informania Limited, P.O. Box 1359, London W5 3ZP, England. FAX 44-1730-265398. E-mail: 100060,172@compuserve.com. abstr.; bibl.; illus. **Document type:** abstracting/indexing, academic/scholarly publication.
●Available only on CD-ROM.
Description: Covers 220 of the principal Third World biomedical journals. Provides searchable abstracts and bibliographical data with full-text images, including illustrations and graphs.

610 310   US   ISSN 1074-8849
R11
FACTS ABOUT FAMILY PRACTICE. 1987. a. $60 to non-members; members $40. American Academy of Family Physicians, 8880 Ward Pkwy., Kansas City, MO 64114. TEL 800-274-2237. Ed. Gordon Schmittling. circ. 3,500. (back issues avail.)
Description: Provides statistics on family medicine, such as income, patient visits, ratio of physicians to population. Designed for use by the medical community.

FIRE STATISTICS UNITED KINGDOM. see *FIRE PREVENTION — Abstracting, Bibliographies, Statistics*

610 362   UK   ISSN 1350-9497
THE FITZHUGH DIRECTORY OF N H S TRUSTS. FINANCIAL INFORMATION. 1993. a. £195. (Norwich Union Healthcare, W A F Health Care Consultant Ltd.) Health Care Information Services, 12 Riverview Grove, London W4 3QJ, England. TEL 0181-995-1752. FAX 0181-742-2418. Ed. William Fitzhugh. charts; illus. **Document type:** directory.
—BLDSC (3948.417000).
Description: Summarizes the financial activities of institutions receiving N.H.S. funds and lists key personnel for each. Features articles by leading experts.

617.643   NZ   ISSN 0015-4725
QP535.F1   CODEN: FLUOA4
FLUORIDE. 1968. q. $50 (effective 1995 & 1996). International Society for Fluoride Research, 81 A Landscape Rd., Mount Eden, Auckland, New Zealand. TEL 64-9-6307114. E-mail: j.colquhoun@auckland.as.nz. Ed.Bd. bk.rev.; abstr.; bibl.; charts; illus.; stat. circ. 600. (also avail. in microform from UMI; reprint service avail. from ISI,UMI) **Indexed:** Biol.Abstr., C.I.S. Abstr., Cadscan, Chem.Abstr., Curr.Adv.Ecol.Sci., Curr.Cont., Dairy Sci.Abstr., Excerp.Med., Field Crop Abstr., Food Sci.& Tech.Abstr., Ind.Sci.Rev., Ind.Vet., INIS Atomind., Lead Abstr., Nutr.Abstr., Ocean.Abstr., Pollut.Abstr., Sci.Cit.Ind., Soils & Fert., Vet.Bull., Zincscan. **Document type:** academic/scholarly publication.
—BLDSC (3962.262800); CASDDS; Faxon; Genuine Article; UMI. **CCC.**
Description: Reports on biological, chemical, ecological, industrial, toxicological and clinical aspects of inorganic and organic fluoride compounds.
Refereed Serial

617.1   US   ISSN 1069-7004
FOCUS ON: SPORTS SCIENCE AND MEDICINE. m. $215. Institute for Scientific Information, 3501 Market St., Philadelphia, PA 19104. TEL 215-386-0100. FAX 215-386-2991. (U.K. addr.: Brunel Science Park, Brunel University, Uxbridge UB6 3PQ, England) (diskette format) **Document type:** academic/scholarly publication, bibliography.
Description: Provides bibliographic data and English-language author abstracts from international scholarly research journals and conference proceedings.

617   FR
FRANCE. SERVICE D'ETUDE DES STRATEGIES ET DES STATISTIQUES INDUSTRIELLES. RESULTATS TRIMESTRIELS DES ENQUETES DE BRANCHE. FABRICATION DE MATERIEL MEDICO-CHIRURGICAL ET DES PROTHESES. q. 180 F. (foreign 210 F.) (effective 1991). Service d'Etude des Strategies et des Statistiques Industrielles (SESSI), 85 Bd. du Montparnasse, 75270 Paris Cedex 06, France. TEL 45-56-42-34. FAX 45-56-40-71. stat.
Description: Provides detailed industry-wide performance statistics for comparative evaluations.

FRITZ-HUESER-INSTITUT FUER DEUTSCHE UND AUSLAENDISCHE ARBEITERLITERATUR. INFORMATIONEN. see *LITERATURE — Abstracting, Bibliographies, Statistics*

617   JA
GEKA SHUDANKAI SHOROKUSHU/TOKYO SURGICAL SOCIETY. ABSTRACTS. (Text in Japanese) 4/yr. Geka Shudankai, Tokyo Daigaku Igakubu Dai 1 Geka, 3-1, Hongo 7-chome, Bunkyo-ku, Tokyo 113, Japan. **Document type:** abstracting/indexing.

575.1   UK   ISSN 1356-1308
▼**GENE THERAPY (SHEFFIELD).** 1995. s-m. (diskette m.). £110 (diskette £115; both £175) (effective 1995). S U B I S, Mansion House, 19 Kingfield Rd., Sheffield S11 9AS, England. TEL 0114-2554433. FAX 0114-4626. E-mail: admin@sheffac.demon.co.uk. (also avail. in diskette format) **Document type:** abstracting/indexing.
Description: Current awareness service for researchers in clinical and life sciences.

619   US
GENERAL CLINICAL RESEARCH CENTERS; a research resources directory. 1978. biennial. free. U.S. National Institutes of Health, National Center for Research Resources, Westwood Bldg., Rm. 10A15, 5333 Westbard Ave., Bethesda, MD 20892. TEL 301-594-7938. circ. 9,000. **Document type:** government publication, directory.
Description: Directory of clinical research centers.

GESUNDHEITSFOERDERUNG. see *PHYSICAL FITNESS AND HYGIENE — Abstracting, Bibliographies, Statistics*

GREAT BRITAIN. GOVERNMENT STATISTICAL SERVICE. ABORTION STATISTICS. see *BIRTH CONTROL — Abstracting, Bibliographies, Statistics*

MEDICAL SCIENCES — ABSTRACTING, BIBLIOGRAPHIES, STATISTICS

616.99 UK ISSN 0143-4829
RC279.G7
GREAT BRITAIN. GOVERNMENT STATISTICAL SERVICE. CANCER STATISTICS REGISTRATIONS. ENGLAND AND WALES. 1979. a.? (Department of Health, Statistics Division) Government Statistical Service, SD2, Rm. 804, Hannibal House, Elephant and Castle, London SE1 6TE, England. TEL 0171-972-2193. (Orders to: Department of Health Leaflets, P.O. Box 21, Stanmore, Mddx. HA7 1AY, England) **Document type:** government publication.

616.04 UK ISSN 0265-3567
GREAT BRITAIN. GOVERNMENT STATISTICAL SERVICE. CONGENITAL MALFORMATION STATISTICS NOTIFICATIONS. 1983. a.? (Department of Health, Statistics Division) Government Statistical Service, SD2, Rm. 804, Hannibal House, Elephant and Castle, London SE1 6TE, England. TEL 0171-972-2193. (Orders to: Department of Health Leaflets, P.O. Box 21, Stanmore, Mddx. HA7 1AY, England) **Document type:** government publication.

616.863 310 UK ISSN 0143-1463
HV5840.G7
GREAT BRITAIN. HOME OFFICE. STATISTICS OF THE MISUSE OF DRUGS: SEIZURES AND OFFENDERS DEALT WITH, UNITED KINGDOM (YEAR). 1978. a. Home Office, 50 Queen Anne's Gate, London SW1H 9AT, England.
Former titles (until 1992): Great Britain. Home Office. Statistics of the Misuse of Drugs in the United Kingdom: Seizures and Offenders Dealt with; (until 1986): Great Britain. Home Office. Statistics of the Misuse of Drugs in the United Kingdom, Supplementary Tables.

016 616 UK
GROWTH FACTORS & CYTOKINES - CLINICAL. 1985. s-m. (diskette m.) £115 (diskette £115; both £175) (effective 1996). S U B I S, Mansion House, 19 Kingfield Rd., Sheffield S11 9AS, England. TEL 0114-2554433. FAX 0114-2554626. E-mail: admin@sheffac.demon.co.uk. (also avail. in diskette format) **Document type:** abstracting/indexing.
—CCC.
Supersedes in part: Growth Factors and Cytokines (ISSN 0964-7554); Which supersedes: Growth Factors (ISSN 0268-1595); Cytokines (ISSN 0960-3212); Which was formerly (until 1990): Lymphokines (ISSN 0264-9586)
Description: Current awareness service for researchers in clinical and life sciences.

616.1 US
HANDBOOK OF HYPERLIPIDAEMIA. 1990. a. $59.95. Current Science, 400 Market St., Ste. 700, Philadelphia, PA 19106. TEL 215-574-2210; 800-552-5866. FAX 215-574-3533. (And: Current Science Ltd., 34-42 Cleveland St., London W1P 6LB, England. TEL 0171-323-0323. FAX 0171-636-6911) Ed. G.R. Thompson. illus.
Document type: academic/scholarly publication.
Description: For lipid and cardiovascular specialists as well as the general practitioner. Covers all aspects of hyperlipidemia including pathophysiology, classification and clinical practice.

610 US ISSN 0163-0458
HEALTH DEVICES ALERTS; a summary of reported problems, hazards, recalls, and updates. (Includes: Health Devices Alerts Action Items; Health Devices Alerts Abstracts; Health Devices Alerts F D A Data; Health Devices Alerts Implants; Health Devices Alerts Hazards Bulletin) 1976. w. $595. (Emergency Care Research Institute) E C R I, 5200 Butler Pike, Plymouth Meeting, PA 19462. TEL 610-825-6000. FAX 610-834-1275. abstr. (back issues avail.)
●Also available online. Vendor(s): Knight-Ridder, Inc. (File no.198).
Also available on CD-ROM.
—BLDSC (4274.963500). **CCC.**
Description: Includes over 250,000 reports from international sources, focusing on problems with equipment, disposables, in vitro diagnostics, implants, and other critical devices.
Refereed Serial

HEALTH DEVICES SOURCEBOOK. see *MEDICAL SCIENCES*

610.73 016
HEALTH INDEX. (Not avail. in printed format) updated m. $80 per hour on BRS and DIALOG; $94.80 on Data-Star; $1600 on CD-ROM. Information Access Company (Subsidiary of: Thomson Corporation), 362 Lakeside Dr., Foster City, CA 94404. TEL 415-378-5200; 800-227-8431. FAX 415-378-5369. **Document type:** abstracting/indexing.
●Also available online. Vendor(s): Ovid Technologies (HEAL), Data-Star (HLTH), Knight-Ridder, Inc. (File no.149).
Also available on CD-ROM.

610 016.05 US ISSN 1077-9469
▼**HEALTH INDUSTRY QUICKSOURCE;** a complete descriptive reference to healthcare information resources. 1994. a. $225 (effective Nov. 1994). QuickSource Press, 10 Pelham Ave., Nanuet, NY 10954-3428. TEL 800-576-4342. Ed. Mary Jeanne Cilurzo; Pub John F. Vellardito. **Document type:** bibliography, directory.
●Also available on CD-ROM.

610 015 US ISSN 0162-0843
CODEN: HSSED4
HEALTH SCIENCES SERIALS. 1979. q. $19 (foreign $23.75) (effective 1995). U.S. National Library of Medicine, 8600 Rockville Pike, Bethesda, MD 20894. (Subscr. to: Superintendent of Documents, U.S. Government Printing Office, Box 371954, Pittsburgh, PA 15250-7954. TEL 202-512-1800. FAX 202-512-2250) (microfiche) **Indexed:** MEDOC.
Document type: bibliography, government publication.
●Also available online. Vendor(s): National Library of Medicine.
—BLDSC (4275.106710); CASDDS.
Description: Assists health sciences librarians in identifying serial titles and locating the nearest library from which they can be obtained on interlibrary loan.

360 614 UK ISSN 0268-0459
HEALTH SERVICE ABSTRACTS. 1974. m. £36 (rest of Europe £48; overseas £59.50). Department of Health, Library and Information Services, Health Service Information Unit, Rm. 5C07, Quarry House, Quarry Hill, Leeds LS2 7UE, England. TEL 0113-254-5072. FAX 0113-254-5084. (Subscr. to: Health Publications Unit, Department of Health, Manchester Rd., Heywood, Lancs. OL10 2PZ, England) Eds. Helen Wolfenden, Ray Ward. bibl. circ. 1,500. **Document type:** abstracting/indexing, government publication.
●Also available online. Vendor(s): Data-Star.
—BLDSC (4275.106745); UMI. **CCC.**
Incorporates (in May 1985): Hospital Abstracts (ISSN 0018-5507); Current Literature on Health Services (ISSN 0141-0571); Current Literature on General Medical Practice.
Description: Summarizes books, reports, journal articles, and other publications on the nonclinical aspects of health services, with emphasis on the U.K. Covers such topics as health service administration, policy and planning, economics and finance, compensation, and ethics.

610 US ISSN 0361-4468
RA407.3
HEALTH, UNITED STATES. a. price varies. U.S. National Center for Health Statistics, Data Dissemination Branch, 6525 Belcrest Rd., Hyattsville, MD 20782. TEL 301-436-8500. (Orders to: Superintendent of Documents, U.S. Government Printing Office, Box 371954, Pittsburgh, PA 15250-7954. TEL 202-512-1800. FAX 202-512-2250; Or: Bernan, 4611-F Assembly Dr., Lanham, MD 20706. TEL 301-459-7666. FAX 301-459-0056) **Document type:** government publication.

610 US ISSN 1073-0303
HEALTHCARE QUALITY ABSTRACTS. 1993. m. $98. C O R Healthcare Resources, Box 40959, Santa Barbara, CA 93140. TEL 805-564-2177. Ed. Dean H. Anderson. **Document type:** abstracting/indexing.
Description: Contains abstracts of quality improvement articles selected from more than 140 periodicals.

HELEN K. MUSSALLEM LIBRARY SELECTED ACQUISITIONS LIST. see *LIBRARY AND INFORMATION SCIENCES — Abstracting, Bibliographies, Statistics*

HIGH PERFORMANCE LIQUID CHROMATOGRAPHY. see *CHEMISTRY — Abstracting, Bibliographies, Statistics*

616.6 JA
HOKKAIDO TOSEKI RYOHO GAKKAI PUROGURAMU ENDAI SHOROKU/HOKKAIDO SOCIETY FOR DIALYSIS THERAPY. PROGRAM AND ABSTRACTS. (Text in Japanese) a. Hokkaido Toseki Ryoho Gakkai, 3, Nishi 7-chome, Kita 1-jo, Chuo-ku, Sapporo-shi, Hokkaido 090, Japan. **Document type:** abstracting/indexing.

616.07 JA
HOSHASEN EIKYO KENKYUJO HAPPYO RONBUN MOKUROKU/RADIATION EFFECTS RESEARCH FOUNDATION. BIBLIOGRAPHY OF PUBLISHED PAPERS. (Text in Japanese) 1960. a. Radiation Effects Research Foundation, 5-2, Hijiyama Koen, Minami-ku, Hiroshima-shi, Hiroshima-ken 732, Japan. **Document type:** bibliography.

HUMAN REPRODUCTION UPDATE. see *BIOLOGY — Abstracting, Bibliographies, Statistics*

610 016 HU ISSN 0441-4438
HUNGARIAN MEDICAL BIBLIOGRAPHY; abstracts. (Text in English) 1961. s-a. 2400 Ft.($30) Orszagos Orvostudomanyi Informacios Intezet es Konyvtar - National Institute for Medical Information and Library of Medicine, Szentkiralyi u. 21, 1088 Budapest, Hungary. TEL 36-1-117-6352. FAX 36-1-266-9710. Ed. Julia Angyal; Pub. Dr. Alexander Fedinecz. circ. 320. **Document type:** bibliography.
—BLDSC (4337.035000).

610 FR ISSN 1011-8624
IMMUNIZATIONS/VACCINATIONS/VACUNACIONES. (Text in English, French, Spanish) 1977. 3/yr. 360 F. for 2 yrs. Centre International de l'Enfance - International Children's Center, Chateau de Longchamp, Bois de Boulogne, 75016 Paris, France. TEL 1-45-20-79-92. FAX 1-45-25-73-67. **Document type:** abstracting/indexing.
Description: Abstracts on program evaluation, investigation of new vaccines, immunization policies, epidemiological impact, technical aspects: vaccinal associations, schedules, cold chain, logistics.

IMMUNOASSAY. see *CHEMISTRY — Abstracting, Bibliographies, Statistics*

615.37 016 US ISSN 0307-112X
QR180
IMMUNOLOGY ABSTRACTS. 1976. m. $945 (foreign $995). Cambridge Scientific Abstracts, 7200 Wisconsin Ave., 6th Fl., Bethesda, MD 20814. TEL 301-961-6750. FAX 301-961-6720. E-mail: market@csa.com. Ed.Bd; Pub. Ted Caris. adv.; abstr.; index. (also avail. in magnetic tape; back issues avail.) **Indexed:** Cal.Tiss.Abstr., Chemorec.Abstr., Comput.& Info.Sys., Oncol.Abstr., Pollut.Abstr. **Document type:** abstracting/indexing.
●Also available online. Vendor(s): Knight-Ridder, Inc. (File no.76/LIFE SCIENCES COLLECTION), STN International (LIFESCI).
Also available on CD-ROM. Producer(s): SilverPlatter Information, Inc..
—BLDSC (4369.701000).
Description: Covers immune systems in humans and animals, both basic research and clinical applications.

MEDICAL SCIENCES — ABSTRACTING, BIBLIOGRAPHIES, STATISTICS

610 016   US   ISSN 0019-3879
Z6660
INDEX MEDICUS. (Compiled annually in Cumulated Index Medicus (ISSN 0090-1423). Medical Subject Headings (MSH) is published as Part 2 of the Jan. Index Medicus.) 1960. m. $260 (foreign $325) (includes List of Journals Indexed in Index Medicus and Medical Subject Headings). U.S. National Library of Medicine, 8600 Rockville Pike, Bethesda, MD 20894. (Subscr. to: Superintendent of Documents, U.S. Government Printing Office, Box 371954, Pittsburgh, PA 15250-7954. TEL 202-512-1800. FAX 202-512-2250) circ. 6,000. (also avail. in microform from UMI,PMC) **Indexed:** JAMA, MEDOC, Popul.Ind. **Document type:** abstracting/indexing, bibliography, government publication.
●Also available online. Vendor(s): Knight-Ridder, Inc. (File nos.154 & 155/MEDLINE), National Library of Medicine, Ovid Technologies (MESH, MESZ), STN International (MEDLINE).
Also available on CD-ROM. Producer(s): Cambridge Scientific Abstracts (Compact Cambridge MEDLINE), Knight-Ridder, Inc. (DIALOG OnDisc MEDLINE), SilverPlatter Information, Inc. (MEDLINE).
—BLDSC (4382.500000); UMI.
Description: Compiles and lists articles from 3,000 of the world's leading biomedical journals published in 36 languages.

610   RU   ISSN 0206-0515
INDEX OF CURRENT MEDICAL LITERATURE IN THE U S S R; including the medical demographic statistics of the U S S R. s-m. N P O Soyuzmedinform, Moskvoretskaya Nab 2A, 109240 Moscow, Russia.
Description: Covers all publications in the biomedical sciences in the USSR.

617.6 016   US   ISSN 0019-3992
Z6668
INDEX TO DENTAL LITERATURE; an alphabetical author and subject index to dental literature. q. (annual cumulation). $250 (including bound vol.). American Dental Association, Department of Library Services, 211 E. Chicago Ave., Chicago, IL 60611. TEL 312-440-2500. FAX 312-440-2550. circ. 1,100. (also avail. in microform from UMI; reprint service avail. from UMI) **Document type:** abstracting/indexing.
●Also available online. Vendor(s): Ovid Technologies (MESH, MESZ), Knight-Ridder, Inc. (File nos.154 & 155/MEDLINE), National Library of Medicine, STN International (MEDLINE).
Also available on CD-ROM. Producer(s): Cambridge Scientific Abstracts (Compact Cambridge MEDLINE), Knight-Ridder, Inc. (DIALOG OnDisc MEDLINE), SilverPlatter Information, Inc. (MEDLINE).
—BLDSC (4377.800000); UMI.

617.6 016   AG   ISSN 0325-0679
INDICE DE LA LITERATURA DENTAL EN CASTELLANO. 1950. a. $40. Asociacion Odontologica Argentina, Junin 959, Buenos Aires, Argentina. TEL 541-9611062. FAX 541-9611110. E-mail: postmaster@asoda.sld.ar. bibl. circ. 300. **Document type:** abstracting/indexing.
●Also available on CD-ROM.
Supersedes: Indice de la Literatura Dental Periodica en Castellano y Portugues.

610 016   SP   ISSN 0019-7068
INDICE MEDICO ESPANOL. 1965. 3/yr. 5000 ptas. to individuals; institutions 6000 ptas.; foreign 7000 ptas. (Instituto de Estudios Documentales e Historicos sobre la Ciencia) Generalitat Valenciana, Conselleria de Sanitat i Consum, Avda. Blasco Ibanez - 17, 46010 Valencia, Spain. TEL 96-361-06-54. FAX 96-3613975. Dir. Maria-Luz Terrada Ferrandis. circ. 2,000. (reprint service avail.) **Indexed:** Nutr.Abstr. **Document type:** abstracting/indexing.
●Also available online.
Also available on CD-ROM.
Description: Two issues each year list Spanish medical bibliographic references and the third lists Spanish authors and their works.

016.6176   US   ISSN 0534-669X
INTERNATIONAL ASSOCIATION FOR DENTAL RESEARCH. ABSTRACTS OF THE GENERAL MEETING. Variant title: Program and Abstracts of Papers. (Special issue of: Journal of Dental Research (ISSN 0022-0345)) 1919. a. $30. International Association for Dental Research, 1619 Duke St., Alexandria, VA 22314. TEL 703-548-0066. (Co-sponsor: American Association for Dental Research) Ed. Mark C. Herzberg. adv. circ. 9,500. (also avail. in microform from UMI) **Indexed:** Dent.Abstr. **Document type:** proceedings.
—CCC.

340.6 016   US   ISSN 0098-2393
INTERNATIONAL BIBLIOGRAPHY OF THE FORENSIC SCIENCES.* 1975. biennial. $25. International Reference Organization in Forensic Medicine and Sciences, c/o William G. Eckert, M.D., Ed., 1877 Claudia Ave., Simi Valley, CA 93065-3642. TEL 316-268-5000.

617.11 016   US   ISSN 0090-0575
Z6667.B8
INTERNATIONAL BIBLIOGRAPHY ON BURNS.* 1969. a., latest 1985. $25. National Institute for Burn Medicine, P.O. Box 15138, Ann Arbor, MI 48106-5138. TEL 313-769-9000. Ed. Dr. Irving Feller. circ. 1,000. **Document type:** bibliography.

610.73 016   US   ISSN 0020-8124
Z6675.N7
INTERNATIONAL NURSING INDEX. 1966. q. $280 (foreign $310). (American Nurses' Association) American Journal of Nursing Co., 555 W. 57th St., New York, NY 10019. TEL 212-582-8820. Ed. Frederick W. Pattison. index. circ. 1,917. (also avail. in microform from UMI; reprint service avail. from UMI) **Indexed:** JAMA. **Document type:** abstracting/indexing.
●Also available online. Vendor(s): Ovid Technologies, Knight-Ridder, Inc. (File nos.154 & 155/MEDLINE), National Library of Medicine, STN International (MEDLINE).
Also available on CD-ROM. Producer(s): Cambridge Scientific Abstracts (Compact Cambridge MEDLINE), Knight-Ridder, Inc. (DIALOG OnDisc MEDLINE), SilverPlatter Information, Inc. (MEDLINE).
—BLDSC (4544.449000); UMI.
Description: Covers over 270 international nursing journals.

INTERNATIONAL RARE BOOK PRICES - SCIENCES & MEDICINE. see *PUBLISHING AND BOOK TRADE — Abstracting, Bibliographies, Statistics*

610 362   JA   ISSN 0911-8411
JAPAN. MINISTRY OF HEALTH AND WELFARE. STATISTICS AND INFORMATION DEPARTMENT. REPORT ON ACTIVITIES OF PUBLIC HEALTH CENTERS. Key Title: Hokenjo Un'ei Hokoku. a. 3090 Yen. Ministry of Health and Welfare, Statistics and Information Department - Koseisho Daijin Kanbo Tokei Johobu, 7-3 Ichigaya-Honmura-cho, Shinjuku-ku, Tokyo 162, Japan. TEL 03-3260-3181. FAX 03-3269-8824. (Subscr. to: Health & Welfare Statistics Association, 5-13-14 Roppongi, Minato-ku, Tokyo, Japan. TEL 03-3586-3361. FAX 03-3584-4710) **Document type:** government publication.
Formerly (until 1960): Hokenjo Un'ei Hokoku Nenpo (ISSN 0437-6633)

JATROS DERMATOLOGIE. see *MEDICAL SCIENCES — Dermatology And Venereology*

JATROS GYNAEKOLOGIE. see *MEDICAL SCIENCES — Obstetrics And Gynecology*

JATROS H N O. see *MEDICAL SCIENCES — Otorhinolaryngology*

JATROS NEUROLOGIE PSYCHIATRIE UND PSYCHOTHERAPIE. see *MEDICAL SCIENCES — Psychiatry And Neurology*

JATROS ORTHOPAEDIE - RHEUMATOLOGIE - SPORTMEDIZIN. see *MEDICAL SCIENCES — Orthopedics And Traumatology*

JATROS PAEDIATRIE. see *MEDICAL SCIENCES — Pediatrics*

JATROS UROLOGIE. see *MEDICAL SCIENCES — Urology And Nephrology*

616.3   BG   ISSN 0253-8768
CODEN: JDDREM
JOURNAL OF DIARRHOEAL DISEASES RESEARCH. 1983. q. $70 for SAARC countries; elsewhere $100. International Centre for Diarrhoeal Disease Research, Bangladesh, G.P.O. Box 128, Dhaka 1000, Bangladesh. TEL 600171-78. FAX 880-2-883116. TELEX 675612 ICDD BJ. E-mail: msik%cholera@external.ait.ac.th. Ed. R. Eeckels. bk.rev.; bibl. circ. 450.
—BLDSC (4969.460000); Faxon; Genuine Article; SWETS; UnCover. **CCC**.
Description: Publishes review articles, original research articles, short communications, preliminary communications, and letters dealing with all aspects of diarrheal diseases.

610 016   GW   ISSN 0022-9113
KARTEI DER PRAKTISCHEN MEDIZIN;* unabhaengige Referatenzeitschrift des in- und auslaendischen Fachschrifttums. 1927. s-m. DM.58. Hippokrates Verlag GmbH, Postfach 300504, 70445 Stuttgart, Germany. TEL 0711-8931-0. FAX 0711-8931453. bk.rev.; abstr.; illus.; index. (cards) **Document type:** abstracting/indexing.

618   US   ISSN 0896-4467
KEY OBSTETRICS AND GYNECOLOGY. 1988. q. $75 to individuals (foreign $89); institutions $112.50 (foreign $126.50); students $47.25 (foreign $61.25). Mosby - Year Book, Inc. (Subsidiary of: Times Mirror Company), 11830 Westline Industrial Dr., St. Louis, MO 63146. TEL 314-872-8370; 800-325-4177. FAX 314-432-1380. TELEX 44-2402.
—CCC.
Description: Provides abstracts from the world's scientific literature covering new diagnostic techniques, new therapeutic approaches, and new issues, trends, discoveries, and developments.

616.6   US   ISSN 0940-7936
CODEN: KIDEET
KIDNEY (NEW YORK, 1992); a current survey of world literature. 1992. bi-m. $116 (effective 1996). Springer-Verlag, Journals, 175 Fifth Ave., New York, NY 10010. TEL 212-460-1500. FAX 212-473-6272. (N. American subscr. to: Journal Fulfillment Services, Box 2485, Secaucus, NJ 07096-2491. TEL 800-777-4643; Subscr. outside N. America: Heidelberger Platz 3, 1000 Berlin 33, Germany. TEL 030-8207-1. FAX 030-82140091) Eds. J.A.L. Arruda, George Dunea. adv.: B&W page $650, color page $1525; trim 8 1/4 x 11. circ. 3,000. (reprint service avail.) **Document type:** abstracting/indexing.
Description: Summarizes the most important articles in the field.
Refereed Serial

618.92 016   GW   ISSN 0340-5877
DER KINDERARZT. 1953. bi-m. DM.160. (Berufsverband der Kinderaerzte Deutschlands e.V.) Hansisches Verlagskontor H. Scheffler, 23547 Luebeck, Germany. Eds. Dr. H. Olbing, Dr. K. Gritz. **Indexed:** Dok.Arbeitsmed. **Document type:** academic/scholarly publication.
—BLDSC (5095.580000).

618.92   JA
KITA NIHON SHONIKA GAKKAI SHOROKUSHU/PEDIATRICS SOCIETY OF NORTH JAPAN. ABSTRACTS. (Text in Japanese) a. Kita Nihon Shonika Gakkai, Asahikawa Ika Daigaku Shonikagaku Kyoshitsu, 3-11, 5 Go, Nihikagura 4 Sen, Asahikawa-shi, Hokkaido 078, Japan.

610 016   KO   ISSN 0047-360X
KOREAN MEDICAL ABSTRACTS. (Text in English) 1971. q. $25. Korea Institute for Economics and Technology, P.O. Box 250, 206-9 Cheongryangri-Dong, Dongdaimun-Ku, S. Korea. abstr.; index. circ. 400. (also avail. in microfilm; reprint service avail. from UMI)

MEDICAL SCIENCES — ABSTRACTING, BIBLIOGRAPHIES, STATISTICS

016 610   BL
Z6661.L29
LILACS-CD-ROM. (Literatura Latinoamericana y del Caribe en Ciencias de la Salud) (Text in English, Portuguese and Spanish) 1979. q. $150 in Latin America; elsewhere $200. (Panamerican Health Organization) Latin American and Caribbean Center on Health Sciences Information (BIREME), Rua Botucatu, 862, Caixa Postal 20.381, V. Clementino, 04023-062 Sao Paulo, SP, Brazil. TEL 011-5492611. FAX 011-5711919. TELEX 11-22143 OPAS BR. E-mail: bireme@BRFAPESP.BITNET. (Affiliate: World Health Organization) abstr.; bibl. circ. 500. (back issues avail.) Document type: bibliography.
●Available only on CD-ROM.
Formerly (until 1992): Index Medicus Latinoamericano (ISSN 0100-4743)
Description: Contains abstracts of articles from more than 650 Latin American titles.

610 016   SW   ISSN 0075-9813
LIST BIO-MED; biomedical serials in Nordic libraries. (Text in English) 1965. irreg. SEK 350. Karolinska Institutets Bibliotek och Informationscentral, P.O. Box 200, S-171 77 Stockholm, Sweden. FAX 46-8-348793. circ. 500. Document type: bibliography.

610.73   CN   ISSN 0844-0999
LIST OF CANADIAN NURSING-RELATED PERIODICALS. (Text in English, French) a. Can.$5. Canadian Nurses Association - Association des Infirmieres et Infirmiers du Canada, 50 Driveway, Ottawa, ON K2P 1E2, Canada. TEL 613-237-2133. FAX 613-237-3520. Document type: catalog.
Description: Catalog of Canadian periodicals in nursing, listed alphabetically. Information includes titles, the frequency of publication, where the periodicals may be obtained and the approximate cost.

610   US   ISSN 0093-3821
Z6660   CODEN: LJIMDR
LIST OF JOURNALS INDEXED IN INDEX MEDICUS. 1960. a. $16 (foreign $20). U.S. National Library of Medicine, 8600 Rockville Pike, Bethesda, MD 20894. (Orders to: Superintendent of Documents, U.S. Government Printing Office, Box 371954, Pittsburgh, PA 15250-7954. TEL 202-512-1800. FAX 202-512-2250; Or: Bernan, 4611-F Assembly Dr., Lanham, MD 20706. TEL 301-459-7666. FAX 301-459-0056) circ. 3,500. Document type: bibliography, government publication.
—BLDSC (5233.400000); CASDDS.
Description: Lists the 3,000 journals indexed in Index Medicus as of January 1990.

610 015   US   ISSN 0736-7139
Z6660
LIST OF SERIALS INDEXED FOR ONLINE USERS. 1980. a. $24 in N. America; overseas $48. U.S. National Library of Medicine, 8600 Rockville Pike, Bethesda, MD 20894. (Orders to: National Technical Information Service, 5285 Port Royal Rd., Springfield, VA 22161. TEL 703-487-4650. FAX 703-321-8547; Or: Bernan, 4611-F Assembly Dr., Lanham, MD 20706. TEL 301-459-7666. FAX 301-459-0056) Document type: bibliography, government publication.
●Also available online. Vendor(s): National Library of Medicine.
Formerly: List of Serials and Monographs Indexed for Online Users (ISSN 0196-755X)
Description: Provides complete bibliographic information on serials and congress proceedings. Contains about 7,606 titles listed alphabetically by abbreviated title followed by full title.

610 614.7   US   ISSN 1065-0490
CODEN: LAHEE4
LITERATURE ABSTRACTS: HEALTH & ENVIRONMENT. (Part of: Literature Abstracts) w. American Petroleum Institute, Central Abstracting & Information Services, 275 Seventh Ave., New York, NY 10001-6708. TEL 212-366-4040. FAX 212-366-4298. Document type: abstracting/indexing.
Formerly (until 1991): A P I Abstracts - Health and Environment.

LUNGE UND ATMUNG. see *MEDICAL SCIENCES — Respiratory Diseases*

610 011   AT   ISSN 1035-5693
M I M S DISEASE INDEX. biennial. Aus.$90. M I M S Australia, 48 Albany St., Crows Nest, N.S.W. 2065, Australia.

610 016   SA   ISSN 0580-6755
M I M S MEDICAL SPECIALITIES. (Monthly Index of Medical Specialties) Key Title: Mims (Pretoria). 1960. m. M I M S, Division of Times Media Limited, P.O. Box 2059, Pretoria 0001, South Africa. TEL 27-12-3485010. FAX 27-12-477716. Eds. R.J. van Rooyen, J.R. Sayman. adv.; index, cum.index; circ. 7,610 (paid). Indexed: Curr.Adv.Ecol.Sci.
Formerly: M I M S (ISSN 0027-0431)
Description: An index containing medicines available in South Africa in pharmacological order, alphabetically.

610 016   HU   ISSN 0025-0252
MAGYAR ORVOSI BIBLIOGRAFIA; bibliographia medica Hungarica. 1957. bi-m. 2450 Ft. Orszagos Orvostudomanyi Informacios Intezet es Konyvtar - National Institute for Medical Information and Library of Medicine, Szentkiralyi u. 21, 1088 Budapest, Hungary. TEL 36-1-117-6352. FAX 36-1-266-9710. Ed. Julia Angyal; Pub. Dr. Alexander Fedinecz. bibl.; index. circ. 350. Document type: bibliography.

MAKERERE UNIVERSITY. ALBERT COOK LIBRARY. LIBRARY BULLETIN AND ACCESSION LIST. see *LIBRARY AND INFORMATION SCIENCES — Abstracting, Bibliographies, Statistics*

MANAGED HEALTH CARE OVERVIEW. see *INSURANCE — Abstracting, Bibliographies, Statistics*

610   GW   ISSN 0940-9866
MEDBOOK; Medienfuehrer fuer junge Mediziner. 1991. s-a. Varus Verlag Birgit Laube, Koenigswintererstr. 552, 53227 Bonn, Germany. TEL 0228-440015. FAX 0228-440017. Ed. Detlef Mett. adv.; page DM.1387; trim 275 x 180. circ. 16,000. (back issues avail.) Document type: academic/scholarly publication.

MEDEXPRES. see *PUBLIC HEALTH AND SAFETY — Abstracting, Bibliographies, Statistics*

613.7 614.8   US   ISSN 0730-7810
MEDICAL ABSTRACTS NEWSLETTER; your direct pipeline to the latest breakthroughs in health care. 1981. m. $24.95. Communi-T Publications, Box 2170, Teaneck, NJ 07666. TEL 201-836-5030. FAX 201-836-5030. Ed. Toni L. Goldfarb; Pub. Toni L. Goldfarb. Indexed: CHNI. Document type: newsletter, consumer publication.

610 016   US   ISSN 0000-085X
Z6658
MEDICAL AND HEALTH CARE BOOKS AND SERIALS IN PRINT; an index to literature in health sciences. (Issued in 2 vols.) 1972. a. $229.95. R.R. Bowker, A Reed Reference Publishing company, 121 Chanlon Rd., New Providence, NJ 07974. TEL 908-464-6800. FAX 908-665-3502. TELEX 138 755. (Subscr. to: Order Dept., Box 31, New Providence, NJ 07974-9903. TEL 800-521-8110) (also avail. in magnetic tape) Document type: bibliography, directory.
●Also available online. Vendor(s): Knight-Ridder, Inc.; Ovid Technologies (BBIP,ULRI).
Also available on CD-ROM.
—BLDSC (5525.955000). CCC.
Former titles (until 1985): Medical Books and Serials in Print (ISSN 0000-0574); (until 1978): Medical Books in Print (ISSN 0076-5929)
Description: Provides a comprehensive reference to currently published books and international serials in the biomedical and specialized health sciences, for professionals, students, librarians and others in the health sciences community. Provides bibliographic and ordering information, book classifications by subject, author and title, with an index to publishers and distributors; serial publications are classified by subject and title.

610.285   US   ISSN 1063-1178
MEDICAL & PHARMACEUTICAL BIOTECHNOLOGY ABSTRACTS. 1984. bi-m. $275 (foreign $285). Cambridge Scientific Abstracts, 7200 Wisconsin Ave., 6th Fl., Bethesda, MD 20814. TEL 301-961-6700. FAX 301-961-6720. E-mail: market@csa.com. Pub. Ted Caris. Document type: abstracting/indexing.
●Also available online. Vendor(s): Knight-Ridder, Inc. (File no.76/LIFE SCIENCES COLLECTION), STN International (LIFESCI).
Also available on CD-ROM. Producer(s): SilverPlatter Information, Inc..
—BLDSC (5525.989000).
Supersedes in part (in 1993): Biotechnology Research Abstracts (ISSN 0733-5709)

616.5   US   ISSN 0944-5196
CODEN: MSDEEJ
▼**MEDICAL & SURGICAL DERMATOLOGY;** a critical guide to world literature. 1994. bi-m. $132 (effective 1996). Springer-Verlag, Journals, 175 Fifth Ave., New York, NY 10010. TEL 212-460-1500. FAX 212-473-6272. (Subscr. in N. America to: Journal Fulfillment Services, Box 2485, Secaucus, NJ 07096-2491. TEL 800-777-4643. FAX 201-348-4505; Subscr. outside N. America to: Heidelberger Platz 3, 1000 Berlin 33, Germany. TEL 030-8207-0. FAX 030-8214091) Eds. Kenneth A. Arndt, Robert S. Stern. illus. (also avail. in microform from UMI; back issues avail.; reprint service avail.) Document type: academic/scholarly publication, abstracting/indexing.
Description: Abstracts 75-100 important articles from more than 160 medical journals and comments on the clinical and therapeutic issues facing practicing dermatologists.
Refereed Serial

016.61   II   ISSN 0025-7060
MEDICAL BOOK NEWS; a guide to new books. (Text in English) 1967. bi-m. Rs.200($50) Medical Publications, 6 Owners Court, Near Strand Cinema, Colaba, Bombay 400 005, India. TEL 022-233962. FAX 022-202-2267. TELEX 11-2466-5863-KTKIN. Ed. Dr. Champaklal K. Parikh. adv.; bk.rev. circ. 3,000.
Description: To be used by institutions as a basis for selection of books to be purchased.

MEDICAL CARE RESEARCH AND REVIEW. see *PUBLIC HEALTH AND SAFETY — Abstracting, Bibliographies, Statistics*

610 016   II   ISSN 0025-7109
MEDICAL CHECKLIST. 1966. bi-m. Rs.150($30) K.K. Roy (Private) Ltd., 55 Gariahat Rd., P.O. Box 10210, Calcutta 700 019, India. Ed. K.K. Roy. adv.; bk.rev.; bibl.; index. circ. 1,750. (looseleaf format)

MEDICAL COMPANIES GUIDE TO JAPAN. see *PHARMACY AND PHARMACOLOGY — Abstracting, Bibliographies, Statistics*

610   US   ISSN 0147-5711
Z695.1.M48
MEDICAL SUBJECT HEADINGS - ANNOTATED ALPHABETIC LIST. (Supplement avail.: Medical Subject Headings - Supplementary Chemical Records (Year) (ISSN 0897-3994)) a. $42 for print edition (foreign $84); microfiche edition $24 (foreign $48). U.S. National Library of Medicine, 8600 Rockville Pike, Bethesda, MD 20894. (Orders to: National Technical Information Service, U.S. Department of Commerce, 5285 Port Royal Rd., Springfield, VA 22161. TEL 703-487-4650. FAX 703-321-8547; Or: Bernan, 4611-F Assembly Dr., Lanham, MD 20706. TEL 301-459-7666. FAX 301-459-0056) (also avail. in microfiche) Document type: government publication.

MEDICAL SCIENCES — ABSTRACTING, BIBLIOGRAPHIES, STATISTICS

610 540 US ISSN 0891-3994
MEDICAL SUBJECT HEADINGS - SUPPLEMENTARY CHEMICAL RECORDS (YEAR). (Supplement to: Medical Headings - Annotated Alphabetic List (Year) (ISSN 0147-5711)) a. $50 for print edition (foreign $100); microfiche edition $23 (foreign $46). U.S. National Library of Medicine, 8600 Rockville Pike, Bethesda, MD 20894. (Orders to: National Technical Information Service, 5285 Port Royal Rd., Springfield, VA 22161. TEL 703-487-4650. FAX 703-321-8547; Or: Bernan, 4611-F Assembly Dr., Lanham, MD 20706. TEL 301-459-7666. FAX 301-459-0056) (also avail. in microfiche) **Document type:** government publication.
Description: Assists indexers and users of Index Medicus and Medline in obtaining entries that are more specific than those found in Medical Subject Headings. Lists approximately 22,000 chemicals.

610 US ISSN 0147-099X
Z695.1.M48
MEDICAL SUBJECT HEADINGS - TREE STRUCTURE (YEAR). a. $39 for print edition (foreign $78); microfiche edition $18 (foreign $36). U.S. National Library of Medicine, 8600 Rockville Pike, MD 20894. (Orders to: National Technical Information Service, 5285 Port Royal Rd., Springfield, VA 22161. TEL 703-487-4650. FAX 703-321-8547; Or: Bernan, 4611-F Assembly Dr., Lanham, MD 20706. TEL 301-459-7666. FAX 301-459-0056) (also avail. in microfiche) **Document type:** government publication.
Description: Contains all the Medical Subject Headings currently in use among the National Library of Medicine indexers, catalogers, and searchers.

400 610 UK
▼**MEDICINAL AND AROMATIC PLANTS.** 1994. irreg. CAB International, Wallingford, Oxon. OX10 8DE, England. TEL 01491-832111. FAX 01491-833508. TELEX 847964 COMAGG G. E-mail: cabi@cabi.org. (Subscr. in N. America to: CAB International, 845 N. Park Ave., Tucson, AZ 85719. TEL 800-528-4841. FAX 602-621-3816) (also avail. in diskette format) **Document type:** bibliography.
Description: Annotated bibliographies covering medicinal, aromatic and pesticidal plants.

610 II ISSN 0250-4367
MEDICINAL AND AROMATIC PLANTS ABSTRACTS. (Text in English) 1979. bi-m. Rs.450($200) Council of Scientific and Industrial Research, Publications & Information Directorate, Hillside Rd., New Delhi 110 012, India. TEL 11-5726014. FAX 11-5787062. TELEX 031-77271. E-mail: pid@sirnet.d.ernet.in. Ed. H.C. Jain. adv.; bk.rev. circ. 400. **Indexed:** Hort.Abstr. **Document type:** abstracting/indexing.
●Also available online.
Description: Reports current world literature on medicinal and aromatic plants. Covers about 600 journals published in 22 languages from 55 countries of the world.

618 DK ISSN 0904-1966
RG503.2.D4
MEDICINSK FOEDSELSSTATISTIK OG MISDANNELSESSTATISTIK. (Included in the series: Vitalstatistik) 1973. biennial. DKK 60. Sundhedsstyrelsen, Amaliegade 13, 1012 Copenhagen K, Denmark. (Subscr. to: Statens Informationtjeneste, P.O. Box 1103, 1009 Copenhagen K, Denmark)
Formerly: Medicinsk Foedselsstatistik (ISSN 0107-7597)

610 JA
MEDIFAX INDEX. (Text in Japanese) 1986. m. membership. Yakugyo Jiho Co., Ltd., 2-36, Kanda Jinbocho, Chiyoda-ku, Tokyo 101, Japan.

610 016 016 GW
MEDIZIN IM UMWELTSCHUTZ. 1977. 4/yr. DM.52. Landesinstitut fuer den Oeffentlichen Gesundheitsdienst Nordrhein-Westfalen, Westerfeldstr. 15, 33611 Bielefeld, Germany. TEL 0521-8007265. FAX 0521-8007200. (Subscr. to: Postfach 201012, 33548 Bielefeld, Germany) Ed. Eva-Maria Dreitzel. bk.rev.; cum.index. circ. 330. **Document type:** abstracting/indexing.
Formerly: Dokumentation Medizin im Umweltschutz (ISSN 0342-0795)

610 011 GW
MEDIZINISCHER LITERATUR ANZEIGER; bibliographische Zeitschrift fuer medizinische Neuerscheinungen. 1950. m. DM.22.80. Dustri-Verlag Dr. Karl Feistle, Bahnhofstr. 9, 82041 Deisenhofen, Germany. TEL 089-6138610. FAX 089-6135412. Ed. Joerg Feistle. circ. 6,000. **Document type:** bibliography.
Description: Bibliography of new medical books.

610 016.5 US
MEDLINE PROFESSIONAL - C D. (Compact Disc) bi-m. $695 for single user. SilverPlatter Information, Inc., 100 River Ridge Dr., Norwood, MA 02062. TEL 617-769-2599; 800-343-0064. FAX 617-769-8763. (U.K. addr.: 10 Barley Mow Passage, Chiswick, London W4 4PH, England. TEL 44-181-995-8242) **Document type:** abstracting/indexing.
●Available only on CD-ROM.
Formerly: ClinMed - C D.
Description: A subset of the entire MEDLINE database focusing on clinical medicine. Includes citations from more than 300 journals, primarily in English.

610 US ISSN 0097-9732
MEDOC: INDEX TO U S GOVERNMENT PUBLICATIONS IN THE MEDICAL AND HEALTH SCIENCES. 1975. q. $110 (foreign $115). Spencer S. Eccles Health Sciences Library, University of Utah, Bldg. 589, Salt Lake City, UT 84112. TEL 801-581-5268. FAX 801-581-3632. Ed. Michael Thelin. bk.rev. circ. 400. (also avail. in microfiche) **Document type:** abstracting/indexing.
Description: Includes abstracts of selected documents.

MENTAL HEALTH STATISTICAL NOTES. see SOCIAL SERVICES AND WELFARE — Abstracting, Bibliographies, Statistics

616.89 UK ISSN 0260-5252
RA790.7.G7
MENTAL HEALTH STATISTICS FOR WALES. 1981. a. £5. Welsh Office, Statistical Directorate, New Crown Bldg., Cathays Park, Cardiff CF1 3NQ, Wales. TEL 01222-825044. FAX 01222-825350. TELEX 498228. Ed. E. Swires-Hennessy. stat. circ. 550. **Document type:** government publication.
—BLDSC (5678.589000). CCC.
Description: Specifics on mental illness and mental handicap services in Wales.

574.28 658.403 US ISSN 1060-8788
N C B I NEWS. 1991. 3/yr. free. U.S. National Center for Biotechnology Information, National Library of Medicine, Bldg. 38A, Rm. 8N-803, 8600 Rockville Pike, Bethesda, MD 20894. TEL 301-496-2475. FAX 301-480-9241. E-mail: info@ncbi.nlm.nih.gov. circ. 25,000. **Document type:** newsletter, government publication.
Description: Informs the biomedical community about N.C.B.I. research activities and the availability of molecular biology database and software services.

610.28 016 US
N T I S ALERTS: BIOMEDICAL TECHNOLOGY & HUMAN FACTORS ENGINEERING. w. $135 (foreign $195). U.S. National Technical Information Service, 5285 Port Royal Rd., Springfield, VA 22161. TEL 703-487-4630. FAX 703-321-8547. TELEX 64616. abstr.; index, cum.index. (back issues avail.)
Former titles: Abstract Newsletter: Biomedical Technology and Human Factors Engineering (ISSN 0163-1497); Weekly Abstract Newsletter: Biomedical Technology and Human Factors Engineering; Weekly Government Abstracts. Biomedical Technology and Human Factors Engineering; Weekly Government Abstracts. Biomedical Technology and Engineering (ISSN 0364-4952)

N T I S ALERTS: MEDICINE & BIOLOGY. (U.S. National Technical Information Service) see BIOLOGY — Abstracting, Bibliographies, Statistics

016 610 US ISSN 1052-9063
Z6660
NATIONAL LIBRARY OF MEDICINE. CURRENT BIBLIOGRAPHIES IN MEDICINE. 1966. irreg. (approx. 7/yr.). $47 (foreign $58.75) (effective 1995). U.S. National Library of Medicine, Reference Section, 8600 Rockville Pike, Bethesda, MD 20894. (Orders to: Superintendent of Documents, U.S. Government Printing Office, Box 371954, Pittsburgh, PA 15250-7954. TEL 202-512-1800. FAX 202-512-2250) circ. 1,000. **Document type:** bibliography, government publication.
Formerly: National Library of Medicine. Literature Search Series (ISSN 0083-2251)
Description: Documents approximately 7 bibliographies per year on a variety of biomedical topics, excluding AIDS (see AIDS Bibliography) similar to those found in the N.L.M. Literature Search Series.

610 016 US ISSN 0027-9641
NATIONAL LIBRARY OF MEDICINE. CURRENT CATALOG. (Also issued: N.L.M. Current Catalog Quarterly) 1966. q. (with a. cumulation). $34 (foreign $42.50); annual cumulation $76 (foreign $95). U.S. National Library of Medicine, 8600 Rockville Pike, Bethesda, MD 20894. (Orders to: Superintendent of Documents, U.S. Government Printing Office, Box 371954, Pittsburgh, PA 15250-7954. TEL 202-512-1800. FAX 202-512-2250) **Indexed:** MEDOC, Popul.Ind. **Document type:** bibliography, government publication.
Incorporates (1965-1980): Notes for Medical Catalogers (ISSN 0078-2025)
Description: Lists monographs and serials cataloged by the National Library of Medicine by subject and name.

616.8 US ISSN 1057-6096
NEUROSCIENCE CITATION INDEX. bi-m. $1450. Institute for Scientific Information, 3501 Market St., Philadelphia, PA 19104. TEL 215-386-0100. FAX 215-386-2991. (U.K. addr.: Brunel Science Park, Brunel University, Uxbridge UB6 3PQ, England) (also avail. in magnetic tape) **Document type:** academic/scholarly publication, bibliography.
●Also available on CD-ROM.
Description: Provides bibliographic data, cited references, related records and English-language author abstracts for international scholarly research journals and conference proceedings.

610 020 US
NEW ENGLAND SOUNDING LINE. 1991. bi-m. free. National Network of Libraries of Medicine, New England Region, Univ. of Connecticut Health Center, 263 Farmington Ave., Farmington, CT 06030-5370. TEL 203-679-4500. FAX 203-679-1305. Ed. Janet A. Ohles. **Document type:** newsletter.
Description: Covers activities of the National Network of Libraries of Medicine New England Region.

610 174 US ISSN 0361-6347
Z6675.E8
NEW TITLES IN BIOETHICS. 1975. q. $20 (foreign $30). Kennedy Institute of Ethics, National Reference Center for Bioethics Literature, Georgetown University, Washington, DC 20057-1065. TEL 202-687-3885. FAX 202-687-6770. Ed. Lucinda Fitch-Huttlinger. circ. 2,000. **Document type:** bibliography.
Description: Includes the Kampelman Collection of Jewish Ethics, the Shriver Collection of Christian Ethics and updates to the Syllabus Exchange catalog.

312.3 NZ
NEW ZEALAND HEALTH INFORMATION SERVICE. CANCER: NEW REGISTRATIONS AND DEATHS. a. NZ.$30. New Zealand Health Information Service, Ministry of Health, 133 Molesworth St., P.O. Box 5013, Wellington, New Zealand. TEL 04-496-2000. FAX 04-496-2040. stat.; circ. controlled.
Former titles: New Zealand. Health Statistical Services. Cancer Data: New Registrations and Deaths (ISSN 1171-6509); Cancer Data: Deaths and Cases Reported (ISSN 0548-9415)

MEDICAL SCIENCES — ABSTRACTING, BIBLIOGRAPHIES, STATISTICS 4305

616.8   NZ   ISSN 0548-992X
RC451.N4
NEW ZEALAND HEALTH INFORMATION SERVICE. MENTAL HEALTH DATA. Key Title: Mental Health Data. a. NZ.$30. New Zealand Health Information Service, Ministry of Health, 133 Molesworth St., P.O. Box 5013, Wellington, New Zealand. TEL 04-496-2188. FAX 04-496-2340. circ. controlled.
   Formerly: New Zealand. Health Statistical Services. Mental Health Data.

617.7 615.7   JA
NIHON GAN YAKURI GAKKAI PUROGURAMU KOEN YOSHISHU/JAPANESE SOCIETY FOR OCULAR PHARMACOLOGY. PROGRAM AND ABSTRACTS OF THE MEETING. (Text in Japanese) 1981. a. Nihon Gan Yakuri Gakkai, Tokyo Daigaku Igakubu Gankagaku Kyoshitsu, 3-1, Hongo 7-chome, Bunkyo-ku, Tokyo 113, Japan. **Document type:** abstracting/indexing.

617   JA
NIHON GEKAKEI RENGO GAKKAI GAKUJUTSU SHUKAI SHOROKUGO/JAPANESE COLLEGE OF SURGEONS. ABSTRACTS OF MEETING. (Text in English, Japanese) 1975. a. membership. Nihon Gekakei Rengo Gakkai, 4-3, Iidabashi 3-chome, Chiyoda-ku, Tokyo 102, Japan. **Document type:** abstracting/indexing.

617   JA   ISSN 0385-7883
NIHON GEKAKEI RENGO GAKKAISHI/JAPANESE COLLEGE OF SURGEONS. JOURNAL. (Text in English, Japanese) 1976. irreg. Nihon Gekakei Rengo Gakkai, 4-3, Iidabashi 3-chome, Chiyoda-ku, Tokyo 102, Japan.

612   JA
NIHON JIKKEN DOBUTSU GAKKAI SOKAI KOEN YOSHISHU/JAPANESE ASSOCIATION FOR LABORATORY ANIMAL SCIENCE. ABSTRACTS OF GENERAL MEETING. (Text in Japanese) a. Nihon Jikken Dobutsu Gakkai - Japanese Association for Laboratory Animal Science, Kanda Nagatani Manshon, 602, 8-10 Iwamotocho 2-chome, Chiyoda-ku, Tokyo 101, Japan. **Document type:** abstracting/indexing.

610   JA
NIHON KAIBOGAKU BUNKENSHU/ABSTRACTS OF JAPANESE ANATOMY. (Text in Japanese) 1936. every 2 yrs. Nihon Kaibo Gakkai - Japanese Association of Anatomists, c/o Nihon Gakkai Jimu Senta, 16-9, Honkomagome 5-chome, Bunkyo-ku, Tokyo 113, Japan. **Document type:** abstracting/indexing.

618 617   JA
NIHON NO SHINKEI GEKA GAKKAI SOKAI SHOROKUSHU/JAPAN NEUROSURGICAL SOCIETY. ABSTRACTS OF THE ANNUAL MEETING. (Text in English, Japanese) a. Nihon No shinkei Geka Gakkai, c/o Kyoto Daigaku Igakubu No Shinkei Geka, Yosida Konoecho, Sakyo-ku, Kyoto 606-01, Japan.

617   JA   ISSN 0285-1474
NIHON SHINZO KEKKAN GEKA GAKKAI GAKUJUTSU SOKAI NITTEI TO ENDAI SHOROKUSHU/JAPANESE SOCIETY FOR CARDIOVASCULAR SURGERY. ABSTRACTS OF MEETING. (Text in English, Japanese) a. Nihon Shinzo Kekkan Geka Gakkai, c/o Tokyo Daigaku Igakubu Kyobu Geka Kyoshitsu, 3-1, Hongo 7-chome, Bunkyo-ku, Tokyo 113, Japan. **Document type:** abstracting/indexing.

610   NO   ISSN 0333-3701
HA1501 subser.
NORWAY. STATISTISK SENTRALBYRAA. HELSEINSTITUSJONER. (Subseries of: Norges Offisielle Statistikk) 1980. a. NOK 70 (effective 1996). Statistisk Sentralbyraa, P.O. Box 8131-Dep., 0033 Oslo 1, Norway. TEL 02-864500. FAX 02-864973. circ. 850. **Document type:** government publication.

610.69   NO   ISSN 0800-403X
NORWAY. STATISTISK SENTRALBYRAA. HELSEPERSONELLSTATISTIKK. (Subseries of: Norges Offisielle Statistikk) 1979. biennial. Statistisk Sentralbyraa, P.O. Box 8131-Dep., N-0033 Oslo, Norway. TEL 47-22-864500. FAX 47-22-864976. circ. 2,000.
   Supersedes: Norway. Statistisk Sentralbyraa. Legestatistikk (ISSN 0377-8886)

616.21 016   IT   ISSN 1121-4163
NOTIZARIO BIBLIOGRAFICO DI AUDIOLOGIA O R L E FONIATRIA. 1967. s-a. free. Centro Ricerche e Studi Amplifon, Via Ripamonti, 133, 20141 Milan, Italy. TEL 02-57472361. FAX 02-57400384. TELEX 02-57400384. Ed. Isabella Costa. adv. contact: A.M. Holland. bk.rev. circ. 2,000. (back issues avail) **Document type:** academic/scholarly publication.
   Formerly: Notiziario Bibliografico di Audiologia (ISSN 0392-3711)

610 016   XR   ISSN 0029-5205
Z6660
NOVINKY LITERATURY: ZDRAVOTNICTVI. 1955. 10/yr. 100 Kc. Narodni Lekarska Knihovna, Sokolska 31, 121 32 Prague 2, Czech Republic. TEL 2491-5775. FAX 2491-4625. Ed. M. Hulovcova. circ. 250. (tabloid format) **Document type:** bibliography.

016 610.73   US   ISSN 0195-3354
NURSING ABSTRACTS. 1979. bi-m. $340 in U.S. & Canada; elsewhere $385. Nursing Abstracts Co., Inc., Box 295, Forest Hills, NY 11375. FAX 718-268-8872. Ed. Diana Dolgins. index. (back issues avail.) **Document type:** abstracting/indexing.
   Description: Provides clear 5-8 line abstracts of articles appearing in 82 nursing journals. Geared to all health professionals, educators, students and researchers.

610.73 016   UK   ISSN 0300-9947
NURSING BIBLIOGRAPHY. 1972. m. £58 (foreign £68). Royal College of Nursing, Library and Information Services, 20 Cavendish Sq., London W1M 0AB, England. TEL 071-409-3333. FAX 071-355-1379. circ. 700. **Document type:** bibliography.
—BLDSC (6187.039000).

610.73   UK   ISSN 0141-3899
NURSING RESEARCH ABSTRACTS. 1978. q. £20. Departments of Health and Social Security, Library & Information Services, Rm. 5E05, Quarry House, Quarry Hill, Leeds LS2 7UE, England. TEL 0532-545080. FAX 0532-545084. (Subscr. to: D H S S Publications, No. 2 Site, Manchester Rd., Heywood, Lancs. OL10 2PZ, England) Ed. Debra Jesssop. **Document type:** abstracting/indexing, government publication.
—BLDSC (6187.112000). CCC.

618   JA
NYUSEN HINYU KENKYUKAI KOEN YOSHISHU/SOCIETY FOR MAMMARY GLANDS AND LACTATION RESEARCH. ABSTRACTS OF THE MEETING. (Text in Japanese) a. Nyusen Hinyu Kenkyukai, Tokyo Daigaku Nogakubu Dobutsu Ikusyu Hanshokugakka, 1-1, Yayoi 1-chome, Bunkyo-ku, Tokyo 113, Japan. **Document type:** abstracting/indexing.

616.99   US   ISSN 1062-5720
O N S NURSING SCAN IN ONCOLOGY. 1992. bi-m. $45 to individuals (foreign $60); institutions $68 (foreign $83) (effective 1996). (Oncology Nursing Society) Nursecom, Inc., 1211 Locust St., Philadelphia, PA 19107. TEL 215-545-7222. FAX 215-545-8107. Ed. Karen Hasey Dow; Pub. Margo C. Neal. abstr. **Document type:** academic/scholarly publication, abstracting/indexing.
—BLDSC (6261.580000).
   Description: Addresses topics in oncology nursing with commentary on applications to nursing practice. *Refereed Serial*

OBSTETRIC ANESTHESIA DIGEST. see *MEDICAL SCIENCES — Anaesthesiology*

615.82   UK   ISSN 0950-6675
OCCUPATIONAL THERAPY INDEX. m. £53 (outside Europe £69) (effective 1995). British Library, Medical Information Centre, Boston Spa, Wetherby, W. Yorks. LS23 7BQ, England. TEL 01937-546039. FAX 01937-546458. E-mail: maggie.taylor@bl.uk. index. **Document type:** abstracting/indexing.
   ●Also available online.
—BLDSC (6231.254500).
   Description: Current awareness service for occupational therapy journals.

616.994 575.1   UK   ISSN 0950-0561
ONCOGENES. 1987. s-m. (diskette m.) £115 (diskette £115; both £175) (effective 1995). S U B I S, Mansion House, 19 Kingfield Rd., Sheffield S11 9AS, England. TEL 0114-2554433. FAX 0114-2554626. E-mail: admin@sheffac.demon.co.uk. (also avail. in diskette format) **Document type:** abstracting/indexing.
—CCC.
   Description: Current awareness service for researchers. Covers oncogenes and neoplastic cell transformation.

616.4 011   US   ISSN 1043-8963
RC268.42
ONCOGENES AND GROWTH FACTORS ABSTRACTS. 1989. q. $275 (foreign $285). Cambridge Scientific Abstracts, 7200 Wisconsin Ave., 6th Fl., Bethesda, MD 20814. TEL 301-961-6750. FAX 301-961-6720. E-mail: market@csa.com. Pub. Ted Caris. abstr.; index. (also avail. in magnetic tape; back issues avail.) **Document type:** abstracting/indexing.
   ●Also available online. Vendor(s): Knight-Ridder, Inc. (File no.76), STN International (LIFESCI).
Also available on CD-ROM. Producer(s): SilverPlatter Information, Inc..
   Description: Covers worldwide research into the molecular basis of malignant transformation.

617 016   US   ISSN 0733-4060
ONGOING CURRENT BIBLIOGRAPHY OF PLASTIC & RECONSTRUCTIVE SURGERY. 1973. q. $60 (foreign $75) (effective 1995). Creative Products, Inc., 23 Pinewood Farm Ct., Owings Mills, MD 21117. TEL 410-252-4022. FAX 410-252-3142. (Co-sponsors: American Society of Plastic and Reconstructive Surgeons; Plastic Surgery Educational Foundation; U.S. National Library of Medicine) Ed. Ron Markow. circ. 1,000. (looseleaf format; back issues avail.) **Document type:** bibliography.
   ●Also available online. Vendor(s): National Library of Medicine.
   Former titles (until 1980): Current Bibliography of Plastic and Reconstructive Surgery (ISSN 0149-5348); until 1976): Ongoing Current Bibliography of Plastic and Reconstructive Surgery (ISSN 0360-1722)
   Description: Publishes current citations from the MEDLARS database in the field of plastic and reconstructive surgery.

617.7 016   UK   ISSN 0030-3720
Z6669
OPHTHALMIC LITERATURE. 1947. q. £204($325) (effective 1996). (Institute of Ophthalmology) Butterworth - Heinemann, Part of the Reed Elsevier group, Linacre House, Jordan Hill, Oxford OX2 8DP, England. TEL 0865-310366. FAX 0865-310898. TELEX 83111 BHPOXF G. (Subscr. to: Elsevier Science Ltd., P.O. Box 800, Kidlington, Oxford OX5 1DX, England. TEL 44-865-843000. FAX 44-865-843010; Subscr. in U.S. and Canada to: Elsevier Science, 660 White Plains Rd., Tarrytown, NY 10591-5153. TEL 914-524-9200. FAX 914-333-2444) Ed.Bd. adv.; bk.rev.; index. (also avail. in microform from UMI; reprint service avail. from UMI) **Document type:** abstracting/indexing.
—UMI.
   Description: Abstracts the world literature on all aspects of ophthalmology and optometry.

610   JA   ISSN 0913-4751
OSAKA UNIVERSITY. RESEARCH INSTITUTE FOR MICROBIAL DISEASES. ANNUAL REPORTS. 1986. a. free. Osaka Daigaku, Biseibutsubyo Kenkyujo - Osaka University, Research Institute for Microbial Diseases, 3-1 Yamadaoka, Suita-shi, Osaka 565, Japan. TEL 06-877-5121. FAX 06-876-1017. Ed. Kumao Toyoshima. abstr.
—BLDSC (1410.645000).
   Description: Provides abstracts of papers published in the previous year from various departments of the institute.

MEDICAL SCIENCES — ABSTRACTING, BIBLIOGRAPHIES, STATISTICS

616.4 UK ISSN 1351-5330
OXYTOCIN AND VASOPRESSIN. 1980. s-m. (diskette m.). £85 (diskette £115; both £175) (effective 1995). S U B I S, Mansion House, 19 Kingfield Rd., Sheffield S11 9AS, England. TEL 0114-2554433. FAX 0114-2554626. E-mail: admin@sheffac.demon.co.uk. (also avail. in diskette format) Document type: abstracting/indexing.
—CCC.
Formerly (until 1993): Neurohypophysical Hormones (ISSN 0143-4276)
Description: Current awareness service for researchers. Covers oxytocin, vasopressin and neurophysin.

616.4 016 FR ISSN 1146-5522
P A S C A L E 64: ENDOCRINOLOGIE HUMAINE ET EXPERIMENTALE. ENDOCRINOPATHIES. (Printed format ceased Jan. 1995) (Text in English, French) 1984. 10/yr. Centre National de la Recherche Scientifique, Institut de l'Information Scientifique et Technique, 2 allee du Parc de Brabois, 54514 Vandoeuvre-Les-Nancy Cedex, France. TEL 83-50-46-00. FAX 83-50-46-50. adv. contact: Veronique Guinvarc'h. index, cum.index. Document type: bibliography.
●Also available online. Vendor(s): European Space Agency (File no.14), Knight-Ridder, Inc. (File no.144), Telesystemes - Questel.
Also available on CD-ROM.
Former titles: P A S C A L Explore. E 64: Endocrinologie Humaine et Experimentale. Endocrinopathies (ISSN 0761-2168); P A S C A L Explore. Part 64: Endocrinologie Humaine et Experimentale. Endocrinopathies; Supersedes in part: Bulletin Signaletique. Part 361: Reproduction. Gynecologie. Obstetrique. Embryologie. Endocrinologie (ISSN 0245-9884)

150 616.89 016 Z7203 FR ISSN 1146-5530
P A S C A L E 65: PSYCHOLOGIE, PSYCHOPATHOLOGIE, PSYCHIATRIE. (Printed format ceased Jan. 1995) (Text in English, French) 1984. 10/yr. Centre National de la Recherche Scientifique, Institut de l'Information Scientifique et Technique, 2 allee du Parc de Brabois, 54514 Vandoeuvre-Les-Nancy Cedex, France. TEL 83-50-46-00. FAX 83-50-46-50. adv. contact: Veronique Guinvarc'h. abstr.; index, cum.index. (also avail. in microfiche) Document type: bibliography.
●Also available online. Vendor(s): European Space Agency (File no.14), Knight-Ridder, Inc. (File no.144), Telesystemes - Questel.
Also available on CD-ROM.
Former titles: P A S C A L Explore. E 65: Psychologie, Psychopathologie, Psychiatrie (ISSN 0761-2176); P A S C A L Explore. Part 65: Psychologie, Psychopathologie, Psychiatrie; Which supersedes: Bulletin Signaletique. Part 390: Psychologie. Psychopathologie. Psychiatrie (ISSN 0007-5531)

617.7 016 FR ISSN 1146-5557
P A S C A L E 71: OPHTALMOLOGIE. (Printed format ceased Jan. 1995) (Text in English, French) 1984. 10/yr. 1040 F. (outside EC 1095 F.). Centre National de la Recherche Scientifique, Institut de l'Information Scientifique et Technique, 2 allee du Parc de Brabois, 54514 Vandoeuvre-Les-Nancy Cedex, France. TEL 83-50-46-00. FAX 83-50-46-50. adv. contact: Veronique Guinvarc'h. abstr.; index, cum.index. (also avail. in microfiche) Document type: bibliography.
●Also available online. Vendor(s): European Space Agency (File no.14), Knight-Ridder, Inc. (File no. 144), Telesystemes - Questel.
Also available on CD-ROM.
Former titles: P A S C A L Explore. E 17: Ophtalmologie (ISSN 0761-2184); P A S C A L Explore. Part 71: Ophtalmologie; Which supersedes: Bulletin Signaletique. Part 346: Ophtalmologie (ISSN 0301-3324); Which supersedes in part: Bulletin Signaletique. Part 350. Pathologie Generale et Experimentale.

616.21 016 FR ISSN 1146-5565
P A S C A L E 72: OTORHINOLARYNGOLOGIE. STOMATOLOGIE. PATHOLOGIE CERVICOFACIALE. (Printed format ceased Jan. 1995) (Text in English, French) 1984. 10/yr. Centre National de la Recherche Scientifique, Institut de l'Information Scientifique et Technique, 2 allee du Parc de Brabois, 54514 Vandoeuvre-Les-Nancy, France. TEL 83-50-46-00. FAX 83-50-46-50. adv. contact: Veronique Guinvarc'h. index, cum.index. (also avail. in microfiche) Document type: bibliography.
●Also available online. Vendor(s): European Space Agency (File no.14), Knight-Ridder, Inc. (File no.144), Telesystemes - Questel.
Also available on CD-ROM.
Former titles: P A S C A L Explore. E 72: Otorhinolaryngologie. Stomatologie. Pathologie Cervicofaciale (ISSN 0761-2192); P A S C A L Explore. Part 72: Otorhinolaryngologie. Stomatologie. Pathologie Cervicofaciale; Which supersedes: Bulletin Signaletique. Part 347: Oto-Rhino-Laryngologie, Stomatologie, Pathologie Cervicofaciale (ISSN 0301-3375); Which supersedes in part: Bulletin Signaletique. Part 350. Pathologie Generale et Experimentale.

616.5 016 FR ISSN 1146-5573
P A S C A L E 73: DERMATOLOGIE. MALADIES SEXUELLEMENT TRANSMISSIBLES. (Printed format ceased Jan. 1995) (Text in English, French) 1984. 10/yr. Centre National de la Recherche Scientifique, Institut de l'Information Scientifique et Technique, 2 allee du Parc de Brabois, 54514 Vandoeuvre-Les-Nancy, France. TEL 83-50-46-00. FAX 83-50-46-50. adv. contact: Veronique Guinvarc'h. abstr.; index, cum.index. (also avail. in microfiche) Document type: bibliography.
●Also available online. Vendor(s): European Space Agency (File no.14), Knight-Ridder, Inc. (File no.144), Telesystemes - Questel.
Also available on CD-ROM.
Former titles: P A S C A L Explore. E 73: Dermatologie. Maladies Sexuellement Transmissibles (ISSN 0761-2206); P A S C A L Explore. Part 73: Dermatologie. Maladies Sexuellement Transmissibles; Which supersedes (1972-1984): Bulletin Signaletique. Part 348: Dermatologie - Venerologie (ISSN 0301-3383); Which supersedes in part: Bulletin Signaletique. Part 350. Pathologie Generale et Experimentale.

616.2 016 FR ISSN 1146-5581
P A S C A L E 74: PNEUMOLOGIE. (Printed format ceased Jan. 1995) (Text in English, French) 1984. 10/yr. Centre National de la Recherche Scientifique, Institut de l'Information Scientifique et Technique, 2 allee du Parc de Brabois, 54514 Vandoeuvre-Les-Nancy Cedex, France. TEL 83-50-46-00. FAX 83-50-46-50. adv. contact: Veronique Guinvarc'h. abstr.; index, cum.index. (also avail. in microfiche) Document type: bibliography.
●Also available online. Vendor(s): European Space Agency (File no.14), Knight-Ridder, Inc. (File no.144), Telesystemes - Questel.
Also available on CD-ROM.
Former titles: P A S C A L Explore. E 74: Pneumologie (ISSN 0761-2214); P A S C A L Explore. Part 74: Pneumologie; Which supersedes in part: Bulletin Signaletique. Part 362: Maladies de l'Appareil Respiratoire du Coeur et des Vaisseaux. Chirurgie Thoracique et Vasculaire (ISSN 0301-3391); Which supersedes in part: Bulletin Signaletique. Part 350: Pathologie Generale et Experimentale.

616.2 016 FR ISSN 1146-559X
P A S C A L E 75: CARDIOLOGIE ET APPAREIL CIRCULATOIRE. (Printed format ceased Jan. 1995) 1984. 10/yr. Centre National de la Recherche Scientifique, Institut de l'Information Scientifique et Technique, 2 allee du Parc de Brabois, 54514 Vandoeuvre-Les-Nancy Cedex, France. TEL 83-50-46-00. FAX 83-50-46-50. adv. contact: Veronique Guinvarc'h. Document type: bibliography.
●Also available online. Vendor(s): European Space Agency (File no.14), Knight-Ridder, Inc. (File no.144), Telesystemes - Questel.
Also available on CD-ROM.
Former titles: P A S C A L Explore. E 75: Cardiologie et Appareil Circulatoire (ISSN 0761-2222); P A S C A L Explore. Part 75: Cardiologie et Appareil Circulatoire; Which supersedes in part: Bulletin Signaletique. Part 352: Maladies de l'Appareil Respiratoire, du Coeur et des Vaisseaux. Chirurgie Thoracique et Vasculaire.

616.3 617 016 FR ISSN 1146-5603
P A S C A L E 76: GASTROENTEROLOGIE, FOIE, PANCREAS, ABDOMEN. (Printed format ceased Jan. 1995) (Text in English, French) 1973. 10/yr. Centre National de la Recherche Scientifique, Institut de l'Information Scientifique et Technique, 2 allee du Parc de Brabois, 54514 Vandoeuvre-Les-Nancy Cedex, France. TEL 83-50-46-00. FAX 83-50-46-50. adv. contact: Veronique Guinvarc'h. index, cum.index. (also avail. in microfiche) Document type: bibliography.
●Also available online. Vendor(s): European Space Agency (File no.14), Knight-Ridder, Inc. (File no.144), Telesystemes - Questel.
Also available on CD-ROM.
Former titles: P A S C A L Explore. E 76: Gastroenterologie, Foie, Pancreas, Abdomen (ISSN 0761-2230); P A S C A L Explore. Part 76: Gastroenterologie, Foie, Pancreas, Abdomen; Which supersedes (in 1984): Bulletin Signaletique. Part 354: Maladies de l'Appareil Digestif. Chirurgie Abdominale (ISSN 0301-3405); Which supersedes in part: Bulletin Signaletique. Part 350. Pathologie Generale et Experimentale.

616.6 016 617 FR ISSN 1146-5611
P A S C A L E 77: NEPHROLOGIE. VOIES URINAIRES. (Printed format ceased Jan. 1995) (Text in English, French) 1973. 10/yr. Centre National de la Recherche Scientifique, Institut de l'Information Scientifique et Technique, 2 allee du Parc de Brabois, 54514 Vandoeuvre-Les-Nancy Cedex, France. TEL 83-50-46-00. FAX 83-50-46-50. adv. contact: Veronique Guinvarc'h. abstr.; index, cum.index. (also avail. in microfiche) Document type: bibliography.
●Also available online. Vendor(s): European Space Agency (File no.14), Knight-Ridder, Inc. (File no.144), Telesystemes - Questel.
Also available on CD-ROM.
Former titles: P A S C A L Explore. E 77: Nephrologie. Voies Urinaires (ISSN 0761-2249); P A S C A L Explore. Part 77: Nephrologie. Voies Urinaires; Which supersedes (in 1984): Bulletin Signaletique. Part 355: Maladies des Reins et des Voies Urinaires - Chirurgie de l'Appareil Urinaire; Which was formerly: Bulletin Signaletique. Part 355: Maladies des Reins et des Voies Urinaires. Chirurgie (ISSN 0301-3413); Supersedes in part: Bulletin Signaletique. Part 350. Pathologie Generale et Experimentale.

616.8 016 FR ISSN 1146-562X
P A S C A L E 78: NEUROLOGIE. (Printed format ceased Jan. 1995) (Text in English, French) 1973. 10/yr. Centre National de la Recherche Scientifique, Institut de l'Information Scientifique et Technique, 2 allee du Parc de Brabois, 54514 Vandoeuvre-Les-Nancy Cedex, France. TEL 83-50-46-00. FAX 83-50-46-50. adv. contact: Veronique Guinvarc'h. abstr.; index, cum.index. (also avail. in microform) Document type: bibliography.
●Also available online. Vendor(s): European Space Agency (File no.14), Knight-Ridder, Inc. (File no.144), Telesystemes - Questel.
Also available on CD-ROM.
Former titles: P A S C A L Explore. E 78: Neurologie (ISSN 0761-2257); P A S C A L Explore. Part 78: Neurologie; Supersedes (in 1984): Bulletin Signaletique. Part 356: Maladies du Systeme Nerveux Myopathies-Neurochirurgie (ISSN 0301-3421); Which supersedes in part: Bulletin Signaletique. Part 350. Pathologie Generale et Experimentale.

MEDICAL SCIENCES — ABSTRACTING, BIBLIOGRAPHIES, STATISTICS

617.3 016   FR   ISSN 1146-5638
P A S C A L E 79: PATHOLOGIE ET PHYSIOLOGIE OSTEOARTICULAIRES. (Printed format ceased Jan. 1995) (Text in English, French) 1973. 10/yr. Centre National de la Recherche Scientifique, Institut de l'Information Scientifique et Technique, 2 allee du Parc de Brabois, 54514 Vandoeuvre-Les-Nancy Cedex, France. TEL 83-50-46-00. FAX 83-50-46-50. adv. contact: Veronique Guinvarc'h. abstr.; index, cum.index. (also avail. in microfiche) **Document type:** bibliography.
●Also available online. Vendor(s): European Space Agency (File no.14), Knight-Ridder, Inc. (File no.144), Telesystemes - Questel.
Also available on CD-ROM.
    Former titles: P A S C A L Explore. E 79: Pathologie et Physiologie Osteoarticulaires (ISSN 0761-2265); P A S C A L Explore. Part 79: Pathologie et Physiologie Osteoarticulaires; Which supersedes (in 1984): Bulletin Signaletique. Part 357: Maladies des Os et des Articulations. Chirurgie Orthopedique. Traumatologie (ISSN 0301-343X); Which superseded in part: Bulletin Signaletique. Part 350. Pathologie Generale et Experimentale.

616.15 016   FR   ISSN 1146-5646
P A S C A L E 80: HEMATOLOGIE. (Printed format ceased Jan. 1995) (Text in English, French) 1973. 10/yr. Centre National de la Recherche Scientifique, Institut de l'Information Scientifique et Technique, 2 allee du Parc de Brabois, 54514 Vandoeuvre-Les-Nancy Cedex, France. TEL 83-50-46-00. FAX 83-50-46-50. adv. contact: Veronique Guinvarc'h. (also avail. in microfiche) **Document type:** bibliography.
●Also available online. Vendor(s): European Space Agency (File no.14), Knight-Ridder, Inc. (File no.144), Telesystemes - Questel.
Also available on CD-ROM.
    Former titles: P A S C A L Explore. E 80: Hematologie (ISSN 0761-2273); P A S C A L Explore. Part 80: Hematologie; Supersedes (in 1984): Bulletin Signaletique. Part 359: Maladies du Sang (ISSN 0301-3448); Which supersedes in part: Bulletin Signaletique. Part 350. Pathologie Generale et Experimentale.

616.4 016   FR   ISSN 1146-5662
P A S C A L E 82: GYNECOLOGIE, OBSTETRIQUE, ANDROLOGIE. (Printed format ceased Jan. 1995) (Text in English, French) 1984. 10/yr. Centre National de la Recherche Scientifique, Institut de l'Information Scientifique et Technique, 2 allee du Parc de Brabois, 54514 Vandoeuvre-Les-Nancy Cedex, France. TEL 83-50-46-00. FAX 83-50-46-50. adv. contact: Veronique Guinvarc'h. (also avail. in microfiche) **Document type:** bibliography.
●Also available online. Vendor(s): European Space Agency (File no.14), Knight-Ridder, Inc. (File no.144), Telesystemes - Questel.
Also available on CD-ROM.
    Former titles: P A S C A L Explore. E 82: Gynecologie. Obstetrique. Andrologie (ISSN 0761-229X); P A S C A L Explore. Part 82: Gynecologie. Obstetrique. Andrologie; Supersedes in part: Bulletin Signaletique. Part 361: Reproduction. Gynecologie. Obstetrique. Embryologie. Endocrinologie (ISSN 0245-9884)

617.96 016   FR   ISSN 1146-5670
P A S C A L E 83: ANESTHESIE ET REANIMATION. (Printed format ceased Jan. 1995) (Text in English, French) 1972. 10/yr. Centre National de la Recherche Scientifique, Institut de l'Information Scientifique et Technique, 2 allee du Parc de Brabois, 54514 Vandoeuvre-Les-Nancy Cedex, France. TEL 83-50-46-00. FAX 83-50-46-50. adv. contact: Veronique Guinvarc'h. abstr.; index, cum.index. (also avail. in microfiche) **Document type:** bibliography.
●Also available online. Vendor(s): European Space Agency (File no.14), Knight-Ridder, Inc. (File no.144), Telesystemes - Questel.
Also available on CD-ROM.
    Former titles: P A S C A L Explore. E 83: Anesthesie et Reanimation (ISSN 0761-2303); P A S C A L Explore. Part 83: Anesthesie et Reanimation; Supersedes (in 1984): Bulletin Signaletique. Part 349: Anesthesie. Reanimation (ISSN 0301-133X); Bulletin Signaletique. Part 350. Pathologie Generale et Experimentale (ISSN 0007-5469)

610 016 574   FR   ISSN 1146-5689
P A S C A L E 84: GENIE BIOMEDICAL. INFORMATIQUE BIOMEDICALE. (Printed format ceased Jan. 1995) (Text in English, French) 1972. 10/yr. Centre National de la Recherche Scientifique, Institut de l'Information Scientifique et Technique, 2 allee du Parc de Brabois, 54514 Vandoeuvre-Les-Nancy Cedex, France. TEL 83-50-46-00. FAX 83-50-46-50. adv. contact: Veronique Guinvarc'h. abstr.; index, cum.index. (also avail. in microfiche) **Document type:** bibliography.
●Also available online. Vendor(s): European Space Agency (File no.14), Knight-Ridder, Inc. (File no.144), Telesystemes - Questel.
Also available on CD-ROM.
    Former titles: P A S C A L Explore. E 84: Genie Biomedical. Informatique Biomedicale (ISSN 0761-2311); P A S C A L Explore. Part 84: Genie Biomedical. Informatique Biomedicale; Supersedes (in 1984): Bulletin Signaletique. Part 310: Genie Biomedical. Informatique Biomedicale. Physique Biomedicale (ISSN 0398-9941)

616.994 016   FR   ISSN 1146-5697
P A S C A L E 89: CANCER. (Printed format ceased Jan. 1995) (Text in English, French) 1968. 10/yr. Centre National de la Recherche Scientifique, Institut de l'Information Scientifique et Technique, 2 allee du Parc de Brabois, 54514 Vandoeuvre-les-Nancy Cedex, France. TEL 83-50-46-00. FAX 83-50-46-50. (Co-sponsor: Institut Gustave Roussy (Villejuif). adv. contact: Veronique Guinvarc'h. (also avail. in microfiche) **Document type:** bibliography.
●Also available online. Vendor(s): European Space Agency (File no.14), Knight-Ridder, Inc. (File no.144), Telesystemes - Questel.
Also available on CD-ROM.
    Former titles (until 1990): P A S C A L Explore. E 89: Cancer (ISSN 0246-1188); (until 1985): P A S C A L Thema. T 251: Cancerologie (ISSN 0761-1706); (until 1984): Bulletin Signaletique 251: Cancernet, Cancerologie, Oncology (ISSN 0245-9566); Cancer (ISSN 0007-5477); Bibliographie Internationale du Cancer (ISSN 1140-6038).

616.4 016   FR   ISSN 1146-5271
P A S C A L F 54: REPRODUCTION DES VERTEBRES, EMBRYOLOGIE DES VERTEBRES ET DES INVERTEBRES. (Printed format ceased Jan. 1995) (Text in English, French) 1984. 10/yr. Centre National de la Recherche Scientifique, Institut de l'Information Scientifique et Technique, 2 allee du Parc de Brabois, 54514 Vandoeuvre-Les-Nancy Cedex, France. TEL 83-50-46-00. FAX 83-50-46-50. adv. contact: Veronique Guinvarc'h. (also avail. in microfiche) **Document type:** bibliography.
●Also available online. Vendor(s): European Space Agency (File no.14), Knight-Ridder, Inc. (File no.144), Telesystemes - Questel.
Also available on CD-ROM.
    Former titles: P A S C A L Folio. F 54: Reproduction des Vertebres. Embryologie des Vertebres et des Invertebres (ISSN 0761-1919); P A S C A L Folio. Part 54: Reproduction des Vertebres. Embryologie des Vertebres et des Invertebres; Which superseded in part: Bulletin Signaletique. Part 361: Reproduction. Gynecologie. Obstetrique. Embryologie. Endocrinologie (ISSN 0245-9884); Which was formerly: Bulletin Signaletique. Part 361: Reproduction. Embryologie. Endocrinologie (ISSN 0180-9989); Bulletin Signaletique. Part 361. Endocrinologie et Reproduction (ISSN 0007-5493)

660 574.285   FR   ISSN 1146-5034
P A S C A L T 215: BIOTECHNOLOGIES. (Printed format ceased Jan. 1995) (Text in English, French) 1984. 10/yr. Centre National de la Recherche Scientifique, Institut de l'Information Scientifique et Technique, 2 allee du Parc de Brabois, 54514 Vandoeuvre-les-Nancy Cedex, France. TEL 83-50-46-00. FAX 83-50-46-50. Ed.Bd. adv. contact: Veronique Guinvarc'h. abstr.; index, cum.index. (also avail. in microform) **Document type:** bibliography.
●Also available online. Vendor(s): European Space Agency (File no.14), Knight-Ridder, Inc. (File no.144), Telesystemes - Questel.
Also available on CD-ROM.
    Former titles: P A S C A L Thema. T 215: Biotechnologies (Editions Francaises) (ISSN 0761-165X); P A S C A L Thema. Part 215. Biotechnologies (Editions Francaises); Which superseded (in 1984): Bulletin Signaletique. Part 215: Biotechnologies (French Edition) (ISSN 0245-954X)

610 616.07   FR   ISSN 1146-5050
P A S C A L T 235: MEDECINE TROPICALE. (Printed format ceased Jan. 1995) (Text in English, French) 1982. 10/yr. Centre National de la Recherche Scientifique, Institut de l'Information Scientifique et Technique, 2 allee du Parc de Brabois, 54514 Vandoeuvre-Les-Nancy Cedex, France. TEL 83-50-46-00. FAX 83-50-46-50. adv. contact: Veronique Guinvarc'h. abstr.; index, cum.index. (also avail. in microfiche) **Document type:** bibliography.
●Also available online. Vendor(s): European Space Agency (File no.14), Knight-Ridder, Inc. (File no.144), Telesystemes - Questel.
Also available on CD-ROM.
    Former titles: P A S C A L Thema. T 235: Medecine Tropicale (ISSN 0761-1676); P A S C A L Thema. Part 235: Medecine Tropicale; Which superseded (in 1984): Bulletin Signaletique. Part 233: Medecine Tropicale (ISSN 0245-9558)

P H L S LIBRARY BULLETIN. (Public Health Laboratory Service) see *MEDICAL SCIENCES — Communicable Diseases*

016.6168   US   ISSN 1080-5621
▼**PAIN MEDICINE JOURNAL CLUB JOURNAL.** 1995. bi-m. $85 to individuals (foreign $94); institutions $125 (foreign $134) (effective 1996); newsstand price: $24. Lippincott - Raven Press, 227 E. Washington Sq., Philadelphia, PA 19106. TEL 215-238-4200. Ed.Bd. **Document type:** abstracting/indexing.
    Description: Provides summaries, with commentaries, of current world literature in pain medicine and related fields.

610   UK   ISSN 0961-4591
PALLIATIVE CARE INDEX. m. £53 (outside Europe £63) (effective 1995). British Library, Medical Information Centre, Boston Spa, Wetherby, W. Yorks. LS23 7BQ, England. TEL 01937-546039. FAX 01937-546458. E-mail: maggie.taylor@bl.uk. index. **Document type:** abstracting/indexing.
—BLDSC (6345.562055).
    Formerly: Terminal Care Index (ISSN 0953-6779)
    Description: Features abstracts on terminal and palliative care, hospice, symptom control, legal and ethical aspects of death, bereavement and psychosocial aspects of palliative care.

610   UK   ISSN 0957-4190
PAPILLOMAVIRUS REPORT. 1990. bi-m. £54($110) to individuals; institutions £74($155). Leeds Medical Information, University of Leeds, Leeds LS2 9JT, England. TEL 01532-335550. FAX 01532-334381. (Subscr. to: Royal Society of Medicine Press Ltd., 1 Wimpole St., London W1M 8AE, England. TEL 0171-290-2900. FAX 0171-290-2929) Ed. C. Lacey. bibl. **Document type:** academic/scholarly publication, bibliography.
—BLDSC (6403.165000).
    Description: Contains bibliographic information, including abstracts and authors' addresses, for papers on all aspects of papillomavirus infection in humans and animals published worldwide.

591   UK   ISSN 0964-7570
PARASITOLOGY (SHEFFIELD). 1992. s-m. (diskette m.). £115 (diskette £115; both £175) (effective 1995). S U B I S, Mansion House, 19 Kingfield Rd., Sheffield S11 9AS, England. TEL 0114-2554433. FAX 0114-2554626. E-mail: admin@sheffac.demon.co.uk. (also avail. in diskette format) **Document type:** abstracting/indexing.

MEDICAL SCIENCES — ABSTRACTING, BIBLIOGRAPHIES, STATISTICS

618.92   US   ISSN 1059-0870
PEDIATRIC EMERGENCY & CRITICAL CARE; a clinical update for those who care for infants and children. 1988. m. $55 to individuals; institutions $85; residents and nurses $35. Riverpress, Inc., Box 23, Jersey City, NJ 07303-0023. TEL 201-434-5073. FAX 201-434-7230. Ed. Douglas W.E. Wagner. circ. 1,700. (looseleaf format) **Document type:** newsletter.
—CCC.
    Formerly (until vol.5, 1992): Pediatric Trauma and Acute Care (ISSN 0894-1122)
    Description: Digest of clinically useful literature and papers; each abstract has an expert's comment focusing on the clinical point.
    Refereed Serial

618.92   US   ISSN 1071-5711
PEDIATRIC PRIMARY CARE; practical pediatrics for the pediatric practitioner. 1987. m. $45 to individuals; institutions $80; residents and nurses $30. Riverpress, Inc., Box 23, Jersey City, NJ 07303-0023. TEL 201-434-5073. FAX 201-434-7230. Ed. Douglas W.E. Wagner. (looseleaf format; back issues avail.) **Document type:** newsletter.
—CCC.
    Formerly (until vol.7, no.8, 1993): Pediatric Therapeutics and Toxicology (ISSN 0893-6218)
    Description: Digest of clinically useful articles; each abstract has an expert's comment focusing on the clinical point.
    Refereed Serial

616.4 574.8   UK   ISSN 0268-1552
PEPTIDE HORMONE RECEPTORS. 1986. m. £75 (effective 1995). S U B I S, Mansion House, 19 Kingfield Rd., Sheffield S11 9AS, England. TEL 0114-2554433. FAX 0114-2554626. E-mail: admin@sheffac.demon.co.uk. **Document type:** abstracting/indexing.
—CCC.
    Description: Current awareness service for researchers. Covers receptors for gastrointestinal hormones, hypothalamic and pituitary hormones, placental hormones, angiotensin, and growth factors.

610   US   ISSN 1045-2338
Z695.1.M48
PERMUTED MEDICAL SUBJECT HEADINGS (YEAR). q. $35 for print edition (foreign $70); microfiche edition $17 (foreign $34). U.S. National Library of Medicine, 8600 Rockville Pike, Bethesda, MD 20894. (Oders to: National Technical Information Service, 5285 Port Royal Rd., Springfield, VA 22161. TEL 703-487-4650. FAX 703-3218547; Or: Bernan, 4611-F Assembly Dr., Lanham, MD 20706. TEL 301-459-7666. FAX 301-459-0056) (also avail. in microfiche) **Document type:** government publication.
    Description: Displays all terms for the National Library of Medicine's Medical Subject Headings for the year.

610 615   HK   ISSN 0218-4206
PHILIPPINES INDEX OF MEDICAL SPECIALITIES. Short title: P I M S. (Text in English) 1972. 3/yr. S.$60 (foreign $27) (effective 1993). MediMedia Asia (Subsidiary of: MediMedia Pacific Ltd.), 1501 Tung Sun Commercial Centre, 194-200 Lockhart Rd., Wanchai, Hong Kong. TEL 852-511-0765. FAX 852-507-3817. (Alt. addr.: MIMS Asia, 15 McCallum St., 04-01, Natwest Centre, Singapore 0106, Singapore. TEL 65-223-3788) Ed. Shirley C. Cocabo. adv.: color page S$5439; adv. contact: Annie T. Fuentes. circ. 22,000. **Document type:** directory, trade publication.
    Description: Indexes brief prescribing information on pharmaceutical products available in Philippines for doctors.

610   US   ISSN 0731-0315
RA410.7
PHYSICIAN CHARACTERISTICS & DISTRIBUTION IN THE U S. 1943. a. $99.95 to non-members; members $75.95. American Medical Association, 515 N. State St., Chicago, IL 60610. TEL 312-464-5000; 800-262-2350. FAX 312-464-4184. Ed. G.A. Roback. (also avail. in microfiche from CIS) **Indexed:** SRI. **Document type:** bulletin.
    Former titles: Physician Characteristics and Distribution; Physician Distribution and Medical Licensure in the U S (ISSN 0364-6610); Distribution of Physicians in the U S (ISSN 0146-4558); Distribution of Physicians, Hospital, Hospital Beds in the U S (ISSN 0419-4357)

658   US
PHYSICIAN EXECUTIVE REVIEW; quarterly abstracts from medical management literature. 1975. q. $70 to non-members; members $35. American College of Physician Executives, Two Urban Centre, Ste. 200, 4890 W. Kennedy Blvd., Tampa, FL 33609. TEL 813-287-2000. FAX 813-287-8993. Ed. Susan Quinn. circ. 900. **Document type:** abstracting/indexing.
    Former titles: Vantage Report; Medical Director.
    Description: Contains 20-30 abstracts prepared by college members on articles on medical management issues and management publications.

615.82   UK   ISSN 0950-6659
PHYSIOTHERAPY INDEX. m. £53 (outside Europe £69) (effective 1995). British Library, Medical Information Centre, Boston Spa, Wetherby, W. Yorks. LS23 7BQ, England. TEL 01937-546039. FAX 01937-546458. E-mail: maggie.taylor@bl.uk. **Document type:** abstracting/indexing.
●Also available online.
—BLDSC (6489.107000).
    Description: Current awareness service for physical therapy journals.

574 610   UK   ISSN 0142-8268
PLATELETS (SHEFFIELD). 1976. s-m. (diskette m.). £110 (diskette £115; both £175) (effective 1995). S U B I S, Mansion House, 19 Kingfield Rd., Sheffield S11 9AS, England. TEL 0114-2554433. FAX 0114-2554626. E-mail: admin@sheffac.demon.co.uk. (also avail. in diskette format) **Document type:** abstracting/indexing.
—CCC.
    Description: Current awareness service for researchers. Covers thrombocytopoiesis, pharmacology, aggregation, structure, biochemistry and functions of platelets.

016.617585   UK   ISSN 1354-9979
▼**PODIATRY INDEX.** 1994. q. £40 (outside Europe £59). British Library, Medical Information Centre, Boston Spa, Wetherby, W. Yorks. LS23 7BQ, England. TEL 01937-546039. FAX 01937-4546458. E-mail: maggie.taylor@bl.uk. Pub. Maggie Taylor. **Document type:** abstracting/indexing, bibliography.
    Description: Abstracts clinical and research articles on podiatric care.

016.61   XR   ISSN 1210-7182
CODEN: POUSE
POHYBOVE USTROJI. 1957. q. Narodni Lekarska Knihovna - National Medical Library, Sokolska 31, 121 32 Prague 2, Czech Republic. TEL 2-299956. bk.rev. **Indexed:** Excerp.Med. (1995-). **Document type:** abstracting/indexing.
    Formerly (until 1993): Referatovy Vyber z Ortopedie, Traumatologie a Pribuznych Oboru (ISSN 0034-2823)

616.07 574.2   PL   ISSN 1233-9687
CODEN: PAPOAC
POLISH JOURNAL OF PATHOLOGY. 1950. q. $60. Polskie Towarzystwo Patologow - Polish Society of Pathologists, Ul. Grzegorzecka 16, 31-531 Krakow, Poland. TEL 48-12-211564. FAX 48-12-215210. E-mail: mpstachu@cyf-kr.dcu.pl. (Co-sponsor: International Academy of Pathology, Polish Division) Ed. Jerzy Stachura. bk.rev.; illus.; index. circ. 700. **Indexed:** Biol.Abstr., Chem.Abstr., Excerp.Med., Ind.Med. **Document type:** abstracting/indexing, academic/scholarly publication.
—CASDDS.
    Formerly (until 1993): Patologia Polska (ISSN 0031-3114)
    Description: Contains papers reporting experimental research in pathology.
    Refereed Serial

616.4   NO   ISSN 0906-9666
QP1
PROGRAM OF PLENARY SESSIONS AND ADVANCE ABSTRACTS OF SHORT COMMUNICATIONS. (Subseries of: Acta Endocrinologica. Supplementum (ISSN 0300-9750)) 1971. irreg. price varies; free to subscribers to Acta Endocrinologica. Scandinavian University Press, P.O. Box 2959 Toeyen, N-0608 Oslo, Norway. TEL 47-22-57-54-00. FAX 47-22-57-53-53. (U.S. addr.: Scandinavian University Press, 200 Meacham Ave., Elmont, N.Y. 11003. TEL 516-352-7300) **Indexed:** Biol.Abstr., Curr.Cont., Ind.Med., Nutr.Abstr.
    Formerly (until 1984): Acta Endocrinologica Congress. Advance Abstracts of Short Papers (ISSN 0302-9522)

PROGRESS IN PALLIATIVE CARE. see *MEDICAL SCIENCES — Oncology*

616.4 574.192   UK   ISSN 0142-8276
PROLACTIN. s-m. (diskette m.). £85 (diskette £115; both £175) (effective 1995). S U B I S, Mansion House, 19 Kingfield Rd., Sheffield S11 9AS, England. TEL 0114-2554433. FAX 0114-2554626. E-mail: admin@sheffac.demon.co.uk. (also avail. in diskette format; looseleaf format; back issues avail.) **Document type:** abstracting/indexing.
—CCC.
    Description: Current awareness service for researchers in clinical and life sciences.

593 016   UK   ISSN 0309-1287
PROTOZOOLOGICAL ABSTRACTS. 1977. m. £325($585) (effective 1996). CAB International, Wallingford, Oxon. OX10 8DE, England. TEL 01491-832111. FAX 01491-833508. TELEX 487964 COMAGG G. E-mail: cabi@cabi.org. (U.S. subscr. to: CAB International, North American Office, 845 N. Park Ave., Tucson, AZ 85719. TEL 800-528-4841) circ. 500. (also avail. in diskette format; back issues avail.) **Indexed:** Abstr.Hyg., Ind.Vet., Rev.Appl.Entomol., Sport Fish.Abstr., Trop.Dis.Bull., Vet.Bull., Wild.Rev. **Document type:** abstracting/indexing.
●Also available online. Vendor(s): CISTI, DIMDI, European Space Agency (File nos.16 & 124/CAB), Knight-Ridder, Inc., Ovid Technologies (VETR).
    Description: Covers all protozoan diseases, many endemic to the tropics, affecting humans and animals.

610   US   ISSN 1058-6660
PSYCSCAN: NEUROPSYCHOLOGY. q. $64 to non-members (foreign $64): members $19.50 (foreign $27.50); institutions $99 (foreign $129). American Psychological Association, 750 First St., N.E., Washington, DC 20002-4242. TEL 202-336-5560. FAX 202-336-5568. circ. 3,800. **Document type:** abstracting/indexing.
    Description: Pulls approximately 2,500 news items of information from scholarly books and journals that are reviewed and included in the database.

610   JA   ISSN 0285-4694
PURASUMIN BUNKEN MOKUROKU/BIBLIOGRAPHY OF PLASMIN. (Text in English, Japanese) bi-m. (Kokusai Igaku Joho Senta - International Medical Information Center) Daiichi Seiyaku Co., Ltd., 14-10, Nihonbashi 3-chome, Chuo-ku, Tokyo 103, Japan. **Document type:** bibliography.

616.97 016   RU   ISSN 0202-9154
REFERATIVNYI ZHURNAL. IMMUNOLOGIYA - ALLERGOLOGIYA. 1978. m. $315 (effective 1996). Vsesoyuznyi Institut Nauchno-Tekhnicheskoi Informatsii (VINITI), Baltiiskaya ul. 14, Moscow A-219, Russia. (Dist. by: Mezhdunarodnaya Kniga, B. Yakimanka 39, 117049 Moscow, Russia) **Document type:** abstracting/indexing.

610 016   RU   ISSN 0034-2475
REFERATIVNYI ZHURNAL. MEDITSINSKAYA GEOGRAFIYA. m. $119 (effective 1996). Vsesoyuznyi Institut Nauchno-Tekhnicheskoi Informatsii (VINITI), Baltiiskaya ul., 14, Moscow A-219, Russia. (Subscr. to: Mezhdunarodnaya Kniga, Dimitrova ul. 39, 113095 Moscow, Russia) **Document type:** abstracting/indexing.

REFERATIVNYI ZHURNAL. OBSHCHIE VOPROSY PATOLOGICHESKOI ANATOMII. see *BIOLOGY — Abstracting, Bibliographies, Statistics*

616.992 016   RU   ISSN 0869-4117
REFERATIVNYI ZHURNAL. ONKOLOGIYA. 1961. m. 168 Rub. (210 Rub. including index). Vsesoyuznyi Institut Nauchno-Tekhnicheskoi Informatsii (VINITI), Baltiiskaya ul., 14, Moscow A-219, Russia. (Subscr. to: Mezhdunarodnaya Kniga, Dimitrova ul. 39, 113095 Moscow, Russia) **Document type:** abstracting/indexing.
—BLDSC (0142.106000).

MEDICAL SCIENCES — ABSTRACTING, BIBLIOGRAPHIES, STATISTICS

574.19 016   RU   ISSN 0131-355X
QH652.A1   CODEN: RZRBDD
REFERATIVNYI ZHURNAL. RADIATSIONNAYA BIOLOGIYA. 1973. m. 56 Rub. (60 Rub. including index). Vsesoyuznyi Institut Nauchno-Tekhnicheskoi Informatsii (VINITI), Baltiiskaya ul., 14, Moscow A-219, Russia. (Subscr. to: Mezhdunarodnaya Kniga, Dimitrova ul. 39, 113095 Moscow, Russia) **Indexed:** Chem.Abstr. **Document type:** abstracting/indexing. —CASDDS.

617.96 016   XR   ISSN 0034-2688
REFERATOVY VYBER Z ANESTESIOLOGIE A RESUSCITACE/ABSTRACTS OF ANESTHESIOLOGY AND RESUSCITATION. 1954. bi-m. 150 Kc. Narodni Lekarska Knihovna, Sokolska 31, 121 32 Prague 2, Czech Republic. TEL 2491-5774. FAX 2491-4625. Ed. J. Drabkova. circ. 1,270. **Document type:** abstracting/indexing.

617 016   XR   ISSN 0034-2696
REFERATOVY VYBER Z CHIRURGIE/ABSTRACTS OF SURGERY. 1969. bi-m. 150 Kc. 150 Kc. Narodni Lekarska Knihovna, Sokolska 31, 121 32 Prague 2, Czech Republic. TEL 2491-5775. FAX 2491-4625. Ed. O. Vojtisek. circ. 590. **Document type:** abstracting/indexing.

616.9 016   XR   ISSN 0034-270X
REFERATOVY VYBER Z CHOROB INFEKCNICH/ABSTRACTS OF INFECTIOUS DISEASES. 1960. q. 100 Kc. Narodni Lekarska Knihovna, Sokolska 31, 121 32 Prague 2, Czech Republic. TEL 2491-5775. FAX 2491-4625. Ed. J. Vanista. circ. 455. **Document type:** abstracting/indexing.

616.5 616.9 016   XR   ISSN 0139-648X
REFERATOVY VYBER Z DERMATOVENEROLOGIE/ABSTRACTS OF DERMATOLOGY AND VENEROLOGY. 1959. q. 100 Kc. Narodni Lekarska Knihovna, Sokolska 31, 121 32 Prague 2, Czech Republic. TEL 2491-5775. FAX 2491-4625. Ed. T. Frej. circ. 460. **Document type:** abstracting/indexing.
    Formerly (until 1976): Referatovy Vyber z Dermatovenerologie a Pribuznych Oboru (ISSN 0034-2718)

616.3 016   XR   ISSN 0034-2742
REFERATOVY VYBER Z GASTROENTEROLOGIE/ABSTRACTS OF GASTROENTEROLOGY. 1965. q. 100 Kc. Narodni Lekarska Knihovna, Sokolska 31, 121 32 Prague 2, Czech Republic. TEL 2491-5775. FAX 2491-4625. Ed. J. Stransky. circ. 410. **Document type:** abstracting/indexing.

616.1 016   XR   ISSN 0139-6536
REFERATOVY VYBER Z KARDIOLOGIE/ABSTRACTS OF CARDIOLOGY. 1960. bi-m. 100 Kc. Narodni Lekarska Knihovna, Sokolska 31, 121 32 Prague 2, Czech Republic. TEL 2491-5775. FAX 2491-4625. Ed. J. Pokorny. bk.rev. circ. 620. (tabloid format) **Document type:** abstracting/indexing.
    Formerly (until 1975): Referatovy Vyber z Kardiologie, Fysiologie a Patologie Obehoveho Ustroji (ISSN 0034-2769)

616.8 016   XR   ISSN 0034-2793
REFERATOVY VYBER Z NEUROLOGIE/ABSTRACTS OF NEUROLOGY. 1969. q. 100 Kc. Narodni Lekarska Knihovna, Sokolska 31, 121 32 Prague 2, Czech Republic. TEL 2491-5775. FAX 2491-4625. Ed. J. Simek. circ. 490. **Document type:** abstracting/indexing.

617.7 016   XR   ISSN 0034-2807
REFERATOVY VYBER Z OFTALMOLOGIE/ABSTRACTS OF OPHTHALMOLOGY. 1969. q. 100 Kc. Narodni Lekarska Knihovna, Sokolska 31, 121 32 Prague 2, Czech Republic. TEL 2491-5775. FAX 2491-4625. Ed. H. Kraus. bk.rev. circ. 440. **Document type:** abstracting/indexing.

618.92 016   XR   ISSN 0034-2858
REFERATOVY VYBER Z PEDIATRIE/ABSTRACTS OF PEDIATRICS. 1959. bi-m. 150 Kc. Narodni Lekarska Knihovna, Sokolska 31, 121 32 Prague 2, Czech Republic. TEL 2491-5775. FAX 2491-4625. Ed. M. Frank. circ. 615. **Document type:** abstracting/indexing.

616.246 016   XR   ISSN 0034-2890
REFERATOVY VYBER Z PNEUMOLOGIE A TUBERKULOSY/ABSTRACTS OF PNEUMOLOGY AND TUBERCULOSIS. 1956. q. 100 Kc. Narodni Lekarska Knihovna, Sokolska 31, 121 32 Prague 2, Czech Republic. TEL 2491-5775. FAX 2491-4625. Ed. B. Fuchs. circ. 375. **Document type:** abstracting/indexing.

618 016   XR   ISSN 0034-2866
REFERATOVY VYBER Z PORODNICTVI A GYNEKOLOGIE/ABSTRACTS OF OBSTETRICS AND GYNECOLOGY. 1962. bi-m. 150 Kc. Narodni Lekarska Knihovna, Sokolska 31, 121 32 Prague 2, Czech Republic. TEL 2491-5775. FAX 2491-4625. Ed. V. Trnka. circ. 715. **Document type:** abstracting/indexing.

615.842 016   XR   ISSN 0862-2183
REFERATOVY VYBER Z RADIODIAGNOSTIKY/ABSTRACTS OF RADIOLOGY. 1955. q. 100 Kc. Narodni Lekarska Knihovna, Sokolska 31, 121 32 Prague 2, Czech Republic. TEL 2491-5775. FAX 2491-4625. Ed. S. Vesin. circ. 340. **Document type:** abstracting/indexing.
    Formerly (until 1985): Referatovy Veber z Rentgenologie (ISSN 0034-2874)

616.742 016   XR   ISSN 0034-2882
REFERATOVY VYBER Z REVMATOLOGIE/ABSTRACTS OF RHEUMATOLOGY. 1961. q. 100 Kc. Narodni Lekarska Knihovna, Sokolska 31, 121 32 Prague 2, Czech Republic. TEL 2491-5775. FAX 2491-4625. Ed. R. Bardfeld. bk.rev. circ. 380. **Document type:** abstracting/indexing.

616.6   XR   ISSN 0139-9322
REFERATOVY VYBER Z UROLOGIE/ABSTRACTS OF UROLOGY. 1979. q. 100 Kc. Narodni Lekarska Knihovna, Sokolska 31, 121 32 Prague 2, Czech Republic. TEL 2491-5775. FAX 2491-4625. Ed. P. Verner. circ. 500. **Document type:** abstracting/indexing.
    Description: Abstracts of medical journal articles from around the world.

617.1 790 016   XR
REFERATOVY VYBER ZE SPORTOVNI MEDICINY A LECEBNE REHABILITACE/ABSTRACTS OF SPORTS MEDICINE AND REHABILITATION. 1964. q. 100 Kc. Narodni Lekarska Knihovna, Sokolska 31, 121 32 Prague 2, Czech Republic. TEL 2491-5775. FAX 2491-4625. Ed. M. Pribil. circ. 495. **Document type:** abstracting/indexing.
    Formerly: Referatovy Vyber ze Sportovni Mediciny - Abstracts of Sports Medicine (ISSN 0034-2904)
    Description: Abstracts of medical journal articles from around the world.

610   UK   ISSN 0955-0984
REHABILITATION INDEX. 1988. m. £53 (outside Europe £69) (effective 1995). British Library, Medical Information Centre, Boston Spa, Wetherby, W. Yorks. LS23 7BQ, England. TEL 01937-546520. FAX 01937-546458. E-mail: maggie.taylor@bl.uk. index. **Document type:** abstracting/indexing.
    ●Also available online.
    —BLDSC (7350.243000).
    Description: Current awareness index of rehabilitation professional journals.

616.4   UK   ISSN 0142-8314
RELEASING HORMONES. 1978. s-m. (diskette m.) £85 (diskette £115; both £175) (effective 1995). S U B I S, Mansion House, 19 Kingfield Rd., Sheffield S11 9AS, England. TEL 0114-2554433. FAX 0114-2554626. E-mail: admin@sheffac.demon.co.uk. (also avail. in diskette format) **Document type:** abstracting/indexing.
    —CCC.
    Description: Current awareness service for researchers. Covers buserelin, corticotropin releasing hormone, LH-ESH releasing hormone, somatotropin releasing hormone, and thyrotropin releasing hormone.

619   US
RESOURCES FOR COMPARATIVE BIOMEDICAL RESEARCH; a research resources directory. 1978. biennial. free. U.S. National Institutes of Health, National Center for Research Resources, Westwood Bldg. Rm. 10A15, 5333 Westbard Ave., Bethesda, MD 20892. TEL 301-594-7938. circ. 9,000. **Document type:** government publication, directory.
    Formerly: Animal Resources.
    Description: Source directory of animals used for research purposes.

610   CU   ISSN 0864-2184
RESUMENES MEDICOS. Short title: ResuMed. (Text in Spanish; summaries in English, Spanish) 1987. s-a. $26 in S. America; N. America $28; elsewhere $30. Ministerio de Salud Publica, Centro Nacional de Informacion de Ciencias Medicas, Calle E No. 452, e-19 y 21, Plaza de la Revolucion, Apdo. 6520, Havana, Cuba. TEL 809-23-5338. (Dist. by: Ediciones Cubanas, Obispo No. 527, Apdo. 605, Havana, Cuba) Ed. Sara Perez. circ. 1,000.
    Description: Covers the fields of basic, preventive and clinical medical science and public health and safety.

581 615.8   UK
▼**REVIEW OF AROMATIC AND MEDICINAL PLANTS.** 1995. bi-m. £125($230) (effective 1996). CAB International, Wallingford, Oxon. OX10 8DE, England. TEL 44-1491-832111. FAX 44-1491-826090. E-mail: cabi@cabi.org. (U.S. subscr. to: CAB International, 845 N. Park Ave., Tucson, AZ 85719. TEL 800-528-4841. FAX 520-621-3816) (also avail. in diskette format; back issues avail.) **Document type:** abstracting/indexing.
    ●Also available online.

618.202   UK   ISSN 0260-5848
ROYAL COLLEGE OF MIDWIVES. CURRENT AWARENESS SERVICE; recent literature on midwifery. 1980. q. £20 to individuals; institutions £34(foreign £40). Royal College of Midwives Trust, Library, 15 Mansfield St., London W1M 0BE, England. TEL 0171-872-5100. FAX 0171-872-5101. Ed. Mrs. Jan Ayres. circ. 450. **Document type:** abstracting/indexing.

SELECTED ABSTRACTS ON OCCUPATIONAL DISEASES. see OCCUPATIONAL HEALTH AND SAFETY — Abstracting, Bibliographies, Statistics

610   US
SELECTED PERIODICALS FOR THE MEDICAL LIBRARY. 1967. a. free to qualified personnel. Ebsco Industries, Inc., Title Information Department, 5724 Hwy. 280 East, Birmingham, AL 35242. TEL 205-991-6600. FAX 205-995-1518. (Subscr. to: EBSCO Subscription Services, Box 2543, Birmingham, AL 35201. TEL 800-826-3024) Ed. Erdeal Moore. adv.; tr.lit. circ. 18,000.

619 574.28 616.97   US
SEQUENCES OF PROTEINS OF IMMUNOLOGICAL INTEREST. irreg., 5th edition, 1994. $30 in N. America (overseas $51). U.S. National Center for Biotechnology Information, National Library of Medicine, Bldg. 38A, Rm. 8N-803, 8600 Rockville Pike, Bethesda, MD 20894. TEL 301-496-2475. FAX 301-480-9241. E-mail: info@ncbi.nlm.nih.gov. (Subscr. to: National Technical Information Service, 5285 Port Royal Rd., Springfield, VA 22161. TEL 703-487-4650. FAX 703-321-8547) charts. **Document type:** academic/scholarly publication, government publication.
    Description: Discusses N.I.H. research in this area; includes summary distribution tables, variability plots, protein index, antibody specificity index, and general reference index.

610 011   US   ISSN 1041-2832
Z6664.A1
SICKNESS AND WELLNESS PUBLICATIONS. 1989. triennial. $89.50. John Gordon Burke Publisher, Inc., Box 1492, Evanston, IL 60204-1492. TEL 708-866-8625. **Document type:** directory.
    ●Also available online.
    Description: Directory of newsletters indexed by type of disease and medical condition written for the layperson who has an interest in a specific disease or medical condition.

616.1   RU   ISSN 0234-9760
SIGNAL'NAYA INFORMATSIYA. ISHEMICHESKAYA BOLEZN' SERDTSA. 1987. m. 6.60 Rub. Vsesoyuznyi Institut Nauchno-Tekhnicheskoi Informatsii (VINITI), Baltiiskaya ul. 14, A-219 Moscow, Russia. **Document type:** abstracting/indexing.

610   RU   ISSN 0234-9752
SIGNAL'NAYA INFORMATSIYA. NEIROPEPTIDY. 1987. m. 6.80 Rub. Vsesoyuznyi Institut Nauchno-Tekhnicheskoi Informatsii (VINITI), Baltiiskaya ul. 14, A-219 Moscow, Russia. **Document type:** abstracting/indexing.

MEDICAL SCIENCES — ABSTRACTING, BIBLIOGRAPHIES, STATISTICS

SISTER COMMUNITIES HEALTH PROFILES OF THE U S - MEXICO BORDER/PERFILES DE SALUD DE LAS COMUNIDADES HERMANAS DE LA FRONTERA MEXICO - ESTADOS UNIDOS. see *PUBLIC HEALTH AND SAFETY — Abstracting, Bibliographies, Statistics*

617.7   US   ISSN 1055-6575
SLIDE ATLAS OF CURRENT OPHTHALMOLOGY (YEAR). (Supplement to: Current Opinion in Ophthalmology) bi-m. $299.95. Current Science, 400 Market St., Ste. 700, Philadelphia, PA 19106. TEL 215-574-2210; 800-552-5866. FAX 215-574-3533. (And: Current Science Ltd., 34-42 Cleveland St., London W1P 6LB, England. TEL 0171-323-0323. FAX 0171-636-6911) Ed. G.W. Weinstein. (looseleaf format) **Document type:** academic/scholarly publication.

617.3   US   ISSN 1055-6583
SLIDE ATLAS OF CURRENT ORTHOPAEDICS (YEAR). (Supplement to: Current Opinion in Orthopaedics) bi-m. $299.95. Current Science, 400 Market St., Ste. 700, Philadelphia, PA 19106. TEL 215-574-2210; 800-552-5866. FAX 215-574-3533. (And: Current Science Ltd., 34-42 Cleveland St., London W1P 6LB, England. TEL 0171-323-0323. FAX 0171-636-6911) Ed. W.R.J. Rennie. (looseleaf format) **Document type:** academic/scholarly publication.

616.3   US
SLIDE ATLAS OF GASTROINTESTINAL ENDOSCOPY (YEAR). (Supplement to: Annual of Gastrointestinal Endoscopy) bi-m. $195. Current Science, 400 Market St., Ste. 700, Philadelphia, PA 19106. TEL 215-574-2210; 800-552-5866. FAX 215-574-3533. (And: Current Science Ltd., 34-42 Cleveland St., London W1P 6LB, England. TEL 0171-323-0323. FAX 0171-636-6911) Ed.Bd. (looseleaf format) **Document type:** academic/scholarly publication.

615.53 316.8   SA
SOUTH AFRICA. CENTRAL STATISTICAL SERVICE. CENSUS OF MEDICAL, DENTAL AND OTHER HEALTH SERVICES - CHIROPRACTORS, HOMEOPATHS, NATUROPATHS, OSTEOPATHS AND HERBALISTS. (Report No. 93-06-01) irreg., latest 1987. R.4.40 (foreign R.4.80). Central Statistical Service - Sentrale Statistiekdiens, Private Bag X44, Pretoria 0001, South Africa. TEL 27-12-310-8911. FAX 27-12-310-8500. (Orders to: Government Printing Works, Private Bag X85, Pretoria 0001, South Africa) **Document type:** government publication.

610 316.8   SA
SOUTH AFRICA. CENTRAL STATISTICAL SERVICE. CENSUS OF MEDICAL, DENTAL AND OTHER HEALTH SERVICES - DOCTORS. (Report No. 93-02-01) irreg., latest 1987. R.4.40 (foreign R.4.80). Central Statistical Service - Sentrale Statistiekdiens, Private Bag X44, Pretoria 0001, South Africa. TEL 27-12-310-8911. FAX 27-12-310-8500. (Orders to: Government Printing Works, Private Bag X85, Pretoria 0001, South Africa) **Document type:** government publication.

617.6 316.8   SA
SOUTH AFRICA. CENTRAL STATISTICAL SERVICE. CENSUS OF MEDICAL, DENTAL AND OTHER HEALTH SERVICES - DENTISTS. (Report No. 93-03-01) irreg., latest 1987. R.4.40 (foreign R.4.80). Central Statistical Service - Sentrale Statistiekdiens, Private Bag X44, Pretoria 0001, South Africa. TEL 27-12-310-8911. FAX 27-12-310-8500. (Orders to: Government Printing Works, Private Bag X85, Pretoria 001, South Africa) **Document type:** government publication.

610 316.8   SA
SOUTH AFRICA. CENTRAL STATISTICAL SERVICE. CENSUS OF MEDICAL, DENTAL AND OTHER HEALTH SERVICES - SUPPLEMENTARY HEALTH SERVICES AND DENTAL TECHNICIANS. (Report No. 93-05-01) irreg., latest 1987. R.4.40 (foreign R.4.80). Central Statistical Service - Sentrale Statistiekdiens, Private Bag X44, Pretoria 0001, South Africa. TEL 27-12-310-8911. FAX 27-12-310-8500. (Orders to: Government Printing Works, Private Bag X85, Pretoria 0001, South Africa) **Document type:** government publication.

610 316.8   SA
SOUTH AFRICA. CENTRAL STATISTICAL SERVICE. STATISTICAL RELEASE. CENSUS OF AUXILIARY, HEALTH SERVICES AND DENTAL TECHNICIANS (YEAR). (No. P9306) irreg., latest 1987. free. Central Statistical Service - Sentrale Statistiekdiens, Private Bag X44, Pretoria 0001, South Africa. TEL 27-12-310-8911. FAX 27-12-310-8500. **Document type:** government publication.

610 316.8   SA
SOUTH AFRICA. CENTRAL STATISTICAL SERVICE. STATISTICAL RELEASE. CENSUS OF CHIROPRACTORS AND HOMEOPATHS. (No. P9306) irreg., latest 1987. free. Central Statistical Service - Sentrale Statistiekdiens, Private Bag X44, Pretoria 0001, South Africa. TEL 27-12-310-8911. FAX 27-12-310-8500. **Document type:** government publication.

610 316.8   SA
SOUTH AFRICA. CENTRAL STATISTICAL SERVICE. STATISTICAL RELEASE. CENSUS OF DOCTORS (YEAR). (No. P9302) irreg., latest 1987. free. Central Statistical Service - Sentrale Statistiekdiens, Private Bag X44, Pretoria 0001, South Africa. TEL 27-12-310-8911. FAX 27-12-310-8500. **Document type:** government publication.

610 316.81   SA
SOUTH AFRICA. CENTRAL STATISTICAL SERVICE. STATISTICAL RELEASE. CENSUS OF DENTISTS (YEAR). (No. P9303) irreg., latest 1987. free. Central Statistical Service - Sentrale Statistiekdiens, Private Bag X44, Pretoria 0001, South Africa. TEL 27-12-310-8911. FAX 27-12-310-8500. **Document type:** government publication.

610 011   GW   ISSN 0932-5034
SOZIALMEDIZIN. (Text in English or German) 1987. irreg. DM.13 per no. Landesinstitut fuer den Oeffentlichen Gesundheitsdienst des Landes Nordrhein-Westfalen, Westerfeldstr. 35-37, 33611 Bielefeld, Germany. TEL 0521-8007264. FAX 0521-8007200. (Subscr. to: Postfach 201012, 33548 Bielefeld, Germany) circ. 350. **Document type:** abstracting/indexing.

617.1   UK   ISSN 0967-7755
SPORTS PHYSIOLOGY AND MEDICINE. 1993. m. £75. S U B I S, Mansion House, 19 Kingfield Rd., Sheffield S11 9AS, England. TEL 0114-255-4433. FAX 0114-255-4626. E-mail: admin@sheffac.demon.co.uk. **Document type:** abstracting/indexing.
Description: Current awareness service for researchers in clinical and life sciences.

610 016   UK   ISSN 0277-6715
RA409   CODEN: SMEDDA
STATISTICS IN MEDICINE. 1982. 25/yr. $1195 (foreign $1195) (effective 1996). John Wiley & Sons Ltd., Journals, Baffins Ln., Chichester, W. Sussex PO19 1UD, England. TEL 01243-779777. FAX 01243-776128. TELEX 86290 WIBOOK G. (Subscr. in the Americas to: John Wiley & Sons, Inc., 605 Third Ave., New York, NY 10158. TEL 212-850-6645. FAX 212-850-6021) Ed.Bd. adv.; bk.rev.; charts; illus.; stat.; index. circ. 1,448. (also avail. in microform from UMI; back issues avail.; reprint service avail. from SWZ,UMI) **Indexed:** Abstr.Hyg., ASCA, Biostat., Comput.Abstr., Curr.Cont., Curr.Ind.Stat., Diar.Dis.Res., Dok.Arbeitsmed., Excerp.Med., Ind.Med., Oper.Res.Manage.Sci., Qual.Contr.Appl.Stat., Stat.Theor.Meth.Abstr. **Document type:** academic/scholarly publication.
—BLDSC (8453.576000); Faxon; Genuine Article; SWETS; UMI; UnCover. **CCC.**
Description: Covers all aspects of the collection, analysis, presentation and interpretation of medical data.
Refereed Serial

610.73   DK   ISSN 0108-9714
STATISTIK OM SUNDHEDSPLEJERSKERNES VIRKSOMHED. (Subseries of: Primaer Sundhedstjenestestatistik) 1983. irreg. DKK 75. Sundhedsstyrelsen, Amaliegade 13, 1012 Copenhagen K, Denmark. (Subscr. to: Statens Informationstjeneste, P.O. Box 1103, 1009 Copenhagen K, Denmark) illus.

610.73   CN   ISSN 0843-1167
SUGGESTED LIST OF PERIODICALS FOR NURSES FOR THE CANADIAN HEALTH SCIENCE LIBRARY. a. Can.$5. Canadian Nurses Association - Association des Infirmieres et Infirmiers du Canada, 50 Driveway, Ottawa, ON K2P 1E2, Canada. TEL 613-237-2133. FAX 613-237-3520. **Document type:** catalog, bibliography.
Description: A list of suggested and recommended periodicals in nursing published in Canada, the U.S., Switzerland, England and France. Information includes titles, where periodicals may be obtained and the approximate cost.

617.96 016   US   ISSN 0039-6206
RD81.A1   CODEN: SANEA5
SURVEY OF ANESTHESIOLOGY. 1957. bi-m. $87 to individuals; institutions $112 (effective 1995). Williams & Wilkins, 428 E. Preston St., Baltimore, MD 21202. TEL 410-528-4000; 800-638-6423. FAX 410-528-4312. TELEX 87699. Ed. Burnell R. Brown, Jr., M.D. adv.; bk.rev.; abstr. circ. 3,000. (also avail. in microfilm from WWS) **Indexed:** Curr.Adv.Ecol.Sci. **Document type:** academic/scholarly publication, abstracting/indexing.
—BLDSC (8548.834400); SWETS; UnCover. **CCC.**
Description: Abstracts anesthesiology-related literature from around the world.

617.7 016   US   ISSN 0039-6257
         CODEN: SUOPAD
SURVEY OF OPHTHALMOLOGY. 1956. bi-m. $60 to individuals (Canada $70; elsewhere $100); institutions $95 (Canada $105; elsewhere $160). Survey of Ophthalmology, Inc., 7 Kent St., Ste. 4, Brookline, MA 02146. TEL 617-566-2138. FAX 617-566-4019. Ed. Dr. Bernard Schwartz; Pub. Susan Erickson. adv. contact: Ina Orenstein. bk.rev.; abstr.; charts; illus.; index. circ. 11,024. (also avail. in microform from MIM,UMI,WWS; back issues avail.; reprint service avail. from UMI) **Indexed:** ASCA, Biol.Abstr., Chem.Abstr., Curr.Adv.Cancer Res., Curr.Cont., Excerp.Med., Ind.Med., Ophthal.Lit., Rev.Plant Path. **Document type:** academic/scholarly publication.
—BLDSC (8550.770000); CASDDS; EMDOCS; Faxon; Genuine Article; SWETS; UMI; UnCover. **CCC.**
Description: Contains articles in a review format that enables opthamologists to maintain a critical awareness about the volume of literature in the field. Integrates and interprets the information on subjects selected for their clinical importance.
Refereed Serial

SWEDEN. STATISTISKA CENTRALBYRAAN. STATISTISKA MEDDELANDEN. SUBGROUP HS (PUBLIC HEALTH AND MEDICAL CARE). see *PUBLIC HEALTH AND SAFETY — Abstracting, Bibliographies, Statistics*

616.988   UK   ISSN 0041-3240
TROPICAL DISEASES BULLETIN. 1912. m. £180($325) (effective 1996). CAB International, Wallingford, Oxon. OX10 8DE, England. TEL 01491-832111. FAX 01491-833508. TELEX 847964 COMAGG G. E-mail: cabi@cabi.org. Ed. C.A. Brown. adv.; bk.rev.; abstr.; index. circ. 720. (also avail. in diskette format; microform from PMC) **Indexed:** Biol.Abstr., Curr.Adv.Ecol.Sci., Helminthol.Abstr., Ind.Med., Ind.Vet., Nutr.Abstr., Rev.Appl.Entomol., Rev.Plant Path., Vet.Bull. **Document type:** bulletin.
●Also available online. Vendor(s): DIMDI.
—BLDSC (9056.000000).

TUMOUR MARKER UPDATE. see *MEDICAL SCIENCES — Oncology*

016.6   US   ISSN 0276-7570
U C M P QUARTERLY. 1973. q. $260 in the U.S. and Canada; elsewhere $290. Medical Library Center of New York, 5 E. 102nd St., 7th Fl., New York, NY 10029-5288. FAX 212-876-6697. Ed. Robert Dempsey. circ. 720. (microfiche) **Document type:** catalog.
Incorporates (1966-1976): Union Catalog of Medical Periodicals (ISSN 0090-0672)

MEDICAL SCIENCES — ALLERGOLOGY AND IMMUNOLOGY

619   US
R854.U5
U.S. NATIONAL INSTITUTES OF HEALTH. NATIONAL CENTER FOR RESEARCH RESOURCES. PROGRAM HIGHLIGHTS. 1978. a. free. U.S. National Institutes of Health, National Center for Research Resources, Westwood Bldg., Rm. 10A15, 5333 Westbard Ave., Bethesda, MD 20892. TEL 301-594-7938. circ. 11,000. **Document type:** government publication.
Formerly: U.S. National Institutes of Health. Division of Research Resources. Program Highlights (ISSN 0278-5374)
Description: Annual report of the National Center for Research Resources.

610 016   IR
UNIVERSITY OF TEHERAN. FACULTY OF HEALTH. INSTITUTE OF RESEARCH. LIST OF PUBLICATIONS RECEIVED IN THE LIBRARY/DANESHGAH-E TEHRAN. DANESHKADE-YE BEDASHT VA ANSTITU TAHQIQAT-E BEHDASHTI. AKHBAR-E KETABKHANEH VA SURAT-E NASHRIYAT-E RESIDEH.* (Text in English, Persian) 1946. m. free. University of Teheran, Faculty of Health, P.O. Box 1310, Teheran 5, Iran.

610   RH   ISSN 1021-5549
UTANO - ZIMBABWE; an annotated health information bibliography. 1993. 2/yr. $20 (free to health institutions). (University of Zimbabwe Medical Library) Box MP45, Mount Pleasant, Harare, Zimbabwe. TEL 263-4-791631. FAX 263-4-795019. Ed. Sabelo Mapasure. circ. 500. **Document type:** bibliography.

VIOLENCE & ABUSE ABSTRACTS; current literature in interpersonal violence. see *SOCIOLOGY — Abstracting, Bibliographies, Statistics*

616.92 016 576.64   US   ISSN 0896-5919
QR360
VIROLOGY AND AIDS ABSTRACTS. 1967. m. $845 (foreign $900). Cambridge Scientific Abstracts, 7200 Wisconsin Ave., 6th Fl., Bethesda, MD 20814. TEL 301-961-6750. FAX 301-961-6720. E-mail: market@csa.com. Ed.Bd; Pub. Ted Caris. adv.; bk.rev.; abstr.; index. (also avail. in magnetic tape; back issues avail.) **Indexed:** Cal.Tiss.Abstr., Chemorec.Abstr., Comput.& Info.Sys., Oncol.Abstr., Pollut.Abstr. **Document type:** abstracting/indexing.
•Also available online. Vendor(s): Knight-Ridder, Inc. (File no.76/LIFE SCIENCES COLLECTION), STN International (LIFESCI).
Also available on CD-ROM. Producer(s): SilverPlatter Information, Inc..
Formerly: Virology Abstracts (ISSN 0042-6830)
Description: Covers viruses of humans, animals and plants, with emphasis on AIDS.

617.7   UK   ISSN 0142-8543
VISION (SHEFFIELD). 1981. s-m. (diskette m.) £115 (diskette £115; both £175) (effective 1995). S U B I S, Mansion House, 19 Kingfield Rd., Sheffield S11 9AS, England. TEL 0114-2554433. FAX 0114-2554626. E-mail: admin@sheffac.demon.co.uk. (also avail. in diskette format) **Document type:** abstracting/indexing.
—CCC.
Description: Current awareness service for researchers in clinical and life sciences. Studies the structure, function, and pharmacology of the eye and its transmitters.

610 016   XR
VYBER NOVINEK BRNENSKYCH KNIHOVEN. SERIE B: LEKARSTVI. 1974. 6/yr. 18 Kc. (49 Kc. for 7 vols. series: A-G). Moravska Zemska Knihovna, Kounicova 5-7, 601 87 Brno, Czech Republic. Ed. Lenka Karlovska. circ. 300.
Formerly: Statni Vedecka Knihovna. Vyber Novinek. Serie B: Lekarstvi.

617.6   US   ISSN 0048-3389
WESTERN SOCIETY OF PERIODONTOLOGY. JOURNAL. PERIODONTAL ABSTRACTS. 1957. q. $60 (Canada and Mexico $70; elsewhere $75) (effective 1996). Western Society of Periodontology, 9010 Reseda Blvd., Ste.204, Northridge, CA 91324-3921. TEL 818-993-5093. FAX 818-993-5094. Ed. Thomas N. Sims. adv.; bk.rev. circ. 2,200. (back issues avail.) **Indexed:** Curr.Tit.Dent., Dent.Ind. **Document type:** abstracting/indexing.

610   CC
YIXUE WENZHAI/MEDICAL ABSTRACTS. (Text in Chinese) bi-m. Guangxi Yixue Qingbao Yanjiusuo - Guangxi Institute of Medical Information, 20 Gucheng Lu, Nanning, Guangxi 530022, People's Republic of China. TEL 29823. Ed. Ma Banghai. **Document type:** abstracting/indexing.

616.21 016   GW   ISSN 0340-5214
ZENTRALBLATT HALS-, NASEN- UND OHRENHEILKUNDE, PLASTISCHE CHIRURGIE AN KOPF UND HALS/OTO-RHINO-LARYNGOLOGY, PLASTIC SURGERY OF HEAD AND NECK. (Text in English, German) 13/yr. DM.4964($3607) (effective 1996). (Deutsche Gesellschaft fuer Hals,- Nasen-, Ohrenheilkunde, Kopf- und Halschirurgie) Springer-Verlag, Heidelberger Platz 3, 14197 Berlin, Germany. TEL 030-8207-0. FAX 030-8214091. E-mail: orders@springer.de. (Subscr. in N. America to: Springer-Verlag New York, Inc., 44 Hartz Way, Secaucus, NJ 07096-2491. TEL 201-348-4033. FAX 201-348-4505) Eds. H.J. Denecke, U.F. Denecke-Singer. (also avail. in microform from UMI; reprint service avail. from ISI) **Document type:** abstracting/indexing.
—UMI. CCC.
Formerly: Zentralblatt fuer Hals-, Nasen- und Ohrenheilkunde Sowie Deren Grenzgebiete (ISSN 0044-4200)

616.5 016   GW   ISSN 0343-3048
ZENTRALBLATT HAUT- UND GESCHLECHTSKRANKHEITEN/DERMATOLOGY, VENEROLOGY, ANDROLOGY. (Text in English, German) 1921. 13/yr. DM.5828($4235) (effective 1996). (Deutsche Dermatologische Gesellschaft) Springer-Verlag, Heidelberger Platz 3, 14197 Berlin, Germany. TEL 030-8207-0. FAX 030-8214091. E-mail: orders@springer.de. (Subscr. in N. America to: Springer-Verlag New York, Inc., 44 Hartz Way, Secaucus, NJ 07096-2491. TEL 201-348-4033. FAX 201-348-4505) (Co-sponsor: Vereinigung Deutschsprachiger Dermatologen) Eds. R. Clorius, G. Landes. (also avail. in microform from UMI; reprint service avail. from ISI) **Document type:** abstracting/indexing.
—SWETS; UMI. CCC.
Formerly (until 1977): Zentralblatt fuer Haut- und Geschlechtskrankheiten Sowie Deren Grenzgebiete (ISSN 0044-4219)

616.8 016   GW   ISSN 0722-3064
ZENTRALBLATT NEUROLOGIE - PSYCHIATRIE/NEUROLOGY - PSYCHIATRY. (Supplement avail.: Neurology, Pyschiatry and Brain Research (ISSN 0941-9500)) (Text in English, German) 52/yr. DM.9916($7206) (effective 1996). (Archiv fuer Psychiatrie und Nervenkrankheiten) Springer-Verlag, Heidelberger Platz 3, 14197 Berlin, Germany. TEL 030-8207-0. FAX 030-8214091. E-mail: orders@springer.de. (Subscr. in N. America to: Springer-Verlag New York, Inc., 44 Hartz Way, Secaucus, NJ 07096-2491. TEL 201-348-4033. FAX 201-348-4505) (Co-sponsor: Gesamtverbande Deutscher Nervenaerzte) Eds. H. Kornhuber, G. Huber. (also avail. in microform from UMI; reprint service avail. from ISI) **Document type:** abstracting/indexing.
—UMI. CCC.
Formerly: Zentralblatt fuer die Gesamte Neurologie und Psychiatrie (ISSN 0044-412X)

617.7 016   GW   ISSN 0722-9933
ZENTRALBLATT OPHTHALMOLOGIE/OPHTHALMOLOGY. (Text in English, German) 13/yr. DM.2689($1954) (effective 1996). Springer-Verlag, Heidelberger Platz 3, 14197 Berlin, Germany. TEL 030-8207-0. FAX 030-8214091. E-mail: orders@springer.de. (Subscr. in N. America to: Springer-Verlag New York, Inc., 44 Hartz Way, Secaucus, NJ 07096-2491. TEL 201-348-4033. FAX 201-348-4505) Ed.Bd. (also avail. in microform from UMI; reprint service avail. from ISI) **Document type:** abstracting/indexing.
—UMI. CCC.
Formerly: Zentralblatt fuer die Gesamte Ophthalmologie und ihre Grenzgebiete (ISSN 0044-4138)

614.19 016   GW   ISSN 0722-3056
RA1001
ZENTRALBLATT RECHTSMEDIZIN/LEGAL MEDICINE. (Text in English, German) 1970. 26/yr. (in 2 vols., 13 nos./vol.) DM.5290($3844) (effective 1996). (Deutsche Gesellschaft fuer Rechtsmedizin) Springer-Verlag, Heidelberger Platz 3, 14197 Berlin, Germany. TEL 030-8207-0. FAX 030-8214091. E-mail: orders@springer.de. (Subscr. in N. America to: Springer-Verlag New York, Inc., 44 Hartz Way, Secaucus, NJ 07096-2491. TEL 201-348-4033. FAX 201-348-4505) Ed.Bd. (also avail. in microform from UMI; back issues avail.; reprint service avail. from ISI) **Indexed:** Ind.Med. **Document type:** abstracting/indexing.
—UMI. CCC.
Formerly: Zentralblatt fuer die Gesamte Rechtsmedizin und ihre Grenzgebiete (ISSN 0044-4154); Which supersedes: Deutsche Zeitschrift fuer die Gesamte Gerichtliche Medizin. Abstract Section.

617 016   GW   ISSN 0722-6985
ZENTRALORGAN CHIRURGIE/SURGERY. (Text in English, German) 26/yr. (in 2 vols., 13 nos./vol.). DM.3994($2902) (effective 1996). (Deutsche Gesellschaft fuer Chirurgie) Springer-Verlag, Heidelberger Platz 3, 14197 Berlin, Germany. TEL 030-8207-0. FAX 030-8214091. E-mail: orders@springer.de. (Subscr. in N. America to: Springer-Verlag New York, Inc., 44 Hartz Way, Secaucus, NJ 07096-2491. TEL 201-348-4033. FAX 201-348-4505) Ed.Bd. (also avail. in microform from UMI; reprint service avail. from ISI) **Document type:** abstracting/indexing.
—UMI. CCC.
Formerly: Zentralorgan fuer die Gesamte Chirurgie und ihre Grenzgebiete (ISSN 0044-4308)

610   CC
ZHONGGUO YIXUE WENZHAI (ERKEXUE)/CHINA MEDICAL ABSTRACTS (PEDIATRICS). (Text in Chinese) bi-m. $48. Liaoning Provincial Institute of Medical Information, Information Retrieval Office, 79 Jixian Jie, Heping-qu, Shenyang, Liaoning 110005, People's Republic of China. TEL 362837. Ed. Lin He. **Document type:** academic/scholarly publication, abstracting/indexing.

618   CC   ISSN 1001-1315
ZHONGGUO YIXUE WENZHAI (JIHUA SHENGYU, FUCHAN KEXUE)/CHINA MEDICAL ABSTRACTS (BIRTH CONTROL AND GYNECOLOGY). (Text in Chinese) q. Sichuan Yixue Qingbao Yanjiusuo - Sichuan Medical Science Information Research Institute, 34, Wangjiaguai Jie, Chengdu, Sichuan 610041, People's Republic of China. TEL 28790. Ed. Song Wenli. **Document type:** abstracting/indexing.

617.6   CC
ZHONGGUO YIXUE WENZHAI (KOUQIANG YIXUE)/CHINA MEDICAL ABSTRACTS (STOMATOLOGY). (Text in Chinese) q. Nanjing Yixueyuan - Nanjing Institute of Medical Sciences, 140 Hanzhong Lu, Nanjing, Jiangsu 210029, People's Republic of China. TEL 649141. Ed. Yin Liqiao. **Document type:** abstracting/indexing.

616   CC   ISSN 1001-4136
ZHONGGUO YIXUE WENZHAI (NEIKE XUE). English edition: China Medical Abstracts (Internal Medicine) (ISSN 1000-9086) (Text in Chinese) bi-m. $26. Guangxi Yixue Kexue Qibaosuo - Guangxi Institute of Medical Science Information, 20 Gucheng Lu, Nanning, Guangxi 530022, People's Republic of China. TEL 86-771-5864744. (Dist. outside China by: Guoji Shudian - China International Book Trading Corp., P.O. Box 399, Beijing, P.R.C.) Ed. Lin Zhongchang. **Document type:** abstracting/indexing.

MEDICAL SCIENCES — Allergology And Immunology

616.97   US
A A O A NEWS. 1981. q. free. American Academy of Otolaryngic Allergy, 8455 Colesville Rd., Ste. 745, Silver Spring, MD 20910. Ed. Dr. Richard L. Mabay. adv.; tr.lit. circ. 12,000. (back issues avail.)
Description: Developments in otolaryngic allergy for physicians and allied health practitioners.

ACTA MICROBIOLOGICA ET IMMUNOLOGICA HUNGARICA. see *BIOLOGY — Microbiology*

ADVANCES IN HOST DEFENSE MECHANISMS. see *MEDICAL SCIENCES — Communicable Diseases*

MEDICAL SCIENCES — ALLERGOLOGY AND IMMUNOLOGY

616.97 US ISSN 0065-2776
QR180 CODEN: ADIMAV
ADVANCES IN IMMUNOLOGY. 1961. irreg., vol.53, 1993. Academic Press, Inc., 525 B St., Ste. 1900, San Diego, CA 92101-4495. TEL 619-231-0926. FAX 619-699-6715. (Subscr. to: Order Dept., 6277 Sea Harbor Dr., 4th Fl., Orlando, FL 32887. TEL 800-321-5068) Eds. W.H. Taliaferro, J.H. Humphrey. index. (reprint service avail. from ISI) **Indexed:** Abstr.Hyg., Anim.Breed.Abstr., Biol.Abstr., Chem.Abstr., Curr.Adv.Ecol.Sci., Dairy Sci.Abstr., Diar.Dis.Res., Excerp.Med., Helminthol.Abstr., Ind.Med., Ind.Sci.Rev., Ind.Vet., Nutr.Abstr., Sci.Cit.Ind., Telegen, Trop.Dis.Bull., Vet.Bull. —BLDSC (0709.100000); CASDDS; EMDOCS; Faxon; SWETS; UnCover. **CCC.**

616.97 UK ISSN 0960-5428
QP356.47 CODEN: ADNIEE
ADVANCES IN NEUROIMMUNOLOGY. 1991. q. £237($377) (effective 1996). Elsevier Science Ltd., Pergamon, P.O. Box 800, Kidlington, Oxford OX5 1DX, England. TEL 44-1865-843000. FAX 44-1865-843010. E-mail: nlinfo-f@elsevier.nl; usinfo-f@elsevier.com; forinfo-kyf04035@niftyserve.or.jp; Site addr.: http://www.elsevier.nl/. (Subscr. in U.S. and Canada to: Elsevier Science, 660 White Plains Rd., Tarrytown, NY 10591-5153. TEL 914-524-9200. FAX 914-333-2444) Eds. George B. Stefano, Eric M. Smith. (also avail. in microform from UMI) **Indexed:** Excerp.Med. (1994-), Ind.Med. (1994-). **Document type:** academic/scholarly publication. —BLDSC (0709.479000); CASDDS; Genuine Article; SWETS; UMI. **CCC.**
Description: Publishes comprehensive reviews on significant research into the interactions between the nervous and immune systems, from both basic and clinical standpoints.
Refereed Serial

AIDS ALERT. see *MEDICAL SCIENCES — Communicable Diseases*

AIDS RESEARCH AND HUMAN RETROVIRUSES. see *MEDICAL SCIENCES — Communicable Diseases*

616.97 GW ISSN 0931-2579
AKTUELLE IMMUNOLOGIE. 1986. irreg., vol.11, 1993. W. Zuckschwerdt Verlag GmbH, Industriestr. 17, 82110 Germering, Germany. TEL 089-894349-0. FAX 089-89434950. Ed. G. Gross. **Document type:** academic/scholarly publication.

616.97 MX ISSN 0002-5151
CODEN: ALEGAF
ALERGIA. (Text in Spanish; summaries in English) 1953. bi-m. $120. Sociedad Mexicana de Alergia e Inmunologia, A.C., Fuente Emperador 6, Tecamachalco, Deleg. Naucalpan, 53950 Edo. de Mexico, Mexico. FAX 251-3975. Ed. Jesus Perez Martin. adv.; bk.rev. circ. 3,000. **Indexed:** Biol.Abstr., Chem.Abstr., Dent.Ind., Excerp.Med., Ind.Med. **Document type:** academic/scholarly publication. —BLDSC (7840.857000).
Description: Original research articles in clinical case studies on allergy and immunology.

616.97 SW ISSN 0002-5747
ALLERGIA. 1957. bi-m. SEK 120 (effective 1991). Riksfoerbundet mot Astma-Allergi (RmA) - Swedish National Federation Against Allergy, P.O. Box 49098, S-100 28 Stockholm, Sweden. Ed. Christian Palme. adv.; bk.rev.; charts; illus. circ. 20,000.

616.97 US ISSN 1053-1092
CODEN: ADITEM
ALLERGIC DISEASE AND THERAPY. 1990. irreg., vol.7, 1994. price varies. Marcel Dekker, Inc., 270 Madison Ave., New York, NY 10016. TEL 212-696-9000. FAX 212-685-4540. TELEX 421419. —BLDSC (0790.500000).

615.37 616.97 FR ISSN 0397-9148
ALLERGIE ET IMMUNOLOGIE.* 1969. q. 300 F. (students 200 F.). Nouvelles Editions Medicales Francaises, B.P. 451, 95005 Clergy Poutoise Cedex, France. Ed. G.M. Halpern. adv.; bk.rev. circ. 5,000. **Indexed:** Apic.Abstr., Biol.Abstr., Excerp.Med., Ind.Med., Nutr.Abstr. —BLDSC (0790.600000); SWETS.

616.97 GW ISSN 0941-8849
CODEN: ALJOE
ALLERGO JOURNAL. 1992. 6/yr. DM.98. M M V Medizin Verlag, Neumarkter Str. 18, 81673 Munich, Germany. TEL 089-43189647. FAX 089-43189633. **Indexed:** Excerp.Med. (1994-). **Document type:** academic/scholarly publication. —BLDSC (0790.925000).

616.97 615.37 SP ISSN 0301-0546
CODEN: AGIMBJ
ALLERGOLOGIA ET IMMUNOPATHOLOGIA. (Supplement avail. (ISSN 0211-6448)) (Text in English, Spanish) 1972. bi-m. 10900 ptas.($110) (effective 1995). Editorial Garsi, S.A., Juan Bravo 46, 28006 Madrid, Spain. TEL 34-1-4021212. FAX 34-1-4020954. Dir. A. Olive. circ. 3,000. **Indexed:** Biol.Abstr., Chem.Abstr., CINAHL, Curr.Adv.Ecol.Sci., Dent.Ind., Excerp.Med., Helminthol.Abstr., Ind.Med.Esp., Ind.Med., Nutr.Abstr., Protozool.Abstr., Rev.Med.& Vet.Mycol. —BLDSC (0790.930000); CASDDS; SWETS. **CCC.**

616.97 SZ ISSN 0065-6372
ALLERGOLOGICUM; TRANSACTIONS OF THE COLLEGIUM INTERNATIONALE. (Supplement to: International Archives of Allergy and Applied Immunology) (Text in English) 1955. a. (Collegium Internationale Allergologicum) S. Karger AG, Allschwilerstr. 10, P.O. Box, CH-4009 Basel, Switzerland. TEL 061-3061111. FAX 061-3061234. E-mail: Karger@Karger.ch. Ed. Basel Karger. **Indexed:** Curr.Cont. **Document type:** proceedings.
Refereed Serial

616.97 GW ISSN 0344-5062
CODEN: ALLRDI
ALLERGOLOGIE. 1978. m. DM.228($172) Dustri-Verlag Dr. Karl Feistle, Bahnhofstr. 9, 82041 Deisenhofen, Germany. TEL 089-613861-0. FAX 089-6135412. Ed. Dr. L. Jaeger. **Indexed:** Apic.Abstr., Biol.Abstr., Chem.Abstr., Curr.Adv.Ecol.Sci., Curr.Cont., Excerp.Med., Rev.Med.& Vet.Mycol. **Document type:** academic/scholarly publication. —BLDSC (0790.940000); CASDDS; Genuine Article. **CCC.**

616.97 AT ISSN 1323-8930
CODEN: ARERAM
ALLERGOLOGY INTERNATIONAL. 1952. q. Aus.$268($190) (18000 Yen) (effective 1996). (Japanese Society of Allergology, AT - Nihon Arerugi Gakkai) Blackwell Science Pty Ltd, P.O. Box 378, Carlton South, Vic. 3053, Australia. TEL 61-3-93470300. FAX 61-3-93493016. adv.; bk.rev. circ. 6,800. **Indexed:** Apic.Abstr., Chem.Abstr., Dent.Ind., Excerp.Med., Ind.Med., INIS Atomind. **Document type:** academic/scholarly publication. —BLDSC (4650.785000); CASDDS; EMDOCS.
Formerly (until vol.45): Japanese Journal of Allergology (ISSN 0021-4884)
Refereed Serial

616.97 DK ISSN 0105-4538
CODEN: LLRGDY
ALLERGY; European journal of allergy and immunology. (Text in English) 1948. 12/yr. DKK 2300 (incl. supplements) (effective 1996). (European Academy of Allergology and Clinical Immunology) Munksgaard International Publishers Ltd., 35 Noerre Soegade, P.O. Box 2148, DK-1016 Copenhagen K, Denmark. TEL 33-127030. FAX 33-129387. Ed. S. G. O. Johansson. adv.; bk.rev.; bibl.; charts; illus.; index. circ. 2,600. (also avail. in microform from SWZ; reprint service avail. from ISI) **Indexed:** Biol.Abstr., Biotech.Abstr., C.I.S. Abstr., Chem.Abstr., Curr.Adv.Ecol.Sci., Curr.Adv.Genetics & Molec.Biol., Curr.Cont., Dairy Sci.Abstr., Dent.Ind., Dok.Arbeitsmed., Excerp.Med., Helminthol.Abstr., Ind.Med., Ind.Sci.Rev., INIS Atomind., Med.& Surg.Dermat., NRN, Nutr.Abstr., Rev.Med.& Vet.Mycol., Risk Abstr., Sci.Cit.Ind., Weed Abstr. —BLDSC (0790.945000); ADONIS; CASDDS; Faxon; Genuine Article; SWETS; UnCover. **CCC.**
Formerly: Acta Allergologica (ISSN 0001-5148)
Refereed Serial

616.97 DK ISSN 0108-1675
CODEN: ALSUET
ALLERGY. SUPPLEMENTUM. (Text in English) 1950. irreg. (European Academy of Allergology and Clinical Immunology) Munksgaard International Publishers Ltd., 35 Noerre Soegade, P.O. Box 2148, DK-1016 Copenhagen K, Denmark. TEL 33-127030. FAX 33-129387. adv. (reprint service avail. from ISI) **Indexed:** Biol.Abstr., Curr.Cont., Excerp.Med. —BLDSC (0790.946000); ADONIS. **CCC.**
Formerly: Acta Allergologica. Supplementum (ISSN 0065-096X)

616.97 CN ISSN 0824-1333
ALLERGY ALERT. 1980. q. Can.$15. Allergy Foundation of Canada, Box 1904, Saskatoon, SK S7K 3S5, Canada. TEL 306-652-1608. Ed. Sandy Woynarski. bk.rev. circ. 550. **Document type:** newsletter.

616.97 US ISSN 0838-1925
ALLERGY & CLINICAL IMMUNOLOGY NEWS. Short title: A C I News. 1989. bi-m. $68 to individuals; institutions $78; IAACI members $44. (International Association of Allergology and Clinical Immunology) Hogrefe & Huber Publishers, Box 2487, Kirkland, WA 98083. TEL 206-820-1500. FAX 206-823-8324. Ed. A.L. de Weck. adv. circ. 3,700. (back issues avail.) **Document type:** academic/scholarly publication. —BLDSC (0791.040000); SWETS. **CCC.**
Description: Includes clinical trends and practice, research trends and notes, reports on meetings, forum, people and calendar of events.

616.9 664 US
ALLERGY HOTLINE. m. $35. Hotline Printing and Publishing, Box 161132, Altamonte Springs, FL 32716. TEL 407-628-1377. FAX 407-628-9935. Ed. Dennis Blank. bk.rev. circ. 1,700. **Document type:** newsletter.

616.97 US ISSN 1046-9354
CODEN: ALPRE5
ALLERGY PROCEEDINGS. 1980. bi-m. $72 to individuals; institutions $102. Ocean Side Publications, Inc., 95 Pitman St., Providence, RI 02906. TEL 401-331-2510. FAX 401-331-5138. Ed. Dr. Guy A. Settipane. adv. circ. 3,000. (back issues avail.) **Indexed:** Chem.Abstr., Curr.Adv.Ecol.Sci., Curr.Cont., Ind.Med., Ind.Vet., Small Anim.Abstr. **Document type:** academic/scholarly publication, proceedings. —BLDSC (0791.081000); CASDDS; Faxon; Genuine Article; SWETS. **CCC.**
Former titles: New England and Regional Allergy Proceedings; New England Society of Allergy. Proceedings (ISSN 0276-7511)

616.97 US
AMERICAN ACADEMY OF ALLERGY. POLLEN AND MOLD COMMITTEE. STATISTICAL REPORT. 1973. a. free. Ross Laboratories, 625 Cleveland Ave., Columbus, OH 43216. TEL 614-227-3333. Ed. Bill Rohn. circ. 100. **Indexed:** Biol.Abstr., Nutr.Abstr.

616.97 618.92 US ISSN 0899-7411
AMERICAN JOURNAL OF ASTHMA & ALLERGY FOR PEDIATRICIANS. 1987. q. $55 to individuals; institutions $70; foreign $100. Slack, Inc., 6900 Grove Rd., Thorofare, NJ 08086-9447. TEL 609-848-1000. FAX 609-853-5991. Ed. Dr. Jacob Hen, Jr. adv. circ. 800.
Refereed Serial

616.97 618 DK ISSN 1046-7408
QP252.5 CODEN: AJRIE8
AMERICAN JOURNAL OF REPRODUCTIVE IMMUNOLOGY. (Text in English) 1980. 12/yr. DKK 2600 (effective 1996). (American Society of Reproductive Immunology, US) Munksgaard International Publishers Ltd., P.O. Box 2148, DK-1016 Copenhagen K, Denmark. (U.S. addr.: 238 Main Street, Cambridge, MA 02142-9740. TEL 45-33-12-70-30) Ed. Norbert Gleicher. adv.; bibl.; charts; illus.; index. circ. 600. (reprint service avail.) **Indexed:** Anim.Breed.Abstr., Biol.Abstr., Chem.Abstr., Curr.Adv.Ecol.Sci., Curr.Cont., Dairy Sci.Abstr., Excerp.Med., Ind.Med., Ind.Sci.Rev., Ind.Vet., INIS Atomind., Kidney, Pig News & Info., Sci.Cit.Ind.
●Also available online.
—BLDSC (0836.500000); CASDDS; Faxon; Genuine Article; SWETS; UnCover. **CCC.**
Former titles (until 1989): American Journal of Reproductive Immunology and Microbiology (ISSN 8755-8920); (until 1985): American Journal of Reproductive Immunology (ISSN 0271-7352)
Refereed Serial

MEDICAL SCIENCES — ALLERGOLOGY AND IMMUNOLOGY

616.97 US
CODEN: ANAEA3
ANNALS OF ALLERGY, ASTHMA, & IMMUNOLOGY. 1943. m. $50 to individuals; institutions $75; foreign 478. American College of Allergy, Asthma, & Immunology, 85 W. Algonquin Rd., Ste. 550, Arlington Heights, IL 60005-4425. TEL 708-427-1200. Ed. Dr. R. Michael Sly. adv.; bk.rev.; bibl.; charts; illus.; index; circ. 6,200 (paid). (also avail. in microform from UMI) **Indexed:** Abstr.Inter.Med., Apic.Abstr., Biol.Abstr., Biotech.Abstr., C.I.S. Abstr., Chem.Abstr., CINAHL, Curr.Adv.Ecol.Sci., Curr.Cont., Dairy Sci.Abstr., Dent.Ind., Dent.Ind., Excerp.Med., Food Sci.& Tech.Abstr., Helminthol.Abstr., Ind.Med., Ind.Sci.Rev., Med.& Surg.Dermat., NRN, Nutr.Abstr., Potato Abstr., Rev.Appl.Entomol., Rev.Med.& Vet.Mycol., Rev.Plant Path., Sci.Cit.Ind., Soyabean Abstr., Sugar Ind.Abstr. **Document type:** academic/scholarly publication.
—CASDDS; Genuine Article; SWETS; UMI; UnCover. **CCC.**
Formerly (until 1995): Annals of Allergy (ISSN 0003-4738)
Description: Contains case reports, reviews, reports of original research, brief abstracts of articles published elsewhere and abstracts presented at the annual meeting of the college.
Refereed Serial

616.97 US ISSN 0732-0582
QR180 CODEN: ARIMDU
ANNUAL REVIEW OF IMMUNOLOGY. 1983. a. $48 (foreign $53) (effective Jan. 1995). Annual Reviews Inc., 4139 El Camino Way, Box 10139, Palo Alto, CA 94303-0139. TEL 415-493-4400. FAX 415-855-9815. E-mail: annrevu@class.org. Ed. William E. Paul. adv. contact: Elizabeth Kao. bibl.; index, cum.index. (also avail. in microform from UMI; back issues avail.; reprint service avail.) **Indexed:** Abstr.Hyg., Anim.Breed.Abstr., Biol.Abstr., Chem.Abstr., Curr.Adv.Ecol.Sci., Diar.Dis.Res., Ind.Sci.Rev., Ind.Vet., Protozool.Abstr., Sci.Cit.Ind. **Document type:** academic/scholarly publication.
—BLDSC (1522.565800); CASDDS; Faxon; Genuine Article; SWETS; UMI; UnCover. **CCC.**
Description: Original critical reviews of the significant primary literature and current developments in immunology.

ANTIBODY, IMMUNOCONJUGATES, AND RADIOPHARMACEUTICALS. see *MEDICAL SCIENCES — Oncology*

616.97 616.2 JA ISSN 0287-0185
ARERUGIA. 1968. irreg. free. Japan Allergy Foundation, 6-8 Minamidai, Sagamihara, Kanagawa Prefecture, Japan. Ed. Prof. A. Kumagai. circ. 4,500.

616.97 US ISSN 0899-7470
ASTHMA AND ALLERGY ADVOCATE. 1985. q. $70. American Academy of Allergy, Asthma and Immunology, 611 E. Wells St., Milwaukee, WI 53202. TEL 414-272-6071. FAX 414-276-3349. Ed. S.E. Kaluzny-Petroff. bk.rev.; charts; illus.; stat. circ. 75,000. (looseleaf format) **Document type:** newsletter.
Description: Patient newsletter with information in the field.

616.97 US
ASTHMA RESOURCES DIRECTORY. 1990. irreg. (every 2-3 yrs.). $29.95. Allergy Publications, Inc., Box 640, Menlo Park, CA 94026-0640. TEL 415-322-1663. Ed. Carol Rudoff. adv. **Document type:** directory.
Description: Presents information on allergens that may trigger asthma symptoms, organizations and programs that provide support, information, education or products and services to asthma patients, doctors and treatment centers for asthma, and libraries or organizations with allergy specialty departments, databases and publications on asthma.

616.97 NO ISSN 0801-3799
ASTMA ALLERGI. 1961. 6/yr. NOK 160. Norges Astma- og Allergiforbund, Industrist. 36, 0357 Oslo 3, Norway. TEL 02-460613. FAX 02-698152. Eds. Ernst Pettersen, Tove T. Tveit. adv.; bk.rev.; illus.; pat. circ. 25,000.
—**CCC.**
Formerly: Astma- og Allergi-Nytt (ISSN 0004-6086)

616.97 DK ISSN 0900-4262
ASTMA ALLERGI BLADET.* 1971. q. DKK 100. Danmarks Astma - Allergiforbund, Hovedvej 9 C, 2600 Glostrup, Denmark. adv.; bk.rev. circ. 15,000.

AUSTRALIA. BUREAU OF STATISTICS. CHILDREN'S IMMUNISATION. see *MEDICAL SCIENCES — Abstracting, Bibliographies, Statistics*

616.97 616.7 UK ISSN 0142-8365
AUTOIMMUNE DISEASES. s-m. (diskette m.). £115 (diskette £115; both £175) (effective 1995). S U B I S, Mansion House, 19 Kingfield Rd., Sheffield S11 9AS, England. TEL 0114-2554433. FAX 0114-2554626. E-mail: admin@sheffac.demon.co.uk. (also avail. in diskette format; looseleaf format; back issues avail.) **Document type:** abstracting/indexing.
—**CCC.**
Description: Current awareness service for researchers in clinical and life sciences.

616.97 US ISSN 0891-6934
QR188.3 CODEN: AUIMEI
AUTOIMMUNITY. 1988. 12/yr. (in 3 vols., 4 nos./vol.). 106 ECU per vol. (effective 1996). Harwood Academic Publishers, c/o International Publishers Distributor, 820 Town Center Dr., PA 19047. TEL 215-750-2642. FAX 215-750-6343. (Subscr. to: International Publishers Distributor, P.O. Box 90, Reading, Berkshire RG1 8JL, England. TEL 44-734-560-080) Ed. Terence J. Wilkin. index. (also avail. in microform; back issues avail.) **Indexed:** Diab.Cont., Ind.Med.
—BLDSC (1828.345000); Faxon; SWETS. **CCC.**
Description: For researchers and clinicians interested in all aspects of auto immune disease.
Refereed Serial

615.37 SZ ISSN 0301-3782
QR180
BASEL INSTITUTE FOR IMMUNOLOGY. ANNUAL REPORT. (Text in English) 1972. a. free to libraries and immunologists. Basel Institute for Immunology, Grenzacherstr. 487, CH-4058 Basel, Switzerland. TEL 061-6051232. FAX 061-6051353. Ed. C.M. Steinberg. circ. 8,000. **Indexed:** Biol.Abstr. **Document type:** academic/scholarly publication.
—ADONIS.
Description: Presents research reports on all aspects of basic immunology.

616.97 US ISSN 0889-1591
QP356.47 CODEN: BBIMEW
BRAIN, BEHAVIOR, AND IMMUNITY. 1987. q. $231 (foreign $258) (effective 1996). Academic Press, Inc., Journal Division, 525 B St., Ste. 1900, San Diego, CA 92101-4495. TEL 619-230-1840. FAX 619-699-6800. (Subscr. to: Box 620000, Orlando, FL 32891-8340. TEL 800-543-9534) Ed. Robert Ader. (back issues avail.) **Indexed:** Psychol.Abstr. (1987-). **Document type:** academic/scholarly publication.
—BLDSC (2268.101000); CASDDS; Faxon; Genuine Article; SWETS; UnCover. **CCC.**
Description: Concerned with the interaction between the nervous system and the immune system at the molecular, cellular, and organismic levels. Addresses the relationships among behavioral, neural, and immunoregulatory processes.
Refereed Serial

C A SELECTS. ALLERGY AND ANTIALLERGIC AGENTS. see *MEDICAL SCIENCES — Abstracting, Bibliographies, Statistics*

C A SELECTS. IMMUNOCHEMICAL METHODS. see *MEDICAL SCIENCES — Abstracting, Bibliographies, Statistics*

615.37 CN ISSN 0068-9653
CANADIAN SOCIETY FOR IMMUNOLOGY. BULLETIN. (Text in English, French) 1967. q. membership. Canadian Society for Immunology, c/o Department of Immunology, University of Manitoba, 730 William Ave., Winnipeg, Man. R3E 0W3, Canada. TEL 204-788-6793. FAX 204-772-7924. Ed. Dr. Kent T. Hayglass. adv.; bk.rev. circ. 500. (also avail. in microform from UMI; reprint service avail. from UMI) **Document type:** bulletin.
—UMI.

CELIAC NEWS. see *MEDICAL SCIENCES — Gastroenterology*

615.37 574.8 US ISSN 0008-8749
QR185.C4 CODEN: CLIMB8
CELLULAR IMMUNOLOGY. 1970. 16/yr. $1550 (foreign $1852) (effective 1996). Academic Press, Inc., Journal Division, 525 B St., Ste. 1900, San Diego, CA 92101-4495. TEL 619-230-1840. FAX 619-699-6800. (Subscr. to: Box 620000, Orlando, FL 32891-8340. TEL 800-543-9534) Ed. H. Sherwood Lawrence. index. (back issues avail.) **Indexed:** Abstr.Hyg., Anim.Breed.Abstr., Biol.Abstr., Chem.Abstr., Curr.Adv.Cancer Res., Curr.Adv.Ecol.Sci., Curr.Cont., Dairy Sci.Abstr., Dent.Ind., Excerp.Med., Helminthol.Abstr., Ind.Med., Ind.Sci.Rev., Ind.Vet., INIS Atomind., Protozool.Abstr., Rev.Med.& Vet.Mycol., Rev.Plant Path., Small Anim.Abstr., Trop.Dis.Bull., Vet.Bull. **Document type:** academic/scholarly publication.
—BLDSC (3097.930000); ADONIS; CASDDS; Faxon; Genuine Article; SWETS; UnCover. **CCC.**
Description: Publishes original investigations concerned with the immunological activities of cells in experimental or clinical situations.
Refereed Serial

616.97 SZ ISSN 1015-0145
CODEN: CHMIEP
CHEMICAL IMMUNOLOGY. (Text in English) 1939. irreg. (approx. 1/yr.). price varies. S. Karger AG, Allschwilerstr. 10, P.O. Box, CH-4009 Basel, Switzerland. TEL 061-3061111. FAX 061-3061234. E-mail: Karger@Karger.ch. Ed.Bd. (back issues avail.) **Indexed:** Biol.Abstr., Chem.Abstr., Curr.Adv.Ecol.Sci., Curr.Cont., Excerp.Med., Ind.Med., Ind.Sci.Rev. **Document type:** academic/scholarly publication.
—BLDSC (3146.750000); CASDDS; Faxon; Genuine Article; SWETS; UnCover. **CCC.**
Formerly (until 1989): Progress in Allergy (ISSN 0079-6034)
Refereed Serial

CHINESE JOURNAL OF MICROBIOLOGY AND IMMUNOLOGY. see *BIOLOGY — Microbiology*

616.97 576 US ISSN 1071-412X
RB46.5 CODEN: CDIMEN
▼**CLINICAL AND DIAGNOSTIC LABORATORY IMMUNOLOGY.** 1994. bi-m. $230 (Canada $246; elsewhere $267) (effective 1996). American Society for Microbiology, 1325 Massachusetts Ave., N.W., Washington, DC 20005. TEL 202-942-9319. FAX 202-942-9346. Ed. Steven D. Douglas. (back issues avail., reprint service avail. from UMI) **Indexed:** Excerp.Med. (1995-). **Document type:** academic/scholarly publication.
●Also available on CD-ROM.
—BLDSC (3286.248800); CASDDS; SWETS. **CCC.**
Description: Covers human immune response assessment, including indication for testing, methods used, and interpretation of the results.
Refereed Serial

616.97 UK ISSN 0954-7894
CODEN: CLEAEN
CLINICAL AND EXPERIMENTAL ALLERGY. 1971. bi-m. £386 in Europe; elsewhere £424($678) (effective 1996). (British Society for Allergy & Clinical Immunology) Blackwell Science Ltd., Osney Mead, Oxford OX2 0EL, England. TEL 01865-240201. FAX 01865-721205. TELEX 83355 MEDBOK G. Eds. A.B. Kay, S.T. Holgate. adv.; bk.rev.; illus.; index. circ. 1,600. (also avail. in microform from UMI; back issues avail; reprint service avail. from ISI) **Indexed:** Abstr.Hyg., Apic.Abstr., ASCA, Biol.Abstr., Biotech.Abstr., C.I.S. Abstr., Chem.Abstr., Curr.Adv.Ecol.Sci., Curr.Cont., Dairy Sci.Abstr., Dok.Arbeitsmed., Excerp.Med., Helminthol.Abstr., Ind.Med., Ind.Sci.Rev., INIS Atomind., Lab.Haz.Bull., Med.& Surg.Dermat., NRN, Rev.Appl.Entomol., Rev.Med.& Vet.Mycol., Sci.Cit.Ind., Trop.Dis.Bull. **Document type:** academic/scholarly publication.
—BLDSC (3286.249700); ADONIS; CASDDS; Faxon; Genuine Article; SWETS; UMI; UnCover. **CCC.**
Formerly (until Jan. 1989): Clinical Allergy (ISSN 0009-9090)
Refereed Serial

616.97 UK ISSN 0960-2178
CLINICAL AND EXPERIMENTAL ALLERGY. SUPPLEMENT. irreg. (British Society for Allergy and Clinical Immunology) Blackwell Science Ltd., Osney Mead, Oxford OX2 0EL, England. TEL 01865-240201. FAX 01865-721205. TELEX 83355 MEDBOK G. **Document type:** academic/scholarly publication.
—ADONIS.

MEDICAL SCIENCES — ALLERGOLOGY AND IMMUNOLOGY

615.37   UK   ISSN 0009-9104
RC583   CODEN: CEXIAL
CLINICAL AND EXPERIMENTAL IMMUNOLOGY.
(Supplement avail. (ISSN 0964-2536)) 1966. m. £489.50 with archival CD-ROM in Europe; elsewhere £538($860) (effective 1996). (British Society for Immunology) Blackwell Science Ltd., Osney Mead, Oxford OX2 0EL, England. TEL 44-1865-206206. FAX 44-1865-721205. TELEX 83355-MEDBOK-G. Eds. R.A. Thompsen, P.J. Lachmann. adv.; bibl.; charts; illus.; index. circ. 1,900. (also avail. in microform from UMI; back issues avail.; reprint service avail. from ISI) **Indexed:** Abstr.Hyg., Anim.Breed.Abstr., ASCA, Biol.Abstr., Biotech.Abstr., Chem.Abstr., Curr.Adv.Cancer Res., Curr.Adv.Ecol.Sci., Curr.Adv.Genetics & Molec.Biol., Curr.Cont., Dairy Sci.Abstr., Dent.Ind., Diar.Dis.Res., Excerp.Med., Helminthol.Abstr., Ind.Med., Ind.Sci.Rev., Ind.Vet., Nutr.Abstr., Protozool.Abstr., Rev.Med.& Vet.Mycol., Rev.Plant Path., Sci.Cit.Ind, Telegen, Trop.Dis.Bull., Vet.Bull. **Document type:** academic/scholarly publication.
●Also available on CD-ROM.
—BLDSC (3286.251000); ADONIS; CASDDS; Faxon; Genuine Article; SWETS; UMI; UnCover. **CCC.**
Refereed Serial

616.97   UK   ISSN 0964-2536
CLINICAL AND EXPERIMENTAL IMMUNOLOGY. SUPPLEMENT. irreg. Blackwell Science Ltd., Osney Mead, Oxford OX2 0EL, England. TEL 01865-240201. FAX 01865-721205. TELEX 83355 MEDBOK G. **Indexed:** Excerp.Med. (1992-). **Document type:** academic/scholarly publication.
—ADONIS.

615.37   US   ISSN 0090-1229
RC583   CODEN: CLIIAT
CLINICAL IMMUNOLOGY AND IMMUNOPATHOLOGY. 1972. m. $868 (foreign $1051) (effective 1996). Academic Press, Inc., Journal Division, 525 B St., Ste. 1900, San Diego, CA 92101-4495. TEL 619-230-1840. FAX 619-699-6800. (Subscr. to: Box 620000, Rolando, FL 32891-8340. TEL 800-543-9534) Ed. Noel Rose. adv.; illus.; index. (back issues avail.) **Indexed:** Biol.Abstr., Chem.Abstr., Curr.Adv.Ecol.Sci., Curr.Adv.Genetics & Molec.Biol., Curr.Cont., Dairy Sci.Abstr., Dent.Ind., Excerp.Med., Helminthol.Abstr., Ind.Med., Ind.Sci.Rev., Ind.Vet., INIS Atomind., Med.& Surg.Dermat., Nutr.Abstr., Rev.Med.& Vet.Mycol., Sci.Cit.Ind., Vet.Bull. **Document type:** academic/scholarly publication.
—BLDSC (3286.293000); ADONIS; CASDDS; EMDOCS; Faxon; Genuine Article; SWETS; UnCover. **CCC.**
Description: Publishes original research on the molecular and cellular bases of immunological diseases.

616.97   US   ISSN 0197-1859
                         CODEN: CIMNDC
CLINICAL IMMUNOLOGY NEWSLETTER. 1980. m. $207 to institutions in U.S.; $265 to institutions outside the Americas (effective 1996). Elsevier Science Inc., 655 Ave. of the Americas, New York, NY 10010. TEL 212-989-5800. FAX 212-633-3990. TELEX 420643 AEP UI. (Subscr. to: Box 882, Madison Sq. Sta., New York, NY 10159-0882) Eds. Alan L. Landay, Henry Homburger. **Indexed:** Abstr.Hyg., Biol.Abstr., Excerp.Med., Ind.Vet. **Document type:** newsletter.
—BLDSC (3286.293400); SWETS. **CCC.**
Description: For clinical immunologists, clinical pathologists, microbiologists, and infectious disease physicians.
Refereed Serial

615.37   US   ISSN 1075-3273
CLINICAL IMMUNOLOGY SPECTRUM. bi-m. membership. (Clinical Immunology Society) T M Marketing, 105 N. Main St., Hackensack, NJ 07601. TEL 201-342-6511. FAX 201-342-9502. (Subscr. to: Clinical Immunology Society, 6900 Grove Rd., Thorofare, NJ 08086. TEL 609-848-1000) Ed. Dr. Andrew Saxon. circ. 10,000. **Document type:** academic/scholarly publication.

CLINICAL IMMUNOTHERAPEUTICS. see *PHARMACY AND PHARMACOLOGY*

616.96   US   ISSN 1080-0549
                         CODEN: CRVADD
CLINICAL REVIEWS IN ALLERGY & IMMUNOLOGY. 1983. q. $190 (foreign $245) (effective 1995). Humana Press Inc., 999 Riverview Dr., Ste. 208, Totowa, NJ 07512. TEL 201-256-1699. FAX 201-256-8341. (Dist. in Japan by: Maruzen Co. Ltd., Journals Div., P.O. Box 5050, Tokyo 100-31, Japan. TEL 03-32758591. FAX 03-32781937) Ed. Dr. M. Eric Gershwin. adv. contact: Thomas B. Lanigan, Jr. abstr.; bibl.; charts; illus.; index. (also avail. in microform; back issues avail.) **Indexed:** Biol.Abstr., Chem.Abstr., Curr.Adv.Ecol.Sci., Curr.Cont., Dok.Arbeitsmed., Excerp.Med., Ind.Med., Ind.Sci.Rev., Rev.Med.& Vet.Mycol., Sci.Cit.Ind. **Document type:** academic/scholarly publication.
—BLDSC (3286.374520); CASDDS; Faxon; Genuine Article; UnCover. **CCC.**
Formerly (until vol.13, 1995): Clinical Reviews in Allergy (ISSN 0731-8235)
Description: Provides comprehensive coverage of subjects critical to the study of allergy and immunology. Each issue is thematic with the articles designed for immediate clinical use.
Refereed Serial

616.97   SZ   ISSN 1021-6286
COMPLEMENT PROFILES. (Text in English) 1993. irreg., vol.1, 1993. S. Karger AG, Allschwilerstr. 10, P.O. Box, CH-4009 Basel, Switzerland. TEL 061-3061111. FAX 061-3061234. Eds. J.M. Cruse, R.E. Lewis. **Document type:** monographic series.

616.97   US   ISSN 0149-1148
                         CODEN: COIMDV
COMPREHENSIVE IMMUNOLOGY. irreg., latest vol.9. price varies. Plenum Publishing Corp., 233 Spring St., New York, NY 10013-1578. TEL 212-620-8000. FAX 212-463-0742. TELEX 23-421139. Eds. Robert A. Good, Stacey B. Day. **Indexed:** Biol.Abstr., Chem.Abstr. **Document type:** monographic series.
—CASDDS.
Refereed Serial

616.97 574.2   US   ISSN 0093-4054
QR180   CODEN: CTIBBV
CONTEMPORARY TOPICS IN IMMUNOBIOLOGY. 1972. irreg., vol.15, 1985. price varies. Plenum Publishing Corp., 233 Spring St., New York, NY 10013-1578. TEL 212-620-8000. FAX 212-463-0742. TELEX 23-421139. illus. **Indexed:** ASCA, Biol.Abstr., Ind.Med., INIS Atomind., Int.Sci.Rev., Sci.Cit.Ind. **Document type:** monographic series.
—CASDDS. **CCC.**
Refereed Serial

615.37   US   ISSN 0090-8800
QR180   CODEN: CTMIB4
CONTEMPORARY TOPICS IN MOLECULAR IMMUNOLOGY. 1972. irreg., vol.10, 1985. price varies. Plenum Publishing Corp., 233 Spring St., New York, NY 10013-1578. TEL 212-620-8047. FAX 212-463-0742. TELEX 23-421139. Ed. F.P. Inman. **Indexed:** Biol.Abstr., Curr.Adv.Ecol.Sci., Ind.Med., Ind.Sci.Rev., Sci.Cit.Ind. **Document type:** monographic series.
—CASDDS.
Refereed Serial

615.37 576   SZ   ISSN 0301-3081
                         CODEN: CMIMBF
CONTRIBUTIONS TO MICROBIOLOGY AND IMMUNOLOGY. (Text in English) 1973. irreg. (approx. 1/yr.). price varies. S. Karger AG, Allschwilerstr. 10, P.O. Box, CH-4009 Basel, Switzerland. TEL 061-3061111. FAX 061-3061234. E-mail: Karger@Karger.ch. Eds. J.M. Cruse, R.E. Lewis Jr. (reprint service avail. from ISI) **Indexed:** Biol.Abstr., Chem.Abstr., Curr.Cont., Ind.Med., Ind.Vet., Protozool.Abstr., Vet.Bull. **Document type:** academic/scholarly publication.
—BLDSC (3460.500000); CASDDS. **CCC.**
Supersedes: Bibliotheca Microbiologia (ISSN 0067-8058)
Refereed Serial

616.97   US   ISSN 1040-8401
QR180   CODEN: CCRIDE
CRITICAL REVIEWS IN IMMUNOLOGY. 1980. q. $84 to individuals; institutions $299 (effective 1996). Begell House Inc., 79 Madison Ave., Ste. 1201, New York, NY 10016-7892. TEL 212-213-8368. FAX 212-725-1999. E-mail: 74353.2052@compuserve.com. Ed. M.Z. Atassi. circ. 270. (back issues avail.) **Indexed:** Anim.Breed.Abstr., Biol.Abstr., Chem.Abstr., Curr.Adv.Ecol.Sci., Curr.Cont., Excerp.Med., Helminthol.Abstr., Ind.Med., Ind.Sci.Rev., Ind.Vet., Sci.Cit.Ind., Telegen. **Document type:** academic/scholarly publication.
—BLDSC (3487.477000); CASDDS; Faxon; Genuine Article; SWETS; UnCover. **CCC.**
Formerly: C R C Critical Reviews in Immunology (ISSN 0197-3355)
Description: Presents a multidisciplinary overview of contemporary immunology, bringing together molecular immunology and immunobiology.
Refereed Serial

CURRENT ADVANCES IN IMMUNOLOGY & INFECTIOUS DISEASES. see *MEDICAL SCIENCES — Abstracting, Bibliographies, Statistics*

CURRENT OPINION IN IMMUNOLOGY. see *MEDICAL SCIENCES — Abstracting, Bibliographies, Statistics*

576.64 616.9   US
CURRENT PROTOCOLS IN IMMUNOLOGY. base vol. plus q. updates. $395 (Canada $422.65); update service $160 (Canada $171.20); CD-ROM version $486 (Canada $520.02) (effective 1995). John Wiley & Sons, Inc., Journals, 605 Third Ave., New York, NY 10158. TEL 212-850-6645. FAX 212-850-6021. (Subscr. to: Box 2535, Secaucus, NJ 07096-2535) **Document type:** academic/scholarly publication.
●Also available on CD-ROM.

CYTOKINE. see *BIOLOGY — Genetics*

616.87   UK   ISSN 1355-6568
▼**CYTOKINES AND MOLECULAR THERAPY.** 1995. q. £125 (foreign £130). Martin Dunitz Ltd., The Livery House, 7-9 Pratt St., London NW1 0AE, England. TEL 0171-482-2202. Eds. Moshe Talpaz, Friedhelm Herrmann. adv.: B&W page £550, color page £850; adv. contact: Ruth Dunitz. bk.rev.; index. (back issues avail.) **Indexed:** Chem.Abstr., Genet.Abstr. **Document type:** academic/scholarly publication.
—BLDSC (3506.786000).
Refereed Serial

616.969   DK   ISSN 0900-2219
DANSK SELSKAB FOR MYKOPATOLOGI. MEDDELESER. 3/yr. (Dansk Selskab for Mykopatologi - Danish Society for Mycopatology) Dansk BiblioteksCenter as, Tempovej 7-11, DK-2750 Ballerup, Denmark.

MEDICAL SCIENCES — ALLERGOLOGY AND IMMUNOLOGY

616.079 574.29   UK   ISSN 0145-305X
QR180   CODEN: DCIMDQ
DEVELOPMENTAL AND COMPARATIVE IMMUNOLOGY; ontogeny - phylogeny - aging. Title originally announced as: Journal of Developmental and Comparative Immunology. 1977. bi-m. £517($823) (effective 1996). (International Society of Developmental and Comparative Immunology) Elsevier Science Ltd., Pergamon, P.O. Box 800, Kidlington, Oxford OX5 1DX, England. TEL 44-1865-843000. FAX 44-1865-843010. E-mail: nlinfo-f@elsevier.nl; usinfo-f@elsevier.com; forinfo-kyf04035@niftyserve.or.jp; Site addr.: http://www.elsevier.nl/. (Subscr. in U.S. and Canada to: Elsevier Science, 660 White Plains Rd., Tarrytown, NY 10591-5153. TEL 914-524-9200. FAX 914-333-2444) Eds. L.W. Clem, G.W. Warr. adv.; bibl.; charts; illus.; index, cum.index. circ. 1,020. (also avail. in microfilm from UMI; back issues avail.; reprint service avail. from UMI) **Indexed**: Anim.Breed.Abstr., Biol.Abstr., Chem.Abstr., Curr.Adv.Ecol.Sci., Curr.Cont., Dairy Sci.Abstr., Excerp.Med., Helminthol.Abstr., Ind.Med., Ind.Sci.Rev., Ind.Vet., INIS Atomind., Poult.Abstr., Protozool.Abstr., Sci.Cit.Ind., Vet.Bull., W.R.C.Inf. **Document type**: academic/scholarly publication.
—BLDSC (3579.051000); CASDDS; Faxon; Genuine Article; SWETS; UMI; UnCover. **CCC**.
    Description: Publishes original research addressing the development and maturation of the immune system in the broadest sense, emphasizing ontogenetic (including aging) and phylogenetic aspects, including recognition mechanisms, cellular interactions, immunoglobins, and products of T cells and macrophages.
    Refereed Serial

616.97   US   ISSN 1044-6672
QR184.5   CODEN: DEIMDQ
DEVELOPMENTAL IMMUNOLOGY. 1990. 8/yr. (in 2 vols., 4 nos./vol.). 91 ECU per vol. (effective 1996). Harwood Academic Publishers, c/o International Publisher Distributor, 820 Town Center Dr., Langhorne, PA 19047. TEL 215-750-2642. FAX 215-750-6343. (Subscr. to : International Publishers Distributor, PO Box 90, Reading, Berkshire, RG1 8JL, England. TEL 44-173-456-8316) Ed. Dr. Roland Scollay. (also avail. in microform) **Indexed**: Excerp.Med. (1994-), Ind.Med. (1992-). **Document type**: academic/scholarly publication.
—BLDSC (3579.054700); CASDDS; UnCover. **CCC**.
    Refereed Serial

DEVELOPMENTS IN HEMATOLOGY AND IMMUNOLOGY.
see *MEDICAL SCIENCES* — *Hematology*

616.97   IT   ISSN 0392-6699
    CODEN: EOSSDJ
EOS; rivista di immunologia ed immunofarmacologia. (Text and summaries in English and Italian) 1981. q. L.90000($90) Sigma-Tau SpA, Via Pontina, Rm. 30,400, 00040 Pomezia, Rome, Italy. FAX 6-9108260. Ed. Claudio De Simone. bk.rev.; index. circ. 4,100. (back issues avail.) **Indexed**: Apic.Abstr., Chem.Abstr., Curr.Cont., Excerp.Med., Sci.Cit.Ind.
—BLDSC (3793.030000); CASDDS; Genuine Article.

615.37   GW   ISSN 0014-2980
QR180   CODEN: EJIMAF
EUROPEAN JOURNAL OF IMMUNOLOGY. (Text in English) 1970. m. DM.1385($850) (effective 1996). V C H Verlagsgesellschaft mbH, Postfach 101161, 69451 Weinheim, Germany. TEL 06201-606-147. FAX 06201-606117. TELEX 465516-VCHWH-D. (U.S. addr.: V C H Publishers Inc., 220 E. 23rd St., New York, NY 10010-4606. TEL 212-683-8333) Ed. L. Leclercq-Reth. circ. 2,000. (also avail. in microfilm from VCI; reprint service avail. from ISI) **Indexed**: Abstr.Hyg., Anim.Breed.Abstr., Biol.Abstr., Biotech.Abstr., Chem.Abstr., Curr.Adv.Cell & Devel.Biol., Curr.Adv.Ecol.Sci., Curr.Adv.Genetics & Molec.Biol., Curr.Cont., Dairy Sci.Abstr., Excerp.Med., Helminthol.Abstr., Ind.Med., Ind.Sci.Rev., Ind.Vet., Pig News & Info., Poult.Abstr., Protozool.Abstr., Rev.Med.& Vet.Mycol., Telegen, Trop.Dis.Bull., Vet.Bull. **Document type**: academic/scholarly publication.
—BLDSC (3829.730100); CASDDS; Faxon; Genuine Article; SWETS; UnCover. **CCC**.

EXCHANGE. see *MEDICAL SCIENCES* — *Dermatology And Venereology*

EXERCISE IMMUNOLOGY REVIEW. see *MEDICAL SCIENCES* — *Sports Medicine*

F E M S. IMMUNOLOGY AND MEDICAL MICROBIOLOGY. (Federation of European Microbiological Societies) see *BIOLOGY* — *Microbiology*

615.37   GW   ISSN 0016-6006
DIE GELBEN HEFTE. 1961. q. DM.28. (Immunbiologische Informationen) Medizinische Verlagsgesellschaft mbH, Postfach 1732, 35007 Marburg, Germany. TEL 06421-24044. Ed. Dr. Dietmar Nedde. illus.; cum.index. circ. 120,000. **Document type**: academic/scholarly publication.

616.97   IT   ISSN 1120-6373
GIORNALE ITALIANO DI ALLERGOLOGIA E IMMUNOLOGIA CLINICA. (Text in Italian; summaries in English, Italian) 1991. bi-m. L.100000($100) Editrice Kurtis s.r.l., Via L. Zoja, 30, 20153 Milan, Italy. TEL 39-2-48202740. FAX 39-2-48201219. Ed. G. Valesini. adv.: B&W page L.2700000, color page L.3350000; trim 200 x 260.
—BLDSC (4178.138000).
    Description: Publishes original studies on allergological and immunological subjects.

616.97   UK   ISSN 0969-3653
    CODEN: GLDIEI
▼**GLYCOSYLATION AND DISEASE**. 1994. bi-m. £175($295) to institutions (effective 1995). Rapid Communications of Oxford Ltd. (Subsidiary of: International Thomson Ltd.), The Old Malthouse, Paradise St., Oxford OX1 1LD, England. TEL 01865-790447. FAX 01865-244012. E-mail: rapidcom@vax.oxford.ac.uk. (N. American addr.: 115 Fifth Ave., 4th Fl., New York, NY 10003. TEL 212-780-6234) Ed. Dr. G.A. Turner. adv. **Document type**: academic/scholarly publication.
●Also available on CD-ROM.
—ADONIS; CASDDS. **CCC**.
    Description: Covers all aspects of glycosylation (e.g., glycoproteins, glycolipids, proteoglycans, and glycation), as they relate to immunologic diseases, infections, inflammations, arthritic conditions, metabolic disorders, cancerous tumors and neurological impairment.

GROWTH FACTORS & CYTOKINES - CLINICAL. see *MEDICAL SCIENCES* — *Abstracting, Bibliographies, Statistics*

616   UK
GROWTH FACTORS & CYTOKINES - RESEARCH. m. £120 (diskette £115; both £175) (effective 1996). S U B I S, Mansion House, 19 Kingfield Rd., Sheffield S11 9AS, England. TEL 0114-255-4433. FAX 0114-255-4626. E-mail: subis@sheffac.demon.co.uk. (also avail. in diskette format) **Document type**: abstracting/indexing.
    Supersedes in part: Growth Factors and Cytokines (ISSN 0964-7554)

616.97 614.4   US
HEPATITIS B COALITION NEWS. irreg. (2-4/yr.). donation. Immunization Action Coalition, 1573 Selby Ave., Ste. 229, St. Paul, MN 55104. TEL 612-647-9009. FAX 612-647-9131. E-mail: wexle001@maroon.tc.umn.edu. Ed. Deborah Wexler. circ. 65,000. **Document type**: newsletter.
●Also available online.
    Description: Features articles and reprintable resources on all aspects of hepatitis B.

HIV PREVENTION NEWS. see *MEDICAL SCIENCES* — *Communicable Diseases*

HOKKAIDO UNIVERSITY. INSTITUTE OF IMMUNOLOGICAL SCIENCE. BULLETIN. see *MEDICAL SCIENCES* — *Respiratory Diseases*

616.97   US   ISSN 0198-8859
QR180   CODEN: HUIMDQ
HUMAN IMMUNOLOGY. 1980. 14/yr. $765 to institutions (effective 1996). (American Society for Histocompatibility and Immunogenetics) Elsevier Science Inc., 655 Ave. of the Americas, New York, NY 10010. TEL 212-989-5800. FAX 212-633-3990. TELEX 420643 AEP UI. (Subscr. to: Box 882, Madison Sq. Sta., New York, NY 10159-0882) Ed.Bd. (also avail. in microform from UMI) **Indexed**: Biol.Abstr., Chem.Abstr., Curr.Adv.Cancer Res., Curr.Adv.Genetics & Molec.Biol., Curr.Cont., Excerp.Med., Helminthol.Abstr., Ind.Med., Ind.Sci.Rev., Sci.Cit.Ind. **Document type**: academic/scholarly publication.
—BLDSC (4336.160000); CASDDS; Faxon; Genuine Article; SWETS; UnCover. **CCC**.
    Description: Provides information on the immune system of man and the analogous systems of other vertebrates, emphasizing topics in histocompatibility and immunogenetics.
    Refereed Serial

574.29 616.07   US   ISSN 0272-457X
QR185.8.H93   CODEN: HYBRDY
HYBRIDOMA, a journal of molecular immunology and experimental and clinical immunotherapy. 1981. bi-m. $230 (foreign $282). Mary Ann Liebert, Inc. Publishers, 2 Madison Ave., Larchmont, NY 10538. TEL 914-834-3100. FAX 914-834-3688. E-mail: Liebert@pipeline.com. Ed. Dr. Zenon Steplewski. adv. circ. 800. **Indexed**: Biol.Abstr., Biotech.Abstr., Chem.Abstr., Curr.Adv.Cancer Res., Curr.Adv.Ecol.Sci., Curr.Biotech.Abstr., Dairy Sci.Abstr., Excerp.Med., Ind.Med., Ind.Sci.Rev., Ind.Vet., Poult.Abstr., Sci.Cit.Ind., Telegen, Vet.Bull. **Document type**: academic/scholarly publication.
—BLDSC (4340.385000); CASDDS; Faxon; Genuine Article; SWETS; UnCover.
    Incorporates (in 1990): Monoclonal Antibodies (ISSN 1047-871X); Formerly (until 1990): Monoclonal Antibody News (ISSN 0272-4588)
    Description: Publishes research in molecular immunology and experimental and clinical immunotherapy. Includes papers on the application of monoclonal antibodies for diagnostics and therapy, and original articles on various aspects of hybridoma research.
    Refereed Serial

615.37   GW   ISSN 0340-1162
    CODEN: IMINDI
IMMUNITAET UND INFEKTION; Zeitschrift fuer Klinische Immunologie, Klinische Mikrobiologie. 1973. 6/yr. DM.102 (Europe DM.111). (Deutsche Gesellschaft fuer Hygiene und Mikrobiologie) Richard Pflaum Verlag GmbH und Co. KG, Lazarettstr. 4, 80636 Munich, Germany. TEL 089-12607-0. FAX 089-12607-200. (Subscr. to: Postfach 190737, 80607 Munich, Germany) Eds. K. Federlin, H. Finger. adv.; bk.rev. circ. 8,000. (also avail. in microform from UMI; back issues avail.; reprint service avail. from UMI) **Indexed**: Abstr.Hyg., Biol.Abstr., Chem.Abstr., Curr.Adv.Ecol.Sci., Curr.Adv.Genetics & Molec.Biol., Curr.Cont., Excerp.Med., Helminthol.Abstr., Ind.Med., INIS Atomind., Trop.Dis.Bull. **Document type**: academic/scholarly publication.
—BLDSC (4369.646000); CASDDS; Faxon; Genuine Article; SWETS. **CCC**.

574.29 616.07   US   ISSN 1074-7613
    CODEN: IUNIEH
▼**IMMUNITY**. 1994. m. Cell Press, 50 Church St., Cambridge, MA 02138. TEL 617-661-7060. FAX 617-661-7061. **Indexed**: Excerp.Med. (1995-). **Document type**: academic/scholarly publication.
—BLDSC (4369.649000); CASDDS; SWETS.

IMMUNO-ANALYSE ET BIOLOGIE SPECIALISEE. see *BIOLOGY*

MEDICAL SCIENCES — ALLERGOLOGY AND IMMUNOLOGY

616.07 NE ISSN 0926-2067
THE IMMUNOASSAY KIT DIRECTORY. SERIES A: CLINICAL CHEMISTRY. (Text in English) 1991. 5/yr. fl.980 to institutions; $560 to institutions in U.S. (effective 1996). Kluwer Academic Publishers, Postbus 17, 3300 AA Dordrecht, Netherlands. TEL 31-78-392392. FAX 31-78-392254. TELEX 29245 KAPG NL. E-mail: SERVICES@WKAP.NL. (Dist. by: Kluwer Academic Publishers Group, P.O. Box 322, 3300 AH Dordrecht, Netherlands. TEL 31-78-392392. FAX 31-78-546474; N. America dist. addr.: Box 358, Accord Sta., Hingham, MA 02018-0358. TEL 617-871-6600. FAX 617-871-6528) Ed. Dr. John Seth. (back issues avail.) **Document type:** directory.
—UMI. **CCC.**
Description: Comprehensive, independent reference source listing commercially available immunoassay kits, including information on assay and sample type, number of tests, antibodies and antigens used, sensitivity, and limitations.
Refereed Serial

616 NE ISSN 1381-5067
▼**THE IMMUNOASSAY KIT DIRECTORY. SERIES B: INFECTIOUS DISEASES.** (Text in English) 1995. 3/yr. fl.850 to institutions; $486 to institutions in U.S. (effective 1996). Kluwer Academic Publishers, Postbus 17, 3300 AA Dordrecht, Netherlands. TEL 31-78-392392. FAX 31-78-392254. E-mail: SERVICES@WKAP.NL. (Dist. by: Kluwer Academic Publishers Group, P.O. Box 322, 3300 AH Dordrecht, Netherlands. TEL 31-78-392392. FAX 31-78-546474) Ed. Hugh Young. **Document type:** directory.
Description: Provides an independent reference source on immmunoassay kits for the diagnosis of clinically important infectious diseases.

615.37 GW ISSN 0171-2985
QR180 CODEN: IMMND4
IMMUNOBIOLOGY. (Supplement avail. (ISSN 0722-6365)) (Text and summaries in English) 1909. irreg. (2 nos./vol.) DM.956 (foreign DM.972. Gustav Fischer Verlag, Wollgrasweg 49, 70599 Stuttgart, Germany. TEL 0711-458030. FAX 0711-4580334. TELEX 7111488-FIBUCH. (Subscr. to: Postfach 720143, 70577 Stuttgart, Germany; U.S. address: VCH Publishers, Inc., 303 N.W. 12th Ave., Deerfield Beach, FL 33442-1788) Ed. D. Gemsa. circ. 900. (also avail. in microform from PMC) **Indexed:** Anim.Breed.Abstr., Biol.Abstr., Chem.Abstr., Curr.Adv.Genetics & Molec.Biol., Excerp.Med., Ind.Med., Ind.Vet., Poult.Abstr., Vet.Bull. **Document type:** academic/scholarly publication.
—BLDSC (4369.656000); CASDDS; Faxon; Genuine Article; SWETS; UMI; UnCover. **CCC.**
Former titles: Zeitschrift fuer Immunitaetsforschung - Immunologie; Zeitschrift fuer Immunitaetsforschung, Experimentelle und Klinische Immunologie (ISSN 0300-872X)

616.97 US ISSN 1067-795X
QR188.35 CODEN: IUNOEZ
IMMUNODEFICIENCY. 1988. 4/yr. (in 1 vol., 4 nos./vol.). 141 ECU (effective 1996). Harwood Academic Publishers, c/o International Publishers Distributor, 820 Town Center Dr., Langhorne, PA 19047. TEL 215-750-2642. FAX 215-750-6343. (Subscr. to: International Publishers Distributor, PO Box 90, Reading, Berkshire, RG1 8JL, England. TEL 44-173-456-8316) Eds. Fred Rosen, Maxime Seligmann. (also avail. in microform) **Document type:** academic/scholarly publication.
—BLDSC (4369.663600); CASDDS; SWETS. **CCC.**
Formerly (until 1993): Immunodeficiency Reviews (ISSN 0893-5300)
Refereed Serial

IMMUNOFACTS VACCINES & IMMUNOLOGIC DRUGS. see PHARMACY AND PHARMACOLOGY

616.97 615.37 GW ISSN 0093-7711
QR184
IMMUNOGENETICS. (Text in English) 1974. 12/yr. (in 2 vols., 6 nos./vol.). DM.1656($1203) (effective 1996). Springer-Verlag, Heidelberger Platz 3, 14197 Berlin, Germany. TEL 030-8207-0. FAX 030-8214091. E-mail: orders@springer.de. (Subscr. in. N. America to: Springer-Verlag New York, Inc., 44 Hartz Way, Secaucus, NJ 07096-2491. TEL 201-348-4033. Fax 201-348-4505) Eds. J. Klein, E. Moeller. (also avail. in microform from UMI; reprint service avail. from ISI) **Indexed:** Anim.Breed.Abstr., Biol.Abstr., Biotech.Abstr., Chem.Abstr., Curr.Adv.Ecol.Sci., Curr.Adv.Genetics & Molec.Biol., Curr.Cont., Dent.Ind., Excerp.Med., Helminthol.Abstr., Ind.Med., Ind.Sci.Rev., Ind.Vet., Pig News & Info., Poult.Abstr., Rev.Med.& Vet.Mycol., Sci.Cit.Ind., Small Anim.Abstr., Vet.Bull. **Document type:** academic/scholarly publication.
—BLDSC (4369.665000); CASDDS; EMDOCS; Faxon; Genuine Article; SWETS; UMI; UnCover. **CCC.**
Description: Covers the areas of immunogenetics of cell interaction and tissue differentiation and development, phylogeny of alloantigens, and genetic control of immune response and disease susceptibility.

616.97 SZ ISSN 0257-277X
CODEN: IMRSEB
IMMUNOLOGIC RESEARCH; a selective reference to current research and practice. (Text in English) 1982. q. 144.90 SFr.($111.30) to individuals; institutions 414 SFr.($318) (effective 1996). S. Karger AG, Allschwilerstr. 10, P.O. Box, CH-4009 Basel, Switzerland. TEL 061-3061111. FAX 061-3061234. E-mail: Karger@Karger.ch. Ed. J.M. Cruse. circ. 800. (also avail. in microform from UMI; back issues avail.) **Indexed:** Anim.Breed.Abstr., ASCA, Chem.Abstr., Curr.Adv.Ecol.Sci., Dent.Ind., Excerp.Med., Ind.Med., Ind.Vet., Pig News & Info., Telegen. **Document type:** academic/scholarly publication.
—BLDSC (4369.677800); CASDDS; Faxon; Genuine Article; SWETS; UnCover. **CCC.**
Formerly: Survey of Immunologic Research (ISSN 0252-9564)
Refereed Serial

576 US ISSN 0882-0139
QR180 CODEN: IMINEJ
IMMUNOLOGICAL INVESTIGATIONS; a journal of molecular and cellular immunology. 1972. 6/yr. $317.50 to individuals; institutions $635. Marcel Dekker Journals, 270 Madison Ave., New York, NY 10016. TEL 212-696-9000. FAX 212-685-4540. TELEX 421419. (Subscr. to: Box 5017, Monticello, NY 12701) Ed. Carel J. Van Oss. adv.; bk.rev.; charts; illus.; index. (also avail. in microform from RPI) **Indexed:** Anim.Breed.Abstr., Biol.Abstr., Chem.Abstr., Curr.Adv.Cell & Devel.Biol., Curr.Adv.Ecol.Sci., Curr.Cont., Dairy Sci.Abstr., Excerp.Med., Helminthol.Abstr., Ind.Med., Ind.Sci.Rev., Ind.Vet., Sci.Cit.Ind., Telegen. **Document type:** academic/scholarly publication.
—BLDSC (4369.682500); CASDDS; Faxon; Genuine Article; SWETS; UMI; UnCover. **CCC.**
Formerly: Immunological Communications (ISSN 0090-0877); Incorporates (1982-1985): Clinical Immunology Reviews (ISSN 0277-9366)
Refereed Serial

617 612 DK ISSN 0105-2896
CODEN: IMRED2
IMMUNOLOGICAL REVIEWS. (Text in English) 1969. bi-m. DKK 2300 (effective 1996). Munksgaard International Publishers Ltd., 35 Noerre Soegade, P.O. Box 2148, DK-1016 Copenhagen K, Denmark. TEL 33-127030. FAX 33-129387. Ed. Goeran Moeller. adv.; illus. circ. 2,100. (reprint service avail. from ISI) **Indexed:** Anim.Breed.Abstr., Biol.Abstr., Chem.Abstr., Curr.Adv.Ecol.Sci., Curr.Adv.Genetics & Molec.Biol., Curr.Biotech.Abstr., Curr.Cont., Excerp.Med., Helminthol.Abstr., Ind.Med., Ind.Sci.Rev., Sci.Cit.Ind., Telegen.
—BLDSC (4369.687000); ADONIS; CASDDS; Faxon; Genuine Article; SWETS; UnCover. **CCC.**
Formerly: Transplantation Reviews (ISSN 0082-5948)
Refereed Serial

616.97 CN ISSN 1192-5612
CODEN: INOLEG
▼**IMMUNOLOGIST.** 1994. 6/yr. $68 to individuals; institutions $78; IVIS $44. (International Union of Immunological Societies) Hogrefe & Huber Publishers, Box 2487, Kirkland. TEL 206-820-1500; 800-228-3749. FAX 206-823-8324. Ed. J.B. Natvig. circ. 1,800. **Document type:** academic/scholarly publication.
—BLDSC (4369.688000); CASDDS. **CCC.**
Description: Serves as a forum for all matters immunological, including society news and official proposals and discussions, as well as for interesting arguments, critical analyses of products, meeting reports and the latest clinical or research techniques.

616.97 RU ISSN 0206-4952
CODEN: IMUNDA
IMMUNOLOGIYA/IMMUNOLOGY. 1980. bi-m. $135 (effective 1996). (Akademiya Meditsinskikh Nauk Rossii) Izdatel'stvo Meditsina, Petroverigskii pereulok 6-8, 101000 Moscow, Russia. (Dist. by: Mezhdunarodnaya Kniga, B. Yakimanka 39, 117079 Moscow, Russia. TEL 7-095-2384600. FAX 7-095-2384634) Ed. R.M. Khaitov. **Indexed:** Biol.Abstr., Chem.Abstr., Excerp.Med., INIS Atomind.
—BLDSC (0086.168250); CASDDS.
Description: Publishes data on original investigations in immunogenetics, molecular and cellular immunology, immunochemistry, biochemistry of immunogenesis, immunomorphology, functional bases of immunity, immunology of allergic reaction, clinical immunology and immunopathology.

576 UK ISSN 0019-2805
QR180 CODEN: IMMUAM
IMMUNOLOGY. 1958. m. £357 in Europe; elsewhere £393($628) (effective 1996). (British Society for Immunology) Blackwell Science Ltd., Osney Mead, Oxford OX2 OEL, England. TEL 01865-240201. FAX 01865-721205. TELEX 83355 MEDBOK G. Ed. M.W. Steward. adv.; bk.rev.; bibl.; charts; illus.; index. circ. 2,000. (also avail. in microform from UMI; back issues avail.; reprint service avail. from ISI) **Indexed:** Abstr.Hyg., Anim.Breed.Abstr., Biol.Abstr., Biotech.Abstr., Chem.Abstr., Curr.Adv.Biochem., Curr.Adv.Ecol.Sci., Curr.Cont., Dairy Sci.Abstr., Dent.Ind., Diar.Dis.Res., Excerp.Med., Helminthol.Abstr., Ind.Med., Ind.Sci.Rev., Ind.Vet., INIS Atomind., NRN, Nutr.Abstr., Pig News & Info., Rev.Med.& Vet.Mycol., Sci.Cit.Ind., Telegen, Trop.Dis.Bull., Vet.Bull. **Document type:** academic/scholarly publication.
—BLDSC (4369.700000); ADONIS; CASDDS; EMDOCS; Faxon; Genuine Article; SWETS; UMI; UnCover. **CCC.**
Refereed Serial

616.97 US ISSN 0889-8561
CODEN: INCAEP
IMMUNOLOGY AND ALLERGY CLINICS OF NORTH AMERICA. 1981. q. $120 (foreign $145) (effective 1996). W.B. Saunders Co. (Subsidiary of: Harcourt Brace & Company), Curtis Center, 3rd Fl., Independence Sq. W., Philadelphia, PA 19106-3399. TEL 215-238-7800. FAX 215-238-6445. (Subscr. to: Periodicals Fulfillment, W.B. Saunders Co., 6277 Sea Harbor Dr., 4th Fl., Orlando, FL 32891-4800. TEL 800-654-2452. FAX 215-800-874-6418) Ed. June Eberharter. **Indexed:** Chem.Abstr., Curr.Adv.Ecol.Sci., Excerp.Med., Helminthol.Abstr., Ind.Sci.Rev., Sci.Cit.Ind., Sugar Ind.Abstr. **Document type:** academic/scholarly publication.
—BLDSC (4369.701500); CASDDS; Faxon; Genuine Article; SWETS; UMI; UnCover. **CCC.**
Formerly: Clinics in Immunology and Allergy (ISSN 0260-4639)

616.97 US ISSN 0194-7508
RC581
IMMUNOLOGY AND ALLERGY PRACTICE. 1978. m. $55 (foreign $82). (American Association for Clinical Immunology and Allergy) Macor Publishing Co., 116 W. 32nd St., New York, NY 10001. TEL 212-736-6688. FAX 212-564-1763. Ed. Dr. Sidney Frielander. adv. **Indexed:** Excerp.Med.
—Faxon; UnCover. **CCC.**
Description: Contains clinical, research, and review articles of interest to allergists and other related specialists.

MEDICAL SCIENCES — ALLERGOLOGY AND IMMUNOLOGY

616.97 574   **AT**   **ISSN 0818-9641**
QH301   **CODEN: ICBIEZ**
IMMUNOLOGY AND CELL BIOLOGY. 1924. bi-m. Aus.$340 (foreign Aus.$408) (effective 1996). Blackwell Science Pty Ltd, P.O. Box 378, Carlton, Vic. 3053, Australia. TEL 61-3-93470300. FAX 61-3-93493016. Ed. Chris Parish. charts; illus.; index. circ. 1,700. (also avail. in microfiche from JAI; microfilm from UMI,PMC) **Indexed:** Abstr.Hyg., Anim.Breed.Abstr., Biol.Abstr., Chem.Abstr., Curr.Adv.Cancer Res., Curr.Adv.Ecol.Sci., Curr.Biotech.Abstr., Curr.Cont., Dairy Sci.Abstr., Dent.Ind., Diar.Dis.Res., Excerp.Med., Field Crop Abstr., Helminthol.Abstr., Herb.Abstr., Ind.Med., Ind.Sci.Rev., Ind.Vet., Nutr.Abstr., Protozool.Abstr., Sci.Cit.Ind., Trop.Dis.Bull., Vet.Bull. **Document type:** academic/scholarly publication.
—BLDSC (4369.702400); ADONIS; CASDDS; Faxon; Genuine Article; SWETS; UMI; UnCover. **CCC.**
Formerly: Australian Journal of Experimental Biology and Medical Science (ISSN 0004-945X)
Description: Covers original research, methods or concepts in the broad fields of immunology and cell biology.

IMMUNOLOGY AND INFECTIOUS DISEASES. see MEDICAL SCIENCES — Communicable Diseases

616.97   **NE**
IMMUNOLOGY AND MEDICINE. (Text in English) irreg., vol.21, 1994. price varies. Kluwer Academic Publishers, Postbus 17, 3300 AA Dordrecht, Netherlands. TEL 31-78-392392. FAX 31-78-392254. TELEX 29245 KAPG NL. (Dist. by: Kluwer Academic Publishers Group, P.O. Box 322, 3300 AH Dordrecht, Netherlands. TEL 31-78-392392. FAX 31-78-546474; N. America dist. addr.: Box 358, Accord Sta., Hingham, MA 02018-0358. TEL 617-871-6600. FAX 617-871-6528) Ed. Keith Whaley. **Document type:** monographic series.
Refereed Serial

616.97   **NE**   **ISSN 0165-2478**
                     CODEN: IMLED6
IMMUNOLOGY LETTERS; for the rapid publication of short reports in immunology. (Text in English) 1979. 15/yr. fl.2805($1710) (effective 1996). (European Federation of Immunological Societies (E.F.I.S.)) Elsevier Science B.V., P.O. Box 211, 1000 AE Amsterdam, Netherlands. TEL 31-20-4853911. FAX 31-20-4853598. TELEX 18582 ESPA NL. E-mail: nlinfo-f@elsevier.nl; usinfo-f@elsevier.com; forinfo-kyf04035@niftyserve.or.jp; Site addr.: http://www.elsevier.nl/. (Subscr. in U.S. and Canada to: Elsevier Science Inc., Box 882, Madison Sq. Sta., New York, NY 10159. TEL 212-989-5800. FAX 212-633-3990) Ed.Bd. adv.; bk.rev. circ. 500. (also avail. in microform from UMI; back issues avail.) **Indexed:** Anim.Breed.Abstr., Biol.Abstr., Chem.Abstr., Curr.Adv.Cancer Res., Curr.Adv.Cell & Devel.Biol., Curr.Adv.Ecol.Sci., Curr.Adv.Genetics & Molec.Biol., Curr.Cont., Excerp.Med., Helminthol.Abstr., Ind.Med., Ind.Sci.Rev., Ind.Vet., Sci.Cit.Ind., Telegen, Vet.Bull. **Document type:** academic/scholarly publication.
—BLDSC (4369.705000); ADONIS; CASDDS; Faxon; Genuine Article; SWETS; UnCover. **CCC.**
Description: Publishes research articles and minireviews on all aspects of immunology.
Refereed Serial

616.97   **US**
IMMUNOLOGY SERIES. 1973. irreg., vol.61, 1994. price varies. Marcel Dekker, Inc., 270 Madison Ave., New York, NY 10016. TEL 212-696-9000. FAX 212-685-4540. TELEX 421419.

616.97   **UK**   **ISSN 0167-5699**
                     CODEN: IMTOD8
IMMUNOLOGY TODAY. Library compendium: Immunology Today (Reference Edition) (ISSN 0167-4919) (Text in English) 1980. m. £386($614) to institutions; with electronic access £521($829) (effective 1996). Elsevier Science Ltd., P.O. Box 800, Kidlington, Oxford OX5 1DX, England. TEL 44-1865-843000. FAX 44-1865-843010. E-mail: nlinfo-f@elsevier.nl; usinfo-f@elsevier.com; forinfo-kyf04035@niftyserve.or.jp; Site addr.: http://www.elsevier.nl/. (Subscr. in U.S. and Canada to: Elsevier Science, 660 White Plains Rd., Tarrytown, NY, 10591-5153. TEL 914-524-9200. FAX 914-333-2444) Ed. Robert Brines. adv.; bk.rev.; charts; illus.; index. circ. 4,000. (back issues avail.; reprint service avail. from SWZ) **Indexed:** Abstr.Hyg., Anim.Breed.Abstr., Biol.Abstr., Chem.Abstr., Curr.Cont., Dairy Sci.Abstr., Diar.Dis.Res., Excerp.Med., Food Sci.& Tech.Abstr., Helminthol.Abstr., Ind.Sci.Rev., Ind.Vet., Protozool.Abstr., Sci.Cit.Ind., Telegen, Vet.Bull. **Document type:** academic/scholarly publication.
● Also available online. Vendor(s): OCLC.
—BLDSC (4369.745000); ADONIS; Faxon; SWETS. **CCC.**
Description: For immunologists and transplantation researchers, and all other scientists with an interest in the theory, practice, applications and techniques of modern immunology.

616.97   **UK**   **ISSN 0167-4919**
                     CODEN: IMTOD8
IMMUNOLOGY TODAY (REFERENCE EDITION). 1980. a. £345($514) includes Immunology Today (effective 1995). Elsevier Science Ltd., P.O. Box 800, Kidlington, Oxford OX5 1DX, England. TEL 44-1865-843000. FAX 44-1865-843010. E-mail: nlinfo-f@elsevier.nl; usinfo-f@elsevier.com; forinfo-kyf04035@niftyserve.or.jp; Site addr.: http://www.elsevier.nl/. (Subscr. in U.S. and Canada to: Elsevier Science, 660 White Plains Rd., Tarrytown, NY 10591-5153. TEL 914-524-9200. FAX 914-333-2444) Ed. Robert Brines. (also avail. in microform from UMI; back issues avail.) **Document type:** academic/scholarly publication.
—CASDDS; Genuine Article; UnCover. **CCC.**
Description: Compendium of archival material from Immunology Today.
Refereed Serial

616.97   **NE**   **ISSN 0162-3109**
                     CODEN: IMMUDP
IMMUNOPHARMACOLOGY. 1979. 9/yr. fl. 1626($992) (effective 1996). Elsevier Science B.V., P.O. Box 211, 1000 AE Amsterdam, Netherlands. TEL 31-20-4853911. FAX 31-20-4853598. TELEX 18582 ESPA NL. E-mail: nlinfo-f@elsevier.nl; usinfo-f@elsevier.com; forinfo-kyf04035@niftyserve.or.jp; Site addr.: http://www.elsevier.nl/. (Subscr. in U.S. and Canada to: Elsevier Science Inc., Box 882, Madison Sq. Sta., New York, NY 10159-0882. TEL 212-989-5800. FAX 212-633-3990) Ed. Dr. J.R. Battisto. (also avail. in microform from UMI) **Indexed:** Biol.Abstr., Biotech.Abstr., Chem.Abstr., Curr.Adv.Cancer Res., Curr.Adv.Ecol.Sci., Curr.Cont., Excerp.Med., Helminthol.Abstr., Ind.Med., Ind.Sci.Rev., Int.Abstr.Biol.Sci., Sci.Cit.Ind. **Document type:** academic/scholarly publication.
—BLDSC (4369.760000); ADONIS; CASDDS; Faxon; Genuine Article; SWETS; UnCover. **CCC.**
Description: Covers immunology, pharmacology and toxicology.
Refereed Serial

616.9 660   **NE**   **ISSN 1380-2933**
                     CODEN: IOTEER
▼**IMMUNOTECHNOLOGY;** an international journal of immunological engineering. (Text in English) 1995. q. fl. 440($268) (effective 1996). Elsevier Science B.V., P.O. Box 211, 1000 AE Amsterdam, Netherlands. TEL 31-20-4853911. FAX 31-20-4853598. (Subscr. in U.S. and Canada to: Elsevier Science Inc., Box 882, Madison Sq. Sta., New York, NY 10159-0882. TEL 212-989-5800. FAX 212-633-3990) Ed. Carl A.K. Borrebaeck. (also avail. in microform from UMI; back issues avail.) **Document type:** academic/scholarly publication.
—CCC.
Description: Publishes scientific reports on the application of biotechnology to cells and molecules of the immune system.
Refereed Serial

616   **II**   **ISSN 0255-0857**
                     CODEN: IJMMEF
INDIAN JOURNAL OF MEDICAL MICROBIOLOGY. (Text in English) 1983. q. Rs.75($20) Indian Association of Medical Microbiologists, c/o Dept. of Experimental Medicine, Postgraduate Institute of Medical Education and Research, Chandigarh - 160 012, India. Ed. N.K. Ganguly. **Indexed:** Chem.Abstr., Diar.Dis.Res., Excerp.Med.
—BLDSC (4416.400000); CASDDS.

616.97   **SZ**   **ISSN 1016-4901**
                     CODEN: IENVEC
INDOOR ENVIRONMENT. (Text in English) 1992. 6/yr. 176.40 SFr.($135.80) to individuals; institutions 504 SFr.($388) (effective 1996). (Indoor Air International) S. Karger AG, Allschwilerstr. 10, P.O. Box, CH-4009 Basel, Switzerland. TEL 061-3061111. FAX 061-3061234. E-mail: Karger@Karger.ch. Ed. J.A. Hoskins. (also avail. in microform from UMI) **Document type:** academic/scholarly publication.
—BLDSC (4438.047100); CASDDS; Genuine Article; UnCover. **CCC.**
Description: Publishes original reports on topics pertaining to the quality of indoor air and environment, and how these might affect the health, performance, efficiency and comfort of persons so exposed.
Refereed Serial

616.97   **US**   **ISSN 0019-9567**
QR1.A47   **CODEN: INFIBR**
INFECTION AND IMMUNITY. CD-ROM edition (ISSN 1070-6313) 1970. m. $419 (Canada $448; elsewhere $451) (effective 1996). American Society for Microbiology, 1325 Massachusetts Ave., N.W., Washington, DC 20005. TEL 202-737-3600. Ed. Vincent A. Fischetti. adv.; charts; stat.; index. circ. 6,650. (also avail. in microform from UMI; back issues avail.; reprint service avail. from UMI) **Indexed:** Abstr.Hyg., Anim.Breed.Abstr., Biol.Abstr., Biotech.Abstr., Chem.Abstr., Curr.Adv.Genetics & Molec.Biol., Curr.Cont., Curr.Tit.Dent., Dairy Sci.Abstr., Dent.Ind., Diar.Dis.Res., Dok.Arbeitsmed., Excerp.Med., Food Sci.& Tech.Abstr., Helminthol.Abstr., Ind.Med., Ind.Sci.Rev., Ind.Vet., INIS Atomind., Med.& Surg.Dermat., Nutr.Abstr., Pig News & Info., Poult.Abstr., Protozool.Abstr., Rev.Med.& Vet.Mycol., Rev.Plant Path., Sci.Cit.Ind., Small Anim.Abstr., Soils & Fert., Telegen, Trop.Dis.Bull., Vet.Bull. **Document type:** academic/scholarly publication.
● Also available on CD-ROM.
—BLDSC (4478.720000); CASDDS; EMDOCS; Faxon; Genuine Article; SWETS; UMI; UnCover. **CCC.**
Description: Directed toward immunologists, epidemiologists, pathologists, and clinicians.
Refereed Serial

INFECTIOUS DISEASES IN OBSTETRICS AND GYNECOLOGY. see MEDICAL SCIENCES — Obstetrics And Gynecology

616.97   **SP**   **ISSN 0213-9626**
                     CODEN: INMNEC
INMUNOLOGIA. (Text in English, Spanish; summaries in English) 1982. q. 4400 ptas.($35) to non-members. (Sociedad Espanola de Inmunologia) Ediciones Doyma, S.A., Travesera de Gracia, 17-21, 08021 Barcelona, Spain. TEL 34-1-200-07-11. FAX 34-1-209-11-36. TELEX 51964 INK-E. Dirs. T. Gallart, J.R. Regueiro Gonzalez. adv.: page 180000 ptas.; trim 210 x 280; adv. contact: Marte Vidal. circ. 2,000. (reprint service avail. from UMI) **Indexed:** Curr.Adv.Ecol.Sci., Curr.Adv.Genetics & Molec.Biol., Curr.Cont., Ind.Med.Esp., Ind.Sci.Rev., Sci.Cit.Ind.
—BLDSC (4515.276000); CASDDS; UMI.
Former titles (until 1986): Revista Doyma de Inmunologia (ISSN 0213-540X); (until 1985): Inmunologia (ISSN 0212-5765)
Description: Covers the basic aspects and clinical application in immunology.

MEDICAL SCIENCES — ALLERGOLOGY AND IMMUNOLOGY

616.97 UK ISSN 0965-2310
CODEN: IANWEL
INTERNATIONAL ANTIVIRAL NEWS. Abbreviated title: I A V N. 1993. 10/yr. £100($165) to individuals; institutions £200 ($330) (effective 1994). University of Cambridge, Department of Veterinary Medicine, Madingley Rd., Cambridge CB3 OES, England. TEL 01223-330810. FAX 01223-332998. Ed. Hugh J. Field. adv.; bk.rev. circ. 150. **Indexed:** Excerp.Med. (1994-). **Document type:** newsletter.
—BLDSC (4535.940000).
Description: Covers developments in immunology.

615.37 616.97 SZ ISSN 1018-2438
RC583. CODEN: IAAIEG
INTERNATIONAL ARCHIVES OF ALLERGY AND IMMUNOLOGY. (Text in English) 1950. m. (3 vols./yr.). 1287 SFr.($990) to individuals; institutions 2145 SFr.(£1650) (effective 1996). S. Karger AG, Allschwilerstr. 10, P.O. Box, CH-4009 Basel, Switzerland. TEL 061-3061111. FAX 061-3061234. E-mail: Karger@Karger.ch. Ed. G. Wick. adv.; bk.rev.; abstr.; bibl.; illus. circ. 1,400. (also avail. in microfilm from UMI) **Indexed:** Anim.Breed.Abstr., Biol.Abstr., Biotech.Abstr., C.I.S. Abstr., Chem.Abstr., Curr.Adv.Ecol.Sci., Curr.Cont., Dairy Sci.Abstr., Dent.Ind., Dok.Arbeitsmed., Excerp.Med., Forest Prod.Abstr., Helminthol.Abstr., Ind.Med., Ind.Sci.Rev., Ind.Vet., NRN, Nutr.Abstr., Pig News & Info., Rev.Med.& Vet.Mycol., Rev.Plant Path., Sci.Cit.Ind., Vet.Bull. **Document type:** academic/scholarly publication.
—BLDSC (4536.050000); CASDDS; Faxon; Genuine Article; SWETS; UnCover. **CCC.**
Formerly: International Archives of Allergy and Applied Immunology (ISSN 0020-5915)
Refereed Serial

616.97 UK ISSN 0953-8178
CODEN: INIMEN
INTERNATIONAL IMMUNOLOGY. 1989. m. £325($550) (effective 1996). Oxford University Press, Oxford Journals, Walton St., Oxford OX2 6DP, England. TEL 01865-267907. FAX 01865-267773. TELEX 837330-OXPRES-G. E-mail: jnlorders@oup.co.uk. (U.S. subscr. to: Oxford University Press Inc., 2001 Evans Rd., Cary, NC 27513. TEL 919-677-0977. FAX 919-677-1714) Ed. Tomio Tada. adv. circ. 1,000. **Document type:** academic/scholarly publication.
—BLDSC (4541.038930); CASDDS; Genuine Article; SWETS; UMI; UnCover. **CCC.**
Description: Publishes a broad range of experimental and theoretical studies in molecular and cellular immunology conducted in laboratories throughout the world.

616.97 615.19 IT ISSN 0394-6320
CODEN: IJIPE4
INTERNATIONAL JOURNAL OF IMMUNOPATHOLOGY AND PHARMACOLOGY. 1988. 3/yr. L.49000($49) to individuals; institutions L.190000 ($190) (effective 1995). Biomedical Research Press, s.a.s., c/o Universita di Chieti, Depto. di Immunologia, Via dei Vestini, Italy. TEL 39-871-355293. FAX 39-871-561635. Ed. Dr. Pio Conti. adv. contact: Renato Barbacane. circ. 600. **Indexed:** Curr.Cont., Excerp.Med. **Document type:** academic/scholarly publication.
—BLDSC (4542.300500); CASDDS; Genuine Article.
Refereed Serial

INTERNATIONAL JOURNAL OF IMMUNOPHARMACOLOGY.
see *PHARMACY AND PHARMACOLOGY*

616.97 SZ ISSN 0255-9625
CODEN: IJIMET
INTERNATIONAL JOURNAL OF IMMUNOTHERAPY. Short title: Immunotherapy. 1985. q. 250 SFr. Bioscience Ediprint Inc., Rue Alexandre-Gavard 16, CH-1227 Carouge-Geneva, Switzerland. TEL 022-3003383. FAX 022-3002489. TELEX 423355-BIOS-CH. Ed. Prof. A. Bertelli. (reprint service avail. from UMI) **Indexed:** Excerp.Med., Telegen.
—BLDSC (4542.302000); CASDDS; Faxon; Genuine Article; SWETS; UMI. **CCC.**

616.97 US ISSN 0883-0185
CODEN: IRIMEH
INTERNATIONAL REVIEWS OF IMMUNOLOGY. 1986. 8/yr. (in 2 vol., 4 nos./vol.). 141 ECU per vol. (effective 1996). Harwood Academic Publishers, c/o International Publishers Distributor, 820 Town Center Dr., Langhorne, PA 19047. TEL 215-750-2642. FAX 215-750-6343. (Subscr. to: International Publishers Distributor, PO Box 90, Reading, Berkshire, RG1 8JL, England. TEL 44-173-456-8316) Ed. Dr. Constantin Bona.
—BLDSC (4547.310000); Faxon; SWETS. **CCC.**
Refereed Serial

615.37 576 IT ISSN 0021-2547
CODEN: BISMAP
ISTITUTO SIEROTERAPICO MILANESE. BOLLETTINO; archivio di microbiologia ed immunologia. (Text and summaries in English and Italian) vol.49, 1970. bi-m. L.20000. Istituto Sieroterapico Milanese, Via Darwin 20, 20143 Milan, Italy. Ed. Augusto De Barbieri. adv.; bk.rev.; charts; illus.; stat. circ. 2,000. **Indexed:** Biol.Abstr., Curr.Adv.Ecol.Sci., Curr.Cont., Dairy Sci.Abstr., Excerp.Med., Helminthol.Abstr., Ind.Med., Ind.Vet., Nutr.Abstr., Protozool.Abstr., Sci.Cit.Ind, Trop.Dis.Bull., Vet.Bull.
—CASDDS.

616.97 SZ
JA! - WIR ATMEN. 1989. 6/yr. 20 SFr. Vereinigung das Band, Gryphenhuebeliweg 40, CH-3000 Bern 6, Switzerland. TEL 031-3521138. FAX 031-3516185. Ed. Zuzana Fajfr. bk.rev. circ. 10,000. **Document type:** bulletin.
Formerly: Band.

JAPANESE JOURNAL OF MEDICAL MYCOLOGY/NIHON ISHINKIN GAKKAI ZASSHI. see *BIOLOGY — Microbiology*

589.2 FR ISSN 1156-5233
CODEN: JMYME
JOURNAL DE MYCOLOGIE MEDICALE. (Supplement avail. (ISSN 1166-7680)) (Text in English, French) 1960. q. 756 F. (foreign 968 F.) (effective 1996). (Societe Francaise de Mycologie Medicale) Masson - Periodiques, Villa Laromiguiere, 75005 Paris, France. TEL 1-40-46-62-00. FAX 1-40-46-62-01. Ed. E. Drouhet. adv.; bk.rev.; illus. circ. 1,000. **Indexed:** Biol.Abstr., Excerp.Med. (1994-), Ind.Vet., Rev.Med.& Vet.Mycol., Rev.Plant Path., Small Anim.Abstr., Vet.Bull. **Document type:** academic/scholarly publication.
—BLDSC (5021.169000); SWETS.
Formerly (until 1991): Societe Francaise de Mycologie Medicale. Bulletin (ISSN 0037-9336)
Description: Aims to improve understanding of fungal diseases and mycoses that have developed in recent years and unravel the complications they cause.

616.97 615.37 US ISSN 0091-6749
CODEN: JACIBY
JOURNAL OF ALLERGY AND CLINICAL IMMUNOLOGY. (Supplements avail.) 1929. m. $115 to individuals (Canada $159.43; elsewhere $149); institutions $220 (Canada $271.78; elsewhere 254); students, residents $54 (Canada $94.16; elsewhere $88) (effective 1996); newsstand price: $10.50. (American Academy of Allergy and Immunology) Mosby - Year Book, Inc. (Subsidiary of: Times Mirror Company), 11830 Westline Industrial Dr., St. Louis, MO 63146-3318. TEL 314-872-8370; 800-325-4177. FAX 314-872-9164. TELEX 44-2402. Ed. Dr. Philip S. Norman. adv.: B&W page $1040, color page $2100; trim 8 1/8 x 10 7/8. abstr.; charts; illus.; index. circ. 13,062. (also avail. in microfilm from UMI,PMC; reprint service avail. from UMI) **Indexed:** AIM, Apic.Abstr., ASCA, Biol.Abstr., Biol.Dig., Biotech.Abstr., Chem.Abstr., Curr.Cont., Dairy Sci.Abstr., Dok.Arbeitsmed., Excerp.Med., Fababean Abstr., Helminthol.Abstr., I.P.A., Ind.Med., Ind.Sci.Rev., Ind.Vet., INIS Atomind., Med.& Surg.Dermat., NRN, Nutr.Abstr., Rev.Appl.Entomol., Rev.Med.& Vet.Mycol., Rev.Plant Path., Sci.Cit.Ind., Seed Abstr., Small Anim.Abstr., Soyabean Abstr., Triticale Abstr., Weed Abstr.
●Also available online. Vendor(s): Ovid Technologies.
—BLDSC (4927.100000); ADONIS; CASDDS; EMDOCS; Faxon; Genuine Article; SWETS; UMI; UnCover. **CCC.**
Formerly: Journal of Allergy (ISSN 0021-8707); Incorporates: Allergy Abstracts.
Description: Articles on the clinical manifestations of allergies for the clinical allergist and immunologist, dermatologist, general practitioner, pediatrician and otolaryngologist.
Refereed Serial

616.97 UK ISSN 0896-8411
QR188.3 CODEN: JOAUEP
JOURNAL OF AUTOIMMUNITY. bi-m. £225 (effective 1996). Academic Press Ltd. (Subsidiary of: Harcourt Brace & Company Ltd.), 24-28 Oval Rd., London NW1 7DX, England. TEL 44-171-267-4466. FAX 44-171-482-2293. TELEX 25775 ACPRES G. (Subscr. to: Harcourt Brace & Company Ltd., Foots Cray High St., Sidcup, Kent DA14 5HP, England. TEL 44-181-300-3322. FAX 44-171-309-0807) Ed. J.F. Bach. index. **Document type:** academic/scholarly publication.
—BLDSC (4949.555000); ADONIS; Faxon; Genuine Article; SWETS; UnCover. **CCC.**
Description: Publishes papers on all aspects of autoimmunity and its diverse aspects.

616.97 UK ISSN 0141-2760
CODEN: JLIMDJ
JOURNAL OF CLINICAL & LABORATORY IMMUNOLOGY. 1978. m. £395 (foreign £485). Teviot Scientific Publications Ltd., 82 Great King St., Edinburgh EH3 6QU, Scotland. TEL 031-332-8764. FAX 031-343-2633. Ed. Dr. W. James Irvine. adv.; bk.rev. **Indexed:** Chem.Abstr., Curr.Cont., Dairy Sci.Abstr., Excerp.Med., Helminthol.Abstr., Ind.Med., Ind.Sci.Rev., Ind.Vet., Rev.Med.& Vet.Mycol., Sci.Cit.Ind., Vet.Bull. **Document type:** academic/scholarly publication.
—BLDSC (4958.380700); CASDDS; Genuine Article; SWETS; UnCover. **CCC.**

616.97 US ISSN 0271-9142
RC581 CODEN: JCIMDO
JOURNAL OF CLINICAL IMMUNOLOGY. 1981. bi-m. $365 (foreign $425) (effective 1996). Plenum Publishing Corp., 233 Spring St., New York, NY 10013-1578. TEL 212-620-8000. FAX 212-463-0742. TELEX 23-421139. Ed. Sudhir Gupta. adv.; bk.rev.; illus. (also avail. in microfilm from JSC; back issues avail.) **Indexed:** Biol.Abstr., Chem.Abstr., Curr.Adv.Cancer Res., Curr.Cont., Dent.Ind., Diar.Dis.Res., Excerp.Med., Ind.Med., Ind.Sci.Rev., INIS Atomind., Sci.Cit.Ind. **Document type:** academic/scholarly publication.
—BLDSC (4958.490000); ADONIS; CASDDS; Faxon; Genuine Article; SWETS; UMI; UnCover. **CCC.**
Refereed Serial

MEDICAL SCIENCES — ALLERGOLOGY AND IMMUNOLOGY

616.97 US CODEN: JCLIES
JOURNAL OF CLINICAL LIGAND ASSAY. 1978. q. $85. (Clinical Ligand Assay Society) Kellner-McCaffery Associates, Inc., 150 Fifth Ave., Ste. 840, New York, NY 10011. TEL 212-741-0280. Ed. George Johnson. adv.; bk.rev. circ. 1,600. (also avail. in microfilm; microfiche; microform from UMI) **Indexed:** Chem.Abstr., Excerp.Med. **Document type:** academic/scholarly publication.
—BLDSC (4958.489000); CASDDS; Faxon; Genuine Article; SWETS; UMI.
Former titles: Journal of Clinical Immunoassay (ISSN 0736-4393); (until 1983): Ligand Quarterly (ISSN 0199-4794)
Refereed Serial

616 576.2 NE ISSN 0022-1759
QR183 CODEN: JIMMBG
JOURNAL OF IMMUNOLOGICAL METHODS. (Text in English) 1971. 22/yr. fl.4972($3032) (effective 1996). Elsevier Science B.V., P.O. Box 211, 1000 AE Amsterdam, Netherlands. TEL 31-20-4853911. FAX 31-20-4853598. TELEX 18582 ESPA NL. E-mail: nlinfo-f@elsevier.nl; usinfo-f@elsevier.com; forinfo-kyf04035@niftyserve.or.jp; Site addr.: http://www.elsevier.nl/. (Subscr. in U.S. and Canada to: Elsevier Science Inc., Box 882, Madison Sq. Sta., New York, NY 10159-0882. TEL 212-989-5800. FAX 212-633-3990) Eds. M. Turner, V. Nussenzweig. adv.; bk.rev.; illus.; index. circ. 2,500. (also avail. in microform from UMI; reprint service avail. from ISI) **Indexed:** Abstr.Hyg., Anim.Breed.Abstr., Apic.Abstr., Biol.Abstr., Chem.Abstr., Curr.Adv.Cancer Res., Curr.Adv.Cell & Devel.Biol., Curr.Adv.Ecol.Sci., Curr.Adv.Biotech.Abstr., Curr.Cont., Dairy Sci.Abstr., Dent.Ind., Excerp.Med., Helminthol.Abstr., Ind.Med., Ind.Sci.Rev., Ind.Vet., INIS Atomind., Nutr.Abstr., Poult.Abstr., Protozool.Abstr., Rev.Med.& Vet.Mycol., Rev.Plant Path., Risk Abstr., Sci.Cit.Ind., Telegen, Trop.Dis.Bull., Vet.Bull. **Document type:** academic/scholarly publication.
—BLDSC (5004.600000); ADONIS; CASDDS; EMDOCS; Faxon; Genuine Article; SWETS; UnCover. CCC.
Refereed Serial

615.37 US ISSN 0022-1767
QR180 CODEN: JOIMA3
JOURNAL OF IMMUNOLOGY. 1916. s-m. $170 to individuals (foreign $260); institutions $300 (foreign $390) (effective 1995). American Association of Immunologists, 9650 Rockville Pike, Bethesda, MD 20814. TEL 301-530-7178. FAX 301-571-1831. (Subscr. to: Fulco, Box 3000, Denville, NJ 07843. TEL 201-627-2997. FAX 201-627-5872) Ed. Dr. Peter Lipsky. adv.; bibl.; illus. circ. 8,600. (also avail. in microform from UMI) **Indexed:** Abstr.Hyg., AIM, Anim.Breed.Abstr, Apic.Abstr., Behav.Med.Abstr., Biol.Abstr., Biotech.Abstr., Chem.Abstr., Curr.Adv.Biochem., Curr.Adv.Cancer Res., Curr.Adv.Cell & Devel.Biol., Curr.Adv.Ecol.Sci., Curr.Adv.Genetics & Molec.Biol., Curr.Biotech.Abstr., Dairy Sci.Abstr., Dent.Ind., Diar.Dis.Res., Excerp.Med., Helminthol.Abstr., Ind.Med., Ind.Sci.Rev., Ind.Vet., INIS Atomind., Int.Aerosp.Abstr., Kidney, Med.& Surg.Dermat., Nutr.Abstr., Pig News & Info., Poult.Abstr., Protozool.Abstr., Rev.Appl.Entomol., Rev.Med.& Vet.Mycol., Rev.Plant Path., Sci.Cit.Ind., Telegen, Trop.Dis.Bull., Vet.Bull. **Document type:** academic/scholarly publication.
—BLDSC (5005.000000); CASDDS; EMDOCS; Faxon; Genuine Article; SWETS; UMI; UnCover. CCC.
Refereed Serial

616.02 US ISSN 1067-5582
RM270 CODEN: JIEIEZ
JOURNAL OF IMMUNOTHERAPY WITH EMPHASIS ON TUMOR IMMUNOLOGY. 1982. 8/yr. $208 to individuals (foreign $267); institutions $385 (foreign 467P (effective 1996); newsstand price: $60. (Society for Biological Therapy) Raven Press (Subsidiary of: Wolters Kluwer N.V.), 1185 Ave. of the Americas, New York, NY 10036. TEL 212-930-9500. FAX 212-869-3495. Ed. Steven A. Rosenberg. adv. contact: Phyllis Noyes. bk.rev.; illus.; index. circ. 1,300. (back issues avail.; reprint service avail. from UMI) **Indexed:** Chem.Abstr., Excerp.Med., Ind.Med., Ind.Sci.Rev., INIS Atomind., Sci.Cit.Ind. **Document type:** academic/scholarly publication.
—BLDSC (5005.040000); CASDDS; Faxon; Genuine Article; SWETS; UMI; UnCover. CCC.
Former titles: Journal of Immunotherapy (ISSN 1053-8550); (until 1991): Journal of Biological Response Modifiers (ISSN 0732-6580)
Description: Publishes laboratory, preclinical, and clinical reports on mechanisms and methods in immunotherapy.
Refereed Serial

616.97 US ISSN 1079-9907
QR187.5 CODEN: JICRFJ
JOURNAL OF INTERFERON & CYTOKINE RESEARCH. 1980. bi-m. $299 (foreign $354). (International Society for Interferon Research) Mary Ann Liebert, Inc. Publishers, 2 Madison Ave., Larchmont, NY 10538. TEL 914-834-3100. FAX 914-834-3688. E-mail: Liebert@pipeline.com. Ed. Philip I. Marcus. adv. (reprint service avail. from ISI; back issues avail.) **Indexed:** Anim.Breed.Abstr., Biol.Abstr., Chem.Abstr., Curr.Adv.Cell & Devel.Biol., Curr.Adv.Ecol.Sci., Curr.Adv.Genetics & Molec.Biol., Curr.Biotech.Abstr., Excerp.Med., Ind.Med., Ind.Sci.Rev., Ind.Vet., Pig News & Info., Rev.Med.& Vet.Mycol., Sci.Cit.Ind., Telegen, Vet.Bull. **Document type:** academic/scholarly publication.
—BLDSC (5007.548300); CASDDS; Faxon; Genuine Article; UnCover.
Formed by the merger of (1980-1985): Journal of Interferon Research (ISSN 0197-8357);
(1991-1995): Lymphokine and Cytokine Research (ISSN 1056-5477)
Description: Publishes original articles on varied aspects of interferon research and clinical applications.
Refereed Serial

616.97 SP ISSN 1018-9068
CODEN: JIAIEF
JOURNAL OF INVESTIGATIONAL ALLERGOLOGY AND CLINICAL IMMUNOLOGY. (Text in English) 1991. bi-m. $100 (effective 1996). (International Association of Asthmology) J.R. Prous, S.A. International Publishers, Apdo. de Correos 540, 08080 Barcelona, Spain. TEL 343-459-2220. FAX 343-458-1535. (Co-sponsor: Sociedad Latinoamericana de Alergia e Inmunología) **Indexed:** Excerp.Med. (1993-), Ind.Med. (1993-). **Document type:** academic/scholarly publication.
—BLDSC (5007.980000); Genuine Article.

JOURNAL OF NEUROIMMUNOLOGY. see MEDICAL SCIENCES — Psychiatry And Neurology

616.97 US ISSN 1049-5150
QP141.A1 CODEN: JNUIEE
JOURNAL OF NUTRITIONAL IMMUNOLOGY. 1992. q. $120 (foreign $168) (effective 1996). Haworth Press, Inc., 10 Alice St., Binghamton, NY 13904. TEL 607-722-5857; 800-342-9678. FAX 607-722-1424. TELEX 4932599. Ed. Jullian E. Spallholz. adv.; bk.rev. (also avail. in microfiche from UMI; reprint service avail. from HAW) **Indexed:** Biostat., Excerp.Med. (1993-). **Document type:** academic/scholarly publication.
—BLDSC (5024.735000); CASDDS; Haworth; UnCover.
Description: Provides a forum for research scientists that bridges the disciplines of nutrition and immunology.
Refereed Serial

616.97 618 IE ISSN 0165-0378
CODEN: JRIMDR
JOURNAL OF REPRODUCTIVE IMMUNOLOGY. (Text in English) 1979. 9/yr. I£462($730) (effective 1996). (International Society for Immunology of Reproduction) Elsevier Science Ireland Ltd., P.O. Box 85, Limerick, Ireland. TEL 353-61-471944. FAX 353-61-472144. (Subscr. in U.S. and Canada to: Elsevier Science Inc., Box 882, Madison Sq. Sta., New York, NY 10159. TEL 212-989-5800. FAX 212-633-3990) Eds. W.D. Billington, A.E. Beer. adv.; bk.rev. (also avail. in microform from UMI; reprint service avail. from SWZ) **Indexed:** Anim.Breed.Abstr., Biol.Abstr., Chem.Abstr., Curr.Adv.Ecol.Sci., Curr.Cont., Dairy Sci.Abstr., Excerp.Med., Ind.Med., Ind.Sci.Rev., Ind.Vet., INIS Atomind., Pig News & Info., Vet.Bull. **Document type:** academic/scholarly publication.
—BLDSC (5049.670000); CASDDS; Faxon; Genuine Article; SWETS; UnCover. CCC.
Refereed Serial

THE JOURNAL OF VETERINARY AND CLINICAL IMMUNOLOGY. see VETERINARY SCIENCE

616.97 JA ISSN 0916-8966
KAFUNSHO KENKYUKAI KAIHO/POLLEN ALLERGY AND PREVENTION. (Text in Japanese) 1990. a. Kafunsho Kenkyukai - Society of Pollen Allergy and Prevention, Toyama Ika Yakka Daigaku, Igakubu Koshu Eiseigaku Kyoshitsu, 2630 Sugitani, Toyama-shi, Toyama-ken 930-01, Japan.

616.97 610 UK ISSN 0142-8160
LEUCOCYTES. 1976. s-m. (diskette m.) £120 (diskette £115; both £175) (effective 1995). S U B I S, Mansion House, 19 Kingfield Rd., Sheffield S11 9AS, England. TEL 0114-2554433. FAX 0114-2554626. E-mail: admin@sheffac.demon.co.uk. bk.rev. (also avail. in diskette format) **Document type:** abstracting/indexing.
—CCC.
Description: Current awareness service for researchers. Covers leucocytes: structure, biochemistry, function, granulopoiesis, adherence and migration.

LUNG LINE LETTER. see MEDICAL SCIENCES — Respiratory Diseases

616.97 611 UK ISSN 0142-8179
LYMPHOCYTES. 1976. m. £75 (effective 1995). S U B I S, Mansion House, 19 Kingfield Rd., Sheffield S11 9AS, England. TEL 0114-2554433. FAX 0114-2554626. E-mail: admin@sheffac.demon.co.uk. **Document type:** abstracting/indexing.
—CCC.
Description: Current awareness service for researchers in clinical and life sciences. Covers helper and suppressor cells, transformation, T-lymphocytes, B-lymphocytes, T-cell receptors.

616.7 CN ISSN 0315-1131
M S CANADA. 1974. q. Can.$10 (foreign Can.$12). Multiple Sclerosis Society of Canada, 250 Bloor St. E., Ste. 820, Toronto, ON M4W 3P9, Canada. TEL 416-922-6065. FAX 416-922-7538. Ed. Deanna Groetzinger. bk.rev. circ. 26,000. **Document type:** newsletter.
Description: Provides information on M S research, how to cope with multiple sclerosis, and activities of the Society.

616.97 UK ISSN 0142-8195
MACROPHAGES. 1976. s-m. (diskette m.) £110 (diskette £115; both £175) (effective 1995). S U B I S, Mansion House, 19 Kingfield Rd., Sheffield S11 9AS, England. TEL 0114-2554433. FAX 0114-2554626. E-mail: admin@sheffac.demon.co.uk. bk.rev. (also avail. in diskette format) **Document type:** abstracting/indexing.
—CCC.
Description: Current awareness service for researchers in clinical and life sciences. Covers the biochemistry, structure and function of monocytopoiesis, macrophages, monocytes.

MANUAL OF BIOLOGICAL MARKERS OF DISEASE. see BIOLOGY — Physiology

MEDICAL SCIENCES — ALLERGOLOGY AND IMMUNOLOGY

616 615.37 GW ISSN 0300-8584
CODEN: MMIYAO
MEDICAL MICROBIOLOGY AND IMMUNOLOGY. (Text in English) 1886. 4/yr. DM.825($599) (effective 1996). Springer-Verlag, Heidelberger Platz 3, 14197 Berlin, Germany. TEL 030-8207-0. FAX 030-8214091. E-mail: orders@springer.de. (Subscr. in N. America to: Springer-Verlag New York, Inc., 44 Hartz Way, Secaucus, NJ 07096-2491. TEL 201-348-4033. FAX 201-348-4505) Ed.Bd. (also avail. in microform from UMI; reprint service avail. from ISI) **Indexed:** Biol.Abstr., Chem.Abstr., Curr.Adv.Ecol.Sci., Curr.Cont., Excerp.Med., Helminthol.Abstr., Ind.Med., Ind.Sci.Rev., Ind.Vet., INIS Atomind., Rev.Plant Path., Telegen, Trop.Dis.Bull., Vet.Bull. **Document type:** academic/scholarly publication.
—BLDSC (5529.990000); ADONIS; CASDDS; Faxon; Genuine Article; SWETS; UMI; UnCover. **CCC.**
Formerly: Zeitschrift fuer Medizinische Mikrobiologie und Immunologie (ISSN 0044-3077)
Description: Covers a broad spectrum of the interrelationships between micro-organisms and the human host, with special emphasis on medical virology and immunology, and how they relate to the mechanisms of pathogenesis.

MEDICAL SCIENTIFIC UPDATE. see MEDICAL SCIENCES — Respiratory Diseases

616.97 JA ISSN 0917-0774
MEN-EKI IMMUNOLOJI FURONTIA/IMMUNOLOGY FRONTIER. (Text in Japanese) 1991. 6/yr. 1100 Yen per no. Medikaru Rebyusha - Medical Review Co., Ltd., 7-3, Hiranomachi 1-chome, Chuo-ku, Osaka 541, Japan.

616.97 JA ISSN 0914-8639
MEN'EKI KAKU IGAKU/IMMUNONUCLEAR MEDICINE. (Text in Japanese) 1986. s-a. Men'eki Kaku Igaku Kenkyukai - Immunonuclear Medicine Study Group, Kitasato Daigaku Igakubu Hoshasenka, 15-1, Kitasato 1-chome, Sagamihara-shi, Kanagawa-ken 228, Japan.

616.97 576 UK ISSN 0891-060X
QR171.A1 CODEN: MEHDE6
MICROBIAL ECOLOGY IN HEALTH & DISEASE. 1988. bi-m. $475 (foreign $475) (effective 1996). John Wiley & Sons Ltd., Journals, Baffins Ln., Chichester, W. Sussex PO19 1UD, England. TEL 01243-779777. FAX 01243-776128. (Subscr. in the Americas to: John Wiley & Sons, Inc., 605 Third Ave., New York, NY 10158. TEL 212-850-6645. FAX 212-850-6021) Ed. S.P. Borriello. adv.; bk.rev. circ. 173. (also avail. in microform from UMI; back issues avail.; reprint service avail. from SWZ) **Indexed:** Curr.Adv.Cancer Res., Diar.Dis.Res., Ind.Med. **Document type:** academic/scholarly publication.
—BLDSC (5756.922000); Faxon; Genuine Article; UMI; UnCover. **CCC.**
Description: Draws together research on various human microbial ecosystems to increase understanding of their role in health and disease.
Refereed Serial

MOLECULAR IMMUNOLOGY. see BIOLOGY — Biological Chemistry

616.97 UK ISSN 0261-4960
MONOCLONAL ANTIBODIES. 1981. s-m. (diskette m.). £115 (diskette £115; both £175) (effective 1995). S U B I S, Mansion House, 19 Kingfield Rd., Sheffield S11 9AS, England. TEL 0114-2554433. FAX 0114-2554626. E-mail: admin@sheffac.demon.co.uk. bk.rev. (also avail. in diskette format) **Document type:** abstracting/indexing.
—CCC.
Description: Current awareness service for researchers. Covers antibodies, molecules and cell types. Includes information on assays and separation techniques using MAB's.

616.97 SZ ISSN 0077-0760
CODEN: MOALAR
MONOGRAPHS IN ALLERGY. (Text in English) 1966. irreg. varies. S. Karger AG, Allschwilerstr. 10, P.O. Box, CH-4009 Basel, Switzerland. TEL 061-3061111. FAX 061-3061234. E-mail: Karger@Karger.ch. Eds. L.A. Hanson, F. Shakib. (reprint service avail. from ISI) **Indexed:** Apic.Abstr., Biol.Abstr., Chem.Abstr., Curr.Cont., Dent.Ind., Ind.Med., Ind.Sci.Rev., Rev.Med.& Vet.Mycol. **Document type:** monographic series.
—BLDSC (5914.975000); CASDDS; Faxon; Genuine Article; SWETS. **CCC.**
Refereed Serial

616.9 US ISSN 1068-7629
MUCOSAL IMMUNOLOGY UPDATE. 1993. q. $45 to individuals (foreign $57); institutions $70 (foreign $89) (effective 1996); newsstand price: $23. (Society for Mucosal Immunology) Lippincott - Raven Publishers, 227 E. Washington Sq., Philadelphia, PA 19106. TEL 215-238-4200. Eds. Hiroshi Kiyono, Peter B. Ernst. adv. contact: Phyllis Noyes. charts; illus. circ. 700. **Document type:** newsletter.
—CCC.
Description: Presents minireviews, abstracts from meetings and society news.

N O H A NEWS. (Nutrition for Optimal Health Association) see NUTRITION AND DIETETICS

616.97 614.4 US
NEEDLE TIPS. irreg. (2-4/yr.). Immunization Action Coalition, 1573 Selby Ave., Ste. 229, St. Paul, MN 55104. TEL 612-647-9009. FAX 612-647-9131. E-mail: wexle.001@maroon.tc.umn.edu. Ed. Deborah Wexler. circ. 65,000. **Document type:** newsletter.
●Also available online.
Description: Features articles and reprintable resources on immunizations for vaccine-preventable diseases.

616.97 616.8 SZ ISSN 1021-7401
CODEN: NROIEM
▼**NEUROIMMUNOMODULATION.** (Text in English) 1994. bi-m. 250.25 SFr.($192.50) to individuals; institutions 715 SFr.($550) (effective 1996). S. Karger AG, Allschwilerstr. 10, P.O. Box, CH-4009 Basel, Switzerland. TEL 061-3061111. FAX 061-3061234. E-mail: Karger@Karger.ch. (Subscr. in U.S. to: S. Karger Publishers, Inc., 26 W. Avon Rd., Box 529, Farmington, CT 06085) Eds. S.M. McCann, J.M. Lipton. circ. 1,000. (also avail. in microform from UMI) **Indexed:** Excerp.Med. (1995-). **Document type:** academic/scholarly publication.
—BLDSC (6081.373400); CASDDS; Genuine Article.
Description: Explores the way in which the nervous system interacts with the immune system via neural, hormonal, and paracrine actions.
Refereed Serial

NEW TRENDS IN LIPID MEDIATORS RESEARCH. see PHARMACY AND PHARMACOLOGY

616.97 US ISSN 0899-7489
NEWS & NOTES (MILWAUKEE). 1943. q. membership. American Academy of Allergy, Asthma and Immunology, 611 E. Wells St., Milwaukee, WI 53202. TEL 414-272-6071. FAX 414-276-3349. Ed. S.E. Kaluzny-Petroff. adv.: B&W page $703; adv. contact: S.E. Kaluzny-Petroff. charts; illus.; stat. circ. 5,500.
Description: Covers membership and educational activities.

OCULAR IMMUNOLOGY AND INFLAMMATION. see MEDICAL SCIENCES — Ophthalmology And Optometry

616.97 US ISSN 0000-1538
RC583
OFFICIAL AMERICAN BOARD OF MEDICAL SPECIALTIES (A B M S) DIRECTORY OF BOARD CERTIFIED ALLERGISTS AND IMMUNOLOGISTS. 1985. biennial. $99.95. Marquis Who's Who, A Reed Reference Publishing company, 121 Chanlon Rd., New Providence, NJ 07974. TEL 908-464-6800. FAX 908-665-2889. (Subscr. to: Order Dept., Box 31, New Providence, NJ 07974-9903. TEL 800-521-8110) Ed. Roy Crego. **Document type:** directory.
Formerly (until 1994): A B M S Directory of Certified Allergy and Immunology Physicians (ISSN 0883-2994)
Description: Biographical sketches of U.S. certified medical specialists sorted geographically with alpha index.

ORAL MICROBIOLOGY AND IMMUNOLOGY. see BIOLOGY — Microbiology

PARASITE IMMUNOLOGY. see MEDICAL SCIENCES — Communicable Diseases

PEDIATRIC ALLERGY AND IMMUNOLOGY. see MEDICAL SCIENCES — Pediatrics

PEDIATRIC ALLERGY AND IMMUNOLOGY. SUPPLEMENTUM. see MEDICAL SCIENCES — Pediatrics

PEDIATRIC ASTHMA, ALLERGY & IMMUNOLOGY. see MEDICAL SCIENCES — Pediatrics

615.37 US
PERSPECTIVES IN IMMUNOLOGY; a series of publications based on symposia. 1969. irreg., no.10, 1981. Academic Press, Inc., 525 B St., Ste. 1900, San Diego, CA 92101-4495. TEL 619-231-0926. FAX 619-699-6715. (Subscr. to: Order Dept., 6277 Sea Harbor Dr., 4th Fl., Orlando, FL 32887. TEL 800-321-5068) (reprint service avail. from ISI)
Refereed Serial

615.37 PL ISSN 1233-0167
QR180 CODEN: PJIME4
POLISH JOURNAL OF IMMUNOLOGY. (Text mainly in Polish; occasionally in English; summaries in English) 1969. q. $20. Polskie Towarzystwo Immunologiczne, c/o Samodzielna Pracownia Immunologii, Centrum Zdrowia Dziecka, Al. Dzieci Polskich 20, 07-736 Warsaw, Poland. Ed. Prof. Kazimierz Madalisnki. bk.rev.; illus. circ. 1,170. **Indexed:** Biol.Abstr., Biotech.Abstr., Chem.Abstr., Excerp.Med., INIS Atomind.
—CASDDS.
Former titles (until 1992): Immunologia Polska (ISSN 0324-8534); Annals of Immunology (ISSN 0044-8338)

616.97 CN ISSN 0831-0998
PRACTICAL ALLERGY & IMMUNOLOGY; practical journal of allergy for the family practitioner. 1986. bi-m. Can.$60 (U.S. $72; elsewhere $94). Medicopea International Inc., 3333 Cote Vertu Blvd., Ste. 300, St. Laurent, PQ H4R 2N1, Canada. TEL 514-333-4561. FAX 514-336-1129. Ed.Bd. adv. contact: Sara Wilkins. bk.rev.; illus.; index; circ. 3,600 (controlled). (back issues avail.) **Document type:** trade publication.

PSORI NEWSLETTER. see MEDICAL SCIENCES — Dermatology And Venereology

MEDICAL SCIENCES — ALLERGOLOGY AND IMMUNOLOGY

615.37 FR ISSN 0923-2494
CODEN: RIMME5
RESEARCH IN IMMUNOLOGY. (Text in English) 1887. 9/yr. 1930 F. in France; foreign 2335 F.($456) (effective 1996). (Institut Pasteur) Editions Scientifiques Elsevier, 141 rue de Javel, 75747 Paris, France. TEL 33-1-45589063. (Subscr. in U.S. and Canada to: Elsevier Science Inc., Box 882, Madison Sq. Sta., New York, NY 10159. TEL 212-989-5800) Eds. P. Kourilsky, P. Truffa-Bachi. index. (also avail. in microform from RPI,PMC; reprint service avail. from ISI) **Indexed:** Abstr.Hyg., Anim.Breed.Abstr., Biol.Abstr., Bull.Signal., Chem.Abstr., Curr.Adv.Ecol.Sci., Curr.Cont., Dairy Sci.Abstr., Dent.Ind., Excerp.Med., Helminthol.Abstr., Ind.Med., Ind.Sci.Rev., Ind.Vet., INIS Atomind., Pig News & Info., Rev.Med.& Vet.Mycol., Sci.Cit.Ind., Trop.Dis.Bull., Vet.Bull. **Document type:** academic/scholarly publication.
—BLDSC (7741.325000); ADONIS; CASDDS; Faxon; Genuine Article; SWETS; UnCover. **CCC.**
Former titles (until 1988): Institut Pasteur. Annales. Immunologie (ISSN 0769-2625); (until 1985): Annales d'Immunologie (ISSN 0300-4910); Supersedes in part: Institut Pasteur. Annales (ISSN 0020-2444).
Description: Publishes full-length articles on all aspects of immunology, including immunochemistry, cellular immunology, immunogenetics and transplantation immunopathology.
Refereed Serial

616.97 NE ISSN 0167-6091
CODEN: RMIMDC
RESEARCH MONOGRAPHS IN IMMUNOLOGY. 1980. irreg., vol.12, 1989. price varies. Elsevier Science B.V., Books Division, P.O. Box 211, 1000 AE Amsterdam, Netherlands. TEL 31-20-4853911. FAX 31-20-4853705. TELEX 18582 ESPA NL. E-mail: nlinfo-f@elsevier.nl; usinfo-f@elsevier.com; forinfo-kyf04035@niftyserve.or.jp; Site addr.: http://www.elsevier.nl/. (Subscr. in U.S. and Canada to: Elsevier Science Inc., Box 882, Madison Sq. Sta., New York, NY 10159. TEL 212-989-5800) **Document type:** monographic series.
—BLDSC (7743.356100); CASDDS.
Refereed Serial

REVIEWS IN MEDICAL VIROLOGY. see *BIOLOGY — Microbiology*

REVISTA ARGENTINA DE MICROBIOLOGIA. see *BIOLOGY — Microbiology*

616.97 SP ISSN 0214-1477
CODEN: REACEN
REVISTA ESPANOLA DE ALERGOLOGIA E INMUNOLOGIA CLINICA. vol.6, 1991. 6/yr. (Sociedad Espanola de Alergologia e Inmunologia Clinica.) Saned, S.A., Paseo de la Habana 202-bis, 28036 Madrid, Spain. TEL 1-3594092. Ed. Manuel Martin Esteban. **Indexed:** Excerp.Med.
—BLDSC (7853.852000).

616.97 FR ISSN 0335-7457
REVUE FRANCAISE D'ALLERGOLOGIE ET IMMUNOLOGIE CLINIQUE. 1961. 4/yr. 660 F. to individuals (foreign 870 F.); students 330 F. (foreign 440 F.). (Societe Francaise d'Allergologie) Expansion Scientifique, 31 bd. de la Tour Maubourg, 75007 Paris, France. TEL 40-62-64-00. FAX 45-55-69-20. Ed. Dr. Sclafer. adv.; bk.rev.; abstr.; bibl.; charts. circ. 3,000. (also avail. in microform from UMI; reprint service avail. from UMI) **Indexed:** Biol.Abstr., C.I.S. Abstr., Chem.Abstr., Curr.Adv.Ecol.Sci., Curr.Cont., Ind.Med., Rev.Med.& Vet.Mycol., Rev.Plant Path.
—BLDSC (7902.470000); Genuine Article; UMI. **CCC.**
Former titles: Revue Francaise d'Allergologie et Immunologie; Revue Francaise d'Allergologie (ISSN 0035-2845); Revue Francaise d'Allergie.

616.07 RM ISSN 1220-8485
576 CODEN: RAMIE5
ROMANIAN ARCHIVES OF MICROBIOLOGY AND IMMUNOLOGY. (Text in English; summaries in English, French) 1928. q. $150 (effective 1993). Institutul Cantacuzino R A, P.O. Box 1-525, Spl. Independentei 103, 70100 Bucharest, Rumania. TEL 01-6383800. FAX 01-3122720. bk.rev.; charts; illus.; index. circ. 1,000. (back issues avail.) **Indexed:** Abstr.Hyg., Biol.Abstr., Bull.Signal., Chem.Abstr., Excerp.Med., Ind.Med., Ind.Vet., INIS Atomind., Rev.Appl.Entomol., Trop.Dis.Bull., Vet.Bull. **Document type:** academic/scholarly publication.
—BLDSC (1640.850000); CASDDS; Faxon.
Formerly (until 1991): Archives Roumaines de Pathologie Experimentale et de Microbiologie (ISSN 0004-0037).

616.97 UK ISSN 0300-9475
QR180 CODEN: SJIMAX
SCANDINAVIAN JOURNAL OF IMMUNOLOGY. (Supplement avail. (ISSN 0301-6323)) 1972. m. £289($462) (effective 1996). Blackwell Science Ltd., Osney Mead, Oxford OX2 OEL, England. TEL 01865-240201. FAX 01865-721205. TELEX 83355 MEDBOK G. Eds. M. Harboe, J.B. Natvig. adv. circ. 1,500. (also avail. in microform from UMI; back issues avail.; reprint service avail. from ISI) **Indexed:** Anim.Breed.Abstr., ASCA, Biol.Abstr., Chem.Abstr., Curr.Adv.Biochem., Curr.Adv.Cancer Res., Curr.Adv.Cell & Devel.Biol., Curr.Adv.Ecol.Sci., Curr.Adv.Genetics & Molec.Biol., Curr.Cont., Dairy Sci.Abstr., Excerp.Med., Helminthol.Abstr., Ind.Med., Ind.Vet., Protozool.Abstr., Sci.Cit.Ind., Vet.Bull. **Document type:** academic/scholarly publication.
—BLDSC (8087.516800); ADONIS; CASDDS; Faxon; Genuine Article; SWETS; UMI; UnCover. **CCC.**
Refereed Serial

616.97 UK ISSN 0301-6323
CODEN: SJISDK
SCANDINAVIAN JOURNAL OF IMMUNOLOGY. SUPPLEMENT. 1973. irreg. Blackwell Science Ltd., Osney Mead, Oxford OX2 OEL, England. TEL 01865-240201. FAX 01865-7221205. TELEX 83355 MEDBOK G. **Indexed:** Excerp.Med. (1993-). **Document type:** academic/scholarly publication.
—BLDSC (8087.516900); ADONIS; CASDDS. **CCC.**

SEMINARS IN DIAGNOSTIC PATHOLOGY. see *MEDICAL SCIENCES*

574 UK ISSN 1044-5323
CODEN: SEIME2
SEMINARS IN IMMUNOLOGY. 1989. bi-m. £115 (effective 1996). Academic Press Ltd. (Subsidiary of: Harcourt Brace & Company Ltd.), 24-28 Oval Rd., London NW1 7DX, England. TEL 44-171-267-4466. FAX 44-171-482-2293. TELEX 25775 ACPRES G. (Subscr. to: Harcourt Brace & Company Ltd., Foots Cray High St., Sidcup, Kent DA14 5HP, England. TEL 44-181-300-3322. FAX 44-181-309-0807) Ed. Michael Julian. **Indexed:** Chem.Abstr., Ind.Med. **Document type:** academic/scholarly publication.
—BLDSC (8239.451000); CASDDS; SWETS; UnCover. **CCC.**
Description: Reviews the latest news in R&D in studies of the human immune system.

SEMINARS IN OTOLARYNGIC ALLERGY. see *MEDICAL SCIENCES — Otorhinolaryngology*

616.97 AT
SENSITIVITY MATTERS. 1982. q. Aus.$25. Allergy and Environmental Sensitivity Support and Research Association, P.O. Box 298, Ringwood, Vic. 3134, Australia. TEL 03-888-1382. Ed. Catherine McIver. adv.; bk.rev. circ. 400. (back issues avail.) **Document type:** newsletter.
Formerly (until 1994): A A A News (ISSN 0817-1300).
Description: Covers the treatment and management of allergy and sensitivity related diseases (asthma, eczema, Multiple Chemical Sensitivity, Chronic Fatigue Syndrome, hayfever, ADHD) as well as local and overseas news and activities.

SEQUENCES OF PROTEINS OF IMMUNOLOGICAL INTEREST. see *MEDICAL SCIENCES — Abstracting, Bibliographies, Statistics*

616.97 US
SJOGREN'S SYNDROME FOUNDATION INC.; the moisture seekers newsletter. 1984. m. $25 (Canada $30; elsewhere $35). Sjogen's Syndrome Foundation Inc., c/o Rita M. May, Exec. Dir., 333 N. Broadway, Ste. 2000, NY 11753-2007. TEL 516-933-6365; 800-4SJ-OGRE. FAX 516-933-6368. circ. 11,000. (tabloid format; back issues avail.) **Document type:** newsletter.
Description: Informs patients and medical professionals about all aspects of Sjogren's syndrome, including the various manifestations of the disorder, treatment modalities, news on research developments, important legislation, and advice on how to live more comfortably and prevent or prolong the onset of major debilitating consequences. Provides information on support groups and on meetings and symposia.
Refereed Serial

616.97 GW ISSN 0344-4325
CODEN: SSIMDV
SPRINGER SEMINARS IN IMMUNOPATHOLOGY. (Text in English) 1978. 4/yr. DM.548($398) (effective 1996). Springer-Verlag, Heidelberger Platz 3, 14197 Berlin, Germany. TEL 030-8207-0. FAX 030-8214091. E-mail: orders@springer.de. (Subscr. in N. America to: Springer-Verlag New York, Inc., 44 Hartz Way, Secaucus, NJ 07096-2491. TEL 201-348-4033. FAX 201-348-4505) Eds. P.A. Miescher, H.L. Spiegelberg. charts; illus.; index. (also avail. in microform from UMI; back issues avail.; reprint service avail. from ISI) **Indexed:** Abstr.Hyg., Anim.Breed.Abstr., ASCA, Chem.Abstr., Curr.Adv.Ecol.Sci., Curr.Adv.Genetics & Molec.Biol., Curr.Cont., Excerp.Med., Helminthol.Abstr., Ind.Med., Trop.Dis.Bull. **Document type:** academic/scholarly publication.
—BLDSC (8424.730000); ADONIS; CASDDS; Faxon; Genuine Article; SWETS; UMI; UnCover. **CCC.**
Description: Offers up-to-date developments in the field of immunopathology.

616.97 UK ISSN 0967-0149
RM270 CODEN: THIMEY
▼**THERAPEUTIC IMMUNOLOGY.** 1994. bi-m. £62.50 to individuals (outside Europe £68.50($106)); institutions £144 (outside Europe £159($255)) (effective 1996). Blackwell Science Ltd., Osney Mead, Oxford OX2 OEL, England. TEL 01865-240201. FAX 01865-721205. TELEX 83355 MEDBOK G. Eds. E. Vitetta, H. Waldmann. adv.; bk.rev.; bibl.; illus.; index. (also avail. in microform from UMI; back issues avail.) **Indexed:** Excerp.Med. (1995-). **Document type:** academic/scholarly publication.
—BLDSC (8814.660000); CASDDS; UMI. **CCC.**
Refereed Serial

616.97 NE ISSN 0165-6090
CODEN: THYMDB
THYMUS; journal of T-cell biology. (Text in English) 1979. q. fl.311 to institutions; $199 to institutions in U.S. (effective 1996). Kluwer Academic Publishers, Postbus 17, 3300 AA Dordrecht, Netherlands. TEL 31-78-392392. FAX 31-78-392254. TELEX 29245 KAPG NL. E-mail: SERVICES@WKAP.NL. (Dist. by: Kluwer Academic Publishers Group, P.O. Box 322, 3300 AH Dordrecht, Netherlands. TEL 31-78-392392. FAX 31-78-546474; N. America dist. addr.: Box 358, Accord Sta., Hingham, MA 02018-0358. TEL 617-871-6600. FAX 617-871-6528) Ed. Ada M. Kruisbeek. adv. (also avail. in microform from UMI; back issues avail.) **Indexed:** ASCA, Biol.Abstr., Chem.Abstr., Curr.Adv.Ecol.Sci., Curr.Cont., Excerp.Med., Ind.Med., Ind.Vet., Protozool.Abstr., Sci.Cit.Ind., Sport Fish.Abstr., Vet.Bull., Wild.Rev. **Document type:** academic/scholarly publication.
—BLDSC (8820.381500); CASDDS; Faxon; Genuine Article; SWETS; UMI; UnCover. **CCC.**
Description: Publishes articles dealing with a wide range of subjects relating to T-cell biology, including molecular and cellular immunology, pharmacology and cytokines, immuno-deficiencies and AIDS, and immune-mediated diseases.
Refereed Serial

MEDICAL SCIENCES — ANAESTHESIOLOGY

616.97   US   ISSN 0896-341X
CODEN: THUPEZ
THYMUS UPDATE. irreg., latest vol.4. price varies. Harwood Academic Publishers, c/o International Publishers Distributor, 820 Town Center Dr., Langhorne, PA 19047. TEL 215-750-2642. FAX 215-750-6343. (Subscr. to: International Publishers Distributor, Box 90, Reading, Berkshire RG1 8JL, England. TEL 44-173-456-8316) Eds. M.D. Kendall, M.A. Ritter. (also avail. in microform) **Document type:** monographic series.
Refereed Serial

616.97   UK   ISSN 0966-3274
CODEN: TRIME2
TRANSPLANT IMMUNOLOGY. 1993. q. £71($129) to individuals; institutions £150 ($270) (effective 1996). Arnold (Subsidiary of: Hodder Headline plc.), 338 Euston Rd., London NW1 3BH, England. TEL 0171-873-6000. FAX 0171-873-6325. (Subscr. to: Turpin Distribution Services Ltd., Blackhorse Rd., Letchworth, Herts. SG6 1HN, England. TEL 01462-672555. FAX 01462-480947) **Indexed:** Excerp.Med. (1994-), Ind.Med. (1994-). **Document type:** academic/scholarly publication.
—BLDSC (9024.988500); CASDDS.

TRANSPLANTATION. see *MEDICAL SCIENCES — Surgery*

U K PRODUCT REVIEW. see *BIOLOGY — Biological Chemistry*

616.97   GW   ISSN 0945-7526
UMWELT UND GESUNDHEIT. q. DM.24. (Allergie Verein in Europa) Karl F. Haug Verlag GmbH, Fritz-Frey-Str. 21, 69121 Heidelberg, Germany. TEL 06221-4062-0. FAX 06221-400727. TELEX 461683-HVVFM-D. (Subscr. to: Postfach 102840, 69018 Heidelberg, Germany) Ed. R. Zienczyk. adv. contact: G. Werner. **Document type:** academic/scholarly publication.
Formerly (until 1994): Allergothek (ISSN 0938-5983)

616.97   UK   ISSN 0264-410X
CODEN: VACCDE
VACCINE. 1983. 18/yr. £645($1026) (£870($1384) with electronic access) (effective 1996). Butterworth - Heinemann, Part of the Reed Elsevier group, Linacre House, Jordan Hill, Oxford OX2 8DP, England. TEL 01865-310366. FAX 01865-310898. TELEX 83111 BHPOXF G. E-mail: nlinfo-f@elsevier.nl; usinfo-f@elsevier.com; Site addr: http://www.elsevier.nl/. (Subscr. to: Elsevier Science Ltd., P.O. Box 800, Kidlington, Oxford OX5 1DX, England. TEL 44-1865-843000. FAX 44-1865-843010; Subscr. in U.S. and Canada to: Elsevier Science, 660 White Plains Rd., Tarrytown, NY 10591-5153. TEL 914-524-9200. FAX 914-333-2444) Ed. R.E. Spier. adv.; bk.rev.; abstr.; bibl.; charts; illus.; pat.; stat.; index. (also avail. in microform from UMI; back issues avail.) **Indexed:** Abstr.Hyg., Chem.Abstr., Curr.Adv.Ecol.Sci., Curr.Adv.Genetics & Molec.Biol., Curr.Biotech.Abstr., Curr.Cont., Diar.Dis.Res., Dok.Arbeitsmed., Excerp.Med., Ind.Med., Ind.Vet., Poult.Abstr., Small Anim.Abstr., Telegen, Vet.Bull. **Document type:** academic/scholarly publication.
●Also available online.
—BLDSC (9138.628000); ADONIS; CASDDS; Faxon; Genuine Article; SWETS; UMI; UnCover. **CCC.**
Description: Covers research and development, production and use of both human and veterinary vaccines.
Refereed Serial

616.97   US   ISSN 1056-7909
CODEN: VAREES
VACCINE RESEARCH. 1992. q. $149 (foreign $189). Mary Ann Liebert, Inc. Publishers, 2 Madison Ave., Larchmont, NY 10538. TEL 914-834-3100. FAX 914-834-3688. E-mail: Liebert@pipeline.com. Ed. Michael G. Hanna. **Indexed:** Excerp.Med. (1993-). **Document type:** academic/scholarly publication.
—BLDSC (9138.635000); CASDDS; SWETS.
Description: Publishes original investigative and theoretical papers describing principles and technologies that can be applied to the development of new vaccines and the improvement of safety and efficacy of existing vaccines as well as important biological and immunologic principles relevant to host-vaccine interactions.

616.96   US   ISSN 0899-4056
QR189   CODEN: VMAVEA
VACCINES (YEAR). a. Cold Spring Harbor Laboratory Press, Publications Department, Box 100, Cold Spring Harbor, NY 11724. TEL 800-843-4388; 800-843-4388. FAX 516-349-1946. (reprint service avail.) **Document type:** monographic series.
—BLDSC (9138.650000).

VETERINARY IMMUNOLOGY AND IMMUNOPATHOLOGY; an international journal of comparative immunology. see *VETERINARY SCIENCE*

616.97   US   ISSN 0882-8245
CODEN: VIIMET
VIRAL IMMUNOLOGY. vol.2, 1989. q. $155 (foreign $195). Mary Ann Liebert, Inc. Publishers, 2 Madison Ave., Larchmont, NY 10538. TEL 914-834-3100. FAX 914-834-3688. E-mail: Liebert@pipeline.com. Ed. Constantin A. Bona. abstr.; charts; stat. (reprint service avail.) **Document type:** academic/scholarly publication.
—BLDSC (9237.876000); CASDDS; Faxon; Genuine Article; SWETS; UnCover.
Description: Covers human and animal viral immunology. Includes research and development of viral vaccines. Features regular mini-reviews of all relevant literature.
Refereed Serial

615.65   SZ   ISSN 0042-9007
CODEN: VOSAAD
VOX SANGUINIS; international journal of transfusion medicine. (Text in English) 1956. 8/yr. (2 vols./yr.). 334.80 SFr.($258) to individuals; institutions 558 SFr.($430) (effective 1996). (International Society of Blood Transfusion) S. Karger AG, Allschwilerstr. 10, P.O. Box, CH-4009 Basel, Switzerland. TEL 061-3061111. FAX 061-3061234. E-mail: Karger@Karger.ch. (Co-sponsor: League of Red Cross Societies) Ed. C.P. Engelfriet. adv.; bibl.; charts; illus.; index. circ. 2,900. (also avail. in microform) **Indexed:** Abstr.Hyg., Anim.Breed.Abstr., Biol.Abstr., Chem.Abstr., Curr.Adv.Ecol.Sci., Curr.Cont., Dairy Sci.Abstr., Dent.Ind., Excerp.Med., Helminthol.Abstr., Ind.Med., Ind.Vet., Nutr.Abstr., Risk Abstr., Trop.Dis.Bull., Vet.Bull. **Document type:** academic/scholarly publication.
—BLDSC (9258.700000); CASDDS; EMDOCS; Faxon; Genuine Article; SWETS; UnCover. **CCC.**
Refereed Serial

616.97   SZ   ISSN 0256-2308
QR180
YEAR IN IMMUNOLOGY. 1982. a. price varies. S. Karger AG, Allschwilerstr. 10, P.O. Box, CH-4009 Basel, Switzerland. TEL 061-3061111. FAX 061-3061234. E-mail: Karger@Karger.ch. Eds. J.M. Cruse, R.E. Lewis Jr. **Indexed:** Anim.Breed.Abstr., Biol.Abstr., Curr.Cont. **Document type:** academic/scholarly publication.
—BLDSC (9371.628470); Faxon. **CCC.**
Description: Provides updates on current developments of various aspects in immunologic research.
Refereed Serial

616.97   GW   ISSN 0343-8554
CODEN: ZELYDR
ZEITSCHRIFT FUER LYMPHOLOGIE; Ergebnisse aus Forschung, Klinik und Praxis. 1977. 2/yr. DM.117($88) (German Society of Lymphology) F.K. Schattauer Verlagsgesellschaft mbH, Lenzhalde 3, 70192 Stuttgart, Germany. TEL 0711-22987-0. FAX 0711-22987-50. Ed.Bd. adv.; bk.rev. circ. 1,200. **Document type:** academic/scholarly publication.
—BLDSC (5010.660000); Faxon; Genuine Article; SWETS. **CCC.**

616.97   CC
ZHONGGUO MEIJIE SHENGWUXUE JI KONGZHI ZAZHI. (Text in Chinese) bi-m. Zhonghua Yufang Yixuehui - China Preventive Medical Society, 16, Hepingli Zhongjie, Beijing 100013, People's Republic of China. TEL 4218457. Ed. Wang Chengxin.

616.97   CC
ZHONGGUO MIANYIXUE ZAZHI/CHINESE JOURNAL OF IMMUNOLOGY. (Text in Chinese) bi-m. Jilin Sheng Weisheng Ting - Jilin Provincial Bureau of Health, Fu 2, Dong Minzhu Dajie, Changchun, Jilin 130061, People's Republic of China. TEL 825027. Ed. Xie Guangwen.
Refereed Serial

616.97   CC   ISSN 0254-5101
CODEN: ZWMZDP
ZHONGHUA WEISHENGWUXUE HE MIANYIXUE ZAZHI/CHINESE JOURNAL OF MICROBIOLOGY AND IMMUNOLOGY. (Text in Chinese) 1981. bi-m. (Beijing Shengwu Zhipin Yanjiusuo - Beijing Institute of Biological Products) Chinese Medical Association - Zhonghua Yixuehui, P.O. Box 2258, 42 Dongsi Xidajie, Beijing 100710. TEL 1-550394. Ed. Li Hemin. **Indexed:** Biodet.Abstr., Excerp.Med. (1993-).
—BLDSC (3180.430500); CASDDS.

MEDICAL SCIENCES — Anaesthesiology

617.96   GW
CODEN: AINNDT
A I N S - ANAESTHESIOLOGIE INTENSIVMEDIZIN NOTFALLMEDIZIN SCHMERZTHERAPIE. (Text in German; summaries in English, German) 1966. 8/yr. DM.314 (members DM.251.20). (Deutsche Gesellschaft fuer Anaesthesiologie und Intensivmedizin) Georg Thieme Verlag, Ruedigerstr. 14, 70469 Stuttgart, Germany. TEL 0711-8931-0. FAX 0711-8931298. (Subscr. to: Postfach 104853, 70042 Stuttgart, Germany) Ed. O.H. Just. adv.; bk.rev; bibl.; charts; illus.; stat.; index. circ. 5,100. (reprint service avail. from UMI) **Indexed:** Curr.Cont., Excerp.Med., Ind.Med., INIS Atomind., Sci.Cit.Ind. **Document type:** academic/scholarly publication.
—BLDSC (0897.895000); CASDDS; SWETS; UMI. **CCC.**
Former titles: Anaesthesie - Intensivtherapie - Notfallmedizin - Schmerztherapie (ISSN 0939-2661); (until 1990): Anaesthesie - Intensivtherapie - Notfallmedizin (ISSN 0174-1837); (until 1980): Praktische Anaesthesie (ISSN 0302-7600); (until 1974): Zeitschrift fuer Praktische Anaesthesie, Wiederbelebung und Intensivtherapie (ISSN 0044-3387)

612   US   ISSN 1057-1590
A P S BULLETIN. 1991. bi-m. membership. American Pain Society, 5700 Old Orchard Rd., 1st Fl., Skokie, IL 60077-1057. TEL 708-966-5595. FAX 708-966-9418. Ed. Richard Chapman. adv.: page $575; 7 x 10; adv. contact: Michelle Ginocchio. bk.rev.; charts; illus.; stat. circ. 3,000. **Document type:** academic/scholarly publication, newsletter.
Description: Covers clinical and scientific research in pain.

617.96   US   ISSN 0363-471X
A S A REFRESHER COURSES IN ANESTHESIOLOGY. 1973. a. $23.95 to individuals (foreign $26.95); institutions $$29.95 (foreign $32.95) (effective 1996). (American Society of Anesthesiologists) Lippincott - Raven Publishers, 227 E. Washington Sq., Philadelphia, PA 19106. TEL 215-238-4200. Ed. Dr. Paul G. Barash. (also avail. in microform from UMI)
—BLDSC (7333.765000); UMI. **CCC.**

617.96   BE   ISSN 0001-5164
CODEN: AABEAJ
ACTA ANAESTHESIOLOGICA BELGICA. (Supplements avail.) vol.17, 1966. 4/yr. 2200 BEF (foreign 2500 BEF)(effective 1992). Association des Societes Scientifiques Medicales Belges - Vereiniging van de Belgische Medische Wetenschappelijke Genootschappen, Av. Circulaire 138A, B-1180 Brussels, Belgium. TEL 02-374-5158. Ed. Dr. G. Rolly. **Indexed:** Biol.Abstr., Chem.Abstr., Dent.Ind., Excerp.Med., Ind.Med.
—BLDSC (0593.600000); CASDDS; Faxon; SWETS; UnCover.

617.96   IT   ISSN 0374-4965
CODEN: AANIBO
ACTA ANAESTHESIOLOGICA ITALICA; rivista di anestesia e cure pre e post-operatorie. (Supplement avail. s-a.: Anaesthesia and Intensive Care in Italy) (Text in Italian; summaries in English) 1949. q. L.120000 includes supplements (effective 1995). Tipografia Editrice la Garangola, Via Montona 4, 35137 Padua, Italy. FAX 39-49-8751743. adv.; abstr.; illus.; index. (back issues avail.) **Indexed:** Biol.Abstr., Chem.Abstr., Excerp.Med., Ind.Med.
—BLDSC (0593.620000); CASDDS.
Formerly (until 1971): Acta Anaesthesiologica (ISSN 0001-5156)

MEDICAL SCIENCES — ANAESTHESIOLOGY

617.96 DK ISSN 0001-5172
CODEN: AANEAB
ACTA ANAESTHESIOLOGICA SCANDINAVICA. (Text and summaries in English) 1957. 8/yr. DKK 1100 (incl. supplements) (effective 1996). (Scandinavian Society of Anaesthesiology) Munksgaard International Publishers Ltd., Noerre Soegade, P.O. Box 2148, DK-1016 Copenhagen K, Denmark. TEL 33-127030. FAX 33-129387. Ed. Sven Erik Gisvold. adv.; bibl.; charts; illus.; stat.; index. circ. 3,500. (reprint service avail. from ISI) **Indexed:** ASCA, Biol.Abstr., Biotech.Abstr., Chem.Abstr., Curr.Adv.Ecol.Sci., Curr.Cont., Curr.Tit.Dent., Dent.Ind., Dok.Arbeitsmed., Excerp.Med., Ind.Med., Ind.Sci.Rev., INIS Atomind., Sci.Cit.Ind.
—BLDSC (0593.650000); ADONIS; CASDDS; Faxon; Genuine Article; SWETS; UnCover. **CCC.**
Refereed Serial

617.96 DK ISSN 0515-2720
CODEN: AASXAP
ACTA ANAESTHESIOLOGICA SCANDINAVICA. SUPPLEMENTUM. (Text in English) irreg. free with subscription to Acta Anaesthesiologica Scandinavica. (Scandinavian Society of Anaesthesiology) Munksgaard International Publishers Ltd., Journals Division, 35 Noerre Soegade, P.O. Box 2148, DK-1016 Copenhagen K, Denmark. TEL 45-33-12-70-30. FAX 45-33-12-93-87. **Indexed:** Biol.Abstr., Chem.Abstr., Curr.Adv.Ecol.Sci., Curr.Cont., Excerp.Med., Ind.Med., INIS Atomind.
—BLDSC (0593.651000); ADONIS; CASDDS; Faxon; SWETS; UnCover. **CCC.**

617.96 US ISSN 0737-6146
RD78.3
ADVANCES IN ANAESTHESIA. 1982. a. $71.95 (residents $40) (effective 1996). Mosby - Year Book, Inc. (Chicago) (Subsidiary of: Times Mirror Company), 200 N. LaSalle St., Chicago, IL 60601-1080. TEL 312-726-9733. FAX 312-726-6075. TELEX 206155. (Subscr. to: 11830 Westline Industrial Dr., St. Louis, MO 63146. TEL 800-325-4177) Ed. Carol L. Lake.
—BLDSC (0698.850000); Faxon; UnCover. **CCC.**
Description: Presents a collection of original, fully referenced articles from experts in the field.

617.96 US ISSN 1078-4500
RD78.3 CODEN: AJANF7
THE AMERICAN JOURNAL OF ANESTHESIOLOGY. 1973. bi-m. $124 to institutions outside the Americas; $103 to institutions in U.S (effective 1996). Excerpta Medica, Inc., Core Publishing Division (Subsidiary of: Reed Elsevier Medical group), 105 Raider Blvd., Belle Mead, NJ 08520. TEL 908-874-8550. FAX 908-874-0707. (Subscr. to: Box 3085, Princeton, NJ 08543-3085) Ed. Andrew Voynow. adv.; bk.rev.; charts; illus.; circ. 18,045 (controlled). (also avail. in microform from UMI) **Indexed:** Excerp.Med.
—BLDSC (0821.040000); EMDOCS; Faxon. **CCC.**
Former titles (until 1995): Anesthesiology Review (ISSN 0093-4437)

617.96 US ISSN 0270-5877
AMERICAN SOCIETY OF ANESTHESIOLOGISTS NEWSLETTER. 1938. m. $12 to non-members. American Society of Anesthesiologists, 520 N. Northwest Hwy., Park Ridge, IL 60068-2573. TEL 708-825-5586. FAX 708-825-1692. Ed. Dr. Erwin Lear. index. circ. 34,000. **Document type:** newsletter.
Description: Covers subjects of interest to anesthesiologists.

617.96 UK ISSN 0003-2409
CODEN: ANASAB
ANAESTHESIA (LONDON). 1945. m. £68 in Europe (rest of world $122) to individuals; institutions £175 in Europe (rest of world $315). (Association of Anaesthetists of Great Britain and Ireland) W.B. Saunders Co. Ltd. (Subsidiary of: Harcourt Brace & Company Ltd.), 24-28 Oval Rd., London NW1 7DX, England. TEL 0171-267-4466. FAX 0171-482-2293. TELEX 25775-ACPRES-G. (Subscr. to: Harcourt Brace & Company Ltd., Foots Cray High St., Sidcup, Kent DA14 5HP, England. TEL 0181-300-3322. FAX 0181-309-0807; US, Canadian, and Mexican subscr. to: W.B. Saunders Co., Journal Subscription Fulfillment, 6277 Sea Harbor Dr., Orlando, FL 32887-4800. TEL 800-654-2452. FAX 800-874-6418) Ed. M. Morgan. adv.; bk.rev.; bibl.; illus.; index. (back issues avail.; reprint service avail. from ISI) **Indexed:** AIM, Biol.Abstr., Biotech.Abstr., Chem.Abstr., Curr.Adv.Ecol.Sci., Curr.Cont., Excerp.Med., Ind.Med., Ind.Sci.Rev., Int.Nurs.Ind., Nutr.Abstr., Rev.Plant Path., Sci.Cit.Ind. **Document type:** academic/scholarly publication.
—BLDSC (0859.900000); CASDDS; Faxon; Genuine Article; SWETS; UMI; UnCover. **CCC.**
Description: Covers practical techniques of general and local anaesthesia, pre- and postoperative management, resuscitation and intensive care, and acute and chronic pain therapy.

617.96 AT ISSN 0310-057X
ANAESTHESIA AND INTENSIVE CARE. 1972. bi-m. $144 (foreign $244) (effective 1996). Australian Society of Anaesthetists, P.O. Box 600, Edgecliff, N.S.W. 2027, Australia. TEL 61-2-327-4022. FAX 61-2-327-7666. Ed. J. Roberts. adv.; bk.rev.; bibl.; charts; illus.; index. circ. 3,800. (also avail. in microfiche from UMI; back issues avail.) **Indexed:** Biol.Abstr., CINAHL, Curr.Adv.Ecol.Sci., Curr.Cont., Excerp.Med., Ind.Med., Nutr.Abstr. **Document type:** academic/scholarly publication.
—BLDSC (0859.901500); Faxon; Genuine Article; SWETS; UMI; UnCover.
Description: Presents original articles of scientific and clinical interest in the specialties of anaesthesia, intensive care, pain therapy and related disciplines.

617.96 IT
ANAESTHESIA AND INTENSIVE CARE IN ITALY. (Supplement to: Acta Anaesthesiologica Italica) vol.40, 1989. s-a. L.120000 includes Acta Anaesthesiologica Italica (effective 1995). Tipografia Editrice la Garangola, Via Montona, 4, 35137 Padua, Italy. FAX 39-49-8751743.

617.96 JO ISSN 0259-1162
CODEN: AESRE
ANAESTHESIA ESSAYS AND RESEARCHES. (Text in Arabic, English) 1985. a. $18. (Pan-Arabic Scientific Committee) Dar Ammar for Publication, P.O. Box 921691, Petra Market, Amman, Jordan. TEL 01-652437. TELEX 55545 JUST JO. Ed. Dr. M. Takrouri. adv.; bk.rev. circ. 3,000. **Indexed:** Excerp.Med. (until 1993). **Document type:** academic/scholarly publication.
Description: Specialized research journal published by the Arabic Scientific Committee on anaesthesia and intensive care.

617 GW ISSN 0170-5334
CODEN: ATIMDA
ANAESTHESIOLOGIE UND INTENSIVMEDIZIN. 1970. m. DM.96 (effective 1996). (Deutsche Gesellschaft fuer Anaesthesiologie und Intensivmedizin, Berufsverband Deutscher Anaesthesisten) Perimed - Spitta Medizinische Verlagsgesellschaft mbH, Ammonitenstr. 1, 72336 Balingen, Germany. TEL 07433-952-0. FAX 07433-952185. Ed. H.W. Opderbecke. circ. 13,000. **Indexed:** Biol.Abstr., Chem.Abstr. **Document type:** academic/scholarly publication.
—BLDSC (0897.905000); Genuine Article.
Formerly: Anaesthesiologische Informationen.

617.96 US ISSN 0171-1814
CODEN: ANIMD2
ANAESTHESIOLOGIE UND INTENSIVMEDIZIN/ANAESTHESIOLOGY AND INTENSIVE CARE MEDICINE. (Text in German; contributions in English and French) 1963. irreg., vol.212, 1989. price varies. Springer-Verlag, 175 Fifth Ave., New York, NY 10010. TEL 212-460-1500. FAX 212-473-6272. (Also: Berlin, Heidelberg, Tokyo and Vienna) (reprint service avail. from ISI) **Document type:** monographic series.
—BLDSC (0859.909000); CASDDS. **CCC.**
Formerly: Anaesthesiology and Resuscitation (ISSN 0066-1341)

617.96 GW ISSN 0323-4983
CODEN: ANREDN
ANAESTHESIOLOGIE UND REANIMATION; Zeitschrift fuer Anaesthesiologie, Intensivtherapie, Notfallmedizin und Schmerztherapie. (Text in English and German; summaries in English) 1976. bi-m. DM.150. (Gesellschaft fuer Anaesthesiologie und Intensivmedizin) Selecta Verlagsgesellschaft mbH, Postfach 4240, 65032 Wiesbaden, Germany. TEL 0611-17050. Ed. G. Benad. circ. 1,200. **Indexed:** Excerp.Med. **Document type:** academic/scholarly publication.
—BLDSC (0859.904700); CASDDS; SWETS. **CCC.**

617.96 GW ISSN 0003-2417
CODEN: ANATAE
DER ANAESTHESIST. (Supplement avail.: Regional-Anaesthesie) 1952. 12/yr. DM.478($347) (effective 1996). (Deutschen Gesellschaft fuer Anaesthesiologie und Intensivmedizin) Springer-Verlag, Heidelberger Platz 3, 14197 Berlin, Germany. TEL 030-8207-0. FAX 030-8214091. E-mail: orders@springer.de. (Subscr. in N. America to: Springer-Verlag New York, Inc., 44 Hartz Way, Secaucus, NJ 07096-2491. TEL 201-348-4033) (Co-sponsors: Oesterreichischen Gesellschaft fuer Anaesthesiologie, Reanimation und Intensivtherapie, Schweizerischen Gesellschaft fuer Anaesthesiologie und Reanimation) Ed. A. Doenicke. adv.; bk.rev.; abstr.; bibl.; charts; illus.; index. (also avail. in microform from UMI; back issues avail.; reprint service avail. from ISI) **Indexed:** Abstr.Health Care Manage.Stud., Biol.Abstr., Biotech.Abstr., Chem.Abstr., Curr.Cont., Dent.Ind., Excerp.Med., Ind.Med., Ind.Sci.Rev., INIS Atomind., Sci.Cit.Ind. **Document type:** academic/scholarly publication.
—BLDSC (0859.920000); ADONIS; CASDDS; Faxon; Genuine Article; SWETS; UMI. **CCC.**

ANAESTHETIC PHARMACOLOGY REVIEW. see *PHARMACY AND PHARMACOLOGY*

617.96 MX ISSN 1405-0056
ANESTESIA EN MEXICO. (Text in Spanish; summaries in English, Spanish) 1989. bi-m. $55. (Federacion Mexicana de Sociedades de Anestesiologia) Obsidiana Editores, S.A., Czda. de Tlalpan 2365, Col. Ciudad Jardin, 04370 Mexico DF, Mexico. TEL 6899133. FAX 6896545. Ed. Dr. Orlando Tamariz; Pub. Jorge Godoy. circ. 3,000. **Document type:** academic/scholarly publication.
Description: Contains original articles, research reports, review articles, clinical cases, and notices related to anesthesiology.

617.96 IT ISSN 0392-5854
ANESTESISTA. 1978. bi-m. Associazione Anestesisti Rianimatori Ospedalieri Italiani, Via Poliziano 69, 00184 Rome, Italy. Ed. Alessandro Pesce.

MEDICAL SCIENCES — ANAESTHESIOLOGY

617   RU   ISSN 0201-7563
CODEN: AREAD8
ANESTEZIOLOGIYA I REANIMATOLOGIYA/ANESTHESIOLOGY AND REANIMATOLOGY. 1956. bi-m. $89 (effective 1996). (Nauchnoe Obshchestvo Anesteziologov i Reanimatologov) Izdatel'stvo Meditsina, Petroverigskii pereulok 6-8, 101000 Moscow, Russia. (Dist. by: Mezhdunarodnaya Kniga, B. Yakimanka 39, 117049 Moscow, Russia. TEL 7-095-2384600. FAX 7-095-2384634) (Co-sponsor: Ministerstvo Zdravookhraneniya) Dir. R.N. Lebedeva. adv. contact: O.V. Vlasova. bk.rev.; index. **Indexed:** Biol.Abstr., Chem.Abstr., Excerp.Med., Ind.Med.
—BLDSC (0006.650000); CASDDS.
Formerly (until 1977): Eksperimental'naya Khirurgiya i Anesteziologiya (ISSN 0013-3329)
Description: Covers general anesthesiology in surgery, intensive treatment and resuscitation. Presents the progressive methods used in anesthesiology and reanimatology in obstetrics, gynecology, pediatrics, stomatology, otolaryngology, and surgery in the outpatient practice.

617.96   US   ISSN 0003-2999
RD81.A1   CODEN: AACRAT
ANESTHESIA AND ANALGESIA. (Supplement avail.) 1922. m. $157 to individuals; institutions foreign $267) (effective 1995). (International Anesthesia Research Society) Williams & Wilkins, 428 E. Preston St., Baltimore, MD 21202. TEL 410-528-4000; 800-638-6423. FAX 410-528-4312. (Co-sponsor: Society of Cardiovascular Anesthesiologists) Ed. Dr. Ronald D. Miller. adv.; bk.rev.; bibl.; charts; illus.; index. circ. 22,700. (also avail. in microfilm from PMC) **Indexed:** Abstr.Health Care Manage.Stud., AIM, Biol.Abstr., Biotech.Abstr., C.I.S Abstract, Chem.Abstr., CINAHL, Curr.Adv.Ecol.Sci., Curr.Cont., Dent.Abstr., Dent.Ind., Excerp.Med., Ind.Med., Ind.Sci.Rev., Sci.Cit.Ind. **Document type:** academic/scholarly publication.
●Also available online. Vendor(s): Ovid Technologies.
—BLDSC (0900.500000); CASDDS; Faxon; Genuine Article; SWETS; UMI; UnCover. **CCC.**
Formerly: Current Researches in Anesthesia and Analgesia.
Description: Publishes original research and clinical articles, providing researchers, practicing physicians, and allied medical personnel in anesthesiology and related fields with a wealth of information to keep them up to date with the latest issues and advances in the field.
Refereed Serial

617.96   US   ISSN 1057-4123
ANESTHESIA COMPUTERFILE. m. $225 to individuals (foreign $290); institutions $245 (foreign $310) (effective 1994). (Dannemiller Memorial Educational Foundation) W.B. Saunders Co. (Subsidiary of: Harcourt Brace & Company), Curtis Center, 3rd Fl., Independence Sq. W., Philadelphia, PA 19106-3399. TEL 215-238-7800. FAX 215-238-6445. (Subscr. to: Periodicals Fulfillment, W.B. Saunders Co., 6277 Sea Harbor Dr., 4th Fl., Orlando, FL 32891-4800. TEL 800-654-2452. FAX 800-874-6418) Ed. Dr. Vincent Collins. (diskette format; also avail. in looseleaf format (ISSN 0740-1914)) **Document type:** abstracting/indexing.
Description: Reviews articles on research and development in anesthesiology from more than 750 medical journals.

617.96   US   ISSN 0740-1914
ANESTHESIA FILE NOTEBOOK. m. $225 to individuals (foreign $290); institutions $245 (foreign $310) (includes binder) (effective 1994). (Dannemiller Memorial Educational Foundation) W.B. Saunders Co. (Subsidiary of: Harcourt Brace & Company), Curtis Center, 3rd Fl., Independence Sq. W., Philadelphia, PA 19106-3399. TEL 215-238-7800. FAX 215-238-6445. (Subscr. to: Periodicals Fulfillment, W.B. Saunders Co., 6277 Sea Harbor Dr., 4th Fl., Orlando, FL 32891-4800. TEL 800-654-2452. FAX 800-874-6418) Ed. Dr. Vincent Collins. (looseleaf format; also avail. in diskette format (ISSN 1057-4123)) **Document type:** abstracting/indexing.
Description: Reviews articles on research and developments in anesthesiology from more than 750 medical journals.

617.96   US   ISSN 1050-8775
KF2910.A53
ANESTHESIA MALPRACTICE PROTECTOR. 1989. m. $219. American Health Consultants, Inc., Six Piedmont Center, Ste. 400, Atlanta, GA 30305. TEL 800-688-2421. FAX 800-284-3291. Ed. Mark Lewyn. index. circ. 680. **Document type:** newsletter.
Incorporates (in 1991): Anesthesia Alert.

ANESTHESIA PROGRESS; a journal for pain and anxiety control. see *MEDICAL SCIENCES — Dentistry*

617.96   FR   ISSN 0996-8296
ANESTHESIE - REANIMATION PRATIQUE. 1989. m. (10/yr.). 350 F. L.E.N. Medical, 48 bis, av. Kleber, 75116 Paris, France. TEL 47-55-06-06. FAX 47-55-69-41. TELEX 640 748. Ed. Dr. Francois Gaudillat. **Document type:** newspaper.

617.96   US   ISSN 0003-3022
CODEN: ANESAV
ANESTHESIOLOGY. 1940. m. $130 to individuals (foreign $205); institutions $220 (foreign $295) (effective 1996). (American Society of Anesthesiologists) Lippincott - Raven Publishers, 227 E. Washington Sq., Philadelphia, PA 19106. TEL 215-238-4200. Ed. Dr. Lawrence J. Saidman. adv.; bk.rev.; illus.; cum.index. circ. 39,168. (also avail. in microform from UMI; reprint service avail. from UMI) **Indexed:** AIM, Biol.Abstr., Biotech.Abstr., Chem.Abstr., CINAHL, Curr.Adv.Ecol.Sci., Curr.Cont., Excerp.Med., Ind.Med., Ind.Sci.Rev., Ind.Vet., INIS Atomind., Int.Nurs.Ind., Med.& Surg.Dermat., Pig News & Info., Risk Abstr., Sci.Cit.Ind., SSCI, Vet.Bull.
●Also available online. Vendor(s): Ovid Technologies.
—BLDSC (0900.600000); CASDDS; Faxon; Genuine Article; SWETS; UMI; UnCover. **CCC.**
Refereed Serial

617.96   US   ISSN 0889-8537
CODEN: CLIAD8
ANESTHESIOLOGY CLINICS OF NORTH AMERICA. 1987. q. $120 (foreign $155) (effective 1996). W.B. Saunders Co. (Subsidiary of: Harcourt Brace & Company), The Curtis Center, 3rd Fl., Independence Sq. W., Philadelphia, PA 19106-3399. TEL 215-238-7800. FAX 215-238-6445. (Subscr. to: W.B. Saunders Co., Periodicals Fulfillment, 6277 Sea Harbor Dr., 4th Fl., Orlando, FL 32887-4800. TEL 800-654-2452. FAX 800-874-6418) Ed. Dr. Jonathan L. Benumof. **Document type:** academic/scholarly publication.
—BLDSC (0900.725000); CASDDS; Genuine Article; SWETS; UMI; UnCover. **CCC.**
Supersedes in part (in 1986): Clinics in Anaesthesiology (ISSN 0261-9881)
Description: Each issue treats a topic on the administration of anesthesia.

617.96 346   US   ISSN 0738-1018
KF2910.A53
ANESTHESIOLOGY MALPRACTICE REPORTER. 1981-199? m. $128. Public Reporting Services, Inc., 332 Bleecker St., Ste. 424, New York, NY 10014. TEL 212-989-8303. Ed. Joan Fabricant; Pub. Joan Fabricant.

617.96   US   ISSN 0747-4679
ANESTHESIOLOGY NEWS. 1975. m. $28. McMahon Publishing Co., 148 W. 24th St., 8th Fl., New York, NY 10011. TEL 212-620-4600. FAX 212-620-5928. Ed. Kenneth J. Zeserson. adv.: B&W page $2100, color page $3600; bleed 8 1/4 x 11 1/4. circ. 17,500. (tabloid format)
—BLDSC (0900.750000).
Formerly (until 1979?): Anesthesia Staff News.

617.96   US   ISSN 1063-8571
ANESTHESIOLOGY RESIDENT. 1992. bi-m. $44. Slack, Inc., 6900 Grove Rd., Thorofare, NJ 08086. TEL 609-848-1000. FAX 609-853-5991. adv.: B&W page $1325, color page $2675; trim 8 1/8 x 10 7/8. circ. 8,200.

617.96   FR   ISSN 0750-7658
CODEN: AFAREO
ANNALES FRANCAISES D'ANESTHESIE ET DE REANIMATION. 1939. 7/yr. $254 (effective 1996). (Societe Francaise d'Anesthesie, d'Analgesie et de Reanimation) Masson - Periodiques, Villa Laromiguiere, 75005 Paris, France. TEL 1-40-46-62-00. FAX 1-40-46-62-01. Ed. J.C. Otteni. adv.; bk.abstr.; abstr.; charts; illus. circ. 5,500. (reprint service avail. from ISI) **Indexed:** Biol.Abstr., Biotech.Abstr., Chem.Abstr., Dent.Ind., Excerp.Med., Ind.Med., Nutr.Abstr. **Document type:** academic/scholarly publication.
—BLDSC (0973.800000); CASDDS; Faxon; Genuine Article; SWETS; UMI. **CCC.**
Formerly: Anesthesie, Analgesie, Reanimation (ISSN 0003-3014)

617.96 615.804   II   ISSN 0301-0368
CODEN: AAARDM
ASIAN ARCHIVES OF ANAESTHESIOLOGY AND RESUSCITATION. (Text in English) 1971. q. $100. National Association of Critical Care Medicine, 147, North Ave., New Delhi 110001, India. TEL 3014755. Ed. Dr. N.P. Singh. adv.; bk.rev.; bibl.; charts; illus. circ. 2,000. (back issues avail.) **Indexed:** Biol.Abstr., Chem.Abstr.
—CASDDS; UnCover.
Formerly (1973): Archives of Anaesthesiology and Resuscitation.

617.96   US   ISSN 0271-1265
AUDIO-DIGEST ANESTHESIOLOGY. 1958. s-m. $168. Audio-Digest Foundation (Subsidiary of: California Medical Association), 1577 E. Chevy Chase Dr., Glendale, CA 91206. TEL 213-245-8505. FAX 818-240-7379. (audio cassette)
Refereed Serial

617.96   UK   CODEN: BJANAD
B J A: INTERNATIONAL JOURNAL OF ANAESTHESIA. 1923. m. £149($223) Professional & Scientific Publications, B.M.A. House, Tavistock Sq., London WC1H 9JR, England. TEL 0171-383-4499. FAX 0171-383-6662. (N. American subscr. to: Box 580, Franklin, MA 02038. TEL 800-2-FON-BMJ. FAX 800-2-FAX-BMJ) Ed. G. Smith. adv.; bk.rev.; bibl.; charts; illus.; index. (also avail. in microfilm from UMI; reprint service avail. from SWZ) **Indexed:** Biol.Abstr., Biotech.Abstr., Chem.Abstr., Curr.Adv.Ecol.Sci., Curr.Cont., Dairy Sci.Abstr., Dent.Ind., Dok.Arbeitsmed., Excerp.Med., Helminthol.Abstr., Ind.Med., Ind.Sci.Rev., Ind.Vet., Nutr.Abstr., Risk Abstr., Sci.Cit.Ind., Small Anim.Abstr., Vet.Bull. **Document type:** academic/scholarly publication.
—BLDSC (2303.900000); CASDDS; Faxon; Genuine Article; SWETS; UMI; UnCover.
Formerly: British Journal of Anaesthesia (ISSN 0007-0912)
Refereed Serial

617.96   UK   ISSN 0950-3501
CODEN: CLIAD8
BAILLIERE'S CLINICAL ANAESTHESIOLOGY. 1986. q. £70 to individuals; institutions £80. Bailliere Tindall - W.B. Saunders Co. Ltd. (Subsidiary of: Harcourt Brace & Company Ltd.), 24-28 Oval Rd., London NW1 7DX, England. TEL 0171-267-4466. FAX 0171-482-2293. TELEX 25775 ACPRES G. (Subscr. to: Journals Subscriptions Fulfillment, Foots Cray High St., Sidcup, Kent DA14 5HP, England. TEL 0181-300-3322. FAX 0181-309-0807; Subscr. in N. America to: W.B. Saunders Co., Journal Subscription Fulfillment, 6277 Sea Harbor Dr., 4th Fl., Orlando, FL 32887-4800. TEL 800-874-6418) (also avail. in microform from UMI) **Indexed:** Abstr.Health Care Manage.Stud., Curr.Adv.Ecol.Sci., Excerp.Med. **Document type:** academic/scholarly publication.
—BLDSC (1856.717000); CASDDS; Genuine Article; SWETS; UMI. **CCC.**
Supersedes in part (in 1986): Clinics in Anaesthesiology (ISSN 0261-9881)
Refereed Serial

617.96 610.73   US
BREATHLINE.* bi-m. membership. Uniformed Services Academy of Family Physicians, 4211 Dover Rd., Richmond, VA 23221-3267. TEL 804-379-5516. bk.rev.

MEDICAL SCIENCES — ANAESTHESIOLOGY

617.96 US
BRISTOL-MYERS - SQUIBB SYMPOSIUM ON PAIN RESEARCH SERIES. 1991. irreg., latest 1993. price varies. Raven Press (Subsidiary of: Wolters Kluwer N.V.), 1185 Ave. of the Americas, New York, NY 10036. TEL 212-930-9500. FAX 212-869-3495.
Document type: proceedings.

BUNBEN TO MASUI/JOURNAL OF OBSTETRICS AND ANESTHESIA. see *MEDICAL SCIENCES — Obstetrics And Gynecology*

617.96 610.73 US ISSN 1048-2687
 CODEN: CCFAFY
C R N A: THE CLINICAL FORUM FOR NURSE ANESTHETISTS. 1990. q. $92 (foreign $119) (effective 1996). W.B. Saunders Co. (Subsidiary of: Harcourt Brace & Company), Curtis Center, 3rd Fl., Independence Sq. W., Philadelphia, PA 19106-3399. TEL 215-238-7800. FAX 215-238-6445. (Subscr. to: Periodicals Fulfillment, W.B. Saunders Co., 6277 Sea Harbor Dr., 4th Fl., Orlando, FL 32891-4800. TEL 800-654-2452. FAX 800-874-6418) Ed. Mary Jeanette Mannino; Pub. Joan W. Blumberg. adv.: B&W page $625, color page $1575; 7 x 10. abstr. circ. 1,437. (back issues avail.) Indexed: CINAHL. Document type: academic/scholarly publication.
—BLDSC (3487.494700). **CCC.**
Description: Provides nurse anesthetists with in-depth updates of clinical advances, as well as with abstracts, including commentary of the recent literature in anesthesiology.

617.96 FR ISSN 0007-9685
 CODEN: CAANBU
CAHIERS D'ANESTHESIOLOGIE. 1953. 6/yr. 600 F. (foreign 835 F.) (effective 1996). Arnette Blackwell, 1 rue de Lille, 75007 Paris, France. TEL 33-1-44-86-07-70. FAX 33-1-44-86-07-66. Ed. St. Maurice. adv.; bk.rev.; index. circ. 3,005. Indexed: Biol.Abstr., Excerp.Med., Ind.Med.
—BLDSC (2948.620000); CASDDS; Faxon; SWETS; UMI. **CCC.**

617.96 CN ISSN 0832-610X
 CODEN: CJOAEP
CANADIAN JOURNAL OF ANAESTHESIA/JOURNAL CANADIEN D'ANESTHESIE. (Text in English and French) 1954. 12/yr. Can.$156 to individuals; institutions $204. Canadian Anaesthetists' Society - Societe Canadienne des Anesthesistes, 1 Eglinton Ave., E., Ste. 208, Toronto, ON M4P 3A1, Canada. TEL 416-480-0602. FAX 416-480-0320. Ed. Dr. David R. Bevan. adv. contact: Neil Hutton. bk.rev.; bibl.; charts; illus.; index; circ. 5,040 (paid). (also avail. in microform from UMI; back issues avail; reprint service avail. from UMI) Indexed: Biol.Abstr., Chem.Abstr., CINAHL, Curr.Adv.Ecol.Sci., Curr.Cont., Dent.Ind., Excerp.Med., Ind.Med., Ind.Sci.Rev., INIS Atomind., Kidney, Sci.Cit.Ind. Document type: academic/scholarly publication.
—BLDSC (3028.300000); CASDDS; Faxon; Genuine Article; SWETS; UMI; UnCover. **CCC.**
Formerly (until 1986): Canadian Anaesthetists' Society. Journal (ISSN 0008-2856)

CLINICAL JOURNAL OF PAIN. see *MEDICAL SCIENCES — Psychiatry And Neurology*

617.96 SP
CLINICAS DE ANESTESIOLOGIA DE NORTEAMERICA. 1991. 4/yr. 14416 ptas. (effective 1990). Interamericana de Espana, S.A., Manuel Ferrero, 13, 28036 Madrid, Spain. TEL 315-0340. FAX 733-6627.

617.96 UK ISSN 0953-7112
 CODEN: CCCAEI
CURRENT ANAESTHESIA AND CRITICAL CARE. 1989. q. £77($128) to individuals; institutions £144 ($237) (effective 1995). Churchill Livingstone Journals (Subsidiary of: Pearson Professional), Robert Stevenson House, 1-3 Baxter's Pl., Leith Walk, Edinburgh EH1 3AF, Scotland. TEL 0131-556-2424. FAX 0131-459-1177. (Subscr. to: Longman Group, Journals Subscr. Dept, P.O. Box 77, Fourth Ave., Harlow, Essex CM19 5AA, England. TEL 01279-623760; U.S. subscr. to: Churchill Livingstone, 650 Ave. of the Americas, New York, NY 10011. TEL 212-206-5000) Ed. B.J. Pollard. adv. contact: David Dunnachie. circ. 1,100. Document type: academic/scholarly publication.
—BLDSC (3494.128000). **CCC.**
Description: Reviews articles of interest to anesthesiologists.

CURRENT OPINION IN ANAESTHESIOLOGY. see *MEDICAL SCIENCES — Abstracting, Bibliographies, Statistics*

617.96 NE ISSN 0924-5294
 CODEN: DCCAET
DEVELOPMENTS IN CRITICAL CARE MEDICINE AND ANESTHESIOLOGY. (Text in English) 1982. irreg., vol.28, 1993. price varies. Kluwer Academic Publishers, Postbus 17, 3300 AA Dordrecht, Netherlands. TEL 31-78-392392. FAX 31-78-392254. TELEX 29245 KAPG NL. (Dist. by: Kluwer Academic Publishers Group, P.O. Box 322, 3300 AH Dordrecht, Netherlands. TEL 31-78-392292. FAX 31-78-546474; N. America dist. addr.: Box 358, Accord Sta., Hingham, MA 02018-0358. TEL 617-871-6600. FAX 617-871-6528) Document type: monographic series.
—BLDSC (3579.070000).
Refereed Serial

617.96 SP ISSN 0071-2671
EUROPEAN CONGRESS OF ANAESTHESIOLOGY. PROCEEDINGS. (Proceedings published in host countries) 1962. quadrennial, 4th, Madrid, 1974. (World Federation of Societies of Anaesthesiologists) European Congress of Anaesthesiology, c/o Professor Arias, Arapiles 16, Madrid, Spain. Document type: proceedings.

617.96 UK ISSN 0265-0215
 CODEN: EJANEG
EUROPEAN JOURNAL OF ANAESTHESIOLOGY. (Supplement avail. (ISSN 0952-1941)) 1984. bi-m. £317($510) (effective 1996). (European Academy of Anaesthesiology) Blackwell Science Ltd., Osney Mead, Oxford OX2 0EL, England. TEL 01865-206206. FAX 01865-206219. TELEX 83355 MEDBOK G. Ed. M.D. Vickers. adv.; bk.rev.; abstr.; bibl.; illus.; index. circ. 750. (also avail. in microform from UMI; back issues avail.) Indexed: Curr.Adv.Ecol.Sci., Excerp.Med. Document type: academic/scholarly publication.
—BLDSC (3829.722200); CASDDS; Faxon; Genuine Article; SWETS; UMI; UnCover. **CCC.**
Refereed Serial

617.96 UK ISSN 0952-1941
 CODEN: EJSUEP
EUROPEAN JOURNAL OF ANAESTHESIOLOGY. SUPPLEMENT. 1987. irreg. price varies. (European Academy of Anaesthesiology) Blackwell Science Ltd., Osney Mead, Oxford OX2 0EL, England. TEL 01865-240201. FAX 01865-721205. TELEX 83355 MEDBOK G. Indexed: Excerp.Med., Ind.Med. Document type: academic/scholarly publication, monographic series.
—BLDSC (3829.722202).

EUROPEAN JOURNAL OF PAIN. see *MEDICAL SCIENCES*

617.96 IT ISSN 0391-5670
GIORNALE DI ANESTESIA STOMATOLOGICA. 1972? q. L.82000($99) (effective 1994). (Associazione Italiana di Anestesia Odontostomatologica) Masson S.p.A., Divisione Periodici, Via Statuto 2-4, 20121 Milan, Italy. TEL 02-67637-1. FAX 02-6367211. Ed. Giuseppe Saba. adv.: B&W page L.1370000, color page L.2150000; 193 x 265. circ. 1,000. Document type: academic/scholarly publication.
—BLDSC (4176.855000).

617.96 II ISSN 0019-5049
INDIAN JOURNAL OF ANAESTHESIA.* (Text in English) 1953. q. $35. Indian Society of Anaesthetists, c/o Dr. D. Das Gupta, Department of Anaesthesia, K.E.M. Hospital, Parel, Bombay, India. adv.; bk.rev.; abstr.; bibl.; charts; illus.; stat.; index. circ. 2,000. (tabloid format) Indexed: Biol.Abstr.
—Faxon.

617.96 US ISSN 0020-5907
RD81.A1 CODEN: IACLAV
INTERNATIONAL ANESTHESIOLOGY CLINICS. 1963. q. $135 to individuals (foreign $120); institutions $150 (foreign $194); residents $99 (foreign $120) (effective Oct. 1994). Little, Brown and Company, Medical Journals, 34 Beacon St., Boston, MA 02108. TEL 617-859-5500. FAX 617-859-0629. Ed. Dr. Thomas W. Feeley. charts; illus.; stat.; index. circ. 3,000. (also avail. in microform from UMI; reprint service avail. from UMI; back issues avail.) Indexed: Biol.Abstr., CINAHL, Curr.Cont., Dent.Ind., Excerp.Med., Ind.Med., Sci.Cit.Ind.
—BLDSC (4535.750000); CASDDS; EMDOCS; Faxon; Genuine Article; SWETS; UMI; UnCover. **CCC.**
Description: Focuses on a single topic in each issue. Presents discussions of physiology, pharmacology of the agents, clinical application of techniques, and causes and treatments of complications.

617.96 610 NE ISSN 0167-9945
 CODEN: IJMCEJ
INTERNATIONAL JOURNAL OF CLINICAL MONITORING AND COMPUTING. (Text and summaries in English) 1984. q. fl.413 to institutions; $264 to institutions in U.S. (effective 1996). (European Society for Computing and Technology in Anaesthesia and Intensive Care) Kluwer Academic Publishers, Postbus 17, 3300 AA Dordrecht, Netherlands. TEL 31-78-392392. FAX 31-78-392254. TELEX 29245 KAPG NL. E-mail: SERVICES@WKAP.NL. (Dist. by: Kluwer Academic Publishers Group, P.O. Box 322, 3300 AH Dordrecht, Netherlands. TEL 31-78-392392. FAX 31-78-546474; N. America dist. addr.: Box 358, Accord Sta., Hingham, MA 02018-0358. TEL 617-871-6600. FAX 617-871-6528) Ed. Likka Kalli. adv.; bk.rev. (also avail. in microform from UMI; reprint service avail. from SWZ) Indexed: ASCA, Curr.Cont., Excerp.Med., Ind.Med., INSPEC (1987-). Document type: academic/scholarly publication.
—BLDSC (4542.170300); Faxon; Genuine Article; SWETS; UMI; UnCover. **CCC.**
Description: Publishes original articles and reviews on topics relating to clinical and experimental monitoring and the use of computers in patient care.
Refereed Serial

INTERNATIONAL JOURNAL OF OBSTETRIC ANESTHESIA. see *MEDICAL SCIENCES — Obstetrics And Gynecology*

617.96 GW ISSN 0941-5424
JAHRBUCH DER ANAESTHESIOLOGIE UND INTENSIVMEDIZIN. (Text in German; summaries in English, German) 1991. a. DM.126.40. Biermann Verlag GmbH, Englerstr. 18, 53909 Zuelpich, Germany. TEL 02252-9410-0. FAX 02252-941015. Ed. P. Lawin. (back issues avail.) Document type: academic/scholarly publication.

617.96 JA ISSN 0021-4892
 CODEN: MASUAC
JAPANESE JOURNAL OF ANESTHESIOLOGY/MASUI. (Text in Japanese; summaries in English) 1952. q. (Japan Society of Anesthesiology - Nippon Masui Gakkai) Springer-Verlag Tokyo, 3-13, Hongo 3-chome, Bunkyo-ku, Tokyo 113, Japan. TEL 03-3812-0617. FAX 03-3812-4699. (Subscr. to: Springer-Verlag, Heidelberger Platz3, D-1000 Berlin 33, Germany. TEL 030-8207-1; N. American subscr. to: Springer-Verlag New York Inc., Service Center Secaucus, 44 Hartz Way, Secaucus, NJ 07096-2491. TEL 201-348-4033) Ed. Y. Shimada. (also avail. in microform from UMI) Indexed: Dent.Ind., Excerp.Med., Ind.Med., INIS Atomind. Document type: academic/scholarly publication.
—BLDSC (4650.810000); EMDOCS.
Description: Contains original articles, clinical reports, short communications and announcements.

617.96 GW ISSN 0941-4223
▼**JOURNAL FUER ANAESTHESIE UND INTENSIVBEHANDLUNG.** (Text and summaries in English, German) 1994. q. DM.30($20) Pabst Science Publishers, Am Eichengrund 28, 49525 Lengerich, Germany. TEL 05484-308. FAX 05484-550. Ed. Wolfgang Pabst. adv.; bk.rev. Document type: academic/scholarly publication.

MEDICAL SCIENCES — ANAESTHESIOLOGY

617.96   GW
JOURNAL OF ANESTHESIA. (Text in English) q. DM.260. Springer-Verlag, Heidelberger Platz 3, 14197 Berlin, Germany. TEL 030-8207-0. FAX 030-8214091. E-mail: orders@springer.de. (Subscr. in N. America to: Springer-Verlag New York, Inc., 44 Hartz Way, Secaucus, NJ 07096-2491. TEL 201-348-4033. FAX 201-348-4505) **Document type:** academic/scholarly publication.

617.96   JA   ISSN 0913-8668
                            CODEN: JANEEC
JOURNAL OF ANESTHESIA. (Text in English) 1987. q. DM.260($188) (effective 1996). (Japan Society of Anesthesiology - Nihon Masui Gakkai) Springer-Verlag Tokyo, 3-13 Hongo, 3-chome, Bunkyo-ku, Tokyo 113, Japan, 113 Tokyo, Japan. TEL 03-3812-0617. FAX 03-3812-4699. (Subscr. in N. America to: Springer-Verlag New York Inc., Service Center Secaucus, 44 Hartz Way, Secaucus, NJ 07096-2491. TEL 201-348-4033) **Indexed:** Excerp.Med. (1993-). **Document type:** academic/scholarly publication.
—BLDSC (4935.360000).

JOURNAL OF CARDIOTHORACIC AND VASCULAR ANESTHESIA. see *MEDICAL SCIENCES — Cardiovascular Diseases*

617.96   US   ISSN 0952-8180
                            CODEN: JCLBE7
JOURNAL OF CLINICAL ANESTHESIA; an international journal of anesthesia practice. 1988. 8/yr. $255 to institutions (effective 1996). Butterworth - Heinemann, Part of the Reed Elsevier group, 313 Washington St., Newton, MA 02158. TEL 617-928-2500; 800-366-2665. FAX 617-928-2610. TELEX 880052. (Subscr. to: Elsevier Science Inc., Box 882, Madison Sq. Sta., New York, NY 10159-0882. TEL 212-989-5800. FAX 212-633-3990) Ed. Dr. Richard J. Kitz. adv.; bk.rev.; charts; illus.; index. (also avail. in microform from UMI; back issues avail.) **Document type:** academic/scholarly publication.
—BLDSC (4958.381070); Genuine Article; SWETS; UMI. **CCC.**
    Description: Serves as a forum for practical clinical information for the anesthesiologist from the resident level onward.
    Refereed Serial

JOURNAL OF CLINICAL MONITORING. see *MEDICAL SCIENCES*

617.96 617   US   ISSN 0898-4921
                            CODEN: JNANEV
JOURNAL OF NEUROSURGICAL ANESTHESIOLOGY. 1989. q. $125 to individuals (foreign $190); institutions $205 (foreign $232) (effective 1996); newsstand price: $59. (Society for Neurosurgical Anesthesiology and Critical Care) Lippincott - Raven Publishers, 276 E. Washington Sq., Philadelphia, PA 19106. TEL 215-238-4200. Ed. James E. Cottrell. adv. contact: Phyllis Noyes. charts; illus. circ. 2,000. **Indexed:** Excerp.Med., Ind.Med. (1992-). **Document type:** academic/scholarly publication.
—BLDSC (5022.150000); Faxon; Genuine Article; SWETS; UMI. **CCC.**
    Description: Features articles on new drugs, equipment, and procedures, and presents reports of major clinical and laboratory research projects.
    Refereed Serial

615 610.73   US   ISSN 0885-3924
RB127
JOURNAL OF PAIN AND SYMPTOM MANAGEMENT. (Supplement avail.) 1982. m. $345 to institutions (effective 1996). (University of Wisconsin-Madison, Department of Anesthesiology) Elsevier Science Inc., 655 Ave. of the Americas, New York, NY 10010. TEL 212-989-5800. FAX 212-633-3990. TELEX 420643 AEP UI. (Subscr. to: Box 882, Madison Sq. Sta., New York, NY 10159-0882) Eds. George Heidrich, Russell K. Portenoy. adv.; bk.rev.; index. circ. 3,200. (also avail. in microform from UMI; back issues avail.) **Indexed:** Behav.Med.Abstr., Child Devel.Abstr., CINAHL, Curr.Adv.Ecol.Sci., Excerp.Med, Int.Nurs.Ind., Nurs.Abstr., Psychol.Abstr. (1986-). **Document type:** academic/scholarly publication.
—BLDSC (5027.790000); Genuine Article; SWETS; UnCover. **CCC.**
    Formerly (until 1985): P R N Forum (ISSN 0743-345X)
    Description: Provides the professional with the results of important new research on pain and its clinical management.
    Refereed Serial

JOURNAL OF POST ANESTHESIA NURSING. see *MEDICAL SCIENCES — Nurses And Nursing*

617.96   CC
LINCHUANG MAZUIXUE ZAZHI/JOURNAL OF CLINICAL ANESTHESIOLOGY. (Text in Chinese, abstracts in English) 1985. bi-m. Y15. Zhonghua Yixuehui, Nanjing Fenhui - Chinese Society of Medical Sciences, Nanjing Chapter, 291 Zhongshan Lu, Nanjing, Jiangsu 210008, People's Republic of China. TEL 303848. Ed. Li Dexin. **Document type:** academic/scholarly publication.

617.96   JA   ISSN 0385-1664
MASUI TO SOSEI/ANESTHESIA AND RESUSCITATION. (Text in Japanese) 1965. q. Hiroshima Masui Igakkai, c/o Hiroshima University, School of Medicine, Dept. of Anesthesiology & Critical Care Medicine, Minami-ku, Hiroshima 734, Japan. **Document type:** academic/scholarly publication.
    Formerly (until 1970): Hiroshima Masui Igakkai Zasshi - Hiroshima Journal of Anesthesia (ISSN 0440-8764)

617.96   IT   ISSN 0375-9393
                            CODEN: MIANAP
MINERVA ANESTESIOLOGICA. Variant title: Giornale Italiano di Anestesia e di Analgesia. (Text in Italian; summaries in English, Italian) 1935. m. $110 to individuals; institutions $150 (effective 1995). (Societa Italiana di Anestesia, Analgesia, Rianimazione e Terapia Intensiva) Edizioni Minerva Medica, Corso Bramante 83-85, 10126 Turin, Italy. TEL 39-11-678282. FAX 39-11-3121736. Ed. R. Pattono; Pub. Alberto Oliaro. adv.: B&W page $1300, color page $2200; trim 190 x 270; adv. contact: F. Filippo. bk.rev.; bibl.; charts; illus.; index. (also avail. in microform from UMI) **Indexed:** Biol.Abstr., Chem.Abstr., Dent.Ind., Excerp.Med., Ind.Med. **Document type:** academic/scholarly publication.
—BLDSC (5794.040000); CASDDS; Faxon; SWETS; UMI.
    Description: Covers anesthesiology, analgesia, resuscitation and intensive care.
    Refereed Serial

617.96   NE   ISSN 0303-254X
                            CODEN: MOAND2
MONOGRAPHS IN ANAESTHESIOLOGY. 1974. irreg., vol.21, 1991. price varies. Elsevier Science B.V., Books Division, P.O. Box 211, 1000 AE Amsterdam, Netherlands. TEL 31-20-4853911. FAX 31-20-4853705. TELEX 18582 ESPA NL. E-mail: nlinfo-f@elsevier.nl; usinfo-f@elsevier.com; forinfo-kyf04035@niftyserve.or.jp; Site addr.: http://www.elsevier.nl/. (Subscr. in U.S. and Canada to: Elsevier Science Inc., Box 882, Madison Sq. Sta., New York, NY 10159. TEL 212-989-5800) Ed. T.E.J. Healy. (back issues avail.) **Indexed:** Biol.Abstr., Chem.Abstr. **Document type:** monographic series.
—BLDSC (5914.975900); CASDDS; Faxon.
    Refereed Serial

617.96   US   ISSN 0095-2273
N Y S S A SPHERE. 1948. q. $40. New York State Society of Anesthesiologists, Inc., 41 E. 42nd St., No. 703, New York, NY 10017. TEL 212-867-7140. FAX 212-867-7153. Ed. Dr. Mark J. Lema. adv.; bk.rev.; abstr.; charts; illus.; tr.lit.; circ. 3,200 (controlled). **Document type:** academic/scholarly publication, newsletter.
    Former titles: N Y S S A Bulletin (ISSN 0027-7169); New York State Society of Anesthesiologists. Bulletin (ISSN 0095-2265)
    Description: Publishes articles and news relating to the practice of anesthesiology, including case reports, review articles, drug profiles, historical articles and meeting news.

617.6   JA   ISSN 0386-5835
                            CODEN: NSMZDZ
NIHON SHIKA MASUI GAKKAI ZASSHI/JAPANESE DENTAL SOCIETY OF ANESTHESIOLOGY. JOURNAL. (Text in English, Japanese) 1973. 4/yr. 10000 Yen. Nihon Shika Masui Gakkai - Japanese Dental Society of Anesthesiology, Osaka University, 1-8 Yamadoaka, Suita, 565 Osaka, Japan. TEL 03-3947-8891. FAX 03-3947-8341. Ed. Hideo Matsuura. adv. circ. 2,050. **Indexed:** Excerp.Med. (1993-). **Document type:** academic/scholarly publication.
●Also available on CD-ROM.
—BLDSC (4809.260000); CASDDS. **CCC.**
    Description: Contains scientific articles related to dental anesthesia, fundamentals of anesthesiology and the general management of the dental patients with some underlying systemic diseases.
    Refereed Serial

618.2 617.96   US   ISSN 0275-665X
                            CODEN: OADIDS
OBSTETRIC ANESTHESIA DIGEST. 1981. q. $92 to individuals (foreign $112); institutions $120 (foreign $142) (effective 1996); newsstand price: $37. Lippincott - Raven Publishers, 227 E. Washington Sq., Philadelphia, PA 19106. TEL 215-238-4200. Ed. Dr. Gerard M. Bassell. adv. contact: Phyllis Noyes. bk.rev. circ. 800. (also avail. in microform from UMI) **Document type:** academic/scholarly publication, abstracting/indexing.
—BLDSC (6208.155000); UMI. **CCC.**
    Description: Provides annotated abstracts from world literature pertaining to the administration of anaesthesia during the perinatal period.
    Refereed Serial

617.96   US   ISSN 0000-1546
RD78.62.U6
OFFICIAL AMERICAN BOARD OF MEDICAL SPECIALTIES (A B M S) DIRECTORY OF BOARD CERTIFIED ANESTHESIOLOGISTS. 1985. biennial. $119.95. Marquis Who's Who, A Reed Reference Publishing company, 121 Chanlon Rd., New Providence, NJ 07974. TEL 908-464-6800. FAX 908-665-2898. (Subscr. to: Order Dept., Box 31, New Providence, NJ 07974-9903. TEL 800-521-8110) Ed. Roy Crego. **Document type:** directory.
    Formerly (until 1994): A B M S Directory of Certified Anesthesiologists (ISSN 0883-122X)
    Description: Biographical sketches of U.S. certified medical specialists sorted alphabetically with geographical index.

P A S C A L E 83: ANESTHESIE ET REANIMATION. see *MEDICAL SCIENCES — Abstracting, Bibliographies, Statistics*

616.99 618.92   FR   ISSN 1155-5645
PAEDIATRIC ANAESTHESIA. 1991. q. 720 F.($146) to individuals; institutions 990 F.($200) (effective 1996). Arnette Blackwell, 1 rue de Lille, 75007 Paris, France. TEL 33-1-44-86-07-70. FAX 33-1-44-76-07-66.
—BLDSC (6333.399705). **CCC.**

617.96   NE   ISSN 0169-1112
                            CODEN: PACLEA
THE PAIN CLINIC. (Text in English) 1986. q. DM.270 (effective 1996). V S P, P.O. Box 346, 3700 AH Zeist, Netherlands. TEL 31-30-6925790. FAX 31-30-6932081. E-mail: 100341.2372@compuserve.com. adv.; bk.rev. (back issues avail.) **Document type:** academic/scholarly publication.
—BLDSC (6333.798800); SWETS.
    Description: Focuses on the clinical methods used and the problems involved in the diagnosis and treatment of persistent and recurrent types of pain.
    Refereed Serial

617.96   NE
THE PAIN CLINIC (PROCEEDINGS). (Text in English) 1985. irreg., vol.4, 1992. price varies. (Pain Clinic Symposium) V S P, P.O. Box 346, 3700 AH Zeist, Netherlands. TEL 31-3404-25790. FAX 31-3404-32081. (Dist. in U.S. and Canada by: Books International Inc., Box 605, herndon, VA 22070. TEL 703-435-7064. FAX 703-689-0660) Ed.Bd. (back issues avail.) **Document type:** proceedings.

PAIN MEDICINE JOURNAL CLUB JOURNAL. see *MEDICAL SCIENCES — Abstracting, Bibliographies, Statistics*

POSTGRADUATE SURGERY: MIDDLE EAST. see *MEDICAL SCIENCES — Surgery*

MEDICAL SCIENCES — CARDIOVASCULAR DISEASES 4327

617.96 US ISSN 0889-4698
RD82.5
PROBLEMS IN ANESTHESIA. 1987. q. $98 to individuals (foreign $123); institutions $133 (foreign $168); newsstand price: $46. Lippincott - Raven Publisher, 227 E. Washington Sq., Philadelphia, PA 19106. TEL 215-238-4200. Eds. Dr. Robert R. Kirby, Dr. David L. Brown. circ. 3,000. (also avail. in microform from UMI) **Document type:** academic/scholarly publication.
—BLDSC (6617.876900); SWETS; UMI. **CCC.**

617.96 US ISSN 0891-5784
PROGRESS IN ANESTHESIOLOGY (PHILADELPHIA). m. $295 to individuals (foreign $360); institutions $325 (foreign $390) (effective 1994). (Dannemiller Memorial Educational Foundation) W.B. Saunders Co. (Subsidiary of: Harcourt Brace & Company), Curtis Center, 3rd Fl., Independence Sq. W., Philadelphia, PA 19106-3399. TEL 215-238-7800. FAX 215-238-6445. (Subscr. to: Periodicals Fulfillment, W.B. Saunders Co., 6277 Sea Harbor Dr., 4th Fl., Orlando, FL 32891-4800. TEL 800-654-2452. FAX 800-874-6418) Ed. Dr. James B. Eisenkraft. **Document type:** academic/scholarly publication.
Formerly (until 1987): Clinical Anesthesiology (ISSN 0883-0282)
Description: Explores a topic in detail and offers clinical advice and information on the latest techniques and technologies.

617.96 617.3 FR ISSN 1164-6756
REANIMATION URGENCES. 1991. bi-m. 1160 F. (foreign 1490 F.) (effective 1995). (Societe Francophone d'Urgences Medicales) Arnette Blackwell, 1 rue de Lille, 75007 Paris, France. TEL 33-1-44-86-07-70. FAX 33-1-44-83-07-66. (Co-sponsor: Societe de Reanimation de Langue Francaise)
—BLDSC (7303.557000). **CCC.**

617.96 US ISSN 0146-521X
RD84 CODEN: RGANDZ
REGIONAL ANESTHESIA. 1975. bi-m. $102 to individuals (foreign $134); institutions $136 (foreign $168). (American Society of Regional Anesthesia) Churchill Livingstone International, 650 Avenue of the Americas, New York, NY 10011. TEL 212-206-5000. Ed. Dr. Gerard W. Ostheimer. adv.; illus.; index. circ. 11,000. (also avail. in microform from UMI; back issues avail.) **Indexed:** Excerp.Med. (1993-). **Document type:** academic/scholarly publication.
—BLDSC (7336.572200); CASDDS; Faxon; Genuine Article; SWETS; UMI; UnCover. **CCC.**
Description: Contains original articles, case reports, and other material relevant to practitioners concerned with local anesthetics, regional anesthesia, and pain management.

617.96 TU
REJYONAL ANESTEZI BULTEN. 1993. bi-m. Rejyonal Anestezi Dernegi, c/o Dr. Serdar Erdine, Ed., Istanbul Tip Fakultesi, Agri Merkezi, Capa Kliniklari, 34390 Istanbul, Turkey. TEL 90-212-6350135. FAX 90-212-6310541. adv.; abstr. **Document type:** bulletin, newsletter.
Description: Reports on news, medical and technical issues affecting regional anesthesiologists, with summaries in Turkish of recent articles appearing in international literature.

RESUSCITATION; an interdisciplinary journal for the dissemination of clinical and basic science research relating to acute care medicine and cardiopulmonary resuscitation. see MEDICAL SCIENCES — Respiratory Diseases

617.96 BL ISSN 0034-7094
CODEN: RBANAV
REVISTA BRASILEIRA DE ANESTESIOLOGIA. (Annual English edition avail.) (Text in Portuguese; summaries in English, Portuguese and Spanish) 1951. bi-m. Cz.$51.64($120) (Sociedade Brasileira de Anestesiologia) Cidade - Editora Cientifica Ltda., c/o Dr. Antonio Leite Oliva Filho, Ed., Rua Professor Alfredo Gomes 36, 22251 Rio de Janeiro, Brazil. TEL 021-266-6324. adv.; bk.rev.; charts; illus.; stat. circ. 4,500. (also avail. in microform from UMI; reprint service avail. from UMI) **Indexed:** Biol.Abstr., Chem.Abstr., Excerp.Med., Ind.Med. **Document type:** academic/scholarly publication.
—CASDDS; EMDOCS; Faxon.
Description: Original papers and articles on anaesthesiology.

617.96 BL ISSN 0104-0014
REVISTA BRASILEIRA DE ANESTESIOLOGIA - INTERNATIONAL ISSUE/BRAZILIAN JOURNAL OF ANESTHESIOLOGY - INTERNATIONAL ISSUE. (Text in English) 1990. a. $20. (Sociedade Brasileira de Anestesiologia) Cidade - Editora Cientifica Ltda., c/o Dr. Antonio Leite Oliva Filho, Ed., Rua Professor Alfredo Gomes 36, 22251 Rio de Janeiro, Brazil. TEL 021-266-6324. FAX 021-2665888. circ. 2,000.
●Also available on CD-ROM.
Description: Selected articles translated in full from the previous year's issues, plus summaries of all of the year's other articles.

617.96 CK ISSN 0120-3347
REVISTA COLOMBIANA DE ANESTESIOLOGIA. 1973. q. $20. Sociedad Colombiana de Anestesiologia y Reanimacion, Apdo. Aereo 11206, Bogota, Colombia. TEL 2-883985. FAX 2-454481. Ed. Julio Enrique Pena. adv.; bk.rev. circ. 1,000. (back issues avail.)

617.96 SP ISSN 0034-9356
CODEN: REANBJ
REVISTA ESPANOLA DE ANESTESIOLOGIA Y REANIMACION. (Text in Spanish; summaries in English) 1953. m. (10/yr.). 5200 ptas.($45) to non-members. (Sociedad Espanola de Anestesiologia - Reanimacion y Terapia del Dolor) Ediciones Doyma, S.A., Travesera de Gracia, 17-21, 08021 Barcelona, Spain. TEL 34-1-200-07-11. FAX 34-1-209-11-36. TELEX 51964 INK-E. Ed. R. Garcia Guasch. adv.: page 200000 ptas.; trim 210 x 280; adv. contact: Marte Vidal. bk.rev.; abstr.; charts; illus.; stat. circ. 5,000. (reprint service avail. from UMI) **Indexed:** Biol.Abstr., Dent.Ind., Excerpt.Med., Ind.Med., Ind.Med.Esp.
—BLDSC (7853.910000); CASDDS; EMDOCS; SWETS; UMI. **CCC.**
Formerly: Revista Espanola de Anestesiologia.
Description: Diffuses information on the clinical and experimental work of Spanish anesthesiologists.

617.96 MX ISSN 0185-1012
REVISTA MEXICANA DE ANESTESIOLOGIA. (Text in Spanish; summaries in English and Spanish) 1952. q. Mex.$50,000($60) Sociedad Mexicana de Anestesiologia A.C., Av. Insurgentes Sur 636-502, Col. del Valle, Deleg. Benito Juarez, 03100 Mexico, D.F., Mexico. TEL 669-14-57. adv.; bk.rev.; charts; illus.; stat.; index. circ. 1,000. (back issues avail.) **Indexed:** Excerp.Med., Ind.Med. **Document type:** academic/scholarly publication.
—BLDSC (7866.200000).

617 UK
ROYAL COLLEGE OF ANAESTHETISTS. NEWSLETTER. 1965. bi-m. membership. Royal College of Anaesthetists, 48-49 Russel Sq., London WC1B 4JY, England. TEL 0171-813-1900. FAX 0171-813-1876. circ. 6,000 (controlled). **Document type:** newsletter.
Former titles: Royal College of Surgeons of England. Faculty of Anaesthetists. Dean's Newsletter; Royal College of Surgeons of England. Faculty of Anaesthetists. Newsletter.
Description: Report to Fellows and Members of College. Covers activities, events, and personalities.

617.96 SZ
S B A P - A S I A BULLETIN. (Text in French, German, Italian) 1978. q. 56 SFr. Hoelderlinstr. 17, CH-9008 St. Gallen, Switzerland. TEL 071-253330. FAX 071-253321. Ed. D. Barthlome. adv. contact: Hermi Loehnert. bk.rev. circ. 1,000. **Document type:** bulletin.
Formerly (until 1992): S F A - A S A Bulletin.

617.96 US ISSN 0277-0326
CODEN: SEANDW
SEMINARS IN ANESTHESIA. 1982 (Mar.). q. $135 (foreign $165) (effective 1996). W.B. Saunders Co. (Subsidiary of: Harcourt Brace & Company), Curtis Center, 3rd Fl., Independence Sq. W., Philadelphia, PA 19106-3399. TEL 215-238-7800. FAX 215-238-6445. (Subscr. to: Periodicals Fulfillment, W.B. Saunders Co., 6277 Sea Harbor Dr., 4th Fl., Orlando, FL 32891-4800. TEL 800-654-2452. FAX 800-874-6418) Ed. Dr. Ronald L. Katz; Pub. Joan W. Blumberg. adv.: B&W page $790; color page $1790; 7 x 10. bibl.; charts; illus.; index. circ. 2,628. **Indexed:** ASCA, Chem.Abstr., Curr.Cont., Sci.Cit.Ind. **Document type:** academic/scholarly publication.
●Also available online.
—BLDSC (8239.447600); CASDDS; Genuine Article; SWETS; UMI; UnCover. **CCC.**
Description: In each issue, experts discuss a single topic from their clinical experience.

SEMINARS IN HEADACHE MANAGEMENT. see PSYCHOLOGY

617.96 SP ISSN 1134-8046
▼**SOCIEDAD ESPANOLA DEL DOLOR. REVISTA.** 1994. bi-m. 5300 ptas.($65) (effective 1995). Editorial Garsi, S.A., Juan Bravo 46, 28006 Madrid, Spain. TEL 34-1-4021212. FAX 34-1-4020954.

617.96 US ISSN 8756-8578
TECHNOLOGY FOR ANESTHESIA. m. $95. (Emergency Care Research Institute) E C R I, 5200 Butler Pike, Plymouth Meeting, PA 19462. TEL 610-825-6000. FAX 610-834-1275. Ed. Michele Moscarella. **Document type:** trade publication.
—CCC.
Former titles: Technology of Anesthesiology; Health Devices Update: Anesthesiology.
Description: Covers news and development of technology for anesthesia. Summarizes comparative product evaluations, principles of device operation, and reported medical device problems and recalls. *Refereed Serial*

617 TU ISSN 1016-5150
CODEN: TANRE
TURK ANESTEZIYOLOJI VE REANIMASYON CEMIYETI DERGISI. 1972. q. (Turk Anesteziyoloji ve Reanimasyon Cemiyeti - Turkish Anaesthesiology and Reanimation Society) Logos Yayincilik Ticaret A.S., Yildiz Posta Cad., Sinan Apt. No. 36 D 66-67, Gayrettepe 80280 - Istanbul, Turkey. TEL 90-212-2880541. Ed. Dr. Mois Bahar. adv. contact: Ipek Karisman. **Indexed:** Excerp.Med.
—BLDSC (9071.888500).

617.96 US
YEAR BOOK OF ANESTHESIOLOGY AND PAIN MANAGEMENT. 1961. a. $72.95 (residents $35) (effective 1996). Mosby - Year Book, Inc., Continuity Division, 200 N. LaSalle, Chicago, IL 60601. TEL 312-726-9733. FAX 312-726-6075. TELEX 206155. Ed. John H. Tinker. illus. (reprint service avail.)
●Also available online. Vendor(s): Ovid Technologies. Also available on CD-ROM.
Formerly: Year Book of Anesthesia (ISSN 0084-3652)

617.96 CC
ZHONGHUA MAZUIXUE ZAZHI/CHINESE JOURNAL OF ANAESTHESIOLOGY. (Text in Chinese) q. $1.30 per no. Guoji Shudian, Qikan Bu - Chinese International Book Trading Corp., Chegongzhuang Xilu 21, P.O. Box 399, Beijing 100044, People's Republic of China. **Indexed:** Chem.Abstr., ExtraMED. **Document type:** academic/scholarly publication.
●Also available on CD-ROM.

MEDICAL SCIENCES — Cardiovascular Diseases

A C C CURRENT JOURNAL REVIEW. (American College of Cardiology) see MEDICAL SCIENCES — Abstracting, Bibliographies, Statistics

MEDICAL SCIENCES — CARDIOVASCULAR DISEASES

616.1 US
A C C E L; audio cassette journal of clinical cardiology. 1969. m. $150 to non-members; members $125. American College of Cardiology, 9111 Old Georgetown Rd., Bethesda, MD 20814-1699. TEL 301-897-5400; 800-253-4636. FAX 301-897-9745. Ed. Dr. Sylvan L. Weinberg. index. circ. 7,500. (audio cassette) **Indexed:** Risk Abstr. **Document type:** academic/scholarly publication.
Former titles: A C C E L for Physicians; A C C E S S (ISSN 0001-0626)
Description: Brings up-to-date reports on diagnosis, treatment, and research as well as editorials, and in-depth coverage of conferences and meetins in the U.S. and abroad.

616.1 BE ISSN 0001-5385
CODEN: ACCAAQ
ACTA CARDIOLOGICA; journal international de cardiologie - international journal of cardiology. (Supplements avail.) (Text in English) 1946. bi-m. 3100 BEF. Association des Societes Scientifiques Medicales Belges - Vereiniging van de Belgische Wetenschappelijke Genootschappen, Av. Circulaire, 138A, B-1180 Brussels, Belgium. TEL 02-375-58-92. FAX 02-374-96-28. Eds. J. Lequime, H. Kesteloot. adv.; bk.rev.; charts; illus.; index. circ. 900. **Indexed:** ASCA, Biol.Abstr., Biotech.Abstr., Chem.Abstr., Curr.Cont., Excerp.Med., Ind.Med.
—BLDSC (0608.400000); Faxon; Genuine Article; SWETS; UnCover.
Description: Papers on fundamental, clinical, epidemiological and nutritional research in the field of cardiovascular disease.

616.1 IT ISSN 0392-9698
ACTA CARDIOLOGICA MEDITERANEA. (Text in English, Italian) 1960. 3/yr. L.40000($40) Carbone Editore, Via G. Daita, 29, 90139 Palermo, Italy. TEL 091-321273. FAX 91-321782. adv.; abstr.; bibl.; illus.; stat; index. circ. 3,000.
—BLDSC (0608.403000).
Description: Discusses and reviews clinical cases of cardiovascular diseases.

616 FR ISSN 0245-8659
ACTUALITES D'ANGEIOLOGIE. 1976. m. (10/yr.). 550 F. P D G Communication, 30 rue d'Armaille, 75017 Paris, France. TEL 40-55-05-95. FAX 45-74-65-67. adv.; charts; illus.
—BLDSC (0677.167000).
Formerly (until 1978): Actualites d'Angeiologie et de Pathologie Vasculaire (ISSN 0397-2003)

616.1 NE ISSN 0884-6863
RC685.C6
ACUTE CORONARY CARE. (Text in English) 1985. a. price varies. Kluwer Academic Publishers Group, Postbus 17, 3300 AA Dordrecht, Netherlands. TEL 31-78-392392. FAX 31-78-392254. TELEX 29245 KAPG NL. (Dist. by: Kluwer Academic Publishers Group, P.O. Box 322, 3300 AH Dordrecht, Netherlands. TEL 31-78-392392. FAX 31-78-546474; N. America dist. addr.: Box 358, Accord Sta., Hingham, MA 02018-0358. TEL 617-871-6600. FAX 617-871-6528) **Document type:** monographic series.
—BLDSC (0678.070000).
Refereed Serial

616.1 US ISSN 1041-7974
ADVANCED CARDIAC LIFE SUPPORT. m. $179. American Health Consultants, Inc., Six Piedmont Center, Ste. 400, 3525 Piedmont Rd., N.E., Atlanta, GA 30305. TEL 800-688-2421. FAX 800-284-3291. Ed. Dr. Mikel A. Rothenberg. circ. 920. **Document type:** newsletter.
Description: Offers a concise review of articles and reports on advanced cardiac life support.
Refereed Serial

616.1 US
ADVANCES IN CARDIAC SURGERY. 1989. a. $82.95 (residents $40) (effective 1996). Mosby - Year Book, Inc. (Chicago) (Subsidiary of: Times Mirror Company), 200 N. LaSalle St., Chicago, IL 60601-1080. TEL 312-726-9733. FAX 312-726-6075. TELEX 206155. (Subscr. to: 11830 Westline Industrial Dr., St. Louis, MO 63146. TEL 800-325-4177) Ed. Dr. Robert B. Karp. **Indexed:** Ind.Med. (1993-). **Document type:** academic/scholarly publication.
—BLDSC (0702.200000).
Formerly: Advances in Cardiovascular Surgery (ISSN 0889-5074)
Description: Presents a collection of original and fully referenced articles from experts in the field.

616.1 SZ ISSN 0065-2326
RC681.A25 CODEN: ACDYB2
ADVANCES IN CARDIOLOGY. (Text in English) 1956. irreg. (approx. 2/yr.). price varies. S. Karger AG, Allschwilerstr. 10, P.O. Box, CH-4009 Basel, Switzerland. TEL 061-3061111. FAX 061-3061234. E-mail: Karger@Karger.ch. Ed. J. Kellermann. (reprint service avail. from ISI) **Indexed:** Biol.Abstr., Chem.Abstr., CINAHL, Curr.Adv.Ecol.Sci., Curr.Cont., Excerp.Med., Ind.Med. **Document type:** academic/scholarly publication.
—BLDSC (0702.300000); CASDDS; EMDOCS; Faxon; SWETS. **CCC**.
Refereed Serial

616.1 SZ ISSN 0378-6900
CODEN: ACAPDU
ADVANCES IN CARDIOVASCULAR PHYSICS. (Text in English) irreg. price varies. S. Karger AG, Allschwilerstr. 10, P.O. Box, CH-4009 Basel, Switzerland. TEL 061-3061111. FAX 061-3061234. E-mail: Karger@Karger.ch. Ed. D.N. Ghista. charts. (reprint service avail. from ISI) **Indexed:** Biol.Abstr., Chem.Abstr., Curr.Cont., Ind.Med. **Document type:** academic/scholarly publication.
—CASDDS; Faxon. **CCC**.
Refereed Serial

ADVANCES IN VASCULAR SURGERY. see *MEDICAL SCIENCES — Surgery*

616.1 378 US
AFFILIATES IN TRAINING. 1983. bi-m. $10. American College of Cardiology, 9111 Old Georgetown Rd., Bethesda, MD 20814. TEL 301-897-5400; 800-253-4636. FAX 301-897-9745. Ed. Sharon Ballas. charts. circ. 4,000. **Document type:** newsletter.
Description: Covers new directions in managed care, opportunities in subspecialization, positions available, meeting updates, board exams. Aimed towards doctors in cardiovascular fellowships and their training directors.

ALGOLOGIA. see *MEDICAL SCIENCES — Psychiatry And Neurology*

616.12 US ISSN 0735-1097
CODEN: JACCDI
AMERICAN COLLEGE OF CARDIOLOGY. JOURNAL. Key Title: Journal of the American College of Cardiology. 14/yr. $198 to institutions in U.S.; $290 to institutions outside the Americas; $413 to institutions in Europe; $483 to institutions in Japan (effective 1996). (American College of Cardiology) Elsevier Science Inc., 655 Ave. of the Americas, New York, NY 10010. TEL 212-989-5800. FAX 212-633-3990. TELEX 420643 AEP UI. (Subscr. to: Box 882, Madison Sq. Sta., New York, NY 10159-0882) Ed. Dr. Simon Dack. adv. (also avail. in microform from UMI; back issues avail.) **Indexed:** AIM, Biol.Abstr., Chem.Abstr., CINAHL, Curr.Cont., Dent.Ind., Excerp.Med., Ind.Med., INIS Atomind., NRN, Risk Abstr., Sci.Cit.Ind. **Document type:** academic/scholarly publication.
●Also available online. Vendor(s): Ovid Technologies.
—BLDSC (4685.500000); ADONIS; CASDDS; Faxon; Genuine Article; SWETS; UnCover. **CCC**.
Description: Publishes original clinical and experimental reports on all aspects of cardiovascular disease.
Refereed Serial

616.1 US
AMERICAN COLLEGE OF CARDIOLOGY. SYMPOSIA. (Supplement to: American College of Cardiology. Journal (ISSN 0735-1097)) 1973. a. Elsevier Science Inc., 655 Ave. of the Americas, New York, NY 10010. TEL 212-989-5800. FAX 212-633-3990. TELEX 420643 AEP UI. (Subscr. to: Box 882, Madison Sq. Sta., New York, NY 10159-0882) **Document type:** proceedings.

616.1 US
AMERICAN COLLEGE OF CARDIOLOGY SCIENTIFIC SESSION NEWS. 1982. 5/yr. American College of Cardiology, 9111 Old Georgetown Rd., Bethesda, MD 20814. TEL 301-897-2627. FAX 301-897-9745. Ed. Sharon Ballasward. adv. contact: Sharon Ballas. circ. 41,000 (controlled). (tabloid format; back issues avail.) **Document type:** newsletter.
Formerly: American College of Cardiology Annual Scientific Session News.
Description: For attendees of the college's Annual Scientific Session. Highlights clinical presentations events and activities of the meetings as well as activities within the city.

616.1 US ISSN 0065-8502
AMERICAN HEART ASSOCIATION. SCIENTIFIC SESSIONS. ABSTRACTS. 1927. a. $15 (foreign $25). American Heart Association, Committee on Scientific Sessions Program, 7272 Greenville Ave., Dallas, TX 75231-4596. TEL 214-706-1253. FAX 214-691-6342. adv.; index. circ. 40,000. (also avail. in microfiche; reprint service avail. from UMI) **Document type:** abstracting/indexing.
—**CCC**.

616.6 US
AMERICAN HEART ASSOCIATION. SUPPLEMENTS. 1960. irreg. $10 (foreign $15). American Heart Association, 7272 Greenville Ave., Dallas, TX 75231-4596. TEL 214-706-1310. FAX 214-691-2704. (Subscr. to: Box 843543, Dallas, TX 75284-3543) (reprint service avail. from UMI) **Indexed:** Biol.Abstr., Ind.Med. **Document type:** monographic series.
Formerly: American Heart Association. Monographs (ISSN 0065-8499)
Description: Provides proceedings of council meetings and significant research related to cardiovascular disease and cerebral circulation.
Refereed Serial

616.1 US ISSN 0002-8703
RC681.A1 CODEN: AHJOA2
AMERICAN HEART JOURNAL; the international publication for the study of the heart and circulation. 1925. m. $121 to individuals (Canada $165.85; elsewhere $155); institutions $235 (Canada $287.83; elsewhere $269); students, residents $51 (Canada $90.95; elsewhere $85) (effective 1996); newsstand price: $11. Mosby - Year Book, Inc. (Subsidiary of: Times Mirror Company), 11830 Westline Industrial Dr., St. Louis, MO 63146-3318. TEL 314-872-8370; 800-325-4177. FAX 314-432-1380. TELEX 44-2402. Ed. Dr. Dean T. Mason. adv.: B&W page $1100, color page $2060; trim 8 1/8 x 10 7/8. bibl.; charts; illus.; s-a. index. circ. 8,031. (also avail. in microfilm from PMC,UMI; reprint service avail. from UMI) **Indexed:** Abstr.Hyg., Abstr.Inter.Med., AIM, ASCA, Behav.Med.Abstr., Biol.Abstr., Biotech.Abstr., Chem.Abstr., CINAHL, Curr.Adv.Ecol.Sci., Curr.Cont., Dairy Sci.Abstr., Diab.Cont., Excerp.Med., Helminthol.Abstr., I.P.A., Ind.Med., Ind.Sci.Rev., INIS Atomind., Kidney, NRN, Rev.Plant Path., Risk Abstr., Sci.Cit.Ind., Trop.Dis.Bull.
●Also available online. Vendor(s): Ovid Technologies.
—BLDSC (0817.000000); ADONIS; CASDDS; Faxon; Genuine Article; SWETS; UMI; UnCover. **CCC**.
Description: For those concerned with the diagnosis and management of cardiovascular disease.
Refereed Serial

MEDICAL SCIENCES — CARDIOVASCULAR DISEASES

616.1 US ISSN 0887-7971
CODEN: AJCIEZ
AMERICAN JOURNAL OF CARDIAC IMAGING. 1987. q. $195 (foreign $225) (effective 1996). W.B. Saunders Co. (Subsidiary of: Harcourt Brace & Company), Curtis Center. 3rd Fl., Independence Sq. W., Philadelphia, PA 19106-3399. TEL 215-238-7800. FAX 215-238-6445. (Subscr. to: Periodicals Fulfillment, W.B. Saunders Co., 6277 Sea Harbor Dr., 4th Fl., Orlando, FL 32891-4800. TEL 800-654-2452. FAX 800-874-6418) Ed. Dr. James T. Valano; Pub. Joan W. Blumberg. adv.: B&W page $735, color $1685; 7 x 10. bk.rev.; abstr.; bibl.; charts; illus. circ. 1,107. **Indexed:** Excerp.Med., Ind.Med. (1993-). **Document type:** academic/scholarly publication.
—BLDSC (0822.475000); CASDDS; Faxon; SWETS; UMI; UnCover. **CCC**.
Description: Presents original symposium contributions, case studies, and current review articles on two-dimensional and Doppler echocardiography, digital angiography, magnetic resonance imaging, PET and CAT scanning, radionuclide techniques, and related modalities.
Refereed Serial

616.1 US ISSN 0002-9149
RC681.A1 CODEN: AJCDAG
AMERICAN JOURNAL OF CARDIOLOGY. 1958. 24/yr. $260 to institutions outside the Americas; $160 to institutions in U.S (effective 1996). Excerpta Medica, Inc. (Subsidiary of: Reed Elsevier Medical group), 105 Raider Blvd., Belle Mead, NJ 08502. TEL 908-874-8550. FAX 908-874-8419. (Subscr. to: Box 3085, Princeton, NJ 08543-3085) Eds. Dr. William C. Roberts, Judy Wagner. adv.; bk.rev.; bibl.; charts; illus.; index. circ. 30,050. (also avail. in microform) **Indexed:** Abstr.Hyg., Abstr.Inter.Med., AIM, Behav.Med.Abstr., Biol.Abstr., Biotech.Abstr., C.I.S.Abstr., CINAHL, Curr.Adv.Ecol.Sci., Curr.Cont., Dent.Ind., Dok.Arbeitsmed., Excerp.Med., Helminthol.Abstr., I.P.A., Ind.Med., Ind.Sci.Rev., Kidney, NRN, Nutr.Abstr., Risk Abstr., Sci.Cit.Ind., Trop.Dis.Bull. **Document type:** academic/scholarly publication.
●Also available online. Vendor(s): Ovid Technologies, Lexis-Nexis.
—BLDSC (0822.500000); ADONIS; CASDDS; Faxon; Genuine Article; SWETS; UMI; UnCover. **CCC**.
Description: Explores and highlights advances in diagnosis and treatment of cardiovascular disease, stressing a practical, clinical approach to cardiology.
Refereed Serial

616.1 US ISSN 0887-8005
RC669.9 CODEN: AJCPEM
AMERICAN JOURNAL OF CARDIOVASCULAR PATHOLOGY. 1987. q. $115 to individuals; institutions $145 (effective 1996). Field & Wood, Medical Periodicals, Inc., Box 975, Blue Bell, PA 19422. TEL 610-828-4010. FAX 215-482-0226. Ed. Colin M. Bloor. **Indexed:** Excerp.Med. **Document type:** academic/scholarly publication.
—BLDSC (0822.520000); CASDDS; SWETS; UnCover.
Refereed Serial

616.12 612.67 US
AMERICAN JOURNAL OF GERIATRIC CARDIOLOGY. 1992. bi-m. $60 to individuals (foreign $75); institutions $75 (foreign $90) (effective 1993). Cardiovascular Reviews & Reports, Inc., 777 W. Putnam Ave., Greenwich, CT 06830-5014. TEL 203-531-0450. FAX 203-531-0533. Ed. Suzanne DelGallo. adv.: B&W page $2200, color page $3240; trim 7 7/8 x 10 3/4. circ. 20,000. **Indexed:** Excerp.Med. (1993-).
Description: Devoted to the study of heart disease in the elderly.
Refereed Serial

618 US ISSN 0895-7061
CODEN: AJHYE6
AMERICAN JOURNAL OF HYPERTENSION. 1988. m. $255 to institutions in U.S.; $315 to institutions outside the Americas; $345 to institutions in Europe; $368 to institutions in Japan (effective 1996). (American Society of Hypertension) Elsevier Science Inc., 655 Ave. of the Americas, New York, NY 10010. TEL 212-989-5800. FAX 212-633-3990. TELEX 420643 AEP UI. (Subscr. to: Box 882, Madison Sq. Sta., New York, NY 10159-0882) Ed. John H. Laragh. (also avail. in microform from UMI) **Indexed:** Curr.Cont., Excerp.Med., Ind.Med., Kidney. **Document type:** academic/scholarly publication.
—BLDSC (0826.400000); ADONIS; CASDDS; Faxon; Genuine Article; SWETS; UnCover. **CCC**.
Incorporates (1985-1987): Journal of Clinical Hypertension (ISSN 0748-450X)
Description: Offers wide coverage of experimental and clinical hypertension and related cardiovascular diseases.
Refereed Serial

616.12 SZ ISSN 0258-4425
CODEN: AJNCE4
AMERICAN JOURNAL OF NONINVASIVE CARDIOLOGY. (Text in English) 6/yr. 165 SFr.($107.40) to individuals; institutions 443 SFr.($307). S. Karger AG, Allschwilerstr. 10, P.O. Box, CH-4009 Basel, Switzerland. TEL 061-3061111. FAX 061-3061234. E-mail: Karger@Karger.ch. (U.S. addr.: S. Karger, 79 Fifth Ave., New York, NY 10003) Ed. H.D. Spodick. circ. 950. (also avail. in microform from UMI) **Indexed:** Excerp.Med. **Document type:** academic/scholarly publication.
—BLDSC (0828.410000); Faxon; Genuine Article; SWETS. **CCC**.
Refereed Serial

574.1 US ISSN 0363-6135
QP101.2
AMERICAN JOURNAL OF PHYSIOLOGY: HEART AND CIRCULATORY PHYSIOLOGY.[1] 1977. m. $367 to individuals (Canada and Mexico $347; elsewhere $407); institutions $468 (Canada and Mexico $500; elsewhere $568); members $154. American Physiological Society, 9650 Rockville Pike, Bethesda, MD 20814. TEL 301-530-7164. FAX 301-571-1814. Ed. Brenda Rauner. circ. 720. (also avail. in microform from UMI; reprint service aval. from UMI) **Indexed:** Abstr.Hyg., Biol.Abstr., Biol.& Agr.Ind., Biotech.Abstr., Chem.Abstr., Curr.Cont., Dent.Ind., Excerp.Med., Helminthol.Abstr., Ind.Med., Ind.Sci.Rev., Ind.Vet., Int.Abstr.Biol.Sci., Key Word Ind.Wildl.Res., Nutr.Abstr., Ref.Zh., Sci.Cit.Ind., Trop.Dis.Bull., Vet.Bull. **Document type:** academic/scholarly publication.
—SWETS; UMI. **CCC**.
Description: Presents experimental and theoretical studies of cardiovascular function at all levels of organization ranging from the intact animal to the cellular, subcellular, and molecular levels.
Refereed Serial

616.01 US ISSN 0894-7317
CODEN: JSECEJ
AMERICAN SOCIETY OF ECHOCARDIOGRAPHY. JOURNAL. 1988. bi-m. $83 to individuals (Canada $109.14; elsewhere $102); institutions $111 (Canada $139.10; elsewhere $130); students, residents $40 (Canada $63.13; elsewhere $59) (effective 1996); newsstand price: 14.50. (American Society of Echocardiography (ASE)) Mosby - Year Book, Inc. (Subsidiary of: Times Mirror Company), 11830 Westline Industrial Dr., St. Louis, MO 63146-3318. TEL 314-872-8370; 800-325-4177. FAX 314-432-1380. TELEX 44-2402. Ed. Dr. Harvey Feigenbaum. adv.: B&W page $940, color page $1855; trim 8 1/4 x 11. s-a. index. circ. 7,568. (also avail. in microform from UMI; reprint service avail. from UMI)
—BLDSC (4692.680000); SWETS; UMI. **CCC**.

616.132 US ISSN 0898-672X
CODEN: ASHSEH
AMERICAN SOCIETY OF HYPERTENSION. SYMPOSIUM SERIES. 1987. irreg., latest vol.3. price varies. Raven Press (Subsidiary of: Wolters Kluwer N.V.), 1185 Ave. of the Americas, New York, NY 10036. TEL 212-930-9500. FAX 212-869-3495. (reprint service avail. from UMI) **Document type:** monographic series.
—BLDSC (0857.490500); CASDDS.
Refereed Serial

616.1 617 SP
▼**ANALES DE CIRUGIA CARDIACA Y CIRUGIA VASCULAR.** 1995. q. Editorial Rocas, Muntaner 393, pral. 2a, 08021 Barcelona, Spain. TEL 39-3-2001389. FAX 39-3-2021958. circ. 3,000 (paid). **Document type:** trade publication.

616.1 574 FR ISSN 0003-3049
ANGEIOLOGIE. (Text in English or French; summaries in English, French) 1948-1993; resumed 1995. q. (plus supplements). 618 F. (foreign 752 F.) (effective 1995). (Societe Francaise d'Angeiologie) Editions E S K A, 27 rue Dunois, 75013 Paris, France. TEL 44-06-80-42. FAX 44-24-06-94. (Co-sponsor: Union Internationale d'Angeiologie) Ed.Bd. adv.; bk.rev. circ. 3,800. **Indexed:** Excerp.Med. (until 1993). **Document type:** academic/scholarly publication.
—BLDSC (0900.900000); Faxon. **CCC**.
Formerly (until 1951): Societe d'Angeiologie et Histopathologie. Annales (ISSN 0399-0494)
Description: Treats all theoretical and clinical aspects of cardiovascular disease for specialists and general practioners alike.

616.1 US ISSN 0003-3197
RC691 CODEN: ANGIAB
ANGIOLOGY. 1950. m. $145 to individuals (overseas $165); institutions $190 (overseas $210) (effective 1996). (American College of Angiology) Westminster Publications, Inc., 708 Glen Cove Ave., Glen Head, NY 11545. TEL 516-759-0025. FAX 516-759-5524. adv.; bk.rev. circ. 6,028. **Indexed:** Biol.Abstr., Biotech.Abstr., Chem.Abstr., Curr.Adv.Ecol.Sci., Curr.Cont., Excerp.Med., Ind.Med., Ind.Sci.Rev., INIS Atomind., Nutr.Abstr., Sci.Cit.Ind. **Document type:** academic/scholarly publication.
—BLDSC (0902.700000); CASDDS; Faxon; SWETS; UnCover.
Description: Contains original papers relating to cerebrovascular, cardiovascular and peripheral vascular diseases.
Refereed Serial

616.13 FR ISSN 0003-3928
CODEN: ACAABH
ANNALES DE CARDIOLOGIE ET D'ANGEIOLOGIE. (Summaries in English) 1952. 10/yr. 785 F. to individuals (foreign 1035 F.); students 390 F. (foreign 605 F.). Expansion Scientifique, 31 bd. de la Tour Maubourg, 75007 Paris, France. TEL 40-62-64-00. FAX 45-55-69-20. Eds. J.J. Welti, M. Grivaux. adv.; bk.rev.; abstr.; bibl.; illus. circ. 2,800. (also avail. in microform) **Indexed:** Biol.Abstr., Chem.Abstr., Curr.Cont., Dent.Ind., Excerp.Med., Ind.Med., Ind.Sci.Rev., Sci.Cit.Ind.
—BLDSC (0969.500000); Genuine Article; SWETS. **CCC**.
Formerly: Actualities Cardiologiques et Angeiologiques Internationales.

617.41 FR ISSN 0066-2054
CODEN: ACSSBP
ANNALES DE CHIRURGIE THORACIQUE ET CARDIO-VASCULAIRE. (Supplement to: Annales de Chirurgie) (Text in English, French) 1962. 2/yr. (Societe de Chirurgie Thoracique de Langue Francaise) Expansion Scientifique, 31 bd. de la Tour Maubourg, 75007 Paris, France. TEL 40-62-64-00. FAX 45-55-69-20. adv.; bk.rev. circ. 3,500. **Indexed:** Biol.Abstr., Curr.Cont., Ind.Med.

ANNALS OF VASCULAR SURGERY; international journal of vascular surgery. see *MEDICAL SCIENCES — Surgery*

ANNUAL OF CARDIAC SURGERY. see *MEDICAL SCIENCES — Abstracting, Bibliographies, Statistics*

616.1 JA
ANNUAL REVIEW JUNKANKI/ANNUAL REVIEW. CIRCULATORY ORGAN. (Text in Japanese) 1988. a. 7828 Yen. Chugai Igakusha, 62, Yaraicho, Shinjuku-ku, Tokyo 162, Japan.

MEDICAL SCIENCES — CARDIOVASCULAR DISEASES

616.1   FR   ISSN 0003-9683
CODEN: AMCVAN
ARCHIVES DES MALADIES DU COEUR ET DES VAISSEAUX. 1908. m. J.B. Bailliere Editeur, 37 av. des Champs Elysees, 75008 Paris, France. TEL 33-1-49536900. Ed. Dr. Gerard Roux-Dessarps. adv.; bk.rev.; abstr.; charts; illus.; index. circ. 4,300. (also avail. in microform) **Indexed:** Biol.Abstr., C.I.S. Abstr., Chem.Abstr., Curr.Adv.Ecol.Sci., Excerp.Med., Helminthol.Abstr., Ind.Med., Ind.Sci.Rev., Nutr.Abstr., Sci.Cit.Ind. **Document type:** academic/scholarly publication.
—BLDSC (1637.370000); Genuine Article; SWETS. **CCC.**

ARCHIVIO DI CHIRURGIA TORACICA E CARDIOVASCOLARE. see *MEDICAL SCIENCES — Surgery*

616.12   IT   ISSN 1120-8635
ARGOMENTI DI CARDIOLOGIA. 1990. q. L.8200($58) (effective 1994). Masson S.p.A., Divisione Periodici, Via Statuto 2-4, 20121 Milan, Italy. TEL 02-6367-1. FAX 02-6367-211. Ed. Alberto Zanchetti. adv.; B&W page L.3750000, color page L.6100000; trim 175 x 245. circ. 15,000. **Document type:** academic/scholarly publication.

616.12   BL   ISSN 0066-782X
CODEN: ABCAAJ
ARQUIVOS BRASILEIROS DE CARDIOLOGIA. (Articles in several languages; summaries in English) 1948. m. $150. Arquivos Brasileiros de Cardiologia, Rua Itapeva, 574, 8, 01332 Sao Paulo, SP, Brazil. Ed. Joao Pimenta. adv.; bk.rev. circ. 6,000. **Indexed:** Biol.Abstr., Chem.Abstr., Excerp.Med., Ind.Med., Protozool.Abstr.
—BLDSC (1695.160000); CASDDS; EMDOCS; Faxon.

616.1   FR   ISSN 0293-5090
ARTERES ET VEINES. 1982. 6/yr. 280 F. to individuals (foreign 340 F.); students 180 F. (foreign 300 F.) (effective 1996). (Arteres et Veines) Publications Medicales, 77 bis, rue des Chesneaux, 95160 Montmorency, France. TEL 34-17-68-88. FAX 34-28-17-59. Ed. A. Castillo Fenoy. adv. contact: A. Castillo Fenoy. bk.rev.; illus.
—BLDSC (1733.492500).

616.136   US   ISSN 1079-5642
RC692   CODEN: ATVBFA
ARTERIOSCLEROSIS, THROMBOSIS AND VASCULAR BIOLOGY. 1981. bi-m. $218 (foreign $260) (effective 1996). American Heart Association, 7272 Greenville Ave., Dallas, TX 75231-4596. TEL 214-706-1310. FAX 214-691-6342. (Subscr. to: Box 843543, Dallas, TX 75284-3543) Ed. Dr. Alan M. Fogelman. adv.; index. circ. 1,740. (also avail. in microform from UMI; back issues avail.) **Indexed:** Biol.Abstr., Curr.Adv.Ecol.Sci., Curr.Adv.Genetics & Molec.Biol., Excerp.Med., Ind.Med., Ind.Sci.Rev., NRN, Poult.Abstr., Sci.Cit.Ind.
—BLDSC (1733.670000); CASDDS; Faxon; Genuine Article; SWETS; UMI; UnCover. **CCC.**
Former titles (until 1994): Arteriosclerosis and Thrombosis (ISSN 1049-8834); Arteriosclerosis (ISSN 0276-5047)
Description: Relates original research and reviews on the biology, prevention, and impact of vascular diseases.
Refereed Serial

616.1   US   ISSN 0098-6127
RC691   CODEN: ARTEDR
ARTERY; an international journal for rapid communication of arterial research. 1974. 6/yr. Artery Publishing, 13998 West Ave., E., Fulton, MI 49052. adv.; bk.rev.; illus. (also avail. in microfilm from PMC) **Indexed:** Biol.Abstr., Chem.Abstr., Curr.Adv.Ecol.Sci., Curr.Cont., Dairy Sci.Abstr., Excerp.Med., Ind.Med., Nutr.Abstr., Sci.Cit.Ind. **Document type:** academic/scholarly publication.
—BLDSC (1733.703000); CASDDS; EMDOCS; Faxon; Genuine Article; SWETS; UnCover.
Refereed Serial

616.1   SI   ISSN 0218-4923
ASIAN CARDIOVASCULAR & THORACIC ANNALS. (Text in English) 1993. q. $60 in Asia-Pacific, Africa & Middle East; Americas & Europe $120. Asia Publishing Exchange Pte. Ltd., 40 St. Thomas Walk, Ste. 07-01, St. Thomas Ct., Singapore 0923, Singapore. TEL 65-235-2425. FAX 65-736-1149. adv. contact: X. **Document type:** academic/scholarly publication.
—BLDSC (1742.403530).
Description: Covers Asia-Pacific Rim research and contributions to cardiovascular and theoracic knowledge. Focuses on the Asian patient population and medical facilities.

616.1   IO   ISSN 0587-5471
ASIAN PACIFIC CONGRESS OF CARDIOLOGY. SYMPOSIA. * irreg. Asian-Pacific Society of Cardiology, c/o Cardiac Centre, Jalan Diponegoro 69, Jakarta, Indonesia. (Symposia from 4th Congress: 1968, pub. by Academic Press, US) **Indexed:** Biol.Abstr.

616.1   IE   ISSN 0021-9150
CODEN: ATHSBL
ATHEROSCLEROSIS; international journal for research and investigation on atherosclerosis and related diseases. 1961. 16/yr. I£1328($2098) (effective 1996). (International Atherosclerosis Society) Elsevier Science Ireland Ltd., P.O. Box 85, Limerick, Ireland. TEL 353-61-471944. FAX 353-61-472144. (Subscr. in U.S. and Canada to: Elsevier Science Publishing Co., Inc., Box 882, Madison Sq. Sta., New York, NY 10159. TEL 212-989-5800. FAX 212-633-3990) Ed.Bd. adv.; charts; illus.; index. **Indexed:** Biol.Abstr., Bull.Signal., Chem.Abstr., Curr.Adv.Biochem., Curr.Cont., Excerp.Med., Ind.Med., INIS Atomind., NRN, Poult.Abstr., Rice Abstr., Vet.Bull. **Document type:** academic/scholarly publication.
—BLDSC (1765.874000); ADONIS; CASDDS; EMDOCS; Faxon; Genuine Article; SWETS; UnCover. **CCC.**
Formerly: Journal of Atherosclerosis Research.
Description: Brings together research and clinical papers related to the focal accumulation of collagen, lipids, complex carbohydrates, blood and blood products, fibrous tissue and calcium deposits in the intima of arteris, its medical complications, related phenomena and diseases.
Refereed Serial

616.136   US   ISSN 0362-1650
RC692   CODEN: ATHEDF
ATHEROSCLEROSIS REVIEWS. 1975. irreg., latest vol.25. price varies. Raven Press (Subsidiary of: Wolters Kluwer N.V.), 1185 Ave. of the Americas, New York, NY 10036. TEL 212-930-9500. FAX 212-869-3495. Eds. Antonio Gotto, Jr., Rodolfo Paoletti. (reprint service avail. from UMI) **Indexed:** Biol.Abstr., Chem.Abstr., Curr.Cont., Ind.Sci.Rev., Sci.Cit.Ind. **Document type:** monographic series.
—BLDSC (1765.878200); CASDDS; Faxon; SWETS; UnCover.
Refereed Serial

616.1   US
BASIC AND CLINICAL CARDIOLOGY SERIES. 1981. irreg., vol.11, 1988. price varies. Marcel Dekker, Inc., 270 Madison Ave., New York, NY 10016. TEL 212-696-9000. FAX 212-685-4540. TELEX 421419.
Refereed Serial

616.1   GW   ISSN 0300-8428
RC633.A1   CODEN: BRCAB7
BASIC RESEARCH IN CARDIOLOGY. (Text in English) 1938. bi-m. DM.908($659) (effective 1996). Dr. Dietrich Steinkopff Verlag, Saalbaustr. 12, 64283 Darmstadt, Germany. TEL 06151-1745-0. FAX 06151-174510. (Subscr. to: Postfach 111442, 64229 Darmstadt, Germany; Subscr. in Austria to: Minerva Wissenschaftliche Buchhandlung GmbH, Sachsenplatz 4-6, A-1201, Austria; subscr. in Japan to: Eastern Book Service, Inc., 37-3, Hongo 3-chome, Bunkyo-ku, Tokyo 113, Japan; subscr. in N. America to: Springer-Verlag, Journals, 175 Fifth Ave., New York, NY 10010; subscr. in Switzerland to: Freihofer AG, Weinbergstr. 109, CH-8033 Zurich, Switzerland) Ed. G. Heusch. adv.; charts; illus.; pat.; index. circ. 2,000. (also avail. in microform from UMI) **Indexed:** Biol.Abstr., Chem.Abstr., Curr.Adv.Ecol.Sci., Curr.Cont., Excerp.Med., Ind.Med., Ind.Sci.Rev., INIS Atomind., Nutr.Abstr., Sci.Cit.Ind. **Document type:** academic/scholarly publication.
—BLDSC (1864.080000); CASDDS; Faxon; Genuine Article; SWETS; UMI; UnCover. **CCC.**

616.1   SZ   ISSN 0067-7906
CODEN: BCSCAL
BIBLIOTHECA CARDIOLOGICA. (Text in English) 1939. irreg. S. Karger AG, Allschwilerstr. 10, P.O. Box, CH-4009 Basel, Switzerland. TEL 061-3061111. FAX 061-3061234. E-mail: Karger@Karger.ch. Ed. A. Maseri. (reprint service avail. from ISI) **Indexed:** Biol.Abstr., Chem.Abstr., Curr.Cont., Ind.Med. **Document type:** academic/scholarly publication.
—CASDDS. **CCC.**
Refereed Serial

BLOOD COAGULATION FACTORS; current awareness service for researchers in life sciences. see *MEDICAL SCIENCES — Abstracting, Bibliographies, Statistics*

616.1   NO   ISSN 0803-7051
CODEN: BLPREG
BLOOD PRESSURE; for the advancement of hypertension research. (Supplement avail. (ISSN 0803-8023)) (Text in English) 1991. 6/yr. NOK 1035 in Nordic countries; elsewhere $177 (effective 1996). (Scandinavian Foundation for Cardiovascular Research) Scandinavian University Press, P.O. Box 2959 Toeyen, N-0608 Oslo, Norway. TEL 47-22-57-54-00. FAX 47-22-57-53-53. Ed. Lennart Hansson. **Indexed:** Excerp.Med. (1993-), Ind.Med. (1993-). **Document type:** academic/scholarly publication.
—BLDSC (2113.034000); CASDDS.
Description: Covers essential research from basic science to clinical discipline related to blood pressure research, including the physiology and pathophysiology of cerebrocardiovascular diseases, and renal hypertensive diseases.

616.1   NO   ISSN 0803-8023
CODEN: BPSUEY
BLOOD PRESSURE. SUPPLEMENT. (Text in English) 1991. irreg. (Scandinavian Foundation for Cardiovascular Research) Scandinavian University Press, P.O. Box 2959 Toeyen, N-0608 Oslo, Norway. TEL 47-22-57-54-00. FAX 47-22-57-53-53. **Indexed:** Excerp.Med. (1994-), Ind.Med. (1993-). **Document type:** academic/scholarly publication.
—BLDSC (2113.034100).

616.1   UK   ISSN 0969-6113
BRITISH JOURNAL OF CARDIOLOGY. 1993. m. £48 (foreign £72) to individuals; institutions £75 (foreign £110). Milestone Medical Media, The Media Suite, 3 Tyers Gate, London SE1 3HX, England. TEL 0171-403-6753. FAX 0171-378-1208. Ed.Bd. **Indexed:** Excerp.Med. (1995-). **Document type:** academic/scholarly publication.
—BLDSC (2307.010000).

C A SELECTS. ANTIARRHYTHMICS. see *MEDICAL SCIENCES — Abstracting, Bibliographies, Statistics*

616.1   IT   ISSN 1120-0421
C I - CARDIOVASCULAR IMAGING. 1989. q. $110. C E P I - Centro Editoriale Pubblicitario Italiano S.r.l., Via N. Tartaglia 3, 00197 Rome, Italy. TEL 39-6-8082101. FAX 39-6-8072458. Ed. Armando Dagianti. adv. contact: Marina Buongiorno. bk.rev. **Indexed:** Excerp.Med. (1993-). **Document type:** academic/scholarly publication.
—BLDSC (3051.464000).

616.1   US
C P DIGEST. (Cardiovascular Pulmonary) bi-m. $35. American Society of Cardiovascular Professionals - Society for Cardiovascular Management, 120 Falcon Dr., Unit 3, Fredericksburg, VA 22408. TEL 703-891-0079. FAX 703-898-2393. Ed. Peggy McElgunn. adv. circ. 3,000.

616.1   GW   ISSN 0940-8770
C V. (Cardiovascular); European journal of cardiovascular disease. (Text in English, French, German, Italian, Spanish) 1988. bi-m. DM.142. (Society for Advances in Cardiovascular Medicine e.V.) Miranda Communications GmbH, Guenterstalstr. 3, 79102 Freiburg, Germany. TEL 0761-74094. FAX 0761-75422. Ed. Dr. H.W. Heiss. adv.; bk.rev. circ. 15,000. (back issues avail.)
Formerly (until 1991): C V World Report (ISSN 0934-0815)

MEDICAL SCIENCES — CARDIOVASCULAR DISEASES 4331

616.1 CN ISSN 0828-282X
CODEN: CJCAEX
CANADIAN JOURNAL OF CARDIOLOGY. 1985. 11/yr. Can.$110 (foreign $157) to individuals; institutions Can.$212 (foreign $275). (Canadian Cardiovascular Society) Pulsus Group Inc., 2902 S. Sheridan Way, Oakville, ON L6J 7L6, Canada. TEL 905-829-4770. FAX 905-829-4799. Eds. Drs. R.E. Beamish, R.E. Blakley. adv.; bk.rev.; abstr.; bibl.; charts; illus.; index; circ. 16,000. (back issues avail.) **Indexed:** Biol.Abstr., Chem.Abstr., Curr.Cont., Excerp.Med., Ind.Med., NRN. **Document type:** trade publication.
—BLDSC (3030.500000); CASDDS; Faxon; Genuine Article; SWETS; UnCover. **CCC.**
Description: Original studies in the area of cardiovascular medicine.
Refereed Serial

CANADIAN JOURNAL OF CARDIOVASCULAR NURSING. see *MEDICAL SCIENCES — Nurses And Nursing*

CARDIAC ALERT. see *PHYSICAL FITNESS AND HYGIENE*

616.1 JA ISSN 0915-874X
CARDIAC PRACTICE. (Text in Japanese) 1990. 4/yr. 1990 Yen per no. Medikary Rebyusha - Medical Review Co., Ltd., 7-3, Hiranomachi 1-chome, Chuo-ku, Osaka 541, Japan.

616.1 US
CARDIO INTERNATIONAL. 1993. q. free to qualified personnel. Miller Freeman, Inc. (Subsidiary of: United Newspapers), 600 Harrison St., San Francisco, CA 94107. TEL 415-905-2200. FAX 415-905-2233. Ed. Joe Kornfeld. circ. 10,000.

616.1 US
CARDIO INTERVENTION. 1991. q. Miller Freeman, Inc. (Subsidiary of: United Newspapers), 600 Harrison St., San Francisco, CA 94107. TEL 415-905-2200. FAX 415-905-2235. Ed. Steve Stiles. adv.: B&W page $2450, color page $3770; trim 8 1/8 x 10 7/8. adv. circ. 10,000.
Description: Covers the field of interventional cardiology: angioplasty, angiography, and other therapeutic and diagnostic lab procedures.

616.1 IT ISSN 0393-1978
CODEN: CARDDJ
CARDIOLOGIA. (Summaries in English, French, German) 1955. m. $25. Societa Italiana di Cardiologia, Corso Francia 197, 00191 Rome, Italy. Ed. Antonio Strano. adv.; bk.rev.; charts; illus.; index. circ. 1,600. **Indexed:** Biol.Abstr., Chem.Abstr., Excerp.Med., Ind.Med.
—BLDSC (3051.272000); CASDDS; Faxon.
Formerly: Societa Italiana di Cardiologia. Bollettino (ISSN 0037-878X)

616.1 SP ISSN 1130-4014
CODEN: CAHIE
CARDIOLOGIA E HIPERTENSION. 6/yr. Saned, S.A., Paseo de la Habana 202-bis, 28036 Madrid, Spain. TEL 1-3594092. Ed. Makim Huerta. **Indexed:** Excerp.Med. (1992-).
—BLDSC (3051.285000).

616.12 IT ISSN 0945-8298
▼**LA CARDIOLOGIA NELLA PRATICA CLINICA.** 1994. q. L.120000. Springer-Verlag Milan, Via Podgora 4, 20122 Milan, Italy. TEL 39-2-55194656. FAX 39-2-55193360. Ed. E. Ambrosioni. (also avail. in microform from UMI; reprint service avail.) **Document type:** academic/scholarly publication.
—BLDSC (3051.351000).
Description: Bridges the gap between the research and clinical developments in the cardiology.
Refereed Serial

616.12 FR ISSN 0983-4532
CARDIOLOGIE. 1987. 6/yr. 230 Fr. Maloine Editeur, 27 rue de l'Ecole de Medecine, 75006 Paris, France. (Subscr. to: Publicite Batard, 38 rue Pascal, 75013 Paris, France) Ed. N. Gofstein. adv.; bk.rev.

616.12 NE ISSN 0929-7456
CARDIOLOGIE. (Text in Dutch, English) 1994. 11/yr. fl.163 (Belgium 3200 BEF; elsewhere $100). (Nederlandse Vereniging voor Cardiologie) Mediselect B.V., Postbus 28091, 2828 ZH Hoogland, Netherlands. TEL 31-33-808020. FAX 31-33-805881. (Co-sponsor: Nederlandse Hartstichting) Ed. E.E. van der Wall; Pub. J. Blom. adv. **Document type:** academic/scholarly publication.
—BLDSC (3051.355000).
Formed by the merger of (1987-1994): Nederlands Tijdschrift voor Cardiologie (ISSN 0921-4674); (1988-1994): Netherlands Journal of Cardiology (ISSN 0921-5018)
Description: Publishes article of interest to cardiologists and specialists in related fields.

616.1 FR ISSN 0766-3633
CARDIOLOGIE PRATIQUE. (Supplement avail.) 1985. w. (40/yr.). 300 F. L.E.N. Medical, 48 bis, av. Kleber, 75016 Paris, France. TEL 47-55-06-06. FAX 47-55-69-41. TELEX 640 748. Ed. Dr. J. Chapsal. **Document type:** newspaper.

CARDIOLOGIST'S COMPENDIUM OF DRUG THERAPY. see *PHARMACY AND PHARMACOLOGY*

616.12 FR ISSN 0769-0819
LE CARDIOLOGUE. 1965. m. (10/yr.). 550 F. P D G Communication, 30 rue d'Armaille, 75017 Paris, France. TEL 40-55-05-95. FAX 45-74-65-67.

616.1 SZ ISSN 0008-6312
RC681.A1 CODEN: CAGYAO
CARDIOLOGY; international journal of cardiovascular medicine, surgery and pathology. (Text in English) 1937. bi-m. 143.10 SFr.($110.10) to individuals; institutions 954 SFr.($734) (effective 1996). S. Karger AG, Allschwilerstr. 10, P.O. Box, CH-4009 Basel, Switzerland. TEL 061-3061111. FAX 061-3061234. E-mail: Karger@Karger.ch. Ed. J.S. Alpert. adv.; bk.rev.; charts; illus.; index. circ. 1,300. (also avail. in microfilm from PMC) **Indexed:** Biol.Abstr., Biotech.Abstr., Chem.Abstr., Curr.Adv.Ecol.Sci., Curr.Cont., Excerp.Med., Helminthol.Abstr., Ind.Med., Ind.Sci.Rev., Nutr.Abstr., Protozool.Abstr. **Document type:** academic/scholarly publication.
—BLDSC (3051.410000); CASDDS; Faxon; Genuine Article; SWETS; UnCover. **CCC.**
Formerly: Cardiologia.
Refereed Serial

616.1 US
CARDIOLOGY (BETHESDA). 1972. m. $59. American College of Cardiology, Communications Department, 9111 Old Georgetown Rd., Bethesda, MD 20814. TEL 301-897-5400. FAX 301-897-9745. Ed. Suzanne H. Howard. adv. contact: Sharon Ballas. charts. circ. 23,000. (looseleaf format) **Indexed:** Protozool.Abstr. **Document type:** newspaper.
Description: Describes the activities, services and products of the American College of Cardiology and provides information of interest to those involved in the practice of cardiovascular medicine.

616.2 US ISSN 0275-0066
RC681.A1
CARDIOLOGY (YEAR). 1981. a. $85. Butterworth - Heinemann, Part of the Reed Elsevier group, 313 Washington St., Newton, MA 02158. TEL 617-928-2500; 800-366-2665. FAX 617-928-2610. TELEX 880052. Ed.Bd. bibl.; charts; illus.; index. (also avail. in microform from UMI; back issues avail.) **Indexed:** Chem.Abstr., NRN, Protozool.Abstr., Sci.Cit.Ind. **Document type:** academic/scholarly publication, monographic series.
—BLDSC (3051.415000).

616.12 US ISSN 0888-8418
CARDIOLOGY BOARD REVIEW. 1984. m. $60 free to qualified personnels. M R A Publications, Inc., 3 Greenwich Office Park, Greenwich, CT 06831-5154. TEL 203-629-3550. FAX 203-629-2536. Ed. Dr. Peter F. Cohn. adv.: B&W page $3080, color page $3620; trim 8 1/8 x 11. bk.rev.; bibl.; charts; illus. circ. 32,129. (back issues avail.) **Indexed:** Excerp.Med.
Description: Revised and updated articles that originally appeared in the literature of cardiology.
Refereed Serial

616.12 US ISSN 0733-8651
RC681.A1 CODEN: CACLE3
CARDIOLOGY CLINICS. 1983. q. $120 (foreign $149) (effective 1996). W.B. Saunders Co. (Subsidiary of: Harcourt Brace & Company), Curtis Center, 3rd Fl., Independence Sq. W., Philadelphia, PA 19106-3399. TEL 215-238-7800. FAX 215-238-6445. (Subscr. to: Periodicals Fulfillment, W.B. Saunders Co., 6277 Sea Harbor Dr., 4th Fl., Orlando, FL 32891-4800. TEL 800-654-2452. FAX 800-874-6418) Ed. Dr. Michael H. Crawford. (also avail. in microform from UMI) **Indexed:** CINAHL, Curr.Adv.Ecol.Sci., Excerp.Med., INIS Atomind. **Document type:** academic/scholarly publication.
●Also available online. Vendor(s): Ovid Technologies.
—BLDSC (3051.417000); Genuine Article; SWETS; UMI; UnCover. **CCC.**
Description: Each issue discusses an aspect of heart disease in detail.

616.12 CN ISSN 0844-5575
CARDIOLOGY IN PRACTICE. 1989. m. $48. M P I Medical Publishing Inc., 14 Ronan Ave., Toronto, ON M4N 2X9, Canada. TEL 416-481-6384. Ed. Dr. Harry Rakowski. adv. circ. 22,028. (tabloid format)

616.12 US ISSN 1061-5377
CODEN: CRVIE
CARDIOLOGY IN REVIEW. 1993. bi-m. $95 to individuals; institutions $145 (effective 1995). Williams & Wilkins, 382 E. Preston St., Baltimore, MD 21202. TEL 410-528-4000; 800-638-6423. FAX 410-528-4312. Ed. Dr. Douglas P. Zipes. circ. 3,500. (also avail. in microfilm from WWS) **Indexed:** Excerp.Med. 1995-). **Document type:** academic/scholarly publication.
—BLDSC (3051.433800). **CCC.**
Description: Covers pathogenesis, diagnosis, clinical course, prevention and treatment of cardiovascular disorders.

616.1 US ISSN 1058-3661
CARDIOLOGY IN THE ELDERLY. 1993. bi-m $144.95 to individuals; institutions $295; residents $99.95. Current Science, 400 Market St., Ste. 700, Philadelphia, PA 19106. TEL 215-574-2210; 800-552-5866. FAX 215-574-3533. (And: Current Science Ltd., 34-42 Cleveland St., London W1P 6LB, England. TEL 0171-323-0323. FAX 0171-636-6911) Eds. A. John Camm, Franz H. Messerli. adv.: B&W page $580; color page $1980; trim 8 1/2 x 11; adv. contact: Steven Miller. illus. circ. 1,235. **Indexed:** Excerp.Med. (1995-). **Document type:** academic/scholarly publication.
—BLDSC (3051.431000); ADONIS; Genuine Article. **CCC.**
Description: Directed toward researchers and practicing cardiologists working with the elderly. Covers the foremost data and research. Each issue features a bibliography of the current world literature published during the previous month.

CARDIOLOGY JOURNAL CLUB JOURNAL. see *MEDICAL SCIENCES — Abstracting, Bibliographies, Statistics*

616.1 US ISSN 0163-1675
RC681.A1
CARDIOLOGY UPDATE; reviews for physicians. 1979. irreg., latest 1990. price varies. Elsevier Science Inc., 655 Ave. of the Americas, New York, NY 10010. TEL 212-989-5800. FAX 212-633-3990. TELEX 420643 AEP UI. Ed. E. Rapaport. **Document type:** academic/scholarly publication.
Refereed Serial

616.1 IT ISSN 0390-5403
CARDIOSTIMOLAZIONE. (Text in English and Italian) 1983. q. $120. (Italian Society of Cardiac Pacing) Edizioni Luigi Pozzi s.r.l., Via Panama 68, 00198 Rome, Italy. TEL 39-6-8553548. FAX 39-6-8554105. Ed. F. Bellocci. adv.; bk.rev. circ. 5,000.
Description: Covers cardiology and cardiac pacing.

MEDICAL SCIENCES — CARDIOVASCULAR DISEASES

616.1   US   ISSN 1046-1795
CARDIOTHORACIC AND VASCULAR ANESTHESIA UPDATE. a. $136 to individuals (foreign $157); institutions $136 (foreign $157) (effective 1994). W.B. Saunders Co. (Subsidiary of: Harcourt Brace & Company), Curtis Center, 3rd Fl., Independence Sq. W., Philadelphia, PA 19106-3399. TEL 215-238-7800. FAX 215-238-6445. (Subscr. to: Periodicals Fulfillment, W.B. Saunders Co., 6277 Sea Harbor Dr., 4th Fl., Orlando, FL 32891-4800. TEL 800-654-2452. FAX 800-874-6418) Ed. Dr. Joel Kaplan. (looseleaf format) **Document type:** academic/scholarly publication.
—BLDSC (3051.437250); UMI. **CCC.**
Description: Reviews current problems or procedures in the field.

616.1   US   ISSN 1041-5521
CARDIOTHORACIC SURGERY SERIES. 1986. irreg., vol.3, 1987. price varies. Marcel Dekker, Inc., 270 Madison Ave., New York, NY 10016. TEL 212-696-9000. FAX 212-685-4540. TELEX 421419.
Refereed Serial

616.1   SP   ISSN 1133-6846
CARDIOVASCULAR; actualidad internacional en enfermedades del cardiacas. 1980. m. (13/yr.). 4820 ptas.($48) Haymarket, S.A., Travesera Gracia 17-21, 5o 2o, 08022 Barcelona, Spain. TEL 3-237-22-66. FAX 3-237-66-88. Ed. Dr. F.B. Ferrer Ruscalleda. circ. 10,000.
Formerly (until 1993): Cardiovascular Reviews and Reports (Edicion Espanola) (ISSN 0211-6553)

616.1   US   ISSN 0174-1551
CODEN: CAIRDG
CARDIOVASCULAR AND INTERVENTIONAL RADIOLOGY; a journal of imaging in diagnosis and treatment. 1977. 6/yr. $218 (effective 1996). (European College of Angiography) Springer-Verlag, Journals, 175 Fifth Ave., New York, NY 10010. TEL 212-460-1500. FAX 212-473-6272. (N. American subscr. to: Journal Fulfillment Services, Box 2485, Secaucus, NJ 07096-2491. TEL 800-777-4643. FAX 201-348-4505; Subscr. outside N. America: Heidelberger Platz 3, 1000 Berlin 33, Germany. TEL 030-8207-1. FAX 030-8214091) (Co-sponsors: European Society of Cardiovascular and International Radiology; North American Society of Cardiac Radiology) Ed. Klemens Barth. adv.; bk.rev.; illus. (also avail. in microform from UMI; reprint service avail. from ISI) **Indexed:** Curr.Cont., Excerp.Med., Ind.Med., INIS Atomind., Kidney. **Document type:** academic/scholarly publication.
●Also available online. Vendor(s): FIZ Technik.
—BLDSC (3051.438000); Faxon; Genuine Article; SWETS; UMI; UnCover. **CCC.**
Formerly: Cardiovascular Radiology (ISSN 0342-7196)
Description: Examines developments in the diagnostic techniques of this specialty.
Refereed Serial

CARDIOVASCULAR DRUG ALERTS. see *PHARMACY AND PHARMACOLOGY*

615   US   ISSN 0897-5957
CODEN: CDREEA
CARDIOVASCULAR DRUG REVIEWS. 1983. 4/yr. Neva Press Inc., Box 347, Branford, CT 06405. TEL 203-272-5338. **Indexed:** Excerp.Med. **Document type:** academic/scholarly publication.
—BLDSC (3051.461500); CASDDS; Genuine Article; SWETS. **CCC.**
Former titles (until 1988): New Cardiovascular Drugs (ISSN 0891-3692); (until 1985): New Drugs Annual, Cardiovascular Drugs (ISSN 0742-387X)

616.1   US   ISSN 0920-3206
RM345   CODEN: CDTHET
CARDIOVASCULAR DRUGS AND THERAPY. 1987. bi-m. fl.637 to institutions; $409 to institutions in U.S. (effective 1996). (International Society of Cardiovascular Pharmacotherapy) Kluwer Academic Publishers Boston, Box 358, Accord Sta., Hingham, MA 02018-0358. TEL 617-871-6300. FAX 617-871-6528. (Dist. outside N. America by: Kluwer Academic Publishers Group, P.O. Box 322, 3300 AH Dordrecht, Netherlands. TEL 31-78-392392. FAX 31-78-546474) Eds. Lionel H. Opie, Elliot Rapaport. adv.; bk.rev. (also avail. in microform from UMI; back issues avail.; reprint service avail. from SWZ,UMI) **Indexed:** Biol.Abstr., Curr.Cont., Excerp.Med., Ind.Med., Inpharma, Int.Abstr.Biol.Sci., Reac., Sci.Cit.Ind. **Document type:** academic/scholarly publication.
—BLDSC (3051.462500); ADONIS; CASDDS; Faxon; Genuine Article; SWETS; UMI; UnCover. **CCC.**
Description: Articles on laboratory investigators and clinical studies related to cardiovascular drug therapy.
Refereed Serial

616.1   AT
CARDIOVASCULAR GUIDELINES. 1991. irreg. (every 2-3 years). Aus.$18. Victorian Medical Postgraduate Foundation Inc., Therapeutics Committee, Chelsea House, Level 3, 55 Flemington Rd., N. Melbourne, Vic. 3051, Australia. TEL 03-329-1566. FAX 03-326-5632. (Co-sponsor: Victorian Drug Usage Advisory Committee) bk.rev. **Document type:** academic/scholarly publication.
Description: Gives concrete recommendations for rational therapy of cardiovascular disease and where necessary justifies the choice.

616.1   SA   ISSN 1015-9657
CODEN: CJSAE
CARDIOVASCULAR JOURNAL OF SOUTHERN AFRICA. 1990. 5/yr. (Medical Association of South Africa) M A S A Publications, Private Bag X1, Pinelands 7430, South Africa. TEL 27-21-531-3081. FAX 27-21-531-4126. **Indexed:** Excerp.Med. (1995-). **Document type:** academic/scholarly publication.

616.1   US   ISSN 1054-8807
CODEN: CATHE8
CARDIOVASCULAR PATHOLOGY. 1992. bi-m. $267 to institutions (effective 1996). (Society for Cardiovascular Pathology) Elsevier Science Inc., 655 Ave. of the Americas, New York, NY 10010. TEL 212-989-5800. FAX 212-633-3990. TELEX 42063 AEP UI. (Subscr. to: Box 882, Madison Sq. Sta., New York, NY 10159-0882) Ed. Dr. Stephen M. Factor. (also avail. in microform from UMI; back issues avail.) **Indexed:** Excerp.Med. (1994-). **Document type:** academic/scholarly publication.
—BLDSC (3051.470700); CASDDS; Genuine Article; SWETS; UnCover. **CCC.**
Description: Papers on disease-oriented morphology and pathobiology from pathologists and investigators in the cardiovascular field.
Refereed Serial

CARDIOVASCULAR PHARMACOLOGY. see *PHARMACY AND PHARMACOLOGY*

CARDIOVASCULAR PHYSIOLOGY. see *BIOLOGY — Physiology*

616.1   NE   ISSN 0008-6363
CODEN: CVREAU
CARDIOVASCULAR RESEARCH. (Text in English) 1967. m. fl.840($512) (effective 1996). Elsevier Science B.V., P.O. Box 211, 1000 AE Amsterdam, Netherlands. TEL 31-20-4853911. FAX 31-20-4853598.
E-mail: nlinfo-f@elsevier.nl; usinfo-f@elsevier.com; forinfo-kyf04035@niftyserve.or.jp; Site addr.: http://www.elsevier.nl/. (Subscr. in U.S. and Canada to: Elsevier Science, Box 882, Madison Sq. Sta., New York, NY 10159-0882. TEL 212-989-5800. FAX 212-633-3950) (Co-sponsor: British Cardiac Society) Ed. David J. Hearse. adv.; abstr.; index. (also avail. in microform from UMI; reprint service avail. from UMI) **Indexed:** Biol.Abstr., Biotech.Abstr., Chem.Abstr., Curr.Adv.Ecol.Sci., Curr.Cont., Excerp.Med., Helminthol.Abstr., Ind.Med., Ind.Sci.Rev., NRN, Nutr.Abstr., Sci.Cit.Ind. **Document type:** academic/scholarly publication.
—BLDSC (3051.490000); ADONIS; CASDDS; Faxon; Genuine Article; SWETS; UMI; UnCover. **CCC.**
Incorporates (1990-1995): Cardioscience (ISSN 1015-5007)
Description: Strives to promote links between fundamental research and clinical cardiology,and to enhance the understanding of the pathophysiology of cardiovascular disease with an international scope.
Refereed Serial

616.1   US   ISSN 0197-3118
CARDIOVASCULAR REVIEWS & REPORTS. 1980. m. $65 to individuals (foreign $80); institutions $80 (foreign $95). Cardiovascular Reviews & Reports, Inc., 777 W. Putnam Ave., Greenwich, CT 06830-5014. TEL 203-531-0450. FAX 203-531-0533. Ed. Dr. John H. Laragh. adv. circ. 70,026. (back issues avail.) **Indexed:** Excerp.Med., NRN.
—BLDSC (3051.513000); Faxon; SWETS; UMI.
Refereed Serial

616.12   US   ISSN 1130-7501
CODEN: CRFAE2
CARDIOVASCULAR RISK FACTORS; an international journal. 1991. q. $98 to individuals (foreign $106); institutions $220 (foreign $236) (effective 1996). Lippincott - Raven Press, 227 E. Washington Sq., Philadelphia, PA 19106. TEL 215-238-4200. Ed. A. Fernandez-Cruz, W. Castelli. **Indexed:** Excerp.Med. (1992-). **Document type:** academic/scholarly publication.
—BLDSC (3051.514000).
Description: Publishes original research and review articles on factors important to the prevention of coronary heart disease and other diseases of the heart and blood vessels.
Refereed Serial

617.41   US   ISSN 0069-0406
CARDIOVASCULAR SURGERY. (Subseries of: American Heart Association Journals) 1962. a. $10 (foreign $20). American Heart Association, Council on Cardiovascular Surgery, 7272 Greenville Ave., Dallas, TX 75231-4596. TEL 214-706-1310. FAX 214-691-6342. (Subscr. to: Box 843543, Dallas, TX 75284-3543) adv. circ. 23,000. **Indexed:** Ind.Med. **Document type:** monographic series.
Refereed Serial

616.1 617   UK   ISSN 0967-2109
CARDIOVASCULAR SURGERY. 1993. bi-m. £145($231) (effective 1996). (International Society for Cardiovascular Surgery) Butterworth - Heinemann, Part of the Reed Elsevier group, Linacre House, Jordan Hill, Oxford OX2 8DP, England. TEL 0865-310366. FAX 0865-310898. TELEX 83111 BHPOXF G. (Subscr. to: Elsevier Science Ltd., P.O. Box 800, Kidlington, Oxford OX5 1DX, England. TEL 44-865-843000. FAX 44-865-843010; Subscr. in U.S. and Canada to: Elsevier Science, 660 White Plains Rd., Tarrytown, NY 10591-5153. TEL 914-524-9200. FAX 914-333-2444) (also avail. in microform from UMI; back issues avail.) **Indexed:** Excerp.Med. (1994-), Ind.Med. (1994-). **Document type:** academic/scholarly publication.
—BLDSC (3051.515050); SWETS; UMI. **CCC.**
Refereed Serial

MEDICAL SCIENCES — CARDIOVASCULAR DISEASES 4333

616.1 US ISSN 0098-6569
RC683 CODEN: CCDID
CATHETERIZATION AND CARDIOVASCULAR DIAGNOSIS. 1975. m. $936 (foreign $1122) (effective 1996). John Wiley & Sons, Inc., Journals, 605 Third Ave., New York, NY 10158. TEL 212-850-6645. FAX 212-850-6021. TELEX 12-7063. E-mail: SUBINFO@JWILEY.COM. (Subscr. outside the Americas to: John Wiley & Sons Ltd., Baffins Ln., Chichester, W. Sussex PO19 1UD, England. TEL 44-1243-779777. FAX 44-1243-776128) Ed. Dr. Frank J. Hildner. adv.; bibl.; charts; illus. (also avail. in microform from UMI; back issues avail.; reprint service avail. from ISI) **Indexed:** Biol.Abstr., Curr.Cont., Excerp.Med., Ind.Med., Ind.Sci.Rev., INIS Atomind., Sci.Cit.Ind. **Document type:** academic/scholarly publication.
—BLDSC (3092.990000); EMDOCS; Faxon; Genuine Article; SWETS; UnCover. **CCC.**
Description: Devoted to invasive cardiology, Emphasizes angioplasty and the newest techniques of interventional cardiology.
Refereed Serial

CHEST; the cardiopulmonary and critical care journal. see *MEDICAL SCIENCES — Respiratory Diseases*

616.12 US ISSN 0894-5853
CODEN: CCRDEY
CHOICES IN CARDIOLOGY. 1988. bi-m. $48 (effective 1995). Choices Publishing Group, Inc., 129 Washington St., Hoboken, NJ 07030. TEL 201-792-1900. FAX 201-792-3955. Ed. Dr. Alfred F. Parisi. adv. contact: H. Thomas McCarren. circ. 17,000 (controlled). **Indexed:** Excerp.Med. (1994-).
Refereed Serial

616.1 016 US ISSN 0009-7322
RC681.A1 CODEN: CIRCAZ
CIRCULATION (DALLAS). (Supplement avail. (ISSN 0069-4193)) 1950. m. $236 (foreign $362) (effective 1996). American Heart Association, 7272 Greenville Ave., Dallas, TX 75231-4596. TEL 214-706-1310. FAX 214-691-6342. (Subscr. to: Box 843543, Dallas, TX 75284-3543) Ed. Dr. John Ross Jr. adv.; abstr.; bibl.; illus.; index. circ. 25,000. (also avail. in microform from PMC,UMI; back issues avail.; reprint service avail. from UMI) **Indexed:** Abstr.Hyg., Abstr.Inter.Med., AIM, Behav.Med.Abstr., Biol.Abstr., Biotech.Abstr., C.I.S. Abstr., Chem.Abstr., CINAHL, Curr.Adv.Ecol.Sci., Curr.Cont., Excerp.Med., Ind.Med., Ind.Sci.Rev., Int.Nurs.Ind., Kidney, NRN, Nutr.Abstr., Pig News & Info., Protozool.Abstr., Risk Abstr., Sci.Cit.Ind., Trop.Dis.Bull. **Document type:** academic/scholarly publication.
●Also available online. Vendor(s): Ovid Technologies (JWAT).
—BLDSC (3265.200000); CASDDS; Faxon; Genuine Article; SWETS; UMI; UnCover. **CCC.**
Description: For cardiologists and internists; presents clinical and laboratory research relevant to cardiovascular diseases.
Refereed Serial

616.1 SP ISSN 1134-5187
▼**CIRCULATION (EDICION ESPANOLA).** 1994. 8/yr. 10500 ptas.($115) (effective 1995). Editorial Garsi, S.A., Juan Bravo 46, 28006 Madrid, Spain. TEL 34-1-4021212. FAX 34-1-4020954.

616.1 US ISSN 0069-4193
CODEN: CISUAQ
CIRCULATION. SUPPLEMENT. 1964. irreg., latest 1993. included in subscr. to Circulation. American Heart Association, 7272 Greenville Ave., Dallas, TX 75231-4596. TEL 214-706-1310. FAX 214-691-6342. (Subscr. to: Box 8483543, Dallas, TX 75284-3543) adv. circ. 27,000. (reprint service avail. from UMI) **Indexed:** Ind.Med. **Document type:** academic/scholarly publication.
—CASDDS.

616.1 US ISSN 0009-7330
RC681.A1 CODEN: CIRUAL
CIRCULATION RESEARCH. (Irregular supplement avail.) 1953. m. $270 (foreign $336) (effective 1996). American Heart Association, 7272 Greenville Ave., Dallas, TX 75231-4596. TEL 214-706-1310. FAX 214-691-6342. (Subscr. to: Box 843543, Dallas, TX 75284-3543) Ed. Dr. Stephen Vather. adv.; charts; illus.; stat.; index. circ. 3,750. (also avail. in microform from MIM,PMC,UMI; back issues avail.; reprint service avail. from UMI) **Indexed:** Biol.Abstr., Biotech.Abstr., Chem.Abstr., Curr.Adv.Biochem., Curr.Adv.Cell & Devel.Biol., Curr.Adv.Ecol.Sci., Curr.Cont., Diab.Cont., Excerp.Med., Ind.Med., Ind.Sci.Rev., Ind.Vet., INIS Atomind., NRN, Nutr.Abstr., Sci.Cit.Ind., Vet.Bull.
●Also available online. Vendor(s): Ovid Technologies.
—BLDSC (3265.300000); CASDDS; Faxon; Genuine Article; SWETS; UMI; UnCover. **CCC.**
Description: Documents research advances in basic science, research, and experimental medicine.
Refereed Serial

616.1 IT ISSN 0392-1344
CLINICA & TERAPIA CARDIOVASCOLARE. (Text in Italian; summaries in English) 1980. q. L.60000($60) C I C Edizioni Internazionali s.r.l., Via L. Spallanzani 11, 00161 Rome, Italy. TEL 06-8412673. FAX 06-44242033. TELEX 622099 CIC. Dirs. A. Dagianti, G. Ricci. **Indexed:** Chem.Abstr., Excerp.Med.
—BLDSC (3286.203500). **CCC.**

616.1 SP ISSN 0212-1808
CODEN: CCAREP
CLINICA CARDIOVASCULAR. 1982. 6/yr. 5000 ptas.($100) (Europe $60). (Universidad de Navarra (Pamplona)) Alpe Editores, S.A., Pedro Rico, 27, 28029 Madrid, Spain. TEL 34-1-7338811. FAX 34-1-3159652. Eds. Dr. Plaza, Dr. Tormo; Pub. A. Alvarez. adv.; color page 160000 ptas.; trim 210 x 280; adv. contact: C. Alvarez. circ. 6,500 (controlled).
—BLDSC (3286.190000). **CCC.**

616.136 SP ISSN 0214-9168
CLINICA E INVESTIGACION EN ARTERIOSCLEROSIS. (Includes a supplement) q. 4400 ptas.($35) to non-members. (Sociedad Espanola de Arteriosclerosis) Ediciones Doyma S.A., Travesera de Gracia, 17-21, 08021 Barcelona, Spain. TEL 34-1-200-07-11. FAX 34-1-209-11-36. TELEX 51964 INK E. Ed. R. Carmena Rodriguez. adv.: page 180000 ptas.; trim 210 x 280; adv. contact: Olga Gomez. circ. 2,000.
Description: Covers basic science aspects such as etiology, epidemiology, physiopathology, and the diagnosis and treatment of arteriosclerosis and related processes.

616.1 US ISSN 1064-1963
RC685.H8 CODEN: CEHYER
CLINICAL AND EXPERIMENTAL HYPERTENSION. 1978. 8/yr. $1195. Marcel Dekker Journals, 270 Madison Ave., New York, NY 10016. TEL 212-696-9000. FAX 212-685-4540. TELEX 421419. (Subscr. to: Box 5017, Monticello, NY 12701) Ed. Mustafa F. Lokhandwala. adv. contact: Eridania Perez. bk.rev.; index. (also avail. in microform from RPI; back issues avail.) **Indexed:** Biol.Dig., Biotech.Abstr., Chem.Abstr., Curr.Adv.Cell & Devel.Biol., Curr.Adv.Ecol.Sci., Curr.Adv.Genetics & Molec.Biol., Curr.Cont., Dent.Ind., Excerp.Med., Ind.Med., Ind.Sci.Rev., NRN, Sci.Cit.Ind. **Document type:** academic/scholarly publication.
—BLDSC (3286.250500); ADONIS; CASDDS; Faxon; Genuine Article; SWETS; UMI. **CCC.**
Formerly: Clinical and Experimental Hypertension. Part A: Theory and Practice (ISSN 0730-0077); Which supersedes in part: Clinical and Experimental Hypertension (ISSN 0148-3927)
Refereed Serial

616.1 US ISSN 0160-9289
CODEN: CLCADC
CLINICAL CARDIOLOGY; international journal for cardiovascular diseases. 1978. m. $80 (foreign $126.50). Clinical Cardiology Publishing Company, Inc., Box 832, Mahwah, NJ 07430-0832. TEL 201-818-1010. FAX 201-818-0086. TELEX 220883 TAUR. Ed. Dr. C. Richard Conti; Pub. Tony Bourgholtzer. adv. contact: Lillian Conly. bk.rev. circ. 31,683. **Indexed:** Biol.Abstr., Curr.Cont., Excerp.Med., Ind.Med., Ind.Sci.Rev., INIS Atomind., NRN, Sci.Cit.Ind. **Document type:** trade publication.
—BLDSC (3286.265000); CASDDS; Faxon; Genuine Article; SWETS; UnCover. **CCC.**
Description: Provides a forum for the coordination of clinical research in cardiology and cardiovascular surgery; also publishes the results of experimental studies closely related to clinical problems.
Refereed Serial

616.1 US ISSN 0741-4218
CLINICAL CARDIOLOGY ALERT. 1982. m. $115. American Health Consultants, Inc., Six Piedmont Center, Ste. 400, Atlanta, GA 30305. TEL 800-688-2421. FAX 800-284-3291. Ed. Dr. Michael Crawford. index. circ. 2,265. (also avail. in audio cassette; reprint service avail.) **Document type:** newsletter.
Formerly: Cardiology Alert.
Description: Provides the latest advances and clinical developments in cardiology and cardiovascular disease.

616.1 SP
CLINICAS CARDIOLOGICAS DE NORTEAMERICA. Spanish translation of: Cardiology Clinics of North America. 1984. 4/yr. 13144 ptas.($80) Interamericana de Espana, S.A., Division de Ciencias de la Salud de McGraw-Hill, Calle Manuel Ferrero, 13, 28036 Madrid, Spain. TEL 315-0340. FAX 733-6627. charts; illus.; cum.index.

CLINICIAN'S MANUAL ON HYPERLIPIDEMIA (YEAR). see *MEDICAL SCIENCES — Abstracting, Bibliographies, Statistics*

CLINICIAN'S MANUAL ON HYPERTENSION (YEAR). see *MEDICAL SCIENCES — Abstracting, Bibliographies, Statistics*

COEUR ET SANTE. see *PHYSICAL FITNESS AND HYGIENE*

616.12 US ISSN 8756-9086
CONNECTIVE ISSUES. 1984. q. $25 membership. National Marfan Foundation, 382 Main St., Pt. Washington, NY 11050. TEL 516-883-8712; 800-862-7326. FAX 516-883-8712. Ed. Eileen Masciak. circ. 12,000. (back issues avail.) **Document type:** newsletter.
Description: Provides information on the Marfan syndrome, an inherited disorder of connective tissue that can cause heart disease, orthopedic problems and blindness.

616.1 IT
CONTROVERSIES IN CARDIOLOGY. vol.3, no.3, 1991. q. Zambon Group S.p.A., Via Lillo del Duca 10, Bresso (MI), Italy. Ed. Germano Marchetti.

616.1 XR ISSN 0010-8650
CODEN: COVAAN
COR ET VASA; international journal of cardiology. (Text in English, French, and German; separate edition in Russian) 1958. 6/yr. 90 Kc. (Ceska Kardiologicka Spolecnost) Praha Publishing Ltd., Anglicka 19, 120 00 Prague 2, Czech Republic. FAX 42-0-2-202788. (Dist. in Western countries by: Karger Libri A G, Petersgraben 31, CH-4011 Basel, Switzerland) (Co-sponsor: Klinika Kardiologie) Ed. Eva Kolencikova. adv.; bk.rev.; index. **Indexed:** Biol.Abstr., Chem.Abstr., Curr.Adv.Ecol.Sci., Curr.Cont., Excerp.Med., Ind.Med., Nutr.Abstr.
—BLDSC (3470.250000); CASDDS; Faxon; Genuine Article; SWETS.

616.1 GW
▼**COR EUROPAEUM;** european journal for cardiac interventions. (Text in English) 1994. q. DM.232($139) Ecomed Verlagsgesellschaft AG & Co. KG, Rudolff-Diesel-Str. 3, 86899 Landsberg, Germany. TEL 08191-125500. FAX 08191-125513. Ed. Felix Unger. adv. contact: Luitgard Ruile. circ. 2,000 (paid). **Document type:** academic/scholarly publication.
Description: Provides insight into all facets of cardiac interventions.

MEDICAL SCIENCES — CARDIOVASCULAR DISEASES

CORE JOURNALS IN CARDIOLOGY. see *MEDICAL SCIENCES — Abstracting, Bibliographies, Statistics*

CORONARY ARTERY DISEASE. see *MEDICAL SCIENCES — Abstracting, Bibliographies, Statistics*

616.1   IT
CUORE; rivista di cardiochirurgia e cardiologia. vol.11, 1994. bi-m. (Mediterranean Association of Cardiology and Cardiac Surgery) Casa Editrice Scientifica Internazionale, Via Cremona 19, 00161 Rome, Italy. TEL 39-6-44290783. FAX 39-6-44241-598.
   Refereed Serial

616.12   IT
CUORE E SALUTE. 6/yr. Centro Lotta contra l'Infarto, Viale Bruno Buozzi 60, 00197 Rome, Italy. TEL 39-6-3218205. FAX 39-6-3221068. Ed. Franco Fontanini. adv.: B&W page L.2700000, color page L.3500000; 190 x 260; adv. contact: Sandra del Papa. circ. 41,000. cols./p.: 2.

616.1   615   US   ISSN 1070-4345
RM345
CURRENT CARDIOVASCULAR DRUGS (YEAR). 1992. biennial. $39.95. Current Science, 400 Market St., Ste. 700, Philadelphia, PA 19106. TEL 312-733-2980; 800-892-7456. FAX 312-733-3107. (And: Current Science Ltd., 34-42 Cleveland St., London W1P 6LB, England. TEL 0171-323-0323. FAX 0171-636-6911) Ed.Bd. illus. **Document type:** academic/scholarly publication.
   Description: Guide to cardiovascular drugs; includes introductions to each drug class; information on each approved drug describing dosage guidelines and prescribing information and a full reference list.

CURRENT CRITICAL PROBLEMS IN VASCULAR SURGERY. see *MEDICAL SCIENCES — Surgery*

CURRENT OPINION IN CARDIOLOGY. see *MEDICAL SCIENCES — Abstracting, Bibliographies, Statistics*

CURRENT OPINION IN LIPIDOLOGY. see *MEDICAL SCIENCES — Abstracting, Bibliographies, Statistics*

616.12   US   ISSN 0146-2806
CURRENT PROBLEMS IN CARDIOLOGY. Short title: C P C. 1976. m. $78 to individuals (foreign $87); institutions $100 (foreign $109); students $45 (foreign $54); (effective Jan. 1994). Mosby - Year Book, Inc. (Subsidiary of: Times Mirror Company), 11830 Westline Indusrial Dr., St. Louis, MO 63146. TEL 314-872-8370; 800-325-4177. FAX 314-432-1380. Ed. Robert A. O'Rourke. cum.index. circ. 3,708. (also avail. in microform from UMI; back issues avail.; reprint service avail. from UMI) **Indexed:** Curr.Cont., Excerp.Med., Ind.Med., SSCI.
—BLDSC (3501.347000); Genuine Article; SWETS; UMI; UnCover. **CCC.**
   Description: A fully referenced monographic journal that consists of original review articles on practical clinical topics.

616.1   NE
CURRENT STATUS OF CLINICAL CARDIOLOGY. 1985. irreg., latest 1990. Kluwer Academic Publishers, Postbus 17, 3300 AA Dordrecht, Netherlands. TEL 31-78-392392. FAX 31-78-392254. (Dist. by: Kluwer Academic Publishers Group, P.O. Box 322, 3300 AH Dordrecht, Netherlands. TEL 31-78-392392. FAX 31-78-546474; N. America dist. addr.: Box 358, Accord Sta., Hingham, MA 02018-0358. TEL 617-871-6600. FAX 617-871-6528) (back issues avail.) **Document type:** monographic series.
   Refereed Serial

616.1   NE
CURRENT TOPICS IN CARDIOLOGY. (Text in English) 1990. irreg., vol.3, 1992. price varies. Elsevier Science B.V., Books Division, P.O. Box 211, 1000 AE Amsterdam, Netherlands. TEL 31-20-4853911. FAX 31-20-4853705. E-mail: nlinfo-f@elsevier.nl; usinfo-f@elsevier.com; forinfo-kyf04035@niftyserve.or.jp; Site addr.: http://www.elsevier.nl/. (Subscr. in U.S. and Canada to: Elsevier Science Inc., Box 882, Madison Sq. Sta., New York, NY 10159-0882. TEL 212-989-5800. FAX 212-633-3680) **Document type:** monographic series.
   Refereed Serial

616.1   UK
CURRENT TOPICS IN HYPERTENSION. irreg., latest 1994. £4. Graffham Press Ltd., 6 York Pl., Edinburgh EH1 3EP, Scotland. TEL 0131-556-7887. FAX 0131-556-1129. **Document type:** proceedings.

616.1   US   ISSN 1054-917X
CURRENTS IN EMERGENCY CARDIAC CARE. 1990. q. $12 to individuals (foreign $16); institutions $20 (foreign $24). American Heart Association, Citizen CPR Foundation, 7272 Greenville Ave., Dallas, TX 75231-4596. TEL 214-706-1310. FAX 214-691-6342. E-mail: fgse@amhrt.org. (Subscr. to: Box 843543, Dallas, TX 75284-3543) Ed. F.G. Stoddard. **Document type:** newsletter.
—**CCC.**
   Description: For EMS personnel and healthcare professionals. Offers scientific information about ideas, developments, and trends in emergency cardiac care.

616.1   US   ISSN 1046-6959
DEVELOPMENTS IN CARDIOLOGY. m. $150 to individuals (foreign $215); institutions $160 ($225). (Dannemiller Memorial Educational Foundation) W.B. Saunders (Subsidiary of: Harcourt Brace & Company), Curtis Center, Independence Sq. W., Philadelphia, PA 19106-3399. TEL 215-238-7800. FAX 215-238-6445. (Subscr. to: Periodicals Fulfillment, W.B. Saunders Co., 6277 Sea Harbor Dr., 4th Fl., Orlando, FL 32891-4800. TEL 800-654-2452. FAX 800-874-6418) Ed. Dr. Gregory L. Freeman. **Document type:** academic/scholarly publication.
   Supersedes (in 1989): Progress in Cardiology (Philadelphia) (ISSN 1041-3375)
   Description: Keeps readers up to date on the developments in the diagnosis and treatment of heart-related diseases.

616.1   NE   ISSN 0166-9842
CODEN: DCMEDM
DEVELOPMENTS IN CARDIOVASCULAR MEDICINE. (Text in English) 1979. irreg., vol.156, 1994. price varies. Kluwer Academic Publishers, Postbus 17, 3300 AA Dordrecht, Netherlands. TEL 31-78-392392. FAX 31-78-392254. TELEX 29245 KAPG NL. (Dist. by: Kluwer Academic Publishers Group, P.O. Box 322, 3300 AH Dordrecht, Netherlands. TEL 31-78-392392. FAX 31-78-546474; N. America dist. addr.: Box 358, Accord Sta., Hingham, MA 02018-0358. TEL 617-871-6600. FAX 617-871-6528) **Indexed:** INSPEC. **Document type:** monographic series.
—BLDSC (3579.067400); CASDDS.
   Refereed Serial

615.65   IT   ISSN 0012-544X
DONO. 1959. 9/yr. free. Associazione Friulana Donatori di Sangue, Ospedale General Regionale, Piazza della Misericordia, 33100 Udine, Italy. TEL 0432-481818. Ed. Gianpaolo Sbaiz. illus.; stat. circ. 44,000.
   Description: Contains health information and news of the organization.

616.12   GW   ISSN 0170-8287
CODEN: EEGLE5
E E G LABOR. (Text in German; summaries in English and German) q. DM.136 (foreign DM.140). (Fachvereinigung der Elektrophysiologischen Assistenten e.V.) Gustav Fischer Verlag, Wollgrasweg 49, 70599 Stuttgart, Germany. TEL 0711-458030. FAX 0711-4580334. TELEX 7111488-FIBUCH. (Subscr. to: Postfach 720143, 70577 Stuttgart, Germany; U.S. address: VCH Publishers Inc., 303 N.W. 12th Ave., Deerfield Beach, FL 33442-1788) **Indexed:** Excerp.Med. **Document type:** academic/scholarly publication.
—BLDSC (3663.395500); UMI. **CCC.**

616.12   US   ISSN 0742-2822
ECHOCARDIOGRAPHY; a journal of cardiovascular ultrasound and allied techniques. 1984. bi-m. $130 (foreign $160) (effective 1995). Futura Publishing Company, Inc., 135 Bedford Rd., Box 418, Armonk, NY 10504. TEL 914-273-1014; 800-877-8761. FAX 914-273-1015. Ed. Dr. Navin C. Nanda. adv.: B&W page $775, color page $1625; trim 8 1/4 x 10 7/8; adv. contact: Suzanne Fath. bk.rev.; abstr. circ. 2,449. **Indexed:** Curr.Cont. **Document type:** academic/scholarly publication.
—BLDSC (3647.572500); ADONIS; Faxon; Genuine Article; UnCover. **CCC.**
   Description: Contains articles on specific applications of diagnostic ultrasound and other related techniques. Includes special topics, case reports, and news items.
   Refereed Serial

616.11   FR   ISSN 1251-3571
▼**ETUDES & EVALUATIONS CARDIO-VASCULAIRES.** 1994. m. 400 (foreign 550 F.) (effective 1996). Apex, 62, av. Foch, 92250 La Garenne-Colombes, France. TEL 33-1-47-80-94-60. FAX 33-1-41-19-67-63. Ed. Jean Louis Gayet. adv. contact: Rene Michel. bk.rev. **Document type:** newspaper.
—BLDSC (3818.851000).
   Description: For cardiovascular specialists wishing to keep up with the latest studies and opinions.

EUROPEAN CONGRESS OF CARDIOLOGY. ABSTRACTS OF PAPERS. see *MEDICAL SCIENCES — Abstracting, Bibliographies, Statistics*

616.1   UK   ISSN 0423-7242
EUROPEAN CONGRESS OF CARDIOLOGY. PROCEEDINGS. 1952. a. (European Society of Cardiology, SZ) Academic Press Ltd. (Subsidiary of: Harcourt Brace & Company Ltd.), 24-28 Oval Rd., London NW1 7DX, England. TEL 44-171-267-4466. FAX 44-171-482-2293. TELEX 25775 ACPRES G. (Subscr. to: Harcourt Brace & Company Ltd., Foots Cray High St., Sidcup, Kent DA14 5HP, England. TEL 44-181-300-3322) **Document type:** proceedings.

616.1   UK   ISSN 0195-668X
CODEN: EHJODF
EUROPEAN HEART JOURNAL. (Supplement avail.: European Congress of Cardiology. Abstracts of Papers (ISSN 0421-7527)) 1980. m. £83 in Europe (rest of world $150) to individuals; institutions £225 in Europe (rest of world $405). (European Society of Cardiology) W.B. Saunders Ltd. (Subsidiary of: Harcourt Brace & Company Ltd.), 24-28 Oval Rd., London NW1 7DX, England. TEL 0171-267-4466. FAX 0171-482-2293. TELEX 25775-ACPRES-G. (Subscr. to: Harcourt Brace & Company Ltd., Foots Cray High St., Sidcup, Kent DA14 5HP, England. TEL 0181-300-3322. FAX 0181-309-0807; US, Canadian, and Mexican subscr. to: W.B. Saunders Co., Journal Subscription Fulfillment, 6277 Sea Harbor Dr., 4th Fl., Orlando, FL 32887-4800. TEL 800-654-2452) Ed. H.E. Kulbertus. adv.; illus.; index. **Indexed:** Biotech.Abstr., Chem.Abstr., Curr.Cont., Dok.Arbeitsmed., Excerp.Med., Ind.Med., Ind.Sci.Rev., Sci.Cit.Ind. **Document type:** academic/scholarly publication.
—BLDSC (3829.717500); CASDDS; Faxon; Genuine Article; SWETS; UnCover. **CCC.**
   Description: Directed to practicing cardiologists publishing original papers on all aspects of cardiovascular medicine, surgery, and basic research.

616.2   GW   ISSN 0939-6780
CODEN: EJCEEX
EUROPEAN JOURNAL OF CARDIAC PACING AND ELECTROPHYSIOLOGY. (Text in English) 1991. q. DM.195 (foreign DM.255). E B M Erdmann-Brenger GmbH, Postfach 810225, 81902 Munich, Germany. TEL 089-935779. FAX 089-9301943. Ed. Richard Sutton. adv.: B&W page DM.4500, color page DM.7485; trim 210 x 280; adv. contact: K. Brenger. **Document type:** academic/scholarly publication.
—BLDSC (3829.725500). **CCC.**

MEDICAL SCIENCES — CARDIOVASCULAR DISEASES

616.1   GW   ISSN 1010-7940
EUROPEAN JOURNAL OF CARDIO-THORACIC SURGERY. (Text in English) 1989. 12/yr. DM.498($361) (effective 1996). Springer-Verlag, Heidelberger Platz 3, 14197 Berlin, Germany. TEL 030-8207-0. FAX 030-8214091. E-mail: orders@springer.de. (Subscr. in N. America to: Springer-Verlag New York, Inc., 44 Hartz Way, Secaucus, NJ 07096-2491. TEL 201-348-4033. FAX 201-348-4505) Ed. H.G. Borst. **Document type:** academic/scholarly publication.
—BLDSC (3829.725620); Faxon; Genuine Article; SWETS; UMI; UnCover. **CCC.**
Description: Documents progress made in cardiac and thoracic surgery, reporting on clinical and experimental advances relating to surgery of the heart, great vessels, and the chest.

616.1   UK   ISSN 1078-5884
CODEN: EJVSFZ
EUROPEAN JOURNAL OF VASCULAR AND ENDOVASCULAR SURGERY. 8/yr. £84 in Europe (rest of world $126) to individuals; institutions £205 in Europe (rest of world $369). (European Society for Vascular Surgery) W.B. Saunders Ltd. (Subsidiary of: Harcourt Brace & Co. Ltd.), 24-28 Oval Rd., London NW1 7DX, England. TEL 0171-267-4466. FAX 0171-482-2293. TELEX 25775-ACPRES-G. (Subscr. to: Harcourt Brace & Co. Ltd., Foots Cray High St., Sidcup, Kent DA14 5HP, England. TEL 0181-300-3322. FAX 0181-309-0807; Subscr. in N. America to: W.B. Saunders Co., Journal Subscription Fulfilment, 6277 Sea Harbor Dr., 4th Fl., Orlando, FL 32887-4800. TEL 800-654-2452. FAX 800-874-6418) Ed. D. Bergqvist. adv.; bk.rev.; circ. 2,250. **Indexed:** Excerp.Med. **Document type:** academic/scholarly publication.
—BLDSC (3829.747280); Genuine Article; SWETS; UnCover. **CCC.**
Formerly: European Journal of Vascular Surgery (ISSN 0950-821X)
Description: Covers all aspects of diagnosis, investigation, and management of vascular disorders. Includes papers on technical aspects of vascular surgery.

616.1   NE   ISSN 0928-0529
EUROPEAN VIDEO JOURNAL OF CARDIOLOGY. 1993. 6/yr. fl.753 to institutions; $482 to institutions in U.S. (effective 1996). (European Society of Cardiology) Kluwer Academic Publishers, Postbus 17, 3300 AA Dordrecht, Netherlands. TEL 31-78-392392. FAX 31-78-392254. E-mail: SERVICES@WKAP.NL. (Dist. by: Kluwer Academic Publishers Group, P.O. Box 322, 3300 AH Dordrecht, Netherlands. TEL 31-78-392392. FAX 31-78-546474; N. America dist. addr.: Box 358, Accord Sta., Hingham, MA 02018-0358. TEL 617-871-6600. FAX 617-871-6528) Ed. Lars Ryden. (video cassette; 45 minutes) **Document type:** academic/scholarly publication.
—**CCC.**
Description: Provides in-depth coverage of recent advances in the broad field of cardiology.
Refereed Serial

615.65   FR   ISSN 0253-1321
F I O D S REVUE. (Editions in English, French, Spanish) 1967. q. 100 F. (Federation Internationale des Organisations de Donneurs de Sang Benevoles - International Federation of Blood Donors Organizations) F I O D S, c/o Vico Fresia, Dir., 34 place Raoul Dautry, 75748 Paris Cedex 15, France. TEL 45-38-71-93. FAX 43-20-33-87. Ed. Jean Gallard. adv.; bk.rev.; illus. circ. 5,000.
Formerly (until 1980): Don Universel du Sang (ISSN 0012-5407)

616.1   US   ISSN 1067-5264
CODEN: FCCAEH
FUNDAMENTAL AND CLINICAL CARDIOLOGY. 1991. irreg., vol.24, 1995. price varies. Marcel Dekker, Inc., 270 Madison Ave., New York, NY 10016. TEL 212-696-9000. FAX 212-685-4540. TELEX 421419.
—BLDSC (4056.031500); CASDDS. **CCC.**

616.136   IT   ISSN 0017-0224
CODEN: GIARA5
GIORNALE DELL'ARTERIOSCLEROSI.* (Supplement to: Giornale de Gerontologia) (Text in Italian; summaries in English) 1965-1972; N.S. 1976. 3/yr. L.30000. (Societa Italiana di Gerontologia e Geriatria) Boehringer Mannheim Italia SpA, Via S. Uguzzone 5, 20126 Milan, Italy. Ed. G. Gentili. adv.; bk.rev.; abstr.; bibl.; charts; illus.; index. circ. 5,000. **Indexed:** Chem.Abstr. Excerp.Med.
—BLDSC (4176.870000); CASDDS; UMI.
Description: Features original articles, reviews and letters on topics of physiopathology, clinics and the therapy of arteriosclerosis.

616.13   IT   ISSN 0392-1387
GIORNALE ITALIANO DI ANGIOLOGIA. (Text in Italian; summaries in English) 1981. q. L.60000($60) C I C Edizioni Internazionali s.r.l., Via L. Spallanzani 11, 00161 Rome, Italy. TEL 06-8412673. FAX 06-44242033. TELEX 622099 CIC. Dir. P. Pola. adv.; bk.rev. **Indexed:** Excerp.Med.
—BLDSC (4178.140000). **CCC.**

616.1   IT   ISSN 0046-5968
CODEN: GICDA7
GIORNALE ITALIANO DI CARDIOLOGIA. 1971. m. L.150000($200) Piccin Editore, Via Altinate 107, 35100 Padua, Italy. TEL 049-655566. FAX 049-8750693. Ed. E. Geraci. adv.; B&W page L.3900000, color page L.5600000; trim 195 x 270. bk.rev.; illus. circ. 10,000. **Indexed:** Biol.Abstr., Chem.Abstr., Excerp.Med., Ind.Med.
—BLDSC (4178.150000); CASDDS; EMDOCS; Faxon; SWETS.
Formed by the merger of: Cuore e Circolazione; Folia Cardiologica; Malattie Cardiovascolari.

H L B NEWSLETTER; reporting on heart, lung and blood disease research program, policy development. see MEDICAL SCIENCES — Experimental Medicine, Laboratory Technique

HAEMOSTASIS; international journal on haemostasis and thrombosis research. see MEDICAL SCIENCES — Hematology

HANDBOOK OF HYPERLIPIDAEMIA. see MEDICAL SCIENCES — Abstracting, Bibliographies, Statistics

616.1   NE   ISSN 0301-8202
HART BULLETIN. 1970. bi-m. (Dutch Heart Association) Reed HealthCare (Subsidiary of: Reed Elsevier plc), P.O. Box 1126, 1000 BC Amsterdam, Netherlands. TEL 31-20-5153350. FAX 31-20-5153354. Ed. Dr. J.A.E. v.d. Feen. adv. contact: G.J.M. van den Akker. circ. 18,000.
—SWETS.
Description: For general practitioners, internists, cardiologists and pharmacologists.
Refereed Serial

616.1   US   ISSN 1051-5313
HARVARD HEART LETTER. 1990. m. $32. (Harvard Medical School) Harvard Health Publications Group, 164 Longwood Ave., Boston, MA 02115. TEL 800-829-9171. FAX 617-432-1506. E-mail: jrudin@warren.med.edu. (Subscr. to: Box 420235, Palm Coast, FL 32142-0235) Ed. Dr. Thomas Lee. **Document type:** newsletter.
●Also available online. Vendor(s): Information Access Co..
Description: Features articles and information on cardiovascular health for the lay reader.

616.1   US
HEALTHY HEART. (In two eds.: Physicians' ed. and Patients' ed.) 1988. q. Medical Economics Publishing Co., Inc., Five Paragon Dr., Montvale, NJ 07645. TEL 201-358-7200. FAX 201-573-1045. circ. 10,000.

HEALTHY WEIGHT JOURNAL; research, news and commentary across the weight spectrum. see NUTRITION AND DIETETICS

616.1   GW   ISSN 0179-342X
HEART & CIRCULATION; diseases of heart and cardiovascular system. (Text in English) 1986. q. P M I Verlagsgruppe GmbH, August-Schanz-Str. 21, 60433 Frankfurt a.M., Germany. TEL 069-5480000. FAX 069-54800077. Ed. Peter Hoffmann. circ. 20,000. (back issues avail.) **Document type:** academic/scholarly publication.

616.1   CN
HEART AND STROKE FOUNDATION OF CANADA. ANNUAL REPORT. (Text in English, French) 1956. a. free. Heart and Stroke Foundation of Canada, 160 George St., Ste. 200, Ottawa, ON K1N 9M2, Canada. TEL 613-241-4361. FAX 613-241-3278. Ed. J. Fox. circ. 3,000.
Formerly: Canadian Heart Foundation. Annual Report (ISSN 0068-8851)

616.1   JA   ISSN 0910-8327
CODEN: HEVEEO
HEART AND VESSELS; an international journal. (Text in English) 1985. bi-m. 32000($232) (effective 1996). (Heart Institute of Japan, Tokyo) Springer-Verlag Tokyo, 3-13 Hongo, 3-chome, Bunkyo-ku, Tokyo 113, Japan. TEL 03-3812-0617. FAX 03-3812-4699. (Subscr. in N. America to: Springer-Verlag New York Inc., Service Center, Secaucus 4, Hartz Way, Secaucus, NJ 07096-2491. TEL 201-348-4033) (Co-sponsor: Tokyo Women's Medical College) Ed. Atsuyoshi Takao. adv.: B&W page 70000 Yen. bk.rev.; index. circ. 1,000. (also avail. in microform from UMI; back issues avail.; reprint service avail. UMI) **Indexed:** Chem.Abstr., Excerp.Med., Ind.Med. **Document type:** academic/scholarly publication.
—BLDSC (4275.297000); CASDDS; Faxon; Genuine Article; SWETS; UMI; UnCover. **CCC.**
Description: Publishes research, ideas, methods, and techniques on cardiovascular diseases.

616.1   II   ISSN 0046-7111
HEART CARE. (Text in English) 1970. m. Rs.10($6) (Society for the Prevention of Heart Disease and Rehabilitation) Praga Publications, 43 Sundar Mahal, Churchgate, Bombay 400020, India. Ed. C.V. Shah. adv.; bk.rev.; charts; illus. circ. 3,000.

616.1   SP
HEART DISEASE AND STROKE (EDICION ESPANOLA). bi-m. 5800 ptas.($48) (effective 1995). Editorial Garsi, S.A., Juan Bravo 46, 28006 Madrid, Spain. TEL 34-1-4021212. FAX 34-1-4020954.

616.1   US   ISSN 8755-7673
CODEN: HEFAEY
HEART FAILURE. 1984. bi-m. $40 to individuals (foreign $45); institutions $50 (foreign $65) (effective 1994). (Albert Einstein College of Medicine) LeJacq Communications, Inc., 777 W. Putnam Ave., Greenwich, CT 06830-5014. TEL 203-531-0450. Ed. Dr. John E. Strobeck. adv.; bk.rev.; abstr.; bibl.; illus. circ. 50,000. **Indexed:** Excerp.Med.
—BLDSC (4275.340000); UMI.

616.1   US   ISSN 1382-4147
▼**HEART FAILURE REVIEWS.** Announced for publication in 1996. q. fl.428 to institutions; $274 to institutions in U.S. (effective 1996). Kluwer Academic Publishers Boston, Box 358, Accord Sta., Hingham, MA 02018-0358. TEL 617-871-6600. FAX 617-871-6528. (Subscr. outside N. America to: Kluwer Academic Publishers Group., P.O. Box 322, 3300 AH Dordrecht, Netherlands. TEL 31-78-392392. FAX 31-78-546474) **Document type:** academic/scholarly publication.
Refereed Serial

616.1   UK
HEART JOURNAL. 1939. m. £190($309) (British Cardiac Society) B M J Publishing Group, B.M.A. House, Tavistock Sq., London WC1H 9JR, England. TEL 0171-383-6270. FAX 0171-383-6402. (N. American subscr. to: Box 408, Franklin, MA 02038. TEL 800-2-FON-BMJ. FAX 800-2-FAX-BMJ) Ed. M.J. Davies. adv. contact: Sheila Rowe. bk.rev.; abstr.; charts; illus.; index, cum.index: 1939-1955; 1956-1967. (also avail. in microform from UMI) **Indexed:** Abstr.Hyg., AIM, Behav.Med.Abstr., Biol.Abstr., Biotech.Abstr., C.I.S. Abstr., Chem.Abstr., CINAHL, Curr.Adv.Ecol.Sci., Curr.Cont., Dent.Ind., Diab.Cont., Excerp.Med., Helminthol.Abstr., Ind.Med., INIS Atomind., NRN, Nutr.Abstr., Risk Abstr., Sci.Cit.Ind., Trop.Dis.Bull. **Document type:** academic/scholarly publication.
●Also available online. Vendor(s): Ovid Technologies.
—BLDSC (2301.300000); ADONIS; Faxon; Genuine Article; SWETS; UMI; UnCover. **CCC.**
Formerly (until 1995): British Heart Journal (ISSN 0007-0769)
Description: Concentrates on providing current clinical information on cardiac diseases, conditions, and research.
Refereed Serial

MEDICAL SCIENCES — CARDIOVASCULAR DISEASES

616.1　US　ISSN 8755-5271
HEARTLINE. 1972. m. $29. Coronary Club, Inc., 9500 Euclid Ave., E37, Cleveland, OH 44195-5058. TEL 216-444-3690. FAX 216-444-9385. (Co-sponsor: Cleveland Clinic Educational Foundation) Ed. Dr. Fredric J. Pashkow. bk.rev.; index. circ. 10,000. (looseleaf format; back issues avail.) **Document type:** consumer publication.
　Formerly (until 1985): Coronary Club Bulletin.
　Description: Provides current information on heart problems for the lay public.

616.1　GR　ISSN 1011-7970
　　　　　　CODEN: HLKEA
HELLENIKE KARDIOLOGIKE EPITHEORESIS/HELLENIC CARDIOLOGICAL REVIEW. Variant title: Hellenic Journal of Cardiology. (Text in Greek; summaries in English) 1960. 6/yr. Hellenic Cardiological Society, Sisini 17, 115 28 Athens, Greece. TEL 30-1-7221633. **Indexed:** Excerp.Med.

616.12　GW　ISSN 0340-9937
　　　　　　CODEN: HERZDW
HERZ; kardiovaskulaere Erkraenkungen. 1976. bi-m. DM.216($156) (effective 1996). Urban and Vogel, Lindwurmstr. 95, 80337 Munich, Germany. TEL 089-53292-0. FAX 089-53292-100. (Subscr. to: Postfach 152209, 80052 Munich, Germany) Ed.Bd. circ. 4,000. **Indexed:** Curr.Cont., Excerp.Med., Ind.Med. **Document type:** academic/scholarly publication.
　—BLDSC (4300.396000); Faxon; Genuine Article; SWETS; UMI; UnCover. **CCC.**

616.1　GW　ISSN 0046-7324
　　　　　　CODEN: HZKLAV
HERZ KREISLAUF; Zeitschrift fuer Kardiologie und Angiologie in Klinik und Praxis. 1969. m. DM.192 (Europe DM.210). (Deutsche Gesellschaft fuer Praevention und Rehabilitation von Herz-Kreislauf-Erkrankungen e.V.) Richard Pflaum Verlag GmbH und Co. KG, Lazarettstr. 4, 80636 Munich, Germany. TEL 089-12607-0. FAX 089-12607-200. (Subscr. to: Postfach 190737, 80607 Munich, Germany) Ed. K.W. Westermann. adv.; bk.rev.; bibl.; charts; illus. circ. 32,000. **Indexed:** Chem.Abstr., Curr.Cont., Excerp.Med., Ind.Sci.Rev., INIS Atomind., Sci.Cit.Ind. **Document type:** academic/scholarly publication.
　—BLDSC (4300.420000); CASDDS; EMDOCS; Genuine Article. **CCC.**

616.1　GW　ISSN 0944-260X
HERZ UND GESUNDHEIT. ceased 1986; resumed 1991. 4/yr. DM.24. (Deutsche Herzhilfe e.V.) Verlag fuer Medizin Dr. Ewald Fischer GmbH, Fritz-Frey-Str. 21, 69121 Heidelberg, Germany. TEL 06221-4062-0. Eds. A. Kroedel, P. Mand. **Document type:** academic/scholarly publication.

616.1　GW　ISSN 0938-7412
HERZSCHRITTMACHERTHERAPIE UND ELEKTROPHYSIOLOGIE. (Text in German; summaries in English) 1990. q. DM.182($132) (effective 1996). Dr. Dietrich Steinkopff Verlag, Saalbaustr. 12, 64283 Darmstadt, Germany. TEL 06151-1745-0. FAX 06151-174510. (Subscr. to: Postfach 111442, 64229 Darmstadt, Germany; Subscr. in N. America to: Springer-Verlag New York, Inc., Box 2485, Secaucus, NJ 07096-2491. TEL 201-348-4033) Ed. H. Klein. adv.; bk.rev.; bibl.; charts; illus. circ. 1,500. **Document type:** academic/scholarly publication.
　—UMI. **CCC.**

616.1　IT　ISSN 1120-9879
HIGH BLOOD PRESSURE AND CARDIOVASCULAR PREVENTION/IPERTENSIONE E PREVENZIONE CARDIOVASCOLARE. (Text in English) 1992. q. L.80000($80) Editrice Kurtis s.r.l., Via Luigi Zoja 30, 20153 Milan, Italy. TEL 39-2-48202740. FAX 39-2-48201219. Ed. B. Ambrosioni. adv.: B&W page L.5900000, color page L.7350000; trim 200 x 260. circ. 12,000.
　—BLDSC (4307.284500).
　Description: Publishes papers reporting original clinical and basic research on hypertension and other cardiovascular risk factors.

HIROSAKI DAIGAKU IGAKUBU EISEIGAKU KYOSHITSU GYOSEKISHU. see *MEDICAL SCIENCES*

616.1 616.2　SW
HJAERT-LUNGFONDEN; Kvartalsskrift. 1906. q. SEK 45($6) Hjaert-Lung-Fonden - Swedish Heart Lung Foundation, Kungsgatan 30, S-111 35 Stockholm, Sweden. TEL 46-8-411-01-74. FAX 46-8-723-17-25. Ed. Bjoern Lilliehoeoek. circ. 10,000. (back issues avail.)
　Formerly: Hjaerta Kaerl Lungor (ISSN 0280-4638)

616.1　IC　ISSN 1022-4955
HJARTAVERND. 1964. s-a. ISK 200($5) (effective 1992). Hjartavernd, Lagmuli 9, 108 Reykjavik, Iceland. TEL 354-581-3755. FAX 354-581-2295. Ed. S. Helgason. charts; illus.; cum.index. circ. 3,000. (back issues avail.)
　Description: Features articles on cardiovascular disease and the risk factor in Iceland.

616.1　DK　ISSN 0105-9785
HJERTEFORENINGEN. 1978. a. free. Hjerteforeningen, Hauser Plads 10, 1127 Copenhagen K, Denmark. illus.

616.1　DK　ISSN 0108-8904
HJERTENYT; orientering om sundhed og praeventiv medicin. 1982. irreg. free. Hjerteforeningen, Hauser Plads 10, 1127 Copenhagen K, Denmark.

616.1　US　ISSN 0194-911X
RC685.H8　CODEN: HPRTDN
HYPERTENSION. 1979. m. $198 (foreign $244) (effective 1996). American Heart Association, 7272 Greenville Ave., Dallas, TX 75231-4596. TEL 214-706-1310. FAX 214-691-6342. (Subscr. to: Box 843543, Dallas, TX 75284-3543) Ed. Dr. Allyn L. Mark. adv.; index. circ. 4,600. (also avail. in microform from UMI; back issues avail.; reprint service avail. from UMI) **Indexed:** Biol.Abstr., Biotech.Abstr., Curr.Adv.Genetics & Molec.Biol., Curr.Cont., Dent.Ind., Excerp.Med., Ind.Med., Ind.Sci.Rev., INIS Atomind., Kidney, Risk Abstr.
　—BLDSC (4352.629000); CASDDS; Faxon; Genuine Article; SWETS; UMI; UnCover. **CCC.**
　Incorporates (1957-1977): Council for High Blood Pressure Research. Proceedings (ISSN 0073-425X)
　Description: For cardiologists, internists, and researchers; reports clinical and laboratory investigations in hypertension.
　Refereed Serial

616.1　UK　ISSN 0143-117X
HYPERTENSION. m. £75 (effective 1995). S U B I S, Mansion House, 19 Kingfield Rd., Sheffield S11 9AS, England. TEL 0114-2554433. FAX 0114-2554626. E-mail: admin@sheffac.demon.co.uk. (looseleaf format; back issues avail.) **Document type:** abstracting/indexing.
　—CCC.
　Description: Current awareness service for researchers in clinical and life sciences.

616.132　US　ISSN 0956-2311
HYPERTENSION ANNUAL (YEAR); clinical reviews for the clinician. a. $24.95. (International Society of Hypertension) Current Science, 800 Market St., Ste. 700, Philadelphia, PA 19106. TEL 215-574-2210; 800-552-5866. FAX 215-574-3533. (And: Current Science Ltd., 34-42 Cleveland St., London W1P 6LB, England. TEL 0171-323-0323. FAX 0171-636-6911) Ed. L. Hansson. **Document type:** academic/scholarly publication.
　Formerly (until 1986): Hypertension Yearbook (ISSN 0950-2319)

616.1 618.2　US　ISSN 1064-1955
RG580.H9　CODEN: HYPPEV
HYPERTENSION IN PREGNANCY. 1982. 3/yr. $415. (International Society for the Study of Hypertension in Pregnancy) Marcel Dekker Journals, 270 Madison Ave., New York, NY 10016. TEL 212-696-9000. FAX 212-685-4540. TELEX 421419. (Subscr. to: Box 5017, Monticello, NY 12701) Eds. W.M. Barron, Olavi Ylikorkala. (also avail. in microform from RPI) **Indexed:** Biol.Dig., Biotech.Abstr., Chem.Abstr., Curr.Adv.Ecol.Sci., Excerp.Med., Ind.Sci.Rev., Kidney, Sci.Cit.Ind. **Document type:** academic/scholarly publication.
　—BLDSC (4352.635260); ADONIS; CASDDS; Faxon; Genuine Article; SWETS; UMI; UnCover. **CCC.**
　Formerly: Clinical and Experimental Hypertension. Part B: Hypertension in Pregnancy (ISSN 0730-0085); Which supersedes in part: Clinical and Experimental Hypertension (ISSN 0148-3927)
　Refereed Serial

616.1　JA　ISSN 0916-9636
　　　　　　CODEN: HRESE4
HYPERTENSION RESEARCH - CLINICAL AND EXPERIMENTAL. 1978. q. $120 (effective 1996). Japanese Society of Hypertension, Center for Academic Societies Osaka - Nihon Koketsuatsu Gakkai, Senri Life Science Center Bldg., 14th Fl., 1-4-2 Shinsenrihigashi-machi, Toyonaka 565, Japan. TEL 6-873-2301. FAX 6-873-2300. E-mail: HBHO1424@nifryserve.or.jp. Ed. Tatsuo Kokubu. adv. **Indexed:** Biol.Abstr., Chem.Abstr., Curr.Cont., Excerp.Med. (1993-), Ind.Med., Sci.Cit.Ind. **Document type:** academic/scholarly publication.
　—CASDDS.
　Formerly (until 1991): Koketsuatsu (ISSN 0288-0032)
　Description: Publishes articles on worldwide research topics of hypertension.

616.1　II　ISSN 0019-4832
RC681
INDIAN HEART JOURNAL. (Text in English) 1949. bi-m. Rs.10($15) Cardiological Society of India, Bombay Mutual Terrace, 534 Sandhurst Bridge, Bombay 400007, India. Ed. Shantilal Shah. bk.rev.; abstr.; illus. circ. 1,500. **Indexed:** Biol.Abstr., Chem.Abstr., Excerp.Med., Ind.Med., INIS Atomind., NRN.
　—BLDSC (4409.400000); EMDOCS; Faxon.

616.12　FR　ISSN 0220-2476
INFORMATION CARDIOLOGIQUE. English edition: Editorials in Cardiology (ISSN 1259-492X) (Editions in English, French) 1978. 11/yr. 420 F. to individuals (foreign 490 F.); students 290 F. (foreign 360 F.) (effective 1996). (Centre Cardiologique du Nord) Publications Medicales, 77 bis, rue des Chesneaux, 95160 Montmorency, France. TEL 34-17-68-88. FAX 34-28-17-59. Ed. Dr. A. Castillo Fenoy. adv. contact: A. Castillo Fenoy. bk.rev. circ. 2,500.
　—BLDSC (4485.640000).

616.12　IT
INFORMAZIONE CARDIOLOGICA. m. Viale Verdi, 18, 28100 Novara, Italy. TEL 39-321-36331. Ed. Dr. Paolo Rossi. circ. 7,000.

616.1　MX　ISSN 0020-3785
　　　　　　CODEN: AICMA2
INSTITUTO DE CARDIOLOGIA DE MEXICO. ARCHIVOS. (Text in Spanish; summaries in English and French) 1930. bi-m. Mex.$180($75) Instituto Nacional de Cardiología "Ignacio Chavez" - National Institute of Cardiology "Ignacio Chavez", Oficina de Publicaciones, Juan Badiano No.1, Tlalpan, 14080 Mexico D.F., Mexico. TEL 52-5-732911 ext. 310. FAX 52-5-730994. Eds. Drs. Eduardo Salazar, Alfredo de Micheli. adv.; bk.rev.; charts; illus.; stat.; index. circ. 2,500. **Indexed:** Biol.Abstr., Chem.Abstr., Curr.Adv.Ecol.Sci., Dent.Ind., Excerp.Med., Ind.Med.
　●Also available on CD-ROM.
　—BLDSC (1651.500000); EMDOCS.

INTERNAL MEDICINE NEWS & CARDIOLOGY NEWS. see *MEDICAL SCIENCES — Internal Medicine*

616.1　IT　ISSN 0392-9590
　　　　　　CODEN: INANEK
INTERNATIONAL ANGIOLOGY. (Text in English) $90 to individuals; institutions $140 (effective 1995). (International Union of Angiology) Edizioni Minerva Medica, Corso Bramante 83-85, 10126 Turin, Italy. TEL 39-11-678282. FAX 39-11-3121736. Ed. P. Balas; Pub. Alberto Oliaro. adv.: B&W page $1100, color page $1900; trim 215 x 280; adv. contact: F. Filippo. circ. 5,000 (paid). **Indexed:** ASCA, Curr.Cont., Excerp.Med., Ind.Med., Sci.Cit.Ind. **Document type:** academic/scholarly publication.
　—BLDSC (4535.770000); Faxon; Genuine Article; SWETS; UnCover.
　Description: Addresses latest news concerning the vascular system, vascular pathophysiology and therapy.
　Refereed Serial

616.12　US　ISSN 0173-0282
INTERNATIONAL BOEHRINGER MANNHEIM. SYMPOSIA. 1976. irreg. price varies. Springer-Verlag, 175 Fifth Ave., New York, NY 10010. TEL 212-460-1500. FAX 212-473-6272. (reprint service avail. from ISI) **Document type:** proceedings.

MEDICAL SCIENCES — CARDIOVASCULAR DISEASES

616.13 GR ISSN 0074-347X
INTERNATIONAL CONGRESS OF ANGIOLOGY.
PROCEEDINGS. 1952. biennial, 16th, 1992, Paris. International Union of Angiology, c/o Prof. Panayotis Balas, 4 Hiraklitou St., 10673 Athens, Greece. **Document type:** proceedings.

616.1 617 US ISSN 1061-1711
CODEN: IJAGE5
INTERNATIONAL JOURNAL OF ANGIOLOGY. 1992. q. $135 (effective 1996). (International College of Angiology) Springer-Verlag, Journals, 175 Fifth Ave., New York, NY 10010. TEL 212-460-1500. FAX 212-473-6272. (Subscr. in N. America to: Journal Fulfillment Services, Box 2485, Secaucus, NJ 07096-2491. TEL 800-777-4643. FAX 201-348-4505; Subscr. outside N. America to: Springer-Verlag, Heidelberger Platz 3, 14197 Berlin, Germany. TEL 030-8207-0. FAX 030-8214091) Ed. Dr. John B. Chang. adv.: B&W page $450, color page $950; trim 8 1/4 x 11; adv. contact: Robert Vrooman. abstr.; charts; illus.; index. circ. 1,200. (also avail. in microform from UMI; back issues avail.) **Indexed:** Excerp.Med. (1995-). **Document type:** academic/scholarly publication.
—BLDSC (4542.081500); ADONIS.
Description: Dedicated to promoting multidisciplinary approaches to all aspects of vascular diseases aimed at clinicians and scientists in cardiovascular surgery and medicine.
Refereed Serial

616.1 NE ISSN 0167-9899
CODEN: IJCIEL
INTERNATIONAL JOURNAL OF CARDIAC IMAGING. (Text in English) 1984. q. fl.420 to institutions; $269 to institutions in U.S. (effective 1996). Kluwer Academic Publishers, Postbus 17, 3300 AA Dordrecht, Netherlands. TEL 31-78-392392. FAX 31-78-392254. TELEX 29245 KAPG NL. E-mail: SERVICES@WKAP.NL. (Dist. by: Kluwer Academic Publishers Group, P.O. Box 322, 3300 AH Dordrecht, Netherlands. TEL 31-78-392392. FAX 31-78-546474; N. America dist. addr.: Box 358, Accord Sta., Hingham, MA 02018-0358. TEL 617-871-6600. FAX 617-871-6528) Eds. G.B. John Mancini, Johan H.C. Reiber. adv.; bk.rev. (also avail. in microform from UMI; reprint service avail. from SWZ) **Indexed:** Excerp.Med., Ind.Med. **Document type:** academic/scholarly publication.
—BLDSC (4542.157000); Faxon; Genuine Article; SWETS; UMI; UnCover. **CCC.**
Formerly: International Journal of Cardiovascular Imaging.
Description: Provides a forum for communications on the basic and applied technologies relating to video and digital image acquisition and analysis, and the clinical applications of imaging modalities in the diagnosis and treatment of cardiovascular disease.
Refereed Serial

616.1 IE ISSN 0167-5273
CODEN: IJCDD5
INTERNATIONAL JOURNAL OF CARDIOLOGY. 1973. 15/yr. I£760($1201) (effective 1996). Elsevier Science Ireland Ltd., P.O. Box 85, Limerick, Ireland. TEL 353-61-471944. FAX 353-61-472144. (Subscr. in U.S. and Canada to: Elsevier Science Inc., Box 882, Madison Sq. Sta., New York, NY 10159. TEL 212-989-5800. FAX 212-633-3990) Ed.Bd. bk.rev.; illus. (also avail. in microform from UMI; back issues avail.) **Indexed:** Biol.Abstr., Biotech.Abstr., Chem.Abstr., Curr.Adv.Ecol.Sci., Curr.Cont., Dent.Ind., Excerp.Med., Ind.Med., Ind.Sci.Rev., Kidney, NRN, Rev.Med.& Vet.Mycol., Sci.Cit.Ind. **Document type:** academic/scholarly publication.
—BLDSC (4542.158000); ADONIS; CASDDS; Faxon; Genuine Article; SWETS; UMI; UnCover. **CCC.**
Formerly: European Journal of Cardiology (ISSN 0301-4711); Incorporates: Association of European Paediatric Cardiologists. Proceedings (ISSN 0066-9547).
Description: For clinical practitioners and research workers in cardiovascular research and surgery, clinical cardiology and paediatric cardiology.
Refereed Serial

616.1 US
▼**INTERNATIONAL JOURNAL OF CARDIOVASCULAR IMAGING & INTERVENTION.** Announced forp ublication in 1996. q. $135 to individuals; institutions $185 (effective 1996). Field & Wood, Medical Periodicals, Inc., Box 975, Blue Bell, PA 19422. TEL 610-828-4010. FAX 215-482-0226. Eds. Dr. Michael Rees, Dr. Lewis Wexler. **Document type:** academic/scholarly publication.
Refereed Serial

616.12 IT ISSN 0393-6066
CODEN: ISCAE
INTERNATIONAL JOURNAL OF SPORTS CARDIOLOGY. 1984. s-a. (Italian Society of Sports Cardiology) C E P I - Centro Editoriale Pubblicitario Italiana S.r.l., Via N. Tartaglia 3, 00197 Rome, Italy. TEL 6-8077011. Ed. Antonio Venerando. **Indexed:** Excerp.Med. (until 1992; 1995-), NRN, Sportsearch (1984-).
—UnCover.

INTERNATIONAL SOCIETY OF BLOOD TRANSFUSION. PROCEEDINGS OF THE CONGRESS. see *MEDICAL SCIENCES — Hematology*

616.12 617 JA
INTERNATIONAL SOCIETY OF CARDIO-THORACIC SURGEONS. ANNUAL MEETING. (Text in English, Japanese) a. International Society of Cardio-Thoracic Surgeons - Kokusai Shinzo Kyobu Geka Gakkai, Fujita Gakuen Hoken Eisei Daigaku, Kyobu Gekagaku Kyoshitsu, 1-98, Dengakugakubo, Kutsukakecho, Toyoake-shi, Aichi-ken 470-11, Japan.

616.1 US ISSN 0074-8765
INTERNATIONAL SYMPOSIUM ON ATHEROSCLEROSIS. PROCEEDINGS. irreg. price varies. Springer-Verlag, 175 Fifth Ave., New York, NY 10010. TEL 212-460-1500. FAX 212-473-6272. (Also: Berlin, Heidelberg, Tokyo and Vienna) **Document type:** proceedings.

616.1 NE ISSN 0926-9649
INTERVENTIONAL CARDIOLOGY. (Text in English) 1991. irreg. price varies. Kluwer Academic Publishers, Postbus 17, 3300 AA Dordrecht, Netherlands. TEL 31-78-392392. FAX 31-78-392254. TELEX 29245 KAPG NL. (Dist. by: Kluwer Academic Publishers Group, P.O. Box 322, 3300 AH Dordrecht, Netherlands. TEL 31-78-392392. FAX 31-78-546474; N. America dist. addr.: Box 358, Accord Sta., Hingham, MA 02018-0358. TEL 617-871-6600. FAX 617-871-6528) Ed. Amar S. Kapoor. **Document type:** monographic series.
Refereed Serial

616.1 US ISSN 1063-4282
CODEN: ICANEB
INTERVENTIONAL CARDIOLOGY NEWSLETTER. 1993. bi-m. $110 to institutions in U.S.; $137 to institutions outside the Americas (effective 1996). Elsevier Science Inc., 655 Ave. of the Americas, New York, NY 10010. TEL 212-633-3950. FAX 212-633-3990. (Subscr. to: Box 882, Madison Sq. Sta., New York, NY 10159-0882) Ed.Bd. (also avail. in microform from UMI; back issues avail.) **Document type:** newsletter.
—BLDSC (4557.471853). **CCC.**

616.1 JA ISSN 0912-4837
JAKUNENSHA SHINSHIKKAN TAISAKU KYOGIKAISHI/YOUNGER CARDIAC DISEASE COUNTERMEASURE ASSOCIATION. JOURNAL. (Text in Japanese) 1973. s-a. Jakunensha Shinshikkan Taisaku Kyogikai, Kyoto Junkankibyo Yobokai, Onmae Higashi, Marutamachi Dori, Nakagyo-ku, Kyoto 604, Japan.

616.1 JA ISSN 0386-2682
JAPAN ATHEROSCLEROSIS SOCIETY. JOURNAL/DOMYAKU KOKA. (Text in English, Japanese) 1973. q. Japan Atherosclerosis Society - Nihon Domyaku Koka Gakkai, 3-2-29-401, Shibaura, Minato-ku, Tokyo 108, Japan. TEL 81-3-3455-4439. FAX 81-3-3798-1372. **Document type:** academic/scholarly publication.
—BLDSC (4804.615000).

616.1 JA ISSN 0047-1828
RC681 CODEN: JCIRA2
JAPANESE CIRCULATION JOURNAL. (Title varies: Nippon Journal of Angio-Cardiology) (Text in English) 1935. m. 20000 Yen. Japanese Circulation Society - Nihon Junkanki Gakkai, Kinki Invention Center, 14 Yoshida Kawahara-cho, Sakyo-ku, Kyoto 606, Japan. TEL 075-751-8643. FAX 075-771-3060. E-mail: KGE01125@Niftyserve.or.jp. Ed. Chuichi Kawai. adv. circ. 14,000. **Indexed:** Biol.Abstr., Chem.Abstr., Curr.Cont., Excerp.Med., Ind.Med., INIS Atomind., Nutr.Abstr., Sci.Cit.Ind. **Document type:** academic/scholarly publication.
—BLDSC (4650.750000); CASDDS; EMDOCS; Faxon; Genuine Article; SWETS; UnCover.

616.1 JA
JAPANESE CIRCULATION JOURNAL SUPPLEMENT. (Text in Japanese) irreg. (3-4/yr.). Japanese Circulation Society - Nihon Junkanki Gakkai, Kinki Invention Center, 14 Yoshida Kawahara-cho, Sakyo-ku, Kyoto 606, Japan. TEL 075-751-8643. FAX 075-771-3060. Ed. Tsuneaki Sugimoto. **Document type:** academic/scholarly publication.

616.1 JA ISSN 0021-4868
CODEN: JHEJAR
JAPANESE HEART JOURNAL. (Text in English) 1960. bi-m. 529 SFr. (effective 1996). (University of Tokyo, Faculty of Medicine, Department of Internal Medicine - Tokyo Daigaku Igakubu Dai-2-Naika) Nankodo Co. Ltd., 42-6, Hongo 3-chome, Bunkyo-ku, Tokyo 113, Japan. TEL 03-3811-7239. FAX 03-3811-7230. TELEX 963475. (Dist. outside Japan by: Baltzer Science Publishers B.V., Asterweg 1A, 1031 HL Amsterdam, Netherlands. TEL 31-20-6370061. FAX 31-20-6323651; Subscr. in N. America to: Baltzer Science Publishers, Box 8577, Red Bank, NJ 07701-8577) Ed. Dr. S. Murao. adv.; bk.rev.; charts; illus.; index. circ. 1,000. (also avail. in microfilm from UMI; reprint service avail. from UMI) **Indexed:** Biol.Abstr., Chem.Abstr., Curr. Cont., Excerp.Med., Ind.Med., Ind.Sci.Rev., INIS Atomind., NRN, Sci.Cit.Ind. **Document type:** academic/scholarly publication.
—BLDSC (4650.770000); CASDDS; EMDOCS; Faxon; Genuine Article; SWETS; UMI; UnCover.

617.41 JA ISSN 0914-8922
CODEN: JJICFB
JAPANESE JOURNAL OF INTERVENTIONAL CARDIOLOGY. (Text in Japanese) 1988. q. (Nihon Shinkekkan Keiseijutsu Kenkukai) Miwa Shoten, 30-3 Hakusan, 2-chome, Bunkyo-ku, Tokyo 112, Japan. TEL 3-3816-7796. **Indexed:** Excerp.Med. (1995-).
Supersedes: Nihon Kandomyaku Keiseijutsu Kenkyukaishi.

610 616.1 GW
JATROS KARDIOLOGIE - MIT KARDIOLOGISCHE KLINIK. 1983. 12/yr. DM.90. P M I Verlagsgruppe GmbH, August-Schanz-Str. 21, 60433 Frankfurt a.M., Germany. TEL 069-548000-0. FAX 069-54800077. TELEX 412952-PMI-D. Ed.Bd. circ. 4,000. **Document type:** academic/scholarly publication.
Former titles: Jatros Kardiologie - Hypertonie und Artherosklerose (ISSN 0943-3341); Kardio (ISSN 0724-9187)

616.65 JA ISSN 0915-0188
JIKOKETSU YUKETSU/JAPANESE SOCIETY OF AUTOLOGOUS BLOOD TRANSFUSION. JOURNAL. (Text in English, Japanese) 1987. s-a. 5000 Yen membership. Nihon Jikoketsu Yuketsu Kenkyukai, Kawasaki Ika Daigaku Masuika, 577, Matsushima, Kurashiki-shi, Okayama-ken 701-01, Japan. TEL 086-462-111. FAX 086-462-1199. Ed. M. Takaori.

616 FR ISSN 0398-0499
JOURNAL DES MALADIES VASCULAIRES. 1976. q. 898 F. (foreign 1103 F.) (effective 1996). (College Francais de Pathologie Vasculaire) Masson - Periodiques, Villa Laromiguiere, 75005 Paris, France. TEL 1-40-46-62-00. FAX 1-40-46-62-01. Ed. Vayssairat. circ. 2,000. (also avail. in microform from UMI; reprint service avail. from ISI) **Indexed:** Excerp.Med., Ind.Med., Ind.Sci.Rev., Sci.Cit.Ind. **Document type:** academic/scholarly publication.
—BLDSC (5010.850000); Faxon; Genuine Article; SWETS; UMI. **CCC.**
Description: Publishes texts of the annual congress of the college, original work selected by the editorial committee and the best postgraduate courses of the faculty.

MEDICAL SCIENCES — CARDIOVASCULAR DISEASES

616.1 UK ISSN 0951-1830
JOURNAL OF AMBULATORY MONITORING. 1988. q. £121($199) (effective 1996). Taylor & Francis Ltd., Rankine Rd., Basingstoke, Hants. RG24 8PR, England. TEL 44-1256-840366. FAX 44-1256-479438. TELEX 858540. E-mail: info@tandf.co.uk. (Subscr. in N. America to: Taylor & Francis Inc., 1900 Frost Rd., Ste. 101, Bristol, PA 19007-1598. TEL 800-821-8312. FAX 215-785-5515) Eds. S.J. Meldrum, S. Stern. **Document type:** academic/scholarly publication.
—BLDSC (4927.230200); Ei. **CCC.**
Description: Covers ambulatory, or personal, monitoring in the broadest sense. In addition to the established field of ECG monitoring this will include blood pressure, oesophageal pH, EEG, and the emerging fields of radio and transtelephonic monitoring.
Refereed Serial

616.1 JA ISSN 1340-3478
CODEN: JATHEH
▼**JOURNAL OF ATHEROSCLEROSIS AND THROMBOSIS.** (Text in English) 1994. q. Japan Atherosclerosis Society, 3-2-29-401, Shibarura, Minato-ku, Tokyo 108, Japan. TEL 81-3-3455-4439. FAX 81-3-3798-1372. Ed. Yoshiya Hata.
—BLDSC (4947.790000); CASDDS.
Description: Contains original articles, reviews, and information on conferences related to atherosclerosis and thrombosis, and their risk factors.

616.12 US ISSN 1071-9164
▼**JOURNAL OF CARDIAC FAILURE.** 1994. q. $115 to individuals (foreign $140); institutions $145 (foreign $170). Churchill Livingstone International, 650 Ave. of the Americas, New York, NY 10011. TEL 212-206-5040. FAX 212-727-7808. Ed. Jay Cohn; Pub. Jane Grochowski. **Document type:** academic/scholarly publication.
—BLDSC (4954.862000).
Description: Features original and review articles on clinical research, basic human studies, animal studies, and bench research, with potential clinical application to heart failure.
Refereed Serial

616.1 US ISSN 0886-0440
JOURNAL OF CARDIAC SURGERY. 1986. bi-m. $115 (foreign $143) (effective 1995). Futura Publishing Company, Inc., 135 Bedford Rd., Box 418, Armonk, NY 10504-0418. TEL 914-273-1014; 800-877-8761. FAX 914-273-1015. Ed. Dr. Lawrence H. Cohn. adv.: B&W page $810, color page $1745; trim 8 1/4 x 10 7/8; adv. contact: Maureen Sonntag. bk.rev.; abstr. circ. 2,417. (back issues avail.) Indexed: Excerp.Med., Ind.Med. (1992-). **Document type:** academic/scholarly publication.
—BLDSC (4954.863500); ADONIS; Faxon; Genuine Article; SWETS; UnCover. **CCC.**
Incorporates (1981-199?): Modern Technics in Surgery. Head and Neck Surgery (ISSN 0271-8219); (1979-199?): Modern Technics in Surgery. Neurosurgery (ISSN 0163-7617); (1980-199?): Modern Technics in Surgery. Urologic Surgery (ISSN 0193-8568)
Description: Includes technical papers and review articles on a wide variety of cardiac surgical techniques for both congenital and acquired conditions.
Refereed Serial

616.1 US ISSN 0883-9212
RC681.A1
JOURNAL OF CARDIOPULMONARY REHABILITATION. bi-m. $69 to individuals (foreign $110); institutions $140 (foreign $170) (effective 1996); newsstand price: $30. (American Association of Cardiovascular & Pulmonary Rehabilitation) Lippincott - Raven Publishers, 227 E. Washington Sq., Philadelphia, PA 19105. TEL 215-238-4200. (Subscr. to: 12107 Insurance Way, Hagerstown, MD 21740) Ed. Dr. Barry A. Franklin; Pub. Lisa M. Marshall. adv. contact: Jennifer Bass. bk.rev. circ. 3,934. (also avail. in microform from UMI; back issues avail.) **Indexed:** Phys.Ed.Ind. **Document type:** academic/scholarly publication.
—BLDSC (4954.864500); Faxon; SWETS; UMI; UnCover. **CCC.**
Formerly: Journal of Cardiac Rehabilitation (ISSN 0275-1429)
Description: Covers articles in peripheral, vascular, and pulmonary rehabilitation.
Refereed Serial

616.1 US ISSN 1053-0770
CODEN: JCVAEK
JOURNAL OF CARDIOTHORACIC AND VASCULAR ANESTHESIA. 1987. bi-m. $186 (foreign $232) (effective 1996). W.B. Saunders Co. (Subsidiary of: Harcourt Brace & Company), The Curtis Center, 3rd Fl., Independence Sq. W., Philadelphia, PA 19106-3399. TEL 215-238-7800. FAX 215-238-6445. (Subscr. to: Periodicals Fulfillment, W.B. Saunders Co., 6277 Sea Harbor Dr., 4th Fl., Orlando, FL 32891-4800. TEL 800-654-2452. FAX 800-874-6418) Ed. Dr. Joel A. Kaplan; Pub. Joan W. Blumberg. adv.: B&W page $835, color page $1835; 7 x 10. bk.rev.; abstr.; bibl.; charts; illus.; index. circ. 3,648. (back issues avail.) **Indexed:** Excerp.Med. **Document type:** academic/scholarly publication.
—BLDSC (4954.864700); Genuine Article; SWETS; UMI; UnCover. **CCC.**
Formerly: Journal of Cardiothoracic Anesthesia (ISSN 0888-6296)
Description: Primarily aimed at anesthesiologists who deal with patients undergoing heart, throat, or blood vessel surgery.
Refereed Serial

616.1 619 US ISSN 1073-7774
CODEN: JCDPE9
JOURNAL OF CARDIOVASCULAR DIAGNOSIS AND PROCEDURES. 1982. q. $178 (foreign $217). Mary Ann Liebert, Inc. Publishers, 2 Madison Ave., Larchmont, NY 10538. TEL 914-834-3100. FAX 914-834-3688. E-mail: Liebert@pipeline.com. Ed. Michelle Nanna. adv.; bk.rev. (back issues avail.) **Indexed:** Curr.Cont., Excerp.Med. **Document type:** academic/scholarly publication.
—Faxon; Genuine Article; SWETS; UnCover.
Former titles (until 1994): Journal of Cardiovascular Technology (ISSN 1043-4356); *(until 1989):* Journal of Cardiovascular Ultrasonography (ISSN 0730-8396)
Description: Publishes articles on both diagnostic and therapeutic applications of new technologies to cardiovascular disease.
Refereed Serial

616.1 US ISSN 1045-3873
CODEN: JCELE2
JOURNAL OF CARDIOVASCULAR ELECTROPHYSIOLOGY. 1990. m. $135 (foreign $180) (effective 1995). Futura Publishing Company, Inc., 135 Bedford Rd., Box 418, Armonk, NY 10504-0418. TEL 914-273-1014; 800-877-8761. FAX 914-273-1015. Ed. Dr. Douglas P. Zipes. adv.: B&W page $911, color page $1876; trim 8 1/4 x 10 7/8; adv. contact: Maureen Sonntag. bk.rev.; abstr. circ. 3,164. **Indexed:** Ind.Med. (1993-). **Document type:** academic/scholarly publication.
—BLDSC (4954.866000); ADONIS; Faxon; Genuine Article; SWETS; UnCover. **CCC.**
Description: Devoted to the study of the electrophysiology of the heart and its blood vessels.
Refereed Serial

616.12 US ISSN 1053-5330
RA975.5.C3
JOURNAL OF CARDIOVASCULAR MANAGEMENT. 1990. bi-m. $48 in the U.S.; Canada $56; elsewhere $66. Knolls Publishing Group, Inc., 201 Littleton Rd., Ste. 100, Morris Plains, NJ 07950-2932. TEL 201-285-0855. FAX 201-285-1472. Ed. Nancy Salerno-Davis. adv. contact: Stuart G. Mann. circ. 11,564.
—BLDSC (4954.866900).
Description: Facilitates the dissemination of information and ideas among those professionals involved with the day-to-day management and administrative duties in hospital cardiovascular departments.

616.12 610.73 US ISSN 0889-4655
JOURNAL OF CARDIOVASCULAR NURSING. 1986. q. $68 (foreign $82). Aspen Publishers, Inc., 200 Orchard Ridge Dr., Gaithersburg, MD 20878. TEL 301-417-7500. FAX 301-417-7550. **Indexed:** CINAHL, Ind.Med. (1993-), Nurs.Abstr.
—BLDSC (4954.867500); Faxon; SWETS; UMI; UnCover. **CCC.**

JOURNAL OF CARDIOVASCULAR PHARMACOLOGY. see *PHARMACY AND PHARMACOLOGY*

616.1 US ISSN 1350-6277
CODEN: JCRIE
▼**JOURNAL OF CARDIOVASCULAR RISK.** 1994. bi-m. $144.95 to individuals; institutions $295; residents $99.95. Current Science, 400 Market St., Ste. 700, Philadelphia, PA 19106-2199. TEL 215-574-2210; 800-552-5866. FAX 215-574-3533. (And: Current Science Ltd., 34-42 Cleveland St., London W1P 6LB, England. TEL 0171-323-0323. FAX 0171-636-6911) Eds. A.M. Gotto Jr., P. Sleight. (back issues avail.) **Indexed:** Excerp.Med. (1995-). **Document type:** academic/scholarly publication.
—BLDSC (4954.869000); ADONIS.

616.1 IT ISSN 0021-9509
CODEN: JCVSA2
JOURNAL OF CARDIOVASCULAR SURGERY. (Text in English) 1960. bi-m. $110 to individuals; institutions $150 (effective 1995). (International Society of Cardiothoracic Surgeons) Edizioni Minerva Medica, Corso Bramante 83-85, 10126 Turin, Italy. TEL 011-678282. FAX 011-3121736. Ed. L. Castellani; Pub. Alberto Oliaro. adv.: B&W page $1100, color page $1900; trim 215 x 280; adv. contact: F. Filippo. bk.rev.; bibl.; charts; illus.; index; circ. 5,000 (paid). (also avail. in microform from SWZ; back issues avail.) **Indexed:** Biol.Abstr., Chem.Abstr., Curr.Cont., Excerp.Med., Ind.Med., Sci.Cit.Ind. **Document type:** academic/scholarly publication.
—BLDSC (4954.870000); EMDOCS; Faxon; Genuine Article; SWETS; UnCover.
Description: Covers pathophysiology and therapy of surgical diseases of the chest and heart, the blood vessels and cardiorespiratory system.
Refereed Serial

616.1 US
JOURNAL OF CARDIOVASCULAR TECHNOLOGY. 1970. s-a. $45. American Society of Cardiovascular Professionals - Society for Cardiovascular Management, 120 Falcon Dr., Unit 3, Fredericksburg, VA 22408. TEL 703-891-0079. FAX 703-898-2393. Ed. Dr. John Cissik. adv.; index. circ. 3,200. (back issues avail.)
Formerly: Journal of Cardiovascular and Pulmonary Technology (ISSN 0893-2972); *Supersedes* (in 1985): Analyzer (ISSN 0146-5449)

JOURNAL OF CRITICAL CARE. see *MEDICAL SCIENCES — Orthopedics And Traumatology*

616.1 US ISSN 0022-0736
RC681.A1 CODEN: JECAB4
JOURNAL OF ELECTROCARDIOLOGY. 1968. q. $95 to individuals (foreign $130); institutions $145 (foreign $187). Churchill Livingstone International, 650 Ave. of the Americas, New York, NY 10011. TEL 212-206-5040. FAX 212-727-7808. TELEX 662266. Ed. Dr. Ronald H. Selvester. adv.; bk.rev.; charts; illus.; index. circ. 1,000. (also avail. in microfilm from UMI; reprint service avail. from UMI, ISI) **Indexed:** Biol.Abstr., Curr.Cont., Excerp.Med., Ind.Med., Ind.Sci.Rev., INIS Atomind., Sci.Cit.Ind. **Document type:** academic/scholarly publication.
—BLDSC (4974.750000); EMDOCS; Faxon; Genuine Article; SWETS; UMI; UnCover. **CCC.**
Description: Devoted to the clinical and experimental studies of the electrical activities of the heart.
Refereed Serial

616.125 UK ISSN 0966-8519
CODEN: JHVDEU
JOURNAL OF HEART VALVE DISEASE. 1992. bi-m. £97 to individuals; institutions $167 (effective 1995). I C R Publishers Ltd., 9 West End Ct., West End Ave., Pinner, Middx. HA5 1BP, England. TEL 0181-8663117. Ed. Dr. Endre Bodnar. circ. 5,200. **Indexed:** Excerp.Med. (1994-), Ind.Med. (1993-). **Document type:** academic/scholarly publication.
—BLDSC (4996.876000).
Description: Covers all topics related to heart valves, and the prevention, pathology, diagnosis, and treatment of heart-valve disease.
Refereed Serial

MEDICAL SCIENCES — CARDIOVASCULAR DISEASES 4339

616.1 UK ISSN 0950-9240
RC685.H8
JOURNAL OF HUMAN HYPERTENSION. 1987. m. £105 to individuals; institutions £245. Stockton Press (Subsidiary of: Macmillan Press Ltd.), Houndmills, Basingstoke, Hants RG21 2XS, England. TEL 01256-817245. FAX 01256-28339. Ed. D.G. Beevers. adv. contact: Michael Rowley. bk.rev.; index. (also avail. in microfilm from UMI; back issues avail.) **Indexed:** Curr.Cont., Excerp.Med., Ind.Med., Kidney. **Document type:** academic/scholarly publication.
—BLDSC (5003.416000); Faxon; Genuine Article; SWETS; UMI; UnCover. **CCC.**

616.132 US ISSN 0263-6352
CODEN: JOHYD3
JOURNAL OF HYPERTENSION. (Supplement avail. (ISSN 0952-1178)) 1982. m. $160 to individuals; institutions $295; residents $99.95. (International Society of Hypertension) Current Science, 400 Market St., Ste. 700, Philadelphia, PA 19106. TEL 215-574-2210; 800-552-5866. FAX 215-574-3533. (And: Current Science Ltd., 34-42 Cleveland St., London W1P 6LB, England. TEL 0171-323-0323. FAX 0171-636-6911) Ed. A. Zanchetti. adv.; bibl.; illus. circ. 3,575. **Indexed:** Behav.Med.Abstr., Curr.Adv.Biochem., Curr.Adv.Cancer Res., Excerp.Med., Ind.Med., Kidney. **Document type:** academic/scholarly publication.
—BLDSC (5004.510000); ADONIS; CASDDS; Faxon; Genuine Article; SWETS; UnCover. **CCC.**
Description: Presents original papers ranging from studies in clinical care to the investigation of experimental hypertension. Includes review articles with annotated bibliographies, plus a bibliography of the current current world literature published during the previous year.

616.132 UK ISSN 0952-1178
JOURNAL OF HYPERTENSION. SUPPLEMENT. (Supplement to: Journal of Hypertension (ISSN 0263-6352)) 1983. irreg. (International Society of Hypertension) Current Science, 400 Market St., Ste. 700, Philadelphia, PA 19106. TEL 215-574-2210; 800-552-5866. FAX 215-574-3533. (And: Current Science Ltd., 34-42 Cleveland St., London W1P 6LB, England. TEL 44-171-323-0323. FAX 44-171-636-6911) **Indexed:** Excerp.Med. (1995-), Ind.Med. (1983-). **Document type:** academic/scholarly publication.
—BLDSC (5004.510010).

616.1 US ISSN 1078-7852
RC685.C18 CODEN: CRSHAG
JOURNAL OF INFLAMMATION. 1974. m. $996 (foreign $1182) (effective 1996). (Shock Society) John Wiley & Sons, Inc., Journals, 605 Third Ave., New York, NY 10158. TEL 212-850-6645. FAX 212-850-6021. TELEX 12-7063. E-mail: SUBINFO@JWILEY.COM. (Subscr. outside the Americas to: John Wiley & Sons Ltd., Baffins Ln., Chichester, W. Sussex PO19 1UD, England. TEL 44-1243-779777. FAX 44-1243-776128) Ed. James P. Filkins. adv.; bibl.; illus.; index. (also avail. in microform from UMI; back issues avail.) **Indexed:** Biol.Abstr., Chem.Abstr., Curr.Adv.Ecol.Sci., Curr.Cont., Excerp.Med., Ind.Med., Ind.Sci.Rev., Ind.Vet., INIS Atomind., Sci.Cit.Ind., Small Anim.Abstr., Vet.Bull. **Document type:** academic/scholarly publication.
●Also available online.
—BLDSC (3265.320000); CASDDS; EMDOCS; Faxon; Genuine Article; SWETS; UnCover. **CCC.**
Formerly (until 1995): Circulatory Shock (ISSN 0092-6213)
Description: Devoted to basic and clinical research on shock and low-flow states.
Refereed Serial

616.1 US ISSN 0896-4327
JOURNAL OF INTERVENTIONAL CARDIOLOGY. 1988. bi-m. $98 (foreign $126) (effective 1995). Futura Publishing Company, Inc., 135 Bedford Rd., Box 418, Armonk, NY 10504-0418. TEL 914-273-1014. FAX 914-273-1015. Ed. Dr. Gerald C. Timmis. adv.: B&W page $925, color page $1860; trim 8 1/4 x 10 7/8; adv. contact: Suzanne Fath. bk.rev. circ. 2,333. **Indexed:** Curr.Cont., Excerp.Med. (1995-). **Document type:** academic/scholarly publication.
—BLDSC (5007.696000); ADONIS; Genuine Article; UnCover. **CCC.**
Description: Provides the latest information on interventional cardiology, including diagnostics, monitoring, therapeutic techniques and equipment.
Refereed Serial

616.1 US ISSN 1042-3931
JOURNAL OF INVASIVE CARDIOLOGY. 1988. 9/yr. $90 (foreign $126). Health Management Publications, Inc., 550 American Ave., King of Prussia, PA 19406-1441. TEL 215-337-4466; 800-237-7285. FAX 215-337-0890. Ed. Dr. Richard Shaw. adv. **Document type:** trade publication.
—BLDSC (5007.800000); Genuine Article.
Description: Covers cardiac catheterization, coronary and peripheral angioplasty, including thrombolytic and associated therapy.
Refereed Serial

616.1 UK ISSN 0022-2828
RC681.A1 CODEN: JMCDAY
JOURNAL OF MOLECULAR AND CELLULAR CARDIOLOGY. 1970. m. £795 (effective 1996). (International Society for Heart Research) Academic Press Ltd. (Subsidiary of: Harcourt Brace & Company Ltd.), 24-28 Oval Rd., London NW1 7DX, England. TEL 44-171-267-4466. FAX 44-171-482-2293. TELEX 25775 ACPRES G. (Subscr. to: Harcourt Brace & Company Ltd., Foots Cray High St., Sidcup, Kent DA14 5HP, England. TEL 44-181-300-3322. FAX 44-181-309-0807) Ed. N.R. Alpert. index. **Indexed:** Apic.Abstr., Biol.Abstr., Biotech.Abstr., Chem.Abstr., Curr.Adv.Biochem., Curr.Adv.Cell & Devel.Biol., Curr.Adv.Ecol.Sci., Curr.Adv.Genetics & Molec.Biol., Dent.Ind., Excerp.Med., Helminthol.Abstr., Ind.Med., Ind.Sci.Rev. **Document type:** academic/scholarly publication.
—BLDSC (5020.690000); ADONIS; CASDDS; EMDOCS; Faxon; Genuine Article; SWETS; UnCover. **CCC.**
Description: Provides a forum for research papers dealing with the molecular biology, physiology, pharmacology, and pathophysiology of the heart and cardiovascular system.

616.13 US ISSN 1045-7984
CODEN: JMYIER
JOURNAL OF MYOCARDIAL ISCHEMIA. 1989. 10/yr. $60 to individuals (foreign $75); institutions $90 (effective 1995). P R R, Inc., 17 Prospect St., Huntington, NY 11743. TEL 516-424-8900. FAX 516-424-8503. Ed. Dr. Carl J. Pepine; Pub. Tiberius H. Schuldner. adv.: B&W page $2290, color page $3540; trim 7 7/8 x 10 3/4. index; circ. 27,833 (controlled). **Indexed:** Excerp.Med. (1993-).
—BLDSC (5021.172500). **CCC.**
Description: Forum for reports and reviews on the diagnosis and treatment of angina, silent ischemia, atherosclerosis and acute myocardial infarction.

616.1 NE ISSN 0929-5305
CODEN: JTTHFF
▼**JOURNAL OF THROMBOSIS AND THROMBOLYSIS;** an international journal for clinician-scientists. (Text in English) 1994. q. fl.448 to institutions; $287 to institutions in U.S. (effective 1996). Kluwer Academic Publishers, Postbus 17, 3300 AA Dordrecht, Netherlands. TEL 31-78-392392. FAX 31-78-392254. TELEX 29245 KAPG NL. E-mail: SERVICES@WKAP.NL. (Dist. by: Kluwer Academic Publishers Group, P.O. Box 322, 3300 AH Dordrecht, Netherlands. TEL 31-78-392392. FAX 31-78-546474; N. America dist. addr.: Box 358, Accord Sta., Hingham, MA 02018-0358. TEL 617-871-6600. FAX 617-871-6528) Ed. Dr. Richard T. Becker. **Document type:** academic/scholarly publication.
—BLDSC (5069.350000); CASDDS. **CCC.**
Description: Publishes original papers integrating basic science and clinical investigation of thrombotic disorders.
Refereed Serial

616.1 UK ISSN 1353-8012
▼**JOURNAL OF VASCULAR INVESTIGATION.** 1995. q. £99 to individuals; institutions £175. Churchill Livingstone Journals (Subsidiary of: Pearson Professional), Robert Stevenson House, 1-3 Baxter's Pl., Leith Walk, Edinburgh EH1 3AF, Scotland. TEL 0131-556-2424. FAX 0131-558-1278. Eds. Eugene Strandness, Robert Reneman. adv. contact: David Dunnachie. **Document type:** academic/scholarly publication.
—BLDSC (5072.267000).

616.1 574 US ISSN 1042-5268
CODEN: JVBIE9
JOURNAL OF VASCULAR MEDICINE AND BIOLOGY. 1988. bi-m. $130 to individuals; institutions $170. (Society of Vascular Medicine and Biology) Blackwell Scientific Publications, Inc., 238 Main St., Ste. 501, Cambridge, MA 02142-1413. TEL 617-876-7000. FAX 617-876-7022. Ed. Dr. Mark V. Creager. **Document type:** academic/scholarly publication.
—BLDSC (5072.268000); UMI; UnCover. **CCC.**
Description: Focuses on the blood vessel - the biology and pathology - including the vascular wall and blood components.
Refereed Serial

JOURNAL OF VASCULAR NURSING. see *MEDICAL SCIENCES — Nurses And Nursing*

JOURNAL OF VASCULAR SURGERY. see *MEDICAL SCIENCES — Surgery*

616.1 US ISSN 1044-4122
CODEN: JVTEEJ
JOURNAL OF VASCULAR TECHNOLOGY. 1979. bi-m. $100 (Canada $100; elsewhere $125) (effective 1996). Society of Vascular Technology, 4601 Presidents Dr., Ste. 260, Lanham, MD 20706-4365. TEL 301-459-7550; 800-SVT-VEIN. FAX 301-459-5651. Ed. Ann Marie Kwpinski; Pub. Patricia I. Horner. adv.: B&W page $706; color page $1306; trim 7 x 9 3/8; adv. contact: John R. Avellanet. bk.rev. circ. 10,000. (back issues avail.) **Indexed:** Excerp.Med. (1993-). **Document type:** academic/scholarly publication.
—BLDSC (5072.271000).
Formerly (until 1986): Bruit (ISSN 0739-8670)
Description: Provides an educational service for practicing noninvasive vascular technologists, technologists involved in supervision and education in a clinical setting, physicians, surgeons, researchers, manufacturers, and other health care professionals. Covers advances in the field, case studies, and opinions.
Refereed Serial

616.1 PL ISSN 0022-9032
KARDIOLOGIA POLSKA. (Text in Polish; summaries in English) 1958. m. $120. Polskie Towarzystwo Kardiologiczne, Ul. Grenadierow 51-59, 04-073 Warsaw, Poland. TEL 48-22-101738. Ed. Leszek Ceremuzynski. adv.; bk.rev. circ. 3,000. **Indexed:** Biol.Abstr, Chem.Abstr., Excerp.Med., Ind.Med., INIS Atomind.
—BLDSC (5085.700000); EMDOCS.

616.1 JA ISSN 0911-4637
KEKKAN/JAPANESE JOURNAL OF CIRCULATION RESEARCH. (Text in Japanese) 1976. 4/yr. Nihon Myakkan Sado Busshitsu Gakkai - Japanese Society for Circulation Research, Nagoya Daigaku Igakubu Yakuri Kyoshitsu, 65, Tsurumaicho, Showa-ku, Nagoya-shi, Aichi-ken 466, Japan.

616.1 JA ISSN 0917-5318
KEKKAN TO NAIHI/BLOOD VESSEL & ENDOTHELIUM. (Text in Japanese) 1991. 6/yr. 1900 Yen per no. Medikaru Rebyusha - Medical Review Co., Ltd., 7-3, Hiranomachi 1-chome, Chuo-ku, Osaka 541, Japan.

LIVEWELL. see *PHYSICAL FITNESS AND HYGIENE*

616.1 BL
MEDISOM: CARDIOLOGY. 1976. bi-m. $90. Editora Medisom, Ltda., Rua Sao Paulino 224, Caixa Postal 7650, 01064-970 Sao Paulo, Brazil. FAX 55-11-572-5957. Ed. Dr. Philip Querido. adv. (audio cassette)

616.1 NE ISSN 0167-725X
CODEN: MACDDK
METABOLIC ASPECTS OF CARDIOVASCULAR DISEASE. 1981. irreg., vol.3, 1984. price varies. Elsevier Science B.V., Books Division, P.O. Box 211, 1000 AE Amsterdam, Netherlands. TEL 31-20-4853911. FAX 31-20-4853705. TELEX 18582 ESPA NL. E-mail: nlinfo-f@elsevier.nl; usinfo-f@elsevier.nl; forinfo-kyf04035@niftyserve.or.jp; Site addr.: http://www.elsevier.nl/. (Subscr. in U.S. and Canada to: Elsevier Science Inc., Box 882, Madison Sq. Sta., New York, NY 10159. TEL 212-989-5800) **Document type:** monographic series.
—CASDDS.
Refereed Serial

MEDICAL SCIENCES — CARDIOVASCULAR DISEASES

616.1 US ISSN 0026-2862
RC681.A1 CODEN: MIVRA6
MICROVASCULAR RESEARCH; an international journal. 1968. bi-m. $522 (foreign $617) (effective 1996). Academic Press, Inc., Journal Division, 525 B St., Ste. 1900, San Diego, CA 92101-4495. TEL 619-230-1840. FAX 619-699-6800. (Subscr. to: Box 620000, Orlando, FL 32891-8340. TEL 800-543-9534) Ed. David Shepro. adv.; charts; illus.; index. (back issues avail.) **Indexed:** Biol.Abstr., Chem.Abstr., Curr.Adv.Ecol.Sci., Curr.Cont., Dent.Ind., Excerp.Med., Ind.Med., Ind.Sci.Rev., Ind.Vet., Pig News & Info., Vet.Bull. **Document type:** academic/scholarly publication.
—BLDSC (5761.060000); ADONIS; CASDDS; EMDOCS; Faxon; Genuine Article; SWETS; UnCover. **CCC.**
   Description: Disseminates information related to the microvascular field.
   Refereed Serial

616.1 IT ISSN 0391-3627
CODEN: MIANFU
MINERVA ANGIOLOGICA. q. $90 to individuals; institutions $140 (effective 1995). (Societa Italiana di Patologia Vascolare) Edizioni Minerva Medica, Corso Bramante 83-85, 10126 Turin, Italy. TEL 39-11-678282. FAX 39-11-3121736. (Co-sponsors: Gruppo Italiano di Ultrasonologia Vascolare; Societa Italiana di Flebologia Clinica e Sperimentale; Societa Italiana di Linfangiologia) Ed. A. Oliaro. adv.: B&W page $1300, color page $2200; trim 190 x 270; adv. contact: F. Filippo. circ. 3,000 (paid). **Indexed:** Ind.Med. **Document type:** academic/scholarly publication.
—BLDSC (5794.050000).
   Description: Covers angiological pathophysiology, clinical medicine, and therapy.
   Refereed Serial

616.1 IT ISSN 0026-4725
MINERVA CARDIOANGIOLOGICA; rivista mensile di clinica e terapia medica e chirurgica delle malattie del cuore e dei vasi. (Text in Italian; summaries in English, Italian) 1953. m. $110 to individuals; institutions $150 (effective 1995). Edizioni Minerva Medica, Corso Bramante 83-85, 10126 Turin, Italy. TEL 39-11-678282. FAX 39-11-3121736. Ed. Alberto Oliaro; Ed. Alberto Oliaro. adv.: B&W page $1100, color page $1900; trim 190 x 270; adv. contact: F. Filippo. abstr.; bibl.; illus.; circ. 4,000 (paid). (also avail. in microform from UMI) **Indexed:** Biol.Abstr., Chem.Abstr., Curr.Adv.Ecol.Sci., Curr.Cont., Dent.Ind., Excerp.Med., Ind.Med., Nutr.Abstr. **Document type:** academic/scholarly publication.
—BLDSC (5794.060000); EMDOCS; Faxon; SWETS; UMI.
   Description: Covers pathophysiology, clinical medicine and therapy of heart and vessels.
   Refereed Serial

616.1 DK ISSN 0109-0690
MOTIONSBLADET; magazine for the Runners Club of the Danish Heart Foundation. 1974. bi-m. DKK 100. Hjerteforeningens Motionsklub, Paradisvejen 44, 8600 Silkeborg, Denmark. TEL 06-837114. Ed. Soeren Staehr. adv.; bk.rev.; illus. circ. 6,000.
   Formerly: Hjerteforeningens Motionsblad (ISSN 0109-0704)

616.1 610 JA ISSN 0387-1126
MYAKKANGAKU/JAPANESE COLLEGE OF ANGIOLOGY. JOURNAL. (Text in Japanese; summaries in English, Japanese) 1961. m. (Nihon Myakkan Gakkai - Japanese College of Angiology) Bunkodo Co., Ltd., 2-7, Hongo 7-chome, Bunkyo-ku, Tokyo 113, Japan. **Indexed:** INIS Atomind. **Document type:** academic/scholarly publication.

N M C D. (Nutrition, Metabolism and Cardiovascular Diseases) see *NUTRITION AND DIETETICS*

616.1 AT
NATIONAL HEART FOUNDATION OF AUSTRALIA. ANNUAL REPORT (YEAR). a. National Heart Foundation of Australia, P.O. Box 2, Woden, A.C.T. 2606, Australia. TEL 61-2-82-2144. FAX 61-2-282-5147.

616.1 NE
NEW CLINICAL APPLICATIONS IN CARDIOLOGY. (Text in English) irreg. price varies. Kluwer Academic Publishers, Postbus 17, 3300 AA Dordrecht, Netherlands. TEL 31-78-392392. FAX 31-78-392254. TELEX 29245 KAPG NL. (Dist. by: Kluwer Academic Publishers Group, P.O. Box 322, 3300 AH Dordrecht, Netherlands. TEL 31-78-392392. FAX 31-78-546474; N. America dist. addr.: Box 358, Accord Sta., Hingham, MA 02018-0358. TEL 617-871-6600. FAX 617-871-6528) **Document type:** monographic series.

616.1 IT ISSN 0393-5302
NEW TRENDS IN ARRHYTHMIAS. (Text in English) 1985. q. L.70000($70) (effective 1993). (Italian Group of Arrhythmology) C I C Edizioni Internazionali s.r.l., Via L. Spallanzani, 11, 00161 Rome, Italy. TEL 06-8412673. FAX 06-8845590. Ed. Francesco Furlanello. adv.; bk.rev. (back issues avail.) **Indexed:** Excerp.Med.
—BLDSC (6089.000500). **CCC.**
   Description: Publishes original research papers regarding cardiovascular diseases. Includes proceedings of congresses.

616.1 US
NEWSPAPER OF CARDIOLOGY. 1982. m. $46. McMahon Group, 148 W. 24th St., New York, NY 10011. TEL 212-620-4600. FAX 212-620-5928. Ed. William Dunnett. adv. contact: Ward Byrne. circ. 35,000. (tabloid format)
   Formerly: Cardiovascular News.
   Description: Features research developments.

616.1 GW ISSN 0300-5224
CODEN: NIHOD9
NIEREN- UND HOCHDRUCKKRANKHEITEN. 1972. m. DM.228($172) Dustri-Verlag Dr. Karl Feistle, Bahnhofstr. 9, 82041 Deisenhofen, Germany. TEL 089-613861-0. FAX 089-613-5412. Ed. Dr. H. Brass. **Indexed:** Biol.Abstr., Chem.Abstr., Curr.Adv.Ecol.Sci., Curr.Cont., Excerp.Med. **Document type:** academic/scholarly publication.
—CASDDS; Genuine Article. **CCC.**

616.1 MX ISSN 1405-2229
NUEVA CARDIOLOGIA. (Text in Spanish, summaries in English) 1987. m. Mex.$290($90) (Instituto Nacional de Cardiologia) Obsidiana Editores, S.A., Czda. de Tlalpan 2365, Col. Ciudad Jardin, 04370 Mexico DF, Mexico. TEL 6899133. FAX 6896545. Eds. Dr. Fause Attie, Dr. Paris Troyo. circ. 1,430 (paid); 570 (controlled). **Document type:** academic/scholarly publication.
   Description: Publishes works presented orally at the general sessions of the institute.

616.1 US ISSN 0147-8389
RC684.P3 CODEN: PPCED
P A C E. (Pacing and Clinical Electrophysiology) 1978. m. $160 (foreign $208) (effective 1995). Futura Publishing Company, Inc., 135 Bedford Rd., Box 418, Armonk, NY 10504-0418. TEL 914-273-1014; 800-877-8761. FAX 914-973-1015. (Co-sponsors: North American Society of Pacing and Clinical Electrophysiology; Asian-Pacific Working Group on Cardiac Pacing) Ed. Dr. Seymour Furman. adv.: B&W page $1107, color page $2072; trim 8 1/4 x 10 7/8; adv. contact: Maureen Sonntag. bk.rev.; abstr.; bibl.; charts; illus.; pat.; stat.; index, cum.index. circ. 6,616. **Indexed:** Biol.Abstr., Chem.Abstr., Curr.Cont., Excerp.Med., Ind.Med. **Document type:** academic/scholarly publication.
—BLDSC (6328.210000); ADONIS; Faxon; Genuine Article; SWETS; UnCover.
   Description: Information regarding the major advances in clinical cardiac pacing, electrophysiology, electrostimulation, biostimulation, and implantable devices.
   Refereed Serial

P A S C A L E 75: CARDIOLOGIE ET APPAREIL CIRCULATOIRE. see *MEDICAL SCIENCES — Abstracting, Bibliographies, Statistics*

616.1 PK ISSN 0048-2706
PAKISTAN HEART JOURNAL. (Text in English) 1968. q. Rs.200($25) Pakistan Cardiac Society, c/o National Institute of Cardiovascular Diseases, Jinnah Hospital Rd., Karachi, Pakistan. Ed. Azhar M.A. Faruqui. adv.; bk.rev.; bibl.; charts; illus. circ. 1,000. **Document type:** academic/scholarly publication.
—BLDSC (6340.842000).
   Description: Covers cardiac science in Pakistan with original papers and review papers.

618.92 616.12 US ISSN 0172-0643
RJ421 CODEN: PECAD4
PEDIATRIC CARDIOLOGY. 1979. q. $180 (effective 1996). Springer-Verlag, Journals, 175 Fifth Ave., New York, NY 10010. TEL 212-460-1500. FAX 212-473-6272. (Subscr. in N. America to: Journal Fulfillment Services, Box 2485, Secaucus, NJ 07096-2491. TEL 800-777-4643. FAX 201-348-4505; Elsewhere: Springer-Verlag, Heidelberger Platz 3, 14197 Berlin, Germany. TEL 030-8207-1. FAX 030-821-4091) Ed. I. Carr. circ. 890. (also avail. in microform from UMI; reprint service avail. from ISI) **Indexed:** Curr.Cont., Dent.Ind., Excerp.Med., Ind.Med. **Document type:** academic/scholarly publication.
—BLDSC (6417.535000); Faxon; Genuine Article; SWETS; UMI; UnCover. **CCC.**
   Description: Devoted exclusively to the diagnosis and management of heart disease in young people. Presents research reports and the latest clinical information from across the entire field.
   Refereed Serial

616.1 UK ISSN 0267-6591
CODEN: PERFER
PERFUSION. 1986. bi-m. £96($165) to individuals; institutions £242 ($395) (effective 1996). Arnold (Subsidiary of: Hodder Headline plc.), 338 Euston Rd., London NW1 3BH, England. TEL 0171-873-6000. FAX 0171-873-6325. (Subscr. to: Turpin Distribution Services Ltd., Blackhorse Rd., Letchworth, Herts. SG6 1HN, England. TEL 01462-672555. FAX 01462-480947) Ed. Prof. K.M. Taylor. adv.; bk.rev.; index. **Indexed:** Excerp.Med., Ind.Med. (1993-). **Document type:** academic/scholarly publication.
—BLDSC (6425.020000); UnCover. **CCC.**
   Description: Dedicated to the advancement of knowledge and clinical practice in the field of extracorporeal circulation.

616.1 US
PERFUSION REVIEW. 1992. q. D M R Publishing, Box 85099, Los Angeles, CA 90072. TEL 213-464-3891. FAX 213-463-1959. adv.: B&W page $800, color page $1600; trim 8 1/2 x 10 7/8. circ. 3,000. **Document type:** trade publication.

616.12 CN ISSN 0828-6396
PERSPECTIVES IN CARDIOLOGY. 1985. 9/yr. S T A Communications Inc., 955 boul. St. Jean, Ste. 306, Pointe-Claire, PQ H9R 5K3, Canada. TEL 514-695-7623. FAX 514-695-8554. Ed. Paul Brand. adv. circ. 22,000.

616.132 US ISSN 0898-6770
PERSPECTIVES IN HYPERTENSION SERIES. 1987. irreg., latest vol.3. price varies. Raven Press (Subsidiary of: Wolters Kluwer N.V.), 1185 Ave. of the Americas, New York, NY 10036. TEL 212-930-9500. FAX 212-869-3495. Ed.Bd. (reprint service avail. from UMI) **Document type:** monographic series.
   Refereed Serial

616.1 UK ISSN 0268-3555
CODEN: PHLEEF
PHLEBOLOGY. 1986. q. £110($176) (effective 1996). (International Union of Phlebology) Springer-Verlag, Springer House, 8 Alexandra Rd., Wimbledon, London SW19 7JZ, England. TEL 081-944-2942. FAX 081-947-4651. (Subscr. in N. America to: Springer-Verlag New York, Inc., Box 2485, Secaucus, NJ 07096-2491. TEL 201-348-4033) Ed. David Negus. index. circ. 700. (back issues avail.) **Indexed:** Curr.Cont., Excerp.Med., Ind.Med. **Document type:** academic/scholarly publication.
—BLDSC (6465.101100); Genuine Article; UMI. **CCC.**

616.1 US ISSN 0363-5104
RC681.A1 CODEN: PRCRDA
PRIMARY CARDIOLOGY; cardiovascular medicine for the internist and cardiologist. 1975. m. $69. P W Communications, Inc., 400 Plaza Dr., Secaucus, NJ 07094. TEL 201-865-7500. Ed. Frederick Robin; Pub. John Molluso. illus. (also avail. in microform from UMI; reprint service avail. from UMI) **Indexed:** Excerp.Med. **Document type:** trade publication.
—BLDSC (6612.907500); Faxon; UMI; UnCover.
   Incorporates (as of 1986): Cardiovascular Medicine; Which was formerly titled: Journal of Cardiovascular Medicine (ISSN 0199-6614); (1976-1980): Cardiovascular Medicine (ISSN 0145-403X)
   Refereed Serial

MEDICAL SCIENCES — CARDIOVASCULAR DISEASES

616.12   IT   ISSN 0393-6139
PRIMARY CARDIOLOGY (EDIZIONE ITALIANA). 1986. bi-m. E S I Stampa Medica s.r.l., L.go Volontari del Sangue 10, 20097 S. Donato Milanese (MI), Italy. TEL 39-2-5274241. FAX 39-2-55600670. adv.: Ornella/Galbiati. circ. 37,000.

616.1   US   ISSN 0146-6917
RC388.5   CODEN: CERDDD
PRINCETON RESEARCH CONFERENCES ON CEREBROVASCULAR DISEASES. Key Title: Cerebrovascular Diseases. 1976. irreg., latest 16th. price varies. Raven Press (Subsidiary of: Wolters Kluwer N.V.), 1185 Ave. of the Americas, New York, NY 10036. TEL 212-930-9500. FAX 212-869-3495. index. (reprint service avail. from UMI) **Indexed:** Chem.Abstr. **Document type:** proceedings.
—CASDDS.
    Formerly: Princeton Conference on Cerebrovascular Diseases; Supersedes (1954-1974): Cerebral Vascular Diseases. Conference (ISSN 0069-2255)
    Refereed Serial

616.1   SZ   ISSN 0254-5195
                CODEN: MFKLDH
PROGRESS IN APPLIED MICROCIRCULATION. (Text in English) 1983. irreg. (1-2/yr.). price varies. S. Karger AG, Allschwilerstr. 10, P.O. Box, CH-4009 Basel, Switzerland. TEL 061-3061111. FAX 061-3061234. E-mail: Karger@Karger.ch. Ed. K. Messmer. **Indexed:** Chem.Abstr. **Document type:** academic/scholarly publication.
—CASDDS. **CCC.**
    Description: Series that confronts some of the most challenging problems of microcirculation research and demonstrates how their solutions can alter clinical practice.
    Refereed Serial

616.1   US   ISSN 0033-0620
                CODEN: PCVDAN
PROGRESS IN CARDIOVASCULAR DISEASES. Italian translation: Progressi in Patologia Cardiovascolare (IT ISSN 0033-0701) (French and Spanish translations also avail.) 1958. bi-m. $184 (foreign $244) (effective 1996). W.B. Saunders Co. (Subsidiary of: Harcourt Brace & Company), Curtis Center, 3rd Fl., Independence Sq. W., Philadelphia, PA 19106-3399. TEL 215-238-7800. FAX 215-238-6445. (Subscr. to: Periodicals Fulfillment, W.B. Saunders Co., 6277 Sea Harbor Dr., 4th Fl., Orlando, FL 32891-4800. TEL 800-654-2452. FAX 800-874-6418) Eds. Drs. Michael Lesch, Edmund H. Sonnenblick; Pub. Joan W. Blumberg. adv.: B&W page $870, color page $1705; 7 x 10. bibl.; charts; illus.; index. circ. 4,042. **Indexed:** AIM, Biol.Abstr., Chem.Abstr., Curr.Adv.Ecol.Sci., Curr.Cont., Curr.Cont., Excerp.Med., Ind.Med., Ind.Sci.Rev., Nutr.Abstr., Sci.Cit.Ind. **Document type:** academic/scholarly publication.
●Also available online. Vendor(s): Lexis-Nexis.
—BLDSC (6866.650000); CASDDS; EMDOCS; Faxon; Genuine Article; SWETS; UMI; UnCover. **CCC.**
    Description: Each issue covers a single major topic, which experts discuss from various perspectives.
    Refereed Serial

616.12 610.73   US   ISSN 0889-7204
PROGRESS IN CARDIOVASCULAR NURSING. 1986. q. $50 to individuals (foreign $70); institutions $70 (foreign $90). Medquest Communications, Inc., 629 Euclid Ave., Ste. 500, Cleveland, OH 44114-3003. TEL 216-522-9700. FAX 216-522-9707. Ed. Marguerite M. Engler; Pub. John H. Whaley III. **Indexed:** CINAHL, Ind.Med. (1993-).
—BLDSC (6866.660000); UMI; UnCover. **CCC.**
    Description: Reflects current practice in caring for the cardiac patient; emphasis on research, new therapies and technologies.
    Refereed Serial

616.1   US
PROGRESS IN CORONARY SINUS INTERVENTIONS. 1986. irreg. price varies. Springer-Verlag, 175 Fifth Ave., New York, NY 10010. TEL 212-460-1500. FAX 212-473-6272. (Dist. in Germany by: Dr. Dietrich Steinkopff Verlag, Darmstadt, Germany) (reprint service avail. from ISI) **Document type:** monographic series.

616.1   NE   ISSN 0923-4020
PROGRESS IN HYPERTENSION. (Text in English) 1988. irreg., vol.2, 1992. price varies. V S P, P.O. Box 346, 3700 AH Zeist, Netherlands. TEL 31-3404-25790. FAX 31-3404-32081. (Dist. in U.S. and Canada by: Books International Inc., Box 605, Herndon, VA 22070. TEL 703-435-7064. FAX 703-689-0660) Ed. H. Saito. (back issues avail.) **Document type:** monographic series.
—BLDSC (6868.439000).

616.1 618.92   IE   ISSN 1058-9813
PROGRESS IN PEDIATRIC CARDIOLOGY. 1992. bi-m. I£160($253) (effective 1996). Elsevier Science Ireland Ltd., P.O. Box 85, Limerick, Ireland. TEL 353-31-471944. FAX 353-61-472144. (Subscr. in U.S. and Canada to; Elsevier Science, Box 882, Madison Sq. Sta., New York, NY 10159-0882. TEL 212-989-5800. FAX 212-633-3990) Ed. Dr. William W. Miller. (also avail. in microform from UMI; back issues avail.) **Document type:** academic/scholarly publication.
—BLDSC (6872.440000); Genuine Article; UMI. **CCC.**
    Description: Presents information and opinion important to the understanding and management of cardiovascular disease in children.
    Refereed Serial

616.1   IT   ISSN 0033-0701
PROGRESSI IN PATOLOGIA CARDIOVASCOLARE. Italian translation of: Progress in Cardiovascular Disease (US ISSN 0033-0620) 1957. bi-m. L.396000($240) (effective 1996). Pensiero Scientifico Editore s.r.l., Via Bradano 3-C, 00199 Rome, Italy. TEL 06-86207158. FAX 06-86207160. Ed. Piero Lega. adv.; bk.rev.; bibl.; charts; cum.index. circ. 1,000. **Document type:** academic/scholarly publication.

616.1   US
PULMONARY AND CRITICAL CARE MEDICINE. biennial. $55 (foreign $65). Hanley & Belfus, Inc., 210 S. 13th St., Philadelphia, PA 19107. TEL 215-546-7293. FAX 215-790-9330. Ed.Bd.
    Refereed Serial

616.1   UK   ISSN 0143-2435
RECENT ADVANCES IN CARDIOLOGY. 1929. irreg. Churchill Livingstone Medical Journals, Robert Stevenson House, 1-3 Baxter's Pl., Leith Walk, Edinburgh EH1 3AF, Scotland. TEL 0131-556-2424. FAX 0131-459-1177. **Document type:** academic/scholarly publication.

REFERATOVY VYBER Z KARDIOLOGIE/ABSTRACTS OF CARDIOLOGY. see MEDICAL SCIENCES — *Abstracting, Bibliographies, Statistics*

616.1   AG   ISSN 0034-6993
REVISTA ARGENTINA DE ANGIOLOGIA.* (Text in Spanish; summaries in English) 1967. q. Arg.$20($8) (Argentine Society of Angiology) Plantie Talleres Graficos S.A., Juan B. Alberdi 571, Buenos Aires, Argentina. Ed. Dr. Miguel Angel Lucas. adv.; bk.rev.; abstr.; bibl.; charts; illus.; stat. circ. 1,500. (also avail. in microform from UMI; reprint service avail. from UMI) **Indexed:** Biol.Abstr.

616.12   CU   ISSN 0864-2168
REVISTA CUBANA DE CARDIOLOGIA Y CIRUGIA CARDIOVASCULAR. s-a. $30 in S. America; N. America $32; elsewhere $34. Ministerio de Salud Publica, Centro Nacional de Informacion de Ciencias Medicas, Calle E, No. 452 e-19 y 21, Plaza de la Revolucion, Apdo. 6520, Havana, Cuba. TEL 809-32-5338. (Dist. by: Ediciones Cubanas, Obispo No. 526, Apdo. 605, Havana, Cuba) Ed. Sara Perez. circ. 1,300.
    Formerly (until 1987): Boletin de Cardiologia y Cirugia Cardiovascular.

REVISTA DE NUTRICION Y ATEROSCLEROSIS. see *NUTRITION AND DIETETICS*

616.1   SP   ISSN 0300-8932
                CODEN: RCDOAM
REVISTA ESPANOLA DE CARDIOLOGIA. (Supplement avail. (ISSN 1131-3587)) (Text in Spanish; summaries in English, Spanish) 1958. m. 7900 ptas.($57) to non-members. (Sociedad Espanola de Cardiologia) Ediciones Doyma S.A., Travesera de Gracia, 17-21, 08021 Barcelona, Spain. TEL 34-1-200-07-11. FAX 34-1-209-11-36. TELEX 51964 INK E. Ed. F. Fernandez Aviles. adv.: page 300000 ptas.; trim 210 x 180; adv. contact: Anna Pahissa. bk.rev.; index. circ. 4,000. **Indexed:** Chem.Abstr., Excerp.Med, Ind.Med.Esp., Ind.Med.
—BLDSC (7853.930000); CASDDS; UMI.
    Description: Covers cardiac physiopathology and the diagnostic and therapeutic resources applicable to heart disease.

616.1   SP   ISSN 0214-3941
REVISTA IBEROAMERICANA DE TROMBOSIS Y HEMOSTASIA. (Supplement avail. (ISSN 0214-395X)) 1988. q. 7200 ptas.($69) (effective 1995). Editorial Garsi S.A., Juan Bravo 46, 28006 Madrid, Spain. TEL 34-1-4021212. FAX 34-1-4020954. Ed. Justo Aznar. circ. 1,000.
—BLDSC (7858.843000).

616.12   SP   ISSN 0210-8755
                CODEN: RLCEEK
REVISTA LATINA DE CARDIOLOGIA. 6/yr. Principe de Vergara 112, 1o G, 28002 Madrid, Spain. TEL 1-563-73-06. FAX 1-563-23-93. Ed. Dr. Valles de Lema.
—BLDSC (7863.250000).

REVUE DE PNEUMOLOGIE CLINIQUE; le poumon et le coeur. see MEDICAL SCIENCES — *Respiratory Diseases*

616.12   FR   ISSN 1146-6537
REVUE DU CARDIOLOGUE PRATICIEN. 1989. 8/yr. 500 F. (foreign 727 F.) (effective 1996). Masson - Periodiques, Villa Laromiguiere, 75005 Paris, France. TEL 1-40-46-62-00. FAX 1-40-46-62-01. Ed. Francois Jan. adv. circ. 6,000. **Document type:** academic/scholarly publication.
    Description: Aids the general practitioner in day-to-day concerns about treating cardiology patients.

616.1   SU   ISSN 1018-077X
SAUDI HEART JOURNAL. (Text in English) 1989. 2/yr. free. (Saudi Heart Foundation - Jam'iah Asdiqa' al-Qalb al-Khairiyyah) King Abdul Aziz University Hospital, P.O. Box 6615, Jeddah 21452, Saudi Arabia. TEL 966-2-6697043. FAX 966-2-6697043. Ed. Dr. Hassan Raffa. adv.: B&W page SRI.5000. circ. 5,000. **Indexed:** Excerp.Med. (1993-), ExtraMED. **Document type:** academic/scholarly publication.
●Also available on CD-ROM.
—BLDSC (8076.974200).
    Formerly (until vol.2, no.1, 1990): Saudi Heart Bulletin.
    Description: Publishes research articles of interest, case reprots, reviews, discussions of new operative techniques and medical matters relating to the human heart.
    Refereed Serial

SCRIPTA SCIENTIFICA MEDICA. see MEDICAL SCIENCES — *Oncology*

SEMINARS IN HEMATOLOGY. see MEDICAL SCIENCES — *Hematology*

SEMINARS IN THORACIC AND CARDIOVASCULAR SURGERY. see MEDICAL SCIENCES — *Surgery*

SEMINARS IN VASCULAR SURGERY. see MEDICAL SCIENCES — *Surgery*

616.12   JA   ISSN 0911-0836
                CODEN: SHPEEY
SHINZO PESHINGU/JAPANESE JOURNAL OF CARDIAC PACING AND ELECTROPHYSIOLOGY. (Text in Japanese) 1984. q. 4000 Yen per no. Nihon Shinzo Peshingu Gakkai - Japanese Cardiac Pacing Society, Tokyo Joshi Ika Daigaku, Fuzoku Nihon Shinzo Ketsuatsu Kenkyujo, 8-1, Ichigaya Kawadacho, Shinjuku-ku, Tokyo 162, Japan. **Indexed:** Excerp.Med.
—BLDSC (4651.280000).

SIGNAL'NAYA INFORMATSIYA. ISHEMICHESKAYA BOLEZN' SERDTSA. see MEDICAL SCIENCES — *Abstracting, Bibliographies, Statistics*

MEDICAL SCIENCES — CARDIOVASCULAR DISEASES

SMOOTH MUSCLE. see *BIOLOGY — Physiology*

616.1 FR ISSN 0395-403X
SOCIETE FRANCAISE DE CARDIOLOGIE. BULLETIN D'INFORMATIONS. 1976. q. membership. Grou-Radenez-Joly, 19 rue des Saints Peres, 75006 Paris, France. Ed. Dr. A. Barrillon. adv. circ. 1,800. **Indexed:** I.P.A.
●Also available online.

616.1 US
SPECTRUM (LANHAM). q. $25 to non-members (outside N. America $30). Society of Vascular Technology, 4601 Presidents Dr., Ste. 260, Lanham, MD 20706-4365. TEL 301-459-7550; 800-SVT-VEIN. FAX 301-459-5651. Ed. Carol Ann Faull; Pub. Patricia I. Horner. adv.: page $550; 7 1/2 x 9 1/2. circ. 5,000. **Document type:** newsletter.
Description: Covers technological, social, economic, and legislative news of interest to medical professionals in the field. Reviews new products, reports chapter news, and lists forthcoming events and educational programs.

616.1 US ISSN 0039-2499
RC388.5 CODEN: SJCCA7
STROKE; a journal of cerebral circulation. 1970. m. $198 (foreign $246) (effective 1996). American Heart Association, 7272 Greenville Ave., Dallas, TX 75231-4596. TEL 214-706-1310. FAX 214-691-6342. (Subscr. to: Box 843543, Dallas, TX 75284-3543) Ed. Dr. Mark Dyken. adv.: abstr.; charts; illus.; index. circ. 6,200. (also avail. in microform from UMI,MIM; back issues avail.; reprint service avail. from UMI) **Indexed:** ASCA, Biol.Abstr., Biotech.Abstr., Chem.Abstr., Curr.Adv.Ecol.Sci., Curr.Cont., Dent.Ind., Excerp.Med., Ind.Med., Nutr.Abstr., Rehabil.Lit.
●Also available online. Vendor(s): Ovid Technologies.
—BLDSC (8474.900000); CASDDS; EMDOCS; Faxon; Genuine Article; SWETS; UMI; UnCover. **CCC.**
Description: For neurologists and internists. Includes articles on prevention, diagnosis, treatment and rehabilitation of stroke victims.
Refereed Serial

616.1 US ISSN 1047-014X
STROKE CONNECTION. 1980. bi-m. $8. A H A Stroke Connection, 7272 Greenville Ave., Dallas, TX 75231. TEL 214-706-1332. FAX 214-696-5211. adv.; bk.rev. circ. 5,000.
Description: For stroke survivors, caregivers, and professionals. Focuses on the lay population's ability to deal with various aspects of stroke-prevention, rehabilitation, and personal expenses.

616.1 FI ISSN 0039-7571
SYDAN. (Text in Finnish, Swedish) 1958. 7/yr. FIM 100 to non-members. Suomen Sydantautiliitto - Finnish Heart Association, Oltermannintie 8, P.O. Box 50, FIN-00621 Helsinki, Finland.
TEL 358-0-752-7521. FAX 358-0-752-752-50. Eds. Mauri Akkanen, Marjatta Karvinen. adv.: B&W page FIM 14400, color page FIM 20200. bk.rev. circ. 115,000. (tabloid format)
Description: Reports on the prevention, treatment and rehabilitation of cardio-vascular diseases and the activities of the association.

616.1 FR ISSN 1143-4171
SYNTHESE MEDICALE CARDIOLOGIE. 10/yr. 150 F. Editions Techniques et Medicales, 18 rue des Huissiers, 92200 Neuilly-sur-Seine, France. TEL 47-47-74-74. FAX 47-47-71-03. Ed. Guy-Vincent Heugas. adv.; charts. circ. 7,000.
Description: Covers current cardiology news.

616.12 US ISSN 8756-8586
TECHNOLOGY FOR CARDIOLOGY. m. $95. (Emergency Care Research Institute) E C R I, 5200 Butler Pike, Plymouth Meeting, PA 19462. TEL 610-825-6000. FAX 610-834-1275. Ed. Michele Moscarella.
Document type: newsletter.
—CCC.
Formerly: Health Devices Update: Cardiology.
Description: Contains technology-related information about cardiology for healthcare professionals.
Refereed Serial

616.1 US ISSN 0730-2347
CODEN: THIJDO
TEXAS HEART INSTITUTE JOURNAL. 1974. q. $25 (foreign $35). Texas Heart Institute, Publications & Communications, MC 1-194, Box 20345, Houston, TX 77225-0345. TEL 713-794-6630. FAX 713-791-3714. Ed. Dr. Robert J. Hall. adv. contact: Kathleen Denk. bk.rev.; illus.; stat. circ. 23,000. (also avail. in microform from UMI; back issues avail.; reprint service avail.) **Indexed:** ASCA, ASCA, Biol.Abstr., Curr.Cont., Excerp.Med., Helminthol.Abstr., Ind.Med. (1992-), Rev.Med.& Vet.Mycol. **Document type:** academic/scholarly publication.
●Also available online.
—BLDSC (8798.865000); Faxon; Genuine Article; SWETS; UMI; UnCover.
Formerly: Cardiovascular Diseases (ISSN 0093-3546)
Refereed Serial

616.1 GW ISSN 0340-6245
CODEN: THHADQ
THROMBOSIS AND HAEMOSTASIS. 1957. 12/yr. DM.480($366) to individuals; institutions DM.604($446). (International Society on Thrombosis and Haemostasis) F.K. Schattauer Verlagsgesellschaft mbH, Lenzhalde 3, 70192 Stuttgart, Germany. TEL 0711-22987-0. FAX 0711-22987-50. circ. 3,500. **Indexed:** ASCA, Biol.Abstr., Biotech.Abstr., Chem.Abstr., Curr.Adv.Cancer Res., Curr.Adv.Ecol.Sci., Curr.Cont., Dairy Sci.Abstr., Dent.Ind., Helminthol.Abstr., Ind.Med., Ind.Vet., Nutr.Abstr., Vet.Bull. **Document type:** academic/scholarly publication.
—BLDSC (8820.344000); CASDDS; Faxon; Genuine Article; SWETS; UnCover.
Formerly: Thrombosis et Diathesis Haemorrhagica (ISSN 0040-6597)

616.1 UK ISSN 0049-3848
CODEN: THBRAA
THROMBOSIS RESEARCH; an international journal on vascular obstruction, hemorrhage and hemostasis. (Text in English, French, German and Russian; summaries in English) 1972. 24/yr.
£1150($1829) (effective 1996). Elsevier Science Ltd., Pergamon, P.O. Box 800, Kidlington, Oxford OX5 1DX, England. TEL 44-1865-843000. FAX 44-1865-843010. E-mail: nlinfo-f@elsevier.nl; usinfo-f@elsevier.com; forinfo-kyf04035@niftyserve.or.jp; Site addr.: http://www.elsevier.nl/. (Subscr. in U.S. and Canada to: Elsevier Science, 660 White Plains Rd., Tarrytown, NY 10591-5153. TEL 914-524-9200. FAX 914-333-2444) Eds. Birger Blombak, Calvin M. Redman. adv.; bk.rev.; charts; illus.; index. circ. 700. (also avail. in microfilm from UMI) **Indexed:** ASCA, Biol.Abstr., Biotech.Abstr., Chem.Abstr., Curr.Adv.Biochem., Curr.Adv.Cell & Devel.Biol., Curr.Adv.Ecol.Sci., Curr.Cont., Dairy Sci.Abstr., Dent.Ind., Excerp.Med., Ind.Med., Nutr.Abstr., Risk Abstr. **Document type:** academic/scholarly publication.
—BLDSC (8820.365000); ADONIS; CASDDS; EMDOCS; Faxon; Genuine Article; SWETS; UMI; UnCover. **CCC.**
Description: Forum for the rapid dissemination of original research on thrombosis, hemostasis and fibrinolysis.
Refereed Serial

616.1 615.82 US ISSN 1074-9357
▼**TOPICS IN STROKE REHABILITATION.** 1994. q. $68. Aspen Publishers, Inc., 200 Orchard Ridge Dr., Ste. 200, Gaithersburg, MD 20878.
TEL 800-638-8437. Ed. Lenda P. Hill. (also avail. in microform from UMI; back issues avail.; reprint service avail. from UMI)
—BLDSC (8867.490300). **CCC.**
Description: Devoted to the study and dissemination of theoretical and practical information related to the subject of stroke rehabilitation. Reviews and reports common clinical practices, state-of-the-art concepts, and new developments in stroke patient care and research.
Refereed Serial

616.1 US ISSN 1050-1738
CODEN: TCMDEQ
TRENDS IN CARDIOVASCULAR MEDICINE. 1991. 8/yr. $264 to institutions in U.S.; $304 to institutions outside the Americas (effective 1996). Elsevier Science Inc., 655 Ave. of Americas, New York, NY 10010. TEL 212-989-5800. FAX 212-633-3990. TELEX 420643 AEP Ul. (Subscr. to: Box 882, Madison Sq. Sta., New York, NY 10159-0882) Ed.Bd. (also avail. in microform from UMI; back issues avail.) **Indexed:** Excerp.Med. (1992-). **Document type:** academic/scholarly publication.
—BLDSC (9049.549000); CASDDS; Genuine Article; SWETS. **CCC.**
Description: Designed to help clinical cardiologists and basic researchers keep up with advances in cardiovascular research.
Refereed Serial

616.13 IT ISSN 1120-2963
TROMBOSI & ARTEROSCLEROSI. 1990. bi-m. L.70000($120) Piccin Editore, Via Altinate 107, 35121 Padua, Italy. TEL 049-655566.
FAX 049-8750693. adv.: B&W page L.4000000, color page L.6000000; trim 195 x 270. circ. 11,930.
—BLDSC (9050.829000).

616.1 TU ISSN 1016-5169
CODEN: TKDAE
TURK KARDIYOLOJI DERNEGI ARSIVI. 1972. q. (Turk Kardiyoloji Dernegi) Logos Yayincilik Ticaret A.S., Yildiz Posta Cad., Sinan Apt. No. 36 D 66-67, Gayrettepe 80280 - Istanbul, Turkey.
TEL 90-212-2880541. Ed. Dr. Altan Onat. adv. contact: Ipek Karisman. **Indexed:** Excerp.Med.

616.1 US ISSN 0301-1526
CODEN: VASAAH
VASA; Zeitschrift fuer Gefaesskrankheiten - journal of vascular diseases. (Text in English or German) 1972. q. $103. Hogrefe & Huber Publishers, Box 2487, Kirkland, WA 98083. TEL 206-820-1500. FAX 206-823-8324. Ed. Dr. H.J. Leu. adv.; bk.rev.; abstr.; charts; illus.; index. circ. 1,300. **Indexed:** Biol.Abstr., Curr.Cont., Excerp.Med., Ind.Med. **Document type:** academic/scholarly publication.
—BLDSC (9148.300000); Faxon; Genuine Article; SWETS. **CCC.**
Formerly: Zentralblatt fuer Phlebologie (ISSN 0044-426X)
Description: Contains case reports, overviews and congress information.

616.1 UK ISSN 1358-863X
CODEN: VMEREI
VASCULAR MEDICINE. 1990; N.S. 1996. q. £85($125) to individuals; institutions £125 ($199) (effective 1996). Arnold (Subsidiary of: Hodder Headline plc.), 338 Euston Rd., London NW1 3BH, England. TEL 0171-873-6000.
FAX 0171-873-6325. (Subscr. to: Turpin Distribution Services Ltd., Blackhorse Rd., Letchworth, Herts. SG6 1HN, England. TEL 01462-672555. FAX 01462-480947) **Indexed:** Excerp.Med. (1992-). **Document type:** academic/scholarly publication.
—BLDSC (9148.852000). **CCC.**
Supersedes (in 1995): Vascular Medicine Review (ISSN 0954-2582)

VASCULAR SURGERY (GLEN HEAD). see *MEDICAL SCIENCES — Surgery*

VASCULAR SURGERY OUTLOOK. see *MEDICAL SCIENCES — Surgery*

616.1 US ISSN 1052-2174
VIDEO JOURNAL OF ECHOCARDIOGRAPHY. (Includes 4 video cassettes.) 1987. q. $250 (Canada $270; elsewhere $290) (effective 1994). Dynamedia, Inc., 2 Fulham Court, Silver Spring, MD 20902-3016. TEL 301-649-6886. FAX 301-649-3447. Ed. S.B. Ritter. adv. circ. 1,000. (back issues avail.)
—CCC.
Supersedes in part (in 1991): Dynamic Cardiovascular Imaging (ISSN 0891-9313)
Description: Covers ultrasound imaging. Consists of tutorials, reviews, case reports and original research.
Refereed Serial

VOX SANGUINIS; international journal of transfusion medicine. see *MEDICAL SCIENCES — Allergology And Immunology*

MEDICAL SCIENCES — CHIROPRACTIC, HOMEOPATHY, OSTEOPATHY

616.12   CC
XINXUEGUANBINGXUE JINZHAN/ADVANCES IN CARDIOVASCULAR DISEASE. (Text in Chinese) 1980. q. Chengdu Yixue Qingbao Yanjiusuo - Chengdu Medical Science Information Research Institute, 54 Tidu Jie, Chengdu, Sichuan 610016, People's Republic of China. TEL 673735. (Co-sponsor: Chengdu Xinxueguanbing Yanjiushi - Chengdu Cardiovascular Disease Research Office) Ed. Du Chuan-li. circ. 10,000.

616.1005   US   ISSN 0145-4145
RC681.A1
YEAR BOOK OF CARDIOLOGY. 1968. a. $74.95 (residents $35) (effective 1996). Mosby - Year Book, Inc., Continuity Division, 200 N. LaSalle, Chicago, IL 60601. TEL 312-726-9733. FAX 312-726-6075. TELEX 206155. Ed. Dr. Robert C. Schlant. illus. (reprint service avail.)
●Also available online. Vendor(s): Ovid Technologies. Also available on CD-ROM. Producer(s): SilverPlatter Information, Inc. (ClinMED-CD).
—BLDSC (9411.617000); SWETS.
Former titles: Year Book of Cardiovascular Medicine (ISSN 0360-6023); Year Book of Cardiovascular Medicine and Surgery (ISSN 0084-3687); Supersedes in part title issued 1962-1967 as: Year Book of Cardiovascular and Renal Disease.

616.1 617   US   ISSN 0749-4041
RD598.5
YEAR BOOK OF VASCULAR SURGERY. a. $72.95 (residents $35) (effective 1996). Mosby - Year Book, Inc., Continuity Division, 200 N. LaSalle, Chicago, IL 60601. TEL 312-726-9733. FAX 312-726-6075. TELEX 312-726-6075. Ed. Dr. John M. Porter.
●Also available online. Vendor(s): Ovid Technologies.
—BLDSC (9417.580000).

ZEITSCHRIFT FUER HERZ, THORAX- UND GEFAESSCHIRURGIE. see *MEDICAL SCIENCES — Surgery*

616.1   GW   ISSN 0300-5860
CODEN: ZKRDAX
ZEITSCHRIFT FUER KARDIOLOGIE. (Text in German; summaries in English) 1909. m. DM.558($405) (effective 1996). (Deutsche Gesellschaft fuer Kardiologie - Herz- und Kreislaufforschung) Dr. Dietrich Steinkopff Verlag, Saalbaustr. 12, 64283 Darmstadt, Germany. TEL 06151-1745-0. FAX 06151-174510. (Dist. by: Springer GmbH & Co., Auftragsbearbeitung, Heidelberger Platz 3, 14197 Berlin, Germany. TEL 030-8207212; Subscr. in N. America to: Springer-Verlag New York, Inc., 175 Fifth Ave., New York, NY 10010. TEL 212-460-1500) Ed.Bd. adv.; bk.rev.; bibl.; charts; illus.; index. circ. 3,000. (also avail. in microform from UMI; back issues avail.) **Indexed:** Biol.Abstr., Biotech.Abstr., Chem.Abstr., Curr. Cont., Curr.Adv.Ecol.Sci., Excerp.Med., Ind.Med., Nutr.Abstr. **Document type:** academic/scholarly publication.
—BLDSC (9467.430000); ADONIS; CASDDS; Genuine Article; SWETS; UMI. **CCC.**
Formerly: Zeitschrift fuer Kreislaufforschung (ISSN 0044-295X)

616.12   CC   ISSN 0253-3758
CODEN: CHHCDF
ZHONGHUA XIN-XUEGUANBING ZAZHI/CHINESE JOURNAL OF CARDIOLOGY. (Text in Chinese, English) q. $3.50 per no. Chinese Medical Association - Zhonghua Yixuehui, P.O. Box 2588, 42 Donsi Xidajie, Beijing 100710, People's Republic of China. TEL 1-550394. **Indexed:** Biol.Abstr., Chem.Abstr., Excerp.Med., ExtraMED, Ind.Med. **Document type:** academic/scholarly publication.
●Also available on CD-ROM.
—BLDSC (3180.298000); CASDDS.

MEDICAL SCIENCES — Chiropractic, Homeopathy, Osteopathy

A A C O M ORGANIZATIONAL GUIDE. (American Association of Colleges of Osteopathic Medicine) see *EDUCATION — School Organization And Administration*

615.633   US
A A O A ACCENTS. 1941. q. (Auxiliary to the American Osteopathic Association) McVey Marketing & Advertising, Box 569, Flint, MI 48501-0569. TEL 313-735-7892. FAX 313-735-4226. (Subscr. to: 142 E. Ontario St., Chicago, IL 60611) Ed. Mary M. Balog. circ. 1,900.
Description: For spouses of osteopathic physicians. Covers issues pertinent to the osteopathic profession.

615.53   US
A A O JOURNAL. 1991. q. $25. American Academy of Osteopathy, 3500 DePauw Blvd., Ste. 1080, Indianapolis, IN 46268-1136. TEL 317-879-1881. FAX 317-879-0563. Ed. Raymond J. Hruby. adv. circ. 3,500. (back issues avail.) **Document type:** abstracting/indexing.
Formerly: A A O Newsletter.
Description: Includes clinically related articles that illustrate the art and science of osteopathic practice.

A F H H A INSIDER. (American Federation of Home Health Agencies) see *MEDICAL SCIENCES — Nurses And Nursing*

615.533   US
A O A YEARBOOK AND DIRECTORY OF OSTEOPATHIC PHYSICIANS. 1908. a. $50. American Osteopathic Association, 142 E. Ontario St., Chicago, IL 60611. TEL 312-280-5800. Ed. Thomas Wesley Allen. adv.; stat.; index. circ. 35,000. (also avail. in microfiche from CIS) **Indexed:** SRI.
Formerly: Yearbook and Directory of Osteopathic Physicians (ISSN 0084-358X)

ACTA BIOLOGICA; Zeitschrift fuer angewandte Homoeo-Phytotherapie, Ganzheitsbehandlungen und Sondermethoden der Medizin. see *BIOLOGY*

615.63   US
▼**ADVANCES IN CHIROPRACTIC.** 1994. a. $66.95 (residents $40) (effective 1996). Mosby - Year Book, Inc. (Chicago) (Subsidiary of: Times Mirror Company), 200 N. LaSalle St., Chicago, IL 60601-1080. TEL 312-726-9733. FAX 312-726-6075. TELEX 206155.

615.532   GW   ISSN 0002-5887
ALLGEMEINE HOMOEOPATHISCHE ZEITUNG. 1832. 6/yr. DM.105 (students DM.57). (Deutscher Zentralverein Homoeopathischer Aerzte e.V.) Karl F. Haug Verlag GmbH, Fritz-Frey-Str. 21, 69121 Heidelberg, Germany. TEL 06221-4062-0. FAX 06221-400727. TELEX 461683-HVVFMD. (Subscr. to: Postfach 102840, 69018 Heidelberg, Germany) Ed. Karl-Heinz Gebhardt. **Indexed:** Excerp.Med. **Document type:** bulletin.
—BLDSC (0791.780000). **CCC.**

615.532   SW   ISSN 1104-4551
ALTERNATIV. 1991. irreg. (1-2/yr.). SEK 500 membership. Letitimerade Sjukskoeterskors Riksfoerening foer Homeopati, Nortullsg. 15, S-113 27 Stockholm, Sweden.

ALTERNATIV MEDICIN. see *ALTERNATIVE MEDICINE*

ALTERNATIVE HEALTH PRACTITIONER; the journal of complementary and natural care. see *ALTERNATIVE MEDICINE*

615.533   US   ISSN 0732-703X
AMERICAN ACADEMY OF OSTEOPATHY YEARBOOK. Variant title: Yearbook of Selected Osteopathic Papers. 1943. a. $40. American Academy of Osteopathy, 3500 DePauw Blvd., Ste. 1080, Indianapolis, IN 46268-1136. TEL 317-879-1881. FAX 317-879-0563. Ed. Myron C. Beal. illus.; cum.index 1972, 1977; circ. 1,600 (controlled). **Document type:** monographic series.

615.53   US
AMERICAN ASSOCIATION OF OSTEOPATHIC SPECIALISTS. NEWSLETTER. 1979. bi-m. $7.50. American Association of Osteopathic Specialists, Inc., 804 Main St., Ste. F, Forest Park, GA 30050. TEL 404-363-8263. FAX 404-361-2285. Ed. D.S. Strickland. adv. circ. 2,000. (looseleaf format) **Document type:** newsletter.
Former titles: American Association of Osteopathic Specialists. Journal; A A O S Newsletter.

615.53 612.3   US   ISSN 0194-6536
AMERICAN CHIROPRACTOR. 1979. m. $56. (American Chiropractor Magazine) Busch Publishing, 5005 Rivera Ct., Ft. Wayne, IN 46825. TEL 219-484-9600. Ed. Lana K. Stewart. adv.: B&W page $1545, color page $2195; trim 7 x 10; adv. contact: Elaine Fortmeyer. bk.rev. circ. 35,000. (also avail. in microform from UMI)
—BLDSC (0812.425000); UMI.
Description: Covers chiropractice and adjuctive health care procedures.

615.53   US   ISSN 0002-8967
RX1
AMERICAN INSTITUTE OF HOMEOPATHY. JOURNAL. 1907. q. $35 (outside N. America $45). American Institute of Homeopathy, 1585 Glencoe St., Ste. 44, Denver, CO 80220. TEL 303-898-5477. Ed. Dr. George Guess. adv.; bk.rev.; index. circ. 550. **Document type:** trade publication.
—BLDSC (4686.730000); UnCover.
Description: Presents articles of historical interest, current research, and case studies. Includes listing of foreign and U.S. homeopathic organizations and upcoming homeopathic conferences and meetings.

AMERICAN JOURNAL OF NONINVASIVE CARDIOLOGY. see *MEDICAL SCIENCES — Cardiovascular Diseases*

ANNALES DE KINESITHERAPIE. see *MEDICAL SCIENCES — Sports Medicine*

615.33   GW   ISSN 0940-9963
ARCHIV FUER HOMOEOPATHIK. 1992. q. DM.63 (foreign DM.72; students DM.56). Dynamis-Verlag GbR, Am Vogelherd 18, 46147 Oberhausen, Germany. TEL 0208-676525. FAX 0208-677047. Eds. Michael Terlinden, Stefan Reis. adv.; bk.rev. **Document type:** trade publication.
—BLDSC (1612.675000).

615.53   US
BEACON (IOWA). 1967. m. $20. Palmer Chiropractic College, 1000 Brady St., P C C Box 66, Davenport, IA 52803. Ed. Nils Heubach. circ. 3,000.

615.53   GW   ISSN 0340-8671
BIOLOGISCHE MEDIZIN. (Text in English, German, Italian, Polish, Russian, Spanish) 1962. bi-m. DM.30. Aurelia Verlag GmbH, Dr.-Reckeweg-Str. 2-4, 76532 Baden-Baden, Germany. TEL 07221-50102. FAX 07221-501420. Ed. Peter Hamlcik. adv.: B&W page DM.6600, color page DM.10452; trim 260 x 178. circ. 46,000. **Document type:** academic/scholarly publication.
—BLDSC (2083.700000).

615.532   UK   ISSN 0007-0785
BRITISH HOMOEOPATHIC JOURNAL. 1911. q. £36($80) Faculty of Homoeopathy, 2 Powis Pl., Great Ormond St., London WC1N 3HT, England. TEL 0171-833-1197. FAX 0171-278-7900. Ed. P. Fisher. adv. contact: A. Irwin. bk.rev.; index. circ. 1,500. (also avail. in microform from UMI; reprint service avail. from UMI) **Indexed:** Excerp.Med. **Document type:** academic/scholarly publication.
—BLDSC (2301.340000); UMI; UnCover.
Description: Covers all works of homoeopathy with emphasis on scientific research, clinical homoeopathy, provings and historical articles.
Refereed Serial

CAHIERS DE KINESITHERAPIE; revue d'enseignement post-scolaire et de documentation technique. see *MEDICAL SCIENCES — Physical Medicine And Rehabilitation*

615.53   US   ISSN 1060-1155
CALIFORNIA CHIROPRACTIC ASSOCIATION JOURNAL. 1985. m. $50. California Chiropractic Association, 7801 Folsom Blvd., Ste. 375, Sacramento, CA 95826. TEL 916-387-0177. FAX 916-387-6222. Ed. Don C. Meadows. adv. **Document type:** trade publication.
Formerly (until 1991): California Chiropractic Journal (ISSN 0899-0204)
Description: Promotes chiropractic and general health progress.
Refereed Serial

MEDICAL SCIENCES — CHIROPRACTIC, HOMEOPATHY, OSTEOPATHY

615.534   CN   ISSN 0008-3194
CANADIAN CHIROPRACTIC ASSOCIATION. JOURNAL. Abbreviated title: J C C A (Journal of the Canadian Chiropractic Association). 1957. q. Can.$58 (foreign Can.$75). Canadian Chiropractic Association, 1396 Eglinton Ave. W., Toronto, ON M6C 2E4, Canada. TEL 416-781-5656. FAX 416-781-7344. Ed. Allan Gotlib. adv.; bk.rev.; charts; illus.; stat. circ. 4,000. (reprint service avail. from UMI) **Document type:** academic/scholarly publication.
—BLDSC (4723.003000); Faxon; UMI. **CCC**.

615.53   US   ISSN 0897-6058
CHIROPRACTIC; the journal of chiropractic research, study and clinical investigation. 1988. q. $60. Busch Publishing, 5005 Riviera Court, Fort Wayne, IN 46825. TEL 219-484-9600. Ed. Dr. Brian A. McMaster. adv.; B&W page $750, color page $1400; trim 7 x 10. bk.rev.; abstr.; index. circ. 4,000. (also avail. in microfiche; back issues avail.) **Document type:** academic/scholarly publication.
—BLDSC (3181.143000).
Incorporates (in 1989): Journal of Chiropractic Research (ISSN 1044-1050); Which was formerly (1984-1988): Palmer College of Chiropractic. Research Forum (ISSN 0743-6300)
Description: Dedicated to the advancement of chiropractic health care principles and practice. Seeks to fulfill this purpose by the critical review and publication of original research and scholarly work relating to its scientific bases and clinical applications.

615.53 920 900   US   ISSN 0736-4377
RZ221
CHIROPRACTIC HISTORY. 1981. s-a. $50. Association for the History of Chiropractic, 1000 Brady St., Davenport, IA 52803. TEL 319-326-9656. FAX 319-326-8414. Ed. Russell W. Gibbons. adv. contact: Russell Gibbons. bk.rev. circ. 300. (back issues avail.) **Document type:** academic/scholarly publication.
●Also available online. Vendor(s): National Library of Medicine.
—BLDSC (3181.144000).
Description: Contains professional papers delivered at the annual historical conference.
Refereed Serial

615.53   US
THE CHIROPRACTIC JOURNAL. 1986. m. 2950 N. Dobson Rd., Ste. 1, Chandler, AZ 85224-1800. TEL 602-786-9235; 800-347-1011. FAX 602-732-9313. Pub. Terry A. Rondberg. adv.: B&W page $2,490; color page $2,990; adv. contact: Linda C. Bevel. circ. 60,000 (controlled). (tabloid format) **Document type:** newspaper, trade publication.
Description: Includes information on practice enhancement, legislative developments, insurance regulations, products and other topics of professional interest.

615.534   AT   ISSN 1036-0913
CHIROPRACTIC JOURNAL OF AUSTRALIA. 1966. q. Aus.$65 (foreign individuals Aus.$85; institutions Aus.$120) (effective 1995). Chiropractors' Association of Australia, P.O. Box 748, Wagga Wagga, N.S.W. 2650, Australia. TEL 61-69-21-3238. FAX 61-69-21-8869. Eds. Rolf E. Peters, Mary Ann Chance. adv.; bk.rev. circ. 1,800. (also avail. in microform from UMI; back issues avail.) **Indexed:** Aus.P.A.I.S. **Document type:** academic/scholarly publication.
—BLDSC (3181.144050); UMI; UnCover.
Formerly (until 1991): Australian Chiropractors Association. Journal (ISSN 0045-0359)
Description: Contains original investigations, case studies, literature reviews, clinical procedures, chiropractic history and commentary; seeks to cultivate professional dialogue and awareness in areas relevant to the practice of chiropractic in Australia.
Refereed Serial

615.53   US   ISSN 1041-2360
CHIROPRACTIC PRODUCTS. 1985. 8/yr. $16 (foreign $40) (free to qualified personnel). Novicom, Inc., 20000 Mariner Ave., Ste. 480, Torrance, CA 90503. TEL 310-793-4141. FAX 310-793-4138. Ed. Julie Craig. adv.: B&W page $1545, color page $2145; trim 8 3/8 x 10 7/8. bk.rev.; charts; illus.; circ. 35,059 (controlled). **Document type:** trade publication.
Description: Covers news of product releases, topics of interest to professionals in the field, and special features.

615.53 617.1   US   ISSN 0889-6976
CODEN: CHSMEX
CHIROPRACTIC SPORTS MEDICINE. 1987. q. $65 to individuals; institutions $95 (effective 1995). Williams & Wilkins, 428 E. Preston St., Baltimore, MD 21202. TEL 410-528-4000; 800-638-6423. FAX 410-528-4312. Ed. Dr. Robert H. Hazel, Jr. circ. 3,000. (also avail. in microfilm from WWS) **Indexed:** Excerp.Med. **Document type:** academic/scholarly publication.
—BLDSC (3181.144200); Genuine Article. **CCC**.
Description: Covers chiropractic advances in sports injury treatment, athletic training and injury prevention.
Refereed Serial

615.543   US   ISSN 0899-3467
CHIROPRACTIC TECHNIQUE. 1989. q. $65 to individuals; institutions $92 (effective 1995). (National College of Chiropractic) Williams & Wilkins, 428 E. Preston St., Baltimore, MD 21202. TEL 410-528-4000; 800-638-6423. FAX 410-528-4312. Ed. Thomas F. Bergman. circ. 1,900. (also avail. in microfilm from WWS) **Document type:** academic/scholarly publication, trade publication.
—**CCC**.
Description: Focuses on traditional, time-tested procedures, as well as innovative concepts in manipulative and physiological therapeutics.
Refereed Serial

615.53   AT   ISSN 1037-8839
CHIROPRACTORS' ASSOCIATION OF AUSTRALIA. MEMBERSHIP DIRECTORY. 1938. a. Aus.$20. Chiropractors' Association of Australia, Editorial Office, P.O. Box 241, Springwood, N.S.W 2777, Australia. TEL 047-515644. FAX 047-515856. Ed. Terry Deane. circ. 1,500. **Document type:** directory.
Formerly (until 1992): Australian Chiropractor's Association. Membership Directory (ISSN 0728-7291)
Description: Listing of the Association's members.

615.53 200   US
CHRISTIAN CHIROPRACTOR. 1953. bi-m. membership. Christian Chiropractors Association, 3200 S. Lemay Ave., Fort Collins, CO 80525-3605. TEL 303-482-1404; 800-999-1970. FAX 303-482-1404. Ed. Ronald Murphy. circ. 1,300. (back issues avail.) **Document type:** newsletter.

615.53 200   US
CHRISTIAN CHIROPRACTORS ASSOCIATION JOURNAL. 1953. bi-m. membership. Christian Chiropractors Association, 3200 S. Lemay Ave., Fort Collins, CO 80525-3605. TEL 800-999-1970. FAX 303-482-1404. circ. 1,200.
Formerly: Christian Chiropractors Association Bulletin.

615.533   UK   ISSN 0268-0033
CODEN: CLBIEW
CLINICAL BIOMECHANICS. 1968. 8/yr. £230($366) (effective 1996). (Osteopathic Association of Great Britain) Butterworth - Heinemann, Part of the Reed Elsevier group, Linacre House, Jordan Hill, Oxford OX2 8DP, England. TEL 0865-310366. FAX 0865-310898. TELEX 83111 BHPOXF G. (Subscr. to: Elsevier Science Ltd., P.O. Box 800, Kidlington, Oxford OX5 1DX, England. TEL 44-865-843000. FAX 44-865-843010; Subscr. in U.S. and Canada to: Elsevier Science, 660 White Plains Rd., Tarrytown, NY 10591-5153. TEL 914-524-9200. FAX 914-333-2444) Ed. A. Kim Burton. adv.; bk.rev.; abstr.; illus.; index. circ. 750. (also avail. in microform from UMI; back issues avail.) **Indexed:** Curr.Adv.Ecol.Sci., Curr.Cont., Excerp.Med. **Document type:** academic/scholarly publication.
—BLDSC (3286.262800); Ei; Faxon; Genuine Article; SWETS; UMI. **CCC**.
Formerly (until 1986): British Osteopathic Journal.
Description: Multidisciplinary journal of original research papers, reviews and abstracts on clinical aspects of biomechanics related to dysfunction of the musculoskeletal system.
Refereed Serial

COLLEGE INFORMATION BOOKLET. see *EDUCATION — Higher Education*

615.53 615.89   UK   ISSN 0965-2299
CODEN: CTHMES
COMPLEMENTARY THERAPIES IN MEDICINE. 1993. q. £80($124) to non-member individuals; institutions £104 ($162); members £26 ($45) (effective 1995). Churchill Livingstone Journals (Subsidiary of: Pearson Professional), Robert Stevenson House, 1-3 Baxter's Pl., Leith Walk, Edinburgh EH1 3AF, Scotland. TEL 0131-556-2424. FAX 0131-459-1177. (Subscr to: Pearson Professional Ltd., P.O. Box 77, Fourth Ave., Harlow, Essex CM19 5AA, England. TEL 01279-623760; U.S. subscr. to: Churchill Livingstone, 650 Ave. of the Americas, New York, NY 10011. TEL 212-206-5000) Ed. Dr. George Lewith. adv. contact: David Dunnachie. bk.rev. circ. 410. **Indexed:** Excerp.Med. (1994-). **Document type:** academic/scholarly publication.
—BLDSC (3364.203750).
Description: Aimed at general practitioners, nurses, and other medical professionals interested in chiropractics, acupuncture, and homeopathic and osteopathic medicine.

615.53 617.3   US   ISSN 1041-469X
D.C. TRACTS. 1989. q. $125 to individuals; institutions $195 (effective 1995; typically set in Oct.). Data Trace Chiropractic Publishers, Inc., 110 West Rd., Ste. 227, Baltimore, MD 21204-2316. TEL 301-494-4994. FAX 301-494-0515. Ed. Bruce Gundersen.
—**CCC**.
Description: A continuing education program for chiropractors providing condensations of current chiropractic literature. Each issue includes a 90-minute audiotape lecture by experts and a 20-question continuing education exam.

615.533 340   US   ISSN 0011-5088
THE D.O.. (Doctor of Osteopath); a publication for osteopathic physicians and surgeons. 1960. m. $20. American Osteopathic Association, 142 E. Ontario St., Chicago, IL 60611. TEL 312-280-5800. Ed. Thomas Wesley Allen. adv.; bk.rev.; stat. circ. 38,000. **Indexed:** Chem.Abstr.
—BLDSC (3605.780000).
Supersedes: Forum of Osteopathy.
Description: For practicing physicians. Contains articles on legislative developments and news of the profession and its members.

DEBTS AND CAREER PLANS OF OSTEOPATHIC MEDICAL STUDENTS. see *EDUCATION — Higher Education*

615.53   US   ISSN 0415-8407
DIGEST OF CHIROPRACTIC ECONOMICS. 1958. bi-m. $27. Chiropractic News Publishing Corp., 29229 W. 6 Mile Rd., Livonia, MI 48152. TEL 313-427-5720. FAX 313-427-2760. Ed. Keith Tosolt; Pub. Gaynold M. Maly. adv.; bk.rev. circ. 22,000. (back issues avail.) **Document type:** trade publication.
—BLDSC (3586.879500).
Description: Business and practice management for the doctor of chiropractic.

615.53   US
DYNAMIC CHIROPRACTIC. 1983. fortn. free to qualified personnel. Non-Profit Motion Palpation Institute, 21541 Surveyor Circle, Box 6100, Huntington, CA 92646. TEL 714-960-6577. Ed. Donald M. Petersen, Jr. (tabloid format)

615.53   UK   ISSN 0263-9114
CODEN: EJCHE8
EUROPEAN JOURNAL OF CHIROPRACTIC. 1953. 3/yr. European Chiropractors' Union, c/o Simon Leyson, Ed., 16 Uplands Crescent, Swansea SA2 OPB, Wales. adv.; bk.rev.; bibl.; charts; illus. circ. 1,650. (also avail. in microform from UMI; back issues avail.) **Document type:** academic/scholarly publication.
—BLDSC (3829.725900); UMI. **CCC**.
Refereed Serial

615.532   II   ISSN 0015-0827
FIFTY MILLESIMAL NEWS LETTER; the journal of pure homoeopathy. (Text and summaries in English) 1969. q. Rs.6($2) Hahnemann Homoeopathic Pharmacy, Hahnemann House, College Rd., Kottayam, India. Ed. Dr. Ramanial P. Patel. adv.; bk.rev. circ. 1,600.

DIE FUNKTIONSKRANKHEITEN DES BEWEGUNGSAPPARATES; Zeitschrift fuer interdisziplinaere Diagnostik und Therapie. see *MEDICAL SCIENCES — Orthopedics And Traumatology*

MEDICAL SCIENCES — CHIROPRACTIC, HOMEOPATHY, OSTEOPATHY

615.53 GW ISSN 0931-5527
GERMAN JOURNAL OF HOMEOPATHY. (Text in English) 1987. q. DM.93. Barthel & Barthel Publishing, Schatzlgasse 31, 82335 Berg, Germany. TEL 08151-51085. FAX 08151-51086. Ed. Dr. Michael Barthel. circ. 1,000.
—BLDSC (4162.120730).

GOOD LIFE TIMES; choices in health, education and the arts. see NEW AGE PUBLICATIONS

165.53 II ISSN 0379-8151
HAHNEMANNIAN HOMOEOPATHIC SANDESH. 1977. m. Rs.90($20) Delhi Homoeopathic Medical Association, J-3, 188-A, Nehru Market, Rajouri Garden, New Delhi 110027, India. TEL 5450550. Ed. Hira Singh Namdhari. adv.; bk.rev. circ. 1,500.
Document type: trade publication.

610 UK ISSN 0965-1292
HEALTH AND HOMOEOPATHY. 1980. q. £3. Hahnemann Society for the Promotion of Homoeopathy, Two Powis Pl., Great Ormond St., London WC1N 3HT, England. illus.
Formerly: Homoeopathy Today (ISSN 0261-2828)

HEALTH WORLD. see ALTERNATIVE MEDICINE

615.53 GW ISSN 0177-8617
HEILPRAXIS - MAGAZIN. 1982. m. DM.60. Medizinische Praxis-Verlagsgesellschaft mbH, Basler Str. 19, 79189 Bad Krozingen, Germany. TEL 07633-14081. circ. 6,500.

HERBA POLONICA. see BIOLOGY — Botany

615.532 II ISSN 0377-4902
HOMEOPATHIC HERALD. (Text in English) 1940. m. Rs.9. 73 Netaji Subhas Rd., Calcutta 700001, India.

615.532 NE ISSN 1380-5096
HOMEOPATHIE. 1889. bi-m. fl.39.50. Koninklijke Vereniging tot Bevordering der Homeopathie in Nederland (KVHN) Kroon Uitgevers bv, Postbus 46, 6980 AA Doesburg, Netherlands. TEL 31-8334-79570. (Editorial addr.: KVHN, Postbus 90003, 1006 BA Amsterdam, Netherlands. TEL 31-20-6178308. FAX 31-20-6178249) adv.; bk.rev.; abstr.; bibl.; illus.; stat.; index. circ. 10,000.
Former titles (until 1994): Tijdschrift Homeopathie (ISSN 0920-4113); (until 1986): Homeopathisch Tijdschrift (ISSN 0378-6048); (until 1976): Homoeopathisch Maandblad (ISSN 0018-4489)
Description: Publishes articles relating to homeopathic medicine, including case studies and discussions of diagnosis, treatment, health policy.

615.532 FR ISSN 1244-2356
HOMEOPATHIE EUROPEENNE. (Text in French; summaries in English, French) 1912. 6/yr. 590 F. (foreign 690 F.). (Centre Homeopathique de France) Meditions Carline, 1 et 3 rue du Depart, 75014 Paris, France. TEL 1-40-64-00-75.
FAX 1-43-22-26-99. Eds. Dr. Poitevin, Dr. Dupre. adv. contact: Soizyk Brault. bk.rev.; bibl.; index.
—BLDSC (4326.176387). CCC.
Formed by the 1993 merger of: Homeopathie (ISSN 0762-638X) & Medecin Homeopathe (ISSN 0990-7483) & Homeopathie Francaise (ISSN 0018-4225)

615.532 SW ISSN 0280-3356
HOMEOPRAKTIKERN. 1979. Q. SEK 100 membership. Svenska Homeopraktikers Riksfoerbund (SHR), Gladiolusg. 6 B, S-431 61 Moelndal, Sweden.

615.532 II ISSN 0046-7812
HOMEOPATHIC WORLD. (Text in English) 1964. m. Rs.35. Sundar Homoeo Sadan, 113 Netaji Subhas Rd., Calcutta 1, India. TEL 387632. Ed. Sri Abinash Das. adv.; bk.rev. circ. 1,500.

615.532 II ISSN 0046-7820
HOMOEOPATHY; for health and life. (Text in English and Tamil) 1948. m. Rs.5($3) Indian Institute of Homoeopaths, c/o Dr. R.J. Murty, Murty Gardens, Srinagar Colony, Kumbakonam, India. Eds. Dr. R.J. Murty, Sri R. Srinivasan. circ. 2,000.

615.532 UK ISSN 1351-4903
HOMOEOPATHY. 1932. bi-m. £15 (foreign £20) (effective 1995). British Homoeopathic Association, 27a Devonshire St., London W1N 1RJ, England. TEL 0171-935-2163. Ed. Enid Segall. adv.; bk.rev. circ. 5,500. **Indexed:** Curr.Adv.Ecol.Sci. **Document type:** consumer publication.
—BLDSC (4326.343300).

615.53 II
HOMOEOPATHY HERITAGE 9. (Text in English) 1976. m. Rs.100 in India & Nepal; Bangladesh Rs.200; elsewhere $25. B. Jain Publishers Pvt. Ltd., 1921 Chuna Mandi, St. 10th, Pahar Ganj, New Delhi 110055, India. TEL 11-7770430. FAX 11-7510471. (Subscr. to: P.O. Box 5775, New Delhi 110055, India) Ed. Dr. S.P. Dey. adv.; bk.rev. circ. 10,000. (back issues avail.) **Document type:** academic/scholarly publication.
—BLDSC (4326.341910).
Formerly (until 1993): Homoeopathic Heritage (ISSN 0970-6038)
Description: Covers homeopathic research on preventative and curative medicine.

370 US ISSN 0899-9260
I C A REVIEW; international review of Chiropractic. 1944. bi-m. $50. International Chiropractors Association, 1110 N. Glebe Rd., Ste. 1000, Arlington, VA 22201. Ed. Molly Rangnath. adv.; bk.rev.; illus.; index. circ. 10,000.
Formerly (until 1985): International Review of Chiropractic (ISSN 0738-6850)
Description: Scientific and general articles on chiropractic and health-related issues.

615.532 II ISSN 0019-4867
INDIAN HOMOEOPATHIC GAZETTE. 1961. q. Rs.4($1.50) Med-House, Chowghat, S. India. Ed. Dr. Mathews. adv.; bk.rev.; bibl.; index. circ. 3,000.
Indexed: Amer.Hist.& Life, Hist.Abstr.

615.532 II ISSN 0019-5243
INDIAN JOURNAL OF HOMOEOPATHIC MEDICINE. (Text in English) 1967. q. Rs.80($25) (effective 1996). Homeopathic Education Society, Gadkari Marg, Vile Parle West, Bombay 400 056, India. TEL 620-1135. Ed. P.M. Barvalla. adv.: B&W page Rs.750. bk.rev.; abstr.; index. circ. 2,000. **Document type:** academic/scholarly publication.
—BLDSC (4414.800000).
Incorporates: Indian Journal of Homoeopathy (ISSN 0537-202X); Journal of Homoeopathic Medicine.
Description: Contains detailed discussion on concepts and articles on clinical research, and homoeopathic education.

615.533 US ISSN 0098-6151
RZ301 CODEN: JAOAAZ
J A O A: JOURNAL OF THE AMERICAN OSTEOPATHIC ASSOCIATION. 1901. m. $20. American Osteopathic Association, 142 E. Ontario St., Chicago, IL 60611. TEL 312-280-5800. FAX 312-280-5893. Ed. Thomas Wesley Allen. adv.; bk.rev.; abstr.; charts; illus.; index, cum.index 1901-1956; 1956-1965. circ. 38,000. (also avail. in microfilm from UMI; reprint service avail. from UMI) **Indexed:** Biol.Abstr., C.I.S. Abstr., Chem.Abstr., Curr.Cont., Dok.Arbeitsmed., Excerp.Med., Ind.Med., INIS Atomind., Med. Care Rev., Nutr.Abstr.
—BLDSC (4689.400000); EMDOCS; Faxon; Genuine Article; SWETS; UMI; UnCover.
Formerly: American Osteopathic Association. Journal (ISSN 0003-0287)
Refereed Serial

J N M S: JOURNAL OF THE NEUROMUSCULOSKELETAL SYSTEM. see MEDICAL SCIENCES — Psychiatry And Neurology

615.53 GW ISSN 0943-4259
JATROS NATURHEILKUNDE. 1992. m. DM.90. P M I Verlagsgruppe GmbH, August-Schanz-Str. 21, 60433 Frankfurt a.M., Germany. TEL 069-5480000. FAX 069-54800077. Ed. Peter Hoffmann. circ. 5,800. **Document type:** academic/scholarly publication.

JOURNAL OF BACK AND MUSCULOSKELETAL REHABILITATION. see MEDICAL SCIENCES — Orthopedics And Traumatology

615.543 US ISSN 0744-9984
JOURNAL OF CHIROPRACTIC. 1930. m. $80 (foreign $100). American Chiropractic Association, Inc., 8229 Maryland Ave., St. Louis, MO 63105. TEL 314-862-7800. FAX 314-721-5171. Ed. Irvin Davis. adv.: B&W page $1460, color page $1960; trim 8 1/8 x 10 5/8; adv. contact: Lee Clark. bk.rev.; charts; illus.; index. circ. 23,161. (also avail. in microform from UMI; reprint service avail. from UMI) **Document type:** trade publication.
—UMI.
Formerly (until 1981): A C A Journal of Chiropractic (ISSN 0044-7609); Supersedes (in 1964): National Chiropractic Journal.
Description: Discusses current procedures, research and developments in the field of chiropractic and in related fields of interest to chiropractors.
Refereed Serial

615 617.3 US ISSN 0161-4754
RM724
JOURNAL OF MANIPULATIVE AND PHYSIOLOGICAL THERAPEUTICS. Abbreviated title: J M P T. 1978. 9/yr. $82 to individuals; institutions $110 (effective 1995). (National College of Chiropractic) Williams & Wilkins, 428 E. Preston St., Baltimore, MD 21202. TEL 410-528-4000; 800-638-6423. FAX 410-528-4312. Ed. Dr. Dana J. Lawrence. adv.; bk.rev. circ. 3,756. (also avail. in microfilm from WWS; back issues avail.) **Indexed:** Apic.Abstr., Biol.Abstr., Curr.Cont., Dent.Ind., Excerp.Med., Ind.Med. **Document type:** academic/scholarly publication.
—BLDSC (5011.600000); Faxon; Genuine Article; SWETS; UnCover. CCC.
Description: Deals with chiropractic medicine issues such as manipulation, physical therapy and other conservative treatment methods.
Refereed Serial

JOURNAL OF MUSCULOSKELETAL PAIN. see MEDICAL SCIENCES — Orthopedics And Traumatology

615.532 II ISSN 0300-3957
KERALA HOMOEO JOURNAL. (Text and summaries in English) 1971. q. Rs.8. All Kerala Homeopathic Physicians Association, Kanjikuzhy, Kottayam 4, Kerala, India. (Co-sponsor: Indian Homoeo Chemists Federation) Ed. Dr. T.R. Sivan Tholoor. adv.; bk.rev.; abstr.; stat. circ. 15,890.

615.53 378 US
LOS ANGELES COLLEGE OF CHIROPRACTIC. NEWS & ALUMNI REPORT. 1977. q. free. Los Angeles College of Chiropractic, 16200 E. Amber Valley Dr., Box 1166, Whittier, CA 90604-1166. TEL 310-947-8755. FAX 310-947-5724. Ed. Steven E. Reifel. adv. circ. 6,000. **Document type:** newsletter.
Description: News, announcements, and notes on the activities and people associated with the College.

MODERNES LEBEN - NATUERLICHES HEILEN; Monatsblaetter fuer naturgemaesse Lebenspflege, Homoeopathie und Naturheilkunde. see ALTERNATIVE MEDICINE

615.533 US ISSN 0892-0249
N J A O P S JOURNAL. 1901. 6/yr. $25. New Jersey Association of Osteopathic Physicians and Surgeons, 1212 Stuyvesant Ave., Trenton, NJ 08618. TEL 609-393-8114. (Affiliate: American Osteopathic Association) adv.; bk.rev.; illus. circ. 1,650.
Formerly: New Jersey Association of Osteopathic Physicians and Surgeons. Journal (ISSN 0028-5528)

NATIONAL DIRECTORY OF CHIROPRACTIC. see BUSINESS AND ECONOMICS — Trade And Industrial Directories

615.53 SA
NEW HOMOEOPATHIC NEWSLETTER OF SOUTH AFRICA. 1957. irreg. R.25. Homoeopathic Society of S.A., P.O. Box 9658, Johannesburg 2000, South Africa.
Document type: newsletter.
Formerly (until Nov. 1992): Homoeopathic Newsletter of South Africa.

615.53 JA ISSN 0912-1110
NIPPON KAIROPURAKUTIKKU GAKKAI ZASSHI/JAPAN JOURNAL OF CHIROPRACTIC SCIENCE. (Text in Japanese) 1984. s-a. 4000 Yen per no. Rinsho Kairopurakutikku Gakkai - Association of Clinical Chiropractic, Nihon Kairopurakutikku Renmei, 5-9, Aoyama 3-chome, Minato-ku, Tokyo 105, Japan.

MEDICAL SCIENCES — COMMUNICABLE DISEASES

NURSES IN TRANSITION. see *MEDICAL SCIENCES — Nurses And Nursing*

615.532   II   ISSN 0048-2242
ORISSA HOMOEOPATHIC BULLETIN; bilingual monthly magazine. (Text in English and Oriya) 1969. m. Rs.40($20) Natabar Naik, Ed. & Pub., Tilottame Homoeo House, P.O. Jagatsinghpur, Cuttack 754 103, Orissa, India. TEL 754103. adv.; bk.rev. circ. 500. (also avail. in microform from UMI; reprint service avail. from UMI)

617.3   US   ISSN 0030-591X
ORTHOPOD. 1960. 2/yr. free to qualified personnel. American Osteopathic Academy of Orthopedics, 2500 Hollywood Blvd., No. 212, Hollywood, FL 33020-6615. TEL 305-922-1110. Ed. Dr. Daniel L. Morrison. adv. contact: Margaret S. Moore. illus. circ. 1,100. (processed) **Document type:** academic/scholarly publication, bulletin.

OSTEOPATHIC MEDICAL EDUCATION: A HANDBOOK FOR MINORITY APPLICANTS. see *EDUCATION — Higher Education*

615.53   US
OSTEOPATHIC MEDICAL NEWS.* m. Compendium Publishing Company Inc., Box 505, Jamesburg, NJ 08831. TEL 215-860-9560. FAX 215-860-9558. Ed. Letha Strothers. circ. 31,494.

PENNSYLVANIA OSTEOPATHIC MEDICAL ASSOCIATION. JOURNAL. see *MEDICAL SCIENCES*

615.53   SP   ISSN 0212-7393
PODOSCOPIO. 1984. 6/yr. 5000 ptas. (effective 1994). C. San Bernardo 74, 28015 Madrid, Spain. TEL 522-8763. Ed. Manuel Meneses Garde. adv. contact: A. Cros. circ. 3,600.

615.53   SZ
PRO CHIROPRAKTIK. q. Stampachgasse 6, CH-3065 Bollingen, Switzerland. TEL 031-585210. FAX 031-587246. Ed. Rudolf Weber. circ. 13,475.

615.532   BE   ISSN 0035-0885
                              CODEN: RBHOD4
REVUE BELGE D'HOMOEOPATHIE. 1949. a. 2000 BEF. Societe Royale Belge d'Homoeopathie, 7 Ave. Cardinal Micara, B-1160 Brussels, Belgium. TEL 32-2-735-35-25. FAX 32-2-242-75-55. Ed. Dr. Ch. Schepens. adv.; bk.rev.; bibl.; illus.; index. circ. 2,000. **Document type:** bulletin, academic/scholarly publication.
—BLDSC (7891.930000).

615.53   US   ISSN 1068-2953
SECOND OPINION (DUNWOODY). Key Title: Dr. William Campbell Douglass' Second Opinion. 1976. m. $49. 1350 Center Dr., Ste. 100, Dunwoody, GA 30338. TEL 404-399-5617; 800-728-2288. FAX 404-399-0815. Dr. William Campbell Douglass; Pub. Wallis W. Wood. bk.rev. circ. 60,000. **Document type:** newsletter.
Incorporates: Doctor's People; Which was formerly: People's Doctor.

SELECTED SOURCES OF FINANCIAL AID FOR OSTEOPATHIC MEDICAL STUDENTS. see *EDUCATION — Higher Education*

615.533   JA   ISSN 0910-1225
SOGO SEIKOTSU/SYNTHESIS OSTEOPATHY. (Text in Japanese) 1984. q. 1500 Yen per no. Medikaru Puresu - Medical Press Ltd., 43-9, Sakuradai 3-chome, Nerima-ku, Tokyo 176, Japan.

SOUTH AFRICA. CENTRAL STATISTICAL SERVICE. CENSUS OF MEDICAL, DENTAL AND OTHER HEALTH SERVICES - CHIROPRACTORS, HOMEOPATHS, NATUROPATHS, OSTEOPATHS AND HERBALISTS. see *MEDICAL SCIENCES — Abstracting, Bibliographies, Statistics*

615.53   US
SPINAL COLUMN.* 6/yr. $10. Palmer College of Chiropractic, 1000 Brady St., Davenport, IA 52803. TEL 319-326-9662. adv.

615.534   US
▼**STAYING WELL.** 1994. bi-m. $14.95. Foundation for Chiropractic Education and Research, 66 Washington Ave., Des Moines, IA 50314. TEL 800-622-6309. Ed. Robin Merrifield. **Document type:** newsletter.

615.53   US
TEXAS CHIROPRACTIC REVIEW. 1974. q. $50. Texas Chiropractic College, Alumni Association, 5912 Spencer Hwy., Pasadena, TX 77505. TEL 713-487-1170; 800-TCC-ALUM. FAX 713-487-2009. Ed. Suzanne M. Powell. adv. circ. 5,000. (back issues avail.) **Document type:** newsletter.
Description: Contains articles on pertinent legislation and on supporting alumni.

615.53   US   ISSN 0275-1453
TEXAS D O. 1945. m. $35. Texas Osteopathic Medical Association, 1 Financial Center, 1717 N. 1H35, Ste. 100, Round Rock, TX 78664-2901. TEL 817-336-0549. FAX 817-336-8801. Ed. Terry R. Boucher. adv. circ. 2,650. **Document type:** trade publication.
—UMI.
Formerly (until 1980): Association: Journal of Texas Osteopathic Medical Association (ISSN 0275-1445)

615.53   US
TEXAS JOURNAL OF CHIROPRACTIC. m. $36. Texas Chiropractic Association, 1601 Rio Grande, Ste. 420, Austin, TX 78701. TEL 512-477-9292. FAX 512-477-9296. Ed. Dr. Chris Dalrymple. adv. contact: Christine M. Lehmann. circ. 1,650. **Document type:** trade publication, academic/scholarly publication.

TIJDSCHRIFT VOOR INTEGRALE GENEESKUNDE. see *ALTERNATIVE MEDICINE*

615.543   US   ISSN 0091-2360
RZ201
TODAY'S CHIROPRACTIC. 1971. bi-m. $24 in U.S.; Canada $28; elsewhere $33. Life College, 1269 Barclay Circle, Marietta, GA 30060. TEL 404-424-0554. FAX 404-419-0568. Ed. James B. Panter. adv. contact: Cheryl Diduro. bk.rev.; charts; illus. circ. 37,000. **Document type:** trade publication.
—BLDSC (8859.727800); UMI.

615.534   US   ISSN 1073-2837
▼**TOPICS IN CLINICAL CHIROPRACTIC.** 1994. q. $58 in U.S. & Canada. Aspen Publishers, Inc., 200 Orchard Ridge Dr., Gaithersburg, MD 20878. TEL 301-471-7500; 800-638-8437. FAX 301-417-7550. Eds. Jane Coyle Garwood, Sandra L. Lunsford; Pub. Michael B. Brown. adv. contact: Frances S. Ray. (also avail. in microform from UMI; reprint service avail. from UMI)
—BLDSC (8867.432660). **CCC.**
Refereed Serial

TOUCH FOR HEALTH. see *PHYSICAL FITNESS AND HYGIENE*

615.533   US   ISSN 1046-4948
TRIAD (FARMINGTON). 1989. bi-m. $30. Michigan Association of Osteopathic Physicians and Surgeons, Inc., 33100 Freedom Rd., Farmington, MI 48336. TEL 313-476-2800. FAX 313-476-1834. Ed. Mark E. Scheible. adv.; bk.rev.; charts; illus. circ. 3,200. —**CCC.**
Formerly (until Aug. 1989): Michigan Osteopathic Journal (ISSN 0026-2374)
Description: Covers association activities.

615.53   US   ISSN 1066-484X
RZ201
YEAR BOOK OF CHIROPRACTIC. 1994. a. $61.95 (residents $40) (effective 1996). Mosby - Year Book, Inc. (Chicago) (Subsidiary of: Times Mirror Company), 200 N. LaSalle St., Chicago, IL 60601-1080. TEL 312-726-9733. FAX 312-726-6075. TELEX 2066075. Ed. Dana Lawrence.

615.532   GW   ISSN 0935-0853
ZEITSCHRIFT FUER KLASSISCHE HOMOEOPATHIE; kritisches Organ fuer Homoeopathie. (Text in German; summaries in English) 1957. 6/yr. DM.105 (students DM.57). Karl F. Haug Verlag GmbH, Fritz-Frey-Str. 21, 69121 Heidelberg, Germany. TEL 06221-4062-0. (Subscr. to: Postfach 102840, 69018 Heidelberg, Germany) Ed. Dr. T. Genneper. adv.; bk.rev. circ. 2,800. **Document type:** academic/scholarly publication.
—BLDSC (9467.719000). **CCC.**
Former titles: Klassische Homoepathie (ISSN 0301-1402); (until 1971): Acta Homeopathica (ISSN 0001-5881)

MEDICAL SCIENCES — Communicable Diseases

614.8   US
A L M INTERNATIONAL ANNUAL REPORT. a. American Leprosy Missions International, 1 ALM Way, Greenville, SC 29601. TEL 803-271-7040. FAX 803-271-7062. **Document type:** corporate report.
Formerly: American Leprosy Missions Annual Report.

619.9   AT   ISSN 1031-4873
ACCENT.* 1988. m. free. A I D S Council of South Australia, Inc., P.O. Box 907, Norwood, S.A. 5067, Australia. TEL 08-223-6322. FAX 08-232-0715. Ed. Kenton Penley. circ. 250.
Description: For staff, volunteers and general members of AIDS Council of SA. Includes current information about HIV infection and AIDS.

616.998   SZ   ISSN 0001-5938
                                   CODEN: ALEPA8
ACTA LEPROLOGICA; revue editee par le comite international executif de l'Ordre S.M. de Malte. (Text in English, French, Spanish) 1960. s-a. $50. Ordre de Malte pour l'Assistance aux Lepreux, 3 Place Claparede, CH-1205 Geneva, Switzerland. TEL 022-468687. FAX 022-3470861. Ed. J-M. Decazes. adv.; bk.rev.; bibl. circ. 2,000. **Indexed:** Excerp.Med., Ind.Med. **Document type:** academic/scholarly publication.
—BLDSC (0629.100000); CASDDS; Faxon.
Description: Technical journal devoted to leprosy research, its treatment and prevention, drug therapy and health education. Contains articles about survey methodology, and recent technological and medical developments. Also includes reports of events and list of courses.

616.9   IT   ISSN 0392-9515
ACTA MEDITERRANEA DI PATOLOGIA INFETTIVA E TROPICALE. (Text in English, Italian) 1960. 3/yr. L.40000($40) Carbone Editore, Via G. Daita, 29, 90139 Palermo, Italy. TEL 091-321-273. FAX 091-321782. adv.; abstr.; bibl.; illus.; stat.; index. circ. 3,000.
Description: Reviews clinical cases of communicable and tropical diseases.

616.988   NE   ISSN 0001-706X
Q3   CODEN: ACTRAQ
ACTA TROPICA; journal of biomedical sciences. (Text in English, French and German; summaries in English) 1944. m. fl.1515($924) (effective 1996). (Schweizerisches Tropeninstitut - Swiss Tropical Institute) Elsevier Science B.V., P.O. Box 211, 1000 AE Amsterdam, Netherlands. TEL 31-20-4853911. FAX 31-20-4853598. TELEX 18582 ESPA NL. E-mail: nlinfo-f@elsevier.nl; usinfo-f@elsevier.com; forinfo-kyf04035@niftyserve.or.jp; Site addr.: http://www.elsevier.nl/. (Subscr. in U.S. and Canada to: Elsevier Science Inc., Box 882, Madison Sq. Sta., New York, NY 10159-0882. TEL 212-989-5800. FAX 212-633-3990) Ed. H. Hecker. adv.; bk.rev.; abstr.; charts; illus.; index. (back issues avail.) **Indexed:** Abstr.Hyg., Biol.Abstr., Biotech.Abstr., Chem.Abstr., Curr.Adv.Ecol.Sci., Curr.Cont., Excerp.Med., Helminthol.Abstr., Ind.Med., Ind.Sci.Rev., Ind.Vet., Key Word Ind.Wildl.Res., Nutr.Abstr., Plant Breed.Abstr., Protozool.Abstr., Rev.Appl.Entomol., Rice Abstr., Sci.Cit.Ind., Sport Fish.Abstr., Trop.Dis.Bull., Vet.Bull., Wild.Rev., Zoo.Rec. **Document type:** academic/scholarly publication.
—BLDSC (0666.000000); CASDDS; Ei; Faxon; Genuine Article; SWETS; UMI; UnCover. **CCC.**
Description: Details every aspect of biomedical sciences relevant to humans, including veterinary medicine and biology in the tropics.
Refereed Serial

ACTA VIROLOGICA; international journal. see *BIOLOGY — Microbiology*

616.9   US   ISSN 0732-0566
                                   CODEN: AHDMD3
ADVANCES IN HOST DEFENSE MECHANISMS. 1983. irreg., latest vol.9. price varies. Raven Press (Subsidiary of: Wolters Kluwer N.V.), 1185 Ave. of the Americas, New York, NY 10036. TEL 212-930-9500. FAX 212-869-3495. Eds. John I. Gallin, Anthony S. Fauci. (reprint service avail. from UMI) **Document type:** monographic series.
—BLDSC (0709.063000); CASDDS; Faxon.

MEDICAL SCIENCES — COMMUNICABLE DISEASES

616.9 618.92 US ISSN 0884-9404
CODEN: APIDEO
ADVANCES IN PEDIATRIC INFECTIOUS DISEASES. 1986. a. $68.95 (residents $40) (effective 1996). Mosby - Year Book, Inc. (Chicago) (Subsidiary of: Times Mirror Company), 200 N. LaSalle St., Chicago, IL 60601-1080. TEL 312-726-9733. FAX 312-726-6075. TELEX 206155. (Subscr. to: 11830 Westline Industrial Dr., St. Louis, MO 63146. TEL 800-325-4177) Ed. Dr. Stephen C. Aronoff. —BLDSC (0709.588500). **CCC.**
Description: Presents a collection of original, fully referenced clinical reviews and articles from the experts in the field.

ADVANCES IN VIRUS RESEARCH. see *BIOLOGY — Microbiology*

616.9 US ISSN 0269-9370
RC607.A26 CODEN: AIDSET
AIDS. (Acquired Immune Deficiency Syndrome) (Supplement avail.: AIDS (Year) (ISSN 1350-2840)) 1987. m. $144.95 to individuals; institutions $345; residents $99.95. Current Science, 400 Market St., Ste. 700, Philadelphia, PA 19106. TEL 215-574-2210; 800-552-5866. FAX 215-574-3533. (And: Current Science Ltd., 34-42 Cleveland St., London W1P 6LB, England. TEL 0171-3230323. FAX 0171-636-6911) Ed.Bd. adv.; bibl.; illus. circ. 4,430. **Indexed:** Excerp.Med., Med.& Surg.Dermat., Psychol.Abstr. (1988-). **Document type:** academic/scholarly publication.
●Also available on CD-ROM.
—BLDSC (0773.083000); ADONIS; CASDDS; Faxon; Genuine Article; SWETS; UnCover. **CCC.**
Description: Publishes original papers on all aspects of acquired immunodeficiency syndrome, AIDS. Features rapid publication of the latest in the clinical and scientific aspects of the disease.

AIDS (YEAR); a year in review. see *MEDICAL SCIENCES — Abstracting, Bibliographies, Statistics*

AIDS ABSTRACTS; international literature on acquired immunodeficiency syndrome and related retroviruses. see *MEDICAL SCIENCES — Abstracting, Bibliographies, Statistics*

616.9 US ISSN 0887-0292
AIDS ALERT. (Acquired Immune Deficiency Syndrome) 1986. m. $239. American Health Consultants, Inc., Six Piedmont Center, Ste. 400, Atlanta, GA 30305. TEL 800-688-2421. FAX 800-284-3291. Ed. Skip Connett. circ. 2,130. (reprint service avail.) **Indexed:** CINAHL. **Document type:** newsletter.
—BLDSC (0773.083070); SWETS. **CCC.**
Incorporates: AIDS Medical Report.
Description: Information source for frontline health care workers in the AIDS epidemic.
Refereed Serial

AIDS & FLORIDA LAW. see *LAW*

614 ZA
AIDS & HEALTH NEWS. no.5, 1991. bi-m. K.5 per no. Kara Counseling and Training Trust, P.O. Box 37559, Lusaka, Zambia. Ed. Oliver Kanene. **Document type:** newspaper.

616.9 340 US ISSN 0887-3852
RA644.A25
AIDS & PUBLIC POLICY JOURNAL. (Acquired Immune Deficiency Syndrome) 1986. q. $55 to individuals; institutions $105. University Publishing Group, Inc., 107 E. Church St., Frederick, MD 21701. TEL 800-654-8188. Ed. Dr. Alvin Novick. **Indexed:** Excerp.Med. (1992-), Soc.Sci.Ind. (1994-). **Document type:** academic/scholarly publication.
—BLDSC (0773.083090).
Description: Addresses the social, political, ethical, and legal issues in public health and health policy, especially as they relate to AIDS. Draws from a variety of disciplines and intellectual perspectives, including medicine, law, philosophy, business, and the social sciences.
Refereed Serial

AIDS & SOCIETY. see *SOCIAL SERVICES AND WELFARE*

AIDS & T B WEEKLY ABSTRACTS FROM CONFERENCE PROCEEDINGS. see *MEDICAL SCIENCES — Abstracting, Bibliographies, Statistics*

AIDS & T B WEEKLY ARTICLE SUMMARIES. see *MEDICAL SCIENCES — Abstracting, Bibliographies, Statistics*

AIDS BIBLIOGRAPHY (BETHESDA). see *MEDICAL SCIENCES — Abstracting, Bibliographies, Statistics*

616.99 US ISSN 1068-4174
RA644.A25
AIDS BOOK REVIEW JOURNAL. 1993. irreg. (1-2/mo.). free. University of Illinois at Chicago, Library, Box 8198, Chicago, IL 60680-8198. TEL 312-996-2730. FAX 312-413-0424. E-mail: U50095@uicvm.uic.edu. Ed. H. Robert Malinowsky. bk.rev. circ. 400. **Document type:** academic/scholarly publication.
●Available only online.
Description: Reviews books and videos on AIDS, STDs, and safe sex.

616.9 US
AIDS BULLETIN. irreg., 4th ed., 1990. $15 to non-members; members $10. American Correctional Health Services Association, 11 W. Monument Ave., Box 2307, Dayton, OH 45401. TEL 513-223-9630.
Description: Discusses CDC classification system for HTLV-III - LAV infections; the case definition of AIDS, CDC AIDS update, sample history and physical examination, guidelines for prevention of transmission of HIV and Hepatitis B virus to healthcare and public-safety workers.

614 SA ISSN 1019-8334
AIDS BULLETIN. 1992. q. R.45.60 (foreign R.50); free to non-profit organizations. Medical Research Council, P.O. Box 19070, Tygerberg 7505, South Africa. TEL 27-21-938-0205. FAX 27-21-938-0395. Ed. Michelle Galloway. bk.rev. circ. 1,600. **Document type:** bulletin.
Description: Provides information on AIDS education, prevention, care and research of interest to policymakers, personnel managers, researchers, education centers and the information industry.

616.9 UK ISSN 0954-0121
RC607.A26 CODEN: AIDCEF
AIDS CARE; psychological and socio-medical aspects of AIDS-HIV. Online edition (ISSN 1360-0451) 1989. 6/yr. £72 to individuals; institutions £234 (effective 1996). Carfax Publishing Co., P.O. Box 25, Abingdon, Oxon. OX14 3UE, England. TEL 01235-555335. FAX 01235-553559. (Subscr. in N. America to: Carfax Publishing Co., 875-81 Massachusetts Ave., Cambridge, MA 02139) Ed.Bd. adv.; bk.rev. (also avail. in microfiche) **Indexed:** Mult.Ed.Abstr., Psychol.Abstr. (1989-). **Document type:** academic/scholarly publication.
●Also available online.
—BLDSC (0773.083190); ADONIS; Genuine Article; SWETS; UMI; UnCover. **CCC.**
Description: Examines the biopsychosocial aspects of AIDS and HIV infection.
Refereed Serial

616.9 US ISSN 1043-1543
AIDS CLINICAL CARE. 1989. m. $89 in U.S.; elsewhere $117. Massachusetts Medical Society, Publishing Division, 1440 Main St., Waltham, MA 02154. TEL 617-893-3800; 800-843-6356. FAX 617-893-8103. Ed. Deborah Cotton. adv. contact: Art Wilschek. charts; illus.; stat.; index. circ. 30,000. (back issues avail.) **Document type:** academic/scholarly publication, newsletter.
—BLDSC (0773.083193).
Description: Brings the latest developments in the diagnosis and treatment of HIV-related diseases to the practicing clinician.

616.9 US ISSN 1045-2877
RC607.A26 CODEN: ACLREO
AIDS CLINICAL REVIEW. 1989. a. price varies. Marcel Dekker, Inc., 270 Madison Ave., New York, NY 10016. TEL 212-696-9000. FAX 212-685-4540. TELEX 421419.
—BLDSC (0773.083196). **CCC.**

616.9 362.1 US ISSN 0893-7613
RA644.A25
THE AIDS CRISIS. (Subseries of: S I R S Critical Issues (ISSN 0893-7605)) 1985. a. price varies; a. supplement $17. Social Issues Resource Series, Box 2348, Boca Raton, FL 33427-2348. TEL 407-994-0079; 800-232-7477. FAX 407-994-4704. cum.index: 1985-1991. (looseleaf format; also avail. in microfiche; back issues avail.)
Description: Reprints landmark articles following the development of the AIDS crisis from a variety of medical, social, ethical, legal, and economic perspectives.

616.9 US ISSN 1065-6162
RC607.A26
AIDS DIRECTORY. 1992. a. $250. L R P Publications, 747 Dresher Rd., Box 980, Horsham, PA 19044-0980. TEL 215-784-0941; 800-341-7874. FAX 215-784-9639. Ed. Jackie Peddigree; Pub. Ken Kahn. **Document type:** directory.
—BLDSC (0773.083280). **CCC.**
Description: Profiles of 1,500 organizations including the first interdisciplinary compilation of leaders in the struggle against AIDS, those who care for people with HIV disease, funding sources, and government agencies (federal, state, and regional).

616.97 615.5 UK ISSN 1354-5493
AIDS DIRECTORY. 1987. s-a. £80 (rest of Europe £90; elsewhere £100). N A M Publications, 52 Eurolink Centre, 49 Effra Rd., London SW2 1BZ, England. TEL 0171-737-1846. FAX 0171-737-6190. E-mail: info@nam.org.uk. Eds. Philip Browning, Andrea Cordani. **Document type:** directory.
Description: Information on all HIV and AIDS services in the UK.

616.9 US ISSN 0899-9546
RA644.A25 CODEN: AEPREO
AIDS EDUCATION AND PREVENTION. (Acquired Immune Deficiency Syndrome); an interdisciplinary journal. 1989. bi-m. $37.50 (foreign $67.50) to individuals; institutions $115 (foreign $145) (effective 1995). (International Society of AIDS Education) Guilford Publications, Inc., 72 Spring St., 4th Fl., New York, NY 10012. TEL 212-431-9800. FAX 212-966-6708. Ed. Dr. Francisco Sy; Pub. Robert Matloff. adv. contact: Marian Robinson. circ. 1,700. (reprint service avail. from UMI) **Indexed:** CINAHL, Psychol.Abstr. (1989-), Soc.Work Res.& Abstr.
—BLDSC (0773.083360); Faxon; Genuine Article; SWETS; UMI; UnCover. **CCC.**
Description: Provides information on prevention of AIDS geared towards all professionals: epidemiologists, physicians, health educators, psychologists, social workers, counselors and legislators.
Refereed Serial

616.9 US ISSN 0898-5030
RC607.A26
AIDS - HIV TREATMENT DIRECTORY; experimental and approved agents and methods. 1987. q. $44 (foreign $66). American Foundation for AIDS Research, 733 Third Ave., 12th Ave., New York, NY 10017-3204. TEL 212-682-7440. FAX 212-682-9812. (Subscr. to: 6020 N. Lindbergh Blvd., St. Louis, MO 63042. TEL 314-731-4554) Eds. Drs. Donald I. Abrams, Michael H. Grieco. **Document type:** directory.
Description: Comprehensive source of information on treatments in development for AIDS-HIV infections and neoplasms.

614 616.96 US ISSN 0891-7426
AIDS INFORMATION EXCHANGE. (Acquired Immune Deficiency Syndrome) 1984. q. $50 for 2 yrs.; qualified personnel free. U.S. Conference of Mayors, Office of Public Affairs, 1620 Eye St., N.W., Washington, DC 20006. TEL 202-293-7330. FAX 202-293-2352. (Co-sponsor: U.S. Department of Health and Human Services) Ed. P.M. Jones. bk.rev.; charts; illus. **Document type:** government publication.
Description: Provides information on innovative and effective AIDS-related policies and programs.
Refereed Serial

616.9 SZ ISSN 1021-321X
AIDS INFOTHEK. French edition: S I D A Infotheque (ISSN 1017-8791) (Editions in French, German) 1989. bi-m. 40 SFr. AIDS Info Docu Schweiz, Schauplatzgasse 26, CH-3001 Bern, Switzerland. TEL 031-3121266. FAX 031-3116414. Ed. Christa Brunswicker. bk.rev.; video rev.; index (1989-1994). circ. 22,000. **Document type:** bulletin.

AIDS LAW & LITIGATION REPORTER. see *LAW*

AIDS LAW REVIEW QUARTERLY. see *LAW*

THE AIDS LEADER. see *PUBLIC HEALTH AND SAFETY*

MEDICAL SCIENCES — COMMUNICABLE DISEASES

616.9
AIDS LETTER. (Acquired Immune Deficiency Syndrome) bi-m. £16($32) Royal Society of Medicine Press Ltd., 1 Wimpole St., London W1M 8AE, England. TEL 0171-290-2900. FAX 0171-290-2929. Ed. Dr. Victor G. Daniels. **Document type:** academic/scholarly publication.
—BLDSC (0773.083490).
Description: Includes information about research and treatment for AIDS; and related political and social issues.

610   US   ISSN 0893-1526
RC607.A26
AIDS LITERATURE & NEWS REVIEW. m. $195 to individuals; institutions and libraries $225. University Publishing Group, Inc., 107 E. Church St., Frederick, MD 21701. TEL 800-654-8188. (back issues avail.) **Document type:** newsletter.
Description: Provides monthly coverage of AIDS-related articles, developments, and news from more than 500 journals and periodicals. Serves as a reference tool for physicians, attorneys, scientists, policymakers, researchers, health care professionals, administrators, and managers.

AIDS LITIGATION REPORTER; the national journal of record of AIDS-related litigation. see *LAW*

616.9   UK   ISSN 0268-8360
AIDS NEWSLETTER. (Acquired Immune Deficiency Syndrome) 1986. m. £106($190) (effective 1996). CAB International, Wallingford, Oxon. OX10 8DE, England. TEL 01491-832111. FAX 01491-833508. TELEX 847964 COMAGG G. E-mail: cabi@cabi.org. (U.S. subscr. to: CAB International, 845 N. Park Ave., Tucson, AZ 85719. TEL 800-528-4841. FAX 520-621-3816) Eds. D.W. FitzSimons, C.J. Akehurst. circ. 750. **Document type:** newsletter.
●Also available online. Vendor(s): DIMDI.
—BLDSC (0773.083800).

616   US   ISSN 0893-5068
RC607.A26   CODEN: APACEF
AIDS PATIENT CARE. 1987. bi-m. $89 (foreign $129). Mary Ann Liebert, Inc. Publishers, 2 Madison Ave., Larchmont, NY 10538. TEL 914-834-3100. FAX 914-834-3688. E-mail: liebert@pipeline.com. (back issues avail.) **Indexed:** CINAHL, Hlth.Ind., Telegen. **Document type:** academic/scholarly publication.
—BLDSC (0773.083870); Genuine Article; SWETS; UnCover.
Description: Covers the full spectrum of health care for patients with AIDS and ARC. Provides guidelines and critical resources.
Refereed Serial

AIDS POLICY AND LAW; the bi-weekly newsletter on legislation, regulation, and litigation concerning AIDS. see *LAW*

616.9   US
AIDS PREVENTION AND MENTAL HEALTH. 1993. irreg. price varies. Plenum Publishing Corp., 233 Spring St., New York, NY 10013-1578. TEL 212-620-8000. FAX 212-463-0742. TELEX 23-421139. **Document type:** monographic series.
Description: Presents current research and clinical applications dealing with the preventive, social and psychological aspects of HIV and AIDS.
Refereed Serial

616.9   US   ISSN 1053-0894
RC607.A26
AIDS READER. 1991. bi-m. S C P Communications, Inc., 134 W. 29th St., New York, NY 10001-5304.

616.9   US
AIDS REFERENCE GUIDE. 1988. m. (in 2 vols. with 12 updates & 12 newsletters). $354. Atlantic Information Services, Inc., 1050 17th St., N.W., Ste. 480, Washington, DC 20036-5500. TEL 202-775-9008. FAX 202-331-9542. (looseleaf format)
Description: Information source tracking the cost, financing and impact of AIDS by monitoring the experiences and findings of hundreds of AIDS programs and projects.

616.97 615.5   UK
AIDS REFERENCE MANUAL. 1987. a. £29.95 (rest of Europe £34.95; elsewhere £39.95). N A M Publications, 52 Eurolink Centre, 49 Effra Rd., London SW2 1BZ, England. TEL 0171-737-1846. FAX 0171-737-6190. E-mail: info@nam.org.uk. Ed. Keith Alcorn. **Document type:** bulletin.
Description: Contains comprehensive information on all nonmedical aspects of HIV and AIDS.

616.97   US   ISSN 0889-2229
RC607.A26   CODEN: ARHRE7
AIDS RESEARCH AND HUMAN RETROVIRUSES. 1983. m. $300 (foreign $375). Mary Ann Liebert, Inc. Publishers, 2 Madison Ave., Larchmont, NY 10358. TEL 914-834-3100. FAX 914-384-3688. E-mail: Liebert@pipeline.com. Ed. Dani Bolognesi. adv. **Indexed:** Curr.Adv.Ecol.Sci., Med.& Surg.Dermat., Protozool.Abstr., Rev.Med.& Vet.Mycol., Telegen. **Document type:** academic/scholarly publication.
—BLDSC (0773.089000); CASDDS; Faxon; Genuine Article; SWETS; UnCover.
Formerly (until 1987): AIDS Research (ISSN 0737-6006)
Description: Provides studies of new viruses pertaining to cancer, degenerative diseases, and the immune system.
Refereed Serial

616.9   US   ISSN 1056-1080
RC607.A26   CODEN: ARRVEZ
AIDS RESEARCH REVIEWS. 1991. irreg., vol.3, 1993. price varies. Marcel Dekker, Inc., 270 Madison Ave., New York, NY 10016. TEL 212-696-9000. FAX 212-685-4540. TELEX 421419.
—CASDDS.

616.7   US
AIDS THERAPIES. 1987. m. $995. Charles W. Henderson, Ed. & Pub., Box 5528, Atlanta, GA 31107-0528. TEL 404-377-8895. FAX 404-378-5411. TELEX 78-2661. (Subscr. to: Box 830409, Birmingham, AL 35283-0409. TEL 800-633-4931. FAX 205-995-1588) Ed Daniel J. DeNoon. index. (looseleaf format)
Description: Incorporates the latest information available on treatment protocols, experimental drugs, clinical trials and advances on the horizon. Includes a guide to opportunistic infections of AIDS.

616.97 615.5   UK
▼**AIDS TRAINERS DIRECTORY.** 1994. a. £9.95 (outside Europe £14.95). N A M Publications, 52 Eurolink Centre, 49 Effra Rd., London SW2 1BZ, England. TEL 0171-737-1846. FAX 0171-737-6190. E-mail: info@nam.org.uk. Eds. Philip Browning, Andrea Cordani. **Document type:** directory.

616.9   US   ISSN 1052-4207
AIDS TREATMENT NEWS. 1986. s-m. $100 to individuals; institutions $230; low income individuals $45. A T N Publications, Box 411256, San Francisco, CA 94141. TEL 415-255-0588; 800-873-2812. FAX 415-255-4659. Ed. John S. James. bk.rev. circ. 6,000. (looseleaf format; back issues avail.) **Document type:** newsletter.
Description: Chronicles current developments in experimental and alternative treatments.

616.97 615.5   UK   ISSN 0969-4706
AIDS TREATMENT UPDATE. 1992. m. £35 (rest of Europe £40; elsewhere £50). N A M Publications, 52 Eurolink Centre, 49 Effra Rd., London SW2 1BZ, England. TEL 0171-737-1846. FAX 0171-737-6190. E-mail: info@nam.org.uk. Ed. Edward King. **Document type:** bulletin.
Description: Covers all new trials, treatments conferences, newly published research and changes in drugs licensing, as well as offering regular expert opinions.

616.9   CN
AIDS UPDATE. q. Ministry of Health, Centre for Disease Control, 828 W. 10th Ave., Vancouver, BC V5Z 1L8, Canada. **Document type:** government publication.

616.97 574 330   US   ISSN 1069-1456
AIDS WEEKLY; a complete weekly report privately circulated. 1985. w. (48/yr.). $995 (foreign $1195). Charles W. Henderson, Ed. & Pub., Box 5528, Atlanta, GA 31107-0528. TEL 404-377-8895. FAX 205-991-1479. TELEX 78-2661. (Subscr. to: Box 830409, Birmingham, AL 35283-0409. TEL 800-633-4931. FAX 205-995-1588) adv.; bk.rev.; index. (also avail. in microform from UMI; back issues avail.) **Document type:** newsletter.
●Also available online. Vendor(s): Data-Star (PTS NEWSLETTER DATABASE), Knight-Ridder, Inc. (File no.636), Information Access Co., NewsNet (HH14).
—BLDSC (0773.096900); UMI. **CCC.**
Formerly (until 1991): C D C - AIDS Weekly (ISSN 0884-903X); Incorporates (in 1988): Brown University S T D Update.
Description: Covers all aspects of AIDS, including research, treatments, psychosocial and prevention issues and politics.

ALERT (LOS ANGELES). see *SOCIAL SERVICES AND WELFARE*

616.9   US
AM F A R REPORT. 1985. q. free. American Foundation for A I D S Research, 733 Third Ave., 12th Fl., New York, NY 10017-3204. TEL 212-682-7440. FAX 212-682-9812. (Los Angeles Office: 5900 Wilshire Blvd., 23rd. Fl., Los Angeles, CA 90036) circ. 60,000.

614.4   US   ISSN 0196-6553
RA969
AMERICAN JOURNAL OF INFECTION CONTROL. Variant title: A J I C. 1973. bi-m. $53 to individuals (Canada $71.69; elsewhere $67); institutions $141 (Canada $165.85; elsewhere $155); students, residents $29 (Canada $46.01; elsewhere $43) (effective 1996); newsstand price: $10. (Association for Professionals in Infection Control and Epidemiology, Inc.) Mosby - Year Book, Inc. (Subsidiary of: Times Mirror Company), 11830 Westline Industrial Dr., St. Louis, MO 63146-3318. TEL 314-872-8370; 800-325-4177. FAX 314-432-1380-3318. TELEX 44-2402. Eds. Dr. Bruce H. Hamory, Elaine Larson. adv.: B&W page $1230, color page $2275; trim 8 1/8 x 10 7/8. bk.rev.; film rev.; abstr.; bibl.; charts; illus.; stat.; index. circ. 15,000. (also avail. in microfilm from UMI; back issues avail.; reprint service avail. from UMI) **Indexed:** ASCA, Biol.Abstr., CINAHL, Curr.Adv.Ecol.Sci., Curr.Cont., Dok.Arbeitsmed., Excerp.Med., Helminthol.Abstr., Ind.Med., INIS Atomind., Int.Nurs.Ind, Nurs.Abstr., Rev.Med.& Vet.Mycol.
—BLDSC (0826.761000); ADONIS; Faxon; Genuine Article; SWETS; UMI; UnCover. **CCC.**
Former titles: A P I C Bulletin; A P I C Journal (ISSN 0161-6005); A P I C Newsletter.
Description: Serves infection control practitioners and hospital epidemiologists concerned with the control of infection associated with hospitals and extended-care facilities.

616.988   US   ISSN 0002-9637
RC960   CODEN: AJTHAB
AMERICAN JOURNAL OF TROPICAL MEDICINE AND HYGIENE. 1921. m. $300 (overseas $385) (effective 1996). American Society of Tropical Medicine and Hygiene, 3088 Briarcliff Rd., Ste. 11A, Atlanta, GA 30329. TEL 404-636-3621. FAX 404-633-5737. Ed. Dr. McWilson Warren. adv.; bk.rev.; bibl.; charts; illus. circ. 4,300. **Indexed:** Abstr.Anthropol., Abstr.Hyg., AIM, Biol.Abstr., Biotech.Abstr., Chem.Abstr., Curr.Adv.Ecol.Sci., Curr.Adv.Genetics & Molec.Biol., Curr.Cont., Dairy Sci.Abstr., Dent.Ind., Diar.Dis.Res., Excerp.Med., Helminthol.Abstr., I.P.A., Ind.Med., Ind.Sci.Rev., Ind.Vet., INIS Atomind., Med.& Surg.Dermat., Nutr.Abstr., Pig News & Info., Poult.Abstr., Protozool.Abstr., Rev.Appl.Entomol., Sci.Cit.Ind., Small Anim.Abstr., So.Pac.Per.Ind., Sport Fish.Abstr., Trop.Dis.Bull., Vet.Bull., Wild.Rev., Zoo.Rec. **Document type:** academic/scholarly publication.
—BLDSC (0839.000000); CASDDS; Faxon; Genuine Article; SWETS; UnCover. **CCC.**
Supersedes in part (in 1951): American Journal of Tropical Medicine (ISSN 0096-6746)

MEDICAL SCIENCES — COMMUNICABLE DISEASES

616.998   UK   ISSN 0003-4983
RC960   CODEN: ATMPA2
ANNALS OF TROPICAL MEDICINE AND PARASITOLOGY. 1907. 6/yr. £119 in Europe (rest of world $218) to individuals; institutions £167 in Europe (rest of world $300). (Liverpool School of Tropical Medicine) W.B. Saunders Ltd. (Subsidiary of: Harcourt Brace & Company Ltd.), 24-28 Oval Rd., London NW1 7DX, England. TEL 0171-267-4466. FAX 0171-482-2293. TELEX 25775-ACPRES-G. (Subscr. to: Harcourt Brace & Company Ltd., Foots Cray High St., Sidcup, Kent DA14 5HP, England. TEL 0181-300-3322. FAX 800-874-6418; US, Canadian, and Mexican subscr. to: W.B. Saunders & Co., Journal Subscription Fulfillment, 6277 Sea Harbor Dr., 4th Fl. Orlando, FL 32887-4800. TEL 800-654-2452) Ed. Dr. W. Crewe. adv.; bibl.; illus.; index. (also avail. in microform from UMI,PMC; back issues avail.) **Indexed:** Abstr.Hyg., Biol.Abstr., Biotech.Abstr., Chem.Abstr., Curr.Adv.Ecol.Sci., Curr.Cont., Dairy Sci.Abstr., Dent.Ind., Diar.Dis.Res., Excerp.Med., Helminthol.Abstr., Ind.Med., Ind.Sci.Rev., Ind.Vet., Nutr.Abstr., Protozool.Abstr., Rev.Appl.Entomol., Rev.Plant Path., Sci.Cit.Ind., Sport Fish.Abstr., Trop.Dis.Bull., Vet.Bull., Wild.Rev., Zoo.Rec. **Document type:** academic/scholarly publication.
—BLDSC (1045.000000); CASDDS; Faxon; Genuine Article; SWETS; UnCover. **CCC.**
Description: Deals with tropical diseases and medical and veterinary parasitology in their broadest aspects.

616.9   US   ISSN 1069-417X
CODEN: AIDIEX
ANTIMICROBICS AND INFECTIOUS DISEASES NEWSLETTER. 1982. m. $238 to institutions in U.S.; $296 to institutions outside the Americas (effective 1996). Elsevier Science Inc., 655 Ave. of the Americas, New York, NY 10010. TEL 212-989-5800. FAX 212-633-3990. TELEX 420643 AEP UI. (Subscr. to: Box 882, Madison Sq. Sta., New York, NY 10159-0882) Ed. Dr. Charles W. Stratton. (also avail. in microform from UMI) **Indexed:** Abstr.Hyg., Biol.Abstr., Diar.Dis.Res., Excerp.Med. **Document type:** newsletter.
—BLDSC (1549.252000); CASDDS; Faxon; SWETS. **CCC.**
Formed by the 1993 merger of: Antimicrobic Newsletter (ISSN 0738-1751) & I D N - Infectious Diseases Newsletter (ISSN 0278-2316)
Description: For professionals and researchers in clinical microbiology, infectious diseases, clinical pharmacology, and clinical pharmacy.
Refereed Serial

ANTIVIRAL AGENTS BULLETIN; antiviral drug and vaccine development information. see *PHARMACY AND PHARMACOLOGY*

ANTIVIRAL RESEARCH; a multidisciplinary journal of antiviral agents, natural host defence mechanisms, interferons and antiviral vaccines. see *BIOLOGY — Microbiology*

616.96   GW   ISSN 0943-0938
QL757   CODEN: APPAEG
APPLIED PARASITOLOGY. (Text in English, German) 1960. q. DM.236 (foreign DM.244). Gustav Fischer Verlag Jena, Villengang 2, 07745 Jena, Germany. TEL 03641-626444. FAX 03641-626500. (Subscr. to: Postfach 100537, 07705 Jena, Germany) Ed. Klaus Odening. adv.; bk.rev.; bibl.; charts; illus.; index. (reprint service avail. from ISI) **Indexed:** Abstr.Hyg., Bio-Contr.News & Info., Biol.Abstr., Chem.Abstr., Dent.Ind., Excerp.Med., Helminthol.Abstr., Ind.Med., Ind.Vet., Protozool.Abstr., Ref.Zh., Rev.Appl.Entomol., Soils & Fert., Trop.Dis.Bull., Vet.Bull. **Document type:** academic/scholarly publication.
—BLDSC (1576.305000); CASDDS; Faxon. **CCC.**
Formerly (until 1992): Angewandte Parasitologie (ISSN 0003-3162)

616.9   US
ARBOVIRUS SURVEILLANCE SUMMARY. 1992. bi-m. U.S. Centers for Disease Control and Prevention, National Center for Infectious Diseases, Division of Vector-Borne Infectious Diseases, Box 2087, Ft. Collins, CO 80522. charts. **Document type:** government publication, newsletter.
Description: Discusses U.S. government programs to identify areas at risk to arbovirus and other vector-borne deseases and to control the spread of disease.

616.9   US   ISSN 1071-0906
ARCHIVES OF S T D - HIV RESEARCH; an international journal. 1987. 4/yr. $180 to individuals (foreign $190); institutions $200 (foreign $210) (effective 1996). Reproductive Health Center, 78 Surfsong Rd., Kiawah Island, SC 29455. TEL 803-768-5556. FAX 803-768-6494. Ed.Bd. **Indexed:** Excerp.Med. **Document type:** academic/scholarly publication.
—BLDSC (1643.169000); CASDDS; Faxon.
Formerly (until 1992): Archives of AIDS Research (ISSN 0899-4811)
Refereed Serial

616.019 576.64   AU   ISSN 0304-8608
QR360   CODEN: ARVIDF
ARCHIVES OF VIROLOGY. (Supplement avail. (ISSN 0939-1983) 1939. 12/yr. DM.2354($1710) (effective 1996). Springer-Verlag, Sachsenplatz 4-6, Postfach 89, A-1201 Vienna, Austria. TEL 0222-3302415. FAX 0222-3302426. (Subscr. in N. America to: Springer-Verlag New York, Inc., 44 Hartz Way, Secaucus, NJ 07096-2491. TEL 201-348-4033. FAX 201-348-4505) Ed. J.W. Almond. adv.; charts; illus.; index. (also avail. in microform from UMI; reprint service avail. from ISI) **Indexed:** Abstr.Hyg., Biol.Abstr., Biotech.Abstr., Chem.Abstr., Curr.Adv.Ecol.Sci., Curr.Cont., Dairy Sci.Abstr., Dent.Ind., Excerp.Med., Ind.Med., Ind.Sci.Rev., Ind.Vet., INIS Atomind., Med.& Surg.Dermat., Pig News & Info., Rev.Appl.Entomol., Sci.Cit.Ind., Small Anim.Abstr., Sport Fish.Abstr., Trop.Dis.Bull., Vet.Bull., Wild.Rev., Zoo.Rec. **Document type:** academic/scholarly publication.
—BLDSC (1643.600000); ADONIS; CASDDS; Faxon; Genuine Article; SWETS; UMI; UnCover. **CCC.**
Formerly: Archiv fuer die Gesamte Virusforschung (ISSN 0003-9012)

616.019 576.64   AU   ISSN 0939-1983
CODEN: AVISE9
ARCHIVES OF VIROLOGY. SUPPLEMENTUM. (Text in English) 1991. irreg. Springer-Verlag, Sachsenplatz 4-6, Postfach 89, A-1201 Vienna, Austria. TEL 0222-3302415. FAX 0222-3302426. (Subscr. in N. America to: Springer-Verlag New York, Inc., 44 Hartz Way, Secaucus, NJ 07096-2491. TEL 201-348-4033. FAX 201-348-4505) **Document type:** monographic series.
—BLDSC (1643.610000); ADONIS; CASDDS; SWETS.

ART & UNDERSTANDING; the international magazine of literature and art about AIDS. see *LITERATURE*

610.73   US   ISSN 1055-3290
ASSOCIATION OF NURSES IN AIDS CARE. JOURNAL. Key Title: Journal of the Association of Nurses in AIDS Care. Short title: J A N A C. 1989. bi-m. $52 to individuals (foreign $62); institutions $62 (foreign $78). Nursecom Inc., 1211 Locust St., Philadelphia, PA 19107. TEL 215-545-7222. FAX 215-545-8107. Ed. Jeanne Kalinoski; Pub. Margo C. Neal. noc.: B&W page $875, color page $2175; trim 8 1/4 x 10 3/4. bk.rev. circ. 4,200. (also avail. in microform from UMI) **Indexed:** CINAHL, Ind.Med. (1992-), Int.Nurs.Ind. **Document type:** academic/scholarly publication.
—BLDSC (4645.870000); UMI; UnCover.
Description: Articles focus on clinical practice, health services, education, research, and social issues related to the care of persons with HIV infection or AIDS.
Refereed Serial

AUSTRALIAN JOURNAL OF PUBLIC HEALTH. see *PUBLIC HEALTH AND SAFETY*

AUTOIMMUNITY. see *MEDICAL SCIENCES — Allergology And Immunology*

616.9   UK   ISSN 1071-6564
CODEN: BCIDFD
▼**BAILLIERE'S CLINICAL INFECTIOUS DISEASES.** 1994. 3/yr. £58 to individuals; institutions £78. Bailliere Tindall - W.B. Saunders Co. Ltd. (Subsidiary of: Harcourt Brace & Company Ltd.), 24-28 Oval Rd., London NW1 7DX, England. TEL 0171-237-4466. FAX 0171-482-2293. TELEX 25775 ACPRES G. (Subscr. to: Journals Subscription Fulfillment, Foots Cray High St., Sidcup, Kent DA14 5HP, England. TEL 0181-300-3322. FAX 0181-309-0807; Subscr. in N. America to: W.B. Saunders Co., Journal Subscription Fulfillment, 6277 Sea Harbor Dr., 4th Fl., Orlando, FL 32887-4800. TEL 800-874-6418) **Indexed:** Excerp.Med. (1995-). **Document type:** academic/scholarly publication.
—BLDSC (1856.724200).
Refereed Serial

616.9   US
BEING ALIVE NEWSLETTER. m. $24. Being Alive, People with HIV - AIDS Action Coalition, 3626 Sunset Blvd., Los Angeles, CA 90026. TEL 213-667-3262. FAX 213-667-2735. Ed. Jim Stoecker. circ. 11,000. **Document type:** newsletter.

BLOOD WEEKLY. see *MEDICAL SCIENCES — Hematology*

616.97   US   ISSN 1048-4396
BODY POSITIVE. 1987. m. $35 donation. Body Positive, New York, 19 Fulton St., Ste. 308B, New York, NY 10038. TEL 212-566-7333. FAX 212-566-4539. Ed. Frank Carbone; Pub. Kathryn Clark. circ. 5,000 (paid); 10,000 (controlled). **Document type:** newsletter, directory.

616.96 574.524   CL   ISSN 0365-9402
CODEN: BCPRAH
BOLETIN CHILENO DE PARASITOLOGIA. (Text in Spanish; abstracts in English) 1946. s-a. $20 (effective 1996). Universidad de Chile, Departamento de Parasitologia, Casilla No. 9183, Santiago, Chile. TEL 56-2-7370081 ext. 5340. Ed. Dr. Hugo Schenone. adv.; bk.rev.; charts; illus.; index. circ. 1,000. **Indexed:** Abstr.Hyg., Biol.Abstr., Chem.Abstr., Excerp.Med., Helminthol.Abstr., Ind.Med., Ind.Vet., Protozool.Abstr., Rev.Appl.Entomol., Small Anim.Abstr., Sport Fish.Abstr., Trop.Dis.Bull., Vet.Bull., Wild.Rev., Zoo.Rec. **Document type:** bulletin.
—BLDSC (2203.000000); Faxon; UMI.
Description: Includes subjects dealing with biology, epidemiology, clinics, laboratory and prevention of parasitoses.
Refereed Serial

BOTSWANA. MINISTRY OF HEALTH. EPIDEMIOLOGICAL BULLETIN. see *PUBLIC HEALTH AND SAFETY*

616.9   NE   ISSN 0925-711X
BULLETIN INFECTIEZIEKTEN. 1990. 13/yr. free. (Rijksinstituut voor Volksgezondheid en Milieuhygiene) Inspectie voor de Gezondheidszorg, Postbus 5406, 2280 HK Rijswijk, Netherlands. TEL 31-70-3405972. FAX 31-70-3405974. (Co-sponsor: Geneeskundige Hoofdinspectie) **Document type:** government publication, bulletin.

610   IQ   ISSN 0007-4845
BULLETIN OF ENDEMIC DISEASES. 1954. s-a. ID.3000($12) Endemic Diseases Institute, Alwiyah, P.O. Box 1178, Baghdad, Iraq. TEL 719-2033. Ed. Najat Abbas Ali. adv. circ. 1,000. **Indexed:** Abstr.Hyg., Biol.Abstr., Excerp.Med., Helminthol.Abstr., Ind.Med., Protozool.Abstr., Rev.Appl.Entomol., Trop.Dis.Bull.

616.9   UK   ISSN 1356-0832
BULLETIN OF TROPICAL MEDICINE AND INTERNATIONAL HEALTH. 3/yr. membership. Royal Society of Tropical Medicine and Hygiene, Manson House, 26 Portland Pl., London W1N 4EY, England. TEL 0171-580-2127. FAX 0171-436-1389. adv.: B&W page £500, color page £1000. **Document type:** bulletin.
Formerly (until 1994): Royal Society of Tropical Medicine and Hygiene. Newsletter.

C A SELECTS. AIDS AND RELATED IMMUNODEFICIENCIES. see *MEDICAL SCIENCES — Abstracting, Bibliographies, Statistics*

C D C HIV-AIDS SURVEILLANCE REPORTS. see *MEDICAL SCIENCES — Abstracting, Bibliographies, Statistics*

MEDICAL SCIENCES — COMMUNICABLE DISEASES

614.4241 616.9   UK   ISSN 1350-9349
C D R REVIEW. (Communicable Disease Report) 1967. m. £73 (overseas £95). Public Health Laboratory Service, 61 Colindale Ave., London NW9 5HT, England. TEL 0181-200-6868. FAX 0181-200-7868. Ed. Dr. Stuart Handysides. circ. 4,000 (paid). **Indexed:** Ind.Med. (1993-). **Document type:** academic/scholarly publication.
—BLDSC (3096.526800).
  Supersedes in part (in 1991): Communicable Disease Report. Weekly Edition (ISSN 0144-3186)

614.4241 616.905   UK
C D R SUPPLEMENT. (Communicable Disease Report) 1983. irreg. Public Health Laboratory Service, 61 Colindale Ave., London NW9 5HT, England. TEL 0181-200-6868. FAX 0181-200-7868. Ed. Dr. Stuart Handysides. **Indexed:** Ind.Med (1993-). **Document type:** monographic series.

614.4241 616.9   UK   ISSN 1350-9357
C D R WEEKLY. (Communicable Disease Report) 1967. w. £73 (overseas £95). Public Health Laboratory Service, 61 Colindale Ave., London NW9 5HT, England. TEL 0181-200-4400. FAX 0181-200-7868. Ed. Dr. Stuart Handysides. circ. 4,000. **Indexed:** Ind.Med. (1993-). **Document type:** bulletin.
—BLDSC (3096.526850).
  Supersedes in part (in 1991): Communicable Disease Report. Weekly Edition (ISSN 0144-3186)

616.9   US
CALIFORNIA MORBIDITY; bi-weekly report from the Infectious Disease Branch. 1968. bi-w. Department of Health Services, Infectious Disease Branch, 2151 Berkeley Way, Berkeley, CA 94704-1011. TEL 510-540-2566. index. circ. 4,000.

616.9   CN   ISSN 1188-0325
CANADIAN AIDS NEWS/SIDA: REALITES; the new facts of life - les faits. (Text in English, French) 1991. bi-m. free. Canadian Public Health Association, 1565 Carling Ave., Ste. 400, Ottawa, ON K1Z 8R1. TEL 613-725-3769. FAX 613-725-9826. Ed. Judy Redpath. bk.rev. circ. 10,000. **Document type:** newsletter.
  Formed by the merger of: C H News (ISSN 1186-1347) & New Facts of Life (ISSN 0841-9396)
  Description: Covers issues related to HIV-AIDS prevention in schools, the workplace, health care workers, testing and innovative education strategies for AIDS education workers.

616.9   CN   ISSN 1183-5702
CANADIAN JOURNAL OF INFECTION CONTROL. 1986. 4/yr. Can.$17($28) (foreign Can.$35). (Community and Hospital Infection Control Association) Pulsus Group Inc., 2902 S. Sheridan Way, Oakville, ON L6J 7L6, Canada. TEL 905-829-4770. FAX 905-829-4799. Ed. Pauline W. Fallis. adv.: B&W page Can.$2165; trim 8 1/8 x 10 7/8. circ. 3,000 (controlled). **Indexed:** CINAHL. **Document type:** trade publication.
—BLDSC (3031.735000).
  Formerly (until 1990): Infection Control Canada (ISSN 0833-076X)
  Refereed Serial

616.9   CN   ISSN 1180-2332
                            CODEN: CJDIES
CANADIAN JOURNAL OF INFECTIOUS DISEASES/JOURNAL CANADIEN DES MALADIES INFECTIEUSES. 1990. 6/yr. Can.$61($90) (foreign $160) to individuals; institutions Can.$84($125) (foreign $210). (Canadian Infectious Disease Society) Pulsus Group Inc., 2902 S. Sheridan Way, Oakville, ON L6J 7L6, Canada. TEL 905-829-4770. FAX 905-829-4799. Ed. L.E. Nicolle. adv.; bk.rev. circ. 7,000. **Indexed:** Excerp.Med. (1994-). **Document type:** academic/scholarly publication.
—BLDSC (3031.740000); Faxon. **CCC.**
  Description: Provides experimental and original clinical papers, case reports, editorials, news and meeting announcements and reports.
  Refereed Serial

616.9   NE   ISSN 0928-0197
CLINICAL AND DIAGNOSTIC VIROLOGY. (Text in English) 1993. 9/yr. fl.1392($849) (effective 1996). Elsevier Science B.V., P.O. Box 211, 1000 AE Amsterdam, Netherlands. TEL 31-20-4853911. FAX 31-20-4853598. TELEX 18582 ESPA NL. E-mail: nlinfo-f@elsevier.nl; usinfo-f@elsevier.com; forinfo-kyf04035@niftyserve.or.jp; Site addr.: http://www.elsevier.nl/. (Subscr. in U.S. and Canada to: Elsevier Science Inc., Box 882, Madison Sq. Sta., New York, NY 10159. TEL 212-989-5800. FAX 212-633-3990) Eds. M. Chernesky, P. Leinikki. adv.; bk.rev.; index. (also avail. in microform from UMI; back issues avail.) **Indexed:** Excerp.Med. (1994-). **Document type:** academic/scholarly publication.
—BLDSC (3286.249000). **CCC.**
  Description: Publishes papers on all aspects of human virology directly pertaining to virus-induced clinical conditions, covering epidemiology, pathogenesis, diagnosis and detection, and prevention and treatment.
  Refereed Serial

616.9   US   ISSN 1058-4838
RC110   CODEN: CIDIEL
CLINICAL INFECTIOUS DISEASES. 1979. m. $89 to individuals; institutions $205. (Infectious Diseases Society of America) University of Chicago Press, Journals Division, 5720 S. Woodlawn Ave., Chicago, IL 60637. TEL 312-753-3347. FAX 312-753-0811. (Subscr. to: Box 37005, Chicago, IL 60637) Ed. Sidney M. Finegold. adv. circ. 8,700. (also avail. in microform from UMI,PMC; reprint service avail. from UMI,ISI) **Indexed:** Abstr.Hyg., Biol.Dig., Chem.Abstr., Curr.Cont., Dent.Ind., Diar.Dis.Res., Dok.Arbeitsmed., Excerp.Med., Helminthol.Abstr., Ind.Med., Ind.Vet., Kidney, Med.& Surg.Dermat., Pig News & Info., Protozool.Abstr., Rev.Med.& Vet.Mycol., Sci.Cit.Ind., Sport Fish.Abstr., Trop.Dis.Bull., Vet.Bull., Wild.Rev. **Document type:** academic/scholarly publication.
—BLDSC (3286.293860); CASDDS; Faxon; Genuine Article; SWETS; UMI; UnCover. **CCC.**
  Formerly (until 1991): Reviews of Infectious Diseases (ISSN 0162-0886)
  Refereed Serial

CLINICAL TOPICS IN INFECTIOUS DISEASE. see *MEDICAL SCIENCES*

614.49   AT   ISSN 0725-3141
COMMUNICABLE DISEASES INTELLIGENCE. 1978. fortn. free. Department of Health, Housing, Local Government and Community Services, G.P.O. Box 9848, Canberra, A.C.T. 2601, Australia. TEL 06-289-7808. FAX 062-816-946. TELEX 61209. Ed. Robert Hall. stat.; index. circ. 4,200. (back issues avail.) **Document type:** government publication, bulletin.
—BLDSC (3341.347800).
  Description: Communicable disease epidemiology, surveillance and alert for health professionals.

COMPLICATIONS IN SURGERY. see *MEDICAL SCIENCES — Surgery*

CURRENT ADVANCES IN IMMUNOLOGY & INFECTIOUS DISEASES. see *MEDICAL SCIENCES — Abstracting, Bibliographies, Statistics*

CURRENT AIDS LITERATURE. see *MEDICAL SCIENCES — Abstracting, Bibliographies, Statistics*

616.9   UK   ISSN 0195-3842
RC111
CURRENT CLINICAL TOPICS IN INFECTIOUS DISEASES. 1980. a. $45. Blackwell Science Ltd., Osney Mead, Oxford OX2 OEL, England. TEL 01865-240201. FAX 01865-721205. TELEX 83355 MEDBOK G. Eds. Dr. Jack Remington, Dr. Morton Swartz. illus. **Document type:** academic/scholarly publication.
—BLDSC (3496.056000).

CURRENT OPINION IN INFECTIOUS DISEASES. see *MEDICAL SCIENCES — Abstracting, Bibliographies, Statistics*

CURRENT OPINION IN SURGICAL INFECTIONS. see *MEDICAL SCIENCES — Surgery*

616.9   US   ISSN 0177-4204
                           CODEN: CTMMEJ
CURRENT TOPICS IN MEDICAL MYCOLOGY. 1985. irreg. price varies. Springer-Verlag, 175 Fifth Ave., New York, NY 10010. TEL 212-460-1500. FAX 212-473-6272. (Also: Berlin, Heidelberg, Tokyo) **Document type:** monographic series.
—BLDSC (3504.884960); CASDDS. **CCC.**
  Description: Reports on research and developments in pharmaceutical uses of fungi.

616.0194   NE   ISSN 0924-5367
DEVELOPMENTS IN MEDICAL VIROLOGY. (Text in English) 1985. irreg. price varies. Kluwer Academic Publishers, Postbus 17, 3300 AA Dordrecht, Netherlands. TEL 31-78-392392. FAX 31-78-392254. TELEX 29245 KAPG NL. (Dist. by: Kluwer Academic Publishers Group, P.O. Box 322, 3300 AH Dordrecht, Netherlands. TEL 31-78-392392. FAX 31-78-546474; N. America dist. addr.: Box 358, Accord Sta., Hingham, MA 02018-0358. TEL 617-871-6600. FAX 617-871-6528) **Document type:** monographic series.
—Faxon.
  Refereed Serial

DEVELOPMENTS IN MOLECULAR VIROLOGY. see *BIOLOGY — Microbiology*

DIAGNOSTIC MICROBIOLOGY AND INFECTIOUS DISEASE. see *BIOLOGY — Microbiology*

616.9   US   ISSN 1064-1815
THE DOUBLE HELIX. 1975. q. free. National Foundation for Infectious Diseases, 4733 Bethesda Ave., Ste. 750, Bethesda, MD 20814. TEL 301-656-0003. FAX 301-907-0878. Eds. Leonard Novick, Dr. John Utz. circ. 18,000. **Document type:** newsletter.

DRUG RESISTANCE WEEKLY. see *PHARMACY AND PHARMACOLOGY*

616.9   TZ
EAST AFRICAN INSTITUTE OF MALARIA AND VECTORBORNE DISEASES. ANNUAL REPORT. (Text in English) a. East African Institute of Malaria and Vectorborne Diseases, P.O. Box 4, Amani, Tanzania. **Indexed:** Biol.Abstr., Rev.Appl.Entomol.

616.988   UA   ISSN 0301-8849
                            CODEN: EJBLAB
EGYPTIAN JOURNAL OF BILHARZIASIS. (Text in English; summaries in Arabic and English) 1974. s-a. $57 (effective 1996). (Egyptian Society of Tropical Medicine and Parasitology, Research Department) National Information and Documentation Centre (NIDOC), Tahrir St., Dokki, Awqaf P.O., Cairo, Egypt. TEL 20-2-701696. (Co-sponsor: General Society for Combat of Bilharziasis) Ed. Z. Shaker. adv.; charts; illus. circ. 1,000. (reprint service avail. from IRC) **Indexed:** Biol.Abstr., Chem.Abstr., Excerp.Med., Ind.Med. **Document type:** academic/scholarly publication.
—BLDSC (3664.280000); CASDDS.

616.9   UA   ISSN 0253-5890
                            CODEN: JESPDT
EGYPTIAN SOCIETY OF PARASITOLOGY. JOURNAL. 1972. s-a. Egyptian Society of Parasitology, Tager Bldg, Ozoris St., Garden City, Cairo, Egypt. **Indexed:** Irr.& Drain.Abstr., Zoo.Rec. **Document type:** academic/scholarly publication.
—BLDSC (4735.910000).

616.9 576   MX   ISSN 1405-0994
ENFERMEDADES INFECCIOSAS Y MICROBIOLOGIA. (Text in Spanish; summaries in English, Spanish) 1980. bi-m. $55. Obsidiana Editores, S.A., Czda. de Tlalpan 2365, Col. Ciudad Jardin, 04370 Mexico DF, Mexico. TEL 6899133. FAX 6896545. (Co-sponsors: Asociacion Mexicana de Infectologia; Consejo Nacional de Certificacion en Infectologia) Eds. Dr. Jose Ruiloba Benitez, Dr. Jose Sifuentes Osornio; Pub. Jorge Godoy. circ. 3,900. **Document type:** academic/scholarly publication.
  Description: Contains original articles, research reports, review articles, clinical cases and notices related to infectious diseases.

MEDICAL SCIENCES — COMMUNICABLE DISEASES 4351

616.9   SP   ISSN 0213-005X
CODEN: EIMCE2
ENFERMEDADES INFECCIOSAS Y MICROBIOLOGIA CLINICA. (Text in Spanish; summaries in English) 1982. m. (10/yr). 6900 ptas.($57) to non-members. (Sociedad Espanola de Enfermedades Infecciosas y Microbiologia Clinica) Ediciones Doyma, S,A, Travesera de Gracia, 17-21, 08021 Barcelona, Spain. TEL 34-1-200-07-11. FAX 34-1-209-11-36. TELEX 51964 INK-E. Dir. V. Ausina Ruiz. adv.: page 210000 ptas.; trim 210 x 280; adv. contact: Marte Vidal. circ. 3,500. (reprint service avail. from UMI) **Indexed:** Ind.Med.Esp.
—BLDSC (3747.900500); UMI. **CCC.**
Formerly: Enfermedades Infecciosas (ISSN 0212-5218)
Description: Diffuses investigative works, clinical and microbiological, related to infectious pathology. Contributes to the continuing education of professionals.

616.9   SI   ISSN 0218-0103
EPIDEMIOLOGICAL NEWS BULLETIN. (Text in English) 1974. m. Ministry of Health, Committee on Epidemic Diseases, Quarantine & Epidemiology Dept., 40 Scotts Rd., Environment Bldg., Singapore 0922, Singapore. TEL 7329758. FAX 7319866. Ed. Goh Kee Tai. stat. circ. 2,500. **Indexed:** ExtraMED. **Document type:** bulletin.
●Also available on CD-ROM.
—BLDSC (3793.566000).
Description: Provides and updates information on infectious diseases and other public health issues for medical practitioners in Singapore.

616.9 576   UK   ISSN 0950-2688
RA421   CODEN: EPINEU
EPIDEMIOLOGY AND INFECTION. 1901. bi-m. £190($352) (effective 1996). (Society for the Study of Infectious Diseases) Cambridge University Press, Edinburgh Bldg., Shaftesbury Rd., Cambridge CB2 2RU, England. TEL 01223-312393. FAX 01223-315052. TELEX 851817256. (N. American addr.: Cambridge University Press, Journals Dept., 40 W. 20th St., New York, NY 10011. TEL 212-924-3900. FAX 212-691-3239) (Co-sponsor: British Society for the Study of Infection) Ed.Bd. adv.; bk.rev.; charts; illus.; index. (also avail. in microform from UMI,PMC; back issues avail.; reprint service avail. from UMI) **Indexed:** Abstr.Health Care Manage.Stud., Abstr.Hyg., Art.Hosp.& Tour., Art.Hosp.& Tour., Biodet.Abstr., Biol.Abstr., Biostat., Br.Tech.Ind., Chem.Abstr., Curr.Adv.Ecol.Sci., Curr.Adv.Genetics & Molec.Biol., Curr.Cont., Dairy Sci.Abstr., Diar.Dis.Res., Excerp.Med., Food Sci.& Tech.Abstr., Geo.Abstr. Helminthol.Abstr, Ind.Med., Ind.Sci.Rev., Ind.Vet., Int.Abstr.Biol.Sci., Lab.Haz.Bull., Nutr.Abstr., Pig News & Info., Poult.Abstr., Protozool.Abstr., Rev.Appl.Entomol., Rev.Plant Path., Rice Abstr., Risk Abstr., Sel.Water Res.Abstr., Small Anim.Abstr., Sport Fish.Abstr., Trop.Dis.Bull., Vet.Bull., W.R.C.Inf., Wild.Rev., Zoo.Rec. **Document type:** academic/scholarly publication.
—BLDSC (3793.600000); CASDDS; Faxon; Genuine Article; SWETS; UMI; UnCover. **CCC.**
Formerly (until 1987): Journal of Hygiene (ISSN 0022-1724)
Description: Contains original findings in the fields of microbiology and infectious disease. Emphasis is on epidemiology, prevention and control.

616.9   UK   ISSN 0969-9252
▼**EPSTEIN-BARR VIRUS REPORT.** 1995. bi-m. £54 to individuals; institutions £74. Leeds Medical Information, University of Leeds, Leeds LS2 9JT, England. TEL 0113-233-5550. FAX 0113-233-5568. (Subscr. to: Royal Society of Medicine Press Ltd., 1 Wimpole St., London W1M 8AE, England. TEL 0171-290-2927. FAX 0171-290-2929) Ed. Lawrence Young. **Document type:** academic/scholarly publication.
—BLDSC (3794.399220).
Description: Locates and reports the scientific and research literature on Epstein-Barr Virus internationally.

616.9   FR
EUROPEAN CENTRE FOR THE EPIDEMIOLOGICAL MONITORING OF AIDS. QUARTERLY REPORT/CENTRE EUROPEEN POUR LA SURVEILLANCE EPIDEMIOLOGIQUE DU SIDA. RAPPORT TRIMESTRIEL. (Text in English, French) q. European Centre for the Epidemiological Monitoring of AIDS - Centre Europeen pour la Surveillance Epidemiologique du SIDA, Hopital National de Saint-Maurice, 14 rue du Val d'Osne, 94410 Saint-Maurice, France. TEL 43-96-65-45. FAX 43-96-50-81. TELEX 219 000. E-mail: EARN::"DUBOIS__D@FRCCRM51".

616.97 615.5   UK
EUROPEAN UNION AIDS DIRECTORY. (Editions in English, French, German, Italian, Spanish) a. £29.95 (outside Europe £34.95). N A M Publications, 52 Eurolink Centre, 49 Effra Rd., London SW2 1BZ, England. TEL 0171-737-1846. FAX 0171-737-6190. E-mail: info@nam.org.uk. Ed. Brian Cooper. **Document type:** directory.
Description: Information on all non-governmental HIV and AIDS services in the European Union.

616.9 340   US   ISSN 1042-4652
KF3803.A54
THE EXCHANGE (SAN FRANCISCO).* 1986. 3/yr. $35 includes membership. National Lawyers Guild, AIDS Network, 55 Ave. of the Americas, No. NLG, New York, NY 10013-1601. Ed. Eileen Hansen.

616.96   US   ISSN 0014-4894
QL757   CODEN: EXPAAA
EXPERIMENTAL PARASITOLOGY. 1952. 9/yr. $533 (foreign $634) (effective 1996). Academic Press, Inc., Journal Division, 525 B St., Ste. 1900, San Diego, CA 92101-4495. TEL 619-230-1840. FAX 619-699-6800. (Subscr. to: Box 620000, Orlando, FL 32891-8340. TEL 800-543-9534) Ed. Dyann F. Wirth. adv.; bibl.; illus.; index. (back issues avail.) **Indexed:** Abstr.Hyg., Bio-Contr.News & Info., Biol.Abstr., Biotech.Abstr., Chem.Abstr., Curr.Adv.Ecol.Sci., Curr.Cont., Dent.Ind., Excerp.Med. (1993-), Helminthol.Abstr., Ind.Med., Ind.Sci.Rev., Ind.Vet., INIS Atomind., Nutr.Abstr., Pig News & Info., Poult.Abstr., Protozool.Abstr., Rev.Appl.Entomol., Sci.Cit.Ind., Small Anim.Abstr., Sport Fish.Abstr., Trop.Dis.Bull., Vet.Bull., Wild.Rev., Zoo.Rec. **Document type:** academic/scholarly publication.
—BLDSC (3840.000000); ADONIS; CASDDS; Faxon; Genuine Article; SWETS; UnCover. **CCC.**
Description: Emphasizes modern approaches to parasitology, including molecular biology and immunology.
Refereed Serial

616.9   US
FEDERAL FUNDING TO FIGHT AIDS. 1991. irreg. $59.50. Government Information Services, 4301 N. Fairfax Dr., Ste. 875, Arlington, VA 22203-1627. TEL 703-528-1000. FAX 703-528-6060. Ed. Amy McAuliffe. (looseleaf format)
Description: Describes all the federal government grants and financial aid programs to fight the AIDS epidemic.

610   US   ISSN 1047-0719
FOCUS (SAN FRANCISCO); a guide to AIDS research & counseling. 1985. m. $36 to individuals (foreign $48); institutions $90 (foreign $110). AIDS Health Project, University of California, San Francisco, Box 0884, San Francisco, CA 94143-0884. TEL 415-476-6430. FAX 415-476-7996. Ed. Robert Marks. bk.rev.; circ. 2,000 (paid). **Document type:** academic/scholarly publication, newsletter.
●Also available online.
—BLDSC (3964.199500).
Description: Reviews the mental health and counseling aspects of AIDS and HIV disease. Puts medical, epidemiological, and social aspects of the epidemic in the context of HIV-related counseling and psychotherapy.

616.96 574.524   XR   ISSN 0015-5683
CODEN: FPARA9
FOLIA PARASITOLOGICA. (Text and summaries in English) 1966. q. $60 to individuals; institutions $180 (effective 1994). Academy of Sciences of the Czech Republic, Parasitological Institute, Branisovska 31, 37005 Ceske Budejovice, Czech Republic. TEL 0042-38-41158. E-mail: paru@entu.cas.cz. Ed. Jiri Lom. bk.rev.; bibl.; charts; illus.; index. circ. 850. **Indexed:** Abstr.Hyg., Biol.Abstr., Chem.Abstr., Curr.Adv.Ecol.Sci., Curr.Cont., Curr.Ref.Fish Res., Excerp.Med., Helminthol.Abstr., Ind.Med., Ind.Sci.Rev., Ind.Vet., Pig News & Info., Poult.Abstr., Protozool.Abstr., Rev.Appl.Entomol., Sci.Cit.Ind., Soils & Fert., Trop.Dis.Bull., Vet.Bull. **Document type:** academic/scholarly publication.
—BLDSC (3971.850000); CASDDS; Faxon; Genuine Article; SWETS. **CCC.**
Formerly (until 1965): Ceskoslovenska Parasitologie.
Description: Includes papers on human and veterinary parasitology and on the biology, morphology, ultrastructure, physiology and biochemistry of parasites.
Refereed Serial

616.9   US   ISSN 1077-1824
RC607.A26
G M H C TREATMENT ISSUES; newsletter of experimental AIDS therapies. 1987. m. $35 to individuals; institutions and foreign $70 (effective 1996). (Gay Men's Health Crisis, Inc.) G M H C, Inc., Department of Medical Information, 129 W. 20th St., New York, NY 10011. FAX 212-337-3656. Ed. David Gilden. circ. 18,000. **Document type:** newsletter.
Formerly: Treatment Issues (ISSN 1050-625X)
Description: Addresses the various medical aspects of AIDS, including experimental treatments, descriptions of opportunistic infections often seen in AIDS, drug licensing issues, and medical articles of general interest to people who are HIV-infected.

GAY MEN'S HEALTH CRISIS. see *MEDICAL SCIENCES — Experimental Medicine, Laboratory Technique*

616.96   IT   ISSN 0017-0321
CODEN: GMIPAX
GIORNALE DI MALATTIE INFETTIVE E PARASSITARIE. 1948. m. L.250000 (effective 1996). (Societa Italiana per lo Studio delle Malattie Infettive e Parassitarie) Edizioni Arti Grafische Valsesiane s.a.s, Ospedale L. Sacco, 1o Div. Mal. Infettive, Via G.B. Grassi 74, 20157 Milan, Italy. TEL 35-799-452. Ed. Prof. Francesco Milazzo. adv.; bk.rev.; abstr.; bibl.; charts; illus.; stat.; index. cum.index. circ. 1,350. (reprint service avail. from IRC) **Indexed:** Abstr.Hyg., Biol.Abstr., Chem.Abstr., Curr.Adv.Ecol.Sci., Dent.Ind., Excerp.Med., Helminthol.Abstr., Ind.Vet., Protozool.Abstr., Rev.Med.& Vet.Mycol., Trop.Dis.Bull.
—BLDSC (4178.330000); CASDDS; SWETS.

616.9   UN   ISSN 1020-007X
RA644.A25
GLOBAL AIDSNEWS; newsletter of the World Health Organization global programme on AIDS. Arabic edition: Akhbar al-Aydz al-'Alamiyyah (ISSN 1020-0061); French edition: SIDA - O M S le Point (ISSN 1020-0088) 1992. q. free. World Health Organization, Global Programme on AIDS, CH-1211 Geneva 27, Switzerland. TEL 791-4650. FAX 0791-0107. E-mail: lewisd@who.ch. Ed. David Lewis. circ. 32,000 (23,000 English ed.; 7,000 French ed.; 2,000 Arabic ed.). **Document type:** newsletter.
—BLDSC (4195.338000).
Description: Provides news about AIDS and action by the WHO and its partners to curtail the HIV-AIDS pandemic and alleviate the suffering of those affected.

616.998   US
GLOBAL MISSIONS. 1943. 3/yr. International Christian Leprosy Mission, Inc., Box 23353, Portland, OR 97223. Ed. Dr. De-Ann Pillers. circ. 1,650. **Document type:** bulletin.

GLYCOSYLATION AND DISEASE. see *MEDICAL SCIENCES — Allergology And Immunology*

MEDICAL SCIENCES — COMMUNICABLE DISEASES

616.998   BL   ISSN 0100-3283
CODEN: HAINDP
HANSENOLOGIA INTERNATIONALIS. (Text in English, French, Italian, Portuguese or Spanish) 1976. s-a. exchange basis. Instituto de Saude, Biblioteca, Caixa Postal 8027, 01051 Sao Paulo, SP, Brazil. Ed. Teresa A.E. Kliemann. bk.rev.; bibl.; charts; illus.; stat. circ. 2,000. **Indexed:** Biol.Abstr., Excerp.Med., Ind.Med. (until 1992), Trop.Dis.Bull.
    Supersedes (1933-1970): Revista Brasileira de Leprologia.
    Description: Articles, news, correspondence and more on Hansen's disease, leprosy.

HARVARD AIDS INSTITUTE SERIES ON GENE REGULATION OF HUMAN RETROVIRUSES. see BIOLOGY — Genetics

HEALTH INFORMATION BULLETIN. see PUBLIC HEALTH AND SAFETY

616.9   US   ISSN 1064-4873
THE HELPER. 1979. q. $25 to individuals; institutions $50. Herpes Resource Center, (Subsidiary of: American Social Health Association), Box 13827, Research Triangle Park, NC 27709. TEL 919-361-8485. FAX 919-361-8425. Ed. Charles Ebel. bk.rev. circ. 15,000. **Document type:** newsletter.
    Description: Presents emerging issues in the treatment of herpes simplex. Covers both scientific breakthroughs and psychosocial aspects.

616.97 615.6   UK   ISSN 1357-6410
HIV AND AIDS TREATMENTS DIRECTORY. 1987. s-a. £55 (Europe £65; rest of world £75). N A M Publications, 52 Eurolink Centre, 49 Effra Rd., London SW1 2BZ, England. TEL 0171-737-1846. FAX 0171-737-6190. E-mail: info@nam.org.uk. Ed. Edward King. **Document type:** directory.
    Description: Comprehensive information on all treatments for HIV and AIDS.

616.9   US
HIV FUNDING WATCH. (Human Immunodeficiency Virus) m. free to Texas residents. Department of Health, Reprographics & Library Services Division, 1100 W. 49th St., Austin, TX 78756-3199. TEL 512-458-7684. FAX 512-458-7683. circ. controlled. **Document type:** newsletter, government publication.
    Description: Reports on HIV-related funding to organizations in Texas.

616.9   US
HIV PREVENTION NEWS. 1988. q. free. Department of Health, HIV Division, 1100 W. 49th St., Austin, TX 78756. TEL 512-458-7304. FAX 512-458-7434. Ed. Margaret Dugan. circ. 3,000. (back issues avail.) **Document type:** newsletter, government publication.
    Description: Statewide news on HIV and AIDS, resources for health education and risk reduction.

016.6   US   ISSN 0197-8160
RB155
HUMAN GENETICS, INFORMATIONAL AND EDUCATIONAL MATERIALS. SUPPLEMENT. 1980. a. U.S. Public Health Service, 5600 Fishers Lane, Rockville, MD 20857. TEL 301-444-6656.

616.98   NE   ISSN 0169-3727
CODEN: HPDIEN
HUMAN PARASITIC DISEASES. (Text in English) 1985. irreg., vol.4, 1991. price varies. Elsevier Science B.V., Books Division, P.O. Box 211, 1000 AE Amsterdam, Netherlands. TEL 31-20-4853911. FAX 31-20-4853705. TELEX 18582 ESPA NL. E-mail: nlinfo-f@elsevier.nl; usinfo-f@elsevier.com; forinfo-kyf04035@niftyserve.or.jp; Site addr.: http://www.elsevier.nl/. (Subscr. in U.S. and Canada to: Elsevier Science Inc., Box 882, Madison Sq. Sta., New York, NY 10159. TEL 212-989-5800) (back issues avail.) **Document type:** monographic series.
—BLDSC (4336.259000). **CCC.**
Refereed Serial

616.9 616.97   UK   ISSN 0959-4957
CODEN: IINDEK
IMMUNOLOGY AND INFECTIOUS DISEASES. 1991. q. £250($425) to institutions (effective 1995). Rapid Communications of Oxford Ltd., The Old Malthouse, Paradise St., Oxford OX1 1LD, England. TEL 01865-790447. FAX 01865-244012. E-mail: rapidcom@vax.oxford.ac.uk. Ed. R.K. Chandra. adv. contact: Julie Gribben. (reprint service avail.) **Indexed:** Diar.Dis.Res. **Document type:** academic/scholarly publication.
—BLDSC (4369.703500); ADONIS; CASDDS; SWETS. **CCC.**
    Description: Covers all aspects of the relationship between the immune system and microbial infections.

616.998   CN
IN ACTION. 1973. q. free. Leprosy Mission Canada, 40 Wynford Dr., Ste. 216, Don Mills, ON M3C 1J5, Canada. TEL 416-441-3618. FAX 416-441-0203. Ed. Nicholas Hunter. bk.rev.; video rev. circ. 14,000. **Document type:** bulletin, academic/scholarly publication, newsletter.

INDIAN JOURNAL OF DERMATOLOGY, VENEREOLOGY AND LEPROLOGY. see MEDICAL SCIENCES — Dermatology And Venereology

616.96 574.524   II   ISSN 0019-5227
QL386
INDIAN JOURNAL OF HELMINTHOLOGY. 1948. s-a. Rs.20($40) Helminthological Society of India, Prints India, 11 Darya Ganj, New Delhi 110 002, India. Ed. Dr. G.S. Thapar. illus. (back issues avail.) **Indexed:** Biol.Abstr., Helminthol.Abstr., Ind.Vet., Vet.Bull.
—BLDSC (4414.000000); Faxon; UnCover.

616.998   II   ISSN 0254-9395
RC154.7.I6
INDIAN JOURNAL OF LEPROSY. (Text in English) 1929. q. Rs.60 (Europe, Africa & Asia £12; elsewhere $22). Indian Leprosy Association - Hind Kusht Nivaran Sangh, 1, Red Cross Road, New Delhi 110 001, India. TEL 3714748. Ed. Dr. H. Srinivasan. adv.; bk.rev.; abstr.; charts; illus.; stat.; index. circ. 1,750. **Indexed:** Abstr.Hyg., Biol.Abstr., Dent.Ind., Excerp.Med., ExtraMED, Ind.Med., Indian Sci.Abstr., Trop.Dis.Bull.
● Also available on CD-ROM.
—BLDSC (4415.850000); Faxon; SWETS; UnCover.
    Formerly (until 1984): Leprosy in India (ISSN 0024-1024)

616.9   II   ISSN 0367-8326
RC164.I3   CODEN: IJMAA9
INDIAN JOURNAL OF MALARIOLOGY. (Text in English) 1947-1963; resumed 1981. q. Rs.75($20) Indian Council of Medical Research, Malaria Research Center, 22, Sham Nath Marg, Delhi 110 054, India. TEL 91-11-2528455. FAX 91-11-7234234. TELEX 31-65518 MRC IN. Ed. V.P. Sharma. bk.rev. circ. 350. **Indexed:** Excerp.Med., ExtraMED, Ind.Med., Protozool.Abstr., Rev.Appl.Entomol. **Document type:** academic/scholarly publication.
● Also available on CD-ROM.
—BLDSC (4416.000000); Faxon; UnCover.
    Description: Contains original research articles, short notes and reviews on all fields of malariology.

616.9   US   ISSN 0899-823X
RA969   CODEN: ICEPE3
INFECTION CONTROL & HOSPITAL EPIDEMIOLOGY. 1980. m. $70 to individuals; institutions $80. Slack, Inc., 6900 Grove Rd., Thorofare, NJ 08086. TEL 609-848-1000. FAX 609-853-5991. adv. circ. 5,000. (also avail. in microform from UMI) **Indexed:** Biol.Abstr., Chem.Abstr., CINAHL, Curr.Adv.Ecol.Sci., Curr.Cont., Diar.Dis.Res., Dok.Arbeitsmed., Helminthol.Abstr., Ind.Med., Int.Nurs.Ind., Nurs.Abstr., Rev.Med.& Vet.Mycol.
—BLDSC (4478.721050); CASDDS; Faxon; Genuine Article; SWETS; UMI; UnCover. **CCC.**
    Formerly: Infection Control (ISSN 0195-9417)
Refereed Serial

616.6   US   ISSN 1074-2905
▼**INFECTION CONTROL WEEKLY.** 1994. w. $995. Charles W. Henderson, Ed. & Pub., Box 5528, Atlanta, GA 31107-0528. TEL 404-377-8895. FAX 404-378-5411. TELEX 78-2661. (Subscr. to: Box 830409, Birmingham, AL 35283-0409. TEL 800-633-4931. FAX 205-995-1588) (also avail. in microform from UMI) **Document type:** newsletter.
—UMI. **CCC.**
    Description: Focuses on nosocomial infections originating in hospitals, prisons and other high-risk sites. Topics include the identification, treatment and control of various acquired infections, from AIDS to TB, surgical site infections, nosocomial candida infections, hospital epidemiology, hospital policies, CDC guidelines.

616.9   UK
▼**INFECTIONS.** 1994. 3/yr. £23 (overseas £29) (effective 1995). Hayward Medical Communications Ltd., 44 Earlham St., Covent Garden, London WC2H 9LA, England. TEL 44-171-240-4493. FAX 44-171-240-4479. (Subscr. to: Essex House, Cromwell Park, Chipping Norton, Oxon. OX7 4SR, England. TEL 44-1608-645564. FAX 44-1608-645645) **Document type:** academic/scholarly publication.

616.9   US   ISSN 0749-6524
CODEN: INMDEG
INFECTIONS IN MEDICINE; infectious disease in medical and family practice. 1984. m. $50 to individuals; residents and students $30. S C P Communications, Inc., 134 W. 29th St., New York, NY 10001-5304. TEL 212-714-1740. adv.; circ. 61,693 (controlled).
—BLDSC (4478.721550); Genuine Article. **CCC.**

616.9 576   US   ISSN 1056-2044
CODEN: IADIEV
INFECTIOUS AGENTS AND DISEASE. 1992. q. $95 to individuals (foreign $113); institutions $135 (foreign $165) (effective 1996); newsstand price: $42. Lippincott - Raven Press, 227 E. Washington Sq., Philadelphia, PA 19106. TEL 215-238-4200. Ed. Bernard Roizman. adv. contact: Phyllis Noyes. bk.rev.; charts; illus. (reprint service avail. from UMI) **Indexed:** Diar.Dis.Res., Excerp.Med. (1993-), Ind.Med. (1994-). **Document type:** academic/scholarly publication.
—BLDSC (4478.721680); CASDDS; Genuine Article; SWETS; UMI. **CCC.**
    Description: Publishes major interdisciplinary review articles in infectious disease and related disciplines, and commentaries on significant and controversial issues.
Refereed Serial

616.9   US   ISSN 0739-7348
INFECTIOUS DISEASE ALERT. 1981. s-m. $116. American Health Consultants, Inc., Six Piedmont Center, Ste. 400, Atlanta, GA 30305. TEL 404-262-7436; 800-688-2421. FAX 800-284-3291. Ed. Dr. Stanley Deresinski. index. circ. 2,380. (reprint service avail.) **Document type:** newsletter.
—**CCC.**
    Incorporates (in 1991): A I D S Clinical Digest.

616.9   US   ISSN 1043-2981
CODEN: IDTHER
INFECTIOUS DISEASE AND THERAPY SERIES. 1989. irreg., vol.15, 1994. price varies. Marcel Dekker, Inc., 270 Madison Ave., New York, NY 10016. TEL 212-696-9000. FAX 212-685-4540. TELEX 421419. **Document type:** monographic series.
—BLDSC (4478.721800); CASDDS.

616.9   US   ISSN 0891-5520
RC109   CODEN: IDCAEN
INFECTIOUS DISEASE CLINICS OF NORTH AMERICA. Title varies slightly: Infectious Disease Clinics. 1987. q. $122 (foreign $145) (effective 1996). W.B. Saunders Co. (Subsidiary of: Harcourt Brace & Company), Curtis Center, 3rd Fl., Independence Sq. W., Philadelphia, PA 19106-3399. TEL 215-238-7800. FAX 215-238-6445. (Subscr. to: Periodicals Fulfillment, W.B. Saunders Co., 6277 Sea Harbor Dr., 4th Fl., Orlando, FL 32887-4800. TEL 800-654-2452. FAX 800-874-6418) Ed. Sandra Masse. index. (also avail. in microform from UMI; back issues avail.) **Indexed:** Excerp.Med. (1992-). **Document type:** academic/scholarly publication.
—BLDSC (4478.722000); Faxon; Genuine Article; SWETS; UMI; UnCover. **CCC.**
    Description: Disucusses a topic on the diagnosis or treatment of infectious diseases in each issue.

MEDICAL SCIENCES — COMMUNICABLE DISEASES

616.9 610   US   ISSN 1056-9251
INFECTIOUS DISEASE NEWS. 1988. m. $110 to individuals (foreign $146); institutions $120 (foreign $156). Slack, Inc., 6900 Grove Rd., Thorofare, NJ 08086-9447. TEL 609-848-1000. FAX 609-853-5991.

616.9   US   ISSN 0162-6493
INFECTIOUS DISEASE PRACTICE. 1977. m. $89 (foreign $111). M B C Publications, Winthrop University Hospital, 222 Station Plaza N., Ste. 432, Mineola, NY 11501-3432. TEL 516-663-4435. FAX 513-663-2753. Ed. Dr. Burke A. Cunha. circ. 700. (back issues avail.)
—CCC.
Description: For physicians in practice or research. Each issue focuses on a specific disease presenting symptoms, differential diagnosis, clinical course, management, and treatment or prevention.

616.9 576   GW   ISSN 0934-8379
INFEKTIONS KLINIK - MIKROBIOLOGIE UND KRANKENHAUSHYGIENE. 1988. bi-m. DM.60. Universmed Verlag, August-Schanz-Str. 21, 60433 Frankfurt a.M., Germany. TEL 069-5480000. Ed. Peter Hoffmann. adv.; bk.rev. avail. circ. 9,500. (back issues avail.)
Description: Interviews, congress reports and patient information about communicable diseases.

616.9   BU   ISSN 0861-8259
                        CODEN: EMIBA3
INFEKTOLOGIIA/INFECTOLOGY. (Text in Bulgarian; summaries in English) q. 30 lv. Natsionalen Tsentar po Zarasni i Parasitni Bolesti - National Center of Infectious and Parasitic Diseases, Bul. Yanko Sakazov 26, 1504 Sofia, Bulgaria. TEL 395-2-4347399. FAX 359-2-442260. Ed. Borban Petrunov. adv. circ. 1,000. **Indexed:** Abstr.Bulg.Sci.Med.Lit., BSL Biol.
—BLDSC (0086.565000); CASDDS.
Formerly (until 1992): Epidemiologiia, Mikrobiologiia i Infektsiozni Bolesti (ISSN 0425-1482)

616.01 589.9   FR   ISSN 0020-2452
R108   CODEN: BIPAA8
INSTITUT PASTEUR. BULLETIN. (Supplement avail.) (Text and summaries in English, French) 1903. q. 965 F. in France; foreign 1135 F.($222) (effective 1996). Editions Scientifiques Elsevier, 141 rue de Javel, 75747 Paris, France. TEL 33-1-45589063. (Subscr. in U.S. and Canada to: Elsevier Science Inc., Box 882, Madison Sq. Sta., New York, NY 10159. TEL 212-989-5800) Ed. P. Meyer. adv.; bk.rev.; index. circ. 1,300. (also avail. in microform from UMI,PMC; reprint service avail. from ISI) **Indexed:** Abstr.Hyg., Biol.Abstr., Bull.Signal., Curr.Adv.Ecol.Sci., Curr.Cont., Dairy Sci.Abstr., Excerp.Med., Helminthol.Abstr., Ind.Vet., Trop.Dis.Bull., Vet.Bull. **Document type:** academic/scholarly publication, bulletin.
—BLDSC (2575.000000); ADONIS; CASDDS; EMDOCS; Faxon; Genuine Article; SWETS. **CCC.**
Description: Presents reviews on all aspects of microbiology, immunology and infectious diseases, and aims at providing researchers and teaching staff in these fields.
Refereed Serial

616.01 576.64   AE   ISSN 0020-2460
INSTITUT PASTEUR D'ALGERIE. ARCHIVES. (Text in English and French) 1921. a. 30 din.($6) Institut Pasteur d'Algerie, Rue du Docteur Laveran, Algiers, Algeria. TEL 67-25-02. TELEX 65337. bibl.; charts; illus.; stat.; index. circ. 1,000. (also avail. in microfilm) **Indexed:** Bio-Contr.News & Info., Biol.Abstr., Dairy Sci.Abstr., Excerp.Med., Helminthol.Abstr., Ind.Med., Ind.Vet., Protozool.Abstr., Rev.Appl.Entomol., Trop.Dis.Bull., Vet.Bull.

INSTITUT PASTEUR DE MADAGASCAR. ARCHIVES. see
BIOLOGY — Microbiology

616.01 576   GR   ISSN 0004-6620
INSTITUT PASTEUR HELLENIQUE. (Text in French; summaries in English and Greek) 1923. a. free. Institut Pasteur Hellenique, 127 Ave. de la Reine Sophie, Athens 618, Greece. Dir. Charles Serie. adv. circ. 1,500. **Indexed:** Abstr.Hyg., Biol.Abstr., Ind.Vet., Trop.Dis.Bull., Vet.Bull.

INSTITUTO DE HIGIENE E MEDICINA TROPICAL. ANAIS.
see *PUBLIC HEALTH AND SAFETY*

616.988   BL   ISSN 0036-4665
                        CODEN: RMTSAE
INSTITUTO DE MEDICINA TROPICAL DE SAO PAULO. REVISTA. (Text and summaries in English, Portuguese and Spanish) 1959. bi-m. $200. Instituto de Medicina Tropical de Sao Paulo, Universidad de Sao Paulo, Ave. Dr. Eneias C. Aguiar 470, 05403 Sao Paulo, Brazil. Ed. Thales F. de Brito. adv.; bk.rev.; abstr.; illus.; index. circ. 1,300. (also avail. in microform from UMI; back issues avail.) **Indexed:** Abstr.Hyg., B.R.I., Biol.Abstr., Bull.Anal.Ent.Med.Vet., Curr.Adv.Ecol.Sci., Curr.Cont., Dent.Ind., Excerp.Med., Helminthol.Abstr., Ind.Med., Ind.Vet., Protozool.Abstr., Rev.Appl.Entomol., Rev.Med.& Vet.Mycol., Rev.Plant Path., Sci.Cit.Ind., Trop.Dis.Bull, Vet.Bull.
—BLDSC (7819.850000); CASDDS; EMDOCS; Genuine Article; UMI.

616.988   PL   ISSN 0324-8542
                        CODEN: BIMGDE
INSTYTUT MEDYCYNY MORSKIEJ I TROPIKALNEJ W GDYNI. BULLETIN/INSTITUTE OF MARITIME AND TROPICAL MEDICINE IN GDYNIA. BULLETIN. (Text and summaries in English) 1948. q. $30 (effective 1995 & 1996). Instytut Medycyny Morskiej i Tropikalnej w Gdyni, Ul. Powstania Styczniowego 9B, 81-519 Gdynia-Radlowo, Poland. TEL 48-58-223011. FAX 48-58-223354. (Co-sponsor: Ministry of Health and Social Welfare) Ed. S. Tomaszunas. adv.; bk.rev. circ. 550. **Indexed:** Abstr.Hyg., Anal.Abstr., Biol.Abstr., C.I.S. Abstr., Chem.Abstr., Excerp.Med., Ind.Med., Protozool.Abstr., Rev.Appl.Entomol., Rev.Med.& Vet.Mycol., Trop.Dis.Bull. **Document type:** academic/scholarly publication, bulletin.
—BLDSC (2580.890500); CASDDS.
Formerly (until 1974): Instytut Medycyny Morskiej w Gdansku. Biuletyn - Institute of Marine Medicine in Gdansk. Bulletin (ISSN 0020-4463)
Description: Covers occupational diseases and maritime hygiene related to the work of seamen, fishermen and maritime ports personnel; parasitology, bacteriology, sea water control.

616.96   PL   ISSN 0074-3356
INTERNATIONAL COMMISSION ON TRICHINELLOSIS. PROCEEDINGS. (Published as a No. of "Wiadomosci Parazytologiczne") 1962. irreg. price varies. (Polskie Towarzystwo Parazytologiczne) Wiadomosci Parazytologiczne, Ul. Przybyszewskiego 63, 51-148 Wroclaw, Poland. TEL 48-71-247214. Ed. J. Zlotorzycka. bk.rev. circ. 800. **Document type:** proceedings.

616.9   NE   ISSN 0074-4212
INTERNATIONAL CONGRESSES ON TROPICAL MEDICINE AND MALARIA. (PROCEEDINGS). (Proceedings issued at discretion of host country; none issued for 8th, 1968, Teheran) 1948. quadrennial, 13th, 1992, Bangkok. International Federation for Tropical Medicine, c/o Dr. Wm. A. Sodeman, Sec.-Gen., Medical College of Ohio, Box 10008, Toledo, OH 43699-0008. circ. 1,500. **Document type:** proceedings.

616.96 574.524   UK   ISSN 0020-7519
QL757   CODEN: IJPYBT
INTERNATIONAL JOURNAL FOR PARASITOLOGY. 1971. m. £550($875) (effective 1996). (Australian Society for Parasitology, AT) Elsevier Science Ltd., Pergamon, P.O. Box 800, Kidlington, Oxford OX5 1DX, England. TEL 44-1865-843000. FAX 44-1865-843010.
E-mail: nlinfo-f@elsevier.nl; usinfo-f@elsevier.com; forinfo-kyf04035@niftyserve.or.jp; Site addr.: http://www.elsevier.nl/. (Subscr. in U.S. and Canada to: Elsevier Science, 660 White Plains Rd., Tarrytown, NY 10591-5153. TEL 914-524-9200. FAX 914-333-2444) Ed. J.F.A. Sprent. adv.; bk.rev. circ. 1,250. (also avail. in microform from UMI; reprint service avail. from UMI) **Indexed:** Anim.Breed.Abstr., Chem.Abstr., Curr.Adv.Ecol.Sci., Dent.Ind., Excerp.Med., Helminthol.Abstr., Ind.Med., Ind.Sci.Rev., Ind.Vet., Ocean.Abstr., Poult.Abstr., Protozool.Abstr., Sci.Cit.Ind., Small Anim.Abstr., Sport Fish.Abstr., Vet.Bull., Wild.Rev., Zoo.Rec. **Document type:** academic/scholarly publication.
—BLDSC (4542.449000); ADONIS; CASDDS; EMDOCS; Faxon; Genuine Article; SWETS; UMI; UnCover. **CCC.**
Description: Serves as an international medium for the communication of scientific contributions in the field of parasitology.
Refereed Serial

616.9   CN   ISSN 1201-9712
▼**INTERNATIONAL JOURNAL OF INFECTIOUS DISEASES.** Announced for publication in 1996. q. $55 to individuals ($65 outside U.S. and Canada); institutions $83 ($93 outside U.S. and Canada) (effective 1996). (International Society of Infectious Diseases) Decker Periodicals, P.O. Box 620, LCD 1, Hamilton, ON L8N 3K7, Canada. TEL 905-522-7017; 800-568-7281. FAX 905-522-7839. E-mail: decker@io.org. (U.S. addr.: Box 785, Lewiston, NY 14092-0785) **Document type:** academic/scholarly publication.

616.998   US   ISSN 0148-916X
                        CODEN: IJLEAG
INTERNATIONAL JOURNAL OF LEPROSY AND OTHER MYCOBACTERIAL DISEASES. 1933. q. $120 (effective 1996). International Leprosy Association, One ALM Way, Greenville, SC 29601. TEL 803-271-7040. FAX 803-271-7062. Ed. Robert C. Hastings. adv. contact: Robert Hastings. bk.rev.; abstr.; bibl.; charts; illus.; index. circ. 1,300. (also avail. in microform from UMI; back issues avail.; reprint service avail. from UMI) **Indexed:** Abstr.Hyg., Biol.Abstr., Chem.Abstr., Curr.Adv.Ecol.Sci., Curr.Cont., Excerp.Med., Helminthol.Abstr., Ind.Med., Ind.Sci.Rev., Med.& Surg.Dermat., Sci.Cit.Ind., Trop.Dis.Bull.
—BLDSC (4542.319000); CASDDS; Faxon; Genuine Article; SWETS; UMI; UnCover.
Formerly: International Journal of Leprosy (ISSN 0020-7349)

616.9   UK   ISSN 0956-4624
RC201.A1   CODEN: INSAE3
INTERNATIONAL JOURNAL OF S T D & AIDS. 1990. bi-m. £72($128) to individuals; institutions £98($172). Royal Society of Medicine Press Ltd., 1 Wimpole St., London W1M 8AE, England. TEL 0171-290-2900. FAX 0171-290-2929. Ed. W.W. Dinsmore. adv.; bk.rev.; illus.; index. circ. 900. **Indexed:** Psychol.Abstr. (1993-). **Document type:** academic/scholarly publication.
—BLDSC (4542.681350); ADONIS; Faxon; Genuine Article; SWETS; UnCover. **CCC.**
Description: Clinically oriented forum for papers on both the traditional sexually transmissible diseases (STD) and AIDS.
Refereed Serial

616.97 615.5   UK   ISSN 1357-2873
▼**INTERNATIONAL UPDATE.** 1995. a. £9.95 (outside Europe £14.95). N A M Publications, 52 Eurolink Centre, 49 Effra Rd., London SW2 1BZ, England. TEL 0171-737-1846. FAX 0171-737-6190. E-mail: info@nam.org.uk. Ed. Brian Cooper. **Document type:** bulletin.
Description: Information on HIV and AIDS organizations throughout the world.

616.9   JA   ISSN 0387-5911
                        CODEN: KSSZAT
JAPANESE ASSOCIATION FOR INFECTIOUS DISEASES. JOURNAL/KANSENSHOGAKU ZASSHI. (Text in Japanese; summaries in English) 1911. m. membership. Japanese Association for Infectious Diseases - Nihon Kansensho Gakkai, Sankei Bldg., 6F, 1-8-7 Ebisu, Shibuya-ku, Tokyo 150, Japan. adv.; charts; illus. **Indexed:** Biol.Abstr., Chem.Abstr., Dent.Ind., Excerp.Med., Ind.Med., INIS Atomind., Rev.Med.& Vet.Mycol.
—BLDSC (4808.800000); CASDDS.
Formerly (until 1970): Nippon Densembyo Gakkai Zasshi (ISSN 0021-4817)

616.01   JA   ISSN 0021-4930
                        CODEN: NSKZAM
JAPANESE JOURNAL OF BACTERIOLOGY/NIHON SAIKINGAKU ZASSHI. (Text in English) 1944. q. 18540 Yen. (Japanese Society for Bacteriology - Nihon Saikin Gakkai) Business Center for Academic Societies Japan, 5-16-9 Honkomagome, Bunkyo-ku, Tokyo 113, Japan. TEL 03-5814-5811. FAX 03-5814-5822. TELEX 2722268 BCJSP J. adv.; bk.rev.; bibl.; charts. circ. 3,700. **Indexed:** Abstr.Hyg., Biol.Abstr., Chem.Abstr., Dairy Sci.Abstr., Excerp.Med., Food Sci.& Tech.Abstr., Hort.Abstr., Ind.Med., INIS Atomind., Jap.per.Ind., Rev.Med.& Vet.Mycol., Rev.Plant Path., Trop.Dis.Bull. **Document type:** academic/scholarly publication.
—BLDSC (4651.000000); CASDDS.

MEDICAL SCIENCES — COMMUNICABLE DISEASES

616.998   JA   ISSN 0386-3980
CODEN: NRGZDW
JAPANESE JOURNAL OF LEPROSY. (Text mainly in Japanese; summaries in English) 1930. q. 5000 Yen($15) Japanese Leprosy Association - Nihon Rai Gakukai, 2-1, Aobacho 4-chome, Higashimurayama-shi, Tokyo 189, Japan. Ed. Dr. Masahide Abe. adv.; bk.rev.; charts; illus.; index. circ. 700. **Indexed:** Abstr.Hyg., Chem.Abstr., Excerp.Med., Ind.Med., Trop.Dis.Bull.
—BLDSC (4655.870000); CASDDS.
Formerly (until vol.46, no.1): Leppro (ISSN 0024-1008)

616.96   JA   ISSN 0021-5171
CODEN: KISZAR
JAPANESE JOURNAL OF PARASITOLOGY/KISEICHUGAKU ZASSHI. (Text in English or Japanese; summaries in English) 1951. bi-m. $133. Japanese Society of Parasitology, c/o Dept. of Medical Zoology, Tokyo Medical and Dental University, 1-5-45 Yushima, Bunkyo-ku, Tokyo 113, Japan. TEL 81-3-3813-6111. FAX 81-3-5684-2849. E-mail: ocha.mzoo@med.tmd.ac.jp. (Dist. by: Business Center for Academic Societies Japan, 5-16-9 Honkomagome, Bunkyo-ku, Tokyo 113, Japan. TEL 03-5814-5811. FAX 03-5814-5822) Ed. Koichiro Fujita. adv.; charts; illus. circ. 1,250. (also avail. in microform from UMI; reprint service avail. from UMI) **Indexed:** Abstr.Hyg., Biotech.Abstr., Chem.Abstr., Excerp.Med., Helminthol.Abstr., Ind.Med., Ind.Vet., INIS Atomind., Pig News & Info., Poult.Abstr., Trop.Dis.Bull., Vet.Bull. **Document type:** academic/scholarly publication.
—BLDSC (4656.900000); CASDDS; UMI; UnCover.

616.988   JA   ISSN 0304-2146
JAPANESE JOURNAL OF TROPICAL MEDICINE AND HYGIENE. (Text in English) 1959. q. 7000 Yen. Japanese Society of Tropical Medicine - Nihon Nettai Igakkai, c/o Institute of Tropical Medicine, Nagasaki University, 12-4, Sakamoto-machi, Nagasaki 852, Japan. Ed. Hideyo Itakura. abstr. circ. 700. (reprint service avail.) **Indexed:** Abstr.Hyg., Diar.Dis.Res.
—BLDSC (4658.970000).
Formerly (until 1973): Japanese Journal of Tropical Medicine.

616.9792   US   ISSN 1077-9450
RC607.A26   CODEN: JDSRET
JOURNAL OF ACQUIRED IMMUNE DEFICIENCY SYNDROMES AND HUMAN RETROVIROLOGY. 1988. 15/yr. $178 to individuals (foreign $178); institutions $455 (foreign $490) (effective 1996); newsstand price: $34. (International Retrovirology Association) Lippincott - Raven Publishers, 227 E. Washington Sq., Philadelphia, PA 19106. TEL 215-238-4200. Ed.Bd. adv. contact: Phyllis Noyes. bibl. circ. 3,000. (reprint service avail. from UMI) **Indexed:** ASCA, Biol.Abstr., CINAHL, Curr.Cont., Excerp.Med., Ind.Med., Med.& Surg.Dermat., Sci.Cit.Ind. **Document type:** academic/scholarly publication.
—BLDSC (4918.933100); CASDDS; Faxon; Genuine Article; SWETS; UMI; UnCover. **CCC.**
Formerly (until vol.8, 1995): Journal of Acquired Immune Deficiency Syndromes (ISSN 0894-9255)
Description: Provides results of clinical trials, case reports, reviews of current research, discussions of national policy issues and a literature citation index.
Refereed Serial

616.9   UK   ISSN 0305-7453
CODEN: JACHDX
JOURNAL OF ANTIMICROBIAL CHEMOTHERAPY. 1975. 12/yr. (2 vols./yr.) £190 in Europe (rest of world $353) to individuals; institutions £262 in Europe (rest of world $472). (British Society for Antimicrobial Chemotherapy) W.B. Saunders Ltd. (Subsidiary of: Harcourt Brace & Company Ltd.), 24-28 Oval Rd., London NW1 7DX, England. TEL 0171-267-4466. FAX 0171-482-2293. TELEX 25775-ACPRES-G. (Subscr. to: Harcourt Brace & Company Ltd., Journals Subscriptions, Foots Cray High St., Sidcup, Kent DA14 5HP, England. TEL 0181-300-3322. FAX 0181-309-0807; US, Canadian, and Mexican subscr. to: W.B. Saunders Co., Journals Subscription Fulfillment, 6277 Sea Harbor Dr., Orlando, FL 32887-4800. TEL 800-654-2452. FAX 800-874-6418) Ed. R.G. Finch. adv.; illus.; charts; index. **Indexed:** Abstr.Hyg., Biol.Abstr., Biotech.Abstr., Chem.Abstr., Curr.Cont., Dairy Sci.Abstr., Dent.Ind., Diar.Dis.Res., Excerp.Med., Helminthol.Abstr., I.P.A., Ind.Med., Ind.Sci.Rev., Ind.Vet., INIS Atomind., Med.& Surg.Dermat., Protozool.Abstr., Rev.Med.& Vet.Mycol., Rev.Plant Path., Sci.Cit.Ind., Trop.Dis.Bull., Vet.Bull. **Document type:** academic/scholarly publication.
—BLDSC (4939.100000); ADONIS; CASDDS; Faxon; Genuine Article; SWETS; UnCover. **CCC.**
Description: Presents original articles about laboratory and clinical aspects of the use of antimicrobials, including antibacterial, antiviral, antifungal, antihelminthic, and antiprotozoal agents; also includes reviews, articles, Working Party reports, and corresondence on related subjects.

610   II   ISSN 0019-5138
CODEN: JCDSBF
JOURNAL OF COMMUNICABLE DISEASES. (Text in English) 1969. q. Rs.40($10) Indian Society for Malaria and Other Communicable Diseases, 22 Alipur Rd., Delhi 110006, India. **Indexed:** Abstr.Hyg., Biol.Abstr., Diar.Dis.Res., Excerp.Med., Helminthol.Abstr., IDA, Ind.Med., Ind.Vet., Protozool.Abstr., Rev.Appl.Entomol., Trop.Dis.Bull., Vet.Bull.
—BLDSC (4961.450000); Faxon; SWETS; UnCover.

616.96   UK   ISSN 0022-149X
CODEN: JOHLAT
JOURNAL OF HELMINTHOLOGY. 1923. q. £125($255) (effective 1996). (International Institute of Parasitology) CAB International, Wallingford, Oxon OX10 8DE, England. TEL 44-1491-832111. FAX 44-1491-826090. E-mail: cabi@cabi.org. (U.S. subscr. to: CAB International, 845 N. Park Ave., Tucson, AZ 85719. TEL 800-528-4841. FAX 520-621-3816) Ed. R. Muller. adv. contact: Claire Gilman. bk.rev.; charts; illus. circ. 485. (back issues avail.) **Indexed:** Abstr.Hyg., Biol.Abstr., Biotech.Abstr., Chem.Abstr., Curr.Adv.Ecol.Sci., Curr.Cont., Curr.Ref.Fish Res., Ecol.Abstr., Excerp.Med., Helminthol.Abstr., IDA, Ind.Med., Ind.Sci.Rev., Ind.Vet., INIS Atomind., Nutr.Abstr., Pig News & Info., Poult.Abstr., Protozool.Abstr., Rev.Appl.Entomol., Sci.Cit.Ind., Small Anim.Abstr., Sport Fish.Abstr., Trop.Dis.Bull., Vet.Bull., Wild.Rev., Zoo.Rec. **Document type:** academic/scholarly publication.
—BLDSC (4997.000000); CASDDS; EMDOCS; Faxon; Genuine Article; SWETS; UnCover.
Refereed Serial

616.9   UK   ISSN 0195-6701
CODEN: JHINDS
JOURNAL OF HOSPITAL INFECTION. 1980. 12/yr. (3 vols./yr.) £147 in Europe (rest of world $271) to individuals; institutions £199 in Europe (rest of world $358). (Hospital Infection Society) W.B. Saunders Ltd. (Subsidiary of: Harcourt Brace & Company Ltd.), 24-28 Oval Rd., London NW1 7DX, England. TEL 0171-267-4466. FAX 0171-482-2293. TELEX 25775-ACPRES-G. (Subscr. to: Harcourt Brace & Company Ltd., Foots Cray High St., Sidcup, Kent DA14 5HP, England. TEL 0181-300-3322. FAX 0181-309-0807; US, Canadian, and Mexican subscr. to: W.B. /Saunders Co., Journal Fulfillment, 6277 Sea Harbor Dr., 4th Fl., Orlando, FL 32887-4800. TEL 800-654-2452. FAX 800-874-6418) Ed. T.R. Rogers. adv.; bk.rev.; illus. **Indexed:** Abstr.Health Care Manage.Stud., Abstr.Hyg., ASCA, CINAHL, Curr.Adv.Ecol.Sci., Dent.Ind., Dok.Arbeitsmed., Excerp.Med., Ind.Med., Ind.Sci.Rev., Sci.Cit.Ind., Trop.Dis.Bull. **Document type:** academic/scholarly publication.
—BLDSC (5003.285000); Faxon; Genuine Article; SWETS; UnCover. **CCC.**
Description: Provides a forum for original observations of international significance in all aspects of hospital infection.

616.9   UK   ISSN 0163-4453
CODEN: JINFD2
JOURNAL OF INFECTION. 1979. bi-m. (2 vols./yr.) £58 to individuals (outside Europe $106); institutions £144 (outside Europe $266). (British Society for the Study of Infection) W.B. Saunders Ltd. (Subsidiary of: Harcourt Brace & Company Ltd.), 24-28 Oval Rd., London, NW1 7DX, England. TEL 0171-267-4466. FAX 0171-482-2293. TELEX 25775-ACPRES-G. (Subscr. to: Harcourt Brace & Company Ltd., Foots Cray High St., Sidcup, Kent DA14 5HP, England. TEL 0181-300-3322. FAX 0181-309-0807; US, Canadian, and Mexican subscr. to: W.B. Saunders Co., Journal Subscription Fulfillment, 6277 Sea Harbor Dr., 4th Fl., Orlando, FL 32887-4800. TEL 800-654-2452. FAX 800-874-6418) Ed. B.K. Mandal. adv.; bk.rev.; illus.; index. **Indexed:** Abstr.Hyg., Biotech.Abstr., Chem.Abstr., Curr.Adv.Cancer Res., Curr.Adv.Ecol.Sci., Curr.Cont., Dairy Sci.Abstr., Dent.Ind., Dok.Arbeitsmed., Excerp.Med., Helminthol.Abstr., I.P.A., Ind.Med., Ind.Sci.Rev., Ind.Vet., Med.& Surg.Dermat., Protozool.Abstr., Rev.Med.& Vet.Mycol., Sci.Cit.Ind., Trop.Dis.Bull., Vet.Bull. **Document type:** academic/scholarly publication.
●Also available online.
—BLDSC (5006.690000); CASDDS; Faxon; Genuine Article; SWETS; UnCover. **CCC.**
Description: Publishes papers that reflect the diverse nature of infection and seeks to brings together the views of clinicians, microbiologists, epidemiologists, molecular biologists, and other researchers in the field.

616.9   US   ISSN 0022-1899
CODEN: JIDIAQ
JOURNAL OF INFECTIOUS DISEASES. 1904. m. (2 vols./yr.) $89 to individuals; institutions $205. (Infectious Diseases Society of America) University of Chicago Press, Journals Division, 5720 S. Woodlawn Ave., Chicago, IL 60637. TEL 312-753-3347. FAX 312-753-0811. TELEX 25-4603. (Subscr. to: Box 37005, Chicago, IL 60637) Ed. Marvin Turck. adv.; bibl.; charts; illus.; index. circ. 9,900. (also avail. in microform from UMI,PMC; reprint service avail. from UMI,ISI) **Indexed:** Abstr.Health Care Manage.Stud., Abstr.Hyg., AIM, Biol.Abstr., Biol.Dig., Biotech.Abstr., Chem.Abstr., CINAHL, Curr.Adv.Ecol.Sci., Curr.Adv.Genetics & Molec.Biol., Curr.Cont., Dairy Sci.Abstr., Dent.Ind., Diar.Dis.Res., Dok.Arbeitsmed., Excerp.Med., Helminthol.Abstr., I.P.A., Ind.Med., Ind.Sci.Rev., Ind.Vet., INIS Atomind., Int.Abstr.Biol.Sci., Med.& Surg.Dermat., Nutr.Abstr., Protozool.Abstr., Rev.Med.& Vet.Mycol., Risk Abstr., Sci.Cit.Ind., Small Anim.Abstr., Sport Fish.Abstr., Trop.Dis.Bull., Vet.Bull., W.R.C.Inf., Wild.Rev., Zoo.Rec. **Document type:** academic/scholarly publication.
●Also available online. Vendor(s): Ovid Technologies (JWAT).
—BLDSC (5006.700000); CASDDS; EMDOCS; Faxon; Genuine Article; SWETS; UMI; UnCover. **CCC.**
Refereed Serial

MEDICAL SCIENCES — COMMUNICABLE DISEASES

616.969   UK   ISSN 0268-1218
RC117   CODEN: JMVMEO
JOURNAL OF MEDICAL & VETERINARY MYCOLOGY. (Supplement avail. (ISSN 0966-8454)) 1963. bi-m. £306 (outside Europe £338($544)) (effective 1996). (International Society for Human and Animal Mycology) Blackwell Science Ltd., Osney Mead, Oxford OX2 0EL, England. TEL 01865-240201. FAX 01865-721205. TELEX 83355 MEDBOK G. Ed. E.G.V. Evans. bk.rev.; abstr.; bibl.; charts; illus.; index. circ. 1,150. (also avail. in microform from UMI; back issues avail.) **Indexed:** Abstr.Hyg., Biol.Abstr., Curr.Adv.Ecol.Sci., Curr.Cont., Dairy Sci.Abstr., Dent.Ind., Excerp.Med., Ind.Med., Ind.Vet., Rev.Med.& Vet.Mycol., Rev.Plant Path., Small Anim.Abstr., So.Pac.Per.Ind., Soils & Fert., Sport Fish.Abstr., Vet.Bull., Wild.Rev., Zoo.Rec. **Document type:** academic/scholarly publication.
—BLDSC (5017.048200); ADONIS; CASDDS; Faxon; Genuine Article; SWETS; UMI; UnCover. **CCC.**
    Formerly (until 1986): Sabouraudia: Journal of Medical and Veterinary Mycology (ISSN 0036-2174)
    Refereed Serial

616.969   UK   ISSN 0966-8454
CODEN: JMVSE
JOURNAL OF MEDICAL AND VETERINARY MYCOLOGY. SUPPLEMENT. irreg. price varies. (International Society for Human and Animal Mycology) Blackwell Science Ltd., Osney Mead, Oxford OX2 0EL, England. TEL 01865-240201. FAX 01865-721205. TELEX 83355 MEDBOK G. (back issues avail.) **Indexed:** Excerp.Med. (1994-). **Document type:** academic/scholarly publication.
—ADONIS.
    Refereed Serial

616.968   US   ISSN 0022-2585
RA639.5   CODEN: JMENA6
JOURNAL OF MEDICAL ENTOMOLOGY. 1964. bi-m. $75 to individuals (foreign $95); institutions $150 (foreign $170); members $25 (foreign $40). Entomological Society of America, 9301 Annapolis Rd., Lanham, MD 20706. TEL 301-731-4535. FAX 301-731-4538. (Subscr. to: Box 177, Hyattsville, MD 20781-0177) Eds. C. Dayton Steelman, William K. Reisen. bk.rev.; bibl.; charts; illus.; maps; index. circ. 1,600. (also avail. in microform from UMI; back issues avail.; reprint service avail. from UMI) **Indexed:** Abstr.Hyg., Bio-Contr.News & Info., Biol.Abstr., Biol.Dig., Biotech.Abstr., Chem.Abstr., Curr.Adv.Ecol.Sci., Curr.Cont., Dent.Ind., Entomol.Abstr., Environ.Per.Bibl., Excerp.Med., Helminthol.Abstr., Ind.Med., Ind.Sci.Rev., Ind.Vet., INIS Atomind., Poult.Abstr., Protozool.Abstr., Rev.Appl.Entomol., Sci.Cit.Ind., Small Anim.Abstr., So.Pac.Per.Ind., Sport Fish.Abstr., Trop.Dis.Bull., Vet.Bull., Wild.Rev., Zoo.Rec. **Document type:** academic/scholarly publication.
—BLDSC (5017.060000); CASDDS; Faxon; Genuine Article; SWETS; UMI; UnCover. **CCC.**
    Description: Covers all phases of medical entomology.
    Refereed Serial

606.9   UK   ISSN 0969-1413
▼**JOURNAL OF MEDICAL SCREENING.** 1994. q. £92($145) B M J Publishing Group, B.M.A. House, Tavistock Sq., London WC1H 9JR, England. TEL 0171-383-6270. FAX 0171-383-6402. (N. American subscr. to: Box 480, Franklin, MA 02038. TEL 800-2-FON-BMJ. FAX 800-2-FAX-BMJ) Ed. N. Wald. adv. contact: Sheila Rowe. bk.rev.; abstr.; charts; illus.; index. **Document type:** academic/scholarly publication.
—BLDSC (5017.087250).
    Description: Covers all aspects of medical screening. Aims to bring together specialist groups conducting screening research and to establish a liaison with health authorities and policymakers.
    Refereed Serial

JOURNAL OF NEURO-AIDS. see *MEDICAL SCIENCES — Psychiatry And Neurology*

616.96 574.524   US   ISSN 0022-3395
QL757   CODEN: JOPAA2
JOURNAL OF PARASITOLOGY. 1914. bi-m. $125 (foreign $130). American Society of Parasitologists, Dept. of Biology, Wake Forest Univ., P.O. Box 7629, Winston-Salem, NC 27109. TEL 919-759-5323. FAX 919-759-6008. Ed. Gerald Esch. adv.; bk.rev.; bibl.; illus.; index, cum.index. circ. 2,800. (also avail. in microform from UMI,PMC; reprint service avail. from UMI) **Indexed:** Abstr.Hyg., Bio-Contr.News & Info., Biol.Abstr., Biol.& Agr.Ind., Biotech.Abstr., Chem.Abstr., Curr.Adv.Ecol.Sci., Curr.Cont., Curr.Ref.Fish Res., Diar.Dis.Res., Ecol.Abstr., Excerp.Med., Helminthol.Abstr., Ind.Med., Ind.Sci.Rev., Ind.Vet., INIS Atomind., Nutr.Abstr., Pig News & Info., Poult.Abstr., Protozool.Abstr., Rev.Appl.Entomol., Small Anim.Abstr., Soils & Fert., Sport Fish.Abstr., SSCI, Trop.Dis.Bull., W.R.C.Inf., Wild.Rev., Zoo.Rec. **Document type:** academic/scholarly publication.
—BLDSC (5029.000000); CASDDS; EMDOCS; Faxon; SWETS; UnCover.
    Description: Results of research, primarily on animal parasitology.

JOURNAL OF PHARMACEUTICAL CARE IN INFECTIOUS DISEASE MANAGEMENT. see *PHARMACY AND PHARMACOLOGY*

616.988   UA   ISSN 1110-0796
JOURNAL OF TROPICAL MEDICINE. Abbreviated title: J T M. (Text in English) vol.1, no.3, 1991. irreg. Royal Society of Tropical Medicine & Hygiene, Egyptian Branch, Tager Bldg., 1 Ozoris St., Garden City, Cairo, Egypt. TEL 3541857. Ed. S.M. Kabil. **Document type:** academic/scholarly publication.
—BLDSC (5070.900000).
    Refereed Serial

616.96 574.524   JA   ISSN 0915-5007
KISEICHU BUNRUI KEITAI DANWAKAI KAIHO/JAPANESE SOCIETY FOR SYSTEMATIC PARASITOLOGY. CIRCULAR. (Text in Japanese) 1983. a. Kiseichu Bunrui Keitai Danwakai - Japanese Society for Systematic Parasitology, c/o Mr. Masaaki Machida, Kokuritsu Kagaku Hakubutsukan, Dobutsu Kenkyubu, 23-1 Hyakunincho, Shinjuku-ku, Tokyo 169, Japan.

614 616.998   JA   ISSN 0454-2029
KOKURITSU TAMA KENKYUJO NENPO/NATIONAL INSTITUTE FOR LEPROSY RESEARCH ANNUAL REPORT. (Text in Japanese) 1955. a. free. Kokuritsu Tama Kenkyujo - National Institute for Leprosy Research, 2-1 Aoba-cho 4-chome, Higashi-murayama-shi, Tokyo 189, Japan. TEL 0423-91-8211. FAX 0423-94-9092. adv. contact: Hajime Saito. **Document type:** academic/scholarly publication.

616.96   KO   ISSN 0023-4001
QL757   CODEN: KSCHAV
KOREAN JOURNAL OF PARASITOLOGY. (Text in English, Korean) 1963. q. 20000 Won($30) (effective 1996). Korean Society for Parasitology, c/o Dept. of Parasitology, College of Medicine, Seoul National University, Seoul 110 799, S. Korea. TEL 82-2-740-8348. FAX 82-2-765-6142. Ed. Soon-Hyung Lee. abstr.; charts; illus. circ. 1,000. (back issues avail.) **Indexed:** Abstr.Hyg., Biol.Abstr., Diar.Dis.Res., Excerp.Med., Helminthol.Abstr., Ind.Vet., Protozool.Abstr., Rev.Appl.Entomol., Rev.Med.& Vet.Mycol., Trop.Dis.Bull., Vet.Bull. **Document type:** academic/scholarly publication.
—BLDSC (5113.570000).
    Description: Contains original papers of research articles, case records, and brief communications on parasites of humans or animals, and host-parasite relations.

616.9   JA   ISSN 0910-6073
CODEN: KKZAE5
KOSANKINBYO KENKYUSHO ZASSHI. (Text in Japanese) 1949. q. exchange basis. Tohoku Daigaku, Kosankinbyo Kenkyusho Kenyukai - Tohoku University, Research Institute for Tuberculosis, Leprosy, and Cancer, Seiryo-machi, Aoba-ku, Sendai 980, Japan. **Indexed:** Excerp.Med. (1992-). **Document type:** academic/scholarly publication.
    Formerly (until 1984): Kosankinbyo Kenkyu Zasshi - Journal of Tuberculosis and Leprosy (ISSN 0368-6078)

616.998   II
KUSHT VINASHAK. (Text in English, Hindi) m. Rs.30 (foreign $8) (effective 1993). Indian Leprosy Association, Hind Kusht Nivaran Sangh, 1, Red Cross Rd., New Delhi 110 001, India. TEL 3714748.

616.9   UK   ISSN 0305-7518
CODEN: LEREAA
LEPROSY REVIEW. 1927. q. £30($56) British Leprosy Relief Association, Fairfax House, Causton Rd., Colchester, Essex CO1 1PU, England. TEL 01206-562286. FAX 01206-762151. Ed. J.L. Turk. adv.; bk.rev. circ. 1,800. (also avail. in microform from SWZ) **Indexed:** Abstr.Hyg., Biol.Abstr., Chem.Abstr., Curr.Adv.Ecol.Sci., Curr.Cont., Ind.Med., Ind.Sci.Rev., Med.& Surg.Dermat., Rev.Med.& Vet.Mycol., Trop.Dis.Bull. **Document type:** academic/scholarly publication.
—BLDSC (5183.300000); CASDDS; Genuine Article; SWETS; UnCover. **CCC.**

614.49 616.96   FR   ISSN 0399-077X
MEDECINE ET MALADIES INFECTIEUSES; revue francaise d'epidemiologie, de pathologie infectieuse et parasitaire. (Supplement avail. (ISSN 1166-8237)) (Text in French; summaries in English and French) 1971. m. 630 F. (foreign 750 F.). Societe Francaise d'Editions Medicales, 22-24 rue du Chateau des Rentiers, 75013 Paris, France. TEL 45-83-50-54. FAX 45-83-13-54. Ed. Colette Gallula. bk.rev.; bibl.; charts; illus.; index. circ. 5,000. (back issues avail.) **Indexed:** Bull.Signal., Curr.Adv.Cancer Res., Curr.Cont., Excerp.Med., Forest.Abstr., Forest Prod.Abstr., Helminthol.Abstr., Ind.Vet., Pig News & Info., Protozool.Abstr., Rev.Med.& Vet.Mycol., Vet.Bull.
—BLDSC (5487.732000); Genuine Article; SWETS; UMI.

616.988   FR   ISSN 0025-682X
CODEN: METRA2
MEDECINE TROPICALE. (Summaries in English, French) 1941. q. 160 F. (foreign 180 F.). Institut de Medecine Tropicale, Parc du Pharo, 13007 Marseille, France. TEL 91-52-35-68. FAX 91-59-44-77. Ed. B. Maistre. adv.; bk.rev.; bibl.; charts; illus.; stat.; index. circ. 1,500. **Indexed:** Abstr.Hyg., Biol.Abstr., Chem.Abstr., Excerp.Med., Helminthol.Abstr., Ind.Med., Nutr.Abstr., Protozool.Abstr., Rev.Appl.Entomol., Rev.Med.& Vet.Mycol., Rev.Plant Path., Trop.Dis.Bull.
—BLDSC (5488.000000); CASDDS; EMDOCS; Faxon; SWETS.

616   US   ISSN 1043-1837
CODEN: MEVIEN
MEDICAL VIROLOGY. Represents: International Symposium on Medical Virology. Proceedings. 1982. a., vol.10, 1991. price varies. Plenum Publishing Corp., 233 Spring St., New York, NY 10013-1578. TEL 212-620-8000. FAX 212-463-0742. TELEX 23-421139. **Document type:** proceedings.
—CASDDS.

616.9   IT
MEDITERRANEAN JOURNAL OF INFECTIOUS AND PARASITIC DISEASES. (Text in English) 1986. q. L.70000($70) (effective 1991). (Mediterranean Society of Infectious and Parasitic Diseases) C I C Edizioni Internazionali s.r.l., Via L Spallanzani, 11, 00161 Rome, Italy. TEL 06-8412673. FAX 06-8845590. Ed. F. De Rosa. adv. (back issues avail.) **Indexed:** Excerp.Med. (1992-).
—BLDSC (5534.735000).
    Formerly (until 1991): Therapy of Infectious Diseases (ISSN 0394-025X)
    Description: Publishes original research papers and case reports, and proceedings of congresses.

616.96   AG   ISSN 0524-952X
MUSEO ARGENTINO DE CIENCIAS NATURALES "BERNARDINO RIVADAVIA." INSTITUTO NACIONAL DE INVESTIGACION DE LAS CIENCIAS NATURALES. REVISTA. PARASITOLOGIA. 1968. irreg., vol.2, no.5, 1980. Museo Argentino de Ciencias Naturales "Bernardino Rivadavia", Instituto Nacional de Investigacion de las Ciencias Naturales, Avda. Angel Gallardo 470, Casilla de Correo 220-Sucursal 5, Buenos Aires, Argentina.

MEDICAL SCIENCES — COMMUNICABLE DISEASES

616.9   NO   ISSN 0332-5652
CODEN: NIAND5
N I P H ANNALS. (Text in English) 1978. s-a.
NOK 100($20) National Institute for Public Health, Geitmyrsveien 75, N-0462 Oslo 4, Norway.
FAX 47-22-35-36-05. TELEX 72400 FOTEX N. Ed. Stian Erichsen. circ. 800. (back issues avail.)
Indexed: Abstr.Hyg., Biol.Abstr., Chem.Abstr., Excerp.Med., Ind.Med., Trop.Dis.Bull.
—BLDSC (6113.247000); CASDDS; Faxon.
Description: Covers public health and medical research in Norway.

616.9   US
NATIONAL COUNCIL OF LA RAZA. AIDS NEWSLETTER.* q. free. National Council of La Raza, 1111 19th St., N.W., Washington, DC 20036-3603.
TEL 202-289-1380. FAX 202-289-8173. Ed. Miguel Serrez. **Document type:** newsletter.
Description: Covers medical and legislative news of AIDS with a focus on the Hispanic community. Also disseminates news of the NCLR AIDS Center's activities.

NIHON SANFUJINKA KANSENSHO KENKYUKAI GAKUJUTSU KOENKAI KIROKUSHI/CONFERENCE ON OBSTETRICAL AND GYNECOLOGICAL INFECTION. PROCEEDINGS. see *MEDICAL SCIENCES — Obstetrics And Gynecology*

616.9 576   UK   ISSN 0141-9692
P H L S DIRECTORY. 1980. a. £5.95. Public Health Laboratory Service, 61 Colindale Ave., London NW9 5HT, England. TEL 0181-200-1295.
FAX 0181-200-7868. circ. 10,000. **Document type:** directory.

616.9 576   UK   ISSN 0968-1280
P H L S FOOD AND ENVIRONMENT BULLETIN. 1991. m. £40 (Europe £49; elsewhere £67). Public Health Laboratory Service, 61 Colindale Ave., London NW9 5HT, England. TEL 0181-200-4400.
FAX 0181-200-7875. Ed. Margaret Clennett.
Document type: bibliography.
Formerly: P H L S Food and Environmental Microbiology Bulletin.

616.9   UK   ISSN 0958-1316
P H L S HIV BULLETIN. 1989. m. £40 (Europe £49; elsewhere £67). Public Health Laboratory Service, 61 Colindale Ave., London NW9 5HT, England. TEL 0181-200-4400. FAX 0181-200-7875. Ed. Margaret Clennett. circ. 500. **Document type:** bibliography.
Description: Microbiological and epidemiological aspects of AIDS and HIV.

616.3 576 628   UK   ISSN 0267-6850
P H L S LIBRARY BULLETIN. 1948. w. £53 (Europe £93; elsewhere £132). Public Health Laboratory Service, 61 Colindale Ave., London NW9 5HT, England. TEL 0181-200-4400.
FAX 0181-200-7875. Ed. Margaret Clennett. circ. 1,000. **Document type:** bibliography.
Description: Compiled specifically with the public health and medical laboratory microbiologist in mind. Lists authors and titles of 350 relevant papers published in over 300 of the world's journals.

616.9 576 628   UK   ISSN 0265-3400
P H L S MICROBIOLOGY DIGEST. 1983. q. £25 (Europe £25; elsewhere £30). Public Health Laboratory Service, 61 Colindale Ave., London NW9 5HT, England. TEL 0181-200-1295.
FAX 0181-200-8130. Ed. C. Murphy. adv.; B&W page £350. bk.rev. circ. 1,500. **Indexed:** Ind.Vet., Small Anim.Abstr., Vet.Bull. **Document type:** academic/scholarly publication.
—BLDSC (6465.101700).
Description: Written by specialists for both specialists and non-specialists. Focuses on communicable diseases.

P P O UPDATE. (Principles and Practices of Oncology) see *MEDICAL SCIENCES — Oncology*

616.9   US   ISSN 1069-3637
P W A COALITION NEWSLINE.* (People with AIDS) 1985. m. $35 (free to persons with AIDS or ARC). P W A Coalition Inc., 245 Eighth Ave., No. 316, New York, NY 10016-1607. TEL 212-532-0290.
FAX 212-696-9127. Ed. Bree Scott-Hartland. circ. 15,000. **Document type:** newsletter.
Description: Reports new developments dealing with the health crisis as well as alternative treatments, and personal perspectives of people with AIDS and HIV infection.

616.9   US
P W ALIVE.* q. free. Sabathani Community Center, Box 80216, Minneapolis, MN 55408-8216.
TEL 612-823-8205. Ed. Jim Maurer.
Description: A journal by, for, and about persons affected by AIDS.

616.9   NL   ISSN 1018-2152
PACIFIC AIDS ALERT BULLETIN. French edition: Alerte au SIDA Oceanie (ISSN 1023-1730) (Text in English) 1991. q. South Pacific Commission - Commission de Pacifique Sud, B.P. D5, Noumea, Cedex, New Caledonia. TEL 687-262000.
FAX 687-263818. TELEX 3139 NM SOPACOM. **Document type:** newsletter.

616.9 574   UK   ISSN 0141-9838
CODEN: PAIMD8
PARASITE IMMUNOLOGY. 1979. m. £363 in Europe; elsewhere £399($638) (effective 1996). Blackwell Science Ltd., Osney Mead, Oxford OX2 0EL, England. TEL 01865-206206.
FAX 01865-206219. TELEX 83355 MEDBOK G. Eds. G.A.T. Targett, D. Wakelin. adv.; bibl.; charts; illus.; index. circ. 550. (also avail. in microform from UMI; back issues avail.; reprint service avail. from ISI) **Indexed:** Abstr.Hyg., ASCA, Biol.Abstr., Curr.Adv.Ecol.Sci., Curr.Adv.Genetics & Molec.Biol., Curr.Cont., Diar.Dis.Res., Excerp.Med., Helminthol.Abstr., Ind.Med., Ind.Vet., Protozool.Abstr., Sci.Cit.Ind., Trop.Dis.Bull., Vet.Bull. **Document type:** academic/scholarly publication.
—BLDSC (6404.940000); ADONIS; CASDDS; Faxon; Genuine Article; SWETS; UMI; UnCover. **CCC.**
Refereed Serial

574.5   UK   ISSN 0031-1820
CODEN: PARAAE
PARASITOLOGY (CAMBRIDGE). (Two supplements avail.) 1908. 10/yr. £292($540) (effective 1996). Cambridge University Press, Edinburgh Bldg., Shaftesbury Rd., Cambridge CB2 2RU, England. TEL 01223-312393. FAX 01223-315052. TELEX 851817256. (N. American addr.: Cambridge University Press, Journals Dept., 40 W. 20th St., New York, NY 10011. TEL 212-924-3900. FAX 212-691-3239) Eds. F.E.G. Cox, C. Arme. adv.; bk.rev.; index. (also avail. in microfiche from IDC,BHP; microfilm from UMI; back issues avail.)
Indexed: Abstr.Hyg., Anim.Breed.Abstr., Biol.Abstr., Biotech.Abstr., Chem.Abstr., Curr.Adv.Ecol.Sci., Curr.Cont., Dairy Sci.Abstr., Ecol.Abstr., Excerp.Med., Geo.Abstr., Helminthol.Abstr., IDA, Ind.Med., Ind.Vet., Int.Abstr.Biol.Sci, Nutr.Abstr., Potato Abstr., Rev.Appl.Entomol., Sport Fish.Abstr., Trop.Dis.Bull., Vet.Bull., Wild.Rev., Zoo.Rec. **Document type:** academic/scholarly publication.
—BLDSC (6406.000000); ADONIS; CASDDS; EMDOCS; Faxon; Genuine Article; SWETS; UMI; UnCover. **CCC.**
Description: Publishes papers on all aspects of pure and applied parasitology, including biochemical, immunological, physiological, and ecological topics, with emphasis on parasites and their control.

616.96 574.524   GW   ISSN 0932-0113
QL757   CODEN: PARREZ
PARASITOLOGY RESEARCH. (Text in English, French and German; summaries in English) 1928. 8/yr. DM.2298($1670) (effective 1996). (Deutschen Gesellschaft fuer Parasitologie) Springer-Verlag, Heidelberger Platz 3, 14197 Berlin, Germany.
TEL 030-8207-0. FAX 030-8214091. E-mail: orders@springer.de. (Subscr. in N. America to: Springer-Verlag New York, Inc., 44 Hartz Way, Secaucus, NJ 07096-2491. TEL 201-348-4033. FAX 201-348-4505) Eds. B. Chobotar, H. Mehlhorn. adv.; charts; illus. (also avail. in microform from UMI; back issues avail.; reprint service avail. from ISI) **Indexed:** Abstr.Hyg., Biol.Abstr., Biotech.Abstr., Chem.Abstr., Curr.Adv.Ecol.Sci., Curr.Cont., Excerp.Med., Helminthol.Abstr., Ind.Med., Ind.Vet., Poult.Abstr., Protozool.Abstr., Trop.Dis.Bull. **Document type:** academic/scholarly publication.
—BLDSC (6406.120000); ADONIS; CASDDS; EMDOCS; Faxon; Genuine Article; SWETS; UMI; UnCover. **CCC.**
Formerly: Zeitschrift fuer Parasitenkunde (ISSN 0044-3255).
Description: Presents information on the latest developments in parasitology research, with special emphasis on practical aspects such as immunodiagnosis, chemotherapy, and epidemiology. Includes review articles that provide an overview of current advances.

576.15 616.9   UK   ISSN 0169-4758
CODEN: PATOE2
PARASITOLOGY TODAY; international review journal in the field of medical and veterinary parasites. Library compendium: Parasitology Today (Reference Edition) (ISSN 0169-4707) 1985. m. £386 to institutions; $614 to institutions (effective 1996). Elsevier Science Ltd., P.O. Box 800, Kidlington, Oxford OX5 1DX, England. TEL 44-1865-843010.
FAX 44-1865-843010.
E-mail: nlinfo-f@elsevier.nl; usinfo-f@elsevier.com; forinfo-kyf04035@niftyserve.or.jp; Site addr.: http://www.elsevier.nl/. (Subscr. in U.S. and Canada to: Elsevier Science, 660 White Plains Rd., Tarrytown, NY 10591-5153. TEL 914-524-9200. FAX 914-333-2444) Ed. Theresa Saklatvala. adv.; bk.rev.; illus.; index. circ. 4,600. (back issues avail.)
Indexed: Anim.Breed.Abstr., Biol.Abstr., Curr.Adv.Ecol.Sci., Curr.Cont., Dairy Sci.Abstr., Diar.Dis.Res., Excerp.Med., Ind.Vet., Poult.Abstr., Protozool.Abstr., Sport Fish.Abstr., Trop.Dis.Bull., Vet.Bull., Wild.Rev., Zoo.Rec. **Document type:** academic/scholarly publication.
—BLDSC (6406.120300); ADONIS; CASDDS; Faxon; Genuine Article. **CCC.**
Description: Interdisciplinary forum for communications in all aspects of current field and laboratory research in parasitology from molecular biology to ecology.
Refereed Serial

576.15 616.9   UK   ISSN 0169-4707
PARASITOLOGY TODAY (REFERENCE EDITION). 1985. a. £345($514) includes m. Parasitology Today (effective 1994). Elsevier Science Ltd., P.O. Box 800, Kidlington, Oxford OX5 1DX, England.
TEL 44-1865-843000. FAX 44-1865-843010.
E-mail: nlinfo-f@elsevier.nl; usinfo-f@elsevier.com; forinfo-kyf04035@niftyserve.or.jp; Sute addr.: http://www.elsevier.nl/. (Subscr. in U.S. and Canada to: Elsevier Science, 660 White Plains Rd., Tarrytown, NY 10591-5153. TEL 914-524-9200. FAX 914-333-2444) Ed. Theresa Saklatvala. (back issues avail.) **Document type:** academic/scholarly publication.
—Faxon; SWETS; UnCover. **CCC.**
Description: Compendium of archival material from Parasitology Today.
Refereed Serial

616.96 574.524   IT   ISSN 0048-2951
QL757   CODEN: PSSGAR
PARASSITOLOGIA. (Text in English, French and Italian; summaries in English) 1959. 3/yr. L.150000 (effective 1994). (Societa Italiana di Parassitologia) Lombardo Editore, Via Verona, 22, 00161 Rome, Italy. TEL 39-6-44290974. FAX 39-6-44238543. Ed. M. Coluzzi. adv.; index. (also avail. in microform) **Indexed:** Abstr.Hyg., Biol.Abstr., Chem.Abstr., Excerp.Med., Helminthol.Abstr., Ind.Med., Ind.Vet., Protozool.Abstr., Rev.Appl.Entomol., Trop.Dis.Bull., Vet.Bull. **Document type:** academic/scholarly publication.
—BLDSC (6406.130000); CASDDS; Faxon; UnCover.

616.96 574.524   RU   ISSN 0031-1847
QL757   CODEN: PAZGA4
PARAZITOLOGIYA/PARASITOLOGY. 1966. bi-m. $96 (effective 1996). (Rossiiskaya Akademiya Nauk) Izdatel'stvo Nauka, 90 Profsoyuznaya ul., 117864 Moscow, Russia. index. (also avail. in microfiche from BHP) **Indexed:** Abstr.Hyg., Apic.Abstr., Bio-Contr.News & Info., Biol.Abstr., Chem.Abstr., Curr.Adv.Ecol.Sci., Curr.Cont., Excerp.Med., Helminthol.Abstr., Ind.Med., Ind.Vet., Protozool.Abstr., Rev.Appl.Entomol., Trop.Dis.Bull., Vet.Bull.
—BLDSC (0129.130000); CASDDS; Genuine Article. **CCC.**

616.998   UK   ISSN 0308-745X
PARTNERS; magazine for paramedical workers. (Text in Bengali, Chinese, English, French) 1976. s-a. free. Leprosy Mission International, 80 Windmill Rd., Brentford, Mddx. TW8 0QH, England. Eds. Christine Smith, June Nash. bk.rev. circ. 30,000. **Indexed:** Curr.Adv.Ecol.Sci., Rehabil.Lit., Trop.Dis.Bull.
Description: Provides health information for health workers involved in leprosy.

MEDICAL SCIENCES — COMMUNICABLE DISEASES

618.92 US ISSN 1045-5418
RJ387.A25 CODEN: PAHIEQ
PEDIATRIC AIDS AND HIV INFECTION: FETUS TO ADOLESCENT. 1990. bi-m. $97 (foreign $137). Mary Ann Liebert, Inc. Publishers, 2 Madison Ave., Larchmont, NY 10538. TEL 914-834-3100. FAX 914-834-3688. E-mail: Liebert@pipeline.com. Eds. Mhairi G. MacDonald, Dr. Harold M. Ginzburg. **Indexed:** CINAHL, Excerp.Med. (1992-). **Document type:** academic/scholarly publication.
—BLDSC (6417.525000); Genuine Article.
Description: Covers methods of diagnosis and treatment of HIV infection. Includes epidemiology, molecular biology, clinical presentation, diagnosis and treatment, pathology, virology, reproductive, psychosocial, and relevant legal and community needs.

THE PEDIATRIC INFECTIOUS DISEASE JOURNAL. see MEDICAL SCIENCES — Pediatrics

PEDIATRIC PATHOLOGY & LABORATORY MEDICINE. see MEDICAL SCIENCES — Pediatrics

616.998 PH
PHILIPPINE JOURNAL OF DERMATOLOGY AND LEPROSY. (Text and summaries in English) 1966. s-a. exchange basis. Dermatology Research and Training, Ministry of Health, Manila, Philippines. Ed. Perpetua D. Reyes Javier. bk.rev.; abstr.; illus. circ. 500.
Formerly: Philippine Journal of Leprosy (ISSN 0031-7632)

616.9 051 US
PLUS (CHICAGO); the magazine about life and HIV. 1993. bi-m. $30. Plus Magazine, Inc., 945 W. George St., Chicago, IL 60657-9974. TEL 312-929-9761. Ed. Brett Grodeck. adv.: B&W page $1500. circ. 30,000. **Document type:** consumer publication.

616.9 362 SA ISSN 1022-5277
POSITIVE OUTLOOK; the thinking person's AIDS awareness magazine. (Text in English, occasional articles in Zulu) 1993. q. R.10 to individuals; institutions R.50 (£20/$30) outside Southern Africa). AIDS Training, Information & Counselling Centre (ATICC), 42 Havelock Rd., Pietermaritzburg 3201, South Africa. TEL 27-331-942111. FAX 27-331-42345. (Co-sponsors: P A A G) Ed. Greg Wood. bk.rev.; illus. circ. 500. **Document type:** bulletin.

POZ. see PUBLIC HEALTH AND SAFETY

616.9 US ISSN 1042-363X
CODEN: PAPAE8
PROGRESS IN AIDS PATHOLOGY. 1989. irreg., vol.3, 1995. $135 to individuals; institutions $170 (effective 1996). Field & Wood, Medical Periodicals, Inc., Box 975, Blue Bell, PA 19422. TEL 610-828-4010. FAX 215-482-0226. Eds. Drs. H. Rotterdam, M.A. Greco. **Indexed:** Curr.Cont., Ind.Med.
—BLDSC (6865.902300).
Refereed Serial

610 576.64 SZ ISSN 0079-645X
RC114.5 CODEN: PMVIA6
PROGRESS IN MEDICAL VIROLOGY. (Text in English) 1958. irreg. (approx. 1/yr.). price varies. S. Karger AG, Allschwilerstr. 10, P.O. Box, CH-4009 Basel, Switzerland. TEL 061-3061111. FAX 061-3061234. E-mail: Karger@Karger.ch. Ed. W.P. Parks. (reprint service avail. from ISI) **Indexed:** Abstr.Hyg., Biol.Abstr., Chem.Abstr., Curr.Adv.Ecol.Sci., Curr.Cont., Dent.Ind., Ind.Med., Ind.Sci.Rev., Ind.Vet., Vet.Bull. **Document type:** academic/scholarly publication.
—BLDSC (6868.960000); CASDDS; Faxon; Genuine Article; SWETS; UnCover. **CCC.**
Refereed Serial

616.9 614 UK ISSN 0142-3517
PUBLIC HEALTH LABORATORY SERVICE BOARD. BIENNIAL REPORT. 1975. biennial. Public Health Laboratory Service, 61 Colindale Ave., London NW9 5HT, England. TEL 0181-200-1295. FAX 0181-200-8130. Ed. J. McBride. circ. 1,500. (also avail. in microform; MI) **Document type:** corporate report.
—BLDSC (2046.200000).
Formerly: Public Health Laboratory Service Board. Year Book (ISSN 0306-1531)

PUBLIC HEALTH NEWS. see PUBLIC HEALTH AND SAFETY

READING AIDS. see LITERATURE

616.9 FR ISSN 0923-2516
CODEN: RESVEY
RESEARCH IN VIROLOGY. (Text in English) 1886. bi-m. 1425 F. in France; foreign 1710 F.($334) (effective 1996). (Institut Pasteur) Editions Scientifiques Elsevier, 141 rue de Javel, 75747 Paris, France. TEL 33-1-45589063. (Subscr. in U.S. and Canada to: Elsevier Science Inc., Box 882, Madison Sq. Sta., New York, NY 10159. TEL 212-989-5800) Ed. P. Tiollais. index. (also avail. in microform from UMI; back issues avail.) **Indexed:** Abstr.Hyg., Biol.Abstr., Bull.Signal., Chem.Abstr., Curr.Adv.Ecol.Sci., Curr.Adv.Genetics & Molec.Biol., Curr.Cont., Excerp.Med., Ind.Sci.Rev., Ind.Vet., INIS Atomind., Sci.Cit.Ind., Trop.Dis.Bull., Vet.Bull. **Document type:** academic/scholarly publication.
—BLDSC (7774.120000); ADONIS; CASDDS; Faxon; Genuine Article; SWETS; UnCover. **CCC.**
Former titles (until 1988): Institut Pasteur. Annales. Virologie (ISSN 0769-2617); Annales de Virologie (ISSN 0242-5017)
Description: Publishes editorials, full-length articles, technical and brief notes on molecular virology, virus-cell interactions, viral oncogenesis, medical virology and epidemiology.
Refereed Serial

616.988 CU ISSN 0375-0760
CODEN: RCMTBF
REVISTA CUBANA DE MEDICINA TROPICAL. (Text in Spanish; summaries in English, Spanish) 1945. 3/yr. $30 in S. America; N. America $32; elsewhere $34. Ministerio de Salud Publica, Centro Nacional de Informacion de Ciencias Medicas, Calle E No. 452, e 19 y 21, Plaza de la Revolucion, Apdo. 6520, Havana, Cuba. TEL 32-5556-60. (Dist. by: Ediciones Cubanas, Obispo No. 461, Apdo. 605, Havana, Cuba) Ed. Ivette Cabrera. bibl.; charts; illus.; index. circ. 1,000. **Indexed:** Abstr.Hyg., Biol.Abstr., Chem.Abstr., Curr.Adv.Ecol.Sci., Excerp.Med., Helminthol.Abstr., Ind.Med., Nutr.Abstr., Protozool.Abstr., Repindex, Rev.Med.& Vet.Mycol., Trop.Dis.Bull.
—BLDSC (7852.121000).
Formerly (until 1966): Medicina Tropical (ISSN 0025-794X)

REVISTA DE IGIENA, BACTERIOLOGIE, VIRUSOLOGIE, PARAZITOLOGIE, PNEUMOFTIZIOLOGIE. BACTERIOLOGIE, VIRUSOLOGIE, PARAZITOLOGIE, EPIDEMIOLOGIE. see BIOLOGY — Microbiology

REVISTA DE IGIENA, BACTERIOLOGIE, VIRUSOLOGIE, PARAZITOLOGIE, PNEUMOFTIZIOLOGIE. see MEDICAL SCIENCES — Respiratory Diseases

616.988 EC ISSN 0048-7775
REVISTA ECUATORIANA DE HIGIENE Y MEDICINA TROPICAL. 1944. q. exchange basis. Instituto Nacional de Higiene y Medicina Tropical "Leopoldo Izquieta Perez", Casilla de Correos No. 3961, Guayaquil, Ecuador. Ed.Bd. illus. circ. 3,500. (reprint service avail. from ISI) **Indexed:** Biol.Abstr., Ind.Med., Rev.Appl.Entomol.

616.019 576.64 RM ISSN 1018-0532
CODEN: RRVIEX
REVUE ROUMAINE DE VIROLOGIE/RUMANIAN JOURNAL OF VIROLOGY. (Text in English, French, German and Russian) 1964. 4/yr. 200 lei($55) (Academia de Stiinte Medicale) Editura Academiei Romane, Calea Victoriei 125, 79717 Bucharest, Rumania. TEL 50-76-80. (Dist. by: Rompresfilatelia, Calea Grivitei 64-66, P.O. Box 12-201, 78104 Bucharest, Rumania) Ed. N. Cajal. bk.rev. circ. 800. **Indexed:** Abstr.Hyg., Biol.Abstr., Chem.Abstr., Excerp.Med., Ind.Vet., Poult.Abstr., Trop.Dis.Bull., Vet.Bull., Virol.Abstr.
—CASDDS.
Former titles: Revue Roumaine de Medecine. Serie Virologie; Revue Roumaine de Virologie; Revue Roumaine d'Inframicrobiologie (ISSN 0035-4082)

616.96 574.524 IT ISSN 0035-6387
QL757 CODEN: RPSTAX
RIVISTA DI PARASSITOLOGIA. (Text in English, French, German, Italian and Spanish) 1937. 3/yr. $60. Istituto di Parassitologia, Universita di Messina, Via Cesare Battisti 48, 98100 Messina, Italy. TEL 090-673136. adv.; bk.rev.; charts; illus.; index. circ. 600. **Indexed:** Abstr.Hyg., Biol.Abstr., Chem.Abstr., Excerp.Med., Helminthol.Abstr., Ind.Vet., Rev.Appl.Entomol., Rev.Med.& Vet.Mycol., Trop.Dis.Bull., Vet.Bull.
—BLDSC (7992.200000); CASDDS; Faxon; UnCover.

616.9 US
ROYAL COLLEGE OF PHYSICIANS AND SURGEONS OF USA. JOURNAL. 1987. s-a. $75 to non-members; members $50; institutions $100. Royal College of Physicians and Surgeons of USA, 16126 E. Warren, Box 24224, Detroit, MI 48224. TEL 313-882-0641. FAX 313-882-5110. Ed. Ben Allie. adv.; bk.rev. **Document type:** academic/scholarly publication.
Formerly: American Academy of Tropical Medicine and Surgery. Journal (ISSN 0891-544X)
Description: Offers practical approaches to diagnosis and treatment of tropical diseases as a continuing education to physicians in tropical countries.

616.988 UK ISSN 0035-9203
CODEN: TRSTAZ
ROYAL SOCIETY OF TROPICAL MEDICINE AND HYGIENE. TRANSACTIONS. 1907. bi-m. £120. Royal Society of Tropical Medicine and Hygiene, Manson House, 26 Portland Pl., London W1N 4EY, England. TEL 0171-580-2127. FAX 0171-436-1389. Ed. Dr. J.R. Baker. adv.: B&W page £500, color page £1000. bibl.; charts; illus.; index. circ. 3,800. **Indexed:** Abstr.Hyg., Biol.Abstr., Chem.Abstr., Curr.Adv.Cancer Res., Curr.Adv.Ecol.Sci., Curr.Adv.Genetics & Molec.Biol., Dairy Sci.Abstr., Dent.Ind., Diar.Dis.Res., Excerp.Med., Helminthol.Abstr., Ind.Med., Ind.Vet., Med.& Surg.Dermat., Nutr.Abstr., Protozool.Abstr., Rev.Appl.Entomol., Rev.Med.& Vet.Mycol., Rev.Plant Path., Risk Abstr., Sel.Water Res.Abstr., So.Pac.Per.Ind., Sport Fish.Abstr., Trop.Dis.Bull., Vet.Bull., Wild.Rev., Zoo.Rec. **Document type:** academic/scholarly publication, proceedings.
—BLDSC (9003.000000); CASDDS; EMDOCS; Faxon; Genuine Article; SWETS; UnCover. **CCC.**

616.988 UK ISSN 0080-4711
ROYAL SOCIETY OF TROPICAL MEDICINE AND HYGIENE, LONDON. YEARBOOK. 1908. a. £20. Royal Society of Tropical Medicine and Hygiene, Manson House, 26 Portland Pl., London W1N 4EY, England. TEL 0171-580-2127. FAX 0171-436-1389. Ed. C.R. Guest. adv.; bk.rev. circ. 3,500. **Indexed:** Curr.Cont. **Document type:** directory.
—CCC.

616.9 SP
S E I SIDA. (Sindrome de Inmunologia Deficiente Adquirido) 1990. 12/yr. 5000 ptas. Sociedad Espanola Interdisciplinaria del SIDA, Principe de Vergara 112, 1o G, 28002 Madrid, Spain. TEL 34-1-5637306. FAX 34-1-5632393. Ed. Dr. Najera Morrondo. adv. circ. 3,500.

616 NO ISSN 0036-5548
CODEN: SJIDB7
SCANDINAVIAN JOURNAL OF INFECTIOUS DISEASES. (Supplement avail. (ISSN 0300-8878)) (Text in English) 1969. 6/yr. NOK 1250 in Nordic countries; elsewhere $214 (effective 1996). Scandinavian University Press, P.O. Box 2959 Toeyen, N-0608 Oslo, Norway. TEL 47-22-57-54-00. FAX 47-22-57-53-53. (U.S. addr.: Scandinavian University Press, 200 Meacham Ave., Elmont, NY 11003. TEL 516-352-7300) Eds. Ola Weiland, Stellan Bengtsson. adv. circ. 2,100. **Indexed:** Abstr.Hyg., ASCA, Biol.Abstr., Biol.Dig., Biotech.Abstr., Chem.Abstr., CINAHL, Curr.Adv.Ecol.Sci., Curr.Cont., Dent.Ind., Diar.Dis.Res., Dok.Arbeitsmed., Excerp.Med., Helminthol.Abstr., Ind.Med., Ind.Vet., Med.& Surg.Dermat., Protozool.Abstr., Rev.Med.& Vet.Mycol., Rev.Plant Path., Trop.Dis.Bull. **Document type:** academic/scholarly publication.
—BLDSC (8087.517000); CASDDS; EMDOCS; Faxon; Genuine Article; SWETS; UnCover. **CCC.**
Description: Publishes original papers on clinical aspects of infectious diseases.

MEDICAL SCIENCES — COMMUNICABLE DISEASES

616.9   NO   ISSN 0300-8878
CODEN: SJISAH
SCANDINAVIAN JOURNAL OF INFECTIOUS DISEASES. SUPPLEMENTUM. 1970. irreg. free to Journal subscribers. Scandinavian University Press, P.O. Box 2959 Toeyen, N-0608 Oslo, Norway. TEL 47-22-57-54-00. FAX 47-22-57-53-53. (U.S. addr.: Scandinavian University Press, 200 Meacham Ave., Elmont, NY 11003. TEL 516-352-7300) **Indexed:** Excerp.Med. (1988-). **Document type:** academic/scholarly publication.
—BLDSC (8087.517100); CASDDS; Faxon; SWETS.

SEMINARS IN DIAGNOSTIC PATHOLOGY. see *MEDICAL SCIENCES*

SEMINARS IN PEDIATRIC INFECTIOUS DISEASES. see *MEDICAL SCIENCES — Pediatrics*

616.9   UK   ISSN 0888-0786
CODEN: SIIDE3
SERODIAGNOSIS AND IMMUNOTHERAPY IN INFECTIOUS DISEASE. 1987. q. fl.362($221) (effective 1996). Butterworth - Heinemann, Part of the Reed Elsevier group, Linacre House, Jordan Hill, Oxford OX2 8DP, England. TEL 0865-310366. FAX 0865-310898. TELEX 83111 BHPOXF G. (Subscr. to: Elsevier Science Ltd., P.O. Box 800, Kidlington, Oxford OX5 1DX, England. TEL 44-865-843000. FAX 44-865-843010; Subscr. in U.S. and Canada to: Elsevier Science, 660 White Plains Rd., Tarrytown, NY 10591-5153. TEL 914-524-9200. FAX 914-333-2444) Ed. J.P. Burnie. (also avail. in microform from UMI; back issues avail.) **Indexed:** Excerp.Med., Vet.Bull. **Document type:** academic/scholarly publication.
—BLDSC (8250.356000); UMI. **CCC.**
Refereed Serial

616.9 917.306   US
SIDA; todo lo que usted debe saber. (Text in Spanish) m. Latin American News and Book Inc., 614 Franklin St., Box 2109, Elizabeth, NJ 07207. TEL 908-355-8835. FAX 908-527-9160. Ed. Jesus M. Tenreiro. adv.: B&W page $650; trim 6 3/4 x 9 1/2. circ. 45,000.
Description: Gives preventative measures, medical views and interviews, and news of recent research and advancements.

616.9   US
SIDA AHORA.* (Text in Spanish) 1989. q. P W A Coalition Inc., 245 Eighth Ave., No. 316, New York, NY 10016. TEL 212-532-0290. FAX 212-447-1508.
Description: Written for the Latino community; contains original personal stories, legal and medical information about AIDS, editorial observation, and political coverage.

616.988   BL   ISSN 0037-8682
SOCIEDADE BRASILEIRA DE MEDICINA TROPICAL. REVISTA. (Text in Portuguese; summaries in English, French or German) 1967. bi-m. Cr.$35($15) Sociedade Brasileira de Medicina Tropical, Rua Laura de Araujo 36, P.O. Box 1859, Rio de Janeiro, Brazil. Ed. Dr. Lea Camillo-Coura. adv.; abstr.; bibl.; charts; index; circ. controlled. **Indexed:** Abstr.Hyg., Biol.Abstr., Excerp.Med., Trop.Dis.Bull.
—BLDSC (7834.200000); EMDOCS.
Formerly: Jornal Brasileiro de Medicina Tropical.

616.988   TH   ISSN 0125-1562
CODEN: SJTMAK
SOUTHEAST ASIAN JOURNAL OF TROPICAL MEDICINE AND PUBLIC HEALTH. (Text in English) 1970. q. $50. Southeast Asian Ministers of Education Organisation (SEAMEO), Regional Tropical Medicine & Public Health Network (TROPMED), 420-6 Rajvithi Rd., Bangkok 10400, Thailand. TEL 66-2-2457193. FAX 66-2-2477721. Ed. Chev Kidson. adv.; bk.rev.; abstr.; bibl.; illus.; index. circ. 1,000. (also avail. in microform from UMI; reprint service avail. from UMI) **Indexed:** Abstr.Hyg., Biol.Abstr., Chem.Abstr., Diar.Dis.Res., Excerp.Med., ExtraMED, Helminthol.Abstr., Ind.Med., Ind.Vet., Nutr.Abstr., Protozool.Abstr., Rev.Appl.Entomol., Rev.Med.& Vet.Mycol., Rev.Plant Path., Sel.Water Res.Abstr., Trop.Dis.Bull., Vet.Bull. **Document type:** academic/scholarly publication.
●Also available on CD-ROM.
—CASDDS; EMDOCS; SWETS.

SPAIN. MINISTERIO DE AGRICULTURA, PESCA Y ALIMENTACION. BOLETIN DE SANIDAD VEGETAL. PLAGAS. see *AGRICULTURE — Crop Production And Soil*

616.9   US   ISSN 0895-755X
SPOTLIGHT ON AIDS.* 1988? 12/yr. $20. Odyssey Institute Corporation, Concerned Physicians Network, 5 Hedley Rd., Westport, CT 06880.
Formerly: Odyssey Institute Journal.

616.998   US   ISSN 0049-2116
CODEN: STARC
THE STAR (CARVILLE); radiating the light of truth on Hansen's disease. 1941. bi-m. $2. National Hansen's Disease Center, Box 325, Point Clair Br., Carville, LA 70721. TEL 504-642-5559. Ed. Manuel Faris. bk.rev.; charts; illus. circ. 70,000. (also avail. in microform from UMI; reprint service avail. from UMI) **Indexed:** Excerp.Med., Rehabil.Lit.
—BLDSC (8434.560000); EMDOCS; UMI; UnCover.

616.96   US
STUDIES IN INFECTIOUS DISEASES RESEARCH. 1975. irreg., latest 1989. price varies. University of Chicago Press, 5801 S. Ellis Ave., Chicago, IL 60637. TEL 312-702-7899. (Subscr. to: 11030 Langley Ave., Chicago, IL 60628)
Refereed Serial

616.9   US   ISSN 1065-982X
T B WEEKLY. (Tuberculosis) 1993. w. $995. Charles W. Henderson, Ed. & Pub., Box 5528, Atlanta, GA 31107-0528. TEL 404-377-8895. FAX 404-378-5411. TELEX 78-2661. (Subscr. to: Box 830409, Birmingham, AL 35283-0409. TEL 800-633-4931. FAX 205-995-1588) (also avail. in microform from UMI) **Document type:** newsletter.
●Also available online. Vendor(s): CompuServe, Inc., Data-Star, Dow Jones News Retrieval, Knight-Ridder, Inc., NewsNet, Ovid Technologies.
—UMI. **CCC.**
Description: Concentrates on tuberculosis-related news and research worldwide, with original reporting, reviews of periodicals and journal articles, calendars of upcoming professional meetings. Topics include TB control programs, vaccine development, the dual epidemics of AIDS and TB, and government roles and responses.

616.9 362.1   NE   ISSN 0928-2998
TIJDSCHRIFT VOOR HYGIENE EN INFEKTIEPREVENTIE. 1981. bi-m. fl.48. Stichting Tijdschrift Hygiene en Infektiepreventie, Kennedystraat 4A, 6921 CW Duiven, Netherlands. TEL 31-8367-63743. circ. 800 (paid). **Document type:** academic/scholarly publication.
—SWETS.
Formerly (until 1992): Ziekenhuishygiene en Infektiepreventie.
Description: Publishes original papers on all aspects of hospital hygiene and infection prevention, investigations, reviews of the literature, and communications about practical problems in infection prevention.

610   US   ISSN 0171-2160
CODEN: TIDID3
TOPICS IN INFECTIOUS DISEASES. 1975. irreg. price varies. Springer-Verlag, 175 Fifth Ave., New York, NY 10010. TEL 212-460-1500. FAX 212-473-6272. (Also: Berlin, Heidelberg, Tokyo and Vienna) (reprint service avail. from ISI) **Indexed:** Chem.Abstr. **Document type:** monographic series.
—CASDDS.

616.988   UK   ISSN 0049-4755
RC960   CODEN: TPDCAV
TROPICAL DOCTOR; a journal of modern medical practice. 1971. q. £32 (foreign £36($70)). Royal Society of Medicine Press Ltd., 1 Wimpole St., London W1M 8AE, England. TEL 0171-290-2900. FAX 0171-290-2929. Ed.Bd. bk.rev.; illus. circ. 2,000. (reprint service avail. from ISI) **Indexed:** Abstr.Hyg., Abstr.Rural Dev.Trop., Biol.Abstr., Curr.Adv.Ecol.Sci., Curr.Cont., Diar.Dis.Res., Excerp.Med., Helminthol.Abstr., Ind.Med., Nutr.Abstr., Rev.Med.& Vet.Mycol., Rice Abstr., So.Pac.Per.Ind., Trop.Dis.Bull. **Document type:** academic/scholarly publication.
—BLDSC (9056.060000); ADONIS; EMDOCS; Faxon; Genuine Article; SWETS; UMI; UnCover. **CCC.**
Description: Publishes contributions on the prevention, management and treatment of prevalent diseases in developing countries and on the promotion of health.
Refereed Serial

616.988   JA   ISSN 0041-3267
TROPICAL MEDICINE/NETTAI IGAKU. (Text in English) 1959. q. exchange basis only. Nagasaki Daigaku, Nettai Igaku Kenkyujo - Nagasaki University, Institute of Tropical Medicine, 12-4 Sakamoto-machi, Nagasaki 852, Japan. Ed.Bd. abstr.; charts; illus.; index. circ. 450. **Indexed:** Abstr.Hyg., Biol.Abstr., Diar.Dis.Res., Excerp.Med., Helminthol.Abstr., Ind.Vet., Protozool.Abstr., Rev.Appl.Entomol., Trop.Dis.Bull., Vet.Bull. **Document type:** academic/scholarly publication.
Formerly: Endemic Diseases Bulletin of Nagasaki University.
Refereed Serial

616.988   US   ISSN 0041-3275
RC960   CODEN: TMHNAT
TROPICAL MEDICINE AND HYGIENE NEWS. 1952. bi-m. membership. American Society of Tropical Medicine and Hygiene (Washington), 6436 31st St., N.W., Washington, DC 20015. TEL 301-496-6721. FAX 301-402-3255. Ed. Dr. Karl A. Western. bk.rev.; circ. 2,400 (controlled). **Indexed:** Abstr.Hyg., Biol.Abstr., Helminthol.Abstr., Protozool.Abstr., Trop.Dis.Bull. **Document type:** newsletter.

TROPICAL MEDICINE & INTERNATIONAL HEALTH. see *PUBLIC HEALTH AND SAFETY*

616.9   TH
TROPMED SEMINARS ON TROPICAL MEDICINE. PROCEEDINGS. (Text in English) irreg., no.29, 1986. $10. Southeast Asian Ministers of Education Organisation (SEAMEO), Regional Tropical Medicine & Public Health Network (TROPMED), 420-6 Rajvithi Road, Bangkok 10400, Thailand. TEL 66-2-2457193. FAX 66-2-2477721. circ. 500. **Document type:** proceedings.
Former titles: Tropmed Seminars on Parasitology and Tropical Medicine. Proceedings; Southeast Asian Seminar on Parasitology and Tropical Medicine. Proceedings (ISSN 0085-6517)

610   US   ISSN 0361-6800
RC110
U.S. ARMY MEDICAL RESEARCH INSTITUTE OF INFECTIOUS DISEASES. ANNUAL PROGRESS REPORT. Key Title: Annual Progress Report - U.S. Army Medical Research Institute of Infectious Diseases. 1968. a. free. U.S. Army Medical Research Institute of Infectious Diseases, Fort Detrick, Frederick, MD 21701. TEL 301-663-8000. (Orders to: NTIS, Springfield, VA 22151) Ed. K. Kenyon. **Document type:** government publication.

616.9   US
U.S. CENTERS FOR DISEASE CONTROL. DIPHTHERIA SURVEILLANCE REPORT. 1962. irreg. U.S. Centers for Disease Control, Dept. of Health and Human Services, 1600 Clifton Rd., NE, Atlanta, GA 30333. TEL 404-639-3311. charts; stat. (looseleaf format) **Document type:** government publication.

616.998   US
U.S. CENTERS FOR DISEASE CONTROL. LEPROSY SURVEILLANCE REPORT. 1970. irreg., no.2, 1972. U.S. Centers for Disease Control, Dept. of Health and Human Services, 1600 Clifton Rd., N.E., Atlanta, GA 30333. TEL 404-639-3311. charts; stat. **Document type:** government publication.

616.9   US   ISSN 0501-8390
U.S. CENTERS FOR DISEASE CONTROL. MALARIA SURVEILLANCE REPORT. 1955. a. free. U.S. Centers for Disease Control, Department of Health and Human Services, 1600 Clifton Rd., N.E., Atlanta, GA 30333. TEL 404-488-7760. Ed. Dr. Jane R. Zucker. circ. 2,000. **Document type:** government publication.

VACCINE WEEKLY. see *PHARMACY AND PHARMACOLOGY*

VIROLOGY. see *BIOLOGY — Microbiology*

VIROLOGY MONOGRAPHS/VIRUSFORSCHUNG IN EINZELDARSTELLUNGEN. see *BIOLOGY — Microbiology*

VIRUS/UIRUSU. see *BIOLOGY — Microbiology*

616.9 UN ISSN 1011-5773
CODEN: WASEEA
W H O AIDS SERIES. French edition: Serie O M S sur le SIDA (ISSN 1011-5781); Spanish edition: O M S SIDA Serie (ISSN 1020-0274) 1988. irreg. World Health Organization, Distribution and Sales, 1211 Geneva 27, Switzerland. TEL 41-22-791-2476. FAX 41-22-791-4857. TELEX 27821-OMS. circ. 4,000. **Document type:** monographic series.
—BLDSC (9311.596000); SWETS.
Description: Features documents and reports issued by the WHO Global Programme on AIDS.

W O R L D; a newsletter by, for and about women facing HIV disease. (Women Organized to Respond to Life-Threatening Diseases) see *WOMEN'S HEALTH*

WEEKLY EPIDEMIOLOGICAL RECORD. see *PUBLIC HEALTH AND SAFETY*

616.9 US
WISCONSIN AIDS UPDATE. q. Department of Health and Social Services, Division of Health, Box 309, Madison, WI 53702. TEL 608-267-5287. **Document type:** government publication.

614.8 US
WORD & DEED. 1976. 4/yr. free. American Leprosy Missions International Partnership, 1 ALM Way, Greenville, SC 29601. TEL 803-271-7040; 800-543-3131. FAX 803-271-7062. Ed. Susan S. Renault. circ. 70,000. **Document type:** newsletter.
Formerly: Crossways.
Description: News and features on the international effort to fight leprosy.

616.9 US ISSN 0743-9261
RC109 CODEN: YBIDEK
YEAR BOOK OF INFECTIOUS DISEASES. 1986. a. $74.95 (residents $35) (effective 1996). Mosby - Year Book, Inc. (Chicago) (Subsidiary of: Times Mirror Company), 200 N. LaSalle St., Chicago, IL 60601-1080. TEL 312-726-9733. FAX 312-726-6075. TELEX 206155. Ed. Gerald Keusch. illus.
● Also available online. Vendor(s): Ovid Technologies.
—BLDSC (9413.450000).

610 KO ISSN 0375-5207
CODEN: YRTMA6
YONSEI REPORTS ON TROPICAL MEDICINE. (Text in English) 1970. a. exchange basis. Yonsei University, Institute of Tropical Medicine, C.P.O. Box 8044, Seoul 120-752, S. Korea. TEL 02-361-5290. FAX 02-363-8676. Ed. Kyung-il Im. adv.; abstr.; bibl.; charts; stat. (tabloid format) **Indexed:** Biol.Abstr., Excerp.Med., Protozool.Abstr. **Document type:** academic/scholarly publication.
—BLDSC (9421.120000).

616.96 574.524 GW ISSN 0934-8840
QR46 CODEN: ZEBAE8
ZENTRALBLATT FUER BAKTERIOLOGIE. irreg. (2 nos./vol.). DM.1052 (foreign DM.1068). Gustav Fischer Verlag, Wollgrasweg 49, 70599 Stuttgart, Germany. TEL 0711-458030. FAX 0711-4580334. TELEX 7111488-FIBUCH. (Subscr. to: Postfach 720143, 70577 Stuttgart, Germany; U.S. address: VCH Publishers, Inc., 303 N.W. 12th Ave., Deerfield Beach, FL 33442-1788) Ed. G. Hennebelg. (also avail. in microfilm from VCI) **Indexed:** Biol.Abstr., Chem.Abstr., Dent.Ind., Helminthol.Abstr., Ind.Med., Poult.Abstr., Rev.Appl.Entomol. **Document type:** academic/scholarly publication.
—BLDSC (9500.970000); CASDDS; Faxon; Genuine Article; SWETS; UMI. **CCC.**
Formerly: Zentralblatt fuer Bakteriologie, Parasitenkunde, Infektionskrankheiten und Hygiene. Series A: Medizinische Mikrobiologie und Parasitologie (ISSN 0174-3031)

MEDICAL SCIENCES — Computer Applications

ADVANCES IN CONNECTIONIST AND NEURAL COMPUTATION THEORY. see *COMPUTERS — Artificial Intelligence*

ADVANCES IN CONTROL NETWORKS AND LARGE SCALE PARALLEL DISTRIBUTED PROCESSING MODELS. see *COMPUTERS — Artificial Intelligence*

616.075 NE ISSN 0925-5206
CODEN: ADECEJ
ADVANCES IN ECHO-CONTRAST; ultrasound imaging innovations, echo-enhancing agents, clinical impact. (Text in English) 1991. q. fl.144 to institutions; $93 to institutions in U.S. (effective 1996). Kluwer Academic Publishers, Postbus 17, 3300 AA Dordrecht, Netherlands. TEL 31-78-392392. FAX 31-78-392254. TELEX 29245 KAPG NL. E-mail: SERVICES@WKAP.NL. (Dist. by: Kluwer Academic Publishers Group, P.O. Box 322, 3300 AH Dordrecht, Netherlands. TEL 31-78-392392. FAX 31-78-546474; N. America dist. addr.: Box 358, Accord Sta., Hingham, MA 02018-0358. TEL 617-871-6600. FAX 617-871-6528) Ed.Bd. (also avail. in microfilm from UMI; back issues avail.) **Indexed:** Excerp.Med. (1995-). **Document type:** academic/scholarly publication.
—BLDSC (0704.480000); UMI. **CCC.**
Refereed Serial

ADVANCES IN M R I - CONTRAST; MRI innovations, contrast-enhancing agents, clinical impact. see *MEDICAL SCIENCES — Radiology And Nuclear Medicine*

610 US ISSN 1067-5027
R858.A1
▼**AMERICAN MEDICAL INFORMATICS ASSOCIATION. JOURNAL.** Abbreviated title: J A M I A. 1994. bi-m. $98 to individuals (foreign $108); institutions $175 (foreign $185). Hanley & Belfus, Inc., 210 S. 13th St., Philadelphia, PA 19107. TEL 215-546-7293. FAX 215-790-9330. Ed. Dr. William W. Stead. adv. contact: Diane R. Sherel. circ. 3,000 (paid). (back issues avail.)
—BLDSC (4689.025000). **CCC.**
Description: Presents state-of-the-art material to assist physicians, informaticians, scientists, nurses and other health care professionals to develop and apply medical informatics to patient care, teaching, research, and health care administration.
Refereed Serial

006.3 610 NE ISSN 0933-3657
CODEN: AIMEEW
ARTIFICIAL INTELLIGENCE IN MEDICINE. 1989. bi-m. fl.480($293) (effective 1996). Elsevier Science B.V., P.O. Box 211, 1000 AC Amsterdam, Netherlands. TEL 31-20-4853911. FAX 31-20-4853598. TELEX 18582 ESPA NL. E-mail: nlinfo-f@elsevier.nl; usinfo-f@elsevier.com; forinfo-kyf04035@niftyserve.or.jp; Site addr.: http://www.elsevier.nl/. (Subscr. in U.S. and Canada to: Elsevier Science Inc., Box 882, Madison Sq. Sta., New York, NY 10159. TEL 212-989-5800. FAX 212-633-3990) Eds. D.G. Bobrow, M. Brady. adv.; bk.rev. circ. 1,500. (also avail. in microform from UMI; back issues avail.) **Indexed:** Comput.Abstr., Excerp.Med. (1992-), Ind.Med. (1993-), INSPEC (1989-). **Document type:** academic/scholarly publication.
—BLDSC (1735.036800); Ei; Genuine Article; SWETS. **CCC.**
Description: Publishes original articles from a wide variety of interdisciplinary perspectives concerning the theory and practice of medical artificial intelligence.
Refereed Serial

610 001.6 US ISSN 0095-0963
R858.A1 CODEN: AUMDC7
AUTOMEDICA; a multinational journal for automation in the medical sciences. 1974. 4/yr. (in 1 vol.). 286 ECU to individuals (effective 1996). Gordon and Breach Science Publishers, c/o International Publishers Distributor, 820 Town Center Dr., Langhorne, PA 19047. TEL 215-750-2642. FAX 215-750-6343. (Subscr. to: International Publishers Distributor, P.O. Box 90, Reading, Berkshire RG1 8JL, England. TEL 44-173-456-8316) Ed. Barry W. Hyndman. adv.; bk.rev.; abstr.; bibl.; charts; illus.; index, cum.index. (also avail. in microform) **Indexed:** Bioeng.Abstr., Biol.Abstr., Chem.Abstr., Comput.Abstr., Comput.Rev., INSPEC (1974-1990).
—BLDSC (1831.770000); Faxon; SWETS. **CCC.**
Refereed Serial

610 UK
BRITISH JOURNAL OF HEALTHCARE COMPUTING & INFORMATION MANAGEMENT. 1984. 10/yr. £45 (rest of Europe £55; overseas £60) (effective 1996). B J H C Ltd., 45 Woodland Grove, Weybridge, Surrey KT13 9EQ, England. TEL 01932-820282. FAX 01932-858035. E-mail: bjhc@bcs.org.uk. Ed. Jenny Roberts; Pub. Dr. H. de Glanville. adv. contact: Simon Rodwell. circ. 11,570. (back issues avail.) **Indexed:** INSPEC (1994-). **Document type:** trade publication.
—Genuine Article.
Formerly: British Journal of Healthcare Computing (ISSN 0265-5217)
Description: Contains news, news analysis, features, articles, and case histories covering the application of information management and technology to healthcare.

610 CN
▼**CANADIAN MEDICAL INFORMATICS MAGAZINE.** (Text in English, French) 1994. 4/yr. M I M Publishing, Box 64, 325 A Vanier Blvd., Bathurst, NB E2A 3Z1, Canada. TEL 506-548-4085; 800-665-4811. FAX 506-548-3204. Ed. Hermel Vienneau. adv.: B&W page Can.$3050, color page Can.$4500; trim 8 1/8 x 10 7/8. circ. 47,750.

COGNITIVE BRAIN RESEARCH. see *MEDICAL SCIENCES — Psychiatry And Neurology*

610.28 616 IE ISSN 0169-2607
CODEN: CMPBEK
COMPUTER METHODS AND PROGRAMS IN BIOMEDICINE; an international journal devoted to the development, implementation and exchange of computing methodology and software systems in biomedical research and medical practice. 1970. 9/yr. I£576($910) (effective 1996). Elsevier Science Ireland Ltd., P.O. Box 85, Limerick, Ireland. TEL 353-61-471944. FAX 353-61-472144. (Subscr. in U.S. and Canada to: Elsevier Science Inc., Box 882 Madison Sq. Sta., New York, NY 10159. TEL 212-989-5800. FAX 212-633-3990) Ed. W. Schneider. bk.rev.; charts. (also avail. in microform from UMI) **Indexed:** Biol.Abstr., Compumath, Comput.Abstr., Curr.Adv.Ecol.Sci., Curr.Cont., Cyb.Abstr., Excerp.Med., Ind.Med., Ind.Sci.Rev., INSPEC (1970-), Sci.Cit.Ind., Stat.Theor.Meth.Abstr., Telegen. **Document type:** academic/scholarly publication.
—BLDSC (3394.095000); Ei; Faxon; Genuine Article; SWETS; UnCover. **CCC.**
Incorporates: Journal of Biomedical Measurement Informatics and Control; Formerly (until 1985): Computer Programs in Biomedicine (ISSN 0010-468X)
Description: For all life science researchers, clinicians, statisticians, health scientists, computer scientists, programmers and bio-engineers, engaged in applying and teaching biomedical information processing.
Refereed Serial

MEDICAL SCIENCES — COMPUTER APPLICATIONS

610   UK   ISSN 0895-6111
CODEN: CMIGEY
COMPUTERIZED MEDICAL IMAGING AND GRAPHICS; the international journal on imaging and image archiving in all medical specialties. 1977. bi-m. £515($819) (effective 1996). (Computerized Medical Imaging and Graphics Society) Elsevier Science Ltd., Pergamon, P.O. Box 800, Kidlington, Oxford OX5 1DX, England. TEL 44-1865-843000. FAX 44-1865-843010.
E-mail: nlinfo-f@elsevier.nl; usinfo-f@elsevier.com; forinfo-kyf04035@niftyserve.or.jp; Site addr.: http://www.elsevier.nl/. (Subscr. in U.S. and Canada to: Elsevier Science, 660 White Plains Rd., Tarrytown, NY 10591-5153. TEL 914-524-9200. FAX 914-333-2444) Ed. Robert S. Ledley. adv. circ. 1,500. (also avail. in microfilm from UMI) **Indexed**: Biol.Abstr., Comput.Cont., Curr.Cont., Dent.Ind., Excerp.Med., Ind.Med., Ind.Sci.Rev., INIS Atomind., INSPEC, Protozool.Abstr., Rev.Med.& Vet.Mycol., Sci.Cit.Ind. **Document type**: academic/scholarly publication.
—BLDSC (3394.586000); Ei; Faxon; Genuine Article; SWETS; UMI; UnCover. **CCC**.
Former titles (until 1988): Computerized Radiology (ISSN 0730-4862); (until 1982): Computerized Tomography (ISSN 0363-8235)
Description: Discusses new developments in computerized medical imaging and graphics and the application of these to patient care. Publishes research results in medical imaging techniques, modalities, analysis and clinical applications of medical images.
Refereed Serial

610.28 004   US   ISSN 0010-4809
CODEN: CBMRB7
COMPUTERS AND BIOMEDICAL RESEARCH. 1969. bi-m. $274 (foreign $333) (effective 1996). (American Medical Informatics Association) Academic Press, Inc., Journal Division, 525 B. St., Ste. 1900, San Diego, CA 92101-4495. TEL 619-230-1840. FAX 619-699-6800. (Subscr. to: Box 620000, Orlando, FL 32891-8340. TEL 800-543-9534) Ed. T. Allan Pryor. adv.; charts; illus. (back issues avail.) **Indexed**: Abstr.Hyg., Anim.Breed.Abstr., Appl.Mech.Rev., Biol.Abstr., Biostat., Chem.Abstr., Compumath, Comput.Cont., Comput.Rev., Curr.Adv.Ecol.Sci., Curr.Cont., Excerp.Med., Ind.Med., Ind.Sci.Rev., Ind.Vet., INIS Atomind., INSPEC, Risk Abstr., Sci.Cit.Ind., Trop.Dis.Bull., Vet.Bull. **Document type**: academic/scholarly publication.
—BLDSC (3394.660000); ADONIS; CASDDS; Ei; Faxon; Genuine Article; SWETS; UnCover. **CCC**.
Description: Provides researchers with current information concerning the use of computers in biomedicine.
Refereed Serial

610.285 004   US   ISSN 0163-0547
CODEN: CMPMDI
COMPUTERS AND MEDICINE.* 1972. m. $127. Medical Group News Inc., P.O. Box 11147, Chicago, IL 60611-0147. TEL 708-446-3100. Ed. Carol Brierly. adv.; bk.rev.; charts; illus.; cum.index. circ. 4,000. (back issues avail.) **Indexed**: Comput.Cont., Comput.Lit.Ind., INSPEC (until 1983), LAMP, MEDSOC.
—Faxon; UnCover.
Description: For medical personnel interested in computer applications. Articles cover current computer technology in medicine, medical education, practice management, and hospitals.

COMPUTERS IN BIOLOGY AND MEDICINE; an international journal. see BIOLOGY — Computer Applications

621.3 616   US   ISSN 0276-6574
RC683.5.D36   CODEN: COCADX
COMPUTERS IN CARDIOLOGY. 1974. a. price varies. (Institute of Electrical and Electronics Engineers, Inc.) I E E E Computer Society Press, 10662 Los Vaqueros Circle, Los Alamitos, CA 90720-1264. TEL 714-821-8380. FAX 714-821-4641. (Co-sponsors: U.S. National Institutes of Health; European Society of Cardiology) Ed. Cat Harris; Pub. Matt Loeb. adv. contact: Frieda Koester. **Indexed**: INSPEC. **Document type**: proceedings.
—BLDSC (3394.895000); Ei; Faxon; UMI. **CCC**.
Description: Presents topics of mutual interest to computer scientists and cardiologists.

610.73   US   ISSN 0736-8593
COMPUTERS IN NURSING. Abbreviated title: C I N. bi-m. $54 to individuals (foreign $85); institutions $125 (foreign $165) (effective 1996). Lippincott - Raven Publishers, 227 E. Washington Sq., Philadelphia, PA 19106. TEL 215-238-4200. Ed. Leslie H. Nicoll. adv.; illus.; index. circ. 3,617. (also avail. in microform from UMI) **Indexed**: CINAHL, Ind.Med., Int.Nurs.Ind., Nurs.Abstr. **Document type**: trade publication.
—BLDSC (3394.925500); Faxon; Genuine Article; SWETS; UMI; UnCover. **CCC**.

610 621.381   US   ISSN 0739-6201
COMPUTERTALK DIRECTORY OF MEDICAL COMPUTER SYSTEMS. 1983. 2/yr. $35. ComputerTalk Associates, Inc., 482 Norristown Rd., Ste. 112, Blue Bell, PA 19422. TEL 610-825-7686. FAX 610-825-7641. Ed. Neil R. Bauman. adv. circ. 195,521. (back issues avail.) **Document type**: directory.
Formerly: ComputerTalk Directory of Medical Systems.
Description: A compilation of information on available medical computer systems. Information contained in product profiles written by vendors. Features articles on the applications of computer systems to medical practices.

COMPUTERTALK FOR THE PHARMACIST. see PHARMACY AND PHARMACOLOGY — Computer Applications

COMPUTERTALK PHARMACY SYSTEMS BUYERS GUIDE. see PHARMACY AND PHARMACOLOGY — Computer Applications

610.28   NE   ISSN 0920-3907
COMPUTING IN BIOMEDICINE. 1987. irreg. price varies. Elsevier Science B.V., Books Division, P.O. Box 211, 1000 AE Amsterdam, Netherlands. TEL 31-20-4853911. FAX 31-20-4853705. TELEX 18582 ESPA NL.
E-mail: nlinfo-f@elsevier.nl; usinfo-f@elsevier.com; forinfo-kyf04035@niftyserve.or.jp; Site addr.: http://www.elsevier.nl/. (Subscr. in U.S. and Canada to: Elsevier Science Inc., Box 882, Madison Sq. Sta., New York, NY 10159. TEL 212-989-5800) **Document type**: monographic series.
Refereed Serial

610 621.381 001.642   US
CYBERLOG; library of applied medical software. 1985. q. $99.95 per program (includes text and software). Cardinal Health Systems, Inc., 4600 W. 77th St., Ste. 150, Edina, MN 55435. TEL 800-328-0180. FAX 612-835-7141. Ed.Bd.
Description: Library and interactive software for physicians. Each program is devoted to a single topic, presented by prominent experts and organizations.

610   US   ISSN 1043-1012
DECISIONS IN IMAGING ECONOMICS.* 1988. q. Curant Communications, Inc., 4676 Admiralty Way, Ste. 202, Marina Del Rey, CA 90292-6603. TEL 213-479-1769. FAX 213-301-3329. Ed. Roger Backlar. circ. 40,000. **Document type**: trade publication.
Formerly (until 1989): Decisions in Technology Economics (ISSN 0898-6096)

617.6 621.381   US   ISSN 0738-9744
DENTAL COMPUTER NEWSLETTER. 1978. q. $20. Andent, Inc., 1000 North Ave., Waukegan, IL 60085. TEL 708-223-5077. Ed. E.J. Neiburger. adv.; bk.rev.; illus. circ. 3,000. **Indexed**: LAMP. **Document type**: newsletter.
Description: For dentists and other medical practitioners interested in office computers. Offers notes on hardware, software, peripherals and integration with office personnel.

617.6   US
DENTISTS' COMPUTER NEWS. 1981. 12/yr. Charles Mann & Associates, Microcomputer Division, 113 Wattenbarger Rd., Sweetwater, TN 37874-6135. TEL 619-365-9718. FAX 615-228-1567. Ed. Ray Burr. bk.rev. circ. 101,711.

610   UK
▼**HEALTH INFORMATICS**. 1995. q. £38 to individuals; institutions £78. Churchill Livingstone Journals (Subsidiary of: Pearson Professional), Robert Stevenson House, 1-3 Baxter's Pl., Leith Walk, Edinburgh EH1 3AF, Scotland. TEL 0131-556-2424. FAX 0131-459-1177. (Subscr. to: Pearson Professional Ltd., P.O. Box 77, Fourth Ave., Harlow, Essex CM19 5AA, England. TEL 01279-623760; U.S. subscr. to: Churchill Livingstone, 650 Ave. of the Americas, New York, NY 10011. TEL 212-206-5000) Ed. Chris Dowd. adv. contact: David Dunnachie. bk.rev. **Document type**: academic/scholarly publication.
Description: Publishes original and commissioned papers, reports, reviews, and announcements on all aspects of information technology applicable to physicians, nurses, hospital administrators and other health care professionals.

610   UK   ISSN 0969-0719
HEALTH INFORMATICS EUROPE. 1993. bi-m. £235 to institutions worldwide (effective 1996). B J H C Ltd., 45 Woodland Grove, Weybridge, Surrey KT13 9EQ, England. TEL 01932-820282. FAX 01932-858035. E-mail: bjhc@bcs.org.uk. (back issues avail.) **Document type**: bulletin.
—BLDSC (4275.016800).
Description: Contains news and commentary on key issues in health informatics across Europe.

610 658 R858.A1   US   ISSN 1074-4770
CODEN: HMTEE2
HEALTH MANAGEMENT TECHNOLOGY. 1980. m. $34 (Canada and Mexico $54; elsewhere $94). Argus Inc., 6151 Powers Ferry Rd., N.W., Atlanta, GA 30339-2491. TEL 404-955-2500. FAX 404-955-0400. (Subscr. to: Box 41528, Nashville, TN 37204. TEL 615-377-3322) Ed. Michael Stefanchik. adv.; bk.rev.; charts; illus.; stat. circ. 21,880. (also avail. in microfiche; reprint service avail. from UMI) **Indexed**: ABI Inform., Abstr.Health Care Manage.Stud., Comput.Dtbs., I.P.A., INSPEC. **Document type**: trade publication.
●Also available online. Vendor(s): Knight-Ridder, Inc., University Microfilms International.
—Faxon; SWETS; UMI; UnCover. **CCC**.
Former titles (until 1994): Computers in Healthcare (ISSN 0745-1075); (until 1982): Computers in Hospitals (ISSN 0274-631X)
Description: For healthcare systems professionals. Features articles on systems applications for hospitals and other health facilities.

610   UK
HEALTHCARE COMPUTING CONFERENCE PROCEEDINGS. a. £45. B J H C Ltd., 45 Woodland Grove, Weybridge, Surrey KT13 9EQ, England. TEL 01932-820282. FAX 01932-858035. E-mail: bjhc@bcs.org.uk. **Document type**: proceedings.
Description: Concentrates on a particular aspect of health care computing.

610   US   ISSN 1050-9135
HEALTHCARE INFORMATICS. 1984. m. $28. Health Data Analysis, Inc., 2902 Evergreen Pkwy., No. 100, Evergreen, CO 80439-2830. TEL 303-674-2774. FAX 303-674-3134. Ed. Bill W. Childs; Pub. Gary Voreis. adv.: B&W page $2800, color page $3790; adv. contact: Al Elliot, Bob Zavodsky. tr.lit. circ. 30,000. (back issues avail.) **Document type**: trade publication.
—BLDSC (4275.247850); Genuine Article; UnCover.
Former titles (until Jan. 1990): U S Healthcare (ISSN 1040-3973); (until Aug. 1988): Healthcare Computing and Communications (ISSN 8750-149X)
Description: Features for computer and communications for the healthcare field. Contains articles on telecommunications, managed care, new products, applications and systems market for healthcare administrators and medical professionals.

MEDICAL SCIENCES — COMPUTER APPLICATIONS

610 001.6   US
I E E E ENGINEERING IN MEDICINE AND BIOLOGY SOCIETY. INTERNATIONAL CONFERENCE. 1979. a. price varies. (I E E E, Engineering in Medicine and Biology Society) Institute of Electrical and Electronics Engineers, Inc., 345 E. 47th St., New York, NY 10017-2394. FAX 908-981-9667. (Subscr. to: Box 1331, 445 Hoes Lane, Piscataway, NJ 08855-1331)
    Former titles: I E E E Engineering in Medicine and Biology Society. Conference; (until 1984): Frontiers of Engineering and Computing in Health Care; Which was formed by the merger of (1981-1982): I E E E Frontiers of Computers in Medicine; (1979-1982): I E E E Frontiers of Engineering in Health Care.

I F M B E NEWS. (M) (International Federation for Medical and Biological Engineering) see *BIOLOGY — Bioengineering*

610   FR   ISSN 1156-5802
INFORMATIQUE ET SANTE. 1990. 4/yr. 380 F. (foreign 490 F.). P G Promotion, 17 rue Childebert, 69002 Lyon, France. TEL 78-42-67-70. FAX 78-42-37-70. Ed. Antoine Servetti. adv. contact: Joelle Courret. circ. 2,000.
    Description: Studies data-processing in the medical field, covering computing systems, research, communication systems, office automation.

610   US
INTERACTIVE HEALTHCARE C A I DIRECTORY. $59 (foreign $69) (effective May 1995). Stewart Publishing, Inc., 6471 Merritt Ct., Alexandria, VA 22312. TEL 703-354-8155. FAX 703-354-2177. software rev. **Document type:** directory.
    Description: Lists more than 450 computer-assisted instruction programs in the health care sciences for IBM and Macintosh computers.

610   US   ISSN 1074-6064
R119.9
INTERACTIVE HEALTHCARE C D - R O M DIRECTORY. a. $59 (foreign $69) (effective May 1995). Stewart Publishing, Inc., 6471 Merritt Ct., Alexandria, VA 22312. TEL 703-354-8155. FAX 703-354-2177. software rev. **Document type:** directory.
    Description: Lists more than 230 CD-ROM, CD-I, and MMCD titles in the health sciences.

610 384.3   US
▼**INTERACTIVE HEALTHCARE INTERNET DIRECTORY.** 1995. a. $59 (overseas $69) (effective June 1995). Stewart Publishing, Inc., 6471 Merritt Ct., Alexandria, VA 22312. TEL 703-354-8155. FAX 703-354-2177. **Document type:** directory.
    Description: Lists health-related services found on the Internet.

610   US   ISSN 1048-0501
INTERACTIVE HEALTHCARE NEWSLETTER. 1985. m. $70 (overseas $85). Stewart Publishing, Inc., 6471 Merritt Ct., Alexandria, VA 22312. TEL 703-354-8155. FAX 703-354-2177. Ed. Scott Alan Stewart. **Document type:** newsletter.
    Formerly (until 1989): MedicalDisc Reporter (ISSN 0882-4665)
    Description: Covers the use of videodisc, CD-ROM, multimedia, and related technology in the health sciences.

610   US
INTERACTIVE HEALTHCARE VIDEODISC DIRECTORY. a. $59 (foreign $69) (effective May 1995). Stewart Publishing, Inc., 6471 Merritt Ct., Alexandria, VA 22312. TEL 703-354-8155. FAX 703-354-2177. software rev. **Document type:** directory.
    Description: Lists nearly 500 proprietary and commercial videodisc projects developed for the medical sciences.

610.285 574   IE   ISSN 0020-7101
CODEN: IJBCBT
INTERNATIONAL JOURNAL OF BIO-MEDICAL COMPUTING. 1970. m. I£652($1030) (effective 1996). Elsevier Science Ireland Ltd., P.O. Box 85, Limerick, Ireland. TEL 353-61-471944. FAX 353-61-472144. (Subscr. in U.S. and Canada to: Elsevier Science Inc. Box 882, Madison Sq. Sta., New York, NY 10159. TEL 212-989-5800. FAX 212-633-3990) Eds. J.G. Llaurado, A. Hasman. charts; illus.; index. **Indexed:** Biol.Abstr., Biostat., Chem.Abstr., Compumath, Comput.Cont., Comput.Rev., Curr.Adv.Ecol.Sci., Curr.Cont., Eng.Ind., Excerp.Med., Ind.Med., INSPEC (1974-), Math.R., Sci.Cit.Ind. **Document type:** academic/scholarly publication.
    —BLDSC (4542.152000); CASDDS; Ei; EMDOCS; Faxon; Genuine Article; SWETS; UnCover. **CCC.**
    Description: For those working in computing applied to the medical and life sciences.
    Refereed Serial

INTERNATIONAL JOURNAL OF CLINICAL MONITORING AND COMPUTING. see *MEDICAL SCIENCES — Anaesthesiology*

610   US   ISSN 0090-1091
CODEN: JCLCB
JOURNAL OF CLINICAL COMPUTING.* 1971. bi-m. $30. Journal of Clinical Computing, Inc., 75 Cambridge Parkway, PH-6, Cambridge, MA 02142-1237. Ed. E.R. Gabrieli. adv.; bk.rev. circ. 700. (back issues avail.) **Indexed:** Comput.Cont., Cyb.Abstr., Excerp.Med., INSPEC.
    —BLDSC (4958.387000); Ei; EMDOCS; Faxon; SWETS.

JOURNAL OF COMPUTER ASSISTED TOMOGRAPHY; a radiological journal dedicated to the basic and clinical aspects of reconstructive tomography. see *MEDICAL SCIENCES — Radiology And Nuclear Medicine*

JOURNAL OF DIGITAL IMAGING. see *MEDICAL SCIENCES — Radiology And Nuclear Medicine*

JOURNAL OF IMAGE GUIDED SURGERY. see *MEDICAL SCIENCES — Surgery*

JOURNAL OF MEDICAL EDUCATION TECHNOLOGIES. see *EDUCATION — Computer Applications*

610 004   US   ISSN 0148-5598
R858.A1   CODEN: JMSYDA
JOURNAL OF MEDICAL SYSTEMS. 1977. bi-m. $365 (foreign $425) (effective 1989). Plenum Publishing Corp., 233 Spring St., New York, NY 10013-1578. TEL 212-620-8000. FAX 212-463-0742. TELEX 23-421139. Ed. Dr. Ralph R. Grams. adv. (also avail. in microfilm from JSC; back issues avail.) **Indexed:** Biol.Abstr., CINAHL, Curr.Cont., Excerp.Med., Ind.Med., INIS Atomind., Med.Care Rev. **Document type:** academic/scholarly publication.
    —BLDSC (5017.088000); Faxon; Genuine Article; SWETS; UMI; UnCover. **CCC.**
    Refereed Serial

M COMPUTING. see *COMPUTERS — Computer Programming*

610 621.381   US   ISSN 0724-6811
R858.A1
M.D. COMPUTING (NEW YORK); computers in medical practice. 1983. bi-m. $125 (effective 1996). (American Association for Medical Systems and Informatics) Springer-Verlag, Journals, 175 Fifth Ave., New York, NY 10010. TEL 212-460-1500. FAX 212-473-4262. E-mail: bbrash@springer-ny.com. (N. American subscr. to: Journal Fulfillment Services, Box 2485, Secaucus, NJ 07096-2491. TEL 800-777-4643. FAX 201-348-4505; Elsewhere to: Springer-Verlag, Heidelberger Platz 3, 1000 Berlin 3, Germany. TEL 030-8207-0. FAX 030-821-4091) Ed. W.V. Slack; Pub. Jolanda von Hagen. adv. contact: Bob Vrooman. illus.; tr.lit. (also avail. in microform from UMI; back issues avail.; reprint service avail. from ISI) **Indexed:** CINAHL, Comput.Dtbs., Comput.Lit.Ind., Curr.Cont., Excerp.Med. (until 1993), Ind.Med., INSPEC, Microcomp.Ind. **Document type:** academic/scholarly publication.
    —BLDSC (5413.509920); Faxon; Genuine Article; SWETS; UnCover. **CCC.**
    Supersedes (in July 1985): Medical Computer Journal; **Formerly:** Medcomp: Computers in Medicine.
    Description: Covers the various uses of microcomputing in the medical field - from software to clinical applications.
    Refereed Serial

M LINK. see *COMPUTERS — Computer Programming*

MEDICAL & BIOLOGICAL ENGINEERING & COMPUTING. see *BIOLOGY — Bioengineering*

MEDICAL ARTIFICIAL INTELLIGENCE. see *COMPUTERS — Artificial Intelligence*

610   UK   ISSN 0307-7640
CODEN: MINFDZ
MEDICAL INFORMATICS. 1976. q. £200($330) (effective 1996). Taylor and Francis Ltd., Rankine Rd., Basingstoke, Hants. RG24 8PR, England. TEL 44-1256-840366. FAX 44-1256-479438. TELEX 858540. E-mail: info@tandf.co.uk. (Subscr. in N. America to: Taylor & Francis Inc., 1900 Frost Rd., Ste. 101, Bristol, PA 19007-1598. TEL 800-821-8312. FAX 215-785-5515) Ed. J.A. Newell. adv.; bk.rev. (back issues avail.) **Indexed:** Abstr.Hum.Comp.Inter., Art.Int.Abstr., Biol.Abstr., CAD CAM Abstr., CINAHL, Comput.Lit.Ind., Curr.Cont., Excerp.Med., Helminthol.Abstr., Hosp.Lit.Ind., Ind.Med., INSPEC. **Document type:** academic/scholarly publication.
    —BLDSC (5527.553000); Ei; Faxon; Genuine Article; SWETS; UnCover. **CCC.**
    Description: Not only serves as a focus for most aspects of the application of computers to medicine, but promotes the application of analysis, inference and reasoning to medical information.
    Refereed Serial

610   US
MEDICAL INTELLIGENCE. 1990. 12/yr. $745 in US and Canada; elsewhere $900. Gallifrey Publishing, Box 155, Vicksburg, MI 49097. TEL 616-649-3772. Ed. Dr. Derek F. Stubbs.
    Description: For investors and researchers exploring the interrelationships between medicine and technology and current and future advances in medical therapy.

610   US
MICRO M D NEWSLETTER.* 1983. 12/yr. Micro M D Publishing, 170 University Ave. W, Waterloo, Ontario, Canada N2L 3E9. Ed. Terry Polevoy. adv.; bk.rev. circ. 1,500.
    ●Also available online. Vendor(s): CompuServe, Inc., NewsNet.
    Formerly: Micro M D Journal.

610 621.381   US
MICRO MEDICAL NEWSLETTER. 1981. 12/yr. Charles Mann & Associates, Microcomputer Division, 113 Wattenbarger, Sweetwater, TN 37874-6135. TEL 619-365-9718. FAX 619-228-1567. Ed. Ray Burr. bk.rev. circ. 171,214. **Document type:** newsletter.

MEDICAL SCIENCES — DENTISTRY

610 US ISSN 0748-2051
MICROPSYCH NETWORK; computer applications in psychology. 1985. bi-m. $20 (foreign $30). (Professional Resource Exchange, Inc.) Human Technology Interface, Ink Press, 163 Wood Wedge Way, Sanford, NC 27330. Ed. Emory Sadler. adv.; bk.rev. circ. 500. (back issues avail.)
Description: Publishes computer-related material that psychologists will find useful; articles about using computers in clinical practice, the classroom, and research laboratory, and reviews of software and original programs.

MONOGRAFIAS DE DIAGNOSTICO POR IMAGEN. see *MEDICAL SCIENCES — Radiology And Nuclear Medicine*

610 US ISSN 0273-4974
NATIONAL REPORT ON COMPUTERS AND HEALTH. 1980. 25/yr. $427. United Communications Group, 11300 Rockville Pike, Ste. 1100, Rockville, MD 20852-3030. TEL 301-816-8950. FAX 301-816-8945. Ed. Bob Gough. (back issues avail.) Indexed: Tel.Alert.
●Also available online. Vendor(s): Data-Star, Knight-Ridder, Inc..
—CCC.
Description: Features articles pertaining to new software, technologies in the fast changing field of hospital data processing and clinical information systems.

NEURAL COMPUTATION. see *COMPUTERS — Artificial Intelligence*

610 US ISSN 0891-8163
PHYSICIANS & COMPUTERS. 1982. m. $28 (Canada $34; international $48) (effective 1995). Moorhead Publications, Inc., 810 S. Waukegan Rd., Ste. 200, Lake Forest, IL 60045-2672. TEL 708-615-8333. FAX 708-615-8345. Ed. Rogers H. Piercy; Pub. Thomas J. Moorhead. adv.: B&W page $2650, color page $3300; trim 8 1/8 x 10 3/4. tr.lit. circ. 90,131. (reprint service avail.) Document type: trade publication.
—BLDSC (6476.361580).
Description: For physicians who have little or no computer experience. Articles cover applications to office management and clinical medicine environment.

RADIOLOGIC TECHNOLOGY. see *MEDICAL SCIENCES — Radiology And Nuclear Medicine*

610 011 FR ISSN 1169-6176
REPERTOIRE INTERNATIONAL DES BANQUES DE DONNEES BIOMEDICALES. 1991. irreg. 370 F. (Ministere de la Recherche et de l'Espace) Editions F L A Consultants, 27 rue de la Vistule, 75013 Paris, France. TEL 45-82-75-75. FAX 45-82-46-04. Ed. Madeleine Wolff-Terroine. adv. contact: Beatrice Riou. Document type: directory.
Description: A directory of worldwide databases in the field of medical, pharmaceutical and biological sciences with a description of each database.

651.8 US
S I G B I O NEWSLETTER. 1970. q. $30 to non-members; members $20. Association for Computing Machinery, Special Interest Group on Biomedical Computing, 1515 Broadway, 17th Fl., New York, NY 10036. TEL 212-869-7440. FAX 212-302-5826. Ed. Cathy Rubens. bk.rev. circ. 1,000. Indexed: Abstr.Hum.Comp.Inter., INSPEC. Document type: newsletter.

610 US ISSN 1071-1910
THE SINGER REPORT ON MANAGED CARE SYSTEMS AND TECHNOLOGY. 1991. every 6 wks. $395. Charles J. Singer & Co., 401 Edgewater Pl., Ste. 580, Wakefield, MA 01880. TEL 617-246-7585. FAX 617-246-7737. E-mail: RLUHR@AOL.COM. Ed. Rich Luhr. circ. 2,000 (paid). (also avail. in diskette format; back issues avail.) Document type: newsletter.
Description: Covers developments in the design and use of computer systems in managed health care organizations.

STUDIES IN HEALTH TECHNOLOGY AND INFORMATICS. see *MEDICAL SCIENCES*

610.285 004 US ISSN 0195-4210
R858.A2 CODEN: PCMCDC
SYMPOSIUM ON COMPUTER APPLICATIONS IN MEDICAL CARE. PROCEEDINGS. 1977. a. $65. American Medical Informatics Association, 4915 St. Elmo Ave., Ste. 302, Bethesda, MD 20814. TEL 301-657-1291. FAX 301-657-1296. circ. 3,000. Indexed: Ind.Med. (1992-), INSPEC. Document type: proceedings.
—BLDSC (1534.946800); SWETS; UMI.
Refereed Serial

651.8 610.28 US ISSN 1063-973X
R864
TOWARD AN ELECTRONIC PATIENT RECORD; updates on standards and developments. 1992. 10/yr. $145 (foreign $165). Medical Records Institute, Box 289, Newtonville, MA 02160. TEL 617-964-3923. FAX 617-964-3926. Ed. C. Peter Waegemann. circ. 500 (paid). (back issues avail.) Document type: newsletter.

MEDICAL SCIENCES — Dentistry

617.6 BL
A B E S P BOLETIM. 1972. q. Cr.$200($13) Associacao Brasileira de Endodontia, Seccao Sao Paulo, Praca Amadeu Amaral 47-8, Sao Paulo, SP, Brazil. Ed. Antonio Elias Makaron. adv.; circ. 2,500 (controlled).

617.6 CN ISSN 0820-5949
A C F D FORUM. (Text mainly in English; occasionally in French) 1968. 3/yr. membership. Association of Canadian Faculties of Dentistry, Central Office, Ste. 109, Alta Vista Dr., Ottawa, ON K1G 3Y6, Canada. TEL 604-228-3413. FAX 604-228-6698. Ed. R.M. Shah. bk.rev. circ. 700. (processed) Document type: newsletter.
Formerly: Association of Canadian Faculties of Dentistry. Newsletter (ISSN 0044-9555)

617.6 US ISSN 0001-0855
RK1
A D A NEWS. 1970. 22/yr. $45 to non-members (foreign $65). American Dental Association, 211 E. Chicago Ave., Chicago, IL 60611. TEL 312-440-2500. FAX 312-440-3538. adv. circ. 140,000. (also avail. in microform from UMI) Document type: newsletter.

617.6 CN ISSN 0849-5866
A D A NEWSLETTER. 1967. irreg. membership. Alberta Dental Association, 209-1610 37th S.W., Calgary, AB T3C 3P1, Canada. Ed. Dr. John Aitken. adv. circ. 1,375. Document type: newsletter.
Formerly: A D A News Information (ISSN 0383-6355)

617.6 MX ISSN 0001-0944
A D M. 1943. bi-m. $100 (effective 1996). Asociacion Dental Mexicana, A.C., Ezequiel Montes No. 92, Col. Revolucion, Delegacion Cuauhtemoc, Mexico, D.F. 06030, Mexico. TEL 52-5-29400095. FAX 52-5-2945143. (Co-sponsor: Federacion Nacional de Colegios de Cirujanos Dentistas) Ed. Elias Grego Samra. adv.; abstr.; charts; illus. circ. 3,000. Indexed: Chem.Abstr., Ind.Med., INIS Atomind. Document type: academic/scholarly publication.
—BLDSC (7802.195000).
Refereed Serial

617.6 US ISSN 0194-729X
A G D IMPACT. 1973. 11/yr. $20 to individuals; institutions $32. Academy of General Dentistry, 211 E. Chicago Ave., Ste. 1200, Chicago, IL 60611. TEL 312-440-4300. FAX 312-440-0559. Ed. Dr. William W. Howard. adv.: B&W page $1785, color page $2885; adv. contact: Todd Goldman. illus. circ. 33,000. Document type: trade publication.
—CCC.
Description: Features issues, controversies, legislation and trends that affect the practice of general dentistry.

617.6 IT ISSN 0001-1908
A M D I BOLLETTINO.* vol.16, 1970. m. Associazione Medici Dentisti Italiani, Via Savoia 78, Rome, Italy. Ed. Ermano Ricci. adv.; charts.

617.6 US ISSN 0277-3619
RK58.5
A S D A HANDBOOK. a. $20 (foreign $35). American Student Dental Association, 211 E. Chicago Ave., Ste. 840, Chicago, IL 60611. TEL 312-440-2795. adv. circ. 18,000.
Description: Reference guide for dental students. Contains information on applying to dental schools, financial aid, ASDA membership benefits, post doctorial opportunities.

617.6 US ISSN 0277-3627
A S D A NEWS (YEAR). 1971. m. (Sep.-May). $20 (foreign $30). American Student Dental Association, 211 E. Chicago Ave., Chicago, IL 60611. TEL 312-440-2795. Ed. Lisa Coghlan. adv. circ. 15,000. (tabloid format) Indexed: Dent.Abstr., Dent.Ind. Document type: newspaper.
Former titles (until 1981): New Dentist; (until 1979): A S D A News (ISSN 0161-8431); A S D A Newsletter (ISSN 0044-8052)
Description: Assortment of dental, association and student news, viewpoints, features, and numerous pieces.

617.6 US
A S D A TODAY. 1980. q. membership. American Society for Dental Aesthetics, 635 Madison Ave., New York, NY 10022. TEL 212-371-4575. Ed. Melvin S. Babad. circ. 3,000 (controlled). Document type: newsletter.
Formerly: American Association for Dental Aesthetics Newsletter.
Description: Covers porcelain laminates, bonding, new dental materials and techniques presented on the post graduate level of advanced dentistry.

617.6 US ISSN 1050-0758
ACCESS (CHICAGO). 10/yr. American Dental Hygienists Association, 444 N. Michigan Ave., Ste. 3400, Chicago, IL 60611. TEL 312-440-8929. FAX 312-440-8900. Ed. Rosetta Gervasi. circ. 30,000. Document type: trade publication.
Formerly (until 1987): A D H A Access (ISSN 0894-9042)

617.6 618.92 DR ISSN 0252-1032
ACTA DE ODONTOLOGIA PEDIATRICA; una revista internacional para la odontologia pediatrica. (Text in English and Spanish) 1979. s-a. $25 foreign; free to qualified personnel. Centro de Odontologia Pediatrica, Jose Joaquin Perez No. 101 - Zona 1, Apartado Postal 2753, Santo Domingo, Dominican Republic. TEL 809-689-4277. Ed. Dr. Fredrico Garcia-Godoy. adv.: B&W page $780, color page $12400; 8 1/2 x 11. bk.rev. circ. 2,300. Indexed: Dent.Ind., Ind.Med. Document type: academic/scholarly publication.

617.6 NO ISSN 0001-6357
CODEN: AOSCAQ
ACTA ODONTOLOGICA SCANDINAVICA; Scandinavian dental research journal. (Text in English) 1939. bi-m. NOK 1250 in Nordic countries; elsewhere $220 (incl. supplements) (effective 1996). Scandinavian University Press, P.O. Box 2959 Toeyen, N-0608 Oslo, Norway. TEL 47-22-57-54-00. FAX 47-22-57-53-53. (U.S. addr.: Scandinavian University Press, 200 Meacham Ave., Elmont, NY 11003. TEL 516-352-7300) Ed. Gunnar E. Carlsson. adv.; bibl.; charts; illus.; index. circ. 1,000. (also avail. in microform from UMI; back issues avail.; reprint service avail. SWZ) Indexed: Abstr.Health Care Manage.Stud., Biol.Abstr., Chem.Abstr., Curr.Adv.Ecol.Sci., Curr.Cont., Curr.Tit.Dent., Dent.Ind., Energy Res.Abstr, Excerp.Med., Ind.Med., Ind.Sci.Rev., INIS Atomind., Nucl.Sci.Abstr., Sci.Cit.Ind.
—BLDSC (0641.630000); CASDDS; Faxon; Genuine Article; SWETS; UMI; UnCover. CCC.
Description: Presents dental research in the Scandinavian countries to an international forum.

617.6 BE ISSN 0001-7000
CODEN: ASBEBA
ACTA STOMATOLOGICA BELGICA. (Text in Flemish and French; summaries in English, Flemish, French and German) vol.67, 1970. 4/yr. 1800 Fr. (foreign 2000 Fr.) (effective 1992). Association des Societes Scientifiques Medicales Belges - Vereiniging van de Belgische Medische Wetenschappelijke Genootschappen, Av. Circulaire 138A, B-1180 Brussels, Belgium. TEL 02-374-5158. bk.rev.; abstr.; bibl.; illus.; index. Indexed: Biol.Abstr., Dent.Ind., Excerp.Med., Ind.Med.
—BLDSC (0663.380000); Faxon.

MEDICAL SCIENCES — DENTISTRY

617.6   CI   ISSN 0001-7019
ACTA STOMATOLOGICA CROATICA. (Text in Croatian or English; summaries in English) 1966. q. $30. Hrvatski Lijecnicki Zbor, Vinogradska 97, 4100 Zagreb, Croatia. Ed. Vladimir Lapter. adv.; bk.rev.; charts; illus. circ. 2,000. **Indexed:** Biol.Abstr., Dent.Ind.

617.6   FR   ISSN 0001-7817
CODEN: ACOPAR
ACTUALITES ODONTO-STOMATOLOGIQUES. (Text in French; summaries in English, German, Italian, Portuguese, Russian and Spanish) 1946. 4/yr. 705 F. to individuals; students 415 F. Groupe C D P, 77 rue de Richelieu, 75002 Paris, France. TEL 42-61-50-65. FAX 42-61-31-95. TELEX 210 717 F. Ed. C. Hubert Ouvrard. adv. contact: Chantal Daly. **Indexed:** Biol.Abstr., Chem.Abstr., Curr.Cont., Dent.Ind., Ind.Med.
—CASDDS; Faxon; SWETS.

ADMISSION REQUIREMENTS OF U S AND CANADIAN DENTAL SCHOOLS. see EDUCATION — Guides To Schools And Colleges

617.6   US   ISSN 0895-9374
ADVANCES IN DENTAL RESEARCH. (Supplement to: Journal of Dental Research (ISSN 0022-0345)) 1987. irreg. (2-6/yr.) included in subscription to Journal of Dental Research. (International Association for Dental Research) American Association for Dental Research, 1619 Duke St., Alexandria, VA 22314-3406. TEL 703-548-0066. FAX 703-548-1883. Ed. Dr. Arthur R. Hand. cum.index every 3 yrs. circ. 3,000. (also avail. in microform from UMI; back issues avail.; reprint service avail. from UMI) **Indexed:** Biol.Abstr., Chem.Abstr., Curr.Cont., Dairy Sci.Abstr., Dent.Abstr., Dent.Ind., Excerp.Med., Ind.Med., Ind.Sci.Rev., Met.Abstr., Nutr.Abstr., Sci.Cit.Ind., World Alum.Abstr. **Document type:** academic/scholarly publication.
—BLDSC (0704.242200); Faxon; SWETS; UnCover. **CCC.**
Incorporates: International Conference on Oral Biology. Proceedings (ISSN 0074-3216)
Description: Provides a forum for detailed exploration and timely discussion of significant research developments in the sciences relevant to dentistry and to the chemistry, biology, and function of the oral cavity in health and disease.

617.6   JA   ISSN 0044-6912
CODEN: AGDSAB
AICHI-GAKUIN JOURNAL OF DENTAL SCIENCE. (Text in Japanese; summaries in English) 1964. q. 5000 Yen($20) per no. Aichi-Gakuin Society of Dental Science, School of Dentistry, Aichi-Gakuin University, 1-100 Kusumoto-cho, Chikusa-ku, Nagoya 464, Japan. Ed. Jiro Hasegawa; Pub. Hajime Hanamura. adv. contact: Yoichiro Kameya. bk.rev.; abstr.; charts; stat. circ. 4,000. **Indexed:** Biol.Abstr., Dent.Ind. **Document type:** academic/scholarly publication.
—BLDSC (0773.074200); CASDDS.

617.6   US   ISSN 0002-3701
AKRON DENTAL SOCIETY. BULLETIN. vol.29, 1970. 8/yr. $40 (foreign $60). Akron Dental Society, 440 Grant St., Akron, OH 44311. TEL 216-376-3551. Ed. Samuel N. Pupino. adv. contact: Nancy L. Seigfreid. circ. 450.

617.6   US   ISSN 0002-4198
ALABAMA DENTAL ASSOCIATION. JOURNAL. 1917. q. $24 (foreign $35). Alabama Dental Association, 3915 Old Shell Rd., Mobile, AL 36608. TEL 205-342-6410. Ed. Dr. John H. Mosteller. adv.; bk.rev.; bibl.; charts; illus. circ. 1,650. (also avail. in microform from UMI; reprint service avail. from UMI) **Indexed:** Dent.Abstr., Dent.Ind.
—BLDSC (4683.030000); UMI.

617.6   UA
ALEXANDRIA DENTAL JOURNAL/MAGALLAT AL-ISKANDIRIYYAH LI-TIBB AL-ASNAN. vol.14, 1989. q. Alexandria University, Faculty of Dentistry, 22 Sharia al-Gaish, Al-Shatby, Alexandria, Egypt.

617.6   US   ISSN 0002-6417
ALPHA OMEGAN.* 1908. q. $30 (foreign $40). Alpha Omega International Fraternity, 1314 Bedford Ave., Ste. 206, Baltimore, MD 21208-3737. TEL 212-683-4155. FAX 212-683-0027. Ed. Dr. Roger Spott. adv.; bk.rev. circ. 8,000. (back issues avail.)
—BLDSC (0802.091000); Faxon.
Description: Scientific and membership information.

617.643   US   ISSN 0886-1064
AMERICAN ACADEMY OF GNATHOLOGIC ORTHOPEDICS. JOURNAL. 1984. q. $50. American Academy of Gnathologic Orthopedics, Box 548, Richmond, TX 77406-0548. TEL 713-341-5250. Ed. L.M. Alderson. adv. contact: L.M. Alderson. circ. 400. (back issues avail.) **Document type:** academic/scholarly publication.

AMERICAN ASSOCIATION OF DENTAL EDITORS. NEWSLETTER. see JOURNALISM

617.6   US   ISSN 0002-7421
AMERICAN ASSOCIATION OF DENTAL EXAMINERS. BOARD BULLETIN. 1965. q. $10. American Association of Dental Examiners, 211 E. Chicago Ave., Ste. 844, Chicago, IL 60611. TEL 312-440-7464. FAX 312-440-7494. Ed. Ronald Maitland. illus.; circ. 1,100 (controlled). **Document type:** bulletin.

617.6   US
AMERICAN ASSOCIATION OF WOMEN DENTISTS. CHRONICLE. 1964. 6/yr. $30 (effective 1993). American Association of Women Dentists, 401 N. Michigan Ave., Chicago, IL 60611-4267. TEL 312-644-6610. FAX 312-527-6640. Ed. Dr. Kate Hakala. adv.; bk.rev.; circ. 2,200 (controlled). **Document type:** newsletter.
Former titles (until 1980): American Association of Women Dentists. Journal; (until 1978): Association of American Women Dentists. Newsletter.

617.6   US   ISSN 0002-7979
RK1
AMERICAN COLLEGE OF DENTISTS. JOURNAL. 1934. q. $30. American College of Dentists, 839 Quince Orchard Blvd., Gaithersburg, MD 20878. TEL 301-977-3223. FAX 301-977-3330. Ed. David W. Chambers. bk.rev.; index. circ. 5,300. (also avail. in microform from UMI; reprint service avail. from UMI) **Indexed:** Curr.Tit.Dent., Dent.Abstr., Dent.Ind., Ind.Med.
—BLDSC (4685.700000); Faxon; UMI; UnCover. *Refereed Serial*

617.6   US   ISSN 0002-8177
RK1.   CODEN: JADSAY
AMERICAN DENTAL ASSOCIATION. JOURNAL. 1913. m. $85 to non-members; members $25 (foreign $105). American Dental Association, 211 E. Chicago Ave., Chicago, IL 60611. TEL 312-440-2500. FAX 312-440-3538. Ed. Dr. Lawrence Meskin; Pub. Laura A. Kosden. adv. contact: Duane Billek. charts; illus.; stat.; s-a. index. circ. 140,000. (also avail. in microform from UMI; back issues avail.; reprint service avail. from UMI) **Indexed:** Abstr.Health Care Manage.Stud., Behav.Med.Abstr., Biol.Abstr., C.I.S.Abstr., Chem.Abstr., Curr.Adv.Ecol.Sci., Curr.Cont., Curr.Tit.Dent., Dent.Abstr., Dent.Ind., Dok.Arbeitsmed., Helminthol.Abstr., Hosp.Lit.Ind., Ind.Med., INIS Atomind., Med.Care Rev., NRN, Nutr.Abstr., Rev.Med.& Vet.Mycol. **Document type:** academic/scholarly publication.
—BLDSC (4686.075000); CASDDS; Faxon; Genuine Article; SWETS; UMI; UnCover. **CCC.**
Description: Provides the latest scientific information and news about dentistry. A mix of articles that are relevant to the dental practitioner and in the forefront of dental research.
Refereed Serial

617.6   US
AMERICAN DENTAL ASSOCIATION. TRANSACTION SERIES: ANNUAL REPORTS AND RESOLUTIONS, SUPPLEMENTS ONE AND TWO, TRANSACTIONS. a. price varies. American Dental Association, 211 E. Chicago Ave., Chicago, IL 60611. TEL 312-440-2500. FAX 312-440-3538. **Document type:** corporate report.
Formerly: American Dental Association. Annual Reports and Resolutions (ISSN 0090-3329)

617.6   US   ISSN 0065-8073
RK37
AMERICAN DENTAL DIRECTORY. 1947. a. $110. American Dental Association, 211 E. Chicago Ave., Chicago, IL 60611. TEL 312-440-2500. FAX 312-440-3538. **Document type:** directory.

617.6   US   ISSN 0894-8275
CODEN: AJDEES
AMERICAN JOURNAL OF DENTISTRY. 1988. bi-m. $50 (Canada and Mexico $75; elsewhere $95). Mosher & Linder, Inc., 9859 IH 10 W., Ste. 107-489, San Antonio, TX 78230. TEL 210-493-9660. Ed. Franklin Garcia-Godoy.
—BLDSC (0824.230000); SWETS; UnCover.

617.643   US   ISSN 0889-5406
RK1   CODEN: AJOOEB
AMERICAN JOURNAL OF ORTHODONTICS AND DENTOFACIAL ORTHOPEDICS. French edition (ISSN 1145-0541) 1915. m. $100 to individuals (Canada $135.89; elsewhere $127); institutions $207 (Canada $250.38; elsewhere $234); students, residents $47 (Canada $79.18; elsewhere $74) (effective 1996); newsstand price: $10. (American Association of Orthodontists) Mosby - Year Book, Inc. (Subsidiary of: Times Mirror Company), 11830 Westline Industrial Dr., St. Louis, MO 63146-3318. TEL 314-872-8370; 800-325-4177. FAX 314-432-1380. TELEX 44-2402. (Co-sponsor: American Board of Orthodontics) Ed. Dr. T.M. Graber. adv.: B&W page $1455, color page $2665; trim 8 1/8 x 10 7/8. s-a. index. circ. 16,803. (also avail. in microfilm from UMI; reprint service avail. from UMI) **Indexed:** ASCA, Biol.Abstr., Curr.Cont., Curr.Tit.Dent., Dent.Ind., Excerp.Med., Ind.Med., Ind.Sci.Rev., INIS Atomind., Sci.Cit.Ind.
—BLDSC (0829.152000); Faxon; Genuine Article; SWETS; UMI; UnCover. **CCC.**
Formerly (until 1986): American Journal of Orthodontics (ISSN 0096-6347); Which incorporates: International Journal of Orthodontics (ISSN 0020-7500); (1938-1937): American Journal of Orthodontics and Oral Surgery (ISSN 0002-9416)
Description: International research covering all phases of orthodontic treatment.
Refereed Serial

617.6   US   ISSN 1062-8746
AMERICAN ORTHODONTIC SOCIETY. WIRELINE.* 1978. q. American Orthodontic Society, 11884 Greenville Ave., No. 112, Dallas, TX 75243-3537. TEL 214-343-0805. FAX 214-343-1628. Ed. Bret Cullers. adv.; circ. 15,000 (controlled). (looseleaf format; back issues avail.) **Document type:** trade publication.
Formerly: American Orthodontic Society. Newsletter.
Description: Provides information relating to changes within the organization; and dental and orthodontic information.

617.6   US   ISSN 0164-1700
AMERICAN SOCIETY FOR THE ADVANCEMENT OF ANESTHESIA IN DENTISTRY. PROCEEDINGS. Variant title: Pain Control in Dentistry. 1972. s-a. $40. American Society for the Advancement of Anesthesia in Dentistry, 475 White Plains Rd., Eastchester, NY 10707. TEL 914-961-8136. Ed. R. Antonio Reyes-Guerra. adv.; bk.rev. circ. 650. **Document type:** proceedings.

617.6   SP   ISSN 1134-3605
ANALES DE ODONTOESTOMATOLOGIA. 1987. 5/yr. 5500 ptas.($108) (effective 1995). Editorial Rocas, Muntaner 393, pral. 2a, 08021 Barcelona, Spain. TEL 39-3-2001389. FAX 39-3-2021958. Ed. J.M. Ustreli i Torrent. circ. 3,000. **Document type:** trade publication.
Formerly (until 1994): Odontostomatologia e Implantoprotesi (Edicion Espanola) (ISSN 0213-9898)

M

MEDICAL SCIENCES — DENTISTRY

617.6   US   ISSN 0003-3006
CODEN: ANPRBG
ANESTHESIA PROGRESS; a journal for pain and anxiety control. 1957. q. $185 to institutions (effective 1996). (American Dental Society of Anesthesiology) Elsevier Science Inc., 655 Ave. of the Americas, New York, NY 10010. TEL 212-989-5800. FAX 212-633-3990. TELEX 420643 AEP Ul. (Subscr. to: Box 882, Madison Sq. Sta., New York, NY 10159-0882) Ed. Raymond A. Dionne. adv.; bk.rev.; abstr.; bibl.; charts; illus.; stat.; index. circ. 4,000. (also avail. in microform from UMI) **Indexed:** Biol.Abstr., Curr.Tit.Dent., Dent.Abstr., Dent.Ind., Excerp.Med., Oral Res.Abstr. **Document type:** academic/scholarly publication.
—BLDSC (0900.520000); Faxon; SWETS. **CCC.**
    Formerly: American Dental Society of Anesthesiology. Journal.
    Description: Directed to practicing dentists. Devoted to the management of pain and anxiety in dental outpatients.
    Refereed Serial

617.6   US   ISSN 0003-3219
CODEN: ANORA
ANGLE ORTHODONTIST. 1931. bi-m. $60 (foreign $70) (effective 1996). (Edward H. Angle Society of Orthodontists, Inc.) Angle Orthodontists Research & Education Foundation, Inc., Box 2577, Appleton, WI 54913-2577. TEL 414-738-6938. FAX 414-830-2468. Ed. Dr. John S. Kloehn. charts; illus.; index. circ. 5,000. (also avail. in microform from UMI; microfiche; back issues avail.) **Indexed:** Curr.Cont., Curr.Tit.Dent., Dent.Abstr., Dent.Ind., Excerp.Med., Ind.Med., Ind.Sci.Rev., Sci.Cit.Ind. **Document type:** academic/scholarly publication.
—BLDSC (0902.750000); Faxon; SWETS; UMI; UnCover.
    Description: Covers all phases of orthodontic treatment as well as the basic sciences related to orthodontics.

617.6   US   ISSN 0003-4770
ANNALS OF DENTISTRY. 1934. s-a. $20 (foreign $22). New York Academy of Dentistry, Box 522, Hackensack, NJ 07602-0522. TEL 201-440-4498. FAX 201-440-7963. Ed. Murray A. Cantor. bk.rev.; charts; illus. circ. 750. **Indexed:** Curr.Tit.Dent., Dent.Abstr., Dent.Ind., Ind.Med., NRN. **Document type:** academic/scholarly publication.
—BLDSC (1040.350000); Faxon; SWETS; UnCover.

617.6   FR   ISSN 0066-2712
ANNUAIRE DENTAIRE. 1936. a. 450 F.($75) Editions de Chabassol, 30 rue de Gramont, 75002 Paris, France. TEL 42-97-50-30. FAX 42-86-02-81. Ed. B. Laloup. adv. circ. 6,500.

618   US   ISSN 0147-0264
ANNUAL REPORT ON ADVANCED DENTAL EDUCATION. 1972. a. $20 to non-members; members $10. American Dental Association, 211 E. Chicago Ave., Chicago, IL 60611. TEL 312-440-2674. FAX 312-440-3538. (also avail. in microfiche from CIS) **Indexed:** SRI. **Document type:** academic/scholarly publication.

617.6   GW
ARAB DENTAL/ALAM TUB AL-ASNAN. (Text in Arabic) 1989. q. DM.32($21) Beta Verlag GmbH, Postfach 140121, 53056 Bonn, Germany. TEL 0228-91937-0. FAX 0228-252067. TELEX 8869536-BETA-D. Ed. Dr. Rabih Nahas. adv.; B&W page DM.4770; trim 250 x 178. charts; illus. circ. 7,500. **Indexed:** ExtraMED. **Document type:** academic/scholarly publication.
●Also available on CD-ROM.

617.6   UK   ISSN 0003-9969
RK1   CODEN: AOBIAR
ARCHIVES OF ORAL BIOLOGY; a multidisciplinary journal in oral research. (Text in English, French, and German) 1959. m. £870($1384) (effective 1996). Elsevier Science Ltd., Pergamon, P.O. Box 800, Kidlington, Oxford OX5 1DX, England. TEL 44-1865-843000. FAX 44-1865-843010. E-mail: nlinfo-f@elsevier.nl; usinfo-f@elsevier.com; forinfo-kyf04035@niftyserve.or.jp; Site addr.: http://www.elsevier.nl/. (Subscr. in U.S. and Canada to: Elsevier Science, 660 White Plains Rd., Tarrytown, NY 10591-5153. TEL 914-524-9200. FAX 914-333-2444) Eds. D.B. Ferguson, Dr. Edward J. Kollar. adv.; bk.rev.; charts; illus.; index. circ. 1,250. (also avail. in microfilm from UMI; back issues avail.) **Indexed:** Abstr.Anthropol., Biol.Abstr., Chem.Abstr., Curr.Adv.Biochem., Curr.Adv.Cell & Devel.Biol., Curr.Adv.Ecol.Sci., Curr.Cont., Curr.Tit.Dent., Dairy Sci.Abstr., Dent.Ind., Excerp.Med., Ind.Med., Ind.Sci.Rev., Ind.Vet., INIS Atomind., Med.& Surg.Dermat., NRN, Nutr.Abstr., Rev.Med.& Vet.Mycol., Rev.Plant Path., Sci.Cit.Ind., Small Anim.Abstr., Triticale Abstr., Vet.Bull. **Document type:** academic/scholarly publication.
—BLDSC (1638.475000); CASDDS; Faxon; Genuine Article; SWETS; UMI; UnCover. **CCC.**
    Description: Publishes research results on every aspect of the oral and dental tissues and bone from the entire range of vertebrates.
    Refereed Serial

617.6   US   ISSN 0004-1769
ARKANSAS DENTAL JOURNAL.* 1930. q. $5 to non-members; members $4. Arkansas State Dental Association, 2501 Crestwood Rd., Ste. 205, N. Little Rock, AR 72116-7613. Ed. R.L. Smith, Jr. adv.; bk.rev.; abstr.; illus. circ. 1,100. (also avail. in microfilm from UMI) **Indexed:** Dent.Ind.
—UMI.

617.6   FR   ISSN 0571-1525
ART DENTAIRE LIBERAL. 1974. bi-m. 400 F. Federation des Chirurgiens-Dentistes de France, 15 bis, av. Foch, 77500 Chelles, France. TEL 60-20-53-45. FAX 60-20-99-83. Ed. Pierre Petit. adv. contact: Henri Parfait. bk.rev. circ. 18,000. **Document type:** bulletin.

617.6   FR   ISSN 1146-0717
ART ET TECHNIQUE DENTAIRES. 1990. 6/yr. Groupe C D P, 77 rue de Richelieu, 75002 Paris, France. TEL 42-61-50-65. FAX 42-61-31-95. Ed. Christian Moullin. adv. contact: Chantal Daly. circ. 3,000.

617.6   US   ISSN 0272-9067
ARTICULATOR. 1971. m. membership. North Central Ohio Dental Society, 2355 W. State Rte. 18, Triffin, OH 44883. TEL 419-447-0253. FAX 419-447-2054. Ed. Robert J. Dornauer. circ. 108. (looseleaf format) **Document type:** newsletter.

617.6   GW   ISSN 0720-972X
DER ARTIKULATOR; Zeitschrift der Kritische Zahnmedizin. 1976. q. DM.10. Vereinigung Demokratische Zahnmedizin e.V., Koelnstr. 198, 53111 Bonn, Germany. TEL 0228-693327. FAX 0228-690474. **Document type:** academic/scholarly publication.

617.6   JA   ISSN 0915-6992
ASIAN JOURNAL OF ORAL AND MAXILLOFACIAL SURGERY. (Text in English) 1989. s-a. Asian Association of Oral and Maxillofacial Surgeons - Ajia Koku Gaku Ganmen Geka Gakkai, Tsurumi Daigaku Shigakubu, Koku Gekagaku Kyoshitsu, 1-3, Tsurumi 2-chome, Tsurumi-ku, Yokohama-shi, Kanagawa-ken 230, Japan.

617.6   AG   ISSN 0004-4881
CODEN: RAOABM
ASOCIACION ODONTOLOGICA ARGENTINA. REVISTA. 1898. q. $80. Asociacion Odontologica Argentina, Junin 959, 1113 Buenos Aires, Argentina. TEL 541-961-1062. FAX 541-961-1110. E-mail: postmaster@asoda.sld.ar. Ed. Eugenio Henry. adv.; bk.rev.; abstr.; bibl.; charts; illus.; index. circ. 7,500. **Indexed:** Dent.Ind. **Document type:** academic/scholarly publication.
—BLDSC (7804.425000).

617.6   FR
ASSISTANCE ET LE PROTHESISTE DENTAIRES. bi-m. Syndicat National des Assistantes et Prothesistes Dentaires, 21 rue Defresne Bast, 95100 Argenteuil, France. Ed. M. Hachmanian. adv.

617.6   BL
ASSOCIACAO PAULISTA DE CIRURGIOES DENTISTAS. JOURNAL. 1957. m. free to members and qualified personnel. Associacao Paulista de Cirurgioes Dentistas - Sao Paulo State Dental Association, Rua Humaita 389, 01321 Sao Paulo, SP, Brazil. Ed. F. Tornelli. adv.; circ. 23,500 (controlled). (tabloid format; back issues avail.)

617.6   BL   ISSN 0004-5276
ASSOCIACAO PAULISTA DE CIRURGIOES DENTISTAS. REVISTA. 1947. bi-m. $15. Associacao Paulista de Cirurgioes Dentistas - Sao Paulo State Dental Association, Rua Humaita 389, C.P. 2523, 01321 Sao Paulo, SP, Brazil. Ed. Julio Jorge D'Albuquerque Lossio. adv.; bk.rev.; cum.index. circ. 23,500. (also avail. in microfilm) **Indexed:** Dent.Ind.

617.6 617   US   ISSN 1061-3315
ATLAS OF THE ORAL AND MAXILLOFACIAL SURGERY CLINICS OF NORTH AMERICA. 1993. s-a. $70 to subscribers of Oral and Maxillofacial Clinics of North America (foreign $90); nonsubscribers $90 (foreign $110) (effective 1994). W.B. Saunders Co. (Subsidiary of: Harcourt Brace & Company), Curtis Center, 3rd Fl., Independence Sq. W., Philadelphia, PA 19106-3399. TEL 215-238-7800. FAX 215-238-6445. (Subscr. to: Periodicals Fulfillment, W.B. Saunders Co., 6277 Sea Harbor Dr., 4th Fl., Orlando, FL 32891-4800. TEL 800-654-2452. FAX 800-874-6418) Ed. Dr. Leon A. Assnel. illus. (back issues avail.) **Document type:** academic/scholarly publication.
—UMI.
    Description: Contains detailed line drawings and photographs, along with articles on various aspects of a single type of surgery or a surgical problem.

618   AT
AUSTRALIAN DENTAL ASSOCIATION. DENTAL BULLETIN. 1964. 10/yr. Aus.$2. Australian Dental Association, Western Australian Branch, 14 Altona St., West Perth, W.A. 6005, Australia. Ed. P.J. Colgan.

617.6   AT   ISSN 0810-7440
AUSTRALIAN DENTAL ASSOCIATION. NEWS BULLETIN. 11/yr. Aus.$77 (foreign Aus.$91). Australian Dental Association, 75 Lithgow St., St. Leonards, N.S.W. 2065, Australia. TEL 02-906-4412. FAX 02-906-4917. Ed. J. Green. adv.: B&W page $755, color page $1657; trim 200 x 270. bk.rev.; circ. 7,600 (paid). **Document type:** newsletter.

617.6   AT   ISSN 0045-0421
CODEN: ADEJA2
AUSTRALIAN DENTAL JOURNAL. 1956. bi-m. Aus.$96. Australian Dental Association, Inc., P.O. Box 520, St. Leonards, N.S.W. 2065, Australia. FAX 02-906-4617. Ed. J.K. Harcourt. adv.; bk.rev.; index. circ. 7,500. (also avail. in microfilm from UMI; back issues avail.; reprint service avail. from UMI) **Indexed:** Biol.Abstr., C.I.S. Abstr., Chem.Abstr., Curr.Adv.Cancer Res., Curr.Adv.Ecol.Sci., Curr.Cont., Curr.Tit.Dent., Dent.Abstr., Dent.Ind., Excerp.Med., Ind.Med., Ind.Sci.Rev., NRN, Sci.Cit.Ind., So.Pac.Per.Ind. **Document type:** academic/scholarly publication.
—BLDSC (1798.450000); CASDDS; EMDOCS; Faxon; SWETS; UMI; UnCover.

617.6 658   AT   ISSN 1320-2340
AUSTRALIAN DENTAL PRACTICE MAGAZINE. 1980. q. plus 2 special issues Auxiliary. Aus.$95. Main Street Publishing Pty. Ltd., P.O. Box 1481, Sydney, N.S.W. 2001, Australia. TEL 61-2-4385333. FAX 61-2-4382999. Ed. Ann Ly. adv.; bk.rev. circ. 3,000. (back issues avail.) **Document type:** trade publication.
    Formerly (until 1990): Dental Reporter (ISSN 0727-7261)
    Description: Covers news, practice management, tax, team building, issues affecting effective business management.

617.6   AT   ISSN 0587-3908
AUSTRALIAN ORTHODONTIC JOURNAL. 1967. s-a. Aus.$50. Australian Society of Orthodontists, 28 Bramble St., Bendigo, Vic. 3550, Australia. TEL 61-54-430877. FAX 61-54-416983. Ed. Brian W. Lee. adv. circ. 750. **Indexed:** Dent.Ind., NRN. **Document type:** academic/scholarly publication.
—UnCover.
    Description: Includes scientific and clinical articles.

MEDICAL SCIENCES — DENTISTRY

617.6   AT   ISSN 0819-0887
AUSTRALIAN PROSTHODONTIC JOURNAL. 1971. a. Aus.$35 (foreign Aus.$40). Australian Prosthodontic Society, Westmead Hospital Dental Clinical School, Westmead, N.S.W. 2145, Australia.
TEL 61-2-633-7157. FAX 61-2-633-4759. Ed. Roland Bryant. adv.; bk.rev. circ. 1,000. **Document type:** academic/scholarly publication.
—BLDSC (1818.340000).
Formerly (until 1987): Australian Prosthodontic Society. Bulletin (ISSN 0816-4460)
Description: Covers all aspect of prosthodontics.

617.6   AT   ISSN 0313-7384
AUSTRALIAN SOCIETY OF ENDODONTOLOGY. NEWSLETTER. 1965. 3/yr. membership (Aus.$4 per no. for institutions only). Australian Society of Endodontology Inc., Ste. 301, 60 Park St., Sydney, N.S.W. 2000, Australia. Ed. Dr. Steven A. Cohn. adv.; bk.rev. circ. 500.

617.6   GW   ISSN 0005-3473
B Z B. (Bayerisches Zahnaerzteblatt) 1961. m. DM.170.80 (foreign DM.190) (effective 1996). (Bayerische Landeszahnaerztekammer) Urban und Vogel, Lindwurmstr. 95, 80337 Munich, Germany. TEL 089-53292140. FAX 089-53292100. Ed. Ursel Meenzen. adv.; bk.rev.; abstr.; bibl.; illus.; index. circ. 11,300. **Indexed:** Dent.Ind. **Document type:** academic/scholarly publication.

617.6   US   ISSN 0005-7258
BAYLOR DENTAL JOURNAL. 1951. 2/yr. free to qualified personnel. Baylor College of Dentistry, Office of Alumni and Public Affairs, 3302 Gaston Ave., Dallas, TX 75246. TEL 214-828-8214. FAX 214-828-8906. Ed. Carolyn Cox. abstr.; illus.; circ. 7,000 (controlled). **Indexed:** Dent.Ind. **Document type:** academic/scholarly publication.
—BLDSC (1871.240000).
Description: Alumni publication with dental features, college and alumni news.

617.6   US   ISSN 0092-9832
BERGEN COUNTY DENTAL SOCIETY. NEWSLETTER. 1920. m. $12 (foreign $18). Bergen County Dental Society, 1060 Main St., River Edge, NJ 07661. Ed. Thomas DiLauro. adv. contact: Stanley Markman. circ. 700 (controlled). (back issues avail.) **Indexed:** Dent.Ind. **Document type:** newsletter.
Formerly: Bergen County Dental Society. Journal.
Description: Provides Bergen county dentists with social, societal, political, and legislative information; includes scientific sessions.

617.6 610   CN   ISSN 0882-1852
BIOLOGICAL THERAPIES IN DENTISTRY. 1985. bi-m. $45 to individuals (outside US & Canada $68); institutions $68 (outside US & Canada $90) (effective 1996). Decker Periodicals, P.o. Box 620, LCD 1, Hamilton, ON L8N 3K7, Canada.
TEL 905-522-7017; 800-568-7281.
FAX 905-522-7839. E-mail: decker@io.org. (U.S. addr.: Box 785, Lewiston, NY 14092-0785) circ. 322. (also avail. in microform from UMI)
—UMI. **CCC.**
Description: Keeps the dental profession up-to-date with current developments in dental therapeutics.

617.6   DK   ISSN 0905-006X
RK55.C5
BOERNE- OG UNGDOMSTANDPLEJEN I DANMARK. (Subseries: Primaer Sundhedstjenestestatistik) 1983. irreg. DKK 60. Sundhedsstyrelsen, Amaliegade 13, 1012 Copenhagen K, Denmark. (Subscr. to: Statens information, P.O. Box 1103, 1009 Copenhagen K, Denmark)
Formerly: Boernetandplejen i Danmark (ISSN 0108-6618)

617.6   BL   ISSN 0045-2378
BOLETIM DE MATERIAIS DENTARIOS.* (Text in Portuguese; summaries in English) 1969. s-a. Universidade Estadual de Campinas, Faculdade de Odontologia de Piracicaba, Sao Paulo, Brazil. illus. **Indexed:** Dent.Ind.

617.643   FR
BREF INFO. 2/yr. Promo U.N., 80-82 rue de la Roquette, 75011 Paris, France. TEL 49-29-46-19. FAX 49-29-46-26. Ed. Robert-Frederic Dumont. circ. 5,000. **Document type:** corporate report.

617.6   UK   ISSN 0007-0610
                   CODEN: BDJOHJ
BRITISH DENTAL JOURNAL. 1880. s-m. £212. British Dental Association, 64 Wimpole St., London W1M 8AL, England. TEL 0171-935-0875.
FAX 0171-224-0603. Ed. M. Grace. adv. contact: Stephen McAuley. bk.rev.; abstr.; charts; illus.; s-a. index. circ. 18,000. (also avail. in microform from UMI) **Indexed:** Abstr.Hyg., Biol.Abstr., C.I.S. Abstr., Chem.Abstr., Curr.Adv.Cancer Res., Curr.Adv.Ecol.Sci., Curr.Cont., Curr.Tit.Dent., Dent.Abstr., Dent.Ind., Ind.Med., Ind.Sci.Rev., Met.Abstr., NRN, Nutr.Abstr., Risk Abstr., Sci.Cit.Ind., Sugar Ind.Abstr., Trop.Dis.Bull., World Alum.Abstr. **Document type:** academic/scholarly publication.
—BLDSC (2299.000000); Faxon; Genuine Article; SWETS; UMI; UnCover.
Refereed Serial

BRITISH DENTAL NURSES' JOURNAL. see *MEDICAL SCIENCES — Surgery*

617.6   UK   ISSN 0266-4356
BRITISH JOURNAL OF ORAL AND MAXILLOFACIAL SURGERY. 1963. bi-m. £69($114) to individuals (outside Europe £71); institutions £130 (outside Europe £212) (effective 1995). (British Association of Oral and Maxillofacial Surgeons) Churchill Livingstone Journals (Subsidiary of: Pearson Professional), Robert Stevenson House, 1-3 Baxter's Pl., Leith Walk, Edinburgh EH1 3AF, Scotland. TEL 0131-556-2424.
FAX 0131-459-1177. (Subscr. to: Pearson Professional Ltd., P.O. Box 77, Fourth Ave., Harlow, Essex CM19 5AA, England. TEL 01279-623760; U.S. subscr: Churchill Livingstone, 650 Ave. of the Americas, New York, NY 10011. TEL 212-206-5000) Ed. P. Ward-Booth. adv. contact: David Dunnachie. bk.rev.; charts; illus.; index. circ. 1,970. (also avail. in microform from UMI) **Indexed:** Biol.Abstr., Curr.Adv.Ecol.Sci., Curr.Cont., Curr.Tit.Dent., Dent.Abstr., Dent.Ind., Excerp.Med., Ind.Med., Ind.Sci.Rev., Res.High.Educ.Abstr., Sci.Cit.Ind. **Document type:** academic/scholarly publication.
—BLDSC (2314.200000); Faxon; Genuine Article; SWETS; UnCover. **CCC.**
Formerly: British Journal of Oral Surgery (ISSN 0007-117X)
Description: Provides contemporary information on developments within the scope of oral and maxillofacial surgery.

617.643   UK   ISSN 0301-228X
BRITISH JOURNAL OF ORTHODONTICS. 1974. q. £80($140) (effective 1996). (British Society of the Study of Orthodontics) Oxford University Press, Oxford Journals, Walton St., Oxford OX2 6DP, England. TEL 01865-267907.
FAX 01865-267773. TELEX 837330-OXPRES-G. E-mail: jnlorders@oup.co.uk. (U.S. subscr. to: Oxford University Press Inc., 2001 Evans Rd., Cary, NC 27513. TEL 919-677-0977. FAX 919-677-1714) (Co-sponsor: British Association of Orthodontists) Ed. R.J. Edler. adv.; bk.rev.; index. circ. 2,150. (also avail. in microform from UMI) **Indexed:** Curr.Adv.Ecol.Sci., Curr.Tit.Dent., Dent.Abstr., Dent.Ind., Ind.Med. **Document type:** academic/scholarly publication.
—BLDSC (2314.500000); Faxon; SWETS; UMI; UnCover. **CCC.**
Description: Contains original articles, reviews, critical commentaries, editorials, and correspondence on features of orthodontic practice and teaching and research.

617.6   UK   ISSN 0957-7173
BRITISH SOCIETY OF DENTAL AND MAXILLOFACIAL RADIOLOGY. PROCEEDINGS. 1978. a. £20. British Society of Dental and Maxillofacial Radiology, University of Manchester Dental School, Radiology Dept., Higher Cambridge St., Manchester M15 6FH, England. TEL 061-275-6690. FAX 061-275-6776. bk.rev. circ. 200.
—BLDSC (6668.100000).
Formerly (until 1986): British Society of Dental and Maxillofacial Radiology. Newsletter.

BULLETIN OF DENTAL EDUCATION. see *EDUCATION — Higher Education*

617.6   US   ISSN 0007-5132
BULLETIN OF THE HISTORY OF DENTISTRY. 1952. 3/yr. $35. American Academy of the History of Dentistry, c/o Aletha Kowitz, 100 S. Vail Ave., Arlington Heights, IL 60005-1866. TEL 708-670-7561. Ed. H.T. Loevy. adv.; bk.rev.; bibl.; illus.; cum.index every 5 yrs. circ. 800. (also avail. in microform from UMI; reprint service avail. from UMI; back issues avail.) **Indexed:** Curr.Tit.Dent., Dent.Abstr., Dent.Ind., Ind.Med. **Document type:** academic/scholarly publication.
—BLDSC (2855.980000); UMI; UnCover.
Description: Covers all areas relating to dental history.
Refereed Serial

617.6   US   ISSN 1048-3594
C D A UPDATE. 1989. m. $24. California Dental Association, Box 13749, Sacramento, CA 95853. TEL 916-443-3382. FAX 916-443-2943. Ed. Douglas Curley. adv. contact: Ingrid Landis. circ. 17,000. (tabloid format; back issues avail.)

617.6   BL   ISSN 0104-4923
C E C A D E NEWS. (Centro de Estudios da Carie Dentaria) (Text in Portuguese; summaries in English, Portuguese) 1993. 3/yr. Universidade de Sao Paulo, Faculdade de Odontologia de Bauru, Al. Dr. O.P. Brisolla, 9-75, 17043 Bauru, SP, Brazil.
TEL 55-142-234133 ext. 218.
FAX 55-142-230415. TELEX 142314 FOBU. Ed. Dr. Maria Francesca T.B. Bijella. bibl.

617.6   FR   ISSN 0397-1643
CAHIERS DE PROTHESE. 4/yr. Groupe C D P, 77 rue de Richelieu, 75002 Paris, France. TEL 42-61-50-65. FAX 42-61-31-95. Ed. C. Knellesen. adv. contact: Chantal Daly. circ. 6,500.
—BLDSC (2952.113000).

617.6   US   ISSN 0008-0977
CALIFORNIA DENTAL ASSOCIATION. JOURNAL. 1918. m. $60 to non-members; members $24; foreign $40. California Dental Association, Box 13749, Sacramento, CA 95853. TEL 916-443-0505.
FAX 916-443-2943. Ed. Jack Conley. adv.: B&W page $1650, color page $2400; adv. contact: Ingrid Landis. bk.rev.; charts; illus. circ. 18,000. **Indexed:** Curr.Tit.Dent., Dent.Abstr., Dent.Ind., INIS Atomind.
Incorporates (in 1973): Southern California Dental Association. Journal (ISSN 0049-156X); Which was formerly (1934-1966): Southern California State Dental Association. Journal (ISSN 0098-7115); S C D A Newsletter; Composite.
Description: Provides dentists with scientific, technique-oriented and practice management information.

617.6   CN   ISSN 1199-1666
CANADIAN DENTAL ASSISTANTS ASSOCIATION. JOURNAL. 1956. 2/yr. Can.$20 (foreign Can.$30). Canadian Dental Assistants Association, 869-871 Dundas St., London, ON N5W 2Z8, Canada.
TEL 519-679-1582; 800-345-5137.
FAX 519-679-8494. Ed. Charlotte Peer Miller. adv.; bk.rev. circ. 3,000 (back issues avail.)
Document type: trade publication.
Formerly: Canadian Dental Assistants Association (ISSN 0833-8264)

617.6   CN   ISSN 0709-8936
                   CODEN: JCDAAS
CANADIAN DENTAL ASSOCIATION. JOURNAL/ASSOCIATION DENTAIRE CANADIENNE. JOURNAL. (Text in English, French) 1935. m. Can.$48($53) (foreign $58). Canadian Dental Association, 1815 Alta Vista Dr., Ottawa, ON K1G 3Y6, Canada. TEL 613-523-1770.
FAX 613-523-7736. Ed. Dr. P.R. Crawford. adv. contact: Janet Duffield. bk.rev.; abstr.; charts; index. circ. 17,800. **Indexed:** Biol.Abstr., Chem.Abstr., Curr.Tit.Dent., Dent.Abstr., Dent.Ind., Dok.Arbeitsmed., Ind.Med., NRN, Nutr.Abstr. **Document type:** academic/scholarly publication.
—BLDSC (4723.010000); Faxon; SWETS; UnCover. **CCC.**
Former titles (until 1979): Dental Journal (ISSN 0382-8514); Canadian Dental Association. Journal (ISSN 0008-3372)
Description: Clinical and scientific articles directed toward general practitioners.
Refereed Serial

MEDICAL SCIENCES — DENTISTRY

617.6   CN   ISSN 0834-1494
CANADIAN DENTAL HYGIENISTS ASSOCIATION. PROBE. 1967. bi-m. Can.$69.55 (foreign Can.$110). Canadian Dental Hygienists Association, 96 Centrepointe Dr., Nepean, ON K2G 6B1, Canada. TEL 613-224-5515. FAX 613-224-7283. (Subscr. to: Keith Health Care Communications, 1382 Hurontario St., Mississauga, ON L5G 3H4, Canada. TEL 905-278-6700. FAX 905-278-4850) Ed. Janice Edgar. adv.: B&W page Can.$825, color page Can.$1405; trim 8 1/2 x 11. bk.rev.; charts; illus. circ. 6,500. **Indexed:** Dent.Ind. **Document type:** bulletin.
—BLDSC (6617.275000). **CCC.**
Formerly: Canadian Dental Hygienist (ISSN 0008-3380)
Refereed Serial

617.6   SZ   ISSN 0008-6568
                       CODEN: CAREBK
CARIES RESEARCH. (Text in English) 1967. bi-m. 375.60 SFr.($289.20) to individuals; institutions 626 SFr.($482) (effective 1996). (European Organization for Caries Research) S. Karger AG, Allschwilerstr. 10, P.O. Box, CH-4009 Basel, Switzerland. TEL 061-3061111. FAX 061-3061234. E-mail: Karger@Karger.ch. Ed. J. Tenoviro. adv.; bibl.; charts; illus.; index. circ. 1,450. (also avail. in microform; reprint service avail. from ISI) **Indexed:** Apic.Abstr., Biol.Abstr., Chem.Abstr., Curr.Adv.Ecol.Sci., Curr.Cont., Curr.Tit.Dent., Dairy Sci.Abstr., Dent.Abstr., Dent.Ind., Excerp.Med., Food Sci.& Tech.Abstr., Ind.Med., Ind.Sci.Rev., NRN, Nutr.Abstr., Sci.Cit.Ind., Sugar Ind.Abstr. **Document type:** academic/scholarly publication.
—BLDSC (3053.200000); CASDDS; Faxon; Genuine Article; SWETS; UnCover. **CCC.**
Description: Coverage of human and animal experimental work for the researcher; clinical trials of interest to the practicing dentist.
Refereed Serial

617.6   US
CASE WESTERN RESERVE UNIVERSITY. SCHOOL OF DENTISTRY. ALUMNI MAGAZINE. 1985. s-a. free. Case Western Reserve University, School of Dentistry, 2123 Abington Rd., Cleveland, OH 44106. TEL 216-368-3480. FAX 216-368-3204. Ed. Mary Wirtz Juhnke. adv.; bk.rev.; illus. circ. 3,500.
Former titles: Case Western Reserve University. School of Dentistry. Dental Alumni News; Case Western Reserve University. School of Dentistry. Dental Alumni Newsletter; Case Western Reserve University. School of Dentistry. Dental Alumni News; Case Western Reserve University. School of Dentistry. Dental Alumni Bulletin (ISSN 0043-4140); Western Reserve University Dental Alumni Bulletin.
Description: Covers dental advancement and school status, university and alumni news.

617.6   ES   ISSN 0008-9907
CENTRO AMERICA ODONTOLOGICA. 1965. q. membership. Editorial Zavaleta, 23 Av. N. 1214, San Salvador, El Salvador. Ed. Dr. J. Benjamin Zavaleta. adv.; bk.rev.

617.6   XR   ISSN 1210-7891
CESKA STOMATOLOGIE. (Text in Czech or Slovak; summaries in English and Russian) 1900. bi-m. $48.60. (Ceska Lekarska Spolecnost J.E. Purkyne) Nakladatelske Stredisko C L S J.E. Purkyne, Sokolska 31, 120 26 Prague 2, Czech Republic. FAX 42-2-202788. (Dist. by: Artia, Ve Smeckach 30, 111 27 Prague 1, Czech Republic) (Co-sponsor: Ceska Stomatologicka Spolecnost) Ed. E. Jirava. adv.; bk.rev.; abstr.; charts; illus.; index, cum.index. **Indexed:** Chem.Abstr., Dent.Abstr., Dent.Ind., Ind.Med., INIS Atomind., Nutr.Abstr., Protozool.Abstr. —CCC.
Formerly (until 1994): Ceskoslovenska Stomatologie (ISSN 0009-0654)

617.6   US   ISSN 0091-1666
CHICAGO DENTAL SOCIETY REVIEW. 1920. m. (11/yr.). $25 to non-members; members $17; institutions $30; foreign $45. Chicago Dental Society, 401 N. Michigan Ave., Ste. 300, Chicago, IL 60611-4205. TEL 312-836-7300. FAX 312-836-7337. Ed. Roger H. Scholle. adv.: B&W page $840; trim 8 3/8 x 10 7/8. bk.rev.; illus. circ. 8,000. (also avail. in microform from UMI; reprint service avail. from UMI) **Indexed:** Dent.Abstr., Dent.Ind.
—BLDSC (3096.530000); UMI.
Formerly: Chicago Dental Society Fortnightly Review (ISSN 0009-353X)
Description: Covers a wide range of topics to assist practicing dentists including: clinical and scientific subjects; local, state and national news and meetings; news and programs of the Chicago Dental Society and its nine branches.

CHIKEN ISHIYAKU JOHO/INVESTIGATIONAL DRUG INFORMATION. MEDICAL AND DENTAL. see *PHARMACY AND PHARMACOLOGY*

CHIRURGIA MAXILLOFACIALIS ET PLASTICA/MAXILLOFACIAL AND PLASTIC SURGERY. see *MEDICAL SCIENCES — Surgery*

617.6   FR   ISSN 0009-4838
CHIRURGIEN-DENTISTE DE FRANCE. vol.46, 1976. w. 450 F. non-members; members 225 F. (foreign 925 F.). Confederation Nationale des Syndicats Dentaires, 22 av. de Villiers, 75017 Paris, France. TEL 47-66-02-32. Ed. Georges-Ericc Ernouf. adv.; bk.rev.; illus.; s-a. index. circ. 21,000. **Indexed:** Dent.Ind., Dok.Arbeitsmed. **Document type:** academic/scholarly publication, trade publication.
—CCC.

617.6   US   ISSN 0894-0975
CINCINNATI DENTAL SOCIETY BULLETIN. 1930. m. $25. Cincinnati Dental Society, 9200 Montgomery Rd., Ste. 21A, Cincinnati, OH 45242. TEL 513-984-3443. FAX 513-984-3047. Ed. John B. Bennett. adv. contact: Beverly G. Fortner. circ. 700. **Document type:** trade publication.
Description: Contains information about dentistry on the local, state and national levels for member dentists.

617.6   AG   ISSN 0325-7479
CIRCULO ARGENTINO DE ODONTOLOGIA. REVISTA. 1950. q. $40. Circulo Argentino de Odontologia, Eduardo Acevedo 54, 1901 Buenos Aires, Argentina. TEL 901-5488. FAX 901-9311. Ed. Nilda Belardi. circ. 3,000. **Indexed:** Dent.Ind.

617.6   AG   ISSN 0045-6942
CIRCULO ODONTOLOGICO DE CORDOBA. REVISTA. 1936. 3/yr. free. Circulo Odontologico de Cordoba, Direccion y Administracion, 27 de Abril 887, T.E. 46207, Cordoba, Argentina. Ed. Dr. Ramon Ocanto. illus. circ. 1,800. **Indexed:** Dent.Ind.

617.6   AG   ISSN 0009-7357
CIRCULO ODONTOLOGICO DE ROSARIO. REVISTA. (Text in Spanish; summaries in English) 1929. q. membership or exchange basis. Circulo Odontologico de Rosario, Rioja 2471, Rosario, Argentina. Ed. Dr. Natalio Grynberg. adv.; bk.rev.; bibl.; illus. circ. 1,000. (also avail. in microfiche) **Indexed:** Dent.Ind.

CLEFT PALATE - CRANIOFACIAL JOURNAL; an international journal of craniofacial anomalies. see *MEDICAL SCIENCES — Surgery*

617.6   FR   ISSN 0998-3392
CLINIC - ODONTOLOGIA. 1980. 6/yr. Groupe C D P, 77 rue de Richelieu, 75002 Paris, France. TEL 42-61-50-65. FAX 42-61-31-95. Ed. Christian Knellesen. adv. contact: Chantal Daly. circ. 8,000.
Formerly (until 1988): Odontologia (ISSN 0244-9331)

617.6   IT   ISSN 0393-7593
CLINICA ODONTOIATRICA DEL NORD AMERICA. 3/yr. L.120000($180) Piccin Editore, Via Altinate 107, 35100 Padua, Italy. TEL 049-655566. FAX 049-8750693. (reprint service avail. from UMI) **Indexed:** Excerp.Med.

617.6   US   ISSN 1057-5480
CLINICAL DENTAL BRIEFINGS; timesaving summaries of significant clinical literature. 1987. m. $108. Boston University, Goldman School of Graduate Dentistry, 100 E. Newton St., Boston, MA 02118. TEL 617-638-4677. Ed. Abigail M. Obenchain. abstr.; tr.lit. circ. 1,168. (back issues avail.)
Formerly (until 1991): Dental Watch (ISSN 0893-665X)
Description: Summaries of literature and dental news.

617.6   DK   ISSN 0905-7161
CLINICAL ORAL IMPLANTS RESEARCH. (Text in English) 1990. q. DKK 1100 (effective 1996). (European Association for Osseointegration) Munksgaard International Publishers Ltd., 35 Noerre Soegade, P.O. Box 2148, DK-1016 Copenhagen K, Denmark. TEL 45-33-12-70-30. FAX 45-33-12-93-87. Ed. Niklaus P. Lang. adv.; illus. circ. 3,200. (reprint service avail.)
—BLDSC (3286.318000); Genuine Article; SWETS; UnCover. **CCC.**
Refereed Serial

617.6   SP
CLINICAS ODONTOLOGICAS DE NORTEAMERICA. Spanish translation of: Dental Clinics of North America. 1973. 4/yr. 15264 ptas.($113) (effective 1990). Interamericana de Espana, S.A., Division de Ciencias de la Salud de McGraw-Hill, Calle Manuel Ferrero, 13, 28036 Madrid, Spain. TEL 315-0340. FAX 733-6627. charts; illus.; index.

617.6   US   ISSN 0010-1559
COLORADO DENTAL ASSOCIATION. JOURNAL. 1922. 4/yr. $25 to individuals (foreign $35); libraries $20 (foreign $30) (effective 1995). Colorado Dental Association, 3690 S. Yosemite, Ste. 100, Denver, CO 80237-1808. TEL 303-740-6900. FAX 303-740-7989. Ed. Stewart Whitmarsh. adv. contact: Barbara White Melin. bk.rev.; circ. 3,000 (paid). **Indexed:** Dent.Abstr., Dent.Ind.
—BLDSC (4730.800000); UnCover.

617.6
COMMUNICATOR (JOHNSTOWN). 1971. q. American Academy of Dental Practice Administration, First United Federal Bldg., 227 Franklyn St., Ste. 220, Johnstown, PA 15901. Ed. W.F. Hrin. circ. 1,100.

617.6   US
COMMUNIQUE (IOWA CITY). q. American Association of Public Health, c/o Marsha Cunningham, Ed., College of Dentistry, University of Iowa, Iowa City, IA 52242. (reprint service avail. from UMI)

617.6   UK   ISSN 0265-539X
                       CODEN: CDHEES
COMMUNITY DENTAL HEALTH. 1984. q. £76 to non-member individuals (outside Europe £83); members £61 (outside Europe £66.50) (effective 1995). (British Association for the Study of Community Dentistry) F D I World Dental Press Ltd., 7 Carlisle St., London W1V 5RG, England. TEL 0171-935-7852. FAX 0171-486-0183. Ed. M.C. Downer. adv.; bk.rev.; abstr. circ. 1,000. **Indexed:** Curr.Adv.Ecol.Sci., Curr.Tit.Dent. **Document type:** academic/scholarly publication.
—BLDSC (3363.608900); SWETS; UMI.
Description: Contains papers, articles, abstracts, and news on all aspects of community and public health dentistry.

617.6   DK   ISSN 0301-5661
                       CODEN: CDOEAP
COMMUNITY DENTISTRY AND ORAL EPIDEMIOLOGY. (Text in English) 1973. bi-m. DKK 1400 (incl. supplements) (effective 1996). Munksgaard International Publishers Ltd., 35 Noerre Soegade, P.O. Box 2148, DK-1016 Copenhagen K, Denmark. TEL 33-12-70-30. FAX 33-12-93-87. Ed. Ole Fejerskov. adv.; bk.rev.; illus. circ. 1,000. (also avail. in microform from SWZ; reprint service avail. from ISI,SWZ) **Indexed:** Biol.Abstr., Curr.Cont., Curr.Tit.Dent., Dent.Abstr., Dent.Ind., Dok.Arbeitsmed., Excerp.Med., Ind.Med., Ind.Sci.Rev., NRN, Nutr.Abstr., Sci.Cit.Ind.
—BLDSC (3363.609000); Faxon; Genuine Article; SWETS; UnCover. **CCC.**
Refereed Serial

MEDICAL SCIENCES — DENTISTRY 4367

617.6　　　US　ISSN 0894-1009
COMPENDIUM OF CONTINUING EDUCATION IN DENTISTRY. Key Title: Compendium (Newtown, Pa.) 1980. 12/yr. $96 (effective 1996). (University of Pennsylvania, School of Dental Medicine) Dental Learning Systems Co., Inc., P.O. Box 500, Jamesburg, NJ 08831-0505. TEL 908-656-1143. FAX 908-656-1146. adv.: page $3365; trim 7 x 10. bk.rev. circ. 60,588. (back issues avail.) **Indexed:** Curr.Tit.Dent., Dent.Abstr., Dent.Ind.
—BLDSC (3363.958000); SWETS.
Former titles (until 1986): Compendium of Continuing Education in Dentistry (ISSN 0734-0338); (until 1980): Compendium on Continuing Education in General Dentistry (ISSN 0196-1756)
Description: Published for generalists and specialists in private practice who wish to expand their knowledge in a variety of dental specialties.

617.6　　　AG　ISSN 0325-2426
CONECTOR. 1971. q. Arg.$4500($45) Instituto de Implantodontologia, Callao 433-3e, Buenos Aires, Argentina. Ed. Carlos Alberto Rillos. adv.; bk.rev.; abstr.; bibl.; illus.; stat. circ. 10,000. (back issues avail.)

617.6　　　US　ISSN 0010-6232
CONNECTICUT STATE DENTAL ASSOCIATION. JOURNAL. vol.27, 1953. q. $15 to non-members. Connecticut State Dental Association, 131 New London Tpke., Glastonbury, CT 06033. TEL 203-659-2623. Ed. Howard I. Mark. adv.; bk.rev.; charts; illus.; circ. 3,000 (controlled). **Indexed:** Dent.Abstr., Dent.Ind. **Document type:** trade publication.
—BLDSC (4731.900000).

617.6　　　US　ISSN 0010-7301
RK97
CONTACT POINT. 1924. q. free. University of the Pacific, School of Dentistry, 2155 Webster St., San Francisco, CA 94115. TEL 415-929-6400. Ed. David W. Chambers. adv.; illus. circ. 6,700. **Indexed:** Chem.Abstr., Dent.Ind.

617.6　　　AG　ISSN 0069-9799
COOPERADOR DENTAL.* 1933. irreg. membership. Cooperativa Dental Argentina, M.T. de Alvear 2167, Buenos Aires, Argentina. Eds. H.B. Ferreri, Horacio Martinez. adv.; bk.rev. circ. 6,000.

617.6　　　US　ISSN 1045-4411
CODEN: CROMEF
CRITICAL REVIEWS IN ORAL BIOLOGY AND MEDICINE. 1989. q. $79.95 to individuals; institutions $195. (American Association of Oral Biologists) Begell House Inc., 79 Madison Ave., Ste. 1201, New York, NY 10016-7892. TEL 212-213-8368. FAX 212-725-1999. Ed. Olav F. Alvares. **Indexed:** Excerp.Med. **Document type:** academic/scholarly publication.
—BLDSC (3487.479500); Genuine Article; SWETS. CCC.
Description: Analyzes the field of oral biology and medicine in the form of review articles of interest to a broad base of scientists engaged in dental research.

CURRENT OPINION IN COSMETIC DENTISTRY. see MEDICAL SCIENCES — Abstracting, Bibliographies, Statistics

CURRENT OPINION IN PERIODONTOLOGY. see MEDICAL SCIENCES — Abstracting, Bibliographies, Statistics

CURRENT TITLES IN DENTISTRY. see MEDICAL SCIENCES — Abstracting, Bibliographies, Statistics

617.6　　　PL　ISSN 0011-4553
CODEN: CZSTA6
CZASOPISMO STOMATOLOGICZNE.* 1948. m. $132. Polskie Towarzystwo Stomatologiczne - Polish Dental Society, Ul. Polorska 21, 90-202 Lodz, Poland. TEL 48-42-321738. (Dist. by: Ars Polona-Ruch, Krakowskie Przedmiescie 7, 00-068 Warsaw, Poland) Ed. Kazimierz Stawinski. circ. 2,500. **Indexed:** Biol.Abstr., Chem.Abstr., Dent.Abstr., Dent.Ind., Dok.Arbeitsmed., Excerp.Med., Ind.Med., INIS Atomind.
—BLDSC (3507.300000); CASDDS.

617.6　　　US
D.L.A.N.Y. NEWSLETTER. 1939. bi-m. $12. Dental Laboratory Association of State of New York, 1 Barstpw Rd., Ste. P-20, Great Neck, NY 11021. TEL 516-829-1144. FAX 516-829-1988. Ed. Teresa M. Sager. adv.; bk.rev.; illus.; stat. circ. 10,000. **Document type:** trade publication, newsletter.
Formerly (until 1989): Dental Laboratory News (ISSN 0011-8664)

617.6　　　CN　ISSN 0418-3010
DALHOUSIE DENTAL JOURNAL. 1961. a. free. Dalhousie Dental Students Society, Dalhousie University, Halifax, NS B3H 4H8, Canada. TEL 902-424-2211. Ed.Bd. adv. circ. 1,000. (back issues avail.)

617.6　　　DK
DENS. 1910. m. Tandteknikenen Foereningen, Upsalagade 20B, DK-2100 Copenhagen OE, Denmark. FAX 009-45-35432104. adv. circ. 800.

617.6　　　GW　ISSN 0177-7483
DENT - TAX; Ratgeber fuer den Zahnarzt. 1980. q. DM.28. Pharmedtax Verlagsgesellschaft mbH, Marienburgerstr. 22, 5000 Cologne 51, Germany. TEL 0221-376950. Ed. Peter John von Freyend. adv.; bk.rev. circ. 28,500.
—BLDSC (5915.905000).

617.6　　　FR
DENTAIRE - HEBDO. 42/yr. Union des Jeunes Chirurgiens-Dentistes, 14 rue Etex, 75018 Paris, France. TEL 46-27-45-39. Ed. Gilles Drain. circ. 10,000.

617.6　　　US
DENTAL ADMISSION TESTING PROGRAM. 1951. a. free. American Dental Association, 211 E. Chicago Ave., Chicago, IL 60611. TEL 312-440-2500. FAX 312-440-3538. Ed. Dr. Gene A. Kramer. circ. 110,000. **Document type:** academic/scholarly publication.

617.6　　　US　ISSN 0733-9836
DENTAL ASEPSIS REVIEW. 1980. m. $10 (foreign $13). Indiana University School of Dentistry, Department of Oral Microbiology, 1121 W. Michigan St., Indianapolis, IN 46202. TEL 317-274-4561. FAX 317-274-5425. Eds. Chris H. Miller, Charles J. Palenik. bk.rev.; index. circ. 1,100. (looseleaf format; back issues avail.)

617.6　　　US　ISSN 0011-8508
CODEN: DEASEJ
DENTAL ASSISTANT JOURNAL. 1931. 5/yr. $30 (foreign $35) to non-members. American Dental Assistants Association, 203 N. La Salle St., Ste. 1320, Chicago, IL 60601-1210. TEL 312-541-1550. FAX 312-541-1496. Ed. Michael Shaneyfelt. adv. contact: Dolorez Lopez. bk.rev.; abstr.; illus.; circ. 15,000 (controlled). (also avail. in microform from UMI; back issues avail.) **Indexed:** Curr.Tit.Dent., Dent.Abstr., Dent.Ind., Oral Res.Abstr. **Document type:** academic/scholarly publication, trade publication.
—UMI.
Description: Contains technical and theoretical articles specifically written for and directed to the dental assistant. Includes office management articles and news of advances in dentistry.

617.6　　　SA　ISSN 0011-8516
CODEN: DASJAG
DENTAL ASSOCIATION OF SOUTH AFRICA. JOURNAL/TANDHEELKUNDIGE VERENIGING VAN SUID-AFRIKA. TYDSKRIF. (Text and summaries in Afrikaans, English) 1922. m. R.500 (effective 1996). Dental Association of South Africa - Tandheelkundige Vereniging van Suid-Afrika, Private Bag 1, Houghton 2041, South Africa. TEL 27-11-6424687. FAX 27-11-6425718. Ed. Dr. Helmut Heydt. adv.; bk.rev.; charts; illus.; index. circ. 3,750. (back issues avail.) **Indexed:** Biol.Abstr., Dent.Abstr., Dent.Ind., I.P.A., Ind.S.A.Per., INIS Atomind. **Document type:** academic/scholarly publication.
—CASDDS.
Description: Original scientific research articles of interest to association members.

617.6　　　TH　ISSN 0045-9917
DENTAL ASSOCIATION OF THAILAND. JOURNAL. 1949. bi-m. $100. Dental Association of Thailand, 71-58 Soi Prangthip, Lardprao, Bangkapi, Bangkok 10310, Thailand. (Mailing addr.: P.O. Box 355, Samsen Nai, Bangkok 10400, Thailand) Ed. Dr. Porjai Ruangsri. illus. (reprint service avail. from IRC) **Indexed:** Dent.Ind.
—BLDSC (4732.750000).

617.6　　　IT　ISSN 0011-8524
DENTAL CADMOS; rivista quindicinale di odontoiatria e tecnica dentaria. 1933. fortn. L.165000($222) (effective 1994). Masson S.p.A., Divisione Periodici, Via Statuto 2-4, 20121 Milan, Italy. TEL 02-6367-1. FAX 02-6367211. Ed. Carlo Guastamacchia. adv.: B&W page L.2700000, color page L.4100000; trim 193 x 265. bk.rev.; index. circ. 21,000. **Indexed:** Dent.Ind., Ind.Med. **Document type:** academic/scholarly publication.
—BLDSC (3553.260000).

617.6　　　US　ISSN 0011-8532
RK1　CODEN: DCNAAC
DENTAL CLINICS OF NORTH AMERICA. Title varies slightly: Dental Clinics. 1956. q. $110 (foreign $135) (effective 1996). W.B. Saunders Co. (Subsidiary of: Harcourt Brace & Company), Curtis Center, 3rd Fl., Independence Sq. W., Philadelphia, PA 19106-3399. TEL 215-238-7800. FAX 215-238-6445. (Subscr. to: Periodicals Fulfillment, W.B. Saunders Co., 6277 Sea Harbor Dr., 4th Fl., Orlando, FL 32891-4800. TEL 800-654-2452. FAX 800-874-6418) Ed. Susan Short. illus.; index, cum.index every 3 yr. (also avail. in microform from MIM,UMI; reprint service avail. from ISI,UMI) **Indexed:** Curr.Cont., Dent.Ind., Excerp.Med., Ind.Med., INIS Atomind., Nutr.Abstr. **Document type:** academic/scholarly publication.
—BLDSC (3553.290000); CASDDS; Faxon; SWETS; UMI; UnCover. CCC.

DENTAL COMPUTER NEWSLETTER. see MEDICAL SCIENCES — Computer Applications

617.6　　　II　ISSN 0970-4167
DENTAL DIALOGUE. 1974. a. $5. Government Dental College & Hospital, Nagpur 440 003, India. Ed. Dr. V.K. Hazarey. circ. 1,500. **Indexed:** Dent.Ind.

617.6　　　GW　ISSN 0011-8575
DENTAL ECHO. (Text in English, French, German, Italian and Spanish) 1950. every 6 weeks. DM.144. Dental Echo Verlag GmbH, Wieblingerstr. 41, 69214 Eppelheim, Germany. TEL 06221-768492. FAX 06221-768592. Ed. Dr. Karlheinz Kimmel. adv.; bk.rev.; charts; illus. circ. 4,500. **Indexed:** Biol.Abstr., Dent.Ind.

617.6　　　US　ISSN 0011-8583
RK1
DENTAL ECONOMICS. 1911. m. $58 (foreign $76) (effective 1995). PennWell Publishing Co., Dental Economics Division, Box 3408, Tulsa, OK 74101. TEL 918-835-3161. FAX 918-831-9804. Ed. Dick Hale; Pub. Dick Hale. adv. contact: LaVerne Lewis. illus.; index. circ. 111,718. **Indexed:** Account.Ind. (1987-), Dent.Abstr., Dent.Ind. **Document type:** trade publication.
●Also available online. Vendor(s): University Microfilms International.
—BLDSC (3553.321000); UMI; UnCover. CCC.
Formerly: Oral Hygiene.
Description: Helps dentists combine their clinical skills and product knowledge with sound management decisions. Includes articles on marketing, financial and investment information.

617.6　　　CN　ISSN 0070-3656
DENTAL GUIDE (DON MILLS). 1965. a. Can.$12.84 (foreign $12). Southam Magazine Group, 1450 Don Mills Rd., Don Mills, ON M3B 2X7, Canada. TEL 416-445-6641. FAX 416-442-2261. adv. circ. 13,663.

DENTAL GUIDE (SCARBOROUGH); the CE planner for the dental profession. see MEETINGS AND CONGRESSES

M

ULRICH'S INTERNATIONAL PERIODICALS DIRECTORY 1996

MEDICAL SCIENCES — DENTISTRY

617.6   UK   ISSN 0011-8605
DENTAL HEALTH. 1962. bi-m. £45 (effective 1995). British Dental Hygienists' Association, St. Luke, Maywood Dr., Portsmouth Rd., Camberley, Surrey GU15 1LH, England. TEL 01276-677156. FAX 01276-671185. Ed. Caroline Clitter. adv.: B&W page £307; trim 210 x 298; adv. contact: Freda Rimini. bk.rev.; charts; illus.; index; circ. 2,000 (controlled). (also avail. in microform from UMI; reprint service avail. from UMI) **Indexed:** Biol.Abstr., Dent.Ind., NRN.
—BLDSC (3553.325000); UMI.
Refereed Serial

617.6   US   ISSN 1047-3823
DENTAL HEALTH ADVISER. q. Whittle Communications L.P., 333 Main Ave., Knoxville, TN 37902. TEL 615-595-5300. Ed. Wayne Christensen.
Description: Provides information regarding diet, dental hygiene and other areas of concern for dental patients, such as gum disease, braces and infant dental care.

617.6   UK   ISSN 0958-6687
DENTAL HISTORIAN. s-a. £12. Lindsay Society for the History of Dentistry, c/o Christine Hillam, University of Liverpool, Department of Clinical Dental Sciences, Pembroke Pl., Liverpool L3 5PS, England. **Document type:** academic/scholarly publication.
—BLDSC (3553.330600).

617.6   US   ISSN 0070-3664
DENTAL IMAGES. 1961. 3/yr. free. Marquette University, School of Dentistry, 604 N. 16th St., Milwaukee, WI 53233. TEL 414-288-7738. Ed. Dr. Robert B. Morris. adv. contact: Carol Trecek. circ. 8,400. **Indexed:** Dent.Ind.
Description: For alumni and friends. Covers the school, the university, and the alumni.

617.6   US   ISSN 1062-0346
DENTAL IMPLANTOLOGY UPDATE. 1990. m. $209. American Health Consultants, Inc., Six Piedmont Center, Ste. 400, Atlanta, GA 30305. TEL 404-262-7436; 800-688-2421. FAX 800-284-3291. Ed. Morton Perel. circ. 1,140. **Document type:** newsletter.
—BLDSC (3553.332200).
Description: Practical information for both general dentists and specialists on materials, procedures and techniques.

617.6   US   ISSN 8750-9539
DENTAL LAB MANAGEMENT TODAY.* 1984. 10/yr. $17 (foreign $75). Dental Lab Publications, Inc., 731 Main St., No. AZ, Monrue, CT 06788-2872. TEL 203-866-3302. FAX 203-838-3454. Ed. Maribeth Marsico. adv.: B&W page $1870, color page $10500; trim 10 3/4 x 14. tr.lit. circ. 19,500. (reprint service avail.)
Description: Provides management & marketing strategies for dental laboratory decision makers.

617.6   US   ISSN 0146-9738
DENTAL LAB PRODUCTS. 1976. bi-m. $24 (foreign $30). Medical Economics Publishing Co., Inc., Five Paragon Dr., Montvale, NJ 07645. TEL 201-358-7200. FAX 201-573-1045. Ed. D. Kaplan. adv.; bk.rev.; illus.; tr.lit. circ. 20,983. (tabloid format; also avail. in microform from UMI) **Document type:** trade publication.
—UMI.
Description: Provides news, new products and step-by-step procedures for dental laboratory owners and managers.

617.6   GW   ISSN 0011-8656
DAS DENTAL-LABOR; internationales Fachblatt fuer die gesamte Zahntechnik und ihre Randgebiete. 1953. m. DM.114 (foreign DM.126). Verlag Neuer Merkur GmbH, Ingolstaedter Str. 63a, 80939 Munich, Germany. TEL 089-318905-0. FAX 089-31890553. Ed. Dr. Joerg Lingenberg. adv.; bk.rev.; charts; illus.; pat.; stat.; index. circ. 17,000. (tabloid format) **Indexed:** Curr.Tit.Dent., Dent.Ind. **Document type:** academic/scholarly publication.

617.6   DK   ISSN 0070-3672
DENTAL LABORATORIE BLADET. 1949. 4/yr. DKK 150. (Association of Dental Laboratories in Denmark - Danske Dental Laboratorier) D L B -Bladforlag A-S, Rentemestervej 64, DK-2400 Copenhagen NV, Denmark. TEL 31-10-76-83. FAX 38-33-16-07. Eds. Vibeke Fialla, Alf Rasmussen. adv.; bk.rev. circ. 500.

617.6   UK   ISSN 0957-5138
DENTAL LABORATORY. (Supplement avail.) 1975. m. £24 (registered dental technicians £16) (foreign £48); newsstand price: £2. Dental Laboratories Association Ltd., Chapel House, Noel St., Nottingham NG7 6AS, England. TEL 01602-704321. FAX 01602-422675. Ed. Bill Courtney. adv.: page £300; adv. contact: Bill Courtney. bk.rev. circ. 3,000. **Document type:** trade publication.
Description: Contains articles of interest to dental labs, DLA news and more.

617.6   US
DENTAL LABORATORY CONFERENCE. NEWS & VIEWS.* 1976. q. membership. Dental Laboratory Conference, Packman Gitman Market, Box 3427, Maple Glen, PA 19002-8427. FAX 215-546-9595. Ed. Robert C. Gitman. adv. circ. 700. (back issues avail.)

DENTAL LABORATORY REVIEW BUYER'S GUIDE. see *MEDICAL SCIENCES — Experimental Medicine, Laboratory Technique*

617.6   US   ISSN 0109-5641
         CODEN: DEMAEP
DENTAL MATERIALS. 1985. 6/yr. $175 to non-members. Academy of Dental Materials, 3302 Gaston Ave., Box 640677, Dallas, TX 75244-0677. TEL 214-828-8278. FAX 214-828-8458. Ed. Dr. Victoria A. Marker. adv.: B&W page $350, color page $1650; adv. contact: Victoria A. Marker. bk.rev.; index. circ. 780. (also avail. in microfilm from UMI; back issues avail.) **Indexed:** Curr.Tit.Dent., Dent.Abstr. **Document type:** academic/scholarly publication.
—BLDSC (3553.365800); CASDDS; Faxon; SWETS; UnCover.
Description: Devoted to the materials used in dentistry; covers all aspects of dental materials science, such as laboratory, clinical, and animal testing of materials and their components, as well as instruments and equipment; interactions of dental materials, testing methods, and protocols.
Refereed Serial

617.6   IT
DENTAL MATERIALS. 10/yr. Via A. Saffi 7, 20123 Milan, Italy. TEL 2-46-94-696. FAX 2-46-94-805. Ed. Dr. Gabriele.

617.6   PH   ISSN 0011-8699
DENTAL MIRROR;* journal of Philippine dentistry. vol.2, 1965. s-a. Philippine Medical - Dental Publications, c/o Philippine Medical Association, PMA Bldg., North Ave., Quezon City, Philippines. Ed. P.V. Norona. adv.

617.1   US   ISSN 1049-4871
DENTAL OFFICE; today's newsletter for the dental staff. 1981. m. $58. Stevens Publishing Corporation, 3630 J.H. Kultgen Frwy., Waco, TX 76706. TEL 817-776-9000. FAX 817-776-9018. Ed. Kathy Witherspoon; Pub. Marc Scheiner. adv.; tr.lit. circ. 7,000. **Indexed:** Dent.Ind. **Document type:** newsletter.
—BLDSC (3553.367500). CCC.
Formerly: Dental Assisting.

617.6   JA   ISSN 0011-8702
DENTAL OUTLOOK/SHIKAI TENBO. (Text in Japanese) 1921. m. 1300 Yen per no. Ishiyaku Publishers, Inc., 7-10 Honkomagome 1-chome, Bunkyo-ku, Tokyo 113, Japan. Ed. Hiroshi Miura. adv.; bk.rev.; abstr.; charts; illus.; s-a. index. circ. 24,500. **Indexed:** Dent.Ind.
—BLDSC (3553.370000).

617.6   UK   ISSN 0011-8710
DENTAL PRACTICE; the journal of modern techniques, equipment and materials. vol.2, 1970. s-m. £32.50 (foreign £46) (effective 1996). A.E. Morgan Publications Ltd., Stanley House, 9 West St., Epsom, Surrey KT18 7RL, England. TEL 01372-741411. FAX 01372-744493. Ed. Mary Newing; Pub. Terence Morgan. adv. contact: Barry Hollamby. bk.rev.; abstr.; charts; illus. circ. 23,300. (tabloid format; also avail. in microform from UMI; reprint service avail. from UMI) **Indexed:** Curr.Tit.Dent., Dent.Ind. **Document type:** trade publication.
—BLDSC (3553.372300); SWETS; UMI.
Incorporating: Dental News.
Description: Entertaining and informative reading for dentists including up-to-date articles on products and news.

617.6 658   CN   ISSN 0827-1305
DENTAL PRACTICE MANAGEMENT. 1985. q. Can.$16.85($19.50) (foreign $32). Southam Magazine Group, 1450 Don Mills Rd., Don Mills, ON M3B 2X7, Canada. TEL 416-445-6641. FAX 416-442-2261. Ed. Janet Bonellie. adv. contact: Lorraine Collinson. circ. 16,910. (back issues avail.) **Indexed:** Dent.Abstr.
—BLDSC (3553.372700); UnCover.
Description: Provides business management information to dentists, hygienists, dental assistants and office managers. Covers topics from investment planning to life-style issues.

617.6   US   ISSN 0011-8737
         CODEN: DPREE3
DENTAL PRODUCTS REPORT; trends in dentistry. 1967. 11/yr. $66 (foreign $88). Medical Economics Publishing Co., Inc., Five Paragon Dr., Montvale, NJ 07645. TEL 201-358-7246. FAX 201-573-0344. Ed. Jeanne K. Matson. adv.; bk.rev.; illus.; tr.lit.; circ. 147,801 (controlled). (tabloid format; also avail. in microform from UMI) **Document type:** trade publication.
—UMI.
Formerly: Dental Products Annual Report (ISSN 0070-3702)
Description: Focuses on the latest innovations in products, literature, techniques, continuing education opportunities and services of interest to practicing dentists.

617.6   SP   ISSN 0212-3738
DENTAL PROTESIS. bi-m. 5000 ptas. Federacion Espanola de Protesicos Dentales, Doctor Fleming 44, Of. 7, 28036 Madrid, Spain. TEL 1-457-91-09. FAX 1-345-78-33. Ed. Carlos Buitrago Alvaro. adv.: B&W page 75000 ptas., color page 95000 ptas.; trim 170 x 250. circ. 5,000.

617.6   HK   ISSN 1016-5037
DENTAL REVIEW; continuing clinical education journal for practising dentists in Asia. (Text in English) 1989. bi-m. $36 (effective Jan. 1993). MediMedia Asia (Subsidiary of: MediMedia Pacific Ltd.), 1501 Tung Sun Commercial Centre, 194-200 Lockhart Rd., Wanchai, Hong Kong. TEL 852-511-0765. FAX 852-507-3817. (Alt. addr.: MIMS Asia, 15 McCallum St., 04-01, Natwest Centre, Singapore 0106, Singapore. TEL 65-223-3788) Ed. H. Edward Lyon. adv.: color page $2527; adv. contact: Mary Ng. index. circ. 12,200. (back issues avail.) **Document type:** trade publication.
Description: Contains abstracts and reviews of articles in dentistry published for continuing education of dentists in Asia.
Refereed Serial

617.6   PH
DENTAL SERVICE QUARTERLY. 4/yr. Philippines Dental Society, Armed Forces, 23 Zamboanga St., Diliman, Quezon City, Philippines. adv. circ. 1,200.

617.6   US
DENTAL SOCIETY OF WESTERN PENNSYLVANIA. BULLETIN. 1900. bi-m. $36. Dental Society of Western Pennsylvania, 900 Cedar Ave., Pittsburgh, PA 15212. TEL 412-321-5810. FAX 412-321-7719. Ed. Dr. Joel A. Casar. adv.; bk.rev.; charts; illus. circ. 1,600. **Indexed:** Dent.Ind. **Document type:** bulletin.
Formerly: Odontological Bulletin (ISSN 0029-8433)

617.6   CN   ISSN 1183-9996
DENTAL STUDY CLUB; journal of dental continuing education. bi-m. $70 to individuals (outside US & Canada $100); institutions $100 (outside US & Canada $135) (effective 1996). (Continuing Dental Education Foundation) Decker Periodicals, P.O. Box 620, LCD 1, Hamilton, ON L8N 3K7, Canada. TEL 905-522-7017. FAX 905-522-7839. E-mail: decker@io.org. (U.S. addr.: Box 785, Lewiston, NY 14092) Ed. Dr. William F. Wathen. abstr.
Description: Presents abstracts and expert reviews from 60 dental journals.

617.6   SA
DENTAL SUMMARIES. (UK & US editions avail.) (Text in English) 1988. bi-m. M I M S, Division of Times Media Limited, P.O. Box 2059, Pretoria 0001, South Africa. TEL 27-12-3485010. FAX 27-12-477716. Ed. D. Verwagen. adv.; charts; illus.; circ. 800 (paid). (back issues avail.)
Description: Summarizes important papers from international journals.

MEDICAL SCIENCES — DENTISTRY

617.6 US ISSN 0895-318X
DENTAL TEAMWORK. bi-m. $30 (foreign $45). American Dental Association, 211 E. Chicago Ave., Ste. 840, Chicago, IL 60611-2616. TEL 312-440-2500. FAX 312-440-2550. Ed. Linda Sprouls. circ. 90,110. **Document type:** trade publication.
—BLDSC (3553.490000). **CCC.**

617.6 UK ISSN 0011-8796
DENTAL TECHNICIAN. 1948. m. £13.90 (foreign £19.50) (effective 1996). A.E. Morgan Publications Ltd., Stanley House, 9 West St., Epsom, Surrey KT18 7RL, England. TEL 01372-741411. FAX 01372-744493. Ed. D. Ritchie; Pub. Terence Morgan. adv. contact: Barry Hollamby. bk.rev.; illus. circ. 3,500. **Indexed:** Br.Ceram.Abstr., Curr.Tit.Dent., Dent.Ind. **Document type:** directory.
—SWETS.
Description: Listing of suppliers and contacts for dental technicians.

617.6 UK
DENTAL TECHNICIAN YEARBOOK & DIRECTORY. 1979. a. £7.70. A.E. Morgan Publications Ltd., Stanley House, 9 West St., Epsom, Surrey KT18 7RL, England. TEL 01372-741411. FAX 01372-744493. Ed. D. Ritchie; Pub. Terence Morgan. adv. contact: Barry Hollamby. **Document type:** directory.

617.3 UK ISSN 0305-5000
DENTAL UPDATE. 1972. 10/yr. £45 (Europe £59; overseas £62; students £20). George Warman Publications, Warman House, 20 Leas Rd., Guilford, Surrey GU1 4QT, England. TEL 01483-304944. Ed. Susan Joyce. adv.; bk.rev.; cum.index. circ. 8,500. **Indexed:** Curr.Adv.Ecol.Sci., Curr.Tit.Dent., Dent.Ind. **Document type:** trade publication.
—BLDSC (3553.515000); Faxon; SWETS; UMI.
Description: Provides dentists with in-depth clinical information on orthodontics, preventative, restorative and conservative dentistry.

617.6 SA ISSN 1011-5986
DENTAL UPDATE; the journal for the general dental practitioner. UK edition: Dental Update (ISSN 0305-5000) (Text in English) 1987. m. R.100. George Warman Publications (Pty.) Ltd., P.O. Box 3847, Cape Town 8000, South Africa. TEL 27-21-24-5320. FAX 27-21-261-332. Ed. A. Rademeyer. adv. circ. 2,300. (back issues avail.) **Document type:** trade publication.
Description: Clinical journal for the continuing education of dentists.

617.6 CN ISSN 0822-1596
DENTALETTER. 10/yr. Can.$137. M P L Communications Inc., 700-133 Richmond St. W., Toronto, ON M5H 3M8, Canada. TEL 416-869-1177. FAX 416-869-0456. **Document type:** newsletter.
Description: Professional source letter for the dentist.

617.6 SZ
DENTALHYGIENE. 1976. 6/yr. 65 SFr. Swiss Dental Hygienists' Association, Oberstadt 11, CH-6204 Sempach, Switzerland. TEL 041-993385. FAX 041-993381. Ed. Vreni Steinegger. adv.; bk.rev. circ. 2,000. **Document type:** academic/scholarly publication.
Formerly: Dentalhygienikerin.

617.6 SA ISSN 0259-563X
DENTEKSA. (Text in Afrikaans, English) 1980. q. (Dental Laboratories Association of South Africa) M I M S, Division of Times Media Limited, P.O. Box 2059, Pretoria 0001, South Africa. TEL 27-12-3485010. FAX 27-12-477716. Ed. A. Hacquebord. adv.; bk.rev.; charts; illus.; index. circ. 663. **Indexed:** Ind.S.A.Per.
Description: A journal for the dental technician.

617.6 UK ISSN 0266-3414
DENTIST. m. £29. Reed Business Publishing Group, Carew Division (Subsidiary of: Reed International PLC), Quadrant House, The Quadrant, Sutton, Surrey SM2 5AS, England. TEL 081-661-3500. Ed. Jennifer C. Dyer. (back issues avail.)
—CCC.

617.643 IT
DENTISTA MODERNO. m. (except July & Aug.). L.100000. Utet Periodici Scientifici s.r.l., Via P. Giuria 20, 10125 Turin, Italy. TEL 39-2-29003555. FAX 39-2-6599049. Ed. Paolo Pegoraro. adv.: B&W page L.2640000, color page L.3795000; trim 185 x 250; adv. contact: Corrado Trevisani. circ. 22,600.

617.6 US ISSN 0277-3635
CODEN: DENTEJ
DENTISTRY (YEAR). 1981. q. $16 (foreign $24). American Student Dental Association, 211 E. Chicago Ave., Ste. 840, Chicago, IL 60611. TEL 312-440-2795. adv. rates page $950; trim 8 1/4 X 10 7/8. circ. 15,000. (reprint service avail.) **Document type:** academic/scholarly publication, trade publication.
—BLDSC (3553.544000); UnCover.
Description: For dental students and young dental professionals. Discusses issues, trends and new developments in dentistry.

617.6 US ISSN 1078-7658
▼**DENTISTRY AND MANAGED CARE NEWS.** 1994. bi-m. $100 to institutions outside the Americas; $65 to institutions in U.S (effective 1996). Excerpta Medica, Inc., Knolls Group (Subsidiary of: Reed Elsevier Medical group), 201 Littleton Rd., Ste. 100, Morris Plains, NJ 07950-2932. TEL 201-285-0855. FAX 201-285-1472. Ed. Nancy Salerno-Davis. adv.; illus. (tabloid format) **Document type:** trade publication.
Description: Provides current information to dentists and dental industry professionals concerning managed care, management, administrative and financial issues.

617.6 JA ISSN 0070-3737
DENTISTRY IN JAPAN. (Text in English) 1968. a. membership. (Japanese Association for Dental Science - Nihon Shika Igakkai) Japan Dental Association, 4-1-20 Kudan-Kita, Chiyoda-ku, Tokyo 102, Japan. FAX 03-3262-9885. Ed. I. Ishikawa. circ. 1,300 (controlled). **Document type:** academic/scholarly publication.
—BLDSC (3553.545000).

617.6 US
DENTISTRY IN SOUTH DAKOTA. 1962. m. $20 to non-members (effective 1995). South Dakota Dental Association, 330 S. Poplar Ave., Box 1194, Pierre, SD 57501-1194. TEL 605-224-9133. FAX 605-224-9168. Ed. Trudy Feigum. adv.; circ. 500 (controlled). **Document type:** newsletter.
Formerly (until 1995): South Dakota Dental Association. Newsletter (ISSN 0038-3287)

617.6 US ISSN 8750-2186
DENTISTRY TODAY. 1982. 11/yr. $40. Dentistry Today, Inc., 26 Park St., Montclair, NJ 07042. TEL 201-783-3190. FAX 201-783-6835. Ed. Ted Fetner; Pub. Paul Radcliffe. adv.; tr.lit. circ. 140,000. **Document type:** trade publication.
—BLDSC (3553.546500).

DENTISTS' COMPUTER NEWS. see *MEDICAL SCIENCES — Computer Applications*

617.6 US
DENTIST'S PATIENT NEWSLETTER. 1983. q. $495 per quarter for 1000 copies. Doctor's Press, Box 10488, Lancaster, PA 17605-0488. TEL 717-393-1010; 800-233-0196. Ed. Kim Conlin; Pub. Cindy A. Young. adv. contact: Rem Jackson. index. **Document type:** newsletter.
Description: Provides dental health information for dentists to use to market their practice.

617.6 US ISSN 0011-9601
DETROIT DENTAL BULLETIN. 1939. m. (8/yr.) $25 to non-members. Detroit District Dental Society, 7430 2nd Ave., Ste. 420, Detroit, MI 48202. TEL 313-871-3500. FAX 313-871-3503. Ed. Edward H. Hirisch. adv.; bk.rev.; abstr. circ. 1,400. **Indexed:** Dent.Ind. **Document type:** trade publication, bulletin.
—BLDSC (3561.500000).

617.6 GW ISSN 0012-1029
CODEN: DZZEA7
DEUTSCHE ZAHNAERZTLICHE ZEITSCHRIFT. (Text in German; summaries in English) 1946. m. DM.272.40. (Deutsche Gesellschaft fuer Zahn-, Mund- und Kieferheilkunde) Carl Hanser Verlag, Kolbergerstr. 22, 81679 Munich, Germany. TEL 089-998300. FAX 089-984809. (Subscr. to: Postfach 860420, 81631 Munich, Germany) Ed.Bd. adv.; bk.rev.; abstr.; charts; illus. circ. 5,300. **Indexed:** Biol.Abstr., Chem.Abstr., Curr.Cont., Curr.Tit.Dent., Dent.Ind., Ind.Med., INIS Atomind. **Document type:** trade publication.
—BLDSC (3575.694000); CASDDS; Genuine Article; SWETS. **CCC.**

617.643 GW ISSN 0178-7276
DEUTSCHE ZEITSCHRIFT FUER BIOLOGISCHE ZAHNMEDIZIN; Archiv fuer ganzheitliche Stomatologie. 1984. q. DM.75 (students DM.57). Karl F. Haug Verlag GmbH, Fritz-Frey-Str. 21, 69121 Heidelberg, Germany. TEL 06221-4062-0. FAX 06221-400727. TELEX 461683-HVVFMD. (Subscr. to: Postfach 102840, 69018 Heidelberg, Germany) Ed. Dr. Christoph Herrmann. adv.: B&W page DM.3280, color page DM.6040; trim 172 x 257; adv. contact: Juergen Schulz. circ. 10,867. **Document type:** academic/scholarly publication.

617.6 GW ISSN 0343-3137
DEUTSCHE ZEITSCHRIFT FUER MUND, KIEFER- UND GESICHTSCHIRURGIE. (Text in German; summaries in English) 1977. bi-m. DM.357. (Deutsche Gesellschaft fuer Mund- Kiefer- und Gesichtschirurgie) Carl Hanser Verlag, Kolbergerstr. 22, 81679 Munich, Germany. TEL 089-998300. FAX 089-984809. (Subscr. to: Postfach 860420, 81631 Munich, Germany) (Co-sponsor: Berufsverband Deutscher Aerzte fuer Mund-Kiefer-Gesichtschirurgie e.V.) adv.; bk.rev.; abstr.; charts; illus. circ. 1,350. **Indexed:** Curr.Tit.Dent. **Document type:** trade publication.
—BLDSC (3575.815000); SWETS. **CCC.**

DEUTSCHER KONGRESS KALENDER ZAHNMEDIZINER. see *MEETINGS AND CONGRESSES*

617.6 GW ISSN 0344-2926
DEUTSCHER ZAHNAERZTEKALENDER. 1941. a. DM.56. Carl Hanser Verlag, Kolbergerstr. 22, 81679 Munich, Germany. TEL 089-998300. FAX 089-984809. (Subscr. to: Postfach 860420, 81631 Munich, Germany) Ed. Dr. Werner Ketterl. adv. circ. 6,000. **Document type:** trade publication.

617.5 MX
DICCIONARIO DE ESPECIALIDADES ODONTOLOGICAS. 1984. a. Ediciones P L M, S.A. de C.V., San Bernadino 17, Colonia del Valle, 03100 Mexico D.F., Mexico. TEL 687-1311. FAX 536-5027. TELEX 01772912 EPLM ME. Ed. Patricia Calderon. circ. 5,000.

617.6 SW ISSN 0281-5168
DINA TAENDER; en vaentrumstidning fraan Tandvaernet. 1959. q. SEK 90 includes membership (effective 1990). Tandvaernet, P.O. Box 3198, S400 10 Goeteborg, Sweden. Ed. Ove Sjoestroem. adv. contact: Ronald Durghram. **Document type:** consumer publication, newspaper.
Formerly (until 1983): Tandvaernsnytt.

617.6 US
DISTRIBUTION OF DENTISTS IN THE U S. triennial. $100 to non-members; members $25. American Dental Association, Survey Center, 211 E. Chicago Ave., Chicago, IL 60611. TEL 312-440-2500. FAX 312-440-2550. **Document type:** monographic series.

617.6 US
DISTRICT OF COLUMBIA DENTAL SOCIETY. NEWSLETTER. 1915. 10/yr. membership. District of Columbia Dental Society, 502 C St., N.E., Washington, DC 20002-5810. TEL 202-547-7613. FAX 202-546-1482. Ed. Maggie DiJulio. adv. circ. 850. **Document type:** newsletter.
Description: Contains news of particular interest to District of Columbia and surrounding metropolitan area practitioners, such as Society activities, legislative and political developments, community activities, as well as news of general interest.

MEDICAL SCIENCES — DENTISTRY

617.643 IT
DOCTOR OS. 9/yr. L.50000. Ariesdue s.r.l., Via Airoldi 9, 22060 Carimatee (CO), Italy. TEL 39-31-792135. FAX 39-31-7907432. Ed. Sergio Porro. circ. 21,000.

617.634 IT
DOSSIER DEL DENTISTA MODERNO. irreg. (7-8/yr.) Utet Periodici Scientifici s.r.l., Via P. Giuria 20, 10125 Turin, Italy. TEL 39-2-29003555. FAX 39-2-6599049. Ed. Paolo Pegoraro. adv.: B&W page L.2640000, color page L.3795000; trim 185 x 250; adv. contact: Corrado Trevisan. circ. 22,470.

617.6 US ISSN 0012-8759
EASTERN DENTAL SOCIETY BULLETIN.* vol.11, 1968. m. membership. Eastern Dental Society, c/o Tim Wong, D.D.S., 85 4th Ave., New York, NY 10003. bk.rev.; illus.

617.6 UA ISSN 0070-9484
EGYPTIAN DENTAL JOURNAL. (Text in English; summaries in Arabic) 1955. q. $36. Egyptian Dental Association, Dar el Hekma, 42 Kasr el-Eini St., Cairo, Egypt. Ed. Dr. M. el Sadeek. Indexed: Biol.Abstr., Dent.Ind.

617.6 GR
ELLINIKI ODONTIATRIKI OMOSPONDIA. ENEMEROTIKO DELTIO/HELLENIC DENTAL ASSOCIATION. JOURNAL. (Text in Greek) bi-m. free to qualified personnel. Hellenic Dental Association, Themistokleous 38, 106 78 Athens, Greece. TEL 30-1-3803-816. FAX 30-1-3834-385. Ed. Dimitrios Damoulis. Document type: academic/scholarly publication.

617.6 FR ISSN 1168-5476
ENDO; revue Francaise d'endodontie. 4/yr. Groupe C D P, 77 rue de Richelieu, 75002 Paris, France. TEL 42-61-50-65. FAX 42-61-31-95. Ed. Jean-Marie Laurichesse. adv. contact: Chantal Daly. circ. 3,000.
—BLDSC (3740.420000).
Formerly (until 1992): Revue Francaise d'Endodontie (ISSN 0294-1813)

617.6 SP ISSN 1130-9903
ENDODONCIA. (Text in Spanish; summaries in English) 1982. q. 3600 ptas.($26) (Asociacion Espanola de Endodoncia) Ediciones Ergon, S.A., Pza. Josep Pallach 10, 1o 1o, 08035 Barcelona, Spain. TEL 4285500. FAX 4285660. (Subscr. to: Ergon, C. Antonio Lopez Aguado 1, 28029 Madrid, Spain) adv.; bk.rev.; index. (back issues avail.)
—BLDSC (3743.098000).
Formerly: Revista Espanola de Endodoncia (ISSN 0212-4688)

617.6 DK ISSN 0109-2502
CODEN: EDTRED
ENDODONTICS & DENTAL TRAUMATOLOGY. (Supplements avail.) (Text and summaries in English) 1985. bi-m. DKK 1200 (effective 1996). (International Association for Dental Traumatology) Munksgaard International Publishers Ltd., 35 Noerre Soegade, P.O. Box 2148, DK-1016 Copenhagen K, Denmark. TEL 33-127030. FAX 33-129387. Ed. Leif Tronstad. adv.; bk.rev.; illus. circ. 800. (back issues avail.) Indexed: Chem.Abstr., Curr.Cont., Curr.Tit.Dent., Dent.Abstr., Excerp.Med.
—BLDSC (3743.120000); CASDDS; Faxon; Genuine Article; SWETS; UnCover. **CCC.**
Refereed Serial

617.6 GW ISSN 0940-9505
ENDODONTIE; Zeitschrift fuer die Praxis. 1992. 4/yr. DM.168 (foreign DM.178). Quintessenz Verlags GmbH, Ifenpfad 2-4, 12107 Berlin, Germany. TEL 030-74006-0. FAX 030-7415080. Ed.Bd. adv. contact: Gudrun Matthes. Document type: trade publication.
—BLDSC (3743.150000).

617.6 BL
EQUIPE DE ODONTOLOGIA SANITARIA. BOLETIM.* (Text in Portuguese; occasionally in Spanish) 1964. 4/yr. free. Departamento da Saude, Esplanada dos Ministerios, Bloco 11, 70058 Brasilia, D.F., Brazil. Ed. Dr. Antonio Motta Gimenez. bibl.; charts; stat.; circ. 1,000 (controlled). (looseleaf format)
Formerly: Servico de Odontologia Sanitaria. Boletim (ISSN 0037-2722)

617.6 US ISSN 1045-9812
ESTHETIC DENTISTRY UPDATE (PHILADELPHIA); endorsed by the American Academy of Cosmetic Dentistry. 1990. bi-m. $125 (foreign $152) (effective 1996). W.B. Saunders Co. (Subsidiary of: Harcourt Brace & Company), The Curtis Center, 3rd Fl., Independence Sq. W., Philadelphia, PA 19106-3399. TEL 215-238-7807. FAX 215-238-6445. (Subscr. to: W.B. Saunders Co., Periodicals Dept., 6277 Sea Harbor Dr., 4th Fl., Orlando, FL 32887-4800. TEL 800-654-2452. FAX 800-874-6418) Ed. Dr. Roger P. Levin; Pub. Joan W. Blumberg. adv.: B&W page $580, color page $1380, 7 x 10; adv. contact: Steve Gray. illus. circ. 1,390. Document type: academic/scholarly publication.
—BLDSC (3812.569600). **CCC.**
Description: Provides information on restorative dentistry to practitioners seeking to expand their practices.
Refereed Serial

617.6 DK
CODEN: SJDRAN
EUROPEAN JOURNAL OF ORAL SCIENCES. (Text and summaries in English) 1893. 6/yr. DKK 1350 (effective 1996). (Nordiska Odontologiska Foreningen) Munksgaard International Publishers Ltd., 35 Noerre Soegade, P.O. Box 2148, DK-1016 Copenhagen K, Denmark. TEL 33-127030. FAX 33-129387. Ed. J.J. Pindborg. adv.; illus.; index. circ. 1,400. (also avail. in microform from SWZ; reprint service avail. from ISI,SWZ) Indexed: Biol.Abstr., Chem.Abstr., Curr.Adv.Ecol.Sci., Curr.Cont., Curr.Tit.Dent., Dent.Abstr., Dent.Ind., Excerp.Med., Ind.Med., Med.& Surg.Dermat., Nutr.Abstr., Risk Abstr., Sugar Ind.Abstr.
—CASDDS; EMDOCS; Faxon; Genuine Article; UnCover. **CCC.**
Former titles: Scandinavian Journal of Dental Research (ISSN 0029-845X); (until 1970): Odontologisk Tidskrift (ISSN 0472-514X)
Refereed Serial

617.6 UK ISSN 0141-5387
EUROPEAN JOURNAL OF ORTHODONTICS. 1979. bi-m. £120($195) (effective 1996). (European Association of Orthodontics) Oxford University Press, Oxford Journals, Walton St., Oxford OX2 6DP, England. TEL 01865-267907. FAX 01865-267773. TELEX 837330-OXPRES-G. E-mail: jnlorders@oup.co.uk. (U.S. subscr. to: Oxford University Press Inc., 2001 Evans Rd., Cary, NC 27513. TEL 919-677-0977. FAX 919-677-1714) Ed. Fraser McDonald. adv.; bk.rev. circ. 2,600. Indexed: Biol.Abstr., Curr.Cont., Dent.Ind., Excerp.Med., Ind.Med. Document type: academic/scholarly publication.
—BLDSC (3829.733300); Faxon; Genuine Article; SWETS; UMI; UnCover. **CCC.**
Description: Presents research or clinical papers of interest to all orthodontists.

617.6 UK ISSN 0965-7452
EUROPEAN JOURNAL OF PROSTHODONTICS AND RESTORATIVE DENTISTRY. (Abbreviated title: E J P R D) 1962. q. £37.50 to non-member individuals (outside Europe £34); members £30 (outside Europe £34); institutions £65 (outside Europe £70) (effective 1995). (F D I World Dental Federation) F D I World Dental Press Ltd., 7 Carlisle St., London W1V 5RG, England. TEL 0171-935-7852. FAX 0171-486-0183. Co-sponsor: Dutch Society of Prosthetic Dentistry) Ed. Paul S. Wright. adv.; bk.rev. circ. 1,500. (tabloid format) Document type: academic/scholarly publication.
—BLDSC (3829.737550); SWETS.
Former titles (until 1992): Restorative Dentistry; Anglo-Continental Dental Society. Journal (ISSN 0003-3324)
Description: Covers all aspects of prosthodontics and restorative dentistry.

617.6 NE ISSN 0928-4109
EXKIES; vaktijdschrift voor tandartsen en tandtechnici. 1981. 8/yr. fl.135. Van Zuiden Communications B.V., Postbus 2122, 2400 CC Alphen aan den Rijn, Netherlands. TEL 31-1720-76191. FAX 31-1720-71882. Dir. L.J. van Zuiden. circ. 6,000. Document type: trade publication.

617.6 US ISSN 0894-7929
EXPLORER (FALLS CHURCH). 1974. m. $15 (foreign $20). National Association of Dental Assistants, 900 S. Washington St., Ste. G13, Falls Church, VA 22046. TEL 703-237-8616. Ed. S. Young. circ. 3,000.

617.6 US
EXPLORER (LAKE WORTH). 1972. s-a. free. Atlantic Coast District Dental Association, 5700 Lake Worth Rd., Ste. 206, Lake Worth, FL 33463. TEL 407-968-7714. FAX 407-968-4834. Ed. Dr. Richard Masella. adv. contact: Catherine Sanson. tr.lit. circ. 1,600. Indexed: Biol.Abstr., Biol.Dig., GeoRef. Document type: newsletter.

617.6 UK
F D I WORLD. (Editions in English, French, German, Spanish) 1952. bi-m. £30 to non-members in Europe; elsewhere £35 (effective 1995). (Federation Dentaire Internationale - World Dental Federation) F D I World Dental Press Ltd., 7 Carlisle St., London W1V 5RG, England. TEL 0171-935-7852. FAX 0171-486-0183. Ed. Dr. Stephen Hancocks. adv.; illus. circ. 17,000. Document type: newsletter.
Former titles (until 1992): F D I Dental World (ISSN 0965-9986) & F D I News; F D I Newsletter (ISSN 0014-5777)
Description: Includes clinical articles, dental news from around the world, news of F.D.I. activities, and the trade industry; also contains features and congress news.

317.3 UK
F D I WORLD DENTAL PRESS. TECHNICAL REPORTS. irreg. price varies. (F D I World Dental Federation) F D I World Dental Press Ltd., 7 Carlisle St., London W1V 5RG, England. TEL 0171-935-7852. FAX 0171-486-0183. Document type: monographic series.
Description: Discusses clinical aspects of dental care.

617.6 US
FACETS (SAN DIEGO). 1930. m. $20. San Diego County Dental Society, 1275 W. Morena Blvd., Ste.B, San Diego, CA 92110-3837. TEL 619-275-7188. FAX 619-275-0646. Ed. Dr. David M. Donnelly. adv. contact: Shirlee Smith. circ. 1,300. Indexed: Dent.Ind. Document type: newsletter.
Former titles: San Diego County Dental Society. News; San Diego County Dental Society. Bulletin (ISSN 0036-4010)
Description: Provides in-house information to the membership.

617.6 BL
FACULDADE DE ODONTOLOGIA DE BAURU. REVISTA. (Text in Portuguese; abstracts in English, Portuguese) 1993. a. Cr.$15 (effective 1994). Universidade de Sao Paulo, Faculdade de Odontologia de Bauru, Al. Dr. O.P. Brisolla, 9-75, C.P. 73, 17043-101 Bauru, SP, Brazil. TEL 55-142-234133. FAX 55-142-230415. TELEX 142314 FOBU. bibl.

617.6 BL
FACULDADE DE ODONTOLOGIA DE LINS. REVISTA. (Text in Portuguese; summaries in English, Portuguese) vol.6, 1993. s-a. Faculdade de Odontologia de Lins, Rua Tenente Florencio Pupo Neto, 300, Jd. Americano, 16400-000 Lins, SP, Brazil. TEL 0145-225088. FAX 0145-224611. adv.; bibl.; charts; illus. circ. 1,000. Document type: academic/scholarly publication.

617.6 BL ISSN 0048-3419
FACULDADE DE ODONTOLOGIA DE PERNAMBUCO. REVISTA. (Text in Portuguese; summaries in English, Portuguese) 1968. s-a. free. Faculdade de Odontologia de Pernambuco, Biblioteca, Av. General Newton Cavalcanti, 1650, Camarajibe, Pernambuco, Brazil. illus.; index. Indexed: Dent.Ind.

617.6 BL
FACULDADE DE ODONTOLOGIA DE PORTO ALEGRE. REVISTA. (Text in Portuguese; summaries in English) 1958. s-a. exchange basis only. Universidade Federal do Rio Grande do Sul, Faculdade de Odontologia, Ramiro Barcelos 2492, P.O. Box 1118, 90000 Porto Alegre, Brazil. TEL 55-512-255784. TELEX 051-1055. Eds. Jorge H. Brito, Pantelis Varvaki Rados. adv. circ. 3,500. (back issues avail.) Indexed: Bibliogr.Bras.Odontol., Dent.Ind. Document type: academic/scholarly publication.
Formerly: Universidade Federal do Rio Grande do Sul. Faculdade de Odontologia. Revista (ISSN 0477-6763)
Description: Covers orthodontics, dental oclusion, pathology, preventive dentistry and dental care.

MEDICAL SCIENCES — DENTISTRY

617.6 069 AG
FACULTAD DE ODONTOLOGIA DE BUENOS AIRES. MUSEO Y CENTRO DE ESTUDIOS HISTORICOS. REVISTA. 1986. s-a. Facultad de Odontologia de Buenos Aires, Museo y Centro de Estudios Historicos, Marcelo T. de Alvear 2142, 1122 Buenos Aires, Argentina. TEL 54-1-9619080. FAX 54-1-9620176.

617.6 CK ISSN 0046-354X
FEDERACION ODONTOLOGICA COLOMBIANA. REVISTA. 1950. 4/yr. Federacion Odontologica Colombiana, Calle 71 No. 11-10, Of 1101, Apdo. Aereo 52925, Bogota, Colombia. Ed. Edmundo Alberto Noguera. adv.; illus. **Indexed:** Dent.Ind., Ind.Med.
—BLDSC (7815.800000).

617.6 FR ISSN 1163-1325
FEDERATION NATIONALE INDEPENDANTE DES SYNDICATS DES PERSONNELS DES CABINETS ET LABORATOIRES DENTAIRES. BULLETIN NATIONAL. 1945. 6/yr. 163 rue Saint Honore, 75001 Paris, France. TEL 42-66-37-75. Ed. Louis Vergnaud. adv. circ. 1,800.
Formerly (until 1991): Mecanicien en Prothese Dentaire (ISSN 1163-1600)

FINLAND. LAAKINTOHALLITUS. LAAKARIT - LAKKARE. see MEDICAL SCIENCES

614 US ISSN 0092-3664
TD467
FLUORIDATION CENSUS. 1954. quinquennial. U.S. Center for Prevention Services, Division of Oral Health, Program Services Branch, 1600 Clifton Rd., N.E., F-10, Atlanta, GA 30333. TEL 404-639-8377. FAX 404-639-8617. **Document type:** government publication.

FLUORIDE. see MEDICAL SCIENCES — Abstracting, Bibliographies, Statistics

617.6 US ISSN 1042-2528
FOCUS ON OHIO DENTISTRY. m. $30 to non-members & libraries (foreign $45); members $15 (effective 1994). Ohio Dental Association, 1370 Dublin Rd., Columbus, OH 43215-1098. TEL 614-486-2700. (Subscr. to: Dept. 367, Box 182039, Columbus, OH 43218-2039) **Document type:** newsletter.

617.6 SZ
FOLIA ODONTOLOGICA. (Text in French, German) q. CH-8808 Pfaeffikon, Switzerland. TEL 01-7849693. circ. 3,200.

617.6 US ISSN 0071-9285
LJ105.P75
FRATER OF PSI OMEGA. 1901. 3/yr. membership. Psi Omega Fraternity, 6730 Commerce Rd., Orchard Lake, MI 48324. TEL 810-363-4818. Ed. Christina E. Angott. circ. 8,500. **Document type:** newsletter.

617.6 GW ISSN 0340-1766
DER FREIE ZAHNARZT. 1958. m. DM.3. (Freier Verband Deutscher Zahnaerzte e.V.) Kern und Birner GmbH und Co., Werrastr. 4, 60486 Frankfurt a.M., Germany. Ed. Hubertus Foester. adv.; bk.rev. circ. 50,000. **Indexed:** Curr.Tit.Dent., Dent.Ind. **Document type:** trade publication.
Formerly: Monatsschrift Deutscher Zahnaerzte (ISSN 0047-7842)

617.643 SZ ISSN 0301-536X
CODEN: FROPBK
FRONTIERS OF ORAL PHYSIOLOGY. (Text in English) 1974. irreg. price varies. S. Karger AG, Allschwilerstr. 10, P.O. Box, CH-4009 Basel, Switzerland. TEL 061-3061111. FAX 061-3061234. E-mail: Karger@Karger.ch. Ed. D.B. Ferguson. (reprint service avail. from ISI) **Indexed:** Biol.Abstr., Chem.Abstr., Ind.Med. **Document type:** academic/scholarly publication.
—BLDSC (4042.045000); CASDDS; Faxon. **CCC.**
Description: Aids for specialists who wish to expand with the field of dental medicine.
Refereed Serial

617.6 US ISSN 8756-3150
FUNCTIONAL ORTHODONTIST; a journal of functional jaw orthopedics. vol.4, 1987. bi-m. $69. c/o The AAFO, 106 S. Kent St., Winchester, VA 22601. TEL 703-662-2200. Ed. Dr. Craig C. Stoner.
—BLDSC (4055.630000); UnCover.

617.6 US ISSN 0884-6898
G M D A BULLETIN.* 1934. q. $30 (foreign $40). Greater Milwaukee Dental Association, 111 E. Wisconsin Ave., Ste. 1300, Milwaukee, WI 53202-4807. TEL 414-461-0230. Ed. R.F. Johnson. adv.; charts; illus. circ. 1,000. **Indexed:** Dent.Ind.
—BLDSC (4196.370000).
Formerly: Greater Milwaukee Dental Bulletin (ISSN 0017-3754)

617.6 US ISSN 1063-3324
G P. (General Practitioner) m. $139. American Health Consultants, Inc., Six Piedmont Center, Ste. 400, Atlanta, GA 30305. TEL 404-262-7436. FAX 404-262-7837. Ed. Mike Coleman. circ. 1,730. **Document type:** newsletter.
Incorporates (in 1992): Cosmetic Dentistry for G Ps & Dental Practice Success; Which incorporated (in 1990): American Health Consultants. Press Report; Former titles: Dental Update on Practice Management; Dental Management Update; Incorporates (1990-1991): Dentist's Malpractice Protector; (1989-1991): Endodontics for G Ps; (1989-1991): Soft Tissue Care for G Ps.
Description: Covers clinical topics of interest to the general dentist such as aesthetic dentistry, periodontics, endodontics, implant dentistry, pediatric dentistry and orthodontics.

617.6 SP
GACETA DENTAL. 12/yr. Pues S.L., Pinos Alta 15, 1o, 28029 Madrid, Spain. TEL 1-314-78-13. FAX 1-315-19-60. Ed. Manuel Manzano Martin. circ. 17,000.

617.6 UK ISSN 0072-0674
GENERAL DENTAL COUNCIL. DENTISTS REGISTER. 1878. a. £15.50 (overseas £18.50). General Dental Council, 37 Wimpole St., London W1M 8DQ, England. TEL 0171-486-2171. FAX 0171-224-3294. Ed. Jean Dineen. (back issues avail.) **Document type:** directory.

617.6 UK ISSN 0072-0682
GENERAL DENTAL COUNCIL. MINUTES OF THE PROCEEDINGS. 1956. a. £10. General Dental Council, 37 Wimpole St., London W1M 8DQ, England. TEL 0171-486-2171. FAX 0171-224-3294. **Document type:** proceedings.

617.6 UK
GENERAL DENTAL TREATMENT. 1983. s-a. £40($66) (effective 1995). Churchill Livingstone Journals (Subsidiary of: Pearson Professional), Robert Stevenson House, 1-3 Baxter's Pl., Leith Walk, Edinburgh EH1 3AF, Scotland. TEL 0131-556-2424. FAX 0131-459-1177. (Subscr. to: Pearson Professional Ltd., P.O. Box 77, Fourth Ave., Harlow, Essex CM19 5AA, England. TEL 01279-623760; U.S. subscr. to: Churchill Livingstone, 650 Ave. of the Americas, New York, NY 10011. TEL 212-206-5000) Eds. Drs. W.M. Tay, E. Lynch. adv. contact: David Dunnachie. **Document type:** academic/scholarly publication.
Description: Provides updates on materials, techniques, and drugs commonplace in dentistry.

617.6 US ISSN 0363-6771
GENERAL DENTISTRY. 1952. bi-m. $40 (foreign 60) (effective 1996). Academy of General Dentistry, 211 E. Chicago Ave., Ste. 1200, Chicago, IL 60611. TEL 312-440-4300. FAX 312-440-0559. Ed. Dr. William W. Howard. adv.: B&W page $2600, color page $3700; adv. contact: Todd Goldman. bk.rev.; illus.; index. circ. 45,000. (also avail. in microform from UMI) **Indexed:** Biol.Abstr., Dent.Ind., Energy Res.Abstr. **Document type:** trade publication.
—BLDSC (4103.430000); SWETS; UMI; UnCover. **CCC.**
Former titles: Academy of General Dentistry. Journal (ISSN 0001-4265); Academy of General Dentistry. Bulletin (ISSN 0098-3810)
Description: Offers clinical data and management information for the general dentist.
Refereed Serial

617.6 UK ISSN 0734-0664
CODEN: GRDND6
GERODONTOLOGY; an international journal. 1982-1991; resumed. s-a. £22 to non-member individuals (outside Europe £24); members £18 (outside Europe £20); institutions £30 (outside Europe £32) (effective 1995). F D I World Dental Press Ltd., 7 Carlisle St., London W1V 5RG, England. TEL 0171-935-7852. FAX 0171-486-0183. Ed. Dr. M.R. Heath. adv.; bk.rev. circ. 1,000. **Indexed:** Biol.Abstr., Chem.Abstr., Curr.Adv.Ecol.Sci., Curr.Cont., Dent.Abstr., Excerp.Med., NRN. **Document type:** academic/scholarly publication.
—BLDSC (4162.179500); CASDDS; UMI; UnCover.
Description: Provides a publication for dental research in gerodontology at the clinical and basic sciences level. Deals with dentistry for the aging and the aged adult.
Refereed Serial

617.6 IT ISSN 0393-067X
GIORNALE DELL'ODONTOIATRA/DENTAL FLASH. 1984. 18/yr. L.6000($26) (effective 1994). Masson S.p.A., Divisione Periodici, Via Statuto 2-4, 20121 Milan, Italy. TEL 02-6367-1. FAX 02-6367-211. adv.: B&W page L.3490000, color page L.5400000; trim 285 x 420. circ. 25,000. (tabloid format)

617.643 IT ISSN 1122-1038
GIORNALE DI STOMATOLOGIA E DI ORTOGNATODONZIA. 1982. q. $50. Poliambulatorio Odontoiatrico Riunito S.r.l., P.za Castello, 9, 31046 Oderzo (TV), Italy. Dir. Dr. Lorenzo Favero. adv.; bk.rev. circ. 5,000.
—BLDSC (4178.775000).

617.643 IT
GIOVANE ODONTOIATRIA. Cover title: G O - Giovane Odontoiatria. 1984. q. L.37000($47) (effective 1994). (Associazione Italiana Studenti in Odontoiatria) Masson S.p.A., Divisione Periodici, Via Statuto 2-4, 20121 Milan, Italy. TEL 02-6367-1. FAX 02-6367211. adv.: color page L.1900000; trim 250 x 377. circ. 2,200. **Document type:** academic/scholarly publication.
Formerly: Bollettino Nazionale A I S O (ISSN 1120-8686)

617.6 US ISSN 1062-0265
GREATER HOUSTON DENTAL SOCIETY. JOURNAL. vol.64, no.6, 1993. 9/yr. 50. Greater Houston Dental Society, One Greenway Plaza, Ste. 110, Houston, TX 77046. TEL 713-961-4337. FAX 713-961-3617. Ed. Dr. Janet Harrison. adv. contact: Charlotte Childress. circ. 1,700. **Document type:** academic/scholarly publication.
—BLDSC (4757.639000).
Refereed Serial

616.7 BE ISSN 0303-7479
CODEN: BGEODI
GROUPEMENT INTERNATIONAL POUR LA RECHERCHE EN STOMATOLOGIE ET ODONTOLOGIE. BULLETIN. q. 3000 BEF. Groupement International Pour la Recherche Stomatologie et Odontologie - International Group for Research in Stomatology and Odontology, Institut de Stomatologie, Hospital Universitaire Saint-Pierre, Rue Haute 322, 1000 Brussels, Belgium. Ed. N. Dourov. **Indexed:** Curr.Adv.Ecol.Sci., Excerp.Med., Ind.Med. **Document type:** bulletin.

617.6 TU ISSN 0250-5207
HACETTEPE DIS HEKIMLIGI FAKULTESI DERGISI/HACETTEPE FACULTY OF DENTISTRY JOURNAL. (Text in Turkish; summaries in English, French or German) 1977. q. Hacettepe Universitesi, Dis Hekimligi Fakultesi - Hacettepe University, Faculty of Dentistry, Ankara, Turkey. Ed. Aytekin Bilge. **Document type:** academic/scholarly publication.
Description: Keeps dentists informed on research being done in the field of dentistry and related areas.

617.6 US
HARTFORD DENTAL SOCIETY NEWSLETTER. m. membership. Hartford Dental Society, 230 Scarborough St., Hartford, CT 06105. TEL 203-523-8657. FAX 203-523-8657. Ed. Dr. Judd B. Fink. circ. 600 (controlled). (looseleaf format) **Document type:** newsletter.
Description: Announces upcoming meetings and programs, lists new members, course offerings, provides comment and editorial.

MEDICAL SCIENCES — DENTISTRY

617.6   US   ISSN 1062-029X
HARVARD DENTAL BULLETIN. 1940. 2/yr. free. Harvard School of Dental Medicine, 188 Longwood Ave., Boston, MA 02115. TEL 617-432-1533. FAX 617-432-4266. (Co-sponsor: Harvard Dental Alumni Association) Ed. Henry D. Epstein. illus.; circ. 2,500 (controlled). **Indexed:** Ind.Med.
—BLDSC (4265.886100).
Formerly (until 1990): Harvard Dental Alumni Bulletin (ISSN 0046-6891); **Supersedes:** Harvard Dental Record.
Description: Provides information on teaching, research and clinical activities of the school. Articles on students, faculty and alumni.

617.6   US   ISSN 0073-1021
HAWAII DENTAL ASSOCIATION. TRANSACTIONS. a. (typically set in Jan.). Hawaii Dental Association, 1000 Bishop St., Ste. 805, Honolulu, HI 96813. TEL 808-536-2135. FAX 808-536-2137.

617.6   US   ISSN 0891-9933
HAWAII DENTAL JOURNAL. 1967. m. $20 (foreign $25) (typically set in Jan.). Hawaii Dental Association, 1000 Bishop St., Ste. 805, Honolulu, HI 96813. TEL 808-536-2135. FAX 808-536-2137. Ed. Dr. Martin Nweeia. adv.; illus.; circ. 950 (controlled). **Indexed:** Dent.Abstr., Dent.Ind.
Formerly: Hawaii State Dental Association. Journal (ISSN 0017-8616)

617.3   US   ISSN 0073-1404
HAYES DIRECTORY OF DENTAL SUPPLY HOUSES. 1935. a. $80. Edward N. Hayes, Publisher, 4229 Birch St., Newport Beach, CA 92660. TEL 714-756-9063. FAX 714-756-0921. **Document type:** directory.

HEALTHSTATE. see *MEDICAL SCIENCES*

617.6   GR   ISSN 1011-4181
HELLENIC STOMATOLOGICAL REVIEW. (Text in Greek; summaries in English) 1957. q. Dr.4000($30) Hellenic Dental Association, 38 Themistocleous St, Athens 106-78, Greece. TEL 30-1-3803-816. FAX 30-1-3834-385. Ed.Bd. adv.; bk.rev.; bibl.; charts; illus.; index. circ. 7,000. **Document type:** academic/scholarly publication.
—BLDSC (4285.458200).
Former titles: Hellenic Stomatological Annals; Acta Stomatologica Hellenica.

617.6   JA   ISSN 0046-7472
                 CODEN: HUDJAN
HIROSHIMA UNIVERSITY DENTAL SOCIETY. JOURNAL/HIROSHIMA DAIGAKU SHIGAKU ZASSHI. (Text in English or Japanese) 1969. s-a. $12. Hiroshima Daigaku Shigakkai - Hiroshima University Dental Society, Hiroshima Daigaku, 2-3 Kasumi 1-chome, Minami-ku, Hiroshima 734, Japan. Ed. Nobuo Nagasaka. adv.; illus. (also avail. in microform from UMI; reprint service avail. from UMI) **Indexed:** Chem.Abstr., Dent.Ind., INIS Atomind.
—BLDSC (4758.330000); CASDDS; UMI.

617.6   CC   ISSN 1000-1182
HUAXI KOUQIANG YIXUE ZAZHI/WEST CHINA JOURNAL OF STOMATOLOGY. (Text in Chinese; summaries in English) 1983. q. Y7.2. Huaxi Yike Daxue - West China University of Medical Sciences, 14, Remin Nanlu 3 Duan, Chengdu, Sichuan 610041, People's Republic of China. FAX 028-583252. (Co-sponsor: Sichuan Branch of the Chinese Medical Association) Ed. Wang Hanzhang.

617.6   US
I A O STRAIGHT TALK. 1968. m. $15 (foreign $20). International Association for Orthodontics, 1100 Lake St., Ste. 240, Oak Park, IL 60301-1035. TEL 708-445-0320. FAX 708-445-0321. Ed. Joanna Carey. circ. 2,100 (controlled). (tabloid format; back issues avail.) **Document type:** newsletter.
Formerly: Bandelette.
Description: Contains news and concerns of association members.

617.6   US   ISSN 0018-8875
I C D LETTERETTE. Alternate issues titled: I C D Newsletter. vol.2, 1970. membership. International College of Dentists, c/o Dr. William E. Hawkins, Ed., 320 W. Indian School Rd., Phoenix, AZ 85013. TEL 602-248-9445. circ. 6,000.

617.6   US   ISSN 0019-1973
ILLINOIS DENTAL JOURNAL. 1905. bi-m. $30 to non-members (foreign $40); members $20. Illinois State Dental Society, 1010 S. Second St., Springfield, IL 62704-3005, TEL 217-525-1406. FAX 217-525-8872. Ed. Mary Byers. adv.: B&W page $638, color page $1588; trim 8 1/2 x 11. illus.; index; circ. 6,000 (controlled). (also avail. in microfilm from UMI; reprint service avail.) **Indexed:** Chem.Abstr., Dent.Abstr., Dent.Ind.
—BLDSC (4365.120000); UMI.
Description: Publishes activities, legislative updates, newsbriefs, new product reviews of interest to Illinois dentists.

617.6   US   ISSN 1056-6163
IMPLANT DENTISTRY. q. $99 to individuals (foreign $119); institutions $124 (foreign $144) (effective 1995). (International Congress of Oral Implantologists) Williams & Wilkins, 428 E. Preston St., Baltimore, MD 21202. TEL 410-528-4000; 800-638-6423. FAX 410-528-4312. Ed. Dr. Sheldon Winkler. adv. contact: Cristophe Nalton. bk.rev. circ. 3,847. **Document type:** academic/scholarly publication.
—BLDSC (4371.436300); UnCover. **CCC.**
Former titles (until 1992): International Journal of Oral Implantology (ISSN 1048-1842); Implantologist (ISSN 0190-2024)
Description: Scientific, clinical, educational and research articles on oral implantology and related dental and medical topics.
Refereed Serial

617.6   US   ISSN 1059-3489
IMPLANT SOCIETY; dedicated to the highest quality dentistry. 1990. bi-m. $125. Implant Society, Inc., Box 1264, Westborough, MA 01581. TEL 617-621-7170. FAX 508-366-3637. Pub. Richard Ciambrone. **Document type:** academic/scholarly publication.
—BLDSC (4371.436500).

617.7   GW
IMPLANTOLOGIE. 4/yr. DM.178 (foreign DM.188), Quintessenz Verlags GmbH, Ifenpfad 2-4, 12107 Berlin, Germany. TEL 030-7400646. FAX 030-7415080. **Document type:** academic/scholarly publication.

617.6   II   ISSN 0019-4611
INDIAN DENTAL ASSOCIATION. JOURNAL. (Text in English) 1925. m. Rs.60($30) Indian Dental Association, 532, 10th Main, 5th Block, Jayanagar, Bangalore 560 041, India. TEL 643838. Ed. K.G. Ghorpade. adv.: B&W page Rs.2500, color page Rs.5000. bk.rev.; abstr.; charts; illus.; index. circ. 3,000. **Indexed:** Dent.Abstr., Dent.Ind.
Former titles (until 1966): All India Dental Association. Journal (ISSN 0377-0516); (until 1947): Indian Dental Journal (ISSN 0971-1147)

617.6   II   ISSN 0970-4388
INDIAN SOCIETY OF PEDODONTICS AND PREVENTIVE DENTISTRY. JOURNAL. (Text in English) 1983. q. Rs.225 to individuals; institutions Rs.600; foreign $26. Indian Society of Pedodontics and Preventive Dentistry, c/o H.S. Chawka, Ed., Dept. of Dentistry, P.G.I.M.E.R., Chandigarh 160012, India. Ed. H.S. Chawla.
—BLDSC (4768.900000).

617.6   US   ISSN 0019-6568
                 CODEN: IDNJBY
INDIANA DENTAL ASSOCIATION. JOURNAL. 1921. q. $25 (foreign $27) (effective 1996). Indiana Dental Association, Box 2467, Indianapolis, IN 46206-2467. TEL 317-634-2610. FAX 317-634-2612. Ed. Dr. Phillip E. O'Shaughnessy. adv.; bk.rev.; charts. circ. 3,000. **Indexed:** Dent.Abstr., Dent.Ind. **Document type:** trade publication.
—BLDSC (4769.070000).
Refereed Serial

617.6   US
INDIANAPOLIS DISTRICT DENTAL SOCIETY. NEWSLETTER. vol.11, 1957. q. $35. Indianapolis District Dental Society, 3901 N. Meridian St., no.10, Indianapolis, IN 46208-4026. TEL 317-923-8421. FAX 317-923-8575. Ed. Dr. Desiree Dimond. adv.; bk.rev. circ. 860. **Document type:** newsletter.
Formerly: Indianapolis District Dental Society. Journal (ISSN 0073-7135)

INDICE DE LA LITERATURA DENTAL EN CASTELLANO. see *MEDICAL SCIENCES — Abstracting, Bibliographies, Statistics*

617.6   IT
INFODENT. 1989? m. B & C s.r.l., Str. Teverina Km 3600, 01100 Viterbo, Italy. TEL 0761-251372. FAX 0761-352198. adv.: color page L.1900000; trim 210 x 297. circ. 8,404.

617.6   FR   ISSN 0020-0018
INFORMATION DENTAIRE; hebdomadaire independant. 1918. 44/yr. 780 F. Information Dentaire, 42, rue Vignon, 75009 Paris Cedex 09, France. TEL 42-66-24-07. FAX 42-66-26-07. Dir. Yves Leroux. adv.; bk.rev.; abstr.; illus. circ. 15,000. (reprint service avail. from ISI) **Indexed:** Biol.Abstr., Chem.Abstr., Curr.Tit.Dent., Dent.Ind., Dok.Arbeitsmed.
—BLDSC (4493.530000); UMI.

617.43   GW   ISSN 0020-0336
INFORMATIONEN AUS ORTHODONTIE UND KIEFERORTHOPAEDIE. 1968. q. DM.228 (foreign DM.232). Huethig GmbH, Postfach 102869, 69018 Heidelberg, Germany. TEL 06221-489281. FAX 06221-489205. TELEX 461727-HUEHDD. Ed.Bd. adv.: B&W page DM.1690; trim 210 x 275; adv. contact: Micheline Cohen. bk.rev.; illus. circ. 2,400. **Indexed:** Dent.Ind. **Document type:** academic/scholarly publication.

617.6 618.97   US   ISSN 0887-6304
INTERFACE (CHICAGO, 1984). 1984. q. $25. American Society for Geriatric Dentistry, 211 E. Chicago Ave., Chicago, IL 60611. TEL 312-440-2660. Ed. Roger E. Oppenheimer. adv. contact: John S. Rutkavskas. circ. 600. **Document type:** newsletter.

INTERNATIONAL ASSOCIATION FOR DENTAL RESEARCH. ABSTRACTS OF THE GENERAL MEETING. see *MEDICAL SCIENCES — Abstracting, Bibliographies, Statistics*

617.6   UK   ISSN 0257-2796
INTERNATIONAL COLLEGE OF DENTISTS. EUROPEAN SECTION. NEWSLETTER. 1956. a. membership. (International College of Dentists) F D I World Dental Press Ltd., 7 Carlisle St., London W1V 5RG, England. TEL 0171-935-7852. FAX 0171-486-0183. Ed. Dr. M. Seward. bk.rev. circ. 600. **Document type:** newsletter.

617.6   US   ISSN 1057-5235
INTERNATIONAL COMMUNICATOR. 1976. 2/yr. Academy of Dentistry International, 5125 MacArthur Blvd., N.W., Ste. 50, Washington, DC 20016-3315. TEL 202-364-8349. Ed. Dr. Henry J. Sazima. circ. 1,800 (controlled). (tabloid format) **Document type:** newsletter.
Description: Informs membership of news, actions of the Board of Regents, and meetings.

617.6   UK   ISSN 0020-6539
                 CODEN: IDJOAS
INTERNATIONAL DENTAL JOURNAL. (Text in English; abstracts in French, German, Spanish) 1951. bi-m. £55 non-member individuals (outside Europe £60); members £85; institutions £90 (outside Europe £95) (effective 1995). F D I World Dental Press Ltd., 7 Carlisle St., London W1V 5RG, England. TEL 0171-935-7852. FAX 0171-486-0183. TELEX 83111 BHPOXF G. Ed. Dr. Margaret Seward. adv.; bk.rev.; illus.; abstr.; index. circ. 3,000. (also avail. in microfilm from UMI; reprint service avail. from UMI) **Indexed:** Biol.Abstr., Chem.Abstr., Curr.Adv.Ecol.Sci., Curr.Cont., Curr.Tit.Dent., Dent.Ind., Dok.Arbeitsmed., Ind.Med., Ind.Sci.Rev., NRN, Nutr.Abstr., Sci.Cit.Ind. **Document type:** academic/scholarly publication.
—BLDSC (4539.520000); CASDDS; Faxon; SWETS; UMI; UnCover. **CCC.**
Description: Presents a selection of Transactions of the F.D.I. Annual World Dental Congress and other suitable manuscripts on clinical dentistry of international interest and significance.
Refereed Serial

617.6 UK ISSN 0143-2885
CODEN: IENJEA
INTERNATIONAL ENDODONTIC JOURNAL. vol.14, 1981. bi-m. £137.50 in Europe; elsewhere £151.50($244) (effective 1996). (British Endodontic Society) Blackwell Science Ltd., Osney Mead, Oxford OX2 0EL, England. TEL 01865-206206. FAX 01865-206219. TELEX 83355 MEDBOK G. (Co-sponsor: Netherlands Society for Endodontology; European Soociety of Endodontology) Ed. W.P. Saunders. adv.; bibl.; illus.; index. circ. 2,150. (back issues avail.) Indexed: Curr.Tit.Dent., Dent.Ind. Document type: academic/scholarly publication.
—BLDSC (4539.975000); Faxon; Genuine Article; SWETS; UMI; UnCover. **CCC.**
Formerly (until 1980): British Endodontic Society Journal (ISSN 0007-0653)
Refereed Serial

617.6 617 US ISSN 0742-1931
CODEN: IAOSEE
INTERNATIONAL JOURNAL OF ADULT ORTHODONTICS AND ORTHOGNATHIC SURGERY. 1986. 4/yr. $88 (foreign $108) (effective 1996). Quintessence Publishing Co., Inc., 551 Kimberly Dr., Carol Stream, IL 60188-1881. TEL 708-682-3223. FAX 708-682-3288. Eds. Dr. Robert Vanarsdall, Dr. Raymond White; Pub. H.W. Haase. adv. contact: William G. Hartman. charts; illus.; index. circ. 3,500. (back issues avail.) Indexed: Curr.Tit.Dent., Dent.Abstr. Document type: academic/scholarly publication.
—BLDSC (4541.571000); Faxon; SWETS; UnCover. **CCC.**
Description: Conveys advances in orthodontics and orthognathic surgery care of interest to general practitioners, orthodontists, oral surgeons and periodontists.
Refereed Serial

617.6 US ISSN 0882-2786
CODEN: IJOIED
INTERNATIONAL JOURNAL OF ORAL & MAXILLOFACIAL IMPLANTS. 1986. bi-m. $106 (foreign $141) (effective 1996). (Academy of Osseointegration) Quintessence Publishing Co., Inc., 551 Kimberly Dr., Carol Stream, IL 60188-1881. TEL 708-682-3223. FAX 708-682-3288. Ed. Dr. William Laney; Pub. H.W. Haase. adv. contact: William G. Hartman. charts; illus.; index. circ. 6,464. (back issues avail.) Indexed: Dent.Abstr., Excerp.Med. Document type: academic/scholarly publication.
—BLDSC (4542.429600); Faxon; SWETS; UnCover. **CCC.**
Description: Tracks developments in reconstructive dentistry and implantology by compiling research, technology, clinical applications, symposia proceedings and review treatises.
Refereed Serial

617.6 DK ISSN 0901-5027
CODEN: IJOSE9
INTERNATIONAL JOURNAL OF ORAL & MAXILLOFACIAL SURGERY. (Text in English) 1972. bi-m. DKK 1650 (incl. supplements) (effective 1996). (International Association of Oral and Maxillofacial Surgeons) Munksgaard International Publishers Ltd., 35 Noerre Soegade, P.O. Box 2148, DK-1016 Copenhagen K, Denmark. TEL 33-127030. FAX 33-129387. Ed. P. Stoelinga. adv.; bk.rev.; charts; illus. circ. 2,800. (reprint service avail. from ISI,SWZ) Indexed: Biol.Abstr., C.I.J.E., Chem.Abstr., Curr.Cont., Curr.Tit.Dent., Dent.Abstr., Dent.Ind., Excerp.Med., Ind.Med., Ind.Sci.Rev., Ind.Vet., INIS Atomind., Nutr.Abstr.
—BLDSC (4542.429800); CASDDS; Faxon; Genuine Article; SWETS; UnCover. **CCC.**
Formerly: International Journal of Oral Surgery (ISSN 0300-9785)
Refereed Serial

617.6 UK ISSN 0960-7439
CODEN: IJPDE3
INTERNATIONAL JOURNAL OF PAEDIATRIC DENTISTRY. 1971. q. £155 in Europe; elsewhere £177.50($275) (effective 1996). (British Society of Paedodontic Dentistry) Blackwell Science Ltd., Osney Mead, Oxford OX2 0EL, England. TEL 01865-240201. FAX 01865-721205. TELEX 83355 MEDBOK G. (Co-sponsor: International Association of Paedodontic Dentistry) Ed. R.J. Andlaw. adv.; bk.rev.; abstr.; illus.; index. circ. 1,500. (also avail. in microform from UMI; back issues avail.) Document type: academic/scholarly publication.
—SWETS; UMI. **CCC.**
Incorporates (in 1991): International Association of Dentistry for Children. Journal (ISSN 0309-6858); Former titles: Journal of Paediatric Dentistry (ISSN 0267-2073); British Paedodontic Society. Proceedings (ISSN 0308-4922)
Refereed Serial

617.6 US ISSN 0198-7569
INTERNATIONAL JOURNAL OF PERIODONTICS & RESTORATIVE DENTISTRY. (Editions in English, French, German, Italian, Japanese) 1981. bi-m. $168 (foreign $208) (effective 1996). Quintessence Publishing Co., Inc., 551 Kimberly Dr., Carol Stream, IL 60188-1881. TEL 708-682-3223. FAX 708-682-3288. Eds. Dr. Gerald M. Kramer, Dr. Myron Nevins; Pub. H.W. Haase. adv. contact: William G. Hartman. charts; illus.; index. circ. 6,000. (back issues avail.) Indexed: Curr.Tit.Dent., Dent.Abstr. Document type: academic/scholarly publication.
—BLDSC (4542.452400); SWETS; UnCover. **CCC.**
Description: Clinically oriented coverage of the relationship between a healthy periodontium and precise restorations.
Refereed Serial

617.6 US ISSN 0893-2174
CODEN: IJLPEJ
INTERNATIONAL JOURNAL OF PROSTHODONTICS. 1988. 6/yr. $106 (foreign $141) (effective 1996). (International College of Prosthodontists) Quintessence Publishing Co., Inc., 551 Kimberly Dr., Carol Stream, IL 60188-1881. TEL 708-682-3223. FAX 708-682-3288. Ed. Dr. Jack D. Preston; Pub. H.W. Haase. adv. contact: William G. Hartman. charts; illus.; index. circ. 3,500. (back issues avail.) Document type: academic/scholarly publication.
—BLDSC (4542.488000); SWETS. **CCC.**
Description: Provides prosthodontists throughout the world with research articles on prosthodontics and interrelated disciplines.
Refereed Serial

INTERNATIONAL JOURNAL OF PSYCHOSOMATICS. see MEDICAL SCIENCES

617.6 GW ISSN 0721-0051
INTERNATIONALES JOURNAL FUER PARADONTOLOGIE & RESTAURATIVE ZAHNHEILKUND. English edition: International Journal of Periodontics & Restorative Dentistry (ISSN 0198-7569); French edition: Revue International de Parodontie et Dentisterie Restauratrice (ISSN 0721-0078); Italian edition: Revista Internazionale di Parodontologia y Odontoiatria Ricostruttiva (ISSN 0721-006X); Spanish edition: Revista Internacional de Periodoncia y Odontologia Restauradora (ISSN 0275-2867) (Text in German) 1981. bi-m. DM.310 (foreign DM.340). Quintessenz Verlags GmbH, Ifenpfad 2-4, 12107 Berlin, Germany. TEL 030-74006-46. FAX 030-7415080. TELEX 183815-QUINT-D. Indexed: Curr.Tit.Dent. Document type: academic/scholarly publication.

617.6 US ISSN 0021-0498
IOWA DENTAL JOURNAL. vol.15, 1929. 4/yr. $30 (foreign $35). Iowa Dental Association, 333 Insurance Exchange Bldg., Des Moines, IA 50309. TEL 515-282-7250. FAX 515-282-7256. Ed. R.W. Harpster. adv.; bk.rev.; charts; illus.; stat. circ. 2,250. Indexed: Curr.Tit.Dent., Dent.Abstr., Dent.Ind.
—BLDSC (4565.700000).

ISHI SHIKAISHI YAKUZAISHI CHOSA/SURVEY ON PHYSICIANS, DENTISTS AND PHARMACEUTISTS. see MEDICAL SCIENCES

617.6 JA ISSN 0385-1311
IWATE MEDICAL UNIVERSITY. DENTAL JOURNAL/IWATE IKA DAIGAKU SHIGAKU ZASSHI. (Text in Japanese; summaries in English) 1976. 3/yr. 4000 Yen($32) Iwate Medical University, Dental Society, c/o Iwate Ika Daigaku Shigakubu, 3-27, Chuo-dori 1-chome, Morioka 020, Japan. TEL 0196-51-5111. FAX 0196-52-4131. Ed. Dr. Yohichiro Nozaka; Pub. Takashi A. Suzuki. circ. 900. (back issues avail.) Indexed: INIS Atomind. Document type: academic/scholarly publication.

617.7 IT ISSN 0393-800X
J D. (Junior Dental); rivista d'informazione dentale. 1986. q. free. Imadent s.n.c., Via Locana 14-A, 10143 Turin, Italy. TEL 39-11-747718. Ed. Federico Manassero. adv.; bk.rev.; illus.; index. circ. 16,000. Document type: newspaper.

617.6 CN ISSN 0845-9320
J D Q: JOURNAL DENTAIRE DU QUEBEC. (Text in English and French) 1963. m. Can.$58.70 (foreign Can.$72.10). Ordre des Dentistes du Quebec, 625, Rene-Levesque Ouest, 15th Fl., Montreal, PQ H3B 1R2, Canada. TEL 514-875-8511. FAX 514-393-9248. Ed. Denis Forest. adv. contact: Suzanne Chartrand. bk.rev.; charts; illus.; cum.index: 1963-1966. circ. 4,800. Indexed: Dent.Ind., Pt.de Rep. (1988-). Document type: academic/scholarly publication.
—BLDSC (4968.400000).
Formerly (until 1987): Journal Dentaire du Quebec (ISSN 0021-7999)

617.6 JM
JAMAICA DENTAL ASSOCIATION. NEWSLETTER. irreg. Jamaica Dental Association, P.O. Box 19, Kingston 5, Jamaica, W.I. Document type: newsletter.

617.6 IR
JAME'E DANDANPEZESHKI IRAN. NAMAH-I/IRANIAN DENTAL ASSOCIATION. BULLETIN. m. (Iranian Dental Association) Hamid Adeli-Najafi, Ed. & Pub., No. 94, W. P...zi Str., Nasr Place, P.O. Box 14155-3695, Tehr..., Iran. TEL 98-21-639591. FAX 98-21-639592.

617.6 JA ISSN 0047-1763
CODEN: NISIA9
JAPAN DENTAL ASSOCIATION. JOURNAL/NIHON SHIKA ISHIKAI ZASSHI. (Text in Japanese) 1948. m. 4800 Yen($50) Japan Dental Association - Nihon Shika Igakkai, 4-1-20 Kudan-Kita, Chiyoda-ku, Tokyo 102, Japan. Ed. Dr. M. Nishimura. adv.; illus.; index. circ. 58,000. (also avail. in microform from UMI; reprint service avail. from UMI) Indexed: Dent.Ind., Ind.Med. Document type: academic/scholarly publication.
—CASDDS; UMI.

617.643 JA ISSN 0021-454X
JAPAN ORTHODONTIC SOCIETY. JOURNAL/NIHON KYOSEI SHIKA GAKKAI ZASSHI. (Text in Japanese; summaries in English) 1932. bi-m. 8000 Yen($18) Japan Orthodontic Society - Nihon Kyosei Shika Gakkai, c/o Oral health Association of Japan, 1-44-2 Komagome, Toshima-ku, Tokyo 170, Japan. Ed. Yoshii Suzuki. adv. Indexed: Dent.Ind.
—BLDSC (4805.670000).

617.6 JA ISSN 0021-5163
CODEN: NGGZAK
JAPANESE JOURNAL OF ORAL AND MAXILLOFACIAL SURGERY. Key Title: Nippon Koku Geka Gakkai Zasshi. (Text mainly in Japanese) 1954. bi-m. Japanese Society of Oral and Maxillofacial Surgeons - Nippon Koku Geka Gakkai, 1-15-2-502 Nakasato, Kita-ku, Tokyo 114, Japan. adv.; charts; illus.; index; circ. 2,500 (controlled). Indexed: Dent.Ind., INIS Atomind.
—BLDSC (4656.785000).
Formerly: Japanese Journal of Oral Surgery (ISSN 0454-1693)

617.6 FR ISSN 0301-3952
CODEN: JBBUA3
JOURNAL DE BIOLOGIE BUCCALE. (Text in English, French; summaries in English, French, German) 1973. q. 720 F. Societe d'Edition de l'Information Dentaire, 42 rue Vignon, 75442 Paris Cedex 09, France. TEL 88-36-25-26. FAX 88-24-00-69. Ed. Robert Frank. adv.; bk.rev. circ. 1,565. (reprint service avail. from ISI) Indexed: Biol.Abstr., Chem.Abstr., Curr.Cont., Dent.Ind., Excerp.Med., Helminthol.Abstr., Ind.Med., Ind.Sci.Rev., Nutr.Abstr., Sci.Cit.Ind.
—CASDDS; Faxon; UMI.

MEDICAL SCIENCES — DENTISTRY

617.6   FR
JOURNAL DE PARODONTOLOGIE ET D'IMPLANTOLOGIE ORALE. (Text in English, French) 1982. 4/yr. 640 F. to non-members (foreign 670 F.); members 560 F. (foreign 590 F.). (Societe Francaise de Parodontologie) Groupe C D P, 77 rue de Richelieu, 75002 Paris, France. TEL 42-61-50-65. FAX 42-61-31-95. Ed. H.S. Koskas. adv. contact: Chantal Daly. circ. 3,500.
    Formerly: Journal de Parodontologie (ISSN 0750-1838)
    Description: For specialists and general practitioners interested in the connective tissues of the teeth and their influence on odontology and general health.

617.643   US   ISSN 0022-3875
JOURNAL OF CLINICAL ORTHODONTICS. 1967. m. $118 to individuals (foreign $145); institutions $155 (foreign $190). J C O Inc., 1828 Pearl St., Boulder, CO 80302. FAX 303-443-9356. Ed. Larry White. adv. contact: Lynn Bollinger. bk.rev. circ. 11,000. (back issues avail.) Indexed: Curr.Tit.Dent., Dent.Abstr., Dent.Ind. Document type: academic/scholarly publication.
    —BLDSC (4958.630000); Faxon; SWETS; UnCover.

617.6 618.92   US   ISSN 1053-4628
RK55.C5   CODEN: JCPDEX
JOURNAL OF CLINICAL PEDIATRIC DENTISTRY. 1977. q. $117 to individuals (foreign $137); institutions $129 (foreign $149) (effective 1995). Tufts University, School of Dental Medicine, Dept. of Pediatric Dentistry, 1 Kneeland St., Boston, MA 02111. TEL 617-956-6902. (Subscr. to: Box 830259, Birmingham, AL 35283-0259. TEL 205-995-1567) Ed. Dr. George E. White. bk.rev.; index. circ. 2,600. (also avail. in microform from UMI; reprint service avail. from UMI) Indexed: Behav.Med.Abstr., Biol.Abstr., Chem.Abstr., Dent.Ind., Excerp.Med. Document type: academic/scholarly publication.
    —BLDSC (4958.665000); CASDDS; Faxon; SWETS; UMI; UnCover.
    Formerly: Journal of Pedodontics (ISSN 0145-5508)
    Refereed Serial

617.6   DK   ISSN 0303-6979
    CODEN: JCPEDZ
JOURNAL OF CLINICAL PERIODONTOLOGY. (Text in English; summaries in German and French) 1974. 10/yr. DKK 1300 (effective 1996). Munksgaard International Publishers Ltd., 35 Noerre Soegade, P.O. Box 2148, DK-1016 Copenhagen K, Denmark. TEL 33-127030. FAX 33-129387. Ed. Jan Lindhe. adv.; illus. circ. 11,000. (also avail. in microform from SWZ; reprint service avail. from ISI,SWZ) Indexed: Biol.Abstr., Chem.Abstr., Curr.Cont., Curr.Tit.Dent., Dent.Abstr., Dent.Ind., Excerp.Med., Ind.Med., Ind.Sci.Rev., Sci.Cit.Ind.
    —BLDSC (4958.672000); CASDDS; Faxon; Genuine Article; SWETS; UnCover. CCC.
    Refereed Serial

JOURNAL OF DENTAL EDUCATION. see EDUCATION — Teaching Methods And Curriculum

617.6   US   ISSN 1043-254X
RK1
JOURNAL OF DENTAL HYGIENE. 1927. 9/yr. $40. American Dental Hygienists' Association, 444 N. Michigan Ave., Ste. 3400, Chicago, IL 60611. TEL 312-440-8900. FAX 312-440-8929. Ed. Nancy Sisty-LePeau. adv.; bk.rev.; abstr.; bibl.; charts; illus.; stat.; index. circ. 30,000. (also avail. in microform from UMI; reprint service avail. from UMI) Indexed: Biol.Abstr., Curr.Tit.Dent., Dent.Abstr., Dent.Ind.
    —BLDSC (4968.470000); SWETS; UMI; UnCover.
    Former titles (until Oct. 1988): Dental Hygiene (ISSN 0091-3979); American Dental Hygienists Association. Journal (ISSN 0002-8185)
    Description: Scientific journal with articles pertaining to dental hygiene practice, education, and research.
    Refereed Serial

617.6   JA   ISSN 0285-0508
JOURNAL OF DENTAL HYGIENE. (Text in Japanese) 1981. m. 850 Yen per no. Ishiyaku Publishers, Inc., 7-10 Honkomagome 1-chome, Bunkyo-ku, Tokyo 113, Japan. Ed. Hiroshi Miura. adv.; bk.rev.; charts; illus. circ. 15,000.

617.6   US   ISSN 0022-0345
RK1   CODEN: JDREAF
JOURNAL OF DENTAL RESEARCH. (Supplements avail.: Advances in Dental Research (ISSN 0895-9374)) 1919. m. $350 (foreign $360). (International Association for Dental Research) American Association for Dental Research, 1619 Duke St., Alexandria, VA 22314-3406. TEL 703-548-0066. FAX 703-548-1883. Ed. Dr. Mark Herzberg. adv.: B&W page $945, color page $1690; trim 7 x 10; adv. contact: Bill Stevenson. charts; illus.; stat.; index. circ. 7,237. (also avail. in microform from UMI,PMC; back issues avail.; reprint service avail. from UMI) Indexed: Biol.Abstr., Chem.Abstr., Curr.Cont., Curr.Tit.Dent., Dairy Sci.Abstr., Dent.Abstr., Dent.Ind., Excerp.Med., Ind.Med., Ind.Sci.Rev., INIS Atomind., Met.Abstr., NRN, Nutr.Abstr., Rev.Med.& Vet.Mycol., Sci.Cit.Ind., World Alum.Abstr. Document type: academic/scholarly publication.
    —BLDSC (4968.500000); ADONIS; CASDDS; EMDOCS; Faxon; Genuine Article; SWETS; UMI; UnCover. CCC.
    Description: Original research on the oral cavity, its contiguous parts and its impact on the total human organism in health and disease.
    Refereed Serial

617.6   UK   ISSN 0300-5712
    CODEN: JDENAB
JOURNAL OF DENTISTRY. 1972. bi-m. £235($374) (effective 1996). Butterworth - Heinemann, Part of the Reed Elsevier group, Linacre House, Jordan Hill, Oxford OX2 8DP, England. TEL 44-865-310366. FAX 44-865-310898. TELEX 83111 BHPOXF G. (Subscr. to: Elsevier Science Ltd., P.O. Box 800, Kidlington, Oxford OX5 1DX, England. TEL 44-865-843000. FAX 44-865-843010; Subscr. in U.S. and Canada to: Elsevier Science, 660 White Plains Rd., Tarrytown, NY 10591-5153. TEL 914-524-9200. FAX 914-333-2444) Ed. Nairn H.F. Wilson. bk.rev.; illus.; index. (also avail. in microform from UMI; reprint service avail. from UMI; back issues avail.) Indexed: Chem.Abstr., Curr.Cont., Curr.Tit.Dent., Dent.Ind., Ind.Med., Ind.Sci.Rev., NRN, Nutr.Abstr., Sci.Cit.Ind. Document type: academic/scholarly publication.
    —BLDSC (4968.670000); CASDDS; Faxon; Genuine Article; SWETS; UMI; UnCover. CCC.
    Incorporates: Quarterly Dental Review (ISSN 0033-5479); Dental Practitioner and Dental Record (ISSN 0011-8729)
    Description: Reports on all issues relating to research, innovations and the practice of restorative dentistry, including dental materials science.
    Refereed Serial

617.64 618.92   US   ISSN 0022-0353
    CODEN: JDCHAH
JOURNAL OF DENTISTRY FOR CHILDREN. 1933. bi-m. $90 to individuals (foreign $110); institutions $105 (foreign $135). American Society of Dentistry for Children, 875 N. Michigan Ave., Ste. 4040, Chicago, IL 60611-1901. TEL 312-943-1244. FAX 312-943-5341. Ed. Dr. George W. Teuscher. adv.; bk.rev.; abstr.; charts; illus.; stat.; index. circ. 10,000. (also avail. in microform from UMI,WWS; reprint service avail. from KTO,UMI) Indexed: Behav.Med.Abstr., Biol.Abstr., Chem.Abstr., Chic.Per.Ind., Curr.Tit.Dent., Dent.Abstr., Dent.Ind., Ind.Med., Ind.Sci.Rev., Nutr.Abstr., Sci.Cit.Ind. Document type: academic/scholarly publication.
    —BLDSC (1739.600000); Faxon; Genuine Article; SWETS; UMI; UnCover.
    Refereed Serial

617.6   US   ISSN 0099-2399
RK351
THE JOURNAL OF ENDODONTICS. 1975. m. $65 to individuals; institutions $103 (effective 1995). (American Association of Endodontics) Williams & Wilkins, 428 E. Preston St., Baltimore, MD 21202. TEL 410-528-4000; 800-638-6423. FAX 410-528-4312. Ed. Dr. Henry J. Van Hassel. abstr.; illus.; index. circ. 6,633. (also avail. in microform from PMC; reprint service avail.) Indexed: Biol.Abstr., Curr.Tit.Dent., Dent.Abstr., Dent.Ind., Excerp.Med. Document type: academic/scholarly publication.
    —BLDSC (4978.200000); Faxon; Genuine Article; SWETS; UnCover. CCC.
    Description: Explores methods of pulp conservation, root canal instrumentation and endodontic treatment.
    Refereed Serial

617.6   CN   ISSN 1040-1466
JOURNAL OF ESTHETIC DENTISTRY. 1988. bi-m. $135 to individuals (outside US & Canada $195); institutions $190 (outside US & Canada $215) (effective 1996). Decker Periodicals, P.O. Box 620, LCD 1, Hamilton, ON L8N 3K7, Canada. TEL 416-522-7017. FAX 416-522-7839. (U.S. address: Box 785, Lewiston, NY 14092) (Co-sponsors: American Academy of Esthetic Dentistry; European Academy of Esthetic Dentistry) adv. circ. 25,000. Document type: academic/scholarly publication.
    —BLDSC (4979.555000); SWETS.
    Description: Provides information relative to the fields of esthetic and geriatric dentistry.

617.643   US   ISSN 1048-1990
JOURNAL OF GENERAL ORTHODONTICS. 1990. q. $40 (foreign $60). International Association for Orthodontics, 1100 Lake St., Ste. 240, Oak Park, IL 60301-1035. TEL 708-445-0320. FAX 708-445-0321. adv.; bk.rev.; circ. 3,500 (controlled). Document type: trade publication.
    Description: Contains scientific and clinical articles on orthodontic techniques.

617.6   GW   ISSN 0891-8171
THE JOURNAL OF GNATHOLOGY. (Text in English) 1981. a. $28. (International Academy of Gnathology) Quintessenz Verlags GmbH, Ifenpfad 2-4, 12107 Berlin, Germany. TEL 030-74006-0. FAX 030-7415080. Ed. Dr. Axel Bauer. adv.: B&W page DM.1980; trim 280 x 210; adv. contact: Marlies Kauffeldt. Document type: academic/scholarly publication.

617.6   US   ISSN 0278-2391
RK1   CODEN: JOMSDA
JOURNAL OF ORAL AND MAXILLOFACIAL SURGERY. 1943. m. $90 to individuals (foreign $146); institutions $112 (foreign $158) (effective 1995). (American Association of Oral and Maxillofacial Surgeons) W.B. Saunders Co. (Subsidiary of: Harcourt Brace & Company), Curtis Center, 3rd Fl., Independence Sq. W., Philadelphia, PA 19106-3399. TEL 215-238-7800. FAX 215-238-6445. (Subscr. to: Periodicals Fulfillment, W.B. Saunders Co., 6277 Sea Harbor Dr., 4th Fl., Orlando, FL 32891-4800. TEL 800-654-2452. FAX 800-874-6418) Ed. Dr. Daniel M. Laskin; Pub. Joan W. Blumberg. adv.: B&W page $1510, color page $2585; 7 x 10. bk.rev.; abstr.; bibl.; charts; illus.; index; circ. 10,003 (paid). (also avail. in microform from UMI; reprint service avail. from UMI) Indexed: AIM, Biol.Abstr., Chem.Abstr., Curr.Cont., Curr.Tit.Dent., Dent.Abstr., Dent.Ind., Excerp.Med., Helminthol.Abstr., Ind.Med., Ind.Sci.Rev., INIS Atomind., Med.& Surg.Dermat. Document type: academic/scholarly publication.
    —BLDSC (5026.385000); Faxon; Genuine Article; SWETS; UMI; UnCover. CCC.
    Former titles (until 1982): Journal of Oral Surgery (ISSN 0022-3255); Journal of Oral Surgery, Anesthesia and Hospital Dental Service (ISSN 0095-9618)
    Description: Serves oral and maxillofacial surgeons and other health care professionals interested in the field with scientific reports, case studies, news articles, and editorials.
    Refereed Serial

617.6   US   ISSN 0160-6972
JOURNAL OF ORAL IMPLANTOLOGY. 1970. q. $100 (effective 1996). (American Academy of Implant Dentistry) International Association for Dental Research, 1619 Duke St., Alexandria, VA 22314. TEL 703-548-0066. (Co-sponsor: American Association for Dental Research) Ed. A. Norman Cranin. adv.; bk.rev.; illus. circ. 3,000. (also avail. in microform from UMI; back issues avail.) Indexed: Dent.Ind. Document type: academic/scholarly publication.
    —BLDSC (5026.410000); Faxon; SWETS; UMI; UnCover.
    Formerly (until 1977): Oral Implantology (ISSN 0048-2064); Which incorporates: American Academy of Implant Dentistry. Newsletter.
    Description: Brings information of interest on all areas of implant dentistry to scientists, clinicians, laboratory owners, technicians, manufacturers, and educators.

MEDICAL SCIENCES — DENTISTRY

617.6   DK   ISSN 0904-2512
CODEN: JPMEEA
JOURNAL OF ORAL PATHOLOGY & MEDICINE. (Text in English) 1972. 10/yr. DKK 2800 (effective 1996). (International Association of Oral Pathologists) Munksgaard International Publishers Ltd., 35 Noerre Soegade, P.O. Box 2148, DK-1016 Copenhagen K, Denmark. TEL 33-127030. FAX 33-129387. (Co-sponsor: American Academy of Oral Pathology) Ed. Colin Smith. adv.; bk.rev.; charts; illus.; bibl. circ. 900. (also avail. in microform from SWZ; reprint service avail. from ISI,SWZ) **Indexed:** Biol.Abstr., Chem.Abstr., Curr.Adv.Ecol.Sci., Curr.Cont., Curr.Tit.Dent., Dent.Abstr., Dent.Ind., Excerp.Med., Ind.Med., Ind.Sci.Rev., INIS Atomind., Med.& Surg.Dermat., Nutr.Abstr., Rev.Med.& Vet.Mycol., Rev.Plant Path.
—BLDSC (5026.435000); CASDDS; Faxon; Genuine Article; SWETS; UnCover. **CCC.**
   Formerly: Journal of Oral Pathology (ISSN 0300-9777)
   Refereed Serial

617.6   UK   ISSN 0305-182X
CODEN: JORHBY
JOURNAL OF ORAL REHABILITATION; clinical dental science and materials. 1974. bi-m. £365 (outside Europe £402($647)) (effective 1996). Blackwell Science Ltd., Osney Mead, Oxford OX2 0EL, England. TEL 01865-240201. FAX 01865-721205. TELEX 83355 MEDBOK G. Ed. A.S.T. Franks. adv.; bk.rev.; bibl.; illus.; index. circ. 500. (also avail. in microform from UMI; back issues avail.; reprint service avail. from ISI) **Indexed:** ASCA, Behav.Med.Abstr., Chem.Abstr., Curr.Cont., Curr.Tit.Dent., Dent.Abstr., Dent.Ind., Excerp.Med., Ind.Med., Ind.Sci.Rev., Rev.Med.& Vet.Mycol., Sci.Cit.Ind. **Document type:** academic/scholarly publication.
—BLDSC (5026.440000); CASDDS; Genuine Article; SWETS; UMI; UnCover. **CCC.**
   Refereed Serial

617.6   US   ISSN 1064-6655
CODEN: JOROEO
JOURNAL OF OROFACIAL PAIN. 1987. 4/yr. $72 (foreign $92) (effective 1996). (American Academy of Orofacial Pain) Quintessence Publishing Co., Inc., 551 Kimberly Dr., Carol Stream, IL 60188-1881. TEL 708-682-3223. FAX 708-682-3288. (Co-sponsor: European Academy of Craniomandibular Disorders) Ed. Dr. Charles McNeill; Pub. H.W. Haase. adv. contact: William B. Hartwell. charts; illus.; index. circ. 3,000. (back issues avail.) **Indexed:** Dent.Abstr. **Document type:** academic/scholarly publication.
—BLDSC (5027.530000); Faxon; SWETS; UnCover. **CCC.**
   Formerly (until 1993): Journal of Craniomandibular Disorders (ISSN 0890-2739)
   Description: Research, clinical material and treatment therapies on facial pain, headaches, occlusion, physiology and physical therapy.
   Refereed Serial

617.632   DK   ISSN 0022-3484
RK361.A1   CODEN: JPDRAY
JOURNAL OF PERIODONTAL RESEARCH. (Supplements avail.) (Text in English) 1966. 8/yr. DKK 1800 (effective 1996). Munksgaard International Publishers Ltd., 35 Noerre Soegade, P.O. Box 2148, DK-1016 Copenhagen K, Denmark. TEL 33-127030. FAX 33-129387. Ed. Roy C. Page. adv.; bibl.; charts; illus. circ. 1,100. (also avail. in microform from SWZ; reprint service avail. from ISI,SWZ) **Indexed:** Biol.Abstr., Chem.Abstr., Curr.Adv.Ecol.Sci., Curr.Cont., Curr.Tit.Dent., Dairy Sci.Abstr., Dent.Abstr., Dent.Ind., Excerp.Med., Ind.Med., Ind.Sci.Rev., INIS Atomind.
—BLDSC (5030.600000); CASDDS; EMDOCS; Faxon; Genuine Article; SWETS; UnCover. **CCC.**
   Refereed Serial

617.632   US   ISSN 0022-3492
RK1.A512   CODEN: JOPRAJ
JOURNAL OF PERIODONTOLOGY. 1930. m. $90 to individuals in US and Canada (elsewhere $100); institutions $125 in US and Canada (elsewhere $150) (effective 1995). American Academy of Periodontology, 737 N. Michigan, Ste. 800, Chicago, IL 60611. TEL 312-573-3220. FAX 312-573-3225. Ed. Robert Genco. adv. contact: Kelly Wool. abstr.; bibl.; illus.; index. circ. 8,000. (also avail. in microform from UMI,PMC; back issues avail.; reprint service avail. from UMI) **Indexed:** Biol.Abstr., Chem.Abstr., Curr.Adv.Ecol.Sci., Curr.Cont., Curr.Tit.Dent., Dent.Abstr., Dent.Ind., Excerp.Med., Ind.Med., Ind.Sci.Rev., INIS Atomind., Nutr.Abstr., Rev.Med.& Vet.Mycol. **Document type:** academic/scholarly publication.
—BLDSC (5030.700000); CASDDS; EMDOCS; Faxon; Genuine Article; SWETS; UMI; UnCover. **CCC.**
   Formerly: Journal of Periodontology - Periodontics.
   Refereed Serial

617.6   US   ISSN 1072-7965
JOURNAL OF PRACTICAL HYGIENE. 1991. 6/yr. $28. Montage Media Corp., 70 Hill Top Rd., Ramsey, NJ 07446. TEL 201-236-0700. FAX 201-236-1339. adv.; B&W page $3900, color page $5100; trim 8 1/8 x 10 7/8. circ. 60,000. **Document type:** trade publication.
   Description: Clinical publication disseminating information on practical applications of soft tissue management and oral hygiene, as well as applications in restorative and implant treatments.
   Refereed Serial

617.69   US   ISSN 0022-3913
RK1   CODEN: JPDEAT
JOURNAL OF PROSTHETIC DENTISTRY. 1951. m. $99 to individuals (Canada $138.03; elsewhere $129); institutions $198 (Canada $243.96; elsewhere $228); students, residents $53 (Canada $88.81; elsewhere $83) (effective 1996); newsstand price: $10. (Academy of Prosthodontics) Mosby - Year Book, Inc. (Subsidiary of: Times Mirror Company), 11830 Westline Industrial Dr., St. Louis, MO 63146-3318. TEL 314-872-8370; 800-325-4177. FAX 314-432-1380. TELEX 44-2402. (Co-sponsors: American Prosthodontic Society; Pacific Coast Society of Prosthodontists) Ed. Dr. Glen P. McGivney. adv.; B&W page $1205, color page $2230; trim 8 1/8 x 10 7/8. bk.rev.; charts; illus.; s-a. index. circ. 10,685. (also avail. in microfilm from UMI; back issues avail.; reprint service avail. from UMI) **Indexed:** ASCA, Biol.Abstr., Br.Ceram.Abstr., Ceram.Abstr., Chem.Abstr., Curr.Adv.Ecol.Sci., Curr.Cont., Curr.Tit.Dent., Dent.Abstr., Dent.Ind., Ind.Med., Ind.Sci.Rev., INIS Atomind., Sci.Cit.Ind.
—BLDSC (5042.900000); CASDDS; Faxon; Genuine Article; SWETS; UMI; UnCover. **CCC.**
   Description: New techniques, evaluation of dental materials, and patient psychology relevant to practitioners of prosthetic dentistry.
   Refereed Serial

617.6   US   ISSN 1059-941X
JOURNAL OF PROSTHODONTICS. 1992. q. $118 (foreign $136) (effective 1996). (American College of Prosthodontists) W.B. Saunders Co. (Subsidiary of: Harcourt Brace & Company), Curtis Center, 3rd Fl., Independence Sq. W., Philadelphia, PA 19106-3399. TEL 215-238-7800. FAX 215-238-6445. (Subscr. to: Periodicals Fulfillment, W.B. Saunders Co., 6277 Sea Harbor Dr., 4th Fl., Orlando, FL 32891-4800. TEL 800-654-2452. FAX 800-874-6418) Ed. Dr. Patrick M. Lloyd; Pub. Joan W. Blumberg. adv.; B&W page $875, color page $1775; 7 x 10. circ. 2,921. **Document type:** academic/scholarly publication.
—BLDSC (5042.920000). **CCC.**
   Description: Contains original articles, reviews of new techniques and instrumentation, and instructive case reports.
   Refereed Serial

617.6 614.8   US   ISSN 0022-4006
RK52   CODEN: JPHDAC
JOURNAL OF PUBLIC HEALTH DENTISTRY. 1941. q. $85 (foreign $90). American Association of Public Health Dentistry, 10619 Jousting Ln., Richmond, VA 23235. Ed. R. Gary Rozier. adv.; bk.rev.; bibl.; charts; illus.; stat. circ. 1,200. (also avail. in microform from UMI; reprint service avail. from UMI) **Indexed:** Abstr.Health Care Manage.Stud., Biol.Abstr., Curr.Cont., Curr.Tit.Dent., Dent.Abstr., Dent.Ind., Excerp.Med., Ind.Med., Ind.Sci.Rev. **Document type:** academic/scholarly publication.
—BLDSC (5043.550000); Faxon; Genuine Article; SWETS; UMI; UnCover.
   Former titles: Public Health Dentistry; American Association of Public Health Dentists. Bulletin.

617.6   JA   ISSN 0385-1443
CODEN: BKDCD5
KANAGAWA DENTAL COLLEGE. BULLETIN. (Text in English) 1973. s-a. free. Kanagawa Dental College Society - Kanagawa Shika Daigaku Gakkai, 82 Inaoka-cho, Yokosuka, Kanagawa-ken, Japan. TEL 0468-25-1500. FAX 0468-23-9415. Ed. Akiya Yamanaka. circ. 1,000. **Document type:** bulletin.
—BLDSC (2597.959000); CASDDS.

617.6   JA   ISSN 0454-8302
CODEN: KSHGDM
KANAGAWA SHIGAKU/KANAGAWA ODONTOLOGICAL SOCIETY. JOURNAL. 1967. q. 1500 Yen. Kanagawa Dental College Society - Kanagawa Shika Daigaku Gakkai, 82 Inaoka-cho, Yokosuka, Kanagawa-ken, Japan. TEL 0468-25-1500. FAX 0468-23-9415. Ed. Tsugio Iwamoto. circ. 3,000. **Indexed:** INIS Atomind.
—BLDSC (4810.229000); CASDDS.

617.6   US   ISSN 0888-7063
KANSAS DENTAL ASSOCIATION. JOURNAL. vol.57, 1973. q. $35. Kansas Dental Association, 5200 S.W. Huntoon St., Topeka, KS 66604-2365. Ed. Dr. Ron Price. adv.; illus. circ. 1,200. **Indexed:** Dent.Abstr., Dent.Ind., Med. Care Rev.
   Formerly (until July 1981): Kansas State Dental Association. Journal (ISSN 0022-8796)

617.6   US   ISSN 0744-396X
KENTUCKY DENTAL ASSOCIATION. JOURNAL.* 1949. bi-m. $20. Kentucky Dental Association, 1725 Hillcrest Dr., Madisonville, KY 42431. Ed. Joe W. Jones, Jr. adv.; bk.rev.; illus. circ. 1,900. **Indexed:** Dent.Abstr., Dent.Ind.

617.6   US
KERN COUNTY DENTAL SOCIETY OCCLUSAL REGISTER. 1967. bi-m. free. Kern County Dental Society, 1701 Westwind Dr., Ste. 209, Bakersfield, CA 93301. TEL 805-327-2666. FAX 805-327-1229. Ed. Dr. Karen Yoon. adv.; charts; illus.; stat. circ. 180. (looseleaf format)
   Formerly: Kern County Dental Society Newsletter (ISSN 0023-0634)

617.6   SW   ISSN 0281-7020
KLINIK OCH TERAPI FOER TANDLAEKARE. 1970-1976; resumed 1980-1987; resumed 1991. s-a. Astra Laekemedel AB, S-151 85 Soedertaelje, Sweden.
   Formerly (until 1982): Astranytt.

617.6   JA   ISSN 0023-2831
CODEN: KEGZA7
KOKU EISEI GAKKAI ZASSHI/JOURNAL OF DENTAL HEALTH. (Text mainly in Japanese; summaries in English) 1953. q. (Koku Eisei Gakkai - Japanese Society for Dental Health) Tokyo Medical and Dental University, School of Dentistry, Dept. of Preventive Dentistry, Yushima 1-chome, Bunkyo-ku, Tokyo 113, Japan. Ed. Masao Onisi. adv.; index. **Indexed:** Biol.Abstr., Chem.Abstr., Dent.Ind.
—BLDSC (4968.460000).

617.6   KO   ISSN 0023-3927
KOREA RESEARCH SOCIETY FOR DENTAL MATERIALS. JOURNAL.* (Text in Korean; summaries and contents page in English) 1966. q. free. Seoul National University, College of Dentistry, San 56-1, Sinlim-dong, Kwanak-ku, Seoul 151-742, S. Korea. Ed. Dr. Yang-Shok Yoo. adv.; abstr.; bibl.; charts; illus.

MEDICAL SCIENCES — DENTISTRY

617.6   KO
KOREAN DENTAL ASSOCIATION. JOURNAL. (Text in English and Korean) 1962. m. $60. Korean Dental Association, P.O. Box 41, Yongdungpo, Seoul 150-650, S. Korea. TEL 2-635-3351. FAX 2-671-3624. Ed. S.R. Lee. adv. circ. 7,000. **Indexed:** Dent.Ind.

617.6   FI   ISSN 0023-5717
KUSPI. 1961. m. FIM 50. Turun Hammaslaaketieteenkandidaattiseura, Lemminkaisenkatu 2, 20520 Turku 52, Finland. Ed. Riitta Saarikivi. adv.; bk.rev.; charts; illus.; circ. 2,600 (controlled).

617.6   RU
KVINTESSENTSIYA; mezhdunarodnyi stomatologicheskii zhurnal. (Text in Russian) 1991. 6/yr. 14 Rub. per issue. c/o Yu.E. Shirokov, Ed., Abonementnyi yashchik 212, 125190 Moscow, Russia. TEL 203-99-88.

617.6   HK   ISSN 1022-7970
▼**LATIN AMERICAN DENTAL NEWS.** (Text in English, Spanish) 1994. q. MediMedia Asia (Subsidiary of: MediMedia Pacific Ltd.), 1501 Tung Sun Commercial Centre, 194-200 Lockhart Rd., Wanchai, Hong Kong. TEL 852-511-0765. FAX 852-507-3817. **Document type:** trade publication.

617.6   US   ISSN 0023-9062
LAVENDER BAND. 1961. bi-m. $20 to non-members. Iowa Dental Hygienists' Association, 4498 Pepperwood Hill S.E., Cedar Rapids, IA 52403. TEL 319-365-5735. FAX 319-365-8299. Ed. Alice Brown. adv. circ. 575. **Document type:** newsletter.

617.6   US   ISSN 0024-6786
LOUISIANA DENTAL ASSOCIATION. JOURNAL. vol.23, 1966. q. $15. Louisiana Dental Association, 8510 Line Ave., Shreveport, LA 71106. FAX 318-869-3111. (Or: Mng. Ed., Dr. David Austin, 230 Carroll, Shreveport, LA 71105) Ed. Dr. Gary L. Roberts. adv.; illus. circ. 1,650. **Indexed:** Dent.Abstr., Dent.Ind.

617.6   SW   ISSN 0076-3438
LUND UNIVERSITY. SCHOOL OF DENTISTRY. FACULTY OF ODONTOLOGY. ANNUAL PUBLICATIONS. (Text in English) 1958. a. free. Lund University, Faculty of Odontology, School of Dentistry, 214 21 Malmoe, Sweden. FAX 46-40-92-53-59. Ed. Krister Nilner. bk.rev. circ. 750. **Document type:** academic/scholarly publication.

617.6   US   ISSN 0738-4556
M D S NEWS. 1964. 6/yr. $20. Massachusetts Dental Society, 83 Speen St., Natick, MA 01760-4144. TEL 508-651-7511. FAX 508-653-7115. Ed. Margaret Quinlan. circ. 4,250. (looseleaf format; back issues avail.)

617.6   IO   ISSN 0024-9548
MADJALAH PERSATUAN DOKTER GIGI INDONESIA.* (Summaries in English) 1951. 4/yr. $10. Indonesian Dental Association, Jalan Prapatan 14, Jakarta, Indonesia. Ed. Geri Pandjaitan. circ. 1,000.

617.6   IR
MAJDA. (Text in Farsi; summaries in English) 1964. 3/yr. membership. (Iranian Dental Association) Hamid Adeli-Najafi, Ed. & Pub., No. 94, W. Piroozi Str., Nasr Place, P.O. Box 14155-3695, Tehran, Iran. TEL 98-21-639591. FAX 98-21-639592.
    Formerly: Iranian Dental Association. Journal - Jame'e-Ye Dandanpezeshkan-e Iran. Majalleh.

617.6   TU   ISSN 1018-5992
MARMARA UNIVERSITY. FACULTY OF DENTISTRY. JOURNAL. Key Title: Journal of Marmara University Dental Faculty. (Text in English) 1990. a. $15. Marmara University, Faculty of Dentistry, Buyukciftlik Sok. No. 6, 80200 Nisantasi - Istanbul, Turkey. TEL 90-212-2483697. FAX 90-212-2465247. TELEX 27826 MUDH TR. Eds. Dr. B.G.H. Levers, Dr. Selcuk Yilmaz. circ. 1,300. (back issues avail.) **Document type:** academic/scholarly publication.
—BLDSC (4821.200000).
    Refereed Serial

617.6   US   ISSN 0025-4355
MARYLAND STATE DENTAL ASSOCIATION. JOURNAL. 1958. 4/yr. $24 (foreign $30). Maryland State Dental Association, 6450 Dobbin Rd., Columbia Business Center, Columbia, MD 21045-4744. TEL 301-964-2880. FAX 301-964-0583. Ed. Dr. Bernard Gordon. adv.; bk.rev.; charts; illus.; stat.; index. circ. 2,600. **Indexed:** Dent.Abstr., Dent.Ind.
—BLDSC (4821.310000).

617.6   US   ISSN 0025-4800
MASSACHUSETTS DENTAL SOCIETY. JOURNAL. 1951. q. $12 to non-members; members $3. Massachusetts Dental Society, 83 Speen St., Natick, MA 01760-4144. TEL 508-651-7511. FAX 508-653-7115. Ed. Dr. Norman Becker. adv.; bk.rev.; illus.; abstr. circ. 4,166. **Indexed:** Dent.Ind.
—BLDSC (4821.600000).

MATSUMOTO SHIGAKU/MATSUMOTO DENTAL COLLEGE SOCIETY. JOURNAL. see *BIOLOGY*

617.6   GW   ISSN 0940-2500
MED. DENT. MAGAZIN; der Wegbegleiter vom Studienanfaenger zum Praxisgruender. 1987. bi-m. DM.24. H.P. Kuechenmeister Hochschulverlag, Daldorferstr. 15, 24635 Rickling, Germany. TEL 04328-208. FAX 04328-1516. Ed. Hans-Peter Kuechenmeister. adv.; bk.rev. circ. 13,000. **Document type:** academic/scholarly publication.

MEDICAL AND DENTAL ASSOCIATION OF BOTSWANA. JOURNAL. see *MEDICAL SCIENCES*

MEDICAL MALPRACTICE: HANDLING DENTAL CASES. see *LAW — Civil Law*

617.6   CI   ISSN 0025-7966
MEDICINAR; strucni i znanstveni casopis Saveza Studenata. (Text in Croatian, English) 1946. 2/yr. $28. Sveuciliste u Zagrebu, Medicinski Fakultet, Salata 3b, 41000 Zagreb, Croatia. TEL 041 271-188. Ed. Dinka Pavicic. adv.; bk.rev.; abstr.; bibl.; charts; illus.; stat.; index. circ. 3,500.

617.6 610   JA   ISSN 0916-0701
                              CODEN: MDSZEI
MEIKAI UNIVERSITY SCHOOL OF DENTISTRY. JOURNAL. (Text and summaries in English, Japanese) 1972. 3/yr. Meikai University, School of Dentistry, 1-1 Keyakidai, Sakado, Saitama 350-02, Japan. TEL 81-492-85-5511. FAX 81-492-87-6657. Ed. Naomi Minami. circ. 1,000. **Document type:** bulletin.
—BLDSC (4824.365000); CASDDS.
    Formerly: Josai Shika Daigaku Kiyo (ISSN 0301-2662)
    Description: Focuses on oral tumors, cleansing agents, head and neck cancer and osteotomy. Includes case reports.
    Refereed Serial

617.6   US   ISSN 0026-2102
MICHIGAN DENTAL ASSOCIATION. JOURNAL. 1919. 9/yr. $15 to college libraries; non-members $70. Michigan Dental Association, 230 N. Washington Sq., Ste. 208, Lansing, MI 48933. TEL 517-372-9070. FAX 517-372-0008. Ed. Dr. William Chase. adv.; illus. circ. 6,300. **Indexed:** Abstr.Health Care Manage.Stud., Biol.Abstr., Dent.Abstr., Dent.Ind. **Document type:** trade publication.
—BLDSC (4825.600000).
    Former titles (1951-1968): Michigan State Dental Association. Journal (ISSN 0098-7107); Michigan State Dental Society. Journal.

617.6   US   ISSN 0047-7095
MICHIGAN DENTAL HYGIENIST ASSOCIATION. BULLETIN. 1973. q. $12 (foreign $18). Michigan Dental Hygienists Association, 1609 E. Kalamazoo St., Ste. 11, Lansing, MI 48912. TEL 517-484-1352. Ed. Anne Gwozdek. adv.; bk.rev.; illus. circ. 1,200. **Indexed:** Dent.Ind. **Document type:** trade publication.

617.6   US   ISSN 0026-3478
MIDWESTERN DENTIST.* 1925. m. (except June, July, Aug.). $18 (only to qualified personnel in the U.S.). Greater Kansas City Dental Society, 5907 Raytown Traffic Light, Kansas City, MO 64133. TEL 816-737-5353. Ed. Dr. Robert Nelson. adv.; bk.rev.; circ. 800 (controlled).
    Former titles (until 1959): Kansas City District Dental Society. Journal; (until 1947): Kansas City Dental Society Bulletin; (until 1932): Kansas City Dental Society. Monthly Bulletin.

617.6   IT   ISSN 0394-168X
MINERVA ORTOGNATODONTICA; rivista trimestrale di ortognatodonzia, gnatologia, odontoiatria preventiva. q. $90 to individuals; institutions $140 (effective 1995). Edizioni Minerva Medica, Corso Bramante 83-85, 10126 Turin, Italy. TEL 39-11-678282. FAX 39-11-3121736. Ed. P. Bracco; Pub. Alberto Oliaro. adv.: B&W page $1100, color page $1900; trim 190 x 270; adv. contact: F. Filippo. circ. 2,000 (paid). **Document type:** academic/scholarly publication.
—BLDSC (5794.307000).
    Formerly: Minerva Odontoiatrica.
    Description: Covers orthognathodontics, gnathology, and preventive dentistry.
    Refereed Serial

617.6   IT   ISSN 0026-4970
MINERVA STOMATOLOGICA. (Text in Italian; summaries in English, Italian) 1952. m. $130 to individuals; institutions $160 (effective 1995). (Societa Italiana di Odontostomatologia e Chirurgia Maxillo-Facciale) Edizioni Minerva Medica, Corso Bramante 83-85, 10126 Turin, Italy. TEL 39-11-678282. FAX 39-11-3121736. Ed. R. Modica; Pub. Alberto Oliaro. adv.: B&W page $1100, color page $1900; trim 190 x 270; adv. contact: F. Filippo. bk.rev.; abstr.; bibl.; charts; illus.; index; circ. 3,000 (paid). (also avail. in microform from UMI) **Indexed:** Biol.Abstr., Chem.Abstr., Dent.Ind., Excerp.Med., Ind.Med. **Document type:** academic/scholarly publication.
—BLDSC (5794.600000); Faxon; UMI.
    Description: Covers odontostomatology and maxillofacial surgery.
    Refereed Serial

617.6   CE
MIRROR AND PROBE.* (Text in English; summaries in Sinhala and Tamil) 1963. a. Dental Students' Association, University of Sri Lanka, University Park, Peradeniya, Sri Lanka. adv.; charts; illus.; stat.; circ. controlled.

617.6   US   ISSN 0887-4646
MISSOURI DENTAL JOURNAL. 1921. bi-m. $12 to non-members; members $5 (foreign $18). Missouri Dental Association, 230 W. McCarty St., Box 1707, Jefferson City, MO 65102. TEL 314-634-3436. Ed. Dr. Elizabeth Ward. adv.: B&W page $326; trim 7 1/4 x 9 1/2; adv. contact: Jean Pfeifer. bk.rev.; illus. circ. 2,700. (also avail. in microform from UMI; reprint service avail. from UMI) **Indexed:** Dent.Abstr., Dent.Ind., Med.Care Rev.
—BLDSC (5829.052500); UMI.
    Former titles: Missouri Dental Association Journal (ISSN 0273-3463); M D A Journal (ISSN 0199-6584); Missouri Dental Association. Journal (ISSN 0026-6523)

617.6   US
MOMENTUM (ROCHESTER). 1974. q. Eastman Dental Center, 625 Elmwood Ave., Rochester, NY 14620. TEL 716-275-5064. FAX 716-244-8772. Ed. Teresa A. O'Loughlin. circ. 1,800.

617.6   BE
MONDE DENTAIRE. Dutch edition: Tandartsen Wereld. (Text in French) 1982. bi-m. 1000 BEF. C.E.P. s.r.l., Av. de Tervuren 298, 1150 Brussels, Belgium. TEL 32-2-7623458. FAX 32-2-7716351. Ed. Emmanuel M.G. Steinbach. adv.; illus.; index. circ. 9,600. (back issues avail.) **Document type:** trade publication.

617.6   IT   ISSN 0391-2000
                              CODEN: MOORDG
MONDO ORTODONTICO; rivista internazionale di ortognatodonzia. 1975. bi-m. L.139000($196) Masson S.p.A., Divisione Periodici, Via Statuto 2-4, 20121 Milan, Italy. TEL 02-6367-1. FAX 02-6367211. adv.: B&W page L.1150000, color page L.1900000; trim 193 x 265. circ. 4,500. **Indexed:** Biol.Abstr., Dent.Ind., Excerp.Med. **Document type:** academic/scholarly publication.
—BLDSC (5908.235000).

MEDICAL SCIENCES — DENTISTRY

617.6   SZ   ISSN 0077-0892
CODEN: MGUSCU
MONOGRAPHS IN ORAL SCIENCE. (Text in English) 1972. irreg. (approx. 1/yr.) price varies. S. Karger AG, Allschwilerstr. 10, P.O. Box, CH-4009 Basel, Switzerland. TEL 061-3061111. FAX 061-3061234. E-mail: Karger@Karger.ch. Ed. H.M. Myers. (reprint service avail. from ISI) **Indexed:** Biol.Abstr., Chem.Abstr., Curr.Cont., Ind.Med. **Document type:** monographic series.
—BLDSC (5915.830000). **CCC.**
   Description: Summaries of important topics in oral biology.
   Refereed Serial

617.6   US   ISSN 0027-0156
MONTGOMERY - BUCKS DENTAL SOCIETY. BULLETIN. 1955. 7/yr. membership. Montgomery - Bucks County Dental Society, 625 N. Charlotte St., Pottstown, PA 19464. TEL 215-326-3610. FAX 215-326-3494. Ed. Dr. Jeffrey Sameroff. adv.; bk.rev.; bibl. circ. 800. **Indexed:** Dent.Ind. **Document type:** bulletin.

617.6   US
MOUTHPIECE (CHICAGO). 1983. q. $56 to non-members; members $40. American Dental Association, 211 E. Chicago Ave., Chicago, IL 60611. TEL 312-440-2602. FAX 312-440-2550. Ed. Alanna Gordon. illus. **Indexed:** Sports Per.Ind. **Document type:** trade publication.

617.6   US
MOUTHPIECE (SAN MATEO). 1965. m. $15. San Mateo County Dental Society, 1941 O'Farrel St., Ste. 9, San Mateo, CA 94403. TEL 415-345-5714. FAX 415-345-2820. Ed. Dr. Michael A. Njo. adv. circ. 525.
   Formerly: San Mateo County Dental Society. Bulletin (ISSN 0080-598X)
   Description: General information for dentists with emphasis on local impact.

617.6   NO   ISSN 0047-8377
MUNNPLEIEN. 1916. 4/yr. NOK 300. Norsk Tannvern - Oral Health of Norway, Elisenberg vn. 12, N-0265 Oslo, Norway. TEL 47-22-44-28-66. FAX 47-22-56-36-93. Ed. Gerd M. Brandt. adv.; bk.rev. circ. 5,000. **Indexed:** Dent.Ind.

617.6   US   ISSN 0027-6545
N H D S NEWSLETTER. 1939. bi-m. membership. New Hampshire Dental Society, Box 2229, Concord, NH 03301-1772. Ed. Dr. James P. Cassidy. adv.; bk.rev.; illus.; stat. circ. 600. **Indexed:** Dent.Abstr. **Document type:** newsletter.

N S T A NEWSLETTER. (National Spasmodic Torticollis Association) see *MEDICAL SCIENCES — Psychiatry And Neurology*

617.6   US
NASSAU COUNTY DENTAL SOCIETY. NEWSLETTER. 1949. m. $10. Tenth District Dental Society Headquarters, 377 Oak St., No. 205, Garden City, NY 11530-6543. TEL 516-764-9620. FAX 516-227-1114. Ed. Dr. Steven Kerpen. adv.; bk.rev.; circ. 2,000 (controlled). **Document type:** bulletin.
   Former titles (until 1994): Nassau Dental News; (until 1984): Nassau County Dental Society. Bulletin; (until 1981): Tenth District Dental Society of the State of New York. Bulletin (ISSN 0070-3729)
   Refereed Serial

617.6   US
NATIONAL ASSOCIATION OF DENTAL LABORATORIES. MEMBERSHIP MEMO. q. membership. National Association of Dental Laboratories, 555 E. Braddock Rd., Alexandria, VA 22314-2106. TEL 703-683-5263. FAX 703-549-4788. **Document type:** newsletter.

NATIONAL FLUORIDATION NEWS; covering reports on research into the toxicity of fluoride, news on accidents, election outcomes and general information on the issue. see *ENVIRONMENTAL STUDIES*

NATIONAL MEDICAL AND DENTAL ASSOCIATION. BULLETIN. see *MEDICAL SCIENCES*

617.6   NE   ISSN 0028-2111
NEDERLANDS TANDARTSENBLAD. 1942. fortn. fl.155. Nederlandse Maatschappij tot Bevordering der Tandheelkunde, Postbus 2000, 3430 CA Nieuwegein, Netherlands. TEL 31-3402-76251. FAX 31-3402-41500. adv.; bk.rev.; index. circ. 8,600. **Document type:** trade publication.
—SWETS.

617.6   NE   ISSN 0028-2200
CODEN: NTTAAX
NEDERLANDS TIJDSCHRIFT VOOR TANDHEELKUNDE. 1894. 12/yr. free to qualified personnel. Wegener Tijl Tijdschriften Groep B.V., Postbus 9943, 1006 AP Amsterdam, Netherlands. TEL 31-20-5182828. FAX 31-20-5182843. Ed. Dr. I. van der Waal. adv.; bk.rev.; illus.; tr.lit.; index. circ. 5,536. **Indexed:** Biol.Abstr., Dent.Ind. **Document type:** trade publication.
—SWETS.

617.6   US
NEW DENTIST. 1993. bi-m. Slack, Inc., 6900 Grove Rd., Thorofare, NJ 08086. TEL 609-848-1000. FAX 609-853-5991. adv.: B&W page $1850, color page $3050; trim 8 1/8 x 10 7/8. circ. 12,000.

617.6   US   ISSN 0093-7347
NEW JERSEY DENTAL ASSOCIATION. JOURNAL. 1912. q. $50 to non-members; members $20. New Jersey Dental Association, 1 Dental Plaza, N. Brunswick, NJ 08902. TEL 908-821-9400. FAX 908-821-1082. Eds. Harvey S. Nisselson, Carl T. Buscher; Philip J. Cocuzza. adv. contact: Magdalena C. Burgos. bk.rev.; bibl.; charts; illus.; stat. circ. 5,000. **Indexed:** Dent.Abstr., Dent.Ind. **Document type:** academic/scholarly publication.
—BLDSC (4832.200000).

617.6   US   ISSN 0028-7571
NEW YORK STATE DENTAL JOURNAL. N.S. 1933. m. (Oct.-May); bi-m. (Jun.-Sep.). $48 to non-members; members $5; foreign $85 (effective 1992). Dental Society of the State of New York, 7 Elk St., Albany, NY 12207-1066. TEL 518-465-0044. FAX 518-427-0461. Ed. Sheridan B. Albert. adv. contact: Mayfrances McCarthy. bk.rev.; bibl.; illus.; stat.; index. circ. 15,286. (also avail. in microform from UMI; reprint service avail. from UMI) **Indexed:** Biol.Abstr., Chem.Abstr., Curr.Tit.Dent., Dent.Abstr., Dent.Ind., Dok.Arbeitsmed., Excerp.Med., Ind.Med., Med.Care Rev. **Document type:** trade publication.
—BLDSC (6089.730000); Faxon; UMI.
   Description: Features scientific articles covering research reports, case studies, and experiences with new techniques. Includes general and technical information of interest to dental practitioners.

617.6   NZ   ISSN 0028-8047
CODEN: NZDJAM
NEW ZEALAND DENTAL JOURNAL. 1905. q. NZ.$75 (foreign NZ.$95) (effective 1994). New Zealand Dental Association, P.O. Box 647, Dunedin, New Zealand. TEL 64-03-479-7115. FAX 64-03-479-0673. Ed. R.H. Brown. adv.; bk.rev.; abstr.; charts; illus.; index. circ. 1,660. **Indexed:** Biol.Abstr., Dent.Abstr., Dent.Ind., Excerp.Med., Ind.Med. **Document type:** academic/scholarly publication.
—BLDSC (6089.970000); Faxon; UnCover. **CCC.**

617.632   NZ   ISSN 0111-1485
NEW ZEALAND SOCIETY OF PERIODONTOLOGY. JOURNAL. 1956. s-a. NZ.$80 (effective 1995). New Zealand Society of Periodontology, P.O. Box 647, Dunedin, New Zealand. TEL 64-3-4797-108. FAX 64-3-4790-673. Ed. Angela Pack. adv.; bk.rev.; stat. circ. 600. **Indexed:** Curr.Tit.Dent., Dent.Ind. **Document type:** academic/scholarly publication.
—BLDSC (4833.070000). **CCC.**
   Formerly: New Zealand Society of Periodontology. Bulletin (ISSN 0028-8705)
   Refereed Serial

617.6   US
NEWS AND VIEWS (BETHESDA). 1972. q. membership. American College of Dentists, 839-J Quince Orchard Blvd., Bethesda, MD 20878. TEL 301-977-3223. FAX 301-977-3330. Ed. Sherry Keramidas. (tabloid format; back issues avail.)
   Description: Covers the activities and projects of the College and its 41 sections.

617.6   JA   ISSN 0385-0102
NICHIDAI SHIGAKU/NIHON UNIVERSITY DENTAL JOURNAL. (Text in Japanese; summaries in English) 1921. bi-m. 3000 Yen. Nihon Daigaku Shigakukai, c/o Mayumi Nomura, Secy., Nihon University, School of Dentistry, 1-8-13 Kanda Surugadai, Chiyoda-ku, Tokyo 101, Japan. FAX 0-3219-8310. Ed. Yoshihiko Moriya. circ. 2,150.

617.6   JA   ISSN 0029-0297
CODEN: NKOGAV
NIHON KOKUKA GAKKAI ZASSHI/JAPANESE STOMATOLOGICAL SOCIETY. JOURNAL. (Text in Japanese) 1952. q. 5200 Yen($3.50) Nihon Kokuka Gakkai - Japanese Stomatological Society, Department of Oral Surgery, School of Medicine, University of Tokyo, 7-3-1 Hongo, Bunkyo-ku, Tokyo 113, Japan. Ed.Bd. circ. 1,900. **Indexed:** Chem.Abstr., Ind.Med.
—BLDSC (4809.550000); CASDDS.

NIHON SHIKA MASUI GAKKAI ZASSHI/JAPANESE DENTAL SOCIETY OF ANESTHESIOLOGY. JOURNAL. see *MEDICAL SCIENCES — Anaesthesiology*

617.6   JA   ISSN 0385-0110
CODEN: NSKADI
NIHON SHISHUBYO GAKKAI KAISHI/JAPANESE ASSOCIATION OF PERIODONTOLOGY. JOURNAL. 1968. q. 5000 Yen. Nihon Shishubyo Gakkai, Koku Hoken Kyokai, 44-2, Komagome 1-chome, Toshima-ku, Tokyo 170, Japan. Ed. Tadashi Nakashizuka. adv.; bk.rev. **Indexed:** Chem.Abstr., Dent.Ind., Eng.Ind.
—CASDDS.

617.6   JA   ISSN 0385-0145
CODEN: NKOKDC
NIHON UNIVERSITY. JOURNAL OF ORAL SCIENCE/NICHIDAI KOKU KAGAKU. 1975. q. exchange basis. Nihon University, School of Dentistry at Matsudo, 870-1 Sakaecho, Nishi-2, Matsudo-shi, Chiba-ken 271, Japan. Ed. Tadamasa Iwasawa. index. circ. 900. **Document type:** academic/scholarly publication.
—BLDSC (6113.150000); CASDDS.

617.6   JA   ISSN 0029-0432
CODEN: JNUDAT
NIHON UNIVERSITY. SCHOOL OF DENTISTRY. JOURNAL/NIHON DAIGAKU SHIGAKUBU OBUN ZASSHI. (Text in English) 1958. q. exchange basis. Nihon University, School of Dentistry - Nihon Daigaku Shigakubu, 1-8-13 Kanda Surugadai, Chiyoda-ku, Tokyo 101, Japan. FAX 03-3219-8310. Ed. Itaru Moro. bk.rev.; abstr.; charts; illus.; index. circ. 1,200. **Indexed:** Biol.Abstr., Chem.Abstr., Curr.Tit.Dent., Dent.Ind., Ind.Med., INIS Atomind., Med.Abstr. **Document type:** academic/scholarly publication.
—BLDSC (4833.400000); CASDDS; UnCover.
   Description: Contains academic research papers and case reports.

617.6   JA   ISSN 0549-5245
NIPPON DENTAL UNIVERSITY. ANNUAL PUBLICATIONS. (Text in English) 1964. a. exchange basis. Society of the Nippon Dental University - Nihon Shika Daigaku Shigakkai, 9-20 Fujimi 1-chome, Chiyoda-ku, Tokyo 102, Japan. FAX 03-264-8745. Ed. Kazuko Saito. circ. 2,000. **Document type:** academic/scholarly publication.
—BLDSC (1093.502000).
   Formerly: Society of Nippon Dental College. Annual Publications.

617.6   NO   ISSN 0029-2303
NORSKE TANNLEGEFORENINGS TIDENDE. (Text in Norwegian; summaries in English) 1890. 20/yr. NOK 925. Norske Tannlegeforening - Norwegian Dental Association, P.O. Box 3063 Elisenberg, 0207 Oslo, Norway. TEL 47-22-55-13-50. FAX 47-22-55-11-09. Ed. Gudrun Sangnes. adv. contact: Nina Smedstad. bk.rev.; charts; illus.; stat.; tr.lit.; index. circ. 5,200. **Indexed:** Dent.Abstr., Dent.Ind., Ind.Med. **Document type:** academic/scholarly publication.
—BLDSC (6147.800000).
   Former titles (until 1946): Norges Tannlaegeforbunds Tidsskrift (ISSN 0801-4477); (until 1941): Norske Tannlaegeforenings Tidsskrift (ISSN 0801-4469)

MEDICAL SCIENCES — DENTISTRY

617.6 US
NORTH CAROLINA DENTAL REVIEW. 1983. s-a. $10. University of North Carolina, School of Dentistry, Brauer Hall, Rm. 410, CB 7450, Chapel Hill, NC 27599-7450. TEL 919-966-2730. FAX 919-966-4049. E-mail: SKG.DENTCE@MHS.UNC.edu. (Co-sponsor: U N C Dental Alumni Association) Ed. Sharon K. Grayden. adv.; circ. 6,200 (controlled). **Document type:** academic/scholarly publication.
  Description: Supports the school's missions of dental education, patient care, research and service.

617.6 US ISSN 0029-2915
RK1
NORTHWEST DENTISTRY. 1930. bi-m. $20 to non-members. Minnesota Dental Association, 2236 Marshall Ave., St. Paul, MN 55104. TEL 612-646-7457. FAX 612-646-8246. (Co-sponsors: North Dakota Dental Association; South Dakota Dental Society) Ed. Richard A. Johnson. adv. circ. 3,472. **Indexed:** Dent.Ind.
  —BLDSC (6151.710000); Faxon; UnCover.

617.6 CN
NOVA SCOTIA DENTIST. 1985. bi-m. membership. Nova Scotia Dental Association, 5991 Spring Garden Road, Ste 604, Halifax, NS B3H 1Y6, Canada. TEL 902-420-0088. FAX 902-423-6537. Ed. D.V. Pamenter. adv. contact: Steve Jennex. circ. 1,000. **Document type:** newsletter.
  Formerly (until 1985): Nova Scotia Dental Association. Newsletter.

617.6 US
O D A NEWSLETTER. vol.17, 1987. q. $20 to non-members; members $15 (includes subscr. to Journal of the Oregon Dental Association). Oregon Dental Association, 17898 S.W. McEwan Rd., Portland, OR 97224. Ed. Dr. James P. Fratzke. **Document type:** newsletter.

617.6 FR ISSN 0251-172X
ODONTO-STOMATOLOGIE TROPICALE/TROPICAL DENTAL JOURNAL. (Text in English, French) 1978. q. 303 F.($72) Universite de Bordeaux 2, Departement Sante et Developpement, c/o Jean-Louis Miquel, Universite de Bordeaux 2, 146, rue Leo-Saignat, 33076 Bordeaux Cedex, France. TEL 56-96-28-93. FAX 56-24-46-82. TELEX IN UB2 572 237 F. (Co-sponsor: Commonwealth Foundation) Ed. J.L. Miquel. adv.; bk.rev.; charts; index. circ. 2,500. (back issues avail.; reprint service avail. from IRC) **Indexed:** Biol.Abstr., So.Pac.Per.Ind.
  —BLDSC (9055.800000); SWETS.
  Formerly: Secretariat de Sante Dentaire de l'Afrique. Revue.
  Description: Addresses numerous oral health problems in various tropical countries and efforts to treat them.

617.6 IT ISSN 0393-7631
ODONTOIATRIA OGGI. 1984. bi-m. L.135000($180) Piccin Editore, Via Altinate 107, 35100 Padua, Italy. TEL 049-655566. FAX 049-8750693. Ed. Prof. E. Gianni. adv.; B&W page L.1900000, color page L.2700000; trim 210 x 280. circ. 5,000.

618 IT ISSN 0390-6000
ODONTOIATRIA PRATICA. 1966. q. L.8000. Sabatelli Editori, Piazza Diaz 11, 17100 Savona, Italy. Ed. Raffaello Rastelli. adv.; bk.rev.; abstr.; bibl.; illus. circ. 1,500. (back issues avail.)

617.6 DK ISSN 0105-0141
ODONTOLOGI. (Text in Danish, Norwegian and Swedish) 1976. a. price varies. Munksgaard International Publishers Ltd., Book Division, 35 Noerre Soegade, P.O. Box 2148, DK-1016 Copenhagen K, Denmark. TEL 45-33-12-70-30. FAX 45-33-12-93-87. illus.

617.6 CL ISSN 0029-8417
ODONTOLOGIA CHILENA. 1954. s-a. free. (Colegio de Dentistas de Chile) Editorial Universitaria, Avda. Santa Maria 1990, Casilla 3444 Correo Central, Santiago, Chile. Ed. Dr. Juan Montagna Concha. adv.; bibl.; charts; illus.; stat.; tr.mk. circ. 3,500. **Indexed:** Dent.Ind.

617.6 UY ISSN 0029-8425
ODONTOLOGIA URUGUAYA. vol.21, 1965. s-a. membership. Asociacion Odontologica Uruguaya, Durazno 937-39, Montevideo, Uruguay. TEL 901572. Ed.Bd. adv.; bk.rev.; bibl.; charts; illus.; stat. circ. 3,000.

617.6 FI ISSN 0078-3358
ODONTOLOGISKA SAMFUNDET I FINLAND. AARSBOK. 1946. a. Fmk.50. Odontologiska Samfundets i Finland, Bergmansg. 11 D 11, SF-00140 Helsinki 14, Finland. adv.; bk.rev. circ. 500. **Indexed:** Biol.Abstr.

617.6 PN ISSN 0472-5158
ODONTOLOGO. (Text in Spanish; abstracts in English) 1975. 2/yr. $24. Asociacion Odontologica Panamena - Panamanian Dental Association, Apdo. 6777, Zona 5, Panama, Panama. TEL 507-269-1603. FAX 507-269-3749. Ed. Dr. Amalia Membreno. adv.; circ. 750 (controlled). **Document type:** trade publication.
  Refereed Serial

617.6 BL ISSN 0100-0187
ODONTOLOGO MODERNO; a revista dos cursos. 6/yr. Editora de Publicacoes Cientificas Ltda., Rua Major Suckow, 30 a 36, 20911 Rio de Janeiro RJ, Brazil. TEL 021-201-3722. FAX 021-261-3749. Ed. Almir L. de Fonseca. adv.; abstr.; bibl.; illus.; cum.index. circ. 15,000.
  Formerly (until 1973): Manual do Odontologo Moderno (ISSN 0100-0438)

617.6 IT ISSN 0391-3783
ODONTOSTOMATOLOGIA E IMPLANTOPROTESI. 1974. m. foreign L.280000 (effective 1995). Stammer S.p.A., Via della Liberazione, 1, 20068 Peschiera Borromeo (MI), Italy. TEL 02-55-30-26-06. FAX 02-55-30-27-00. adv.; bk.rev. circ. 20,000. **Indexed:** Dent.Ind.

617.6 GR ISSN 0029-8506
ODONTOSTOMATOLOGICAL PROGRESS. (Text in Greek; summaries in English) 1947. bi-m. $60. Society of Odontostomatological Research, 70 Micras Asias St., Athens 11527, Greece. Ed. B.G. Tsatsas. adv.; bk.rev.; charts; illus. circ. 3,000.

617.6 AU ISSN 0029-9596
OESTERREICHISCHE ZAHNAERZTE - ZEITUNG. 1950. m. Bundesfachgruppe fuer Zahn-, Mund- und Kieferheilkunde, Weihburgstrasse 1012, A-1010 Vienna, Austria. adv.; bk.rev.; charts; stat. circ. 4,900. **Document type:** newsletter.
  Incorporates (1949-1989): Oesterreichische Dentistenzeitschrift (ISSN 0029-9006)

617.6 AU
DAS OESTERREICHISCHE ZAHNTECHNIKERHANDWERK. 1955. q. S.280. (Bundesinnung der Zahntechniker) Oesterreichischer Wirtschaftsverlag, Nikolsdorfergasse 7-11, 1050 Vienna, Austria. TEL 0222-555585. TELEX 1-11669. Ed. Ingeborg Reisner. tr.lit. circ. 1,000.
  Former titles: Oesterreichische Zahntechniker; Oesterreichische Zahnprothetik; Oesterreichische Zahntechnikerhandwerk.

617.6 US ISSN 0030-087X
OHIO DENTAL JOURNAL. 1927. 2/yr. $30 to non-members & libraries (foreign $45). Ohio Dental Association, 1370 Dublin Rd., Columbus, OH 43215-1098. TEL 614-486-2700. (Subscr. to: Department 367, Box 182039, Columbus, OH 43218-2039) Ed. Donald F. Bowers. adv.; illus.; circ. 5,300 (controlled). **Indexed:** Dent.Abstr., Dent.Ind. **Document type:** trade publication.
  —BLDSC (6245.800000).

617.6 US ISSN 0164-9442
OKLAHOMA DENTAL ASSOCIATION JOURNAL. vol.64, 1973. q. $12 (foreign $18). Oklahoma Dental Association, 629 N.W. Expressway, Oklahoma City, OK 73118. TEL 405-848-8873. Ed. Jerome Miller. adv.; illus. circ. 1,600. **Indexed:** Dent.Abstr., Dent.Ind.
  Former titles: Your Oklahoma Dental Association. Journal; Oklahoma State Dental Association. Journal (ISSN 0030-1868)

617.6 US ISSN 0030-2201
OMAHA DISTRICT DENTAL SOCIETY. CHRONICLE. 1936. m. (10/yr.). $10. (Omaha District Dental Society) Barnhart Press, Dundee Professional Bldg., Ste. 403, 119 N. 51st St., Omaha, NE 68132. TEL 402-544-1322. Ed. Dr. Douglas O. deShazer. adv.; bk.rev.; abstr.; charts; illus. circ. 2,600. **Indexed:** Dent.Ind. **Document type:** academic/scholarly publication.

617.6 CN ISSN 0300-5275
ONTARIO DENTIST. 1925. m. Can.$70. Ontario Dental Association, 4 New St., Toronto, ON M5R 1P6, Canada. TEL 416-922-3900. FAX 416-922-9005. Ed. Dr. James Shosenberg; Pub. Peter James. adv. contact: Marnie Boggs. bk.rev.; bibl.; illus. circ. 6,500. **Indexed:** Dent.Abstr., Dent.Ind.
  —BLDSC (6261.890000); Faxon.
  Formerly: Ontario Dental Association. Journal (ISSN 0030-2864)

617.6 US ISSN 0361-7734
RK501
OPERATIVE DENTISTRY. Variant title: Journal of Operative Dentistry. (Supplements avail.) 1976. bi-m. $55 to individuals (foreign $65); students $25 (foreign $34). (Academy of Operative Dentistry) University of Washington, School of Dentistry, SM-57, Seattle, WA 98195-0001. TEL 206-543-5913. FAX 206-543-7783. (Alt. ed. addr.: R.J. Werner, Box 177, Menominie, WI 54751) (Co-sponsor: American Academy of Gold Foil Operators) Ed. Dr. Richard B. McCoy. bk.rev.; illus.; circ. 2,000 (paid). (also avail. in microfilm from UMI; back issues avail.) **Indexed:** Curr.Cont., Curr.Tit.Dent., Dent.Abstr., Dent.Ind. **Document type:** academic/scholarly publication.
  —BLDSC (6269.375000); Faxon; Genuine Article; SWETS; UMI; UnCover.
  Supersedes: American Academy of Gold Foil Operators. Journal (ISSN 0002-7146)

617.6 US
ORACLE. 1964. m. $2. Napa-Solano Dental Society, 1023 Empire St., Fairfield, CA 94533-5706. Ed. Dr. Robert E. Sprott. adv. circ. 195.
  Formerly: Napa-Solano Dental Society. District Six. Newsletter (ISSN 0027-7800)
  Description: Contains organization news.

ORAL AND MAXILLOFACIAL SURGERY CLINICS OF NORTH AMERICA. see *MEDICAL SCIENCES — Surgery*

617.6 UK ISSN 1354-523X
▼**ORAL DISEASES.** 1995. q. £50($75) to individuals; institutions in E.U. £125(elsewhere £135). Stockton Press (Subsidiary of: Macmillan Press Ltd.), Houndmills, Basingstoke, Hants RG21 2XS, England. TEL 01256-817245. FAX 01256-28339. Ed. Newell Johnson; Pub. Jayne Marks. adv. contact: Michael Rowley. **Document type:** academic/scholarly publication.
  —BLDSC (6277.470000). CCC.

617.6 CN ISSN 0030-4204
ORAL HEALTH; clinical journal devoted to the advancement of the dental profession. 1911. m. Can.$42.80($46) (foreign $75). Southam Magazine Group, 1450 Don Mills Rd., Don Mills, ON M3B 2X7, Canada. TEL 416-445-6641. FAX 416-442-2077. Ed. Janet Bonellie. adv.; bk.rev.; abstr.; illus. circ. 15,000. **Indexed:** Chem.Abstr., Dent.Abstr., Dent.Ind.
  —BLDSC (6277.500000); Faxon. CCC.
  Description: Consists of clinical articles, abstracts from the world's dental literature.

617.6 615.842 JA ISSN 0911-6028
ORAL RADIOLOGY. Japanese edition: Shika Hoshasen (ISSN 0389-9705) (Text in English) 1985. 2/yr. (in one vol.) 5000 Yen. Nihon Shika Hoshasen Gakkai - Japanese Society for Oral and Maxillofacial Radiology, Faculty of Dentistry, Osaka University, 1-8, Yamadaoka, Suita, Osaka 565, Japan. Ed. Kanji Kishi. **Document type:** academic/scholarly publication.
  —BLDSC (6277.595000).

MEDICAL SCIENCES — DENTISTRY 4379

617.6 US
RD1 CODEN: OSOMAE
ORAL SURGERY, ORAL MEDICINE, ORAL PATHOLOGY, ORAL RADIOLOGY, AND ENDODONTICS. 1948. m. $97 to individuals (Canada $132.68; elsewhere $124); institutions $207 (Canada 250.38; elsewhere $234); students, residents $46 (Canada $78.11; elsewhere $73) (effective 1996); newsstand price: $10. (American Academy of Oral Pathology) Mosby - Year Book, Inc. (Subsidiary of: Times Mirror Company), 11830 Westline Industrial Dr., St. Louis, MO 63146-3318. TEL 314-872-8370; 800-325-4177. FAX 314-432-1380. TELEX 44-2402. (Co-sponsors: American Academy of Dental Radiology; American Institute of Oral Biology) Ed. Larry J. Peterson. adv.: B&W page $990, color page $1885; trim 8 1/8 x 10 7/8. bk.rev.; abstr.; illus.; s-a. index. circ. 7,634. (also avail. in microfilm from UMI; reprint service avail. from UMI) **Indexed:** Apic.Abstr., ASCA, Chem.Abstr., Curr.Adv.Cancer Res., Curr.Adv.Ecol.Sci., Curr.Cont., Curr.Tit.Dent., Dent.Abstr., Dent.Ind., Excerp.Med., Helminthol.Abstr., Ind.Med., Med.& Surg.Dermat., Nutr.Abstr., Rev.Med.& Vet.Mycol., Rev.Plant Path., Sci.Cit.Ind.
—BLDSC (6277.800000); CASDDS; EMDOCS; Genuine Article; UMI; UnCover. **CCC.**
Formerly: Oral Surgery, Oral Medicine, Oral Pathology (ISSN 0030-4220)
Description: Comprehensive coverage of the field including identification of abnormalities and use of specialized diagnostic techniques.
Refereed Serial

617.6 GW ISSN 0724-4991
ORALPROPHYLAXE. 1984. q. DM.32. (Verein fuer Zahnhygiene e.V.) Zahnaerztlicher Fachverlag GmbH, Mont-Cenis-Str. 5, 44623 Herne, Germany. TEL 02323-593141. circ. 5,000.
—BLDSC (6277.808000).
Description: Contains current information and research concerning dental and mouth hygiene. Covers flouride, toothpaste research, and childrens' dental care.

617.6 FR ISSN 0755-2378
ORDRE NATIONAL DES CHIRURGIENS- DENTISTES. CONSEIL NATIONAL. BULLETIN OFFICIEL. 1976. q. 190 F. Ordre National des Chirurgiens- Dentistes, Conseil National, 22, rue Emile-Menier, 75116 Paris, France. TEL 45-53-40-05. Dir. M.A. Rochais. charts; illus.

617.6 US
OREGON DENTAL ASSOCIATION. DENTAL OFFICE SAFETY & HEALTH MANUAL. a. membership. Oregon Dental Association, 17898 S.W. McEwan Rd., Portland, OR 97224. TEL 503-620-3230.
Description: Provides information for dentist and dental office staff concerning potential occupational hazards and compliance with Oregon OSHA rules and regulations.

617.6 US
OREGON DENTAL ASSOCIATION. JOURNAL. 1930. q. $20 to non-members; members $15 (includes ODA newsletter). Oregon Dental Association, 17898 S.W. McEwan Rd., Portland, OR 97224. TEL 503-620-3230. Ed. Dr. Marion S. Ratliff. adv.; bk.rev.; charts; illus. circ. 2,000. **Indexed:** Dent.Abstr., Dent.Ind. **Document type:** trade publication.
Formerly: Oregon State Dental Journal.
Description: Covers the current news in the science of dentistry.

617.643 US ISSN 0895-5034
ORTHODONTIC REVIEW. 1987. q. $93. University of Missouri at Kansas City, School of Dentistry, 650 E. 25th St., Kansas City, MO 64108. TEL 816-235-5602. Ed. Dr. Richard Ackerman.

617.6 FR ISSN 0078-6608
ORTHODONTIE FRANCAISE. (1921-1962 called also Comptes Rendus du Congres Annuel) 1921. a. 1500 F. (effective Jan. 1994). Societe d'Information et Diffusion, Librarie Internationale, 9 rue Christine, 75006 Paris, France. TEL 43-29-31-01. FAX 43-29-32-62. (back issues avail.) **Indexed:** Ind.Med. **Document type:** academic/scholarly publication.

617.6 AG ISSN 0030-5936
ORTODONCIA. (Text in Spanish; summaries in English, French, German and Spanish) 1937. s-a. $56. Sociedad Argentina de Ortodoncia, Montevideo 971, 1019 Buenos Aires, Argentina. TEL 811-5569. Ed. Dr. Marcos M. Rose. adv.: page $400. bk.rev.; abstr.; bibl.; charts; illus.; stat.; index. circ. 1,500. **Indexed:** Biol.Abstr., Dent.Ind.

617.6 BL ISSN 0030-5944
ORTODONTIA.* (Text in Portuguese; summaries in English) 1968. 3/yr. exchange basis. Sociedade Paulista de Ortodontia, R. do Livramento, 243, 01321 Sao Paulo, SP, Brazil. Dir. Dr. Julio W. Vigorito. adv.: page $400. bk.rev.; bibl.; charts; illus.; index. circ. 5,000. (also avail. in microform) **Indexed:** Dent.Ind.
Description: Presents results of research in orthodontics.

617.6 JA ISSN 0473-4629
CODEN: ODSZA2
OSAKA DAIGAKU SHIGAKU ZASSHI/OSAKA UNIVERSITY DENTAL SOCIETY. JOURNAL. (Text in Japanese) 1956. s-a. 3000 Yen. Osaka Daigaku Shigakkai - Osaka University Dental Society, 1-8 Yamadaoka, Suita, Osaka 565, Japan. TEL 06-876-5711. FAX 06-876-7931. Ed. Yoshio Shigenaga. adv. circ. 1,700. **Indexed:** Dent.Ind., Excerp.Med.
—BLDSC (4839.370000).
Description: Contains mini-reviews, original articles, and case reports on dental science.

617.6 JA ISSN 0475-2058
CODEN: JODUA2
OSAKA DENTAL UNIVERSITY. JOURNAL. (Text and summaries in English) 1967. s-a. exchange basis. Osaka Dental University - Osaka Shika Daigaku, 5-31, Otemae 1-chome, Chuo-ku, Osaka 540, Japan. FAX 06-943-5656. Ed. Akio Tanaka. abstr.; charts; illus.; stat.; tr.lit.; index. (back issues avail.) **Indexed:** Biol.Abstr., Chem.Abstr., Curr.Tit.Dent., Dent.Ind., Excerp.Med., Ind.Med., Oral Res.Abstr. **Document type:** academic/scholarly publication.
—BLDSC (4838.500000); CASDDS; UnCover.

617.6 JA ISSN 0030-6150
CODEN: SIGAAE
OSAKA ODONTOLOGICAL SOCIETY. JOURNAL/SHIKA IGAKU. (Text in Japanese; summaries in English) 1930. bi-m. $6.50. Osaka Odontological Society - Osaka Shika Gakkai, 1-47 Kyobashi Higashiku, Osaka 540, Japan. adv.; charts; illus. **Indexed:** Biol.Abstr., Chem.Abstr.
—BLDSC (4839.300000); CASDDS. **CCC.**
Description: Contains numerous studies in dental research, including new technologies and treatments.

617.6 PK ISSN 0030-9710
CODEN: PKDRAV
PAKISTAN DENTAL REVIEW. (Text in English) 1951. q. $30. 26 Shahrah-e-Quaid-e-Azam, Lahore 54000, Pakistan. Ed. S. Eckbelle. adv.; bk.rev.; bibl.; charts; illus.; stat.; index. circ. 5,000. **Indexed:** Biol.Abstr., Dent.Ind.

PANKEY-GRAM. see COLLEGE AND ALUMNI

617.6 IT
PARODONTOLOGIA E STOMATOLOGIA NUOVA. (Text in Italian; summaries in English, French and German) vol.9, 1965. q. L.50000. Istituto Clinico di Odontostomatologia, Viale Benedetto 15, Genoa, Italy. Eds. I. Jonata, F. Torrielli. adv.; bk.rev.; charts; illus.; index. **Indexed:** Chem.Abstr.
Formerly: Stomatologica (ISSN 0039-1727)

617.6 GW ISSN 0937-1532
PARODONTOLOGIE. 1990. q. DM.178 (foreign DM.193). Quintessenz Verlags GmbH, Ifenpfad 2-4, 12107 Berlin, Germany. TEL 030-74006-46. FAX 030-7415080. **Indexed:** Curr.Tit.Dent. **Document type:** academic/scholarly publication.

617.6 US
PASSAIC COUNTY DENTAL SOCIETY NEWSLETTER. 1979. m. (Oct.-May). $40. Passaic County Dental Society, 999 McBride Ave., 2nd Fl., W. Paterson, NJ 07424. Ed. Dr. Stuart Katz. adv. circ. 300. **Indexed:** Dent.Ind. **Document type:** newsletter.
Formerly (until 1981): Passaic County Dental Society. Bulletin (ISSN 0079-0125)

617.6 618.92 JA ISSN 0917-2394
PEDIATRIC DENTAL JOURNAL. Variant title: International Journal of Japanese Society of Pediatric Dentistry. (Text in English) 1991. a. $10. Japanese Society of Pediatric Dentistry, Oral Health Association, 1-44-2 Komagome, Toshima-ku, Tokyo, Japan. Ed. Mizuho Nishino.
—BLDSC (6417.575000).
Description: Promotes research, practice and education specifically related to pediatric dentistry.

617.6 US ISSN 0164-1263
CODEN: PEDEDL
PEDIATRIC DENTISTRY. 1979. bi-m. $80. American Academy of Pediatric Dentistry, 211 E. Chicago Ave., Ste. 700, Chicago, IL 60611-2616. TEL 312-337-2169. FAX 312-337-6329. Ed. Dr. Paul S. Casamassimo. adv.: B&W page $380; trim 8 1/4 x 10 7/8. bk.rev.; circ. 4,210 (paid). **Indexed:** Behav.Med.Abstr., Biol.Abstr., Curr.Tit.Dent., Dent.Abstr., Dent.Ind. **Document type:** trade publication.
—BLDSC (6417.580000); Faxon; SWETS.
Description: Promotes the practice, education, and research of pediatric dentistry.
Refereed Serial

617.6 618.92 US ISSN 1046-2791
PEDIATRIC DENTISTRY TODAY. bi-m. $20 (foreign $30) membership. American Academy of Pediatric Dentistry, 211 E. Chicago Ave., Ste. 700, Chicago, IL 60611-2616. TEL 312-337-2169. FAX 312-337-6329. Ed. Amy Fox. adv.: B&W page $228; trim 8 1/2 x 11. circ. 3,100. (back issues avail.; reprint service avail.) **Document type:** newsletter.

617.6 US ISSN 0031-4331
PENN DENTAL JOURNAL. 1897. s-a. $40 (typically set in Jul.). University of Pennsylvania, School of Dental Medicine, 4001 Spruce St., Philadelphia, PA 19104. TEL 215-898-5243. FAX 215-898-8951. Ed. Tobe Amsterdam. adv.; bk.rev.; charts; illus.; index. circ. 7,500. (also avail. in microform from UMI) **Indexed:** Dent.Ind. **Document type:** academic/scholarly publication.
Description: A progressive, clinical journal of dentistry, containing articles by faculty and students.

617.6 US ISSN 0031-4439
RK1
PENNSYLVANIA DENTAL JOURNAL. 1933. 6/yr. $12 (foreign $36). Pennsylvania Dental Association, Box 3341, Harrisburg, PA 17105. TEL 717-234-5941. FAX 717-232-7169. Ed. Dr. Judith McFadden. adv.: B&W page $442.75, color page $990.38; trim 7 x 10. index. circ. 7,000. (also avail. in microfilm from UMI; reprint service avail. from UMI) **Indexed:** Dent.Abstr., Dent.Ind., Med.Care Rev. **Document type:** trade publication.
—BLDSC (6421.705000); Faxon; UMI.
Description: Covers topics of interest to members of the dental professions: dentistry techniques, breakthroughs, governmental regulations, and other items.
Refereed Serial

617.6 US
PENNSYLVANIA SOCIETY OF DENTISTRY FOR CHILDREN NEWSLETTER. 1968. 4/yr. Pennsylvania Society of Dentistry for Children, c/o Dr. W.F. Hrin, Ed., 227 Franklin St., Ste. 220, Johnstown, PA 15901. circ. 1,100. **Document type:** newsletter.

617.695 FI ISSN 0359-2189
PERFIS. 1982. q. FIM 50($10) Perfis Oy, PL 625, FIN-20101 Turku, Finland. TEL 358-21-232-24-20. FAX 358-21-233-11-48. Ed. Ilkka Pekanheimo. adv.: B&W page FIM 5300. circ. 13,000. (back issues avail.) **Document type:** trade publication.

617.6 SP
PERIODONCIA. (Text in Spanish; summaries in English) 1991. 3/yr. 3000 ptas. (Sociedad Espanola de Periodoncia) Ediciones Ergon S.A., Pza. Josep Pallach 10, 1o 1o, 08035 Barcelona, Spain. TEL 4285500. FAX 4285660. (Subscr. to: Ergon, C. Antonio Lopez Aguado 1, 28029 Madrid, Spain) adv.; bk.rev.; index. (back issues avail.)

MEDICAL SCIENCES — DENTISTRY

617.632 CN ISSN 1195-2008
▼**PERIODONTAL INSIGHTS**; a newsletter for the dental team. 1994. q. $55 to individuals (outside N. America $85); institutions $85 (outside N. America $115) (effective 1996). Decker Periodicals, P.O. Box 620, LCD 1, Hamilton, ON L8N 3K7, Canada. TEL 905-522-7017; 800-568-7281.
FAX 905-522-7839. E-mail: decker@io.org. (U.S. addr.: Box 785, Lewiston, NY 14092-0785) **Document type:** newsletter.

618 AT ISSN 0726-5247
PERIODONTOLOGY. 1967. s-a. Aus.$40. Australian Society of Periodontology, Dept. of Dentistry, University of Queensland, Brisbane, Qld. 4000, Australia. TEL 61-7-365-8055.
FAX 61-7-365-8199. E-mail: P.Bartold@mailbox.uq.oz.au. Ed. P.M. Bartold. adv.; bk.rev.; circ. 400 (paid). **Document type:** trade publication.
Formerly (until 1980): A S P Newsletter.
Description: Publishes clinical papers, original research, review articles, case reports and items of general interest in the field of periodontology.
Refereed Serial

617.632 DK ISSN 0906-6713
PERIODONTOLOGY 2000. (Text in English) 1993. 3/yr. DKK 1000 (effective 1996). Munksgaard International Publishers Ltd., 35 Noerre Soegade, P.O. Box 2148, DK-1016 Copenhagen K, Denmark. TEL 45-33-12-70-30. FAX 45-33-12-93-87. Ed. Joergen Slots. adv.; illus. (reprint service avail.)
Document type: academic/scholarly publication.
—BLDSC (6426.452300); SWETS. **CCC.**
Refereed Serial

617.6 US ISSN 0031-7268
PHILADELPHIA COUNTY DENTAL SOCIETY. BULLETIN. 1936. 6/yr. membership. Philadelphia County Dental Society, 225 E. Washington Sq., Philadelphia, PA 19106. TEL 215-925-6050.
FAX 215-925-6998. Ed. Dr. James H. Dyen. adv.; illus. circ. 2,500. **Indexed:** Dent.Ind., Med.Care Rev.

617.6 PH ISSN 0031-7497
PHILIPPINE DENTAL ASSOCIATION. JOURNAL. 1908. q. P.200 to non-members (foreign $25). Philippines Dental Association, Ayala Ave. corner Kamagong St., Makati, Metro Manila, Philippines. TEL 818-6144. FAX 816-3034. Ed. Dr. Francisco M. Herbosa. adv. contact: Leo G. Espina. bk.rev.; bibl.; illus.; index. circ. 5,000. (back issues avail.) **Indexed:** Dent.Ind., ExtraMED. **Document type:** academic/scholarly publication.
●Also available on CD-ROM.

617.6 GW ISSN 0174-5980
PHILLIP JOURNAL. 1983. bi-m. DM.180. Phillip Verlag, Maximilianstrasse 52, 80538 Munich, Germany. FAX 089-222268. (Dist. by: PAN-Adress Direktmarketing GmbH, Semmelweisstrasse 8, 8033 Planegg, Germany) Ed. Dr. J. Schmidseder. adv.; bk.rev. circ. 6,500.
—BLDSC (6450.100000).
Formerly: Philip Journal fuer Restaurative Zahnmedizin.

617.6 BL ISSN 0102-9460
PONTIFICIA UNIVERSIDADE CATOLICA DO RIO GRANDE DO SUL. REVISTA ODONTOCIENCIA. 1986. 2/yr. Cr.$10($20) Editora da P U C R S, c/o Antoninho M. Naime, Caixa Postal 12001, 90620 Porto Alegre RS, Brazil. circ. 1,000.

617.6 UK ISSN 0959-6666
POSTGRADUATE DENTIST: MIDDLE EAST. 1990. q. £20 (outside Europe £30) (effective 1996). Barker Publications Ltd., Barker House, 539 London Rd., Isleworth, Mddx. TW7 4DA, England.
TEL 44-181-847-1774. FAX 44-181-568-2766. TELEX 24667 IMPEMP G. Ed. David Croser. adv.; bk.rev.; charts; illus. circ. 6,150. (back issues avail.) **Document type:** academic/scholarly publication.
Description: Contains specially commissioned postgraduate-level review articles on all aspects of clinical dentistry for practicing dentists in the Middle East.

617.6 MX ISSN 0185-5905
PRACTICA ODONTOLOGICA. 1979. m. Mundo Medico, S.A., Ejercito Nacional 381, 11520 Mexico DF, Mexico. TEL 525-5451798. FAX 525-2036418. Ed. Maria Beatriz Elizalde Vergara.
—BLDSC (6593.809000).

617.632 US ISSN 1042-2722
PRACTICAL PERIODONTICS AND AESTHETIC DENTISTRY. 1988. 9/yr. $65 (typically set in Jan.). Montage Media Corp., 70 Hilltop Rd., Ramsey, NJ 07446-1119. TEL 201-236-0070.
FAX 201-236-1339. Ed. Roland W. Meffert; Pub. Stephen E. Sweeney. adv.: B&W page $4264, color page $5464; trim 8 1/8 x 10 7/8. circ. 84,000. **Document type:** trade publication.
—BLDSC (6595.340000).
Description: Presents practical applications of soft tissue management and all aspects of restorative and aesthetic dentistry.

617.69 JA ISSN 0018-6341
PRACTICE IN PROSTHODONTICS/HOTETSU RINSHO. (Text in Japanese) 1968. bi-m. 1300 Yen per no. Ishiyaku Publishers, Inc., 7-10 Honkomagome 1-chome, Bunkyo-ku, Tokyo 113, Japan. Ed. Hiroshi Miura. adv.; bk.rev.; index. circ. 16,200. **Indexed:** Dent.Ind.

617.6 XR ISSN 0032-6720
PRAKTICKE ZUBNI LEKARSTVI. 1952. 10/yr. $45.10. (Ceska Lekarska Stomatologicka Spolecnost J.E. Purkyne) Nakladatelske Strediska C L S J.E. Purkyne, Sokolska 31, 120 26 Prague 2, Czech Republic. FAX 42-0-2-202788. (Dist. by: Artia, Ve Smeckach 30, 111 27 Prague 1, Czech Republic) (Co-sponsor: Ceskoslovenska Stomatologicka Spolecnost) Ed. Dr. V. Sicha. bk.rev.; abstr.
—BLDSC (6598.600000). **CCC.**

617.6 362.1 SW ISSN 1103-1727
PRAKTIKAN. 1986. 10/yr. Praktikertjaenst, P.O. Box 1304, S-111 83 Stockholm, Sweden.

617.6 GW ISSN 0931-6965
PRAKTISCHE KIEFERORTHOPAEDIE; die Zeitschrift aus Praxis und Wissenschaft. 1987. q. DM.183 (foreign DM.200). Quintessenz Verlags GmbH, Ifenpfad 2-4, 12107 Berlin, Germany. TEL 030-74006-46.
FAX 030-7415080. Eds. Prof. Rainer-Reginald Miethke, Prof. Dieter Drescher. circ. 3,000. (back issues avail.) **Document type:** academic/scholarly publication.
Description: Further education for dentists and orthodontists.

617.6 IT ISSN 0393-9960
PREVENZIONE E ASSISTANZA DENTALE. 1975. bi-m. L.61000($97) (effective 1994). Masson S.p.A., Divisione Periodici, Via Statuto 2-4, 20121 Milan, Italy. TEL 02-6367-1. FAX 02-6367211. Ed. Carlo Guastamacchia. adv.; B&W page L.1150000, color page L.1850000; trim 193 x 265. circ. 5,000. **Document type:** academic/scholarly publication.
—BLDSC (6612.795300).
Formerly (until 1985): Prevenzione Stomatologica (ISSN 0390-1033)

617.6 US ISSN 1079-0187
PREVIEW (COLLINSVILLE). 1991. s-a. free. Stehman Publications, 300 W. Main St., Collinsville, IL 62234. TEL 618-345-7559. FAX 618-345-8915. Ed. James J. Stehman; Pub. James J. Stehman. adv.: B&W page $1775, color page $2750 (spring issue); B&W page $1175, color page $1950 (fall issue); trim 8 1/8 x 10 7/8. circ. (controlled). **Document type:** trade publication.
Description: Covers practice set-up and management, dental equipment and material selection, office design, practice purchase, associateship, and advanced dental education.

617.6 UK ISSN 1355-7610
▼**PRIMARY DENTAL CARE**. 1994. fortn. £130 (overseas £142). Royal College of Surgeons of England, Faculty of General Dental Practitioners, 35-43 Lincoln's Inn Fields, London WC2A 3PN, England. TEL 0171-405-3474.
FAX 0171-831-7999. Ed. Julian Scott. **Document type:** academic/scholarly publication.
—BLDSC (6612.908570).

617.6 UK ISSN 0032-9185
THE PROBE. 1959. m. £30($60) (overseas £40). Nexus Media Ltd., Warwick House, Azalea Dr., Swanley, Kent BR8 8HY, England.
TEL 01322-660070. FAX 01322-667633. adv.; bk.rev. circ. 20,000. **Indexed:** Dent.Ind. **Document type:** academic/scholarly publication.

617.6 AT ISSN 0079-5631
PROBE. 1949. a. Aus.$15. Adelaide University Dental Students Society (AUDSS), School of Dentistry, Undergraduate Mailbox, 5th Fl., Dental Hospital, Frome Rd., Adelaide, S.A. 5000, Australia. TEL 618-223-9211. FAX 61-8-232-4061. Eds. M. Bilski, K. Tabalotny. adv.; bk.rev.; circ. 220 (paid). **Document type:** newsletter.

617.6 GW ISSN 0932-4488
PRODENT; Zahntechnik-Gesundheit-Soziales-Arbeit. 1988. q. DM.180. Deutscher Zahntechniker Verband e.V., Bundesgeschaeftsstelle, Am Bach 6-8, 33617 Bielefeld, Germany. TEL 0521-179674. Ed. Dr. Ulrich Weisemann. adv.; bk.rev. circ. 3,500. (back issues avail.)

617.6 US ISSN 0033-1236
RK1
PROOFS; the magazine of dental sales. 1918. 10/yr. $18 (Canada & Mexico $25; elsewhere $65) (effective 1995). PennWell Publishing Co., Dental Economics Division, Box 3408, Tulsa, OK 74101. TEL 918-835-3161. FAX 918-831-9804. Ed. Mary Elizabeth Good; Pub. Dick Hale. adv. contact: LaVerne Lewis. illus. circ. 6,100. **Document type:** trade publication.
—UMI.
Description: Directed to dental sales and marketing sales personnel and staff, and to key executives and marketing personnel of dental manufacturing firms.

617.6 613.7 US
PROPHYWAYS.* 1951. 4/yr. $25. Florida Dental Hygienists' Association, Inc., 335 Beard St., Tallahassee, FL 32303-6227. Ed. Toni Barketti. adv.; illus.; tr.lit. circ. 2,300. (tabloid format; back issues avail.)
Formerly: Prophygram.

617.6 PL ISSN 0033-1783
PROTETYKA STOMATOLOGICZNA.* 1965. bi-m. $87. Polskie Towarzystwo Stomatologiczne - Polish Stomatological Society, Ul. Pomorska 21, 90-202 Lodz, Poland. TEL 48-42-321738. (Dist. by: Ars Polona-Ruch, Krakowskie Przedmiescie 7, 00-068 Warsaw, Poland) Ed. E. Spiechowicz. adv.; bk.rev.; abstr.; charts; illus.; pat.; tr.mk.; index, cum.index. circ. 3,000. **Indexed:** Dent.Ind.
Description: Deals with clinical and laboratory prosthetics.

617.6 US ISSN 1060-1341
Q D T. (Editions in English, German, Italian and Japanese) 1976. a. $56. Quintessence Publishing Co., Inc., 551 Kimberly Dr., Carol Stream, IL 60188-1881. TEL 708-682-3223.
FAX 708-682-3288. Ed. John Sorenson; Pub. H.W. Haase. adv. contact: William G. Hartman. illus.; index. **Indexed:** Dent.Abstr., Dent.Ind. **Document type:** academic/scholarly publication.
—BLDSC (7163.591440). **CCC.**
Former titles: Q D T Yearbook (ISSN 0896-6532); (until 1987): Quintessence of Dental Technology (ISSN 0362-0913)

617.6 US
QUEENS COUNTY DENTAL SOCIETY. BULLETIN. 1962. 6/yr. $30. Queens County Dental Society, 86-90 188th St., Jamaica, NY 11423.
TEL 718-454-8344. FAX 718-454-8818. Ed. Alan N. Queen. adv.; bk.rev.; illus. circ. 1,500. **Indexed:** Dent.Ind. **Document type:** bulletin.
Formerly: Eleventh District Dental Society. Bulletin (ISSN 0013-6166)
Description: Covers news of the Society and the dental profession.

617.6 SP ISSN 0214-0985
QUINTESSENCE (EDICION ESPANOLA); publicacion internacional de odontologia. 1988. m. (10/yr.). 11400 ptas.($100) (free to qualified personnel). Ediciones Doyma S.A., Travesera de Gracia, 17-21, 08021 Barcelona, Spain. TEL 34-1-200-07-11. FAX 34-1-209-11-36. TELEX 51964 INK E. Dir. S. Campi Schoeller. adv.: page 230000 ptas.; trim 210 x 280; adv. contact: Marte Vidal. circ. 6,700.
Description: Contains scientific and technical information from clinical centers in Europe and N. America. Covers hygiene and prophylaxis, implantology, periodontics, pediatric dentistry, maxofacial surgery and prothesis.

MEDICAL SCIENCES — DENTISTRY 4381

617.6 US ISSN 0033-6572
QUINTESSENCE INTERNATIONAL. (Text in English) 1970. m. $98 (foreign $128) (effective 1996). Quintessence Publishing Co., Inc., 551 Kimberly Dr., Carol Stream, IL 60188-1881. TEL 708-682-3223. FAX 708-682-3288. Ed. Dr. Richard J. Simonsen; Pub. H.W. Haase. adv. contact: William E. Hartman. circ. 21,000. **Indexed:** Curr.Tit.Dent., Dent.Abstr., Dent.Ind. **Document type:** academic/scholarly publication, trade publication.
—BLDSC (7218.120000); SWETS. **CCC.**
  Incorporates: Dental Digest (ISSN 0011-8567)
  Description: Targeted at general practitioners. Covers all areas of dentistry, including oral surgery, clinical communication, preventive and pediatric dentistry, practice administration, and clinical communication.
  Refereed Serial

617.6 SP ISSN 1130-5339
QUINTESSENCE TECNICA (EDICION ESPANOLA); publicacion internacional de protesis dental. Spanish translation of: Quintessenz der Zahntechnik. 1990. m. 7500 ptas.($66) Ediciones Doyma S.A., Travesera de Gracia, 17-21, 08021 Barcelona, Spain. TEL 34-1-200-07-11. FAX 34-1-209-11-36. TELEX 51964 INK E. Dir. G. Sierra del Hoyo. adv.: page 160000 ptas.; trim 150 x 210; adv. contact: Marte Vidal. circ. 4,500.
  Description: Covers dental prosthesis. Contains photographs and schematics of new techniques to facilitate their immediate practical application.

617.6 GW ISSN 0033-6580
DIE QUINTESSENZ (BERLIN); die Monatszeitschrift fuer den praktizierenden Zahnarzt. 1950. m. DM.228 (foreign DM.240). Quintessenz Verlags GmbH, Ifenpfad 2-4, 12107 Berlin, Germany. TEL 030-74006-46. FAX 030-7415080. TELEX 183815-QUINT-D. **Indexed:** Curr.Tit.Dent., Dok.Arbeitsmed. **Document type:** academic/scholarly publication.

617.6 GW ISSN 0340-4641
QUINTESSENZ DER ZAHNTECHNIK. 1975. m. DM.198 (foreign DM.208). Quintessenz Verlags GmbH, Ifenpfad 2-4, 12107 Berlin, Germany. TEL 030-74006-46. FAX 030-7415080. TELEX 183815-QUINT-D. **Indexed:** Curr.Tit.Dent., Dok.Arbeitsmed. **Document type:** academic/scholarly publication.
—BLDSC (7218.160000).

617.6 GW ISSN 0033-6599
QUINTESSENZ JOURNAL; Zeitschrift fuer die Zahnarzthelferin. 1971. m. DM.138 (foreign DM.146). Quintessenz Verlags GmbH, Ifenpfad 2-4, 12107 Berlin, Germany. TEL 030-74006-46. FAX 030-7415080. TELEX 183815-QUINT-D. **Indexed:** Dent.Ind., Dok.Arbeitsmed., So.Pac.Per.Ind. **Document type:** academic/scholarly publication.
—BLDSC (7218.145000).

617.6 US ISSN 0279-7720
R D H. (Registered Dental Hygienist); the national magazine for dental hygiene professionals. 1981. m. $48. Stevens Publishing Corporation, 3630 J.H. Kultgen Frwy., Waco, TX 76706. TEL 817-776-9000. FAX 817-779-9018. Ed. Kathleen Witherspoon; Pub. Marc Sheiner. adv. contact: John Ward. circ. 65,000. **Document type:** trade publication.
—BLDSC (7300.251200). **CCC.**

617.6 FR ISSN 0997-3397
R F P D ACTUALITES - REVUE FRANCAISE DES PROTHESISTES DENTAIRES. 10/yr. 80 rue de la Roquette, 75011 Paris, France. TEL 49-29-46-19. FAX 49-29-46-26. Ed. Robert-Frederic Dumont. adv.: B&W page 2800 F., color page 8900 F.; 210 x 270. circ. 6,000.
—BLDSC (7960.052900).

617.6 IT ISSN 0048-6787
RASSEGNA ODONTOTECNICA. 1954. bi-m. L.120000 (foreign L.240000). Sindacato Nazionale Odontotecnici, Via Termopili 12, 20127 Milan, Italy. Dir. Francesco Palladini. **Indexed:** Dent.Ind. **Document type:** corporate report.

617.6 IT ISSN 0033-9911
RASSEGNA TRIMESTRALE DI ODONTOIATRIA. (Text in Italian; summaries in English, French and German) 1920. q. L.5000. Istituto Stomatologico Italiano, Via della Pace 21, 20122 Milan, Italy. Ed. Oscar Hoffer. adv.; charts; illus.; index. **Indexed:** Biol.Abstr., Ind.Med.

617.6 FR ISSN 0999-5021
REALITES CLINIQUES; revue europeenne d'odontologie. 1990. irreg. Societe Editrice de la Revue Realites Cliniques, 42 rue Vignon, 75009 Paris, France. TEL 42-66-24-07. FAX 42-66-26-07. Ed. Jean-Jacques Lasfargues.
—BLDSC (7303.287500).

617.6 BL ISSN 0034-7272
REVISTA BRASILEIRA DE ODONTOLOGIA. (Text in Portuguese; summaries in English and Portuguese) 1942. bi-m. Cr.$2000($15) Associacao Brasileira de Odontologia, Secao do Rio de Janeiro, Rua Barao de Sertorio, 75, CEP 20261, Rio de Janeiro RJ, Brazil. TEL 021-293-5322. FAX 021-293-3893. Ed. Francisco Nader. adv.; bk.rev.; abstr. circ. 15,000. (back issues avail.) **Indexed:** Biol.Abstr.

617.6 CU ISSN 0034-7507
REVISTA CUBANA DE ESTOMATOLOGIA. (Text in Spanish; summaries in English, French, Spanish) 1965. s-a. $30 in S. America; N. America $32; elsewhere $34. Ministerio de Salud Publica, Centro Nacional de Informacion de Ciencias Medicas, Calle E No. 452, e-19 y 21, Plaza de la Revolucion, Apdo. 6520, Havana, Cuba. TEL 809-32-5338. (Dist. by: Ediciones Cubanas, Obispo No. 527, Apdo. 605, Havana, Cuba) Ed. Grisell Concepcion. bibl.; abstr.; charts; illus.; index. circ. 2,500. **Indexed:** Biol.Abstr., Dent.Ind., Ind.Med.
—BLDSC (7852.105000).

617.643 CU ISSN 0864-3784
REVISTA CUBANA DE ORTODONCIA. (Text in Spanish; summaries in English, Spanish) 1985. s-a. $9. Ministerio de Salud Publica, Centro Nacional de Informacion de Ciencias Medicas, Calle E No. 452, e-19 y 21, Plaza de la Revolucion, Apdo. 6520, Havana, Cuba. TEL 809-32-5338. (Dist. by: Ediciones Cubanas, Obispo No. 527, Apdo. 6520, Havana, Cuba) (Co-sponsor: Sociedad Cubana de Ortodoncia) Ed. Fidel Araujo. circ. 1,000. **Document type:** government publication.
  Description: Covers the field of orthodontics and related specialties.

617.6 SP ISSN 1130-0094
REVISTA DE ACTUALIDAD ODONTO ESTOMATOLOGICA ESPANOLA. 1954. m. (10/yr.). 10900 ptas.($125) (effective 1995). (Consejo General de Colegios de Odontologos y Estomatologos de Espana) Editorial Garsi, S.A., Juan Bravo 46, 28006 Madrid, Spain. TEL 34-1-4021212. FAX 34-1-4020954. Dir. Jose A. del Pozo del Olmo. adv.; bk.rev.; bibl.; illus. circ. 14,000. **Indexed:** Dent.Ind., Ind.Med.Esp.
—BLDSC (7835.625000).
  Former titles (until 1990): Revista de Actualidades de Estomatologica Espanola (ISSN 0212-9701); (until 1983): Boletin de Informacion Dental (ISSN 0006-6311)

617.6 RM ISSN 0377-7871
CODEN: RCOSDO
REVISTA DE CHIRURGIE, ONCOLOGIE, RADIOLOGIE, O.R.L., OFTALMOLOGIE, STOMATOLOGIE. STOMATOLOGIE. (Text in Rumanian; summaries in English, French, German, Russian) 1954. 4/yr. $20. Uniunea Societatilor de Stiinte Medicale din Republica Socialista Rumania, Str. Progresului No. 8-10, Sectorul 1, Bucharest 70754, Rumania. (Subscr. to: ILEXIM, Str. 13 Decembrie Nr. 3, P.O. Box 136-137, Bucharest, Rumania) Ed:Bd. adv.; bk.rev.; abstr.; bibl.; charts; illus.; index. **Indexed:** Biol.Abstr., Chem.Abstr., Dent.Ind., Ind.Med.
—CASDDS.
  Supersedes: Stomatologia (ISSN 0039-1719)

617.6 SP ISSN 0210-0576
REVISTA ESPANOLA DE ORTODONCIA. 1971. 4/yr. 5000 ptas.($60) (foreign 7000 ptas.) (effective 1992). Publicidad Permanyer, Mallorca 310, 08037 Barcelona, Spain. TEL 34-3-2075920. FAX 34-3-4576642. Dir. Arturo Costa. adv.; bk.rev.; abstr.; bibl. circ. 1,000. (back issues avail.) **Indexed:** Dent.Abstr., Ind.Med.Esp.

617.6 SP ISSN 1133-1615
REVISTA ESPANOLA ODONTOESTOMATOLOGICA DE IMPLANTES. 1993. q. 5500 ptas.($108) (effective 1995). Editorial Rocas, Muntaner 393, pral. 2a, 08021 Barcelona, Spain. TEL 39-3-2001389. FAX 39-3-2021958. **Document type:** trade publication.

617.6 BL ISSN 0034-9542
REVISTA GAUCHA DE ODONTOLOGIA. (Text in Portuguese; summaries in English) 1953. q. $21. Estrada da Ponta Grossa 5311, Porto Alegre, 9000 Rio Grande do Sul, Brazil. Ed. Ricardo Cauduro Neto. adv.; bk.rev.; abstr.; bibl.; illus.; index. circ. 22,680. **Indexed:** Dent.Ind.

617.6 CK ISSN 0120-2855
REVISTA ODONTOLOGIA. 1963. 3/yr. Universidad Nacional de Colombia, Facultad de Odontologia, Ciudad Universitaria, Bogota, Colombia. Ed. Oscar Monroy Vega. adv.; bibl.; illus. circ. 2,000.
  Formerly: Odontologia (ISSN 0029-8409)

617.5 BL ISSN 0100-705X
REVISTA PAULISTA DE ODONTOLOGIA. 1979. 6/yr. $50. Sindicato dos Odontologistas do Estado de Sao Paulo, Rua Humaita 349-1a, sobreloja, 01321-010 Sao Paulo SP, Brazil. TEL 011-37-7567. FAX 011-37-0727. Ed. Henrique Motilinsky. adv.: B&W page $1130, color page $1350; trim 210 x 280; adv. contact: Ernesto Leme Filho. circ. 15,000.

617.6 PO ISSN 0035-0397
REVISTA PORTUGUESA DE ESTOMATOLOGIA E CIRURGIA MAXILO-FACIAL. (Text in Portuguese; summaries in English and French) 1944. q. Esc.5000 (effective 1995 & 1996). Sociedade Portuguesa de Estomatologia e Medicina Dentaria, Av. Rainha D. Amelia 36, 1600 Lisbon, Portugal. TEL 351-1-7593948. Ed. Dr. Carlos Portugal. adv. contact: Luis Lopes. bk.rev.; abstr.; bibl.; charts; illus.; stat.; index. circ. 1,800. **Indexed:** Biol.Abstr., Dent.Ind., Ind.Med.
  Refereed Serial

617.6 BE ISSN 0775-0293
REVUE BELGE DE MEDECINE DENTAIRE. Dutch edition: Belgisch Tijdschrift voor Tandheelkunde (ISSN 0775-0285) (Text in French) 1946. q. 1600 BEF (foreign 1800 BEF). Societe Francophone Belge de Medecine Dentaire a.s.b.l., Bd. Gen. Jacques 221, B-1050 Brussels, Belgium. TEL 02-647-41-37. FAX 02-640-29-15. adv.; bk.rev.; index. circ. 3,500. **Indexed:** Ind.Med. **Document type:** academic/scholarly publication.
—BLDSC (7891.975000); Faxon.
  Supersedes in part (in 1984): Revue Belge de Medecine Dentaire (ISSN 0035-080X); Which was formed by the 1962 merger of: Revue Belge de Science Dentaire (ISSN 0770-0059); Journal Dentaire Belge (ISSN 0770-0008)

617.6 FR ISSN 0300-9815
REVUE D'ODONTO-STOMATOLOGIE. (Text in French; summaries in English) 1954. bi-m. 920 Fr. (effective 1995). Societe Odontologique de Paris, 239 rue du Faubourg Saint-Martin, 75010 Paris, France. TEL 42-09-29-13. FAX 42-09-29-08. Ed. Dr. Gerard Mandel. adv. contact: Louis Verchere. bk.rev.; bibl.; charts; illus.; tr.lit.; index, cum.index: 1954-1961. **Indexed:** Chem.Abstr., Curr.Tit.Dent., Dent.Ind., Ind.Med. **Document type:** newspaper.
—BLDSC (7938.710000); Faxon. **CCC.**
  Formerly: Revue Francaise d'Odonto-Stomatologie (ISSN 0035-3043)

617.6 FR ISSN 0035-2470
REVUE D'ODONTO-STOMATOLOGIE DU MIDI DE LA FRANCE. (Text in French; summaries in English) 1937. 4/yr. $45. Faculte de Medecine, 3 ter. Place de la Victoire, 33076 Bordeaux Cedex, France. Ed. P. Benoit. adv.; bk.rev.; abstr.; bibl.; charts. circ. 2,000. **Indexed:** Dent.Ind.

617.6 FR ISSN 0721-0078
REVUE INTERNATIONALE DE PARODONTIE ET DENTISTERIE RESTAURATRICE. (Text in English, French, German, Italian, Japanese, Spanish) 6/yr. Groupe C D P, 77 rue de Richelieu, 75002 Paris, France. TEL 42-61-50-65. FAX 42-61-31-95. Ed. Christian Knellesen. adv. contact: Chantal Daly. circ. 1,700.

617.6 FR ISSN 0035-4147
REVUE STOMATO-ODONTOLOGIQUE DU NORD DE LA FRANCE.* vol.25, 1970. q. 25 F. Place de Verdun, 59 Lille, France. adv.; illus.; index. **Indexed:** Biol.Abstr.

MEDICAL SCIENCES — DENTISTRY

617.6 US
CODEN: RIDJEJ
RHODE ISLAND DENTAL ASSOCIATION. JOURNAL. 1968. q. $15. Rhode Island Dental Association, 200 Centerville Pl., Warwick, RI 02886. TEL 401-732-6833. Ed. Dr. Jan Feldman. adv.; bk.rev.; illus. circ. 700. **Indexed:** Dent.Ind. **Document type:** trade publication.
  Formerly (until 1975): Rhode Island State Dental Society. Journal (ISSN 0035-4643)

617.6 US
RHODE ISLAND DENTAL ASSOCIATION. NEWSLETTER. 1972. s-a. membership only. Rhode Island Dental Association, 200 Centerville Pl., Warwick, RI 02886. TEL 401-732-6833. Ed. Valerie G. Donnelly. circ. 600.

617.6 IT ISSN 0391-5611
RIVISTA ITALIANA DEGLI ODONTOTECNICI - DENTAL PRESS. 1964. 9/yr. L.89000($137) (effective 1994). Masson S.p.A., Divisione Periodici, Via Statuto 2-4, 20121 Milan, Italy. TEL 02-6367-1. FAX 02-6367211. Ed. Maurizio Camandena. adv.; B&W page L.1130000, color page L.1850000; 193 x 265. bk.rev. circ. 7,000. **Indexed:** Dent.Ind. **Document type:** academic/scholarly publication.
  Former titles (until 1983): Dental Press (ISSN 0391-5883); (until 1965): Rivista Italiana degli Odontotecnici.

617.6 613.92 IT ISSN 1120-8716
RIVISTA ITALIANA DI ODONTOIATRIA INFANTILE. 1990. q. L.72000($97) (effective 1994). (Societa Italiana di Odontoiatria Infantile) Masson Italia Periodici, Via Statuto 2-4, 20121 Milan, Italy. TEL 02-6367-1. FAX 02-6367-211. Ed. Giovanni Dolci. adv.; B&W page L.1100000, color page L.1800000; trim 157 x 229. circ. 1,500. **Document type:** academic/scholarly publication.
  —BLDSC (7987.442900).

617.6 IT ISSN 0035-6905
RIVISTA ITALIANA DI STOMATOLOGIA.* 1931. m. L.65000. (Associazione Medici Dentisti Italiani) Attualita Dentale S.r.l., Via L. da Viadana 9, 20122 Milan, Italy. bk.rev. circ. 15,000. **Indexed:** Dent.Ind.

617.6 UK
ROLLS OF DENTAL AUXILIARIES. a. £8. General Dental Council, 37 Wimpole St., London W1M 8DQ, England. TEL 0171-486-2171. FAX 0171-224-3294. (back issues avail.)
  Formerly: Rolls of Ancilliary Dental Workers.

617.6 AT ISSN 0158-1570
ROYAL AUSTRALASIAN COLLEGE OF DENTAL SURGEONS. ANNALS. 1967. irreg., vol.11, 1992. Aus.$45. Royal Australasian College of Dental Surgeons, 64 Castlereagh St., Sydney, N.S.W. 2000, Australia. TEL 61-2-232-3800. FAX 61-2-221-8108. Ed. John Harcourt. circ. 1,500. **Document type:** academic/scholarly publication.
  —BLDSC (1031.492000).
  Former titles: Royal Australian College of Dental Surgeons. Annals (ISSN 0312-7923); Australian College of Dental Surgeons. Annals. (ISSN 0004-8895)

617.6 UK ISSN 0049-1160
S A A D DIGEST. 1970. q. £28. Society for the Advancement of Anaesthesia in Dentistry, 53 Wimpole St., London W1M 7DP, England. Ed. Andrea Wraith. adv.; bk.rev.; illus. circ. 1,500. **Indexed:** Curr.Adv.Ecol.Sci. **Document type:** academic/scholarly publication.
  —BLDSC (8055.110000).

SAARLAENDISCHES AERZTEBLATT. see *MEDICAL SCIENCES*

617.6 US
SAN ANTONIO DISTRICT DENTAL SOCIETY NEWSLETTER. 1970. m. $40. San Antonio District Dental Society, 202 W. French Pl., San Antonio, TX 78212. TEL 512-732-1264. Ed. Dr. Dave C. Bensh. adv.; illus. circ. 1,100. **Indexed:** Dent.Ind.
  Supersedes (1946-1970): San Antonio District Dental Society. Journal (ISSN 0036-3979)

617.6 SZ ISSN 1011-4203
SCHWEIZER MONATSSCHRIFT FUER ZAHNMEDIZIN. (Text in English, French, German and Italian) 1891. m. 250 SFr. Schweizerische Zahnaerztegesellschaft, Postfach, CH-3000 Bern 8, Switzerland. TEL 031-3120377. FAX 031-3113534. Ed.Bd. adv.; bk.rev.; abstr.; bibl.; charts; illus.; index. circ. 4,300. **Indexed:** Biol.Abstr., Chem.Abstr., Curr.Adv.Ecol.Sci., Curr.Tit.Dent., Dent.Ind., Excerp.Med., Ind.Med. **Document type:** academic/scholarly publication.
  —CASDDS; SWETS.
  Formerly: Schweizerische Monatsschrift fuer Zahnheilkunde (ISSN 0036-7702); Which included: Helvetica Odontologica Acta (ISSN 0018-0211); Helvetica Odontologica Acta. Supplementum (ISSN 0073-1803)

617.6 US ISSN 0037-0452
SEATTLE - KING COUNTY DENTAL SOCIETY. JOURNAL. 1962. m. (Aug.-May). $16. Journal and Bulletin Agency, Box 10249, Bainbridge Island, WA 98110. TEL 206-682-7813. adv.; B&W page $140; trim 4 3/4 x 7 1/2. bk.rev. circ. 1,500. **Indexed:** Dent.Ind.
  Formerly: Seattle District Dental Society. Journal.

SELECTED READINGS IN ORAL AND MAXILLOFACIAL SURGERY. see *MEDICAL SCIENCES — Surgery*

617.6 IT
SELEZIONE ODONTOIATRICA. q. L.125000($135) Piccin Editore, Via Altinate 107, 35121 Padua, Italy. TEL 049-655566. FAX 049-8750693.

617.643 US ISSN 1073-8746
▼**SEMINARS IN ORTHODONTICS.** 1995. q. $99 (foreign $119) (effective 1996). W.B. Saunders Co. (Subsidiary of: Harcourt Brace & Company), Curtis Center, 3rd Fl., Independence Sq. W., Philadelphia, PA 19106-3399. TEL 215-238-7800. FAX 215-238-6445. (Subscr. to: Periodicals Fulfillment, W.B. Saunders Co., 6277 Sea Harbor Dr., 4th Fl., Orlando, FL 32891-4800. TEL 800-654-2452. FAX 800-574-6418) Ed. Dr. P. Lionel Sadowsky. adv. **Document type:** academic/scholarly publication.
  Description: Provides authoritative, up-to-date coverage of innovative techniques, new instruments and other products, and new uses for existing material.

617.6 IR
SHAHEED BEHESHTI UNIVERSITY. FACULTY OF DENTISTRY. JOURNAL. (Text in Farsi) 1968. q. Shaheed Beheshti University, Faculty of Dentistry, Shahid Chamran Ave., Evin, Teheran 19834, Iran. TEL 021-21411. TELEX 215464. Ed. Dr. Ali- A. Bahreman. adv.
  Formerly (until 1983): National University of Iran. Dental School. Journal (ISSN 0011-8745)

617.6 JA ISSN 0029-8484
CODEN: SHIGAZ
SHIGAKU/ODONTOLOGY. (Text in Japanese; summaries in English) 1941. 6/yr. 6000 Yen. Society of the Nippon Dental University - Nihon Shika Daigaku Shigakkai, 9-20 Fujimi 1-chome, Chiyoda-ku, Tokyo 102, Japan. FAX 03-264-8745. Ed. Shigeo Aiyama. charts; illus. circ. 2,650. **Indexed:** Amer.Hist.& Life (until 1992), Biol.Abstr., Chem.Abstr., Dent.Ind., Hist.Abstr. (until 1992). **Document type:** academic/scholarly publication.
  —BLDSC (6235.230000); CASDDS.

617.6 JA ISSN 0037-3710
CODEN: SHGKA3
SHIKA GAKUHO/TOKYO DENTAL COLLEGE SOCIETY JOURNAL. (Text in English and Japanese) 1895. m. 5000 Yen($8.60) Tokyo Shika Daigaku Gakkai - Tokyo Dental College Society, Tokyo Dental College, 2-2 Masago 1-chome, Chiba 260, Japan. (Order from: Maruzen Co., Ltd., 2-3-10 Nihonbashi, Chuo-ku, Tokyo 103, Japan; or their Import and Export Department, P.O. Box 5050, Tokyo International, Tokyo 100-31, Japan) Ed. Dr. Tetsuya Kanatake. adv.; bk.rev.; abstr.; bibl.; charts; illus.; stat.; tr.lit.; index. circ. 4,600. **Indexed:** Biol.Abstr., Dent.Ind., Excerp.Med.
  —BLDSC (4908.920000); CASDDS.

617.6 JA ISSN 0389-1895
CODEN: SHGKD6
SHIKA GIKO/JOURNAL OF DENTAL TECHNICS. (Special issues avail.) (Text in Japanese) 1973. m. 1200 Yen per no. Ishiyaku Publishers, Inc., 7-10 Honkagome 1-chome, Bunkyo-ku, Tokyo 113, Japan. Ed. Hiroshi Miura. adv.; bk.rev.; charts; illus. circ. 20,000. **Indexed:** Chem.Abstr.
  —CASDDS.

617.6 615.84 JA ISSN 0389-9705
SHIKA HOSHASEN. English edition: Oral Radiology (ISSN 0911-6028) (Text in Japanese) 1960. q. 10000 Yen (includes English editions). Nihon Shika Hoshasen Gakkai - Japanese Society for Oral and Maxillofacial Radiology, Faculty of Dentistry, Osaka University, 1-8, Yamadaoka, Suita, Osaka 565, Japan. **Document type:** academic/scholarly publication.
  —BLDSC (3553.430000).

SIERRA LEONE MEDICAL AND DENTAL ASSOCIATION. JOURNAL. see *MEDICAL SCIENCES*

617.643 CK ISSN 0037-8453
SOCIEDAD COLOMBIANA DE ORTODONCIA. REVISTA.* 1963. q. free. Sociedad Colombiana de Ortodoncia, Carrera 9a, No. 52A-46, Bogota D.E., Colombia. Ed. Dr. Carlos Perez Martinez. adv.; bk.rev.; charts; illus.; index. circ. 1,000.

617.6 SP ISSN 0213-831X
SOPRODEN. 1985. q. 6000 ptas.($65) (effective 1995). (Sociedad Espanola de Protesicos Dentales) Editorial Garsi, S.A., Juan Bravo 46, 28006 Madrid, Spain. TEL 34-1-4021212. FAX 34-1-4020954. Ed. J. Tevar Montero. circ. 5,000.

SOUTH AFRICA. CENTRAL STATISTICAL SERVICE. CENSUS OF MEDICAL, DENTAL AND OTHER HEALTH SERVICES - DENTISTS. see *MEDICAL SCIENCES — Abstracting, Bibliographies, Statistics*

617.6 US ISSN 0038-3945
SOUTHERN CALIFORNIA DENTAL LABORATORY ASSOCIATION. BULLETIN. 1944. bi-m. $5. Southern California Dental Laboratory Association, 3333 Glendale Blvd., Ste. 4, Los Angeles, CA 90039. TEL 213-661-2188. Ed. James C. Powell. adv.; illus. circ. 2,000.
  Formerly: Southern California State Dental Laboratory Association Bulletin.

617.6 US ISSN 0275-1879
RK55.H28
SPECIAL CARE IN DENTISTRY; managing special patients, settings, and situations. 1981. bi-m. $55 to individuals (foreign $85); institutions $92 (foreign $122). (Federation of Special Care Organizations) Federation of Special Care Organizations in Dentistry, 211 E. Chicago Ave., Chicago, IL 60611. TEL 312-440-2661. (Co-sponsors: Academy of Dentistry for Persons with Disabilities; American Association of Hospital Dentists; American Society for Geriatric Dentistry) circ. 2,500. (also avail. in microform from UMI; back issues avail.) **Indexed:** CINAHL, Curr.Tit.Dent., Dent.Abstr., Dent.Ind. **Document type:** academic/scholarly publication.
  —BLDSC (8365.680000); UMI; UnCover.
  Formed by merger of (1974-1981): Journal of Dentistry for the Handicapped (ISSN 0163-8629); (1967-1981): Journal of Hospital Dental Practice (ISSN 0022-1600); (1966-1981): American Society for Geriatric Dentistry. Journal (ISSN 0003-1054)
  Description: Provides oral health care professionals with information to enhance their ability to address special patient needs.
  Refereed Serial

617.6 NE ISSN 0922-310X
STANDBY; vaktijdschrift voor tandartsassistenten. 1988. 6/yr. fl.65. Chameleon c.v., Looiersgracht 63, 1016 WC Amsterdam, Netherlands. TEL 31-20-6271738. FAX 31-20-4203631. Ed. S. Menheere. circ. 2,500. **Document type:** trade publication.

MEDICAL SCIENCES — DENTISTRY

617.6   PO   ISSN 0870-4287
STOMA; cadernos de estomatologia, cirurgia maxilo-facial e medicina dentaria. 1986. q. Esc.8500 in Europe; elsewhere Esc.9500 (effective 1996). Edicoes Valde-Mecum, Lda., Calcada do Tijolo, 45, 1200 Lisbon, Portugal. TEL 351-1-3420518. FAX 351-1-3420682. TELEX 64989 USUS P. Ed. Dr. Pedro Graca Castel-Branco. adv. contact: Joaquim Azevedo. circ. 3,000.
—BLDSC (8465.863000).
Description: Publishes scientific works on dentistry, maxillo traumatology, dental surgery and dental forensic sciences. Includes information on new products and services, meetings and congresses.

617.6   IT   ISSN 1120-9402
STOMATOLOGIA MEDITERRANEA; rivista trimestrale di odontoiatria e chirurgia maxillo-facciale. (Text in Italian; summaries in English) 1981. q. L.70000($80) Via Emerico Amari 32, 90139 Palermo, Italy. TEL 091-32-82-69. Ed. Giuseppe Messina. adv.; bk.rev.; bibl.; charts; illus.; stat. circ. 1,500.
—BLDSC (8465.901000).

617.6   BU   ISSN 0491-0982
CODEN: STMYAN
STOMATOLOGIJA. (Text in Bulgarian; summaries in English, Russian) 1951. bi-m. 16 lv. (Ministerstvo na Narodnoto Zdrave) Izdatelstvo Meditsina i Fizkultura, 11 Pl. Slaveikov, Sofia, Bulgaria. (Distr. by: Hemus, 6 Rouski Bvld., 1000 Sofia, Bulgaria) (Co-sponsor: Nauchno Druzhestvo po Stomatologija) Ed. E. Atanassova. circ. 2,581. **Indexed:** Abstr.Bulg.Sci.Med.Lit.
—CASDDS.

617.6   YU   ISSN 0039-1743
CODEN: SGLSAB
STOMATOLOSKI GLASNIK SRBIJE. (Text in Serbian; summaries in English, French and German) 1954. bi-m. $25. Srpsko Lekarsko Drustvo, Dzordza Vasingtona 19, Belgrade, Yugoslavia. Ed. Dr. Miroslav Pajic. adv.; bk.rev.; charts; illus. circ. 2,000. **Indexed:** Dent.Ind.
—BLDSC (8465.920000); CASDDS.

617.6   US
SUFFOLK DENTISTRY. vol.16, 1970. bi-m. $12. Suffolk County Dental Society, 850 Veterans Memorial Hwy., Hauppauge, NY 11788. TEL 516-265-6924. Ed. Dr. Charles S. Leibowitz. adv. contact: Dr. Charles S. Leibowitz. bk.rev. circ. 1,100. **Document type:** newsletter.
Formerly: Suffolk County Dental Society. Bulletin (ISSN 0039-4688)

617.6   US
SURGICAL UPDATE. 1985. 3/yr. American Association of Oral and Maxillofacial Surgeons, 9700 W. Bryn Mawr Ave., Rosemont, IL 60018. TEL 708-678-6200. FAX 708-678-6286. Ed.Bd. circ. 150,000 (controlled). (back issues avail.) **Document type:** newsletter.
Description: Provides information on oral and maxillofacial surgery for general dentists.
Refereed Serial

617.6   US
SURVEY OF DENTAL PRACTICE. a. $200 for set to non-members; members $75. American Dental Association, Survey Center, 211 E. Chicago Ave., Chicago, IL 60611. TEL 312-440-2500. FAX 312-440-2550. **Indexed:** SRI. **Document type:** trade publication.

617.6   SW   ISSN 0348-0011
SVENSK SJUKHUSTANDLAEKARTIDNING. 1976. q. SEK 100 (effective 1991). Svensk Sjukhustandlaekarfoerening, Sjukhustandvaarden Oral Medicin-Pedodonti, Oestra Sjukhuset, S-416 85 Goeteborg, Sweden. TEL 031-374842. FAX 031-253974. Ed. Johan Blomgren. **Document type:** academic/scholarly publication.

617.6   SW   ISSN 0347-9994
CODEN: SDJOD5
SWEDISH DENTAL JOURNAL. (Supplement avail. (ISSN 0348-6672)) (Text in English) 1908. bi-m. SEK 450 in Sweden; elsewhere SEK 500. Sveriges Tandlaekarfoerbund - Swedish Dental Association, P.O. Box 5843, S-102 48 Stockholm, Sweden. TEL 46-8-666-15-00. Ed. Dr. Goeran Koch. adv.: B&W page SEK 4000, color page SEK 20000; trim 165 x 240. bk.rev.; charts; illus.; index, cum.index: 1908-1953. circ. 11,000. **Indexed:** ASCA, Biol.Abstr., Chem.Abstr., Curr.Adv.Ecol.Sci., Curr.Cont., Curr.Tit.Dent., Dent.Abstr., Dent.Ind., Excerp.Med., Ind.Med.
—BLDSC (8573.865000); CASDDS; Faxon; Genuine Article; SWETS; UMI; UnCover.
Formed by the merger of: Odontologisk Revy (ISSN 0029-8441); Svensk Tandlaekare-Tidskrift (ISSN 0039-6745)

617.6   NE   ISSN 0167-1685
TANDARTSPRAKTIJK; onafhankelijk vaktijdschrift voor tandartsen. 1979. 10/yr. fl.79. Wegener Tijl Tijdschriften Groep B.V., Postbus 9943, 1006 AP AMsterdam, Netherlands. TEL 31-20-5182828. FAX 31-20-5182843. Ed. J.G. Advokaat. adv.; circ. 6,000 (paid). **Document type:** trade publication.

617.6   SW   ISSN 0349-9456
TANDHYGIENISTBLADET. 1977. bi-m. SEK 95 (effective 1991). Sveriges Tandhygienistfoerening (STHF), P.O. Box 4243, S-102 63 Stockholm, Sweden.

617.6   DK   ISSN 0039-9353
TANDLAEGEBLADET/DANISH DENTAL JOURNAL. 1897. 18/yr. DKK 1020. Dansk Tandlaegeforening - Danish Dental Association, Amaliegade 17, Postboks 143, 1004 Copenhagen K, Denmark. Eds. J.J. Pindborg, Chr. Nissen. adv.; bk.rev.; index. circ. 6,995. **Indexed:** Dent.Ind., Ind.Med.
—BLDSC (8601.700000).

617.6   DK   ISSN 0901-9898
TANDLAEGERNES NYE TIDSSKRIFT. Variant title: T N T. 1976. m. membership. Tandlaegernes Nye Landsforening - T N L, Kompagnistraede 14 D, DK-1208 Copenhagen K, Denmark. TEL 45-33-14-00-65. FAX 45-33-14-03-24. Ed. Peter Simonsen. adv. contact: Michael Diepeveen. bk.rev.; illus. circ. 1,500. **Document type:** trade publication.
Former titles (until 1986): D B - D Bat (ISSN 0109-3592); (until 1980): D Bat (ISSN 0109-4475)

617.6   SW   ISSN 0039-6982
TANDLAEKARTIDNINGEN. 1909. every 3 wks. SEK 950 in the Nordic countries; elsewhere SEK 1100. Sveriges Tandlaekarfoerbund - Swedish Dental Association, P.O. Box 5843, S-102 48 Stockholm, Sweden. TEL 46-8-666-15-00. FAX 46-8-662-58-42. Ed. Staffan Olsson. adv.: B&W page SEK 13000, color page SEK 27000; trim 200 x 272. bk.rev.; illus.; stat.; index. circ. 11,545. **Indexed:** Dent.Ind.
—BLDSC (8601.750000).
Formerly (until 1971): Sveriges Tandlaekarfoerbunds Tidning.

617.6 331.8   DK   ISSN 0900-257X
TANDPLEJEREN. 1976. m. DKK 240. Dansk Tandplejerforening, Sundhedsorganisationernes Hus, Noerre Voldgade 90, DK-1358 Copenhagen K, Denmark. TEL 45-33-13-82-11. FAX 45-33-93-82-14. Ed. Eva Lis Pedersen. adv. circ. 1,300. **Document type:** trade publication.

617.6   SW   ISSN 0346-2617
TANDSKOETERSKETIDNINGEN. 1946. q. SEK 100 (effective 1990). Svenska Tandskoeterskefoerbundet, P.O. Box 30102, S104 25 Stockholm, Sweden.
Formerly (until vol.3, 1974): Svenska Tandskoeterskefoerbundets Tidskrift.

617.6   SW   ISSN 0039-9361
TANDTEKNIKERN. 1932. m. SEK 700 (effective 1995). Tandteknikerfoerbundet, P.O. Box 6060, S-164 06 Kista, Sweden. TEL 46-8-751-88-67. FAX 46-8-752-6036. Ed. Kerstin Orsen. adv.: B&W page SEK 4450. circ. 2,000. **Document type:** trade publication.

617.6   US   ISSN 0040-3385
CODEN: JTDAAB
TENNESSEE DENTAL ASSOCIATION. JOURNAL. 1919. q. $9.50 (Canada $20; elsewhere $25). Tennessee Dental Association, 2104 Sunset Pl., Box 120188, Nashville, TN 37212. TEL 615-383-8962. Ed. Dr. Stephen Brooks. adv. contact: Sharon Melvin. bk.rev.; illus.; index. circ. 2,100. (back issues avail.) **Indexed:** Dent.Abstr., Dent.Ind. **Document type:** trade publication.
—BLDSC (4907.100000); Faxon.
Formerly: Tennessee State Dental Association. Journal.

617.6   US
TENTH TIMES. 1962. m. $15. Texas Dental Association, Tenth District Dental Society, 3303 Northland, No. 313, Austin, TX 78731. TEL 512-452-9296. Ed. Dr. Mark Sweeney. adv.; circ. 450 (controlled).
Formerly: Austin Dental News (ISSN 0004-8267)

617.6   US
TEXAS DENTAL ASSISTANTS ASSOCIATION. BULLETIN. 1955? 3/yr. $10. Texas Dental Assistants Association, 4948 Colonial Park Dr., Haltom City, TX 76117-1009. TEL 817-281-3949. Ed. Dennise Jennings. adv.; illus. circ. 500. **Indexed:** Dent.Ind. **Document type:** newsletter.
Former titles: Texas Dental Assistants Association. Newsletter; Texas Dental Assistants Association. Bulletin (ISSN 0049-3503)
Description: Information for Association members.

617.6   US   ISSN 0040-4284
TEXAS DENTAL JOURNAL. 1883. m. $82.50 to non-ADA members; members $49.50 (foreign $82.50). Texas Dental Association, 1946 S. Interregional, Austin, TX 78704. TEL 512-443-3675. FAX 512-443-3031. Ed. Dr. Douglas B. Willingham. adv.; bk.rev.; film rev.; charts; illus.; stat. circ. 7,200. **Indexed:** Dent.Abstr., Dent.Ind.
—BLDSC (8798.690000); Faxon.

617.6   US
THIRTIETH DISTRICT DENTAL SOCIETY, FRESNO, CALIFORNIA. BULLETIN. 1953. 6/yr. Fresno-Madera Dental Society, 371 E. Bullard Ave., Ste. 120, Fresno, CA 93710-5217. FAX 209-224-1098. Ed. Dr. John Cornell. adv. circ. 600. **Document type:** newsletter.
Former titles: Thirteenth District Dental Society. Bulletin; Fifth District Dental Society. Bulletin (ISSN 0071-9544)

617.6   GW   ISSN 0939-5687
THUERINGER ZAHNAERZTEBLATT.* 1991. m. DM.88 (foreign DM.102). Ilmtal Verlag, Zeughausstr., 99438 Bad Berka, Germany. **Document type:** academic/scholarly publication.

617.6   SW   ISSN 0348-6117
TIDSKRIFT FOER ODONTOLOGISK PEDAGOGIK. 1978. 3/yr. SEK 55 (effective 1991). Svensk Odontologisk Pedagogisk Foerening, c/o G. Sundin, Institutionen foer Protetik, P.O. Box 4064, S-141 04 Huddinge, Sweden.

617.6   US   ISSN 1048-5317
TODAY'S F D A. 1989. m. $32.10 (foreign $48.15). Florida Dental Association, 1111 E. Tennessee St., Ste. 102, Tallahassee, FL 32308-6914. TEL 904-681-3629. FAX 904-561-0504. Ed. Dr. Bert V. Dannheisser, Jr. adv. contact: Carolyn Sullenberger. bk.rev.; charts; illus. circ. 6,800. (tabloid format) **Indexed:** Dent.Ind. **Document type:** trade publication.
—BLDSC (8859.737800).
Incorporates (in July-Aug. 1989): Dental Team; Formed by the 1989 merger of: Dental Times Dispatch (ISSN 0886-5094) & Florida Dental Journal (ISSN 0015-3990); Which was formerly titled (1938-1967): Florida State Dental Society. Journal (ISSN 0360-1676); F D A Dispatch; F D A Intaglio.
Description: Contains news, features, commentary, and scientific information for the Florida dentist.
Refereed Serial

MEDICAL SCIENCES — DENTISTRY

617.6 JA ISSN 0040-8891
CODEN: BTDCAV
TOKYO DENTAL COLLEGE. BULLETIN/TOKYO SHIKA DAIGAKU OBUN KIYO. (Text in English) 1960. q. 6000 Yen. Tokyo Shika Daigaku - Tokyo Dental College, 1-2-2, Masago, Mihama, Chiba 261, Japan. Ed. Tatsuya Ishikawa. charts; illus. circ. 1,000. (also avail. in microfiche) **Indexed:** Biol.Abstr., Curr.Adv.Ecol.Sci., Curr.Tit.Dent., Dent.Abstr., Dent.Ind., INIS Atomind. **Document type:** bulletin.
—BLDSC (2780.300000); CASDDS; UnCover. **CCC.**

TOKYO MEDICAL AND DENTAL UNIVERSITY. INSTITUTE FOR MEDICAL AND DENTAL ENGINEERING. REPORTS/IYO KIZAI KENKYUJO HOKOKU. see *MEDICAL SCIENCES*

617.6 US ISSN 0746-8962
RK1.N28
TRENDS & TECHNIQUES IN THE CONTEMPORARY DENTAL LABORATORY. 1954. 10/yr. $40 (foreign $50). National Association of Dental Laboratories, 555 E. Braddock Rd., Alexandria, VA 22314-2106. TEL 703-683-5263. FAX 703-549-4788. Ed. Jason Warholic. adv.; bk.rev.; illus. circ. 17,000. **Indexed:** Dent.Ind. **Document type:** trade publication.
—BLDSC (9049.539600).
  Former titles: N A D L Journal (ISSN 0360-5361); N A C D L Journal (ISSN 0027-5735)
  Description: Published for dental technicians and laboratory owners. Covers technical issues, association activities and business management, as well as industry news and new products.

617.6 UY ISSN 0083-4785
UNIVERSIDAD DE LA REPUBLICA. FACULTAD DE ODONTOLOGIA. ANALES. (Supplements accompany some numbers) 1955. irreg. exchange basis. Universidad de la Republica, Facultad de Odontologia, Gral. las Heras 1925, Montevideo, Uruguay. **Indexed:** Biol.Abstr., Dent.Ind.

617.6 VE
UNIVERSIDAD DE LOS ANDES. FACULTAD DE ODONTOLOGIA. REVISTA.* 1958. s-a. exchange basis. Universidad de los Andes, Facultad de Odontologia, Via los Chorras de Milla, C.P. 5101, Merida, Venezuela. illus.
  Formerly: Revista Odontologica de Merida (ISSN 0035-0273)

617.6 AG ISSN 0325-1071
UNIVERSIDAD NACIONAL DE CORDOBA. FACULTAD DE ODONTOLOGIA. REVISTA. (Text in Spanish; summaries in English, Spanish) 1966. s-a. exchange. Universidad Nacional de Cordoba, Facultad de Odontologia, Casilla de Correo 458, 5000 Cordoba, Argentina. Dir. Dr. Juan Carlos Albera. adv.; bk.rev.; bibl.; charts; illus. circ. 350. **Indexed:** Dent.Ind., Ind.Med.
  Supersedes: Revista Odontologica (ISSN 0035-0257)

617.6 BL ISSN 0103-0663
CODEN: ROUPES
UNIVERSIDADE DE SAO PAULO. REVISTA DE ODONTOLOGIA. (Text and abstracts in English and Portuguese) 1987. 4/yr. Cr.$20($20) or exchange basis (effective 1995). Universidade de Sao Paulo, Faculdade de Odontologia, Av. Lineu Prestes, 2227, C.P. 8216, 05508-900 Sao Paulo, SP, Brazil. TEL 55-11-8187861. FAX 55-11-818-7413. Ed. Esther Goldenberg Birman. adv.; bk.rev.; abstr.; bibl.; charts; illus.; stat. circ. 2,000. (reprint service avail. from UMI) **Indexed:** Biol.Abstr., Chem.Abstr., Dent.Ind.
—BLDSC (7869.090000); CASDDS; UMI.
  Formed by the merger of (1968-1986): Estomatologia e Cultura (ISSN 0014-1364); (1964-1986): Faculdade de Odontologia de Ribeirao Preto. Revista (ISSN 0102-129X); Which was formerly (until 1983): Faculdade de Farmacia e Odontologia de Ribeirao Preto. Revista (ISSN 0006-9418); (until 1970): Faculdade de Farmacia e Odontologia de Ribeirao Preto. Boletim (ISSN 0080-2913); (1963-1986): Universidade de Sao Paulo. Faculdade de Odontologia. Revista (ISSN 0581-6866); Which superseded in part (1939-1962): Universidade de Sao Paulo. Faculdade de Farmacia. Anais (ISSN 0365-2181)

617.6 BL ISSN 0101-1774
CODEN: ROUNDL
UNIVERSIDADE ESTADUAL PAULISTA. REVISTA DE ODONTOLOGIA. Key Title: Revista de Odontologia da Unesp. (Text in Portuguese; summaries in English and Portuguese) 1979. a. $30 or exchange basis. Universidade Estadual Paulista, Av. Vicente Ferreira, 1278, Caixa Postal 603, 17515-901 Marilia SP, Brazil. TEL 0144-33-1844. FAX 0144-22-2504. TELEX 1119016 UJME BR. Ed.Bd. bibl.; charts; illus.; stat.; circ. 1,000 (controlled). (back issues avail.) **Indexed:** Bibliogr.Bras.Odontol., Biol.Abstr. **Document type:** academic/scholarly publication.
—BLDSC (7869.080000); CASDDS.
  Formed by the merger of (1972-1979): Universidade Estadual Paulista. Faculdade de Odontologia de Aracatuba. Revista (ISSN 0300-1350); Which was formerly: Revista F O A (ISSN 0300-2837); (1967-1979): Faculdade de dontologia de Araraquara. Revista (ISSN 0101-1820); Which was formerly (until 1977): Faculdade de Farmacia e Odontologia de Araraquara. Revista (ISSN 0014-6684); (1972-1977): Faculdade de Odontologia de Sao Jose dos Campos. Revista (ISSN 0301-1119)
  Description: Publishes original articles in the study and research of odontology.

617.6 BL ISSN 0102-5902
CODEN: ACECDB
UNIVERSIDADE FEDERAL DE MINAS GERAIS. CURSO DE ODONTOLOGIA. ARQUIVOS DO CENTRO DE ESTUDOS. (Text in Portuguese; summaries in English) 1964. s-a. Cr.$20 per no. or exchange basis. Universidade Federal de Minas Gerais, Faculdade de Odontologia, Rua Conde Linhares 141, 30000 Belo Horizonte, Minas Gerais, Brazil. Ed. Mario Lucio Jardim Parreira. bibl.; charts; illus. **Indexed:** Biol.Abstr., Chem.Abstr., Dent.Ind., Oral Res.Abstr.
—BLDSC (1685.400000).

617.6 BL ISSN 0083-3908
UNIVERSIDADE FEDERAL DE PERNAMBUCO. FACULDADE DE ODONTOLOGIA. ANAIS. (Text in Portuguese; summaries in English) 1960. a. Universidade Federal de Pernambuco, Faculdade de Odontologia, Recife, Pernambuco, Brazil.
  Continues (with vol.5): Universidade do Recife. Faculdade de Odontologia. Anais.

617.6 BL ISSN 0041-8919
UNIVERSIDADE FEDERAL DO RIO DE JANEIRO. FACULDADE DE ODONTOLOGIA. ANAIS.* (Text in Portuguese; summaries in English) 1947. Universidade Federal do Rio de Janeiro, Faculdade de Odontologia, Ilha da Cidade Universitaria, Rio de Janeiro, Brazil. illus.; stat.; circ. controlled. **Indexed:** Biol.Abstr.

617.6 US ISSN 0076-843X
UNIVERSITY OF MICHIGAN. SCHOOL OF DENTISTRY. ALUMNI BULLETIN. 1937. a. University of Michigan, School of Dentistry, Ann Arbor, MI 48104. TEL 313-764-1817. Ed. Charles C. Kelsey. circ. 6,000. **Indexed:** Dent.Ind.

617.6 US
UPDATE (GAINESVILLE). 1967. 3/yr. free to qualified personnel. University of Florida, College of Dentistry, Box J-405 JHMHC, Gainesville, FL 32610. TEL 904-392-4431. FAX 904-392-3070. Ed. Linda Mealiea. circ. 2,100.

617.6 VE ISSN 0042-3424
VENEZUELA ODONTOLOGIA. 1934. bi-m. Colegio de Odontologos de Venezuela, Junta Directiva, Av. Guanare, Las Palmas, Apdo. 1341, Caracas 105, Venezuela. TEL 782.15.54. adv.; bk.rev.; charts; illus.; index. circ. 2,000. **Indexed:** Dent.Ind.

617.6 US ISSN 0049-6472
VIRGINIA DENTAL JOURNAL. 1924. q. $12 to non-members. Virginia Dental Association, c/o Francis F. Carr, Jr., D.D.S., Ed., Box 6906, Richmond, VA 23230. TEL 804-358-4927. FAX 804-353-7342. adv.; bk.rev.; charts; illus. circ. 2,900. **Indexed:** Dent.Ind., Ind.Med.
—BLDSC (9238.400000).
  Continues: Virginia Dental Association. Bulletin.

617.6 US ISSN 1046-9338
CODEN: WDJOEG
W D A JOURNAL. vol.49, 1973. m. $35 to libraries and dental agencies (foreign $65). Wisconsin Dental Association, 111 E. Wisconsin Ave., Ste. 1300, Milwaukee, Milwaukee, WI 53202. TEL 414-276-4520. FAX 414-276-8431. Ed. Dennis W. Engel, D.D.S. adv. contact: Richard Brandtjen. charts; illus.; circ. 3,100 (controlled). (processed) **Indexed:** Dent.Abstr., Dent.Ind., Med.Care Rev. **Document type:** academic/scholarly publication.
—BLDSC (9325.666500).
  Former titles (until 1988): Wisconsin Dental Association. Journal (ISSN 0887-9699); Wisconsin State Dental Society. Journal (ISSN 0043-6674)

617.6 US
W S D A MEMBERSHIP DIRECTORY & RESOURCE GUIDE. 1934. a. (included with W S D A News (ISSN 1064-0835)). Washington State Dental Association, 2033 Sixth Ave., No. 333, Seattle, WA 98121-2514. TEL 206-448-1914. adv. circ. 3,500. **Indexed:** Dent.Ind. **Document type:** directory, trade publication.
  Formerly (until 1993): Washington State Dental Journal. Membership Roster (ISSN 0083-7431)

617.6 US ISSN 1064-0835
W S D A NEWS. 1960. 11/yr. $40 (foreign $50) (includes W S D A Membership Directory & Resource Guide). Washington State Dental Association, 2033 Sixth Ave., No. 333, Seattle, WA 98121-2514. TEL 206-448-1914. Ed. Dr. Richard J. Mielke. adv. contact: Kerry Alexander. illus. circ. 3,900. **Document type:** newsletter.
  Description: Contains brief articles of interest to members.

617.6 JA ISSN 0386-1449
WAY. 1975. q. Kawamura Dental Clinic, Matsuzakaya, 2-chome, Kyobashi, Higashi-ku, Osaka, Japan.

617.6 US ISSN 0043-3225
WEST VIRGINIA DENTAL JOURNAL. vol.40, 1966. q. $10. West Virginia Dental Association, 300 Capitol St., K V Bldg., Ste. 1002, Charleston, WV 25301. TEL 304-925-7201. Ed. R.D. Smith. adv.; bk.rev.; illus. circ. 1,100. **Indexed:** Dent.Abstr., Dent.Ind., Med.Care Rev.
—BLDSC (9299.800000).

WESTERN SOCIETY OF PERIODONTOLOGY. JOURNAL. PERIODONTAL ABSTRACTS. see *MEDICAL SCIENCES — Abstracting, Bibliographies, Statistics*

617.6 US
WESTVIEWS. 1972. 8/yr. $10. Western Dental Society, 6242 Westchester Pkwy, No. 220, Los Angeles, CA 90045. FAX 213-641-3258. Ed. Victor Pineschi. adv. circ. 910. (tabloid format)
  Formerly: Western Dental Society. Newsletter.

617.6 US
RK37
WHO'S WHO IN BLACK DENTISTRY IN AMERICA. triennial with a. supplements. $125. Aqua Dynamics Ltd., 1317 E. Bramblestone Ave., Norfolk, VA 23510. TEL 804-627-3100. FAX 804-627-2907. Ed. Lord Cecil Rhodes. stat. **Document type:** directory.
  Formerly: Rhodes Directory of Black Dentists Registered in the United States (ISSN 0090-7995)

617.6 US
WORD OF MOUTH (SAN FRANCISCO). 1975. q. free to program purchasers and brokers. c/o Delta Dental Plan of CA, Box 7736, San Francisco, CA 94120. TEL 415-972-8300. Ed. Jeannine Rucker. adv.; circ. 6,000 (controlled). **Document type:** newsletter.
  Description: Provides news and dental health tips for California dental program purchasers and brokers.

617.6 US ISSN 0049-8262
XI PSI PHI QUARTERLY.* 1906. q. $6. Xi Psi Phi Fraternity, c/o Dr. Leighton A. Wier, Ed., 104 Magnolia Ave., San Antonio, TX 78212. TEL 512-733-1961. bk.rev.; illus. circ. 3,000. **Indexed:** Dent.Ind.

MEDICAL SCIENCES — DERMATOLOGY AND VENEREOLOGY

617.6058 US ISSN 0084-3717
RK16
YEAR BOOK OF DENTISTRY. 1936. a. $66.95 (residents $35) (effective 1996). Mosby - Year Book, Inc., Continuity Division, 200 N. LaSalle, Chicago, IL 60601. TEL 312-726-9733. FAX 312-726-6075. TELEX 206155. Ed. Dr. Lawrence Meskin. illus. (reprint service avail.) Indexed: Curr.Adv.Ecol.Sci. ●Also available online. Vendor(s): Ovid Technologies. Also available on CD-ROM.
—BLDSC (9411.625000); Faxon.

617.6 JA ISSN 0914-9554
YOKOHAMA GAKU GANMEN KOKU GEKA GAKKAISHI/YOKOHAMA JOURNAL OF ORAL AND MAXILLOFACIAL SURGERY. (Text in Japanese; summaries in English) 1988. s-a. Yokohama Gaku Ganmen Koku Geka Gakkai - Yokohama Society of Oral and Maxillofacial Surgery, Yokohama Shiritsu Daigaku Igakubu Koku Gekagaku Koza, 3-46, Urafunecho, Minami-ku, Yokohama-shi, Kanagawa-ken 232, Japan.

617.6 GW
Z F N SEMINARPROGRAMM. a. Zahnaerztliches Fortbildungszentrum Niedersachsen, Hildesheimerstr. 35, 30169 Hannover, Germany. TEL 0511-8112-303. FAX 0511-8112-106. Ed. Herbert Buettner. adv.

617.6 GW ISSN 0044-166X
Z W R. (Zahnaerztliche Welt Rundschau); das Deutsche Zahnaerzteblatt. 1891. m. DM.220 (foreign DM.244). Huethig Verlag, Postfach 102869, 69018 Heidelberg, Germany. TEL 06221-489281. FAX 06221-489205. TELEX 461727-HUEHDD. Ed. Dr. Cornelia Gins. adv.; B&W page DM.3310; trim 210 x 297; adv. contact: Micheline Cohen. bk.rev.; illus.; index. circ. 15,000. Indexed: Biol.Abstr., Chem.Abstr., Curr.Tit.Dent., Dent.Ind., Ind.Med. Document type: trade publication.
—SWETS. CCC.
Incorporates (1968-1986): Zahnarzt (ISSN 0044-1678); (1948-1971): Stoma (ISSN 0039-1697); Formerly (until 1970): Z W R - Zahnaerztliche Welt, Zahnaerztliche Rundschau (ISSN 0301-1607)
Description: Professional journal for dentists, dental technicians and their support staff.

617.6 GW ISSN 0340-3017
ZAHNAERZTEBLATT BADEN-WUERTTEMBERG. 1972. m. DM.185.40 (foreign DM.219.60) (effective 1995). (Landeszahnaerztekammer Baden-Wuerttemberg) Verlagsgemeinschaft Gentner Verlag - Strobel Verlag, Forststr. 131, 70193 Stuttgart, Germany. TEL 0711-63672-0. FAX 0711-63672-11. Eds. H.-H. Holfeld, J. Glueck. adv. contact: G. Reuchen. circ. 9,900. Indexed: Dent.Ind. Document type: academic/scholarly publication.

617.6 GW ISSN 0938-8486
ZAHNAERZTEBLATT SACHSEN. 1989. m. DM.109.80 (foreign DM.133.20) (effective 1995). (Landeszahnaerztekammer Sachsen) Verlagsgemeinschaft Gentner Verlag - Strobel Verlag, Forststr. 131, 70193 Stuttgart, Germany. TEL 0711-63672-0. FAX 0711-6367211. adv. contact: G. Keuchen. circ. 4,800. Document type: academic/scholarly publication.

617.6 GW ISSN 0341-8995
ZAHNAERZTLICHE MITTEILUNGEN. 1910. s-m. DM.276 (students DM.70.40). (Bundesverband der Deutschen Zahnaerzte e.V.) Deutscher Aerzte-Verlag GmbH, Postfach 400265, 50832 Cologne, Germany. TEL 02234-7011-0. FAX 02234-7011444. adv.; bk.rev.; charts; illus.; stat.; tr.lit.; index. circ. 71,817. Indexed: Curr.Tit.Dent., Dent.Ind., Ind.Med. Document type: trade publication.
—SWETS.

617.6 GW ISSN 0044-1651
ZAHNAERZTLICHE PRAXIS. 1949. m. DM.132. Reed Elsevier Deutschland GmbH (Subsidiary of: Reed Elsevier group), Hans-Cornelius Str. 4, 82166 Graefelfing, Germany. TEL 089-8917-0. FAX 089-853799. Ed. Burkhard Bierschenck; Pub. Wolfram Haase. adv. contact: Elke Mueller. bk.rev.; charts; illus.; index. Indexed: Curr.Tit.Dent., Dent.Ind. Document type: trade publication.
—BLDSC (9425.720000); UMI. CCC.

617.6 GW ISSN 0934-9634
DIE ZAHNARZTHELFERIN. 1987. m. DM.66. Friedrich Kiehl Verlag GmbH, Pfaustr. 13, 67063 Ludwigshafen, Germany. TEL 0621-63502-0. FAX 0621-6350222. Ed. Lothar Kurz. circ. 8,200 (paid). Document type: trade publication.

617.6 SZ ISSN 0044-1686
DIE ZAHNTECHNIK. (Text in French, German and Italian) 1942. 6/yr. 75 SFr. Schweizerische Zahntechniker-Vereinigung, Heidenbuehl 2, CH-8840 Einsiedeln, Switzerland. TEL 055-531074. Ed. W. Meyer. adv. contact: Paul Rickenbacher. bk.rev.; abstr.; bibl.; charts; illus.; stat.; cum.index. circ. 5,000. Indexed: Curr.Tit.Dent., Dent.Ind. Document type: newsletter.

617.6 AU ISSN 0175-7784
ZEITSCHRIFT FUER STOMATOLOGIE. (Supplement avail. (ISSN 0178-4595)) 1903. 10/yr. DM.276($200) (effective 1996). Springer-Verlag, Sachsenplatz 4-6, Postfach 89, A-1201 Vienna, Austria. TEL 0222-3302415. FAX 0222-3302426. (Subscr. in N. America to: Springer-Verlag New York, Inc., 44 Hartz Way, Secaucus, NJ 07096-2491. TEL 201-348-4033. FAX 201-348-4505) Eds. Drs. G. Watzek, M. Matejka. adv.; bk.rev.; bibl.; illus.; index. circ. 3,500. (also avail. in microform; back issues avail.) Indexed: Biol.Abstr., Curr.Cont., Curr.Tit.Dent., Dent.Ind. Document type: academic/scholarly publication.
—Faxon; UMI. CCC.
Formerly: Oesterreichische Zeitschrift fuer Stomatologie (ISSN 0029-9642)

617.7 GW
ZEITSCHRIFT FUER ZAHNAERZTLICHE IMPLANTOLOGIE. (Text in German; summaries in English) 1984. q. DM.218. (Deutsche Gesellschaft fuer Zahn-, Mund- und Kieferheilkunde) Carl Hanser Verlag, Kolbergerstr. 22, 81679 Munich, Germany. TEL 089-998300. FAX 089-984809. (Subscr. to: Postfach 860420, 81631 Munich, Germany) Ed.Bd. adv.; bk.rev.; charts; illus. circ. 1,700. (reprint service avail. from SCH) Indexed: Curr.Tit.Dent. Document type: trade publication.
—CCC.
Formerly: Fortschritte der Zahnaerztliche Implantologie (ISSN 0177-3348)

ZHONGGUO YIXUE WENZHAI (KOUQIANG YIXUE)/CHINA MEDICAL ABSTRACTS (STOMATOLOGY). see *MEDICAL SCIENCES — Abstracting, Bibliographies, Statistics*

617.6 XV ISSN 0044-4928
CODEN: ZOVEAG
ZOBOZDRAVSTVENI VESTNIK. (Text in Slovenian; summaries in English and German) 1946. bi-m. 100 din.($20.85) Drustvo Zobozdravstvenih Delavcev Slovenije, Hrvatski trg 6, Ljubljana, Slovenia. Ed. Rajko Sedej. adv.; bk.rev.; illus.; index. circ. 1,500. Indexed: Chem.Abstr., Dent.Ind.
—BLDSC (9514.950000); CASDDS.

MEDICAL SCIENCES — Dermatology And Venereology

616.5 616.95 NO ISSN 0001-5555
CODEN: ADVEA4
ACTA DERMATO-VENEREOLOGICA. (Supplements avail.) (Text and summaries in English) 1920. 6/yr. NOK 1135 in Nordic countries; elsewhere $195 (effective 1996). Scandinavian University Press, P.O. Box 2959 Toeyen, N-0608 Oslo, Norway. TEL 47-22-57-54-00. FAX 47-22-57-53-53. (U.S. addr.: Scandinavian University Press, 200 Meecham Ave., Elmont, NY 11003. TEL 516-352-7300) Ed. Lennart Juhlin. adv.; illus.; index. circ. 1,600. Indexed: Abstr.Hyg., ASCA, Biol.Abstr., Biotech.Abstr., C.I.S. Abstr., Chem.Abstr., Curr.Adv.Cancer Res., Curr.Adv.Ecol.Sci., Curr.Cont., Dairy Sci.Abstr., Dent.Ind., Dok.Arbeitsmed., Excerp.Med., Helminthol.Abstr., Ind.Med., Ind.Sci.Rev., Kidney, Med.& Surg.Dermat., Nucl.Sci.Abstr., Nutr.Abstr., Protozool.Abstr., Rev.Med.& Vet.Mycol., Rev.Plant Path., Sci.Cit.Ind., Trop.Dis.Bull.
—BLDSC (0612.320000); ADONIS; CASDDS; Faxon; Genuine Article; SWETS; UnCover.
Description: Focuses on clinical and experimental research in the field of dermatology and venereology.

616.5 NO ISSN 0365-8341
CODEN: AVSUAR
ACTA DERMATO-VENEREOLOGICA. SUPPLEMENTUM. (Supplement to: Acta Dermato-Venereologica (ISSN 0001-5555)) 1929. irreg. Scandinavian University Press, P.O. Box 2959, N-0608 Oslo, Norway. TEL 47-22-57-54-00. FAX 47-22-57-53-53. (U.S. addr.: Scandinavian University Press, 200 Meecham Ave., Elmont, NY 11003. TEL 516-352-7300) Document type: academic/scholarly publication, monographic series.
—BLDSC (0612.322000); ADONIS; CASDDS; Faxon; SWETS; UnCover.

616.5 JA ISSN 0065-1176
ACTA DERMATOLOGICA/HIFUKA KIYO. (Issues for 1923-1961 have title: Acta Dermatologica: Dermatologia, Syphilidologia et Urologia) (Articles in Japanese with some English; table of contents and summaries in English) 1923. q. 3000 Yen or exchange basis. Kyoto University, Faculty of Medicine, Department of Dermatology - Kyoto Daiguku Igakubu Hifuka Kyoshitsu, 54 Shogoin Kawara-cho, Sakyo-ku, Kyoto 606, Japan. Ed. Sadao Imamura. bk.rev. circ. 1,000. Indexed: Biol.Abstr., Excerp.Med., INIS Atomind.
—BLDSC (0612.300000); EMDOCS.

616 CI ISSN 1330-027X
ACTA DERMATOLOGICA CROATICA. q. Croatian Dermatological Society, Vinogradska 29, 41000 Zagreb, Croatia. (Co-sponsor: Hravatska Akademija Medicinskih Znanosti) Indexed: Excerp.Med. (1994-). Document type: academic/scholarly publication.

616 XV ISSN 1318-4458
ACTA DERMATOVENEROLOGICA ALPINA, PANONICA ET ADRIATICA. 1974. q. DM.70. Slovene Medical Society, Dermatological Section, Dermatoloska Klinika, Zaloska c.2, 61000 Ljubljana, Slovenia. Ed. A. Kansky. adv.; bk.rev. circ. 500. Indexed: Biol.Abstr., Excerp.Med. (1994-). Document type: academic/scholarly publication.
—BLDSC (0612.328000).
Formerly (until 1992): Acta Dermatovenerologica Iugoslavica (ISSN 0302-4466)

616.5 SP ISSN 0001-7310
ACTAS DERMOSIFILIOGRAFICAS. m. (10/yr.). 10900 ptas.($125) (effective 1995). (Academia Espanola de Dermatologia y Sifiliografia) Editorial Garsi, S.A., Juan Bravo 46, 28006 Madrid, Spain. TEL 34-1-4021212. FAX 34-1-4020954. Ed. Dr. Miguel Armijo Moreno. adv.; bk.rev.; illus.; index. circ. 1,500. Indexed: Chem.Abstr., Dent.Ind., Excerp.Med., Ind.Med.Esp., Ind.Med., Med.& Surg.Dermat., Rev.Med.& Vet.Mycol., Rev.Plant Path.
—BLDSC (0612.330000); Faxon.

616.5 SP ISSN 0210-279X
ACTUALIDAD DERMATOLOGICA. 1962. 11/yr. Corcega 83, 6o 2a, 08029 Barcelona, Spain. TEL 3-439-25-41.

616.5 US ISSN 0882-0880
CODEN: ADDEEK
ADVANCES IN DERMATOLOGY. 1986. a. $64.95 (residents $40) (effective 1996). Mosby - Year Book, Inc. (Chicago) (Subsidiary of: Times Mirror Company), 200 N. LaSalle St., Chicago, IL 60601-1080. TEL 312-726-9733. FAX 312-726-6075. TELEX 206155. (Subscr. to: 11830 Westline Industrial Dr., St. Louis, MO 63146. TEL 800-325-4177) Ed. Dr. Jeffrey P. Callen. illus.
—BLDSC (0704.242300); Faxon; SWETS; UnCover. CCC.
Description: Presents a collection of fully referenced articles from experts in dermatology.

MEDICAL SCIENCES — DERMATOLOGY AND VENEREOLOGY

616.5 US ISSN 1076-2191
ADVANCES IN WOUND CARE;* the journal for prevention and healing. 1988. bi-m. $28 ($40 to Canada; elsewhere $50) (effective 1994). S - N Publications, Inc., Box 908, Spring House, PA 19477-0903. TEL 708-426-6100. FAX 708-426-6146. Ed. Roberta S. Abruzzese. adv.; tr.lit. circ. 6,500. (reprint service avail.) **Indexed:** CINAHL, Int.Nurs.Ind., Med.& Surg.Dermat. **Document type:** academic/scholarly publication.
—SWETS. **CCC.**
Formerly (until 1994): Decubitus: The Journal of Skin Ulcers (ISSN 0898-1655)
Description: Examines medical and technical developments of interest to physicians, nurses, and specialists responsible for the treatment of pressure ulcers, with reports of current research, legal and professional issues.
Refereed Serial

AIDS INFORMATION EXCHANGE. see *MEDICAL SCIENCES — Communicable Diseases*

616.5 GW ISSN 0340-2541
AKTUELLE DERMATOLOGIE; Andrologie - Phlebologie - Proktologie - Venerologie - Allergologie - Mykologie. 1975. m. DM.234. Georg Thieme Verlag, Ruedigerstr. 14, 70469 Stuttgart, Germany. TEL 0711-8931-0. FAX 0711-8931298. (Subscr. to: Postfach 104853, 70042 Stuttgart, Germany) Ed.Bd. adv.; index. circ. 2,700. (reprint service avail. from UMI) **Indexed:** Biol.Abstr., Excerp.Med. **Document type:** academic/scholarly publication.
—BLDSC (0785.729700); UMI. **CCC.**

616.5 US ISSN 0190-9622
RL1 CODEN: JAADDB
AMERICAN ACADEMY OF DERMATOLOGY. JOURNAL. (Supplements avail.) 1979. m. $133 to individuals (Canada $180.83; elsewhere $169); institutions $230 (Canada $248.62; elsewhere $266); students, residents $61 (Canada $103.79; elsewhere $97) (effective 1996); newsstand price: $13.50. (American Academy of Dermatology) Mosby - Year Book, Inc. (Subsidiary of: Times Mirror Company), 11830 Westline Industrial Dr., St. Louis, MO 63146-3318. TEL 314-872-8370; 800-325-4177. FAX 314-432-1380. TELEX 44-2402. Ed. Dr. Richard Dobson. adv.: B&W page $1495, color page $2690; trim 8 1/8 x 10 7/8. bk.rev.; s-a. index. circ. 17,614. (also avail. in microfilm from UMI; reprint service avail. from UMI) **Indexed:** ASCA, Biol.Abstr., Curr.Adv.Cancer Res., Curr.Cont., Dok.Arbeitsmed., Excerp.Med., Helminthol.Abstr., Ind.Med., INIS Atomind., Kidney, Lab.Haz.Bull., Med.& Surg.Dermat., NRN, Protozool.Abstr., Rev.Med.& Vet.Mycol., Sci.Cit.Ind., Small Anim.Abstr.
—BLDSC (4683.703000); Faxon; Genuine Article; SWETS; UMI; UnCover. **CCC.**
Description: Provides a clinical perspective on manifestations of skin disease.
Refereed Serial

616.5 US ISSN 1046-199X
CODEN: AJCDFL
AMERICAN JOURNAL OF CONTACT DERMATITIS. 1990. q. $159 (foreign $185) (effective 1996). (American Contact Dermatitis Society) W.B. Saunders Co. (Subsidiary of: Harcourt Brace & Company), Curtis Center, 3rd Fl., Independence Sq. W., Philadelphia, PA 19106-3399. TEL 215-238-7800. FAX 215-238-6445. (Subscr. to: Periodicals Fulfillment, W.B. Saunders Co., 6277 Sea Harbor Dr., 4th Fl., Orlando, FL 32819-4800. TEL 800-654-2452. FAX 800-874-6418) Ed. Dr. Walter G. Larsen; Pub. Joan W. Blumberg. adv.: B&W page $700, color page $1650; 7 x 10. bk.rev.; abstr. circ. 841. (back issues avail.) **Indexed:** Excerp.Med. (1995-), Med.& Surg.Dermat. **Document type:** academic/scholarly publication.
—BLDSC (0824.150000); UMI; UnCover. **CCC.**
Description: Provides clinically focused articles on diagnosing and treating dermatologic conditions caused by irritants and allergic reactions.
Refereed Serial

AMERICAN JOURNAL OF DERMATOPATHOLOGY. see *MEDICAL SCIENCES*

616.5 BL ISSN 0365-0596
CODEN: ABDEB3
ANAIS BRASILEIROS DE DERMATOLOGIA. (Text in Portuguese; summaries in English, Portuguese) 1925. bi-m. Cr.$150000($60) or exchange basis. Sociedade Brasileira de Dermatologia, Caixa Postal 389, 20001-970 Rio de Janeiro, Brazil. TEL 55-21-2222648. (Orders to: ECN-Editora Cientifica Nacional Ltda., Caixa Postal 590, 20241-180 Rio de Janeiro, Brazil) Ed. R.D. Azulay. adv.; bk.rev.; abstr.; bibl.; charts; illus.; stat.; index, cum.index. circ. 3,000. (also avail. in microform from UMI; back issues avail.) **Indexed:** Abstr.Hyg., Biol.Abstr., Chem.Abstr., Curr.Cont., Excerp.Med., Ind.Med., Rev.Med.& Vet.Mycol., Trop.Dis.Bull.
—Faxon; UMI.
Description: Original research papers in dermatology.

616.5 616.951 FR ISSN 0151-9638
CODEN: ADVED7
ANNALES DE DERMATOLOGIE ET DE VENEREOLOGIE. (Text in French; summaries in English) 1869. 11/yr. 1170 F. (foreign 1428 F.) (effective 1996). (Societe Francaise de Dermatologie et de Venereologie) Masson - Periodiques, Villa Laromiguiere, 75005 Paris, France. TEL 1-40-46-62-00. FAX 1-40-46-62-01. Ed. E. Grosshans. adv.; bk.rev.; abstr.; illus.; index. circ. 3,900. (also avail. in microform from UMI; reprint service avail. from ISI) **Indexed:** Biol.Abstr., C.I.S. Abstr., Chem.Abstr., Curr.Adv.Ecol.Sci., Curr.Cont., Dent.Ind., Excerp.Med., Helminthol.Abstr., Ind.Med., Ind.Sci.Rev., Lab.Haz.Bull., Med.& Surg.Dermat., Protozool.Abstr., Rev.Med.& Vet.Mycol., Rev.Plant Path., Sci.Cit.Ind. **Document type:** academic/scholarly publication.
—BLDSC (0971.600000); Genuine Article; SWETS; UMI. **CCC.**
Former titles: Annales de Dermatologie et de Syphiligraphie; Societe Francaise de Dermatologie et de Syphiligraphie. Bulletin (ISSN 0003-3979)
Description: Publishes original work from numerous schools of dermatology. Provides both clinical and therapeutic points of view.

616.5 IT ISSN 0003-4703
ANNALI ITALIANI DI DERMATOLOGIA CLINICA E SPERIMENTALE. (Text in English, Italian) 1945. q. L.264000($160) (effective 1996). Pensiero Scientifico Editore s.r.l., Via Bradano 3-C, 00199 Rome, Italy. TEL 06-86207158. FAX 06-86207160. Ed. Paolo Lisi. adv.; bk.rev.; circ. 1,200 (controlled). **Indexed:** Biol.Abstr., Chem.Abstr., Excerp.Med., Ind.Med. **Document type:** academic/scholarly publication.
—Faxon.

616.5 616.95 KO ISSN 1013-9087
CODEN: ANDEEM
ANNALS OF DERMATOLOGY. (Text in English) 1989. q. 40000 Won($50) Korean Dermatological Association, 401 Sindonga Jonghap-Sangka, 491 Suecho-dong, Suecho-ku, Seoul 137-070, S. Korea. TEL 02-567-0284. FAX 02-552-4203. (Editorial addr.: c/o Department of Dermatology, 134, Shinchon-dong, Seodaemun-ku, Seoul 120-752, S. Korea) (Co-sponsor: Korean Federation of Science & Technology Societies) Ed. Yoon-Kee Park. adv.
—BLDSC (1040.351000).

616.5 GW ISSN 0340-3696
CODEN: ADMFAU
ARCHIVES OF DERMATOLOGICAL RESEARCH. (Text in English) 1869. 8/yr. DM.1398($1015) (effective 1996). (Deutsche Dermatologische Gesellschaft) Springer-Verlag, Heidelberger Platz 3, 14197 Berlin, Germany. TEL 030-8207-0. FAX 030-8214091. E-mail: orders@springer.de. (Subscr. in N. America to: Springer-Verlag New York, Inc., 44 Hartz Way, Secaucus, NJ 07096-2491. TEL 201-348-4033. FAX 201-348-4505) Ed. E. Christophers. adv.; bibl.; charts; illus.; index. (also avail. in microfilm from UMI; back issues avail.; reprint service avail. from ISI) **Indexed:** Biol.Abstr., Biotech.Abstr., Chem.Abstr., Curr.Adv.Ecol.Sci., Curr.Cont., Dairy Sci.Abstr., Excerp.Med., Helminthol.Abstr., Ind.Med., Ind.Sci.Rev., Med.& Surg.Dermat., NRN, Nutr.Abstr., Ornam.Hort., Rev.Appl.Entomol., Rev.Plant Path., Risk Abstr., Sci.Cit.Ind. **Document type:** academic/scholarly publication.
—BLDSC (1634.130000); CASDDS; Faxon; Genuine Article; SWETS; UMI; UnCover. **CCC.**
Former titles: Archiv fuer Dermatologische Forschung (ISSN 0003-9187); Archiv fuer Klinische und Experimentelle Dermatologie.
Description: Publishes original contributions in the field of experimental dermatology, including biochemistry, morphology and immunology of the skin.

616.5 US ISSN 0003-987X
CODEN: ARDEAC
ARCHIVES OF DERMATOLOGY. Spanish translation: Archives of Dermatology (Edicion Espanola) (SP ISSN 1130-1910) 1920. m. $135 (foreign $175). American Medical Association, 515 N. State St., Chicago, IL 60610. TEL 312-464-5000; 800-262-2350. FAX 312-464-4184. Ed. Dr. Kenneth A. Arndt. bk.rev.; abstr.; charts; illus.; index. circ. 14,500. (also avail. in microform from UMI) **Indexed:** Abstr.Hyg., Abstr.Inter.Med., AIM, Biol.Abstr., Biotech.Abstr., C.I.S.Abstr., Chem.Abstr., Curr.Adv.Cancer Res., Curr.Adv.Ecol.Sci., Curr.Adv.Genetics & Molec.Biol., Curr.Cont., Dairy Sci.Abstr., Dent.Ind., Dok.Arbeitsmed., Excerp.Med., Helminthol.Abstr., I.P.A., Ind.Med., Ind.Sci.Rev., INIS Atomind., Med.& Surg.Dermat., NRN, Nutr.Abstr., Protozool.Abstr., Rev.Appl.Entomol., Rev.Med.& Vet.Mycol., Sci.Cit.Ind., Trop.Dis.Bull. **Document type:** academic/scholarly publication.
●Also available online. Vendor(s): Lexis-Nexis.
—BLDSC (1634.150000); CASDDS; Faxon; Genuine Article; SWETS; UMI; UnCover. **CCC.**
Description: Enhances the understanding of skin and its diseases by publishing original articles.
Refereed Serial

616.5 SP ISSN 1130-1910
ARCHIVES OF DERMATOLOGY (EDICION ESPANOLA). Spanish translation of: Archives of Dermatology (US ISSN 0003-987X) bi-m. 6900 ptas.($35) (American Medical Association, US) Ediciones Doyma S.A., Travesera de Gracia, 17-21, 08021 Barcelona, Spain. TEL 34-1-200-07-11. FAX 34-1-209-11-36. TELEX 51964 INK E. Ed. J.M. Mascaro Ballester. adv.: page 180000 ptas.; trim 210 x 280; adv. contact: Olga Gomez. circ. 2,000. **Indexed:** Sci.Cit.Ind.
Description: Contains translations of articles on investigative dermatology from the American edition.

616.5 AG ISSN 0066-6750
ARCHIVOS ARGENTINOS DE DERMATOLOGIA. (Text in Spanish; abstracts in English) 1951. bi-m. $140 (effective Jan. 1995). Paraguay 1307, 4 38, 1057 Buenos Aires, Argentina. TEL 541-01-813-4698. Ed. Fernando M. Stengel. adv. contact: Dagoberto Pierini. bk.rev.; circ. 1,600 (controlled). **Indexed:** Bull.Signal., Excerp.Med., Ind.Med. **Document type:** academic/scholarly publication.
—BLDSC (1654.150000).

616.5 IT
ARGOMENTI DI DERMATOLOGIA. 1992. 3/yr. L.8500($61) (effective 1994). Masson S.p.A., Divisione Periodici, Via Statuto 2-4, 20121 Milan, Italy. TEL 02-63671. FAX 02-6367-211. Ed. Benvenuto Giannotti. adv.: B&W page L.2350000, color page L.3850000.

MEDICAL SCIENCES — DERMATOLOGY AND VENEREOLOGY   4387

616.5   AT   ISSN 0004-8380
CODEN: AJDEBP
AUSTRALASIAN JOURNAL OF DERMATOLOGY. 1951. 3/yr. Aus.$170 (foreign Aus.$239) (effective 1996. (Australasian College of Dermatologists) Blackwell Science Pty Ltd, P.O. Box 378, Carlton, Vic. 3053, Australia. TEL 61-3-93470300. FAX 61-3-93473016. Ed. D. Dyall-Smith. adv.: B&W page $720, color page $1510; trim 275 x 210; adv. contact: Chris Hum. bk.rev. circ. 600. **Indexed:** Biol.Abstr., Chem.Abstr., Curr.Cont., Dent.Ind., Excerp.Med., Ind.Med., Med.& Surg.Dermat., NRN, Nutr.Abstr., Rev.Plant.Path.
—BLDSC (1794.900000); SWETS; UnCover.
Formerly: Australian Journal of Dermatology.
Description: Presents research and review articles on recent advances in therapeutics and pharmacology - dealing with normal and pathological skin conditions.

616.5   UK   ISSN 0007-0963
CODEN: BJDEAZ
BRITISH JOURNAL OF DERMATOLOGY. 1886. m. £285 in Europe; elsewhere £312($499) (effective 1996). (British Association of Dermatologists) Blackwell Science Ltd., Osney Mead, Oxford OX2 OEL, England. TEL 01865-240201. FAX 01865-721205. TELEX 83355 MEDBOK G. Ed. D.A. Burns. adv.; bk.rev.; abstr.; bibl.; illus.; index. circ. 3,500. (also avail. in microform from UMI; back issues avail.; reprint service avail. from ISI) **Indexed:** Abstr.Hyg., Abstr.Inter.Med., ASCA, Biol.Abstr., Biotech.Abstr., C.I.S. Abstr., Chem.Abstr., Curr.Adv.Cancer Res., Curr.Adv.Genetics & Molec.Biol., Curr.Cont., Dent.Ind., Excerp.Med., Helminthol.Abstr., I.P.A., Ind.Med., Ind.Sci.Rev., Ind.Vet., INIS Atomind., Lab.Haz.Bull., Med.& Surg.Dermat., NRN, Nutr.Abstr., Pig News & Info., Rev.Med.& Vet.Mycol., Rev.Plant Path., Sci.Cit.Ind., Triticale Abstr., Trop.Dis.Bull. **Document type:** academic/scholarly publication.
●Also available online.
—BLDSC (2307.400000); ADONIS; CASDDS; Faxon; Genuine Article; SWETS; UMI; UnCover. **CCC.**
Refereed Serial

616.5   UK   ISSN 0366-077X
CODEN: BJDSA9
BRITISH JOURNAL OF DERMATOLOGY. SUPPLEMENT. 1969. irreg. free. (British Association of Dermatologists) Blackwell Science Ltd., Osney Mead, Oxford OX2 OEL, England. TEL 01865-240201. FAX 01865-721205. TELEX 83355 MEDBOK G. Ed. R.M. Mackie. adv. circ. 3,500. (also avail. in microform from UMI) **Indexed:** ASCA, Biol.Abstr., Chem.Abstr., Curr.Cont., Excerp.Med., Helminthol.Abstr., I.P.A., Ind.Med., Nutr.Abstr., Rev.Plant Path., Sci.Cit.Ind. **Document type:** academic/scholarly publication.
—BLDSC (2307.405000); ADONIS; CASDDS; SWETS. **CCC.**

616.5   CN   ISSN 0843-4247
CANADIAN JOURNAL OF DERMATOLOGY; for primary care physicians and the specialist. 1986. 6/yr. Can.$60($67) Rodar Publishing Inc., 8102 Trans Canada Hwy., St. Laurent, PQ H4S 1J4, Canada. TEL 514-333-5350. Ed. W. Alan Dodd; Pub. Bob Fauteux. adv.; bk.rev.; charts; illus.; index; circ. 9,640 (controlled). (also avail. in microfilm; back issues avail.; reprint service avail. from MML) **Indexed:** Can.B.P.I., CMI.
—BLDSC (3031.133000).
Formerly (until 1989): Contemporary Dermatology (ISSN 0836-1207)
Refereed Serial

CELIAC NEWS. see *MEDICAL SCIENCES — Gastroenterology*

616.5   XR
CODEN: CEDEAB
CESKO-SLOVENSKA DERMATOLOGIE. (Text in Czech or Slovak; summaries in English and Russian) 1925. 6/yr. $48.60. (Ceska Lekarska Spolecnost J.E. Purkyne - Czech Medical Society) Nakladatelske Stredisko C L S J.E. Purkyne, Sokolska 31, 120 26 Prague 2, Czech Republic. FAX 42-0-202788. (Dist. by: Artia, Ve Smeckach 30, 111 27 Prague 1, Czech Republic) (Co-sponsor: Ceska Dermato-Venerologicka Spolecnost) Ed. Michaela Malinova. adv.; bk.rev. **Indexed:** Biol.Abstr., C.I.S. Abstr., Chem.Abstr., Curr.Adv.Ecol.Sci., Excerp.Med., Ind.Med.
—BLDSC (3120.550000); CASDDS. **CCC.**
Formerly (until 1993): Ceskoslovenska Dermatologie (ISSN 0009-0514)

616.5   IT   ISSN 0011-1759
CHRONICA DERMATOLOGICA. (Text in Italian; summaries in English and Italian) 1946. bi-m. free to qualified personnel. Istituto Dermopatico dell'Immacolata, Via Monti di Creta, 104, 00167 Rome, Italy. FAX 39-6-66464437. Dir. Rino Cavalieri. adv.; bk.rev.; abstr.; bibl.; charts; illus.; stat.; index; circ. 7,000 (controlled). **Indexed:** Excerp.Med. **Document type:** academic/scholarly publication.
Formerly: I D I Cronache.

616.5   UK   ISSN 0307-6938
CODEN: CEDEDE
CLINICAL AND EXPERIMENTAL DERMATOLOGY. 1976. bi-m. £234 in Europe; elsewhere £258($415) (effective 1996). Blackwell Science Ltd., Osney Mead, Oxford OX2 OEL, England. TEL 01865-206206. FAX 01865-206219. TELEX 83355 MEDBOK G. Ed. S.M. Breathnach. circ. 950. (also avail. in microform from UMI; back issues avail.; reprint service avail. from ISI) **Indexed:** ASCA, Biotech.Abstr., Chem.Abstr., Curr.Adv.Ecol.Sci., Curr.Cont., Dent.Ind., Dok.Arbeitsmed., Excerp.Med., Helminthol.Abstr., Ind.Med., Ind.Sci.Rev., Ind.Vet., Med.& Surg.Dermat., NRN, Nutr.Abstr., Protozool.Abstr., Rev.Med.& Vet.Mycol., Rev.Plant Path., Sci.Cit.Ind., Small Anim.Abstr. **Document type:** academic/scholarly publication.
—BLDSC (3286.250000); ADONIS; CASDDS; Faxon; Genuine Article; SWETS; UMI; UnCover. **CCC.**
Formerly (until 1976): St. John's Hospital Dermatological Society. Transactions (ISSN 0036-2891)
Refereed Serial

616.5   UK   ISSN 0966-3487
CLINICAL AND EXPERIMENTAL DERMATOLOGY. SUPPLEMENT. irreg. Blackwell Science Ltd., Osney Mead, Oxford OX2 OEL, England. TEL 01865-240201. FAX 01865-721205. TELEX 83355 MEDBOK G. **Indexed:** Excerp.Med. (1993-). **Document type:** academic/scholarly publication.
—ADONIS.

616.5   JA   ISSN 0018-1404
CLINICAL DERMATOLOGY/HIFUKA NO RINSHO. (Text in Japanese) 1959. m. 1950 Yen per no. Kanehara & Co., Ltd., 2-31-14 Yushima, Bunkyo-ku, Tokyo 113, Japan. Ed. Dr. Kenichi Ueno. bk.rev.; illus.; index. circ. 4,500. **Indexed:** INIS Atomind.
—BLDSC (7971.620000).

616.5   US   ISSN 0738-081X
RL1
CLINICS IN DERMATOLOGY. 1983. bi-m. $325 to institutions (effective 1996). Elsevier Science Inc., 655 Ave. of the Americas, New York, NY 10010. TEL 212-989-5800. FAX 212-633-3990. TELEX 420643 AEP UI. (Subscr. to: Box 882, Madison Sq. Sta., New York, NY 10159-0882) Ed. Lawrence Charles Parish. illus.; index. circ. 1,500. (also avail. in microform from UMI) **Indexed:** Excerp.Med., Ind.Med., Rev.Med.& Vet.Mycol. **Document type:** academic/scholarly publication.
—BLDSC (3286.548000); Faxon; Genuine Article; SWETS; UnCover. **CCC.**
Description: Provides information on the treatment and care of skin disorders.
Refereed Serial

616.5   DK   ISSN 0105-1873
CODEN: CODEDG
CONTACT DERMATITIS; environmental and occupational dermatitis. (Text in English) 1975. 10/yr. DKK 1700 (effective 1996). (European Society of Contact Dematitis) Munksgaard International Publishers Ltd., 35 Noerre Soegade, P.O. Box 2148, DK-1016 Copenhagen K, Denmark. TEL 33-127030. FAX 33-129387. Ed. Dr. Richard Rycroft. bk.rev.; illus. circ. 1,800. (also avail. in microform from SWZ; reprint service avail. from ISI,SWZ) **Indexed:** Abstr.Hyg., Biol.Abstr., C.I.S. Abstr., Chem.Abstr., Curr.Adv.Ecol.Sci., Curr.Cont., Dent.Ind., Dok.Arbeitsmed., Excerp.Med., Hort.Abstr., Ind.Hyg.Dig., Ind.Med., Ind.Sci.Rev., Lab.Haz.Bull., Med.& Surg.Dermat., Sci.Cit.Ind., Sugar Ind.Abstr., Trop.Dis.Bull. **Document type:** academic/scholarly publication.
—BLDSC (3424.960000); CASDDS; EMDOCS; Faxon; Genuine Article; SWETS; UnCover. **CCC.**
Refereed Serial

CORE JOURNALS IN DERMATOLOGY. see *MEDICAL SCIENCES — Abstracting, Bibliographies, Statistics*

616.5   US   ISSN 1041-3766
COSMETIC DERMATOLOGY. m. $100 to institutions outside the Americas; $85 to institutions in U.S (effective 1996). Excerpta Medica, Inc., Knolls Group, 201 Littleton Rd., Ste. 100, Morris Plains, NJ 07950-2932. TEL 201-285-0855. FAX 201-285-1472. (Subscr. to: Box 3000, Denville, NJ 07834) Ed. Kathleen Kurtz. circ. 13,403 (controlled). **Indexed:** Med.& Surg.Dermat.
—BLDSC (3477.174690). **CCC.**
Description: Presents news and clinical information focusing on the cosmetic aspects of dermatology. Includes coverage of clinical meetings and industry events as well as news from Washington, DC, legal information and new products.

616.5   US   ISSN 1068-381X
CURRENT OPINION IN DERMATOLOGY. 1993. a. $99.95 to individuals; institutions $215.95; residents $52.95. Current Science, 400 Market St., Ste. 700, Philadelphia, PA 19106. TEL 215-574-2210; 800-552-5866. FAX 215-574-3533. (And: Current Science Ltd., 34-42 Cleveland St., London W1P 5LB, England. TEL 0171-323-0323. FAX 0171-636-6911) Eds. M.V. Dahl, P.J. Lynch. **Document type:** academic/scholarly publication.
●Also available online. Vendor(s): OCLC.
Also available on CD-ROM.
—BLDSC (3500.774050); ADONIS. **CCC.**

616.5   SZ   ISSN 0070-2064
CODEN: APDEBX
CURRENT PROBLEMS IN DERMATOLOGY. (Text in English) 1959. irreg., approx. a. price varies. S. Karger AG, Allschwilerstr. 10, P.O. Box, CH-4009 Basel, Switzerland. TEL 061-3061111. FAX 061-3061234. E-mail: Karger@Karger.ch. Ed. G. Burg. (reprint service avail. from ISI) **Indexed:** Biol.Abstr., Chem.Abstr., Curr.Cont., Dent.Ind., Ind.Med. **Document type:** academic/scholarly publication.
—BLDSC (3501.370000); CASDDS; Faxon; SWETS; UnCover. **CCC.**
Description: Contains reports from the most active areas of dermatology and skin research.
Refereed Serial

616.5   US   ISSN 1040-0486
CURRENT PROBLEMS IN DERMATOLOGY. 1989. bi-m. $65 to individuals (foreign $71); institutions $90 (foreign $96); students $40 (foreign $46) (effective Jan. 1994). Mosby Year - Book, Inc. (Subsidiary of: Times Mirror Company), 11830 Westline Industrial Dr., St. Louis, MO 63146. TEL 800-325-4177. Ed. Jeffrey P. Callen. circ. 1,703.
—UMI. **CCC.**
Description: Covers current concerns of the dermatologist in everyday practice.

616.5   US   ISSN 0011-4162
RL1   CODEN: CUTIB
CUTIS; cutaneous medicine for the practitioner. 1965. m. $158 to institutions outside the Americas; $121 to institutions in U.S (effective 1996). Excerpta Medica, Inc. (Subsidiary of: Reed Elsevier Medical group), 105 Raider Blvd., Belle Mead, NJ 08502. TEL 908-874-8550. FAX 908-874-8419. (Subscr. to: Box 3085, Princeton, NJ 08543-3085) Ed. Sharon Finch. adv.; bk.rev.; charts; illus. circ. 49,300. (also avail. in microform from UMI; reprint service avail. from UMI) **Indexed:** Abstr.Inter.Med., Curr.Cont., Dent.Ind., Excerp.Med., Helminthol.Abstr., Ind.Med., Ind.Sci.Rev., INIS Atomind., Med.& Surg.Dermat., NRN, Nutr.Abstr., Protozool.Abstr., Rev.Med.& Vet.Mycol., Sci.Cit.Ind. **Document type:** academic/scholarly publication, trade publication.
—BLDSC (3506.150000); Faxon; Genuine Article; SWETS; UMI; UnCover. **CCC.**
Description: Provides practical information on skin diseases and allergies, with clinical observations and discussions of therapeutic techniques.
Refereed Serial

616.5   TU   ISSN 1019-214X
CODEN: DHFAE
DERI HASTALIKLARI VE FRENGI ARSIVI/TURKISH ARCHIVES OF DERMATOLOGY AND SYPHILOLOGY. (Text in Turkish) 1967. q. Deri ve Zuhrevi Hastaliklar Dernegi, Dermatoloji Anabilim Dali - Istanbul Association of Dermatology and Venereology, Capa, Istanbul, Turkey. TEL 90-1-8245487. **Indexed:** Excerp.Med.

MEDICAL SCIENCES — DERMATOLOGY AND VENEREOLOGY

616.5   MX   ISSN 0185-4038
DERMATOLOGIA; revista mexicana. (Text in Spanish; summaries in English, Spanish) 1952. bi-m. $55. (Sociedad Mexicana de Dermatologia) Obsidiana Editores, S.A., Czda. de Tlalpan 2365, Col. Ciudad Jardin, 04370 Mexico, D.F., Mexico. TEL 6899133. FAX 6896545. (Co-sponsor: Academia Mexicana de Dermatologia) Eds. Dr. Roberto Arenas, Dr. Clemente Moreno-Collado. bk.rev.; cum.index: 1952-1981. circ. 2,400. **Indexed:** Biol.Abstr., Excerp.Med., Trop.Dis.Bull. **Document type:** academic/scholarly publication.
—BLDSC (3555.000000).
  Description: Contains original articles, revision articles, clinical cases, and notices.

616.5   IT   ISSN 0392-1395
DERMATOLOGIA CLINICA. (Text in Italian; summaries in English) q. L.50000($60) C I C Edizioni Internazionali s.r.l., Via L. Spallanzani 11, 00161 Rome, Italy. TEL 06-8412673. FAX 06-44242033. TELEX 622099 CIC. Dir. O.A. Carlesimo. **Indexed:** Excerp.Med.
—BLDSC (3555.110000). **CCC.**

616.5   SP   ISSN 1130-605X
DERMATOLOGIA COSMETICA. 1990. q. 7300 ptas.($72) (effective 1995). (Grupo Espanol de Dermatologia Cosmetica) Editorial Garsi, S.A., Juan Bravo 46, 28006 Madrid, Spain. TEL 34-1-4021212. FAX 34-1-4020954.

616.5 616.95   BU   ISSN 0417-0792
                           CODEN: DVENA3
DERMATOLOGIA I VENEROLOGIA. (Text in Bulgarian; summaries in Russian and English) 1962. q. 15 lv.($5) (Ministerstvo na Narodnoto Zdrave) Izdatelstvo Meditsina i Fizkultura, 11, Pl. Slaveikov, Sofia, Bulgaria. (Dist by: Hemus, 6, Rouski Blvd., 1000 Sofia, Bulgaria) (Co-sponsor: Nauchno Druzhestvo po Dermatologia) Ed. N.Z. Catkov. circ. 988. **Indexed:** Abstr.Bulg.Sci.Med.Lit., Biol.Abstr., C.I.S. Abstr., Chem.Abstr., Excerp.Med. (until 1993).
—CASDDS.

616.5   US   ISSN 0733-8635
RL1
DERMATOLOGIC CLINICS. 1983. q. $145 (foreign $170) (effective 1996). W.B. Saunders Co. (Subsidiary of: Harcourt Brace & Company), Curtis Center, 3rd Fl., Independence Sq. W., Philadelphia, PA 19106-3399. TEL 215-238-7800. FAX 215-238-6445. (Subscr. to: Periodicals Fulfillment, W.B. Saunders Co., 6277 Sea Harbor Dr., 4th Fl., Orlando, FL 32891-4800. TEL 800-654-2452. FAX 800-874-6418) Ed. Helaine Barron. (also avail. in microform from UMI) **Indexed:** Excerp.Med., Ornam.Hort. **Document type:** academic/scholarly publication.
—BLDSC (3555.138000); Faxon; Genuine Article; SWETS; UMI; UnCover. **CCC.**
  Description: Each issue covers a single topic of skin disease or therapy in detail.

DERMATOLOGIC SURGERY. see *MEDICAL SCIENCES — Surgery*

616.5   DK
▼**DERMATOLOGIC THERAPY 2000.** (Text in English) 1996. q. DKK 800 (effective 1996). Munksgaard International Publishers Ltd., 35 Noerre Soegade, P.O. Box 1248, DK-1016 Copenhagen K, Denmark. TEL 45-33-12-70-30. FAX 45-33-12-93-87. E-mail: fsub@mail.munksgaard.dk.

616.5   FR   ISSN 0982-8567
DERMATOLOGIE PRATIQUE. 1986. bi-m. (20/yr.). 250 F. L.E.N. Medical, 48 bis, av. Kleber, 75016 Paris, France. TEL 47-55-06-06. FAX 47-55-69-41. TELEX 640 748. Ed. Dr. C. P. Morel. circ. 4,200. **Document type:** newspaper.

616.5   IT
IL DERMATOLOGO. 10/yr. L.25000($25) C I C Edizioni Internazionali s.r.l., Via L. Spallanzani 11, 00161 Rome, Italy. TEL 06-8412673. FAX 06-44242033. TELEX 622099 CIC. adv.; bk.rev.
  Formerly: Dermatologo Ospedaliero (ISSN 0391-8912)

616.5   SZ   ISSN 1018-8665
                           CODEN: DERAEG
DERMATOLOGY; international journal for clinical and investigative dermatology. (Text in English) 1893. 8/yr. (in 2 vols.). 513.60 SFr.($394.80) to individuals; institutions 856 SFr.($658) (effective 1996). S. Karger AG, Allschwilerstr. 10, P.O. Box, CH-4009 Basel, Switzerland. TEL 061-3061111. FAX 061-3061234. E-mail: Karger@Karger.ch. (Co-sponsors: Belgian Society for Dermatology and Syphiligraphy, Schweizerisch Gesellschaft fuer Dermatologie und Venerologie) Ed. J.H. Saurat. adv.; bk.rev.; bibl.; illus.; index. circ. 2,350. (also avail. in microform from UMI,PMC) **Indexed:** Biol.Abstr., Biotech.Abstr., C.I.S. Abstr., Chem.Abstr., Curr.Adv.Ecol.Sci., Curr.Cont., Dent.Ind., Excerp.Med., Helminthol.Abstr., Ind.Med., Ind.Sci.Rev., Med.& Surg.Dermat., NRN, Nutr.Abstr., Rev.Plant Path., Sci.Cit.Ind. **Document type:** academic/scholarly publication.
—BLDSC (3555.213000); CASDDS; Faxon; Genuine Article; SWETS; UnCover. **CCC.**
  Formerly: Dermatologica (ISSN 0011-9075)
Refereed Serial

616.5   US   ISSN 0742-3217
                           CODEN: DERMEI
DERMATOLOGY. 1982. irreg., vol.7, 1986. price varies. Marcel Dekker, Inc., 270 Madison Ave., New York, NY 10016. TEL 212-696-9000. FAX 212-685-4540. TELEX 421419. Eds. Charles D. Calnan, Howard I. Mailbach.
—CASDDS.
Refereed Serial

616.5   UK   ISSN 0262-5504
DERMATOLOGY IN PRACTICE. 1982-1990; resumed 1994. bi-m. £45 (overseas £501 (effective 1995). Hayward Medical Communications Ltd., 44 Earlham St., Covent Garden, London WC2H 9LA, England. TEL 44-171-240-4493. FAX 44-171-240-4479. (Subscr. to: Essex House, Cromwell Park, Chipping Norton, Oxon. OX7 5SR, England. TEL 44-1608-645564. FAX 44-1608-645645) bk.rev.; illus. circ. 21,000. **Document type:** academic/scholarly publication.
—BLDSC (3555.232980).

616.5   US   ISSN 1060-3441
DERMATOLOGY NURSING. bi-m. $28 to individuals (foreign $41); institutions $38 (foreign $51). (Dermatology Nurses' Association) Jannetti Publications, Inc., East Holly Ave., Box 56, Pitman, NJ 08071-0056. TEL 609-589-2319. FAX 609-589-7463. **Indexed:** CINAHL.
—BLDSC (3555.232600).
Refereed Serial

616.5   US   ISSN 0196-6197
                           CODEN: DETIEG
DERMATOLOGY TIMES. 1979. m. $75. Advanstar Communications, Inc., 7500 Old Oak Blvd., Cleveland, OH 44130. TEL 216-826-2839. FAX 216-891-2726. (Subscr. to: 1 E. First St., Duluth, MN 55802. TEL 800-346-0085) circ. 7,562. (tabloid format; also avail. in microform from UMI) **Document type:** trade publication.
●Also available online. Vendor(s): Knight-Ridder, Inc..
—BLDSC (3555.233600); UMI. **CCC.**
  Description: Industry news and developments, meeting announcements and classifieds for office-based and hospital-based dermatology professionals.

616.5   CN
DERMATOLOGY TIMES OF CANADA. 1992. 9/yr. Can.$75 (foreign Can.$125). C T C Communications Corp., 1 Yonge St., Ste. 1801, Toronto, ON M5E 1W7, Canada. TEL 416-869-3862. FAX 416-369-0515. Ed. Dr. W. Stuart Maddin; Pub. Mitchell Shannon. adv.: B&W page Can.$1800, color page Can.$3000; trim 11 x 16. circ. 5,585.

616.5   GW   ISSN 0343-2432
                           CODEN: DBUMDB
DERMATOSEN IN BERUF UND UMWELT. (Text in English and German; summaries in English, French and German) 1952. bi-m. DM.75. Editio Cantor, Postfach 1255, 88341 Aulendorf, Germany. TEL 07525-2060. FAX 07525-20680. Ed.Bd. adv.; bk.rev.; abstr.; bibl.; charts; illus.; index. circ. 6,850. (reprint service avail. from IRC,ISI; back issues avail.) **Indexed:** Abstr.Hyg., Biol.Abstr., C.I.S. Abstr., Chem.Abstr., Excerp.Med., Ind.Med., INIS Atomind., Protozool.Abstr., Trop.Dis.Bull.
—BLDSC (3555.234000); CASDDS; Faxon; Genuine Article; SWETS. **CCC.**
  Formerly: Berufs-Dermatosen (ISSN 0005-9498)

616.5 616.95   US
DIALOGUES IN DERMATOLOGY; the audiojournal of dermatology. 1977. m. $180 to non-members; members $130. American Academy of Dermatology, 930 N. Meacham Rd., Shcaumburg, IL 60173-4965. TEL 708-330-0230. FAX 708-330-0050. Ed. Dr. Stephen P. Stone. bibl.; illus.; cum.index: 1977-present. circ. 2,500. (back issues avail.; avail. in audio cassette only) **Document type:** academic/scholarly publication.
  Description: Features interviews with experts on recent advances in the field of dermatology.

616.5   SA
DISEASES OF THE SKIN. vol.5, 1991. 4/yr. R.50. Helm Publishing Co. (Pty.) Ltd., P.O. Box 41706, Craighall 2024, South Africa. TEL 011-788-0612.

616.5 646.7   US
ELECTROLYSIS WORLD.* 1982. q. membership. American Electrolysis Association, 7332 E. Camelback Rd., No. D, Scottsdale, AZ 85251. TEL 602-945-4245. Ed. Gail J. Walker. circ. 1,700. (back issues avail.)

616   NE   ISSN 0926-9959
                           CODEN: JEAVEQ
EUROPEAN ACADEMY OF DERMATOLOGY AND VENEREOLOGY. JOURNAL. Key Title: Journal of the European Academy of Dermatology and Venereology. Short title: J E A D V. (Supplement avail. (ISSN 0929-0168)) 1992. bi-m. fl.926($565) (effective 1996). Elsevier Science B.V., P.O. Box 211, 1000 AE Amsterdam, Netherlands. TEL 31-20-4853598. TELEX 18582 ESPA NL. E-mail: nlinfo-f@elsevier.nl; usinfo-f@elsevier.com; forinfo-kyf04035@niftyserve.or.jp; Site addr.: http://www.elsevier.nl/. (Subscr. in U.S. and Canada to: Elsevier Science Inc., Box 882, Madison Sq. Sta., New York, NY 10159. TEL 212-989-5800. FAX 212-633-33990) Eds. T. Lotti, D. Freedman. (also avail. in microform from UMI; back issues avail.) **Indexed:** Excerp.Med. (1992-), Med.& Surg.Dermat. **Document type:** academic/scholarly publication.
—BLDSC (4741.624000). **CCC.**
  Description: Broad-based articles of general relevance for the practicing dermato-venereologist.
Refereed Serial

616   NE   ISSN 0929-0168
EUROPEAN ACADEMY OF DERMATOLOGY AND VENEREOLOGY. JOURNAL. SUPPLEMENT. Key Title: JEADV. Journal of the European Academy of Dermatology and Venereology. Supplement. (Text in English) 1992. irreg. Elsevier Science B.V., Books Division, P.O. Box 211, 1000 AE Amsterdam, Netherlands. TEL 31-20-4853911.
FAX 31-20-4853705.
E-mail: nlinfo-f@elsevier.nl; usinfo-f@elsevier.com; forinfo-kyf04035@niftyserve.or.jp; Site addr.: http://www.elsevier.nl/. (Subscr. in U.S. and Canada to: Elsevier Science Inc., Box 882, Madison Sq. Sta., New York, NY 10159-0882. TEL 212-989-5800. FAX 212-633-3680) **Document type:** monographic series.
Refereed Serial

616.5   IT   ISSN 1122-7672
                           CODEN: EPDDE
EUROPEAN JOURNAL OF PEDIATRIC DERMATOLOGY. Key Title: P D. European Journal of Pediatric Dermatology (English Ed.). Italian edition (ISSN 1122-7788) (Text in English) 1991. 4/yr. European Society for Pediatric Dermatology, Via C. Colombo 40, 70045 Torre a Mare (Bari), Italy. **Indexed:** Excerp.Med. (1991-). **Document type:** academic/scholarly publication.
  Supersedes (1982-1989): Pediatric Dermatology News (ISSN 1122-8644)

MEDICAL SCIENCES — DERMATOLOGY AND VENEREOLOGY

616.5 618.92   IT   ISSN 1122-7788
EUROPEAN JOURNAL OF PEDIATRIC DERMATOLOGY (EDIZIONE ITALIANA). Key Title: P D. European Journal of Pediatric Dermatology (Ed. Italiana). English edition (ISSN 1122-7672) 1991. 4/yr. European Society for Pediatric Dermatology, Via C. Colombo 40, 70045 Torre a Mare (Bari), Italy.
Supersedes (1982-1989): Bollettino di Dermatologia Pediatrica (ISSN 1122-5793)

616.5   UK   ISSN 0951-9785
EXCHANGE. 1976. q. £7. National Eczema Society, Tavistock House North, Tavistock Sq., London WC1H 9SR, England. TEL 01-388-4097. Ed. Freda Houlton. adv.; bk.rev. circ. 10,000.

616.5 616.95   DK   ISSN 0906-6705
CODEN: EXDEEY
EXPERIMENTAL DERMATOLOGY. (Text in English) 1992. 6/yr. DKK 1200 (effective 1996). Munksgaard International Publishers Ltd., 35 Noerre Soegade, P.O. Box 2148, DK-1016 Copenhagen K, Denmark. TEL 45-33-12-70-30. FAX 45-33-12093-87. Eds. T.A. Luger, G.L. Vejlsgaard. adv.; illus. (reprint service avail.) **Indexed:** Excerp.Med. (1993-), Ind.Med. (1994-). **Document type:** academic/scholarly publication.
—BLDSC (3839.070000); CASDDS; SWETS. **CCC.**
Refereed Serial

EXTRACTA DERMATOLOGICA; weltweit Auserlesen. see *MEDICAL SCIENCES — Abstracting, Bibliographies, Statistics*

616.5 616.95   US   ISSN 0071-7932
FORTSCHRITTE DER PRAKTISCHEN DERMATOLOGIE UND VENEROLOGIE. 1952. irreg. price varies. Springer-Verlag, 175 Fifth Ave., New York, NY 10010. TEL 212-460-1500. FAX 212-473-6272. (Also: Berlin, Heidelberg, Tokyo and Vienna) (reprint service avail. from ISI) **Document type:** monographic series.
—BLDSC (4023.055000).

616.951   UK   ISSN 0266-4348
CODEN: GEMEE2
GENITOURINARY MEDICINE; the journal of sexual health, STDs and HIV. 1925. bi-m. £136($237) B M J Publishing Group, B.M.A. House, Tavistock Sq., London WC1H 9JR, England. TEL 0171-383-3270. FAX 0171-383-6402. (N. American subscr. to: Box 480, Franklin, MA 02038. TEL 800-2-FON-BMJ. FAX 800-2-FAX-BMJ) Ed. A. Mindel. adv. contact: Sheila Rowe. bk.rev.; abstr.; charts; illus.; index. (also avail. in microform from UMI) **Indexed:** Abstr.Hyg., Biol.Abstr., Biotech.Abstr., Chem.Abstr., Curr.Adv.Ecol.Sci., Curr.Cont., Dent.Ind., Excerp.Med., Helminthol.Abstr., Ind.Med., Ind.Sci.Rev., Med.& Surg.Dermat., Protozool.Abstr., Rev.Plant Path., Sci.Cit.Ind., Trop.Dis.Bull. **Document type:** academic/scholarly publication.
●Also available online. Vendor(s): Ovid Technologies.
—BLDSC (4116.218000); ADONIS; CASDDS; Faxon; Genuine Article; SWETS; UMI; UnCover. **CCC.**
Former titles (until 1984): British Journal of Venereal Diseases (ISSN 0007-134X); Incorporates: International Union against the Venereal Diseases and the Treponematoses. Proceedings of Assemblies (ISSN 0074-9230)
Description: Presents an international forum for experts in the clinical, microbiological, immunological, behavioral, epidemiological, social, and historical aspects of sexually transmitted diseases.
Refereed Serial

616.5 618.92   IT   ISSN 1120-0499
GIORNALE INTERNAZIONALE DI DERMATOLOGIA PEDIATRICA. (Text in Italian; summaries in English) 1989. q. L.60000($60) C I C Edizioni Internazionali s.r.l., Via L. Spallanzani, 11, 00161 Rome, Italy. TEL 06-8412673. FAX 06-44242033. TELEX 622099 CIC I. Dir. F. Rantuccio.

616.5 616.951   IT   ISSN 0392-0488
CODEN: GIDVDZ
GIORNALE ITALIANO DI DERMATOLOGIA E VENEREOLOGIA. (Text in Italian; summaries in English, Italian) 1866. bi-m. $130 to individuals; institutions $160 (effective 1995). (Societa Italiana di Dermatologia e Venereologia) Edizioni Minerva Medica, Corso Bramante 83-85, 10126 Turin, Italy. TEL 39-11-678282. FAX 39-11-3121736. Ed. M. Pippione; Pub. Alberto Oliaro. adv.: B&W page $1300, color page $2200; trim 215 x 280; adv. contact: F. Filippo. abstr.; bibl.; charts; illus.; index; circ. 3,000 (paid). (also avail. in microform) **Indexed:** Biol.Abstr., C.I.S. Abstr., Chem.Abstr., Dent.Ind., Excerp.Med., Ind.Med., Med.& Surg.Dermat., Soils & Fert. **Document type:** academic/scholarly publication.
—BLDSC (4178.214000); CASDDS; EMDOCS; Faxon; SWETS.
Supersedes (in 1979): Giornale Italiano di Dermatologia. Minerva Dermatologica (ISSN 0300-1318); Which was formed by the 1969 merger of: Giornale Italiano di Dermatologia (ISSN 0376-0901); Minerva Dermatologica (ISSN 0026-4741); Which was formerly (until 1950): Dermosifilografo (ISSN 0366-886X); Cosmetologia.
Description: Covers dermatological and venereological biology, histology, clinical medicine and therapy.

HANSENOLOGIA INTERNATIONALIS. see *MEDICAL SCIENCES — Communicable Diseases*

616.5 616.95   GW   ISSN 0017-8470
CODEN: HAUTAW
DER HAUTARZT; Zeitschrift fuer Dermatologie, Allergologie, Venerologie und verwandte Gebiete. (Supplements avail.) (Text in German) 1950. 12/yr. DM.498($361) (effective 1996). Springer-Verlag, Heidelberger Platz 3, 14197 Berlin, Germany. TEL 030-8207-0. FAX 030-8214091. E-mail: orders@springer.de. (Subscr. in N. America to: Springer-Verlag New York, Inc., 44 Hartz Way, Secaucus, NJ 07096-2491. TEL 201-348-4033. FAX 201-348-4505) Ed.Bd. adv.; bk.rev.; illus.; index. (also avail. in microform from UMI; back issues avail.; reprint service avail. from ISI) **Indexed:** Biol.Abstr., Biotech.Abstr., Chem.Abstr., Curr.Adv.Cancer Res., Curr.Cont., Dent.Ind., Dok.Arbeitsmed., Excerp.Med., Ind.Med., Med.& Surg.Dermat., Nutr.Abstr., Protozool.Abstr., Rev.Med.& Vet.Mycol., Sci.Cit.Ind. **Document type:** academic/scholarly publication.
—BLDSC (4273.760000); CASDDS; Faxon; Genuine Article; SWETS; UMI. **CCC.**
Refereed Serial

616.5   GW   ISSN 0933-7385
HAUTFREUND. 1986. bi-m. DM.54. (Deutscher Neurodermitiker Bund e.V.) Verlag fuer Medizin Dr. Ewald Fischer GmbH, Fritz-Frey-Str. 21, 69121 Heidelberg, Germany. TEL 06221-4062-0. Ed. E. Ruge. circ. 5,650. (back issues avail.) **Document type:** academic/scholarly publication.

616.5   GW   ISSN 0930-7109
HAUTNAH; Dermatologie aus der Praxis. (Text in German; summaries in English and German) 1985. bi-m. DM.94. Medi-A-Derm Verlag GmbH, Heidenkampsweg 74, 20097 Hamburg, Germany. TEL 040-232334. FAX 040-230292. Ed. Michael Friedrich. adv. contact: Michael Friedrich. bk.rev. circ. 7,800. **Document type:** academic/scholarly publication.

616.5   JA
HIFU SHIKKAN SAISHIN NO CHIRYO. (Text in Japanese) 1987. biennial. 7000 Yen per no. Nankodo Co., Ltd., 42-6-Hongo 3-chome, Bunkyo-ku, Tokyo 113, Japan.

616.5   US
ICHTHYOSIS FOCUS. 1981. q. $35 membership. Foundation for Ichthyosis and Related Skin Types, Inc., Box 20921, Raleigh, NC 27619-0921. TEL 800-545-3286. Ed. Nicholas Gattuccio. circ. 2,500. (back issues avail.) **Document type:** newsletter.
Description: Provides information on rare skin diseases for patients, physicians and health workers.

616.5 616.951   II   ISSN 0378-6323
CODEN: IJDLDY
INDIAN JOURNAL OF DERMATOLOGY, VENEREOLOGY AND LEPROLOGY. (Text in English) 1935. bi-m. Rs.500($100) (effective 1996). Indian Association of Dermatologists, Venereologists and Leprologists, c/o Dr. Gurmohan Singh, Ed., New D-7, Banaras Hindu University, Varanasi 221 005, India. TEL 0542-310845. adv. contact: S.S. Pawdey. bk.rev.; charts; illus.; stat.; index. circ. 2,000. (also avail. in microform from UMI; reprint service avail. from UMI) **Indexed:** Biol.Abstr., Chem.Abstr., Excerp.Med., ExtraMED, Indian Sci.Abstr., Rev.Plant Path. **Document type:** academic/scholarly publication.
●Also available on CD-ROM.
—BLDSC (4411.610000); Faxon; UMI; UnCover.
Supersedes (in 1976): Indian Journal of Dermatology and Venereology (ISSN 0019-5162)

616.5   CN   ISSN 0011-9059
RL1   CODEN: IJDEBB
INTERNATIONAL JOURNAL OF DERMATOLOGY. 1962. m. $118 to individuals (outside US & Canada $139); institutions $155 (outside US & Canada $182) (effective 1996). (International Society of Dermatology: Tropical, Geographic, and Ecologic) Decker Periodicals, P.O. Box 820, LCD 1, Hamilton, ON L8N 3K7, Canada. TEL 905-522-7017; 800-568-7281. E-mail: decker@io.org. (U.S. addr.: Box 785, Lewiston, NY 14092-0785) Ed. Dr. Lawrence C. Parish. adv.; illus.; index. circ. 9,714. (also avail. in microform from UMI) **Indexed:** Biol.Abstr., Chem.Abstr., Curr.Adv.Ecol.Sci., Curr.Cont., Dent.Ind., Dok.Arbeitsmed., Excerp.Med., Helminthol.Abstr., Ind.Med., Ind.Sci.Rev., INIS Atomind., Med.& Surg.Dermat., NRN, Protozool.Abstr., Rev.Med.& Vet.Mycol., Sci.Cit.Ind., SSCI. **Document type:** academic/scholarly publication.
—BLDSC (4542.185000); CASDDS; Faxon; Genuine Article; SWETS; UMI; UnCover. **CCC.**
Formerly: Dermatologia Internationalis.
Refereed Serial

616.5   IT   ISSN 0021-292X
ITALIAN GENERAL REVIEW OF DERMATOLOGY. (Text in English and Italian) vol.10, 1970. q. $60. (Centro Servizi Segreteria) Sigred S.r.l., Via Lapini 1, 50136 Florence, Italy. TEL 39-55670369. FAX 3955-660236. Ed. E. Panconesi. adv.; bk.rev.; abstr.; charts; illus. circ. 3,300. **Indexed:** Excerp.Med., Ind.Med.
—Faxon.

616.5   JA   ISSN 0021-4973
JAPANESE JOURNAL OF CLINICAL DERMATOLOGY/RINSHO HIFUKA. (Text in Japanese) 1946. m. 30330 Yen($233) Igaku-Shoin Ltd., 5-24-3 Hongo, Bunkyo-ku, Tokyo 113-91, Japan. TEL 03-817-5716. Ed. Yoshio Sato. circ. 3,500.
—BLDSC (4651.373000).

616.5   JA   ISSN 0021-499X
CODEN: NHKZAD
JAPANESE JOURNAL OF DERMATOLOGY: SERIES A. Key Title: Nihon Hifuka Gakkai Zasshi. (Text in Japanese) 1901. m. 7000 Yen. Japanese Dermatological Association - Nihon Hifuka Gakkai, Taisei Bldg., 14-10 Hongo 3-chome, Bunkyo-ku, Tokyo 113, Japan. Dir. M. Takenouchi. bk.rev.; charts; illus.; index. **Indexed:** Biol.Abstr., Chem.Abstr., Dent.Ind., Ind.Med., Rev.Med.& Vet.Mycol.
Document type: academic/scholarly publication.
—BLDSC (4651.550000); CASDDS.
Former titles (until 1957): Hifuka Seibyoka Zasshi (ISSN 0368-3524); (until 1942): Hifuka Hinyokika Zasshi (ISSN 0368-2846)

616.5   GW   ISSN 0932-8661
JATROS DERMATOLOGIE. 1987. 12/yr. DM.90. P M I Verlagsgruppe GmbH, August-Schanz-Str. 21, 60433 Frankfurt a.M., Germany. TEL 069-5480000. FAX 069-54800077. TELEX 412952-PMI-D. Ed. Peter Hoffmann. circ. 3,000. (back issues avail.) **Document type:** academic/scholarly publication.
Description: A seminar paper journal containing summaries of dermatologic articles, interviews and Congress reports.

MEDICAL SCIENCES — DERMATOLOGY AND VENEREOLOGY

616.5 FR ISSN 1167-1122
CODEN: EJDEE4
JOURNAL EUROPEEN DE DERMATOLOGIE/EUROPEAN JOURNAL OF DERMATOLOGY. (Text in English) 1991. 8/yr. 100 F. to individuals; institutions 1700 F.; students 500 F. (effective 1995). John Libbey Eurotext, 127 av de la Republique, 92120 Montrouge, France. TEL 1-46-73-06-60. FAX 1-40-84-09-99. (Subscr. to: A T E I, 23-25 rue Fernand Combette, 93100 Montreuil sous Bois, France. TEL 48-59-58-11. FAX 48-59-57-99) Ed. Jean Thivolet. **Indexed:** Curr.Cont., Excerp.Med. (1993-). **Document type:** academic/scholarly publication.
—BLDSC (3668.416000); CASDDS; Genuine Article; SWETS.
Description: Provides up-to-date information and works in all fields of dermatology and skin biology.

616.5 IT ISSN 0392-8543
CODEN: JACOEL
JOURNAL OF APPLIED COSMETICS; quarterly review of cosmetic dermatology. 1983. q. $60. International Ediemme, Via Innocenzo XI, 41, 00165 Rome, Italy. TEL 39378788. Ed. P. Morganti. adv.; bk.rev. circ. 5,000. **Indexed:** Excerp.Med.
—BLDSC (4942.380000); CASDDS; Ei; SWETS.

616.5 DK ISSN 0303-6987
CODEN: JCUPBN
JOURNAL OF CUTANEOUS PATHOLOGY. (Text and summaries in English) 1974. bi-m. DKK 980 to individuals; institutions DKK 1800 (incl. supplements) (effective 1996). (American Society for Dermatopathology, US) Munksgaard International Publishers Ltd., 35 Noerre Soegade, P.O. Box 2148, DK-1016 Copenhagen K, Denmark. TEL 33-127030. FAX 33-129387. Ed. Philip Cooper. adv.; bibl.; charts; illus. circ. 1,800. (reprint service avail. from ISI) **Indexed:** Biol.Abstr., Chem.Abstr., Curr.Adv.Biochem., Curr.Cont., Dent.Ind., Excerp.Med., Helminthol.Abstr., Ind.Med., Ind.Sci.Rev., INIS Atomind., Med.& Surg.Dermat., Nutr.Abstr., Rev.Plant Path., Sci.Cit.Ind.
—BLDSC (4965.960000); Faxon; Genuine Article; SWETS; UnCover. **CCC.**
Refereed Serial

616.5 IE ISSN 0923-1811
CODEN: JDSCEI
JOURNAL OF DERMATOLOGICAL SCIENCE. (Text in English) 1990. bi-m. I£280($442) (effective 1996). (Japanese Society for Investigative Dermatology, JA) Elsevier Science Ireland Ltd., P.O. Box 85, Limerick, Ireland. TEL 353-61-471944. FAX 353-61-472144. (Subscr. in U.S. and Canada to: Elsevier Science Inc., Box 882, Madion Sq. Sta., New York, NY 10159. TEL 212-989-5800. FAX 212-633-3990) Ed. Hideoki Ogawa. adv.; bk.rev. circ. 1,500. (back issues avail.) **Indexed:** Biol.Abstr., Excerp.Med., Ind.Med., Med.& Surg.Dermat. **Document type:** academic/scholarly publication.
—BLDSC (4968.766500); CASDDS; SWETS. **CCC.**
Description: Publishes manuscripts covering the entire scope of dermatology, from molecular studies to clinical investigations.
Refereed Serial

616.5 UK ISSN 0954-6634
CODEN: JDTREY
JOURNAL OF DERMATOLOGICAL TREATMENT. 1989. 4/yr. £60 to individuals; institutions £120. Stockton Press (Subsidiary of: Macmillan Press Ltd.), Houndmills, Basingstoke, Hants RG21 2XS, England. TEL 01256-817245. FAX 01256-28339. (Co-publisher: Martin Dunitz Ltd.) Ed. Richard Marks. adv. contact: Michael Rowley. **Indexed:** Excerp.Med., Med.& Surg.Dermat. **Document type:** academic/scholarly publication.
—BLDSC (4968.767000); Faxon; SWETS; UMI. **CCC.**
Description: All aspects of the treatment of skin disorders.

616.5 JA ISSN 0385-2407
CODEN: JDMYAG
JOURNAL OF DERMATOLOGY. (Text in English) 1974. m. Japanese Dermatological Association - Nihon Hifuka Gakkai, Taisei Bldg., 14-10 Hongo 3-chome, Bunkyo-ku, Tokyo 113, Japan. TEL 3-3811-5099. Dir. M. Takenouchi. bk.rev.; charts; illus.; index. **Indexed:** Biol.Abstr., Chem.Abstr., Dent.Ind., Excerp.Med., Ind.Med., Med.& Surg.Dermat., Rev.Med.& Vet.Mycol. **Document type:** academic/scholarly publication.
—BLDSC (4968.770000); CASDDS; Faxon; SWETS.
Supersedes (1963-1972): Japanese Journal of Dermatology: Series B (ISSN 0368-282X)

JOURNAL OF GERIATRIC DERMATOLOGY. see *GERONTOLOGY AND GERIATRICS*

616.5 US ISSN 0022-202X
RL1 CODEN: JIDEAE
JOURNAL OF INVESTIGATIVE DERMATOLOGY. 1938. m. $360 to institutions (foreign $420) (effective 1996). (Society of Investigative Dermatology, Inc.) Blackwell Science Inc., 238 Main St., Cambridge, MA 02142. TEL 617-876-7022; 800-759-6102. FAX 617-492-5263. (Co-sponsor: European Society for Dermatological Research) Ed. Dr. David Norris. adv.; bk.rev.; bibl.; illus.; index. circ. 4,800. (also avail. in microform from WWS) **Indexed:** Abstr.Hyg., Biol.Abstr., Biotech.Abstr., C.I.S. Abstr., Chem.Abstr., Curr.Adv.Biochem., Curr.Adv.Cancer Res., Curr.Adv.Cell & Devel.Biol., Curr.Adv.Ecol.Sci., Curr.Adv.Genetics & Molec.Biol., Curr.Cont., Dent.Ind., Excerp.Med., I.P.A., Ind.Med., Ind.Sci.Rev., Ind.Vet., INIS Atomind., Med.& Surg.Dermat., Nutr.Abstr., Pig News & Info., Sci.Cit.Ind., Small Anim.Abstr., Vet.Bull. **Document type:** academic/scholarly publication.
●Also available online.
—BLDSC (5008.000000); ADONIS; CASDDS; EMDOCS; Faxon; Genuine Article; SWETS; UnCover. **CCC.**
Description: Presents original papers and reviews pertinent to the normal and abnormal function of the skin.
Refereed Serial

616.5 UK ISSN 0965-206X
JOURNAL OF TISSUE VIABILITY. 1981. q. £20 (outside the E.C. £30); hospitals £50; corporate £110. Tissue Viability Society, c/o Wessex Rehabilitation Association, Salisbury District Hospital, Salisbury, Wilts. SP2 8BJ, England. TEL 01722-336262. FAX 01722-325904. Ed. K.S. Gebhardt. adv.; page £140; adv. contact: J. Gisby. bk.rev. (back issues avail.) **Document type:** academic/scholarly publication.
—BLDSC (5069.540000).
Formerly (until 1991): Care - Science and Practice (ISSN 0268-0009)
Refereed Serial

JOURNAL OF TOXICOLOGY. CUTANEOUS AND OCULAR TOXICOLOGY. see *PHARMACY AND PHARMACOLOGY*

616.5 KO ISSN 0494-4739
CODEN: TPKCAW
KOREAN JOURNAL OF DERMATOLOGY/TAEHAN P'IBU KWAHAKHOE CHI. (Text mainly in Korean, occasionally in English; contents and summaries in English) 1960. bi-m. 40000 Won($50) Korean Dermatological Association - Taehan P'ibu Kwahakhoe, No. 401, Sindonga Jonghap-Sangka, 1334, Seocho-dong, Seocho-ku, Seoul 137-070, S. Korea. TEL 02-567-0284. FAX 02-552-4203. Ed. Hyung-Ok Kim. adv.; bk.rev.; bibl.; charts. circ. 900. (back issues avail.) **Indexed:** Biol.Abstr., Chem.Abstr., Excerp.Med. **Document type:** academic/scholarly publication.
—BLDSC (5113.530000); CASDDS.

616.5 IT
LEXICON VEVY EUROPE SKIN CARE INSTANT REPORTS. 1984. 4/yr. free to qualified personnel. Vevy Europe S.p.A., Casella Postale 81570, 16131 Genoa, Italy. TEL 39-10-5221515. FAX 39-10-5221530. TELEX 281257 VEVY I. E-mail: vevy001@it.net. (Co-sponsor: Skin Applied Sciences Associates) Ed. Dr. Giorgio Rialdi. bk.rev.; circ. 12,900 (controlled). **Document type:** trade publication.
Formerly (until 1989): Lexicon Vevy Skin Care Instant Reports.
Description: Contains international information on dermo-pharmaceutics, cosmetics and toiletries.

616.5 CC ISSN 1000-4963
LINCHUANG PIFUKE ZAZHI/JOURNAL OF CLINICAL DERMATOLOGY. (Text in Chinese, abstracts in English) 1972. bi-m. $30. Jiangsu Sheng Renmin Yiyuan - Jiangsu People's Hospital, 300 Guangzhou Lu, Nanjing, Jiangsu 210029, People's Republic of China. TEL 8625-303836. FAX 8625-6612555. Ed. Zhao Bian. adv.; bk.rev. circ. 20,000. **Indexed:** ExtraMED, Rev.Med.& Vet.Mycol. **Document type:** academic/scholarly publication.
●Also available on CD-ROM.
—BLDSC (4958.391000).
Description: Contains original papers on clinical and laboratory studies, therapies, case reports and reviews.

MEDICAL & SURGICAL DERMATOLOGY; a critical guide to world literature. see *MEDICAL SCIENCES — Abstracting, Bibliographies, Statistics*

611 SP ISSN 0210-5187
MEDICINA CUTANEA IBERO-LATINO-AMERICANA. 1973. 8/yr. 10500 ptas.($111) (effective 1995). (Colegio Ibero-Latino-Americano de Dermatologia, AG) Editorial Garsi, S.A., Juan Bravo 46, 28006 Madrid, Spain. TEL 34-1-4021212. FAX 34-1-4020954. (Subscr. to: Prof. Jose M. Mascaro, Casanova 143, Barcelona 36, Spain) Ed. Jose Maria Mascaro. adv.; bk.rev. circ. 3,000. **Indexed:** Biol.Abstr., Dent.Ind., Excerp.Med., Ind.Med., Med.& Surg.Dermat. **Document type:** academic/scholarly publication.
—Faxon.
Formed by the merger of: Medicina Cutanea (ISSN 0025-7788); Dermatologia Ibero Latino-Americano (ISSN 0011-9040)

616.5 BL
MEDISOM: DERMATOLOGY. 1982. bi-m. $90. Editora Medisom, Ltda., Rua Sao Paulino 224, Caixa Postal 7650, 01064-970 Sao Paulo, Brazil. FAX 55-11-572-5957. Ed. Dr. Philip Querido. adv. (audio cassette)

616.5 616.99 US
MELANOMA LETTER. q. $25 donation. Skin Cancer Foundation, 245 Fifth Ave., Ste. 2402, New York, NY 10016. TEL 212-725-5176. FAX 212-725-5751. Ed. Joyce Weisbach Ayoub. **Document type:** bulletin, newsletter.
Description: Features articles by prominent medical authorities to inform health care professionals of the latest advances in melanoma research and treatment.

616.5 SP ISSN 0214-4735
CODEN: MONDE4
MONOGRAFIAS DE DERMATOLOGIA. 7/yr. 8500 ptas. to individuals; institutions 10000 ptas; foreign 18500 ptas.($185). Grupo Aula Medica, S.A., C.I. Venecia 2, Alfa III, Isabel Colbrana, s-n, 28050 Madrid, Spain. TEL 34-1-3588657. FAX 34-1-3589067. Ed. J.A. Ruiz. adv. contact: J.A. de la Fuente. **Indexed:** Excerp.Med. **Document type:** monographic series.
—BLDSC (5912.655500).

616.5 616.4 646.7 US ISSN 0894-1769
NATIONAL ALOPECIA AREATA FOUNDATION NEWSLETTER. 1981. bi-m. $35. National Alopecia Areata Foundation, 710 C St., Ste. 11, San Rafael, CA 94901. TEL 415-456-4644. FAX 415-456-4274. Ed. Vicki Kalabokes. adv. circ. 6,000. (back issues avail.) **Document type:** newsletter.

616.5 US ISSN 8756-2243
RL321
NATIONAL PSORIASIS FOUNDATION. ANNUAL REPORT. a. donation. National Psoriasis Foundation, 6600 S.W. 92nd Ave., Ste. 300, Portland, OR 97223. TEL 503-244-7404. FAX 503-245-0626. Ed. Sheri Decker. circ. 33,000. **Document type:** corporate report.
Description: Provides a summary of the foundation's major activities, programs, and research involvement, in addition to financial statements.

616.5 US ISSN 1040-0060
NATIONAL PSORIASIS FOUNDATION. BULLETIN. 1968. bi-m. donation. National Psoriasis Foundation, 6600 S.W. 92nd Ave., Ste. 300, Portland, OR 97223. TEL 503-244-7404. FAX 503-245-0626. Ed. Serith Decker. circ. 33,000. **Document type:** bulletin.
Description: Provides information on psoriasis treatments and includes news of the Foundation's research and activities.

MEDICAL SCIENCES — DERMATOLOGY AND VENEREOLOGY

NETWORK (DURHAM). see *BIRTH CONTROL*

616.5   JA   ISSN 0386-9784
CODEN: NNHIAN
NISHINIHON JOURNAL OF DERMATOLOGY/NISHINIHON HIFUKA. (Text in Japanese; summaries in English) 1933. bi-m. 8000 Yen. Kyushu University, Faculty of Medicine, Department of Dermatology, Maidashi 3-1-1, Higashi-ku, Fukuoka 812, Japan. TEL 81-92-641-1151. FAX 81-92-651-0165. Ed. Yoshiaki Hori. adv.; bk.rev.; bibl.; charts; illus. circ. 3,500. **Indexed:** Biol.Abstr., Chem.Abstr., Excerp.Med., Ind.Med. **Document type:** academic/scholarly publication.
—BLDSC (6113.603000).
    Supersedes in part: Dermatology and Urology - Hifu to Hinyo (ISSN 0011-9091)

616   FR   ISSN 0752-5370
CODEN: NODEE
NOUVELLES DERMATOLOGIQUES. 1982. bi-m. Presse Communication Intercontinental Medecine, 2 Place Golbery, 6700 Strasbourg, France. TEL 88604600. **Indexed:** Excerp.Med. (1994-).
—BLDSC (6176.762000).

616.5   US   ISSN 0000-1422
RL43
OFFICIAL AMERICAN BOARD OF MEDICAL SPECIALTIES (A B M S) DIRECTORY OF BOARD CERTIFIED DERMATOLOGISTS. 1984. biennial. $99.95. Marquis Who's Who, A Reed Reference Publishing company, 121 Chanlon Rd., New Providence, NJ 07974. TEL 908-464-6800. FAX 908-665-2898. (Subscr. to: Order Dept., Box 31, New Providence, NJ 0794-9903. TEL 800-521-8110) Ed. Roy Crego. **Document type:** directory.
    Formerly (until 1992): A B M S Directory of Certified Dermatologists (ISSN 0884-1489)
    Description: Biographical sketches of U.S. certified medical specialists sorted alphabetically with a geographical index.

P A S C A L E 73: DERMATOLOGIE. MALADIES SEXUELLEMENT TRANSMISSIBLES. see *MEDICAL SCIENCES — Abstracting, Bibliographies, Statistics*

616.5   SW   ISSN 0345-9616
P S O AKTUELLT. 1963. q. SEK 100 (effective 1991). Svenska Psoriasisfoerbundet, Roekerigatan 19, 121 62 Johanneshov, Sweden. TEL 08-6003636. FAX 08-6002284. Ed. Gunilla Qwerin Helling. adv.; bk.rev. circ. 20,000.

PARAPHARMEX. see *PHARMACY AND PHARMACOLOGY*

616.5 618.92   US   ISSN 0736-8046
PEDIATRIC DERMATOLOGY. 1983. bi-m. $285 (foreign $315) (effective 1996). (Society for Pediatric Dermatology) Blackwell Science Inc., 238 Main St., Cambridge, MA 02142-1413. TEL 617-876-7022. FAX 617-492-5263. (Co-sponsor: International Society of Pediatric Dermatology) Eds. Drs. N. Esterly, Lawrence M. Solomon. adv.; bk.rev. circ. 1,300. **Indexed:** Ind.Med., Med.& Surg.Dermat. **Document type:** academic/scholarly publication.
—BLDSC (6417.582000); Faxon; Genuine Article; SWETS; UMI; UnCover. **CCC.**
    Refereed Serial

616.5   SZ   ISSN 1011-291X
CODEN: PHSKEY
PHARMACOLOGY AND THE SKIN. (Text in English) 1987. irreg. price varies. S. Karger AG, Allschwilerstr. 10, P.O. Box, CH-4009 Basel, Switzerland. TEL 061-3061111. FAX 061-3061234. E-mail: Karger@Karger.ch. Eds. B. Shroot, H. Schaefer. **Document type:** academic/scholarly publication.
—BLDSC (6447.061500); CASDDS. **CCC.**
    Description: Spotlights topics at the center of interest in skin pharmacology.
    Refereed Serial

616.5 615   US
PHARMACY NEWS; a consumer newsletter to advance awareness while saving time and money. 1989. 3/yr. membership. National Psoriasis Foundation, 6600 S.W. 92nd Ave., Ste. 300, Portland, OR 97223. TEL 503-244-7404. FAX 503-245-0626. Ed. Sherith Decker. adv. **Document type:** newsletter, catalog.
    Description: Contains articles on psoriasis treatment and new product reviews. Includes a catalog of products from Medic Pharmacy available to members.

616.5   DK   ISSN 0905-4383
CODEN: PPPHEW
PHOTODERMATOLOGY, PHOTOIMMUNOLOGY & PHOTOMEDICINE. (Text and summaries in English) 1984. bi-m. DKK 1200 (effective 1996). Munksgaard International Publishers Ltd., 35 Noerre Soegade, P.O. Box 2148, DK-1016 Copenhagen K, Denmark. TEL 33-127030. FAX 33-129387. Ed. Paul Bergstresser. adv.; bk.rev.; illus. circ. 600. **Indexed:** Chem.Abstr., Curr.Adv.Ecol.Sci., Curr.Cont., Excerp.Med., Ind.Med.
—BLDSC (6465.991500); CASDDS; Faxon; Genuine Article; SWETS; UnCover. **CCC.**
    Formerly: Photodermatology (ISSN 0108-9684)
    Refereed Serial

616.5   SP   ISSN 0213-9251
PIEL. 1986. m. (10/yr.) 6700 ptas.($57) (free to qualified personnel). Ediciones Doyma, S.A., Travesera de Gracia, 17-21, 08021 Barcelona, Spain. TEL 34-1-200-07-11. FAX 34-1-209-11-36. TELEX 51964 INK-E. Dir. Carlos Ferrandiz Foraster. adv.: page 230000 ptas.; trim 210 x 280; adv. contact: Anna Pahissa. circ. 3,500. (reprint service avail. from UMI) **Indexed:** Ind.Med.Esp.
    Description: Offers articles for the continuing education of physicians concerned with dermatology.

616.5   US   ISSN 0033-0639
PROGRESS IN DERMATOLOGY.* 1966. 4/yr. membership. Dermatology Foundation, 1560 Sherman Ave., Ste. 302, Evanston, IL 60201-4802. Ed. Dr. Thomas Lawley. adv.; circ. 3,000 (controlled). (looseleaf format)

616.5   PL   ISSN 0033-2526
CODEN: PRDEA7
PRZEGLAD DERMATOLOGICZNY. (Text in Polish; summaries in English) 1959. bi-m. $120. (Polskie Towarzystwo Dermatologiczne) Sanmedica, Nowy Zjazd 1, Warsaw, Poland. TEL 48-22-215180. FAX 48-22-215180. (Dist. by: Ars Polona-Ruch, Krakowskie Przedmiescie 7, Warsaw, Poland) Ed. Maria Blaszczyk. bk.rev.; abstr.; charts; illus.; index. **Indexed:** Biol.Abstr., Chem.Abstr., Dent.Ind., Dok.Arbeitsmed., Excerp.Med., Ind.Med., Rev.Med.& Vet.Mycol.
—BLDSC (6939.700000); CASDDS; EMDOCS.
    Description: Addresses skin problems and sexually transmitted diseases.

616.5   GW   ISSN 0931-1521
PSO MAGAZIN. 1973. 6/yr. membership. Deutscher Psoriasis Bund e.V., Oberaltenallee 20a, 22081 Hamburg, Germany. TEL 040-2270985. FAX 040-2270986. Ed. Peter Dlugi. adv. **Document type:** academic/scholarly publication.
    Formerly: Psoriasis Magazin.

616.5   AT
PSORI NEWSLETTER. 1979. bi-m. membership. Psoriasis Association of Victoria, Inc., P.O. Box 1151, Glen Waverley, Vic. 3150, Australia. TEL 61-3-6635983. FAX 61-3-6393575. Ed. Helen McNair. circ. 500. (back issues avail.) **Document type:** newsletter.
    Formerly (until 1986): Skin and Psoriasis Newsletter (ISSN 1030-7257)
    Description: Articles by dermatologists directed to the general public.

616.5   US
PSORIASIS NEWSLETTER. 1980. s-a. free. Psoriasis Research Institute, 600 Town and Country Village, Palo Alto, CA 94301-2326. TEL 415-326-1848. FAX 415-326-1262. E-mail: 71162.1233@compuserve.com. Ed. Dr. Warren Gibson. circ. 14,000. **Document type:** newsletter.
    Description: Reports research advances in the field of dermatology relevant to psoriasis. Directed to the general public.

616.526   DK   ISSN 0909-2757
PSORIASIS NYT. 1974. q. Danmarks Psoriasis Forening, Copenhagen, Denmark.
    Formerly (until Aug., 1992): Dansk Psoriasis Tidsskrift (ISSN 0105-0370)

616.5   IT   ISSN 0033-9490
CODEN: RDSIAI
RASSEGNA DI DERMATOLOGIA E SIFILOGRAFIA. 1948. s-a. L.30000 (foreign L.60000) (effective 1994). Casa Editrice Maccari, Via Trento, 53, 43100 Parma, Italy. FAX 039-521-771268. circ. 1,200. **Indexed:** Excerp.Med. 1994-). **Document type:** academic/scholarly publication.
—EMDOCS.

REFERATOVY VYBER Z DERMATOVENEROLOGIE/ABSTRACTS OF DERMATOLOGY AND VENEROLOGY. see *MEDICAL SCIENCES — Abstracting, Bibliographies, Statistics*

REVISTA DE MEDICINA INTERNA, NEUROLOGIE, PSIHIATRIE, NEURO-CHIRURGIE, DERMATO-VENEROLOGIE. SERIES NEUROLOGIE, PSIHIATRIE, NEUROCHIRUGIE. see *MEDICAL SCIENCES — Psychiatry And Neurology*

616.9   JA
S T D: JAPANESE JOURNAL OF THE SEXUALLY TRANSMITTED DISEASES. (Text in Japanese) 1921. q. 2000 Yen. Japanese Association for the Prevention of Venereal Diseases - Nihon Seibyo Yobo Kyokai, 3-14-10 Hongo, Bunkyo-ku, Tokyo 113, Japan. FAX 03-3814-4117. Ed. Tadao Niijima. adv.; stat. circ. 880. **Document type:** academic/scholarly publication.
    Formerly (until vol.64, 1983): V D: Japanese Journal of Venereal Diseases.

616.5   US   ISSN 0278-145X
CODEN: SDERDN
SEMINARS IN DERMATOLOGY. 1982. q. $138 (foreign $177) (effective 1996). W.B. Saunders Co. (Subsidiary of: Harcourt Brace & Company), Curtis Center, 3rd Fl., Independence Sq. W., Philadelphia, PA 19106-3399. TEL 215-238-7800. FAX 215-238-6445. (Subscr. to: Periodicals Fulfillment, W.B. Saunders Co., 6277 Sea Harbor Dr., 4th Fl., Orlando, FL 32891-4800. TEL 800-654-2452. FAX 800-874-6418) Ed. Dr. Howard I. Maibach; Pub. Joan W. Blumberg. adv.: B&W page $760, color page $1710; 7 x 10. bibl.; charts; illus.; stat.; index. (also avail. in microform from UMI; back issues avail.) **Indexed:** ASCA, Curr.Cont., Med.& Surg.Dermat. **Document type:** academic/scholarly publication.
    ●Also available online.
—BLDSC (8239.448800); Faxon; Genuine Article; SWETS; UMI; UnCover. **CCC.**
    Description: Each issue focuses on a single aspect of the field from several angles as it applies to daily practice.

616.951   US   ISSN 0148-5717
RC201.A1   CODEN: STRDDM
SEXUALLY TRANSMITTED DISEASES. 1974. bi-m. $150 to individuals (foreign $160); institutions $200 (foreign $245) (effective 1996); newsstand price: $42. (American Venereal Disease Association) Lippincott - Raven Publishers, 227 E. Washington Sq., Philadelphia, PA 19106. TEL 215-238-4200. Ed. Julius Schachter; Pub. Marcia E. Serepy. adv. contact: Susan Eidson. illus.; index. circ. 1,578. **Indexed:** Chem.Abstr., CINAHL, Curr.Adv.Ecol.Sci., Curr.Cont., Dent.Ind., Excerp.Med. (1993-), Helminthol.Abstr., Ind.Med., Med.& Surg.Dermat., Sci.Cit.Ind., SSCI.
    ●Also available online. Vendor(s): Lexis-Nexis, Ovid Technologies.
—BLDSC (8254.486500); Faxon; Genuine Article; SWETS; UMI; UnCover. **CCC.**
    Formerly: American Venereal Disease Association. Journal (ISSN 0095-148X)
    Refereed Serial

616.5   US   ISSN 0037-6337
CODEN: SKANB4
SKIN & ALLERGY NEWS. 1970. m. $70. International Medical News Group, 12230 Wilkins Ave., Rockville, MD 20852. TEL 301-816-8700. Ed. Richard Camer. adv.; bk.rev. circ. 17,500. (tabloid format; also avail. in microform from UMI) **Document type:** newspaper.
—BLDSC (8295.910000); UMI.

SKIN CANCER FOUNDATION JOURNAL. see *MEDICAL SCIENCES — Oncology*

616.5   US   ISSN 0898-6525
SKIN INC; business and science for skin care professionals. 1988. 6/yr. $46 (Canada $54; elsewhere $72) (effective until Aug.31, 1996). Allured Publishing, 362 S. Schmale Rd., Carol Stream, IL 60188-2787. TEL 708-653-2155. FAX 708-653-2192. TELEX 910-253-2133. Ed. Jean Allured. adv.; bk.rev.; index. circ. 15,000. (back issues avail.) **Document type:** trade publication.
    Description: For the aesthetician and skin care professional. Includes treatments, physiology and business articles.

SKIN PHARMACOLOGY. see *PHARMACY AND PHARMACOLOGY*

MEDICAL SCIENCES — ENDOCRINOLOGY

616.5   JA   ISSN 0018-1390
CODEN: HIFUAG
SKIN RESEARCH/HIFU. (Text in Japanese; summaries in English) 1959. bi-m. 5000 Yen($35) Osaka Dermatological Association - Nihon Hifukagakkai Osaka Chihokai, c/o Osaka University School of Medicine, Dept. of Dermatology, 1-1-50 Fukushima, Fukushima-ku, Osaka 553, Japan. Ed. Dr. Minoru Yasuhara. adv.; index. circ. 1,050. **Indexed:** Biol.Abstr., Chem.Abstr., INIS Atomind.
—BLDSC (8295.940000); CASDDS.

616.5   DK
▼**SKIN RESEARCH AND TECHNOLOGY.** (Text in English) 1995. q. DKK 900 (effective 1996). Munksgaard International Publishers Ltd., 35 Noerre Soegade, P.O. Box 1248, DK-1016 Copenhagen K, Denmark. TEL 45-33-12-70-30. FAX 45-33-12-93-87. E-mail: fsub@mail.munksgaard.dk.

616.5   SA   ISSN 1015-8782
SOUTHERN AFRICAN JOURNAL OF EPIDEMIOLOGY AND INFECTION. 1982. q. R.100 (effective 1995 & 1996). P.O. Box 1038, Johannesburg 2000, South Africa. TEL 27-11-4899021. FAX 27-11-4899012. (Co-sponsors: Epidemiological Society of Southern Africa; Infections Diseases Society of Southern Africa; Sexually Transmitted Diseases Society of Southern Africa; South African Institute for Medical Research) Ed. H.J. Koornhoff. adv.; bk.rev.; charts; illus. circ. 1,800. (back issues avail.) **Document type:** academic/scholarly publication.
—BLDSC (8352.592000).
Incorporates: Southern African Journal of Sexually Transmitted Diseases.
Description: Contains articles on infectious diseases, sexually transmitted diseases and epidemiology.
Refereed Serial

616.5   IT   ISSN 1121-1946
CODEN: GSDOE
GLI SPECIALIZZATI OGGI - DERMATOLOGIA. 1986. q. L.25000. E S I Stampa Medica s.r.l., Casella Postale 42, Lgo. Volontari del Sangue 10, 20097 S. Donato, Milan, Italy. TEL 39-2-5274241. FAX 39-2-55600670. TELEX 324894. Ed. Diego Onestinghel. adv.: B&W page L.5200000, color page L.6800000; trim 162 x 242; adv. contact: Ornella Galbiati. bk.rev. circ. 8,700. **Indexed:** Excerp.Med.
—BLDSC (8404.918500).
Formerly (until 1992): Dermatologia Oggi (ISSN 0394-2503)

616.5   US
SUN & SKIN NEWS. q. $25 donation. Skin Cancer Foundation, 245 Fifth Ave., Ste. 2402, New York, NY 10016. TEL 212-725-5176. FAX 212-725-5751. Ed. Joyce Weisbach Ayoub. **Document type:** newsletter.
Description: Alerts the general public on sun protection, skin health, and skin cancer prevention and treatment.

668.5 616.5   GW   ISSN 0939-0448
CODEN: TWDEEM
T W DERMATOLOGIE; Fachzeitschrift fuer kosmetische Dermatologie. 1971. 6/yr. DM.74 (foreign DM.100). Verlag G. Braun GmbH, Karl-Friedrich-Str. 14-18, 76133 Karlsruhe, Germany. TEL 0721-165-0. FAX 0721-165191. TELEX 7826904-VGB-D. circ. 5,000. **Indexed:** Chem.Abstr., Excerp.Med. (until 1988; 1994-). **Document type:** trade publication.
—BLDSC (9076.749000); CASDDS.
Former titles: Aerztliche Kosmetologie (ISSN 0340-5702); Kosmetologie.

TOILETRIES, FRAGRANCES AND SKIN CARE: THE ROSE SHEET. see BEAUTY CULTURE — Perfumes And Cosmetics

616.5   TU
TURKISH JOURNAL OF DERMATOPATHOLOGY. q? Turkish Society of Dermatopathology, Mithatpasa Cad. 16-11, Yenisehir, 06420 Ankara, Turkey. **Indexed:** Excerp.Med. (1994-). **Document type:** academic/scholarly publication.

616.95   AT   ISSN 1032-1012
CODEN: VNERE
VENEREOLOGY. 1988. q. Aus.$50 to individuals (foreign Aus.$70); institutions Aus.$80 (foreign Aus.$100) (effective thru 1996). Venereology Publishing Inc., 580 Swanston St., Carlton, Vic. 3053, Australia. TEL 61-3-94792718. FAX 61-3-94792750. E-mail: B.Cairns@latrobe.edu.au. **Indexed:** Excerp.Med. (1994-). **Document type:** academic/scholarly publication.
—BLDSC (9154.425400).

VETERINARY DERMATOLOGY; an international journal. see VETERINARY SCIENCE

616.5 617   US   ISSN 1059-0587
YEAR BOOK OF DERMATOLOGIC SURGERY. 1992. a. $72.95 (residents $35) (effective 1996). Mosby - Year Book, Inc. (Chicago) (Subsidiary of: Times Mirror Company), 200 N. LaSalle St., Chicago, IL 60601. TEL 312-726-9733. Ed. Dr. Neil Swanson. ●Also available online. Vendor(s): Ovid Technologies.
—BLDSC (9411.627000).

616.505   US   ISSN 0093-3619
RL26
YEAR BOOK OF DERMATOLOGY. 1933. a. $74.95 (residents $35) (effective 1996). Mosby - Year Book, Inc., Continuity Division, 200 N. LaSalle, Chicago, IL 60601. TEL 312-726-9733. FAX 312-726-6075. TELEX 206155. Eds. Drs. Arthur Sober, Thomas B. Fitzpatrick. illus. (reprint service avail.) **Indexed:** Biol.Abstr., Curr.Adv.Ecol.Sci. ●Also available online. Vendor(s): Ovid Technologies. —SWETS.
Formerly: Year Book of Dermatology and Syphilology (ISSN 0093-3627)

616.5   GW
CODEN: DMONBP
ZEITSCHRIFT FUER DERMATOLOGIE. 1892. a. DM.40 (students DM.30). Juergen Hartmann Verlag GmbH, Seefeld 18, 91093 Hessdorf-Klebheim, Germany. TEL 09135-7123-0. FAX 09135-712340. Ed.Bd. adv. contact: E. Michel. bk.rev.; bibl.; charts; illus.; stat.; index. **Indexed:** Biol.Abstr., C.I.S.Abstr., Chem.Abstr., Curr.Adv.Ecol.Sci., Dent.Ind., Excerp.Med., Hort.Abstr., Ind.Med., INIS Atomind., Rev.Plant Path. **Document type:** academic/scholarly publication.
—BLDSC (9457.652730); CASDDS; Faxon; SWETS. CCC.
Former titles: Zeitschrift fuer Dermatologie und deren Grenzgebiete (ISSN 0946-4115); (until 1994): Dermatologische Monatsschrift (ISSN 0011-9083); Dermatologische Wochenschrift.

610   GW   ISSN 0301-0481
CODEN: ZHKRAJ
ZEITSCHRIFT FUER HAUTKRANKHEITEN H UND G. 1946. m. DM.327($242) to individuals in Europe (rest of world DM.395($293)); institutions in Europe DM.480($356) (rest of world DM.548($406)) (effective 1996). (Berliner Dermatologische Gesellschaft) Blackwell Wissenschaft, Kurfuerstendamm 57, 10707 Berlin, Germany. TEL 030-32790624. FAX 030-32790610. Eds. T. Krieg, H. Merk. adv. contact: Jutta Weber-Pianka. bk.rev.; charts; illus.; tr.lit.; index. circ. 4,000. **Indexed:** A.D.& D., Biol.Abstr., Biotech.Abstr., Curr.Cont., Dent.Ind., Excerp.Med., Helminthol.Abstr., Ind.Med., Rev.Med.& Vet.Mycol., Rev.Plant Path. **Document type:** academic/scholarly publication.
—BLDSC (9464.322000); CASDDS; Faxon; Genuine Article; SWETS; UMI. CCC.
Formerly: Zeitschrift fuer Haut- und Geschlechtskrankheiten (ISSN 0044-2844)
Description: Covers all aspects of clinical dermatology.
Refereed Serial

ZENTRALBLATT HAUT- UND GESCHLECHTSKRANKHEITEN/DERMATOLOGY, VENEROLOGY, ANDROLOGY. see MEDICAL SCIENCES — Abstracting, Bibliographies, Statistics

ZHONGGUO SHAOSHANG CHUANGSHANG ZAZHI/CHINESE JOURNAL OF BURNS AND WOUNDS. see MEDICAL SCIENCES — Orthopedics And Traumatology

MEDICAL SCIENCES — Endocrinology

616.462   GW   ISSN 0940-5429
CODEN: ACDAEZ
ACTA DIABETOLOGICA; an international journal devoted to the study of clinical and experimental diabetes and metabolism. (Text in English) 1964. q. DM.386($280) (effective 1996). Springer-Verlag, Heidelberger Platz 3, 14197 Berlin, Germany. TEL 030-8207-0. FAX 030-8214091. E-mail: orders@springer.de. (Subscr. in N. America to: Springer-Verlag New York, Inc., 44 Hartz Way, Secaucus, NJ 07096-2491. TEL 201-348-4033) Ed. G. Pozza. bk.rev.; abstr.; bibl.; illus.; index. circ. 5,000. (also avail. in microfiche from UMI) **Indexed:** ASCA, Biol.Abstr., Bull.Signal., Chem.Abstr., Curr.Adv.Ecol.Sci., Curr.Cont., Diab.Cont., Diab.Lit.Ind., Excerp.Med., Ind.Med., Ind.Sci.Rev., Nutr.Abstr., Ref.Zh., Sci.Cit.Ind., Sugar Ind.Abstr. **Document type:** academic/scholarly publication.
—BLDSC (0612.399900); CASDDS; Faxon; Genuine Article; SWETS; UMI. CCC.
Formerly (until 1991): Acta Diabetologica Latina (ISSN 0001-5563)

616.4   AG   ISSN 0065-1192
ACTA ENDOCRINOLOGICA PANAMERICANA.* 1970. irreg. Panamerican Federation of Endocrine Societies, c/o Dr. Noe Altschuler, 25 de Mayo no. 648, Vicente Lopez, Buenos Aires, Argentina.

616.4 618.2 610.73   IT   ISSN 0001-6004
CODEN: AMAXBK
ACTA MEDICA AUXOLOGICA. (Text in English, Italian) 1969. 3/yr. L.99000($86) Centro Auxologico Italiano, Via Ariosto 13, 20145 Milan, Italy. TEL 39-2-58211203. FAX 39-2-48009009. (Subscr. to: Editrice Vita e Pensiero, Largo Gemelli, 1, 20123 Milan, Italy) Ed. Francesco Morabito. adv.; bk.rev.; abstr.; bibl.; illus.; index. circ. 3,000. **Indexed:** Biol.Abstr., Curr.Adv.Ecol.Sci., Curr.Cont., Excerp.Med., Ind.Med., Nutr.Abstr., Psychol.Abstr. **Document type:** academic/scholarly publication.
—BLDSC (0633.200000).

ACTUALITES REPRODUCTION HUMAINE. see MEDICAL SCIENCES — Obstetrics And Gynecology

616.4   US   ISSN 1049-6734
RC648.a1
ADVANCES IN ENDOCRINOLOGY AND METABOLISM. 1990. a. $72.95 (residents $40) (effective 1996). Mosby - Year Book, Inc. (Chicago) (Subsidiary of: Times Mirror Company), 200 N. Lasalle St., Chicago, IL 60601-1080. TEL 312-726-9733. FAX 312-726-6075. TELEX 206155. (Subscr. to: 11830 Westline Industrial Dr., St. Louis, MO 63146. TEL 800-325-4177) Ed. Dr. Ernest L. Mazzaferri.
—BLDSC (0705.250000). CCC.
Description: Provides referenced articles that enable clinical endocrinologists to incorporate new data in the day-to-day management of endocrine and metabolic disease.

616.4   US
RC620.A1   CODEN: AMTDAK
ADVANCES IN METABOLISM. 1964. irreg., vol.12, 1988. Academic Press, Inc., 525 B St., Ste. 1900, San Diego, CA 92101-4495. TEL 619-231-0926. FAX 619-699-6715. (Subscr. to: Order Dept., 6277 Sea Harbor Dr., 4th Fl., Orlando, FL 32887. TEL 800-321-5068) (reprint service avail. from ISI) **Indexed:** Biol.Abstr., Curr.Adv.Ecol.Sci.
—CASDDS.
Formerly (until vol.11): Advances in Metabolic Disorders (ISSN 0065-2903); Which supersedes: Advances in Metabolic Disorders. Supplements (ISSN 0587-4394)
Refereed Serial

AMERICAN JOURNAL OF KIDNEY DISEASES. see MEDICAL SCIENCES — Urology And Nephrology

MEDICAL SCIENCES — ENDOCRINOLOGY

616.4   FR   ISSN 0003-4266
CODEN: ANENAG
ANNALES D'ENDOCRINOLOGIE. (Text and summaries in English, French) 1939. bi-m. 1152 F. (foreign 1423 F.) (effective 1996). (Societe Francaise d'Endocrinologie) Masson - Periodiques, Villa Laromiguiere, 75005 Paris, France. TEL 1-40-46-62-00. FAX 1-40-46-62-01. Ed. P.J. Leclere. adv.; bk.rev.; illus.; index. circ. 1,500. (tabloid format; also avail. in microform from UMI; reprint service avail. from ISI) Indexed: Anim.Breed.Abstr., Biol.Abstr., Chem.Abstr., Curr.Adv.Ecol.Sci., Curr.Cont., Dairy Sci.Abstr., Excerp.Med., Ind.Med., Ind.Sci.Rev., Ind.Vet., INIS Atomind., Nutr.Abstr., Sci.Cit.Ind. **Document type:** academic/scholarly publication.
—BLDSC (0972.000000); CASDDS; Genuine Article; SWETS; UMI. **CCC.**
    Description: Publishes reports of meetings of Belgian and French societies, original articles, biological and clinical notes and commentaries.

616.4   JA
ANNUAL REVIEW NAIBUNPI TAISHA/ANNUAL REVIEW. ENDOCRINE AND METABOLISM. (Text in Japanese) a. 8652 Yen. Chugai Igakusha, 62, Yaraicho, Shinjuku-ku, Tokyo 162, Japan.

616.4   BL   ISSN 0004-2730
CODEN: ABENAY
ARQUIVOS BRASILEIROS DE ENDOCRINOLOGIA E METABOLOGIA. (Text in English, French, Portuguese and Spanish) 1951-1973; resumed 1978. q. free. Universidade de Sao Paulo, Faculdade de Medicina, Av. Dr. Arnaldo 455, Cx. Postal 8100, 01246 Sao Paulo, Brazil. Ed. Antonio Roberto Chacra. bk.rev.; bibl.; charts; illus.; index. **Indexed:** Biol.Abstr., Chem.Abstr., Excerp.Med., Ind.Med., Nutr.Abstr.
—CASDDS

ATRIAL NATRIURETIC FACTORS. see *MEDICAL SCIENCES — Abstracting, Bibliographies, Statistics*

616.4   UK   ISSN 0950-351X
BAILLIERE'S CLINICAL ENDOCRINOLOGY AND METABOLISM. 1987. q. £76 to individuals; institutions £87. Bailliere Tindall - W.B. Saunders Co. Ltd. (Subsidiary of: Harcourt Brace & Company Ltd.), 24-28 Oval Rd., London NW1 7DX, England. TEL 0171-267-4466. FAX 0171-482-2293. TELEX 25775 ACPRES G. (Subscr. to: Journals Subscriptions Fulfillment, Foots Cray High St., Sidcup, Kent DA14 5HP, England. TEL 0181-300-3322. FAX 0181-309-0807; Subscr. in N. America to: W.B. Saunders Co., Journal Subscription Fulfillment, 6277 Sea Harbor Dr., 4th Fl., Orlando, FL 32887-4800. TEL 800-874-6418) **Indexed:** Diab.Cont., Excerp.Med. **Document type:** academic/scholarly publication.
—BLDSC (1856.720000); Faxon; Genuine Article; SWETS; UnCover. **CCC.**
    Refereed Serial

616.462   UK   ISSN 0005-4216
BALANCE. 1935. bi-m. membership. British Diabetic Association, 10 Queen Anne St., London W1M 0BD, England. TEL 0171-323-1531. FAX 0171-637-3644. Ed. Lesley Hallett. adv.; bk.rev.; illus. circ. 140,000.
    Description: For people with diabetes and their families: medical and dietary information and research news.

616.4   US   ISSN 0891-2068
RC648.A1
BASIC & CLINICAL ENDOCRINOLOGY. 1981. irreg., vol.9, 1987. Marcel Dekker, Inc., 270 Madison Ave., New York, NY 10016. TEL 212-696-9000. FAX 212-685-4540. TELEX 421419. **Indexed:** Chem.Abstr.
    Refereed Serial

BONE. see *MEDICAL SCIENCES — Orthopedics And Traumatology*

616.462   CN
CANADIAN JOURNAL OF DIABETES CARE. (Text in English; summaries in English, French) q. Can.$26.75. Canadian Diabetes Association, 15 Toronto St., Ste. 1001, Toronto, ON M5C 2E3, Canada. TEL 416-363-3373. FAX 416-363-3393. Ed. Gillian Seaman. adv. contact: Tom Lowell. bk.rev.; circ. 1,500 (controlled).
—CCC.
    Formerly: Beta Release (ISSN 0710-0248)
    Refereed Serial

CHRONOBIOLOGIA. see *BIOLOGY*

616.46   US   ISSN 0891-8929
CODEN: CLDIE8
CLINICAL DIABETES. 1983. bi-m. $15 (foreign $21). American Diabetes Association, 1660 Duke St., Alexandria, VA 22314. TEL 703-549-1500. FAX 703-836-7439. TELEX 901132. Ed.Bd. circ. 40,000. **Indexed:** Diab.Cont.
● Also available online. Vendor(s): Ovid Technologies.
—BLDSC (3286.272700); SWETS; UMI. **CCC.**
    Refereed Serial

616.4   UK   ISSN 0300-0664
CODEN: CLECAP
CLINICAL ENDOCRINOLOGY. 1972. m. £385 (outside Europe £423($680)) (effective 1996). Blackwell Science Ltd., Osney Mead, Oxford OX2 0EL, England. TEL 01865-240201. FAX 01865-721205. TELEX 83355 MEDBOK G. Ed.Bd. adv.; bk.rev.; index. circ. 1,550. (also avail. in microform from UMI; back issues avail.; reprint service avail. from ISI) **Indexed:** Abstr.Inter.Med., ASCA, Biol.Abstr., Biotech.Abstr., Chem.Abstr., Curr.Adv.Ecol.Sci., Curr.Adv.Genetics & Molec.Biol., Curr.Cont., Dairy Sci.Abstr., Diab.Cont., Excerp.Med., Ind.Med., Ind.Sci.Rev., INIS Atomind., Nutr.Abstr., Sci.Cit.Ind. **Document type:** academic/scholarly publication.
—BLDSC (3286.278000); ADONIS; CASDDS; Faxon; Genuine Article; SWETS; UMI; UnCover. **CCC.**
    Refereed Serial

616.462   US
CLINICAL PRACTICE RECOMMENDATIONS. (Supplement to: Diabetes Care) a. $8. American Diabetes Association, 1660 Duke St., Alexandria, VA 22314. TEL 703-549-1500. FAX 703-836-7439. TELEX 901132.

616.4   US   ISSN 1050-3374
CLINICAL SURVEYS IN ENDOCRINOLOGY. 1987. irreg., vol.2, 1988. price varies. Plenum Publishing Corp., 233 Spring St., New York, NY 10013-1578. TEL 212-620-8000. FAX 212-463-0742. TELEX 23-421139. Ed. C.R. Kannan. (back issues avail.) **Document type:** monographic series.
    Refereed Serial

616.4   US   ISSN 0160-242X
COMPREHENSIVE ENDOCRINOLOGY. 1978. irreg., latest 1994. Raven Press (Subsidiary of: Wolters Kluwer N.V.), 1185 Ave. of the Americas, New York, NY 10036. TEL 212-930-9500. FAX 212-869-3495. Ed. Luciano Martini. (reprint service avail. from UMI) **Document type:** monographic series.

616.4   SZ   ISSN 0255-7983
CONCEPTS IN IMMUNOPATHOLOGY; series in immunoregulation research. 1985. irreg. price varies. S. Karger AG, Allschwilerstr. 10, P.O. Box, CH-4009 Basel, Switzerland. TEL 061-3061111. FAX 061-3061234. E-mail: Karger@Karger.ch. Eds. J.M. Cruse, R.E. Lewis Jr. **Document type:** academic/scholarly publication.
—BLDSC (3399.413100). **CCC.**
    Refereed Serial

616.4   US   ISSN 0196-8653
QP187.A1   CODEN: CNEND7
CONTEMPORARY ENDOCRINOLOGY. 1976. irreg., vol.2, 1985. Plenum Publishing Corp., 233 Spring St., New York, NY 10013-1578. TEL 212-620-8000. FAX 212-463-0742. TELEX 23-421139. Ed. Sidney H. Ingbar. (back issues avail.) **Indexed:** Chem.Abstr. **Document type:** monographic series.
—CASDDS.
    Formerly (until 1979): Year in Endocrinology (ISSN 0146-4078)
    Refereed Serial

616.4   US   ISSN 0193-340X
RC627.5   CODEN: CONMDM
CONTEMPORARY METABOLISM; analytical reviews of basic & clinical progress. 1976. irreg., vol.2, 1982. Plenum Publishing Corp., 233 Spring St., New York, NY 10013-1578. TEL 212-620-8000. FAX 212-463-0742. TELEX 23-421139. Ed. Norbert Freinkel. **Document type:** monographic series.
—CASDDS.
    Formerly: Year in Metabolism (ISSN 0147-4189)

616.4   GW   ISSN 0933-002X
CORTISON SPIEGEL. 1988. q. P M I Verlagsgruppe GmbH, August-Schanz-Str. 21, 60433 Frankfurt a.M., Germany. TEL 069-5480000. FAX 069-548000-77. TELEX 412952-PMI-D. Ed. E. Merck. circ. 60,000. (back issues avail.) **Document type:** academic/scholarly publication.

CURRENT ADVANCES IN ENDOCRINOLOGY & METABOLISM. see *MEDICAL SCIENCES — Abstracting, Bibliographies, Statistics*

616.4   JA   ISSN 0912-2249
CURRENT CONCEPTS IN MAGNESIUM METABOLISM/MAGUNESHUMU TAISHA KONNICHI NO KANAEKATA. (Text in Japanese) 1985. q. Standard McIntyre - Sutandado Mkkintaiya, 3-7, Irifune 2-chome, Chuo-ku, Tokyo 104, Japan.

616.4   NE   ISSN 1061-2793
CURRENT ENDOCRINOLOGY. 1981. irreg., latest 1986. price varies. Elsevier Science B.V., Books Division, P.O. Box 211, 1000 AE Amsterdam, Netherlands. TEL 31-20-4853911. FAX 31-20-4853705. TELEX 18582 ESPA NL. E-mail: nlinfo-f@elsevier.nl; usinfo-f@elsevier.com; forinfo-kyf04035@niftyserve.or.jp; Site addr.: http://www.elsevier.nl/. (Subscr. in U.S. and Canada to: Elsevier Science Inc., Box 882, Madison Sq. Sta., New York, NY 10159. TEL 212-989-5800) (reprint service avail. from ISI) **Document type:** monographic series.
    Refereed Serial

616.4   US   ISSN 1068-3097
CODEN: CENDES
▼**CURRENT OPINION IN ENDOCRINOLOGY & DIABETES.** 1994. bi-m. $129.95 to individuals; institutions $259.95; residents $52.95. Current Science, 400 Market St., Ste. 700, Philadelphia, PA 19106-2199. TEL 215-574-2210; 800-552-5866. FAX 215-574-2270. (And: Current Science Ltd., 34-42 Cleveland St., London W1P 6LB, England. TEL 0171-323-0323. FAX 0171-636-6911) Ed. Peter O. Kohler. adv. contact: Steven Miller. **Document type:** academic/scholarly publication.
● Also available online. Vendor(s): OCLC.
Also available on CD-ROM.
—BLDSC (3500.774200); ADONIS; CASDDS. **CCC.**

616.4   US   ISSN 0091-7397
RC648.A1   CODEN: CTEEAJ
CURRENT TOPICS IN EXPERIMENTAL ENDOCRINOLOGY. 1972. irreg., vol.5, 1983. Academic Press, Inc., 525 B St., Ste. 1900, San Diego, CA 92101-4495. TEL 619-231-0926. FAX 619-699-6715. (Subscr. to: Order Dept., 6277 Sea Harbor Dr., 4th Fl., Orlando, FL 32887. TEL 800-321-5068) Eds. L. Martini, V.H.T. James. (reprint service avail. from ISI) **Indexed:** Biol.Abstr., Curr.Adv.Ecol.Sci., Excerp.Med., Ind.Med.
—CASDDS.
    Refereed Serial

CURRENT TOPICS IN NEUROENDOCRINOLOGY. see *MEDICAL SCIENCES — Psychiatry And Neurology*

CYTOKINE AND GROWTH FACTOR REVIEWS. see *BIOLOGY — Microscopy*

616.4   NE   ISSN 0165-1900
CODEN: DENDD4
DEVELOPMENTS IN ENDOCRINOLOGY (AMSTERDAM). 1977. irreg., vol.16, 1985. price varies. Elsevier Science B.V., Books Division, P.O. Box 211, 1000 AE Amsterdam, Netherlands. TEL 31-20-4853911. FAX 31-20-4853705. TELEX 18582 ESPA NL. E-mail: nlinfo-f@elsevier.nl; usinfo-f@elsevier.com; forinfo-kyf04035@niftyserve.or.jp; Site addr.: http://www.elsevier.nl/. (Subscr. in U.S. and Canada to: Elsevier Science Inc., Box 882, Madison Sq. Sta., New York, NY 10159. TEL 212-989-5800) **Indexed:** Chem.Abstr. **Document type:** monographic series.
—CASDDS.
    Refereed Serial

616.46   IT   ISSN 0394-901X
DIABETE. 1989. q. L.80000($80) (Italian Society of Diabetology) Editrice Kurtis s.r.l., Via L. Zoja, 30, 20153 Milan, Italy. TEL 39-2-48202740. FAX 39-2-48201219. Ed. Riccardo Vigneri. adv.: B&W page L.5150000, color page L.6450000; trim 210 x 280.
—BLDSC (3579.577000).

MEDICAL SCIENCES — ENDOCRINOLOGY

616.462   FR   ISSN 0338-1684
CODEN: DIMEDU
DIABETE & METABOLISME. (Text in English, French) 1975. bi-m. 940 F. (foreign 1236 F.) (effective 1996). Masson - Periodiques, Villa Laromiguiere, 75005 Paris, France. TEL 1-40-46-62-00. FAX 1-40-46-62-01. Ed. P. Sai. adv.; illus.; index. circ. 1,500. (also avail. in microform from UMI; reprint service avail. from ISI) Indexed: Apic.Abstr., Biol.Abstr., Chem.Abstr., Curr.Adv.Ecol.Sci., Curr.Cont., Diab.Cont., Excerp.Med., Ind.Med., Ind.Sci.Rev., Nutr.Abstr., Risk Abstr., Sci.Cit.Ind. **Document type:** academic/scholarly publication.
—BLDSC (3579.585000); CASDDS; Faxon; Genuine Article; SWETS; UMI; UnCover. **CCC.**
   Formerly: Diabete (ISSN 0012-1770)
   Description: Presents original clinical and laboratory work of high quality.

616.46   IT
DIABETE, OGGI E DOMANI. 4/yr. Via S. Uguzzone 5, 20126 Milan, Italy. TEL 2-25-28-447. FAX 2-252-82-20. TELEX 321339 BMM. Ed. Rodolfo Colarizi. circ. 130,000.

616.462   FI   ISSN 0046-0192
DIABETES. 1948. 10/yr. FIM 130($32) Finnish Diabetes Association, Kirjoniementie 15, 33680 Tampere, Finland. TEL 358-31-28-60-111. FAX 358-31-3600-462. Ed. Tarja Sampo-Makinen. adv.; illus. circ. 50,000. Indexed: Abstr.Inter.Med., Curr.Adv.Biochem., NRN.
   Description: Directed to diabetics.

616.462   US   ISSN 0012-1797
RC660.A1   CODEN: DIAEAZ
DIABETES. 1952. m. $100 (foreign $156). American Diabetes Association, 1660 Duke St., Alexandria, VA 22314. TEL 703-549-1500. FAX 703-836-7439. TELEX 901132. Ed.Bd. adv.; abstr.; charts; illus.; index. circ. 10,000. (also avail. in microform from UMI,PMC; reprint service avail. from UMI) Indexed: Abstr.Hyg., Abstr.Inter.Med., AIM, Biol.Abstr., Biotech.Abstr., Chem.Abstr., Curr.Adv.Biochem., Curr.Adv.Cancer Res., Curr.Adv.Cell & Devel.Biol., Curr.Adv.Ecol.Sci., Curr.Adv.Genetics & Molec.Biol., Diab.Cont., Excerp.Med., Ind.Med., Ind.Sci.Rev., INIS Atomind., Kidney, Nutr.Abstr., Sci.Cit.Ind., So.Pac.Per.Ind., Trop.Dis.Bull.
●Also available online. Vendor(s): Ovid Technologies.
—BLDSC (3579.600000); CASDDS; Faxon; Genuine Article; SWETS; UMI; UnCover. **CCC.**
   Refereed Serial

616.462   DK   ISSN 0901-3652
DIABETES. 1941. 6/yr. DKK 110. Diabetesforeningen - Danish Diabetes Association, Filosofgangen 24, DK-5000 Odense, Denmark. TEL 45-66-12-90-06. FAX 45-66-13-58-83. Ed. Flemming Kjaersgaard Johansen. adv.; B&W page DKK 8295, color page DKK 15855. circ. 35,000.
   Former titles (until 1985): Tidsskrift for Sukkersyge (ISSN 0900-3215); (until 1948): Landsforeningen for Sukkersyge (ISSN 0909-6949)

616.462   SW   ISSN 0419-0459
DIABETES. 1948. bi-m. SEK 175. Svenska Diabetesfoerbundet, P.O. Box 1545, S-171 20 Solna, Sweden. TEL 46-8-629-85-80. Eds. Ann-Sofie Lindberg, Ulla Ernstroem. adv.; B&W page SEK 12200, color page SEK 18000. circ. 35,200. cols./p.: 3; pp./issue: 40.

616.4   US   ISSN 1068-8099
DIABETES ADVISOR. 1993. bi-m. American Diabetes Association, 1660 Duke St., Alexandria, VA 22314. TEL 703-549-1500. FAX 703-836-7439. TELEX 901132. circ. 100,000.

616.4   NE   ISSN 0168-9282
CODEN: DIANEW
DIABETES ANNUAL. 1985. a., latest vol.7, 1993. price varies. Elsevier Science B.V., Books Division, P.O. Box 211, 1000 AE Amsterdam, Netherlands. TEL 31-20-4853911. FAX 31-20-4853705. TELEX 18582 ESPA NL. E-mail: nlinfo-f@elsevier.nl; usinfo-f@elsevier.com; forinfo-kyf04035@niftyserve.or.jp; Site addr.: http://www.elsevier.nl/. (Subscr. in U.S. and Canada to: Elsevier Science Inc., Box 882, Madison Sq. Sta., New York, NY 10159. TEL 212-989-5800) Eds. K.G.M.M. Alberti, L.P. Krall. **Document type:** monographic series.
—BLDSC (3579.600520).
   Refereed Serial

616.462   US   ISSN 0149-5992
RC660.A1   CODEN: DICAD2
DIABETES CARE. (Supplement avail.: Clinical Practice Recommendations) 1978. 12/yr. $75 (foreign $107). American Diabetes Association, 1660 Duke St., Alexandria, VA 22314. TEL 703-549-1500. FAX 703-836-7439. TELEX 901132. Ed.Bd. adv.; bk.rev.; charts; illus.; stat.; index. circ. 11,500. (also avail. in microform from UMI; reprint service avail. from UMI) Indexed: Abstr.Inter.Med., Behav.Med.Abstr., Chem.Abstr., CINAHL, Curr.Cont., Diab.Cont., Excerp.Med., Ind.Med., Ind.Sci.Rev., Kidney, NRN, Rev.Med.& Vet.Mycol., Sci.Cit.Ind., Sugar Ind.Abstr.
●Also available online. Vendor(s): Ovid Technologies.
—BLDSC (3579.600600); CASDDS; Faxon; Genuine Article; SWETS; UMI; UnCover. **CCC.**
   Description: Presents the latest clinical research from top researchers, including analysis and comments on what the new findings mean for you and your patients.
   Refereed Serial

DIABETES CONTENTS. see *MEDICAL SCIENCES — Abstracting, Bibliographies, Statistics*

616.4   US
DIABETES COUNTDOWN. 1982. q. $25. Juvenile Diabetes Foundation International, 432 Park Ave. S., New York, NY 10016. TEL 212-889-7575. FAX 212-532-8791. Ed. Julie Mettenburg. adv. circ. 240,042. **Document type:** consumer publication.
   Description: Offers the latest information in diabetes research and treatment, as the foundation strives for a cure.

616.462   CN   ISSN 0703-5764
DIABETES DIALOGUE. 1954. q. Can.$15 membership. Canadian Diabetes Association, 15 Toronto St., Ste. 1001, Toronto, ON M5C 2E3, Canada. TEL 416-363-3373. FAX 416-363-3393. Ed. Dr. Robert Silver. adv.; bk.rev.; illus. circ. 59,398. (also avail. in audio cassette) **Document type:** consumer publication.
—BLDSC (3579.600630).
   Formerly (until vol.24, 1977): C D A Newsletter (ISSN 0007-8018)
   Description: Geared to readers with both Type 1 (insulin dependent) and Type 2 (non-insulin dependent) diabetics. Covers topics such as exercise, nutrition, food choices, foot care, health care, medical updates, research, life-style management, travel, book reviews, advice columns, skin care, products and policy statements.

616.462   US   ISSN 0095-8301
RC660.A1
DIABETES FORECAST. 1948. m. $24 (Canada and Mexico $39; elsewhere $49). American Diabetes Association, 1660 Duke St., Alexandria, VA 22314. TEL 703-549-1500. FAX 703-836-7439. TELEX 901132. Ed.Bd. adv.; bk.rev.; charts; illus. circ. 280,000. (reprint service avail.) Indexed: CHNI, CINAHL, Hlth.Ind.
—BLDSC (3579.600670); Faxon; SWETS; UnCover. **CCC.**
   Formerly: A.D.A. Forecast (ISSN 0001-0847)

616.462   JA   ISSN 0915-6593
DIABETES FRONTIER. (Text in Japanese) 1990. 6/yr. 2060 Yen. Medikaru Rebyusha - Medical Review Co., Ltd., 7-3, Hiranomachi 1-chome, Chuo-ku, Osaka 541, Japan. TEL 06-223-1468. Ed. Mitsuaki Matsuoka. **Document type:** academic/scholarly publication.
—BLDSC (3579.600680).

616.462   US   ISSN 0893-5939
DIABETES IN THE NEWS.* 1962. 6/yr. $12. Miles Laboratories, Inc., Ames Education Service, 1560 N. Sandburg Terr., Apt. 1402, Chicago, IL 60610-1338. FAX 312-664-9770. Ed. Morton B. Stone. adv.; bk.rev. circ. 90,000. (also avail. in microform from UMI) Indexed: Hlth.Ind.
—UMI.
   Former titles: D I T N: Diabetes in the News (ISSN 8750-1244); (until 1972): Diabetes in the News (ISSN 0012-1800)

616.462   GW   ISSN 0341-8812
CODEN: DIJODB
DIABETES-JOURNAL. 1951. m. DM.67.20. (Deutscher Diabetikerbund e.V.) Verlag Kirchheim und Co. GmbH, Kaiserstr. 41, 55116 Mainz, Germany. TEL 06131-96070-0. FAX 06131-9607070. Ed. H. Mehnert. adv.; bk.rev.; charts; illus. circ. 51,500. Indexed: Chem.Abstr. **Document type:** academic/scholarly publication.
—CASDDS; SWETS. **CCC.**
   Formerly: Diabetiker (ISSN 0012-1851)

DIABETES MELLITUS. see *MEDICAL SCIENCES — Abstracting, Bibliographies, Statistics*

616.4   UK   ISSN 0742-4221
CODEN: DMREEG
DIABETES - METABOLISM REVIEWS. 1985. q. $375 (foreign $375) (effective 1996). John Wiley & Sons Ltd., Journals, Baffins Ln., Chichester, W. Sussex PO19 1UD, England. TEL 01243-779777. FAX 01243-776128. TELEX 86290 WIBOOK G. (Subscr. in the Americas to: John Wiley & Sons, Inc., 605 Third Ave., New York, NY 10158. TEL 212-850-6645. FAX 212-850-6021) Ed. D. Andreani. circ. 457. (also avail. in microform from UMI; back issues avail.; reprint service avail. from SWZ) Indexed: Curr.Cont., Diab.Cont., Excerp.Med., INIS Atomind. **Document type:** academic/scholarly publication.
—BLDSC (3579.601900); ADONIS; CASDDS; Faxon; Genuine Article; SWETS; UMI; UnCover. **CCC.**
   Description: Covers clinical and basic scientific advances in edocrinology, insulin secretion, resistance, ketone metabolism, obesity and lipid metabolism, pathogenesis and cellular action of insulin.
   Refereed Serial

616.46 612.3   IT   ISSN 0394-3402
DIABETES, NUTRITION & METABOLISM, CLINICAL AND EXPERIMENTAL. (Text in English) 1988. bi-m. L.100000($100) Editrice Kurtis s.r.l., Via. L. Zoja, 30, 20153 Milan, Italy. TEL 39-2-48202740. FAX 39-2-48201219. Ed. P. Brunetti. adv.: B&W page L.2700000, color page L.3400000; trim 200 x 260. Indexed: Curr.Cont., Diab.Cont.
—BLDSC (3579.601950); Genuine Article.
   Description: Publishes original papers on diabetes, nutrition and metabolism research.

616.46   US
DIABETES PATH FINDER. 1978. q. $12. American Diabetes Association, Washington Affiliate, Inc., 557 Roy St., Lower Lever, Seattle, WA 98109. TEL 206-282-4616; 800-628-8808. FAX 206-282-4729. Ed. Clair Sagiv. bk.rev.; circ. 15,000 (controlled). (tabloid format)
   Formerly (until 1994): W A News.

616.4   UK   ISSN 1056-053X
CODEN: DPTHEM
DIABETES PREVENTION AND THERAPY. Variant title: I D I G Newsletter. 1987. q. $95 (foreign $95) (effective 1996). (International Diabetes Immunotherapy Group) John Wiley & Sons Ltd., Journals, Baffins Ln., Chichester, W. Sussex PO19 1UD, England. TEL 01243-779777. FAX 01243-776128. TELEX 86290 WIBOOK G. (Subscr. in the Americas to: John Wiley & Sons, Inc., 605 Third Ave., New York, NY 10158. TEL 212-850-6645. FAX 212-850-6021) Ed. Paolo Pozzilli. (also avail. in microform from UMI; back issues avail.) **Document type:** academic/scholarly publication.
   Refereed Serial

616.4   IE   ISSN 0168-8227
CODEN: DRCPE9
DIABETES RESEARCH AND CLINICAL PRACTICE. m. I£688($1087) (effective 1996). (International Diabetes Federation) Elsevier Science Ireland Ltd., P.O. Box 85, Limerick, Ireland. TEL 353-61-471944. FAX 353-61-472144. (Subscr. in U.S. and Canada to: Elsevier Science Inc., Box 882, Madison Sq. Sta., New York, NY 10159. TEL 212-989-5800. FAX 212-633-3990) Ed. S. Baba. (back issues avail.) Indexed: Diab.Cont., Excerp.Med., NRN. **Document type:** academic/scholarly publication.
—BLDSC (3579.603700); CASDDS; Faxon; Genuine Article; SWETS; UnCover. **CCC.**
   Description: Covers diabetes research, experimental biology, molecular biology and immunology, clinical practice, epidemiology and diabetes education.
   Refereed Serial

MEDICAL SCIENCES — ENDOCRINOLOGY

616.46 UK ISSN 0265-5985
CODEN: DIREEM
DIABETES RESEARCH: CLINICAL & EXPERIMENTAL.
1984. m. £395 (foreign £485). Teviot Scientific Publications Ltd., 82 Great King St., Edinburgh EH3 6QU, Scotland. TEL 031-332-8764. FAX 031-343-2633. Ed. W. James Irvine. adv.; bk.rev. **Indexed:** Curr.Adv.Cell & Devel.Biol., Curr.Adv.Ecol.Sci., Curr.Cont., Excerp.Med. **Document type:** academic/scholarly publication.
—BLDSC (3579.603600); CASDDS; Faxon; Genuine Article; SWETS; UnCover. **CCC.**

616.4 US ISSN 1066-9442
RC660.A1 CODEN: DBRVEO
DIABETES REVIEWS. 1993. q. $30 (foreign $41). American Diabetes Association, 1660 Duke St., Alexandria, VA 22314. TEL 703-549-1500. FAX 703-683-2890. TELEX 901132. Ed. Dr. Ralph A. DeFronzo. **Indexed:** Excerp.Med. (1994-).
—BLDSC (3579.603840); SWETS.

616.46 613.7 US ISSN 0741-6253
CODEN: DSMAEL
DIABETES SELF-MANAGEMENT. 1983. m. $18. R.A. Rapaport Publishing, Inc., 150 W. 22nd St., New York, NY 10011. TEL 212-989-0200. FAX 212-989-4786. (Subscr. to: Box 52890, Boulder, CO 80322-2890. TEL 800-234-0923) Ed. James Hazlett; Pub. Richard A. Rapaport. adv.; B&W page $8900; adv. contact: Kathy Jones. charts; illus.; circ. 305,000 (paid); 30,000 (controlled). (also avail. in audio cassette; back issues avail.) **Document type:** consumer publication.
Description: Practical and instructive "how-to" information for people with diabetes.
Refereed Serial

616.46 US ISSN 1040-9165
RC660.A1
DIABETES SPECTRUM; from research to practice. 1988. bi-m. $30 (foreign $45). American Diabetes Association, 1660 Duke St., Alexandria, VA 22314. TEL 703-549-1500. FAX 703-836-7439. TELEX 901132. Ed.Bd. adv.; bk.rev.; illus. circ. 10,500.
—BLDSC (3579.603950); UMI. **CCC.**
Refereed Serial

616.4 GW ISSN 0942-0037
DIABETES UND STOFFWECHSEL. (Text in German; summaries in English, German) 1992. bi-m. DM.150. Verlag Kirchheim und Co. GmbH, Kaiserstr. 41, 55116 Mainz, Germany. TEL 06131-96070-0. FAX 06131-9607070. Eds. Prof. E. Standl, Prof. B. Willms. adv. contact: Andreas Goerner. bk.rev.; index; circ. 13,000. (back issues avail.) **Indexed:** Excerp.Med. (1995-). **Document type:** academic/scholarly publication.
—BLDSC (3579.604100).

616.462 US
DIABETES UPDATE. 1955. 4/yr. $10 to non-members (foreign $20). Greater Boston Diabetes Society Inc., 1330 Beacon St., Ste. 345, Brookline, MA 02146. TEL 617-731-2972. Ed. Thelma Gruenbaum. adv.; bk.rev. circ. 4,000.
Former titles (until 1985): Diabetes Dialogue; Diabetes Newsletter (ISSN 0012-1827)
Description: News, information, and announcements pertaining to the members and activities of the Greater Boston Diabetes Society with medical and nutritional information on inhibiting and controlling the disorder and information about diet and exercise to help prevent or delay the onset of diabetes.

616.46 US
THE DIABETESCARE GUIDE.* 1991. s-a. $4. Health Care Publishing, Ltd., 84 Clinton Ave., Nyack, NY 10960-4604. TEL 212-489-2273. FAX 212-489-2476. adv.: B&W page $12025, color page $14450; trim 5 1/4 x 7 1/2; adv. contact: Glenn Meyerson. circ. 200,000. (back issues avail.)
Description: Reference guide distributed to newly diagnosed adults. Covers the practical aspects of controlling and managing diabetes.

616.462 II ISSN 0970-4035
CODEN: JDAIBB
DIABETIC ASSOCIATION OF INDIA. JOURNAL. EDUCATION SECTION. 1960. q. Diabetic Association of India, S.L. Raheja Hospital, Raheja Rugnalaya Marg., Mahim, Bombay 400 016, India. **Indexed:** Excerp.Med. (until 19??).
—BLDSC (4734.541000); CASDDS.
Supersedes in part (in 1988): Diabetic Association of India. Journal (ISSN 0304-4513); Which was formerly (until 1974): Madhumeh (ISSN 0024-9424)

616.462 II ISSN 0970-4027
CODEN: JDAIB
DIABETIC ASSOCIATION OF INDIA. JOURNAL. SCIENTIFIC SECTION. (Text in English) 1960. q. Diabetic Association of India, S.L. Raheja Hospital, Raheja Rugnalaya Marg, Mahim, Bombay 400 016, India. adv.; bk.rev.; illus. circ. 3,000. **Indexed:** Biol.Abstr., Excerp.Med.
—BLDSC (4734.542000); CASDDS.
Supersedes in part (in 1988): Diabetic Association of India. Journal (ISSN 0304-4513); Which was formerly (until 1974): Madhumeh (ISSN 0024-9424)

616.46 616.3
610.73 UK ISSN 0742-3071
CODEN: DIMEEV
DIABETIC MEDICINE. 1984. m. $455 (foreign $455) (effective 1996). (British Diabetic Association) John Wiley & Sons Ltd., Journals, Baffins Ln., Chichester, W. Sussex PO19 1UD, England. TEL 01243-779777. FAX 01243-776128. TELEX 86290 WIBOOK G. (Subscr. in the Americas to: John Wiley & Sons, Inc., 605 Third Ave., New York, NY 10158. TEL 212-850-6645. FAX 212-850-6021) Ed. A. Boulton. adv.; bk.rev. circ. 1,352. (also avail. in microform from UMI; back issues avail.; reprint service avail. from SWZ) **Indexed:** Behav.Med.Abstr., CINAHL, Curr.Adv.Ecol.Sci., Curr.Cont., Diab.Cont., Excerp.Med., Ind.Med., NRN, Rev.Med.& Vet.Mycol., Triticale Abstr. **Document type:** academic/scholarly publication.
—BLDSC (3579.606000); ADONIS; Faxon; Genuine Article; SWETS; UMI; UnCover. **CCC.**
Description: Designed as an information exchange on all aspects of diabetes mellitus and aims to interest everyone helping diabetic patients whether through fundamental research or better health care.
Refereed Serial

616.46 US
DIABETIC READER; we read to know we're not alone. 1981. s-a. $6. Prana Publications & Paraphernalia, 5623 Matilija Ave., Van Nuys, CA 91401. TEL 818-780-1308. FAX 818-786-7359. E-mail: prana@earthspirit.org. Eds. June Biermann, Barbara Toohey; Pubs. June Biermann, Barbara Toohey. adv.; bk.rev.; circ. 40,000 (paid).
Formerly (until 1991): Health-O-Gram.
Description: Offers support, advice, and practical information to persons with diabetes and family members.

616.4 US ISSN 0899-2398
THE DIABETIC TRAVELER. 1987. q. $18.95 (foreign $21.95). Box 8223 - RW, Stamford, CT 06905. TEL 203-327-5832. Ed. Maury E. Rosenbaum. adv.; bk.rev.; index. circ. 2,500. (looseleaf format; back issues avail.) **Document type:** newsletter.
Description: Provides hints to assist individuals with diabetes in planning safe travel.
Refereed Serial

616.46 NO ISSN 0419-0505
DIABETIKEREN. 1950. 6/yr. NOK 210. Norges Diabetesforbund - Norwegian Diabetic Association, P.O. Box 6442, Etterstad, N-0605 Oslo, Norway. TEL 47-22-65-45-50. FAX 47-22-63-06-88. Ed. Bjoernar Allgot. adv.; bk.rev. circ. 25,000.

616.462 GW ISSN 0012-186X
RC660.A1 CODEN: DBTGAJ
DIABETOLOGIA; clinical and experimental diabetes and metabolism. (Text in English) 1965. 12/yr. DM.1048($761) (effective 1996). (European Association for the Study of Diabetes) Springer-Verlag, Heidelberger Platz 3, 14197 Berlin, Germany. TEL 030-8207-0. FAX 030-8214091. E-mail: orders@springer.de. (Subscr. in N. America to: Springer-Verlag New York, Inc., 44 Hartz Way, Secaucus, NJ 07096-2491. TEL 201-348-4033. FAX 201-348-4505) Ed. C. Hellerstroem. adv.; bibl.; charts; illus.; tr.lit. (also avail. in microform from UMI; back issues avail.; reprint service avail. from ISI) **Indexed:** Behav.Med.Abstr., Biol.Abstr., Biotech.Abstr., Chem.Abstr., Curr.Adv.Cell & Devel.Biol., Curr.Adv.Ecol.Sci., Curr.Adv.Genetics & Molec.Biol., Curr.Cont., Diab.Cont., Excerp.Med., Ind.Med., Ind.Sci.Rev., NRN, Nutr.Abstr., Sci.Cit.Ind., Small.Anim.Abstr. **Document type:** academic/scholarly publication.
—BLDSC (3579.615000); ADONIS; CASDDS; Faxon; Genuine Article; SWETS; UMI; UnCover. **CCC.**
Description: Reports of clinical and experimental work on all aspects of diabetes research and related medicine, metabolic diseases, and physiology.

616.46 619 CI ISSN 0350-1892
DIABETOLOGIA CROATICA. (Text and summaries in Croatian, English) 1972. q. $12. Vuk Vrhovac Institute for Diabetes, Endocrinology and Metabolic Diseases, Krijesnice b.b., 41000 Zagreb, Croatia. Ed. Zdenko Skrabalo. bk.rev. circ. 1,000. **Indexed:** Biol.Abstr., Chem.Abstr., Excerp.Med.
—BLDSC (0050.533000).

616.4 GW ISSN 0171-8045
DIABETOLOGIE INFORMATIONEN. 4/yr. DM.56. (Deutsche Diabetes Gesellschaft) Schmidt-Roemhild Verlag, Mengstr. 16, 23552 Luebeck, Germany. TEL 0451-1605-0. FAX 0451-1605253. **Document type:** bulletin.

DOMESTIC ANIMAL ENDOCRINOLOGY. see *VETERINARY SCIENCE*

616.4 UA ISSN 0070-9506
EGYPTIAN SOCIETY OF ENDOCRINOLOGY AND METABOLISM. JOURNAL.* (Text in English) 1955-1968; resumed 1971. irreg. Egyptian Society of Endocrinology and Metabolism, 42 Sharia Kasr el-Aini, Cairo, Egypt.

616.4 591.142 UK ISSN 1355-008X
ENDOCRINE. 1993. m. Macmillan Press Ltd., Houndmills, Basingstoke, Hants RG21 2XS, England. TEL 44-1256-817245. **Indexed:** Excerp.Med. (1995-). **Document type:** academic/scholarly publication.
—BLDSC (3740.440000); Genuine Article.
Formerly (until 1994): Endocrine Journal (ISSN 0969-711X)

616.4 JA ISSN 0918-8959
CODEN: ECJPAE
ENDOCRINE JOURNAL. (Text in English) 1954. bi-m. 10000 Yen($70) to individuals; institutions $100. Japan Endocrine Society - Nihon Naibunpi Gakkai, Department of Veterinary Physiology, Veterinary Medical Science, University of Tokyo, 1-1-1 Yayoi Bunkyo-ku, Tokyo 113, Japan. FAX 011-81-3-815-4266. (Overseas Dist. by: Japan Publications Trading Co., Ltd., P.O. Box 5030, Tokyo International, Tokyo 100-31, Japan) Ed. Michio Takahashi. adv.; bk.rev.; abstr.; charts; illus.; index. circ. 1,000. (back issues avail.) **Indexed:** Anim.Breed.Abstr., Biol.Abstr., Chem.Abstr., Curr.Adv.Ecol.Sci., Curr.Cont., Curr.Ref.Fish Res., Dairy Sci.Abstr., Dent.Ind., Excerp.Med., Ind.Med., Ind.Vet., Nutr.Abstr., Sci.Cit.Ind., Vet.Bull. **Document type:** academic/scholarly publication.
—BLDSC (3740.453000); CASDDS; Faxon; Genuine Article; SWETS; UnCover.
Formerly (until Feb. 1993): Endocrinologia Japonica (ISSN 0013-7219)
Description: Publishes papers which contribute either experimentally, theoretically or clinically to knowlege in the field of endocrinology.
Refereed Serial

MEDICAL SCIENCES — ENDOCRINOLOGY

616.4 US ISSN 1046-3976
RC648.A1 CODEN: ENPAFD
ENDOCRINE PATHOLOGY. 1989. q. $310 (foreign $340) (effective 1996). (Endocrine Pathology Society) Humana Press Inc., 999 Riverview Dr., Ste. 208, Totowa, NJ 07512. TEL 201-256-1699. FAX 201-256-8341. (Dist. in Japan by: Maruzen Co. Ltd., Journals Div., P.O. Box 5050, Tokyo 100-31, Japan. TEL 03-3275-8591. FAX 03-3278-1937) Ed. Ricardo V. Lloyd. adv. contact: Thomas B. Lanigan, Jr. bk.rev.; abstr.; bibl.; charts; illus.; index. **Document type:** academic/scholarly publication.
—BLDSC (3740.460000); CASDDS; Genuine Article; UMI. **CCC.**
Description: Focuses on the diagnostic aspects of endocrine pathology and new developments in the diagnostic applications of molecular biology and immunohistochemistry to endocrine pathology.
Refereed Serial

616.4 XO ISSN 1210-0668
CODEN: EREGE3
ENDOCRINE REGULATIONS. (Text and summaries in English) 1967. q. $19. (Slovenska Akademia Vied) Veda, Publishing House of the Slovak Academy of Sciences, Klemensova 19, 814 30 Bratislava, Slovakia. (Dist. in Western countries by: Karger-Libri AG, Scientific Booksellers, Arnold-Bocklin-Strasse 25, CH-4000 Basel 11, Switzerland) Eds. L. Macho, P. Langer. bk.rev.; charts; illus.; stat.; index. circ. 800. **Indexed:** Biol.Abstr., Chem.Abstr., Curr.Adv.Ecol.Sci., Curr.Cont., Dairy Sci.Abstr., Endocrin.Ind., Excerp.Med., Ind.Med., Ind.Sci.Rev., Ind.Vet., INIS Atomind., Nutr.Abstr., Pig News & Info., Ref.Zh., Sci.Cit.Ind., Vet.Bull.
—BLDSC (3740.467000); CASDDS; Faxon; SWETS.
Formerly (until 1991): Endocrinologia Experimentalis (ISSN 0013-7200).
Description: Publishes original works that deal with the contemporary problems of experimental endocrinology of morphologic, physiologic, biochemical, pathophysiological or pharmacologic character.

616.4 UK ISSN 1351-0088
CODEN: ERCAE9
ENDOCRINE - RELATED CANCER. q. £100($160) (effective 1996). (Society for Endocrinology) Journal of Endocrinology Ltd., 17-18 The Courtyard, Woodlands, Almondsbury, Bristol BS12 4NQ, England. TEL 01454-616046. FAX 01454-616071. E-mail: soc-endoc@bristol.ac.uk. (Dist. by: Turpin Distribution Services Ltd., Blackhorse Rd., Letchworth, Herts. SG6 1HN, England. TEL 01462-672555. FAX 01462-480947) Ed. V.H.T. James. **Indexed:** Excerp.Med. **Document type:** academic/scholarly publication.
—BLDSC (3740.467500); CASDDS.
Formerly (until 1993): Reviews on Endocrine - Related Cancer (ISSN 0260-0897).
Description: International forum for the presentation of all types of basic, clinical, and experimental investigations and observations which concern endocrine-related cancers.

616.4 US ISSN 0743-5800
QP187.A1 CODEN: ENRSE8
ENDOCRINE RESEARCH. 1964. 4/yr. $450. Marcel Dekker Journals, 270 Madison Ave., New York, NY 10016. TEL 212-696-9000. FAX 212-685-4540. TELEX 421419. (Subscr. to: Box 5017, Monticello, NY 12701) Ed. Alexander C. Brownie. adv. (also avail. in microform from RPI) **Indexed:** Anim.Breed.Abstr., ASCA, Biol.Abstr., Chem.Abstr., Curr.Adv.Ecol.Sci., Curr.Cont., Dairy Sci.Abstr., Excerp.Med., Ind.Med., Ind.Sci.Rev., INIS Atomind., Nutr.Abstr., Pig News & Info., Sci.Cit.Ind. **Document type:** academic/scholarly publication.
—BLDSC (3740.469000); CASDDS; Faxon; Genuine Article; SWETS; UMI; UnCover. **CCC.**
Formerly: Endocrine Research Communications (ISSN 0093-6391); Supersedes: Endocrinological Communications.
Refereed Serial

616.4 US ISSN 0163-769X
QP187.A1 CODEN: ERVIDP
ENDOCRINE REVIEWS. 1980. q. $195 (foreign $225) (effective 1996). Endocrine Society, 4350 East West Hwy., Ste. 500, Bethesda, MD 20814-4410. TEL 301-941-0200. FAX 301-941-0259. Ed.Bd. adv. circ. 4,800. (also avail. in microform from WWS) **Indexed:** Anim.Breed.Abstr., Chem.Abstr., Curr.Adv.Ecol.Sci., Diab.Cont., Excerp.Med., Ind.Med., Ind.Sci.Rev., Pig News & Info., Poult.Abstr., Sci.Cit.Ind. **Document type:** academic/scholarly publication.
—BLDSC (3740.480000); ADONIS; CASDDS; Faxon; Genuine Article; SWETS; UnCover. **CCC.**
Description: Review articles explore clinical and experimental endocrinology topics.

616.4 AT ISSN 0312-4738
CODEN: ESAUAS
ENDOCRINE SOCIETY OF AUSTRALIA. PROCEEDINGS. 1958. a. Aus.$36. Endocrine Society of Australia, Ewen Downie Metabolic Unit, Alfred Hospital, Commercial Rd., Prahran, Vic. 3181, Australia. TEL 61-3-2762460. FAX 61-3-2763782. Ed. D.J. Topliss. adv. circ. 700. **Indexed:** Biol.Abstr., Excerp.Med. **Document type:** proceedings.
—CASDDS.

616.4 SP ISSN 0211-2299
CODEN: ENDCDP
ENDOCRINOLOGIA. (Text in Spanish; summaries in English) 1953. m. (10/yr.) 6900 ptas.($57) to non-members. (Sociedad Espanola de Endocrinologia) Ediciones Doyma S.A., Traversera de Gracia, 17-21, 08021 Barcelona, Spain. TEL 34-1-200-07-11. FAX 34-1-209-11-36. TELEX 51964 INK-E. Ed. R. Gomis Barbera. adv.: page 180000 ptas.; trim 210 x 180; adv. contact: Marte Vidal. circ. 2,000. (reprint service avail. from UMI) **Indexed:** Excerp.Med., Ind.Med.Esp.
—BLDSC (3740.485000); CASDDS; UMI.
Description: Publishes clinical and experimental research in endocrinology.

616.4 XV ISSN 0351-1677
ENDOCRINOLOGIA IUGOSLAVICA. (Text in Serbo-Croatian; summaries in English) 1977. s-a. 1800 din.($20) (Raziskovalna Skupnost Slovenija) Tiskarna Tone Tomsic, Gregorciceua 25a, 61000 Ljubljana, Slovenia. (Subscr. to: Nusa Bambic, Dispanzer za Diabetike, UKC Njegoseva 4, 61000 Ljubljana, Slovenia) Ed. Andreja Kocijancic. adv.; bk.rev. circ. 400.
Description: Research reports on clinical endocrinology and diabetology for internists, endocrinologists, gynecologists and pediatricians.

616.4 US ISSN 1051-2144
CODEN: EDOCEB
THE ENDOCRINOLOGIST. 1991. bi-m. $86 to individuals; institutions $145 (effective 1995). Williams & Wilkins, 428 E. Preston St., Baltimore, MD 21202. TEL 410-528-4000; 800-638-6423. FAX 410-528-4312. Ed. Dr. Lynn Loriaux. circ. 3,700. **Indexed:** Excerp.Med. (1993-). **Document type:** academic/scholarly publication.
—BLDSC (3741.750000); Genuine Article. **CCC.**
Description: Directed exclusively to clinicians interested in practical applications of new discoveries in endocrinology, diabetes, and metabolism.
Refereed Serial

616.4 US ISSN 0013-7227
QP187 CODEN: ENDOAO
ENDOCRINOLOGY. 1917. m. $410 (foreign $500) (effective 1996). Endocrine Society, 4350 East West Hwy., Ste. 500, Bethesda, MD 20814-4410. TEL 301-941-0200. FAX 301-941-0259. Ed.Bd. adv.; bibl.; charts; illus.; index. circ. 5,800. (also avail. in microform from PMC; reprint service avail.) **Indexed:** AIM, Anim.Breed.Abstr., Biol.Abstr., Biotech.Abstr., Chem.Abstr., Curr.Adv.Biochem., Curr.Adv.Cancer Res., Curr.Adv.Cell & Devel.Biol., Curr.Adv.Ecol.Sci., Curr.Adv.Genetics & Molec.Biol., Curr.Cont., Curr.Cont., Curr.Ref.Fish Res., Dairy Sci.Abstr., Dent.Ind., Excerp.Med., Ind.Med., Ind.Sci.Rev., Ind.Vet., INIS Atomind., Nutr.Abstr., Pig News & Info., Poult.Abstr., Rev.Med.& Vet.Mycol., Sci.Cit.Ind., Small.Anim.Abstr., Soyabean Abstr., Sport Fish.Abstr., Trop.Dis.Bull., Vet.Bull., Wild.Rev., Zoo.Rec. **Document type:** academic/scholarly publication.
—BLDSC (3742.000000); ADONIS; CASDDS; Faxon; Genuine Article; SWETS; UnCover. **CCC.**
Description: Covers all aspects of research on endocrine glands and their hormones.
Refereed Serial

616.4 UK ISSN 1074-939X
CODEN: ENDMEM
▼**ENDOCRINOLOGY AND METABOLISM.** (Supplement avail.) 1994. q. £45 to individuals (outside Europe $80); institutions £95 (outside Europe $170). Bailliere Tindall - W.B. Saunders Co. Ltd. (Subsidiary of: Harcourt Brace & Company Ltd.), 24-28 Oval Rd., London NW1 7DX, England. TEL 0171-267-4466. FAX 0171-482-2293. TELEX 25775 ACPRES G. (Subscr. to: Harcourt Brace & Company, Journal Subscription Fulfillment, Foots Cray High St., Sidcup, Kent DA14 5HP, England. TEL 0181-300-3322. FAX 0181-309-0807; Subscr. in N. America to: Periodicals Fulfillment, W.B. Saunders Co., 6277 Sea Harbor Dr., 4th Fl., Orlando, FL 32887-4800. TEL 800-654-2452. FAX 800-874-6418) Ed. P.H. Soenksen. adv. **Indexed:** Excerp.Med. (1995-). **Document type:** academic/scholarly publication.
—BLDSC (3743.045000); CASDDS.
Formerly (until 1995): Clinical and Experimental Metabolism.
Refereed Serial

616.4 UK
▼**ENDOCRINOLOGY AND METABOLISM. SUPPLEMENT.** 1994. bi-m. £65($120) in the U.K. and rest of Europe. Bailliere Tindall - W.B. Saunders Co. Ltd. (Subsidiary of: Harcourt, Brace & Company Ltd.), 24-28 Oval Rd., London NW1 7DX, England. TEL 0171-267-4466. FAX 0171-482-2293. TELEX 25775 ACPRES G. (Subscr. to: Journals Subscription Department, Harcourt, Brace & Company Ltd., Foots Cray High St., Sidcup, Kent DA14 5HP, England. TEL 0181-300-3322. FAX 0181-309-0807; Subscr. in N. America to: W.B. Saunders Co., Journals Subscription Fulfillment, 6277 Sea Harbor Dr., 4th Fl., Orlando, FL 32887-4800. TEL 800-874-6418) Ed. P.H. Soenksen. adv. **Document type:** academic/scholarly publication.
Refereed Serial

616.4 US ISSN 0889-8529
RC648.A1 CODEN: ECNAER
ENDOCRINOLOGY AND METABOLISM CLINICS OF NORTH AMERICA. 1972. q. $127 (foreign $150) (effective 1996). W.B. Saunders Co. (Subsidiary of: Harcourt Brace & Company), Curtis Center, 3rd Fl., Independence Sq. W., Philadelphia, PA 19106-3399. TEL 215-238-7800. FAX 215-238-6445. (Subscr. to: Periodicals Fulfillment, W.B. Saunders Co., 6277 Sea Harbor Dr., 4th Fl., Orlando, FL 32891-4800. TEL 800-654-2452. FAX 800-874-6418) Ed. Ruth Savitz. **Indexed:** Biol.Abstr., Chem.Abstr., Curr.Adv.Ecol.Sci., Dent.Ind., Excerp.Med., Ind.Med., Ind.Sci.Rev., Nutr.Abstr., Sci.Cit.Ind. **Document type:** academic/scholarly publication.
—BLDSC (3743.052000); CASDDS; Faxon; Genuine Article; SWETS; UMI; UnCover. **CCC.**
Formerly: Clinics in Endocrinology and Metabolism (ISSN 0300-595X)

616.4 GW ISSN 0721-667X
ENDOKRINOLOGIE - INFORMATIONEN.* (Text in German; summaries in English) 1977. bi-m. DM.66. Deutsche Gesellschaft fuer Endokrinologie, Postfach, 13342 Berlin, Germany. Ed. Dr. O.-A. Mueller. circ. 1,400. **Document type:** academic/scholarly publication.

616.4 PL ISSN 0423-104X
CODEN: EDPKA2
ENDOKRYNOLOGIA POLSKA. (Text in Polish; summaries in English and Russian) 1951. bi-m. $30. Polskie Towarzystwo Endokrynologiczne - Polish Endocrinological Association, Pl. Starynkiewicza 3, 02-015 Warsaw, Poland. (Dist. by: Ars Polona, Krakowskie Przedmiescie 7, 00-068 Warsaw, Poland) Ed. Zbigniew Szybinski. adv.; bk.rev.; bibl.; charts; illus.; index. **Indexed:** Anim.Breed.Abstr., Biol.Abstr., Chem.Abstr., Dent.Ind., Excerp.Med. (until 1993), Ind.Med., INIS Atomind.
—BLDSC (3743.300000); CASDDS.
Description: Papers on practical and theoretical aspects of Polish research on endocrinology.

ENZYME AND PROTEIN. see BIOLOGY — Biological Chemistry

MEDICAL SCIENCES — ENDOCRINOLOGY

616.4 NO ISSN 0804-4643
QP187.A1 CODEN: EJOEEP
EUROPEAN JOURNAL OF ENDOCRINOLOGY. (Supplement avail. (ISSN 0804-4635)) (Text in English) 1948. 12/yr. NOK 2250 in Nordic countries; elsewhere $430 (effective 1996). Scandinavian University Press, P.O. Box 2959 Toeyen, N-0608 Oslo, Norway. TEL 47-22-57-54-00.
FAX 47-22-57-53-53. Ed. Albert G. Burger. abstr.; charts; illus.; index. circ. 1,800. **Indexed:** Abstr.Inter.Med., Anim.Breed.Abstr., ASCA, Behav.Med.Abstr., Biol.Abstr., Biotech.Abstr., C.I.S. Abstr., Chem.Abstr., Curr.Adv.Cancer Res., Curr.Adv.Cell & Devel.Biol., Curr.Adv.Ecol.Sci., Curr.Adv.Genetics & Molec.Biol., Curr.Cont., Dairy Sci.Abstr., Dent.Ind., Diab.Cont., Excerp.Med., Ind.Med., Ind.Sci.Rev., Ind.Vet., INIS Atomind., Nutr.Abstr., Pig News & Info., Sci.Cit.Ind., Small Anim.Abstr., Sport Fish.Abstr., Vet.Bull., Wild.Rev., Zoo.Rec. **Document type:** academic/scholarly publication.
—BLDSC (3829.728700); ADONIS; CASDDS; Faxon; Genuine Article; SWETS; UnCover. **CCC.**
Formerly (until 1994): Acta Endocrinologica (ISSN 0001-5598)
Description: Publishes original scientific papers and critical reviews within clinical and experimental endocrinology.
Refereed Serial

616.4 NO ISSN 0804-4635
QP1 CODEN: EJESE
EUROPEAN JOURNAL OF ENDOCRINOLOGY. SUPPLEMENT. 1948. irreg., latest 1995. Scandinavian University Press, P.O. Box 2959 Toeyen, N-0608 Oslo, Norway.
TEL 47-22-57-54-00. FAX 47-22-57-53-53. abstr.; illus. **Indexed:** Biol.Abstr., Chem.Abstr., Curr.Adv.Ecol.Sci., Dairy Sci.Abstr., Excerp.Med. (1993-), Ind.Med., INIS Atomind., Nutr.Abstr.
—BLDSC (3829.728710); ADONIS; CASDDS; Faxon; SWETS; UnCover.
Formerly (until 1994): Acta Endocrinologica. Supplementum (ISSN 0300-9750)

616.4 GW ISSN 0947-7349
QP187.A1 CODEN: EXCEDS
EXPERIMENTAL AND CLINICAL ENDOCRINOLOGY AND DIABETES. (Text in English) 1928. 6/yr. DM.272 (foreign DM.280). (Deutsche Gesellschaft fuer Endokrinologie) Johann Ambrosius Barth, Postfach 102869, 69018 Heidelberg, Germany.
TEL 06221-489281. FAX 06221-489205. Eds. K. Voigt, H. Schatz. adv.: B&W page DM.1500; trim 210 x 275; adv. contact: Petra Schoene. abstr.; bibl.; charts; illus.; index. circ. 2,000. **Indexed:** Anim.Breed.Abstr., Biol.Abstr., Biotech.Abstr., Chem.Abstr., Curr.Adv.Cancer Res., Curr.Cont., Dairy Sci.Abstr., Dent.Ind., Dok.Arbeitsmed., Excerp.Med., Ind.Med., Ind.Sci.Rev., Ind.Vet., INIS Atomind., Nutr.Abstr., Pig News & Info., Sci.Cit.Ind., Vet.Bull. **Document type:** academic/scholarly publication.
—BLDSC (3838.630100); CASDDS; Faxon; Genuine Article; UMI; UnCover. **CCC.**
Former titles: Experimental and Clinical Endocrinology (ISSN 0232-7384); Endokrinologie (ISSN 0013-7251)
Description: Covers the entire field of endocrinology from molecular biology to the clinic.

616.4 SZ ISSN 0251-5342
CODEN: FDIADJ
FRONTIERS IN DIABETES. (Text in English) irreg. price varies. S. Karger AG, Allschwilerstr. 10, P.O. Box, CH-4009 Basel, Switzerland. TEL 061-3061111.
FAX 061-3061234. E-mail: Karger@Karger.ch. Ed. F. Belfiore. (reprint service avail. from ISI) **Indexed:** Biol.Abstr. **Document type:** academic/scholarly publication.
—BLDSC (4042.003000); CASDDS. **CCC.**
Description: Provides a reference tool for workers who need convenient, well-ordered access to the latest information.
Refereed Serial

616.4 616.8 US ISSN 0091-3022
QP187.A1 CODEN: FNEDA7
FRONTIERS IN NEUROENDOCRINOLOGY. 1962. q. $260 (foreign $308) (effective 1996). Academic Press, Inc., 528 B. St., Ste. 1900, San Diego, CA 92101-4495. TEL 619-230-1840.
FAX 619-699-6800. TELEX 181726. (Subscr. to: Box 620000, Orlando, FL 32891-8340. TEL 800-543-9534) Eds. L. Martini, William F. Ganong. (reprint service avail. from UMI) **Indexed:** Biol.Abstr., Chem.Abstr., Curr.Cont., Excerp.Med., Ind.Med. (1992-), Ind.Sci.Rev., Sci.Cit.Ind. **Document type:** academic/scholarly publication.
—BLDSC (4042.040000); CASDDS; EMDOCS; Faxon; Genuine Article; SWETS; UnCover. **CCC.**
Description: Contains review coverage of major clinical issues.
Refereed Serial

616.4 SZ ISSN 0301-3073
CODEN: FHRSA7
FRONTIERS OF HORMONE RESEARCH. (Text in English) 1972. irreg. price varies. S. Karger AG, Allschwilerstr. 10, P.O. Box, CH-4009 Basel, Switzerland. TEL 061-3061111.
FAX 061-3061234. E-mail: Karger@Karger.ch. Ed. A. Grossman. (reprint service avail. from ISI) **Indexed:** Biol.Abstr., Chem.Abstr., Curr.Cont., Ind.Med., Ind.Sci.Rev., Ind.Vet., Sci.Cit.Ind., Small Anim.Abstr., Vet.Bull. **Document type:** academic/scholarly publication.
—BLDSC (4042.025000); Faxon; Genuine Article. **CCC.**
Formerly: Monographs in Hormone Research (ISSN 0077-0868)
Description: Information on how findings from hormone research can be used in clinical medicine.
Refereed Serial

616.4 US ISSN 0016-6480
QP187 CODEN: GCENA5
GENERAL AND COMPARATIVE ENDOCRINOLOGY; an international journal. 1961. m. $934 (foreign $1066) (effective 1996). Academic Press, Inc., Journal Division, 525 B St., Ste. 1900, San Diego, CA 92101-4495. TEL 619-230-1840.
FAX 619-699-6800. (Subscr. to: Box 620000, Orlando, FL 32891-8340. TEL 800-543-9534) Eds. Ian W. Henderson, Frank L. Moore. adv.; bk.rev.; bibl.; charts; illus.; index. (back issues avail.) **Indexed:** Anim.Breed.Abstr., Biol.Abstr., Chem.Abstr., Curr.Adv.Cell & Devel.Biol., Curr.Adv.Ecol.Sci., Curr.Cont., Excerp.Med., Helminthol.Abstr., Ind.Med., Ind.Sci.Rev., INIS Atomind., Nutr.Abstr., Poult.Abstr., Rev.Appl.Entomol., Sport Fish.Abstr., Vet.Bull., Wild.Rev., Zoo.Rec. **Document type:** academic/scholarly publication.
—BLDSC (4097.400000); CASDDS; Faxon; Genuine Article; SWETS; UnCover. **CCC.**
Description: Devoted to basic endocrinological research; emphasizes fundamental research; features occasional brief reviews that deal with a particular field or problem.
Refereed Serial

616.46 IT ISSN 0391-7525
CODEN: GIDIDU
GIORNALE ITALIANO DI DIABETOLOGIA.* (Text in Italian; summaries in English, Italian, Spanish) 1981. q. L.30000($35) Boehringer Mannheim Italia S.p.A., Via S. Uguzzone 5, 20126 Milan, Italy. Ed. G. Gentili. adv.; bk.rev.; abstr.; charts; illus.; stat.; index. circ. 2,300. **Indexed:** Chem.Abstr., Excerp.Med.
—BLDSC (4178.214300); CASDDS.
Description: Features original articles, reviews and edited letters on topics of physiopathology, clinics, and the therapy of diabetic illnesses. Includes columns on domestic and international cultural, social and sanitary-political activities for the diabetic.

GROWTH FACTORS & CYTOKINES - CLINICAL. see *MEDICAL SCIENCES — Abstracting, Bibliographies, Statistics*

GROWTH FACTORS & CYTOKINES - RESEARCH. see *MEDICAL SCIENCES — Allergology And Immunology*

616.4 UK ISSN 0956-523X
CODEN: GREGEP
GROWTH REGULATION. 1991. q. £129($206) to individuals; institutions £161 ($257) (effective 1995). Churchill Livingstone Journals (Subsidiary of: Pearson Professional), Robert Stevenson House, 1-3 Baxter's Pl., Leith Walk, Edinburgh EH1 3AF, Scotland. TEL 0131-556-2424.
FAX 0131-459-1177. (Subscr. to: Pearson Professional Ltd., P.O. Box 77, Harlow, Essex CM19 5BQ, England. TEL 01279-623760; U.S. subscr. to: Churchill Livingstone, 650 Ave. of the Americas, New York, NY 10011. TEL 212-206-5000) Ed. D. Schuster. adv. contact: David Dunnachie. **Indexed:** Excerp.Med. (1993-), Ind.Med. (1992-). **Document type:** academic/scholarly publication.
—BLDSC (4223.047000); CASDDS; Genuine Article. **CCC.**
Description: Publishes research articles and topical mini-reviews concerning all aspects of growth-promoting and growth-inhibiting hormones and factors, whether in whole animals or in tissues and cells.
Refereed Serial

612.4008042 UK ISSN 0951-3590
GYNECOLOGICAL ENDOCRINOLOGY. 1987. bi-m. £75($130) to individuals; institutions £140($240) (effective 1996). (International Society of Gynecological Endocrinology) Parthenon Publishing Group, Casterton Hall, Carnforth, Lancs LA6 2LA, England. TEL 44-15242-72084.
FAX 44-15242-71587. (In U.S.: Box 1564, Pearl River, NY 10965. TEL 914-735-9363. FAX 914-735-1385) Ed. A.R. Genazzani. circ. 1,200 (paid). (back issues avail.) **Indexed:** Excerp.Med., Ind.Med. **Document type:** academic/scholarly publication.
—BLDSC (4233.720000); Genuine Article; SWETS.
Refereed Serial

616.4 US
HOMEOSTASIS QUARTERLY.* 1971. q. $5. Hypoglycemia Foundation, Inc., Adrenal Metabolic Research Society, 32 Sunrise Ter., Clifton Park, NY 12065-2327. Ed. Marilyn Hamilton Light. bk.rev. circ. 5,000. (tabloid format)

616.4 GW ISSN 0018-5043
QP801.H7 CODEN: HMMRA2
HORMONE AND METABOLIC RESEARCH. (Supplement Series (ISSN 0170-5903)) (Text in English, French and German; summaries in English) 1969. m. DM.396. (German Society of Endocrinology) Georg Thieme Verlag, Ruedigerstr. 14, 70469 Stuttgart, Germany. TEL 0711-8931-0. FAX 0711-8931298. (Subscr. to: Postfach 104853, 70042 Stuttgart, Germany) Eds. E.F. Pfeiffer, G.M. Reaven. adv.; bibl.; charts; illus.; stat.; index. circ. 1,500. (also avail. in microform from UMI; reprint service avail. from UMI) **Indexed:** Anim.Breed.Abstr., Apic.Abstr., Biol.Abstr., Biotech.Abstr., Chem.Abstr., Curr.Adv.Biochem., Curr.Adv.Cell & Devel.Biol., Curr.Adv.Ecol.Sci., Curr.Cont., Dairy Sci.Abstr., Dent.Ind., Diab.Cont., Excerp.Med., Ind.Med., Ind.Sci.Rev., Ind.Vet., INIS Atomind., Nutr.Abstr., Pig News & Info., Poult.Abstr., Risk Abstr., Sci.Cit.Ind., Vet.Bull. **Document type:** academic/scholarly publication.
—BLDSC (4327.300000); ADONIS; CASDDS; Faxon; Genuine Article; SWETS; UMI; UnCover. **CCC.**

616.4 GW ISSN 0170-5903
CODEN: HMRSAU
HORMONE AND METABOLIC RESEARCH. SUPPLEMENT. irreg. (German Society of Endocrinology) Georg Thieme Verlag, Ruedigerstr. 14, 70469 Stuttgart, Germany. TEL 0711-8931-0. FAX 0711-8391298. (Subscr. to: Postfach 104853, 70042 Stuttgart, Germany) (back issues avail.) **Indexed:** Excerp.Med. (1994-), Ind.Med. **Document type:** monographic series.
—BLDSC (4327.310000); CASDDS; Faxon.

HORMONE FRONTIER IN GYNECOLOGY. see *MEDICAL SCIENCES — Obstetrics And Gynecology*

MEDICAL SCIENCES — ENDOCRINOLOGY

616.4 SZ ISSN 0301-0163
QP187.A1 CODEN: HRMRA3
HORMONE RESEARCH; international journal of experimental and clinical endocrinology. (Text in English) 1970. 12/yr.(2 vols.). 550.80 SFr.($423.60) to individuals; institutions 918 SFr.($706) (effective 1996). S. Karger AG, Allschwilerstr. 10, P.O. Box, CH-4009 Basel, Switzerland. TEL 061-3061111. FAX 061-3061234. E-mail: Karger@Karger.ch. Ed. J. Girard. adv.; bk.rev.; bibl.; charts; stat. circ. 1,000. (also avail. in microform) **Indexed**: Anim.Breed.Abstr., Biol.Abstr., Biotech.Abstr., Chem.Abstr., Curr.Adv.Ecol.Sci., Curr.Cont., Dairy Sci.Abstr., Dent.Ind., Diab.Cont., Excerp.Med., Ind.Med., Ind.Sci.Rev., Nutr.Abstr., Pig News & Info., Sci.Cit.Ind. **Document type**: academic/scholarly publication.
—BLDSC (4327.400000); CASDDS; Faxon; Genuine Article; SWETS; UnCover. **CCC**.
Incorporates: Hormones (ISSN 0018-5051); Steroids and Lipids Research (ISSN 0300-0621); Which was formerly: Steroidologica (ISSN 0049-2221)
Refereed Serial

616.4 156 US ISSN 0018-506X
QP187.A1 CODEN: HOBEAO
HORMONES AND BEHAVIOR. 1969. q. $268 (foreign $327) (effective 1996). Academic Press, Inc., Journal Division, 525 B St., Ste. 1900, San Diego, CA 92101-4495. TEL 619-230-1840. FAX 619-699-6800. (Subscr. to: Box 620000, Orlando, FL 32891-8340. TEL 800-543-9534) Ed. Robert W. Goy. adv. bk.rev. (back issues avail.) **Indexed**: Abstr.Anthropol., Anim.Breed.Abstr., Biol.Abstr., Chem.Abstr., Curr.Adv.Ecol.Sci., Curr.Cont., Dairy.Sci.Abstr., Excerp.Med., Ind.Med., Ind.Sci.Rev., Mid.East: Abstr.& Ind., Nutr.Abstr., Poult.Abstr., Psychol.Abstr. (1971-). **Document type**: academic/scholarly publication.
—BLDSC (4328.050000); ADONIS; CASDDS; Faxon; Genuine Article; SWETS; UnCover. **CCC**.
Description: Publishes original articles concerned with behavioral systems that are known to be hormonally influenced.
Refereed Serial

616.4 JA ISSN 0045-7167
CODEN: HORIAE
HORUMON TO RINSHO/CLINICAL ENDOCRINOLOGY. (Text in Japanese) 1953. m. 2000 Yen per no. Igaku no Sekaisha, 12-4, Kudan Kita 1-chome, Chiyoda-ku, Tokyo 102, Japan. **Indexed**: Chem.Abstr., INIS Atomind., Jap.Per.Ind.
—BLDSC (3286.279000); CASDDS.

HUMAN REPRODUCTION. see *MEDICAL SCIENCES — Obstetrics And Gynecology*

616.33 JA ISSN 0289-2057
I-BUNPI KENKYUKAISHI/JAPANESE SOCIETY OF GASTRIC SECRETION RESEARCH. PROCEEDINGS. Variant title: I-bunpi Kenkyukai Kiroku. (Text in Japanese) 1971. a. 3000 Yen (effective Apr. 1993). Japanese Society of Gastric Secretion Research - I-bunpi Kenkyukai, c/o Tokyo Jikaijai Ika Daigaku Dai-2 Geka, 25-8, 3-chome, Nishi-Shinbashi, Minato-ku, Tokyo 105, Japan. TEL 03-3433-1111. FAX 03-3435-8677. Ed. Teruaki Aoki. adv. contact: Teruaki Aoki. circ. 1,000. (back issues avail.) **Document type**: proceedings.

616.462 BE ISSN 0306-4980
CODEN: IDFBD6
I D F BULLETIN. 4/yr. $40 includes I D F Newsletter. International Diabetes Federation, 1 rue Defacqz, 1050 Brussels, Belgium. TEL 32-2-5385511. FAX 32-2-5385514. TELEX 65080 INAC B. Ed.Bd. adv.; bk.rev. circ. 6,000. (back issues avail.) **Indexed**: Diab.Cont. **Document type**: bulletin.
—BLDSC (4362.460100).
Description: Covers diabetes, health economics, and relevant developments in endocrinology and medicine.

616.462 BE ISSN 1015-1753
I D F DIRECTORY. triennial, 3rd ed., 1994. $80. International Diabetes Federation, 1 rue Defacqz, 1050 Brussels, Belgium. TEL 32-2-5385511. FAX 32-2-5385514. TELEX 65080 INAC B. **Document type**: directory.
Incorporates (in 1994): International Diabetes Federation. Triennial Report; Which was formerly: International Diabetes Federation. Proceedings of Congress (ISSN 0074-4522)

616.462 BE
I D F NEWS BULLETIN. q. $25 includes I D F Bulletin. International Diabetes Federation, 1 rue Defacqz, 1050 Brussels, Belgium. TEL 32-2-5385511. FAX 32-2-5385514. TELEX 65080 INAC B. Ed.Bd. circ. 3,000. **Document type**: bulletin.

616.462 UK
INTERNATIONAL DIABETES DIGEST. 1989. q. £30($50) (effective 1995). F S G Communications Ltd., Vine House, Fair Green, Reach, Cambridge CB5 0JD, England. TEL 01638-743633. FAX 01638-743998. Eds. G. Alberti, G. Gill. adv. contact: Mark Temple-Smith. circ. 5,000 (controlled). **Document type**: academic/scholarly publication.
Formerly: Practical Diabetes Digest (ISSN 0960-8893)
Description: Contains original and review articles for physicians and others treating diabetes in the Middle East and Africa.

616.3 US ISSN 0169-4197
CODEN: IJPNEX
INTERNATIONAL JOURNAL OF PANCREATOLOGY. 1986. bi-m. $360 (foreign $390) (effective 1996). (International Association of Pancreatology) Humana Press Inc., 999 Riverview Dr., Ste. 208, Totowa, NJ 07512. TEL 201-256-1699. FAX 201-256-8341. (Dist. in Japan by: Maruzen Co. Ltd., Journals Div., P.O. Box 5050, Tokyo 100-31, Japan. TEL 03-32758591. FAX 03-32781937) Ed. Dr. Parviz M. Pour. adv. contact: Thomas B. Lanigan, Jr. bk.rev.; abstr.; bibl.; charts; illus.; index. (back issues avail.) **Indexed**: Biol.Abstr., Curr.Cont., Excerp.Med., Ind.Med., Sci.Cit.Ind. **Document type**: academic/scholarly publication.
—BLDSC (4542.441000); CASDDS; Faxon; Genuine Article; SWETS; UnCover. **CCC**.
Description: Multidisciplinary forum for original clinical research on the exocrine and endocrine pancreas.
Refereed Serial

616.4 GW ISSN 0943-1675
INTERNATIONAL JOURNAL OF THYMOLOGY. (Text in English) 1993. 2/yr. Thymus Medizinischer Fachbuchverlag, Rudolf-Huch-Strasse 14, 38667 Bad Harzburg, Germany. TEL 49-5322-2033. **Indexed**: Excerp.Med. (1995-). **Document type**: academic/scholarly publication.
—BLDSC (4542.695300).

616.15 US ISSN 0895-7762
IRONIC BLOOD; information on iron overload. 1981. bi-m. free. Iron Overload Diseases Association, Inc., International Consortium, 433 Westwind Dr., N. Palm Beach, FL 33408. TEL 407-840-8512. FAX 407-842-9881. Ed. Roberta Crawford. circ. 8,000. (back issues avail.) **Document type**: newsletter.
Description: Contains the latest information about hemochromatosis and other iron overload diseases for doctors, patients, and the public.

616.462 JA ISSN 0021-437X
CODEN: TONYA4
JAPAN DIABETES SOCIETY. JOURNAL/TONYOBYO. (Text in Japanese; summaries in English) 1958. m. 20550 Yen($65) Japan Diabetes Society - Nihon Tonyobyo Gakkai, Sky Bldg., Rm. 403, 3-38-11 Hongo, Bunkyo-ku, Tokyo 113, Japan. Ed. Dr. K. Yamashita. adv.; charts; index. circ. 4,800. **Indexed**: Biol.Abstr., Chem.Abstr., Diab.Cont., Excerp.Med. **Document type**: academic/scholarly publication.
—BLDSC (4804.840000); CASDDS; EMDOCS.
Formerly: Japan Diabetic Society. Journal.

616.4 574 JA ISSN 0913-9036
CODEN: PJSEEU
JAPAN SOCIETY FOR COMPARATIVE ENDOCRINOLOGY. PROCEEDINGS. (Text in English) 1986. a. 3000 Yen. Japan Society for Comparative Endocrinology - Nihon Hikaku Naibunpi Gakkai, c/o Zoology Institute, Faculty of Science, University of Tokyo, 3-1 Hongo 7-chome, Bunkyo-ku, Tokyo 113, Japan. TEL 03-3812-2111. FAX 81-3-3816-1965. Ed. Yuichi Sasayama. circ. 600. (back issues avail.) **Document type**: proceedings.
—BLDSC (6742.312000).

616.462 US
JOSLIN MAGAZINE. 1985. 4/yr. $25. Joslin Diabetes Center, Inc., One Joslin Pl., Boston, MA 02215. TEL 617-732-2415. FAX 617-732-2664. Ed. Julie F. Rafferty. illus. circ. 17,000. (back issues avail.)
Former titles: Joslin Diabetes Center Newsletter; Joslin Diabetes Foundation. Newsletter (ISSN 0021-7611)
Description: Covers articles on patient care and research on diabetics and its complications.

616.4 SZ
JOURNAL DES DIABETIQUES. (Text in French) 1962. 5/yr. 30 SFr. 2 Rue du Moulin, CH-2740 Moutier, Switzerland. TEL 032-935908. FAX 032-936234. Ed. J.J. Grimm. adv.; bk.rev. circ. 7,000. **Document type**: academic/scholarly publication.

616.4 GW ISSN 0914-8779
CODEN: JBMME4
JOURNAL OF BONE AND MINERAL METABOLISM. Japanese edition: Nihon Kotsu Taisha Gakkai Zasshi (ISSN 0910-0067) (Text in English) 1988. 4/yr. DM.260($188) (effective 1996). (Nihon Kotsu Taisha Gakkai - Japan Society for Bone and Metabolism Research) Springer-Verlag, Heidelberger Platz 3, 14197 Berlin, Germany. TEL 030-8207-1. FAX 030-8214091. (Subscr. in N. America to: Springer-Verlag New York, Inc., 44 Hartz Way, Secaucus, NJ 07096-2491. TEL 201-348-4033. FAX 201-348-4505) Ed. R. Suzuki. **Indexed**: Chem.Abstr.
—BLDSC (4954.255500); CASDDS.

616.4 US ISSN 0021-972X
CODEN: JCEMAZ
JOURNAL OF CLINICAL ENDOCRINOLOGY AND METABOLISM. 1941. m. $295 (foreign $345) (effective 1996). Endocrine Society, 4350 East West Hwy., Ste. 500, Bethesda, MD 20814-4410. TEL 301-941-0200. FAX 301-941-0259. Ed.Bd. adv.; charts; illus. circ. 9,400. (also avail. in microform from PMC; reprint service avail.) **Indexed**: AIM, Behav.Med.Abstr., Biol.Abstr., Biotech.Abstr., Chem.Abstr., Curr.Adv.Biochem., Curr.Adv.Cancer Res., Curr.Adv.Cell & Devel.Biol., Curr.Adv.Genetics & Molec.Biol., Curr.Cont., Dairy Sci.Abstr., Dent.Ind., Diab.Cont., Diar.Dis.Res., Excerp.Med., Food Sci.& Tech.Abstr., Helminthol.Abstr., Ind.Med., Ind.Sci.Rev., INIS Atomind., Kidney, Med.& Surg.Dermat., Nutr.Abstr., Risk Abstr., Sci.Cit.Ind, Sport Fish.Abstr., Wild.Rev. **Document type**: academic/scholarly publication.
—BLDSC (4958.400000); ADONIS; CASDDS; EMDOCS; Faxon; Genuine Article; SWETS; UnCover. **CCC**.
Description: Information on the clinical applications of endocrine research.
Refereed Serial

616.4 US ISSN 1056-8727
CODEN: JDICE2
JOURNAL OF DIABETES AND ITS COMPLICATIONS. 1987. bi-m. $292 to institutions (effective 1996). Elsevier Science Inc., 655 Ave. of the Americas, New York, NY 10010. TEL 212-989-5800. FAX 212-633-3990. TELEX 420643 AEP UI. (Subscr. to: Box 882, Madison Sq. Sta., New York, NY 10159-0882) Ed. Eli A. Friedman. (also avail. in microform from UMI; back issues avail.) **Indexed**: Diab.Cont., Excerp.Med., Ind.Med. **Document type**: academic/scholarly publication.
—BLDSC (4969.407000); Faxon; Genuine Article; SWETS. **CCC**.
Formerly (until 1992): Journal of Diabetic Complications (ISSN 0891-6632)
Description: Publishes original contributions developed from clinical investigation, as well as brief review articles.
Refereed Serial

MEDICAL SCIENCES — ENDOCRINOLOGY

616.4   IT   ISSN 0391-4097
CODEN: JEIND7
JOURNAL OF ENDOCRINOLOGICAL INVESTIGATION.
(Supplement avail. (ISSN 1121-1369)) (Text in English) 1978. 11/yr. L.140000 (foreign $140). (Societa Italiana di Endocrinologia - Italian Society of Endocrinology) Editrice Kurtis s.r.l., Via L. Zoja, 30, 20153 Milan, Italy. TEL 39-2-48202740. FAX 39-2-48201219. Ed. Aldo Pinchera. adv.: B&W page L.1900000, color page L.2350000; trim 200 x 260. charts; illus.; stat. **Indexed:** Curr.Adv.Biochem., Curr.Adv.Cell & Devel.Biol., Curr.Cont., Dairy Sci.Abstr., Excerp.Med., Ind.Med., Med.& Surg.Dermat. **Document type:** academic/scholarly publication.
—BLDSC (4977.900000); CASDDS; Faxon; Genuine Article; SWETS; UnCover.
Description: Publishes original studies on clinical and experimental research in endocrinology and related fields.

616.4   IT   ISSN 1121-1369
JOURNAL OF ENDOCRINOLOGICAL INVESTIGATION. SUPPLEMENT. 1991. q. (Societa Italiana di Endocrinologia - Italian Society of Endocrinology) Editrice Kurtis s.r.l., Via L. Zoja, 30, 20153 Milan, Italy. TEL 39-2-48202740. FAX 39-2-48201219. **Document type:** academic/scholarly publication.
—SWETS.

616.4   UK   ISSN 0022-0795
QP187.A1   CODEN: JOENAK
JOURNAL OF ENDOCRINOLOGY. 1939. m. (4 vols. per year). £285 (N. and S. America $515; elsewhere £315) (effective 1996). (Society for Endocrinology) Journal of Endocrinology Ltd., 17-18 The Courtyard, Woodlands, Almondsbury, Bristol BS12 4NQ, England. TEL 01454-616046. FAX 01454-616071. E-mail: soc-endoc@bristol.ac.uk. (Dist. by: Turpin Distribution Centre, Blackhorse Rd., Letchworth, Herts. SG6 1HN, England. TEL 01462-672555. FAX 01462-480947) Ed. Prof. A. McNeilly. adv.; bibl.; charts; illus.; index, cum.index: vols.1-20, 21-40. circ. 2,200. (also avail. in microform from PMC) **Indexed:** Anal.Abstr., Anim.Breed.Abstr., Behav.Med.Abstr., Biol.Abstr., Biotech.Abstr., Chem.Biol., Curr.Adv.Biochem., Curr.Adv.Cell & Devel.Biol., Curr.Adv.Genetics & Molec.Biol., Curr.Cont., Curr.Ref.Fish Res., Dairy Sci.Abstr., Dent.Ind., Diab.Cont., Excerp.Med., Ind.Med., Ind.Sci.Rev., Ind.Vet., INIS Atomind., Kidney, Mass Spectr.Bull., NRN, Nutr.Abstr., Poult.Abstr., Sci.Cit.Ind., Sport Fish.Abstr., Vet.Bull., Wild.Rev., Zoo.Rec. **Document type:** academic/scholarly publication.
—BLDSC (4978.000000); CASDDS; EMDOCS; Faxon; Genuine Article; SWETS; UnCover. **CCC**.

616.4   UK   ISSN 0968-0519
QP632.E4   CODEN: JENREB
▼**JOURNAL OF ENDOTOXIN RESEARCH.** 1994. q. £299($463) (effective 1995). Churchill Livingstone Journals (Subsidiary of: Pearson Professional), Robert Stevenson House, 1-3 Baxter's Pl., Leith Walk, Edinburgh EH1 3AF, Scotland. TEL 0131-556-2424. FAX 0131-459-1177. (Subscr. to: Pearson Professional Ltd., P.O. Box 77, Fourth Ave., Harlow, Essex CM19 5AA, England. TEL 01279-623760; U.S. subscr. to: Churchill Livingstone, 650 Ave. of the Americas, New York, NY 10011. TEL 212-206-5000) Ed. David C. Morrison. adv. contact: David Dunneallie. bk.rev.; bibl. **Indexed:** Excerp.Med. (1995-). **Document type:** academic/scholarly publication.
—BLDSC (4978.205000); CASDDS.
Description: Covers developments in endotoxin research.

616.4   UK   ISSN 0952-5041
QP187.3.M64   CODEN: JMLEEI
JOURNAL OF MOLECULAR ENDOCRINOLOGY. 1988. bi-m (in 2 vols.). £160 (N. and S. America $310; elsewhere £185) (effective 1996). (Society for Endocrinology) Journal of Endocrinology Ltd., 17-18 The Courtyard, Woodlands, Almondsbury, Bristol BS12 4NQ, England. TEL 01454-616046. FAX 01454-616071. E-mail: soc-endoc@bristol.ac.uk. (Subscr. to: Turpin Distribution Centre, Blackhorse Rd., Letchworth, Herts. SG6 1HN, England. TEL 01462-672555. FAX 01462-480947) Ed. B.L. Brown. charts; illus.; index. circ. 550. **Indexed:** Diab.Cont., Excerp.Med. **Document type:** academic/scholarly publication.
—BLDSC (5020.709000); CASDDS; Faxon; Genuine Article; SWETS; UnCover. **CCC**.
Description: Publishes research and review papers on molecular and cellular aspects of endocrine and related systems.

JOURNAL OF NEUROENDOCRINOLOGY. see *MEDICAL SCIENCES — Psychiatry And Neurology*

616.4   618.92   UK
CODEN: JPENEV
JOURNAL OF PEDIATRIC ENDOCRINOLOGY & METABOLISM. (Text in English) 1985. q. $250 (effective 1996). Freund Publishing House Ltd., Ste. 500, Chesham House, 150 Regent St., London W1R 5FA, England. (Alt addr.: P.O. Box 35010, Tel Aviv, Israel. TEL 972-3-5625840) Ed. Z. Laron. adv.; bk.rev. circ. 1,000. (back issues avail.) **Indexed:** Curr.Adv.Ecol.Sci., Excerp.Med., Ind.Med. (1993-), Kidney. **Document type:** academic/scholarly publication.
—CASDDS; Faxon; UnCover.
Formerly: Journal of Pediatric Endocrinology (ISSN 0334-018X)

616.4   JA   ISSN 0289-4947
CODEN: PRCTEH
JOURNAL OF PRACTICAL DIABETES; practice. (Text in Japanese) 1984. q. 800 Yen per no. Ishiyaku Publishers, Inc., 7-10 Honkomagome 1-chome, Bunkyo-ku, Tokyo 113, Japan. Ed. Hiroshi Miura. adv.; bk.rev.; charts; illus. circ. 10,000.

616.4   FR   ISSN 0075-4439
CODEN: JDBHAC
JOURNEES ANNUELLES DE DIABETOLOGIE DE L'HOTEL DIEU. 1961. a. price varies. (Hotel-Dieu, Clinique Medico-Sociale du Diabete et des Maladies Metaboliques) Flammarion Medecine Sciences, 4 rue Casimir Delavigne, 75006 Paris, France. (U.S. subscr. addr. S.F.P.A., c/o M. Benech, 14 E. 60 St., New York, NY 10022) Ed. Dr. Rathery. **Indexed:** Biol.Abstr., Chem.Abstr., Dent.Ind., Ind.Med.
—BLDSC (5072.940000); CASDDS; Faxon. **CCC**.

616.4   II   ISSN 0971-5053
CODEN: LSAEE
LIFE SCIENCE ADVANCES: EXPERIMENTAL & CLINICAL ENDOCRINOLOGY. Key Title: Experimental & Clinical Endocrinology - Life Science Advances. (Text in English) 1982. 4/yr. Council of Scientific Research Integration, T.C. 28-408 (3), Vilayal Gardens, Kaithamukku, 695 024 Trivandrum, India. TEL 91-471-77305. **Indexed:** Excerp.Med. (1994-). **Document type:** academic/scholarly publication.

616.4   GW   ISSN 0024-7766
RC646   CODEN: LYMPBN
LYMPHOLOGY. 1968. q. International Society of Lymphology, c/o Univ. of Arizona, Dept. of Surgery - Trauma, 1501 N. Campbell, Tucson, AZ 85724. TEL 602-626-6118. Ed. Dr. Charles L. Witte. adv.; abstr.; charts; illus.; stat.; index. circ. 1,100. (reprint service avail. from UMI) **Indexed:** Biol.Abstr., Chem.Abstr., Curr.Adv.Cancer Res., Curr.Adv.Ecol.Sci., Curr.Cont., Dairy Sci.Abstr., Dent.Ind., Excerp.Med., Helminthol.Abstr., Ind.Med., Ind.Sci.Rev., INIS Atomind., Sci.Cit.Ind., Vet.Bull.
—BLDSC (5311.300000); CASDDS; EMDOCS; Faxon; Genuine Article; SWETS; UMI. **CCC**.
Refereed Serial

616.4   JA   ISSN 0913-4867
CODEN: MAGUEO
MAGUNESHUMU/JAPANESE SOCIETY FOR MAGNESIUM RESEARCH. JOURNAL. (Text in English, Japanese; summaries in English) 1982. s-a. Nihon Maguneshumu Kenkyukai, Kyoto Daigaku Igakubu Eiseigaku Kyoshitsu, Yoshida Konoecho, Sakyo-ku, Kyoto 606-01, Japan. **Indexed:** Chem.Abstr.
—BLDSC (4809.464000); CASDDS.

MENOPAUSE. see *MEDICAL SCIENCES — Obstetrics And Gynecology*

616.4   574.133   US   ISSN 0026-0495
RB147   CODEN: METAAJ
METABOLISM: CLINICAL AND EXPERIMENTAL. 1952. m. $251 (foreign $345) (effective 1996). W.B. Saunders Co. (Subsidiary of: Harcourt Brace & Company), Curtis Center, 3rd Fl., Independence Sq. W., Philadelphia, PA 19106-3399. TEL 215-238-7800. FAX 215-238-6445. (Subscr. to: Periodicals Fulfillment, W.B. Saunders Co., 6277 Sea Harbor Dr., 4th Fl., Orlando, FL 32891-4800. TEL 800-654-2452. FAX 800-874-6418) Ed. Dr. James B. Field; Pub. Joan W. Blumberg. adv.: B&W page $800, color page $1750; 7 x 10. abstr.; bibl.; charts; illus.; index. circ. 3,011. **Indexed:** Abstr.Hyg., Biol.Abstr., Biotech.Abstr., Chem.Abstr., Curr.Adv.Biochem., Curr.Adv.Cell & Devel.Biol., Curr.Adv.Ecol.Sci., Curr.Cont., Diab.Cont., Excerp.Med., Helminthol.Abstr., Ind.Med., Ind.Vet., INIS Atomind., Nutr.Abstr., Trop.Dis.Bull. **Document type:** academic/scholarly publication.
●Also available online.
—BLDSC (5683.300000); CASDDS; EMDOCS; Faxon; Genuine Article; SWETS; UMI; UnCover. **CCC**.
Description: Reports on research into the metabolic aspects of nutrition, endocrines, genetics, dystrophies, diabetes, and gout.
Refereed Serial

616.4   IT   ISSN 0391-1977
CODEN: MNREDJ
MINERVA ENDOCRINOLOGICA; rivista trimestrale di fisiopatologia e clinica delle ghiandole endocrine. 1976. q. $90 to individuals; institutions $140 (effective 1995). Edizioni Minerva Medica, Corso Bramante 83-85, 10126 Turin, Italy. TEL 39-11-678282. FAX 39-11-3121736. Ed. G.H. Molinatti; Pub. Alberto Oliaro. adv.: B&W page $1100, color page $1900; trim 190 x 270; adv. contact: F. Filippo. **Indexed:** Chem.Abstr., Ind.Med. **Document type:** academic/scholarly publication.
—BLDSC (5794.153000); CASDDS; Faxon.
Refereed Serial

616.4   IE   ISSN 0303-7207
QP187.A1   CODEN: MCEND6
MOLECULAR AND CELLULAR ENDOCRINOLOGY; an international journal integrating all aspects related to the biochemical effects, synthesis and secretions of extracellular signals (hormones, neurotransmitters, etc.) and to the understanding of cellular regulatory mechanisms involved in hormonal control. 1974. 20/yr. I£1450($2291) (effective 1996). Elsevier Science Ireland Ltd., P.O. Box 85, Limerick, Ireland. TEL 353-61-471944. FAX 353-61-472144. (Subscr. in U.S. and Canada to: Elsevier Science Inc., Box 882, Madison Sq. Sta., New York, NY 10159. TEL 212-989-5800. FAX 212-633-3990) Ed. B.A. Cooke. (also avail. in microform from UMI) **Indexed:** Anim.Breed.Abstr., Biol.Abstr., Chem.Abstr., Curr.Adv.Biochem., Curr.Adv.Cell & Devel.Biol., Curr.Adv.Ecol.Sci., Curr.Adv.Genetics & Molec.Biol., Curr.Cont., Dairy Sci.Abstr., Excerp.Med., Ind.Med., Ind.Sci.Rev., Nutr.Abstr., Poult.Abstr. **Document type:** academic/scholarly publication.
—BLDSC (5900.760000); CASDDS; Faxon; Genuine Article; SWETS; UnCover. **CCC**.
Refereed Serial

616.4   US   ISSN 0888-8809
QP187.3.M64   CODEN: MOENEN
MOLECULAR ENDOCRINOLOGY. m. $295 (foreign $345) (effective 1996). Endocrine Society, 4350 East West Hwy., Ste. 500, Bethesda, MD 20814-4410. TEL 301-941-0200. FAX 301-941-0259. Ed. Dr. E. Brad Thompson. circ. 1,900. (also avail. in microform from WWS; back issues avail.) **Indexed:** Anim.Breed.Abstr., Curr.Adv.Biochem., Curr.Adv.Cancer Res., Curr.Adv.Cell & Devel.Biol., Curr.Adv.Genetics & Molec.Biol., Poult.Abstr., Sport Fish.Abstr., Wild.Rev. **Document type:** academic/scholarly publication.
—BLDSC (5900.817390); ADONIS; CASDDS; Faxon; Genuine Article; SWETS; UnCover. **CCC**.
Description: Forum for molecular and cellular biologists investigating the molecular mechanisms of cellular regulatory processes.
Refereed Serial

MEDICAL SCIENCES — ENDOCRINOLOGY

616.4   JA   ISSN 0918-6557
CODEN: MOLMEL
MOLECULAR MEDICINE. (Text in Japanese) 1964. m. 2500 Yen per no. Nakayama Shoten, 25-14, Hakusan 1-chome, Bunkyo-ku, Tokyo 113, Japan. TEL 81-3-3813-1103. FAX 81-3-3814-6336. Ed. Nobuko Itowi. adv. contact: Shiho Nakamura. **Indexed:** Chem.Abstr., INIS Atomind., Jap.Per.Ind. —BLDSC (5900.817950).
    Formerly (until vol.30, no.1, 1993): Taisha - Metabolism and Diseases (ISSN 0372-1566)

616.4   US   ISSN 0077-1015
CODEN: MOENBK
MONOGRAPHS ON ENDOCRINOLOGY. 1967. irreg. price varies. Springer-Verlag, 175 Fifth Ave., New York, NY 10010. TEL 212-460-1500. FAX 212-473-6272. (Also: Berlin, Heidelberg, Tokyo and Vienna) (reprint service avail. from ISI) **Indexed:** Biol.Abstr., Chem.Abstr., Ind.Med. **Document type:** monographic series.
—CASDDS.

616.4   UK   ISSN 0047-8385
MURMUR. 1922. 3/yr. free to qualified medical students. Cambridge University Medical Society, Department of Anatomy, Cambridge University, Cambridge CB2 9DT, England. TEL 01223-60160. Eds. Kate Wynne, Rob Weinkore. adv. contact: Ben Silverman. bk.rev.; circ. 750 (controlled). **Document type:** academic/scholarly publication.

616.4 617   JA   ISSN 0914-9953
NAIBUNPI GEKA/ENDOCRINE SURGERY. (Text in English, Japanese; summaries in English) 1984. q. 15100 Yen. Intermerc Co., Ltd., 39-15-104, Eifuku 1-chome, Suginami-ku, Tokyo 168, Japan. TEL 03-5376-2820. FAX 03-5376-5790. **Indexed:** INIS Atomind.

616   JA
NAIBUNPIGAKU NO SHINPO/ADVANCES IN ENDOCRINOLOGY. (Text in English, Japanese; summaries in Japanese) 1983. a. 6500 Yen. Topuko Shuppanbu - Topco Ltd., 5-2-302, Kojimachi 2-chome, Chiyoda-ku, Tokyo 102, Japan.

NATIONAL ALOPECIA AREATA FOUNDATION NEWSLETTER. see MEDICAL SCIENCES — Dermatology And Venereology

NEUROENDOCRINE PERSPECTIVES. see MEDICAL SCIENCES — Psychiatry And Neurology

616.4 616.8   SZ   ISSN 0028-3835
QP187.A1   CODEN: NUNDAJ
NEUROENDOCRINOLOGY; international journal for basic and clinical studies on neuroendocrine relationships. (Text in English) 1965. m. (2 vols./yr.). 1056 SFr.($812.40) to individuals; institutions1760 SFr.($1354) (effective 1996). (International Society of Neuroendocrinology) S. Karger AG, Allschwilerstr. 10, P.O. Box, CH-4009 Basel, Switzerland. TEL 061-3061111. FAX 061-3061234. E-mail: Karger@Karger.ch. Ed. C. Kordon. adv.; illus. circ. 1,650. (also avail. in microform) **Indexed:** Anim.Breed.Abstr., Biol.Abstr., Biotech.Abstr., Chem.Abstr., Curr.Adv.Cell & Devel.Biol., Curr.Adv.Ecol.Sci., Curr.Adv.Genetics & Molec.Biol., Curr.Cont., Dairy Sci.Abstr., Excerp.Med., Ind.Med., Ind.Sci.Rev., Ind.Vet., Int.Aerosp.Abstr., Poult.Abstr., Pub.Fish.Abstr., Vet.Bull., Wild.Rev., Zoo.Rec. **Document type:** academic/scholarly publication.
—BLDSC (6081.370000); CASDDS; EMDOCS; Faxon; Genuine Article; SWETS; UnCover. **CCC.**
Refereed Serial

NIHON DAEKISEN GAKKAISHI/JAPAN SALIVARY GLAND SOCIETY. JOURNAL. see BIOLOGY — Physiology

616.4   JA   ISSN 0913-9044
NIHON HIKAKU NAIBUNPI GAKKAI NYUSU/JAPAN SOCIETY FOR COMPARATIVE ENDOCRINOLOGY. NEWSLETTER. (Text in Japanese) 1975. q. Nihon Hikaku Naibunpi Gakkai, Tokyo Daigaku Rigakubu Dobutsugaku Kyoshitsu, 3-1, Hongo 7-chome, Bunkyo-ku, Tokyo 113, Japan. Ed. Yuichi Sasayama. adv. contact: Inoue Kinji. **Document type:** newsletter.

616.4   JA   ISSN 0910-0067
CODEN: NKTZEF
NIHON KOTSU TAISHA GAKKAI ZASSHI. English edition: Journal of Bone and Mineral Metabolism (ISSN 0914-8779) (Text in Japanese) 1983. q. 1500 Yen per no. Nihon Kotsu Taisha Gakkai - Japan Society for Bone and Metabolism Research, Nihon Konbenshon Sabisu, 2-1, Uchisaiwaicho 2-chome, Chiyoda-ku, Tokyo 100, Japan.
—CASDDS.

616.4   JA   ISSN 0029-0661
CODEN: NNGZAZ
NIHON NAIBUNPI GAKKAI ZASSHI/FOLIA ENDOCRINOLOGICA JAPONICA. (Text in Japanese; summaries in English) 1925. m. 700 Yen per no. Nihon Naibunpi Gakkai - Japan Endocrine Society, Kinki Chiho Hatsumei Center, 14, Yoshida Kawara-machi, Sakyo-ku, Kyoto 606, Japan. adv.; bk.rev. **Indexed:** Anim.Breed.Abstr., Biol.Abstr., Dent.Ind., Excerp.Med., Ind.Med., Pig News & Info. —BLDSC (3969.700000); CASDDS; Genuine Article.

NIHON SHONI NAIBUNPI GAKKAI PUROGURAMU SHOROKUSHU/JAPANESE SOCIETY FOR PEDIATRIC ENDOCRINOLOGY. ANNUAL MEETING. see MEDICAL SCIENCES — Pediatrics

616.4   JA   ISSN 0912-2532
NO CHO HORUMON GAKKAI NYUSU/NEWS OF THE BRAIN-GUT HORMONE RESEARCH. (Text in Japanese) 1986. q. No Cho Horumon Gakkai - Society of Brain-Gut Hormone Research, Niigata Daigaku Igakubu Dai 3 Kaibogaku Kyoshitsu, 757, Ichibancho, Asahimachi Dori, Niigata-shi, Niigata-ken 951, Japan.

616.4   FR   ISSN 0985-0562
CODEN: NCMEEV
NUTRITION CLINIQUE ET METABOLISME. 1987. q. 580 F. to individuals; institutions 745 F.; foreign 805 F.(163) (effective 1996). Arnette Blackwell, 1 rue de Lille, 75007 Paris, France. TEL 33-1-44-86-07-70. FAX 33-1-44-86-07-66. —BLDSC (6188.133000); UMI. **CCC.**

616.46   IT   ISSN 1122-2255
OBIETTIVO DIABETE; rassegna di diabetologia, metabolismo e nutrizione clinica. (Text in English, Italian) 1991. q. L.90000($150) (effective 1995). Casa Editrice Idelson, Via A. De Gasperi 55, 80133 Naples, Italy. TEL 39-81-5524733. FAX 39-81-5518295. Ed. Renato Carleo.

OXYTOCIN AND VASOPRESSIN. see MEDICAL SCIENCES — Abstracting, Bibliographies, Statistics

616.4   US   ISSN 0885-3177
CODEN: PANCE4
PANCREAS. 1986. bi-m. $373 to individuals (foreign $468); institutions $620 (foreign $676) (effective 1996); newsstand price: $86. Lippincott - Raven Publishers, 227 E. Washington Sq., Philadelphia, PA 19106. TEL 215-238-4200. Ed. Dr. Vay Liang W. Go. adv. contact: Phyllis Noyes. bk.rev.; charts; illus.; index. circ. 1,500. (back issues avail.; reprint service avail. from UMI) **Indexed:** Curr.Adv.Biochem., Curr.Adv.Cell & Devel.Biol., Excerp.Med., Ind.Med. **Document type:** academic/scholarly publication.
—BLDSC (6357.351500); CASDDS; Faxon; Genuine Article; SWETS; UMI; UnCover. **CCC.**
    Description: Publishes both basic and clinical work on the exocrine and endocrine pancreas, their interrelationship, and consequences in disease states.
Refereed Serial

PANCREATIC AND SALIVARY SECRETION. see BIOLOGY — Physiology

616.4   SZ   ISSN 0304-4254
CODEN: PAENDP
PEDIATRIC AND ADOLESCENT ENDOCRINOLOGY. (Text in English) 1976. irreg. price varies. S. Karger AG, Allschwilerstr. 10, P.O. Box, CH-4009 Basel, Switzerland. TEL 061-3061111. FAX 061-3061234. E-mail: Karger@Karger.ch. Ed. Z. Laron. (reprint service avail. from ISI) **Indexed:** Biol.Abstr., Chem.Abstr., Curr.Adv.Ecol.Sci. **Document type:** academic/scholarly publication.
—BLDSC (6417.528000); CASDDS. **CCC.**
Refereed Serial

PEPTIDE HORMONE RECEPTORS. see MEDICAL SCIENCES — Abstracting, Bibliographies, Statistics

616.462   CN   ISSN 0384-7810
PLEIN SOLEIL. 1958. q. Can.$20. Association du Diabete du Quebec Inc., 5635 rue Sherbrooke E., Montreal, PQ H1N 1A3, Canada. TEL 514-259-3422. FAX 514-259-9286. Ed. Anne Leblanc. adv. contact: Yvan Gagne. bk.rev. circ. 15,000. (also avail. in audio cassette) **Indexed:** Pt.de Rep. (1979-). **Document type:** consumer publication.
    Formerly: Survivre (ISSN 0562-7087)

616.5   UK   ISSN 1357-8170
PRACTICAL DIABETES INTERNATIONAL; the international journal for diabetes care teams worldwide. 1984. bi-m. £36 to institutions (free to qualified personnel in UK) (Europe £42; USA $90; elsewhere £54). (Newbourne Group) P M H Publications Ltd., P.O. Box 100, Chichester, W. Sussex PO19 1XR, England. TEL 44-1243-576444. FAX 44-1243-576456. Ed. Dr. Ken Shaw; Pub. James Wroe. circ. 10,000. **Indexed:** Diab.Cont. **Document type:** academic/scholarly publication.
—BLDSC (6593.980157).
    Formerly (until vol.12, 1995): Practical Diabetes (ISSN 0266-447X)
    Description: Delivers important educational service to all health professionals involved in diabetes care.

616.4   US   ISSN 0730-3491
PRACTICAL DIABETOLOGY. 1982. q. $48 (effective 1992). R.A. Rapaport Publishing, Inc., 150 W. 22nd St., New York, NY 10011. TEL 212-989-0200. FAX 212-989-4786. Ed. Dr. Daniel L. Lorber; Pub. Richard A. Rapaport. adv.; B&W page $4800; adv. contact: Kathy Jones. circ. 52,000 (controlled). (back issues avail.) **Document type:** academic/scholarly publication.
—BLDSC (6593.980300).
    Description: Practical diabetes information for the busy physician and pharmacist.
Refereed Serial

616.4 612.405   RU   ISSN 0375-9660
CODEN: PROEAS
PROBLEMY ENDOKRINOLOGII/PROBLEMS OF ENDOCRINOLOGY. (Text in Russian; summaries in English) 1955. bi-m. $89 (effective 1996). (Endokrinologicheskii Nauchnyi Tsentr) Izdatel'stvo Meditsina, Petroverigskii pereulok 6-8, 101000 Moscow, Russia. (Dist. by: Mezhdunarodnaya Kniga, B. Yakimanka 39, 117049 Moscow, Russia. TEL 7-095-2384600. FAX 7-095-2384634) (Co-sponsor: Ministerstvo Zdravookhraneniya) Ed. V.P. Fedotov. adv. contact: T.A. Pokrovskaya. bk.rev. (tabloid format) **Indexed:** Biol.Abstr., Biotech.Abstr., Chem.Abstr., Excerp.Med., Ind.Med., Int.Aerosp.Abstr., Nutr.Abstr.
—BLDSC (0133.980000); CASDDS.
    Formerly: Problemy Endokrinologii i Gormonoterapii (ISSN 0032-9509)
    Description: Covers the most pressing problems of modern endocrinology, such as chemical structure, biosynthesis and metabolism of hormones, the mechanism of their action at cellular and molecular levels, as well as the pathogenesis and clinical picture of endocrine diseases and new methods of their diagnosis and treatment.

PROGRAM OF PLENARY SESSIONS AND ADVANCE ABSTRACTS OF SHORT COMMUNICATIONS. see MEDICAL SCIENCES — Abstracting, Bibliographies, Statistics

616.4   SP
PROGRAMA DE DIABETES. 6/yr. General Lopez Pozas 8, 28036 Madrid, Spain. TEL 1-2504489.

616.4   US   ISSN 0890-7048
CODEN: PERTEZ
PROGRESS IN ENDOCRINE RESEARCH AND THERAPY. 1984. irreg., latest vol.5. price varies. Raven Press (Subsidiary of: Wolters Kluwer N.V.), 1185 Ave. of the Americas, New York, NY 10036. TEL 212-930-9500. FAX 212-869-3495. (reprint service avail. from UMI) **Document type:** proceedings.
—CASDDS.
Refereed Serial

PROLACTIN. see MEDICAL SCIENCES — Abstracting, Bibliographies, Statistics

MEDICAL SCIENCES — ENDOCRINOLOGY

616.4 US ISSN 0090-6980
QP801.P68 CODEN: PRGLBA
PROSTAGLANDINS. 1972. m. $525 to institutions (effective 1996). Butterworth - Heinemann, Part of the Reed Elsevier group, 313 Washington St., Newton, MA 02158. TEL 617-928-2500; 800-366-2665. FAX 617-928-2610. TELEX 880052. (Subscr. to: Elsevier Science Inc., Box 882, Madison Sq. Sta., New York, NY 10159-0882. TEL 212-989-5800. FAX 212-633-3990) Ed. Peter W. Ramwell. (also avail. in microform from UMI,PMC; back issues avail.) **Indexed:** Anal.Abstr., Anim.Breed.Abstr., Biol.Abstr., Biotech.Abstr., Chem.Abstr., Curr.Adv.Biochem., Curr.Adv.Cancer Res., Curr.Adv.Cell & Devel.Biol., Curr.Adv.Ecol.Sci., Curr.Chem.React., Curr.Cont., Dairy Sci.Abstr., Dent.Ind., Excerp.Med., Helminthol.Abstr., Ind.Chem., Ind.Med., Ind.Vet., Mass Spectr.Bull., Nutr.Abstr., Pig News & Info., Telegen, Vet.Bull. **Document type:** academic/scholarly publication.
—BLDSC (6935.180000); ADONIS; CASDDS; EMDOCS; Faxon; Genuine Article; SWETS; UMI. **CCC.**
  Description: Covers all areas of prostaglandin research, including chemistry, endocrinology, immunology, and oncology.
  Refereed Serial

616.4 UK ISSN 0142-8284
PROSTAGLANDINS - BIOLOGY. 1979. s-m. (diskette m.). £115 (diskette £115; both £175) (effective 1995). S U B I S, Mansion House, 19 Kingfield Rd., Sheffield S11 9AS, England. TEL 0114-2554433. FAX 0114-2554626. E-mail: admin@sheffac.demon.co.uk. (also avail. in diskette format) **Document type:** abstracting/indexing.
—**CCC.**
  Description: Current awareness service for researchers. Covers prostaglandin precursors, production, release, effects, medical uses and metabolism.

616.4 UK ISSN 0952-3278
CODEN: PLEAEU
PROSTAGLANDINS, LEUKOTRIENES AND ESSENTIAL FATTY ACIDS. 1978. m. £1001($1657) (effective 1995). Churchill Livingstone Journals (Subsidiary of: Pearson Professional), Robert Stevenson House, 1-3 Baxter's Pl., Leith Walk, Edinburgh EH1 3AF, Scotland. TEL 0131-556-2424. FAX 0131-459-1177. (Subscr. to: Pearson Professional Ltd., P.O. Box 77, Fourth Ave., Harlow, Essex CM19 5AA, England. TEL 01279-623760; U.S. subscr. to: Churchill Livingstone, 650 Ave. of the Americas, New York, NY 10011. TEL 212-206-5000) Ed. Dr. David F. Horrobin. adv. contact: David Dunnachie. circ. 450. (also avail. in microform from UMI; back issues avail.) **Indexed:** Anim.Breed.Abstr., Chem.Abstr., Curr.Adv.Ecol.Sci., Curr.Cont., Dairy Sci.Abstr., Excerp.Med., Ind.Med., Poult.Abstr. **Document type:** academic/scholarly publication.
—BLDSC (6935.190900); ADONIS; CASDDS; Faxon; Genuine Article; SWETS; UnCover. **CCC.**
  Former titles (until 1988): Prostaglandins, Leukotrienes and Medicine (ISSN 0262-1746); Prostaglandins and Medicine (ISSN 0161-4630)

PSYCHONEUROENDOCRINOLOGY. see *MEDICAL SCIENCES — Psychiatry And Neurology*

616.4 UK ISSN 0140-9123
RC648.A1 CODEN: RAEMDA
RECENT ADVANCES IN ENDOCRINOLOGY AND METABOLISM. 1978. irreg. Churchill Livingstone Medical Journals, Robert Stevenson House, 1-3 Baxter's Pl., Leith Walk, Edinburgh EH1 3AF, Scotland. TEL 0131-556-2424. FAX 0131-459-1177. **Document type:** academic/scholarly publication.
—CASDDS.

616.4 574.192 US ISSN 0079-9963
QP187 CODEN: RPHRA6
RECENT PROGRESS IN HORMONE RESEARCH. PROCEEDINGS OF THE LAURENTIAN HORMONE CONFERENCE. 1947. irreg., vol.48, 1993. Academic Press, Inc., 525 B St., Ste. 1900, San Diego, CA 92101-4495. TEL 619-231-0926. FAX 619-699-6715. (Subscr. to: Order Dept., 6277 Sea Harbor Dr., 4th Fl., Orlando, FL 32887. TEL 800-321-5068) Ed. Roy O. Greep. index, cum.index: vols.1-10 (1947-1954). (reprint service avail. from ISI) **Indexed:** Anim.Breed.Abstr., Biol.Abstr., Chem.Abstr., Dairy Sci.Abstr., Excerp.Med., Ind.Med., Ind.Vet., Nutr.Abstr., Vet.Bull. **Document type:** proceedings.
—BLDSC (7305.000000); CASDDS; Faxon; SWETS; UnCover. **CCC.**
  Refereed Serial

RELEASING HORMONES. see *MEDICAL SCIENCES — Abstracting, Bibliographies, Statistics*

RENIN, ANGIOTENSIN & KININS. see *BIOLOGY — Physiology*

REPRODUCTION HUMAINE ET HORMONES. see *MEDICAL SCIENCES — Obstetrics And Gynecology*

616.4 CU ISSN 0864-4462
REVISTA CUBANA DE ENDOCRINOLOGIA. (Text in Spanish, summaries in English, Spanish) s-a. $30 in S. America; N. America $32; elsewhere $34. Ministerio de Salud Publica, Centro Nacional de Informacion de Ciencias Medicas, Calle E No. 452, e-19 y 21, Plaza de la Revolucion, Apdo. 6520, Havana, Cuba. TEL 809-32-5338. (Dist. by: Ediciones Cubanas, Obispo No. 527, Apdo. 605, Havana, Cuba) (Co-sponsor: Instituto Nacional de Endocrinologia y Enfermedades Metabolicas) Ed. Milagros de los Reyes. circ. 1,000.
  Description: Covers the fields of endocrinology, metabolic illnesses and related specialties.

616.4 FR ISSN 0048-8062
CODEN: RECNAS
REVUE FRANCAISE D'ENDOCRINOLOGIE CLINIQUE, NUTRITION ET METABOLISME. (Text in French; some summaries in English) 1960. bi-m. Editions de Medecine Pratique, 4 rue Louis-Armand, 92600 Asnieres, France. TEL 33-1-47910910. illus. **Indexed:** Biol.Abstr., C.I.S. Abstr., Chem.Abstr., Excerp.Med., Ind.Med.
—BLDSC (7903.800000); CASDDS; EMDOCS. **CCC.**

616.4 JA ISSN 0910-4186
CODEN: RINPEJ
RINPAGAKU/JAPANESE JOURNAL OF LYMPHOLOGY. (Text in English, Japanese; summaries in English) 1978. 2/yr. 6000 Yen. Nihon Rinpa Gakkai - Japanese Society of Lymphology, Tokyo Ika Daigaku Dai 1 Kaibogaku Kyoshitsu, 1-1, Shinjuku 6-chome, Shinjuku-ku, Tokyo 160, Japan. **Indexed:** Chem.Abstr., INIS Atomind.
—CASDDS.

616.4 RM ISSN 1221-356X
CODEN: RJENE9
ROMANIAN JOURNAL OF ENDOCRINOLOGY/REVUE ROUMAINE D'ENDOCRINOLOGIE. (Text in English, French, German, Russian or Spanish) 1964. q. 200 lei($55) (Academia de Stiinte Medicale) Editura Academiei Romane, Calea Victoriei 125, 79717 Bucharest, Rumania. (Dist. by: Rompresfilatelia, Calea Grivitei 64-66, P.O. Box 12-201, 78104 Bucharest, Rumania) Ed. Marcela Pitis. adv.; bk.rev.; abstr.; bibl.; illus.; index. circ. 1,050. **Indexed:** Biol.Abstr., Chem.Abstr., Curr.Adv.Ecol.Sci., Curr.Cont., Excerp.Med. (until 1993), Ind.Med. **Document type:** academic/scholarly publication.
—CASDDS.
  Former titles (until 1992): Endocrinologie (ISSN 1220-4722); (until 1987): Revue Roumaine de Medecine. Serie Endocrinologie (ISSN 0253-1801); (until 1975): Revue Roumaine d'Endocrinologie (ISSN 0035-4015)
  Description: Presents original papers (studies and researches in experimental and clinical endocrinology), short articles on unusual cases and techniques, editorials and endocrinological news.

616.462 SA
S A DIABETIESE TYDSKRIF/S A DIABETIC JOURNAL. (Text in Afrikaans, English) 1992. q. Dia Kure, Posbus 1908, Bloemfontein 9300, South Africa. illus.

616.4 GW ISSN 0720-065X
DIE SCHILDDRUESE. 1976. irreg. P M I Verlagsgruppe GmbH, August-Schanz-Str. 6, 60433 Frankfurt a.M., Germany. TEL 069-548000-0. FAX 069-548000-77. TELEX 412952-PMI-D. circ. 30,000. **Document type:** academic/scholarly publication.

616.4 US ISSN 0882-5815
RC963.A1
SEMINARS IN REPRODUCTIVE ENDOCRINOLOGY. q. $91 to individuals (foreign $116); institutions $127 (foreign $152). Thieme Medical Publishers, Inc., 381 Park Ave., S., Ste. 1501, New York, NY 10016. TEL 212-683-5088. FAX 212-779-9020. Ed. Dr. Leon Speroff. adv.; abstr.; bibl.; illus. circ. 1,900. **Indexed:** Curr.Adv.Cell & Devel.Biol., Curr.Adv.Ecol.Sci., Curr.Adv.Genetics & Molec.Biol.
—BLDSC (8239.457700); Genuine Article; SWETS; UMI; UnCover. **CCC.**
  Formerly: Reproductive Endocrinology (ISSN 0734-8630)

SEMINARS IN RESPIRATORY INFECTIONS. see *MEDICAL SCIENCES — Respiratory Diseases*

616.4 CK ISSN 0120-1182
SOCIEDAD COLOMBIANA DE ENDOCRINOLOGIA. REVISTA. (Text in Spanish; summaries in English and Spanish) 1958. s-a. $6. Sociedad Colombiana de Endocrinologia, Apdo. Aereo 29714, Bogota, D.E., Colombia. Ed. Dr. Alfredo F. Jacome. adv.; index. circ. 2,000. **Indexed:** Biol.Abstr.

STEROID RECEPTORS. see *BIOLOGY — Cytology And Histology*

616.46 US
▼**TEAMWORK.** 1995. 3/yr. (free to qualified personnel). Joslin Center for Diabetes, St. Luke's Roosevelt Hospital Center, 425 W. 59th St., New York, NY 10019. TEL 212-523-8353. FAX 212-523-2617. Ed. Genie Agins. illus. circ. 15,000. **Document type:** newsletter.
  Description: Provides information that will enable people with diabetes to live better. Informs about activities and events at the Joslin Center.

616.6 612.4 CN ISSN 0832-7076
THYROBULLETIN. 1980. q. Can.$15 membership. Thyroid Foundation of Canada, 1040 Gardiner's Rd., Kingston, ON K7P 1R7, Canada. TEL 613-634-3426. FAX 613-634-3483. Ed. Robert Mactavish. circ. 3,700. (back issues avail.) **Document type:** academic/scholarly publication, bulletin.
  Description: Aims to awaken public interest in and awareness of thyroid disease, to lend moral support to patients and their families, and to assist in fund-raising for thyroid disease research.

616.44 US ISSN 1050-7256
CODEN: THYRER
THYROID. 1991. q. $145 (foreign $185). (American Thyroid Association) Mary Ann Liebert, Inc., 1651 Third Ave., New York, NY 10128. TEL 212-289-2300. FAX 212-289-4697. **Indexed:** Excerp.Med. (1992-), Ind.Med. (1992-). **Document type:** academic/scholarly publication.
—BLDSC (8820.383300); Genuine Article; SWETS; UnCover.
  Description: Covers all aspects of thyroid medicine, from the molecular biology of the cell to clinical management of thyroid disorders.

616.4 610 UK ISSN 0142-8349
THYROID HORMONES. 1976. s-m. (diskette m.). £110 (diskette £115; both £175) (effective 1995). S U B I S, Mansion House, 19 Kingfield Rd., Sheffield S11 9AS, England. TEL 0114-2554433. FAX 0114-2554626. E-mail: admin@sheffac.demon.co.uk. (also avail. in diskette format) **Document type:** abstracting/indexing.
—**CCC.**
  Description: Current awareness service for researchers. Covers hormone synthesis and secretion, receptors, effects, and hypothalamic-pituitary control of thyroid function.

MEDICAL SCIENCES — EXPERIMENTAL MEDICINE, LABORATORY TECHNIQUE

616.44 IT ISSN 1121-7596
THYROIDOLOGY: CLINICAL AND EXPERIMENTAL. 1989. 3/yr. L.40000($30) to individuals; institutions L.50000 ($40) (effective 1995). Pacini Editore s.r.l., Via A. Gherardesca 1, 56121 Ospedaletto (Pisa), Italy. TEL 39-50-982439. FAX 39-50-983906. Ed. A. Carpi. **Document type:** academic/scholarly publication.
—BLDSC (8820.384500).

616.46 US ISSN 1043-2760
RC648.A1 CODEN: TENME4
TRENDS IN ENDOCRINOLOGY AND METABOLISM. 1990. 10/yr. $250 to institutions in U.S.; $290 to institutions outside the Americas (effective 1996). Elsevier Science Inc., 655 Ave. of the Americas, New York, NY 10010. TEL 212-989-5800. FAX 212-633-3990. TELEX 420643 AEP UI. (Subscr. to: Box 882, Madison Sq. Sta., New York, NY 10159-0882) Ed.Bd. (also avail. in microform from UMI; back issues avail.) **Indexed:** Excerp.Med. **Document type:** academic/scholarly publication.
—BLDSC (9049.590500); CASDDS; Faxon; Genuine Article; SWETS; UnCover. **CCC.**
Description: Attempts to keep the researcher and the clinician informed of advances across the field of endocrinology, with emphasis on research. Features include endocrine rounds, journal club, and emergency techniques.
Refereed Serial

616 BU ISSN 0506-2772
CODEN: VTBLAU
VATRECHNI BOLESTI. (Text in Bulgarian; summaries in English, Russian) bi-m. 24 lv. (Ministerstvo na Narodnoto Zdrave) Izdatelstvo Meditsina i Fizkultura, 11 Pl. Slaveikov, Sofia, Bulgaria. (Dist. by: Hemus, 6 Rouski Blvd., 1000 Sofia, Bulgaria) (Co-sponsor: Nauchno Druzhestvo po Vatresni Bolesti) Ed. N. Belovezdov. circ. 2,584. **Indexed:** Abstr.Bulg.Sci.Med.Lit.
—CASDDS.

VOICE OF THE DIABETIC; a support and information network. see *HANDICAPPED — Visually Impaired*

616.4058 US ISSN 0084-3741
RC648
YEAR BOOK OF ENDOCRINOLOGY. 1950. a. $72.95 (residents $35) (effective 1996). Mosby - Year Book, Inc., Continuity Division, 200 N. LaSalle, Chicago, IL 60601. TEL 312-726-9733. FAX 312-726-6075. TELEX 206155. Ed. Dr. John D. Bagdade. (reprint service avail.) **Indexed:** Anim.Breed.Abstr.; Curr.Adv.Ecol.Sci.
●Also available on CD-ROM. Producer(s): SilverPlatter Information, Inc.
—BLDSC (9411.690000). **CCC.**

616.4 CC ISSN 1000-6699
CODEN: ZNDZEK
ZHONGHUA NEIFENMI DAIXIE ZAZHI/CHINESE JOURNAL OF ENDOCRINOLOGY AND METABOLISM. (Text in Chinese; summaries in Chinese and English) 1985. q. Y12 (foreign $10). Shanghai Institute of Endocrinology - Shanghai-shi Neifenmi Yanjiusuo, 197 Ruijin Lu Sec. 2, Shanghai, People's Republic of China. TEL 8610-8232343. FAX 8610-8211656. (Co-sponsor: Chinese Medical Association - Zhonghua Yixue Hui) Eds. Chen Jialun, Zhang Daqing. adv. circ. 10,000. (back issues avail.) **Indexed:** ExtraMED. **Document type:** academic/scholarly publication.
●Also available on CD-ROM.
—CASDDS.

MEDICAL SCIENCES — Experimental Medicine, Laboratory Technique

616 US
A A B BULLETIN. 1965. bi-m. membership. American Association of Bioanalysts, 818 Olive St., Ste. 918, St. Louis, MO 63101. TEL 314-241-1445. Ed. Mark S. Birenbaum. circ. 1,700 (controlled). (tabloid format) **Document type:** newsletter.

A A M I NEWS. (Association for the Advancement of Medical Instrumentation) see *INSTRUMENTS*

616 574.8 US ISSN 0732-8753
RB155.6
A C T INTERNATIONAL CYTOGENETICS LABORATORY DIRECTORY. a. $60. Association of Cytogenetic Technologists, c/o A C T Association Manager, Box 15945-288, Lenexa, KS 66285. TEL 913-541-9077. FAX 913-541-0156. Ed. Turid Knutsen. circ. 1,700. **Document type:** directory.

A I CH E EQUIPMENT TESTING PROCEDURES. (American Institute of Chemical Engineers) see *ENGINEERING — Chemical Engineering*

A I CH E PARTICLE SIZE CLASSIFIER TEST PROCEDURE. (American Institute of Chemical Engineers) see *ENGINEERING — Chemical Engineering*

A I M S NEWSLETTER. (Australian Institute of Medical Scientists) see *MEDICAL SCIENCES*

616.15 AT
A I M S SELF ASSESSMENT PROGRAMMES SERIES. 1988. s-a. Aus.$25. Australian Institute of Medical Scientists, P.O. Box 450, Toowong, Qld. 4066, Australia. TEL 61-7-371-3370. FAX 61-7-870-4857. Ed. Brendon Walker. adv. contact: Brendon Walker. circ. 400. (back issues avail.)
Formerly: A I M L S Self Assessment Programmes Series (ISSN 1031-7074)

616 II
A M T CHRONICLE. q. Association of Medical Technologists, 55 Harish Mukherjee, Calcutta 25, India.

A S A I O JOURNAL. (American Society for Artificial Internal Organs, Inc.) see *MEDICAL SCIENCES*

619 US
A S C L S TODAY. 1965. 11/yr. American Society for Clinical Laboratory Science, 7910 Woodmont Ave., Ste. 1301, Bethesda, MD 20814-3015. TEL 301-657-2768. FAX 301-657-2909. Ed. Anne Salassi. circ. 20,000. **Document type:** newsletter.
Former titles (until 1993): A S M T Today (ISSN 0895-3597); A S M T News (ISSN 0001-2564)

ABSTRACTS: CELLULAR PATHOLOGY. see *MEDICAL SCIENCES — Abstracting, Bibliographies, Statistics*

ACTA TOXICOLOGICA ET THERAPEUTICA; international journal of toxicology, pharmacology and therapy. see *ENVIRONMENTAL STUDIES — Toxicology And Environmental Safety*

619 US
ADVANCE FOR ADMINISTRATORS OF THE LABORATORY. 1992. bi-m. Merion Publications, 650 Park Ave., Box 61556, King of Prussia, PA 19406. TEL 610-265-7812. FAX 610-265-8971. E-mail: blammey@merion.com. Ed. Theresa Steltzer. adv.: B&W or color page $1764; trim 8 1/2 x 11. circ. 28,500. **Document type:** trade publication.

651 US
ADVANCE FOR MEDICAL LABORATORY PROFESSIONALS. 1989. w. Merion Publications, 650 Park Ave., Box 61556, King of Prussia, PA 19406. TEL 610-265-7812. FAX 610-265-8971. E-mail: blammey@merion.com. Ed. Bette Mooney. adv.: B&W page $1444, color page $2144; trim 10 x 13 1/4. circ. 88,500. **Document type:** trade publication.

619 016 UK ISSN 0261-1929
QH301 CODEN: AALADQ
ALTERNATIVES TO LABORATORY ANIMALS: A T L A. (Supplement avail.: Animal Experimentation. Improvements and Alternatives) 1973. 6/yr. £65($130) Fund for the Replacement of Animals in Medical Experiments, Russel & Burch House, 96 N. Sherwood St., Nottingham NG1 4EE, England. TEL 0115-958-4740. FAX 0115-950-3570. Ed. Dr. Michael Ball. adv.; bk.rev.; bibl. circ. 850. (back issues avail.) **Indexed:** Abstr.Hyg., Biol.Abstr., Curr.Adv.Ecol.Sci., Ind.Vet., Vet.Bull. **Document type:** academic/scholarly publication.
—BLDSC (1765.890900); CASDDS; Faxon; Genuine Article; SWETS. **CCC.**
Formerly (until 1983): A T L A Abstracts (ISSN 0306-2465)
Description: Covers all aspects of the development, validation, introduction and implementation of alternatives to the use of laboratory animals in biomedical research and toxicity testing.

616 US
AMERICAN ASSOCIATION OF BIOANALYSTS. PROFICIENCY TESTING SERVICE. TEST OF THE MONTH. 1970. irreg. membership. American Association of Bioanalysts, 205 W. Levee, Brownsville, TX 78520. TEL 512-546-5313. Ed. Nicholas T. Serafy. charts; illus.; circ. 4,500 (controlled). (tabloid format) **Document type:** academic/scholarly publication.

AMERICAN BIOTECHNOLOGY LABORATORY. see *BIOLOGY — Biotechnology*

619 US ISSN 8750-9490
CODEN: ACPREA
AMERICAN CLINICAL LABORATORY. (Includes a. Buyers' Guide) 1982. m. $215 (foreign $252). International Scientific Communications, Inc., 30 Controls Dr., Box 870, Shelton, CT 06484-0870. TEL 203-926-9300. FAX 203-926-9310. (U.K. subscr. to: I.S.C. House, Progress Business Centre, 5 Whittle Pkwy., Slough, Berks. SL1 6DQ, England. TEL 0628-668881. FAX 0628-669199) Ed. Brian Howard. adv.; bk.rev.; charts; illus.; stat.; tr.lit.; circ. 62,050 (controlled). **Document type:** academic/scholarly publication.
—CASDDS.
Formerly: American Clinical Products Review.

619 US
AMERICAN COLLEGE OF LABORATORY ANIMAL MEDICINE SERIES. 1974. irreg. Academic Press, Inc., 525 B St., Ste. 1900, San Diego, CA 92101-4495. TEL 619-231-6616. FAX 619-699-6715. (Subscr. to: Order Dept., 6277 Sea Harbor Dr., 4th Fl., Orlando, FL 32887. TEL 800-321-5068) (back issues avail.) **Document type:** monographic series.
Refereed Serial

619 US
AMERICAN CRYONICS. 1984. s-a. $35 includes The Immortalist. American Cryonics Society, Box 761, Cupertino, CA 95015-0761. TEL 408-446-4425. FAX 408-725-0385. (Subscr. to: c/o Jim Yount, VP, Box 1509, Cupertino, CA 95015) Ed. Peter Christiansen. adv.; bk.rev. circ. 500. **Document type:** newsletter.
Former titles: A C S Notebook; A C S Journal.
Description: Reports on cryonics, cryobiology, and life extension; articles speculating on future medicine, and life; how current discoveries may change lifestyles.

616 UK ISSN 0965-2329
AMERICAN JOURNAL OF CLINICAL RESEARCH. 1992. irreg. £125 (outside Europe £175) (effective 1995). Brookwood Medical Publications, Orchard House, Brookwood, Surrey GU24 OAT, England. TEL 01483-797975. FAX 01483-797915. **Indexed:** Excerp.Med. (1993-). **Document type:** academic/scholarly publication.
—BLDSC (0824.040000).
Description: Publishes primarily clinical trials.
Refereed Serial

AMERICAN JOURNAL OF EMERGENCY MEDICINE. see *MEDICAL SCIENCES — Orthopedics And Traumatology*

AMERICAN POLYGRAPH ASSOCIATION NEWSLETTER. see *CRIMINOLOGY AND LAW ENFORCEMENT*

616 NE ISSN 0166-7688
ANALYSE. Bound with: International Association of Medical Laboratory Technologists. Newsletter. 1946. m. fl.135. Vereniging van Medische Analisten - Association of Medical Laboratory Technologists, Wilhelminapark 52, 3581 NM Utrecht, Netherlands. TEL 31-30-522881. FAX 31-30-541814. (Co-sponsor: International Association of Medical Technologists) Ed. Mrs. W.M.H.M. van den Eertwegh. adv.; bk.rev.; illus.; index; circ. 3,500 (controlled). **Indexed:** INIS Atomind. **Document type:** academic/scholarly publication.
Formerly: Tijdschrift voor Medische Analisten.

619 JA ISSN 0910-0911
ANIMARUZU NYUSU/ANIMALS NEWS. (Text in Japanese) 1978. a. Niigata Daigaku, Igakubu, Fuzoku Dobutsu Jikken Shisetsu - Niigata University, School of Medicine, Facilities for Comparative Medicine and Animal Experimentation, 757, Asahimachi Dori Ichibancho, Niigata-shi, Niigata-ken 951, Japan.

MEDICAL SCIENCES — EXPERIMENTAL MEDICINE, LABORATORY TECHNIQUE

616 JA ISSN 0915-3667
ANITEKKUSU/LABORATORY ANIMAL TECHNOLOGY AND SCIENCE. (Text in Japanese) 1989. bi-m. 1100 Yen per no. Kenseisha Inc., 6-4, Kakigaracho 1-chome, Nihonbashi, Chuo-ku, Tokyo 103, Japan.

ANLEITUNG FUER DIE CHEMISCHE LABORATORIUMSPRAXIS - CHEMICAL LABORATORY PRACTICE. see *CHEMISTRY*

616 CN ISSN 0709-8502
CODEN: ABCQD2
ANNALES DE BIOCHIMIE CLINIQUE DU QUEBEC. (Text in French) 1980. q. free. Societe Quebecoise de Biochimie Clinique, c/o Marc Letellier, Ed., Dept. de Biochimie Clinique, C H U S, Sherbrooke, PQ J1H 5N4, Canada. TEL 819-563-5555. FAX 819-820-6414. adv.; bk.rev.; abstr.; index. circ. 900. (back issues avail.) Indexed: Biol.Abstr., Chem.Abstr., Curr.Adv.Ecol.Sci. Document type: academic/scholarly publication.
—BLDSC (0967.590000); CASDDS.
   Description: Studies clinical biochemistry.
   Refereed Serial

616 US ISSN 0091-7370
RB37.A1 CODEN: ACLSCP
ANNALS OF CLINICAL AND LABORATORY SCIENCE. 1971. bi-m. $70 to individuals (foreign $105); institutions $105 (foreign $115). (Association of Clinical Scientists) Institute for Clinical Science, 1833 Delancey Pl., Philadelphia, PA 19103. TEL 215-829-7068. FAX 215-829-3094. Ed. Dr. F. William Sunderman. adv.; bk.rev.; abstr.; charts; illus.; index. circ. 2,000. Indexed: Biol.Abstr., Chem.Abstr., Curr.Adv.Cancer Res., Curr.Adv.Ecol.Sci., Curr.Cont., Dent.Ind., Dok.Arbeitsmed., Excerp.Med., Ind.Med., Ind.Sci.Rev., INIS Atomind., Nutr.Abstr.
—BLDSC (1040.228000); CASDDS; EMDOCS; Faxon; Genuine Article; SWETS; UnCover. **CCC.**

619 UK ISSN 1350-4266
▼**ANNALS OF EXPERIMENTAL AND CLINICAL MEDICINE.** (Supplement avail.) 1994. bi-m. £80 (includes supplements). Graffham Press Ltd., 6 York Pl., Edinburgh EH1 3EP, Scotland. TEL 0131-556-7887. FAX 0131-556-1129. Ed. Patrick Daly. illus.; stat. Document type: academic/scholarly publication.
—BLDSC (1040.530000).
   Refereed Serial

616 UK ISSN 0785-3890
CODEN: ANMDEU
ANNALS OF MEDICINE. 1969. bi-m. £195($314) (effective 1996). (Finnish Medical Society Duodecim) Blackwell Science Ltd., Osney Mead, Oxford OX2 0EL, England. TEL 01865-240201. FAX 01865-721205. TELEX 83355 MEDBOK G. Ed. Leena Peltonen. adv.; bk.rev.; charts; illus.; index. circ. 1,200. (also avail. in microform from UMI; back issues avail.) Indexed: Abstr.Hyg., Biol.Abstr., Chem.Abstr., Child Devel.Abstr., Curr.Adv.Ecol.Sci., Curr.Cont., Dairy Sci.Abstr., Diar.Dis.Res., Excerp.Med., Helminthol.Abstr., Ind.Med., Ind.Sci.Rev., Med.& Surg.Dermat., NRN, Nutr.Abstr., Psychol.Abstr. (1989-), Risk Abstr., Sci.Cit.Ind., Trop.Dis.Bull. Document type: academic/scholarly publication.
—BLDSC (1043.131000); CASDDS; Faxon; Genuine Article; SWETS; UMI; UnCover. **CCC.**
   Formed by the merger of (1969-1989): Annals of Clinical Research (ISSN 0003-4762); Which was formed by the merger of: Annales Paediatriae Fenniae (ISSN 0570-1732); Annales Medicinae Internae Fenniae (ISSN 0365-4362); (1974-1989): Medical Biology (ISSN 0302-2137); Which supersedes: Annales Medicinae Experimentalis et Biologiae Fenniae (ISSN 0003-4479).
   Refereed Serial

616 FR ISSN 0245-1913
ANNUAIRE DES LABORATOIRES D'ANALYSES DE BIOLOGIE MEDICALE DE FRANCE. a. Labo-France, 7 rue Godot de Mauroy, 75009 Paris, France. adv.
   Formerly (until 1979): Annuaire des Laboratoires d'Analyses de France (ISSN 0300-0613)

ANNUAIRE FOURNI-LABO RECHERCHE (YEAR); fondementale et appliquee. see *BUSINESS AND ECONOMICS — Trade And Industrial Directories*

APPLIED CYTOGENETICS. see *BIOLOGY — Genetics*

APPLIED NURSING RESEARCH. see *MEDICAL SCIENCES — Nurses And Nursing*

APPLIED RADIATION AND ISOTOPES; including data, instrumentation and methods for use in agriculture, industry and medicine. see *PHYSICS — Nuclear Physics*

ARCHIVES OF PATHOLOGY & LABORATORY MEDICINE. see *MEDICAL SCIENCES*

ARQUIVOS DE CIRURGIA CLINICA E EXPERIMENTAL. see *MEDICAL SCIENCES — Surgery*

610.28 660 US ISSN 1073-1199
R856.A1 CODEN: ABSBE4
ARTIFICIAL CELLS, BLOOD SUBSTITUTES, AND IMMOBILIZATION BIOTECHNOLOGY. 1973. 6/yr. $775 per vol. Marcel Dekker Journals, 270 Madison Ave., New York, NY 10016. TEL 212-696-9000. FAX 212-685-4540. TELEX 421419. (Subscr. to: Box 5017, Monticello, NY 12701) Ed. T.M.S. Chang. adv. contact: Eridania Perez. illus. (also avail. in microform from RPI) Indexed: Bioeng.Abstr., Biol.Abstr., Chem.Abstr., Curr.Cont., Dent.Ind., Excerp.Med., Ind.Med., Ind.Sci.Rev., INSPEC (1991-), Met.Abstr., Sci.Cit.Ind., World Alum.Abstr. Document type: academic/scholarly publication.
—BLDSC (1735.022500); CASDDS; Ei; Faxon; Genuine Article; SWETS; UMI; UnCover. **CCC.**
   Former titles (until 1993): Biomaterials, Artificial Cells and Immobilization Biotechnology (ISSN 1055-7172); (until 1991): Biomaterials, Artificial Cells and Artificial Organs; (until 1987): Biomaterials, Medical Devices, and Artificial Organs (ISSN 0890-5533)
   Description: Focuses on medical instrumentation.
   Refereed Serial

619 US ISSN 0160-564X
RD130 CODEN: ARORD7
ARTIFICIAL ORGANS. 1977. m. $540 (foreign $580) (effective 1996). (International Society for Artificial Organs) Blackwell Science Inc., 238 Main St., Cambridge, MA 02142-1413. TEL 617-876-7022. FAX 617-492-5263. Ed. Dr. Yukihiko Nose. adv.; bk.rev.; charts; illus.; index. circ. 1,400. (back issues avail.) Indexed: Biol.Abstr., Chem.Abstr., Curr.Cont., Dent.Ind., Excerp.Med, Ind.Med, Ind.Sci.Rev., Sci.Cit.Ind. Document type: academic/scholarly publication.
—BLDSC (1735.052000); ADONIS; CASDDS; Faxon; Genuine Article; SWETS; UMI; UnCover. **CCC.**
   Description: Multidisciplinary journal publishing reports on the design, performance and evaluation of biomaterials and devices used in artificial organs for the medical, scientific and engineering communities; includes relevant coverage of biomechanics, bioelectronics, hemodynamics, and plasmapheresis.
   Refereed Serial

ASSOCIATION OF TALENT AGENTS. NEWSLETTER. see *THEATER*

619 530 AT ISSN 0158-9938
CODEN: AUPMDI
AUSTRALASIAN PHYSICAL & ENGINEERING SCIENCES IN MEDICINE. 1977. q. Aus.$45 to individuals; institutions Aus.$75 (effective 1993). Australasian College of Physical Scientists and Engineers in Medicine, Physics Dept., Queensland University of Technoloiy, G.P.O. Box 2434, Brisbane, Qld. 4001, Australia. Ed. Dr. T. van Doorn. adv. contact: S. Pinneri. bk.rev.; index. circ. 450. (back issues avail.) Indexed: Chem.Abstr., Excerp.Med., Ind.Med., INIS Atomind., INSPEC (1980-). Document type: academic/scholarly publication.
—BLDSC (1796.030000); CASDDS; Ei; Faxon; UnCover.
   Formerly: Australasian Physical Sciences in Medicine.
   Description: Covers applications of the physical sciences and engineering on medicine and biology; papers, reviews, technical reports and letters.
   Refereed Serial

AUSTRALIAN JOURNAL OF MEDICAL SCIENCE. see *MEDICAL SCIENCES*

B B A - GENE STRUCTURE AND EXPRESSION. see *BIOLOGY — Genetics*

B B A - MOLECULAR CELL RESEARCH. see *BIOLOGY — Biophysics*

BASIC PATTERNS IN UNION CONTRACTS. see *LAW — Corporate Law*

BIOELECTRONICS AND BIOSENSORS. see *BIOLOGY — Biophysics*

BIOLOGICAL RESEARCH. see *BIOLOGY*

616 RU
BIOLOGIYA LABORATORNYKH ZHIVOTNYKH. irreg. 2 Rub. (Rossiiskaya Akademiya Meditsinskikh Nauk, Nauchno-Issledovatel'skaya Laboratoriya Eksperimental'no-Biologicheskikh Modelei) Izdatel'stvo Meditsina, Petroverigskii per. 6-8, 101838 Moscow, Russia. bibl.

619 UK ISSN 0269-3879
CODEN: BICHE2
BIOMEDICAL CHROMATOGRAPHY. 1986. bi-m. £645 (foreign £645) (effective 1996). John Wiley & Sons Ltd., Journals, Baffins Ln., Chichester, W. Sussex PO19 1UD, England. TEL 01243-779777. FAX 01243-776128. TELEX 86290 WIBOOK G. (Subscr. in the Americas to: John Wiley & Sons, Inc., 605 Third Ave., New York, NY 10158. TEL 212-850-6645. FAX 212-850-6021) Eds. E.F. Hounsell, C.K. Lim. circ. 157. (also avail. in microform from UMI; reprint service avail. from SWZ) Indexed: Chem.Abstr., Curr.Cont., Excerp.Med. Document type: academic/scholarly publication.
—BLDSC (2087.758000); CASDDS; Ei; Faxon; Genuine Article; SWETS; UMI; UnCover. **CCC.**
   Description: Devoted to the publication of original papers on the applications of chromatography and allied techniques in the biological and medical sciences.

BIOMEDICAL PRODUCTS. see *MEDICAL SCIENCES*

619 US
BIONICS.* 1988. q. $20. Bionics Industry Association, c/o Ben Campbell, Ed., 917 S. Park St., Owosso, MI 48867-4422. TEL 517-485-7800. adv.; film rev.; charts; illus.; pat.; tr.lit.; cum.index: 1989-1990. circ. 4,000. (also avail. in microfilm)
   Description: Reports on bionics, bio-sensors, artificial organs, cybernetics, industrial and governmental research, investment news.

BIOPSY INTERPRETATION SERIES. see *MEDICAL SCIENCES*

BIOTECHNOLOGY SOFTWARE; the interface between researchers and computers. see *BIOLOGY — Biotechnology*

619 UK ISSN 0268-3369
CODEN: BMTRE9
BONE MARROW TRANSPLANTATION. 1986. m. £135($199) to individuals; institutions £290(foreign £300($405)). Stockton Press (Subsidiary of: Macmillan Press Ltd.), Houndmills, Basingstoke, Hants RG21 2XS, England. TEL 01256-817245. FAX 01256-28339. Eds. John Goldman, Robert Peter Gale; Pub. Jayne Marks. adv. contact: Michael Rowley. abstr.; illus.; index. Indexed: Curr.Adv.Cancer Res., Curr.Adv.Cell & Devel.Biol., Curr.Adv.Ecol.Sci., Curr.Adv.Genetics & Molec.Biol., Curr.Cont., Excerp.Med., Ind.Med., Med.& Surg.Dermat., Protozool.Abstr., Rev.Med.& Vet.Mycol. Document type: academic/scholarly publication.
—BLDSC (2247.358000); Faxon; Genuine Article; SWETS; UMI; UnCover. **CCC.**
   Description: Clinical results of bone marrow transplantation in man and experimental results with animals.

BRAIN PATHOLOGY. see *MEDICAL SCIENCES — Psychiatry And Neurology*

MEDICAL SCIENCES — EXPERIMENTAL MEDICINE, LABORATORY TECHNIQUE

616   UK   ISSN 0967-4845
CODEN: BJMSEO
BRITISH JOURNAL OF BIOMEDICAL SCIENCE. 1951. q. £95 (foreign £100($190)). (Institute of Biomedical Science) Royal Society of Medicine Press Ltd., 1 Wimpole St., London W1M 8AE, England. TEL 0171-290-2900. FAX 0171-290-2929. Ed. A.D. Farr. adv.; bk.rev.; abstr.; bibl.; charts; illus.; index. circ. 15,000. Indexed: Abstr.Hyg., Biol.Abstr., Chem.Abstr., CINAHL, Curr.Adv.Cancer Res., Curr.Adv.Ecol.Sci., Curr.Cont., Diar.Dis.Res., Excerp.Med., Helminthol.Abstr., Ind.Med., Ind.Sci.Rev., Ind.Vet., INIS Atomind., Med.& Surg.Dermat., Nutr.Abstr., Rev.Med.& Vet.Mycol., Rev.Plant Path., Telegen, Trop.Dis.Bull., Vet.Bull. **Document type:** academic/scholarly publication.
—BLDSC (2306.730000); CASDDS; Genuine Article; SWETS; UMI; UnCover. **CCC.**
Former titles: Medical Laboratory Sciences (ISSN 0308-3616); Medical Laboratory Technology (ISSN 0022-2607); Journal of Medical Laboratory Technology.
Refereed Serial

542 681.2   US   ISSN 0093-8076
RB36.2
C L R. (Clinical Laboratory Reference) 1974. a. $29 (foreign $35). (Medical Laboratory Observer) Medical Economics Publishing Co., Inc., Five Paragon Dr., Montvale, NJ 07645. TEL 201-358-7200. FAX 201-573-0344. Ed. Robert J. Fitzgibbon. adv.; circ. 59,000 (controlled). (reprint service avail.) **Document type:** trade publication.
Description: Includes product information on diagnostic reagents, test systems, instruments, and equipment for the medical laboratory.

C M B E S - S C G B NEWSLETTER. see *MEDICAL SCIENCES*

619   CN   ISSN 0045-4354
CANADIAN ASSOCIATION FOR LABORATORY ANIMAL SCIENCE NEWSLETTER. (Text and summaries in English and French) 1968. bi-m. membership. Canadian Association for Laboratory Animal Science (CALAS), c/o Dr. Donald G. McKay, Biosciences Animal Service, University of Alberta, Edmonton, Alta. T6G 2E9, Canada. Ed. M. Buckley. adv.; bk.rev.; bibl.; charts; illus.; circ. 1,000 (controlled). **Document type:** newsletter.

CANADIAN JOURNAL OF CARDIOLOGY. see *MEDICAL SCIENCES — Cardiovascular Diseases*

616   CN   ISSN 0008-4158
CODEN: CJMTAY
CANADIAN JOURNAL OF MEDICAL TECHNOLOGY. French edition (ISSN 0828-7643) 1938. 4/yr. Can.$19.26 (foreign Can.$20) (effective 1996). Canadian Society of Laboratory Technologists, P.O. Box 2830 LCD 1, Hamilton, ON L8N 3N8, Canada. TEL 905-528-8642. FAX 905-528-4968. Ed. Nancy McBride. adv.; bk.rev.; bibl.; charts; illus.; index. circ. 24,000. Indexed: Biol.Abstr., Chem.Abstr., CINAHL, Curr.Adv.Ecol.Sci., Curr.Cont., Helminthol.Abstr., Ind.Med., Nutr.Abstr., Rev.Med.& Vet.Mycol., Sci.Cit.Ind. **Document type:** trade publication.
—BLDSC (3032.600000); CASDDS; UnCover. **CCC.**
Description: Explores medical laboratory technology, management and education.

616   CN   ISSN 0381-5838
CANADIAN SOCIETY OF LABORATORY TECHNOLOGISTS. BULLETIN/ASSOCIATION CANADIENNE DES TECHNOLOGISTES DE LABORATOIRE. BULLETIN. (Text in English, French) 1951. m. membership. Canadian Society of Laboratory Technologists, P.O. Box 2830 LCD 1, Hamilton, ON L8N 3N8, Canada. TEL 905-528-8642. FAX 905-528-4968. Ed. K. Davis. circ. 22,000. **Document type:** newsletter.
Description: Includes society information, job advertisements, continuing education opportunities, examination information and public relations data.

CELL AND TISSUE CULTURE: LABORATORY PROCEDURES. see *BIOLOGY — Cytology And Histology*

CELL DEATH AND PROLIFERATION. see *BIOLOGY — Cytology And Histology*

CHEMIE-INGENIEUR-TECHNIK; Verfahrenstechnik, Technische Chemie, Apparatewaren, Biotechnologie. see *ENGINEERING — Chemical Engineering*

619 636   US   ISSN 0277-0393
CLINICAL ENGINEERING INFORMATION SERVICE. 1977. bi-m. $110 (outside the U.S. and Canada $130) (effective 1996). Scientific Enterprises, Inc., 5104 Randolph Rd., N. Little Rock, AR 72116-6836. TEL 501-771-1775. FAX 501-771-1775. Ed. Dr. David Simmons. bk.rev.; charts; illus.; stat.; index. (looseleaf format; back issues avail.) **Document type:** newsletter.
Description: Covers technical topics and maintenance management for engineers and technicians.
Refereed Serial

616   US   ISSN 0197-8454
CODEN: CLLEE2
CLINICAL LAB LETTER. 1980. s-m. (m. in Jan. & Aug.). $252 (foreign $288). Quest Publishing Co., Inc., A Division of Raven Press Ltd. (Subsidiary of: Wolters Kluwer N.V.), 1351 Titan Way, Brea, CA 92621. TEL 714-738-6400. FAX 714-525-6258. (Subscr. to: Raven Press, 1185 Ave. of the Americas, New York, NY 10036. TEL 212-930-9500. FAX 212-869-3495) Ed. Marty Matisoff; Pub. Mary Waltham. bk.rev.; tr.lit.; index. (back issues avail.) **Document type:** newsletter.
—UMI. **CCC.**
Description: Published for clinical lab personnel. Covers latest diagnostic technology, safety hazards, recalls, legislation, standards, products, legal issues and education.

619   BE
CLINICAL LABORATORY INTERNATIONAL. 1977. 9/yr. $95 (free to qualified personnel) Pan European Publishing Co. (Subsidiary of: Reed Elsevier plc), Rue Verte 216, B-1210 Brussels, Belgium. TEL 32-2-2402611. FAX 32-2-2427111. TELEX 25828. Ed. Y. Cordonnier. adv.; bk.rev.; circ. 30,012 (controlled). (tabloid format) **Document type:** trade publication.
Description: Reports exclusively on what is new in clinical laboratory instrumentation, equipment and reagents in the international market.

616 658   US   ISSN 0888-7950
CLINICAL LABORATORY MANAGEMENT REVIEW. 1987. bi-m. $60 to individuals (foreign $85); institutions $85 (foreign $110). Clinical Laboratory Management Association, 9 Old Lincoln Hwy., Ste. 201, Malvern, PA 19355-2135. TEL 610-647-8970. FAX 610-889-9731. Ed. Patricia Bergbauer. adv. contact: Garth Thompson. circ. 8,500. (also avail. in microform from WWS) Indexed: Ind.Med. **Document type:** academic/scholarly publication.
—BLDSC (3286.295870); Genuine Article.
Description: Geared toward the clinical laboratory manager. Includes general management, federal regulations, and general health care issues.
Refereed Serial

616   US
CLINICAL LABORATORY METHODS AND TECHNIQUES. 1991. q? $125 to individuals; institutions $159 (effective 1993). Field & Wood, Medical Periodicals, Inc., Box 975, Blue Bell, PA 19422. TEL 610-828-4010. FAX 610-482-0226. Ed. Dr. Sun. **Document type:** academic/scholarly publication.
Refereed Serial

681   US
CLINICAL LABORATORY PRODUCT COMPARISON SYSTEM. m. $695. (Emergency Care Research Institute) E C R I, 5200 Butler Pike, Plymouth Meeting, PA 19462. TEL 610-825-6000. FAX 610-834-1275. Ed. Garrett Hayner. (looseleaf format)
●Also available on CD-ROM. Producer(s): Knight-Ridder, Inc.
Description: Covers laboratory instrumentation, such as amino acid and blood chemistry analyzers, to labware washers and centrifuges.
Refereed Serial

616   US   ISSN 0894-959X
CLINICAL LABORATORY SCIENCE. 1988. bi-m. $40 to individuals; institutions $60; foreign $80. American Society for Clinical Laboratory Science, 7910 Woodmont Ave., Ste. 1301, Bethesda, MD 20814-3015. TEL 301-657-2768. FAX 301-657-2909. Ed. L. Michael Posey. adv.; bk.rev. circ. 22,000. (also avail. in microform from UMI; back issues avail.) Indexed: Rev.Med.& Vet.Mycol. **Document type:** trade publication.
—BLDSC (3286.295880); Faxon; SWETS; UMI; UnCover.
Description: Written for all medical technologists, including senior management, mid-level supervisors, and staff technologists. Editorial is based on the common body of knowledge that unites all clinical laboratory scientists, and articles cover all subspecialties of medical technology.

619   UK   ISSN 1355-2910
CODEN: CMPAFI
▼**CLINICAL MOLECULAR PATHOLOGY.** 1995. bi-m. £80($126) B M J Publishing Group, B.M.A. House, Tavistock Sq., London WC1H 9HR, England. TEL 0171-383-4499. FAX 0171-383-6661. (N. American subscr. to: Box 408, Franklin, MA 02038. TEL 800-2-FON-BMJ. FAX 800-2-FAX-BMJ) Eds. J. Crocker, D. Burnett. adv. contact: Sheila Rowe. bk.rev.; abstr.; charts; illus.; index. (also avail. in microfilm from UMI; reprint service avail. from UMI) **Document type:** academic/scholarly publication.
●Also available online. Vendor(s): Ovid Technologies.
—CASDDS.
Refereed Serial

619   US   ISSN 0272-2712
RB37.A1   CODEN: CLMED6
CLINICS IN LABORATORY MEDICINE. 1981. q. $110 (foreign $135) (effective 1996). W.B. Saunders Co. (Subsidiary of: Harcourt Brace & Company), Curtis Center, 3rd Fl., Independence Sq. W., Philadelphia, PA 19106-3399. TEL 215-238-7800. FAX 215-238-6445. (Subscr. to: Periodicals Fulfillment, W.B. Saunders Co., 6277 Sea Harbor Dr., 4th Fl., Orlando, FL 32891-4800. TEL 800-654-2452. FAX 800-874-6418) Ed. Sandy Hitchens. (also avail. in microform from UMI) Indexed: ASCA, Curr.Adv.Ecol.Sci., Dok.Arbeitsmed., Excerp.Med., Ind.Med. **Document type:** academic/scholarly publication.
—BLDSC (3286.575000); Faxon; Genuine Article; SWETS; UMI; UnCover. **CCC.**

616   US   ISSN 1060-0558
CONTEMPORARY TOPICS IN LABORATORY ANIMAL SCIENCE. 1961. 6/yr. $70 (foreign $100). American Association for Laboratory Animal Science, 70 Timber Creek Dr., Ste. 5, Cordova, TN 38018. TEL 901-754-8620. circ. 6,500. (processed) **Document type:** academic/scholarly publication.
—BLDSC (0537.309200); Genuine Article.
Formerly (until Dec. 1991): A A L A S Bulletin (ISSN 1056-1471)

619   US   ISSN 0197-2456
R850.A1   CODEN: CCLTDH
CONTROLLED CLINICAL TRIALS; design, methods, and analysis. 1979. bi-m. $346 to institutions (effective 1996). (Society for Clinical Trials) Elsevier Science Inc., 655 Ave. of the Americas, New York, NY 10010. TEL 212-989-5800. FAX 212-633-3990. TELEX 420643 AEP UI. (Subscr. to: Box 882, Madison Sq. Sta., New York, NY 10159-0882) Ed. C.L. Meinert. (also avail. in microform from UMI) Indexed: Abstr.Hyg., Behav.Med.Abstr., Biol.Abstr., Biostat., Biotech.Abstr., Curr.Adv.Ecol.Sci., Curr.Cont., Diar.Dis.Res., Excerp.Med., Ind.Med., Ind.Sci.Rev., Oper.Res.Manage.Sci., Qual.Contr.Appl.Stat., Sci.Cit.Ind. **Document type:** academic/scholarly publication.
—BLDSC (3463.060000); ADONIS; Faxon; Genuine Article; SWETS; UnCover. **CCC.**
Description: Provides current information on the design, methods, and operational aspects of controlled clinical trials and follow-up studies.
Refereed Serial

619   US   ISSN 1054-4305
CRYONICS.* q. $3.50 per no. Alcor Life Extension Foundation, 7895 E. Acoma Dr., Ste. 110, Scottsdale, AZ 85260-6916.
Description: Covers the new medical and legal developments of the cryonics movement.

MEDICAL SCIENCES — EXPERIMENTAL MEDICINE, LABORATORY TECHNIQUE

619 US ISSN 0892-5798
CURRENT COMMENTS; the newsletter of discovery and innovation. 1986. 10/yr. $145. Chocorua Group, Box 193, Woodstock, CT 06281.
TEL 203-928-3692. Ed. Thompson E. Upham.
Indexed: ABC.
Description: Emerging research and innovation in life sciences.

CURRENT TOPICS IN DRUG RESEARCH. see *PHARMACY AND PHARMACOLOGY*

D.L.A.N.Y. NEWSLETTER. (Dental Laboratory Association of State of New York) see *MEDICAL SCIENCES — Dentistry*

D N A PROBES. see *BIOLOGY — Genetics*

DECHEMA MONOGRAPHIEN. see *CHEMISTRY — Analytical Chemistry*

618 US
DENTAL LABORATORY REVIEW BUYER'S GUIDE. 1975. a. $6. Dental Survey Publications (Subsidiary of: Harcourt Brace Jovanovich, Inc.), 7500 Old Oak Blvd., Cleveland, OH 44130. TEL 216-243-8100. adv. circ. 17,264.
Formerly: Dental Laboratory Buyer's Guide.

DEVICES & DIAGNOSTICS LETTER. see *MEDICAL SCIENCES*

DIABETOLOGIA CROATICA. see *MEDICAL SCIENCES — Endocrinology*

616 GW ISSN 0178-8345
CODEN: DILAEE
DIAGNOSE UND LABOR. 1950. q. DM.28. Die Medizinische Verlags GmbH, Gartenstr. 179, 60596 Frankfurt a.M., Germany. TEL 069-638204. FAX 069-636976. Eds. Dr. Bicker, Dr. Knoop. circ. 22,000. (back issues avail.) **Document type:** catalog.
—CASDDS.
Formerly (until 1985): Laboratoriumsblaetter (ISSN 0023-673X)

616 US ISSN 1070-3608
CODEN: DTENER
▼**DIAGNOSTIC AND THERAPEUTIC ENDOSCOPY.** 1994. 4/yr. 80 ECU (effective 1996). Harwood Academic Publishers, c/o International Publishers Distributor, 820 Town Center Dr., Langhorne, PA 19047.
TEL 215-750-2642; 800-545-8398. (Subscr. to: International Publishers Distributor, P.O. Box 90, Reading, Berkshire RG1 8JL, England. TEL 44-173-456-8316) (back issues avail.) **Indexed:** Excerp.Med. (1995-). **Document type:** academic/scholarly publication.

DIAGNOSTYKA LABORATORYJNA. see *MEDICAL SCIENCES*

619 US
DIRECTORY OF FEDERAL LABORATORY RESOURCES AND TECHNOLOGIES. biennial. $65 in N. America; elsewhere $130. U.S. National Technical Information Service, 5285 Port Royal Rd., Springfield, VA 22161. TEL 703-487-4630. FAX 703-321-8547. TELEX 64617. Ed. Ed Lehmann. **Document type:** directory.
Description: Includes detailed summaries of over 1,100 resources and descriptions of over 90 technical information centers.

619 US
DRUG AND DEVICE PRODUCT APPROVAL LIST. m. $150 in the U.S., Canada, Mexico; elsewhere $300. U.S. Food and Drug Administration, Office of Public Affairs, 5600 Fisher's Ln., Rockville, MD 20857. TEL 301-443-3220. (Orders to: National Technical Information Service, 5285 Port Royal Rd., Springfield, VA 22161. TEL 703-487-4650. FAX 703-321-8547) **Document type:** government publication.
Description: Lists the most recent new drug approvals, new animal and drug devices, and licenses issued for biological products.

DRUG TARGETING. see *PHARMACY AND PHARMACOLOGY*

619 UA ISSN 1012-5558
CODEN: EJBEDR
EGYPTIAN JOURNAL OF BIOMEDICAL ENGINEERING. (Text in English; summaries in Arabic and English) 1980. a. $32 (effective 1996). (Egyptian Society of Biomedical Engineering, Research Department) National Information and Documentation Centre (NIDOC), Tahrir Street, Dokki, Awqaf P.O., Cairo, Egypt. TEL 20-2-701696. Ed. M.Y. Saada. charts; illus. circ. 1,000. (reprint service avail. from IRC) **Indexed:** INSPEC (1982-). **Document type:** academic/scholarly publication.

619 JA ISSN 0915-5422
EIJU SOGO BYOIN KIYO/EIJU GENERAL HOSPITAL. JOURNAL. (Text in Japanese) 1989. a. Raifu Ekusutenshon Kenkyujo - Research Institute for Life Extension, 11-7, Motoasakusa 2-chome, Taito-ku, Tokyo 111, Japan.

ELECTRON MICROSCOPY IN BIOLOGY AND MEDICINE. see *BIOLOGY — Microscopy*

619 340 US ISSN 1070-2504
ENVIRONMENTAL LABORATORY WASHINGTON REPORT. 1990. bi-w. $349 (foreign $317). L R P Publications, 747 Dresher Rd., Box 980, Horsham, PA 19044-0980. TEL 215-784-0860; 800-341-7874. FAX 215-784-9639. Ed. Audrey Ross. index. (back issues avail.) **Document type:** newsletter.
—CCC.
Formerly: Laboratory Regulation News (ISSN 1048-0706)
Description: Reports on regulations of environmental testing written exclusively for lab managers, directors and quality assurance professionals. Covers federal regulations as well as consumers and insurance groups.

619 US ISSN 0888-7128
EUROPEAN CLINICAL LABORATORY. (Includes a. Buyers' Guide) 1982. 7/yr. $162 (foreign $147). International Scientific Communications, Inc., 30 Controls Dr., Box 870, Shelton, CT 06484-0870. TEL 203-926-9300. FAX 203-926-9310. (U.K. subscr. to: I.S.C. House, Progress Business Centre, 5 Whittle Pkwy., Slough SL1 6DQ, England. TEL 0628-668881. FAX 0628-669199) Ed. Brian Howard. adv.; bk.rev.; charts; illus.; stat.; tr.lit.; circ. 32,801 (controlled). **Indexed:** ABC, Anal.Abstr., Lab.Haz.Bull. **Document type:** trade publication.
Formerly: International Clinical Products Review.

616 IT ISSN 1122-8652
CODEN: EJLME
EUROPEAN JOURNAL OF LABORATORY MEDICINE. (Text in English) 1987. 6/yr. T H Editing, Via C. Colombo 63, 10129 Turin, Italy. TEL 39-11-500497. **Indexed:** Excerp.Med. (1994-). **Document type:** academic/scholarly publication.
Formerly (until 1993): Progressi in Medicina di Laboratorio (ISSN 1120-995X)

EXPERIMENTAL AND CLINICAL IMMUNOGENETICS. see *BIOLOGY — Genetics*

619 JA ISSN 0007-5124
CODEN: JIDOAA
EXPERIMENTAL ANIMALS/JIKKEN DOBUTSU. (Text in English and Japanese; summaries in English) 1952. q. $70. Japanese Association for Laboratory Animal Science - Nihon Jikken Dobutsu Gakkai, c/o Tokyo Daigaku Nogakubu, Juigaku-ka, 1-1-1 Yayoi, Bunkyo-ku, Tokyo 113, Japan. FAX 03-5800-6925. (Dist. by: Kinokuniya Company, Inc., 3-17-7 Shinjuku, Shingjuku-ku, Tokyo 160-91, Japan. TEL 03-3354-0131) Ed. Shigeru Sugano. adv.; bk.rev.; charts; illus.; cum.index. circ. 2,300. **Indexed:** Anim.Breed.Abstr., Biol.Abstr., Chem.Abstr., Curr.Adv.Ecol.Sci., Dent.Ind., Excerp.Med., Ind.Med., Ind.Vet., Poult.Abstr., Small Anim.Abstr., Vet.Bull. **Document type:** academic/scholarly publication.
—BLDSC (3838.730000); CASDDS; Genuine Article; SWETS; UMI. **CCC.**
Formerly: Bulletin of the Experimental Animals.

FERTILITAET, STERILITAET, IN-VITRO-FERTILISATION, SEXUALITAET, KONTRAZEPTION. see *MEDICAL SCIENCES — Obstetrics And Gynecology*

619 UK ISSN 0268-9499
CODEN: FBRIE7
FIBRINOLYSIS. 1987. bi-m. £242($399) (effective 1995). Churchill Livingstone Journals (Subsidiary of: Pearson Professional), Robert Stevenson House, 1-3 Baxter's Pl., Leith Walk, Edinburgh EH1 3AF, Scotland. TEL 0131-556-2424. FAX 0131-459-1177. (Subscr. to: Pearson Professional Ltd., P.O. Box 77, Fourth Ave., Harlow, Essex CM19 5AA, England. TEL 01279-623760; U.S. subscr. to: Churchill Livingstone, 650 Ave. of the Americas, New York, NY 10011. TEL 212-206-5000) Eds. J.F. Davidson, I.D. Walker. adv. contact: David Dunnachie. circ. 650.
Document type: academic/scholarly publication.
—BLDSC (3918.118000); ADONIS; CASDDS; Genuine Article; SWETS. **CCC.**
Formerly: Journal of Fibrinolysis.
Description: Covers molecular biology of fibrinolysis and clinical trials of thrombolytic agents.

619 PO ISSN 0374-7638
CODEN: FAUCAR
FOLIA ANATOMICA UNIVERSITATIS CONIMBRICENSIS. (Text in English, French and Portuguese) 1926. a. free or exchange basis. Imprensa de Coimbra, Ltd., Largo de S. Salvador, Coimbra, Portugal. Ed. A. Simoes de Carvalho. bibl.; illus.; index. **Indexed:** Biol.Abstr.

619 IT ISSN 1121-8142
CODEN: FTCME
FORUM: TRENDS IN EXPERIMENTAL AND CLINICAL MEDICINE. Key Title: Forum (Genova). 1991. bi-m. L.120000 (Europe $100, elsewhere $130) to individuals; institutions L.180000 (Europe $150; elsewhere $180). Scuola Superiore di Oncologia e Scienze Biomediche, Piazza della Vittoria 15-1, 16121 Genova, Italy. TEL 39-10-5458611. FAX 39-10-541761. Ed. Luigi Frati. circ. 6,000. **Indexed:** Excerp.Med. (1993-). **Document type:** academic/scholarly publication.
—BLDSC (4024.117000).
Refereed Serial

FUJIAN ZHONGYI YAO/FUJIAN JOURNAL OF TRADITIONAL CHINESE MEDICINE. see *ALTERNATIVE MEDICINE*

616 GW ISSN 0016-3538
CODEN: GITEAR
G I T; Fachzeitschrift fuer das Laboratorium. (Summaries in English and German) 1957. m. DM.160 (students DM.80). G I T Verlag GmbH, Roesslerstr. 90, 64293 Darmstadt, Germany. TEL 06151-8090-0. FAX 06151-809045. Ed. Ernst Giebeler. adv.: B&W page DM.7950, color page DM.10830; trim 185 x 260; adv. contact: Heinz Beckmann. bk.rev.; charts; illus.; pat.; tr.lit.; index. circ. 25,000. **Indexed:** Chem.Abstr., Dok.Arbeitsmed., Excerp.Med., INIS Atomind., Sugar Ind.Abstr. **Document type:** trade publication.
—BLDSC (4179.652000); CASDDS; SWETS.

619 616.9 US
GAY MEN'S HEALTH CRISIS. 1989. a. $30. G M H C, Inc., 129 W. 20th St., 2nd Fl., New York, NY 10011-0022. TEL 212-337-3693. FAX 337-3656. circ. 30,000. **Document type:** newsletter.
Description: Devoted to providing reliable information on experimental therapies for people living with AIDS and HIV infections.

GENE AMPLIFICATION AND ANALYSIS SERIES. see *BIOLOGY — Genetics*

GENERAL CLINICAL RESEARCH CENTERS; a research resources directory. see *MEDICAL SCIENCES — Abstracting, Bibliographies, Statistics*

GENOME PRIORITY REPORTS. see *BIOLOGY — Genetics*

616 US
GUIDE FOR THE CARE AND USE OF LABORATORY ANIMALS. 1963. irreg. free. U.S. National Institutes of Health, National Center for Research Resources, Westwood Bldg., Rm. 10A15, 5333 Westbard Ave., Bethesda, MD 20892. TEL 301-594-7938. (Subscr. to: Supt. of Documents, Washington, DC 20402) **Document type:** government publication.
Formerly (until 1972): Guide for Laboratory Animal Facilities and Care (ISSN 0072-8098)
Description: Contains guidelines articles on the care and proper use of laboratory research animals.

MEDICAL SCIENCES — EXPERIMENTAL MEDICINE, LABORATORY TECHNIQUE

610   GY
GUYANA ASSOCIATION OF MEDICAL TECHNOLOGISTS. NEWSLETTER. s-a. Guyana Association of Medical Technologists, Central Medical Laboratory, Public Hospital, Middle St., Georgetown, Guyana.

GYNECOLOGIC ENDOSCOPY. see *MEDICAL SCIENCES — Obstetrics And Gynecology*

619   US   ISSN 0887-3712
H L B NEWSLETTER; reporting on heart, lung and blood disease research program, policy development. 1985. 24/yr. $296 (foreign $346). Nathaniel Polster, Ed. & Pub., 821 Delaware Ave., S.W., Washington, DC 20024. TEL 202-488-7533. bk.rev. **Document type:** newsletter.

HAYASTANI BZHSHKAGITUTYUN/MEDITSINSKAYA NAUK ARMENII/ARMENIAN MEDICAL JOURNAL. see *MEDICAL SCIENCES*

619   US   ISSN 0885-0615
R853.H8
HUMAN RESEARCH REPORT; protecting researchers and research subjects. 1986. m. $177 (Canada & Mexico $184; elsewhere $214) (effective 1996). Deem Corporation, Box 44069, Omaha, NE 68144-0069. TEL 402-895-5748; 800-786-5748. FAX 402-895-2306. Ed. Dennis M. Maloney. (back issues avail.) **Document type:** newsletter.
    Description: Contains notices and explanations of research regulations, ethics, laws, lawsuits and Federal funding in biomedical and behavioral research.

619 574 591   US   ISSN 0018-9960
QL55
I L A R NEWS. 1957. q. free to qualified personnel. Institute of Laboratory Animal Resources, 2101 Constitution Ave., N.W., Washington, DC 20418. TEL 202-334-2590. FAX 202-334-1687. Ed. Mara L. Glenshaw. bk.rev.; bibl.; illus. circ. 3,500. (back issues avail.) **Indexed:** Ind.Vet., Sport Fish.Abstr., Vet.Bull., Wild.Rev. **Document type:** academic/scholarly publication.
    —BLDSC (4364.050000); Faxon; UnCover.
    Formerly: Information on Laboratory Animals for Research.
    Description: Articles on animal models, issues of interest to animal care and use committees, information on alternatives, adjuncts and refinements to the use of animals, letters to the editor, announcements of new books and meetings.
Refereed Serial

619   US   ISSN 0193-7758
I R B: A REVIEW OF HUMAN SUBJECTS RESEARCH. (Institutional Review Board) 1979. bi-m. $40 to individuals; libraries $65; institutions $260 for 20 copies. Hastings Center, 255 Elm Rd., Briarcliff Manor, NY 10510. TEL 914-762-8500. FAX 914-762-2124. Ed. Robert J. Levine. bk.rev.; bibl. circ. 5,000. (back issues avail.) **Indexed:** Psychol.Abstr. (1984-). **Document type:** academic/scholarly publication.
    —BLDSC (4567.631000); UnCover.

619   US   ISSN 1079-7823
THE IMMORTALIST. 1970. m. $25. Immortalist Society, 24355 Sorrentino Court, Clinton Township, MI 48035. TEL 810-791-5961. FAX 810-791-5961. E-mail: cryonics@AOL.com. (And: Box 1509, Cupertino, CA 95015. TEL 408-734-4200) (Co-sponsor: American Cryonics Society) Ed. Mae Ettinger. bk.rev. circ. 420. **Document type:** newsletter.
    Formerly: Outlook.
    Description: Contains news, information, conjecture, and opinion related to cryonics and life extension.

IMMUNOHISTOCHEMISTRY. see *BIOLOGY — Cytology And Histology*

619   GR   ISSN 0258-851X
CODEN: IVIVE4
IN VIVO; international journal of in vivo research. 1987. bi-m. Dr.408($230) to individuals; institutions Dr.680. John D. Delinassios, Ed. & Pub., Km. 1, Kapandritiou-Kalamou, P.O. Box 22, 190 14 Kapandriti, Attica, Greece. TEL 30-1-2016-380. adv.; index. circ. 420. (back issues avail.) **Indexed:** Excerp.Med. **Document type:** academic/scholarly publication.
    —BLDSC (4372.507000); CASDDS; Genuine Article; SWETS. **CCC.**
    Description: Takes a multidisciplinary approach to the study of biomedical research involving experimental systems. Covers oncology, chemotherapy, pharmacology, immunology, radiology, toxicology, genetics, cytology, endocrinology biotechnology, comparative pathology, and nutrition.

616   FR
INFORMATION DES LABORATOIRES. 4/yr. C G N, 32 rue Saint-Marc, 75002 Paris, France. TEL 42-60-51-58. FAX 46-28-36-10. TELEX 220 064. Ed. Albert Willemetz. circ. 6,000.

619 574   FR   ISSN 0989-8735
INFORMATION DU TECHNICIEN BIOLOGISTE. 4/yr. 318 F. (foreign 428 F.). Doin Editeurs, 6 rue de Mezieres, 75006 Paris, France. TEL 1-45481210. FAX 1-45444331. **Document type:** academic/scholarly publication.

INSTITUTION OF CHEMISTS (INDIA). JOURNAL. see *CHEMISTRY*

INSTITUTION OF CHEMISTS (INDIA). PROCEEDINGS. see *CHEMISTRY*

INSTRUMENTATION SCIENCE & TECHNOLOGY. see *CHEMISTRY — Analytical Chemistry*

INTERNATIONAL BIOTECHNOLOGY LABORATORY. see *BIOLOGY — Biotechnology*

INTERNATIONAL JOURNAL OF ARTIFICIAL ORGANS. see *MEDICAL SCIENCES*

INTERNATIONAL JOURNAL OF CLINICAL AND LABORATORY RESEARCH; an international multidisciplinary journal devoted to research pertinent to human biology and disease. see *MEDICAL SCIENCES*

INTERNATIONAL JOURNAL OF COSMETIC SCIENCE. see *BEAUTY CULTURE — Perfumes And Cosmetics*

619   UK   ISSN 0266-4623
R855
INTERNATIONAL JOURNAL OF TECHNOLOGY ASSESSMENT IN HEALTH CARE. 1985. q. £92($142) (effective 1996). (International Society for Technology Assessment in Health Care) Cambridge University Press, Edinburgh Bldg., Shaftesbury Rd., Cambridge CB2 2RU, England. TEL 01223-312393. FAX 01223-315052. TELEX 851817256. (N. American addr.: Cambridge University Press, Journals Dept., 40 W. 20th St., New York, NY 10011. TEL 212-924-3900. FAX 212-691-3239) Eds. Egon Jonsson, Stanley J. Reiser. adv.; bk.rev. (also avail. in microform from UMI; back issues avail.; reprint service avail. from SWZ) **Indexed:** Abstr.Health Care Manage.Stud., Excerp.Med. **Document type:** academic/scholarly publication.
    —BLDSC (4542.693300); Faxon; Genuine Article; SWETS; UMI; UnCover. **CCC.**
    Description: Forum for professionals interested in the assessment of medical technology, its consequences for patients and its impact on society.

616 542   UK   ISSN 0143-5140
INTERNATIONAL LABMATE. 1976. bi-m. £70. International Labmate Ltd., Newgate, Sandpit Ln., St. Albans, Herts. AL4 0BS, England. TEL 01727-858840. FAX 01727-840310. (Alt. addr.: 12 Alban Park, Hatfield Rd., St. Albans, Herts. AL4 0JJ, England) Ed. Michael H. Pattison. adv. contact: Christine Carroll. stat.; tr.lit. circ. 45,463. (back issues avail.) **Document type:** trade publication.
    —BLDSC (4542.702850).

INTERNATIONAL PRESS CUTTING SERVICE: SCIENTIFIC INSTRUMENTS, LABORATORY EQUIPMENT & CHEMICALS. see *INSTRUMENTS*

616   US
INTERNATIONAL SOCIETY FOR CLINICAL LABORATORY TECHNOLOGY NEWSLETTER. bi-m. $55. International Society for Clinical Laboratory Technology, 818 Olive St., Ste. 918, St. Louis, MO 63101-1598. TEL 314-241-1445. Ed. Mark S. Birenbaum. adv. circ. 6,000. (looseleaf format; back issues avail.) **Document type:** newsletter.
    Description: Provides information on meetings, conventions, legislative and regulatory issues and developments, news from other laboratories, state activities, continuing education programs and technical information.

619   IS   ISSN 0333-5739
ISRAEL INSTITUTE OF ANIMAL SCIENCE. SCIENTIFIC ACTIVITIES. (Text in English and Hebrew) 1971. triennial. $20 (effective 1993). Agricultural Research Organization, Israel Institute of Animal Science, Volcani Centre, P.O. Box 6, Bet Dagan 50250, Israel. TEL 972-3-9683215. FAX 972-3-993998. **Indexed:** Biol.Abstr.

J E O L NEWS: ANALYTICAL INSTRUMENTATION. (Japan Electron Optics Laboratory News) see *INSTRUMENTS*

J E O L NEWS: ELECTRON OPTICS INSTRUMENTATION. see *INSTRUMENTS*

619   JA   ISSN 0021-4965
JAPANESE JOURNAL OF CLINICAL AND EXPERIMENTAL MEDICINE/RINSHO TO KENKYU. (Text in English and Japanese) 1924. m. 11760 Yen($40) Daido Gakkan Shuppan-bu, Kyushu University Medical School, 3576 Hako Zaki, Higashi-ku, Fukuoka 812, Japan. **Indexed:** Biol.Abstr.
    —BLDSC (4651.370000).
    Description: Covers clinical and experimental medicine.

619   JA   ISSN 0910-7967
CODEN: JICHBJ
JIKKEN CHIRYO/EXPERIMENT & THERAPY. (Text in Japanese) 1921. q. 5100 Yen. Takeda Yakuhin Kogyo K.K. - Takeda Chemical Industries, Ltd., 4-1-1 Doshomachi, Chuo-ku, Osaka 541, Japan. **Document type:** academic/scholarly publication.
    —CASDDS.

JOURNAL OF APPLIED ANIMAL WELFARE SCIENCE. see *ANIMAL WELFARE*

619   US   ISSN 1045-4861
CODEN: JABIEW
JOURNAL OF APPLIED BIOMATERIALS. 1990. q. $196 to institutions (Canada and Mexico $236; elsewhere $251) (effective 1995). (Society for Biomaterials) John Wiley & Sons, Inc., Journals, 605 Third Ave., New York, NY 10158-0012. TEL 212-850-6645. FAX 212-850-6021. TELEX 12-7063. (Subscr. outside the Americas to: John Wiley & Sons, Ltd., Baffins Ln., Chichester, W. Sussex PO19 1UD, England. TEL 44-1243-779777. FAX 44-1243-776128) Ed. Harold Alexander. (also avail. in microform from UMI; back issues avail.) **Indexed:** Curr.Cont., Intl.Polym.Sci.& Tech., RAPRA. **Document type:** academic/scholarly publication.
    —BLDSC (4940.650000); CASDDS; Ei; Genuine Article; SWETS; UMI; UnCover. **CCC.**
    Description: Covers medical device development, implant retrieval and analysis, government regulations, liability and legal issues.

JOURNAL OF CARDIOVASCULAR DIAGNOSIS AND PROCEDURES. see *MEDICAL SCIENCES — Cardiovascular Diseases*

MEDICAL SCIENCES — EXPERIMENTAL MEDICINE, LABORATORY TECHNIQUE

619 US ISSN 0887-8013
CODEN: JCANEM
JOURNAL OF CLINICAL LABORATORY ANALYSIS. 1987. bi-m. $528 (foreign $621) (effective 1996). John Wiley & Sons, Inc., Journals, 605 Third Ave., New York, NY 10158. TEL 212-850-6645. FAX 212-850-6021. TELEX 12-7063. E-mail: SUBINFO@JWILEY.COM. (Subscr. outside the Americas to: John Wiley & Sons, Ltd., Baffins Ln., Chichester, W. Sussex PO19 1UD, England. TEL 44-1243-779777. FAX 44-1243-776128) Eds. Dr. Robert M. Nakamura, Ralph A. Reisfeld. (also avail. in microform from UMI; back issues avail.) **Indexed:** Biol.Abstr., Chem.Abstr., Curr.Cont., Ind.Med. **Document type:** academic/scholarly publication.
—BLDSC (4958.520000); CASDDS; Faxon; Genuine Article; SWETS; UnCover. **CCC.**
Description: Includes articles about immunochemistry, toxicology, hematology, immunopathology, microbiology, genetic testing, immunohematology, and clinical chemistry.
Refereed Serial

619 GW ISSN 0939-8600
CODEN: JEXSEU
JOURNAL OF EXPERIMENTAL ANIMAL SCIENCE. (Text in English, German) 1961. q. DM.266 (foreign DM.274). Gustav Fischer Verlag Jena, Villengang 2, 07745 Jena, Germany. TEL 03641-626444. FAX 03641-626500. (Subscr. to: Postfach 100537, 07705 Jena, Germany) Ed. H.-J. Hedrich. adv.; bk.rev.; abstr.; bibl.; charts; illus.; index, cum.index: vols.1-25. (reprint service avail. from ISI) **Indexed:** Anim.Breed.Abstr., Bibl.Agri., Biol.Abstr., Biotech.Abstr., Chem.Abstr., Curr.Adv.Cancer Res., Curr.Adv.Ecol.Sci., Curr.Adv.Genetics & Molec.Biol., Curr.Cont., Dairy Sci.Abstr., Dent.Ind., Excerp.Med., Helminthol.Abstr., Ind.Med., Ind.Vet., Nutr.Abstr., Pig News & Info., Protozool.Abstr., Ref.Zh., Small Anim.Abstr., Vet.Bull. **Document type:** academic/scholarly publication.
—BLDSC (4979.850000); CASDDS; Faxon; Genuine Article; SWETS. **CCC.**
Formerly (until 1991): Zeitschrift fuer Versuchstierkunde (ISSN 0044-3697)

610 US ISSN 0022-1007
CODEN: JEMEAV
JOURNAL OF EXPERIMENTAL MEDICINE. 1896. m. (2 vols./yr. 6 nos./vol.) $225 (effective 1994). Rockefeller University Press, 222 E. 70th St., New York, NY 10021. TEL 212-327-8572. FAX 212-327-7944. (Subscr. to: Box 5108, GPO, New York, NY 10087-5108) Ed.Bd. charts; illus. circ. 3,769. (also avail. in microform from UMI,PMC; reprint service avail. from ISI,UMI) **Indexed:** Anim.Breed.Abstr., Biol.Abstr., Biotech.Abstr., Chem.Abstr., Curr.Adv.Cancer Res., Curr.Adv.Cell & Devel.Biol., Curr.Adv.Genetics & Molec.Biol., Curr.Cont., Dairy Sci.Abstr., Diar.Dis.Res., Excerp.Med., Helminthol.Abstr., Ind.Med., Ind.Sci.Rev., Ind.Vet., INIS Atomind., Med.& Surg.Dermat., Nutr.Abstr., Poult.Abstr., Protozool.Abstr., Rev.Med.& Vet.Mycol., Sci.Cit.Ind., Trop.Dis.Bull., Vet.Bull. **Document type:** academic/scholarly publication.
—BLDSC (4982.000000); CASDDS; EMDOCS; Faxon; Genuine Article; SWETS; UMI; UnCover. **CCC.**
Description: Provides significant research in immunology and experimental medicine.
Refereed Serial

610 US ISSN 0022-2143
R11 CODEN: JLCMAK
JOURNAL OF LABORATORY AND CLINICAL MEDICINE. 1915. m. $101 to individuals (foreign $122); institutions $196 (foreign $217); students $48 (foreign $69). (Central Society for Clinical Research) Mosby - Year Book, Inc. (Subsidiary of: Times Mirror Company), 11830 Westline Industrial Dr., St. Louis, MO 63146. TEL 314-872-8370; 800-325-4177. FAX 314-432-1380. TELEX 44-2402. Ed. Dr. Harry S. Jacob. adv.; abstr.; bibl.; charts; illus.; s-a. index. circ. 3,500. (also avail. in microform from UMI,PMC; reprint service avail. from UMI) **Indexed:** Abstr.Hyg., AIM, ASCA, Biol.Abstr., Biotech.Abstr., Chem.Abstr., Curr.Adv.Biochem., Curr.Adv.Cancer Res., Curr.Adv.Ecol.Sci., Curr.Cont., Dairy Sci.Abstr., Diar.Dis.Res., Excerp.Med., Helminthol.Abstr., Ind.Med., Ind.Sci.Rev., Ind.Vet., INIS Atomind., Kidney, Med.& Surg.Dermat., Nutr.Abstr., Rev.Med.& Vet.Mycol., Rev.Plant Path., Sci.Cit.Ind., Telegen, Trop.Dis.Bull., Vet.Bull.
●Also available online. Vendor(s): Ovid Technologies.
—BLDSC (5010.000000); ADONIS; CASDDS; EMDOCS; Faxon; Genuine Article; SWETS; UMI; UnCover. **CCC.**
Description: Information on clinical investigation and research with advanced information on hematology, nephrology, organ transplantation, cardiology and immunology.
Refereed Serial

JOURNAL OF MICROSURGERY. see *MEDICAL SCIENCES — Surgery*

619 US ISSN 0896-548X
CODEN: JTEMEM
THE JOURNAL OF TRACE ELEMENTS IN EXPERIMENTAL MEDICINE. 1988. q. $298 (foreign $360) (effective 1996). (International Society for Trace Element Research in Humans) John Wiley & Sons, Inc., Journals, 605 Third Ave., New York, NY 10158. TEL 212-850-6645. FAX 212-850-6021. TELEX 12-7063. E-mail: SUBINFO@JWILEY.COM. (Subscr. outside the Americas to: John Wiley & Sons, Ltd., Baffins Ln., Chichester, W. Sussex PO19 1UD, England. TEL 44-1243-779777. FAX 44-1243-776128) Ed. Ananda S. Prasad. (also avail. in microform from UMI; back issues avail.) **Indexed:** Chem.Abstr., Excerp.Med. **Document type:** academic/scholarly publication.
—BLDSC (5069.744300); CASDDS; Genuine Article; SWETS.
Description: Focuses on the role of trace elements in human health and disease. Provides special attention to their clinical, nutritional, biochemical, immunological, and toxicological aspects.
Refereed Serial

619 JA ISSN 0301-2611
CODEN: KTGIDU
KENSA TO GIJUTSU/MODERN MEDICAL LABORATORY. (Text in Japanese) 1973. m. 13020 Yen($100) Igaku-Shoin Ltd., 5-24-3 Hongo, Bunkyo-ku, Tokyo 113-91, Japan. TEL 03-817-5713. Ed.Bd. circ. 8,500.
—CASDDS.

610 HU ISSN 0023-1878
R850 CODEN: KIORAH
KISERLETES ORVOSTUDOMANY. 1949. bi-m. $43.50. Magyar Elettani Tarsasag, Puskin u. 9, Budapest 8, Hungary. (Subscr. to: Kultura, P.O. Box 149, H-1389 Budapest, Hungary) Ed. Peter Balint. adv.; bk.rev.; charts; illus. **Indexed:** Biol.Abstr., Chem.Abstr., Excerp.Med., Ind.Med., INIS Atomind. —CASDDS.

616 RU ISSN 0869-2084
RB1 CODEN: KLDIES
KLINICHESKAYA LABORATORNAYA DIAGNOSTIKA. 1955. bi-m. $80 (effective 1996). (Soyuz Nauchnykh Obshchestv Klinichekoi Laboratornoi Diagnostiki) Izdatel'stvo Meditsina, Petroverigskii pereulok 6-8, 101000 Moscow, Russia. (Dist. by: Mezhdunarodnaya Kniga, B. Yakimanka 39, 117049 Moscow, Russia. TEL 7-095-2384600. FAX 7-095-2384634; Dist. in U.S. by: Victor Kamkin Inc., 4956 Boiling Brook Pkwy, Rockville, MD 20852. TEL 301-881-5973) (Co-sponsor: Ministerstvo Zdravookhraneniya) Ed. V.V. Men'shikov. bk.rev.; bibl. **Indexed:** Anal.Abstr., Biol.Abstr., Chem.Abstr., Dent.Ind., Ind.Med. (until 1992), INIS Atomind., Nutr.Abstr.
—BLDSC (0089.238000); CASDDS; Genuine Article. **CCC.**
Formerly: Laboratornoe Delo (ISSN 0023-6748)
Description: Covers clinical laboratory diagnosis - hematology, cytology, coagulation, biochemistry, immunology.

616 GW ISSN 0941-2131
CODEN: KLLAEA
KLINISCHES LABOR/CLINICAL LABORATORY. (Text and summaries in English and German) 1955. 10/yr. $130. Verlag Klinisches Labor, Im Breitspiel 15, 69126 Heidelberg, Germany. TEL 06221-3432133. FAX 06221-300291. Ed. H. Schmidt-Gayk. adv. contact: Ellen Buck. bk.rev.; bibl.; charts; illus.; cum.index; circ. 3,000. circ. 2,000 (paid). (back issues avail.) **Indexed:** Biol.Abstr., Chem.Abstr., Curr.Adv.Ecol.Sci., Curr.Cont., Excerp.Med., Ind.Med., INIS Atomind. **Document type:** academic/scholarly publication.
—BLDSC (5099.502000); CASDDS; Genuine Article; SWETS.
Formerly: Aerztliche Laboratorium (ISSN 0001-9526)
Description: Publication for physicians concerning the latest research and findings in medical laboratories. Covers all fields of medicine and includes announcements of events and list of suppliers.
Refereed Serial

542 SA
L M S - LABORATORY EQUIPMENT BUYERS GUIDE. (Laboratory Marketing Spectrum) (Text in English) 1989. a. R.110. George Warman Publications (Pty.) Ltd., P.O. Box 3847, Cape Town 8000, South Africa. TEL 27-21-245320. FAX 27-21-261332. Ed. Anne Duncan. **Document type:** trade publication.
Description: Guide for buyers of laboratory equipment.

619 SA ISSN 1013-1205
L M S - LABORATORY MARKETING SPECTRUM; new developments in laboratory equipment. (Text in English) 1982. bi-m. George Warman Publications (Pty.) Ltd., P.O. Box 3847, Cape Town 8000, South Africa. TEL 27-21-245320. FAX 27-21-261332. Ed. Anne Duncan. adv.; bk.rev.; index; circ. 5,800 (controlled). (back issues avail.) **Document type:** trade publication.
Description: Provides product data on laboratory equipment and materials.

619 US ISSN 0093-7355
LAB ANIMAL. 1972. 11/yr. $70. Nature Publishing Co. (Subsidiary of: Macmillan Magazines, Ltd.), 65 Bleecker St., New York, NY 10012-2467. TEL 212-477-9600. (Subscr. to: Lab Animal Subscription Fulfillment, Box 1710, Riverton, NJ 08077-7310) Ed. Julia Schuloff; Pub. James Skowrenski. adv. contact: Sharon Gellman. bk.rev.; charts; illus.; tr.lit. circ. 10,500.
—BLDSC (5137.700000); Faxon; Genuine Article; UMI.
Refereed Serial

542 GW ISSN 0343-9100
LAB-COMPACT SERVICE; Direktinformation Labortechnik. 1971. 4/yr. free to qualified personnel. G I T Verlag GmbH, Roesslerstr. 90, 64293 Darmstadt, Germany. TEL 06151-8090-0. FAX 06151-809045. Ed. Ernst Giebeler. adv.; illus.; tr.lit. circ. 14,000. **Document type:** trade publication.
Description: Consists of requests-for-information postcards.

MEDICAL SCIENCES — EXPERIMENTAL MEDICINE, LABORATORY TECHNIQUE

619   US
LAB HOTLINE. 1965. m. free. University of Iowa, University Hygienic Laboratory, Oakdale Campus, Iowa City, IA 52242. TEL 319-335-4500. FAX 319-335-4555. E-mail: theald@uhl.uiowa.edu. Ed. Tex Heald. charts; stat. circ. 1,000. **Document type:** academic/scholarly publication.

619   NE   ISSN 0368-7368
LAB INSTRUMENTEN; maandblad voor het wetenschappelijk klinisch chemische en industriele laboratorium. 1964. m. fl.110. Uitgeverij Adex, Postbus 328, 3760 AH Soest, Netherlands. TEL 31-2155-10034. FAX 31-2155-25576. Ed. Dr. G.J. de Jong. adv.; bk.rev.; illus. circ. 3,500. **Document type:** trade publication.
—SWETS.
Description: Covers new technological research and development in laboratory instruments. Includes new product listings.

619   BE   ISSN 0775-602X
LAB PRODUCTS INTERNATIONAL. 1987. 8/yr. $95 (free to qualified personnel). Pan European Publishing Co. (Subsidiary of: Reed Elsevier plc), Rue Verte 216, B-1210 Brussels, Belgium. TEL 32-2-2402611. FAX 32-2-242711. TELEX 25828 B. Ed. S. Soukias. adv.; bk.rev.; circ. 50,000 (controlled). **Document type:** trade publication.
Description: Informs its readers about the latest laboratory products being introduced into the European market from around the world.

616   US   ISSN 1045-7313
LAB REPORT; a monthly update on laboratory diagnosis. 1979. m. $99 (effective 1995 & 1996). G & R Publications, Inc., 185 Devonshire St., No. 9, Boston, MA 02110-1727. Ed. Dr. Raymond Gambino. bibl.; charts; index. circ. 2,500. (looseleaf format; back issues avail.; reprint service avail.) **Document type:** newsletter.
—CCC.
Formerly (until Sep. 1989): Lab Report for Physicians Newsletter (ISSN 0278-5161)

616   US   ISSN 1068-1760
LABMEDICA INTERNATIONAL. (Text in English; summaries in French, German, Italian, Spanish) 1982. 6/yr. $120. Globetech Publishing, 30 Cannon Rd., Wilton, CT 06897. TEL 203-762-3432. FAX 203-762-8640. TELEX 4972075 TECHCOM. Ed. Dr. John A. Koepke; Pub. Marc Gueron. adv. contact: Chrys Emery. bk.rev.; index; circ. 26,000. **Document type:** trade publication.
Former titles (until 1990): LabMedica (ISSN 1054-0970); (until 1984): Medilab.
Description: Covers the latest developments in laboratory technology, including: microbiology, clinical chemistry, hematology and immunology.
Refereed Serial

LABNEWS. see *SCIENCES: COMPREHENSIVE WORKS*

542   GW   ISSN 0344-5208
LABO; Kennziffer-Zeitschrift fuer Labortechnik. (Supplement avail.: Labo-Plus) 1970. 12/yr. free. Verlag Hoppenstedt GmbH, Havelstr. 9, 64295 Darmstadt, Germany. TEL 06151-380-0. FAX 06151-380-360. Ed. Rainer Jupe. adv.; bk.rev.; circ. 16,000 (controlled). **Document type:** trade publication.

616   SZ
LABOR AND MEDIZIN. 1973. 11/yr. 80 SFr. Swiss Association of Medical Laboratory Technologists, Chemin de Carles, CH-2035 Corcelles, Switzerland. TEL 038-318838. FAX 038-305766. Ed. Jacqueline Merlotti. adv.; bk.rev. circ. 2,900. **Document type:** academic/scholarly publication.

616   SZ
LABOR FLASH. 10/yr. Kretz AG, Postfach, CH-8706 Feldmeilen, Switzerland. TEL 01-9237656. FAX 01-9237657. Ed. H. Zullinger. adv.; B&W page 2550 SFr., color page 3590 SFr.; trim 185 x 265; adv. contact: Esther Kretz. circ. 6,400. **Document type:** trade publication.

658.5   GW
LABOR 2000. (Supplement to: Labor-Praxis (ISSN 0344-1733)) 1977. s-a. DM.20. Vogel Verlag und Druck GmbH & Co. KG, Max-Planck-Str. 7-9, 97082 Wuerzburg, Germany. TEL 0931-4182145. FAX 0931-4182640. adv. contact: Wolfgang Hartmann. circ. 14,000(controlled). **Indexed:** Chem.Abstr., Excerp.Med. **Document type:** bulletin.
—CCC.
Formerly: Labor Praxis in der Medizin (ISSN 0171-4279)

616   SW   ISSN 0345-696X
LABORATORIET. Variant title: Tidskriften Laboratoriet. 1955. 6/yr. SEK 175. Institutet foer Biomedicinsk Laboratorievetenskap, Adolf Fredriks Kyrkogata 11, S-111 37 Stockholm, Sweden. TEL 46-8-240131. FAX 46-8-240124. Ed. Barbro Soederberg. adv.; bk.rev.; circ. 12,428 (controlled). **Document type:** bulletin.

616   NE   ISSN 0924-4433
LABORATORIUM PRAKTIJK. 1979. 10/yr. fl.137 (foreign fl.340) (effective 1995). Ten Hagen & Stam b.v. (Subsidiary of: Wolters Kluwer N.V.), Postbus 34, 2501 AG The Hague, Netherlands. TEL 31-70-3045700. FAX 31-70-3045812. adv.: B&W page fl.3190, color page fl.6640; trim 297 x 210; adv. contact: Herman Voois. circ. 4,674. **Document type:** trade publication.
—SWETS.
Former titles (until 1992): Lab - A B C (ISSN 0168-7417); (until 1983): Para Medica (ISSN 0927-0582)
Description: Covers developments, new methods and techniques of interest to laboratory staff and management.

616.07   GW   ISSN 0342-3026
CODEN: LABOD3
LABORATORIUMS MEDIZIN. (Text and summaries in English, German) 1976. 11/yr. DM.231($171) in Europe; rest of world DM.319($236) (effective 1996). (Deutschen Gesellschaft fuer Laboratoriumsmedizin e.V.) Blackwell Wissenschaft, Kurfuerstendamm 57, 10707 Berlin, Germany. TEL 030-32790624. FAX 030-32790610. Ed. Lothar Thomas. adv.: B&W page DM.3500, color page DM.6200; trim 178 x 250; adv. contact: Jutta Weber-Pianka. charts; illus. circ. 7,000. **Indexed:** Chem.Abstr. **Document type:** academic/scholarly publication.
—BLDSC (5137.974000); CASDDS; SWETS. CCC.
Description: Covers chemical and microbiological analysis of body fluids, evaluation of diagnostic tools, and quality assurance of medical therapies.
Refereed Serial

616   UK   ISSN 0458-5933
CODEN: LAHBA
LABORATORY ANIMAL HANDBOOKS. 1968. irreg. price varies. Laboratory Animals Ltd., c/o Royal Society of Medicine Press Ltd., 1 Wimpole St., London W1M 8AE, England. TEL 0171-209-2900. **Indexed:** Biol.Abstr., Excerp.Med. **Document type:** monographic series.
—BLDSC (5138.530000).
Formerly (until 1969): Laboratory Animal Symposia (ISSN 0374-8855)

619   US   ISSN 0023-6764
CODEN: LBASAE
LABORATORY ANIMAL SCIENCE. 1950. bi-m. $70 (foreign $100). American Association for Laboratory Animal Science, 70 Timber Creek Dr., Ste. 5, Cordova, TN 38018. TEL 901-754-8620. Ed. Abigail Smith. charts; illus.; index. circ. 4,500. (also avail. in microform from PMC) **Indexed:** Anim.Breed.Abstr., Biol.Abstr., Biotech.Abstr., Chem.Abstr., Curr.Adv.Ecol.Sci., Curr.Cont., Dairy Sci.Abstr., Dent.Ind., Diar.Dis.Res., Excerp.Med., Helminthol.Abstr., Ind.Med., Ind.Sci.Rev., Ind.Vet., INIS Atomind., Nutr.Abstr., Pig News & Info., Protozool.Abstr., Rev.Med.& Vet.Mycol., Rev.Plant Path., Small Anim.Abstr., Sport Fish.Abstr., Vet.Bull., Wild.Rev., Zoo.Rec.
—BLDSC (5138.540000); CASDDS; EMDOCS; Faxon; Genuine Article; SWETS; UnCover.
Formerly: Laboratory Animal Care.
Refereed Serial

619   UK   ISSN 0023-6772
SF405.5   CODEN: LBANAX
LABORATORY ANIMALS. 1966. q. £85 (foreign £89($160)). (Laboratory Animal Science Association) Royal Society of Medicine Press Ltd., 1 Wimpole St., London W1M 8AE, England. TEL 0171-290-2900. FAX 0171-290-2929. adv.; bk.rev.; charts; illus.; index. circ. 1,700. **Indexed:** Anim.Breed.Abstr., Biol.Abstr., Chem.Abstr., Curr.Adv.Cell & Devel.Biol., Curr.Adv.Ecol.Sci., Curr.Cont., Dairy Sci.Abstr., Excerp.Med., Helminthol.Abstr., Ind.Med., Ind.Sci.Rev., Ind.Vet., Nutr.Abstr., Poult.Abstr., Rev.Med.& Vet.Mycol., Rev.Plant Path., Sport Fish.Abstr., Vet.Bull., Wild.Rev., Zoo.Rec. **Document type:** academic/scholarly publication.
—BLDSC (5138.600000); CASDDS; EMDOCS; Faxon; Genuine Article; SWETS; UnCover. CCC.
Description: Provides an international forum for the publication of research carried out by scientists primarily concerned with the care, welfare and science of laboratory animals.
Refereed Serial

619   UK   ISSN 0309-7382
LABORATORY ANIMALS. BUYERS GUIDE. 1977. irreg. Laboratory Animals Ltd., c/o Royal Society of Medicine Press Ltd., 1 Wimpole St., London W1M 8AE, England. TEL 0171-290-2900. FAX 0171-290-2929. **Document type:** bulletin.

619   CN   ISSN 0381-6729
LABORATORY BUYERS GUIDE. a. Can.$74.90 (foreign Can.$70). Southam Magazine Group, 1450 Don Mills Rd., Don Mills, ON M3B 2X9, Canada. TEL 416-445-6641. FAX 416-442-2261. Ed. Rita Tate. adv.
Description: Lists suppliers of laboratory equipment and chemicals, major manufacturers along with their Canadian sales agents. Includes alphabetical listing of allied products and an advertisers index.

542   US   ISSN 0023-6810
LABORATORY EQUIPMENT. 1964. m. (13/yr.). $36 (Canada $38.52; Mexico $36; elsewhere $54) (effective 1996). Gordon Publications, Inc., Part of Cahners Publishing Company, Division of Reed Elsevier Inc., 301 Gibraltar Dr., Box 650, Morris Plains, NJ 07950-0650. TEL 201-292-5100. FAX 201-898-9281. Ed. Helen Robinson. adv.: B&W page $8235, color page $10280. illus. circ. 120,000. (tabloid format; also avail. in microform from UMI) **Indexed:** Curr.Pack.Abstr., Graph.Arts Lit.Abstr., World Text.Abstr.
—UMI. CCC.
Description: Reaches managers, supervisors and research directors with buying responsibility in laboratories located in industry, government and universities.

542   UK   ISSN 0023-6829
Q185   CODEN: LEQDA2
LABORATORY EQUIPMENT DIGEST. 1963. m. $120. Morgan-Grampian (Process Press) Ltd. (Subsidiary of: Morgan-Grampian plc), Morgan-Grampian House, 30 Calderwood St., London SE18 6QH, England. TEL 0181-855-7777. FAX 0181-316-3422. Ed. Zack Goldring. adv. contact: Rob Hancocks. bk.rev.; charts; illus.; tr.lit. circ. 17,009. **Indexed:** Art & Archaeol.Tech.Abstr., Excerp.Med., INSPEC, Met.Abstr., World Surf.Coat. **Document type:** trade publication.
—BLDSC (5139.500000); SWETS.

MEDICAL SCIENCES — EXPERIMENTAL MEDICINE, LABORATORY TECHNIQUE

616 US ISSN 0023-6837
RB1 CODEN: LAINAW
LABORATORY INVESTIGATION; a journal of experimental methods and pathology. 1952. m. $147 to individuals; institutions $249. (United States and Canadian Academy of Pathology) Williams & Wilkins, 428 E. Preston St., Baltimore, MD 21202. TEL 410-528-4000; 800-638-6423. FAX 410-528-4312. TELEX 87669. Ed. Dr. Emanuel Rubin. adv.; abstr.; bibl.; charts; illus. circ. 3,260. (also avail. in microfilm from WWS) **Indexed:** Biol.Abstr., Chem.Abstr., Curr.Adv.Cancer Res., Curr.Adv.Cell & Devel.Biol., Curr.Adv.Ecol.Sci., Curr.Adv.Genetics & Molec.Biol., Curr.Cont., Dairy Sci.Abstr., Dent.Ind., Diar.Dis.Res., Excerp.Med., Helminthol.Abstr., Ind.Med., Ind.Sci.Rev., Ind.Vet., INIS Atomind., Nutr.Abstr., Pig News & Info., Protozool.Abstr., Small Anim.Abstr., Sport Fish.Abstr., Vet.Bull., Wild.Rev. **Document type:** academic/scholarly publication.
—BLDSC (5140.000000); CASDDS; EMDOCS; Faxon; Genuine Article; SWETS; UnCover. **CCC.**
Description: Experimental, anatomical and comparative pathology, cytologic and histologic methods, tissue culturing for pathologists and laboratory technicians.
Refereed Serial

616.07 US ISSN 0007-5027
RB37.A1 CODEN: LBMEBX
LABORATORY MEDICINE. 1965. m. $50. American Society of Clinical Pathologists, 2100 W. Harrison St., Chicago, IL 60612. TEL 312-738-4860. FAX 312-738-0101. Ed. Pamela Cassidy. adv. contact: Joe Dingee. bk.rev.; charts; illus.; stat.; tr.lit. circ. 166,000. (also avail. in microform from UMI; back issues avail., reprint service avail.) **Indexed:** C.I.S. Abstr., Chem.Abstr., Curr.Adv.Cell & Devel.Biol., Curr.Adv.Ecol.Sci., Curr.Adv.Genetics & Molec.Biol., Curr.Cont., Excerp.Med. **Document type:** academic/scholarly publication, bulletin.
—BLDSC (5140.400000); CASDDS; Faxon; Genuine Article; SWETS; UMI; UnCover.
Formerly (until 1970): Bulletin of Pathology; Incorporates: Technical Improvement Service Bulletin.
Description: Devoted to the continuing education of laboratory professionals. Presents original scientific articles from laboratory professionals containing both theoretical and practical information on the most recent ideas and the latest research.
Refereed Serial

619 AT ISSN 0727-7245
LABORATORY NEWS. m. Aus.$48 (foreign Aus.$80). Business Press International Pty. Ltd., 1-5 Railway St., Chatsweed, N.S.W. 2067, Australia. TEL 02-372-5222. FAX 02-419-7399. Ed. John Collett. adv.; illus. circ. 8,300. (tabloid format) **Indexed:** Br.Ceram.Abstr., Curr.Biotech.Abstr., Lab.Haz.Bull., Mass Spectr.Bull., World Surf.Coat.

619 UK ISSN 0266-7169
CODEN: LANEEY
LABORATORY NEWS. 1971. fortn. £125. E M A P Maclaren Ltd., P.O. Box 109, Maclaren House, Scarbrook Rd., Croydon CR9 1QH, England. TEL 0181-688-7788. FAX 0181-688-9300. Ed. Alex Crawford. adv.; bk.rev. circ. 16,000. **Indexed:** ABC, Curr.Biotech.Abstr.
—BLDSC (5140.570000); Faxon; SWETS.
Description: Provides news of experimental medicine and laboratory technique.

616 542 UK ISSN 0023-6853
Q183 CODEN: LABPA3
LABORATORY PRACTICE; research techniques and equipment. (Text in English; summaries in French, German) 1952. m. £39($170) United Trade Press Ltd., U.T.P. House, 33-35 Bowling Green Ln., London EC1R 0DA, England. TEL 01-837 1212. Ed. Richard Davies. adv.; bk.rev.; abstr.; charts; illus.; index, cum.index. circ. 15,669. **Indexed:** Abstr.Hyg., Anal.Abstr., Biol.Abstr., Br.Ceram.Abstr., Br.Tech.Ind., Chem.Abstr., Curr.Adv.Ecol.Sci., Dairy Sci.Abstr., Excerp.Med., Field Crop Abstr., Fluidex, Food Sci.& Tech.Abstr., Herb.Abstr., Hort.Abstr., Ind.Vet., INIS Atomind., INSPEC, Lab.Haz.Bull., Mass Spectr.Bull., Met.Abstr., RAPRA, Soils & Fert., Trop.Dis.Bull., Vet.Bull., W.R.C.Inf., World Surf.Coat.
—CASDDS; Faxon; UnCover.

616 CN ISSN 0047-3855
LABORATORY PRODUCT NEWS. 1971. 7/yr. Can.$27.82($49) (foreign $80). Southam Magazine Group, 1450 Don Mills Rd., Don Mills, ON M3B 2X7, Canada. TEL 416-445-6641. FAX 416-442-2261. Ed. Rita Tate. adv.; circ. 18,677 (controlled). **Document type:** trade publication.
Description: Provides concise product data for buyers, specifiers and users of laboratory equipment. Industrial, hospital, university, private and government users are informed about the latest equipment suitable for their particular branch of science.

619 US ISSN 0272-3778
LABORATORY REGULATION MANUAL. 1976. q. $675 (foreign $810). Aspen Publishers, Inc., 200 Orchard Ridge Dr., Gaithersburg, MD 20878. TEL 301-417-7500. FAX 301-417-7550.

LABORATORY TECHNIQUES IN BIOCHEMISTRY AND MOLECULAR BIOLOGY. see *BIOLOGY — Biological Chemistry*

LABORATORY YELLOW PAGES. see *BUSINESS AND ECONOMICS — Trade And Industrial Directories*

619 GW ISSN 0170-2572
LABORMEDIZIN. 1978. bi-m. DM.90 (students DM.45). G I T Verlag GmbH, Roesslerstr. 90, 64293 Darmstadt, Germany. TEL 06151-8090-0. FAX 06151-809045. Ed. Walter Depner. adv.: B&W page DM.5640, color page DM.8160; trim 185 x 260; adv. contact: Frank Urban. circ. 11,000. **Indexed:** INIS Atomind. **Document type:** academic/scholarly publication.

619 GW ISSN 0344-1733
CODEN: LAPRDE
LABORPRAXIS. 1977. m. DM.198. Vogel Verlag und Druck GmbH & Co. KG, Max-Planck-Str. 7-9, 97082 Wuerzburg, Germany. TEL 0931-4182145. FAX 0931-4182640. (Subscr. to: Vogel Verlag, 97064 Wuerzburg, Germany; Dist. in U.S. by: Vogel Europublishing, Inc., 19927 Villa Dr., Sonora, CA 95370. TEL 209-533-3555. FAX 209-533-9555) Ed. Dieter Kneucker. adv.: B&W page DM.6670, color page DM.8810; trim 270 x 190; adv. contact: Wolfgang Hartmann. bk.rev.; circ. 20,000 (controlled). **Indexed:** INIS Atomind. **Document type:** trade publication.
—BLDSC (5141.942000); CASDDS; SWETS. **CCC.**

542 SZ
LABORSCOPE; Messtechnik - Regelung und Steuerung - Datentechnik. 1974. 8/yr. free in Switzerland (foreign 60 SFr.). Verlag Binkert AG, CH-4335 Laufenburg, Switzerland. TEL 064-697272. FAX 064-697333. Ed. Ludwig Binkert. adv. contact: Ludwig Binkert. bk.rev.; illus. circ. 6,250. **Document type:** trade publication.

619 621.329 IT ISSN 1121-0656
CODEN: LASTE2
LASER AND TECHNOLOGY; clinical and experimental. (Text in Italian; abstracts in English) 1991. 3/yr. L.80000($80) (effective 1994). Wichtig Editore s.r.l., Via Friuli, 72-73, 20135 Milan, Italy. TEL 02-5452306. FAX 02-5451843.
—CASDDS.

681 GW ISSN 0938-765X
CODEN: LASMEF
LASERMEDIZIN. 1985. irreg. DM.280 (foreign DM.284). Gustav Fischer Verlag, Wollgrasweg 49, 70599 Stuttgart, Germany. TEL 0711-458030. FAX 0711-4580334. TELEX 7111488-FIBUCH-D. (Subscr. to: Postfach 720143, 70577 Stuttgart, Germany) **Document type:** academic/scholarly publication.
—BLDSC (5156.597000).

616 US ISSN 0580-7247
RB36 CODEN: MLOBAC
M L O. (Medical Laboratory Observer) 1969. m. $65 (foreign $75). Medical Economics Publishing Co., Inc., Five Paragon Dr., Montvale, NJ 07645. TEL 201-358-7200. FAX 201-573-0344. Ed. Robert J. Fitzgibbon. adv.; charts; illus.; stat.; index. circ. 59,000. (also avail. in microform from UMI) **Indexed:** Bus.Ind., CINAHL, Tr.& Indus.Ind.
—BLDSC (5529.387000); Genuine Article; UMI. **CCC.**
Description: Improves the management skills of clinical lab supervisors.

M T A - FACHZEITSCHRIFT FUER TECHNISCHE ASSISTENTEN DER MEDIZIN; Monatszeitschrift fuer MTA's, Labormediziner, Fachleute Radio-Diagnostik, Lehrer und Studenten. (Medizinisch-Technische Assistenten) see *MEDICAL SCIENCES*

619 US ISSN 1060-7609
M T TODAY. (Medical Technologist) 1991. fortn. free. Valley Forge Press, 1288 Valley Forge Rd., Box 1135, Valley Forge, PA 19482. TEL 610-935-3302; 800-9VF-PRES. FAX 215-935-3072. E-mail: vpfedit@aol.com. Ed. Gregg McQueen. bk.rev.; charts; illus.; circ. 60,000 (controlled).
Description: Contains items of general interest to medical laboratory professionals, managers and educators.

MADE IN EUROPE - MEDICAL EQUIPMENT AND SUPPLY GUIDE. see *MEDICAL SCIENCES*

616 US ISSN 1048-5007
MANAGEMENT BRIEFS. 1979. s-m. $37. Clinical Laboratory Management Association, 9 Old Lincoln Hwy., Ste. 201, Malvern, PA 19355-2135. TEL 610-647-8970. FAX 610-889-9731. Ed. Jennifer Begley. adv. contact: Jennifer Begley. circ. 8,500 (controlled). **Indexed:** Excerp.Med. **Document type:** academic/scholarly publication, newsletter.
Formerly (until 1989): Clinical Laboratory Management Newsletter.
Description: To keep association members updated on general healthcare management issues.

MEDICAL AND RADIOLOGICAL DEVICES GUIDANCE MANUAL. see *PUBLIC HEALTH AND SAFETY*

619 681 US ISSN 1060-8338
MEDICAL DEVICE APPROVAL LETTER.* 1992. m. $495. Washington Information Source, 6506 Old Stage Rd., Ste. 100, Rockville, MD 20852-4326. TEL 301-770-5553. Ed. Kenneth Reid. bk.rev. **Document type:** newsletter.
—CCC.

MEDICAL DEVICE ESTABLISHMENT REGISTRATION MASTER FILE. see *PUBLIC HEALTH AND SAFETY*

MEDICAL DEVICE PROBLEMS REPORT FROM THE D E N: REPORTS FROM MEDICAL DEVICE USERS. see *PUBLIC HEALTH AND SAFETY*

MEDICAL DEVICE REPORTING FROM THE D E N: REPORTS FROM MEDICAL DEVICE MANUFACTURERS. see *PUBLIC HEALTH AND SAFETY*

610 UK ISSN 0140-3028
CODEN: MLWODQ
MEDICAL LABORATORY WORLD. 1977. 11/yr. £48($178) (foreign £90). Wilmington Publishing, Wilmington House, Church Hill, Dartford, Kent UA2 7EF, England. TEL 0322-277788. FAX 0322-276476. (Subscr. to: Ferrari House, 258 Field End Rd., Ruislip, Middx HA4 9UX, England. TEL 081-868-4499) Ed. Julian Page. circ. 9,974. **Indexed:** ABC, Br.Tech.Ind., Chem.Abstr.
—BLDSC (5529.420000); CASDDS.

619 SA ISSN 1011-5528
MEDICAL TECHNOLOGY S A. 1987. 2/yr. R.45 (foreign R.50). (Society of Medical Laboratory Technologists of South Africa - Vereniging van Geneeskundige Laboratorium Tengnoloe van Suid-Afrika) Medical Technology News, P.O. Box 253, Rondebosch 7700, South Africa. TEL 27-21-4610054. Ed. G.W. Wikeley. adv. contact: C.J. Blom. charts; illus.; tr.lit. circ. 2,100. (back issues avail.) **Document type:** academic/scholarly publication.
Description: Publishes original papers on any aspect of medical laboratory science or related disciplines.
Refereed Serial

MEDICAL ULTRASOUND TECHNOLOGY. see *MEDICAL SCIENCES — Radiology And Nuclear Medicine*

MICROSURGERY. see *MEDICAL SCIENCES — Surgery*

MEDICAL SCIENCES — EXPERIMENTAL MEDICINE, LABORATORY TECHNIQUE

619 540 UK ISSN 0890-8508
RB43.7 CODEN: MCPRE6
MOLECULAR AND CELLULAR PROBES; the location, diagnosis, and monitoring of disease by nucleic acid techniques. 1987. bi-m. £145 (effective 1996). Academic Press Ltd. (Subsidiary of: Harcourt Brace & Company Ltd.), 24-28 Oval Rd., London NW1 7DX, England. TEL 44-171-267-4466. FAX 44-171-482-2293. TELEX 25775 ACPRES G. (Subscr. to: Harcourt Brace & Company Ltd., Foots Cray High St., Sidcup, Kent DA14 5HP, England. TEL 44-181-300-3322. FAX 44-181-309-0807) Ed. D.J.H. Brock, R.H. Yolken. index. (back issues avail.) **Indexed:** Anim.Breed.Abstr., Excerp.Med. (1993-), Ind.Vet. **Document type:** academic/scholarly publication.
—BLDSC (5900.761000); ADONIS; CASDDS; Faxon; Genuine Article; SWETS; UnCover. **CCC.**
Description: Examines location, diagnosis, and monitoring of both infectious and inherited diseases.

619 616 BU
MOLEKULIARNA MEDITSINA. (Text in Bulgarian; summaries in English, Russian) 1963. q. 360 lv. Tsentar za Informatsiia po Meditsina, 1, Sv. Georgi Sofiiski St., 1431 Sofia, Bulgaria. TEL 359-2-522342. Ed. L. Sirakov. circ. 200. **Indexed:** Abstr.Bulg.Sci.Med.Lit., BSL Biol., Curr.Adv.Ecol.Sci., Excerp.Med. (until 1993). **Document type:** academic/scholarly publication.
—CASDDS.
Formerly (until 1995): Eksperimentalna Medicina i Morfologija (ISSN 0367-0643)
Description: Publishes original articles on experimental medicine, molecular biology and morphology.

MONOCLONAL ANTIBODIES. see MEDICAL SCIENCES — Allergology And Immunology

619 US ISSN 0177-7475
MONOGRAPHS ON PATHOLOGY OF LABORATORY ANIMALS. 1983. irreg. price varies. (International Life Sciences Institute) Springer-Verlag, 175 Fifth Ave., New York, NY 10010. TEL 212-460-1500. FAX 212-473-6272. (Also: Berlin, Heidelberg, Tokyo and Vienna) Ed. T.C. Jones. **Document type:** monographic series.

N A P A M A NEWS. (National Association of Performing Arts Managers and Agents) see THEATER

619 NE
NEDERLANDSE VERENIGING VOOR KLINISCHE CHEMIE. ALMANAK. a. membership. Nederlandse Vereniging voor Klinische Chemie, Vredenburg 139A, 4th Fl., 3511 BG Utrecht, Netherlands. TEL 31-30-328623. adv. circ. 650.

NIHON JIKKEN DOBUTSU GAKKAI SOKAI KOEN YOSHISHU/JAPANESE ASSOCIATION FOR LABORATORY ANIMAL SCIENCE. ABSTRACTS OF GENERAL MEETING. see MEDICAL SCIENCES — Abstracting, Bibliographies, Statistics

619 JA ISSN 0913-2139
NIHON JIKKEN DOBUTSU GIJUTSUSHA KYOKAI HOKKAIDO SHIBU KAISHI/JAPANESE ASSOCIATION FOR EXPERIMENTAL ANIMAL TECHNOLOGISTS. HOKKAIDO BRANCH. JOURNAL. (Text in Japanese) 1977. a. Nihon Jikken Dobutsu Gijutsusha Kyokai, Hokkaido Shibu - Japanese Association for Experimental Animal Technologists, Hokkaido Branch, Hokkaido Daigaku Igakubu Fuzoku Dobutsu Jikken Shisetsu, Nishi 7-chome, Kita 15-jo, Kita-ku, Sapporo-shi, Hokkaido 060, Japan.

616 US ISSN 0048-069X
NORTH DAKOTA SOCIETY OF MEDICAL TECHNOLOGISTS. NEWSLETTER. vol.24, 1972. q. $6 to non-members. (North Dakota Society for Medical Technology) University of North Dakota, Department of Pathology, Grand Forks, ND 58201. TEL 701-777-2563. FAX 701-772-9636. Eds. Eileen Nelson, Linda Larson. adv.; bk.rev.; film rev.; bibl.; charts; illus. circ. 400. (tabloid format) **Indexed:** Ind.Med. **Document type:** newsletter.

NURSE RESEARCHER. see MEDICAL SCIENCES — Nurses And Nursing

542 CN ISSN 0832-5332
O S M T UPDATE. 1985. 6/yr. Ontario Society of Medical Technologists, 234 Eglinton Ave. E., Ste. 600, Toronto, Ont. M4P 1K5, Canada. Ed. Richard C. Lafferty. adv.; bk.rev.; circ. 5,180 (controlled).

PERITONEAL DIALYSIS INTERNATIONAL. see MEDICAL SCIENCES

619.05 US ISSN 1053-8984
QL55
PERSPECTIVES ON MEDICAL RESEARCH. 1989. irreg. $10 per no. to non-members. Medical Research Modernization Committee, Box 2751, New York, NY 10163. TEL 216-832-3904. FAX 216-283-6702. Ed. Dr. Stephen R. Kaufman. bk.rev.; circ. 1,200. (back issues avail.) **Document type:** academic/scholarly publication.
—BLDSC (6428.144400).
Formerly (until 1990): Perspectives on Animal Research (ISSN 1045-0424)
Description: Critically evaluates various research methods to assess their scientific validity and clinical utility.
Refereed Serial

619 UK ISSN 0966-4068
PORTLAND PRESS PROCEEDINGS. 1992. irreg., vol.9, 1995. Portland Press Ltd., 59 Portland Place, London W1N 3AJ, England. TEL 0171-580-5530. FAX 0171-323-1136. E-mail: sales@portlandpress.co.uk. (Subscr. to: Commerce Way, P.O. Box 32, Colchester, Essex CO2 8HP, England. TEL 01206-796351. FAX 01206-799331) Ed. J.H. Botting. (back issues avail.) **Document type:** proceedings.
—BLDSC (6555.657000).
Refereed Serial

PREPARATIVE BIOTRANSFORMATIONS: WHOLE CELL AND ISOLATED ENZYMES IN ORGANIC SYNTHESIS. see BIOLOGY — Cytology And Histology

PROCEDURES IN ELECTRON MICROSCOPY. see BIOLOGY — Microscopy

616 IT
RASSEGNA DI MEDICINA DEI LAVORATORI. q. L.80000 (foreign L.160000) (effective 1993). Ediesse s.r.l., Via dei Frentani, 4-A, 00185 Rome, Italy. TEL 06-448701. FAX 06-44481260.

610 IT ISSN 0033-9555
CODEN: RMSPAY
RASSEGNA DI MEDICINA SPERIMENTALE. (Text in English and Italian) 1953. m. L.60000($100) (effective 1995). Casa Editrice Idelson, Via A. de Gasperi 55, 80133 Naples, Italy. TEL 39-81-5524733. FAX 39-81-5518295. Ed. Giovanni de Franciscis. bk.rev.; charts; illus.; stat. **Indexed:** Biol.Abstr., Chem.Abstr., Curr.Adv.Ecol.Sci., Excerp.Med.
—BLDSC (7294.440000); CASDDS; EMDOCS; UMI.
Description: Features research papers covering a wide variety of topics in experimental medicine.

RAVEN PRESS SERIES IN PHYSIOLOGY. see BIOLOGY — Physiology

619 574.192 UK
▼**REDOX REPORT.** 1994. q. £100($155) to individuals; insitutions £200 ($310) (effective 1995). Churchill Livingstone Journals (Subsidiary of: Pearson Professional), Robert Stevenson House, 103 Baxter's Pl., Leith Walk, Edinburgh EH1 3AF, Scotland. TEL 0131-556-2424. FAX 0131-459-1177. (Subscr. to: Pearson Professional, Ltd., P.O. Box 77, Fourth Ave., Harlow, Essex CM19 5AA, England. TEL 01279-623760; U.S. subscr. to: Churchill Livingstone, 650 Ave. of the Americas, New York, NY 10011. TEL 212-206-5000) Ed.Bd. adv. contact: David Dunnachie. bk.rev. **Document type:** academic/scholarly publication.
Description: Publishes reviews, research articles, hypotheses, debates, and correspondence on the role of free radicals, oxidative stress, activated oxygen, peroxidative, and redox processes, primarily in human biology and pathology.

610 GW ISSN 0300-9130
R850.A1 CODEN: REXMAS
RESEARCH IN EXPERIMENTAL MEDICINE. (Text in English) vol.155, 1971. 6/yr. DM.1136($825) (effective 1996). Springer-Verlag, Heidelberger Platz 3, 14197 Berlin, Germany. TEL 030-8207-0. FAX 030-8214091. E-mail: orders@springer.de. (Subscr. in N. America to: Springer-Verlag New York, Inc., 44 Hartz Way, Secaucus, NJ 07096-2491. TEL 201-348-4033. FAX 201-348-4505) Ed. F.D. Goebel. (also avail. in microform from UMI; back issues avail.; reprint service avail. from ISI) **Indexed:** Biol.Abstr., Biotech.Abstr., Chem.Abstr., Curr.Adv.Cancer Res., Curr.Adv.Ecol.Sci., Curr.Cont., Dairy Sci.Abstr., Dent.Ind., Excerp.Med., Helminthol.Abstr., Ind.Med., Ind.Vet., Nutr.Abstr., Vet.Bull. **Document type:** academic/scholarly publication.
—BLDSC (7740.200000); ADONIS; CASDDS; Faxon; Genuine Article; SWETS; UMI; UnCover. **CCC.**
Formerly: Zeitschrift fuer die Gesamte Experimentelle Medizin Einschliesslich Experimenteller Chirurgie (ISSN 0044-2534)
Description: Original papers and research reports cover experimental medicine and surgery, internal medicine, surgery, endocrinology, pathology, anesthesiology, biochemistry, physiology, and pharmacology.
Refereed Serial

RESOURCES FOR COMPARATIVE BIOMEDICAL RESEARCH; a research resources directory. see MEDICAL SCIENCES — Abstracting, Bibliographies, Statistics

619 SP ISSN 0214-3429
CODEN: RESQEJ
REVISTA ESPANOLA DE QUIMIOTERAPIA/SPANISH JOURNAL OF CHEMOTHERAPY. (Text in Spanish; abstracts in English, Spanish) 1988. q. $75 (effective 1995). (Sociedad Espanola de Quimioterapia - Spanish Society for Chemotherapy) J.R. Prous, S.A. International Publishers, Apdo. de Correos, 540, 08080 Barcelona, Spain. TEL 343-459-2220. FAX 343-458-1535. Ed. M. Gobernado. adv. contact: P. Blancafort. circ. 3,000. (back issues avail.)
—BLDSC (7854.230000).

619 616 FR ISSN 0296-5321
REVUE DES LABORATOIRES D'ESSAIS. 1978. q. A.S.T.E., 8 rue Roquepine, 75008 Paris, France. TEL 42-66-58-29. FAX 42-66-12-06. Ed. Jean Delatte. circ. 3,000.
Formerly (until 1984): Association pour la Developpement des Sciences et Techniques de l'Environnement. Revue (ISSN 0249-6658)

619 JA ISSN 0485-1420
CODEN: RNKNAT
RINSHO KENSA/JOURNAL OF MEDICAL TECHNOLOGY. (Text in Japanese) 1957. m. 17700 Yen($136) Igaku-Shoin Ltd., 5-24-3 Hongo, Bunkyo-ku, Tokyo 113-91, Japan. TEL 03-817-5712. Ed.Bd. circ. 12,000.
—BLDSC (5017.090000); CASDDS.

S E R B OFFICIAL REPORTER. (State Employment Relations Board) see LAW

616 FR ISSN 0339-722X
CODEN: STALDT
S T A L. (Sciences et Techniques de l'Animal de Laboratoire) (Text in English, French) 1976. q. 350 F. Societe Francaise d'Experimentation Animale (SFEA), Centre d'Experimentation Animale et de Recherches Chirurgicales, 6 rue du General-Sarrail, 94000 Creteil, France. TEL 31-47-02-00. (Subscr. to: C. Bugiani, Laboratoire Roussel-Uclaf, 102, route de Noisy, 93230 Romainville, France. TEL 1-48-91-51-90) Ed. J. Duteil. adv.; bk.rev. circ. 1,000. **Indexed:** ASCA, Biol.Abstr., Curr.Adv.Ecol.Sci., Curr.Cont., Helminthol.Abstr., Ind.Vet., Int.Aerosp.Abstr., Met.Abstr., Vet.Bull.
—BLDSC (8430.123000).
Formerly: Association des Techniciens d'Animaux de Laboratoire. Bulletin Trimestriel (ISSN 0339-7238)

MEDICAL SCIENCES — FORENSIC SCIENCES

616   **NO**   ISSN 0036-5513
RB1   CODEN: SJCLAY
SCANDINAVIAN JOURNAL OF CLINICAL & LABORATORY INVESTIGATION. (Text in English) 1949. 8/yr. NOK 1600 in Nordic countries; elsewhere $282 (effective 1996). (Scandinavian Society for Clinical Chemistry) Scandinavian University Press, P.O. Box 2959 Toeyen, N-0608 Oslo, Norway. TEL 47-22-57-54-00. FAX 47-22-57-53-53. (U.S. addr.: Scandinavian University Press, 200 Meecham Ave., Elmont, NY 11003. TEL 516-352-7300) Ed. O. Stokke. adv.; bibl.; charts; illus.; index. circ. 1,200. (also avail. in microform from UMI; back issues avail.; reprint service avail. from ISI) **Indexed:** Abstr.Hyg., ASCA, Biol.Abstr., Biotech.Abstr., C.I.S. Abstr., Chem.Abstr., Curr.Adv.Cancer Res., Curr.Adv.Ecol.Sci., Curr.Cont., Dairy Sci.Abstr., Excerp.Med., Helminthol.Abstr., Ind.Med., Ind.Vet., Nutr.Abstr., Pig News & Info., Sci.Cit.Ind., Trop.Dis.Bull., Vet.Bull. **Document type:** academic/scholarly publication.
—BLDSC (8087.500000); ADONIS; CASDDS; EMDOCS; Faxon; Genuine Article; SWETS; UMI; UnCover. **CCC.**
Refereed Serial

616   **UK**   ISSN 0085-591X
                     CODEN: SJCLAY
SCANDINAVIAN JOURNAL OF CLINICAL AND LABORATORY INVESTIGATION. SUPPLEMENT. (Text in English) 1951. irreg. (Scandinavian Society for Clinical Chemistry and Clinical Physiology) Blackwell Science Ltd., Osney Mead, Oxford OX2 0EL, England. TEL 01865-240201. FAX 01865-721205. TELEX 83355 MEDBOK G. Ed. O. Stokke. adv. circ. 1,200. (also avail. in microform from UMI; back issues avail.; reprint service avail. from ISI) **Indexed:** Biol.Abstr., Chem.Abstr., Curr.Adv.Biochem., Curr.Adv.Cell & Devel.Biol., Curr.Adv.Ecol.Sci., Curr.Cont., Excerp.Med., Ind.Med., Nutr.Abstr. **Document type:** academic/scholarly publication.
—BLDSC (8087.505000); ADONIS; CASDDS; EMDOCS; Faxon; SWETS. **CCC.**

SCANNING MICROSCOPY; an international journal of scanning electron microscopy, related techniques, and applications. see *BIOLOGY — Microscopy*

616   **SZ**   ISSN 0253-5211
                     CODEN: SSLADA
SCHWEIZERISCHE LABORATORIUMS ZEITSCHRIFT. (Text in French, German, Italian) 10/yr. 85 SFr. (foreign 116 SFr.). Schweizerischer Laborpersonal Verband, Postfach, CH-4002 Basel, Switzerland. TEL 061-3242759. FAX 061-8515332. Ed. Christian Beerli. adv.: B&W page 1475 SFr., color page 1500 SFr. circ. 3,500. **Document type:** trade publication.
—BLDSC (8117.855000); CASDDS.

542   **US**
SCIENCE SUPPLY NEWS.* 1972. q. free. Markson Science Inc., Box 1359, Hillsboro, TX 97123-1359. Ed. Alec Trode. adv.; illus. circ. 500,000.

619   **US**   ISSN 1068-6746
R11   CODEN: SASMFP
▼**SCIENTIFIC AMERICAN SCIENCE & MEDICINE.** 1994. bi-m. $59 (foreign $65); newsstand price $9.95. Scientific American, Inc., 415 Madison Ave., New York, NY 10017-1111. TEL 212-754-0050. FAX 212-754-1138. (Subscr. to: Box 3182, Harlan, IA 51593-0373. TEL 800-888-0028) Ed. Albert E. Meier. illus. (reprint service avail.) **Document type:** academic/scholarly publication.
—BLDSC (8175.240000); CASDDS. **CCC.**
Description: Provides medical scientists with an opportunity to interpret their biomedical research to a wide audience.

SCRIPTA SCIENTIFICA MEDICA. see *MEDICAL SCIENCES — Oncology*

SEMINARS IN NUCLEAR MEDICINE. see *MEDICAL SCIENCES — Radiology And Nuclear Medicine*

619   **IT**   ISSN 0390-8283
SOCIETA MEDICO CHIRURGICA DE PAVIA. BOLLETTINO. (Text in Italian; summaries in English, Italian) 1886. q. Societa Medico Chirurgica de Pavia, Palazzo Universita, Strada Nuova, 65, 27100 Pavia, Italy. TEL 0382-422932. (Co-sponsor: Universita di Pavia, Facolta Medica) Ed. Vittorio Malamavi. bibl. circ. 300.

SOCIETY FOR CRYOBIOLOGY. NEWS NOTES. see *BIOLOGY — Biophysics*

SOCIETY FOR EXPERIMENTAL BIOLOGY AND MEDICINE. PROCEEDINGS. see *BIOLOGY*

SOUTHERN CALIFORNIA DENTAL LABORATORY ASSOCIATION. BULLETIN. see *MEDICAL SCIENCES — Dentistry*

616   **FR**   ISSN 0766-5725
                     CODEN: TEBIEY
TECHNIQUE ET BIOLOGIE; revue de documentation scientifique et d'information professionnelle. 1975. bi-m. 350 F. (foreign 500 F.). Societe Francaise d'Editions Medicales, 22-24 rue du Chateau des Rentiers, 75013 Paris, France. TEL 45-83-50-54. FAX 45-83-13-54. Ed. Colette Gallula. adv.; charts; illus. **Indexed:** C.I.S. Abstr., Chem.Abstr.
—BLDSC (8739.250000); CASDDS; SWETS. **CCC.**
Formerly: Technicien Biologiste (ISSN 0337-9965)

TECHNIQUES OF CHEMISTRY. see *CHEMISTRY*

619   **UK**   ISSN 0144-8633
                     CODEN: TMMEDU
TECHNIQUES OF MEASUREMENT IN MEDICINE SERIES. 1978. irreg., no.7, 1982. price varies. Cambridge University Press, Edinburgh Bldg., Shaftesbury Rd., Cambridge CB2 2RU, England. TEL 01223-312393. FAX 01223-315052. TELEX 851817256. (N. American addr.: Cambridge University Press, Journals Dept., 40 W. 20th St., New York, NY 10011. TEL 212-924-3900. FAX 212-691-3239) **Indexed:** Biol.Abstr. **Document type:** monographic series.

616   **SP**   ISSN 0371-5728
                     CODEN: TCLBAB
TECNICAS DE LABORATORIO. 1969. 10/yr. 8800 ptas.($99) (effective 1995). Publica, S.A., Ecuador, 75, entlo., 08029 Barcelona, Spain. TEL 34-3-3215046. FAX 34-3-4391027. Ed. Carlos Romagosa. adv.; bk.rev.; bibl.; charts; illus. circ. 3,000. **Indexed:** Chem.Abstr., Ind.Med.Esp., Ind.SST. **Document type:** trade publication.
—BLDSC (8762.710000); CASDDS. **CCC.**

TISSUE CULTURE. see *BIOLOGY — Cytology And Histology*

610   **JA**   ISSN 0040-8727
                     CODEN: TJEMAO
TOHOKU JOURNAL OF EXPERIMENTAL MEDICINE. (Text in English, French and German) 1920. m. (3 vols./yr.) $410. Tohoku University Medical Press, 2-1 Seiryou-machi, Aoba-ku, Seindai 980-77, Japan. TEL 81-22-274-111. FAX 81-22-272-6293. Ed. Hiroshi Satoh. abstr.; bibl.; charts; illus. circ. 800. (also avail. in microform from UMI,PMC; reprint service avail. from UMI) **Indexed:** Abstr.Hyg., ASCA, Biol.Abstr., C.I.S. Abstr., Chem.Abstr., Curr.Adv.Ecol.Sci., Curr.Cont., Dairy Sci.Abstr., Dent.Ind., Excerp.Med., Helminthol.Abstr., Ind.Med., Nutr.Abstr., Risk Abstr., Sci.Cit.Ind., Trop.Dis.Bull. **Document type:** academic/scholarly publication.
—BLDSC (8861.000000); CASDDS; EMDOCS; Faxon; Genuine Article; SWETS; UMI; UnCover. **CCC.**

610   **JA**   ISSN 0040-8875
                     CODEN: TJXMAH
TOKUSHIMA JOURNAL OF EXPERIMENTAL MEDICINE. (Text in English and European languages) 1954. s-a. exchange basis. Tokushima Daigaku, Igakubu - Tokushima University, School of Medicine, 18-15 Kuramoto-cho 3-chome, Tokushima-shi, Tokushima-ken 770, Japan. TEL 0886-33-7183. FAX 0886-31-9495. Ed. Kenji Shima. charts; illus. **Indexed:** Abstr.Hyg., Biol.Abstr., Chem.Abstr., Curr.Adv.Ecol.Sci., Excerp.Med., Ind.Med., Nutr.Abstr., Trop.Dis.Bull. **Document type:** academic/scholarly publication.
—BLDSC (8862.900000); CASDDS; EMDOCS; UnCover.

TRANSPLANTATION PROCEEDINGS. see *MEDICAL SCIENCES — Surgery*

ULTRASTRUCTURAL PATHOLOGY. see *BIOLOGY — Cytology And Histology*

U.S. NATIONAL INSTITUTES OF HEALTH. NATIONAL CENTER FOR RESEARCH RESOURCES. PROGRAM HIGHLIGHTS. see *MEDICAL SCIENCES — Abstracting, Bibliographies, Statistics*

619 591   **GW**   ISSN 0300-1016
VERSUCHSTIERKUNDE. (Text in English, German) 1972. irreg. price varies. Verlag Paul Parey (Berlin), Seelbuschring 9-17, 12105 Berlin, Germany. TEL 030-70784-0. FAX 030-70784199. Eds. M. Merkenschlager, K. Gaertner. bibl.; illus.; index. (back issues avail.) **Document type:** academic/scholarly publication.

YAOWU SHIPIN FENXI/JOURNAL OF FOOD AND DRUG ANALYSIS. see *FOOD AND FOOD INDUSTRIES*

ZAVODSKAYA LABORATORIYA; zhurnal po analiticheskoi khimii, fizicheskim, matematicheskim i mekhanicheskim metodam issledovaniya materialov. see *CHEMISTRY — Analytical Chemistry*

MEDICAL SCIENCES — Forensic Sciences

614.19   **US**   ISSN 0739-7666
RA1001.A35
ACADEMY NEWS. 1955. bi-m. $15 to non-members. American Academy of Forensic Sciences, Box 669, Colorado Springs, CO 80901. TEL 719-939-1100. FAX 719-636-1993. Ed. Brenda K. Papke. adv. circ. 3,600. (back issues avail.) **Document type:** newsletter.

ACCIDENT RECONSTRUCTION JOURNAL. see *LAW*

ACTA CRIMINOLOGIAE ET MEDICAE LEGALIS JAPONICA/HANZAIGAKU ZASSHI. see *CRIMINOLOGY AND LAW ENFORCEMENT*

340.6   **BE**   ISSN 0065-1397
ACTA MEDICINAE LEGALIS ET SOCIALIS. (Represents proceedings of its triennial world congress and its interim international meetings; not published 1969-1971) (Text in English, French) 1948. a. 1800 BEF (effective 1994). International Academy of Legal Medicine and Social Medicine, c/o Elizabeth Francson, Perm.Secr. & Treas., Avenue Nicolair, 49A-8, B-4802 Verviers, Belgium. TEL 32-87-229821. circ. 450. **Indexed:** Biol.Abstr., Chem.Abstr., Ind.Med. **Document type:** proceedings.
—BLDSC (0635.800000).

614.19   **TU**   ISSN 1018-5275
                     CODEN: ATDEE
ADLI TIP DERGISI. 1985. 3/yr. (Ministry of Justice) Council of Forensic Medicine of Turkey, Cerrahpasa Medical Faculty, 34303 Istanbul, Turkey. TEL 5880873. **Indexed:** Excerp.Med. (1994-).
—BLDSC (0681.746000).

ALCOHOL, DRUGS AND DRIVING. see *DRUG ABUSE AND ALCOHOLISM*

614.19   **US**   ISSN 0195-7910
RA1001
AMERICAN JOURNAL OF FORENSIC MEDICINE AND PATHOLOGY. 1980. q. $150 to individuals (foreign $191); institutions $230 (foreign $276) (effective 1996). (National Association of Medical Examiners) Lippincott - Raven Press (Subsidiary of: Wolters Kluwer N.V.), 227 E. Washington Sq., Philadelphia, PA 19106. TEL 215-238-4200. Ed. Dr. Vincent J.M. DiMaio. adv. contact: Phyllis Noyes. bk.rev.; charts; illus.; stat.; index. circ. 2,000. (also avail. in microform; back issues avail.; reprint service avail. from UMI) **Indexed:** Abstr.Anthropol., C.L.I., Curr.Cont., Dent.Ind., Excerp.Med., Ind.Med., INIS Atomind., Leg.Per. **Document type:** academic/scholarly publication.
—BLDSC (0824.630000); Faxon; Genuine Article; SWETS; UMI; UnCover. **CCC.**
Description: Features original articles on new examination and documentation procedures, case reports, new devices, and medico-legal aspects.
Refereed Serial

MEDICAL SCIENCES — FORENSIC SCIENCES

616.8 340   US   ISSN 0163-1942
RA1151
AMERICAN JOURNAL OF FORENSIC PSYCHIATRY.* (Supplement avail.: Dementia) 1978. q. $65 to individuals (foreign $80). (American College of Forensic Psychiatry) Edward Miller, Ed. & Pub., Box 560, Shaftsbury, VT 05262-0560. TEL 714-831-0236. bk.rev. circ. 1,000. (also avail. in microfilm from WSH,PMC; microfiche; reprint service avail. from WSH) **Indexed:** Abstr.Bk.Rev.Curr.Leg.Per., Psychol.Abstr. (1983-).
—BLDSC (0824.640000); UnCover.
Description: For psychiatrists used as expert witnesses in civil and criminal court cases.
Refereed Serial

614.19   FR   ISSN 0242-6110
TX501   CODEN: AFETDF
ANNALES DES FALSIFICATIONS DE L'EXPERTISE CHIMIQUE ET TOXICOLOGIQUE. 1907. m. (10/yr.). Societe des Expert-Chimistes de France, 3.5 rue du General Foy, 75008 Paris, France. adv. circ. 2,000. **Indexed:** Biol.Abstr., Chem.Abstr., Dairy Sci.Abstr., Nutr.Abstr., Packag.Sci.Tech., Sugar Ind.Abstr. **Document type:** academic/scholarly publication.
—BLDSC (0972.980000); CASDDS; SWETS.
Supersedes (in 1979): Annales des Falsifications et de l'Expertise Chimique (ISSN 0003-4274); Annales des Falsifications et des Fraudes.

614.19   GW   ISSN 0570-5886
ARBEITSMETHODEN DER MEDIZINISCHEN UND NATURWISSENSCHAFTLICHEN KRIMINALISTIK. 1962. irreg., vol.19, 1993. price varies. Schmidt-Roemhild Verlag, Mengstr. 16, 23552 Luebeck, Germany. TEL 0451-1605-0. FAX 0451-1605253. TELEX 26536-MSRD. **Document type:** academic/scholarly publication.

ARCHIVUM IMMUNOLOGIAE ET THERAPIAE EXPERIMENTALIS. see *MEDICAL SCIENCES*

614.19 364   PL   ISSN 0324-8267
                        CODEN: AMSKA2
ARCHIWUM MEDYCYNY SADOWEJ I KRIMINOLOGII. 1950. q. Polskie Towarzystwo Medycyny Sadowej i Kryminalnej, Ul. Grzegorzewska 16, 31-581 Krakow, Poland. TEL 48-12-210851. Ed. Jerzy Kurz.
—BLDSC (1661.370000); CASDDS.
Formerly (until 1966): Archiwum Medycyny Sadowej, Psychiatrii Sadowej i Kryminalistyki (ISSN 0402-9178).
Description: Covers forensic medicine and criminology.

614.19   AT   ISSN 0045-0618
K1   CODEN: AJFSB9
AUSTRALIAN JOURNAL OF FORENSIC SCIENCES. 1968. biennial. Aus.$60. Australian Academy of Forensic Sciences, c/o McGraw-Hill Book Company Australia, Distributor, 4 Barcoo St., Roseville, N.S.W. 2069, Australia. TEL 02-417-4288. FAX 02-417-5687. TELEX 120849. Ed. David Bell. adv.; bk.rev. circ. 400. **Indexed:** Aus.P.A.I.S., C.L.I., Chem.Abstr., Excerp.Med., L.R.I. **Document type:** academic/scholarly publication.
—BLDSC (1808.100000); CASDDS; UnCover.
Description: Interdisciplinary forum on law, medicine and science.

340.6   AU   ISSN 0067-5016
RA1001   CODEN: BEGMA5
BEITRAEGE ZUR GERICHTLICHEN MEDIZIN. 1911. a. price varies. Franz Deuticke Verlag GmbH, Schwarzenbergstr. 5, A-1010 Vienna, Austria. TEL 0222-51405-0. Ed. W. Holczobek. cum.index (vols. 1-20 in vol. 20; vols. 21-30 in vol. 31). circ. 250. (back issues avail.) **Indexed:** Chem.Abstr., Dent.Ind., Excerp.Med., Ind.Med. **Document type:** academic/scholarly publication.
—BLDSC (1883.700000); CASDDS; EMDOCS; Faxon; SWETS.

340.6   US   ISSN 0009-7446
KF3821.A59
CITATION; current legal developments relating to medicine and allied professions. 1958. s-m. $120. (American Medical Association, Health Law Division) Citation Publishing Corp., Box 3538 RFD, Long Grove, IL 60047. TEL 708-438-2020. FAX 708-438-2299. Ed. Sheri Thomsen; Pub. Dean E. Snyder. index. circ. 1,000. (looseleaf format) **Indexed:** I.P.A. **Document type:** newsletter.
—Faxon.

614.19   US   ISSN 0743-1872
HV8073
CRIME LABORATORY DIGEST. vol.11, 1984. q. free. U.S. Federal Bureau of Investigation Laboratory, FSRTC, F B I Academy, Quantico, VA 22135. (Co-sponsor: American Society of Crime Laboratory Directors (ASCLD)) Ed. Barry L. Brown. circ. 3,000.
—Faxon; Genuine Article; UnCover.
Description: Covers all aspects of forensic science.

CRIMINALIST'S SOURCE BOOK. see *CRIMINOLOGY AND LAW ENFORCEMENT — Abstracting, Bibliographies, Statistics*

614.19 364   NE
ELSEVIER SERIES IN FORENSIC AND POLICE SCIENCE. 1981. irreg., vol.7, 1992. price varies. Elsevier Science B.V., Books Division, P.O. Box 211, 1000 AE Amsterdam, Netherlands. TEL 31-20-4853911. FAX 31-20-4853705. TELEX 18582 ESPA NL. E-mail: nlinfo-f@elsevier.nl; usinfo-f@elsevier.com; forinfo-kyf04035@niftyserve.or.jp; Site addr.: http://www.elsevier.nl/. (Subscr. in U.S. and Canada to: Elsevier Science Inc., Box 882, Madison Sq. Sta., New York, NY 10159. TEL 212-989-5800) **Document type:** monographic series.
Refereed Serial

614.19 364   NE
ELSEVIER SERIES IN PRACTICAL ASPECTS OF CRIMINAL & FORENSIC INVESTIGATION. (Text in English) 1983. irreg., latest 1992. price varies. Elsevier Science B.V., Books Division, P.O. Box 211, 1000 AE Amsterdam, Netherlands. TEL 31-20-4853911. FAX 31-20-4853705. TELEX 18582 ESPA NL. E-mail: nlinfo-f@elsevier.nl; usinfo-f@elsevier.com; forinfo-kyf04035@niftyserve.or.jp; Site addr.: http://www.elsevier.nl/. (Subscr. in U.S. and Canada to: Elsevier Science Inc., Box 882, Madison Sq. Sta., New York, NY 10159. TEL 212-989-5800) (back issues avail.) **Document type:** monographic series.
Refereed Serial

THE EXPERT AND THE LAW. see *LAW*

FINGERPRINT WORLD. see *CRIMINOLOGY AND LAW ENFORCEMENT*

614.19   AU   ISSN 0724-844X
FORENSIA; interdisziplinaere Jahrbuch fuer Psychiatrie, Psychologie, Kriminologie und Recht. vol.4, 1983. a. price varies. (Gesellschaft Oesterreichischer Nervenaerzte und Psychiater) Springer-Verlag, Sachsenplatz 4-6, Postfach 89, A-1201 Vienna, Austria. TEL 0222-3302415. FAX 0222-3302426. Ed. G. Harrer. (also avail. in microform from UMI; reprint service avail from ISI) **Indexed:** Excerp.Med. **Document type:** monographic series.
—UMI. **CCC.**

363.2   IE   ISSN 0379-0738
RA1001   CODEN: FSINDR
FORENSIC SCIENCE INTERNATIONAL; an international journal dedicated to the applications of science to the administration of justice. 1972. 21/yr. I£728($1150) (effective 1996). Elsevier Science Ireland Ltd., P.O. Box 85, Limerick, Ireland. TEL 353-61-471944. FAX 353-61-472144. (Subscr. in U.S. and Canada to: Elsevier Science Inc., Box 882, Madison Sq. Sta., New York, NY 10159. TEL 212-989-5800. FAX 212-633-3990) Ed. B. Knight. charts; illus. (also avail. in microform from UMI; reprint service avail. from WSH) **Indexed:** Abstr.Anthropol., Abstr.Crim.& Pen., Biol.Abstr., Bull.Signal., C.L.I., Chem.Abstr., Crim.Just.Abstr., Curr.Cont., Dent.Ind., Excerp.Med., Hlth.Ind., HRIS, Ind.Med., L.R.I., Leg.Per., Sci.Cit.Ind., SSCI. **Document type:** academic/scholarly publication.
—BLDSC (3987.764000); CASDDS; Faxon; Genuine Article; SWETS; UnCover. **CCC.**
Former titles (until vol.13, no.1, 1979): Forensic Science (ISSN 0300-9432); Journal of Forensic Medicine (ISSN 0022-1171)
Description: Publishes original contributions in the many different scientific disciplines pertaining to the forensic sciences.
Refereed Serial

614.19   US   ISSN 0930-1461
HV8073   CODEN: FSPRE7
FORENSIC SCIENCE PROGRESS. 1986. irreg. price varies. Springer-Verlag, 175 Fifth Ave., New York, NY 10010. TEL 212-460-1550. FAX 212-473-6272. (Also: Berlin, Heidelberg, Tokyo and Vienna) (reprint service avail. form ISI) **Document type:** academic/scholarly publication.
—BLDSC (3987.765000); CASDDS.

340   US   ISSN 0192-3145
KF195.E96
FORENSIC SERVICES DIRECTORY; national register of experts, engineers, scientific advisors, medical specialists, technical consultants and sources of specialized knowledge. 1980. a. $117.50. National Forensic Center, 17 Temple Terr., Lawrenceville, NJ 08648. TEL 609-883-0550. Ed. Betty S. Lipscher. adv. **Document type:** directory.
●Also available online. Vendor(s): Lexis-Nexis, West Services, Inc.

340.6   CN   ISSN 0226-8841
KE3646.A13
HEALTH LAW IN CANADA. 1980. q. Can.$135. Butterworths Canada Ltd., Part of the Reed Elsevier group, 75 Clegg Rd., Markham, ON L6G 1A1, Canada. TEL 905-479-2665. FAX 905-479-2826. Ed. Gilbert Sharpe. **Indexed:** C.L.I., Hlth.Ind., Ind.Can.L.P.L., L.R.I. **Document type:** trade publication.
—Faxon; UnCover. **CCC.**
Description: Covers all major aspects of Canadian health law.

614.19   JA   ISSN 0289-0755
HOIGAKU NO JISSAI TO KENKYU/RESEARCH AND PRACTICE IN FORENSIC MEDICINE. (Text in English, Japanese; summaries in English) 1954. a. 5000 Yen. Tohoku Daigaku, Igakubu Hoigaku Danwakai - Tohoku University, School of Medicine, Department of Forensic Medicine, Sendai-shi, Miyagi-ken 980, Japan. TEL 022-274-1111. FAX 022-272-7273. Ed. Kaoru Sagisaka. circ. 1,000. (back issues avail.) **Document type:** academic/scholarly publication.
—BLDSC (7715.695000).

614.19   II   ISSN 0970-1982
RA1001   CODEN: IJFSEW
INDIAN JOURNAL OF FORENSIC SCIENCES. 1985. q. Rs.120($24) (free to members). Forensic Science Society of India, Forensic House, Kamarajar Salai, Madras 600 004, India. TEL 845085. Ed. P. Chandra Sekharan. adv. circ. 1,000. **Indexed:** Abstr.Crim.& Pen.
—BLDSC (4412.650000); CASDDS.
Formerly (until 1987): Forensic Science Society of India. Journal.
Description: Information geared to scientists, pathologists, police surgeons and members of the legal profession interested in forensic sciences.

340.6   US
INFORM QUARTERLY NEWSLETTER.* 1969. q. $25. International Reference Organization in Forensic Medicine & Sciences, c/o Dr. William G. Eckert, Ed., 3114 State St. Dr., New Orleans, LA 70125-4241. bibl. circ. 1,500. (looseleaf format) **Indexed:** Excerp.Med.
Formerly: Inform - Letter (ISSN 0019-9702)

INFORMATION EXCHANGE. see *MEDICAL SCIENCES — Pediatrics*

614.19 340   CK   ISSN 0120-0097
RA1001   CODEN: RINCDD
INSTITUTO NACIONAL DE MEDICINA LEGAL DE COLOMBIA. REVISTA. 1975. s-a. Col.$4000 or exchange basis (effective 1995). Instituto Nacional de Medicina Legal y Ciencias Forenses, Division de Desarrollo Tecnologico y Normalizacion, Calle 7A, 12-61 Bogota, DC, Colombia. TEL 571-2-339883. FAX 571-2-338534. Ed. Ricardo Mora Izquierdo. circ. 2,000. **Indexed:** Excerp.Med. **Document type:** academic/scholarly publication.
—CASDDS.
Refereed Serial

340.6   BE   ISSN 0074-1248
INTERNATIONAL ACADEMY OF LEGAL MEDICINE AND OF SOCIAL MEDICINE. (CONGRESS REPORTS). (Subseries of: Acta Medicinae Legalis et Socialis (ISSN 0065-1397). triennial, 16th, 1994, Strasbourg. International Academy of Legal Medicine and Social Medicine, c/o Elizabeth Francson, Perm.Secr. & Treas., Avenue Nicolai, 49A-8, B-4802 Verviers, Belgium. TEL 32-87-229821. **Document type:** proceedings.

614.19   BE   ISSN 1016-829X
INTERNATIONAL ACADEMY OF LEGAL MEDICINE AND SOCIAL MEDICINE. NEWSLETTER. 3/yr. free. International Academy of Legal and Social Medicine, c/o Elizabeth Francson, Perm.Secr. & Treas., Avenue Nicolai, 49A-8, B-4802 Verviers, Belgium. TEL 32-87-229821. bk.rev. **Document type:** newsletter.

MEDICAL SCIENCES — FORENSIC SCIENCES

614.19 GW ISSN 0937-9827
RA1001 CODEN: IJLMEA
INTERNATIONAL JOURNAL OF LEGAL MEDICINE. (Text in English) 1922. 6/yr. DM.894($649) (effective 1996). (Deutsche Gesellschaft fuer Rechtsmedizin) Springer-Verlag, Heidelberger Platz 3, 14197 Berlin, Germany. TEL 030-8207-0. FAX 030-8214091. E-mail: orders@springer.de. (Subscr. in N. America to: Springer-Verlag New York, Inc., 44 Hartz Way, Secaucus, NJ 07096-2491. TEL 201-348-4033. FAX 201-348-4505) Ed. B. Brinkmann. adv.; illus.; index. (also avail. in microform from UMI; back issues avail.; reprint service avail. from ISI) **Indexed:** Biol.Abstr., C.L.I., Chem.Abstr., Curr.Cont., Excerp.Med., Ind.Med., L.R.I., Leg.Per. **Document type:** academic/scholarly publication.
—BLDSC (4542.315500); CASDDS; Faxon; Genuine Article; SWETS; UMI. **CCC.**
Former titles (until 1992): Zeitschrift fuer Rechtsmedizin - Journal of Legal Medicine (ISSN 0044-3433); Deutsche Zeitschrift fuer die Gesamte Gerichtliche Medizin.
Description: Provides research articles in the areas of forensic pathology, clinical forensic pathology, forensic hemogenetics and stain identification, forensic toxicology, and traffic medicine.

614.19 NO
INTERNATIONAL SYMPOSIUM ON WOUND BALLISTICS. PROCEEDINGS. (Supplement to: Acta Chirurgica Scandinavica) 3rd, 1978. irreg. $42. Scandinavian University Press, P.O. Box 2959 Toeyen, N-0608 Oslo, Norway. TEL 47-22-57-54-00. FAX 47-22-57-53-53. Ed. T. Seeman. illus. **Document type:** proceedings.

614.19 JA ISSN 0915-9606
CODEN: HOCHE8
JAPANESE JOURNAL OF FORENSIC TOXICOLOGY/HO CHUDOKU. (Text in English, Japanese) 1990. 3/yr. Japanese Association of Forensic Toxicology - Nihon Ho Chudoku Gakkai, Showa University, Faculty of Pharmaceutical, Dept. of Toxicology, 1-5-8, Hatanodai, Shinagawa-ku, Tokyo 142, Japan. TEL 03-3784-8205. FAX 03-3784-8246. Ed. Osamu Suzuki. **Indexed:** Excerp.Med. (1993-). **Document type:** academic/scholarly publication.
—BLDSC (4651.955000); CASDDS.

614.19 JA ISSN 0047-1887
CODEN: NHOZAX
JAPANESE JOURNAL OF LEGAL MEDICINE/NIPPON HOIGAKU ZASSHI. (Supplements accompany some numbers) (Table of contents and summaries in English) 1944. bi-m. $49.50. Medico-Legal Society of Japan - Nihon Hoi Gakkai, Faculty of Medicine, University of Tokyo, 7-3-1 Hongo, Bunkyo-ku, Tokyo 13, Japan. (Subscr. to: Japan Publications Trading Co., Box 5030, Tokyo International, Tokyo 100-31, Japan) illus. **Indexed:** Chem.Abstr., Dent.Ind., Excerp.Med., Ind.Med.
—BLDSC (4655.850000); CASDDS; EMDOCS.

340.6 615.9 FR ISSN 0249-6208
RA1001 CODEN: JMLMD7
JOURNAL DE MEDECINE LEGALE DROIT MEDICAL; expertise medicale, deontologie, urgence medicale. 1957. 8/yr. 1008 F. to individuals (foreign 1226 F.); institutions 1167 F. (foreign 1400 F.) (effective 1995). Editions E S K A, 27 rue Dunois, 75013 Paris, France. TEL 44-06-80-42. FAX 44-24-06-94. (Co-sponsors: Association Lyonnaise de Medecine Legale; Association Lyonnaise d'Economie Medicale) Ed. D. Malicier. adv.; bk.rev.; index. circ. 1,900. (reprint service avail. from ISI) **Indexed:** Biol.Abstr., C.I.S. Abstr., Chem.Abstr., Curr.Cont., Excerp.Med., I.P.A. **Document type:** academic/scholarly publication.
●Also available online.
—CASDDS; Genuine Article; SWETS. **CCC.**
Supersedes in part (in 1981): Medecine Legale, Toxicologie, Urgence Medicale, Centre Anti-Poisons (ISSN 0241-6751); Which was formerly (until 1980): Bulletin de Medecine Legale, Toxicologie (ISSN 0181-0154); (until 1978): Bulletin de Medecine Legale, Urgence Medicale, Centre Anti-Poisons (ISSN 0395-4374); (until 1976): Bulletin de Medecine Legale et de Toxicologie Medicale (ISSN 0007-4365); (until 1964): Bulletin de Medicine Legale (ISSN 0994-8430).
Description: Explores and reports on public regulations affecting medical activities and the relationship between public administration and the practice of medicine.

614.19 364 UK ISSN 1353-1131
JOURNAL OF CLINICAL FORENSIC MEDICINE. 1972. q. £69($106) to individuals; institutions £107 ($166) (effective 1995). (Association of Police Surgeons) Churchill Livingstone Journals (Subsidiary of: Pearson Professional), Robert Stevenson House, 1-3 Baxter's Pl., Leith Walk, Edinburgh EH1 3AF, Scotland. TEL 0131-556-2424.
FAX 0131-459-1177. (Subscr. to: Pearson Professional Ltd., P.O. Box 77, Fourth Ave., Harlow, Essex CM19 5AA, England. TEL 01279-623760; U.S. subscr. to: Churchill Livingstone, 650 Ave. of the Americas, New York, NY 10011. TEL 212-206-5000) Ed. Jason Payne-James. adv. contact: David Dunnachie. bk.rev. **Document type:** academic/scholarly publication.
—BLDSC (4958.460000).
Formerly (until 1994): Police Surgeon (ISSN 0308-0242)
Description: Provides a forum for the rapid publication of topical articles on the clinical aspects of forensic medical work.

JOURNAL OF EVIDENCE PHOTOGRAPHY. see *PHOTOGRAPHY*

614.19 US ISSN 0895-173X
HV8073 CODEN: JFIDFK
JOURNAL OF FORENSIC IDENTIFICATION. 1988. bi-m. $70 to individuals; institutions $90 (foreign $110) (effective 1993). International Association for Identification, Box 2423-0247, Alameda, CA 94501. TEL 510-865-2174. FAX 510-865-2167. Ed. David Grieve. index; circ. 3,800 (paid).
—BLDSC (4984.588000); UMI.
Description: Devoted to the publication of information about forensic identification in it various disciplines, including document examination, imprint evidence, polygraph examination, crime scene investigation, forensic reconstruction, blood stain pattern identification, and other pertinent subjects.
Refereed Serial

614.19 CC ISSN 1004-5619
JOURNAL OF FORENSIC MEDICINE/FAYIXUE ZAZHI. (Text in Chinese; summaries in English) 1985. q. $55 (effective 1996). Ministry of Justice, Institute of Forensic Sciences, 1347 West Guangfu Rd., Shanghai 200063, People's Republic of China. TEL 021-2440148. FAX 021-2442691. Ed. Zhang Peng. adv.: B&W page $300, color page $600. bk.rev.; circ. 5,000 (paid). (reprint service avail. from WSH) **Document type:** academic/scholarly publication.
Description: Publishes original contributions in the fields of forensic pathology, histochemistry, serology, toxicology, odontology, psychiatry and anthropology.
Refereed Serial

JOURNAL OF FORENSIC PSYCHIATRY. see *MEDICAL SCIENCES — Psychiatry And Neurology*

340.6 614.19 US ISSN 0022-1198
RA1001 CODEN: JFSCAS
JOURNAL OF FORENSIC SCIENCES. 1956. bi-m. $124. (American Academy of Forensic Sciences) American Society for Testing and Materials, 1916 Race St., Philadelphia, PA 19103. TEL 215-299-5400.
FAX 215-977-9679. Ed. Abel M. Dominguez. adv.; bk.rev.; charts; illus.; index. circ. 4,200. (also avail. in microform from UMI; reprint service avail. from UMI,WSH) **Indexed:** Abstr.Bk.Rev.Curr.Leg.Per., Abstr.Bull.Inst.Pap.Chem., Abstr.Crim.& Pen., Art & Archaeol.Tech.Abstr., Biol.Abstr., C.L.I., Chem.Abstr., CJPI, Crim.Just.Abstr., Curr.Cont., Dent.Ind., Excerp.Med., Hlth.Ind., HRIS, Ind.Med., INIS Atomind., L.R.I., Leg.Per., Mass Spectr.Bull., Psychol.Abstr. (1989-), W.R.C.Inf. **Document type:** academic/scholarly publication.
—BLDSC (4984.600000); CASDDS; EMDOCS; Faxon; Genuine Article; SWETS; UMI; UnCover. **CCC.**
Supersedes: What's New in Forensic Sciences (ISSN 0511-8662)
Refereed Serial

610 US ISSN 1081-5589
JOURNAL OF INVESTIGATIVE MEDICINE. 1953. 4/yr. $95 to non-members; institutions $100; foreign $120. (American Federation for Clinical Research) Slack, Inc., 6900 Grove Rd., Thorofare, NJ 08086. TEL 609-848-1000. FAX 609-853-5991. Ed. Barbara L. Hempstead. adv.; abstr.; illus.; index. circ. 11,675. (also avail. in microform from UMI) **Indexed:** Biol.Abstr., Biotech.Abstr., Chem.Abstr., Curr.Adv.Ecol.Sci., Curr.Cont., Diar.Dis.Res., Excerp.Med., Helminthol.Abstr., Ind.Med., Ind.Sci.Rev., Med.& Surg.Dermat., NRN, Risk Abstr., Sci.Cit.Ind., Telegen.
—Genuine Article; SWETS; UMI; UnCover. **CCC.**
Formerly (until Dec. 1994): Clinical Research (ISSN 0009-9279)
Refereed Serial

614 340 IT ISSN 0394-8218
CODEN: JUMEE
JURA MEDICA. 1988. q. Edizioni Colosseum, Via Monte Zebio 25, 00195 Rome, Italy. TEL 6-3703825. **Indexed:** Excerp.Med. (1995-).

614.19 JA ISSN 0285-7960
IN PROCESS
KAGAKU KEISATSU KENKYUJO HOKOKU HOKAGAKU HEN/NATIONAL RESEARCH INSTITUTE OF POLICE SCIENCE. REPORT. RESEARCH OF FORENSIC SCIENCE. (Text in Japanese; summaries in English) 1948. q. Kagaku Keisatsu Kenkyujo - National Research Institute of Police Science, 6 Sanban-cho, Chiyoda-ku, Tokyo 102, Japan. Ed. Shoichi Yada. circ. 1,000. **Indexed:** Crim.Just.Abstr., INIS Atomind., Psychol.Abstr.
—BLDSC (7570.222600).
Formerly: National Research Institute of Police Science. Report (ISSN 0451-1980)

616 SZ ISSN 1019-4231
LABOLIFE. (Text in English, French, German, Italian) 1992. 6/yr. 30 SFr. Degra AG, Postfach 415, CH-6343 Rotkreuz, Switzerland. TEL 042-644860. FAX 042-645323. Ed. Peter Hagemann; Pub. Rolf Ruegg. adv. contact: Prisca Ruegg. **Document type:** academic/scholarly publication.

LEBENSMITTELCHEMIE. see *FOOD AND FOOD INDUSTRIES*

LEGAL AND CRIMINOLOGICAL PSYCHOLOGY. see *PSYCHOLOGY*

614.190971 US ISSN 0703-1211
LEGAL MEDICAL QUARTERLY. 1977. q. $95 (foeign $105) (effective 1995 & 1996). Jonah Publications, 558 Pleasant St., 3rd Fl., New Bedford, MA 02740. TEL 508-994-5515.
FAX 508-992-8772. Ed. David A. Silverman. (back issues avail.; reprint service avail. from RRI,WSH) **Indexed:** C.L.I., I.P.A., Ind.Can.L.P.L., L.R.I., Leg.Per.
—BLDSC (5181.329000).

340.6 US ISSN 0197-9981
RA1001
LEGAL MEDICINE. 1969-1987; resumed 1989. a. Butterworth Legal Publishers (Salem) (Subsidiary of: Reed Elsevier plc), 8 Industrial Way, Bldg. C, Salem, NH 03079. TEL 800-548-4001.
FAX 603-898-9858. Ed. Cyril H. Wecht. **Indexed:** C.L.I., Excerp.Med., Hlth.Ind., Ind.Med., L.R.I.
—BLDSC (5181.329950); UnCover. **CCC.**
Formerly: Legal Medicine Annual (ISSN 0075-8590)
Description: Contains a collection of articles which addresses a variety of subjects in the fields of legal medicine and the forensic sciences.

614 363.2 FR ISSN 1246-7391
MEDECINE ET DROIT. 1993. bi-m. 575 F. in France; foreign 640 F.($125) (effective 1996). Editions Scientifiques Elsevier, 141 rue de Javel, 75747 Paris, France. TEL 33-1-45589063. (Subscr. in U.S. and Canada to: Elsevier Science Inc., Box 882, Madison Sq. Sta., New York, NY 10159-0882. TEL 212-989-5800. FAX 212-633-3990) (also avail. in microform from UMI) **Document type:** academic/scholarly publication.

340.6 614.19 II ISSN 0047-6536
MEDICAL NEWS, MEDICINE AND LAW. (Text in English) 1970. m. Rs.15($7.50) Joshi Hospital, 778 Shivajinagar, Poona 411004, Maharashtra, India. Ed. Dr. L.B. Joshi. bk.rev. circ. 2,500. (also avail. in microfilm from UMI)

MEDICAL SCIENCES — FORENSIC SCIENCES

MEDICINE AND LAW; an international journal. see *LAW*

614.19   UK   ISSN 0025-8024
K13   CODEN: MDSLA6
MEDICINE, SCIENCE AND THE LAW. 1960. q. £55 (overseas £65) (effective 1994-1995). (British Academy of Forensic Science) Chiltern Publishing, 34 Aylesbury End, Beaconsfield, Bucks HP9 1LW, England. TEL 44-494-678914.
FAX 44-494-678914. Eds. Hazel Powell, Alex Reeve. adv.; bk.rev. circ. 1,600. (reprint service avail. from WSH) **Indexed:** Abstr.Crim.& Pen., Adol.Ment.Hlth.Abstr., Anal.Abstr., Biol.Abstr., C.I.S. Abstr., C.L.I., Chem.Abstr., Curr.Adv.Ecol.Sci., Dent.Ind., Euro.LJI, Excerp.Med., Hlth.Ind., HRIS, Ind.Med., Ind.Sci.Rev., L.R.I., Leg.Per, LJI, Nutr.Abstr., Risk Abstr., SSCI. **Document type:** academic/scholarly publication.
—BLDSC (5534.100000); CASDDS; EMDOCS; Faxon; Genuine Article; SWETS; UnCover. **CCC.**
Description: Publishes original contributions on topics in the forensic sciences and medico-legal issues.
Refereed Serial

614.19   UK   ISSN 0025-8172
MEDICO-LEGAL JOURNAL. 1932. q. £32. (Medico-Legal Society) Dramrite Printers Ltd., 175 Bermondsey St., Southwark, London SE1 3UW, England.
TEL 0171-831-0801. FAX 0171-405-1387. Ed. Diana Brahams. adv. contact: Diana Brahams. bk.rev.; abstr.; index. circ. 1,000. **Indexed:** Abstr.Bk.Rev.Curr.Leg.Per., ASSIA, Br.Hum.Ind., C.L.I., Chem.Abstr., CINAHL, Euro.LJI, Excerp.Med., Ind.Med., L.R.I., Leg.Per., LJI. **Document type:** academic/scholarly publication.
—BLDSC (5534.200000); Faxon; SWETS.

340.6   CE
MEDICO-LEGAL SOCIETY OF SRI LANKA. PROCEEDINGS. irreg. Medico-Legal Society of Sri Lanka, 111 Francis Rd., Colombo 10, Sri Lanka. **Document type:** proceedings.

614   US
MEDICOLEGAL-GRAM. 1980. m. Board of Medicolegal Investigations, Office of the Chief Medical Examiner, Box 26901, 800 Northeast 13th St., Oklahoma City, OK 73190. TEL 405-848-6841. Ed. Dr. Fred B. Jordan. illus. circ. 1,000.
Supersedes (1972-1979): Oklahoma Journal of Forensic Medicine (ISSN 0363-2679)

614.19   GW   ISSN 0723-8886
KK6206.A13
MEDIZINRECHT. 1983. 12/yr. DM.620($450) (effective 1996). (Deutsche Gesellschaft fuer Medizinrecht) Springer-Verlag, Heidelberger Platz 3, 14197 Berlin, Germany. TEL 030-8207-0. FAX 030-8214091. E-mail: orders@springer.de. (Subscr. in N. America to: Springer-Verlag New York, Inc., 44 Hartz Way, Secaucus, NJ 07096-2491. TEL 201-348-4033. FAX 201-348-4505) (Co-publisher: C.H. Beck'sche Verlagsbuchhandlung) adv.: B&W page DM.1740, color page DM.3480; trim 260 x 186. **Document type:** academic/scholarly publication.
—SWETS; UMI. **CCC.**
Formerly: Med R-Medizinrecht.

MICROSCOPE. see *BIOLOGY — Microscopy*

340.6   IT   ISSN 0026-4849
HV6004
MINERVA MEDICOLEGALE; archivio di antropologia criminale. (Text in Italian; summaries in English, Italian) 1880. q. $90 to individuals; institutions $140 (effective 1995). Edizioni Minerva Medica, Corso Bramante 83-85, Turin, Italy.
TEL 39-11-678282. FAX 39-11-3121736. Ed. P.L. Baima-Bollone; Pub. Alberto Oliaro. adv.: B&W page $1100, color page $1900; trim 190 x 270; adv. contact: F. Filippo. bk.rev.; charts; illus.; index; circ. 2,000 (paid). (also avail. in microform from UMI) **Indexed:** C.I.S. Abstr., Chem.Abstr., Excerp.Med., Ind.Med. **Document type:** academic/scholarly publication.
—BLDSC (5794.260000); UMI.
Description: Covers forensic medicine, criminal anthropology and insurance medicine.

614.19   NE   ISSN 0927-2216
MODUS; tijdschrift voor recherche en forensische wetenschappen. 1992. 6/yr. fl.115 (fl.72 to police professionals). Vuga Uitgeverij B.V., P.O. Box 16400, 2500 The Hague, Netherlands.
TEL 31-70-3614011. FAX 31-70-3632338. (Co-sponsors: Recherchschool; Divisie Centrale Recherche Informatie; Gerechtelijk Laboratorium; Forensisch Medisch Genootschap; Stichting Landelijk Kontakt van Technische Recherche- en Forensische Wetenschappen; Ministerie van Justitie) Ed.Bd. adv.: B&W page fl.1115, color page fl.2735; trim 210 x 297. illus. **Document type:** trade publication.
Incorporates (1982-1992): Nederlands Forensisch Tijdschrift (ISSN 0920-363X)
Description: Covers current issues, technical developments and other topics relating to forensic sciences.

344.73 614.19   US   ISSN 1052-309X
K14
NATIONAL MEDICAL-LEGAL JOURNAL; dedicated to innovative career opportunities and defensive legal strategies. 1990. q. Medical - Legal Consulting Institute, Inc., Box 27087, Houston, TX 77227-7087. TEL 713-961-3078; 800-880-0944. adv. **Document type:** newsletter.
—BLDSC (6027.095000).

614.19   US   ISSN 0000-1619
RB10
OFFICIAL AMERICAN BOARD OF MEDICAL SPECIALTIES (A B M S) DIRECTORY OF BOARD CERTIFIED PATHOLOGISTS. 1985. biennial. $119.95. Marquis Who's Who, A Reed Reference Publishing Company, 121 Chanlon Rd., New Providence, NJ 07974.
TEL 908-464-6800. FAX 908-665-2898. (Subscr. to: Order Dept., Box 31, New Providence, NJ 07974-9903. TEL 800-521-8110) Ed. Roy Crego. **Document type:** directory.
Formerly: A B M S Directory of Certified Pathologists (ISSN 0883-1203)
Description: Biographical sketches of U.S. certified medical specialists sorted alphabetically with a geographical index.

RECHT & PSYCHIATRIE. see *PSYCHOLOGY*

610   GW   ISSN 0937-9819
RECHTSMEDIZIN. 1991. 4/yr. DM.368($267) (effective 1996). (Deutschen Gesellschaft fuer Rechtsmedizin) Springer-Verlag, Heidelberger Platz 3, 14197 Berlin, Germany. TEL 030-8207-0. FAX 030-8214091. E-mail: orders@springer.de. (Subscr. in N. America to: Springer-Verlag New York, Inc., 44 Hartz Way, Secaucus, NJ 07095-2491. TEL 201-348-4033. FAX 201-348-4505) **Document type:** academic/scholarly publication.
—BLDSC (7309.453000); UMI. **CCC.**

REGULATORY TOXICOLOGY AND PHARMACOLOGY. see *ENVIRONMENTAL STUDIES — Toxicology And Environmental Safety*

340.6 614   RM   ISSN 1221-8618
CODEN: RMLGB
REVISTA DE MEDICINA LEGALA/ROMANIAN JOURNAL OF LEGAL MEDICINE. 1993. q. Societatea de Medicina Legala din Romania, Sos. Vitan-Birzesti 9, 75669 Bucharest, Rumania. TEL 1-6343890. **Indexed:** Excerp.Med. (1995-). **Document type:** academic/scholarly publication.

340.6   SP   ISSN 0377-4732
REVISTA ESPANOLA DE MEDICINA LEGAL. 1974. bi-m. 1000 ptas. Asociacion Nacional de Medicos Forenses, Goya 99, Madrid 9, Spain. bk.rev. circ. 1,000. **Indexed:** Abstr.Crim.& Pen., Ind.Med.Esp.

614.19   FR
REVUE FRANCAISE DU DOMMAGE CORPOREL. 1975. q. 360 F. (Federation Francaise des Associations de Medecins-Conseils de Societes d'Assurances) J. B. Bailliere Editeur, 37 av. des Champs Elysees, 75008 Paris, France. TEL 33-1-49536900. Ed. C. Rousseau. bibl.; charts; illus.; stat.; index.

RIDGE DETAIL IN NATURE. see *CRIMINOLOGY AND LAW ENFORCEMENT*

614.19   IT
RIVISTA ITALIANA DI MEDICINA LEGALE. 1979. q. L.100000 (foreign L.150000). Casa Editrice Dott. A. Giuffre, Via Busto Arsizio 40, 20151 Milan, Italy. TEL 02-38000905. FAX 02-38009582. Ed. Francesco Introna. adv.; bk.rev.; index. circ. 2,200. (back issues avail.) **Indexed:** Excerp.Med.

340.6 614.19   UK   ISSN 1355-0306
CODEN: SJUSFE
SCIENCE AND JUSTICE. 1960. q. £90($220) Forensic Science Society, 18-A Mount Parade, Harrogate, N. Yorks. HG1 1BX, England. Ed. B. Caddy. adv.; bk.rev.; charts; illus.; index. circ. 2,600. **Indexed:** Abstr.Crim.& Pen., Biol.Abstr., C.L.I., Chem.Abstr., Curr.Adv.Ecol.Sci., Curr.Adv.Genetics & Molec.Biol., Curr.Cont., Excerp.Med., Hlth.Ind., Ind.Med., Ind.Vet., L.R.I., Mass Spectr.Bull., Vet.Bull. **Document type:** academic/scholarly publication.
—BLDSC (8134.129500); CASDDS; Faxon; Genuine Article; SWETS; UnCover.
Formerly: Forensic Science Society. Journal (ISSN 0015-7368)
Description: Seeks to advance the study, application and standing of forensic science and to facilitate cooperation among persons interested in forensic science throughout the world.

SCIENTIFIC SLEUTHING REVIEW; a quarterly of forensic science in law enforcement. see *LAW — Criminal Law*

614.19 368   IT
SOCIETA LOMBARDA DI MEDICINA LEGALE E DELLE ASSICURAZIONI. ARCHIVIO. 1965. q. L.15000. Universita degli Studi di Milano, Istituto di Medicina Legale, Via Mangiagalli 37, Milan, Italy. Dir. A. Fornari.

610   RU   ISSN 0039-4521
CODEN: SMEZA5
SUDEBNOMEDITSINSKAYA EKSPERTIZA/MEDICO-LEGAL EXPERT TESTIMONY. (Text in Russian; contents page and summaries in English) 1958. q. $47 (effective 1996). (Ministerstvo Zdravookhraneniya) Izdatel'stvo Meditsina, Petroverigskii pereulok 6-8, 101000 Moscow, Russia. (Dist. by: Mezhdunarodnaya Kniga, B. Yakimanka 39, 117049 Moscow, Russia. TEL 7-095-2384600. FAX 7-095-2384634) Ed. V.V. Tomilin. adv.; bk.rev.; abstr.; charts; illus. circ. 18,800. **Indexed:** Biol.Abstr., Chem.Abstr., Dent.Ind., Excerp.Med., Ind.Med.
—BLDSC (0174.500000); CASDDS; EMDOCS.
Description: Concerned with the theory and practice of forensic medicine. Examines the problems of thanatology, traumatology, toxicology, serology, forensic obstetrics, stomatology, psychiatry, chemistry, history of forensic medicine and certain problems of criminology and legal laws as they relate to forensic medicine.

SYNOPSIS (COLUMBIA). see *MEDICAL SCIENCES — Pediatrics*

614.19 364   US   ISSN 1055-0305
RA1121   CODEN: WBREFD
WOUND BALLISTICS REVIEW. 1991. 2/yr. $40. International Wound Ballistics Association, Box 701, El Segunao, CA 90245. TEL 310-640-6065. Ed. Martin Fackler. bk.rev.; abstr.; charts; illus. circ. 600. (back issues avail.) **Document type:** academic/scholarly publication.
Description: Looks at the effects of projectiles on tissue, medical treatment of ballistic trauma, law enforcement equipment and procedures. Also studies projectile design, testing and evaluation.
Refereed Serial

614.19   IT   ISSN 0044-1570
CODEN: ZACCAL
ZACCHIA; archivio di medicina legale, sociale e criminologica. (Text and summeries in English or Italian, French, German, Spanish) 1921. q. L.20000($40) (Universita degli Studi di Roma, Istituto di Medicina Legale) Societa Editrice Universo, Via G.B. Morgagni 1, 00161 Rome, Italy. Ed. Prof. Cesare Gerin. adv.; bk.rev.; abstr.; bibl.; charts; illus.; stat.; index. circ. 900. **Indexed:** Biol.Abstr., Chem.Abstr., Excerp.Med., Ind.Med.
—BLDSC (9425.200000); CASDDS; EMDOCS.

ZENTRALBLATT RECHTSMEDIZIN/LEGAL MEDICINE. see *MEDICAL SCIENCES — Abstracting, Bibliographies, Statistics*

614.1   CC   ISSN 1001-5728
ZHONGGUO FAYIXUE ZAZHI/CHINESE JOURNAL OF FORENSIC SCIENCES. (Text in Chinese) 1986. q. Y2.55 per no. Zhongguo Fayi Xuehui - Forensic Medicine Association of China, No. 17, Muxidi Nanli, Beijing 100038, People's Republic of China. TEL 01-3264488. Ed. Wu Jiayi. adv.; bk.rev. circ. 3,000. **Document type:** academic/scholarly publication.

MEDICAL SCIENCES — Gastroenterology

616.3 616.07   US   ISSN 0942-8925
    CODEN: ABIMEL
ABDOMINAL IMAGING; a journal of diagnostic imaging. 1976. bi-m. $244 (effective 1996). Springer-Verlag, Journals, 175 Fifth Ave., New York, NY 10010. TEL 212-460-1500. FAX 212-473-6272. (N. American subscr. to: Journal Fulfillment Services, Box 2485, Secaucus, NJ 07096-2491. TEL 800-777-4643. FAX 201-348-4505; Elsewhere: Heidelberger Platz 3, 1000 Berlin 33, Germany. TEL 030-8207-1. FAX 030-8214091) Eds. Morton A. Meyers, Gary G. Ghahremani. (also avail. in microform from UMI; reprint service avail.) Indexed: Curr.Cont., Excerp.Med., Helminthol.Abstr., Ind.Med., Ind.Sci.Rev., INIS Atomind., Rev.Med.& Vet.Mycol., Sci.Cit.Ind. Document type: academic/scholarly publication.
—BLDSC (0537.809800); Faxon; Genuine Article; SWETS; UMI; UnCover. **CCC.**
    Formerly: Gastrointestinal Radiology (ISSN 0364-2356); Incorporates (in 1993): Urologic Radiology (ISSN 0171-1091)
    Description: Brings together previously disparate information of value to radiologists, internists, and surgeons involved in diagnostic imaging of the alimentary tract.
    Refereed Serial

616.4 616.3   FR   ISSN 0240-642X
    CODEN: AENDD5
ACTA ENDOSCOPICA. (Text in English, French) 1970. bi-m. 930 F. (foreign 970 F.) Endoscopica, 127 rue St. Dizier, 54000 Nancy, France. TEL 83-37-44-38. FAX 83-35-34-53. (Co-sponsors: Societe Medicale d'Imagerie, Enseignement et Recherche; Interamerican Society for Digestive Endoscopy) Ed. Fernand Vicari. adv. contact: Lydie Devred. bk.rev. circ. 4,500. Indexed: Excerp.Med. Document type: academic/scholarly publication.
—BLDSC (0614.620000). **CCC.**

616.3   PL   ISSN 0867-4140
ACTA ENDOSCOPICA POLONA. 1991. q. 180000 Zl. Krakowskie Stowarzyszwnie im. Ludwika Rydygiera, Ul. Kopernika 40, 31-501, Krakow, Poland. TEL 48-12-213583. Ed. Tadeusz Popiela. adv. Indexed: Excerp.Med. (1993-).

616.3   BE   ISSN 0001-5644
    CODEN: AGEBAX
ACTA GASTRO-ENTEROLOGICA BELGICA. (Supplements avail.) (Text usually in French; occasionally in English or German) 1933. 6/yr. 2400 BEF (foreign 2750 BEF). Association des Societes Scientifiques Medicales Belges - Vereiniging van de Belgische Medische Wetenschappelijke Genootschappen, Av. Circulaire 138A, B-1180 Brussels, Belgium. TEL 32-2-374-5158. adv.; bk.rev.; abstr.; bibl.; charts; illus.; index. circ. 1,000. Indexed: ASCA, Biol.Abstr., Chem.Abstr., Curr.Adv.Cancer Res., Curr.Cont., Excerp.Med., Helminthol.Abstr., Ind.Med., Nutr.Abstr.
—BLDSC (0616.700000); CASDDS; Genuine Article; SWETS.

616.3   AG   ISSN 0300-9033
    CODEN: AGLTBL
ACTA GASTROENTEROLOGICA LATINOAMERICANA. 1969. 5/yr. $75 (effective 1996). Juncal 2134, Planta Baja B 1125, Buenos Aires, Argentina. TEL 0541-8250050. FAX 0541-822-2139. Eds. Pablo Mazure, Mauricio Schraler. adv.; bk.rev. circ. 3,500. Indexed: Biol.Abstr., Chem.Abstr., Excerp.Med., Ind.Med. Document type: academic/scholarly publication.
—BLDSC (0616.730000); CASDDS; Faxon.
    Description: Original research papers in gastroenterology.

616.3   UK   ISSN 0269-2813
    CODEN: APTHEN
ALIMENTARY PHARMACOLOGY AND THERAPEUTICS. 1987. bi-m. £165($265) (effective 1996). Blackwell Science Ltd., Osney Mead, Oxford OX2 OEL, England. TEL 01865-206206. FAX 01865-206219. TELEX 83355 MEDBOK G. Eds. R.E. Pounder, W.L. Peterson. adv.; bk.rev.; illus.; index. circ. 6,500. (also avail. in microform from UMI; back issues avail.) Indexed: Excerp.Med. Document type: academic/scholarly publication.
—BLDSC (0787.886000); ADONIS; CASDDS; Faxon; Genuine Article; SWETS; UMI; UnCover. **CCC.**
    Refereed Serial

616.3   UK   ISSN 0953-0673
ALIMENTARY PHARMACOLOGY AND THERAPEUTICS. SUPPLEMENT. 1987. irreg. Blackwell Science Ltd., Osney Mead, Oxford OX2 OEL, England. TEL 01865-240201. FAX 01865-721205. TELEX 83355 MEDBOK G. Document type: academic/scholarly publication.
—ADONIS.

617.5   US   ISSN 0065-7204
AMERICAN ASSOCIATION OF GENITO-URINARY SURGEONS. TRANSACTIONS. a. American Association of Genito-Urinary Surgeons, 22 W. Greene St., Baltimore, MD 21201. (also avail. in microform from UMI) Indexed: Ind.Med.

616.3   US   ISSN 0002-9270
RC799   CODEN: AJGAAR
AMERICAN JOURNAL OF GASTROENTEROLOGY. 1934. m. $149 to individuals; institutions $199 (effective 1995). (American College of Gastroenterology, Inc.) Williams & Wilkins, 428 E. Preston St., Baltimore, MD 21202. TEL 410-528-4000; 800-638-6423. FAX 410-528-4312. Ed. Dr. R.K. Zetterman. adv.; bk.rev.; abstr.; bibl.; illus.; stat.; index. circ. 9,620. (also avail. in microform; microfilm from WWS) Indexed: Behav.Med.Abstr., Biol.Abstr., Biotech.Abstr., Chem.Abstr., Curr.Adv.Cancer Res., Curr.Adv.Ecol.Sci., Curr.Cont., Dent.Ind., Diar.Dis.Res., Excerp.Med., Helminthol.Abstr., Ind.Med., Ind.Sci.Rev., INIS Atomind., Nutr.Abstr., Protozool.Abstr., Rev.Plant Path., Sci.Cit.Ind., Sugar Ind.Abstr., Triticale Abstr. Document type: academic/scholarly publication.
—BLDSC (0824.650000); CASDDS; Faxon; Genuine Article; SWETS; UnCover. **CCC.**
    Description: Contains articles and reviews of current topics for gastroenterologists and internists.
    Refereed Serial

616.3   FR   ISSN 0066-2070
    CODEN: AGHPBN
ANNALES DE GASTROENTEROLOGIE ET D'HEPATOLOGIE. 1963. 6/yr. 990 F. to individuals (foreign 1380 F.); students 495 F. (foreign 700 F.) Expansion Scientifique, 31 bd. de la Tour Maubourg, 75007 Paris, France. TEL 40-62-64-00. FAX 45-55-69-20. Ed. Guy Albot. adv.; bk.rev. circ. 3,500. Indexed: Biol.Abstr., Curr.Cont., Excerp.Med., Helminthol.Abstr., INIS Atomind., Rev.Med.& Vet.Mycol.
—BLDSC (0974.500000); EMDOCS; Genuine Article; SWETS. **CCC.**
    Incorporates: Actualites Hepato-Gastro-Enterologiques de l'Hotel Dieu.

ANNUAL OF GASTROINTESTINAL ENDOSCOPY. see MEDICAL SCIENCES — Abstracting, Bibliographies, Statistics

616.3   YU   ISSN 0354-2440
    CODEN: ARGAE
ARCHIVES OF GASTROENTEROHEPATOLOGY. (Text and summaries in English and Serbo-Croatian) 1982. q. 1200 din.($28) Srpsko Lekarsko Drustvo, Dzordza Vasingtona 19, 11000 Belgrade, Yugoslavia. TEL 011-346-090. Ed. Obren Popovic. adv.; abstr.; bibl.; charts; illus.; pat.; stat. circ. 800. Indexed: Excerp.Med.
—BLDSC (1634.335000).
    Formerly: Gastroenterohepatoloski Arhiv (ISSN 0352-082X)
    Description: Basic and clinical studies of the digestive tract and liver.

616.3   AG   ISSN 0004-0517
ARCHIVOS ARGENTINOS ENFERMEDADES DEL APARATO DIGESTIVO. vol. 46, 1971. bi-m. $25. Sociedad Argentina de Gastroenterologia, Jeronimo Salguero 88 A, 1177 Buenos Aires, Argentina. TEL 983-0863. FAX 981-4936. Ed. Dr. Leonardo Pinchuck. adv.; bk.rev. circ. 1,350.

616.3   IT   ISSN 1120-8651
ARGOMENTI DI GASTROENTEROLOGIA CLINICA. 1988. 8/yr. L.12000($53) (effective 1994). Masson S.p.A., Divisione Periodici, Via Statuto 2-4, 20121 Milan, Italy. TEL 02-6367-1. FAX 02-6367-211. Ed. Gabriele Bianchi Porro. adv.: B&W page L.3750000, color page L.6100000; trim 195 x 265. circ. 13,000. Indexed: Excerp.Med.
—BLDSC (1664.344950).

616.3   BL   ISSN 0004-2803
    CODEN: ARQGAF
ARQUIVOS DE GASTROENTEROLOGIA. (Text in Portuguese; summaries in English, French, Portuguese and Spanish) 1964. q. $50 (effective 1996). Instituto Brasileiro de Estudos e Pesquisas de Gastroenterologia - Brazilian Institute for Studies and Research in Gastroenterology, Rua Dr. Seng 320, 01331-020 Sao Paulo SP, Brazil. TEL 55-11-2882119. FAX 55-11-2892768. (Co-sponsor: Brazilian Society of Digestive Mobility) Ed. Nelson Henrique Michelsohn. adv.; bk.rev.; charts; illus.; index; circ. 5,000 (controlled). (also avail. in microfilm from UMI; reprint service avail. from IRC.UMI) Indexed: Abstr.Hyg., Biol.Abstr., Chem.Abstr., Dairy Sci.Abstr., Diar.Dis.Res., Excerp.Med., Gastroenterol.Abstr.& Cit., Ind.Med., Nutr.Abstr., Protozool.Abstr., Soyabean Abstr., Trop.Dis.Bull.
—BLDSC (1695.430000); CASDDS; UMI.
    Description: Publishes original papers, review articles, and case reports concerning all aspects of the digestive tract, including the liver.
    Refereed Serial

616.3   BL   ISSN 0101-8531
ARS CVRANDI GASTRO. 1978. bi-m. Elea Ciencia Editorial Ltda., Rua Barao de Uba 48, CEP 20260 Rio de Janeiro RJ, Brazil. TEL 293-2112. Ed. J.G. Alves. circ. 4,500.

616.3   US   ISSN 0892-9386
AUDIO-DIGEST GASTROENTEROLOGY. 1987. m. $84. Audio-Digest Foundation (Subsidiary of: California Medical Association), 1577 E. Chevy Chase Dr., Glendale, CA 91206. TEL 213-245-8505. FAX 818-240-7379. Ed. Claron L. Oakley. circ. controlled. (audio cassette)
    Refereed Serial

616.3   UK   ISSN 0950-3528
BAILLIERE'S CLINICAL GASTROENTEROLOGY. 1987. q. £76 to individuals; institutions £87. Bailliere Tindall - W.B. Saunders Co. Ltd. (Subsidiary of: Harcourt Brace & Company Ltd.), 24-28 Oval Rd., London NW1 7DX, England. TEL 0171-267-4466. FAX 0171-482-2293. TELEX 25775 ACPRES G. (Subscr. to: Journals Subscription Fulfillment, Foots Cray High St., Sidcup, Kent DA14 5HP, England. TEL 0181-300-3322. FAX 0181-309-0807; Subscr. in N. America to: W.B. Saunders Co., Journal Subscription Fulfillment, 6277 Sea Harbor Dr., 4th Fl., Orlando, FL 32887-4800. TEL 800-874-6418) Document type: academic/scholarly publication.
—BLDSC (1856.722000); Genuine Article; SWETS; UnCover. **CCC.**
    Refereed Serial

617.5   CN   ISSN 1192-0890
C A E T JOURNAL. 1988. q. Can.$32.10 (in U.S. Can.$45; elsewhere Can.$60). Canadian Association for Enterostomal Therapy - Association Canadienne des Stomotherapeutes, Mount Sinai Hospital, 600 University Ave., Ottawa, ON H5G 1X5, Canada. Ed. Sue Russell. adv. contact: Mario Morin. circ. 200. Document type: academic/scholarly publication.
—BLDSC (2947.371500).
    Refereed Serial

616.3   US
C C F A COMMUNIQUE. q. membership. Crohn's and Colitis Foundation of America, Inc., Philadelphia - Delaware Valley Chapter, 521 Bustleton Pike, Feasterville Trevose, PA 19053-6051. TEL 215-396-9100. FAX 215-396-1170. Ed. Barbara Berman. Document type: newsletter.

MEDICAL SCIENCES — GASTROENTEROLOGY

616.3   CN   ISSN 0835-7900
CANADIAN JOURNAL OF GASTROENTEROLOGY. 1987. 6/yr. Can.$90($61) (foreign $160) to individuals; institutions Can.$125 ($84)(foreign $180). Pulsus Group Inc., 2902 S. Sheridan Way, Oakville, ON L6J 7L6, Canada. TEL 905-829-4770. FAX 905-829-4799. Eds. Dr. C.N. Williams, A.B.R. Thomson. adv.; bk.rev.; circ. 18,000 (controlled). **Indexed:** Excerp.Med. **Document type:** academic/scholarly publication.
—BLDSC (3031.550000); Genuine Article; SWETS; UnCover. **CCC.**
    Description: Original papers, case reports and reviews pertaining to gastroenterology and hepatology.
    Refereed Serial

616.3   CN   ISSN 0833-1464
CELIAC NEWS. 1986. q. Can.$25($30) Canadian Celiac Association, 6519 B Mississauga Rd., Mississauga, ON L5N 1A6, Canada. TEL 905-567-7195. FAX 905-567-0710. Ed. Judi Sennett. adv. contact: Judi Sennett. bk.rev. circ. 3,500. (also avail. in diskette format; back issues avail.) **Document type:** newsletter.
    Description: Provides information on celiac disease and dermatitis herpetiformis for the purposes of education and updating.

616.3   XR   ISSN 1210-7824
                     CODEN: CKGAAM
CESKA A SLOVENSKA GASTROENTEROLOGIE/CZECH AND SLOVAK GASTROENTEROLOGY. (Text in Czech and Slovak; summaries in English and Russian) 1947. 8/yr. $65.30. (Ceska Lekarska Spolecnost J.E. Purkyne - Czech Medical Society) Nakladateske Stredisko C L S J.E. Purkyne, Sokolska 31, 120 26 Prague 2, Czech Republic. FAX 42-0-2-202788. (Dist. by: Artia, Ve Smeckach 30, 111 27 Prague 1, Czech Republic) Ed. Zdenek Maratka. adv.; bk.rev.; abstr.; charts; illus.; index. circ. 900. **Indexed:** Biol.Abstr., C.I.S. Abstr., Chem.Abstr., Curr.Adv.Ecol.Sci., Excerp.Med., Food Sci.& Tech.Abstr., Ind.Med., Nutr.Abstr.
—BLDSC (3120.258400); CASDDS. **CCC.**
    Formerly (until Aug. 1994): Cesko-Slovenska Gastroenterologie a Vyziva (ISSN 0009-0565)

616.3   IT   ISSN 0009-4765
CHIRURGIA GASTROENTEROLOGICA (ITALIAN EDITION); rassegna trimestrale di chirurgia dell'apparato digerente e degli organi addominali. (Text in Italian; summaries in English and Italian) 1967. q. L.90000($80) (effective 1995). Giovanni Battista Grassi, C.P. 4236, 00100 Rome Appio, Italy. FAX 06-70454246. adv.; bk.rev. **Indexed:** Excerp.Med.
—BLDSC (3181.186000).

616.3   SZ   ISSN 0177-9990
CHIRURGISCHE GASTROENTEROLOGIE. 1985. 4/yr. 76.50 SFr.($59) to individuals; institutions 153 SFr.($118) (effective 1996). S. Karger AG, Allschwilerstr. 10, P.O. Box, CH-4009 Basel, Switzerland. TEL 061-3061111. FAX 061-3061234. E-mail: Karger@Karger.ch. Ed. K.-J. Paquet. (also avail. in microform from UMI) **Indexed:** Excerp.Med. (1995-). **Document type:** academic/scholarly publication.
—BLDSC (3181.470700); Genuine Article.
    Refereed Serial

CLINICAL NUTRITION. see *NUTRITION AND DIETETICS*

COLON AND RECTAL SURGERY OUTLOOK. see *MEDICAL SCIENCES — Surgery*

616.3   GW   ISSN 0174-2442
COLOPROCTOLOGY. (Text in German) 1979. bi-m. DM.228($165) (effective 1996). (Berufsverband der Coloproktologen Deutschland) Urban und Vogel, Lindwurmstr. 95, 80337 Munich, Germany. TEL 089-53292-0. FAX 089-53292100. (Co-sponsor: Deutsche Gesellschaft fuer Koloproktologie) Ed. T. Hager. adv.; bk.rev.; index. circ. 4,000. (back issues avail.) **Document type:** academic/scholarly publication.
—BLDSC (3320.408800). **CCC.**
    Formerly: Proktologie (ISSN 0174-240X)
    Description: Covers case reports and techniques in proctology. Includes new product information, calendar of events and reviews of journal articles.

616.3   GW   ISSN 0174-2450
COLOPROCTOLOGY (INTERNATIONAL EDITION). (Text in English) 1979. bi-m. DM.228($165) (effective 1996). (Berufsverband fuer Coloproktologen Deutschlands) Urban und Vogel, Lindwurmstr. 95, 80337 Munich, Germany. TEL 089-53292-0. FAX 089-53292100. (Dist. by: Springer-Verlag, Heidelberger Platz 3, 14197 Berlin, Germany. TEL 030-8207-1. FAX 030-8214091; Subscr. in N. America to: Springer-Verlag New York, Inc., 44 Hartz Way, Secaucus, NY 07099-2491. TEL 201-348-4033. FAX 201-348-4505) (Co-sponsor: Deutsche Gesellschaft fuer Koloproktologie) Ed. T. Hagen. **Document type:** academic/scholarly publication.
—BLDSC (3302.480800).
    Formerly (until 1980): Proctology (International Edition) (ISSN 0174-2418)

CORE JOURNALS IN GASTROENTEROLOGY. see *MEDICAL SCIENCES — Abstracting, Bibliographies, Statistics*

616.3   CI   ISSN 0353-9296
                     CODEN: CJGHE6
CROATIAN JOURNAL OF GASTROENTEROLOGY AND HEPATOLOGY. 1992. q. Medicinska Naklada Co., Vlaska 69, HR-41000 Zagreb, Croatia. TEL 41-447255. **Indexed:** Excerp.Med. (1993-).
—BLDSC (3487.498100).

616.3   US   ISSN 0198-8085
RC799   CODEN: CUGADR
CURRENT GASTROENTEROLOGY. 1980. a. $77.95 (residents $40) (effective 1996). Mosby - Year Book, Inc. (Chicago) (Subsidiary of: Times Mirror Company), 200 N. LaSalle St., Chicago, IL 60601-1080. TEL 312-726-9733. FAX 312-726-6075. TELEX 206155. (Subscr. to: 11830 Westline Industrial Dr., St. Louis, MO 63146. TEL 800-325-4177) Ed. Dr. Gary Gitnick. illus.
—BLDSC (3496.920000); CASDDS. **CCC.**
    Description: Surveys developments in gastroenterology and provides synopses of the past twelve months of medical literature.

616.3   US   ISSN 0198-8093
RC845   CODEN: CUHEDA
CURRENT HEPATOLOGY. 1980. a. $82.95 (residents $40) (effective 1996). Mosby - Year Book, Inc. (Chicago) (Subsidiary of: Times Mirror Company), 200 N. LaSalle St., Chicago, IL 60601-1080. TEL 312-726-9733. FAX 312-726-6075. TELEX 206155. (Subscr. to: 11830 Westline Industrial Dr., St. Louis, MO 63146. TEL 800-325-4177) Ed. Dr. Gary L. Gitnick.
—BLDSC (3497.430000); CASDDS; Faxon. **CCC.**
    Description: Surveys developments in hepatology and provides synopses of the past twelve months of medical literature.

CURRENT OPINION IN GASTROENTEROLOGY. see *MEDICAL SCIENCES — Abstracting, Bibliographies, Statistics*

616.3   NE   ISSN 0167-935X
DEVELOPMENTS IN GASTROENTEROLOGY. (Text in English) 1981. irreg., vol.13, 1991. price varies. Kluwer Academic Publishers, Postbus 17, 3300 AA Dordrecht, Netherlands. TEL 31-78-3923292. FAX 31-78-392254. TELEX 29245 KAPG NL. (Dist. by: Kluwer Academic Publishers Group, P.O. Box 322, 3300 AH Dordrecht, Netherlands. TEL 31-78-392392. FAX 31-78-546474; N. America dist. addr.: Box 358, Accord Sta., Hingham, MA 02018-0358. TEL 617-871-6600. FAX 617-871-6528) **Document type:** monographic series.
—BLDSC (3579.071870).
    Refereed Serial

DIABETIC MEDICINE. see *MEDICAL SCIENCES — Endocrinology*

DIARRHOEAL DISEASES/MALADIES DIARRHEIQUES. see *MEDICAL SCIENCES — Abstracting, Bibliographies, Statistics*

616.3   SZ   ISSN 0012-2823
QP141.A1   CODEN: DIGEBW
DIGESTION; international journal of gastroenterology. (Text in English) 1968. bi-m. 519 SFr.($399.60) to individuals; institutions 866 SFr.($666) (effective 1996). S. Karger AG, Allschwilerstr. 10, P.O. Box, CH-4009 Basel, Switzerland. TEL 061-3061111. FAX 061-3061234. E-mail: Karger@Karger.ch. Ed. R. Arnold. adv.; bibl.; illus. circ. 1,250. (also avail. in microform) **Indexed:** Biol.Abstr., Chem.Abstr., Curr.Adv.Ecol.Sci., Curr.Cont., Dairy Sci.Abstr., Dent.Ind., Excerp.Med., Helminthol.Abstr., Ind.Med., Ind.Sci.Rev., NRN, Nutr.Abstr., Protozool.Abstr., Sci.Cit.Ind. **Document type:** academic/scholarly publication.
—BLDSC (3588.345000); CASDDS; Faxon; Genuine Article; SWETS; UnCover. **CCC.**
    Formerly: Gastroenterologia.
    Refereed Serial

616.3   SZ   ISSN 0257-2753
                     CODEN: DIDIEW
DIGESTIVE DISEASES; current concepts in research and practice. (Text in English) 1983. bi-m. 260.50 SFr.($200.50) to individuals; institutions 521 SFr.($401) (effective 1996). S. Karger AG, Allschwilerstr. 10, P.O. Box, CH-4009 Basel, Switzerland. TEL 061-3061111. FAX 061-3061234. E-mail: Karger@Karger.ch. Ed. S.R. Achem. adv.; illus.; index. circ. 800. **Indexed:** Chem.Abstr., Curr.Cont., NRN. **Document type:** academic/scholarly publication.
—BLDSC (3588.346000); CASDDS; Genuine Article; SWETS. **CCC.**
    Formerly: Survey of Digestive Diseases (ISSN 0253-4398)
    Refereed Serial

616.3   US   ISSN 0163-2116
RC799   CODEN: DDSCDJ
DIGESTIVE DISEASES AND SCIENCES. 1934. m. $495 (foreign $580) (effective 1996). Plenum Publishing Corp., 233 Spring St., New York, NY 10013-1578. TEL 212-620-8000. FAX 212-463-0742. TELEX 23-421139. Ed. Richard L. Wechsler. adv.; bk.rev. (also avail. in microfilm from JSC; back issues avail.) **Indexed:** Abstr.Inter.Med., AIM, Behav.Med.Abstr., Biol.Abstr., Chem.Abstr., Curr.Adv.Cancer Res., Curr.Adv.Ecol.Sci., Curr.Adv.Genetics & Molec.Biol., Curr.Cont., Dairy Sci.Abstr., Dent.Ind., Diar.Dis.Res., Excerp.Med., Fababean Abstr., Helminthol.Abstr., Ind.Med., Ind.Sci.Rev., Ind.Vet., INIS Atomind., Maize Abstr., NRN, Nutr.Abstr., Ref.Zh., Rev.Med.& Vet.Mycol., Sci.Cit.Ind., Small.Anim.Abstr., Triticale Abstr., Vet.Bull. **Document type:** academic/scholarly publication.
—BLDSC (3588.346100); ADONIS; CASDDS; Faxon; Genuine Article; SWETS; UMI; UnCover. **CCC.**
    Formerly (until vol.24, no.1, 1979): American Journal of Digestive Diseases (ISSN 0002-9211)
    Refereed Serial

616.3   JA   ISSN 0915-5635
DIGESTIVE ENDOSCOPY. (Text in English) 1989. q. 9000 Yen (foreign $90). Japan Gastroenterological Endoscopy Society, Taimei Bldg., 3-22, Kanda Ogawa-machi, Chiyoda-ku, Tokyo 101, Japan. TEL 81-3-3291-4111. FAX 81-3-3291-5568. Ed. T. Miwa. adv.; abstr. circ. 1,000. **Document type:** academic/scholarly publication.
—BLDSC (3588.346200).
    Description: Includes case reports, editorial opinions and news items that may be of interest to endoscopists.

616.3   JA   ISSN 0912-0505
                     CODEN: EFDDE
ENDOSCOPIC FORUM FOR DIGESTIVE DISEASE/NIHON SHOKAKI NAISHIKYO GAKKAI KOSHIN'ETSU CHIHOKAI ZASSHI. (Text in various languages) 1986. a. Japanese Journal of Cancer and Chemotherapy Publishers, Inc., 1-8-9 Yaesu, Chuo-ku, Tokyo 103, Japan. TEL 81-3-3278-0052. FAX 81-3-3281-0435. **Indexed:** Excerp.Med. (1993-). **Document type:** academic/scholarly publication.

MEDICAL SCIENCES — GASTROENTEROLOGY

616.3   GW   ISSN 0013-726X
CODEN: ENDCAM
ENDOSCOPY. (Text in English, German; summaries in English) 1969. 9/yr. DM.378. (European Society of Gastrointestinal Endoscopy) Georg Thieme Verlag, Ruedigerstr. 14, 70469 Stuttgart, Germany. TEL 0711-8931-0. FAX 0711-8931298. (Subscr. to: Postfach 104853, 70042 Stuttgart, Germany; Subscr. in U.S. to: Thieme Medical Publishers, Inc., 381 Park Ave. S., New York, NY 10016) Ed.Bd. adv.; bk.rev.; abstr.; bibl.; charts; illus.; stat.; index. circ. 2,900. (also avail. in microform from UMI; reprint service avail. from UMI) **Indexed:** Biol.Abstr., Curr.Cont., Dent.Ind., Excerp.Med., Helminthol.Abstr., Ind.Med., Ind.Sci.Rev., INIS Atomind., Nutr.Abstr., Sci.Cit.Ind. **Document type:** academic/scholarly publication.
—BLDSC (3743.600000); Faxon; Genuine Article; SWETS; UMI; UnCover. **CCC.**

616.3   GW   ISSN 0933-811X
CODEN: ENDHE7
ENDSKOPIE HEUTE; forum bildgebener verfahren. 1988. q. DM.106. Demeter Verlag GmbH und Co. KG, Bussardstr. 5, 82166 Graefelfing, Germany. TEL 089-85463-0. FAX 089-8543347. Eds. Drs. R. Ottenjann, J.F. Riemann. circ. 2,500. **Document type:** academic/scholarly publication.
—BLDSC (3743.630000).

616.362   IT
CODEN: EPATA4
EPATOLOGIA E MALATTIE DEL RICAMBIO. 1955. 3/yr. L.48000 (foreign L.96000). Societa Editrice Universo, Via G.B. Morgagni 1, 00161 Rome, Italy. **Indexed:** Biol.Abstr., Chem.Abstr., Excerp.Med.
—CASDDS.
Formerly (until 1984): Epatologia (ISSN 0013-9475)

EUROPEAN JOURNAL OF GASTROENTEROLOGY AND HEPATOLOGY. see MEDICAL SCIENCES — Abstracting, Bibliographies, Statistics

616.3   UK   ISSN 0353-9245
CODEN: ECGAEQ
EXPERIMENTAL AND CLINICAL GASTROENTEROLOGY. 1991. 4/yr. £188($281) (effective 1995). Elsevier Science Ltd., Pergamon, P.O. Box 800, Kidlington, Oxford OX5 1DX, England. TEL 44-1865-843000. FAX 44-1865-843010.
E-mail: nlinfo-f@elsevier.nl; usinfo-f@elsevier.com; forinfo-kyf04035@niftyserve.or.jp; Site addr.: http://www.elsevier.nl/. (Subscr. in U.S. and Canada to: Elsevier Science, 660 White Plains Rd., Tarrytown, NY 10591-5153. TEL 914-524-9200. FAX 914-333-2444) Eds. Predrag Sikiric, Gyula Moszik. (also avail. in microform from UMI; back issues avail.) **Document type:** academic/scholarly publication.
—BLDSC (3838.634000); CASDDS; UMI. **CCC.**
Description: Systematic presentations of experimental and clinical studies in gastroenterology.
Refereed Serial

616.3   US   ISSN 0897-6759
FOUNDATION FOCUS. 1977. 3/yr. $25 membership. Crohn's & Colitis Foundation of America, Inc., 386 Park Ave. S., New York, NY 10016-7374. TEL 212-685-3440; 800-932-2423. FAX 212-779-4098. Ed. Barbara Rosenstein. adv.; bk.rev. circ. 50,000. (back issues avail.) **Document type:** newsletter.
Description: Features stories about coping with Crohn's disease (ileitis) and ulcerative colitis; articles on CCFX-sponsored research and education programs; medical news and profiles of individuals.

616.3   SZ
CODEN: FGREDT
FRONTIERS OF GASTROINTESTINAL RESEARCH. (Text in English) 1960. irreg. price varies. S. Karger AG, Allschwilerstr. 10, P.O. Box, CH-4009 Basel, Switzerland. TEL 061-3061111. FAX 061-3061234. E-mail: Karger@Karger.ch. Ed. P. Rozen. (reprint service avail. from ISI) **Indexed:** Biol.Abstr., Chem.Abstr., Curr.Cont., Ind.Med. **Document type:** academic/scholarly publication.
—BLDSC (4042.022000); CASDDS.
Formerly: Bibliotheca Gastroenterologica (ISSN 0302-0665)
Refereed Serial

616.3   VE   ISSN 0016-3503
G E N. (Text in English, Spanish) 1946. q. Bs.4000($70) Sociedad Venezolana de Gastroenterologia - Venezuelan Society of Gastroenterology, Torre del Colegio, Piso 2, Av. Jose Maria Vargas, Santa Fe Norte, Caracas 1080, Venezuela. TEL 58-2-9765520. FAX 58-2-9799380. (Or: Apdo. 51890, Sabana Grande, Caracas 1050 A, Venezuela) Ed. Dr. Mercedes Alvarado. adv.; bk.rev.; abstr.; bibl.; charts; illus. circ. 1,200. **Indexed:** Abstr.Hyg., Biol.Abstr., Excerp.Med., Helminthol.Abstr., Ind.Med., Trop.Dis.Bull. **Document type:** academic/scholarly publication.
—BLDSC (4096.385000).

G I CANCER; an international journal on gastrointestinal oncology. (Gastrointestinal) see MEDICAL SCIENCES — Oncology

G I G NEWSLETTER. (Gluten Intolerance Group of North America) see NUTRITION AND DIETETICS

GASTRIC SECRETION. see BIOLOGY — Physiology

616.3   FR   ISSN 0399-8320
CODEN: GCBIDC
GASTRO-ENTEROLOGIE CLINIQUE ET BIOLOGIQUE. (Text in French; summaries in English) 1907. 10/yr. 1114 F. (foreign 1341 F.) (effective 1996). (Societe Nationale Francaise de Gastro-Enterologie) Masson - Periodiques, Villa Laromiguiere, 75005 Paris, France. TEL 1-40-46-62-00. FAX 1-40-46-62-01. Ed. Dr. Robaszkiewicz. adv.; bk.rev.; illus.; index. circ. 4,500. (reprint service avail. from ISI) **Indexed:** Biol.Abstr., Chem.Abstr., Curr.Adv.Biochem., Curr.Adv.Cancer Res., Curr.Adv.Ecol.Sci., Curr.Adv.Genetics & Molec.Biol., Curr.Cont., Dairy Sci.Abstr., Dent.Ind., Excerp.Med., Helminthol.Abstr., Ind.Med., Nutr.Abstr., Protozool.Abstr., Risk Abstr. **Document type:** academic/scholarly publication.
—BLDSC (4088.973000); CASDDS; Faxon; Genuine Article; SWETS; UMI. **CCC.**
Former titles: Archives Francaises des Maladies de l'Appareil Digestif (ISSN 0003-9772); Biologie et Gastro-Enterologie (ISSN 0006-3258); Archives Francaises des Maladies de l'Appareil Digestif et des Maladies de la Nutrition.
Description: Publishes original work, clinical radiological laboratory and pathological documents related to gastroenterology, laboratory or experimental research on the digestive tract and related glands.

616.3   FR   ISSN 0995-7278
GASTRO ENTEROLOGIE PRATIQUE. 1989. m. (10/yr.). 200 F. L.E.N. Medical, 48 bis, rue Kleber, 75016 Paris, France. TEL 47-55-06-06. FAX 47-55-69-41. TELEX 640 748. Ed. Philippe Levy. **Document type:** newspaper.

616.3   FR   ISSN 0016-5077
GASTRO-ENTEROLOGIE QUOTIDIENNE. 1967. 3/yr. free. Laboratoires Beaufour, 18 Place Doguereau, 28100 Dreux, France. Ed. P. Bernades. adv.; illus.; tr.mk. circ. 30,000.

616.3   IT   ISSN 1120-3757
GASTROENTEROLOGIA CLINICA. Italian translation of: Clinics in Gastroenterology. 1972. bi-m. L.264000($160) (effective 1996). Pensiero Scientifico Editore s.r.l., Via Bradano 3-C, 00199 Rome, Italy. TEL 06-86207158. FAX 06-86207160. Eds. G. Rossi, G. Pippa. circ. 800. **Document type:** academic/scholarly publication.

616.3   SP   ISSN 0210-5705
CODEN: GHEPDF
GASTROENTEROLOGIA Y HEPATOLOGIA. (Text in Spanish; summaries in English) 1978. m. (10/yr.). 6900 ptas.($57) (free to qualified personnel). Ediciones Doyma S.A., Travesera de Gracia 17-21, 08021 Barcelona, Spain. TEL 34-1-200-07-11. FAX 34-1-209-11-36. TELEX 51964 INK-E. Ed. Dr. J. Rodes Teixidor. adv.: page 200000 ptas.; trim 210 x 280; adv. contact: Eulalia Valls. circ. 2,500. (reprint service avail. from UMI) **Indexed:** Excerp.Med., Ind.Med.Esp.
—BLDSC (4088.955000); UMI. **CCC.**
Description: Covers gastroenterology, hepatology and pathology of the digestive tract, liver, pancreas and biliary paths.

616.3   JA   ISSN 0387-1207
GASTROENTEROLOGICAL ENDOSCOPY. (Text in Japanese) 1958. m. 12000 Yen($120) membership only. Nihon Shokaki Naishikyo Gakkai - Japan Gastroenterological Endoscopy Society, Taimei Bldg., 3-22, Kanda Ogawa-machi, Chiyoda-ku, Tokyo 101, Japan. TEL 03-3291-4111. FAX 03-3291-5568. Ed. Saburo Oshiba. adv.; charts; illus. circ. 24,000. **Indexed:** Excerp.Med. **Document type:** academic/scholarly publication.
—BLDSC (4088.965000).
Description: Reports investigations relating to endoscopic diagnosis and treatment of digestive diseases.

616.3   US   ISSN 1065-2477
CODEN: GASTFG
GASTROENTEROLOGIST; The Gastroenterologist. 1993. q. $87 to individuals (foreign $116); institutions $151 (foreing $182); resident $52 (foreign $81). Little, Brown and Company, Medical Journals, 34 Beacon St., Boston, MA 02108. TEL 617-859-5000. FAX 617-859-0629. Ed. Dr. Martin H. Floch. adv.: B&W page $660, color page $1530; trim 8 1/2 x 11. circ. 1,925. **Indexed:** Excerp.Med. (1995-), Ind.Med. (1994-). **Document type:** trade publication.
—BLDSC (4088.993400). **CCC.**
Description: Covers the latest in diagnosis and treatment in gastroenterology and nutrition through review articles. Other sections include New Techniques, Therapeutic Recommendations, and Grand Rounds.

616.3   IT   ISSN 0391-8939
IL GASTROENTEROLOGO. 10/yr. L.25000($25) C I C Edizioni Internazionali s.r.l., Via L. Spallanzani 11, 00161 Rome, Italy. TEL 06-8412673. FAX 06-44242033. TELEX 622099 CIC.

616.3   US   ISSN 0016-5085
RC799   CODEN: GASTAB
GASTROENTEROLOGY; a journal devoted to the clinical and basic studies of the digestive tract and liver. (Supplement avail.) 1943. m. $304 (foreign $381) (effective 1996). (American Gastroenterological Association) W.B. Saunders Co. (Subsidiary of: Harcourt Brace & Company), Curtis Center, 3rd Fl., Independence Sq. W., PA 19106-3399. TEL 215-238-7800. FAX 215-238-6445. (Subscr. to: Periodicals Fulfillment, W.B. Saunders Co., 6277 Sea Harbor Dr., 4th Fl., Orlando, FL 32887-4800. TEL 800-654-2452. FAX 800-874-6418) Ed. Dr. Nicholas F. LaRusso; Pub. Joan W. Blumberg. adv.: B&W page $1805, color page $3605; 7 x 10. bk.rev.; abstr.; charts; illus.; cum.index. circ. 16,494. (also avail. in microform from UMI,WWS; reprint service avail. from UMI) **Indexed:** Abstr.Hyg., Abstr.Inter.Med., AIM, Behav.Med.Abstr., Biol.Abstr., Biotech.Abstr., C.I.S. Abstr., Chem.Abstr., Curr.Adv.Biochem., Curr.Adv.Cancer Res, Curr.Adv.Cell & Devel.Biol., Curr.Adv.Ecol.Sci., Curr.Cont., Dent.Ind., Diar.Dis.Res., Excerp.Med., Food Sci.& Tech.Abstr., Helminthol.Abstr., Ind.Med., Ind.Sci.Rev., Ind.Vet., INIS Atomind., Kidney, Med.& Surg.Dermat., NRN, Nutr.Abstr., Pig News & Info., Risk Abstr., Sci.Cit.Ind., Small Anim.Abstr., Soyabean Abstr., Vet.Bull. **Document type:** academic/scholarly publication.
●Also available online. Vendor(s): Ovid Technologies.
—BLDSC (4089.000000); CASDDS; Faxon; Genuine Article; SWETS; UMI; UnCover. **CCC.**
Description: Provides clinical coverage of all areas of the digestive tract, including the liver.
Refereed Serial

616.35   US   ISSN 0883-8348
RC864.A1
GASTROENTEROLOGY AND ENDOSCOPY NEWS. 1950. m. (International Academy of Proctology) McMahon Group, 148 W. 24th St., New York, NY 10011. TEL 212-620-4600. FAX 212-620-5928. Ed. Cornelia Kean. adv.; bk.rev.; bibl.; illus.; index. circ. 8,000. (also avail. in microform from UMI) **Indexed:** Biol.Abstr., Curr.Cont., Excerp.Med., Ind.Med. **Document type:** academic/scholarly publication.
—BLDSC (4089.025000); Genuine Article; UMI.
Former titles (until 1985): American Journal of Proctology, Gastroenterology, and Colon and Rectal Surgery (ISSN 0162-6566); (until 1977): American Journal of Proctology (ISSN 0002-9521)
Refereed Serial

MEDICAL SCIENCES — GASTROENTEROLOGY

616.3   US   ISSN 0889-8553
RC799   CODEN: GCNAEF
GASTROENTEROLOGY CLINICS OF NORTH AMERICA. 1972. q. $129 (foreign $154) (effective 1996). W.B. Saunders Co. (Subsidiary of: Harcourt Brace & Company), Curtis Center, 3rd Fl., Independence Sq. W., Philadelphia, PA 19106-3399. TEL 215-238-7800. FAX 215-238-6445. (Subscr. to: Periodicals Fulfillment, W.B. Saunders Co., 6277 Sea Harbor Dr., 4th Fl., Orlando, FL 32891-4800. TEL 800-654-2452. FAX 800-874-6418) Ed. Kelly Thomas. **Indexed:** Biol.Abstr., Chem.Abstr., Curr.Adv.Ecol.Sci., Dent.Ind., Diar.Dis.Res., Excerp.Med., Helminthol.Abstr., Ind.Med., Ind.Sci.Rev., INIS Atomind., Sci.Cit.Ind. **Document type:** academic/scholarly publication.
—BLDSC (4089.031500); CASDDS; Faxon; Genuine Article; SWETS; UMI; UnCover. **CCC.**
Formerly: Clinics in Gastroenterology (ISSN 0300-5089)

616.3   UK   ISSN 0966-6311
GASTROENTEROLOGY IN PRACTICE. Abbreviated title: G I P. 1990. 5/yr. £38 (overseas £42) (effective 1995). Hayward Medical Communications Ltd., 44 Earlham St., Covent Garden, London WC2H 7LA, England. TEL 44-171-240-4493. FAX 44-171-240-4479. (Subscr. to: Essex House, Cromwell Park, Chipping Norton, Oxon. OX7 5SR, England. TEL 44-1608-645564. FAX 44-1608-645645) Ed.Bd. adv.; bk.rev. circ. 21,000. **Document type:** academic/scholarly publication.
Supersedes in part (in 1990): Gastroenterology and Rheumatology in Practice (ISSN 0959-3314); Which was formed by the merger of (1983-1990): Gastroenterology in Practice (ISSN 0264-7478); (1981-1990): Rheumatology in Practice (ISSN 0262-5512)

616.3   IT   ISSN 0950-5911
CODEN: GASIEG
GASTROENTEROLOGY INTERNATIONAL. (Text in English) 1988. q. $100 to individuals; institutions $150. International University Press, Via Monte delle Gioie 22, 00199 Rome, Italy. TEL 39-6-86211027. FAX 39-6-86211026. Ed. Sydney F. Phillips. adv.: B&W page $1200, color page $2150; trim 179 x 235; adv. contact: Isabella Leonardo. circ. 3,000. (reprint service avail.) **Document type:** academic/scholarly publication.
—BLDSC (4089.032000).
Description: Publishes reports from international working teams, composed of leading clinicians and appointed by the editors, on controversial clinical topics. Provides information on the activities of the major international gastroenterological organizations.

616.3   IT   ISSN 1120-4818
GASTROENTEROLOGY INTERNATIONAL (ITALIAN EDITION). 1990. q. $70 to individuals; institutions $120. International University Press, Via Monte delle Gioie 22, 00199 Rome, Italy. TEL 39-6-86211027. FAX 39-6-86211026. Ed. Sidney F. Phillips. adv.: B&W page $2550, color page $5050; adv. contact: Isabella Leonardo. circ. 10,000. (reprint service avail.) **Document type:** academic/scholarly publication.
Description: Devoted to education and international cooperation in the field of digestive disease.

616.3   US   ISSN 1042-895X
RC804.E6   CODEN: GANUER
GASTROENTEROLOGY NURSING. 1977. bi-m. $69 to individuals; institutions $99 (effective 1995). (Society of Gastroenterology Nurses and Associates) Williams & Wilkins, 428 E. Preston St., Baltimore, MD 21202. TEL 410-528-4000; 800-638-6423. FAX 410-528-4312. Ed. Belinda Puetz. adv.; bk.rev. circ. 7,740. (also avail. in microfilm from WWS; back issues avail.) **Indexed:** CINAHL. **Document type:** academic/scholarly publication.
—BLDSC (4089.032300); Faxon. **CCC.**
Formerly: S G A Journal (ISSN 0149-6212)
Description: Describes new procedures, techniques and equipment for gastroenterology nurses and associates.

616.3   US   ISSN 0898-4670
GASTROENTEROLOGY SERIES. 1983. irreg., vol.2, 1986. Marcel Dekker, Inc., 270 Madison Ave., New York, NY 10016. TEL 212-696-9000. FAX 212-685-4540. TELEX 421419. **Document type:** monographic series.
Refereed Serial

616.3   US   ISSN 0016-5107
RC804.E6   CODEN: GAENBQ
GASTROINTESTINAL ENDOSCOPY. 1953. m. $108 to individuals (foreign $153); institutions $144 (foreign $189); students $60 (foreign$105); newsstand price: $10. Mosby - Year Book, Inc. (Subsidiary of: Times Mirror Company), c/o Dr. Charles J. Lightdale, Ed., Columbia-Presbyterian Medical Center, 630 W. 168th St., New York, NY 10032. TEL 201-592-0529. FAX 201-592-7354. Ed. Dr. Charles J. Lightdale. adv.: B&W page $840; trim 8 1/8 x 10 1/8. bk.rev.; abstr.; index. circ. 9,725. (also avail. in microfilm from WWS; reprint service avail.) **Indexed:** Biol.Abstr., CINAHL, Curr.Adv.Cancer Res., Curr.Cont., Excerp.Med., Helminthol.Abstr., Ind.Med., Ind.Sci.Rev., INIS Atomind., Protozool.Abstr., Rev.Med.& Vet.Mycol., Sci.Cit.Ind., Sugar Ind.Abstr. **Document type:** academic/scholarly publication.
—BLDSC (4089.050000); Genuine Article; SWETS; UMI; UnCover. **CCC.**
Formerly: Bulletin of Gastrointestinal Endoscopy.
Description: Current papers in endoscopy for gastroenterologists and general surgeons.
Refereed Serial

616.3   US   ISSN 1052-5157
CODEN: GECNED
GASTROINTESTINAL ENDOSCOPY CLINICS OF NORTH AMERICA. 1991. q. $120 (foreign $147) (effective 1996). W.B. Saunders Co. (Subsidiary of: Harcourt Brace & Company), Curtis Center, 3rd Fl., Independence Sq. W., Philadelphia, PA 19106-3399. TEL 215-238-7800. FAX 215-238-6445. (Suscr. to: Periodicals Fulfillment, W.B. Saunders Co., 6277 Sea Harbor Dr., 4th Fl., Orlando, FL 32887-4800. TEL 800-654-2452. FAX 800-874-6418) Ed. Naina Chohan. (also avail. in microform from UMI) **Indexed:** Excerp.Med. (1993-), Ind.Med. (1994-). **Document type:** academic/scholarly publication.
—BLDSC (4089.052000); UMI.
Description: Each issue focuses on the treatment or diagnosis of a condition or disease of the digestive tract.

616.3   UK   ISSN 0142-8101
GASTROINTESTINAL HORMONES. 1977. s-m. (diskette m.). £105 (diskette £115; both £175) (effective 1995). S U B I S, Mansion House, 19 Kingfield Rd., Sheffield S11 9AS, England. TEL 0114-2554433. FAX 0114-2554626. E-mail: admin@sheffac.demon.co.uk. (also avail. in diskette format) **Document type:** abstracting/indexing.
—CCC.
Description: Current awareness service for researchers. Covers gastrin, bombesin, G-I-polypeptide, secretin, motilin, VIP, pancreatic polypeptide and other hormones.

616.3   SP   ISSN 0211-058X
GASTRUM PATOLOGIA DEL APARATO DIGESTIVO. 1977. 12/yr. 6000 ptas. Antonio Lopez Aguado 4, 28029 Madrid, Spain. TEL 1-314-43-38. FAX 1-314-44-99. Ed. Dr. Jose Mora Sainz. adv. circ. 2,838. **Document type:** monographic series.

616.3   IT   ISSN 0394-0225
GIORNALE ITALIANO DI ENDOSCOPIA DIGESTIVA. (Text in Italian; summaries in English) 1978. q. L.79000($98) (effective 1994). (Societa Italiana di Endoscopia Digestiva) Masson S.p.A., Divisione Periodici, Via Statuto 2-4, 20121 Milan, Italy. TEL 02-63671. FAX 02-6367211. Ed. Lorenzo Cestari. adv.: B&W page L.1650000, color page L.2400000; trim 167 x 222. circ. 1,500. (reprint service avail. from UMI) **Indexed:** Excerp.Med. **Document type:** academic/scholarly publication.
—BLDSC (4178.214600).
Formerly (until 1980): Giornale di Gastroenterologia ed Endoscopia (ISSN 0394-0489)

616.3   UK   ISSN 0017-5749
CODEN: GUTTAK
GUT. 1960. m. £191($309) (British Society of Gastroenterology) B M J Publishing Group, B.M.A. House, Tavistock Sq., London WC1H 9JR, England. TEL 0171-387-4499. FAX 0171-383-6661. (N. American subscr. to: Box 480, Franklin, MA 02038. TEL 800-2-FON-BMJ. FAX 800-2-FAX-BMJ) Ed. R.N. Allan. adv. contact: Sheila Rowe. bk.rev.; charts; illus.; index. (also avail. in microform from UMI; reprint service avail. from UMI) **Indexed:** AIM, Behav.Med.Abstr., Biol.Abstr., Biotech.Abstr., Chem.Abstr., Curr.Adv.Ecol.Sci., Dent.Ind., Diar.Dis.Res., Excerp.Med., Helminthol.Abstr., I.P.A., Ind.Med., Ind.Sci.Rev., Ind.Vet., INIS Atomind., NRN, Nutr.Abstr., Sci.Cit.Ind., Triticale Abstr., Vet.Bull. **Document type:** academic/scholarly publication.
●Also available online. Vendor(s): Ovid Technologies.
—BLDSC (4232.400000); ADONIS; CASDDS; Faxon; Genuine Article; SWETS; UMI; UnCover. **CCC.**
Description: Covers all diseases of the alimentary tract, liver, biliary tree, and pancreas.
Refereed Serial

616.3   GR   ISSN 1012-0424
HELLENIKE GASTROENTEROLOGIA/HELLENIC JOURNAL OF GASTROENTEROLOGY. (Text in English) 1988. q. Dr.4000($50) to individuals; libraries Dr.6000. (Hellenike Gastroenterologike Etaireia - Hellenic Society of Gastroenterology) Beta Medical Publishers Ltd., Adrianiou 3, 115 25 Athens, Greece. TEL 30-1-7232-302. FAX 30-1-7232-302. Ed. Dr. John A. Karagiannis. adv. contact: A. Vassilakou. bk.rev.; circ. 2,000 (paid). **Indexed:** Excerp.Med. (1994-). **Document type:** academic/scholarly publication.
●Also available on CD-ROM.
—BLDSC (4285.436000).
Refereed Serial

616.3   FR   ISSN 1253-7020
▼**HEPATO - GASTRO.** 1994. 6/yr. 460 F. to individuals; institutions 690 F.; students 250 F. (effective 1995). John Libbey Eurotext, 127 av de la Republique, 92120 Montrouge, France. TEL 1-46-73-06-60. FAX 1-40-84-09-99. (Subscr. to: ATEI, 23-25 rue Fernand-Combette, 93100 Montreuil, France. TEL 48-59-58-11) Eds. Jean Paul Galmiche, Jean-Pierre Benhamou. circ. 1,000.
Description: Used as a training and updating tool in digestive pathology. Includes bibliographical synopses, mini-reviews and annotated clinical cases.

616.3   GW   ISSN 0172-6390
CODEN: HEGAD4
HEPATO-GASTROENTEROLOGY. (Text in English; summaries in English and German) 1954. bi-m. DM.278. Georg Thieme Verlag, Ruedigerstr. 14, 70469 Stuttgart, Germany. TEL 0711-8931-0. FAX 0711-8931298. (Subscr. to: Postfach 104853, 70042 Stuttgart, Germany) Ed.Bd. adv.; bk.rev.; abstr.; bibl.; charts; illus.; stat.; index. circ. 2,700. (also avail. in microform from UMI; back issues avail.; reprint service avail. from UMI) **Indexed:** Biol.Abstr., Chem.Abstr., Curr.Adv.Ecol.Sci., Dent.Ind., Excerp.Med., Helminthol.Abstr., Ind.Med., Ind.Sci.Rev., INIS Atomind., Nutr.Abstr., Sci.Cit.Ind. **Document type:** academic/scholarly publication.
—BLDSC (4295.835000); ADONIS; CASDDS; Faxon; Genuine Article; SWETS; UMI; UnCover. **CCC.**
Former titles: Acta Hepato-Gastroenterologica (ISSN 0300-970X); Acta Hepato- Splenologica (ISSN 0001-5822)

MEDICAL SCIENCES — GASTROENTEROLOGY

616.362 US ISSN 0270-9139
RC845 CODEN: HPTLD9
HEPATOLOGY. 1981. m. $423 (foreign $473) (effective 1996). (American Association for the Study of Liver Diseases) W.B. Saunders Co., Curtis Center, 3rd Fl., Indpendence Sq. W., Philadelphia, PA 19106-3399. TEL 215-238-7800. FAX 215-238-6445. (Subscr. to: Periodicals Fulfillment, W.B. Saunders Co., 6277 Sea Harbor Dr., 4th Fl., Orlando, FL 32891-4800. TEL 800-654-2452. FAX 800-874-6418) Ed. Dr. Paul D. Berk; Pub. Joan W. Blumberg. adv.: B&W page $640; 7 x 10. bk.rev. circ. 5,721. (also avail. in microform from WWS; back issues avail.) **Indexed:** Curr.Adv.Cancer Res., Curr.Adv.Ecol.Sci., Curr.Cont., Excerp.Med., Ind.Med., Ind.Sci.Rev., Ind.Vet., INIS Atomind., Kidney, Poult.Abstr., Rev.Med.& Vet.Mycol., Risk Abstr., Sci.Cit.Ind, Sugar Ind.Abstr., Vet.Bull. **Document type:** academic/scholarly publication.
—BLDSC (4295.836000); CASDDS; Faxon; Genuine Article; SWETS; UMI; UnCover. **CCC.**
Description: Examines hepatitis, gallstone formation, drug injury, liver physiology and disease. For gastroenterologists and internists.
Refereed Serial

616.3 JA ISSN 0536-2180
I TO CHO/STOMACH AND INTESTINE. (Text in Japanese; captions and summaries in English) 1966. m. 22710 Yen($175) Igaku-Shoin Ltd., 5-24-3 Hongo, Bunkyo-ku, Tokyo 113-91, Japan. TEL 03-817-5714. Ed.Bd. circ. 15,000. **Indexed:** INIS Atomind.
●Also available online. Vendor(s): JICST.
—BLDSC (8465.870000).

616.3 UK ISSN 1352-8513
▼**ILLUSTRATED CASE REPORTS IN GASTROENTEROLOGY.** 1994. q. £75($139) to individuals; institutions in the E.U. £130 (N. America $245; elsewhere £155) (effective 1995). Chapman & Hall, Journals Department (Subsidiary of: International Thomson Publishing Group), 2-6 Boundary Row, London SE1 8HN, England. TEL 0171-865-0066. FAX 0171-522-9323. TELEX 290164 CHAPMA G. E-mail: journal@chall.mhs.compuserve.com. (Subscr. to: International Thomson Publishing Services Ltd., Cheriton House, North Way, Andover, Hants. SP10 5BE, England. TEL 01264-342713. FAX 01264-342807; Subscr. in N. America to: Chapman & Hall, Journals Promotion Department, One Penn Plaza, 41st Fl., New York, NY 10119. TEL 212-564-1060. FAX 212-564-1505) Ed. K.R.F. Schiller. adv.; illus. (reprint service avail.) **Document type:** academic/scholarly publication.
—BLDSC (4367.015000). **CCC.**
Description: Covers all research and clinical aspects of gastroenterology.
Refereed Serial

616.3 II ISSN 0970-0935
INDIAN JOURNAL OF COLO-PROCTOLOGY. (Text in English) 1986. s-a. Rs.80($20) Association of Colon and Rectal Surgeons of India, 30 Circus Ave., Calcutta 700 017, India. TEL 33-249776. Ed. Dr. Syed Abdul Momen. adv.; bk.rev.; index. circ. 500. **Document type:** academic/scholarly publication.

616.3 II ISSN 0254-8860
INDIAN JOURNAL OF GASTROENTEROLOGY. (Supplement avail.: Proceedings of Annual Conference) (Text in English) 1982. q. Rs.250 (foreign $50). Indian Society of Gastroenterology, 23, Bombay Mutual Terrace, 534 Sandhurst Bridge, Bombay 400 007, India. TEL 3613344. Ed. Subhash R. Naik. adv.; bk.rev.; abstr.; bibl. circ. 1,000. (back issues avail.) **Indexed:** Abstr.Hyg., Diar.Dis.Res., Excerp.Med., Ind.Med.
—BLDSC (4412.760000); Faxon. **CCC.**

616.3 II
INDIAN SOCIETY OF GASTROENTEROLOGY. PROCEEDINGS OF THE ANNUAL CONFERENCE. (Supplement to: Indian Journal of Gastroenterology) 1962. a. $20. Indian Society of Gastroenterology, 23, Bombay Mutual Terrace, 534 Sandhurst Bridge, Bombay 400 007, India. TEL 8113344. Ed. Dr. S.R. Naik. adv.; bk.rev. circ. 500. **Indexed:** Excerp.Med., Ind.Med.

616.3 US ISSN 1078-0998
INFLAMMATORY BOWEL DISEASES. 1976. 4/yr. $92 to individuals (foreign $103); institutions $116 (foreign $125) (effective 1996); newsstand price: $32. (Crohn's & Colitis Foundation of America, Inc.) Lippincott - Raven Press, 227 E. Washington Sq., Philadelphia, PA 19106. TEL 215-238-4200. Eds. Dr. Robert Burakoff, Dr. Richard P. MacDermott. bk.rev.; abstr.; bibl. circ. 14,000. (back issues avail.) **Document type:** academic/scholarly publication.
—BLDSC (4478.845400).
Former titles (until 1995): Progress in Inflammatory Bowel Disease; (until 1990): I B D News.
Description: Articles on basic research and clinical studies related to Crohn's disease and ulcerative colitis, also known as inflammatory bowel disease.

616.3 US ISSN 1047-5028
CODEN: IDITE8
INFLAMMATORY DISEASE AND THERAPY. 1989. irreg., vol.12, 1993. price varies. Marcel Dekker, Inc., 270 Madison Ave., New York, NY 10016. TEL 212-696-9000. FAX 212-685-4540. TELEX 421419. Ed. Furst.
—BLDSC (4478.845500); CASDDS. **CCC.**

616.362 IE ISSN 0928-4346
CODEN: IHCOEP
INTERNATIONAL HEPATOLOGY COMMUNICATIONS; an international journal for the rapid dissemination of original short communications in hepatology. (Text in English) 1993. m. I£420($664) (effective 1996). Elsevier Science Ireland Ltd., P.O. Box 85, Limerick, Ireland. TEL 353-61-471944. FAX 353-61-472144. (Subscr. in U.S. and Canada to: Elsevier Science Inc., Box 882, Madison Sq. Sta., New York, NY 10159-0882. TEL 212-989-5800. FAX 212-633-3990) Eds. T. Tsujii, G. Toda. (also avail. in microform from UMI; back issues avail.) **Indexed:** Excerp.Med. (1994-). **Document type:** academic/scholarly publication.
—BLDSC (4540.721950); Genuine Article. **CCC.**
Previously announced as: Hepatology Letters.
Description: Publishes reports of basic and clinical research in the field of hepatology, and mini-reviews on selected aspects of hepatology undergoing rapid change.
Refereed Serial

INTERNATIONAL JOURNAL OF PANCREATOLOGY. see *MEDICAL SCIENCES — Endocrinology*

616.9233005 CN ISSN 1188-4525
INTERNATIONAL SEMINARS IN PAEDIATRIC GASTROENTEROLOGY AND NUTRITION. 1990. q. $52 to individuals (outside US & Canada $79); institutions $78 (outside US & Canada $105) (effective 1996). Decker Periodicals, P.O. Box 620, LCD 1, Hamilton, ON L8N 3K7, Canada. TEL 905-522-7017; 800-568-7281. FAX 905-522-7839. E-mail: decker@io.org. Ed. W. Allan Walker. **Document type:** academic/scholarly publication.
Formerly (until 1992): Seminars in Paediatric Gastroenterology and Nutrition (ISSN 1188-0244)
Description: Offers a review of current investigation and clinical practice in the nutritional management of children.

616.3 UK ISSN 0261-4995
INTESTINAL FUNCTION. 1965. s-m. (diskette m.) £115 (diskette £115; both £175) (effective 1995). S U B I S, Mansion House, 19 Kingfield Rd., Sheffield S11 9AS, England. TEL 0114-2554433. FAX 0114-2554626. E-mail: admin@sheffac.demon.co.uk. (also avail. in diskette format) **Document type:** abstracting/indexing.
—UMI. **CCC.**
Former titles (until 1981): Intestinal Absorption (ISSN 0306-3003); Intestinal Absorption and Related Topics.
Description: Current awareness service for researchers. Covers intestinal transport, structure, physiology, motility and biochemistry.

616.3 IT ISSN 0392-0623
CODEN: ITJGDH
ITALIAN JOURNAL OF GASTROENTEROLOGY. (Text in English; summaries in English and Italian) 1969. m. (9/yr.) $130 to individuals; institutions $200. (Italian Society of Gastroenterology) International University Press, Via Monte delle Gioie 22, 00199 Rome, Italy. TEL 39-6-86211027. FAX 39-6-86211026. Ed. Romano Garratu. adv.: B&W page $1400, color page $2150; trim 179 x 235; adv. contact: Isabella Leonardo. bk.rev.; index, cum.index. circ. 2,000. (also avail. in microform from UMI; reprint service avail.) **Indexed:** Curr.Cont., Diar.Dis.Res., Excerp.Med., Ind.Med., Nutr.Abstr., Rev.Med.& Vet.Mycol., Sci.Cit.Ind. **Document type:** academic/scholarly publication.
—BLDSC (4588.340400); CASDDS; Faxon; Genuine Article; SWETS; UMI.
Former titles: Rendiconti di Gastroenterologia (ISSN 0300-0877); (until 1971): Rendiconti Romani di Gastro-Enterologia (ISSN 0300-0524); (until 1970): Rendiconti delle Romane di Gastro-Enterology.
Description: Publishes original articles concerning basic and clinical research, case reports, editorials, articles discussing hypothese and interpretations, and the proceedings of the national congresses on gastroenterology and hepatology.

616.3 GW
▼**JAHRBUCH DER GASTROENTEROLOGIE.** (Text in German; summaries in English, German) 1994. a. DM.126.40. Biermann Verlag GmbH, Nideggenerstr. 18, 53909 Zuelpich, Germany. TEL 02252-9410-0. FAX 02252-941015. Eds. G. Strohmeyer, C. Niederau. **Document type:** academic/scholarly publication.

616.3 US ISSN 0192-0790
RC799
JOURNAL OF CLINICAL GASTROENTEROLOGY. 1979. 8/yr. $134 to individuals (foreign $190); institutions $252 (foreign $292) (effective 1996); newsstand price: $38. Lippincott - Raven Publishers, 276 E. Washington Sq., Philadelphia, PA 19106. TEL 215-238-4200. Ed. Dr. Howard M. Spiro. adv. contact: Phyllis Noyes. bk.rev.; charts; illus.; stat.; index. circ. 2,500. (back issues avail.; reprint service avail. from UMI) **Indexed:** Curr.Adv.Cancer Res., Curr.Cont., Excerp.Med., Helminthol.Abstr., Ind.Med., Ind.Sci.Rev., NRN, Sci.Cit.Ind. **Document type:** academic/scholarly publication.
—BLDSC (4958.470000); Faxon; Genuine Article; SWETS; UMI; UnCover. **CCC.**
Description: Focuses on essential advances in the field of digestive diseases that relate directly to clinical practice and patient care problems.
Refereed Serial

JOURNAL OF DIARRHOEAL DISEASES RESEARCH. see *MEDICAL SCIENCES — Abstracting, Bibliographies, Statistics*

616.3 JA ISSN 0944-1174
CODEN: JOGAET
JOURNAL OF GASTROENTEROLOGY. (Text in English) 1966. bi-m. DM.280($203) (effective 1996). (Japanese Society of Gastroenterology - Nihon Shokakibyo Gakkai) Springer-Verlag Tokyo, 3-13 Hongo 3-chome, Bunkyo-ku, Tokyo 113, Japan. TEL 03-3812-0617. FAX 03-3812-4699. (N. America subscr. to: Springer-Verlag New York Inc., Service Center Secaucus 44, Hartz Way, Secaucus, NJ 07096-2491. TEL 201-348-4033) Ed. Tsune Yoshi. adv.; abstr. circ. 1,500. **Indexed:** Biol.Abstr., Chem.Abstr., Excerp.Med., Ind.Med., INIS Atomind. **Document type:** academic/scholarly publication.
—BLDSC (4987.610000); CASDDS; Genuine Article; SWETS.
Formerly (until 1994): Gastroenterologia Japonica (ISSN 0435-1339)
Description: Publishes original papers, case reports, reports of multi-center trials, and review articles on all aspects of the field of gastroenterology.

MEDICAL SCIENCES — GASTROENTEROLOGY

616.3 AT ISSN 0815-9319
CODEN: JGHEEO
JOURNAL OF GASTROENTEROLOGY AND HEPATOLOGY. 1986. bi-m. Aus.$395($320) (effective 1996). Blackwell Science Pty Ltd, P.O. Box 378, Carlton, Vic. 3053, Australia. TEL 61-3-93470300. FAX 61-3-93493016. Ed.Bd. adv.: B&W page $720, color page $1510; trim 275 x 210. illus.; index. circ. 1,500. (also avail. in microform from UMI; back issues avail.; reprint service avail. from UMI) **Indexed:** Chem.Abstr., Curr.Adv.Cancer Res., Curr.Cont., Excerp.Med., Ind.Med., Sci.Cit.Ind. **Document type:** academic/scholarly publication.
—BLDSC (4987.615000); ADONIS; CASDDS; Faxon; Genuine Article; SWETS; UMI; UnCover. **CCC.**
Description: Covers original contributions concerned with clinical practice and research in the fields of gastroenterology and hepatology.

616.3 DK ISSN 0168-8278
CODEN: JOHEEC
JOURNAL OF HEPATOLOGY. (Text and summaries in English) 1985. 12/yr. (in 2 vols.; 6 nos./vol.). DKK 900 to individuals; institutions DKK 4500 (incl. supplements) (effective 1996). (European Association for the Study of the Liver) Munksgaard International Publishers Ltd., 35 Noerre Soegade, P.O. Box 2148, DK-1016 Copenhagen K, Denmark. TEL 33-127030. FAX 33-129387. Ed. Jean-Pierre Benhamou. adv.; bk.rev.; illus.; index. (back issues avail.; reprint service avail. from ISI,SWZ) **Indexed:** Curr.Adv.Cell & Devel.Biol., Curr.Adv.Ecol.Sci., Excerp.Med., INIS Atomind., Rev.Med.& Vet.Mycol., Sci.Cit.Ind. **Document type:** academic/scholarly publication.
—BLDSC (4997.700000); ADONIS; CASDDS; Faxon; Genuine Article; SWETS; UnCover. **CCC.**
Description: Publishes original papers and reviews concerned with practice and research in the field of hepatology.
Refereed Serial

616.3 612.3 US ISSN 0277-2116
CODEN: JPGND6
JOURNAL OF PEDIATRIC GASTROENTEROLOGY AND NUTRITION. 1982. 8/yr. $195 to individuals (foreign $211); institutions $376 (foreign $471) (effective 1996); newsstand price: $60. Lippincott - Raven Press, 276 E. Washington Sq., Philadelphia, PA 19106. TEL 215-238-4200. (Co-sponsors: North American Society for Pediatric Gastroenterology and Nutrition; European Society for Pediatric Gastroenterology and Nutrition) Eds. William F. Balistreri, Michael Lentze. adv. contact: Phyllis Noyes. bk.rev.; charts; illus.; index. circ. 2,000. (back issues avail.; reprint service avail. from UMI) **Indexed:** C.C.I.P., Chem.Abstr., Curr.Adv.Ecol.Sci., Dent.Ind., Diar.Dis.Res., Excerp.Med., Ind.Med., Ind.Sci.Rev., Ind.Vet., Maize Abstr., Pig News & Info., Protozool.Abstr., Soyabean Abstr., Triticale Abstr. **Document type:** academic/scholarly publication.
—BLDSC (5030.175000); CASDDS; Faxon; Genuine Article; SWETS; UnCover. **CCC.**
Description: Reports of studies on nutrition, normal and abnormal functions of the alimentary tract and associated organs, with emphasis on development and its relation to infant and childhood nutrition.
Refereed Serial

JOURNAL OF PEPTIDE SCIENCE. see *BIOLOGY — Biological Chemistry*

616.362 JA ISSN 0451-4203
CODEN: KNZOA
KANZO/ACTA HEPATOLOGICA JAPONICA. (Text in Japanese, summaries in English, Japanese) 1960. m. Nihon Kanzo Gakkai - Japanese Society of Hepatology, 28-10 Hongo 3-chome, Bunkyo-ku, Tokyo 113, Japan. TEL 03-3812-1567. **Indexed:** Chem.Abstr., Excerp.Med. **Document type:** academic/scholarly publication.
—BLDSC (0623.550000); CASDDS.

616.3 GW ISSN 0940-9092
KONTINENZ; Zeitschrift fuer Funktionsstoerungen von Blase und Darm. 1992. bi-m. DM.104. Hippokrates Verlag GmbH, Postfach 300504, 70445 Stuttgart, Germany. TEL 0711-8931-0. FAX 0711-8931453. Ed. W. Jost. **Document type:** academic/scholarly publication.

616.3 GW ISSN 0300-8622
CODEN: LBMDAT
LEBER MAGEN DARM; zeitschrift fuer angewandte gastroenterologie und stoffwechsel. 1971. 6/yr. DM.120.60 (Europe DM.129.60). Richard Pflaum Verlag GmbH und Co. KG, Lazarettstr. 4, 80636 Munich, Germany. TEL 089-12607-0. FAX 089-12607-200. (Subscr. to: Postfach 190737, 80607 Munich, Germany) Ed. P. Fruehmorgen. adv.; bk.rev. circ. 16,000. **Indexed:** Curr.Cont., Excerp.Med., Helminthol.Abstr., Ind.Med., Ind.Sci.Rev., Nutr.Abstr. **Document type:** academic/scholarly publication.
—BLDSC (5179.660000); CASDDS; Faxon; Genuine Article; SWETS; UMI. **CCC.**
Incorporates: Innere Medizin (ISSN 0303-4305)

LIFELINELETTER. see *NUTRITION AND DIETETICS*

616.3 DK ISSN 0106-9543
CODEN: LIVEDR
LIVER; an international journal. (Text in English) 1981. bi-m. DKK 1400 (effective 1996). Munksgaard International Publishers Ltd., 35 Noerre Soegade, P.O. Box 2148, DK-1016 Copenhagen K, Denmark. TEL 33-127030. FAX 33-129387. Ed. Dr. Valeer Desmet. adv.; bk.rev.; illus.; stat.; index. circ. 800. (reprint service avail. from ISI) **Indexed:** Biol.Abstr., Curr.Adv.Biochem., Curr.Adv.Cell & Devel.Biol., Curr.Cont., Excerp.Med., Ind.Med., Rev.Med.& Vet.Mycol.
—BLDSC (5280.400000); Faxon; Genuine Article; SWETS; UnCover. **CCC.**
Refereed Serial

617 616.362 US ISSN 1074-3022
▼**LIVER TRANSPLANTATION AND SURGERY.** 1995. bi-m. $90 to individuals (foreign $110); institutions $140 (foreign $160); students $40 (foreign $50). (American Association for the Study of Liver Diseases) W.B. Saunders Co. (Subsidiary of: Harcourt Brace & Company), Curtis Center, 3rd Fl., Independence Sq., W., Philadelphia, PA 19106-3399. TEL 215-238-7800. FAX 215-238-3445. (Subscr. to: Journals Fulfillment, W.B. Saunders Co., 6277 Sea Harbor Dr., 4th Fl., Orlando, FL 32891-4800. TEL 800-654-2452. FAX 800-800-874-6418) (Co-sponsor: International Liver Transplantation Society) Eds. Drs. Byers. W. Shaw, Jr., Michael F. Sorrell. **Document type:** academic/scholarly publication.
—BLDSC (5280.525000).
Description: Discusses surgical techniques, clinical investigations, and drug research in the subspecialties of liver transplantation and surgery.
Refereed Serial

616.02 US
LIVER UPDATE. 1988. irreg. (2-4/yr.). $175. American Liver Foundation, 1425 Pompton Ave., Cedar Grove, NJ 07009-1043. TEL 201-256-2550. Ed. Dr. Anna Mae Diehl. circ. 70,000 (controlled). **Document type:** academic/scholarly publication.

616.3 574 US
LIVING HEALTHY;* learning to live with digestive disease. 1979. bi-m. $30. American Digestive Disease Society, 60 E 42nd St., Ste. 411, New York, NY 10165-0015. Ed. Martin I. Hassner. bibl.; charts; illus. circ. 14,000. (back issues avail.)

616.3 FR ISSN 0047-6412
CODEN: MCDGBC
MEDECINE ET CHIRURGIE DIGESTIVES. (Text in English, French; summaries in English, French, German, Spanish) 1972. bi-m. 550 F. (foreign 600 F.); students 300 F. (Hopital Saint Antoine, Centre d'Enseignement d'Hepatologie) B.C. Diffusion, 116 av. des Champs-Elysees, 75008 Paris, France. TEL 44-21-80-26. FAX 44-21-82-99. Eds. J. Caroli, B. Chevrel. adv.; bk.rev.; abstr.; bibl.; illus.; index. circ. 2,200. **Indexed:** Biol.Abstr., Bull.Signal., C.I.S. Abstr., Curr.Cont., Excerp.Med., Helminthol.Abstr., Ind.Med., Nutr.Abstr.
—BLDSC (5487.729000); CASDDS; EMDOCS; SWETS; UMI. **CCC.**
Description: Scientific journal covering research articles, statistics, treatments and medication available with respect to gastrointestinal ailments.

616.3 BL
MEDISOM: GASTROENTEROLOGY. 1979. bi-m. $90. Editora Medisom, Ltda., Rua Sao Paulino 224, Caixa Postal 7650, 01064-970 Sao Paulo, Brazil. FAX 55-11-572-5957. Ed. Dr. Philip Querido. adv. (audio cassette)

616.3 IT ISSN 1121-421X
RC799 CODEN: MDGADI
MINERVA GASTROENTEROLOGICA E DIETOLOGICA; rivista trimestrale di gastroenterologia e nutrizione clinica. (Text in Italian; summaries in English, Italian) 1960. q. $90 to individuals; institutions $140 (effective 1995). Edizioni Minerva Medica, Corso Bramante 83-85, 10126 Turin, Italy. TEL 39-11-678282. FAX 39-11-3121736. Ed. M. Rizzetto; Pub. A. Oliaro. adv.: B&W page $1100, color page $1900; trim 190 x 270; adv. contact: F. Filippo. bk.rev.; bibl.; charts; illus.; index; circ. 3,000 (paid). (also avail. in microform from UMI) **Indexed:** Biol.Abstr., Chem.Abstr., Dent.Ind., Excerp.Med., Ind.Med., Nutr.Abstr. **Document type:** academic/scholarly publication.
—BLDSC (5794.178000); CASDDS; EMDOCS; UMI.
Formerly (until 1990): Minerva Dietologica e Gastroenterologica (ISSN 0391-1993); Which was formed by the merger of: Minerva Dietologica (ISSN 0026-475X); Minerva Gastroenterologica (ISSN 0026-4776)
Refereed Serial

616.3 UK ISSN 0969-935X
N A C C NEWS. 1990. 2/yr. National Association for Colitis and Crohn's Disease, 4 Beaumont House, Sutton Rd., St. Albans, Herts AL1 5HH, England. TEL 01727-844296. Ed. Maureen Lakeman. adv.; bk.rev. **Document type:** newsletter.

616.3 UK ISSN 0144-6967
N A C C NEWSLETTER. 1980. 4/yr. membership. National Association for Colitis and Crohn's Disease, 4 Beaumont House, Sutton Rd., St. Albans, Herts AL1 5HH, England. TEL 01727-844296. adv.; bk.rev. circ. 21,000. **Document type:** newsletter.
Description: Includes reports of inflammatory bowel disease lectures, activities of over 60 area groups in Great Britain, research progress, fundraising and members' letters.

616.3 UK ISSN 1350-1925
CODEN: NMOTEK
NEUROGASTROENTEROLOGY AND MOTILITY. 1989. q. £78 to individuals (outside Europe £85($137)); institutions £123 (outside Europe £135($217)) (effective 1996). (European Gastrointestinal Motility Society) Blackwell Science Ltd., Osney Mead, Oxford OX2 0EL, England. TEL 01865-206206. FAX 01865-206219. TELEX 83355 MEDBOK G. Eds. M. Read, D. Grundy. adv.; bk.rev.; abstr.; bibl.; illus.; index. circ. 850. (also avail. in microform from UMI; back issues avail.) **Document type:** academic/scholarly publication.
—BLDSC (6081.371450); ADONIS; Genuine Article; UMI; UnCover. **CCC.**
Formerly (until 1994): Journal of Gastrointestinal Motility (ISSN 1043-4518)
Refereed Serial

616.3 NE
NEW CLINICAL APPLICATIONS IN GASTROENTEROLOGY. (Text in English) irreg. price varies. Kluwer Academic Publishers, Postbus 17, 3300 AA Dordrecht, Netherlands. TEL 31-78-392392. FAX 31-78-392254. TELEX 29245 KAPG NL. (Dist. by: Kluwer Academic Publishers Group, P.O. Box 322, 3300 AH Dordrecht, Netherlands. TEL 31-78-392392. FAX 31-78-546474; N. America dist. addr.: Box 358, Accord Sta., Hingham, MA 02018-0358. TEL 617-871-6600. FAX 617-871-6528) **Document type:** monographic series.
Refereed Serial

NIHON KIKAN SHOKUDOKA GAKKAI KAIHO/JAPAN BRONCHO-ESOPHAGOLOGICAL SOCIETY. JOURNAL. see *MEDICAL SCIENCES — Respiratory Diseases*

616.3 JA ISSN 0386-9768
NIHON SHOKAKI GEKA GAKKAI ZASSHI/JAPANESE JOURNAL OF GASTROENTEROLOGICAL SURGERY. (Text in Japanese; summaries in English, Japanese) 1969. m. 1000 Yen per no. Nihon Shokaki Geka Gakkai - Japanese Society of Gastroenterological Surgery, 2-4, Kudan Minami 2-chome, Chiyoda-ku, Tokyo 102, Japan. **Indexed:** INIS Atomind.

MEDICAL SCIENCES — GASTROENTEROLOGY

616.3 JA ISSN 0047-1801
CODEN: NDKGAU
NIPPON DAICHO KOMONBYO GAKKAI ZASSHI/JAPAN SOCIETY OF COLO-PROCTOLOGY. JOURNAL. 1940. 10/yr. Nippon Daicho Komonbyo Gakkai - Japan Society of Colo-Proctology, 11-1 Omori-Nishi 6-chome, Ota-ku, Tokyo 143, Japan. TEL 03-3762-4151. **Indexed:** Excerp.Med. **Document type:** academic/scholarly publication.
—EMDOCS.

617 US ISSN 0000-1414
RD10.U6
OFFICIAL AMERICAN BOARD OF MEDICAL SPECIALTIES (A B M S) DIRECTORY OF BOARD CERTIFIED COLON AND RECTAL SURGEONS. 1985. biennial. $99.95. Marquis Who's Who, A Reed Reference Publishing company, 121 Chanlon Rd., New Providence, NJ 07974. TEL 908-464-6800. FAX 908-665-2898. (Subscr. to: Order Dept., Box 31, New Providence, NJ 07974-9903. TEL 800-521-8110) Ed. Roy Crego. **Document type:** directory.
Formerly (until 1992): A B M S Directory of Certified Colon and Rectal Surgeons (ISSN 0884-1470)
Description: Biographical sketches of U.S. certified medical specialists sorted alphabetically with a geographical index.

P A S C A L E 76: GASTROENTEROLOGIE, FOIE, PANCREAS, ABDOMEN. see MEDICAL SCIENCES — Abstracting, Bibliographies, Statistics

PANCREAS. see MEDICAL SCIENCES — Endocrinology

PERSPECTIVES IN COLON & RECTAL SURGERY. see MEDICAL SCIENCES — Surgery

616.3 US ISSN 0277-4208
CODEN: PRGAEE
PRACTICAL GASTROENTEROLOGY; for the busy internist. 1977. 10/yr. $115 (foreign $160) (effective Jan. 1991). Shugar Publishing, 32 Mill Rd., Westhampton Beach, NY 11978-0947. TEL 516-288-4404. FAX 516-288-4435. Ed. Andrew Kiburis; Pub. Gerald R. Shugar. adv.: B&W page $4664; adv. contact: Vivian Mahlen. bk.rev.; film rev.; charts; illus.; index; circ. 32,000 (controlled). (also avail. in microfilm from UMI; back issues avail.; reprint service avail. from ISI,UMI) **Indexed:** Curr.Cont., Excerp.Med. **Document type:** trade publication.
—BLDSC (6594.062000); Faxon; UMI. **CCC.**
Former titles: Primary Care Physician's Guide to Practical Gastroenterology (ISSN 0163-7894); Physician's Guide to Practical Gastroenterology (ISSN 0149-9912)
Description: For the gastroenterologist, rheumatologist, and busy internist on the diagnosis, therapy and management of digestive disorders. Includes articles on topics that the practitioner encounters in daily practice.
Refereed Serial

616.362 US ISSN 1060-913X
RC845 CODEN: PLVDAI
PROGRESS IN LIVER DISEASE. 1961. 1/yr. $125 (foreign $154) (effective 1996). W.B. Saunders Co. (Subsidiary of: Harcourt Brace & Company), Curtis Center, 3rd Fl., PA 19106-3399. TEL 215-238-7800. FAX 215-238-6445. (Subscr. to: Periodicals Fulfillment, W.B. Saunders Co., 6277 Sea Harbor Dr., 4th Fl., Orlando, FL 32891-4800. TEL 800-654-2452. FAX 800-874-6418) Eds. Drs. James L. Boyer, Robert K. Ockner. index. **Indexed:** ASCA, Biol.Abstr., Chem.Abstr., Curr.Adv.Ecol.Sci., Excerp.Med. (1994-), Ind.Med., Ind.Sci.Rev. **Document type:** academic/scholarly publication, monographic series.
—BLDSC (6868.650000); CASDDS; Faxon; UMI. **CCC.**
Supersedes (in 1991): Progress in Liver Diseases (ISSN 0079-6409)
Description: Reviews advances in clinical research and practice in the diagnosis and treatment of liver diseases and conditions.
Refereed Serial

616.3 UK ISSN 0141-5581
RC799 CODEN: RAGADI
RECENT ADVANCES IN GASTROENTEROLOGY. 1965. irreg. Churchill Livingstone Medical Journals, Robert Stevenson House, 1-3 Baxter's Pl., Leith Walk, Edinburgh EH1 3AF, Scotland. TEL 0131-556-2424. FAX 0131-459-1177. **Document type:** academic/scholarly publication.
—BLDSC (7303.835000); CASDDS.

REFERATOVY VYBER Z GASTROENTEROLOGIE/ABSTRACTS OF GASTROENTEROLOGY. see MEDICAL SCIENCES — Abstracting, Bibliographies, Statistics

616.3 MX ISSN 0375-0906
CODEN: RGMXA
REVISTA DE GASTROENTEROLOGIA DE MEXICO. (Text in Spanish; summaries in English, Spanish) 1935. q. $80. (Asociacion Mexicana de Gastroenterologia) Obsidiana Editores, S.A., Czda. de Tlalpan 2365, Col. Ciudad Jardin, 04370 Mexico DF, Mexico. TEL 6899133. FAX 6896545. Eds. Dr. Roberto de la Garza-Villasenor, Dr. Eduardo Marin-Lopez; Pub. Jorge Godoy. circ. 2,400. **Document type:** academic/scholarly publication.
●Also available on CD-ROM.
—BLDSC (7856.520000).
Description: Contains original articles, research reports, review articles, clinical cases, and notices related to gastroenterology.

616.3 SP ISSN 1130-0108
CODEN: REDIE
REVISTA ESPANOLA DE LAS ENFERMEDADES DIGESTIVAS. (Supplement avail. (ISSN 1130-4588)) (Text in Spanish; summaries in English and Spanish) 1918. 6/yr. 11600 ptas.($130) (effective 1995). (Sociedad Espanola de Patologia Digestiva) Editorial Garsi, S.A., Juan Bravo 46, 28006 Madrid, Spain. TEL 34-1-4021212. FAX 34-1-4020954. Ed. Dr. F. Vilardell. adv.; bk.rev.; abstr.; bibl.; charts; illus.; stat. circ. 3,500. (also avail. in microfilm from UMI; reprint service avail. from UMI) **Indexed:** Biol.Abstr., Chem.Abstr., Curr.Cont., Excerp.Med., Helminthol.Abstr., Ind.Med., Nutr.Abstr., Protozool.Abstr.
—BLDSC (7853.970000); CASDDS; Genuine Article; SWETS; UMI. **CCC.**
Former titles (until 1989): Revista Espanola de las Enfermedades del Aparato Digestivo (ISSN 0034-9437); (until 1967): Revista Espanola de las Enfermedades del Aparato Digestivo y de la Nutricion (ISSN 0370-4343); And (until 1934): Archivos Espanoles de las Enfermedades del Aparato Digestivo y de la Nutricion (ISSN 0210-1556).

616.3 FR ISSN 0035-2888
REVUE FRANCAISE DE GASTRO ENTEROLOGIE. m. (10/yr.). 260 F. to individuals (foreign 340 F.); students 230 F. Galliena Promotion, 58 A, Rue du Dessous des Berges, 75013 Paris, France. TEL 45-84-97-66. FAX 45-84-92-56. **Indexed:** Excerp.Med.
—BLDSC (7904.140000); EMDOCS.

616.3 IT ISSN 0035-6255
RIVISTA DI GASTROENTEROLOGIA. (Text in Italian; summaries in English) 1949. s-a. L.30000 (foreign L.60000) (effective 1994). Casa Editrice Maccari, Via Trento 53, 43100 Parma, Italy. FAX 039-521-771268. Ed.Bd. adv.; bk.rev. circ. 1,200. **Indexed:** Chem.Abstr., Excerp.Med.
—UMI.

616.3 NO ISSN 0036-5521
CODEN: SJGRA4
SCANDINAVIAN JOURNAL OF GASTROENTEROLOGY. (Editions in Chinese, English and Spanish) 1966. 12/yr. NOK 2700 in Nordic countries; elsewhere $525 (effective 1996). Scandinavian University Press, P.O. Box 2959 Toeyen, N-0608 Oslo, Norway. TEL 47-22-57-54-00. FAX 47-22-57-53-53. (U.S. addr.: Scandinavian University Press, 200 Meacham Ave., Elmont, NY 11003. TEL 516-352-7300) Ed.Bd. adv.; bk.rev.; charts; illus.; index. circ. 1,700. (also avail. in microform from UMI) **Indexed:** Biol.Abstr., Biotech.Abstr., Chem.Abstr, Curr.Adv.Cancer Res., Curr.Adv.Ecol.Sci., Curr.Adv.Genetics & Molec.Biol., Curr.Cont., Dairy Sci.Abstr., Dent.Ind., Diar.Dis.Res., Excerp.Med., Helminthol.Abstr., Ind.Med., Nutr.Abstr., Protozool.Abstr., Sci.Cit.Ind., Sugar Ind.Abstr. **Document type:** academic/scholarly publication.
—BLDSC (8087.507000); ADONIS; CASDDS; EMDOCS; Faxon; Genuine Article; SWETS; UMI. **CCC.**
Description: Membership journal for the gastroenterologic societies of Denmark, Finland, Iceland, Norway and Sweden.

616.3 NO ISSN 0085-5928
CODEN: SJGSB8
SCANDINAVIAN JOURNAL OF GASTROENTEROLOGY. SUPPLEMENT. (Text in English) 1968. irreg. $414 (includes Scandinavian Journal of Gastroenterology). Scandinavian University Press, P.O. Box 2959 Toeyen, N-0608 Oslo, Norway. TEL 47-22-57-54-00. FAX 47-22-57-53-53. (U.S. addr.: Scandinavian University Press, 200 Meacham Ave., Elmont, NY 11003. TEL 516-352-7300) Ed. E. Gjone. circ. 1,700. (also avail. in microform from UMI; back issues avail.; reprint service avail. from ISI) **Indexed:** Biol.Abstr., Chem.Abstr., Curr.Adv.Ecol.Sci., Dent.Ind., Excerp.Med., Ind.Med., Nutr.Abstr.
—BLDSC (8087.508000); ADONIS; CASDDS; EMDOCS; Faxon; SWETS; UMI; UnCover. **CCC.**

616.3 IT
SELECTA MEDICA GASTROENTEROLOGIA. 1993. s-a.? L.89000($118) (effective 1994). Masson S.p.A., Divisione Periodici, Via Statuto 2-4, 20121 Milan, Italy. TEL 02-6367-1. FAX 02-6367211. Ed. Gabriele Bianchi Porro. adv.: B&W page L.2500000, color page L.3800000. circ. 5,000.

SEMINARS IN COLON AND RECTAL SURGERY. see MEDICAL SCIENCES — Surgery

616.3 US ISSN 1049-5118
CODEN: SGDIED
SEMINARS IN GASTROINTESTINAL DISEASE. 1990. q. $133 (foreign $166) (effective 1996). W.B. Saunders Co. (Subsidiary of: Harcourt Brace & Company), Curtis Center, 3rd Fl., Independence Sq. W., Philadelphia, PA 19106-3399. TEL 215-238-7800. FAX 215-238-6445. (Subscr. to: Periodicals Fulfillment, W.B. Saunders Co., 6277 Sea Harbor Dr., 4th Fl., Orlando, FL 32891-4800. TEL 800-654-2452. FAX 800-874-6418) Eds. Marvin Seisenger, John Fordtran; Pub. Joan W. Blumberg. **Indexed:** Excerp.Med. (1993-), Ind.Med. (1994-). **Document type:** academic/scholarly publication.
—BLDSC (8239.449600); UMI. **CCC.**
Description: Serves specialists caring for patients suffering disorders of the digestive tract and liver by focusing on a single topic in each issue on treatment options, complications, and alternative approaches.

616.3 US ISSN 0272-8087
CODEN: SLDIEE
SEMINARS IN LIVER DISEASES. 1981. q. $93 to individuals (foreign $118); institutions $125 (foreign $150). Thieme Medical Publishers, Inc., 381 Park Ave., S., Ste. 1501, New York, NY 10016. TEL 212-683-5088. FAX 212-779-9020. Ed. Dr. M. Rothschild. adv.; abstr. circ. 2,800. (also avail. in microform from UMI; reprint service avail. from UMI) **Indexed:** Abstr.Hyg., Curr.Adv.Genetics & Molec.Biol., Ind.Med. **Document type:** academic/scholarly publication.
—BLDSC (8239.454000); Faxon; Genuine Article; SWETS; UMI; UnCover. **CCC.**

616.3 JA ISSN 0387-2645
SHOKAKI GEKA/GASTROENTEROLOGICAL SURGERY. (Text in Japanese; table of contents in English) 1978. m. 1900 Yen per no. Herusu Publishing Co. Inc., 2-3, Nakano 2-chome, Nakano-ku, Tokyo 164, Japan. Eds. Keizo Shogenji, Aki Ishibashi.
—BLDSC (4088.966000).

616.3 JA ISSN 0915-3217
SHOKAKI NAISHIKYO/ENDOSCOPIA DIGESTIVA. (Text in English, Japanese) 1989. m. 32400 Yen. Tokyo Igakusha Ltd., 35-4 Hongo 3-chome, Bunkyo-ku, Tokyo 113, Japan. TEL 03-3814-8541. FAX 03-3811-6135.
—BLDSC (3743.550000).

616.3 JA ISSN 0389-9403
SHOKAKI NAISHIKYO NO SHINPO/PROGRESS OF DIGESTIVE ENDOSCOPY. (Text in Japanese; summaries in English) 1972. s-a. 10300 Yen. Kyowa Kikaku Tsushin, 2-20 Shinbashi, Minato-ku, Tokyo 105, Japan. TEL 03-3575-0181. charts; illus. circ. 2,000. (back issues avail.)
—BLDSC (6868.155000).

SLIDE ATLAS OF GASTROINTESTINAL ENDOSCOPY (YEAR). see MEDICAL SCIENCES — Abstracting, Bibliographies, Statistics

SMOOTH MUSCLE. see BIOLOGY — Physiology

MEDICAL SCIENCES — HEMATOLOGY

616.3   SP
SOCIEDAD VALENCIANA DE PATOLOGIA DIGESTIVA. q. 5000 ptas.($50) (effective 1995). Editorial Garsi, S.A., Juan Bravo 46, 28006 Madrid, Spain. TEL 34-1-4021212. FAX 34-1-4020954.

616.3   IT
GLI SPECIALIZZATI. GASTROENTEROLOGIA. 1990. q. L.25000. E S I Stampa Medica s.r.l., Casella Postale 42, Lgo. Volontari del Sangue 10, 20097 S. Donato, Milan, Italy. TEL 39-2-5274241. FAX 39-2-55600670. TELEX 324-894. Ed. Diego Onestinghel. adv.: B&W page L.5200000, color page L.6800000; trim 171 x 235; adv. contact: Ornella Galbiati. bk.rev. circ. 5,900.
  Formerly: Gastroenterologia Oggi (ISSN 1120-3641)

SURGICAL LAPAROSCOPY AND ENDOSCOPY. see *MEDICAL SCIENCES — Surgery*

616.3   GW   ISSN 0303-6294
TIPS FUER DIE GASTROENTEROLOGISCHE PRAXIS. 1974. s-a. (Gesellschaft fuer Gastroenterologie in Bayern e.V.) Demeter Verlag GmbH und Co. KG, Bussardstr. 5, 82166 Graefelfing, Germany. TEL 089-85463-0. FAX 089-8543347. circ. 2,500. **Document type:** academic/scholarly publication.

616.3   US
TOPICS IN GASTROENTEROLOGY. 1979. irreg., latest 1992. price varies. Plenum Publishing Corp., 233 Spring St., New York, NY 10013-1578. TEL 212-620-8000. FAX 212-463-0742. TELEX 23-421139. Ed. Howard M. Spiro. **Indexed:** Biol.Abstr. **Document type:** monographic series.
  Refereed Serial

VATRECHNI BOLESTI. see *MEDICAL SCIENCES — Endocrinology*

616.3   US
WORLD GASTROENTEROLOGY NEWS. 1993. 3/yr. Current Science, 400 Market St., Ste. 700, Philadelphia, PA 19106. TEL 215-574-2285; 800-552-5866. FAX 215-574-2270. (And: Current Science Ltd., 34-42 Cleveland St., London W1P 6LB, England. TEL 0171-323-0323. FAX 0171-636-6911) Ed. Meinhard Classen. adv.: B&W page $4250; color page $5245; trim 8 1/2 x 11; adv. contact: Steve Miller. illus. circ. 38,525. **Document type:** academic/scholarly publication, newsletter.
  Description: Covers topics of interest to practicing gastroenterologists worldwide.

616.3   US   ISSN 0739-5930
RC799
YEAR BOOK OF DIGESTIVE DISEASES. a. $72.95 (residents $35) (effective 1996). Mosby - Year Book, Inc., Continuity Division, 200 N. LaSalle, Chicago, IL 60601. TEL 312-726-9746. FAX 312-726-6933. TELEX 206155. Eds. Drs. Norton J. Greenberger, Frank G. Moody. illus.
  ●Also available online. Vendor(s): Ovid Technologies.
  —BLDSC (9411.629700).

616   GW   ISSN 0044-2771
CODEN: ZGASAX
ZEITSCHRIFT FUER GASTROENTEROLOGIE. 1963. m. DM.219. (Deutsche Gesellschaft fuer Verdauungs- und Stoffwechselkrankheiten) Demeter Verlag GmbH und Co. KG, Bussardstr. 5, 82166 Graefelfing, Germany. TEL 089-85463-0. FAX 089-8543347. (Co-sponsors: Deutsche Gesellschaft fuer Gastroenterologische Endoskopie; Oesterreichische Gesellschaft fuer Gastroenterologie) Ed. Dr. F.W. Caspary. adv.; bk.rev.; abstr.; charts; illus.; stat.; tr.lit. circ. 2,000. **Indexed:** Biol.Abstr., Chem.Abstr., Curr.Cont., Excerp.Med., Helminthol.Abstr., Ind.Med., Nutr.Abstr. **Document type:** academic/scholarly publication.
  —BLDSC (9462.350000); CASDDS; EMDOCS; Genuine Article; SWETS. **CCC.**

616.3   CC   ISSN 1000-1174
ZHONGGUO GANGCHANGBING ZAZHI/CHINESE JOURNAL OF COLO-PROCTOLOGY. (Text in Chinese; abstracts in Chinese, English) 1981. bi-m. $120. Zhongguo Gangchangbing Zazhi Bianjibu, No. 42, Wenhua Xilu, Jinan, Shandong 250011, People's Republic of China. TEL 0531-2963276. Ed. Huang Naijian. adv. contact: Li Wenfu. circ. 15,000 (paid). **Document type:** academic/scholarly publication.
  Description: Covers the latest achievements in scientific research on the prevention, diagnosis and treatment of anorectal diseases in China.
  Refereed Serial

616.3   CC   ISSN 1013-7696
CODEN: CMHCE
ZHONGHUA MINGUO XIAOHUA XIYI XUEHUI ZAZHI/GASTROENTEROLOGICAL SOCIETY OF TAIWAN. JOURNAL. 1982. q. Zhonghua Minguo Xiaohua Xiyi Xuehui - Gastroenterological Society of the Republic of China, Taita Jing-fu Alumni Bldg., 2nd Fl., 7 Chung-San South Rd., Taipei, Taiwan. TEL 02-3119062. FAX 02-3114182. Ed. Shiann Pan; Pub. Teh-Hong Wang. **Indexed:** Excerp.Med. **Document type:** trade publication.
  —BLDSC (3180.330000).

616.3   CC   ISSN 0254-1432
ZHONGHUA XIAOHUA ZAZHI/CHINESE JOURNAL OF DIGESTION. (Text in Chinese; abstracts in Chinese, English) bi-m. $48.22. Zhonghua Yixuehui, Shanghai Fenhui - Chinese Medical Association, Shanghai Branch, 1623 Beijing Xilu, Shanghai 200040, People's Republic of China. TEL 2531885. Ed. Jiang Shaoji. circ. 13,000. (reprint service avail.) **Indexed:** ExtraMED.
  ●Also available on CD-ROM.
  —BLDSC (3180.317000).

MEDICAL SCIENCES — Hematology

616.15   SZ   ISSN 0001-5792
CODEN: ACHAAH
ACTA HAEMATOLOGICA. (Text in English) 1948. 8/yr. (2 vols. per yr.). 496.80 SFr.($381.60) to individuals; institutions 818 SFr.($636) (effective 1996). S. Karger AG, Allschwilerstr. 10, P.O. Box, CH-4009 Basel, Switzerland. TEL 061-3061111. FAX 061-3061234. E-mail: Karger@Karger.ch. Eds. B. Ramot, I. Ben-Bassat. adv.; bk.rev.; abstr.; illus.; index. circ. 1,600. **Indexed:** ASCA, Biol.Abstr., Chem.Abstr., Curr.Adv.Cancer Res., Curr.Adv.Ecol.Sci., Curr.Cont., Excerp.Med., Ind.Med., Ind.Sci.Rev., Ind.Vet., Nutr.Abstr., Sci.Cit.Ind., Telegen, Vet.Bull. **Document type:** academic/scholarly publication.
  —BLDSC (0623.000000); CASDDS; Faxon; Genuine Article; SWETS; UnCover. **CCC.**
  Refereed Serial

616.15   PL   ISSN 0001-5814
CODEN: AHPLBO
ACTA HAEMATOLOGICA POLONICA. (Text and summaries in English and Polish) 1970. 4/yr. $60. Instytut Hematologii i Transfuzjologii, Ul. Chocimska 5, 00-957 Warsaw, Poland. (Dist. by: Il Klinika Chorob Wewnetrznych A.M., ul. Pabianicka 62, 93-513 Lodz, Poland) (Co-sponsor: Polskie Towarzystwo Hematologow i Transfuzjologow) Ed. Tadeusz Robak. adv.; bk.rev.; index. (processed; also avail. in cards) **Indexed:** Biol.Abstr., Chem.Abstr., Excerp.Med., Ind.Med., INIS Atomind.
  —CASDDS.
  Description: Features case reports on hematology, transfusion and immunology.

616.1   US   ISSN 0361-8609
QP91   CODEN: AJHEDD
AMERICAN JOURNAL OF HEMATOLOGY. 1976. m. $1200 (foreign $1386) (effective 1996). John Wiley & Sons, Inc., Journals, 605 Third Ave., New York, NY 10158. TEL 212-850-6645. FAX 212-850-6021. TELEX 12-7063. E-mail: SUBINFO@JWILEY.COM. (Subscr. outside the Americas to: John Wiley & Sons Ltd., Baffins Ln., Chichester, W. Sussex PO19 1UD, England. TEL 44-1243-779777. FAX 44-1243-776128) Ed. Ananda S. Prasad. adv.; bibl.; illus. (also avail. in microform from UMI; back issues avail.; reprint service avail. from ISI) **Indexed:** Abstr.Hyg., Abstr.Inter.Med., Biol.Abstr., Chem.Abstr., Curr.Adv.Ecol.Sci., Curr.Adv.Genetics & Molec.Biol., Curr.Cont., Dent.Ind., Excerp.Med., Helminthol.Abstr., Ind.Med., Ind.Sci.Rev., INIS Atomind, Nutr.Abstr., Protozool.Abstr., Sci.Cit.Ind., Trop.Dis.Bull. **Document type:** academic/scholarly publication.
  —BLDSC (0824.800000); ADONIS; CASDDS; Faxon; Genuine Article; SWETS; UnCover. **CCC.**
  Description: Provides broad coverage of both human and animal hematological topics and publishes original contributions from investigators and clinicians in hematology, as well as related areas such as immunology, blood banking, genetics, chemotherapy, and cell biology.
  Refereed Serial

AMERICAN JOURNAL OF KIDNEY DISEASES. see *MEDICAL SCIENCES — Urology And Nephrology*

616.15   GW   ISSN 0721-9318
ANGIO;* Gefaesschirurgie - Angiologie - Angioradiologie. (Text in German; summaries in English) 1979. bi-m. DM.110. Klinikum r.d. Isar, Ismaningerstr. 22, 81675 Munich, Germany. Ed. Dr. P.C. Maurer. circ. 1,500. **Document type:** academic/scholarly publication.

616.15   GW   ISSN 0939-5555
CODEN: ANHEE8
ANNALS OF HEMATOLOGY. (Supplement avail.: Haematolgie und Bluttransfusion (ISSN 0440-0607)) (Text in English) 1950. 12/yr.(in 2 vols., 6 nos./vol.). DM.1460($1061) (effective 1996). Springer-Verlag, Heidelberger Platz 3, 14197 Berlin, Germany. TEL 030-8207-0. FAX 030-8214091. E-mail: orders@springer.de. (Subscr. in N. America to: Springer-Verlag New York, Inc., 44 Hartz Way, Secaucus, NJ 07096-2491. TEL 201-348-4033) (Co-sponsors: Deutsche Gesellschaft fuer Haematologie und Onkologie; Deutsche Gesellschaft fuer Transfusionsmedizin und Immunhaematologie) Ed. R. Willemze. adv.; bk.rev.; abstr.; bibl.; charts; illus.; index. (also avail. in microform from UMI; reprint service avail. from ISI) **Indexed:** Biol.Abstr., Chem.Abstr., Curr.Adv.Cancer Res., Curr.Adv.Ecol.Sci., Curr.Cont., Excerp.Med., Helminthol.Abstr., Ind.Med., Ind.Sci.Rev., Ind.Vet., INIS Atomind., Kidney, Nutr.Abstr., Protozool.Abstr., Sci.Cit.Ind., Vet.Bull. **Document type:** academic/scholarly publication.
  —BLDSC (1040.855000); CASDDS; Genuine Article; SWETS; UMI; UnCover. **CCC.**
  Formerly (until 1991): Blut (ISSN 0006-5242)
  Description: Covers the entire spectrum of clinical and experimental hematology, hemostasiology, immunohematology and blood transfusion, including the diagnosis and treatment of hematopoietic and lymphatic neoplasis and of bone marrow transplantation.

616.15   JA
ANNUAL REVIEW KETSUEKI/ANNUAL REVIEW. BLOOD. (Text in Japanese) 1988. a. 6386 Yen. Chugai Igakusha, 62, Yaraicho, Shinjuku-ku, Tokyo 162, Japan.

616.15   US
APLASTIC ANEMIA FOUNDATION OF AMERICA. NEWSLETTER. 1987. q. free. Aplastic Anemia Foundation of America, Box 22689, Baltimore, MD 21203. TEL 800-747-2820. Ed. Marilyn Baker. circ. 6,000. (back issues avail.) **Document type:** newsletter.

MEDICAL SCIENCES — HEMATOLOGY

616.15   CN
ARTERIAL BLOOD GAS ANALYSIS. s-a. $149 to individuals; institutions $200. (American Association of Critical-Care Nurses) Decker Periodicals, P.O. Box 620, L.C.D. 1, Hamilton, ON L8N 3K7, Canada. TEL 905-522-7017. FAX 905-522-7839. (U.S. addr.: Box 785, Lewiston, NY 14092-0785) Ed. Mary E. Mancini. (diskette format)
Description: Step-by-step approach to interpretation and management techniques for new nurses and respiratory therapists.

616.5   UK   ISSN 0950-3536
BAILLIERE'S CLINICAL HAEMATOLOGY. 1987. q. £76 to individuals; institutions £87. Bailliere Tindall - W.B. Saunders Co. Ltd. (Subsidiary of: Harcourt Brace & Company Ltd.), 24-28 Oval Rd., London NW1 7DX, England. TEL 0171-267-4466. FAX 0171-482-2293. TELEX 25775 ACPRES G. (Subscr. to: Journals Subscriptions Fulfillment, Foots Cray High St., Sidcup, Kent DA14 5HP, England. TEL 0181-300-3322. FAX 0181-309-0807; Subscr. in N. America to; W.B. Saunders Co., Journal Subscription Fulfillment, 6277 Sea Harbor Dr., 4th Fl., Orlando, FL 32887-4800. TEL 800-574-2293) **Document type:** academic/scholarly publication.
—BLDSC (1856.723000); Faxon; Genuine Article; SWETS; UnCover. **CCC.**
Refereed Serial

616.15   YU   ISSN 0523-6150
BILTEN ZA HEMATOLOGIJU I TRANSFUZIJU. 1973. a. 200 din. Zavod za Transfuziju Krvi, Belgrade, Svetosavska 39, Belgrade, Yugoslavia. (Co-sponsor: Udruzenje Hematologa i Transfuziologa Jugoslavije) Ed. Budimir Dinic. adv. circ. 500. **Indexed:** Ind.Med.

616.15   **610.28**   SP   ISSN 0210-895X
CODEN: BCHED9
BIOLOGIA & CLINICA HEMATOLOGICA. Abbreviated title: B C H. (Text in English, Spanish) 1979. q. 4900 ptas. (effective 1996). Springer-Verlag Iberica S.A., C. Provenza 388, 1a, 08025 Barcelona, Spain. TEL 34-3-4570227. FAX 34-3-4571502. E-mail: barcelona@spint.compuserve.com. Ed. Angel Remacha. adv.: B&W page 35000 ptas., color page 65000 ptas.; adv. contact: J. Arellano. bk.rev. circ. 1,200. (also avail. in microform from UMI; reprint service avail.) **Document type:** academic/scholarly publication.
—CASDDS.
Description: Publishes research and clinical papers on all aspects of hematology and biomedical research, including hemostasis, blood transfusions, and oncology.
Refereed Serial

616.5   **574.192**   US   ISSN 0006-4971
RB145   CODEN: BLOOAW
BLOOD. 1945. 24/yr. $477 (foreign $572) (effective 1996). (American Society of Hematology) W.B. Saunders Co. (Subsidiary of: Harcourt Brace & Company), Curtis Center, 3rd Fl., Independence Sq. W., Philadelphia, PA 19106-3399. TEL 215-238-7800. FAX 215-238-6445. (Subscr. to: Periodicals Fulfillment, W.B. Saunders Co., 6277 Sea Harbor Dr., 4th Fl., Orlando FL 32891-4800. TEL 800-654-2452. FAX 800-874-6418) Ed. Dr. James D. Griffin; Pub. Joan W. Blumberg. adv.: B&W page £1480, color page $2630; 7 x 10. bk.rev.; abstr.; bibl.; charts; illus.; index. circ. 13,922. **Indexed:** Abstr.Hyg., Abstr.Inter.Med., AIM, Anim.Breed.Abstr., Biol.Abstr., Biotech.Abstr., Chem.Abstr., Curr.Adv.Cancer Res., Curr.Adv.Ecol.Sci., Curr.Cont., Dairy Sci.Abstr., Dent.Ind., Excerp.Med., Helminthol.Abstr., Ind.Med., Ind.Sci.Rev., Ind.Vet., INIS Atomind., Nutr.Abstr., Protozool.Abstr., Rev.Med.& Vet.Mycol., Risk Abstr., Sci.Cit.Ind., Small Anim.Abstr., Telegen, Trop.Dis.Bull. **Document type:** academic/scholarly publication.
●Also available online. Vendor(s): Ovid Technologies, Lexis-Nexis.
—BLDSC (2112.000000); CASDDS; Faxon; Genuine Article; SWETS; UMI; UnCover. **CCC.**
Formerly: Blood: The Journal of Hematology.
Description: Publishes original articles relating to all phases of hematology
Refereed Serial

616.1   US   ISSN 0340-4684
CODEN: BLCEDD
BLOOD CELLS. 1975. 3/yr. $196 (effective 1995). Springer-Verlag, Journals, 175 Fifth Ave., New York, NY 10010. TEL 212-460-1500.
FAX 212-473-6272. (N. American subscr. to: Journal Fulfillment Services, Box 2485, Secaucus, NJ 07096-2491. TEL 800-777-4643. FAX 201-348-4505; Elsewhere: Heidelberger Platz 3, 1000 Berlin 33, Germany. TEL 030-8207-1. FAX 030-8214091) Ed. B.S. Bull. adv. (also avail. in microform from UMI; reprint service avail.) **Indexed:** Anim.Breed.Abstr., Chem.Abstr., Curr.Adv.Cell & Devel.Biol., Curr.Adv.Ecol.Sci., Curr.Adv.Genetics & Molec.Biol., Curr.Cont., Excerp.Med., Ind.Med., Ind.Sci.Rev., INIS Atomind., Sci.Cit.Ind. **Document type:** academic/scholarly publication.
—BLDSC (2112.200000); ADONIS; CASDDS; Faxon; Genuine Article; SWETS; UMI; UnCover. **CCC.**
Description: Aimed at researchers involved in physiology, ultrastructure, immunology, and biophysics of blood cells.
Refereed Serial

616.15   UK   ISSN 0957-5235
CODEN: BLFIE7
BLOOD COAGULATION AND FIBRINOLYSIS; international journal in haemostasis and thrombosis. 1990. 8/yr. £365($625) to institutions (effective 1995). Rapid Communications of Oxford Ltd., The Old Malthouse, Paradise St., Oxford OX1 1LD, England. TEL 01865-790447. FAX 01865-244012. E-mail: rapidcom@vax.oxford.ac.uk. Ed. John Francis. adv. contact: Julie Gribben. bk.rev. **Indexed:** Excerp.Med. (1993-), Ind.Med., Sci.Cit.Ind. **Document type:** academic/scholarly publication.
●Also available on CD-ROM.
—BLDSC (2112.650000); ADONIS; CASDDS; Genuine Article; SWETS; UnCover. **CCC.**

BLOOD COAGULATION FACTORS; current awareness service for researchers in life sciences. see *MEDICAL SCIENCES — Abstracting, Bibliographies, Statistics*

616.15   SZ   ISSN 0253-5068
CODEN: BLPUDO
BLOOD PURIFICATION. (Text and summaries in English) 1983. bi-m. 275.40 SFr.($211.80) to individuals; institutions 459 SFR.($353) (effective 1996). S. Karger AG, Allschwilerstr. 10, P.O. Box, CH-4009 Basel, Switzerland. TEL 061-3061111.
FAX 061-3061234. E-mail: Karger@Karger.ch. Ed. L.W. Henderson. adv.; illus.; index. circ. 950. (also avail. in microform from UMI; back issues avail.) **Indexed:** Curr.Cont., Excerp.Med. **Document type:** academic/scholarly publication.
—BLDSC (2113.037000); CASDDS; Faxon; Genuine Article; UnCover. **CCC.**
Refereed Serial

616.15   UK   ISSN 0268-960X
CODEN: BLOREB
BLOOD REVIEWS. 1987. q. £109($180) (effective 1995). Churchill Livingstone Journals (Subsidiary of: Pearson Professional), Robert Stevenson House, 1-3 Baxter's Pl., Leith Walk, Edinburgh EH1 3AF, Scotland. TEL 0131-556-2424.
FAX 0131-459-1177. (Subscr. to: Pearson Professional Ltd., P.O. Box 77, Fourth Ave., Harlow, Essex CM19 5AA, England. TEL 01279-623760; U.S. subscr. to: Churchill Livingstone, 650 Ave. of the Americas, New York, NY 10011. TEL 212-206-5000) Eds. Ian Franklin, Jacob Rowe. adv. contact: David Dunnachie. circ. 990. **Document type:** academic/scholarly publication.
—BLDSC (2113.038000); Faxon; Genuine Article; SWETS; UnCover. **CCC.**
Description: Covers all aspects of hematology - current ideas in clinical and laboratory practice.

616.15   II   ISSN 0006-5005
BLOOD THERAPY JOURNAL INTERNATIONAL; committed to the cause of eradication of blood diseases & cancer. (Text in English and Hindi; summaries in English) 1965. bi-m. Rs.120($50) Institute of Haematology, 11, 6-B Pusa Road, New Delhi 110 005, India. TEL 91-11-2246228.
FAX 91-11-2247189. Ed. Dr. V.B. Lal. adv.; bk.rev.; abstr.; bibl.; charts; illus. circ. 3,000.
Supersedes (in 1980): Blood Therapy Journal.
Refereed Serial

BLOOD TRANSFUSION. see *MEDICAL SCIENCES — Abstracting, Bibliographies, Statistics*

616.6   US   ISSN 1065-6073
BLOOD WEEKLY. 1993. w. $995. Charles W. Henderson, Ed. & Pub., Box 5528, Atlanta, GA 31107-0528. TEL 404-377-8895.
FAX 404-378-5411. TELEX 78-2661. (Subscr. to: Box 830409, Birmingham, AL 35283-0409. TEL 800-633-4931. FAX 205-995-1588) (also avail. in microform from UMI) **Document type:** newsletter.
●Also available online. Vendor(s): CompuServe, Inc., Data-Star, Dow Jones News Retrieval, Knight-Ridder, Inc., NewsNet, Ovid Technologies.
—UMI. **CCC.**
Description: Concentrates on blood-related news and research worldwide, with original reporting, reviews of periodicals and journal articles and calendars of forthcoming professional meetings. Covers blood products and substitutes, blood-related diseases, including AIDS, tissue transplants and blood-borne pathogens.

616.15   UK   ISSN 0007-1048
CODEN: BJHEAL
BRITISH JOURNAL OF HAEMATOLOGY. 1955. m. £345 in Europe; elsewhere £380($612) (effective 1996). Blackwell Science Ltd., Osney Mead, Oxford OX2 0EL, England. TEL 44-1865-206206.
FAX 44-1865-721205. TELEX 83355-MEDBOK-G. Ed. I. Peake. adv.; bk.rev.; bibl.; charts; illus.; index. circ. 3,800. (also avail. in microform from UMI; back issues avail.; reprint service avail. from ISI) **Indexed:** Abstr.Hyg., ASCA, Biol.Abstr., Chem.Abstr., Curr.Adv.Biochem., Curr.Adv.Cancer Res., Curr.Adv.Cell & Devel.Biol., Curr.Adv.Ecol.Sci., Curr.Adv.Genetics & Molec.Biol., Curr.Cont., Dairy Sci.Abstr., Dent.Ind., Excerp.Med., Helminthol.Abstr., Ind.Med., Ind.Sci.Rev., Ind.Vet., INIS Atomind., Nutr.Abstr., Protozool.Abstr., Sci.Cit.Ind., Telegen, Trop.Dis.Bull., Vet.Bull. **Document type:** academic/scholarly publication.
—BLDSC (2309.000000); ADONIS; CASDDS; Faxon; Genuine Article; SWETS; UMI; UnCover. **CCC.**
Refereed Serial

616.15   UK   ISSN 0963-1860
BRITISH JOURNAL OF HAEMATOLOGY. SUPPLEMENT. irreg. Blackwell Science Ltd., Osney Mead, Oxford OX2 0EL, England. TEL 01865-240201.
FAX 01865-721205. TELEX 83355 MEDBOK G. **Indexed:** Excerp.Med. **Document type:** academic/scholarly publication.
—ADONIS.

613.7 616.15   US
C C B C NEWSLETTER. 1978. w. $192 (foreign $240). Council of Community Blood Centers, 725 15th St., N.W., Ste. 700, Washington, DC 20005-2109. TEL 202-393-5725. FAX 202-393-1282. Ed. Jane M. Starkey. bk.rev.; index. circ. 400. (back issues avail.) **Document type:** newsletter.
Description: Current events and trends in community blood services and transfusion medicine.

616.15   CN   ISSN 0840-5360
CANADIAN RED CROSS SOCIETY. BLOOD SERVICES. ANNUAL REPORT. French edition: Societe Canadienne de la Croix-Rouge. Services Transfusionnels. Rapport Annuel (ISSN 0840-6103) (Text in English and French) 1946. a. free. Canadian Red Cross Society, National Headquarters, 5700 Cancross Court, Mississauga, ON L5R 3E9, Canada. TEL 416-890-1000. circ. 6,000.
Formerly (until 1986): Canadian Red Cross Blood Transfusion Service. Annual Report (ISSN 0708-7047)

CEREBROVASCULAR DISEASES. see *MEDICAL SCIENCES — Psychiatry And Neurology*

616.15   US   ISSN 1076-0296
▼**CLINICAL AND APPLIED THROMBOSIS - HEMOSTASIS.** 1995. q. $95 (foreign $105) (effective 1995). (International Academy of Clinical and Applied Thrombosis - Hemostasis) Lippincott - Raven Press, 227 E. Washington Sq., Philadelphia, PA 19106. TEL 215-238-4200. Ed. Dr. Rodger L. Bick. (also avail. in microform from UMI; back issues avail.) **Document type:** academic/scholarly publication.
—BLDSC (3286.247800).
Description: Publishes the latest results of new clinical trials and studies, discussions of new pharmacologic methodologies, and new management strategies.

MEDICAL SCIENCES — HEMATOLOGY

616.15   UK   ISSN 0141-9854
CODEN: CLHAD3
CLINICAL AND LABORATORY HAEMATOLOGY. 1979. q. £186.50 in Europe; elsewhere £205 ($330) (effective 1996). Blackwell Science Ltd., Osney Mead, Oxford OX2 0EL, England. TEL 01865-206206. FAX 01865-206219. TELEX 83355 MEDBOK G. Ed. J.M. England. adv.; bk.rev.; abstr.; bibl.; charts; illus.; index. circ. 750. (also avail. in microform from UMI; back issues avail.; reprint service avail. from ISI) **Indexed:** ASCA, Curr.Adv.Ecol.Sci., Curr.Cont., Excerp.Med., Ind.Med., Ind.Sci.Rev., Sci.Cit.Ind. **Document type:** academic/scholarly publication.
—BLDSC (3286.253200); ADONIS; CASDDS; Faxon; Genuine Article; SWETS; UMI; UnCover. **CCC.**
Refereed Serial

616.15   UK   ISSN 0271-5198
QP105   CODEN: CLHEDF
CLINICAL HEMORHEOLOGY. (Companion journal to: Biorheology) 1981. bi-m. £390($621) (effective 1996). (International Society of Biorheology) Elsevier Science Ltd., Pergamon, P.O. Box 800, Kidlington, Oxford OX5 1DX, England. TEL 44-1865-843000. FAX 44-1865-843010. E-mail: nlinfo-f@elsevier.nl; usinfo-f@elsevier.com; forinfo-kyf04035@niftyserve.or.jp; Site addr.: http://www.elsevier.nl/. (Subscr. in U.S. and Canada to: Elsevier Science, 660 White Plains Rd., Tarrytown, NY 10591-5153. TEL 914-524-9200. FAX 914-333-2444) Eds. S. Witte, J.F. Stoltz. adv. (also avail. in microfilm from UMI) **Indexed:** Chem.Abstr., Curr.Adv.Ecol.Sci., Curr.Cont., Excerp.Med., Helminthol.Abstr. **Document type:** academic/scholarly publication.
—BLDSC (3286.290000); CASDDS; Faxon; Genuine Article; SWETS; UMI; UnCover. **CCC.**
Description: Topics covered include pathogenesis, symptomatology, and diagnostic, prophylactic and therapeutic methods.
Refereed Serial

616.15   IT   ISSN 0393-487X
CLOT AND HEMATOLOGIC MALIGNANCIES; journal of blood coagulation, hemostasis, thrombosis, hemorheology, and malignant hemopathies. (Text in Italian) 1981. bi-m. L.27($27) Via le Unita d'Italia 743, 74029 Talsano, Italy. Ed. Teodoro Ripa. adv.; bk.rev.; index. circ. 2,500.
Formerly: Clot.

616.15   615.9   UK   ISSN 0938-7714
CODEN: CHAIEX
COMPARATIVE HAEMATOLOGY INTERNATIONAL. 1991. 4/yr. £148($237) (effective 1996). Springer-Verlag, Springer House, 8 Alexandra Rd., London SW19 7JZ, England. TEL 081-944-2942. FAX 081-947-4651. (U.S. subscr. to: Springer-Verlag New York, Inc., Box 2485, Secaucus, NJ 07096-2491. TEL 201-348-4033) Ed.Bd. (back issues avail.) **Indexed:** Excerp.Med. (1993-). **Document type:** academic/scholarly publication.
—BLDSC (3363.782200); CASDDS; Genuine Article; UMI. **CCC.**
Description: Publishes papers encompassing the entire spectrum of comparative haematology, including immunological, toxicological and cellular aspects, data from human, veterinary and zoological studies, as well as experimental and diagnostic studies.
Refereed Serial

616.15   US   ISSN 0197-3649
RB145   CODEN: CHONDF
CONTEMPORARY HEMATOLOGY - ONCOLOGY. 1977. irreg., vol.3, 1984. Plenum Publishing Corp., 233 Spring St., New York, NY 10013-1578. TEL 212-620-8000. FAX 212-463-0742611. Ed.Bd. **Indexed:** Biol.Abstr. **Document type:** monographic series.
—CASDDS.
Formerly: Year in Hematology (ISSN 0160-7014)
Refereed Serial

616.15   UK   ISSN 0956-2257
CRITICAL ISCHAEMIA. 1990. q. £60 (overseas £65). Cambridge Medical Publications Ltd., Wicker House, High St., Worthing, W. Sussex BN11 1DJ, England. TEL 01903-205884. FAX 01903-234862. TELEX 878372 PPSLTD G. Ed.Bd. **Indexed:** Excerp.Med. (1993-). **Document type:** academic/scholarly publication.
—BLDSC (3487.454100).
Description: Contains review articles and commentary on all aspects of critical limb ischemia and peripheral arterial occlusive disease, including pathophysiology, biochemistry, surgery, and clinical treatment.

CRITICAL REVIEWS IN ONCOLOGY - HEMATOLOGY. see *MEDICAL SCIENCES — Oncology*

616.15   US   ISSN 1065-6251
RC633.A1
▼**CURRENT OPINION IN HEMATOLOGY.** 1994. bi-m. $159.95 to individuals; institutions $323.95; residents $55. Current Science, 400 Market St., Ste. 700, Philadelphia, PA 19106. TEL 215-574-2210; 800-552-5866. FAX 215-574-3533. (And: Current Science Ltd., 34-42 Cleveland St., London W1P 6LB, England. TEL 0171-323-0323. FAX 0171-636-3911) **Document type:** academic/scholarly publication.
●Also available online. Vendor(s): OCLC.
Also available on CD-ROM.
—BLDSC (3500.775200); ADONIS. **CCC.**

616.1   SZ   ISSN 0258-0330
CODEN: CSHTE8
CURRENT STUDIES IN HEMATOLOGY AND BLOOD TRANSFUSION. (Text in English) 1955. irreg. (approx. 1/yr.). price varies. (European Society of Hematology) S. Karger AG, Allschwilerstr. 10, P.O. Box, CH-4009 Basel, Switzerland. TEL 061-3061111. FAX 061-3061234. E-mail: Karger@Karger.ch. Eds. J. Leikola, P. Lundsgaard-Hansen. (reprint service avail. from ISI) **Indexed:** Biol.Abstr., Chem.Abstr., Curr.Cont., Excerp.Med., Ind.Med. **Document type:** academic/scholarly publication.
—BLDSC (3504.041000); CASDDS; Faxon; SWETS. **CCC.**
Formerly: Bibliotheca Haematologica.
Description: Presents current data in areas of hematology and transfusion medicine where problems are far from solved.
Refereed Serial

616.15 576   JA
CURRENTS IN HEMATOIMMUNOLOGY. (Text in Japanese) 1985. q. Ekuseputa Medika K.K. - Excerpta Medica Ltd., Tokyo, 15-23, Nishiazabu 4-chome, Minato-ku, Tokyo 106, Japan.

616.15   GW   ISSN 0931-5551
DEUTSCHE GESELLSCHAFT FUER ANGIOLOGIE. MITTEILUNGEN. q. DM.48. Demeter Verlag GmbH und Co. KG, Bussardstr. 5, 82166 Graefelfing, Germany. TEL 089-85463-0. FAX 089-8543347. circ. 1,000. **Document type:** newsletter.

616.15   NE   ISSN 0167-9201
CODEN: DHIMDR
DEVELOPMENTS IN HEMATOLOGY AND IMMUNOLOGY. (Text in English) 1980. irreg., vol.28, 1993. price varies. Kluwer Academic Publishers, Postbus 17, 3300 AA Dordrecht, Netherlands. TEL 31-78-392392. FAX 31-78-392254. TELEX 29245 KAPG NL. (Dist. by: Kluwer Academic Publishers Group, P.O. Box 322, 3300 AH Dordrecht, Netherlands. TEL 31-78-392392. FAX 31-78-546474; N. America dist. addr.: Box 358, Accord Sta., Hingham, MA 02018-0358. TEL 617-871-6600. FAX 617-871-6528) **Document type:** monographic series, proceedings.
—BLDSC (3579.075400); CASDDS.
Formerly (until 1982): Developments in Hematology (ISSN 0167-448X)
Refereed Serial

ERYTHROCYTES. see *MEDICAL SCIENCES — Abstracting, Bibliographies, Statistics*

616.15   UK   ISSN 0956-6309
CODEN: ERYTE
ERYTHROPOIESIS; new dimensions in the treatment of anaemia. 1989. q. (Janssen-Cilag) Adis International Ltd., Chowley Oak Ln., Tattenhall, Chester, Ches. CH3 9GA, England. TEL 01829-771155. FAX 01829-770330. Ed. Stephen Winter; Pub. Nikki McKevitt. abstr.; circ. 9,000 (controlled). **Indexed:** Excerp.Med. (1995-). **Document type:** academic/scholarly publication.
—BLDSC (3810.885000).
Description: Discusses recent research into the production of red blood cells and developments in the treatment of anemia.
Refereed Serial

616.15   DK   ISSN 0902-4441
CODEN: EJHAEC
EUROPEAN JOURNAL OF HAEMATOLOGY. (Text in English) 1964. 10/yr. DKK 2500 (incl. supplements) (effective 1996). Munksgaard International Publishers Ltd., P.O. Box 2148, DK-1016 Copenhagen K, Denmark. TEL 33-127030. FAX 33-129387. Ed. Inge Olsson. adv.; bk.rev.; bibl.; charts; illus. circ. 1,200. (reprint service avail. from ISI) **Indexed:** ASCA, Biol.Abstr., Chem.Abstr., Curr.Adv.Ecol.Sci., Curr.Cont., Dairy Sci.Abstr., Dent.Ind., Excerp.Med., Helminthol.Abstr., Ind.Med., Nutr.Abstr.
—BLDSC (3829.729700); ADONIS; CASDDS; Faxon; Genuine Article; SWETS; UnCover. **CCC.**
Formerly: Scandinavian Journal of Haematology (ISSN 0036-553X)
Refereed Serial

616.15   DK   ISSN 0902-4506
CODEN: EJHSEW
EUROPEAN JOURNAL OF HAEMATOLOGY. SUPPLEMENTUM. (Text in English) 1964. irreg. free with subscription to European Journal of Haematology. Munksgaard International Publishers Ltd., P.O. Box 2148, DK-1016 Copenhagen K, Denmark. TEL 33-127030. FAX 33-129387. Ed. Inge Olsson. adv. (reprint service avail. from ISI) **Indexed:** Biol.Abstr., Chem.Abstr., Curr.Cont., Excerp.Med., Ind.Med., Nutr.Abstr.
—BLDSC (3829.729800); ADONIS; CASDDS. **CCC.**
Formerly: Scandinavian Journal of Haematology. Supplementum (ISSN 0080-6722)
Refereed Serial

616.15   US   ISSN 0301-472X
CODEN: EXHMA6
EXPERIMENTAL HEMATOLOGY. (Includes supplements of Meeting Proceedings, published irreg.) 1973. 13/yr. $313 (foreign $333). (International Society for Experimental Hematology) Kluge Carden Jennings Publishing Co. Ltd., 853 W. Main St., Charlottesville, VA 22903-3420. TEL 804-979-4913. FAX 804-979-4025. Ed. Peter Quesenberry. adv. contact: Tammi Bourgee. circ. 1,700 (paid). (reprint service avail. from ISI) **Indexed:** Biol.Abstr., Chem.Abstr., Curr.Adv.Cell & Devel.Biol., Curr.Adv.Ecol.Sci., Curr.Cont., Dent.Ind., Excerp.Med., Ind.Med., Ind.Sci.Rev., INIS Atomind., Sci.Cit.Ind. **Document type:** academic/scholarly publication.
—BLDSC (3839.360000); CASDDS; Faxon; Genuine Article; SWETS; UnCover. **CCC.**

FEDERAZIONE DELLE SOCIETA MEDICO-SCIENTIFICHE ITALIANE. CONGRESSI (YEAR). see *MEDICAL SCIENCES*

616.15   RU   ISSN 0234-5730
CODEN: GETRE8
GEMATOLOGIYA I TRANSFUSIOLOGIYA/HEMATOLOGY AND TRANSFUSIOLOGY. 1956. bi-m. $92 (effective 1996). (Nauchnoe Obshchestvo Gematologov i Transfuziologov) Izdatel'stvo Meditsina, Petroverigskii pereulok 6-8, 101000 Moscow, Russia. (Dist. by: Mezhdunarodnaya Kniga, B. Yakimanka 39, 117049 Moscow, Russia. TEL 7-095-2384600. FAX 7-095-2384634) (Co-sponsor: Ministerstvo Zdravookhraneniya) Ed. A.I. Vorobyev. **Indexed:** Biol.Abstr., Chem.Abstr., Excerp.Med., Ind.Med., INIS Atomind., Nutr.Abstr.
—BLDSC (0047.072000); CASDDS; Genuine Article. **CCC.**
Formerly (until 1983): Problemy Gematologii i Perelivaniya Krovi (ISSN 0552-2080)
Description: Publishes original theoretical and clinical investigations, reviews and clinical notes concerning different problems of hematology and blood transfusion.

MEDICAL SCIENCES — HEMATOLOGY

616.15 CC ISSN 1001-1013
GUOWAI YIXUE (SHUXUE YU XUEYEXUE FENCE)/FOREIGN MEDICAL SCIENCES (BLOOD TRANSFUSION AND BLOOD). (Text in Chinese) 1979. bi-m. Chinese Academy of Medical Sciences, Blood Transfusion Research Institute, San Xiang, Xiaojiacun, Renmin Beilu, Chengdu, Sichuan 610081, People's Republic of China. TEL 331031-43.

H L B NEWSLETTER; reporting on heart, lung and blood disease research program, policy development. see MEDICAL SCIENCES — Experimental Medicine, Laboratory Technique

616.15 HU ISSN 0017-6559
CODEN: HAEMBY
HAEMATOLOGIA; international quarterly of haematology. (Text in English) 1967. q. DM.360 (effective 1996). (Magyar Tudomanyos Akademia) Akademiai Kiado, Publishing House of the Hungarian Academy of Sciences, P.O. Box 245, H-1519 Budapest, Hungary. TEL 181-2134. FAX 166-6466. TELEX 22-6228 AKNYO H. (Co-publisher and distributor: V S P, P.O. Box 346, 3700 AH Zeist, Netherlands. TEL 31-30-6925790. FAX 31-30-6932081) Ed. Susan R. Hollan. adv.; bk.rev. (back issues avail.) **Indexed:** Biol.Abstr., Chem.Abstr., Curr.Adv.Ecol.Sci., Curr.Adv.Genetics & Molec.Biol., Curr.Cont., Excerp.Med., Ind.Med., Ind.Sci.Rev., Sci.Cit.Ind. **Document type:** academic/scholarly publication.
—BLDSC (4237.800000); CASDDS; Faxon; SWETS; UnCover.
Description: Publishes original papers, preliminary reports and reviews of basic and clinical research in hematology and related fields, including immunology, blood transfusion, transplantation and oncology.
Refereed Serial

616.1 IT ISSN 0390-6078
CODEN: HAEMAX
HAEMATOLOGICA. (Text and summaries in English) 1914. bi-m. L.445500($270) (effective 1996). (Societa Italiana di Ematologia) Pensiero Scientifico Editore s.r.l., Via Bradano 3-C, 00199 Rome, Italy. TEL 06-862071853. FAX 06-86207160. Ed. Edoardo Ascari. adv.; bk.rev.; abstr.; bibl.; charts; illus.; index. circ. 2,000. (back issues avail.) reprint service avail. from ISI) **Indexed:** Biol.Abstr., Chem.Abstr., Curr.Adv.Cell & Devel.Biol., Curr.Adv.Ecol.Sci., Curr.Adv.Genetics & Molec.Biol., Curr.Cont., Excerp.Med., Ind.Med., INIS Atomind., Rev.Med.& Vet.Mycol., Sci.Cit.Ind. **Document type:** academic/scholarly publication.
—BLDSC (4238.000000); CASDDS; Faxon; Genuine Article; SWETS; UMI.

616.15 US ISSN 0440-0607
CODEN: HABLAF
HAEMATOLOGIE UND BLUTTRANSFUSION. (Supplement to: Annals of Hematology (ISSN 0939-5555)) (Text in English or German) 1962. irreg. price varies. Springer-Verlag, 175 Fifth Ave., New York, NY 10010. TEL 212-460-1500. FAX 212-473-6272. (Also: Berlin, Heidelberg, Tokyo and Vienna) Eds. W. Stich, G. Ruhenstroth-Bauer. adv. (also avail. in microform from UMI; reprint service avail. from ISI) **Indexed:** Chem.Abstr. **Document type:** academic/scholarly publication.
—BLDSC (4241.210000); CASDDS; Faxon. **CCC**
Formerly: Haematology and Blood Transfusion (ISSN 0171-7111)

616.1572 UK ISSN 1351-8216
▼**HAEMOPHILIA.** (Supplement avail. (ISSN 1355-0691)) 1994. q. £110 in Europe; elsewhere £121($195) (effective 1996). (World Federation of Haemophilia) Blackwell Science Ltd., Osney Mead, Oxford OX2 0EL, England. TEL 44-1865-206206. FAX 44-1865-721205. TELEX 83355 MEDBOK G. (back issues avail.) **Document type:** academic/scholarly publication.
—BLDSC (4238.086500). **CCC**
Refereed Serial

615.1572 UK ISSN 1355-0691
▼**HAEMOPHILIA. SUPPLEMENT.** 1994. irreg. (World Federation of Haemophilia) Blackwell Science Ltd., Osney Mead, Oxford OX2 0EL, England. TEL 44-1865-206206. FAX 44-1865-721205. TELEX 83355 MEDBOK G. (back issues avail.) **Document type:** academic/scholarly publication.

616.15 AT
HAEMOPHILIA FOUNDATION, VICTORIA. NEWSLETTER. 1955. q. Aus.$10. Haemophilia Foundation, Victoria, 1216 Toorak Rd., Hartwell, Vic. 3125, Australia. TEL 61-3 889-0200. FAX 61-3-889-6120. Ed. B. Spence. bk.rev. circ. 400. (looseleaf format; back issues avail.) **Document type:** newsletter.
Formerly: Haemophilia Society of Victoria. Newsletter.
Description: Information for parents and people with haemophilia.

616.15 GW ISSN 0720-9355
CODEN: HAEMD2
HAEMOSTASEOLOGIE; Diagnostik, Therapie und Grundlagenforschung von Haemorrhagien und Thromboembolien. 1981. q. DM.178($130.60) F.K. Schattauer Verlagsgesellschaft mbH, Lenzhalde 3, 70192 Stuttgart, Germany. TEL 0711-22987-0. FAX 0711-22987-50. Ed.Bd. circ. 3,200. **Indexed:** Excerp.Med. **Document type:** academic/scholarly publication.
—CASDDS. **CCC**

616.15 SZ ISSN 0301-0147
CODEN: HMTSB7
HAEMOSTASIS; international journal on haemostasis and thrombosis research. (Text in English) 1973. bi-m. 275.40 SFr.($211.80) to individuals; institutions 459 SFr.($353) (effective 1996). S. Karger AG, Allschwilerstr. 10, P.O. Box, CH-4009 Basel, Switzerland. TEL 061-3061111. FAX 061-3061234. E-mail: Karger@Karger.ch. Ed. H.C. Hemker. adv.; bk.rev. circ. 1,150. (also avail. in microform) **Indexed:** Biol.Abstr., Chem.Abstr., Curr.Adv.Biochem., Curr.Adv.Cancer Res., Curr.Adv.Cell & Devel.Biol., Curr.Adv.Ecol.Sci., Curr.Cont., Excerp.Med., Helminthol.Abstr., Ind.Med., Ind.Sci.Rev., Kidney, Sci.Cit.Ind. **Document type:** academic/scholarly publication.
—BLDSC (4238.090000); CASDDS; Faxon; Genuine Article; SWETS; UnCover. **CCC**
Formerly: Coagulation (ISSN 0009-9902)
Refereed Serial

616.15 616.99 US ISSN 1067-2370
HEM-ONC ANNALS; the journal of continuing education in hematology & oncology. 1993. bi-m. $80 to individuals (Canada $98; elsewhere $116); institutions $90 (Canada $108; elsewhere $126). Slack, Inc., 6900 Grove Rd., Thorofare, NJ 08086. TEL 609-848-1000. FAX 609-853-5991. Ed. John S. MacDonald. adv.: B&W page $1850, color page $2050; trim 8 1/8 x 10 7/8. illus. circ. 22,800. (back issues avail.) **Document type:** academic/scholarly publication.
—BLDSC (4290.950000).

660 US ISSN 0886-0238
CODEN: HEPAEG
HEMATOLOGIC PATHOLOGY. 4/yr. $225 to individuals; institutions $450. Marcel Dekker Journals, 270 Madison Ave., New York, NY 10016. TEL 212-696-9000. FAX 212-685-4540. TELEX 421419 MARDEEK. (Subscr. to: Box 5017, Monticello, NY 12701) Ed. Sanford A. Stass. (microform) **Indexed:** Curr.Adv.Genetics & Molec.Biol., Excerp.Med. **Document type:** academic/scholarly publication.
—BLDSC (4291.300000); Faxon; Genuine Article; SWETS; UMI; UnCover. **CCC**
Refereed Serial

616.15 UK ISSN 0278-0232
CODEN: HAONDL
HEMATOLOGICAL ONCOLOGY. 1983. q. $495 (foreign $495) (effective 1996). John Wiley & Sons Ltd., Journals, Baffins Ln., Chichester, W. Sussex PO19 1UD, England. TEL 01243-779777. FAX 01243-776128. (Subscr. in the Americas to: John Wiley & Sons, Inc., 605 Third Ave., New York, NY 10158. TEL 212-850-6645. FAX 212-850-6021) Ed.Bd. adv.; bk.rev.; charts; illus.; index. circ. 309. (also avail. in microform from UMI; back issues avail.; reprint service avail. from SWZ,UMI) **Indexed:** Chem.Abstr., Curr.Adv.Ecol.Sci., Curr.Adv.Genetics & Molec.Biol., Curr.Cont., Excerp.Med., Ind.Med., Telegen. **Document type:** academic/scholarly publication.
—BLDSC (4291.550000); ADONIS; CASDDS; Faxon; Genuine Article; SWETS; UMI; UnCover. **CCC**
Description: Presents a variety of clinical and scientific specialties concerned with neoplastic disease of the hemopoietic system, and any neoplastic or related process that may directly or indirectly involve the hemopoietic system.

616.1 FR
▼**HEMATOLOGIE.** 1995. bi-m. 460 F. to individuals (rest of Europe 530 F.); elsewhere 590 F.); institutions 780 F. (rest of Europe 850 F.; elsewhere 910 F.). John Libbey Eurotext, 127 ave. de la Republique, 92120 Montrouge, France. TEL 33-1-46730660. FAX 33-1-40840999. Ed. Francois Sigaux. **Document type:** academic/scholarly publication.
Refereed Serial

616.15 US ISSN 0882-8083
CODEN: HRCOEG
HEMATOLOGY REVIEWS AND COMMUNICATIONS; an international journal. 1985. 8/yr. (in 2 vols., 4 nos./vol.). 151 ECU per vol. (effective 1996). Harwood Academic Publishers, c/o International Publishers Distributor, 820 Town Center Dr., Langhorne, PA 19047. TEL 215-750-2642. FAX 215-750-6343. (Subscr. to: International Publishers Distributor, PO Box 90, Reading, Berkshire, RG1 8JL, England. TEL 44-173-456-8316) Ed. Stuart Roath. (also avail. in microform) **Indexed:** Excerp.Med. **Document type:** academic/scholarly publication.
—BLDSC (4291.620000). **CCC**
Refereed Serial

616.15 US
HEMATOLOGY SERIES. irreg., vol.16, 1993. Marcel Dekker, Inc., 270 Madison Ave., New York, NY 10016. TEL 212-696-9000. FAX 212-658-4540. TELEX 421419. Ed. Kenneth M. Brinkhous. **Document type:** monographic series.
Refereed Serial

616.15 US ISSN 0363-0269
RC641.7.H35 CODEN: HEMOD8
HEMOGLOBIN; international journal for hemoglobin research. 1977. 6/yr. $665. Marcel Dekker Journals, 270 Madison Ave., New York, NY 10016. TEL 212-696-9000. FAX 212-685-4540. TELEX 421419. (Subscr. to: Box 5017, Monticello, NY 12701) Ed. Abdullah Kutdar. (also avail. in microform from RPI) **Indexed:** Chem.Abstr., Curr.Adv.Ecol.Sci., Curr.Cont., Excerp.Med., Ind.Sci.Rev., Sci.Cit.Ind. **Document type:** academic/scholarly publication.
—BLDSC (4295.040000); CASDDS; Faxon; Genuine Article; SWETS; UMI; UnCover. **CCC**
Refereed Serial

616.15 CN ISSN 0046-7251
HEMOPHILIA TODAY. (Editions in English, French) 1964. q. free. Canadian Hemophilia Society, 1450 City Councillors, Ste. 840, Montreal, PQ H3A 2E6, Canada. TEL 514-848-0503. FAX 514-848-9661. Ed. Barry Issac. circ. 6,000.

616.15 613.2 SZ ISSN 1019-8466
CODEN: IFTRE3
INFUSIONSTHERAPIE UND TRANSFUSIONSMEDIZIN. (Supplements avail.: Beitraege zur Infusionstherapie und Klinischen Ernaehrung - Forschung und Praxis) (Text in German; summaries in English and German) 1974. bi-m. 142 SFr.($109) to individuals; institutions 124 SFr.($109) (effective 1996). (Deutsche Arbeitsgemeinschaft fuer Kuenstliche Ernaehrung) S. Karger AG, Allschwilerstr. 10, P.O. Box, CH-4009 Basel, Switzerland. TEL 061-3061111. FAX 061-3061234. E-mail: Karger@Karger.ch. (Co-sponsors: Oesterreichische Arbeitsgemeinschaft fuer Klinische Ernaehrung; Deutsche Gesellschaft fuer Transfusionsmedizin und Immunhaematologie) Ed.Bd. adv.; illus.; index. circ. 11,000. (also avail. in microform from UMI) **Indexed:** Biol.Abstr., Chem.Abstr., Curr.Cont., Excerp.Med., Ind.Med., Ind.Sci.Rev., Nutr.Abstr., Sci.Cit.Ind. **Document type:** academic/scholarly publication.
—BLDSC (4499.563000); CASDDS; Genuine Article; SWETS. **CCC**
Former titles: Infusionstherapie (ISSN 1011-6966); Internationale Zeitschrift fuer Infusionstherapie, Klinische Ernaehrung und Transfusionmedizin; Infusionstherapie und Klinische Ernaehrung - Forschung und Praxis (ISSN 0378-0791); Infusionstherapie und Klinische Ernaehrung (ISSN 0301-3243); Infusionstherapie.
Refereed Serial

MEDICAL SCIENCES — HEMATOLOGY

616.15   BL   ISSN 0103-3263
INSTITUTO ESTADUAL DE HEMATOLOGIA ARTHUR DE SIQUEIRA CAVALCANTI. REVISTA. (Text in Portuguese; summaries in English) 1971. s.a. exchange basis. Instituto Estadual de Hematologia Arthur de Siqueira Cavalcanti, Biblioteca, Rua Frei Caneca, 08, Centro - CEP 20211, RJ, Brazil. TEL 021-242-6080. FAX 021-252-3739. Ed. Jose Moreira Pereira. bk.rev.; bibl.; charts. circ. 1,000. (reprint service avail. from IRC) **Indexed:** Excerp.Med.
    Formerly (until vol.4, no.2, 1976): Instituto Estadual de Hematologia Arthur de Siqueira Cavalcanti. Boletim (ISSN 0046-9963)

INTERNATIONAL ANGIOLOGY. see *MEDICAL SCIENCES — Cardiovascular Diseases*

612.1   US   ISSN 0074-3682
INTERNATIONAL CONGRESS OF HEMATOLOGY. PROCEEDINGS. (Proceedings Published in host country) 1958. biennial, 24th, 1992, London. International Society of Hematology, c/o Dr. Robert Kyle, Mayo Clinic, Rochester, MN 55905. circ. 2,000. **Document type:** proceedings.

616.15   IE   ISSN 0925-5710
                         CODEN: IJHEEY
INTERNATIONAL JOURNAL OF HEMATOLOGY. (Text in English) 1938. 8/yr. I£244($386) (effective 1996). (Japanese Society of Hematology, JA) Elsevier Science Ireland Ltd., P.O. Box 85, Limerick, Ireland. TEL 353-61-471944. FAX 353-61-472144. (Subscr. in U.S. and Canada to: Elsevier Science Inc., Box 882, Madison Sq. Sta., New York, NY 10159. TEL 212-989-5800. FAX 212-633-3990) Eds. H. Uchino, E. Yoshida. adv.; bk.rev. circ. 5,000. (also avail. in microform from UMI) **Indexed:** ASCA, Biol.Abstr., Curr.Adv.Biochem., Curr.Adv.Cancer Res., Curr.Adv.Cell & Devel.Biol., Curr.Adv.Ecol.Sci., Curr.Cont., Dent.Ind., Excerp.Med., Ind.Med., Nutr.Abstr. **Document type:** academic/scholarly publication.
    —BLDSC (4542.280400); CASDDS; Genuine Article; SWETS. **CCC.**
    Formerly (until 1991): Acta Haematologica Japonica (ISSN 0001-5806)
    Description: Publishes original papers and reviews of international origin in basic and clinical hematology.
    Refereed Serial

INTERNATIONAL JOURNAL OF PEDIATRIC HEMATOLOGY - ONCOLOGY. see *MEDICAL SCIENCES — Oncology*

616.5 612.1   FR   ISSN 0074-8528
INTERNATIONAL SOCIETY OF BLOOD TRANSFUSION. PROCEEDINGS OF THE CONGRESS. biennial, 22nd, 1992, Sao Paolo. Societe Internationale de Transfusion Sanguine - International Society of Blood Transfusion, c/o C N T S, B.P. 100, 91943 Les Ulis Cedex, France. TEL 69-07-20-40. FAX 69-07-41-85. TELEX 603218. circ. controlled. **Indexed:** Biol.Abstr. **Document type:** proceedings.

IRON METABOLISM. see *BIOLOGY — Biological Chemistry*

IRONIC BLOOD; information on iron overload. see *MEDICAL SCIENCES — Endocrinology*

616.15   CN   ISSN 0715-8602
JOURNAL: NEWS OF THE BLOOD PROGRAMME IN CANADA. (Text in English and French) 1983. q. free. Canadian Red Cross Society, National Headquarters, 5700 Cancross Court, Mississauga, Ont. L5R 3E9, Canada. TEL 416-890-1000. circ. 4,000.

616.15   US   ISSN 1061-6128
                         CODEN: JOEMEL
JOURNAL OF HEMATOTHERAPY. 1993. q. $114 (foreign $154). (International Society for Hematotherapy and Graft Engineering) Mary Ann Liebert, Inc. Publishers, 2 Madison Ave., Larchmont, NY 10538. TEL 914-834-3100. FAX 914-834-3688. E-mail: Liebert@pipeline.com. Eds. Adrian P. Gee, Nancy H. Collins. **Indexed:** Excerp.Med. (1993-), Ind.Med. (1994-). **Document type:** academic/scholarly publication.
    —BLDSC (4997.600000).
    Description: Focuses on a specific area of clinical research that ranges over several disciplines; that of ex vivo manipulation of hematopoietic cells for in vivo therapy.
    Refereed Serial

JOURNAL OF PEDIATRIC HEMATOLOGY - ONCOLOGY. see *MEDICAL SCIENCES — Oncology*

616   JA
KENKETSU JIGYO NO GENKYO/BLOOD DONATION IN NARA PREFECTURE. (Text in Japanese) a. Naraken Hoken Kankyobu - Nara Prefectural Government, Public Health and Environment Affairs Department, Noboriojicho, Nara-shi, Nara-ken 630, Japan.

616.15   JA   ISSN 0913-9532
KESSEI HANNO NO AYUMI/STUDY REPORT OF SERUM REACTION. (Text in Japanese) 1972. irreg. Nihon Toketsu Kanso Kenkyujo - Japan Lyophilization Laboratory, 2-6, Kohinata 4-chome, Bunkyo-ku, Tokyo 112, Japan. TEL 03-5800-5310. FAX 03-5800-5306. TELEX 2322357 BCGLAB J. Ed. Kuniyoshi Kikuchi. **Document type:** academic/scholarly publication.

616.15   JA
KETSUEKI JIGYO/BLOOD PROGRAMME. (Text in Japanese) q. 1000 Yen per no. Nihon Ketsueki Jigyo Gakkai - Society for Japanese Blood Programme, Nihon Sekijujisha Ketsueki Jigyobu, 1-3, Shiba Daimon 1-chome, Minato-ku, Tokyo 105, Japan.

616   JA   ISSN 0915-8529
KETSUEKI SHUYOKA/HEMATOLOGY & ONCOLOGY. (Text in Japanese) 1990. m. 1950 Yen per no. Kagaku Hyoronsha, 2-11, Kanda Tacho, Chiyoda-ku, Tokyo 101, Japan.

616.15   JA
KETSUEKIGAKU SEMINA/SEMINAR IN HEMATOLOGY. (Text in Japanese) 1983. a. membership. Osaka Shiritsu Daigaku, Byoin Ketsueki Kenkyukai, Osaka Shiritsu Daigaku Igakubu Fuzoku Byoin, 4-54 Asahimachi 1-chome, Abeno-ku, Osaka 545, Japan.

616.15   JA   ISSN 0451-1611
KYUSHU HEMATOLOGICAL SOCIETY. JOURNAL/KYUSHU KETSUEKI KENKYU DOKOKAI-SHI. (Text in English, Japanese; summaries in English) 1952. s-a. 5000 Yen($39) Kyushu University, Faculty of Dentistry, Department of Oral Pathology, 3-1-1 Maidashi, Higashi-ku, Fukuoka 812, Japan. Ed. Norizo Hashimoto. adv. circ. 640. (back issues avail.) **Indexed:** Biol.Abstr., Excerp.Med., INIS Atomind.
    Description: Publishes histological and pathological research on the hematopoietic organs and clinical studies on the hematological diseases.

616.15   UK   ISSN 0887-6924
                         CODEN: LEUKED
LEUKEMIA. 1987. m. (Leukemia Society of America) Macmillan Press Ltd., Brunel Rd., Houndmills, Basingstoke, Hants RG21 2XS, England. TEL 44-1256-29242. (Co-sponsor: Leukemia Research Fund) Eds. Dr. C. Nicole Muller-Berat, Sven-Aage Killman. adv. circ. 800. (also avail. in microform from PMC) **Indexed:** Curr.Adv.Cell & Devel.Biol., Curr.Adv.Genetics & Molec.Biol., Excerp.Med., Ind.Med., Telegen. **Document type:** academic/scholarly publication.
    —BLDSC (5185.249000); CASDDS; Faxon; Genuine Article; SWETS; UMI; UnCover. **CCC.**
    Description: Articles on leukemia, germane diseases and normal hemopoiesis by specialists.
    Refereed Serial

616.15   US   ISSN 1042-8194
                         CODEN: LELYEA
LEUKEMIA AND LYMPHOMA. 18/yr. (in 3 vols., 6 nos./vol.). 106 ECU per vol. (effective 1996). Harwood Academic Publishers, c/o International Publishers Distributor, 820 Town CenterDr., Langhorne, PA 19047. TEL 215-750-2642. FAX 215-750-6343. (Subscr. to: International Publishers Distributor, PO Box 90, Reading, Berkshire, RG1 8JL, England. TEL 44-173-456-8316) Ed. Aaron Polliak. (also avail. in microform) **Indexed:** Excerp.Med., Ind.Med. (1992-). **Document type:** academic/scholarly publication.
    —BLDSC (5185.251500); Genuine Article; SWETS; UnCover. **CCC.**
    Description: Offers clinical-pathologic correlation and brings together clinical and laboratory data on lymphomas, leukemias, and allied disorders, including myeloma and myelodysplastic syndromes.
    Refereed Serial

616   UK   ISSN 0145-2126
                         CODEN: LEREDD
LEUKEMIA RESEARCH. 1977. m. £750($1193) (effective 1996). Elsevier Science Ltd., Pergamon, P.O. Box 800, Kidlington, Oxford OX5 1DX, England. TEL 44-1865-843000. FAX 44-1865-843010. E-mail: nlinfo-f@elsevier.nl; usinfo-f@elsevier.com; forinfo-kyf04035@niftyserve.or.jp; Site addr.: http://www.elsevier.nl/. (Subscr. in U.S. and Canada to: Elsevier Science, 660 White Plains Rd., Tarrytown, NY 10591-5153. TEL 914-524-9200. FAX 914-333-2444) Eds. Peter Reizenstein, Terry Hamblin. adv.; bk.rev.; abstr.; bibl.; charts; illus.; index. circ. 1,100. (also avail. in microfilm from UMI; back issues avail.) **Indexed:** Biol.Abstr., Chem.Abstr., Curr.Adv.Ecol.Sci., Curr.Cont., Excerp.Med., Ind.Med., Ind.Sci.Rev., INIS Atomind., Risk Abstr., Telegen, Vet.Bull. **Document type:** academic/scholarly publication.
    —BLDSC (5185.270000); CASDDS; Faxon; Genuine Article; SWETS; UMI; UnCover. **CCC.**
    Description: Integrates basic research in leukemia with recent reports of clinical applications.
    Refereed Serial

M T TODAY. (Medical Technologist) see *MEDICAL SCIENCES — Experimental Medicine, Laboratory Technique*

616.15 574.192   US   ISSN 0740-9451
QP106.6   CODEN: MELYEL
MICROCIRCULATION, ENDOTHELIUM AND LYMPHATICS.* 1984. bi-m. $230 (foreign $288). B M A Publications, Box 562, 31 Willows Rd., Ayer, MA 01432-0562. TEL 212-270-2194. adv.; abstr.; illus.; index. (also avail. in microform from UMI; back issues avail.) **Indexed:** Chem.Abstr., Curr.Cont. **Document type:** academic/scholarly publication.
    —CASDDS; Faxon; Genuine Article; UMI. **CCC.**
    Refereed Serial

616   JA   ISSN 0914-0956
NIHON SEKIJUJISHA KETSUEKI JIGYOBU KENKYU HOKOKU/JAPANESE RED CROSS SOCIETY. BLOOD PROGRAMME BUREAU. RESEARCH REPORT. (Text in Japanese) a. Nihon Sekijujisha, Ketsueki Jigyobu, 5-3, Shiba Daimon 1-chome, Minato-ku, Tokyo 105, Japan.

616.15   FR   ISSN 0029-4810
                         CODEN: NRFHA4
NOUVELLE REVUE FRANCAISE D'HEMATOLOGIE/JOURNAL OF EXPERIMENTAL AND CLINICAL HEMATOLOGY. (Text in English; summaries in English and French) 1946. bi-m. 1960 F.($412) (effective 1996). (Societe Francaise d'Hematologie) Springer-Verlag France, 26, rue des Carmes, 75005 Paris. TEL 44-41-15-8057. (Subscr. in N. America to: Springer-Verlag New York, Inc., Box 2485, Secaucus, NJ 07096-2491. TEL 201-348-4033) Eds. J.L Binet, J.P. Cazenave. adv.; bk.rev.; illus.; index. (also avail. in microform from UMI; reprint service avail. from ISI) **Indexed:** Biol.Abstr., Chem.Abstr., Curr.Adv.Cancer Res., Curr.Adv.Ecol.Sci., Curr.Cont., Dent.Ind., Excerp.Med., Ind.Med., Ind.Sci.Rev., Nutr.Abstr., Rev.Med.& Vet.Mycol. **Document type:** academic/scholarly publication.
    —BLDSC (6176.800000); CASDDS; EMDOCS; Faxon; Genuine Article; SWETS; UMI. **CCC.**
    Description: Provides editorials, original articles, and congress reports on the clinical, genetic, and experimental aspects of hematology. For physiologists, pathologists, oncologists, and physicians.

P A S C A L E 80: HEMATOLOGIE. see *MEDICAL SCIENCES — Abstracting, Bibliographies, Statistics*

P H - O FORUM; news - updates in Pediatric Hematology - Oncology. see *MEDICAL SCIENCES — Pediatrics*

PEDIATRIC HEMATOLOGY & ONCOLOGY. see *MEDICAL SCIENCES — Pediatrics*

PEDIATRIC HEMATOLOGY - ONCOLOGY SERIES. see *MEDICAL SCIENCES — Oncology*

PLATELETS (EDINBURGH). see *BIOLOGY — Biological Chemistry*

PLATELETS (SHEFFIELD). see *MEDICAL SCIENCES — Abstracting, Bibliographies, Statistics*

PROGRESS IN CARDIOVASCULAR DISEASES. see *MEDICAL SCIENCES — Cardiovascular Diseases*

MEDICAL SCIENCES — HEMATOLOGY

616.15 US
PSYCHOSOCIAL NEWS. s-a. free to qualified personnel. National Hemophilia Foundation, Mental Health Committee, Soho Bldg., Ste. 303, 110 Greene St., New York, NY 10012. FAX 212-966-9247. Eds. Regina Bussing, Mike Lammer. circ. 600. **Document type:** newsletter.

616.15 US ISSN 0272-507X
RB145 CODEN: REHEDT
REVIEWS OF HEMATOLOGY. 1980. irreg. $69.95. P J D Publications Ltd., Box 966, Westbury, NY 11590. TEL 516-626-0650. FAX 516-626-5546. Ed. Dr. Julian L. Ambrus; Pub. Barbara Sankar. (back issues avail.) **Indexed:** Biol.Abstr., Chem.Abstr., Curr.Cont. **Document type:** academic/scholarly publication.
—CASDDS.
Description: Provides information of value to hematologists, biochemists and other medical scientists.
Refereed Serial

616.15 CU ISSN 0864-0289
REVISTA CUBANA DE HEMATOLOGIA, INMUNOLOGIA Y HEMATERAPIA. (Text in Spanish; summaries in English, Spanish) s-a. C.$4($3) Ministerio de Salud Publica, Centro Nacional de Informacion de Ciencias Medicas, Calle E No. 452, e-19 y 21, Plaza de la Revolucion, Apdo. 6520, Havana, Cuba. TEL 809-32-5338. (Dist. by: Ediciones Cubanas, Obispo No. 527, Apdo. 605, Havana, Cuba) Ed. Ivette Cabrera. adv.; charts; illus.; stat.; index. circ. 1,200.
Description: Covers immunology, hematologic and hematopoietic system diseases, AIDS research and the application of hemotherapy techniques.

REVISTA IBEROAMERICANA DE TROMBOSIS Y HEMOSTASIA. see *MEDICAL SCIENCES — Cardiovascular Diseases*

616.15 FR ISSN 0999-7385
CODEN: STVAEY
SANG THROMBOSE VAISSEAUX. Abbreviated title: S T V. 10/yr. 445 F. to individuals; institutions 785 F.; students 285 F. (effective 1995). John Libbey Eurotext, 127 av de la Republique, 92120 Montrouge, France. TEL 1-46-73-06-60. FAX 1-40-84-09-99. (Subscr. to: A T E I, 23-25 rue Fernand Combette, 93100 Montreuil sous Bois, France. TEL 48-59-58-11. FAX 48-59-57-99) Ed. Gerard Tobelem. **Document type:** academic/scholarly publication.
—BLDSC (8073.160000).
Description: Studies fundamental and practical aspects of blood and vascular problems.

616.1 SP ISSN 0036-4355
RC633.A1 CODEN: SNGRAW
SANGRE; trabajos de hematologia y hemoterapia. (Text mainly in Spanish; summaries in English and Spanish) 1956. bi-m. 5300 ptas.($70) Revista Sangre, S.A., P.O. Box 687, Gral Sueiro 35, pral.dcha, 50008 Zaragoza, Spain. TEL 76-222638. FAX 76-222638. Ed. M. Giralt. adv.; bk.rev.; index. circ. 2,200. (back issues avail.) **Indexed:** Biol.Abstr., Chem.Abstr., Curr.Adv.Genetics & Molec.Biol., Curr.Cont., Dent.Ind., Excerp.Med., Ind.Med., Ind.Med.Esp., Nutr.Abstr.
—BLDSC (8073.200000); CASDDS; EMDOCS; Genuine Article; SWETS. CCC.

616.15 US ISSN 0037-1963
RC633.A1 CODEN: SEHEA3
SEMINARS IN HEMATOLOGY. 1964. q. $134 (foreign $173) (effective 1996). W.B. Saunders Co. (Subsidiary of: Harcourt Brace & Company), Curtis Center, 3rd Fl., Independence Sq. W., Philadelphia, PA 19106-3399. TEL 215-238-7800. FAX 215-238-6445. (Subscr. to: Periodicals Fulfillment, W.B. Saunders Co., 6277 Sea Harbor Dr., 4th Fl., Orlando, FL 32891-4800. TEL 800-654-2452. FAX 800-874-6418) Eds. Drs. Peter A. Miescher, Ernst R. Jaffe; Pub. Joan W. Blumberg. adv.: B&W page $1050, color page $2050; 7 x 10. bibl.; charts; illus.; index. circ. 6,377. (also avail. in microform from SWZ) **Indexed:** Biol.Abstr., Chem.Abstr., Curr.Adv.Cancer Res., Curr.Adv.Ecol.Sci., Curr.Cont., Excerp.Med., Ind.Med., Nutr.Abstr. **Document type:** academic/scholarly publication.
●Also available online. Vendor(s): Lexis-Nexis.
—BLDSC (8239.450000); CASDDS; EMDOCS; Faxon; Genuine Article; SWETS; UMI; UnCover. CCC.
Description: Publishes original articles of current importance in clinical hematology and related fields.

SEMINARS IN NEPHROLOGY. see *MEDICAL SCIENCES — Urology And Nephrology*

616.15 US ISSN 0094-6176
CODEN: STHMBV
SEMINARS IN THROMBOSIS AND HEMOSTASIS. q. $95 to individuals (foreign $120); institutions $125 (foreign $150). Thieme Medical Publishers, Inc., 381 Park Ave. S., Ste. 1501, New York, NY 10016. TEL 212-683-5088. FAX 212-779-9020. Ed. Dr. Eberhard F. Mammen. circ. 2,100. (also avail. in microform from UMI; reprint service avail. from UMI) **Indexed:** ASCA, Biol.Abstr., Chem.Abstr., Curr.Adv.Ecol.Sci., Excerp.Med., Ind.Med. **Document type:** academic/scholarly publication.
—BLDSC (8239.480000); ADONIS; CASDDS; EMDOCS; Faxon; Genuine Article; SWETS; UMI; UnCover. CCC.

LA STILLA; organo di stampa dell'A.V.I.S. provinciale di Montova. see *SOCIAL SERVICES AND WELFARE*

TETSU TAISHA KENKYUKAI PUROGURAMU SHOROKUSHU/CONFERENCE ON CURRENT TOPICS FOR IRON METABOLISM. PROGRAM AND ABSTRACTS. see *BIOLOGY — Biological Chemistry*

616.1 FR ISSN 1246-7820
CODEN: RFTID6
TRANSFUSION CLINIQUE ET BIOLOGIQUE. 1958. 6/yr. 980 F. (foreign 1240 F.). (Societe Francaise de Transfusion Sanguine) Arnette Blackwell, 1 rue de Lille, 75007 Paris, France. TEL 33-1-44-86-07-70. FAX 33-1-44-86-07-66. Eds. Philippe Rouger, Jean-Yves Muller. bk.rev.; index. circ. 1,000. (also avail. in microform from UMI; reprint service avail. from UMI) **Indexed:** Biol.Abstr., Chem.Abstr., Curr.Cont., Dent.Ind., Excerp.Med., Ind.Med.
—BLDSC (9020.705000); CASDDS; Faxon; Genuine Article; SWETS; UMI. CCC.
Former titles (until 1994): Revue Francaise de Transfusion et d'Hemobiologie (ISSN 1140-4639); (until 1989): Revue Francaise de Transfusion et Immuno-Hematologie (ISSN 0338-4535); (until 1975): Revue Francaise de Transfusion (ISSN 0035-2977); Transfusion.

616.15 UK ISSN 0958-7578
CODEN: TRMDET
TRANSFUSION MEDICINE. 1991. q. £99 (outside Europe £109($175)) (effective 1996). (British Blood Transfusion Society) Blackwell Science Ltd., Osney Mead, Oxford OX2 0EL, England. TEL 01865-206206. FAX 01865-206219. TELEX 83355 MEDBOK G. Ed. A.H. Waters. adv.; bk.rev.; illus.; index. circ. 1,700. (also avail. in microform from UMI; back issues avail.) **Indexed:** Ind.Med. (1993-). **Document type:** academic/scholarly publication.
—BLDSC (9020.706000); Genuine Article; SWETS; UMI. CCC.
Refereed Serial

616.15 US ISSN 0887-7963
CODEN: TMEREU
TRANSFUSION MEDICINE REVIEWS. 1987 (Apr.). q. $112 (foreign $148) (effective 1996). W.B. Saunders Co. (Subsidiary of: Harcourt Brace & Company), Curtis Center, 3rd Fl., Independence Sq. W., Philadelphia, PA 19106. TEL 215-238-7800. FAX 215-238-6445. (Subscr. to: Periodicals Fulfillment, W.B. Saunders Co., 6277 Sea Harbor Dr., 4th Fl., Orlando, FL 32891-3399. TEL 800-654-2452. FAX 800-874-6418) Ed. Dr. Morris A. Blajchman; Pub. Joan W. Blumberg. adv.: B&W page $670, color page $1570; 7 x 10. abstr.; bibl.; charts; illus.; index. circ. 1,619. **Indexed:** Excerp.Med. (1993-), Ind.Med. (1992-). **Document type:** academic/scholarly publication.
—BLDSC (9020.707000); Faxon; Genuine Article; SWETS; UMI; UnCover. CCC.
Description: Provides a forum for important clinical and research topics in the field.

616.15 UK ISSN 0955-3886
CODEN: TRASEE
TRANSFUSION SCIENCE. q. £260($414) (effective 1996). (European Society for Haemapheresis) Elsevier Science Ltd., Pergamon, P.O. Box 800, Kidlington, Oxford OX5 1DX, England. TEL 44-1865-843000. FAX 44-1865-843010. E-mail: nlinfo-f@elsevier.nl; usinfo-f@elsevier.com; forinfo-kyf04035@niftyserve.or.jp; Site addr.: http://www.elsevier.nl/. (Subscr. in U.S. and Canada to: Elsevier Science, 660 White Plains Rd., Tarrytown, NY 10591-5153. TEL 914-524-9200. FAX 914-333-2444) Ed. Dr. Gail Rock. circ. 2,000. (also avail. in microfilm from UMI) **Indexed:** Excerp.Med. **Document type:** academic/scholarly publication.
—BLDSC (9020.710000); Faxon; Genuine Article; UMI; UnCover. CCC.
Formerly: Plasma Therapy and Transfusion Technology; Incorporates: Apheresis Bulletin.
Description: Presents scientific and clinical studies in the areas of immunohematology, transfusion practice and apheresis.
Refereed Serial

616.15 FR ISSN 1015-3276
TRANSFUSION TODAY. French edition (ISSN 1015-3284); Spanish edition (ISSN 1015-3292) (Text in English) 1989. q. membership. Societe Internationale de Tranfusion Sanguine - International Society of Blood Transfusion, c/o C N T S, B.P. 100, 91943 Les Ulis Cedex, France. TEL 69-07-20-40. FAX 69-07-41-85. Ed. Bahman Habibi. adv.; bk.rev. circ. 7,000.
Description: Articles on blood transfusion and related topics.

616.15 IT ISSN 0041-1787
CODEN: TRSABD
LA TRASFUSIONE DEL SANGUE. (Text in Italian; summaries in English, Italian) 1956. bi-m. L.75000 to individuals; institutions L.90000($147). (Societa Italiana di Immunoematologia e Associazione Italiana Centri Trasfusionali) S I M T I Edizione, Viale Brianza 6, 20127 Milan, Italy. TEL 39-2-26148759. FAX 39-2-26145813. (Edit. addr.: c/o Servizio Trasfusionale, Ospedale Galliera, Mura delle Cappuccine, 14, 16128 Genova, Italy. TEL 39-10-564395. FAX 39-10-5632544) Ed. Dr. Giorgio Reali. adv. contact: Gianalfredo Sciorelli. bk.rev.; abstr.; bibl.; charts; illus.; index. circ. 700. **Indexed:** Biol.Abstr., Excerp.Med. **Document type:** academic/scholarly publication.
—BLDSC (9026.710000); CASDDS.

VATRECHNI BOLESTI. see *MEDICAL SCIENCES — Endocrinology*

616.15 US ISSN 0882-5998
RB145 CODEN: YBHEEI
YEAR BOOK OF HEMATOLOGY. a. $74.95 (residents $35) (effective 1996). Mosby - Year Book, Inc., Continuity Division, 200 N. LaSalle, Chicago, IL 60601. TEL 312-726-9733. FAX 312-726-6075. TELEX 206155. Ed. Dr. Jerry L. Spivak. illus. (reprint service avail.)
●Also available online. Vendor(s): Ovid Technologies.
—BLDSC (9413.050000).

616.15 CC ISSN 0253-2727
CODEN: CHTCD7
ZHONGHUA XUEYEXUE ZAZHI/CHINESE JOURNAL OF HEMATOLOGY. (Text in Chinese; abstracts in Chinese, English) 1980. m. $75.60 (effective 1995). Zhongguo Yixue Kexueyuan, Xueye Yanjiusuo - Chinese Academy of Medical Sciences, Institute of Hematology, 288 Nanjing Lu, Tianjin 300020, People's Republic of China. TEL 86-22-704167. FAX 86-22-706542. (Subscr. to: China International Book Trading Corp., P.O. Box 399, Beijing, P.R. China) Ed. Li Jiazeng. adv.: B&W page $1400, color page $3000; adv. contact: Zhang Zhifang. circ. 10,000. **Indexed:** ExtraMED. **Document type:** academic/scholarly publication.
●Also available on CD-ROM.
—CASDDS.
Description: Covers the latest development on hematology in China. Contains original articles, case reports and laboratory techniques.

MEDICAL SCIENCES — Hypnosis

154.7 616.891   US   ISSN 0002-9157
RC490   CODEN: AJHNA3
AMERICAN JOURNAL OF CLINICAL HYPNOSIS. 1958. q. $30 to individuals (foreign $37.60); institutions $45 (foreign $52.60). American Society of Clinical Hypnosis, 2200 E. Devon Ave., Ste. 291, Des Plaines, IL 60018-4501. TEL 708-297-3317. FAX 708-297-7309. Ed. Edward Frischholz. bk.rev.; index, cum.index. circ. 5,000. (also avail. in microform from UMI; back issues avail.; reprint service avail. from UMI) **Indexed:** Adol.Ment.Hlth.Abstr., Behav.Med.Abstr., Bibl.Ind., Biol.Abstr., Curr.Cont., Excerp.Med., Ind.Med., Mid.East: Abstr.& Ind., Psychol.Abstr. (1966-), SSCI. **Document type:** academic/scholarly publication.
—BLDSC (0822.800000); Faxon; Genuine Article; SWETS; UMI; UnCover.

159.7 616.891   US   ISSN 0517-5178
AMERICAN SOCIETY OF CLINICAL HYPNOSIS. DIRECTORY. s-a. price varies. American Society of Clinical Hypnosis, 2200 E. Devon Ave., Ste. 291, Des Plaines, IL 60018-4501. TEL 708-297-3317. FAX 708-297-7309. **Document type:** directory.

616.891   AT   ISSN 0156-0417
CODEN: AJCHDV
AUSTRALIAN JOURNAL OF CLINICAL AND EXPERIMENTAL HYPNOSIS. 1977. s-a. Aus.$25 to individuals (foreign Aus.$30); institutions Aus.$40 (foreign Aus.$45) (effective thru 1996). Australian Society of Hypnosis, Edward Wilson Bldg., Austin Hospital, Heidelberg 3084, Australia. FAX 613-4596244. Ed. Dr. Barry J. Evans. bk.rev. circ. 1,100. (back issues avail.) **Indexed:** Excerp.Med., Ind.Med., Psychol.Abstr. (1978-), Sci.Cit.Ind. **Document type:** academic/scholarly publication.
—BLDSC (1806.200000); UnCover.
Former titles: Australian Society of Hypnosis. Journal; Australian Society of Clinical and Experimental Hypnosis. Journal.

616.891   AT   ISSN 0810-0713
AUSTRALIAN JOURNAL OF CLINICAL HYPNOTHERAPY AND HYPNOSIS. 1980. s-a. Aus.$25 to individuals; institutions and libraries Aus.$31; foreign Aus.$38. (Australian Society of Clinical Hypnotherapists) Australian Academic Press Pty. Ltd., 32 Jeays St., Bowen Hills, Qld. 4006, Australia. TEL 61-7-257-1176. FAX 61-7-252-5908. Ed. Zoltan A. Kelemen. bk.rev. (also avail. in microform from UMI; back issues avail.) **Indexed:** Excerp.Med., Psychol.Abstr. (1980-).
—BLDSC (1806.353000); UMI.
Description: Publishes original clinical, research, review, theoretical, historical and related reports dealing with the professional application of hypnosis and hypnotherapy.

COMPREHENSIVE PSYCHIATRY. see *MEDICAL SCIENCES — Psychiatry And Neurology*

616.89   UK   ISSN 0960-5290
CODEN: COHYET
CONTEMPORARY HYPNOSIS. 1983. 3/yr. £95 to individuals; institutions £49 (effective 1996). (British Society of Experimental and Clinical Hypnosis) Whurr Publishers Ltd., 19b Compton Terrace, London N1 2UN, England. TEL 0171-359-5979. FAX 0171-226-5290. (Subscr. to: Turpin Distribution Services Ltd., Blackhorse Rd., Letchworth, Herts. SG6 1HN, England. TEL 01462-672555. FAX 01462-480947; Subscr. in N. America to: Whurr Publishers Ltd., Box 1897, Lawrence, KS 66044-8897. TEL 913-843-1221. FAX 913-843-1274) Ed. Brian Fellows. adv.: page £150; adv. contact: Sarah Vicary. bk.rev.; index. circ. 400. (back issues avail.) **Indexed:** Behav.Med.Abstr., Psychol.Abstr. (1982-). **Document type:** academic/scholarly publication.
—BLDSC (3425.182900); ADONIS; UMI.
Formerly: British Journal of Experimental and Clinical Hypnosis (ISSN 0265-1033)
Description: Covers all aspects of theory, research and practice of hypnosis.

616.891   GW   ISSN 0933-1093
EXPERIMENTELLE UND KLINISCHE HYPNOSE. (Text in German; summaries in English, German) 1983. s-a. DM.22. (Deutsche Gesellschaft fuer Hypnose) Verlag Dr. Dieter Winkler, Katharinastr. 37, 44793 Bochum, Germany. TEL 0234-17508. Ed. Hans-Christian Kossak. adv.; bk.rev. circ. 700. (back issues avail.) **Indexed:** Psychol.Abstr. (1987-). **Document type:** academic/scholarly publication.
Description: For medical or psychiatric professionals interested in using hypnosis as a therapeutic method.

616.891 370.15   US   ISSN 0882-8652
HYPNOTHERAPY TODAY. 1980. q. membership only. American Association of Professional Hypnotherapists, Box 29, Boones Mill, VA 24065. TEL 540-334-3035. Ed. William S. Brink. bk.rev. circ. 2,000. **Document type:** newsletter.
Description: Studies the therapeutic uses of hypnosis for the body, mind and spiritual needs.

154.7 616.891   US   ISSN 0020-7144
RC490   CODEN: IJEHAO
INTERNATIONAL JOURNAL OF CLINICAL AND EXPERIMENTAL HYPNOSIS. (Text in English; summaries in French, German and Spanish) 1953. q. $64 to individuals; institutions $139 (effective Sep. 1995). (Society for Clinical and Experimental Hypnosis) Sage Publications, Inc., 2455 Teller Rd., Thousand Oaks, CA 91320. TEL 805-499-0721. E-mail: libraries@sagepub.com. (Overseas subscr. to: Sage Publications Ltd., 6 Bonhill St., London EC2A 4PU, England; Sage Publications India Pvt. Ltd., P.O. Box 4215, Delhi 110 048, India) Ed. Dr. Fred H. Frankel. cum.index. circ. 2,500. (also avail. in microfilm from UMI; back issues avail.; reprint service avail. from UMI) **Indexed:** Adol.Ment.Hlth.Abstr., Behav.Med.Abstr., Biol.Abstr., Curr.Cont., Excerp.Med., Ind.Med., Ind.Sci.Rev., Mid.East: Abstr.& Ind., Psychol.Abstr. (1959-), Sci.Cit.Ind., Soc.Work Res.& Abstr., SSCI, Viol.& Abuse Abstr. **Document type:** academic/scholarly publication.
—BLDSC (4542.170000); EMDOCS; Faxon; SWETS; UMI; UnCover.
Formerly: Clinical and Experimental Hypnosis.
Description: Publishes research papers dealing with hypnosis in psychology, psychiatry, the medical and dental specialties, and related studies.

616.891   US
▼**JOURNAL OF CLINICAL HYPNOTHERAPY AND HYPNOANALYSIS.** 1994. q. $42.50 to individuals (foreign $86.50); institutions $70 (foreign $104). International Universities Press, Inc., 59 Boston Post Rd., Box 1524, Madison, CT 06443-1524. TEL 203-245-4000. FAX 203-245-07756. Ed. Milton V. Kline. **Indexed:** Excerp.Med. (1995-). **Document type:** academic/scholarly publication.
Description: Focuses exclusively on clinical work with patients. Features original scientific papers on the psychodynamic aspects of the hypnotherapeutic process and hypnotic states.

615.8   US
▼**JOURNAL OF HYPNOTHERAPY AND HYPNOANALYSIS.** 1994. q. $42.50 to individuals (foreign $86.50); institutions $70 (foreign $104). (International Society for Medical and Psychological Hypnosis) International Universities Press, Inc., 59 Boston Post Rd., Box 1524, Madison, CT 06443-1524. TEL 203-245-4000. FAX 203-245-0775. (Co-sponsor: Institute for Research in Hypnosis and Psychotherapy) Ed. Milton V. Kline. **Document type:** academic/scholarly publication.

KWARTAALSCHRIFT VOOR DIRECTIEVE THERAPIE EN HYPNOSE. see *PSYCHOLOGY*

154.7 616.8 614.58   US   ISSN 0894-5098
RC490
MEDICAL HYPNOANALYSIS JOURNAL. 1980. q. $27 (foreign $39). (American Academy of Medical Hypnoanalysts) A A M H, 125 Liberty St., Ste. 403, Springfield, MA 01103-1109. TEL 413-786-0707. FAX 413-786-0618. film rev.; tr.lit.; cum.index; circ. 500 (paid). (back issues avail.) **Indexed:** Psychol.Abstr. (1986-). **Document type:** academic/scholarly publication, trade publication.
—BLDSC (5527.525000); Faxon.
Description: Provides educational and practical information for the psychotherapist using hypnosis.

616.8   US
NATIONAL REGISTER OF PROFESSIONAL HYPNOTHERAPISTS. 1983. a. membership. American Association of Professional Hypnotherapists, Box 29, Boones Mill, VA 24065. TEL 540-334-3035. Ed. William Brink. circ. 2,000. **Document type:** directory.
Description: Lists hypnotherapy practitioners state-by-state and in 20 foreign countries.

616.891   US
NEW YORK SOCIETY OF ETHICAL HYPNOSIS. NEWSLETTER.* 4/yr. $10. New York Society of Ethical Hypnosis, c/o Carol Styron-Gore, Ed., Box 818, Skyland, NC 28776-0818. **Document type:** newsletter.

PARAPSYCHOLOGY, HYPNOSIS & ALTERNATIVE HEALTH. see *PARAPSYCHOLOGY AND OCCULTISM*

154.7 616.891   US   ISSN 0583-8975
S C E H NEWSLETTER.* 1955. q. $10. Society for Clinical and Experimental Hypnosis, S C E H Central Office, 8335 Allison Pointe Trail, Ste. 250, Indianapolis, IN 46250. TEL 703-556-9222. FAX 703-556-8729. Ed. Dr. Roseann Mulligan. bk.rev. circ. 1,200. **Document type:** newsletter.

SEMINARS IN ANESTHESIA. see *MEDICAL SCIENCES — Anaesthesiology*

MEDICAL SCIENCES — Internal Medicine

see also *Medical Sciences–Cardiovascular Diseases; Medical Sciences–Communicable Diseases; Medical Sciences–Endocrinology; Medical Sciences–Gastroenterology; Medical Sciences–Hematology; Medical Sciences–Oncology; Medical Sciences–Respiratory Diseases; Medical Sciences–Rheumatology; Medical Sciences–Urology and Nephrology*

A C P JOURNAL CLUB. (American College of Physicians) see *MEDICAL SCIENCES — Abstracting, Bibliographies, Statistics*

616   US   ISSN 0065-2822
RC46   CODEN: AIMNAL
ADVANCES IN INTERNAL MEDICINE. 1954. a. $72.95 (residents $40) (effective 1996). Mosby - Year Book, Inc. (Chicago) (Subsidiary of: Times Mirror Company), 200 N. LaSalle St., Chicago, IL 60601-1080. TEL 312-726-9733. FAX 312-726-6075. TELEX 206155. (Subscr. to: 11830 Westline Industrial Dr., St. Louis, MO 63146. TEL 800-325-4177) Ed. Robert W. Schirer. (also avail. in microfilm from UMI; reprint service avail. from UMI) **Indexed:** Biol.Abstr., Chem.Abstr., Curr.Adv.Ecol.Sci., Curr.Adv.Genetics & Molec.Biol., Dent.Ind., Diar.Dis.Res., Ind.Med., Ind.Sci.Rev., INIS Atomind., Sci.Cit.Ind.
—BLDSC (0709.250000); CASDDS; Faxon; Genuine Article; SWETS; UMI; UnCover. **CCC.**
Description: Presents a collection of original fully referenced clinical reviews from the experts in the field.

616.02   SP   ISSN 0212-7199
ANALES DE MEDICINA INTERNA. m. 7500 ptas. (effective 1996). (Sociedad Espanola de Medicina Interna) Aran Ediciones, S.A., Avda. General Peron 20, 5o Dcha., 28020 Madrid, Spain. TEL 34-1-5332525. FAX 34-1-5332123. Ed. Dr. J. Portugal Alvarez. circ. 7,764.
—BLDSC (0890.018000).

MEDICAL SCIENCES — INTERNAL MEDICINE

616.026   FR   ISSN 0003-410X
CODEN: AMDIBO
ANNALES DE MEDECINE INTERNE. 1848. 8/yr. 1540 F. (foreign 1817 F.) (effective 1996). (Societe Medicale des Hopitaux de Paris) Masson - Periodiques, Villa Laromiguiere, 75005 Paris, France. TEL 1-40-46-62-00. FAX 1-40-46-62-01. Ed. P. Guillevin. adv.; index. circ. 1,500. (also avail. in microform from UMI; reprint service avail. from ISI) **Indexed:** Biol.Abstr., Bull.Signal., C.I.S. Abstr., Chem.Abstr., Curr.Cont., Dent.Ind., Excerp.Med., Helminthol.Abstr., Ind.Med., INIS Atomind., Protozool.Abstr., Rev.Med.& Vet.Mycol., Rev.Plant Path., Sci.Cit.Ind. **Document type:** academic/scholarly publication.
—BLDSC (0981.800000); CASDDS; Faxon; Genuine Article; SWETS; UMI. **CCC.**
Supersedes: Societe Medicale des Hopitaux de Paris. Bulletins et Memoires.
Description: Covers equipment, techniques, and economic surveys relating to medical bioengineering.

616.02   IT   ISSN 0393-9340
ANNALI ITALIANI DI MEDICINA INTERNA. 1986. q. $90. C E P I - Centro Editoriale Pubblicitario Italiano S.r.l., Via N. Tartaglia 3, 00197 Rome, Italy. TEL 39-6-8082101. FAX 39-6-8072458. Ed. Alberico Borghetti. adv. contact: Enzo Buongiorno. bk.rev. **Document type:** academic/scholarly publication, proceedings.
—BLDSC (1014.460000).

616.026   US   ISSN 0003-4819
R11   CODEN: AIMEAS
ANNALS OF INTERNAL MEDICINE. (Supplement avail.: A C P Journal Club (ISSN 1056-8751)) 1922. s-m. $92 (Canada $119; Japan $159; W. Europe $150; elsewhere $145). American College of Physicians, Independence Mall W., Sixth St. at Race, Philadelphia, PA 19106-1572. TEL 215-351-2400. FAX 215-351-2644. Ed. Frank Davidoff. adv.: B&W page $4600. bk.rev.; charts; illus.; index, cum.index. circ. 100,000. (also avail. in microform from UMI,PMC) **Indexed:** Abstr.Health Care Manage.Stud., Abstr.Hyg., Abstr.Inter.Med., AIM, Behav.Med.Abstr., Biol.Abstr., Biotech.Abstr., C.I.S. Abstr., Chem.Abstr., CINAHL, Curr.Adv.Cancer Res., Curr.Adv.Ecol.Sci., Curr.Cont., Dairy Sci.Abstr., Dent.Ind., Diab.Cont., Diar.Dis.Res., Dok.Arbeitsmed., Excerp.Med., FAMLI, Helminthol.Abstr., Hosp.Lit.Ind., I.P.A., Ind.Med., Ind.Sci.Rev., INIS Atomind., Int.Nurs.Ind., Kidney, Med.& Surg.Dermat., Med.Care Rev., NRN, Nutr.Abstr., Protozool.Abstr., Rev.Med.& Vet.Mycol., Rev.Plant Path., Risk Abstr., Sci.Cit.Ind., Trop.Dis.Bull. **Document type:** academic/scholarly publication.
●Also available online. Vendor(s): Ovid Technologies. Also available on CD-ROM.
—BLDSC (1041.200000); CASDDS; Faxon; Genuine Article; SWETS; UMI; UnCover. **CCC.**
Refereed Serial

616   US   ISSN 0003-9926
CODEN: AIMDAP
ARCHIVES OF INTERNAL MEDICINE. 1908. m. $115 (foreign $160). American Medical Association, 515 N. State St., Chicago, IL 60610. TEL 312-464-5000; 800-262-2350. FAX 312-464-5831. Ed. Dr. James E. Dalen. adv.; bk.rev.; charts; illus.; index. circ. 100,000. (also avail. in microform from UMI,PMC) **Indexed:** Abstr.Health Care Manage.Stud., Abstr.Hyg., Abstr.Inter.Med., AIM, Biol.Abstr., Biotech.Abstr., C.I.S.Abstr., Chem.Abstr., CINAHL, Curr.Adv.Cancer Res., Curr.Adv.Ecol.Sci., Curr.Cont., Curr.Lit.Fam.Plan., Dairy Sci.Abstr., Dent.Ind., Diab.Cont., Diar.Dis.Res., Dok.Arbeitsmed., Excerp.Med., Helminthol.Abstr., Hosp.Lit.Ind., I.P.A., Ind.Hyg.Dig., Ind.Med., Ind.Sci.Rev., Ind.Vet., INIS Atomind., Int.Nurs.Ind., Kidney, Med.& Surg.Dermat., NRN, Nutr.Abstr., Poult.Abstr., Protozool.Abstr., Rev.Med.& Vet.Mycol., Rev.Plant Path., Sci.Cit.Ind., Trop.Dis.Bull., Vet.Bull. **Document type:** academic/scholarly publication.
●Also available online. Vendor(s): Lexis-Nexis.
—BLDSC (1634.850000); CASDDS; Faxon; Genuine Article; SWETS; UMI; UnCover. **CCC.**
Refereed Serial

616   IT   ISSN 0004-010X
CODEN: AMITAD
ARCHIVIO DI MEDICINA INTERNA. 1949. bi-m. L.60000 (foreign L.120000) (effective 1994). Casa Editrice Maccari, Via Trento 53, 43100 Parma, Italy. FAX 039-521-771268. circ. 1,600. **Indexed:** Excerp.Med.
—BLDSC (1647.650000); UMI.

616.07   IT   ISSN 0004-0193
CODEN: AMPCAV
ARCHIVIO E. MARAGLIANO DI PATOLOGIA E CLINICA.* vol.28, 1972. bi-m. L.5000. Universita degli Studi di Genova, Istituto Scientifico di Medicina Interna, 16132 Genoa, Italy. **Indexed:** Biol.Abstr., Chem.Abstr., Excerp.Med., Ind.Med.

616 016   US   ISSN 0271-1303
AUDIO-DIGEST INTERNAL MEDICINE. 1954. s-m. $168. Audio-Digest Foundation (Subsidiary of: California Medical Association), 1577 E. Chevy Chase Dr., Glendale, CA 91206. TEL 213-245-8505. FAX 818-240-7379. Ed. Claron L. Oakley. index; circ. controlled. (audio cassette)
Refereed Serial

BIO-REGULADORES/REVIEWS ON BIO-REGULATORS. see *BIOLOGY — Bioengineering*

616   UK   ISSN 0956-3075
CODEN: CICAEQ
CLINICAL INTENSIVE CARE; international journal of critical care medicine. 1989. bi-m. £70 to individuals in the U.K. and Europe £70 (in the U.S. $110; elsewhere £82); institutions in the U.K. and Europe £95 (in the U.S. $150; elsewhere £112). Castle House Publications Ltd., 28-30 Church Rd., Tunbridge Wells, Kent TN1 1JP, England. TEL 01892-539606. FAX 01892-517005. bk.rev.; index. **Indexed:** Excerp.Med. **Document type:** academic/scholarly publication.
—BLDSC (3286.293910).

616   US   ISSN 1042-9646
CONTEMPORARY INTERNAL MEDICINE. 1989. 12/yr. $85. Aegean Communications, Inc., 666 Glenbrook Rd., Stamford, CT 06906-1439. TEL 203-353-0111. FAX 203-353-1975. Pub. Mark Brauca. adv. circ. 90,000 (controlled). **Document type:** trade publication.
Description: Provides clinically practical and authoritative information in areas of high interest to internists and specialist physicians.

616   UK   ISSN 0968-6053
▼**CURRENT DIAGNOSTIC PATHOLOGY.** 1994. q. £80($132) to individuals; institutions £150 ($248) (effective 1995). Churchill Livingstone Journals (Subsidiary of: Pearson Professional), Robert Stevenson House, 1-3 Baxter's Pl., Leith Walk, Edinburgh EH1 3AF, Scotland. TEL 0131-556-2424. FAX 0131-459-1177. (Subscr. to: Pearson Professional Ltd., P.O. Box 77, Fourth Ave., Harlow, Essex CM19 5AA, England. TEL 01279-623760; U.S. subscr. to: Churchill Livingstone, 650 Ave. of the Americas, New York, NY 10011. TEL 212-206-5000) Ed. Kristin Henry. adv. contact: David Dunnachie. bk.rev. **Document type:** academic/scholarly publication.
—BLDSC (3496.315000).
Description: Covers the research and diagnosis of various internal diseases.

616   NE   ISSN 0272-1465
CURRENT HISTOPATHOLOGY. (Text in English) irreg., vol.23, 1993. price varies. Kluwer Academic Publishers, Postbus 17, 3300 AA Dordrecht, Netherlands. TEL 31-78-392392. FAX 31-78-392254. TELEX 29245 KAPG NL. (Dist. by: Kluwer Academic Publishers Group, P.O. Box 322, 3300 AH Dordrecht, Netherlands. TEL 31-78-392392. FAX 31-78-546474; N. America dist. addr.: Box 358, Accord Sta., Hingham, MA 02018-0358. TEL 617-871-6600. FAX 617-871-6528) **Document type:** monographic series.
—BLDSC (3497.435000).
Refereed Serial

615.82   US
DIRECTORY OF MEDICAL REHABILITATION FACILITIES. 1990. a. $195. H C I A Inc. - Co-publisher: NovaCare, 300 E. Lombard St., Baltimore, MD 21202. TEL 800-568-3280. FAX 410-539-5220. **Document type:** directory.
Formerly: Directory of Medical Rehabilitation Programs (ISSN 1063-1712)
Description: Identifies more than 1,100 U.S. medical rehabilitation programs, including hospital-based, free-standing, outpatient and specialty programs.

ENDOSCOPIC FORUM FOR DIGESTIVE DISEASE/NIHON SHOKAKI NAISHIKYO GAKKAI KOSHIN'ETSU CHIHOKAI ZASSHI. see *MEDICAL SCIENCES — Gastroenterology*

616.026 618.92   US   ISSN 0071-111X
ERGEBNISSE DER INNEREN MEDIZIN UND KINDERHEILKUNDE. NEW SERIES/ADVANCES IN INTERNAL MEDICINE AND PEDIATRICS. (Text in German; occasionally in English) 1949. irreg. price varies. Springer-Verlag, 175 Fifth Ave., New York, NY 10010. TEL 212-460-1500. FAX 212-473-6272. (Also: Berlin, Heidelberg, Tokyo and Vienna) (reprint service avail. from ISI) **Indexed:** Ind.Med. **Document type:** monographic series.
—Faxon.
Description: Covers internal medicine.

616   IT   ISSN 0953-6205
CODEN: EJIMEJ
EUROPEAN JOURNAL OF INTERNAL MEDICINE. (Supplement avail. (ISSN 1121-8967)) (Text in English; summaries in French) 1990. q. $200. Edizioni Luigi Pozzi s.r.l., Via Panama 68, 00198 Rome, Italy. TEL 39-6-8553548. FAX 39-6-8554105. Ed. U. Carcassi. circ. 1,200. **Indexed:** Excerp.Med.
—BLDSC (3829.730700); UMI.
Description: Covers all aspects of internal medicine.

616   IT   ISSN 1121-8967
CODEN: EJMSE
EUROPEAN JOURNAL OF MEDICINE. SUPPLEMENT. irreg. Edizione Luigi Pozzi s.r.l., Via Panama 68, 00198 Rome, Italy. TEL 39-6-8553548. FAX 39-6-8554105. **Indexed:** Excerp.Med. (1994-).

616   UK
▼**EUROPEAN JOURNAL OF PALLIATIVE CARE.** 1994. q. £21 to member individuals (outside Europe £32); non-member individuals £28 (outside Europe £42); member institutions £100 (outside Europe £120 ($185)) (effective 1995). (European Association for Palliative Care) Hayward Medical Communications Ltd., Essex House, Cromwell Park, Chipping Norton, Oxon. OX7 5SR, England. TEL 44-171-240-4493. FAX 44-171-240-4479. (Subscr. to: Essex House, Cromwell Park, Chipping Norton, Oxon. OX7 5SR, England. TEL 44-1608-645564. FAX 44-1608-645645) **Document type:** academic/scholarly publication.
Description: Covers the many clinical and social aspects of palliative care.

EXCERPTA MEDICA. SECTION 6: INTERNAL MEDICINE. see *MEDICAL SCIENCES — Abstracting, Bibliographies, Statistics*

616   US
▼**FOCUS & OPINION IN INTERNAL MEDICINE.** 1994. q. $68 to individuals; institutions $112.50; residents $43 (effective 1996). Mosby - Year Book, Inc. (Chicago) (Subsidiary of: Times Mirror Company), 200 N. LaSalle St., Chicago, IL 60601-1080. TEL 312-726-9733. FAX 312-726-6075. TELEX 206155. Ed. Jay H. Stein.

616   GW   ISSN 0931-1130
FORTSCHRITTE IN DER HOCHDRUCKFORSCHUNG. 1986. irreg., vol.5, 1992. DM.29.80. W. Zuckschwerdt Verlag GmbH, Industriestr. 17, 82110 Germering, Germany. TEL 089-894349-0. FAX 089-89434950. Ed. J. Rosenthal. **Document type:** academic/scholarly publication.

616   CC
GUOWAI YIXUE (NEIKEXUE FENCE)/FOREIGN MEDICAL SCIENCES (INTERNAL MEDICINE). (Text in Chinese) m. Zhongshan Yike Daxue - Sun Yat-sen Medical University, 74 Zhongshan Erlu, Guangzhou, Guangdong 510089, People's Republic of China. TEL 778223. Ed. Liang Sudi.

616.1   II   ISSN 0377-9343
INDIAN JOURNAL OF CHEST DISEASES AND ALLIED SCIENCES. (Text in English) 1959. q. Rs.200($50) University of Delhi, Vallabhbhai Patel Chest Institute, P.O. Box 2101, Delhi 110 007, India. TEL 7257102. (Co-sponsor: National College of Chest Physicians) Ed. Dr. A.S. Paintal. adv.: B&W page Rs.900; trim 19 1/2 x 13. bk.rev. circ. 1,000. **Indexed:** Biol.Abstr., Chem.Abstr., Curr.Cont., Dent.Ind., Dok.Arbeitsmed., Excerp.Med. (until 19??), ExtraMED, Helminthol.Abstr., Ind.Med. **Document type:** academic/scholarly publication.
●Also available on CD-ROM.
—BLDSC (4410.710000); Faxon; UnCover. **CCC.**
Formerly (until vol.18, Jan. 1976): Indian Journal of Chest Diseases.
Description: Covers internal medicine.

MEDICAL SCIENCES — INTERNAL MEDICINE

616   AU   ISSN 0936-8507
INTENSIVMEDIZINISCHES SEMINAR. 1989. irreg., vol.7, 1994. Springer-Verlag, Sachsenplatz 4-6, Postfach 89, A-1201 Vienna, Austria. TEL 0222-3302415. FAX 0222-3302426. Eds. K. Lenz, A.N. Laggner. **Document type:** academic/scholarly publication.
—BLDSC (4531.847300).

616   US   ISSN 1056-9286
R11   **CODEN: IMEIEI**
INTERNAL MEDICINE. Variant title: I M. 1980. 12/yr. $75 (foreign $99). Medical Economics, 5 Paragon Dr., Montvale, NJ 07645. TEL 201-358-7200. Ed. Deborah Kaplan. circ. 92,770. (also avail. in microform from UMI). **Indexed:** Excerp.Med.
—BLDSC (4368.580000); UMI. **CCC.**
Formerly (until 1990): Internal Medicine for the Specialist (ISSN 0273-6608)
Description: Presents current approach to diagnostic and management problems of particular interest to internists, with emphasis on cardiovascular and pulmonary medicine, gastroenterology, infectious disease, rheumatology, oncology, nephrology and allergy.

616   JA   ISSN 0918-2918
                         CODEN: IEDIEP
INTERNAL MEDICINE (TOKYO, 1992). (Text in English) 1962. m. 20000 Yen to non-members; members 3000 Yen (foreign $270) (effective 1. Japanese Society of Internal Medicine - Nihon Naika Gakkai, Hongo Daiichi Bldg., 34-3, 3-chome, Bunkyo-ku, Tokyo 113, Japan. TEL 3-3813-5991. FAX 3-3818-1556. (Dist. to non-members by: Nankodo Co. Ltd., 42-6, 3-chome Hongo, Bunkyo-ku, Tokyo 113, Japan. TEL 03-3811-7239. FAX 03-3811-7230; Dist. overseas by: Japan Publications Trading Co., Ltd., Box 5030 Tokyo International, Tokyo 100-31, Japan. TEL 81-3-3292-3753. FAX 81-3-3292-0410) Ed. Takao Saruta. abstr.; charts; illus. circ. 7,400. **Indexed:** Biol.Abstr., Chem.Abstr., Curr.Cont., Excerp.Med., Helminthol.Abstr., Ind.Med., INIS Atomind., Nutr.Abstr. **Document type:** academic/scholarly publication.
—BLDSC (4534.880000); CASDDS; Faxon; Genuine Article.
Formerly (until 1992): Japanese Journal of Medicine (ISSN 0021-5120)

616   US   ISSN 0195-315X
INTERNAL MEDICINE ALERT. 1979. s-m. $116. American Health Consultants, Inc., Six Piedmont Center, Ste. 400, Atlanta, GA 30305. TEL 404-262-7436; 800-688-2421. FAX 800-284-3291. Ed. Dr. Stephen A. Brunton. index. circ. 6,345. (also avail. in audio cassette; reprint service avail.) **Document type:** newsletter.
—CCC.
Incorporates (1985-1991): Diagnostic Testing Alert (ISSN 8756-7474)

616   US
INTERNAL MEDICINE BULLETIN. 1993. bi-w. $89 to individuals (foreign $153); institutions $99 (foreign $153) (effective 1994). W.B. Saunders Co, (Subsidiary of: Harcourt Brace & Company), Curtis Center, 3rd Fl., Independence Sq. W., Philadelphia, PA 19106-3399. TEL 215-238-7800. FAX 215-238-6445. (Subscr. to: Periodicals Fulfillment, W.B. Saunders Co., 6277 Sea Harbor Dr., 4th Fl., Orlando, FL 32891-4800. TEL 800-654-2452. FAX 800-874-6418) Ed. Dr. Malcolm S. Thaler. abstr. (back issues avail.) **Document type:** academic/scholarly publication.
Description: Provides physicans in internal medicine and family practice with concise reviews of the most important articles in the professional literature.

616   IT
INTERNAL MEDICINE; CLINICAL AND LABORATORY. 1993. s-a. L.40000($40) to individuals; institutions L.50000($50) (effective 1995). Pacini Editore s.r.l., Via A. Gherardesca 1, 56121 Ospedaletto (Pisa), Italy. TEL 39-50-982439. FAX 39-50-983906. Eds. A. Sagripanti, A. Capri.

616   US   ISSN 0274-5542
INTERNAL MEDICINE NEWS & CARDIOLOGY NEWS. 1968. s-m. $96. International Medical News Group, 12230 Wilkins Ave., Rockville, MD 20852. TEL 301-816-8700. Ed. Johanna H. Weekley. adv.; bk.rev. circ. 98,000. (tabloid format; also avail. in microform from UMI) **Document type:** newspaper.
—UMI.
Former titles (until 1980): Internal Medicine News (ISSN 0099-152X); Internal Medicine and Diagnosis News (ISSN 0012-1908); Diagnosis News.
Description: Covers internal medicine and associated specialties.

616.02   US   ISSN 1058-1685
INTERNAL MEDICINE RESIDENT. 1992. bi-m. Slack, Inc., 6900 Grove Rd., Thorofare, NJ 08086. TEL 609-848-1000. FAX 609-853-5991. Ed. Laura Ronge. adv. circ. 21,900.
Description: Contains information on career, life-style and business issues facing residents.

616   US
INTERNAL MEDICINE WORLD REPORT. 21/yr. $75. Medical World Business Press, Inc., 241 Forsgate Dr., CN 505, Jamesburg, NJ 08831. TEL 908-656-1140. FAX 908-656-1142. Ed. Karen Rosenberg. adv. contact: Jack Cittarelli. circ. 105,000. **Document type:** newspaper.

616   GW   ISSN 0020-9554
                          CODEN: INTEAG
DER INTERNIST. 1960. 12/yr. DM.398($289) (effective 1996). (Berufsverband Deutscher Internisten) Springer-Verlag, Heidelberger Platz 3, 14197 Berlin, Germany. TEL 030-8207-0. FAX 030-8214091. E-mail: orders@springer.de. (Subscr. in N. America to: Springer-Verlag New York, Inc., 44 Hartz Way, Secaucus, NJ 07096-2491. TEL 201-348-4033. FAX 201-348-4505) Ed. G. Budelmann. adv.; bk.rev.; charts; illus.; index, cum.index. (also avail. in microform from UMI; back issues avail.; reprint service avail. from ISI) **Indexed:** Biol.Abstr., Biotech.Abstr., Curr.Cont., Excerp.Med., Ind.Med., Ind.Sci.Rev., Nutr.Abstr. **Document type:** academic/scholarly publication.
—BLDSC (4557.200000); ADONIS; CASDDS; EMDOCS; Genuine Article; SWETS; UMI. **CCC.**

616 330.9   US
INTERNIST: HEALTH POLICY IN PRACTICE. 1959. 10/yr. $24 to non-members (foreign $30). American Society of Internal Medicine, 2011 Pennsylvania Ave., N.W., Ste. 800, Washington, DC 20006-1808. TEL 202-835-2746. FAX 202-835-0441. Ed. Dr. C. Burns Roehrig. adv.; charts; illus.; stat. circ. 29,500. (also avail. in microform from UMI; reprint service avail. from UMI) **Indexed:** C.I.S. Abstr., Chem.Abstr., Hosp.Lit.Ind., Med.Care Rev., Sci.Cit.Ind. **Document type:** trade publication.
—UMI; UnCover.
Formerly (until 1986): Internist (ISSN 0020-9546)
Description: Analysis and reports on current health policy, medical socioeconomic trends and issues affecting the practice of medicine.

616   IT   ISSN 1121-9017
                          CODEN: IRNIE
L'INTERNISTA; giornale di medicina interna. (Text and abstracts in English, Italian) 1993. 3/yr. $60 (effective 1995). (Ospedale Niguarda - Ca Grande) Editore P C A, Via Clerici 12, 20032 Brusuglio di Corman (MI), Italy. TEL 39-2-66300802. FAX 39-2-6151239. Pub. Gianfranco Boldrini. adv.: color page L.5000000; adv. contact: Liliana Succio. bk.rev. circ. 2,000. **Indexed:** Excerp.Med. (1994-).
Description: Provides editorials, reviews, original clinical works and case reports, news, scientific notes, and letters to the editor.
Refereed Serial

616   GW   ISSN 0020-9570
                          CODEN: INPXAJ
INTERNISTISCHE PRAXIS; taegliche Praxis der gesamten Inneren Medizin. 1961. 4/yr. DM.280. Hans Marseille Verlag GmbH, Buerkleinstr. 12, 80538 Munich, Germany. TEL 089-227988. FAX 089-2904643. Eds. H. Feiereis, R. Saller. bk.rev.; abstr.; bibl.; charts; illus.; index, cum.index every 5 yrs. circ. 4,800. (also avail. in microfilm from UMI; reprint service avail. from UMI) **Indexed:** Biol.Abstr., Excerp.Med., Ind.Med. **Document type:** academic/scholarly publication.
—BLDSC (4557.220000); Faxon; SWETS. **CCC.**
Description: Practical information of interest to specialists in internal medicine. Features the latest research in the field. Includes questions and answers.

616.02   GW   ISSN 0344-4201
DIE INTERNISTISCHE WELT. (Supplement to: Die Medizinische Welt (ISSN 0025-8512)) 1978. 4/yr. F.K. Schattauer Verlagsgesellschaft mbH, Lenzhalde 3, 70192 Stuttgart, Germany. TEL 0711-22987-0. FAX 0711-22987-50. Ed. G. Oehler. **Indexed:** Excerp.Med. **Document type:** bulletin.
—SWETS. **CCC.**

616   US   ISSN 0164-6419
INTERNIST'S INTERCOM. m. membership only. American Society of Internal Medicine, 2011 Pennsylvania Ave., N.W., Ste. 800, Washington, DC 20006-1808. TEL 202-835-2746. FAX 202-835-0441. Ed. Barbara Lauter. circ. 29,500. **Document type:** newsletter.
Description: Covers the socioeconomics of internal medicine practice.

616   JA   ISSN 0021-4809
                          CODEN: NAHOAI
JAPANESE ARCHIVES OF INTERNAL MEDICINE/NAIKAHOKAN. (Text in Japanese; summaries in English) 1954. m. $30. Kyoto University, Medical Faculty, Department of Internal Medicine - Kyoto Daigaku Igakubu, 54 Shogoin, Kawara-machi, Kyoto 606, Japan. TEL 075-751-3153. FAX 075-771-2309. Ed. Dr. Tadashi Kano. adv.; bk.rev.; abstr.; charts; illus. circ. 500. **Indexed:** Chem.Ind., Dent.Ind., Excerp.Med., Ind.Med. **Document type:** academic/scholarly publication.
—BLDSC (4650.600000); CASDDS; EMDOCS.

616   JA   ISSN 0301-1542
                          CODEN: NKYZA2
JAPANESE JOURNAL OF THORACIC DISEASES. Key Title: Nihon Kyobu Shikkan Gakkai Zasshi. (Text in Japanese, summaries in English, Japanese) 1963. m. Japanese Society of Chest Diseases - Nihon Kyobu Shikkan Gakkai, YK Hongo Bldg., 4th Fl., 1-11 Hongo 4-chome, Bunkyoku, Tokyo 113. TEL 03-3816-0102. **Indexed:** Biol.Abstr., Excerp.Med., Ind.Med., INIS Atomind. **Document type:** academic/scholarly publication.
—BLDSC (4658.870000).

616   JA   ISSN 0021-5384
                          CODEN: NNGAAS
JAPANESE SOCIETY OF INTERNAL MEDICINE. JOURNAL/NIHON NAIKA GAKKAI ZASSHI. (Text in Japanese) 1913. m. 9000 Yen to non-members. Japanese Society of Internal Medicine - Nihon Naika Gakkai, Hongo Daiichi Bldg., 34-3, 3-chome, Bunkyo-ku, Tokyo 113, Japan. Ed. Takao Saruta. adv.; charts; illus.; index, cum.index. circ. 67,500. **Indexed:** Biol.Abstr., Curr.Cont., Dent.Ind., Ind.Med. **Document type:** academic/scholarly publication.
—BLDSC (4809.460000); CASDDS.
Description: Covers internal medicine.

616   US   ISSN 0884-8734
R11   **CODEN: JGIMEJ**
JOURNAL OF GENERAL INTERNAL MEDICINE. m. $78 to individuals (foreign $88); institutions $98 (foreign $108). (American College of Physicians, Society for General Internal Medicine) Hanley & Belfus, Inc., 210 S. 13th St., Philadelphia, PA 19107. TEL 215-546-7293. FAX 215-790-9330. Ed. Sankey Williams. circ. 3,000. **Indexed:** Behav.Med.Abstr., Excerp.Med.
—BLDSC (4987.827000); Faxon; Genuine Article; SWETS; UnCover. **CCC.**
Description: Focuses on the training and practice of the general internist.
Refereed Serial

610	UK	ISSN 0954-6820
		CODEN: JINMEO

JOURNAL OF INTERNAL MEDICINE. (Supplements avail.) 1869. m. £225($362) (effective 1996). Blackwell Science Ltd., Osney Mead, Oxford OX2 0EL, England. TEL 01865-240201. FAX 01865-721205. TELEX 83355 MEDBOK G. Ed. Lars-Erik Boettiger. adv.; abstr.; bibl.; charts; illus.; index. cum.index: vols.52-140. circ. 2,900. (also avail. in microform from UMI; back issues avail.) **Indexed:** Abstr.Inter.Med., ASCA, Biol.Abstr., Biotech.Abstr., C.I.S. Abstr., Chem.Abstr., Curr.Adv.Ecol.Sci., Curr.Cont., Dairy Sci.Abstr., Dent.Ind., Diar.Dis.Res., Energy Ind., Energy Info.Abstr., Excerp.Med., Helminthol.Abstr., Ind.Med., Ind.Sci.Rev., Kidney, Med.& Surg.Dermat., NRN, Nutr.Abstr., Risk Abstr., Sci.Cit.Ind. **Document type:** academic/scholarly publication.
—BLDSC (5007.548700); ADONIS; CASDDS; Faxon; Genuine Article; SWETS; UMI; UnCover. **CCC.**
Formerly (until 1989): Acta Medica Scandinavica (ISSN 0001-6101)
Refereed Serial

616	UK	ISSN 0955-7873
		CODEN: JIMSE3

JOURNAL OF INTERNAL MEDICINE. SUPPLEMENT. 1989. q. Blackwell Science Ltd., Osney Mead, Oxford OX2 0EL, England. TEL 01865-206206. FAX 01865-206219. TELEX 83355 MEDBOK G. **Indexed:** Excerp.Med. **Document type:** academic/scholarly publication.
—BLDSC (5007.548800); ADONIS; CASDDS; SWETS.

616	KO	ISSN 0494-4712
R97.7.K6		CODEN: TNHCA3

KOREAN JOURNAL OF INTERNAL MEDICINE/DAIHAN NAIGWA HAGHOI JABJI. 1958. m. Korean Association of Internal Medicine - Daihan Naigwa Haghoi, P.O. Box 2062, Korean Medical Association Bldg., 140-031 Seoul, S. Korea. **Indexed:** Excerp.Med. (1993-). **Document type:** academic/scholarly publication.
—BLDSC (5113.560000); CASDDS.

616.02	SP	ISSN 0212-1514

M T A MEDICINA INTERNA. (Metodos Terapeutico-diagnosticos de Actualidad) 1983. m. $75 (effective 1995). J.R. Prous, S.A. International Publishers, Apdo. de Correos 540, 08080 Barcelona, Spain. TEL 343-459-2220. FAX 343-458-1535. Ed. A. Urbano Marquez. adv. contact: P. Blancafort. index. circ. 2,500. (back issues avail.)
Description: Source of practical and current information for internists.

616.07	US	ISSN 0076-2881

MAJOR PROBLEMS IN PATHOLOGY. 1970. irreg. price varies. W.B. Saunders Co. (Subsidiary of Harcourt Brace & Company), The Curtis Center, 3rd Fl., Independence Sq. W., Philadelphia, PA 19106-3399. TEL 215-238-7800. FAX 215-238-6445. (Subscr. to: Periodicals Fulfillment, W.B. Saunders Co., 6277 Sea Harbor Dr., 4th Fl., Orlando, FL 32891-4800. TEL 800-654-2452. FAX 800-874-6418) Ed. J.L. Bennington. **Document type:** academic/scholarly publication.
—BLDSC (5353.690000).
Description: Discusses hurdles pathologists are likely to encounter in their practices.

616	JA	ISSN 0025-7699
		CODEN: MDCHBH

MEDICINA; journal of internal medicine. (Text in Japanese; title in English) 1964. m. 25230 Yen($194) Igaku-Shoin Ltd., 5-24-3 Hongo, Bunkyo-ku, Tokyo 113-91, Japan. TEL 03-3817-5717. adv.; charts; illus.; index. circ. 19,000. **Indexed:** Chem.Abstr.
—BLDSC (5532.400000); CASDDS.

616.026	RM	ISSN 1220-5818

MEDICINA INTERNA. (Text in Rumanian; summaries in English, French, German, Russian) 1905. q. $20. Uniunea Societatilor de Stiinte Medicale din Republica Socialista Rumania, Str. Progresului No. 8, 70754 Bucharest, Rumania. (Subscr. to: ILEXIM, Str. 13 Decembrie Nr. 3, P.O. Box 136-137, Bucharest, Rumania) Ed.Bd. adv.; bk.rev.; abstr.; bibl.; charts; illus. **Indexed:** Biol.Abstr., Chem.Abstr., Dent.Ind., Ind.Med.
Former titles (until 1991): Revista de Medicina Interna, Neurologie, Psihiatrie, Neuro-Chirurgie, Dermato-Venerologie. Series Medicina Interna (ISSN 1220-0905); (until 1974): Medicina Interna (ISSN 0025-7869); (until 1954): Revista Stiintelor Medicale (ISSN 1013-414X)

616	MX	ISSN 0186-4866

MEDICINA INTERNA. (Text in Spanish; summaries in English, Spanish) 1985. q. $40. (Asociacion de Medicina Interna de Mexico) Obsidiana Editores, S.A., Czda. de Tlalpan 2365, Col. Ciudad Jardin, 04370 Mexico DF, Mexico. TEL 6899133. FAX 6896545. Eds. Dr. Manuel Ramiro-Hernandez, Dr. Oscar Saita-Kamino; Pub. Jorge Godoy. circ. 3,000. **Document type:** academic/scholarly publication.
Description: Contains original articles, research reports, review articles, clinical cases and notices related to internal medicine.

616	IT	ISSN 0026-4806
R61		CODEN: MIMEAO

MINERVA MEDICA; rivista mensile di medicina interna. (In 10 parts) (Text in Italian; summaries in English, Italian) 1909. m. $110 to individuals; institutions $150 (effective 1995). Edizioni Minerva Medica, Corso Bramante 83-85, 10126 Turin, Italy. TEL 39-11-678282. FAX 39-11-3121736. Ed. M.L. Benzo; Pub. Alberto Oliaro. adv.: B&W page $1100, color $1900; trim 190 x 270; adv. contact: F. Filippo. bibl.; illus.; circ. 5,000 (paid). (also avail. in microform from UMI) **Indexed:** Biol.Abstr., Biotech.Abstr., C.I.S. Abstr., Chem.Abstr., Curr.Adv.Cancer Res., Curr.Adv.Ecol.Sci., Curr.Cont., Dent.Ind., Dok.Arbeitsmed., Excerp.Med., Helminthol.Abstr., Ind.Med., Nutr.Abstr., Rev.Med.& Vet.Mycol. **Document type:** academic/scholarly publication.
—BLDSC (5794.250000); CASDDS; EMDOCS; Faxon; SWETS; UMI.
Refereed Serial

616	JA	ISSN 0022-1961

NAIKA/INTERNAL MEDICINE (TOKYO, 1958). (Text in Japanese) 1958. m. 30750 Yen (foreign 46000 Yen). Nankodo Co., Ltd., 42-6, Hongo 3-chome, Bunkyo-ku, Tokyo 113, Japan. TEL 03-3811-7239. FAX 03-3811-7230. Ed. Kiyoshi Kurokawa. adv.; charts; illus.; s-a. index. circ. 13,000. **Indexed:** Biol.Abstr., Curr.Adv.Cancer Res.
—BLDSC (4534.890000).
Description: Covers internal medicine.

616	CH	ISSN 1016-7390
R97.7.C5		

NEIKE XUEZHI/JOURNAL OF INTERNAL MEDICINE R O C. (Text in Chinese) 1990. q. Zhonghua Minguo Neike Yixuehui - Society of Internal Medicine R O C, Hsin Hai Rd., Section 1, No. 1, 7th Fl., Taipei, Taiwan 10718, Republic of China.
—BLDSC (5007.548850).

616	NE	ISSN 0300-2977
		CODEN: NLJMAV

NETHERLANDS JOURNAL OF MEDICINE. (Text in English) 1958. m. fl.1062($648) (effective 1996). (Nederlandse Internisten Vereniging - Netherlands Association of Internal Medicine) Elsevier Science B.V., P.O. Box 211, 1000 AE Amsterdam, Netherlands. TEL 31-20-4853911. FAX 31-20-4853598. TELEX 18582 ESPA NL. E-mail: nlinfo-f@elsevier.nl; usinfo-f@elsevier.com; forinfo-kyf04035@niftyserve.or.jp; Site addr.: http://www.elsevier.nl/. (Subscr. in U.S. and Canada to: Elsevier Science Inc., Box 882, Madison Sq. Sta., New York, NY 10159-0882. TEL 212-989-5800. FAX 212-633-3990) Ed. P.W. De Leeuw. adv.; bk.rev.; bibl.; charts; illus. circ. 1,600. (also avail. in microform from UMI) **Indexed:** Biol.Abstr., Chem.Abstr., Curr.Adv.Biochem., Curr.Cont., Excerp.Med., Helminthol.Abstr., Ind.Med., Nutr.Abstr., Sugar Ind.Abstr. **Document type:** academic/scholarly publication.
—BLDSC (6077.003000); CASDDS; Faxon; Genuine Article; SWETS. **CCC.**
Formerly (until 1973): Folia Medica Neerlandica (ISSN 0015-5624)
Description: Publishes original articles and reviews in all relevant fields of internal medicine.
Refereed Serial

610	US	ISSN 0000-1562
R712.A1		

OFFICIAL AMERICAN BOARD OF MEDICAL SPECIALTIES (A B M S) DIRECTORY OF BOARD CERTIFIED INTERNISTS. 1985. biennial. $169.95. Marquis Who's Who, A Reed Reference Publishing company, 121 Chanlon Rd., New Providence, NJ 07974. TEL 908-464-6800. FAX 908-665-2898. (Subscr. to: Order Dept., Box 31, New Providence, NJ 07974-9903. TEL 800-521-8110) Ed. Roy Crego. **Document type:** directory.
Formerly: A B M S Directory of Certified Internists (ISSN 0884-6448)
Description: Biographical sketches of U.S. certified specialists sorted geographically with alpha index.

616	PH	ISSN 0556-0071

PHILIPPINE JOURNAL OF INTERNAL MEDICINE. (Text in English) 1963. bi-m. Philippine College of Physicians, Facilities Central Bldg., 548 Shaw Blvd., Mandaluyong, Metro Manila, Philippines. TEL 2-780233. **Indexed:** Excerp.Med., ExtraMED. **Document type:** academic/scholarly publication.
●Also available on CD-ROM.

616.026	PL	ISSN 0032-3772
		CODEN: PAMWAL

POLSKIE ARCHIWUM MEDYCYNY WEWNETRZNEJ/POLISH ARCHIVES OF INTERNAL MEDICINE. (Text in English or Polish; summaries in English) 1923. m. $100. Towarzystwo Internistow Polskich - Polish Society of Internal Medicine, Ul. Edukacji 1-2, 43-100 Tychy, Poland. TEL 47-32-277723. Ed. Tadeusz Orlowski. adv.; bk.rev.; charts; illus.; index. circ. 4,100. (back issues avail.) **Indexed:** Biol.Abstr., Chem.Abstr., Dent.Ind., Excerp.Med. (until 1993; 1995-), Ind.Med. **Document type:** academic/scholarly publication.
—BLDSC (6546.500000); CASDDS; EMDOCS.
Description: Covers internal medicine.

616	FR	ISSN 0248-8663
		CODEN: RMEIDE

REVUE DE MEDECINE INTERNE. 1962; N.S. 1980. m. 1315 F. in France; foreign 1475 F.($288) (effective 1996). (Societe Francaise de Medecine Interne) Editions Scientifiques Elsevier, 141 rue de Javel, 75747 Paris, France. TEL 33-1-45589063. (Subscr. in U.S. and Canada to: Elsevier Science Inc., Box 882, Madison Sq. Sta., New York, NY 10159-0882. TEL 212-989-5800. FAX 212-633-3990) adv.; bk.rev.; illus.; index. (also avail. in microform from UMI) **Indexed:** Biol.Abstr., C.I.S. Abstr., Chem.Abstr., Curr.Adv.Ecol.Sci., Curr.Cont., Excerp.Med., Ind.Med., Nutr.Abstr., Rev.Med.& Vet.Mycol. **Document type:** academic/scholarly publication.
—BLDSC (7930.940000); Faxon; Genuine Article; SWETS. **CCC.**
Formerly (until 1980): Coeur et Medecine Interne (ISSN 0010-0234)
Description: Covers internal medicine.

MEDICAL SCIENCES — NURSES AND NURSING

616.026   RM   ISSN 1220-4749
                     CODEN: RRINEH
ROMANIAN JOURNAL OF INTERNAL MEDICINE/REVUE ROUMAINE DE MEDECINE INTERNE. (Text in English, French, German or Russian) 1964. 4/yr. 200 lei($55) (Academia de Stiinte Medicale) Editura Academiei Romane, Calea Victoriei 125, 79717 Bucharest, Rumania. (Dist. by: Rompresfilatelia, Calea Grivitei 64-66, P.O. Box 12-201, 78104 Bucharest, Rumania) Ed. S. Purice. bk.rev.; charts; illus.; index. circ. 1,500. (also avail. in microform from UMI; reprint service avail. from UMI) **Indexed:** Biol.Abstr., Chem.Abstr., Curr.Cont., Excerp.Med., Helminthol.Abstr., Ind.Med., Nutr.Abstr. **Document type:** academic/scholarly publication.
   —BLDSC (8019.632000); CASDDS; Faxon; UMI.
   Formerly (until 1990): Revue Roumaine de Medecine. Serie Medecine Interne (ISSN 0377-1202); Which supersedes in part (in 1975): Revue Roumaine de Medecine (ISSN 0303-822X); Which was formed by the 1974 merger of: Revue Roumaine de Neurologie et de Psychiatrie (ISSN 0301-7303); Which was formerly titled (1964-1974): Revue Roumaine de Neurologie (ISSN 0035-3981) & Revue Roumaine d'Endocrinologie (ISSN 0035-4015) & Revue Roumaine de Medecine Interne (ISSN 0035-3973); Which was formerly titled (1964-1974): Revue de Sciences Medicales (ISSN 0484-8632).
   Description: Contains reviews, articles, results of experimental studies and new book information.

616   CC   ISSN 1001-084X
SHIYONG NEIKE ZAZHI/JOURNAL OF PRACTICAL INTERNAL MEDICINE. (Text in Chinese; abstracts in English) 1981. m. $60. Shiyong Yixue Zazhishe - Applied Medical Science Journal Publishing House, 44-1, Jixian St., Heping District, Shenyang, Liaoning 110005, People's Republic of China. TEL 024-3864398. Ed. Yu Runjia. adv. circ. 88,000. **Document type:** academic/scholarly publication.
   Description: Features new developments and methods of practical diagnosis, treatment and prevention of internal diseases.
   Refereed Serial

ZHONGGUO YIXUE WENZHAI (NEIKE XUE). see *MEDICAL SCIENCES — Abstracting, Bibliographies, Statistics*

616.02   CC
ZHONGHUA NEIKE ZAZHI/CHINESE JOURNAL OF INTERNAL MEDICINE. (Text in Chinese) m. $3 per no. Guoji Shudian, Qikan Bu - China International Book Trading Corp., Chegongzhuang Xilu 21, P.O. Box 399, Beijing 100044, People's Republic of China. **Indexed:** Chem.Abstr., ExtraMED, Ind.Med. **Document type:** academic/scholarly publication.
   ●Also available on CD-ROM.

MEDICAL SCIENCES — Nurses And Nursing

see also Gerontology and Geriatrics; Hospitals

A A C N NURSING SCAN IN CRITICAL CARE. see *MEDICAL SCIENCES — Abstracting, Bibliographies, Statistics*

610.73   US   ISSN 0094-6354
                     CODEN: ANJOEE
A A N A JOURNAL. 1933. bi-m. $24. (American Association of Nurse Anesthetists) A A N A Publishing, Inc., 222 S. Prospect, Park Ridge, IL 60068. TEL 708-692-7050. FAX 708-692-6968. Ed. Betty Colitti-Stuffers. adv.; bk.rev. circ. 24,000. (also avail. in microform from MIM,PMC,UMI) **Indexed:** CINAHL, Excerp.Med., Hosp.Lit.Ind., Int.Nurs.Ind.
   —BLDSC (0537.340000); EMDOCS; Faxon; SWETS; UMI; UnCover.
   Formerly: American Association of Nurse Anesthetists. Journal (ISSN 0002-7448)

610.73   US
A A N N SYNAPSE. bi-m. membership only. American Association of Neuroscience Nurses, 224 N. Des Plaines, Ste. 601, Chicago, IL 60661. TEL 312-993-0043. FAX 312-993-0362. E-mail: Bergfeld@aol.com. Ed. Tracy Bergfeld. circ. 4,000. **Document type:** newsletter.

610.73   CN   ISSN 0001-0197
A.A.R.N. NEWSLETTER. 1948. 11/yr. Can.$35 (foreign Can.$40). Alberta Association of Registered Nurses, 11620-168 St., Edmonton, AB T5M 4A6, Canada. TEL 403-451-0043. FAX 403-452-3276. Ed. Evelyn Henderson. adv.: B&W page Can.$1300, color page Can.$1750; 7 3/4 x 10; adv. contact: Jan Henry. bk.rev.; illus.; stat.; circ. 27,777 (controlled). **Indexed:** CINAHL, Int.Nurs.Ind. **Document type:** newsletter.
   —BLDSC (0537.537700). **CCC.**
   Description: Provides information on current trends and issues in nursing in Alberta. Lists educational and career opportunities and a calendar of events.

610.73   US   ISSN 1046-7041
A B N F JOURNAL. 1990. 5/yr. $75 to individuals; institutions $125 (effective 1996). (Association of Black Nursing Faculty in Higher Education, Inc.) Tucker Publications, Inc., Box 580, Lisle, IL 60532. TEL 708-969-3809. FAX 708-969-3895. Ed. Dr. Sallie Tucker-Allen; Pub. Dr. Sallie Tucker-Allen. adv. contact: S. Monique Allen. bk.rev.; circ. 450 (paid). **Indexed:** CINAHL, Int.Nurs.Ind. **Document type:** academic/scholarly publication.
   —BLDSC (0549.610000).
   Refereed Serial

A C O R N JOURNAL. (Australian Confederation of Operating Room Nurses) see *HOSPITALS*

613.7 615.53   US
A F H H A INSIDER. 1984. m. free to members. American Federation of Home Health Agencies, 1320 Fenwick Lane, Ste. 100, Silver Spring, MD 20910. TEL 301-588-1454. FAX 301-588-4732. Ed. Ann Howard. adv.; bk.rev. circ. 500. (looseleaf format; back issues avail.)
   Description: Explores home health care industry issues.

610.73   US   ISSN 0898-4646
A J N GUIDE; to nursing career opportunities. 1982. a. free. American Journal of Nursing Co., 555 W. 57th St., New York, NY 10019. TEL 212-582-8820. FAX 212-586-5462. adv. circ. 150,000.

610.73   CK   ISSN 0120-1832
A N E C. 1966. irreg. $7. Asociacion Nacional de Enfermeras de Colombia, Apdo. Aereo No. 059871, Bogota, D.E., Colombia. Ed.Bd. adv.; bk.rev.; illus. circ. 1,500,811. **Indexed:** Int.Nurs.Ind.
   Formerly: Asociacion Nacional de Enfermeras de Colombia. A N E C. Revista.

610.73 616.1   US   ISSN 8750-0779
RC902.A1
A N N A JOURNAL. 1974. bi-m. $28 to individuals; (foreign $41); institutions $40 (foreign $53). (American Nephrology Nurses' Association) Jannetti Publications, Inc., East Holly Ave., Box 56, Pitman, NJ 08071-0056. TEL 609-589-2319. FAX 609-589-7463. Ed. Sally Downs McCulloch. adv.; bk.rev. circ. 5,743. **Indexed:** CINAHL, Int.Nurs.Ind., Nurs.Abstr.
   —BLDSC (0905.346600); Faxon; SWETS; UnCover. **CCC.**
   Formerly (until 1984): American Association of Nephrology Nurses and Technicians. Journal.

610.73   PH   ISSN 0065-0676
A N P H I PAPERS. (Text in English) 1966. a. P.30($10) Academy of Nursing of the Philippines, College of Nursing, University of the Philippines, Padre Faura, Manila, Philippines. TEL 58-49-39. Ed. Cecilia M. Laurente. bk.rev. circ. 400. (also avail. in microform from UMI) **Indexed:** CINAHL, Int.Nurs.Ind. **Document type:** academic/scholarly publication.
   —UMI.

610.73   UK   ISSN 0960-8508
A N S A JOURNAL. 1988. 3/yr. £12.50. Association of Nurses in Substance Abuse, 18 St. Johns St., Bury St. Edmunds, Suffolk IP33 1SJ, England. TEL 0284-762377. FAX 0284-724374. Ed. Alan Staff. adv.; bk.rev.; circ. 400 (controlled). **Document type:** academic/scholarly publication.
   —BLDSC (1541.844700).
   Description: Carries information about the activities of the association; provides features and abstracts about substance misuse and conference course information.

A O N E'S LEADERSHIP PROSPECTIVES. (American Organization of Nurse Executives) see *MEDICAL SCIENCES — Abstracting, Bibliographies, Statistics*

610.73   US   ISSN 0001-2092
RD99.A1   CODEN: AOJOEL
A O R N JOURNAL. 1963. m. $50 to non-members; members $20; foreign $60. Association of Operating Room Nurses, Inc., c/o Peggy S. Lehr, 2170 S. Parker Rd., Ste. 300, Denver, CO 80231. TEL 303-755-6300. FAX 303-750-3441. TELEX 910-320-2273. Ed. Beverly P. Giordano. adv. contact: Denise Belua. bk.rev.; abstr.; bibl.; charts; illus.; stat.; index, cum.index. circ. 50,389. (also avail. in microfilm from UMI) **Indexed:** Abstr.Health Care Manage.Stud., CINAHL, Hosp.Lit.Ind., I.P.A., Ind.Med., Int.Nurs.Ind., Nurs.Abstr. **Document type:** trade publication.
   —BLDSC (1567.727000); Faxon; SWETS; UMI; UnCover. **CCC.**
   Supersedes: O R Nursing.
   Description: Contains clinical information, research articles, and perioperative nursing standards of practice.

610.73   CN   ISSN 1182-8897
A R N N ACCESS. 1981. q. $10. Association of Registered Nurses of Newfoundland, 55 Military Rd., P.O. Box 6116, St. John's, NF A1C 5X8, Canada. TEL 709-753-6040. FAX 709-753-4940. adv. circ. 6,300. **Document type:** newsletter.
   Former titles (until 1990): A R N N News News (ISSN 0822-7160); (until 1981): News! News! News! (ISSN 0319-7611)

610.73   US   ISSN 1075-5764
A R N NEWS. 1976. 10/yr. Association of Rehabilitation Nurses, 5700 Old Orchard Rd., 1st Fl., Skokie, IL 60077-1057. TEL 708-966-3433. FAX 708-966-9418. Ed. Joann Abkemeier. adv. circ. 11,000. **Document type:** newsletter.
   Description: Focuses on association news, upcoming educational events, committee functions, and new items of interest to those in the field of nursing and the specialty of rehabilitation nursing.

A SORN NEWS. (American Society of Ophthalmic Registered Nurses, Inc.) see *MEDICAL SCIENCES — Ophthalmology And Optometry*

610.73 618   US   ISSN 1066-2944
A W H O N N NEWSLETTER. (Former name of issuing body: N A A C O G: The Organization for Obstetric, Gynecologic, & Neonatal Nurses) 1974. m. $30 (foreign $45) (effective 1993). Association of Women's Health, Obstetric, and Neonatal Nurses, 409 12th St., S.W., Ste. 300, Washington, DC 20024. TEL 202-638-0026. Ed. Connie S. Helminger. adv.; index. circ. 27,000. (back issues avail.) **Document type:** newsletter.
   Formerly (until 1993): N A A C O G Newsletter (ISSN 0889-0579)
   Description: For nurses and others interested in women's health nursing issues

610.73   UK   ISSN 0965-2302
ACCIDENT AND EMERGENCY NURSING. 1993. q. £52($86) to individuals; institutions £99 ($164) (effective 1995). Churchill Livingstone Journals (Subsidiary of: Pearson Professional), Robert Stevenson House, 1-3 Baxter's Pl., Leith Walk, Edinburgh EH1 3AF, Scotland. TEL 0131-556-2424. FAX 0131-459-1177. (Subscr. to: Pearson Professional Ltd., P.O. Box 77, Fourth Ave., Harlow, Essex CM19 5AA, England. TEL 01279-623760; U.S. subscr. to: Churchill Livingstone, 650 Ave. of the Americas, New York, NY 10011. TEL 212-206-5000) Ed. Bob Wright. adv. contact: David Dunnachie. bk.rev. circ. 725. **Document type:** academic/scholarly publication.
   —BLDSC (0573.137000).
   Description: Covers various topics in emergency-care nursing.

610.73   IS   ISSN 0048-1165
HA-ACHOTE BE-YISRAEL/NURSE IN ISRAEL. (Text in Hebrew) 1948. q. $3. National Association of Nurses in Israel, Box 303, Tel-Aviv, Israel. Ed.Bd. adv.; illus. circ. 10,000. **Indexed:** Ind.Heb.Per., Ind.Med.

ACTA MEDICA AUXOLOGICA. see *MEDICAL SCIENCES — Endocrinology*

MEDICAL SCIENCES — NURSES AND NURSING 4433

610.73 US ISSN 1073-886X
CODEN: ADNUFH
ADDICTIONS NURSING. 1989. q. $95 (foreign $135). Mary Ann Liebert, Inc. Publishers, 2 Madison Ave., Larchmont, NY 10538. TEL 914-834-3100. FAX 914-834-3688. E-mail: Liebert@pipeline.com. Ed. Madeline A. Naegle. **Indexed:** CINAHL. **Document type:** academic/scholarly publication.
—BLDSC (0678.728000).
Formerly (until 1994): Addictions Nursing Network (ISSN 0899-9112)
Description: Recognizes the major role of nurses in identifying and intervening with drug and alcohol abuse. Provides current information on serious major health problems, as well as specialties of addictions nursing.

610.73 US ISSN 0161-9268
RT1
ADVANCES IN NURSING SCIENCE. 1978. q. $68 (foreign $82). Aspen Publishers, Inc., 200 Orchard Ridge Dr., Gaithersburg, MD 20878. TEL 301-417-7500. FAX 301-417-7550. (Subscr. addr.: 7201 Mckinney Circle, Frederich, MD 21701. TEL 800-234-1660) adv. contact: Frances S. Ray. index; circ. 3,277 (paid). (back issues avail.) **Indexed:** Behav.Med.Abstr., CINAHL, IMFL, Ind.Med., Nurs.Abstr., Psychol.Abstr. (1984-). **Document type:** academic/scholarly publication.
—BLDSC (0709.508000); Faxon; Genuine Article; SWETS; UMI; UnCover. **CCC.**
Refereed Serial

610.73 US ISSN 0002-4546
ALASKA NURSE. 1951. q. $7 to non-members. Alaska Nurses Association, 237 E. Third Ave., Anchorage, AK 99501. TEL 907-274-0827. FAX 907-272-0292. Ed. Kathy North. adv.; bk.rev.; illus. circ. 500. **Indexed:** CINAHL, Int.Nurs.Ind.

610.73 GW ISSN 0002-6573
ALTENHEIM; Organ der gemeinnuetzigen und privaten Alten- und Altenpflegeheime. 1962. m. DM.123 (foreign DM.144). Vincentz Verlag, Schiffgraben 43, 30175 Hannover, Germany. TEL 0511-9909823. FAX 0511-9909829. (Subscr. to: Postfach 6247, 30062 Hannover, Germany) Ed. Reinhard Hein. adv.; bk.rev.; charts; illus.; stat.; index. circ. 8,130. (tabloid format) **Indexed:** Dok.Arbeitsmed. **Document type:** bulletin.
—**CCC.**

610.73 GW ISSN 0341-0455
ALTENPFLEGE. 1976. m. DM.75 (foreign DM.94.80). (Fachkraefte in Ambulanter und Stationaerer Altenhilfe) Vincentz Verlag, Schiffgraben 43, 30175 Hannover, Germany. TEL 0511-9909830. FAX 0511-9909871. (Subscr. to: Postfach 6247, 30062 Hannover, Germany) Ed. Wolfgang Bergmann. adv.; bk.rev.; charts; illus.; stat.; index. circ. 29,317. (tabloid format) **Document type:** bulletin.
—**CCC.**

610.73 US ISSN 1041-2972
RT82.8 CODEN: JANPEB
AMERICAN ACADEMY OF NURSE PRACTITIONERS. JOURNAL. 1988. q. $39 to individuals (foreign $45); institutions $50 (foreign $60). Slack, Inc., 6900 Grove Rd., Thorofare, NJ 08086. TEL 609-848-1000.
—BLDSC (4683.731500); UMI.
Description: Captures what's happening in clinical practice, management, education, research and legislation.
Refereed Serial

610.73 340 US ISSN 1065-3449
AMERICAN ASSOCIATION OF LEGAL NURSE CONSULTANTS NETWORK;* news for the legal nurse consultant. 1990. q. $24. American Association of Legal Nurse Consultants, 444 N. Michigan Ave., Ste. 1240, Chicago, IL 60611-3901. TEL 312-670-0550. FAX 312-661-0769. Ed. Rebecca Dawson. adv.; bk.rev. circ. 1,000. (tabloid format; back issues avail.) **Indexed:** CINAHL.
Description: Provides a forum for continuing education, facilities and exchange of information; establishes a communication network for its members; it also functions as a resource to other professional organizations of similar interest.

610.73 US ISSN 0891-0162
RC966
AMERICAN ASSOCIATION OF OCCUPATIONAL HEALTH NURSES JOURNAL. Abbreviated title: A A O H N Journal. 1953. m. $40 to individuals; institutions $53. (American Association of Occupational Health Nurses, Inc.) Slack, Inc., 6900 Grove Rd., Thorofare, NJ 08086. TEL 609-848-1000.
FAX 609-853-5991. adv.; bk.rev.; charts; illus.; index. circ. 14,000. (also avail. in microfilm) **Indexed:** C.I.S. Abstr., CINAHL, Excerp.Med., Ind.Hyg.Dig., Int.Nurs.Ind., Noise Pollut.Publ.Abstr., Nurs.Abstr.
—BLDSC (0537.501300); Faxon; Genuine Article; SWETS; UMI; UnCover. **CCC.**
Former titles: Occupational Health Nursing (ISSN 0029-7933); (1953-1968): American Association of Industrial Nurses Journal (ISSN 0098-6097)
Refereed Serial

610.73 616 US ISSN 1062-3264
AMERICAN JOURNAL OF CRITICAL CARE. 1992. bi-m. $45 to individuals (Canada and Mexico $52; elsewhere $60); institutions $110 (Canada and Mexico $126; elsewhere $163) (effective 1993). American Association of Critical Care Nurses, 101 Columbia, Aliso Viejo, CA 92656. TEL 714-362-2000. FAX 714-362-2020. (Subscr. to: Box 626, Holmes, PA 19043. TEL 800-345-8112) adv.; B&W page $2610, color page $3685; trim 8 7/8 x 10 7/8. circ. 74,000. **Indexed:** Ind.Med. (1993-). **Document type:** academic/scholarly publication.
●Also available on CD-ROM. Producer(s): SilverPlatter Information, Inc.
—BLDSC (0824.210000). **CCC.**
Description: Communicates important advances in clinical science and research in critical care.
Refereed Serial

610.73 US ISSN 0002-936X
RT1
AMERICAN JOURNAL OF NURSING. 1900. m. $22.97 to individuals; institutions $45. (American Nurses' Association) American Journal of Nursing Co., 555 W. 57th St., New York, NY 10019. TEL 212-582-8820. FAX 212-586-5462. Dir. Martin DiCarlantonio. adv.: page $7040; adv. contact: Joan Harrigan. bk.rev.; bibl.; charts; illus.; tr.lit.; index, cum.index: 1961-65, 1966-70, 1971-75. circ. 233,000. (also avail. in microform from PMC,UMI; reprint service avail. from UMI) **Indexed:** Abstr.Health Care Manage.Stud., Acad.Ind., Adol.Ment.Hlth.Abstr., AIM, ASSIA, Chem.Abstr., CINAHL, CLOA, Curr.Cont., Curr.Lit.Fam.Plan., Dent.Ind., Dok.Arbeitsmed., Except.Child.Educ.Abstr., Gen.Sci.Ind., Hlth.Ind., Hosp.Lit.Ind., I.P.A., IMFL, Ind.Med., Ind.Sci.Rev., Int.Nurs.Ind., Med.Care Rev., Nurs.Abstr., Nutr.Abstr., P.A.I.S., Psychol.Abstr., Risk Abstr., Sci.Cit.Ind., Soc.Sci.Ind., Soc.Work Res.& Abstr., SSCI, Tr.& Indus.Ind.
●Also available online. Vendor(s): University Microfilms International.
—BLDSC (0828.500000); Faxon; SWETS; UMI; UnCover.
Description: Emphasizes the latest technological advances affecting nursing care for registered nurses.
Refereed Serial

610.73 US ISSN 0098-1486
THE AMERICAN NURSE. 1969. 10/yr. $20. American Nurses Association, 600 Maryland Ave. S.W., Ste. 100, Washington, DC 20024-2571. TEL 202-554-4444. FAX 202-554-2262. Ed. Mandy Mikulencak. adv. circ. 200,000. (also avail. in microform from UMI; reprint service avail. from UMI) **Indexed:** CINAHL, Hosp.Lit.Ind., Int.Nurs.Ind., Nurs.Abstr. **Document type:** trade publication.
—UMI.
Formerly (until 1974): A N A in Action (ISSN 0587-3053)

610.73 616.89 US ISSN 1078-3903
▼**AMERICAN PSYCHIATRIC NURSES ASSOCIATION. JOURNAL.** 1995. bi-m. $42 to individuals (Canada $57.78; elsewhere $54); institutions $75 (Canada $93.09; elsewhere $87); students $21 (Canada $35.31; elsewhere $33) (effective 1996). Mosby - Year Book, Inc. (Subsidiary of: Times Mirror Company), 11830 Westline Industrial Dr., St. Louis, MO 63146-3318. TEL 314-872-8370. FAX 314-872-9164. adv.; B&W page $660, color page $1440; trim 8 1/4 x 11. circ. 3,908.
Description: Covers a blend of clinical and research topics, practice challenges, and changes occurring in this ever-changing field.

610.73.5 US ISSN 0739-6686
ANNUAL REVIEW OF NURSING RESEARCH. 1984. a. price varies. Springer Publishing Company, 536 Broadway, New York, NY 10012-3955. TEL 212-431-4370. FAX 212-941-7842. Ed. Joyce J. Fitzpatrick. circ. 1,212. **Indexed:** CINAHL, Int.Nurs.Ind. **Document type:** academic/scholarly publication.
—BLDSC (1524.200000); Faxon; SWETS; UnCover.
Description: Focuses on developments in nursing.

610.73 616 US ISSN 0897-1897
CODEN: ANUREA
APPLIED NURSING RESEARCH. 1988. q. $87 (foreign $137) (effective 1996). W.B. Saunders Co. (Subsidiary of: Harcourt Brace & Company), Curtis Center, 3rd Fl., Independence Sq. W., Philadelphia, PA 19106-3399. TEL 215-238-7800. FAX 215-238-6445. (Subscr. to: Periodicals Fulfillment, W.B. Saunders Co., 6277 Sea Harbor Dr., 4th Fl., Orlando, FL 32891-4800. TEL 800-654-2452. FAX 800-874-6418) Ed. Joyce J. Fitzpatrick; Pub. Joan W. Blumberg. adv.: B&W page $545, color page $1315; 7 x 10; adv. contact: Steve Gray. circ. 1,779. **Indexed:** CINAHL, Ind.Med. (1993-). **Document type:** academic/scholarly publication.
—BLDSC (1576.236000); Faxon; Genuine Article; SWETS; UMI; UnCover. **CCC.**
Description: Devoted to advancing nursing as a research-based profession and bridging the gap between research and practice in nursing.

610.73 616.8 US ISSN 0883-9417
ARCHIVES OF PSYCHIATRIC NURSING. 1987 (Feb.). bi-m. $72 (foreign $99) (effective 1996). (Society for Education and Research in Psychiatric-Mental Health Nursing) W.B. Saunders Co. (Subsidiary of: Harcourt Brace & Company), Curtis Center, 3rd Fl., Independence Sq. W., Philadelphia, PA 19106-3399. TEL 215-238-7800. FAX 215-238-6445. (Subscr. to: Periodicals Fulfillment, W.B. Saunders Co., 6277 Sea Harbor Dr., 4th Fl., Orlando, FL 32891-4800. TEL 800-654-2452. FAX 800-874-6418) Ed. Judith B. Krauss; Pub. Joan W. Blumberg. adv.: B&W page $710, color $1610; 7 x 10; adv. contact: Steve Gray. bk.rev.; abstr.; bibl.; charts; illus.; index. circ. 3,223. **Indexed:** CINAHL, Nurs.Abstr., Psychol.Abstr. (1988-). **Document type:** academic/scholarly publication.
—BLDSC (1640.410000); Faxon; SWETS; UMI; UnCover. **CCC.**
Description: Approaches the field from the broadest possible perspective through articles and case reports relating to theories, practices, and research applications.
Refereed Serial

610.73 US ISSN 0004-1599
ARIZONA NURSE. vol.23, 1970. 6/yr. $30. Arizona Nurses Association, 1850 E. Southern Ave., Ste. 1, Tempe, AZ 85282. FAX 602-839-4780. Ed. Jennifer McAfee. adv.; bk.rev.; illus. circ. 2,000. (also avail. in microfilm from UMI; reprint service avail. from UMI) **Indexed:** CINAHL, Int.Nurs.Ind. **Document type:** newsletter.
—BLDSC (1740.440000); UMI.

ARTHRITIS CARE AND RESEARCH. see MEDICAL SCIENCES — Rheumatology

610.73 GW ISSN 0931-5853
DIE ARZTHELFERIN. 1963. m. Friedrich Kiehl Verlag GmbH, Pfaustr. 13, 67063 Ludwigshafen, Germany. Ed. Lothar Kurz; Pub. Ernst Kleyboldt. bk.rev.; index. circ. 14,000. **Document type:** academic/scholarly publication.
—**CCC.**
Incorporates (in 1989): Helferin des Arztes (ISSN 0017-9949)

610.73 US
ASPEN'S ADVISOR FOR NURSE EXECUTIVES. 1985. m. $155 (foreign $186). Aspen Publishers, Inc., 200 Orchard Ridge Dr., Gaithersburg, MD 20878. TEL 301-417-7500. FAX 301-417-7550. **Indexed:** CINAHL. **Document type:** newsletter.
—BLDSC (1745.932000); UMI.
Former titles: Aspen's Nurse Executive Network; (until 1993): Aspen's Advisor for Nurse Executives (ISSN 0883-9743)
Description: Covers strategies, financial techniques, new ventures, human resources, and legislative legal and labor issues, all presented from the perspective of the Nurse Executive.

MEDICAL SCIENCES — NURSES AND NURSING

610.73   IT   ISSN 0393-7550
ASSISTENZA INFERMIERISTICA DEL NORD AMERICA. q. L.110000($125) Piccin Editore, Via Altinate 107, 35100 Padua, Italy. TEL 049-655566. FAX 049-8750693. (reprint service avail. from UMI)

610.73 378   US
ASSOCIATE DEGREE EDUCATION FOR NURSING. 1972. a. $5.95. National League for Nursing, 350 Hudson St., New York, NY 10014. TEL 212-989-9393.
Formerly: National League for Nursing. Associate Degree Education for Nursing (ISSN 0077-5118)

ASSOCIATION OF MEDICAL WOMEN IN INDIA. JOURNAL. see *WOMEN'S HEALTH*

ASSOCIATION OF NURSES IN AIDS CARE. JOURNAL. see *MEDICAL SCIENCES — Communicable Diseases*

610.73 618.92   AT   ISSN 1036-5060
AUSTRALIA PAEDIATRIC NURSE JOURNAL. Abbreviated title: A P N J. 1988-1993; resumed 1994. 3/yr. Queensland Paediatric Nurses Association, c/o Education Centre, Royal Children's Hospital, Herston Rd., Herston, Qld. 4029, Australia.
—BLDSC (1817.530000).
Formerly (until 1991); Queensland Paediatric Nurses Association Journal (ISSN 1035-2600)
Description: Provides a means for the publication of articles in the field of healthcare for infants, children, and their families. Promotes the sharing of information among networks of nurses and other health care providers to improve the quality of care.

AUSTRALIAN AND NEW ZEALAND JOURNAL OF MENTAL HEALTH NURSING. see *MEDICAL SCIENCES — Psychiatry And Neurology*

610.73   AT   ISSN 0813-0531
AUSTRALIAN JOURNAL OF ADVANCED NURSING. 1983. q. Aus.$55 to non-members; members Aus.$35; libraries Aus.$60; foreign Aus.$65. Australian Nursing Federation, 373-375 St. Georges Rd., North Fitzroy, Vic. 3068, Australia. TEL 03-482-2722. FAX 03-482-2330. Ed. Natalie Newman. circ. 1,600. **Indexed:** CINAHL, Int.Nurs.Ind. **Document type:** academic/scholarly publication.
—BLDSC (1801.830000). **CCC**.
Description: Covers nursing research and allied philosophical study.

AUSTRALIAN JOURNAL OF EMERGENCY CARE. see *MEDICAL SCIENCES — Orthopedics And Traumatology*

AUSTRALIAN JOURNAL OF RURAL HEALTH. see *PUBLIC HEALTH AND SAFETY*

610.73   AT   ISSN 1320-3185
RT15
AUSTRALIAN NURSING JOURNAL. 1962. 10/yr. Aus.$33 to non-members; members Aus.$15.40; foreign Aus.$50. Australian Nursing Federation, 373-375 St. Georges Rd., North Fitzroy, Vic. 3068, Australia. TEL 03-482-2722. FAX 03-482-2330. Ed. Amanda Tattam. adv.; bk.rev. circ. 47,000. (also avail. in microfiche from UMI; reprint service avail. from UMI) **Indexed:** CINAHL, Int.Nurs.Ind., NRN.
—BLDSC (1815.830000); UMI; UnCover.
Formerly: Australian Nurses' Journal (ISSN 0045-0758)
Description: Multi-purpose professional and trade union nursing journal.

610.73   FR   ISSN 0240-6411
AVENIR ET SANTE; la revue des infirmieres liberales. 1971. m. (10/yr.). 400 F. to non-members, students and retirees; members 250 F.; institutions 800 F. Federation Nationale des Infirmiers et Infirmieres, 7 rue Godot de Mauroy, 75009 Paris, France. TEL 47-42-94-13. FAX 47-42-90-82. Ed. Veronique Veillon. adv. circ. 12,916.

610.73   UK
BAILLIERE'S NURSES' DICTIONARY. 1912. irreg., vol. 21, 1990. £3.50 (effective 1994). Bailliere Tindall - W.B. Saunders Co. Ltd. (Subsidiary of: Harcourt Brace & Company Ltd.), 24-28 Oval Rd., London NW1 7DX, England. TEL 0171-267-4466. FAX 0171-482-2293. TELEX 25775 ACPRES G. (Orders to: Harcourt Brace & Company Ltd., Foots Cray High St., Sidcup, Kent DA14 5HP, England. TEL 0181-300-3322. FAX 0181-309-0807; Orders in N. America to: W.B. Saunders Co., 6277 Sea Harbor Dr., 4th Fl., Orlando, FL 32887-4800. TEL 800-874-6418) (back issues avail.) **Document type:** academic/scholarly publication.

610.73   BB   ISSN 0572-6042
BARBADOS NURSING JOURNAL. a. membership. Barbados Registered Nurses Association, Gibson House, Spry Street, Bridgetown, Barbados, W.I.

BARNBLADET; tidskrift foer Sveriges barnsjukskoeterskor. see *MEDICAL SCIENCES — Pediatrics*

610.73 310.412   US   ISSN 1071-2984
BEGINNINGS (RALEIGH). 1981. m. (10/yr.). $16. American Holistic Nurses' Association, 4101 Lake Boone Trail, Ste. 201, Raleigh, NC 27607. TEL 800-278-AHNA. FAX 919-787-4916. Ed. Sue Collins, R.N. adv. contact: Paige Landry. bk.rev.; tr.lit. circ. 3,000. (back issues avail.) **Document type:** academic/scholarly publication.
—BLDSC (1876.607000).
Description: Promotes the education of nurses and the public in the concepts and practice of health of the whole person.

BETHLEM AND MAUDSLEY GAZETTE. see *MEDICAL SCIENCES — Psychiatry And Neurology*

BIRTH; issues in perinatal care and education. see *MEDICAL SCIENCES — Obstetrics And Gynecology*

BLAETTER AUS DEM HENRIETTENSTIFT. see *HOSPITALS*

BREATHLINE. see *MEDICAL SCIENCES — Anaesthesiology*

610.73   UK   ISSN 0966-0461
RT1
BRITISH JOURNAL OF NURSING. 1979. fortn. £50 (overseas £100). Mark Allen Publishing Ltd., Croxted Mews, 288 Croxted Rd., London SE24 9BY, England. TEL 0181-671-7521. FAX 0181-671-1722. Ed. George Castledine; Pub. Mark Allen. adv. contact: Adrian Johnston. **Indexed:** CINAHL, Curr.Adv.Ecol.Sci., Int.Nurs.Ind., Nurs.Abstr., Tr.& Indus.Ind. **Document type:** academic/scholarly publication.
—BLDSC (2311.980100); SWETS; UMI. **CCC**.
Formerly: Nursing (ISSN 0142-0372)

610.73   UK   ISSN 1353-0224
BRITISH JOURNAL OF THEATRE NURSING. 1965. m. £30 (foreign £40). National Association of Theatre Nurses, 22 Mount Parade, Harrogate HG1 1BX, England. TEL 01423-508079. FAX 01423-531613. Ed. Kate Nightingale. adv. contact: John Matthews. bk.rev.; circ. 6,000 (controlled). (back issues avail.) **Indexed:** CINAHL, Int.Nurs.Ind. **Document type:** academic/scholarly publication.
—BLDSC (2325.700000); UnCover.
Formerly (until 1991): N A T News (ISSN 0027-6049)
Description: News and research articles on the technological, administrative, and procedural aspects of providing care and services to patients in the operating room, with announcements of the activities and membership of the association.

610.73 616.6   CN
C A N N T JOURNAL/JOURNAL C A N N T.* (Text in English, French) q. Can.$30. (Canadian Association of Nephrology Nurses and Technicians - Association Canadienne des Infirmiers-Infirmieres et Techniciens-nnes en Nephrologie) Pappin Communications, The Victoria Centre, 84 Isabella St., Pembroke, ON K8A 5S5, Canada. TEL 613-735-0952. FAX 613-735-7983. Ed. Leanne Dekker. **Indexed:** CINAHL.

610.73   NE   ISSN 0920-2811
C F O - MAGAZINE; league issue for nurses and other people working the health and social welfare field. Key Title: CFO Magazine (Ed. Overheid). C F O Magazine (Ed. Trendvolgers) (ISSN 0920-282X) 1948. fortn. fl.76.20. (Christelijke Federatie Overheidspersoneel) C N V Bond voor Overheid, Gezondheid, Welzijn en Sociale Werkvoorziening, Seekant 35, 2586 AA The Hague, Netherlands. TEL 31-70-3582582. FAX 31-70-3547163. adv.; bk.rev. circ. 18,000.
—SWETS.
Formed by the 1986 merger of: C F O - Krant (ISSN 0169-4804); Welzijn (ISSN 0165-8379); Which was formerly: Volksgezondheid.

610.73   BE   ISSN 0007-8417
C I C I A M S NEWS - NOUVELLES - NACHRICHTEN. (Text in English, French and German) 1964. 3/yr. 1200 BEF($40) International Catholic Committee of Nurses and Medico Social Assistants - C I C I A M S - Comite International Catholique des Infirmieres et des Assistantes Medico-Sociales, 43, Sq. Vergote, 1040 Brussels, Belgium. TEL 32-2-7321050. FAX 32-2-7348460. adv.; bk.rev.; bibl.; illus. circ. 700.
—BLDSC (3192.450000).

610.73   CN
C I N A.* 1975. q. Can.$32.10($37.45) (foreign Can$48.15). (Canadian Intravenous Nurses Association) Pappin Communications, The Victoria Centre, 84 Isabella St., Pembroke, ON K8A 5S5, Canada. TEL 613-735-0952. Ed. Dianne Lopponen. adv. contact: Bruce Pappin. **Indexed:** CINAHL.

C N N T NEWSLETTER. (Council of Nephrology Nurses & Technicians) see *MEDICAL SCIENCES — Urology And Nephrology*

C O N A JOURNAL. (Canadian Orthopaedic Nurses Association) see *MEDICAL SCIENCES — Orthopedics And Traumatology*

C R N A: THE CLINICAL FORUM FOR NURSE ANESTHETISTS. see *MEDICAL SCIENCES — Anaesthesiology*

610.73   US   ISSN 0008-1310
CALIFORNIA NURSE. 1904. m. $30. California Nurses' Association, 1145 Market St., Ste. 1100, San Francisco, CA 94103-1545. TEL 415-864-4141. FAX 415-431-1011. Ed. Jennifer L. Watson. adv.: page $1300; 10 x 13. circ. 25,000. (tabloid format; also avail. in microfilm from UMI; reprint service avail. from UMI, ISI) **Indexed:** Cal.Per.Ind. (1978-), CINAHL, Int.Nurs.Ind. **Document type:** bulletin.
—BLDSC (3015.085000); UMI.
Formerly: C N A Bulletin.

610.73   US
CALIFORNIA SCHOOL NURSE. 3/yr. Health Information Publications, Inc., 92 S. Highland Ave., Ossining, NY 10562. TEL 914-762-6498. Ed. Barbara Bradstock. circ. 1,888.

610.73   CN   ISSN 0843-6096
CANADIAN JOURNAL OF CARDIOVASCULAR NURSING. (Text in English or French) 1973. q. Can.$28 to individuals; institutions $42; students $20. Canadian Council of Cardiovascular Nurses, 160 George St., Ste. 200, Ottawa, ON K1N 9M2, Canada. TEL 613-241-4361. FAX 416-241-3278. Ed. Ellen Rukholm. adv.; bk.rev. circ. 1,200. **Indexed:** CINAHL.
—BLDSC (3030.600000).
Supersedes (in Apr. 1989): Canadian Bulletin of Cardiovascular Nursing (ISSN 0831-4462)
Description: Concerned with health care issues related to cardiovascular diseases.
Refereed Serial

610.73   CN   ISSN 0838-2948
CANADIAN JOURNAL OF NURSING ADMINISTRATION. 1988. q. Can.$28. Health Media Inc., 14453 29A Ave., White Rock, BC V4A 9K8, Canada. TEL 604-535-7933. Ed. Jan Dick. **Indexed:** CINAHL, Nurs.Abstr.
—BLDSC (3033.350000).
Description: For Canadian nurse administrators, managers and educators.
Refereed Serial

MEDICAL SCIENCES — NURSES AND NURSING

610.73   CN   ISSN 0844-5621
CODEN: CJNRE3
THE CANADIAN JOURNAL OF NURSING RESEARCH/REVUE CANADIENNE DE RECHERCHE EN SCIENCES INFIRMIERES. (Text in English and French) 1969. q. Can.$61 to individuals (foreign Can.$65); institutions Can.$107 (foreign Can.$108); students Can.$38.50 (foreign $55). McGill University, School of Nursing, 3506 University St., Montreal, PQ H3A 2A7, Canada. TEL 514-392-4160. FAX 514-398-8455. E-mail: cylg@musicA.mcgill.ca. Ed. Laurie Gottleib. adv.; B&W page Can.$275. bk.rev. circ. 1,200. **Indexed:** Abstr.Health Care Manage.Stud., CINAHL, Hosp.Abstr., Int.Nurs.Ind., Nurs.Abstr., Nurs.Abstr., Pt.de Rep. (1988-), Sociol.Abstr., SOPODA. **Document type:** academic/scholarly publication.
—BLDSC (3033.400000); Faxon; UnCover.
Formerly: Nursing Papers - Perspectives en Nursing (ISSN 0318-1006)
Description: Provides a forum for research and articles relevant to nursing and health. Covers clinical research, methodological issues, education research, and theory.
Refereed Serial

610.73   CN
CANADIAN NURSE - L'INFIRMIERE CANADIENNE. 1905. 11/yr. Can.$36 (US Can.$50, elsewhere Can.$60). Canadian Nurses Association - Association des Infirmieres et Infirmiers du Canada, 50 Driveway, Ottawa, ON K2P 1E2, Canada. TEL 613-237-2133. FAX 613-237-3520. Ed. Heather Broughton. adv.; bk.rev.; film rev.; bibl.; charts; illus.; stat.; tr.lit.; index. circ. 104,000. (also avail. in microfilm from UMI,PMC; reprint service avail. from UMI) **Indexed:** Can.B.P.I., Can.Per.Ind., CINAHL, CMI, Hosp.Abstr., Int.Nurs.Ind., Nurs.Abstr., Pt.de Rep. (1979-).
—BLDSC (3043.110000); SWETS; UMI; UnCover. **CCC.**
Formed by the merger of: Infirmiere Canadienne (ISSN 0019-9605) & Canadian Nurse (ISSN 0008-4581)

CANADIAN NURSES ASSOCIATION. HELEN K. MUSSALLEM LIBRARY. PERIODICAL HOLDINGS. see *MEDICAL SCIENCES — Abstracting, Bibliographies, Statistics*

610.73   CN
CANADIAN NURSING MANAGEMENT. 1987. 10/yr. Can.$109. M P L Communications Inc., 700-133 Richmond St., W., Toronto, ON M5H 2M8, Canada. TEL 416-869-1177. FAX 416-869-0456. Ed. John Hobel. circ. 800. **Document type:** newsletter.

610.73 616.99   CN   ISSN 1181-912X
CANADIAN ONCOLOGY NURSING JOURNAL/REVUE CANADIENNE DE NURSING ONCOLOGIQUE.* (Texts and summaries in English, French) 1991. 4/yr. Can.$44.94 to individuals; institutions Can.$64.20; foreign Can.$75. (Canadian Association of Nurses in Ocology - Association Canadienne des Infirmieres en Oncologie) Pappin Communications, The Victoria Centre, 84 Isabella St., Pembroke, ON K8A 5S5, Canada. TEL 613-735-0952. FAX 613-735-7983. (Subscr. to: S. Burlein-Hall, 214 Lake Driveway W., Ajax, ON L1S 5A1, Canada) Ed. Beverley Page. adv.; B&W page Can.$860, color page Can.$1310; trim 8 1/2 x 11. circ. 1,100. **Indexed:** CINAHL. **Document type:** academic/scholarly publication, newsletter.
—BLDSC (3043.176000).
Description: Covers clinical oncology nursing practice, education and research. Also serves as newsletter and networking vehicle for nurses.
Refereed Serial

610.73   CN   ISSN 0712-6778
CANADIAN OPERATING ROOM NURSING JOURNAL. 1983. 4/yr. Can.$16($22) (Operating Room Nurses Association of Canada) Health Media Inc., 14453 29A Ave., White Rock, BC V4A 9K8, Canada. TEL 604-535-7933. Ed. Agnes Forster. circ. 4,020. **Indexed:** CINAHL.
—BLDSC (3043.177000). **CCC.**

610.73 616.99   US   ISSN 0162-220X
RC266
CANCER NURSING; an international journal for cancer care. 1978. bi-m. $44 to individuals; institutions $84 (effective 1995). Lippincott - Raven Press, 227 E. Washington Sq., Philadelphia, PA 19106. TEL 215-238-4200. Ed. Carol Reed-Ash. adv. contact: Phyllis Noyes. bk.rev.; charts; illus.; stat.; tr.lit. circ. 7,300. (also avail. in microform; back issues avail.; reprint service avail. from UMI) **Indexed:** CINAHL, Dent.Ind., Int.Nurs.Ind., Nurs.Abstr. **Document type:** academic/scholarly publication.
—BLDSC (3046.491000); Faxon; Genuine Article; SWETS; UMI; UnCover. **CCC.**
Description: Covers problems arising in the care of cancer patients.
Refereed Serial

610.73 616.99   US   ISSN 0734-1873
CANCER NURSING NEWS. 1982. q. free. American Cancer Society, Inc., 1599 Clifton Rd., N.E., Atlanta, GA 30329. TEL 404-329-7617. Ed. Patricia Greene. circ. 90,000.
Description: Provides information and educational resources on the care of cancer patients.

610.73   US
CAPITAL NURSING. 1984. q. District of Columbia Nurses Association, 5100 Wisconsin Ave., N.W., Ste. 306, Washington, DC 20016. TEL 202-244-2705. FAX 202-362-8285. Ed. Evelyn Sommers. adv.; page $1000; adv. contact: Nancy Kofie. index; circ. 15,000 (controlled). (back issues avail.)
Description: Covers news and activities of the Association.

610.736   US   ISSN 0008-6355
CARDIOVASCULAR NURSING. 1965. bi-m. $6 to individuals (foreign $15); institutions $11 (foreign $20). American Heart Association, 7272 Greenville Ave., Dallas, TX 75231-4596. TEL 214-706-1310. FAX 214-691-6342. (Subscr. to: Box 843543, Dallas, TX 75284-3543) Ed. Kathleen King. charts; illus. circ. 54,000. (also avail. in microform from UMI; reprint service avail. from UMI; back issues avail.) **Indexed:** CINAHL, Int.Nurs.Ind., Nurs.Abstr.
—BLDSC (3051.470000); UMI; UnCover. **CCC.**
Description: Discusses new developments in care for patients with heart disease.
Refereed Serial

610.73   CN   ISSN 0843-9966
CARE CONNECTION. 1985. q. Can.$23.50 (foreign Can.$29). Registered Practical Nurses Association of Ontario (RPNAO), 5025 Orbitor Dr., Ste. 200, Bldg. 4, Mississauga, ON L4W 4Y5, Canada. TEL 905-602-4664. FAX 905-602-4666. Ed. Kelly Zimmer-Goodine. adv.; B&W page Can.$438; trim 8 1/2 x 11. bk.rev.; illus.; tr.lit. circ. 5,500. (back issues avail.) **Document type:** trade publication.
Former titles: Bedside Specialist (ISSN 0835-6203); Green Band.
Description: Contains educational articles and health care issue updates.

610.73   VI
CARIBBEAN CHRONICLE.* bi-m. Caribbean Nurses Organization, P.O. Box 583, Christiansted, St. Croix, VI 00820.

610.73   US
CARIBBEAN NURSES ORGANIZATION. NEWSLETTER.* q. Caribbean Nurses Organization, P.O. Box 583, Christiansted, St. Croix 00820, Virgin Islands, USA.

610.73   CN
CARING. 1945. bi-m. membership. Manitoba Association of Licensed Practical Nurses, P.O. Box 249, Transcona, 615 Kernaghan Ave., Winnipeg, MB R2C 2Z9, Canada. TEL 204-222-6743. FAX 204-224-0166. adv.
Formerly (until Dec.1990): Nurses News.

658 610   US   ISSN 0738-467X
RA645.3   CODEN: CARGET
CARING (WASHINGTON). 1982. m. $45. National Association for Home Care, 519 C St., N.E., Washington, DC 20002-5809. TEL 202-547-5277. FAX 202-547-7518. Ed. Heather Dittbrenner. adv.; bk.rev.; charts; stat.; index. circ. 5,927. (back issues avail.) **Indexed:** Abstr.Health Care Manage.Stud., CINAHL, Hosp.Lit.Ind.
—BLDSC (3053.222000); Faxon; UnCover.
Supersedes: Home Health Review (ISSN 0193-2683)
Description: Contains articles, special sections and departments covering national and international aspects of the home care field.

613   GW   ISSN 0948-003X
CARITAS UND PFLEGE. q. DM.30. Caritas-Gemeinschaft fuer Pflege- und Sozialberufe e.V., Maria-Theresia-Str. 10, 79102 Freiburg, Germany. TEL 0761-70861-0. FAX 0761-7086116. Ed. Renate Heinzmann. adv. circ. 4,500.
Former titles (until 1993): Caritas-Gemeinschaft. Publication; Caritasschwester.

610.73   US   ISSN 0069-2778
CHART. 1904. 6/yr. $25 to institutions. Illinois Nurses Association, 300 S. Wacker Dr., Ste. 2200, Chicago, IL 60606-6701. TEL 312-360-2300. FAX 312-36093808. Ed. Pamela Towne. adv. circ. 9,100. (also avail. in microfilm from UMI) **Indexed:** CINAHL, Int.Nurs.Ind. **Document type:** trade publication.
—BLDSC (3129.960000); UMI.
Description: Covers health care and professional issues of importance to all nurses.

610.73   US   ISSN 0199-2066
CHICAGO NURSE. 1946. 5/yr. $10. Chicago Nurses' Association, 203 N. Wabash, Ste. 818, Chicago, IL 60601-2415. TEL 312-263-2708. FAX 312-726-6337. Ed. Renata Hornick. adv.: page $300. bk.rev. circ. 1,400. **Document type:** newsletter.
Former titles (until 1979): Chicago District; First (ISSN 0015-2749)

610.73   US   ISSN 0887-6274
CLINICAL NURSE SPECIALIST. 1987. bi-m. $74 to individuals; institutions $95 (effective 1995). Williams & Wilkins, 428 E. Preston St., Baltimore, MD 21202. TEL 410-528-4000; 800-638-6423. FAX 410-528-4312. Eds. Pauline E. Beecroft, Patricia Sparacino. adv. circ. 3,600. (also avail. in microfilm from WWS) **Indexed:** CINAHL, Nurs.Abstr. **Document type:** academic/scholarly publication.
—BLDSC (3286.314100); Faxon; SWETS; UnCover. **CCC.**
Description: Information for the clinician, consultant, executive, peer, and patient educator.
Refereed Serial

610.73   US   ISSN 1054-7738
RT81.5   CODEN: CNREFD
CLINICAL NURSING RESEARCH. 1992. q. $49 to individuals; institutions $138 (effective Sep. 1995). (University of Alberta, CN) Sage Publications, Inc., 2455 Teller Rd., Thousand Oaks, CA 91320. TEL 805-499-0721. FAX 805-499-0871. E-mail: libraries@sagepub.com. (Overseas subscr. to: Sage Publications Ltd., 6 Bonhill St., London EC2A 4PU, England; Sage Publications India Pvt. Ltd., P.O. Box 4215, New Delhi 110 048, India) Eds. Marilynn J. Wood, Patricia Hayes. circ. 1,250. (back issues avail.; reprint service avail.) **Indexed:** Viol.& Abuse Abstr. **Document type:** academic/scholarly publication.
—BLDSC (3286.314150); Faxon; UnCover. **CCC.**
Description: Provides an international forum for scholarly research focusing on clinical nursing practice, including the clinical application of research findings.
Refereed Serial

610.73   SP
COLECCION LIBROS DE ENFERMERIA. 1975. irreg., no.12, 1988. price varies. (Universidad de Navarra, Escuela de Enfermeras) Ediciones Universidad de Navarra, S.A., Apdo. 396, 31080 Pamplona, Spain. TEL 94 825 6850.

MEDICAL SCIENCES — NURSES AND NURSING

610.73   MX   ISSN 0045-7329
COLEGIO NACIONAL DE ENFERMERAS. REVISTA. 1967. 3/yr. $21 (effective Jan. 1992). Colegio Nacional de Enfermeras, Obrero Mundial 229, Mexico, D.F., Mexico. TEL 5-43-66-37. illus. **Indexed:** Int.Nurs.Ind.
Formerly: Asociacion Mexicana de Enfermeras. Revista.

610.73   SA
COLIMPEX PAEDIATRIC EXECUPAD. (Text in Afrikaans and English) a. free to qualified personnel. Colimpex Africa (Pty) Ltd., P.O. Box 5838, Johannesburg 2000, South Africa. adv.

610.73   US   ISSN 0010-1680
COLORADO NURSE. vol.73, 1973. q. $20 (foreign $27). Colorado Nurses Association, 5453 E. Evans Place, Denver, CO 80222. TEL 303-757-7483. FAX 303-757-2679. Ed. Alison Biggs. adv.; bk.rev.; illus. circ. 36,000. **Indexed:** CINAHL, Int.Nurs.Ind. **Document type:** newsletter.

610.73   US   ISSN 0069-634X
COLUMBIA UNIVERSITY - PRESBYTERIAN HOSPITAL SCHOOL OF NURSING. ALUMNAE ASSOCIATION. MAGAZINE.* 1906. 3/yr. $1 to non-members. Columbia University, School of Nursing, 617 W. 168th St., New York, NY 10032. TEL 212-854-1754. Ed. Ria Hawks. circ. 2,700.

COMMUNITY NURSE. see *MEDICAL SCIENCES*

362 051   US   ISSN 1070-0323
COMPLEAT NURSE. 1991. m. $12. Box 640345, San Francisco, CA 94164. TEL 415-292-7371. FAX 415-292-7314. Ed. J. Rankin. adv.; bk.rev. circ. 750.
Description: Publishes news, features, poetry and other materials of interest to nurses and their patients.

610.73 618.202   UK
▼**COMPLEMENTARY THERAPIES IN NURSING & MIDWIFERY.** 1995. bi-m. £20 to individuals; institutions £65. Churchill Livingstone Journals (Subsidiary of: Pearson Professional), Robert Stevenson House, 1-3 Baxter's Pl., Leith Walk, Edinburgh EH1 3AF, Scotland. TEL 0131-556-2224. FAX 0131-459-1177. (Subscr. to: Pearson Professional Ltd., P.O. Box 77, Fourth Ave., Harlow, Essex CM19 5AA, England. TEL 01279-623760; U.S. subscr. to: Churchill Livingstone, 650 Ave. of the Americas, New York, NY 10011. TEL 212-206-5000) Ed. D. Rankin. adv. contact: David Dunnachie. bk.rev. **Document type:** academic/scholarly publication.
Description: Publishes articles on all aspects of individual therapies and includes origiginal research in nursing practice.

COMPUTERS IN NURSING. see *MEDICAL SCIENCES — Computer Applications*

610.73   CN
CONCERN. 1968. 6/yr. ProWest Publications, No. 208, 438 Victoria Ave. E., Regina, SK S4N 0N7, Canada. TEL 306-352-3400. FAX 306-525-0960. adv. circ. 9,700.

610.73   US   ISSN 0278-4092
CONNECTICUT NURSING NEWS. 1921. m. $30 (effective Jan. 1995). Connecticut Nurses Association, 377 Research Pkwy., Ste. 2D, Meriden, CT 06450-7160. TEL 203-238-1207. Ed. Mary L. Welch. adv.; illus. circ. 2,000. (also avail. in microform from UMI; reprint service avail. from UMI) **Indexed:** CINAHL, Int.Nurs.Ind. **Document type:** newspaper.
—UMI.
Formerly: Nursing News (ISSN 0029-652X)

CONTINUING EDUCATION IN NURSING: A DIRECTORY/FORMATION CONTINUEE EN SOINS INFIRMIERES: REPERTOIRE. see *EDUCATION — Higher Education*

610.73   US   ISSN 1078-4535
CREATIVE NURSING. 1980. 6/yr. $25. Creative Nursing Management, Inc., Box 8286, Minneapolis, MN 55408. TEL 612-823-0637. Ed. Claire Manthey Haukkala. **Document type:** trade publication.
Formerly (until Sep. 1994): Primarily Nursing (ISSN 0739-4446)

610.73   US   ISSN 0279-5442
                 CODEN: CCNUEV
CRITICAL CARE NURSE. 1980. 6/yr. $27 to individuals in US, Canada and Mexico $31, elsewhere $37; institutions in US $45, Canada and Mexico $55, elsewhere $65. American Association of Critical Care Nurses, 101 Columbia, Aliso Viejo, CA 92656. TEL 714-362-2000. (Subscr. to: Box 611, Holmes, PA 19043. TEL 800-345-8112) Ed. Joann Grif Alspach. adv.; bk.rev. circ. 110,000. (reprint service avail. from UMI) **Indexed:** CINAHL, Int.Nurs.Ind., Nurs.Abstr. **Document type:** academic/scholarly publication.
—BLDSC (3487.451100); Faxon; SWETS; UMI; UnCover. **CCC.**
Description: Provides current information and perspectives on a wide range of topics in critical care nursing.
Refereed Serial

610.7   US   ISSN 0899-5885
RT120.I5
CRITICAL CARE NURSING CLINICS OF NORTH AMERICA. 1989. q. $75 (foreign $91) (effective 1996). W.B. Saunders Co. (Subsidiary of: Harcourt Brace & Company), The Curtis Center, 3rd Fl., Independence Sq. W., Philadelphia, PA 19106-3399. TEL 215-238-7800. FAX 215-238-6445. (Subscr. to: W.B. Saunders Co., Periodicals Fulfillment, 6277 Sea Harbor Dr., 4th Fl., Orlando, FL 32891-4800. TEL 800-654-2452. FAX 800-874-6418) Ed. Helaine Barron. index. (also avail. in microform from UMI; back issues avail.) **Document type:** academic/scholarly publication.
—BLDSC (3487.451175); UMI; UnCover.
Description: Each issue addresses a single specific topic in the field.

610   US   ISSN 0887-9303
                 CODEN: CCNQEJ
CRITICAL CARE NURSING QUARTERLY. 1978. q. $66 (foreign $79). Aspen Publishers, Inc., 200 Orchard Ridge Dr., Gaithersburg, MD 20878. TEL 301-417-7500. FAX 301-417-7550. (also avail. in microform from UMI; reprint service avail. from UMI) **Indexed:** Biol.Abstr., CINAHL, Excerp.Med., IMFL, Nurs.Abstr., Psychol.Abstr. **Document type:** academic/scholarly publication.
—BLDSC (3487.451200); Faxon; SWETS; UMI; UnCover. **CCC.**
Formerly: Critical Care Quarterly (ISSN 0160-2551)
Description: Presents current, proven, hands-on procedures for improving clinical practice.

610.73   US
DELAWARE NURSES' ASSOCIATION REPORTER. 1968. 10/yr. $15 (foreign $25). Delaware Nurses Association, 2634 Capitol Trail, Ste. C, Newark, DE 19711. TEL 302-368-2333. Ed. Karen Morin. adv.: B&W page $150; trim 9 1/2 x 7 1/4. bk.rev. circ. 1,000. **Indexed:** CINAHL. **Document type:** newsletter.
Supersedes: Delaware Nurse (ISSN 0070-3281)

DIABETIC MEDICINE. see *MEDICAL SCIENCES — Endocrinology*

DIALAESEN; tidningen foer Svenska dialyskoeterskor. see *MEDICAL SCIENCES — Urology And Nephrology*

610.73   US   ISSN 0730-4625
DIMENSIONS OF CRITICAL CARE NURSING. Abbreviated title: D C C N. 1982. bi-m. $45 to individuals; institutions $78 (effective 1996). Hall Johnson Communications, Inc., 9737 W. Ohio Ave., Lakewood, CO 80226. TEL 303-988-0056. Ed. Suzanne Hall Johnson. adv.; illus.; index. circ. 3,000. **Indexed:** CINAHL, Int.Nurs.Ind., Nurs.Abstr.
—BLDSC (3588.471200); Faxon; SWETS; UMI; UnCover. **CCC.**
Refereed Serial

610.73   US   ISSN 1062-8835
DIRECTORY OF NURSE-MIDWIFERY PRACTICES (YEAR). a. $4.95. American College of Nurse-Midwives, 818 Connecticut Ave., Ste. 900, Washington, DC 20006. TEL 202-728-9860. FAX 202-728-9897. Ed. John Boggess. adv. circ. 6,000. **Document type:** directory.
Formerly: Registry of Nurse-Midwifery Services and Practices.

610.73   DQ
DOMINICA NURSES ASSOCIATION. NEWSLETTER. q. membership. Dominica Nurses Association, Roseau, Dominica, W.I. **Document type:** newsletter.

DRUGS AND DEVICE RECALL BULLETIN. see *PHARMACY AND PHARMACOLOGY*

E D T N A - E R C A JOURNAL (ENGLISH EDITION). (European Dialysis and Transplant Nurses Association, European Renal Care Association) see *MEDICAL SCIENCES — Urology And Nephrology*

610.73 618   UK
E N B NEWS. 1991. q. free. English National Board for Nursing, Midwifery, and Health Visiting, Victory House, 170 Tottenham Ct. Rd., London W1P 0HA, England. TEL 0171-388-3131. FAX 0171-383-4031. adv.; circ. 20,000 (controlled). **Document type:** newsletter.
Formerly (until 1990): Feedback.

610.73 378   CN   ISSN 1191-176X
EDUFACTS. French edition: Eduneuf (ISSN 1187-7669) 4/yr. Can.$2. Canadian Nurses Association - Association des Infirmieres et Infirmiers du Canada, 50 Driveway, Ottawa, ON K2P 1E2, Canada. TEL 613-237-2133. FAX 613-237-3520. **Document type:** newsletter.
Formerly: Entry to Practice.
Description: Covers news in nursing education across Canada.

610.73   UK
▼**EMERGENCY NURSE.** 1994. q. £35 (overseas £40). (R C N Accident & Emergency Nursing Association) R C N Publishing Co., 17-19 Peterborough Rd., Harrow-on-the-Hill, Middlesex HA1 2AX, England. TEL 0181-423-1066. FAX 0181-423-3867. (Subscr. to: Nursing Standard, Glynteg House, Station Terrace, Ely, Cardiff CF5 4XG, Wales. TEL 01222-553411. FAX 01222-576208) Ed. Brian Dolan. **Document type:** trade publication.

610 340   US   ISSN 0098-1516
KF2915.N8
EMERGENCY NURSE LEGAL BULLETIN. Abbreviated title: E N L B. 1975. q. $20. Med-Law Publishers, Inc., Box 293, Westville, NJ 08093. TEL 609-848-3817. FAX 609-848-1431. Ed. Dr. James E. George. **Indexed:** CINAHL, Int.Nurs.Ind. **Document type:** newsletter, bulletin.
—BLDSC (3733.193000); UnCover.

610.73   BL
ENFERMAGEM; o jornal brasileiro de enfermagem. 1977. bi-m. $50. (Associacao Brasileira de Enfermagem) Cidade - Editora Cientifica Ltda., Rua Mexico, 90-2 andar, 20031 Rio de Janeiro RJ, Brazil. TEL 021-240-4578. Ed. Fernando Moyses. adv. circ. 31,000.

610.73   MX   ISSN 0185-0970
ENFERMERA AL DIA. 1976. m. Mex.$90($40) Intersistemas S.A. de C.V., Fernando Alencastre No. 110 Lomas de Virreyes, 11000 Mexico D.F., Mexico. TEL 525-540-0798. FAX 525-540-3764. Ed. Dr. Elvia Espino B; Pub. Pedro Vera-Cervera. adv. contact: Miguel Alberto Gonzalez. charts. circ. 10,000. **Document type:** academic/scholarly publication.

610.73   MX
ENFERMERAS.* 1953. q. Mex.$20 per no. Colegio Nacional de Enfermeras, Obrero Mundial 229, Mexico, D.F., Mexico. Ed. Margarita Navarro Salazar. adv.

610.73   SP   ISSN 0211-9005
ENFERMERIA CIENTIFICA. 12/yr. Francisca Armanda 38, 28047 Madrid, Spain. TEL 1-255-68-09. FAX 1-46-48-613. Ed. Jesus Sanchez Martos.

610.73   SP   ISSN 1130-8621
ENFERMERIA CLINICA. 1990. bi-m. 4700 ptas.($43) Ediciones Doyma S.A., Travesera de Gracia 17-21, 08021 Barcelona, Spain. TEL 34-1-200-07-11. FAX 34-1-209-11-36. TELEX 51964 INK E. Ed. P. Vilagrasa. adv. page 210000 ptas.; trim 210 x 280; adv. contact: Anna Pahissa. circ. 6,000.
Description: Studies clinical nursing to promote a solution to the health problems of individuals, families and communities. Contributes to the theoretical and practical development of the profession in Spain.

MEDICAL SCIENCES — NURSES AND NURSING

610.73　　　　　SP　　ISSN 1130-2399
ENFERMERIA INTENSIVA. 1990. q. 4800 ptas.($50) (effective 1995). (Sociedad Espanola de Enfermeria Intensiva y Unidades Coronarias) Editorial Garsi, S.A., Juan Bravo 46, 28006 Madrid, Spain. TEL 34-1-4021212. FAX 34-1-4020954. adv.; bk.rev.; index. (back issues avail.)

610.73　　　　　CN　　ISSN 1180-4920
ENTRANCE REQUIREMENTS FOR NURSING EDUCATION PROGRAMS IN CANADA. a. Can.$20. Canadian Nurses Association - Association des Infirmieres et Infirmiers du Canada, 50 Driveway, Ottawa, ON K2P 1E2, Canada. TEL 613-237-2133. FAX 613-237-3520.
　　Formed by the 1990 merger of: Entrance Requirements for Diploma Schools of Nursing and Schools of Practical Nursing (ISSN 0710-2976) & Nursing Programs and Entrance Requirements at Canadian Universities (ISSN 0229-7345); Which was formed by the 1982 merger of: Nursing Programs Offered at Canadian Universities (ISSN 0706-3873); Outline of General Academic Requirements for Programs in Nursing at Canadian Universities (ISSN 0708-7683); Which was formerly: Outline of General Academic Entrance Requirements for Basic Programmes in Nursing Canadian Universities (ISSN 0706-3903); Nursing Programs Offered at Canadian University was formerly: Programs Offered at Canadian University Schools of Nursing (ISSN 0381-923X); Entrance Requirements for Diploma Schools of Nursing and Schools of Practical Nursing was formerly (until 1981): General Entrance Requirements for Schools of Nursing and Practical Nursing (ISSN 0706-3865); (until 1978): Entrance Requirements for Schools of Nursing and Schools of Practical Nursing (ISSN 0319-4787).

610.73　　　　　UK　　ISSN 1358-8621
▼**EUROPEAN NURSE.** Announced for publication in 1996. q. £70($110) (effective 1996). Arnold (Subsidiary of: Hodder Headline plc.), 338 Euston Rd., London NW1 3BH, England. TEL 44-171-873-6000. FAX 44-171-873-6325. (Subscr. to: Turpin Distribution Services Ltd., Blackhorse Rd., Letchworth, Herts. SG6 1HN, England. TEL 44-1462-672555. FAX 44-1462-480947) **Document type:** academic/scholarly publication.

610.73　　　　　BE　　ISSN 0774-935X
F.N.I.B. - INFO/N.V.B.V. - INFO. (Text in Dutch, French) 1921. bi-m. 1500 BEF. Federation Nationale Neutre des Infirmieres Belges - Nationaal Verbond van Belgische Verpleegsters, 18 rue de la Source, 1060 Brussels, Belgium. TEL 32-2-5370193. Ed. Bernard Fadeur. adv.; illus. (tabloid format)
　　—BLDSC (3964.175550).
　　Former titles (until 1987): Flash-informations (ISSN 0771-8187); (until 1983): F.N.I.B. - N.V.B.V. (ISSN 0301-0813); (until 1971): Infirmiere (ISSN 0019-9591)

610.73　　　　　　　ISSN 0172-5238
FACHSCHWESTER - FACHPFLEGER. 1975. irreg. price varies. Springer-Verlag, 175 Fifth Ave., New York, NY 10010. TEL 212-460-1500. FAX 212-473-6272. (Also: Berlin, Heidelberg, Tokyo and Vienna) (reprint service avail. from ISI) **Document type:** monographic series.

610.73　615.82　SP　ISSN 0211-5638
FISIOTERAPIA. (Text in Spanish; summaries in English) 1979. q. 5900 ptas.($63) (effective 1995). (Asociacion Espanola de Fisioterapeutas) Editorial Garsi, S.A., Juan Bravo 46, 28006 Madrid, Spain. TEL 34-1-4021212. FAX 34-1-4020954. adv.; bk.rev.; index.

610.73　　　　　US　　ISSN 0015-4199
FLORIDA NURSE. 1952. m. $15 (foreign $20). Florida Nurses Association, 1235 E. Concord St., Box 536985, Orlando, FL 32853-6985. TEL 407-896-3261. FAX 407-896-9042. Eds. Paula Massey, Karen Rogers. adv. contact: Karen Rogers. bk.rev.; illus. circ. 8,500. (reprint service avail. from UMI) **Indexed:** CINAHL, Int.Nurs.Ind. **Document type:** newsletter.
　　—BLDSC (3956.080000); UMI.
　　Description: Covers legislative, health policy, regulatory, labor, educational, and administrative issues that affect the registered nursing profession throughout the state.

610.73　　　　　US
FLORIDA NURSING NEWS.* (In 2 editions: South Florida and Gulf-Central) 1981. fortn. $9.95. Nursing News, Inc., 2750 S.W. 140th Terrace, Ft. Lauderdale, FL 33330-1175. FAX 305-748-3663. Ed. Steven Ricci. adv. circ. 55,000.

610.73　　　　　SW　　ISSN 0283-913X
FOERETAGSSKOETERSKAN. 1972. q. SEK 250. (Riksfoereningen foer Foeretagsskoeterskor, c/o Inger Nyman) Tunavaegen 16, S-862 32 Kvissleby, Sweden. FAX 46-60-181980. Ed. Inger Gradling. adv. contact: Anita Ericson. **Document type:** newsletter.
　　Supersedes: Industriskoeterskan.

610.73　　　　　US　　ISSN 0016-2116
FRONTIER NURSING SERVICE QUARTERLY BULLETIN. 1925. q. $5 to individuals; institutions $10. Frontier Nursing Service, Inc., 100 Wendover Rd., Wendover, KY 41775. TEL 606-672-2317. FAX 606-672-3022. Ed. Barb Gibson. adv.; illus. circ. 7,000. (tabloid format; also avail. in microform from UMI; back issues avail.) **Indexed:** CINAHL, Int.Nurs.Ind. **Document type:** bulletin.
　　—BLDSC (4041.200000); Faxon; UMI.
　　Description: Overview of the Frontier Nursing Service of Eastern Kentucky.

610.73　　　　　US　　ISSN 0016-8335
GEORGIA NURSING. 1945. 10/yr. $25. Georgia Nurses Association, 1362 W. Peachtree St., Atlanta, GA 30309. TEL 404-876-4624. Ed. Mary Mallison. adv. circ. 3,000. **Indexed:** CINAHL, Int.Nurs.Ind. **Document type:** newsletter.
　　—BLDSC (4158.457000); UMI.

GERIATRIC NURSING; American journal of care for the aging. see *GERONTOLOGY AND GERIATRICS*

610.73　　　　　SP
GEROKOMOS. 3/yr. 4200 ptas.($48) (effective 1995). Editorial Garsi, S.A., Juan Bravo 46, 28006 Madrid, Spain. TEL 34-1-4021212. FAX 34-1-4020954.

610.73　　　　　BE　　ISSN 0778-4457
GEST HOME; la revue des gestionnaires et du personnel soignant des maisons de repos, centres hopitaliers, c.p.a.s., centre de sante et de soins. (Text in Dutch, French) 1986. q. 450 BEF. Socorema s.c.r.l, Rue du Merlo, 28, 1180 Brussels, Belgium. TEL 02-376-62-28. FAX 02-376-12-80. Ed. J. Laffineur-Brouhon. adv.; bk.rev. circ. 5,000.
　　Description: Intended to serve those involved and working in the health care profession, nursing homes, rehabilitation centers, and hospitals.

610.73　371.42　US
GRADUATING NURSE. 1991. 3/yr. Peterson's - C O G Publishing, 16030 Ventura Blvd., Ste. 560, Encino, CA 91346. TEL 818-789-5293. FAX 818-789-5488. Ed. Al Austin. adv.: B&W page $4150; trim 8 x 10 3/4. circ. 29,658.
　　Description: Covers career development, emerging technologies, areas of specialization and personal growth.

610.73　　　　　UK　　ISSN 0262-172X
H V A CURRENT AWARENESS BULLETIN. 1981. q. £6 to non-members; members £12. Health Visitors' Association, 50 Southwark St., London SE1 1UN, England. Ed. E. Burke. circ. 850. **Document type:** abstracting/indexing, bibliography.

610.73　　　　　CN
HAND IN HAND. 4/yr. Can.$51 membership. Saskatchewan Association of Licensed Practical Nurses, 2310 Smith, Regina, SK S4P 2P6, Canada. TEL 306-525-1436. FAX 306-347-7784. circ. 2,600. **Document type:** newsletter.
　　Formerly: S N A A Newsletter.

610.73　　　　　UK
HANDBOOK OF PRACTICE NURSING. 1992. 3/yr. £32($53) (effective 1995). Churchill Livingstone Journals (Subsidiary of: Pearson Professional), Robert Stevenson House, 1-3 Baxter's Pl., Leith Walk, Edinburgh EH1 3AF, England. TEL 0131-556-2424. FAX 0131-459-1177. (Subscr. to: Pearson Professional Ltd., P.O. Box 77, Fourth Ave., Harlow, Essex CM19 5AA, England. TEL 01279-623760; U.S. subscr to: Churchill Livingstone, 650 Ave. of the Americas, New York, NY 10011. TEL 212-206-5000) Ed.Bd. adv. contact: David Dunnachie. bk.rev. (looseleaf format) **Document type:** academic/scholarly publication.
　　Description: Provides updates on materials, techniques, and drugs commonplace in nursing.

610.73　　　　　US　　ISSN 0731-3381
RA971
HEALTH CARE SUPERVISOR. 1982. 4/yr. $104 (foreign $125). Aspen Publishers, Inc., 200 Orchard Ridge Dr., Gaithersburg, MD 20878. TEL 301-417-7500. FAX 301-417-7550. Ed. Charles R. McConnell. **Indexed:** ABI Inform., CINAHL, Diar.Dis.Res.
　　●Also available online. Vendor(s): University Microfilms International.
　　—BLDSC (4274.949500); Faxon; UMI; UnCover. CCC.
　　Formerly: Health Care Supervisors Journal.

HEALTH CAREER POST. see *HOSPITALS*

HEALTH MANPOWER MANAGEMENT. see *BUSINESS AND ECONOMICS — Management*

610.73　　　　　UK　　ISSN 0017-9140
RT97
HEALTH VISITOR. 1927. m. £51. (Health Visitors' Association) Professional & Scientific Publications, BMA House, Tavistock Sq., London WC1H 9JR, England. TEL 0171-383-6640. FAX 0171-383-6662. Ed. N. Robin. adv.; bk.rev.; film rev.; illus.; index. circ. 18,000. (also avail. in microfilm from UMI; reprint service avail. from UMI) **Indexed:** Abstr.Hyg., ASSIA, CINAHL, Curr.Adv.Ecol.Sci., Dent.Ind., Int.Nurs.Ind., Mult.Ed.Abstr., Sp.Ed.Needs Abstr., Trop.Dis.Bull. **Document type:** academic/scholarly publication.
　　—BLDSC (4275.245000); UMI.
　　Refereed Serial

610.73　　　　　US　　ISSN 0199-8552
HEALTHWIRE. 1980. bi-m. membership. (American Federation of Teachers) Federation of Nurses and Health Professionals (Subsidiary of: American Federation of Teachers), 555 New Jersey Ave., N.W., Washington, DC 20001. TEL 202-879-4430. Ed. Trish Gorman. adv. contact: Sharon Wright. circ. 63,000. **Document type:** newsletter.
　　Description: Describes membership and local union activities, provides readers with national union news and an update on activities organized at the national level. Covers topics of interest to health care professionals and provides information on professional development workshops, conferences and publications.

616.12　　　　　US　　ISSN 0147-9563
RC681.A1　　　　　　CODEN: HELUAI
HEART & LUNG; the journal of acute and critical care. 1972. bi-m. $39 to individuals (Canada $57.78; elsewhere $54); institutions $127 (Canada $151.94; elsewhere $142); students $21 (Canada $38.52; elsewhere $36) (effective 1996); newsstand price: $8.50. Mosby - Year Book, Inc. (Subsidiary of: Times Mirror Company), 11830 Westline Industrial Dr., St. Louis, MO 63146-3318. TEL 314-872-8370; 800-325-4177. FAX 314-432-1380. TELEX 44-2402. Ed. Kathleen S. Stone. adv.: B&W page $680, color page $1310; trim 8 1/8 x 10 7/8. adv.; charts; illus.; index. circ. 6,893. (also avail. in microfilm from UMI; reprint service avail. from UMI) **Indexed:** Abstr.Health Care Manage.Stud., AIM, ASCA, Behav.Med.Abstr., Biol.Abstr., Chem.Abstr, CINAHL, Curr.Adv.Ecol.Sci., Curr.Cont., Excerp.Med., Hosp.Lit.Ind., Ind.Med., Ind.Sci.Rev., INIS Atomind., Int.Nurs.Ind., Nurs.Abstr., RILM.
　　●Also available online. Vendor(s): Ovid Technologies.
　　—BLDSC (4275.295000); ADONIS; CASDDS; Faxon; Genuine Article; SWETS; UMI; UnCover. **CCC**.
　　Description: Scientific nursing journal with practical articles on critical care.
　　Refereed Serial

MEDICAL SCIENCES — NURSES AND NURSING

610.73 UK ISSN 0960-2348
HISTORY OF NURSING JOURNAL. 1983. 4/yr. £60 (foreign £80). (Royal College of Nursing) R C N Publishing Co., 17-19 Peterborough Rd., Harrow-on-the-Hill, Middlesex HA1 2AX, England. TEL 0181-423-1066. FAX 0181-423-4302. (Subscr. to: Nursing Standard, Glynteg House, Station Terrace, Ely, Cardiff CF5 4XG, Wales. TEL 01222-553411. FAX 01222-576208) Ed. Dr. M.E. Baly. bk.rev. circ. 200. (back issues avail.) **Document type:** bulletin.
—BLDSC (4318.388100).
Formerly: History of Nursing Bulletin (ISSN 0265-3834)

610.73 NO ISSN 0332-7841
HJELPEPLEIEREN. 1967. 16/yr. NOK 375. Norsk Hjelpepleierforbund, P.O. Box 151, Brun, N-0611 Oslo 1, Norway. FAX 645602. Ed. Erling Lat. adv. contact: Lillian Lindberg. bk.rev.; circ. 48,000 (controlled). **Document type:** trade publication.
—CCC.

610.73 IC ISSN 0250-4731
HJUKRUN. 1925. q. $30. Hjukrunarfelag Islands - Icelandic Nurses' Association, Sudurlandsbraut 22, 108 Reykjavik, Iceland. TEL 354-568-7575. FAX 354-568-0727. Eds. Lilja Oskarsdottir, Stefania Sigurjonsdottir. adv.; bk.rev.; illus. circ. 2,200. **Indexed:** Int.Nurs.Ind. **Document type:** newsletter, trade publication.
Former titles (until Jan. 1978): Hjukrunarfelag Islands. Timarit (ISSN 0046-7634); Hjukrunarkvennabladid.

610.73 616 FI ISSN 0786-5686
HOITOTIEDE. 1989. q. FIM 160 in Nordic countries; elsewhere FIM 250 (effective 1995). Sairaanhoitajien Koulutusaatio - S H K S, Sitratori 5, FIN-00420 Helsinki, Finland. TEL 358-0-566-8640. FAX 358-0-531-504. Ed. Maija Hentinen. adv.; B&W page FIM 2000.
—BLDSC (4322.216500).

610.73 JA ISSN 0018-3369
HOKENFU NO KEKKAKU TENBO/REVIEW OF TUBERCULOSIS FOR PUBLIC HEALTH NURSE. (Text in Japanese) 1963. s-a. 3090 Yen. Japan Anti-Tuberculosis Association - Kekkaku Yobokai, 3-12 Misaki-cho 1-chome, Chiyoda-ku, Tokyo 101, Japan. FAX 03-3292-9208. Ed. Dr. Masakazu Aoki. adv.; bk.rev.; charts; illus.; stat. circ. 1,500.

610.73 JA ISSN 0047-1844
HOKENFU ZASSHI/JAPANESE JOURNAL FOR PUBLIC HEALTH NURSE. (Text in Japanese) 1951. m. 12090 Yen($93) Igaku-Shoin Ltd., 5-24-3 Hongo, Bunkyo-ku, Tokyo 113-91, Japan. TEL 03-817-5776. Ed.Bd. circ. 8,500.
—BLDSC (4658.420000).

610.73 US ISSN 0887-9311
HOLISTIC NURSING PRACTICE. 1979. q. $75 (foreign $90). Aspen Publishers, Inc., 200 Orchard Ridge Dr., Gaithersburg, MD 20878. TEL 301-417-7500. FAX 301-417-7550. **Indexed:** CINAHL, IMFL, Int.Nurs.Ind., Nurs.Abstr. **Document type:** academic/scholarly publication.
—BLDSC (4322.302600); Faxon; SWETS; UMI; UnCover. CCC.
Formerly (until 1985): Topics in Clinical Nursing (ISSN 0164-0534)

610.73 GW ISSN 0944-1360
HOME CARE; Journal fuer Ausserklinische Betreuung und Pflege. 1993. 4/yr. DM.20. M M V Medizin Verlag, Neumarkter Str. 18, 81673 Munich, Germany. TEL 089-43189-0. FAX 089-43189633. **Document type:** academic/scholarly publication.

610.73 US ISSN 1045-1242
HOMECARE NEWS. m. National Association for Home Care, 519 C St., N.E., Washington, DC 20002-5809. TEL 202-547-7424. FAX 202-547-3540. Ed. Val Halamandaris. circ. 13,500. **Document type:** newspaper.

610.73 HK ISSN 0073-3253
HONG KONG NURSING JOURNAL/HSIANG KANG HU LI TSA CHIH. Key Title: Xianggang Huli Zazhi. (Text in Chinese and English) 1965. s-a. membership. Hong Kong Nurses Association, Hong Kong, Hong Kong. TEL 5-729255. bk.rev. circ. 4,500. **Indexed:** CINAHL.
—BLDSC (4326.402000).

HOSPITAL AND NURSING YEARBOOK OF SOUTHERN AFRICA. see *HOSPITALS*

HOSPITAL NEWS DELAWARE VALLEY. see *HOSPITALS*

HOSPITAL PHARMACY DIRECTOR'S MONTHLY MANAGEMENT SERIES. see *PHARMACY AND PHARMACOLOGY*

610.73 NE ISSN 1013-1779
I C H S INFORMATION BULLETIN. irreg., approx. 3-4/yr. International Council of Homehelp Services, c/o R. Kalfsbeek, Exec. Sec., Postbus 100, 3980 CC Bunnik, Netherlands. TEL 31-3405-96211. FAX 31-3405-63994. **Document type:** bulletin.

610.73 US
I N S NEWSLINE. 1973. bi-m. membership. Intravenous Nurses Society, Two Brighton St., Belmont, MA 02178. TEL 617-489-5205. FAX 617-489-0656. adv. contact: Stephen W. Forbes. bk.rev.; stat. circ. 8,000.
Former titles: I N S Update; N I T A Update.

610.73 378 US ISSN 0743-5150
CODEN: IMNSEP
IMAGE: JOURNAL OF NURSING SCHOLARSHIP. 1967. q. $16 to individuals (Canada and Mexico $21; elsewhere $26); institutions £25 (Canada and Mexico $30; elsewhere $35). Sigma Theta Tau International Honor Society of Nursing, 550 W. North St., Indianapolis, IN 46202. TEL 317-634-8171. FAX 317-634-8188. Ed. Beverly Henry. adv. circ. 100,000. (also avail. in microfiche; back issues avail.) **Indexed:** CINAHL, Ind.Med. (1993-), Int.Nurs.Ind., Nurs.Abstr., Psychol.Abstr. (1983-). **Document type:** academic/scholarly publication.
—BLDSC (4368.990100); Faxon; SWETS; UMI; UnCover.
Formerly: Image (ISSN 0363-2792)
Description: Presents cutting-edge thinking from top writers and researchers in nursing.
Refereed Serial

610.73 US ISSN 0019-3062
IMPRINT (NEW YORK). 1968. 5/yr. $15. National Student Nurses' Association, 555 W. 57 St., New York, NY 10019. TEL 212-581-2211. Ed. Caroline Jaffe. adv.; illus.; index. circ. 34,000. **Indexed:** CINAHL, Int.Nurs.Ind.
—BLDSC (4371.486500); Faxon; UnCover.
Formerly: N S N A Newsletter.
Description: Provides organization news.

INDUSTRIAL HEALTH FOUNDATION. NURSING SERIES. BULLETINS. see *OCCUPATIONAL HEALTH AND SAFETY*

610 UK ISSN 0956-9510
INFECTION CONTROL YEARBOOK. a. £30. (Infection Control Nurses Association) C M A Medical Data Ltd., Cambridge Research Laboratories, 181A Huntingdon Rd., Cambridge CB3 0DJ, England. TEL 0223-277709. FAX 0223-276444. **Document type:** directory.
—BLDSC (4478.721300).
Description: Contains a complete listing of full time infection control nurses and other members of staff who have control of infection as one of their responsibilities. Members are listed alphabetically by both name and hospital.

610.73 CN ISSN 0822-8558
L'INFIRMIERE AUXILIAIRE. (Text in French) 1928. 3/yr. Can.$10. Corporation Professionnelle de Infirmieres et Infirmiers, Auxiliaires du Quebec, 531 Sherbrooke E., Montreal, PQ H2L 1K2, Canada. TEL 514-282-9511. FAX 514-282-0631. adv.; bk.rev.; charts; illus.; index. circ. 21,000.
Former titles: Auxiliaire (ISSN 0703-9484); Revue des Infirmieres et Infirmiers du Quebec; Cahiers du Nursing (ISSN 0008-0179)

610.73 CN ISSN 1195-2695
INFIRMIERE DU QUEBEC. (Text in English and French) 1976. 6/yr. $36 to individuals; institutions $47; students $20. Order of Nurses of Quebec - Ordre des Infirmieres et Infirmiers du Quebec, 4200 Dorchester Blvd. W., Montreal, PQ H3Z 1V4, Canada. TEL 514-762-1667. FAX 514-769-9490. Ed. Guylaine Chabot. adv.: B&W page Can.$1885, color page Can.$3225; trim 8 1/8 x 10 7/8; adv. contact: Ghislaine Brunet. bk.rev.; illus.; circ. 61,803 (controlled). **Indexed:** Can.Per.Ind., Int.Nurs.Ind., Pt.de Rep. (1982-).
Former titles (until Sep. 1993): Nursing Quebec (ISSN 0381-6419); (until 1980): Order of Nurses of Quebec. News and Notes (ISSN 0319-2636)

610.73 CN ISSN 0846-524X
INFO NURSING. (Text in English, French) 1967. 5/yr. Can.$25 (foreign $30). Nurses Association of New Brunswick - Association des Infirmieres et Infirmiers du Nouveau-Brunswick, 165 Regent St., Fredericton, NB E3B 3W5, Canada. TEL 506-458-8731. FAX 506-459-2838. Ed. George Bergeron. adv. contact: George Bergeron. bk.rev.; illus. circ. 8,900. **Document type:** newsletter.
—BLDSC (4478.876830).
Former titles (until 1989): Info - Nurses Association of New Brunswick (ISSN 0842-3210); (until 1984): Info - New Brunswick Association of Registered Nurses (ISSN 0382-5574); (until 1975): N B A R N News (ISSN 0382-5566)

610.73 BE
INFO-NURSING. m. 1500 BEF. Association Nationale Catholique du Nursing, Av. Hippocrate 91, B-1200 Brussels, Belgium. TEL 32-2-7625618. FAX 32-2-7725219. Ed. Hans Sabine. **Document type:** bulletin.

INFORMATIONSDIENST KRANKENHAUSWESEN/HEALTH CARE INFORMATION SERVICE. see *HOSPITALS*

INSIGHT (SAN FRANCISCO). see *MEDICAL SCIENCES — Ophthalmology And Optometry*

610.73 UK ISSN 0964-3397
INTENSIVE AND CRITICAL CARE NURSING. 1985. q. £147($230) (effective 1995). (B A C C N) Churchill Livingstone Journals, Robert Stevenson House, 1-3 Baxter's Pl., Leith Walk, Edinburgh EH1 3AF, Scotland. TEL 0131-556-2424. FAX 0131-459-1177. (Subscr. to: Pearson Professional Ltd., P.O. Box 77 Fourth Ave., Harlow, Essex CM19 5AA, England. TEL 01279-623760; U.S. subscr. to: Churchill Livingstone, 650 Ave. of the Americas, New York, NY 10011. TEL 212-206-5000) Ed. Pat Ashworth. adv. contact: David Dunnachie. circ. 4,000. **Indexed:** CINAHL. **Document type:** academic/scholarly publication.
—BLDSC (4531.836000); Faxon; SWETS; UnCover. CCC.
Formerly (until Mar. 1992): Intensive Care Nursing (ISSN 0266-612X)

INTENSIVE CARING UNLIMITED. see *CHILDREN AND YOUTH — About*

005.3029 610.73 US
INTERACTIVE HEALTHCARE DIRECTORY OF EDUCATIONAL SOFTWARE FOR NURSING. 1987. biennial. $59 (foreign $69) (effective May 1995). Stewart Publishing, Inc., 6471 Merritt Ct., Alexandria, VA 22312. TEL 703-354-8155. FAX 703-354-2177. Ed. Christine Bolwell. software rev. **Document type:** directory.
Description: Reviews more than 300 computer-based programs for nurses.

610.73 005.3029 US
INTERACTIVE HEALTHCARE NURSING DIRECTORY. a. $59 (foreign $69) (effective May 1995). Stewart Publishing, Inc., 6471 Merritt Ct., Alexandria, VA 22312. TEL 703-354-8155. FAX 703-354-2177. Ed. Christine Bolwell. **Document type:** directory.
Description: Lists nearly 600 computer-assisted instruction programs for nursing education, along with brief annotations for each.

MEDICAL SCIENCES — NURSES AND NURSING

610.73   FR   ISSN 0242-3960
INTERBLOC; la revue des infirmiers et infirmieres de salles d'operations. q. 152 F. (effective 1996). Masson - Periodiques, Villa Laromiguiere, 75005 Paris, France. TEL 1-40-46-62-00.
FAX 1-40-46-62-01. Ed. A. Blanchart. circ. 2,500.
Document type: academic/scholarly publication.
—CCC.
Formerly: Journal of Operating Theatre Male and Female Nurses.
Description: Topics covered include hygiene, surgical technique and technology, and legal and professional aspects.

610.73   NE   ISSN 0074-4360
INTERNATIONAL COUNCIL OF HOMEHELP SERVICES. REPORTS OF CONGRESS. 1959. quadrennial, 8th, Noordwijkerhout, NE, 1989. International Council of Homehelp Services, c/o R. Kalfsbeek, Exec. Sec., Postbus 100, 3980 CC Bunnik, Netherlands. TEL 31-3405-96211. FAX 31-3405-63994.
Document type: proceedings.

610.73   AT   ISSN 1322-7114
▼**INTERNATIONAL JOURNAL OF NURSING PRACTICE.** 1995. q. Aus.$175($175) (effective 1996). Blackwell Science Pty Ltd, P.O. Box 378, Carlto South, Vic. 3053, Australia. TEL 61-3-93470300. FAX 61-3-93493016. (back issues avail.) **Document type:** academic/scholarly publication.

610.730   UK   ISSN 0020-7489
RT1   CODEN: IJNUA6
INTERNATIONAL JOURNAL OF NURSING STUDIES. 1965. bi-m. £285($454) (effective 1996). Elsevier Science Ltd., Pergamon, P.O. Box 800, Kidlington, Oxford OX5 1DX, England. TEL 44-1865-843000. FAX 44-1865-843010.
E-mail: nlinfo-f@elsevier.nl; usinfo-f@elsevier.com; forinfo-kyf04035@niftyserve.or.jp; Site addr.: http://www.elsevier.nl/. (Subscr. in U.S. and Canada to: Elsevier Science, 660 White Plains Rd., Tarrytown, NY 10591-5153. TEL 914-524-9200. FAX 914-333-2444) Ed. Rosemary Crow. adv.; bk.rev.; charts; illus.; index. circ. 1,150. (also avail. in microfilm from UMI; reprint service avail. from UMI) **Indexed:** Abstr.Health Care Manage.Stud., CINAHL, Curr.Cont., Ind.Med., Int.Nurs.Ind., Psychol.Abstr. (1982-), SSCI, Tech.Educ.Abstr.
Document type: academic/scholarly publication.
—BLDSC (4542.407000); Faxon; Genuine Article; SWETS; UMI; UnCover. **CCC.**
Description: Covers worldwide changes and developments in nursing.
Refereed Serial

610.73   UK   ISSN 1357-6321
▼**INTERNATIONAL JOURNAL OF PALLIATIVE NURSING.** 1995. q. £38 (overseas £60). Mark Allen Publishing Ltd., Croxted Mews, 288 Croxted Rd., London SE24 9BY, England. TEL 0181-671-7521.
FAX 0181-671-1722. Ed. Jeanette Webber; Pub. Mark Allen. adv. contact: Adrian Johnston. **Document type:** academic/scholarly publication.

610.73 617.1   US
▼**INTERNATIONAL JOURNAL OF TRAUMA NURSING.** 1995. q. $40 to individuals (Canada $66.34; elsewhere $62); institutions $75 (Canada $103.79; elsewhere $97); students $21 (Canada $46.01; elsewhere $43) (effective 1996); newsstand price: 10. Mosby - Year Book, Inc. (Subsidiary of: Times Mirror Company), 11830 Westline Industrial Dr., St.Louis, MO 63146. TEL 314-872-8370.
FAX 314-872-9164. Ed. Judith Stoner Halpern. adv.: B&W page $500, color page $1335; trim 8 1/4 x 11; adv. contact: Jo Ann Anzalone. circ. 1,200. **Document type:** academic/scholarly publication.
Description: Written especially for the nursing professionals working in trauma care, from scene of injury through rehabilitation. Original articles focus on topics of key interest to readers and are clinically relevant to trauma nurses.

610.73   SZ   ISSN 0020-8132
RT1
INTERNATIONAL NURSING REVIEW. 1926. 6/yr. 50 SFr. International Council of Nurses, 3 place Jean-Marteau, CH-1201 Geneva, Switzerland. TEL 022-7312960. FAX 022-7381036. Ed. Nancy Vatre. adv.; bk.rev.; illus.; index. circ. 3,500. (also avail. in microform from UMI; reprint service avail. from UMI) **Indexed:** Abstr.Health Care Manage.Stud., ASSIA, CINAHL, Ind.Med., Int.Nurs.Ind. **Document type:** academic/scholarly publication.
—BLDSC (4544.500000); Faxon; SWETS; UMI; UnCover.

610.73   CK   ISSN 0120-5307
INVESTIGACION Y EDUCACION EN ENFERMERIA. 1983. s-a. Col.4000($20) (typically set in Sept.). Universidad de Antioquia, Facultad de Enfermeria, Apdo. Aereo 1226, Carrera 53, no. 62-65, Medellin, Colombia. TEL 5742-110058. FAX 5742-638282. Ed. Beatriz Zuluaga A. adv. contact: Luz Angela Ramirez. bk.rev.; bibl.; circ. 1,000 (controlled). **Document type:** academic/scholarly publication.
Description: Publishes works of importance from Latin American institutions.

610.73   IE   ISSN 0790-7257
IRISH NURSING FORUM & HEALTH SERVICES. 6/yr. 127 Lower Baggot St., Dublin 2, Ireland. TEL 789318. FAX 767072. Ed. Eivlin Roden.

610.73   US   ISSN 0146-0862
                   CODEN: ICNUDS
ISSUES IN COMPREHENSIVE PEDIATRIC NURSING. 1976. q. £60($99) (effective 1996). Taylor & Francis Inc., 1900 Frost Rd., Ste. 101, Bristol, PA 19007-1598. TEL 215-785-5800; 800-821-8312. FAX 215-785-5515. (Subscr. in Europe to: Taylor & Francis Ltd., Rankine Rd., Basingstoke, Hants. RG24 8PR, England. TEL 44-1256-840366. FAX 44-1256-479438) Ed. Chandice Covington. adv.; bk.rev.; bibl.; charts; illus.; index. circ. 1,200. (back issues avail.; reprint service avail. from UMI) **Indexed:** CINAHL, Int.Nurs.Ind., J.of Abstr.Int.Educ., Psychol.Abstr. (1981-), Sage Fam.Stud.Abstr., Sociol.Abstr. **Document type:** academic/scholarly publication.
—BLDSC (4584.160000); Faxon; SWETS; UnCover. **CCC.**
Description: Publishes articles pertinent to the critical aspects of pediatric nursing.
Refereed Serial

616.8   US   ISSN 0161-2840
                 CODEN: IHNUDT
ISSUES IN MENTAL HEALTH NURSING. 1978. bi-m. £98($162) (effective 1996). Taylor & Francis Inc., 1900 Frost Rd., Ste. 101, Bristol, PA 19007-1598. TEL 215-785-5800; 800-821-8312.
FAX 215-785-5515. (Taylor & Francis Ltd., Rankine Rd., Basingstoke, Hants. RG24 8PR, England. TEL 44-1256-840366. FAX 44-1256-479438) Ed. Mary Swanson Crockett. adv.; bk.rev.; film rev.; bibl.; charts; illus.; index. circ. 600. (back issues avail.; reprint service avail. from UMI) **Indexed:** CINAHL, Int.Nurs.Ind., J.of Abstr.Int.Educ., Nurs.Abstr., Psychol.Abstr. (1981-), Sage Fam.Stud.Abstr., Sociol.Abstr. **Document type:** academic/scholarly publication.
—BLDSC (4584.305000); Faxon; UnCover. **CCC.**
Description: Presents practical information about psychosocial and mental health issues in nursing.
Refereed Serial

610.73   JA   ISSN 0912-3741
J J N SUPESHARU/J J N SPECIAL. (Text in Japanese) 1986. irreg. 1545 Yen($12) per no. Igaku-Shoin Ltd., 5-24-3 Hongo, Bunkyo-ku, Tokyo 113-91, Japan. TEL 03-817-5771. Ed.Bd. circ. 30,000.

618   US   ISSN 0884-2175
RG951   CODEN: JOGNEY
J O G N N. (Journal of Obstetric, Gynecologic and Neonatal Nursing) 1972. 9/yr. $60 to individuals (foreign $105); institutions $170 (foreign $200) (effective 1996); newsstand price: $24. (Association of Women's Health, Obstetric and Neonatal Nurses) Lippincott - Raven Publishers, 227 E. Washington Sq., Philadelphia, PA 19106. TEL 215-238-4200. Ed. Dr. Karen B. Haller; Pub. Lisa R. Marshall. adv. contact: Kathleen Phelan. circ. 24,042. (also avail. in microform from UMI) **Indexed:** CINAHL, Ind.Med., Int.Nurs.Ind., Nurs.Abstr.
—BLDSC (4670.352000); Faxon; SWETS; UMI; UnCover. **CCC.**
Former titles: J O G N Nursing (ISSN 0090-0311); Nurses Association of the American College of Obstetricians and Gynecologists. Bulletin News (ISSN 0044-7641); Nurses Association of A.C.O.G. Bulletin (ISSN 0095-2982)

610.73   JM   ISSN 0021-4140
JAMAICAN NURSE. 1961. 3/yr. $25. Nurses Association of Jamaica, Mary Seacole Annex, 4 Trevennion Park Rd., P.O. Box 277, Kingston 5, Jamaica, W.I. TEL 809-92-95213. Ed. Murleene Anderson. adv.; bk.rev.; charts; illus.; cum.index. circ. 2,500. **Indexed:** CINAHL, Int.Nurs.Ind.
—BLDSC (4645.150000).

610.73   JA   ISSN 0389-8326
JAPANESE JOURNAL OF NURSING. (Text in Japanese) 1981. m. 9600 Yen. Gakken Co. Ltd., 40-5, 4-chome, Kamiikedai, Ohta-ku, Tokyo 145, Japan. Ed. Hisashi Nakamura. **Indexed:** Dent.Ind.

610.73 371.42   JA   ISSN 0911-0844
JAPANESE NURSING ASSOCIATION RESEARCH REPORT. (Text in Japanese; summaries in English) 1975. irreg. 1500 Yen. Japanese Nursing Association, 8-2, 5-chome, Jingumae, Shibuya-ku, Tokyo 150, Japan. Ed. Kazuo Fujita.
Description: Reports on status of nursing personnel.

610.73   US   ISSN 0002-6700
JOHNS HOPKINS HOSPITAL SCHOOL OF NURSING. ALUMNI MAGAZINE.* vol.70, 1971. q. $6. Johns Hopkins Hospital School of Nursing, c/o Allie Saularn, 515 N. Washington, Baltimore, MD 21205. Ed. Mary Kuntz. adv.; illus. (tabloid format) **Indexed:** CINAHL.

JOSANPU ZASSHI/JAPANESE JOURNAL FOR MIDWIVES. see *MEDICAL SCIENCES — Obstetrics And Gynecology*

610.73   FR   ISSN 1251-943X
▼**JOURNAL DE L'INFIRMIERE.** 1994. m. (10/yr.). (Croix-Rouge Francaise) Editions de l'Infirmiere Croix-Rouge, Villa Laromiguiere, 75005 Paris, France. TEL 40-46-62-18. FAX 40-46-62-01. Ed. Michel Guennerin. adv. contact: Marie-Pierre Cancel. circ. 30,000.

610.73   UK   ISSN 0309-2402
RT1
JOURNAL OF ADVANCED NURSING. 1976. m. £68.50 to individuals in Europe; elsewhere £75($120); institutions £297 in Europe; elsewhere £327($526) (effective 1996). Blackwell Science Ltd., Osney Mead, Oxford OX2 0EL, England.
TEL 01865-206206. FAX 01865-206219. TELEX 83355 MEDBOK G. Ed. J.P. Smith. adv.; bk.rev.; bibl.; illus.; index. circ. 2,700. (also avail. in microform from UMI; back issues avail; reprint service avail. from ISI) **Indexed:** Abstr.Health Care Manage.Stud., ASCA, ASSIA, Behav.Med.Abstr., CINAHL, Curr.Cont., Excerp.Med., Ind.Med., Int.Nurs.Ind., Mult.Ed.Abstr., Res.High.Educ.Abstr., Risk Abstr., SSCI, Tech.Educ.Abstr. **Document type:** academic/scholarly publication.
—BLDSC (4918.947000); Faxon; Genuine Article; SWETS; UMI; UnCover. **CCC.**
Refereed Serial

JOURNAL OF CARDIOVASCULAR NURSING. see *MEDICAL SCIENCES — Cardiovascular Diseases*

MEDICAL SCIENCES — NURSES AND NURSING

616.89 155.4   US   ISSN 1073-6077
RJ499.A1
JOURNAL OF CHILD AND ADOLESCENT PSYCHIATRIC NURSING. 1987-1991; resumed 1994. q. $43 to individuals (foreign $52); institutions $70 (foreign $82) (effective 1996). Nursecom, Inc., 1211 Locust St., Philadelphia, PA 19107. TEL 215-545-7222. FAX 215-545-1807. Eds. Elizabeth Poster, Brooke Randell. circ. 1,700. **Document type:** academic/scholarly publication.
—BLDSC (4957.423500); UMI; UnCover.
Formerly: Journal of Child and Adolescent Psychiatric and Mental Health Nursing (ISSN 0897-9685)
Description: Professional forum for nurses involved in promoting the mental health of children and adolescents and caring for emotionally disturbed youth and their families.
Refereed Serial

610.73   US   ISSN 0743-2550
JOURNAL OF CHRISTIAN NURSING. 1951. q. $19.95 (foreign $22.45) (effective 1996). Inter-Varsity Christian Fellowship, Nurses Christian Fellowship, 430 E. Plaza Dr., Westmont, IL 60559. TEL 708-887-2500. (Subscr. to: Box 1650, Downers Grove, IL 60515; Alt. addr.: 5206 Main St., Box 1650, Downers Grove, IL 60515) Ed. Judy Shelly. adv.; bk.rev.; abstr.; cum.index. circ. 12,000. (also avail. in microform from UMI) **Indexed:** CINAHL, Int.Nurs.Ind., Nurs.Abstr.
—BLDSC (4958.275000); UMI; UnCover.
Formerly (until 1984): Nurses Lamp.
Description: Offers biblical based articles to help nurses and students meet patients spiritual needs and ethical dilemmas and helps them grow spiritually.

610.73   UK   ISSN 0962-1067
CODEN: JCCNEW
JOURNAL OF CLINICAL NURSING. 1992. bi-m. £39 to individuals (outside Europe £43($69)); institutions £133.50 (outside Europe £147($237)) (effective 1996). Blackwell Science Ltd., Osney Mead, Oxford OX3 0EL, England. TEL 01865-240201. FAX 01865-721205. TELEX 83355 MEDBOK G. Ed. Mary Watkins. bk.rev.; bibl.; index. circ. 600. (also avail. in microform from UMI; back issues avail.) **Document type:** academic/scholarly publication.
—BLDSC (4958.595000); UMI. **CCC.**
Refereed Serial

610.73   US   ISSN 0737-0016
JOURNAL OF COMMUNITY HEALTH NURSING. 1984. q. $29.50 to individuals (foreign $54.50); institutions $185 (foreign $210). Lawrence Erlbaum Associates, Inc., 10 Industrial Dr., Mahwah, NJ 07430-2262. TEL 201-236-9500. FAX 201-236-0072. Eds. Arlene Cairns, Alice Schroeder. adv.: page $475; 6 x 9. bk.rev.; abstr.; charts; illus. **Indexed:** CINAHL, Excerp.Med., Ind.Med. (1993-), Int.Nurs.Ind. **Document type:** academic/scholarly publication.
—BLDSC (4961.722000); Faxon; SWETS; UMI; UnCover.
Description: Focuses on health care issues relevant to all aspects of community practice - schools, homes, visiting nursing services, clinics, hospices, education, and public health administration.
Refereed Serial

610.73   UK
JOURNAL OF COMMUNITY NURSING. 1977. m. £33 (foreign £62). P T M Publishers Ltd., 282 High St., Sutton, Surrey SM1 1PQ, England. TEL 0181-642-0162. FAX 0181-643-2275. Ed. Fiona Meehan; Pub. Peter Mell. adv. contact: Peter Mell. bk.rev. circ. 25,000. **Document type:** trade publication.
—BLDSC (4961.730000).
Former titles: Journal of District Nursing (ISSN 0263-4465); Journal of Community Nursing (ISSN 0140-0908)
Refereed Serial

610.73   US   ISSN 0022-0124
RT90
JOURNAL OF CONTINUING EDUCATION IN NURSING. 1970. bi-m. $42 to individuals; institutions $52. Slack, Inc., 6900 Grove Rd., Thorofare, NJ 08086. TEL 609-848-1000. FAX 609-853-5991. Ed. Patricia S. Yoder Wide. adv.; bk.rev. circ. 3,800. (also avail. in microform from UMI; reprint service avail. from UMI) **Indexed:** C.I.J.E., CINAHL, Cont.Pg.Educ., Educ.Ind., Int.Nurs.Ind., Nurs.Abstr., Tech.Educ.Abstr.
—BLDSC (4965.246000); Faxon; SWETS; UMI; UnCover.

610.73   US   ISSN 0099-1767
RT120.E4
JOURNAL OF EMERGENCY NURSING. Key Title: JEN, Journal of Emergency Nursing. Variant title: J E N. (Supplement avail.) 1975. bi-m. $52 to individuals (Canada $78.62; elsewhere $66); institutions $138 (Canada $162.64; elsewhere $152); students, residents $29 (Canada $46.01; elsewhere $43) (effective 1996); newsstand price: $10. (Emergency Nurses Association) Mosby - Year Book, Inc. (Subsidiary of: Times Mirror Company), 11830 Westline Industrial Dr., St. Louis, MO 63146-3318. TEL 314-872-8370; 800-325-4177. FAX 314-432-1380. TELEX 44-2402. Ed. Gail Pisarcik Lenehan. adv.: B&W page $1430, color page $2435; trim 8 1/8 x 10 7/8. bk.rev.; illus.; index. circ. 29,433. (also avail. in microfilm from UMI; reprint service avail. from UMI) **Indexed:** CINAHL, Int.Nurs.Ind., Nurs.Abstr.
—BLDSC (4977.300000); Faxon; SWETS; UMI; UnCover. **CCC.**
Description: Information on emergency care with articles written and reviewed by emergency nurses.

610.73   US   ISSN 1074-8407
RT120.F34
▼**JOURNAL OF FAMILY NURSING.** 1995. q. $55 to individuals; institutions $138 (effective Sep. 1995). (University of Calgary, Faculty of Nursing, CN) Sage Publications, Inc., 2455 Teller Rd., Thousand Oaks, CA 91320. TEL 805-499-0721. FAX 805-499-0871. E-mail: libraries@sagepub.com. (Overseas subscr. to: Sage Publications Ltd., 6 Bonhill St., London EC2A 4PU, England; Sage Publications India Pvt. Ltd., Box 4215, New Delhi 110 048, India) Ed. Janice M. Bell. adv.; bk.rev. (back issues avail.; reprint service avail.) **Document type:** academic/scholarly publication.
—BLDSC (4983.720000). **CCC.**
Description: Publishes empirical and theoretical analyses and scholarly work on nursing research, education, and policy issues pertaining to family health and illness.
Refereed Serial

JOURNAL OF GERONTOLOGICAL NURSING. see *GERONTOLOGY AND GERIATRICS*

610.73   US   ISSN 0898-0101
RT42   CODEN: JHNUF8
JOURNAL OF HOLISTIC NURSING. 1983. q. $49 to individuals; institutions $106 (effective Sep. 1995). (American Holistic Nurses' Association) Sage Publications, Inc., 2455 Teller Rd., Thousand Oaks, CA 91320. TEL 805-499-0721. FAX 805-499-0871. E-mail: libraries@sagepub.com. (Overseas subscr. to: Sage Publications Ltd., 6 Bonhill St., London EC2A 4PU, England; Sage Publications India Pvt. Ltd., P.O. Box 4215, New Delhi 110 048, India) Eds. Imelda Clements, Henry Plawecki. index. circ. 3,600. (back issues avail.; reprint service avail.) **Indexed:** Viol.& Abuse Abstr. **Document type:** academic/scholarly publication.
—BLDSC (5002.710000); Faxon; UnCover.
Description: Offers a holistic nursing foundation for practitioners and educators through shared research and clinical experience; publishes original work and disseminates the ideals of holistic nursing to the health care community.

658   US   ISSN 0896-5846
JOURNAL OF INTRAVENOUS NURSING. 1978. bi-m. $70 to individuals (foreign $85); institutions $120 (foreign $145) (effective 1996); newsstand price: $26. (Intravenous Nurses Society) J.B. Lippincott Co., E. Washington Sq., Philadelphia, PA 19106. TEL 215-238-4200. (Subscr. to: Insurance Way, Hagerstown, MD 21740) Ed. Mary Larkin. adv.: B&W page $1770; 7 x 10. abstr.; bibl.; charts; illus.; index. circ. 10,107. (also avail. in microform from UMI; back issues avail.) **Indexed:** CINAHL, Excerp.Med., Int.Nurs.Ind., Nurs.Abstr.
—BLDSC (5007.698000); Faxon; SWETS; UMI; UnCover. **CCC.**
Formerly (until 1988): N I T A (ISSN 0160-3930)
Description: News of Society activities and clinical developments affecting intravenous therapy practice.
Refereed Serial

610.73   US   ISSN 0194-1658
JOURNAL OF INTRAVENOUS THERAPY. 1976. bi-m. $24 (foreign $38) (effective 1995-1996). (I.V. Therapy Association of the USA) Medical Education Consultants, Box 67159, Los Angeles, CA 90067. TEL 213-475-5141. Ed. William J. Kurdi; Pub. William J. Kurdi. adv. contact: Kevin J. Kurdi. bk.rev. circ. 1,000. **Document type:** academic/scholarly publication.
—BLDSC (5007.700000).

610.73   US   ISSN 0888-0395
RC350.5   CODEN: JNNUEF
JOURNAL OF NEUROSCIENCE NURSING. 1969. bi-m. $45 to individuals; institutions $60 (effective 1995). American Association of Neuroscience Nurses, 224 N. Des Plaines, Ste. 601, Chicago, IL 60661. TEL 312-993-0043. FAX 312-993-0962. E-mail: Bergfeld@aol.com. Ed. Christina Stewart-Amidi. adv.; bk.rev.; illus. circ. 5,700. (also avail. in microform from UMI; reprint service avail. from UMI) **Indexed:** CINAHL, Hosp.Lit.Ind., Ind.Med., INIS Atomind., Int.Nurs.Ind., Nurs.Abstr. **Document type:** trade publication.
—BLDSC (5022.085000); Faxon; SWETS; UMI; UnCover. **CCC.**
Formerly (until 1986): Journal of Neurosurgical Nursing (ISSN 0047-2603)
Refereed Serial

JOURNAL OF NURSE-MIDWIFERY. see *MEDICAL SCIENCES — Obstetrics And Gynecology*

610.73   CH   ISSN 0047-262X
JOURNAL OF NURSING/HU LI TSA CHIH. (Text in Chinese; titles and table of contents in English) 1954. q. $35. Nurses' Association of the Republic of China, 12th Fl., No.315, Hsinyi Rd. Sec. 4, Taipei, Taiwan 10657, Republic of China. FAX 02-701-9817. Ed. Chuan-Min Lee. adv.; bk.rev.; illus. circ. 15,000. **Indexed:** Int.Nurs.Ind.

610.73   US   ISSN 0002-0443
RT89   CODEN: JNUAA
JOURNAL OF NURSING ADMINISTRATION. Abbreviated title: J O N A. 1971. 11/yr. $65 to individuals (foreign $105); institutions $175 (foreign $225) (effective 1996); newsstand price: $22. Lippincott - Raven Publishers, 227 E. Washington Sq., Philadelphia, PA 19106. TEL 215-238-4200. Ed. Suzanne Smith Blancett; Pub. Lisa R. Marshall. adv. contact: Kathleen Phelan. index. circ. 11,397. (also avail. in microform from UMI) **Indexed:** Abstr.Health Care Manage.Stud., AIM, C.I.J.E., CINAHL, Hosp.Lit.Ind., Ind.Med., Int.Nurs.Ind., Nurs.Abstr.
—BLDSC (5023.700000); Faxon; Genuine Article; SWETS; UMI; UnCover. **CCC.**

610.73   US   ISSN 1057-3631
RT85.5
JOURNAL OF NURSING CARE QUALITY. 1986. q. $81 (foreign $97). Aspen Publishers, Inc., 200 Orchard Ridge Dr., Gaithersburg, MD 20878. TEL 301-417-7500. FAX 301-417-7550. (Subscr. to: 7201 McKinney Circle, Frederick, MD 21701) circ. 6,000. (also avail. in microfiche; back issues avail.) **Indexed:** CINAHL, Curr.Cont., Ind.Med. (1993-), Int.Nurs.Ind., Nurs.Abstr.
—BLDSC (5023.770000); Faxon; SWETS; UMI; UnCover. **CCC.**
Formerly (until 1991): Journal of Nursing Quality Assurance (ISSN 0889-4647)
Description: Nursing QA programs, especially in the application of QA principles and concepts in the practice setting.

MEDICAL SCIENCES — NURSES AND NURSING

610.73   US   ISSN 0022-3158
JOURNAL OF NURSING EDUCATION. 1962. 9/yr. $42 to individuals; institutions $52. Slack, Inc., 6900 Grove Rd., Thorofare, NJ 08086. TEL 609-848-1000. FAX 609-853-5991. Ed. Reba de Tornyay. adv.; illus.; index. circ. 4,300. (also avail. in microform from UMI; reprint service avail. from UMI) **Indexed:** CINAHL, Educ.Ind., Hosp.Lit.Ind., Ind.Med., Ind.Sci.Rev., Int.Nurs.Ind., Nurs.Abstr.
—BLDSC (5023.800000); Faxon; SWETS; UMI; UnCover.
   Formerly (until 1983): J N E: Journal of Nursing Education (ISSN 0148-4834)
   Description: Presents study and teaching methods.

610.73 340   US   ISSN 1073-7472
K10
JOURNAL OF NURSING LAW. 1993. q. $75 to individuals (foreign $95); institutions $145. K R M Information Services, Inc., 200 Spring St., Eau Claire, WI 54703. TEL 715-833-5208. FAX 715-836-0031. Ed. Mark Helland. abstr. (back issues avail.) **Document type:** academic/scholarly publication.

610.73 658   UK   ISSN 0966-0429
                CODEN: JNMNEN
JOURNAL OF NURSING MANAGEMENT. 1993. bi-m. £33 to individuals (outside Europe £37($59)); institutions £109 (outside Europe £120($193) (effective 1996). Blackwell Science Ltd., Osney Mead, Oxford OX2 0EL, England. TEL 01865-240201. FAX 01865-721205. TELEX 83355 MEDBOK G. Ed. A.M. Palmer. adv.; bk.rev.; bibl.; illus.; index. circ. 500. (also avail. in microform from UMI; back issues avail.) **Document type:** academic/scholarly publication.
—BLDSC (5023.830000); UMI. **CCC**.
   Refereed Serial

610.73   US   ISSN 1061-3749
JOURNAL OF NURSING MEASUREMENT. 1993. s-a. $29 to individuals (foreign $34); institutions $55 (foreign $64) (effective 1996). Springer Publishing Company, 526 Broadway, New York, NY 10012-3955. TEL 212-431-4370. FAX 212-941-7842. Eds. Ora L. Strickland, Ada Sue Hinshaw. bk.rev. **Document type:** trade publication, academic/scholarly publication.
—BLDSC (5023.832000).
   Description: Provides a forum for disseminating information on instruments, tools, approaches, and procedures developed or used to measure variables in nursing, sppanning practice, education, and research.
   Refereed Serial

658   US   ISSN 0882-0627
JOURNAL OF NURSING STAFF DEVELOPMENT. 1985. bi-m. $57 to individuals (foreign $85); institutions $145 (foreign $175) (effective 1996); newsstand price: $31. Lippincott - Raven Publishers, 227 E. Washington Sq., Philadelphia, PA 19106. TEL 215-238-4200. Ed. Belinda E. Puetz; Pub. Marcia E. Serepy. adv. contact: Susan Eidson. illus.; index. circ. 4,361. (also avail. in microform from UMI) **Indexed:** CINAHL.
—BLDSC (5023.900000); Faxon; Genuine Article; SWETS; UMI; UnCover. **CCC**.

610.73   US   ISSN 0744-7132
JOURNAL OF OPHTHALMIC NURSING & TECHNOLOGY. 1982. bi-m. $32 to individuals; institutions $44. Slack, Inc., 6900 Grove Rd., Thorofare, NJ 08086. TEL 609-848-1000. FAX 609-853-5991. Ed. Heather Boyd-Monk. adv. circ. 3,000. **Indexed:** CINAHL, Int.Nurs.Ind., Nurs.Abstr.
—BLDSC (5026.344000); Faxon; UnCover.

JOURNAL OF PAIN AND SYMPTOM MANAGEMENT. see MEDICAL SCIENCES — Anaesthesiology

610.73   US   ISSN 0882-5963
                CODEN: JLPNEO
JOURNAL OF PEDIATRIC NURSING; nursing care of children and families. 1986 (Feb.). bi-m. $87 (foreign $129) (effective 1996). W.B. Saunders Co. (Subsidiary of: Harcourt Brace & Company), Curtis Center, 3rd Fl., Independence Sq. W., Philadelphia, PA 19106-3399. TEL 215-238-7800. FAX 215-238-6445. (Subscr. to: Periodicals Fulfillment, W.B. Saunders Co., 6277 Sea Harbor Dr., 4th Fl., Orlando, FL 32891-4800. TEL 800-654-2452. FAX 800-874-6418) Ed. Cecily Lynn Betz; Pub. Joan W. Blumberg. adv.: B&W page $715, color page$1665; 7 x 10. bk.rev.; bibl.; charts; illus.; index. circ. 3,004. **Indexed:** CINAHL, Ind.Med. (1993-). **Document type:** academic/scholarly publication.
—BLDSC (5030.190000); Faxon; SWETS; UMI; UnCover. **CCC**.
   Description: Taking a family-centered approach, presents comprehensive discussions of topics of interest to pediatric and maternal nurses from several points of view.
   Refereed Serial

JOURNAL OF PEDIATRIC ONCOLOGY NURSING. see MEDICAL SCIENCES — Oncology

610.73 618.2   US   ISSN 0893-2190
                CODEN: JPNNE8
JOURNAL OF PERINATAL AND NEONATAL NURSING. 1987. q. $67 (foreign $80). Aspen Publishers, Inc., 200 Orchard Ridge Dr., Gaithersburg, MD 20878. TEL 301-417-7500. FAX 301-417-7550. **Indexed:** CINAHL, IMFL, Nurs.Abstr.
—BLDSC (5030.548000); Faxon; SWETS; UMI; UnCover. **CCC**.

610.73 617.96   US   ISSN 0883-9433
JOURNAL OF POST ANESTHESIA NURSING. 1986. bi-m. $98 (foreign $139) (effective 1996). (American Society of Post Anesthesia Nurses) W.B. Saunders Co. (Subsidiary of: Harcourt Brace & Company), Curtis Center, 3rd Fl., Independence Sq., Philadelphia, PA 19106-3399. TEL 215-238-7800. FAX 215-238-6445. (Subscr. to: Periodicals Fulfillment, W.B. Saunders Co., 6277 Sea Harbor Dr., 4th Fl. Orlando, FL 32891-4800. TEL 800-654-2452. FAX 800-874-6418) Ed. Susan Goodwin; Pub. Joan W. Blumberg. adv.: B&W page $830, color page $1830; 7 x 10. bibl.; charts; illus.; cum.index. circ. 11,980. **Indexed:** CINAHL. **Document type:** academic/scholarly publication.
—BLDSC (5041.148400); Faxon; UMI; UnCover. **CCC**.
   Description: Aimed primarily at nurses engaged in the practice of postsurgical nursing and the management of patients in postanesthesia care units; covers standards of care, educational resources, pharmacology, and legal and ethical issues.
   Refereed Serial

610.73   US   ISSN 0022-3867
JOURNAL OF PRACTICAL NURSING. 1951. q. $15 (foreign $25) (effective 1994). National Association for Practical Nurse Education and Service, Inc., 1400 Spring St., Ste. 310, Silver Spring, MD 20910. TEL 301-588-2491. FAX 301-588-2839. Ed. Matthew Green. adv.; bk.rev.; abstr.; bibl.; charts; illus.; stat.; index. cum.index. circ. 13,000. (also avail. in microform from UMI; reprint service avail. from UMI) **Indexed:** CINAHL, Dent.Ind., Hosp.Lit.Ind., Int.Nurs.Ind., Rehabil.Lit
—BLDSC (5041.600000); Faxon; UMI; UnCover.
   Refereed Serial

610.73   US   ISSN 8755-7223
RT1   CODEN: JPNUET
JOURNAL OF PROFESSIONAL NURSING. 1985. bi-m. $124 (foreign $155) (effective 1996). (American Association of Colleges of Nursing) W.B. Saunders Co. (Subsidiary of: Harcourt Brace & Company), Curtis Center, 3rd Fl., Independence Sq. W., Philadelphia, PA 19106-3399. TEL 215-238-7800. FAX 215-238-6445. (Subscr. to: Periodicals Fulfillment, W.B. Saunders Co., 6277 Sea Harbor Dr., 4th Fl., Orlando, FL 32891-4800. TEL 800-654-2452. FAX 800-874-6418) Ed. Laurel Archer Copp; Pub. Joan W. Blumberg. adv.: B&W page $620, color page $1460; 7 x 10; adv. contact: Steve Gray. bk.rev. circ. 2,348. (back issues avail.) **Indexed:** CINAHL, Nurs.Abstr. **Document type:** academic/scholarly publication.
—BLDSC (5042.697000); Faxon; SWETS; UMI; UnCover. **CCC**.
   Description: Addresses the practice, research, and policy roles of nurses through general articles, research articles, reviews, and editorials.

610.736   US   ISSN 0279-3695
RC440
JOURNAL OF PSYCHOSOCIAL NURSING AND MENTAL HEALTH SERVICES. 1962. m. $44 to individuals; institutions $54. Slack, Inc., 6900 Grove Rd., Thorofare, NJ 08086. TEL 609-848-1000. FAX 609-853-5991. Ed. Shirley Smoyak. adv.; bk.rev.; charts; illus.; index. circ. 12,800. (also avail. in microform from UMI; reprint service avail. from UMI) **Indexed:** Adol.Ment.Hlth.Abstr., C.I.N.L., Chic.Per.Ind., Ind.Med., Int.Nurs.Ind., Mid.East: Abstr.& Ind., Nurs.Abstr., Psychol.Abstr.
—BLDSC (5043.475000); Faxon; Genuine Article; SWETS; UMI; UnCover.
   Former titles: Journal of Psychiatric Nursing and Mental Health Services (ISSN 0360-5973); Journal of Psychiatric Nursing (ISSN 0022-3948)

610.73 371   US   ISSN 1059-8405
JOURNAL OF SCHOOL NURSING. 1970; N.S. 1985. q. $60 to non-members; members $10. (National Association of School Nurses, Inc.) Health Information Publications, Inc., 92 S. Highland Ave., Ossining, NY 10562. TEL 914-762-6498. FAX 914-762-1234. (Subscr. to: National Association of School Nurses, Inc., Box 1300, Scarborough, ME 04070-1300. TEL 207-883-2117) Ed. Carole Passarelli. adv.: B&W page $1430; color page $2200; trim 8 1/4 x 11. circ. 8,000 (paid). **Indexed:** CINAHL. **Document type:** academic/scholarly publication.
—BLDSC (5052.665000).
   Formerly (until vol.7, no.3, 1991): School Nurse (ISSN 0048-945X)

610.73   US   ISSN 1043-6596
JOURNAL OF TRANSCULTURAL NURSING. 1989. s-a. $60 to institutions; members $70; student and retirees $45 (effective 1996) (includes Transcultural Nursing Newsletter). Transcultural Nursing Society, 601 N. Wenona, Bay City, MI 48706. TEL 517-684-7381. FAX 517-684-1248. E-mail: 70536,1754@compuserve.com. (Subscr. to: Transcultural Nursing Society, Madonna University, College of Nursing, 36600 School Dr., Livonia, MI 48150. TEL 313-454-7642. FAX 313-591-8356) Ed. M. McFarland. adv.; bk.rev. (back issues avail.) **Indexed:** CINAHL.
—BLDSC (5069.795000).
   Description: Serves as an international forum for researchers who desire to share their ideas regarding transcultural nursing.
   Refereed Serial

610.73   US   ISSN 1076-4747
▼**JOURNAL OF TRAUMA NURSING.** 1994. q. $42 to individuals (foreign $58); institutions $52 (foreign $68) (effective 1996). Nursecom Inc., 1211 Locust St., Philadelphia, PA 19107. TEL 215-545-7222; 800-242-6757. FAX 215-545-8107. Ed. Connie Walleck. (back issues avail.) **Document type:** academic/scholarly publication.

MEDICAL SCIENCES — NURSES AND NURSING

610.736 616.1   US   ISSN 1062-0303
JOURNAL OF VASCULAR NURSING. 1982. q. $50 to individuals (Canada $64.20; elsewhere $60); institutions $77 (Canada $93.09; elsewhere $87); student, residents $25 (Canada $37.45; elsewhere $35) (effective 1996); newsstand price: $13. (Society for Vascular Nursing) Mosby - Year Book, Inc. (Subsidiary of: Times Mirror Company), 11830 Westline Industrial Dr., St. Louis, MO 63146-3318. TEL 314-872-8370; 800-325-4177. FAX 314-432-1380. Eds. Victoria A. Fahey, Janice D. Nunnelee. adv.; B&W page $765, color page $1515; trim 8 1/4 x 11. circ. 1,553.
—BLDSC (5072.268500); UMI. **CCC.**

610.73   NZ   ISSN 1173-2032
KAI TIAKI: NURSING NEW ZEALAND. 1993; N.S. 1995. m. NZ.$50. New Zealand Nurses' Organisation, P.O. Box 2128, Wellington, New Zealand. TEL 64-4-385-0847. FAX 64-4-382-9993. Eds. Teresa O'Connor, Kathy Stodart. adv.; bk.rev.; charts; illus.; stat.; circ. 24,000 (controlled). **Indexed:** CINAHL, Int.Nurs.Ind.
—BLDSC (5081.173000); Faxon; UMI; UnCover. **CCC.**
Formerly (until Feb. 1995): Nursing New Zealand (ISSN 1172-1979); Formed by the merger of (1909-1993): New Zealand Nursing Journal (ISSN 0028-8535); (1982-1993): N Z N U News (ISSN 0111-865X); Which was formed by the merger of (1979-1982): N.Z. Nurses News (ISSN 0111-297X) and New Zealand Nurses Union News.
Description: Contains information on professional issues and issues concerning nurses' pay and conditions. Includes clinical and research articles, news and events and reports from staff around the country.
Refereed Serial

610.73   JA   ISSN 0022-8362
KANGO/NURSING. (Text in Japanese; summaries in English) 1949. m. 8400 Yen($30) Japanese Nursing Association - Nihon Kango Kyokai Shuppanka, 8-11, 5-chome, Jingumae, Shibuya-ku, Tokyo 150, Japan. Ed. Yaeko Inada. adv.; bk.rev.; abstr.; bibl.; charts; film rev.; illus.; play rev.; stat.; index, cum.index. circ. 50,000. **Indexed:** Int.Nurs.Ind.
—BLDSC (5085.356000).

610.73   JA   ISSN 0385-5988
KANGO GAKUSEI/NURSE STUDENT. 1951. m.(plus suppl.). 11400 Yen. Medical Friend Co. Ltd. - Mejikaru Furendo Sha, 2-4, 3-chome, Kudan-Kita, Chiyoda-ku, Tokyo 102, Japan. FAX 03-3261-6602. Ed. Kazuhazu Ogura. circ. 30,000. (also avail. in microfiche; back issues avail.)
Description: Learning guide and drills for student nurses.

610.7   JA   ISSN 0449-752X
KANGO GIJUTSU/JAPANESE JOURNAL OF NURSING ARTS. (Text in Japanese) 1950. m.(plus 4 supplements). 17600 Yen($133) Medical Friend Co., Ltd. - Mejikaru Furendo Sha, 2-4, 3-chome, Kudan-Kita, Chiyoda-ku, Tokyo 102, Japan. FAX 03-3261-6602. Ed.Bd. adv.; bk.rev.; illus.; index. circ. 100,000. (also avail. in microfiche) **Indexed:** Dent.Ind., Int.Nurs.Ind.
—BLDSC (4656.740500).
Description: Case analyses and literature in clinical nursing.

610.73   JA   ISSN 0022-8370
KANGO KENKYU/JAPANESE JOURNAL OF NURSING RESEARCH. (Text in Japanese) 1968. q. 7760 Yen($60) Igaku-Shoin Ltd., 5-24-3 Hongo, Bunkyo-ku, Tokyo 113-91, Japan. TEL 03-817-5775. Ed.Bd. circ. 8,000. **Indexed:** Int.Nurs.Ind.
—BLDSC (4656.745000).

610.73   JA   ISSN 0047-1895
KANGO KYOIKU/JAPANESE JOURNAL OF NURSING EDUCATION. (Text in Japanese) 1960. m. 12630 Yen($97) Igaku-Shoin Ltd., 5-24-3 Hongo, Bunkyo-ku, Tokyo 113-91, Japan. TEL 03-817-5775. illus. circ. 10,000. **Indexed:** Int.Nurs.Ind.

610.73   JA   ISSN 0385-549X
KANGO TENBO/JAPANESE JOURNAL OF NURSING SCIENCE. (Supplement avail.) (Text in Japanese) 1976. m. 18000 Yen. Medical Friend Co. Ltd. - Mejikaru Furendo-Sha, 2-4, 3-chome, Kudan-Kita, Chiyoda-ku, Tokyo 102, Japan. FAX 03-3261-6602. Ed. Kazuhazu Ogura. index. circ. 30,000. (also avail. in microfiche; back issues avail.) **Indexed:** Int.Nurs.Ind.
—BLDSC (4656.746000).
Description: Administrative issues of nursing and various discussions on nursing education.

610.73   JA   ISSN 0387-351X
KANGOGAKU ZASSHI/NURSING MAGAZINE. (Text in Japanese) 1946. m. 9960 Yen($77) Igaku-Shoin Ltd., 5-24-3 Hongo, Bunkyo-ku, Tokyo 113-91, Japan. TEL 03-817-5771. Ed.Bd. circ. 50,000.

610.73   US   ISSN 0022-8710
KANSAS NURSE. vol.48, 1973. 10/yr. $30 to non-members (foreign $40). Kansas State Nurses Association, 700 S.W. Jackson, Ste. 601, Topeka, KS 66603-3731. TEL 913-233-8638. Ed. Dawn L. Reid. adv.; bk.rev.; illus. circ. 2,360. (also avail. in microform from UMI; reprint service avail. from UMI) **Indexed:** CINAHL, Int.Nurs.Ind. **Document type:** trade publication.
—BLDSC (5085.648000); UMI.

610.73   US   ISSN 0742-8367
KENTUCKY NURSE. 1952. q. $18 (foreign $24). Kentucky Nurses Association, Box 2616, Louisville, KY 40201. TEL 502-637-2546. FAX 502-637-8236. Ed. Ida Slusher. adv.; bk.rev.; circ. 2,800 (controlled). (also avail. in microfiche from UMI) **Indexed:** CINAHL. **Document type:** newsletter.
—BLDSC (5089.653500); UMI.
Formerly: Kentucky Nurse Association Newsletter (ISSN 0023-0316)

610.73   KE   ISSN 0301-0333
KENYA NURSING JOURNAL. 1972. s-a. EAs.7.50($1) per no. National Nurses Association of Kenya, P.O. Box 49422, Nairobi, Kenya. Ed. J. B. Khachina. adv.; bk.rev. circ. 2,750. (back issues avail.) **Indexed:** Int.Nurs.Ind.

610.73 618.92   GW   ISSN 0723-2276
KINDERKRANKENSCHWESTER. 1982. m. DM.64. Schmidt-Roemhild Verlag, Mengstr.16, 22552 Luebeck, Germany. TEL 0451-1605-0. FAX 0451-1605280. adv.; bk.rev. circ. 17,000. (back issues avail.) **Document type:** trade publication.
—BLDSC (5095.637000).

610.73   DK   ISSN 0902-2767
KLINISK SYGEPLEJE. 1987. bi-m. DKK 230 (effective 1996). Munksgaard International Publishers Ltd., Noerre Soegade 35, P.O. Box 2148, DK-1016 Copenhagen K, Denmark. TEL 45-33-12-70-30. FAX 45-33-12-93-87. Ed. Marion Thorning. adv.: B&W page $350; trim 6 1/2 x 9. index. circ. 4,500. (back issues avail.) **Document type:** academic/scholarly publication.

610.73   KO   ISSN 0047-3618
RT1
KOREAN NURSE/TAEHAN KANHO. 1961. bi-m. $1.49. Korean Nurses' Association, 88-7 Sanglim-Dong, Choong Ku, Seoul, S. Korea. Ed. San-Cho Chun. adv.; bk.rev.; illus. **Indexed:** ExtraMED, Int.Nurs.Ind.
●Also available on CD-ROM.
—BLDSC (5113.602000).

KRANKENDIENST; Zeitschrift fuer kath. Krankenhaeuser, Sozialstationen und Pflegeberufe. see HOSPITALS

610.73   GW   ISSN 0174-108X
KRANKENPFLEGE JOURNAL; Krankenhaus Magazin. 1963. m. DM.36.40. Die Schwestern Revue GmbH, Am Schwarzenberg 28, 8700 Wuerzburg, Germany. Ed. Knut Wenzel Backe. adv.; illus. **Indexed:** Int.Nurs.Ind.
—BLDSC (5118.146600).
Formerly: Schwestern Revue (ISSN 0048-9549)

610.73   JA   ISSN 0388-5585
KURINIKARU SUTADI/CLINICAL STUDY. (Text in Japanese) 1980. m. (plus 2 supplements). 15000 Yen. Medical Friend Co. Ltd. - Mejikaru Furendo Sha, 2-4, 3-chome, Kudan-Kita, Tokyo 102, Japan. TEL 03-3261-6602. Ed. Kazuhazu Ogura. index. circ. 60,000. (also avail. in microfiche; back issues avail.) **Indexed:** Int.Nurs.Ind.
Description: Case studies in nursing process and miscellanies for novice nurses and student nurses.

610.73   CN
L P N ASSOCIATION OF BRITISH COLUMBIA NEWSLETTER.* 1957. q. free to members. Licensed Practical Nurses of British Columbia, P.O. Box 44, Lake Errock B.C. V0M 190, Canada. TEL 604-754-3428. Judy Wild.

610.7   AT   ISSN 0047-3936
LAMP. 1943. m. Aus.$55. New South Wales Nurses Association, 43 Australia St., Camperdown, N.S.W. 2050, Australia. TEL 02-550-3244. FAX 02-550-3667. Ed. Patricia Staunton. adv.; bk.rev. circ. 39,500. (also avail. in microfiche) **Indexed:** CINAHL, Int.Nurs.Ind. **Document type:** trade publication.
—BLDSC (5145.050000).
Description: Features industrial and professional news and development of interest to nurses.

610.73 618.97   AU   ISSN 1024-6908
LAZARUS; Oesterreichs Zeitschrift fuer Kranken- und Altenpflege. 1986. m. S.550. Verein Lazarus Press, Doppel 29, A-3062 Kirchstetten, Austria. TEL 02743-8797. Ed. Erich Hofer. adv.: B&W page S.22000, color page S.30000; trim 191 x 251; adv. contact: Erich Hofer. bk.rev. circ. 20,000. **Document type:** bulletin.

610.73 340   US   ISSN 8756-0054
LEGISLATIVE NETWORK FOR NURSES. 1984. s-m. $210 (effective Sep. 1992). Business Publishers, Inc., 951 Pershing Dr., Silver Spring, MD 20910-4464. TEL 301-587-6300. FAX 301-585-9075. Ed. B.K. Morris. (looseleaf format) **Document type:** newsletter.
●Also available online. Vendor(s): NewsNet.
—**CCC.**
Description: Regulations and how they impact the nursing profession - salaries, training, recruiting and unionizing.

610.73   UK   ISSN 0263-4945
LIBRARIES FOR NURSING BULLETIN. 1981. q. £10 (students £5). Libraries for Nursing Group, c/o Robin Snowball, Radcliffe Infirmary, Oxford OX2 6HE, England. TEL 01865-224478. Eds. Paul Moorbath, Maurice Wakeham. adv. contact: Robin Snowball. bk.rev./ circ. 200 (paid). **Document type:** bulletin.
—BLDSC (5186.094000).

610.73   US
LICENSED PRACTICAL NURSE.* 1968-1982 (July); resumed 1984. m. $12 to individuals; institutions $18. McClain Publishing Co., Box 10619, Charlotte, NC 28212-5677. Ed. Debbie Egan. adv.; bk.rev.; charts; illus.; index. cum.index. circ. 65,000. (processed; also avail. in microform from UMI; reprint service avail. from UMI) **Indexed:** C.I.N.L., Hosp.Lit.Ind., I.P.A., Int.Nurs.Ind.
●Also available online.
—UMI. **CCC.**
Former titles: Journal of Nursing Care (ISSN 0162-7155); Nursing Care (ISSN 0091-2379); Bedside Nurse (ISSN 0005-7665)

LINK (WOODLAND HILLS). see MEDICAL SCIENCES — Psychiatry And Neurology

LIST OF CANADIAN NURSING-RELATED PERIODICALS. see MEDICAL SCIENCES — Abstracting, Bibliographies, Statistics

610.73   US
LOUISIANA. STATE BOARD OF NURSING. REPORT (CALENDAR YEAR). 1973. a. $25. State Board of Nursing, 912 Pere Marquette Bldg., New Orleans, LA 70112. TEL 504-568-5464. FAX 504-568-5467. Dir. Barbara L. Morvant. circ. 150. **Document type:** government publication.
Formerly (until 1976): Louisiana. State Board of Nurse Examiners. Report (ISSN 0095-5884)

MEDICAL SCIENCES — NURSES AND NURSING

610.73   US   ISSN 0361-929X
RG951   CODEN: MCNNEI
M C N: AMERICAN JOURNAL OF MATERNAL CHILD NURSING. 1976. bi-m. $23 to individuals; institutions $30. American Journal of Nursing Co., 555 W. 57th St., New York, NY 10019. TEL 212-582-8820. Ed. Barbara E. Bishop, R.N. adv.; bk.rev.; bibl.; charts; illus.; index. circ. 37,500. (also avail. in microform from UMI; reprint service avail. from UMI) **Indexed:** CINAHL, IMFL, Ind.Med., Int.Nurs.Ind., Nurs.Abstr.
●Also available online.
—BLDSC (5413.499800); Faxon; SWETS; UMI; UnCover.

610.73 362   NE   ISSN 0165-2923
M G Z. (Maatschappelijke Gezondheidszorg) 1973. m. Misset (Subsidiary of: Reed Elsevier plc), Postbus 4, 7000 BA Doetinchem, Netherlands. TEL 31-8340-49911. FAX 31-8340-63638. (Editorial addr.: Postbus 100, 3980 CC Bunnik, Netherlands. TEL 31-3405-96390. FAX 31-3405-63994) adv.: B&W page fl.2178, color page fl.4768; trim 210 x 297; adv. contact: Cor van Nek. bk.rev.; illus.; index. circ. 5,900. **Document type:** trade publication.
Formed by the merger of (1910-1972): Gezondheidszorg (ISSN 0016-9528); Katholieke Gezondheidszorg (ISSN 0022-9369); Oranje - Groene Kruis.
Description: For professionals in home care and preventive health care, including district nurses, midwives, dieticians, doctors, and home nursing services.

610.73   US
M L N NEW DIRECTIONS.* 1975. 2-4/yr. $30. Minnesota League for Nursing, Box 24713, Minneapolis, MN 55424-0713. Ed. Adella Espelien. adv. circ. 400. **Document type:** newsletter.
Formerly: M L N Bulletin - Newsletter; Which supersedes (1953-1975): M L N Bulletin (ISSN 0047-7508)

610.73   US   ISSN 0047-6080
MARYLAND NURSE. 1970. 8/yr. $12. Maryland Nurses Association, Airport Square, 849 International Dr., Ste. 255, Linthicum Heights, MD 21090. TEL 410-859-3000. FAX 410-859-3001. Ed. Nancy McCashen. adv. contact: Marie Ciarpella. bk.rev. circ. 5,000. (also avail. in microfilm from UMI) **Indexed:** CINAHL, Int.Nurs.Ind. **Document type:** newspaper.
—BLDSC (5383.518000); UMI.
Supersedes: Maryland Nurses News.

610.73   US   ISSN 0163-0784
MASSACHUSETTS NURSE. 1932. m. $12. Massachusetts Nurses Association, 340 Turnpike St., 2nd Fl., Canton, MA 02021-2700. FAX 617-821-4445. Ed. Lynette Aznavourian. adv.; bk.rev.; charts; illus. circ. 18,000. **Indexed:** CINAHL, Int.Nurs.Ind.
Formerly (until vol. 44, 1975): Massachusetts Nurses Association. Bulletin (ISSN 0025-4843)

610.73   US   ISSN 0090-0702
RJ245   CODEN: MCNJA2
MATERNAL - CHILD NURSING JOURNAL. 1972. q. $43 to individuals (foreign $59); institutions $50 (foreign $66) (effectie 1996). Nursecom, Inc., 1211 Locust St., Philadelphia, PA 19107. TEL 215-545-7222. FAX 215-545-8107. Ed. Corinne Barnes; Pub. Margo C. Neal. adv.: B&W page $825, color page $2125; trim 8 1/4 x 10 3/4. bk.rev. circ. 2,500. (also avail. in microform from UMI; reprint service avail. from UMI, WSH) **Indexed:** CINAHL, Excerpt.Med., Ind.Med., Nurs.Abstr., Psychol.Abstr. (1972-). **Document type:** academic/scholarly publication.
—BLDSC (5399.275000); Faxon; SWETS; UMI; UnCover.
Description: Articles on the professional care of mothers and children for the expert nurse practitioner.
Refereed Serial

MEDIA PROFILES: HEALTH SCIENCES EDITION. see *MEDICAL SCIENCES*

610.73   RU   ISSN 0869-7760
CODEN: MESEAQ
MEDITSINSKAYA POMOSHCH/MEDICAL CARE. 1942. bi-m. $46 (effective 1996). (Ministerstvo Zdravookhraneniya) Izdatel'stvo Meditsina, Petroverigskii pereulok 6-8, 101000 Moscow, Russia. (Dist. by: Mezhdunarodnaya Kniga, B. Yakimanka 39, 117049 Moscow, Russia. TEL 7-095-2384600. FAX 7-095-2384634) (Co-sponsor: A-O Pharmapeks) Ed. O.V. Aleksandrov. adv. contact: L.A. Shestakova. bk.rev.; index. **Indexed:** Biol.Abstr., Chem.Abstr., Dent.Ind., Int.Nurs.Ind.
—BLDSC (0104.700000).
Formerly (until 1993): Meditsinskaya Sestra (ISSN 0025-8342)
Description: Publishes articles on the care of patients, medical technique, sanitary education.

MEDSURG NURSING. see *MEDICAL SCIENCES — Surgery*

610.73   SA
MEMBRANE. 1979. s-a. free. Renal Care Society of Southern Africa, Heldokruin, Roodepoort 1726, South Africa. illus. circ. 200. **Indexed:** Ind.S.A.Per.

MENTAL HEALTH NURSING JOURNAL. see *MEDICAL SCIENCES — Psychiatry And Neurology*

610.73   US   ISSN 0026-2366
MICHIGAN NURSE. 1924. 11/yr. $33 (foreign $50). Michigan Nurses Association, 2310 Jolly Oak Rd., Okemos, MI 48864-3546. TEL 517-349-5640. FAX 517-349-5818. Ed. Tina Steger Gratz. adv.; illus.; index. circ. 10,000. (also avail. in microform from UMI) **Indexed:** CINAHL, Int.Nurs.Ind., Mich.Mag.Ind. **Document type:** newsletter.
—BLDSC (5755.540000); UMI.

MIDWIFERY. see *MEDICAL SCIENCES — Obstetrics And Gynecology*

610.73   TS
MINBAR AL-TAMRID/NURSING FORUM. (Text in Arabic, English) 1987. 5/yr. free. Ministry of Health, School of Nursing - Wizarat al-Sihhah, Madrasat al-Tamrid, P.O. Box 3798, Abu Dhabi, United Arab Emirates. TEL 668591. FAX 665472. TELEX 22678 MEDAD EM. Ed. Nabil Kronfol. circ. 1,000 (controlled).
Description: Scientific articles in the field of nursing, and news of interest to the nursing profession.

610.73   US   ISSN 1068-5685
CODEN: MISNFI
MINIMALLY INVASIVE SURGICAL NURSING. q. $75 (foreign $109). Mary Ann Liebert, Inc. Publishers, 2 Madison Ave., Larchmont, NY 10538. TEL 914-834-3100. FAX 914-834-3688. E-mail: Liebert@pipeline.com. Ed. Carolyn Mackety. **Indexed:** CINAHL. **Document type:** academic/scholarly publication.
—BLDSC (5797.712000).
Formerly: Laser Nursing (ISSN 0888-6075)
Description: For nurses who work with patients receiving laser therapy. Covers safety, administration, diagnostic and therapeutic applications, and responsibilities pertaining to preoperative and postoperative patient care.

610.73   US   ISSN 0026-5586
MINNESOTA NURSING ACCENT. Variant title: M N A Accent. 1927. 10/yr. $25 to non-members. Minnesota Nurses Association, 1295 Bandana Blvd., Ste. 140, St. Paul, MN 55108. FAX 612-646-4807. Ed. Marilyn Cunningham. adv.; bk.rev.; illus. circ. 14,000. **Indexed:** CINAHL, Int.Nurs.Ind. **Document type:** newsletter.

MINORITY NURSE PROFESSIONAL. see *OCCUPATIONS AND CAREERS*

610.73   US   ISSN 0026-6388
MISSISSIPPI R N. 1939. bi-m. $18. Mississippi Nurses' Association, 135 Bounds St., Jackson, MS 39206. TEL 601-982-9182. FAX 601-982-9183. Ed. Betty Dickson. adv.; bk.rev.; illus. circ. 2,000. **Indexed:** CINAHL, Int.Nurs.Ind. **Document type:** newsletter.

610.73   US   ISSN 0026-6655
MISSOURI NURSE.* 1932. 6/yr. $25 to non-members (foreign $30). Missouri Nurses Association, P.O. Box 105228, Jefferson City, MO 65110-5228. TEL 314-636-4623. FAX 314-636-9576. Ed. Kay Fulwider. adv.; illus. circ. 3,000. **Indexed:** CINAHL, Int.Nurs.Ind. **Document type:** trade publication.
—BLDSC (5829.085000).
Description: Disseminates information regarding policies, positions and activities of the Association; strives to provide a forum for discussion of nursing issues relevant to Association members.

610.73   US   ISSN 1047-4757
N A S NEWSLETTER. 1986. 5/yr. membership. (National Association of School Nurses, Inc.) Health Information Publications, Inc., 92 S. Highland Ave., Ossining, NY 10562. TEL 914-762-6498. FAX 914-762-0239. (Subscr. to: Box 1300, Scarborough, ME 04070-1300. TEL 207-883-2117) Ed. Beverly Farquhar. adv.: B&W page $945, color page $1745; trim 8 1/4 x 11. circ. 7,100. **Document type:** newsletter.
Description: Covers news, issues, conferences and resources of interest to school nurses.

610.73   US   ISSN 1069-6903
N P NEWS. 1993. 6/yr. free. Elsevier Science Inc., 655 Ave. of the Americas, New York, NY 10010. TEL 212-633-3875. FAX 212-633-3762. TELEX 420643 AEP UI. Ed. Joan Stanley. adv. contact: Andrea Cernichiari. illus. circ. 20,000. (tabloid format) **Document type:** newsletter.
●Also available online. Vendor(s): University Microfilms International.
Description: Covers health care, politics, and general information affecting the roles and practices of nurse practitioners.

610.73   UK
NATIONAL ASSOCIATION OF FAMILY PLANNING NURSES JOURNAL. 1980. 2/yr. £18. National Association of Family Planning Nurses, 19 Whitacre Rd., Knowle, Solihull, W. Midlands B93 9HW, England. TEL 01564-770032. Ed. Gill O'Connor. adv.; bk.rev. **Document type:** newsletter.
Formerly: National Association of Family Planning Nurses Newsletter.

610.73   US   ISSN 0028-1921
NEBRASKA NURSE.* 1947. q. $10. Nebraska Nurses' Association, 1430 South St., No. 202, Lincoln, NE 68502-2446. TEL 402-475-3859. Ed. Donna R. Baker. adv.; charts; illus. circ. 24,000. **Indexed:** CINAHL, Int.Nurs.Ind. **Document type:** newsletter.

610.73   US   ISSN 0730-0832
Discard   CODEN: NEONEE
NEONATAL NETWORK; the journal of neonatal nursing. 1982. 8/yr. $38 to individuals (Canada $44; elsewhere $56); institutions $50 (foreign $56) (effective 1996). Neonatal Network, 1304 Southpoint Blvd., Ste. 280, Petaluma, CA 94954-6859. TEL 707-762-2646. FAX 707-762-0401. E-mail: neonatal82@aol.com. Ed. Charles Rait. adv.; bk.rev.; index. circ. 18,000. (back issues avail.) **Indexed:** CINAHL, Ind.Med., Int.Nurs.Ind. **Document type:** academic/scholarly publication.
—BLDSC (6075.624000); SWETS; UnCover.
Refereed Serial

610.73   US   ISSN 0273-4117
NEVADA R N-FORMATION. Variant title: Nevada Registered Nurse Information. 1931. q. $15. Nevada Nurses Association, 3660 Baker Ln., Reno, NV 89509-5409. FAX 702-825-3555. adv. circ. 11,000. (back issues avail.) **Indexed:** CINAHL, Int.Nurs.Ind.

610.73   US   ISSN 0196-4895
NEW JERSEY NURSE. vol.26, 1970. 10/yr. $20 (effective 1993). New Jersey State Nurses' Association, 320 W. State St., Trenton, NJ 08618. TEL 609-392-4884. FAX 609-396-2330. Ed. Dorothy Flemming. adv.; bk.rev. circ. 6,000. **Indexed:** CINAHL, Int.Nurs.Ind. **Document type:** newsletter.
Formerly: N J S N A Newsletter (ISSN 0028-5870)
Description: News and information of interest to association members.

MEDICAL SCIENCES — NURSES AND NURSING

610.73   IE
THE NEW WORLD OF IRISH NURSING. 8/m. £15. (Irish Nurses' Organization) In Ireland Publishing, 25 Sibthorpe Ln., Dublin 6, Ireland. TEL 01-604805. FAX 01-604615. (Co-sponsor: National Council of Nurses of Ireland) Ed. P.J. Madden. circ. 14,000. (processed) Indexed: ASSIA, CINAHL, Int.Nurs.Ind.
    Former titles (until 1993): World of Irish Nursing; Incorporates: Irish Nurses' Journal (ISSN 0021-1338); Irish Nursing and Hospital World.

610.73 371   US
NEW YORK STATE ASSOCIATION OF SCHOOL NURSES COMMUNICATOR. s-a. membership. Health Information Publications, Inc., 92 S. Highland Ave., Ossining, NY 10562. TEL 914-762-6498. FAX 914-762-0239. Ed. Ruth Papagni. adv.: B&W page $500. circ. 800 (paid). **Document type:** newsletter.

610.73   US   ISSN 0028-7644
                     CODEN: JNYNA
NEW YORK STATE NURSES ASSOCIATION. JOURNAL. 1970. q. $24. New York State Nurses Association, 46 Cornell Rd., Latham, NY 12110-1403. TEL 518-782-9400. FAX 518-782-9533. Ed. Anne Schott. adv.; bk.rev.; abstr.; bibl.; charts; illus.; stat. circ. 35,000. (also avail. in microform from UMI; back issues avail.) Indexed: CINAHL, Int.Nurs.Ind., Soc.Work Res.& Abstr. **Document type:** academic/scholarly publication.
—BLDSC (4832.940000); Faxon.
    Formerly: New York State Nurse.
    Description: Publishes research reports and scholarly articles on nurses and nursing.
    Refereed Serial

610.73   US   ISSN 0028-7652
NEW YORK STATE NURSES ASSOCIATION. REPORT. 1969. 10/yr. $24. New York State Nurses Association, 46 Cornell Rd., Latham, NY 12110-1403. TEL 518-782-9400. FAX 518-782-9533. Ed. Anne Schott. adv.; charts; illus.; stat. circ. 35,000. (tabloid format; back issues avail.) **Document type:** newsletter.
    Incorporates (in 1978): N Y S N A Legislative Bulletin.
    Description: Covers news of interest to nurses, and reports activities of the Association.

610.73   NZ   ISSN 0110-7968
NEW ZEALAND NURSING FORUM. 1973-199?; resumed Aug. 1995. q. NZ.$45. Nurses Society of New Zealand., P.O. Box 3195, Auckland 1, New Zealand. TEL 64-9-8178412. FAX 64-9-817-6833. Ed. David Wills. adv.; bk.rev.; abstr.; bibl.; charts; illus.; stat. circ. 12,500. Indexed: C.I.N.L., Int.Nurs.Ind. **Document type:** academic/scholarly publication.
—BLDSC (6096.345000). CCC.
    Formerly (until 1978): Nursing Forum (ISSN 0110-0890)
    Description: Original papers, abstracts and reviews on nursing.

610.73   NR   ISSN 0331-4448
NIGERIAN NURSE. 1973. bi-m. $13.50. (National Association of Nigeria Nurses and Midwives) Literamed Publications Nigeria, Ltd., Oregun Village, Private Mail Bag 21068, Ikeja, Nigeria. TEL 234-1-962512. FAX 234-1-961037. Ed. Anu Adegoroye; Pub. O.M. Lawal-Solarin. bibl.; illus. circ. 10,000. Indexed: CINAHL. **Document type:** academic/scholarly publication.

610.73   US   ISSN 0894-5780
NIGHTINGALE. 1973. m. $15 or membership. National Association of Physician Nurses, 900 S. Washington St., Ste. G-13, Falls Church, VA 22046. TEL 703-237-8616. stat.; tr.lit. (back issues avail.)

610.73   JA   ISSN 0917-513X
NIHON KANGO GAKKAISHI/JOURNAL OF JAPANESE NURSING RESEARCH. (Text in Japanese) 1991. s-a. 750 Yen. Nihon Kango Gakkai - Society of Japanese Nursing Research, Japanese Nursing Association, 5-8-11 Jingumae, Shibuya-ku, Tokyo 150, Japan. TEL 03-3499-7335. FAX 03-3499-5943. Ed. Kayoko Matsumoto. adv. contact: Toshiaki Okuno. **Document type:** academic/scholarly publication.
—BLDSC (5009.250000).
    Description: Publishes selected papers presented at the JNA Nursing Research Conferences.

610.73   SZ
NOVA. (Text in French, German, Italian) 11/yr. Schweizerische Verband der Krankenpflegerinnen und Krankenpfleger, Obergrundstr. 44, CH-6003 Luzern, Switzerland. TEL 041-227822. FAX 041-227820. circ. 6,000.

610.73   HU   ISSN 0864-7003
NOVER; az apolas elmelete es gyakorlata. 1988. bi-m. 600 Ft. Orszagos Orvostudomanyi Inormacios Intezet es Konyvtar - National Institute for Medical Information and Library of Medicine, Szentkiralyi u. 21, 1088 Budapest, Hungary. TEL 36-1-384133. FAX 36-1-2669710. Ed. Katalin Vittay Fedinecz; Pub. Dr. Alexander Fedinecz. adv.: B&W page 20000 Ft., color page 30000 Ft.; adv. contact: Ilona Borbas. bk.rev.; index. circ. 3,500. **Document type:** academic/scholarly publication.
—BLDSC (6180.365000).
    Description: Directed at the continuing education of nurses, nursing theory and practice.

610.73   SP   ISSN 0210-8275
NUEVA ENFERMERIA. m. free to qualified personnel. Consejo Nacional de Ayudantes Tecnicos Sanitarios y Diplomados en Enfermeria, Buen Suceso 6, 2o, 28008 Madrid, Spain. TEL 1-541-60-73. Ed. Luis A. Jurjo Alonso. adv.; bk.rev. Indexed: Int.Nurs.Ind. **Document type:** bulletin.
    Formerly (until 1979): A T S Boletin Cultural e Informativo (ISSN 0210-8186); Which was formed by the merger of (1928-1977): Boletin Oficial de los Practicantes de Medicina y Cirugia (ISSN 0210-833X); Boletin de las Enfermeras Espanoles y A T S de Espana (ISSN 0304-9213); Which was formerly (1963-1968): Caridad, Ciencia y Arte (ISSN 0069-0546)

610.73   CN   ISSN 0382-8476
NURSCENE. 1967. 6/yr. Can.$30. (foreign Can.$40). Manitoba Association of Registered Nurses, 647 Broadway, Winnipeg, MB R3C 0X2, Canada. TEL 204-774-3477. FAX 204-775-6052. Ed. Heather McLaughlin. adv.: B&W page Can.$825. bk.rev.; circ. 11,000 (controlled). **Document type:** trade publication.
    Formerly: Marnews.
    Description: Includes articles on healthcare, profiles of nurses, updates on education, seminars, meetings and forums dealing with the provision and administration of healthcare in Manitoba and elsewhere.

610.73 070.4   US   ISSN 1054-2353
RT24
NURSE AUTHOR AND EDITOR. 1991. q. $48 (Canada $58; elsewhere $66) (effective 1996). Hall Johnson Communications, Inc., 9737 W. Ohio Ave., Lakewood, CO 80226. TEL 303-988-0056. Ed. Suzanne Hall Johnson. Indexed: CINAHL. **Document type:** newsletter.
—CCC.
    Description: Offers advice on writing and editing articles and books for nursing publications.

610.73   UK   ISSN 0260-6917
NURSE EDUCATION TODAY. 1981. bi-m. £40($61) to individuals; institutions £165 ($260) (effective 1995). Churchill Livingstone Journals (Subsidiary of: Pearson Professional), Robert Stevenson House, 1-3 Baxter's Pl., Leith Walk, Edinburgh EH3 3AF, Scotland. TEL 0131-556-2424. FAX 0131-459-1177. (Subscr. to: Longman Group Ltd., Journals Subscr. Dept., Fourth Ave., Harlow, Essex CM19 5AA, England. TEL 01279-623760; U.S. subscr. to: Churchill Livingstone, 650 Ave. of the Americas, New York, NY 10011. TEL 212-206-5000) Ed. Peter Birchenall. adv. contact: David Dunnachie. bk.rev.; illus. circ. 990. (also avail. in microform from UMI; back issues avail.) Indexed: CINAHL, Mult.Ed.Abstr., Sociol.Educ.Abstr., Tech.Educ.Abstr. **Document type:** academic/scholarly publication.
—BLDSC (6187.028400); Faxon; Genuine Article; SWETS. CCC.

610.73   US   ISSN 0363-3624
RT71   CODEN: NUEDEC
NURSE EDUCATOR. 1976. bi-m. $52 to individuals (foreign $85); institutions $110 (foreign $145) (effective 1996); newsstand price: 26. Lippincott - Raven Publishers, 227 E. Washington Sq., Philadelphia, PA 19106. TEL 215-238-4200. Ed. Suzanne Smith Blancett; Pub. Lisa R. Marshall. adv. contact: Susan Eidson. bk.rev.; index. circ. 3,416. (also avail. in microform from UMI) Indexed: C.I.J.E., CINAHL, Int.Nurs.Ind., Nurs.Abstr.
—BLDSC (6187.028500); Faxon; SWETS; UMI; UnCover. CCC.

610.73   US   ISSN 0361-1817
RT1   CODEN: NRPRDJ
THE NURSE PRACTITIONER; the American journal of primary health care. 1975. 12/yr. $75 to institutions (foreign $94) (effective 1995). Elsevier Science Inc., 655 Ave. of the Americas, New York, NY 10010. TEL 212-989-5800. FAX 212-633-3990. (Subscr. to: Box 882, Madison Sq. Sta., New York, NY 10159-0882) Ed. Linda J. Pearson. adv.; charts; illus.; stat.; index. circ. 13,500. (also avail. in microform from UMI; reprint service avail. from UMI) Indexed: CINAHL, Curr.Lit.Fam.Plan., FAMLI, Hosp.Lit.Ind., I.P.A., Ind.Med., Int.Nurs.Ind., Nurs.Abstr. **Document type:** trade publication.
●Also available online.
—BLDSC (6187.028700); Faxon; SWETS; UnCover. CCC.
    Refereed Serial

610.73   US   ISSN 1045-5485
NURSE PRACTITIONER FORUM. 1990. q. $67 (foreign $99) (effective 1996). W.B. Saunders Co. (Subsidiary of: Harcourt Brace & Company), Curtis Center, 3rd Fl., Independence Sq. W., Philadelphia, PA 19106-3399. TEL 215-238-7800. FAX 215-238-6445. (Subscr. to: Periodicals Fulfillment, W.B. Saunders Co., 6277 Sea Harbor Dr., 4th Fl., Orlando, FL 32891-4800. TEL 800-654-2452. FAX 800-874-6418) Ed. Charon A. Pierson; Pub. Joan W. Blumberg. adv.: B&W page $620, color page $1445; 7 x 10; adv. contact: Steve Gray. circ. 1,961. Indexed: CINAHL. **Document type:** academic/scholarly publication.
—BLDSC (6187.028720). CCC.
    Description: Each issue covers a single clinical topic, emphasizing diagnostic and therapeutic measures performed by the nurse practitioner.

610.73 616   UK   ISSN 1351-5578
NURSE RESEARCHER. 1993. q. £27 (overseas £48). R C N Publishing Co., Viking House, 17-19 Peterborough Rd., Harrow, Middlesex HA1 2AX, England. TEL 0181-423-1066. FAX 0181-423-3867. (Subscr. to: Glynteg House, Station Terrace, Ely, Cardiff CF5 4XG, Wales. TEL 01222-553411, FAX 01222-576208) Ed. Alex Mathieson; Pub. Alison Dunn. (back issues avail.) **Document type:** academic/scholarly publication.
—BLDSC (6187.028730).
    Description: Contains authoritative papers on the appropriate application and relevance of research methods to nursing.
    Refereed Serial

610.73 340   US   ISSN 0196-6790
KFC615.A15
THE NURSE, THE PATIENT AND THE LAW; the journal of nursing law & risk management. 1977-1983; resumed 1984. m. $250 (effective Jan. 1994). Cox Publications, Box 20316, Billings, MT 59104-0316. TEL 406-256-8822. Ed. Meridith B. Cox. index. circ. 1,046. Indexed: CINAHL.
    Description: Discusses nursing negligence cases from a risk management perspective; keeps readers current on new standards of care, new methods to reduce or eliminate risks and new laws affecting patient care and nursing practice.
    Refereed Serial

610.73   CN   ISSN 0849-3383
NURSE TO NURSE. 1961. q. Can.$30. Registered Nurses Association of Nova Scotia, 120 Eileen Stubbs Ave., Ste. 104, Dartmouth, NS B3B 1Y1, Canada. TEL 902-468-9744. FAX 902-468-9510. Ed. Marie Dauphinee-Booth. adv. contact: Colleen Burke. bk.rev. circ. 10,000. **Document type:** academic/scholarly publication, newsletter.
    Formerly (until 1990): R N A N S Bulletin (ISSN 0319-4604)
    Refereed Serial

MEDICAL SCIENCES — NURSES AND NURSING 4445

610.73 615 US ISSN 0191-2291
NURSES' DRUG ALERT. 1976. m. $24 (Canada $30; elsewhere $35) (effective 1996). M.J. Powers & Co., 65 Madison Ave., Morristown, NJ 07960-6088. TEL 201-898-1200. FAX 201-898-1201. Ed. Sally Wicklund. index. (looseleaf format; back issues avail.) **Indexed:** CINAHL, Nurs.Abstr. **Document type:** newsletter.
—BLDSC (6187.034000).

610.73 615.53
NURSES IN TRANSITION.* 4/yr. $5. c/o Marta Johnson, Box 104, Glencoe, CA 95232. Ed. Claudia Deyton.

610.73 US ISSN 1063-2859
NURSEWEEK. 1986. bi-m. $40 (free to qualified personnel). 1156 Aster Ave., Ste. C, Sunnyvale, CA 94086-6801. TEL 408-249-5877. FAX 408-249-8204. Ed. Clarice Hutchison. adv. circ. 190,000. **Document type:** trade publication.
Formerly: California Nursing Review.
Description: For experienced, career-oriented nurses in hospitals and other California health care facilities.

610.73 PO
NURSING. 12/yr. Rua D. Estefania 32, 1000 Lisbon, Portugal. TEL 1-572763. FAX 1-522643. Ed. Antonio Panciarelli. circ. 15,000.

610.73 US ISSN 0360-4039
RT1
NURSING (YEAR). 1971. m. $42 (effective 1995). Springhouse Corporation (Subsidiary of: Reed Elsevier Medical group plc.), 1111 Bethlehem Pike, Box 908, Springhouse, PA 19477. TEL 215-646-8700; 800-346-7844. FAX 215-653-0826. (Subscr. to.: Box 2021, Marion, OH 43305-9974) Pub. Maryanne Wagner. adv. contact: Mary Wardlaw. bibl.; charts; illus.; index. circ. 442,626. (also avail. in microform from UMI; back issues avail.) **Indexed:** CINAHL, Curr.Lit.Fam.Plan., Gen.Sci.Ind., Hosp.Lit.Ind., Ind.Med., Int.Nurs.Ind., Nurs.Abstr., Tr.& Indus.Ind. **Document type:** trade publication.
—BLDSC (6187.037500); Faxon; SWETS; UMI; UnCover. **CCC.**
Description: Provides a how-to journal for nurses focusing on clinical, management, legal, ethical, and professional issues. Includes special sections for hospital, critical care, and continuing care.

610.73 IT
NURSING (YEAR). q. Systems Comunicazioni, Via Olanda, 6, 20083 Gaggiano (MI), Italy. TEL 02-90811814. FAX 02-90841682. adv.: B&W page L.1300000, color page L.2000000; trim 180 x 240. circ. 5,000.

610.73 NE ISSN 1381-5911
▼**NURSING (YEAR).** Key Title: Nursing (Maarssen). (Text in Dutch) 1994. m. Misset (Subsidiary of: Reed Elsevier plc), Postbus 4, 7000 BA Doetinchem, Netherlands. TEL 31-8340-49371. FAX 31-8340-63638. (Editorial addr.: Postbus 1110, 3600 BC Maarssen, Netherlands. TEL 31-3465-58277. FAX 31-3465-58255) adv.: B&W page fl.4250, color page fl.7100; trim 215 x 285; adv. contact: Cor van Nek. illus. circ. 30,000. **Document type:** trade publication.
—SWETS.
Description: Professional magazine for nurses.

NURSING (YEAR) CAREER DIRECTORY. see BUSINESS AND ECONOMICS — Trade And Industrial Directories

610.73 US ISSN 0273-320X
RM301.12
NURSING (YEAR) DRUG HANDBOOK. a. $25.95 (effective 1995). Springhouse Corporation (Subsidiary of: Reed Elsevier Medical group plc.), 1111 Bethlehem Pike, Box 908, Springhouse, PA 19477-0908. TEL 215-646-8700; 800-346-7844. FAX 215-646-4508. Pub. Minnie Rose. **Document type:** trade publication.

610.73 SP ISSN 0212-5382
NURSING (YEAR) (EDICION ESPANOLA). 1983. m. (10/yr.). 5900 ptas.($55) (free to qualified personnel). Ediciones Doyma, S.A., Travesera de Gracia, 17-21, 08021 Barcelona, Spain. TEL 34-1-200-07-11. FAX 34-1-209-11-36. TELEX 51694 INK-E. (U.S. publisher: Springhouse Corporation, 1111 Bethlehem Pike, Springhouse, PA 19477) Dir. Margarita Peya. adv.: page 330000 ptas.; trim 200 x 273; adv. contact: Julio Esteva. circ. 29,000. (reprint service avail. from UMI)
Description: Covers nursing within and outside of the hospital environment. Serves the continuing education needs of nurses on a scientific and technical level.

NURSING ABSTRACTS. see MEDICAL SCIENCES — Abstracting, Bibliographies, Statistics

610.73 US ISSN 0363-9568
RT89
NURSING ADMINISTRATION QUARTERLY. 1976. q. $97 (foreign $117). Aspen Publishers, Inc., 200 Orchard Ridge Dr., Gaithersburg, MD 20878. TEL 301-417-7500. FAX 301-417-7550. Ed.Bd. (also avail. in microform from UMI; reprint service avail. from UMI) **Indexed:** Abstr.Health Care Manage.Stud., CINAHL, Int.Nurs.Ind., Nurs.Abstr.
—BLDSC (6187.038400); Faxon; SWETS; UMI. **CCC.**

610.73 US ISSN 0276-5284
RT1
NURSING AND HEALTH CARE. 1952. m. (10/yr.). institutions $60. National League for Nursing, 350 Hudson St., New York, NY 10014. TEL 212-989-9393. Ed. Ellen Fahy. illus. circ. 16,000. (also avail. in microform from UMI; microfiche from CIS; reprint service avail. from UMI) **Indexed:** CINAHL, Int.Nurs.Ind., Med.Care Rev., Nurs.Abstr., SRI. **Document type:** academic/scholarly publication.
—BLDSC (6187.038800); Faxon; Genuine Article; SWETS; UMI; UnCover. **CCC.**
Supersedes (1952-1980): N L N News (ISSN 0027-6804)
Description: Contains organization news and articles on health care issues and trends.

610.73 AT ISSN 1033-6303
▼**NURSING AND HEALTH SCIENCE EDUCATION.** 1994. s-a. $60 to individuals; institutions $120. James Nicholas Publishers, P.O. Box 244, Albert Park, Vic. 3206, Australia. TEL 61-3-696-5545. FAX 613-699-2040. Ed. Rea Zajda. adv.; bk.rev.; index. **Document type:** academic/scholarly publication.
Description: To provide nursing practitioners, nursing educators, hospital administrators and health science educators with current and innovative theory and practice in various major areas of nursing and health science education.
Refereed Serial

610.73 US
NURSING ARCHIVES NEWS. 1981. a. Boston University, Mugar Memorial Library, Department of Special Collections, Nursing Archives, Charles River Campus, 771 Commonwealth Ave., Boston, MA 02215. TEL 617-353-3696. FAX 617-353-2838. bk.rev. circ. 300. (back issues avail.) **Document type:** newsletter.
Description: Information for the Nursing Archives Associates membership and others about the activities of the Nursing Archives.

610.73 CN ISSN 1185-3638
NURSING B C. 1968. 5/yr. Can.$53.50 to non-members. Registered Nurses Association of British Columbia, 2855 Arbutus St, Vancouver, BC V6J 3Y8, Canada. TEL 604-736-7331. FAX 604-738-2272. Ed. Bruce Wells. adv. contact: Doug Davison. bk.rev.; illus.; circ. 35,000 (controlled). (also avail. in microform from UMI; reprint service avail. from UMI) **Indexed:** CINAHL, Int.Nurs.Ind. **Document type:** academic/scholarly publication.
—BLDSC (6187.038950); UMI.
Formerly: R N A B C News (ISSN 0048-7104)
Description: Contains news about nurses and nursing in Canada. Covers health issues.

610.73 US ISSN 0029-6465
RT1 CODEN: NCNAAK
NURSING CLINICS OF NORTH AMERICA. 1966. q. $85 (foreign $106) (effective 1996). W.B. Saunders Co. (Subsidiary of: Harcourt Brace & Company), Curtis Center, 3rd Fl., Independence Sq. W., Philadelphia, PA 19106-3399. TEL 215-238-7800. FAX 215-238-6445. (Subscr. to: Periodicals Fulfillment, W.B. Saunders Co., 6277 Sea Harbor Dr., 4th Fl., Orlando, FL 32891-4800. TEL 800-654-2452. FAX 800-874-6418) Ed. Sandy Masse. index. (also avail. in microform from UMI; reprint service avail. from UMI,ISI) **Indexed:** Abstr.Health Care Manage.Stud., AIM, Chem.Abstr., CINAHL, Curr.Cont., Excerp.Med., Hosp.Lit.Ind., Ind.Med., Int.Nurs.Ind., Nurs.Abstr.
—BLDSC (6187.040000); Faxon; Genuine Article; SWETS; UMI; UnCover. **CCC.**
Description: Aimed at students and graduate nurses.

610.73 US ISSN 0895-2809
NURSING CONNECTIONS; a forum for collaboration among nurses in pratice, education, research & administration. 1988. q. $58 to individuals (foreign $125); libraries $75 (foreign $140). Washington Hospital Center, Division of Nursing, 110 Irving St., N.W., Washington, DC 20010. TEL 202-877-3048. FAX 202-877-8082. Ed. Molly Billingsley. adv.; circ. 1,500 (paid). **Indexed:** CINAHL, Nurs.Abstr. **Document type:** academic/scholarly publication.
—BLDSC (6187.042000).
Refereed Serial

610.73 US ISSN 0894-3656
RT79
NURSING DATA REVIEW. a. $36.95. National League for Nursing, 350 Hudson St., New York, NY 10014. TEL 212-989-9393.
Former titles: N L N Nursing Data Book (ISSN 0748-5573); (until 1980): N L N Nursing Data Book: Statistical Information on Nursing Education and Newly Licensed Nurses; Some Statistics on Baccalaureate and Higher Degree Programs in Nursing (ISSN 0081-203X)

610.73 US ISSN 1046-7459
RT48.6
NURSING DIAGNOSIS. 1974. q. $45 to individuals (foreign $61); insitutions $72 (foreign $88) (effective 1996). (North American Nursing Diagnosis Association) Nursecom, Inc., 1211 Locust St., Philadelphia, PA 19107. TEL 215-545-7222. FAX 215-545-8107. Ed. Noreen Fritsch; Pub. Margo C. Neal. (also avail. in microform from UMI) **Indexed:** CINAHL.
—BLDSC (6187.043000); SWETS; UMI; UnCover.
Formerly (until 1990): Nursing Diagnosis Newsletter (ISSN 0890-7188)

610.73 US ISSN 0746-1739
NURSING ECONOMICS. bi-m. $30 to individuals (foreign $43); institutions $45 (foreign $58). Jannetti Publications, Inc., East Holly Ave., Box 56, Pitman, NJ 08071-0056. TEL 609-589-2319. FAX 609-589-7463. **Indexed:** CINAHL, Nurs.Abstr.
—BLDSC (6187.046800); Faxon; Genuine Article; SWETS; UnCover. **CCC.**

610.73 371.394 US ISSN 0893-1356
RT50.5
NURSING EDUCATORS MICROWORLD.* 1986. bi-m. $74 (effective 1992). Nursing Educators MicroWorld, 1620 Saratoga Ave., Ste. 214, San Jose, CA 95129-5113. FAX 408-741-5987. Ed. Christine Bolwell. index. (back issues avail.) **Indexed:** CINAHL. **Document type:** newsletter.
Description: Provides information on applications of microcomputers in nursing instruction and administration, for nurse educators in hospitals and schools.

610.73 UK ISSN 0969-7330
▼**NURSING ETHICS;** an international journal for health care professionals. 1994. q. £31($56) to individuals; institutions £75 ($135) (effective 1996). Arnold (Subsidiary of: Hodder Headline plc.), 338 Euston Rd., London NW1 3BH, England. TEL 0171-873-6000. FAX 0171-873-6325. (Subscr. to: Turpin Distribution Services Ltd., Blackhorse Rd., Letchworth, Herts. SG6 1HN, England. TEL 01462-672555. FAX 01462-480947) Ed. Verena Tschudin. **Document type:** academic/scholarly publication, trade publication.
—BLDSC (6187.046970).
Refereed Serial

MEDICAL SCIENCES — NURSES AND NURSING

610.73 US
NURSING FACULTY CENSUS. 1988. biennial. $19.95. National League for Nursing, 350 Hudson St., New York, NY 10014. TEL 212-989-9393.

610.73 US ISSN 0029-6473
RT1 CODEN: NUFOA
NURSING FORUM. 1961. q. $43 to individuals (foreign $59); institutions $56 (foreign $72) (effective 1996). Nursecom Inc., 1211 Locust St., Philadelphia, PA 19107. TEL 215-545-7222. FAX 215-545-8107. Ed. Lynda Juall Carpenito; Pub. Margo C. Neal. adv.: B&W page $825, color page $2125; trim 8 1/4 x 10 7/8. bk.rev.; charts; illus.; index. circ. 2,050. (also avail. in microform from UMI; reprint service avail. from UMI) **Indexed:** CINAHL, Excerp.Med., Hosp.Lit.Ind., Ind.Med., Int.Nurs.Ind. **Document type:** academic/scholarly publication.
—BLDSC (6187.050000); Faxon; SWETS; UMI; UnCover.
Description: Professional nursing journal presenting innovative ideas and emerging issues in nursing.
Refereed Serial

610.73 US ISSN 1062-8061
RT31
NURSING HISTORY REVIEW. 1993. a. $50. (American Association for the History of Nursing) University of Pennsylvania Press, Blockley Hall, 13th Fl., 418 Service Dr., Philadelphia, PA 19104. TEL 215-898-6261. Ed. Joan E. Lynaugh. bk.rev. **Indexed:** Amer.Hist.& Life (1993-), Hist.Abstr. (1993-), Ind.Med. (1994-). **Document type:** academic/scholarly publication.
—BLDSC (6187.051000); Genuine Article.
Description: Traces new and developing work in the fields of nursing and health care history.

330 US
NURSING HOME PRACTITIONER. 1993. bi-m. $50 (Canada & Mexico $55; elsewhere $60). Medquest Communications, Inc., 629 Euclid Ave., Ste. 500, Cleveland, OH 44114-3003. TEL 216-522-9700. FAX 216-522-9707. Ed. Dr. Leslie S. Libow; Pub. John H. Whaley III. adv. contact: Mark Goodman.
Description: Seeks to help nursing home practitioners, primary care physicians and consultant pharmacists to meet the ever increasing demands on clinical skills and knowledge.

610.73 US ISSN 1061-4753
RA997.A1
NURSING HOMES; long term care management. 1950. 9/yr. $50 (Canada and Mexico $55; elsewhere $60). Medquest Communications, Inc., 629 Euclid Ave., Ste. 500, Cleveland, OH 44114-3003. TEL 216-522-9700. FAX 216-522-9707. Ed. Richard Peck; Pub. John H. Whaley III. adv.; illus.; stat. circ. 45,000. (also avail. in microform from UMI; back issues avail.; reprint service avail.) **Indexed:** Account.Ind. (1974-), B.P.I., Bus.Ind., CINAHL, Hosp.Lit.Ind., I.P.A., Int.Nurs.Ind., Rehabil.Lit., Tr.& Indus.Ind.
●Also available online. Vendor(s): Knight-Ridder, Inc., University Microfilms International.
—BLDSC (6187.060000); Faxon; UMI; UnCover. CCC.
Former titles: Nursing Homes and Senior Citizen Care (ISSN 0896-6915); (until 1986): Nursing Homes (ISSN 0029-649X)
Description: For professionals in planning, directing, organizing and delivering long-term care in the proprietary nursing home field.

610.73 AT ISSN 1320-7881
▼**NURSING INQUIRY.** 1994. q. Aus.$195($195) (effective 1996). Blackwell Science Pty Ltd, P.O. Box 378, Carlton South, Vic. 3053, Australia. TEL 61-3-93470300. FAX 61-3-93493016. (back issues avail.) **Document type:** academic/scholarly publication.

610.73 CE
NURSING JOURNAL. a. Sri Lanka Nurses Association, Post Basic School of Nursing, Regent St., Colombo 10, Sri Lanka. **Indexed:** CINAHL.

610.73 II ISSN 0029-6503
RT13
NURSING JOURNAL OF INDIA. (Text in English and Hindi) 1910. m. Rs.200($40) Trained Nurses Association of India, L-17 Green Park, New Delhi 110016, India. TEL 91-11-666665. FAX 91-11-6858304. Ed. N. Nagpal. adv.; bk.rev.; charts; illus.; index. circ. 31,000. (also avail. in microfilm from UMI; reprint service avail. from UMI) **Indexed:** CINAHL, Int.Nurs.Ind.
—BLDSC (6187.080000); UMI.

610.73 US ISSN 1076-1632
▼**NURSING LEADERSHIP FORUM.** 1995. 3/yr. $39 to individuals (foreign $44); institutions $78 (foreign $87) (effective 1996). Springer Publishing Company, 536 Broadway, New York, NY 10012-3955. TEL 212-431-4370. FAX 212-941-7842. Ed. Barbara Stevens Barnum. **Document type:** trade publication.
—BLDSC (6187.091550).
Description: Aimed at nurses in management positions in practice, education, research, administration, or politics.
Refereed Serial

610.73 US ISSN 0744-6314
NURSING MANAGEMENT.* 1970. m. $25 (free to qualified personnel; $32 to Canada; elsewhere $45). S - N Publications, Inc., Box 908, Spring House, PA 19477-0903. TEL 708-426-6100. FAX 708-426-6146. Ed. Leah Curtin. adv.; bk.rev.; index; circ. 135,000 (controlled). (also avail. in microform from UMI; reprint service avail. from UMI) **Indexed:** ABI Inform, CINAHL, Hosp.Lit.Ind., Int.Nurs.Ind., Nurs.Abstr.
—BLDSC (6187.094000); Faxon; Genuine Article; SWETS; UMI; UnCover. **CCC.**
Formerly (until 1981): Supervisor Nurse (ISSN 0039-5870)
Description: Covers all aspects of nursing management and related medical, legal, personnel and ethical issues.
Refereed Serial

610.73 UK ISSN 1354-5760
NURSING MANAGEMENT. 1979. 10/yr. £55 (foreign £70). (Royal College of Nursing) R C N Publishing Co., Viking House, 17-19 Peterborough Rd., Harrow-on-the-Hill, Middlesex HA1 2AX, England. TEL 0181-423-1066. FAX 0181-423-3867. (Subscr. to: RCN Membership Records Dept., Glynteg House, Station Terrace, Cardiff CF5 4XG, Wales. TEL 01222-553411. FAX 01222-576208) Ed. John Naish. circ. 1,500. (also avail. in microform from UMI) **Indexed:** ASSIA, CINAHL, Curr.Cont. **Document type:** trade publication.
—BLDSC (6187.093500); UMI.
Former titles (until 1994): Senior Nurse (ISSN 0265-9999); (until 1984): Nursing Focus (ISSN 0144-4069)
Description: For senior clinical nurses and administrative nurse managers.
Refereed Serial

610.73 SA ISSN 1018-9238
NURSING NEWS/VERPLEEGNUUS. 1978. m. R.80 (effective 1995). South African Nursing Association, P.O. Box 1280, Pretoria 0001, South Africa. TEL 27-12-3432315. FAX 27-12-3440750. Ed. Elna Rademeyer. adv.: B&W page R.3360, color page R.4840; bleed 210 x 273. illus. circ. 88,000. **Indexed:** CINAHL. **Document type:** trade publication.
Supersedes (1935-1978): South African Nursing Journal (ISSN 0038-2507)
Description: Nursing magazine including news and educational articles.
Refereed Serial

610.73 US ISSN 0029-6538
NURSING NEWS (CONCORD). 1949. 6/yr. $20 (foreign $30). New Hampshire Nurses' Association, 48 West St., Concord, NH 03301. TEL 603-225-3783. Ed. Sara McNeil. adv. circ. 850. **Indexed:** Int.Nurs.Ind. **Document type:** newsletter.
—BLDSC (6187.104000).

610.73 US ISSN 0029-6546
NURSING NEWS (FLORAL PARK). 1944. 5/yr. membership. Nurses Association of the Counties of Long Island, 99 Tulip Ave., No. 404, Floral Park, NY 11001-1959. TEL 718-783-4433. Ed. Barbara J. Malon. adv.; illus. circ. 5,000. **Document type:** trade publication, newsletter.

610.73 US
NURSING OPPORTUNITIES. (Supplement to: R N Magazine) 1970. a. $9.95 (foreign $15). (R N Magazine) Medical Economics Publishing Co., Inc., Five Paragon Dr., Montvale, NJ 07645. TEL 201-358-7200. FAX 201-573-8979. adv.; bk.rev. circ. 130,000. (also avail. in microform from UMI)
Description: Features comprehensive profiles of hundreds of hospitals emphasizing specific employment opportunities for nurses, and related information.

610.73 US ISSN 0029-6554
RT1
NURSING OUTLOOK. 1953. bi-m. $37 to individuals (Canada $54.57; elsewhere $51); institutions $58 (Canada $77.04; elsewhere $72); students $21 (Canada $37.45; elsewhere $35) (effective 1996); newsstand price: $8. (American Academy of Nursing) Mosby Year - Book, Inc. (Subsidiary of: Times Mirror Company), 11830 Westline Industrial Dr., St. Louis, MO 63146-3318. TEL 314-872-8370; 800-325-4177. FAX 314-432-1380. (Subscr. to: Journal Subscription Service, 11830 Westline Industrial Dr., St. Louis, MO 63146. TEL 800-325-4177) Ed. Carole A. Anderson. adv.: B&W page $990, color page $1855; trim 8 1/8 x 10 7/8. bk.rev.; charts; illus.; tr.lit.; index. circ. 8,400. (also avail. in microform from UMI; reprint service avail. from UMI) **Indexed:** Abstr.Hosp.Manage.Stud., AIM, ASSIA, C.I.J.E., C.I.S. Abstr., CINAHL, Curr.Lit.Fam.Plan., Except.Child Educ.Abstr., Hosp.Lit.Ind., I.P.A., Ind.Med., Int.Nurs.Ind., Med.Care Rev., Nurs.Abstr., Psychol.Abstr., Rehabil.Lit., Soc.Sci.Ind., Soc.Work Res.& Abstr., SSCI.
●Also available online.
—BLDSC (6187.108000); Faxon; Genuine Article; SWETS; UMI; UnCover. **CCC.**

610.73 US ISSN 0886-8948
NURSING PULSE OF NEW ENGLAND. fortn. $7.50. 104 Charles St., Box 682, Boston, MA 02114. TEL 617-523-5123.
Description: News magazine for nurses.

610.73 362.1 US ISSN 1055-6818
RT85.5
NURSING QUALITY CONNECTION. 1992. bi-m. $49.95 to individuals; institutions $65 (effective 1996). Mosby - Year Book, Inc. (Chicago) (Subsidiary of: Times Mirror Company), 200 N. LaSalle St., Chicago, IL 60601-1080. TEL 312-726-9733. FAX 312-726-6075. TELEX 206155. **Document type:** newsletter.
—BLDSC (6187.109280).

610.73 SA ISSN 0258-1647
NURSING R S A VERPLEGING; magazine for today's nurse - die moderne verpleegkunidge se tydskrif. (Text and summaries in Afrikaans, English) 1986. m. R.89 (foreign R.105($32)) (effective 1995). (South African Nursing Association) M A S A Publications, Private Bag X1, Pinelands 7430, Cape Town, South Africa. TEL 27-21-531-3081q. FAX 27-21-531-4126. Ed. Lilian Medlen; Pub. Peter Roberts. adv.; bk.rev.; abstr.; bibl.; charts; illus. circ. 30,000. (reprint service avail. from IRC) **Indexed:** CINAHL, Ind.S.A.Per., Int.Nurs.Ind. **Document type:** academic/scholarly publication.
—BLDSC (6187.116310); SWETS; UMI.
Incorporates: Curationis (ISSN 0379-8577)
Description: Covers a broad spectrum of issues of interest to nursing professionals, including practical, technical, historical and theoretical topics.

610.73 658.3 US ISSN 1051-4341
NURSING RECRUITMENT & RETENTION; strategies and resources for the nursing professional. 1988. m. $330. Business Publishers, Inc., 951 Pershing Dr., Silver Spring, MD 20910-4464. TEL 301-587-6300. FAX 301-585-9075. Ed. B.K. Morris. (looseleaf format; back issues avail.) **Document type:** newsletter.
●Also available online. Vendor(s): NewsNet.
—CCC.
Description: Teaches health care managers how to recruit and retain qualified nurses for their staff.

610.73 US ISSN 0029-6562
RT1 CODEN: NURNA
NURSING RESEARCH. 1952. bi-m. $35 to individuals; institutions $70. American Journal of Nursing Co., 555 W. 57th St., New York, NY 10019. TEL 212-582-8820. Ed. Florence D. Downs, R.N. adv.; bk.rev.; abstr.; charts; stat.; index. cum.index: 1952-1963. circ. 11,000. (also avail. in microform from UMI; reprint service avail. from UMI) **Indexed:** Abstr.Health Care Manage.Stud., AIM, ASSIA, Behav.Med.Abstr., Child Devel.Abstr., CINAHL, Curr.Cont., Dent.Ind., Excerp.Med., Hosp.Lit.Ind., I.P.A., IMFL, Ind.Med., Ind.Sci.Rev., Int.Nurs.Ind., Med.Care Rev., MEDSOC, Ment.Retard.Abstr., Mid.East: Abstr.& Ind., Mult.Ed.Abstr., Nucl.Sci.Abstr., Nurs.Abstr., Psychol.Abstr. (1952-), Risk Abstr., Soc.Work Res.& Abstr., Sp.Ed.Needs Abstr., SSCI, Stud.Wom.Abstr.
●Also available online.
—BLDSC (6187.110000); Faxon; SWETS; UMI; UnCover.

NURSING RESEARCH ABSTRACTS. see *MEDICAL SCIENCES — Abstracting, Bibliographies, Statistics*

610.73 US ISSN 0894-3184
NURSING SCIENCE QUARTERLY; theory, research and practice. 1988. q. $50 to individuals (foreign $60); institutions $70 (foreign $80); students $25 (foreign $35) (effective 1993). Chestnut House Publications, Box 633, Pittsburgh, PA 15230. TEL 412-391-8585. FAX 412-391-8458. Ed. Rosemarie Rizzo Parse. adv. contact: Jean M. Furgivele. bk.rev.; adv.; abstr.; bibl.; charts; illus.; stat.; index. (also avail. in microform from WWS; back issues avail.) **Indexed:** CINAHL, Nurs.Abstr. **Document type:** academic/scholarly publication.
—BLDSC (6187.116340); Faxon; UnCover.
Description: Covers key aspects of nursing science, such as theoretical dilemmas, research issues, and practice applications.
Refereed Serial

610.73 730 658.3 US ISSN 1057-8323
RT90
NURSING STAFF DEVELOPMENT INSIDER. 1992. bi-m. $39.95 to individuals; institutions $55.10 (effective 1996). Mosby - Year Book, Inc. (Chicago) (Subsidiary of: Times Mirror Company), 200 N. LaSalle St., Chicago, IL 60601-1080. TEL 312-726-9733. FAX 312-726-6075. TELEX 206155. Ed. Donna Richards Sheridan. **Document type:** newsletter.
—BLDSC (6187.116450).
Description: Features original articles and commentary on issues pertinent to nursing staff development.

610.73 UK ISSN 0029-6570
CODEN: NSTAEU
NURSING STANDARD. 1968. w. £65 (overseas £70). (Royal College of Nursing) R C N Publishing Co., 17-19 Peterborough Rd., Harrow-on-the-Hill, Middlesex HA1 2AX, England. TEL 0181-423-1066. FAX 0181-423-4302. (Subscr. to: Nursing Standard, Glynteg House, Station Terrace, Ely, Cardiff CF5 4XG, Wales. TEL 01222-553411. FAX 01222-576208) Ed. Norah Casey. adv. contact: Brian Dorans. bk.rev.; illus. circ. 70,000. (reprint service avail. from IRC) **Indexed:** CINAHL, Int.Nurs.Ind. **Document type:** academic/scholarly publication.
—BLDSC (6187.116700); SWETS.
Incorporated: Lampada (ISSN 0266-8769); Tradimus (ISSN 0269-0977)

610.73 US
NURSING STUDENT CENSUS. 1987. a. $19.95. National League for Nursing, 350 Hudson St., New York, NY 10014. TEL 212-989-9393.

610.73 II
NURSING TECHNOLOGY. 1991. bi-m. Rs.640($45) K.K. Roy (Private) Ltd., 55 Gariahat Road, P.O. Box 10210, Calcutta 700 019, India. Ed. K.K. Roy. adv.; abstr.; bibl.; index. circ. 2,240.

610.73 UK ISSN 0954-7762
NURSING TIMES. 1905. w. £56($160) Macmillan Magazines Ltd., 4 Little Essex St., London WC2R 3LF, England. TEL 071-836-6633. FAX 071-379-4204. Ed. John Gilbert. adv.; bk.rev.; illus.; index. circ. 87,348. (also avail. in microform from UMI; reprint service avail. from UMI) **Indexed:** Abstr.Health Care Manage.Stud., ASSIA, C.I.S. Abstr., CINAHL, Curr.Adv.Ecol.Sci., Dent.Ind., Hosp.Abstr., Hosp.Lit.Ind., Ind.Med., Int.Nurs.Ind., Sp.Ed.Needs Abstr. **Document type:** consumer publication.
—BLDSC (6187.121000); Faxon; SWETS; UMI; UnCover. **CCC.**
Formerly (until 1987): Nursing Times, Nursing Mirror (ISSN 0269-7289); Which was formed by the 1985 merger of: Nursing Times (ISSN 0029-6589); Nursing Mirror (ISSN 0029-6511); Which incorporates (in 1978): Nursing Mirror and Midwives Journal (ISSN 0143-2524); Which was formerly: Queen's Nursing Journal (ISSN 0301-0821); District Nursing (ISSN 0012-4044).

610.73 US
NURSINGWORLD JOURNAL NURSING JOB GUIDE. 1979. a. $75. Prime National Publishing Corp., 470 Boston Post Rd., Weston, MA 02193. TEL 617-899-2702. Ed. P. Patrick Gates. adv.; charts; illus.; stat. circ. 3,000. (back issues avail.) **Document type:** directory.
Former titles: Nursingworld Journal Annual Hospital Directory; Nursing Job News: Annual Hospital Directory; Nursing Job News: Nursing Job Guide to Over 7000 Hospitals (ISSN 0162-9069)

610.73 CN ISSN 0834-9088
O N A NEWS. 1974. m. free. Ontario Nurses' Association, 85 Grenville St., Ste. 600, Toronto, ON M5S 3A2, Canada. TEL 416-964-8833. FAX 416-964-8864. Ed. Melanie Pottins. circ. 50,000. **Document type:** newsletter.
Formerly (until 1987): Ontario Nurses Association. Newsletter (ISSN 0704-8009)
Description: For staff nurses in hospitals, homes for the aged and community health nurses.

O N S NURSING SCAN IN ONCOLOGY. (Oncology Nursing Society) see *MEDICAL SCIENCES — Abstracting, Bibliographies, Statistics*

613.62 610.73 CN
O O H N A JOURNAL. 1980. 3/yr. Can.$19($20) Ontario Occupational Health Nurses Association, Ste. 605, 302 The East Mall, Etobicoke, ON M9B 6C7, Canada. TEL 613-239-6462. FAX 613-239-5462. Ed. Ken Dykeman. adv. contact: Ken Dykeman. bk.rev.; bibl.; charts; illus.; stat. **Document type:** trade publication.

O R L - HEAD AND NECK NURSING. see *MEDICAL SCIENCES — Otorhinolaryngology*

610.73 FR ISSN 1163-4634
OBJECTIF SOINS; la revue professionnelle du nouveau science de soins infirmieres. 1992. 10/yr. Editions Lamarre-Poinat, 47 rue St. Andre des Arts, 75006 Paris, France. Ed. Christian Moreau; Pub. Thierry Verret. adv. contact: Pascale Bernanose.

610.73 UK ISSN 0279-7917
OCCUPATIONAL HEALTH; a journal for the occupational health team. 1949. m. £55($99) to institutions. Aldwych Publishing plc., 230-234 Long Ln., London SE1 4QE, England. Ed. D.E. Little. adv.; bk.rev.; illus.; index. (also avail. in microform from UMI) **Indexed:** ASSIA, C.I.S Abstr., CINAHL, Curr.Adv.Ecol.Sci., Excerp.Med., Int.Nurs.Ind., Lab.Haz.Bull. **Document type:** academic/scholarly publication.
—BLDSC (6228.849000); EMDOCS; Faxon; SWETS; UMI. **CCC.**
Refereed Serial

610.73 AU ISSN 0303-4461
OESTERREICHISCHE KRANKENPFLEGEZEITSCHRIFT. 1948. 10/yr. S.330 (foreign S.360). Oesterreichischer Krankenpflegeverband, Mollgasse 3a, A-1180 Vienna, Austria. TEL 0222-346397. Ed. Ulrike Sokol. adv.; bk.rev.; abstr.; illus. circ. 8,000. **Indexed:** Int.Nurs.Ind.
—BLDSC (6307.810000); Faxon.

610.7 AU
OESTERREICHISCHER KRANKENPFLEGERVERBAND. FORTBILDUNGSPROGRAMM. 1969. a. free. Oesterreichischer Krankenpflegeverband, Mollgasse 3a, A-1180 Vienna, Austria. TEL 0222-346397. Ed. Marianne Kriegl. circ. 10,000.

OFFICIEL DE LA SAGE-FEMME. see *MEDICAL SCIENCES — Obstetrics And Gynecology*

610.73 US ISSN 0030-0993
OHIO NURSES REVIEW. 1926. bi-m. $25 (foreign $30). Ohio Nurses Association, 4000 E. Main St., Columbus, OH 43213-2983. TEL 614-237-5414. FAX 614-237-6074. Ed. Carol A. Jenkins. adv.: B&W page $580; 7 x 10. index; circ. 9,000 (controlled). **Indexed:** CINAHL, Int.Nurs.Ind.
—BLDSC (6247.150000).

OMVAARDAREN. see *SOCIAL SERVICES AND WELFARE*

610.73 616.99 US ISSN 0190-535X
ONCOLOGY NURSING FORUM. 1974. 10/yr. $95 (foreign $110) (effective 1996). (Oncology Nursing Society) Oncology Nursing Press, Inc., 501 Holiday Dr., Pittsburgh, PA 15220-2749. TEL 412-921-7373. FAX 412-921-2131. Ed. Rose Mary Carroll-Johnson. adv.; bk.rev.; index. circ. 26,000. (also avail. in microfilm from UMI; back issues avail.) **Indexed:** CINAHL, Int.Nurs.Ind., Nurs.Abstr. **Document type:** academic/scholarly publication.
—BLDSC (6256.980000); Faxon; SWETS; UMI; UnCover.
Description: Contains news related to developments in oncology nursing practice, technology, and research. Focuses on promoting a positive image of professional specialized nursing.
Refereed Serial

610.73 US ISSN 1072-7639
ONLINE JOURNAL OF KNOWLEDGE SYNTHESIS FOR NURSING. 1993. irreg. (updated approx. bi-w.). $60 to individuals; institutions $250. Sigma Theta Tau International Honor Society of Nursing, 550 W. North St., Indianapolis, IN 46202. TEL 317-634-8171. FAX 317-634-8188. Ed. Jane Barnsteiner. abstr.; bibl.; charts; stat. (back issues avail.) **Indexed:** Curr.Cont. (1994-), SSCI (1994-). **Document type:** academic/scholarly publication.
●Available only online. Vendor(s): OCLC.
—Genuine Article.
Description: Provides critical reviews of research literature of interest to clinical nurses, academicians and researchers.
Refereed Serial

610.73 617 UK ISSN 0961-1258
OPPORTUNITIES FOR THEATRE STAFF & OTHER SPECIALISTS. 1980. fortn. Newton Mann Ltd., Stretton Rd., Tansley Matlock, Derbyshire DE4 5GE, England. TEL 01629-583941. FAX 01629-580479. Ed. Vicky Stevens; Pub. N.P. Mann. adv. contact: John Eaton. circ. 5,000. **Document type:** newsletter.

610.73 US ISSN 0030-4751
RT1
OREGON NURSE. 1932. 4/yr. $16 (effective 1994). Oregon Nurses Association, 9600 S.W. Oak St., Ste. 550, Portland, OR 97223-6599. FAX 503-293-0013. Ed. Sandy Marron. adv. contact: Cathi Liston. bk.rev.; illus. circ. 5,500. **Indexed:** CINAHL, Int.Nurs.Ind. **Document type:** newsletter.
—BLDSC (6281.600000).

610.73 617.3 US ISSN 0744-6020
ORTHOPAEDIC NURSING JOURNAL; national association of orthopaedic nurses. 1981. bi-m. $24 to individuals (foreign $37); institutions $36 (foreign $49). (National Association of Orthopaedic Nurses) Jannetti Publications, Inc., East Holly Ave., Box 56, Pitman, NJ 08071-0056. TEL 609-589-2319. FAX 609-589-7463. Ed. Ann Maher. adv.; bk.rev. circ. 10,000. **Indexed:** Nurs.Abstr.
—BLDSC (6296.125300); Faxon; UnCover. **CCC.**

610.73 UK ISSN 0269-9079
PAEDIATRIC NURSING. 1988. 10/yr. £35 (overseas £60). (Royal College of Nursing) R C N Publishing Co., Viking House, 17-19 Peterborough Rd., Harrow-on-the-Hill, Middlesex HA1 2AX, England. TEL 0181-423-1066. FAX 0181-423-3867. (Subscr. to: RCN Membership Records Dept., Glynteg House, Station Terrace, Cardiff CF5 4XG, Wales. TEL 01222-553411. FAX 01222-576208) Ed. Rosemary Rogers. adv. circ. 4,500. **Document type:** trade publication.
Refereed Serial

MEDICAL SCIENCES — NURSES AND NURSING

610.73   PK   ISSN 0078-8376
PAKISTAN NURSING AND HEALTH REVIEW. 1951. q. Pakistan Nurses Federation, c/o College of Nursing, Jinnah Postgraduate Medical Centre, Karachi 35, Pakistan. Ed. Mushtaq Ahmad. circ. 2,000. **Indexed:** Int.Nurs.Ind.

PALLIATIVE CARE TODAY; the journal for today's palliative care team. see *MEDICAL SCIENCES — Oncology*

610.73   US   ISSN 0886-9006
PEDIATRIC NURSE PRACTITIONER. bi-m. National Association of Pediatric Nurse Associates and Practitioners, 1101 Kings Hwy. N., No. 206, Cherry Hill, NJ 08034. TEL 609-667-1773. FAX 609-667-7187. Ed. Timothy W. Gordon. circ. 4,000. **Document type:** trade publication.

610.73   US   ISSN 0097-9805
RJ245   CODEN: PENUEI
PEDIATRIC NURSING. 1975. bi-m. $24 to individuals (foreign $37); institutions $32 (foreign $45). Jannetti Publications, Inc., East Holly Ave., Box 56, Pitman, NJ 08071-0056. TEL 609-589-2319. FAX 609-589-7463. Ed. Veronica Feeg. adv.; bk.rev.; illus. circ. 8,763. (also avail. in microfilm from UMI; reprint service avail. from UMI) **Indexed:** CINAHL, Dent.Ind., Int.Nurs.Ind., Nurs.Abstr.
—BLDSC (6417.605300); Faxon; SWETS; UMI; UnCover. **CCC.**

610.73   US   ISSN 0031-4617
PENNSYLVANIA NURSE. 1946. 11/yr. (Nov./Dec. combined). $15. Pennsylvania Nurses Association, Editorial Board, Box 68525, Harrisburg, PA 17106-8525. TEL 717-657-1222. FAX 717-657-3796. Ed. Christine E. Finnegan. adv.; bk.rev.; illus. circ. 9,000. (tabloid format) **Indexed:** CINAHL, Int.Nurs.Ind. **Document type:** newsletter.
—BLDSC (6421.747000).

PERSPECTIVES (TORONTO). see *GERONTOLOGY AND GERIATRICS*

610.736   US   ISSN 0031-5990
RC475   CODEN: PEPYA
PERSPECTIVES IN PSYCHIATRIC CARE. 1963. q. $43 to individuals (foreign $59); institutions $56 (foreign $72) (effective 1996). Nursecom Inc., 1211 Locust St., Philadelphia, PA 19107. TEL 215-545-7222. FAX 215-545-8107. Ed. Norine Kerr; Pub. Margo C. Neal. adv.: B&W page $825, color page $2125; trim 8 1/8 x 10 7/8. bk.rev.; index. circ. 2,580. (also avail. in microfilm from UMI; reprint service avail. from UMI) **Indexed:** CINAHL, Excerp.Med., Hosp.Lit.Ind., Ind.Med., Int.Nurs.Ind., Nurs.Abstr., Psychol.Abstr. (1972-). **Document type:** academic/scholarly publication.
—BLDSC (6428.160000); Faxon; SWETS; UMI; UnCover.
Description: Focuses on research, clinical practice, trends and innovations in psychiatric and mental-health nursing.
Refereed Serial

610.73 616.2   US   ISSN 1075-5756
PERSPECTIVES IN RESPIRATORY NURSING. 1990. q. $35 (effective 1994). Respiratory Nursing Society, 5700 Old Orchard Rd., 1st Fl., Skokie, IL 60077-1057. TEL 708-966-8673. Ed. Michelle Geiger-Bronsky. adv.: B&W page $295; trim 8 1/2 x 11; adv. contact: Michelle Ginocchio. bk.rev.; charts; index. circ. 1,200. (back issues avail.) **Indexed:** CINAHL. **Document type:** newsletter.
Description: Publishes news and clinical reports of interest to respiratory nurses and therapists.

610.73   US
PERSPECTIVES ON ADDICTIONS NURSING. q. $20 to non-members. National Nurses Society on Addictions, 4101 Lake Boone Trail, Ste. 201, Raleigh, NC 27607. TEL 919-783-5871. FAX 919-787-4916. **Document type:** newsletter.
Description: Presents clinical and research articles relevant to addictions nursing.

610.73   SZ   ISSN 1012-5302
PFLEGE; die wissenschaftliche Zeitschrift fuer Pflegeberufe. 1988. q. 84 SFr. (foreign 96 SFr.). Verlag Hans Huber, Laenggassstr. 76, CH-3000 Bern 9, Switzerland. TEL 031-3004500. FAX 031-3004590. Eds. Dr. S. Kaeppeli, M. Meier. circ. 3,000. **Document type:** academic/scholarly publication.

610.73   GW   ISSN 0944-8918
PFLEGE AKTUELL. 1946. m. DM.69. Deutscher Berufsverband fuer Pflegeberufe, Hauptstr. 392, 65760 Eschborn, Germany. TEL 06173-63016. FAX 06173-640913. Ed. Eva-Maria Krampe. adv.; bk.rev.; illus.; index. circ. 33,000. **Indexed:** Dok.Arbeitsmed., Int.Nurs.Ind. **Document type:** trade publication.
—BLDSC (6440.711000).
Formerly (until 1993): Krankenpflege (ISSN 0002-1008)

610.73   GW   ISSN 0945-1129
PFLEGEZEITSCHRIFT. 1948. m. DM.104.40 (students DM.67.20). W. Kohlhammer GmbH, Hessbruehlstr. 69, 70565 Stuttgart, Germany. TEL 0711-7863-1. FAX 0711-7863263. Ed. Paul-Werner Schreiner. bk.rev. circ. 20,000. **Indexed:** Dok.Arbeitsmed. **Document type:** academic/scholarly publication.
—BLDSC (6440.715000). **CCC.**
Former titles: Deutsche Krankenpflege-Zeitschrift (ISSN 0012-074X); Deutsche Schwesternzeitung.

PHARMACY HEALTH-LINE. see *PHARMACY AND PHARMACOLOGY*

610.73   PH   ISSN 0048-3818
PHILIPPINE JOURNAL OF NURSING. 1953. q. P.25($15) Philippine Nurses Association, 1663 F. Tirena Benitez St., Malate, Manila 2801, Philippines. TEL 583092. Ed. Cecilia M. Laurente. adv.; bk.rev.; illus. circ. 13,000. **Indexed:** CINAHL, Ind.Phil.Per., Int.Nurs.Ind.
—BLDSC (6455.629000).
Formerly: Filipino Nurse.

610.73 618   PL   ISSN 0048-4148
PIELEGNIARKA I POLOZNA. 1958. m. 180000 Zl. Wydawnictwo Auxilium Spolka z o.o., Ul. Koszykowa 8, 00-562 Warsaw, Poland. TEL 48-22-215066. (Dist. by: Ars Polona-Ruch, Krakowskie Przedmiescie 7, Warsaw, Poland. TEL 48-22-267622) Ed. Irena Kosobudzka. adv.; bk.rev.; illus. circ. 35,000. **Indexed:** Int.Nurs.Ind.
Formed by the merger of: Pielegniarka Polska; Polozna.

610.73   PL   ISSN 0860-8466
PIELEGNIARSTWO POLSKIE. (Text and summaries in English, Polish) 1989. irreg. price varies. (Ministerstwo Zdrowia i Opieki Spolecznej) Wydawnictwo Naukowe P W N - Polish Scientific Publishers P W N Ltd., Ul. Miodowa 10, 00-251 Warsaw, Poland. TEL 48-22-260207. FAX 48-22-260950. (Dist. by: Redakcja Pielenaisto Polskie, c/o Akademia Medyczna, Wydzial Pielegniarski, ul. Dabrowskiego 79, 60-529 Poznan, Poland) Ed. Laura Wolowicka.

610.73 617.95   US   ISSN 0741-5206
              CODEN: PSNUEE
PLASTIC SURGICAL NURSING. q. $28 to individuals (foreign $36); institutions $35 (foreign $43). (American Society of Plastic and Reconstructive Surgical Nurses) Jannetti Publications, Inc., East Holly Ave., Box 56, Pitman, NJ 08071-0056. TEL 609-589-2319. FAX 609-689-7463. **Indexed:** CINAHL, Nurs.Abstr.
—BLDSC (6528.938100). **CCC.**

610.73 617   US   ISSN 1066-8977
POST ANESTHESIA AND AMBULATORY SURGERY NURSING UPDATE. 1993. bi-m. $92 (foreign $108) (effective 1996). W.B. Saunders Co. (Subsidiary of: Harcourt Brace & Company), Curtis Center, 3rd Fl., Independence Sq. W., Philadelphia, PA 19106-3399. TEL 215-238-7800. FAX 215-238-6445. (Subscr. to: Periodicals Fulfillment, W.B. Saunders Co., 6277 Sea Harbor Dr., 4th Fl., Orlando, FL 32891-4800. TEL 800-654-2452. FAX 800-874-6418) Ed. Nancy Burden. **Document type:** newsletter, abstracting/indexing.
—UMI. **CCC.**
Description: Informs post-anesthesia nurses, nurse anesthetists, and nurses in ambulatory surgery about developments in their field. Also summarizes current literature.

610.73   UK   ISSN 0953-6612
PRACTICE NURSE. 1988. 22/yr. £35. Reed Business Publishing Group, Reed Healthcare Communications (Subsidiary of: Reed Elsevier group), Quadrant House, The Quadrant, Sutton, Surrey SM2 5AS, England. TEL 081-652-8879. FAX 081-652-8946. Ed. Carolyn Scott. adv.; index. circ. 6,500. **Document type:** trade publication.
—BLDSC (6597.170000).
Description: Information on patient care and management in general practice.

610.73   UK   ISSN 0964-9271
PRACTICE NURSING. 1990. fortn. £44 (overseas £90). Mark Allen Publishing Ltd., Croxted Mews, 288 Croxted Rd., London SE24 9BY, England. TEL 0181-671-7521. FAX 0181-671-1722. Ed. Elizabeth Gledhill; Pub. Mark Allen. **Document type:** academic/scholarly publication.
—BLDSC (6597.175000).

610.73   US   ISSN 0032-6666
PRAIRIE ROSE. 1931. q. $10. (North Dakota Nurses Association) Arthur Davis Agency, 517 Washington St., Box 216, Cedar Falls, IA 50613. FAX 319-277-4055. (Subscr. to: 212 N. 4th St., Bismarck, ND 58501. TEL 701-223-1385) Ed. Ida H. Rigley. adv.; bk.rev. circ. 12,000. **Indexed:** CINAHL, Int.Nurs.Ind.

PRAXIS NAH. see *MEDICAL SCIENCES — Surgery*

610.73   CN   ISSN 1197-2297
PRE & POST NATAL NEWS. 1987. q. Professional Publishing Associates, 269 Richmond St. W., Toronto, ON M5V 1X1, Canada. TEL 416-596-8680. FAX 416-596-1991. Ed. Winifred Honsburger. adv. circ. 6,821. **Document type:** newsletter.
Formerly: Canadian Childbirth Educator (ISSN 0835-586X)

610.73   US   ISSN 1044-4025
PRO RE NATA. 1975. q. $12 to non-members. (Utah Nurses Association) Art Davis Associates, Box 216, Cedar Falls, IA 50613. TEL 801-322-3439. Ed. Pam Gurrell. adv.; circ. 15,000 (controlled). **Indexed:** CINAHL.
Former titles (until 1987): One on One (ISSN 0270-6628); U N A Communique; Utah Nurse.
Description: Preofeesional journal for nurses in Utah.

614   UK   ISSN 0964-4156
PROFESSIONAL CARE OF MOTHER & CHILD. 1965. m. (10/yr.) £25 (rest of Europe £48; elsewhere £60). P M H Publications Ltd., P.O. Box 100, Chichester, W. Sussex PO19 1XR, England. Ed. Pat Souwen; Pub. Peter Harkness. adv.; bk.rev.; index. circ. 5,330. **Indexed:** ASSIA, CINAHL, Dent.Ind., Int.Nurs.Ind. **Document type:** academic/scholarly publication.
—BLDSC (6857.395000); Faxon; UnCover.
Former titles: Midwife, Health and Community Nurse (ISSN 0306-9699); Midwife and Health Visitor (ISSN 0026-3516)

610.73   US   ISSN 0033-0140
R728.8
PROFESSIONAL MEDICAL ASSISTANT. Cover title: P M A. 1956. bi-m. $30. American Association of Medical Assistants, Inc., 20 N. Wacker Dr., Ste. 1575, Chicago, IL 60606-2903. TEL 312-899-1500; 800-228-2262. FAX 312-899-1259. Ed. Jean Lynch. adv.: B&W page $900, color page $1750; trim 7 1/2 x 10; adv. contact: James Gillespie. bk.rev.; illus.; index. circ. 14,000. (also avail. in microform from UMI) **Indexed:** CINAHL. **Document type:** bulletin.
—BLDSC (6541.079200); Faxon; UMI; UnCover.
Formerly: A A M A Bulletin.
Description: Educational articles of interest to medical assistants in the office, hospital, clinic or school setting.

610.73   SI   ISSN 0218-0995
PROFESSIONAL NURSE. 1972. q. S.40. Singapore Trained Nurses' Association, Manhattan House, No. 09-13, 151 Chin Swee Rd., Singapore 0316, Singapore. TEL 7333984. FAX 7340137. Ed. Kiak Kong Sim. adv. circ. 2,600. **Indexed:** CINAHL, Int.Nurs.Ind.
Former titles (until 1987): Nursing Journal of Singapore - Berita Jururawat (ISSN 0067-5814); S T N A Newsletter.

MEDICAL SCIENCES — NURSES AND NURSING

610.73 UK ISSN 0266-8130
RT1
THE PROFESSIONAL NURSE. 1985. m. £33.50 to individuals; institutions £47. Macmillan Magazines Ltd., 4 Little Essex St., London WC2R 3LF, England. TEL 0171-836-6633. FAX 0171-379-4204. Ed. Andrew Heenan; Pub. Simon Warne. adv. contact: Sarah Deakin. bk.rev.; index; circ. 50,000 (paid). (back issues avail.) Indexed: CINAHL. Document type: academic/scholarly publication.
—BLDSC (6860.300000); SWETS. **CCC.**
Description: Primarily clinical magazine with the aim of keeping nurses up to date on practice issues and improving their effectiveness.

610.73 UK ISSN 0969-434X
PROFESSIONAL UPDATE. 1993. 10/yr. £25($38) to individuals; institutions £69 ($107) (effective 1995). Churchill Livingstone Journals (Subsidiary of: Pearson Professional Ltd.), Robert Stevenson House, 1-3 Baxter's Pl., Leith Walk, Edinburgh EH1 3AF, Scotland. TEL 0131-556-2424. FAX 0131-459-1177. (Subscr. to: Pearson Professional Ltd., P.O. Box 77, Fourth Ave., Harlow, Essex CM19 5AA, England. TEL 01279-623760; U.S. subscr. to: Churchill Livingstone, 650 Ave. of the Americas, New York, NY 10011. TEL 212-206-5000) Ed. Neil Kenworthy. adv. contact: David Dunnachie. bk.rev. circ. 500. Document type: newsletter.
Description: Provides information and news of interest to professional nurses.

610.73 US ISSN 0734-1431
PROGRAM PLANS: NURSING BASIC SERIES. 1979. m. $84. (Educational Planning Services Corp.) E P S C O, Box 930, E. Sandwich, MA 02537. TEL 508-888-3257. FAX 508-833-1676. Ed. Jessica D. Terrill. bk.rev.; bibl.; charts; illus.; stat.; index. circ. 3,000. (looseleaf format; back issues avail.) Document type: trade publication.
—**CCC.**
Description: For training non-professional staff in health service facilities.

PROGRESS IN CARDIOVASCULAR NURSING. see MEDICAL SCIENCES — Cardiovascular Diseases

610.73 574.16 SZ ISSN 0254-105X
CODEN: PRBMEP
PROGRESS IN REPRODUCTIVE BIOLOGY AND MEDICINE. (Text in English) 1976. irreg. (approx. 1/yr.) price varies. S. Karger AG, Allschwilerstr. 10, P.O. Box, CH-4009 Basel, Switzerland. TEL 061-3061111. FAX 061-3061234. E-mail: Karger@Karger.ch. Ed. M. L'Hermite. (reprint service avail. from ISI) Indexed: Biol.Abstr., Chem.Abstr., Curr.Cont., Dairy Sci.Abstr. Document type: academic/scholarly publication.
—BLDSC (6924.518500); CASDDS; Faxon. **CCC.**
Formerly: Progress in Reproductive Biology (ISSN 0304-4262)
Description: Represents some of the most significant recent work relevant to reproductive biology and medicine.
Refereed Serial

610.73 362 CN
PROVIDERS; the journal of long term care. 1993. bi-m. (O A N H S S) Kenilworth Publishing Inc., 80 W. Beaver Creek, Ste. 18, Richmond Hill, ON L4B 1H3, Canada. TEL 905-771-7333. FAX 905-771-7336. Ed.Bd. adv.: B&W page Can.$1400, color page Can.$2150; trim 8 1/8 x 10 3/4. circ. 4,000. Document type: trade publication.

610.73 CN
PSYCHIATRIC NURSES ASSOCIATION OF NOVA SCOTIA. NEWSLETTER.* q. c/o Psychiatric Nurses Association of Canada, 509 Pandora Ave. W., Winnipeg, MB R2C 1M8, Canada. Document type: newsletter.

610.73 US ISSN 0737-1209
PUBLIC HEALTH NURSING. bi-m. $150 (foreign $180) (effective 1996). Blackwell Science Inc., 238 Main St., Cambridge, MA 02142-1413. TEL 617-876-7022. FAX 617-492-5263. Indexed: CINAHL, Curr.Cont., Ind.Med., Nurs.Abstr., Psychol.Abstr. (1993-).
—BLDSC (6964.760000); Faxon; Genuine Article; SWETS; UMI; UnCover. **CCC.**

610.73 CN ISSN 1197-4745
PULSE - CANADIAN HEALTH CARE GUILD. Short title: C H C G Pulse. (Text in English) 1976. q. Can.$16 to non-members. Canadian Health Care Guild - Guilde Canadienne de la Sante, 17410-107th Ave., No. 200, Edmonton, AB T5S 1E9, Canada. TEL 403-483-8126; 800-252-7984. FAX 403-484-3341. Ed. Mark Fitton. adv. circ. 7,000. Document type: newsletter.
Former titles (until 1990): Pulse - Canadian Health Care Association (ISSN 1197-4737); (until 1989): Pulse - Alberta Association of Registered Nursing Assistants (ISSN 1197-4729); Former titles (until 1988): A A R N A Pulse (ISSN 0706-2192); (until 1978): Alberta Association of Registered Nursing Assistants. Bulletin (ISSN 0705-7008); (until 1977): Alberta Certified Nursing Aide Association. Bulletin (ISSN 0044-7102)
Description: News of interest to members of CHCG and others in the health care professions.

QUALITY OF CARE. see MEDICAL SCIENCES — Psychiatry And Neurology

610.73 US ISSN 0196-3805
QUICKENING. bi-m. membership only. American College of Nurse-Midwives, 818 Connecticut Ave., Ste. 900, Washington, DC 20005. TEL 202-728-9860. FAX 202-728-9897. circ. 5,000. Document type: directory.

610.73 US ISSN 0033-7021
RT1
R N. (Registered Nurse) 1937. m. $35 (foreign $50). Medical Economics Publishing Co., Inc., Five Paragon Dr., Montvale, NJ 07645. TEL 201-358-7200. FAX 201-573-8979. (Subscr. to: Box 57140, Boulder, CO 80322-7140) Ed. Marianne Mattera. adv.; bk.rev.; index. circ. 285,000. (also avail. in microform from RPI,UMI; reprint service avail.) Indexed: Acad.Ind., Bus.Ind., CINAHL, Curr.Lit.Fam.Plan., Gen.Sci.Ind., Hlth.Ind., Hosp.Lit.Ind., Int.Nurs.Ind., Nurs.Abstr., Tr.& Indus.Ind.
●Also available online. Vendor(s): University Microfilms International.
—BLDSC (7993.980000); Faxon; SWETS; UMI; UnCover. **CCC.**
Description: Articles of interest to registered nurses, particularly those in the hospital environment.

610.73 US ISSN 0192-298X
R.N. IDAHO. 1942. 4/yr. $25 to non-members; foreign $30. Idaho Nurses Association, 200 N. 4th St., Ste. 20, Boise, ID 83702-6001. TEL 208-345-0500. FAX 208-345-1163. Ed. Kathy Stockton. adv. circ. 600.
Former titles: Gem State R.N. Newsletter; Gem State R.N. (ISSN 0072-0569); Idaho State Bulletin.

614.253 FR ISSN 0297-2964
RECHERCHE EN SOINS INFIRMIERS. 1985. q. 430 F. (foreign 520 F.) (effective 1994). (Association de Recherche en Soins Infirmiers) Mallet Conseil, 2 place Antonin Jutard, 69003 Lyon, France. TEL 78-95-10-11. Ed. Monique Formarier.

610.73 US
RECRUITMENT, RETENTION & RESTRUCTURING REPORT; strategies for recruiters, managers, r&r committees, & human resource directors. 1988. bi-m. $128 (effective 1996). Hall Johnson Communications, Inc., 9737 W. Ohio Ave., Lakewood, CO 80226. TEL 303-988-0056. Ed. Suzanne Hall Johnson. adv.; bk.rev.; abstr.; bibl.; charts. Indexed: CINAHL. Document type: newsletter.
—**CCC.**
Formerly (until 1994): Recruitment and Retention Report (ISSN 1044-0666)
Description: Offers strategies for nursing recruitment, retention, restructuring, and improving nurse satisfaction.

REFLECTIONS (INDIANAPOLIS). see CLUBS

REGAN REPORT ON NURSING LAW. see LAW

610.73 CN ISSN 0840-8831
REGISTERED NURSE. q. Can.$19.50($26) (foreign $39). (Registered Nurses' Association of Ontario) Kenilworth Publishing Inc., 80 West Beaver Creek, Toronto, ON L4B 1H3, Canada. TEL 905-771-7333. FAX 905-771-7336. adv.: B&W page Can.$1215, color page Can.$2015; trim 8 1/8 x 10 3/4. circ. 26,000. Indexed: CINAHL.
—BLDSC (7344.160000). **CCC.**
Description: Acts as a forum between the Association and its members, discussing ethical, legal, moral, professional and economic issues within the profession.

610.73 615.82 US ISSN 0278-4807
RT120.R4
REHABILITATION NURSING. 1975. bi-m. $50 to individuals; institutions $75; Canada $75; elsewhere $90. Association of Rehabilitation Nurses, 5700 Old Orchard Rd., 1st Fl., Skokie, IL 60077-1057. TEL 708-966-3433. FAX 708-966-9418. Ed. Belinda Puetz. adv.; bk.rev.; charts; illus.; index. circ. 13,000. (also avail. in microform from UMI; back issues avail.; reprint service avail. from UMI) Indexed: CINAHL, Int.Nurs.Ind., Nurs.Abstr. Document type: academic/scholarly publication.
—BLDSC (7350.285000); Faxon; SWETS; UMI; UnCover.
Formerly (until 1981): A R N Journal (ISSN 0362-3505)

610.73 625.82 US ISSN 1070-5767
RT120.R4
REHABILITATION NURSING RESEARCH. 1992. s-a. $60 to non-members; institutions $75; members $40. Association of Rehabilitation Nurses, 5700 Old Orchard Rd., 1st Fl., Skokie, IL 60077-1057. TEL 708-966-3433. Ed. Belinda E. Puetz. Document type: trade publication.
—BLDSC (7350.286000).

610.73 US
REPORTS ON LONG TERM CARE. 1972. bi-w. $365. Faulkner & Gray, Healthcare Information Center (Subsidiary of: Thomson Publishing Group), 1133 15th St., N.W., Ste. 450, Washington, DC 20005. TEL 202-828-4150. FAX 202-828-2352. Ed. Karen Migdail. (looseleaf format)
●Also available online. Vendor(s): Knight-Ridder, Inc., NewsNet (HH26).
Former titles (until 1994): Long Term Care Management (ISSN 0743-1422); (until 1984): Long Term Care (ISSN 0192-7701); Washington Report on Long Term Care (ISSN 0091-7311)
Description: Covers legal, medical, economic, and ethical issues in long term patient management.

610.73 US ISSN 0160-6891
RT81.5
RESEARCH IN NURSING & HEALTH. 1978. bi-m. $336 (foreign $429) (effective 1996). John Wiley & Sons, Inc., Journals, 605 Third Ave., New York, NY 10158. TEL 212-850-6645. FAX 212-850-6021. TELEX 12-7063. (Subscr. outside the Americas to: John Wiley & Sons Ltd., Baffins Ln., Chichester, W. Sussex PO19 1UD, England. TEL 44-1243-779777. FAX 44-1243-776128) Ed. Marilyn T. Oberst. circ. 1,650. (also avail. in microform from UMI; back issues avail.; reprint service avail. from UMI) Indexed: Behav.Med.Abstr., CINAHL, Curr.Cont., Ind.Med., Int.Nurs.Ind., Nurs.Abstr., Psychol.Abstr. (1980-), Sociol.Abstr., SSCI. Document type: academic/scholarly publication.
—BLDSC (7750.150000); Faxon; Genuine Article; SWETS; UMI; UnCover. **CCC.**
Description: Covers nursing practice, education and administration.
Refereed Serial

610.73 UK
RESOURCES FOR NURSING RESEARCH. irreg., vol.2, 1994. £45. (Library Association) Library Association Publishing Ltd., 7 Ridgmount St., London WC1E 7AE, England. TEL 0171-636-7543. FAX 0171-636-3627. E-mail: lapublishing@lahq.org.uk. (Dist. by: Bookpoint Ltd., 39 Milton Park, Abingdon, Oxon OX14 4TD, England. TEL 01235-400400. FAX 01235-832068) Ed.Bd. Document type: directory.

MEDICAL SCIENCES — NURSES AND NURSING

610.73 US ISSN 1040-3957
RESPONSE (LEBANON).* 1988. m. $19.95. c/o D.J. Russell, Pub., 1002 Smith Ave., Lebanon, PA 17042-7144. Ed. Terrilynn M. Quillen. adv.; bk.rev.; charts; illus.; pat. circ. 600. (back issues avail.)
Description: Potpourri of clinical data, personal insights and humor. For all nurses: active, retired, students, or those with advanced degrees.

610.73 BL ISSN 0034-7167
REVISTA BRASILEIRA DE ENFERMAGEM. (Abstract in English) 1938. q. $30. Brazilian Nursing Association, Av. L2 Norte Q. 603, Modulo B, Brasilia, DF, Brazil. Ed. Maria Helia de Almeidago. circ. 2,400. **Indexed:** Int.Nurs.Ind.

610.73 CU ISSN 0864-0319
RT7.C9
REVISTA CUBANA DE ENFERMERIA. (Text in Spanish; summaries in English, French, Spanish) 1985. s-a. $26 in S. America; N. America $28; elsewhere $30. Ministerio de Salud Publica, Centro Nacional de Informacion de Ciencias Medicas, Calle E No. 452, e-19 y 21, Plaza de la Revolucion, Apdo. 6520, Havana, Cuba. TEL 809-32-5338. (Dist. by: Ediciones Cubanas, Obispo No. 527, Apdo. 605, Havana, Cuba) Ed. Fredesvinda Blanco. bibl.; charts; illus.; index. circ. 2,500.
—BLDSC (7852.104000).

658 SP ISSN 0210-5020
REVISTA ROL DE ENFERMERIA. 1978. 12/yr. 7260 ptas.($67) Ediciones Rol, S.A., Marco Aurelio 8, 08006 Barcelona, Spain. TEL 34-3-2008033. FAX 34-3-2002762. Ed. Nestor Bereciartu. circ. 25,000. **Document type:** newsletter.
—BLDSC (7870.510000).
Description: Updates, developments, and research in nursing in hospitals, first aid, teaching, public health, health administration and management.

610.73 US ISSN 1059-0927
REVOLUTION: THE JOURNAL OF NURSE EMPOWERMENT. 1991. q. $24.95 to individuals (Canada $34.95); institutions $44.95. A.D. Von Publishers, Inc., 56 McArthur Ave., Staten Island, NY 10312. TEL 800-331-6534. FAX 718-317-0858. Ed. Joan Swirsky; Pub. Laura Gasparis Vonfrolio. adv.; B&W page $2000; adv. contact: Roe Livosi. circ. 10,000. **Document type:** trade publication.
—BLDSC (7874.348000).
Description: Focuses on contemporary nursing issues, such as the roles of care, education, research and advocacy for AIDS patients; the relationship between nursing and feminism; media neglect of nurses; legislative matters; entrepreneurship; and sexism on the job.
Refereed Serial

610.73 FR ISSN 0987-8947
REVUE DE L'AIDE-SOIGNANTE. 11/yr. 230 F. to individuals (foreign 270 F.); students 185 F. (foreign 215 F.). Expansion Scientifique, 31 bd. de la Tour Maubourg, 75007 Paris, France. TEL 40-62-64-00. FAX 45-55-69-20.

610.73 FR ISSN 0397-7900
REVUE DE L'INFIRMIERE. 1951. 20/yr. 370 F. to individuals (foreign 580 F.); students 295 F. (foreign 480 F.). Expansion Scientifique, 31 bd. de la Tour Maubourg, 75007 Paris, France. TEL 40-62-64-00. FAX 45-55-69-20. Ed. Nadine Wehrlin. adv.; bk.rev.; charts; illus.; index. circ. 60,000. **Indexed:** Dent.Ind., Int.Nurs.Ind., Pt.de Rep. (1979-).
—BLDSC (7924.170000). **CCC.**
Formerly: Revue de l'Infirmiere et de l'Assistante Sociale (ISSN 0035-144X)

610.73 IT ISSN 1120-3803
RIVISTA DELL'INFERMIERE. q. L.214500($130) (effective 1996). Pensiero Scientifico Editore s.r.l., Via Bradano 3-C, 00199 Rome, Italy. TEL 06-86207158. FAX 06-86207160. circ. 3,000. **Indexed:** Int.Nurs.Ind. **Document type:** academic/scholarly publication.
—BLDSC (7986.810000).

610.73 PH ISSN 0048-9123
SANTO TOMAS NURSING JOURNAL; devoted to the collegiate programmes of nursing in the Philippines. 1962-1976; resumed 1978. s-a. $8. University of Santo Tomas, College of Nursing, Espana St., Manila, Philippines. Ed. Conchita Torres-Maceda. adv.; bk.rev.; illus. circ. 2,000. **Indexed:** CINAHL, Int.Nurs.Ind.

610.73 CN ISSN 0836-7310
SASKATCHEWAN CONCE R N. 1948. bi-m. Can.$15 (foreign $25). Saskatchewan Registered Nurses' Association, 2066 Retallack St., Regina, SK S4T 2K2, Canada. TEL 306-527-4643. FAX 306-525-0849. Ed. Joy Johnson. adv.; bk.rev. circ. 10,000.
Formerly (until 1987): Saskatchewan Registered Nurses' Association. Bulletin (ISSN 0319-8499)
Description: Information about the association's activities in nursing education.

610.73 CN
SASKATCHEWAN PSYCHIATRIC NURSES' ASSOCIATION. R P NEWS. q. Can.$10. Registered Psychiatric Nurses Association of Saskatchewan, 2631 28th Ave., Ste. 101, Parliament Pl., Regina, SK S4S 6X3, Canada. TEL 306-586-4617. FAX 306-586-6000. Ed. Barbara Wright. circ. 1,400.
Formerly: Saskatchewan Psychiatric Nurses' Association. Newsletter.

610.73 US ISSN 0889-7182
SCHOLARLY INQUIRY FOR NURSING PRACTICE; an international journal. 1986. q. $42 to individuals (foreign $47); institutions $79 (foreign $87) (effective 1996). Springer Publishing Company, 536 Broadway, New York, NY 10012-3955. TEL 212-431-4370. FAX 212-941-7842. Ed.Bd. adv.; bk.rev. (back issues avail.) **Indexed:** Behav.Med.Abstr., CINAHL, Ind.Med. (1993-), Int.Nurs.Ind., Psychol.Abstr. (1987-). **Document type:** trade publication.
—BLDSC (8092.540300); Faxon; SWETS; UnCover. **CCC.**
Description: Publishes original manuscripts concerned with the development and testing or theory relevant to nursing practice to facilitate the integration of theory, research and practice.
Refereed Serial

610.73 US ISSN 1048-3896
SCHOOL HOUSE ALERT.* 1984. m. (10/yr.). $25. Box 13716, San Antonio, TX 78213-0716. TEL 512-433-7327.

610.73 371 US
SCHOOL NURSE NEWS; current issues affecting school nurses. vol.11, 1994. 5/yr. Health Information Publications, Inc., 92 S. Highland Ave., Ossining, NY 10562. TEL 914-762-6498. FAX 914-762-0239. Ed. Kathleen Yasas. adv.; B&W page $1100, color page $1900; trim 11 1/4 x 14 5/8; adv. contact: Rhonda Guthoff. illus.; circ. 5,000 (paid). (tabloid format) **Document type:** trade publication.
Description: Reports on current medical and professional developments of interest to school nurses.

610.73 SZ
SCHWEIZER HEBAMME. (Text in French, German) m. Schweizer Hebammenverband, Flurstr. 26, CH-3000 Bern 22, Switzerland. TEL 031-3326340. circ. 2,400. **Document type:** newsletter.

610.73 GW ISSN 0340-5303
DIE SCHWESTER - DER PFLEGER. 1962. m. DM.75. Bibliomed - Medizinische Verlagsgesellschaft mbH, Carl-Braun-Str. 15, 34201 Melsungen, Germany. FAX 05661-8360. Ed.Bd. adv.; bk.rev. circ. 47,000. **Indexed:** Dok.Arbeitsmed. **Document type:** academic/scholarly publication.
—SWETS.

610.73 US ISSN 1066-3851
RT89
SEMINARS FOR NURSE MANAGERS. 1993. q. $75 (foreign $109) (effective 1996). W.B. Saunders Co. (Subsidiary of: Harcourt Brace & Company), Curtis Center, 3rd Fl., Independence Sq. W., Philadelphia, PA 19106-3399. TEL 215-238-7800. FAX 215-238-6445. (Subscr. to: Periodicals Fulfillment, W.B. Saunders Co., 6277 Sea Harbor Dr., 4th Fl., Orlando, FL 32891-4800. TEL 800-654-2452. FAX 800-874-6418) Ed. Roxane B. Spitzer-Lehman; Pub. Joan W. Blumberg. adv.: B&W page $550, color page $1300; 7 x 10; adv. contact: Steve Gray. circ. 2,000. (back issues avail.) **Document type:** academic/scholarly publication.
—BLDSC (8239.456050); UMI.
Description: Provides detailed reviews of the challenges nurse managers face; each issue covers a single topic in detail through clinical review articles and regular columns.

610.73 616.992 US ISSN 0749-2081
SEMINARS IN ONCOLOGY NURSING. 1985. q. $99 (foreign $132) (effective 1996). W.B. Saunders Co. (Subsidiary of: Harcourt Brace & Company), Curtis Center, 3rd Fl., Independence Sq. W., Philadelphia, PA 19106-3399. TEL 215-238-7800. FAX 215-238-6445. (Subscr. to: Periodicals Fulfillment, W.B. Saunders Co., 6277 Sea Harbor Dr., 4th Fl., Orlando, FL 32891-4800. TEL 800-654-2452. FAX 800-874-6418) Ed. Connie H. Yarbro; Pub. Joan W. Blumberg. adv.: B&W page $725, color page $1725; 7 x 10. bibl.; charts; illus.; index. circ. 2,866. **Indexed:** CINAHL, Nurs.Abstr. **Document type:** academic/scholarly publication.
—BLDSC (8239.456600); Faxon; SWETS; UMI; UnCover. **CCC.**
Description: Each issue focuses on a single theme on cancer patient nursing.

610.73 617 US ISSN 1056-8670
SEMINARS IN PERIOPERATIVE NURSING. 1992. q. $79 (foreign $112) (effective 1996). W.B. Saunders Co. (Subsidiary of: Harcourt Brace & Company), The Curtis Center, 3rd Fl., Independence Sq. W., Philadelphia, PA 19106-3399. TEL 215-238-7800. FAX 215-238-6445. (Subscr. to: Periodicals Fulfillment, W.B. Saunders Co., 6277 Sea Harbor Dr., 4th Fl., Orlando, FL 32891-4800. TEL 800-654-2452. FAX 800-874-6418) Ed. Nancy Girard; Pub. Joan W. Blumberg. adv.: B&W page $565, color page $1340; 6 x 9 1/2; adv. contact: Cindy Gray. circ. 1,512. **Document type:** academic/scholarly publication.
—BLDSC (8239.456900). **CCC.**
Description: Reviews a clinical topic of operating room nursing in each issue.

610.73 CN ISSN 1192-5299
SERVO. (Text in English, French) 1967. 3/yr. Can.$5. Association of Hospital Auxiliaries of the Province of Quebec, 505 Maisonneuve W., Ste. 400, Montreal, PQ H3A 3C2, Canada. TEL 514-842-4861. FAX 514-873-5415. circ. 300. (back issues avail.) **Document type:** newsletter.
Description: For hospital auxiliary volunteers.

610.73 JA ISSN 0038-0660
SOGO KANGO; comprehensive nursing quarterly. (Text in Japanese) 1966. q. 3200 Yen. Gendaisha Publishing Co, Ltd., 514 Waseda, Tsurumaki-cho, Shinjukuku, Tokyo 162, Japan. Ed. Yoshio Takeuchi. adv.; bk.rev. circ. 12,000. **Indexed:** Int.Nurs.Ind.

910.73 617 FR ISSN 0249-6429
SOINS - CHIRURGIE. 1981. 7/yr. 275 F. to individuals; institutions 480 F.; students 240 F. (effective 1996). Masson - Periodiques, Villa Laromiguiere, 75005 Paris, France. TEL 40-46-62-55. FAX 40-46-62-01. Eds. Bernard Goddet, C. Toucheboeuf. adv. circ. 5,000. **Document type:** academic/scholarly publication.
—BLDSC (8327.117240).

610.73 FR ISSN 1163-4723
SOINS - FORMATION, PEDAGOGIE, ENCADREMENT. 4/yr. 350 F. (effective 1996). Massons - Periodiques, Villa Laromiguiere, 75005 Paris, France. TEL 40-46-62-55. FAX 40-46-62-01. Ed. L. Goumarre. circ. 5,000. **Document type:** academic/scholarly publication.
Description: Looks at the initial and continuing education of nurses.

610.73 FR ISSN 1259-4792
SOINS - PEDIATRIE, PUERICULTURE. 1980. 6/yr. 260 F. to individuals; institutions 460 F.; students 230 F. (effective 1996). Masson - Periodiques, Villa Laromiguiere, 75005 Paris, France. TEL 40-46-62-55. FAX 40-46-62-01. Eds. B. Goddet, C. Toucheboeuf. adv. circ. 5,000. **Document type:** academic/scholarly publication.
Former titles (until 1995): Soins - Gynecologie, Obstetrique, Puericulture, Pediatrie (ISSN 0766-1193); (until 1981): Soins - Gynecologie, Obstetrique, Puericulture (ISSN 0151-6655)
Description: Each issue covers a clinical case.

MEDICAL SCIENCES — NURSES AND NURSING

610.73 616.8   FR   ISSN 0241-6972
SOINS - PSYCHIATRIE. 1980. 8/yr. 300 F. to individuals; institutions 500 F.; students 260 F. (effective 1996). Masson - Periodiques, Villa Laromiguiere, 75005 Paris, France. TEL 40-46-62-55. FAX 40-46-62-01. Eds. Bernard Goddet, C. Toucheboeuf. adv. circ. 5,000. **Document type:** academic/scholarly publication.
—BLDSC (8327.117600).
Description: Specializes in the training of psychiatric nurses.

610.73   FR   ISSN 0038-0814
SOINS - REVUE GENERALE. 1956. 10/yr. 340 F. to individuals; institutions 585 F.; students 290 F. (effective 1996). Masson - Periodiques, Villa Laromiguiere, 75005 Paris, France. TEL 40-46-62-55. FAX 40-46-62-01. Eds. B. Goddet, C. Toucheboeuf. adv.; bk.rev. circ. 35,000. **Indexed:** Int.Nurs.Ind., Pt.de Rep. (1979-). **Document type:** academic/scholarly publication.
—BLDSC (8327.117000); SWETS.
Description: Covers management, communication, health, psychology, education as they relate to nursing and nurses.

610.73   US
SPRINGER SERIES ON ADVANCED PRACTICE NURSING. 1993. irreg. price varies. Springer Publishing Company, 536 Broadway, New York, NY 10012-3955. TEL 212-431-1370. FAX 212-941-7842. Ed. Terry T. Fulmer. **Document type:** monographic series.

SPRINGER SERIES ON GERIATRIC NURSING. see *GERONTOLOGY AND GERIATRICS*

610.73 371.3   US   ISSN 0272-1473
SPRINGER SERIES ON THE TEACHING OF NURSING. 1977. irreg., latest 1994. price varies. Springer Publishing Company, 536 Broadway, New York, NY 10012-3955. TEL 212-431-4370. FAX 212-941-7842. Ed. Patricia Moccia. **Document type:** monographic series.
—BLDSC (8424.780000).
Description: Deals with various aspects of professional training in nursing.

610.73   US   ISSN 0038-9986
STAT (MADISON). 1941. m. $45 membership. Wisconsin Nurses Association, 6117 Monona Dr., Madison, WI 53716-3932. FAX 608-221-2788. Ed. Susan Carter. adv.; illus. circ. 2,700. **Indexed:** C.I.N.L. Int.Nurs.Ind. **Document type:** newsletter.

610.73   US   ISSN 0081-4423
RT74
STATE-APPROVED SCHOOLS OF NURSING - L.P.N. - L.V.N. 1958. a. $21.95. National League for Nursing, 350 Hudson St., New York, NY 10014. TEL 212-989-9393. (also avail. in microfiche from CIS) **Indexed:** SRI.
Formerly (1959-1966): State-Approved Schools of Practical and Vocational Nursing (ISSN 0095-6570)

610.73   US   ISSN 0081-4431
STATE-APPROVED SCHOOLS OF NURSING - R.N. a. $26.95. National League for Nursing, 350 Hudson St., New York, NY 10014. TEL 212-989-9393. (also avail. in microfiche from CIS) **Indexed:** SRI.

610.73   UK   ISSN 0302-1440
STUDY OF NURSING CARE: RESEARCH PROJECT SERIES. 1973. irreg. price varies. Royal College of Nursing, 20 Cavendish Sq., London W1M 0AB, England. TEL 071-409-3333. FAX 071-408-0190. bibl. **Document type:** monographic series.

SUGGESTED LIST OF PERIODICALS FOR NURSES FOR THE CANADIAN HEALTH SCIENCE LIBRARY. see *MEDICAL SCIENCES — Abstracting, Bibliographies, Statistics*

610.73 617   UK   ISSN 0954-8947
SURGICAL NURSE. bi-m. £22.80 (foreign £30). The Medicine Group (Journals) Ltd., Publishing House, 62 Stert St., Abingdon, Oxon. OX14 3UQ, England. TEL 01235-555770. FAX 01235-554691. Ed.Bd. adv. contact: Christian Benzing. **Document type:** academic/scholarly publication.
—BLDSC (8548.241000).

610.73   DK   ISSN 0049-3856
SYGEPLEJERSKEN. 1901. w. DKK 772($30) Dansk Sygeplejeraad - Danish Nurses' Organization, Vimmelskaftet 38, Postbox 1084, DK-1008 Copenhagen K, Denmark. Ed. Peter Hjorth. adv.; bk.rev.; illus. circ. 62,000. **Indexed:** Dent.Ind., Ind.Med., Int.Nurs.Ind.

610.73   NO   ISSN 0802-9768
SYKEPLEIEN. FAG. (Includes Sykepleien. Journalen) 6/yr. DKK 520. Norsk Sykepleierforbund, P.O. Box 2633, St. Hanshaugen, N-0131 Oslo, Norway. FAX 47-22-38-35-36. Ed. Morten E. Mathiesen. adv. contact: Maud P. Kaino. bk.rev.; circ. 50,000 (controlled). **Document type:** academic/scholarly publication.
—CCC.
Supersedes in part (in 1990): Sykepleien (ISSN 0039-7628)

610.73 331.88   NO   ISSN 0802-9776
SYKEPLEIEN. JOURNALEN. (Includes Sykepleien. Fag) 1912. 21/yr. NOK 595. Norsk Sykepleierforbund, P.O. Box 2633, St. Hanshaugen, N-0131 Oslo, Norway. FAX 47-22-38-35-36. Ed. Morten E. Mathiesen. adv. contact: Maud P. Kaino. bk.rev.; circ. 51,094 (controlled). **Indexed:** Dent.Ind., Int.Nurs.Ind. **Document type:** trade publication.
—BLDSC (5072.823000). **CCC.**
Supersedes in part (in 1990): Sykepleien (ISSN 0039-7628)

610.73   US   ISSN 0039-9620
TAR HEEL NURSE. 1939. bi-m $25 (foreign $50). North Carolina Nurses Association, Box 12025, Raleigh, NC 27605. TEL 919-821-4250. FAX 919-829-5807. Ed. Hazel Browning Moore. adv.; charts; illus. circ. 3,500. (also avail. in microform from UMI; reprint service avail. from UMI) **Indexed:** CINAHL, Int.Nurs.Ind. **Document type:** trade publication.
—UMI.

610.73   US   ISSN 1055-9620
TECHNOLOGY FOR CRITICAL CARE NURSES. 1986. bi-m. $95 (Canada $105; elsewhere $125). (Emergency Care Research Institute) E C R I, 5200 Butler Pike, Plymouth Meeting, PA 19462. TEL 610-825-6000. FAX 610-834-1274. Ed. Michele Moscharella. **Document type:** trade publication.
—CCC.
Formerly (until 1990): Technology for Nursing (ISSN 0890-9059)
Description: Covers new and emerging healthcare technologies, product reviews, hazard reports on the dangers of commonly used devices, news highlights and alerts to minimize risk.
Refereed Serial

610.73   US   ISSN 1059-454X
TECHNOLOGY FOR EMERGENCY CARE NURSES. bi-m. $95 (Canada $105; elsewhere $125). (Emergency Care Research Institute) E C R I, 5200 Butler Pike, Plymouth Meeting, PA 19462. TEL 610-825-6000. FAX 610-834-1275. Ed. Michele Moscarella. **Document type:** newsletter.
—CCC.
Former titles: Technology for Emergency Medicine (ISSN 8756-8594); Health Devices Update: Emergency Medicine.
Description: Features descriptions of new and emerging technologies, device hazards and recalls for healthcare professionals involved in emergency care.
Refereed Serial

610.73   FI   ISSN 0358-4038
TEHY. (Text in Finnish, Swedish) 1925. s-m. Fmk.370. Union of Health Professionals - Terveydenhuoltoalan Ammattijaresto Tehy, Asemamiehenkatu 4, 00520 Helsinki, Finland. TEL 90-1551. FAX 90-1483038. TELEX 122505. Ed. Sinikka Pitko. adv.; bk.rev.; film rev.; bibl.; charts; illus. circ. 73,000.
Former titles (until 1981): Laboratoriohoitaja; Lastenhoitajalehti (ISSN 0355-5089); Sairaanhoitaja - Sjukskoterskan (ISSN 0036-3278); Sairaanhoitajalehti.

610.73   US   ISSN 1053-3134
TENNESSEE NURSE. 1934. q. $20. Tennessee Nurses Association, 545 Mainstream Dr., Ste. 405, Nashville, TN 37228-1201. TEL 615-254-0350. FAX 615-254-0303. Ed. Anita Naprer. adv.; bk.rev.; illus. circ. 5,000. (also avail. in microform from UMI) **Indexed:** CINAHL, Int.Nurs.Ind. **Document type:** academic/scholarly publication.
—UMI.
Formerly (until 1990): Tennessee Nurses Association. Bulletin (ISSN 0040-3342)
Refereed Serial

610.73   US   ISSN 0095-036X
TEXAS NURSING. 1925. m. $30. Texas Nurses Association, 7600 Burnet Rd., No. 440, Austin, TX 78757-1241. TEL 512-452-0645. FAX 512-452-0648. Ed. John Lewis Brown. adv.; bk.rev. circ. 6,000. (also avail. in microform; back issues avail.) **Indexed:** CINAHL, Int.Nurs.Ind. **Document type:** trade publication.
—BLDSC (8799.560000); UMI.

610.73   DK   ISSN 0900-3002
TIDSKRIFT FOR SYGEPLEJEFORSKNING. 1985. s-a. DKK 150 (effective 1996). Dansk Selskab for Sygeplejeforskning - Danish Nursing Research Society, P.O. Box 37, DK-2930 Klampenborg, Denmark. Ed. Helle Plovg. Hansen. adv.; bk.rev. circ. 1,000. **Document type:** academic/scholarly publication.

610.73   NE   ISSN 0921-5832
TIJDSCHRIFT VOOR VERZORGENDEN. 1968. m. fl.57.50 (students fl.42). Uitgeverij De Tijdstroom b.v, Postbus 19135, 3501 DC Utrecht, Netherlands. TEL 31-30-586900. FAX 31-30-586950. adv.; bk.rev.; tr.lit.; index. circ. 10,050. **Indexed:** Int.Nurs.Ind.
—SWETS.
Former titles (until 1988): B K Z (ISSN 0169-7765); (until 1983): Tijdschrift voor Bejaarden-, Kraam- en Ziekenverzorging (ISSN 0049-3880)

610.73   NE   ISSN 0303-6456
TIJDSCHRIFT VOOR ZIEKENVERPLEGING. Short title: T v Z. 1890. fortn. fl.114 (students fl.82.50). (Stichting Publikaties voor Verpleegkundigen en Verzorgenden) Uitgeverij De Tijdstroom b.v., Postbus 19135, 301 DC Utrecht, Netherlands. TEL 31-30-586900. FAX 31-30-586950. adv.; bk.rev.; charts; illus.; index. circ. 18,000. **Indexed:** C.I.S. Abstr., Dent.Ind., Int.Nurs.Ind.
—SWETS.
Formerly: Stichting Tijdschriften voor Verpleegkundigen en Verzorgenden. Jaarboekje.

610.73   US   ISSN 0194-5181
TODAY'S O R NURSE. 1979. m. $30 to individuals; institutions $40. Slack, Inc., 6900 Grove Rd., Thorofare, NJ 08086. TEL 609-848-1000. FAX 609-853-5991. Ed. Rose Marie McWilliams. adv.; bk.rev. circ. 8,000. (back issues avail.) **Indexed:** CINAHL, Dent.Ind., Int.Nurs.Ind., Nurs.Abstr.
—BLDSC (8859.764000); SWETS; UMI; UnCover. **CCC.**

610.73   US
TRANSCULTURAL NURSING NEWSLETTER. s-a. membership (includes Journal of Transcultural Nursing). Transcultural Nursing Society, 601 N. Wenona, Bay City, MI 48706. TEL 517-684-7381. FAX 517-684-1248. E-mail: 70536,1754@compuserve.com. (Subscr. to: Transcultural Nursing Society, Madonna University, College of Nursing, 36600 Schoolcraft Dr., Livonia, MI 48150. TEL 313-454-7642. FAX 313-591-8356) Ed. M. McFarland. **Document type:** newsletter.

610.73   BL   ISSN 0080-6234
UNIVERSIDADE DE SAO PAULO. ESCOLA DE ENFERMAGEM. REVISTA. 1967. q. $70. Universidade de Sao Paulo, Escola de Enfermagem, Av. Dr. Eneas de Carvalho Aguiar, 419, SP, Caixa Postal 5751, 05403 Sao Paulo, Brazil. FAX 011-280-8213. index, cum.index; circ. 1,000 (controlled). **Indexed:** Ind.Med., Int.Nurs.Ind.
—BLDSC (7805.530000).

MEDICAL SCIENCES — OBSTETRICS AND GYNECOLOGY

610.73 375   AT   ISSN 1036-0700
UNIVERSITY OF TECHNOLOGY, SYDNEY. FACULTY OF NURSING HANDBOOK. 1990. a. Aus.$5 (foreign Aus.$10). University of Technology, Sydney, P.O. Box 123, City Campus, Broadway, N.S.W. 2007, Australia. TEL 02-330-1990. FAX 02-330-1551. circ. 3,000.
Description: Contains details about the faculty, schools, staff, courses, and other information pertaining to nursing students.

UROLOGIC NURSING. see MEDICAL SCIENCES — Urology And Nephrology

610.73   VI   ISSN 0049-6464
V I N A QUARTERLY.* 1964. q. Virgin Islands Nurses Association, Box 2866, Charlotte Amalie, St. Thomas, Virgin Islands. illus. **Indexed:** Int.Nurs.Ind.

610.73   US
V N A B NEWSLETTER. 1970. 4/yr. free. Visiting Nurse Association of Brooklyn, Department of Development and Public Relations, 138 South Oxford St., Brooklyn, NY 11217. TEL 718-230-6927. FAX 718-636-7572. Ed. Elanor Brand. charts; illus. circ. 5,000.
Former titles: V N A Newsletter; In Step with the Visiting Nurse Association of Brooklyn (ISSN 0046-8770)
Description: Covers news and services of the Visiting Nurse Association of Brooklyn.

610.73   CN
V O N CANADA ANNUAL REPORT (YEAR). a. Victorian Order of Nurses for Canada, 5 Blackburn Ave., Ottawa, ON K1N 8A2, Canada. TEL 613-233-5694. Ed. Ruth Mellor. adv. contact: Patty Lascelle. **Document type:** corporate report.

610.73   CN   ISSN 0846-135X
V O N CANADA REPORT. q. Victorian Order of Nurses for Canada, 5 Blackburn Ave., Ottawa, ON K1N 8A2, Canada. TEL 613-233-5694. Ed. Ruth Mellor. adv. contact: Patty Lascelle. **Document type:** newsletter.
Description: Reports on VON's commitment to innovative community based nursing and other health care and support services.

610.73   NO   ISSN 0107-4083
VAARD I NORDEN; sygeplejevidenskab, omvaardnadsforskning og udvikling. (Text in Danish, English, Norwegian, Swedish; abstracts in English) 1981. q. NOK 250 (students NOK 150). Sygeplejerskernes Samarbejde i Norden - Northern Nurses Federation, P.O. Box 2681, St. Hanshaugen, N-131 Oslo 1, Norway. TEL 47-22-38-20-00. FAX 47-22-38-54-47. Ed. Randi Annikki Mortensen. bk.rev. circ. 2,500.
●Also available online. Vendor(s): Ovid Technologies, Data-Star, Knight-Ridder, Inc.
Also available on CD-ROM. Producer(s): SilverPlatter Information, Inc.
—BLDSC (9146.090000).
Description: Focuses on development and research in nursing in the Nordic countries.
Refereed Serial

610.73   US   ISSN 0191-1880
VERMONT REGISTERED NURSE. 1934. q. $18 (typically set in Dec.). Vermont State Nurses' Association, 1 Main St., No. 26, Winooski, VT 05404-2230. TEL 802-655-7123. FAX 802-655-7187. Ed. Bonnie Stiles. adv.: page $165. circ. 500. **Indexed:** CINAHL, Int.Nurs.Ind. **Document type:** newsletter.
Description: Contains association news and feature articles for members.

610.73 373.246   NE   ISSN 0920-3273
VERPLEEGKUNDE; nederlandse-vlaams tijdschrift voor verpleegkundigen. 1986. q. fl.67.50 to individuals; institutions fl.101.50; students fl.50.30. Uitgeverij De Tijdstroom b.v., Postbus 19135, 3501 DC Utrecht, Netherlands. TEL 31-30-586900. FAX 31-30-586950. Ed. C.L.M. Wiebnga. adv.; bk.rev. circ. 2,500. **Document type:** academic/scholarly publication.
—BLDSC (9194.810000); SWETS.
Description: Covers case studies, research and items of interest to nursing leaders and teachers.

610.73   BE
VERPLEEGKUNDIGEN EN GEMEENSCHAPSZORG; tijdschriften voor verpleegkundigen en gemeenschapszorg. (Text in Flemish) 1944. bi-m. 1700 BEF (effective 1993). N.V.K.V.V., Vergote Sq. 43, 1040 Brussels, Belgium. TEL 32-2-732-1050. FAX 32-2-732-8460. adv.; bk.rev.; bibl.; charts; illus.; stat. circ. 9,000. (back issues avail.)

610.73   RM   ISSN 0042-5036
       CODEN: VMRMDX
VIATA MEDICALA - CADRE MEDII. (Text in Rumanian; summaries in English, French, German, Russian) 1953. 12/yr. $20. Uniunea Societatilor de Stiinte Medicale din Republica Socialista Rumania, Str. Progresului No. 8, Bucharest, Rumania. (Subscr. to: ILEXIM, Str. 13 Decembrie Nr. 3, P.O. Box 136-137, Bucharest, Rumania) Ed.Bd. adv.; bk.rev.; abstr. **Indexed:** Biol.Abstr., C.I.S. Abstr., Dent.Ind., Excerp.Med., Int.Nurs.Ind.
—CASDDS.
Formerly: Munca Sanitaria (ISSN 0027-318X)

VITAL SIGNS PHARMACY SERVICES NEWSLETTER. see PHARMACY AND PHARMACOLOGY

616.86 610.73   CI   ISSN 0352-3721
VJESNIK MEDICINSKIH SESTARA I MEDICINSKIH TEHNICARA HRVATSKE. (Text in Croatian) 1933. 6/yr. $10. Savez Drustava Medicinskih Sestara SR Hrvatske, Butkoviceva 4, 51000 Rijeka, Croatia. Ed. Mirjana Longhino. adv.; bk.rev.; charts; illus.; pat.; index. circ. 13,500.
Former titles (until 1982): Vjesnik Drustava Medicinskih Sestara i Medicinskih Tehnicara SR Hrvatske (ISSN 0351-6687); (until 1969): Vjesnik Drustva Diplomiranih Sestara NR Hrvatske; Sestrinska Rijec.

610.73   US   ISSN 0734-5666
WASHINGTON NURSE. 1929. bi-m. $20 (Canada and Mexico $26; elsewhere $39). Washington State Nurses Association, 2505 Second Ave., Ste. 500, Seattle, WA 98121-1460. TEL 206-443-9762. FAX 206-728-2074. Ed. Denise Shepard. adv. contact: Denise Shepard. bk.rev.; circ. 7,500 (paid). (back issues avail.) **Indexed:** CINAHL, Int.Nurs.Ind. **Document type:** trade publication.
—BLDSC (9263.210000).
Supersedes (in 1977): W S N A Mini Journal.
Description: Provides information about professional, educational, ethical, legal, economic, and legislative issues affecting the practice of nursing.

610.73   US   ISSN 1074-8091
WEST VIRGINIA NURSE. 1927. q. $15. West Virginia Nurses Association, Box 1946, Charleston, WV 25327-1946. Ed. Carol S. Fulks. adv.; illus. circ. 2,200. **Indexed:** CINAHL, Int.Nurs.Ind.
Formerly: Weather Vane (ISSN 0043-1664)

610.73   US   ISSN 0193-9459
WESTERN JOURNAL OF NURSING RESEARCH; an international forum for communciating nursing research. 1979. bi-m. $74 to individuals; institutions $220 (effective Sep. 1995). Sage Publications, Inc., 2455 Teller Rd., Thousand Oaks, CA 91320. TEL 805-499-0721. FAX 805-499-0871. E-mail: libraries@sagepub.com. (Overseas subscr. to: Sage Publications Ltd., 6 Bonhill St., London EC2A 4PU, England; Sage Publications India Pvt. Ltd., P.O. Box 4215, New Delhi 110 048, India) Ed. Pamela J. Brink. adv.; bk.rev.; film rev.; abstr.; bibl.; illus.; stat.; cum.index. circ. 2,000. (back issues avail.) reprint service avail.) **Indexed:** Behav.Med.Abstr., CINAHL, Ind.Med., Int.Nurs.Ind., Psychol.Abstr. (1991-), Viol.& Abuse Abstr. **Document type:** academic/scholarly publication.
—BLDSC (9300.835000); Faxon; SWETS; UMI; UnCover. CCC.
Description: Provides a forum for scholarly debate and for research and theoretical papers. Clinical studies have commentaries and rebuttals.

610.73   UK
WESTMINSTER HOSPITAL NURSES' LEAGUE. PUBLICATION. a. membership. Westminster Hospital Nurses' League, Queen Mary Nurses' Home, Page St., Westminster, London SW1, England.

610.73 920   US
WHO'S WHO IN AMERICAN NURSING. 1984. biennial, 6th ed., 1995. $169.95. Marquis Who's Who, A Reed Reference Publishing company, 121 Chanlon Rd., New Providence, NJ 07974. TEL 908-464-6800. FAX 908-665-6688. TELEX 138 755. (Subscr. to: Order Dept., Box 31, New Providence, NJ 07974-9903. TEL 800-521-8110) (also avail. in magnetic tape) **Document type:** directory.
●Also available on CD-ROM. Producer(s): Bowker - Reed Reference Electronic Publishing.
Formed by the 1991 merger of: Who's Who in American Nursing. Administrators, Educators, and Other Nursing Professionals (ISSN 1062-2411) & Who's Who in American Nursing. Primary Care Nurses in Clinical Settings (ISSN 1062-242X); Which was formerly (until 1989): Who's Who in American Nursing (ISSN 0740-7912)
Description: Lists biographies of over 26,000 leading American primary care nurses, nursing administrators, educators, researchers, and other specialists. These individuals are indexed by city and state within their specialties.

610.73   US
WYOMING NURSE. 1926. q. $15. Wyoming Nurses Association, 1603 Capitol Ave., No. 305, Cheyenne, WY 82001. TEL 307-635-3955. FAX 307-635-2173. Lori Sweers, Exec. Dir. adv. circ. 6,000. (processed) **Document type:** newsletter.
Formerly: Wyoming Nurses Newsletter (ISSN 0084-3164)

610.73   ZA
ZAMBIA NURSE. 1965. 3/yr. K.5. (Zambia Nurses Association) Mission Press, Ndola, P.O. Box 2104, Kitwe, Zambia. Eds. N. Booth, P.S. Chibuye. adv.; bk.rev. circ. 1,000. **Indexed:** CINAHL, Int.Nurs.Ind.

610.73   XV   ISSN 0350-9516
ZDRAVSTVENI OBZORNIK. (Text in Slovenian; summaries in English, Slovenian) 1966. q. 3000 din. Zveza Drustev Medicinskih Sester Slovenije, Vidovdanska 9, 61000 Ljubjana, Slovenia. TEL 061 316-055. Ed. Dunja Kalcic. adv.; bk.rev.; index. circ. 5,000. (back issues avail.)

MEDICAL SCIENCES — Obstetrics And Gynecology

see also Women's Health

A C O G CURRENT JOURNAL REVIEW. (American College of Obstetricians and Gynecologists) see MEDICAL SCIENCES — Abstracting, Bibliographies, Statistics

618   CN
A C O G INTERACTIONS: PROGRAMS IN CLINICAL DECISION MAKING. 1988. bi-m. $375 to non-fellows; fellows $325; jr. fellows $175. (American College of Obstetricians and Gynecologists) Decker Periodicals, P.O. Box 620, LCD 1, Hamilton, ON L8N 3K7, Caanada. TEL 905-522-7017. FAX 905-522-7839. (U.S. addr.: Box 785, Lewiston, NY 14092-0785) Ed. Dr. Honor M. Wolfe. abstr. (diskette format)
Description: Focuses on a challenging clinical topic in OB-GYN and combines case studies, animated color graphics, management options and references.

618   US   ISSN 0400-048X
A C O G NEWSLETTER. 1952. m. membership. American College of Obstetricians and Gynecologists, 409 12th St., S.W., Washington, DC 20024. TEL 202-863-2423. FAX 202-479-6826. Ed. Patrick Tucker. adv.; charts; illus.; circ. 35,000 (controlled). **Document type:** newsletter.
—CCC.

A I U M REPORTER. (American Institute of Ultrasound in Medicine) see MEDICAL SCIENCES — Radiology And Nuclear Medicine

618   AT   ISSN 1321-0335
A M B A JOURNAL. 1974. 5/yr. Aus.$10 (foreign Aus.$22). Australian Multiple Birth Association Inc., P.O. Box 105, Coogee, N.S.W. 2034, Australia. TEL 61-49-468030. Ed. Jenny Noonan. circ. 200. **Document type:** newsletter.
Description: Publishes articles relevant to multiple births, multiple birth clubs, multiple birth research, information, personal experiences, activities of the association.

MEDICAL SCIENCES — OBSTETRICS AND GYNECOLOGY

A W H O N N NEWSLETTER. (Association of Women's Health, Obstetric, and Neonatal Nurses) see *MEDICAL SCIENCES — Nurses And Nursing*

ACTA CHIRURGICA MEDITERRANEA. see *MEDICAL SCIENCES — Surgery*

618 SP ISSN 0001-5776
CODEN: ACGLA
ACTA GINECOLOGICA. Spanish translation of: Journal of Gynaecology & Obstetrics. (Text in Spanish; summaries in English) 1958. 10/yr. 8000 ptas. (foreign $100). Editores Medicos, S.A., Gabriela Mistral 2, 28035 Madrid, Spain. TEL 34-1-3860033. FAX 34-1-3739907. adv.; bk.rev.; illus.; index. circ. 2,000. **Indexed:** Biol.Abstr., Chem.Abstr., Excerp.Med., Helminthol.Abstr., Ind.Med.Esp., Ind.Med.
—BLDSC (0622.600000); SWETS.

ACTA MEDICA AUXOLOGICA. see *MEDICAL SCIENCES — Endocrinology*

618 DK ISSN 0001-6349
CODEN: AOGSAE
ACTA OBSTETRICA ET GYNECOLOGICA SCANDINAVICA. (Text in English) 1921. 10/yr. DKK 1825 (incl. supplements) (effective 1996). (Scandinavian Association of Obstetricians and Gynecologists) Munksgaard International Publishers Ltd., 35 Noerre Soegade, P.O. Box 2148, DK-1016 Copenhagen K, Denmark. TEL 33-127030. FAX 33129387. Ed. Viggo Fischer Rasmussen. adv.; bk.rev.; bibl.; charts; illus.; cum.index: 1922-1952; 1953-1962. circ. 4,500. (also avail. in microfiche; back issues avail.) **Indexed:** Biol.Abstr., Biotech.Abstr., Chem.Abstr., Curr.Adv.Ecol.Sci., Curr.Cont., Curr.Lit.Fam.Plan., Dairy Sci.Abstr., Excerp.Med., Ind.Med., NRN, Nutr.Abstr., Risk Abstr., Sci.Cit.Ind.
—BLDSC (0641.600000); ADONIS; CASDDS; Faxon; Genuine Article; SWETS; UnCover. **CCC.**
Formerly (until 1925): Acta Gynecologica Scandinavica.

618 DK ISSN 0300-8835
CODEN: AGSSAI
ACTA OBSTETRICA ET GYNECOLOGICA SCANDINAVICA. SUPPLEMENT. (Text in English) irreg. free to subscribers of Acta Obstetrica et Gynecologica Scandinavica. (Scandinavian Association of Obstetricians and Gynecologists) Munksgaard International Publishers Ltd., 35 Noerre Soegade, P.O. Box 2148, DK-1016 Copenhagen K, Denmark. TEL 33-127030. FAX 33-129387. **Indexed:** Biol.Abstr., Chem.Abstr., Curr.Adv.Ecol.Sci., Dairy Sci.Abstr., Excerp.Med., Helminthol.Abstr., Ind.Med., Ind.Sci.Rev., Nutr.Abstr.
—BLDSC (0641.605000); ADONIS; CASDDS; Faxon; SWETS. **CCC.**

618 TU ISSN 0252-9696
CODEN: ARTUD7
ACTA REPRODUCTIVA TURCICA. (Text and summaries in English) 1979-19??; resumed vol.14, no.1, 1992. q. TL.110000 (effective 1993). Hacettepe University, Department of Gynecology and Obstetrics, Ankara, Turkey. (Co-sponsor: Hacettepe University, Department of Public Health) Ed. Dr. Husnu A. Kisnisci. adv.; abstr.; charts; illus. circ. 1,000. **Indexed:** Bibl.Repro., Biol.Abstr. **Document type:** academic/scholarly publication.
—BLDSC (0662.530000).
Description: Publishes original research studies in obstetrics and gynecology, reproductive biology, public health, and related fields, including endocrinology, pediatrics, surgery and population studies.
Refereed Serial

618 616.4 FR ISSN 1243-6933
ACTUALITES REPRODUCTION HUMAINE. 1993. bi-m. (plus 6 supplements). 335 F. (foreign 446 F.) (effective 1995). Editions E S K A, 27 rue Dunios, 75013 Paris, France. TEL 44-06-80-42. FAX 44-24-06-94. Ed. Dr. Henri Rozenbaum. **Document type:** academic/scholarly publication.
Description: Covers developments in obstetrics and gynecology. Publishes conference proceedings, reports new protocols, and offers critical commentary in original articles

ADOLESCENT AND PEDIATRIC GYNECOLOGY. see *MEDICAL SCIENCES — Pediatrics*

618 616.6 NE
ADVANCES IN REPRODUCTIVE HEALTH CARE. (Text in English) irreg. price varies. Kluwer Academic Publishers, Postbus 17, 3300 AA Dordrecht, Netherlands. TEL 31-78-392392. FAX 31-78-392254. TELEX 29245 KAPG NL. (Dist. by: Kluwer Academic Publishers Group, P.O. Box 322, 3300 AH Dordrecht, Netherlands. TEL 31-78-392392. FAX 31-78-546474; N. America dist. addr.: Box 358, Accord Sta., Hingham, MA 02018-0358. TEL 617-871-6600. FAX 617-871-6528) **Document type:** monographic series.
Refereed Serial

618.2 GW
AERZTLICHER RATGEBER FUER WERDENDE UND JUNGE MUETTER; die Schwangerschaft, Geburt und Babyzeit. 1964. 3/yr. free. Wort und Bild Verlag Konradshoehe GmbH, Konradshoehe, 82065 Baierbrunn, Germany. TEL 089-74433-0. FAX 089-74433155. Ed. Rolf Becker. adv.; circ. 240,000 (controlled). **Document type:** consumer publication.

618 JA ISSN 0917-0162
AICHI BOSEI EISEI GAKKAISHI/AICHI JOURNAL OF MATERNAL HEALTH. (Text in Japanese) 1985. a. 2000 Yen. Aichi Bosei Eisei Gakkai - Aichi Society of Maternal Health, Nagoya Daigaku Iryo Gijutsu Tanki Daigaku, 1-20, Taiko Minami 1-chome, Higashi-ku, Nagoya-shi, Aichi-ken 461, Japan. TEL 052-723-1111. FAX 052-723-0290. Ed. Miyoko Ogiso. adv.; bk.rev.; film rev.; software rev.; bibl.; illus. circ. 300. **Document type:** bulletin.

618 JA
AKITA SANFUJINKA IHO/AKITA JOURNAL OF OBSTETRICIANS AND GYNECOLOGISTS. (Text in Japanese) 1976. bi-m. free. Nihon Sanka Fujinka Gakkai, Akita Chiho Bukai - Japan Society of Obstetrics and Gynecology, Akita Branch, Akita-ken Ishi Kaikan, 6-6, Senshu Kubota-cho, Akita-shi, Akita-ken 010, Japan. TEL 81-188-33-7401. FAX 81-188-32-1356. Ed. Toshiya Ohkura. circ. 100. **Document type:** bulletin.

618 BU ISSN 0324-0959
CODEN: AKGIBP
AKUSERSTVO I GINEKOLOGIJA. (Text in Bulgarian; summaries in English, Russian) bi-m. 16 lv. (Ministerstvo na Narodnoto Zdrave) Izdatelstvo Meditsina i Fizkultura, 11 Pl. Slaveikov, Sofia, Bulgaria. (Dist. by: Hemus, 6 Rouski Blvd., 1000 Sofia, Bulgaria) (Co-sponsor: Nauchno Druzhestvo po Akuserstvo i Ginekologija) Ed. K. Mirkov. circ. 2,213. **Indexed:** Abstr.Bulg.Sci.Med.Lit., Excerp.Med.
—BLDSC (0006.300000); CASDDS.

618 RU ISSN 0300-9092
AKUSHERSTVO I GINEKOLOGIYA/OBSTETRICS AND GYNECOLOGY. (Text in Russian; summaries in English) 1922. bi-m. $86 (effective 1996). (Nauchnyi Tsentr Akusherstva, Ginekologii i Perinatologii) Izdatel'stvo Meditsina, Petroverigskii pereulok 6-8, 101000 Moscow, Russia. (Dist. by: Mezhdunarodnaya Kniga, B. Yakimanka 39, 117049 Moscow, Russia. TEL 7-095-2384600. FAX 7-095-2384634) (Co-sponsor: Ministerstvo Zdravookhraneniya) Ed. A.P. Kiryushchenkov. adv.: N.V.Biyatova. bk.rev.; illus.; index. **Indexed:** Abstr.Bulg.Sci.Med.Lit., Biol.Abstr., Chem.Abstr., Dairy Sci.Abstr., Excerp.Med., Ind.Med., INIS Atomind., Nutr.Abstr.
—BLDSC (0006.200000). **CCC.**
Description: Publishes original and survey papers dealing with modern scientific achievements in the field of obstetrics and gynecology. Covers physiology and pathology of the fetus and the newborn, scientific and practical problems of diagnosis, treatment of complications in pregnancy, labor and gynecologic diseases.

AMERICAN ASSOCIATION OF GENITO-URINARY SURGEONS. TRANSACTIONS. see *MEDICAL SCIENCES — Gastroenterology*

618 US ISSN 1074-3804
CODEN: JAALF3
AMERICAN ASSOCIATION OF GYNECOLOGIC LAPAROSCOPISTS. JOURNAL. 1993. 4/yr. $100 to non-members (Canada & Mexico $115; elsewhere $122); institutions $125 (Canada & Mexico $140; elsewhere $162) (effective 1995). American Association of Gynecologic Laparoscopists, 13021 E. Florence Ave., Santa Fe Springs, CA 90670-4505. TEL 310-946-9774; 800-554-2245. Ed. Karen Cook. **Indexed:** Excerp.Med. (1995-). **Document type:** academic/scholarly publication.

618 US ISSN 0895-3643
AMERICAN JOURNAL OF GYNECOLOGIC HEALTH. 1987. bi-m. $55 (foreign $82). (Association of Reproductive Health Professionals) Macor Publishing Co., 116 W. 32nd St., New York, NY 10001-3212. TEL 212-736-6688. FAX 212-564-1763. Ed. Dr. Michael R. Spence.
—CCC.

618 US ISSN 0002-9378
RG1 CODEN: AJOGAH
AMERICAN JOURNAL OF OBSTETRICS AND GYNECOLOGY. 1920. m. $137 to individuals (Canada $186.18; elsewhere $174); institutions $247 (Canada $303.88; elsewhere $284); students, residents $63 (Canada $107; elsewhere $100) (effective 1996); newsstand price: $14. (American Gynecological and Obstetrical Society) Mosby - Year Book, Inc. (Subsidiary of: Times Mirror Company), 11830 Westline Industrial Dr., St. Louis, MO 63146-3318. TEL 314-872-8370; 800-325-4177. FAX 314-432-1380. TELEX 44-2402. (Co-sponsor: American Board of Obstetrics and Gynecology) Ed.Bd. adv.: B&W page $1350, color page $2375; trim 8 1/8 x 10 7/8. illus.; s-a. index. circ. 17,066. (also avail. in microfilm from UMI,PMC; reprint service avail. from UMI) **Indexed:** AIM, Anim.Breed.Abstr., ASCA, Behav.Med.Abstr., Bibl.Dev.Med.& Child Neur., Biol.Abstr., Biol.Dig., Biotech.Abstr., C.C.I.Ob.Gyn., Chem.Abstr., CINAHL, Curr.Adv.Biochem., Curr.Adv.Cancer Res., Curr.Adv.Cell & Devel.Biol., Curr.Adv.Ecol.Sci., Curr.Adv.Genetics & Molec.Biol., Curr.Cont., Curr.Lit.Fam.Plan., Dairy Sci.Abstr., Diab.Cont., Dok.Arbeitsmed., Excerp.Med., FAMLI, Helminthol.Abstr., I.P.A., Ind.Med., Ind.Sci.Rev., Ind.Vet., INIS Atomind., Int.Nurs.Ind., Kidney, Med.& Surg.Dermat., NRN, Nutr.Abstr., Rev.Med.& Vet.Mycol., Rev.Plant Path., Risk Abstr., Sage Fam.Stud.Abstr., Sci.Cit.Ind, Vet.Bull.
●Also available online. Vendor(s): Ovid Technologies.
—BLDSC (0828.700000); ADONIS; CASDDS; Faxon; Genuine Article; SWETS; UMI; UnCover. **CCC.**
Description: Articles devoted to obstetrics, gynecology, fetuses, the placenta and the newborn.
Refereed Serial

618.3 US ISSN 0735-1631
RG600
AMERICAN JOURNAL OF PERINATOLOGY. 1983. bi-m. $99 to individuals (foreign $124); institutions $137 (foreign $162). Thieme Medical Publishers, Inc., 381 Park Ave., S., Ste. 1501, New York, NY 10016. TEL 212-683-5088. FAX 212-779-9020. Ed. Dr. Peter A.M. Auld. bk.rev. circ. 1,600. **Indexed:** Bibl.Dev.Med.& Child Neur., CINAHL, Excerp.Med. **Document type:** academic/scholarly publication.
—BLDSC (0829.900000); Faxon; Genuine Article; SWETS; UMI; UnCover. **CCC.**
Refereed Serial

AMERICAN JOURNAL OF REPRODUCTIVE IMMUNOLOGY. see *MEDICAL SCIENCES — Allergology And Immunology*

ANNALES CHIRURGIAE ET GYNAECOLOGIAE. see *MEDICAL SCIENCES — Surgery*

618 IT ISSN 0300-0087
CODEN: AOGMAU
ANNALI DI OSTETRICIA GINECOLOGIA MEDICINA PERINATALE. (Summaries in English, Italian) 1879. bi-m. L.70000 (foreign L.100000). (Universita degli Studi di Milano, Clinica Ostetrica e Ginecologica) Istituti Clinici di Perfezionamento, Via Daverio 6, 20122 Milan, Italy. Ed. Prof. G.B. Candiani. adv.; bibl.; charts; illus.; index. **Indexed:** Biol.Abstr., Chem.Abstr., Excerp.Med., Ind.Med.
—BLDSC (1016.190000); CASDDS.
Formerly (until 1971): Annali di Ostetricia e Ginecologia (ISSN 0003-4657)

MEDICAL SCIENCES — OBSTETRICS AND GYNECOLOGY

618   JA   ISSN 0913-8307
AOMORIKEN RINSHO SANFUJINKA IKAISHI/AOMORI SOCIETY OF OBSTETRICIANS AND GYNECOLOGISTS. JOURNAL. (Text in English, Japanese; summaries in English) 1986. s-a. Aomoriken Rinsho Sanfujinka Ikai, Hirosaki Daigaku Igakubu Sanfujinka Kyoshitsu, 5, Zaifu-cho, Hirosaki-shi, Aomori-ken 036, Japan.

APPLIED CYTOGENETICS. see *BIOLOGY — Genetics*

618.92   UK
ARCHIVES OF DISEASE IN CHILDHOOD. FETAL AND NEONATAL EDITION. (Supplement to: Archives of Disease in Childhood (ISSN 0003-9888)) 1988. bi-m. £54($85) B M J Publishing Group, B.M.A. House, Tavistock Sq., London WC1H 9JR, England. TEL 0171-383-4499. FAX 0171-383-6661. (N. American subscr. to: Box 408, Franklin, MA 02038. TEL 800-2-FON-BMJ. FAX 800-2-FAX-BMJ) Eds. M. Chiswick, H. Marcovitch. adv. contact: Sheila Rowe. bk.rev.; abstr.; charts; illus.; index. (also avail. in microfilm from UMI; reprint service avail. from UMI) **Document type:** academic/scholarly publication.
●Also available online. Vendor(s): Ovid Technologies.
   Description: Focuses on research in neonatology, genetics, fetal medicine, neurodevelopmental medicine, fetal physiology, and perinatal epidemiology.

618.1   GW   ISSN 0932-0067
                        CODEN: AGOBEJ
ARCHIVES OF GYNECOLOGY AND OBSTETRICS. (Text in English) 1870. 8/yr. (in 2 vols., 4 nos./vol.). DM.1144($831) (effective 1996). (Deutschen Gesellschaft fuer Gynaekologie und Geburtshilfe) Springer-Verlag, Heidelberger Platz 3, 14197 Berlin, Germany. TEL 030-8207-0. FAX 030-8214091. E-mail: orders@springer.de. (Subscr. in N. America to: Springer-Verlag New York, Inc., 44 Hartz Way, Secaucus, NJ 07096-2491. TEL 201-348-4033. FAX 201-348-4505) Ed.Bd. adv.; bibl.; charts; illus.; index. (also avail. in microfilm from UMI; back issues avail.; reprint service avail. from ISI) **Indexed:** Anim.Breed.Abstr., Biol.Abstr., Chem.Abstr., Curr.Adv.Cancer Res., Curr.Adv.Cell & Devel.Biol., Curr.Adv.Ecol.Sci., Curr.Cont., Dairy Sci.Abstr., Excerp.Med., Ind.Med., Ind.Sci.Rev., INIS Atomind., NRN, Nutr.Abstr., Sci.Cit.Ind. **Document type:** academic/scholarly publication.
—BLDSC (1634.404000); CASDDS; Faxon; Genuine Article; SWETS; UMI; UnCover. **CCC.**
   Former titles: Archives of Gynecology (ISSN 0170-9925); Archiv fuer Gynaekologie (ISSN 0003-9128)
   Description: Informs about the latest advances in the field.
   Refereed Serial

618   IT   ISSN 0004-0126
                        CODEN: AOGNAX
ARCHIVIO DI OSTETRICIA E GINECOLOGIA. vol.80, 1975. bi-m. $90. Universita di Napoli, Clinica Ostetrica e Ginecologica, Via S. Andrea delle Dame 2, 80138 Naples, Italy. Ed. Enzo Martella. **Indexed:** Biol.Abstr., Chem.Abstr., Excerp.Med., Ind.Med.
—CASDDS.

ASIAN AND PACIFIC WOMEN'S RESOURCE AND ACTION SERIES. see *WOMEN'S INTERESTS*

618   US   ISSN 1051-2446
                        CODEN: AEPEEJ
ASSISTED REPRODUCTION REVIEWS. 1991. q. $158 to individuals; institutions $180 (effective 1995). Williams & Wilkins, 428 E. Preston St., Baltimore, MD 21202. TEL 410-528-4000; 800-638-6423. FAX 410-528-4312. Ed. Dr. Alan H. DeCherney. (also avail. in microfilm from WWS) **Indexed:** Excerp.Med. (1993-). **Document type:** academic/scholarly publication.
—BLDSC (1746.661938). **CCC.**
   Description: Publishes reviews covering advances in reproductive medicine directed to obstetricians, gynecologists, urologists, endocrinologists and biologists.

618.2   FR
ASSOCIATION DES SAGES-FEMMES DE LA MATERNITE DE NANCY. BULLETIN. 1946. q. 75 F. Association des Sages-Femmes de l'Ecole d'Accouchement de la Maternite de Nancy, Rue de Docteur-Heydendreich, 54000 Nancy, France. Dir. Mme Poutas. adv. circ. 1,400.

618   IT   ISSN 0004-7317
ATTUALITA DI OSTETRICIA E GINECOLOGIA. (Text in Italian; summaries in English, French, German, Italian) 1955. bi-m. L.20000. (Universita degli Studi di Padova, Facolta di Medicina e Chirurgia) Societa Editrice Universo, Via G.B. Morgagni 1, 00161 Rome, Italy. Ed. Giuseppe Vecchietti. **Indexed:** Biol.Abstr.

618   US   ISSN 0271-129X
AUDIO-DIGEST OBSTETRICS - GYNECOLOGY. 1954. s-m. $168. Audio-Digest Foundation (Subsidiary of: California Medical Association), 1577 E. Chevy Chase Dr., Glendale, CA 91206. TEL 213-245-8505. FAX 818-240-7379. Ed. Claron L. Oakley. circ. controlled. (audio cassette)
—UnCover.
   Refereed Serial

618   AT   ISSN 0004-8666
                        CODEN: AZOGBS
AUSTRALIAN AND NEW ZEALAND JOURNAL OF OBSTETRICS AND GYNAECOLOGY. 1961. q. Aus.$70 (overseas Aus.$75) (effective 1995). Royal Australian College of Obstetricians & Gynecologists, 254 Albert St., Melbourne, Vic. 3002, Australia. TEL 61-3-417-1699. FAX 61-3-419-0672. (Co-sponsor: RACOG Research) Ed. Norman A. Beischer. adv.; bk.rev.; charts; illus.; index. circ. 4,500. (back issues avail.) **Indexed:** Bibl.Dev.Med.& Child Neur., Biol.Abstr., Curr.Adv.Ecol.Sci., Curr.Cont., Excerp.Med., Helminthol.Abstr., Ind.Med., NRN, Nutr.Abstr., So.Pac.Per.Ind.
—BLDSC (1796.890000); CASDDS; Faxon; Genuine Article; SWETS; UMI.

BABY CONNECTION NEWS JOURNAL; for new and expectant parents and their children 0-5 years. see *CHILDREN AND YOUTH — About*

649   US
BABY ON THE WAY. 1990. a. free. Time Inc. Ventures, Baby Talk, 25 W. 43rd St., New York, NY 10036. TEL 212-840-4200. adv. contact: Lori Fromm. circ. 1,800,000. **Document type:** consumer publication.
   Description: Guide to a healthy pregnancy, labor and delivery, and taking care of a newborn.

649 618   US
BABY ON THE WAY: BASICS. 1991. a. free. (American College of Obstetricians and Gynecologists) Time Inc. Ventures, Baby Talk, 25 W. 43rd St., New York, NY 10036. TEL 212-840-4200. adv. contact: Lori Fromm. circ. 500,000. **Document type:** consumer publication.
   Description: Contains information for expectant mothers with low reading ability, in easy-to-read format.

618   UK   ISSN 0950-3552
BAILLIERE'S CLINICAL OBSTETRICS AND GYNAECOLOGY. 1987. q. £76 to individuals; institutions £87. Bailliere Tindall - W.B. Saunders Co. Ltd. (Subsidiary of: Harcourt Brace & Company Ltd.), 24-28 Oval Rd., London NW1 7DX, England. TEL 0171-267-4466. FAX 0171-482-2293. TELEX 25775 ACPRES G. (Subscr. to: Journals Subscriptions Fulfillment, Foots Cray High St., Sidcup, Kent DA14 5HP, England. TEL 0181-300-3322. FAX 0181-309-0807; Subscr. in N. America to: W.B. Saunders Co., 6277 Sea Harbor Dr., 4th Fl., Orlando, FL 32887-4800. TEL 800-874-6418) **Document type:** academic/scholarly publication.
—BLDSC (1856.725000); Genuine Article; SWETS; UnCover. **CCC.**
   Refereed Serial

618.2   UK
BAILLIERE'S MIDWIVES' DICTIONARY. 1951. irreg., vol. 8, 1992. £4.95 (effective 1994). Bailliere Tindall - W.B. Saunders Co. Ltd. (Subsidiary of: Harcourt Brace & Company Ltd.), 24-28 Oval Rd., London MW1 7DX, England. TEL 0171-267-4466. FAX 0171-482-2293. TELEX 25775 ACPRES G. (Orders to: Harcourt Brace & Company Ltd., Foots Cray High St., Sidcup, Kent DA14 5HP, England. TEL 0181-300-3322. FAX 0181-309-0807; Orders in N. America to: W.B. Saunders Co., 6277 Sea Harbor Dr., 4th Fl., Orlando, FL 32887-4800. TEL 800-874-6418) (back issues avail.) **Document type:** academic/scholarly publication.

BELIZE FAMILY HEALTH SURVEY. see *MEDICAL SCIENCES — Abstracting, Bibliographies, Statistics*

BERICHTE GYNAEKOLOGIE - GEBURTSHILFE/GYNECOLOGY - OBSTETRICS. see *MEDICAL SCIENCES — Abstracting, Bibliographies, Statistics*

574.33 618   SZ   ISSN 0006-3126
RJ251   CODEN: BNEOBV
BIOLOGY OF THE NEONATE; fetal and neonatal research. (Text in English) 1959. m. (2 vols./yr.). 604.80 SFr.($465.60) to individuals; institutions 1008 SFr. ($776) (effective 1996). S. Karger AG, Allschwilerstr. 10, P.O. Box, CH-4009 Basel, Switzerland. TEL 061-3061111. FAX 061-3061234. E-mail: Karger@Karger.ch. Ed. J.P. Relier. adv.; bibl.; charts; illus. circ. 1,150. (also avail. in microform from UMI) **Indexed:** Anim.Breed.Abstr., Bibl.Dev.Med.& Child Neur., Biol.Abstr., Chem.Abstr., Curr.Adv.Ecol.Sci., Curr.Cont., Dairy Sci.Abstr., Dent.Ind., Excerp.Med., Ind.Med., Ind.Sci.Rev., Ind.Vet., Nutr.Abstr., Pig News & Info., Sci.Cit.Ind, Vet.Bull. **Document type:** academic/scholarly publication.
—BLDSC (2087.100000); CASDDS; Faxon; Genuine Article; SWETS; UnCover. **CCC.**
   Incorporates (in 1995): Developmental Pharmacology and Therapeutics (ISSN 0379-8305); Formerly: Biologia Neonatorum.
   Description: Highlights aspects of embryology.
   Refereed Serial

301.4 618   US   ISSN 0730-7659
RG651
BIRTH; issues in perinatal care and education. 1973. 4/yr. $110 (foreign $135) (effective 1996). Blackwell Science inc., 238 Main St., Cambridge, MA 02142-1413. TEL 617-876-7022. FAX 617-492-5263. Ed. Diony Young. adv.; bk.rev. circ. 3,500. (also avail. in microform from UMI; back issues avail.; reprint service avail. from UMI,ISI) **Indexed:** CINAHL, Curr.Cont., Dok.Arbeitsmed., Ind.Med., Int.Nurs.Ind., NRN, Psychol.Abstr.
—BLDSC (2094.081000); Faxon; Genuine Article; UMI; UnCover. **CCC.**
   Formerly (until 1981): Birth and the Family Journal (ISSN 0098-860X)
   Description: Covers education and technology regarding childbirth for childbirth educators, midwives and physicians.

618   AT   ISSN 1032-9625
BIRTH. 1989. a. Aus.$5.95 (foreign Aus.$9.50). Magazine House Pty. Ltd., P.O. Box 1067, Crows Nest, N.S.W. 2065, Australia. TEL 61-2-438-2399. FAX 61-2-436-3014. Ed. Carol Fallows. adv.; bk.rev. circ. 40,000. **Document type:** consumer publication.
   Description: Offers important information for expectant mothers.

618   US   ISSN 0890-3255
BIRTH GAZETTE. 1977; N.S. 1985. q. $30 to individuals (foreign $35); institutions $40 (foreign $45). Second Foundation, 42, The Farm, Summertown, TN 38483. TEL 615-964-2519. Ed. Ina May Gaskin; Pub. Ina May Gaskin. adv. contact: Pamela Hunt. bk.rev.; illus.; stat. circ. 3,000. (also avail. in microform from UMI; reprint service avail. from UMI) **Indexed:** CINAHL.
—BLDSC (2094.092300).
   Formerly (until vol.11, no.4, 1985): Practicing Midwife (ISSN 0733-8317)
   Description: Covers midwifery, childbirth issues, and access to maternity care.

BIRTH PSYCHOLOGY BULLETIN. see *PSYCHOLOGY*

BOSHI KAGAKU RYOHO/CHEMOTHERAPY FOR MOTHER AND CHILD. see *MEDICAL SCIENCES — Pediatrics*

618   CN   ISSN 1183-0670
BOUNTY PREGNANCY GUIDE. French edition: Guide Bounty de la Grossesse (ISSN 1183-0689) 1990. s-a. Bounty Family Publications Ltd., 746 Warden Ave., No. 2, Scarborough, ON M1L 4A2, Canada. TEL 416-750-1165. FAX 416-750-7266. Ed. Alan Donaldson. adv. circ. 320,000 (255,000 English ed., 65,000 French ed.).

618   US
BOUNTY PREGNANCY GUIDE.* 1989. q. $8. Health Care Publishing, Ltd., 84 Clinton Ave., Nyack, NY 10960-4604. TEL 212-489-2476. FAX 212-489-2476. Ed. Robert Egleton. adv.: B&W page $27067, color page $33609; trim 5 1/4 x 7 1/2; adv. contact: Glenn Meyerson. circ. 525,000. (back issues avail.) **Document type:** consumer publication.

MEDICAL SCIENCES — OBSTETRICS AND GYNECOLOGY 4455

618.1   UK   ISSN 0960-9776
THE BREAST. 1992. q. £159($263) (effective 1995). Churchill Livingstone Journals (Subsidiary of: Pearson Professional), Robert Stevenson House, 1-3 Baxter's Pl., Leith Walk, Edinburgh EH1 3AF, Scotland. TEL 0131-556-2424.
FAX 0131-558-1177. (Subscr. to: Pearson Professional Ltd., P.O. Box 77, Fourth Ave., Harlow, Essex CM19 5AA, England. TEL 01279-623760; U.S. subscr. to: Churchill Livingstone, 650 Ave. of the Americas, New York, NY 10011. TEL 212-206-5000) Ed. J. Michael Dixon. adv. contact: David Dunnachie. abstr.; bibl. circ. 955. **Indexed:** Excerp.Med. (1993-). **Document type:** academic/scholarly publication.
—BLDSC (2277.492700).
Description: Covers the physiology of the normal breast and the etiology, biology, investigation, medical and surgical treatment and management of benign and malignant breast diseases.

BREAST CANCER; evolution of concepts. see *MEDICAL SCIENCES — Oncology*

618.1   US   ISSN 1075-122X
▼**THE BREAST JOURNAL.** 1995. bi-m. $140 (foreign $170) (effective 1996). Blackwell Science Inc., 238 Main St., Cambridge, MA 02142.
TEL 617-876-7022; 800-759-6102.
FAX 617-492-5263. (back issues avail.) **Document type:** academic/scholarly publication.

618   UK   ISSN 0969-4900
BRITISH JOURNAL OF MIDWIFERY. 1993. m. £35 (overseas £80). Mark Allen Publishing Ltd., Croxted Mews, 288 Croxted Rd., London SE24 9BY, England. TEL 0181-671-7521.
FAX 0181-671-1722. Ed. Christine Henderson; Pub. Mark Allen. adv. contact: Ian White. **Document type:** academic/scholarly publication.
—BLDSC (2311.885000).

618   UK   ISSN 0306-5456
CODEN: BJOGAS
BRITISH JOURNAL OF OBSTETRICS & GYNAECOLOGY. 1902. m. £129 in Europe; elsewhere £142($229) (effective 1996). (Royal College of Obstetricians and Gynaecologists) Blackwell Science Ltd., Osney Mead, Oxford OX2 0EL, England. TEL 01865-240201.
FAX 01865-721205. TELEX 83355 MEDBOK G. Ed. G. Chamberlain. adv.; bk.rev.; abstr.; bibl.; charts; illus.; index. circ. 6,000. (back issues avail., reprint service avail. from UMI) **Indexed:** AIM, ASCA, Bibl.Dev.Med.& Child Neur., Biol.Abstr., Biotech.Abstr., Chem.Abstr., CINAHL, Curr.Adv.Cancer Res., Curr.Adv.Ecol.Sci., Curr.Cont., Curr.Lit.Fam.Plan., Dairy Sci.Abstr., Dent.Ind., Diab.Cont., Excerp.Med., Helminthol.Abstr., I.P.A., Ind.Med., Ind.Sci.Rev., Nut.Vet., Kidney, Med.& Surg.Dermat., NRN, Nutr.Abstr. Risk Abstr., Sci.Cit.Ind, Vet.Bull.
● Also available online. Vendor(s): Ovid Technologies.
—BLDSC (2312.300000); ADONIS; CASDDS; Faxon; Genuine Article; SWETS; UMI. **CCC.**
Formerly: Journal of Obstetrics and Gynaecology of the British Commonwealth (ISSN 0022-3204)
Refereed Serial

618 016   UK   ISSN 0140-7686
BRITISH JOURNAL OF OBSTETRICS & GYNAECOLOGY. SUPPLEMENT. 1977. irreg. (Royal College of Obstetricians and Gynaecologists) Blackwell Science Ltd., Osney Mead, Oxford OX2 0EL, England. TEL 01865-240201. FAX 01865-721205. TELEX 83355 MEDBOK G. **Document type:** academic/scholarly publication.
—BLDSC (2312.310000); ADONIS; SWETS; UnCover. **CCC.**

618.1   GW   ISSN 0068-337X
CODEN: BUFZBG
BUECHEREI DES FRAUENARZTES. (Supplement to: Zeitschrift fuer Geburtshilfe und Perinatologie) 1956. irreg., vol.43, 1992. price varies. Ferdinand Enke Verlag, Postfach 300366, 70443 Stuttgart, Germany. TEL 0711-135798-0.
FAX 0711-135798-30. TELEX 07252275-GTV-D. Ed. G. Martius. (reprint service avail. from IRC) **Indexed:** Chem.Abstr.
—CASDDS.

618.2 617.96   JA   ISSN 0387-2653
BUNBEN TO MASUI/JOURNAL OF OBSTETRICS AND ANESTHESIA. (Text in Japanese; summaries in English) 1961. irreg. (Mutsu Bunben Kenkyukai - Institute of Obstetrical Anesthesia) Kokuseido Publishing Co., Ltd., 23-5-202, Hongo 3-chome, Bunkyo-ku, Tokyo 113, Japan.

618   CN   ISSN 1183-2517
CANADIAN JOURNAL OF OB-GYN & WOMEN'S HEALTH CARE; for physicians dealing with today's issues. 1984. 6/yr. $60. Rodar Publishing Inc., 8102 Trans Canada Hwy., St. Laurent, PQ H4S 1Z4, Canada. TEL 514-333-5350. adv.; circ. 17,000 (controlled). **Indexed:** Can.B.P.I., CMI.
Former titles (until Jun. 1991): Canadian Journal of Ob-Gyn (ISSN 0843-4255); (until 1989): Contemporary Ob-Gyn (ISSN 0829-9161)
Description: Covers all areas of reproductive medicine, childbirth, sexually transmitted diseases, menopause, PMS, and ovarian cancer.

618   XR   ISSN 1210-7832
CESKA GYNEKOLOGIE. (Text in Czech or Slovak; summaries in English and Russian) 1936. 10/yr. $62.60. (Ceska Lekarska Spolecnost J.E. Purkyne - Czech Medical Society) Nakladatelske Stredisko C L S J.E. Purkyne, Sokolska 31, 120 26 Prague 2, Czech Republic. FAX 42-0-2-202788. (Dist. by: Artia, Ve Smeckach 30, 111 27 Prague 1, Czech Republic) (Co-sponsor: Ceska Spolecnost Gynekologicka a Porodnicka) Ed. Dr. K. Balak. bk.rev. **Indexed:** Biol.Abstr., Excerp.Med., Ind.Med.
—BLDSC (3122.220000). **CCC.**
Formerly: Ceskoslovenska Gynekologie (ISSN 0374-6852)

618   CE
CEYLON COLLEGE OF OBSTETRICIANS AND GYNAECOLOGISTS. JOURNAL. (Text in English) q. Rs.25. Ceylon College of Obstetricians and Gynaecologists, C.M.A. House, 6 Wijerama Mawatha, Colombo 7, Sri Lanka.

618   US
CHILDBIRTH (YEAR). 1984. a. Cahners Publishing Company (New York), Childcare Group, Division of Elsevier Inc., 249 W. 17th St., New York, NY 10011. TEL 212-645-0067. FAX 212-463-6410. (Dist. by: Neodata Services, Box 2971, Boulder, CO 80329) Ed. Judith Nolte. adv. circ. 2,000,000. **Document type:** consumer publication.
Description: Answers the questions of couples approaching the birth of their child. The magazine's four sections include: the last three months of pregnancy, getting ready for baby, labor and birth, and life with baby.

618.2 375   US
CHILDBIRTH INSTRUCTOR. 1990. q. $17.97. Cradle Publishing, Inc., 52 Vanderbilt Ave., Ste. 501, New York, NY 10017-3808. TEL 212-986-1422.
FAX 212-986-0816. Ed. Colleen Davis Gardephe. adv.: B&W page $3880. circ. 5,000 (paid); 10,000 (controlled). **Document type:** trade publication.
Description: Contains information, ideas and advice on teaching techniques for professionals who educate parents for childbirth and parenting.

618.45   US
CHILDBIRTH WITHOUT PAIN EDUCATION ASSOCIATION. MEMO. 1960. bi-m. membership. Childbirth Without Pain Education Association, 20134 Snowden, Detroit, MI 48235. TEL 313-341-3816. Dir. Flora Hommel. adv.; bk.rev.; tr.mk. circ. 3,000. (processed) **Document type:** newsletter.
Formerly: Childbirth Without Pain Education Association. Newsletter (ISSN 0009-4048)

618   SP   ISSN 0210-573X
CODEN: CIGODJ
CLINICA E INVESTIGACION EN GINECOLOGIA Y OBSTETRICIA. (Text in Spanish; summaries in English) 1974. m. (10/yr). 6900 ptas.($57) (free to qualified personnel). Ediciones Doyma S.A., Travesera de Gracia 17-21, 08021 Barcelona, Spain. TEL 34-1-200-07-11. FAX 34-1-209-11-36. TELEX 51964 INK-E. Ed. J. Esteban-Altirriba. adv.: page 180000 ptas.; trim 210 x 280; adv. contact: Olga Gomez. circ. 3,000. (reprint service avail. from UMI) **Indexed:** Excerp.Med., Ind.Med.Esp.
—BLDSC (3286.202000); UMI.
Description: Covers the early detection of gynecological diseases, the improvement of family planning methods, the treatment of sterility and infertility, and the mother-child relationship during pregnancy.

618   IT   ISSN 0390-6663
CODEN: CEOGA4
CLINICAL AND EXPERIMENTAL OBSTETRICS AND GYNECOLOGY. (Text and summaries in English) 1974. q. $150 to individuals; institutions $250. Studi Ostetrico Ginecologici s.r.l., Galleria Storione 2-A, 35128 Padua, Italy. TEL 39-49-8758644.
FAX 39-49-8752018. Ed. Prof. Antonio Onnis. (back issues avail.) **Indexed:** Biol.Abstr., Chem.Abstr., Excerp.Med., Ind.Med. **Document type:** academic/scholarly publication.
—BLDSC (3286.251900); CASDDS; Faxon; SWETS. **CCC.**
Refereed Serial

618   US   ISSN 1043-0660
CODEN: CCOGFT
CLINICAL CONSULTATIONS IN OBSTETRICS AND GYNECOLOGY. 1989. q. $125 (foreign $145) (effective 1996). W.B. Saunders Co. (Subsidiary of: Harcourt Brace & Company), Curtis Center, 3rd. Fl., Independence Sq. W., Philadelphia, PA 19106-3399. TEL 215-238-7800.
FAX 215-238-6445. (Subscr. to: Periodicals Fulfillment, W.B. Saunders Co., 6277 Sea Harbor Dr., 4th Fl., Orlando, FL 32891-4800. TEL 800-654-2452. FAX 800-874-6418) Ed. Dr. Ronald A. Chez; Pub. Joan W. Blumberg. adv.: B&W page $625, color page $1575; 7 x 10. circ. 1,254. **Indexed:** Excerp.Med. (1995-). **Document type:** academic/scholarly publication.
—UMI. **CCC.**
Description: Aimed at obstetrics and gynecology practitioners, each issue reviews a single topic in the care of patients.

CLINICAL CYTOGENETICS. see *BIOLOGY — Genetics*

618   UK   ISSN 0962-8827
CODEN: CDYSEJ
CLINICAL DYSMORPHOLOGY. 1992. q. £57($89) to individuals; institutions in the E.U. £150 (N. America $255; elsewhere £165) (effective 1995). Chapman & Hall, Journals Department (Subsidiary of: International Thomson Publishing Group), 2-6 Boundary Row, London SE1 8HN, England.
TEL 0171-865-0066. FAX 0171-522-9623. TELEX 290164 CHAPMA G. E-mail: journal@chall.mhs.compuserve.com. (Dist. by: International Thomson Publishing Services Ltd., Cheriton House, North Way, Andover, Hants. SP10 5BE, England. TEL 01264-342713. FAX 01264-342807; N. American subscr. to: Chapman & Hall, Journals Promotion Department, One Penn Plaza, 41st Fl., New York, NY 10119. TEL 212-564-1060. FAX 212-564-1505) Ed.Bd. adv.; bk.rev.; illus. (reprint service avail.) **Indexed:** Excerp.Med. (1994-), Ind.Med. (1993-). **Document type:** academic/scholarly publication.
—BLDSC (3286.273700); ADONIS; Genuine Article. **CCC.**
Description: Devoted to publishing reports of multiple congenital anomaly syndromes, original studies and review articles on etiology, clinical delineation, genetic mapping, and molecular embryology of birth defects.
Refereed Serial

618   US   ISSN 0009-9201
RG101   CODEN: COGYAK
CLINICAL OBSTETRICS AND GYNECOLOGY. 1958. q. $115 to individuals (foreign $153); institutions $219 (foreign $255) (effective 1996). Lippincott - Raven Publishers, 227 E. Washington Sq., Philadelphia, PA 19106. TEL 215-238-4200. Ed. Dr. James R. Scott. circ. 8,406. (also avail. in microform from UMI) **Indexed:** Bibl.Dev.Med.& Child Neur., Biol.Abstr., C.C.I.Ob.Gyn., Chem.Abstr, Curr.Adv.Cancer Res., Curr.Adv.Ecol.Sci., Curr.Cont., Dok.Arbeitsmed., Excerp.Med., Hosp.Lit.Ind., Ind.Med., Ind.Sci.Rev., INIS Atomind.
—BLDSC (3286.316000); CASDDS; Faxon; Genuine Article; SWETS; UMI; UnCover. **CCC.**
Refereed Serial

618   US   ISSN 0178-0328
CLINICAL PERSPECTIVES IN OBSTETRICS AND GYNECOLOGY. 1983. irreg. price varies. Springer-Verlag, 175 Fifth Ave., New York, NY 10010. TEL 212-460-1500. FAX 212-473-6272. (Also: Berlin, Heidelberg, Tokyo and Vienna) **Document type:** monographic series.

MEDICAL SCIENCES — OBSTETRICS AND GYNECOLOGY

618 US ISSN 1043-3198
CODEN: CPGYEV
CLINICAL PRACTICE OF GYNECOLOGY. 1991. 3/yr. Elsevier Science Inc., 655 Ave. of Americas, New York, NY 10010. TEL 212-989-5800. Ed. Michael S. Baggish. **Document type:** academic/scholarly publication.
—CCC.
Description: Covers all aspects of gynecology from diagnosis to treatment.
Refereed Serial

618 SP
CLINICAS DE PERINATOLOGIA DE NORTEAMERICA. Spanish translation of: Clinics in Perinatology. 1974. 4/yr. 14204 ptas.($104) (effective 1990). Interamericana de Espana, S.A., Division de Ciencias de la Salud de McGraw-Hill, Calle Manuel Ferrero, 13, 28036 Madrid, Spain. TEL 315-0340. FAX 733-6627. charts; illus.; cum.index.

618 SP ISSN 0009-9333
CLINICAS OBSTETRICAS Y GINECOLOGICAS DE NORTEAMERICA. Spanish translation of: Clinical Obstetrics and Gynecology (US ISSN 0009-9201) 1964. 4/yr. 17596 ptas.($129) (effective 1990). Interamericana de Espana, S.A., Division de Ciencias de la Salud de McGraw-Hill, Calle Manuel Ferrero, 13, 28036 Madrid, Spain. TEL 315-0340. FAX 733-6627. charts; illus.; cum.index.

618 US ISSN 0095-5108
CODEN: CLPEDL
CLINICS IN PERINATOLOGY. 1974. q. $108 (foreign $134) (effective 1996). W.B. Saunders Co. (Subsidiary of: Harcourt Brace & Company), Curtis Center, 3rd Fl., Independence Sq. W., Philadelphia, PA 19106-3399. TEL 215-238-7800. FAX 215-238-6445. (Subscr. to: Periodicals Fulfillment, W.B. Saunders Co., 6277 Sea Harbor Dr., 4th Fl., Orlando, FL 32891-4800. TEL 800-654-2452. FAX 800-874-6418) Ed. Sandy Hitchens. (reprint service avail. from UMI, ISI) **Indexed:** Bibl.Dev.Med.& Child Neur.; Biol.Abstr., Chem.Abstr., CINAHL, Curr.Adv.Ecol.Sci., Dent.Ind., Excerp.Med., Helminthol.Abstr., Ind.Med., Ind.Sci.Rev., INIS Atomind., Sci.Cit.Ind. **Document type:** academic/scholarly publication.
—BLDSC (3286.585000); CASDDS; EMDOCS; Faxon; Genuine Article; SWETS; UMI; UnCover. **CCC.**

CLIO; eine feministische Zeitschrift zur gesundheitlichen Selbsthilfe. see WOMEN'S HEALTH

THE COLPOSCOPIST. see MEDICAL SCIENCES — Oncology

COMBINED CUMULATIVE INDEX TO OBSTETRICS AND GYNECOLOGY. see MEDICAL SCIENCES — Abstracting, Bibliographies, Statistics

618 649 US ISSN 0829-8564
THE COMPLEAT MOTHER; the magazine of pregnancy, birth and breastfeeding. 1985. q. 12. Compleat Mother, 720 4th Ave. N.W., Box 209, Minot, ND 58702. TEL 701-852-2822. Ed. Jody McLaughlin. adv.: B&W page $350. bk.rev. circ. 20,000. **Document type:** consumer publication.

COMPLEMENTARY THERAPIES IN NURSING & MIDWIFERY. see MEDICAL SCIENCES — Nurses And Nursing

618 US ISSN 0090-3159
RG1
CONTEMPORARY OB-GYN. 1973. m. (plus 1 special issues). $89 (foreign $115). Medical Economics, Five Paragon Dr., Montvale, NJ 07645. TEL 800-526-4870. FAX 201-358-7260. Ed. Mary Hale. adv.; charts; illus.; stat.; index. circ. 39,255. (also avail. in microfilm from UMI) **Indexed:** Curr.Cont., Curr.Lit.Fam.Plan.
—BLDSC (3425.196000); Genuine Article; SWETS; UMI; UnCover. **CCC.**
Description: Sets the standards for women's health. Includes practical advice by leading authorities in the ob-gyn field emphasizing clinical problems.
Refereed Serial

618 CN ISSN 1194-7519
CONTEMPORARY OB-GYN. 1993. 6/yr. Can.$38 (foreign Can.$54). Thomson Healthcare Communications, 1120 Birchmount Rd., Ste. 200, Scarborough, ON M1K 5G4, Canada. TEL 416-750-8900. FAX 416-751-8126. Ed. Vil Meere. adv.: B&W page Can.$1695, color page Can.$2790; trim 8 1/8 x 10 7/8; adv. contact: Alexandra Hamilton. circ. 10,832.

618.1 UK ISSN 0953-9182
CODEN: CROGEV
CONTEMPORARY REVIEWS IN OBSTETRICS AND GYNAECOLOGY. 1989. 4/yr. £50($78) to individuals; institutions £100($155) (effective 1996). Parthenon Publishing Group, Casterton Hall, Carnforth, Lncs LA6 2LA, England. TEL 44-15242-72084. FAX 44-15242-71587. (In U.S.: Box 1564, Pearl Pearl River, NY 10965. TEL 914-735-9363) adv.; bk.rev. (also avail. in microform from UMI; back issues avail.) **Indexed:** Excerp.Med. **Document type:** academic/scholarly publication.
—BLDSC (3425.300100). **CCC.**
Description: Aims to provide an up-to-date source on the latest trends and developments in obstetrics and gynaecology.
Refereed Serial

CONTRACEPTION. see BIRTH CONTROL

618.1 618.2 SZ ISSN 0304-4246
CODEN: CGOBD6
CONTRIBUTIONS TO GYNECOLOGY AND OBSTETRICS. (Text in English) 1950. irreg. (approx. a.) price varies. S. Karger AG, Allschwilerstr. 10, P.O. Box, CH-4009 Basel, Switzerland. TEL 061-3061111. FAX 061-3061234. E-mail: Karger@Karger.ch. Eds. P.J. Keller, G. Zador. (reprint service avail. from ISI; back issues avail.) **Indexed:** Biol.Abstr., Chem.Abstr., Curr.Adv.Ecol.Sci., Curr.Cont., Excerp.Med., Ind.Med. **Document type:** academic/scholarly publication.
—BLDSC (3458.610000); CASDDS; Genuine Article. **CCC.**
Formerly: Advances in Obstetrics and Gynaecology (ISSN 0065-2997)
Refereed Serial

618 EC
CUADERNOS DE SALUD DE LA MUJER. 1990. q. $10. Centreo de Estudios y Asesoria en Salud, Calle Roca 549, Dpto. 602, Quito, Ecuador. TEL 593-2-466714. FAX 593-2-566714. (Co-sponsor: Panamerican Health Organization) Ed. De. Jose Yepez. bk.rev.; bibl.; illus.

618.2 US ISSN 1051-077X
RG1
CURRENT OBSTETRIC MEDICINE. 1991. biennial. $64.95 (residents $40) (effective 1996). Mosby - Year Book, Inc. (Chicago) (Subsidiary of: Times Mirror Company), 200 N. LaSalle St., Chicago, IL 60601-1080. TEL 312-726-9733. FAX 312-726-6075. TELEX 206155. (Subscr. to: 11830 Westline Industrial Dr., St. Louis, MO 63146) Ed. Dr. Richard Lee.
—BLDSC (3500.712000).
Description: Geared toward the general physician. Surveys developments in obstetric medicine through a synopsis of the past twelve months of medical literature.

618 UK ISSN 0957-5847
CURRENT OBSTETRICS AND GYNAECOLOGY. 1991. q. £60($96) to individuals; institutions £89 ($180) (effective 1995). Churchill Livingstone Journals (Subsidiary of: Pearson Professional), Robert Stevenson House, 1-3 Baxter's Pl., Leith Walk, Edinburgh EH1 3AF, Scotland. TEL 0131-556-2424. FAX 0131-459-1177. (Subscr. to: Pearson Professional Ltd., P.O. Box 77, Harlow, Essex CM19 5AA, England. TEL 01279-623760; U.S. subscr. to: Churchill Livingstone, 650 Ave. of the Americas, New York, NY 10011. TEL 212-206-5000) Ed. E.M. Symonds. adv. contact: David Dunnachie. circ. 890. **Indexed:** Excerp.Med. (1995-). **Document type:** academic/scholarly publication.
—BLDSC (3500.715000). **CCC.**
Description: Provides reviews on themes of current interest and educational values for both practicing clinicians and training grade staff; includes self-evaluation sections for the examination candidate.

618 IT
CURRENT OBSTETRICS AND GYNAECOLOGY - EDIZIONE ITALIANA. 1992. q. Gruppo Editoriale Faenza Editrice S.p.A., Via Pier. de Crescenai 44, 48018 Faenza RA, Italy. TEL 39-546-663488. FAX 39-546-660440. adv.: B&W page L.3850000, color page L.5170000.

CURRENT OPINION IN OBSTETRICS & GYNECOLOGY. see MEDICAL SCIENCES — Abstracting, Bibliographies, Statistics

618 US ISSN 8756-0410
CODEN: CPOIEN
CURRENT PROBLEMS IN OBSTETRICS AND GYNECOLOGY AND FERTILITY. 1978. bi-m. $68 to individuals (foreign $74); institutions $90 (foreign $96); students $43 (foreign $49) (effective Jan. 1994). Mosby - Year Book, Inc. (Subsidiary of: Times Mirror Company), 11830 Westline Industrial Dr., St. Louis, MO 63146. TEL 314-872-8370; 800-325-4177. FAX 314-432-1380. Ed. Robert L. Barbieri. cum.index. circ. 1,600. (also avail. in microform from UMI; reprint service avail. from UMI) **Indexed:** Excerp.Med., Ind.Med.
—BLDSC (3501.387200); CASDDS; Genuine Article; SWETS; UMI; UnCover. **CCC.**
Formerly: Current Problems in Obstetrics and Gynecology (ISSN 0147-1988)
Description: Provides clinical monographic reviews in obstetrics, gynecology and fertility.

618 NE ISSN 1058-8051
CURRENT TOPICS IN OBSTETRICS & GYNECOLOGY. (Text in English) 1989. irreg., vol. 6, 1992. price varies. Elsevier Science B.V., Books Division, P.O. Box 211, 1000 AE Amsterdam, Netherlands. TEL 31-20-4853911. FAX 31-20-4853705. E-mail: nlinfo-f@elsevier.nl; usinfo-f@elsevier.com; forinfo-kyf04035@niftyserve.or.jp; Site addr.: http://www.elsevier.nl/. (Subscr. in U.S. and Canada to: Elsevier Science Inc., Box 882, Madison Sq. Sta., New York, NY 10159-0882. TEL 212-989-5800. FAX 212-633-3680) **Document type:** monographic series.
Refereed Serial

618 GW ISSN 0012-026X
DEUTSCHE HEBAMMEN-ZEITSCHRIFT; Fachblatt fuer Hebammern und Entbindungspfleger. 1886. m. DM.63. (Bund Deutscher Hebammen) Elwin Staude Verlag GmbH, Fuchsrain 18A, 30657 Hannover, Germany. Ed. Dr. H. W. Vasterling. adv.; bk.rev.; charts; illus.; stat.; index. circ. 9,200.
—CCC.

618 UK ISSN 1351-8402
▼**THE DIPLOMATE.** 1994. q. £40($68) (effective 1996). (Royal College of Obstetricians and Gynaecologists) Parthenon Publishing Group, Casterton Hall, Carnforth, Lancs LA6 2LA, England. TEL 015242-72084. FAX 015242-71587. (In U.S.: Box 1564, Pearl River, NY 10965. TEL 914-735-936321) Ed. John Studd. (back issues avail.) **Document type:** academic/scholarly publication.
—BLDSC (3589.342000).

E N B NEWS. (English National Board for Nursing, Midwifery, and Health Visiting) see MEDICAL SCIENCES — Nurses And Nursing

MEDICAL SCIENCES — OBSTETRICS AND GYNECOLOGY

618.2   IE   ISSN 0378-3782
RG600   CODEN: EHDEDN
EARLY HUMAN DEVELOPMENT; an international journal concerned with the continuity of fetal and post natal life. 1977. 9/yr. I£435($687) (effective 1996). Elsevier Science Ireland Ltd., P.O. Box 85, Limerick, Ireland. TEL 353-61-471944. FAX 353-61-472144. (Subscr. in U.S. and Canada to: Elsevier Science Inc., Box 882, Madison Sq. Sta., New York, NY 10159. TEL 212-989-5800. FAX 212-633-3990) Ed. David R. Harvey. adv.; bk.rev. (also avail. in microform from UMI) **Indexed:** Abstr.Hyg., Bibl.Dev.Med.& Child Neur., Biol.Abstr., Chem.Abstr., CINAHL, Curr.Adv.Cell & Devel.Biol., Curr.Adv.Ecol.Sci., Curr.Cont., Dairy Sci.Abstr., Excerp.Med., Ind.Med., Ind.Sci.Rev., Nutr.Abstr., Psychol.Abstr. (1979-), Sci.Cit.Ind., Trop.Dis.Bull. **Document type:** academic/scholarly publication.
—BLDSC (3642.983000); CASDDS; Faxon; Genuine Article; SWETS; UnCover. **CCC.**
   Description: Publishes original research papers with particular emphasis on the continuum between fetal life and the perinatal period; aspects of postnatal growth influenced by early events; and the safeguarding of the quality of human survival.
Refereed Serial

618   UK   ISSN 1354-4195
▼**EARLY PREGNANCY BIOLOGY & MEDICINE**. 1995. q. £85($130) to individuals; institutions £150 ($225) (effective 1996). (Society for the Investigation of Early Pregnancy) Parthenon Publishing Group, Casterton Hall, Carnforth, Lancs. LA6 2LA, England. TEL 44-152-427-2084. FAX 44-152-427-1587. (U.S. subscr. to: Box 1564, Pearl River, NY 10965. TEL 914-735-9363) Ed. Dr. Eytan R. Barnea. adv. contact: Julia Tissington. (back issues avail.) **Document type:** academic/scholarly publication.
Refereed Serial

618   US
EMBARAZO/PREGNANCY. (Text in Spanish) 1990. s-a. Gruner & Jahr U.S.A. Publishing, 685 Third Ave., New York, NY 10017. TEL 212-878-8700. Ed. Elvia Delgado. circ. 200,000. **Document type:** consumer publication.
   Description: Provides information for expectant Hispanic mothers.

618.1   US   ISSN 0897-1870
ENDOMETRIOSIS ASSOCIATION NEWSLETTER. 1980. bi-m. $25. Endometriosis Association, Inc., 8585 N. 76th Pl., Milwaukee, WI 53223. TEL 414-355-2200. FAX 414-355-6065. Ed. Mary Lou Ballweg. bk.rev. circ. 10,000. (reprint service avail.) **Document type:** newsletter.
   Formerly: Endometriosis Association International Newsletter.
   Description: Discusses endometriosis, a disease affecting women primarily in their reproductive years.

EUROPEAN JOURNAL OF GYNECOLOGICAL ONCOLOGY. see MEDICAL SCIENCES — Oncology

618   IE   ISSN 0301-2115
      CODEN: EOGRAL
EUROPEAN JOURNAL OF OBSTETRICS & GYNECOLOGY AND REPRODUCTIVE BIOLOGY. (Supplement avail. (ISSN 0921-8750)) 1971. m. I£936($1479) (effective 1996). (European Association of Gynaecologists and Obstetricians) Elsevier Science Ireland Ltd., P.O. Box 85, Limerick, Ireland. TEL 353-61-471944. FAX 353-61-472144. (Subscr. in U.S. and Canada to: Elsevier Science Inc., Box 882, Madison Sq. Sta., New York, NY 10159. TEL 212-989-5800. FAX 212-633-3990) Ed. Dr. T.K.A.B. Eskes. adv.; bk.rev.; bibl.; charts. (also avail. in microform from UMI) **Indexed:** Biol.Abstr., Chem.Abstr., Curr.Adv.Cancer Res., Curr.Adv.Ecol.Sci., Curr.Cont., Dairy Sci.Abstr., Dent.Ind., Excerp.Med., Ind.Med., Ind.Sci.Rev., NRN, Nutr.Abstr., Rev.Med.& Vet.Mycol., Sci.Cit.Ind. **Document type:** academic/scholarly publication.
—BLDSC (3829.733000); CASDDS; EMDOCS; Faxon; Genuine Article; SWETS; UnCover. **CCC.**
   Formerly: European Journal of Obstetrics and Gynecology (ISSN 0028-2243)
   Description: Serves both the clinical practitioner and researcher by publishing studies, case reports and reviews of developments, as well as basic biochemical, physiological, embryological and genetic research related to human reproduction.
Refereed Serial

618   US   ISSN 0014-472X
EXPECTING. 1967. q. free. Gruner & Jahr U.S.A. Publishing, 685 Third Ave., New York, NY 10017. TEL 908-549-6344. FAX 908-548-1717. Ed. Maija Johnson. adv.; bk.rev.; illus.; circ. 1,300,000 (controlled). (also avail. in microform from UMI; reprint service avail. from UMI) **Document type:** consumer publication.

FAMILY PLANNING ASSOCIATION OF FIJI. NEWS. see BIRTH CONTROL

301.426   US   ISSN 0014-7354
HQ763   CODEN: FPGPA
FAMILY PLANNING PERSPECTIVES. 1969. bi-m. $32 to individuals; institutions $42; foreign $52 (effective 1994). Alan Guttmacher Institute, 120 Wall St., New York, NY 10005. TEL 212-248-1111. FAX 212-248-1951. Ed. Olivia Nordberg. adv.; bk.rev.; charts; illus.; index, cum.index: 1969-1988. circ. 10,000. (also avail. in microform from UMI,CIS; reprint service avail. from UMI) **Indexed:** Abstr.Anthropol., Adol.Ment.Hlth.Abstr., Biol.Abstr., Biol.Dig., C.I.N.L., Curr.Cont., Curr.Lit.Fam.Plan., Environ.Abstr., Excerp.Med., Human Resour.Abstr., IMFL, Ind.Med., Mid.East: Abstr.& Ind., Mult.Ed.Abstr., P.A.I.S., Popul.Ind., Psychol.Abstr., Risk Abstr., Sage Fam.Stud.Abstr., Soc.Work Res.& Abstr., SRI, SSCI, Stud.Wom.Abstr. **Document type:** academic/scholarly publication.
● Also available online. Vendor(s): University Microfilms International.
—BLDSC (3865.572000); CIS; Faxon; Genuine Article; SWETS; UMI; UnCover.
   Description: Focuses on the country's most pressing reproductive health issues, providing key findings from the institute's research and work of other distinguished social scientists.
Refereed Serial

618.2 649   US
FAMILY WAYS; education resources for pregnancy to parenthood. m. free to qualified individuals. 30 West Advertising (Subsidiary of: Wyeth-Ayerst), 130 Radnor-Chester Rd., St. Davids, PA 19087. TEL 610-902-2800; 800-234-WAYS. Ed.Bd.
   Description: Provides mothers and mothers-to-be advice on feeding baby and other parenthood issues.

618   JA   ISSN 0915-6852
FEMALE PATIENT.* (Text in Japanese) 1988. q. Churchill Livingstone Japan K.K., K.I.T. Bldg., 2-8-16 Yutenji, Meguro-ku, Tokyo 153, Japan.

618.1   US   ISSN 0888-2401
RG1   CODEN: FPPME5
FEMALE PATIENT: PRACTICAL OB-GYN MEDICINE; total health care for women. 1976. m. $100 to institutions outside the Americas; $79 to institutions in U.S (effective 1996). Excerpta Medica, Inc., Core Publishing Division (Subsidiary of: Reed Elsevier Medical group), 105 Raider Blvd., Belle Mead, NJ 08503. TEL 908-874-8550. FAX 908-874-0707. (Subscr. to: Box 3085, Princeton, NJ 08543-3085) illus. circ. 87,000. (also avail. in microform from UMI; reprint service avail. from UMI) **Indexed:** Curr.Lit.Fam.Plan., FAMLI.
—BLDSC (3905.168000); UMI. **CCC.**
   Supersedes in part (in 1981): Female Patient (ISSN 0364-1198)

618   BL
FEMINA. 1972. bi-m. Elea Cientia Editorial Ltda., Rua Barao de Uba 48, CEP 20260 Rio de Janiero RJ, Brazil. TEL 293-2112. Ed. J.C. Nahoum. circ. 8,000.

618 619   GW   ISSN 0179-1796
      CODEN: FSIKEJ
FERTILITAET, STERILITAET, IN-VITRO-FERTILISATION, SEXUALITAET, KONTRAZEPTION. 1985. 4/yr. DM.298($216) (effective 1996). Springer-Verlag, Heidelberger Platz 3, 14197 Berlin, Germany. TEL 030-2807-0. FAX 030-8214091. E-mail: orders@springer.de. (Subscr. in N. America to: Springer-Verlag New York, Inc., 44 Hartz Way, Secaucus, NJ 07096-2491. TEL 201-348-4033. FAX 201-348-4505) Eds. L. Mettler, H.W. Michelmann. (also avail. in microform from UMI; back issues avail.; reprint service avail. from ISI) **Indexed:** Biotech.Abstr. **Document type:** academic/scholarly publication.
—CASDDS; UMI. **CCC.**

618.178   US   ISSN 0015-0282
RC889   CODEN: FESTAS
FERTILITY AND STERILITY. 1949. m. $120 to individuals (foreign $165); institutions $175 (foreign $220). American Society for Reproductive Medicine, 1209 Montgomery Hwy., Birmingham, AL 35216-2809. TEL 205-978-5000. FAX 205-930-9905. (Co-sponsors: Pacific Coast Fertility Society, Canadian Fertility Society) Ed. Dr. Roger D. Kempers. adv.; bk.rev.; bibl.; charts; illus.; index, cum.index: vols.1-50. circ. 14,000. **Indexed:** Anim.Breed.Abstr., Biol.Abstr., C.C.I.Ob.Gyn., Chem.Abstr., Curr.Adv.Cancer Res., Curr.Adv.Cell & Devel.Biol., Curr.Adv.Ecol.Sci., Curr.Cont., Curr.Lit.Fam.Plan., Dairy Sci.Abstr., Dent.Ind., Excerp.Med., Helminthol.Abstr., I.P.A., Ind.Med., Ind.Sci.Rev., Ind.Vet., INIS Atomind., Med.& Surg.Dermat., Nutr.Abstr., Risk Abstr., Sci.Cit.Ind., Vet.Bull. **Document type:** academic/scholarly publication.
—BLDSC (3909.750000); CASDDS; Faxon; Genuine Article; SWETS; UnCover.
   Description: Includes ethical guidelines governing the new reproductive technologies; protocols for management and standards and guidelines for practice as determined by the ASRM Practice Committee.
Refereed Serial

618   UK   ISSN 0965-5395
      CODEN: FMMREI
FETAL AND MATERNAL MEDICINE REVIEW. 1989. q. £87($156) (effective 1996). Cambridge University Press, Edinburgh Bldg., Shaftesbury Rd., Cambridge CB2 2RU, England. TEL 01223-312393. FAX 01223-315052. TELEX 851817556. (N. American addr.: Cambridge University Press, Journals Dept., 40 W. 20th St. New York, NY 10011. TEL 212-924-3900. FAX 212-691-3239) Ed. William Dunlop. adv. (back issues avail.) **Indexed:** Excerp.Med. (1993-). **Document type:** academic/scholarly publication.
—BLDSC (3910.846000); UMI. **CCC.**
   Formerly (until 1993): Fetal Medicine Review (ISSN 0953-8267)
   Description: Aims to bring together all multidisciplinary interests and approaches appropriate to the advancement of knowledge and clinical practice in obstetrics.
Refereed Serial

618   SZ   ISSN 1015-3837
      CODEN: FDTHES
FETAL DIAGNOSIS AND THERAPY; clinical advances and basic research. 1986. bi-m. 312.60 SFr.($240.60) to individuals; institutions 521 SFr.($401) (effective 1996). (International Fetal Medicine and Surgery Society) S. Karger AG, Allschwilerstr. 10, P.O. Box, CH-4009 Basel, Switzerland. TEL 061-3061111. FAX 061-3061234. E-mail: Karger@Karger.ch. (U.S. and Canada subscr. to: S. Karger Publishers, Inc., 79 Fifth Ave., New York, NY, 10003, U.S.A.) Eds. M. Michejda, S. Uzan. circ. 800. (also avail. in microform from UMI) **Indexed:** Excerp.Med. **Document type:** academic/scholarly publication.
—BLDSC (3910.848000); Faxon; Genuine Article; SWETS; UnCover. **CCC.**
   Formerly: Fetal Therapy (ISSN 0257-2788)
Refereed Serial

FIRST YEAR OF LIFE; a guide to your baby's growth and development month by month. see CHILDREN AND YOUTH — About

618 376   US
FOCAL POINT.* 1972. bi-m. $10. National Association of Childbirth Education, 2931 Tennessee, Riverside, CA 92506. Ed. Gretchen Wetzel. adv.; bk.rev. circ. 350. (looseleaf format; back issues avail.)

618.4   SW
FOEDSEL & FOERAELDRASKAP. 1981. q. SEK 200 (effective 1995). Foereningen Foeda Hemma, c/o Whitaker, Fatburs Brunnsg. 20, S-118 28 Stockholm, Sweden. TEL 46-8-720-11-56. E-mail: fof@nytta.se. Eds. Anna Whitaker, Diane Sjoegren. adv.; bk.rev. circ. 3,600.
   Formerly (until 1994): Foeda Hemma (ISSN 0282-4272)

MEDICAL SCIENCES — OBSTETRICS AND GYNECOLOGY

618.1 GW ISSN 0016-0237
DER FRAUENARZT. 1951. 9/yr. DM.198. (Berufsverband der Frauenaerzte e.V.) Demeter Verlag GmbH und Co. KG, Bussardstr. 8, 82166 Graefelfing, Germany. TEL 089-85463-0. FAX 089-8543347. adv.; bk.rev.; bibl.; illus. circ. 5,300. **Document type:** academic/scholarly publication.
—SWETS.

A FRIEND INDEED; for women in the prime of life/pour les femmes dans la force de l'age. see WOMEN'S INTERESTS

618 GW ISSN 0016-5751
CODEN: GEFRA2
GEBURTSHILFE UND FRAUENHEILKUNDE; Ergebnisse der Forschung fuer die Praxis. (Text in German; summaries in English and German) 1940. m. DM.308. Georg Thieme Verlag, Ruedigerstr. 14, 70469 Stuttgart, Germany. TEL 0711-8931-0. FAX 0711-8931298. (Subscr. to: Postfach 104853, 70042 Stuttgart, Germany) Ed. K. Holzmann. adv.; bk.rev.; abstr.; bibl.; stat.; index. circ. 6,500. (reprint service avail. from UMI) **Indexed:** Biol.Abstr., Biotech.Abstr., Chem.Abstr., Curr.Adv.Cancer Res., Curr.Cont., Excerp.Med., Ind.Med., Ind.Sci.Rev., INIS Atomind., Sci.Cit.Ind. **Document type:** academic/scholarly publication.
—BLDSC (4095.650000); CASDDS; Faxon; Genuine Article; SWETS; UMI. **CCC.**

618 US ISSN 0744-0596
GENESIS (WASHINGTON). 1966. q. $30 to non-member institutions. American Society for Psychoprophylaxis in Obstetrics, Inc. (ASPO Lamaze), 1200 19th St., N.W., Washington, DC 20036. TEL 202-857-1128. FAX 202-223-4579. Ed. Robert Scaer. adv. contact: Megan Thompson. bk.rev. circ. 4,000. **Document type:** newsletter.
Former titles: A.S.P.O. Genesis; (until 1978): Conceptions; A.S.P.O. Newsletter.

GERIATRIC GYNECOLOGY. see GERONTOLOGY AND GERIATRICS

618 JA ISSN 0915-7557
GIFUKEN BOSEI EISEU GAKKAI ZASSHI/GIFU JOURNAL OF MATERNAL HEALTH. (Text in English, Japanese; summaries in Japanese) 1989. 3/yr. Gifuken Bosei Eiseu Gakkai - Gifu Society of Maternal Health, Gifu Daigaku Igakubu Sanfujinkagaku Kyoshitsu, 40, Tsukasa-cho, Gifu-shi, Gifu-ken 500, Japan.

618.1 SP ISSN 0211-6901
GINE DIPS; revista mensual hispano-americana de obstetricia y ginecologia. (Text mainly in Spanish; summaries in English and Spanish) 1970. m. 5000 ptas.($108) (effective 1995). (Facultad de Medicina de Barcelona, Departamento de Ostetricia y Ginecologia) Editorial Rocas, Muntaner 393, pral. 4, 08021 Barcelona, Spain. TEL 39-3-2001389. FAX 39-3-2021958. Dir. M. Carreras Roca. adv.; abstr.; bibl.; charts; illus.; stat. **Indexed:** Excerp.Med. (1995-), Ind.Med.Esp. **Document type:** trade publication.
—BLDSC (4176.280000).

618 IT ISSN 0392-2944
CODEN: GICLDY
GINECOLOGIA CLINICA. (Text in Italian; summaries in English) 1980. q. L.80000($90) (from Italy L.120000) (effective 1995). Studi Ostetrico Ginecologici s.r.l., Galleria Storione 2A, 35123 Padua, Italy. TEL 39-49-8758644. FAX 39-49-8752018. (Dist. by: La Garangola, Via Montona 4, 35137 Padua, Italy. FAX 39-49-8751743) Ed. A. Onnis. adv. (back issues avail.) **Indexed:** Biol.Abstr. **Document type:** academic/scholarly publication.
—BLDSC (4176.330000).
Refereed Serial

618 MX ISSN 0300-9041
CODEN: GOMEAY
GINECOLOGIA Y OBSTETRICIA DE MEXICO. 1946. m. Asociacion Mexicana de Ginecologia y Obstetricia, Ave. Amsterdam 214-PH2, Col. Hipodromo, Deleg. Cuauhtemoc, 06100 Mexico D.F., Mexico. TEL 5645463. **Indexed:** Excerp.Med. **Document type:** academic/scholarly publication.
—BLDSC (4176.400000); CASDDS.

618 SP
GINECOLOGIA Y OBSTETRICIA TEMAS ACTUALES. Spanish translation of: Clinics in Obstetrics and Gynecology. (Supplements: Clinicas Obstetricas y Ginecologicas) 1974. 4/yr. 17384 ptas.($128) (effective 1990). Interamericana de Espana, S.A., Division de Ciencias de la Salud de McGraw-Hill, Calle Manuel Ferrero, 13, 28036 Madrid, Spain. TEL 315-0340. FAX 733-6627. charts; illus.; index. **Indexed:** Excerp.Med.

618.1 IT ISSN 0391-8920
GINECORAMA. 10/yr. L.25000($25) C I C Edizioni Internazionali s.r.l., Via L. Spallanzani 11, 00161 Rome, Italy. TEL 06-8412673. FAX 06-44242033. TELEX 622099 CIC.

618.1 PL ISSN 0017-0011
CODEN: GIPOA3
GINEKOLOGIA POLSKA.* (Text in Polish; summaries in English, Russian) 1922. m. $180. Polskie Towarzystwo Ginekologiczne - Polish Society of Gynaecology, Ul. Czerniakowska 231, 01-416 Warsaw, Poland. (Subscr. to: RSW Prasa-Ksiazka-Ruch, Centrala Kolportazu Prasy i Wydawnictw, ul. Towarowa 28, 00-958 Warsaw, Poland) Ed. Z. Slomko. adv.; bk.rev.; abstr.; bibl.; charts; illus.; index; cum.index. circ. 2,600. **Indexed:** Biol.Abstr., Chem.Abstr., Curr.Adv.Ecol.Sci., Dok.Arbeitsmed., Excerp.Med., Ind.Med., INIS Atomind.
—BLDSC (4176.500000); CASDDS.

618 IT ISSN 0391-9013
GIORNALE ITALIANO DI OSTETRICIA E GINECOLOGIA. (Text in Italian; summaries in English) m. L.90000($90) C I C Edizioni Internazionali s.r.l., Via L. Spallanzani 11, 00161 Rome, Italy. TEL 06-8412673. FAX 06-44242033. TELEX 622099 CIC. **Indexed:** Excerp.Med.
—BLDSC (4178.237000). **CCC.**

GREAT BRITAIN. GOVERNMENT STATISTICAL SERVICE. ABORTION STATISTICS. see BIRTH CONTROL — *Abstracting, Bibliographies, Statistics*

618 301.412 CN ISSN 0823-9266
GREAT EXPECTATIONS. 1972. q. Can.$12($18) Professional Publishing Associates, 269 Richmond St. W., Toronto, ON M5V 1X1, Canada. TEL 416-596-8680. FAX 416-596-1991. Ed. Fran Fearnley. adv.; bk.rev. circ. 150,000. **Document type:** consumer publication.

618 US
GUIDE FOR EXPECTANT PARENTS. 1979. s-a. free. Educational Programs, Inc., 8003 Old York Rd., Elkins Park, PA 19117-1410. TEL 215-635-1700. FAX 215-635-6455. Ed. Deana C. Jamroz. adv. circ. 850,000. (back issues avail.)
Description: For pregnant women in prenatal education classes.

618 US
GUIDELINES FOR PERINATAL CARE. 1983. irreg., 3rd ed., 1992. $39.95. American Academy of Pediatrics, 141 Northwest Point Blvd., Box 927, Elk Grove Village, IL 60009-0927. TEL 708-228-5005; 800-433-9016. FAX 708-228-1281. (Co-sponsor: American College of Obstetricians and Gynecologists) **Document type:** monographic series.
Description: Guidelines for care of pregnant women, fetuses, and neonates including discussion of preconceptional and antenatal screening, adoption, perinatal infections, and fetal monitoring.

618 CC
GUOWAI YIXUE (FUCHAN KEXUE FENCE)/FOREIGN MEDICAL SCIENCES (GYNECOLOGY & OBSTETRICS). (Text in Chinese) Tianjin Yixue Keji Qingbao Yanjiusuo - Tianjin Institute of Medical Science Information, 131, Chengdu Dao, Heping-qu, Tianjin 300050, People's Republic of China. TEL 302570. Ed. Yu Aifeng.

618 FR ISSN 0240-172X
GYN OBS - LA MEDECINE ET LA FEMME. 21/yr. 600 F. (foreign 800 F.). 55 rue des Petits-Champs, 75001 Paris, France. TEL 42-96-97-25. Ed. Christian Rayr. circ. 10,000.

618 CI ISSN 1330-0091
GYNAECOLOGIA ET PERINATOLOGIA. (Text in Serbo-Croatian; summaries in English) 1960. bi-m. $30. Udruzenje Ginekologa-Opstetricara Jugoslavije, Petrova 13, 41000 Zagreb, Croatia. TEL 041-444-279. Ed. Dr. Zdravko Pavlic. adv.; bk.rev.; bibl.; charts; illus.; index. circ. 1,700. **Indexed:** Biol.Abstr., Dent.Ind., Excerp.Med., Ind.Med. **Document type:** academic/scholarly publication.
—BLDSC (4233.505000).
Former titles (until 1992): Jugoslavenska Ginekologija i Perinatologija (ISSN 0352-5562); (until 1985): Jugoslavenska Ginekologija i Opsteltricija (ISSN 0017-002X); Ginekologija i Opstetricija.

618 UK ISSN 0962-1091
CODEN: GYNEEB
GYNAECOLOGICAL ENDOSCOPY. 1992. q. £169 (outside Europe £187/$298) (effective 1996). (Brtish Society for Gynaecological Endoscopy) Blackwell Science Ltd., Osney Mead, Oxford OX2 OEL, England. TEL 01865-240201. FAX 01865-721205. TELEX 83355 MEDBOK G. Ed. R. Garry. adv.; bk.rev.; abstr.; bibl.; illus.; index. circ. 1,250. (also avail. in microform from UMI; back issues avail.) **Indexed:** Excerp.Med. (1993-). **Document type:** academic/scholarly publication.
—BLDSC (4233.510000); ADONIS; UMI. **CCC.**
Refereed Serial

618.1 GW ISSN 0017-5994
CODEN: GYNKAP
DER GYNAEKOLOGE. (Text in German) 1968. 6/yr. DM.358($260) (effective 1996). Springer-Verlag, Heidelberger Platz 3, 14197 Berlin, Germany. TEL 030-8207-0. FAX 030-8214091. E-mail: orders@springer.de. (Subscr. in N. America to: Springer-Verlag New York, Inc., 44 Hartz Way, Secaucus, NJ 07096-2491. TEL 201-348-4033. FAX 201-348-4505) Ed.Bd. adv. (also avail. in microform from UMI; back issues avail.; reprint service avail. from ISI) **Indexed:** Biol.Abstr., Curr.Adv.Ecol.Sci., Curr.Cont., Excerp.Med., Ind.Med., INIS Atomind. **Document type:** academic/scholarly publication.
—BLDSC (4233.550000); Faxon; Genuine Article; SWETS; UMI. **CCC.**

618.1 SZ ISSN 1018-8843
CODEN: GGRUEL
GYNAEKOLOGISCH - GEBURTSHILFLICHE RUNDSCHAU. (Supplements avail.) (Text in English, French and German) 1964. q. 221.40 SFr.($170.40) to individuals; institutions 369 SFr.($284) (effective 1996). (Oesterreichische Gesellschaft fuer Gynaekologie und Geburtshilfe) S. Karger AG, Allschwilerstr. 10, P.O. Box, CH-4009 Basel, Switzerland. TEL 061-3061111. FAX 061-3061234. E-mail: Karger@Karger.ch. Ed.Bd. adv.; illus. circ. 1,500. (reprint service avail. from ISI; back issues avail.) **Indexed:** Biol.Abstr., Ind.Med. **Document type:** academic/scholarly publication.
—BLDSC (4233.565000); Faxon; Genuine Article. **CCC.**
Formerly: Gynaekologische Rundschau (ISSN 0017-6001)
Refereed Serial

618 GW ISSN 0341-8677
GYNAEKOLOGISCHE PRAXIS. 4/yr. DM.280. Hans Marseille Verlag GmbH, Buerkleinstr. 12, 80538 Munich, Germany. TEL 089-227988. FAX 089-2904643. Ed. W. Siebert. **Document type:** academic/scholarly publication.
—BLDSC (4233.570000); SWETS. **CCC.**

MEDICAL SCIENCES — OBSTETRICS AND GYNECOLOGY

618   SZ   ISSN 0378-7346
CODEN: GOBIDS
GYNECOLOGIC AND OBSTETRIC INVESTIGATION. (Text in English) 1895. 8/yr. (2 vols./yr.). 568.80 SFr.($438) to individuals; institutions 948 SFr.($730) (effective 1996). S. Karger AG, Allschwilerstr. 10, P.O. Box, CH-4009 Basel, Switzerland. TEL 061-3061111. FAX 061-3061234. E-mail: Karger@Karger.ch. Ed. G. Zador. adv.; bibl.; illus.; index. circ. 950. (also avail. in microform; back issues avail.) **Indexed:** Anim.Breed.Abstr., Biol.Abstr., Chem.Abstr., Curr.Adv.Ecol.Sci., Curr.Cont., Dairy Sci.Abstr., Excerp.Med., Ind.Med., Ind.Sci.Rev., NRN, Sci.Cit.Ind. **Document type:** academic/scholarly publication.
—BLDSC (4233.650000); CASDDS; Faxon; Genuine Article; SWETS; UnCover. **CCC.**
  Former titles: Gynecologic Investigation (ISSN 0017-5986); Gynaecologia.
Refereed Serial

618.1   NE   ISSN 0922-5064
GYNECOLOGIC ENDOSCOPY. (Text in English) 1988. irreg., vol.2, 1990. price varies. Elsevier Science B.V., Books Division, P.O. Box 211, 1000 AE Amsterdam, Netherlands. TEL 31-20-4853911. FAX 31-20-4853705. TELEX 18582 ESPA NL. E-mail: nlinfo-f@elsevier.nl; usinfo-f@elsevier.com; forinfo-kyf04035@niftyserve.or.jp; Site addr.: http://www.elsevier.nl./. (Subscr. in U.S. and Canada to: Elsevier Science Inc., Box 882, Madison Sq. Sta., New York, NY 10159. TEL 212-989-5800) (back issues avail.) **Document type:** monographic series.
Refereed Serial

618 617   US
GYNECOLOGIC LASER AND ADVANCED TECHNOLOGY SOCIETY. MEMBERSHIP NEWSLETTER. 1993. s-a. $95 membership (effective 1995). Gynecologic Laser & Advanced Technology Society, 6900 Grove Rd., Thorofare, NJ 08086. TEL 609-848-1000. FAX 609-848-5274. Ed. Dr. Dan C. Martin. bk.rev. circ. 1,000. (back issues avail.) **Document type:** newsletter.
  Description: Reports and analyzes developments in surgical procedures, complications, instruments and other trends of interest.

618.1   US   ISSN 0090-8258
RC280.G5   CODEN: GYNOA3
GYNECOLOGIC ONCOLOGY; an international journal. 1972. m. $926 (foreign $1088) (effective 1996). Academic Press, Inc., Journal Division, 525 B St., Ste. 1900, San Diego, CA 92101-4495. TEL 619-230-1840. FAX 619-699-6800. (Subscr. to: Box 620000, Orlando, FL 32891-8340. TEL 800-543-9534) Ed. David Gershenson. adv.; index. (back issues avail.) **Indexed:** Apic.Abstr., Biol.Abstr., Chem.Abstr., Curr.Adv.Ecol.Sci., Curr.Cont., Excerp.Med., Ind.Med., Ind.Sci.Rev., INIS Atomind., NRN, Sci.Cit.Ind. **Document type:** academic/scholarly publication.
—BLDSC (4233.710000); CASDDS; EMDOCS; Faxon; Genuine Article; SWETS; UnCover. **CCC.**
  Description: Serves as an archive devoted to the publication of clinical and investigative articles that concern tumors of the female reproductive tract.
Refereed Serial

GYNECOLOGICAL ENDOCRINOLOGY. see *MEDICAL SCIENCES — Endocrinology*

618   FR   ISSN 1167-2420
GYNECOLOGIE INTERNATIONALE; recherche et clinique en gynecologie obstetrique. 1992. 10/yr. 300 F. Presence et Communication Medicales, 11 rue de Rome, 75008 Paris, France. TEL 44-70-75-00. FAX 44-70-75-09. Ed. Dr. Jacques Halimi. adv. contact: Francine Fleury. circ. 8,000. **Document type:** academic/scholarly publication.
—BLDSC (4233.760000); UMI.
Refereed Serial

618   FR
GYNECOLOGIE PRATIQUE. 1988. m. (10/yr.). 200 F. L.E.N. Medical, 48 bis, av. Kleber, 75016 Paris, France. TEL 47-55-06-06. FAX 47-55-69-41. TELEX 640 748. Ed. Dr. D. Zarca. circ. 7,800.
  Formerly: Gynecologie Obstetrique Pratique (ISSN 0988-6990)

618.1   FR   ISSN 1250-3347
CODEN: GRGYE
GYNECOLOGIE - REVUE MASSON DU GYNECOLOGUE. (Text in French; summaries in English) 1950. 8/yr. 750 F. (foreign 927 F.) (effective 1996). (Societe Francaise de Gynecologie) Masson - Periodiques, Villa Laromiguiere, 75005 Paris, France. TEL 1-40-46-62-00. FAX 1-40-46-62-01. (Co-sponsor: Federation Internationale de Gynecologie et du Partheriologie) Ed. Hoang-Mgnoc Minh. adv.; bk.rev.; abstr.; bibl.; charts; illus.; stat.; index. circ. 6,000. (reprint service avail. from ISI) **Indexed:** Biol.Abstr., Excerp.Med., Ind.Med. **Document type:** academic/scholarly publication.
—BLDSC (4233.785000); UMI. **CCC.**
  Formed by the 1993 merger of: Revue du Gynecologue Obstetricien (ISSN 1141-5886) & Gynecologie (ISSN 0301-2204); Which was formerly: Gynecologie Pratique (ISSN 0017-6028)
  Description: Publishes original papers, general reviews, and round tables.

618.1 301.5   US   ISSN 0892-628X
H E R S NEWSLETTER. 1982. q. $20. (Hysterectomy Educational Resources & Services) H E R S Foundation, 422 Bryn Mawr Ave., Bala Cynwyd, PA 19004. TEL 610-667-7757. FAX 610-667-8096. Ed. Nora W. Coffey. bk.rev.; abstr.; stat.; cum.index. circ. 15,000. (back issues avail.) **Document type:** academic/scholarly publication, newsletter.
  Description: Medical and scientific reviews discussing alternatives and consequences of hysterectomies.

HEALTH CARE FOR WOMEN, INTERNATIONAL. see *WOMEN'S HEALTH*

HEALTH LAW LITIGATION REPORTER; the monthly national journal of record reporting general medical malpractice, obstetrical and gynecological litigation. see *LAW — Civil Law*

618.202   GW   ISSN 0932-8122
DIE HEBAMME; Fortbildungszeitschrift fuer Hebammen und Entbindungspfleger. 1988. q. DM.62. Ferdinand Enke Verlag, Postfach 300366, 70443 Stuttgart, Germany. TEL 0711-135798-0. FAX 0711-135798-30. TELEX 07252275-GTV-D. Eds. G. Martius, J.W. Dudenhausen. (reprint service avail. from IRC) **Document type:** academic/scholarly publication.

618   JA   ISSN 0367-6277
HOKKAIDO SANKA FUJINKA GAKKAI KAISHI/HOKKAIDO OBSTETRICAL AND GYNECOLOGICAL SOCIETY. JOURNAL. (Text in Japanese) 1950. a. 8000 Yen. Nihon Sanfujinka Gakkai, Hokkaido Chiho Bukai - Japan Society of Obstetrics and Gynecology, Hokkaido Branch, c/o Hokkaido Daigaku Igakubu Sanfujinka Kyoshitsu, Nishi 7-chome, Kita 15-jo, Kita-ku, Sapporo-shi, Hokkaido 060, Japan. TEL 011-716-1161. FAX 011-707-5767. Ed. Hiroshi Satoh. circ. 650. **Document type:** academic/scholarly publication.

618 616.4   JA   ISSN 1340-220X
HORMONE FRONTIER IN GYNECOLOGY. (Text in Japanese) 1993. 2/yr. 2060 Yen per no. Medikaru Rebyusha - Medical Review Co., Ltd., 7-3, Hiranomachi 1-chome, Chuo-ku, Osaka 541, Japan.

618   UK
HUMAN CONCERN NEWSPAPER. 1968. q. membership. Society for the Protection of Unborn Children, 7 Tufton St., Westminster, London SW1P 3QN, England. TEL 071-222-5845. FAX 071-222-0630. Ed. Phyllis Bowman. adv.; bk.rev.; stat. circ. 65,000. (tabloid format) **Document type:** newspaper.
  Formerly: Society for the Protection of Unborn Children. Bulletin.

HUMAN DEVELOPMENT. see *PSYCHOLOGY*

618 616.4   UK   ISSN 0268-1161
CODEN: HUREEE
HUMAN REPRODUCTION. 1986. m. £400($750) (effective 1996). (European Society of Human Reproduction and Embryology, EI) Oxford University Press, Oxford Journals, Walton St., Oxford OX2 6DP, England. TEL 01865-267907. FAX 01865-267773. TELEX 837330-OXPRES-G. E-mail: jnlorders@oup.co.uk. (U.S. subscr. to: Oxford University Press Inc., 2001 Evans Rd., Cary, NC 27513. TEL 919-677-0977. FAX 919-677-1714) Ed. R.G. Edwards. adv.; bk.rev.; illus.; index. circ. 1,950. (back issues avail.; reprint service avail. from SWZ) **Indexed:** Bibl.Repro., Biol.Abstr., Chem.Abstr., Curr.Adv.Ecol.Sci., Curr.Cont., Excerp.Med., Ind.Med., Sci.Cit.Ind. **Document type:** academic/scholarly publication.
—BLDSC (4336.431000); CASDDS; Faxon; Genuine Article; SWETS; UMI; UnCover. **CCC.**
  Description: For scientists and clinicians working in international human reproduction research and practice.

HYPERTENSION IN PREGNANCY. see *MEDICAL SCIENCES — Cardiovascular Diseases*

618   US   ISSN 1064-7449
CODEN: IDOGEX
INFECTIOUS DISEASES IN OBSTETRICS AND GYNECOLOGY. 1993. bi-m. $95 (foreign $188) (effective 1996). John Wiley & Sons, Inc., Journals, 605 Third Ave., New York, NY 10158. TEL 212-850-6645. FAX 212-850-6021. TELEX 12-7063. E-mail: SUBINFO@JWILEY.COM. (Subscr. outside the Americas to: John Wiley & Sons Ltd., Baffins Ln., Chichester, W. Sussex PO19 1UD, England. TEL 44-1243-779777. FAX 44-1243-776128) Ed. Dr. Sebastian Faro. adv. contact: Roberta Frederick. (also avail. in microform from UMI; back issues avail.) **Document type:** academic/scholarly publication.
—BLDSC (4478.729100).
Refereed Serial

618   US   ISSN 0160-7626
RC889   CODEN: INFEDH
INFERTILITY; an interdisciplinary journal devoted to the rapid communication of clinical aspects of human infertility. 1978. q. $65 to individuals; institutions $147 (foreign $157). c/o Dr. Louis A. Mucelli, Ed., 614 2nd Ave., Ste. H, New York, NY 10016. TEL 212-684-4242. FAX 212-684-4290. adv.; charts; illus.; index. (back issues avail.) reprint service avail. from UMI) **Indexed:** Biol.Abstr., Chem.Abstr., Curr.Adv.Ecol.Sci., Curr.Cont., Excerp.Med., I.P.A. **Document type:** academic/scholarly publication.
•Also available online.
—CASDDS; Faxon; SWETS; UMI; UnCover. **CCC.**
  Description: Female infertility, andrology, endocrinology, genetics, extra-corporeal fertilization and other aspects of human fertility.
Refereed Serial

618   US   ISSN 1047-9422
RG133.5   CODEN: IRMCF8
INFERTILITY AND REPRODUCTIVE MEDICINE CLINICS OF NORTH AMERICA. 1990. q. $113 (foreign $147) (effective 1996). W.B. Saunders Co. (Subsidiary of: Harcourt Brace & Company), The Curtis Center, 3rd Fl., Independence Sq. W., Philadelphia, PA 19106-3399. TEL 215-238-7800. FAX 215-238-6445. (Subscr. to: Periodicals Fulfillment, W.B. Saunders Co., 6277 Sea Harbor Dr., 4th Fl., Orlando, FL 32891-4800. TEL 800-654-2452. FAX 800-874-6418) Ed. Naina Chohan. index. (also avail. in microform from UMI; back issues avail.) **Indexed:** Excerp.Med. (1995-). **Document type:** academic/scholarly publication.
—BLDSC (4478.791000); UMI.
  Description: Each issue approaches a specific topic in the field.

610.73   UK   ISSN 0074-2880
INTERNATIONAL CONFEDERATION OF MIDWIVES. CONGRESS REPORTS. triennial, 23rd, Vancouver, 1993. £25. International Confederation of Midwives - Confederation Internationale des Sages-femmes, c/o Joan Walker, Gen.-Gen., 10 Barley Mow Passage, Chiswick, London W4 4PH, England. TEL 0181-994-6477. FAX 0181-995-1332. **Document type:** proceedings.

MEDICAL SCIENCES — OBSTETRICS AND GYNECOLOGY

618 UK
INTERNATIONAL CONFEDERATION OF MIDWIVES. NEWSLETTER. q. £12. International Confederation of Midwives, c/o Joan Walker, Sec.-Gen., 10 Barley Mow Passage, Chiswick, London W4 4PH, England. TEL 0181-994-6477. FAX 0181-995-1332. **Document type:** newsletter.

618 UK
INTERNATIONAL CONFEDERATION OF MIDWIVES. POSITION STATEMENTS. 1990. 3/yr. £0.50 per no. International Confederation of Midwives, c/o Joan Walker, Sec.-Gen., 10 Barley Mow Passage, Chiswick, London W4 4PH, England. TEL 0181-994-6477. FAX 0181-995-1332. **Document type:** monographic series.

618.202 UK
INTERNATIONAL CONFEDERATION OF MIDWIVES. TRIENNIAL REPORT. 1993. £2. International Confederation of Midwives, c/o Joan Walker, Sec.-Treas., 10 Barley Mow Passage, Chiswick, London W4 4PH, England. TEL 0181-994-6477. FAX 0181-995-1332.

618 US ISSN 0443-9058
INTERNATIONAL CORRESPONDENCE SOCIETY OF OBSTETRICS AND GYNECOLOGY. COLLECTED LETTERS. 1959-19?? m. $97 (foreign $125). (International Correspondence Society of Obstetrics and Gynecology) Laux Company, Inc., 63 Great Rd., Maynard, MA 01754. TEL 617-897-5552. FAX 508-897-6824. Ed. Dr. Richard E. Hunter. circ. 1,465. (looseleaf format; back issues avail.) —CCC.
Formerly: Ob-Gyn Collected Letters (ISSN 0472-397X)

301.426 US ISSN 0190-3187
HQ763
INTERNATIONAL FAMILY PLANNING PERSPECTIVES. French edition: Perspectives Internationales sur le Planning Familial. Spanish edition: Perspectivas Internacionales en Planificacion Familiar (ISSN 0190-3195) 1975. q. $30 to individuals; institutions $40; foreign $46 (effective 1995). Alan Guttmacher Institute, 120 Wall St., New York, NY 10005. TEL 212-248-1111. FAX 212-248-1951. Ed. Olivia Nordberg. charts; illus.; stat. circ. 20,000. (also avail. in microfilm from UMI; reprint service avail. from UMI) **Indexed:** Abstr.Hyg., Abstr.Rural Dev.Trop., Curr.Lit.Fam.Plan., Excerp.Med., Mult.Ed.Abstr., P.A.I.S., Popul.Ind., SRI, Stud.Wom.Abstr., Trop.Dis.Bull. **Document type:** academic/scholarly publication.
—BLDSC (4540.150000); UMI; UnCover.
Former titles (until vol.4, no.4, 1978): International Family Planning Perspectives and Digest (ISSN 0162-2749); (until vol.3, no.4, 1977): International Family Planning Digest.
Description: Highlights population research and program achievements of prime interest to those concerned with the growing family planning challenges faced by developing countries.
Refereed Serial

618 US ISSN 0887-8625
INTERNATIONAL JOURNAL OF CHILDBIRTH EDUCATION. 1961. q. $25. International Childbirth Education Association, Box 20048, Minneapolis, MN 55420-0048. TEL 612-854-8660. FAX 612-854-8772. Ed. Trudy Keller. adv. contact: Doris Olson. bk.rev.; bibl. circ. 12,000. **Indexed:** CINAHL, Curr.Lit.Fam.Plan. **Document type:** consumer publication.
—BLDSC (4542.165400).
Formerly (until 1986): I C E A News (ISSN 0445-0485)
Description: Covers maternity and infant care.
Refereed Serial

618 IE ISSN 0020-7292
RG1 CODEN: IJGOAL
INTERNATIONAL JOURNAL OF GYNAECOLOGY AND OBSTETRICS. (Text in English) 1963. m. I£584($923) (effective 1996). (International Federation of Gynaecology and Obstetrics) Elsevier Science Ireland Ltd., P.O. Box 85, Limerick, Ireland. TEL 353-61-471944. FAX 353-61-472144. (Subscr. in U.S. and Canada to: Elsevier Science Inc., Box 882, Madison Sq. Sta., New York, NY 10159. TEL 212-989-5800) (Co-sponsor: Family Health International) Ed. J.J. Sciarra. adv.; bibl.; illus.; index. circ. 4,000. (also avail. in microform from UMI) **Indexed:** Biol.Abstr., Chem.Abstr., Curr.Adv.Ecol.Sci., Curr.Cont., Curr.Lit.Fam.Plan., Dent.Ind., Excerp.Med., Ind.Med., Ind.Sci.Rev., INIS Atomind., NRN, Sci.Cit.Ind. **Document type:** academic/scholarly publication.
—BLDSC (4542.273000); CASDDS; EMDOCS; Faxon; Genuine Article; SWETS; UnCover. **CCC.**
Supersedes: International Federation of Gynaecology and Obstetrics. Journal (ISSN 0020-6695)
Description: Publishes articles on all aspects of basic and clinical research in the fields of obstetrics and gynecology and related subjects, with emphasis on matters of worldwide interest.
Refereed Serial

618 616.99 US ISSN 1048-891X
CODEN: IJGCEN
INTERNATIONAL JOURNAL OF GYNECOLOGICAL CANCER. 1991. bi-m. $295 (foreign $345) (effective 1996). (International Gynecological Cancer Society) Blackwell Science Inc., 238 Main St., Cambridge, MA 02142-1413. TEL 617-876-7022. FAX 617-492-5263. Ed. Harold Fox. **Indexed:** Excerp.Med. (1993-). **Document type:** academic/scholarly publication.
—BLDSC (4542.273500); Genuine Article; SWETS; UMI. **CCC.**
Description: Interdisciplinary journal covering gynecology, oncology, radiation therapy and pathology.

618.1 US ISSN 0277-1691
INTERNATIONAL JOURNAL OF GYNECOLOGICAL PATHOLOGY. 1982. q. $186 to individuals (foreign $238); institutions $273 (foreign $335) (effective 1996); newsstand price: $85. (International Society of Gynecological Pathologists) Lippincott - Raven Press, 227 E. Washington Sq., Philadelphia, PA 19106. TEL 215-238-4200. Ed. Dr. Philip B. Clement. adv. contact: Phyllis Noyes. index. circ. 1,500. (reprint service avail. from UMI) **Indexed:** Curr.Adv.Cancer Res., Excerp.Med., Ind.Med., Ind.Sci.Rev., Sci.Cit.Ind. **Document type:** academic/scholarly publication.
—BLDSC (4542.274000); Faxon; Genuine Article; SWETS; UMI; UnCover. **CCC.**
Description: Reports on advances in the understanding and management of gynecological disease.
Refereed Serial

618 UK ISSN 0959-289X
CODEN: IOANER
INTERNATIONAL JOURNAL OF OBSTETRIC ANESTHESIA. q. £67($107) to individuals; institutions £103 ($165) (effective 1995). Churchill Livingstone Journals (Subsidiary of: Pearson Professional), Robert Stevenson House, 1-3 Baxter's Pl., Leith Walk, Edinburgh EH1 3AF, Scotland. TEL 0131-556-2424. FAX 0131-459-1177. (Subscr. to: Pearson Professional Ltd., P.O. Box 77, Fourth Ave., Harlow, Essex CM19 5AA, England. TEL 01279-623760; U.S. subscr. to: Churchill Livingstone, 650 Ave. of the Americas, New York, NY 10011. TEL 212-206-5000) Eds. F. Reynolds, S.C. Hughes. adv. contact: David Dunnachie. circ. 625. **Indexed:** Excerp.Med. (1993-). **Document type:** academic/scholarly publication.
—BLDSC (4542.410500). **CCC.**
Description: Presents research papers on obstetric anaesthesia, analgesia and related topics.
Refereed Serial

618 GW ISSN 0943-5417
INTERNATIONAL JOURNAL OF PRENATAL AND PERINATAL PSYCHOLOGY AND MEDICINE. (Text in English) 1989. 4/yr. DM.120 to individuals; institutions £160. Mattes Verlag GmbH, Postfach 103866, 69028 Heidelberg, Germany. TEL 06221-459321. FAX 06221-459322. Eds. P. Fedor-Freybergh, L. Janus; Pub. Kurt Mattes. adv.; bk.rev. **Document type:** academic/scholarly publication.
—BLDSC (4542.481800).
Formerly (until 1993): International Journal of Prenatal and Perinatal Studies (ISSN 0954-8629)

618 616.6 UK ISSN 0937-3462
CODEN: IUJOEF
INTERNATIONAL UROGYNECOLOGY JOURNAL. 1990. 6/yr. £190($305) (effective 1996). Springer-Verlag, Springer House, 8 Alexandra Rd., London SW19 7JZ, England. TEL 081-944-2942. FAX 081-947-4651. (U.S. subscr. to: Springer-Verlag New York, Inc., Box 2485, Secaucus, NJ 07096-2491. TEL 201-348-4033) Ed. O.C. Ortiz. (also avail. in microform from UMI; back issues avail.) **Indexed:** Excerp.Med. (1993-). **Document type:** academic/scholarly publication.
—BLDSC (4551.567800).
Description: Emphasizes a clinical approach to urogynecological topics of interest to urologists, gynaecologists, nurses and basic scientists.
Refereed Serial

618 IS ISSN 0792-4569
ISRAEL JOURNAL OF OBSTETRICS & GYNECOLOGY. (Text in English) 1990. q. $80. (Israel Society of Obstetrics & Gynecology) Menachem Horowitz Publishing, 22 Shlomzion Hamalca St., Tel Aviv 62276, Israel. TEL 972-3-448676. FAX 972-3-449422. Ed. Dr. M. Lancet. adv.; bk.rev. circ. 2,000. (back issues avail.) **Document type:** academic/scholarly publication.
Refereed Serial

618 IT ISSN 1121-8339
ITALIAN JOURNAL OF GYNAECOLOGY & OBSTETRICS. 1989. q. Societa Italiana di Ginecologia e Ostetricia, Via dei Soldati 25, 00186 Rome, Italy.
—BLDSC (4588.340430).

618 360 JA
J A O G NEWS. (Text in Japanese) 1949. m. 10000 Yen. Japan Association of Obstetricians & Gynecologists - Japan Association for Maternal Welfare, 1-2, Ichigaya Sadohara-cho, Shinjuku-ku, Tokyo 162, Japan. TEL 03-3269-4739. FAX 03-3269-4730. Ed. Kawakami Seiji; Pub. Sakamoto Shoichi. circ. 14,800. **Document type:** newsletter.
Former titles (until May 1995): Nihon Bosei Hogo Sanfujinka Ikai; (until Mar. 1994): Nichibo Iho (ISSN 0288-8270)

J O G N N. (Journal of Obstetric, Gynecologic and Neonatal Nursing) see MEDICAL SCIENCES — Nurses And Nursing

618 GW ISSN 0941-5246
JAHRBUCH DER GYNAEKOLOGIE UND GEBURTSHILFE. (Text in German; summaries in English, German) 1991. a. DM.126.40. Biermann Verlag GmbH, Nideggenerstr. 18, 53909 Zuelpich, Germany. TEL 02252-9410-0. FAX 02252-941015. Ed. W. Schmidt. (back issues avail.) **Document type:** academic/scholarly publication.

618.202 JM
JAMAICA MIDWIVES ASSOCIATION. NEWSLETTER. bi-m. membership. Jamaica Midwives Association, c/o Victoria Jubilee Hospital, Kingston, Jamaica, W.I.

618 GW ISSN 0177-9109
JATROS GYNAEKOLOGIE. 1985. 12/yr. DM.90. P M I Verlagsgruppe GmbH, August-Schanz-Str. 21, 60433 Frankfurt a.M., Germany. TEL 069-5480000. FAX 069-54800077. Ed. Peter Hoffman. circ. 7,850. (back issues avail.) **Document type:** academic/scholarly publication.
Description: Seminar paper journal with summaries of original articles, interviews and Congress reports.

MEDICAL SCIENCES — OBSTETRICS AND GYNECOLOGY

618   TU   ISSN 1016-5126
CODEN: JODEE
JINEKOLOJI VE OBSTETRIK DERGISI. 1987. q. Logos Yayincilik Ticaret A.S., Yildiz Posta Cad., Sinan Apt. No.36 D 66-67, Gayrettepe 80280 - Istanbul, Turkey. TEL 90-212-2880541. Ed. Dr. Turgay Atasu. adv. contact: Ipek Karisman. **Indexed:** Excerp.Med. (1994-).

618.2   SW   ISSN 0021-7468
JORDEMODERN/MIDWIFE. 1888. m. SEK 230. Svenska Barnmorskefoerbundet - Swedish Association of Midwives, Ostermalmsg. 19, 114 26 Stockholm, Sweden. TEL 46-8-10-70-88. FAX 46-8-29-49-46. Ed. Anita Karlsson. adv.; bk.rev.; illus. circ. 6,700. **Indexed:** Int.Nurs.Ind.
—BLDSC (4673.940000).

618.1   BL   ISSN 0368-1416
CODEN: JBGCA8
JORNAL BRASILEIRO DE GINECOLOGIA. (Text and summaries in English and Portuguese) 1935. m. $180. (Universidade Federal do Rio de Janeiro, Centro de Estudos da Maternidade) Cidade - Editora Cientifica Ltda., Rua Mexico 90, 2 and., 20031 Rio de Janeiro, RJ, Brazil. Ed. Fernando Moyses. adv.; bk.rev.; bibl.; charts; illus. circ. 12,000. **Indexed:** Biol.Abstr., Excerp.Med., Ind.Med.
—BLDSC (4674.637000).

618.202   JA   ISSN 0389-9063
JOSANPU/JAPANESE MIDWIFE. (Text in Japanese) 1947. 4/yr. 6300 Yen per no. Nihon Josanpukai Shuppanbu - Japan Midwives Association, 8-21, Fujimi-cho 1-chome, Chiyoda-ku, Tokyo 102, Japan. TEL 813-3262-9923. FAX 813-3262-8933. Ed. Shigeko Horiuchi. **Document type:** trade publication.

618.202 610.73   JA   ISSN 0047-1836
JOSANPU ZASSHI/JAPANESE JOURNAL FOR MIDWIVES. 1952. m. 11160 Yen($86) Igaku Shoin Ltd., 24-3, Hongo 5-chome, Bunkyo-ku, Tokyo 113-91, Japan. TEL 03-817-5775. adv.; illus. circ. 12,000. **Indexed:** Int.Nurs.Ind.
—BLDSC (4656.510000).

618   FR   ISSN 0368-2315
CODEN: JGOBAC
JOURNAL DE GYNECOLOGIE OBSTETRIQUE ET BIOLOGIE DE LA REPRODUCTION. (Text in French; summaries in English and French) 1920. 8/yr. 906 F. (foreign 1104 F.) (effective 1996). Masson - Periodiques, Villa Laromiguiere, 75005 Paris, France. TEL 1-40-46-62-00. FAX 1-40-46-62-01. Ed. G. Magnin. adv.; bk.rev.; abstr.; illus.; index. circ. 5,000. (also avail. in microform from UMI; reprint service avail. from ISI) **Indexed:** Biol.Abstr., Chem.Abstr., Excerp.Med., Ind.Med., Nutr.Abstr. **Document type:** academic/scholarly publication.
—BLDSC (4996.600000); CASDDS; Faxon; SWETS; UMI. **CCC.**
Formerly: Gynecologie et Obstetrique et Federation des Societes de Gynecologie et d'Obstetrique. Bulletin (ISSN 0017-601X)
Description: Focuses on the entire field of medical and surgical gynecology as well as obstetrics and perinatal medicine.

618   US   ISSN 1058-0468
RG135   CODEN: JARGE4
JOURNAL OF ASSISTED REPRODUCTION AND GENETICS. 1984. 10/yr. $475 (foreign $555) (effective 1996). Plenum Publishing Corp., 233 Spring St., New York, NY 10013-1578. TEL 212-620-8000. FAX 212-463-0742. TELEX 23-421139. Ed. Norbert Gleicher. adv. (also avail. in microform from JSC; back issues avail.) **Indexed:** Excerp.Med., INIS Atomind. **Document type:** academic/scholarly publication.
—BLDSC (4947.286000); Faxon; Genuine Article; SWETS; UMI; UnCover. **CCC.**
Formerly (until 1992): Journal of In Vitro Fertilization and Embryo Transfer (ISSN 0740-7769)
Description: Covers research in the reproductive sciences, including assisted reproduction technologies, genetics of early gestation, relevant contributions from laboratory sciences affecting diagnosis and treatment of infertility, preimplantation genetics, and controversies in assisted reproduction.
Refereed Serial

618 612   UK   ISSN 0141-9846
CODEN: JDPHDH
JOURNAL OF DEVELOPMENTAL PHYSIOLOGY. 1979. m. £172($320) Caxton Communications Ltd., Unit 8, Central Park Business Centre, Bellfiedl Rd., High Wycombe, Bucks HP13 5HG, England. TEL 44-1494-473405. Ed. Colin T. Jones. adv.; bk.rev.; index. circ. 200. (also avail. in microform from UMI) **Indexed:** Biol.Abstr., Chem.Abstr., Curr.Cont., Dent.Ind., Excerp.Med., Ind.Med., Ind.Sci.Rev., Ind.Vet., Sci.Cit.Ind., Vet.Bull. **Document type:** academic/scholarly publication.
—CASDDS; Faxon; Genuine Article; SWETS; UMI; UnCover.
Description: Papers describing the results of pregnancy, the fetus, or the neonate of humans or experimental animals.

JOURNAL OF DIAGNOSTIC MEDICAL SONOGRAPHY. see *MEDICAL SCIENCES — Radiology And Nuclear Medicine*

618   US   ISSN 1042-4067
CODEN: JGYSEF
JOURNAL OF GYNECOLOGIC SURGERY. 1984. q. $155 (foreign $195). (Gynecologic Laser Society) Mary Ann Liebert, Inc. Publishers, 2 Madison Ave., Larchmont, NY 10538. TEL 914-834-3100. FAX 914-834-3688. E-mail: Liebert@pipeline.com. (Co-sponsors: International Society for Gynecologic Endocrinology; British Society for Cervical Pathology) Ed. Michael S. Baggish. adv.; bk.rev.; abstr. **Indexed:** Curr.Adv.Cancer Res., Excerp.Med. **Document type:** academic/scholarly publication.
—BLDSC (4996.595000); Faxon; Genuine Article; SWETS.
Formerly (until 1989): Colposcopy and Gynecologic Laser Surgery (ISSN 0741-6113)
Description: Deals with all aspects of operative and office gynecology, including colposcopy, endoscopy (hysteroscopy and laparoscopy), laser and conventional surgery, female urology, microsurgery, and in vitro fertilization.
Refereed Serial

618.1   US   ISSN 1069-2673
▼**JOURNAL OF GYNECOLOGIC TECHNIQUES.** 1995. q. $89 to individuals (foreign $114); institutions $135 (foreign $160). Churchill Livingstone International, 650 Ave. of the Americas, New York, NY 10011. TEL 212-206-5040. FAX 212-727-7808. Ed. Jonathan Berek; Pub. Jane Grochowski. **Document type:** academic/scholarly publication.
—**CCC.**
Description: Features original and review articles on techniques and methods, particularly those that are innovative, and general advances in diagnostic, operative, and other therapeutic techniques related to the specialty of gynecology.
Refereed Serial

610.73 618   US   ISSN 0890-3344
CODEN: JHLAE5
JOURNAL OF HUMAN LACTATION. 1984. q. $215 (foreign $250) (effective 1996). (International Lactation Consultants Association) Human Sciences Press, Inc. (Subsidiary of: Plenum Publishing Corp.), 233 Spring St., New York, NY 10013. TEL 212-620-8000. FAX 212-463-0742. TELEX 23-421139. Ed. Kathleen G. Auerbach. adv.; bk.rev.; film rev.; bibl.; index. circ. 2,000. (back issues avail.) **Indexed:** CINAHL, IMFL, Int.Nurs.Ind. **Document type:** academic/scholarly publication.
—BLDSC (5003.417000); Faxon; UnCover. **CCC.**
Formerly (until 1985): Consultants' Corner.
Description: Publishes scientific articles and commentaries on human lactation and breastfeeding, and discussions of clinical case reports relevant to practicing lactation consultants.
Refereed Serial

618.1   US
▼**JOURNAL OF MAMMARY GLAND BIOLOGY AND NEOPLASIA.** Announced for publication in 1996. q. $145 (foreign $170) (effective 1996). Plenum Publishing Corp., 233 Spring St., New York, NY 10013-1578. TEL 212-620-8000. FAX 212-463-0742. TELEX 23-421139. **Document type:** academic/scholarly publication.
Refereed Serial

618.2   US   ISSN 0939-6322
CODEN: JMFIEY
JOURNAL OF MATERNAL - FETAL INVESTIGATION. 1991. q. $184 (effective 1996). Springer-Verlag, Journals, 175 Fifth Ave., New York, NY 10010. TEL 212-460-1500. FAX 212-473-6272. (N. American subscr. to: Journal Fulfillment Services, Box 2485, Secaucus, NJ 07096-2491. TEL 800-777-4643. FAX 201-348-4505; Elsewhere: Springer-Verlag, Heidelberger Platz 3, 14197 Berlin, Germany. TEL 030-8207-1. FAX 030-8214091) (Co-sponsors: French Society of Ultrasound in Medicine and Biology; International Perinatal Doppler Society; Japanese Society of Biomedical Engineering in Obstetrics and Gynecology; Spanish Association of Perinatal Medicine) Ed. Dev Maulik. circ. 1,500. (also avail. in microform from UMI; reprint service avail.) **Indexed:** Excerp.Med. (1994-). **Document type:** academic/scholarly publication.
—BLDSC (5012.335000); Genuine Article; UMI. **CCC.**
Description: Publishes original research relevant to the various aspects of maternal and fetal care, including basic and clinical investigations, biophysical and biomedical diagnostic techniques, clinical trials, epidemiological, ethical and liability issues, as well as health care policies relating to maternal and infant health.
Refereed Serial

618.2   US   ISSN 1057-0802
CODEN: JMFMEC
THE JOURNAL OF MATERNAL - FETAL MEDICINE. 1992. bi-m. $156 (foreign $249) (effective 1996). John Wiley & Sons, Inc., Journals, 605 Third Ave., New York, NY 10158-0012. TEL 212-850-6645. FAX 212-850-6021. TELEX 12-7063. E-mail: SUBINFO@JWILEY.COM. (Subscr. outside the Americas to: John Wiley & Sons Ltd., Baffins Ln., Chichester, W. Sussex PO19 1UD, England. TEL 44-1243-779777. FAX 44-1243-776128) Eds. Roy H. Petrie, Hung N. Winn. (also avail. in microform from UMI; back issues avail.) **Indexed:** Chem.Abstr., Excerp.Med. (1993-). **Document type:** academic/scholarly publication.
—BLDSC (5012.340000); CASDDS; SWETS. **CCC.**
Description: Provides expert coverage of all aspects of modern maternal-fetal medicine, including the pathophysiology of the placenta, the pregnant patient, the fetus, and the neonate in both normal and abnormal states.
Refereed Serial

610.73 618   US   ISSN 0091-2182
CODEN: JNUMEQ
JOURNAL OF NURSE-MIDWIFERY. 1955. bi-m. $175 to institutions (effective 1996). (American College of Nurse-Midwives) Elsevier Science Inc., 655 Ave. of the Americas, New York, NY 10010. TEL 212-989-5800. FAX 212-633-3990. TELEX 420643 AEP UI. (Subscr. to: Box 882, Madison Sq. Sta., New York, NY, 10159-0882) Ed. Mary Ann Shah. adv.; bk.rev.; bibl.; charts; illus.; cum.index. (also avail. in microform from UMI) **Indexed:** ASSIA, C.I.N.L., Curr.Cont., Excerp.Med., Ind.Med., Int.Nurs.Ind., Nurs.Abstr., SSCI. **Document type:** academic/scholarly publication.
—BLDSC (5023.650000); Faxon; Genuine Article; SWETS; UnCover. **CCC.**
Former titles: American College of Nurse-Midwives. Bulletin (ISSN 0002-8002); (until 1969): American College of Nurse-Midwifery. Bulletin (ISSN 0098-3721)
Description: Includes the presentation of current knowledge in the fields of nurse-midwifery, parent-child health, obstetric, well-woman gynecology, family planning and neonatology.
Refereed Serial

618   UK   ISSN 0144-3615
CODEN: JOGYDW
JOURNAL OF OBSTETRICS AND GYNAECOLOGY. 1980. bi-m. £52 to individuals; institutions £134 (effective 1996). (Institute of Obstetrics and Gynaecology Trust) Carfax Publishing Co., P.O. Box 25, Abingdon, Oxon. OX14 3UE, England. TEL 01235-555335. FAX 01235-553559. (Subscr. in N. America to: Carfax Publishing Co., 875-81 Massachusetts Ave., Cambridge, MA 02139) Ed. Prof. D.F. Hawkins. adv.; bk.rev.; index. circ. 500. **Indexed:** Chem.Abstr., Curr.Adv.Cancer Res., Curr.Adv.Ecol.Sci., Curr.Cont., Excerp.Med. **Document type:** academic/scholarly publication.
—BLDSC (5025.400000); CASDDS; Faxon; SWETS; UMI; UnCover. **CCC.**
Refereed Serial

MEDICAL SCIENCES — OBSTETRICS AND GYNECOLOGY

618   JA
CODEN: AOJGDU
JOURNAL OF OBSTETRICS AND GYNAECOLOGY. (Text in English) 1970. 6/yr. membership. (Juntendo University, School of Medicine, Department of Obstetrics and Gynaecology) University of Tokyo Press - Tokyo Daigaku Shuppankai, 3-1, Hongo 7-chome, Bunkyo-ku, Tokyo 113, Japan. **Indexed:** Chem.Abstr., Excerp.Med. (1993-), ExtraMED, Ind.Med., INIS Atomind. **Document type:** academic/scholarly publication.
●Also available on CD-ROM.
—BLDSC (1742.256000); CASDDS.
Formerly: Asia - Oceania Journal of Obstetrics and Gynaecology (ISSN 0389-2328)

618   II   ISSN 0022-3190
CODEN: JOBYA4
JOURNAL OF OBSTETRICS AND GYNAECOLOGY OF INDIA. 1950. bi-m. Rs.600($35) Federation of Obstetric & Gynaecological Societies of India, Purandare Griha, 31 C, Dr. N.A. Purandare Marg, Bombay 400 007, India. TEL 811-04-46. Ed. Dr. V.N. Purandare. adv.; bk.rev.; charts; illus.; stat. circ. 8,600. (reprint service avail. from IRC) **Indexed:** Biol.Abstr., Chem.Abstr, ExtraMED. **Document type:** academic/scholarly publication.
●Also available on CD-ROM.
—CASDDS; Faxon.

618   CH
JOURNAL OF OBSTETRICS AND GYNECOLOGY OF THE REPUBLIC OF CHINA. (Text and summaries in Chinese and English) 1962. q. NT.$320. Association of Obstetrics and Gynecology of the Republic of China, No.1 Chang-Te St., Taipei, Taiwan, Republic of China. Ed. Pei-Chuan Ouyang. adv. circ. 1,600. (also avail. in microform from UMI; reprint service avail. from UMI)

JOURNAL OF PEDIATRIC & PERINATAL NUTRITION. see
MEDICAL SCIENCES — Pediatrics

JOURNAL OF PEDIATRIC SURGERY. see MEDICAL SCIENCES — Surgery

JOURNAL OF PERINATAL AND NEONATAL NURSING. see MEDICAL SCIENCES — Nurses And Nursing

618   GW   ISSN 0300-5577
CODEN: JPEMAO
JOURNAL OF PERINATAL MEDICINE. 1973. 6/yr. DM.498. Walter de Gruyter und Co., Genthiner Str. 13, 10785 Berlin, Germany. TEL 030-26005-0. FAX 030-26005251. TELEX 184027. (U.S. addr.: Walter de Gruyter, Inc., 200 Saw Mill River Rd., Hawthorne, NY 10532. TEL 914-747-0110) Ed.Bd. adv. **Indexed:** Bibl.Dev.Med.& Child Neur., Biol.Abstr., Chem.Abstr., Curr.Adv.Biochem., Curr.Adv.Ecol.Sci., Curr.Cont., Dairy Sci.Abstr., Excerp.Med., Ind.Med., Ind.Sci.Rev., INIS Atomind., Nutr.Abstr. **Document type:** academic/scholarly publication.
—BLDSC (5030.550000); CASDDS; Faxon; Genuine Article; SWETS; UnCover. **CCC**.

618.3   US   ISSN 0743-8346
CODEN: JOPEEI
JOURNAL OF PERINATOLOGY. 1981. bi-m. $66 to individuals (Canada $86.70; elsewhere $81); institutions $111 (Canada $134.82; elsewhere $126); students $35 (Canada $53.50; elsewhere $50) (effective 1996); newsstand price: $14.50. (National Perinatal Association) Mosby - Year Book, Inc. (Subsidiary of: Times Mirror Company), St. Louis, MO 63146-3318. TEL 314-872-8370; 800-453-4351. FAX 314-432-1380. (Co-sponsor: California Perinatal Association) Ed. Dr. Gilbert I. Martin. adv.: B&W page $710, color page $1610; trim 8 1/4 x 11. bk.rev.; charts; illus.; index. circ. 3,500. (also avail. in microform from UMI; back issues avail.) **Indexed:** C.C.I.P., Ind.Med., Int.Abstr.Biol.Sci. **Document type:** academic/scholarly publication.
—BLDSC (5030.570000); Faxon; SWETS; UMI; UnCover. **CCC**.
Description: Contains original clinical articles, commentaries, current concepts, case reports, editorials, and letters on all aspects of perinatal medicine from pregnancy through neonatal period.
Refereed Serial

618   UK   ISSN 0167-482X
CODEN: JPOGD
JOURNAL OF PSYCHOSOMATIC OBSTETRICS AND GYNAECOLOGY. (Text in English) 1982. q. £75($135) to individuals; institutions £150($250) (effective 1996). (International Society of Psychosomatic Obstetrics and Gynaecology) Parthenon Publishing Group, Casterton Hall, Casterton, Carnforth, Lancs LA6 2LA, England. TEL 44-15242-72084. FAX 44-15242-71587. (In U.S.: Box 1564, Pearl River, NY 10965. TEL 914-735-9363) Ed. Eylard V. Van Hall. bk.rev.; charts; illus.; circ. 1,000 (paid). (back issues avail.) **Indexed:** Curr.Cont., Dok.Arbeitsmed., Excerp.Med., Ind.Med. (1993-), Psychol.Abstr., Sci.Cit.Ind. **Document type:** academic/scholarly publication.
—BLDSC (5043.479000); Faxon; Genuine Article; SWETS; UnCover. **CCC**.
Refereed Serial

JOURNAL OF REPRODUCTIVE IMMUNOLOGY. see MEDICAL SCIENCES — Allergology And Immunology

618.05   US   ISSN 0024-7758
RG1   CODEN: JRPMAP
JOURNAL OF REPRODUCTIVE MEDICINE; for the obstetrician and gynecologist. 1968. m. $190 (foreign $220) (effective 1996). Journal of Reproductive Medicine, Inc., 8342 Olive Blvd., St. Louis, MO 63132. TEL 314-991-4440. FAX 314-991-4654. adv.; bk.rev.; illus.; index. circ. 29,686. (also avail. in microform from UMI,PMC; back issues avail.; reprint service avail. from ISI) **Indexed:** Anim.Breed.Abstr., Biol.Abstr., C.C.I.Ob.Gyn., Chem.Abstr., CINAHL, Curr.Adv.Ecol.Sci., Curr.Cont., Curr.Lit.Fam.Plan., Excerp.Med., Ind.Med., Ind.Sci.Rev., INIS Atomind., Med.& Surg.Dermat., Nutr.Abstr., Rev.Med.& Vet.Mycol.
—BLDSC (5409.700000); CASDDS; EMDOCS; Faxon; Genuine Article; SWETS; UMI; UnCover. **CCC**.
Continues: Lying-in (ISSN 0096-7033)
Refereed Serial

618   JA   ISSN 0916-2747
KAGAKU RYOHO KENKYUJO KIYO/INSTITUTE OF CHEMOTHERAPY. BULLETIN. (Text in English, Japanese) 1989. a. Kagaku Ryoho Kenkyujo, 1-14, Konodai 6-chome, Ichikawa-shi, Chiba-ken 272, Japan.

618 615   JA   ISSN 0913-2384
CODEN: KRRYEI
KAGAKU RYOHO NO RYOIKI/ANTIBIOTICS AND CHEMOTHERAPY. (Text in Japanese; summaries in English) m. 2884 Yen per no. (Kagaku Ryoho Kenkyukai - Committee of Chemotherapy) Iyaku Janarusha - Medicine & Drug Journal Co., Ltd., 2-8, Hiranocho 3-chome, Chuo-ku, Osaka 541, Japan. **Indexed:** Chem.Abstr. **Document type:** academic/scholarly publication.
—BLDSC (1546.995500); CASDDS.

KEY OBSTETRICS AND GYNECOLOGY. see MEDICAL SCIENCES — Abstracting, Bibliographies, Statistics

KIND ERNAEHRUNG UMWELT. see MEDICAL SCIENCES — Pediatrics

618.202   JA   ISSN 0917-3641
KYOTO DAIGAKU JOSANPU DOSOKAISHI/MIDWIVES ASSOCIATION OF KYOTO UNIVERSITY. ANNALS. (Text in Japanese) a. Kyoto Daigaku Josanpu Dosokai, Kyoto Daigaku Igakubu, Fanfujinkagaku Kyoshitsu, Shogoin Kawaramachi, Sakyo-ku, Kyoto-shi, Kyoto 606, Japan.

618   US
LAMAZE PARENTS' MAGAZINE. 1983. s-a. free to qualified personnel. (American Society for Psychoprophylaxis in Obstetrics, Inc.) Lamaze Publishing Co., 372 Danbury Rd., Wilton, CT 06897-2523. TEL 203-834-2711. FAX 203-761-8696. Ed. Carole Sherwood. adv.; circ. 2,200,000 (controlled). **Document type:** consumer publication.
Description: Offers prenatal and postpartum information to expectant couples who are preparing for birth through Lamaze classes.

618.45   US
LAMAZEBABY. 1993. s-a. Lamaze Publishing Co., 372 Danbury Rd., Wilton, CT 06897-2523. TEL 203-834-2711. FAX 203-761-8696. Ed. Carole Sherwood. adv.; B&W page $43100, color page $56300; trim 7 7/8 x 10 3/4. circ. 1,500,000 (controlled). **Document type:** consumer publication.

LAPAROSCOPIC SURGERY. see MEDICAL SCIENCES — Surgery

618.12   IC
LJOSMAEDRABLADID. 1922. 3/yr. ISK 550($17) Ljosmaedrafelagid, Grettisgata 89, 105 Reykjavik, Iceland. TEL 354-561-7399. FAX 354-562-9106. Ed. Hanna S. Antoniusdottir. circ. 550. **Document type:** trade publication.

618   IT
LUCINA. 1934. m. free. Federazione Nazionale dei Collegi delle Ostetriche, Piazza Tarquinia 5-D, 00183 Rome, Italy. Ed. Berta Comitini. adv. circ. 20,000. **Document type:** bulletin.

618.202   UK   ISSN 0961-5555
M I D I R S MIDWIFERY DIGEST. 1986. q. $105. Midwives Information and Resource Service, 9 Elmdale Rd., Clifton, Bristol, Avon BS8 1SL, England. TEL 01272-251791. FAX 01272-251792. adv. (back issues avail.) **Document type:** academic/scholarly publication.
Formerly (until 1991): M I D I R S Information Pack (ISSN 0955-8683)
Description: Enables midwives and other childbirth professionals to keep up to date with the latest research and information in the field.

M I D S NEWSLETTER. (Miscarriage, Infant Death, and Stillbirth) see WOMEN'S STUDIES

M O M MAGAZINE. (Mothers and Others for Midwives) see WOMEN'S HEALTH

610   HU   ISSN 0025-021X
CODEN: MNLAA8
MAGYAR NOORVOSOK LAPJA. (Summaries in English, German and Russian) bi-m. Magyar Noovos Tarsasag, P.O. Box 112, Szabolcs u 35, 1135 Budapest, Hungary. TEL 1-1296726. (Subscr. to: Kultura, Box 149, H-1389 Budapest, Hungary) Ed. Dr. Istvan Gati. bibl.; charts; illus. **Indexed:** Chem.Abstr., Excerp.Med., Ind.Med., INIS Atomind.
—BLDSC (5345.010000); CASDDS; EMDOCS.

613.9   MY   ISSN 0127-3213
MALAYSIAN JOURNAL OF REPRODUCTIVE HEALTH. (Text in English) 1983. a. $25. National Population and Family Development Board, Box 10416, Jalan Raja Laut, 50712 Kuala Lumpur, Malaysia. TEL 2937555. TELEX POPMAL MA 31911. Ed. Dr. Mohd Ismail Thambi. circ. 618. **Document type:** government publication.
—BLDSC (5356.068800).
Description: Discusses various aspects of reproductive health.

MATERNAL & CHILD HEALTH; the journal of family medicine. see MEDICAL SCIENCES — Pediatrics

MEALEY'S LITIGATION REPORT: NORPLANT. see LAW — Corporate Law

MEDICAL - LEGAL ASPECTS OF BREAST IMPLANTS. see LAW — Civil Law

MEDICAL MALPRACTICE: HANDLING OBSTETRIC AND NEONATAL CASES. see LAW — Civil Law

618.1   BL
MEDISOM: GYNECOLOGY. 1975. bi-m. $90. Editora Medisom, Ltda., Rua Sao Paulino 224, Caixa Postal 7650, 01064-970 Sao Paulo, Brazil. FAX 55-11-572-5957. Ed. Dr. Philip Querido. adv. (audio cassette)

618   US   ISSN 1072-3714
▼**MENOPAUSE.** 1994. q. $95 to individuals (foreign $106); institutions $116 (foreign $126) (effective 1996); newsstand price: $33. (North American Menopause Society) Lippincott - Raven Publishers, 227 W. Washington Sq., Philadelphia, PA 19106. TEL 215-238-4200. Eds. Isaac Schiff, Wulf H. Utian. adv. contact: Phyllis Noyes. charts; illus. (also avail. in microform from UMI; back issues avail.) **Document type:** academic/scholarly publication.
—BLDSC (5678.457030); UMI. **CCC**.
Description: Forum for new research and scholarly material relating to all aspects of the human female menopause, from physiological, pathological, sociocultural and medical perspectives.
Refereed Serial

MENOPAUSE NEWS. see GERONTOLOGY AND GERIATRICS

MEDICAL SCIENCES — OBSTETRICS AND GYNECOLOGY

618 UK ISSN 0266-6138
MIDWIFERY. (Text in English) 1984. q. £30($46) to individuals; institutions £405 ($169) (effective 1995). Churchill Livingstone Journals (Subsidiary of: Pearson Professional), Robert Stevenson House, 1-3 Baxter's Pl., Leith Walk, Edinburgh EH1 3AF, Scotland. TEL 0131-556-2424.
FAX 0131-459-1177. (Subscr. to: Pearson Professional Ltd., P.O. Box 77, Fourth Ave., Harlow, Essex CM19 5AA, England. TEL 01279-623760; U.S. subscr. to: Churchill Livingstone, 650 Ave. of the Americas, New York, NY 10011. TEL 212-206-5000) Ed. Ann Thomson. adv. contact: David Dunnachie. bk.rev. circ. 1,100. (back issues avail.) **Indexed:** CINAHL, Curr.Adv.Ecol.Sci. **Document type:** academic/scholarly publication.
—BLDSC (5761.449220); Faxon; SWETS; UnCover. CCC.

618.202 US
MIDWIFERY TODAY AND CHILDBIRTH EDUCATION. 1987. q. $32 (effective Jan. 1991). Box 2672, Eugene, OR 97402. TEL 503-344-7438.
FAX 503-344-1422. Ed. Jan Tritten. adv.; bk.rev.; film rev.; abstr.; charts; illus.; stat.; tr.lit. circ. 5,500.
—BLDSC (5761.449240).
Formerly: Midwifery Today (ISSN 0891-7701)
Description: Directed to professionals and non-professionals alike; balances technical articles with personal accounts and photography to present a wide range of options and perspectives on current birth care issues.

618.202 UK ISSN 1355-8404
MIDWIVES. 1887. m. £20.50 (Europe £26). (Royal College of Midwives) Nursing Notes Ltd., 120 High Rd., E. Finchley, London N2 8AG, England. TEL 0181-442-0801. FAX 0181-442-0623. (Subscr. to: TG Scott Subscriber Services, 6 Bourne Enterprise Centre, Wrotham Rd., Borough Green, Kent TN15 8DG, England. TEL 01732-884023.
FAX 01732-884034) Ed. Ann Graveley. adv. contact: Philip New. bk.rev.; index. circ. 35,000. (also avail. in microform from UMI; reprint service avail. from UMI) **Indexed:** ASSIA, CINAHL, Curr.Adv.Ecol.Sci., Int.Nurs.Ind. **Document type:** bulletin.
—BLDSC (5761.449380); Faxon; SWETS.
Formerly (until 1995): Midwives Chronicle (ISSN 0026-3524)

618 JA
MIEKEN SANFUJINKA IHO/MIE SOCIETY OF OBSTETRICIANS AND GYNECOLOGISTS. ANNUAL BULLETIN. (Text in Japanese) 1982. a. Mieken Sanfujinka Ikai, c/o Mr. Mizuno, 97-52, Otani-cho, Tsu-shi, Mie-ken 514, Japan. **Document type:** bulletin.

618 IT ISSN 0026-4784
MINERVA GINECOLOGICA. (Text in Italian; summaries in English and Italian) 1949. m. $110 to individuals; institutions $150 (effective 1995). (Societa Piemontese e Valdostana di Ostetrica e Ginecologia) Edizioni Minerva Medica, Corso Bramante 83-85, 10126 Turin, Italy. TEL 39-11-678282.
FAX 39-11-3121736. Ed. Alberto Oliaro; Pub. Alberto Oliaro. adv.: B&W page $1300, color page $2200; trim 190 x 270; adv. contact: F. Filippo. bk.rev.; bibl.; charts; illus.; index; circ. 4,000 (paid). (also avail. in microform from UMI) **Indexed:** Biol.Abstr., Chem.Abstr., Excerp.Med., Helminthol.Abstr., Ind.Med. **Document type:** academic/scholarly publication.
—BLDSC (5794.185000); EMDOCS; Faxon; SWETS; UMI.
Incorporates: Folia Gynaecologica; Ginecologia; Aggiornamenti di Ostetricia e Ginecologia (ISSN 0002-0931)
Refereed Serial

618 UK ISSN 0963-276X
MODERN MIDWIFE. 1991. m. £100 (Europe £120; elsewhere £145) (effective 1994). Hayward Medical Communications Ltd., 44 Earlham St, Covent Garden, London WC2H 9LA, England.
TEL 44-171-240-4493. FAX 44-171-240-4479. (Subscr. to: Essex House, Cromwell Park, Chipping Norton, Oxon. OX7 5SR, England. TEL 44-1608-645564. FAX 44-1608-645645) **Document type:** academic/scholarly publication.
—BLDSC (5890.150000).

MOTHERING. see *WOMEN'S HEALTH*

618 US ISSN 0192-1223
N A P S A C NEWS. 1976. q. $20. National Association of Parents and Professionals for Safe Alternatives in Childbirth, International, Rt. 1, Box 646, Marble Hill, MO 63764. TEL 314-238-2010. Eds. David & Lee Stewart. adv.; bk.rev. circ. 1,500.
Description: Information on parenting, breastfeeding, pregnancy, family health and the dangers of traditional medicine.

618.1 JA
NAGANOKEN SANKA FUJINKA IKAIHO/GYNECOLOGICAL SOCIETY OF NAGANO. BULLETIN. (Text in Japanese) 1962. s-a. free. Naganoken Sanka Fujinka Ikai, Shinshu Daigaku Igakubu Sanfujinka Kyoshitsu, 1-1, Asahi 3-chome, Matsumoto-shi, Nagano-ken 390, Japan. Ed. Hiroo Linumd. **Document type:** bulletin.

618.2 US
NATIONAL PERINATAL ASSOCIATION. BULLETIN. 1980. q. $15 to non-members. National Perinatal Association, 3500 E. Fletcher Ave., Ste. 209, Tampa, FL 33613-4712. TEL 813-971-1008.
FAX 813-971-9306. Ed. Julie A. Leachman. adv.; bk.rev. circ. 1,500. (tabloid format) **Document type:** newsletter.
Description: Information for association members.

618 618.92 US ISSN 1062-2454
NEONATAL INTENSIVE CARE; the journal of perinatalogy/neonatology. 1988. 6/yr. Goldstein and Associates Publishing, Inc., 1150 Yale St., Ste. 12, Santa Monica, CA 90403-4738.
TEL 213-828-1309. Ed. Les Plesko. adv. **Indexed:** CINAHL.
—BLDSC (6075.623500).
Description: Covers diagnostic techniques, case studies and research findings in perinatology and neonatology.
Refereed Serial

NEONATAL NETWORK; the journal of neonatal nursing. see *MEDICAL SCIENCES — Nurses And Nursing*

NETWORK (DURHAM). see *BIRTH CONTROL*

618 NE
NEW CLINICAL APPLICATIONS IN GYNAECOLOGY. (Text in English) irreg. price varies. Kluwer Academic Publishers, Postbus 17, 3300 AA Dordrecht, Netherlands. TEL 31-78-392392.
FAX 31-78-392254. TELEX 29245 KAPG NL. (Dist. by: Kluwer Academic Publishers Group, P.O. Box 322, 3300 AH Dordrecht, Netherlands. TEL 31-78-392392. FAX 31-78-546474; N. America dist. addr.: Box 358, Accord Sta., Hingham, MA 02018-0358. TEL 617-871-6600. FAX 617-871-6528) **Document type:** monographic series.

618 UK ISSN 0263-5429
NEW GENERATION. 1982. q. £6. National Childbirth Trust, Alexandra House, Oldham Terrace, Acton, London W3 6NH, England. TEL 0181-992-8637. FAX 0181-992-5929. Ed. Daphne Metland. bk.rev. circ. 30,000. **Document type:** consumer publication.
—BLDSC (6084.210900).

618 UK ISSN 1350-2735
NEW GENERATION DIGEST. 1993. q. £6. National Childbirth Trust, Alexandra House, Oldham Terrance, Acton, London W3 6NH, England.
TEL 0181-992-8637. FAX 0181-466-5307. Ed. Jane Moody. **Document type:** consumer publication.
—BLDSC (6084.211300).

NEW MOTHER; including new father news. see *CHILDREN AND YOUTH — About*

618 613.9 AT ISSN 1030-3987
NEW PARENT. 1968. q. Aus.$20. Parents Centers Australia, 71 Grand Ave., Westmead, N.S.W. 2150, Australia. TEL 02-633 5899. Ed. Beth Mitchell. adv.; bk.rev. circ. 2,000.
Description: Provides information to general public about birthing and parenting options and practices.

618.1 JA
NIHON FUJINKA BYORI KORUPOSUKOPI GAKKAI ZASSHI/JAPAN SOCIETY OF GYNECOLOGIC PATHOLOGY AND COLPOSCOPY. JOURNAL. (Text in Japanese; summaries in English, Japanese) 1982. s-a. Nihon Fujinka Byori Koruposukopi Gakkai, Keio Gijuku Daigaku Igakubu Sanfujinkagaku Kyoshitsu, 35, Shinano-machi, Shinjuku-ku, Tokyo 160, Japan.

618.178 JA ISSN 0029-0629
CODEN: NFGZAD
NIHON FUNIN GAKKAI ZASSHI/JAPANESE JOURNAL OF FERTILITY AND STERILITY.* (Text in Japanese; summaries in English) 1956. q. 9000 Yen. Nihon Funin Gakukai - Japanese Society of Fertility and Sterility, c/o Japan Medical Association, Bunkyo-ku, Tokyo 113, Japan. Ed. Keiko Ashihara. adv. circ. 2,000. (back issues avail.) **Indexed:** Anim.Breed.Abstr., Biol.Abstr., Chem.Abstr., Excerp.Med.
—BLDSC (4651.940000); CASDDS; EMDOCS.

618.202 JA ISSN 0917-6357
NIHON JOSAN GAKKAISHI/JAPAN ACADEMY OF MIDWIFERY. JOURNAL. (Text in Japanese; summaries in English, Japanese) 1987. s-a. Nihon Josan Gakkai, Tokyo Josanpu Kaikan, 8-21, Fujimi 1-chome, Chiyoda-ku, Tokyo 102, Japan.

618 JA ISSN 0914-6776
NIHON JUSEI CHAKUSHO GAKKAI ZASSHI/JOURNAL OF FERTILIZATION AND IMPLANTATION. (Text in English, Japanese) a. 6000 Yen. Nihon Jusei Chakusho Gakkai - Japan Society of Fertilization and Implantation, c/o Konbekkusu, 9-14, Azabudai 1-chome, Minato-ku, Tokyo 106, Japan.

618 616.9 JA ISSN 0918-4031
NIHON SANFUJINKA KANSENSHO KENKYUKAI GAKUJUTSU KOENKAI KIROKUSHI/CONFERENCE ON OBSTETRICAL AND GYNECOLOGICAL INFECTION. PROCEEDINGS. (Text in Japanese; summaries in English, Japanese) 1983. a. Nihon Sanfujinka Kansensho Kenkyukai - Japan Association of Obstetrical and Gynecological Infection, Koto Byoin Sanfujinka, 8-5, Oshima 6-chome, Koto-ku, Tokyo 136, Japan. **Document type:** academic/scholarly publication, proceedings.

618 JA ISSN 0916-8796
NIHON SANFUJINKA SHINSEIJI KETSUEKI GAKKAISHI/JAPANESE JOURNAL OF OBSTETRICAL, GYNECOLOGICAL AND NEONATAL HEMATOLOGY. (Text in English, Japanese) 1977. q. 8000 Yen. Japanese Society of Obstetrical, Gynecological and Neonatal Hematology, Hamamatsu University, School of Medicine, Department of Obstetrics and Gynecology, 3600 Handa-cho, Hamamatsu 431-31, Japan. TEL 053-435-2309. FAX 053-435-2308. E-mail: terao@hama-med.ac.jp. Ed. Terao Toshihiko. adv. contact: Maeda Makoto. bk.rev. circ. 1,500. **Document type:** academic/scholarly publication.
Description: Contains papers with laboratory or clinical orientation, case reports and revew articles.
Refereed Serial

618 JA ISSN 0546-1790
NIHON SANKA FUJINKA GAKKAI CHUGOKU SHINKOKU GODO CHIHO BUKAI ZASSHI/JAPAN SOCIETY OF OBSTETRICS AND GYNECOLOGY. CHUGOKU AND SHIKOKU DISTRICTS JOURNAL. (Text in Japanese) 1951. s-a. Nihon Sanka Fujinka Gakkai, Chuoku Shikoku Godo Chiho Bukai, c/o Okayama Daigaku Igakubu Sanfujinkagaku Kyoshitsu, 5-1, Shikada-cho 2-chome, Okayama-shi, Okayama-ken 700, Japan. **Indexed:** INIS Atomind.

618 JA ISSN 0910-2485
NIHON SANKA FUJINKA GAKKAI KANAGAWA CHIHO BUKAI KAISHI/JAPAN SOCIETY OF OBSTETRICS AND GYNECOLOGY. KANAGAWA DISTRICT JOURNAL. (Text in Japanese) 1964. s-a. Nihon Sanka Fujinka Gakkai, Kanagawa Chiho Bukai, Kanagawaken Ishi Kaikan, 4-104, Hanasaki-cho, Nishi-ku, Yokohama-shi, Kanagawa-ken 220, Japan.

618 JA ISSN 0285-8096
CODEN: NKRKES
NIHON SANKA FUJINKA GAKKAI KANTO RENGO CHIHO BUKAI KAIHO/KANTO JOURNAL OF OBSTETRICS AND GYNECOLOGY. (Text in Japanese) 1964. s-a. Nihon Sanka Fujinka Gakkai, Kanto Rengo Chiho Bukai - Japan Society of Obstetrics and Gynecology, Kanto Branch, Hoken Kaikan Bekkan, 1-1, Ichigaya Sadohara-cho, Shinjuku-ku, Tokyo 162, Japan. **Indexed:** Chem.Abstr.
—CASDDS.

MEDICAL SCIENCES — OBSTETRICS AND GYNECOLOGY

618 JA
NIHON SANKA FUJINKA GAKKAI KUMAMOTO CHIHO BUKAI ZASSHI/JAPAN SOCIETY OF OBSTETRICS AND GYNECOLOGY. KUMAMOTO DISTRICT JOURNAL. (Text in Japanese) 1949. a. 13000 Yen for 5 yrs. Nihon Sanka Fujinka Gakkai, Kumamoto Chiho Bukai, c/o Kumamoto Daigaku Igakubu Sanfujinka Kyoshitsu, 1-1, Honjo 1-chome, Kumamoto-shi, Kumamoto-ken 860, Japan. Ed. H. Okamura. adv. **Document type:** academic/scholarly publication.

618 JA ISSN 0913-2368
NIHON SANKA FUJINKA GAKKAI KYUSHU RENGO CHIHO BUKAI ZASSHI/JAPAN SOCIETY OF OBSTETRICS AND GYNECOLOGY. KYUSHU DISTRICT JOURNAL. (Text in Japanese) a. Nihon Sanka Fujinka Gakkai, Kyushu Rengo Chiho Bukai - Japan Society of Obstetrics and Gynecology, Kurume Daigaku Igakubu Sanfujinkagaku Kyoshitsu, 67, Asahi-cho, Kurume-shi, Fukuoka-ken 830, Japan.

618 JA ISSN 0285-3485
NIHON SANKA FUJINKA GAKKAI NIIGATA CHIHO BUKAI KAISSHI/JAPAN SOCIETY OF OBSTETRICS AND GYNECOLOGY. NIIGATA DISTRICTS JOURNAL. (Text in Japanese) 1972. q. membership. Nihon Sanka Fujinka Gakkai, Niigata Chiho Bukai, c/o Niigata Daigaku Igakubu Sanfujinka Kyoshitsu, 1-757, Asahi-machi Dori, Niigata-shi, Niigata-ken 951, Japan.

618 JA ISSN 0911-6281
NIHON SANKA FUJINKA GAKKAI SAITAMA CHIHO BUKAI KAISHI/JAPAN SOCIETY OF OBSTETRICS AND GYNECOLOGY. SAITAMA DISTRICT JOURNAL. (Text in Japanese) 1971. s-a. 2500 Yen per no. Nihon Sanka Fujinka Gakkai, Saitama Chiho Bukai, Saitama Kenmin Kenko Senta, 5-1, Naka-cho 3-chome, Urawa-shi, Saitama-ken 336, Japan.

618 JA ISSN 0288-5751
NIHON SANKA FUJINKA GAKKAI TOKYO CHIHO BUKAI KAISHI/TOKYO JOURNAL OF OBSTETRICS AND GYNECOLOGY. (Text in Japanese) 1952. q. Nihon Sanka Fujinka Gakkai, Tokyo Chiho Bunkai, Hoken Kaikan Bekkan, 1-1, Ichigaya Sadohara-cho, Shinjuku-ku, Tokyo 162, Japan.

618 JA ISSN 0300-9165
CODEN: NISFAY
NIHON SANKA FUJINKA GAKKAI ZASSHI/ACTA OBSTETRICA ET GYNAECOLOGICA JAPONICA. (Text in English, Japanese) 1949. m. 1100 Yen. Nihon Sanka Fujinka Gakkai - Japan Society of Obstetrics and Gynecology, Hoken Kaikan Bekkan, 1-1, Ichigaya Sadohara-cho, Shinjuku-ku, Tokyo 162, Japan. adv.; bibl.; charts; index. circ. 2,500. **Indexed:** Anim.Breed.Abstr., Biol.Abstr., Chem.Abstr., Excerp.Med., Ind.Med., INIS Atomind.
—BLDSC (0641.571000); CASDDS; Genuine Article.
Incorporates (in 1969): Acta Obstetrica et Gynaecologica Japonica (ISSN 0001-6330); Which was formerly (1954-1968): Japanese Obstetrical and Gynecological Society. Journal (ISSN 0388-0486)

618 JA
NIHON SANKA FUJINKA NAISHIKYO GAKKAI ZASSHI/JAPANESE JOURNAL OF GYNECOLOGIC AND OBSTETRIC ENDOSCOPY. (Text in Japanese) 1985. irreg. Nihon Sanka Fujinka Naishinkyo Gakkai - Japan Endoscopy Society of Obstetrics and Gynecology, c/o Mr. Iwata, Kawasaki Byoin Sanfujinka, 12-1, Shinkawa Dori, Kawasaki-ku, Kawasaki-shi, Kanagawa-ken 210.

618 JA
NISSANFUKAI TOHOKU RENGO CHIHO BUKAIHO/TOHOKU JOURNAL OF OBSTETRICS AND GYNECOLOGY. (Text in Japanese) a. Nihon Sanka Fujinka Gakkai, Tohoku Rengo Chiho Bukai - Japan Society of Obstetrics and Gynecology, Tohoku Branch, Tohoku Daigaku Igakubu Sankafujinka Kyoshitsu, 1-1, Seiryo-cho, Aoba-ku, Sendai-shi, Miyagi-ken 980, Japan.

618 US
NUEVA VIDA/A NEW LIFE. (Text in Spanish) 1990. a. Gruner & Jahr U.S.A. Publishing, 685 Third Ave., New York, NY 10017. TEL 212-878-8700. Ed. Elvia Delgado. circ. 450,000. **Document type:** consumer publication.
Description: Provides information on newborn baby care for Hispanic mothers.

NYUSEN HINYU KENKYUKAI KOEN YOSHISHU/SOCIETY FOR MAMMARY GLANDS AND LACTATION RESEARCH. ABSTRACTS OF THE MEETING. see *MEDICAL SCIENCES — Abstracting, Bibliographies, Statistics*

618 658 US ISSN 1044-307X
O B G MANAGEMENT. (Obstetrics and Gynecology) 1989. m. $65. Dowden Publishing Company, 110 Summit Ave., Montvale, NJ 07645. TEL 201-391-9100. FAX 201-391-2778. Ed. Mark Dowden. adv.; circ. 31,500 (controlled).
—CCC.
Description: Provides information on how to run an ob-gyn medical practice better. Covers malpractice, practice management, fees, reimbursement, government regulation, technology, ethics and patient relations.

618 US ISSN 0743-8354
RG1
OB-GYN CLINICAL ALERT. 1982. m. $115. American Health Consultants, Inc., Six Piedmont Center, Ste. 400, Atlanta, GA 30305. TEL 404-262-7436; 800-688-2421. FAX 800-284-3291. Ed. Dr. Leon Speroff. index. circ. 2,810. (also avail. in audio cassette; reprint service avail.) **Document type:** newsletter.
—CCC.

618 US ISSN 0029-7437
RG1
OB-GYN NEWS. 1966. s-m. $96. International Medical News Group, 12230 Wilkins Ave., Rockville, MD 20852. TEL 301-816-8700. Ed. Sheila Callahan. adv.; bk.rev.; circ. 31,000 (controlled). (tabloid format; also avail. in microform from UMI) **Indexed:** Curr.Lit.Fam.Plan. **Document type:** newspaper.
—UMI.

618 US ISSN 1058-1677
OB-GYN RESIDENT. 1992. bi-m. $40. Slack, Inc., 6900 Grove Rd., Thorofare, NJ 08086. TEL 609-848-1000. Ed. Laura Ronge. adv. circ. 5,189.
Description: Guide to career, lifestyle and business issues facing residents.

OBSTETRIC ANESTHESIA DIGEST. see *MEDICAL SCIENCES — Anaesthesiology*

618 US ISSN 0029-7828
RG1 CODEN: OGSUA8
OBSTETRICAL & GYNECOLOGICAL SURVEY. 1946. m. $99 to individuals; institutions $154 (effective 1995). Williams & Wilkins, 428 E. Preston St., Baltimore, MD 21202. TEL 410-528-4000; 800-638-6423. FAX 410-528-4312. TELEX 87669. Ed.Bd. adv.; bk.rev.; abstr.; bibl.; charts; illus. circ. 9,900. (also avail. in microfilm from WWS) **Indexed:** Biol.Abstr., C.C.I.Ob.Gyn., Chem.Abstr., Curr.Adv.Cancer Res., Curr.Adv.Ecol.Sci., Curr.Lit.Fam.Plan., Dok.Arbeitsmed., Excerp.Med., Ind.Med., Med.& Surg.Dermat. **Document type:** academic/scholarly publication, abstracting/indexing.
—BLDSC (6208.172000); CASDDS; EMDOCS; Faxon; Genuine Article; UnCover. **CCC.**
Description: Reviews articles and in-depth condensations of important obstetrical and gynecological articles from nearly 100 U.S. and international journals.

618 SP ISSN 1130-7919
OBSTETRICIA Y GINECOLOGIA ESPANOLA. 1991. bi-m. Obstetricia y Ginecologia Espanola, S.L., C. Maestro Lope 59, 46100 Burjassot (Valencia), Spain. TEL 363-82-02. FAX 363-85-52. Ed. F. Bonilla-Musoles.
—BLDSC (6208.174500).

618 US ISSN 0029-7844
RG1 CODEN: OBGNAS
OBSTETRICS AND GYNECOLOGY. 1952. m. $232 to institutions in U.S.; $322 to institutions outside the Americas; $397 to institutions in Europe; $432 to institutions in Japan (effective 1996). (American College of Obstetricians and Gynecologists) Elsevier Science Inc., 655 Ave. of the Americas, New York, NY 10010. TEL 212-989-5800. FAX 212-633-3990. TELEX 420643 AEP UI. (Subscr. to: Box 882, Madison Sq. Sta., New York, NY 10159-0882) Ed. Dr. Roy M. Pitkin. adv.; bk.rev.; bibl.; charts; illus.; s-a. index. (also avail. in microform from UMI,WWS; reprint service avail. from UMI) **Indexed:** AIM, Behav.Med.Abstr., Bibl.Dev.Med.& Child Neur., Biol.Abstr., Biotech.Abstr., C.C.I.Ob.Gyn., Chem.Abstr., CINAHL, Curr.Adv.Cancer Res., Curr.Adv.Ecol.Sci., Curr.Adv.Genetics & Molec.Biol., Curr.Cont., Curr.Lit.Fam.Plan., Dairy Sci.Abstr., Dent.Ind., Diab.Cont., Excerp.Med., Helminthol.Abstr., I.P.A., Ind.Med., Int.Nurs.Ind., Kidney, Med.& Surg.Dermat., Nutr.Abstr., Risk Abstr., Sci.Cit.Ind. **Document type:** academic/scholarly publication.
●Also available online. Vendor(s): Ovid Technologies.
—BLDSC (6208.200000); ADONIS; CASDDS; EMDOCS; Faxon; Genuine Article; SWETS; UnCover. **CCC.**
Description: Provides information on current developments in women's health care.
Refereed Serial

618 US ISSN 0889-8545
CODEN: OGCAE8
OBSTETRICS AND GYNECOLOGY CLINICS OF NORTH AMERICA. 1974. q. $130 (foreign $155) (effective 1996). W.B. Saunders Co. (Subsidiary of: Harcourt Brace & Company), Curtis Center, 3rd Fl., Independence Sq. W., Philadelphia, PA 19106-3399. TEL 215-238-7800. FAX 215-238-6445. (Subscr. to: Periodicals Fulfillment, W.B. Saunders Co., 6277 Sea Harbor Dr., 4th Fl., Orlando, FL 32891-4800. TEL 800-654-2452. FAX 800-874-6418) Ed. Helaine Barron. **Indexed:** Bibl.Dev.Med.& Child Neur., Biol.Abstr., CINAHL, Curr.Adv.Ecol.Sci., Curr.Lit.Fam.Plan., Dok.Arbeitsmed., Excerp.Med., Ind.Med., Ind.Sci.Rev., Sci.Cit.Ind. **Document type:** academic/scholarly publication.
—BLDSC (6208.206300); Faxon; Genuine Article; SWETS; UMI; UnCover. **CCC.**
Formerly: Clinics in Obstetrics and Gynaecology (ISSN 0306-3356)
Description: Each issue addresses a single topic in obstetric and gynecological care.
Refereed Serial

618 US ISSN 0000-1589
RG33.U6
OFFICIAL AMERICAN BOARD OF MEDICAL SPECIALTIES (A B M S) DIRECTORY OF BOARD CERTIFIED OBSTETRICIANS AND GYNECOLOGISTS. 1985. biennial. $169.95. Marquis Who's Who, A Reed Reference Publishing company, 121 Chanlon Rd., New Providence, NJ 07974. TEL 908-464-6800. FAX 908-665-2898. (Subscr. to: Order Dept., Box 31, New Providence, NJ 07974-9903. TEL 800-521-8110) Ed. Roy Crego. **Document type:** directory.
Formerly: A B M S Directory of Certified Obstetricians and Gynecologists (ISSN 0884-1535)
Description: Biographical sketches of U.S. certified medical specialists sorted geographically with alpha index.

618 FR ISSN 0223-4211
OFFICIEL DE LA SAGE-FEMME.* 1953. 10/yr. 330 F. Organisation Nationale des Syndicats de Sages Femmes (ONSSF), 7 rue Rougemont, 75009 Paris, France. TEL 48-24-50-20. FAX 45-23-19-61. adv. circ. 3,500.

618 JA
ONCHIKAI KAIHO/NEWS OF ONCHIKAI. (Text in Japanese) a. Onchikai, Kyoto Daigaku Igakubu, Fuzoku Byoin Sanfujinkagaku Kyoshitsu, 54, Kawara-cho Shogoin, Sakyo-ku, Kyoto-shi, Kyoto 606, Japan.

ONCOLOGY & CHEMOTHERAPY. see *MEDICAL SCIENCES — Oncology*

MEDICAL SCIENCES — OBSTETRICS AND GYNECOLOGY 4465

618 JA
OSAKA SOCIETY OF OBSTETRICIANS AND GYNECOLOGISTS. JOURNAL. (Text in Japanese) 1977. biennial. Osaka Society of Obstetricians and Gynecologists - Osaka Sanfujinka Ikai, 8-25, Karakiyomachi, Tennoji-ku, Osaka-shi, Osaka 543, Japan.

P A S C A L E 82: GYNECOLOGIE, OBSTETRIQUE, ANDROLOGIE. see *MEDICAL SCIENCES — Abstracting, Bibliographies, Statistics*

PAEDIATRIA CROATICA. see *MEDICAL SCIENCES — Pediatrics*

PEDI KAI NEI GONIS. see *MEDICAL SCIENCES — Pediatrics*

PEDIATRIYA, AKUSHERSTVO TA GINEKOLOGIYA. see *MEDICAL SCIENCES — Pediatrics*

618 JA ISSN 0910-8718
PERINATAL CARE. (Text in Japanese) 1982. m. 1600 Yen per no. Medika Shuppan - Medicus Publishing Inc., 18-24, Hiroshiba-cho, Suita-shi, Osaka 564, Japan.

618 US ISSN 0160-7219
PERINATAL PRESS; for persons dedicated to improving the health care of the pregnant woman, fetus and newborn. 1977. 6/yr. $21 (Canada $29; elsewhere $34). Perinatal Press, Inc., Box 710698, San Diego, CA 92171-0698. Ed. Dr. J.M. Schneider. bk.rev.; abstr.; charts; illus.; stat.; index. circ. 6,000. (looseleaf format; also avail. in microfilm from UMI; back issues avail.) **Indexed:** CINAHL.
—BLDSC (6425.126000); UMI.

618.9 GW ISSN 0936-7160
CODEN: PEMDEU
PERINATALMEDIZIN. 1989. 4/yr. DM.140($101) (effective 1996). (Deutschen Gesellschaft fuer Perinatale Medizin) Springer-Verlag, Heidelberger Platz 3, 14197 Berlin, Germany. TEL 030-8207-0. FAX 030-8214091. E-mail: orders@springer.de. (Subscr. in N. America to: Springer-Verlag New York, Inc., 44 Hartz Way, Secaucus, NJ 07096-2491. TEL 201-348-4033. FAX 201-348-4505) Ed. J.W. Dudenhausen. **Document type:** academic/scholarly publication.
—BLDSC (6425.121500); SWETS; UMI. **CCC.**

618 JA ISSN 0910-3570
PERINATOLOGY SYMPOSIUM. (Text in Japanese) 1984. a. 6000 Yen. (Japan Society of Perinatology - Nihon Shusanki Gakkai) Medical View Co., Ltd., 2-30, Ichigaya Honmra-cho, Shinjuku-ku, Tokyo 162, Japan.

613.9 US ISSN 0190-3195
PERSPECTIVAS INTERNACIONALES EN PLANIFICACION FAMILIAR. English edition: International Family Planning Perspectives (ISSN 0190-3187); French edition: Perspectives Internationales sur le Planning Familial. (Text in Spanish) a. $10 (effective 1995). Alan Guttmacher Institute, 120 Wall St., New York, NY 10005. TEL 212-248-1111. FAX 212-248-1951. Ed. Olivia Schieffelin Nordberg. bk.rev. **Indexed:** Hisp.Amer.Per.Ind. (1994-).
Description: Focuses on the population concerns of Latin America.

301.426 US
PERSPECTIVES INTERNATIONALES SUR LE PLANNING FAMILIAL. English edition: International Family Planning Perspectives (ISSN 0190-3187); Spanish edition: Perspectivas Internacionales en Planificacion Familiar (ISSN 0190-3195) (Text in French) a. $10 (effective 1995). Alan Guttmacher Institute, 120 Wall St., New York, NY 10005. TEL 212-248-1111. FAX 212-248-1951. Ed. Olivia Schieffelin Nordberg. bk.rev.
Description: Focuses on the population concerns of francophone Africa.

PIELEGNIARKA I POLOZNA. see *MEDICAL SCIENCES — Nurses And Nursing*

PLACENTA. see *BIOLOGY — Physiology*

618.2 613.9 US ISSN 0883-3095
RG635 CODEN: PPPJE4
PRE- AND PERI-NATAL PSYCHOLOGY JOURNAL. 1986. q. $225 (foreign $265) (effective 1996). (Pre- and Peri-Natal Psychology Association of North America) Human Sciences Press, Inc. (Subsidiary of: Plenum Publishing Corp.), 233 Spring St., New York, NY 10013-1578. TEL 212-620-8000.
FAX 212-463-0742. TELEX 23-421139. Ed. Ruth Carter. adv. (reprint service avail. from UMI) **Indexed:** IMFL, Psychol.Abstr. (1986-). **Document type:** academic/scholarly publication.
—BLDSC (6603.620000); UMI. **CCC.**
Description: Explores the psychological dimensions of human reproduction and pregnancy and the mental and emotional development of the unborn and newborn child.
Refereed Serial

618 AT ISSN 1035-5448
PREGNANCY. 1986. q. Aus.$5.95 (foreign Aus.$9.50). Magazine House Pty. Ltd., P.O. Box 1067, Crows Nest, N.S.W. 2065, Australia. TEL 61-2-438-2399. FAX 61-2-436-3014. Ed. Carol Fallows. adv.; bk.rev. circ. 45,000. **Document type:** consumer publication.
Formerly: Pregnancy, Birth and the Next 6 Months (ISSN 0817-2420)
Description: Covers birth process, moods of pregnancy, exercises, beauty, breastfeeding, and choosing a birth place.

618 UK ISSN 1359-8635
PRENATAL AND NEONATAL MEDICINE. Announced for publication in 1996. q. £65($100) to individuals; institutions £120($190) (effective 1996). Parthenon Publishing Group, Casterton Hall, Carnforth, Lancs LA6 2LA, England.
TEL 44-12542-72084. FAX 44-15242-71587. (U.S. subscr. to: Box 1564, Pearl River, NY 10965. TEL 914-735-9363) Ed. Dr. Dian Carlo di Renzo. adv.
Refereed Serial

618 UK ISSN 0197-3851
CODEN: PRDIDM
PRENATAL DIAGNOSIS. 1981. 13/yr. $825 (foreign $825) (effective 1996). John Wiley & Sons Ltd., Journals, Baffins Ln., Chichester, W. Sussex PO19 1UD, England. TEL 01243-779777.
FAX 01243-776128. TELEX 86290 WIBOOK G. (Subscr. in the Americas to: John Wiley & Sons, Inc., 605 Third Ave., New York, NY 10158. TEL 212-850-6645. FAX 212-850-6021) Ed. M.A. Ferguson-Smith. adv. circ. 1,072. (also avail. in microform from UMI; back issues avail.; reprint service avail. from ISI,SWZ,UMI) **Indexed:** Bibl.Dev.Med.& Child Neur., Biol.Abstr., Chem.Abstr., Curr.Adv.Ecol.Sci., Curr.Adv.Genetics & Molec.Biol., Curr.Cont., Dent.Ind., Excerp.Med., Ind.Med., Med.& Surg.Dermat. **Document type:** academic/scholarly publication.
—BLDSC (6607.646000); ADONIS; CASDDS; Faxon; Genuine Article; SWETS; UMI; UnCover. **CCC.**
Description: Communicates the results of original research in a variety of clinical and scientific specialties concerned with in-utero diagnosis of fetal abnormality in man resulting from genetic and environmental factors.
Refereed Serial

618.2 US
PRENATAL EDUCATOR. q. free to qualified personnel. E P I Inc., 8003 Old York Rd., Elkins Park, PA 19117. TEL 215-635-1700. Ed. Deana Jamroz. adv.; tr.lit. circ. 8,540.
Description: For health care professionals who instruct prenatal education classes, as well as couples expecting the birth of a child. Covers advances in medicine, classroom techniques, and relevant consumer product information.

618 US ISSN 1068-607X
▼**PRIMARY CARE UPDATE FOR O B - GYNS.** 1994. bi-m. $115 to institutions in U.S.; $159 to institutions outside the Americas (effective 1996). (American College of Obstetricians and Gynecologists) Elsevier Science Inc., 655 Ave. of the Americas, New York, NY 10010. TEL 212-989-5800.
FAX 212-633-3990. TELEX 420643 AEP UI. (Subscr. to: Box 882, Madison Sq. Sta., New York, NY 10159-0882) Ed. Dr. V.L. Seltzer. (also avail. in microform from UMI; back issues avail.) **Indexed:** Excerp.Med. (1995-). **Document type:** academic/scholarly publication.
—BLDSC (6612.908450). **CCC.**
Description: Serves as a current resource on primary and preventive health care for women, focusing on practical clinical information pertaining to the diagnosis, treatment and management of non-OB/Gyn disorders in women.
Refereed Serial

618 US
PRINCIPLES AND TECHNIQUES IN GYNECOLOGIC SURGERY SERIES. 1992. irreg., latest 1993. price varies. Raven Press (Subsidiary of: Wolters Kluwer N.V.), 1185 Ave. of the Americas, New York, NY 10036. TEL 212-930-9500. FAX 212-869-3495. Ed. Luis E. Sanz. **Document type:** monographic series.

PROFESSIONAL CARE OF MOTHER & CHILD. see *MEDICAL SCIENCES — Nurses And Nursing*

618 IT
PROGESSI CLINICI: GINECOLOGIA E OSTETRICIA. q. L.180000($180) Piccin Editore, Via Altinate 107, 35121 Padua, Italy. TEL 049-655566.
FAX 049-8750693.

618 SP ISSN 0304-5013
PROGRESOS DE OBSTETRICIA Y GINECOLOGIA. (Text in Spanish; summaries in English) 1958. m. 10900 ptas.($105) (effective 1995). (Sociedad Espanola de Ginecologia e Obstetricia) Editorial Garsi, S.A., Juan Bravo 46, 28006 Madrid, Spain. TEL 34-1-4021212. FAX 34-1-4020954. Eds. Santiago Dexeus, Jesus Gonzalez-Merlo. adv.; bk.rev.; index. circ. 3,000. (back issues avail.) **Indexed:** Excerp.Med., Ind.Med.Esp.

618 SP ISSN 1130-0523
PROGRESOS EN DIAGNOSTICO PRENATAL. (Text in Spanish; summaries in English) 1989. 8/yr. 8900 ptas.($85) (effective 1995). (Asociacion Espanola de Diagnostico Prenatal) Editorial Garsi, S.A., Juan Bravo 46, 28006 Madrid, Spain. TEL 34-1-4021212. FAX 34-1-4020954. adv.; bk.rev.; index. circ. 2,000. (back issues avail.)

PROLIFE NEWS. see *PUBLIC HEALTH AND SAFETY*

618 IT ISSN 0033-491X
QUADERNI DI CLINICA OSTETRICA E GINECOLOGICA. (Text in Italian; summaries in English) 1946. bi-m. L.60000 (foreign L.120000) (effective 1994). Casa Editrice Maccari, Via Trento 53, 43100 Parma, Italy. FAX 039-521-771268. Eds. Giuseppe Dellepiane, Eugenio Maurizio. circ. 1,600. **Indexed:** Chem.Abstr., Excerp.Med., Ind.Med.
—BLDSC (7165.900000).

618.2 GW
RATGEBER FUER SCHWANGERE UND JUNGE MUETTER. 1973. a. Informedia Verlags GmbH, Eupenerstr. 165, Postfach 450569, 5000 Cologne 41, Germany. TEL 0221-49810. FAX 0221-4981258. TELEX 8882071. Ed. Hildegard Schuster. charts; illus.

618 FR ISSN 1244-8168
CODEN: RGOBE2
REFERENCES EN GYNECOLOGIE OBSTETRIQUE. 1993. 10/yr. Editions Mellet, 25 av. de Trudaine, 75009 Paris, France. TEL 33-1-42821562. **Indexed:** Excerp.Med. (1994-).

MEDICAL SCIENCES — OBSTETRICS AND GYNECOLOGY

618 616.4   FR   ISSN 0994-3919
CODEN: RHHOE
REPRODUCTION HUMAINE ET HORMONES. 1988?
10/yr. 335 F. (foreign 446 F.) (effective 1995).
Editions E S K A, 27 rue Dunois, 75013 Paris,
France. TEL 44-06-80-42. FAX 44-24-06-94. Ed.
Dr. Henri Rozenbaum. **Indexed:** Excerp.Med. (1994-).
Document type: academic/scholarly publication.
—BLDSC (7713.605000).
Description: Publishes both cutting edge articles on
the discoveries in the field and practical syntheses
and analyses on contemporary issues in gynecologie.

612.6   UK   ISSN 0962-2799
QP251   CODEN: RMERE8
REPRODUCTIVE MEDICINE REVIEW. 1992. 3/yr.
£96($148) (effective 1996). Cambridge University
Press, Edinburgh Bldg., Shaftsbury Rd., Cambridge
CB2 2RU, England. TEL 44-1223-325968.
FAX 44-1223-325959. (N. American addr.:
Cambridge University Press, Journals Dept., 40 W.
20th St., New York, NY 10011. TEL
212-924-3900. FAX 212-691-3239) adv.; bk.rev.
Indexed: Excerp.Med. (1994-). **Document type:**
academic/scholarly publication.
—BLDSC (7713.706200).
Description: Addresses topics of interest to
obstetricians involved in reproductive medinince,
reproductive endocrinologists, clinitians in fertility
and in-vitro fertilization clinics, and scientific staff in
all these areas.

REPRODUCTIVE TOXICOLOGY. see ENVIRONMENTAL
STUDIES — Toxicology And Environmental Safety

618.3   US   ISSN 0362-5699
RG600   CODEN: PPMED7
REVIEWS IN PERINATAL MEDICINE. 1976. a. price
varies. Raven Press (Subsidiary of: Wolters Kluwer
N.V.), 1185 Ave. of the Americas, New York, NY
10036. TEL 212-930-9500. FAX 212-869-3495.
Eds. Emile M. Scarpelli, Ermelando V. Cosmi. (reprint
service avail. from UMI) **Indexed:** Biol.Abstr.
Document type: monographic series.
—CASDDS.
Refereed Serial

618   BL   ISSN 0100-7203
CODEN: RBGODX
REVISTA BRASILEIRA DE GINECOLOGIA E OBSTETRICIA.*
1979. q. Elea Projetos Graficos e Editorais Ltda., Rio
de Janeiro, Brazil. Ed. Euvaldo Amaral. adv. circ.
8,500.
—BLDSC (7845.050000); CASDDS.

618   CL   ISSN 0048-766X
REVISTA CHILENA DE OBSTETRICIA Y GINECOLOGIA.*
1961. bi-m. Sociedad Chilena de Obstetricia y
Ginecologia, Mac - Iver 721 Of. 8, Casilla 639,
Santiago, Chile. illus. **Indexed:** Chem.Abstr.,
Excerp.Med., Ind.Med.
—BLDSC (7848.930000).
Supersedes: Sociedad Chilena de Obstetricia y
Ginecologia. Boletin.

618   CK   ISSN 0034-7434
**REVISTA COLOMBIANA DE OBSTETRICIA Y
GINECOLOGIA.** 1950. bi-m. Col.2000($50)
Sociedad Colombiana de Obstetricia y Ginecologia,
Carrera 23 No.39-82, Apdo. Aereo 14961 y
34188, Bogota, Colombia. (Co-sponsor: Federacion
Colombiana de Sociedades de Obstetricia y
Ginecologia) Eds. Jose Gabriel Acuna, Enrique
Archila. adv.; bk.rev.; bibl.; charts; illus.; index. circ.
2,000. **Indexed:** Biol.Abstr., Excerp.Med., Ind.Med.
—BLDSC (7851.405000); EMDOCS.

618   CU   ISSN 0138-600X
REVISTA CUBANA DE OBSTETRICIA Y GINECOLOGIA.
(Text in Spanish; summaries in English, Spanish)
1975. s-a. $30 in S. America; N. America $32;
elsewhere $34. Ministerio de Salud Publica, Centro
Nacional de Informacion de Ciencias Medicas, Calle
E No. 452, e-19 y 21, Plaza de al Revolucion, Apdo.
6520, Havana, Cuba. TEL 809-32-5338. (Dist. by:
Ediciones Cubanas, Obispo No. 527, Apdo. 605,
Havana, Cuba) Ed. Fredesvinda Blanco. bibl.; charts;
illus.; index. circ. 1,500.

618   VE   ISSN 0048-7732
**REVISTA DE OBSTETRICIA Y GINECOLOGIA DE
VENEZUELA.** 1941. q. $50. Sociedad de Obstetricia
y Ginecologia de Venezuela, Biblioteca, Apartado
20081, Avenida San Martin, Caracas, Venezuela.
TEL 58-2-4510895. Ed. Dr. Itic Zighelboim. adv.;
bk.rev. circ. 2,000. **Indexed:** Biol.Abstr., Chem.Abstr.,
Excerp.Med., Ind.Med.
—BLDSC (7869.020000); EMDOCS.

618   RM   ISSN 0029-781X
**REVISTA DE PEDIATRIE, OBSTETRICA, GINECOLOGIE.
OBSTETRICA SI GINECOLOGIE.** (Text in Rumanian;
summaries in English, French, German, Russian)
1953. 4/yr. $20. Uniunea Societatilor de Stiinte
Medicale din Republica Socialista Rumania, Str.
Progresului No. 8, Bucharest, Rumania. (Subscr. to:
ILEXIM, Str. 13 Decembrie Nr. 3, P.O. Box 136-137,
Bucharest, Rumania) Ed.Bd. adv.; bk.rev.; bibl.;
charts; illus. **Indexed:** Biol.Abstr., Chem.Abstr.,
Dent.Ind.

618   SP   ISSN 0214-1582
REVISTA DE SENOLOGIA Y PATOLOGIA MAMARIA. q.
9000 ptas.($90) (effective 1995). (Asociacion
Espanola de Senologia y Patologia Mamaria)
Editorial Garsi, S.A., Juan Bravo 46, 28006 Madrid,
Spain. TEL 34-1-4021212. FAX 34-1-4020954.
Ed.Bd. circ. 1,000.

618   SP   ISSN 0034-9445
CODEN: REOGAX
REVISTA ESPANOLA DE OBSTETRICIA Y GINECOLOGIA.
(Text in Spanish; summaries in English, Spanish)
1944. bi-m. 6000 ptas. (Asociacion de Obstetricia y
Ginecologia) Editorial Facta, Menedez y Pelayo 5-7,
46010 Valencia, Spain. Ed. Dr. F. Gomar Sancho.
adv.; bk.rev.; bibl.; charts; illus. circ. 3,500. **Indexed:**
Biol.Abstr., Chem.Abstr., Dairy Sci.Abstr.,
Ind.Med.Esp., Ind.Med.
—CASDDS. **CCC.**

618.45   US
▼**REVISTA LAMAZE PARA PADRES.** (Text in Spanish)
1994. s-a. Lamaze Publishing Co., 372 Danbury
Rd., Wilton, CT 06897-2523. TEL 203-834-2711.
FAX 203-761-8696. circ. 250,000. **Document type:**
consumer publication.
Description: Offers information to expectant
couples on prenatal and postpartum care through
Lamaze classes.

618   FR   ISSN 0035-290X
CODEN: RFGOAO
**REVUE FRANCAISE DE GYNECOLOGIE ET
D'OBSTETRIQUE.** (Text in French; summaries in
English, French and German) 1906. 10/yr. 940 F.
to individuals (foreign 1200 F.); students 470 F.
(foreign 655 F.). Expansion Scientifique, 31 bd. de
la Tour Maubourg, 75007 Paris, France.
TEL 40-62-64-00. FAX 45-55-69-20. Eds. Y.
Malinas, J. Seneze. adv.; bk.rev.; abstr.; charts; illus.;
stat.; tr.lit. circ. 5,000. (also avail. in microform from
UMI; reprint service avail. from UMI) **Indexed:**
Biol.Abstr., Chem.Abstr., Curr.Cont., Excerp.Med.,
Ind.Med., Rev.Plant Path.
—BLDSC (7904.170000); CASDDS; EMDOCS;
Faxon; SWETS; UMI. **CCC.**

618   JA   ISSN 0386-9865
CODEN: RFUSA4
**RINSHO FUJINKA SANKA/CLINICAL GYNECOLOGY AND
OBSTETRICS.** 1946. m. 2200 Yen($190) per no.
Igaku Shoin Ltd., 24-3, Hongo 5-chome, Bunkyo-ku,
Tokyo 113-91, Japan. TEL 03-817-5709. Ed.Bd.
circ. 3,000. **Indexed:** Biol.Abstr., Chem.Abstr., INIS
Atomind.
—BLDSC (3286.289000); CASDDS.

618   IT
RISVEGLIO OSTETRICO. 1922. m. L.8000. Editoriale
Emme 3, Corso Venezia 24, 20122 Milan, Italy.
TEL 2-66-91-97. adv. circ. 20,000.

**ROYAL COLLEGE OF MIDWIVES. CURRENT AWARENESS
SERVICE**; recent literature on midwifery. see
MEDICAL SCIENCES — Abstracting, Bibliographies,
Statistics

S H A R E NEWSLETTER. see PSYCHOLOGY

618   JA   ISSN 0912-2966
**SAITAMAKEN SANFUJINKA IKAIHO/SAITAMA SOCIETY
OF OBSTETRICIANS AND GYNECOLOGISTS.** (Text in
Japanese) 1970. a. Saitamaken Sanfujinka Ikai,
Saitamaken Ishikai, 5-1, Naka-cho 3-chome,
Urawa-shi, Saitama-ken 336, Japan.

618   JA   ISSN 0558-471X
CODEN: RKAKDK
**SANFUJINKA CHIRYO/OBSTETRICAL AND
GYNECOLOGICAL THERAPY.** (Text in Japanese)
1960. m. $350. Nagai Shoten Co., Ltd., 21-15,
Fukushima 8-chome, Fukushima-ku, Osaka-shi,
Osaka 553, Japan. Ed. T. Nagai. **Indexed:** INIS
Atomind. **Document type:** academic/scholarly
publication.
—BLDSC (6208.173000); CASDDS.

618   JA   ISSN 0913-865X
**SANFUJINKA KANPO KENKYU NO AYUMI/RECENT
PROGRESS OF KANPO MEDICINE IN OBSTETRICS AND
GYNECOLOGY.** (Text in Japanese) 1984. a.
2000 Yen. Shindan to Chiryosha, 4-1, Marunouchi
2-chome, Chiyoda-ku, Tokyo 100, Japan.

618 617   JA
**SANFUJINKA MAIKURO SAJARI GAKKAI
ZASSHI/JAPANESE JOURNAL OF GYNECOLOGICAL
MICROSURGERY.** (Text in Japanese) a. Sanfujinka
Maikuro Sajari Gakkai - Japan Society for
Gynecological Microsurgery, Tokai Daigaku Igakubu
Sanfujinka Kyoshitsu, 143, Shimokasuya,
Isehara-shi, Kanagawa-ken, Japan.

618   JA   ISSN 0558-4728
**SANFUJINKA NO JISSAI/OBSTETRICAL AND
GYNECOLOGICAL PRACTICE.** (Text in Japanese)
1952. m. 2000 Yen per no. Kanehara Shuppan
Ltd., 31-14, Yushima 2-chome, Bunkyo-ku, Tokyo
113-91, Japan. **Indexed:** INIS Atomind.

618   JA   ISSN 0386-9873
CODEN: SASEAU
**SANFUJINKA NO SEKAI/WORLD OF OBSTETRICS AND
GYNECOLOGY.** (Text in Japanese) 1949. m.
1900 Yen per no. Igaku no Sekaisha, 12-4, Kudan
Kita 1-chome, Chiyoda-ku, Tokyo 102, Japan.
Indexed: Chem.Abstr., INIS Atomind.
—CASDDS.

618 617   JA   ISSN 0915-8375
**SANFUJINKA SHUJUTSU/GYNECOLOGIC AND OBSTETRIC
SURGERY.** (Text in Japanese) 1990. a. 7000 Yen.
Medical View Co., Ltd., 2-30, Ichigaya Honmura-cho,
Shinjuku-ku, Tokyo 162, Japan.

618   JA   ISSN 0386-9792
CODEN: OBGYAR
SANKA TO FUJINKA/OBSTETRICS AND GYNECOLOGY.
(Text in Japanese) 1933. m. 1900 Yen per no.
Shindan to Chiryosha, 4-1, Marunouchi 2-chome,
Chiyoda-ku, Tokyo 100, Japan. **Indexed:** INIS
Atomind.
—BLDSC (6208.205000); CASDDS.

618.2   IE   ISSN 0925-6164
CODEN: SCRFEC
SCREENING. (Text in English) 1992. q. I£161($254)
(effective 1996). (International Society of Neonatal
Screening) Elsevier Science Ireland Ltd., P.O. Box 85,
Limerick, Ireland. TEL 353-61-471944.
FAX 353-61-472144. (Subscr. in U.S. and Canada
to: Elsevier Science Inc., Box 882, Madison Sq. Sta.,
New York, NY 10159-0882. TEL 212-989-5800.
FAX 212-633-3990) Eds. H. Naruse, H. Levy. adv.;
abstr.; illus.; stat. (also avail. in microform from UMI;
back issues avail.) **Indexed:** Excerp.Med. (1993-).
Document type: academic/scholarly publication.
—BLDSC (8211.815570); CASDDS; Genuine
Article. **CCC.**
Previously announced as: International Journal of
Neonatal and Later Screening.
Description: Provides scientific, technical and
medical information about newborn screening and all
other population based screening, including all types
of mass screening for genetic and non-genetic
diseases.
Refereed Serial

SEMINARS IN LAPAROSCOPIC SURGERY. see MEDICAL
SCIENCES — Surgery

SEMINARS IN PERINATOLOGY. see MEDICAL
SCIENCES — Pediatrics

618   CN   ISSN 0840-6006
SHATTERED DREAMS. 1987. q. Can.$16($18) Born to
Love, 15 Silas Hill Dr., North York, ON M2J 2X8,
Canada. TEL 416-499-8309. FAX 416-499-5606.
Ed. Debbie Anderson. bk.rev.; bibl. circ. 1,000. (back
issues avail.) **Document type:** newsletter.
Description: Offers support, information, sharing
and hope for the future to parents experiencing
miscarriage.

MEDICAL SCIENCES — OBSTETRICS AND GYNECOLOGY

618   CC   ISSN 1001-0858
SHIYONG FUKE YU CHANKE ZAZHI/JOURNAL OF PRACTICAL GYNECOLOGY AND OBSTETRICS. (Text in Chinese; abstracts in English) 1985. bi-m. $30. Shiyong Yixue Zazhishe - Applied Medical Science Journal Publishing House, 44-1, Jixian St., Heping District, Shenyang, Liaoning 110005, People's Republic of China. TEL 024-3864398. Ed. Wang Dezhi. adv. circ. 57,000. **Document type:** academic/scholarly publication.
Description: Features new developments and methods of practical diagnosis, treatment, and prevention of gynecological and obstetrical diseases.
Refereed Serial

618   JA   ISSN 0386-9881
CODEN: SHUIAX
SHUSANKI IGAKU/PERINATAL MEDICINE. (Text in Japanese) 1971. m. 2200 Yen per no. (effective Jan. 1994). Tokyo Igakusha Ltd., 35-4, Hongo 3-chome, Bunkyo-ku, Tokyo 113, Japan. TEL 03-3811-4119. FAX 03-3811-6135. **Document type:** academic/scholarly publication.
—CASDDS.

618   SI   ISSN 0129-3273
CODEN: SJOGDE
SINGAPORE JOURNAL OF OBSTETRICS & GYNAECOLOGY. vol.6, 1967. 3/yr. $25 to individuals; medical students $6. Obstetrical and Gynaecological Society of Singapore, c/o National University Hospital, Dept. of O & G, Lower Kent Ridge Road, Singapore 0511, Singapore. TEL 7724267. FAX 779-4753. Ed. Dilip K. Sen. adv.; bk.rev.; charts; illus. circ. 1,000. (reprint service avail. from ISI) **Indexed:** ASCA, Biol.Abstr., Chem.Abstr., Curr.Cont., ExtraMED. **Document type:** academic/scholarly publication.
●Also available on CD-ROM.
—BLDSC (8285.463800); CASDDS.
Formerly: Kandang Kerbau Hospital Bulletin (ISSN 0022-8346)
Description: Original and review articles on all aspects of obstetrics and gynaecology.

618.1 618.2   BL
SINOPSE DE GINECOLOGIA E OBSTETRICIA. (Text in English and Portuguese) vol.5, 1973. bi-m. Moreira Jr. Editora Ltda., Rua Henrique Martins, 493, 04504 Sao Paulo, Brazil. Ed.Bd. adv.

618.2   FR
SOCIETE FRANCAISE DE PSYCHO-PROPHYLAXIE OBSTETRICALE. BULLETIN OFFICIEL. 1959. q. 350 F. Societe Internationale de Psycho-Prophylaxie Obstetricale, 31 rue Saint-Guillaume, 75007 Paris, France. Ed. Daniel Lipszyc. adv.; bk.rev. **Document type:** bulletin.
Formerly: Societe Internationale de Psycho-Prophylaxie Obstetricale. Bulletin Officiel (ISSN 0037-9468)

618   BE   ISSN 0037-9522
SOCIETE ROYALE BELGE DE GYNECOLOGIE ET D'OBSTETRIQUE. BULLETIN.* vol.36, 1966. bi-m. Societe Royale Belge de Gynecologie et d'Obstetrique, 309 Ave. Moliere, Brussels 6, Belgium. adv. **Indexed:** Biol.Abstr.

618   US   ISSN 1071-5576
CODEN: JSGIED
▼**SOCIETY FOR GYNECOLOGIC INVESTIGATION. JOURNAL.** 1994. bi-m. $199 to institutions in U.S.; $243 to institutions outside the Americas (effective 1996). Elsevier Science Inc., 1155 Ave. of the Americas, New York, NY 10010. TEL 212-633-3950. FAX 212-633-3990. (Subscr. to: Box 882, Madison Sq. Sta., New York, NY 10159-0882. TEL 212-989-5800) Ed. Dr. R.A. Lobo. adv. (also avail. in microform from UMI; back issues avail.) **Indexed:** Excerp.Med. (1995-). **Document type:** academic/scholarly publication.
—BLDSC (4888.100000); CASDDS. **CCC.**
Description: Publishes timely and important scientific papers in all aspects of reproductive biology, including the disciplines of perinatology, obstetrics, gynecology, infertility and other related fields.
Refereed Serial

618   CN   ISSN 0849-5831
SOCIETY OF OBSTETRICIANS AND GYNECOLOGISTS OF CANADA. JOURNAL. Key Title: Journal S O G C. (Text in English, French) 1980. 12/yr. Can.$85 (US $100, elsewhere $107). (Society of Obstetricians and Gynecologists of Canada) Ribosome Communications, 55 Charles St., W., Ste. 3104, Toronto, ON M5S 2W9, Canada. TEL 416-925-7715. FAX 416-323-3064. Ed. Dr. P.J. Taylor; Pub. Adrian Stein. adv. contact: C. Norman Cook. bk.rev.; circ. 200 (paid); 15,000 (controlled).
—BLDSC (4898.450000).
Refereed Serial

618.202   US
SPECIAL DELIVERY. 1977. q. $20. Association of Labor Assistants & Childbirth Educators, Informed Birth and Parenting, Box 382724, Cambridge, MA 02238. TEL 617-441-2500. Ed. Laine Gerritsen. adv. contact: Jessica Porter. bk.rev.; illus.; circ. 2,000 (paid). (back issues avail.) **Indexed:** Hlth.Ind. **Document type:** consumer publication.
●Also available online. Vendor(s): Information Access Co.
Description: Discusses midwifery alternatives in birth, parenting, early childhood education.

618.1   IT
GLI SPECIALIZZATI. GINECOLOGIA. 1990. q. L.25000. E S I Stampa Medica s.r.l., Casella Postale 42, Lgo. Volontari del Sangue 10, 20097 S. Donato, Milan, Italy. TEL 39-2-5274241. FAX 39-2-55600670. TELEX 324894. Ed. Diego Onestinghel. adv.: B&W page L.5200000, color page L.6800000; trim 171 x 235; adv. contact: Ornella Galbiati. bk.rev. circ. 8,870.
Formerly: Ginecologia Oggi (ISSN 1120-365X)

618 346.01   US   ISSN 1046-6703
KF3771.Z95
STATE REPRODUCTIVE HEALTH MONITOR; legislative proposals and actions. q. $100 to individuals; institutions $120; foreign $113. Alan Guttmacher Institute, 120 Wall St., New York, NY 10005. TEL 212-248-1111. FAX 212-248-1951.
Description: Compiles state legislation dealing with reproductive health.

SURGICAL LAPAROSCOPY AND ENDOSCOPY. see MEDICAL SCIENCES — Surgery

618   GW   ISSN 0935-3208
CODEN: TWGYE
T W GYNAEKOLOGIE. 1988. bi-m. DM.74 (foreign DM.100). Verlag G. Braun GmbH, Karl-Friedrich-Str. 14-18, 76133 Karlsruhe, Germany. TEL 0721-165-0. FAX 0721-165191. **Indexed:** Excerp.Med. **Document type:** trade publication.
—BLDSC (9076.749200).

618.202   DK   ISSN 0106-1836
TIDSSKRIFT FOR JORDEMOEDRE. m. Almindelige Danske Jordemoderforening, Noerre Voldgade 90, DK-1358 Copenhagen K, Denmark. Ed. Inge Jensen. adv. circ. 2,000.

618   NE   ISSN 0921-7304
CODEN: TIFEE
TIJDSCHRIFT VOOR FERTILITEITSONDERZOEK. 1987. q. Reed HealthCare (Subsidiary of: Reed Elsevier plc), P.O. Box 1126, 1000 BC Amsterdam, Netherlands. TEL 31-20-5153350. FAX 31-20-5153354. Ed. Dr. A.Th. Alberda. adv. contact: G.J.M. van den Akker. circ. 2,000. **Indexed:** Excerp.Med. (1994-).
Description: For gynaecologists and gynaecologists in training in the Benelux.
Refereed Serial

618   JA   ISSN 0915-7204
TOKAI SANKA FUJINKA GAKKAI ZASSHI/TOKAI JOURNAL OF OBSTETRICS AND GYNECOLOGY. (Text in English, Japanese) 1981. a. Tokai Sanka Fujinka Gakkai - Tokai Society of Obstetrics and Gynecology, Nogoya Daigaku Iryo Gijutsu Tanki Daigakubu, 1-20, Daiko Minami 1-chome, Higashi-ku, Nagoya-shi, Aichi-ken 461.

618.1   SP   ISSN 0040-8867
TOKO-GINECOLOGIA PRACTICA. 1936. m. (10/yr.). 5900 ptas.($70) (effective 1995). Editorial Garsi, S.A., Juan Bravo 46, 28006 Madrid, Spain. TEL 34-1-4021212. FAX 34-1-4020954. Ed. J. Cruz Hermida. adv.; bk.rev.; charts; stat. circ. 3,000. **Indexed:** Biol.Abstr., Excerp.Med., Ind.Med.Esp., Nutr.Abstr.
—BLDSC (8862.885000); EMDOCS.

618   US   ISSN 0891-9925
CODEN: TRREEN
TROPHOBLAST RESEARCH. 1984. irreg., vol.4, 1990. price varies. Plenum Publishing Corp., 233 Spring St., New York, NY 10013-1578. TEL 212-620-8000. FAX 212-463-0742. TELEX 23-421139. Eds. Richard K. Miller, Henry A. Thiede. (back issues avail.) **Indexed:** Chem.Abstr. (1984-). **Document type:** monographic series, proceedings.
—BLDSC (9051.930000); CASDDS.
Refereed Serial

618   NR   ISSN 0189-5117
TROPICAL JOURNAL OF OBSTETRICS AND GYNAECOLOGY. (Text in English) 1981. s-a. $10. (Society of Gynaecology and Obstetrics of Nigeria) Literamed Nigeria Ltd., Plot 45, Alausa, Oregun Village, P.M.B. 21068, Ikeja, Lagos, Nigeria. Ed. V.E. Aimaku. circ. 1,000.

618   IT   ISSN 0393-7801
ULTRASONICA. (Text in Italian; summaries in English) 1986. q. L.60000($60) (Societa Italiana di Ecografia Ostetrica e Ginecologica) C I C Edizioni Internazionali s.r.l., Via L. Spallanzani, 11, 00161 Rome, Italy. TEL 06-8412673. FAX 06-44242033. TELEX 622099 CIC I. (Co-sponsor: Societa Italiana di Ecografia Pediatrica) Dir. C. Giorlandino.
—BLDSC (9082.792000).

618 616.07   UK   ISSN 0960-7692
ULTRASOUND IN OBSTETRICS & GYNECOLOGY. 1991. m. £210($350) to individuals; institutions £300($510) (effective 1996). (International Society of Ultrasound in Obstetrics and Gynecology) Parthenon Publishing Group, Casterton Hall, Carnforth, Lancs LA6 2LA, England. TEL 44-15242-72084. FAX 44-15242-71587. (In U.S.: Box 1564, Pearl River, NY 10965. TEL 914-735-9363) Ed. Stuart Campbell. bk.rev. (back issues avail.) **Indexed:** ASCA, Curr.Cont., Excerp.Med., Sci.Cit.Ind. **Document type:** academic/scholarly publication.
—BLDSC (9082.815300); Genuine Article; SWETS.
Description: Publishes clinical research in the field.
Refereed Serial

618.1   SA   ISSN 0254-184X
UNIVERSITY OF CAPE TOWN. DEPARTMENT OF OBSTETRICS AND GYNAECOLOGY. ANNUAL REPORT. (Text in English) 1952. a. free. University of Cape Town, Department of Obstetrics and Gynaecology, Medical School, Anzio Rd., Observatory, Cape Town 7925, South Africa. TEL 27-21-4066114. FAX 27-21-4486921. (Co-sponsor: Cape Provincial Administration) Ed. Herman A. van Coeverden de Groot. circ. 100. **Document type:** corporate report.
Formerly: University of Cape Town. Department of Gynaecology. Annual Report (ISSN 0069-0228)
Description: Lists personnel, research in progress, publications and programs available in the department.

618 616.6   IT   ISSN 1121-3086
CODEN: UIJOFU
UROGYNAECOLOGIA INTERNATIONAL JOURNAL. 1987. 3/yr. (Associazione Italiana di Urologia Ginecologica) Associato all'U S P I - Unione Stampa Periodica Italia, Pallonetto S. Chiara 8, 80134 Naples, Italy. TEL 81-446146. **Indexed:** Excerp.Med. (1995-). **Document type:** academic/scholarly publication.
—BLDSC (9124.397000).

VIDEO JOURNAL OF COLOR FLOW IMAGING. see MEDICAL SCIENCES — Radiology And Nuclear Medicine

618.1 350   US   ISSN 0739-4179
WASHINGTON MEMO (NEW YORK). 1966. 10/yr. $35 to individuals; institutions $45; foreign $60 (effective 1995). Alan Guttmacher Institute, Public Policy Division, 120 Wall St., New York, NY 10005. TEL 212-248-1111. FAX 212-248-1951. Ed. Terry Sollom. bibl.; index. circ. 2,800. (back issues avail.; reprint service avail. from UMI)

WOMEN'S HEALTH ISSUES. see WOMEN'S HEALTH

MEDICAL SCIENCES — ONCOLOGY

616 US ISSN 1077-4084
CODEN: YBINEG
YEAR BOOK OF INFERTILITY AND REPRODUCTIVE ENDOCRINOLOGY. 1989. a. $66.95 (residents $35) (effective 1966). Mosby - Year Book, Inc. (Chicago) (Subsidiary of: Times Mirror Company), 200 N. LaSalle St., Chicago, IL 60601-1080.
TEL 312-726-9733. FAX 312-726-6075. TELEX 206155. Ed. Dr. D. Mishele.
—BLDSC (9413.460000).
 Formerly (until 1994); Year Book of Infertility (ISSN 0896-4475)

618.2 US ISSN 1044-4890
RG631
THE YEAR BOOK OF NEONATAL AND PERINATAL MEDICINE. 1987. a. $72.95 (residents $35) (effective 1996). Mosby - Year Book, Continuity Division, 200 N. LaSalle, Chicago, IL 60601. TEL 312-726-9746. FAX 312-726-6075. TELEX 206155. Ed. Dr. Avroy Fanaroff. illus. (reprint service avail.)
●Also available online. Vendor(s): Ovid Technologies.
—BLDSC (9414.624000).
 Formerly (until 1989): Year Book of Perinatal - Neonatal Medicine (ISSN 8756-5005)

618.1 618.2 US ISSN 0084-3911
RG26 CODEN: YOBGAD
YEAR BOOK OF OBSTETRICS AND GYNECOLOGY. 1933. a. $72.95 (residents $35) (effective 1996). Mosby - Year Book, Inc., Continuity Division, 200 N. LaSalle, Chicago, IL 60601. TEL 312-726-9733. FAX 312-726-6075. TELEX 206155. Ed. Daniel R. Mishell, Jr., M.D. illus. (reprint service avail.) **Indexed:** Curr.Adv.Ecol.Sci.
●Also available online. Vendor(s): Ovid Technologies.
—BLDSC (9414.650000).

618 GW ISSN 0300-967X
RG1 CODEN: ZGPRA3
ZEITSCHRIFT FUER GEBURTSHILFE UND PERINATOLOGIE. (Text in German; summaries in English and German) 1876. s-m. DM.345. Ferdinand Enke Verlag, Postfach 300366, 70443 Stuttgart, Germany. TEL 0711-135798-0. FAX 0711-135798-30. TELEX 07252275-GTV-D. Ed.Bd. adv.; bk.rev.; charts; illus.; index per vol. (also avail. in microfiche from BHP; reprint service avail. from IRC) **Indexed:** Bibl.Dev.Med.& Child Neur., Biol.Abstr., Chem.Abstr., Curr.Cont., Dent.Ind., Excerp.Med., Ind.Med., Nutr.Abstr., Sci.Cit.Ind. **Document type:** monographic series.
—ADONIS; CASDDS; Faxon; Genuine Article; SWETS. **CCC.**
 Formerly: Zeitschrift fuer Geburtshilfe und Gynaekologie (ISSN 0044-278X)

618.1 GW ISSN 0044-4197
CODEN: ZEGYAX
ZENTRALBLATT FUER GYNAEKOLOGIE. (Text in German; summaries in English) 1877. m. DM.306 (foreign DM.322). (Arbeitsgemeinschaft fuer Gynaekologische Endoskopie) Johann Ambrosius Barth, Postfach 102869, 69018 Heidelberg, Germany. TEL 06221-489281. FAX 06221-489205. Ed.Bd. adv.; B&W page DM.2000; trim 210 x 275; adv. contact: Petra Schoene. bk.rev.; charts; illus.; index. circ. 2,000. (also avail. in microfiche from BHP) **Indexed:** Biol.Abstr., Chem.Abstr., Curr.Adv.Cancer Res., Curr.Adv.Ecol.Sci., Curr.Cont., Dent.Ind., Excerp.Med., Ind.Med., Nutr.Abstr. **Document type:** academic/scholarly publication.
—BLDSC (9508.400000); CASDDS; EMDOCS; Faxon; Genuine Article; SWETS; UMI. **CCC.**
 Description: Covers all areas of gynecology and obstetrics.

618 614 CC
ZHONGGUO FUNU JIANKANG/CHINA WOMEN'S HEALTH. (Text in Chinese) bi-m. Liaoning Sheng Weisheng Ting, No.6, Heping Dajie 6 Duan 18 Li, Shenyang, Liaoning 110005, People's Republic of China. TEL 365444. Ed. Qin Xinhua.

618 CC
ZHONGGUO FUYOU BAOJIAN/CHINESE WOMEN AND CHILDREN'S HEALTH. (Text in Chinese) bi-m. Jilin Sheng Weisheng Ting - Jilin Provincial Bureau of Health, Fu 2, Dong Minzhu Dajie, Changchun, Jilin 130061, People's Republic of China. TEL 825027. Ed. He Jiesheng.

ZHONGGUO YIXUE WENZHAI (JIHUA SHENGYU, FUCHAN KEXUE)/CHINA MEDICAL ABSTRACTS (BIRTH CONTROL AND GYNECOLOGY). see *MEDICAL SCIENCES — Abstracting, Bibliographies, Statistics*

618 CC
ZHONGHUA FU-CHANKE ZAZHI/CHINESE JOURNAL OF OBSTETRICS AND GYNECOLOGY. (Text in Chinese) q. $3 per no. Guoji Shudian, Qikan Bu - China International Book Trading Corp., Chegongzhuang Xilu 21, P.O. Box 399, Beijing 100044, People's Republic of China. **Indexed:** Chem.Abstr., ExtraMED, Ind.Med. **Document type:** academic/scholarly publication.
●Also available on CD-ROM.

ZHONGHUA NEIFENMI DAIXIE ZAZHI/CHINESE JOURNAL OF ENDOCRINOLOGY AND METABOLISM. see *MEDICAL SCIENCES — Endocrinology*

MEDICAL SCIENCES — Oncology

616.9 SP ISSN 1133-3871
A.E.C.C.. 1993. q. free. Asociacion Espanola Contra el Cancer, C. Amador de los Rios 5, 28010 Madrid, Spain. TEL 93-319-41-38. FAX 91-319-09-66. Dir. Lolina Perez Caballero. circ. 20,000.
 Description: Cover cancer issues and notices about association activities.

A L R A NEWSLETTER. (Abortion Law Reform Association) see *BIRTH CONTROL*

616.99 340 US
A V A ADVISOR. 1980. q. $25 membership; reduced rate for asbestos victims. Asbestos Victims of America, 4622A W. Walnut, Soquel, CA 95073. TEL 408-476-3646. Ed. H.R. Maurer. adv. circ. 18,000. (looseleaf format; back issues avail.) **Document type:** newsletter.
 Description: Coverage of medical, legal, and social aspects of asbestos, including worker safety, scientific data, medical treatments, laws governing uses and exposure, legislative developments, and legal remedies.

ACOUSTIC NEUROMA ASSOCIATION NOTES. see *MEDICAL SCIENCES — Otorhinolaryngology*

616.994 PE ISSN 1013-5545
ACTA CANCEROLOGICA. (Text in Spanish; summaries in English) 1960; resumed 1987. s-a. S/240($15) Peruvian Society of Cancerology, Av. Angamos Este 2520, Lima 34, Peru. Ed. Dr. Juvenal Sanchez. adv.; bibl.; charts; illus. circ. 500. **Indexed:** Biol.Abstr.
 Description: Covers the study and research of cancer.

616.99 NO ISSN 0284-186X
CODEN: ACTOEL
ACTA ONCOLOGICA. (Supplement avail. (ISSN 1100-1704)) (Text in English) 1921. 8/yr. NOK 1860 in Nordic countries; elsewhere $318 (effective 1996). (Acta Radiologica) Scandinavian University Press, P.O. Box 2959 Toeyen, N-0608 Oslo, Norway. TEL 47-22-57-54-00. FAX 47-22-57-53-53. Ed. Lars-Gunnar Larsson. adv.; bk.rev.; bibl.; illus.; index, cum.index. circ. 3,500. **Indexed:** ASCA, Biol.Abstr., Biotech.Abstr., Chem.Abstr., Curr.Adv.Cell & Devel.Biol., Curr.Adv.Ecol.Sci., Curr.Cont., Dent.Ind., Excerp.Med., Ind.Med., Ind.Sci.Rev., INSPEC (1987-1993), Med.& Surg.Dermat., Sci.Cit.Ind.
—BLDSC (0641.705000); ADONIS; CASDDS; Ei; Faxon; Genuine Article; SWETS; UMI; UnCover. **CCC.**
 Former titles (until 1986): Acta Radiologica. Oncology (ISSN 0349-652X); (until 1979): Acta Radiologica. Oncology, Radiation, Physics, Biology (ISSN 0348-5196); (until 1977): Acta Radiologica. Therapy, Physics, Biology (ISSN 0567-8064); Which superseded in part (in 1962): Acta Radiologica (ISSN 0001-6926).
 Description: Focuses on all fields of clinical cancer research including cancer nursing and psychological and social aspects of cancer.

616.994 IT ISSN 0393-7542
ACTA ONCOLOGICA. (Consists of two sections published in alternative issues) (Editions in English, Italian) bi-m. L.90000($125) (Italian Society for the Prevention and Diagnosis of Tumors) Piccin Editore, Via Altinate 107, 35100 Padua, Italy. TEL 049-655566. FAX 049-8750693. (Co-sponsor: Italian Society for the Treatment of Tumors) Eds. C. Maltoni, L. Caldarola. adv.: B&W page L.3500000, color page L.5000000; 195 x 270. circ. 9,398. (reprint service avail. from UMI) **Indexed:** Excerp.Med.
—Faxon.

616.99 NO ISSN 1100-1704
ACTA ONCOLOGICA. SUPPLEMENT. irreg. Scandinavian University Press, P.O. Box 2959 Toeyen, N-0608 Oslo, Norway. TEL 47-22-57-54-00. FAX 47-22-57-53-53. **Indexed:** Excerp.Med. (1993-). **Document type:** academic/scholarly publication.

616.994 US ISSN 0065-230X
RC267 CODEN: ACRSAJ
ADVANCES IN CANCER RESEARCH. 1953. irreg., vol.61, 1993. Academic Press, Inc., 525 B St., Ste. 1900, San Diego, CA 92101-4495. TEL 619-231-0926. FAX 619-699-6715. (Subscr. to: Order Dept., 6277 Sea Harbor Dr., 4th Fl., Orlando, FL 32887. TEL 800-321-5068) Eds. George Klein, Sidney Weinhouse. (reprint service avail. from ISI) **Indexed:** Biol.Abstr., Biotech.Abstr., Chem.Abstr., Dent.Ind., Excerp.Med., Ind.Med., Ind.Sci.Rev., Ind.Vet., INIS Atomind., Sci.Cit.Ind., Telegen, Vet.Bull. **Document type:** monographic series.
—BLDSC (0701.000000); CASDDS; EMDOCS; Faxon; SWETS; UnCover. **CCC.**
 Refereed Serial

616.99 US ISSN 0178-2134
RC271.I45 CODEN: AICTER
ADVANCES IN IMMUNITY AND CANCER THERAPY. 1985. irreg., vol.2, 1986. price varies. Springer-Verlag, 175 Fifth Ave., New York, NY 10010. TEL 212-460-1500. FAX 212-473-6272. (Also: Berlin, Heidelberg, Tokyo, Vienna) (reprint service avail. from ISI) **Indexed:** INIS Atomind. **Document type:** monographic series.
—BLDSC (0709.095000).

616.99 US ISSN 0735-0104
CODEN: AVONDN
ADVANCES IN VIRAL ONCOLOGY. 1982. irreg., latest vol.8. price varies. Raven Press (Subsidiary of: Wolters Kluwer N.V.), 1185 Ave. of the Americas, New York, NY 10036. TEL 212-930-9500. FAX 212-869-3495. Ed. George Klein. (reprint service avail. from UMI) **Document type:** monographic series.
—BLDSC (0711.900000); CASDDS.
 Refereed Serial

616.99 JA ISSN 0916-068X
AICHI CANCER CENTER RESEARCH INSTITUTE. SCIENTIFIC REPORT. (Text in English) 1968. biennial. free. Aichi Cancer Center Research Institute, Kanakoden, Chikusa-ku, Nagoya 464, Japan. TEL 052-762-6111. FAX 052-763-5233. Ed. Akio Matsukaga. circ. 1,000. **Document type:** government publication.
 Formerly: Aichi Cancer Center Research Institute. Annual Report (ISSN 0374-5295)
 Description: Covers the scientific research activities conducted by the institute.

616.99 CC ISSN 1000-467X
AIZHENG/CANCER. (Text in Chinese) bi-m. Zhongshan Yike Daxue, Zhongliu Yiyuan - Sun Yat-sen Medical University, Oncology Hospital, No. 651, Dongfeng Donglu, Guangzhou, Guangdong 510060, People's Republic of China. TEL 777136. Ed. Guan Zhongzhen.

616.99 GW ISSN 0174-2744
AKTUELLE ONKOLOGIE. 1981. irreg., vol.71, 1993. W. Zuckschwerdt Verlag GmbH, Industriestr. 17, 82110 Germering, Germany. TEL 089-894349-0. FAX 089-89434950. Ed.Bd. **Document type:** academic/scholarly publication.
—BLDSC (0785.778000). **CCC.**

MEDICAL SCIENCES — ONCOLOGY

616.99 US ISSN 0197-016X
AMERICAN ASSOCIATION FOR CANCER RESEARCH. PROCEEDINGS OF THE ANNUAL MEETING. 1953. a. $35 (foreign $39) (effective 1995). American Association for Cancer Research, Public Ledger Bldg., 620 Chestnut St., Philadelphia, PA 19106. TEL 215-440-9300. FAX 215-440-9354. **Document type:** proceedings.
—BLDSC (6841.204900); SWETS; UnCover.
Former titles (until 1974): Annual Meeting of the American Association for Cancer Research. Proceedings (ISSN 0197-0151); (until 1971): American Association for Cancer Research. Proceedings (ISSN 0569-2261)
Description: Publishes papers on original research presented at the annual meeting.
Refereed Serial

616.99 US ISSN 1044-4580
AMERICAN INSTITUTE FOR CANCER RESEARCH NEWSLETTER. 1983. q. free. American Institute for Cancer Research (AICR), 1759 R St., N.W., Washington, DC 20009. TEL 202-328-7744. FAX 202-328-7226. Ed. Christine Murray. bk.rev.; bibl.; charts; illus.; stat.; circ. 1,700,000 (controlled). (looseleaf format; back issues avail.) **Document type:** newsletter.
Description: Covers diet, nutrition, and dietary guidelines for reducing cancer risk.

616.99 US ISSN 0277-3732
CODEN: AJCODI
AMERICAN JOURNAL OF CLINICAL ONCOLOGY; cancer clinical trials. 1978. bi-m. $164 to individuals (foreign 209); institutions $246 (foreign $292) (effective 1996). Raven Press (Subsidiary of: Wolters Kluwer N.V.), 1185 Ave. of the Americas, New York, NY 10036. TEL 212-930-9500. FAX 212-869-3495. Ed. Dr. Luther W. Brady. adv. contact: Phyllis Noyes. bk.rev.; charts; illus.; index. circ. 2,500. (also avail. in microform; back issues avail.; reprint service avail. from UMI) **Indexed:** Biol.Abstr., Biotech.Abstr., Chem.Abstr., Curr.Cont., Dent.Ind., Excerp.Med., Ind.Med., Ind.Sci.Rev., INIS Atomind., Med.& Surg.Dermat., NRN, Sci.Cit.Ind., Telegen. **Document type:** academic/scholarly publication.
—BLDSC (0823.500000); CASDDS; Faxon; Genuine Article; SWETS; UMI; UnCover. **CCC.**
Formerly: Cancer Clinical Trials (ISSN 0190-1206)
Description: Presents pathologic, surgical, and clinical data related to all aspects of metastatic and neoplastic diseases and localized tumors.
Refereed Serial

THE AMERICAN JOURNAL OF HOSPICE & PALLIATIVE CARE. see *GERONTOLOGY AND GERIATRICS*

616.9 612 NE
ANALOGUES IN CANCER AND HUMAN REPRODUCTION. (Text in English) irreg. price varies. Kluwer Academic Publishers, Postbus 17, 3300 AA Dordrecht, Netherlands. TEL 31-78-392392. FAX 31-78-392254. TELEX 29245 KAPG NL. (Dist. by: Kluwer Academic Publishers Group, P.O. Box 322, 3300 AH Dordrecht, Netherlands. TEL 31-78-392392. FAX 31-78-546474; N. America dist. addr.: Box 358, Accord Sta., Hingham, MA 02018-0358. TEL 617-871-6600. FAX 617-871-6528) **Document type:** monographic series.

616.99 NE ISSN 0923-7534
CODEN: ANONE2
ANNALS OF ONCOLOGY. (Text in English) 1990. 10/yr. fl.692 to institutions; $443 to institutions in U.S. (effective 1996). (European Society for Medical Oncology) Kluwer Academic Publishers, Postbus 17, 3300 AA Dordrecht, Netherlands. TEL 31-78-392392. FAX 31-78-392254. TELEX 29245 KAPG NL. E-mail: SERVICES@WKAP.NL. (Dist. by: Kluwer Academic Publishers Group, P.O. Box 322, 3300 AH Dordrecht, Netherlands. TEL 31-78-392392. FAX 31-78-546474; N. America dist. addr.: Box 358, Accord Sta., Hingham, MA 02018-0358. TEL 617-871-6600. FAX 617-871-6528) Ed. F. Cavalli. (also avail. in microform from UMI; back issues avail.; reprint service avail. from SWZ) **Indexed:** ASCA, Bull.Signal., Curr.Cont., Excerp.Med., Ind.Med., Inpharma, Int.Abstr.Biol.Sci., Reac., Sci.Cit.Ind. **Document type:** academic/scholarly publication.
—BLDSC (1043.320000); Faxon; Genuine Article; SWETS; UMI. **CCC.**
Refereed Serial

ANNALS OF SURGICAL ONCOLOGY. see *MEDICAL SCIENCES — Surgery*

616.99 SW ISSN 0348-8799
ANNUAL REPORT ON THE RESULTS OF TREATMENT IN GYNECOLOGICAL CANCER. 1937. triennial. $45. Annual Report, Radiumhemmet, S-171 76 Stockholm, Sweden. TEL 08-328752. Dr. Folke Pettersson. adv.; charts. circ. 2,000. **Indexed:** Excerp.Med. **Document type:** monographic series.
—BLDSC (1515.880000).
Former titles (until 1977): Annual Report on the Results of Treatment in Carcinoma of the Uterus, Vagina and Ovary (ISSN 0346-7503); (until 1973): Annual Report on the Results of Treatment in Carcinoma of the Uterus and Vagina.

616.994 612.015 UK ISSN 0266-9536
CODEN: ACDDEA
ANTI-CANCER DRUG DESIGN. 1985. 8/yr. £225($370) (effective 1996). (Cancer Research Campaign) Oxford University Press, Oxford Journals, Walton St., Oxford OX2 6DP, England. TEL 01865-267907. FAX 01865-267773. TELEX 837330-OXPRES-G. E-mail: jnlorders@oup.co.uk. (U.S. subscr. to: Oxford University Press Inc., 2001 Evans Rd., Cary, NC 27513. TEL 919-677-0977. FAX 919-677-1714) Ed. Stephen Neidle. adv.; index, cum.index. circ. 300. (also avail. in microfilm; back issues avail.) **Indexed:** Chem.Abstr., Curr.Adv.Ecol.Sci., Curr.Cont., Excerp.Med., Ind.Med., Telegen. **Document type:** academic/scholarly publication.
—BLDSC (1547.287000); CASDDS; Faxon; Genuine Article; SWETS; UMI; UnCover. **CCC.**

616.99 UK ISSN 0959-4973
CODEN: ANTDEV
ANTI-CANCER DRUGS; international journal on anti-cancer agents. 1990. bi-m. £295($499) to institutions (effective 1995). Rapid Communications of Oxford Ltd., The Old Malthouse, Paradise St., Oxford OX1 1LD, England. TEL 01865-790447. FAX 01865-244012. E-mail: rapidcom@vax.oxford.ac.uk. Ed. Dr. Mels Sluyser. adv. contact: Julie Gribben. bk.rev. (reprint service avail.) **Indexed:** Chem.Abstr., Excerp.Med. (1993-), Ind.Med., Sci.Cit.Ind. **Document type:** academic/scholarly publication.
●Also available on CD-ROM.
—BLDSC (1547.287300); ADONIS; CASDDS; Genuine Article. **CCC.**
Description: Aims to stimulate and report both clinical and experimental results of research on toxic and non-toxic anti-cancer agents.
Refereed Serial

616.9 RM282.I44 US ISSN 0892-7049
CODEN: AIRAEB
ANTIBODY, IMMUNOCONJUGATES, AND RADIOPHARMACEUTICALS. q. $145 (foreign $185). Mary Ann Liebert, Inc. Publishers, 2 Madison Ave., Larchmont, NY 10538. TEL 914-834-3100. FAX 914-834-3688. E-mail: Liebert@pipeline.com. Ed. Dr. Stanley E. Order. **Indexed:** Excerp.Med. (1993-). **Document type:** academic/scholarly publication.
—BLDSC (1547.271000); CASDDS; Genuine Article; SWETS.
Description: Contains papers and review articles on uses of antibodies, immunoconjugates and radiopharmaceuticals in the diagnosis and treatment of cancer.
Refereed Serial

616.99 GR ISSN 0250-7005
CODEN: ANTRD4
ANTICANCER RESEARCH; international journal of cancer research and treatment. (Text and summaries in English) 1981. bi-m. Dr.500 to individuals (outside Europe Dr.550); institutions Dr.1045 (outside Europe Dr.1095). John G. Delinassios, Ed. & Pub, Km. 1, Kapandritiou-Kalamou, P.O. Box 22, 111 45 Kapandriti, Attica, Greece. TEL 30-1-2016-380. adv.; bk.rev.; index. circ. 1,300. (back issues avail.) **Indexed:** Biol.Abstr., Chem.Abstr., Curr.Adv.Biochem., Curr.Adv.Cell & Devel.Biol., Curr.Adv.Ecol.Sci., Curr.Adv.Genetics & Molec.Biol., Curr.Cont., Excerp.Med., Ind.Med., Ind.Sci.Rev., NRN, Rev.Med.& Vet.Mycol., Sci.Cit.Ind., Telegen. **Document type:** academic/scholarly publication.
—BLDSC (1547.290000); CASDDS; Faxon; Genuine Article; SWETS; UnCover. **CCC.**
Description: Contains high-quality works on all aspects of experimental and clinical cancer research.

616.99 574.192 GW ISSN 0946-4832
CODEN: ADRCEG
ANTIINFECTIVE DRUGS AND CHEMOTHERAPY. q. DM.150. (European Society for Biomodulation and Chemotherapy) Futuramed Publishers GmbH, Postfach 830358, 81703 Munich, Germany. TEL 089-6701434. FAX 089-674047. **Document type:** academic/scholarly publication.
—BLDSC (1547.534480); CASDDS.
Incorporates: Journal on Chemotherapy of Infectious Diseases and Malignancies (ISSN 0724-9004)
Description: Publishes information regarding new therapeutic approaches for treating infection and malignant disease.

616.994 IT ISSN 0004-0266
ARCHIVIO ITALIANO DI PATOLOGIA E CLINICA DEI TUMORI. (Text in English and Italian) vol.14, 1971. q. L.6000. Universita degli Studi di Milano, Istituto di Farmacologia, Via Vanvitelli 32, Milan, Italy. charts; illus. **Indexed:** Biol.Abstr., Chem.Abstr., Ind.Med.

616.9 SP
ASOCIACION ESPAÑOLA CONTRA EL CANCER. MEMORIA. 1958. a. free. Asociacion Española Contra el Cancer, C. Amador de los Rios 5, 28010 Madrid, Spain. TEL 91-319-41-38. FAX 91-319-09-66. charts; stat.
Former titles: Asociacion Española Contra el Cancer. Memoria Tecnico-Administrativa; Asociacion Española Contra el Cancer. Memoria de la Assemblea General (ISSN 0066-8540)

616.99 UK ISSN 1350-9667
▼**AUDIO JOURNAL OF ONCOLOGY.** 1995. q. £69 to inidviduals in the E.U. (N. America $135; elsewhere £80); institutions in the E.U. £130 (N. America $225; elsewhere £145) (effective 1995). Chapman & Hall, Journals Department (Subsidiary of: International Thomson Publishing Group), 2-6 Boundary Row, London SE1 8HN, England. TEL 0171-865-0066. FAX 0171-522-9623. TELEX 290164 CHAPMA G. E-mail: journal@chall.mhs.compuserve.com. (Subscr. to: International Thomson Publishing Services Ltd., Cheriton House, North Way, Andover, Hants. SP10 5BE, England. TEL 01264-342713. FAX 01264-342807; Subscr. in N. America to: Chapman & Hall, Journals Promotion Department, One Penn Plaza, 41st Fl., New York, NY 10119. TEL 212-564-1060. FAX 212-564-1505) Ed.Bd. adv. (audio cassette; reprint service avail.) **Document type:** academic/scholarly publication.
Description: Covers research in cancer.
Refereed Serial

616.994 QD1 NE ISSN 0304-419X
CODEN: BBACE
B B A - REVIEWS ON CANCER. (Section of: Biochimica et Biophysica Acta (ISSN 0006-3002)) vol.605, 1977. bi-m. fl.922($562) (effective 1996). Elsevier Science B.V., P.O. Box 211, 1000 AE Amsterdam, Netherlands. TEL 31-20-4853911. FAX 31-20-4853598. TELEX 18582 ESPA NL. E-mail: nlinfo-f@elsevier.nl; usinfo-f@elsevier.com; forinfo-kyf04035@niftyserve.or.jp; Site addr.: http://www.elsevier.nl/. (Subscr. in U.S. and Canada to: Elsevier Science Inc., Box 882, Madison Sq. Sta., New York, NY 10159-0882. TEL 212-989-5800. FAX 212-633-3990) Ed.Bd. (also avail. in microform from UMI; reprint service avail. from ISI) **Indexed:** Curr.Adv.Ecol.Sci., Excerp.Med., Ind.Vet. **Document type:** academic/scholarly publication.
—ADONIS; Faxon; Genuine Article; SWETS. **CCC.**
Description: Presents critical reviews on new developments in cancer investigation at the biochemical level.
Refereed Serial

616.99 IS
BAMAH (GIVATAYIM); journal for health professionals in the field of cancer. (Text in Hebrew) 1983. irreg. free. Israel Cancer Association, Revivim 7, P.O. Box 437, Givatayim 51304, Israel. TEL 972-3-5717234. FAX 972-3-5719578. Ed. Miri Ziv. circ. 10,000.

BARN OCH CANCER. see *MEDICAL SCIENCES — Pediatrics*

MEDICAL SCIENCES — ONCOLOGY

616.99 NE
BIOSYNTHETIC PRODUCTS FOR CANCER CHEMOTHERAPY. irreg., vol.6, 1989. price varies. Elsevier Science B.V., Books Division, P.O. Box 211, 1000 AE Amsterdam, Netherlands. TEL 31-20-4853911. FAX 31-20-4853705. TELEX 18582 ESPA NL.
E-mail: nlinfo-f@elsevier.nl; usinfo-f@elsevier.com; forinfo-kyf04035@niftyserve.or.jp; Site addr.: http://www.elsevier.nl/. (Subscr. in U.S. and Canada to: Elsevier Science Inc., Box 882, Madison Sq. Sta., New York, NY 10159. TEL 212-989-5800) Ed.Bd. (reprint service avail. from ISI) **Document type:** monographic series.
Refereed Serial

616.99249 US ISSN 1074-6900
▼**BREAST CANCER**; evolution of concepts. Announced for publication in 1996. q. $145 to individuals; institutions $225 (effective 1996). Field & Wood, Medical Periodicals, Inc., Box 975, Blue Bell, PA 19422. TEL 610-828-4010. FAX 215-482-0226. Ed. Dr. Gruhn. **Document type:** academic/scholarly publication.
Refereed Serial

616.99249 US ISSN 0167-6806
CODEN: BCTRD6
BREAST CANCER RESEARCH AND TREATMENT. 1981. 15/yr. fl.1692.50 to institutions; $1032 to institutions in U.S. (effective 1996). Kluwer Academic Publishers Boston, Box 358, Accord Sta., Hingham, MA 02018-0358. TEL 617-871-6600. FAX 617-871-6528. TELEX 200190. (Dist. outside N. America by: Kluwer Academic Publishers Group, P.O. Box 322, 3300 AH Dordrecht, Netherlands. TEL 31-78-392392. FAX 31-78-546474) Ed. Marc E. Lippman. adv.; bk.rev. (also avail. in microform from UMI; back issues avail.; reprint service avail. from SWZ) **Indexed:** ASCA, Biol.Abstr., Bull.Signal., Chem.Abstr., Curr.Adv.Cancer Res., Curr.Adv.Ecol.Sci., Curr.Cont., Excerp.Med., Ind.Med., Ind.Sci.Rev., INIS Atomind., Int.Abstr.Biol.Sci., Sci.Cit.Ind. **Document type:** academic/scholarly publication.
—BLDSC (2277.494000); ADONIS; CASDDS; Faxon; Genuine Article; SWETS; UMI; UnCover. **CCC.**
Refereed Serial

616.99 US
CODEN: BCSYDM
BRISTOL-MEYERS - SQUIBB CANCER SYMPOSIA. 1979. irreg., vol.15, 1993. price varies. Raven Press (Subsidiary of: Wolters Kluwer N.V.), 1185 Ave. of the Americas, New York, NY 10036. TEL 212-930-9500. FAX 212-869-3495. Ed. Stephen K. Carter. (reprint service avail. from ISI) **Indexed:** Chem.Abstr. **Document type:** proceedings.
—CASDDS.
Formerly (until 1990): Bristol-Meyers Cancer Symposia. Proceedings (ISSN 0197-8756)

616.992 CN ISSN 1185-1031
BRITISH COLUMBIA CANCER RESEARCH CENTRE. ANNUAL REPORT. 1950. a. free. British Columbia Cancer Research Centre, 601 W. Tenth Ave., Vancouver, BC V5Z 1L3, Canada.
TEL 604-877-6010. FAX 604-872-4596.
(Co-sponsors: B.C. Cancer Agency; British Columbia Cancer Foundation) circ. 6,000. **Document type:** corporate report.
Former titles (until 1990): British Columbia. Cancer Control Agency. Annual Report (ISSN 0849-4703); British Columbia. Cancer Foundation. Annual Report (ISSN 0068-1423)

616.994 UK ISSN 0007-0920
CODEN: BJCAAI
BRITISH JOURNAL OF CANCER. 1947. m. (2 vols./yr.). £385 in E.C.; elsewhere £420($630). (Cancer Research Campaign) Stockton Press (Subsidiary of: Macmillan Press Ltd.), Houndmills, Basingstoke, Hampshire RG21 2XS, England.
TEL 01256-817245. FAX 01256-28339. Ed. G.E. Adams; Pub. Jayne Marks. adv. contact: Michael Rowley. bk.rev.; illus.; index. circ. 2,000. (also avail. in microform from UMI,PMC; reprint service avail. from UMI) **Indexed:** Abstr.Hyg., Anim.Breed.Abstr., Biol.Abstr., Biotech.Abstr., C.I.S. Abstr., Chem.Abstr., Curr.Adv.Biochem., Curr.Adv.Cell & Devel.Biol., Curr.Adv.Ecol.Sci., Curr.Adv.Genetics & Molec.Biol., Curr.Cont., Dairy Sci.Abstr., Dent.Ind., Dok.Arbeitsmed., Excerp.Med., Ind.Med., Ind.Sci.Rev., Ind.Vet., INIS Atomind., Med.& Surg.Dermat., Nutr.Abstr., Rev.Med.& Vet.Mycol., Rev.Plant Path., Risk Abstr., Sci.Cit.Ind., Small Anim.Abstr., Sugar Ind.Abstr., Vet.Bull. **Document type:** academic/scholarly publication.
—BLDSC (2307.000000); CASDDS; Faxon; Genuine Article; SWETS; UMI; UnCover. **CCC.**
Description: Clinical and experimental aspects of cancer research.

616.994 FR ISSN 0007-4551
CODEN: BUCABS
BULLETIN DU CANCER. (Section avail.: Bulletin du Cancer - Radiotherapie (ISSN 0924-4212)) (Text and summaries in English, French) 1908. m. 1445 F. in France; foreign 1665 F.($325) (effective 1996). (Societe Francaise du Cancer) Editions Scientifiques Elsevier, 141 rue de Javel, 75747 Paris, France. TEL 33-1-45589063. (Subscr. in U.S. and Canada to: Elsevier Science Inc., Box 882, Madison Sq. Sta., New York, NY 10159. TEL 212-989-5800) Ed.Bd. adv.; bk.rev.; illus.; index. circ. 3,500. (also avail. in microform from UMI; reprint service avail. from ISI) **Indexed:** Biol.Abstr., Chem.Abstr., Curr.Adv.Cancer Res., Curr.Adv.Ecol.Sci., Curr.Cont., Dent.Ind., Excerp.Med., Ind.Med., Ind.Sci.Rev., Ind.Vet., INIS Atomind., Nutr.Abstr., Sci.Cit.Ind., Vet.Bull. **Document type:** academic/scholarly publication.
—BLDSC (2837.970000); ADONIS; CASDDS; Faxon; Genuine Article; SWETS. **CCC.**
Formerly: Association Francaise pour l'Etude du Cancer. Bulletin (ISSN 0004-5497)
Description: Publishes original articles on clinical oncology, basic cancer research and related fields. Includes review articles, editorials, brief notes, letters to the editor.
Refereed Serial

616.99 615.84 FR ISSN 0924-4212
CODEN: BCRAEE
BULLETIN DU CANCER - RADIOTHERAPIE. (Section of: Bulletin de Cancer (ISSN 0007-4551)) (Text in French; summaries in English, French) 1990. q. 935 F. in France; foreign 1045 F.($204) (effective 1996). (Societe Francaise de Radiotherapie Oncologique) Editions Scientifiques Elsevier, 141 rue de Javel, 75747 Paris, France.
TEL 33-1-45589063. (Subscr. in U.S. and Canada to: Elsevier Science Inc., Box 882, Madison Sq. Sta., New York, NY 10159. TEL 212-989-5800) Ed.Bd. circ. 3,500. (also avail. in microform from UMI; back issues avail.) **Indexed:** Biol.Abstr., Curr.Cont., Excerp.Med., Ind.Med., Sci.Cit.Ind. **Document type:** academic/scholarly publication.
—BLDSC (2837.975000); ADONIS; SWETS. **CCC.**
Description: Provides a forum within the field of oncology for the dissemination of knowledge in all areas relating to therapeutic radiation oncology: technology, radiophysics, radiobiology and clinical radiotherapy.
Refereed Serial

C A SELECTS. ANTITUMOR AGENTS. see *MEDICAL SCIENCES — Abstracting, Bibliographies, Statistics*

C A SELECTS. NUTRITIONAL ASPECTS OF CANCER. see *MEDICAL SCIENCES — Abstracting, Bibliographies, Statistics*

616.994 US ISSN 0007-9235
RC261 CODEN: CAMCAM
CA - A CANCER JOURNAL FOR CLINICIANS. 1950. bi-m. $70 to individuals; institutions $105; newsstand price: $18. (American Cancer Society, Inc.) Lippincott - Raven Publishers, 227 E. Wqashington Sq., Philadelphia, PA 19106. TEL 215-238-4200. Ed. Dr. Gerard P. Murphy. adv.: B&W page $2860, color page $4140; trim 5 3/8 x 8 5/8; adv. contact: Barbara Nakahara. bibl.; charts; illus.; index, cum.index: 1971-80. circ. 163,292. (also avail. in microform from UMI; reprint service avail. from UMI) **Indexed:** AIM, Biol.Abstr., CINAHL, Curr.Cont., Excerp.Med., Ind.Med., INIS Atomind., Med.& Surg.Dermat. **Document type:** academic/scholarly publication.
—BLDSC (2943.180000); Faxon; Genuine Article; SWETS; UMI; UnCover.
Description: Covers all aspects of cancer management for clinician in primary care, oncology and related specialties.
Refereed Serial

616.99 FR ISSN 0941-3804
CODEN: CIOCE
CAHIERS D'ONCOLOGIE. bi-m. 650 F.($136) (effective 1996). Springer-Verlag France, 26 rue des Carmes, 75005 Paris, France. TEL 43-29-38-87. FAX 43-54-49-08. (Subscr. in N. America to: Springer-Verlag New York, Inc. 44 Hartz Way, Secaucus, NJ 07096-2491. TEL 201-348-4033. FAX 201-348-4505) Ed. D. Khayat. adv. (also avail. in microform; reprint service avail.) **Indexed:** Excerp.Med. (1995-). **Document type:** academic/scholarly publication.
—BLDSC (2950.533000); UMI. **CCC.**
Description: Aims to reduce the time between discovery of new advances and their application.

616.99061 CN ISSN 1183-2509
CANADIAN JOURNAL OF ONCOLOGY. 1991. q. Can.$75($85) (effective 1995). Rodar Publishing Inc., 8102 Trans Canada Hwy., St. Laurent, PQ H4S 1Z4, Canada. TEL 514-333-5350. **Indexed:** Ind.Med. (1994-).

CANADIAN ONCOLOGY NURSING JOURNAL/REVUE CANADIENNE DE NURSING ONCOLOGIQUE. see *MEDICAL SCIENCES — Nurses And Nursing*

616.994 US ISSN 0008-543X
RC261 CODEN: CANCAR
CANCER. 1948. s-m. $145 to individuals (foreign $240); institutions $245 (foreign $385) (effective 1996). (American Cancer Society, Inc.) Lippincott - Raven Publishers, 227 E. Washington Sq., Philadelphia, PA 19106. TEL 215-238-4200. Ed. Dr. Robert V.P. Hutter. adv.; illus.; index. circ. 16,371. (also avail. in microform from UMI) **Indexed:** AIM, Behav.Med.Abstr., Biol.Abstr., Biotech.Abstr., Chem.Abstr., CINAHL, Curr.Adv.Cancer Res., Curr.Adv.Ecol.Sci., Curr.Adv.Genetics & Molec.Biol., Curr.Cont., Dent.Ind, Dok.Arbeitsmed., Excerp.Med., Helminthol.Abstr., Hosp.Lit.Ind., Ind.Med., Ind.Sci.Rev., Ind.Vet., INIS Atomind., Kidney, Med.& Surg.Dermat., NRN, Rev.Med.& Vet.Mycol., Risk Abstr., Sci.Cit.Ind., Small Anim.Abstr., SSCI, Telegen, Vet.Bull.
●Also available on CD-ROM.
—BLDSC (3046.450000); CASDDS; Faxon; Genuine Article; SWETS; UMI; UnCover. **CCC.**
Refereed Serial

616.99 US ISSN 0167-7659
CODEN: CMRED4
CANCER AND METASTASIS REVIEWS. 1981. q. fl.493 to institutions; $316 to institutions in U.S. (effective 1996). Kluwer Academic Publishers Boston, Box 358, Accord Sta., Hingham, MA 02018-0358. TEL 617-871-6600. FAX 617-871-6528. TELEX 200190. (Dist. outside N. America by: Kluwer Academic Publishers Group, P.O. Box 322, 3300 AH Dordrecht, Netherlands. TEL 31-78-392392. FAX 31-78-546474) Ed.Bd. adv.; bk.rev. (also avail. in microform from UMI; back issues avail.; reprint service avail. from SWZ,UMI) **Indexed:** Chem.Abstr., Curr.Adv.Ecol.Sci., Curr.Adv.Genetics & Molec.Biol., Curr.Cont, Excerp.Med., Ind.Med., Ind.Sci.Rev., INIS Atomind., Sci.Cit.Ind. **Document type:** academic/scholarly publication.
—BLDSC (3046.455700); CASDDS; Faxon; Genuine Article; SWETS; UMI; UnCover. **CCC.**
Formerly: Cancer Metastasis.
Refereed Serial

616.994 US ISSN 0305-7232
RC261.A1 CODEN: CABCD4
CANCER BIOCHEMISTRY BIOPHYSICS. 1975. 4/yr. (in 1 vol., 4 nos./vol.). 269 ECU (effective 1996). Gordon and Breach Science Publishers, c/o International Publishers Distributor, 820 Town Center Dr., Langhorne, PA 19047. TEL 215-750-2642. FAX 215-750-6343. (Subscr. to: International Publishers Distributor, P.O. Box 90, Reading, Berkshire RG1 8JL, England. TEL 44-173-456-8316) Ed. Harry Darrow Brown. adv. (also avail. in microform) Indexed: Biol.Abstr., Biotech.Abstr., Chem.Abstr., Curr.Adv.Ecol.Sci., Curr.Cont., Dairy Sci.Abstr., Excerp.Med., Helminthol.Abstr., Ind.Med., Ind.Sci.Rev., Sci.Cit.Ind.
—BLDSC (3046.456000); CASDDS; Faxon; SWETS. CCC.
Refereed Serial

616.9 612 NE
CANCER BIOLOGY AND MEDICINE. (Text in English) irreg., vol.3, 1992. price varies. Kluwer Academic Publishers, Postbus 17, 3300 AA Dordrecht, Netherlands. TEL 31-78-392392. FAX 31-78-392254. TELEX 29245 KAPG NL. (Dist. by: Kluwer Academic Publishers Group, P.O. Box 322, 3300 AH Dordrecht, Netherlands. TEL 31-78-392392. FAX 31-78-546474; N. America dist. addr.: Box 358, Accord Sta., Hingham, MA 02018-0358. TEL 617-871-6600. FAX 617-871-6528) **Document type:** monographic series.

616.99 US ISSN 1062-8401
CODEN: CNBTEB
CANCER BIOTHERAPY. 1983. q. $120 (foreign $160). Mary Ann Liebert, Inc., 1651 Third Ave., New York, NY 10128. TEL 914-834-3100. FAX 914-834-3688. E-mail: Liebert@pipeline.com. Ed. Robert Oldham. Indexed: Chem.Abstr., Curr.Adv.Ecol.Sci., Excerp.Med., Telegen. **Document type:** academic/scholarly publication.
—BLDSC (3046.457500); CASDDS; Faxon; Genuine Article; SWETS; UnCover.
Former titles: Selective Cancer Therapeutics (ISSN 1043-0733); (until 1989): Cancer Drug Delivery (ISSN 0732-9482)
Description: Reports on research and advances in cancer therapy, including more selective delivery of drugs, biologicals, radiopharmaceuticals, and advances in delivery instrumentation and technology.
Refereed Serial

616.99 UK ISSN 0957-5243
CODEN: CCCNEN
CANCER CAUSES & CONTROL; an international journal of studies on cancer in human populations. 1990. bi-m. £295($499) to institutions (effective 1995). Rapid Communications of Oxford Ltd., The Old Malthouse, Paradise St., Oxford OX1 1LD, England. TEL 01865-790447. FAX 01865-244012. E-mail: rapidcom@vax.oxford.ac.uk. Ed. Richard Monson. adv. contact: Julie Gribben. Indexed: Curr.Cont., Excerp.Med. (1993-), Ind.Med. **Document type:** academic/scholarly publication.
●Also available on CD-ROM.
—BLDSC (3046.464150); ADONIS; Genuine Article; UnCover. CCC.
Description: Reports and stimulates new avenues of investigation into the causes, control and subsequent prevention of cancer.

616.99 NE ISSN 0921-4410
CODEN: CCBAED
CANCER CHEMOTHERAPY AND BIOLOGICAL RESPONSE MODIFIERS. 1979. a., vol.14, 1993. price varies. Elsevier Science B.V., Books Division, P.O. Box 211, 1000 AE Amsterdam, Netherlands. TEL 31-20-4853911. FAX 31-20-4853705. TELEX 18582 ESPA NL. E-mail: nlinfo-f@elsevier.nl; usinfo-f@elsevier.com; forinfo-kyf04035@niftyserve.or.jp; Site addr.: http://www.elsevier.nl/. (Subscr. in U.S. and Canada to: Elsevier Science Inc., Box 882, Madison Sq. Sta., New York, NY 10159. TEL 212-989-5800) Ed. H.M. Pinedo. (back issues avail.) **Document type:** monographic series.
—BLDSC (3046.466000); SWETS; UnCover. CCC.
Former titles (until vol.9, 1987): Cancer Chemotherapy Annual; (until vol.2, 1980): Cancer Chemotherapy (ISSN 0167-7853)
Refereed Serial

616.99 GW ISSN 0344-5704
CODEN: CCPHDZ
CANCER CHEMOTHERAPY AND PHARMACOLOGY. (Supplement avail. (ISSN 0943-9404)) (Text in English) 1978. 12/yr. (in 2 vols., 6 nos./vol.). DM.2468($1793) (effective 1996). Springer-Verlag, Heidelberger Platz 3, 14197 Berlin, Germany. TEL 030-8207-0. FAX 030-8214091. E-mail: orders@springer.de. (Subscr. in N. America to: Springer-Verlag New York, Inc., 44 Hartz Way, Secaucus, NJ 07096-2491. TEL 201-348-4033. FAX 201-348-4505) Ed.Bd. adv.; index. (also avail. in microform from UMI; reprint service avail. from ISI) Indexed: Biotech.Abstr., Chem.Abstr., Curr.Adv.Cancer Res., Curr.Adv.Ecol.Sci., Curr.Cont., Dent.Ind., Excerp.Med., Ind.Med., Ind.Sci.Rev., Ind.Vet., INIS Atomind., Sci.Cit.Ind. **Document type:** academic/scholarly publication.
—BLDSC (3046.467000); ADONIS; CASDDS; Faxon; Genuine Article; SWETS; UMI; UnCover. CCC.
Description: Addresses pharmacologic and oncologic concerns on both the experimental and clinical levels.

616.99 GW ISSN 0943-9404
CODEN: CCHSE
CANCER CHEMOTHERAPY AND PHARMACOLOGY. SUPPLEMENT. irreg. Springer-Verlag, Heidelberger Platz 3, 14197 Berlin, Germany. TEL 030-8207-0. FAX 030-8214091. E-mail: orders@springer.de. (In N. America to: Springer-Verlag New York, Inc., 44 Hartz Way, Secaucus, NJ 07096-2491. TEL 201-348-4033. FAX 201-348-4505) Indexed: Excerp.Med. (1995-). **Document type:** academic/scholarly publication.

616.99 US ISSN 1073-2748
CODEN: CACOFD
▼**CANCER CONTROL.** 1994. bi-m. $40 (foreign $65). Moffitt Cancer Center, 12220 Bruce Downs, Rm. 108, West Annex, Tampa, FL 33612. TEL 813-632-1349. FAX 813-632-1380. E-mail: Ccjournal.moffitt.usf.edu. Ed. Peggy Farrell. adv. circ. 29,000. Indexed: Excerp.Med. (1995-).
Description: Each issue contains a series of articles that present original research and review a specific theme.
Refereed Serial

616 US ISSN 0191-3794
CANCER CONTROL JOURNAL. 1973. irreg. membership. Cancer Control Society, Cancer Book House, 2043 N. Berendo, Los Angeles, CA 90027. TEL 213-663-7801. Ed. Lorraine Rosenthal. bk.rev. circ. 10,000. (back issues avail.)

616.994 US ISSN 0361-090X
RC268 CODEN: CDPRD4
CANCER DETECTION AND PREVENTION. 1976. m. $135 to individuals (foreign $185); institutions $440 (foreign $490) (effective 1996). (International Society of Preventive Oncology) Blackwell Science Inc., 238 Main St., Cambridge, MA 02142. TEL 617-876-7022; 800-759-6102. FAX 617-492-5263. (also avail. in microfilm; reprint service avail. from ISI) Indexed: Abstr.Hyg., Biol.Abstr., Chem.Abstr., Curr.Cont., Dent.Ind., Dok.Arbeitsmed., Excerp.Med., Ind.Med., INIS Atomind., Trop.Dis.Bull. **Document type:** academic/scholarly publication.
—BLDSC (3046.477500); CASDDS; Faxon; Genuine Article; SWETS; UnCover. CCC.
Description: Publishes current scientific data on cancer epidemiology, biomarkers, and the identification and management of patients at risk for cancer development.
Refereed Serial

616.99 US ISSN 1055-9965
RC268.48 CODEN: CEBPE4
CANCER EPIDEMIOLOGY, BIOMARKERS & PREVENTION. 1991. bi-m. $85 to individuals (foreign $105); institutions $165 (foreign $185) (effective 1995). American Association for Cancer Research, Public Ledger Bldg., 620 Chestnut St., Philadelphia, PA 19106-3483. TEL 215-440-9300. FAX 215-440-9354. (Subscr. to: Fulco, Box 3000, Denville, NJ 07843. TEL 800-627-2997. FAX 201-627-5872) adv. contact: Lisa Chippendale. circ. 800. Indexed: Excerp.Med. (1993-), Ind.Med. (1992-). **Document type:** academic/scholarly publication.
—BLDSC (3046.477930); CASDDS; SWETS; UnCover.
Description: Contains research on the causes and prevention of cancer in humans.
Refereed Serial

616.994 US ISSN 0069-0147
CANCER FACTS AND FIGURES. 1951. a. free. American Cancer Society, Inc., 1599 Clifton Rd., N.E., Atlanta, GA 30329-4251. TEL 404-329-7911. FAX 404-325-2217. Ed. Beverly Greene. circ. 500,000. (also avail. in microfiche from CIS) **Indexed:** SRI.

616.99 AT ISSN 0311-306X
CANCER FORUM. 1974. 3/yr. free. Australian Cancer Society, Inc., G.P.O. Box 4708, Sydney, N.S.W. 2000, Australia. FAX 61-2-356-4558. Ed. L.A. Wright. adv.; bk.rev.; abstr. circ. 4,000. Indexed: Biol.Abstr., Excerp.Med. (1993-). **Document type:** academic/scholarly publication.
—BLDSC (3046.478200); UnCover.
Refereed Serial

616.99 575.1 US ISSN 0929-1903
CODEN: CGTHEG
▼**CANCER GENE THERAPY.** 1994. 4/yr. $85 to individuals (elsewhere $108); institutions $190 (elsewhere $215). Appleton & Lange, Journal Division (Subsidiary of: Simon & Schuster Company), 25 Van Zant St., Box 5630, Norwalk, CT 06856. TEL 203-838-4400. Ed. Robert E. Sobol. Indexed: Chem.Abstr., Curr.Cont. **Document type:** academic/scholarly publication.
—BLDSC (3046.478350); CASDDS; SWETS. CCC.
Refereed Serial

616.99 575.1 US ISSN 0165-4608
RC268.4 CODEN: CGCYDF
CANCER GENETICS & CYTOGENETICS. 1979. 14/yr. $1695 to institutions (effective 1996). Elsevier Science Inc., 655 Ave. of the Americas, New York, NY 10010. TEL 212-989-5800. FAX 212-633-3990. TELEX 420643 AEP UI. (Subscr. to: Box 882, Madison Sq. Sta., New York, NY 10159-0882) Eds. A.A. Sandberg, H. van den Berghe. (also avail. in microform from UMI; reprint service avail. from SWZ) Indexed: Biol.Abstr., Chem.Abstr., Curr.Adv.Cancer Res., Curr.Adv.Ecol.Sci., Curr.Adv.Genetics & Molec.Biol., Curr.Cont., Dent.Ind., Dok.Arbeitsmed., Excerp.Med., Ind.Med., Ind.Sci.Rev., Sci.Cit.Ind. **Document type:** academic/scholarly publication.
—BLDSC (3046.478400); CASDDS; Faxon; Genuine Article; SWETS; UnCover. CCC.
Description: Covers the cellular and molecular aspects of cancer research.
Refereed Serial

616.9 NE
CANCER GROWTH AND PROGRESSION. (Text in English) irreg. price varies. Kluwer Academic Publishers, Postbus 17, 3300 AA Dordrecht, Netherlands. TEL 31-78-392392. FAX 31-78-392254. TELEX 29245 KAPG NL. (Dist. by: Kluwer Academic Publishers Group, P.O. Box 322, 3300 AH Dordrecht, Netherlands. TEL 31-78-392392. FAX 31-78-546474; N. America dist. addr.: Box 358, Accord Sta., Hingham, MA 02018-0358. TEL 617-871-6600. FAX 617-871-6528) **Document type:** monographic series.

615 619 GW ISSN 0340-7004
CODEN: CIIMDN
CANCER IMMUNOLOGY, IMMUNOTHERAPY; other biological response modifications. (Text in English) 1976. 12/yr. (in 2 vols., 6 nos./vol.). DM.1988($1444) (effective 1996). Springer-Verlag, Heidelberger Platz 3, 14197 Berlin, Germany. TEL 030-8207-0. FAX 030-8214091. E-mail: orders@springer.de. (Subscr. in N. America to: Springer-Verlag New York, Inc., 44 Hartz Way, Secaucus, NJ 07096-2491. TEL 201-348-4033. FAX 201-348-4505) Eds. R.W. Baldwin, E. Mihich. adv. (also avail. in microform from UMI; reprint service avail. from ISI) Indexed: Chem.Abstr., Curr.Adv.Cancer Res., Curr.Adv.Ecol.Sci., Curr.Cont., Excerp.Med., Helminthol.Abstr., Ind.Med., Ind.Sci.Rev., INIS Atomind., Sci.Cit.Ind., Telegen. **Document type:** academic/scholarly publication.
—BLDSC (3046.478600); ADONIS; CASDDS; Faxon; Genuine Article; SWETS; UMI; UnCover. CCC.
Description: Presents the latest research results and clinical findings in oncology and immunology, including the latest developments in understanding tumor-host interactions.

MEDICAL SCIENCES — ONCOLOGY

616.9   CN   ISSN 0315-9884
CANCER IN ONTARIO. 1946. a. free. Ontario Cancer Treatment and Research Foundation, 7 Overlea Blvd., Toronto, ON M4H 1A8, Canada. TEL 416-423-4240. Ed. J.O. Godden. circ. 20,000.
—BLDSC (3046.492000).
    Formerly: Ontario Cancer Treatment and Research Foundation. Annual Report (ISSN 0078-4699)

616.9   PR   ISSN 0896-9035
RC279.P8
CANCER IN PUERTO RICO. (Text in English and Spanish) 1950. a. free. (Department of Health, Cancer Control Program, NCI-BIO Branch) Cancer Registry of Puerto Rico, Department of Health, P.O. Box 9342, Santurce, PR 00657. TEL 809-764-7453. Ed. Dr. Isidro Martinez. adv.; bk.rev. circ. 1,000. **Indexed:** Excerp.Med.

616.9   SW   ISSN 0280-7165
CANCER INCIDENCE IN SWEDEN. 1960. a. (Statistiska Centralbyraan) Fritzes AB, S-106 47 Stockholm, Sweden. TEL 08-690-9090. FAX 08-205021. circ. 2,000.

616.99   US   ISSN 0735-7907
RC261.A1   CODEN: CINVD7
CANCER INVESTIGATION. 1983. 6/yr. $65 to individuals; institutions $595. (Inter-American Society for Chemotherapy, Cancer Section) Marcel Dekker Journals, 270 Madison Ave., New York, NY 10016. TEL 212-696-9000. FAX 212-685-4540. TELEX 421419. (Subscr. to: Box 5017, Monticello, NY 12701) (Co-sponsor: Chemotherapy Foundation) Ed. Dr. Yashar Hirshaut. adv. contact: Eridania Perez. bk.rev.; charts; illus.; index. (also avail. in microform from RPI) **Indexed:** Biol.Abstr., Biol.Dig., Chem.Abstr., Curr.Adv.Ecol.Sci., Curr.Cont., Dok.Arbeitsmed., Excerp.Med., Ind.Med., Ind.Sci.Rev., NRN, Rev.Med.& Vet.Mycol., Sci.Cit.Ind., Telegen. **Document type:** academic/scholarly publication.
—BLDSC (3046.479500); ADONIS; CASDDS; Faxon; Genuine Article; SWETS; UMI; UnCover. **CCC.**
    Refereed Serial

616.99   US   ISSN 1081-4442
▼**THE CANCER JOURNAL FROM SCIENTIFIC AMERICAN.** Abbreviated title: T C J F S A. 1995. bi-m. $99 to individuals (Canada $109; elsewhere $114; airmail $159); institutions $155 (Canada $165; elsewhere $170; airmail $215). Scientific American, Inc., 415 Madison Ave., New York, NY 10017-1111. TEL 212-754-0550. FAX 212-980-3062. Ed.Bd. adv. (back issues avail.) **Document type:** academic/scholarly publication.
●Also available online.
    Description: Presents an integrated view of modern oncology across all disciplines, and reports noteworthy reserach at the interface between laboratory and clinic.
    Refereed Serial

616.994   US   ISSN 0096-3917
CANCER LETTER. (Includes monthly supplement: Cancer Economics) 1974. 48/yr. $255 (foreign $280). Cancer Letter Inc., Box 15189, Washington, DC 20053. TEL 202-543-7665. FAX 202-543-6879. Ed. Kirsten B. Goldberg. bk.rev. **Indexed:** Curr.Adv.Biochem., Curr.Adv.Cancer Res., Curr.Adv.Cell & Devel.Biol. **Document type:** newsletter.
    Description: Covers funding policy and research news about the National Cancer Program.

616.994   IE   ISSN 0304-3835
RC261.A1   CODEN: CALEDQ
CANCER LETTERS; an international journal providing a forum for original and pertinent contributions in cancer research. 1975. 18/yr. i£1278($2019) (effective 1996). Elsevier Science Ireland Ltd., P.O. Box 85, Limerick, Ireland. TEL 353-61-471944. FAX 353-61-472144. (Subscr. in U.S. and Canada to: Elsevier Science Inc., Box 882, Madison Sq. Sta., New York, NY 10159. TEL 212-989-5800. FAX 212-633-3990) Ed.Bd. adv.; charts; illus.; index. (also avail. in microform from UMI; reprint service avail. from SWZ) **Indexed:** Biol.Abstr., Chem.Abstr., Curr.Adv.Biochem., Curr.Adv.Ecol.Sci., Curr.Cont., Dent.Ind., Excerp.Med., Ind.Med., Ind.Sci.Rev., Ind.Vet., INIS Atomind., Med.& Surg.Dermat., NRN, Rev.Med.& Vet.Mycol., Risk Abstr., Sci.Cit.Ind., Small Anim.Abstr., Telegen, Vet.Bull. **Document type:** academic/scholarly publication.
—BLDSC (3046.485000); CASDDS; Faxon; Genuine Article; SWETS; UnCover. **CCC.**
    Description: Covers all areas of cancer research, including: molecular biology of cancer, oncogenes, carcinogenesis, hormones and cancer, viral oncology, chemotherapy, epidemiology, biology of cancer and metastasis.
    Refereed Serial

616.99   UA
CANCER MOLECULAR BIOLOGY. 6/yr. Ain Shams Medical Faculty, Abbassia, Cairo, Egypt. TEL 20-2-2858940. **Indexed:** Excerp.Med. (1995-). **Document type:** academic/scholarly publication.

616.994   US   ISSN 0008-5464
RC261   CODEN: CANEAX
CANCER NEWS. 1947. 3/yr. free to qualified personnel. American Cancer Society, Inc., 1599 Clifton Rd., N.E., Atlanta, GA 30329. TEL 404-329-7936. FAX 404-325-2217. Ed. Jerie Jordan. bk.rev.; illus. circ. 240,000. (also avail. in microform from UMI) **Indexed:** Excerp.Med., Hlth.Ind.
●Also available online. Vendor(s): University Microfilms International.
—Faxon; UMI.
    Description: Contains society news and notes only.

CANCER NURSING; an international journal for cancer care. see *MEDICAL SCIENCES — Nurses And Nursing*

CANCER NURSING NEWS. see *MEDICAL SCIENCES — Nurses And Nursing*

616.99   US   ISSN 1065-4704
CANCER PRACTICE. 1993. bi-m. $39 to individuals (foreign $54); institutions $85 (foreign $95) (effective 1996). Lippincott - Raven Publishers, 227 E. Washington Square, Philadelphia, PA 19106. TEL 215-238-4231. Ed. Genevieve V. Foley. circ. 10,333. (also avail. in microform from UMI) **Indexed:** Excerp.Med. (1995-).
—BLDSC (3046.492906); UMI.
    Refereed Serial

616.99   US
RC268
CANCER PREVENTION INTERNATIONAL. 1990. q. $120 (foreign $145) (effective 1996). Cognizant Communication Corporation, 3 Hartsdale Rd., Elmsford, NY 10523-3701. TEL 914-592-7720. FAX 914-592-8981. Ed. Dr. Daniel W. Nixon. circ. 500. **Document type:** academic/scholarly publication.
—**CCC.**
    Formerly (until 1994): Cancer Prevention (ISSN 1043-8491)
    Description: Discusses malignant disease care management strategies, for oncologists, primary care physicians, nutritionists, epidemiologists, and biomedical researchers.
    Refereed Serial

616.994   US   ISSN 0008-5472
RC261   CODEN: CNREA8
CANCER RESEARCH. 1941. m. $495 to institutions (includes Clinical Cancer Research) (foreign $575) (effective 1995). American Association for Cancer Research, Public Ledger Bldg., 620 Chestnut St., Philadelphia, PA 19106. TEL 215-440-9300. FAX 215-440-9354. (Subscr. to: Fulco, Box 3000, Denville, NJ 07843. TEL 800-875-2997. FAX 201-627-5872) Ed. Dr. Peter N. Magee. adv. contact: Lisa Chippendale. abstr.; bibl.; charts; illus.; index. circ. 7,000. (also avail. in microfilm from PMC) **Indexed:** ABC, Abstr.Hyg., Anim.Breed.Abstr., Biol.Abstr., Biotech.Abstr., Chem.Abstr., Curr.Adv.Biochem., Curr.Adv.Cancer Res., Curr.Adv.Cell & Devel.Biol., Curr.Adv.Ecol.Sci., Curr.Adv.Genetics & Molec.Biol., Curr.Biotech.Abstr., Curr.Cont., Dairy Sci.Abstr., Dent.Ind., Dok.Arbeitsmed., Excerp.Med., Helminthol.Abstr., I.P.A., Ind.Med., Ind.Sci.Rev., Ind.Vet., INIS Atomind., Lab.Haz.Bull., Maize Abstr., Med.& Surg.Dermat., NRN, Nutr.Abstr., Pig News & Info., Poult.Abstr., Rev.Med.& Vet.Mycol., Rev.Plant Path., Risk Abstr., Sci.Cit.Ind., Small Anim.Abstr., Telegen, Trop.Dis.Bull., Vet.Bull. **Document type:** academic/scholarly publication.
—BLDSC (3046.500000); CASDDS; Faxon; Genuine Article; SWETS; UMI; UnCover. **CCC.**
    Refereed Serial

616.994   UK   ISSN 0365-9623
RC261
CANCER RESEARCH CAMPAIGN. ANNUAL REVIEW. 1924. a. free to medical & scientific institutions. Cancer Research Campaign, Cambridge House, 6-10 Cambridge Terr., Regent's Park, London NW1 4JL, England. TEL 071-224-1333. circ. controlled.

616.99   CN
CANCER RESEARCH NEWS. 1984. s-a. free. Canadian Cancer Society, B.C. and Yukon Division, 565 W. 10th Ave., Vancouver, BC V5Z 4J4, Canada. TEL 604-872-4400. FAX 604-879-4533. Ed. Sandra Bishop. circ. 7,500. **Document type:** bulletin.
    Description: Summarizes current research into all aspects of cancer: causation, detection, prevention, treatment, epidemiology, survival.

616.99   US   ISSN 1064-0525
RC261.A1   CODEN: CRTCEA
CANCER RESEARCH, THERAPY AND CONTROL. 1989. 4/yr. (in 1 vol., 4 nos./vol.) 99 ECU (effective 1996). Harwood Academic Publishers, c/o International Publishers Distributor, 820 Town Center Dr., Langhorne, PA 19047. TEL 215-750-2642. FAX 215-750-6343. (Subscr. to: International Publishers Distributor, PO Box 90, Reading, Berkshire, RG1 8JL, England. TEL 44-173-456-8316) Ed. Samuel Gross. (also avail. in microform) **Indexed:** Excerp.Med. (1995-). **Document type:** academic/scholarly publication.
—BLDSC (3046.506000). **CCC.**
    Formerly (until 1992): Cancer Therapy and Control (ISSN 0896-5080)

616.99   US   ISSN 1071-7226
CANCER RESEARCHER WEEKLY; a complete weekly report privately circulated. 1988. w. (48/yr.) $995 (foreign $1195). Charles W. Henderson, Ed. & Pub., Box 5528, Atlanta, GA 31107-0528. TEL 404-377-8895. FAX 404-378-5411. TELEX 78-2661. (Subscr. to: Box 830409, Birmingham, AL 35283-0409. TEL 800-633-4931. FAX 205-995-1588) (also avail. in microform from UMI) **Document type:** newsletter.
●Also available online. Vendor(s): Ovid Technologies, CompuServe, Inc., Data-Star, Knight-Ridder, Inc., Dow Jones News Retrieval, NewsNet (HH15).
—UMI. **CCC.**
    Former titles (until 1993): Cancerweekly (ISSN 1071-7218); (until 1991): N C I Cancer Weekly (ISSN 0896-7385)
    Description: Covers all aspects of cancer research, including AIDS-related cancers.

616.99   US
CANCER REVIEW.* 1980. 3/yr. (Cancer Center at Wadley) Wadley Institute of Molecular Medicine, Box 35988, 9000 Harry Hines, Dallas, TX 75235. TEL 214-351-8111. Ed. Christine Donovan. illus. circ. 50,000.
    Formerly: Quest (Dallas).

616.99   US   ISSN 0261-2429
        CODEN: CASUD7
CANCER SURVEYS; advances and prospects in clinical, epidemiological, and laboratory oncology. 1982. irreg. Cold Spring Harbor Laboratory Press, Publications Department, Box 100, Cold Spring Harbor, NY 11724. TEL 800-843-4388. FAX 516-349-1946. (Subscr. to: Fulfillment Center, 1 Skyline Dr., Plainview, NY 11803. TEL 516-349-1930) Ed. John Tooze. (also avail. in microform from UMI) **Indexed:** Abstr.Hyg., Curr.Adv.Ecol.Sci., Curr.Cont., Excerp.Med., Ind.Sci.Rev., Ind.Vet., Med.& Surg.Dermat., Poult.Abstr., Sci.Cit.Ind., Small Anim.Abstr., Telegen, Vet.Bull. **Document type:** monographic series.
—BLDSC (3046.610000); CASDDS; Faxon; Genuine Article; SWETS; UnCover. **CCC.**
  Description: Provides a comprehensive state and future developments in well-defined areas in oncology. Each issues deals with a specific topic and has guest editors with an expert knowledge of the subject.

616.99   UK   ISSN 0265-1319
CANCER TOPICS; regular news and reviews of cancer therapy. 1972. 3/yr. free. (Lederle Laboratories) Eurocommunica Publications, 4 Bersted Mews, Bersted St., Bognor Regis, W. Sussex PO22 9RR, England. TEL 01234-823180. FAX 01234-823180. Ed. Rod Robinson. adv.; bk.rev.; abstr. circ. 13,000. (back issues avail.) **Document type:** academic/scholarly publication.
—BLDSC (3046.623000). **CCC.**
  Description: Covers all aspects of cancer research and therapy.
  Refereed Serial

CANCER TOPICS ABSTRACTS SERVICE; news on advances in clinical and experimental oncology. see MEDICAL SCIENCES — Abstracting, Bibliographies, Statistics

616.99   NE   ISSN 0927-3042
CANCER TREATMENT AND RESEARCH. (Text in English) 1981. irreg., vol.68, 1993. price varies. Kluwer Academic Publishers, Postbus 17, 3300 AA Dordrecht, Netherlands. TEL 31-78-392392. FAX 31-78-392254. (Dist. by: Kluwer Academic Publishers Group, P.O. Box 322, 3300 AH Dordrecht, Netherlands. TEL 31-78-392392. FAX 31-78-546474; N. America dist. addr.: Box 358, Accord Sta., Hingham, MA 02018-0358. TEL 617-871-6600. FAX 617-871-6528) (back issues avail.) **Document type:** monographic series.
—BLDSC (3046.625000).
  Refereed Serial

616.994   UK   ISSN 0305-7372
        CODEN: CTREDJ
CANCER TREATMENT REVIEWS. 1974. 4/yr. £55 in Europe (rest of world $99) to individuals; institutions £110 in Europe (rest of world $198). W.B. Saunders Co. Ltd. (Subsidiary of: Harcourt Brace & Company Ltd.), 24-28 Oval Rd., London NW1 7DX, England. TEL 0171-267-4466. FAX 0171-482-2293. TELEX 25775-ACPRES-G. (Subscr. to: Harcourt Brace & Company Ltd., Foots Cray High St., Sidcup, Kent DA14 5 HP, England. TEL 0181-300-3322. FAX 0181-309-0807; US, Canadian, and Mexican subscr. to: W.B. Saunders Co., Journal Subscription Fulfillment, 6277 Sea Harbor Dr., 4th Fl., Orlando, FL 32887-4800. TEL 800-654-2452. FAX 800-874-6418) Ed. R. Rubens. adv.; illus.; index. (back issues avail.) **Indexed:** Biol.Abstr., Curr.Cont., Dent.Ind., Excerp.Med., Ind.Med., Ind.Sci.Rev., Sci.Cit.Ind. **Document type:** academic/scholarly publication.
—BLDSC (3046.630000); CASDDS; Faxon; Genuine Article; SWETS; UnCover. **CCC.**
  Description: Devoted to important advances in the field of cancer treatment for oncologists and physicians.

616.99   US   ISSN 1059-3802
CANCER WATCH; the monthly news and educational magazine of cancer research. 1992. m. $30 to individuals (Canada & Mexico $40; elsewhere $50); institutions $55 (Canada & Mexico $65, elsewhere $75). Adenine Press, 2066 Central Ave., Schenectady, NY 12304. TEL 518-456-0784. FAX 518-452-4955. Ed. Dr. M.H. Sarma.
—BLDSC (3046.683000).

616.994   IT   ISSN 0008-5480
CANCRO. (Summaries in English) vol.23, 1970. bi-m. L.4000. Istituto di Oncologia, Via Cavour 31, 10123 Turin, Italy. adv.; bk.rev.; charts; illus. **Indexed:** Biol.Abstr., Chem.Abstr., Dent.Ind., Ind.Med., INIS Atomind.

028.5 616.99   US
CANDLELIGHTERS CHILDHOOD CANCER FOUNDATION PROGRESS REPORTS. 1981. irreg. free. Candlelighters Childhood Cancer Foundation, 7910 Woodmont Ave., Ste. 400, Bethesda, MD 20814. TEL 301-657-8410. circ. 34,000. **Document type:** bulletin.
  Formerly: Candlelighters Foundation Progress Reports.

618.92 616.99   US
CANDLELIGHTERS CHILDHOOD CANCER FOUNDATION QUARTERLY NEWSLETTER. 1970. q. free. Candlelighters Childhood Cancer Foundation, 7910 Woodmont Ave., Ste. 400, Bethesda, MD 20814. TEL 301-657-8410. bk.rev. circ. 35,000. **Indexed:** Rehabil.Lit. **Document type:** newsletter.
  Formerly: Candlelighters Foundation Quarterly Newsletter.
  Description: Provides information and support for families of children and teens with cancer, and for interested health or education professionals as well.

616.99 649   US
CANDLELIGHTERS CHILDHOOD CANCER FOUNDATION YOUTH NEWSLETTER. 1979. q. free. Candlelighters Childhood Cancer Foundation, 7910 Woodmont Ave., Ste. 400, Bethesda, MD 20814. TEL 301-657-8401. circ. 15,000. **Document type:** newsletter.
  Formerly: Candlelighters Foundation Youth Newsletter.
  Description: Contains information and creative expressions by and for young people with cancer, their siblings, and health or education professionals.

616   UK   ISSN 0143-3334
RC268.5   CODEN: CRNGDP
CARCINOGENESIS. 1980. m. £340($560) (effective 1996). Oxford University Press, Oxford Journals, Walton St., Oxford OX2 6DP, England. TEL 01865-267907. FAX 01865-267773. TELEX 837330-OXPRES-G. E-mail: jnlorders@oup.co.uk. (U.S. subscr. to: Oxford University Press Inc., 2001 Evans Rd., Cary, NC 27513. TEL 919-677-0977. FAX 919-677-1714) Ed.Bd. adv.; bk.rev.; illus.; index. circ. 1,000. (back issues avail.; reprint service avail. from SWZ) **Indexed:** Curr.Adv.Cancer Res., Curr.Adv.Cell & Devel.Biol., Curr.Adv.Ecol.Sci., Curr.Adv.Genetics & Molec.Biol., Curr.Cont., Excerp.Med., Ind.Med., INIS Atomind., Rev.Med.& Vet.Mycol., Sci.Cit.Ind. **Document type:** academic/scholarly publication.
—BLDSC (3051.007000); CASDDS; Faxon; Genuine Article; SWETS; UMI; UnCover. **CCC.**
  Description: Multi-disciplinary research journal in the areas of viral, physical and chemical carcinogenesis and mutagenesis.

616   US   ISSN 0147-4006
RC268.5   CODEN: CCSUDL
CARCINOGENESIS; a comprehensive survey. 1976. irreg., latest vol.11. price varies. Raven Press (Subsidiary of: Wolters Kluwer N.V.), 1185 Ave. of the Americas, New York, NY 10036. TEL 212-930-9500. FAX 212-869-3495. (reprint service avail. from UMI) **Indexed:** Biol.Abstr., Chem.Abstr., Dairy Sci.Abstr., Dent.Ind., Dok.Arbeitsmed., Ind.Med., Rev.Med.& Vet.Mycol., Rev.Plant Path., Risk Abstr., Sci.Cit.Ind. **Document type:** monographic series.
—BLDSC (3051.005000); CASDDS. **CCC.**
  Refereed Serial

616.99 591   JA   ISSN 0918-1989
CARCINOLOGICAL SOCIETY OF JAPAN. CANCER. (Text in Japanese) 1991. a. Nihon Kokakurui Gakkai - Carcinological Society of Japan, Tokyo University of Fisheries, Dept. of Aquatic Bioscience, 4-5-7 Konan, Minato-ku, Tokyo 108, Japan. TEL 03-5463-0535. FAX 03-5463-0536.

CELL CONTACT AND COMMUNICATION. see BIOLOGY — Cytology And Histology

616.99   US   ISSN 1044-9523
RC261.A1   CODEN: CGDIE7
CELL GROWTH & DIFFERENTIATION. 1990. m. $95 to individuals (foreign $115); institutions $195 (foreign $215) (effective 1995). American Association for Cancer Research, Public Ledger Bldg., 620 Chestnut St., Philadelphia, PA 19106. TEL 215-440-9300. FAX 215-440-9354. (Subscr. to: Fulco, Box 3000, Denville, NJ 07843. TEL 800-875-2997. FAX 201-627-5872) adv. contact: Lisa Chippendale. **Indexed:** Biol.Abstr., Chem.Abstr., Excerp.Med. (1993-), Ind.Med. **Document type:** academic/scholarly publication.
—BLDSC (3097.790000); CASDDS; Faxon; SWETS; UnCover.
  Refereed Serial

616.99   US
CENTER NEWS. 1975. bi-m. Memorial Sloan-Kettering Cancer Center, Department of Public Affairs, 1275 York Ave., New York, NY 10021. TEL 212-639-3573. FAX 212-639-3576. Ed. Debbie Rosenberg Bush. circ. 250,000 (controlled). **Document type:** newsletter.
  Description: Lay language coverage of treatment advances, basic and clinical research, and other programs and activities at Memorial Sloan-Kettering Cancer Center.

616.99   US
THE CHALLENGE.* 1978. q. $20 membership. Cancer Federation, Box 1298, Banning, CA 92220-0009. TEL 800-982-3270. Ed. John Steinbacher. bk.rev. circ. 2,000. (back issues avail.)
  Description: Covers cancer immunology and biological modifiers.

616.99   GW   ISSN 0940-6735
CHEMOTHERAPIE JOURNAL. 1992. q. DM.80. (Paul-Ehrlich-Gesellschaft fuer Chemotherapie e.V.) Wissenschaftliche Verlagsgesellschaft mbH, Postfach 101061, 70009 Stuttgart, Germany. TEL 0711-25820. FAX 0711-2582290. Eds. A. Dalhoff, K.G. Naber. **Document type:** academic/scholarly publication.

616.99   CC   ISSN 1000-9604
CHINESE JOURNAL OF CANCER RESEARCH/ZHONGGUO AIZHENG YANJIU. (Text in English) 1989. q. $120 (effective 1994). (China Anti-Cancer Association) Beijing Institute for Cancer Research, Da-Hong-Luo-Chang Street, Western District, Beijing, People's Republic of China. TEL 861-603-1122. FAX 861-602-3658. Ed. Ling Qibo. circ. 300. **Document type:** academic/scholarly publication.
—BLDSC (3180.297700).
  Description: Contains research papers, clinical observations and traditional Chinese medicine in the field of cancer research.
  Refereed Serial

616   US
CHOICE (CHULA VISTA). 1975. 4/yr. $16. Committee for Freedom of Choice in Medicine, Inc., c/o American Biologics, 1180 Walnut St., Chula Vista, CA 91911. TEL 619-429-8200. FAX 619-429-8004. Ed. Michael L. Culbert. adv.; bk.rev. circ. 10,000. **Document type:** consumer publication.
  Description: Devoted to news about medicine, medical politics, and "alternative" therapies.

616.99   UK   ISSN 0262-0898
        CODEN: CEXMD2
CLINICAL AND EXPERIMENTAL METASTASIS. 1982. bi-m. £295($499) to institutions (effective 1995). Rapid Communications of Oxford Ltd., The Old Malthouse, Paradise St., Oxford OX1 1LD, England. TEL 01865-790447. FAX 01865-244012. E-mail: rapidcom@vax.oxford.ac.uk. Ed. Kurt Hellmann. adv. contact: Julie Gribben. bk.rev.; index. **Indexed:** Chem.Abstr., Curr.Adv.Ecol.Sci., Curr.Cont., Excerp.Med., Ind.Med., Ind.Sci.Rev., Sci.Cit.Ind. **Document type:** academic/scholarly publication.
●Also available on CD-ROM.
—BLDSC (3286.251400); ADONIS; CASDDS; Faxon; Genuine Article; SWETS; UnCover. **CCC.**
  Description: Focuses on the crucial process of dissemination and metastasis formation.

MEDICAL SCIENCES — ONCOLOGY

616.99 US ISSN 0164-985X
CLINICAL CANCER LETTER. 1978. m. $75 (foreign $90). Cancer Letter Inc., Box 15189, Washington, DC 20003. TEL 202-543-7665. FAX 202-543-6879. Ed. Kirsten B. Goldberg. **Document type:** newsletter.
—BLDSC (3286.264500).
Description: Covers new clinical developments, clinical trials, and research on cancer.

616.99 US ISSN 1078-0432
RC267 CODEN: CCREF4
▼**CLINICAL CANCER RESEARCH.** 1995. m. $495 to institutions (foreign $555) (includes Cancer Research) (effective 1995). American Association for Cancer Research, Public Ledger Bldg., 620 Chestnut St., Philadelphia, PA 19106. TEL 215-440-9300. FAX 215-440-9354. (Subscr. to: Fulco, Box 3000, Denville, NJ 07843. TEL 800-875-2997. FAX 201-627-5872) Ed. Dr. John Mendelsohn. adv. contact: Lisa Chippendale. **Document type:** academic/scholarly publication.
—BLDSC (3286.264750); CASDDS; SWETS; UnCover.
Refereed Serial

616.994 UK ISSN 0936-6555
CODEN: CLIOEH
CLINICAL ONCOLOGY. 1989. 6/yr. £172($276) (effective 1996). (Royal College of Radiologists) Springer-Verlag, Springer House, 8 Alexandra Rd., London SW19 7JZ, England. TEL 081-944-2942. FAX 081-947-4651. (U.S. subscr. to: Springer-Verlag New York, Inc., Box 2485, Secaucus, NJ 07096-2491. TEL 201-348-4033) Ed. T.J. Priestman. (back issues avail.) **Indexed:** Excerp.Med. (1993-). **Document type:** academic/scholarly publication.
—BLDSC (3286.317000); SWETS; UMI. **CCC.**
Description: International, multidisciplinary research covering all aspects of the clinical management of cancer patients.

616.99 US ISSN 0886-7186
CLINICAL ONCOLOGY ALERT. 1986. m. $115. American Health Consultants, Inc., Six Piedmont Center, Ste. 400, Atlanta, GA 30305. TEL 404-262-7436; 800-688-2421. FAX 800-284-3291. Ed. Dr. Dan L. Longo. index. circ. 2,225. (also avail. in audio cassette; reprint service avail.) **Document type:** newsletter.
Refereed Serial

CLINICAL RADIOLOGY. see *MEDICAL SCIENCES — Radiology And Nuclear Medicine*

619 US
THE COLPOSCOPIST. 1968. q. $40. (American Society for Colposcopy and Cervical Pathology) Slack, Inc., 6900 Grove Rd., Thorofare, NJ 08086. TEL 609-848-1000. FAX 609-853-5991. Ed. Dr. K. Noller. adv. (back issues avail.)

616.99 US ISSN 0743-5061
COMMUNITY CANCER PROGRAMS IN THE UNITED STATES. 1980. a. $150. Association of Community Cancer Centers, 11600 Nebel St., Ste. 201, Rockville, MD 20852. TEL 301-984-9496. FAX 301-770-1949. Ed. Lee E. Mortenson. adv. contact: Donald Jewler. (back issues avail.) **Document type:** directory.
Description: Summaries of close to 500 cancer programs in the U.S. Includes medical contacts, a cancer program narrative description, and cancer program data.

616.99 SZ ISSN 0250-3220
CODEN: COONEV
CONTRIBUTIONS TO ONCOLOGY/BEITRAEGE ZUR ONKOLOGIE. (Text in English and German) 1979. irreg. price varies. S. Karger AG, Allschwilerstr. 10, CH-4009 Basel, Switzerland. TEL 061-3061111. FAX 061-3061234. E-mail: Karger@Karger.ch. Eds. J.H. Holzner, W. Queisser. index. **Indexed:** Biol.Abstr., Chem.Abstr., Curr.Cont. **Document type:** academic/scholarly publication.
—BLDSC (1887.090000); CASDDS. **CCC.**
Refereed Serial

616.99 US
COPE; working in oncology. 1985. bi-m. Media America, Inc., Box 682268, Franklin, TN 37068-2268. TEL 615-790-2400. FAX 615-794-0179. Ed. Larry Blaser; Pub. Michael D. Holt. adv.: B&W page $3800. circ. 30,000 (controlled). (back issues avail.) **Document type:** trade publication.
Description: Profiles professionals working in the field of oncology and provides the latest information of interest available.

616.994005 US ISSN 1043-8637
RC261.A1
COPING; living with cancer. 1986. bi-m. $18. Media America, Box 682268, Franklin, TN 37068-2268. TEL 615-790-2400. FAX 615-794-0179. Ed. Tricia Brown; Pub. Michael D. Holt. adv. contact: Paula K. Chadwell. bk.rev. circ. 80,000. (back issues avail.)
Description: Offers feature articles, news reports, profiles and current trend information on oncology prevention, research and issues for people living with cancer.

616.99 US ISSN 0893-9675
CODEN: CRONEI
CRITICAL REVIEWS IN ONCOGENESIS. 1989. q. $99.95 to individuals; institutions $297 (effective 1996). Begell House Inc., 79 Madison Ave., Ste. 1201, New York, NY 10016-7892. TEL 212-725-1999. FAX 212-213-8368. E-mail: 74353.2052@compuserve.com. **Indexed:** Excerp.Med. (1995-). **Document type:** academic/scholarly publication.
—BLDSC (3487.478900); CASDDS; Faxon; Genuine Article; SWETS; UnCover. **CCC.**
Description: Offers a selection of reviews on topics of current interest in the field of basic oncology.

616.99 616.15 IE ISSN 1040-8428
RC254.A1 CODEN: CCRHEC
CRITICAL REVIEWS IN ONCOLOGY - HEMATOLOGY. (Text in English) 1981. m. I£648($1024) (effective 1996). Elsevier Science Ireland Ltd., P.O. Box 85, Limerick, Ireland. TEL 353-61-471944. FAX 353-61-472144. (Subscr. in U.S. and Canada to: Elsevier Science Inc. Box 882, Madison Sq. Sta., New York, NY 10159. TEL 212-989-5800. FAX 212-633-3990) Ed. Stephen Davis. **Indexed:** ASCA, Excerp.Med., Ind.Sci.Rev., Telegen. **Document type:** academic/scholarly publication.
—BLDSC (3487.479000); Faxon; Genuine Article; SWETS. **CCC.**
Formerly: C R C Critical Reviews in Oncology - Hematology (ISSN 0737-9587)
Description: Publishes scholarly, critical reviews in the fields of oncology and hematology.
Refereed Serial

CURRENT ADVANCES IN CANCER RESEARCH. see *MEDICAL SCIENCES — Abstracting, Bibliographies, Statistics*

616.99 GW ISSN 0940-0745
CURRENT CANCER RESEARCH. 1986. irreg. DM.32. Deutsches Krebsforschungszentrum, Im Neuenheimer Feld 280, 69120 Heidelberg, Germany. TEL 06221-422854. FAX 06221-422995. **Document type:** academic/scholarly publication, corporate report.

606.99 UK ISSN 0969-692X
CURRENT CLINICAL CANCER. 1993. m. $156 to individuals; institutions $398 (effective 1995). Carfax Publishing Co., P.O. Box 25, Abingdon, Oxon. OX14 3UE, England. TEL 01235-555335. FAX 01235-553559. (N. American subscr. to: Carfax Publishing Co., 875-81 Massachusetts Ave., Cambridge, MA 02139) Ed. Michael Gallico. (also avail. in diskette format; microfiche; back issues avail.) **Document type:** academic/scholarly publication.
—UMI. **CCC.**

CURRENT OPINION IN ONCOLOGY. see *MEDICAL SCIENCES — Abstracting, Bibliographies, Statistics*

616.99 US ISSN 0147-0272
CODEN: CPRCDJ
CURRENT PROBLEMS IN CANCER. Short title: C P Ca. 1977. bi-m. $65 to individuals (foreign $71); institutions $90 (foreign $90); students $40 (foreign $46). Mosby - Year Book, Inc. (Subsidiary of: Times Mirror Company), 11830 Westline Industrial Dr., St. Louis, MO 63146. TEL 314-872-8370; 800-325-4177. FAX 314-432-1380. Ed. Robert Ozols. index. circ. 1,928. (also avail. in microform from UMI; reprint service avail. from UMI) **Indexed:** Biol.Abstr., Curr.Cont., Dent.Ind., Dok.Arbeitsmed., Ind.Med., INIS Atomind.
—BLDSC (3501.345000); Genuine Article; SWETS; UMI; UnCover. **CCC.**
Description: A fully referenced monographic journal with information from recognized experts on practical clinical care.

616.99 US
CURRENT TREATMENT OF CANCER. 1986. irreg. price varies. Springer-Verlag, 175 Fifth Ave., New York, NY 10010. TEL 212-460-1500. FAX 212-473-6272. (Also: Berlin, Heidelberg, Tokyo, Vienna) (reprint service avail. from ISI) **Document type:** monographic series.

CYTOKINES AND MOLECULAR THERAPY. see *MEDICAL SCIENCES — Allergology And Immunology*

362.1 US ISSN 0095-6775
RC267
DAMON RUNYON - WALTER WINCHELL CANCER RESEARCH FUND. ANNUAL REPORT. Key Title: Annual Report, Damon Runyon - Walter Winchell Cancer Research Fund. 1973. a. free. Damon Runyon Walter Winchell Cancer Research Fund, 131 E. 36th St., New York, NY 10016-3404. circ. 1,000.
Formerly (until 1973): Damon Runyon Memorial Fund for Cancer Research. Annual Report (ISSN 0416-6639)

DERMATOLOGIC SURGERY. see *MEDICAL SCIENCES — Surgery*

616.99 GW ISSN 0932-7479
DEUTSCHE KREBSGESELLSCHAFT. MITTEILUNGEN.* 1986. q. DM.60. Deutsche Krebsgesellschaft, Paul-Ehrlich-Str. 41, 60596 Frankfurt a.M., Germany. circ. 2,400. **Document type:** newsletter.

616.99 GW ISSN 0931-0037
DEUTSCHE ZEITSCHRIFT FUER ONKOLOGIE/JOURNAL OF ONCOLOGY; journal of oncology. (Text in German; summaries in English) bi-m. DM.105 (students DM.87). (Deutsche Gesellschaft fuer Onkologie e.V.) Verlag fuer Medizin Dr. Ewald Fischer GmbH, Fritz-Frey-Str. 21, 69121 Heidelberg, Germany. TEL 06221-4062-0. Ed. Dr. E. Dieter Hager. circ. 5,000. (back issues avail.) **Indexed:** Excerp.Med. **Document type:** academic/scholarly publication.
—BLDSC (3575.830000). **CCC.**
Formerly (until 1987): Krebsgeschehen (ISSN 0340-5672)

616.99 GW ISSN 0932-6235
DEUTSCHES KREBSFORSCHUNGSZENTRUM. RESEARCH REPORT. 1982. biennial. free. Deutsches Krebsforschungszentrum, Im Neuenheimer Feld 280, 69120 Heidelberg, Germany. TEL 06221-422854. FAX 06221-422995. **Document type:** academic/scholarly publication.

616.9 GW ISSN 0070-4229
DEUTSCHES KREBSFORSCHUNGSZENTRUM. VEROEFFENTLICHUNGEN. 1965. a. Deutsches Krebsforschungszentrum, Im Neuenheimer Feld 280, 69120 Heidelberg, Germany. TEL 06221-422854. FAX 06221-422995. TELEX 461562-DKFZ-D. circ. 1,000. **Document type:** academic/scholarly publication.

MEDICAL SCIENCES — ONCOLOGY 4475

616.99 NE ISSN 0163-6146
CODEN: DCREDD
DEVELOPMENTS IN CANCER RESEARCH. 1979. irreg., vol.7, 1982. price varies. Elsevier Science B.V., Books Division, P.O. Box 211, 1000 AE Amsterdam, Netherlands. TEL 31-20-4853911. FAX 31-20-4853705. TELEX 18582 ESPA NL. E-mail: nlinfo-f@elsevier.nl; usinfo-f@elsevier.com; forinfo-kyf04035@niftyserve.or.jp; Site addr.: http://www.elsevier.nl/. (Subscr. in U.S. and Canada to: Elsevier Science Inc., Box 882, Madison Sq. Sta., New York, NY 10159. TEL 212-989-5800) **Document type:** monographic series.
—CASDDS.
Refereed Serial

619.99 NE ISSN 0167-4927
CODEN: DEOND5
DEVELOPMENTS IN ONCOLOGY. 1980. irreg., vol.72, 1993. price varies. Kluwer Academic Publishers, Postbus 17, 3300 AA Dordrecht, Netherlands. TEL 31-78-392392. FAX 31-78-392254. TELEX 29245 KAPG NL. (Dist. by: Kluwer Academic Publishers Group, P.O. Box 322, 3300 AH Dordrecht, Netherlands. TEL 31-78-392392. FAX 31-78-546474; N. America dist. addr.: Box 358, Accord Sta., Hingham, MA 02018-0358. TEL 617-871-6600. FAX 617-871-6528) **Indexed:** Chem.Abstr. **Document type:** monographic series.
—BLDSC (3579.085470); CASDDS. **CCC.**
Refereed Serial

616.99 SZ ISSN 1013-8129
CODEN: DIONEY
DIAGNOSTIC ONCOLOGY. 1991. bi-m. 581 SFr.($387) S. Karger AG, Allschwilerstr. 10, P.O. Box, CH-4009 Basel, Switzerland. TEL 061-306-1111. FAX 061-306-1234. E-mail: Karger@Karger.ch. Ed. A. Malkin. (also avail. in microform from UMI) **Document type:** academic/scholarly publication.
—BLDSC (3579.663500); Genuine Article.
Description: Forum for the latest developments in cancer diagnosis. Multidisciplinary in scope, the journal features clinically relevant contributions from the fields of medical, surgical and radiation oncology; pathology; tumor immunology; and diagnostic imaging.
Refereed Serial

616.99 UN ISSN 0254-2420
LC1041
DIRECTORY OF ON-GOING RESEARCH IN CANCER EPIDEMIOLOGY. (Text in English) 1976. biennial. £46($98) International Agency for Research on Cancer, 150 cours Albert-Thomas, 69372 Lyon Cedex 08, France. TEL 72-73-84-85. FAX 72-73-85-75. TELEX 380023 CIRC F. (Subscr. to: Oxford University Press, Walton St., Oxford OX2 6DP, England) Ed.Bd. circ. 2,300.
Description: Compilation of current research projects in the field of cancer epidemiology.

616.99 NE ISSN 0278-0240
CODEN: DMARD3
DISEASE MARKERS. 1982. 4/yr. fl.730 in Europe (elsewhere $410) (effective 1995). ASFRA B.V., Voorhaven 33, 1135 BL Edam, Netherlands. TEL 31-2993-72751. FAX 31-2993-72877. Ed. C.M. Steel. adv.; bk.rev.; charts; illus.; index. circ. 171. (reprint service avail. from SWZ) **Indexed:** Chem.Abstr., Curr.Adv.Ecol.Sci., Curr.Adv.Genetics & Molec.Biol., Curr.Cont., Excerp.Med., Ind.Med., Telegen. **Document type:** academic/scholarly publication.
—BLDSC (3598.090000); ADONIS; CASDDS; Faxon; Genuine Article; SWETS; UMI; UnCover. **CCC.**
Description: Addresses original research findings and reviews on the subject of the identification of markers associated with the disease process, whether or not they are an integral part of the pathological lesion.

616.99 GW ISSN 0933-128X
EINBLICK. 1987. 4/yr. free. Deutsches Krebsforschungszentrum, Im Neuenheimer Feld 280, 69120 Heidelberg, Germany. TEL 06221-422854. FAX 06221-422995. **Document type:** bulletin.

616.99 KR ISSN 0204-3564
CODEN: EKSODD
EKSPERIMENTAL'NAYA ONKOLOGIYA/EXPERIMENTAL ONCOLOGY; nauchno-tekhnicheskii zhurnal. (Text in Russian; summaries in English and Russian) 1979. bi-m. $98 (effective 1996). (Akademiya Nauk Ukrainy, Otdelenie Biokhimii, Fiziologii i Teoreticheskoi Meditsiny) Vidavnitstvo Naukova Dumka, Vul. Tereshchenkivska 3, 252601 Kiev, Ukraine. TEL 044-224-4068. FAX 044-224-7060. (Dist. by: Mezhdunarodnaya Kniga, B. Yakimanka 39, 117049 Moscow, Russia; Dist. in U.S. by: Victor Kamkin, Inc., 4956 Boiling Brook Pkwy., Rockville, MD 20852. TEL 301-881-5973. FAX 301-881-1637) Ed. V.G. Pinchuk. **Indexed:** Biol.Abstr., Chem.Abstr., Curr.Adv.Ecol.Sci., Excerp.Med., Ind.Med., Ind.Sci.Rev., INIS Atomind., Sci.Cit.Ind.
—BLDSC (0397.998500); CASDDS; Genuine Article.

EMOTION; Wilhelm-Reich-Zeitschrift ueber Triebenergie, Charakterstruktur, Krankheit, Natur und Gesellschaft. see *PSYCHOLOGY*

616.9 US ISSN 8756-1689
CODEN: ENONFD
ENDOCURIETHERAPY - HYPERTHERMIA ONCOLOGY. 1985. q. Endocurietherapy Research Foundation, 2801 Atlantic Ave., Long Beach, CA 90801. TEL 310-933-2929. **Indexed:** Excerp.Med. (1995-). **Document type:** academic/scholarly publication.
—BLDSC (3743.088000).

ENVIRONMENTAL CARCINOGENESIS & ECOTOXICOLOGY REVIEWS. see *ENVIRONMENTAL STUDIES — Toxicology And Environmental Safety*

ETESIA STATISTIKE. EREVNA TOU KARKINOU/ANNUAL STATISTICAL SURVEY OF CANCER. see *MEDICAL SCIENCES — Abstracting, Bibliographies, Statistics*

616.99 NE ISSN 0921-3732
CODEN: ECNEE5
EUROPEAN CANCER NEWS. (Text in English) 1988. 10/yr. fl.261 to institutions; $168 to institutions in U.S. (effective 1996). Kluwer Academic Publishers, Postbus 17, 3300 AA Dordrecht, Netherlands. TEL 31-78-392392. FAX 31-78-392254. TELEX 29245 KAPG NL. E-mail: SERVICES@WKAP.NL. (Dist. by: Kluwer Academic Publishers Group, P.O. Box 322, 3300 AH Dordrecht, Netherlands. TEL 31-78-392392. FAX 31-78-546474; N. America dist. addr.: Box 358, Accord Sta., Hingham, MA 02018-0358. TEL 617-871-6600) Ed. J. Gordon McVie. (also avail. in microform from UMI; back issues avail.; reprint service avail. from SWZ) **Indexed:** ASCA. **Document type:** academic/scholarly publication.
—Genuine Article; UMI. **CCC.**
Description: Provides up-to-date information on the research and treatment of cancer in Europe and around the world.
Refereed Serial

616.994 UK ISSN 0959-8049
RC261.A1 CODEN: EJCAEL
EUROPEAN JOURNAL OF CANCER. Key Title: European Journal of Cancer. Part A: General Topics. 1965. 14/yr. £995($1583) (effective 1996). (Federation of European Cancer Societies) Elsevier Science Ltd., Pergamon, P.O. Box 800, Kidlington, Oxford OX5 1DX, England. TEL 44-1865-843000. FAX 44-1865-843010. E-mail: nlinfo-f@elsevier.nl; usinfo-f@elsevier.com; forinfo-kyf04035@niftyserve.or.jp; Site addr.: http://www.elsevier.nl/. (Subscr. in U.S. and Canada to: Elsevier Science, 660 White Plains Rd., Tarrytown, NY 10591-5153. TEL 914-524-9200. FAX 914-333-2444) (Co-sponsors: European Organization for Research & Treatment of Cancer; European School of Oncology; European Association for Cancer Research) Ed. M.J. Peckham. adv.; bk.rev.; charts; illus.; index. circ. 3,500. (also avail. in microform from UMI; back issues avail.) **Indexed:** Abstr.Health Care Manage.Stud., Biol.Abstr., Biotech.Abstr., Chem.Abstr., Curr.Adv.Biochem., Curr.Adv.Cancer Res., Curr.Adv.Cell & Devel.Biol., Curr.Adv.Ecol.Sci., Curr.Adv.Genetics & Molec.Biol., Curr.Cont., Dairy Sci.Abstr., Dent.Ind., Dok.Arbeitsmed., Excerp.Med., Ind.Med., Ind.Sci.Rev., Ind.Vet., INIS Atomind., Med.& Surg.Dermat., NRN, Rev.Med.& Vet.Mycol., Risk Abstr., Sci.Cit.Ind., Vet.Bull. **Document type:** academic/scholarly publication.
—BLDSC (3829.725102); ADONIS; CASDDS; Faxon; UMI; UnCover. **CCC.**
Former titles (until 1990): European Journal of Cancer and Clinical Oncology (ISSN 0277-5379); (until vol.18, 1982): European Journal of Cancer (ISSN 0014-2964)
Description: Provides an integrated forum for publication of clinical and laboratory research in all specializations of oncology.
Refereed Serial

616.99 UK ISSN 0961-5423
CODEN: EUCAEU
EUROPEAN JOURNAL OF CANCER CARE (ENGLISH EDITION). French edition (ISSN 0961-6438); German edition (ISSN 0961-6446); Italian edition (ISSN 0961-6454); Spanish edition (ISSN 0961-6462) 1992. q. £120 in Europe; elsewhere £132($212) (effective 1996). Blackwell Science Ltd., Osney Mead, Oxford OX2 0EL, England. TEL 44-1865-206206. FAX 44-1865-721205. TELEX 83355 MEDBOK G. Ed. Pat Webb. bk.rev.; bibl.; illus.; index. circ. 1,800. (also avail. in microform from UMI) **Document type:** academic/scholarly publication.
—BLDSC (3829.725350); UMI. **CCC.**
Refereed Serial

616.99 UK ISSN 0961-6462
EUROPEAN JOURNAL OF CANCER CARE (SPANISH EDITION). 1992. q. £80($136) (foreign £88) (effective 1996). Blackwell Science Ltd., Osney Mead, Oxford OX2 0EL, England. TEL 44-1865-206206. FAX 44-1865-721205. **Document type:** academic/scholarly publication.
—**CCC.**
Refereed Serial

616.99 UK ISSN 0964-1955
CODEN: EJCAEL
EUROPEAN JOURNAL OF CANCER PART B: ORAL ONCOLOGY. 1992. bi-m. £280($446) (effective 1996). Elsevier Science Ltd., Pergamon, P.O. Box 800, Kidlington, Oxford OX5 1DX, England. TEL 44-1865-843000. FAX 44-1865-843010. E-mail: nlinfo-f@elsevier.nl; usinfo-f@elsevier.com; forinfo-kyf04035@niftyserve.or.jp; Site addr.: http://www.elsevier.nl/. (Subscr. in U.S., and Canada to: Elsevier Science, 660 White Plains Rd., Tarrytown, NY 10591-5153. TEL 914-524-9200. FAX 914-333-2444) Ed. Crispian Scully. (also avail. in microform from UMI; back issues avail.) **Indexed:** Excerp.Med. (1993-), Ind.Med. (1994-). **Document type:** academic/scholarly publication.
—BLDSC (3829.725120); ADONIS; CASDDS; Faxon; Genuine Article; SWETS; UMI; UnCover. **CCC.**
Description: Discusses issues relating to aetiopathogenesis, epidemiology, prevention and management of oral cancer.
Refereed Serial

MEDICAL SCIENCES — ONCOLOGY

616.99   UK   ISSN 0959-8278
CODEN: EJUPEK
EUROPEAN JOURNAL OF CANCER PREVENTION. 1992. bi-m. £260($445) to institutions (effective 1995). (European Cancer Prevention Organisation) Rapid Communications of Oxford Ltd., The Old Malthouse, Paradise St., Oxford OX1 1LD, England. TEL 01865-790447. FAX 01865-244012. E-mail: rapidcom@vax.oxford.ac.uk. Ed. Michael Hill. adv. contact: Julie Gribben. (reprint service avail.) **Indexed:** Excerp.Med. (1994-), Ind.Med. (1992-). **Document type:** academic/scholarly publication.
●Also available on CD-ROM.
—BLDSC (3829.725400); ADONIS. **CCC.**
    Description: Aims to promote an increased awareness of all aspects of cancer prevention and to stimulate new ideas and innovations.

616.99 618.1   IT   ISSN 0392-2936
CODEN: EJGODE
EUROPEAN JOURNAL OF GYNECOLOGICAL ONCOLOGY. (Text and summaries in English) 1980. bi-m. $200 to individuals; institutions $300. Studi Ostetrico Ginecologici s.r.l., Galleria Storione 2-A, 35128 Padua, Italy. TEL 39-49-8758644. FAX 39-49-8752018. (Co-sponsor: European Society of Gynecological Oncology) Ed. Antonio Onnis. adv.; bk.rev. circ. 600. (back issues avail.) **Indexed:** Biol.Abstr., Excerp.Med., Ind.Med., NRN. **Document type:** academic/scholarly publication.
—BLDSC (3829.729600); Faxon; SWETS; UnCover. **CCC.**
    Refereed Serial

616.994   UK   ISSN 0748-7983
EUROPEAN JOURNAL OF SURGICAL ONCOLOGY. 1975. 6/yr. £90 in Europe (rest of world $168) to individuals; institutions £128 in Europe (rest of world $230). (British Association of Surgical Oncology) W.B. Saunders Ltd. (Subsidiary of: Harcourt Brace & Company Ltd.), 24-28 Oval Rd., London NW1 7DX, England. TEL 0171-267-4466. FAX 0171-482-2293. TELEX 257775-ACPRES-G. (Subscr. to: Harcourt Brace & Company Ltd., Foots Cray High St., Sidcup, Kent DA14 5HP, England. TEL 0181-300-3322. FAX 0181-309-0807; US, Canadian, and Mexican subscr. to: W.B. Saunders Co., Journal Subscription Fulfillment, 6277 Sea Harbor Dr., 4th Fl., Orlando, FL 32887-4800. TEL 800-654-2452. FAX 800-874-6418) (Co-sponsor: European Society of Surgical Oncology) Ed. Ian Burn. adv.; illus.; index. **Indexed:** Biol.Abstr., Curr.Adv.Cancer Res., Curr.Adv.Ecol.Sci., Curr.Adv.Genetics & Molec.Biol., Curr.Cont., Excerp.Med., Ind.Med., INIS Atomind., Nutr.Abstr. **Document type:** academic/scholarly publication.
—BLDSC (3829.745500); Faxon; Genuine Article; SWETS; UnCover. **CCC.**
    Formerly: Clinical Oncology (ISSN 0305-7399)
    Description: Presents original articles and state-of-the-art reviews of interest to surgeons treating patients with cancer.

616   US   ISSN 0146-0447
CODEN: MSECDH
EUROPEAN ORGANIZATION FOR RESEARCH ON TREATMENT OF CANCER. MONOGRAPH SERIES. Short title: E O R T C Monograph Series. 1975. irreg., latest vol.20. price varies. Raven Press (Subsidiary of: Wolters Kluwer N.V.), 1185 Ave. of the Americas, New York, NY 10036. TEL 212-930-9500. FAX 212-869-3495. (reprint service avail. from UMI) **Indexed:** Biol.Abstr., Curr.Cont. **Document type:** monographic series.
—CASDDS.
    Refereed Serial

616.99   GW
EUROPEAN SCHOOL OF ONCOLOGY. MONOGRAPHS. irreg. Springer-Verlag, Heidelberger Platz 3, 14197 Berlin, Germany. TEL 030-8207-0. FAX 030-8214091. Ed. U. Veronesi. **Document type:** monographic series.

616.994   IT   ISSN 0392-047X
FOLIA ONCOLOGICA. (Text in English, Italian; summaries in English) 1978. q. L.50000($50) (effective 1994). (Istituto Scientifico Oncologico) Ciemme, Via Curzio dei Mille, 2, 70122 Bari, Italy. TEL 39-80-5555480. FAX 39-80-5555119. (Subscr. to: I.S.O., Via Amendola 209, 70126 Bari, Italy) Ed. Luigi Marinaccio. bk.rev. circ. 600. **Indexed:** Excerp.Med. **Document type:** academic/scholarly publication.
—BLDSC (3971.790000).

FONDAMENTAL. see *SOCIAL SERVICES AND WELFARE*

616.99 573.21   US   ISSN 1040-0303
FOX CHASE CANCER CENTER. SCIENTIFIC REPORT. 1948. a. free. Fox Chase Cancer Center, 7701 Burholme Ave., Philadelphia, PA 19111. TEL 215-728-6900. FAX 215-728-2412. Ed. Kathy Nelson. circ. 9,000. **Document type:** newsletter.
—BLDSC (8197.249990).
    Formerly: I.C.R. Scientific Report.

FRONTIERS OF RADIATION THERAPY AND ONCOLOGY. see *MEDICAL SCIENCES — Radiology And Nuclear Medicine*

616.99 616.3   US   ISSN 1064-9700
CODEN: GICAE2
G I CANCER. (Gastrointestinal); an international journal on gastrointestinal oncology. 1993. q. 91 ECU (effective 1996). Harwood Academic Publishers, c/o International Publishers Distributor, 820 Town Center Dr.553, PA 19047. TEL 215-750-2642. FAX 215-750-6343. (Subscr. to: International Publishers Distributor, P.O. Box 90, Reading, Berks., RG1 8JL, England. TEL 44-173-456-8316) (also avail. in microform) **Document type:** academic/scholarly publication.
—CCC.
    Description: Features multidisciplinary clinical and laboratory data on gastrointestinal oncology.

616.99   JA
GAN KANJA TO TAISHO RYOHO/SYMPTOM CONTROL IN CANCER PATIENTS. (Text in Japanese) 1989. a. 2000 Yen. Medikaru Rebyusha - Medical Review Co., Ltd., 7-3, Hiranomachi 1-chome, Chuo-ku, Osaka 541, Japan.

615   JA   ISSN 0914-3467
GAN MEN'EKI EIYO/CANCER, IMMUNOLOGY AND NUTRITION. (Text in Japanese) 1987. q. Kyowa Kikaku Ltd., 4-7, Koraibashi 2-chome, Chuo-ku, Osaka 541, Japan.

616.9   JA   ISSN 0385-0684
CODEN: GTKRDX
GAN TO KAGAKU RYOHO/JAPANESE JOURNAL OF CANCER AND CHEMOTHERAPY. (Text in Japanese, summaries in English, Japanese) 1974. m. Japanese Journal of Cancer and Chemotherapy Publishers, Inc., 1-8-9 Yaesu, Chuo-ku, Tokyo 103, Japan. TEL 81-3-3278-0052. FAX 81-3-3281-0435. **Indexed:** Chem.Abstr., Excerp.Med., Ind.Med., INIS Atomind. **Document type:** academic/scholarly publication.
—CASDDS; Genuine Article.

616.9   JA
GANN MONOGRAPHS ON CANCER RESEARCH. (Text in English) 1966. s-a. price varies. (Japanese Cancer Association) Gakkai Shuppan Senta - Japan Scientific Societies Press, 2-10, Hongo 6-chome, Bunkyo-ku, Tokyo 113, Japan. Dir. Tugi Miyazaki. bk.rev. circ. 2,000. **Indexed:** Biol.Abstr., Chem.Abstr., Excerp.Med., INIS Atomind. **Document type:** monographic series.
—EMDOCS.
    Formerly: Gann Monographs (ISSN 0072-0151)
    Description: Includes collected contributions on current topics in cancer problems and allied fields.
    Refereed Serial

GENES, CHROMOSOMES & CANCER. see *BIOLOGY — Genetics*

616.99   IT   ISSN 0392-128X
GIORNALE ITALIANO DI ONCOLOGIA. (Text in Italian; summaries in English) q. L.60000($60) C I C Edizioni Internazionali s.r.l., Via L. Spallanzani 11, 00161 Rome, Italy. TEL 06-8412673. FAX 06-44242033. TELEX 622099 CIC. Dirs. L. Caldarola, C. Maltoni. **Indexed:** Excerp.Med.
—BLDSC (4178.236000). **CCC.**

GREAT BRITAIN. GOVERNMENT STATISTICAL SERVICE. CANCER STATISTICS REGISTRATIONS. ENGLAND AND WALES. see *MEDICAL SCIENCES — Abstracting, Bibliographies, Statistics*

616.99   US
HEALTH VICTORY BULLETIN. 1975. m. $20. Arlin J. Brown Information Center, Inc., Box 251, Fort Belvoir, VA 22060. TEL 703-752-9511. FAX 703-752-4324. Ed. Arlin J. Brown. bk.rev.; index. circ. 300. (back issues avail.) **Document type:** bulletin.
    Formerly (until 1982): Cancer Victory Bulletin.
    Description: Covers current developments in cancer, health and nutrition with emphasis on practical information for the patient.

HEM-ONC ANNALS; the journal of continuing education in hematology & oncology. see *MEDICAL SCIENCES — Hematology*

616.99   US   ISSN 0889-8588
RB145   CODEN: HCNAEQ
HEMATOLOGY - ONCOLOGY CLINICS OF NORTH AMERICA. 1972. bi-m. $140 (foreign $170) (effective 1996). W.B. Saunders Co. (Subsidiary of: Harcourt Brace & Company), Curtis Center, 3rd Fl., Independence Sq. W., Philadelphia, PA 19106-3399. TEL 215-238-7800. FAX 215-238-6445. (Subscr. to: Periodicals Fulfillment, W.B. Saunders Co., 6277 Sea Harbor Dr., 4th Fl., Orlando, FL 32891-4800. TEL 800-654-2452. FAX 800-874-6418) Ed. Naina Chohan. (also avail. in microform from UMI) **Indexed:** Biol.Abstr., Chem.Abstr., CINAHL, Curr.Adv.Ecol.Sci., Excerp.Med., Helminthol.Abstr., Ind.Med., Ind.Sci.Rev., Nutr.Abstr., Sci.Cit.Ind. **Document type:** academic/scholarly publication.
—BLDSC (4291.610000); CASDDS; Faxon; Genuine Article; SWETS; UMI; UnCover. **CCC.**
    Formed by the 1987 merger of: Clinics in Oncology (ISSN 0261-9873); Clinics in Haematology (ISSN 0308-2261)
    Description: Addresses a single topic in the management of patients with cancer and systemic disease.
    Refereed Serial

616.994   US
HERALD OF HOPE. 1960-1976; resumed 19?? q. free. American Cancer Society, Inc., Minnesota Division, 3316 W. 66th St., Edina, MN 55435. TEL 612-925-2772. FAX 612-925-6333. Ed. Nancy Paterson. charts; illus.; pat, stat. circ. 6,500. (processed)
    Formerly: Minnesota Volunteer.

616.994   UK   ISSN 0309-0167
CODEN: HISTDD
HISTOPATHOLOGY. 1977. m. £258 in Europe; elsewhere £285($459) (effective 1996). (International Academy of Pathology, British Division) Blackwell Science Ltd., Osney Mead, Oxford OX2 OEL, England. TEL 01865-206206. FAX 01865-206219. TELEX 83355 MEDBOK G. Ed. R.N.M. MacSween. adv.; bk.rev.; illus.; index. circ. 2,850. (back issues avail.; reprint service avail. from ISI) **Indexed:** ASCA, Biol.Abstr., Curr.Adv.Cancer Res., Curr.Adv.Ecol.Sci., Curr.Cont, Dent.Ind., Dok.Arbeitsmed., Excerp.Med., Helminthol.Abstr., Ind.Med., Ind.Sci.Rev., Med.& Surg.Dermat., Rev.Med.& Vet.Mycol., Sci.Cit.Ind., Vet.Bull. **Document type:** academic/scholarly publication.
—BLDSC (4316.027000); ADONIS; Faxon; Genuine Article; SWETS; UMI; UnCover. **CCC.**
    Refereed Serial

616.9   JA   ISSN 0913-8927
HYOGO KENRITSU SEIJINBYO SENTA KIYO/HYOGO MEDICAL CENTER FOR ADULTS. BULLETIN. (Text in Japanese; summaries in English, Japanese) 1962. a. Hyogo Kenritsu Seijinbyo Senta, 13-17, Kitaoji-cho, Akashi-shi, Hyogo-ken 673, Japan. **Document type:** bulletin.
    Former titles (until 1984): Hyogo Kenritsu Byoin Gan Senta Kiyo - Hyogo Cancer Hospital. Bulletin (ISSN 0387-0944); (until 1973): Hyogoken Gan Senta Nenpo (ISSN 0441-537X)

616.99   NE   ISSN 0928-1606
CODEN: HYONFL
HYPERTHERMIA AND ONCOLOGY. (Text in English) 1988. irreg., vol.4, 1994. price varies. V S P, P.O. Box 346, 3700 AH Zeist, Netherlands. TEL 31-3404-25790. FAX 31-3404-32081. (Dist. in U.S. and Canada by: Books International Inc., Box 605, Herndon, VA 22070. TEL 703-435-7064. FAX 703-689-0660) Eds. M. Urano, E.B. Douple. (back issues avail.) **Document type:** monographic series.
—BLDSC (4352.635500).

616.994 UK
I A QUARTERLY JOURNAL. 1956. q. £12. Ileostomy and Internal Pouch Support Group, Amblehurst House, P.O. Box 23, Mansfield, Notts. NG18 4TT, England. TEL 01623-28099. Ed. David Eades. adv.; pat.; stat. circ. 11,400.

616.99 UN ISSN 0250-8613
I A R C BIENNIAL REPORT. (Editions in English, French) 1987. biennial. 15 SFr. International Agency for Research on Cancer, 150, Cours Albert Thomas, 69372 Lyon Cedex 08, France. TEL 72-73-84-85. FAX 72-73-85-75. TELEX 380023. (Dist. by: World Health Organization, Distribution and Sales Service, 1211 Geneva 27, Switzerland) circ. 3,000. (also avail. in microfiche from CIS) **Indexed:** IIS.
Formerly: I A R C Annual Report.

616.994 UN ISSN 0250-9555
RC268.6 CODEN: IARMB8
I A R C MONOGRAPHS ON THE EVALUATION OF CARCINOGENIC RISK OF CHEMICALS TO HUMANS. (Text in English) 1972. 3/yr. price varies. International Agency for Research on Cancer, 150 cours Albert-Thomas, 69372 Lyon Cedex 08, France. TEL 72-73-84-85. FAX 72-73-85-75. TELEX 380023. (Subscr. addr.: World Health Organization, Distribution and Sales Services, 1211 Geneva 27, Switzerland) **Indexed:** Abstr.Hyg., Anal.Abstr., Biol.Abstr., Curr.Cont., Food Sci.& Tech.Abstr., Ind.Med., NRN, Trop.Dis.Bull.
●Also available on CD-ROM.
—BLDSC (4359.536700). **CCC.**
Formerly (until 1978): I A R C Monographs on the Evaluation of Carcinogenic Risk of Chemicals to Man (ISSN 0301-3944)
Description: Monographs comprise sections on physical and chemical data, technical products, use, occurrence and analysis, carcinogenicity in animals, other biological data, human epidemiological results and evaluations.

616.994 UN ISSN 0300-5038
CODEN: IARCCD
I A R C SCIENTIFIC PUBLICATIONS. 1971. irreg., latest no.132. price varies. International Agency for Research on Cancer, 150 cours Albert-Thomas, 69372 Lyon Cedex 08, France. TEL 72-73-84-85. FAX 72-73-85-75. TELEX 380023. (U.S. subscr. to: Oxford University Press, 200 Madison Ave., New York, NY 10016) Ed. J. Cheney. **Indexed:** Abstr.Hyg., Anal.Abstr., Biol.Abstr., Chem.Abstr., Curr.Cont., Dent.Ind., Dok.Arbeitsmed., Excerp.Med., Food Sci.& Tech.Abstr., Ind.Med., Trop.Dis.Bull. **Document type:** monographic series.
—BLDSC (4359.537000); CASDDS; Faxon.

616.99 UN ISSN 1012-7348
I A R C TECHNICAL REPORTS. 1988. irreg., no.22, 1994. International Agency for Research on Cancer, 150 cours Albert Thomas, 69372 Lyon Cedex 08, France. TEL 72-73-84-85. FAX 72-73-85-75. TELEX 380 023. **Document type:** monographic series.

616.99 362.1 GW ISSN 0724-8016
ILCO-PRAXIS. 1974. q. DM.30. Deutsche Ilco, Kepserstr. 50, 85356 Freising, Germany. FAX 08161-85521. Ed. Helga Englert. adv.; bk.rev. circ. 11,000. **Document type:** newsletter.
Formerly (until 1982): Deutsche Ilco-Praxis (ISSN 0724-8024)

616.994 UK ISSN 0306-4905
IMPERIAL CANCER RESEARCH FUND. SCIENTIFIC REPORT. 1973. a. free to qualified personnel. Imperial Cancer Research Fund, Lincoln's Inn Fields, London WC2A 3PX, England. TEL 0171-269-3206. FAX 0171-269-3084. E-mail: lib__info@icrf.icnet.uk. Ed.Bd. circ. 1,700 (controlled). **Document type:** corporate report.
—BLDSC (8197.900000).

616.99 US
IN TOUCH (PHILADELPHIA). 1984. q. free. Fox Chase Cancer Center, 7701 Burholme Ave., Philadelphia, PA 19111. TEL 215-728-4758.
FAX 215-728-2702. Eds. Denise LaMarra, Susan Tobin. illus. circ. 30,000. **Document type:** newsletter.
Description: Contains news of the center for friends, patients and donors.

IN VITRO CELLULAR & DEVELOPMENTAL BIOLOGY - ANIMAL. see BIOLOGY — Microbiology

IN VITRO CELLULAR & DEVELOPMENTAL BIOLOGY - PLANT. see BIOLOGY — Microbiology

IN VITRO REPORT. see BIOLOGY — Microbiology

616.9 XV ISSN 0079-9580
INCIDENCA RAKA V SLOVENIJI/CANCER INCIDENCE IN SLOVENIA. (Text in English and Slovenian) 1957. a. free. Onkoloski Institut, Zaloska C,2, 61105 Ljubljana, Slovenia. TEL 061 316 490. Ed. Vera Pompe Kirn. index. circ. 800.
Formerly: Rak v Sloveniji. Tabele.

616.994 II ISSN 0019-509X
CODEN: IJCAAR
INDIAN JOURNAL OF CANCER. (Text in English) 1963. q. Rs.120($35) Indian Cancer Society, 74 Jerbai Wadia Rd., Parel, Bombay 400 012, India. TEL 22-412-5238. (Co-sponsor: Indian Association of Oncology) Ed. Dr. D.J. Jussawalla. adv.; bk.rev.; charts; illus.; stat. circ. 1,500. (also avail. in microfilm from UMI; reprint service avail. from IRC,UMI) **Indexed:** Biol.Abstr., Chem.Abstr., Dent.Ind., Excerp.Med. (until 199?), ExtraMED, Ind.Med., INIS Atomind., Vet.Bull. **Document type:** academic/scholarly publication.
●Also available on CD-ROM.
—BLDSC (4410.550000); CASDDS; EMDOCS; Faxon; SWETS; UMI; UnCover.

616.994 MX ISSN 0076-7131
INSTITUTO NACIONAL DE CANCEROLOGIA DE MEXICO. REVISTA. (Text in Spanish; summaries in English) 1954. 4/yr. $40 (foreign $60). (Instituto Nacional de Cancerologia) Editorial Cultura Medica S.A., Casma 576, Col. Lindavista 2C, 07300 Mexico, D.F., Mexico. TEL 525-6280429.
FAX 525-57346662. (Co-sponsors: Sociedad Mexicana de Estudios Oncologicos; Grupo de Estudios y Tratamiento Latinoamericano del Cancer) Ed. Dr. Jaime G. de la Garza Salazar. adv. contact: Alicia Garfias Flores. charts; illus.; stat.; circ. 1,000 (paid). **Indexed:** Excerp.Med., Ind.Med. **Document type:** academic/scholarly publication.
—EMDOCS.
Description: Provides original papers in cancer research.
Refereed Serial

616.994 US ISSN 0020-7136
RC261 CODEN: IJCNAW
INTERNATIONAL JOURNAL OF CANCER. (Text in English, French) 1966. 30/yr. $225 (foreign $225) (effective 1996). (International Union Against Cancer - Union Internationale Contre le Cancer) John Wiley & Sons, Inc., Journals, 605 Third Ave., New York, NY 10158. TEL 212-850-6645.
FAX 212-850-6021. TELEX 12-7063. E-mail: SUBINFO@JWILEY.COM. (Subscr. outside the Americas to: John Wiley & Sons Ltd., Baffins Ln. Chichester, W. Sussex PO19 1UD, England. TEL 44-1243-779777. FAX 44-1243-776128) Ed. N. Odartchenko. adv.; bk.rev.; charts; illus.; s-a. index. (also avail. in microform from UMI; back issues avail.; reprint service avail. from SWZ) **Indexed:** Abstr.Hyg., Biol.Abstr., Biotech.Abstr., C.I.S. Abstr., Chem.Abstr., Curr.Adv.Cell & Devel.Biol., Curr.Adv.Ecol.Sci., Curr.Adv.Genetics & Molec.Biol., Curr.Cont., Dairy Sci.Abstr., Dent. Ind., Dok.Arbeitsmed., Excerp.Med., Helminthol.Abstr., Ind.Med., Ind.Sci.Rev., Ind.Vet., Med.& Surg.Dermat., NRN, Poult.Abstr., Rev.Med.& Vet.Mycol., Risk Abstr., Sci.Cit.Ind., Small Anim.Abstr., Telegen, Trop.Dis.Bull., Vet.Bull. **Document type:** academic/scholarly publication.
—BLDSC (4542.156000); ADONIS; CASDDS; EMDOCS; Faxon; Genuine Article; SWETS; UnCover. **CCC.**
Description: Examines all topics relevant to experimental and clinical cancer research, with an emphasis on fundamental studies that have relevance to the understanding of human cancer.
Refereed Serial

INTERNATIONAL JOURNAL OF GYNECOLOGICAL CANCER. see MEDICAL SCIENCES — Obstetrics And Gynecology

MEDICAL SCIENCES — ONCOLOGY 4477

616.99 UK ISSN 0265-6736
CODEN: IJHYEQ
INTERNATIONAL JOURNAL OF HYPERTHERMIA. bi-m. £312($515) (effective 1996). (North American Hyperthermia Group) Taylor & Francis Ltd., Rankine Rd., Basingstoke, Hants. RG24 8PR, England. TEL 44-1256-840366. FAX 44-1256-479438. TELEX 858540. E-mail: info@tandf.co.uk. (Subscr. in N. America to: Taylor & Francis Inc., 1900 Frost Rd., Ste. 101, Bristol, PA 19007-1598. TEL 800-821-8312. FAX 215-785-5515) Ed.Bd. **Indexed:** Curr.Adv.Cancer Res., Curr.Adv.Cell & Devel.Biol., Curr.Adv.Ecol.Sci., Excerp.Med., INSPEC. **Document type:** academic/scholarly publication.
—BLDSC (4542.297000); CASDDS; Faxon; Genuine Article; UnCover. **CCC.**
Description: Provides a forum for the publication of research and clinical papers on hyperthermia, which fall largely into the three main categories: clinical studies, biological studies and techniques of heat delivery and temperature measurement.
Refereed Serial

616.99 GR ISSN 1019-6439
CODEN: IJONES
INTERNATIONAL JOURNAL OF ONCOLOGY; an international journal devoted to oncology research and cancer treatment. 1992. m. $500 to institutions in Europe (elsewhere $550); individuals in Europe $300 (elsewhere $350) (effective 1995). National Hellenic Research Foundation, Institute of Biological Research and Biotechnology, 48 Vas. Constantinou Ave., Athens 11635, Greece. TEL 30-1-724-1505. FAX 30-1-752-3866. Ed. D.A. Spandidos; Pub. D.A. Spandidos. adv.; bk.rev.; charts; illus. circ. 700. **Indexed:** Chem.Abstr., Curr.Cont., Excerp.Med. (1993-), Med.& Surg.Dermat., Sci.Cit.Ind. **Document type:** academic/scholarly publication.
—BLDSC (4542.424600); CASDDS; Genuine Article; SWETS. **CCC.**
Description: Publishes original high-quality articles and reports in experimental and clinical cancer research.
Refereed Serial

INTERNATIONAL JOURNAL OF PANCREATOLOGY. see MEDICAL SCIENCES — Endocrinology

618.92 616.15 US ISSN 1070-2903
▼**INTERNATIONAL JOURNAL OF PEDIATRIC HEMATOLOGY - ONCOLOGY.** 1994. 6/yr. 90 ECU (effective 1996). Harwood Academic Publishers, c/o International Publishers Distributor, 820 Town Center Dr., Langhorne, PA 19047.
TEL 215-750-2642; 800-545-8398.
FAX 215-750-6343. (Subscr. to: International Publishers Distributor, P.O. Box 90, Reading, Berkshire RG1 8JL, England. TEL 44-173-456-8316) (back issues avail.) **Document type:** academic/scholarly publication.

616.99 574.191 UK ISSN 0955-3002
QH652 CODEN: IJRBE7
INTERNATIONAL JOURNAL OF RADIATION BIOLOGY. (Text and summaries in English, French, German) 1959. m. (2 vols./yr.) £618($1020) (effective 1996). Taylor & Francis Ltd., Rankine Rd., Basingstoke, Hants RG24 8PR, England. TEL 44-1256-840366. FAX 44-1256-479438. TELEX 858540. E-mail: info@tandf.co.uk. (Subscr. in N. America to: Taylor & Francis Inc., 1900 Frost Rd., Ste. 101, Bristol, PA 19007-1598. TEL 800-821-8312. FAX 215-785-5515) Ed. Jolyon H. Hendry. adv.; charts; illus.; index. (also avail. in microform) **Indexed:** Biol.Abstr., Chem.Abstr., Crop Physiol.Abstr., Curr.Adv.Biochem., Curr.Adv.Cancer Res., Curr.Adv.Cell & Devel.Biol., Curr.Adv.Genetics & Molec.Biol., Curr.Cont., Dairy Sci.Abstr., Excerp.Med., Field Crop Abstr., Helminthol.Abstr., Herb.Abstr., Hort.Abstr., Ind.Med., Ind.Vet., INIS Atomind., INSPEC, Nutr.Abstr., Poult.Abstr., Sci.Cit.Ind., Seed Abstr., Vet.Bull. **Document type:** academic/scholarly publication.
—BLDSC (4542.517900); ADONIS; CASDDS; Ei; Faxon; Genuine Article; SWETS; UnCover. **CCC.**
Formerly (until 1988): International Journal of Radiation Biology and Related Studies in Physics, Chemistry and Medicine (ISSN 0020-7616)
Description: Contains original research and review papers on the effects of ionization, ultraviolet and visible radiation, accelerated particles, microwaves, ultrasound and heat and related modalities.
Refereed Serial

INTERNATIONAL JOURNAL OF SURGICAL PATHOLOGY. see MEDICAL SCIENCES — Surgery

MEDICAL SCIENCES — ONCOLOGY

616.99 TU ISSN 0259-840X
INTERNATIONAL QUARTERLY OF CANCER RESEARCH.
(Text in English) 1987. q. $160. Tahsin Yazicioglu, P. Kutusu 1318, Sirkeci, Istanbul 34438, Turkey. Ed. Kenneth D. Tew. adv.; bk.rev. **Indexed:** Biol.Abstr., Chem.Abstr., Curr.Cont., Excerp.Med., Ref.Zh., Sci.Cit.Ind.

616.994 CH ISSN 0074-9206
INTERNATIONAL UNION AGAINST CANCER. PROCEEDINGS OF CONGRESS. quadrennial, 16th, 1994, New Delhi. International Union Against Cancer, SZ - Union Internationale Contre le Cancer, c/o E. Hansen, 3 rue du Conseil-General, CH-1205 Geneva, Switzerland. TEL 022-3201811. FAX 022-3201810. E-mail: uicc@atge.automail.com. **Document type:** proceedings.

616.99 RU ISSN 0202-7127
RC280.B6
ITOGI NAUKI I TEKHNIKI: ONKOLOGIYA. irreg., vol.18, 1989. 6.60 Rub. Vsesoyuznyi Institut Nauchno-Tekhnicheskoi Informatsii (VINITI), Baltiiskaya ul. 14, Moscow A-219, Russia. (Subscr. to: Mezhdunarodnaya Kniga, Dimitrova ul. 39, 113095 Moscow, Russia)
—BLDSC (0127.449000).

J A S T R O NEWSLETTER. (Japanese Society for Therapeutic Radiology and Oncology) see *MEDICAL SCIENCES — Radiology And Nuclear Medicine*

616.994 JA ISSN 0021-4671
CODEN: NGCJAK
JAPAN SOCIETY FOR CANCER THERAPY. JOURNAL. (Text in English, Japanese) 1966. m. 10000 Yen (includes Proceedings of the Congress). Japan Society for Cancer Therapy - Nihon Gan Chiryo Gakkai, c/o Kinki Invention Center, 14 Yoshida, Kawara-cho, Sakyo-ku, Kyoto 606, Japan. TEL 81-75-751-7150. FAX 81-75-761-9724. Ed. Kazue Ozawa. adv.; bk.rev.; abstr.; bibl.; charts; illus. **Indexed:** Biol.Abstr., Dent.Ind., Excerp.Med., Ind.Med.
—BLDSC (4806.500000); CASDDS; EMDOCS.

616.9 JA ISSN 0075-3327
JAPAN SOCIETY FOR CANCER THERAPY. PROCEEDINGS OF THE CONGRESS. (Text in English) 1963. a. included with subcr. to Japan Society for Cancer Therapy. Journal. Japan Society for Cancer Therapy - Nihon Gan Chiryo Gakkai, c/o Kinki Invention Center, 14 Yoshida, Kawara-cho, Sakyo-ku, Kyoto 606, Japan. TEL 81-75-751-7150. FAX 81-75-761-9724. **Document type:** proceedings.

616.994 JA ISSN 0021-4949
CODEN: GANRAE
JAPANESE JOURNAL OF CANCER CLINICS/GAN NO RINSHO. (Text in Japanese; summaries in English) 1954. m. 34820 Yen. Shinohara Publishers, Inc., Yaguchi Bldg., 11-7, Hongo 2-chome, Bunkyo-ku, Tokyo 113, Japan. TEL 03-3816-5311. FAX 03-3816-5314. Ed. Yoshikuni Shinohara. adv.; bk.rev.; abstr.; charts; illus.; index. circ. 3,800. **Indexed:** Chem.Abstr., Dent.Ind., Ind.Med., INIS Atomind., Telegen.
—BLDSC (4651.250000); CASDDS.

616.994 JA ISSN 0910-5050
CODEN: JJCREP
JAPANESE JOURNAL OF CANCER RESEARCH. (Text and summaries in English) 1907. m. 1£405($640) (effective 1996). Japanese Cancer Association, c/o Cancer Institute, 1-37-1 Kami-Ikebukuro, Toshima-ku, Tokyo 170, Japan. TEL 3918-0111. FAX 3918-5776. (Dist. by: Business Center for Academic Societies Japan, 5-16-9, Hongkomagome, Bunkyo-ku, Tokyo; Dist. outside the Far East by: Elsevier Scientific Publishers Ireland Ltd., P.O. Box 85, Limerick, Ireland. TEL 353-61-471944. FAX 353-61-472144; Subscr. in U.S. and Canada to: Elsevier Science Publishing Co., Inc., Box 882, Madison Sq. Sta., New York, NY 10159. TEL 212-989-5800. FAX 212-633-3990) Ed. Takashi Sugimura. adv.; illus.; index. cum.index. circ. 17,500. (also avail. in microform from UMI,PMC; back issues avail.; reprint service avail. from ISI) **Indexed:** Biol.Abstr., Chem.Abstr., Curr.Adv.Biochem., Curr.Adv.Cancer Res., Curr.Adv.Cell & Devel.Biol., Curr.Adv.Ecol.Sci., Curr.Adv.Genetics & Molec.Biol., Dairy Sci.Abstr., Excerp.Med., Ind.Med., Ind.Sci.Rev., Ind.Vet., INIS Atomind., Nutr.Abstr., Rev.Med.& Vet.Mycol., Sci.Cit.Ind. **Document type:** academic/scholarly publication.
—BLDSC (4651.270000); CASDDS; Faxon; Genuine Article; SWETS; UMI; UnCover. **CCC.**
Formerly: Gann (ISSN 0016-450X)
Description: Provides an overview of state of the art cancer research in Japan.

616.994 JA ISSN 0368-2811
CODEN: JJCOAC
JAPANESE JOURNAL OF CLINICAL ONCOLOGY. (Text in English) 1971. 6/yr. 10,000 Yen. Foundation for Promotion of Cancer Research, c/o National Cancer Center Hospital, 1-1, Tsukiji 5-chome, Chuo-ku, Tokyo 104, Japan. TEL 03-3542-2511. FAX 03-3545-3567. Ed. Dr. Takashi Sugimura. bk.rev.; bibl.; charts; illus. circ. 1,100. (reprint service avail. from ISI) **Indexed:** Chem.Abstr., Curr.Cont., Excerp.Med., Ind.Med., INIS Atomind., NRN, Rev.Med.& Vet.Mycol. **Document type:** academic/scholarly publication.
●Also available online. Vendor(s): JICST.
—BLDSC (4651.378000); Faxon; Genuine Article; SWETS; UnCover.

616.99 UK ISSN 0960-9768
JOURNAL OF CANCER CARE. 1992. q. £28($43) to individuals (foreign £29); institutions £95 (overseas £97 (U.S. $153)); (effective 1995). Churchill Livingstone Journals (Subsidiary of: Pearson Professional), Robert Stevenson House, 1-3 Baxter's Pl., Leith Walk, Edinburgh EH1 3AF, Scotland. TEL 0131-556-2424. FAX 0131-459-1177. (Subscr. to: Pearson Professional Ltd., P.O. Box 77, Fourth Ave., Harlow, Essex CM19 5AA, England. TEL 01279-623760; U.S. subscr. to: Churchill Livingstone, 650 Ave. of the Americas, New York, NY 10011. TEL 212-206-5000) Eds. Ann Faulkner, Irene Scott. adv. contact: David Dunnachie. bk.rev.; bibl. circ. 470. **Document type:** academic/scholarly publication.
—BLDSC (4954.842800).
Description: Explores cancer care in hospitals, homes and hospices.

616.99 US ISSN 0885-8195
JOURNAL OF CANCER EDUCATION. 1986. q. $80 to individuals (foreign $90); institutions $150 (foreign $175). (American Association for Cancer Education) Hanley & Belfus, Inc., 210 S. 13th St., Philadelphia, PA 19107. TEL 215-546-7293. FAX 215-790-9330. (Co-sponsor: European Association for Cancer Education) Ed. Richard F. Bakemeier. adv. contact: Diane R. Sherel. index. circ. 6,000. (also avail. in microform from UMI; back issues avail.) **Indexed:** CINAHL, Excerp.Med., Tech.Educ.Abstr. **Document type:** academic/scholarly publication.
—BLDSC (4954.843000); SWETS; UMI; UnCover. **CCC.**
Description: Addresses varied aspects of cancer education for physicians, dentists, nurses, students, social workers and other allied health professionals. Articles include reports of original results of educational research and discussions of current problems and techniques in cancer education.
Refereed Serial

616.994 GW ISSN 0171-5216
CODEN: JCROD7
JOURNAL OF CANCER RESEARCH AND CLINICAL ONCOLOGY. (Supplement avail. (ISSN 0943-9382)) (Text in English) 1903. 12/yr. DM.2192($1593) (effective 1996). (Deutsche Krebsgesellschaft) Springer-Verlag, Heidelberger Platz 3, 14197 Berlin, Germany. TEL 030-8207-0. FAX 030-8214091. E-mail: orders@springer.de. (Subscr. in N. America to: Springer-Verlag New York, Inc., 44 Hartz Way, Secaucus, NJ 07096-2491. TEL 201-348-4033. FAX 201-348-4505) Ed. E. Grundmann. adv. (also avail. in microform from UMI; back issues avail.; reprint service avail. from ISI) **Indexed:** Biol.Abstr., Biotech.Abstr., C.I.S. Abstr., Chem.Abstr., Curr.Adv.Cancer Res., Curr.Cont., Dairy Sci.Abstr., Excerp.Med., Ind.Med., Ind.Sci.Rev., Ind.Vet., INIS Atomind., Med.& Surg.Dermat., NRN, Nutr.Abstr., Protozool.Abstr., Rev.Med.& Vet.Mycol., Sci.Cit.Ind., Vet.Bull. **Document type:** academic/scholarly publication.
—BLDSC (4954.851000); ADONIS; CASDDS; Faxon; Genuine Article; SWETS; UMI; UnCover. **CCC.**
Formerly: Zeitschrift fuer Krebsforschung und Klinische Onkologie (ISSN 0084-5353)
Refereed Serial

616.994 GE ISSN 0943-9382
CODEN: JCCSE
JOURNAL OF CANCER RESEARCH AND CLINICAL ONCOLOGY. SUPPLEMENT. (Text in English) irreg. (Deutsche Krebsgesellschaft) Springer-Verlag, Heidelberger Platz 3, 14197 Berlin, Germany. TEL 030-8207-0. FAX 030-8214091. E-mail: orders@springer.de. (Subscr. in N. America to: Springer-Verlag New York, Inc., 44 Hartz Way, Secaucus, NY 07096-2491. TEL 201-348-4033. FAX 201-348-4505) **Indexed:** Excerp.Med. (1995-). **Document type:** academic/scholarly publication.

616.99 615.8 616.2 IT ISSN 1120-009X
CODEN: JCHEEU
JOURNAL OF CHEMOTHERAPY. (Text in English) 1978. bi-m. L.100000 (foreign $100) (effective 1995-96). (Mediterranean Society of Chemotherapy) E I F T srl, Via XX Settembre 102, 50129 Florence, Italy. TEL 39-55-486147. FAX 39-55-474426. Ed. Piero Periti. circ. 650. **Indexed:** Excerp.Med., Ind.Med. **Document type:** academic/scholarly publication.
—BLDSC (4957.390000); CASDDS; Faxon; Genuine Article; SWETS; UnCover. **CCC.**
Former titles (until 1989): Chemioterapia (ISSN 0392-906X); Which was formed by the 1982 merger of: Chemoterapia Antimicrobica (ISSN 0391-9862); Chemoterapia Oncologica (ISSN 0392-0968)
Description: Publishes original articles on experimental and clinical studies in antimicrobial and oncologic chemotherapy.
Refereed Serial

616.99 US ISSN 0732-183X
RC254.A1 CODEN: JCONDN
JOURNAL OF CLINICAL ONCOLOGY. 1983. m. $258 (foreign $307) (effective 1996). (American Society of Clinical Oncology) W.B. Saunders Co. (Subsidiary of: Harcourt Brace & Company), Curtis Center, 3rd Fl., Independence Sq. W., Philadelphia, PA 19106-3399. TEL 215-238-7800. FAX 215-238-6445. (Subscr. to: Periodicals Fulfillment, W.B. Saunders Co., 6277 Sea Harbor Dr., 4th Fl., Orlando, FL 32891-4800. TEL 800-654-2452. FAX 800-874-6418) Ed. Dr. George P. Canellos; Pub. Joan W. Blumberg. adv.: B&W page $1540, color $2840; 7 x 10. abstr.; bibl.; charts; illus.; index. circ. 16,310. **Indexed:** Abstr.Health Care Manage.Stud., Chem.Abstr., CINAHL, Curr.Cont., Dent.Ind., Excerp.Med., Ind.Med., Ind.Sci.Rev., INIS Atomind., Kidney, Med.& Surg.Dermat., NRN, Rev.Med.& Vet.Mycol., Sci.Cit.Ind. **Document type:** academic/scholarly publication.
●Also available online.
—BLDSC (4958.615000); CASDDS; Faxon; Genuine Article; SWETS; UMI; UnCover. **CCC.**
Description: Contains articles from around the world discussing the diagnosis, management, treatment, and prevention of cancer.
Refereed Serial

MEDICAL SCIENCES — ONCOLOGY

616.99   IT   ISSN 0392-9078
CODEN: JECRDN
JOURNAL OF EXPERIMENTAL AND CLINICAL CANCER RESEARCH. (Text in English) 1982. q. L.100000($100) (effective 1994). Regina Elena Institute for Cancer Research, Via delle Messi d'Oro 156, 00158 Rome, Italy. TEL 06-4985536. FAX 06-4180473. Ed. Dr. Ercole Sega. **Indexed:** Curr.Cont., Ind.Med.
—BLDSC (4979.740000); CASDDS; Faxon; Genuine Article.
Description: Publishes original contributions dealing with basic and applied research in the field of experimental and clinical oncology.

JOURNAL OF MAMMARY GLAND BIOLOGY AND NEOPLASIA. see *MEDICAL SCIENCES — Obstetrics And Gynecology*

616.99   US   ISSN 0167-594X
CODEN: JNODD2
JOURNAL OF NEURO-ONCOLOGY. 1983. m. fl.1374 to institutions; $838 to institutions in U.S. (effective 1996). Kluwer Academic Publishers Boston, Box 358, Accord Sta., Hingham, MA 02018-0358. TEL 617-871-6600. FAX 617-871-6528. TELEX 200190. (Dist. outside N. America by: Kluwer Academic Publishers Group, P.O. Box 322, 3300 AH Dordrecht, Netherlands. TEL 31-78-392392. FAX 31-78-546474) Ed. Dr. Michael D. Walker. adv.; bk.rev. (also avail. in microform from UMI; back issues avail.; reprint service avail. from SWZ,UMI) **Indexed:** ASCA, Chem.Abstr., Curr.Adv.Biochem., Curr.Adv.Cell & Devel.Biol., Curr.Cont., Excerp.Med., Ind.Med., Ind.Sci.Rev., Sci.Cit.Ind. **Document type:** academic/scholarly publication.
—BLDSC (5021.650000); CASDDS; Faxon; Genuine Article; SWETS; UMI; UnCover. **CCC.**
Description: Encompasses basic, applied and clinical investigations in all research areas as they relate to cancer and the central nervous system.
Refereed Serial

JOURNAL OF OCCUPATIONAL MEDICINE AND TOXICOLOGY; an international journal. see *OCCUPATIONAL HEALTH AND SAFETY*

616.99   US   ISSN 1061-9364
JOURNAL OF ONCOLOGY MANAGEMENT. 1992. bi-m. $45 in the U.S.; Canada $54; elsewhere $60. Knolls Publishing Group, Inc., 201 Littleton Rd., Ste. 100, Morris Plains, NJ 07950-2932. TEL 201-285-0855. FAX 201-285-1472. Nancy Salerno-Davis. adv. contact: Stuart G. Mann. circ. 11,564.
—BLDSC (5026.314550).
Description: Disseminates information and ideas among professionals involved in day-to-day management and administrative duties in hospital, university and freestanding cancer programs.

618.92 616.99   US   ISSN 1077-4114
RJ411   CODEN: JPHOFG
JOURNAL OF PEDIATRIC HEMATOLOGY - ONCOLOGY. 1979. q. $152 to individuals (foreign $195); institutions $230 (foreign $281) (effective 1996); newsstand price: $72. (American Society of Pediatric Hematology, Oncology) Lippincott - Raven Press, 276 E. Washington Sq., Philadelphia, PA 19106. TEL 215-238-4200. Ed. Teresa J. Vietti. adv. contact: Phyllis Noyes. bk.rev.; abstr.; bibl.; charts; illus.; stat.; tr.lit.; index. circ. 1,200. (also avail. in microform; back issues avail.; reprint service avail. from UMI) **Indexed:** Curr.Cont., Dent.Ind., Excerp.Med., Ind.Med., Ind.Sci.Rev., INIS Atomind., Sci.Cit.Ind. **Document type:** academic/scholarly publication.
—Faxon; Genuine Article; SWETS; UMI; UnCover. **CCC.**
Formerly (until 1995): American Journal of Pediatric Hematology - Oncology (ISSN 0192-8562)
Description: Reports on advances in the diagnosis and treatment of cancer and blood diseases in children.
Refereed Serial

616.99 610.73   US   ISSN 1043-4542
CODEN: JONUEM
JOURNAL OF PEDIATRIC ONCOLOGY NURSING. 1984. q. $79 (foreign $115) (effective 1996). (Association of Pediatric Oncology Nurses) W.B. Saunders Co. (Subsidiary of: Harcourt Brace & Company), The Curtis Center, 3rd Fl., Independence Sq. W., Philadelphia, PA 19106-3399. TEL 215-238-7800. FAX 215-238-6445. (Subscr. to: W.B. Saunders Co., Periodicals Dept., 6277 Sea Harbor Dr., 4th Fl., Orlando, FL 32887-4800. TEL 800-654-2452. FAX 800-874-6418) Ed. Pamela S. Hinds; Pub. Joan W. Blumberg. adv.: B&W page $710, color page $1660; 7 x 10. bk.rev.; bibl. circ. 2,693. **Indexed:** Ind.Med. (1993-). **Document type:** academic/scholarly publication.
—BLDSC (5030.195000); SWETS; UMI; UnCover. **CCC.**
Description: Stimulates and disseminates research in the treatment of young cancer patients and their families.
Refereed Serial

616.9   US   ISSN 0734-7332
RC261.A1
JOURNAL OF PSYCHOSOCIAL ONCOLOGY. 1983. q. $250 (foreign $350) (effective 1996). Haworth Press, Inc., 10 Alice St., Binghamton, NY 13904. TEL 607-722-5857; 800-342-9678. FAX 607-722-1424. TELEX 4932599. Eds. Grace H. Christ, James R. Zabora. adv.; bk.rev. circ. 991. (also avail. in microfiche from UMI; back issues avail.; reprint service avail. from HAW) **Indexed:** Behav.Med.Abstr., CINAHL, CLOA, Excerp.Med., IMFL, Past.Care & Couns.Abstr., Psychol.Abstr. (1983-), Ref.Zh., Rehabil.Lit., Soc.Work Res.& Abstr., Sp.Ed.Needs Abstr., Stud.Wom.Abstr.
—BLDSC (5043.476000); Haworth; SWETS; UnCover.
Description: Multidisciplinary journal published specifically for health professionals responsible for the psychosocial needs of cancer patients and their families.
Refereed Serial

JOURNAL OF SURGICAL ONCOLOGY. see *MEDICAL SCIENCES — Surgery*

JOURNAL OF TOXICOLOGY AND ENVIRONMENTAL HEALTH. see *ENVIRONMENTAL STUDIES — Toxicology And Environmental Safety*

KAZAKHSKII NAUCHNO-ISSLEDOVATEL'SKII INSTITUT ONKOLOGII I RADIOLOGII. TRUDY. see *MEDICAL SCIENCES — Radiology And Nuclear Medicine*

KETSUEKI SHUYOKA/HEMATOLOGY & ONCOLOGY. see *MEDICAL SCIENCES — Hematology*

KOREAN JOURNAL OF GENETICS. see *BIOLOGY — Genetics*

KOSANKINBYO KENKYUSHO ZASSHI. see *MEDICAL SCIENCES — Communicable Diseases*

616.99   GW   ISSN 0177-0853
KREBSFORSCHUNG HEUTE. 1978. biennial. DM.32. Deutsches Krebsforschungszentrum, Im Neuenheimer Feld 280, 69120 Heidelberg, Germany. TEL 06221-422854. FAX 06221-422995. **Document type:** academic/scholarly publication, corporate report.

616.99   GW
KREBSNACHSORGE UND REHABILITATION. 1989. irreg., vol.4, 1993. W. Zuckerschwerdt Verlag GmbH, Industriestr. 17, 82110 Germering, Germany. TEL 089-894349-0. FAX 089-89434950. Ed. H.G. Delbrueck. **Document type:** academic/scholarly publication.

LEUKEMIA. see *MEDICAL SCIENCES — Hematology*

LEUKEMIA AND LYMPHOMA. see *MEDICAL SCIENCES — Hematology*

LEUKEMIA RESEARCH. see *MEDICAL SCIENCES — Hematology*

616.99   US
LEUKEMIA SOCIETY OF AMERICA. NEWSLINE. 1983. q. free. Leukemia Society of America, Inc., 600 Third Ave., 4th Fl., New York, NY 10016. TEL 212-573-8484. FAX 212-856-9686. Ed. Judy Sandford. bk.rev.; illus.; circ. 50,000 (controlled). (back issues avail.; reprint service avail.) **Document type:** newsletter.
Formerly: Leukemia Society of America. Society News.
Description: To inform patients, volunteers, grantees, and the public about the society's programs and advances in research.

616   CI   ISSN 0300-8142
CODEN: LBOCB3
LIBRI ONCOLOGICI; casopis kancerologa. (Text in Serbo-Croatian; summaries in English) 1972. 3/yr. Ilica 197, 41000 Zagreb, Croatia. TEL 41-572111. **Indexed:** Chem.Abstr., Excerp.Med. **Document type:** academic/scholarly publication.
—BLDSC (5207.350000); CASDDS.

616.99   II   ISSN 0971-5134
LIFE SCIENCE ADVANCES: ONCOLOGY. Key Title: Oncology - Life Science Advances. (Text in English) 1983. 4/yr. Council of Scientific Integration, T.C. 28-408 (3), Vilayil Gardens, Kaithamukku, 695 024 Trivandrum, India. TEL 91-471-77305. **Indexed:** Excerp.Med. (1995-). **Document type:** academic/scholarly publication.

616.99   US
LIVE WELL WITH CANCER. 1982. s-a. $15. Cancer Caring Center, 4117 Liberty Ave., Pittsburgh, PA 15224-1424. TEL 412-622-1212. FAX 412-622-1216. Ed. Rebecca Whitlinger. circ. 10,000. **Document type:** newsletter.
Formerly (until 1988): Cancer Challenge.
Description: Covers current activities related to cancer.

LIVEWELL. see *PHYSICAL FITNESS AND HYGIENE*

616.994   US
LIVINGRIGHT. 1970. 3/yr. free. American Cancer Society, Inc., Florida Division, 3709 W. Jetton Ave., Tampa, FL 33629. TEL 813-253-0541. FAX 813-254-5857. Ed. Sheila Buchert. adv. contact: Sheila H. Buchert. bk.rev.; circ. 300,000 (controlled). **Document type:** consumer publication.
Formerly (until 1990): Florida Cancer News (ISSN 0015-3931)
Description: Health promotion and lifestyle information for the mature audience. Not cancer specific.

616.994   US   ISSN 0459-889X
LOUISIANA CANCER REPORTER. vol.23, 1974. q. free to qualified personnel. American Cancer Society, Inc., Louisiana Division, 2200 Veterans Memorial Blvd., Ste. 214, Kenner, LA 70062-4001. TEL 504-469-0051. Pub. John Dicarlo. circ. 3,000. **Document type:** newsletter.

616.99   IE   ISSN 0169-5002
LUNG CANCER. (Text in English) 1985. bi-m. I£340($537) (effective 1996). (International Association for the Study of Lung Cancer) Elsevier Science Ireland Ltd., P.O. Box 85, Limerick, Ireland. TEL 353-61-471944. FAX 353-61-472144. (Subscr. in U.S. and Canada to: Elsevier Science Inc., Box 882, Madison Sq. Sta., New York, NY 10159. TEL 212-989-5800. FAX 212-633-3990) Ed. H.H. Hansen. **Indexed:** Excerp.Med., Ind.Med. (1994-). **Document type:** academic/scholarly publication.
—BLDSC (5307.245000); Genuine Article; SWETS. **CCC.**
Description: Reports new findings and advances in therapy, etiology and related aspects.
Refereed Serial

616.99   US   ISSN 0160-2454
M.D. ANDERSON CLINICAL CONFERENCES ON CANCER. 1978. a., latest 27th. (University of Texas System Cancer Center) Raven Press (Subsidiary of: Wolters Kluwer N.V.), 1185 Ave. of the Americas, New York, NY 10036. TEL 212-930-9500. FAX 212-869-3495. (Co-sponsor: M.D. Anderson Hospital and Tumor Institute) (reprint service avail. from UMI) **Document type:** proceedings.
Refereed Serial

MEDICAL SCIENCES — ONCOLOGY

616.99 US ISSN 0888-8108
CODEN: UASRER
M.D. ANDERSON SYMPOSIA IN FUNDAMENTAL CANCER RESEARCH. 1947. a., latest 37th. (University of Texas System Cancer Center) Raven Press (Subsidiary of: Wolters Kluwer N.V.), 1185 Ave. of Americas, New York, NY 10036. TEL 212-930-9500. FAX 212-869-3495. (Co-sponsor: M.D. Anderson Hospital and Tumor Insitute) (reprint service avail. from UMI) **Document type:** proceedings.
—CASDDS.
Formerly (until 1985): Annual Symposium on Fundamental Cancer Research (ISSN 0190-1214)
Refereed Serial

616.9 CN ISSN 0076-3802
MANITOBA CANCER TREATMENT AND RESEARCH FOUNDATION. REPORT. 1957. a. free. Manitoba Cancer Treatment and Research Foundation, 100 Olivia St., Winnipeg, MB R3E 0V9, Canada. TEL 204-787-2197. FAX 204-783-6875. circ. 1,000. **Document type:** corporate report.

616.99 614.7 BE ISSN 0302-0800
QH301 CODEN: MBENDX
MEDECINE - BIOLOGIE - ENVIRONNEMENT/MEDICINE - BIOLOGY - ENVIRONMENT/GENEESKUNDE - BIOLOGIE - LEEFMILIEU. (Annual supplement avail.) (Text in Dutch, English, French) 1971. s-a. 1000 BEF($40) (effective 1992). European Institute of Ecology and Cancer, Belgian Section, 24 Bis, Rue des Fripiers, B-1000 Brussels, Belgium. TEL 2-219-0830. FAX 02-219-0636. Ed. Dr. Emile-Gaston Peeters. adv. circ. 3,000.
—CASDDS.
Description: Disseminates information of relevance to medical biology and environmental studies.

616.994 618.92 US ISSN 0098-1532
RC261.A1 CODEN: MPONDB
MEDICAL AND PEDIATRIC ONCOLOGY. (Supplement avail. (ISSN 0740-8226)) 1975. m. $744 (foreign $930) (effective 1996). (International Society of Pediatric Oncology) John Wiley & Sons, Inc., Journals, 605 Third Ave., New York, NY 10158. TEL 212-850-6645. FAX 212-850-6021. TELEX 12-7063. E-mail: SUBINFO@JWILEY.COM. (Subscr. outside the Americas to: John Wiley & Sons Ltd., Baffins Ln., Chichester, W. Sussex PO19 1UD, England. TEL 44-1243-779777. FAX 44-1243-776128) Ed. Alvin M. Mauer. adv.; charts; illus.; index. (also avail. in microform from UMI; back issues avail.; reprint service avail. from ISI) **Indexed:** Biol.Abstr., Curr.Adv.Ecol.Sci., Curr.Cont, Dent.Ind., Excerp.Med., Ind.Med., Ind.Sci.Rev., INIS Atomind. **Document type:** academic/scholarly publication.
●Also available online.
—BLDSC (5525.980000); CASDDS; EMDOCS; Faxon; Genuine Article; SWETS; UnCover. **CCC.**
Description: Provides broad coverage of advances in clinical oncology in children and adults; presents original articles on the diagnosis and treatment of malignant cancerous diseases.
Refereed Serial

616.994 US ISSN 0740-8226
MEDICAL AND PEDIATRIC ONCOLOGY. SUPPLEMENT. 1982. irreg. price varies. (International Society of Pediatric Oncology) John Wiley & Sons, Inc., Journals, 605 Third Ave., New York, NY 10158. TEL 212-850-6645. FAX 212-850-6021. TELEX 12-7063. E-mail: SUBINFO@JWILEY.COM. (Subscr. outside the Americas to: John Wiley & Sons Ltd., Baffins Ln., Chichester, W. Sussex PO19 1UD, England. TEL 44-243-77977. FAX 44-1243-776128) (also avail. in microform from UMI; back issues avail.) **Indexed:** Ind.Med. **Document type:** academic/scholarly publication.
Refereed Serial

MEDICAL - LEGAL ASPECTS OF CANCER LITIGATION. see *LAW — Civil Law*

616.99 UK
CODEN: MOTPE2
MEDICAL ONCOLOGY. 1984. q. £47($95) to individuals; institutions $135 (N. America $270) (effective 1995). Chapman & Hall, Journals Department (Subsidiary of: International Thomson Publishing Group), 2-6 Boundary Row, London SE1 8HN, England. TEL 0171-856-0066. FAX 0171-522-9623. TELEX 2990164 CHAPMA G. E-mail: journal@chall.mhs.compuserve.com. (Subscr. to: International Thomson Publishing Services Ltd., Cheriton House. North Way, Andover, Hants. SP10 5BE, England. TEL 01264-342713. FAX 01264-342713; N. American subscr. to: Chapman & Hall, Journals Promotion Department, One Penn Plaza, 41st Fl., New York, NY 10119. TEL 212-564-1060. FAX 212-564-1505) Eds. Peter Weirnik, Anders Oesterborg. (also avail. in microform from UMI; reprint service avail.) **Indexed:** ASCA, Curr.Adv.Cancer Res., Curr.Adv.Ecol.Sci., Curr.Cont., Excerp.Med. **Document type:** academic/scholarly publication.
—CASDDS; Genuine Article; SWETS; UMI; UnCover. **CCC.**
Formerly (until 1994): Medical Oncology and Tumor Pharmacotherapy (ISSN 0736-0118)
Description: Studies the chemistry, biochemistry, biology, epidemiology, pathology, virology, and genetics of malignant tumors, along with clinical aspects of cancer.
Refereed Serial

MELANOMA LETTER. see *MEDICAL SCIENCES — Dermatology And Venereology*

616.99 UK ISSN 0960-8931
CODEN: MREEEH
MELANOMA RESEARCH. 1990. bi-m. £260($445) to institutions (effective 1995). Rapid Communications of Oxford Ltd., The Old Malthouse, Paradise St., Oxford OX1 1LD, England. TEL 01865-790447. FAX 01865-244012. E-mail: rapidcom@vax.oxford.ac.uk. Ed.Bd. adv. contact: Julie Gribben. (reprint service avail.) **Indexed:** Excerp.Med. (1992-), Ind.Med. (1992-), Med.& Surg.Dermat. **Document type:** academic/scholarly publication.
●Also available on CD-ROM.
—BLDSC (5536.813450); ADONIS; CASDDS; Genuine Article. **CCC.**
Description: Provides an international forum for the rapid dissemination of research on melanoma both at basic and clinical levels

616.99 US ISSN 1060-233X
MESSAGE LINE. 1974. 3/yr. free. American Brain Tumor Association, 2720 S. River Rd., Ste. 146, Des Plaines, IL 60018-4110. TEL 708-827-9910; 800-886-2286. FAX 708-827-9918. Ed.Bd. circ. 31,000. (looseleaf format; back issues avail.) **Document type:** newsletter.
Description: Updates on research advances in the treatment of brain tumors.

METHODS IN CELL SCIENCE. see *BIOLOGY — Microbiology*

MICROBIOS; a prestige international biomedical research journal of chemical and general microbiology. see *BIOLOGY — Microbiology*

616.99 US ISSN 0899-1987
CODEN: MOCAE8
MOLECULAR CARCINOGENESIS. m. $684 (foreign $870) (effective 1996). (University of Texas, M.D. Anderson Cancer Center) John Wiley & Sons, Inc., Journals, 605 Third Ave., New York, NY 10158. TEL 212-850-6645. FAX 212-850-6021. TELEX 12-7063. E-mail: SUBINFO@JWILEY.COM. (Subscr. outside the Americas to: John Wiley & Sons Ltd., Baffins Ln., Chichester, W. Sussex PO19 1UD, England. TEL 44-1243-779777. FAX 44-1243-776128) Eds. Thomas Slaga, Stuart H. Yuspa. (also avail. in microform from UMI; back issues avail.) **Document type:** academic/scholarly publication.
—BLDSC (5900.802000); ADONIS; CASDDS; Faxon; Genuine Article; SWETS; UnCover. **CCC.**
Description: Devoted to the study of the molecular aspects of mechanisms involved in chemical, physical and viral (biological) carcinogenesis.
Refereed Serial

616.99 US ISSN 0270-7950
RC267
N C I FACT BOOK. a. National Cancer Institute, Department of Health and Human Services, Bldg. 31, Rm. 10A16, Bethesda, MD 20892. TEL 301-496-5583. **Document type:** government publication.
Formerly: National Cancer Institute Fact Book.

616.994 US ISSN 0027-8874
CODEN: JNCIEQ
NATIONAL CANCER INSTITUTE. JOURNAL. Abbreviated title: J N C I. 1940. s-m. $100 to members only (foreign $150) (includes irreg. monographs) (effective 1995). U.S. National Cancer Institute, Information Associates Program, 9030 Old Georgetown Rd., Rm. 213, Bethesda, MD 20814. TEL 301-496-4907; 800-NXI-7890. FAX 301-231-6941. E-mail: iap@icib.nci.nih.gov. (Subscr. to: Membership Services, National Cancer Institute, Bldg. 82, Rm. 100, Bethesda, MD 20892. TEL 301-496-2794) Ed. Dr. Barnett Kramer. bibl.; charts; illus.; index. circ. 10,000. (also avail. in microform from MIM,UMI,PMC; microfiche from CIS; reprint service avail. from CIS) **Indexed:** Abstr.Hyg., Amer.Stat.Ind. (1985-), Behav.Med.Abstr., Biol.Abstr., Biotech.Abstr., C.I.S. Abstr., Chem.Abstr., Chic.Per.Ind., CINAHL, Curr.Adv.Biochem., Curr.Adv.Cancer Res., Curr.Adv.Ecol.Sci., Curr.Adv.Genetics & Molec.Biol., Curr.Cont., Dent.Ind., Dok.Arbeitsmed., Excerp.Med., I.P.A., Ind.Med., Ind.U.S.Gov.Per., Ind.Vet., INIS Atomind., Med.& Surg.Dermat., Nutr.Abstr., Poult.Abstr., Rev.Med.& Vet.Mycol., Risk Abstr., Telegen, Triticale Abstr., Vet.Bull. **Document type:** academic/scholarly publication.
●Also available online. Vendor(s): Ovid Technologies, Lexis-Nexis.
—BLDSC (4830.000000); CASDDS; EMDOCS; Faxon; Genuine Article; SWETS; UMI; UnCover.
Incorporated (in 1987): Cancer Treatment Reports (ISSN 0361-5960); Which was formed by the 1976 merger of: Cancer Chemotherapy Reports. Part 1 (ISSN 0069-0112); Cancer Chemotherapy Reports. Part 2 (ISSN 0069-0120); Cancer Chemotherapy Reports. Part 3 (ISSN 0069-0139)
Description: Contains original reports, articles, reviews and commentary on new findings in clinical and laboratory cancer research.
Refereed Serial

616.994 US ISSN 1052-6773
RC261.A2 CODEN: JNCME4
NATIONAL CANCER INSTITUTE. JOURNAL. MONOGRAPHS. Key Title: Journal of the National Cancer Institute. Monographs. 1959. irreg., no.10, 1990. price varies. U.S. National Cancer Institute, Department of Health and Human Services, 9030 Old Georgetown Rd., Bethesda, MD 20814. TEL 301-496-4907. (Subscr. to: Membership Services, National Cancer Institute, Bldg. 82, Rm. 100, Bethesda, MD 20892. TEL 301-496-2794) Ed. Dr. Barnett Kramer. circ. 3,000. (microfiche) **Indexed:** Biol.Abstr., Excerp.Med. (until 1993), Ind.Med. **Document type:** monographic series.
—CASDDS; SWETS.
Former titles (until 1990): N C I Monographs (ISSN 0893-2751); (until 1986): National Cancer Institute. Monographs (ISSN 0083-1921)

616.9 CN ISSN 0077-3689
NATIONAL CANCER INSTITUTE OF CANADA. ANNUAL REPORT. 1947. a. free. National Cancer Institute of Canada, 10 Alcorn Ave., Ste. 200, Toronto, ON M4V 3B1, Canada. TEL 416-961-7223. FAX 416-961-4189. Ed. Dr. M. Wosnick. circ. 1,000.

616.99 SP ISSN 0212-9787
NEOPLASIA; oncologia multidisciplinaria. 1984. bi-m. 5600 ptas.($45) (free to qualified personnel). Ediciones Doyma S.A., Travesera de Gracia, 17-21, 08021 Barcelona, Spain. TEL 34-1-200-07-11. FAX 34-1-209-11-36. TELEX 51964 INK E. Ed. J. Estape Rodriguez. adv.; page 180000 ptas.; trim 210 x 280; adv. contact: Olga Gomez. circ. 2,000. **Indexed:** Excerp.Med. (1993-).
—BLDSC (6075.628000); UMI.
Description: For oncologists, epidemiologists, pathologists, surgeons, internists and specialists interested in oncology and neoplasia.

MEDICAL SCIENCES — ONCOLOGY

616.994   XO   ISSN 0028-2685
CODEN: NEOLA4
NEOPLASMA. (Text in English) 1954. bi-m. $32. Slovak Academy of Sciences, Cancer Research Institute, Spitalska 21, 892 32 Bratislava, Slovakia. (Dist. in Western countries by: Karger-Libri AG, Scientific Booksellers, Arnold-Bocklin-Strasse 25, CH-4000 Basel 11, Switzerland) Ed. Viliam Ujhazy. bk.rev.; charts; illus.; index. **Indexed:** Biol.Abstr., C.I.S. Abstr., Chem.Abstr., Curr.Adv.Cancer Res., Curr.Adv.Genetics & Molec.Biol., Curr.Cont., Dent.Ind., Excerp.Med., Ind.Med., Ind.Sci.Rev., Ind.Vet., Risk Abstr., Vet.Bull.
—BLDSC (6075.630000); CASDDS; EMDOCS; Genuine Article; SWETS; UnCover.
Description: Publishes original works of Czechoslovak and foreign authors in the fields of experimental and clinical oncology. Covers the biochemistry of tumors, the biology and genetics of oncology, and significant causistry. Includes statistics of oncology.

616   US
NORTHWESTERN UNIVERSITY. ROBERT H. LURIE CANCER CENTER. JOURNAL. (Not published 1988-1989) 1977. s-a. free. Northwestern University, Robert H. Lurie Cancer Center, Office of Public Affairs and Communications, Olson Pavilion 8250, 303 E. Chicago Ave., Chicago, IL 60611. TEL 312-908-6346. FAX 312-908-1372. Ed. Dr. Steven T. Rosen. bk.rev.; charts; illus.; index. circ. 2,000. **Document type:** academic/scholarly publication.
Former titles (until vol.2, no.2., 1991): Northwestern University Cancer Center. Journal (ISSN 1049-6025); Supersedes (1977-1987): Cancer Focus (ISSN 0147-1255)
Description: Covers topics of interest to members of the center; faculty and staff of Northwestern University; and oncologists, nurses, clinicians and officials of cancer centers and programs throughout the U.S.
Refereed Serial

616.994   PL   ISSN 0029-540X
CODEN: NOWOAL
NOWOTWORY. (Text in Polish; summaries in English) 1923. q. $80. Maria Curie-Sklodowska Memorial Cancer Center and Institute of Oncology, Ul. Wawelska 15, 00-973 Warsaw, Poland. TEL 48-22-224831. FAX 48-22-222429. TELEX 812704 INONK. (Co-sponsor: Polskie Towarzystwo Onkologiczne) Ed. Jerzy Meyza. bk.rev.; index. circ. 1,000. (reprint service avail.) **Indexed:** Biol.Abstr., Chem.Abstr., Dent.Ind., Excerp.Med., Ind.Med.
—BLDSC (6180.479000); CASDDS; EMDOCS.
Description: Highlights oncology, radio-chemotherapy and surgery, cancer biology, epidemiology and control.

616.39 616.99   US   ISSN 0163-5581
CODEN: NUCADQ
NUTRITION AND CANCER; an international journal. 1978. 6/yr., 2 vols. $130 to individuals (foreign $170); institutions $385 (foreign $425). Lawrence Erlbaum Associates, Inc., 10 Industrial Dr., Mahwah, NJ 07430-2262. TEL 201-236-9500. FAX 201-236-0072. Ed. Dr. Gio B. Gori. adv.: page $425; 6 x 9. bk.rev.; charts; illus. circ. 500. (back issues avail.) **Indexed:** Biol.Abstr., Chem.Abstr., Dairy Sci.Abstr., Dent.Ind., Excerp.Med., Ind.Med., Maize Abstr., Nutr.Abstr., Rev.Med.& Vet.Mycol., Triticale Abstr. **Document type:** academic/scholarly publication.
—BLDSC (6188.045000); CASDDS; Faxon; SWETS; UMI; UnCover.
Description: Reports and reviews current findings on the effect of nutrition on the etiology, therapy, and prevention of cancer.
Refereed Serial

616.99 618.082   JA   ISSN 0911-2251
NYUGAN NO RINSHO/JAPANESE JOURNAL OF BREAST CANCER. (Text in English; summaries in Japanese) 1986. q. 2200 Yen per no. Shinohara Publishers, Inc., 11-7, Hongo 2-chome, Bunkyo-ku, Tokyo 113, Japan. **Indexed:** INIS Atomind.

O N S NURSING SCAN IN ONCOLOGY. (Oncology Nursing Society) see *MEDICAL SCIENCES — Abstracting, Bibliographies, Statistics*

616.99 612.015   UK   ISSN 0950-9232
CODEN: ONCNES
ONCOGENE. 1987. 24/yr. £300 to individuals; institutions £850. Stockton Press (Subsidiary of: Macmillan Press Ltd.), Houndmills, Basingstoke, Hants RG21 2XS, England. TEL 01256-817245. FAX 01256-28339. Ed. John Jenkins; Pub. Jayne Marks. adv. contact: Michael Rowley. index. (also avail. in microfilm from UMI; back issues avail.) **Indexed:** Anim.Breed.Abstr., Curr.Cont., Excerp.Med., Ind.Vet., Small Anim.Abstr., Telegen, Vet.Bull. **Document type:** academic/scholarly publication.
—BLDSC (6256.782000); ADONIS; CASDDS; Faxon; Genuine Article; SWETS; UMI; UnCover. **CCC.**
Description: Studies all aspects of oncogene research and relationships to cancer.

ONCOGENES. see *MEDICAL SCIENCES — Abstracting, Bibliographies, Statistics*

616.99   SP   ISSN 0378-4835
CODEN: NCLGDV
ONCOLOGIA. 1976. m. 10000 ptas.($180) (Europe $100). (Federacion de Sociedades Espanolas de Oncologia) Alpe Editores, S.A., Pedro Rico, 27, 28029 Madrid, Spain. TEL 34-1-7338811. FAX 34-1-3159652. Ed. Dr. Jesus Vicente; Pub. A. Alvarez. adv.: color page 180000 ptas.; 210 x 280; adv. contact: C. Alvarez. charts; illus.; bibl.; circ. 6,000 (controlled). **Indexed:** Biol.Abstr., Chem.Abstr., Excerp.Med., Ind.Med.Esp.
—CASDDS.

616.99   US   ISSN 1070-0900
THE ONCOLOGIST'S POCKET GUIDE. a. $20 (foreign $28) (effective 1994). W.B. Saunders Co. (Subsidiary of: Harcourt Brace & Company), Curtis Center, 3rd Fl., Independence Sq. W., Philadelphia, PA 19106-3399. TEL 215-238-7800. FAX 215-238-6445. (Subscr. to: Periodicals Fulfillment, W.B. Saunders Co., 6277 Sea Harbor Dr., 4th Fl., Orlando, FL 32891-4800. TEL 800-654-2452. FAX 800-874-6418) Ed. Dr. John W. Yarbro. charts. **Document type:** academic/scholarly publication.
Description: Contains data and lists regimens useful to specialists in cancer care.

616.994   SZ   ISSN 0030-2414
RC261   CODEN: ONCOBS
ONCOLOGY; international journal of cancer research and treatment. (Text in English) 1948. bi-m. 528 SFr.($406.20) to individuals; institutions 880 SFr.($677) (effective 1996). S. Karger AG, Allschwilerstr. 10, P.O. Box, CH-4009 Basel, Switzerland. TEL 061-3061111. FAX 061-3061234. E-mail: Karger@Karger.ch. Ed. P.P. Carbone. adv.; bk.rev.; abstr.; index.; charts; illus.; index. circ. 1,500. (also avail. in microform) **Indexed:** Biol.Abstr., Chem.Abstr., Curr.Adv.Ecol.Sci., Curr.Cont., Dairy Sci.Abstr., Dent.Ind., Excerp.Med., Ind.Med., Ind.Vet., Med.& Surg.Dermat., Nutr.Abstr., Telegen, Vet.Bull. **Document type:** academic/scholarly publication.
—BLDSC (6256.900000); CASDDS; EMDOCS; Faxon; Genuine Article; SWETS; UnCover. **CCC.**
Supersedes: Oncologia.
Refereed Serial

616.99   GW
ONCOLOGY. (Text in English) 1992. irreg. vol.3, 1995. Sympomed Medical Publishers, Hohenbrunner Weg 150, 82024 Taufkirchen, Germany. TEL 089-6124411. FAX 089-6123770. **Document type:** monographic series.

616.99   US   ISSN 0890-9091
RC254.A1   CODEN: OCLGE9
ONCOLOGY. 1987. 12/yr. $75 in U.S. and Canada; elsewhere $97. P R R, Inc., 17 Prospect St., Huntington, NY 11743. TEL 516-424-8900. FAX 516-424-8503. Ed. Dr. Robert F. Wittes; Pub. Robert C. Canale. adv.: B&W page $2040, color page $3290; trim 7 7/8 x 10 3/4. cum.index; circ. 26,265 (controlled). **Indexed:** Excerp.Med.
—BLDSC (6256.930000); SWETS. **CCC.**
Description: Publishes articles reviewing recent trends in the clinical practice of oncology, original research or results of trials having clinical relevance.

616.99 618   JA   ISSN 0913-9834
ONCOLOGY & CHEMOTHERAPY. (Text in Japanese) 1985. q. 1500 Yen per no. Research Society on Oncology and Chemotherapy in Gynecology - Nihon Fujinka Akusei Shuyo Kagaku Ryoho Kenkyukai, Kinki Daigaku Igakubu Sanfujinkagaku Kyoshitsu, 377-2, Ono Higashi, Osaka Sayama-shi, Osaka 589, Japan.
Formerly (until 1986): Research Society on Oncology and Chemotherapy in Gynecology (ISSN 0912-1013)

616.99   US   ISSN 1046-3356
ONCOLOGY ISSUES; the journal of cancer program management. 1986. bi-m. $20 to individuals; institutions and libraries $40. Association of Community Cancer Centers, 11600 Nebel St., Ste. 201, Rockville, MD 20852. TEL 301-984-9496. FAX 301-770-1949. Ed. Donald Jewler. adv. contact: William Asmann. circ. 17,000. (back issues avail.) **Document type:** academic/scholarly publication.
—BLDSC (6256.972000).
Description: Provides economic, health policy and planning information to United States cancer programs.

616.99   US   ISSN 1065-2957
ONCOLOGY NEWS INTERNATIONAL. 1992. 12/yr. $70. Pub. Mary Schuldner, 17 Prospect St., Huntington, NY 11743. TEL 516-424-8900. FAX 516-424-8503. Ed. Dr. Martin Abeloff. adv.: B&W page $2880, color page $4080; trim 10 7/8 x 14 3/4. circ. 450 (paid); 26,076 (controlled). (tabloid format)
—CCC.
Description: Publishes timely reports on news and developments from around the world in all areas of interest to the cancer specialist.

ONCOLOGY NURSING FORUM. see *MEDICAL SCIENCES — Nurses And Nursing*

616.99   GR   ISSN 1021-335X
CODEN: OCRPEW
▼**ONCOLOGY REPORTS;** an international journal devoted to fundamental and applied research in oncology. 1994. bi-m. $180 to institutions in Europe (elsewhere $220); individuals in Europe $90 (elsewhere $100) (effective 1995). National Hellenic Research Foundation, Institute of Biological Research and Biotechnology, 48 Vas. Constantinou Ave., 116 35 Athens, Greece. TEL 30-1-724-1505. FAX 30-1-752-3866. Ed. D.A. Spandidos; Pub. D.A. Spandidos. adv.; bk.rev.; index. **Indexed:** Chem.Abstr., Curr.Cont., Excerp.Med. (1995-), Sci.Cit.Ind. **Document type:** academic/scholarly publication.
—BLDSC (6256.983350). **CCC.**
Description: Covers the spectrum of cancer research; aimed at a multidisciplinary readership.
Refereed Serial

616.99   UK   ISSN 0965-0407
RC261.A1   CODEN: ONREE8
ONCOLOGY RESEARCH. 1989. m. $635 to institutions (effective 1996). Elsevier Science Ltd., Pergamon, P.O. Box 800, Kidlington, Oxford OX5 1DX, England. TEL 44-1865-843000. FAX 44-1865-843010. E-mail: nlinfo-f@elsevier.nl; usinfo-f@elsevier.com; forinfo-kyf04035@niftyserve.or.jp; Site addr.: http://www.elsevier.nl/. (Subscr. in U.S. and Canada to: Elsevier Science, 660 White Plains Rd., Tarrytown, NY 10591-5153. TEL 914-524-9200. FAX 914-333-2444) Ed. A.C. Sartorelli. (also avail. in microfilm from UMI; back issues avail.) **Indexed:** Curr.Cont., Excerp.Med., Ind.Med. **Document type:** academic/scholarly publication.
—BLDSC (6256.983400); CASDDS; Faxon; Genuine Article; SWETS; UMI. **CCC.**
Formerly (until 1992): Cancer Communications (ISSN 0955-3541)
Description: Rapid dissemination journal for full research papers and short communications contributing to the understanding of cancer in areas of molecular biology, cell biology, biochemistry, biophysics, genetics, virology, endocrinology and immunology.
Refereed Serial

616.99   UK   ISSN 0265-7945
ONCOLOGY REVIEW. 1984. irreg. Gardiner - Caldwell Communications Ltd., Old Ribbon Mill, Pitt St., Macclesfield, Ches. SK11 7PT, England. TEL 01625-618507. FAX 01625-614161. **Document type:** academic/scholarly publication, monographic series.
—BLDSC (6256.983500).

MEDICAL SCIENCES — ONCOLOGY

616.99 US ISSN 0276-2234
ONCOLOGY TIMES; the independent newspaper for cancer specialists. 1979. m. $95 to individuals (foreign $130); institutions $130 (foreign $165) (effective 1996). Lippincott - Raven Publishers, 227 E. Washington Sq., Philadelphia, PA 19106. TEL 215-238-4200. Ed. Serena Stockwell. adv.; bk.rev.; index. circ. 25,218. (back issues avail.) **Document type:** newspaper.
—BLDSC (6256.984000); UMI. **CCC.**
Description: Covers all aspects of the diagnosis, treatment, and care of the cancer patient.
Refereed Serial

616.99 GW ISSN 0947-8965
▼**DER ONKOLOGE.** 1995. m. DM.198($143) (effective 1996). Springer-Verlag, Heidelberger Platz 3, 14197 Berlin, Germany. TEL 030-8207-0. FAX 030-8214091. (Subscr. in N. America to: Springer-Verlag New York, Inc., 44 Hartz Way, Secaucus, NJ 07096-2491. TEL 201-348-4033. FAX 201-348-4505) **Document type:** academic/scholarly publication.

616 SZ ISSN 0378-584X
CODEN: ONKOD2
ONKOLOGIE; Zeitschrift fuer Krebsforschung und -behandlung. (Text in English and German) bi-m. 142 SFr.($109) to individuals; institutions 142 SFr.($109) (effective 1996). (Deutsche und Oesterreichische Gesellschaft fuer Haematologie und Onkologie) S. Karger AG, Allschwilerstr. 10, P.O. Box, CH-4009 Basel, Switzerland. TEL 061-3061111. FAX 061-3061234. E-mail: Karger@Karger.ch. (Co-sponsor: Oesterreichische Krebsgesellschaft-Krebsliga) Eds. W. Queisser, H. Huber. adv.; illus.; index. circ. 11,000. (also avail. in microform from UMI; back issues avail.) **Indexed:** Biol.Abstr., Curr.Adv.Cancer Res., Curr.Adv.Ecol.Sci., Curr.Cont., Dent.Ind., Excerp.Med., Ind.Med. **Document type:** academic/scholarly publication.
—BLDSC (6260.650000); CASDDS; Faxon; Genuine Article; SWETS. **CCC.**
Formerly: Oesterreichische Zeitschrift fuer Onkologie.
Refereed Serial

616 BU ISSN 0369-7649
CODEN: ONKLAO
ONKOLOGIJA. (Text in Bulgarian; summaries in English and Russian) 1964. q. 10 lv.($6) (Ministerstvo na Narodnoto Zdrave) Izdatelstvo Meditsina i Fizkultura, 11, Pl. Slaveikov, Sofia, Bulgaria. (Dist. by: Hemus, 6, Rouski Blvd., 1000 Sofia, Bulgaria) (Co-sponsor: Nauchno Druzhestvo op Onkologija) Ed. T. Tchernozemski. circ. 713. **Indexed:** Abstr.Bulg.Sci.Med.Lit., Excerp.Med.
—CASDDS.

616 JA
OSAKA UNIVERSITY. INSTITUTE FOR CANCER RESEARCH. ANNUAL REPORT. (Text in English) irreg. exchange basis. Osaka Daigaku, Igakubu Fuzoku Gankenku Shisetsu - Osaka University, Institute for Cancer Research, 3-12 Dojimahama-dori, Fukushima-ku, Osaka-shi 553, Japan.

P A S C A L E 89: CANCER. see *MEDICAL SCIENCES — Abstracting, Bibliographies, Statistics*

P H - O FORUM; news - updates in Pediatric Hematology - Oncology. see *MEDICAL SCIENCES — Pediatrics*

616.9 US
P P O UPDATE. (Principles and Practices of Oncology) 1987. m. $99. Lippincott - Raven Publishers, 227 E. Washington Sq., Philadelphia, PA 19106. TEL 215-238-4200. FAX 215-238-4228. (Subscr. to: 12107 Insurance Way, Hagerstown, MD 21740. TEL 800-777-2295) Ed.Bd. circ. 25,000 (controlled). (looseleaf format)
Description: Provides updated information for the textbook Principles and Practices of Oncology.

616.9 CN ISSN 0828-5535
PACIFIC REPORT NEWSLETTER. 1978. s-a. free. Canadian Cancer Society, B.C. and Yukon Division, 565 W. 10th Ave., Vancouver, BC V5Z 4J4, Canada. TEL 604-872-4400. FAX 604-879-4533. Ed. Debby Alton. illus. **Document type:** newsletter.
Former titles (until 1984): Canadian Cancer Society. B.C. and Yukon Division. Newsletter (ISSN 0708-0999); (until 1978): Canadian Cancer Society. B.C. and Yukon Division. Provincial News (ISSN 0708-1030); (until 196?): Canadian Cancer Society. B.C. Division. Provincial News (ISSN 0045-4516)

THE PAIN CLINIC. see *MEDICAL SCIENCES — Anaesthesiology*

THE PAIN CLINIC (PROCEEDINGS). see *MEDICAL SCIENCES — Anaesthesiology*

616.99 610.73
362.1 UK ISSN 0969-7853
PALLIATIVE CARE TODAY; the journal for today's palliative care team. 1992. q. free to qualified personnel. (N A P P in Palliative Care) C C T Healthcare Communications Ltd., 50-52 Union St., London SE1 1TD, England. TEL 0171-407-9731. FAX 0171-407-7083. Ed. Dr. Ilora Finlay, Dr. John Ellershaw; Pub. Fionnula Russell. bk.rev.; circ. 8,000 (controlled). **Document type:** academic/scholarly publication, trade publication.
—BLDSC (6345.562058).
Description: Discusses various topics in treating and offering comfort to persons with terminal illnesses.
Refereed Serial

PEDIATRIC HEMATOLOGY & ONCOLOGY. see *MEDICAL SCIENCES — Pediatrics*

618.92 616 US ISSN 1054-2086
PEDIATRIC HEMATOLOGY - ONCOLOGY SERIES. 1988. irreg., latest 1990. price varies. Raven Press (Subsidiary of: Wolters Kluwer N.V.), 1185 Ave. of the Americas, New York, NY 10036. TEL 212-930-9500. FAX 212-869-3495. (reprint service avail. from UMI) **Document type:** monographic series.
Refereed Serial

PEDIATRIC PATHOLOGY & LABORATORY MEDICINE. see *MEDICAL SCIENCES — Pediatrics*

616.994 IT ISSN 0069-8520
CODEN: PPQCDL
PERUGIA QUADRENNIAL INTERNATIONAL CONFERENCES ON CANCER. PROCEEDINGS. 1957. quadrennial. price varies. Universita degli Studi di Perugia, Division of Cancer Research, P.O. Box 327, 06100 Perugia, Monteluce, Italy. Ed. Lucio Severi. index. **Document type:** proceedings.
—CASDDS.

616.994 PH ISSN 0031-7608
PHILIPPINE JOURNAL OF CANCER.* vol.12, 1970. q. P.10. Philippine Cancer Society, 310 San Rafael, Manila, Philippines. Ed. Dr. C.P. Manahan. charts; illus.; stat.; index. circ. 1,000. **Indexed:** Chem.Abstr., Ind.Med.

618.92 616.99 US
PHOENIX (BETHESDA). 1993. q. donation. Candlelighters Childhood Cancer Foundation, 7910 Woodmont Ave., Ste. 400, Bethesda, MD 20814. TEL 301-657-8410. Ed. Ellen O'Donnell. circ. 1,300. **Document type:** newsletter.

616.99 US ISSN 0743-8176
RC261.A1
PRIMARY CARE & CANCER. 1981. 10/yr. $60. P R R, Inc., 17 Prospect St., Huntington, NY 11743. TEL 516-424-8900. FAX 516-424-8503. Ed. Dr. Robert F. Wittes; Pub. John J. Coronna. adv.; B&W page $4800, color page $6050; trim 10 7/8 x 14 3/4. charts; illus.; stat.; circ. 70,440 (controlled). (tabloid format; also avail. in microform from UMI; reprint service avail. from UMI)
—BLDSC (6612.908100); Faxon; UMI. **CCC.**
Formerly (until 1984): Your Patient and Cancer (ISSN 0272-6955)
Description: Reports on the latest developments in cancer prevention, early detection, diagnosis, and follow-up.

616.994 CN ISSN 0033-0604
PROGRESS AGAINST CANCER. French edition: Progres Contre le Cancer. 1948. q. free. Canadian Cancer Society, 10 Alcorn Ave., Ste. 200, Toronto, ON M4V 3B1, Canada. TEL 416-961-7223. Ed. Kerstin Ring. illus. circ. 9,000 (8,000 English ed.; 1,000 French ed.). **Document type:** consumer publication.

616 US ISSN 0145-3726
CODEN: PCRTDK
PROGRESS IN CANCER RESEARCH AND THERAPY. 1976. irreg., latest vol.35. price varies. Raven Press (Subsidiary of: Wolters Kluwer N.V.), 1185 Ave. of the Americas, New York, NY 10036. TEL 212-930-9500. FAX 212-869-3495. (reprint service avail. from UMI) **Indexed:** Biol.Abstr., Chem.Abstr., Dairy Sci.Abstr., Hort.Abstr., Nutr.Abstr. **Document type:** proceedings.
—BLDSC (6866.620000); CASDDS.
Refereed Serial

616.994 SZ ISSN 0079-6263
RC254 CODEN: PEXTAR
PROGRESS IN EXPERIMENTAL TUMOR RESEARCH. (Text in English) 1960. irreg. (approx. 1/yr.). price varies. S. Karger AG, Allschwilerstr. 10, P.O. Box, CH-4009 Basel, Switzerland. TEL 061-3061111. FAX 061-3061234. E-mail: Karger@Karger.ch. Ed. C. Unger. (reprint service avail. from ISI, back issues avail.) **Indexed:** Biol.Abstr., Chem.Abstr., Curr.Cont., Ind.Med., Ind.Sci.Rev., Rev.Med.& Vet.Mycol. **Document type:** monographic series.
—CASDDS; Faxon; Genuine Article; SWETS; UnCover. **CCC.**
Description: Overviews of experimental work in key areas of tumor research.
Refereed Serial

616.99 UK ISSN 0969-9260
PROGRESS IN PALLIATIVE CARE. 1993. 6/yr. £43 to individuals; institutions £93. Leeds Medical Information, University of Leeds, Leeds LS2 9JT, England. TEL 0113-233-5550. FAX 0113-233-5568. (Subscr. to: Royal Society of Medicine Services Ltd., 1 Wimpole St., London W1M 8AE, England. TEL 0171-290-2927. FAX 0171-290-2929) Ed. Sam Ahmedzai. **Document type:** academic/scholarly publication.
—BLDSC (6872.285000).
Description: Locates and reports the scholarly literature on all aspects of the management of the problems of end-stage disease, and issues pertinent to living with chronic or progress disease.

616.99 NE ISSN 0924-1914
PROSTAGLANDINS, LEUKOTRIENES AND CANCER. (Text in English) 1985. irreg. price varies. Kluwer Academic Publishers, Postbus 17, 3300 AA Dordrecht, Netherlands. TEL 31-78-392392. FAX 31-78-392254. TELEX 29245 KAPG NL. (Dist. by: Kluwer Academic Publishers Group, P.O. Box 322, 3300 AH Dordrecht, Netherlands. TEL 31-78-392392. FAX 31-78-546474; N. America dist. addr.: Box 358, Accord Sta., Hingham, MA 02018-0358. TEL 617-871-6600. FAX 617-871-6528) **Document type:** monographic series.
Refereed Serial

THE PROSTATE. see *MEDICAL SCIENCES*

PSICOLOGIA ONCOLOGICA/PSYCHO-ONCOLOGY. see *PSYCHOLOGY*

616.99 UK ISSN 1057-9249
RC261.A1 CODEN: POJCEE
PSYCHO-ONCOLOGY; journal of the psychological, social and behavioral dimensions of cancer. 1992. q. $265 (foreign $265) (effective 1996). John Wiley & Sons Ltd., Journals, Baffins Ln., Chichester, W. Sussex PO19 1UD, England. TEL 01243-779777. FAX 01243-776128. TELEX 86290 WIBOOK G. (Subscr. in the Americas to: John Wiley & Sons, Inc., 605 Third Ave., New York, NY 10158. TEL 212-850-6645. FAX 212-850-6021) Eds. Jimmie C. Holland, Maggie Watson. circ. 578. (also avail. in microform from UMI; back issues avail.) **Indexed:** Excerp.Med. (1994-). **Document type:** academic/scholarly publication.
—BLDSC (6946.543200); UMI.
Description: Concerned with the psychological, social, behavioral, and ethical aspects of cancer.
Refereed Serial

PUBLIC HEALTH REVIEWS; an international quarterly. see *PUBLIC HEALTH AND SAFETY*

616.99 IT ISSN 1122-0260
QUADERNI DI CURE PALLIATIVE. 1993. q. L.75000($99) (effective 1994). Masson S.p.A., Via Statuto 2-4, 20121 Milan, Italy. TEL 02-6367-1. FAX 02-6367211. Ed. Marcello Tamburini. adv.: B&W page L.2600000, color page L.4000000. circ. 3,000.

RADIATION MEDICINE; medical imaging and radiation oncology. see *MEDICAL SCIENCES — Radiology And Nuclear Medicine*

616.99 616.842   US   ISSN 1065-7541
                              CODEN: ROINEU
RADIOLOGY ONCOLOGY INVESTIGATIONS. 1993. bi-m. $240 (foreign $333) (effective 1996). John Wiley & Sons, Inc., Journals, 605 Third Ave., New York, NY 10158. TEL 212-850-6645. FAX 212-850-6021. TELEX 12-7063. E-mail: SUBINFO@JWILEY.COM. (Subscr. outside the Americas to: John Wiley & Sons Ltd., Baffins Ln., Chichester, W. Sussex PO19 1UD, England. TEL 44-1243-779777. FAX 44-1243-776128) (also avail. in microform from UMI; back issues avail.) **Document type:** academic/scholarly publication.
—BLDSC (7227.982000); CASDDS.
Refereed Serial

RADIOTHERAPY AND ONCOLOGY. see *MEDICAL SCIENCES — Radiology And Nuclear Medicine*

616.994   US   ISSN 0080-0015
RC261   CODEN: RRCRBU
RECENT RESULTS IN CANCER RESEARCH/FORTSCHRITTE DER KREBSFORSCHUNG. (Text in English; occasionally in French or German) 1965. irreg. price varies. Springer-Verlag, 175 Fifth Ave., New York, NY 10010. TEL 212-460-1500. FAX 212-473-6272. Ed. P. Rentchnick. (reprint service avail. from ISI) **Indexed:** Biol.Abstr., Chem.Abstr., Dent.Ind., Excerp.Med., Ind.Med. **Document type:** academic/scholarly publication.
—BLDSC (7305.090000); CASDDS; Faxon; Genuine Article; SWETS. **CCC.**

616.99   NE   ISSN 0166-8544
RC261.A1
REVIEWS IN CANCER EPIDEMIOLOGY. 1980. irreg., vol.2, 1983. price varies. Elsevier Science B.V., Books Division, P.O. Box 211, 1000 AE Amsterdam, Netherlands. TEL 31-20-4853911. FAX 31-20-4853705. TELEX 18582 ESPA NL. E-mail: nlinfo-f@elsevier.nl; usinfo-f@elsevier.com; forinfo-kyf04035@niftyserve.or.jp; Site addr.: http://www.elsevier.nl/. (Subscr. in U.S. and Canada to: Elsevier Science Inc., Box 882, Madison Sq. Sta., New York, NY 10159. TEL 212-989-5800) **Document type:** monographic series.
Refereed Serial

616.994   BL   ISSN 0034-7116
                              CODEN: RVBCA7
REVISTA BRASILEIRA DE CANCEROLOGIA. (Text in Portuguese; summaries in English and Portuguese) 1947. bi-m. free to qualified personnel; exchange requested. Pro-Onco/INCa-MS, Av. Venezuela 134, bl. A, 9o andar, 20081-310 Rio de Janeiro RJ, Brazil. TEL 55-21-2638565. FAX 55-21-2638297. Ed. Luiz Eduardo Atalecio. adv. contact: Marcos Morais. bibl.; charts; illus. circ. 2,500. **Indexed:** Chem.Abstr, Excerp.Med., Ind.Med. **Document type:** academic/scholarly publication.
—CASDDS.

616.99   CU   ISSN 0864-0297
REVISTA CUBANA DE ONCOLOGIA. (Text in Spanish; summaries in English, Spanish) 1985. s-a. $32 in S. America; N. America $34; elsewhere $36. Ministerio de Salud Publica, Centro Nacional de Informacion de Ciencias Medicas, Calle E No. 452, e-19 y 21, Plaza de la Revolucion, Apdo. 605, Havana, Cuba. TEL 809-32-5338. (Dist. by: Ediciones Cubanas, Obispo No. 527, Apdo. 605, Havana, Cuba) Ed. Frances Saiz. bibl.; charts; illus.; index. circ. 1,000. **Indexed:** Excerp.Med. (until 1993), Ind.Hyg.Dig.

616.994   RM   ISSN 0377-4724
                              CODEN: ONCODU
REVISTA DE CHIRURGIE, ONCOLOGIE, RADIOLOGIE, O.R.L, OFTALMOLOGIE, STOMATOLOGIE. ONCOLOGIE. (Text in Rumanian; summaries in English, French, German, Russian) 1962. 4/yr. $20. Uniunea Societatilor de Stiinte Medicale din Republica Socialista Rumania, Str. Progresului No. 8-10, Sectorul 1, Bucharest 70754, Rumania. (Subscr. to: ILEXIM, Str. 13 Decembrie Nr. 3, P.O. Box 136-137, Bucharest, Rumania) Ed.Bd. adv.; bk.rev.; abstr.; bibl.; charts; illus.; index. **Indexed:** Biol.Abstr., Chem.Abstr.
—CASDDS.
Supersedes in part: Oncologia si Radiologia (ISSN 0030-2406)

RIVISTA DI ANATOMIA PATOLOGICA E DI ONCOLOGIA. see *MEDICAL SCIENCES*

616.994   JA   ISSN 0022-2119
                              CODEN: SKBZAA
SAIBOKAKU BYORIGAKU ZASSHI/JOURNAL OF KARYOPATHOLOGY; tumor and tumor virus. (Text in Japanese; summaries in English) 1953. irreg. $2. Okayama Daigaku, Igakubu Byorigaku Kyoshitsu - Okayama University, School of Medicine, Department of Pathology, 2-5-1 Shikata-cho, Okayama 700, Japan. Ed. Y. Hamazaki. adv. (reprint service avail. from ISI) **Indexed:** Biol.Abstr., Ind.Med.

616.99   IT   ISSN 0393-1447
SARCOIDOSIS; international review of sarcoidosis and other granulomatous disorders. (Text in English) 1984. s-a. $67 (effective 1995). (World Association of Sarcoidosis and Other Granulomatous Disorders) Editore P C A, Via Clerici 12, 20032 Brusuglio di Corman (MI), Italy. TEL 39-2-66300802. FAX 39-2-6151239. Ed. D.G. James; Pub. Gianfranco Boldrini. adv.: color page L.5000000; adv. contact: Liliana Succio. bk.rev. circ. 1,000. **Indexed:** Curr.Cont., Excerp.Med., Ind.Med., Sci.Cit.Ind.
—BLDSC (8076.023000); Genuine Article.
Description: Publishes editorials, original clinical works and case reports, news, scientific notes, and letters to the editor.

616.99   BU   ISSN 0582-3250
                              CODEN: SSCMBX
SCRIPTA SCIENTIFICA MEDICA. (Supplement avail.) (Text in English; summaries in Russian) 1962. a. 10 lv. Medical University, Higher Institute of Medicine, 55 Marin Drinov St., Varna 9002, Bulgaria. (Subscr. to: Martinus Nijhoff International, P.O. Box 269, 2501 AX The Hague, Netherlands. TEL 31-79-684400) Ed. G. Marinov. (back issues avail.) **Indexed:** Abstr.Bulg.Sci.Med.Lit., Abstr.Hyg., Biol.Abstr., BSL Biol., Ref.Zh., Trop.Dis.Bull.
—BLDSC (8213.230000); CASDDS.

616.99 612.015   UK   ISSN 1044-579X
                              CODEN: SECBE7
SEMINARS IN CANCER BIOLOGY. 1989. bi-m. £115 (effective 1996). Academic Press Ltd. (Subsidiary of: Harcourt Brace & Company Ltd.), 24-28 Oval Rd., London NW1 7DX, England. TEL 44-171-267-4466. FAX 44-171-482-2293. TELEX 25775 ACPRES G. (Subscr. to: Harcourt Brace & Company Ltd., Foots Cray High St., Sidcup, Kent DA14 5HP, England. TEL 44-181-300-3322. FAX 44-181-309-0807) **Indexed:** Ind.Med. **Document type:** academic/scholarly publication.
—BLDSC (8239.448340); CASDDS; Genuine Article; SWETS; UnCover. **CCC.**

574.8 616.994   US   ISSN 0093-7754
RC261   CODEN: SOLGAV
SEMINARS IN ONCOLOGY. 1974 (Mar.). bi-m. $178 (foreign $227) (effective 1996). W.B. Saunders Co. (Subsidiary of: Harcourt Brace & Company), Curtis Center, 3rd Fl., Independence Sq. W., Philadelphia, PA 19106-3399. TEL 215-238-7800. FAX 215-238-6445. (Subscr. to: Periodicals Fulfillment, W.B. Saunders Co., 6277 Sea Harbor Dr., 4th Fl., Orlando, FL 32891-4800. TEL 800-654-2452) Ed. Dr. John W. Yarbro; Pub. Joan W. Blumberg. adv.: B&W page $980, color page $1080. bibl.; charts; illus.; index. circ. 9,317. **Indexed:** ASCA, Biol.Abstr., C.I.S. Abstr., Chem.Abstr., Curr.Adv.Cell & Devel.Biol., Curr.Adv.Ecol.Sci., Curr.Adv.Genetics & Molec.Biol., Curr.Cont., Dent.Ind., Excerp.Med., Ind.Med., Sci.Cit.Ind. **Document type:** academic/scholarly publication.
—BLDSC (8239.456500); CASDDS; EMDOCS; Faxon; Genuine Article; SWETS; UMI; UnCover. **CCC.**
Description: Reviews recent developments in cancer applicable to clinical oncology for general physicians.

SEMINARS IN ONCOLOGY NURSING. see *MEDICAL SCIENCES — Nurses And Nursing*

616.99 616.07   US   ISSN 1053-4296
                              CODEN: SRONEO
SEMINARS IN RADIATION ONCOLOGY. 1991 (Oct.). q. $120 (foreign $155) (effective 1996). W.B. Saunders Co. (Subsidiary of: Harcourt Brace & Company), Curtis Center, 3rd Fl., Independence Sq. W., Philadelphia, PA 19106-3399. TEL 215-238-7800. FAX 215-238-6445. (Subscr. to: Periodicals Fulfillment, W.B. Saunders Co., 6277 Sea Harbor Dr., 4th Fl., Orlando, FL 32891-4800. TEL 800-654-2452. FAX 800-874-6418) Ed. Dr. Joel E. Tepper; Pub. Joan W. Blumberg. adv.: B&W page $635, color page $1585; 7 x 10. circ. 2,494. **Indexed:** Excerp.Med. (1993-). **Document type:** academic/scholarly publication.
—BLDSC (8239.457300); SWETS. **CCC.**
Description: Discusses the use of radiation in cancer treatment from both clinical and scientific perspectives.

616.99   US   ISSN 8756-0437
RD651   CODEN: SSONEV
SEMINARS IN SURGICAL ONCOLOGY. 1978. bi-m. $444 (foreign $537) (effective 1996). John Wiley & Sons, Inc., Journals, 605 Third Ave., New York, NY 10158. TEL 212-850-6645. FAX 212-850-6021. TELEX 12-7063. E-mail: SUBINFO@JWILEY.COM. (Subscr. outside the Americas to: John Wiley & Sons, Ltd., Baffins Ln., Chichester, W. Sussex PO19 1UD, England. TEL 44-1243-779777. FAX 44-1243-776128) Ed. Dr. Gerald P. Murphy. adv. (also avail. in microform from UMI; back issues avail.) **Indexed:** Curr.Cont., Excerp.Med., Ind.Med. **Document type:** academic/scholarly publication.
—BLDSC (8239.470000); CASDDS; Faxon; Genuine Article; SWETS; UnCover. **CCC.**
Formerly (until 1985): International Advances in Surgical Oncology (ISSN 0190-1575)
Description: Offers invited review articles about topics in the field of surgical oncology. Each issue focuses on a particular disease entity or therapeutic approach.
Refereed Serial

616.99   US   ISSN 1081-0943
SEMINARS IN UROLOGIC ONCOLOGY. 1983. q. $111 (foreign $137) (effective 1996). W.B. Saunders Co. (Subsidiary of: Harcourt Brace & Company), Curtis Center, 3rd Fl., Independence Sq. W., Philadelphia, PA 19106-3399. TEL 215-238-7800. FAX 215-238-6445. (Subscr. to: Periodicals Fulfillment, W.B. Saunders Co., 6277 Sea Harbor Dr., 4th Fl., Orlando, FL 32891-4800. TEL 800-654-2452. FAX 800-874-6418) Ed. Dr. E. Darracott Vaughan, Jr; Pub. Joan W. Blumberg. adv.: B&W page $745, color page $1695; 7 x 10. bibl.; charts; illus.; index. circ. 1,971. **Indexed:** Ind.Med. **Document type:** academic/scholarly publication.
—BLDSC (8239.486000); SWETS; UnCover. **CCC.**
Formerly (until 1995): Seminars in Urology (ISSN 0730-9147)
Description: Each issue covers a specific area, which experts discuss in detail from their clinical experience.

616.99   CC   ISSN 1001-1692
SHIYONG ZHONGLIU ZAZHI/JOURNAL OF PRACTICAL ONCOLOGY. (Text in Chinese) q. Y4.40. Zhejiang Yike Daxue - Zhejiang Medical University, 157 Yan'an Lu, Hangzhou, Zhejiang 310006, People's Republic of China. TEL 722700. (Dist. outside China by: Guoji Shudian - China International Book Trading Corp., P.O. Box 399, Beijing, P.R.C.) Ed. Zheng Shu.
Refereed Serial

616.99   CC   ISSN 1002-3070
SHIYONG ZHONGLIUXUE ZAZHI/JOURNAL OF APPLIED ONCOLOGY. (Text in Chinese) 1987. q. Y4.80. Heilongjiang Zhonglu Fangzhi Bangongshi - Heilongjiang Cancer Prevention and Treatment Office, Haping Lu, Harbin, Heilongjiang 150040, People's Republic of China. TEL 65003. Ed. Ding Li. circ. 4,000. **Document type:** academic/scholarly publication.

616.99   GW   ISSN 0721-6831
SIGNAL; Leben mit Krebs. 4/yr. DM.28. Verlag fuer Medizin Dr. Ewald Fischer GmbH, Fritz-Frey-Str. 21, 69121 Heidelberg, Germany. TEL 06221-4062-0. Ed. Arndt Kroedel. **Indexed:** Abstr.Engl.Stud. **Document type:** academic/scholarly publication.
—CCC.

MEDICAL SCIENCES — ONCOLOGY

616 US ISSN 0898-6665
SKIN CANCER FOUNDATION JOURNAL. (Includes special edition of: Fourth World Congress of Cancers of the Skin) a. Skin Cancer Foundation, 245 Fifth Ave., Ste. 2402, New York, NY 10016. TEL 212-725-5176. FAX 212-725-5751. Ed. Lucy Kaveler. **Document type:** academic/scholarly publication.
—BLDSC (8295.915100).
Description: Compiles short articles to strengthen public awareness of the importance of prevention and early detection of skin cancer.

616.99 FR ISSN 0753-7417
CODEN: BFCPE
SOCIETE FRANCAISE DE CANCEROLOGIE PRIVEE. BULLETIN. 1982. 4/yr. 850 F. Societe Francaise de Cancerologie Privee, 25 rue Henry-Dunant, 94320 Thiais, France. TEL 1-46-87-20-57. Ed. Dr. H. Lauche. **adv. Indexed:** Excerp.Med. (1993-). **Document type:** bulletin.

616.99 GW ISSN 0941-4355
CODEN: SCCAEO
SUPPORTIVE CARE IN CANCER. (Text in English) 1992. bi-m. DM.298($216) (effective 1996). (Multinational Association of Supportive Care in Cancer) Springer-Verlag, Heidelberger Platz 3, 14197 Berlin, Germany. TEL 030-8207-0. FAX 030-8214091. E-mail: orders@springer.de. (Subscr. in N. America to: Springer-Verlag New York, Inc., 44 Hartz Way, Secaucus, NJ 07096-2491. TEL 201-348-4033. FAX 201-348-4505) Ed. N.K. Aaronson. (also avail. in microform from UMI) **Indexed:** Ind.Med. (1994-). **Document type:** academic/scholarly publication.
—BLDSC (8547.638620); Genuine Article; UMI. CCC.

616.99 GW
SUPPORTIVE MEASURES IN ONCOLOGY. irreg., vol.2, 1994. Georg Thieme Verlag, Ruedigerstr. 14, 70469 Stuttgart, Germany. TEL 0711-8931-0. FAX 0711-8931298. Eds. U. Jehn, H. Berghof. **Document type:** monographic series.

616.99 UK ISSN 0960-7404
CODEN: SUOCEC
SURGICAL ONCOLOGY. 1992. bi-m. £67.50 to individuals (outside Europe £74($115)); institutions £170 (outside Europe £188($303)) (effective 1996). Blackwell Science Ltd., Osney Mead, Oxford OX2 0EL, England. TEL 01865-206206. FAX 01865-206219. TELEX 83355 MEDBOK G. Eds. P.J. Gillou, C.M. Townsend. adv.; bk.rev.; illus.; index. (also avail. in microform from UMI; back issues avail.) **Indexed:** Excerp.Med. (1993-), Ind.Med. (1993-). **Document type:** academic/scholarly publication.
—BLDSC (8548.242000); ADONIS; Genuine Article; UMI. CCC.
Refereed Serial

616.99 617 US ISSN 1055-3207
SURGICAL ONCOLOGY CLINICS OF NORTH AMERICA. 1992. q. $110 (foreign $135) (effective 1996). W.B. Saunders Co. (Subsidiary of: Harcourt Brace & Company), The Curtis Center, 3rd Fl., Independence Sq. W., Philadelphia, PA 19106-3399. TEL 215-238-7800. FAX 215-238-6445. (Subscr. to: Periodicals Fulfillment, W.B. Saunders Co., 6277 Sea Harbor Dr., 4th Fl., Orlando, FL 32887-4800. TEL 800-654-2452. FAX 800-874-6418) Ed. Dr. Blake Cady; Pub. Joan W. Blumberg. adv.; index. (also avail. in microform from UMI; back issues avail.) **Document type:** academic/scholarly publication.
—BLDSC (8548.242100); UMI.
Description: Discusses diagnostic techniques, surgical procedures, and radiation therapy for the treatment of cancer patients.

616.994 FI ISSN 0356-3081
SYOPA/CANCER. (Text in Finnish, Swedish) 1969. 5/yr. FIM 150. Suomen Syopayhdistys - Cancer Society of Finland, Liisankatu 21 B, 00170 Helsinki 17, Finland. FAX 358-0-1351093. adv.; bk.rev. circ. 128,000. **Indexed:** Risk Abstr.
Former titles: Syovantorjunta - Kampen Mot Kraefta - Against Cancer; Terveystyo (ISSN 0049-2787)

616.994 NE ISSN 0166-3925
TIJDSCHRIFT KANKER. 1977. 6/yr. fl.45. (Nederlandse Vereniging tot Steun aan het Koningin Wilhelmina Fonds voor de Kankerbestrijding) Van den Boogaard Uitgeverij B.V., Postbus 24, 5060 AA Oisterwijk, Netherlands. TEL 31-4242-16665. FAX 31-4242-85255. Ed.Bd. adv.; bk.rev. circ. 2,000.
—SWETS.
Formerly: K.W.F. Nieuws (ISSN 0022-7447)

TISSUE CULTURE ASSOCIATION. MONOGRAPH SERIES. see *BIOLOGY — Microbiology*

TISSUE CULTURE ASSOCIATION. PROCEEDINGS. see *BIOLOGY — Microbiology*

616.99 SZ ISSN 1010-4283
CODEN: OBIMD4
TUMOR BIOLOGY. (Text in English) 1980. bi-m. 312.60 SFr.($240.60) to individuals; institutions 521 SFr.($401) (effective 1996). (International Society for Oncodevelopmental Biology and Medicine) S. Karger AG, Allschwilerstr. 10, P.O. Box, CH-4009 Basel, Switzerland. TEL 061-3061111. FAX 061-3061234. E-mail: Karger@Karger.ch. Ed. A.M. Neville. **Indexed:** Curr.Adv.Biochem., Curr.Adv.Cancer Res., Curr.Adv.Cell & Devel.Biol. **Document type:** academic/scholarly publication.
—BLDSC (9070.645500); CASDDS; Faxon; Genuine Article; SWETS; UnCover. CCC.
Former titles: Oncodevelopmental Biology and Medicine (ISSN 0167-1618); Tumour Biology (ISSN 0289-5447)
Refereed Serial

616.99 US
▼**TUMOR DIAGNOSIS.** Announced for publication in 1996. q. $67 to individuals; institutions $95 (effective 1996). Field & Wood, Medical Periodicals, Inc., Box 975, Blue Bell, PA 19422. TEL 610-828-4010. FAX 215-482-0226. Eds. Dr. Jose Russo, Dr. Irma Russo. **Document type:** academic/scholarly publication.
Description: Devoted to the problems involved in the diagnosis of a tumor. Places special emphasis on the utilization of modern techniques of molecular biology.
Refereed Serial

616.994 JA ISSN 0041-4093
CODEN: TUREA6
TUMOR RESEARCH: EXPERIMENTAL AND CLINICAL/GAN KENKYU, JIKKEN TO RINSHO. (Text in English and European languages) 1966. a. exchange basis. Sapporo Ika Daigaku, Fuzoku Gan Kenkyujo - Sapporo Medical University, Cancer Research Institute, Nishi-17-chome, Minami-1-jo, Chuo-ku, Sapporo-shi, Hokkaido 060, Japan. TEL 011-611-2111. FAX 011-615-3099. Ed. Yohichi Mochizuki. abstr.; bibl.; charts; illus.; stat. circ. 550. (also avail. in microfilm from UMI) **Indexed:** Biol.Abstr., Chem.Abstr., Curr.Adv.Ecol.Sci., Excerp.Med. **Document type:** academic/scholarly publication.
—BLDSC (9070.650000); CASDDS; EMDOCS.

616.99 UK ISSN 1351-8488
▼**TUMOR TARGETING.** 1995. q. £59($99) to individuals; institutions in the E.U. £130 (N. America £225; elsewhere £145) (effective 1995). Chapman & Hall, Journals Department (Subsidiary of: International Thomson Publishing Group), 2-6 Boundary Row, London SE1 8HN, England. TEL 0171-865-0066. FAX 0171-522-9623. TELEX 290164 CHAPMA G. E-mail: journal@chall.mhs.compuserve.com. (Subscr. to: International Thomson Publishing Services Ltd., Cheriton House, North Way, Andover, Hants. SP10 5BE, England. TEL 01264-342713. FAX 01264-342807; Subscr. in N. America to: Chapman & Hall, Journals Promotion Department, One Penn Plaza, 41st Fl., New York, NY 10119. TEL 212-564-1060. FAX 212-564-1505) adv. (reprint service avail.) **Document type:** academic/scholarly publication.
—BLDSC (9070.655000). CCC.
Refereed Serial

616.99 GW ISSN 0722-219X
TUMORDIAGNOSTIK & THERAPIE. bi-m. DM.156. Georg Thieme Verlag, Ruedigerstr. 14, 70469 Stuttgart, Germany. TEL 0711-8931-0. FAX 0711-8931298. (Subscr. to: Postfach 104853, 70042 Stuttgart, Germany) Eds. M. Luethgens, S. Seeber. circ. 6,000. **Document type:** academic/scholarly publication.
—BLDSC (9070.675000); Genuine Article; UMI. CCC.

616.994 IT ISSN 0041-4352
TUMORI. (Text in English) 1911. bi-m. L.150000 (effective Jan. 1994). (Istituto Nazionale Tumori) Casa Editrice Ambrosiana, Via Frua 6, 20146 Milan, Italy. TEL 39-2-2390564. FAX 39-2-2362692. Ed. Franco Zunino. bk.rev.; bibl.; charts; illus.; index, cum.index. circ. 2,000. **Indexed:** Biol.Abstr., Chem.Abstr., Curr.Adv.Biochem., Curr.Adv.Cancer Res., Curr.Adv.Ecol.Sci., Curr.Adv.Genetics & Molec.Biol., Curr.Cont., Dent.Ind., Excerp.Med., Ind.Med., Ind.Vet., Risk Abstr., Vet.Bull.

616.99 UK ISSN 0955-5102
TUMOUR MARKER UPDATE. 1989. bi-m. £54($110) to individuals; institutions £74($155) (effective 1996). Leeds Medical Information, University of Leeds, Leeds LS2 9JT, England. TEL 0113-233-5550. FAX 0113-233-5568. (Subscr. to: Royal Society of Medicine Press Ltd., P.O. Box 9002, London W1A 0ZA, England. TEL 0171-290-2927. FAX 0171-290-2929) Ed.Bd. circ. 400. **Document type:** abstracting/indexing, academic/scholarly publication.
Description: Locates and reports the scientific literature on circulating, genetic and immunohistochemical tumor markers from more than 1,000 international biomedical titles.

616.99 TU ISSN 1019-3103
TURKISH JOURNAL OF CANCER. (Text in English) 1967. 4/yr. TL.400000($100) Turkish Association for Cancer Research and Control - Turk Kanser Arastirma ve Savas Kurumu, Atac Sokak No. 21, 06420 Yenisehir, Ankara, Turkey. TEL 90-312-3092908. FAX 90-312-4313958. Ed. Dr. Dincer Firat. adv. contact: Dincer Firat. bk.rev. circ. 1,000. **Document type:** academic/scholarly publication.
—BLDSC (9072.468000).
Formerly (until 1992): Kanser (ISSN 0377-9750)

U I C C INTERNATIONAL CALENDAR OF MEETINGS ON CANCER. (Union Internationale Contre le Cancer) see *MEETINGS AND CONGRESSES*

616.99 SZ
U I C C INTERNATIONAL DIRECTORY OF CANCER INSTITUTES AND ORGANIZATIONS. 1976. quadrennial, 6th ed., 1994. 100 SFr. Union Internationale Contre le Cancer - International Union Against Cancer, 3 rue du Conseil-General, CH-1205 Geneva, Switzerland. TEL 022-3201811. FAX 022-3201810. E-mail: uicc@atge.automail.com. **Document type:** directory.
Formerly: International Directory of Specialized Cancer Research and Treatment Establishments.

ULTRASTRUCTURAL PATHOLOGY. see *BIOLOGY — Cytology And Histology*

616.99 US ISSN 0272-2836
RC268.6
U.S. NATIONAL TOXICOLOGY PROGRAM. ANNUAL REPORT ON CARCINOGENS. 1980. a. U.S. National Toxicology Program, NIEHS-NTP, Box 12233, Research Triangle Park, NC 27709. TEL 919-541-4096. FAX 919-541-2242. E-mail: Jameson@niehs.nih.gov. Ed. C.W. Jameson. **Document type:** government publication.

MEDICAL SCIENCES — OPHTHALMOLOGY AND OPTOMETRY

616.994 US ISSN 1059-2385
UNIVERSITY OF TEXAS. M.D. ANDERSON CANCER CENTER. THE CANCER BULLETIN. 1948. bi-m. $55 (foreign $65). University of Texas, M.D. Anderson Cancer Center, 1515 Holcombe Blvd., No. 227, Houston, TX 77030. TEL 713-792-6014. FAX 713-792-6016. Eds. Drs. Martin N. Raber, Steven P. Tomasovic. bk.rev.; illus.; 5-yr. cum. index. circ. 27,000. (back issues avail.) **Indexed:** Biol.Abstr., Excerp.Med., Ind.Med. **Document type:** academic/scholarly publication.
—BLDSC (3046.460000); Faxon; SWETS; UnCover.
Former titles: M.D. Anderson Hospital and Tumor Institute at Houston. Cancer Bulletin (ISSN 0740-820X); Cancer Bulletin (ISSN 0008-5448)
Description: Informs physicians and other health care professionals of current problems in oncology and new applications and advances in the control of cancer.

616.9 US
UNIVERSITY OF TEXAS. M.D. ANDERSON CANCER CENTER. RESEARCH REPORT. 1955. a. free. University of Texas, M.D. Anderson Cancer Center, Scientific Publications, Box 234, 1515 Holcombe, Houston, TX 77030. TEL 713-792-6014. FAX 713-792-6016. Ed. Diane S. Rivera. circ. 5,500. **Document type:** academic/scholarly publication.
Formerly (until 1977): M.D. Anderson Hospital and Tumor Institute. Research Report (ISSN 0066-1635)
Description: Compendium of research accomplishments at the center.

616.9 US ISSN 1078-1439
▼**UROLOGIC ONCOLOGY.** 1995. bi-m. $185 to institutions (effective 1996). Elsevier Science Inc., 655 Ave. of the Americas, New York, NY 10011. TEL 212-989-5800. FAX 212-633-3990. (Subscr. to: Box 882, Madison Sq. Sta., New York, NY 10159-0882) (back issues avail.) **Document type:** academic/scholarly publication.
Refereed Serial

616.994 FR ISSN 0249-0358
VIVRE. 1923. q. 20 F. Ligue Nationale Francaise Contre le Cancer, 1 av. Stephen Pichon, 75013 Paris, France. Ed. Alain Froissard. adv.; bk.rev.; bibl.; charts; illus.; stat. circ. 300,000. **Indexed:** Biol.Abstr., Ind.Med.
Formerly: Lutte Contre le Cancer (ISSN 0024-7642)
Description: Information on cancer research, prevention, and treatments.

616.99 GW ISSN 0931-8364
WISSENSCHAFTLICHER ERGEBNISBERICHT. 1982. biennial. free. Deutsches Krebsforschungszentrum, Im Neuenheimer Feld 280, 69120 Heidelberg, Germany. TEL 06221-422854. FAX 06221-422995. **Document type:** academic/scholarly publication.

616.994 US ISSN 1040-1741
RC261 **CODEN:** YEONEX
YEAR BOOK OF ONCOLOGY. 1957. a. $74.95 (residents $35) (effective 1996). Mosby - Year Book, Inc., Continuity Division, 200 N. LaSalle, Chicago, IL 60601. TEL 312-726-9733. FAX 312-726-6075. TELEX 206155. Ed. Dr. Joseph Simone. illus. (reprint service avail.)
●Also available online. Vendor(s): Ovid Technologies. Also available on CD-ROM. Producer(s): SilverPlatter Information, Inc.
—BLDSC (9414.665000). CCC.
Formerly: Year Book of Cancer (ISSN 0084-3679)

616.99 CC ISSN 1000-8179
CODEN: ZZLIEP
ZHONGGUO ZHONGLIU LINCHUANG/CHINESE JOURNAL OF CLINICAL ONCOLOGY. (Text in Chinese; abstracts in English) 1963. m. Y4 per no. Tianjin Zhongliu Yanjiusuo, Zhongguo Kang-Ai Xiehui - Tianjin Cancer Institute, China Anti-Cancer Association, Huan-hu-xi Lu, Tiyuanbei, Hexi Qu, Tianjin 300060, People's Republic of China. TEL 86-22-374477. (Dist. overseas by: China Publication Foreign Trading Corp., Tianjin Branch, P.R. China. TEL 86-22-3359984. FAX 86-22-3359958) Ed. Zhang Tian-Ze. adv.: color page Y4000; adv. contact: Hong-Xin Yang. circ. 6,500. **Indexed:** Excerp.Med., ExtraMED. **Document type:** academic/scholarly publication.
●Also available on CD-ROM.
Description: Publishes original articles pertaining to the clinical disciplines of oncology and the related laboratory studies.

ZHONGHUA SHENJING WAIKE ZAZHI/CHINESE JOURNAL OF NEUROSURGERY. see *MEDICAL SCIENCES — Psychiatry And Neurology*

616.99 CC ISSN 0253-3766
CODEN: CCLCDY
ZHONGHUA ZHONGLIU ZAZHI/CHINESE JOURNAL OF ONCOLOGY. (Text in Chinese) bi-m. $3.50 per no. Chinese Medical Association - Zhonghua Yixuehui, P.O. Box 2258, 42 Dongsi Xidajie, Beijing 100710, People's Republic of China. TEL 1-550394. **Indexed:** Biol.Abstr., Excerp.Med., ExtraMED, Ind.Med., Maize Abstr., Rev.Med.& Vet.Mycol. **Document type:** academic/scholarly publication.
●Also available on CD-ROM.
—CASDDS.

MEDICAL SCIENCES — Ophthalmology And Optometry

617.7 610.73 US ISSN 1061-4338
A S O R N NEWS. (Supplement to: Insight (San Francisco) (ISSN 1060-135X) 1992. bi-m. membership. American Society of Ophthalmic Registered Nurses, Inc., Box 193030, San Francisco, CA 94119. TEL 415-561-8513. **Document type:** newsletter.

617.7 CI ISSN 0001-6403
CODEN: AOPIBU
ACTA OPHTHALMOLOGICA IUGOSLAVICA. (Text in Serbo-Croatian; summaries in English, French, German) 1963. s-a. Zbor Lijecnika Hrvatske, Oftalmoloska Sekcija, Subiceva 12, 41000 Zagreb, Croatia. Ed. Dr. Kresimir Cupak. adv.; bk.rev.; abstr.; index. circ. 1,200. **Indexed:** Biol.Abstr., C.I.S. Abstr.
—BLDSC (0641.770000).

617.7 DK ISSN 1395-3907
RE1 **CODEN:** AOSCFV
ACTA OPHTHALMOLOGICA SCANDINAVICA. (Supplement avail. (ISSN 1395-3931)) (Text in English) 1923. bi-m. DKK 1084 in Scandinavia; rest of Europe DKK 1284; elsewhere DKK 1334 (effective 1996). Scriptor Publisher ApS, Soevangsvej 1-5, DK-2650 Hvidovre, Denmark. TEL 45-36-77-41-13. FAX 45-36-77-41-15. Ed. Niels Ehlers. adv.; bibl.; charts; illus.; index, cum.index: vols.1-25. circ. 2,500. **Indexed:** ASCA, Biol.Abstr., Chem.Abstr., Curr.Adv.Cancer Res., Curr.Adv.Ecol.Sci., Curr.Cont., Dok.Arbeitsmed., Excerp.Med., Helminthol.Abstr., Ind.Med., Ind.Sci.Rev., INIS Atomind., Psychol.Abstr., Rev.Med.& Vet.Mycol., Sci.Cit.Ind.
—CASDDS; Faxon; SWETS; UnCover.
Formerly (until 1995): Acta Ophthalmologica (ISSN 0001-639X)

617.7 DK ISSN 1395-3931
RE1
ACTA OPHTHALMOLOGICA SCANDINAVICA. SUPPLEMENTUM. (Text in English) 1932. irreg. free to subscribers to Acta Ophthalmologica. Scriptor Publisher ApS, 1-5 Soevangsvej, DK-2650 Hvidovre, Denmark. TEL 45-36-77-41-13. FAX 45-35-77-41-15. adv. **Indexed:** Biol.Abstr., Curr.Cont., Dent.Ind., Dok.Arbeitsmed., Ind.Med., INIS Atomind.
—BLDSC (0641.755000); Faxon; SWETS; UnCover.
Formerly (until 1995): Acta Ophthalmologica. Supplementum (ISSN 0065-1451)

617.7 658 US ISSN 1060-5991
ADMINISTRATIVE OPHTHALMOLOGY. 1992. q. $45 (effective 1995). American Society of Opthalmic Administrators, 4000 Legato Rd., Ste. 850, Fairfax, VA 22033-4003. TEL 703-591-2222. FAX 703-591-0614. (Subscr. to: Fulco, Box 3000, Denville, NJ 07843. TEL 800-875-2997. FAX 201-627-5872) Ed. Lucy Santiago. adv. contact: Christine Ford. **Document type:** academic/scholarly publication.

617.7 US ISSN 1070-5384
▼**ADVANCES IN CLINICAL OPHTHALMOLOGY.** 1994. a. $90.95 (residents $35) (effective 1996). Mosby - Year Book, Inc. (Chicago) (Subsidiary of: Times Mirror Company), 200 N. LaSalle St., Chicago, IL 60601-1080. TEL 312-726-9733. FAX 312-726-6075. TELEX 206155. Ed. Ronald Burde.

617.7 US ISSN 0276-3508
ADVANCES IN OPHTHALMIC PLASTIC & RECONSTRUCTIVE SURGERY. 1982. irreg. price varies. c/o McGraw Hill, Monterey Ave., Blue Ridge Summit, PA 17294. Ed. Dr. Stephen Bosniak. (also avail. in microform) **Indexed:** Curr.Adv.Ecol.Sci., Curr.Cont. **Document type:** monographic series.
—Faxon. CCC.
Refereed Serial

617.7 IT ISSN 0390-5764
AGGIORNAMENTI DI TERAPIA OFTALMOLOGICA. 1949. q. free to Italian ophthalmologists. Farmigea S.p.A., Via Carmignani, 2, 56127 Pisa, Italy. TEL 39-50-544000. FAX 39-50-544304. adv. contact: Renzo Cannelli. abstr.; circ. 7,200 (controlled). (tabloid format) **Document type:** academic/scholarly publication.
Refereed Serial

617.7 SW ISSN 0348-5730
AKTUELL OPTIK OCH OPTOMETRI. 1979. 10/yr. SEK 495. Swedish Optometric Association, SOR, P.O. Box 274, S-291 23 Kristianstad, Sweden. TEL 46-44-10-22-19. FAX 46-44-10-62-60. Ed. Hans Lundstroem. adv.: B&W page SEK 6600, color page SEK 9130; trim 185 x 265; adv. contact: Jeanette Lindstroem. bk.rev. cols./p.: 3.

617.7 GW ISSN 0942-5276
CODEN: FOOPDZ
AKTUELLE AUGENHEILKUNDE. (Text and summaries in English and German) 1976. bi-m. DM.123. Georg Thieme Verlag, Ruedigerstr. 14, 70469 Stuttgart, Germany. TEL 0711-8931-0. FAX 0711-8931298. (Subscr. to: Postfach 104853, 70042 Stuttgart, Germany) circ. 2,000. **Indexed:** Biol.Abstr., C.I.S. Abstr., Excerp.Med., INIS Atomind. **Document type:** academic/scholarly publication.
—BLDSC (0785.728000). CCC.
Formerly (until 1992): Folia Ophthalmologica (ISSN 0323-4932)

617 II
ALL INDIA OPHTHALMOLOGICAL SOCIETY. PROCEEDINGS. (Text in English) a. All India Ophthalmological Society, 13, Cathedral Rd., Madras 600 086, India.

AMERICAN DIOPTER & DECIBEL SOCIETY. PROCEEDINGS. see *MEDICAL SCIENCES — Otorhinolaryngology*

617.7 US ISSN 0002-9394
RE1 **CODEN:** AJOPAA
AMERICAN JOURNAL OF OPHTHALMOLOGY. 1884. m. $66 to individuals (foreign $99); institutions $99 (foreign $134) (effective 1995). Ophthalmic Publishing Co., 77 W. Wacker Dr., Ste. 660, Chicago, IL 60601-1629. TEL 312-629-1690. FAX 312-629-1744. Ed. Dr. B.R. Straajsma. adv.; bk.rev.; abstr.; bibl.; illus.; index; circ. 17,500 (paid). (also avail. in microform from UMI; reprint service avail. from UMI) **Indexed:** AIM, Biodet.Abstr., Biol.Abstr., Biotech.Abstr., Chem.Abstr., Curr.Adv.Cancer Res., Curr.Adv.Ecol.Sci., Curr.Cont., Dent.Ind., Dok.Arbeitsmed., Excerp.Med., Helminthol.Abstr., Ind.Med., Ind.Sci.Rev., Ind.Vet., INIS Atomind., Kidney, Lab.Haz.Bull., Med.& Surg.Dermat., Nutr.Abstr., Protozool.Abstr., Psychol.Abstr., Rev.Med.& Vet.Mycol., Risk Abstr., Sci.Cit.Ind, Vet.Bull. **Document type:** academic/scholarly publication.
—BLDSC (0828.900000); CASDDS; Faxon; Genuine Article; SWETS; UMI; UnCover.
Refereed Serial

617.7 US ISSN 0065-9533
RE1 **CODEN:** TAOSAT
AMERICAN OPHTHALMOLOGICAL SOCIETY. TRANSACTIONS. 1864. a. $50. American Ophthalmological Society, c/o W. Banks Anderson, M.D., Duke University Eye Center, Durham, NC 27710. FAX 919-684-2230. Ed. Dr. William Tasman. index; circ. 600 (paid). (back issues avail.) **Indexed:** Biol.Abstr., Dent.Ind., Excerp.Med., Ind.Med. **Document type:** academic/scholarly publication, proceedings.
—BLDSC (8893.650000); EMDOCS; SWETS.

MEDICAL SCIENCES — OPHTHALMOLOGY AND OPTOMETRY

617.7   US
AMERICAN OPTICIAN. 1950. 4/yr. membership only. Opticians Association of America, 10341 Democracy Ln., Fairfax, VA 22030-2521. TEL 703-691-8355. FAX 703-691-3929. Ed. Jacqueline Fairbarns. adv. circ. 7,500. **Document type:** newsletter.
  Former titles (until 1992): O A A News Report; Which superseded: O A A News.
  Description: News and education for association members.

617.75   US   ISSN 0003-0244
RE1   CODEN: JAOPBD
AMERICAN OPTOMETRIC ASSOCIATION. JOURNAL. 1928. m. $50 to non-members (foreign $75). American Optometric Association, 243 N. Lindbergh Blvd., St. Louis, MO 63141. TEL 314-991-4100. FAX 314-991-4101. Ed. John G. Classe. adv.: B&W page $3100, color page $4250; trim 8 1/8 x 10 7/8. bk.rev.; abstr.; charts; illus.; stat.; tr.lit.; index, cum.index: 1925-1972. circ. 30,142. **Indexed:** Biol.Abstr., Curr.Cont., Dok.Arbeitsmed., Excerp.Med., Ind.Med. (1992-), INIS Atomind., Psychol.Abstr. (1967-). **Document type:** academic/scholarly publication.
  —BLDSC (4689.370000); Faxon; SWETS; UMI.
  Refereed Serial

617.7   US   ISSN 0094-9620
AMERICAN OPTOMETRIC ASSOCIATION. NEWS. 1961. s-m. $35 (foreign $45). American Optometric Association, 243 N. Lindbergh Blvd., St. Louis, MO 63141. TEL 314-991-4100. FAX 314-991-4101. Ed. Robert Foster. adv.: B&W page $3190, color page $4340; trim 10 3/8 x 15; adv. contact: Andrew Miller. circ. 30,447. (tabloid format) **Document type:** newspaper.
  Description: Covers news of the association for doctors of optometry.

617.7   US   ISSN 0065-955X
CODEN: AOJTAW
AMERICAN ORTHOPTIC JOURNAL. 1950. a. $22 to individuals; institutions $57 (effective 1995). (American Association of Certified Othoptists) University of Wisconsin Press, Journal Division, 114 N. Murray St., Madison, WI 53715. TEL 608-262-4952. FAX 608-262-7560. Ed. Dr. Thomas France. adv.; cum.index: 1950-1960, 1971-1980. circ. 1,300. (also avail. in microform from UMI; back issues avail.; reprint service avail. from UMI) **Indexed:** Biol.Abstr., Excerp.Med. **Document type:** academic/scholarly publication.
  —BLDSC (0847.750000); SWETS; UMI. **CCC.**
  Refereed Serial

617.7   IT   ISSN 0003-4665
CODEN: AOCOAG
ANNALI DI OTTAMOLOGIA E CLINICA OCULISTICA. (Text in Italian; summaries in English, French, German) 1874. m. L.140000 (foreign L.280000) (effective 1994). Casa Editrice Maccari, Via Trento 53, 43100 Parma, Italy. FAX 039-521-771268. adv.; bk.rev.; charts; illus.; index. circ. 2,200. **Indexed:** Chem.Abstr., Excerp.Med., Ind.Med., INIS Atomind.
  —BLDSC (1016.200000); UMI.

617.7   US   ISSN 1079-4794
RE1   CODEN: ANOPB5
ANNALS OF OPHTHALMOLOGY. 1969. bi-m. $120 (foreign $128). American Society of Contemporary Ophthalmology, 233 E. Erie St., Chicago, IL 60611. TEL 708-568-1500; 800-621-4002. FAX 708-568-1527. Eds. Dr. Randall Bellows, Dr. David Bellows. adv.; bk.rev.; bibl.; illus.; index; circ. controlled. **Indexed:** Biol.Abstr., Chem.Abstr., Dent.Ind., Dok.Arbeitsmed., Excerp.Med., Helminthol.Abstr., Ind.Med., INIS Atomind. **Document type:** trade publication.
  —Faxon.
  Incorporated (in 1994): Glaucoma (ISSN 0164-4645); Supersedes: Journal of Experimental and Clinical Ophthalmology.
  Refereed Serial

ANNUARIO OTTICO ITALIANO. see *BUSINESS AND ECONOMICS — Trade And Industrial Directories*

617.7   US   ISSN 0003-9950
RE1   CODEN: AROPAW
ARCHIVES OF OPHTHALMOLOGY. Spanish translation: Archives of Ophthalmology (Edicion Espanola) (SP ISSN 1130-5134) 1869. m. $110 (foreign $150). American Medical Association, 515 N. State St., Chicago, IL 60610. TEL 312-464-5000; 800-262-2350. FAX 312-464-4184. Ed. Dr. Morton F. Goldberg. adv.; bk.rev.; charts; illus.; index. circ. 21,500. (also avail. in microform from UMI,PMC) **Indexed:** Abstr.Inter.Med., AIM, Biol.Abstr., Biotech.Abstr., C.I.S.Abstr., Chem.Abstr., Curr.Adv.Cancer Res., Curr.Adv.Ecol.Sci., Curr.Cont., Dent.Ind., Diab.Cont., Dok.Arbeitsmed., Excerp.Med., Helminthol.Abstr., HRIS, Ind.Med., Ind.Sci.Rev., Ind.Vet., INIS Atomind., Med.& Surg.Dermat., Nutr.Abstr., Protozool.Abstr., Psychol.Abstr., Rev.Med.& Vet.Mycol., Rev.Plant Path., Sci.Cit.Ind., Small Anim.Abstr., Vet.Bull. **Document type:** academic/scholarly publication.
  ●Also available online. Vendor(s): Lexis-Nexis.
  —BLDSC (1638.450000); CASDDS; Faxon; Genuine Article; SWETS; UMI; UnCover. **CCC.**
  Refereed Serial

617.7   SP   ISSN 1130-5134
ARCHIVES OF OPHTHALMOLOGY (EDICION ESPANOLA). Spanish translation of: Archives of Ophthalmology (US ISSN 0003-9950) bi-m. 6500 ptas. (American Medical Association, US) Ediciones Doyma S.A., Travesera de Gracia, 17-21, 08021 Barcelona, Spain. TEL 34-1-200-07-11. FAX 34-1-209-11-36. TELEX 51964 INK E. Ed. J. Murube del Castillo. adv.: page 180000 ptas.; trim 210 x 280; adv. contact: Olga Gomez. circ. 2,500.
  Description: Contains translations of articles from the American edition including editorials, clinical cases, laboratory technique and investigative work.

617.7   AG   ISSN 0066-6777
ARCHIVOS DE OFTALMOLOGIA DE BUENOS AIRES. 1925. q. $30. Sociedad Argentina de Oftalmologia, Viamonte 1464-1 DTO. 2, Buenos Aires, Argentina. adv. circ. 1,500. **Indexed:** Biol.Abstr., Excerp.Med.

617.7   US   ISSN 0194-8172
ARGUS (SAN FRANCISCO). 1978. m. $36. American Academy of Ophthalmology, Box 7424, San Francisco, CA 94120-7424. TEL 415-561-8500. FAX 415-561-8567. Ed. Pamela Beach. adv. contact: Diana Pastore. bk.rev. circ. 21,000. **Document type:** trade publication.
  Description: Highlights health care reform, provides advice on managed care and new health care delivery systems and updates members on academy news and events.

617.7   BL   ISSN 0004-2749
CODEN: AQBOAP
ARQUIVOS BRASILEIROS DE OFTALMOLOGIA. 1938. bi-m. $100. Belfort Editora, Rua Barao de Itapetininga 297, Caixa 4086, Sao Paulo, Brazil. Ed. Rubens Belfort Mattos. adv.; bk.rev.; abstr.; illus. circ. 1,500. **Indexed:** Biol.Abstr., Excerp.Med., Ind.Med.
  —Faxon.

617.7   SI   ISSN 0129-1653
ASIA - PACIFIC JOURNAL OF OPHTHALMOLOGY. 1987. q. $65 to individuals in Asia-Pacific (elsewhere $80); institutions in Asia-Pacific $130 (elsewhere $160). Singapore National Eye Centre, 11 Third Hospital Ave., Singapore 0316, Singapore. TEL 065-227-7255. FAX 065-323-1903. TELEX SNEC RS 22842. Ed. Arthur S.M. Lim. adv.: page $900; trim 205 x 270; adv. contact: Charity Wai. circ. 10,000.
  —BLDSC (1742.260780).
  Incorporates (in 1990): Implants in Ophthalmology (ISSN 0218-0367)
  Description: Disseminates the latest research and development in surgical techniques, complications, management. Includes geographical and historical notes, and information on new implants and instruments.

617.7   US   ISSN 0273-0189
QP474
ASSOCIATION FOR RESEARCH IN VISION AND OPHTHALMOLOGY. SPRING MEETING. (Supplement to: Investigative Ophthalmology and Visual Science (ISSN 0146-0404)) a. Lippincott - Raven Publishers, 227 E. Washington Sq., Philadelphia, PA 19106. TEL 215-238-4200. (Alt. addr.: Association for Research in Vision and Ophthalmology, 9650 Rockville Pike, Bethesda, MD 20814. TEL 301-571-1844) abstr. **Document type:** proceedings.

617.7   JA   ISSN 0910-1810
ATARASHII GANKA/JOURNAL OF THE EYE. (Text in Japanese; summaries in English, Japanese) 1984. m. 1900 Yen per no. Medikaru Aoi Shuppan - Medical Aoi Publisher Inc., 27-1, Hongo 3-chome, Bunkyo-ku, Tokyo 113, Japan. **Indexed:** Chem.Abstr.
  —BLDSC (4983.450000).

617.7 016   US   ISSN 0271-1281
AUDIO-DIGEST OPHTHALMOLOGY. 1963. s-m. $168. Audio-Digest Foundation (Subsidiary of: California Medical Association), 1577 E. Chevy Chase Dr., Glendale, CA 91206. TEL 213-245-8505. FAX 818-240-7379. Ed. Claron L. Oakley. circ. controlled. (audio cassette)
  Refereed Serial

617.7   GW   ISSN 0341-1486
AUGENAERZTLICHE FORTBILDUNG; Jahreskurse fuer die praktische Augenheilkunde. 1977. q. DM.198($143) (effective 1996). Urban und Vogel, Lindwurmstr. 95, 80337 Munich, Germany. TEL 089-53292-0. FAX 089-53292-100. (Subscr. to: Postfach 152209, 80052 Munich, Germany) Ed.Bd. index. circ. 2,000. (back issues avail.) **Document type:** academic/scholarly publication.
  —CCC.

617.7   GW   ISSN 0004-7902
DER AUGENARZT. 1967. 6/yr. (Berufsverband der Augenaerzte Deutschlands e.V.) Dr. R. Kaden Verlag, Poststr. 24-26, 69115 Heidelberg, Germany. TEL 06221-10313. FAX 06221-29910. Eds. Gisa Kemper, Alexander Diehm. adv.: B&W page DM.5270; trim 230 x 178. bk.rev.; abstr.; illus. circ. 7,000. **Document type:** academic/scholarly publication.

617.7   GW   ISSN 0004-7929
DER AUGENOPTIKER. 1946. m. DM.109.20 (foreign DM.124.15). Konradin Verlag Robert Kohlhammer GmbH, Ernst-Mey-Str. 8, 70771 Leinfelden-Echterdingen, Germany. TEL 0711-7594-0. FAX 0711-7594-390. Ed. Martin Graf. adv.: B&W page DM.4300, color page DM.7240; trim 190 x 270; adv. contact: Anna Blum. bk.rev.; bibl.; charts; illus.; stat. circ. 12,740. **Document type:** trade publication.
  —BLDSC (1791.300000).

617.7   GW   ISSN 0004-7937
DER AUGENSPIEGEL; Forum der Augenaerzte. 1955. m. DM.182. Augenspiegel Verlags GmbH, Lintorfer Str. 7-9, 40878 Ratingen, Germany. TEL 02102-23062. FAX 02102-25488. TELEX 8589002-FOC-D. Ed. Dr. Berthold Schwab. adv.; bk.rev.; charts; illus.; mkt.; stat.; tr.lit. circ. 4,000.
  —BLDSC (1791.400000).

617.7   AT   ISSN 0814-9763
CODEN: ANZOEQ
AUSTRALIAN AND NEW ZEALAND JOURNAL OF OPHTHALMOLOGY. q. Aus.$20. Royal Australian College of Ophthalmologists, 27 Commonwealth St., Sydney, N.S.W. 2010, Australia. TEL 61-2-267-7006. Ed. Bruce Langtry. circ. 1,200. (reprint service avail. from ISI) **Indexed:** Biol.Abstr., Curr.Cont., Dent.Ind., Excerp.Med., Ind.Med., Ind.Sci.Rev., Rev.Plant Path., Sci.Cit.Ind.
  —BLDSC (1796.891000); Faxon; Genuine Article. **CCC.**
  Formerly: Australian Journal of Ophthalmology; Incorporates: Australian College of Ophthalmologists Transactions. (ISSN 0067-1789)

617.3   US   ISSN 0067-9283
BLUE BOOK OF OPTOMETRISTS. 1912. biennial. $95. Butterworth - Heinemann, Part of the Reed Elsevier group, 313 Washington St., Newton, MA 02158. TEL 617-928-2500; 800-366-2665. FAX 617-928-2610. TELEX 880052. index. **Document type:** directory.

617.7   IT   ISSN 0006-677X
CODEN: BOOCAH
BOLLETTINO D'OCULISTICA. (Text in Italian; summaries in English and French) 1930. bi-m. L.80000($100) Nuova Casa Editrice Licinio Cappelli di G.E.M. s.r.l., Via Farini, 14, 40126 Bologna, Italy. TEL 39-51-239060. FAX 39-51-239286. Ed. F. D'Ermo. adv.; bk.rev. circ. 2,500. (back issues avail.) **Indexed:** Chem.Abstr., Excerp.Med., Ind.Med.
  —BLDSC (2239.800000); CASDDS.

MEDICAL SCIENCES — OPHTHALMOLOGY AND OPTOMETRY 4487

617.752   GW   ISSN 0933-9264
BRILLEN SPECIAL; Zeitschrift fuer gutes Sehen und besseres Aussehen. 1987. 2/yr. DM.15. Ivy Stoll Verlag, Ridlerstr. 36, 80339 Munich, Germany. TEL 089-509545. FAX 089-503189. Ed. Ivy Stoll. adv.; bk.rev. circ. 103,000. **Document type:** consumer publication.

617.7   UK   ISSN 0007-1161
CODEN: BJOPAL
BRITISH JOURNAL OF OPHTHALMOLOGY. 1917. m. £206($325) B M J Publishing Group, B.M.A. House, Tavistock Sq., London WC1H 9JR, England. TEL 0171-383-6270. FAX 0171-383-6402. (N. American subscr. to: Box 408, Franklin, MA 02038. TEL 800-2-FON-BMJ. FAX 800-2-FAX-BMJ) Ed. J.V. Forester. adv. contact: Sheila Rowe. bk.rev.; abstr.; bibl.; charts; illus.; index. (also avail. in microform from UMI; reprint service avail. from UMI) **Indexed:** Biol.Abstr., Chem.Abstr., Curr.Adv.Cancer Res., Curr.Adv.Ecol.Sci., Curr.Cont., Diab.Cont., Dok.Arbeitsmed., Excerp.Med., Helminthol.Abstr., Ind.Med., Ind.Sci.Rev., INIS Atomind., Nutr.Abstr., Protozool.Abstr., Rev.Med.& Vet. Mycol., Rev.Plant Path., Sci.Cit.Ind. **Document type:** academic/scholarly publication.
—BLDSC (2313.000000); Faxon; Genuine Article; SWETS; UMI; UnCover. **CCC.**
  Formed by the merger of: Ophthalmic Review (ISSN 0266-3066); Ophthalmoscope (ISSN 0266-3430); Royal London (Moorfields) Ophthalmic Hospital Reports (ISSN 0266-2906)
  Description: Presents international papers from both clinicians and laboratory workers in ophthalmology to keep them abreast of trends.
Refereed Serial

617.7   UK   ISSN 1351-6736
BRITISH JOURNAL OF OPTOMETRY AND DISPENSING. 1993. q. £40 (overseas £80). Mark Allen Publishing Ltd., Croxted Mews, 288 Croxted Rd., London SE24 9BY, England. TEL 0181-671-7521. FAX 0181-671-1722. Ed. Rishi Agarwal; Pub. Mark Allen. adv. contact: Ian White. **Document type:** academic/scholarly publication.
—BLDSC (2314.100000).

617.7   UK   ISSN 0068-2314
BRITISH ORTHOPTIC JOURNAL. 1939. a. £28.70 for 1996 edition (rest of world £29.20). British Orthoptic Society, Tavistock House N., Tavistock Sq., London WC1H 9HX, England. TEL 0171-387-7992. FAX 0171-383-2584. Ed. A. Horwood. adv.; bk.rev.; cum.index every 5 yrs. circ. 1,800. (back issues avail.) **Indexed:** Biol.Abstr., Excerp.Med. **Document type:** academic/scholarly publication.
—BLDSC (2332.500000); Faxon; SWETS.
  Description: Subjects covered include orthoptics, binocular vision, ocular motility, pediatric ophthalmology, and neuro-ophthalmology.

617.7   GW   ISSN 0068-3361
BUECHEREI DES AUGENARZTES. (Supplement to: Klinische Monatsblaetter fuer Augenheilkunde) 1938. irreg., no.130, 1992. price varies. Ferdinand Enke Verlag, Postfach 300366, 70443 Stuttgart, Germany. TEL 0711-135798-0. FAX 0711-135798-30. TELEX 07252275-GTV-D. Ed.Bd. (reprint service avail. from IRC) **Indexed:** Ind.Med. **Document type:** monographic series.

BUSINESS RATIO REPORT: OPTICAL INDUSTRY; an industry sector analysis. see *PHYSICS — Optics*

617.7   US   ISSN 0733-8902
RE977.C6   CODEN: CLAJEU
C L A O JOURNAL. 1975. q. $76. (Contact Lens Association of Ophthalmologists) Kellner-McCaffery Associates, Inc., 150 Fifth Ave., New York, NY 10011. TEL 212-741-0280. Ed. Dr. Peter C. Donshik. adv.; bk.rev. circ. 3,300. (also avail. in microform from UMI) **Indexed:** Biol.Abstr., Chem.Abstr., Excerp.Med., Ind.Med., Protozool.Abstr. **Document type:** academic/scholarly publication.
—BLDSC (3274.311000); CASDDS; Faxon; SWETS; UMI; UnCover.
  Former titles: Contact and Intraocular Lens Medical Journal (ISSN 0360-1358); Contact Lens Medical Bulletin (ISSN 0010-728X)
  Description: Research and review articles on contact lenses, and cornea and anterior segment of the eye for vision care professionals.
Refereed Serial

617.75   US   ISSN 0273-804X
CALIFORNIA OPTOMETRY. 1933. s-m. $35 to non-members. California Optometric Association, 801 12th St., Ste. 2020, Sacramento, CA 95814-2930. TEL 916-441-3990. Ed. Margaret Clausen. adv.; bk.rev.; illus. circ. 3,500.
  Former titles (until 1979): California Optometrist (ISSN 0361-7025); California Optometrist Association. Journal (ISSN 0008-1337)

617.7   CN   ISSN 0008-4182
CODEN: CAJOBA
CANADIAN JOURNAL OF OPHTHALMOLOGY/JOURNAL CANADIEN D'OPHTALMOLOGIE. (Text in English, French) 1966. 7/yr. Can.$70($80) (foreign $90) (effective 1996). Canadian Ophthalmological Society, 1525 Carling Ave., No. 610, Ottawa, ON K1Z 8R9, Canada. TEL 613-729-6779. FAX 613-729-7209. Ed. B.J. MacInnis. adv.: B&W page Can.$825, color page Can.$1690; trim 8 1/8 x 10 7/8; adv. contact: Anne Keefer. bk.rev.; illus. circ. 1,300. (also avail. in microform from UMI; reprint service avail. from UMI) **Indexed:** Biol.Abstr., Chem.Abstr., Curr.Cont., Excerp.Med., Ind.Med., Ind.Sci.Rev., Ophthal.Lit., Rev.Plant Path. **Document type:** academic/scholarly publication.
—BLDSC (3033.700000); CASDDS; Genuine Article; SWETS; UMI; UnCover. **CCC.**
  Description: Contains scientific papers presented at annual meetings, and contributions from within and outside Canada.
Refereed Serial

617.7   CN   ISSN 0045-5075
CANADIAN JOURNAL OF OPTOMETRY/REVUE CANADIENNE D'OPTOMETRIE. 1939. q. Can.$40 (foreign Can.$50). Canadian Association of Optometrists, 1785 Alta Vista Dr., Ste. 301, Ottawa, ON K1G 3Y6, Canada. TEL 613-738-4412. FAX 613-738-7161. Ed. Dr. M.J. Samek. adv.: B&W page $650, color page $1850; trim 8 1/2 x 11; adv. contact: Chantale Wall. bk.rev. circ. 4,000. **Document type:** academic/scholarly publication.

617.7   US   ISSN 0178-4781
CODEN: CDBEEW
CELL AND DEVELOPMENTAL BIOLOGY OF THE EYE. 1984. irreg. price varies. Springer-Verlag, 175 Fifth Ave., New York, NY 10010. TEL 212-460-1500. FAX 212-473-6272. (Also: Berlin, Heidelberg, Tokyo and Vienna) Eds. J.B. Sheffield, S.R. Hilfer. **Document type:** academic/scholarly publication.

617.7   XR   ISSN 0009-059X
CESKOSLOVENSKA OFTALMOLOGIE. (Text in Czech or Slovak; summaries in English and Russian) 1943. 6/yr. $48.60. (Ceska Lekarska Spolecnost J.E. Purkyne - Czech Medical Society) Nakladatelske Stredisko C L S J.E. Purkyne, Sokolska 31, 120 26 Prague 2, Czech Republic. FAX 42-2-202788. (Dist. by: Artia, Ve Smeckach 30, 111 27 Prague 1, Czech Republic) (Co-sponsor: Ceskoslovenska Oftalmologicka Spolecnost) Ed. Dr. H. Kraus. adv.; bk.rev.; abstr.; bibl.; illus.; index. **Indexed:** Chem.Abstr., Dent.Ind., Dok.Arbeitsmed., Excerp.Med., Ind.Med., INIS Atomind.
—BLDSC (3122.450000). **CCC.**

617.75   US   ISSN 0147-7633
RE1
CHILTON'S REVIEW OF OPTOMETRY. Variant title: Review of Optometry. 1891. m. $38. Chilton Co., Chilton Way, Radnor, PA 19089. TEL 215-964-4370. Ed. Rich Kirkner. adv.: B&W page $3350, color page $4800; trim 8 x 10 3/4. bk.rev.; illus.; index. (also avail. in microfilm from UMI; microfiche from UMI; reprint service avail. from UMI)
—BLDSC (3172.996000); UMI. **CCC.**
  Formerly (until Apr. 1977): Optical Journal and Review of Optometry (ISSN 0030-3925)
Refereed Serial

617.7   IT   ISSN 0391-8998
CLINICA OCULISTICA E PATOLOGIA OCULARE. (Text in Italian; summaries in English) q. L.60000($60) C I C Edizioni Internazionali s.r.l., Via. L. Spallanzani 11, 00161 Rome, Italy. TEL 06-8412673. FAX 06-44242033. TELEX 622099 CIC. (Co-sponsors: Societa Oftalmologica Meridionale, Societa Oftalmologica Siciliana) Dir. G. Scuderi. **Indexed:** Excerp.Med.
—BLDSC (3286.215700). **CCC.**

617.75   AT   ISSN 0816-4622
CLINICAL AND EXPERIMENTAL OPTOMETRY. 1913. bi-m. Aus.$95. Australian Optometrical Association, 204 Drummond St., Carlton, Vic. 3053, Australia. TEL 61-3-663-6833. FAX 61-3-663-7478. Ed. Dr. Peter Swann. adv.; bk.rev.; abstr.; charts; illus.; stat.; index. circ. 2,600. (back issues avail.) **Indexed:** Excerp.Med. **Document type:** academic/scholarly publication.
—BLDSC (3286.251940); UnCover.
  Incorporates (1934-19??): New South Wales Journal of Optometry (ISSN 0047-9918); Formerly (until 1986): Australian Journal of Optometry (ISSN 0045-0642)
  Description: Publishes original articles, letters to the editor and other items of educational interest.

617.7   IE   ISSN 0953-4431
CODEN: CEVCEV
CLINICAL EYE AND VISION CARE. 1988. q. I£130($205) (effective 1996). Elsevier Science Ireland Ltd., P.O. Box 85, Limerick, Ireland. TEL 353-61-471944; 800-366-2665. FAX 353-61-472144. (Subscr. in U.S. and Canada to: Elsevier Science, P.O. Box 882, Madison Sq. Sta., New York, NY 10159-0882. TEL 212-989-5800. FAX 212-633-3990) Ed. Anthony B. Litwak, O.D. adv.; bk.rev.; abstr.; charts; illus. (also avail. in microform from UMI; back issues avail.) **Document type:** academic/scholarly publication.
—BLDSC (3286.286300); UMI. **CCC.**
  Description: Explains the various modalities of diagnosis and treatment and the management of clinical situations. Features case reports, new advances in disease detection, case presentations and reports, photo-abstracts, ophthalmic pharmaceuticals, instrumentation, and contact lenses.
Refereed Serial

617.7   UK   ISSN 0953-6833
COMMUNITY EYE HEALTH; an international journal to promote eye health worldwide. 1988. s-a. £25($40) International Centre for Eye Health, Institute of Ophthalmology, Bath St., London EC1V 9EL, England. TEL 0171-608-6909. FAX 0171-250-3207. TELEX 926606 ICEH G. Ed. Dr. Murray McGavin. bk.rev. circ. 18,000. **Document type:** academic/scholarly publication.
—BLDSC (3363.624400).

617.7   NE
CONTACT (HANK). (Text in English) 1992. 3/yr. free to qualified personnel. E P S, P.O. Box 40, 4273 ZG Hank, Netherlands. TEL 31-1622-3350. FAX 31-1622-3802. Ed. Wim Aalbers. adv.: B&W page $2500, color page $2750; trim 210 x 297. illus.; circ. 2,000 (controlled). **Document type:** trade publication.
  Description: Covers news affecting the contact lens industry worldwide, including new technologies, manufacturing, marketing and technical issues.

617.7   GW
CONTACT (HEIDELBERG). 1975. 3/yr. Median Verlag GmbH, Postfach 103964, 69029 Heidelberg, Germany. TEL 06221-25731. FAX 06221-25020. circ. 80,000. **Document type:** consumer publication.

617.7   UK   ISSN 0306-9575
CONTACT LENS JOURNAL. 1966. m. £3($75) Libra Publishing Ltd., 14 Fairfield Ave., Datchet, Berks SL3 9NQ, England. Ed. Annette Whibley. adv.; bk.rev.; abstr.; bibl.; charts; illus.; index. circ. 2,000. **Indexed:** Curr.Adv.Ecol.Sci., Excerp.Med.
—BLDSC (3424.974000).
  Formerly: Contact Lens (ISSN 0010-7271)

617.752   US   ISSN 0885-9175
RE977.C6
CONTACT LENS SPECTRUM. 1986. m. $38. Viscom Publications (Subsidiary of: Full Circle Media Corp.), 50 Washington St., Norwalk, CT 06854. TEL 203-838-9100. FAX 203-838-2550. Ed. Joe Barr. adv. circ. 20,792.
—BLDSC (3424.984000).
  Incorporates (1976-1991): Contact Lens Forum (ISSN 0363-1621)
  Description: Provides contact lens professionals with clinical and technical information concerning contact lenses and solutions, guidelines for effective patient care, coverage of industry developments and new products, and analyses of market trends.

CONTACT LENS UPDATE. see *MEDICAL SCIENCES — Abstracting, Bibliographies, Statistics*

M

ULRICH'S INTERNATIONAL PERIODICALS DIRECTORY 1996

MEDICAL SCIENCES — OPHTHALMOLOGY AND OPTOMETRY

CONTACTO. see *MEDICAL SCIENCES — Abstracting, Bibliographies, Statistics*

617.752   GW   ISSN 0171-9599
CODEN: CNTCDF
CONTACTOLOGIA. French edition (ISSN 0171-9602); English edition (ISSN 0936-1235) (Supplement avail.: Contactolgia-Bucherei) 1979. q. DM.138. Ferdinand Enke Verlag, Postfach 300366, 70443 Stuttgart, Germany. TEL 0711-135798-0. FAX 0711-135798-30. TELEX 07252275-GTV-D. Ed.Bd. (reprint service avail. from IRC) **Indexed:** Excerp.Med. **Document type:** academic/scholarly publication.
—Faxon. **CCC**.

617.752   GW   ISSN 0724-6226
CONTACTOLOGIA-BUCHEREI. (Supplement to: Contactologia) 1983. irreg., no.5, 1992. price varies. Ferdinand Enke Verlag, Postfach 300366, 70443 Stuttgart, Germany. TEL 0711-135798-0. FAX 0711-135798-30. TELEX 07252275-GTV-D. Eds. W. Ehrich, R. Heitz. (reprint service avail. from IRC) **Document type:** monographic series.

617.7   US   ISSN 0893-8733
CONTEMPORARY OPHTHALMIC FORUM. 1982. q. $25. Silver Press, Inc., 456 Clinic Dr., Columbus, OH 43210. TEL 614-421-4960. Ed. Dr. Frederick H. Davidorf. adv. circ. 13,600.
Formerly (until 1986): Ophthalmic Forum (ISSN 0734-1652)

617.75   US
CONTEMPORARY OPTOMETRY. 1982. s-a. free to qualified personnel. (Pilkington Visioncare Inc., Sola - Barnes-Hind) Academy Professional Information Services, Inc., 116 W. 32nd St., New York, NY 10001. TEL 212-736-6688. FAX 212-564-1763. Ed. Dr. Garold Edwards. circ. 25,000.
Description: Covers contact lenses.

617.7   US
CONTROVERSIES IN CLINICAL OPHTHALMOLOGY. 1993. irreg. $285 to individuals; institutions $350 (effective 1993). Field & Wood, Medical Periodicals, Inc., Box 975, Blue Bell, PA 19422. TEL 610-828-4010. FAX 610-482-0226. Ed. Dr. Joseph Mauriello. **Document type:** academic/scholarly publication.
Refereed Serial

617.7   US   ISSN 0277-3740
CODEN: CORNDB
CORNEA. 1982. bi-m. $176 to individuals; institutions $246 (effective 1995). (Castroviejo Society) Lippincott - Raven Publishers, 227 E. Washington Sq., Philadelphia, PA 19106. TEL 215-238-4200. Ed. Dr. H. Dwight Cavanagh. adv. contact: Phyllis Noyes. bk.rev.; abstr.; charts; illus.; index. circ. 1,500. (also avail. in microform from UMI; reprint service avail. from UMI) **Indexed:** Chem.Abstr., Excerp.Med., Ind.Med. **Document type:** academic/scholarly publication.
—BLDSC (3470.927500); CASDDS; Faxon; Genuine Article; SWETS; UMI; UnCover. **CCC**.
Refereed Serial

617.7   CN
COUP D'OEIL. 1982. 5/yr. Publedition Inc., 620 Industriel Blvd., St-Jean-sur-Richelieu, PQ J3B 7X4, Canada. TEL 514-856-7821. FAX 514-359-0836. adv.: B&W page Can.$1390, color page Can.:$1955; trim 8 3/4 x 10 7/8. circ. 2,492.

617.7   FR   ISSN 0767-7634
COUP D'OEIL OPHTALMOLOGIQUE. 1985. 6/yr. 450 F. Editions et Regarde Attentivement, 68 bd. des Poilus, 44300 Nantes, France. TEL 40-68-96-06. FAX 40-68-98-76. adv.: B&W page 10900 F., color page 19800 F. bk.rev. circ. 4,000. **Document type:** academic/scholarly publication.

CURRENT CITATIONS ON STRABISMUS, AMBLYOPIA, AND OTHER DISEASES OF OCULAR MOTILITY. see *MEDICAL SCIENCES — Abstracting, Bibliographies, Statistics*

617.7   UK   ISSN 0271-3683
QP476   CODEN: CEYRDM
CURRENT EYE RESEARCH. 1981. m. £320($520) (effective 1996). Oxford University Press, Oxford Journals, Walton St., Oxford OX2 6DP, England. TEL 01865-267907. FAX 01865-267773. TELEX 837330-OXPRES-G. E-mail: jnlorders@oup.co.uk. (U.S. subscr. to: Oxford University Press Inc., 2001 Evans Rd., Cary, NC 27513. TEL 919-677-0977. FAX 919-677-1714) Eds. R. Frank, H. Shichi. adv.; illus.; index. circ. 550. (back issues avail.; reprint service avail. from SWZ) **Indexed:** Curr.Adv.Biochem., Curr.Adv.Cell & Devel.Biol., Curr.Adv.Ecol.Sci., Curr.Cont., Excerp.Med., Ind.Med., Ind.Vet., INIS Atomind., Ophthal.Lit., Rev.Med.& Vet.Mycol., Sci.Cit.Ind., Vet.Bull. **Document type:** academic/scholarly publication.
—BLDSC (3496.570000); CASDDS; Faxon; Genuine Article; SWETS; UMI; UnCover. **CCC**.
Description: Rapidly publishes clinical and basic research on anatomy, physiology, biophysics, biochemistry, developmental biology, microbiology, pharmacology and immunology of the eye.

CURRENT OPINION IN OPHTHALMOLOGY. see *MEDICAL SCIENCES — Abstracting, Bibliographies, Statistics*

617.752   GW   ISSN 0344-7103
RE1   CODEN: DDOPD4
DEUTSCHE OPTIKERZEITUNG. 1945. m. DM.95 (foreign DM.130). Optische Fachveroeffentlichung GmbH, Rohrbacher Str. 57, 69115 Heidelberg, Germany. TEL 06221-184081. FAX 06221-183996. Ed. Dieter Baust. adv.: B&W page DM.3680; trim 185 x 258; adv. contact: Ralf Ritter. bk.rev. circ. 9,999. (back issues avail.) **Document type:** trade publication.
—CASDDS.
Formerly: Sueddeutsche Optikerzeitung.

617.7   SZ   ISSN 0250-3751
CODEN: DEOPDB
DEVELOPMENTS IN OPHTHALMOLOGY. (Text in English and German) 1980. irreg. price varies. S. Karger AG, Allschwilerstr. 10, P.O. Box, CH-4009 Basel, Switzerland. TEL 061-3061111. FAX 061-3061234. E-mail: Karger@Karger.ch. Ed. H. Kaiser. (reprint service avail. from ISI, back issues avail.) **Indexed:** Biol.Abstr., Chem.Abstr., Curr.Cont., Ind.Med. **Document type:** academic/scholarly publication.
—BLDSC (3579.085480); CASDDS; Faxon. **CCC**.
Formed by the merger of: Advances in Ophthalmology (ISSN 0065-3004); Bibliotheca Ophthalmologica (ISSN 0067-8090); Modern Problems in Ophthalmology (ISSN 0077-0078)
Description: Combines reviews with reports on new experimental findings.
Refereed Serial

617.7   MX
DICCIONARIO DE ESPECIALIDADES OFTAMOLOGICAS. 1991. a. Ediciones P L M, S.A. de C.V., San Bernadino 17, Col. del Valle, 03100 Mexico, D.F., Mexico. TEL 687-1766. FAX 536-5027. Ed. Dr. Emilio Rosenstein. circ. 3,000.

617.7   US
DIRECTORY OF CERTIFIED OPHTHALMIC MEDICAL PERSONNEL. 1984. a. $35 (free to qualified personnel). Joint Commission on Allied Health Personnel in Ophthalmology, 2025 Woodlane Dr., St. Paul, MN 55125-2995. TEL 800-284-3937. FAX 612-731-0410. Ed. Beverly Fanning. circ. 12,000. **Document type:** directory.
Formerly: Directory of Certified Ophthalmic Medical Assistants.
Description: Lists every person holding certification with the Commission.

617.7   NE   ISSN 0012-4486
RE14   CODEN: DOOPAA
DOCUMENTA OPHTHALMOLOGICA. (Proceedings supplement avail.) (Text in English) 1938. m. fl.1590 to institutions; $970 to institutions in U.S. (effective 1996). (International Society for Clinical Electrophysiology of Vision) Kluwer Academic Publishers, Postbus 17, 3300 AA Dordrecht, Netherlands. TEL 31-78-392392. FAX 31-78-392254. TELEX 29245 KAPG NL. E-mail: SERVICES@WKAP.NL. (Dist. by: Kluwer Academic Publishers Group, P.O. Box 322, 3300 AH Dordrecht, Netherlands. TEL 31-78-392392. FAX 31-78-546474; N. America dist. addr.: Box 358, Accord Sta., Hingham, MA 02018-0358. TEL 617-871-6600. FAX 617-871-6528) Ed. Prof. L. Missotten. adv.; bk.rev. (also avail. in microform from UMI; reprint service avail. from SWZ) **Indexed:** Biol.Abstr., Chem.Abstr., Curr.Cont., Excerp.Med., Ind.Med., Ind.Sci.Rev., INSPEC (1985-), Nutr.Abstr., Sci.Cit.Ind. **Document type:** academic/scholarly publication.
—BLDSC (3609.560000); CASDDS; Genuine Article; SWETS; UMI; UnCover. **CCC**.
Description: Publishes studies on clinical and non-clinical ophthalmology.
Refereed Serial

617.7   NE   ISSN 0303-6405
CODEN: DOPSBP
DOCUMENTA OPHTHALMOLOGICA PROCEEDINGS SERIES. (Supplement to: Documenta Ophthalmologica (ISSN 0012-4486)) (Text in English) 1973. irreg. price varies. Kluwer Academic Publishers, Postbus 17, 3300 AA Dordrecht, Netherlands. TEL 31-78-392392. FAX 31-78-392254. TELEX 29245 KAPG NL. (Dist. by: Kluwer Academic Publishers Group, P.O. Box 322, 3300 AH Dordrecht, Netherlands. TEL 31-78-392392. FAX 31-78-546474; N. America dist. addr.: Box 358, Accord Sta., Hingham, MA 02018-0358. TEL 617-871-6600. FAX 617-871-6528) **Indexed:** Biol.Abstr., Curr.Adv.Ecol.Sci., Curr.Cont., Nutr.Abstr., Psychol.Abstr. **Document type:** proceedings.
—CASDDS; SWETS.
Refereed Serial

617.7   UK   ISSN 0955-3681
RE451   CODEN: EJISE3
EUROPEAN JOURNAL OF IMPLANT AND REFRACTIVE SURGERY. 1989. bi-m. £78 in Europe (rest of world $120) to individuals; institutions £120 in Europe (rest of world $216). (European Society of Cataract and Refractive Surgeons (ESCRS)) W.B. Saunders Ltd. (Subsidiary of: Harcourt Brace & Company Ltd.), 24-28 Oval Rd., London NW1 7DX, England. TEL 0171-267-4466. FAX 0171-482-2293. TELEX 25775-ACPRES-G. (Subscr. to: Harcourt Brace & Company Ltd., Foots Cray High St., Sidcup, Kent DA14 5HP, England. TEL 0181-300-3322. FAX 0181-309-0807; US, Canadian, and Mexican subscr. to: W.B. Saunders Co., Journal Subscription Fulfillment, 6277 Sea Harbor Dr., 4th Fl., Orlando, FL 32887-4800. TEL 800-654-2452. FAX 800-874-6418) Ed. E. Rosen. (back issues avail.) **Document type:** academic/scholarly publication.
—BLDSC (3829.730200). **CCC**.
Description: Provides a forum for original full papers and rapid communications dealing with all aspects of ocular implants, refractive surgery, and topics of related interest.

617.7   IT   ISSN 1120-6721
CODEN: EJOOEL
EUROPEAN JOURNAL OF OPHTHALMOLOGY. 1991. q. L.140000($140) (effective 1994). Wichtig Editore s.r.l., Via Friuli 72-74, 20135 Milan, Italy. TEL 02-5452306. FAX 02-5451843. **Indexed:** Excerp.Med. (1993-), Ind.Med. (1992-).
—BLDSC (3829.733230). **CCC**.
Description: Covers clinical and basic research in ophthalmology.

617.7   FR   ISSN 0301-326X
EUROPEAN OPHTHALMOLOGICAL SOCIETY. CONGRESS ACTA. (Text in English, French and German) 1960. quadrennial, 9th, 1992, Brussels. (Royal Society of Medicine, London, UK) European Ophthalmological Society, c/o H. Saraux, Service d'Opthalmologie, Hopital St. Antoine, 184, rue du Faubourg St. Antoine, 75012 Paris, France. Ed. P.D. Trevor-Roper. circ. 1,500. **Document type:** proceedings.

MEDICAL SCIENCES — OPHTHALMOLOGY AND OPTOMETRY

617.7   UK   ISSN 0014-4835
QP474   CODEN: EXERA6
EXPERIMENTAL EYE RESEARCH; an international journal devoted to scientific research on the eye. 1961. m. £650 (effective 1996). Academic Press Ltd. (Subsidiary of: Harcourt Brace & Company Ltd.), 24-28 Oval Rd., London, NW1 7DX, England. TEL 44-171-267-4466. FAX 44-171-482-2293. TELEX 25775 ACPRES G. (Subscr. to: Harcourt Brace & Company Ltd., Foots Cray High St., Sidcup, Kent DA14 5HP, England. TEL 44-181-300-3322. FAX 44-181-309-0807) Ed. J.G. Hollyfield. adv.; charts; illus.; stat.; index. (back issues avail.) **Indexed:** Biol.Abstr., Chem.Abstr., Curr.Adv.Biochem., Curr.Adv.Ecol.Sci., Curr.Adv.Genetics & Molec.Biol., Curr.Cont., Dent.Ind., Excerp.Med., Ind.Med., Ind.Sci.Rev., INIS Atomind., Nutr.Abstr., Sci.Cit.Ind. **Document type:** academic/scholarly publication.
—BLDSC (3839.150000); ADONIS; CASDDS; Ei; Faxon; Genuine Article; SWETS; UnCover. **CCC.**
Description: Publishes original research papers on all aspects of the anatomy, physiology, biochemistry, biophysics, molecular biology, pharmacology, developmental biology, microbiology, and immunology of the eye.
Refereed Serial

617.7   UK   ISSN 0950-222X
   CODEN: EYEEEC
EYE. 1880. a. £147($270) College of Ophthalmologists, 2 Bramber Rd., London W14 9PQ, England. TEL 0171-385-6281. FAX 0171-381-1799. (Subscr. to: Professional and Scientific Publications, B.M.A. House, Tavistock Sq., London WC1H 9JH, England) adv.; bk.rev.; index. circ. 3,250. (back issues avail.) **Indexed:** Biol.Abstr., Curr.Cont., Dent.Ind., Excerp.Med., Helminthol.Abstr., Ind.Med.
—BLDSC (3854.566000); CASDDS; Faxon; Genuine Article; SWETS; UnCover.
Formerly (until 1979): Ophthalmological Society of the United Kingdom. Transactions (ISSN 0078-5334)
Refereed Serial

617.7   II   ISSN 0255-4062
EYE CARE. (Text in English) 1979. a. Rs.800($40) (Update in Optics and Contact Lens) Dr. Narendra Kumar, Ed. & Pub., P.O. Box 2812, New Delhi 110 060, India. TEL 5599839. adv.; bk.rev. circ. 1,200.
Description: Annual ocular health guidebook.

617.75   US
EYE ON OREGON. 1934. q. $25. Oregon Optometric Association, 6901 S.E. Lake Rd., Ste. 26, Milwaukie, OR 97267-2195. TEL 503-639-5036. FAX 503-659-4189. Ed. J. Gregg Mindt. bk.rev. (processed) **Document type:** newsletter.
Former titles (until vol.29, no.4, 1992): Oregon Optometry (ISSN 0274-6549); Oregon Optometrist (ISSN 0030-476X)

617.7   CC   ISSN 1000-4432
   CODEN: YAXUE
EYE SCIENCE/YANKE XUEBAO; a view of Chinese ophthalmology. (Text in Chinese, English) q. Sun Yat-sen University of Medical Sciences, Zhongshan Ophthalmic Center, 54 Xianlie Rd., Guangzhou, Guangdong 510060, People's Republic of China. **Indexed:** Excerp.Med. **Document type:** academic/scholarly publication.
—BLDSC (3854.635000).
Refereed Serial

617.7   US
EYE TO EYE. 1971. q. free. International Eye Foundation, 7801 Norfolk Ave., Bethesda, MD 20814. TEL 301-986-1830. FAX 301-986-1876. TELEX 271588 IEF UR. Ed. Molly Cashin. circ. 1,200. (tabloid format) **Document type:** newsletter.
Former titles: International Eye Foundation - Society of Eye Surgeons. Newsletter; Eyelights.

617.7   US   ISSN 0885-9167
EYECARE BUSINESS. 1986. m. Viscom Publications (Subsidiary of: Full Circle Media Corp.), 50 Washington St., Norwalk, CT 06854. TEL 203-838-9100. FAX 203-838-2550. Ed. S. Walter. circ. 40,850.

617.7 362   US   ISSN 0899-7756
FIGHTING BLINDNESS NEWS. 1973. s-a. free. Foundation Fighting Blindness, 1401 Mt. Royal Ave., Baltimore, MD 21217. TEL 410-225-9400. FAX 410-225-3936. Ed. Elinore Tibbetts. circ. 73,000. (also avail. in Braille; audio cassette; large print edition in 14 pt.) **Document type:** newsletter.
Description: Articles on retinitis pigmentosa, macular degeneration and other retinal degenerations. Includes information on research, human services and volunteer activities.

617.7   GW   ISSN 0721-1600
FOCUS; Magazin fuer den erfolgreichen Augenoptiker. 1981. m. DM.145. Spangemacher Verlags GmbH und Co. KG, Lintorfer Str. 7-9, 40878 Ratingen, Germany. TEL 02102-23051. FAX 02102-25488. Ed. Joerg Spangemacher. bk.rev.; charts; illus. circ. 7,500. **Document type:** trade publication.
Description: For optometrists and dispensing opticians: practice management, education and trade relations in political matters.

617.7   JA   ISSN 0015-5667
   CODEN: NGKYA3
FOLIA OPHTHALMOLOGICA JAPONICA/NIHON GANKA KIYO. (Text in Japanese; summaries in English) 1950. m. 25000 Yen (effective 1994). Osaka University Medical School, Department of Ophthalmology, 2-2 Yamadaoka, Suita 565, Japan. TEL 81-6-879-3450. FAX 81-6-879-3459. Ed. Yasuo Tano. adv.; bk.rev. circ. 2,700. (also avail. in microform) **Indexed:** Excerp.Med., Ind.Med. **Document type:** academic/scholarly publication.
—BLDSC (3971.824000); CASDDS.
Refereed Serial

617.7   US   ISSN 1040-8495
FOREFRONT (COLUMBUS); the newsletter for optometric staff. 1988. bi-m. $36 (Canada and Mexico $46; elsewhere $51). Anadem Publishing, Inc., 3620 N. High St., Columbus, OH 43214. TEL 800-633-0055. **Document type:** newsletter.

617.752   US
FRAMES. q. Carmel Communications, Inc., 2 Park Plaza, Ste.900, Irvine, CA 92714-5904. TEL 714-756-2218. FAX 714-756-5322. Ed. Cindy Thomas. circ. 20,395.

617.7 615.7   JA   ISSN 0914-1405
GAN YAKURI/JAPANESE JOURNAL OF OCULAR PHARMACOLOGY. (Text in English, Japanese) 1987. a. Nihon Gan Yakuri Gakkai - Japanese Society for Ocular Pharmacology, Tokyo Daigaku Igakubu Gankagaku Kyoshitsu, 3-1, Hongo 7-chome, Bunkyo-ku, Tokyo 113, Japan.

617.7   JA   ISSN 0386-9601
GANKA RINSHO IHO/JAPANESE REVIEW OF CLINICAL OPHTHALMOLOGY. (Text in Japanese; summaries in English) 1906. m. 15000 Yen. Ganka Rinsho Ihokai - Japanese Society of Clinical Ophthalmology, Teikyo Daigaku Igakubu Gankagaku Kyoshitsu, 11-1, Kaga 2-chome, Itabashi-ku, Tokyo 173, Japan. TEL 03-3964-1211. FAX 03-3963-0303. Ed. Toshio Maruo.
—BLDSC (4661.750000).

617.7   JA   ISSN 0915-5066
GANKA SHUJUTSU KONNICHI NO KANGAEKATA/CURRENT INSIGHTS IN OPHTHALMIC SURGERY. (Text in Japanese) 1989. 4/yr. Sutandado Makkintaiya - Standard McIntyre, 3-7, Irifune 2-chome, Chuo-ku, Tokyo 104, Japan.

617.7   GW   ISSN 0941-2921
   CODEN: GJOPEC
GERMAN JOURNAL OF OPHTHALMOLOGY. (Text in English) 1992. 6/yr. DM.178($129) (effective 1996). (German Ophthalmology Society) Springer-Verlag, Heidelberger Platz 3, 14197 Berlin, Germany. TEL 030-8207-0. FAX 030-8214091. E-mail: orders@springer.de. (Subscr. in N. America to: Springer-Verlag New York, Inc., 44 Hartz Way, Secaucus, NJ 07096-2491. TEL 201-348-4033. FAX 201-348-4505) Ed. M. Spitznas. **Indexed:** Ind.Med. (1992-). **Document type:** academic/scholarly publication.
—BLDSC (4162.120750); CASDDS; UMI. **CCC.**
Description: Original papers and reports on clinical and basic ophthalmological research.
Refereed Serial

617.7   US   ISSN 1072-7906
GLEAMS. 1982. 4/yr. free. Glaucoma Research Foundation, 490 Post, Ste. 830, San Francisco, CA 94102. TEL 415-986-3162; 800-826-6693. FAX 415-986-3763. E-mail: glaucoma@ucsfum.ucsf.edu. Ed. Lisa Wagreich. bk.rev.; charts; illus. circ. 24,000. (tabloid format; back issues avail.) **Document type:** newsletter.
Description: To educate the public and professionals about current glaucoma diagnosis, treatment, and research.
Refereed Serial

617.7   GW   ISSN 0721-832X
   CODEN: GACODL
GRAEFE'S ARCHIVE FOR CLINICAL AND EXPERIMENTAL OPHTHALMOLOGY. (Text in English) 1854. 12/yr. DM.1048($761) (effective 1996). Springer-Verlag, Heidelberger Platz 3, 14197 Berlin, Germany. TEL 030-8207-0. FAX 030-8214091. E-mail: orders@springer.de. (Subscr. in N. America to: Springer-Verlag New York, Inc., 44 Hartz Way, Secaucus, NJ 07096-2491. TEL 201-348-4033. FAX 201-348-4505) Ed.Bd. adv.; bibl.; charts; illus.; index, cum.index: vols.1-138. (also avail. in microform from UMI; back issues avail.; reprint service avail. from ISI) **Indexed:** Apic.Abstr., Biol.Abstr., Chem.Abstr., Curr.Adv.Cell & Devel.Biol., Curr.Cont., Excerp.Med., Ind.Med., INIS Atomind., Nutr.Abstr. **Document type:** academic/scholarly publication.
—BLDSC (4207.850000); CASDDS; Faxon; Genuine Article; SWETS; UMI; UnCover. **CCC.**
Formerly: Albrecht von Graefes Archiv fuer Klinische und Experimentelle Ophthalmologie (ISSN 0065-6100)
Description: Articles by leading ophthalmologists and vision research scientists provide rapid dissemination of clinical and clinically related experimental information.

617.7   GR
GREEK ANNALS OF OPHTHALMOLOGY. (Text in Greek; summaries in English) 1964. q. $30. H. Leontiades Publishing Co., 32 Paraschou St., Athens, Greece. Ed. Dr. S. Liaricos. adv.; bk.rev.; film rev.; abstr.; bibl.; charts; illus.; stat.; tr.lit.; index. circ. 600. **Indexed:** Excerp.Med., Ophthal.Lit.
Formerly: Ofthalmologika Chronika (ISSN 0030-0683)

617.75   US   ISSN 0894-5810
RE1
HIGH PERFORMANCE OPTOMETRY. 1987. m. (except May-June & Nov.-Dec. combined). $69 (Canada & Mexico $79; elsewhere $84). Anadem Publishing, Inc., 3620 N. High St., Columbus, OH 43214. TEL 614-262-2539. index. **Document type:** newsletter.
Description: Summaries of medical and optometry journal articles about diagnosing and treating ocular disease and vision disorders.

617.7   JA   ISSN 0286-7486
HIKAKU GANKA KENKYU/ANIMAL'S EYE RESEARCH. (Text in Japanese) 1982. s-a. membership. Hikaku Ganka Gakkai - Japanese Society of Comparative Ophthalmology, Kokuritsu Yobo Eisei Kenkyujo, Tsukuba Igaku Jikken'yo Reichorui Senta, 1, Yahatadai, Tsukuba-shi, Ibaraki-ken 305, Japan.

617.7   HK   ISSN 1021-8947
HONG KONG OPTICAL. (Text in English) 1992. a. $36 for 2 yrs. in Asia; elsewhere $54. Hong Kong Trade Development Council, 36-39th Fl., Office Tower, Convention Plaza, 1 Harbour Rd., Wanchai, Hong Kong. TEL 852-2584-4333. FAX 852-2824-0249. Ed. Saul Lockhart. circ. 15,000. **Document type:** trade publication.

617.7   II   ISSN 0301-4738
   CODEN: IJOMBM
INDIAN JOURNAL OF OPHTHALMOLOGY. (Text in English) 1953. 4/yr. All India Ophthalmological Society, c/o L.V. Prasad Eye Institute, Road No. 2, Banjara Hills 500 034, Hyderabad, India. illus.; cum.index: vols. 1-5 (1953-58); vols. 11-15 (1963-67). **Indexed:** Dent.Ind., Excerp.Med., ExtraMED, Ind.Med., Rev.Med.& Vet.Mycol. **Document type:** academic/scholarly publication.
●Also available on CD-ROM.
—BLDSC (4417.600000); Faxon; SWETS.
Supersedes (in Sept. 1971): All India Ophthalmological Society. Journal (ISSN 0044-7307)

MEDICAL SCIENCES — OPHTHALMOLOGY AND OPTOMETRY

617.7 — SP
INFORMACION OPTICA. 12/yr. German Perez Carrasco 81, 28027 Madrid, Spain. TEL 1-377-46-40. FAX 1-377-42-86. Ed. Julio Rosas. circ. 10,000.

617.7 610.73 — US — ISSN 1060-135X
INSIGHT (SAN FRANCISCO). (Supplement avail.: A S O R N News (ISSN 1061-4338)) 1977. q. $35 (foreign $45). American Society of Ophthalmic Registered Nurses, Inc., Box 193030, San Francisco, CA 94119. TEL 415-561-8513. Ed. Kay McCoy. adv.; bk.rev. circ. 2,000. **Document type:** newsletter.
—BLDSC (4518.174100).

617.7 — US
INSIGHT (WASHINGTON, 1990). 1961. bi-m. (plus annual newsletter). free. Eye Bank Association of America, 1001 Connecticut Ave., N.W., Ste. 601, Washington, DC 20036. TEL 202-775-4999. FAX 202-429-6036. stat. circ. 5,000. (back issues avail.) **Document type:** newsletter.
Formerly (until 1989): Foresight (Washington, 1961).
Description: Covers latest issues in eye banking and corneal transplantation.

617.7 — SP — ISSN 0020-3645
INSTITUTO BARRAQUER. ANALES. (Text in Spanish; summaries in English, French and Spanish) 1959. q. 10000 ptas. (effective 1994). Instituto Barraquer, Laforja 88, Barcelona, Spain. FAX 343-2099977. TELEX 9948-1 COFBA-E. Ed. Rafael I. Barraquer. adv. contact: Eva Luther. charts; illus. circ. 2,000. **Indexed:** Ophthal.Lit. **Document type:** academic/scholarly publication.

617.7 — US
INTERNATIONAL CONGRESS OF OPHTHALMOLOGY. ABSTRACTS. (Text in English, French, German and Spanish) quadrennial, 1994, 27th, Toronto. International Federation of Ophthalmological Societies, c/o Dr. Bruce E. Spivey, Northwestern Healthcare Network, 980 N. Miichigan Ave., Ste. 1500, Chicago, IL 60611. circ. 8,500 (controlled). (reprint service avail. from ISI) **Indexed:** Curr.Cont., Excerp.Med. **Document type:** proceedings.
Supersedes (in 1994): Acta Concilium Ophthalmologicum (ISSN 0065-115X)
Refereed Serial

617.752 — US — ISSN 0892-8967
RE977.C6 — CODEN: ICCLEF
INTERNATIONAL CONTACT LENS CLINIC. Short title: I C L C. 1973. bi-m. $187 to institutions (effective 1996). Butterworth - Heinemann, Part of the Reed Elsevier group, 313 Washington St., Newton, MA 02158. TEL 617-928-2500; 800-366-2665. FAX 617-928-2610. (Subscr. to: Elsevier Science Inc., Box 882, Madison Sq. Sta., New York, NY 10159-0882. TEL 212-989-5800. FAX 212-633-3990) Eds. Gerald E. Lowther, N. Rex Ghormley. (also avail. in microform from UMI; back issues avail.) **Document type:** academic/scholarly publication.
—BLDSC (4539.435000); Faxon; UMI. **CCC.**
Description: Provides the contact lens practitioner and researcher with clinical and research information relating to the contact lens field.
Refereed Serial

617.7 — NE — ISSN 0165-5701
RE1 — CODEN: INOPDR
INTERNATIONAL OPHTHALMOLOGY. (Text in English) 1978. bi-m. fl.807 to institutions; $518 to institutions in U.S. (effective 1996). Kluwer Academic Publishers, Postbus 17, 3300 AA Dordrecht, Netherlands. TEL 31-78-392392. FAX 31-78-392254. TELEX 29245 KAPG NL. E-mail: SERVICES@WKAP.NL. (Dist. by: Kluwer Academic Publishers Group, P.O. Box 322, 3300 AH Dordrecht, Netherlands. TEL 31-78-392392. FAX 31-78-546474; N. America dist. addr.: Box 358, Accord Sta., Hingham, MA 02018-0358. TEL 617-871-6600. FAX 617-871-6528) Ed.Bd. adv.; bk.rev.; illus. (also avail. in microform from UMI; reprint service avail. from SWZ) **Indexed:** ASCA, Biol.Abstr., Chem.Abstr., Curr.Cont., Excerp.Med., Ind.Med., Ind.Sci.Rev., Sci.Cit.Ind. **Document type:** academic/scholarly publication.
—BLDSC (4544.804000); CASDDS; Faxon; Genuine Article; SWETS; UMI; UnCover. **CCC.**
Description: Publishes articles on all the relevant subspecialties of ophthalmology, with a broad international scope.
Refereed Serial

617.7 — US — ISSN 0020-8167
CODEN: IOPCAV
INTERNATIONAL OPHTHALMOLOGY CLINICS. 1961. q. $135 to individuals (foreign $165); institutions $150 (foreign $198); residents $99 (foreign $120) (effective Oct. 1994). Little, Brown and Company, Medical Journals, 34 Beacon St., Boston, MA 02108. TEL 617-589-5500. FAX 617-589-0629. Eds. Drs. Gilbert L. Smolin, Mitchell H. Friedlaender. charts; illus.; stat.; index. circ. 2,500. (also avail. in microform from UMI; reprint service avail. from UMI; back issues avail.) **Indexed:** ASCA, Biol.Abstr., Curr.Cont., Dent.Ind., Excerp.Med., Ind.Med., INIS Atomind.
—BLDSC (4544.805000); EMDOCS; Faxon; Genuine Article; SWETS; UMI; UnCover. **CCC.**
Description: Covers a single, current topic in ophthalmology with a focus on diagnosis and therapy in each issue.

617.7 — UK
INTERNATIONAL OPTICAL YEAR BOOK. 1903. a. £28. Reed Business Publishing Group (Subsidiary of: Reed Elsevier group), Quadrant House, The Quadrant, Sutton, Surrey SM2 5AS, England. TEL 0181-652-4720. FAX 0181-652-3958. Ed. Philip Mullins. adv.; bibl.; stat. **Document type:** trade publication.

617.7 — US — ISSN 0146-0404
RE1 — CODEN: IOVSDA
INVESTIGATIVE OPHTHALMOLOGY & VISUAL SCIENCE. (Supplement avail.: Association for Research in Vision and Opthamlogy. Spring Meeting (ISSN 0273-0189)) 1962. m. $175 to individuals (foreign $240); institutions $240 (foreign $300) (effective 1996); newsstand price: $26. (Association for Research in Vision and Ophthalmology) Lippincott - Raven Publishers, 227 E. Washington Sq., Philadelphia, PA 19106. TEL 215-238-4200. Ed. Dr. Harry A. Quigley; Pub. Lisa R. Marshall. adv.; Susan/Eidson. illus.; index. circ. 9,541. (also avail. in microform from UMI) **Indexed:** Biol.Abstr., Chem.Abstr., Curr.Adv.Biochem., Curr.Cont., Dent.Ind., Excerp.Med., Helminthol.Abstr., Ind.Med., Ind.Sci.Rev., INIS Atomind., Rev.Med.& Vet.Mycol., Sci.Cit.Ind., Small Anim.Abstr., SSCI. **Document type:** academic/scholarly publication.
—BLDSC (4560.220000); CASDDS; Faxon; Genuine Article; SWETS; UMI; UnCover. **CCC.**
Formerly (until 1977): Investigative Ophthalmology (ISSN 0020-9988)
Refereed Serial

617.75 — US
IOWA JOURNAL OF OPTOMETRY.* q. Iowa Optometric Association, 1454 30th St. Ste 204, West Des Moines, IA 50266-1312. TEL 515-278-1697. FAX 515-278-0016. Ed. Virgil Deering. circ. 600.

617.7 — IE
IRISH COLLEGE OF OPHTHALMOLOGISTS. YEARBOOK. a. Irish College of Ophthalmologists, 10 Hagans Ct., Lad Ln., Dublin 2, Ireland. TEL 01-6785974. FAX 01-6785047. Ed. Robert Acheson. adv. contact: Harriet Duffin. circ. 450. **Document type:** academic/scholarly publication.
Formerly: Irish Faculty of Ophthalmology. Yearbook.

617.7 371.42 — US
J C A H P O OUTLOOK. 1980. 3/yr. $20 (free to qualified personnel). Joint Commission on Allied Health Personnel in Ophthalmology, 2025 Woodlane Dr., St. Paul, MN 55125-2995. TEL 800-284-3937. FAX 612-731-0410. Ed. Beverly Fanning. circ. 29,000.
Description: News related to the Commission including a list of continuing education courses in ophthalmology.

JAHRBUCH FUER BLINDENFREUNDE. see HANDICAPPED — Visually Impaired

617.7 — JA — ISSN 0370-5579
CODEN: RIGAA3
JAPANESE JOURNAL OF CLINICAL OPHTHALMOLOGY/RINSHO GANKA. (Text in Japanese; summaries in English) 1947. m. 29420 Yen($226) Igaku Shoin Ltd., 24-3, Hongo 5-chome, Bunkyo-ku, Tokyo 113-91, Japan. TEL 03-817-5706. Ed. Koichi Shimizu. circ. 5,000. **Indexed:** Biol.Abstr., Excerp.Med., INIS Atomind.
—BLDSC (4651.380000).

617.7 — JA — ISSN 0021-5155
CODEN: JJOPA7
JAPANESE JOURNAL OF OPHTHALMOLOGY. (Text in English) 1957. q. $100. University of Tokyo, School of Medicine, Department of Ophthalmology, 7-3-1 Hongo, Bunkyo-ku, Tokyo 113, Japan. FAX 813-3817-0798. (Dist. by: Business Center for Academic Societies Japan, 5-16-9 Honkomagome, Bunkyo-ku, Tokyo 113, Japan. TEL 03-5814-5811) Ed. Kanjiro Masuda. adv.; bk.rev.; charts; illus. circ. 1,000. (also avail. in microform from UMI; reprint service avail. from UMI) **Indexed:** Biol.Abstr., Chem.Abstr., Curr.Adv.Cell & Devel.Biol., Curr.Cont., Dent.Ind., Excerp.Med., Ind.Med., Ind.Sci.Rev., INIS Atomind., Sci.Cit.Ind. **Document type:** academic/scholarly publication.
●Also available online. Vendor(s): CompuServe, Inc., DataArkiv A.B., JICST.
—BLDSC (4656.770000); CASDDS; EMDOCS; Faxon; Genuine Article; SWETS; UMI; UnCover.
Description: Carries papers on new developments in ophthalmology reported by authors of all nationalities.
Refereed Serial

617.7 — US
JOINT COMMISSION ON ALLIED HEALTH PERSONNEL IN OPHTHALMOLOGY. PRESIDENT'S REPORT. 1983. a. Joint Commission on Allied Health Personnel in Ophthalmology, 2025 Woodlane Dr., St. Paul, MN 55125-2995. TEL 800-284-3837. FAX 612-731-0410. Ed. Beverly Fanning.
Formerly: Joint Commission on Allied Health Personnel in Ophthalmology. Annual Report.
Description: Activities of the Commission.

617.7 — FR — ISSN 0181-5512
JOURNAL FRANCAIS D'OPHTALMOLOGIE. 1881. 10/yr. 1210 F. (foreign 1491 F.) (effective 1996). Masson - Periodiques, Villa Laromiguiere, 75005 Paris, France. TEL 1-40-46-62-00. FAX 1-40-46-62-01. Ed. J.P. Adenis. adv.; bk.rev.; abstr.; bibl.; illus.; index. circ. 3,000. (also avail. in microform from UMI; reprint service avail. from ISI) **Indexed:** Biol.Abstr., Chem.Abstr., Dent.Ind., Excerp.Med., Ind.Med., Rev.Med.& Vet.Mycol. **Document type:** academic/scholarly publication.
—BLDSC (4986.410000); Faxon; Genuine Article; SWETS; UMI. **CCC.**
Formed by the merger of (with vol.210, 1977): Annales d'Oculistique (ISSN 0003-4371); Archives d'Ophtalmologie (ISSN 0003-973X)
Description: Publishes original works, clinical or scientific facts, therapeutic notes, analyses of works, and reports on congresses.

617.7 — FR — ISSN 0240-7914
JOURNAL FRANCAIS D'ORTHOPTIQUE. 1969. a. 100 Fr. Association Francaise des Orthoptistes, Les Roussieres, 01390 St. Andre de Corcy, France. Ed. A.P. Ravault. circ. 2,000.
—BLDSC (4986.420000).

617.7 — US — ISSN 1045-8395
RE960
JOURNAL OF BEHAVIORAL OPTOMETRY.* 1990. bi-m. $50. Optometric Extension Program, 1921 Carnegie Ave., Ste. 3L, Santa Ana, CA 92705-5510. TEL 714-250-8070. FAX 714-250-8157. Ed. Dr. Irwin B. Suchoff. adv.; index. circ. 3,000. (back issues avail.) **Document type:** academic/scholarly publication.
—BLDSC (4951.265000).
Description: Publishes original scholarly and clinical articles in the field of behavioral optometry, with news of issues, meetings and products of interest to the profession.
Refereed Serial

MEDICAL SCIENCES — OPHTHALMOLOGY AND OPTOMETRY

617.7   US   ISSN 0886-3350
CODEN: JCSUEV
JOURNAL OF CATARACT AND REFRACTIVE SURGERY. 1974. bi-m. $60 (foreign $80) (effective 1995). American Society of Cataract and Refractive Surgery, 4000 Legato Rd., Ste. 850, Fairfax, VA 22033-4003. TEL 703-591-2220. FAX 703-591-0614. (Subscr. to: Fulco, Box 3000, Denville, NJ 07843. TEL 800-875-2997. FAX 201-627-5872) Ed. Dr. Stephen A. Obstbaum. adv. contact: Christine Ford. circ. 7,000. **Indexed:** Chem.Abstr., Curr.Cont., Excerp.Med., Ind.Med., INIS Atomind. **Document type:** academic/scholarly publication.
—BLDSC (4954,900000); CASDDS; Faxon; Genuine Article; SWETS; UnCover.
Formerly (until 1986): American Intra-Ocular Implant Society Journal.
Refereed Serial

617.741   US   ISSN 1057-0829
CODEN: JOGLES
JOURNAL OF GLAUCOMA. 1992. bi-m. $130 to individuals (foreign $153); institutions $179 (foreign $200) (effective 1996); newsstand price: $35. Lippincott - Raven Press, 227 E. Washington Sq., Philadelphia, PA 19106. TEL 215-238-4800. Ed. Dr. E. Michael Van Buskirk. adv. contact: Phyllis Noyes. bk.rev.; illus. circ. 1,000. (back issues avail.; reprint service avail. from UMI) **Indexed:** Excerp.Med. (1993-). **Document type:** academic/scholarly publication.
—BLDSC (4996.230000); SWETS; UMI. **CCC.**
Description: Publishes original articles on new approaches to diagnosis, innovations in pharmacological therapy and surgical technique, and basic science advances that affect clinical practice in the treatment of glaucomas.
Refereed Serial

617.7   US   ISSN 1070-8022
CODEN: JNEOEK
JOURNAL OF NEURO-OPHTHALMOLOGY. 1981. q. $142 to individuals (foreign $180); institutions $208 (foreign $249) (effective 1996); newsstand price: $63. (North American Neuro-Ophthalmology Society) Lippincott - Raven Press, 276 E. Washington Sq., Philadelphia, PA 19106. TEL 215-238-4200. Ed. Dr. Ronald M. Burde. adv. contact: Phyllis Noyes. bk.rev.; charts; illus.; stat.; index. circ. 1,200. (back issues avail.; reprint service avail. from UMI) **Indexed:** Dent.Ind., Excerp.Med., Ind.Med. **Document type:** academic/scholarly publication.
—BLDSC (5021.660000); Faxon; Genuine Article; SWETS; UMI; UnCover. **CCC.**
Formerly (until 1994): Journal of Clinical Neuro-Ophthalmology (ISSN 0272-846X)
Description: Reports on recent developments in diagnosing and treating ophthalmic, neurologic, endocrine, inflammatory, and neoplastic conditions affecting the motor and visual systems.
Refereed Serial

617.7 615.7   US   ISSN 8756-3320
CODEN: JOPHER
JOURNAL OF OCULAR PHARMACOLOGY. 1985. q. $139 (foreign $179). Mary Ann Liebert, Inc. Publishers, 2 Madison Ave., Larchmont, NY 10538. TEL 914-834-3100. FAX 914-834-3688. E-mail: Liebert@pipeline.com. Ed. George C.Y. Chiou. adv.; bk.rev. **Document type:** academic/scholarly publication.
—CASDDS; Faxon; Genuine Article; UnCover.
Description: Contains research on all aspects of drug activity pertinent to preventing or controlling diseases of the eye.

617.7   US
▼**JOURNAL OF OCULAR TRAUMA.** Announced for publication in 1996. q. $135 to individuals; institutions $185 (effective 1996). Field & Wood, Medical Periodicals, Inc., Box 975, Blue Bell, PA 19422. TEL 610-828-4010. FAX 215-482-0226. Ed. Dr. Ferenc Kuhn. **Document type:** academic/scholarly publication.
Refereed Serial

JOURNAL OF OPHTHALMIC NURSING & TECHNOLOGY. see MEDICAL SCIENCES — Nurses And Nursing

617.75   US   ISSN 0149-886X
JOURNAL OF OPTOMETRIC VISION DEVELOPMENT. 1970. q. $55 to non-members; members $25. College of Optometrists in Vision Development, Box 285, Chula Vista, CA 91912. TEL 619-425-6191. Ed. Dr. Sidney Groffman. adv.; bk.rev.; abstr.; charts; illus.; bibl.; index. circ. 1,500. **Indexed:** Psychol.Abstr. (1990-). **Document type:** newspaper, trade publication.
—Faxon.

617.7   US   ISSN 0191-3913
CODEN: JPOSDR
JOURNAL OF PEDIATRIC OPHTHALMOLOGY AND STRABISMUS. 1964. bi-m. $85 to individuals; institutions $95. Slack, Inc., 6900 Grove Rd, Thorofare, NJ 08086. TEL 609-848-1000. FAX 609-853-5991. Ed. Dr. Marilyn Miller. adv.; bk.rev.; film rev.; abstr.; bibl.; charts; illus.; stat.; index. circ. 1,500. (also avail. in microform from UMI; reprint service avail. from UMI) **Indexed:** Biol.Abstr., Curr.Cont., Dent.Ind., Excerp.Med., Ind.Med., INIS Atomind.
—BLDSC (5030.210000); Genuine Article; SWETS; UMI; UnCover.
Formerly: Journal of Pediatric Ophthalmology (ISSN 0022-345X)
Refereed Serial

JOURNAL OF TOXICOLOGY. CUTANEOUS AND OCULAR TOXICOLOGY. see PHARMACY AND PHARMACOLOGY

617.7   US   ISSN 1041-0384
JOURNAL OF VISION REHABILITATION. 1985. q. $50. Media Periodicals, Div. of Trozzolo Resources Inc., 1102 Grand Blvd, Ste. 2300, Kansas City, MO 64106-2305. TEL 816-842-8111. FAX 816-842-8188. Eds. Randall T. Jose, Paul B. Freeman. adv.; bk.rev.; index. circ. 500. (back issues avail.; reprint service avail.)
—BLDSC (5072.492000); UnCover.
Description: Provides news and developments that relate to the visually impaired in the fields of health, rehabilittion, and education. Focuses on new devices, diagnostic tests and industry trends.

617.7   JA
KAIGAI GANKA BUNKEN JOHO/OPHTHALMOLOGY UPDATE. (Text in Japanese) q. Santen Seiyaku K.K. - Santen Pharmaceutical Co., Ltd., 9-19, Shimoshinjo 3-chome, Higashiyodogawa-ku, Osaka 533, Japan.

617.75   US   ISSN 1063-1623
KANSAS OPTOMETRIC JOURNAL. 1929. q. $15. Kansas Optometric Association, 1266 S.W. Topeka Blvd., Topeka, KS 66612. Ed. Dr. David R. Reynolds. adv.; bk.rev. circ. 550.

617.7   UK   ISSN 0268-9006
KEY NOTE REPORT: OPHTHALMIC GOODS & SERVICES. Variant title: Ophthalmic Goods & Services. irreg. £185. Key Note Publications Ltd., Field House, 72 Oldfield Rd., Hampton, Middlesex TW12 2HQ, England. TEL 0181-783-0755. FAX 0181-783-1720. **Document type:** trade publication.
●Also available online.
Also available on CD-ROM.

617.7   US   ISSN 0886-8026
KEY OPHTHALMOLOGY. 1985. q. $75 to individuals (foreign $89); institutions $112.50 (foreign $126.50); students $47.25 (foreign $61.25). Mosby - Year Book, Inc. (Subsidiary of: Times Mirror Company), 11830 Westline Industrial Dr., St. Louis, MO 63146. TEL 314-872-8370; 800-325-4177. FAX 314-432-1380. TELEX 44-2402. Ed. Dr. Peter R. Laibson.
—**CCC.**
Description: Surveys and abstracts of key medical literature in ophthalmology with expert commentary.

617.75   US   ISSN 0886-7666
KEYSTONER. 1947. m. membership. Pennsylvania Optometric Association, Box 3312, Harrisburg, PA 17105. TEL 717-233-6455. (Alt. Ed. addr.: 220 Grandview Blvd., Butler, PA 16001. TEL 412-287-3532) Ed. Robert Hall. bk.rev. circ. 175. **Document type:** newsletter.
Description: Contains society news.

617   JA   ISSN 0914-6806
KIKAN GANKA SHUJUTSU/JAPANESE SOCIETY OF OPHTHALMIC SURGEONS. JOURNAL. (Text in Japanese; summaries in English, Japanese) 1988. q. 2000 Yen per no. Medikaru Aoi Shuppan - Medical Aoi Publisher Inc., 27-1, Hongo 3-chome, Bunkyo-ku, Tokyo 113, Japan.

617.7   PL   ISSN 0023-2157
CODEN: KOAOAE
KLINIKA OCZNA. (Text in Polish; summaries in English) 1923. m. $176. (Polskie Towarzystwo Okulistyczne - Polish Ophthalmological Society) Vesalius - Uniwersyteckie Wydawnictwo Medyczne, Ul. Wislisko 1, 31-538 Krakow, Poland. TEL 48-12-213387. (Co-sponsor: Ministersto Zdrowia in Opieki Spolecznej) Ed. Maria Starzycka. adv.; bk.rev.; abstr.; illus.; index. **Indexed:** Biol.Abstr., Chem.Abstr., Dent.Ind., Dok.Arbeitsmed., Excerp.Med., Ind.Med., INIS Atomind. **Document type:** academic/scholarly publication.
—BLDSC (5099.300000); CASDDS; EMDOCS.

617.7   GW   ISSN 0023-2165
CODEN: KMAUAI
KLINISCHE MONATSBLAETTER FUER AUGENHEILKUNDE UND AUGENARZTLICHE FORTBILDUNG. (Supplements avail.) (Text in German; summaries in English and German) 1863. m. (2 vols./yr.) DM.468. Ferdinand Enke Verlag, Postfach 300366, 70443 Stuttgart, Germany. TEL 0711-135798-0. FAX 0711-135798-30. TELEX 07252275-GTV-D. Ed.Bd. adv.; bk.rev.; abstr.; charts; illus.; index. circ. 3,000. (reprint service avail. from IRC) **Indexed:** Biol.Abstr., Chem.Abstr., Curr.Cont., Dent.Ind., Excerp.Med., Helminthol.Abstr., Ind.Med., Ind.Sci.Rev., INIS Atomind., Rev.Med.& Vet.Mycol., Sci.Cit.Ind. **Document type:** academic/scholarly publication.
—BLDSC (5099.450000); EMDOCS; Faxon; Genuine Article; SWETS. **CCC.**

617.7   JA
KOKURITSU KOBE SHIRYOKU SHOGAI SENTA JIGYO NENPO/KOBE VISUAL DISORDER CENTER. BUSINESS REPORT. (Text in Japanese) a. Koseisho, Kokuritsu Kobe Shiryoku Shogai Senta - Ministry of Health and Welfare, Kobe Visual Disorder Center, 1070, Akebonocho, Nishi-ku, Kobe-shi, Hyogo-ken 673, Japan.

617.75   GW   ISSN 0721-5096
DIE KONTAKTLINSE. 1966. 10/yr. DM.160 (foreign DM.172). (Vereinigung Deutscher Contactlinsen-Spezialisten e.V.) Konradin Verlag Robert Kohlhammer GmbH, Ernst-Mey-Str. 8, 70771 Leinfelden-Echterdingen, Germany. TEL 0711-7594-249. FAX 0711-7594-390. Eds. Wolfgang Cagnolati, Hilmar Bussacker. adv.: B&W page DM.2400; trim 190 x 270. bk.rev. circ. 3,968. **Document type:** trade publication.
Description: Publication for specialists devoted to contact lens technology featuring clinical articles, the latest in research and new products.

617.7   NE   ISSN 0922-5307
CODEN: LLOPED
LASERS AND LIGHT IN OPHTHALMOLOGY. (Text in English) 1986. q. 295($165) (effective 1995). Kugler Publications B.V., P.O. Box 11188, 1001 GD Amsterdam, Netherlands. TEL 31-20-6278070. FAX 31-20-6380524. Ed. Dr. J. Marshall. (back issues avail.) **Document type:** academic/scholarly publication.
—BLDSC (5156.667500); SWETS.
Formerly: Lasers in Ophthalmology (ISSN 0920-3265)
Description: Forum covering uses of lasers and light in ophthalmology.

LIGHT (WHEATON). see HANDICAPPED — Visually Impaired

617.7   US
▼**MANAGEMENT & AVOIDANCE OF COMPLICATIONS OF LACRIMAL SURGERY.** Announced for publication in 1996. q. $145 to individuals; institutions $210 (effective 1996). Field & Wood, Medical Periodicals, Inc., Box 975, Blue Bell, PA 19422. TEL 610-828-4010. FAX 215-482-0226. Ed. Dr. Joseph Mauriello. **Document type:** academic/scholarly publication.
Refereed Serial

MEDICAL SCIENCES — OPHTHALMOLOGY AND OPTOMETRY

617.7 CC ISSN 1000-0348
MEIGUO YIXUEHUI YANKE ZAZHI. (Text in Chinese) q. Beijing University of Medical Sciences, Affiliated No. 3 Hospital, Beijing 100083, People's Republic of China. TEL 2017691. (Co-sponsor: Zhonghua Yixuehui - China Medical Science Association) Ed. Li Fengming.

617.7 US ISSN 0882-889X
RE46 CODEN: MPSODY
METABOLIC, PEDIATRIC AND SYSTEMIC OPHTHALMOLOGY; international journal of basic research and clinical applications. 1977. 4/yr. $165 (foreign $190) (effective 1994). (International Society on Metabolic Eye Disease) Opto Education Corp, 105 E. 90th St., New York, NY 10128. TEL 212-427-1246. (Co-sponsor: International Society of Pediatric Ophthalmology) Ed. H. M. Haddad. adv.; bk.rev.; charts; illus.; stat.; index. circ. 1,000. (also avail. in microform from UMI) Indexed: Biol.Abstr., Chem.Abstr., Curr.Adv.Ecol.Sci., Curr.Cont., Dent.Ind., Excerp.Med., Ind.Med., Nutr.Abstr. Document type: academic/scholarly publication.
—BLDSC (5683.287000); CASDDS; SWETS; UMI. CCC.
Former titles (until 1985): Metabolic Ophthalmology, Pediatric and Systemic (ISSN 0883-9522); (until 1984): Metabolic, Pediatric, and Systemic Ophthalmology (ISSN 0277-9382); (until 1982): Metabolic and Pediatric Ophthalmology (ISSN 0191-2771); Metabolic Ophthalmology (ISSN 0361-3674)

617.75 US ISSN 1071-1627
MICHIGAN OPTOMETRIST. 1921. m. $13. Michigan Optometric Association, 530 W. Ionia St., Ste. A, Lansing, MI 48933. FAX 517-482-1611. Ed. William D. Dansby. adv.: B&W page $325; 7 x 9. bk.rev.; charts; stat.; illus. circ. 850.

617.7 IT ISSN 0026-4903
MINERVA OFTALMOLOGICA. (Text in Italian; summaries in English and Italian) 1958. q. $90 to individuals; institutions $140 (effective 1995). Edizioni Minerva Medica, Corso Bramante 83-85, Turin, Italy. TEL 39-11-678282. FAX 39-11-3121736. Ed.Bd; Pub. Alberto Oliaro. adv.: B&W page $1100, color page $1900; trim 190 x 270; adv. contact: F. Filippo. bk.rev.; bibl.; charts; illus.; index; circ. 3,000 (paid). (also avail. in microform from UMI) Indexed: Excerp.Med., Ind.Med. Document type: academic/scholarly publication.
—Faxon; UMI.

617.7 NE ISSN 0167-8612
CODEN: MPTHDI
MONOGRAPHS IN OPHTHALMOLOGY. (Text in English) 1981. irreg., vol.15, 1994. price varies. Kluwer Academic Publishers, Postbus 17, 3300 AA Dordrecht, Netherlands. TEL 31-78-392392. FAX 31-78-392254. TELEX 29245 KAPG NL. (Dist. by: Kluwer Academic Publishers Group, P.O. Box 322, 3300 AH Dordrecht, Netherlands. TEL 31-78-392392. FAX 31-78-546474; N. America dist. addr.: Box 358, Accord Sta., Hingham, MA 02018-0358. TEL 617-871-6600. FAX 617-871-6528) Indexed: Biol.Abstr. Document type: monographic series.
—BLDSC (5915.800000).
Refereed Serial

NATIONAL SOCIETY TO PREVENT BLINDNESS. MEMBER NEWS. see *PUBLIC HEALTH AND SAFETY*

617.7 NE ISSN 0165-8107
NEURO-OPHTHALMOLOGY. (Text in English) 1979. bi-m. fl.524($327) (fl.540 outside EU) (effective 1996). Aeolus Press, Postbus 740, 4116 ZJ Buren, Netherlands. TEL 31-344-572055. FAX 31-344-572562. Ed.Bd. adv.: B&W page fl.600($345); 175 x 240. bk.rev.; index. circ. 800. (also avail. in microform from UMI; back issues avail.; reprint service avail. from UMI) Indexed: Curr.Cont., Excerp.Med., Ind.Sci.Rev. Document type: academic/scholarly publication.
—BLDSC (6081.509000); Faxon; Genuine Article; SWETS; UMI; UnCover. CCC.
Description: Contains review articles, research papers and short communications on diagnostic methods in neuro-ophthalmology, the visual and oculo-motor systems, the pupil, neuro-ophthalmic aspects of the orbit, migraine, and ocular manifestations of neurological diseases.
Refereed Serial

617.75 US ISSN 0028-4807
NEW ENGLAND JOURNAL OF OPTOMETRY. 1949. m. (except Sep.-Jun.). $35 to non-members. New England Council of Optometrists, 101 Tremont St., Boston, MA 02108. TEL 617-542-1233. FAX 617-542-4574. Ed. Dr. Roger Wilson. adv. contact: Jon C. Lundell. bk.rev.; index. circ. 1,360. (also avail. in microfilm from UMI; reprint service avail. from UMI) Indexed: PMR. Document type: academic/scholarly publication.
Description: Publishes articles on multidisciplinary and primary care, clinical comanagement, clinical research, technical developments, case reports, community health and practice management.
Refereed Serial

617.7 US ISSN 0077-8605
CODEN: TNOOA6
NEW ORLEANS ACADEMY OF OPHTHALMOLOGY. TRANSACTIONS. Variant Title--Symposia. a. price varies. New Orleans Academy of Ophthalmology, 2626 Napoleon Ave., New Orleans, LA 70115. TEL 504-899-9955. (Dist. by: Kugler Publications, Box 1498, New York, NY 10009. TEL 212-477-1970. FAX 212-477-0181) Ed.Bd. Indexed: Dent.Ind., Ind.Med. Document type: academic/scholarly publication.

617.7 IT ISSN 0394-3755
CODEN: NTOPEN
NEW TRENDS IN OPHTHALMOLOGY. (Text in English) 1986. q. L.70000($70) (effective 1993). C I C Edizioni Internazionali s.r.l., Via L. Spallanzani, 11, 00161 Rome, Italy. TEL 06-8412673. FAX 06-8845590. Eds. B. Boles Carenini, F. Grignolo. adv.; bk.rev. (back issues avail.) Indexed: Excerp.Med.
—BLDSC (6089.138000).
Description: Publishes original and experimental ophthalmological studies.

617.7 JA ISSN 0374-9851
CODEN: NSIZBD
NIHON CONTACT LENS GAKKAISHI. (Text in Japanese; summaries in English) 1959. q. 8000 Yen (effective 1994). Japan Contact Lens Society, Nihon Ganka Kiyo Kai, 302 Yamamoto Bldg., 3-6 Mihogaoka, Ibaraki 567, Japan. TEL 81-726-23-7878. FAX 81-726-23-6060. Ed. Yasuo Tano. adv.; bk.rev. circ. 1,650. (also avail. in microform) Document type: academic/scholarly publication.
—BLDSC (4804.740000); CASDDS.
Refereed Serial

NIHON GAN YAKURI GAKKAI PUROGURAMU KOEN YOSHISHU/JAPANESE SOCIETY FOR OCULAR PHARMACOLOGY. PROGRAM AND ABSTRACTS OF THE MEETING. see *MEDICAL SCIENCES — Abstracting, Bibliographies, Statistics*

617.7 JA ISSN 0029-0203
CODEN: NGZAA6
NIHON GANKA GAKKAI ZASSHI/JAPANESE OPHTHALMOLOGICAL SOCIETY. JOURNAL. (Text in Japanese; abstracts in English, Japanese) 1897. m. 15000 Yen. Nihon Ganka Gakkai - Japanese Ophthalmological Society, 2-4-11-402 Sarugaku-cho, Chiyoda-ku, Tokyo 101, Japan. TEL 03-3295-2360. FAX 03-3293-9384. E-mail: ytano@ophthal.med.osaka-u.ac.jp. Ed. Yasuo Tano. adv. circ. 11,000. Indexed: Biol.Abstr., Dent.Ind., Excerp.Med., Ind.Med. Document type: academic/scholarly publication.
—BLDSC (4809.365000); CASDDS; EMDOCS.
Refereed Serial

617.7 JA
NIHON GANKOGAKU GAKKAI YOKOSHU/OPHTHALMOLOGICAL OPTICS SOCIETY OF JAPAN. PRELIMINARY PROGRAM. (Text in Japanese) 1964. a. 500 Yen. Nihon Gankogaku Gakkai, Nikon, 2-3 Marunouchi 3-chome, Chiyoda-ku, Tokyo 100, Japan.

617.3 JA ISSN 0915-4302
NIHON HAKUNAISHO GAKKAISHI/JAPANESE SOCIETY FOR CATARACT RESEARCH. JOURNAL. (Text in Japanese; summaries in English, Japanese) 1989. a. Nihon Hakunaisho Gakkai, Fujita Gakuen Hoken Eisei Daigaku Gankagaku Kyoushitsu, 1-98, Dengakugakubo, Kutsukakecho, Tokoake-shi, Aichi-ken 470-11, Japan.

617.3 JA ISSN 0289-3843
NIHON JAKUSHI SHASHI GAKKAI ZASSHI/JAPANESE ASSOCIATION OF STRABISMUS AND AMBLYOPIA. JOURNAL. (Text in Japanese; summaries in English, Japanese) 1973. a. Nihon Jakushi Shashi Gakkai, c/o Teikyo Daigaku Igakubu Ganka Kyoshitsu, 11-1, Kaga 2-chome, Itabashi-ku, Tokyo 173, Japan. (Co-sponsor: Ganka Rinsho Ihokai - Japanese Society of Clinical Ophthalmology)

617.3 JA ISSN 0386-4200
NIHON JAKUSHI SHASHI GAKKAIHO/JAPANESE ASSOCIATION OF STRABISMUS AND AMBLYOPIA. BULLETIN. (Text in Japanese) 1964. irreg. 350 Yen per no. Nihon Jakushi Shashi Gakkai, c/o Teikyo Daigaku Igakubu Ganka Kyoshitsu, 11-1, Kaga 2-chome, Itabashi-ku, Tokyo 173, Japan.

617.3 JA ISSN 0285-1326
NIHON NO GANKA/JAPAN OPHTHALMOLOGISTS ASSOCIATION. JOURNAL. (Text in Japanese) 1967. m. 1500 Yen per no. Nihon Ganka Ikai, 4-11, Sarugakucho 2-chome, Chiyoda-ku, Tokyo 101, Japan.

617.7 JA ISSN 0387-5172
NIHON SHINO KUNRENSHI KYOKAISHI/JAPANESE ORTHOPTIC JOURNAL. (Text in Japanese; summaries in English, Japanese) 1972. a. Nihon Shino Kenrenshi Kyokai - Japanese Association of Certified Orthoptists, 39-11, Narita Higashi 5-chome, Suginmi-ku, Tokyo 166, Japan.

617.7 US
NORTH CENTRAL OPTOMETRIC VIEWPOINT. 1991. q. $50. (North Central State Optometric Council) R.C. Publications, Inc. (Brookfield), Box 604, Brookfield, WI 53008-0604. TEL 414-789-2749. FAX 414-789-9458. Ed. R.A. Koetting. adv.: B&W page $1200, color page $1745; trim 8 1/2 x 11; adv. contact: R.W. Perleberg. circ. 26,200 (controlled). Document type: trade publication.
Description: Offers clinical articles, practice management and industry trends.

617.7 FR ISSN 0983-8201
O P A PRATIQUE. (ORL, Pneumo, Allergo) m. (10/yr.). 200 F. L.E.N. Medical, 48 bis, av. Kleber, 75016 Paris, France. TEL 47-55-06-06. FAX 47-55-69-41. TELEX 640 748. Ed. Olivier de Fenoyl. Document type: newspaper.

617.75 US
THE OBSERVER (JOHNSTON). m. Iowa Optometric Association, 5721 Merle Hay Rd., Rm.14A, Box 64, Johnston, IA 50131. TEL 515-278-1697. FAX 515-278-0016. Ed. Virgil Deering.

617.7 NE ISSN 0927-3948
CODEN: OIINEN
OCULAR IMMUNOLOGY AND INFLAMMATION. (Text in English) 1993. q. fl.376($225) (fl.392 outside EU) (effective 1996). (International Ocular Inflammation Society) Aeolus Press, Postbus 740, 4116 ZJ Buren, Netherlands. TEL 31-344-572055. FAX 31-344-572562. Ed. A. Kijlstra. adv.: B&W page fl.600($345); 175 x 240. circ. 400. (also avail. in microform from UMI; back issues avail.; reprint service avail. from UMI) Indexed: Excerp.Med. 1994-). Document type: academic/scholarly publication.
—BLDSC (6235.154200).
Description: Publishes original research papers, reviews and short communications on all aspects of basic and clinical research pertaining to the ocular inflammatory response and its control by the immune system.
Refereed Serial

617.7 US
OCULAR INFECTIOUS DISEASES. 1993. 3/yr. $135 to individuals; institutions $185 (effective 1996). Field & Wood, Medical Periodicals, Inc., Box 975, Blue Bell, PA 19422. TEL 610-828-4010. FAX 215-482-0226. Eds. Dr. Jeffery B. Robin, Dr. David M. Meisler. Document type: academic/scholarly publication.
Refereed Serial

OCULAR SURGERY NEWS. see *MEDICAL SCIENCES — Surgery*

OCULAR SURGERY NEWS INTERNATIONAL EDITION. see *MEDICAL SCIENCES — Surgery*

MEDICAL SCIENCES — OPHTHALMOLOGY AND OPTOMETRY

617.75 NE ISSN 0029-8328
OCULUS. 1939. m. (11/yr.) fl.95 (foreign fl.170) (effective 1995). (Nederlandse Unie van Optiekbedrijven (NUVO)) Stichting P.R. & Publiciteit Optiekbranche (SPPO), Postbus 677, 2003 RR Haarlem, Netherlands. TEL 31-23-312519. FAX 31-23-320192. Ed. Mariska Blokdijk. adv.: B&W page fl.1025, color page 2055; trim 210 x 297; adv. contact: Eline Walsma. bk.rev.; illus. circ. 2,500. **Indexed:** Avery Ind.Archit.Per. **Document type:** trade publication.

617.7 FR
 CODEN: BSOFAK
OEIL ET LUMIERE. 1949. a. $200. (Societes d'Ophtalmologie de France) Lamy S.A. (Marseille), 150 rue Paradis, 13006 Marseille, France. (Subscr. to: Diffusion Litteraire et Scientifique, 11 rue Moliere, 13001 Marseille, France. TEL 91-33-57-91) Ed. Dr. Korobelnik. adv.; bk.rev.; circ. 2,200 (paid). **Document type:** bulletin.

617.7 US ISSN 0000-1465
RE22
OFFICIAL AMERICAN BOARD OF MEDICAL SPECIALTIES (A B M S) DIRECTORY OF BOARD CERTIFIED OPHTHALMOLOGISTS. 1983. biennial. $99.95. Marquis Who's Who, A Reed Reference Publishing company, 121 Chanlon Rd., New Providence, NJ 07974. TEL 908-464-6800. FAX 908-665-2898. (Subscr. to: Order Dept., Box 31, New Providence, NJ 07974-9903. TEL 800-521-8110) Ed. Roy Crego. **Document type:** directory.
 Formerly (until 1992): A B M S Directory of Certified Ophthalmologists (ISSN 8756-9175)
 Description: Biographical sketches of U.S. certified medical specialists sorted alphabetically with a geographical index.

617.7 DK ISSN 0108-5344
OFTALMOLOG. (Text in Danish, English, Norwegian, Swedish) 1981. q. DKK 195 (free to members) (effective 1996). (Nordiske Oftalmologiske Foreninger) Scriptor Publisher ApS, Soevangsvej 1-5, DK-2650 Hvidovre, Denmark. TEL 45-36-77-41-13. FAX 45-36-77-41-15. (Co-sponsor: Acta Opthalmologica) (back issues avail.)

617.7 IT
▼**OFTALMOLOGIA.** 1994. bi-m. L.100000 (foreign L.200000). Stammer S.p.A., Via della Liberazione 1, 20068 Peschiera Borromeo (MI), Italy. TEL 39-2-55302606. FAX 39-2-55302700. Ed. Maurizio Peruzzi. adv.: B&W page L.1700000, color page L.2720000. circ. 4,750. **Document type:** trade publication.

617.7 KR ISSN 0030-0675
 CODEN: OFZHAV
OFTAL'MOLOGICHESKII ZHURNAL. (Text in Russian; summaries in English) 1946. 8/yr. 17 Rub. (Ministerstvo Zdravookhraneniya) Izdatel'stvo Zdorovya, Ul. Chkalova 65, 252054 Kiev, Ukraine. TEL 044-216-89-08. bk.rev.; bibl.; index. (tabloid format) **Indexed:** Biol.Abstr., Chem.Abstr., Excerp.Med., Ind.Med., Int.Aerosp.Abstr., Rev.Med.& Vet.Mycol.
—BLDSC (0128.620000); CASDDS; EMDOCS.

617.7 RM ISSN 1220-0875
OFTALMOLOGIA. (Text in Rumanian; summaries in English, French, German, Russian) 1957. q. $20. Uniunea Societatilor de Stiinte Medicale din Republica Socialista Rumania, Str. Progresului No. 8-10, Sectorul 1, Bucharest 70754, Rumania. (Subscr. to: ILEXIM, Str. 13 Decembrie Nr. 3, P.O. Box 136-137, Bucharest, Rumania) Ed.Bd. adv.; bk.rev.; index. **Indexed:** Biol.Abstr., Chem.Abstr., Dent.Ind., Excerp.Med. (until 1992), Ind.Med.
—BLDSC (6244.700000).
 Former titles (until 1989): Revista de Chirugie, Oncologie, Radiologie, O.R.L., Oftalmologie, Stomatologie, Urologie (ISSN 1220-0859); (until 1974): Oto-Rino-Laringologie si Oftalmologie (ISSN 0303-5123); Which was formed by the 1974 merger of: Oto-Rino-Laringologie (ISSN 0030-6649); Oftalmologia (ISSN 0030-0667)

617.7 FR ISSN 0989-3105
OPHTALMOLOGIE. 1987. bi-m. 480 F. (foreign 720 F.) (effective 1996). (Societe Francaise d'Ophtalmologie) Masson - Periodiques, Villa Laromiguiere, 75005 Paris, France. TEL 1-40-46-62-00. FAX 1-40-46-62-01. Ed. H. Offret. adv.; bk.rev.; illus.; index. circ. 8,200. **Document type:** academic/scholarly publication.
—BLDSC (6270.850000); SWETS. **CCC**.
 Description: Includes case reports, original articles and reviews.

617.7 FR ISSN 0767-8959
OPHTALMOLOGISTE PRATICIEN. 1972. 5/yr. 15 F. (Association Francaise des Ophtalmologistes Praticiens) Societe Confraternelle d'Editions Medicale, 71 bd. National, 92250 la Garenne Colombes, France. TEL 42-42-00-64. Ed. R. Bideau. adv.; bk.rev. circ. 4,200.

617.75 UK ISSN 0275-5408
RE939.2 CODEN: OPOPD5
OPHTHALMIC AND PHYSIOLOGICAL OPTICS. 1980. bi-m. £340($541) (effective 1996). (British College of Optometrists) Butterworth - Heinemann, Part of the Reed Elsevier group, Linacre House, Jordan Hill, Oxford OX2 8DP, England. TEL 0865-310366. FAX 0865-310898. TELEX 83111 BHPOXF G. (Subscr. to: Elsevier Science Ltd., P.O. Box 800, Kidlington, Oxford OX5 1DX, England. TEL 44-865-843000. FAX 44-865-843010; Subscr. in U.S. and Canada to: Elsevier Science, 660 White Plains Rd., Tarrytown, NY 10591-5153. TEL 914-524-9200. FAX 914-333-2444) Ed. B. Gilmartin. adv.; bk.rev.; charts; illus.; index. (also avail. in microform from UMI; back issues avail.) **Indexed:** Biol.Abstr., Curr.Adv.Ecol.Sci., Curr.Cont., Dent.Ind., Excerp.Med., Ind.Med., INSPEC, Psychol.Abstr. (1981-). **Document type:** academic/scholarly publication.
—BLDSC (6270.870000); Faxon; Genuine Article; SWETS; UMI. **CCC**.
 Supersedes: British Journal of Physiological Optics (ISSN 0007-1218)
 Description: Publishes international and interdisciplinary original research in aspects of pure and applied vision science.
 Refereed Serial

617.7 NE ISSN 0928-6586
▼**OPHTHALMIC EPIDEMIOLOGY.** 1994. 4/yr. fl.361($229) (fl.377 outside EU) (effective 1996). Aeolus Press, Postbus 740, 4116 ZJ Buren, Netherlands. TEL 31-344-572055. FAX 31-344-572562. Ed. J.P. Ganley. adv.: B&W page fl.600($345); 175 x 240. (back issues avail.) **Document type:** academic/scholarly publication.
—BLDSC (6270.880000).
 Description: Publishes research papers in ophthalmic research in the fields of epidemiology, public health, and prevention of blindness.
 Refereed Serial

617.7 618.92 NE ISSN 1381-6810
OPHTHALMIC GENETICS. (Text in English) 1981. q. fl.355($225) (fl.372 outside EU) (effective 1996). (International Society for Genetic Eye Disease, US) Aeolus Press, Postbus 740, 4116 ZJ Buren, Netherlands. TEL 31-344-572055. FAX 31-344-572562. (Co-sponsors: Ophthalmic Genetics Study Club, International Society of Paediatric Ophthalmology) Eds. E. Traboulsi, B. Lorenz. adv.: B&W page fl.600($345); 175 x 240. bk.rev. circ. 500. (also avail. in microform from UMI; back issues avail.) **Indexed:** Curr.Cont., Excerp.Med., Ind.Med. **Document type:** academic/scholarly publication.
—Genuine Article; SWETS; UMI; UnCover. **CCC**.
 Formerly (until vol.15, 1994): Ophthalmic Paediatrics and Genetics (ISSN 1677-6784)
 Description: Contains review articles, research papers, and short communications on genetic ophthalmological problems of the newborn and of children, as well as adults.
 Refereed Serial

617.7 UK
OPHTHALMIC LENS DATA. irreg., latest 1993. £46. S.C. Hardy & Co., Winton House, Beacon Rd., Crowborough, E. Sussex TH16 1AS, England. TEL 01892-782724. FAX 01892-783406. Ed. A.H. Tunnacliffe.
 Description: Provides a reference guide to spectacle lenses available in the U.K.

OPHTHALMIC LITERATURE. see *MEDICAL SCIENCES — Abstracting, Bibliographies, Statistics*

617.7 617 US ISSN 0740-9303
 CODEN: OPRSE
OPHTHALMIC PLASTIC AND RECONSTRUCTIVE SURGERY. 1985. q. $140 to individuals (foreign $174); institutions $220 (foreign $261) (effective 1996); newsstand price: $67. (American Society of Ophthalmic Plastic and Reconstructive Surgery) Lippincott - Raven Publishers, 227 E. Washington Sq., Philadelphia, PA 19106. TEL 215-238-4200. Eds. Bernice Brown, Richard K. Dortzbach. adv. contact: Phyllis Noyes. bk.rev.; illus.; index. circ. 1,200. (back issues avail.) **Indexed:** Excerp.Med., Ind.Med., Med.& Surg.Dermat. **Document type:** academic/scholarly publication.
—BLDSC (6271.430000); Faxon; Genuine Article; SWETS; UMI; UnCover. **CCC**.
 Description: Presents original articles and reviews on diagnostic techniques, surgical instruments and procedures, medical therapies, research findings, and clinical applications.
 Refereed Serial

617.7 CN ISSN 0832-9869
OPHTHALMIC PRACTICE. 1983. bi-m. Can.$60 (US $72, elsewhere $94). Medicopea International Inc., 3333 Cote Vertu Blvd., Ste. 300, St. Laurent, PQ H4R 2N1, Canada. TEL 514-333-4561. FAX 514-336-1129. Ed. Leon Solomen. adv. contact: Sara Wilkins. bk.rev.; index. circ. 1,200 (controlled). **Document type:** trade publication.
 Formerly: Current Canadian Ophthalmic Practice (ISSN 0823-4744)
 Description: Studies ophthalmic surgery, ocular infection, intra-ocular lens implants, pediatric problems, technological advances.

617.7 SZ ISSN 0030-3747
RE58 CODEN: OPRSAQ
OPHTHALMIC RESEARCH; journal for research in experimental and clinical ophthalmology. (Text in English) 1970. bi-m. 357.60 SFr.($274.80) to individuals; institutions 596 SFr.($458) (effective 1996). S. Karger AG, Allschwilerstr. 10, P.O. Box, CH-4009 Basel, Switzerland. TEL 061-3061111. FAX 061-3061234. E-mail: Karger@Karger.ch. Ed. G.F. Vrenson. adv.; charts; illus.; stat.; index. circ. 850. (also avail. in microform) **Indexed:** Biol.Abstr., Chem.Abstr., Chem.Abstr., Curr.Adv.Ecol.Sci., Curr.Cont., Dent.Ind., Excerp.Med., Ind.Med. **Document type:** academic/scholarly publication.
—BLDSC (6271.450000); CASDDS; EMDOCS; Faxon; Genuine Article; SWETS; UnCover. **CCC**.
 Refereed Serial

OPHTHALMIC SURGERY. see *MEDICAL SCIENCES — Surgery*

617.7 GW ISSN 0936-2517
OPHTHALMO CHIRURGIE. 1989. q. DM.138. Dr. R. Kaden Verlag, Poststr. 24-26, 69115 Heidelberg, Germany. TEL 06221-10313. FAX 06221-29910. adv.: B&W page DM.2430; trim 230 x 178; adv. contact: A. Siegmann. bk.rev. circ. 1,200. (back issues avail.) **Document type:** academic/scholarly publication.
—BLDSC (6271.560000).

617.7 BU ISSN 0374-2105
 CODEN: OPTMAI
OPHTHALMOLOGIA. (Text in Bulgarian; summaries in English, Russian) q. 8 lv. (Ministerstvo na Narodnoto Zdrave) Izdatelstvo Meditsina i Fizkultura, 11 Pl. Slaveikov, Sofia, Bulgaria. (Distr. by: Hemus, 6 Rouski Blvd., 1000 Sofia, Bulgaria) (Co-sponsor: Nauchno Druzhestvo po Ophthalmologia) Ed. S. Dabov. circ. 766.
—CASDDS.

617.7 SZ ISSN 0030-3755
RE1 CODEN: OPHTAD
OPHTHALMOLOGICA; international journal of ophthalmology. (Supplement avail.: Bibliotheca Ophthalmologica) (Text in English) 1899. bi-m. 429 SFr.($330) to individuals; institutions 715 SFr.($550) (effective 1996). S. Karger AG, Allschwilerstr. 10, P.O. Box, CH-4009 Basel, Switzerland. TEL 061-3061111. FAX 061-3061234. E-mail: Karger@Karger.ch. Ed. C. Ohrloff. adv.; bk.rev.; bibl.; illus.; index, cum.index vols.96-138. circ. 1,250. (also avail. in microform) **Indexed:** Biol.Abstr., Chem.Abstr., Curr.Cont., Excerp.Med., Helminthol.Abstr., Ind.Med., Nutr.Abstr., Protozool.Abstr., Psychol.Abstr., Rev.Plant Path. **Document type:** academic/scholarly publication.
—BLDSC (6271.600000); CASDDS; EMDOCS; Faxon; Genuine Article; SWETS; UnCover. **CCC**.
 Refereed Serial

MEDICAL SCIENCES — OPHTHALMOLOGY AND OPTOMETRY

617.7 — UA — ISSN 0078-5342
OPHTHALMOLOGICAL SOCIETY OF EGYPT. BULLETIN. (Text in Arabic, English and French) 1902. a. $10. Ophthalmological Society of Egypt, Dar el Hekma, 42 Kasr el-Aini St., Cairo, Egypt. **Indexed:** Excerp.Med., Ind.Med., Ophthal.Lit.

617.7 — GW — ISSN 0941-293X
RE1 — CODEN: OHTHEJ
DER OPHTHALMOLOGIE. 1982. 6/yr. DM.252($183) (effective 1996). Springer-Verlag, Heidelberger Platz 3, 14197 Berlin, Germany. TEL 030-8207-0. FAX 030-8214091. E-mail: orders@springer.de. (Subscr. in N. America to: Springer-Verlag New York, Inc., 44 Hartz Way, Secaucus, NJ 07096-2491. TEL 201-348-4033. FAX 201-348-4505) Ed. H.E. Voelcker. (also avail. in microform from UMI; reprint service avail. from ISI) **Indexed:** Chem.Abstr., Dent.Ind., Dok.Arbeitsmed., Excerp.Med., Ind.Med. **Document type:** academic/scholarly publication.
—BLDSC (6271.585000); CASDDS; Faxon; SWETS; UMI. **CCC.**
Formerly: Fortschritte der Ophthalmologie (ISSN 0723-8045)

617.7 — JA — ISSN 0016-4488
OPHTHALMOLOGY/GANKA. (Text in Japanese) 1959. m. 2000 Yen per no. Kanehara Shuppan Ltd., 2-31-14 Yushima, Bunkyo-ku, Tokyo 113-91, Japan. bk.rev.; cum.index. circ. 5,100. **Indexed:** INIS Atomind., Jap.Per.Ind., Protozool.Abstr.

617.7 616.21 — US — ISSN 0161-6420
OPHTHALMOLOGY. 1907. m. $135 to individuals (foreign $175); institutions $205 (foreign $245) (effective 1966); newsstand price: $22. (American Academy of Ophthalmology) Lippincott - Raven Publishers, 227 E. Washington Sq., Philadelphia, PA 19106. TEL 215-238-4200. Ed. Dr. Donald S. Minkler; Pub. Lisa R. Marshall. illus.; index. circ. 24,110. (also avail. in microform from UMI) **Indexed:** Biol.Abstr., C.I.S. Abstr., Chem.Abstr., Curr.Adv.Cancer Res., Curr.Adv.Ecol.Sci., Curr.Cont., Dent.Ind., Dok.Arbeitsmed., Excerp.Med., Helminthol.Abstr., Hosp.Lit.Ind., Ind.Med., Int.Nurs.Ind., Med.& Surg.Dermat., Protozool.Abstr., Rev.Med.& Vet.Mycol., Sci.Cit.Ind., SSCI. **Document type:** academic/scholarly publication.
—BLDSC (6271.805000); Faxon; Genuine Article; SWETS; UMI; UnCover. **CCC.**
Formerly (until vol.85, 1978): American Academy of Ophthalmology. Transactions-Ophthalmology; Which superseded in part (as of 1975): American Academy of Ophthalmology. Transactions (ISSN 0002-7154)
Refereed Serial

617.7 — US — ISSN 0896-1549
RE1 — CODEN: OCNAF2
OPHTHALMOLOGY CLINICS OF NORTH AMERICA. 1988. q. $145 (foreign $175) (effective 1996). W.B. Saunders Co. (Subsidiary of: Harcourt Brace & Company), The Curtis Center, 3rd Fl., Independence Sq. W., Philadelphia, PA 19106-3399. TEL 215-238-7800. FAX 215-238-6445. (Subscr. to: Periodicals Fulfillment, W.B. Saunders Co., 6277 Sea Harbor Dr., 4th Fl., Orlando, FL 32887-4800. TEL 800-654-2452. FAX 800-874-6418) Ed. Dr. Robert L. Stamper. index. (also avail. in microform from UMI; back issues avail.) **Indexed:** Excerp.Med. (1995-). **Document type:** academic/scholarly publication.
—BLDSC (6271.816000); UMI; UnCover. **CCC.**
Description: Discusses the treatment of eye diseases and conditions.

617.7 — US — ISSN 1067-2346
OPHTHALMOLOGY RESIDENT. 1993. bi-m. Slack, Inc., 6900 Grove Rd., Thorofare, NJ 08086. TEL 609-848-1000. FAX 609-853-5991. adv.: B&W page $1200, color page $2400; trim 8 1/8 x 10 7/8. circ. 1,200.

617.7 — US — ISSN 0193-032X
OPHTHALMOLOGY TIMES. 1976. s-m. $150 (Canada $175; elsewhere $225). Advanstar Communications, Inc., 7500 Old Oak Blvd., Cleveland, OH 44130. TEL 216-826-2839. FAX 216-891-2726. (Subscr. to: 131 W. First St., Duluth, MN 55802. TEL 800-346-0085) Ed. Michael Malley. circ. 15,847. (tabloid format; also avail. in microform from UMI) **Indexed:** Biol.Dig. **Document type:** trade publication.
●Also available online. Vendor(s): Knight-Ridder, Inc.
—BLDSC (6271.833000); UMI. **CCC.**
Description: Features meeting announcements and industry news.

617.7 — US — ISSN 1077-8292
▼**OPHTHALMOLOGY WORLD NEWS.** 1995. m. $84 to individuals (foreign $114); institutions $116 (foreign $161) (effective 1996); newsstand price: $15. Lippincott - Raven Publishers, 227 Washington Sq., Philadelphia, PA 19106. TEL 215-238-4200. Ed. Carol Strickland. circ. 19,287.
Refereed Serial

617.7 — UK — ISSN 0969-0018
OPTICAL PRACTITIONER. 1992. 6/yr. £35 (foreign £45). Optical World Ltd., 200 London Rd., Southend-on-Sea, Essex SS1 1PJ, England. TEL 01702-345443. FAX 01702-431806. Ed. Gerald Ward. adv.: B&W page $1100; trim 8 1/4 x 11; adv. contact: Russell Ward. bk.rev. circ. 5,000. **Document type:** trade publication.
Description: Business management forum for optometrists and dispensing opticians.

617.7 — CN — ISSN 0824-3441
OPTICAL PRISM; Canada's optical goods and services magazine. 1983. 9/yr. Can.$30 (foreign Can.$45) (effective 1995). VezCom Inc., 31 Hastings Dr., Unionville, ON L3R 4Y5, Canada. TEL 905-475-9343. FAX 905-477-2821. Ed. Allan K. Vezina; Pub. Allan K. Vezina. adv.: color page $1952; 8 1/8 x 10 7/8; adv. contact: Monika Raepple-Bingham. bk.rev./ circ. 7,368 (controlled). (back issues avail.) **Document type:** trade publication.
Description: Deals with all aspects of the practitioner's life. Presents a variety of optical information and articles, along with a readers' forum.

617.7 — UK — ISSN 0969-1952
OPTICAL WORLD. 1972. 10/yr. £60 (foreign £85). Optical World Ltd., 200 London Rd., Southend-on-Sea, Essex SS1 1PJ, England. TEL 01702-345443. FAX 01702-431806. TELEX 995701-9-INTCOM-G. Ed. Gerald Ward. adv. contact: Russell Ward. bk.rev.; charts; illus. circ. 4,000. **Document type:** trade publication.
—BLDSC (6273.390000).
Description: International publication of interest to manufacturers, distributors and users of optical machinery and equipment.

617.7 — UK — ISSN 0030-3968
OPTICIAN. 1891. w. £75. Reed Business Publishing Ltd. (Subsidiary of: Reed Elsevier group), Quadrant House, The Quadrant, Sutton, Surrey SM2 5AS, England. TEL 0181-652-4611. FAX 0181-652-4804. (Subscr. to: Quadrant Subscription Services, Oakfield House, Perrymount Rd., Haywards Heath, W. Sussex RH16 3DH, England) Ed. Alison Ewbank. adv.; bk.rev. circ. 6,591. (back issues avail.) **Indexed:** High.Educ.Curr.Aware.Bull. **Document type:** trade publication.
—BLDSC (6273.400000).

617.75 — FR — ISSN 0030-3984
OPTICIEN-LUNETIER; l'optique française. 1952. m. 450 F.($50) Societé d'Editions Lancry, 45 rue de Lancry, 75010 Paris, France. TEL 42-00-90-55. FAX 45-74-76-40. Ed. Alain Brovillard. adv.; bk.rev.; bibl.; illus.; stat.; index. circ. 4,500. **Document type:** newspaper.
Description: Informs readers of the latest technical developments in the field of optometry.

617.75 — DK — ISSN 0900-2944
OPTIKEREN. 1977. a. DKK 244($35) Danmarks Optikerforening, Kongevejs-Centret 2, DK-2970 Hoersholm, Denmark. Ed. Lis Birch. adv.; bk.rev. circ. 800.

617.7 — FI — ISSN 0048-2021
OPTIKKO. 1958. 6/yr. FIM 250 in Scandinavia; elsewhere FIM 350 (effective 1995). Optikko-lehden Kustannus Oy, Mannerheimintie 76 B, 00250 Helsinki, Finland. FAX 90-492147. Ed. Pertti Reijonen. adv.: B&W page FIM 5000, color page FIM 7500; trim 188 x 260; adv. contact: Arja Kupari. bk.rev. circ. 1,300.

617.752 — SP
▼**OPTIMODA.** 1994. m. (11/yr.). 6000 ptas. Astoria Ediciones, S.L., Muntaner, 40-42, 4o 3a, 08011 Barcelona, Spain. TEL 34-3-4517272. FAX 34-3-4543328. circ. 5,000 (paid). **Document type:** trade publication.
Description: Covers the optical industry: frames, lenses, machinery and accessories.

617.75 — FR — ISSN 0988-3525
OPTO. 1954. 11/yr. 591 F. Mediacom Vision, 134 route de Chartres, 91440 Bures sur Yvette, France. FAX 69-28-78-06. Ed. Gerard Larnac; Pub. Jean Paul Roosen. adv. contact: Guy Moulinier. bk.rev.; charts; illus. circ. 3,650. **Indexed:** Vis.Ind. **Document type:** newspaper.
Formerly: Optometrie (ISSN 0030-4115)

617.75 535 — BE
OPTOMAGAZINE. (Supplement avail.) (Editions in Dutch, French) 6/yr. 1700 BEF. Algemene Professionele Opticiensbond van Belgie - Association Professionnelle des Opticiens de Belgique, 26 rue Capitaine Crespel, B-1050 Brussels, Belgium. TEL 32-2-5125526. FAX 32-2-5023402. Ed. Ph. Carlier. adv. circ. 2,500.
Formerly: Association Professionelle des Opticiens de Belgique. Bulletin d'Information Mensuel.

617.7 — US — ISSN 1052-7346
RE959.3
OPTOMETRIC ECONOMICS. 1991. q. $30 to non-members (foreign $55). American Optometric Association, 243 N. Lindbergh Blvd., St. Louis, MO 63141. TEL 314-991-4100. FAX 314-991-4101. Ed. Gene Mitchell. adv.: B&W page $3095, color page $4290; adv. contact: Andrew Miller. charts; illus.; stat.; index. circ. 30,095. **Document type:** trade publication.
Description: Non-clinical journal for optometrists in private practice that covers how to manage an optometric practice.

617.7 — US
RE956
OPTOMETRIC EDUCATION. 1975. q. $20 (foreign $25) (effective 1996). Association of Schools and Colleges of Optometry, 6110 Executive Blvd., Ste. 690, Rockville, MD 20852. TEL 301-231-5944. FAX 301-770-1828. Ed. Patricia C. O'Rourke. adv. contact: Patricia O'Rurke. bk.rev./ index. circ. 3,000. **Indexed:** C.I.J.E. **Document type:** academic/scholarly publication.
—UMI.
Formerly (until Fall 1991): Journal of Optometric Education (ISSN 0098-6917)

617.75 — US — ISSN 0030-4085
OPTOMETRIC MANAGEMENT; the business and marketing magazine for optometry. 1964. m. $37. Cardina Business Media, Inc., 1300 Virginia Dr., Ste. 400, Ft. Washington, PA 19034-3221. TEL 215-643-8138. FAX 215-943-3902. Ed. Sean McKinne y; Pub. Marianne Howatson. adv. contact: Bill Thompson. charts; illus.; tr.lit.; index. circ. 32,000. (also avail. in microform from UMI; reprint service avail. from UMI) **Indexed:** Account.Ind. (1987-). **Document type:** trade publication.
—UMI.

617.75 — US — ISSN 0030-4107
OPTOMETRIC WORLD.* 1912. m. $3. Occidental Publishing Co., Box 955, Palm Springs, CA 92263. Ed. L.D. Bronson. adv.; abstr.; illus. (also avail. in microform from UMI; reprint service avail. from UMI)

617.7 — CN — ISSN 0708-3173
L'OPTOMETRISTE. 1978. 6/yr. free to qualified personnel. Association des Optometristes du Quebec, 133 de la Commune W., 4th Fl., Montreal, PQ H2Y 2C7, Canada. TEL 514-849-8051. FAX 514-849-7201. Ed. Dr. Jean Pierre Lagace. adv.: B&W page Can.$815, color page Can.$940; trim 8 1/8 x 10 7/8. circ. 2,500. **Document type:** trade publication.
Formerly: Opto Magazine.
Description: News for French speaking optometrists in Quebec.

617.75 — US
OPTOMETRIST'S PATIENT NEWSLETTER. 1988. q. $495 per quarter for 1000 copies. Doctor's Press, Box 10488, Lancaster, PA 17605-0488. TEL 717-393-1010. Ed. Kim Conlin. index. **Document type:** newsletter.

MEDICAL SCIENCES — OPHTHALMOLOGY AND OPTOMETRY

617.75 US ISSN 1040-5488
RE1 CODEN: OVSCET
OPTOMETRY AND VISION SCIENCE. 1924. m. $136 (foreign $171) (effective 1996). (American Academy of Optometry) Williams & Wilkins, 428 E. Preston St., Baltimore, MD 21202. TEL 410-528-4000; 800-638-6423. FAX 410-528-4312. TELEX 87669. Ed. Dr. William M. Lyle. adv.; bk.rev.; abstr.; bibl.; charts; illus.; stat.; index. circ. 4,865. (also avail. in microfilm from WWS) **Indexed:** Biol.Abstr., C.I.S. Abstr., Curr.Adv.Ecol.Sci., Curr.Cont., Excerp.Med., Helminthol.Abstr., Ind.Med., INIS Atomind., INSPEC, Psychol.Abstr. **Document type:** academic/scholarly publication.
—BLDSC (6276.450000); Ei; Faxon; Genuine Article; SWETS; UnCover. **CCC.**
Former titles: American Journal of Optometry and Physiological Optics (ISSN 0093-7002); (until 1974): American Journal of Optometry and Archives of American Academy of Optometry.
Description: Presents research and clinical findings in optometry, as well as case reports and instrument and technique reviews.
Refereed Serial

617.7 US ISSN 1050-6918
RE1
OPTOMETRY CLINICS. 1991. q. $77 to individuals (foreign $105); institutions $110 (foreign $146); students $60 (foreign $93). (Prentice Society) Appleton & Lange, Journal Division (Subsidiary of: Simon & Schuster Company), 25 Van Zant St., Box 5630, Norwalk, CT 06856. TEL 203-838-4400. (Subscr. to: Appleton & Lange, Box 118, Pearle River, NY 10965-0118) Ed. Dr. Barbara Jennings. illus.; index. circ. 1,600. (back issues avail.) **Indexed:** Ind.Med. (1992-). **Document type:** academic/scholarly publication.
●Also available online.
—BLDSC (6276.460000). **CCC.**
Description: Each issue devoted to a single topic with articles written on methods of diagnosis and management as well as practical information on the latest techniques and pertinent legal issues.
Refereed Serial

617.7 II ISSN 0048-203X
OPTOMETRY TODAY. (Text in English) 1970. q. Rs.2000($100) Dr. Narendra Kumar, Ed. & Pub., P.O. Box 2812, New Delhi 110 060, India. TEL 5599839. Ed. Dr. Narendra Kumar. adv.; bk.rev.; abstr.; bibl.; tr.lit. circ. 1,200. (also avail. in microform from UMI; reprint service avail. from UMI) **Indexed:** Vis.Ind.
—Faxon.
Incorporating: Indian Optometric Association. Journal.
Description: Ophthalmic medicine quarterly journal.

617.7 UK ISSN 0268-5485
OPTOMETRY TODAY. 1961. fortn. £65 (foreign £85) (effective 1995). Association of Optometrists, Station Approach, Unit 4, Fleet, Hants. GU13 8QY, England. TEL 01252-816266. FAX 01252-816176. Ed. Maureen A. Hunter. adv. contact: Sarah Bradley. bk.rev. circ. 13,686. **Indexed:** C.I.S. Abstr., High.Educ.Curr.Aware.Bull. **Document type:** trade publication.
—BLDSC (6276.480000).
Formerly: Opthalmic Optician (ISSN 0030-3739); Which was formed by the union of: A.O.P. News; And: Diptric News.

617.7 616.21 NE ISSN 0167-6830
ORBIT; an international journal on orbital disorders, oculoplastic and lacrimal surgery. (Text in English) 1981. q. fl.374($235) (fl.391 outside EU) (effective 1996). (International Society on Orbital Disorders) Aeolus Press, Postbus 740, 4116 ZJ Buren, Netherlands. TEL 31-344-572055. FAX 31-344-572562. (Co-sponsor: European Society for Orbital Plastic and Reconstructive Surgery) Eds. M.Ph. Mourits, R. de Keizer. adv.: B&W page fl.600($345); 175 x 240. bk.rev.; index, cum.index. circ. 700. (also avail. in microform from UMI; back issues avail.) **Indexed:** Curr.Cont., Excerp.Med. **Document type:** academic/scholarly publication.
—BLDSC (6277.869600); Faxon; SWETS; UMI; UnCover. **CCC.**
Description: Contains review articles, research papers, and short communications on orbital disorders, ophthalmology, otolaryngology, reconstructive and maxillofacial surgery, endocrinology, radiology, radiotherapy, oncology, neurology, neuro-ophthalmology, neurosurgery, pathology, immunology, and hematology.
Refereed Serial

617.7 IT ISSN 0394-0314
L'OROPTERO; rivista di scienze della visione. (Monographic supplements avail.) (Text in Italian; abstract in English) 1986. q. L.50000 (foreign L.60000) (free to qualified personnel) (effective 1994). Istituto Regionale Studi Ottici e Optometrici, Piazza della Liberta 17, 50059 Vinci (Fi), Italy. TEL 0571-567923. FAX 0571-56520. Ed. Luigi Ferrali. adv. contact: Manola Stefanelli. bk.rev. circ. 6,000. pp./issue: 48. **Document type:** academic/scholarly publication.
Supersedes (after vol.2, 1983): Visione.
Refereed Serial

617.75 IT
OTTICA ITALIANA. 12/yr. National Federation of Opticians, Via Cenisio 32, 20154 Milan, Italy. TEL 2-349-1708. FAX 2-34-91-374. Ed. Giuseppe Ricco. circ. 9,000.

617.7 IT
OTTICO. no.114, 1975. bi-m. L.3000. Associazione Italiana Ottici, Via Giusti 2, 50019 Sesto Fiorentino (FI), Italy. TEL 55-442-090. Ed. Giuseppe Ricco. adv.; bk.rev.; charts; illus. circ. 4,000.

P A S C A L E 71: OPHTALMOLOGIE. see *MEDICAL SCIENCES — Abstracting, Bibliographies, Statistics*

PERCEPTION. see *PSYCHOLOGY*

617.7 PH ISSN 0031-7659
PHILIPPINE JOURNAL OF OPHTHALMOLOGY. 1969. q. P.300($20) Philippine Society of Ophthalmology, Philippine General Hospital, Taft Ave., Manila 1000, Philippines. Ed. Dr. Romeo V. Fajardo. adv.; bk.rev.; abstr.; index. circ. 1,000. (also avail. in microform from UMI; reprint service avail. from UMI) **Indexed:** Biol.Abstr., Chem.Abstr., Excerp.Med. (until 19??), ExtraMED, Ophthal.Lit. **Document type:** academic/scholarly publication.
●Also available on CD-ROM.
—BLDSC (6455.640000).

617.7 US ISSN 0091-6803
RE994
PHYSICIANS' DESK REFERENCE FOR OPHTHALMOLOGY. irreg., 18th ed., 1990. $39.95 (foreign $47.95). Medical Economics Publishing Co., Inc., Five Paragon Dr., Montvale, NJ 07645. TEL 201-358-7246. FAX 201-573-0344.
●Also available online.
Description: Contains product information relating to optometry and ophthalmology.

PHYSIOTHERAPISTS' QUARTERLY. see *HANDICAPPED — Visually Impaired*

617.75 CN ISSN 1181-6058
PRACTICAL OPTOMETRY. bi-m. Can.$60 (U.S. $72; overseas $94). Medicopea International Inc., 3333 Cote Vertu Blvd., Ste. 300, St. Laurent, PQ H4R 2N1, Canada. TEL 514-333-4561. FAX 514-336-1129. Ed. John Jantzi. adv. contact: Sara Wilkins. bk.rev.; illus.; index; circ. 2,300 (controlled). (back issues avail.) **Document type:** trade publication.

617.7 UK ISSN 1350-9462
QP479 CODEN: PRTRES
PROGRESS IN RETINAL AND EYE RESEARCH. 1982. s-a. £299($476) (effective 1996). Elsevier Science Ltd., Pergamon, P.O. Box 800, Kidlington, Oxford OX5 1DX, England. TEL 44-1865-843000. FAX 44-1865-843010. E-mail: nlinfo-f@elsevier.nl; usinfo-f@elsevier.com; forinfo-kyf04035@niftyserve.or.jp; Site addr.: http://www.elsevier.nl/. (Subscr. in U.S. and Canada to: Elsevier Science, 660 White Plains Rd., Tarrytown, NY 10591-5153. TEL 914-524-9200. FAX 914-333-2444) Eds. Neville Osborne, G.J. Chader. (also avail. in microfilm from UMI) **Indexed:** Chem.Abstr., Curr.Adv.Ecol.Sci. **Document type:** monographic series, academic/scholarly publication.
—BLDSC (6924.525590); CASDDS; Faxon; Genuine Article; SWETS; UMI. **CCC.**
Formerly (until 1994): Progress in Retinal Research (ISSN 0278-4327)
Description: Reviews relevant developments and current advances in retinal science for clinicians and scientists.
Refereed Serial

617.7 US ISSN 0146-4582
RE22
RED BOOK OF OPHTHALMOLOGY. biennial. $85. Butterworth - Heinemann, Part of the Reed Elsevier group, 313 Washington St., Newton, MA 02158. TEL 617-928-2500; 800-366-2665. FAX 617-928-2610. TELEX 880052. adv. **Document type:** directory.
Formerly: Red Book of Eye, Ear, Nose and Throat Specialists.

REFERATOVY VYBER Z OFTALMOLOGIE/ABSTRACTS OF OPHTHALMOLOGY. see *MEDICAL SCIENCES — Abstracting, Bibliographies, Statistics*

REFRACTIVE & CORNEAL SURGERY. see *MEDICAL SCIENCES — Surgery*

617.75 378.0025 US
RESIDENCY AND POSTGRADUATE PROGRAMS DIRECTORY. a. Association of Schools and Colleges of Optometry, 6110 Executive Blvd., Ste. 690, Rockville, MD 20852. TEL 301-231-5944. FAX 301-770-1828. **Document type:** directory.

617.7 US ISSN 0275-004X
RE501 CODEN: RETIDX
RETINA; the journal of retinal and vitreous diseases. 1981. 6/yr. $130 to individuals (foreign $175); institutions $216 (foreign $250) (effective 1996); newsstand price: $43. Lippincott - Raven Publishers, 227 E. Washington Sq., Philadelphia, PA 19105. TEL 215-238-4200. Ed. Dr. Alexander J. Brucker; Pub. Marcia E. Serepy. adv. contact: Jennifer Bass. illus.; index. circ. 2,830. (also avail. in microform from UMI) **Indexed:** Curr.Adv.Ecol.Sci., Curr.Cont., Dent.Ind., Excerp.Med. (1993-), Ind.Med. **Document type:** academic/scholarly publication.
—BLDSC (7785.510300); Genuine Article; SWETS; UMI; UnCover. **CCC.**
Refereed Serial

617.7 NE ISSN 0168-8375
CODEN: ROCREC
REVIEWS OF OCULOMOTOR RESEARCH. (Text in English) 1985. irreg., vol.5, 1992. price varies. Elsevier Science B.V., Books Division, P.O. Box 211, 1000 AE Amsterdam, Netherlands. TEL 31-20-4853911. FAX 31-20-4853705. E-mail: nlinfo-f@elsevier.nl; usinfo-f@elsevier.com; forinfo-kyf04035@niftyserve.or.jp; Site addr.: http://www.elsevier.nl/. (Subscr. in U.S. and Canada to: Elsevier Science Inc., Box 882, Madison Sq. Sta., New York, NY 10159. TEL 212-989-5800) (back issues avail.) **Document type:** monographic series.
—BLDSC (7793.802000). **CCC.**
Refereed Serial

617.7 BL ISSN 0034-7280
CODEN: RBOFA9
REVISTA BRASILEIRA DE OFTALMOLOGIA. (Text in Portuguese; summaries in English) 1942. q. $40. Sociedade Brasileira de Oftalmologia, Rua Sao Salvador, 107, Rio de Janeiro ZC 01, Brazil. Ed.Bd. adv.; bk.rev.; abstr.; bibl.; index. circ. 1,000. **Indexed:** Biol.Abstr., Chem.Abstr., Excerp.Med., Ind.Med.
—BLDSC (7845.400000); EMDOCS; Faxon.

MEDICAL SCIENCES — OPHTHALMOLOGY AND OPTOMETRY

618   CU   ISSN 0864-2176
REVISTA CUBANA DE OFTALMOLOGIA. (Text in Spanish; summaries in English, Spanish) 1987. s-a. $30 in S. America; N. America $32; elsewhere $34. Ministerio de Salud Publica, Centro Nacional de Informacion de Ciencias Medicas, Calle E No. 452, e-19 y 21, Plaza de la Revolucion, Apdo. 6520, Habana, Cuba. TEL 809-23-5338. (Dist. by: Ediciones Cubanas, Obispo No. 527, Apdo. 605, Havana, Cuba) (Co-sponsor: Sociedad Cubana de Oftalmologia) Ed. Grisell Concepcion. circ. 1,000.
    Description: Covers ophthalmology and, in particular, the treatment of pigmentary retinosis.

617.7   MX   ISSN 0187-4519
CODEN: RMOFEM
REVISTA MEXICANA DE OFTALMOLOGIA. (Text in Spanish; abstracts in English and Spanish) 1890. bi-m. Mex.$100($100) Sociedad Mexicana de Oftalmologia, Boston, No. 99, Col. Noche Buena, 03720 Mexico D.F., Mexico. TEL 563-93-93. FAX 611-1343. Ed. Dr. Fernando Castanon Nunez. index. circ. 1,000. **Indexed:** Biol.Abstr.

617.7   FR
REVUE DE L'OPHTALMOLOGIE FRANCAISE. 5/yr. 100 F. 1 rue des Pucelles, 67000 Strasbourg, France. TEL 88-36-57-94. FAX 88-25-51-90. Ed. Dr. J.L. Seegmuller. circ. 4,000.

617.7   FR   ISSN 0301-5017
REVUE INTERNATIONALE DU TRACHOME ET DE PATHOLOGIE TROPICALE ET SUBTROPICALE. 1923. q. free. Laboratoires H. Faure, B.P. 131, 07104 Annonay Cedex, France. FAX 75-67-01-74. TELEX 345023. adv.; bibl.; illus. **Indexed:** Abstr.Hyg., Biol.Abstr., Chem.Abstr., Excerp.Med., Ind.Med., Trop.Dis.Bull.
    Former titles: Revue Internationale du Trachome; Revue Internationale du Trachome et des Maladies Oculaires des Pays Tropicaux et Sub Tropicaux (ISSN 0035-3531)

617.7   IT   ISSN 0048-8410
RIVISTA OTO-NEURO-OFTALMOLOGICA.* (Text in Italian; summaries in English, French, German) Clinica Oculistica, Policlinico S. Orsola, Bologna, Italy. illus. **Indexed:** Ind.Med.

617.7   JA   ISSN 0917-4338
RYOKUNAISHO/JAPAN GLAUCOMA SOCIETY. JOURNAL. (Text in English, Japanese) 1990. a. Nihon Ryokunaisho, Miyazaki Ika Daigaku Gankagaku Kyoshitsu, 5200, Kihara, Kiyotakecho, Miyazaki-gun, Miyazaki-ken 889-16, Japan.

617.7 368   US
ST. ANTHONY'S CODING FOR OPHTHALMOLOGY REIMBURSEMENT.* m. $129. St. Anthony's Publishing, Inc., 11410 Isaac Newton Sq., Ste. 700, Reston, VA 22090-5004. TEL 800-632-0123. Ed. Kimberly Fullmer. bk.rev.
    Description: Focuses on coding reimbursement issues that have economic impact on ophthalmology practices.

617.7   SZ
SCHWEIZER OPTIKER. m. Keller und Co. AG, Baselstr. 11, CH-6000 Luzern, Switzerland. TEL 041-281111. FAX 041-222253. TELEX 75522. Ed. Jacques Culand. circ. 2,300.

617.7   UK
SCOTTISH OPTOMETRIST. 1976. m. £28. Scottish Committee of Optometrists, c/o 24 Tweed Crescent, Pean Park, Renfred, Scotland. Ed. Maureen A. Callender. adv.; bk.rev.; charts; illus.; circ. controlled. (tabloid format)
    Formerly (until Jan. 1988): Scottish Ophthalmic Practitioner (ISSN 0308-7670); Supersedes: Optics (ISSN 0048-2013)

617.7   US   ISSN 0882-0538
CODEN: SEOPE7
SEMINARS IN OPHTHALMOLOGY. 1986. q. $139 (foreign $179) (effective 1996). W.B. Saunders Co. (Subsidiary of: Harcourt Brace & Company) Curtis Center, 3rd Fl., Independence Sq. W., Philadelphia, PA 19106-3399. TEL 215-238-7800. FAX 215-238-6445. (Subscr. to: Periodicals Fulfillment, W.B. Saunders Co., 6277 Sea Harbor Dr., 4th Fl., Orlando, FL 32891-4800. TEL 800-654-2452. FAX 800-874-6418) Ed. Dr. Thomas R. Friberg; Pub. Joan W. Blumberg. adv.: B&W page $675, color page $1525; 7 x 10. bibl.; charts; illus.; index. circ. 826. **Document type:** academic/scholarly publication.
    —BLDSC (8239.456650); SWETS; UMI; UnCover. CCC.
    Description: Each issue focuses on a particular therapeutic or surgical technique through high-level clinical reviews geared toward trainee and practicing eye specialists.

617.7   JA
SHIKAKU NO KAGAKU/JAPANESE JOURNAL OF VISUAL SCIENCE. (Text in Japanese; summaries in English) a. 2500 Yen. Nihon Gankogaku Gakkai - Ophthalmological Optics Society of Japan, Nikon, 2-3, Marunouchi 3-chome, Chiyoda-ku, Tokyo 100, Japan.

617.7   JA   ISSN 0287-7767
SHIKAKU SHOGAI KENKYU/NIPPON LIGHTHOUSE WELFARE CENTER FOR THE BLIND. RESEARCH BULLETIN. (Text in Japanese) 1973. s-a. Nippon Raito Hausu Shokugyo Seikatsu Kunren Senta, 4-37, Imazunaka 2-chome, Tsurumi-ku, Osaka 538, Japan.

617.7   JA   ISSN 0289-7024
SHINKEI GANKA/NEURO-OPHTHALMOLOGY JAPAN. (Text in English, Japanese) 1984. q. 4000 Yen per no. Nihon Shinkei Ganka Gakkai - Japanese Neuro-Ophthalmology Society, Kitasato Daigaku Igakubu Ganka, 15-1, Kitasato 1-chome, Sagamihara-shi, Kanagawa-ken 228, Japan. FAX 81-427-78-2357. Ed. Satoshi Ishikawa. **Indexed:** Excerp.Med., INIS Atomind. **Document type:** proceedings.
    —BLDSC (6081.511000).
    Refereed Serial

SIGHT AND SOUND NEWS. see *HOSPITALS*

SKULL BASE SURGERY. see *MEDICAL SCIENCES — Surgery*

SLIDE ATLAS OF CURRENT OPHTHALMOLOGY (YEAR). see *MEDICAL SCIENCES — Abstracting, Bibliographies, Statistics*

117.7   CK   ISSN 0037-8364
SOCIEDAD AMERICANA DE OFTALMOLOGIA Y OPTOMETRIA. ARCHIVOS/AMERICAN SOCIETY FOR OPHTHALMOLOGY AND OPTOMETRY. ARCHIVES. 1958. q. Col.$25000($75) (effective 1995). Sociedad Americana de Oftalmologia y Optometria, Apdo. Aereo 091019, Bogota, D.E. 8, Colombia. Ed. Dr. Angela Ma. Gutierrez. adv.; bk.rev.; illus.; stat.; index, cum.index every 10 yrs. circ. 750. **Indexed:** Biol.Abstr., Excerp.Med.
    —BLDSC (1653.950000).

617.7   SP   ISSN 0365-6691
SOCIEDAD ESPANOLA DE OFTALMOLOGIA. ARCHIVOS. (Text in Spanish; summaries in English, French, German and Spanish) 1940. m. Sociedad Espanola de Oftalmologia, Donoso Cortes 73, 1o, 28015 Madrid, Spain. TEL 1-5445879. adv.; bk.rev.; abstr.; bibl.; illus.; index. circ. 2,000. (back issues avail) **Indexed:** Biol.Abstr., Excerp.Med. **Document type:** academic/scholarly publication.
    —BLDSC (1653.990000). CCC.

617.7   BE   ISSN 0081-0746
SOCIETE BELGE D'OPHTALMOLOGIE. BULLETIN. 1896. q. 3500 BEF. Societe Belge d'Ophtamologie, c/o Hopital Erasme - Ophthalmologie, Route de Lennik 808, 1070 Brussels, Belgium. TEL 32-2-5554514. FAX 32-2-5556737. Ed. Andre P. Zanen. adv. circ. 900. **Indexed:** Biol.Abstr., Dent.Ind., Excerp.Med., Ind.Med. **Document type:** bulletin.
    —BLDSC (2727.220000); EMDOCS; Faxon; SWETS.

617.7   FR   ISSN 0081-1270
SOCIETE D'OPHTALMOLOGIE DE FRANCE. BULLETIN. 1949. bi-m. 1010 F.($200) Diffusion Litteraire et Scientifique, 11 rue Moliere, 13001 Marseille, France. TEL 91-33-57-91. FAX 91-54-87-88. (Subscr. addr.: P.O. Box 47, 13262 Marseille Cedex 07, France) **Indexed:** Biol.Abstr., Chem.Abstr., Ind.Med.
    —BLDSC (2758.240000); Faxon; SWETS.

617.7   US
SOCIETY OF GERIATRIC OPHTHALMOLOGY. NEWSLETTER. 1979. irreg., latest 1988. Society of Geriatric Ophthalmology, c/o Dr. Frank J. Weinstock, 2912 W. Rusc, Canton, OH 44708. FAX 216-497-8990. **Document type:** newsletter.

617.75   SA   ISSN 0378-9411
SOUTH AFRICAN OPTOMETRIST/SUID-AFRIKAANSE OOGKUNDIGE. 1941. q. membership. South African Optometric Association, P.O. Box 3966, Pretoria 0001, South Africa. Ed. W.F. Harris. adv.; bk.rev.; charts; illus. circ. 1,622. **Indexed:** Ind.S.A.Per.
    —BLDSC (8343.500000).

617.75   US   ISSN 0038-4275
RE1
SOUTHERN JOURNAL OF OPTOMETRY. 1959. q. $12. Southern Council of Optometrists, 4661 N. Shallowford Rd., Atlanta, GA 30338. TEL 404-451-8206. Ed. Dr. Lyman Norden. adv.: B&W page $660, color page $1200; 8 3/8 x 11. bk.rev.; abstr.; illus. circ. 5,500.
    —BLDSC (8354.270000); Faxon.
    Refereed Serial

617.7   AU   ISSN 0930-4282
SPEKTRUM DER AUGENHEILKUNDE. (Text in German) 1987. 6/yr. DM.198($143) (effective 1996). (Oesterreichische Ophthalmologische Gesellschaft) Springer-Verlag, Sachsenplatz 4-6, Postfach 89, A-1201 Vienna, Austria. TEL 01-3302415. FAX 01-3302415. (N. American subscr. to: Journal Fulfillment Services, Box 2485, Secaucus, NJ 07096-2491. TEL 800-777-4643. FAX 201-348-4505; Elsewhere: Heidelberger Platz 3, 1000 Berlin 33, Germany. TEL 030-8207-1. FAX 030-821-4091) Ed. P. Drobec. adv.; bk.rev. (also avail. in microform from UMI) **Document type:** academic/scholarly publication.
    —BLDSC (8411.400150); UMI. CCC.
    Description: Informs ophthamologists about developments in research and clinical practice that are relevant to their practices.
    Refereed Serial

617.7   US
SPORTSVISION QUARTERLY. 1991. q. Miller Freeman Inc. (New York) (Subsidiary of: United Newspapers Group), 1515 Broadway, New York, NY 10036. TEL 212-869-1300. FAX 212-302-6273. Ed. Jody Stone. circ. 57,000 (controlled).
    Description: For vision care professionals; covers how to build a sports vision practice.

617.7   NE   ISSN 0927-3972
STRABISMUS. (Text in English) 1993. q. fl.351($222) (fl.367 outside EU) (effective 1996). Aeolus Press, Postbus 740, 4116 ZJ Buren, Netherlands. TEL 31-344-572055. FAX 31-344-572562. Ed.Bd. adv.: B&W page fl.600($345). circ. 400. (also avail. in microform from UMI; back issues avail.; reprint service avail. from UMI) **Document type:** academic/scholarly publication.
    —BLDSC (8467.548000).
    Description: Publishes original papers and review articles on strabismus and related fields including neurophysiology.
    Refereed Serial

STUDIES IN VISUAL INFORMATION PROCESSING. see *MEDICAL SCIENCES — Psychiatry And Neurology*

SUNGLASS ASSOCIATION OF AMERICA. NEWSLETTER. see *CLOTHING TRADE*

617.7   US   ISSN 0738-7644
TEXAS OPTOMETRY. 1945. 3/yr. $12. Texas Optometric Association, 1503 S I H 35, Austin, TX 78741-2502. TEL 512-451-8476. Ed. Clarke Newman. adv.: B&W page $365, color page $965; trim 8 1/8 x 10 7/8. bk.rev.; charts; stat.; illus. circ. 1,600.
    Formerly: Texas Optometric Association. Journal.

THYROBULLETIN. see *MEDICAL SCIENCES — Endocrinology*

TID OG SYN. see *JEWELRY, CLOCKS AND WATCHES*

617.7 TU ISSN 1300-0659
CODEN: TOFGA
TURK OFTALMOLOJI GAZETESI. 1929. bi-m. Turkish Ophthalmological Society, P.O. Box 29, Tesvikiye, 80212 Istanbul, Turkey. TEL 90-212-6351180. Ed. Dr. Ercan Ongor. **Indexed:** Excerp.Med. **Document type:** academic/scholarly publication, bulletin.

V H L FAMILY FORUM. (Von Hippel-Lindau Disease) see *MEDICAL SCIENCES — Psychiatry And Neurology*

617.752 IT ISSN 0392-0453
VEDERE CONTACT INTERNATIONAL. (Text in English and Italian) 1977. q. (plus 1 special issue). L.50000($45) Edizioni Ariminum, Via Negroli 51, 20133 Milan, Italy. TEL 39-2-70102026. FAX 39-2-717346. Ed. Isabella Morpurgo. adv. circ. 5,500. **Document type:** trade publication.
Description: International journal on contactology.

617.7 IT ISSN 0302-6256
VEDERE - INTERNATIONAL; international journal on optics, frame industry and optical instruments. (Text in English, French, Spanish and Italian) 1953. bi-m. (plus 2 special issues). L.100000($85) Edizioni Ariminum, Via Negroli 51, 20133 Milan, Italy. TEL 39-2-70123727. FAX 39-2-717346. Ed. Isabella Morpurgo. adv. circ. 8,500.
Formerly (until 1971): Vedere (ISSN 0503-7565)
Description: Covers the optical industry.

617.752 IT
VEDERE TECH INTERNATIONAL. 1992. bi-m. (plus 2 special issues). L.119000($90) Edizioni Ariminum, Via Negroli 51, 20133 Milan, Italy. TEL 39-2-70102026. FAX 39-2-717346. Ed. Isabella Morpurgo. circ. 4,000. **Document type:** trade publication.
Description: Covers raw materials, machinery, equipment and components for the eyewear industry.

617.7 RU ISSN 0042-465X
CODEN: VEOFA6
VESTNIK OFTAL'MOLOGII/ANNALS OF OPHTHALMOLOGY. (Text in Russian; summaries in English) 1884. q. $58. (Tsentr Retinal'noi Khirurgii) Izdatel'stvo Meditsina, Petroverigskii pereulok 6-8, 101000 Moscow, Russia. (Dist. by: Mezhdunarodnaya Kniga, B. Yakimanka 39, 117049 Moscow, Russia. TEL 7-095-2384600. FAX 7-095-2384634) (Co-sponsor: Ministerstvo Zdravookhraneniya) Ed. M.M. Krasnov. adv. contact: V.I. Sinitsina. bk.rev.; illus.; index. **Indexed:** Biol.Abstr., Chem.Abstr., Curr.Cont., Dent.Ind., Dok.Arbeitsmed., Excerp.Med., Helminthol.Abstr., Ind.Med., Int.Aerosp.Abstr. —BLDSC (0033.600000); CASDDS; EMDOCS; Genuine Article.
Description: Publishes materials on the diagnosis and treatment of eye diseases, hygiene of vision, prevention of ophthalmic infections, history of Russian ophthalmology, organization of ophthalmological aid to the population, as well as the problems of technology.

VETERINARY & COMPARATIVE OPHTHALMOLOGY; an international journal of clinical and investigational ophthalmology. see *VETERINARY SCIENCE*

617.7 US
VIDEO JOURNAL OF CATARACT & REFRACTIVE SURGERY. 1985. q. $220 (foreign $260). Dept. 491, Cincinnati, OH 45296-0491. TEL 513-984-5133. FAX 513-984-4240. (video cassette) **Document type:** trade publication.
Formerly: Audiovisual Journal of Cataracts and Implant Surgery (ISSN 1067-9812)
Description: Features new microsurgical procedures from an international cast of leaders in cataract surgery. Contains one hour of uninterrupted surgical footage recorded through the microscope. Emphasizes surgical techniques, intraocular lenses, complication management, and refractive procedures controversies in cataract surgery.

617.7 JA ISSN 0917-1142
VISION. (Text in Japanese) 1989. q. 2000 Yen per no. Shikaku Kenkyukai - Vision Society of Japan, Tokyo Kogyo Daigaku, Daigakuin Sogo Rikogaku Kenkyuka, 4259, Nagatsudacho, Midori-ku, Yokohama-shi, Kanagawa-ken 227, Japan.

VISION (SHEFFIELD). see *MEDICAL SCIENCES — Abstracting, Bibliographies, Statistics*

617.7 US
VISION QUARTERLY. q. $45 to individuals; institutions $60. Society of Manufacturing Engineers, One SME Dr., Box 930, Dearborn, MI 48121-0930. TEL 313-271-1500. FAX 313-271-2861. TELEX 297742 SME UR (VIA RCA). **Document type:** trade publication.

617.7 UK ISSN 0042-6989
QP474 CODEN: VISRAM
VISION RESEARCH; an international journal for functional aspects of vision. (Text in English, French, German, Russian) 1961. 24/yr. £1069($1700) (effective 1996). (Association for Research in Vision and Ophthalmology) Elsevier Science Ltd., Pergamon, P.O. Box 800, Kidlington, Oxford OX5 1DX, England. TEL 44-1865-843000. FAX 44-1865-843010.
E-mail: nlinfo-f@elsevier.nl; usinfo-f@elsevier.com; forinfo-kyf04035@niftyserve.or.jp; Site addr.: http://www.elsevier.nl/. (Subscr. in U.S. and Canada to: Elsevier Science, 660 White Plains Rd., Tarrytown, NY 10591-5153. TEL 914-524-9200. FAX 914-333-2444) Eds. G. Westheimer, H. Speikreijse. adv.; bk.rev.; charts; illus.; index. circ. 2,500. (also avail. in microfilm from UMI; back issues avail.) **Indexed:** Apic.Abstr., Appl.Mech.Rev., Biol.Abstr., Chem.Abstr., Curr.Adv.Ecol.Sci., Curr.Cont., Curr.Ref.Fish Res., Ergon.Abstr., Excerp.Med., Ind.Med., INSPEC (1987-), Int.Aerosp.Abstr., Int.Build.Serv.Abstr., Nutr.Abstr., Phys.Ber., Psychol.Abstr. (1963-), Sport Fish.Abstr., Wild.Rev. **Document type:** academic/scholarly publication.
—BLDSC (9240.925000); CASDDS; EMDOCS; Faxon; Genuine Article; SWETS; UMI; UnCover. **CCC.**
Incorporates (1986-1993): Clinical Vision Science (ISSN 0887-6169)
Description: Publishes original research in functional aspects of the neurobiology, psychophysics and behavioral physiology of human, vertebrate and invertebrate vision, as well as computational vision research.
Refereed Serial

610 617.7 613.7 US
VISIONARY. 1962. 3/yr. free. Illinois Society for the Prevention of Blindness, 407 S. Dearborn St., Ste. 1000, Chicago, IL 60605-1117. TEL 312-922-8710. FAX 312-922-8713. bk.rev.; charts; illus.; stat. circ. 10,000. (looseleaf format; back issues avail.) **Document type:** newsletter.

617.7 US
VISIONS (CHULA VISTA). bi-m. membership only. College of Optometrists in Vision Development, Box 285, Chula Vista, CA 91912. TEL 619-425-6191. Ed. Robert M. Greenburg. circ. 1,600. **Document type:** directory, newspaper, trade publication.

VISUAL NEUROSCIENCE. see *MEDICAL SCIENCES — Psychiatry And Neurology*

617.7 US ISSN 1077-2863
▼**WILMER RETINA UPDATE.** 1995. bi-m. $70 to individuals (foreign $82); institutions $95 (foreign $112) (effective 1996); newsstand price: $20. Lippincott - Raven Press, 227 Washington Sq., Philadelphia, PA 19106. TEL 215-238-4200. Ed. Dr. Neil M. Bressler. **Document type:** academic/scholarly publication.
Description: Presents case studies that illustrate how the latest evidence from clinical trials can be applied to daily practice.

617.7 US
WISCONSIN OPTOMETRIC ASSOCIATION. JOURNAL. 1956. bi-m. $10. Wisconsin Optometric Association, 5721 Odana Rd., Madison, WI 53719. TEL 608-272-4322. (Affiliate: American Optometric Association) Ed. Dr. Charles Brownlow. adv.; bk.rev. circ. 1,100.

617.7 GW
WISSENSCHAFTLICHE VEREINIGUNG FUER AUGENOPTIK UND OPTOMETRIE. FACHVORTRAEGE DES W V A O JAHRESKONGRESSES. 1952. a. price varies. Wissenschaftliche Vereinigung fuer Augenoptik und Optometrie e.V., Adam-Karrillon-Str. 32, 55118 Mainz, Germany. TEL 06131-613061. FAX 06131-614872. Ed. Hartmut Glaser. adv. **Document type:** academic/scholarly publication.
Formerly: Wissenschaftliche Vereinigung der Augenoptiker. Fachvortraege der Jahrestagungen (ISSN 0084-1005)

617.705 US ISSN 0084-392X
RE6
YEAR BOOK OF OPHTHALMOLOGY. 1901. a. $75.95 (residents $35) (effective 1996). Mosby - Year Book, Inc., Continuity Division, 200 N. LaSalle, Chicago, IL 60601. TEL 312-726-9733. FAX 312-726-6075. TELEX 206155. Ed. Peter R. Laibson, M.D. (reprint service avail.)
●Also available online. Vendor(s): Ovid Technologies.
—BLDSC (9414.670000). **CCC.**

617.7 GW ISSN 0173-2595
CODEN: ZPAUD3
Z P A. (Zeitschrift fuer Praktische Augenheilkunde) 1979. 12/yr. DM.138. Dr. R. Kaden Verlag, Poststr. 24-26, 69115 Heidelberg, Germany. TEL 06221-10313. FAX 06221-29910. adv.; B&W page DM.3800; trim 230 x 178; adv. contact: A. Siegmann. bk.rev. circ. 5,300. (back issues avail.) **Document type:** academic/scholarly publication. —CASDDS.

617.752 GW
ZEISS MARKT - MODE - MEINUNGEN; Informationen fuer Augenoptiker. 1977. 3/yr. gratis. Carl Zeiss Geschaeftsbereich Augenoptik, Postfach 1865, 73408 Aalen, Germany. TEL 07361-591365. Ed.Bd. circ. 7,500. (back issues avail.)

ZENTRALBLATT OPHTHALMOLOGIE/OPHTHALMOLOGY. see *MEDICAL SCIENCES — Abstracting, Bibliographies, Statistics*

617.7 CC ISSN 1005-1015
ZHONGHUA YANDIBING ZAZHI/CHINESE JOURNAL OF OCULAR FUNDUS DISEASES. (Text in Chinese and English) 1985. q. Y14 (foreign $80). West China University of Medical Sciences, 1st Teaching Hospital, No. 37, Guo-Xie-Xiong, Chengdu, Sichuan 610041, People's Republic of China. TEL 551255. FAX 028-582-944. (Dist. outside China by: Guoji Shudian - China International Book Trading Corporation, P.O. Box 399, Beijing, P.R.C.) Ed. Cheng Ren Luo. abstr.; bibl.; charts; illus.; stat.; index. circ. 5,000. (back issues avail.) **Document type:** academic/scholarly publication.
Formerly (until 1992): Yandi Bing - Ocular Fundus (ISSN 1001-4071)
Description: Clinical reports and research works on ocular fundus diseases relating to the infections of the interior eye and systemic involvements.
Refereed Serial

617.7 CC
ZHONGXIYI JIEHE YANKE ZAZHI. (Text in Chinese) q. Wenzhou Yixueyuan - Wenzhou Institute of Medical Sciences, Wenzhou, Zhejiang 325003, People's Republic of China. TEL 34941. Ed. Yao Fangwei.
Description: Covers the combined application of Western and traditional Chinese medicine in ophthalmology.

MEDICAL SCIENCES — Orthopedics And Traumatology

A M S A A NEWSLETTER. (Ambulance and Medical Service Association of America) see *HOSPITALS*

617.585 US ISSN 8750-2585
A P M A NEWS. 1980. m. $50. American Podiatric Medical Association, 9312 Old Georgetown Rd., Bethesda, MD 20814-1698. TEL 301-571-9200. FAX 301-530-2752. Ed. David Zych. adv.; charts; illus.; stat.; tr.lit. circ. 12,800. (tabloid format; back issues avail.) **Document type:** newspaper.
Formerly (until 1984): A P A Report (ISSN 0272-7722)

MEDICAL SCIENCES — ORTHOPEDICS AND TRAUMATOLOGY

616.1   US   ISSN 1069-6563
CODEN: AEMEF5
▼ACADEMIC EMERGENCY MEDICINE. 1994. m. $76 to individuals (foreign $86); institutions $96 (foreign $106). (Society for Academic Emergency Medicine) Hanley & Belfus, Inc., 210 S. 13th St., Philadelphia, PA 19107. TEL 215-546-7293. FAX 215-790-9330. Ed. Jerris R. Hedges. adv. contact: Diane R. Sherel. **Document type:** academic/scholarly publication.
—BLDSC (0570.511250). **CCC.**
Description: Publishes material relevant to the practice, education, and investigation of emergency medicine, and reaches a wide audience of emergency care practitioners and educators.
Refereed Serial

617   XR   ISSN 0001-5415
CODEN: ACOTA7
ACTA CHIRURGIAE ORTHOPAEDICAE ET TRAUMATOLOGIAE CECHOSLOVACA. (Text in Czech or Slovak; summaries in English and Russian) 1934. 6/yr. 66 Kc.($50) (Ceska Spolecnost pro Ortopedii a Traumatologii) Nakladatelstvi a Vydavatelstvi Scientia Medica, spol. s r.o., Chlumova 9, 130 00 Prague 3, Czech Repubic. (Dist. by: Artia, Ve Smeckach 30, 111 27 Prague 1, Czech Republic) Ed. Dr. R. Pavlansky. bk.rev. **Indexed:** Biol.Abstr., C.I.S. Abstr., Dent.Ind., Excerp.Med., Ind.Med.
—BLDSC (0611.050000); CASDDS. **CCC.**

617.3   BE   ISSN 0001-6462
ACTA ORTHOPAEDICA BELGICA. (Supplements avail.) (Text in English and French) 1945. 4/yr. 3000 BEF (foreign 3500 BEF). Association des Societes Scientifiques Medicales Belges - Vereiniging van de Belgische Medische Wetenschappelijke Genootschappen, Av. Circulaire 138A, B-1180 Brussels, Belgium. TEL 02-374-5158. Eds. C. Coutelier, H. Kinzinger. bk.rev.; abstr.; bibl.; index. **Indexed:** Bibl.Dev.Med.& Child Neur., Biol.Abstr., Excerp.Med., Ind.Med. **Document type:** academic/scholarly publication.
—BLDSC (0642.060000); Faxon; SWETS; UnCover.

617.3   DK   ISSN 0001-6470
CODEN: AOSAAK
ACTA ORTHOPAEDICA SCANDINAVICA. (Text in English) 1930. bi-m. NOK 1140 in Nordic countries; elsewhere $193 (effective 1996). (Scandinavian Orthopaedic Association) Scandinavian University Press, P.O. Box 2559-Toeyen, N-0608 Oslo, Norway. TEL 47-22-57-54-00. FAX 47-22-57-53-53. Ed. Goeran H.C. Bauer. adv.; bk.rev.; bibl.; charts; illus.; index. circ. 4,700. (reprint service avail. from ISI,SWZ) **Indexed:** ASCA, Bibl.Dev.Med.& Child Neur., Biol.Abstr., Chem.Abstr., Curr.Adv.Ecol.Sci., Curr.Cont., Dent.Ind., Excerp.Med., Ind.Med., INIS Atomind., Rev.Med.& Vet.Mycol., Sci.Cit.Ind.
—BLDSC (0642.100000); CASDDS; Faxon; Genuine Article; SWETS; UnCover. **CCC.**
Description: Presents original articles of basic research interest, as well as clinical studies in the field of orthopedics and related subdisciplines.
Refereed Serial

617.3   NO   ISSN 0300-8827
CODEN: AOSUAC
ACTA ORTHOPAEDICA SCANDINAVICA. SUPPLEMENTUM. irreg. free to subscribers of Acta Orthopaedica Scandinavica. (Scandinavian Orthopaedic Association) Scandinavian University Press, P.O. Box 2959 Toeyen, N-0608 Oslo, Norway. TEL 47-22-57-54-00. FAX 47-22-57-53-53. adv. (reprint service avail. from ISI) **Indexed:** Biol.Abstr., Curr.Cont., Excerp.Med., Ind.Med.
—BLDSC (0642.105000); Faxon; SWETS; UnCover. **CCC.**

617.3   US   ISSN 1069-7284
ADVANCES IN OPERATIVE ORTHOPAEDICS. 1993. a. $74.95 (residents $40) (effective 1996). Mosby - Year Book, Inc. (Chicago) (Subsidiary of: Times Mirror Company), 200 N. LaSalle St., Chicago, IL 60601-1080. TEL 312-726-9733. FAX 312-726-6075. TELEX 206155. Ed. Richard N. Stauffer.
Description: Presents original, fully-referenced review articles on selected clinical topics in the field of operative orthopaedics.

617.3   US   ISSN 0738-2278
RD701   CODEN: AOSUEG
ADVANCES IN ORTHOPAEDIC SURGERY. 1977. bi-m. $76 to individuals (foreign $118); institutions $165 (foreign $198) (effective 1996). Lippincott - Raven Publishers, 227 E. Washington Sq., Philadelphia, PA 19106. TEL 215-238-4200. Ed. William Cooney. adv. contact: Phyllis Noyes. charts; illus. circ. 2,800. (also avail. in microform; microfilm from WWS; back issues avail.) **Indexed:** Excerp.Med. **Document type:** academic/scholarly publication, abstracting/indexing.
—SWETS; UnCover. **CCC.**
Formerly: Orthopaedic Survey (ISSN 0147-6793)
Description: Each issue contains 20-25 condensations of important recent literature accompanied by original, reviewed editorial commentary.
Refereed Serial

617.1   US
ADVANCES IN TRAUMA AND CRITICAL CARE. 1986. a. $77.95 (residents $40) (effective 1996). Mosby - Year Book, Inc. (Chicago) (Subsidiary of: Times Mirror Company), 200 N. LaSalle St., Chicago, IL 60601-1080. TEL 312-726-9733. FAX 312-726-6075. TELEX 206155. (Subscr. to: 11830 Westline Industrial Dr., St. Louis, MO 63146. TEL 800-325-4177) Ed. Dr. Kimball I. Maull. illus.
—UnCover. **CCC.**
Formerly: Advances in Trauma (ISSN 0886-7755)
Description: Presents a collection of original, fully-referenced review articles on selected clinical topics in the fields of trauma and critical care.

617.1   GW   ISSN 0044-6173
AKTUELLE TRAUMATOLOGIE. (Text in German; summaries in English) 1971. 8/yr. DM.306. Georg Thieme Verlag, Ruedigerstr. 14, 70469 Stuttgart, Germany. TEL 0711-8931-0. FAX 0711-8931298. (Subscr. to: Postfach 104853, 70042 Stuttgart, Germany) Ed.Bd. bk.rev.; index. circ. 2,300. (reprint service avail. from UMI) **Indexed:** Biol.Abstr., Curr.Cont., Dok.Arbeitsmed., Excerp.Med., Ind.Med., Sci.Cit.Ind. **Document type:** academic/scholarly publication.
—BLDSC (0785.885000); EMDOCS; Faxon; UMI. **CCC.**

617.585 378   US
ALUMNUS (NEW YORK).* 1975. q. New York College of Podiatric Medicine, 52 E. 124th St., New York, NY 10035. bk.rev.; illus. circ. 3,000.

AMBULANCE INDUSTRY JOURNAL. see *BUSINESS AND ECONOMICS — Domestic Commerce*

AMBULANCE SERVICE JOURNAL; a professional journal for ambulance and first aid personnel. see *HOSPITALS*

AMBULANCE U K. see *HOSPITALS*

617.3   US   ISSN 1049-9741
AMERICAN ACADEMY OF ORTHOPAEDIC SURGEONS. BULLETIN. 1952. q. membership. American Academy of Orthopaedic Surgeons, 6300 N. River Rd., Rosemont, IL 60018. TEL 708-384-4130. FAX 708-823-8033. E-mail: fox@AAOS.usa.com. Ed. Alvin Nagelberg. circ. 15,000 (controlled). **Document type:** bulletin.
—UMI.

617.3   US   ISSN 0516-8856
AMERICAN ACADEMY OF ORTHOPAEDIC SURGEONS. DIRECTORY. 1933. a. membership only. American Academy of Orthopaedic Surgeons, 6300 N. River Rd., Rosemont, IL 60018. TEL 708-384-4130. FAX 708-823-8033. E-mail: fox@AAOS.usa.com. **Document type:** directory.

617.3   US   ISSN 1067-151X
AMERICAN ACADEMY OF ORTHOPAEDIC SURGEONS. JOURNAL; a comprehensive review. 1993. 6/yr. $66 to individuals (foreign $86); institutions $99 (foreign $108). American Academy of Orthopaedic Surgeons, 6300 N. River Rd., Rosemont, IL 60018. TEL 708-384-4130. FAX 708-823-8033. E-mail: fox@AAOS.usa.com. Ed. Paul D. Psilos. circ. 23,000. **Document type:** academic/scholarly publication, trade publication.
—BLDSC (4683.732000).
Description: Covers the latest developments in the clinical practice of orthopedics, focusing on clinical problem-solving from diagnosis to treatment.
Refereed Serial

617.585   US   ISSN 0737-5409
AMERICAN ACADEMY OF PODIATRY ADMINISTRATION NEWS-LETTER.* vol. 3, 1973. q. $15. American Academy of Podiatry Administration, c/o John V. Cicero, D.P.M., Sec., Ten Meadow Lane, Bloomfield, NJ 07003. (Subscr. to: Dr. Leonard Light, 614 Central Ave., Dunkirk, NY 14048)
Formerly: American Academy of Practice Management in Podiatry. News-Letter.

617.11   US   ISSN 0361-7726
AMERICAN BURN ASSOCIATION. ANNUAL MEETING. PROCEEDING. 1967. a. $25. American Burn Association, c/o Dr. Cleon W. Goodwin, Secy., NY Hospital, Cornell Medical Ctr., 525 E. 68th St., Rm. L-706, New York, NY 10021. TEL 800-548-2876. Ed.Bd. circ. 4,000. (tabloid format; back issues avail.) **Document type:** proceedings.

617.3   US
AMERICAN COLLEGE OF FOOT AND ANKLE ORTHOPEDICS AND MEDICINE NEWSLETTER. 1964. q. $5 to non-members. American College of Foot and Ankle Orthopedics and Medicine, 4603 Hwy. 95 S., Box 39, Cocolalla, ID 83813. TEL 208-683-3900. FAX 208-683-3700. Ed. Judith A. Baerg. bk.rev.; abstr.; charts; illus. circ. 1,100. (looseleaf format) **Document type:** newsletter.
Formerly (until Oct. 1993): American College of Foot Orthopedists Newsletter (ISSN 0002-7987)

AMERICAN COLLEGE OF FOOT SPECIALISTS. ANNUAL YEARBOOK. see *MEDICAL SCIENCES — Surgery*

AMERICAN JOURNAL OF CRITICAL CARE. see *MEDICAL SCIENCES — Nurses And Nursing*

617 619   US   ISSN 0735-6757
CODEN: AJEMEN
AMERICAN JOURNAL OF EMERGENCY MEDICINE. 1983. bi-m. $145 (foreign $195) (effective 1996). W.B. Saunders Co. (Subsidiary of: Harcourt Brace & Company), Curtis Center, 3rd Fl., Independence Sq. W., Philadelphia, PA 19106-3399. TEL 215-238-7800. FAX 215-238-6445. (Subscr. to: Periodicals Fulfillment, W.B. Saunders Co., 6277 Sea Harbor Dr., 4th Fl., Orlando, FL 32891-4800. TEL 800-654-2452. FAX 800-874-6418) Ed. Dr. J. Douglas White; Pub. Joan W. Blumberg. adv.: B&W page $690, color page $1660; 7 x 10. bk.rev.; abstr.; bibl.; charts; illus.; index. circ. 2,574. (also avail. in microform from UMI) **Indexed:** ASCA, CINAHL, Excerp.Med., Med.& Surg.Dermat. **Document type:** academic/scholarly publication.
—BLDSC (0824.480000); Faxon; Genuine Article; SWETS; UMI; UnCover. **CCC.**
Description: Covers all aspects of emergency medicine with clinical articles, case studies, reviews, worldwide news items, and editorials.
Refereed Serial

617.3   US   ISSN 1078-4519
RD701   CODEN: AJORFL
THE AMERICAN JOURNAL OF ORTHOPEDICS. 1972. m. $124 to institutions outside the Americas; $103 to institutions in U.S (effective 1996). Excerpta Medica, Inc., Core Publishing Division (Subsidiary of: Reed Elsevier Medical group), 105 Raider Blvd., Belle Mead, NJ 08052. TEL 908-874-8550. FAX 908-874-0707. (Subscr. to: Box 3085, Princeton, NJ 08543-3085) adv.; bk.rev.; charts; illus.; stat.; index. circ. 25,000. (also avail. in microform from UMI; back issues avail.) **Indexed:** Excerp.Med., Ind.Med.
—BLDSC (0829.190000); EMDOCS; SWETS. **CCC.**
Formerly (until 1995): Orthopaedic Review (ISSN 0094-6591)
Refereed Serial

MEDICAL SCIENCES — ORTHOPEDICS AND TRAUMATOLOGY

617.585 US ISSN 8750-7315
RD563.A2 CODEN: JAPAEA
AMERICAN PODIATRIC MEDICAL ASSOCIATION. JOURNAL. 1907. m. $75. American Podiatric Medical Association, 9312 Old Georgetown Rd., Bethesda, MD 20814-1698. TEL 301-571-9200. FAX 301-530-2752. Ed. Dr. Warren S. Joseph. adv.; bk.rev.; bibl.; illus.; index, cum.index: 1973-1984. circ. 14,000. (also avail. in microfilm) **Indexed:** Biol.Abstr., Curr.Adv.Ecol.Sci., Curr.Cont., Dent.Ind., Excerp.Med., Hosp.Lit.Ind., Ind.Med., INIS Atomind., Int.Nurs.Ind., Med.& Surg.Dermat., Nutr.Abstr., Rev.Med.& Vet.Mycol. **Document type:** academic/scholarly publication.
●Also available online. Vendor(s): National Library of Medicine.
—BLDSC (4692.040000); Faxon; Genuine Article; SWETS; UMI; UnCover.
Incorporates: Podiatric Medicine and Surgery; **Former titles** (until 1984): American Podiatry Association. Journal (ISSN 0003-0538); (until 1957): National Association of Chiropodists. Journal (ISSN 0360-1684); (until 1921): Pedic Items.
Refereed Serial

AMERICAN PODIATRIC MEDICAL WRITERS ASSOCIATION. NEWSLETTER. see *JOURNALISM*

617.3 MX ISSN 0044-8184
ANALES DE ORTOPEDIA Y TRAUMATOLOGIA.* (Text in Spanish; summaries in English and Spanish) vol.5, 1969. q. Mex.$100($10.) Sociedad Mexicana de Ortopedia, Ejercito Nacional 475, Primer Piso, Mexico 17, D.F., Mexico. Ed. Dr. Carlos Hernandez Esquivel. adv.; bibl.; charts; illus.

617.1 FR ISSN 0003-4126
ANNALES DE MEDECINE DES ACCIDENTS ET DU TRAFIC TRAUMATOLOGIE. 1964. bi-m. Institut National de Medecine du Trafic, 21 rue l'Ecole de Medecine, 75006 Paris, France. (Co-sponsor: Societe Francaise de Medecine du Trafic) adv.

616.02 US ISSN 0196-0644
RC86 CODEN: AEMED3
ANNALS OF EMERGENCY MEDICINE. 1972. m. $75 to individuals (Canada $111.28; elsewhere $104); institutions $88 (Canada $125.19; elsewhere $117); students, paramedics, EMT $39 (Canada $72.76; elsewhere $68); newsstand price: $9. (American College of Emergency Physicians) Mosby - Year Book, Inc. (Subsidiary of: Times Mirror Company), 11830 Westline Industrial Dr., S. Louis, MO 63146-3318. TEL 314-872-8370; 800-325-4177. FAX 314-432-1380. Ed. Dr. Joseph F. Waeckerle. adv.; B&W page $2070; trim 8 1/8 x 10 7/8. bk.rev. circ. 22,500. (also avail. in microfilm; reprint service avail. from UMI) **Indexed:** Abstr.Health Care Manage.Stud., AIM, CINAHL, Curr.Cont., Dent.Ind., Excerp.Med., FAMLI, I.P.A., Ind.Med., INIS Atomind., Kidney, Lab.Haz.Bull., Rev.Med.& Vet.Mycol. **Document type:** academic/scholarly publication.
—BLDSC (1040.425000); Faxon; Genuine Article; SWETS; UMI; UnCover. **CCC.**
Formerly: J A C E P (ISSN 0361-1124)
Description: Presents pertinent information encompassing clinical studies, case reports, basic research, and discussion
Refereed Serial

APARATO LOCOMOTOR. see *MEDICAL SCIENCES — Rheumatology*

APUNTS; medicina de l'esport. see *MEDICAL SCIENCES — Sports Medicine*

617.3 GW ISSN 0936-8051
CODEN: AOTSEF
ARCHIVES OF ORTHOPAEDIC AND TRAUMA SURGERY. 1903. 6/yr. DM.848($616) (effective 1996). (Deutsche Gesellschaft fuer Unfallheilkunde, Versicherungs-, Versorgungs- und Verkehrsmedizin) Springer-Verlag, Heidelberger Platz 3, 14197 Berlin, Germany. TEL 030-8207-0. FAX 030-8214091. E-mail: orders@springer.de. (Subscr. in N. America to: Springer-Verlag New York, Inc., 44 Hartz Way, Secaucus, NJ 07096. TEL 201-348-4033. FAX 201-348-4505) Ed. H. Wagner. adv.; bk.rev.; bibl.; charts; illus.; index. (also avail. in microform from ISI) **Indexed:** Biol.Abstr., Chem.Abstr., Curr.Cont., Dent.Ind., Excerp.Med., Ind.Med., Ind.Sci.Rev., INIS Atomind., Sci.Cit.Ind. **Document type:** academic/scholarly publication.
—BLDSC (1638.494900); Faxon; Genuine Article; SWETS; UMI; UnCover. **CCC.**
Former titles: Archives of Orthopaedic and Traumatic Surgery (ISSN 0344-8444); (until 1978): Archiv fuer Orthopaedische und Unfallchirurgie (ISSN 0003-9330)
Description: Reports on the latest advances in all areas of orthopedics, including accident related injuries, experimental bone and joint surgery, and problems related to rehabilitation.

617.3 616.742 IT ISSN 0390-7368
ARCHIVIO DI ORTOPEDIA E REUMATOLOGIA. (Text in Italian; summaries in English) 1884. q. L.200000. (Istituto Ortopedico "Gaetano Pini") Editrice Grafiche Zanini S.r.l., Via Emilia, 41 E, 40011 Anzola dell'Emilia (BO), Italy. TEL 3951-765562. FAX 3951-766060. Ed. Luigi Parrini. adv.; bk.rev.; abstr.; bibl.; illus.; index. circ. 500. **Indexed:** Biol.Abstr., Chem.Abstr., Ind.Med.
—BLDSC (1647.822000).
Formerly: Archivio di Ortopedia (ISSN 0004-0118)

617 US ISSN 0749-8063
CODEN: ARTHE3
ARTHROSCOPY; journal of arthroscopic and related surgery. 1985. bi-m. $247 (foreign $309) (effective 1996). (Arthroscopy Association of North America) W.B. Saunders Co. (Subsidiary of: Harcourt Brace & Company), Curtis Center, 3rd Fl., Independence Sq. W., Philadelphia, PA 19106-3399. TEL 215-238-7800. FAX 215-238-6445. (Subscr. to: Periodicals Fulfillment, W.B. Saunders Co., 6277 Sea Harbor Dr., 4th Fl., Orlando, FL 32891-4800. TEL 800-654-2452. FAX 800-874-6418) (Co-sponsor: International Arthroscopic Association) Ed. Dr. Gary G. Poehling.; Pub. Joan W. Blumberg. adv.; B&W page $1080, color page $2490; 7 x 10; adv. contact: Cindy Gray. bk.rev.; charts; illus.; index. circ. 6,700. (back issues avail.; reprint service avail. from UMI) **Indexed:** Excerp.Med. **Document type:** academic/scholarly publication.
—BLDSC (1733.940000); Genuine Article; SWETS; UnCover. **CCC.**
Description: Explores trends and innovations in both diagnostic and operative arthroscopy.
Refereed Serial

617.1 616.7 JA ISSN 0910-223X
ARTHROSCOPY. (Text in Japanese; summaries in English) 1976. s-a. 5000 Yen($50) Japan Arthroscopic Association, c/o Dept. of Orthopaedic Surgery, School of Medicine, Chiba University, 1-8-1, Inohana, Chuo-ku, Chiba-shi, Chiba 260, Japan. TEL 043-222-7272. FAX 043-226-2338. Ed. Hideshige Moriya. adv. circ. 1,500. (back issues avail.) **Document type:** academic/scholarly publication.
Description: Publishes proceedings of the annual meeting and original papers.

617.3 US ISSN 0748-8947
AUDIO-DIGEST EMERGENCY MEDICINE. 1984. s-m. $168. Audio-Digest Foundation (Subsidiary of: California Medical Association), 1577 E. Chevy Chase Dr., Glendale, CA 91206. TEL 213-245-8505. FAX 818-240-7379. (audio cassette)
Refereed Serial

617.3 US ISSN 0271-132X
AUDIO-DIGEST ORTHOPAEDICS. 1978. m. $84. Audio-Digest Foundation (Subsidiary of: California Medical Association), 1577 E. Chevy Chase Dr., Glendale, CA 91206. TEL 213-245-8505. FAX 818-240-7379. Ed. Claron L. Oakley. circ. controlled. (audio cassette)
Refereed Serial

616.02 610.73 AT ISSN 1322-3127
AUSTRALIAN JOURNAL OF EMERGENCY CARE. 1977. q. Aus.$30 (foreign Aus.$40) (effective 1996). Ambulance Employees Australia, 117-131 Capel St., North Melbourne, Vic. 3051, Australia. TEL 61-3-93295777. FAX 61-3-93295533. (Subscr. to: P.O. Box 60, Carlton South, Vic. 3053, Australia) Ed. Chris Tyler. adv.; bk.rev.; abstr.; bibl.; charts; illus. circ. 5,000. (back issues avail.) **Document type:** academic/scholarly publication.
Formerly (until 1994): Ambulance World (ISSN 0817-4474)
Description: Aimed at ambulance officers, paramedics, emergency doctors, emergency nurses and other emergency care practitioners.
Refereed Serial

616 US ISSN 0894-7376
THE BACK LETTER. Key Title: Backletter. m. $89 (foreign $99) (effective 1995). Quest Publishing Co., Inc., A Division of Raven Press Ltd. (Subsidiary of: Wolters Kluwer N.V.), 1351 Titan Way, Brea, CA 92621. TEL 714-738-6400. FAX 714-525-6258. (Subscr. to: Raven Press, 1185 Ave. of the Americas, New York, NY 10036. TEL 212-930-9500. FAX 212-869-3495) Pub. Mary Waltham. **Document type:** newsletter.
—**CCC.**
Description: Covers all aspects of spine function, disease and injury.

617.533 GW ISSN 0931-6779
BERUFSVERBAND AERZTE FUER ORTHOPAEDIE. INFORMATIONEN.* bi-m. Berufsverband Aerzte fuer Orthopaedie e.V., Am Lindenbaum 6-8, 60433 Frankfurt a.M., Germany. Ed. Dr. Georg Holfelder. circ. 4,000. **Document type:** newsletter.

617.3 JA ISSN 0287-1645
CODEN: SEGEAW
BESSATSU SEIKEI GEKA/ORTHOPEDIC SURGERY. SPECIAL ISSUE. (Text in Japanese) 1982. s-a. 5500 Yen. Nankodo Co., Ltd., 42-6, Hongo 3-chome, Bunkyo-ku, Tokyo 113, Japan. TEL 03-3811-7239. FAX 03-3811-7230.

617.3 CN
BODY CAST.* 1986. q. Can.$26.75($32.10) (outside N. America Can.$37.45). Pappin Communications, The Victoria Centre, 84 Isabella St., Pembroke, ON K8A 5S5, Canada. TEL 613-735-0952. FAX 613-735-7983. (Subscr. to: 4433 Sheppard Ave. E. No. 200, Agincourt, Ont. M1S 1V3, Canada) Ed. Martin McPolin. adv. circ. 1,200. (back issues avail.)

617.6 616.4 US ISSN 8756-3282
QP88.2 CODEN: BONEDL
BONE. (Text in English and French) 1979. m. $1050 to institutions (effective 1996). Elsevier Science Inc., 650 Ave. of the Americas, New York, NY 10010. TEL 212-989-5800. FAX 212-633-3680. TELEX 420643 AEPUI. (Subscr. to: Box 882, Madison Sq. Sta., New York, NY 10159-0882) adv.; abstr.; illus. (also avail. in microfilm from UMI; back issues avail.) **Indexed:** Biol.Abstr., Chem.Abstr., Curr.Adv.Biochem., Curr.Adv.Ecol.Sci., Curr.Cont., Dairy Sci.Abstr., Dent.Ind., Excerp.Med., Ind.Med., Ind.Sci.Rev., Ind.Vet., NRN, Small Anim.Abstr., Vet.Bull. **Document type:** academic/scholarly publication.
—BLDSC (2247.330000); CASDDS; Faxon; Genuine Article; SWETS; UMI; UnCover. **CCC.**
Incorporates (1986-1994): Bone and Mineral (ISSN 0169-6009); **Formerly:** Metabolic Bone Disease and Related Research (ISSN 0221-8747)
Description: Provides an interdisciplinary forum for rapid publication of original experimental or clinical studies and review articles.
Refereed Serial

617.3 JA ISSN 0914-7047
THE BONE. (Text in Japanese) 1987. 4/yr. 1545 Yen per no. Medikaru Rebyusha - Medical Review Co., Ltd., 7-3, Hiranomachi 1-chome, Chuo-ku, Osaka 541, Japan.

MEDICAL SCIENCES — ORTHOPEDICS AND TRAUMATOLOGY

617.533 NE ISSN 0168-051X
QP88.2 CODEN: BMRSDZ
THE BONE AND MINERAL RESEARCH ANNUAL. Key Title: Bone and Mineral Research. 1983. irreg., vol.8, 1994. price varies. Elsevier Science B.V., Books Division, P.O. Box 211, 1000 AE Amsterdam, Netherlands. TEL 31-20-4853911.
FAX 31-20-4853705. TELEX 18582 ESPA NL.
E-mail: nlinfo-f@elsevier.nl; usinfo-f@elsevier.com; forinfo-kyf04035@niftyserve.or.jp; Site addr.: http://www.elsevier.nl/. (Subscr. in U.S. and Canada to: Elsevier Science Inc., Box 882, Madison Sq. Sta., New York, NY 10159. TEL 212-989-5800)
Document type: monographic series.
—BLDSC (2247.340000); CASDDS; Faxon. **CCC.**
 Formerly: Annual Advances in Bone and Mineral Research.
 Refereed Serial

617.3 US
BRISTOL-MYERS - ZIMMER ORTHOPAEDIC SYMPOSIUM SERIES. 1988. irreg., latest 1995. price varies. Raven Press (Subsidiary of: Wolters Kluwer N.V.), 1185 Ave. of the Americas, New York, NY 10036. TEL 212-930-9500. FAX 212-869-3495. **Document type:** proceedings.

617.3 UK ISSN 0267-3258
BRITISH ASSOCIATION FOR IMMEDIATE CARE. JOURNAL. 1977. 3/yr. £20 (effective 1995). British Association for Immediate Care, 7 Black Horse Ln., Ipswich, Suffolk IP1 2EF, England.
TEL 01473-218407. FAX 01473-280585. Ed. B. Robertson. adv.; bk.rev.; film rev.; abstr.; illus.; cum.index. circ. 2,100. (back issues avail.)
Document type: academic/scholarly publication.
—BLDSC (4712.850000).
 Refereed Serial

617.3 GW ISSN 0068-3388
BUECHEREI DES ORTHOPAEDEN. (Supplement to: Zeitschrift fuer Orthopaedie und ihre Grenzgebiete) 1969. irreg., no.60, 1992. price varies. Ferdinand Enke Verlag, Postfach 300366, 70443 Stuttgart, Germany. TEL 0711-135798-0.
FAX 0711-135798-30. TELEX 07252275-GTV-D. Eds. J. Kraemer, K.F. Schlegel. (reprint service avail. from IRC) **Document type:** monographic series.
—Faxon.

617.11 US ISSN 1069-675X
RA975.5.B87
BURN CARE RESOURCES IN NORTH AMERICA. 1984. biennial. $50. American Burn Association, c/o Dr. Cleon W. Goodwin, Secy., NY Hospital, Cornell Medical Ctr., 525 E. 68th St., Rm. L-706, New York, NY 10021. TEL 800-548-2876. Ed.Bd. circ. 4,500.
Document type: directory.
 Description: Lists burn care facilities, skin banks, foundations and available fellowships in U.S. and Canada.

617.95 UK ISSN 0305-4179
 CODEN: BURND8
BURNS; including thermal injury. 1974. 8/yr. £215($342) (effective 1996). (International Society for Burn Injuries) Butterworth - Heinemann, Part of the Reed Elsevier group, Linacre House, Jordan Hill, Oxford OX2 8DP, England. TEL 0865-310366.
FAX 0865-310898. TELEX 83111 BHPOXF G. (Dist by: Elsevier Science Ltd., P.O. Box 800, Kidlington, Oxford OX5 1DX, England. TEL 44-865-843000. FAX 44-865-843010; Subscr. in U.S. and Canada to: Elsevier Science, 660 White Plains Rd., Tarrytown, NY 10591-5153. TEL 914-524-9200. FAX 914-333-2444) Ed. J.W.L. Davies. adv.; bk.rev.; index. circ. 850. (also avail. in microform from UMI; back issues avail.) **Indexed:** Biol.Abstr., Curr.Adv.Cancer Res., Curr.Adv.Ecol.Sci., Curr.Cont., Dent.Ind., Excerp.Med., Ind.Med., Med.& Surg.Dermat., Nutr.Abstr. **Document type:** academic/scholarly publication.
—BLDSC (2931.728000); Faxon; Genuine Article; SWETS; UMI; UnCover. **CCC.**
 Description: Focuses on the scientific, clinical and social aspects of burns. Includes clinical and scientific papers, and case reports.
 Refereed Serial

617 610.73 CN ISSN 0708-6474
C O N A JOURNAL. 1978. q. Can.$35. Canadian Orthopaedic Nurses Association, 43 Wellesley St. E., Toronto, ON M4Y 1H1, Canada. Ed. Brenda Vines. adv.; bk.rev.; index. circ. 600. (back issues avail.) **Indexed:** CINAHL. **Document type:** newsletter.

617.3 UK ISSN 0266-0970
 CODEN: CCILED
CARE OF THE CRITICALLY ILL. 1984. bi-m. £30 to individuals; institutions £40. Mosby Europe Journals Ltd., Lynton House, 7-12 Tavistock Sq., London WC1H 9LB, England. TEL 071-388-7676.
FAX 071-344-0020. TELEX 8814230-MOSBYE. (Subscr. to: Stonehart Subscr. Services, Hainault Rd., Little Heath Romford, Essex RM6 5NP, England) Ed. Dr. David Ryan. adv.: color page £1150; adv. contact: Sally Ricketts. bk.rev. circ. 5,000. **Document type:** academic/scholarly publication.
—BLDSC (3051.549000). **CCC.**
 Description: Directed to doctors and nurses involved with adult intensive care, neonatal and pediatric intensive care, coronary and cardial care, as well as acute trauma.
 Refereed Serial

617.3 JA
CENTRAL JAPAN JOURNAL OF ORTHOPAEDIC SURGERY & TRAUMATOLOGY/CHUBU NIPPON SEIKEI GEKA SAIGAI GEKA GAKKAI ZASSHI. (Text in Japanese; contents page in English) 1958. bi-m. 10000 Yen or exchange basis. Chubu Nihon Seikei Geka Saigai Geka Gakkai, Teramachi, Imadegawa-Sagaru, Kamigyo-ku, Kyoto 602, Japan.
TEL 075-231-7599. FAX 075-231-7499. (Co-sponsor: Central Japan Association of Orthopaedic and Traumatic Surgery) Ed. Takashi Nakamura. adv. rate, 3,600. **Indexed:** INIS Atomind. **Document type:** academic/scholarly publication.
 Formerly (until 1990): Central Japan Journal of Orthopaedic and Traumatic Surgery (ISSN 0008-9443)

CHUBU NIHON SEIKEI GEKA SAIGAI GEKA GAKKAI SHOROKU/CENTRAL JAPAN ORTHOPAEDIC AND TRAUMATIC SURGERY SOCIETY. ABSTRACTS. see *MEDICAL SCIENCES — Abstracting, Bibliographies, Statistics*

617.3 JA ISSN 0915-2695
CHUGOKU SHIKOKU SEIKEI GEKA GAKKAI ZASSHI/CHUGOKU-SHIKOKU ORTHOPAEDIC ASSOCIATION. JOURNAL. (Text in Japanese; summaries in English) 1989. s-a. Chugoku Shikoku Seikei Geka Gakkai, 7-13, Okamachi, Okayama-shi, Okayama-ken 700, Japan.

CLINICAL JOURNAL OF SPORT MEDICINE. see *MEDICAL SCIENCES — Sports Medicine*

617.3 US ISSN 1069-6970
CLINICAL ORTHOPAEDIC SOCIETY. JOURNAL. resumed 1995. bi-m. $175 (foreign $257.50) (effective 1996). (Clinical Orthopaedic Society) John Wiley & Sons, Inc., Journals, 605 Third Ave., New York, NY 10158. TEL 212-850-6645. FAX 212-850-6021. TELEX 12-7063. E-mail: SUBINFO@JWILEY.COM. (Subscr. outside the Americas to: John Wiley & Sons Ltd., Baffins Ln., Chichester, W. Sussex PO19 1UD, England. TEL 44-1243-449777. FAX 44-1243-776128) (also avail. in microform from UMI; back issues avail.) **Document type:** academic/scholarly publication.
 Refereed Serial

617.3 US ISSN 0009-921X
RD701 CODEN: CORTBR
CLINICAL ORTHOPAEDICS AND RELATED RESEARCH. 1952. m. $289 to individuals (foreign $420); institutions $468 (foreign $545) (effective 1996). Lippincott - Raven Publishers, 227 E. Washington Sq., Philadelphia, PA 19106. TEL 215-238-4200. Ed. Dr. Carl T. Brighton. illus.; index. circ. 9,574. (also avail. in microform from UMI) **Indexed:** AIM, Bibl.Dev.Med.& Child Neur., Biol.Abstr., Chem.Abstr., CINAHL, Curr.Adv.Cell & Devel.Biol., Curr.Adv.Ecol.Sci., Curr.Cont., Dent.Ind., Dok.Arbeitsmed., Excerp.Med., Hosp.Lit.Ind., Ind.Med., Ind.Sci.Rev., INIS Atomind., Rev.Med.& Vet.Mycol., Risk Abstr., Sci.Cit.Ind., SSCI.
●Also available online. Vendor(s): Lexis-Nexis, Ovid Technologies.
—BLDSC (3286.323000); CASDDS; Faxon; Genuine Article; SWETS; UMI; UnCover. **CCC.**
 Refereed Serial

617.585 US ISSN 0891-8422
RD563
CLINICS IN PODIATRIC MEDICINE & SURGERY. 1984. q. $120 (foreign $146) (effective 1996). W.B. Saunders Co. (Subsidiary of: Harcourt Brace & Company), Curtis Center, 3rd Fl., Independence Sq. W., Philadelphia, PA 19106-3399.
TEL 215-238-7800. FAX 215-238-6445. (Subscr. to: Periodicals Fulfillment, W.B. Saunders Co., 6277 Sea Harbor Dr., 4th Fl., Orlando, FL 32891-4800. TEL 800-654-2452. FAX 800-874-6418) Ed. Melissa Mitchell. circ. 3,500. (also avail. in microfilm; back issues avail.) **Indexed:** Excerp.Med., INIS Atomind. **Document type:** academic/scholarly publication.
—BLDSC (3286.590500); Faxon; UMI; UnCover. **CCC.**
 Formerly (until 1986): Clinics in Podiatry (ISSN 0742-0668)
 Description: Each issue covers a particular topic of treating foot disorders and conditions.

617.3 US
CONSERVATIVE ORTHOPEDICS INTERNATIONAL ASSOCIATION. NEWS UPDATE - BULLETIN. q. membership. Conservative Orthopedics International Association, 1811 Monroe St., Dearborn, MI 48124-2924. TEL 313-563-0360. Ed. Dr. Stephen Caster. bk.rev. circ. 3,700. (back issues avail.) **Document type:** bulletin.

617 US ISSN 0194-8458
CONTEMPORARY ORTHOPAEDICS. 1979. m. $53 (Canada $63; elsewhere $80). Bobit Publishing Company, 2512 Artesia Blvd., Redondo Beach, CA 90278-3210. TEL 310-376-8788.
FAX 310-376-9043. Ed. Judi Prow. circ. 30,000 (controlled). **Indexed:** Biol.Abstr. **Document type:** academic/scholarly publication.
—BLDSC (3425.197600); UnCover.
 Description: Practical "how-to" clinical information for the teaching and practicing orthopaedic surgeon.
 Refereed Serial

617.3 US
CRANIAL LETTER. 1946. q. $60. Cranial Academy, 3500 Depauw Blvd., Ste. 1080, Indianapolis, IN 46268-1136. TEL 317-879-0713.
FAX 317-879-0718. adv.; bk.rev.; circ. 900 (paid). **Document type:** newsletter.
 Formerly: Cranial Academy Newsletter (ISSN 0011-0825)

617 US ISSN 1070-5295
▼**CURRENT OPINION IN CRITICAL CARE.** 1994. bi-m. $129.95 to individuals; institutions $259.95; residents $55. Current Science, 400 Market St., Ste. 700, Philadelphia, PA 19106-2199.
TEL 215-574-2210; 800-552-5866.
FAX 215-574-3533. (And: Current Science Ltd., 34-42 Cleveland St., London W1P 6LB, England. TEL 0171-323-0323. FAX 0171-636-6911) Eds. R.C. Bone, J.L. Vincent. (back issues avail.) **Document type:** academic/scholarly publication.
●Also available online. Vendor(s): OCLC.
Also available on CD-ROM.
—BLDSC (3500.773800); ADONIS.

CURRENT OPINION IN ORTHOPEDICS. see *MEDICAL SCIENCES — Abstracting, Bibliographies, Statistics*

617.2 UK ISSN 0268-0890
 CODEN: CUOREH
CURRENT ORTHOPAEDICS. 1986. q. £81($130) to individuals; institutions £146 ($234) (effective 1995). Churchill Livingstone Journals (Subsidiary of: Pearson Professional), Robert Stevenson House, 1-3 Baxter's Pl., Leith Walk, Edinburgh EH1 3AF, Scotland. TEL 0131-556-2424.
FAX 0131-459-1177. (Subscr. to: Pearson Professional, Fourth Ave. Harlow, Essex CM19 5AA, England. TEL 01279-623760; U.S. subscr. to: Churchill Livingstone, 650 Ave. of the Americas, New York, NY 10011. TEL 212-206-5000) Ed. R.A. Dickson. adv. contact: David Dunnachie. illus. circ. 1,395. (also avail. in microfilm; back issues avail.; reprint service avail. from UMI) **Indexed:** Excerp.Med. **Document type:** academic/scholarly publication.
—BLDSC (3500.840000); Genuine Article. **CCC.**
 Description: Reviews topics in orthopedics for qualified and trainee orthopedic surgeons.

D.C. TRACTS. see *MEDICAL SCIENCES — Chiropractic, Homeopathy, Osteopathy*

MEDICAL SCIENCES — ORTHOPEDICS AND TRAUMATOLOGY 4501

617.3 UA ISSN 1110-1148
EGYPTIAN ORTHOPAEDIC JOURNAL/AL-MAJALLAH AL-MISRIYYAH LI-JIRAHAT AL-'ITHAM. (Text in Arabic, English, French) 1966. q. $80. Egyptian Orthopaedic Association, P.O. Box 4, Alexandria 21111, Egypt. TEL 20-3-4225626. Ed. Amin M. Rida. adv.; bk.rev.; abstr.; bibl.; charts; illus. circ. 4,000. Indexed: Biol.Abstr., Excerp.Med., ExtraMED. **Document type:** academic/scholarly publication, proceedings.
●Also available on CD-ROM.
—BLDSC (3664.430000).
 Formerly: Egyptian Orthopaedic Journal (ISSN 0013-242X)
 Description: Publishes original research articles, news, and proceedings.

610 US ISSN 0162-5942
RA995.A1
EMERGENCY; the journal of emergency services. 1969. m. $21.95 (foreign $33.95) effective 1991. Hare Publications (Subsidiary of: Dyna Corporation), 6300 Yarrow Dr., Carlsbad, CA 92009-1597. TEL 619-438-2511. FAX 619-931-5809. (Subscr. to: Box 159, Carlsbad, CA 92008) Ed. Doug Fiske. adv. contact: Pat Colatarci. bk.rev.; charts; illus. circ. 26,500. (also avail. in microform from UMI; back issues avail.; reprint service avail. from UMI) **Indexed:** CINAHL. **Document type:** trade publication.
—BLDSC (3733.168000); Faxon; SWETS; UMI.
 Formerly (until 1978): Emergency Product News (ISSN 0098-2180)
 Description: Trade journal for paramedics and EMTs covering topics and trends in EMS.

610 US ISSN 0094-6575
EMERGENCY MEDICAL SERVICES; the journal of emergency care, rescue and transportation. 1972. m. $19.95. Summer Communications Inc., Attn: Barbara Feiner, 7626 Densmore Ave., Van Nuys, CA 91406. TEL 818-786-4367. FAX 818-786-9246. Ed. Barbara Feiner. adv.: B&W page $3501, color page $4341. bk.rev. circ. 45,000. Indexed: CINAHL, Curr.Cont., Ind.Med. **Document type:** academic/scholarly publication.
—BLDSC (3733.187000); Faxon; UnCover.
 Description: Interdisciplinary publication covering critical medical, legal and psychosocial issues for emergency medical technicians, paramedics, administrators, physicians, nurses, and other emergency-care personnel.
 Refereed Serial

610 US ISSN 0013-6654
RC86
EMERGENCY MEDICINE; acute medicine for the primary care physician. 1969. m. $131 to institutions outside the Americas; $89 to institutions in U.S (effective 1996). Excerpta Medica, Inc. (Subsidiary of: Reed Elsevier Medical Group), 105 Raider Blvd., Belle Meade, NJ 08502. TEL 908-874-8550. FAX 908-874-5611. (Subscr. to: Box 3085, Princeton, NJ 08543-3085) Ed. Harry A. Atkins. adv.; bk.rev.; charts; illus.; index. circ. 129,450. (also avail. in microform from UMI; reprint service avail. from UMI) **Indexed:** C.I.N.L., Curr.Cont., Helminthol.Abstr., Hosp.Lit.Ind. **Document type:** academic/scholarly publication, trade publication.
—BLDSC (3733.190000); Genuine Article; SWETS; UMI; UnCover. **CCC.**
 Description: Emphasizes acute care medicine for primary care physicians.

617.1 US ISSN 0733-8627
CODEN: EMCAD7
EMERGENCY MEDICINE CLINICS OF NORTH AMERICA. 1983. q. $120 (foreign $146) (effective 1996). W.B. Saunders Co. (Subsidiary of: Harcourt Brace & Company), Curtis Center, 3rd Fl., Independence Sq. W., Phildelphia, PA 19106-3399. TEL 215-238-7800. FAX 215-238-6445. (Subscr. to: Periodicals Fulfillment, W.B. Saunders Co., 6277 Sea Harbor Dr., 4th Fl., Orlando, FL 32891-4800. TEL 800-654-2452) Ed. Sandy Hitchins. (also avail. in microform from UMI, Dok.Arbeitsmed., Excerp.Med. **Document type:** academic/scholarly publication.
—BLDSC (3733.190400); Faxon; SWETS; UMI; UnCover. **CCC.**

617 UK ISSN 0969-9546
▼**EUROPEAN JOURNAL OF EMERGENCY MEDICINE.** 1994. q. £59($99) to individuals; institutions in the E.U. £130 (N. America $225; elsewhere £145) (effective 1995). (European Society of Emergency Medicine) Chapman & Hall, Journals Department (Subsidiary of: International Thomson Publishing Group), 2-6 Boundary Row, London SE1 8HN, England. TEL 0171-865-0066. FAX 0171-865-9623. TELEX 290164 CHAPMA G. E-mail: journal@chall.mhs.compuserve.com. (Dist. by: International Thomson Publishing Services Ltd., Cheriton House, North Way, Andover, Hants. SP10 5BE England. TEL 01264-342713. FAX 01264-342807; N. American subscr. to: Chapman & Hall, Journals Promotion Department, One Penn Plaza, 41st Fl., New York, NY 10019. TEL 212-564-1060. FAX 212-564-1505) Ed. Herman Delooz. adv. (reprint service avail.) **Document type:** academic/scholarly publication.
—BLDSC (3829.728600). **CCC.**
 Description: Covers all aspects of acute injury and sudden illness, including anaesthesiology, cardiology, disaster medicine, intensive care, internal medicine, orthopedics, pediatrics, and trauma care.
 Refereed Serial

617.3 FR
EUROPEAN JOURNAL OF ORTHOPAEDIC SURGERY. French edition: Revue de Chirurgie Orthopedique et Reparatrice de l'Appareil Moteur (ISSN 0035-1040) 1987. q. foreign 1643 F. (effective 1996). Masson - Periodiques, Villa Laromiguiere, 75005 Paris, France. TEL 1-40-46-62-00. FAX 1-40-46-62-01. Ed. J.M. Thomine. **Document type:** academic/scholarly publication.
 Former titles: Journal of Orthopaedic Surgery (ISSN 1249-0237) & French Journal of Orthopaedic Surgery (ISSN 0981-1974)
 Description: Contains original articles on orthopaedic surgery, anatomy and reconstructive surgery.

617.3 FR
EUROPEAN JOURNAL OF ORTHOPAEDIC SURGERY & TRAUMATOLOGY. (Text in English, French) 1991. 4/yr. 1150 F.($241) (effective 1996). Springer-Verlag France, 26, rue des Carmes, 75005 Paris, France. TEL 44-41-15-80. FAX 43-54-49-08. (U.S. subscr. to: Springer-Verlag New York, Inc., Box 2485, Secaucus, NJ 07096-2491. TEL 201-348-4033) (Co-sponsors: Societe d'Orthopedie et de Traumatologie de l'Est; Groupement d'Etude pour la Chirurgie Osseuse) Eds. H. Coudane, P. Kehr. (also avail. in microform from UMI)
—SWETS; UMI. **CCC.**
 Formerly: Orthopedie - Traumatologie (ISSN 0940-3264)
 Description: Original basic and clinical research articles on all aspects of orthopaedic surgery and traumatology.

EXTRACTA ORTHOPAEDICA; Weltweit Auserlesen. see MEDICAL SCIENCES — Abstracting, Bibliographies, Statistics

617.752 658.8 UK
EYEWEAR: THE INTERNATIONAL MARKET. a. £1595($3190) Euromonitor, 60-61 Britton Rd., London EC1 5NA, England. TEL 0171-251-8024. FAX 0171-608-3149. (Addr. in N. America: Euromonitor International, 122 S. Michigan Ave., Ste. 1200, Chicago, IL 60603. TEL 312-922-1115. FAX 312-922-1157) (looseleaf format) **Document type:** trade publication.
●Also available online. Vendor(s): Data-Star, Knight-Ridder, Inc..
 Formerly (until 1995): Spectacles and Contact Lense: The International Market.
 Description: Analyzes the eye-glass and contact lens market for France, Germany, Italy, Spain, the U.K., the U.S., and Japan.

617.3 616.8 FR ISSN 0223-4696
FLASH-INFORMATIONS. 1978. 3/w. 600 Fr. Centre Technique National d'Etudes et de Recherches sur les Handicapes et les Inadaptations, 236 bis, rue de Tolbisc, 75013 Paris, France. TEL 47-36-74-10. bk.rev.

617.3 DK ISSN 0901-0408
FODTERAPEUTEN. 1932. m. (10/yr.) DKK 145. Landsforeningen af Statsautoriserede Fodterapeuter, Bjelkes Alle 43, 2200 Copenhagen, Denmark. Ed. Anita Ellekjaer Hansen. adv.; bk.rev. circ. 1,600.

617.1 UK ISSN 0958-2592
CODEN: FOOTEE
THE FOOT; international journal of foot surgery. 1991. q. £70($116) to individuals; institutions £148 ($245) (effective 1995). (International College of Foot Medicine and Surgery (CIP)) Churchill Livingstone Journals (Subsidiary of: Pearson Professional), Robert Stevenson House, 1-3 Baxter's Pl., Leith Walk, Edinburgh EH1 3AF, Scotland. TEL 0131-556-2424. FAX 0131-459-1177. (Subscr. to: Pearson Professional Ltd., P.O. Box 77, Fourth Ave., Harlow, Essex CM19 5AA, England. TEL 01279-623760; U.S. subscr. to: Churchill Livingstone, 650 Ave. of the Americas, New York, NY, 10011. TEL 212-206-5000) Eds. T. Duckworth, T.W.D. Smith. adv. contact: David Dunnachie. circ. 5,700. **Indexed:** Excerp.Med. (1993-). **Document type:** academic/scholarly publication.
—BLDSC (3984.840000). **CCC.**
 Description: Contains primary articles and commissioned reviews on disorders of the foot and their medical or surgical treatment.
 Refereed Serial

617.3 US ISSN 1083-7515
▼**FOOT AND ANKLE CLINICS.** Announced for publication in 1996. q. $118 (foreign $135) (effective 1996). W.B. Saunders Co. (Subsidiary of: Harcourt Brace & Co.), Curtis Center, 3rd Fl., Independence Sq. W., Philadelphia, PA 19106-3399. TEL 215-238-7800. FAX 212-238-6445. (Subscr. to: W.B. Saunders Co., Periodicals Dept., 6277 Sea Harbor Dr., 4th Fl., Orlando, FL 32891. TEL 800-654-2452. FAX 800-574-6418) **Document type:** academic/scholarly publication.
 Refereed Serial

617.3 US ISSN 1071-1007
RD781 CODEN: FAINE4
FOOT & ANKLE INTERNATIONAL. 1980. m. $95 to individuals; institutions $110 (effective 1995). (American Orthopaedic Foot and Ankle Society Inc.) Williams & Wilkins, 428 E. Preston St., Baltimore, MD 21202. TEL 410-528-4000; 800-638-6423. FAX 410-528-4312. Ed. Dr. Lowell D. Lutter. adv.; bk.rev. circ. 3,963. (also avail. in microfilm from WWS; back issues avail.) **Indexed:** Curr.Cont., Excerp.Med., Ind.Med., Rev.Med.& Vet.Mycol., Sportsearch (1981-). **Document type:** academic/scholarly publication.
—BLDSC (3984.860000); Genuine Article; SWETS; UnCover. **CCC.**
 Formerly (until 1994): Foot and Ankle (ISSN 0198-0211)
 Description: Focuses on new approaches to foot and ankle disorders and surgical treatment for orthopedic surgeons and podiatrists.
 Refereed Serial

617.3 US ISSN 1068-3100
FOOT AND ANKLE QUARTERLY. 1988. q. $150 to individuals; residents $95; institutions $295 (effective 1993; typically set in Dec.). Data Trace Medical Publishers, Inc., 110 West Rd., Ste. 227, Baltimore, MD 21204. TEL 410-494-4994. FAX 410-494-0515. Ed. Charles Gudas. (also avail. in microform from WWS) **Document type:** academic/scholarly publication.
—**CCC.**
 Formerly (until 1993): Podiatry Tracts (ISSN 0894-6116)
 Description: Provides condensations of current podiatric literature accompanied by in-depth commentaries written by experts on editorial board. Each issue also includes one 90-minute audio tape lecture.

617.3 GW ISSN 0015-816X
FORTSCHRITTE DER KIEFERORTHOPAEDIE. 1931. bi-m. DM.240($174) (effective 1996). (Deutsche Gesellschaft fuer Kieferorthopaedie) Urban and Vogel, Lindwurmstr. 95, 80337 Munich, Germany. TEL 089-53292-0. FAX 089-53292-100. (Subscr. to: Postfach 152209, 80052 Munich, Germany) Eds. Dr. H.G. Sergl, Dr. Eva Holtgrave. adv.; bk.rev.; bibl.; charts; illus.; index. circ. 2,500. **Indexed:** Biol.Abstr., Curr.Adv.Ecol.Sci., Curr.Tit.Dent., Dent.Ind., Excerp.Med., Ind.Med. **Document type:** academic/scholarly publication.
—BLDSC (4021.730000); SWETS; UMI. **CCC.**

MEDICAL SCIENCES — ORTHOPEDICS AND TRAUMATOLOGY

617.3 — GW — ISSN 0258-2015
CODEN: FUBEEE
DIE FUNKTIONSKRANKHEITEN DES BEWEGUNGSAPPARATES; Zeitschrift fuer interdisziplinaere Diagnostik und Therapie. 1986. irreg. (approx 2/yr.). DM.102 (foreign DM.106). (Internationaler Arbeitskreis zur Erforschung der Funktionskrankheiten des Bewegungsapparates e.V.) Gustav Fischer Verlag, Wollgrasweg 49, 70599 Stuttgart, Germany. TEL 0711-458030. FAX 0711-4580334. TELEX 7111488-FIBUCH. (Subscr. to: Postfach 720143, 70577 Stuttgart, Germany; U.S. address: VCH Publishers, Inc., 303 N.W. 12th Ave., Deerfield Beach, FL 33442-1788) Eds. L. Kaeser, F. Vele. **Document type:** academic/scholarly publication.
—BLDSC (4058.372000). **CCC.**

GAIT AND POSTURE. see *MEDICAL SCIENCES*

617.3 — IT — ISSN 0390-0134
GIORNALE ITALIANO DI ORTOPEDIA E TRAUMATOLOGIA. English edition: Italian Journal of Orthopaedics and Traumatology (ISSN 0390-5489) (Supplement avail.) 1975. 4/yr. $200 for Italian ed.; English ed. $110. Aulo Gaggi Editore, Via Andrea Costa 131-5, 40134 Bologna, Italy. TEL 0222-5339614. FAX 0222-638158. TELEX 114506. Ed. P. Perugia. adv.; bk.rev. circ. 4,750. **Indexed:** Biol.Abstr., Dent.Ind., Excerp.Med., Ind.Med., Rev.Med.& Vet.Mycol.
Description: Covers current thought, practice and research in the science of orthopedics and traumatology.

617.1 — FR — ISSN 0992-6739
GUIDE ANNUEL DES S A M U ET S M U R DE FRANCE. (Services d'Aide Medicale Urgente) a. 450 F. (foreign 500 F.). Societe Francaise d'Editions Medicales, 22-24 rue du Chateau des Rentiers, 75013 Paris, France. TEL 45-83-50-54. FAX 45-83-13-54.

617 — JA — ISSN 0917-365X
HAMAMATSU SEIKEI GEKA KIYO/HAMAMATSU UNIVERSITY. ANNUAL OF ORTHOPAEDIC SURGERY. (Text in English, Japanese) 1990. a. Hamamatsu Ika Daigaku, Seikei Gekagaku Kyoshitsu - Hamamatsu University, School of Medicine, Department of Orthopaedics, 3600, Handacho, Hamamatsu-shi, Shizuoka-ken 431-31, Japan.

617 — US — ISSN 0749-0712
HAND CLINICS. 1985. q. $145 (foreign $169) (effective 1996). W.B. Saunders Co. (Subsidiary of: Harcourt Brace & Company), Curtis Center, 3rd Fl., Independence Sq. W., Philadelphia, PA 19106-3399. TEL 215-238-7800. FAX 215-238-6445. (Subscr. to: Periodicals Fulfillment, W.B. Saunders Co., 6277 Sea Harbor Dr., 4th Fl., Orlando, FL 32891-4800. TEL 800-654-2452. FAX 800-874-6418) Ed. Melissa Mitchell. circ. 2,500. (also avail. in microfilm; back issues avail.) **Indexed:** Excerp.Med. **Document type:** academic/scholarly publication.
—BLDSC (4241.558000); Faxon; Genuine Article; SWETS; UMI; UnCover. **CCC.**
Description: Each issue addresses a single topic in the surgical therapy of patients with disorders of the hand.

HEAT SHOCK PROTEINS. see *BIOLOGY — Biological Chemistry*

610 — US — ISSN 0085-1469
CODEN: HUFHAR
HEFTE ZUR UNFALLHEILKUNDE. irreg. price varies. Springer-Verlag, 175 Fifth Ave., New York, NY 10010. TEL 212-460-1500. FAX 212-473-6272. (Also: Berlin, Heidelberg, Tokyo and Vienna) (also avail. in microform from UMI; reprint service avail. from ISI) **Indexed:** Biol.Abstr., Excerp.Med., Ind.Med. **Document type:** academic/scholarly publication.
—SWETS.

617.3 — JA — ISSN 0915-8855
HIGASHINIHON RINSHO SEIKEI GEKA GAKKAI ZASSHI/EASTERN JAPAN JOURNAL OF CLINICAL ORTHOPAEDICS. (Text in Japanese) 1989. irreg. Higashinihon Rinsho Seikei Geka Gakkai - Eastern Japan Society of Clinical Orthopaedics, Nihon Daigaku Igakubu, Seikei Gekagaku Kyoshitsu, 30-1, Oyaguchi Kamicho, Itabashi-ku, Tokyo 173, Japan.

617.3 — JA — ISSN 0389-3634
HIP JOINT. (Text in Japanese) 1975. a. 6000 Yen per no. Nihon Kokansetsu Kenkyukai - Japanese Hip Society, Yamanashi Ika Daigaku Seikei Gekagaku Kyoshitsu, 1110, Shimokato, Tamahocho, Nakakoma-gun, Yamanashi-ken 409-38, Japan.

617.3 — JA — ISSN 0018-3377
HOKKAIDO JOURNAL OF ORTHOPEDIC & TRAUMATIC SURGERY/HOKKAIDO SEIKEI SAIGAI GEKA ZASSHI. (Text in English, Japanese) 1954. a. Hokkaido Orthopedic and Traumatic Surgery Society - Hokkaido Seikei Saigai Geka Gakkai, c/o Hokkaido Daigaku Igakubu Seikei Geka Kyoshitsu, Nishi 7-chome, Kita 15-jo, Kita-ku, Sapporo-shi, Hokkaido 060, Japan. Ed.Bd. circ. 750. **Indexed:** Biol.Abstr., Excerp.Med., INIS Atomind.

617.3 — US
CODEN: BHJDEI
HOSPITAL FOR JOINT DISEASES. BULLETIN. 1940. q. $40. Hospital for Joint Diseases, Bernard Aronson Plaza, 301 E. 17th St., New York, NY 10003. TEL 212-598-6530. FAX 212-260-1203. Ed. Peter L. Ferrara. bk.rev.; charts; illus.; cum.index: 1965-81; 1982-85; 1986-89. circ. 2,500. (reprint service avail. from ISI,UMI) **Indexed:** Bioeng.Abstr., Biol.Abstr., Curr.Cont., Eng.Ind., Excerp.Med., Ind.Med., INIS Atomind. **Document type:** bulletin.
—BLDSC (2555.330000); Ei; Genuine Article; SWETS; UMI. **CCC.**
Former titles (until 1992): Hospital for Joint Diseases Orthopaedic Institute. Bulletin (ISSN 0883-9344); Hospital for Joint Diseases. Bulletin (ISSN 0018-5647)

617.585 — US
HOSPITAL PODIATRIST. 1976. a. membership. American Association of Hospital Podiatrists, c/o Earl L. Cherniak, D.P.M., Ed., 3984 S. Figueroa St., Los Angeles, CA 90037. TEL 213-747-7272. bk.rev. circ. 2,000. (back issues avail.) **Document type:** bulletin.

617.3 — II — ISSN 0019-5413
CODEN: INJOAU
INDIAN JOURNAL OF ORTHOPAEDICS. (Text in English) 1967. s-a. Rs.125($30) (Indian Orthopaedic Association) Banaras Hindu University, Institute of Medical Sciences, Varanasi 221005, India. Eds. Dr. S.M. Tuli, Dr. T.P. Srivastava. adv.; bk.rev.; bibl.; charts; illus.; index. circ. 1,600. **Indexed:** Excerp.Med., Indian Sci.Abstr.
—BLDSC (4417.750000).

617 — UK — ISSN 0020-1383
CODEN: INJUBF
INJURY; British journal of accident surgery. 1969. 10/yr. £250($398) (effective 1996). (Institute of Accident Surgery) Butterworth - Heinemann, Part of the Reed Elsevier group, Linacre House, Jordan Hill, Oxford OX2 8DP, England. TEL 0865-310366. FAX 0865-310898. TELEX 83111 BHPOXF G. (Dist. by: Elsevier Science Ltd., P.O. Box 800, Kidlington, OXford OX5 1DX, England. TEL 44-865-843000. FAX 44-865-843010; Subscr. in U.S. and Canada to: Elsevier Science, 660 White Plains Rd., Tarrytown, NY 10591-5153. TEL 914-524-9200. FAX 914-333-2444) Ed. O.N. Tubbs. adv.; bk.rev.; abstr.; bibl.; illus.; index. (also avail. in microform from UMI; back issues avail.) **Indexed:** Biol.Abstr., Curr.Adv.Ecol.Sci., Curr.Cont., Dent.Ind., Dok.Arbeitsmed., Excerp.Med., Ind.Med., Rev.Med.& Vet.Mycol. **Document type:** academic/scholarly publication.
—BLDSC (4514.400000); EMDOCS; Genuine Article; SWETS; UMI; UnCover. **CCC.**
Description: Deals with all aspects of trauma, including fractures and soft-tissue injuries, and covers problems in the accident unit.
Refereed Serial

617.3 — UK — ISSN 0960-2941
INTERNATIONAL JOURNAL OF ORTHOPAEDIC TRAUMA. 1991. q. £60 to individuals in the U.K. and rest of Europe (the U.S. $95; elsewhere £68); institutions in the U.K. and rest of Europe £85 (the U.S. $145; elsewhere £94). Castle House Publications Ltd., 28-30 Church Rd., Tunbridge Wells, Kent TN1 1JP, England. TEL 01892-539606. FAX 01892-517005. index. **Indexed:** Excerp.Med. **Document type:** academic/scholarly publication.
—BLDSC (4542.440200).

INTERNATIONAL JOURNAL OF TRAUMA NURSING. see *MEDICAL SCIENCES — Nurses And Nursing*

617.3 — GW — ISSN 0341-2695
INTERNATIONAL ORTHOPAEDICS. (Text in English, French) 1977. 6/yr. DM.628($456) (effective 1996). (Societe Internationale de Chirurgie Orthopedique et de Traumatologie, BE - International Society of Orthopaedic Surgery and Traumatology) Springer-Verlag, Heidelberger Platz 3, 14197 Berlin, Germany. TEL 030-8207-0. FAX 030-8214091. E-mail: orders@springer.de. (Subscr. in N. America to: Springer-Verlag New York, Inc., 44 Hartz Way, Secaucus, NJ 07096-2491. TEL 201-348-4033. FAX 201-348-4505) Ed. A. Trias. adv.; illus.; index. (also avail. in microform from UMI; reprint service avail. from ISI) **Indexed:** Curr.Adv.Cancer Res., Curr.Cont., Excerp.Med., Ind.Med., Ind.Sci.Rev., INIS Atomind., Sci.Cit.Ind. **Document type:** academic/scholarly publication.
—BLDSC (4544.856000); Faxon; Genuine Article; SWETS; UMI; UnCover. **CCC.**
Supersedes (1929-1972): International Society of Orthopaedic Surgery and Traumatology. Proceedings of Congresses (ISSN 0074-8552)
Description: Presents articles dealing with clinical orthopedic surgery or basic research directly connected with orthopedic surgery.

ISOKINETICS AND EXERCISE SCIENCE. see *MEDICAL SCIENCES — Sports Medicine*

617.3 — AU — ISSN 0390-5489
CODEN: IJOTD
ITALIAN JOURNAL OF ORTHOPAEDICS AND TRAUMATOLOGY. Italian Edition: Giornale Italiano di Ortopedia e Traumatologia (ISSN 0390-0134) (Text in English) 1975. 4/yr. DM.210.40 (effective 1993). Springer-Verlag, Sachsenplatz 4-6, Postfach 89, 1201 Vienna. TEL 0222-3302415. FAX 0222-3302426. TELEX 114506 SPRIW A. (U.S. subscr. to: Springer-Verlag New York, Inc., Box 2485, Secaucus, NJ 07096-2491. TEL 201-348-4033) (Co-publisher: Aulo Gaggi Editore, IT) Eds. S.G. Monticelli, E.A. Nicoll. (also avail. in microform from UMI) **Indexed:** Excerp.Med. (until 1993). **Document type:** academic/scholarly publication.
—SWETS; UMI; UnCover. **CCC.**
Description: Covers current thought, practice and research in the science of orthopedics and traumatology.

J O H N S: JOURNAL OF OTOLARYNGOLOGY, HEAD AND NECK SURGERY/JIBI INKOKA, TOKEIBU GEKA. see *MEDICAL SCIENCES — Otorhinolaryngology*

617.3 — GW — ISSN 0935-7890
JAHRBUCH DER ORTHOPAEDIE. 1988. a. DM.126.40. Biermann Verlag GmbH, Nideggenerstr. 18, 53909 Zuelpich, Germany. TEL 02252-9410-0. FAX 02252-941015. Eds. R. Venbrocks, G. Salis-Soglio. (back issues avail.) **Document type:** academic/scholarly publication.

617.3 — JA — ISSN 0021-5325
CODEN: NSGZA2
JAPANESE ORTHOPAEDIC ASSOCIATION. JOURNAL/NIPPON SEIKEI GEKA GAKKAI ZASSHI. (Text in English, Japanese) 1926. m. 14000 Yen. Japanese Orthopaedic Association - Nippon Seikei Geka Gakkai, 30-10, Hongo 3-chome, Bunkyo-ku, Tokyo 113, Japan. TEL 03-3816-3671. FAX 03-3818-2337. Ed. Koichiro Hayashi. adv. circ. 18,700. **Indexed:** Chem.Abstr., Dent.Ind., Excerp.Med., Ind.Med. **Document type:** academic/scholarly publication.
—BLDSC (4809.370000); CASDDS; EMDOCS.

617.3 — GW — ISSN 0941-4770
JATROS ORTHOPAEDIE - RHEUMATOLOGIE - SPORTMEDIZIN. 1986. 12/yr. DM.90. P M I Verlagsgruppe GmbH, August-Schanz-Str. 21, 60433 Frankfurt a.M., Germany. TEL 069-5480000. FAX 069-54800077. Ed. Peter Hoffmann. circ. 6,500. (back issues avail.) **Document type:** academic/scholarly publication.
Formerly: Jatros Orthopaedie (ISSN 0930-8326)
Description: Seminar paper journal containing summaries of orthopaedic articles, interviews and Congress reports.

MEDICAL SCIENCES — ORTHOPEDICS AND TRAUMATOLOGY

616 US ISSN 1078-6260
▼**THE JOINT LETTER**. 1995. m. $120 (foreign $135) (effective 1995). Quest Publishing Co., Inc., A Division of Raven Press Ltd. (Subsidiary of: Wolters Kluwer N.V.), 1351 Titan Way, Brea, CA 92621. TEL 714-738-6400. FAX 714-525-6258. (Subscr. to: Raven Press, 1185 Ave. of the Americas, New York, NY 10036. TEL 212-930-9500. FAX 212-869-3495) Pub. Mary Waltham. **Document type:** newsletter.
Description: Covers joint function, disease and injury.

617.3 FR ISSN 0242-648X
JOURNAL DE READAPTATION MEDICALE. q. 578 F. (foreign 798 F.) (effective 1996). Masson - Periodiques, Villa Laromiguiere, 75005 Paris, France. TEL 1-40-46-62-00. FAX 1-40-46-62-01. Ed. J.M. Wirotius. circ. 1,000. **Document type:** academic/scholarly publication.
—BLDSC (5047.460000). **CCC.**
Description: Deals with different therapies, as well as the material problems in kinesitherapy, ergotherapy and orthophony.

616 FR ISSN 0993-9857
CODEN: JEURE
JOURNAL EUROPEEN DES URGENCES/EUROPEAN JOURNAL OF EMERGENCIES. Variant title: J E U R. (Text in English, French) 1988. q. 615 F. (foreign 795 F.) (effective 1996). Masson - Periodiques, Villa Laromiguiere, 75005 Paris, France. TEL 1-40-46-62-00. FAX 1-40-46-62-01. TELEX 202 671 F. (Subscr. to: Masson-Periodiques, Z.I. Vineuil, B.P. 22, 41354 Vineuil, France) Ed. Patrick Barriot. adv. circ. 1,500. (back issues avail.) **Indexed:** Excerp.Med. **Document type:** academic/scholarly publication.
—BLDSC (4979.640500).
Description: Includes original articles, brief reviews, clinical cases and letters. Practical guide to emergency medicine for hospital practitioners.

617 US ISSN 0886-9723
RA645.5
JOURNAL OF AMBULATORY CARE MARKETING. 1980. s-a. $75 (foreign $105) (effective 1996). Haworth Press, Inc., 10 Alice St., Binghamton, NY 13904. TEL 607-722-5857; 800-342-9678. FAX 607-722-1424. Ed. M. Ven Venkatasen. circ. 136. (also avail. in microfiche from UMI; reprint service avail. from HAW,ISI) **Indexed:** Abstr.Health Care Manage.Stud., Bull.Signal., Excerp.Med., Hosp.Abstr., Hosp.Lit.Ind., Med.Care Rev., Ref.Zh., Saf.Sci.Abstr., Soc.Work Res.& Abstr. **Document type:** academic/scholarly publication.
—BLDSC (4927.230000); Faxon; Haworth.
Former titles (until 1987): Emergency Health Services Review (ISSN 0738-6192); Emergency Health Services Quarterly; Emergency Medical Services Quarterly (ISSN 0163-9358)
Description: Focuses on the marketing of traditional emergency health care, urgent and convenient care services, surgicenters, group practices providing emergency ambulatory care, and new sectors of health care, such as HMOs, IPAs, and PPOs that are involved in the provision of ambulatory health care services.
Refereed Serial

617.3 US ISSN 0883-5403
CODEN: JOAREG
JOURNAL OF ARTHROPLASTY. 1986. bi-m. $138 to individuals (foreign $177); institutions $175 (foreign $214). Churchill Livingstone International, 650 Ave. of the America, New York, NY 10011. TEL 212-206-5040. FAX 212-727-7808. TELEX 662266. Ed. Richard Rothman. adv.; charts; illus.; tr.lit.; index. circ. 7,800. (also avail. in microfilm; back issues avail.) **Indexed:** Excerp.Med., Ind.Med. **Document type:** academic/scholarly publication.
—BLDSC (4947.211500); Genuine Article; SWETS; UnCover. **CCC.**
Description: Basic scientific and clinical information on joint replacement surgery. Covers surgical techniques, prosthetic design, biomechanics, biomaterials, metallurgy, and the biologic response to arthroplasty materials in vivo and in vitro.
Refereed Serial

617.3 IE ISSN 1053-8127
CODEN: JBMRFK
JOURNAL OF BACK AND MUSCULOSKELETAL REHABILITATION. 1991. bi-m. I£124($196) (effective 1996). Elsevier Science Ireland Ltd., P.O. Box 85, Limerick, Ireland. TEL 353-61-471944. FAX 353-61-471944. (Subscr. in U.S. and Canada to: Elsevier Science, Box 882, Madison Sq. Sta., New York, NY 10159-0882. TEL 212-989-5800. FAX 212-633-3990) Ed. Dr. Karen Rucker. (also avail. in microform from UMI; back issues avail.) **Document type:** academic/scholarly publication.
—BLDSC (4950.900000); Genuine Article; UMI. **CCC.**
Description: Provides clinicians with a current guide to the assessment, diagnosis, and management of back and musculoskeletal disorders.

617.3 US ISSN 0021-9355
CODEN: JBJSA3
JOURNAL OF BONE AND JOINT SURGERY: AMERICAN VOLUME. 1903. m. $80 (U.K. £55) (effective 1995). Journal of Bone and Joint Surgery, Inc., 20 Pickering St., Needham, MA 02192-3157. TEL 617-449-9738. Ed. Henry R. Cowell. adv.; bk.rev.; bibl.; charts; illus.; index; cum.index every 5 yrs. circ. 38,036. (also avail. in microfilm from UMI; reprint service avail. from UMI) **Indexed:** Abstr.Health Care Manage.Stud., AIM, Bibl.Dev.Med.& Child Neur., Biol.Abstr., Chem.Abstr., CIJE, Curr.Cont., Dent.Ind., Excerp.Med., Ind.Med., Ind.Sci.Rev., INIS Atomind., Nutr.Abstr., Sci.Cit.Ind, Vet.Bull. **Document type:** academic/scholarly publication.
●Also available online. Vendor(s): Ovid Technologies.
—BLDSC (4954.250000); CASDDS; EMDOCS; Faxon; Genuine Article; SWETS; UMI; UnCover.
Supersedes in part: Journal of Bone and Joint Surgery (ISSN 0375-9229)
Refereed Serial

617.3 UK ISSN 0301-620X
CODEN: JBSUAK
JOURNAL OF BONE AND JOINT SURGERY: BRITISH VOLUME. 1948. bi-m. (plus 3 supplements). £38($61) (effective 1996) (includes supplements). British Editorial Society of Bone and Joint Surgery, 22 Buckingham St., London WC2N 6ET, England. TEL 0171-782-0010. FAX 0171-782-0995. (Subscr. in the U.S. to: Journal of Bone and Joint Surgery, Inc., 20 Pickering St., Needham, MA 02192-3157. TEL 617-449-9738) Ed. Philip Fulford. adv. contact: Pam Noble. bk.rev.; bibl.; charts; illus.; index. circ. 30,000. (also avail. in microfilm from UMI; back issues avail.; reprint service avail. from UMI) **Indexed:** AIM, Bibl.Dev.Med.& Child Neur., Biol.Abstr., Chem.Abstr., Curr.Adv.Cancer Res., Dent.Ind., Excerp.Med., Ind.Med., Ind.Sci.Rev., Ind.Vet., Nutr.Abstr., Sci.Cit.Ind, Vet.Bull. **Document type:** academic/scholarly publication.
●Also available on CD-ROM.
—BLDSC (4954.255000); CASDDS; Faxon; Genuine Article; SWETS; UMI.
Description: Devoted to traumatic and orthopedic surgery and rheumatology.
Refereed Serial

617.3 UK ISSN 0968-7300
JOURNAL OF BONE AND JOINT SURGERY: BRITISH VOLUME ON C D - R O M. 1984. a. £209 (effective 1995). British Editorial Society of Bone and Joint Surgery, 22 Buckingham St., London WC2N 6ET, England. TEL 0171-782-0010. FAX 0171-782-0995. Ed. Philip Fulford. adv. contact: Pam Noble. bk.rev. **Document type:** academic/scholarly publication, proceedings.

616.7 US ISSN 0884-0431
CODEN: JBMREJ
JOURNAL OF BONE AND MINERAL RESEARCH. 1986. m. $345 (foreign $395) (effective 1996). (American Society for Bone and Mineral Research) Blackwell Science Inc., 238 Main St., Cambridge, MA 02142. TEL 617-876-7022. FAX 617-492-5263. (Co-sponsor: National Osteoporosis Foundation) **Indexed:** Dairy Sci.Abstr., Kidney. **Document type:** academic/scholarly publication.
—BLDSC (4954.255530); CASDDS; Faxon; Genuine Article; SWETS; UnCover. **CCC.**
Description: Publishes papers on all areas of calcium regulation, skeletal physiology, and metabolic bone diseases.

615.585 UK ISSN 0961-6055
JOURNAL OF BRITISH PODIATRIC MEDICINE; chiropodist. 1914. m. £40. Society of Chiropodists, 53 Welbeck St., London W1M 7HE, England. TEL 071-486-3381. FAX 071-935-6359. Ed. B.L. Berry. adv.; bk.rev.; illus.; index. circ. 7,750. (also avail. in microfilm from UMI) **Indexed:** Curr.Adv.Ecol.Sci. **Document type:** academic/scholarly publication.
—BLDSC (4954.515000); UMI.
Formerly (until 1991): Chiropodist (ISSN 0009-4706)

JOURNAL OF BURN CARE AND REHABILITATION. see *MEDICAL SCIENCES*

610 US ISSN 0883-9441
CODEN: JCCAER
JOURNAL OF CRITICAL CARE. 1986 (Mar.). q. $165 (foreign $199) (effective 1996). W.B. Saunders Co. (Subsidiary of: Harcourt Brace & Company), Curtis Center, 3rd Fl., Independence Sq. W., Philadelphia, PA 19106-3399. TEL 215-238-7800. FAX 215-238-6445. (Subscr. to: Periodicals Fulfillment, W.B. Saunders Co., 6277 Sea Harbor Dr., 4th Fl. Orlando, FL 32891-4800. TEL 800-654-2452. FAX 800-874-6418) Ed. Dr. Michael R. Pinsky; Pub. Joan W. Blumberg. adv.; B&W page $690, color page $1690; 7 x 10. abstr.; bibl.; charts; illus.; index. circ. 1,437. **Indexed:** Excerp.Med., Ind.Med. (1993-). **Document type:** academic/scholarly publication.
—BLDSC (4965.630000); CASDDS; Faxon; Genuine Article; SWETS; UMI; UnCover. **CCC.**
Description: Presents multidisciplinary basic and clinical research, pertinent reviews, ethical and legal controversies, and important abstracts in all specialties and subspecialties of the field.
Refereed Serial

617.3 UK ISSN 0736-4679
JOURNAL OF EMERGENCY MEDICINE. 1983. bi-m. $385 to institutions (effective 1996). (Canadian Association of Emergency Physicians) Elsevier Science Ltd., Pergamon, P.O. Box 800, Kidlington, Oxford OX5 1DX, England. TEL 44-1865-843000. FAX 44-1865-843010. E-mail: nlinfo-f@elsevier.nl; usinfo-f@elsevier.com; forinfo-kyf04035@niftyserve.or.jp; Site addr.: http://www.elsevier.nl/. (Subscr. in U.S. and Canada to: Elsevier Science, 660 White Plains Rd., Tarrytown, NY 10591-5153. TEL 914-524-9200. FAX 914-333-2444) Ed. Peter Rosen. (also avail. in microfilm from UMI; back issues avail.) **Indexed:** CINAHL, Excerp.Med., Ind.Med., Med.& Surg.Dermat., Rev.Med.& Vet.Mycol. **Document type:** academic/scholarly publication.
—BLDSC (4977.250000); Faxon; SWETS; UMI; UnCover. **CCC.**
Refereed Serial

617 US ISSN 0885-9701
JOURNAL OF HEAD TRAUMA REHABILITATION. 1986. q. $99 (foreign $119. Aspen Publishers, Inc., 200 Orchard Ridge Dr., Gaithersburg, MD 20878. TEL 301-417-7500. FAX 301-417-7550. **Indexed:** CINAHL, Excerp.Med., IMFL, Psychol.Abstr. (1986-).
—BLDSC (4996.672000); SWETS; UMI; UnCover. **CCC.**
Refereed Serial

JOURNAL OF MANIPULATIVE AND PHYSIOLOGICAL THERAPEUTICS. see *MEDICAL SCIENCES — Chiropractic, Homeopathy, Osteopathy*

617.3 US ISSN 0899-2517
JOURNAL OF MUSCULOSKELETAL MEDICINE. 1983. m. $70. Cliggott Publishing Co., 55 Holly Hill Ln., Box 4010, Greenwich, CT 06830. TEL 203-661-0600. Ed. Leo Cristofar; Pub. Kenneth Watkins. adv. contact: Kenneth Watkins. circ. 94,000. (reprint service avail.) **Document type:** academic/scholarly publication.
—BLDSC (5021.125000). **CCC.**
Description: Provides practical information on diagnosis and management of a wide variety of common musculoskeletal disorders.
Refereed Serial

MEDICAL SCIENCES — ORTHOPEDICS AND TRAUMATOLOGY

617 US ISSN 1058-2452
RC927.3 CODEN: JMPAEQ
JOURNAL OF MUSCULOSKELETAL PAIN. 1993. q. $90 (foreign $126) (effective 1996). Haworth Press, Inc., 10 Alice St., Binghamton, NY 13904. TEL 607-722-5857; 800-342-9678. FAX 607-722-1424. TELEX 4932599. Ed. I. Jon Russell. adv.; bk.rev.; charts; illus.; stat. (also avail. in microfiche from UMI; reprint service avail. from HAW) **Indexed:** Excerp.Med. (1993-), Ref.Zh. **Document type:** academic/scholarly publication.
—BLDSC (5021.126000); Haworth.
Description: Publishes articles by the vast array of professionals who must deal with acute and chronic musculoskeletal pain.
Refereed Serial

617 US ISSN 0897-7151
CODEN: JNEUE4
JOURNAL OF NEUROTRAUMA. 1984. bi-m. $141 (foreign $181). (Neurotrauma Society) Mary Ann Liebert, Inc. Publishers, 2 Madison Ave., Larchmont, NY 10538. TEL 914-834-3100. FAX 914-834-3688. E-mail: Liebert@pipeline.com. Ed. Dr. John T. Polvishack. adv.; bk.rev. (back issues avail.) **Document type:** academic/scholarly publication.
—BLDSC (5022.270000); Faxon; Genuine Article; SWETS; UnCover.
Formerly: Central Nervous System Trauma (ISSN 0737-5999)
Description: Covers advances in the mechanisms and treatments of neurotrauma of the central and peripheral nervous system. Focuses on neurochemical, neurophysiological, and neuropathological research on spinal cord injury, head trauma, neural injury, and stroke.

JOURNAL OF OCULAR TRAUMA. see *MEDICAL SCIENCES — Ophthalmology And Optometry*

JOURNAL OF ORTHOPAEDIC AND SPORTS PHYSICAL THERAPY. see *MEDICAL SCIENCES — Sports Medicine*

617.3 US ISSN 0736-0266
CODEN: JOREDR
JOURNAL OF ORTHOPAEDIC RESEARCH; a journal for musculoskeletal investigations. 1983. bi-m. $164 to individuals; institutions $231. (Orthopaedic Research Society) Journal of Bone and Joint Surgery, Inc., 20 Pickering St., Needham, MA 02192-3145. TEL 617-734-2835. Eds. Dr. Wayne H. Akeson, Wilson C. Hayes. adv.; illus.; index. circ. 2,500. (back issues avail.) **Indexed:** Curr.Adv.Ecol.Sci., Dok.Arbeitsmed., Excerp.Med., Ind.Med., INIS Atomind. **Document type:** academic/scholarly publication.
—BLDSC (5027.665000); CASDDS; Ei; Faxon; Genuine Article; SWETS; UMI; UnCover. **CCC.**
Description: Covers experimental, theoretical and clinical aspects of orthopaedics.
Refereed Serial

JOURNAL OF ORTHOPAEDIC RHEUMATOLOGY. see *MEDICAL SCIENCES — Rheumatology*

617.3 GW
▼**JOURNAL OF ORTHOPAEDIC SCIENCE.** (Text in English) Announced for publication in 1996. bi-m. DM.260($188) (effective 1996). (Japanese Orthopaedic Association, JA) Springer-Verlag, Heidelberger Platz 3, 14197 Berlin, Germany. TEL 030-8207-0. FAX 030-8214091. (Subscr. in N. America to: Springer-Verlag New York, Inc., 44 Hartz Way, Secaucus, NJ 07096-2491. TEL 201-348-4033. FAX 201-348-4505) **Document type:** academic/scholarly publication.
Description: Documents the latest research and topical debates in all fields of clinical and experimental orthopedics.

617.3 HK ISSN 1022-5536
CODEN: JOTSEC
JOURNAL OF ORTHOPAEDIC SURGERY. (Text in English) 1962. s-a. $60 (effective 1996). (Western Pacific Orthopaedic Association) Hong Kong University Press, 139 Pokfulam Rd., Hong Kong. TEL 8183761. FAX 8728938. (Subscr. to: 4-F MacLehose Medical Rehabilitation Centre, 7 Sha Wan Dr., Sandy Bay, Rokfulam Rd., Hong Kong) Ed. David Fang. adv.; bk.rev.; charts; illus.; circ. 2,000 (controlled). (also avail. in microform from UMI; reprint service avail. from UMI) **Indexed:** Excerp.Med.
—BLDSC (5027.669000); EMDOCS; UMI.
Formerly: Western Pacific Orthopaedic Association. Journal (ISSN 0043-4019)

617.3 UK ISSN 1056-7437
CODEN: JOTTEF
JOURNAL OF ORTHOPAEDIC TECHNIQUES. 1993. q. $85 to individuals (foreign $107); institutions $126 (foreign $148). Stockton Press (Subsidiary of: Macmillan Press Ltd.), Houndmills, Basingstoke, Hampshire RG21 6XS, England. TEL 01256-817245. FAX 01256-28339. circ. 1,000. **Indexed:** Excerp.Med. (1994-). **Document type:** academic/scholarly publication.
—BLDSC (5027.673000). **CCC.**
Description: Forum for innovations and advances in operative and non-operative techniques.
Refereed Serial

617.3 US ISSN 0890-5339
CODEN: JORTE5
JOURNAL OF ORTHOPAEDIC TRAUMA. 1987. bi-m. $145 to individuals (foreign $174); institutions $192 (foreign $232) (effective 1996); newsstand price: $30. (Orthopaedic Trauma Association) Lippincott - Raven Press, 276 E. Washington Sq., Philadelphia, PA 19106. TEL 215-238-4200. (Co-sponsor: International Society for Fracture Repair) Ed. Dr. Philip G. Spiegel. adv. contact: Phyllis Noyes. bk.rev.; charts; illus.; index. circ. 2,000. (back issues avail.; reprint service avail. from UMI) **Indexed:** Ind.Med. **Document type:** academic/scholarly publication.
—BLDSC (5027.675000); Faxon; Genuine Article; SWETS; UMI; UnCover. **CCC.**
Description: Publishes original articles on the diagnosis and management of hard and soft tissue trauma.

JOURNAL OF ORTHOPEDIC SURGICAL TECHNIQUES. see *MEDICAL SCIENCES — Surgery*

617.533 US
JOURNAL OF OSTEOPATHIC MEDICINE.* 1987. m. (except Apr.-May, Nov.-Dec. combined). membership only. (American College of General Practitioners of Osteopathic Medicine and Surgery) In Vivo Inc., 1205 Westlakes Dr., Ste. 150, Berwyn, PA 19312-2405. adv.; circ. 33,000 (controlled). **Document type:** academic/scholarly publication.

617.3 US ISSN 0271-6798
CODEN: JPORDO
JOURNAL OF PEDIATRIC ORTHOPAEDICS. 1981. bi-m. $154 to individuals (foreign $200); institutions $275 (foreign $317) (effective 1996); newsstand price: $55. Lippincott - Raven Publishers, 276 E. Washington Sq., Philadelphia, PA 19106. TEL 215-238-4200. Eds. Dr. Lynn T. Staheli, Dr. Robert N. Hensinger. adv. contact: Phyllis Noyes. bk.rev.; illus.; index. circ. 3,500. (back issues avail.; reprint service avail. from UMI) **Indexed:** Bibl.Dev.Med.& Child Neur., Biol.Abstr., Excerp.Med., Ind.Med., Psychol.Abstr., Rev.Med.& Vet.Mycol. **Document type:** academic/scholarly publication.
—BLDSC (5030.225000); Faxon; Genuine Article; SWETS; UMI; UnCover. **CCC.**
Description: Provides answers to pediatric orthopaedic problems.
Refereed Serial

617.3 US ISSN 1060-152X
JOURNAL OF PEDIATRIC ORTHOPAEDICS, PART B. 1992. q. $125 to individuals (foreign $147); institutions $184 (foreign $202) (effective 1996); newsstand price: $103. (European Paediatric Orthopaedic Society) Lippincott - Raven Press, 276 E. Washington Sq., Philadelphia, PA 19106. TEL 215-238-4200. Ed. Henri Bensahel. adv. contact: Phyllis Noyes. charts; illus. circ. 2,000. (also avail. in microform from UMI) **Document type:** academic/scholarly publication.
—BLDSC (5030.230000); Genuine Article; UMI. **CCC.**
Description: Publishes recent developments in the treatment of musculoskeletal disorders in children, with an emphasis on advances from the European Community.
Refereed Serial

617.3 US ISSN 1040-8800
RD130
JOURNAL OF PROSTHETICS AND ORTHOTICS. 1988. q. $60 (foreign $80) (effective 1996). American Academy of Orthotists and Prosthetists, 1650 King St., Ste. 500, Alexandria, VA 22314. TEL 703-836-7116. FAX 703-836-0838. (Co-sponsor: American Orthotic and Prosthetic Association) Ed. C. Michael Schuch. adv.; bk.rev. circ. 4,600. (also avail. in microfilm from UMI) **Indexed:** CINAHL. **Document type:** academic/scholarly publication.
—BLDSC (5042.910000); Faxon; SWETS; UMI.
Formed by the merger of (1947-1988): Orthotics and Prosthetics (ISSN 0030-5928); Which was formerly (until 1967): Orthopedic and Prosthetic Appliance Journal; (1970-1988): Clinical Prosthetics and Orthotics (ISSN 0735-0090); Which was formerly (until 1982): Newsletter, Prosthetics and Orthotics Clinic (ISSN 0279-6910)
Description: Presents articles and reports from professionals on current topics in orthotics and prosthetics.
Refereed Serial

617.3 US ISSN 0748-7711
RD130 CODEN: JRRDEC
JOURNAL OF REHABILITATION RESEARCH AND DEVELOPMENT. 1964. q. free to qualified personnel. Department of Veterans Affairs, Office of Technology Transfer, 103 S. Gay St., Baltimore, MD 21202. TEL 410-962-1800. FAX 410-962-9670. bk.rev.; abstr.; bibl.; charts; illus.; pat.; stat. circ. 27,000. (also avail. in microform from UMI; reprint service avail. from UMI) **Indexed:** Appl.Mech.Rev., Bioeng.Abstr., Biol.Abstr., Except.Child.Educ.Abstr., Excerp.Med., HRIS, Ind.Med., Rehabil.Lit. **Document type:** government publication.
●Also available online. Vendor(s): University Microfilms International.
—Ei; Faxon; UMI; UnCover.
Former titles: Journal of Rehabilitation R and D; Bulletin of Prosthetics Research (ISSN 0007-506X)

617.3 US ISSN 0895-0385
CODEN: JSDIEW
JOURNAL OF SPINAL DISORDERS. 1985. bi-m. $130 to individuals (foreign $160); institutions $174 (foreign $208) (effective 1996); newsstand price: $36. Lippincott - Raven Press, 276 E. Washington Sq., Philadelphia, PA 19106. TEL 215-238-4200. Eds. Dan M. Spengler, Thomas B. Ducker. adv. contact: Phyllis Noyes. charts; illus. circ. 2,000. (reprint service avail. from UMI) **Indexed:** Excerp.Med., Ind.Med. (1992-). **Document type:** academic/scholarly publication.
—BLDSC (5066.182000); Faxon; Genuine Article; SWETS; UMI. **CCC.**
Description: Features research and clinical articles on diagnosis, management, and treatment of lumbar spine disorders.
Refereed Serial

JOURNAL OF SPORTS TRAUMATOLOGY AND RELATED RESEARCH. see *MEDICAL SCIENCES — Sports Medicine*

617.1 614.49 SW ISSN 0345-5564
JOURNAL OF TRAFFIC MEDICINE; an international journal of traffic safety. (Supplement avail.: Congress Proceedings) (Text in English) 1973. q. 75 SFr. (effective 1993). International Association for Accident and Traffic Medicine, c/o Kjell Roos, IAATM Headquarters, P.O. Box 1644, S-751 46 Uppsala, Sweden. TEL 4618-175-158. FAX 4618-175-031. Ed. James A. Dunbar. adv.; bk.rev.; illus.; stat. circ. 900. **Indexed:** Excerp.Med., HRIS.
—BLDSC (5069.755000).
Refereed Serial

610 JA ISSN 0022-5274
CODEN: KOIGAU
JOURNAL OF TRANSPORTATION MEDICINE; kotsu igaku. (Text in English, Japanese) 1947. bi-m. 7000 Yen. Japanese Association of Transportation Medicine - Nihon Kotsu Igakkai, c/o Business Center for Academic Societies Japan, 5-16-9 Honkomagome, Bunkyo-ku, Tokyo 113, Japan. TEL 03-5814-5811. FAX 03-5814-5822. Ed. Takashi Murayama. adv.; circ. 600 (controlled). **Indexed:** C.I.S. Abstr., Excerp.Med., Ind.Med., INIS Atomind. **Document type:** academic/scholarly publication.
—BLDSC (5070.400000); CASDDS; EMDOCS.

MEDICAL SCIENCES — ORTHOPEDICS AND TRAUMATOLOGY 4505

617 US ISSN 1079-6061
RD92 CODEN: JOTRFA
JOURNAL OF TRAUMA - INJURY, INFECTION AND CRITICAL CARE. 1961. m. $131 to individuals; institutions $171 (effective 1995). (American Association for the Surgery of Trauma) Williams & Wilkins, 428 E. Preston St., Baltimore, MD 21202. TEL 410-528-4000; 800-638-6423. FAX 410-528-4312. TELEX 87669. Ed. Dr. Basil A. Pruitt, Jr. adv.; abstr.; charts; illus.; stat.; tr.lit.; index. circ. 6,570. (also avail. in microfilm from WWS) **Indexed:** AIM, Biol.Abstr., C.I.S. Abstr., C.L.I., Chem.Abstr., CINAHL, Curr.Adv.Ecol.Sci., Curr.Cont., Dent.Ind., Excerp.Med., HRIS, Ind.Med., Ind.Sci.Rev., Ind.Vet., INIS Atomind., Int.Nurs.Ind., L.R.I., Rev.Med.& Vet.Mycol., Sci.Cit.Ind.
●Also available on CD-ROM.
—BLDSC (5070.512000); CASDDS; EMDOCS; Faxon; Genuine Article; SWETS; UnCover. **CCC.**
Formerly: Journal of Trauma (ISSN 0022-5282)
Description: Diagnosis, management and recommendations for surgical approaches to traumatic injury for orthopedic, plastic and general surgeons.
Refereed Serial

JOURNAL OF TRAUMA NURSING. see *MEDICAL SCIENCES — Nurses And Nursing*

JOURNAL OF VETERINARY EMERGENCY AND CRITICAL CARE. see *VETERINARY SCIENCE*

617.1 UK ISSN 0969-0700
JOURNAL OF WOUND CARE. 1992. m. £33 to individuals; institutions £61. Macmillan Magazines, 4 Little Essex St., London WC2R 3LF, England. TEL 0171-836-6633. FAX 0171-240-1227. (Subscr. to: Macmillan Magazines, Brunel Rd., Basingstoke RG21 2XS, England. TEL 01256-29242. FAX 01256-812358) Ed. Suzie Calne. adv. contact: Nic Lewisohn. bk.rev.; charts; illus.; patent.; cum.index. **Document type:** academic/scholarly publication.
—BLDSC (5072.695000). **CCC.**
Refereed Serial

617.3 JA ISSN 0915-1451
KANAGAWA SEIKEI SAIGAI GEKA IKAI ZASSHI/KANAGAWA JOURNAL OF ORTHOPEDICS AND TRAUMATOLOGY. (Text in Japanese) 1988. a. Kanagawa Seikei Saigai Geka Ikai - Kanagawa Society of Orthopedics and Traumatology, Showa Daigaku Fujigaoka Byoin Seikei Geka Kyoshitsu, 1-30, Fujigaoka, Midori-ku, Yokohama-shi, Kanagawa-ken 277, Japan.

617 JA ISSN 0915-7786
KANSAI KANSETSUKYO HIZA KENKYUKAISHI/JOURNAL OF KANSAI ARTHROSCOPY AND KNEE. (Text in Japanese) 1990. a. Kansai Kansetsukyo Hiza Kenkyukai - Kansai Arthroscopy and Knee Society, c/o Kyoto Furitsu Ika Daigaku, Seikei Gekagaku Kyoshitsu, Kajiicho, Hirokoji, Kawaramachi, Kamigyo-ku, Kyoto 602, Japan.

617.3 JA ISSN 0286-5394
KANSETSU GEKA/JOURNAL OF JOINT SURGERY. (Text in Japanese) 1981. bi-m. 1800 Yen per no. Medical View Co., Ltd. - Mejikaru Byusha, 2-30, Ichigaya Honmuracho, Shinjuku-ku, Tokyo 162, Japan.

617.3 JA ISSN 0285-6255
KANSETSU NO GEKA/JOINT SURGERY. (Text in Japanese) 1974. q. 1500 Yen per no. Shizen Kagakusha Co., Ltd., 1-4, Iidabashi 2-chome, Chiyoda-ku, Tokyo 102, Japan.

617.3 JA ISSN 0389-7087
CODEN: KSSZDW
KANTO SEIKEI SAIGAI GEKA GAKKAI ZASSHI/KANTO JOURNAL OF ORTHOPEDICS AND TRAUMATOLOGY. (Text in Japanese) 1970. bi-m. membership. Kanto Seikei Saigai Geka Gakkai - Kanto Society of Orthopedics and Traumatology, Tokyo Jikeikai Ika Daigaku Seikei Gekagaku Kyoshitsu, 25-8, Nishishinbashi 3-chome, Minato-ku, Tokyo 105, Japan. **Indexed:** INIS Atomind.

617.3 JA ISSN 0287-2285
KOSSETSU/FRACTURE. (Text in Japanese) 1978. a. 6000 Yen (effective 1996). Nihon Kossetsu Chiryo Gakkai - Japan Fracture Society, Kitasato Daigaku Igakubu Seikei Geka, 15-1, Kitazato 1-chome, Sagamihara-shi, Kanagawa-ken 228, Japan. Ed. Moritoshi Itoman. **Document type:** proceedings.

KOTSU KANSETSU JINTAI/JOURNAL OF MUSCULOSKELETAL SYSTEM. see *MEDICAL SCIENCES — Rheumatology*

617.3 JA
KOTSU KEITO SHIKKAN KENKYUKAI SHOROKU/JAPANESE SOCIETY FOR SKELETAL DYSPLASIAS. PROCEEDINGS OF THE MEETING. (Text in English, Japanese) 1989. a. Kotsu Keito Shikkan Kenkyukai, Niigata Daigaku Igakubu Seikei Gekagaku Kyoshitsu, 757, Asahimachi Dori Ichibancho, Niigata-shi, Niigata-ken 951, Japan. **Document type:** proceedings.

616 360 UK
L A S NEWS. 1966. m. free to qualified personnel. London Ambulance Service, 220 Waterloo Rd., London SE1 8SD, England. TEL 071-928-0333. FAX 071-401-8969. Ed. Andrew Faith. circ. 3,000. (back issues avail.) **Document type:** newsletter.
Formerly: Londam.

617.3 617.95 HU ISSN 1217-3231
MAGYAR TRAUMATOLOGIA, ORTHOPEDIA, KEZSEBESZET ES PLASZTIKAI SEBESZET. (Text in Hungarian; summaries in English, German, Russian) 1958. q. 1000 Ft. Fiumei ut 17, 1081 Budapest, Hungary. TEL 36-1-1337152. FAX 36-1-1330966. Ed. Tibor Vizkelety. adv.; bk.rev.; charts; illus.; pat.; index. circ. 1,000. **Indexed:** Biol.Abstr., Excerp.Med. (until 1992), Ind.Med., INIS Atomind.
—BLDSC (5345.850000).
Formerly (until no.4, 1992): Magyar Traumatologia, Orthopedia es Helyreallito-Sebeszet (ISSN 0025-0317)

MEALEY'S LITIGATION REPORT: PEDICLE SCREWS. see *LAW — Corporate Law*

MEDICINE AND SPORT SCIENCE. see *MEDICAL SCIENCES — Sports Medicine*

617.3 BL
MEDISOM: ORTHOPEDICS. 1981. bi-m. $90. Editora Medisom, Ltda., Rua Sao Paulino 224, Caixa Postal 7650, 01064-970 Sao Paulo, Brazil. FAX 55-11-572-5957. Ed. R. Philip Querido. adv. (audio cassette)

617.3 GW ISSN 0340-5508
MEDIZINISCH-ORTHOPAEDISCHE TECHNIK. 1880. bi-m. DM.126.70 (foreign DM.153.60) (effective 1995). Verlagsgemeinschaft Gentner Verlag - Strobel Verlag, Forststr. 131, 70193 Stuttgart, Germany. TEL 0711-63672-0. FAX 0711-6367211. Ed. Dr. Grifko. adv. contact: G. Keuchen. bk.rev.; charts; illus.; pat.; index. circ. 3,600. **Document type:** academic/scholarly publication.
—BLDSC (5535.073800). **CCC.**

617.3 IT
CODEN: MIORA5
MINERVA ORTOPEDICA E TRAUMATOLOGICA. (Text in Italian; summaries in English, Italian) 1950. m. $110 to individuals; institutions $150 (effective 1995). (Societa Piemontese - Ligure - Lombarda di Ortopedia e Traumatologia) Edizioni Minerva Medica, Corso Bramante 83-85, Turin, Italy. TEL 39-11-678282. FAX 39-11-3121736. Ed. Alberto Oliaro; Pub. Alberto Oliaro. adv.: B&W page $1300, color page $2200; trim 190 x 270; adv. contact: F. Filippo. bk.rev.; bibl.; charts; illus.; index; circ. 3,000 (paid). **Indexed:** Chem.Abstr., Excerp.Med., Ind.Med. **Document type:** academic/scholarly publication.
—BLDSC (5794.315000); EMDOCS; SWETS.
Formerly: Minerva Ortopedica (ISSN 0026-4911)

617 UK ISSN 1355-3224
▼**MUSCULOSKELETAL MANAGEMENT.** 1995. q. £90 in Europe; elsewhere £99($159) (effective 1996). Blackwell Science Ltd., Osney Mead, Oxford OX2 OEL, England. TEL 44-1865-206206. FAX 44-1865-721205. (back issues avail.) **Document type:** academic/scholarly publication.
—**CCC.**
Refereed Serial

617.3 RU ISSN 0869-8678
N.N. PRIOROV VESNIK TRAVMATOLOGII I ORTOPEDII. (Text in Russian; summaries in English) 1927. q. $80. (Ts N I I Traumatologii i Ortopedii im. N.N. Priorova, Minzdrava R R) Izdatel'stvo Meditsina, Petroverigskii pereulok 6-8, 101000 Moscow, Russia. (Dist. by: Mezhdunarodnaya Kniga, B. Yakomanka 39, 117049 Moscow, Russia. TEL 7-095-2384600. FAX 7-095-2384634) (Co-sponsor: Ministerstvo Zdravookhraneniya) Ed. Yu.G. Shaposhnikov. bk.rev.; bibl. (tabloid format) **Indexed:** Biol.Abstr., Dent.Ind., Excerp.Med., Ind.Med.
Formerly (until 1994): Ortopediya, Travmatologiya i Protezirovanie (ISSN 0030-5987)
Description: Discusses basic theoretical and practical problems of orthopedics, traumatology and prosthetics.

617 NE ISSN 1380-3522
N T S R. (Nederlands Tijdschrift voor Spoedeisende medische hulpverlening en Rampengeneeskunde) 1978. bi-m. fl.37.50($20) H H S Uitgeverij, Postbus 150, 5360 AD Grave, Netherlands. FAX 31-8860-76448. Ed. H.J.J. Berden; Pub. A.M. Janssen. adv. contact: P.G. Hoving. circ. 3,200. (back issues avail.)
Formerly (until 1994): Ambulance (ISSN 0167-9589)
Description: Covers topics relating to emergency medicine and ambulances.

NATIONAL DIRECTORY OF FIRE CHIEFS, RESCUE & EMERGENCY DEPARTMENTS. see *FIRE PREVENTION*

628 US ISSN 0892-6972
NATIONAL DIRECTORY OF HEAD INJURY REHABILITATION SERVICES. 1985. a. $40 (effective 1994). National Head Injury Foundation, 1776 Massachusetts Ave., N.W., Ste. 100, Washington, DC 20036. TEL 202-296-6443. FAX 202-296-8850. **Document type:** directory.
Description: State by state listing of providers of services for people with traumatic brain injury, including rehabilitation programs and individual professionals.

370 US
NATIONAL HEAD INJURY FOUNDATION. CATALOGUE OF EDUCATIONAL MATERIALS. 1987. a. National Head Injury Foundation, 1776 Massachusetts Ave., N.W., Ste. 100, Washington, DC 20036. TEL 202-296-6443. FAX 202-296-8850. **Document type:** catalog.

617.3 617 AU ISSN 0177-7955
NEURO-ORTHOPEDICS. 1986. 2/yr. DM.372($270) (effective 1996). Springer-Verlag, Sachsenplatz 4-6, Postfach 89, A-1201 Vienna, Austria. TEL 0222-330-2415. FAX 0222-330-2426. (N. American subscr. to: Journal Fulfillment Services, Box 2485, Secaucus, NJ 07096-2491. TEL 800-777-4643. FAX 201-348-4505; Subscr. outside N. America to: Springer-Verlag, Heidelberger Platz 3, 14197 Berlin, Germany. TEL 030-8207-0. FAX 030-821-4091) Ed. H. Verbiest. (also avail. in microform from UMI) **Indexed:** Excerp.Med. **Document type:** academic/scholarly publication.
—BLDSC (6081.512000); SWETS; UMI. **CCC.**
Description: Discusses disorders and injuries of the musculo-skeletal system and includes articles on applied research as well as diagnosis and clinical management.

617.1 GW ISSN 0932-3643
NEUROORTHOPAEDIE. (Represents material presented at annual Erlangen Workshops) 1983. irreg., vol.5, 1994. price varies. Springer-Verlag, Heidelberger Platz 3, 14197 Berlin, Germany. TEL 030-820-7448. FAX 030-821-4091. TELEX 183 319 SPBLN D. E-mail: orders@Springer.de. (Subscr. in N. America to: 175 Fifth Ave., New York, NY 10010. TEL 212-460-1500. FAX 212-473-6272) **Document type:** proceedings.

617 US ISSN 1063-7389
CODEN: NEHOFH
NEW HORIZONS (BALTIMORE). Running title: New Horizons: The Science and Practice of Acute Medicine. 1993. q. (Society of Critical Care Medicine) Williams & Wilkins, 428 E. Preston St., Baltimore, MD 21202. TEL 410-528-4000. FAX 410-528-4312. (back issues avail.) **Indexed:** Excerp.Med. (1995-), Ind.Med. (1994-).
—BLDSC (6084.237960). **CCC.**

MEDICAL SCIENCES — ORTHOPEDICS AND TRAUMATOLOGY

617   JA
NIHON GAISHO GAKKAI ZASSHI/JAPANESE ASSOCIATION FOR THE SURGERY OF TRAUMA. JOURNAL. (Text in Japanese; abstracts in English) 1987. 4/yr. 2000 Yen per no. Nihon Gaisho Gakkai, Teikyo Daigaku Kyumei Kyukyu Senta, 11-1, Kaga 2-chome, Itabashi-ku, Tokyo 173, Japan. TEL 81-3-3964-1211. FAX 81-3-5375-0854. Ed. Kazuhiko Maekawa; Pub. Kunio Kobayashi. adv.: page 30000Yen; adv. contact: Toshio Nakatani. circ. 1,200 (controlled). **Document type:** academic/scholarly publication.
—BLDSC (4809.095000).
Formerly (until 1994): Nihon Gaisho Kenkyukaishi (ISSN 0914-4927)
Refereed Serial

617   JA   ISSN 0915-8766
NIHON GAKU TOGAI KINO KENKYUKAISHI/JAPAN ASSOCIATION OF CRANIO-MAUDIBULAR ORTHOPEDICS. JOURNAL. (Text in Japanese; summaries in English) 1988. a. Nihon Gaku Togai Kino Kenkyukai, Okayama Daigaku Shigakubu Shika Hotetsugaku Dai 1 Koza, 5-1, Shikatacho 2-chome, Okayama-shi, Okayama-ken 700, Japan.

617   JA
NIHON KOTSU KANSETSU KANSENSHO KENKYUKAI/JAPANESE SOCIETY FOR STUDY OF BONE AND JOINT INFECTIONS. ANNUAL MEETING. (Text in Japanese) 1978. a. Nihon Kotsu Kansetsu Kansensho Kenkyukai, Dokkyo Ika Daigaku Seikei Gekagaku Kyoshitsu, 880, Kitakobayashi, Mibumachi, Shimotsuga-gun, Tochigi-ken 321-02, Japan.

617   JA   ISSN 0917-4648
NIHON KOTSU KEITAI KEISOKU GAKKAI ZASSHI/JAPANESE SOCIETY OF BONE MORPHOMETRY. JOURNAL. (Text in Japanese; summaries in English, Japanese) 1991. 2/yr. 6000 Yen. Nihon Kotsu Keitai Keisoku Gakkai, Niigata Daigaku Igakubu Seikei Gekagaku Kyoshitsu, Asahimachi Dori 1 Bancho, Niigata-shi, Niigata-ken 951, Japan. Ed. Hideaki akahashi. circ. 1,000 (controlled).

617.3 618   JA   ISSN 0914-6822
NIHON PARAPUREJIA IGAKKAI ZASSHI/JAPAN MEDICAL SOCIETY OF PARAPLEGIA. JOURNAL. (Text in English, Japanese; summaries in English) 1988. a. Nihon Parapureijia Igakkai, Keio Gijuku Daigaku Igakubu Seikei Gekagaku Kyoshitsu, 35, Shinanomachi, Shinjuku-ku, Tokyo 160, Japan.

617.3 616.075   JA   ISSN 0915-7107
NIHON SEIKEI GEKA CHOONPA KENKYUKAI KAISHI/JAPANESE SOCIETY OF ORTHOPEDIC ULTRASONICS. JOURNAL. (Text in Japanese) 1989. a. Nihon Seikei Geka Choonpa Kenkyukai, Osaka Ika Daigaku Seikei Gekagaku Kyoshitsu, 2-7, Daigakumachi, Takatsuki-shi, Osaka 569, Japan.

617   JA   ISSN 0916-1643
NIHON SEIKEI GEKA SUPOTSU IGAKKAISHI/JAPANESE JOURNAL OF ORTHOPEDIC SPORTS MEDICINE. (Text in Japanese) 1982. a. membership. Nihon Seikei Geka Supotsu Igakkai - Japanese Orthopedic Society for Sports Medicine, Yokohama Shiritsu Kowan Byoin Seikei Geka, 2-3, Shin'yamashita 3-chome, Naka-ku, Yokohama-shi, Kanagawa-ken 231.

617.3   JA   ISSN 0917-7132
NIHON SEKITSUI GEKA GAKKAI DAYORI/JAPAN SPINE RESEARCH SOCIETY. NEWS. (Text in Japanese) 1991. s-a. Nihon Sekitsui Geka Gakkai, Keio Gijuku Daigaku Igakubu Seikei Gekagaku Kyoshitsu, 35, Shinanomachi, Shinjuku-ku, Tokyo 160, Japan.

617.3   JA   ISSN 0915-6496
NIHON SEKITSUI GEKA GAKKAI ZASSHI/JAPAN SPINE RESEARCH SOCIETY. JOURNAL. (Text in English, Japanese) 1990. a. Nihon Sekitsui Geka Gakkai, Keio Gijuku Daigaku Igakubu Seikei Gekagaku Kyoshitsu, 35, Shinanomachi, Shinjuku-ku, Tokyo 160, Japan.

NIHON SHONI SEIKEI GEKA GAKKAI ZASSHI/JAPANESE PAEDIATRIC ORTHOPAEDIC ASSOCIATION. JOURNAL.
see *MEDICAL SCIENCES — Pediatrics*

617.3   JA   ISSN 0915-4906
NIHON SOGAI KOTEI KENKYUKAISHI/JAPANESE SOCIETY OF EXTERNAL FIXATION. JOURNAL. (Text in Japanese; summaries in English) 1990. a. Nihon Sogai Kotei Kenkyukai, Asahi Daigaku Murakami Kinen Byoin Seikei Geka Kyoshitsu, 3-23, Hashimotocho, Gihu-shi, Gihu-ken 500, Japan.

617.3   JA   ISSN 0910-5700
NIHON TE NO GEKA GAKKAI ZASSHI/JAPANESE SOCIETY FOR SURGERY OF THE HAND. JOURNAL. (Text in Japanese; summaries in English) 1984. 6/yr. Nihon Te no Geka Gakkai, Kyusyu Daigaku Igakubu Seikei Gekagaku Kyoshitsu, 1-1, Umade 3-chome, Higashi-ku, Fukuoka-shi, Fukuoka-ken 812, Japan.
—BLDSC (4809.518000).

617.3   JA   ISSN 0914-6636
NIIGATA SEIKEI GEKA KENKYUKAI KAISHI/NIIGATA SOCIETY FOR ORTHOPAEDIC SURGERY. ARCHIVES. (Text in Japanese) 1983. a. Niigata Seikei Geka Kenkyukai, Niigata Daigaku Igakubu Seikei Geka Kyoshitsu, 1, Asahimachi Dori, Niigata-shi, Niigata-ken 951, Japan.

617.3   JA   ISSN 0287-1092
NISHINIHON SEKITSUI KENKYUKAISHI/WESTERN JAPANESE RESEARCH SOCIETY FOR SPINE. JOURNAL. (Text in Japanese) a. 6000 Yen. Nishinihon Sekitsui Kenkyukai, Yamaguchi Daigaku Seikei Geka Kyoshitsu, 1144, Ogushi, Ubeshi, Yamaguchi-ken 755, Japan.

610   GW   ISSN 0341-2903
NOTFALLMEDIZIN. 1975. m. DM.120 (effective 1996). Perimed - Spitta Medizinische Verlagsgesellschaft mbH, Ammoninenstr. 1, 72336 Balingen, Germany. TEL 07433-952-0. FAX 07433-952185. Ed.Bd. bk.rev.; abstr.; index. circ. 45,000. **Indexed:** Excerp.Med. **Document type:** academic/scholarly publication.
—BLDSC (6170.050000).

617.3   US   ISSN 1061-4621
O & P ALMANAC; the magazine for the orthotics & prosthetics profession. 1951. m. $35 (foreign $45) (effective 1993). American Orthotic & Prosthetic Association, National Office, 1650 King St., Ste. 500, Alexandria, VA 22314. TEL 703-836-7114. FAX 703-836-0838. Ed. Stacey L. Bell. adv.; circ. 5,900 (paid). (back issues avail.) **Document type:** trade publication.
Formerly (until 1991): American Orthotic and Prosthetic Association. Almanac.
Description: Covers professional, business, association and government activities affecting the field.

617.3   US   ISSN 0000-1597
RD724
OFFICIAL AMERICAN BOARD OF MEDICAL SPECIALTIES (A B M S) DIRECTORY OF BOARD CERTIFIED ORTHOPAEDIC SURGEONS. 1985. biennial. $119.95. Marquis Who's Who, A Reed Reference Publishing company, 121 Chanlon Rd., New Providence, NJ 07974. TEL 908-464-6800. FAX 908-665-2898. (Subscr. to: Order Dept., Box 31, New Providence, NJ 07974-9903. TEL 800-521-8110) Ed. Roy Crego. **Document type:** directory.
Formerly (until 1994): A B M S Directory of Certified Orthopaedic Surgeons (ISSN 0883-1211)
Description: Biographical sketches of U.S. certified medical specialists sorted geographically with alpha index.

617.3   GW   ISSN 0934-6694
OPERATIVE ORTHOPAEDIE UND TRAUMATOLOGIE; Standardeingriffe und neue Verfahren. 1989. q. DM.330($239) (effective 1996). Urban und Vogel, Lindwurmstr. 95, 80337 Munich, Germany. TEL 089-53292-0. FAX 089-53292-100. (Subscr. to: Postfach 152209, 80052 Munich, Germany) Ed.Bd. adv.; bk.rev. circ. 3,500. **Document type:** academic/scholarly publication.

617   US   ISSN 1048-6666
OPERATIVE TECHNIQUES IN ORTHOPAEDICS. 1991. q. $165 (foreign $205) (effective 1996). W.B. Saunders Co. (Subsidiary of: Harcourt Brace & Company), Curtis Center, 3rd Fl., Independence Sq. W., Philadelphia, PA 19106-3399. TEL 215-238-7862. FAX 215-238-6445. (Subscr. to: Periodicals Fulfillment, W.B. Saunders Co., 6277 Sea Harbor Dr., 4th Fl., Orlando, FL 32891-4800. TEL 800-654-2452. FAX 800-874-6418) Ed. Dr. Richard Balderston; Pub. Joan W. Blumberg. adv.: B&W page $600, color page $1425; 7 3/4 x 11; adv. contact: Cindy Gray. illus. circ. 2,590. **Document type:** academic/scholarly publication.
—BLDSC (6269.381500); Faxon. **CCC**.
Description: Treats a clinical condition or surgical procedure in detail in each issue; alternative approaches are also presented.
Refereed Serial

617.3   GW   ISSN 0085-4530
       CODEN: ORHPBG
DER ORTHOPAEDE. 1972. 6/yr. DM.448($325) (effective 1996). Springer-Verlag, Heidelberger Platz 3, 14197 Berlin, Germany. TEL 030-8207-0. FAX 030-8214091. E-mail: orders@springer.de. (Subscr. in N. America to: Springer-Verlag New York, Inc., 44 Hartz Way, Secaucus, NJ 07096-2491. TEL 201-348-4033. FAX 201-348-4505) Ed. R. Bauer. (also avail. in microform from UMI; reprint service avail. from ISI) **Indexed:** Curr.Cont., Excerp.Med., Ind.Med. **Document type:** academic/scholarly publication.
—BLDSC (6296.114000); EMDOCS; Faxon; Genuine Article; SWETS; UMI. **CCC**.

610   JA   ISSN 0387-4095
ORTHOPAEDIC AND TRAUMATIC SURGERY/SEKEI SAIGAI GEKA. (Text in English, Japanese) 1958. m. 1900 Yen per no. Kanehara Shuppan Ltd., 2-31-14 Yushima, Bunkyo-ku, Tokyo 113-91, Japan. Ed. Dr. Yoshio Yamauchi. bk.rev.; index. circ. 7,100. **Indexed:** C.I.S. Abstr., INIS Atomind., Jap.Per.Ind.
Formerly (until 1979): Journal of Accidental Medicine (ISSN 0036-2689)

617.3   JA   ISSN 0289-2855
ORTHOPAEDIC CERAMIC IMPLANTS. (Text in English, Japanese; summaries in English) 1981. a. Seikei Geka Seramikku Inpuranto Kenkyukai, Kokuritsu Osaka Minami Byoin Seikei Geka, 677-2 Kidomachi, Kochinagano-shi, Osaka 586, Japan.

ORTHOPAEDIC NURSING JOURNAL; national association of orthopaedic nurses. see *MEDICAL SCIENCES — Nurses And Nursing*

617.3 615.82   US   ISSN 1059-1516
ORTHOPAEDIC PHYSICAL THERAPY CLINICS OF NORTH AMERICA. 1992. q. $79 (foreign $102) (effective 1996). W.B. Saunders Co. (Subsidiary of: Harcourt Brace & Company), The Curtis Center, Independence Sq. W., Philadelphia, PA 19106-3399. TEL 215-238-7800. FAX 215-238-6445. (Subscr. to: Periodicals Fulfillment, W.B. Saunders Co., 6277 Sea Harbor Dr., 4th Fl., Orlando, FL 32891-4800. TEL 800-654-2452. FAX 800-874-6418) Eds. Z. Annette Inglarsh, Jan K. Richardson. index. (also avail. in microform from UMI; back issues avail.) **Indexed:** Excerp.Med. (1995-). **Document type:** academic/scholarly publication.
—BLDSC (6296.125500); UMI.
Description: Publishes review articles on emerging technologies, new approaches to treatment, and other topics.

617.3 615.82   US
ORTHOPAEDIC PHYSICAL THERAPY PRACTICE. q. Orthopaedic Section A P T A, 505 King St., La Crosse, WI 54601. TEL 608-784-0910. Ed. John Medeiros. circ. 11,083.

617.3   UK   ISSN 0954-4755
ORTHOPAEDIC PRODUCT NEWS. 1987. 5/yr. £20 (foreign £38). Medical Magazines, 9 Sibford Rd., Hook Norton, Oxon. OX15 5LA, England, England. TEL 01608-737504. FAX 01608-730475. E-mail: andrea.editor@orthopod.demon.co.uk. (Subscr. in Germany to: Fasanenstr. 51, 10719 Berlin, Germany. TEL 030-8852678. FAX 030-8818239) Ed. M.J. Whitaker. adv.: color page £1200; adv. contact: M.J. Whitaker. circ. 8,500. (back issues avail.) **Document type:** academic/scholarly publication.
Description: Provides details of new products and reviews of topical products for orthopedic surgeons in Europe.

MEDICAL SCIENCES — ORTHOPEDICS AND TRAUMATOLOGY   4507

617.3   US   ISSN 0162-9379
CODEN: ORTTDM
ORTHOPAEDIC TRANSACTIONS.* 1977. 3/yr. $22.
Journal of Bone and Joint Surgery, Inc., 20 Pickering
St., Needham, MA 02192-3145.
TEL 617-734-2835. illus. **Indexed:** Biol.Abstr.
—BLDSC (6296.126500); SWETS.

617.3   GW   ISSN 0941-2530
ORTHOPAEDICS AND TRAUMATOLOGY; new and
established surgical techniques. (Text in English)
1992. q. DM.330($239) (effective 1996). Urban
und Vogel, Lindwurmstr. 95, 80337 Munich,
Germany. TEL 089-53292-0. FAX 089-53292100.
(Dist. by: Springer-Verlag, Heidelberg Platz 3.
14197 Berlin, Germany. TEL 030-8207-1. FAX
030-8214091; Subscr. in N. America to:
Springer-Verlag New York, Inc., 44 Hartz Way,
Secaucus, NJ 07096-2491. TEL 201-348-4033.
FAX 201-348-4505) Ed. H.K. Uthoff. circ. 3,000.
Document type: academic/scholarly publication.
—BLDSC (6296.128000).

617.533   GW   ISSN 0941-214X
ORTHOPAEDIE MITTEILUNGEN.* 1971. q. DM.60.
Deutsche Gesellschaft fuer Orthopaedie und
Traumatologie, Wilhelm-Kramm-Str. 61a, 50321
Bruehl, Germany. Ed. Dr. Zichney. circ. 2,200.
Document type: academic/scholarly publication.
Formerly (until 1990): Deutsche Gesellschaft fuer
Orthopaedie und Traumatologie. Mitteilungsblatt
(ISSN 0723-8002)

617.3   GW   ISSN 0030-588X
CODEN: OPBAAS
ORTHOPAEDISCHE PRAXIS; mit Traumatologie,
Rheumatologie, physikalischer, physiotherapeutischer
und balneologischer Therapie des
Bewegungsapparates. 1965. m. DM.198 (students
DM.148.50). (Vereinigung Sueddeutscher
Orthopaeden e.V.) Medizinisch-Literarische
Verlagsgesellschaft mbH, Postfach 1151-1152,
29501 Uelzen, Germany. TEL 0581-808151.
FAX 0581-808158. TELEX 91326-AZ-D. Eds. Dr. R.
Faerber, Dr. G. Rompe. adv.; charts; illus.;
index, cum.index. circ. 5,000. (back issues avail.)
Indexed: Excerp.Med. **Document type:**
academic/scholarly publication.
—BLDSC (6296.120000). **CCC**.

617.3   US   ISSN 0030-5898
CODEN: OCLNAQ
ORTHOPEDIC CLINICS OF NORTH AMERICA. 1970. q.
$131 (foreign $155) (effective 1996). W.B.
Saunders Co. (Subsidiary of: Harcourt Brace &
Company), Curtis Center, 3rd Fl., Independence Sq.
W., Philadelphia, PA 19106-3399.
TEL 215-238-7800. FAX 215-238-6445. (Subscr.
to: Periodicals Fulfillment, W.B. Saunders Co., 6277
Sea Harbor Dr., 4th Fl., Orlando, FL 32891-4800.
TEL 800-654-2452. FAX 800-874-6418) Ed.
Melissa Mitchell. charts; illus.; index. (also avail. in
microform from UMI; reprint service avail. from UMI,
ISI) **Indexed:** AIM, Bibl.Dev.Med.& Child Neur.,
Biol.Abstr., CINAHL, Curr.Adv.Ecol.Sci., Curr.Cont.,
Excerp.Med., Ind.Med. **Document type:**
academic/scholarly publication.
—BLDSC (6296.135000); EMDOCS; Faxon;
Genuine Article; SWETS; UMI; UnCover. **CCC**.
Description: Discusses the practice of orthopedic
treatment.
Refereed Serial

617.3   US   ISSN 1056-4543
ORTHOPEDIC RESIDENT. 1991. bi-m. $40. Slack, Inc.,
6900 Grove Rd., Thorofare, NJ 08086.
TEL 609-848-1000. FAX 609-853-5991. Ed. Dr. G.
Dean MacEwen. adv. circ. 3,000.
Description: Guide to career, lifestyle and business
issues facing residents. Covers preparing for boards,
choosing fellowships, establishing a practice and
decision-making.

617.3   US
ORTHOPEDIC SPECIAL EDITION. 1988. m. $50.
McMahon Group, 148 W. 24th St., New York, NY
10011. TEL 212-620-4600. FAX 212-620-5928.
Ed. James La Rossa. adv. circ. 20,384.
Former titles: Orthopedic and Sports Medicine
News; Sports Medicine News.
Description: For orthopedic surgeons and
rheumatologists. Covers arthroscopy, arthroplasty,
pain management, braces, rheumatic disease, and
orthopedic technology.

617.3   JA   ISSN 0030-5901
ORTHOPEDIC SURGERY/SEIKEI GEKA. (Text in Japanese;
title and captions in English) 1950. m. 41900 Yen
(foreign 64000 Yen). Nankodo Co., Ltd., 42-6,
Hongo 3-chome, Bunkyo-ku, Tokyo 113, Japan.
TEL 03-3811-7239. FAX 03-3811-7230. Ed.
Toshinobu Onomura. adv.; charts; illus.; index. circ.
8,500. **Indexed:** Biol.Abstr., Ind.Med.
—BLDSC (6296.140000).

617.3   US   ISSN 0147-7447
RD701
ORTHOPEDICS. 1978. m. $95 to individuals;
institutions $105. Slack, Inc., 6900 Grove Rd.,
Thorofare, NJ 08086. TEL 609-848-1000.
FAX 609-853-5991. Ed. Dr. Robert D'Ambrosia.
adv. circ. 28,000. (back issues avail.) **Indexed:**
Bibl.Dev.Med.& Child Neur., Curr.Cont., Excerp.Med.
—BLDSC (6296.146000); Faxon; Genuine Article;
SWETS; UMI; UnCover.
Refereed Serial

617.3   US   ISSN 0279-5647
ORTHOPEDICS TODAY. 1981. m. $110 to individuals;
institutions $120. Slack, Inc., 6900 Grove Rd.,
Thorofare, NJ 08086. TEL 609-848-1000.
FAX 609-853-5991. Ed. Dr. Robert P. Nirschl. adv.;
illus. circ. 23,800.
● Also available online.
—BLDSC (6296.163000). **CCC**.

685.31 617.3   NE
ORTHOPEDISCHE SCHOENTECHNIEK. 1981. 4/yr. fl.62.
Stichting Voorlichting Orthopedische Schoentechniek,
Postbus 25, 3430 AA Nieuwegein, Netherlands.
TEL 31-30-6051916. FAX 31-30-6051558. Ed.
J.W.M. Lazet. adv.: B&W page fl.715, color page
fl.3410; 163 x 221. bk.rev. circ. 500. **Document
type:** trade publication.
Description: Discusses orthopedic shoes and boots,
foot diseases, and orthopedic surgery.

617.3   IT   ISSN 0392-1417
ORTOPEDIA E TRAUMATOLOGIA OGGI. (Text in Italian;
summaries in English) q. L.60000($60) C I C
Edizioni Internazionali s.r.l., Via L. Spallanzani 11,
00161 Rome, Italy. TEL 06-8412673.
FAX 06-44242033. TELEX 622099 CIC. Dir. V.
Pietrogrande.
—BLDSC (6296.258000). **CCC**.

617.3   BU   ISSN 0473-4378
ORTOPEDIA I TRAUMATOLOGIA. (Text in Bulgarian;
summaries in English, Russian) q. 15 lv.
(Ministerstvo na Narodnoto Zdrave) Izdatelstvo
Meditsina i Fizkultura, 11 Pl. Slaveikov, Sofia,
Bulgaria. (Distr. by: Hemus, 6 Rouski Blvd., 1000
Sofia, Bulgaria) (Co-sponsor: Nauchno Druzhestvo po
Ortopedija i Traumatologija) Ed. D. Djerov. circ. 815.
Indexed: Abstr.Bulg.Sci.Med.Lit.
—BLDSC (0128.280000).

617.3   IT   ISSN 0030-5979
ORTOPEDICI E SANITARI. 1964. m. free. Editgraf s.r.l.,
Via L. del Maino 2, 20146 Milan, Italy.
TEL 39-2-4985947. FAX 39-2-4984625. Ed.
Marcella Boneschi. adv.: B&W page L.1300000.
illus.; pat. circ. 14,000.

617.3   IT
ORTOPEDICO. 1961. bi-m. Editgraf s.r.l., Via Luchino
del Maino 2, 20146 Milan, Italy.
TEL 39-2-4985947. Ed. Marcella Boneschi. adv.:
B&W page L.1000000. circ. 4,500.

617.3   SW   ISSN 0349-733X
ORTOPEDISKT MAGASIN; nordisk tidskrift foer ortopedi
och rehabilitering. 1977. q. SEK 120 (effective
1993). Everoed 13, S-273 93 Tomelilla, Sweden.

617.3   JA   ISSN 0914-8124
ORUSOPEDIKUSU/ORTHOPAEDICS. (Text in Japanese)
1988. m. 2000 Yen per no. (Zennihon Byoin
Shuppankai) Kanehara Shuppan Ltd., 31-14,
Yushima 2-chome, Bunkyo-ku, Tokyo 113-91,
Japan.

617.3   JA   ISSN 0917-8562
**OSAKA SHIDAI SEIKEI GEKA KENKYUKAISHI/OSAKA CITY
UNIVERSITY ORTHOPEDIC SURGERY. BULLETIN.** (Text
in Japanese) 1983. s-a. Osaka Shiritsu Daigaku,
Igakubu, Seikei Gekagaku Kyoshitsu Dosokai - Osaka
City University, Medical School, Department of
Orthopedic Surgery, Alumni Association, 5-7,
Asahimachi 1-chome, Abeno-ku, Osaka 545, Japan.

OSTEOARTHRITIS AND CARTILAGE. see *MEDICAL
SCIENCES* — *Rheumatology*

617.3   SZ   ISSN 1019-1291
OSTEOLOGIE. 1992. q. 260 SFr. (foreign 276 SFr.).
(Deutsche Gesellschaft fuer Osteologie) Verlag Hans
Huber, Laenggassstr. 76, CH-3000 Bern 9,
Switzerland. TEL 031-3004500.
FAX 031-3004590. circ. 2,000. **Document type:**
academic/scholarly publication.
—BLDSC (6303.858920).

617   US   ISSN 0889-5899
RD94
OSTOMY - WOUND MANAGEMENT; the journal of
extended patient care management. 1980. 9/yr.
$36 (foreign $54). Health Management
Publications, Inc., 550 American Ave., King of
Prussia, PA 19406-1441. TEL 215-337-4466;
800-237-7285. FAX 215-337-0890. Ed. Laura
Alexander. adv.; charts; illus.; stat. **Indexed:** CINAHL.
Document type: trade publication.
—BLDSC (6312.377000).
Formerly: Ostomy Management.

OUTREACH (CHICAGO). see *HOSPITALS*

617   US
OXFORD HANDBOOKS IN EMERGENCY MEDICINE. 1991.
irreg., vol.6, 1993. price varies. Oxford University
Press, 200 Madison Ave., New York, NY 10016.
TEL 212-679-7300. Ed.Bd. (back issues avail.)
Document type: monographic series.

PARAPLEGIA. see *MEDICAL SCIENCES* — *Psychiatry
And Neurology*

PEDIATRIC EMERGENCY CARE. see *MEDICAL
SCIENCES* — *Pediatrics*

617.13   US   ISSN 0890-3972
PODIATRIC PRODUCTS. 1984. 6/yr. $12 (foreign $30)
(free to qualified personnel). Novicom, Inc., 20000
Mariner Ave., Ste. 480, Torrance, CA 90503.
TEL 310-793-4141. FAX 310-793-4138. Ed.
Nancy Girardini. adv.: B&W page $1090, color page
$1690; trim 8 3/8 x 10 7/8. bk.rev.; charts; illus.;
circ. 13,000 (controlled). **Document type:** trade
publication.
Formerly (until 1986): Podiatry Products Report.
Description: Product news releases and articles
related to the profession.

617.585   US
PODIATRIST'S PATIENT NEWSLETTER. 1983. q. $495
per quarter for 1000 copies. Doctor's Press, Box
10488, Lancaster, PA 17605-0488.
TEL 717-393-1000. Ed. Kim Conlin; Pub. Cindy A.
Young. adv. contact: Rem Jackson. **Document
type:** newsletter.

PODIATRY INDEX. see *MEDICAL SCIENCES —
Abstracting, Bibliographies, Statistics*

617.585   US
PODIATRY MANAGEMENT MAGAZINE. 1982. 9/yr. $30.
Kane Communications, Inc., 7000 Terminal Square,
Ste. 210, Upper Darby, PA 19082.
TEL 610-734-2420. FAX 610-734-2423. Ed. Dr.
Barry Block. adv.; bk.rev.; pat.; stat. circ. 12,500.
(back issues avail.) **Document type:** trade publication.

617.3   US   ISSN 1045-7860
PODIATRY TODAY. 1988. m. Dowden Publishing
Company, 6838 E. Genesee St., Fayetteville, NY
13066-0507. TEL 315-449-0295.
FAX 315-449-3113. (Adv. to: Dowden Publishing
Co., 110 Summit Ave., Montvale, NJ 07625. TEL
201-391-9100) Ed. Judith A. Rubenstein. adv.:
B&W page $1210; color page $1810. circ. 16,995.
—**CCC**.

POHYBOVE USTROJI. see *MEDICAL SCIENCES —
Abstracting, Bibliographies, Statistics*

PREHOSPITAL AND DISASTER MEDICINE; an
international journal. see *MEDICAL SCIENCES*

617   US
**PRINCIPLES AND TECHNIQUES IN SPINE SURGERY
SERIES.** 1992. irreg., latest 1993. price varies.
Raven Press (Subsidiary of: Wolters Kluwer N.V.),
1185 Ave. of the Americas, New York, NY 10036.
TEL 212-930-9500. FAX 212-869-3495. **Document
type:** monographic series.

MEDICAL SCIENCES — ORTHOPEDICS AND TRAUMATOLOGY

617.3 617.58 DK ISSN 0309-3646
CODEN: POIND7
PROSTHETICS AND ORTHOTICS INTERNATIONAL. (Text in English) 1964. 3/yr. £80. International Society for Prosthetics and Orthotics, Borgervaenget 5, DK-2100 Copenhagen OE, Denmark. TEL 45-31-20-72-60. FAX 45-31-18-16-69. Eds. J. Hughes, Norman A. Jacobs. adv. contact: Norman A. Jacobs. bk.rev.; illus.; index; circ. 3,200 (controlled). **Indexed:** Bibl.Dev.Med.& Child Neur., Biol.Abstr., Curr.Cont., Excerp.Med., Ind.Med., INSPEC (1979-). **Document type:** academic/scholarly publication.
—BLDSC (6935.500000); Faxon; SWETS; UnCover.
Formerly (until 1971): Prosthetics International (ISSN 0555-4837)
Description: Publishes scientific articles on prosthetics, orthotics and related topics.
Refereed Serial

RACHIS; revue de pathologie vertebrale. see *MEDICAL SCIENCES — Rheumatology*

REANIMATION URGENCES. see *MEDICAL SCIENCES — Anaesthesiology*

RECONSTRUCTION SURGERY AND TRAUMATOLOGY. see *MEDICAL SCIENCES — Surgery*

616.02 US ISSN 0732-2933
TL553.8
RESPONSE (FAIRFAX). 1982. q. $12.95 (Canada $15.95; elsewhere $24.95) (effective 1994). National Association for Search and Rescue, Box 3709, Fairfax, VA 22038. TEL 703-352-1349. FAX 703-352-0309. Ed. Judi Schmitt. adv.: B&W page $661, color page $911; trim 8 1/4 x 10 7/8; adv. contact: Mary Harding. bk.rev. circ. 6,000. **Document type:** trade publication.
Description: Provides technical information to the emergency response community at the federal, state and local levels, describing new techniques, procedures, products and technology in the search, rescue and emergency services.
Refereed Serial

617.3 CU
REVISTA CUBANA DE ORTOPEDIA Y TRAUMATOLOGIA. 1987. s-a. $30 in S. America; N. America $32; elsewhere $34. Ministerio de Salud Publica, Centro Nacional de Informacion de Ciencias Medicas, Calle E, No. 452, e 19 y 21, Plaza de la Revolucion, Havana, Cuba. TEL 809-32-5338. (Dist. by: Ediciones Cubanas, Obispo No. 527, Apdo. 605, Havana, Cuba) Ed. Emilio Hernandez. circ. 1,300.

617.3 SP ISSN 0482-5985
REVISTA DE ORTOPEDIA Y TRAUMATOLOGIA. bi-m. 11500 ptas.($123) (effective 1995). (Sociedad Espanola de Cirugia Ortopedica y Traumatologia) Editorial Garsi, S.A., Juan Bravo 46, 28006 Madrid, Spain. TEL 34-1-4021212. FAX 34-1-4020954. Ed. F. Gomez Castresana Bachiller. circ. 4,000.

617.3 SP ISSN 0304-5056
REVISTA ESPANOLA DE CIRUGIA OSTEOARTICULAR. (Text in Spanish; summaries in English and Spanish) 1966. bi-m. 8900 ptas.($83) (effective 1995). Editorial Garsi, S.A., Juan Bravo 46, 28006 Madrid, Spain. TEL 34-1-4021212. FAX 34-1-4020954. Ed. Dr. F. Gomar Sancho. bk.rev. circ. 2,000. **Indexed:** Excerp.Med., Ind.Med.Esp.

617.3 FR ISSN 0337-9736
REVUE D'ORTHOPEDIE DENTO-FACIALE. 1967. q. 755 F. (foreign 890 F.); students 480 F. (Association de la Revue d'Orthopedie Dento-Faciale) Societe d'Information et de Diffusion, Librarie international, 9 rue Christine, 75006 Paris, France. TEL 43-29-31-01. FAX 43-29-32-62. Ed. Y. Barat. adv.; bk.rev. circ. 2,500. **Indexed:** Dent.Ind. **Document type:** academic/scholarly publication.
—BLDSC (7940.070000).

617.3 FR ISSN 0035-1040
REVUE DE CHIRURGIE ORTHOPEDIQUE ET REPARATRICE DE L'APPAREIL MOTEUR. (Text in French; summaries in English) 1890. 8/yr. 826 F. (foreign 998 F.) (effective 1996). Masson - Periodiques, Villa Laromiguiere, 75005 Paris, France. TEL 1-40-46-62-00. FAX 1-40-46-62-01. Ed. J.M. Thomine. bk.rev.; illus.; index. circ. 6,100. (also avail. in microform from UMI; reprint service avail. from ISI) **Indexed:** Bibl.Dev.Med.& Child Neur., Dent.Ind., Excerp.Med., Ind.Med. **Document type:** academic/scholarly publication.
—BLDSC (7897.150000); Genuine Article; SWETS; UMI. **CCC.**
Formerly: Revue d'Orthopedie et de Chirurgie de l'Appareil Moteur (ISSN 1243-2504)
Description: Publishes original articles of clinical facts, technical notes, publication analyses, reports of meetings and congresses.

617.3 JA ISSN 0557-0433
RINSHO SEIKEI GEKA/CLINICAL ORTHOPAEDIC SURGERY. (Text in Japanese) 1966. m. 1900 Yen per no. Igaku Shoin Ltd., 24-3, Hongo 5-chome, Bunkyo-ku, Tokyo 113-91, Japan. TEL 03-3817-5704. Ed.Bd. circ. 9,000.
—BLDSC (3286.319000).

617.3 615.82 IT
RIVISTA DEGLI ARTICOLI SANITARI. 1987. 10/yr. free to qualified personnel. C & V Editrice, Via Vigevano 43, 20144 Milan, Italy. TEL 39-2-89406754. Ed. Roberto Violano. adv.: B&W page L.2100000. bk.rev. circ. 11,000.

617.3 IT ISSN 0035-693X
RIVISTA ITALIANA DI ORTOPEDIA E TRAUMATOLOGIA. 1961. s-a. L.30000 (foreign L.60000) (effective 1994). Casa Editrice Maccari, Via Trento, 53, 43100 Parma, Italy. FAX 039-521-771268. circ. 1,400.

617.3 IT ISSN 0393-5221
RIVISTA ITALIANA DI ORTOPEDIA E TRAUMATOLOGIA PEDIATRICA. 1975. 2/yr. $80. (Italian Society of Paediatric Orthopaedics and Traumatology) Aulo Gaggi Editore, Via Andrea Costa, 131-5, 40134 Bologna, Italy. TEL 0222-5339614. FAX 0222-638158. Ed. A. Dal Monte.

617.3 JA ISSN 0289-1565
SEIKEI GEKA BAIOMEKANIKUSU/JAPANESE SOCIETY FOR ORTHOPAEDIC BIOMECHANICS. PROCEEDINGS OF ANNUAL MEETING. (Text in English, Japanese; summaries in English) 1980. a. 10000 Yen. Seikei Geka Baiomekanikusu Kenkyukai, Osaka Daigaku Igakubu Seikei Geka, 1-50, Fukushima 1-chome, Fukushima-ku Osaka 553, Japan. **Document type:** proceedings.

617.3 JA ISSN 0037-1033
SEIKEI GEKA TO SAIGAI GEKA/ORTHOPEDICS AND TRAUMATOLOGY. (Text in English and Japanese) 1952. s-a. 10000 Yen. Nishi Nihon Seikei Saigai Geka Gakkai - West Japan Society of Orthopedics and Traumatology, c/o Dept. of Orthopedic Surgery, Kyushu University, 3-1-1 Maidashi, Higashi-ku, Fukuoka 812, Japan. Ed. Yoichi Sugioka. adv. circ. 1,000. **Document type:** academic/scholarly publication.

617.3 JA ISSN 0911-6826
SEKICHU HENKEI/SPINAL DEFORMITY. (Text in English, Japanese) 1986. a. Nihon Sokuwansho Kenkyukai - Japanese Scoliosis Society, Chiba Daigaku Igakubu Seikei Geka Kyoshitsu, 8-1, Inohana 1-chome, Chuo-ku, Chiba-shi, Chiba-ken 260.

617.3 JA ISSN 0914-4412
SEKITSUI SEKIZUI JANARU/SPINE AND SPINAL CORD. (Text in Japanese) 1988. m. 1900 Yen per no. Miwa Shoten, 30-3, Hakusan 2-chome, Bunkyo-ku, Tokyo 112, Japan.

617.3 JA ISSN 0914-6024
SEKIZUI GEKA/SPINAL SURGERY. (Text in English, Japanese; summaries in English) 1987. a. 3000 Yen. Nihon Sekizui Geka Kenkyukai Osaka - Japanese Society of Spinal Surgery, Osaka Shiritsu Daigaku Igakubu No Shinkei Gekagaku Kyoshitsu, 5-7, Asahimachi 1-chome, Abeno-ku, Osaka 545, Japan. TEL 06-6452157. FAX 06-6478065. Ed. Akira Hakuba.

SEMINARS IN ARTHRITIS & RHEUMATISM. see *MEDICAL SCIENCES — Rheumatology*

617.3 US ISSN 1045-4527
SEMINARS IN ARTHROPLASTY. 1990. q. $129 (foreign $170) (effective 1996). W.B. Saunders Co. (Subsidiary of: Harcourt Brace & Company), Curtis Center, 3rd Fl., Independence Sq. W., Philadelphia, PA 19106-3399. TEL 215-238-7800. FAX 215-238-6445. (Subscr. to: Periodicals Fulfillment, W.B. Saunders Co., 6277 Sea Harbor Dr., 4th Fl., Orlando, FL 32891-4800. TEL 800-654-2452. FAX 800-874-6418) Ed. Dr. Robert H. Fitzgerald, Jr; Pub. Joan W. Blumberg. adv.: B&W page $610, color page $1430; 7 x 10; adv. contact: Cindy Gray. circ. 2,403. (back issues avail.) **Document type:** academic/scholarly publication.
—BLDSC (8239.448100); UMI. **CCC.**
Description: Covers a single topic of the restorative treatment of the joints in each issue, with emphasis on developments physicians can apply directly to their practices.

SEMINARS IN ROENTGENOLOGY. see *MEDICAL SCIENCES — Radiology And Nuclear Medicine*

617 US ISSN 1040-7383
CODEN: SSPSEH
SEMINARS IN SPINE SURGERY. 1989. q. $129 (foreign $169) (effective 1996). W.B. Saunders Co. (Subsidiary of: Harcourt Brace & Company), The Curtis Center, 3rd Fl., Independence Sq. W., Philadelphia, PA 19106-3399. TEL 215-238-7800. FAX 215-238-6445. (Subscr. to: Periodicals Fulfillment, W.B. Saunders Co., 6277 Sea Harbor Dr., 4th Fl., Orlando, FL 32887-4800. TEL 800-654-2452. FAX 800-874-6418) Ed. Dr. Sam W. Wiesel; Pub. Joan W. Blumberg. adv.: B&W page $600, color page $1400; 7 x 10; adv. contact: Cindy Gray. circ. 2,102. **Document type:** academic/scholarly publication.
—BLDSC (8239.468000). **CCC.**
Description: Addresses a single topic in the management and care of patients with spinal injuries or conditions in each issue.

SEMINARS IN ULTRASOUND, C T AND M R. see *MEDICAL SCIENCES — Radiology And Nuclear Medicine*

617.1 FR ISSN 0399-0265
SERVICES D'AIDE MEDICALE URGENTE. REVUE. Cover title: Revue des S A M U. 1978. 6/yr. 360 F. (foreign 500 F.). (Services d'Aide Medicale Urgente) Societe Francaise d'Editions Medicales, 22-24 rue du Chateau des Rentiers, 75013 Paris, France. TEL 45-83-50-54. FAX 45-83-13-54. Ed. Colette Gallula. adv.; bibl.; charts; illus.

617.3 JA
SHIN JIDAI NO SEIKEI GEKA CHIRYO/ORTHOPAEDIC SURGERY NOW. (Text in Japanese) 1991. q. 6800 Yen. Medical View Co., Ltd. - Mejikaru Byusha, 2-30, Ichigaya Honmuracho, Shinjuku-ku, Tokyo 162, Japan.

SHINKEI GAISHO/NEUROTRAUMATOLOGY. see *MEDICAL SCIENCES — Psychiatry And Neurology*

SLIDE ATLAS OF CURRENT ORTHOPAEDICS (YEAR). see *MEDICAL SCIENCES — Abstracting, Bibliographies, Statistics*

617.2 SP ISSN 0212-0771
SOCIEDAD ANDALUZA DE ORTOPEDIA Y TRAUMATOLOGIA. REVISTA. 1981. s-a. 4200 ptas.($50) (effective 1995). Editorial Garsi, S.A., Juan Bravo 46, 28006 Madrid, Spain. TEL 34-1-4021212. FAX 34-1-4020954. Ed. E. Queipo de Llano Gimenez. circ. 1,000.

617.3 IT ISSN 0394-0713
SOCIETA DI ORTOPEDIA E TRAUMATOLOGIA DELL'ITALIA MERIDIONALE ED INSULARE. ATTI E MEMORIE. (Text in Italian; summaries in English, French) 1937. s-a. L.40000($55) (effective 1995). Casa Editrice Idelson, Via A. DeGasperi, 55, 80133 Naples, Italy. TEL 39-81-5524733. FAX 39-81-5518295. Ed. Nicola Misasi.

617.3 IT
SOCIETA EMILIANA ROMAGNOLA TRIVENETA DI ORTOPEDIA E TRAUMATOLOGIA. ATTI. (Text in Italian; summaries in English) s-a. L.39000. Societa Emiliana Romagnola Triveneta di Ortopedia e Traumatologia, Viale Dei Mille 140, 43100 Parma, Italy. TEL 0521-290191. FAX 0521-291314. TELEX 530476 EMMEVI I. Ed. Dr. L. Cugola. adv. (back issues avail.) **Document type:** proceedings.

MEDICAL SCIENCES — ORTHOPEDICS AND TRAUMATOLOGY

617.3 FR ISSN 0081-1033
SOCIETE FRANCAISE DE CHIRURGIE ORTHOPEDIQUE ET TRAUMATOLOGIQUE. CONFERENCES D'ENSEIGNEMENT. 1967. irreg., latest 1991. price varies. Expansion Scientifique, 31 bd de la Tour Maubourg, 75007 Paris, France. TEL 40-62-64-00. FAX 45-55-69-20. Ed. J. Duparc.

617.3 US ISSN 1059-1052
SOUTHERN ORTHOPAEDIC ASSOCIATION. JOURNAL. 1992. q. $20 to non-members; members $1.25; students $5. Southern Orthopaedic Association, 35 Lake Shore Dr., Box 190088, Birmingham, AL 35219-0088. TEL 800-423-4492. FAX 205-945-1548. Ed. Dr. L. Andrew Koman; Pub. William J. Ranieri. adv. contact: Wendy Ried. circ. 2,400. **Document type:** academic/scholarly publication.
Description: Serves as a forum to present new techniques and procedures, and contains updates about the ongoing educational activities of interest to all practicing orthopedists.
Refereed Serial

610.73 618.92 US
SPINAL CONNECTION. 1984. s-a. National Scoliosis Foundation, 72 Mt. Auburn St., Watertown, MA 02172. TEL 617-926-0397. FAX 617-926-0398. adv.; bk.rev. circ. 22,000. (back issues avail.)
Description: Provides medical information on scoliosis, including an overview of the Foundation's activities and services.

617.375 US ISSN 0362-2436
RD768 CODEN: SPINDD
SPINE (PHILADELPHIA, 1976). 1976. 24/yr. $254 to individuals (foreign $459); institutions $479 (foreign $598) (effective 1996); newsstand price: $26. Lippincott - Raven Publishers, 227 E. Washington Sq., Philadelphia, PA 19106. TEL 215-238-4200. (Subscr. to: 12107 Insurance Way, Hagerstown, MD 21740) Ed. James N. Weinstein. adv.; illus.; index. circ. 9,922. (also avail. in microform from UMI) **Indexed:** Bibl.Dev.Med.& Child Neur., Biol.Abstr., Chem.Abstr., CINAHL, Curr.Adv.Ecol.Sci., Curr.Cont., Dent.Ind., Dok.Arbeitsmed., Excerp.Med., Hosp.Lit.Ind., Ind.Med., Ind.Vet.
—BLDSC (8413.903000); CASDDS; Faxon; Genuine Article; SWETS; UMI; UnCover. **CCC.**

617.375 US ISSN 0887-9869
RD768
SPINE (PHILADELPHIA, 1986); state of the art reviews. 1986. 3/yr. $93 (foreign $103). Hanley & Belfus, Inc., 210 S. 13th St., Philadelphia, PA 19107. TEL 215-546-7293. FAX 215-790-9330.
—BLDSC (8413.902980). **CCC.**
Refereed Serial

617.375 US ISSN 1072-3730
▼**SPINE LETTER.** 1994. m. $59 to individuals (foreign $89); institutions $145 (foreign $160) (effective 1996); newsstand price: $15. Lippincott - Raven Publishers, 227 E. Washington Sq., Philadelphia, PA 19106. TEL 215-238-4200.

SPORTS, EXERCISE AND INJURY. see *MEDICAL SCIENCES — Sports Medicine*

617 US ISSN 1062-8592
SPORTS MEDICINE AND ARTHROSCOPY REVIEW. 1993. q. $105 to individuals (foreign $126); institutions $134 (foreign $156) (effective 1996); newsstand price: $40. Lippincott - Raven Publishers, 227 E. Washington Sq., Philadelphia, PA 19106. TEL 215-238-4200. Eds. W. Dilworth Cannon Jr., Kenneth E. DeHaven. adv. contact: Phyllis Noyes. illus.; index. circ. 1,000. (also avail. in microform; back issues avail.) **Document type:** academic/scholarly publication.
—BLDSC (8419.837370); Genuine Article. **CCC.**
Description: Topic-oriented, invited reviews on issues and techniques in arthroscopy and sports medicine.

SWISS SURGERY/SCHWEIZER CHIRURGIE/CHIRURGIE SUISSE. see *MEDICAL SCIENCES — Surgery*

628 US ISSN 1071-6262
T B I CHALLENGE!. 1982. q. $35 membership ($5 to persons with head injuries). National Head Injury Foundation, 1776 Massachusetts Ave., N.W., Ste. 100, Washington, DC 20036. TEL 202-296-6443. FAX 202-296-8850. Eds. Sue Guzman, Andy Schwarz. circ. 30,000. (back issues avail.)
Formerly: N H I F Newsletter.
Description: Covers topics related to rehabilitation, prevention and legislation as they pertain to the needs and rights of persons with brain injuries and their families.

617.3 US ISSN 0885-9698
TECHNIQUES IN ORTHOPAEDICS. 1986. q. $128 to individuals (foreign $154); institutions $138 (foreign $162) (effective 1996); newsstand price: $42. Lippincott - Raven Publishers, 227 Washington Sq., Philadelphia, PA 19106. TEL 215-238-4200. Ed. Bruce D. Browner. adv. contact: Phyllis Noyes. illus.; index. circ. 2,500. (also avail. in microform; back issues avail.) **Document type:** academic/scholarly publication.
—BLDSC (8745.278000); SWETS; UMI. **CCC.**
Description: Publishes original, technique oriented articles coveing operations, manipulations and instruments being developed and applied in such areas as arthroscopy, arthroplasty and trauma.
Refereed Serial

617.1 FR ISSN 0397-3999
TECHNIQUES ORTHOPEDIQUES. 1976. irreg., latest 1981. 875 F. Expansion Scientifique, 31 bd. de la Tour Maubourg, 75007 Paris, France. TEL 40-62-64-00. FAX 45-55-69-20. Eds. J. Casaing, L. Descamps.

617.3 SP ISSN 0214-4352
TECNICA ORTOPEDICA INTERNACIONAL. Key Title: T O I. (Text in English, Spanish) 1988. q. 5100 ptas.($50) (UK £25) (effective 1995). Editorial Garsi, S.A., Grupo Masson, Principe de Asturias 20, 08012 Barcelona, Spain. TEL 34-3-4154544. FAX 34-3-4161220. Ed. Oriol Cohi. **Document type:** academic/scholarly publication.

617.3 JA ISSN 0917-1789
TOGAI NAIATSU KENKYUKAI HOKOKUSHU/PROGRESS IN RESEARCH ON INTRACRANIAL PRESSURE. (Text in Japanese; summaries in English) 1990. a. Tokai Naiatsu Kenkyukai, c/o Chugai Seiyaku K.K., Iyaku Gakujutsu Dai 3 Bu, 1-9, Kyobashi 2-chome, Chuo-ku, Tokyo 104, Japan.

617.3 JA ISSN 0915-2253
TOHKAI SEIKEI GEKA GAISHO KENKYU KAISHI/TOHKAI ORTHOPAEDIC SOCIETY OF TRAUMATOLOGY. JOURNAL. (Text in Japanese) 1988. a. 5000 Yen to non-members. Tohkai Seikei Geka Gaisho Kenkyukai, Gifu Kenritsu Tajimi Byoin Seikei Geka, 5-161, Maebatacho, Tajimi-shi, Gifu-ken 507, Japan. TEL 0572-22-5311. FAX 0572-25-1246. Ed. Toshiyuki. adv.; circ. 1,000. (controlled). **Document type:** academic/scholarly publication.
●Also available online.
Also available on CD-ROM.
Description: Publishes proceedings of medical meetings and original articles on traumatology, including fractures, dislocations and other injuries in the orthopaedic field.
Refereed Serial

617.3 JA ISSN 0913-476X
TOHKAI SEKITSUI GEKA/JOURNAL TOHKAI SPINAL SURGERY. (Text in Japanese; summaries in English, Japanese) 1987. a. 5000 Yen to non-members. Tohkai Sekitsui Geka Konwakai - Society of Tohkai Spinal Surgery, Gifu Kenritsu Tajimi Byoin, 5-161, Maebbatacho, Tajimi-shi, Gifuken 507, Japan. TEL 0572-22-5311. FAX 0572-25-1246. Ed. Toshiyuki Muro. adv.; circ. 600 (controlled). **Document type:** academic/scholarly publication.
●Also available online.
Also available on CD-ROM.
Description: Contains proceedings of medical meetings, original articles, and historical reviews on spinal surgery.
Refereed Serial

617.3 JA
TOHOKU ARCHIVES OF ORTHOPAEDIC SURGERY AND TRAUMATOLOGY/TOHOKU SEIKEI SAIGAI GEKA KIYO. (Text in Japanese) 1957. s-a. membership. Tohoku Society of Orthopaedic Surgery and Traumatology - Tohoku Seikei Saigai Geka Gakkai, c/o Dept. of Orthopaedic Surgery, Tohoku University School of Medicine, 1-1 Seiryo-machi, Aoba-ku, Sendai 980, Japan. Ed.Bd. bk.rev.; abstr.; bibl.; charts; illus.; index, cum.index. circ. 650 (controlled).
Formerly (until vol. 20, 1977): Tohoku Archivo por Orthopedia Kej Akcidenta Hirurgio (ISSN 0040-8751)

617.3 JA
TOKYO HIZA KANSETSU GAKKAI KAISHI/TOKYO KNEE SOCIETY. PROCEEDINGS OF THE MEETING. (Text in Japanese; summaries in English, Japanese) a. 3000 Yen. Tokyo Hiza Kansetsu Gakkai, Keio Daigaku Igakubu Seikei Gekagaku Kyoshitsu, 35, Shinanomachi, Shinjuku-ku, Tokyo 160, Japan. **Document type:** proceedings.

617.1 SA
TRAUMA & EMERGENCY MEDICINE. vol.8, 1991. 6/yr. R.50. Helm Publishing Co. (Pty.) Ltd., P.O. Box 41706, Craighall 2024, South Africa. TEL 011-788-0612.

TRAUMA QUARTERLY. see *MEDICAL SCIENCES — Surgery*

617.3 US
TRAUMAGRAM. q. membership. American Trauma Society, 8903 Presidental Pkwy., Ste. 512, Upper Marlboro, MD 20772-2656. TEL 301-420-4189. FAX 301-420-0617. Ed. Ruth Pollack. circ. 4,000. **Document type:** newsletter.

TURK ANESTEZIYOLOJI VE REANIMASYON CEMIYETI DERGISI. see *MEDICAL SCIENCES — Anaesthesiology*

616.028 617.1 GW ISSN 0177-5537
R51 CODEN: UNFAE2
DER UNFALLCHIRURG. 1894. 12/yr. DM.498($361) (effective 1996). (Deutsche Gesellschaft fuer Unfallheilkunde) Springer-Verlag, Heidelberger Platz 3, 14197 Berlin, Germany. TEL 030-8207-0. FAX 030-8214091. E-mail: orders@springer.de. (Subscr. in N. America to: Springer-Verlag New York, Inc., 44 Hartz Way, Secaucus, NJ 07096-2491. TEL 201-348-4033. FAX 201-348-4505) Eds. L. Schweiberer, H. Tscherne. (also avail. in microform from UMI; back issues avail.; reprint service avail. from ISI) **Indexed:** Biol.Abstr., Curr.Cont., Excerp.Med., Ind.Med. **Document type:** academic/scholarly publication.
—BLDSC (9090.235280); Faxon; Genuine Article; SWETS; UMI. **CCC.**
Former titles: Unfallheilkunde (ISSN 0341-5694); Monatsschrift fuer Unfallheilkunde (ISSN 0340-1669); Monatsschrift fuer Unfallheilkunde, Versicherungs-, Versorgungs- und Verkehrsmedizin (ISSN 0026-9336)

617.1 GW ISSN 0340-2649
UNFALLCHIRURGIE. (Text in English and German; summaries in English) 1975. 6/yr. DM.279($202) (effective 1996). Urban und Vogel, Lindwurmstr. 95, 80337 Munich, Germany. TEL 089-53292-0. FAX 089-53292-100. (Subscr. to: Postfach 152209, 80052 Munich, Germany) circ. 1,900. **Indexed:** Ind.Med. **Document type:** academic/scholarly publication.
—BLDSC (9090.235300); UMI. **CCC.**

617.1 SP ISSN 1132-4791
URGENCIAS. 11/yr. San Jose 43, Sant Vincenc dels Horts (Barcelona), Spain. TEL 656-05-48. Ed. M. de Aguilar Merlo. circ. 15,000.

VETERINARY AND COMPARATIVE ORTHOPAEDICS AND TRAUMATOLOGY. see *VETERINARY SCIENCE*

617.1 US
WOUND CARE PRODUCTS RESOURCE.* 1992. a. $25. S - N Publications, Inc., Box 908, Spring House, PA 19477-0903. TEL 708-426-6100. FAX 708-426-2083. adv.: B&W page $1250; trim 8 x 10 7/8. circ. 6,500. **Document type:** trade publication.

MEDICAL SCIENCES — OTORHINOLARYNGOLOGY

617.3 UK
WOUND MANAGEMENT. bi-m. P M H Publications Ltd., P.O. Box 100, Chichester, W. Sussex PO19 1XR, England. Ed. Elspeth Lee. **Document type:** academic/scholarly publication.

617.1 US ISSN 1067-1927
CODEN: WREREU
WOUND REPAIR AND REGENERATION. 1993. q. $63 to individuals (Canada $88.28; elsewhere $82.50); institutions $95 (Canada $122.52; elsewhere $114.50); students, residents $31 (Canada $54.04; elsewhere $50.50) (effective 1996); newsstand price: $16.50. (Wound Healing Society) Mosby - Year Book, Inc. (Subsidiary of: Times Mirror Company), 11830 Westline Industrial Dr., St. Louis, MO 63146-3318. TEL 800-325-4177. FAX 314-432-1380. (Co-sponsors: European Tissue Repair Society; Japanese Society for Wound Healing) Ed. Dr. William J. Lindblad. adv.: B&W page $660, color page $1280; trim 8 1/4 x 11. circ. 1,500. (back issues avail.)
—BLDSC (9364.529320); UMI. **CCC.**

616.02 US ISSN 1044-7946
WOUNDS; a compendium of clinical research and practice. bi-m. $60 (foreign $96). Health Management Publications, Inc., 550 American Ave., King of Prussia, PA 19406. TEL 215-337-4466; 800-237-7285. FAX 215-337-0890. **Document type:** trade publication.
—BLDSC (9364.529340); Genuine Article.

617 US ISSN 0271-7964
RC86
YEAR BOOK OF EMERGENCY MEDICINE. 1981. a. $73.95 (residents $35)n(effective 1996). Mosby - Year Book, Inc., Continuity Division, 200 N. LaSalle, Chicago, IL 60601. TEL 312-726-9733. FAX 312-726-6075. TELEX 206155. Ed. Dr. David K. Wagner. (reprint service avail.)
●Also available online. Vendor(s): Ovid Technologies.

YEAR BOOK OF HAND SURGERY. see *MEDICAL SCIENCES — Surgery*

617.305 US ISSN 0276-1092
RD711
YEAR BOOK OF ORTHOPEDICS. 1940. a. $74.95 (residents $35) (effective 1996). Mosby - Year Book, Inc., Continuity Division, 200 N. LaSalle, Chicago, IL 60601. TEL 312-726-9733. FAX 312-726-6075. TELEX 206155. Ed. Clement B. Sledge, M.D. illus. (reprint service avail.)
●Also available online. Vendor(s): Ovid Technologies.
—BLDSC (9414.677000); Faxon; UnCover.
Former titles: Year Book of Orthopedics, Traumatic and Plastic Surgery; Year Book of Orthopedics and Traumatic Surgery (ISSN 0084-3938)

617.585 US ISSN 0742-194X
RD563
YEAR BOOK OF PODIATRIC MEDICINE AND SURGERY. a. $66.95 (residents $35) (effective 1996). Mosby - Year Book, Inc., Continuity Division, 200 N. LaSalle, Chicago, IL 60601. TEL 312-726-9733. FAX 312-726-6075. TELEX 206155. Ed. Stephen J. Kominsky. illus. (reprint service avail.)
—BLDSC (9415.550000).

617.3 GW ISSN 0044-3220
CODEN: ZOIGAP
ZEITSCHRIFT FUER ORTHOPAEDIE UND IHRE GRENZGEBIETE. (Supplement avail.: Bucherei des Orthopaeden) (Text in English and German) 1891. bi-m. DM.468. (Deutsche Gesellschaft fuer Orthopaedie und Traumatologie) Ferdinand Enke Verlag, Postfach 300366, 70443 Stuttgart, Germany. TEL 0711-135798-0. FAX 0711-135798-30. TELEX 07252275-GTV-D. Ed.Bd. adv.; bk.rev.; bibl.; charts; illus.; index. circ. 1,600. (reprint service avail. from IRC) **Indexed:** Biol.Abstr., C.I.S. Abstr., Curr.Adv.Cancer Res., Curr.Cont., Dent.Ind., Excerp.Med., Ind.Med., Sci.Cit.Ind. **Document type:** academic/scholarly publication.
—BLDSC (9475.670000); ADONIS; EMDOCS; Faxon; Genuine Article; SWETS. **CCC.**
Incorporates: Deutsche Gesellschaft fuer Orthopaedie und Ihre Grenzgebiete. Verhandlungen (ISSN 0070-4091)

617.375 CC ISSN 1004-406X
ZHONGGUO JIZHU JISUI ZAZHI/CHINESE JOURNAL OF SPINE AND SPINAL CORD. (Text in Chinese; abstracts in Chinese, English) 1991. bi-m. $24 (effective 1996). Zhong - Ri Youhao Yiyuan - China - Japan Friendship Hospital, Yinghuayuan Dongjie, Beijing 100029, People's Republic of China. TEL 010-4221122. FAX 010-4217749. TELEX 210096 CJFH CN. (Co-sponsor: Chinese Association of Rehabilitation Medicine, Special Board of Spine and Spinal Cord Injury) Ed.Bd. adv.: page $3000. bibl.; illus. **Document type:** academic/scholarly publication.
Description: Covers clinical diagnosis, treatment techniques, rehabilitation techniques and experimental studies, osteonosus, deformation and tumors of spine and spinal cord.

616.02 CC
ZHONGGUO SHAOSHANG CHUANGSHANG ZAZHI/CHINESE JOURNAL OF BURNS AND WOUNDS. (Text in Chinese) q. Zhongguo Shaoshang Chuangshang Keji Zhongxin - Chinese Science and Technology Center for Burns and Wounds, 106 Yong'an Lu, Xuanwu-qu, Beijing 100050, People's Republic of China. TEL 2567733. Ed. Xu Rongxiang.

617.3 CC
ZHONGHUA GUKE ZAZHI/CHINESE JOURNAL OF ORTHOPEDICS. (Text in Chinese) bi-m. $1.50 per no. Guoji Shudian, Qikan Bu - China International Book Trading Corp., Chegongzhuang Xilu 21, P.O. Box 399, Beijing 100044, People's Republic of China. **Indexed:** ExtraMED. **Document type:** academic/scholarly publication.
●Also available on CD-ROM.

617.3 CC ISSN 1001-6015
ZHONGYI ZHENGGU. (Text in Chinese) 1989. q. $8. Luoyang Zhenggu Yanjiusuo, No. 1, Qiming Nanlu, Luoyang, Henan 471002, People's Republic of China. TEL 51838. (Subscr. to: China International Book Trading Corp., P.O. Box 339, Beijing, P.R. China) Ed. Guo Weizhun. **Document type:** academic/scholarly publication.

MEDICAL SCIENCES —
Otorhinolaryngology

A A O A NEWS. (American Academy of Otolaryngic Allergy) see *MEDICAL SCIENCES — Allergology And Immunology*

616.21 US ISSN 0149-8886
RF297
ACADEMY OF REHABILITATIVE AUDIOLOGY. JOURNAL. Short title: J A R A. 1969. a. $20 (overseas $30). Academy of Rehabilitative Audiology, c/o Robert J. Dunlop, Ph.D., JARA Circ. Mgr., Audiology Section (126A), VA Medical Center, Temple, TX 76504. Ed. Patricia Kricos. bk.rev.; circ. 500 (paid). **Indexed:** ERIC, Lang.& Lang.Behav.Abstr., Psychol.Abstr. (1985-), Sociol.Abstr. **Document type:** academic/scholarly publication.
—BLDSC (4674.984000); UnCover.
Description: Forum for the exchange of ideas on, knowledge of, and experience with habilitative and rehabilitative aspects of audiology.
Refereed Serial

616.31 617 US
ACOUSTIC NEUROMA ASSOCIATION NOTES. 1981. q. membership. Acoustic Neuroma Association, Box 12402, Atlanta, GA 30355. TEL 404-237-8023. FAX 404-237-2704. Dir. Linda L.Kees. circ. 4,000. **Document type:** newsletter.
Description: Provides support and information for patients who have had acoustic neuromas or other cranial nerve tumors.

616.21 NO ISSN 0001-6489
CODEN: AOLAAJ
ACTA OTO-LARYNGOLOGICA. (Supplements avail.) (Text in English) 1918. 6/yr. NOK 1625 in Nordic countries; elsewhere $277 (incl. supplements) (effective 1996). (Scandinavian Oto-Laryngological Society) Scandinavian University Press, P.O. Box 2959 Toeyen, N-0608 Oslo, Norway. TEL 47-22-57-54-00. FAX 47-22-57-57-53. (U.S. addr.: Scandinavian University Press, 200 Meacham Ave., Elmont, NY 11003. TEL 516-352-7300) Eds. Boerje Drettner, Carl-Magnus Eneroth. adv.; charts; illus.; index. circ. 2,100. **Indexed:** ASCA, Biol.Abstr., Biotech.Abstr., C.I.S. Abstr., Chem.Abstr., Curr.Adv.Ecol.Sci., Curr.Cont., Dent.Ind., Dok.Arbeitsmed., Energy Res.Abstr., Excerp.Med., Helminthol.Abstr., Hort.Abstr., Ind.Med., Ind.Sci.Rev., Ind.Vet., Lang.& Lang.Behav.Abstr., NBA, Noise Pollut.Publ.Abstr., Nucl.Sci.Abstr., Psychol.Abstr., Sci.Cit.Ind.
—BLDSC (0642.250000); ADONIS; Faxon; Genuine Article; SWETS; UnCover.
Description: Presents original articles of basic research interest, as well as clinical studies in the field of otorhinolaryngology and related subdisciplines.

616.21 NO ISSN 0365-5237
CODEN: AOLSA5
ACTA OTO-LARYNGOLOGICA. SUPPLEMENT. (Supplement to: Acta Oto-Laryngologica) 1918. irreg. (Scandinavian Oto-Laryngological Society) Scandinavian University Press, P.O. Box 2959 Toeyen, N-0608 Oslo, Norway. TEL 47-2-67-76-00. FAX 47-2-67-75-75. adv. circ. 1,900. **Indexed:** Excerp.Med., Ind.Vet.
—BLDSC (0642.255000); ADONIS; Faxon; SWETS; UnCover.

616.21 BE ISSN 0001-6497
CODEN: AORLAE
ACTA OTO-RHINO-LARYNGOLOGICA BELGICA. (Supplements avail.) vol.21,1967. 4/yr. 3000 Fr. (foreign 3200 Fr.). Association des Societes Scientifiques Medicales Belges - Vereiniging van de Belgische Medische Wetenschappelijke Genootschappen, Av. Circulaire 138A, B-1180 Brussels, Belgium. TEL 02-374-5158. Ed. Dr. P. Hennebert. **Indexed:** Biol.Abstr., Chem.Abstr., Dent.Ind., Excerp.Med., Ind.Med., Lang.& Lang.Behav.Abstr., NBA, Rev.Med.& Vet.Mycol.
—BLDSC (0642.270000); Faxon; SWETS.

616.21 IT ISSN 0392-100X
CODEN: AOITDU
ACTA OTORHINOLARYNGOLOGICA ITALICA. (Supplement avail. (ISSN 0393-7976)) 1981. bi-m. L.100000 (foreign L.120000) (effective 1995). Pacini Editore s.r.l., Via A. Gherardesca 1, 56121 Ospedaletto (Pisa), Italy. TEL 39-50-982439. FAX 39-50-983906. Ed. E. de Campora. **Indexed:** Excerp.Med., Ind.Med., NBA.
—BLDSC (0642.280000); Faxon.

616.21 IT ISSN 0393-7976
CODEN: AOTOE
ACTA OTORHINOLARYNGOLOGICA ITALICA. SUPPLEMENT. irreg. Pacini Editore s.r.l., Via A. Gherardesca 1, 56014 Ospedaletto (Pisa), Italy. TEL 050-982439. FAX 050-983906. **Indexed:** Excerp.Med., Ind.Med.
—BLDSC (0642.280100).

616.21 SP ISSN 0001-6519
ACTA OTORRINOLARINGOLOGICA ESPANOLA. 1949. bi-m. 8300 ptas.($96) (effective 1995). (Sociedad Espanola de Otorrinolaringologia) Editorial Garsi, S.A., Juan Bravo 46, 28006 Madrid, Spain. TEL 34-1-4021212. FAX 34-1-4020954. Ed. Teodoro Sacristan Alonso. adv.; bk.rev.; bibl.; charts; illus. circ. 2,500. **Indexed:** Biol.Abstr., Excerp.Med., Ind.Med.Esp.
—BLDSC (0642.300000); Faxon.

616.85 US ISSN 1062-5747
ADVANCE FOR SPEECH - LANGUAGE PATHOLOGISTS AND AUDIOLOGISTS. 1991. fortn. Merion Publications, 650 Park Ave., Box 61556, King of Prussia, PA 19406. TEL 610-265-7812. FAX 610-265-8971. E-mail: blammey@merion.com. Ed. Sherry Fox. adv.: B&W page $995; trim 10 x 13 1/4. circ. 40,177. **Document type:** trade publication.

MEDICAL SCIENCES — OTORHINOLARYNGOLOGY 4511

617.89 SZ ISSN 0254-8747
ADVANCES IN AUDIOLOGY. (Text in English) 1983. irreg. price varies. S. Karger AG, Allschwilerstr. 10, P.O. Box, CH-4009 Basel, Switzerland. TEL 061-3061111. FAX 061-3061234. E-mail: Karger@Karger.ch. Ed. M. Hoke. **Document type:** academic/scholarly publication.
—BLDSC (0699.830000); Faxon. **CCC.**
Refereed Serial

616.21 SZ ISSN 0065-3071
RF16 CODEN: ADORB9
ADVANCES IN OTO-RHINO-LARYNGOLOGY. (Text in English) 1953. irreg. price varies. S. Karger AG, Allschwilerstr. 10, P.O. Box, CH-4009 Basel, Switzerland. TEL 061-3061111. FAX 061-3061234. E-mail: Karger@Karger.ch. Ed.Bd. (reprint service avail. from ISI) **Indexed:** Biol.Abstr., Chem.Abstr., Curr.Cont., Dent.Ind., Ind.Med. **Document type:** academic/scholarly publication.
—BLDSC (0709.570000); CASDDS; Faxon; SWETS. **CCC.**
Refereed Serial

616.21 US ISSN 0887-6916
RF1
ADVANCES IN OTOLARYNGOLOGY - HEAD AND NECK SURGERY. 1987. a. $82.95 (residents $40) (effective 1996). Mosby - Year Book, Inc. (Chicago) (Subsidiary of: Times Mirror Company), 200 N. LaSalle St., Chicago, IL 60601-1080. TEL 312-726-9733. FAX 312-726-6075. TELEX 206155. (Subscr. to: 11830 Westline Industrial Dr., St. Louis, MO 63146. TEL 800-325-4177) Ed. Dr. Eugene N. Myers.
—BLDSC (0709.569000). **CCC.**
Description: Presents a collection of original fully referenced clinical reviews from the experts in the field.

617.89 CN ISSN 1050-0545
RF286 CODEN: JAAAE3
AMERICAN ACADEMY OF AUDIOLOGY. JOURNAL. 1989. bi-m. $105 to individuals (outside US & Canada $140); institutions $145 (outside US & Canada $175) (effective 1996). Decker Periodicals, P.O. Box 620, LCD 1, Hamilton, ON L8N 3K7, Canada. TEL 905-522-7017; 800-568-7281. FAX 905-522-7839. E-mail: decker@io.org. (U.S. addr.: Box 785, Lewiston, NY 14092-0785) Ed. James Jerger. adv. contact: John Birkley. abstr.; circ. 5,600 (paid). (also avail. in microfiche; back issues avail.) **Indexed:** Ind.Med. **Document type:** academic/scholarly publication.
—BLDSC (4683.670000); UnCover. **CCC.**
Description: Features original contributions, abstracts, research reports, case studies and a clinical forum.

616.21 US ISSN 0731-8359
AMERICAN ACADEMY OF OTOLARYNGOLOGY - HEAD AND NECK SURGERY. BULLETIN. 1982. m. $55 to non-members (foreign $65). American Academy of Otolaryngology - Head and Neck Surgery, Inc., One Prince St., Alexandria, VA 22314. TEL 703-836-4444. FAX 703-683-5100. Ed. Dr. Jerome C. Goldstein. adv.: B&W page $750, color page $1600; trim 8 1/2 x 11. charts; stat.; index. circ. 10,000. **Document type:** bulletin.
Description: Features governmental and socioeconomic affairs plus practice management tips and info of interest to otolaryngologists. Provides information about meetings, publications, policies and activities and news. Contains employment listings and a calendar of courses, meetings and workshops.

616.21 US ISSN 0065-7603
AMERICAN BRONCHO-ESOPHAGOLOGICAL ASSOCIATION. TRANSACTIONS.* 1921. a. $40. American Broncho-Esophagological Association, c/o Dr. Stanley M. Shapshay, Ed., Otolaryngology Head & Neck Surgery 850, New England Medical Center, 750 Washington St., Boston, MA 02111. TEL 617-636-1688. circ. 150. **Document type:** proceedings.
—BLDSC (8886.150000).
Description: Publishes all papers presented at the annual spring meeting. Covers diseases of larynx, trachea, and bronchi as well as selected esophageal disorders.

616.21 617.7 US
AMERICAN DIOPTER & DECIBEL SOCIETY. PROCEEDINGS. biennial. free to meeting attendees. American Diopter & Decibel Society, 3518 Fifth Ave., Pittsburgh, PA 15213. TEL 412-647-2227. FAX 412-647-8760. circ. 50. (looseleaf format) **Document type:** proceedings.

616.21 US ISSN 0196-0709
RF1 CODEN: AJOTDP
AMERICAN JOURNAL OF OTOLARYNGOLOGY; head and neck medicine and surgery. 1979. bi-m. $125 (foreign $185) (effective 1996). W.B. Saunders Co. (Subsidiary of: Harcourt Brace & Company), Curtis Center, 3rd Fl., Independence Sq. W., Philadelphia, PA 19106-3399. TEL 215-238-7800. FAX 215-238-6445. (Subscr. to: Periodicals Fulfillment, W.B. Saunders Co., 6277 Sea Harbor Dr., 4th Fl., Orlando, FL 32891-4800. TEL 800-654-2452. FAX 800-874-6418) Ed. Dr. Jonas T. Johnson; Pub. Joan W. Blumberg. adv.: B&W page $695, color page $1595; 7 x 10; adv. contact: Cindy Gray. circ. 1,546. (reprint service avail. from UMI) **Indexed:** Chem.Abstr., CINAHL, Dent.Ind., Excerp.Med., Ind.Med., NBA. **Document type:** academic/scholarly publication.
—BLDSC (0829.300000); CASDDS; Faxon; Genuine Article; SWETS; UMI; UnCover. **CCC.**
Description: Provides original reports on the developments in the fields of otology, neurotology, audiology, allergology, laryngology, speech science, broncoesophagology, facial plastic surgery, and head and neck surgery.
Refereed Serial

616.21 US ISSN 0192-9763
CODEN: AJOTBN
AMERICAN JOURNAL OF OTOLOGY. 1979. bi-m. Lippincott - Raven Press, 227 E. Washington Sq., Philadelphia, PA 19106. TEL 215-238-4200. adv.; bk.rev.; bibl.; illus. circ. 2,000. (also avail. in microform from UMI; back issues avail.) **Indexed:** Biol.Abstr., Dent.Ind., Excerp.Med., Ind.Med., Noise Pollut.Publ.Abstr. **Document type:** academic/scholarly publication.
—BLDSC (0829.400000); ADONIS; Faxon; Genuine Article; SWETS; UMI; UnCover. **CCC.**
Description: Original articles and reviews in otology, neurology and audiology.

616.21 US ISSN 1050-6586
CODEN: AJRHE5
AMERICAN JOURNAL OF RHINOLOGY. 1987. bi-m. $75 to individuals; institutions $105. Ocean Side Publications, Inc., 95 Pitman St., Providence, RI 02906. TEL 401-331-2510. FAX 401-331-5138. Ed. David Kennedy. adv. circ. 3,000. **Document type:** academic/scholarly publication.
—BLDSC (0836.700000); CASDDS; Genuine Article; SWETS. **CCC.**
Description: Clinical discussions regarding medical and surgical aspects of the nose.

636.08 616.21 US
AMERICAN LARYNGOLOGICAL ASSOCIATION. TRANSACTIONS. 1879. a. American Laryngogological Association, Animal Scientific Program, Univ. of Washington, Dept. of Otolaryngology, BB-1165 Health Science Bldg., Seattle, WA 98195-0001. Ed. Ernest A. Weymuller. circ. 300.

617.8 US ISSN 0096-6851
RF1 CODEN: TAOTAW
AMERICAN OTOLOGICAL SOCIETY. TRANSACTIONS. 1868. a. price varies. American Otological Society, c/o Dr. Gregory Matz, Loyola Univ. Medical Ctr., 2160 S. First Ave., Bldg. 105-1870, Maywood, IL 60153. TEL 708-216-8526. Ed. Dr. A. Julianna Gulya. circ. 300. **Document type:** proceedings.
—BLDSC (8893.700000).
Description: Papers presented at the meeting of the society.

616.21 SP ISSN 0303-8874
CODEN: AOIAA4
ANALES OTORRINOLARINGOLOGICOS IBERO-AMERICANOS. (Text in Spanish; summaries in English, French, German) 1950. bi-m. 14402 ptas. (Latin America $144; elsewhere $177) to individuals; libraries 11521 ptas. (foreign $142) (effective 1994). C. Balmes, 24 pral. 1o, 08007 Barcelona, Spain. TEL 317-36-46. Ed. E. Perello Scherdel. adv.; bk.rev.; cum.index: 1950-1973, 1974-1983. circ. 1,000. (reprint service avail. from IRC) **Indexed:** Biol.Abstr., Dent.Ind., Excerp.Med., Ind.Med.
—BLDSC (0890.130000); Faxon.
Formerly (until 1973): Acta Oto-Rino-Laringologica Ibero-Americana (ISSN 0001-6500)

616.21 FR
ANNALES D'OTO-LARYNGOLOGIE. (Text in French; summaries in English) 1875. 8/yr. 1040 F. (foreign 1338 F.) (effective 1996). Masson - Periodiques, Villa Laromiguiere, 75005 Paris, France. TEL 1-40-46-62-00. FAX 1-40-46-62-01. Ed. H. Laccourreye. adv.; bk.rev.; bibl.; illus.; index. circ. 2,000. (also avail. in microform from UMI; reprint service avail. from ISI) **Indexed:** Chem.Abstr., Dent.Ind., Excerp.Med., Ind.Med., Lang.& Lang.Behav.Abstr. **Document type:** academic/scholarly publication.
—BLDSC (0990.700000); Faxon; SWETS; UMI. **CCC.**
Former titles: Annales d'Oto-Laryngologie et de Chirurgie Cervico Faciale (ISSN 0003-438X); (until 1963): Annales d'Oto-Laryngologie et de Chirurgie de la Face (ISSN 0150-9713); (until 1962): Annales d'Oto-Laryngologie (ISSN 0365-4931)
Description: Contains original works devoted to clinical studies and studies of a scientific character. Includes new techniques, reading notes, and analyses.

616.21 US ISSN 0003-4894
RF1 CODEN: AORHA2
ANNALS OF OTOLOGY, RHINOLOGY AND LARYNGOLOGY. 1892. m. $168 (foreign $188) (effective 1996). (American Laryngological Association) Annals Publishing Co., 4507 Laclede Ave., St. Louis, MO 63108. TEL 314-367-4987. FAX 314-367-4988. Ed. Dr. Brian F. McCabe. adv.; bk.rev.; charts; index. circ. 5,900. (also avail. in microfiche; reprint service avail. from UMI) **Indexed:** Abstr.Anthropol., AIM, Biol.Abstr., Chem.Abstr., Curr.Adv.Ecol.Sci., Curr.Cont., Dent.Ind., Dok.Arbeitsmed., Excerp.Med., Ind.Med., Ind.Sci.Rev., INIS Atomind., Lang.& Lang.Behav.Abstr., NBA, Noise Pollut.Publ.Abstr., Nutr.Abstr., Psychol.Abstr., Sci.Cit.Ind. **Document type:** trade publication.
—BLDSC (1043.400000); Faxon; Genuine Article; SWETS; UMI; UnCover.
Description: Publishes original manuscripts of clinical and research importance in otolaryngology - head and neck medicine and surgery, broncho-esophagology, maxillofacial surgery, audiology, speech pathology, and related specialties.
Refereed Serial

616.21 016 US ISSN 0886-4470
RF1 CODEN: AONSEJ
ARCHIVES OF OTOLARYNGOLOGY - HEAD & NECK SURGERY. 1925. m. $125 (foreign $160). American Medical Association, 515 N. State St., Chicago, IL 60610. TEL 312-464-5000; 800-262-2350. FAX 312-464-4184. Ed. Dr. Michael Johns. adv.; bk.rev.; bibl.; charts; illus.; index. circ. 13,000. (also avail. in microform from UMI) **Indexed:** AIM, Biol.Abstr., C.I.S.Abstr., Chem.Abstr., Curr.Cont., Dent.Ind., Except.Child.Educ.Abstr., Excerp.Med., Ind.Med., Ind.Sci.Rev., INIS Atomind., Kidney, Med.& Surg.Dermat., NBA, Noise Pollut.Publ.Abstr., Rev.Med.& Vet.Mycol., Rev.Plant Path., Sci.Cit.Ind. **Document type:** academic/scholarly publication.
●Also available online. Vendor(s): Lexis-Nexis.
—BLDSC (1638.510000); CASDDS; Faxon; Genuine Article; SWETS; UMI; UnCover. **CCC.**
Former titles: Archives of Otolaryngology (ISSN 0003-9977); A.M.A. Archives of Otolaryngology (ISSN 0096-6894)
Refereed Serial

MEDICAL SCIENCES — OTORHINOLARYNGOLOGY

616.2 — IT — ISSN 0066-9865
ASSOCIAZIONE ITALIANA LARINGECTOMIZZATI. ATTI (DEL) CONVEGNO NAZIONALE. 1957. q. Associazione Italiana Laringectomizzati, Via Friuli 28, 20135 Milan, Italy. TEL 02-5510819. Ed. Dr. Giuseppe Sapa.
Description: Addresses all laringectomees and their families with news about Association life and medical advice.

616.21 — US — ISSN 0271-1354
AUDIO-DIGEST OTORHINOLARYNGOLOGY - HEAD AND NECK SURGERY. 1968. s-m. $168. Audio-Digest Foundation (Subsidiary of: California Medical Association), 1577 E. Chevy Chase Dr., Glendale, CA 91206. TEL 213-245-8505. FAX 818-240-7379. (audio cassette)
Former titles: Audio-Digest Otorhinolaryngology - Head and Neck Surgery; Audio-Digest Otorhinolaryngology (ISSN 0030-6673)
Refereed Serial

617.8 — SZ — ISSN 0020-6091
RF290 — CODEN: AUDLAK
AUDIOLOGY; journal of auditory communication. (Text in English; summaries in French) 1962. bi-m. 387 SFr.($266) per vol. (International Society of Audiology) S. Karger AG, Allschwilerstr. 10, P.O. Box, CH-4009 Basel, Switzerland. TEL 061-3061111. FAX 061-3061234. E-mail: Karger@karger.ch. (US addr.: 26 W. Avon Rd., Box 529, Farmington, CT 06085. TEL 203-675-7834) Ed. J.M. Aran. adv.; abstr.; bibl.; illus.; index, cum.index. circ. 1,650. (also avail. in microfilm) **Indexed:** Bibl.Dev.Med.& Child Neur., Biol.Abstr., Curr.Adv.Ecol.Sci., Curr.Cont., Dok.Arbeitsmed., Excerp.Med., Ind.Med., Ind.Sci.Rev., Lang.& Lang.Behav.Abstr., NBA, Noise Pollut.Publ.Abstr., Psychol.Abstr. (1971-), Sci.Cit.Ind. **Document type:** academic/scholarly publication.
—BLDSC (1789.080000); EMDOCS; Faxon; Genuine Article; SWETS; UnCover. **CCC.**
Formerly: International Audiology (ISSN 0538-4915)
Refereed Serial

617.89 — SZ
▼**AUDIOLOGY AND NEUROOTOLOGY.** Announced for publication in 1996. 6/yr. 414 SFr.($318) (effective 1996). S. Karger AG, Allschwilerstr. 10, P.O. Box, CH-4009 Basel, Switzerland. TEL 061-3061111. FAX 061-3061234. E-mail: Karger@karger.ch. (Subscr. in U.S. to: S. Karger Publishers, Inc., 26 W. Avon Rd., Box 529, Farmington, CT 06085. FAX 203-675-7302) **Document type:** academic/scholarly publication.
Refereed Serial

617.89 — JA — ISSN 0303-8106
CODEN: AUJADK
AUDIOLOGY JAPAN. (Text in Japanese; summaries in English) 1958. bi-m. 8000 Yen. Japan Audiological Society - Nihon Chokaku Igakkai, c/o Chateau Takanawa 703, 3-23-14 Takanawa, Minato-ku, Tokyo 108, Japan. FAX 03-3445-5834. TELEX 03-3445-5834. Ed. M. Okamoto. adv. (reprint service avail.) **Indexed:** Biol.Abstr., Excerp.Med.
●Also available online. Vendor(s): JICST.
—BLDSC (1789.083000).
Formerly: Audiology (ISSN 0571-8724)

617.89 — US
AUDIOLOGY TODAY. bi-m. $40 to individuals; institutions $80. American Academy of Audiology, 1735 N. Lynn St., Ste. 950, Arlington, VA 22209-2019. Ed. Jerry Northern. **Document type:** academic/scholarly publication.
Description: Covers academy affairs and clinic practice which offers a series of pragmatic applications in evaluative, diagnostic and rehabilitative services.

616.21 — JA — ISSN 0385-8146
CODEN: ANLADF
AURIS. NASUS. LARYNX. (Text in English, French or German; summaries in English) 1973. q. $30 to individuals; institutions $40. Society for the Promotion of International Otorhinolaryngology - Kokusai Jibi Inkokagaku Shinkokai, Business Center for Academic Societies Japan, 5-16-9 Honkomagome, Bunkyo-ku, Tokyo 113, Japan. TEL 81-3-5814-5801. FAX 81-3-5814-5820. Ed. Dr. Makoto Sakai. adv.; charts; illus. circ. 600. **Indexed:** Biol.Abstr., Dent.Ind., Excerp.Med., Ind.Med. **Document type:** academic/scholarly publication.
—BLDSC (1792.760000).

616.21 — AT — ISSN 1037-2105
CODEN: AJOTEQ
AUSTRALIAN JOURNAL OF OTOLARYNGOLOGY. 1962. a. Aus.$70 (effective 1996). Australian Society of Otolaryngology Head & Neck Surgery Ltd., 33-35 Atchison St., St. Leonards, N.S.W. 2065, Australia. TEL 61-2-94385141. FAX 61-2-99067103. Ed. Dr. G.D. Beaumont. adv.; bk.rev. circ. 1,000. (also avail. in microform from UMI; reprint service avail. from UMI) **Indexed:** DSH Abstr, Excerp.Med. **Document type:** academic/scholarly publication.
—BLDSC (1810.810000); UMI.
Formerly (until 1992): Oto-Laryngological Society of Australia. Journal (ISSN 0030-6614)

616.21 — FR — ISSN 0395-3971
CODEN: CCCADH
CAHIERS D'OTO-RHINOLARYNGOLOGIE, DE CHIRURGIE CERVICO-FACIALE ET D'AUDIOPHONOLOGIE. 1966. 10/yr. 400 F. (foreign 440 F.) (effective 1991). Editions la Simarre, Z.I. No. 2 - rue Joseph-Cugnot, 37300 Joue-les-Tours, France. TEL 47-53-53-66. FAX 47-67-45-05. **Indexed:** NBA.
—BLDSC (2950.602000).
Former titles (until 1976): Cahiers d'O R L et de Chirurgie Cervico-Faciale (ISSN 0395-398X); (until 1973): Cahiers d'Oto-Rhinolaryngologie (ISSN 0373-2827)
Description: Focuses of cervico-facial pathology and anatomy, laryngology, and otology.

CAPTION. see COMMUNICATIONS — Television And Cable

616.21 — UK — ISSN 0307-7772
CODEN: COTSD2
CLINICAL OTOLARYNGOLOGY AND ALLIED SCIENCES. 1976. bi-m. £269.50 in Europe; elsewhere £296.50($477) (effective 1996). Blackwell Science Ltd., Osney Mead, Oxford OX2 OEL, England. TEL 01865-206206. FAX 01865-206219. TELEX 83355 MEDBOK G. Ed. J. Hibbert. adv.; bk.rev.; charts; illus.; index. circ. 1,700. (also avail. in microform from UMI; back issues avail.; reprint service avail. from ISI) **Indexed:** ASCA, Biol.Abstr., Curr.Adv.Ecol.Sci., Curr.Cont., Excerp.Med., Ind.Med., NBA, Sci.Cit.Ind. **Document type:** academic/scholarly publication.
—BLDSC (3286.324000); Faxon; Genuine Article; SWETS; UMI; UnCover. **CCC.**
Refereed Serial

616.21 — SP
CLINICAS OTORRINOLARINGOLOGICAS DE NORTEAMERICA. Spanish translation of Otolaryngologic Clinics of North America. 1986. 6/yr. 19716 ptas.($120) (effective 1990). Interamericana de Espana, S.A., Division de Ciencias de la Salud de McGraw-Hill, Calle Manuel Ferrero, 13, 28036 Madrid, Spain. TEL 315-0340. FAX 733-6627.

CONTACT (BUFFALO). see HANDICAPPED — Hearing Impaired

CORRIERE DEI LARINGECTOMIZZATI. see SOCIAL SERVICES AND WELFARE

616.21 617 — US — ISSN 1068-9508
CODEN: COOSFD
CURRENT OPINION IN OTOLARYNGOLOGY & HEAD AND NECK SURGERY. 1993. bi-m. $129.95 to individuals; institutions $259.95; residents $55. Current Science, 400 Market St., Ste. 700, Philadelphia, PA 19106-2199. TEL 215-574-2210; 800-552-5866. FAX 215-574-3533. (And: Current Science Ltd., 34-42 Cleveland St., London W1P 6LB, England. TEL 0171-323-0323. FAX 0171-636-6911) Eds. Richard Fabian, Jack Gluckman. adv. contact: Steve Miller. **Indexed:** CINAHL, Excerp.Med. (1995-). **Document type:** academic/scholarly publication.
●Also available online. Vendor(s): OCLC.
Also available on CD-ROM.
—BLDSC (3500.776700); ADONIS.

616.21 — UK — ISSN 1120-8694
CODEN: DIESE
DISEASES OF THE ESOPHAGUS. 1988-1992; resumed 1994. q. £156 to individuals (outside Europe £151 ($250)); institutions £191 (outside Europe £191 ($306)) (effective 1995). (International Society for Diseases of the Esophagus) Churchill Livingstone Journals (Subsidiary of: Pearson Professional), Robert Stevenson House, 1-3 Baxter's Pl., Leith Walk, Edinburgh EH1 3AF, Scotland. TEL 0131-556-2424. FAX 0131-459-1177. (Subscr. to: Pearson Professional Ltd., P.O. Box 77, Fourth Ave., Harlow, Essex CM19 5AA, England. TEL 01279-623760; U.S. subscr. to: Churchill Livingstone, 650 Ave. of the Americas, New York, NY 10011. TEL 212-206-5000) Ed. J.R. Siewert. adv. contact: David Dunnachie. bk.rev.; abstr.; bibl. circ. 990. (also avail. in microform from UMI) **Indexed:** Excerp.Med. (until 1992; 1994-). **Document type:** academic/scholarly publication.
—BLDSC (3598.210000). **CCC.**
Incorporates (in Jul. 1993): Gullet (ISSN 0952-0643)
Description: Explores original and review material covering all aspects of esophageal disorders, their etiology, investigation and diagnosis, and both medical and surgical treatment.

617.89 — US — ISSN 0196-0202
RF286 — CODEN: EAHEDS
EAR AND HEARING. 1975. bi-m. $52 to individuals; institutions $94 (effective 1995). (American Auditory Society) Williams & Wilkins, 428 E. Preston St., Baltimore, MD 21202. TEL 410-528-4000; 800-638-6423. FAX 410-528-4312. Ed. Dr. Susan Jerger. adv.; illus.; index. circ. 5,685. (also avail. in microfilm from WWS; back issues avail.) **Indexed:** Chic.Per.Ind., Excerp.Med., Ind.Med., Ind.Sci.Rev., NBA, Noise Pollut.Publ.Abstr., Sci.Cit.Ind. **Document type:** academic/scholarly publication.
—BLDSC (3642.866000); Faxon; Genuine Article; SWETS; UnCover. **CCC.**
Former titles: American Auditory Society. Journal (ISSN 0164-5080); American Audiology Society. Journal (ISSN 0360-9294)
Description: Covers assessment, diagnosis and management of auditory disorders.
Refereed Serial

616.21 — US — ISSN 0145-5613
EAR, NOSE AND THROAT JOURNAL. 1922. m. $100 to individuals (foreign $140); institutions $125 (foreign $160). Medquest Communications, Inc., 629 Euclid Ave., Ste. 500, Cleveland, OH 44114-3003. TEL 216-522-9700. FAX 216-522-9707. Ed. Dr. Jack Pulec; Pub. John H. Whaley III. adv.; bk.rev.; charts; illus.; index. circ. 11,000. (also avail. in microfilm from UMI; reprint service avail.) **Indexed:** Biol.Abstr., Chem.Abstr., Dent.Ind., Excerp.Med., Ind.Med., Rev.Med.& Vet.Mycol.
—BLDSC (3642.867000); Faxon; SWETS; UMI; UnCover. **CCC.**
Formerly: Eye, Ear, Nose and Throat Monthly (ISSN 0014-5491)
Description: Publishes recent, scientific, clinical articles and case reports in otolaryngology and head and neck surgery; provides practical hands-on information for today's busy physician.
Refereed Serial

MEDICAL SCIENCES — OTORHINOLARYNGOLOGY

616.21 GW ISSN 0937-4477
CODEN: EAOTE7
EUROPEAN ARCHIVES OF OTO-RHINO-LARYNGOLOGY. (Text in English or German) 1864. 8/yr. DM.1498($1088) (effective 1996). (European Federation of Oto-Rhino-Laryngological Societies) Springer-Verlag, Heidelberger Platz 3, 14197 Berlin, Germany. TEL 030-8207-0. FAX 030-8214091. E-mail: orders@springer.de. (Subscr. in N. America to: Springer-Verlag New York, Inc., 44 Hartz Way, Secaucus, NJ 07096-2491. TEL 201-348-4033. FAX 201-348-4505) Ed.Bd. adv.; bibl.; charts; illus.; index. (also avail. in microform from UMI; back issues avail.; reprint service avail. from ISI) **Indexed:** Biol.Abstr., Curr.Adv.Ecol.Sci., Curr.Cont., Dent.Ind., Excerp.Med., Ind.Med., Ind.Sci.Rev., INIS Atomind., Sci.Cit.Ind. **Document type:** academic/scholarly publication.
—BLDSC (3829.488540); CASDDS; Faxon; Genuine Article; SWETS; UMI; UnCover. **CCC.**
Former titles: Archives of Oto-Rhino-Laryngology (ISSN 0302-9530); Archiv fuer Klinische und Experimentelle Ohren-, Nasen- und Kehlkopfheilkunde (ISSN 0003-9195)
Description: Focuses on original clinical reports and clinically relevant experimental studies in the fields of oto-rhino-laryngology, and head and neck surgery.

617.8 SZ ISSN 1021-7762
RC423 CODEN: FPLOEP
FOLIA PHONIATRICA ET LOGOPAEDICA; international journal of phoniatrics, speech therapy and communication pathology. (Text in English, French, German; summaries in English) 1947. bi-m. 225.40 SFr.($173.60) to individuals; institutions 322 SFr.($248) (effective 1996). (International Association of Logopedics and Phoniatrics) S. Karger AG, Allschwilerstr. 10, P.O. Box, CH-4009 Basel, Switzerland. TEL 061-3061111. FAX 061-3061234. E-mail: Karger@Karger.ch. Ed.Bd. adv.; bk.rev.; bibl.; charts; illus.; index. circ. 1,600. (also avail. in microform) **Indexed:** Bibl.Dev.Med.& Child Neur., Biol.Abstr., Chem.Abstr., Curr.Cont., Dent.Ind., Excerp.Med., Ind.Med., Lang.& Lang.Behav.Abstr., M.L.A., Mid.East: Abstr.& Ind., NBA, Psychol.Abstr. (1982-), SSCI. **Document type:** academic/scholarly publication.
—BLDSC (3973.560000); Faxon; Genuine Article; SWETS; UnCover. **CCC.**
Formerly: Folia Phoniatrica (ISSN 0015-5705)
Description: Provides a forum for phoniatrics and logopedics.
Refereed Serial

616.21 GW ISSN 0017-6192
CODEN: HBZHAS
H N O (BERLIN). (Hals-, Nasen-, Ohren-Heilkunde) (Text in German; summaries in English and German) 1947. 12/yr. DM.368($267) (effective 1996). (Deutsche Gesellschaft fuer Hals-Nasen-Ohrenheilkunde, Kopf- und Hals-chirurgie) Springer-Verlag, Heidelberger Platz 3, 14197 Berlin, Germany. TEL 030-8207-0. FAX 030-8214091. E-mail: orders@springer.de. (Subscr. in N. America to: Springer-Verlag New York, Inc., 44 Hartz Way, Secaucus, NJ 07096-2491. TEL 201-348-4033. FAX 201-348-4505) Ed. E. Lehnhardt. adv.; bk.rev.; bibl.; charts; illus.; index. (also avail. in microform from UMI; reprint service avail. from ISI) **Indexed:** Biol.Abstr., Curr.Adv.Ecol.Sci., Curr.Cont., Excerp.Med., Ind.Med., INIS Atomind. **Document type:** academic/scholarly publication.
—BLDSC (4319.500000); Faxon; Genuine Article; SWETS; UMI. **CCC.**
Formerly: H N O: Wegweiser fuer Die Fachaerztliche Praxis.

616.21 GW ISSN 0341-9746
H N O (COLOGNE); Mitteilungsblatt. 1950. bi-m. DM.51 (students DM.38.25). (Deutsche Berufsverband der Hals-, Nasen-, Ohrenaerzte e.V.) Deutscher Aerzte-Verlag GmbH, Postfach 400265, 50832 Cologne, Germany. TEL 02234-7011-0. FAX 02234-7011444. adv. circ. 4,567. **Indexed:** Dent.Ind., Excerp.Med. **Document type:** newsletter.

616.21 GW ISSN 0943-0121
H N O AKTUELL. (Hals - Nase - Ohren) 1993. m. DM.118. Dr. R. Kaden Verlag, Poststr. 24-26, 69115 Heidelberg, Germany. TEL 06221-10313. FAX 06221-29910. adv.; page DM.2350; trim 230 x 178; adv. contact: A. Siegmann. index; circ. 4,000. (back issues avail.) **Document type:** academic/scholarly publication.

616.21 GW ISSN 0940-1059
H N O HIGHLIGHTS. 1991. 6/yr. DM.20. M M V Medizin Verlag, Neumarkter Str. 18, 81673 Munich, Germany. TEL 089-43189-0. FAX 089-43189633. **Document type:** academic/scholarly publication.
—Genuine Article; SWETS.

616.21 GW ISSN 0177-1000
H N O - NACHRICHTEN. (Hals-Nasen-Ohren) 1971. bi-m. DM.36($26) (effective 1996). Urban und Vogel, Lindwurmstr. 95, 80337 Munich, Germany. TEL 089-53292-0. FAX 089-53292100. (Subscr. in N. America to: Spreinger-Verlag New York, Inc., 44 Hartz Way, Secaucus, NJ 07096-2491. TEL 201-348-4033. FAX 201-348-4505) circ. 3,200.

616.21 NE ISSN 0378-5955
CODEN: HERED3
HEARING RESEARCH. (Text in English) 1978. 22/yr. fl.4796($2925) (effective 1996). Elsevier Science B.V., P.O. Box 211, 1000 AE Amsterdam, Netherlands. TEL 31-20-4853911. FAX 31-20-4853598. TELEX 18582 ESPA NL. E-mail: nlinfo-f@elsevier.nl; usinfo-f@elsevier.com; forinfo-kyf04035@niftyserve.or.jp; Site addr.: http://www.elsevier.nl/. (Subscr. in U.S. and Canada to: Elsevier Science Inc., Box 882, Madison Sq. Sta., New York, NY 10159-0882. TEL 212-989-5800. FAX 212-633-3990) Ed. A.R. Moeller. adv.; bk.rev. (also avail. in microform from UMI; back issues avail.; reprint service avail. from SWZ) **Indexed:** Biol.Abstr., Chem.Abstr., Curr.Adv.Ecol.Sci., Curr.Cont., Dent.Ind., Excerp.Med., Ind.Med., Ind.Sci.Rev., INSPEC, NBA, Noise Pollut.Publ.Abstr., Sci.Cit.Ind., Sport Fish.Abstr., Wild.Rev. **Document type:** academic/scholarly publication.
—BLDSC (4275.286700); CASDDS; Faxon; Genuine Article; SWETS; UnCover. **CCC.**
Description: Publishes papers concerned with basic auditory mechanisms.
Refereed Serial

616.21 US
HOUSE EAR INSTITUTE. REVIEW. 1966. 3/yr. donation. House Ear Institute, 2100 W. Third St., 5th Fl., Los Angeles, CA 90057. TEL 213-483-4431. FAX 213-483-8789. Ed. Dilys J. Jones. circ. 22,000 (controlled). **Document type:** newsletter.
Formerly: Oto Review.
Description: Informs professionals and the public of new developments and current programs in our hearing research.

I F H O H JOURNAL. (International Federation of the Hard of Hearing) see HANDICAPPED — Hearing Impaired

616.21 II
CODEN: IJOLBJ
INDIAN JOURNAL OF OTOLARYNGOLOGY AND HEAD AND NECK SURGERY. (Text in English) 1948. q. Rs.300($50) (Association of Otolaryngologists of India, West Bengal Branch, 53, Creek Row, Calcutta 700 014, India. TEL 033-27-8092. FAX 033-26-3598. (Alt. addr.: Government Housing Estate, Old Dog Race Course, Blick-LH, Flat 4, Calcutta 700 038, India) Ed. Santanu Banerjee. adv.; bk.rev.; abstr.; index. circ. 1,200. **Indexed:** Biol.Abstr., Excerp.Med.
—BLDSC (4417.800200); CASDDS.
Former titles (until 1993): Indian Journal of Otolaryngology and Head and Neck; Indian Journal of Otolaryngology (ISSN 0019-5421)

616.21 618.92 IE ISSN 0165-5876
CODEN: IPOTDJ
INTERNATIONAL JOURNAL OF PEDIATRIC OTORHINOLARYNGOLOGY. 1979. m. I£652($1030) (effective 1996). Elsevier Science Ireland Ltd., P.O. Box 85, Limerick, Ireland. TEL 353-61-471944. FAX 353-61-472144. (Subscr. in U.S. and Canada to: Elsevier Science Inc., Box 882, Madison Sq. Sta., New York, NY 10159. TEL 212-989-5800. FAX 212-633-3990) Ed. R.J. Ruben. bk.rev. (also avail. in microform from UMI) **Indexed:** Biol.Abstr., Curr.Adv.Cancer Res., Curr.Cont., Dent.Ind., Excerp.Med., Ind.Med., Ind.Sci.Rev., NBA, Sci.Cit.Ind. **Document type:** academic/scholarly publication.
—BLDSC (4542.451000); Faxon; Genuine Article; SWETS; UnCover. **CCC.**
Description: Provides a medium for clinical and basic contributions in all of the areas of pediatric otorhinolaryngology.
Refereed Serial

617 JA ISSN 0910-6820
J O H N S: JOURNAL OF OTOLARYNGOLOGY, HEAD AND NECK SURGERY/JIBI INKOKA, TOKEIBU GEKA. (Text in Japanese) 1985. m. 2200 Yen per no. Tokyo Igakusha Ltd., 35-4, Hongo 3-chome, Bunkyo-ku, Tokyo 113, Japan.

616.21 GW ISSN 0930-8318
JATROS H N O. 1986. 12/yr. DM.90. P M I Verlagsgruppe GmbH, August-Schanz-Str. 21, 60433 Frankfurt a.M., Germany. TEL 069-5480000. FAX 069-54800077. Ed. Peter Hoffmann. circ. 2,900. (back issues avail.) **Document type:** academic/scholarly publication.
Description: Seminar papers with brief summaries of original articles, interviews and congress reports.

616.21 JA ISSN 0914-3491
JIBI INKOKA, TOKEIBU GEKA/OTOLARYNGOLOGY - HEAD AND NECK SURGERY. (Text in Japanese; summaries in English) 1946. m. 28830 Yen($222) Igaku-Shoin Ltd., 5-24-3 Hongo, Bunkyo-ku, Tokyo 113-91, Japan. TEL 03-817-5710. Ed.Bd. circ. 4,000.
●Also available online. Vendor(s): JICST.
—BLDSC (6313.524000).

616.21 FR
JOURNAL FRANCAIS D'OTO-RHINO-LARYNGOLOGIE - AUDIOPHONOLOGIE - CHIRURGIE MAXILLO-FACIALE. bi-m. $156. S E D I P Medical, 75 cours Albert-Thomas, 69447 Lyon Cedex 03, France. TEL 72-35-23-72. FAX 72-35-23-75. Ed. Dr. C. Dubreuil. **Indexed:** Biol.Abstr., Dent.Ind., Ind.Med.
Former titles (until 1990): Journal Francais d'Oto-Rhino-Laryngologie (ISSN 0398-9771); (until 1977): J F O R L (ISSN 0398-9763); (until 1972): Journal Francais d'Oto-Rhino-Laryngologie (ISSN 0368-2218); (until 1967): Journal Francais d'Oto-Rhino-Laryngologie et Chirurgie Maxillo-Faciale (ISSN 0021-8332); (util 1953): Journal Francais d'Oto-Rhino-Laryngologie (ISSN 0398-9755)

617.89 UK ISSN 0963-7133
JOURNAL OF AUDIOLOGICAL MEDICINE. 1992. q. £55($173) to individuals; institutions £50 (effective 1996). (International Society of Physicians in Audiology) Whurr Publishers Ltd., 19b Compton Terrace, London N1 2UN, England. TEL 0171-359-5979. FAX 0171-226-5290. (Subscr. to: Turpin Distribution Services Ltd., Blackhorse Rd., Letchworth, Herts. SG6 1HN, England. TEL 01462-672555. FAX 01462-480947; Subscr. in N. America to: Whurr Publishers Ltd., Box 1897, Lawrence, KS 66044-8897. TEL 913-843-1221. FAX 913-843-1274) Ed.Bd. adv.; page £250; adv. contact: Sarah Vicary. bk.rev. **Indexed:** Excerp.Med. (1993-). **Document type:** academic/scholarly publication.
—BLDSC (4949.295000); ADONIS.
Incorporates: I A P A Bulletin (ISSN 0262-6853)
Description: Provides a forum for the many diverse aspects of audiological medicine: pediatric audiology, auditory electrophysiology, rehabilitation of the adult hearing and balance impaired, and neuro-otology.

JOURNAL OF BRONCHOLOGY. see MEDICAL SCIENCES — Respiratory Diseases

616.21 UK ISSN 0022-2151
CODEN: JLOTAX
JOURNAL OF LARYNGOLOGY AND OTOLOGY. (Supplement avail. (ISSN 0144-2945)) 1887. m. £95($190) Headley Bros. Ltd., Invicta Press, Queen's Rd., Ashford, Kent TN24 8HH, England. TEL 01233-623131. Ed. N. Weir. adv.; bibl.; illus.; index, cum.index every 10 yrs. circ. 2,500. (also avail. in microform from UMI) **Indexed:** AIM, Biol.Abstr., Chem.Abstr., Curr.Adv.Cancer Res., Curr.Adv.Cell & Devel.Biol., Curr.Adv.Ecol.Sci., Curr.Cont., Dent.Ind., Excerp.Med., Helminthol.Abstr., Ind.Med., Ind.Sci.Rev., INIS Atomind., Lang.& Lang.Behav.Abstr., NBA, Nutr.Abstr., Rev.Plant Path., Sci.Cit.Ind. **Document type:** academic/scholarly publication.
—BLDSC (5010.100000); EMDOCS; Faxon; SWETS; UMI; UnCover.

616.21 UK ISSN 0144-2945
JOURNAL OF LARYNGOLOGY AND OTOLOGY. SUPPLEMENT. 1978. irreg. price varies. Headley Bros. Ltd., Invicta Press, Queen's Rd., Ashford, Kent TN24 8HH, England. TEL 01233-623131. Ed. N. Weir. **Indexed:** Ind.Med. **Document type:** academic/scholarly publication.

MEDICAL SCIENCES — OTORHINOLARYNGOLOGY

616.21 — CN — ISSN 0381-6605
CODEN: JOTODX
JOURNAL OF OTOLARYNGOLOGY. (Text in English, French) 1972. bi-m. Can.$90($66) to individuals (foreign $79); institutions Can.$135($99) (foreign $107) (effective 1996). (Canadian Society of Otolaryngology - Head and Neck Surgery) Decker Periodicals, P.o. Box 620, LCD 1, Hamilton, ON L8N 3K7. TEL 905-522-7017. FAX 905-522-7839. bk.rev.; index. circ. 1,200. (tabloid format; also avail. in microfilm from UMI; reprint service avail. from UMI) **Indexed:** Biol.Abstr., Curr.Adv.Cancer Res., Curr.Adv.Cell & Devel.Biol., Curr.Cont., Dok.Arbeitsmed., Excerp.Med., Ind.Med., NBA. **Document type:** academic/scholarly publication.
—BLDSC (5027.710000); Faxon; Genuine Article; SWETS; UMI; UnCover. **CCC.**
Formerly: Canadian Journal of Otolaryngology (ISSN 0045-5083)

616.21 — JA — ISSN 0030-6622
JOURNAL OF OTOLARYNGOLOGY OF JAPAN/NIHON JIBI INKOKA GAKKAI KAIHO. (Text in Japanese; summaries in English) 1890. m. 15600 Yen($160) Oto-Rhino-Laryngological Society of Japan - Nihon Jibi Inkoka Gakkai, c/o Chateau Takanawa, 23-14, 3-chome, Minato-ku, Tokyo 108, Japan. TEL 03-3443-3085. FAX 03-3443-3037. Ed. Yasuya Nomura. adv. circ. 10,500. **Indexed:** Excerp.Med., Ind.Med., Lang.& Lang.Behav.Abstr. **Document type:** academic/scholarly publication.
—BLDSC (5027.720000); EMDOCS.

616.21 — US — ISSN 0892-1997
QP306 CODEN: JOVOEA
JOURNAL OF VOICE. 1987. q. $100 to individuals (foreign $135); institutions $195 (foreign $215) (effective 1996); newsstand price $30. (Voice Foundation) Lippincott - Raven Publishers, 227 E. Washington Sq., Philadelphia, PA 19106. TEL 215-238-4200. Ed. Robert T. Sataloff. adv. contact: Phyllis Noyes. charts; illus. circ. 3,000. (back issues avail.; reprint service avail. from UMI) **Indexed:** Excerp.Med., Ind.Med. (1993-), RILM. **Document type:** academic/scholarly publication.
—BLDSC (5072.512700); Faxon; Genuine Article; SWETS; UMI; UnCover. **CCC.**
Supersedes (1978-1985): Annual Symposium on Care of the Professional Voice. Transcripts.
Description: Publishes articles on the development and care of the professional voice.
Refereed Serial

616.21 — KO — ISSN 1225-035X
CODEN: TIHHEL
KOREAN OTOLARYNGOLOGICAL SOCIETY. JOURNAL. (Text in Korean; abstracts in English) 1958. bi-m. Korean Otolaryngological Society, c/o Young Myung Kim, Dir. of E-Wha Medical Center, College of Medicine, E-Wha Womens University, 70, Chongro 6-ga, Chongro-ku, Seoul 110-126, S. Korea. Ed. Hwoe Young Ahn. adv.; abstr.; charts; illus.; pat.; stat.; circ. 600 (controlled). **Document type:** academic/scholarly publication.
—BLDSC (4812.341400).

616.21 — GW — ISSN 0935-8943
CODEN: LROTEX
LARYNGO- RHINO- OTOLOGIE: Zeitschrift fuer Hals-Nasen-Ohrenheilkunde. (Text in German; summaries in English and German) 1921. m. DM.312 to non-members; members DM.265.20. (Deutsche Gesellschaft fuer Hals-, Nasen-, Ohrenheilkunde, Kopf- und Halschirurgie) Georg Thieme Verlag, Ruedigerstr. 14, 70469 Stuttgart, Germany. TEL 0711-8931-0. FAX 0711-8931298. (Subscr. to: Postfach 104853, 70042 Stuttgart, Germany) (Co-sponsor: Oesterreichische Gesellschaft fuer Hals-Nasen-Ohrenheilkunde, Kopf- und Halschirurgie) Eds. H. Stammberger, E. Kastenbauer. adv.; bk.rev.; abstr.; bibl.; charts; illus.; stat.; index. circ. 3,200. (reprint service avail. from UMI) **Indexed:** Biol.Abstr., C.I.S. Abstr., Curr.Adv.Cancer Res., Curr.Adv.Cell & Devel.Biol., Curr.Cont., Dent.Ind., Excerp.Med., Ind.Med., INIS Atomind., Lang.& Lang.Behav.Abstr., NBA, Sci.Cit.Ind. **Document type:** academic/scholarly publication.
—BLDSC (5156.150000); Faxon; Genuine Article; SWETS; UMI. **CCC.**
Former titles: Laryngologie, Rhinologie, Otologie und ihre Grenzgebiete Vereinigt mit Monatsschrift fuer Ohrenheilkunde (ISSN 0340-1588); Laryngologie, Rhinologie, Otologie und ihre Grenzgebiete (ISSN 0302-9379); Zeitschrift fuer Laryngologie, Rhinologie, Otologie und ihre Grenzgebiete (ISSN 0044-3018); Incorporates (in 1974): Monatschrift fuer Ohrenheilkunde und Laryngo-Rhinologie (ISSN 0026-9328)

616.21 — US — ISSN 0023-852X
CODEN: LARYA8
LARYNGOSCOPE. 1896. m. $110 to individuals (foreign $135); institutions $150 (foreign $175) (effective 1994). (American Laryngological, Rhinological and Otological Society) Triological Society, 10 S. Broadway., Ste. 1401, St. Louis, MO 63102-1741. TEL 314-621-6550. FAX 314-621-6688. Ed. Dr. Byron Bailey. adv.: page $730. bk.rev.; bibl.; illus.; index; circ. 7,800 (paid). (also avail. in microfilm from UMI; reprint service avail. from UMI) **Indexed:** Biol.Abstr., Chem.Abstr., Curr.Adv.Ecol.Sci., Curr.Cont., Dairy Sci.Abstr., Dent.Ind., Dok.Arbeitsmed., Excerp.Med., Ind.Med., Ind.Sci.Rev., INIS Atomind., Med.& Surg.Dermat., NBA, Noise Pollut.Publ.Abstr., Rev.Med.& Vet.Mycol., Rev.Plant Path., Risk Abstr. **Document type:** academic/scholarly publication.
—BLDSC (5156.200000); CASDDS; EMDOCS; Faxon; Genuine Article; SWETS; UMI; UnCover. **CCC.**
Description: Journal comprising medical, clinical and research contributions in otolaryngology, broncho-esophagology, communicative disorders, maxillofacial surgery, head and neck surgery, facial plastic and reconstructive surgery, speech and hearing defects.
Refereed Serial

616.21 — BL
MEDISOM: OTORHINOLARYNGOLOGY. 1980. bi-m. $90. Editora Medisom, Ltda., Rua Sao Paulino 224, Caixa Postal 7650, 01064-970 Sao Paulo, Brazil. FAX 55-11-572-5957. Ed. Dr. Philip Querido. adv. (audio cassette)

616.21 371.9 — US
MINNESOTA SPEECH - LANGUAGE - HEARING ASSOCIATION. NEWSLETTER. 1955. s-a. $25. Minnesota Speech - Language - Hearing Association, Box 26115, St. Louis Park, MN 55426. TEL 612-920-0787. FAX 612-920-6098. Ed. Maxine Slobof. adv. circ. 650. **Document type:** newsletter.
Former titles: Minnesota Speech and Hearing Association. Newsletter; (until 1976): Minnesota Speech and Hearing Association Journal.

617.89 — US
N S S L H A CLINICAL SERIES. no.2, 1971; N.S. 1992. irreg. price varies. National Student Speech Language Hearing Association, 10801 Rockville Pike, Rockville, MD 20852. TEL 301-897-5700. FAX 301-897-7320.

617.89 — US — ISSN 0736-0312
RC423.A1
N S S L H A JOURNAL. 1973. a. $8 to non-members. National Student Speech Language Hearing Association, 10801 Rockville Pike, Rockville, MD 20852. TEL 301-967-5700. FAX 301-897-7350. (back issues avail.) **Document type:** academic/scholarly publication.
—CCC.
Description: Features articles and reports on a variety of current speech-language-hearing topics of special interest to students and practicing clinicians.

616.21 — US — ISSN 0077-8516
NEW JERSEY SPEECH AND HEARING ASSOCIATION. NEWSLETTER.* 1969. irreg. (approx. 4/yr.). $5. New Jersey Speech and Hearing Association, c/o Auriemma, 6 Crest Ln., Warren, NJ 07059-5110. circ. 1,400.

610 — NZ — ISSN 0110-571X
NEW ZEALAND SPEECH-LANGUAGE THERAPISTS JOURNAL. 1946. a. NZ.$7. New Zealand Speech-Language Therapists Association, Special Eudcation Service, P.O. Box 4629, Christchurch 1, New Zealand. Ed. D. Murray Gordon. adv.; bk.rev. circ. 320. (also avail. in microfilm from UMI; reprint service avail. from UMI) **Indexed:** Bibl.Engl.Lang.& Lit., DSH Abstr., Rehabil.Lit.
—BLDSC (6097.499000); UMI. **CCC.**
Formerly (until May 1983): New Zealand Speech Therapists Journal (ISSN 0028-8713)
Description: Covers speech pathology.

NOTIZARIO BIBLIOGRAFICO DI AUDIOLOGIA O R L E FONIATRIA. see *MEDICAL SCIENCES* — Abstracting, Bibliographies, Statistics

616.21 — IT
NUOVA, CLINICA OTORINOLARINGOIATRICA. (Text in Italian; summaries in English, French and German) bi-m. L.40000. Universita degli Studi di Catania, Universita Ospedale Garibaldi, Otorinolaringoiatrica, Catania, Italy. FAX 095-316207. circ. 350. **Indexed:** Biol.Abstr., Dent.Ind., Excerp.Med., Ind.Med., NBA.
Formerly: Clinica Otorinolaringoiatrica (ISSN 0009-904X)

616.2 — SZ — ISSN 0301-1569
CODEN: ORLJAH
O R L; journal for oto-rhino-laryngology and its related specialties. (Text in English) 1938. bi-m. 357.60 SFr.($274.80) to individuals; institutions 596 SFr.($458) (effective 1996). S. Karger AG, Allschwilerstr. 10, P.O. Box, CH-4009 Basel, Switzerland. TEL 061-3061111. FAX 061-3061234. E-mail: Karger@Karger.ch. (U.S. addr.: 26 W. Avon Rd., Box 529, Farmington, CT 06085) Ed. W. Arnold. bk.rev. circ. 850. (also avail. in microfilm; reprint service avail. from UMI) **Indexed:** Biol.Abstr., Chem.Abstr., Curr.Cont., Dent.Ind., Excerp.Med., Ind.Med., NBA, Noise Pollut.Publ.Abstr. **Document type:** academic/scholarly publication.
—BLDSC (6291.378000); CASDDS; Faxon; Genuine Article; SWETS; UnCover. **CCC.**
Formerly: Practica Oto-Rhino-Laryngologica (ISSN 0032-6305)
Refereed Serial

616.21 — SP — ISSN 0210-7309
O.R.L. DIPS; revista internacional de otorrinolaringologia. (Text in Spanish; summaries in English, Spanish) bi-m. 5000 ptas.($108) (effective 1995). Editorial Rocas, Muntaner 393, pral. 2o, 08021 Barcelona, Spain. TEL 39-3-2001389. FAX 39-3-2021958. Dir. Dr. P. Quesada Marin. adv.; bibl.; charts; illus.; stat.; index. circ. 2,800. **Indexed:** Ind.Med.Esp. **Document type:** trade publication.
Description: Original research articles in the science of otorhinolaryngology.

616.21 610.73 — US
O R L - HEAD AND NECK NURSING. 1982. q. (Society of Otorhinolaryngology and Head - Neck Nurses) Health Information Publications, Inc., 92 S. Highland Ave., Ossining, NY 10562. TEL 914-762-6498. FAX 914-762-0239. adv.: B&W page $750; trim 8 1/4 x 11. circ. 970.
Description: Covers the practice of ORL nursing, pertinent research projects and legal issues.
Refereed Serial

MEDICAL SCIENCES — OTORHINOLARYNGOLOGY 4515

616.21 US ISSN 0000-1600
RF28
OFFICIAL AMERICAN BOARD OF MEDICAL SPECIALTIES (A B M S) DIRECTORY OF BOARD CERTIFIED OTOLARYNGOLOGISTS. 1985. biennial. $119.95. Marquis Who's Who, A Reed Reference Publishing company, 121 Chanlon Rd., New Providence, NJ 07974. TEL 908-464-6800. FAX 908-665-2898. (Subscr. to: Order Dept., Box 31, New Providence, NJ 07974-9903. TEL 800-521-8110) Ed. Roy Crego. Document type: directory.
    Formerly: A B M S Directory of Certified Otolaryngologists (ISSN 0883-3001)
    Description: Biographical sketches of U.S. certified medical specialists sorted alphabetically with a geographical index.

617.8 JA ISSN 0030-2813
ONSEI GENGO IGAKU/JAPAN JOURNAL OF LOGOPEDICS AND PHONIATRICS. (Text in Japanese; titles and summaries in English) 1960. 4/yr. membership. Nihon Onsei Gengo Igakkai - Japan Society of Logopedics and Phoniatrics, Hakuo Bldg., 5F, 2-3-10 Kohraku, Bunkyo-ku, Tokyo 112, Japan. FAX 03-5684-5954. Ed. Hiroyuki Fukuda. adv.; bk.rev.; circ. 1,850 (controlled). **Indexed:** Excerp.Med.

616.21 US ISSN 1043-1810
OPERATIVE TECHNIQUES IN OTOLARYNGOLOGY - HEAD AND NECK SURGERY. 1990. q. $133 (foreign $165) (effective 1996). W.B. Saunders Co. (Subsidiary of: Harcourt Brace & Company), Curtis Center, 3rd Fl., Independence Sq. W., Philadelphia, PA 19106-3399. TEL 215-238-7800. (Subscr. to: Periodicals Fulfillment, W.B. Saunders Co., 6277 Sea Harbor Dr., 4th Fl., Orlando, FL 32891-4800. TEL 800-654-2452. FAX 800-874-6418) Ed. Dr. Michael Friedman; Pub. Joan W. Blumberg. adv.; B&W page $600, color $1425; 7 3/4 x 11; adv. contact: Cindy Gray. illus. circ. 1,680. (back issues avail.) **Document type:** academic/scholarly publication.
    —BLDSC (6269.382000). **CCC.**
    Description: Presents detailed illustrations of new surgical procedures and techniques in head and neck surgery.
    Refereed Serial

OPHTHALMOLOGY. see *MEDICAL SCIENCES — Ophthalmology And Optometry*

ORBIT; an international journal on orbital disorders, oculoplastic and lacrimal surgery. see *MEDICAL SCIENCES — Ophthalmology And Optometry*

616.21 610 BE ISSN 0773-4409
OTICA; cahier des gradues en audiologie. (Text in French; summaries in English) 1977. 2/yr. 600 Fr.($40) Groupe Otica, Ave. Edouard Benes 195-15, B-1080 Brussels, Belgium. TEL 425.57.45. (Subscr. to: Otica, Woluweveld 59, B-1940 Sint-Stevens-Woluwe, Belgium) Ed. Gaston Warton Madeira. adv.; bk.rev.; abstr.; bibl. circ. 200. (back issues avail.)

616.21 SZ ISSN 1014-8221
CODEN: OTNOEQ
OTO-RHINO-LARYNGOLOGIA NOVA. 1992. bi-m. 267.50 SFr.($206) to individuals; institutions 535 SFr.($412) (effective 1996). S. Karger AG, Allschwilerstr. 10, P.O. Box, CH-4009 Basel, Switzerland. TEL 061-3061111. FAX 061-3061234. (also avail. in microform from UMI) **Indexed:** Excerp.Med. (1993-). **Document type:** academic/scholarly publication.
    —BLDSC (6313.605000); Genuine Article.

616.21 XR ISSN 1210-7867
CODEN: CEOTA9
OTOLARINOLOGIE A FONIATRIE. (Text in Czech or Slovak; summaries in English and Russian) 1952. q. $48.60. (Ceska Lekarska Spolecnost J.E. Purkyne - Czech Medical Society) Nakladatelske Stredisko C L S J.E. Purkyne, Sokolska 31, 120 26 Prague 2, Czech Republic. (Dist. by: Artia, Ve Smeckach 30, 111 27 Prague 1, Czech Republic) (Co-sponsor: Ceskoslovanska Otorhinolaryngologicka Spolesnost) Eds. P. Skerik, J. Klacansky. bk.rev.; abstr.; index. **Indexed:** C.I.S. Abstr., Dent.Ind., Excerp.Med., Ind.Med.
    —BLDSC (6313.680500); CASDDS. **CCC.**
    Former titles (until 1994): Cesko-Slovenska Otorinologaryngologie a Foniatrie (ISSN 1210-5988); (until 1991): Ceskoslovenska Otolaryngologie (ISSN 0009-0603)

616.21 PL ISSN 0030-6657
CODEN: OTPOAW
OTOLARYNGOLOGIA POLSKA. (Text in Polish; summaries in English and Russian) 1947. bi-m. $87. Polskie Towarzystwo Otolaryngologiczne, Ul. Sklodowskiej 9, 85-094 Bydgoszcz, Poland. TEL 212002. (Dist. by: Ars Polona-Ruch, Krakowskie Przedmiescie 7, Warsaw, Poland) Ed. Zygmunt Szmeja. adv.; bk.rev.; index. **Indexed:** Biol.Abstr., Chem.Abstr., Dent.Ind., Excerp.Med., Ind.Med.
    —CASDDS; EMDOCS.
    Description: Focuses on diseases of the ear, larynx and throat.

616.21 US ISSN 0030-6665
RF1 CODEN: OCNAB
OTOLARYNGOLOGIC CLINICS OF NORTH AMERICA. 1968. bi-m. $160 (foreign $195) (effective 1996). W.B. Saunders Co. (Subsidiary of: Harcourt Brace & Company), Curtis Center, 3rd Fl., Independence Sq. W., Philadelphia, PA 19106-3399. TEL 215-238-7800. FAX 215-238-6445. (Subscr. to: Periodicals Fulfillment, W.B. Saunders Co., 6277 Sea Harbor Dr., 4th Fl., Orlando, FL 32891-4800. TEL 800-654-2452. FAX 800-874-6418) Ed. Susan Short. (also avail. in microform from MIM,UMI; reprint service avail. from UMI,ISI) **Indexed:** Biol.Abstr., Curr.Adv.Cancer Res., Curr.Adv.Ecol.Sci., Curr.Cont., Dent.Ind., Excerp.Med., Ind.Med. **Document type:** academic/scholarly publication.
    —BLDSC (6313.510000); EMDOCS; Faxon; Genuine Article; SWETS; UMI; UnCover. **CCC.**

617.51 US ISSN 0194-5998
CODEN: OHNSDL
OTOLARYNGOLOGY - HEAD AND NECK SURGERY. (Supplement avail.) 1896. m. $131 to individuals (Canada $176.55; elsewhere $165); institutions $219 (Canada $270.71; elsewhere $165); students, residents $63 (Canada $103.79; elsewhere $97) (effective 1996); newsstand price: $12.50. (American Academy of Otolaryngology, Head and Neck Surgery Foundation, Inc.) Mosby - Year Book, Inc. (Subsidiary of: Times Mirror Company), 11830 Westline Industrial Dr., St. Louis, MO 63146-3318. TEL 314-872-8370; 800-325-4177. FAX 314-432-1380. TELEX 44-2402. (Co-sponsor: American Academy of Otolaryngic Allergy) Ed. Dr. J. Gail Neely. adv.: B&W page $760, color page $1685; trim 8 1/8 x 10 7/8. bk.rev.; s-a. index. circ. 11,043. (also avail. in microform from UMI; reprint service avail. from UMI) **Indexed:** ASCA, Biol.Abstr., Chem.Abstr., Curr.Adv.Cell & Devel.Biol., Curr.Cont., Excerp.Med., Ind.Med., NBA, Rev.Plant Path., Sci.Cit.Ind.
    —BLDSC (6313.523000); CASDDS; Faxon; Genuine Article; SWETS; UMI; UnCover. **CCC.**
    Former titles: Otolaryngology; Journal of Otolaryngology and Head and Neck Surgery (ISSN 0161-6439); (until Vol.86, 1978): American Academy of Ophthalmology and Otolaryngology. Transactions-Otolaryngology; Which supersedes in part: American Academy of Ophthalmology and Otolaryngology. Transactions.
    Description: Scientific articles to meet the clinical and continuing educational needs of all specialists in head and neck surgery.
    Refereed Serial

616.21 US ISSN 1070-8049
▼**THE OTOLARYNGOLOGY JOURNAL CLUB JOURNAL.** 1994. bi-m. $102 to individuals (foreign $114); institutions $125 (foreign $131) (effective 1996); newsstand price: $23. Lippincott - Raven Publishers, 227 E. Washington Sq., Philadelphia, PA 19106. TEL 215-238-4200. Ed. Paul Donald. adv. contact: Phyllis Noyes. charts; illus. circ. 1,000. **Document type:** academic/scholarly publication.
    —CCC.
    Description: Presents structured abstracts on key articles from otolaryngology literature, accompanied by original, reviewed editorial commentary.
    Refereed Serial

616.21 JA
OTOLOGIA FUKUOKA - JIBI TO RINSHO. (Text in Japanese; summaries in English, German) 1955. bi-m. 6000 Yen. Otologia Fukuoka Co., Department of Otorhinolaryngology, Kyushu University, Fukuoka 812, Japan. TEL 092-641-1151. FAX 092-651-0975. Ed. Dr. Takuya Uemura. adv.; bk.rev. circ. 1,500. (back issues avail.) **Indexed:** Excerp.Med., INIS Atomind., Lang.& Lang.Behav.Abstr.
    —BLDSC (6313.525000).
    Formerly: Jibi to Rinsho (ISSN 0447-7227)

616.21 618.92 IT ISSN 1120-3455
OTORINOLARINGOLOGIA PEDIATRICA. (Text in Italian; summaries in English) 1989. q. L.60000($60) (Societa Italiana di Otorinolaringologia Pediatrica) C I C Edizioni Internazionali s.r.l., Via L. Spallanzani, 11, 00161 Rome, Italy. TEL 06-8412673. FAX 06-44242033. TELEX 622099 CIC I. Dir. G. Motta.
    —BLDSC (6313.650000).

616.21 IT ISSN 0392-6621
OTORINOLARINGOLOGICA; rivista quadrimestrale di otorinolaringologia, audiologia, foniatria, chirurgia cervico-facciale, maxillo-facciale, plastica ricostruttiva, otoneurochirurgia. (Text in Italian; summaries in English and Italian) 1951. q. $95 to individuals; institutions $145 (effective 1995). Edizioni Minerva Medica, Corso Bramante 83-85, 10126 Turin, Italy. TEL 39-11-678282. FAX 39-11-3121736. Ed. Alberto Oliaro; Pub. Alberto Oliaro. adv.: B&W page $1100, color page $1900; trim 215 x 280; adv. contact: F. Filippo. bk.rev.; bibl.; charts; illus.; index; circ. 3,000 (paid). (also avail. in microform) **Indexed:** Biol.Abstr., Chem.Abstr., Excerp.Med., Ind.Med., INIS Atomind., NBA.
    —BLDSC (6313.635000); EMDOCS.
    Incorporates (in 1981): Minerva Otorinolaringologica (ISSN 0026-4938); Bollettino delle Malattie dell'Orecchio, della Gola, del Naso (ISSN 0392-7024); Otorinolaringologia Italiana; Nuovo Archivio Italiano di Otologia, Rinologia e Laringologia (ISSN 0301-3693); Which was formerly: Archivio Italiano di Otologia, Rinologia e Laringologia (ISSN 0004-0258)
    Description: Covers otorhinolaryngology, audiology, phoniatrics, maxillo-cervicofacial surgery, reconstructive plastic surgery, and otoneurosurgery.
    Refereed Serial

616.21 BU ISSN 0473-5609
OTORINOLARINGOLOGIJA. (Text in Bulgarian; summaries in English, Russian) q. 8 lv. (Ministerstvo na Narodnoto Zdrave) Izdatelstvo Meditsina i Fizkultura, 11 Pl. Slaveikov, Sofia, Bulgaria. (Distr. by: Hemus, 6 Rouski Blvd., 1000 Sofia, Bulgaria) (Co-sponsor: Nauchno Druzhestvo po Otorinolaringologia) Ed. V. Pavlov. circ. 765. **Indexed:** Abstr.Bulg.Sci.Med.Lit.

OTO'S SCOPE. see *BUSINESS AND ECONOMICS — Management*

616.21 US ISSN 1064-0207
OUR VOICE (NEW YORK); a newsletter for the spasmodic dysphonia patient and health professionals. 1989. 2/yr. $20. Our Voice, 365 W. 25th St., Ste. 13E, New York, NY 10001-5816. TEL 212-929-4299. FAX 212-929-4099. (Affiliate: National Spasmodic Dysphonia Association) bk.rev. (back issues avail.) **Document type:** newsletter.
    Description: Covers news about treatment and research regarding spasmodic dysphonia, a voice disorder, including medical conferences, professional and patient articles, and discussions of coping with the disorder.
    Refereed Serial

P A S C A L E 72: OTORHINOLARYNGOLOGIE. STOMATOLOGIE. PATHOLOGIE CERVICOFACIALE. see *MEDICAL SCIENCES — Abstracting, Bibliographies, Statistics*

616.21 CN
P M P : PATIENT OF THE MONTH PROGRAM. (Also avail. in latent-image print version) 1982. 8/yr. $295 to members; non-members $400. (American Academy of Otolaryngology, Head and Neck Surgery) Decker Periodicals, P.O. Box 620, LCD 1, Hamilton, ON L8N 3K7, Canada. TEL 905-522-7017. FAX 905-522-7839. Ed. Dr. William Shockley. abstr.; charts. (also avail. in diskette format)
    Description: Aims to perfect clinical decision-making skills by simulating clinical situations with a personal computer.

MEDICAL SCIENCES — OTORHINOLARYNGOLOGY

616.21 PK ISSN 0257-4985
PAKISTAN JOURNAL OF OTOLARYNGOLOGY. 1985. q. Rs.250($40) (in UK £30) (effective 1994). Pakistan Society of Otolaryngology, c/o Dr. M.H.A. Beg, F.R.C.S., Modern Ear Nose and Throat Hospital, B-10 Block 13-A, Opposite PIA Plaentarium, University Rd., Karachi 74400, Pakistan. TEL 92-21-4971762. FAX 92-21-4971763. adv.; bk.rev. circ. 2,000. **Indexed:** Excerp.Med. (until 19992), ExtraMED. **Document type:** academic/scholarly publication.
●Also available on CD-ROM.
—BLDSC (6341.675000). **CCC.**
Description: Publishes scientific research and articles.

616.21 JA ISSN 0032-6313
CODEN: JIBIAG
PRACTICA OTOLOGICA KYOTO/JIBI INKOKA RINSHO. (Supplement avail. (ISSN 0912-1870)) (Text in Japanese; summaries in English) 1908. m. 10000 Yen. Kyoto University, Faculty of Medicine, Department of Otolaryngology - Kyoto Daigaku Igakubu Jibi Inkoka Kyushitsu, 54 Shogoin Kawara-cho, Sakyo-ku, Kyoto 606, Japan. TEL 095-771-2301. Ed. Iwao Houjo. adv.; abstr.; bibl.; charts; illus.; index. circ. 1,500. **Indexed:** Biol.Abstr., Excerp.Med., INIS Atomind. **Document type:** academic/scholarly publication.
—BLDSC (6593.810000); EMDOCS.

616.21 JA ISSN 0912-1870
CODEN: JIRHET
PRACTICA OTOLOGICA KYOTO. SUPPLEMENT/JIBI INKOKA RINSHO. HOSATSU. (Text in Japanese; summaries in English) 1986. irreg. Kyoto University, Faculty of Medicine, Department of Otolaryngology - Kyoto Daigaku Igakubu Jibi Inkoka Kyushitsu, 54 Shogoin Kawara-cho, Sakto-ku, Kyoto 606, Japan. TEL 095-771-2301. **Indexed:** Excerp.Med. (1994-). **Document type:** academic/scholarly publication.

617 FR ISSN 0034-222X
REEDUCATION ORTHOPHONIQUE. 1963. q. 490 F. to non-members (foreign 550 F.); members 350 F.; students 200 F. (effective 1995). ARPLOEV (Association pour la Reeducation de la Parole, du Langage Oral et Ecrit, et de la Voix), 10 rue de l'Arrivee, 75015 Paris, France. TEL 45-44-48-85. Ed. Lya Caches; Pub. Jacques Roustit. adv.; bk.rev.; bibl.; charts; illus.; stat.; tr.lit. circ. 2,000. **Document type:** academic/scholarly publication.
—BLDSC (7331.430040).
Description: Covers hearing, speech and voice disorders.

616.21 BL ISSN 0034-7299
CODEN: RBORAB
REVISTA BRASILEIRA DE OTO-RINO-LARINGOLOGIA. 1933. q. Sociedade Brasileira de Otorinolaringologia, Rua Visconde de Piraja 330, Grupo 510, Ipanema 22410 RJ, Brazil. TEL 21-287-0893. abstr.; bibl.; illus.; index. **Indexed:** Chem.Abstr., Excerp.Med., Ind.Med.
—EMDOCS.

617.89 420 SP ISSN 0214-4603
REVISTA DE LOGOPEDIA, FONIATRIA Y AUDIOLOGIA. 1982. q. 6200 ptas.($60) (effective 1995). (Asociacion Espanola de Logopedia, Foniatria y Audiologia) Editorial Garsi, S.A., Grupo Masson, Principe de Asturias 20, 08012 Barcelona, Spain. TEL 34-3-4154544. FAX 34-3-4161220. bk.rev.; bibl. circ. 2,000. **Document type:** academic/scholarly publication.
—BLDSC (7863.660000).

616.21 CL ISSN 0716-4084
REVISTA DE OTORRINOLARINGOLOGIA Y CIRUGIA DE CABEZA Y CUELLO. (Text in Spanish; summaries in English) 1941. 3/yr. $30 (foreign $33) (effective 1996). Sociedad Chilena de Otorrinolaringologia, Medicina y Cirugia de Cabeza y Cuello, Casilla 124 Torres de Tajamar, Santiago 9, Chile. TEL 56-2-2354068. Ed. Dr. Juan Viada Lozano. adv. contact: Johanna Otte. bk.rev.; bibl.; charts; illus.; stat.; index. circ. 400. **Indexed:** Biol.Abstr., Chem.Abstr., Excerp.Med. **Document type:** academic/scholarly publication.
Formerly: Revista de Otorrinolaringologia (ISSN 0034-8643)

616.2 VE
REVISTA OTORRINOLARINGOLOGICA. (Text in Spanish; summaries in English) 1965. q. Bs.30($9) Instituto Celis Perez, Apartado Postal 163, Valencia, Venezuela. (Subscr. to: Medicina Libros, Edif. Pax Cruce, Av. Avila y Caracas, Caracas, Venezuela) Ed. Dr. A. Celis Perez. bibl.; index. circ. 500.

616.21 FR ISSN 0035-1334
REVUE DE LARYNGOLOGIE - OTOLOGIE - RHINOLOGIE. (Text and summaries in English and French) 1880. 5/yr. 730 F. to individuals; residents 370 F. Revue de Laryngologie, 114 av. d'Ares, 33074 Bordeaux Cedex, France. TEL 56-24-30-15. FAX 56-96-13-17. Ed. Jacques Verhulst. adv.; bk.rev.; abstr.; bibl.; charts; illus.; stat.; index. circ. 2,200. **Indexed:** Biol.Abstr., Dent.Ind., Excerp.Med., Ind.Med., Lang.& Lang.Behav.Abstr., NBA.
—BLDSC (7926.450000); EMDOCS; SWETS.

616.21 NE ISSN 0300-0729
CODEN: RNGYA8
RHINOLOGY. (Text in English) 1963. q. fl.175 (effective 1994). International Rhinologic Society, c/o Journal Rhinology, Postbus 85500, 3508 GA Utrecht, Netherlands. TEL 31-30-509111. FAX 31-30-507579. Ed. Dr. E.H. Huizing. adv. contact: Dr. J.C.M.J. de Groot. bk.rev.; index. circ. 1,200. (back issues avail.) **Indexed:** Biol.Abstr., Dent.Ind., Excerp.Med., Ind.Med., Rev.Med.& Vet.Mycol. **Document type:** academic/scholarly publication.
—BLDSC (7960.743000); SWETS.
Description: Contains papers dealing with physiology, diagnostics, pathology, medical therapy and surgery of the nose and paranasal sinuses, including allergology.

616.21 617.89 IT ISSN 0392-1360
RIVISTA ITALIANA DI OTORINOLARINGOLOGIA, AUDIOLOGIA E FONIATRIA. (Text in Italian; summaries in English) q. L.60000($60) C I C Edizioni Internazionali s.r.l., Via L. Spallanzani 11, 00161 Rome, Italy. TEL 06-8412673. FAX 06-44242033. TELEX 622099 CIC. Dir. T. Marullo. **Indexed:** Excerp.Med., NBA.
—BLDSC (7987.470000). **CCC.**

617.8 NO ISSN 0105-0397
RF1 CODEN: SNADAS
SCANDINAVIAN AUDIOLOGY. (Supplement avail. (ISSN 0107-8593)) (Text in English) 1952. q. NOK 815 in Nordic countries; elsewhere $149 (effective 1996). (Nordisk Audiologisk Selskab - Nordic Audiological Society) Scandinavian University Press, P.O. Box 2959-Toeyen, N-0608 Oslo, Norway. TEL 47-22-57-54-00. FAX 47-22-57-53-53. (U.S. addr.: Scandinavian University Press, 200 Meacham Ave., Elmont, NY 11003. TEL 516-352-7300) Ed. Einar Laukli. adv.; bk.rev.; index. circ. 1,000. **Indexed:** Acoust.Abstr., Biol.Abstr., Curr.Cont., Dok.Arbeitsmed., DSH Abstr., Excerp.Med., Ind.Med., INSPEC (1979-), Lang.& Lang.Behav.Abstr., Lang.& Lang.Behav.Abstr., Noise Pollut.Publ.Abstr., Psychol.Abstr. (1972-), Risk Abstr. **Document type:** academic/scholarly publication.
—BLDSC (8087.469000); EMDOCS; Faxon; Genuine Article; SWETS. **CCC.**
Former titles (until 1971): Nordisk Audiologi (ISSN 0105-0400); (until 1960): Nordisk Tidsskrift for Praktisk Audiologi (ISSN 0105-1865)

617.8 NO ISSN 0107-8593
CODEN: SAUSBF
SCANDINAVIAN AUDIOLOGY. SUPPLEMENT. (Text in English) 1971. irreg. price varies. (Nordisk Audiologisk Selskab - Nordic Audiological Society) Scandinavian University Press, P.O. Box 2959 - Toeyen, N-0608 Oslo, Norway. TEL 47-22-57-54-00. FAX 47-22-57-53-53. (US addr.: Scandinavian University Press, 200 Meacham Ave., Elmont, NY 11003. TEL 516-352-7300) **Indexed:** Excerp.Med. **Document type:** monographic series.
—BLDSC (8087.471000); SWETS.

617.8 NO ISSN 0803-5032
SCANDINAVIAN JOURNAL OF LOGOPEDICS AND PHONIATRICS. (Text in English; summaries in Danish, Finnish, Norwegian, Swedish) 1936. q. NOK 645 in Nordic countries; elsewhere $115 (effective 1996). (Scandinavian Cooperation Council of Logopedics and Phoniatrics) Scandinavian University Press, P.O. Box 2959 Toeyen, N-0608 Oslo, Norway. TEL 47-22-57-54-00. FAX 47-22-57-53-53. Ed. Peter Kitzing. **Indexed:** Ling.Abstr.
Former titles: Nordisk Tidsskrift for Logopedi og Foniatri (ISSN 0105-1539); (until 1976): Nordisk Tidsskrift for Tale og Stemme (ISSN 0029-1552)
Description: Serves as an international forum for research reports and information within the area of communication disorders.

616 US ISSN 0734-0451
CODEN: SEMHE7
SEMINARS IN HEARING. 1980. q. $63 to individuals (foreign $88); institutions $97 (foreign $130). Thieme Medical Publishers, Inc., 381 Park Ave., S., Ste. 1501, New York, NY 10016. TEL 212-683-5088. FAX 212-779-9020. Ed. Jerry L. Northern. adv. circ. 2,200. (also avail. in microfilm; reprint service avail. from UMI) **Document type:** academic/scholarly publication.
—BLDSC (8239.449800); Faxon; UMI; UnCover. **CCC.**
Supersedes in part: Seminars in Speech, Language and Hearing (ISSN 0196-108X)

616.21 CN ISSN 1198-7421
▼**SEMINARS IN OTOLARYNGIC ALLERGY.** Announced for publication in 1996. q. $52 to individuals ($79 outside N. America); institutions $78 (outside N. America) (effective 1996). Decker Periodicals, P.O. Box 620, LCD 1, Hamilton, ON L8N 3K7, Canada. TEL 905-522-7017; 800-568-7281. FAX 905-522-7839. E-mail: decker@io.org. (U.S. addr.: Box 785, Lewiston, NY 14092-0785) **Document type:** academic/scholarly publication.

617.89 US ISSN 0734-0478
RC423.A1 CODEN: SSLAEB
SEMINARS IN SPEECH AND LANGUAGE. 1980. q. $63 to individuals (foreign $88); institutions $105 (foreign $130). Thieme Medical Publishers, Inc., 381 Park Ave., S., Ste. 1501, New York, NY 10016. TEL 212-683-5088. FAX 212-779-9020. Ed. Richard Curlee. adv.; abstr.; bibl.; illus. circ. 2,000. (also avail. in microfilm; reprint service avail. from UMI) **Document type:** academic/scholarly publication.
—BLDSC (8239.462000); Faxon; UMI; UnCover. **CCC.**
Supersedes in part: Seminars in Speech, Language and Hearing (ISSN 0196-108X)

SIGHT AND SOUND NEWS. see *HOSPITALS*

616.21 SA ISSN 0379-8046
RC423.A1 CODEN: SAJDDJ
SOUTH AFRICAN JOURNAL OF COMMUNICATION DISORDERS/SUID-AFRIKAANSE TYDSKRIF VIR KOMMUNIKASIEAFWYKINGS. (Text mainly in English) 1948. a. R.50. South African Speech - Language - Hearing Association, P.O. Box 600, Wits 2050, South Africa. TEL 27-11-4031892. FAX 27-11-4036689. Ed. B. Louw. adv.; bk.rev. circ. 1,000. **Indexed:** Biol.Abstr., DSH Abstr., Ind.Med., Ind.S.A.Per. **Document type:** academic/scholarly publication.
—BLDSC (8338.851000).
Former titles (until 1974): South African Speech and Hearing Association. Journal (ISSN 0300-9874); Journal of Logopedics (ISSN 0081-2471); South African Logopedic Society. Journal.
Refereed Serial

371 616 GW ISSN 0342-0477
SPRACHE - STIMME - GEHOER; Zeitschrift fuer Kommunikationsstoerungen. 1977. q. DM.79. Georg Thieme Verlag, Ruedigerstr. 14, 70469 Stuttgart, Germany. TEL 0711-8931-0. FAX 0711-8931298. (Subscr. to: Postfach 104853, 70042 Stuttgart, Germany) Ed.Bd. index. circ. 2,500. (reprint service avail. from UMI) **Indexed:** Curr.Cont., Excerp.Med. **Document type:** academic/scholarly publication.
—SWETS; UMI. **CCC.**

MEDICAL SCIENCES — PEDIATRICS

616.21 US
SPRINGER HANDBOOK OF AUDITORY RESEARCH. irreg., vol.3, 1993. Springer-Verlag, Journals, 175 Fifth Ave., New York, NY 10010. TEL 212-460-1500. FAX 212-473-6272. Eds. Richard Fay, Arthur Popper. **Document type:** monographic series.

616.21 CI ISSN 1330-0296
SYMPOSIA OTORHINOLARYNGOLOGICA. (Text in Croatian; summaries in English) 1966. 3/yr. $30. (Klinicka Bolnica "Sestre Milosrdnice", Klinika za Otorinolaringologiju i Cervikofacijalnu Kirurgiju) Zavod za Proucavanje I Zastitu Uha i Disnih Organa, Vinogradska 29, 41000 Zagreb, Croatia. Ed. Ivo Padovan. adv.; bk.rev. circ. 600. **Indexed:** Excerp.Med., Ind.Med.
—BLDSC (8585.629900).
Formerly (until 1991): Symposia Otorhinolaryngologica Iugoslavica (ISSN 0586-9145)

616.21 362.42 US ISSN 0897-6368
TINNITUS TODAY. 1975. q. $25 (foreign $35). American Tinnitus Association, Box 5, Portland, OR 97207. TEL 503-248-9985. FAX 503-248-0024. Ed. Gloria Reich. adv.; bk.rev. circ. 170,000. **Document type:** newsletter.
Formerly (until 1988): A T A Newsletter.
Description: Serves professionals and laypeople with scientific and anecdotal articles.

616.21 US
TRIOLOGISTICS. 1976. 3/yr. (American Laryngological, Rhinological and Otological Society) Triological Society, 10 S. Broadway, Ste. 1401, Saint Louis, MO 63102-1741. TEL 314-621-6550. FAX 314-621-6688. **Document type:** newsletter.
Description: Society information relating to the field of otolaryngology.

616.21 IT ISSN 0042-2371
VALSALVA. (Text in Italian; summaries in English) 1923. q. $100. Edizioni Luigi Pozzi s.r.l., Via Panama 68, 00198 Rome, Italy. TEL 39-6-8553548. FAX 39-6-8554105. Eds. I. de Vincentiis, T. Marullo. adv.; bk.rev. circ. 2,000. **Indexed:** Chem.Abstr., Dent.Ind., Excerp.Med., Ind.Med., NBA.
—BLDSC (9141.800000).
Description: Covers all aspects of otorhinolaryngology.

616.21 US ISSN 1041-892X
RF11
YEAR BOOK OF OTOLARYNGOLOGY - HEAD AND NECK SURGERY. 1900. a. $72.95 (residents $35) (effective 1996). Mosby - Year Book, Inc., Continuity Division, 200 N. LaSalle, Chicago, IL 60601. TEL 312-726-9733. Ed. Dr. John Holt. illus. (reprint service avail.) **Indexed:** Curr.Adv.Ecol.Sci.
—BLDSC (9414.692000).
Supersedes (in 1985): Year Book of Otolaryngology (ISSN 0146-7247); Formerly (1958-1975): Year Book of the Ear, Nose and Throat (ISSN 0084-4055); Supersedes in part: Yearbook of the Eye, Ear, Nose and Throat.

616.21 RU ISSN 0044-4650
CODEN: ZUNBA9
ZHURNAL USHNYKH, NOSOVYKH I GORLOVYKH BOLEZNEI. 1924. bi-m. $13.20. Petroverigskii Per. 6-8, Moscow K-142, Russia. charts; illus.; index. **Indexed:** Biol.Abstr., Chem.Abstr., Ind.Med., Int.Aerosp.Abstr.
—BLDSC (0066.500000); CASDDS; EMDOCS.

MEDICAL SCIENCES — Pediatrics

618.92 US ISSN 1073-0397
A A P NEWS. m. American Academy of Pediatrics, 141 Northwest Point Blvd., Box 927, Elk Grove Village, IL 60009-0927. TEL 708-228-5005; 800-433-9016. FAX 708-228-1281. Ed. Elizabeth Oplatka. adv.: B&W page $2600, color page $3995; trim 11 x 17. charts; illus.; stat. circ. 48,000. (tabloid format) **Document type:** newsletter.
Former titles (until 1985): News and Comment - American Academy of Pediatrics (ISSN 0094-8209); (until 1973): American Academy of Pediatrics. Newsletter (ISSN 0094-8217)
Description: Contains news reports, clinical policy statements, legislation news, and practice management tips.

618.92 US
A A P POLICY REFERENCE GUIDE. 1988. a. $79.95. American Academy of Pediatrics, 141 Northwest Point Blvd., Box 927, Elk Grove Village, IL 60009-0927. TEL 708-228-5005; 800-433-9016. FAX 708-228-1281. **Document type:** bulletin.

ACTA DE ODONTOLOGIA PEDIATRICA; una revista internacional para la odontologia pediatrica. see MEDICAL SCIENCES — Dentistry

618.92 NO ISSN 0803-5253
CODEN: APAEEL
ACTA PAEDIATRICA; an international journal of paediatrics. (Supplement avail. (ISSN 0803-5326)) (Text in English) 1921. m. NOK 2215 in Nordic countries; elsewhere $372 (effective 1996). Scandinavian University Press, P.O. Box 2959 Toeyen, N-0608 Oslo, Norway. TEL 47-22-57-54-00. FAX 47-22-57-53-53. (U.S. addr.: Scandinavian University Press, 200 Meacham Ave., Elmont, NY 11003. TEL 516-352-7300) Ed. Rolf Zetterstroem. adv.; bk.rev.; charts; illus.; index, cum.index: vols.1-30 (1921-1943). circ. 2,200. **Indexed:** ASCA, Bibl.Dev.Med.& Child Neur., Biol.Abstr., C.I.S. Abstr., Chem.Abstr., Curr.Adv.Ecol.Sci., Curr.Adv.Genetics & Molec.Biol., Curr.Cont., Dairy Sci.Abstr., Dent.Ind., Diab.Cont., Diar.Dis.Res., Dok.Arbeitsmed., Excerp.Med., Helminthol.Abstr., Ind.Med., Ind.Sci.Rev., Kidney, Med.& Surg.Dermat., NRN, Nutr.Abstr., Protozool.Abstr., Risk Abstr., Sci.Cit.Ind.
—BLDSC (0642.400000); ADONIS; CASDDS; Faxon; Genuine Article; SWETS; UMI; UnCover. **CCC.**
Former titles (until 1991): Acta Paediatrica Scandinavica (ISSN 0001-656X); Acta Paediatrica.
Description: Covers clinical and experimental research in all fields of paediatrics including developmental physiology.

618.92 HU ISSN 0231-441X
CODEN: APHUDZ
ACTA PAEDIATRICA HUNGARICA. (Text in English) 1960. q. $80 (effective 1992). (Magyar Tudomanyos Akademia) Akademiai Kiado, Publishing House of the Hungarian Academy of Sciences, P.O. Box 245, H-1519 Budapest, Hungary. TEL 181-2134. FAX 166-6466. TELEX 22-6228 AKNYO H. Ed. Miklos Miltenyi. adv.; bk.rev.; bibl.; charts; illus.; index. **Indexed:** Biol.Abstr., Chem.Abstr., Curr.Cont., Excerp.Med., Helminthol.Abstr., Ind.Med., INIS Atomind., Nutr.Abstr.
—BLDSC (0642.415000); CASDDS; Faxon. **CCC.**
Formerly (until 1982): Academiae Scientiarum Hungaricae. Acta Paediatrica (ISSN 0001-6527)
Description: Presents original communications on subjects connected with the theoretical and practical aspects of pediatrics. Includes perinatal medicine, clinical genetics, pediatric surgery and pediatric psychology.

618.92 NO ISSN 0803-5326
CODEN: APUPEI
ACTA PAEDIATRICA, INTERNATIONAL JOURNAL OF PAEDIATRICS, SUPPLEMENT. (Text in English) irreg. Scandinavian University Press, P.O. Box 2959 Toeyen, N-0608 Oslo, Norway. TEL 47-22-57-54-00. FAX 47-22-57-53-53. **Indexed:** Diar.Dis.Res., Excerp.Med.
—BLDSC (0642.402000); ADONIS; CASDDS; SWETS. **CCC.**
Formerly (until 1991): Acta Paediatrica Scandinavica, Supplement (ISSN 0300-8843)

618.92 AT ISSN 0374-5600
CODEN: APDJBE
ACTA PAEDIATRICA JAPONICA. Japanese edition: Nippon Shonika Gakkai Zasshi (ISSN 0001-6543) (Text in English) 1959. bi-m. Aus.$303($215) (19500 Yen) (effective 1996). (Japan Pediatric Society, JA) Blackwell Science Pty Ltd, P.O. Box 378, Carlton, Vic. 3053, Australia. TEL 03-347-0300. FAX 03-347-5001. Ed. N. Kobayashi. adv.: B&W page $720, color page $1510; trim 275 x 210. bk.rev.; abstr.; bibl.; charts; illus.; index. circ. 1,000. (also avail. in microform from UMI; reprint service avail. from ISI) **Indexed:** Biol.Abstr., Chem.Abstr., Curr.Cont., Dairy Sci.Abstr., Excerp.Med., Ind.Med., Kidney, NRN.
—BLDSC (0642.421000); ADONIS; CASDDS; Faxon; Genuine Article; SWETS; UMI. **CCC.**
Description: Contains scientific articles, clinical and laboratory studies, and case reports in the field of paediatrics and child health.

618.92 IT ISSN 0001-6551
ACTA PAEDIATRICA LATINA. (Text and summaries in English, Italian) 1948. q. L.50000 (foreign L.80000) (effective 1995). (Universita degli Studi di Padova, Clinica Pediatrica) Artigianato Grafico Editoriale s.n.c., Via Casorati, 29, 42100 Reggio Emilia, Italy. FAX 39-522-921169. Ed. Ernesto Sartori. adv.; bk.rev.; charts; illus. circ. 3,000. (back issues avail.) **Indexed:** Biol.Abstr., Chem.Abstr., Excerp.Med., Nutr.Abstr.
—BLDSC (0642.424000).

618.92 CH ISSN 0001-6578
CODEN: CHEKAL
ACTA PAEDIATRICA SINICA. Key Title: Zhonghua Minguo Xiao'erke Yixuehui Zazhi. (Text in Chinese; abstracts in Chinese, English) 1960. bi-m. $80 (effective Jan. 1995). Chinese Taipei Pediatric Association, No. 11, Ching-Tao West Road, 4F-4, Taipei, Taiwan 10022, Republic of China. TEL 02-331-4917. FAX 02-314-2184. Ed. Mei-Hwei Chang. adv.; abstr.; stat.; index. circ. 2,200. **Indexed:** Biol.Abstr., Chem.Abstr., Excerp.Med., Ind.Med., Trop.Dis.Bull. **Document type:** academic/scholarly publication, abstracting/indexing.
—BLDSC (0642.435000); CASDDS.
Refereed Serial

618.92 SP ISSN 0001-6640
ACTA PEDIATRICA ESPANOLA. 1943. 11/yr. 1000 ptas. Apolonio Morales 6-8, 28036 Madrid, Spain. TEL 1-403-50-14. FAX 1-457-99-18. TELEX 47331 SNED. Ed. Dr. I. Villa Elizaga. **Indexed:** Chem.Abstr., Excerp.Med., Ind.Med.Esp., Nutr.Abstr.
—BLDSC (0644.300000); Faxon; UMI.

618.92 IT ISSN 0393-6392
ACTA PEDIATRICA MEDITERRANEA. (Text in English, Italian) 1960. 3/yr. L.40000($40) Carbone Editore, Via G. Daita, 29, 90139 Palermo, Italy. TEL 091-321273. FAX 091-321782. adv.; abstr.; bibl.; illus.; stat.; index. circ. 3,000.
Formerly: Archivio Siciliano di Medicina e Chirurgia (Sezione Pediatrica).
Description: Clinical cases of pediatrics and newborns are reviewed and discussed.

618.92 US ISSN 0932-8610
RJ478
ADOLESCENT AND PEDIATRIC GYNECOLOGY. 1988. q. $285 (effective 1996). (North American Society for Pediatric and Adolescent Gynecology) Springer-Verlag, Journals, 175 Fifth Ave., New York, NY 10010. TEL 212-460-1500. FAX 212-473-6272. (Subscr. in N. America to: Journal Fulfillment Services, Box 2485, Secaucus, NJ 079096-2491. TEL 800-777-4643. FAX 201-348-4505; Subscr. outside N. America to: Springer-Verlag, Heidelberger Platz 3, 1000 Berlin 33, Germany. TEL 030-8207-1. FAX 030-8214091) (Co-sponsor: International Federation of Infantile and Juvenile Gynecology) Ed. Joseph S. Sanfilippo. (also avail. in microform from UMI; reprint service avail.) **Indexed:** C.C.I.Ob.Gyn., C.C.I.P. **Document type:** academic/scholarly publication.
—BLDSC (0696.584000); Faxon; Genuine Article; UMI. **CCC.**
Description: Presents papers, case reports, reviews of literature and trends in this medical specialty.
Refereed Serial

618.92 US ISSN 1041-3499
RJ550 CODEN: AMSRER
ADOLESCENT MEDICINE (PHILADELPHIA). 1990. 3/yr. $75 (foreign $85). Hanley & Belfus, Inc., 210 S. 13th St., Philadelphia, PA 19107. TEL 215-546-7293. FAX 215-790-9330. **Indexed:** C.C.I.P.
—BLDSC (0696.588000). **CCC.**
Refereed Serial

ADVANCES IN CHILD DEVELOPMENT AND BEHAVIOR. see PSYCHOLOGY

MEDICAL SCIENCES — PEDIATRICS

618.92   UK
ADVANCES IN DEVELOPMENTAL AND BEHAVIORAL PEDIATRICS. 1980. a. $99. Jessica Kingsley Publishers, 116 Pentonville Rd., London N1 9JB, England. TEL 071-833-2307. FAX 071-837-2917. (Dist. in U.S. by: Taylor & Francis, 1900 Frost Rd., Ste. 101, Bristol PA 19007-1598. TEL 215-785-5800. FAX 215-785-5515) Eds. Mark Wolraich, Donald K. Routh. **Indexed:** Psychol.Abstr. **Document type:** academic/scholarly publication.
Formerly: Advances in Behavioral Pediatrics (ISSN 0198-7069)
Description: Directed to those concerned with behavioural aspects of pediatric medicine and the clinical applications of child and adolescent psychology.
Refereed Serial

618.92   US   ISSN 0732-9598
BF719
ADVANCES IN INFANCY RESEARCH. 1981. a. $37.50 to individuals; institutions $65. Ablex Publishing Corporation, 355 Chestnut St., Norwood, NJ 07648. TEL 201-767-8450. FAX 201-767-6717. TELEX 135-393. Eds. Carolyn Rovee-Collier, Lewis P. Lipsitt. (reprint service avail. from ISI) **Indexed:** Psychol.Abstr. (1981-). **Document type:** academic/scholarly publication.
—BLDSC (0709.120000); Faxon; UnCover.
Refereed Serial

ADVANCES IN PEDIATRIC INFECTIOUS DISEASES. see *MEDICAL SCIENCES — Communicable Diseases*

618.92   US   ISSN 0065-3101
RJ23
ADVANCES IN PEDIATRICS. 1942. a. $66.95 (residents $40) (effective 1996). Mosby - Year Book, Inc. (Chicago) (Subsidiary of: Times Mirror Company), 200 N. LaSalle St., Chicago, IL 60601-1080. TEL 312-726-9733. FAX 312-726-6075. TELEX 206155. (Subscr. to: 11830 Westline Industrial Dr., St. Louis, MO 63146. TEL 800-325-4177) Ed. Dr. Louis A. Barness. illus. (also avail. in microform from UMI; reprint service avail. from UMI) **Indexed:** CINAHL, Curr.Adv.Ecol.Sci., Dent.Ind., Diar.Dis.Res., Ind.Med., INIS Atomind.
—BLDSC (0709.590000); Faxon; SWETS; UMI. **CCC.**
Description: Presents a collection of original, fully referenced clinical review articles in pediatrics.

AERZTLICHER RATGEBER FUER WERDENDE UND JUNGE MUETTER; die Schwangerschaft, Geburt und Babyzeit. see *MEDICAL SCIENCES — Obstetrics And Gynecology*

618.92   IT   ISSN 0002-0958
    CODEN: AGPEAT
AGGIORNAMENTO PEDIATRICO; rivista mensile di pediatria. (Text in Italian; summaries in English, French and German) vol.21, 1970. m. L.34000. Viale Gorizia 24-A, 00198 Rome, Italy. Ed. Dr. V. Genoese. adv.; bk.rev.; abstr.; bibl.; index. circ. 2,500. **Indexed:** Biol.Abstr., Chem.Abstr., Curr.Adv.Ecol.Sci., Excerp.Med.
—BLDSC (0736.280700); CASDDS.

618.92   US   ISSN 0002-7006
AMBULATORY PEDIATRIC ASSOCIATION NEWSLETTER. 1964. 3/yr. membership. Ambulatory Pediatric Association, Department of Pediatrics, c/o Dr. John M. Pascoe, Communications Dir., 600 Highland Ave., Madison, WI 53792. TEL 608-263-9405. FAX 608-263-0440. adv.; bk.rev.; film rev.; circ. 1,500 (controlled). (processed) **Document type:** newsletter.

618.92   US   ISSN 0065-6909
RJ1
AMERICAN ACADEMY OF PEDIATRICS. COMMITTEE ON INFECTIOUS DISEASES. REPORT (YEAR). 1938. irreg., 23rd ed., 1994. $64.95. American Academy of Pediatrics, 141 Northwest Point Blvd., Box 927, Elk Grove Village, IL 60009-0927. TEL 708-228-5005; 800-433-9016. FAX 708-228-1281. **Document type:** monographic series.
●Also available on CD-ROM.
—BLDSC (7405.555000).

AMERICAN JOURNAL OF ASTHMA & ALLERGY FOR PEDIATRICIANS. see *MEDICAL SCIENCES — Allergology And Immunology*

648   SW   ISSN 1102-7207
AMNINGSNYTT. Alternate title: Nya Amningsnytt. 1974. q. SEK 150 (effective 1996). Amningshjaelpen, P.O. Box 3030, S-771 92 Ludvika, Sweden.

ANNA FREUD CENTRE. BULLETIN. see *MEDICAL SCIENCES — Psychiatry And Neurology*

618.92   FR   ISSN 0066-2097
    CODEN: APSHAE
ANNALES DE PEDIATRIE. (Text in French; summaries in English) 1954. 10/yr. 990 F. to individuals (foreign 1370); students 495 F. (foreign 750 F.). (Semaine des Hopitaux) Expansion Scientifique, 31 bd. de la Tour Maubourg, 75007 Paris, France. TEL 40-62-64-00. FAX 45-55-69-20. Ed. Prof. Mozziconacci. circ. 17,500. **Indexed:** Bibl.Dev.Med.& Child Neur., Biol.Abstr., Chem.Abstr., Curr.Adv.Genetics & Molec.Biol., Curr.Cont., Dent.Ind., Excerp.Med., Helminthol.Abstr., Ind.Med., INIS Atomind., Nutr.Abstr., Protozool.Abstr., Rev.Med.& Vet.Mycol. **Document type:** academic/scholarly publication.
—BLDSC (0991.400000); CASDDS; EMDOCS; Faxon; Genuine Article; SWETS.

618.92   UK   ISSN 0272-4936
    CODEN: ATPAD9
ANNALS OF TROPICAL PAEDIATRICS. 1981. q. £58 to individuals; institutions £178 (effective 1996). Carfax Publishing Co., P.O. Box 25, Abingdon, Oxon. OX14 3UE, England. TEL 01235-555335. FAX 01235-553559. (Subscr. in N. America to: Carfax Publishing Co., 875-81 Massachusetts Ave., Cambridge, MA 02139) Ed. R.G. Hendrickse. adv.; bk.rev. (back issues avail.) **Indexed:** Abstr.Hyg., Curr.Adv.Ecol.Sci., Dairy Sci.Abstr., Dent.Ind., Diar.Dis.Res., Excerp.Med., Helminthol.Abstr., Ind.Med., Mult.Ed.Abstr., NRN, Protozool.Abstr., Rev.Med.& Vet.Mycol. **Document type:** academic/scholarly publication.
—BLDSC (1045.100000); Faxon; Genuine Article; SWETS; UMI; UnCover. **CCC.**
Description: Provides an international forum for problems and achievements in child health and pediatrics in the tropics and subtropics.
Refereed Serial

618.92   FR   ISSN 0929-693X
    CODEN: APEDE4
ARCHIVES DE PEDIATRIE. (Text in French; summaries in English, French) 1945. m. 1095 F. in Frnace; foreign 1205 F.($235) (effective 1996). (Societe Francaise de Pediatrie) Editions Scientifiques Elsevier, 141 rue de Javel, 75747 Paris, France. TEL 33-1-45589063. (Subscr. in U.S. and Canada to: Elsevier Science Inc., Box 882, Madison Sq. Sta., New York, NY 10159-0882. TEL 212-989-5800. FAX 212-633-3990) Ed.Bd. adv.; bk.rev.; charts; illus.; index. circ. 3,200. (also avail. in microform from UMI; reprint service avail. from UMI) **Indexed:** Bibl.Dev.Med.& Child Neur., Biol.Abstr., Chem.Abstr., Curr.Adv.Cancer Res., Curr.Adv.Ecol.Sci., Curr.Cont., Dent.Ind., Excerp.Med., Helminthol.Abstr., Ind.Med., Ind.Sci.Rev., Nutr.Abstr., Sci.Cit.Ind. **Document type:** academic/scholarly publication.
—BLDSC (1638.965000); CASDDS; EMDOCS; Faxon; Genuine Article; SWETS; UMI. **CCC.**
Formed by the 1994 merger of: Pediatrie (ISSN 0031-4021) & Archives Francaises de Pediatrie (ISSN 0003-9764)

618.92   II   ISSN 0044-8710
    CODEN: ACHHA4
ARCHIVES OF CHILD HEALTH. 1959. bi-m. Rs.25. Archives of Child Health, 144 Ashutosh Mukherji Rd., Calcutta 25, India. Ed.Bd. adv.; bk.rev.; bibl.; charts; index. **Indexed:** Abstr.Hyg., Biol.Abstr., Excerp.Med., Trop.Dis.Bull.

618.92   UK   ISSN 0003-9888
RJ1   CODEN: ADCHAK
ARCHIVES OF DISEASE IN CHILDHOOD. (Includes supplement: Fetal and Neonatal Edition) 1926. m. (plus bi-m. supplement). £204($322) (British Paediatric Association) B M J Publishing Group, B.M.A. House, Tavistock Sq., London WC1H 9JR, England. TEL 0171-383-6270. FAX 0171-383-6402. (N. American subscr. to: Box 408, Franklin, MA 02038. TEL 800-2-FON-BMJ. FAX 800-2-FAX-BMJ) Eds. M. Chiswick, H. Marcovitch. adv. contact: Sheila Rowe. bk.rev.; charts; illus.; index. (also avail. in microfilm from UMI; reprint service avail. from UMI) **Indexed:** Abstr.Health Care Manage.Stud., Abstr.Hyg., AIM, Biol.Abstr., Chem.Abstr., CINAHL, Curr.Adv.Biochem., Curr.Adv.Ecol.Sci., Curr.Cont., Curr.Lit.Fam.Plan., Dairy Sci.Abstr., Dent.Ind., Diab.Cont., Diar.Dis.Res., Dok.Arbeitsmed., Excerp.Med., Helminthol.Abstr., Ind.Med., Ind.Sci.Rev., Kidney, Med.& Surg.Dermat., NRN, Nutr.Abstr., Psychol.Abstr., Rev.Plant Path., Risk Abstr., Sci.Cit.Ind., Triticale Abstr., Trop.Dis.Bull. **Document type:** academic/scholarly publication.
●Also available online. Vendor(s): Ovid Technologies.
—BLDSC (1634.200000); ADONIS; CASDDS; Faxon; Genuine Article; SWETS; UMI; UnCover. **CCC.**
Supersedes (1904-1944): British Journal of Children's Diseases (ISSN 0366-2837)
Description: Publishes a wide range of papers on all aspects of childhood health and disease for U.K. pediatricians and others worldwide.
Refereed Serial

ARCHIVES OF DISEASE IN CHILDHOOD. FETAL AND NEONATAL EDITION. see *MEDICAL SCIENCES — Obstetrics And Gynecology*

618.92   US   ISSN 1072-4710
RJ1   CODEN: APAMEB
ARCHIVES OF PEDIATRICS & ADOLESCENT MEDICINE. 1911. m. $100 (foreign $135). American Medical Association, 515 N. State St., Chicago, IL 60610. TEL 312-464-5000; 800-262-2350. FAX 312-464-4181. (Editorial addr.: c/o Johns Hopkins School of Medicine, Office of the Senior Associate Dean, 720 Rutland Ave., Ste. 106, Baltimore, MD 21205-2196. TEL 410-614-3100. FAX 410-614-3099) Ed. Dr. Catherine D. DeAngelis. bk.rev.; abstr.; bibl.; charts; illus.; index. circ. 28,500. (also avail. in microform from UMI) **Indexed:** Abstr.Anthropol., Abstr.Hyg., Abstr.Inter.Med., Adol.Ment.Hlth.Abstr., AIM, Bibl.Dev.Med.& Child Neur., Biol.Abstr., Biotech.Abstr., C.C.I.P., Chem.Abstr., CINAHL, Curr.Adv.Ecol.Sci., Curr.Cont., Dairy Sci.Abstr., Diar.Dis.Res., Dok.Arbeitsmed., Except.Child.Educ.Abstr., Excerp.Med., FAMLI, Helminthol.Abstr., HRIS, I.P.A., Ind.Med., Ind.Sci.Rev., INIS Atomind., Kidney, Med.& Surg.Dermat., NRN, Nutr.Abstr., Psychol.Abstr., Rev.Plant Path., Risk Abstr., Sci.Cit.Ind., Soyabean Abstr. **Document type:** academic/scholarly publication.
●Also available online. Vendor(s): Lexis-Nexis.
—BLDSC (1638.960000); CASDDS; Faxon; Genuine Article; SWETS; UMI; UnCover. **CCC.**
Former titles (until Jan. 1994): A J D C - American Journal of Diseases of Children (ISSN 0002-922X); A M A American Journal of Diseases of Children (ISSN 0096-8994)
Description: Publishes original clinical studies, practice commentaries, updates on clinical science and practice management articles. Provides a forum for dialogue on clinical, scientific, advocacy and humanistic issues relevant to the care of pediatric patients from infancy through young adulthood.
Refereed Serial

618.9   SP   ISSN 0402-9054
ARCHIVOS DE PEDIATRIA; revista de formacion medica continuada. (Text in Spanish; summaries in English) 1950. 8/yr. 8600 ptas.($83) (effective 1995). (Universidad de Barcelona, Departamento de Pediatria) Editorial Garsi, S.A., Juan Bravo 46, 28006 Madrid, Spain. TEL 34-1-4021212. FAX 34-1-4020954. Eds. Dr. M. Cruz, Dr. R. Jimenez. adv.; bk.rev.; bibl.; illus.; index. circ. 2,500. (back issues avail.) **Indexed:** Ind.Med.Esp., Nutr.Abstr.
—BLDSC (1655.490000).

MEDICAL SCIENCES — PEDIATRICS

618.92   UY   ISSN 0004-0584
ARCHIVOS DE PEDIATRIA DEL URUGUAY. (Text in Spanish; summaries in English) 1929. q. $50. Sociedad Uruguaya de Pediatria, Casilla de Correo 10906, Montevideo, Uruguay. TEL 79-18-01. FAX 78-52-13. Ed. Dr. Leopoldo F. Peluffo. adv.; bk.rev.; abstr.; bibl.; charts; illus.; index. circ. 1,250. **Indexed:** Biol.Abstr., Excerp.Med., Ind.Med., Nutr.Abstr.

618.92   DR   ISSN 0004-0606
ARCHIVOS DOMINICANOS DE PEDIATRIA. (Text in Spanish; summaries in English) 1965. 3/yr. $15. Sociedad Dominicana de Investigaciones Pediatricas, Fernando Valerio 7, Bella Vista, Santo Domingo, Dominican Republic. TEL 809-532-7663. (Co-sponsors: Academia Americana de Pediatria (Capitulo Dominicano); Hospital de Ninos de Santo Domingo) Dir. Emilio Mena Castro. adv.; bk.rev.; charts; illus.; bibl.; index, cum.index every 10 yrs. circ. 1,500. (reprint service avail.) **Indexed:** Abstr.Hyg., Ind.Med., Trop.Dis.Bull. **Document type:** bulletin.

618.92   VE   ISSN 0004-0649
ARCHIVOS VENEZOLANOS DE PUERICULTURA Y PEDIATRIA. (Text in Spanish; summaries in English) 1939. q. Bs.30. Sociedad Venezolana de Puericultura y Pediatria, Av. Libertador-Edf. La Linca, 9 piso, Ofc. 93a, Caracas 105, Venezuela). Ed. Dr. Eduardo Urdoneta. adv.; bk.rev.; bibl.; charts; illus.; index. circ. 2,000. **Indexed:** Biol.Abstr., Chem.Abstr., Excerp.Med., Nutr.Abstr.

618.92   BL   ISSN 0104-5652
▼**ARQUIVOS BRASILEIROS DE PEDIATRIA.** 1994. bi-m. r.$19 (effective 1995). (Sociedade de Pediatria do Estado de Rio de Janeiro) Editora Cientifica Nacional Ltda., Rua da Gloria, 366, 3o andar, 20241-180 Rio de Janeiro, RJ, Brazil. TEL 55-21-2213235. FAX 55-21-2521691. Ed. Clemax Couto Sant'Anna.

618.92   US   ISSN 0271-1346
AUDIO-DIGEST PEDIATRICS. 1955. s-m. $168. Audio-Digest Foundation (Subsidiary of: California Medical Association), 1577 E. Chevy Chase Dr., Glendale, CA 91206. TEL 213-245-8505. FAX 818-240-7379. (audio cassette)
Refereed Serial

AUSTRALIA. BUREAU OF STATISTICS. CHILDREN'S HEALTH SCREENING. see *MEDICAL SCIENCES — Abstracting, Bibliographies, Statistics*

AUSTRALIA. BUREAU OF STATISTICS. CHILDREN'S IMMUNISATION. see *MEDICAL SCIENCES — Abstracting, Bibliographies, Statistics*

AUSTRALIA PAEDIATRIC NURSE JOURNAL. see *MEDICAL SCIENCES — Nurses And Nursing*

618.92   UK   ISSN 0963-6714
BAILLIERE'S CLINICAL PAEDIATRICS. 1993. q. £70 to individuals; institutions £80. Bailliere Tindall - W.B. Saunders Co. Ltd. (Subsidiary of: Harcourt Brace & Company Ltd.), 24-28 Oval Rd., London NW1 7DX, England. TEL 0171-267-4466. FAX 0171-482-2293. TELEX 25775 ACPRES G. (Subscr. to: Journals Subscriptions Fulfillment, Foots Cray High St., Sidcup, Kent DA14 5HP, England. TEL 0181-300-3322. FAX 0181-309-0807; Subscr. in N. America to: W.B. Saunders Co., Journal Subscription Fulfillment, 6277 Sea Harbor Dr., 4th Fl., Orlando, FL 32887-4800. TEL 800-874-6418) **Document type:** academic/scholarly publication.
—BLDSC (1856.726500).
Refereed Serial

618.92 616.99   SW   ISSN 0284-7507
BARN OCH CANCER. 1987. q. SEK 100 membership. Barncancerfonden, Styrmansg. 43, S-114 54 Stockholm, Sweden.

618.92 610.73   SW   ISSN 0349-1994
BARNBLADET; tidskrift foer Sveriges barnsjukskoeterskor. 1976. q. SEK 100 (effective 1991). (Riksfoereningen foer Barnsjukskoeterskor - Swedish Association of Pediatric Nurses) Via Media, P.O. Box 4075, S-261 04 Landskrona, Sweden. **Document type:** trade publication.

616.8 367   GW   ISSN 0067-5105
BEITRAEGE ZUR KINDERPSYCHOTHERAPIE. 1965. irreg., no.30, 1985. price varies. Ernst Reinhardt Verlag, Kemnatenstr. 46, 80639 Munich, Germany. TEL 089-1783005. FAX 089-1781827. Ed. Gerd Biermann. index. **Document type:** monographic series.

618.92   PL   ISSN 0303-7827
BIBLIOTEKA PEDIATRY.* 1974. irreg. Polskie Towarzystwo Pediatryczne, Ul. Kasprzaka 17, 00-211 Warsaw, Poland. TEL 48-22-323455. Ed. Krystyna Bozkowa.

618.92   SP   ISSN 0214-2597
BOLETIN DE PEDIATRIA. (Text in Spanish; summaries in English and Spanish) 1960. q. 350 ptas.($7) (Sociedad de Pediatria de Asturias, Cantabria, Castilla y Leon, Facultad de Medicina) Editorial Garsi, S.A., Juan Bravo 46, 28006 Madrid, Spain. TEL 34-1-4021212. FAX 34-1-4020954. Ed. Alfredo Blanco. adv.; bk.rev.; abstr.; charts; illus.; index. circ. 2,000.
Formerly (until 1987): Sociedad Castellano-Astur-Leonosa de Pediatria. Boletin (ISSN 0037-8429)

618   JA   ISSN 1341-1780
BOSHI KAGAKU RYOHO/CHEMOTHERAPY FOR MOTHER AND CHILD. (Text in English, Japanese) 1987. bi-m. free to qualified personnel. Boshi Kagaku Ryoho Kenkyujo - Research Institute of Chemotherapy for Mother and Child, 55-12, Ikebukuro 2-chome, Toshima-ku, Tokyo 171, Japan. TEL 03-3980-6139. Ed. Ryochi Fujii. circ. 250 (controlled). **Document type:** monographic series, academic/scholarly publication.
Description: Covers recent trends of worldwide antimicrobial development.

618.92 649   CN   ISSN 1183-0654
BOUNTY INFANT CARE GUIDE. French edition: Guide Bounty des Soins au Nourisson (ISSN 1183-0662) 1990. s-a. Bounty Family Publications Ltd., 746 Warden Ave., No. 2, Scarborough, ON M1L 4A2, Canada. TEL 416-750-1165. FAX 416-750-7266. Ed. Alan Donaldson. adv. circ. 179,891.

618.9 649   US
BOUNTY INFANT CARE GUIDE.* 1989. q. $8. Health Care Publishing, Ltd., 84 Clinton Ave., Nyack, NY 10960-4604. TEL 212-489-2273. FAX 212-489-2476. Ed. Robert Egleton. adv.; B&W page $46297, color page $57156; trim 5 1/4 x 7 1/2; adv. contact: Glenn Meyerson. circ. 950,000. (back issues avail.) **Document type:** consumer publication.

BRAIN AND DEVELOPMENT. see *MEDICAL SCIENCES — Psychiatry And Neurology*

618.92   GW   ISSN 0373-3165
BUECHEREI DES PAEDIATERS. 1972. irreg., no.96, 1993. price varies. Ferdinand Enke Verlag, Postfach 300366, 70443 Stuttgart, Germany. TEL 0711-135798-0. FAX 0711-135798-30. TELEX 07252275-GTV-D. Ed.Bd. (reprint service avail. from IRC) **Indexed:** Nutr.Abstr. **Document type:** monographic series.
Formerly: Archiv fuer Kinderheilkunde. Beihefte (ISSN 0066-6378)

C O N A JOURNAL. (Canadian Orthopaedic Nurses Association) see *MEDICAL SCIENCES — Orthopedics And Traumatology*

618.92   US   ISSN 0882-3421
CALIFORNIA PEDIATRICIAN. 1984. s-a. American Academy of Pediatrics, California District, 4690 Genesse Ave., San Diego, CA 92177. TEL 619-569-5019. FAX 619-560-6340. Ed. Marvin Averback. adv.; B&W page $1500, color page $2500; trim 8 1/2 x 11. circ. 6,500. **Document type:** trade publication.
Description: Covers pediatric health care, practice management, and doctor-patient relationships.

618.92   CN   ISSN 0843-4263
CANADIAN JOURNAL OF PEDIATRICS/JOURNAL CANADIEN DE PEDIATRIE. 1985. 10/yr. Can.$95 (foreign Can.$140). Rodar Publishing Inc., 19180 Trans Canada Hwy., Baie d'Urfe, PQ H4X 9Z9, Canada. TEL 514-457-2673. FAX 514-457-2679. Ed. Dr. Ronald Gold; Pub. Bob Fauteaux. adv.; charts; illus.; circ. 15,800 (controlled). (also avail. in microfilm; back issues avail.) **Indexed:** Can.B.P.I., CMI. **Document type:** academic/scholarly publication.
●Also available online.
—BLDSC (3033.790000).
Formerly (until 1989): Contemporary Pediatrics Canada (ISSN 0832-7831)
Description: Covers issues in neonatology, child psychology, infant nutrition for the general practitioner and the specialists.
Refereed Serial

618.92   CN   ISSN 1199-7044
CANADIAN PAEDIATRIC SOCIETY. ANNUAL REPORT. French edition: Societe Canadienne de Pediatrie. Rapport Annuel (ISSN 1191-1980) (Text in English) a. Canadian Paediatric Society - Societe Canadienne de Pediatrie, 401 Smyth Rd., Ottawa, ON K1H 8L1, Canada. TEL 613-737-2794. FAX 613-737-2794. **Document type:** corporate report.

618.92   CN   ISSN 0831-7682
CANADIAN PAEDIATRIC SOCIETY. NEWS BULLETIN. French edition (ISSN 0831-7674) 1954. bi-m. Can.$60($60) Canadian Paediatric Society, 401 Smyth Rd., Ottawa, ON K1H 8L1, Canada. TEL 613-488-1047. FAX 613-978-7821. Ed. Martine Bernard. adv. contact: Nicole Menzies. bk.rev. circ. 2,500. **Document type:** bulletin.
Description: Promotes the advancement of knowledge of the sciences pertaining to infancy, childhood and adolescence.

CANDLELIGHTERS CHILDHOOD CANCER FOUNDATION QUARTERLY NEWSLETTER. see *MEDICAL SCIENCES — Oncology*

618.92   XR   CODEN: CEPEA3
CESKO-SLOVENSKA PEDIATRIE. (Text in Czech or Slovak; summaries in English and Russian) 1945. 12/yr. $83.30. (Ceska Lekarska Spolecnost - Czech Medical Society) Nakladatelske Strediska C L S J.E. Purkyne, Sokolska 31, 120 26 Prague 2, Czech Republic. FAX 42-0-2-202788. (Dist. by: Artia, Ve Smeckach 30, 111 27 Prague 1, Czech Republic) Ed. Dr. K. Kubat. bk.rev.; abstr. **Indexed:** Chem.Abstr., Child Devel.Abstr., Curr.Adv.Ecol.Sci., Dairy Sci.Abstr., Dent.Ind., Excerp.Med., Ind.Med., INIS Atomind., Nutr.Abstr., Protozool.Abstr. —BLDSC (3122.480000); CASDDS; EMDOCS. **CCC.**
Former titles: Ceskoslovenska Pediatrie (ISSN 0069-2328); Pediatrice Listy.

618   JA
CHIBA DAIGAKU SHONI GEKA NENPO/CHIBA UNIVERSITY. SCHOOL OF MEDICINE. PEDIATRIC SURGICAL DEPARTMENT. ANNUAL REPORT. (Text in Japanese) 1978. a. Chiba Daigaku, Igakubu, 8-1, Inohana 1-chome, Chuo-ku, Chiba-shi, Chiba-ken 260, Japan.

618   US   ISSN 1056-4993
RJ499.A1   CODEN: CAPAF2
CHILD AND ADOLESCENT PSYCHIATRIC CLINICS OF NORTH AMERICA. 1992. q. $120 (foreign $145) (effective 1996). W.B. Saunders Co. (Subsidiary of: Harcourt Brace & Company), The Curtis Center, 3rd Fl., Independence Sq. W., Philadelphia, PA 19106-3399. TEL 215-238-7800. FAX 215-238-6445. (Subscr. to: Periodicals Fulfillment, 6277 Sea Harbor Dr., 4th Fl., Orlando, FL 32891-4800. TEL 800-654-2542. FAX 800-874-6418) Ed. Dr. Melvin Lewis. index. (also avail. in microform from UMI; back issues avail.) **Indexed:** Excerp.Med. (1995-). **Document type:** academic/scholarly publication.
—BLDSC (3172.913600); UMI.

618.92 155.4
616.89   US   ISSN 0193-7421
CHILD BEHAVIOR AND DEVELOPMENT.* 1975. irreg. S P Medical & Scientific Books, Inc. (Subsidiary of: Spectrum Publications, Inc.), c/o Fisher, 200 Park Ave.S., New York, NY 10003-1503.

618.92   UK   ISSN 0305-1862
   CODEN: CCHDDH
CHILD: CARE, HEALTH AND DEVELOPMENT. 1975. bi-m. £127 in Europe; elsewhere £140($225)) (effective 1996). Blackwell Science Ltd., Osney Mead, Oxford OX2 OEL, England. TEL 01865-240201. FAX 01865-721205. TELEX 83355 MEDBOK G. Ed. R.B. Jones. adv.; bk.rev.; bibl.; illus.; index. circ. 750. (also avail. in microform from UMI; back issues avail.; reprint service avail. from ISI) **Indexed:** Abstr.Hyg., ASCA, ASSIA, Bibl.Dev.Med.& Child Neur., Child Devel.Abstr., CINAHL, Curr.Adv.Ecol.Sci., Curr.Cont., Excerp.Med., Ind.Med., Mult.Ed.Abstr., Nutr.Abstr., Psychol.Abstr. (1975-), Psycscan D.P., Sp.Ed.Needs Abstr., SSCI, Yrbk.Assoc.Educ.& Rehab.Blind. **Document type:** academic/scholarly publication.
—BLDSC (3172.925000); Faxon; Genuine Article; SWETS; UMI; UnCover. **CCC.**
Refereed Serial

CHILD PSYCHIATRY AND HUMAN DEVELOPMENT. see *MEDICAL SCIENCES — Psychiatry And Neurology*

MEDICAL SCIENCES — PEDIATRICS

618.92   US
CHILDREN'S HOSPICE INTERNATIONAL NEWSLETTER. q. $35. Children's Hospice International, 700 Princess St., No. LL, Alexandria, VA 22314-2265. TEL 703-684-0330. FAX 703-684-0226. Ed. Julie Frey. circ. 5,000. (back issues avail.) **Document type:** newsletter.
Description: Pediatric hospice care issues.

618.92   US   ISSN 0899-5869
                     CODEN: CHQUED
CHILDREN'S HOSPITAL QUARTERLY; a journal for practicing pediatricians and those who care for the health of children. 1989. q. $195 (foreign $230) (effective 1996). Human Sciences Press, Inc. (Subsidiary of: Plenum Publishing Corp.), 233 Spring St., New York, NY 10013. TEL 212-620-8000. FAX 212-463-0742. TELEX 23-421139. Ed. Philip Lanzkowsky. adv. **Indexed:** IMFL. **Document type:** academic/scholarly publication.
—BLDSC (3172.990210); UMI. **CCC.**
Description: Features the latest information available in the various pediatric subspecialties.
Refereed Serial

CHILD'S NERVOUS SYSTEM. see *MEDICAL SCIENCES — Psychiatry And Neurology*

CHILD'S PLAY. see *CHILDREN AND YOUTH — About*

618.92   IT   ISSN 0009-9058
CLINICA PEDIATRICA. (Text in Italian; summaries in English, French, German and Spanish) 1930. m. $12. Via Massarenti 11, Bologna, Italy. Ed. G. Salvioli. adv.; bk.rev.; abstr.; illus.; index. **Indexed:** Biol.Abstr., Chem.Abstr., Dent.Ind., Excerp.Med.

618.92   IT   ISSN 0393-7615
CLINICA PEDIATRICA DEL NORD AMERICA. bi-m. L.180000($180) Piccin Editore, Via Altinate 107, 35100 Padua, Italy. TEL 049-655566. FAX 049-8750693. (reprint service avail. from UMI)

616.8   US   ISSN 0735-2530
CLINICAL INFANT REPORTS. MONOGRAPH. irreg., latest no.6. price varies. (National Center for Clinical Infant Programs) International Universities Press, Inc., 59 Boston Post Rd., Box 1524, Madison, CT 06443-1524. TEL 203-245-4000. **Indexed:** Psychol.Abstr. **Document type:** monographic series.
Refereed Serial

618.92   US   ISSN 0009-9228
RJ1   CODEN: CPEDAM
CLINICAL PEDIATRICS. 1962. m. $78 to individuals (foreign $98); institutions $98 (foreign $118). Cortlandt Group, Inc., 500 Executive Blvd., Ste. 302, Ossining, NY 10562. TEL 914-762-0647. FAX 914-762-8820. Ed. Dr. Ben H. Brouhard. adv.; illus.; index. circ. 31,481. (also avail. in microform from UMI; back issues avail.) **Indexed:** AIM, Bibl.Dev.Med.& Child Neur., Biol.Abstr., C.C.I.P., Chem.Abstr., Child Devel.Abstr., CINAHL, Curr.Adv.Ecol.Sci., Curr.Cont., Dent.Ind., Diar.Dis.Res., Excerp.Med., Hosp.Lit.Ind., Ind.Med., Ind.Sci.Rev., INIS Atomind., Int.Nurs.Ind., Med.& Surg.Dermat., NRN, Psychol.Abstr. (1982-), Rev.Med.& Vet.Mycol., Sci.Cit.Ind., SSCI. **Document type:** trade publication. ●Also available online. Vendor(s): Lexis-Nexis, Ovid Technologies.
—BLDSC (3286.325000); Faxon; SWETS; UMI; UnCover.
Description: For practitioners in all areas of child care. Contains articles on pediatric practice, clinical research, behavioral and educational problems, community health and subspecialty or affiliated specialty applications.
Refereed Serial

618.92   US
CLINICAL PEDIATRICS SERIES. 1984. irreg., vol.7, 1990. price varies. Marcel Dekker, Inc., 270 Madison Ave., New York, NY 10016. TEL 212-696-9000. FAX 212-685-4540. TELEX 421419. **Document type:** monographic series.
Refereed Serial

618.92   SP
CLINICAS DE ATENCION PRIMARIA DE NORTEAMERICA. Spanish translation of: Primary Care - Clinics in Office Practice. 1988. 4/yr. 13144 ptas.($87) (effective 1990). Interamericana de Espana, S.A., Division de Ciencias de la Salud de McGraw-Hill, Calle Manuel Ferrero, 13, 28036 Madrid, Spain. TEL 315-0340. FAX 733-6627. Ed. Jose Antonio Tapia Granados. charts; illus.; cum.index.
Formerly: Temas Actuales en Medicina General.

618.92   SP
CLINICAS PEDIATRICAS DE NORTEAMERICA. Spanish translation of: Pediatric Clinics of North America (US ISSN 0031-3955) 1964. 4/yr. $111. Interamericana de Espana, S.A., Division de Ciencias de la Salud de McGraw-Hill, Calle Manuel Ferrero, 13, 28036 Madrid, Spain. TEL 1-315-03-40. charts; illus.; index.

612   UK   ISSN 0069-4835
                   CODEN: CDVMAG
CLINICS IN DEVELOPMENTAL MEDICINE. 1959. q. £98($145) (effective 1996). Mac Keith Press, 526-529 High Holborn House, 52-54 High Holborn, London WC1V 6RL. TEL 0171-405-5355. FAX 0171-405-5365. (Dist. by: Cambridge University Press, Edinburgh Bldg., Shaftesbury Rd., Cambridge DB2 2RU, England. TEL 01223-312393. FAX 01223-315052; N. American addr.: Cambridge University Press, Journals Dept., 40 W. 20th St., New York, NY 10011. TEL 212-924-3900. FAX 212-691-3239) Ed. Martin C.O. Bax. **Document type:** monographic series.
—BLDSC (3286.550000); SWETS. **CCC.**
Description: Covers a wide range of circumstances affecting child development. Each thematic volume provides a comprehensive study of the theoretical and clinical aspects of a specific childhood condition or disorder.

618.92   TU   ISSN 0010-0161
                   CODEN: CSHDAO
COCUK SAGLIGI VE HASTALIKLARI DERGISI. (Text in Turkish; summaries in English) 1958. q. $50. Turkish and International Children's Center - Turkiye ve Uluslararasi Cocuk Sagligi Merkezi, P.O. Box 66, Samanpazari, 06240 Ankara, Turkey. TEL 90-312-3242326. FAX 90-312-3112253. TELEX 42999 TCSM TR. (Co-sponsor: Turkish National Pediatric Society) Ed. Dr. Ihsan Dogramaci. bk.rev.; abstr.; bibl.; charts; illus.; index. circ. 1,500. **Indexed:** Biol.Abstr., Excerp.Med. (1992-). **Document type:** academic/scholarly publication.
—BLDSC (3292.760800).
Refereed Serial

COMBINED CUMULATIVE INDEX TO PEDIATRICS. see *MEDICAL SCIENCES — Abstracting, Bibliographies, Statistics*

COMPREHENSIVE MANUALS IN PEDIATRICS. see *MEDICAL SCIENCES — Abstracting, Bibliographies, Statistics*

CONCEPTS IN PEDIATRIC NEUROSURGERY. see *MEDICAL SCIENCES — Psychiatry And Neurology*

618.92   US   ISSN 8750-0507
CONTEMPORARY PEDIATRICS. 1984. m. $79 (foreign $89). Medical Economics, Five Paragon Dr., Montvale, NJ 07645. TEL 201-358-7239. FAX 201-358-7260. (Subscr. to: Box 983, Fairview, NJ 07022) Ed. Catherine Brown. adv.; charts; illus.; stat.; index. circ. 39,000. (also avail. in microform from RPI,UMI; reprint service avail.) **Indexed:** C.C.I.P.
—BLDSC (3425.197900); UMI.
Description: Clinical articles on prevention, diagnosis and treatment of illnesses from infancy through young adulthood; also reports on important trends in pediatric practices, including innovations in practice management.

618.92   CN   ISSN 1182-7076
CONTEMPORARY PEDIATRICS. 1993. 6/yr. Can.$36 (foreign Can.$54). Thomson Healthcare Communications, 1120 Birchmount Rd., Ste. 200, Scarborough, ON M1K 5G4, Canada. TEL 416-751-8900. FAX 416-751-8126. Ed. Vil Meere. adv.; B&W page Can.$1695, color page Can.$2790; trim 8 1/8 x 10 7/8; adv. contact: Alexandra Hamilton. circ. 10,402.

CRITICAL ISSUES IN DEVELOPMENTAL & BEHAVIORAL PEDIATRICS. see *PSYCHOLOGY*

618.92   US   ISSN 0172-1232
CURRENT DIAGNOSTIC PEDIATRICS. 1977. irreg. price varies. Springer-Verlag, 175 Fifth Ave., New York, NY 10010. TEL 212-460-1500. FAX 212-473-6272. (Also: Berlin, Heidelberg, Tokyo and Vienna) Ed. A. Chrispin. (reprint service avail. from ISI) **Document type:** monographic series.

CURRENT OPINION IN PEDIATRICS. see *MEDICAL SCIENCES — Abstracting, Bibliographies, Statistics*

618.92   UK   ISSN 0957-5839
CURRENT PAEDIATRICS. 1991. q. £60($93) to individuals; institutions £155 ($240) (effective 1995). Churchill Livingstone Journals (Subsidiary of: Pearson Professional Ltd.), Robert Stevenson House, 1-3 Baxter's Pl., Leith Walk, Edinburgh EH1 3AF, Scotland. TEL 0131-556-2424. FAX 0131-459-1177. (Subscr. to: Parson Professional Ltd., P.O. Box 77, Fourth Ave., Harlow, Essex CM19 5AA, England. TEL 01279-623760; U.S. subscr. to: Churchill Livingstone, 650 Ave. of the Americas, New York, NY 10011. TEL 212-206-5000) Eds. N. Mann, J. Tyrrell. adv. contact: David Dunnachie. circ. 890. **Document type:** academic/scholarly publication.
—BLDSC (3500.900000). **CCC.**
Description: Provides concise updates on clinical practice, delivery of care, technical procedures, innovations, legal matters and basic science.

618.92   US   ISSN 0045-9380
CURRENT PROBLEMS IN PEDIATRICS. Short title: C P P. 1971. 10/yr. $72 to individuals (foreign $81); institutions $93 (foreign $102); students $44 (foreign $53) (effective Jan. 1994). Mosby - Year Book, Inc. (Subsidiary of: Times Mirror Company), 11830 Westline Industrial Dr., St. Louis, MO 63146. TEL 314-872-8370; 800-325-4177. FAX 314-432-1380. Ed. Norman C. Fost. illus.; cum.index. circ. 2,200. (also avail. in microform from UMI; back issues avail.; reprint service avail. from UMI) **Indexed:** Adol.Ment.Hlth.Abstr., Excerp.Med., Ind.Med.
—BLDSC (3501.390000); EMDOCS; SWETS; UMI; UnCover. **CCC.**
Description: Provides monthly monographic clinical reviews from authorities in the field, intended for practitioners.

618.92   US   ISSN 0893-9020
DAYCARE HEALTH; review and update for early childhood group care. 1987. bi-m. (Oct.-Jun.). $27 (effective 1992-93). Mathanna Publications, Box 5351, Bellingham, WA 98227-9970. TEL 206-671-4350. Ed. Paula B. Kobos, R.N. abstr.; bibl.; index. (looseleaf format; back issues avail.)
Description: Presents current information about health issues in child care.

DEUTSCHE BEHINDERTENZEITSCHRIFT. see *MEDICAL SCIENCES — Psychiatry And Neurology*

618.92 616.8   UK   ISSN 0012-1622
RJ1   CODEN: DMCNAW
DEVELOPMENTAL MEDICINE AND CHILD NEUROLOGY. (Text in English; summaries in French, German, Spanish) 1958. m. £98($145) (effective 1996). (American Academy for Cerebral Palsy and Developmental Medicine, US) Mac Keith Press, 526-529 High Holborn House, 52-54 High Holborn, London WC1V 6RL, England. TEL 0171-405-5355. FAX 0171-405-5365. (Dist. by: Cambridge University Press, Edinburgh Bldg., Shaftesbury Rd., Cambridge CB2 2 RU, England. TEL 01223-312393. FAX 01223-315052; N. American addr.: Cambridge University Press, Journals Dept., 40 W. 20th St., New York, NY 10011. TEL 212-924-3900. FAX 212-691-3239) (Co-sponsor: British Paediatric Neurology Association) Ed. Dr. Martin C.O. Bax. adv.: page $520. bk.rev.; abstr. circ. 5,200. (also avail. in microfilm from UMI; reprint service avail. from UMI) **Indexed:** Abstr.Hyg., Behav.Med.Abstr., Bibl.Dev.Med.& Child Neur., Biol.Abstr., Cadscan, Child Devel.Abstr., CINAHL, Curr.Cont., Dent.Ind., Dok.Arbeitsmed., DSH Abstr., Except.Child.Educ.Abstr., Excerp.Med., Helminthol.Abstr., Ind.Sci.Rev., Lead Abstr., Med.& Surg.Dermat., Ment.Retard.Abstr., NRN, Nutr.Abstr., Psychol.Abstr. (1962-), Rehabil.Lit., Sci.Cit.Ind., Sp.Ed.Needs Abstr., Trop.Dis.Bull., Zincscan. **Document type:** academic/scholarly publication.
—BLDSC (3579.055000); Faxon; Genuine Article; SWETS; UMI; UnCover. **CCC.**
Description: Covers a wide range of clinical topics involving diseases or disabilities of children.
Refereed Serial

MEDICAL SCIENCES — PEDIATRICS

618.92 616.6 US ISSN 0164-9507
DIALOGUES IN PEDIATRIC UROLOGY. 1977. m. $54 (foreign $57). William J. Miller Associates, Inc., 45 Villa Rd., Pearl River, NY 10965. TEL 914-735-7853. FAX 914-735-6628. Ed. Dr. Richard M. Ehrlich. index. circ. 560. (back issues avail.) **Document type:** academic/scholarly publication.
—BLDSC (3579.775850).
Description: Publishes clinical articles on pediatric urology and surgery. Each issue devoted to a specific theme.

618.92 GW
DOCUMENTA PAEDIATRIE. 1976. irreg., vol.21, 1993. DM.24. Schmidt-Roemhild Verlag, Mengstr. 16, 23552 Luebeck, Germany. TEL 0451-1605-0. FAX 0451-1605253. Ed. Dr. Theodor Hellbruegge. **Document type:** monographic series.

EARLY CHILD DEVELOPMENT AND CARE. see *CHILDREN AND YOUTH — About*

EARLY HUMAN DEVELOPMENT; an international journal concerned with the continuity of fetal and post natal life. see *MEDICAL SCIENCES — Obstetrics And Gynecology*

EARLY INTERVENTION. see *EDUCATION — Special Education And Rehabilitation*

618.92 US ISSN 1073-7782
CODEN: EPEDEE
EMERGENCY AND OFFICE PEDIATRICS. bi-m. $70 (foreign $100). Mary Ann Liebert, Inc. Publishers, 2 Madison Ave., Larchmont, NY 10538. TEL 914-834-3100. FAX 914-834-3688. E-mail: Liebert@pipeline.com. Eds. Peter S. Liebert, Andrew P. Mezey. abstr. **Indexed:** CINAHL, Excerp.Med. (1993-). **Document type:** academic/scholarly publication.
Formerly: Emergency Pediatrics (ISSN 1044-3797)
Description: For physicians and nurses who deliver acute and urgent care to children's emergency rooms, offices, clinics and other ambulatory settings. Includes original articles on medical and surgical problems, questions and answers, tips and commentary.

ENFANCE; psychologie, pedagogie, neuro-psychiatrie, sociologie. see *CHILDREN AND YOUTH — About*

ERGEBNISSE DER INNEREN MEDIZIN UND KINDERHEILKUNDE. NEW SERIES/ADVANCES IN INTERNAL MEDICINE AND PEDIATRICS. see *MEDICAL SCIENCES — Internal Medicine*

EUROPEAN JOURNAL OF PEDIATRIC DERMATOLOGY. see *MEDICAL SCIENCES — Dermatology And Venereology*

EUROPEAN JOURNAL OF PEDIATRIC DERMATOLOGY (EDIZIONE ITALIANA). see *MEDICAL SCIENCES — Dermatology And Venereology*

EUROPEAN JOURNAL OF PEDIATRIC SURGERY. see *MEDICAL SCIENCES — Surgery*

EUROPEAN JOURNAL OF PEDIATRIC SURGERY. SUPPLEMENT. see *MEDICAL SCIENCES — Surgery*

618.92 GW ISSN 0340-6199
CODEN: EJPEDT
EUROPEAN JOURNAL OF PEDIATRICS. (Text in English) 1910. 12/yr. DM.2420($1758) (effective 1996). Springer-Verlag, Heidelberger Platz 3, 14197 Berlin, Germany. TEL 030-8207-0. FAX 030-8214091. E-mail: orders@springer.de. (Subscr. in N. America to: Springer-Verlag New York, Inc., 44 Hartz Way, Secaucus, NJ 07096-2491. TEL 201-348-4033. FAX 201-348-4505) Ed. J. Spranger. adv.; charts; illus. (also avail. in microform from UMI; back issues avail.; reprint service avail. from ISI) **Indexed:** Bibl.Dev.Med.& Child Neur., Biol.Abstr., Biotech.Abstr., Chem.Abstr., Curr.Adv.Biochem., Curr.Adv.Ecol.Sci., Curr.Adv.Genetics & Molec.Biol., Curr.Cont., Dairy Sci.Abstr., Dent.Ind., Excerp.Med., Helminthol.Abstr., Ind.Med., Ind.Sci.Rev., Ind.Vet., INIS Atomind., Kidney, Med.& Surg.Dermat., NRN, Nutr.Abstr., Protozool.Abstr., Risk Abstr., Sci.Cit.Ind. **Document type:** academic/scholarly publication.
—BLDSC (3829.733500); ADONIS; CASDDS; Faxon; Genuine Article; SWETS; UMI; UnCover. CCC.
Incorporates: Acta Paediatrica Belgica (ISSN 0001-6535); Helvetica Paediatrica Acta (ISSN 0018-022X); Zeitschrift fuer Kinderheilkunde.
Description: Covers the whole broad field of pediatrics in all its aspects.

FETAL AND MATERNAL MEDICINE REVIEW. see *MEDICAL SCIENCES — Obstetrics And Gynecology*

618.92 US
▼**FOCUS & OPINION IN PEDIATRICS.** 1994. q. $68 to individuals; institutions $112.50; residents $40 (effective 19960. Mosby - Year Book, Inc. (Chicago) (Subsidiary of: Times Mirror Company), 200 N. LaSalle St., Chicago, IL 60601-1080. TEL 312-726-9733. FAX 312-726-6075. TELEX 206155.

FRUEHFOERDERUNG INTERDISZIPLINAER; Zeitschrift fuer Praxis und Theorie der fruehen Hilfe fuer behinderte und entwicklungsauffaellige Kinder. see *MEDICAL SCIENCES — Psychiatry And Neurology*

618.92 IT ISSN 0390-5845
GASLINI; rivista di pediatria e di specialita pediatriche. 3/yr. $90 to individuals; institutions $140 (effective 1995). (Giannina Gaslini Institute) Edizioni Minerva Medica, Corso Bramante 83-85, 10126 Turin, Italy. TEL 011-678282. FAX 011-3121736. Ed. F. Perfumo; Pub. Alberto Oliaro. adv.: B&W page $1100, color page $1900; trim 190 x 270; adv. contact: F. Filippo. circ. 2,000 (paid). **Document type:** academic/scholarly publication.

GIORNALE INTERNAZIONALE DI DERMATOLOGIA PEDIATRICA. see *MEDICAL SCIENCES — Dermatology And Venereology*

618.92 GT ISSN 0017-5064
GUATEMALA PEDIATRICA.* 1960. q. Q.2.($2.) (Asociacion Pediatrica de Guatemala) Imprenta Fray Payo, Ciudad 7, Guatemala. Ed. Dr. Victor A. Argueta von Kaenel. illus. circ. 600.

618.92 CC ISSN 1001-3512
GUOWAI YIXUE (ERKEXUE FENCE)/FOREIGN MEDICAL SCIENCES (PEDIATRICS). (Text in Chinese) 1979. bi-m. Zhongguo Yike Daxue - Chinese University of Medical Sciences, 6, Sanhao Jie 1 Duan, Heping-qu, Shenyang, Liaoning 393501, People's Republic of China. TEL 393501. Ed. Li Yongxu.

618.92 US
HEALTH IN DAY CARE: A MANUAL FOR HEALTH PROFESSIONALS. 1987. irreg. $40. American Academy of Pediatrics, 141 Northwest Point Blvd., Box 927, Elk Grove Village, IL 60009-0927. TEL 708-228-5005; 800-433-9016. FAX 708-228-1281. **Document type:** monographic series.

618.92 HO ISSN 0018-4535
HONDURAS PEDIATRICA. (Text in Spanish; summaries in English) 1963. q. free to qualified personnel. Asociacion Pediatrica Hondurena, P.O. Box 105-C, Tegucigalpa D.C., Honduras. Eds. Dr. Oscar Gonzalez Ardon, Dr. Argentina Alas de Chavez. adv.; abstr.; bibl.; charts; illus.; index. circ. 750.

618.92 AG ISSN 0521-517X
HOSPITAL DE NINOS. REVISTA. 1959. 5/yr. $40. Asociacion Medica del Hospital de Ninos, Gallo 1330, 1425 Buenos Aires, Argentina. Ed. Dr. Jose A. Bodino. adv.; bk.rev. circ. 2,000.

HOSPITAL FOR SICK CHILDREN, TORONTO. RESEARCH INSTITUTE. ANNUAL REPORT. see *MEDICAL SCIENCES*

HOSPITAL INFANTIL DE MEXICO. BOLETIN MEDICO. see *HOSPITALS*

HUMAN DEVELOPMENT. see *PSYCHOLOGY*

IMAGO; giornale italiano de psicopatologia e psichiatria dell'infanzia e dell'adolescenza. see *MEDICAL SCIENCES — Psychiatry And Neurology*

618.92 II ISSN 0019-5456
CODEN: IJPEA2
INDIAN JOURNAL OF PEDIATRICS. (Text in English) 1933. bi-m. Rs.500($60) to individuals; institutions Rs.900($130); students Rs.375($50). All India Institute of Medical Sciences, Department of Pediatrics, Old Operation Theatre Bldg., C1-18 Ansari Nagar, New Delhi 110 029, India. FAX 91-11-6854434. TELEX 31-730-42-AIMS-IN. Ed. Dr. I.C. Verma. adv. contact: G. Rajendran. bk.rev.; abstr.; charts; index. circ. 3,000. (also avail. in microfilm from UMI; reprint service avail. from UMI) **Indexed:** Biol.Abstr., Chem.Abstr., Child Devel.Abstr., Dairy Sci.Abstr., Dent.Ind., Diar.Dis.Res., DSH Abstr., Excerp.Med. (1993-), Ind.Med., Nutr.Abstr., Rural Ext.Educ.& Tr.Abstr. **Document type:** academic/scholarly publication.
—BLDSC (4418.000000); EMDOCS; Faxon; SWETS; UMI.
Description: Features discussions on pediatric emergencies, current issues, clinical and technological techniques, and neonatology. Includes pharmacology and nutrition.

618.92 II ISSN 0019-6061
RJ1 CODEN: INPDAR
INDIAN PEDIATRICS. (Text in English) 1964. m. Rs.250($100) Indian Academy of Pediatrics, PO Box 4509, New Delhi-110016, India. TEL 0291-22567. Ed. Dr. R.N. Srivastava. adv.; bk.rev.; charts; illus. circ. 4,800. (reprint service avail. from IRC) **Indexed:** Biol.Abstr., Chem.Abstr., Curr.Adv.Ecol.Sci., Dairy Sci.Abstr., Dent.Ind., Diar.Dis.Res., Excerp.Med., Helminthol.Abstr., Ind.Med., Indian Sci.Abstr., Maize Abstr., Nutr.Abstr., Triticale Abstr.
—BLDSC (4425.280000); CASDDS; EMDOCS; Faxon; SWETS; UMI; UnCover.
Formed by the merger of (1952-1963): Indian Journal of Child Health (ISSN 0445-7684); (1962-1963): Indian Pediatric Society. Journal (ISSN 0537-2380)

INFANT BEHAVIOR AND DEVELOPMENT; an international & interdisciplinary journal. see *PSYCHOLOGY*

618.92 US ISSN 0163-9641
RJ502.5 CODEN: IMHJDZ
INFANT MENTAL HEALTH JOURNAL. 1980. q. $57.75 to individuals; institutions $109. (Michigan Association for Infant Mental Health) Clinical Psychology Publishing Co., Inc., 4 Conant Sq., Brandon, VT 05733. TEL 802-247-6871. FAX 802-247-6853. Ed. Dr. Joy D. Osofsky. adv. circ. 1,050. (back issues avail.; reprint service avail. from ISI,UMI) **Indexed:** Child Devel.Abstr., Excerp.Med., IMFL, Lang.& Lang.Behav.Abstr., Psychol.Abstr. (1980-), Sociol.Abstr. **Document type:** academic/scholarly publication.
—BLDSC (4478.274000); Faxon; Genuine Article; UMI; UnCover.
Refereed Serial

618.92 613.2 UK ISSN 0965-2272
INFANT NUTRITION. 1991. q. Hayward Medical Communications Ltd., 44 Earlham St., Covent Garden, London WC2H 9LA, England. TEL 44-171-240-4493. FAX 44-171-240-4479. (Subscr. to: Essex House, Cromwell Park, Chipping Norton, Oxon. OX7 5SR, England. TEL 44-1608-645564. FAX 44-1608-645645) circ. controlled. **Document type:** academic/scholarly publication.

618.92 616.8 US ISSN 0886-1315
INFANT SCREENING. 1979. 4/yr. $15 (foreign $18). 3907 Galacia Dr., Austin, TX 78759. TEL 512-345-5685. Ed. Dr. Brad Therrell.

MEDICAL SCIENCES — PEDIATRICS

618.92　　　US　　ISSN 1053-5586
RG580.D76
INFANT - TODDLER INTERVENTION; the transdisciplinary journal. 1991. q. $36 to individuals; institutions $58. Singular Publishing Group, Inc., 4284 41st St., San Diego, CA 92105. TEL 800-521-8545. FAX 800-774-8398. E-mail: singpub@mail.cerfnet.com. Ed. Louis M. Rossetti; Pub. Angie Singh. adv. contact: Angie Singh. bk.rev.; circ. 1,500 (paid). **Document type:** academic/scholarly publication.
—BLDSC (4478.279500).
Description: Provides all members of the early intervention team with information that will enhance the clinical service they provide to infants and toddlers who are at risk or have disabilities.
Refereed Serial

618.92 649　　US　　ISSN 0896-3746
RJ102　　　　　　　　　CODEN: IYCHEL
INFANTS AND YOUNG CHILDREN; an interdisciplinary journal of special care practices. 1988. q. $66 (foreign $79). Aspen Publishers, Inc., 200 Orchard Ridge Dr., Gaithersburg, MD 20878. TEL 301-417-7500. FAX 301-417-7550. **Indexed:** CINAHL, IMFL, Nurs.Abstr.
—BLDSC (4478.283000); Faxon; UMI; UnCover. **CCC.**

618.92　　　US　　ISSN 1044-9779
INFECTIOUS DISEASES IN CHILDREN. 1988. m. $110 to individuals; institutions $120. Slack, Inc., 6900 Grove Rd., Thorofare, NJ 08086-9447. TEL 609-848-1000. FAX 609-853-5991. Ed. Philip A. Brunell. circ. 33,000. (tabloid format)

614.19　　　　US
INFORMATION EXCHANGE. 1983. irreg. National Sudden Infant Death Syndrome Resource Center, 8201 Greensboro Dr., Ste. 600, McLean, VA 22102. TEL 703-821-8955. FAX 703-821-2098. Ed.Bd. circ. 2,600. **Document type:** newsletter.
Description: National forum for exchange of information and resources on SIDS, death investigation, apnea, grief of parents and the role of professionals dealing with families suffering an SIDS loss.
Refereed Serial

618.92　　　　US
INJURY CONTROL FOR CHILDREN AND YOUTH. 1987. irreg. $41.95. American Academy of Pediatrics, 141 Northwest Point Blvd., Box 927, Elk Grove Village, IL 60009-0927. TEL 708-228-5005; 800-433-9016. FAX 708-228-1281. **Document type:** monographic series.

618.92　　　UK　　ISSN 1353-8047
▼**INJURY PREVENTION.** 1995 (Mar.). q. £60($90) to individuals; institutions £100 ($158) worldwide. (International Society for Child and Adolescent Injury Prevention) B M J Publishing Group, B.M.A. House, Tavistock Sq., London WC1H 9JR, England. TEL 0171-383-4499. FAX 0171-383-6661. (N. American subscr. to: Box 408, Franklin, MA 02038. TEL 800-2FON-BMJ. FAX 800-2FAX-BMJ) Ed. I.B. Pless. adv. contact: Sheila Rowe. bk.rev.; charts; illus.; index. (also avail. in microfilm from UMI; reprint service avail. from UMI) **Document type:** academic/scholarly publication.
●Also available online. Vendor(s): Ovid Technologies.
—BLDSC (4514.435000).
Description: Publishes papers that focus on the prevention of unintentional or intentional injury in the young.
Refereed Serial

618.92　　　US　　ISSN 1016-8699
INTERNATIONAL CHILD HEALTH: A DIGEST OF CURRENT INFORMATION. (Text in English) 1990. 4/yr. $48. International Pediatric Association, Univ. of Rochester, School of Medicine, 601 Elmwood Ave., Rm., 4-8104, Rochester, NY 14642-8777. TEL 716-275-0225. FAX 716-273-10387. (Co-sponsors: UNICEF; World Health Organization) Ed.Bd. circ. 6,500. **Indexed:** Diar.Dis.Res.
—BLDSC (4538.617000).

610　　　　US
INTERNATIONAL GUILD FOR INFANT SURVIVAL NEWSLETTER.* (Former name of organization: International Guild for Infant Survival) 1965. bi-m. $1. International Council for Infant Survival, c/o Council of Guilds, 9178 Nadne Wine Circle, Fountain Valley, CA 92708. TEL 319-322-4870. Ed. Mrs. William Reuling. stat. circ. 500.

618.92　　　UK　　ISSN 0334-0139
　　　　　　　　　　　　CODEN: IJAHE8
INTERNATIONAL JOURNAL OF ADOLESCENT MEDICINE AND HEALTH. 1985. q. $230 (effective 1996). Freund Publishing House, Ltd., Ste. 500, Chesham House, 150 Regent St., London W1R 5FA, England. (And: P.O. Box 35010, Tel Aviv, Israel. TEL 972-3-5628540. FAX 972-3-5628538) Ed. E. Chigier. adv.; bk.rev. circ. 1,000. (back issues avail.) **Indexed:** Curr.Adv.Ecol.Sci., Excerp.Med., Psychol.Abstr. (1985-). **Document type:** academic/scholarly publication.
—BLDSC (4541.565000).

INTERNATIONAL JOURNAL OF CHILDBIRTH EDUCATION. see *MEDICAL SCIENCES — Obstetrics And Gynecology*

INTERNATIONAL JOURNAL OF PEDIATRIC HEMATOLOGY - ONCOLOGY. see *MEDICAL SCIENCES — Oncology*

INTERNATIONAL JOURNAL OF PEDIATRIC OTORHINOLARYNGOLOGY. see *MEDICAL SCIENCES — Otorhinolaryngology*

618.92　　　US　　ISSN 0074-7300
INTERNATIONAL PEDIATRIC ASSOCIATION. PROCEEDINGS OF CONGRESS. triennial, 1989, 19th. International Pediatric Association - Association Internationale de Pediatrie, Univ. of Rochester, School of Medicine, 601 Elmwood Ave., Rm. 4-8104, Rochester, NY 14642-8777. TEL 716-275-0225. FAX 716-273-1038. **Document type:** proceedings.

INTERNATIONAL REVIEW OF CHILD NEUROLOGY SERIES. see *MEDICAL SCIENCES — Psychiatry And Neurology*

INTERNATIONAL SEMINARS IN PAEDIATRIC GASTROENTEROLOGY AND NUTRITION. see *MEDICAL SCIENCES — Gastroenterology*

ISSUES IN COMPREHENSIVE PEDIATRIC NURSING. see *MEDICAL SCIENCES — Nurses And Nursing*

618.92　　　　GW
▼**JAHRBUCH DER KINDERHEILKUNDE.** 1995. a. DM.126.40. Biermann Verlag GmbH, Nideggenerstr. 18, 53909 Zuelpich, Germany. TEL 02252-9410-0. FAX 02252-941015. **Document type:** academic/scholarly publication.

618.92　　　JA　　ISSN 0021-518X
JAPANESE JOURNAL OF PEDIATRICS/SHONIKA RINSHO. (Text in Japanese) 1948. m. newsstand price: 1900Yen. Nihon Shoni Iji Shuppansha, Wakodo, 24-18, Nishishinjuku 5-chome, Chiyoda-ku, Tokyo 100, Japan. **Indexed:** Chem.Abstr., INIS Atomind.
—BLDSC (4656.950000).

618.92　　　GW　　ISSN 0177-9095
JATROS PAEDIATRIE. 1985. 12/yr. DM.90. P M I Verlagsgruppe GmbH, August-Schanz-Str. 21, 60433 Frankfurt a.M., Germany. TEL 069-5480000. FAX 069-54800077. Ed. Peter Hoffmann. circ. 5,000. (back issues avail.) **Document type:** academic/scholarly publication.
Description: Seminar paper journal with summaries of pediatric articles, interviews and congress reports.

618.92　　　BL　　ISSN 0021-7557
JORNAL DE PEDIATRIA; orgao oficial. (Text in Portuguese; summaries in English and Portuguese) 1934. bi-m. Sociedade Brasileira de Pediatria, Rua Visconde de Silva 52, Salas 503-504, 2271-090 Rio de Janeiro RJ, Brazil. TEL 21-2862789. adv.; bk.rev.; abstr.; bibl.; charts; illus.; stat.; index. circ. 10,000. (also avail. in microform from UMI; reprint service avail. from UMI) **Indexed:** Biol.Abstr., Excerp.Med., Ind.Med. (until 19??), Nutr.Abstr.
—EMDOCS; UMI.

JOURNAL OF CHILD AND ADOLESCENT GROUP THERAPY. see *MEDICAL SCIENCES — Psychiatry And Neurology*

JOURNAL OF CHILD AND ADOLESCENT PSYCHOPHARMACOLOGY. see *MEDICAL SCIENCES — Psychiatry And Neurology*

JOURNAL OF CHILD NEUROLOGY. see *MEDICAL SCIENCES — Psychiatry And Neurology*

JOURNAL OF CLINICAL PEDIATRIC DENTISTRY. see *MEDICAL SCIENCES — Dentistry*

618.92　　　JA　　ISSN 0035-550X
　　　　　　　　　　　　CODEN: RSHIAY
JOURNAL OF CLINICAL PEDIATRICS/RINSHO SHONI IGAKU. (Text in Japanese) 1953. bi-m. 5000 Yen($6.60) Association for the Care of the Child - Shoni Aiiku Kyokai, c/o Dept. of Pediatrics, School of Medicine, Sapporo Medical University, Minami-1, Nishi-16-chome, Chuo-ku, Sapporo 060, Japan. Ed. Shunzo Chiba. adv.; bk.rev.; abstr.; bibl.; charts; illus.; stat.; index. circ. 575. **Indexed:** Chem.Abstr., Excerp.Med. **Document type:** trade publication.

JOURNAL OF DENTISTRY FOR CHILDREN. see *MEDICAL SCIENCES — Dentistry*

618.92 155.4　US　　ISSN 0196-206X
RJ1　　　　　　　　　　CODEN: JDBPD5
JOURNAL OF DEVELOPMENTAL AND BEHAVIORAL PEDIATRICS. Abbreviated title: J D B P. 1980. bi-m. $114 to individuals; institutions $698 (effective 1995). (Society for Behavioral Pediatrics) Williams & Wilkins, 428 E. Preston St., Baltimore, MD 21202. TEL 410-528-4000; 800-638-6423. FAX 410-528-4312. Ed. Dr. Stanford B. Friedman. adv.; bk.rev. circ. 1,507. (also avail. in microform from WWS) **Indexed:** ASSIA, Behav.Med.Abstr., Bibl.Dev.Med.& Child Neur., Curr.Cont., Excerp.Med., HRIS, IMFL, Ind.Med., Psychol.Abstr. (1980-), Psycscan D.P., SSCI, Viol.& Abuse Abstr., Yrbk.Assoc.Educ.& Rehab.Blind. **Document type:** academic/scholarly publication.
—BLDSC (4969.280000); Faxon; Genuine Article; SWETS; UnCover. **CCC.**
Description: Covers learning disabilities, behavioral reactions of children, and family dynamics. For pediatricians, child psychiatrists and special educators.
Refereed Serial

618.92　　　NE　　ISSN 0141-8955
　　　　　　　　　　　　CODEN: JIMDDP
JOURNAL OF INHERITED METABOLIC DISEASE. 1978. bi-m. fl.681 to institutions; $437 to institutions in U.S. (effective 1996). (Society for the Study of Inborn Errors of Metabolism) Kluwer Academic Publishers, Postbus 17, 3300 AA Dordrecht, Netherlands. TEL 31-78-392392. FAX 31-78-392254. TELEX 29245 KAPG NL. E-mail: SERVICES@WKAP.NL. (Dist. by: Kluwer Academic Publishers Group, P.O. Box 322, 3300 AH Dordrecht, Netherlands. TEL 31-78-392392. FAX 31-78-546474; N. America dist. addr.: Box 358, Accord Sta., Hingham, MA 02018-0358. TEL 617-871-6600. FAX 617-871-6528) Ed.Bd. adv.; bk.rev.; charts; illus.; index. circ. 850. (also avail. in microform from UMI; reprint service avail. from ISI,SWZ) **Indexed:** ASCA, Bibl.Dev.Med.& Child Neur., Biol.Abstr., Bull.Signal., Chem.Abstr., Curr.Adv.Ecol.Sci., Curr.Cont., Excerp.Med., Genet.Abstr., Ind.Med., Ind.Sci.Rev., Int.Abstr.Biol.Sci., Sci.Cit.Ind. **Document type:** academic/scholarly publication.
—BLDSC (5006.950000); CASDDS; Faxon; Genuine Article; SWETS; UMI; UnCover. **CCC.**
Incorporates: Society for the Study of Inborn Errors of Metabolism. Symposia.
Refereed Serial

618.92　　　AT　　ISSN 1034-4810
　　　　　　　　　　　　CODEN: JPCHE3
JOURNAL OF PAEDIATRICS AND CHILD HEALTH. 1965. bi-m. Aus.$246 (foreign Aus.$408) (effective 1996). (Australian College of Paediatrics) Blackwell Science Pty Ltd, P.O. Box 378, Carlton, Vic. 3053, Australia. TEL 61-3-93470300. FAX 61-3-93493016. Ed.Bd. adv.: page $720; trim 275 x 210. bk.rev.; charts; illus.; index. circ. 1,500. (also avail. in microfiche from UMI; back issues avail.; reprint service avail. from UMI) **Indexed:** Adol.Ment.Hlth.Abstr., Bibl.Dev.Med.& Child Neur., Biol.Abstr., Chem.Abstr., Curr.Adv.Ecol.Sci., Curr.Cont., Diar.Dis.Res., Excerp.Med., Helminthol.Abstr., Ind.Med., Ind.Sci.Rev., NRN, Nutr.Abstr., Rev.Med.& Vet.Mycol., Sci.Cit.Ind. **Document type:** academic/scholarly publication.
—BLDSC (5027.778000); ADONIS; CASDDS; Faxon; Genuine Article; SWETS; UMI; UnCover. **CCC.**
Formerly: Australian Paediatric Journal (ISSN 0004-993X)
Description: Covers original contributions concerned with both the formal aspects of paediatric medicine and the broader fields of child health.
Refereed Serial

MEDICAL SCIENCES — PEDIATRICS

618.92 US ISSN 8756-6206
JOURNAL OF PEDIATRIC & PERINATAL NUTRITION. 1987. s-a. $28 to individuals; institutions $36; libraries $45. Haworth Press, Inc., 10 Alice St., Binghamton, NY 13904. TEL 607-722-5857; 800-342-9678. FAX 607-722-1424. TELEX 4932599. Ed. Kathy Rutz. adv.; bk.rev. circ. 228. (also avail. in microfiche from UMI; reprint service avail. from HAW) **Indexed:** Excerp.Med., Human Resour.Abstr., Int.Nurs.Ind., Ref.Zh., Sage Fam.Stud.Abstr., Soc.Work Res.& Abstr.
—Faxon; Haworth.
  Description: Focuses on the nutrition needs of patients in pediatrics and perinatal care; deals with both normal and therapeutic needs, and will assist the practitioner in anticipating conditions that require nutritional management.
  Refereed Serial

JOURNAL OF PEDIATRIC ENDOCRINOLOGY & METABOLISM. see *MEDICAL SCIENCES — Endocrinology*

JOURNAL OF PEDIATRIC GASTROENTEROLOGY AND NUTRITION. see *MEDICAL SCIENCES — Gastroenterology*

618.92 US ISSN 0891-5245
CODEN: JPHCED
JOURNAL OF PEDIATRIC HEALTH CARE. 1987. bi-m. $49 to individuals (Canada $67.41; elsewhere $63); institutions $93 (Canada $114.49; elsewhere $107); students $25 (Canada $41.73; elsewhere $39) (effective 1996); newsstand price: $9.50. (National Association of Pediatric Nurse Associates and Practitioners) Mosby - Year Book, Inc. (Subsidiary of: Times Mirror Company), 11830 Westline Industrial Dr., St. Louis, MO 63146-3318. TEL 314-872-8370; 800-325-4177. FAX 314-432-1380. TELEX 44-2402. Ed. Bobbie Crew Nelms. adv.: B&W page $890, color page $1655; trim 8 1/4 x 11. abstr.; charts; illus.; index. circ. 6,707. (also avail. in microform from UMI; back issues avail.; reprint service avail. from UMI) **Indexed:** CINAHL, Nurs.Abstr.
—BLDSC (5030.180000); SWETS; UMI; UnCover. **CCC.**
  Description: Provides information on examination and developmental assessments, treatment, and coordination of care for various childhood illnesses.
  Refereed Serial

JOURNAL OF PEDIATRIC HEMATOLOGY - ONCOLOGY. see *MEDICAL SCIENCES — Oncology*

JOURNAL OF PEDIATRIC NURSING; nursing care of children and families. see *MEDICAL SCIENCES — Nurses And Nursing*

JOURNAL OF PEDIATRIC ORTHOPAEDICS. see *MEDICAL SCIENCES — Orthopedics And Traumatology*

JOURNAL OF PEDIATRIC ORTHOPAEDICS, PART B. see *MEDICAL SCIENCES — Orthopedics And Traumatology*

JOURNAL OF PEDIATRIC PSYCHOLOGY. see *PSYCHOLOGY*

JOURNAL OF PEDIATRIC SURGERY. see *MEDICAL SCIENCES — Surgery*

618.92 US ISSN 0022-3476
RJ1 CODEN: JOPDAB
JOURNAL OF PEDIATRICS; devoted to the problems and diseases of infancy and childhood. 1932. m. $113 to individuals (Canada $154.08; elsewhere $144); institutions $236 (Canada $285.69; elsewhere $267) (effective 1996); newsstand price: $11. Mosby - Year Book, Inc. (Subsidiary of: Times Mirror Company), 11830 Westline Industrial Dr., St. Louis, MO 63146-3318. TEL 314-872-8370; 800-325-4177. FAX 314-432-1380. TELEX 44-2402. Ed. Dr. Joseph M. Garfunkel. adv.: B&W page $1075, color page $1955; trim 8 1/8 x 10 7/8. bk.rev.; abstr.; bibl.; charts; illus.; s-a. index. circ. 18,348. (also avail. in microfilm from UMI,PMC; reprint service avail. from UMI) **Indexed:** Abstr.Hyg., AIM, ASCA, ASSIA, Behav.Med.Abstr., Bibl.Dev.Med.& Child Neur., Biol.Abstr., Biotech.Abstr., C.C.I.P., Chem.Abstr., Child Devel.Abstr., CINAHL, Curr.Adv.Cancer Res., Curr.Adv.Ecol.Sci., Curr.Cont., Dairy Sci.Abstr., Diab.Cont., Diar.Dis.Res., Dok.Arbeitsmed., Except.Child.Educ.Abstr., Excerp.Med., Food Sci.& Tech.Abstr., Helminthol.Abstr., Hosp.Lit.Ind., I.P.A., IMFL, Ind.Med., Ind.Sci.Rev., INIS Atomind., Kidney, Med.& Surg.Dermat., Nutr.Abstr., Potato Abstr., Protozool.Abstr., Rev.Med.& Vet.Mycol., Rev.Plant Path., Risk Abstr., Sci.Cit.Ind., Soyabean Abstr., Trop.Dis.Bull.
● Also available online. Vendor(s): Ovid Technologies.
—BLDSC (5030.300000); ADONIS; CASDDS; EMDOCS; Faxon; Genuine Article; SWETS; UMI; UnCover. **CCC.**
  Description: Offers practical guidance for physicians who diagnose and treat disorders in infants and children.
  Refereed Serial

JOURNAL OF PERINATOLOGY. see *MEDICAL SCIENCES — Obstetrics And Gynecology*

618.92 614 US
▼**JOURNAL OF SUDDEN INFANT DEATH SYNDROME AND INFANT MORTALITY.** Announced for publication in 1996. q. $150 (foreign $175) (effective 1996). Plenum Publishing Corp., 233 Spring St., New York, NY 10013-1578. TEL 212-620-8000. FAX 212-463-0742. TELEX 23-421139. Ed. Lois M. Roeder. adv. (also avail. in microfilm from JSC) **Document type:** academic/scholarly publication.
  Description: Provides an international forum for presentation and discussion of basic research and clinical studies regarding sudden infant death syndrome and other unexpected deaths in the postnatal period.
  Refereed Serial

618.92 UK ISSN 0142-6338
CODEN: JTRPAO
JOURNAL OF TROPICAL PEDIATRICS. (Supplement avail.) 1954. bi-m. £105($190) (effective 1996). Oxford University Press, Oxford Journals, Walton St., Oxford OX2 6DP, England. TEL 01865-267907. FAX 01865-267773. TELEX 837330-OXPRES-G. E-mail: jnlorders@oup.co.uk. (U.S. subscr. to: Oxford University Press Inc., 2001 Evans Rd., Cary, NC 27513. TEL 919-677-0977. FAX 919-677-1714) Eds. G.J. Ebrahim, E.F.P. Jelliffe. adv.; bk.rev.; charts; illus.; index. circ. 550. **Indexed:** Abstr.Hyg., Abstr.Rural Dev.Trop., Curr.Adv.Ecol.Sci., Curr.Cont., Dairy Sci.Abstr., Dent.Ind., Diar.Dis.Res., Documentatieblad, Excerp.Med., Helminthol.Abstr., Ind.Med., Ind.Sci.Rev., Nutr.Abstr., Protozool.Abstr., Rice Abstr., Rural Devel.Abstr., So.Pac.Per.Ind., Trop.Dis.Bull. **Document type:** academic/scholarly publication.
—BLDSC (5071.090000); Faxon; Genuine Article; SWETS; UMI; UnCover. **CCC.**
  Formerly: Journal of Tropical Pediatrics and Environmental Child Health (ISSN 0300-9920)
  Description: Covers all aspects of child health nutrition, including locality and quality of environment.

618.92 FR ISSN 0399-029X
CODEN: JPPEDO
JOURNEES PARISIENNES DE PEDIATRIE. 1966. a. price varies. (Hopital des Enfants Malades, Centre d'Etudes sur les Maladies du Metabolisme chez l'Enfant) Flammarion Medecine-Sciences, 4 rue Casimir Delavigne, 75006 Paris, France. (U.S. subscr. addr.: S.F.P.A., c/o M. Benech, 14 E. 60th St., New York, NY 10022) Ed. P. Royer.
—CASDDS.

618.92 688.72 GW ISSN 0179-3489
JUNGE FAMILIE. 1969. bi-m. DM.24. Junior-Verlag GmbH und Co. KG, Fehlandstr. 41, 20354 Hamburg, Germany. TEL 040-344434. FAX 040-352540. Ed. Dagmar von Schweinitz. adv. contact: Birgit Koenig. **Document type:** consumer publication.

618.92 CN ISSN 0828-2730
KALEIDOSCOPE (TORONTO). (Text in English) 1984. q. Hospital for Sick Children, 555 University Ave., Toronto, ON M5G 1X8, Canada. TEL 416-598-6377. Ed. Claudia Anderson. circ. 10,000.

618.92 NE ISSN 0169-7072
KIND EN ZIEKENHUIS. 1977. q. fl.50. (Vereniging Kind en Ziekenhuis) Landelijke Vereniging Kind en Ziekenhuis, Aardappelmarkt 3, 3311 BA Dordrecht, Netherlands. TEL 31-78-146363. Ed. B. van Rosendaal. adv.; bk.rev. circ. 2,000.
—SWETS.

618.92 GW ISSN 0943-7665
KIND ERNAEHRUNG UMWELT. 1993. 3/yr. DM.15($10) (effective 1996). Urban und Vogel, Lindwurmstr. 95, 80337 Munich, Germany. TEL 089-53292-0. FAX 089-53292100. (Subscr. in N. America to: Springer-Verlag New York, Inc., 44 Hartz Way, Secaucus, NJ 07096-2491. TEL 201-348-4033. FAX 201-348-4505)

KINDER; das Journal des Kindergartens. see *CHILDREN AND YOUTH — About*

KINDERKRANKENSCHWESTER. see *MEDICAL SCIENCES — Nurses And Nursing*

618.92 GW ISSN 0942-5403
KINDHEIT UND ENTWICKLUNG. 4/yr. DM.98 (foreign DM.108). M M V Medizin Verlag, Sektion Quintessenz, Schillerstr. 7, 80336 Munich, Germany. TEL 089-555808. FAX 089-5501772. **Document type:** academic/scholarly publication.

KITA NIHON SHONIKA GAKKAI SHOROKUSHU/PEDIATRICS SOCIETY OF NORTH JAPAN. ABSTRACTS. see *MEDICAL SCIENCES — Abstracting, Bibliographies, Statistics*

618.92 GW ISSN 0300-8630
CODEN: KLPDB2
KLINISCHE PAEDIATRIE; Zeitschrift fuer Klinik und Praxis. (Text in German; summaries in English and German) 1880. bi-m. DM.338. Ferdinand Enke Verlag, Postfach 300366, 70443 Stuttgart, Germany. TEL 0711-135798-0. FAX 0711-135798-30. TELEX 07252275-GTV-D. Ed.Bd. adv.; bk.rev.; abstr.; charts; illus. circ. 800. (also avail. in microfiche from BHP; reprint service avail. from IRC) **Indexed:** Bibl.Dev.Med.& Child Neur., Biol.Abstr., Biotech.Abstr., Chem.Abstr., Curr.Adv.Ecol.Sci., Curr.Cont., Dairy Sci.Abstr., Excerp.Med., Helminthol.Abstr., Ind.Med., Ind.Sci.Rev., INIS Atomind., Nutr.Abstr., Sci.Cit.Ind., Soyabean Abstr. **Document type:** academic/scholarly publication.
—BLDSC (5099.460000); ADONIS; CASDDS; Genuine Article; SWETS. **CCC.**
  Formerly: Archiv fuer Kinderheilkunde (ISSN 0003-9179)

LJOSMAEDRABLADID. see *MEDICAL SCIENCES — Obstetrics And Gynecology*

LYSOSOMES AND ENDOCYTOSIS. see *BIOLOGY — Biological Chemistry*

618.92 SP ISSN 0210-8135
M T A PEDIATRIA. (Metodos Terapeutico-diagnosticos de Actualidad) 1980. m. $75 (effective 1995). J.R. Prous, S.A. International Publishers, Apdo. Postal 540, 08080 Barcelona, Spain. TEL 343-458-2220. FAX 3-458-1535. Ed. Dr. F. Prandi. adv. contact: P. Blancafort. (back issues avail.)
  Description: Source of practical and current information for the pediatrician and family doctor.

MEDICAL SCIENCES — PEDIATRICS

618.92   UK   ISSN 0262-0200
MATERNAL & CHILD HEALTH; the journal of family medicine. 1976. m. £32 to individuals (rest of Europe £43; elsewhere £64); instititutions £48 (rest of Europe £58; elsewhere £80) (effective 1996). Barker Publications Ltd., Barker House, 539 London Rd., Isleworth, Mddx. TW7 4DA, England. TEL 44-181-847-1774. FAX 44-181-568-2766. TELEX 24667 IMPEMP G. Ed. Dr. David Harvey. adv.; bk.rev.; charts; illus.; circ. 25,000 (controlled). (back issues avail.) **Indexed:** Curr.Adv.Ecol.Sci. **Document type:** academic/scholarly publication.
—BLDSC (5399.272000); SWETS. **CCC.**
Formerly (until 1991): Journal of Maternal and Child Health (ISSN 0308-4426)

618.92   FR   ISSN 0291-0233
MEDECINE ET ENFANCE, ADOLESCENCE. 1981. 10/yr. 160 F. (foreign 250 F.). Edition et Communication Medicales, 23 rue Saint-Ferdinand, 75017 Paris, France. TEL 45-74-44-65. FAX 40-55-94-13. Ed. C. Geselson. adv.; bk.rev. circ. 20,000.
Description: A post-graduate medical journal directed at pediatricians, GP's and institutions.

618.92   FR   ISSN 0025-6773
                  CODEN: MINFAW
MEDECINE INFANTILE; revue de clinique, de therapeutique et d'hygiene sociale de l'enfance. 1894. 8/yr. 460 F. (Comite National de l'Enfance) Editions Maloine, 27 rue de l'Ecole-De-Medecine, 75006 Paris, France. TEL 1-43-25-60-45. TELEX 203 215 F. Ed. R. Perelman. adv.; bk.rev.; abstr.; bibl.; charts; illus. circ. 5,000. **Indexed:** Biol.Abstr., Chem.Abstr., Excerp.Med., Ind.Med., Nutr.Abstr.
—CASDDS; Faxon; UMI.

MEDICAL AND PEDIATRIC ONCOLOGY. see MEDICAL SCIENCES — Oncology

MEDICAL AND PEDIATRIC ONCOLOGY. SUPPLEMENT. see MEDICAL SCIENCES — Oncology

618.92   IT
MEDICO E BAMBINO. 10/yr. (Associazione Culturale Pediatri) Edifarm S.p.A., Viale Sabotino 19-2, 20135 Milan, Italy. TEL 58318401. FAX 28305328. adv.: B&W page L.5800000, color page L.9300000; trim 185 x 250. circ. 54,000.

MIDWIFERY. see MEDICAL SCIENCES — Obstetrics And Gynecology

618.92   IT   ISSN 0026-4946
                  CODEN: MIPEA5
MINERVA PEDIATRICA; rivista mensile di clinica pediatrica, puericultura, auxologia, neuropsichiatria infantile, endocrinologia, diabetologia e chirurgia pediatrica. (Text in Italian; summaries in English, Italian) 1949. m. $110 to individuals; institutions $150 (effective 1995). Edizioni Minerva Medica, Corso Bramante 83-85, 10126 Turin, Italy. TEL 39-11-678282. FAX 39-11-3121736. Eds. G. Bona, N. Nigro; Pub. Alberto Oliaro. adv.: B&W page $1100, color page $1900; trim 190 x 270; adv. contact: F. Filippo. bk.rev.; abstr.; bibl.; illus.; index; circ. 5,000 (paid). (also avail. in microform from UMI) **Indexed:** Biol.Abstr., Chem.Abstr., Curr.Adv.Ecol.Sci., Curr.Cont., Dent.Ind., Excerp.Med., Helminthol.Abstr., Ind.Med., Nutr.Abstr., Rev.Med.& Vet.Mycol. **Document type:** academic/scholarly publication.
—BLDSC (5794.400000); CASDDS; EMDOCS; SWETS; UMI.
Incorporates: Policlinico Infantile; Pediatria del Medico Pratico; Medicina Italiana; Lattante; Rivista di Clinica Pediatrica (ISSN 0035-6077)
Description: Covers pediatric clinical medicine, puericulture, auxology, child psychiatry, endocrinology, diabetology and pediatric surgery.
Refereed Serial

618.92   GW   ISSN 0026-9298
                  CODEN: MOKIAY
MONATSSCHRIFT KINDERHEILKUNDE. 1903. 12/yr. DM.428($311) (effective 1996). (Deutschen Gesellschaft fuer Kinderheilkunde) Springer-Verlag, Heidelberger Platz 3, 14197 Berlin, Germany. TEL 030-8207-0. FAX 030-8214091. E-mail: orders@springer.de. (Subscr. in N. America to: Springer-Verlag New York, Inc., 44 Hartz Way, Secaucus, NJ 07096-2491. TEL 201-348-4033. FAX 201-348-4505) Eds. F. Blaeker, W. Schroeter. adv.; bk.rev.; bibl.; charts. (also avail. in microform from UMI; back issues avail.; reprint service avail. from ISI) **Indexed:** Bibl.Dev.Med.& Child Neur., Biol.Abstr., Chem.Abstr., Curr.Adv.Ecol.Sci., Curr.Cont., Dairy Sci.Abstr., Excerp.Med., Helminthol.Abstr., Ind.Med., Ind.Sci.Rev., Nutr.Abstr., Rev.Med.& Vet.Mycol., Triticale Abstr. **Document type:** academic/scholarly publication.
—BLDSC (5906.400000); CASDDS; EMDOCS; Faxon; Genuine Article; SWETS; UMI. **CCC.**

618.92   SP   ISSN 0212-1603
MONOGRAFIAS DE PEDIATRIA. 1982. 6/yr. Grupo AUla Medica, S.A., C.I. Venecia 2, Alfa III, Oficina 93, Isabel Colbrana s-n, 28050 Madrid, Spain. TEL 34-1-3588657. FAX 34-1-3589067. Ed. Dr. A. Nogales Espert. **Document type:** academic/scholarly publication.

618.92   US   ISSN 1044-4882
MONOGRAPHS IN CLINICAL PEDIATRICS. 1990. irreg, vol.7, 1994. Harwood Academic Publishers, c/o International Publishers Distributor, 820 Town Center Dr., Langhorne, PA 19047. TEL 215-750-2642. FAX 215-750-6343. (Subscr. to: International Publishers Distributor, PO Box 90, Reading, Berkshire, RG1 8JL, England. TEL 44-173-456-8316) Ed. P. Lanzkowsky. **Document type:** monographic series.

618.92   US   ISSN 0886-0270
MONOGRAPHS ON INFANCY. 1981. irreg. price varies. Ablex Publishing Corporation, 355 Chestnut St., Norwood, NJ 07648. TEL 201-767-8450. FAX 201-767-6717. TELEX 135-393. Ed. Lewis P. Lipsitt. **Indexed:** Psychol.Abstr. **Document type:** academic/scholarly publication, monographic series.

618.92   JA   ISSN 0914-2533
N I C U: JAPANESE JOURNAL OF NEONATAL CARE. (Text in Japanese) 1987. m. 19200 Yen. Medika Shuppan - Medicus Publishing Inc., 18-24, Hiroshibacho, Suita-shi, Osaka 564, Japan. TEL 06-385-6911. FAX 06-385-6721.
—BLDSC (6110.130000).

618.92   US   ISSN 1070-3721
N O C I R C NEWSLETTER. 1986. s-a. $15. National Organization of Circumcision Information Resource Centers, Box 2512, San Anselmo, CA 94979-2512. TEL 415-488-9883. Ed. Marilyn Fayre Milos. circ. 20,000. **Document type:** newsletter.
Description: Provides parents, health-care professionals, and other concerned individuals with current medical and legal information on routine neonatal circumcision and female genital mutilation, and focuses on efforts to reduce the frequency of the practice, protecting the rights of infants and children.

NEONATAL INTENSIVE CARE; the journal of perinatalogy/neonatology. see MEDICAL SCIENCES — Obstetrics And Gynecology

NEONATAL NETWORK; the journal of neonatal nursing. see MEDICAL SCIENCES — Nurses And Nursing

616.8   GW   ISSN 0174-304X
                  CODEN: NRPDDB
NEUROPEDIATRICS; journal of pediatric neurobiology, neurology and neurosurgery. (Text in English) 1970. q. DM.348 per vol. Hippokrates Verlag GmbH, Postfach 300504, 70445 Stuttgart, Germany. TEL 0711-8931-0. FAX 0711-8931453. Ed.Bd. adv. circ. 1,200. **Indexed:** Bibl.Dev.Med.& Child Neur., Biol.Abstr, Chem.Abstr., Child Devel.Abstr., Curr.Adv.Ecol.Sci., Curr.Cont., Excerp.Med., Helminthol.Abstr., Ind.Med., Ind.Sci.Rev., Nutr.Abstr. **Document type:** academic/scholarly publication.
—BLDSC (6081.515500); CASDDS; Faxon; Genuine Article; SWETS; UMI; UnCover. **CCC.**
Formerly: Neuropaediatrie (ISSN 0028-3797)

616.8   FR   ISSN 0222-9617
NEUROPSYCHIATRIE DE L'ENFANCE ET DE L'ADOLESCENCE. 1953. 8/yr. 800 F. to individuals (foreign 1080 F.); students 400 F. (foreign 585 F.). (Societe Francaise de Psychiatrie de l'Enfant et de l'Adolescent) Expansion Scientifique, 31 bd. de la Tour Maubourg, 75007 Paris, France. TEL 40-62-64-00. FAX 45-55-69-20. Eds. D. J. Duche, N. Moor. adv.; bk.rev.; bibl.; charts; illus. circ. 5,000. (also avail. in microform) **Indexed:** Biol.Abstr., Curr.Cont., Excerp.Med., Ind.Med., Psychol.Abstr., SSCI.
—BLDSC (6081.536000); Faxon; SWETS. **CCC.**
Formerly: Revue de Neuropsychiatrie Infantile et d'Hygiene Mentale de l'Enfance (ISSN 0035-1628)

THE NEW ADDITION. see CHILDREN AND YOUTH — About

618.92   NE
NEW CLINICAL APPLICATIONS IN PAEDIATRICS. (Text in English) irreg. price varies. Kluwer Academic Publishers, Postbus 17, 3300 AA Dordrecht, Netherlands. TEL 31-78-392392. FAX 31-78-392254. TELEX 29245 KAPG NL. (Dist. by: Kluwer Academic Publishers Group, P.O. Box 322, 3300 AH Dordrecht, Netherlands. TEL 31-78-392392. FAX 31-78-546474; N. America dist. addr.: Box 358, Accord Sta., Hingham, MA 02018-0358. TEL 617-871-6600. FAX 617-871-6528) **Document type:** monographic series.
Refereed Serial

618.92   US   ISSN 0737-4216
NEW YORK PEDIATRICIAN; a forum on issues affecting pediatric practice in New York State. 1983. s-a. membership. American Academy of Pediatrics, District II, Queens Hospital Center, 82-68 164th St., Jamaica, NY 11432. Ed. Dr. Philip W.H. Eskes. adv.; bk.rev.; charts; illus. circ. 3,500. (also avail. in microform)
Formerly: Long Island Pediatrician.

618.92   US
NEWS BRIEF. 1982. q. $25. Parent Care, Inc., 9041 Colgate St., Indianapolis, IN 46268-1210. TEL 317-872-9913. Ed. Sarah Killion. adv.; bk.rev. circ. 1,000. (back issues avail.) **Document type:** newsletter.
Description: Publishes articles by parents and health care professionals relating to premature and critically ill newborns, high risk pregnancies, parent grief, special needs children, and other parenting topics of interest.

618.92   NR   ISSN 0302-4660
                  CODEN: NJPDAK
NIGERIAN JOURNAL OF PAEDIATRICS. 1974. q. £N16($6) (Paediatric Association of Nigeria) Ibadan University Press, University of Ibadan, Dept. of Pediatrics, Ibadan, Nigeria. (Orders to: University College Hospital, c/o Department of Paediatrics, Ibadan, Nigeria) Ed.Bd. adv.; charts; illus. circ. 500. (back issues avail.) **Indexed:** Abstr.Hyg., Biol.Abstr., Excerp.Med. (until 19??), ExtraMED, Trop.Dis.Bull. **Document type:** academic/scholarly publication.
●Also available on CD-ROM.

618.92 610   JA   ISSN 0029-0386
NIHON SHINSEIJI GAKKAI ZASSHI/ACTA NEONATOLOGICA JAPONICA. (Text in Japanese; summaries in English and Japanese) 1965. q. 1000 Yen($2.80) Nihon Shinseiji Gakkai - Japan Society of Neonatology, c/o Nihon University, School of Medicine, Department of Pediatrics, 30-1 Oyaguchi-Kami-machi, Itabashi-ku, Tokyo 173, Japan. Ed. Dr. Kazuo Baba. adv.; bk.rev.; bibl.; cum.index; circ. 4,000 (controlled). **Indexed:** Excerp.Med.
—BLDSC (0639.757000); EMDOCS.

618.92   JA   ISSN 0288-609X
NIHON SHONI GEKA GAKKAI ZASSHI/JAPANESE SOCIETY OF PEDIATRIC SURGEONS. JOURNAL. (Text in Japanese; summaries in English) 1965. 7/yr. 2000 Yen per no. Nihon Shoni Geka Gakkai, Nihon Gakkai Jimu Senta, 16-9, Honkagome 5-chome, Bunkyo-ku, Tokyo 113, Japan.
—BLDSC (4809.476000).

MEDICAL SCIENCES — PEDIATRICS 4525

618.92 616.4 JA
NIHON SHONI NAIBUNPI GAKKAI PUROGURAMU SHOROKUSHU/JAPANESE SOCIETY FOR PEDIATRIC ENDOCRINOLOGY. ANNUAL MEETING. (Text in English, Japanese) 1989. a. Nihon Shoni Naibunpi Gakkai, Asahikawa Ika Daigaku Shonika, 5-3-11, Nishikagura 4-chome, Asahikawa-shi, Hokkaido 078, Japan.

618.92 617.3 JA ISSN 0917-6950
NIHON SHONI SEIKEI GEKA GAKKAI ZASSHI/JAPANESE PAEDIATRIC ORTHOPAEDIC ASSOCIATION. JOURNAL. (Text in English, Japanese) 1991. s-a. 4500 Yen per no. Nihon Shoni Seikei Geka Gakkai, c/o Kokuritsu Shoni Byoin Seikei Geka, 35-31, Taishido 3-chome, Setagaya-ku, Tokyo 154, Japan.

618.92 FR ISSN 0765-5010
NOTES PEDIATRIQUES. 10/yr. Publications R C G, 23 rue Saint-Ferdinand, 75017 Paris, France. TEL 45-72-51-91. Ed. Dr. G. Dutau. circ. 5,000.

618.92 US ISSN 0000-1627
RJ29
OFFICIAL AMERICAN BOARD OF MEDICAL SPECIALTIES (A B M S) DIRECTORY OF BOARD CERTIFIED PEDIATRICIANS. 1984. biennial. $99.95. Marquis Who's Who, A Reed Reference Publishing company, 121 Chanlon Rd., New Providence, NJ 07974. TEL 908-464-6800. FAX 908-665-2898. (Subscr. to: Order Dept., Box 31, New Providence, NJ 07974-9903. TEL 800-521-8110) Ed. Roy Crego. **Document type:** directory.
 Formerly: A B M S Directory of Certified Pediatricians (ISSN 0884-1497)
 Description: Biographical sketches of U.S. certified medical specialists sorted geographically with alpha index.

OPHTHALMIC GENETICS. see *MEDICAL SCIENCES — Ophthalmology And Optometry*

618.92 IT ISSN 0030-6274
OSPEDALI ITALIANI - PEDIATRIA; e specialita chirurgiche. (Text in Italian; abstracts in English, French, German, Italian, Spanish) 1966. bi-m. plus supplements. L.50000($40) (L.40000 without supplements). Giuseppe Caracciolo, Ed. & Pub., Via Cimarosa 180-A, 80127 Naples, Italy. TEL 5569280. bk.rev.; bibl.; charts; illus.; stat.; index, cum.index. circ. 1,000. **Indexed:** Biol.Abstr., Excerp.Med. (until 1993).
 —BLDSC (6301.770000).
 Description: Features research papers on the science of pediatrics and specialized surgery.

OTORINOLARINGOLOGIA PEDIATRICA. see *MEDICAL SCIENCES — Otorhinolaryngology*

618.92 US
P H - O FORUM; news - updates in Pediatric Hematology - Oncology. 1982. bi-m. P H - O Forum, c/o King - Drew Medical Center, Rm. 5101, 12021 S. Wilmington Ave., Los Angeles, CA 90059. TEL 310-668-3850. FAX 310-668-3108. Ed. Carl Pochedly. adv.: page $1000; adv. contact: Carl Pochedly. bk.rev.; circ. 2,200 (controlled). (back issues avail.)

618.92 CI ISSN 1330-1403
CODEN: PCROE
PAEDIATRIA CROATICA. (Text in Croatian) 1957. q. Institut za Zastitu Majki i Djece - Institute for Mother and Child Health, Klaiceva 16, HR-41000 Zagreb, Croatia. TEL 41-440455. FAX 41-451308. Ed. Vladimir Kolbas. adv.; bk.rev. circ. 850. **Indexed:** Excerp.Med.
 Formerly: Arhiv za Zastitu Majke i Djeteta - Archive for Mother and Child Health (ISSN 0004-1289)

PAEDIATRIC ANAESTHESIA. see *MEDICAL SCIENCES — Anaesthesiology*

618.92 UK ISSN 0269-5022
PAEDIATRIC & PERINATAL EPIDEMIOLOGY. 1988. q. £154 (outside Europe £169.50($273)) (effective 1996). (Society for Paediatric Epidemiological Research) Blackwell Science Ltd., Osney Mead, Oxford OX2 0EL, England. TEL 01865-206206. FAX 01865-206219. TELEX 83355 MEDBOK G. Ed.Bd. adv.; bk.rev.; illus.; index, circ. 500. (also avail. in microform from UMI; back issues avail.) **Indexed:** Diar.Dis.Res., Excerp.Med. (1988-), Ind.Med., Med.& Surg.Dermat. **Document type:** academic/scholarly publication.
 —BLDSC (6333.399710); Genuine Article; SWETS; UMI. **CCC.**
 Refereed Serial

618.92 IO ISSN 0030-9311
CODEN: PIDOA8
PAEDIATRICA INDONESIANA; journal of the Indonesian Society of Pediatrician. (Text and summaries in English) 1961. bi-m. $60. Indonesian Society of Pediatrician, c/o Dept. of Child Health, Medical School, University of Indonesia, Jalan Salemba 6, Jakarta 10430, Indonesia. TEL 62-21-314-8610. FAX 61-21-390-7743. Ed. Sudigdo Sastroasmoro. adv.; bk.rev.; abstr.; bibl.; charts; illus.; stat. circ. 2,000. (also avail. in microform from UMI; microfiche; reprint service avail. from UMI) **Indexed:** Abstr.Hyg., Biol.Abstr., Excerp.Med., Ind.Med., Nutr.Abstr., Trop.Dis.Bull. **Document type:** academic/scholarly publication.
 ●Also available on CD-ROM.
 —UMI.

618.92 GW ISSN 0934-1188
PAEDIATRICS IN EUROPE. q. DM.34. Schmidt-Roemhild Verlag, Mengstr. 16, 23552 Luebeck, Germany. TEL 0451-1605-0. FAX 0451-1605253. **Document type:** academic/scholarly publication.

618.92 GW
PAEDIATRIE AKTUELL. 1990. irreg., vol.4, 1993. W. Zuckschwerdt Verlag GmbH, Industriestr. 17, 82110 Germering, Germany. TEL 089-894349-0. FAX 089-89434950. Ed.Bd. **Document type:** academic/scholarly publication.

618.92 US ISSN 0030-932X
CODEN: PRTPE
PAEDIATRIE UND GRENZGEBIETE/PEDIATRICS AND RELATED TOPICS. (Text and summaries in English, German) 1962. bi-m. 116 ECU (effective 1996). Harwood Academic Publishers, c/o International Publishers Distributor, 820 Town Center Dr., Langhorne, PA 19047. TEL 215-750-2642. FAX 215-750-6343. (Subscr. to: International Publishers Distributor, PO Box 90, Reading, Berkshire, RG1 8JL, England. TEL 44-173-456-8316) Eds. B. Schneeweiss, H.W. Ocklitz. bk.rev.; charts; illus.; stat.; index. **Indexed:** Curr.Adv.Ecol.Sci., Excerp.Med., Ind.Med., Nutr.Abstr.
 —BLDSC (6333.200000); EMDOCS; Faxon. **CCC.**

618.92 AU ISSN 0030-9338
CODEN: PAPAB5
PAEDIATRIE UND PAEDOLOGIE. (Text in English, French and German) 1965. 6/yr. DM.358($260) (effective 1996). (Oesterreichischen Gesellschaft fuer Kinder- und Jugendheilkunde) Springer-Verlag, Sachsenplatz 4-6, Postfach 89, A-1201 Vienna, Austria. TEL 0222-330-2415. FAX 0222-330-2426. (N. American subscr. to: Journals Fulfillment Services, Box 2485, Secaucus, NJ 07096-2491. TEL 800-777-4643. FAX 201-348-4505; Elsewhere: Heidelberger Platz 3, 1000 Berlin 33, Germany. TEL 030-8207-1. FAX 030-821-4091) Ed. G. Weippl. bk.rev.; charts; illus.; index. (also avail. in microform from UMI; reprint service avail. from ISI) **Indexed:** Bibl.Dev.Med.& Child Neur., Biol.Abstr., Chem.Abstr., Curr.Adv.Cancer Res., Curr.Cont., Excerp.Med., Ind.Med., Nutr.Abstr. **Document type:** academic/scholarly publication.
 —BLDSC (6333.230000); CASDDS; EMDOCS; Faxon; SWETS; UMI. **CCC.**
 Description: Covers research in children's health and development.

618.92 US ISSN 0300-9556
PAEDIATRIE UND PAEDOLOGIE. SUPPLEMENT. 1972. irreg. price varies. Springer-Verlag, 175 Fifth Ave., New York, NY 10010. TEL 212-460-1500. FAX 212-473-6272. (Also: Berlin, Heidelberg, Tokyo and Vienna) (reprint service avail. from ISI) **Indexed:** Ind.Med. **Document type:** academic/scholarly publication.
 —UMI.

618.92 US
PAEDIATRIE: WEITER- UND FORTBILDUNG. (Text in German) 1980. irreg. price varies. Springer-Verlag, 175 Fifth Ave., New York, NY 10010. TEL 212-460-1500. FAX 212-473-6272. (Also: Berlin, Heidelberg, Tokyo and Vienna) Ed. H. Ewerbeck. (reprint service avail. from ISI) **Document type:** academic/scholarly publication.

618.92 GW ISSN 0030-9346
PAEDIATRISCHE PRAXIS; Zeitschrift fuer Kinder- und Jugendmedizin. 1962. bi-m. DM.280. Hans Marseille Verlag GmbH, Buerkleinstr. 12, 80538 Munich, Germany. TEL 089-227988. FAX 089-2904643. Eds. W. Stoegmann, G.F. Wuendisch. bk.rev.; abstr.; bibl.; charts; illus.; index, cum.index every 5 yrs. circ. 4,500. (also avail. in microfilm from UMI; reprint service avail. from UMI) **Indexed:** Excerp.Med. **Document type:** academic/scholarly publication.
 —BLDSC (6333.300000); SWETS; UMI. **CCC.**
 Description: Practical information of interest to specialists in pediatrics. Features current research, questions and answers, and photographs.

618.92 PK ISSN 0048-2722
PAKISTAN PEDIATRIC JOURNAL.* (Text in English) 1971. q. Rs.10. Association of Pediatricians of Pakistan, 111-D 27-7 Nazimabad, Karachi 18, Pakistan. Dr. Abdul Jamil Khan. adv.; bk.rev.; bibl.; charts; illus.

618.92 GR
PEDI KAI NEI GONIS. 1984. m. Dr.4500($29) International Publications S.A., 14th km. Marathon Ave., Pallini 15344, Greece. TEL 30-1-6667-312. adv. circ. 30,000. (back issues avail.)

618.92 HU ISSN 1216-3821
PEDIATER; az apathy alapitvany gyermekorvosi folyoirata. 1967. q. 280 Ft. Apathy Alapitvany a Gyermekek Gyogyitasaert, Ilka u. 57, 1143 Budapest XIV, Hungary. TEL 122-1626-107. Ed. Peter Kiss. adv.; bk.rev. circ. 1,000. **Document type:** academic/scholarly publication.
 Formerly (until 1992): Magyar Pediater (ISSN 0303-5042)

618.92 FR ISSN 0397-9180
PEDIATRE (PARIS). 1963. bi-m. 550 F. Pediatre Parisien, s.a.r.l., B.P. 132, 75821 Paris Cedex 17, France. TEL 42-67-27-13. FAX 47-54-00-08. (Co-sponsors: SNPF, Groupement des Pediatres; Cercle d'Etudes Pediatriques, Association Francaise Pediatre Ambulatoire) Ed. Dr. Feigelson. adv.; bk.rev. circ. 3,000. (reprint service avail. from ISI) **Indexed:** Excerp.Med. **Document type:** bulletin, abstracting/indexing, proceedings.
 —BLDSC (6417.447000).

618.92 CL ISSN 0375-9563
CODEN: PEDSAQ
PEDIATRIA. (Text in Spanish; summaries in English) 1958. q. Esc.20000($20) Universidad de Chile, Departamento de Pediatria, Zanartu 1085, Santiago, Chile. Ed. Julio Meneghello Rivera. adv.; bk.rev.; abstr.; bibl.; illus.; stat.; index. circ. 1,000. (microform; also avail. in microfilm from UMI; reprint service avail. from UMI) **Indexed:** Dent.Ind., Excerp.Med. (until 1983), Ind.Med., Nutr.Abstr.

618.92 IT ISSN 0031-3890
PEDIATRIA; rivista d'igiene, medicina e chirurgia dell'infanzia. (Text in Italian; summaries in English, French, German, Italian and Spanish) 1893. q. L.6000($14) Universita degli Studi di Napoli, Clinica Pediatrica, S. Andrea delle Dame 4, Naples, Italy. Ed. Prof. Giulio Murano. adv.; bk.rev.; abstr.; illus.; index. **Indexed:** Chem.Abstr., Dent.Ind., Ind.Med., Nutr.Abstr.

618.92 BU ISSN 0479-7876
CODEN: PDTAAB
PEDIATRIA. (Text in Bulgarian; summaries in English and Russian) 1962. bi-m. 24 lv.($7) (Ministerstvo na Narodnoto Zdrave) Izdatelstvo Meditsina i Fizkultura, 11, Pl. Slaveikov, Sofia, Bulgaria. (Dist. by: Hemus, 6, Rouski Blvd., 1000 Sofia, Bulgaria) (Co-sponsor: Nauchno Druzhestvo po Pediatria) Ed. Sh. Ninjo. circ. 1,950. **Indexed:** Abstr.Bulg.Sci.Med.Lit., Dent.Ind., Excerp.Med. (until 1993), Ind.Med.
 —CASDDS.

M

MEDICAL SCIENCES — PEDIATRICS

618.92 CK ISSN 0031-3882
CODEN: PEDSA
PEDIATRIA. 1958. q. Sociedad Colombiana de Pediatria, Hospital Militar Central, Entrepiso 1, Bogota, Colombia. TEL 2883985.
Formerly (until 1965): Sociedad Colombiana de Pediatria y Puericultura. Revista (ISSN 0120-8756)

618.92 BL ISSN 0031-3912
PEDIATRIA E PUERICULTURA.* (Text in Portuguese; summaries in English and French) 1930. 4/yr. Liga Alvaro Bahia contra a Mortalidade Infantil, Avenida Joana Angelica 75, Salvador, Bahia, Brazil. bibl.; charts; illus.; stat. circ. 600.

618.92 BL ISSN 0031-3920
PEDIATRIA MODERNA. (Text in Portuguese; summaries in English, Portuguese, and Spanish) 1966. m. Cr.$160000($250) (free to qualified personnel). Grupo Editorial Moreira Jr., Rua Henrique Martins 493, 04504 Sao Paulo SP, Brazil. TEL 884-9911. FAX 884-9993. Ed. Friederich T. Simon. adv.; bk.rev.; abstr.; bibl.; charts; illus.; stat.; cum.index; circ. 12,000 (controlled). **Indexed:** Biol.Abstr.

618.92 617.3 IT ISSN 0391-898X
PEDIATRIA OGGI MEDICA E CHIRURGICA. (Text in Italian; summaries in English) 10/yr. L.70000($70) (Societa Italiana de Pediatria, Gruppo di Lavoro di Pediatria Ospedaliera) C I C Edizioni Internazionali s.r.l., Via L. Spallanzani 11, 00161 Rome, Italy. TEL 06-8412673. FAX 06-44242033. TELEX 622099 CIC. Dirs. M. Calvani, R. DiToro. **Indexed:** Excerp.Med.
—BLDSC (6417.488000). **CCC.**

618.92 PL ISSN 0031-3939
CODEN: PEPOA6
PEDIATRIA POLSKA. (Text in Polish; summaries in English) 1921. m. $50 for 6 mos. (Polskie Towarzystwo Pediatryczne) Wydawnictwo Medyczne Urban i Partner, Ul. Marii Sklodowskiej-Curie 55-61, 50-950 Wroclaw, Poland. TEL 48-71-225497. FAX 48-71-224391. (Co-sponsor: Instytut Matki i Dziecka) Ed. Teresa Wyszynska. bk.rev.; index. circ. 1,500. **Indexed:** Biol.Abstr., Chem.Abstr., Dent.Ind., Excerp.Med., Ind.Med., Nutr.Abstr.
—BLDSC (6417.500000); CASDDS; EMDOCS.
Description: Publishes original papers on advances in pediatrics as well as clinical reports.
Refereed Serial

618.92 BL ISSN 0031-3947
CODEN: PEPAAW
PEDIATRIA PRATICA; revista de puericultura e clinica infantil. (Text in Portuguese; summaries in English and Spanish) 1930. fortn. Cr.$200($20) (Sociedade de Pediatria de Sao Paulo) Centro de Estudos da Clinica Infantil do Ipiranga, Avda Nazare 1361, Sao Paulo, Brazil. Ed. A.G. de Mattos. adv.; bk.rev.; abstr.; charts; index, cum.index. circ. 3,000. **Indexed:** Biol.Abstr., Chem.Abstr., Excerp.Med., Ind.Med., Nutr.Abstr.

PEDIATRIC AIDS AND HIV INFECTION: FETUS TO ADOLESCENT. see *MEDICAL SCIENCES — Communicable Diseases*

618.92 US ISSN 0160-0184
PEDIATRIC ALERT. 1976. bi-w. $65 to individuals; institutions $85; students $43. Medical Alert, Inc., Box 338, Newton Highlands, MA 02161. Ed. Dr. Allen A. Mitchell. **Document type:** newsletter.

618.92 616.97 DK ISSN 0905-6157
CODEN: PALUEE
PEDIATRIC ALLERGY AND IMMUNOLOGY. (Supplement avail. (ISSN 0906-5784)) (Text in English) 1990. q. DKK 425 to individuals; institutions DKK 1000 (incl. supplements) (effective 1996). (European Society of Pediatric Allergy and Clinical Immunology) Munksgaard International Publishers Ltd., 35 Noerre Soegade, P.O. Box 2148, DK-1016 Copenhagen K, Denmark. TEL 45-33-12-70-30.
FAX 45-33-12-93-87. Ed. Bengt Bjoerksten. adv.; charts; illus. circ. 600. (reprint service avail.) **Indexed:** Excerp.Med., Ind.Med. **Document type:** academic/scholarly publication.
—BLDSC (6417.527000); Faxon; SWETS. **CCC.**
Refereed Serial

618.92 616.97 DK ISSN 0906-5784
CODEN: PAIUE
PEDIATRIC ALLERGY AND IMMUNOLOGY. SUPPLEMENTUM. (Text in English) 1991. irreg. (European Society of Pediatric Allergy and Clinical Immunology) Munksgaard International Publishers Ltd., 35 Norre Soegade, P.O. Box 2148, DK-1016 Copenhagen, Denmark. TEL 45-33-12-70-30.
FAX 45-33-12-93-87. **Indexed:** Excerp.Med. (1994-). **Document type:** academic/scholarly publication.
Refereed Serial

618.92 SZ ISSN 1017-5989
CODEN: PEAMEV
PEDIATRIC AND ADOLESCENT MEDICINE. (Text in English) 1954. irreg. price varies. S. Karger AG, Allschwilerstr. 10, P.O. Box, CH-4009 Basel, Switzerland. TEL 061-3061111.
FAX 061-3061234. E-mail: Karger@Karger.ch. Ed. D. Branski. (reprint service avail. from ISI) **Indexed:** Biol.Abstr., Chem.Abstr., Curr.Cont., Ind.Med.
—BLDSC (6417.528400); CASDDS. **CCC.**
Incorporates (1954-1989): Modern Problems in Paediatrics (ISSN 0077-0086); (1971-1989): Monographs in Paediatrics (ISSN 0077-0914); Which was formerly (1924-1971): Bibliotheca Paediatrica.
Description: A problem-oriented series which seeks to clarify and evaluate difficult and evolving issues in pediatric and adolescent medicine.
Refereed Serial

618.92 US ISSN 0090-4481
RJ1
PEDIATRIC ANNALS; a journal of continuing pediatric education. 1972. m. $85 to individuals; institutions $95. Slack, Inc., 6900 Grove Rd., Thorofare, NJ 08086. TEL 609-848-1000. FAX 609-853-5991. Ed. Dr. Robert A. Hoekelman. adv.; bk.rev.; bibl.; illus.; stat.; index. circ. 33,140. (also avail. in microfilm from UMI; reprint service avail. from UMI;ISI) **Indexed:** Bibl.Dev.Med.& Child Neur., Biol.Abstr., C.C.I.P., CINAHL, Curr.Cont., Excerp.Med., Helminthol.Abstr., Ind.Med.
—BLDSC (6417.530000); Genuine Article; SWETS; UMI; UnCover. **CCC.**

618.92 US ISSN 0883-1874
CODEN: PAAIEP
PEDIATRIC ASTHMA, ALLERGY & IMMUNOLOGY. 1987. bi-m. $143 (foreign $183). Mary Ann Liebert, Inc. Publishers, 2 Madison Ave., Larchmont, NY 10538. TEL 914-834-3100. FAX 914-834-3688. E-mail: Liebert@pipeline.com. Ed. Dr. Jerome M. Hersman. adv. **Indexed:** Excerp.Med. (1993-). **Document type:** academic/scholarly publication.
—BLDSC (6417.532000); Genuine Article; SWETS.
Description: Emphasizes the developmental implications of the morphologic, physiologic, and sociologic components of these problems in infants, children, and adolescents, as well as the impact of the disease processes on their families.

PEDIATRIC CARDIOLOGY. see *MEDICAL SCIENCES — Cardiovascular Diseases*

618.92 II ISSN 0048-3133
PEDIATRIC CLINICS OF INDIA. (Text in English) vol.12, 1977. q. Rs.100. LTMG Hospital, Sion, Bombay 400022, India. Ed. V.B. Athavale. adv.; charts; illus. circ. 500. (also avail. in microfilm from UMI; reprint service avail. from UMI) **Indexed:** Nutr.Abstr.

618.92 US ISSN 0031-3955
RJ23 CODEN: PCNAA8
PEDIATRIC CLINICS OF NORTH AMERICA. Spanish translation: Clinicas Pediatricas de Norteamerica. 1954. bi-m. $110 (foreign $132) (effective 1996). W.B. Saunders Co. (Subsidiary of: Harcourt Brace & Company), Curtis Center, 3rd Fl., Independence Sq. W., Philadelphia, PA 19106-3399.
TEL 215-238-7800. FAX 215-238-6445. (Subscr. to: Periodicals Fulfillment, W.B. Saunders Co., 6277 Sea Harbor Dr., 4th Fl., Orlando, FL 32891-4800. TEL 800-654-2452. FAX 800-874-6418) Ed. Sandra Masse. (also avail. in microform from UMI; reprint service avail. from UMI,ISI) **Indexed:** Adol.Ment.Hlth.Abstr., AIM, Bibl.Dev.Med.& Child Neur., Biol.Abstr., C.C.I.P., Chem.Abstr., CINAHL, Curr.Adv.Cancer Res., Curr.Adv.Ecol.Sci., Curr.Cont., Dairy Sci.Abstr., Diar.Dis.Res., Except.Child.Educ.Abstr., Excerp.Med., Helminthol.Abstr., I.P.A., Ind.Med., Int.Nurs.Ind., Nutr.Abstr. **Document type:** academic/scholarly publication.
—BLDSC (6417.550000); EMDOCS; Faxon; Genuine Article; SWETS; UMI; UnCover. **CCC.**

PEDIATRIC DENTAL JOURNAL. see *MEDICAL SCIENCES — Dentistry*

PEDIATRIC DENTISTRY TODAY. see *MEDICAL SCIENCES — Dentistry*

PEDIATRIC DERMATOLOGY. see *MEDICAL SCIENCES — Dermatology And Venereology*

PEDIATRIC EMERGENCY & CRITICAL CARE; a clinical update for those who care for infants and children. see *MEDICAL SCIENCES — Abstracting, Bibliographies, Statistics*

618.92 616.02 US ISSN 0749-5161
CODEN: PECAE5
PEDIATRIC EMERGENCY CARE. 1985. q. $84 to individuals; institutions $134 (effective 1995). Williams & Wilkins, 428 E. Preston St., Baltimore, MD 21202. TEL 410-528-4000; 800-638-6423. FAX 410-528-4312. TELEX 87669. Eds. Drs. Stephen Ludwig, Gary Fleisher. adv. circ. 2,900. (also avail. in microfilm from WWS; back issues avail.) **Indexed:** CINAHL. **Document type:** academic/scholarly publication.
—BLDSC (6417.586000); Genuine Article; SWETS; UnCover. **CCC.**
Description: Contains clinical information for emergency physicians and pediatricians who care for acutely ill or injured children and adolescents.
Refereed Serial

618.92 US ISSN 0899-8493
PEDIATRIC EXERCISE SCIENCE. Short title: P E S. 1989. q. $40 to individuals (foreign $44); institutions $90 (foreign $94); students $24 (foreign $28). (North American Society of Pediatric Exercise Medicine) Human Kinetics Publishers, Inc., Box 5076, Champaign, IL 61825-5076. TEL 217-351-5076. FAX 217-351-2674. Ed. Dr. Thomas Rowland. adv. contact: Pamela Anderson. bk.rev.; charts. circ. 485. **Indexed:** Child Devel.Abstr., Phys.Ed.Ind., Sportsearch (1990-). **Document type:** academic/scholarly publication.
—BLDSC (6417.590000); Genuine Article; UnCover. **CCC.**
Description: Addresses the importance of exercise during childhood and adolescence to scientists, health-care providers, and physical educators.
Refereed Serial

618.92 US ISSN 0731-5902
CODEN: PEHAEU
PEDIATRIC HABILITATION SERIES. 1980. irreg., vol.8, 1992. price varies. Marcel Dekker, Inc., 270 Madison Ave., New York, NY 10016.
TEL 212-696-9000. FAX 212-685-4540. TELEX 421419.
—BLDSC (6417.598000).
Refereed Serial

618.92 US ISSN 0888-0018
CODEN: PHONEN
PEDIATRIC HEMATOLOGY & ONCOLOGY. 1984. q. £191($315) (effective 1996). Taylor & Francis Inc., 1900 Frost Rd., Ste. 101, Bristol, PA 19007-1598. TEL 215-785-5800; 800-821-8312.
FAX 215-785-5515. (Subscr. in Europe to: Taylor & Francis Ltd., Rankine Rd., Basingstoke, Hants.RG24 8PR, England. TEL 44-1256-840366. FAX 44-1256-479438) Ed. Jorgen Cohn. adv.; bk.rev. circ. 600. (also avail. in microform from UMI; back issues avail.; reprint service avail. from UMI) **Indexed:** Curr.Cont., Excerp.Med., Med.& Surg.Dermat. **Document type:** academic/scholarly publication.
—BLDSC (6417.599500); CASDDS; Faxon; Genuine Article; SWETS; UnCover. **CCC.**
Formerly (until 1986): European Paediatric Haematology and Oncology (ISSN 0800-2789)
Description: Publishes experimental, biochemical and clinical articles covering immunology, pathology and pharmacology.
Refereed Serial

PEDIATRIC HEMATOLOGY - ONCOLOGY SERIES. see *MEDICAL SCIENCES — Oncology*

MEDICAL SCIENCES — PEDIATRICS

618.92 616.9   US   ISSN 0891-3668
CODEN: PIDJEV
THE PEDIATRIC INFECTIOUS DISEASE JOURNAL. m. $93 to individuals; institutions $149. Williams & Wilkins, 428 E. Preston St., Baltimore, MD 21202. TEL 410-528-4000; 800-638-6423. FAX 410-528-4312. TELEX 87669. Eds. Drs. John D. Nelson, George H. McCracken. bk.rev.; index. circ. 16,600. (also avail. in microfilm from WWS) Indexed: Abstr.Hyg., Bibl.Dev.Med.& Child Neur., C.C.I.P., Dent.Ind., Diar.Dis.Res., Dok.Arbeitsmed., Ind.Med., Ind.Vet., Med.& Surg.Dermat., Protozool.Abstr., Rev.Med.& Vet.Mycol., Small Anim.Abstr. Document type: academic/scholarly publication.
—BLDSC (6417.601600); Faxon; Genuine Article; SWETS; UnCover. CCC.
Description: Covers the treatment of viral and bacterial illness in children.
Refereed Serial

PEDIATRIC MENTAL HEALTH. see PSYCHOLOGY

618.92   US   ISSN 0887-8994
PEDIATRIC NEUROLOGY. 1985. 8/yr. $228 to institutions (effective 1996). Elsevier Science Inc., 655 Ave. of the Americas, New York, NY 10010. TEL 212-989-5800. FAX 212-633-3990. (Subscr. to: Box 882, Madison Sq. Sta., new York, NY 10159-0882) Ed. Dr. Kenneth F. Swaiman. adv. (also avail. in microfilm from UMI; back issues avail.) Indexed: Curr.Cont., Excerp.Med., Ind.Med. Document type: academic/scholarly publication.
—BLDSC (6417.604300); Genuine Article; SWETS; UnCover. CCC.
Description: Contains original papers, reviews, case reports, news, and professional announcements which provide current information on diseases affecting the immature nervous system.
Refereed Serial

618.92   US   ISSN 0031-398X
RJ1
PEDIATRIC NEWS. 1967. m. $60. International Medical News Group, 12230 Wilkins Ave., Rockville, MD 20852. TEL 301-816-8700. Ed. Phyllis Schaeffer. adv.; bk.rev.; charts; illus. circ. 35,000. (tabloid format; also avail. in microform from UMI) Document type: newspaper.
—BLDSC (6417.605000); UMI.

618.92   US
PEDIATRIC NUTRITION HANDBOOK. 1979. irreg., 3rd ed., 1992. $51.95. American Academy of Pediatrics, 141 Northwest Point Blvd., Box 927, Elk Grove Village, IL 60009-0927. TEL 708-228-5005; 800-433-9016. FAX 708-228-1281. Document type: monographic series.

618.92   US   ISSN 1077-1042
PEDIATRIC PATHOLOGY & LABORATORY MEDICINE. 1983. bi-m. £282($465) (effective 1996). (Society for Pediatric Pathology) Taylor & Francis Inc., 1900 Frost Rd., Ste. 101, Bristol, PA 19007-1598. TEL 215-785-5800; 800-821-8312. FAX 215-785-5515. (Subscr. in Europe to: Taylor & Francis Ltd., Rankine Rd., Basingstoke, Hants. RG24 8PR, England. TEL 44-1256-840366. FAX 44-1256-479438) (Co-sponsor: International Pediatric Pathology Association) Ed. Dr. Frank Gonzalez-Crussi. adv.; bk.rev.; bibl.; charts; illus.; index. circ. 350. (also avail. in microfilm from UMI; back issues avail.; reprint service avail. from UMI) Indexed: Curr.Adv.Cancer Res., Curr.Adv.Ecol.Sci., Ind.Med. Document type: academic/scholarly publication.
—Faxon; Genuine Article; SWETS; UnCover. CCC.
Formerly (until 1994): Pediatric Pathology (ISSN 0277-0938)
Description: Covers the study of disease in the developing human.
Refereed Serial

618.92 615.82   US   ISSN 0898-5669
CODEN: PPTHEI
PEDIATRIC PHYSICAL THERAPY. 1989. q. $50 to individuals; institutions $88 (effective 1995). (American Physical Therapy Association, Section on Pediatrics) Williams & Wilkins, 428 Preston St., Baltimore, MD 21202. TEL 410-528-4000; 800-638-6423. FAX 410-528-4312. Ed. Ann F. vansant. index. circ. 5,298. (also avail. in microfilm from WWS) Indexed: IMFL. Document type: academic/scholarly publication.
—BLDSC (6417.605700); Faxon. CCC.
Description: Delivers practical information on the full range of pediatric conditions, including developmental, orthopedic and respiratory concerns.
Refereed Serial

PEDIATRIC PRIMARY CARE; practical pediatrics for the pediatric practitioner. see MEDICAL SCIENCES — Abstracting, Bibliographies, Statistics

618.92 616.2   US   ISSN 8755-6863
CODEN: PEPUES
PEDIATRIC PULMONOLOGY. 1985. m. $552 (foreign $738) (effective 1996). John Wiley & Sons, Inc., Journals, 605 Third Ave., New York, NY 10158. TEL 212-850-6645. FAX 212-850-6021. TELEX 12-7063. E-mail: SUBINFO@JWILEY.COM. (Subscr. outside the Americas to: John Wiley & Sons Ltd., Baffins Ln., Chichester, W. Sussex PO19 1UD, England. TEL 44-1243-779777. FAX 44-1243-776128) Ed. George Polgar. adv.; bk.rev. (back issues avail.) Indexed: Biol.Abstr., Curr.Cont., Ind.Med. Document type: academic/scholarly publication.
—BLDSC (6417.605800); Faxon; Genuine Article; SWETS; UMI; UnCover. CCC.
Description: Covers various aspects of respiratory system disorders in infants and children.
Refereed Serial

618.92 615.842   GW   ISSN 0301-0449
CODEN: PDRYA5
PEDIATRIC RADIOLOGY; roentgenology, nuclear medicine, ultrasonics, CT, MRI. (Text in English) 1973. 8/yr. DM.998($725) (effective 1996). Springer-Verlag, Heidelberger Platz 3, 14197 Berlin, Germany. TEL 030-8207-0. FAX 030-8214091. E-mail: orders@springer.de. (Subscr. in N. America to: Springer-Verlag New York, Inc., 44 Hartz Way, Secaucus, NJ 07096-2491. TEL 201-348-4033. FAX 201-348-4505) Eds. W.E. Berdon, P.G. Small. adv. (also avail. in microform from UMI; reprint service avail. from ISI) Indexed: Bibl.Dev.Med.& Child Neur., Chem.Abstr., Curr.Adv.Cancer Res., Curr.Cont., Dent.Ind., Excerp.Med., Ind.Med., Nutr.Abstr., Rev.Med.& Vet.Mycol. Document type: academic/scholarly publication.
—BLDSC (6417.606000); Faxon; Genuine Article; SWETS; UMI; UnCover. CCC.
Description: Reports on the progress and results from all areas of pediatric radiology and related fields.

618.92   US   ISSN 0031-3998
RJ1   CODEN: PEREBL
PEDIATRIC RESEARCH; international journal of human developmental biology. 1967. m. $152 to individuals; institutions $265 (effective 1995). (International Pediatric Research Foundation Inc.) Williams & Wilkins, 428 E. Preston St., Baltimore, MD 21202. TEL 410-528-4000; 800-638-6423. FAX 410-528-4312. TELEX 87669. (Co-sponsors: American Pediatric Society; European Society for Pediatric Research; Society for Pediatric Research) Ed. Dr. George Lister. adv.; bk.rev.; charts; illus.; index. circ. 4,076. (also avail. in microfilm from WWS) Indexed: Bibl.Dev.Med.& Child Neur., Biol.Abstr., C.C.I.P., Chem.Abstr., Chic.Per.Ind., Child Devel.Abstr., Curr.Adv.Biochem., Curr.Adv.Cell & Devel.Biol., Curr.Adv.Ecol.Sci., Curr.Cont., Dairy Sci.Abstr., Dent.Ind., Diar.Dis.Res., Excerp.Med., Helminthol.Abstr., Ind.Med., Kidney, Lang.& Lang.Behav.Abstr., Nutr.Abstr., Pig News & Info., Soyabean Abstr. Document type: academic/scholarly publication.
—BLDSC (6417.620000); CASDDS; EMDOCS; Faxon; Genuine Article; SWETS; UMI; UnCover. CCC.
Description: Covers advances in the understanding and management of pediatric pulmonary, endocrinological, gastroenterological, and nutritional disorders.
Refereed Serial

618.92   US   ISSN 0882-9225
CODEN: PRECEA
PEDIATRIC REVIEWS AND COMMUNICATIONS. 4/yr. (in 1 vol.; 4 nos./vol.). 111 ECU (effective 1996). Harwood Academic Publishers, c/o International Publishers Distributor, 820 Town Center Dr., Langhorne, PA 19047. TEL 215-750-2642. FAX 215-750-6343. (Subscr. to: International Publishers Distributor, PO Box 90, Reading, Berkshire RG1 8JL, England. TEL 44-173-456-8316) Eds. David Burman, Philip Lanzowsky. (also avail. in microform)
—BLDSC (6417.620400). CCC.
Refereed Serial

PEDIATRIC SURGERY INTERNATIONAL. see MEDICAL SCIENCES — Surgery

618.92   US
PEDIATRICIAN. 1984. q. free to qualified personnel. E P I Inc., 8003 Old York Rd., Elkins Park, PA 19117. TEL 215-635-1700. Ed. Deana Jamroz. adv.; tr.lit. circ. 10,565.
Description: For pediatricians and their patient families with pre-school children. Covers advances in neonatal and pediatric medicine, psychology, and dentistry, plus relevant consumer product information.

618.92   US   ISSN 0031-4005
RJ1   CODEN: PEDIAU
PEDIATRICS. Spanish edition (ISSN 0210-5721) (Editions in Arabic, Italian, Portuguese; edition avail. for India) 1948. m. $90 to individuals; institutions $150. American Academy of Pediatrics, 141 Northwest Point Blvd., Box 927, Elk Grove Village, IL 60009-0927. TEL 708-228-5005; 800-433-9016. FAX 708-228-1281. Ed. Dr. Jerold F. Lucey. adv.; bk.rev.; illus.; s-a. index. circ. 54,000. (also avail. in microfiche; back issues avail.; reprint service avail.) Indexed: Abstr.Health Care Manage.Stud., Abstr.Hyg., AIM, Behav.Med.Abstr., Bibl.Dev.Med.& Child Neur., Biol.Abstr., Biotech.Abstr., C.C.I.P., Chem.Abstr., Curr.Adv.Ecol.Sci., Dairy Sci.Abstr., Dent.Ind., Diab.Cont., Dok.Arbeitsmed., Except.Child.Educ.Abstr., Excerp.Med., FAMLI, Food Sci.& Tech.Abstr., Helminthol.Abstr., Hosp.Lit.Ind., I.P.A., Ind.Med., Ind.Vet., Int.Nurs.Ind., Kidney, Med.& Surg.Dermat., Nutr.Abstr., Poult.Abstr., Rev.Med.& Vet.Mycol., Rev.Plant Path., Risk Abstr., Trop.Dis.Bull., Vet.Bull. Document type: bulletin.
•Also available online. Vendor(s): Ovid Technologies, Lexis-Nexis.
Also available on CD-ROM.
—BLDSC (6417.650000); CASDDS; EMDOCS; Faxon; Genuine Article; SWETS; UMI; UnCover. CCC.

648.92   IT   ISSN 1120-7507
PEDIATRICS. 1989. bi-m. Viale Liguria 20 22A, 20143 Milan, Italy. TEL 2-58-10-35-65. FAX 2-581-022-49. Ed. Gianni Ardito.

618.9   SP   ISSN 0210-5721
PEDIATRICS (EDICION ESPANOLA). English edition (ISSN 0031-4005) 1976. m. 7900 ptas.($67) (free to qualified personnel). (American Academy of Pediatrics, US) Ediciones Doyma S.A., Travesera de Gracia 17-21, 08021 Barcelona, Spain. TEL 34-1-200-07-11. FAX 34-1-209-11-36. TELEX 51964 INK-E. Ed. A. Ballabriga Aguado. adv.: page 230000 ptas.; trim 210 x 280; adv. contact: Olga Valls. circ. 5,000. (reprint service avail. from UMI) Indexed: Dok.Arbeitsmed., Vet.Bull.
—CCC.
Description: Covers infectious illnesses, immunity, nutrition, comunity medicine, premature and newborn babies, neurology, psychiatry, cardiology, endocrinology and toxicology.

618.92   US
PEDIATRICS AND THE A A P MEETING PROGRAM. 1948. m. $52. American Academy of Pediatrics, 141 Northwest Point Blvd., Box 927, Elk Grove, IL 60009-0927. TEL 708-228-5005; 800-433-9016. FAX 708-228-1281. Ed.Bd. adv.: B&W page $1650, color page $2900. circ. 49,381. (also avail. in microfilm) Document type: academic/scholarly publication.
Description: Serves as a medium of expression for the general medical profession, especially pediatricians. Provides papers on original research or observations, and contains special feature or review articles in the related fields.

MEDICAL SCIENCES — PEDIATRICS

618.92 649   US   ISSN 0730-6725
PEDIATRICS FOR PARENTS; the monthly newsletter for caring adults. 1980. m. $18. Pediatrics for Parents, Inc., Box 1069, Bangor, ME 04402-1069. TEL 207-942-6212. Ed. Dr. Richard J. Sagall. bk.rev. circ. 1,000. (looseleaf format; also avail. in microform from UMI; back issues avail.) Indexed: Hlth.Ind. **Document type:** newsletter.
—UMI. **CCC.**

618.92   US   ISSN 0191-9601
PEDIATRICS IN REVIEW. 1979. 12/yr. $130 to non-members. American Academy of Pediatrics, 141 Northwest Point Blvd., Box 927, Elk Grove Village, IL 60009-0927. TEL 708-228-5005; 800-433-9016. FAX 708-228-1281. Ed. Robert J. Haggerty, M.D. abstr.; charts; illus.; cum.index. circ. 27,000. (back issues avail.) Indexed: C.C.I.P. **Document type:** trade publication.
—BLDSC (6417.657000); SWETS; UMI; UnCover.
Refereed Serial

618.92   FR   ISSN 0993-9717
PEDIATRIE PRATIQUE. 1988. m. (10/yr.). 200 F. L.E.N. Medical, 48 bis, av. Kleber, 75016 Paris, France. TEL 47-55-06-06. FAX 47-55-69-41. TELEX 640 748. Ed. Jacques de Blic. circ. 7,250. **Document type:** newspaper.

617   TU   ISSN 1016-5142
CODEN: PCEDE
PEDIATRIK CERRAHI DERGISI. 1987. 3/yr. Logos Yayincilik Ticaret A.S., Yildiz Posta Cad., Sinan Apt. No. 36 D 66-67, Gayrettepe 80280 - Istanbul, Turkey. TEL 90-212-2880541. Ed. Dr. Tolga Dagli. adv. contact: Ipek Karisman. Indexed: Excerp.Med.

618.92   SP   ISSN 0211-3465
CODEN: PEDTDW
PEDIATRIKA. 1981. 10/yr. 7500 ptas.($120) (Europe $80). Alpe Editores, S.A., Pedro Rico, 27, 28029 Madrid, Spain. TEL 34-1-7338811. FAX 34-1-3159652. Dir. Dr. I. Polanco Allve; Pub. A. Alvarez. adv.: color page 160000 ptas.; trim 210 x 280; adv. contact: C. Alvarez. bibl.; charts; illus.; circ. 6,500 (controlled). Indexed: Chem.Abstr., Excerp.Med., Ind.Med.Esp.
—BLDSC (6417.694000); CASDDS. **CCC.**

618   KR   ISSN 0031-4048
CODEN: PDAGA2
PEDIATRIYA, AKUSHERSTVO TA GINEKOLOGIYA. (Text in Ukrainian; summary in Russian) 1936. bi-m. $66 (effective 1996). Ministerstvo Zdravookhraneniya Ukraine, Bul. Shevchenko, 19, 252032 Kiev 32. TEL 7-44-244-2886. Ed. Victor M. Sidelnictsov. bk.rev.; index. (tabloid format) Indexed: Biol.Abstr., Chem.Abstr., Ind.Med. **Document type:** academic/scholarly publication.
—CASDDS.
Description: Provides scientific and practical information on pediatrics, obstetrics and gynecology.

618.92   SA   ISSN 1017-1711
PEDMED. (Text in English) 1986. bi-m. R.60. George Warman Publications (Pty.) Ltd., P.O. Box 3847, Cape Town 8000, South Africa. TEL 27-21-245320. FAX 27-21-261332. Ed. Diana Procter. adv. circ. 2,900.
Formerly: South African Paediatrics Magazine.

PENNSYLVANIA SOCIETY OF DENTISTRY FOR CHILDREN NEWSLETTER. see *MEDICAL SCIENCES — Dentistry*

618.92 616.07   SZ   ISSN 0091-2921
RJ49   CODEN: PPEPDY
PERSPECTIVES IN PEDIATRIC PATHOLOGY. (Text in English) 1976. irreg. price varies. S. Karger AG, Allschwilerstr. 10, P.O. Box, CH-4009 Basel, Switzerland. TEL 061-3061111. FAX 061-3061234. E-mail: Karger@Karger.ch. Eds. S. Rosenberg, Dr. Jay Bernstein. Indexed: ASCA, Ind.Med. **Document type:** academic/scholarly publication.
—BLDSC (6428.148000); Faxon; SWETS. **CCC.**
Description: A multidisciplinary approach to selected aspects of pediatric medicine.
Refereed Serial

618.92   PH   ISSN 0031-7667
PHILIPPINE JOURNAL OF PEDIATRICS. (Text in English) 1950. bi-m. P.70($20) Philippine Pediatric Society, PO Box 3527, Manila, Philippines. Ed. Dr. Felix A. Estrada. adv.; bk.rev.; abstr.; index. circ. 2,000. Indexed: Biol.Abstr., Excerp.Med.

PHOENIX (BETHESDA). see *MEDICAL SCIENCES — Oncology*

618.92 615.82   US   ISSN 0194-2638
RJ53.P5   CODEN: POTPDY
PHYSICAL & OCCUPATIONAL THERAPY IN PEDIATRICS; the quarterly journal of developmental therapy. 1980. q. $225 (foreign $315) (effective 1996). Haworth Press, Inc., 10 Alice St., Binghamton, NY 13904. TEL 607-722-5857; 800-342-9678. FAX 607-722-1424. TELEX 4932599. Eds. Irma J. Wilheim. adv.; bk.rev. circ. 981. (also avail. in microfiche from UMI; back issues avail.; reprint service avail. from HAW) Indexed: Biol.Abstr., CINAHL, Excerp.Med., IMFL, Psychol.Abstr. (1980-), Rehabil.Lit., Sage Fam.Stud.Abstr., Viol.& Abuse Abstr., Yrbk.Assoc.Educ.& Rehab.Blind.
—BLDSC (6475.280000); Faxon; Haworth; UnCover.
Description: Brings information to all therapists involved in developmental and physical rehabilitation of infants and children. Covers current clinical research and practical applications.
Refereed Serial

618.92   PL   ISSN 0079-4279
POSTEPY PEDIATRII.* (Text in Polish; summaries in English, Polish, and Russian) 1955. a. Polskie Towarzystwo Pediatryczne, Ul. Kasprzaka 17, 00-211 Warsaw, Poland. TEL 48-22-323455. Ed. Jana Raszka.

618.92   MX
PRACTICA PEDIATRICA. (Text in Spanish; summaries in English) 1929. m. $25. (Sociedad Mexicana de Pediatria) Mundo Medica S.A., Ejercito Nacional 381, Col. Granada, 11520 Mexico DF, Mexico. TEL 52-5-2038111. adv.; bk.rev.; abstr.; illus.; index. circ. 1,250. Indexed: Biol.Abstr., Chem.Abstr., Excerp.Med.
Formerly: Revista Mexicana de Pediatria (ISSN 0035-0052)

618.92   IS   ISSN 0334-7524
PREVENTIVE PEDIATRICS. (Text in English) 1987. q. Freund Publishing House Ltd., P.O. Box 35010, 61 Nachmani St., Tel Aviv 61350, Israel. Ed. D. Tamir. Indexed: Excerp.Med. (1993-).

618.92   US   ISSN 0893-9837
PRIMARY CARE REPORTS. 1989. m. $169. American Health Consultants, Inc., Six Piedmont Center, Ste. 400, 3525 Piedmont Rd., N.E., Atlanta, GA 30305. TEL 404-262-7436. FAX 800-284-3291. (Subscr. to: Box 740056, Atlanta, GA 30374-9822. TEL 800-688-2421) Ed. Dr. Shiranand S. Karkal. circ. 400.
—**CCC.**

618.92 617   US
PRINCIPLES OF PEDIATRIC NEUROSURGERY. 1986. irreg. price varies. Springer-Verlag, 175 Fifth Ave., New York, NY 10010. TEL 212-460-1500. FAX 212-473-6272. (Also: Berlin, Heidelberg, Tokyo and Vienna) (reprint service avail. from ISI) **Document type:** academic/scholarly publication.

618.92   SZ   ISSN 0251-5601
PROGRES EN NEONATOLOGIE. (Text in French) 1980. a. 190 SFr. S. Karger AG, Allschwilerstr. 10, P.O. Box, CH-4009 Basel, Switzerland. TEL 061-3061111. FAX 061-3061234. E-mail: karger@karger.ch. Ed. J.P. Relier. **Document type:** academic/scholarly publication.

PROGRESS IN PEDIATRIC CARDIOLOGY. see *MEDICAL SCIENCES — Cardiovascular Diseases*

618.92   US   ISSN 0079-6654
CODEN: PPDSAZ
PROGRESS IN PEDIATRIC SURGERY. (Text in German; summaries in French) 1971. a. price varies. Springer-Verlag, 175 Fifth Ave., New York, NY 10010. TEL 212-460-1500. FAX 212-473-6272. (Also: Berlin, Heidelberg, Tokyo and Vienna) Indexed: Biol.Abstr., Ind.Med. **Document type:** monographic series.
—BLDSC (6872.600000); Faxon; SWETS. **CCC.**

618.92 155.4   FR   ISSN 0079-726X
CODEN: PSYEAH
PSYCHIATRIE DE L'ENFANT. 1958. s-a. 400 F. (foreign 470 F.) (effective 1996). Presses Universitaires de France, Departement des Revues, 14 Avenue du Bois-de-l'Epine, B.P.90, 91003 Evry Cedex, France. TEL 1-60-77-82-05. FAX 1-60-79-20-45. TELEX PUF 600 474 F. Ed.Bd. cum.index. (reprint service avail. from KTO) Indexed: Excerp.Med. (until 1992), Ind.Med., Psychol.Abstr. (1970-), SSCI.
—BLDSC (6946.243000); Faxon; Genuine Article; SWETS. **CCC.**
Description: Original works in the clinical, technical and social psychological areas.

618.92   II
RECENT ADVANCES IN PEDIATRICS. (Text in English) irreg. Jaypee Brothers Medical Publishers Pvt. Ltd., G-16, EMCA House, 23-23B, Ansari Rd., Daryaganj, New Delhi 110 002, India. Ed. Suraj Gupte. **Document type:** monographic series.

REFERATOVY VYBER Z PEDIATRIE/ABSTRACTS OF PEDIATRICS. see *MEDICAL SCIENCES — Abstracting, Bibliographies, Statistics*

618.92   US   ISSN 1050-964X
CODEN: RPIDE7
THE REPORT OF PEDIATRIC INFECTIOUS DISEASES. 1991. 10/yr. $45 to individuals (foreign $67); institutions $70 (foreign $92). (Pediatric Infectious Diseases Society) Churchill Livingstone International, 650 Ave. of the Americas, New York, NY 10011. TEL 212-206-5040. FAX 212-727-7808. TELEX 332266. Eds. Engine Shapiro, Ellen Wald; Pub. Jane Grochowski. Indexed: Excerp.Med. (1993-). **Document type:** academic/scholarly publication.
—BLDSC (7661.924500); UMI. **CCC.**
Description: Includes articles on issues of importance to practicing physicians responsible for the care of infants and children.

618.92   US   ISSN 1067-2362
RESIDENT IN PEDIATRICS. 1993. bi-m. $40. Slack, Inc., 6900 Grove Rd., Thorofare, NJ 08086. TEL 609-848-1000. FAX 609-853-5991. adv.: B&W page $1500, color page $2750; trim 8 1/8 x 10 7/8. circ. 8,000.

618.92   BL   ISSN 0104-1282
REVISTA BRASILEIRA DE CRESCIMENTO E DESENVOLVIMENTO HUMANO. (Text in Portuguese and Spanish; summaries in English and Portuguese) 1991. s-a. $12. (Centro de Estudos do Crescimento e do Desenvolvimento do Ser Humano) Iglu Editora Ltda., Av. Dr. Arnaldo 715, subsolo, sala 21, 01246-904 Sao Paulo SP, Brazil. TEL 011-280-3233. FAX 011-853-0240. Ed. Denize Cristina de Oliveira. adv.; bk.rev. circ. 2,000. (reprint service avail.) **Document type:** academic/scholarly publication.
Description: Publishes interdisciplinary works in health, education, psychology, sociology and anthropology. Observes the relationship between human growth and developmental processes, highlighting children and adolescents.

618.92   CK   ISSN 0034-7442
REVISTA COLOMBIANA DE PEDIATRIA Y PUERICULTURA. (Text in Spanish; summaries in English) 1941. 4/yr. $12. Apdo. 606, Bogota, Colombia. Ed. Jorge Gamacho Gamba. adv.; bk.rev.; abstr.; bibl.; charts; illus.; index, cum.index. circ. 2,000. (also avail. in microform from UMI; reprint service avail. from IRC,UMI) Indexed: Excerp.Med.
—BLDSC (7851.410000).

618.92   CU   ISSN 0034-7531
REVISTA CUBANA DE PEDIATRIA. (Text in Spanish; summaries in English, Spanish) 1928. 3/yr. $34 in S. America; N. America $36; elsewhere $38. Ministerio de Salud Publica, Centro Nacional de Informacion de Ciencias Medicas, Calle E No. 452, 3-19 y 21, Plaza de la Revolucion, Apdo. 6520, Havana, Cuba. TEL 809-32-5338. (Dist. by: Ediciones Cubanas, Obispo No. 527, Apdo. 605, Havana, Cuba) Ed. Fidel Araujo. bibl.; charts; illus. circ. 2,500. Indexed: Abstr.Hyg., Biol.Abstr., Chem.Abstr., Excerp.Med., Ind.Med., Nutr.Abstr., Trop.Dis.Bull.
—EMDOCS.
Description: Covers child development including infant-newborn issues, child nutrition, respiratory tract diseases, infant mortality, airway obstruction, low birth weight, heart and congenital defects.

MEDICAL SCIENCES — PEDIATRICS

618.92   RM   ISSN 0031-3904
                  CODEN: RPOPD
REVISTA DE PEDIATRIE, OBSTETRICA, GINECOLOGIE. PEDIATRIE. (Text in Rumanian; summaries in English, French, German, Russian) 1952. 4/yr. $15. Uniunea Societatilor de Stiinte Medicale din Republica Socialista Rumania, Str. Progresului 8, R-70754 Bucharest, Rumania. (Subscr. to: ILEXIM, Str. 13 Decembrie Nr. 3, P.O. Box 136-137, Bucharest, Rumania) Ed.Bd. adv.; bk.rev.; abstr.; charts; illus. **Indexed:** Biol.Abstr., Chem.Abstr., Excerp.Med. (until 1993), Ind.Med.

REVISTA DE PSIQUIATRIA INFANTO-JUVENIL. see *MEDICAL SCIENCES — Psychiatry And Neurology*

618.92   SP   ISSN 0034-947X
                  CODEN: REPEAW
REVISTA ESPANOLA DE PEDIATRIA. 1946. bi-m. 6000 ptas.($65) (effective 1995). Editorial Garsi, S.A., Juan Bravo 46, 28006 Madrid, Spain. TEL 34-1-4021212. FAX 34-1-4020954. Ed. Dr. Manuel Hernandez. bk.rev.; abstr.; bibl.; illus. circ. 4,000. **Indexed:** Biol.Abstr., Chem.Abstr., Dairy Sci.Abstr., Excerp.Med., Ind.Med.Esp., Nutr.Abstr. —BLDSC (7854.200000); CASDDS; EMDOCS; Faxon. **CCC.**

618.92   CK   ISSN 0120-6311
REVISTA INTERNACIONAL DE PEDIATRIA. 1984. irreg. (4-6/yr.). (Miami Children's Hospital) Ediciones Lerner Ltda., Calle 8A No.68A-41, Bogota, Colombia. circ. 35,000.
    Formerly (until Dec. 1984): Miami Children's Hospital Journal.

618.92   PO   ISSN 0048-7880
REVISTA PORTUGUESA DE PEDIATRIA E PUERICULTURA. m. Clinica Pediatrica Universitaria de Lisboa, Hospital de Santa Maria, Lisbon, Portugal. illus. **Indexed:** Ind.Med.

618.92   FR   ISSN 0035-1644
                  CODEN: REVPBS
REVUE DE PEDIATRIE. (Text in French; summaries in English, French) 1965. 10/yr. 440 F. (Europe 500 F.; elsewhere 660 F.) Societe Internationale d'Edition Medicale, B.P. 98-41, ave. du Bac, 94210 La Varenne-Saint-Hilaire, France. TEL 49-76-08-56. FAX 49-76-04-81. Ed. Francois Carruzzo. adv.; bk.rev.; bibl.; charts; illus.; stat. circ. 6,000. **Indexed:** Biol.Abstr., Curr.Cont., Excerp.Med. (until 1993), Nutr.Abstr.

618.92   FR   ISSN 0995-1180
REVUE DU PEDIATRE. 1988. 8/yr. 504 F. (foreign 733 F.) (effective 1996). Masson - Periodiques, Villa Laromiguiere, 75005 Paris, France. TEL 1-40-46-62-00. FAX 1-40-46-62-01. Ed. Ph. Letonturier. adv. circ. 6,000. **Document type:** academic/scholarly publication.
    Description: Aids practicing pediatricians in their daily concerns about treating patients.

618.92   FR   ISSN 0048-8135
REVUE INTERNATIONALE DE PEDIATRIE. (Text in French; summaries in English and French) 1969. m. 260 F. to individuals (foreign 340 F.); students 195 F. (foreign 230 F.). Galliena Promotion, 58 A, rue du Dessous des Berges, 75013 Paris, France. TEL 45-84-97-66. **Indexed:** Excerp.Med.

618.92   IT
RIVISTA DI PEDIATRIA PREVENTIVA E SOCIALE. (Text in Italian; summaries in English and Italian) 1951. q. $90 to individuals; institutions $140 (effective 1995). (Societa Italiana di Pediatria Preventiva e Sociale - Nipiologia) Edizioni Minerva Medica, Corso Bramante 83-85, 10126 Turin, Italy. TEL 39-11-678282. FAX 39-11-3121736. Ed. E. Riva; Pub. Alberto Oliaro. adv.; B&W page $1100, color page $1900; trim 190 x 270; adv. contact: F. Filippo. bk.rev.; bibl.; charts; illus.; index; circ. 3,000 (paid). **Indexed:** Biol.Abstr., Chem.Abstr., Ind.Med.
    Former titles: Rivista di Pediatria Preventiva e Sociale - Nipiologia (ISSN 0392-4416); (until 1980): Minerva Nipiologica (ISSN 0026-489X); Nipiopedologia.
    Description: Covers preventive and social pediatrics.
    Refereed Serial

RIVISTA ITALIANA DI ODONTOIATRIA INFANTILE. see *MEDICAL SCIENCES — Dentistry*

618.92   IT
RIVISTA ITALIANA DI PEDIATRIA. 1964. bi-m. L.100000 (foreign L.165000) (effective 1995). Pacini Editore s.r.l., Via A. Gherardesca 1, 46121 Ospedaletto (Pisa), Italy. TEL 39-50-982439. FAX 39-50-983906. Ed. Nicola Principi. **Indexed:** Excerp.Med.

618.92   US
SCHOOL HEALTH: POLICY AND PRACTICE. 1972. irreg., 5th ed., 1993. $44.95. American Academy of Pediatrics, 141 Northwest Point Blvd., Box 927, Elk Grove Village, IL 60009-0927. TEL 708-228-5005; 800-433-9016. FAX 708-228-1281. **Document type:** monographic series.
    Formerly: School Health: A Guide for Health Professionals.

618.92 616.9   US   ISSN 1045-1870
SEMINARS IN PEDIATRIC INFECTIOUS DISEASES. 1990. q. $139 (foreign $169) (effective 1996). W.B. Saunders Co. (Subsidiary of: Harcourt Brace & Company), The Curtis Center, 3rd Fl., Independence Sq. W., Philadelphia, PA 19106-3399. TEL 215-238-7807. (Subscr. to: Periodicals Fulfillment, W.B. Saunders Co., 6277 Sea Harbor Dr., 4th Fl., Orlando, FL 32887-4800. TEL 800-654-2452. FAX 800-874-6418) Ed. Dr. Ralph D. Fegin; Pub. Joan W. Blumberg. adv.; B&W page $630, color page $1480; 7 x 10. circ. 1,186. (back issues avail.) **Document type:** academic/scholarly publication.
—BLDSC (8239.456780); UMI. **CCC.**
    Description: Provides an in-depth update on a new subject, diagnostic technique, or controversial subject in each issue.

SEMINARS IN PEDIATRIC NEUROLOGY. see *MEDICAL SCIENCES — Psychiatry And Neurology*

SEMINARS IN PEDIATRIC SURGERY. see *MEDICAL SCIENCES — Surgery*

618.92   US   ISSN 0146-0005
                  CODEN: SEMPDU
SEMINARS IN PERINATOLOGY. 1977. bi-m. $165 (foreign $209) (effective 1996). W.B. Saunders Co. (Subsidiary of: Harcourt Brace & Company), Curtis Center, 3rd Fl., Independence Sq. W., Philadelphia, PA 19106-3399. TEL 215-238-7800. FAX 215-238-6445. (Subscr. to: Periodicals Fulfillment, W.B. Saunders Co., 6277 Sea Harbor Dr., 4th Fl., Orlando, FL 32891-4800. TEL 800-654-2452. FAX 800-874-6418) Eds. Drs. Robert K. Creasy, Joseph B. Warshaw; Pub. Joan W. Blumberg. adv.; B&W page $690, color $1640; 7 x 10. bibl.; charts; illus.; index. circ. 2,433. **Indexed:** ASCA, Bibl.Dev.Med.& Child Neur., Biol.Abstr., Curr.Cont., Excerp.Med., Ind.Med., Ind.Sci.Rev., Sci.Cit.Ind. **Document type:** academic/scholarly publication.
—BLDSC (8239.456800); Faxon; Genuine Article; SWETS; UMI; UnCover. **CCC.**

618.92   CC   ISSN 1001-0866
SHIYONG ERKE ZAZHI/JOURNAL OF PRACTICAL PEDIATRICS. (Text in Chinese; abstracts in English) 1986. bi-m. $30. Shiyong Yixue Zazhishe - Applied Medical Science Journal Publishing House, 44-1, Jixian St., Heping District, Shenyang, Liaoning 110005, People's Republic of China. TEL 024-3864398. Ed. Xiang Quanshen. circ. 35,000. (reprint service avail.) **Document type:** academic/scholarly publication.
    Description: Features new developments and methods of practical diagnosis, treatment, and prevention of pediatric diseases.
    Refereed Serial

SHONI GEKA/JAPANESE JOURNAL OF PEDIATRIC SURGERY. see *MEDICAL SCIENCES — Surgery*

SHONI HOKEN KENKYU/JOURNAL OF CHILD HEALTH. see *PHYSICAL FITNESS AND HYGIENE*

618.92   JA   ISSN 0583-1180
                  CODEN: SHOIB4
SHONI IGAKU/PEDIATRIC REVIEW. (Text in Japanese; summaries in English) 1968. bi-m. 26460 Yen($204) Igaku-Shoin Ltd., 5-24-3 Hongo, Bunkyo-ku, Tokyo 113-91, Japan. TEL 03-817-5707. Ed.Bd. circ. 3,000.
—BLDSC (6417.620200); CASDDS.

618.92   JA   ISSN 0385-6305
SHONI NAIKA/JAPANESE JOURNAL OF PEDIATRIC MEDICINE. (Text in Japanese) 1969. m. 34800 Yen (effective 1994). Tokyo Igakusha Ltd., 35-4, Hongo 3-chome, Bunkyo-ku, Tokyo 113, Japan. Ed. Naoyoshi Minami. circ. 6,000. **Document type:** academic/scholarly publication.

618.92   JA   ISSN 0037-4121
SHONIKA/CLINICAL PEDIATRICS. (Text in Japanese) 1960. m. 1600 Yen per no. Kanehara & Co., Ltd., 31-14 Yushima 2-chome, Bunkyo-ku, Tokyo 113, Japan. Ed. Dr. Teruji Shinozuka. bk.rev.; index. circ. 6,200. **Indexed:** CINAHL, Curr.Cont., Helminthol.Abstr., Nutr.Abstr.
●Also available online. Vendor(s): Ovid Technologies.

618.92   SI   ISSN 0037-5683
                  CODEN: SPSJBF
SINGAPORE PAEDIATRIC SOCIETY. JOURNAL. 1959. q. Singapore Paediatric Society, Lower Kent Ridge Rd., 0511 Singapore, Singapore. TEL 7724112. adv.; bk.rev. circ. 1,000. **Indexed:** Excerp.Med., Ind.Med. (until 19??). **Document type:** academic/scholarly publication.
—EMDOCS.

618.92   GW   ISSN 0945-7712
                  CODEN: SPKLEI
SOZIALPAEDIATRIE UND KINDERAERZTLICHE PRAXIS. 1979. m. DM.138. (Deutsche Gesellschaft fuer Sozialpaediatrie e.V.) Verlag Kirchheim und Co. GmbH, Kaiserstr. 41, 55116 Mainz, Germany. TEL 06131-96070-0. FAX 06131-9607070. Ed. Dr. Kurt Hartung. adv. contact: Andreas Goerner. circ. 7,100. **Document type:** academic/scholarly publication.
—BLDSC (8361.145600).
    Former titles (until 1993): Sozialpaediatrie in der Paediatrie fuer Praxis und Klinik (ISSN 0944-2375); (until 1992): Sozial Paediatrie in Praxis und Klinik (ISSN 0171-9327)

SPINAL CONNECTION. see *MEDICAL SCIENCES — Orthopedics And Traumatology*

SPORTS MEDICINE: HEALTH CARE FOR YOUNG ATHLETES. see *MEDICAL SCIENCES — Sports Medicine*

614.19   US
SYNOPSIS (COLUMBIA). 1990. q. membership. Sudden Infant Death Syndrome Alliance (SIDS), 1314 Bedford Ave., Ste. 210, Baltimore, MD 21208-3737. TEL 410-653-8226. FAX 410-653-8709. Ed. Phipps Cohe. **Document type:** newsletter.
    Description: Unites families and professionals concerned about SIDS; provides up-to-date information about the syndrome to the general public, particularly to new and expectant parents. Hotline number included.

618.92   GW   ISSN 0935-3216
T W PAEDIATRIE. 1988. bi-m. DM.74 (foreign DM.100). Verlag G. Braun GmbH, Karl-Friedrich-Str. 14-18, 76133 Karlsruhe, Germany. TEL 0721-165-0. FAX 0721-165191. **Indexed:** Excerp.Med. **Document type:** trade publication.
—BLDSC (9076.749600); SWETS.

618.92   TZ   ISSN 0856-311X
TANZANIA JOURNAL OF PAEDIATRICS. 1989. 2/yr. Paediatric Association of Tanzania, P.O. Box 65370, Dar es Salaam, Tanzania. **Indexed:** P.L.E.S.A.

THEIR WORLD. see *EDUCATION — Special Education And Rehabilitation*

618.92   GW
THEMEN DER KINDERHEILKUNDE. 1986. irreg., vol.7, 1993. DM.24. Schmidt-Roemhild Verlag, Mengstr. 16, 23552 Luebeck, Germany. TEL 0451-1605-0. FAX 0451-1605253. **Document type:** monographic series.

THEORY AND RESEARCH IN BEHAVIORAL PEDIATRICS. see *PSYCHOLOGY*

618.92 NE ISSN 0165-1870
TIJDSCHRIFT VOOR JEUGDGEZONDHEIDSZORG. Variant title: J G Z. 1968. 6/yr. fl.67.50. Bohn Stafleu van Loghum B.V. (Subsidiary of: Wolters Kluwer N.V.), Postbus 246, 3990 GA Houten, Netherlands. TEL 31-3403-95711. FAX 31-3403-50903. (Subscr. to: Intermedia, Postbus 4, 2400 MA Alphen aan den Rijn, Netherlands. TEL 31-1720-66811. FAX 31-1720-66770) Ed. S.P. Verloove-Vanhorick. adv.; circ. 2,390 (paid). **Document type:** academic/scholarly publication.
—SWETS.

618.92 NE ISSN 0376-7442
CODEN: TIKID4
TIJDSCHRIFT VOOR KINDERGENEESKUNDE. (Text in Dutch and English) 1932. m. fl.138.50 (students fl.69.25). Bohn Stafleu van Loghum B.V. (Subsidiary of: Wolters Kluwer N.V.), Postbus 246, 3990 GA Houten, Netherlands. TEL 31-3403-95711. FAX 31-3403-50903. Ed. Dr. T.D. Stahlie. adv.; bk.rev.; charts; illus.; stat.; index. circ. 850. **Indexed:** Biol.Abstr., Chem.Abstr., Dent.Ind., Excerp.Med., Ind.Med.
—BLDSC (8842.300000); Faxon; SWETS.
Formerly: Maandschrift voor Kindergeneeskunde (ISSN 0024-869X)

618.92 US ISSN 0892-0435
TOPICS IN PEDIATRICS. 1982. 3/yr. free. Minneapolis Children's Medical Center, 2525 Chicago Ave., S., Minneapolis, MN 55404. TEL 612-863-6222. FAX 612-863-6674. Ed. Dr. John MacDonald. circ. 10,000.
Description: For physicians, nurses, and psychosocial professionals who care for children.

575.1 618.92 US ISSN 0737-5174
TRISOMY 21;* an international, multidisciplinary journal of Downs Syndrome. 1984. q. Eterna International, Inc., Box 6558, Flushing, NY 11365-6558. Ed. Dr. Siegfried M. Pueschel. abstr.; charts; illus.; index.
Refereed Serial

618.92 TU ISSN 0041-4301
TURKISH JOURNAL OF PEDIATRICS. (Text in English) 1958. q. $50. Turkish and International Children's Center - Turkiye ve Uluslararasi Cocuk Sagligi Merkezi, P.O. Box 66, Samanpazari, 06240 Ankara, Turkey. TEL 90-312-3242326. FAX 90-312-3112253. TELEX 42999 TCSM TR. (Co-sponsor: Turkish National Pediatric Society) Ed. Dr. Ihsan Dogramaci. bk.rev.; abstr.; bibl.; charts; illus.; index. circ. 1,500. **Indexed:** Biol.Abstr., Curr.Adv.Ecol.Sci., Dent.Ind., Diar.Dis.Res., Excerp.Med., Ind.Med., Nutr.Abstr. **Document type:** academic/scholarly publication.
—BLDSC (9072.480000); EMDOCS; Faxon; Genuine Article; UMI.
Refereed Serial

618.92 CC ISSN 1002-1213
XINSHENG ERKE ZAZHI/JOURNAL OF NEONATOLOGY. (Text in Chinese) 1986. bi-m. Beijing Medical University, First Clinical Medical College, Women and Children Hospital, Beijing 100034, People's Republic of China. TEL 0086-01-6031122. FAX 0086-01-603-7106. Ed. Huang Demin. **Document type:** academic/scholarly publication.

618.92 US ISSN 1078-5027
YALE CHILDREN'S HEALTH LETTER. m. $45 (foreign $60) (effective 1996). Belvoir Publications, Inc., 75 Holly Hill Ln., Box 2626, Greenwich, CT 06836-2626. TEL 203-661-6111. FAX 203-661-4802.

618.92 US ISSN 0084-3954
RJ16
YEAR BOOK OF PEDIATRICS. 1933. a. $64.95 (residents $35) (effective 1996). Mosby - Year Book, Inc., Continuity Division, 200 N. LaSalle, Chicago, IL 60601. TEL 312-726-9733. FAX 312-726-6075. TELEX 206155. Ed. Dr. James A. Stockman, III. (reprint service avail.) **Indexed:** Curr.Adv.Ecol.Sci., Diar.Dis.Res.
●Also available online. Vendor(s): Ovid Technologies.
—BLDSC (9414.800000); SWETS. **CCC.**

618.92 JA
YOJI EIYO KISO CHOSA KEKKA NO GAIYO/FUNDAMENTAL RESEARCH REPORT OF PEDIATRIC NUTRITION. (Text in Japanese) every 5 yrs. Tokyoto Eiseikyoku, Kenko Suishinbu - Tokyo Metropolitan Government, Bureau of Public Health, Public Health Promotion Division, 8-1 Nishishinjuku 2-chome, Shinjuku-ku, Tokyo 163-01, Japan.
Document type: government publication.

ZHONGGUO YIXUE WENZHAI (ERKEXUE)/CHINA MEDICAL ABSTRACTS (PEDIATRICS). see *MEDICAL SCIENCES — Abstracting, Bibliographies, Statistics*

618.2 CC
ZHONGHUA ERKE ZAZHI/CHINESE JOURNAL OF PEDIATRICS. (Text in Chinese) bi-m. $3 per no. Guoji Shudian, Qikan Bu - China International Book Trading Corp., Chegongzhuang Xilu 21, P.O. Box 399, Beijing, People's Republic of China. **Indexed:** ExtraMED. **Document type:** academic/scholarly publication.
●Also available on CD-ROM.

MEDICAL SCIENCES — Physical Medicine And Rehabilitation

615.82 US
A D T A NEWSLETTER. 1967. q. $12 to non-members. American Dance Therapy Association, 2000 Century Plaza, Ste. 230, Columbia, MD 21044. TEL 301-997-4040. Ed. Judith Fried. bk.rev.; bibl. **Document type:** newsletter.
Description: Contains communications from ADTA President and membership, regional news, committee news, theory and philosophy, listing of courses, workshops, and job opportunities available.

615.8 US ISSN 1053-7597
ADVANCE FOR PHYSICAL THERAPISTS. 1988. w. Merion Publications, 650 Park Ave., Box 61556, King of Prussia, PA 19406. TEL 610-265-7812. FAX 610-265-8971. E-mail: blammey@merion.com. Ed. Linda Jones. adv.; B&W page $1225; trim 10 x 13 1/4. circ. 136,280. **Document type:** trade publication.

615.82 US ISSN 0892-8878
RM735.A1
ADVANCES IN CLINICAL REHABILITATION. 1980-1986 (vol.5); N.S. 1987. irreg. (approx. every 18 mos.). price varies. Springer Publishing Company, 536 Broadway, New York, NY 10012-3955. TEL 212-431-4370. FAX 212-941-7842. Eds. M.C. Eisenberg, R. Grzesiak. circ. 417. **Indexed:** Dok.Arbeitsmed., Ind.Med., Psychol.Abstr. **Document type:** academic/scholarly publication.
—Faxon.
Supersedes: Annual Review of Rehabilitation (ISSN 0197-2251)

613.82 US ISSN 0065-8022
AMERICAN DANCE THERAPY ASSOCIATION. (NO.) ANNUAL CONFERENCE PROCEEDINGS. 1967. a., 27th, 1992. $30 to non-members; members $25. American Dance Therapy Association, 2000 Century Plaza, Ste. 108, Columbia, MD 21044. TEL 301-997-4040.

AMERICAN JOURNAL OF KNEE SURGERY. see *MEDICAL SCIENCES — Surgery*

615.8 US ISSN 0894-9115
RM735.A1 CODEN: AJPREP
AMERICAN JOURNAL OF PHYSICAL MEDICINE AND REHABILITATION. 1921. bi-m. $75 to individuals; institutions $125 (effective 1995). (Association of Academic Physiatrists) Williams & Wilkins, 428 E. Preston St., Baltimore, MD 21202. TEL 410-528-4000; 800-638-6423. FAX 410-528-4312. Ed. Dr. Ernest W. Johnson. adv.; bk.rev.; charts; illus.; tr.lit. circ. 3,850. (microfilm from WWS) **Indexed:** AIM, Behav.Med.Abstr., Bibl.Dev.Med.& Child Neur., Bioeng.Abstr., Biol.Abstr., Chem.Abstr., CINAHL, Curr.Cont., Ergon.Abstr., Excerp.Med., Ind.Med., INIS Atomind., INSPEC (1973-), Int.Sci.Rev., Nutr.Abstr., Psychol.Abstr., Rehabil.Lit., Sci.Cit.Ind., Sportsearch (1988-). **Document type:** academic/scholarly publication.
—BLDSC (0832.160000); ADONIS; Ei; Faxon; Genuine Article; SWETS; UnCover. **CCC.**
Formerly: American Journal of Physical Medicine (ISSN 0002-9491)
Description: Examines acute problems of rehabilitation, their treatment, new methods and equipment.
Refereed Serial

615.8 362 FR ISSN 0168-6054
CODEN: ARMPEQ
ANNALES DE READAPTATION ET DE MEDECINE PHYSIQUE. (Text mainly in French; summaries in English, French) 1957. 8/yr. 1545 F. in France; foreign 1590 F.($311) (effective 1996). (Societe Francaise de Reeducation Fonctionnelle de Readaptation et de Medecine Physique) Editions Scientifiques Elsevier, 141 rue de Javel, 75747 Paris, France. TEL 33-1-45589063. (Subscr. in U.S. and Canada to: Elsevier Science Inc., Box 882, Madison Sq. Sta., New York, NY 10159. TEL 212-989-5800) Ed. M. Perrigot. adv.; bk.rev.; index. circ. 3,000. (also avail. in microform from UMI) **Indexed:** Biol.Abstr., Bull.Signal., Excerp.Med. **Document type:** academic/scholarly publication.
—BLDSC (0995.170000). **CCC.**
Formerly (until 1983): Annales de Medecine Physique (ISSN 0402-4621)
Description: Publishes clinical, paraclinical and basic research papers pertaining to all aspects of the medicine of readaptation and rehabilitation.
Refereed Serial

615.82 JA ISSN 0918-1431
AOMORIKEN SAGYO RYOHO KENKYU/BULLETIN OF AOMORI OCCUPATIONAL THERAPY. (Text in Japanese) 1992. a. Aomoriken Sagyo Ryohoshikai - Association of Aomoriken Occupational Therapists, Hirosaki Daigaku Iryo Gijutsu Tanki Daigakubu, Sagyo Ryohogakka, 66-1 Honcho, Hirosaki-shi, Aomori-ken 036, Japan.

615.8 US ISSN 0003-9993
RM845 CODEN: APMHAI
ARCHIVES OF PHYSICAL MEDICINE AND REHABILITATION. 1920. m. $185 (foreign $219) (effective 1996). (American Congress of Rehabilitation Medicine) W.B. Saunders Co. (Subsidiary of: Harcourt Brace & Co.), Curtis Center, 3rd Fl., Independence Sq. W., Philadelphia, PA 19106-3399. TEL 215-238-7800. FAX 215-238-6445. (Subscr. to: Periodicals Fulfillment, W.B. Saunders Co., 6277 Sea Harbor Dr., 4th Fl., Orlando, FL 32891-4800. TEL 800-654-2452. FAX 874-874-6418) (Co-sponsor: American Academy of Physical Medicine and Rehabilitation) Eds. Drs. Gerald J. Herbison, Carmella Gonella; Pub. Joan W. Blumberg. adv.; B&W page $925, color page $1825; 7 x 10. charts; illus.; index. circ. 10,224. **Indexed:** Abstr.Health Care Manage.Stud., AIM, Behav.Med.Abstr., Bibl.Dev.Med.& Child Neur., Biol.Abstr., C.I.S. Abstr., Chem.Abstr., CINAHL, Curr.Cont., Dent.Ind., Excerp.Med., Hosp.Lit.Ind., Ind.Med., Ind.Sci.Rev., INIS Atomind., JAMA, Lang.& Lang.Behav.Abstr., Phys.Ed.Ind., Rehabil.Lit., Sci.Cit.Ind., Sportsearch (1974-). **Document type:** academic/scholarly publication.
—BLDSC (1639.000000); Faxon; Genuine Article; SWETS; UMI; UnCover. **CCC.**
Description: Concerns the therapeutic use of physical and pharmaceutical agents in providing comprehensive care for persons with disabilities and chronic illnesses.
Refereed Serial

MEDICAL SCIENCES — PHYSICAL MEDICINE AND REHABILITATION

615.8 UK
ASSOCIATION OF PAEDIATRIC CHARTERED PHYSIOTHERAPISTS. JOURNAL. 1973. m. £16. Association of Paediatric Chartered Physiotherapists, 14 Bedford Row, London WC1R 4ED, England. TEL 0171-242-1941. FAX 0171-831-4509. (Co-sponsor: Chartered Society of Physiotherapy) Ed. L. Wakley. circ. 1,200 (controlled). **Document type:** academic/scholarly publication.
Formerly (until 1994): Association of Paediatric Chartered Physiotherapists. Newsletter.
Refereed Serial

615.8 AT ISSN 0004-9514
AUSTRALIAN JOURNAL OF PHYSIOTHERAPY. 1954. q. Aus.$62 (foreign Aus.$90) (effective 1995). Australian Physiotherapy Association, Level 9, 479 St. Kilda Rd., Melbourne, Vic. 3004, Australia. TEL 61-3-866-8366. FAX 61-3-866-2170. Ed. Wendy Cross. adv. contact: Elise Olney. bk.rev.; video rev.; index; circ. 8,300 (controlled). **Indexed:** Excerp.Med. **Document type:** academic/scholarly publication.
—BLDSC (1811.100000); SWETS.
Description: Publishes original scientific articles, new product notes, news, coming events, letters.
Refereed Serial

615.8 AT ISSN 0045-0766
AUSTRALIAN OCCUPATIONAL THERAPY JOURNAL. 1951. q. Aus.$120($120) (effective 1996). Blackwell Science Pty Ltd, P.O. Box 378, Carlton, Vic. 3053, Australia. TEL 61-3-93470300. FAX 61-3-93493016. Ed. Esther May. adv.; bk.rev.; index. circ. 4,000. (also avail. in microfilm from UMI; back issues avail.) **Indexed:** CINAHL, Excerp.Med., Psychol.Abstr. (1991-). **Document type:** academic/scholarly publication.
—BLDSC (1815.950000); EMDOCS; UMI. **CCC.**
Formerly: Australian Association of Occupational Therapists. Journal.

615.82 NE ISSN 0168-9711
BEWEGEN EN HULPVERLENING. 1984. 4/yr. fl.126.50. Bohn Stafleu van Loghum B.V. (Subsidiary of: Wolters Kluwer N.V.), Postbus 246, 3990 GA Houten, Netherlands. TEL 31-3403-95711. FAX 31-3403-50903. adv. **Document type:** academic/scholarly publication.
—SWETS.

BRAILLE JOURNAL OF PHYSIOTHERAPY. see
HANDICAPPED — Visually Impaired

615.82 UK ISSN 1354-8581
▼**BRITISH JOURNAL OF THERAPY & REHABILITATION.** 1994. q. £35 to individuals (overseas £70); institutions £80 (overseas £100). Mark Allen Publishing Ltd, Croxted Mews, 288 Croxted Rd., London SE24 9BY, England. TEL 0181-671-7521. FAX 0181-671-4454. Ed. David Maskill; Pub. Mark Allen. adv. contact: Adrian Johnston. **Document type:** academic/scholarly publication.
—BLDSC (2325.850000).

617.1 615.53 FR ISSN 0007-9782
CAHIERS DE KINESITHERAPIE; revue d'enseignement post-scolaire et de documentation technique. 1962. bi-m. 494 F. (foreign 671 F.) (effective 1996). Masson - Periodiques, Villa Laromiguiere, 75005 Paris, France. TEL 1-40-46-62-00. FAX 1-40-46-62-01. Ed. J. Barthe. adv.; bk.rev. circ. 2,900. (also avail. in microform from UMI) **Indexed:** Biol.Abstr., Chem.Abstr., Excerp.Med. **Document type:** academic/scholarly publication.
—BLDSC (2949.560000); UMI. **CCC.**
Description: Each issue provides thorough knowledge of a particular disease or therapy, for post-graduate learning or review.

615.82 UK
CHIROPODY COMMENT. 1964. q. £8. English Chiropodists Association, 42 Velsheda Rd., Shirley, Solihull, W. Midlands B90 2JN, England. TEL 021-745-1552. Ed. Neil Hailstone. adv.: page £65. bk.rev.; tr.lit. (back issues avail.) **Document type:** academic/scholarly publication.
Refereed Serial

615.8 IT ISSN 0390-8712
CODEN: CLTM-A
CLINICA TERMALE. 1941. bi-m. L.58000 (foreign L.116000). (Associazione Italiana di Idroclimatologia, Talassologia e Terapia Fisica) Societa Editrice Universo, Via G.B. Morgagni 1, 00161 Rome, Italy.

615.82 371.9 US ISSN 0896-9620
RD795 CODEN: CLKIE9
CLINICAL KINESIOLOGY. 1947. q. $25 to non-members (foreign $35); institutions $45 (foreign $55). American Kinesiotherapy Association, c/o Dr. John Drowatzki, Ed., University of Toledo, Dept. of Health Promotion & Human Peformance, 2801 W. Bancroft, Toledo, OH 43606. TEL 419-537-2747. adv.; bk.rev.; bibl.; charts; illus.; index. circ. 1,064. (also avail. in microform from UMI; reprint service avail. from KTO) **Indexed:** Adol.Ment.Hlth.Abstr., Biol.Abstr., CINAHL, Excerp.Med., Hosp.Lit.Ind., HRIS, Ind.Med., Phys.Ed.Ind., Psychol.Abstr., Rehabil.Lit., Sportsearch (1988-), Yrbk.Assoc.Educ.& Rehab.Blind. **Document type:** academic/scholarly publication.
—BLDSC (3286.294700); Faxon; SWETS; UMI; UnCover.
Former titles (until 1987): American Corrective Therapy Journal (ISSN 0002-8088); (until 1967): Association for Physical and Mental Rehabilitation. Journal (ISSN 0098-8448)
Refereed Serial

615.82 UK ISSN 0269-2155
CODEN: CEHAEN
CLINICAL REHABILITATION. 1987. q. £68.50($123) to individuals; institutions £147 ($265) (effective 1996). Arnold (Subsidiary of: Hodder Headline plc.), 338 Euston Rd., London NW1 3BH, England. TEL 0171-873-6000. FAX 0171-973-6325. (Subscr. to: Turpin Distribution Services Ltd., Blackhorse Rd., Letchworth, Herts. SG6 1HN, England. TEL 01462-672555. FAX 01462-480947) adv.; bk.rev. **Indexed:** Excerp.Med. (1993-), Psychol.Abstr. (1987-). **Document type:** academic/scholarly publication.
—BLDSC (3286.351500); Faxon; SWETS.
Description: Provides a forum for ideas and information for persons concerned with rehabilitation.

615.82 US ISSN 0896-2960
CRITICAL REVIEWS IN PHYSICAL & REHABILITATION MEDICINE. 1989. q. $84 to individuals; institutions $295 (effective 1996). Begell House Inc., 79 Madison Ave., Ste. 1201, New York, NY 10016-7892. TEL 212-725-1999. FAX 212-213-8368. E-mail: 74353.2052@compuserve.com. Eds. Martin Grabois, Ernest J. Henley. **Indexed:** Excerp.Med. (1995-). **Document type:** academic/scholarly publication.
—BLDSC (3487.479800); UnCover. **CCC.**
Description: Provides reviews of diagnostic methods, clinical modalities and techniques, and physical and rehabilitative methodologies for specific etiologies amenable to treatment by physical medicine.

616.8 US
DANCE MEDICINE-HEALTH NEWSLETTER.* 1983. q. $15. International Center for Dance Orthopaedics and Dance Therapy, 3742 Whittier Blvd., Los Angeles, CA 90023-1704. TEL 213-261-0326. Ed. Ernest L. Washington, M.D. adv.; bk.rev. circ. 200. (looseleaf format) **Document type:** newsletter.

615.82 DK ISSN 0105-0648
DANSKE FYSIOTERAPEUTER. 1918. 23/yr. DKK 602. Danske Fysioterapeuters Organisation, Norre Voldgade 90, 1358 Copenhagen K, Denmark. TEL 33-13-82-11. FAX 33938214. Ed. Michael Diepeveen. adv.; bk.rev. circ. 7,200.

DISABILITY AND REHABILITATION. see *HANDICAPPED*

615.82 JA ISSN 0919-5602
E I R E C KENKYU HOKOKUSHU. (Text in Japanese; summaries in English) 1986. a. Rehabilitation Engineering Center for Employment Injuries, 10-5, Komei 1-chome, Minato-ku, Nagoya-shi, Aichi-ken 455, Japan. FAX 81-052-652-6275. E-mail: info@eirec3.lwc-eirec.go.jp. **Document type:** academic/scholarly publication.
Formerly (until 1991): Rosai Rihabiriteshon Kogaku Senta Kenkyu Hokokushu (ISSN 0912-7488)

615.82 IT
ERRE COME RIABILITAZIONE. 1990. q. L.30000 (foreign L.35000) (effective 1991). Societa Erre s.r.l., Via Ardeatina 306, 00179 Rome, Italy. TEL 519-16-75. FAX 503-20-97. Ed. Giuseppe Tagliapietra. **Document type:** trade publication.

615.82 IT ISSN 0014-2573
CODEN: EUMPA
EUROPA MEDICOPHYSICA. (Text in English, Italian) 1965. q. $90 to individuals; institutions $140 (effective 1995). (European Federation of Physical Medicine and Rehabilitation) Edizioni Minerva Medica, Corso Bramante 83-85, 10126 Turin, Italy. TEL 39-11-678282. FAX 39-11-3121736. (Co-sponsor: Italian Society of Physical Medicine and Rehabilitation) Ed. F.P. Franchignoni; Pub. Alberto Oliaro. adv.: B&W page $1100, color page $1900; trim 215 x 280; adv. contact: F. Filippo. bk.rev.; bibl.; charts; illus.; index; circ. 3,000 (paid). (also avail. in microform from UMI) **Indexed:** Excerp.Med. (1995-). **Document type:** academic/scholarly publication.
—BLDSC (3829.319500).
Refereed Serial

615.8 GW ISSN 1017-6721
CODEN: EPMRES
EUROPEAN JOURNAL OF PHYSICAL MEDICINE AND REHABILITATION. 1978. 6/yr. DM.265($196) in Europe; rest of world DM.281($208) (effective 1996). (Royal Belgian Society of Physical Medicine and Rehabilitation) Blackwell Wissenschaft, Kurfuerstendamm 57, 10707 Berlin, Germany. TEL 030-327906-0. FAX 030-32790610. (Co-sponsor: Oesterreichische Gesellschaft fuer Physikalische Medizin, Rehabilitation und Grenzgebiete) Eds. Dr. E. Ernst, Dr. G. Vanderstraeten. adv.; bk.rev. circ. 1,500. **Indexed:** Biol.Abstr., Excerp.Med., Ind.Med. **Document type:** academic/scholarly publication.
—BLDSC (3829.734700); ADONIS; Faxon; UMI. **CCC.**
Former titles: Acta Belgica - Medica Physica; Journal Belge de Medecine Physique et de Rehabilitation.

EXCERPTA MEDICA. SECTION 19: REHABILITATION AND PHYSICAL MEDICINE. see *MEDICAL SCIENCES — Abstracting, Bibliographies, Statistics*

FISIOTERAPIA. see *MEDICAL SCIENCES — Nurses And Nursing*

615.82 TU
CODEN: FTRDE
FIZIK TEDAVI REHABILITASYON DERGISI. 4/yr. Turkiye Fiziksel Tip ve Rehabilitasyon Dernegi, Capa, 34390 Istanbul, Turkey. TEL 90-212-5250014. **Indexed:** Excerp.Med. (1995-). **Document type:** academic/scholarly publication.

615.8 NO ISSN 0016-3384
FYSIOTERAPEUTEN. 1933. 14/yr. NOK 650. Norske Fysioterapeuters Forbund, Pilestredet 56, P.O. Box 7009 Majorstua, N-0306 Oslo, Norway. TEL 47-22-697800. FAX 47-22-565825. Ed. Karin Helene Haugen. adv.; bk.rev.; illus. circ. 7,200. **Document type:** trade publication.
—CCC.

615.8 FI ISSN 0789-5232
FYSIOTERAPIA. (Text in Finnish, Swedish; summaries in English) 1954. 8/yr. FIM 305. Suomen Fysioterapeuttiliitto - Finnish Physical Therapy Association, Asemamiehenkatu 4, SF-00520 Helsinki, Finland. TEL 358-0-1496034. FAX 358-0-1483054. Ed. Tarja Mansikkamaki. adv.: B&W page FIM 5460, color page FIM 8750. bk.rev.; charts; illus. circ. 8,000.
Former titles: Laakintavoimistelija (ISSN 0039-5579) & Suomen Laakintavoimistelija.
Description: Covers physiotherapy, movement and health, rehabilitation.

615.8 JA ISSN 0912-1455
HOKKAIDO RIGAKU RYOHO/HOKKAIDO JOURNAL OF PHYSICAL THERAPY. (Text in Japanese) 1984. a. 1500 Yen. Nihon Rigaku Ryohoshi Kyokai, Hokkaido Shikai - Japanese Physical Therapy Association, Hokkaido Chapter, Kokuritsu Ryoyojo Nishi Sapporo Byoin Rigaku Ryohoka, 7, Yamanote 5-jo, Nishi-ku, Sapporo-shi, Hokkaido 063, Japan.

615.82 JA ISSN 0304-2081
HOKKAIDO RIHABIRITESHON GAKKAI ZASSHI/HOKKAIDO REHABILITATION ASSOCIATION. JOURNAL. (Text in Japanese) 1964. a. 1500 Yen. Hokkaido Rihabiriteshon Gakkai, c/o Sapporo Ika Daigaku Eisei Tanki Daigakubu Rigaku Ryoho Gakka, Nishi 17-chome, Minami 3-jo, Chuo-ku, Sapporo-shi, Hokkaido 060, Japan. Ed. Mareo Herayama. **Document type:** academic/scholarly publication.

MEDICAL SCIENCES — PHYSICAL MEDICINE AND REHABILITATION

615.8   JA   ISSN 0915-6429
HOKKAIDO SAGYO RYOHO GAKKAISHI/HOKKAIDO ASSOCIATION OF OCCUPATIONAL THERAPISTS. JOURNAL. (Text in Japanese) 1984. a. Hokkaido Sagyo Ryoho Shikai, Sapporo Ika Daigaku Eisei Tanki Daigakubu, Nishi 17-chome, Minami 3-jo, Chuo-ku, Sapporo-shi, Hokkaido 060, Japan.

615.8   II
INDIAN ASSOCIATION OF PHYSIOTHERAPISTS. JOURNAL. 1965. a. membership. Indian Association of Physiotherapists, c/o Mrs. S.M. Sanghavi, 35 Chowpaty Sea Face, 3rd Fl., Bombay 400007, India. adv.; bk.rev. circ. 500. **Document type:** trade publication.

INDIAN JOURNAL OF OCCUPATIONAL THERAPY. see *OCCUPATIONAL HEALTH AND SAFETY*

INTERNATIONAL JOURNAL OF REHABILITATION RESEARCH. see *HANDICAPPED*

615.8   IS   ISSN 0021-2199
ISRAEL JOURNAL OF PHYSIOTHERAPY. (Text in English and Hebrew) irreg. (3-4/yr.). membership. National Union of Physiotherapists in Israel, 93 Arlozorov St., Tel Aviv, Israel. TEL 03-431111. Ed.Bd. adv.; bk.rev.; charts; illus. circ. 500.

616.07   FR   ISSN 0249-6550
JOURNAL D'ERGOTHERAPIE. 1965. q. 370 F. (foreign 440 F.) (effective 1996). Masson - Periodiques, Villa Laromiguiere, 75005 Paris, France. TEL 1-40-46-62-00. FAX 1-40-46-62-01. Ed. O. Lecluse. circ. 2,100. (also avail. in microform from UMI) **Document type:** academic/scholarly publication.
—UMI. **CCC.**
Description: Publishes theoretical and practical articles dealing with physiotherapy techniques.

JOURNAL OF BACK AND MUSCULOSKELETAL REHABILITATION. see *MEDICAL SCIENCES — Orthopedics And Traumatology*

615.82   US   ISSN 0894-1130
CODEN: JHTHFX
JOURNAL OF HAND THERAPY. 1987. q. $52 to individuals (foreign $62); institutions $62 (foreign $72). (American Society of Hand Therapists) Hanley & Belfus, Inc., 210 S. 13th St., Philadelphia, PA 19107. TEL 215-546-7293. FAX 215-790-9330. Ed. Evelyn Mackin. circ. 4,500. **Indexed:** Ind.Med. (1993-). **Document type:** academic/scholarly publication.
—BLDSC (4996.623500); SWETS; UnCover. **CCC.**
Description: Concerned with post-traumatic and post-surgical rehabilitation of the hand.
Refereed Serial

JOURNAL OF OCCUPATIONAL REHABILITATION. see *OCCUPATIONAL HEALTH AND SAFETY*

JOURNAL OF ORTHOPAEDIC AND SPORTS PHYSICAL THERAPY. see *MEDICAL SCIENCES — Sports Medicine*

615.8   JA   ISSN 0915-5287
JOURNAL OF PHYSICAL THERAPY SCIENCE. (Text in English) 1989. s-a. membership. (Society of Physical Therapy Science - Undo Seiri Kenkyukai) I P E C Inc., 1-2-3 Sugamo, Toshima-ku, Tokyo 170, Japan. TEL 03-5978-4067. FAX 03-5978-4068. (Dist. overseas by: Japan Publications Trading Co., Ltd., P.O. Box 5030, Tokyo International, Tokyo 101, Japan. TEL 03-3292-3753. FAX 03-3292-0410) Ed. Hitoshi Maruyama. abstr.; charts; illus.; index. circ. 1,500. **Document type:** academic/scholarly publication.
—BLDSC (5036.216000).

JOURNAL OF REHABILITATION. see *SOCIAL SERVICES AND WELFARE*

JOURNAL OF REHABILITATION ADMINISTRATION. see *BUSINESS AND ECONOMICS — Management*

JOURNAL OF RHEUMATOLOGY AND MEDICAL REHABILITATION. see *MEDICAL SCIENCES — Rheumatology*

615.82   US
JOURNAL OF SPINAL CORD MEDICINE. 1978. q. American Paraplegia Society, 75-20 Astoria Blvd., Jackson Heights, NY 11370-1177. TEL 718-803-3782. FAX 718-803-0414. Ed. Robert Young. bk.rev. **Document type:** academic/scholarly publication.
Formerly: American Paraplegia Society. Journal (ISSN 0195-2307)
Description: For physicians, researchers and health professionals who work in the spinal cord injury field.
Refereed Serial

JOURNAL OF SPORT REHABILITATION. see *MEDICAL SCIENCES — Sports Medicine*

JOURNAL OF THERAPEUTIC HORTICULTURE. see *GARDENING AND HORTICULTURE*

615.82   FR   ISSN 0755-3951
RM695
JOURNEE DE MEDECINE PHYSIQUE ET DE REEDUCATION. 1958. a. Expansion Scientifique, 15 rue St. Benoit, 75278 Paris Cedex 06, France. TEL 1-45-48-42-60. FAX 1-45-44-81-55. Eds. DeSeze, Debeyre J. Samuel.
Formerly: Journee de Reeducation (ISSN 0075-4420)

615.82   JA
KANAGAWAKEN RIGAKU RYOHOSHIKAI NYUSU/KANAGAWA PHYSICAL THERAPY ASSOCIATION. NEWS. (Text in Japanese) bi-m. Kanagawaken Rigaku Ryohoshikai, c/o Yokohama Shiritsu Daigaku Igakubu, 3-46, Urafunecho, Minami-ku, Yokohama-shi, Kanagawa-ken 232, Japan.

615.82   JA   ISSN 0285-3477
KANAGAWAKEN SOGO RIHABIRITESHON SENTA KIYO/KANAGAWA REHABILITATION CENTER. JOURNAL. (Text in Japanese; summaries in English, Japanese) 1974. a. Kanagawaken Sogo Rihabiriteshon Senta, 516, Nanasawa, Atsugi-shi, Kanagawa-ken 243-01, Japan.

615.82   CC
KANG FU/REHABILITATION. (Text in Chinese) bi-m. Y7.20. (Shanghai Yike Daxue, Jiaoyu Yanjiu Zhongxin - Shanghai University of Medical Sciences, Educational Research Center) Kang Fu Zazhishe, No. 5, Alley 733, Huaihai Zhonglu, Shanghai 200020, People's Republic of China. TEL 3235326. Ed. Yang Zhonghua.

616.07   FR   ISSN 0766-2262
KINE ACTUALITE. 42/yr. 625 F. Societe de Presse et d'Edition de la Kinesitherapie, 24 rue des Petits-Hotels, 75010 Paris, France.
Formerly (until 1984): Kinesitherapie Actualite (ISSN 0754-2038)

615.8   FR   ISSN 0023-1576
CODEN: KNTSAC
KINESITHERAPIE SCIENTIFIQUE. 1965. m. (except Aug.). 630 F. Societe de Presse et d'Edition de la Kinesitherapie, 24 rue des Petits Hotels, 75010 Paris, France. adv.; charts, illus. **Indexed:** Biol.Abstr.
—BLDSC (5096.070000). **CCC.**
Formerly: Kinesitherapie.

THE KNEE. see *BIOLOGY — Physiology*

615.82   JA   ISSN 0912-5825
KOCHI RIHABIRITESHON GAKUIN SOTSUGYO RONBUNSHU/KOCHI REHABILITATION INSTITUTE. COLLEGE OF PHYSICAL THERAPY. BULLETIN OF GRADUATE STUDY. (Text in Japanese) a. Kochi Rihabiriteshon Gakuin, 292, Asahi Tenjincho, Kochi-shi, Kochi-ken 780, Japan.

615.8   GW   ISSN 0023-4494
KRANKENGYMNASTIK; Zeitschrift fuer Physikalische Therapie, Bewegungstherapie, Massage, Praevention und Rehabilitation. 1948. m. DM.150 (Europe DM.174). (Deutscher Verband fuer Physiotherapie - Zentralverband der Krankengymnasten (ZvK) e.V.) Richard Pflaum Verlag GmbH und Co. KG, Lazarettstr. 4, 80636 Munich, Germany. TEL 089-12607-0. FAX 089-12607-200. (Subscr. to: Postfach 190737, 80607 Munich, Germany) Ed. Antje Hueter-Becker. adv.; bk.rev.; abstr.; charts; illus.; index. circ. 34,000. **Indexed:** Excerp.Med. **Document type:** academic/scholarly publication.
—BLDSC (5118.137000). **CCC.**

615.8   JA   ISSN 0915-6739
KYOTO RIGAKU RYOHOSHIKAI KAISHI/KYOTO JOURNAL OF PHYSICAL THERAPY. (Text in English, Japanese) 1971. a. Nihon Rigaku Ryohoshi Kyokai, Kyoto Rigaku Ryohoshikai, Sei Yozefu Seishien, 6, Higashikobaicho, Kita-ku, Kyoto 603, Japan.

615.8   GW   ISSN 0025-2514
MANUELLE MEDIZIN; interdisziplinaere Zeitschrift fuer Arthrologie, Kinesiologie und Chirotherapie. 1963. 6/yr. DM.238($172) (effective 1996). (Deutsche Gesellschaft fuer Manuelle Medizin) Springer-Verlag, Heidelberger Platz 3, 14197 Berlin, Germany. TEL 030-8207-0. FAX 030-8214091. E-mail: orders@springer.de. (Subscr. in N. America to: Springer-Verlag New York, Inc., 44 Hartz Way, Secaucus, NJ 07096-2491. TEL 201-348-4033. FAX 201-348-4505) Ed.Bd. adv.; bk.rev.; index. (also avail. in microform from UMI; reprint service avail. from ISI) **Indexed:** Excerp.Med. **Document type:** academic/scholarly publication.
—BLDSC (5365.766000); EMDOCS; UMI. **CCC.**
Description: Covers physiotherapy.

615.8   AU
MASSEUR. 1985. 4/yr. S.180. (Internationale Vereinigung der Oesterreichischen Masseure) Anna Pichler Verlag, Marchettigasse 6, A-1060 Vienna, Austria. TEL 01-5971652. FAX 01-5870984. Pub. Anna Pichler. adv. contact: Heinz Lasta. **Document type:** academic/scholarly publication.

615.82   SP   ISSN 0214-8714
MEDICINA DE REHABILITACION. 1986. q. 5000 ptas. (foreign $50). (Liga para el Desarrollo de la Rehabilitacion) Editores Medicos, S.A., C. Gabriela Mistral 2, 28035 Madrid, Spain. TEL 34-1-3860033. FAX 34-1-3739907. circ. 3,000. **Document type:** academic/scholarly publication.

615.82   GW   ISSN 0939-3889
CODEN: ZMPHEJ
MEDIZINISCHE PHYSIK. 1990. q. DM.80 (foreign DM.107). Verlag G. Braun GmbH, Karl-Friedrich-Str. 14-18, 76133 Karlsruhe, Germany. TEL 0721-165-0. FAX 0721-165191. **Document type:** trade publication.
—CASDDS.

N A P P S JOURNAL. (National Association of Rehabilitation Professional in the Private Sector) see *EDUCATION — Special Education And Rehabilitation*

615.82   US
N A R F REHABILITATION REPORT. 1982. s-m. membership. National Association of Rehabilitation Facilities, Box 17675, Washington, DC 20041. TEL 703-648-9300. FAX 703-648-0346. Ed. Mark W. Doyon. adv.; circ. 2,000 (controlled). **Document type:** newsletter.
Formerly (until 1992): Medical Rehabilitation Review.

N A R P P S DIRECTORY. (National Association of Rehabilitation Professional in the Private Sector) see *EDUCATION — Special Education And Rehabilitation*

NATIONAL (TORONTO). see *OCCUPATIONAL HEALTH AND SAFETY*

615.8   NZ   ISSN 0303-7193
NEW ZEALAND JOURNAL OF PHYSIOTHERAPY. 1940? 3/yr. NZ.$50. New Zealand Society of Physiotherapists (Inc.), P.O. Box 57-108, Auckland 4, New Zealand. TEL 64-9-6207566. FAX 64-9-6207566. bk.rev.; abstr.; charts; illus.; circ. 1,500 (controlled). **Indexed:** CINAHL. **Document type:** academic/scholarly publication.
—BLDSC (6094.640000).

615.8   NR   ISSN 0331-3735
NIGERIA SOCIETY OF PHYSIOTHERAPY. JOURNAL. Abbreviated title: J N S P. (Text in English) 1972. s-a. £N250($20) Nigeria Society of Physiotherapy, Department of Physiotherapy, College of Medicine, University of Lagos, Idi-Araba, Lagos, Nigeria. FAX 234-1-837630. TELEX 0027636 NG. Ed. Dr. Isaac O. Owoeye. adv. contact: Dr. Isaac O. Owoeye. circ. 1,000. **Document type:** academic/scholarly publication.
Description: Contains articles dealing with the pathology and research aspects of physiotherapy.
Refereed Serial

OCCUPATIONAL THERAPY INDEX. see *MEDICAL SCIENCES — Abstracting, Bibliographies, Statistics*

MEDICAL SCIENCES — PHYSICAL MEDICINE AND REHABILITATION

615.82 US ISSN 0000-1635
RM697.U5
OFFICIAL AMERICAN BOARD OF MEDICAL SPECIALTIES (A B M S) DIRECTORY OF BOARD CERTIFIED PHYSICAL MEDICINE AND REHABILITATION PHYSICIANS. 1985. biennial. $59.95. Marquis Who's Who, A Reed Reference Publishing company, 121 Chanlon Rd., New Providence, NJ 07974. TEL 908-464-6800. FAX 908-665-2898. (Subscr. to: Order Dept., Box 31, New Providence, NJ 07974-9903. TEL 800-521-8110) Ed. Roy Crego. **Document type:** directory.
 Formerly: A B M S Directory of Certified Physical Medicine and Rehabilitation Physicians (ISSN 0883-2986)
 Description: Biographical sketches of U.S. certified medical specialists sorted alphabetically with a geographical index.

ORTHOPAEDIC PHYSICAL THERAPY CLINICS OF NORTH AMERICA. see *MEDICAL SCIENCES — Orthopedics And Traumatology*

ORTHOPAEDIC PHYSICAL THERAPY PRACTICE. see *MEDICAL SCIENCES — Orthopedics And Traumatology*

615.82 617.087 JA ISSN 0916-1163
OSAKA SHIRITSU SHINSHIN SHOGAISHA RIHABIRITESHON SENTA KENKYU KIYO/OSAKA MUNICIPAL REHABILITATION CENTER FOR THE DISABLED. RESEARCH REPORTS. (Text in Japanese) 1986. a. Osaka Shiritsu Shinshin Shogaisha Rehabiriteshon Senta, 2-55, Kire Nishi 6-chome, Hirano-ku, Osaka 547, Japan.

615.82 US ISSN 1065-5077
P T; the magazine of physical therapy. 1993. m. $85 (foreign $110) (effective 1996). American Physical Therapy Association, 1111 N. Fairfax St., Alexandria, VA 22314-1488. TEL 703-684-2782. FAX 703-706-3169. adv.: B&W page $3240, color page $3760; trim 8 1/4 x 10 7/8. circ. 54,033.
 —BLDSC (6946.563020).
 Description: Provides legislative, health care, human interest, and association news and serves as a forum for discussion of professional issues, ideas, and innovations in clinical practice.

615.8 US ISSN 1079-882X
P T TODAY. (Physical Therapy); the nation's contemporary newsmagazine for physical therapy. 1992. w. free to qualified persons. Valley Forge Press, 1288 Valley Forge Rd., Ste. 50, Box 1135, Valley Forge, PA 19482. TEL 610-935-3302; 800-9VF-PRES. FAX 610-935-3072. E-mail: vpfedit@aol.com. Ed. Beverly Hamill; Pub. Michael C. Parella. adv. contact: Renee Luttrell. bk.rev.; illus.; circ. 50,000 (controlled).
 Description: Contains items of professional interest to physical therapists, physical therapist assistants, and physical therapy managers and educators.

PEDIATRIC PHYSICAL THERAPY. see *MEDICAL SCIENCES — Pediatrics*

615.8 US
THE PHYSIATRIST.⁕ 1984. 10/yr. membership. American Academy of Physical Medicine and Rehabilitation, 330 N. Abash Ave., Ste. 2500, Chicago, IL 60611-3514. TEL 312-922-9366. FAX 312-922-6754. adv. circ. 4,300. **Document type:** newsletter.
 Description: Covers education, research, practice, and legislation issues of interest to residents and practitioners in PM&R.

PHYSICAL & OCCUPATIONAL THERAPY IN PEDIATRICS; the quarterly journal of developmental therapy. see *MEDICAL SCIENCES — Pediatrics*

615.82 US ISSN 0888-7357
RD755
PHYSICAL MEDICINE & REHABILITATION; state of the art reviews. Abbreviated title: P M & R. 3/yr. $72 (foreign $82). Hanley & Belfus, Inc., 210 S. 13th St., Philadelphia, PA 19107. TEL 215-546-7293. FAX 215-790-9330. circ. 600. (back issues avail.)
 —BLDSC (6475.635000). **CCC**.
 Refereed Serial

615.82 US ISSN 1047-9651
CODEN: PMRAFZ
PHYSICAL MEDICINE & REHABILITATION CLINICS OF NORTH AMERICA. 1990. q. $108 (foreign $136) (effective 1996). W.B. Saunders Co. (Subsidiary of: Harcourt Brace & Company), The Curtis Center, 3rd Fl., Independence Sq. W., Philadelphia, PA 19106-3399. TEL 215-238-7800. FAX 215-238-6445. (Subscr. to: W.B. Saunders Co., Periodicals Dept., 6277 Sea Harbor Dr., 4th Fl., Orlando, FL 32887-4800. TEL 800-654-2452. FAX 800-874-6418) Ed. Dr. George H. Kraft. index. (also avail. in microform from UMI; back issues avail.) Indexed: Excerp.Med. (1995-). **Document type:** academic/scholarly publication.
 —BLDSC (6475.637000); UMI.

615.8 US ISSN 0031-9023
RM695 CODEN: PTHEA
PHYSICAL THERAPY. 1921. m. $95 (foreign $120) (effective 1996). American Physical Therapy Association, 1111 N. Fairfax St., Alexandria, VA 22314-1488. TEL 703-684-2782. FAX 703-684-7343. Ed. Jules Rothstein. adv.; bk.rev.; abstr.; charts; illus.; index. circ. 53,771. (also avail. in microform from UMI; reprint service avail. from UMI) Indexed: Abstr.Health Care Manage.Stud., AIM, Bibl.Dev.Med.& Child Neur., CINAHL, Curr.Cont., Except.Child Educ.Abstr, Excerp.Med., Hlth.Ind., Hosp.Lit.Ind., Ind.Med., Int.Nurs.Ind., Med.& Surg.Dermat., Phys.Ed.Ind., Sportsearch (1980-).
 ●Also available online. Vendor(s): Central Institute for Scientific & Technical Information, Information Access Co., Ovid Technologies.
 —BLDSC (6476.350000); EMDOCS; Faxon; Genuine Article; SWETS; UMI; UnCover.
 Formerly: American Physical Therapy Association. Journal.
 Description: Contributes to and documents the evolution and expansion of the scientific and professional body of knowledge in physical therapy.
 Refereed Serial

615.8 US ISSN 1059-096X
PHYSICAL THERAPY PRODUCTS. bi-m. $12 (foreign $30) (free to qualified personnel). Novicom, Inc., 20000 Mariner Ave., Ste. 480, Torrance, CA 90503. TEL 310-793-4141. FAX 310-793-4138. Ed. Julie Craig. adv.: B&W page $1595, color page $2295; trim 8 3/8 x 10 7/8. circ. 50,000. **Document type:** trade publication.
 Description: Covers the introductions of new physical therapy products, with advisory columns discussing new procedures, and other topics of interest to professionals.

615.8 US ISSN 1042-2579
PHYSICAL THERAPY TODAY. 1956. q. $46 to individuals; institutions $59. American Physical Therapy Association, Private Practice Section, 1111 N. Fairfax St., Alexandria, VA 22314-1408. TEL 703-684-2782. FAX 703-706-3169. Ed. J.A. Gould. adv.; bk.rev.; illus. circ. 4,500. (also avail. in microform from WWS) **Document type:** academic/scholarly publication, trade publication.
 —CCC.
 Formerly: Whirlpool.
 Description: Addresses business and clinical concerns of physical therapists in private practice.

615.82 GW
PHYSIKALISCHE THERAPIE HEUTE. m. DM.109. Ebert Verlag GmbH, Blankenseer Str. 6-8, 23562 Luebeck, Germany. TEL 0451-501011. FAX 04509-2241. **Document type:** bulletin.

615.8 SZ
PHYSIOTHERAPIE/FISIOTERAPIA. (Text in French, German and Italian) 1933. m. 84 SFr. Schweizerischer Physiotherapeuten-Verband, Oberstadt 11, CH-6204 Sempach-Stadt, Switzerland. TEL 041-993388. FAX 041-993381. Ed. Othmar Wuest; Pub. Hans Walker. adv. contact: Henri Haeckel. bk.rev.; charts; illus.; stat. circ. 6,000. **Document type:** trade publication.
 Formerly: Physiotherapeut (ISSN 0257-7690)

615.8 UK ISSN 0031-9406
PHYSIOTHERAPY. 1915. m. £48 (typically set in Jan.). Chartered Society of Physiotherapy, 14 Bedford Row, London WC1R 4ED, England. TEL 071-242-1941. FAX 071-831-4509. Ed. Jill Whitehouse. adv.; bk.rev.; abstr.; illus.; index. circ. 29,000. Indexed: Bibl.Dev.Med.& Child Neur., CINAHL, Dok.Arbeitsmed., Excerp.Med., Ind.Med. **Document type:** academic/scholarly publication.
 ●Also available online. Vendor(s): Data-Star, MIC-KIBC.
 Also available on CD-ROM. Producer(s): Knight-Ridder, Inc.
 —BLDSC (6489.000000); EMDOCS; Faxon; SWETS; UMI; UnCover.
 Description: Publishes new research on various aspects of physiotherapy.
 Refereed Serial

615.8 CN ISSN 0300-0508
CODEN: PTHCAZ
PHYSIOTHERAPY CANADA. (Text in English, French) 1923. 6/yr. Can.$35($50) Canadian Physiotherapy Association, 890 Yonge St, 9th Fl., Toronto, Ont. M4W 3P4, Canada. TEL 416-924-5312. FAX 416-924-7335. Ed. Diane Charter. adv.; bk.rev.; index. circ. 6,500. (also avail. in microform from UMI; reprint service avail. from UMI) Indexed: Biol.Abstr., C.I.N.L., Excerp.Med., Hosp.Lit.Ind, Rehabil.Lit.
 —BLDSC (6489.100000); Faxon; SWETS; UMI. **CCC**.
 Formerly: Canadian Physiotherapy Association Journal - Association Canadienne de Physiotherapie Revue (ISSN 0008-4751)

615.8 CN
PHYSIOTHERAPY IN TOUCH. 1980. q. $25 to non-members. (Ontario Physiotherapy Association) Upfront Communications, 1 First Canadian Place, Ste. 708, P.O. Box 5, Toronto, Ont. M5X 1A9, Canada. TEL 416-362-2491. FAX 416-362-5344. Ed. Caroline F. Snow. adv.: B&W page Can.$2020, color page Can.$2520. circ. 3,500.
 Former titles (until 1992): Physiotherapy Today (ISSN 0847-9585); Taking Care of O P A Business.

PHYSIOTHERAPY INDEX. see *MEDICAL SCIENCES — Abstracting, Bibliographies, Statistics*

615.8 UK ISSN 1358-2267
▼**PHYSIOTHERAPY RESEARCH INTERNATIONAL.** Announced for publication in 1996. q. £40($150) to individuals; institutions £80 (effective 1996). Whurr Publishers Ltd., 19b Compton Terrace, London N1 2UN, England. TEL 44-171-359-5979. FAX 44-171-226-5290. (Subscr. to: Turpin Distribution Services Ltd., Blackhorse Rd., Letchworth, Herts. SG6 1HN, England. TEL 01462-672555. FAX 01462-480947; Subscr. in N. America to: Whurr Publishers Ltd., Box 1897, Lawrence, KS 66044-8897. TEL 913-843-1221. FAX 913-843-1274) **Document type:** academic/scholarly publication.

615.8 UK ISSN 0959-3985
CODEN: PTHPEA
PHYSIOTHERAPY THEORY AND PRACTICE; an international journal of physical therapy. 1985. q. £45($85) to individuals (outside the E.U. £50); institutions £100 (outside the E.U. £105 ($185)) (effective 1996). Lawrence Erlbaum Associates Ltd., 27 Palmeira Masions, Church Rd., Hove, E. Sussex BN3 2FA, England. TEL 01273-207411. FAX 01273-205612. (Subscr. to: Turpin Distribution Services Ltd., Blackhorse Rd., Letchworth, Herts. SG6 1HN, England. TEL 01462-672555. FAX 01462-480947) Ed. Hilary Baddeley. adv.: page £175; 160 x 220. bk.rev. **Document type:** academic/scholarly publication.
 —BLDSC (6489.140000); SWETS.
 Description: Provides a forum for recent developments and current research in physiotherapy.
 Refereed Serial

MEDICAL SCIENCES — PHYSICAL MEDICINE AND REHABILITATION

615.82   PL   ISSN 0860-6161
POSTEPY REHABILITACJI/ADVANCES IN REHABILITATION. (Text in Polish; summaries in English) 1987. q. price varies. (Akademia Wychowania Fizycznego w Warszawie) Wydawnictwo Naukowe P W N - Polish Scientific Publishers P W N Ltd., Ul. Miodowa 10, 00-251 Warsaw, Poland. TEL 48-22-260207. FAX 48-22-267163. (Dist. by: Ars Polona, Krakowskie Przedmiescie 7, 00-068 Warsaw, Poland) Ed. Aleksander Ronikier.
Description: Publishes papers in therapeutic rehabilitation and related disciplines, information on advances in rehabilitation of various diseases and on new rehabilitation equipment.

PRAEVENTION UND REHABILITATION. see *MEDICAL SCIENCES*

615.82   GW   ISSN 0933-842X
PRAXIS DER KLINISCHEN VERHALTENSMEDIZIN UND REHABILITATION. 1988. q. DM.86. Verlag Modernes Lernen - Dortmund, Hohestr. 39, 44139 Dortmund, Germany. TEL 0231-128008. FAX 0231-125640. Eds. Dr. Manfred Zielke, Dr. Jochen Sturm. adv.; bk.rev. circ. 1,550. **Document type:** academic/scholarly publication.

615.82   GW   ISSN 0932-9692
PRAXIS ERGOTHERAPIE; Fachzeitschrift fuer Beschaeftigungs- und Arbeitstherapie. 6/yr. DM.59. Verlag Modernes Lernen - Dortmund, Borgmann KG, Hohe Str. 39, 44139 Dortmund, Germany. TEL 0231-128008. FAX 0231-125640. Ed. Martina Sankowski. **Document type:** academic/scholarly publication.

PROFESSIONAL READER. see *EDUCATION — Special Education And Rehabilitation*

R A D A R BULLETIN. (Royal Association for Disability and Rehabilitation) see *HANDICAPPED*

615.82 362.15   CN   ISSN 1192-2508
REHAB & COMMUNITY CARE MANAGEMENT. 1992. q. Can.$25.58 (foreign $49.50). B C S Communications Ltd., 101 Thorncliffe Park Dr., Toronto, ON M4H 1M2, Canada. TEL 416-421-7944. FAX 416-421-0966. Ed. H. Dostal. adv.; B&W page Can.$2030, color page Can.$3130; trim 8 1/8 x 10 7/8; adv. contact: Caroline Tapp-McDougall. bk.rev.; circ. 25,000 (controlled). **Document type:** trade publication.
Description: Covers technological advances, therapeutic trends, management issues and government legislative changes for those dedicated to improving the quality of daily life for Canadians challenged by injury, illness or aging.
Refereed Serial

615.82   SP   ISSN 0048-7120
REHABILITACION. (Text in Spanish; summaries in English and Spanish) 1967. bi-m. 9300 ptas.($90) (effective 1995). (Sociedad Espanola de Rehabilitacion) Editorial Garsi, S.A., Juan Bravo 46, 28006 Madrid, Spain. TEL 34-1-4021212. FAX 34-1-4020954. Ed. Dr. I. Bori de Fortuny. adv.; bk.rev.; abstr.; bibl.; illus.; stat.; index. circ. 1,000. (tabloid format) **Indexed:** Excerp.Med.

615.82 362.4   US
REHABILITACION: PREVENCION Y INTEGRACION. (Text in Spanish) 1982. 2/yr. Rehabilitation International, 25 E. 21st St., New York, NY 10010. TEL 212-420-1500. FAX 212-505-0871. TELEX 446412. (Co-sponsor: I N S E R S O) Eds. Luis Reguera, Barbara Duncan. bk.rev. circ. 6,000.
Description: Covers disability and rehabilitation in Latin America, Spain and Portugal.

REHABILITATION ADMINISTRATION. see *EDUCATION — Special Education And Rehabilitation*

REHABILITATION INDEX. see *MEDICAL SCIENCES — Abstracting, Bibliographies, Statistics*

REHABILITATION INTERNATIONAL. WORLD CONGRESS. PROCEEDINGS. see *EDUCATION — Special Education And Rehabilitation*

REHABILITATION NURSING. see *MEDICAL SCIENCES — Nurses And Nursing*

REHABILITATION NURSING RESEARCH. see *MEDICAL SCIENCES — Nurses And Nursing*

REHABILITATION REVIEW. see *EDUCATION — Special Education And Rehabilitation*

615.82   US   ISSN 1054-2280
RM735.A1
REHABILITATION TODAY.* 1991. 9/yr. Sportscape, Inc., 1300 Virginia Dr., No. 400, Ft. Washington, PA 19034-3225. Ed. Michelle Deakin. circ. 25,000.

REIMBURSEMENT NEWS. see *INSURANCE*

615.82   BL
▼**REVISTA DE FISIOTERAPIA.** (Text in Portuguese; abstracts in English, Portuguese) 1994. s-a. Universidade de Sao Paulo, Faculdade de Medicina, Rua Cipotanea, 51, Cidade Univ. A. Salles de Oliveira, 05360-000 Sao Paulo, SP, Brazil. **Document type:** academic/scholarly publication.

615.8   PO
REVISTA FISIOTERAPIA. 4/yr. Rua Portes Santo Antao 81-1o, Lisbon, Portugal. TEL 3475902. FAX 3424304. TELEX 13441 ACL. Ed. Fernando Pedro de Carvalho.

615.82   IT   ISSN 0557-9430
RIABILITAZIONE; rivista di medicina fisica e riabilitazione. 1968. q. L.84800($112) (effective 1994). (Istituto di Terapia Fisica e Riabilitazione dell'Ospedale Niguarda - La Granda) Masson S.p.A., Divisione Periodici, Via Statuto 2-4, 20121 Milan, Italy. TEL 02-6367-1. FAX 02-6367211. Ed. Ivano Colombo. adv.; B&W page L.1500000, color page L.2600000; trim 170 x 240. circ. 2,000. **Indexed:** Biol.Abstr., Excerp.Med. **Document type:** academic/scholarly publication.
—BLDSC (7963.560000).

615.82 371.9   IT
RIABILITAZIONE E APPRENDIMENTO. (Text in Italian; summaries in English) 1980. q. L.90000($150) (effective 1994). Liviana Medicina, Via A. De Gasperi 55, 80133 Naples, Italy. TEL 39-81-5524733. FAX 39-81-5518295. Ed. Carlo Perfetti.
Description: Provides a foundation for the scienze of rehabilitation as a growing discipline in medicine.

615.82   IT
RIABILITAZIONE OGGI. 10/yr. Editrice Spec. Riabilitazione, Via Perugino 26, 20135 Milan, Italy. TEL 2-550-125-35. Ed. Dr. Romualdo Carini. circ. 45,000.

RICERCA & PRATICA. see *PHARMACY AND PHARMACOLOGY*

615.8   JA   ISSN 0915-0552
RIGAKU RYOHO JANARU/JAPANESE JOURNAL OF PHYSICAL THERAPY. (Text in Japanese; summaries in English) 1967. m. 15980 Yen($123) Igaku-Shoin Ltd., 5-24-3 Hongo, Bunkyo-ku, Tokyo 113-91, Japan. TEL 03-3817-5703. Ed.Bd. circ. 7,500. **Document type:** academic/scholarly publication.
●Also available online. Vendor(s): JICST.
Formerly (until 1989): Rigaku Ryoho to Sagyo Ryoho - Japanese Journal of Physical Therapy and Occupational Therapy (ISSN 0386-9849)

615.82   JA   ISSN 0034-351X
RIHABIRITESHON IGAKU/JAPANESE JOURNAL OF REHABILITATION MEDICINE. (Text in Japanese) 1964. m. 22000 Yen($66.90) Japanese Association of Rehabilitation Medicine - Nippon Rihabiriteshon Igakkai, 1-17 Komone, Itabashi-ku, Tokyo, Japan. TEL 03-5966-2031. FAX 03-5966-2033. Ed. Akio Kimura. adv.; index. circ. 6,000. **Document type:** academic/scholarly publication.
●Also available online. Vendor(s): JICST.
Refereed Serial

RIVISTA DEGLI ARTICOLI SANITARI. see *MEDICAL SCIENCES — Orthopedics And Traumatology*

RIVISTA DI CHIRURGIA E RIABILITAZIONE DELLA MANO E DELL'ARTO SUPERIORE. see *MEDICAL SCIENCES — Surgery*

615.8   SA   ISSN 0379-6175
SOUTH AFRICAN JOURNAL OF PHYSIOTHERAPY. (Text in English) 1925. q. R.55 to non-members (foreign R.90). (South African Society of Physiotherapy - Suid-Afrikaanse Fisioterapie Vereiniging) Physiotherapy Publications, P.O. Box 72064, Parkview 2122, South Africa. Ed. J. Beenhakker. adv.; bk.rev. circ. 2,700. (back issues avail.) **Indexed:** Ind.S.A.Per.
—BLDSC (8339.700000).

SPORTS, EXERCISE AND INJURY. see *MEDICAL SCIENCES — Sports Medicine*

615.82 362.4   US   ISSN 0734-6522
SPRINGER SERIES ON REHABILITATION. 1981. irreg., latest 1994. price varies. Springer Publishing Company, 536 Broadway, New York, NY 10012-3955. TEL 212-431-4370. FAX 212-941-7842. Ed. Thomas E. Becker. **Document type:** monographic series.
—BLDSC (8424.773000).
Description: Covers issues in physical rehabilitation.

TEAM REHAB REPORT. see *HANDICAPPED*

615.82 371.9   NE   ISSN 0923-0211
CODEN: TRWEEE
TIJDSCHRIFT VOOR REVALIDATIEWETENSCHAPPEN/JOURNAL OF REHABILITATION SCIENCES. (Text in English) 1988. 4/yr. fl.70 (foreign fl.100) (effective 1995). Van Gorcum en Co. B.V., P.O. Box 43, 9400 AA Assen, Netherlands. TEL 31-5920-46846. FAX 31-5920-72064.
—SWETS.

615.82   JA   ISSN 0388-0168
TOKYO METROPOLITAN REHABILITATION CENTER FOR THE PHYSICALLY AND MENTALLY HANDICAPPED. BULLETIN. (Text in English) 1987. bi-m. Tokyo Metropolitan Rehabilitation Center for the Physically and Mentally Handicapped - Tokyoto Shinshin Shogaisha Fukushi Senta, 17-2, Toyamacho 3-chome, Shinjuku-ku, Tokyo 162, Japan.

TOPICS IN GERIATRIC REHABILITATION. see *GERONTOLOGY AND GERIATRICS*

TOPICS IN STROKE REHABILITATION. see *MEDICAL SCIENCES — Cardiovascular Diseases*

615.89   US
TRAGER INSTITUTE NEWSLETTER. 1979. 3/yr. $45 membership. Trager Institute, 33 Millwood, Mill Valley, CA 94941. TEL 415-388-2688. circ. 2,000 (controlled). **Document type:** newsletter.
Description: Covers various techniques of somatics, a form of pressure therapy.

615.82   US   ISSN 1046-5642
VOICE (FT. LAUDERDALE). 1987. m. $25 (effective 1995). Cary - Joy Communications, 1405 S.E. First St., Ft. Lauderdale, FL 33301. TEL 305-463-5556. FAX 305-463-2674. Ed. Ray Brasted. adv. contact: Melanie Glick. circ. 70,000 (controlled). **Document type:** newspaper.
Description: Contains rehabilitation information for case managers, managed care workers, nurses, physicians, adjusters, consumers with disabilities and caregivers.

615.8   RU   ISSN 0042-8787
CODEN: VKFLAL
VOPROSY KURORTOLOGII, FIZIOTERAPII I LECHEBNOI FIZICHESKOI KUL'TURY/PROBLEMS OF HEALTH RESORTS, PHYSIOTHERAPY AND EXERCISE THERAPY. 1923. bi-m. $45 (effective 1996). (Rossiiskii Nauchnyi Tsentr Reabilitatsii i Fizioterapevtov) Izdatel'stvo Meditsina, Petroverigskii pereulok 6-8, 101000 Moscow, Russia. (Dist. by: Mazhdunarodnaya Kniga, B. Yakimanka 39, 117049 Moscow, Russia. TEL 7-095-2384600. FAX 7-095-2384634) (Co-sponsor: Ministerstvo Zdravookhraneniya) Ed. V.M. Bogolyubov. adv. contact: V.K. Ivannikova. bk.rev.; illus.; index. **Indexed:** Biol.Abstr., Chem.Abstr., Dent.Ind., Ind.Med., Int.Aerosp.Abstr. **Document type:** academic/scholarly publication.
—BLDSC (0043.000000); CASDDS.
Description: Examines the mechanisms of physiological and therapeutic effects of physical and health resort factors, methods and results of their employment; also covers theoretical and practical problems involved in the use of exercise therapy in the complex treatment of different diseases.

615.8   CC   ISSN 0254-1408
RM695
ZHONGHUA LILIAO ZAZHI/CHINESE JOURNAL OF PHYSICAL THERAPY. (Text in Chinese) q. $3 per no. Zhonghua Yixuehui - Chinese Society of Medical Sciences, Tang Gang Zi, Anshan, Liaoning 114048, People's Republic of China. **Indexed:** ExtraMED. **Document type:** academic/scholarly publication.
●Also available on CD-ROM.

MEDICAL SCIENCES — PSYCHIATRY AND NEUROLOGY

610 530   CC   ISSN 0254-1424
ZHONGHUA WULI YIXUE ZAZHI/CHINESE JOURNAL OF PHYSICAL MEDICINE. (Text in Chinese) q. $1.30 per no. Hebei Yixue Yuan - Hebei Academy of Medical Sciences, 5 Chang'an Xilu, Shijiazhuang, Hebei 050017, People's Republic of China. TEL 44121. (Dist. overseas by: Guoji Shudian - China International Book Trading Corporation, P.O. Box 399, Beijing, P.R.C.) **Indexed:** ExtraMED. **Document type:** academic/scholarly publication.
●Also available on CD-ROM.
—BLDSC (3180.475000).

MEDICAL SCIENCES — Psychiatry And Neurology

A B P CONTACT/B V V CONTACT. (Association Belge des Paralyses) see HANDICAPPED

616.8 150   US
A B S A M E NEWSLETTER. 1986. bi-m. membership only. Association for the Behavioral Sciences and Medical Education, 6728 Old McLean, Village Rd., McLean, VA 22101. TEL 703-556-9222. FAX 703-556-8729. Ed. Michael A. Counte. (looseleaf format; back issues avail.) **Document type:** newsletter.

616.8   US
A C O NEWSLETTER. 1968. s-a. $12.50. American College of Orgonomy, Box 490, Princeton, NJ 08542. TEL 908-821-1144. FAX 908-821-0174. Ed. Barbara Koopman. circ. 1,000. (also avail. in microform from UMI) **Document type:** newsletter.

362.2   US   ISSN 0001-1436
A H R C CHRONICLE. 1949. q. membership. Association for the Help of Retarded Children, New York City Chapter, 200 Park Ave. S., New York, NY 10003. TEL 212-254-8203. FAX 212-473-2225. Ed. Shirley Berenstein. adv.; bk.rev.; illus. circ. 15,000. **Document type:** newsletter, consumer publication.
Description: provides information for AHRC families and friends about news in the field and services for the developmentally disabled.

A P S BULLETIN. (American Pain Society) see MEDICAL SCIENCES — Anaesthesiology

616.8 616.2   US
A S D A NEWS. 1978. 3/yr. $30. American Sleep Disorders Association, 1610 14th St., N.W., Ste. 300, Rochester, MN 55901. TEL 507-287-6006. FAX 507-287-6008. E-mail: asda@millcom.com. Ed. Dr. Paul Fredrickson. adv. contact: Michelle Saxton-Felten. bk.rev.; stat.; tr.lit. circ. 2,750. (back issues avail.) **Document type:** newsletter.
●Also available online.
Former titles (until 1993): A P S S Newsletter (ISSN 0897-9375); (until 1986): A S D C Newsletter.
Description: Current information on sleep disorders medicine and research.

616.8   US   ISSN 0886-5620
A S E T NEWSLETTER. 1976. q. membership only. American Society of Electroneurodiagnostic Technologists, Inc., Executive Office, 204 W. Seventh, Carroll, IA 51401. TEL 712-792-2978. Ed. M. Fran Pedelty. circ. 2,600. (looseleaf format)
Description: Contains news of the society, educational articles, and calendar of events.

616.8 378   US   ISSN 1042-9670
RC336   CODEN: JPSEDS
ACADEMIC PSYCHIATRY. 1977. q. $135 (foreign $150) (effective 1996). (American Association of Directors of Psychiatric Residency Training) American Psychiatric Press, Inc., Journals Division, 1400 K St., N.W., Ste. 1101, Washington, DC 20005. TEL 202-682-6240. FAX 202-789-6341. (UK addr.: 17 Belgrave Sq., London SW1X 8PG, England) (Co-sponsor: Association for Academic Psychiatry) Ed. Dr. Samuel J. Keith. adv.; bk.rev.; bibl.; charts; illus. circ. 1,000. (also avail. in microform from UMI; back issues avail.; reprint service avail. from ISI,UMI) **Indexed:** Behav.Med.Abstr., Chicago Psychoanal.Lit.Ind., Cont.Pg.Educ., Curr.Cont., Excerp.Med., Mid.East: Abstr.& Ind., Psychol.Abstr. (1977-), Risk Abstr., Sp.Ed.Needs Abstr., SSCI. **Document type:** consumer publication.
—BLDSC (0570.514150); UMI; UnCover. **CCC**.
Formerly: Journal of Psychiatric Education (ISSN 0363-1907)
Description: Provides a forum for work which furthers knowledge in psychiatric education and stimulates improvements in academic psychiatry.
Refereed Serial

ACTA NEUROCHIRURGICA. see MEDICAL SCIENCES — Surgery

616.8   AU   ISSN 0065-1419
CODEN: ANCSBM
ACTA NEUROCHIRURGICA. SUPPLEMENTUM. (Supplement to: Acta Neurochirugica (ISSN 0001-6268)) 1950. irreg., vol.34, 1984. price varies. Springer-Verlag, Sachsenplatz 4-6, Postfach 89, A-1201 Vienna, Austria. TEL 0222-3302415. FAX 0222-3302426. (N. American subscr. to: Journal Fulfillment Services, Box 2485, Secaucus, NJ 07096. TEL 800-777-4643) Ed. F. Loew. (also avail. in microform from UMI; reprint service avail. from ISI) **Indexed:** Biol.Abstr., Ind.Med., INIS Atomind. **Document type:** academic/scholarly publication.
—BLDSC (0639.851000); ADONIS; Faxon; SWETS; UMI. **CCC**.

616.8   BE   ISSN 0300-9009
RC321   CODEN: ANUBBR
ACTA NEUROLOGICA BELGICA. (Supplements avail.) (Text in English and French) 1900. 5/yr. 2200 Fr. (foreign 2500 Fr.). Association des Societes Scientifiques Medicales Belges - Vereiniging van de Belgische Medische Wetenschappelijke Genootschappen, Av. Circulaire 138A, B-1180 Brussels, Belgium. TEL 02-374-5158. Ed. Dr. Andre Capon. **Indexed:** ASCA, Bibl.& Ind.Geol., Bibl.Dev.Med.& Child Neur., Biol.Abstr., Chem.Abstr., Curr.Cont., Excerp.Med., Ind.Med., Psychol.Abstr. (1981-).
—BLDSC (0639.902000); Faxon; SWETS; UnCover.
Supersedes in part: Acta Neurologica et Psychiatrica Belgica (ISSN 0001-6284)

616.8   DK   ISSN 0001-6314
RC321   CODEN: ANRSAS
ACTA NEUROLOGICA SCANDINAVICA. (Text in English) 1961. m. DKK 2500 (incl. supplements) (effective 1996). Munksgaard International Publishers Ltd., 35 Noerre Soegade, P.O. Box 1248, DK-1016 Copenhagen K, Denmark. TEL 33-127030. FAX 33-129387. Eds. Mogens Dam, Ronald F. Polinsky. adv.; bk.rev.; bibl.; charts; illus.; index. circ. 1,600. (reprint service avail. from ISI) **Indexed:** ASCA, Bibl.Dev.Med.& Child Neur., Biol.Abstr., Biotech.Abstr., Chem.Abstr., Curr.Adv.Ecol.Sci., Curr.Cont., Dent.Ind., Dok.Arbeitsmed., Excerp.Med., Ind.Med., Ind.Sci.Rev., INIS Atomind., Nutr.Abstr., Psychol.Abstr. (1964-), Sci.Cit.Ind.
—BLDSC (0639.910000); ADONIS; CASDDS; Faxon; Genuine Article; SWETS; UnCover. **CCC**.
Supersedes in part: Acta Psychiatrica et Neurologica Scandinavica.
Refereed Serial

616.8   DK   ISSN 0065-1427
CODEN: ANSLAC
ACTA NEUROLOGICA SCANDINAVICA. SUPPLEMENTUM. (Text in English) 1932. irreg. free to subscribers of Acta Neurologica Scandinavica. Munksgaard International Publishers Ltd., 35 Noerre Soegade, P.O. Box 2148, DK-1016 Copenhagen K, Denmark. TEL 33-127030. FAX 33-129387. Eds. Mogens Dam, Ronald F. Polinsky. adv. (reprint service avail. from ISI) **Indexed:** Biol.Abstr., Chem.Abstr., Curr.Adv.Ecol.Sci., Curr.Cont., Excerp.Med., Ind.Med., INIS Atomind.
—BLDSC (0639.912000); ADONIS; CASDDS; EMDOCS; Faxon; SWETS; UnCover. **CCC**.
Refereed Serial

616.8   GW   ISSN 0001-6322
CODEN: ANPTAL
ACTA NEUROPATHOLOGICA. (Text in English) 1961. 12/yr. (in 2 vols., 6 nos./vol.). DM.3598($2614) (effective 1996). (World Federation of Neurology) Springer-Verlag, Heidelberger Platz 3, 14197 Berlin, Germany. TEL 030-8207-0. FAX 030-8214091. E-mail: orders@springer.de. (Subscr. in N. America to: Springer-Verlag New York, Inc., 44 Hartz Way, Secaucus, NJ 07096-2491. TEL 201-348-4033) Ed. K. Jellinger. adv.; bibl.; charts; illus.; index. (also avail. in microform from UMI; reprint service avail. from ISI) **Indexed:** ASCA, Biol.Abstr., Chem.Abstr., Curr.Adv.Ecol.Sci., Curr.Cont., Dent.Ind., Excerp.Med., Helminthol.Abstr., Ind.Med., Ind.Sci.Rev., Ind.Vet., INIS Atomind., Kidney, Nutr.Abstr., Pig News & Info., Poult.Abstr., Protozool.Abstr., Rev.Med.& Vet.Mycol., Sci.Cit.Ind., Small Anim.Abstr. **Document type:** academic/scholarly publication.
—BLDSC (0639.920000); CASDDS; Faxon; Genuine Article; SWETS; UMI; UnCover. **CCC**.
Description: Provides information on subjects related to nerve tissue research based on modern investigative techniques, including histochemistry, electron microscopy, immunology, tissue culture, biophysics, neurochemistry, and experimental neuropathology.

616.8   GW   ISSN 0065-1435
CODEN: ANLSBX
ACTA NEUROPATHOLOGICA. SUPPLEMENT. (Text in English) 1962. irreg. price varies. Springer-Verlag, Heidelberger Platz 3, 14197 Berlin, Germany. TEL 030-8207-0. FAX 030-8214091. E-mail: orders@springer.de. (also avail. in microform from UMI; reprint service avail. from ISI) **Indexed:** Biol.Abstr., Chem.Abstr., Ind.Med., Vet.Bull. **Document type:** monographic series.
—CASDDS.

616.89   NE   ISSN 0924-2708
CODEN: ACTNE
ACTA NEUROPSYCHIATRICA. 1989. 4/yr. (Dutch Interdisciplinary Society of Biological Psychiatry) Reed HealthCare (Subsidiary of: Reed Elsevier plc), P.O. Box 1126, 1000 BC Amsterdam, Netherlands. TEL 31-20-5153350. FAX 31-20-5153354. Ed. Dr. M.J.A.J.M. Hoes. adv. contact: G.J.M. van den Akker. circ. 1,200. **Indexed:** Excerp.Med. (1995-). **Document type:** academic/scholarly publication.
—BLDSC (0639.970000); Genuine Article.
Refereed Serial

616.89   SZ   ISSN 0936-6075
CODEN: ACPDAW
ACTA PAEDOPSYCHIATRICA; international journal of child and adolescent psychiatry. (Text in English) 1934-1984; resumed 1988. q. DM.218($136) Springer-Verlag, Heidelberger Platz 3, 14197 Berlin, Germany. TEL 030-8207-0. FAX 030-8214091. (Subscr. in N. America to: Springer-Verlag New York, Inc., 44 Hartz Way, Secaucus, NJ 07096-2491. TEL 201-348-4033) Ed. Hans G. Reinhard. adv.; bk.rev.; bibl.; charts; illus.; index. circ. 950. **Indexed:** ASCA, Biol.Abstr., Child Devel.Abstr., Curr.Cont., DSH Abstr., Excerp.Med. (until 19??), Ind.Med., Ment.Retard.Abstr., Psychol.Abstr. (1934-), SSCI.
—Faxon; UMI. **CCC**.
Former titles: Acta Paedopsychiatrica (ISSN 0001-6586); (until 1953): Zeitschrift fuer Kinderpsychiatrie (ISSN 0372-8447)

MEDICAL SCIENCES — PSYCHIATRY AND NEUROLOGY

616.89   AG   ISSN 0001-6896
CODEN: APOPAS
ACTA PSIQUIATRICA Y PSICOLOGICA DE AMERICA LATINA. 1954. q. $70 (N. America $98; Europe $102; elsewhere $110) (effective 1994). Fundacion Acta Fondo para la Salud Mental, Malabia 2274 13 A, 1425 Buenos Aires, Argentina. TEL 541-72-3286. FAX 541-856-7108. Dir. Guillermo Vidal. adv. contact: Carlos Foce. bk.rev.; abstr.; charts; illus.; index. circ. 3,000. (reprint service avail. from IRC,ISI,UMI) **Indexed:** ASCA, Biol.Abstr., Chem.Abstr., Curr.Cont., Excerp.Med., Ind.Med., Psychol.Abstr. (1954-), SSCI. **Document type:** academic/scholarly publication.
—BLDSC (0661.399000); UMI.
   Description: Devoted to psychiatry and psychology issues relevant to Latin America.

616.89   DK   ISSN 0001-690X
CODEN: APYSA9
ACTA PSYCHIATRICA SCANDINAVICA. (Text in English) 1926. 12/yr. DKK 2600 (incl. supplements) (effective 1996). Munksgaard International Publishers Ltd., 35 Noerre Soegade, P.O. Box 2148, DK-1016 Copenhagen K. TEL 33-127030. FAX 33-129387. Ed. Jan-Otto Ottosson. adv.; bk.rev.; charts; illus.; index. circ. 1,900. (reprint service avail. from ISI) **Indexed:** Abstr.Crim.& Pen., Abstr.Health Care Manage.Stud., Adol.Ment.Hlth.Abstr., ASCA, Bibl.Dev.Med.& Child Neur., Biol.Abstr., Biotech.Abstr., Chem.Abstr., Curr.Adv.Ecol.Sci., Curr.Cont., Dent.Ind., Dok.Arbeitsmed., Excerp.Med., Ind.Med., Ind.Sci.Rev., INIS Atomind., Kidney, Mid.East: Abstr.& Ind., Psychol.Abstr. (1950-), Risk Abstr., Sci.Cit.Ind., SSCI.
—BLDSC (0661.470000); ADONIS; CASDDS; Faxon; Genuine Article; SWETS; UnCover. **CCC.**
   Supersedes in part: Acta Psychiatrica et Neurologica Scandinavica.
   Refereed Serial

616.8   DK   ISSN 0065-1591
CODEN: ASSUA6
ACTA PSYCHIATRICA SCANDINAVICA. SUPPLEMENTUM. (Text in English) 1932. irreg. free to subscribers of Acta Psychiatrica Scandinavica. Munksgaard International Publishers Ltd., P.O. Box 2148, DK-1016 Copenhagen K, Denmark. TEL 33-127030. FAX 33-129387. Ed. Jan-Otto Ottosson. adv. (reprint service avail. from ISI) **Indexed:** Biol.Abstr., Chem.Abstr., Curr.Adv.Ecol.Sci., Curr.Cont., Excerp.Med., Ind.Med., INIS Atomind., Mid.East: Abstr.& Ind.
—BLDSC (0661.472000); ADONIS; CASDDS; EMDOCS; Faxon; SWETS; UnCover. **CCC.**

616.8   SP   ISSN 0300-5062
CODEN: ALNPAJ
ACTAS LUSO ESPANOLAS DE NEUROLOGIA PSIQUIATRIA Y CIENCIAS AFINES. 1940. bi-m. 5900 ptas.($70) (effective 1995). Editorial Garsi, S.A., Juan Bravo 46, 28006 Madrid, Spain. TEL 34-1-4021212. FAX 34-1-4020954. Ed. J.J. Lopez Ibor. circ. 2,000. **Indexed:** Biol.Abstr., Excerp.Med., Ind.Med., Ind.Med.Esp., Psychol.Abstr. (1966-).
—BLDSC (0629.700000); Genuine Article; SWETS.
   Former titles (until 1971): Actas Luso Espanolas de Neurologia y Psiquiatria (ISSN 0001-7329); (until 1946): Actas Espanolas de Neurologia y Psiquiatria (ISSN 0300-5054)

ACTING OUT. see *SOCIAL SERVICES AND WELFARE*

616.8   US   ISSN 0065-2008
RJ499.A1
ADOLESCENT PSYCHIATRY; development and clinical studies. Represents: American Society for Adolescent Psychiatry. Annals. 1971. a. price varies. (American Society for Adolescent Psychiatry) University of Chicago Press, Journals Division, 5720 S. Woodlawn Ave., Chicago, IL 60637. TEL 312-753-3347. FAX 312-753-0811. TELEX 25-4603. (Orders to: Box 37005, Chicago, IL 60637) Ed. Sherman C. Feinstein. (also avail. in microfilm from PMC; reprint service avail. from UMI) **Indexed:** ASCA, Biol.Abstr., CINAHL, Psychol.Abstr., SSCI. **Document type:** academic/scholarly publication.
—BLDSC (0696.589000); UMI; UnCover.
   Description: Reports on specific clinical and theoretical issues, as well as considerations of social, cultural, and political themes. Contains scholarly articles from contributors in a variety of disciplines.
   Refereed Serial

616.8   SI
ADVANCED SERIES IN NEUROSCIENCE. (Text in English) 1988. irreg., vol. 4, 1994. price varies. World Scientific Publishing Co. Pte. Ltd., Farrer Rd., P.O. Box 128, Singapore 9128, Singapore. TEL 3825663. FAX 3825919. TELEX RS 28561 WSPC. (UK addr.: 73 Lynton Mead, Totteridge, London N20 8DH, England. TEL 44-81-4463356; US addr.: 1060 Main St., Ste. 1B, River Edge, NJ 07661. TEL 800-227-7562) **Document type:** monographic series.

616.8   US   ISSN 0095-4829
ADVANCES AND TECHNICAL STANDARDS IN NEUROSURGERY. 1974. irreg., no.17, 1990. price varies. Springer-Verlag, 175 Fifth Ave., New York, NY 10010. TEL 212-460-1500. FAX 212-473-6272. (Also: Berlin, Heidelberg, Tokyo and Vienna) Ed.Bd. (reprint service avail. from ISI) **Document type:** monographic series.
—BLDSC (0698.820000); Faxon.

616.8   UK   ISSN 0965-1802
ADVANCES IN A L S - M N D. (Amyotrophic Lateral Sclerosis - Motor Neuron Disease) 1991. irreg. Smith-Gordon and Co. Ltd., 16 Gunter Grove, No. 1, London SW10 0UJ, England. TEL 071-351-7042. Ed. Frank Clifford Rose. **Document type:** academic/scholarly publication.
—BLDSC (0698.580000).

ADVANCES IN BIOCHEMICAL PSYCHOPHARMACOLOGY. see *PHARMACY AND PHARMACOLOGY*

616.8   SZ   ISSN 0378-7354
CODEN: ABPSD5
ADVANCES IN BIOLOGICAL PSYCHIATRY. 1978. irreg. (approx. 2/yr.). price varies. S. Karger AG, Allschwilerstr. 10, P.O. Box, CH-4009 Basel, Switzerland. TEL 061-3061111. FAX 061-3061234. E-mail: Karger@Karger.ch. Eds. J. Mendlewicz, H.M. van Praag. (reprint service avail. from ISI) **Indexed:** Biol.Abstr., Chem.Abstr., Curr.Cont., Psychol.Abstr. **Document type:** academic/scholarly publication.
—CASDDS. **CCC.**
   Refereed Serial

ADVANCES IN CHILD NEUROPSYCHOLOGY. see *PSYCHOLOGY*

ADVANCES IN CONNECTIONIST AND NEURAL COMPUTATION THEORY. see *COMPUTERS — Artificial Intelligence*

ADVANCES IN CONSCIOUSNESS RESEARCH. see *PSYCHOLOGY*

ADVANCES IN CONTROL NETWORKS AND LARGE SCALE PARALLEL DISTRIBUTED PROCESSING MODELS. see *COMPUTERS — Artificial Intelligence*

616.8 613.2   UK
ADVANCES IN EATING DISORDERS. 1987. irreg., vol.2, 1989. $88. Jessica Kingsley Publishers, 116 Pentonville Rd., London N1 9JB, England. TEL 071-833-2307. FAX 071-837-2917. (U.S. subscr. to: Taylor & Francis, 1900 Frost Rd., Ste. 101, Bristol, PA 19007-1598. TEL 800-821-8312. FAX 215-785-5515) Ed. William Johnson. **Document type:** monographic series.

616.853   US   ISSN 0892-726X
RC372.A1   CODEN: ADEPDN
ADVANCES IN EPILEPTOLOGY. 1980. irreg., vol.17, 1991. price varies. Raven Press (Subsidiary of: Wolters Kluwer N.V.), 1185 Ave. of the Americas, New York, NY 10036. TEL 212-930-9500. FAX 212-869-3495. (reprint service avail. from UMI) **Document type:** proceedings.
—BLDSC (0706.020000); CASDDS.
   Refereed Serial

ADVANCES IN HUMAN FACTORS - ERGONOMICS. see *PSYCHOLOGY*

ADVANCES IN HUMAN PSYCHOPHARMACOLOGY. see *PHARMACY AND PHARMACOLOGY*

ADVANCES IN NEUROCHEMISTRY. see *BIOLOGY — Biological Chemistry*

616.8   US   ISSN 0091-3952
RC321   CODEN: ADNRA3
ADVANCES IN NEUROLOGY. 1973. irreg., latest vol.69. price varies. Raven Press (Subsidiary of: Wolters Kluwer N.V.), 1185 Ave. of the Americas, New York, NY 10036. TEL 212-930-9500. FAX 212-869-3495. (reprint service avail. from UMI) **Indexed:** Biol.Abstr., Chem.Abstr., Curr.Cont., Dent.Ind., Ind.Med. **Document type:** proceedings.
—BLDSC (0709.482000); CASDDS; Faxon; Genuine Article; SWETS; UnCover. **CCC.**
   Refereed Serial

615.75 616.8   US   ISSN 1057-6592
CODEN: ADNPEZ
ADVANCES IN NEUROPSYCHIATRY AND PSYCHOPHARMACOLOGY. 1991. irreg., vol.2, 1991. price varies. Raven Press (Subsidiary of: Wolters Kluwer N.V.), 1185 Ave. of the Americas, New York, NY 10036. TEL 212-930-9500. FAX 212-869-3495. (reprint service avail. from UMI) **Document type:** monographic series.
—BLDSC (0709.482400).
   Refereed Serial

616.8   US   ISSN 1059-1540
CODEN: ANEUE7
ADVANCES IN NEUROSCIENCE. 1991. irreg., vol.2, 1994. price varies. Raven Press (Subsidiary of: Wolters Kluwer N.V.), 1185 Ave. of the Americas, New York, NY 10036. TEL 212-930-9500. FAX 212-869-3495. (reprint service avail. from UMI) **Document type:** monographic series.
   Refereed Serial

616.8   US   ISSN 0302-2366
CODEN: AVNSBV
ADVANCES IN NEUROSURGERY. (Includes Gesellschaft fuer Neurochirurgie. Proceedings) 1973. irreg., vol.17, 1989. price varies. Springer-Verlag, 175 Fifth Ave., New York, NY 10010. TEL 212-460-1500. FAX 212-473-6272. (Also: Berlin, Heidelberg, Tokyo and Vienna) (reprint service avail. from ISI) **Indexed:** Biol.Abstr., Chem.Abstr. **Document type:** monographic series.
—CASDDS; Faxon.

616.8 617   JA   ISSN 0916-698X
ADVANCES IN NEUROTRAUMA RESEARCH. (Text in English) 1989. a. 3500 Yen. Japanese Society for Neurotrauma Research, Nihon Daigaku no Shinkei Geka, Oyaguchi Kamicho, Itabbashi-ku, Tokyo 173, Japan.

616.8   AU   ISSN 0178-3696
ADVANCES IN NEUROTRAUMATOLOGY. 1985. a. Springer-Verlag, Sachsenplatz 4-6, Postfach 89, A-1201 Vienna, Austria. TEL 0222-3302415. FAX 0222-3302426. **Document type:** monographic series.
—BLDSC (0709.483300).

616.8   US   ISSN 0146-0722
CODEN: APRTDE
ADVANCES IN PAIN RESEARCH AND THERAPY. 1976. irreg., latest vol.21. price varies. Raven Press (Subsidiary of: Wolters Kluwer N.V.), 1185 Ave. of the Americas, New York, NY 10036. TEL 212-930-9500. FAX 212-869-3495. Ed. John J. Bonica. index. (reprint service avail. from UMI) **Indexed:** Biol.Abstr., Chem.Abstr., Curr.Cont., Ind.Sci.Rev., Sci.Cit.Ind. **Document type:** monographic series, proceedings.
—BLDSC (0709.576000); CASDDS; Faxon; Genuine Article; SWETS; UnCover.
   Refereed Serial

ADVANCES IN PERSONALITY ASSESSMENT. see *PSYCHOLOGY*

616.8   UK   ISSN 1355-5146
▼**ADVANCES IN PSYCHIATRIC TREATMENT.** 1994. 6/yr. £50. Royal College of Psychiatrists, 17 Belgrave Sq., London SW1X 8PG, England. TEL 0171-235-2351. FAX 0171-245-1231. (Subscr. to: Royal Society of Medicine Press, 1 Wimpole St., London W1M 8AE, England. TEL 0171-290-2928. FAX 0171-290-2924) Ed. Andrew Simms. adv. contact: Peter Mell. circ. 630. **Document type:** academic/scholarly publication.
—BLDSC (0711.018000).
   Description: Promotes the continuing professional development of consultant psychiatrists.

MEDICAL SCIENCES — PSYCHIATRY AND NEUROLOGY

616.8   SZ   ISSN 0065-3268
ADVANCES IN PSYCHOSOMATIC MEDICINE. (Text in English) 1960. irreg. (approx. 1/yr.). price varies. S. Karger AG, Allschwilerstr. 10, P.O. Box, CH-4009 Basel, Switzerland. TEL 061-3061111. FAX 061-3061234. E-mail: Karger@Karger.ch. Ed. T.N. Wise. (reprint service avail. from ISI, back issues avail.) **Indexed:** Biol.Abstr., Chem.Abstr., Curr.Cont., Ind.Med., SSCI. **Document type:** academic/scholarly publication.
—BLDSC (0711.100000); Faxon; Genuine Article; SWETS. **CCC.**
Refereed Serial

616.85   NE   ISSN 0922-3061
ADVANCES IN SUICIDOLOGY. 1989. irreg. price varies. E.J. Brill, P.O. Box 9000, 2300 PA Leiden, Netherlands. TEL 31-71-5353500. FAX 31-71-5317532. TELEX 39296 BRILL NL. (In N. America: E.J. Brill, 24 Hudson St., Kinderhook, NY 12106. TEL 800-962-4406. FAX 518-758-1959) **Document type:** monographic series.
Description: Scholarly treatment of issues pertaining to the prevention of suicide.

616.8 370.15   US   ISSN 1044-0534
AFTERLOSS; the monthly newsletter to comfort and care for those who mourn. 1989. m. $45. Harbor House (West) Publishers, Inc., 216 E. Victoria St., Santa Barbara, CA 93101. TEL 805-965-0996. FAX 805-965-0986. Ed. Margie Kennedy-Reeves; Pub. Barbara Lesstrang. adv. contact: Raymond George. index. circ. 6,000. (back issues avail.) **Document type:** newsletter, consumer publication.
Description: Deals with the management of and education about grief following the death of a loved one. Functions to help the survivors deal with the death of a spouse, child, other relations and friends.

AGGRESSION AND VIOLENT BEHAVIOR. see *PSYCHOLOGY*

AGING AND COGNITION; a journal of normal and dysfunctional development. see *PSYCHOLOGY*

612   TU   ISSN 1300-0012
AGRI DERGISI; turk algoloji (agri) derneginin yayin organdir. (Text in Turkish, summaries in English) 1989. q. $30. Turk Algoloji Derneginin - Turkish Society of Algology, Istanbul Tip Fakultesi, Agri Merkezi, Capa Klinikleri, 34390 Istanbul, Turkey. TEL 90-212-6350135. FAX 90-212-6310541. Ed. Dr. Serdar Erdine. adv.: page $500; adv. contact: Dr. Suleyman Ozyalcin. abstr.; circ. 1,000 (paid); 500 (controlled). **Indexed:** Excerp.Med. (1993-). **Document type:** academic/scholarly publication.
—BLDSC (0738.780000).
Description: Disseminates research, clinical studies and case reports on pain science in Turkey, with other news relevant to pain study and management.
Refereed Serial

AIDS CARE; psychological and socio-medical aspects of AIDS-HIV. see *MEDICAL SCIENCES — Communicable Diseases*

616.8   GW   ISSN 0302-4350
W1 AK995GN
AKTUELLE NEUROLOGIE. 1974. bi-m. DM.234. Georg Thieme Verlag, Ruedigerstr. 14, 70469 Stuttgart, Germany. TEL 0711-8931-0. FAX 0711-8931298. (Subscr. to: Postfach 104853, 70042 Stuttgart, Germany) Ed.Bd. adv.; index. circ. 1,800. (reprint service avail. from UMI) **Indexed:** Biol.Abstr., Curr.Adv.Genetics & Molec.Biol., Curr.Cont., Excerp.Med., INIS Atomind. **Document type:** academic/scholarly publication.
—BLDSC (0785.775000); Genuine Article; UMI. **CCC.**

616.8 616.1   IT   ISSN 0392-9116
ALGOLOGIA. (Includes supplements) (Text in Italian; summaries in English and Italian) 1982. s-a. free to qualified personnel. Istituto per lo Studio e la Terapia del Dolore (I.S.T.D.), Via del Pergolino 4-6, 50139 Florence, Italy. TEL 39-55-416081. Ed. Pierluigi Zucchi. adv.; bk.rev.; charts; illus. circ. 5,000. (back issues avail.) **Indexed:** Ind.Med., Ref.Zh.
—BLDSC (0787.328000).
Description: Features worldwide research papers on the study of pain. Covers neurology, psychoanalysis and cardiology.

612.67   US   ISSN 0893-0341
RC523   CODEN: ADADE2
ALZHEIMER DISEASE AND ASSOCIATED DISORDERS. 1986. q. $114 to individuals (foreign $143); institutions $180 (foreign $207) (effective 1996). Lippincott - Raven Press, 227 E. Washington Sq., Philadelphia, PA 19106. TEL 215-238-4200. Ed. Peter J. Whitehouse. adv. contact: Phyllis Noyes. bk.rev.; charts; illus. circ. 1,000. (reprint service avail. from UMI) **Indexed:** Psychol.Abstr. (1991-). **Document type:** academic/scholarly publication.
—BLDSC (0806.255300); CASDDS; Faxon; Genuine Article; SWETS; UMI; UnCover. **CCC.**
Description: Provides an international forum for reports of new research findings and approaches to diagnosis and treatment.
Refereed Serial

616.8 618.97 362.1   SW   ISSN 1100-0899
ALZHEIMERFOERENINGEN; et forum foer kontakt och information roerande sjukdomar av Alzheimer-typ. 1987. q. SEK 100 membership. Alzheimerfoereningen i Sverige, Alzheimerfonden, Sunnanv. 14 S, S-222 26 Lund, Sweden.

616.8 618.97   UK   ISSN 1356-918X
▼**ALZHEIMER'S RESEARCH.** 1995. q. £80($137) to individuals; institutions £165($275). (Alzheimer's Research Trust) Rapid Communications of Oxford Ltd., The Old Malthouse, Paradise St., Oxford OX1 1LD, England. TEL 01865-790447. E-mail: rapidcom@vax.oxford.ac.uk. (Subscr. in US to: 115 Fifth Ave., 4th Fl., New York, NY 10003. TEL 212-564-6255. FAX 212-564-6227) Ed. Dr. Sarah-Jane Richards. **Document type:** academic/scholarly publication.

616.8 362.6   US
ALZHEIMER'S RESEARCH REVIEW. q. free to donors. Alzheimer's Disease Research, American Health Assistance Foundation, 15825 Shady Grove Rd., Ste. 140, Rockville, MD 20850. TEL 800-437-AHAF. Ed. Erin Conners. charts; illus. **Document type:** newsletter.
Description: Describes the research into this debilitating disease sponsored by the organization.

AMENTIA; la voix des parents. see *HANDICAPPED*

616.89   US   ISSN 0890-8567
RJ499.A1   CODEN: JAAPEE
AMERICAN ACADEMY OF CHILD AND ADOLESCENT PSYCHIATRY. JOURNAL. 1962. m. $109 to individuals; institutions $199 (effective 1995). Williams & Wilkins, 428 E. Preston St., Baltimore, MD 21202. TEL 410-528-4000; 800-638-6423. FAX 410-528-4312. Ed. Dr. John F. McDermott, Jr. adv. contact: Gayle Miller. bk.rev.; abstr.; bibl.; charts; illus.; index. circ. 9,159. (also avail. in microfilm from WWS) **Indexed:** Adol.Ment.Hlth.Abstr., ASSIA, Behav.Med.Abstr., Bibl.Dev.Med.& Child Neur., C.C.I.P., Child Devel.Abstr., Dent.Ind., Dok.Arbeitsmed., Educ.Ind., Excerp.Med., IMFL, Ind.Med., Mid.East: Abstr.& Ind., NRN, Psychol.Abstr. (1982-), Risk Abstr., Soc.Work Res.& Abstr. **Document type:** academic/scholarly publication.
—BLDSC (4683.690000); Faxon; Genuine Article; SWETS; UnCover. **CCC.**
Formerly: American Academy of Child Psychiatry. Journal (ISSN 0002-7138)
Description: Presents original papers in psychiatric research and the treatment of children and adolescents.
Refereed Serial

616.8   US
AMERICAN ACADEMY OF CLINICAL SEXOLOGISTS. BULLETIN. 1991. q. American Academy of Clinical Sexologists, 1929 18th St., N.W., Ste. 1166, Washington, DC 20008. FAX 407-628-5293. bk.rev.; circ. 1,000 (controlled). **Document type:** newsletter.
Formerly: Cliniscope.
Description: For professional therapists and counselors in the field of sexology.

616.89 340   US   ISSN 0091-634X
RA1151
AMERICAN ACADEMY OF PSYCHIATRY AND THE LAW. BULLETIN. Key Title: Bulletin of the American Academy of Psychiatry and the Law. 1973. q. $50 to individuals; institutions $75. American Academy of Psychiatry and the Law, Box 30, Bloomfield, CT 06002-0030. TEL 203-242-5450. FAX 203-286-0787. Ed. Dr. Seymour Halleck. bk.rev.; bibl. circ. 1,750. (also avail. in microform from UMI,WSH; microfiche from WSH; reprint service avail. from UMI,WSH) **Indexed:** Abstr.Bk.Rev.Curr.Leg.Per., Abstr.Crim.& Pen., Adol.Ment.Hlth.Abstr., C.L.I., Crim.Just.Abstr., Dok.Arbeitsmed., Excerp.Med., Hlth.Ind., Ind.Med., L.R.I., Leg.Cont., Leg.Per., Psychol.Abstr. (1974-). **Document type:** academic/scholarly publication, bulletin.
—BLDSC (2385.230000); EMDOCS; Faxon; UMI; UnCover.

AMERICAN ACADEMY OF PSYCHIATRY AND THE LAW. NEWSLETTER. see *LAW*

AMERICAN ASSOCIATION OF MENTAL HEALTH PROFESSIONALS IN CORRECTIONS. MONOGRAPH SERIES. see *CRIMINOLOGY AND LAW ENFORCEMENT*

616.8   US   ISSN 0895-8033
AMERICAN ASSOCIATION ON MENTAL RETARDATION. NEWS AND NOTES. 1988. bi-m. $35. American Association on Mental Retardation, 444 N. Capitol St., Washington, DC 20001-1512. TEL 202-387-1968. FAX 202-387-2193. Ed. Margaret Seiter. adv. circ. 8,247. (tabloid format; back issues avail.)
Description: For individuals with special needs in the field of mental retardation.

616.8   US
AMERICAN HEALTH INFORMATION MANAGEMENT ASSOCIATION. MENTAL HEALTH SECTION. NEWSLETTER. 1983. q. $25. American Health Information Management Association, Mental Health Section, 919 N. Michigan Ave., Ste. 1400, Chicago, IL 60611-1601. TEL 312-787-2672. FAX 312-787-9793. Ed. Laura Feste. adv. circ. 1,200. (back issues avail.) **Document type:** newsletter.
Formerly (until 1992): From the Couch...
Description: Medical recordkeeping and documentation in the mental health care facilities.

616.89 150   US   ISSN 0065-860X
BF173.A2   CODEN: AMIAAO
AMERICAN IMAGO; a psychoanalytic journal for culture, science and the arts. 1939. q. $29 to individuals; institutions $65. (Association for Applied Psychoanalysis) Johns Hopkins University Press, Journals Publishing Division, 2715 N. Charles St., Baltimore, MD 21218. TEL 410-516-6980. FAX 410-516-6968. Eds. Martin J. Gliserman. adv. contact: Tara Dorai-Berry. bk.rev.; bibl.; charts; illus.; index. circ. 950. (also avail. in microform from UMI,PMC; back issues avail.: from KTO (vols.1-22); from WSU Press (vols.23-43); reprint service avail. from KTO) **Indexed:** Abstr.Engl.Stud., Arts & Hum.Cit.Ind., Bibl.Engl.Lang. & Lit., Biog.Ind., Chem.Abstr., Child.Lit.Abstr., Curr.Cont., Film Lit.Ind. (1974-), Ind.Med., M.L.A., Mag.Ind., Mid.East: Abstr.& Ind., Psychoanal.Abstr., Psychol.Abstr. (1939-), R.G., SSCI.
—BLDSC (0819.300000); Faxon; Genuine Article; SWETS; UMI; UnCover. **CCC.**
Description: Contributors investigate culture, science, and the arts, religion, philosophy, history and education from a psychoanalytic perspective.
Refereed Serial

616.8   US
AMERICAN JOURNAL OF ALZHEIMER'S DISEASE. 1986. bi-m. $109 (foreign $142) (effective 1996. Prime National Publishing Corp., 470 Boston Post Rd., Weston, MA 02193. TEL 617-899-2702. FAX 617-899-4900. Ed. Nancy Stone Hindlian. adv.; bk.rev.; abstr.; bibl.; charts; illus. circ. 3,000. (back issues avail.) **Indexed:** Abstr.Soc.Geront. **Document type:** academic/scholarly publication.
Former titles: American Journal of Alzheimer's Care and Related Disorders and Research (ISSN 0895-5336); (until 1987): American Journal of Alzheimer's Care and Related Disorders (ISSN 0888-4897)
Description: Covers Alzheimer's disease for medical professionals.
Refereed Serial

MEDICAL SCIENCES — PSYCHIATRY AND NEUROLOGY

AMERICAN JOURNAL OF ART THERAPY; art in psychotherapy, education, and rehabilitation. see EDUCATION — Special Education And Rehabilitation

616.804 US ISSN 0002-9238
RC386.5 CODEN: AJETA6
AMERICAN JOURNAL OF E E G TECHNOLOGY. 1960. q. $60 (foreign $70) (effective 1996). American Society of Electroneurodiagnostic Technologists, Inc., Executive Office, 204 W. Seventh, Carroll, IA 51401. TEL 712-792-2978. Ed. Janet Ghigo. adv.; bk.rev.; charts; illus.; index, cum.index. circ. 3,500. (back issues avail.) Indexed: Biol.Abstr., Excerp.Med., INSPEC (1971-), Psychol.Abstr. (1967-).
—BLDSC (0824.400000); Ei; Faxon; Genuine Article; UnCover.
Refereed Serial

AMERICAN JOURNAL OF FORENSIC PSYCHIATRY. see MEDICAL SCIENCES — Forensic Sciences

AMERICAN JOURNAL OF GERIATRIC PSYCHIATRY. see GERONTOLOGY AND GERIATRICS

616.89 US ISSN 0002-953X
RC321 CODEN: AJPSAO
AMERICAN JOURNAL OF PSYCHIATRY. 1844. m. $60 (foreign $90). American Psychiatric Association, 1400 K St., N.W., Washington, DC 20005. TEL 202-682-6020. FAX 202-682-6016. Ed. Nancy C. Andreasen. adv.: B&W page $2700, color page $3900. bk.rev.; bibl.; charts; illus.; index. circ. 44,000. (also avail. in microform from UMI,PMC) Indexed: Abstr.Crim.& Pen., Abstr.Health Care Manage.Stud., AIM, ASSIA, Behav.Med.Abstr., Bibl.Dev.Med.& Child Neur., Biol.Abstr., Biotech.Abstr., C.I.S. Abstr., Chem.Abstr., CINAHL, Crim.Just.Abstr., Curr.Adv.Ecol.Sci., Curr.Cont., Dairy Sci.Abstr., Dent.Ind., Excerp.Med., FAMLI, Hosp.Lit.Ind., HRIS, Ind.Med., Ind.Sci.Rev., Int.Nurs.Ind., Lang.& Lang.Behav.Abstr., Med.Care Rev., Mid.East: Abstr.& Ind., NRN, Nutr.Abstr., Past.Care & Couns.Abstr., Psychol.Abstr. (1928-), Psycscan C.P., Risk Abstr., Soc.Sci.Ind., Soc.Work Res.& Abstr., SSCI.
•Also available online. Vendor(s): Ovid Technologies, University Microfilms International.
—BLDSC (0835.000000); CASDDS; Faxon; Genuine Article; SWETS; UMI; UnCover. CCC.
Description: Presents clinical research and discussion on current psychiatric issues for psychiatrists and other mental health professionals.
Refereed Serial

616.8 US ISSN 0002-9564
RC321 CODEN: AJPTAR
AMERICAN JOURNAL OF PSYCHOTHERAPY.* 1946. q. $50. Association for the Advancement of Psychotherapy, 1300 Morris Park Ave. 402, Bronx, NY 10461-1926. TEL 800-524-4723. Ed. Stanley Lesse. adv.; bk.rev.; abstr.; bibl.; index, cum.index: 1941-1965. circ. 5,000. (also avail. in microform from RPI) Indexed: Abstr.Crim.& Pen., Adol.Ment.Hlth.Abstr., Biol.Abstr., Chem.Abstr., CINAHL, Curr.Adv.Ecol.Sci., Curr.Cont., Excerp.Med., Ind.Med., Ind.Sci.Rev., Lang.& Lang.Behav.Abstr., Mid.East: Abstr.& Ind., Psychol.Abstr. (1947-), Psycscan C.P., Sci.Cit.Ind, SSCI.
•Also available online. Vendor(s): University Microfilms International.
—BLDSC (0835.600000); Faxon; Genuine Article; SWETS; UMI; UnCover.
Refereed Serial

AMERICAN JOURNAL ON ADDICTIONS. see DRUG ABUSE AND ALCOHOLISM

616.858 US ISSN 0895-8017
RC326 CODEN: AJMREA
AMERICAN JOURNAL ON MENTAL RETARDATION. 1876. bi-m. $100 canada $106.; (elsewhere $115) (effective 1996). American Association on Mental Retardation, 444 N. Capitol St., Washington, DC 20001-1512. TEL 202-387-1968. FAX 202-387-2193. Ed. Stephen Schroeder. adv.: B&W page $520. bk.rev.; bibl.; charts; illus.; stat.; index. circ. 11,600. (also avail. in microform from UMI; back issues avail.) Indexed: Adol.Ment.Hlth.Abstr. (1940-), Behav.Med.Abstr., Bibl.Dev.Med.& Child Neur., Bibl.Ind., Biol.Abstr., Bk.Rev.Ind. (1980-), C.I.J.E., Chem.Abstr., Chic.Per.Ind., Child.Bk.Rev.Ind. (1980-), Child Devel.Abstr., Curr.Adv.Ecol.Sci., Curr.Cont., Dent.Ind., Educ.Admin.Abstr., Educ.Ind., Excerp.Med., Ind.Med., Ind.Sci.Rev., Lang.& Lang.Behav.Abstr., Mid.East: Abstr.& Ind., NRN, Psychol.Abstr., Psycscan D.P., Rehabil.Lit., Sci.Cit.Ind., Soc.Work Res.& Abstr., Sp.Ed.Needs Abstr., SSCI.
—BLDSC (0828.280000); Faxon; Genuine Article; SWETS; UMI; UnCover. CCC.
Formerly (until 1987): American Journal of Mental Deficiency (ISSN 0002-9351)
Description: Current research on biological, behavioral and educational sciences in mental retardation and related developmental disabilities.

AMERICAN PARKINSON DISEASE ASSOCIATION. NEWSLETTER. see SOCIAL SERVICES AND WELFARE

920 616.89 US ISSN 0065-9827
RC326
AMERICAN PSYCHIATRIC ASSOCIATION. BIOGRAPHICAL DIRECTORY. irreg. $49.50. American Psychiatric Association, 1400 K St., N.W., Washington, DC 20005.

616.89 US ISSN 0090-1881
AMERICAN PSYCHIATRIC ASSOCIATION. SCIENTIFIC PROCEEDINGS IN SUMMARY FORM. a. $15. (American Psychiatric Association) American Psychiatric Press, Inc., Journals Division, 1400 K St., N.W., Washington, DC 20005. TEL 202-682-6000. FAX 202-789-2648. (UK addr.: 17 Belgrave Sq., London SW1X 8PG, England)

616.89 US ISSN 1048-4159
AMERICAN PSYCHIATRIC ASSOCIATION. TASK FORCE REPORTS. 1970. irreg., no.21, 1982. price varies. (American Psychiatric Association) American Psychiatric Press, Inc., Journals Division, 1400 K St., N.W., Washington, DC 20005. TEL 202-682-6268. FAX 202-789-2648. (UK addr.: 17 Belgrave Sq., London SW1X 8PG, England)

AMERICAN PSYCHIATRIC NURSES ASSOCIATION. JOURNAL. see MEDICAL SCIENCES — Nurses And Nursing

AMERICAN PSYCHOANALYTIC ASSOCIATION. JOURNAL. see PSYCHOLOGY

616.89 US ISSN 0091-7389
AMERICAN PSYCHOPATHOLOGICAL ASSOCIATION. PROCEEDINGS OF THE ANNUAL MEETING. 1945. a. price varies. Guilford Publications, Inc., 72 Spring St., 4th Fl., New York, NY 10012. TEL 212-431-9800; 800-365-7006. FAX 212-966-6708. (reprint service avail. from UMI) Document type: proceedings.

616.8 US
AMERICAN PSYCHOPATHOLOGICAL ASSOCIATION SERIES. 1978. irreg., latest 1991. price varies. Raven Press (Subsidiary of: Wolters Kluwer N.V.), 1185 Ave. of the Americas, New York, NY 10036. TEL 212-930-9500. FAX 212-869-3495. (reprint service avail. from UMI) Document type: proceedings.
Refereed Serial

616.8 US
AMERICAN SOCIETY FOR ADOLESCENT PSYCHIATRY. NEWSLETTER. 1967. 4/yr. $10 or membership. American Society for Adolescent Psychiatry, 4330 East-West Hwy., Ste. 1117, Bethesda, MD 20814. TEL 301-718-6502. FAX 301-656-0989. Ed. Dr. Leonard Henschel. adv.; bk.rev.; stat. circ. 2,700. Document type: newsletter.

616.8 US ISSN 0066-0132
QP356.3
AMERICAN SOCIETY FOR NEUROCHEMISTRY. TRANSACTIONS. 1970. a. $25 (foreign $30). American Society for Neurochemistry, c/o Dr. Bernard Haber, Univ. of Texas Medical Branch, 301 University Blvd., MRB 2143, Galveston, TX 77555-1069. TEL 409-772-2108. FAX 409-772-2920. adv. circ. 1,500. (back issues avail.) Document type: proceedings.
—BLDSC (8898.050000).
Description: Annual meeting of investigators in the American hemisphere in neurochemistry, neurobiology, and molecular biology.

AMYLOID; international journal of experimental and clinical investigation. see MEDICAL SCIENCES — Rheumatology

616.89 SP ISSN 0213-0599
CODEN: APSIEL
ANALES DE PSIQUIATRIA. 10/yr. 6000 ptas. Aran Ediciones, S.A., Avda. General Peron 20, 5o Dcha., 28020 Madrid, Spain. TEL 34-1-5332525. FAX 34-1-5332123. Indexed: Psychol.Abstr. (1992-).

616.8 US ISSN 1071-569X
CODEN: AALGEB
▼**ANALGESIA.** 1994. bi-m. $125 (foreign $145) (effective 1996). Cognizant Communication Corporation, 3 Hartsdale Rd., Elmsford, NY 10523-3701. TEL 914-592-7720. FAX 914-592-8981. Eds. Dr. Robert B. Raffa, Frank Porreca. Indexed: Chem.Abstr., Ind.Med. Document type: academic/scholarly publication.
—BLDSC (0890.239700); CASDDS. CCC.
Description: Covers preclinical studies that are derected toward an aspect of pain pathways (e.g. anatomical, biochemical, molecular, pharmacological or physiological) and their identification; that involve the study of neurotrasmitter of modulators; or that investigate some aspect of known or experimental analgesic-antinociceptive compounds (including side effect).
Refereed Serial

616.8 US ISSN 1057-4131
ANALGESIA COMPUTERFILE. 1991. m. $225 to individuals (foreign $290); institutions $245 (foreign $310) (effective 1994). (Dannemiller Memorial Educational Foundation) W.B. Saunders Co. (Subsidiary of: Harcourt Brace & Company), Curtis Center, 3rd Fl., Independence Sq. W., Philadelphia, PA 19106-3399. TEL 215-238-7800. FAX 215-238-6445. (Subscr. to: Periodicals Fulfillment, W.B. Saunders Co., 6277 Sea Harbor Dr., 4th Fl., Orlando, FL 32891-4800. TEL 800-654-2452. FAX 800-874-6418) Eds. Drs. Steven D. Waldman, Alon P. Winnie. (diskette format; also avail. in looseleaf format) Document type: abstracting/indexing.
Description: Reviews articles on research and developments in pain management from more than 750 medical journals.

616.8 US ISSN 1057-2260
ANALGESIA FILE NOTEBOOK. 1991. m. $225 to individuals (foreign $290); institutions $245 (foreign $310) (includes binder) (effective 1994). (Dannemiller Memorial Educational Foundation) W.B. Saunders Co. (Subsidiary of: Harcourt Brace & Company), Curtis Center, 3rd Fl., Independence Sq. W., Philadelphia, PA 19106-3399. TEL 215-238-7800. FAX 215-238-6445. (Subscr. to: Periodicals Fulfillment, W.B. Saunders Co., 6277 Sea Harbor Dr., 4th Fl., Orlando, FL 32891-4800. TEL 800-654-2452. FAX 800-874-6418) Eds. Drs. Steven D. Waldman, Alon P. Winnie. (looseleaf format; also avail. in diskette format) Document type: abstracting/indexing.
Description: Reviews articles on developments and research in pain management from more than 750 medical journals.

MEDICAL SCIENCES — PSYCHIATRY AND NEUROLOGY

618.2 616.8   UK   ISSN 0267-3061
ANNA FREUD CENTRE. BULLETIN. 1978. q. $50. Anna Freud Centre, 21 Maresfield Gardens, London NW3 5SH, England. FAX 44-71-794-6506. Ed. Clifford Yorke. bk.rev. circ. 400. **Indexed:** Psychol.Abstr. **Document type:** academic/scholarly publication.
—BLDSC (2393.986000).
   Formerly (until 1985): Hampstead Clinic. Bulletin (ISSN 0263-9688)
   Description: For diagnosticians, therapists and social workers. Contains research and clinical papers from the center's psychoanalytic study and treatment of children.

616.8   FR   ISSN 0768-7559
ANNALES DE PSYCHIATRIE. 8/yr. 520 F. (foreign 750 F.) Expansion Scientifique, 31 bd. de la Tour Maubourg, 75007 Paris, France. TEL 40-62-64-00. FAX 45-55-69-20.
—BLDSC (0994.800000).

616.89   IT   ISSN 0003-4606
ANNALI DI FRENIATRIA E SCIENZE AFFINI. 1888; N.S. 1992. s-a. L.60000($80) to individuals; institutions L.80000 (effective 1994). (Centro Studi e Ricerche in Psichiatria) Liviana Medicina, Via A. de Gasperi, 55, 80133 Naples, Italy. TEL 39-81-5524713. FAX 39-81-5518295. Ed. Carmine Munizza. adv.; bk.rev.; abstr.; bibl.; charts; illus.; index. circ. 1,000. **Indexed:** Excerp.Med.
   Description: Contains bibliographic abstracts on the most debated subjects in psychiatry, materials on the courses available at the center, and results of research at the center and other institutes.

616.8 150   US
ANNALS OF BEHAVIORAL SCIENCES AND MEDICAL EDUCATION. a. membership only. Association for the Behavioral Sciences & Medical Education, 6728 Old McLean, Village Dr., McLean, VA 22101. TEL 703-556-9222. FAX 703-556-9729. Ed. Linda Garcia-Shelton. bk.rev.
Refereed Serial

616.8   US   ISSN 1040-1237
RC321   CODEN: APSYEZ
ANNALS OF CLINICAL PSYCHIATRY. 1989. q. $175 (foreign $205) (effective 1996). (American Academy of Clinical Psychiatrists) Plenum Publishing Corp., 233 Spring St., New York, NY 10013-1578. TEL 212-620-8000. FAX 212-463-0742. TELEX 23-421139. Ed. Dr. Charles L. Rich. **Indexed:** Excerp.Med., Ind.Med. (1993-), Psychol.Abstr. (1989-), Sociol.Abstr. **Document type:** academic/scholarly publication.
—BLDSC (1040.245000); SWETS. **CCC**.
   Description: Provides clinical practitioners with the results of current research into the phenomenology and treatment of psychiatric disorders.
Refereed Serial

616.8   US   ISSN 0364-5134
RC321   CODEN: ANNED3
ANNALS OF NEUROLOGY. 1977. m. $152 to individuals (foreign $220); institutions $229 (foreign $304); residents $104 (foreign $169) (effective Nov. 1994). (American Neurological Association) Little, Brown and Company, Medical Journals, 34 Beacon St., Boston, MA 02108. TEL 617-859-5500. FAX 617-859-0629. (Co-sponsor: Child Neurology Society) Ed. Dr. Robert A. Fishman. adv.: B&W page $820; trim 8 1/4 x 11. bk.rev.; abstr.; charts; illus.; stat.; index. circ. 8,700. (also avail. in microform from UMI; back issues avail.; reprint service avail. from UMI) **Indexed:** Abstr.Inter.Med., Behav.Med.Abstr., Bibl.Dev.Med.& Child Neur., Biol.Abstr., Chem.Abstr., Curr.Adv.Ecol.Sci., Curr.Cont., Dent.Ind., Diab.Cont., Dok.Arbeitsmed., Excerp.Med., Ind.Med., Ind.Sci.Rev., INIS Atomind., Nutr.Abstr., Psychol.Abstr. (1989-), Rev.Plant Path., Risk Abstr., Sci.Cit.Ind. **Document type:** academic/scholarly publication, trade publication.
● Also available online. **Vendor(s):** Lexis-Nexis, Ovid Technologies.
—BLDSC (1043.140000); CASDDS; Faxon; Genuine Article; SWETS; UnCover. **CCC**.
   Description: Contains original articles on research and clinical advances, brief communications, neurological progress, and editorials.
Refereed Serial

618.928   US   ISSN 0066-4030
RJ499.A1
ANNUAL PROGRESS IN CHILD PSYCHIATRY AND CHILD DEVELOPMENT. 1968. a. price varies. Brunner-Mazel Publishing Co., 19 Union Sq. W., New York, NY 10003. TEL 212-924-3344. FAX 212-242-6339. **Indexed:** Biol.Abstr., Psychol.Abstr. (1976-). **Document type:** academic/scholarly publication.
—BLDSC (1091.400000); Faxon; UnCover.
   Description: New developments and trends in child psychiatry and development for professionals working with normal and disturbed children.
Refereed Serial

616.8   US   ISSN 0147-006X
QP351   CODEN: ARNSD5
ANNUAL REVIEW OF NEUROSCIENCE. 1978. a. $47 (foreign $52) (effective Jan. 1995). Annual Reviews Inc., 4139 El Camino Way, Box 10139, Palo Alto, CA 94303-0139. TEL 415-493-4400; 800-523-8635. FAX 415-855-9815. TELEX 910-290-0275. E-mail: annrevu@class.org. Ed. W. Maxwell Cowan. bibl.; index, cum.index. (also avail. in microfilm from UMI; back issues avail.; reprint service avail.) **Indexed:** Biol.Abstr., Chem.Abstr., Comput.Abstr., Curr.Adv.Ecol.Sci., Curr.Cont., Excerp.Med., Ind.Med., Ind.Sci.Rev., INSPEC, Psychol.Abstr. (1978-), Sci.Cit.Ind. **Document type:** academic/scholarly publication.
—BLDSC (1523.350000); ADONIS; CASDDS; Faxon; Genuine Article; SWETS; UMI; UnCover. **CCC**.
   Description: Original critical reviews of the significant primary literature and current developments in neuroscience.

616.8   JA
ANNUAL REVIEW SHINKEI/ANNUAL REVIEW. NERVE. (Text in Japanese) 1988. a. 9064 Yen. Chugai Igakusha, 62, Yaraicho, Shinkuku-ku, Tokyo 162, Japan.

ANXIETY. see *PSYCHOLOGY*

616.8   UK   ISSN 0268-7038
RC425
APHASIOLOGY. 1987. 8/yr. £267($440) (effective 1996). Taylor & Francis Ltd., Rankine Rd., Basingstoke, Hants RG24 8PR, England. TEL 44-1256-840366. FAX 441-256-479438. TELEX 858540. E-mail: info@tandf.co.uk. (Subscr. in N. America to: Taylor & Francis Inc., 1900 Frost Rd., Ste. 101, Bristol, PA 19007-1598. TEL 800-821-5800. FAX 215-785-5515) Ed.Bd. bk.rev.; bibl.; charts; illus. (back issues avail.) **Indexed:** Bibl.Ling., Excerp.Med., Lang.& Lang.Behav.Abstr. (1987-), Ling.Abstr., Psychol.Abstr. (1992-). **Document type:** academic/scholarly publication.
—BLDSC (1567.923000); Genuine Article; SWETS; UnCover. **CCC**.
   Description: Information on all aspects of brain damage-related language problems for neurologists, speech therapists, psychologists in universities, and hospitals and clinics.
Refereed Serial

616 616.8   DK
APPLIED NEUROPSYCHOLOGY. 1993. m. DKK 600 (effective 1996). Munksgaard International Publishers Ltd., 35 Noerre Soegade, P.O. Box 1248, DK-1016 Copenhagen K, Denmark. TEL 45-33-12-70-30. FAX 45-33-12-93-87. E-mail: fsub@mail.munksgaard.dk.

APPLIED PSYCHOLINGUISTICS; psychological studies of language processes. see *LINGUISTICS*

616.8   FR   ISSN 0999-792X
APPROCHE NEUROPSYCHOLOGIQUE DES APPRENTISSAGES CHEZ L'ENFANT. Short title: A N A E. (Text in English, French) 5/yr. 680 F. (foreign 1150 F.) P D G Communication, 30 rue d'Armaille, 75017 Paris, France. TEL 40-55-05-95. FAX 45-74-65-67. Ed. Dr. Claude Jeanne Madelin; Pub. Patrick de Gavre. **Indexed:** Psychol.Abstr. (1992-).
—BLDSC (1580.615000).
   Description: For researchers and clinicians.

THE ARC TODAY. see *SOCIAL SERVICES AND WELFARE*

616.8 574.1   IT   ISSN 0003-9829
   CODEN: AIBLAS
ARCHIVES ITALIENNES DE BIOLOGIE; an Italian journal of neuroscience. (Text in English) 1882. q. L.190000($135) (effective 1994). Universita degli Studi di Pisa, Rettorato, Lungarno A. Pacinotti 43, Pisa, Italy. TEL 39-50-920111. FAX 39-50-40834. (Subscr. to: U.P.I.E. di Marlin & C. s.n.c., Pubblicazioni Italiane ed Estere, Borgo Stretto 10, 56100 Pisa, Italy. TEL 39-50-542366) Ed. O. Pompeiano. bk.rev.; abstr.; bibl.; charts; illus.; index; circ. 400 (paid). (also avail. in microfiche from BHP; back issues avail.) **Indexed:** Biol.Abstr., Chem.Abstr., Curr.Adv.Ecol.Sci., Curr.Cont., Excerp.Med., Helminthol.Abstr., Ind.Med., Ind.Sci.Rev., Nutr.Abstr., Phys.Ber., Psychol.Abstr., Sci.Cit.Ind. **Document type:** academic/scholarly publication.
—BLDSC (1637.200000); CASDDS; Faxon; Genuine Article; SWETS; UMI; UnCover.
   Description: Publishes basic research work in neuroanatomy, neurophysiology, neurobiology, neurochemistry and behavioral science.

616.8 150   UK   ISSN 0887-6177
ARCHIVES OF CLINICAL NEUROPSYCHOLOGY. 1986. 8/yr. £187($297) (effective 1996). (National Academy of Neuropsychology, US) Elsevier Science Ltd., Pergamon, P.O. Box 800, Kidlington, Oxford OX5 1DX, England. TEL 44-1865-843000. FAX 44-1865-843010. E-mail: nlinfo-f@elsevier.nl; usinfo-f@elsevier.com; forinfo-kyf04035@niftyserve.or.jp; Site addr.: http://www.elsevier.nl/. (Subscr. in U.S. and Canada to: Elsevier Science, 660 White Plains Rd., Tarrytown, NY 10591-5153. TEL 914-524-9200. FAX 914-333-2444) Ed. Cecil Reynolds. (also avail. in microfilm from UMI; back issues avail.) **Indexed:** Excerp.Med., Psychol.Abstr. (1986-). **Document type:** academic/scholarly publication.
—BLDSC (1634.090000); Genuine Article; SWETS; UMI; UnCover. **CCC**.
   Description: Publishes original contributions dealing with psychological aspects of the etiology, diagnosis and treatment of disorders arising out of dysfunction of the central nervous system.
Refereed Serial

616.89   US   ISSN 0003-990X
RC321   CODEN: ARGPAQ
ARCHIVES OF GENERAL PSYCHIATRY. 1959. m. $90 (foreign $125). American Medical Association, 515 N. State St., Chicago, IL 60610. TEL 312-464-5000; 800-262-2350. FAX 312-464-4184. Ed. Dr. Grayson Norquist. adv.; bk.rev.; bibl.; charts; illus.; index. circ. 38,500. (also avail. in microform from UMI) **Indexed:** Abstr.Health Care Manage.Stud., Adol.Ment.Hlth.Abstr., AIM, Behav.Med.Abstr., Bibl.Dev.Med.& Child Neur., Biol.Abstr., Biotech.Abstr., Chem.Abstr., Child Devel.Abstr., Curr.Adv.Ecol.Sci., Curr.Cont., Dent.Ind., Excerp.Med., I.P.A., IMFL, Ind.Med., Ind.Sci.Rev., Med.& Surg.Dermat., Mid.East: Abstr.& Ind., NRN, Nutr.Abstr., Psychol.Abstr. (1959-), Psyscan C.P., Risk Abstr., Sci.Cit.Ind, SSCI. **Document type:** academic/scholarly publication.
● Also available online. **Vendor(s):** Lexis-Nexis.
—BLDSC (1634.350000); CASDDS; Faxon; Genuine Article; SWETS; UMI; UnCover. **CCC**.
   Description: Publishes clinically relevant science in psychiatry. Includes original articles dealing with the biological origin of mental disorders and pharmaceutical therapy.
Refereed Serial

616.8 016   US   ISSN 0003-9942
RC321   CODEN: ARNEAS
ARCHIVES OF NEUROLOGY. 1959. m. $145 (foreign $185). American Medical Association, 515 N. State St., Chicago, IL 60610. TEL 312-464-5000; 800-262-2350. FAX 312-464-4184. Ed. Dr. Robert J. Joynt. adv.; bk.rev.; charts; illus.; index. circ. 17,500. (also avail. in microform from PMC,UMI) **Indexed:** Abstr.Inter.Med., AIM, Behav.Med.Abstr., Bibl.Dev.Med.& Child Neur., Biol.Abstr., Biotech.Abstr., Chem.Abstr., CINAHL, Curr.Adv.Cancer Res., Curr.Adv.Ecol.Sci., Curr.Adv.Genetics & Molec.Biol., Curr.Cont., Dent.Ind., Dok.Arbeitsmed., Excerp.Med., Ind.Med., Ind.Sci.Rev., INIS Atomind., Med.& Surg.Dermat., Nutr.Abstr., Psychol.Abstr. (1950-), Rev.Med.& Vet.Mycol., Sci.Cit.Ind, So.Pac.Per.Ind. **Document type:** academic/scholarly publication.
● Also available online. **Vendor(s):** Lexis-Nexis.
—BLDSC (1638.400000); CASDDS; Faxon; Genuine Article; SWETS; UMI; UnCover. **CCC**.
Refereed Serial

MEDICAL SCIENCES — PSYCHIATRY AND NEUROLOGY

ARCHIVES OF PSYCHIATRIC NURSING. see *MEDICAL SCIENCES — Nurses And Nursing*

ARCHIVES OF SUICIDE RESEARCH. see *PSYCHOLOGY*

616.89   IT
ARCHIVIO DI PSICHIATRIA GENERALE; l'ospedale psichiatrico. (Text in Italian; summaries in English) 1903. 3/yr. L.90000($150) (effective 1995). Casa Editrice Idelson, Via A. De Gasperi 55, 80133 Naples, Italy. TEL 39-81-5524733. FAX 39-81-5518295. Eds. Alessandro Fiorillo, Franco Rinaldi.
    Former titles (until 1990): Rivista l'Ospedale Pschiatrico; (until 1960): Ospedale Psichiatrico (ISSN 0048-2285)

616.8   IT   ISSN 0004-0150
    CODEN: APNPAD
ARCHIVIO DI PSICOLOGIA, NEUROLOGIA E PSICHIATRIA. (Text in English, French and Italian; summaries in English, French and German) 1940. bi-m. L.131000 (foreign L.183000 ($110)) (effective 1996). (Universita Cattolica del Sacro Cuore, Istituto di Psicologia) Vita e Pensiero, Largo Gemelli 1, 20123 Milan, Italy. TEL 39-2-72342310. FAX 39-2-72342260. TELEX 321033 UCATMI 1. Ed. Leonardo Ancona. adv.; bk.rev.; abstr.; bibl.; charts; illus.; stat.; index. **Indexed:** Biol.Abstr., Ind.Med., Lang.& Lang.Behav.Abstr., Psychol.Abstr. (1950-). **Document type:** academic/scholarly publication.
    —BLDSC (1647.880000); Faxon.
    Description: Covers psychology and neurology.

616.8 364   EC   ISSN 0004-0541
ARCHIVOS DE CRIMINOLOGIA, NEURO-PSIQUIATRIA Y DISCIPLINAS CONEXAS. (Second Series) vol.12, 1964. q. S/3000($5) per no. Universidad Central del Ecuador, Instituto de Criminologia, Apdo. 3663, Quito, Ecuador. TEL 542-971. Dr. Hernando Rosero Cueva. bk.rev.; abstr.; bibl.; charts; illus.; stat.; index. circ. 1,200. (also avail. in microfilm) **Indexed:** Biol.Abstr.

616.8   IT   ISSN 1120-866X
ARGOMENTI DI NEUROLOGIA. 1991. q. L.8300($59) (effective 1994). Masson S.p.A., Divisione Periodici, Via Statuto 2-4, 20121 Milan, Italy. TEL 02-6367-1. FAX 02-6367-211. Ed. Nicola Canal. adv.; B&W page L.3550000, color page L.5900000; trim 175 x 245. circ. 12,000. **Document type:** academic/scholarly publication.

616.89   BL   ISSN 0004-282X
    CODEN: ANPIAM
ARQUIVOS DE NEURO-PSIQUIATRIA. (Text in Portuguese or English) 1943. q. $80 (typically set in Oct.). (Academia Brasileira de Neurologia - Brazilian Academy of Neurology) Associacao Arquivos Neuro-Psiquiatria Dr. Oswaldo Lange, Caixa Postal 8877, 01065-970 Sao Paulo, SP, Brazil. TEL 5511-289-8824. FAX 5511-289-8879. Ed. Dr. Antonio Spina-Franca. adv.; bk.rev.; abstr.; bibl.; charts; index, cum.index: 1943-1982. circ. 1,400. (also avail. in microfilm from UMI) **Indexed:** Biol.Abstr., Dent.Ind., Excerp.Med., Ind.Med., Psychol.Abstr. (1943-).
    ●Also available on CD-ROM.
    —BLDSC (1695.630000); Faxon; Genuine Article; UMI. **CCC.**
    Description: Covers the medical sciences of neurology, applied neuroscience and psychiatry.

616.8 150   BL   ISSN 0103-0809
RA790.7.S25
ARQUIVOS DE SAUDE MENTAL DO ESTADO DE SAO PAULO. (Supplement avail.) (Text in Portuguese; summaries in English) 1924. a. exchange basis. Biblioteca do Hospital de Juqueri, Franco da Rocha E.F.S.J., CEP 07780-000 Sao Paulo, Brazil. TEL 55-11-432-5111. FAX 55-11-432-5444. TELEX 11-79736. Ed. Dr. Maria Tereza G. Freire. bk.rev.; charts; illus. circ. 1,500. **Document type:** academic/scholarly publication.
    —BLDSC (1685.600000).
    Formerly (until 1987): Sao Paulo. Coordenadoria de Saude Mental. Arquivos (ISSN 0101-1693)
    Refereed Serial

616.89   BL   ISSN 0102-7646
ASSOCIACAO BRASILEIRA DE PSIQUIATRIA E ASOCIACION PSIQUIATRICA DE LA AMERICA LATINA. REVISTA. Abbreviated title: Revista A B P - A P A L. (Text in Portuguese; summaries in English, Spanish) 1979. q. $100 (effective 1995). Associacao Brasileira de Psiquiatria, Rua Borges Lagoa, 394, 04038-000 Sao Paulo SP, Brazil. TEL 55-11-549-6699. FAX 55-11-570-6210. (Co-sponsor: Associacao Psiquiatrica da America Latina) Eds. Dr. Helena M. Calil, Sergio Luis Blay. adv.; bk.rev.; bibl.; charts; stat. circ. 3,500. **Indexed:** Biol.Abstr., Excerp.Med., Ind.Med., Psychol.Abstr. (1986-). **Document type:** academic/scholarly publication.
    —EMDOCS.
    Formerly: Revista Brasileira de Psiquiatria.
    Description: Papers on psychiatry and correlated disciplines of general interest to mental health professionals from Brazil and other Latin American countries.
    Refereed Serial

ASSOCIATION FOR APPLIED PSYCHOPHYSIOLOGY AND BIOFEEDBACK. PROCEEDINGS OF THE ANNUAL MEETING. see *PSYCHOLOGY*

ASSOCIATION FOR CHILD PSYCHOANALYSIS. NEWSLETTER. see *CHILDREN AND YOUTH — About*

610   US   ISSN 0091-7443
    CODEN: RPARA5
ASSOCIATION FOR RESEARCH IN NERVOUS AND MENTAL DISEASE. RESEARCH PUBLICATIONS. a., latest vol.72. price varies. Raven Press (Subsidiary of: Wolters Kluwer N.V.), 1185 Ave. of the Americas, New York, NY 10036. TEL 212-930-9500. FAX 212-869-3495. (reprint service avail. from UMI) **Indexed:** Biol.Abstr., Chem.Abstr., Curr.Cont., Dent.Ind., Ind.Med. **Document type:** proceedings.
    —BLDSC (7755.800000); CASDDS; Faxon; SWETS; UnCover.
    Refereed Serial

610 016   US   ISSN 0271-1311
AUDIO-DIGEST PSYCHIATRY. 1971. s-m. $168. Audio-Digest Foundation (Subsidiary of: California Medical Association), 1577 E. Chevy Chase Dr., Glendale, CA 91206. TEL 213-245-8505. FAX 818-240-7379. Ed. Claron L. Oakley. (audio cassette)
    Refereed Serial

AUDIOLOGY AND NEUROOTOLOGY. see *MEDICAL SCIENCES — Otorhinolaryngology*

616.8   US   ISSN 1023-618X
▼**AUDITORY NEUROSCIENCE.** 1995. 4/yr. 83 ECU (effective 1996). Harwood Academic Publishers, c/o International Publishers Distributor, 820 Town Center Dr., Langhorne, PA 19047. TEL 215-750-2642; 800-545-8398. FAX 215-750-6343. (Subscr. to: International Publishers Distributor, P.O. Box 90, Reading, Berkshire RG1 8JL, England. TEL 44-173-456-8316) **Document type:** academic/scholarly publication.

616.858 371.9   AT   ISSN 0726-3864
    CODEN: ANZDDQ
AUSTRALIA AND NEW ZEALAND JOURNAL OF DEVELOPMENTAL DISABILITIES. 1970. q. £40 to individuals; institutions £80 (effective 1996). Australian Society for the Study of Intellectual Disability, Unit for Rehabilitation Studies, Special Education Centre, University of Newcastle, N.S.W. 2308, Australia. TEL 61-49-216274. FAX 61-49-216939. Ed. P.J. Foreman. adv.; bk.rev.; charts; illus.; index. circ. 1,400. (tabloid format; also avail. in microfilm from UMI; reprint service avail. from UMI) **Indexed:** Aus.P.A.I.S., Biol.Abstr., Child Devel.Abstr., Except.Child Educ.Abstr., Excerp.Med., IMFL, Ind.Med., Ment.Retard.Abstr., Mult.Ed.Abstr., Psychol.Abstr. (1970-), Rehabil.Lit., Sp.Ed.Needs Abstr. **Document type:** abstracting/indexing.
    —BLDSC (1796.550000); SWETS; UMI; UnCover.
    Former titles (until vol.7, 1981): Australian Journal of Developmental Disabilities (ISSN 0159-9011); (until vol.6, Mar.1980): Australian Journal of Mental Retardation (ISSN 0045-0634)
    Description: Reports of research in the area of mental retardation and related disabilities.

616.8 610.73   AT
AUSTRALIAN AND NEW ZEALAND JOURNAL OF MENTAL HEALTH NURSING. 1980. q. Aus.$150($150) (effective 1996). Blackwell Science Pty Ltd, P.O. Box 378, Carlton South, Vic. 3053, Australia. TEL 61-3-93470300. FAX 61-3-93493016. **Document type:** academic/scholarly publication.
    Former titles: Australian Journal of Mental Health Nursing (ISSN 1035-8374); (until 1990): Australian Congress of Mental Health Nurses. Journal (ISSN 0727-4173)

616.89   AT   ISSN 0004-8674
RC321   CODEN: ANZPBQ
AUSTRALIAN & NEW ZEALAND JOURNAL OF PSYCHIATRY. (Supplement avail.) 1967. q. Aus.$65 to individuals (foreign Aus.$75); institutions Aus.$90 (foreign Aus.$115). Royal Australian and New Zealand College of Psychiatrists, P.O. Box 126, Karrinyup, W.A. 6018, Australia. TEL 61-9-447-5312. Ed. Sidney Bloch. adv.; bk.rev.; abstr.; charts; illus.; index. circ. 3,100. (back issues avail.) **Indexed:** Adol.Ment.Hlth.Abstr., Aus.Sci.Ind., Biol.Abstr., Curr.Cont., Dok.Arbeitsmed., Excerp.Med., Ind.Med., Mid.East: Abstr.& Ind., Mult.Ed.Abstr., Nutr.Abstr., Psychol.Abstr. (1969-), So.Pac.Per.Ind., Sp.Ed.Needs Abstr., SSCI. **Document type:** academic/scholarly publication.
    —BLDSC (1796.893000); Genuine Article; SWETS. **CCC.**

AUSTRALIAN JOURNAL OF PSYCHOTHERAPY. see *PSYCHOLOGY*

616.89 155   US   ISSN 0893-8474
AUTISM RESEARCH REVIEW INTERNATIONAL. 1987. q. $16 (effective through 1996). Autism Research Institute, 4182 Adams Ave., San Diego, CA 92116. Ed. Bernard Rimland. (back issues avail.) **Document type:** newsletter.
    —BLDSC (1825.569000).
    Description: Covers biomedical and educational research in the field of autism and related disorders.

616.8 910.03   US
B P A QUARTERLY. 1969. q. $20 to individuals; institutions $45. Black Psychiatrists of America, c/o Dr. Issac Slaughter, 2730 Adeline St., Oakland, CA 94607. TEL 510-465-1800. Ed. Dr. William Lawson. adv.: B&W page $1500. bk.rev. circ. 600. **Document type:** academic/scholarly publication, trade publication.
    Former titles: Bottom Line (New York, 1969); Black Psychiatrists of America Newsletter.
    Description: Publishes articles, and reports of professional meetings realting to mental health issues, and treatment concerning minorities and the underserved.

616.8   UK   ISSN 0961-0421
    CODEN: BCNUEK
BAILLIERE'S CLINICAL NEUROLOGY. 1992. 3/yr. £58 to individuals; institutions £66. Bailliere-Tindall (Subsidiary of: Harcourt Brace & Co. Ltd.), 24-29 Oval Rd., London NW1 7DX, England. TEL 44-71-267-4466. FAX 44-71-782-2293. TELEX 25775-ACPRES-G. (Subscr. to: Journals Subscription Fulfilment, Foots Cray High St., Sidcup, Kent DA14 5HP, England. TEL 44-81-300-3322. FAX 44-81-482-2293) **Indexed:** Excerp.Med. (1994-), Ind.Med. (1994-). **Document type:** academic/scholarly publication.
    —BLDSC (1856.724800); Genuine Article.

616.8   UK   ISSN 1074-8806
▼**BAILLIERE'S CLINICAL PSYCHIATRY.** 1995. q. $126 to individuals; institutions $153. Bailliere Tindall - W.B. Saunders Co. Ltd., 24-28 Oval Rd., London NW1 7DX, England. TEL 0171-267-4466. FAX 0171-482-2293. (Subscr. to: Harcourt Brace & Company Ltd., Foots Cray High St., Sidcup, Kent DA14 5HP, England. TEL 0181-300-3322. FAX 0181-309-0807; Subscr. in N. America to: Periodicals Fulfillment, W.B. Saunders Co., 6277 Sea Harbor Dr., 4th Fl., Orlando, FL 32891-4800. TEL 800-654-2452. FAX 800-874-6418) **Document type:** academic/scholarly publication.
    —BLDSC (1856.726800).
    Description: Explores issues in clinical psychiatry.

BEHAVIORAL AND BRAIN SCIENCES; an international journal of current research and theory with open peer commentary. see *PSYCHOLOGY*

MEDICAL SCIENCES — PSYCHIATRY AND NEUROLOGY   **4541**

616.8　　　　　NE　　ISSN 0166-4328
　　　　　　　　　　　CODEN: BBREDI
BEHAVIORAL BRAIN RESEARCH; an international journal. (Text in English) 1980. 14/yr. fl.3626($2211) (effective 1996). Elsevier Science B.V., P.O. Box 211, 1000 AE Amsterdam, Netherlands. TEL 31-20-4853911. FAX 31-20-4853598. TELEX 18582 ESPA NL. E-mail: nlinfo-f@elsevier.nl; usinfo-f@elsevier.com; forinfo-kyf04035@niftyserve.or.jp; Site addr.: http://www.elsevier.nl/. (Subscr.in U.S. and Canada to: Elsevier Science Inc., Box 882, Madison Sq. Sta., New York, NY 10159. TEL 212-989-5800. FAX 212-633-3990) Ed. I. Steele Russell. charts; illus. (also avail. in microform from UMI; reprint service avail. from ISI,SWZ) **Indexed**: Anim.Behav.Abstr., Biol.Abstr., Chem.Abstr., Curr.Cont., Dent.Ind., Excerp.Med., Ind.Med., Psychol.Abstr. (1980-), Yrbk.Assoc.Educ.& Rehab.Blind. **Document type**: academic/scholarly publication.
—BLDSC (1877.320000); CASDDS; Faxon; Genuine Article; SWETS; UnCover. **CCC**.
　Description: Publishes articles in the neurosciences, with special emphasis on neural mechanisms of behaviour.
　Refereed Serial

616.8　　　　　UK　　ISSN 1072-0847
RJ505.B4　　　　　　CODEN: BEHIE2
BEHAVIORAL INTERVENTIONS; theory and practice in residential and community-based clinical programs. 1986. q. £225 (effective 1996). John Wiley & Sons, Ltd., Journals, Baffins Ln., Chichester, W. Sussex PO19 1UD, England. TEL 01243-779777. FAX 01243-776128. TELEX 8620 WIBOOK G. (Subscr. in the Americas to: John Wiley & Sons, Inc., 605 Third Ave., New York, NY 10158. TEL 212-850-6645. FAX 212-850-6021) Ed. Fredrick J. Fuoco. adv. contact: Michael Levermore. circ. 323. (also avail. in microform from UMI; back issues avail.; reprint service avail. from SWZ) **Indexed**: Psychol.Abstr. 1988-). **Document type**: academic/scholarly publication.
—BLDSC (1877.500000); UMI; UnCover. **CCC**.
　Formerly (until 1994): Behavioral Residential Treatment (ISSN 0884-5581)
　Description: Deals specifically with the application of behavioral techniques in residential treatment settings.
　Refereed Serial

BEHAVIORAL MEDICINE; investigations of environmental influences on health and behavior. see *PSYCHOLOGY*

BEHAVIORAL NEUROSCIENCE. see *PSYCHOLOGY*

616.8　　　　　UK　　ISSN 0953-4180
　　　　　　　　　　　CODEN: BNEUEI
BEHAVIOURAL NEUROLOGY. 1988. q. £165($275) to institutions (effective 1995). Rapid Communications of Oxford Ltd., The Old Malthouse, Paradise St., Oxford OX1 1LD, England. TEL 01865-790447. FAX 01865-244012. E-mail: rapidcom@vax.oxford.ac.uk. Ed. H.J. Sagar. adv. contact: Julie Gribben. bk.rev. **Indexed**: Curr.Cont., Excerp.Med. (1993-), Psychol.Abstr. (1988-), Psychol.Abstr. **Document type**: academic/scholarly publication.
●Also available on CD-ROM.
—BLDSC (1877.590000); ADONIS; Genuine Article; UnCover. **CCC**.
　Description: Original and review papers of a predominantly clinical nature, with emphasis on the meaning of expression of disordered human behavior.

619.8　　　　　NE　　ISSN 0376-6357
QL750　　　　　　　　CODEN: BPRODA
BEHAVIOURAL PROCESSES; an international journal of comparative and physiological ethology. (Text in English, French, German) 1976. 9/yr. fl.1443($880) (effective 1996). Elsevier Science B.V., P.O. Box 211, 1000 AE Amsterdam, Netherlands. TEL 31-20-4853911. FAX 31-20-4853598. TELEX 18582 ESPA NL. E-mail: nlinfo-f@elsevier.nl; usinfo-f@elsevier.com; forinfo-kyf04035@niftyserve.or.jp; Site addr.: http://www.elsevier.nl/. (Subscr. in U.S. and Canada to: Elsevier Science Inc., Box 882, Madison Sq. Sta., New York, NY 10159. TEL 212-989-5800. FAX 212-633-3990) Eds. R. Zayan, J.E.R. Staddon. adv.; bk.rev.; bibl.; illus.; index. (also avail. in microform from UMI; reprint service avail. from ISI) **Indexed**: Anim.Behav.Abstr., Biol.Abstr., Curr.Adv.Ecol.Sci., Curr.Cont., Dairy Sci.Abstr., Deep Sea Res.& Oceanogr.Abstr., Excerp.Med., Ind.Sci.Rev., Psychol.Abstr. (1976-), Sci.Cit.Ind., SSCI. **Document type**: academic/scholarly publication.
—BLDSC (1877.700000); CASDDS; Faxon; Genuine Article; SWETS; UnCover. **CCC**.
　Incorporates (1981-1983): Behaviour Analysis Letters.
　Description: Covers comparative ethology, behavioural ecology, theoretical and quantitative ethology, neuroethology, experimental analysis and operant conditioning.
　Refereed Serial

616.8　　　　　UK　　ISSN 0263-9963
BETHLEM AND MAUDSLEY GAZETTE. 1953. q. Bethlem and Maudsley Health Authority, Maudsley Hospital, Denmark Hill, London SE5 8AZ, England. TEL 01-703-6333. Ed. K.R. Lloyd. bk.rev. circ. 3,000.

616.8　　　　　SZ　　ISSN 0067-8147
　　　　　　　　　　　CODEN: BIBPBI
BIBLIOTHECA PSYCHIATRICA. (Text in English and German) 1917. irreg. (approx. 1/yr.). price varies. S. Karger AG, Allschwilerstr. 10, P.O. Box, CH-4009 Basel, Switzerland. TEL 061-3061111. FAX 061-3061234. E-mail: Karger@Karger.ch. Ed. B. Saletu. (reprint service avail. from ISI, back issues avail.) **Indexed**: Biol.Abstr., Chem.Abstr., Curr.Cont., Ind.Med., SSCI. **Document type**: academic/scholarly publication.
—Genuine Article. **CCC**.
　Refereed Serial

BIOFEEDBACK (WHEAT RIDGE). see *PSYCHOLOGY*

616.89 574　　　US　　ISSN 0006-3223
RC321　　　　　　　　CODEN: BIPCBF
BIOLOGICAL PSYCHIATRY; a journal of psychiatric research. 1969. 24/yr. $1124 to institutions (effective 1996). (Society of Biological Psychiatry) Elsevier Science Inc., 655 Ave. of the Americas, New York, NY 10010. TEL 212-989-5800. FAX 212-633-3990. TELEX 420643 AEP UI. (Subscr. to: Box 882, Madison Sq. Sta., New York, NY 10159-0882) Ed. Dr. Joseph Wortis. bk.rev.; charts; illus.; index. (also avail. in microfilm from UMI) **Indexed**: Adol.Ment.Hlth.Abstr., Behav.Med.Abstr., Bibl.Dev.Med.& Child Neur., Biol.Abstr., Chem.Abstr., Curr.Adv.Biochem., Curr.Adv.Ecol.Sci., Curr.Cont., Dairy Sci.Abstr., Dent.Ind., Excerp.Med., Ind.Med., Ind.Sci.Rev., Psychol.Abstr. (1969-), Sci.Cit.Ind. **Document type**: academic/scholarly publication.
—BLDSC (2077.550000); ADONIS; CASDDS; Faxon; Genuine Article; SWETS; UnCover. **CCC**.
　Supersedes: Recent Advances in Biological Psychiatry.
　Description: Covers the whole range of psychiatric research interest.
　Refereed Serial

616.89　　　　　US　　ISSN 1044-422X
BIOLOGICAL THERAPIES IN PSYCHIATRY NEWSLETTER. 1977. m. $52 to individuals (foreign $59); institutions $70 (foreign $77); students $37 (foreign $44). Mosby - Year Book, Inc. (Subsidiary of: Times Mirror Company), 11830 Westline Industrial Dr., St. Louis, MO 63146. TEL 314-872-8370; 800-325-4177. FAX 314-432-1380. Ed. Dr. Alan J. Gelenberg. circ. 6,000. **Document type**: trade publication, newsletter.
—BLDSC (2081.300000). **CCC**.
　Former titles: Biological Therapies in Psychiatry (ISSN 0895-8262); Massachusetts General Hospital Biological Therapies in Psychiatry Newsletter (ISSN 0199-2716)
　Description: Provides updates on the clinical use of psychotropic drugs to practicing psychiatrists, psychiatric house staff, residents, and students.

616.89 574　　　IT　　ISSN 0393-4853
BOLLETTINO DI PSICHIATRIA BIOLOGICA. 1984. 3/yr. L.50000($70) (effective 1995). (Societa Italiana di Psichiatria Biologica) Casa Editrice Idelson, Via A. De Gasperi, 55, 80133 Naples, Italy. TEL 39-81-5524733. FAX 39-81-5518295. Ed. Mario Maj. (back issues avail.)

616.8　　　　　UK　　ISSN 0006-8950
RC321　　　　　　　　CODEN: BRAIAK
BRAIN; a journal of neurology. 1878. bi-m. £140($260) (effective 1996). Oxford University Press, Oxford Journals, Walton St., Oxford OX2 6DP, England. TEL 01865-267907. FAX 01865-267773. TELEX 837330-OXPRES-G. E-mail: jnlorders@oup.co.uk. (U.S. subscr. to: Oxford University Press Inc., 2001 Evans Rd., Cary, NC 27513. TEL 919-677-0977. FAX 919-677-1714) Ed. W.I. McDonald. adv.; bk.rev.; bibl.; illus.; index. circ. 4,250. (also avail. in microform from UMI,PMC; microfiche from IDC; reprint service avail. from SWZ,UMI) **Indexed**: AIM, Bibl.Dev.Med.& Child Neur., Biol.Abstr., Biotech.Abstr., Chem.Abstr., Curr.Adv.Ecol.Sci., Curr.Cont., Diab.Cont., Ergon.Abstr., Excerp.Med., Helminthol.Abstr., Ind.Med., Ind.Sci.Rev., Ind.Vet., Nutr.Abstr., Psychol.Abstr., Sci.Cit.Ind., So.Pac.Per.Ind., Vet.Bull. **Document type**: academic/scholarly publication.
—BLDSC (2268.000000); CASDDS; Faxon; Genuine Article; SWETS; UMI; UnCover. **CCC**.
　Description: Original papers in clinical neurology and related disciplines.

616.8 618.92　　　NE　　ISSN 0387-7604
　　　　　　　　　　　CODEN: NTHAA7
BRAIN AND DEVELOPMENT. Japanese edition: No to Hattatsu. (Text in English) 1969. bi-m. fl.483($295) (effective 1996). (Japanese Society of Child Neurology, JA - Nihon Shoni Shinkei Gakkai) Elsevier Science B.V., P.O. Box 211, 1000 AE Amsterdam, Netherlands. TEL 31-20-4853911. FAX 31-20-4853598. TELEX 18582 ESPA NL. E-mail: nlinfo-f@elsevier.nl; usinfo-f@elsevier.com; forinfo-kyf04035@niftyserve.or.jp; Site addr.: http://www.elsevier.nl/. (Subscr. in U.S. and Canada to: Elsevier Science Inc. Box 882, Madison Sq. Sta., New York, NY 10159-0882. TEL 212-989-5800. FAX 212-633-3990) (also avail. in microform from UMI) **Indexed**: Bibl.Dev.Med.& Child Neur., Curr.Cont., Excerp.Med., Excerp.Med., Ind.Med., INIS Atomind., Int.Abstr.Biol.Sci., Sci.Cit.Ind. **Document type**: academic/scholarly publication.
—BLDSC (2268.032900); CASDDS; EMDOCS; Faxon; Genuine Article; SWETS; UnCover. **CCC**.
　Supersedes in part (in 1979): Brain and Development - No to Hattatsu (ISSN 0029-0831)
　Description: Contains both clinical and basic studies in the field of child neurology.
　Refereed Serial

616.8　　　　　JA　　ISSN 0006-8969
　　　　　　　　　　　CODEN: BRNED8
BRAIN AND NERVE/NO TO SHINKEI. (Text in Japanese; summaries in English) 1948. m. 23520 Yen($181) Igaku-Shoin Ltd., 5-24-3 Hongo, Bunkyo-ku, Tokyo 113-91, Japan. TEL 03-817-5701. Ed.Bd. adv.; bk.rev.; abstr.; cum.index. circ. 4,500. **Indexed**: Biol.Abstr., C.I.S. Abstr., Chem.Abstr., Dent.Ind., Excerp.Med., Ind.Med.
●Also available online. Vendor(s): JICST.
—BLDSC (2268.050000); CASDDS.

MEDICAL SCIENCES — PSYCHIATRY AND NEUROLOGY

616.8   SZ   ISSN 0006-8977
QL750   CODEN: BRBEBE
BRAIN, BEHAVIOR AND EVOLUTION. (Text in English) 1968. m. (in 2 vol.). 913.20 SFr.($702) to individuals; institutions 1522 SFr.($1170) (effective 1996). S. Karger AG, Allschwilerstr. 10, P.O. Box, CH-4009 Basel, Switzerland. TEL 061-3061111. FAX 061-3061234. E-mail: Karger@Karger.ch. Ed. G. Glenn Northcutt. adv.; bibl.; illus.; index. circ. 1,000. (also avail. in microform from RPI) Indexed: Abstr.Anthropol., Biol.Abstr., Curr.Adv.Ecol.Sci., Dent.Ind., Excerp.Med., Ind.Med., Ind.Sci.Rev., Psychol.Abstr. (1971-), Sci.Cit.Ind. **Document type:** academic/scholarly publication.
—BLDSC (2268.100000); Faxon; Genuine Article; SWETS; UnCover. **CCC.**
Refereed Serial

616.8   US
▼**BRAIN IMAGING AND BEHAVIOR;** an international journal. Announced for publication in 1996. q. $150 (foreign $175) (effective 1996). Plenum Publishing Corp., 233 Spring St., New York, NY 10013-1578. TEL 212-620-8000. FAX 212-463-0742. TELEX 23-421139. Eds. Erin D. Bigler, Andrew Kertesz. adv. (also avail. in microfilm from JSC) **Document type:** academic/scholarly publication.
Description: Publishes behavioral research based on a variety of neuroimaging methods.
Refereed Serial

616.8   UK   ISSN 0269-9052
RC387.5   CODEN: BRAIEO
BRAIN INJURY. 1987. 10/yr. £340($560) (effective 1996). Taylor & Francis Ltd., Rankine Rd., Basingstoke, Hants. RG24 8PR, England. TEL 44-1256-840366. FAX 44-1256-479438. TELEX 858540. E-mail: info@tandf.co.uk. (Subscr. in N. America to: Taylor & Francis Inc., 1900 Frost Rd., Ste. 101, Bristol, PA 19007-1598. TEL 800-821-8312. FAX 215-785-5515) Ed. Henry H. Stonnington. Indexed: Excerp.Med., Psychol.Abstr. (1992-). **Document type:** academic/scholarly publication.
—BLDSC (2268.132000); Faxon; Genuine Article; UnCover. **CCC.**
Description: Covers all aspects of brain injury, ranging from basic scientific research to epidemiology, neuropathology, neurosurgical and other medical procedures, assessment methods, rehabilitation, and outcome.
Refereed Serial

616.8   US   ISSN 1072-3927
BP605.N48
BRAIN - MIND; bulletin of breakthroughs. 1975. m. $45 (foreign $55). Interface Press, 4717 N. Figueroa St., Box 42211, Los Angeles, CA 90042. TEL 213-223-2500; 800-553-6463. FAX 213-223-2519. Ed. Marilyn Ferguson. bk.rev.; illus. circ. 4,000. (back issues avail.) Indexed: New.Per.Ind. **Document type:** bulletin.
—BLDSC (2268.137000); UMI.
Former titles: Brain - Mind and Common Sense (ISSN 1064-671X); New Sense Bulletin (ISSN 1057-0705); Incorporates: Brain - Mind Bulletin (ISSN 0273-8546)
Description: Ground-breaking news from the medical, clinical, social, educational, creative and spiritual sciences.

616.8   II   ISSN 0006-8985
BRAIN NEWS.* (Text in English) 1964. s-a. Rs.30.($10.) Indian Brain Research Association, Dept. of Biochemistry, 35 Ballygunge Circular Rd., Calcutta 19, India. Ed. Dr. J.J. Ghosh. adv.; bk.rev. circ. 500. Indexed: Biol.Abstr.

616.8   SZ   ISSN 1015-6305
                       CODEN: BRPAE7
BRAIN PATHOLOGY. (Text in English) 1990. q. 150 SFr. International Society of Neuropathology, P.O. Box, CH-8033 Zurich, Switzerland. TEL 01-2552107. FAX 01-2554402. Ed. Paul Kleihues. adv.; bk.rev. (back issues avail.) Indexed: Excerp.Med. (1993-), Ind.Med. (1993-). **Document type:** academic/scholarly publication.
—BLDSC (2268.175000); CASDDS; Genuine Article.

616.8   NE   ISSN 0006-8993
QP376   CODEN: BRREAP
BRAIN RESEARCH; international multidisciplinary journal devoted to fundamental research in the brain sciences. (Text in English) 1966. 108/yr. (in 53 vols.). fl.19345($10181) includes Brain Research Reviews, Developmental Brain Research, Molecular Brain Research (effective 1995). Elsevier Science B.V., P.O. Box 211, 1000 AE Amsterdam, Netherlands. TEL 31-20-4853911. FAX 31-20-4853598. TELEX 18582 ESPA NL. E-mail: nlinfo-f@elsevier.nl; usinfo-f@elsevier.com; forinfo-kyf04035@niftyserve.or.jp; Site addr.: http://www.elsevier.nl/. (Subscr. in U.S. and Canada to: Elsevier Science Inc., Box 882, Madison Sq. Sta., New York, NY 10159-0882. TEL 212-989-5800. FAX 212-633-3990) Ed. D.P. Purpura. adv.; bk.rev.; abstr.; bibl.; illus.; index, cum.index: 1966-1977. (also avail. in microform from UMI) Indexed: Apic.Abstr., Biol.Abstr., Biotech.Abstr., Chem.Abstr., Curr.Adv.Biochem., Curr.Adv.Cell & Devel.Biol., Curr.Adv.Ecol.Sci., Curr.Cont., Dairy Sci.Abstr., Dent.Ind., Excerp.Med., Helminthol.Abstr., Ind.Med., Ind.Sci.Rev., Ind.Vet., INIS Atomind., Int.Abstr.Biol.Sci., Int.Aerosp.Abstr., Nutr.Abstr., Psychol.Abstr. (1970-), Sci.Cit.Ind., Sport Fish.Abstr., Vet.Bull., Wild.Rev., Zoo.Rec. **Document type:** academic/scholarly publication.
—BLDSC (2268.200000); ADONIS; CASDDS; Faxon; Genuine Article; SWETS; UnCover. **CCC.**
Description: Covers neuroanatomy, neurochemistry, neurophysiology, neuroendocrinology, neuropharmacology, neurotoxicology, neurocommunications, behavioural sciences, neurology and biocybernetics.

618   UK   ISSN 0361-9230
QP376   CODEN: BRBUDU
BRAIN RESEARCH BULLETIN. 1976. 18/yr. $1850 to institutions (effective 1996). Elsevier Science Ltd., Pergamon, P.O. Box 800, Kidlington, Oxford OX5 1DX, England. TEL 44-1865-843000. FAX 44-1865-843010. E-mail: nlinfo-f@elsevier.nl; usinfo-f@elsevier.com; forinfo-kyf04035@niftyserve.or.jp; Site addr.: http://www.elsevier.nl/. (Subscr. in U.S. and Canada to: Elsevier Science, 660 White Plains Rd., Tarrytown, NY 10591-5153. TEL 914-524-9200. FAX 914-333-2444) Ed. Matthew J. Wayner. adv.; bk.rev.; illus.; index. (also avail. in microfilm from UMI; reprint service avail. from ISI,UMI) Indexed: Anim.Behav.Abstr., Biol.Abstr., Chem.Abstr., Curr.Adv.Biochem., Curr.Adv.Cancer Res., Curr.Adv.Ecol.Sci., Curr.Cont., Dent.Ind., Excerp.Med., Helminthol.Abstr., Ind.Med., Ind.Sci.Rev., INIS Atomind., Nutr.Abstr., Psychol.Abstr. (1976-), Sci.Cit.Ind. **Document type:** academic/scholarly publication, bulletin.
—BLDSC (2268.201000); CASDDS; Faxon; Genuine Article; SWETS; UMI; UnCover. **CCC.**
Incorporating: Journal of Electrophysiological Techniques (ISSN 0361-0209)
Description: Broad spectrum of articles in the neurosciences, emphasizing rapid communication of comprehensive articles, meeting reports and special issues.
Refereed Serial

616.8   US
BRAIN RESEARCH FOUNDATION ANNUAL REPORT. (Supplement avail. 3/yr.: Brainwaves Newsletter) 1983. a. Brain Research Foundation, 208 S. LaSalle St., Ste. 1426, Chicago, IL 60604-1102. TEL 312-782-4311. FAX 312-782-6437. Ed. Nancy W. Hohfeler. circ. 1,100. **Document type:** corporate report.
Description: Presents financial statement, year's activities, list of the foundation's grants to scientists at University of Chicago's Brain Research Institute, donors lists, and scientific articles highlighting a specific area of research at the institute.

616.8   NE   ISSN 0165-0173
                       CODEN: BRERD2
BRAIN RESEARCH REVIEWS. (Section of: Brain Research (ISSN 0006-8993)) (Text and summaries in English) 1980. bi-m. fl.904($551) (effective 1996). Elsevier Science B.V., P.O. Box 211, 1000 AE Amsterdam, Netherlands. TEL 31-20-4853911. FAX 31-20-4853598. TELEX 18582 ESPA NL. E-mail: nlinfo-f@elsevier.nl; usinfo-f@elsevier.com; forinfo-kyf04035@niftyserve.or.jp; Site addr.: http://www.elsevier.nl/. (Subscr. in U.S. and Canada to: Elsevier Science Inc., Box 882, Madison Sq. Sta., New York, NY 10159. TEL 212-989-5800. FAX 212-633-3990) Ed. Dr. Dominick P. Purpura. adv. (also avail. in microform from UMI; back issues avail.; reprint service avail. from ISI) Indexed: Biol.Abstr., Biotech.Abstr., Chem.Abstr., Curr.Adv.Cell & Devel.Biol., Curr.Adv.Ecol.Sci., Curr.Cont., Excerp.Med., Ind.Med., Psychol.Abstr. (1979-). **Document type:** academic/scholarly publication.
—BLDSC (2268.205000); ADONIS; CASDDS; Faxon; Genuine Article; SWETS. **CCC.**
Description: Publishes articles and research papers which give analytical surveys that define heuristic hypotheses and provide new insights into brain mechanisms.

616.8   US   ISSN 0896-0267
                       CODEN: BRTOEZ
BRAIN TOPOGRAPHY; journal of functional neurophysiology. 1988. q. $395 (foreign $460) (effective 1996). Human Sciences Press, Inc. (Subsidiary of: Plenum Publishing Corp.), 233 Spring St., New York, NY 10013-1578. TEL 212-620-8000. FAX 212-463-0742. TELEX 23-421139. Ed. Peter K.H. Wong. adv. (also avail. in microform from UMI) Indexed: Psychol.Abstr. (1989-). **Document type:** academic/scholarly publication.
—BLDSC (2268.221200); Faxon; SWETS; UMI; UnCover. **CCC.**
Description: Reviews new research in the areas of E.E.G., M.E.G., pshchiatry, and neuropsychology, and explores new methodology and techniques of data analysis and manipulation.
Refereed Serial

BRILL'S STUDIES IN EPISTEMOLOGY, PSYCHOLOGY AND PSYCHIATRY. see *PHILOSOPHY*

616.8   UK   ISSN 1354-4187
BRITISH JOURNAL OF LEARNING DISABILITIES. 1973. q. £24($52) to individuals; institutions £31 ($67). (British Institute of Learning Disabilities) B I L D Publications, Frankfurt Lodge, Clevedon Hall, Victoria Rd., Clevedon, Avon BS21 7SJ, England. TEL 01275-876519. FAX 01275-343096. Ed. John Harris. adv. circ. 3,500. Indexed: Curr.Adv.Ecol.Sci., Psychol.Abstr. (1993-), Rehabil.Lit., Sp.Ed.Needs Abstr. **Document type:** academic/scholarly publication.
—BLDSC (2311.125000).
Former titles (until 1993): Mental Handicap (ISSN 0261-9997); (until Mar. 1982): Apex (ISSN 0141-2205)
Description: Presents original articles with multidisciplinary appeal covering all aspects of learning disabilities.

BRITISH JOURNAL OF MEDICAL PSYCHOLOGY. see *PSYCHOLOGY*

BRITISH JOURNAL OF PROJECTIVE PSYCHOLOGY. see *PSYCHOLOGY*

616.89 UK ISSN 0007-1250
RC321 CODEN: BJPYAJ
BRITISH JOURNAL OF PSYCHIATRY. 1853. m. £130($210) to individuals; institutions £148($295). Royal College of Psychiatrists, 17 Belgrave Sq., London SW1X 8PG, England. TEL 0171-235-8857. FAX 0171-245-1231. (Subscr. to: Royal Society of Medicine, 1 Wimpole St., London W1M 8AE, England. TEL 0171-290-2928. FAX 0171-290-2924) Ed. Greg Wilkinson. adv. contact: Peter Mell. bk.rev.; bibl.; charts; illus.; index. circ. 12,500. **Indexed:** Abstr.Health Care Manage.Stud., Abstr.Hyg., Adol.Ment.Hlth.Abstr., Bibl.Dev.Med.& Child Neur., Biol.Abstr., Biotech.Abstr., Chem.Abstr., CINAHL, Curr.Adv.Ecol.Sci., Curr.Cont., Diab.Cont., Dok.Arbeitsmed., Excerp.Med., Helminthol.Abstr., I.P.A., IMFL, Ind.Med., Ind.Sci.Rev., Int.Nurs.Ind., Mid.East: Abstr.& Ind., Nutr.Abstr., Psychol.Abstr. (1925-), Risk Abstr., Sci.Cit.Ind., SSCI, Trop.Dis.Bull. **Document type:** academic/scholarly publication.
—BLDSC (2320.800000); ADONIS; CASDDS; Faxon; Genuine Article; SWETS; UnCover. **CCC.**
Description: Covers all branches of psychiatry, with emphasis on the clinical aspects of various topics in field.
Refereed Serial

616.891 UK ISSN 0265-9883
BRITISH JOURNAL OF PSYCHOTHERAPY. 1984. 4/yr. £23 to individuals (foreign £30); institutions £45 (foreign £50). Artesian Books Ltd., 18 Artesian Rd., London W2, England. TEL 44-71-229-2855. FAX 44-71-792-2543. Ed. Jean Arundale. adv.; bk.rev. circ. 2,200. **Indexed:** Psychol.Abstr. (1987-). **Document type:** academic/scholarly publication.
—BLDSC (2321.200000).
Description: Covers clinical and theoretical topics relevant to the psychotherapist practising privately or in institutions. Emphasizes analytical psychotherapy, and the application of psychotherapeutic practice and theory to institutions, society and other settings.

362.4 616.835 UK ISSN 0007-1633
BRITISH POLIO FELLOWSHIP. BULLETIN. 1939. bi-m. £0.20 per no. British Polio Fellowship, 126 Radnor Ave., Bexleyheath, Kent DA16 2BY, England. TEL 081-304-3166. FAX 081-304-3166. Ed. Kathleen M. Dibley. adv.; bk.rev.; illus. circ. 8,000. (tabloid format) **Document type:** bulletin.

616.8 JA ISSN 0917-0898
BUREIN SAIENSU/BRAIN SCIENCE. (Text in Japanese) 1990. q. 1500 Yen. Koseisha Infomeshon Sabisu - Koseisha Information Service, 2-7, Dojima 3-chome, Kita-ku, Osaka 530, Japan.

616.8 JA
BUREIN SAIENSU SAIZENSEN/FRONTIERS OF BRAIN SCIENCE. (Text in Japanese) 1988. a. 2000 Yen. (Burein Saiensu Shinko Zaidan) Kodansha Scientific, 9-25 Shin-Ogawamachi, Shinjyuku-ku, Tokyo 162, Japan.
Formerly (until vol.5, 1992): Burein Saiensu Kenkyu Hokokushu. Brain Science Foundation. Annual Study Report.

616.89 JA ISSN 0910-4798
BYOIN, CHIIKI SEISHIN IGAKU/JAPANESE JOURNAL OF HOSPITAL AND COMMUNITY PSYCHIATRY. (Text in Japanese) 1958. q. Byoin, Chiiki Seishin Igakkai - Japanese Hospital and Community Psychiatry Association, Kokuritsu Seishin Shinkei Senta, 1-1, Ogawa Higashicho 4-chome, Kodaira-shi, Tokyo 187, Japan.
—BLDSC (4655.178000).
Formerly (until 1984): Byoin Seishin Igaku (ISSN 0910-478X)

616.8 617 US
C I N N REPORT. (Former name of issuing body: Chicago NeuroSurgical Center) 1989. 3/yr. Chicago Institute of Neurosurgery and Neuroresearch, 2520 N. Lakeview Ave., Chicago, IL 60614. TEL 312-883-8550. FAX 312-348-9215. Dir. Theodore W. Michalke. **Document type:** trade publication.
Formerly (until 1994): C N C Report.

616.8 CN ISSN 0831-6279
C M T NEWSLETTER; published bimonthly by and for those with Charcot-Marie-Tooth disease. 1984. bi-m. donation. (Personal Muscular Atrophy International Association, Inc.) C M T International, 1 Springbank Dr., St. Catharines, ON L2S 2K1, Canada. TEL 905-687-3630. Ed. Linda D. Crabtree. index. circ. 2,400. (back issues avail.) **Document type:** academic/scholarly publication, newsletter.
Description: For people and health professionals interested in learning more about Charcot-Marie-Tooth disease, a progressive debilitating neuromuscular disorder.

C N S DRUGS. (Central Nervous System) see *PHARMACY AND PHARMACOLOGY*

CAHIERS DE PSYCHOLOGIE CLINIQUE. see *PSYCHOLOGY*

616.8 SZ ISSN 1016-9229
CAHIERS PSYCHIATRIQUES GENEVOIS. 1987. s-a. 50 SFr. (foreign 60 SFr.). Editions Medecine et Hygiene, Case Postale 456, CH-1211 Geneva 4, Switzerland. TEL 022-3469355. FAX 022-3475610. **Document type:** academic/scholarly publication.

616.8 UK ISSN 1350-1461
CAMBRIDGE MEDICAL REVIEWS. NEUROLOGY AND PSYCHIATRY. 1991. irreg., vol.2, 1993. Cambridge University Press, Edinburgh Bldg., Cambridge CB2 2RU, England. TEL 01223-312393. FAX 01223-315052. TELEX 851517256. (N. American addr.: Cambridge University Press, Journals Dept., 40 W. 20th St., New York, NY 10011. TEL 212-924-3900. FAX 212-691-3239) Ed. Robert Kerwin. **Document type:** monographic series.
—BLDSC (3015.962430).

616.8 CN ISSN 0317-1671
RC321 CODEN: CJNSA2
CANADIAN JOURNAL OF NEUROLOGICAL SCIENCES. (Text in English or French, abstracts in English & French) 1974. q. Can.$75($71) (effective 1996). (Canadian Neurological Society) Canadian Journal of Neurological Sciences, Inc., P.O. Box 4220, Sta. C, Calgary, AB T2T 5N1, Canada. TEL 403-229-9575. FAX 403-229-1661. (Co-sponsors: Canadian Neurosurgical Society, Canadian Society of Clinical Neurophysiologists, Canadian Association of Child Neurology) Ed. Dr. J.A. Sharpe. adv.: color page Can.$1392; adv. contact: Sally Gregg. bk.rev.; index; circ. 1,600. (paid). (also avail. in microform from UMI; reprint service avail. from UMI,ISI) **Indexed:** Biol.Abstr., Chem.Abstr., Curr.Adv.Ecol.Sci., Curr.Cont., Dent.Ind., Excerp.Med., Ind.Med., Ind.Sci.Rev., INIS Atomind., Nutr.Abstr., Sci.Cit.Ind., Weed Abstr. **Document type:** academic/scholarly publication.
—BLDSC (3033.300000); CASDDS; Faxon; Genuine Article; SWETS; UMI; UnCover. **CCC.**
Description: Original work in the clinical and basic neurosciences.
Refereed Serial

616.89 CN ISSN 0706-7437
RC321 CODEN: CPAJAK
CANADIAN JOURNAL OF PSYCHIATRY/REVUE CANADIENNE DE PSYCHIATRIE. (Text in English, French) 1956. 10/yr. Can.$80($105) Canadian Psychiatric Association, 237 Argyle Ave., Ste. 200, Ottawa, ON K2P 1B8, Canada. TEL 613-234-2815. FAX 613-234-9857. Ed. Dr. E. Kingstone. adv.: B&W page Can.$970, color page Can.$1880; trim 8 1/8 x 10 7/8; adv. contact: Kim Arial. bk.rev.; bibl.; charts; illus.; index. circ. 3,300. (also avail. in microform from UMI; reprint service avail. from UMI) **Indexed:** Adol.Ment.Hith.Abstr., ASSIA, Bibl.Dev.Med.& Child Neur., Chem.Abstr., Child Devel.Abstr., CINAHL, Curr.Adv.Ecol.Sci., Curr.Cont., Dok.Arbeitsmed., Excerp.Med., Ind.Med., Lang.& Lang.Behav.Abstr., Mid.East: Abstr.& Ind., NRN, Psychol.Abstr. (1961-), Sage Fam.Stud.Abstr., Sage Urb.Stud.Abstr., So.Pac.Per.Ind., Sp.Ed.Needs Abstr., SSCI, Yrbk.Assoc.Educ.& Rehab.Blind. **Document type:** academic/scholarly publication.
—BLDSC (3034.800000); Faxon; Genuine Article; SWETS; UMI; UnCover. **CCC.**
Formerly: Canadian Psychiatric Association Journal (ISSN 0008-4824)
Description: Provides a forum for a broad spectrum of scholarly presentations, case reports, position papers, editorial contributions and current perspectives.
Refereed Serial

616.89 CN ISSN 1195-3330
CANADIAN JOURNAL OF PSYCHOANALYSIS/REVUE CANADIENNE DE PSYCHANALYSE. 1993. s-a. Can.$50 to individuals (foreign $60); institutions Can.$65 (foreign $70). Canadian Psychoanalytic Society - Societe Canadienne de Psychanalyse, 7000 Cote des Neiges, Montreal, PQ H3S 2C1, Canada. TEL 514-738-6105. FAX 514-738-6393. Ed. Eva P. Lester. adv. contact: Nadia Gargour. bk.rev.; circ. 515 (paid). **Document type:** academic/scholarly publication.
—BLDSC (3034.850000).
Refereed Serial

616.8 US ISSN 0272-4340
QP351 CODEN: CMNEDI
CELLULAR & MOLECULAR NEUROBIOLOGY. 1981. bi-m. $395 (foreign $460) (effective 1996). Plenum Publishing Corp., 233 Spring St., New York, NY 10013-1578. TEL 212-620-8000. FAX 212-463-0742. TELEX 23-4211139. Ed. Juan M. Saavedra. adv.; bk.rev. (also avail. in microfilm from JSC; back issues avail.) **Indexed:** Biol.Abstr., Chem.Abstr., Curr.Adv.Ecol.Sci., Curr.Cont., Excerp.Med., Ind.Med., INIS Atomind. **Document type:** academic/scholarly publication.
—BLDSC (3097.925000); CASDDS; Faxon; Genuine Article; SWETS; UMI; UnCover. **CCC.**
Refereed Serial

CELLULAR NEUROBIOLOGY. see *BIOLOGY*

616.8 NO ISSN 0333-1024
CODEN: CEPHDF
CEPHALALGIA; an international journal of headache. (Text in English) 1981. 6/yr. NOK 1530 in Nordic countries; elsewhere $255 (effective 1996). (International Headache Society) Scandinavian University Press, P.O. Box 2959 Toeyen, N-0608 Oslo, Norway. TEL 47-22-57-54-00. FAX 47-22-57-53-53. (U.S. address: Scandinavian University Press, 200 Meacham Ave., Elmont, NY 11003. TEL 516-352-7300) Ed. K.M.A. Welch. adv.; index. circ. 800. (also avail. in microform from UMI; back issues avail.) **Indexed:** Biol.Abstr., Chem.Abstr., Curr.Adv.Ecol.Sci., Curr.Cont., Dent.Ind., Excerp.Med., Ind.Med., INIS Atomind., NRN. **Document type:** academic/scholarly publication.
—BLDSC (3113.691000); ADONIS; CASDDS; Faxon; Genuine Article; SWETS; UMI; UnCover. **CCC.**
Description: Covers migraine and headache research.

616.8 FR ISSN 0264-6900
CODEN: CMCEEW
CEREBRAL CIRCULATION AND METABOLISM/CIRCULATION ET METABOLISME DU CERVEAU. (Text in English, French) 1983. q. 410 F. to individuals (foreign 520 F.); institutions 565 F. (foreign 650 F.) (effective 1995). (Societe Francaise de Circulation et Metabolisme du Cerveau) John Libbey Eurotext, 127 av de la Republique, 92120 Montrouge, France. TEL 1-46-73-06-60. FAX 1-40-84-09-99. (Subscr. to: A T E I, 23-25 rue Fernand Combette, 93100 Montreuil sous Bois, France. TEL 48-59-58-11. FAX 48-59-57-99) Ed. J.C. Depresseux. circ. 500. (back issues avail.) **Indexed:** Curr.Adv.Biochem., Curr.Adv.Cell & Devel.Biol. **Document type:** academic/scholarly publication.
—BLDSC (3265.280000); CASDDS.
Description: Explores the circulation and metabolism of the brain from clinical, physiological, physiopathological and pharmacological approaches.

616.8 US ISSN 1047-3211
QP383
CEREBRAL CORTEX. 1991. bi-m. £165($250) (effective 1996). Oxford University Press, Journals, 2001 Evans Rd., Cary, NC 27513. TEL 919-677-0977; 800-852-7323. FAX 919-677-1714. E-mail: jnlorders@oup-usa.org. (Subscr. outside N. America to: Oxford University Press, Journals, Walton St., Oxford OX2 6DP, England. TEL 44-1865-56767. FAX 44-1865-267773) Eds. Patricia Goldman-Rakic, Pasko Rakic. circ. 350. (back issues avail.) **Indexed:** Excerp.Med. (1993-), Ind.Med. (1992-), Psychol.Abstr. (1991-). **Document type:** academic/scholarly publication.
—BLDSC (3120.027550); Genuine Article; SWETS; UMI. **CCC.**
Description: Interdisciplinary journal publishing papers on the development, organization, plasticity, and function of the cerebral cortex.
Refereed Serial

MEDICAL SCIENCES — PSYCHIATRY AND NEUROLOGY

616.8 **US** **ISSN 1040-8827**
RC386 CODEN: CEMREV
CEREBROVASCULAR AND BRAIN METABOLISM REVIEWS. 1989. q. $168 to individuals (foreign $200); institutions $222 (foreign $266) (effective 1996). Lippincott - Raven Publishers, 227 E. Washington Sq., Philadelphia, PA 19106. TEL 215-238-4200. Ed. A. Murray Harper. adv. contact: Phyllis Noyes. charts; illus. circ. 1,000. (reprint service avail. from UMI) **Document type:** academic/scholarly publication.
—BLDSC (3120.037500); Faxon; Genuine Article; SWETS; UnCover. **CCC.**
  Description: Provides current reviews of topics of interest to neurologists, neurosurgeons, neuroscientists, physiologists, pharmacologists, and general practitioners.
  Refereed Serial

616.8 616.15 **SZ** **ISSN 1015-9770**
CODEN: CDISE7
CEREBROVASCULAR DISEASES. (Text in English) 1991. 6/yr. 214 SFr.($164.80) to individuals; institutions 535 SFr.($412) (effective 1996). S. Karger AG, Allschwilerstr. 10, P.O. Box, CH-4009 Basel, Switzerland. TEL 061-3061111. FAX 061-3061234. E-mail: Karger@Karger.ch. Eds. J. Bogousslavsky, M. Hennerici. (also avail. in microform from UMI) **Document type:** academic/scholarly publication.
—BLDSC (3120.037790); Genuine Article; SWETS. **CCC.**
  Refereed Serial

616.8 617.48 **XR** **ISSN 1210-7859**
CESKA A SLOVENSKA NEUROLOGIE A NEUROCHIRURGIE. (Text in Czech or Slovak; summaries in Czech, English, Russian) 1937. 6/yr. $48.60. (Ceska Lekarska Spolecnost J.E. Purkyne - Czech Medical Society) Nakladatelske Stredisko C L S J.E. Purkyne, Sokolska 31, 120 26 Prague 2, Czech Republic. FAX 42-0-2-202788. (Dist. by: Artia, Ve Smeckach 30, 111 27 Prague 1, Czech Republic) (Co-sponsor: Ceska Neurologicka Spolecnost) Ed. Jiri Dolansky. bk.rev.; abstr.; bibl.; charts; illus.; index. **Indexed:** C.I.S. Abstr., Chem.Abstr., Curr.Adv.Ecol.Sci., Dent.Ind., Excerp.Med., Ind.Med. (until 1992), INIS Atomind. **Document type:** academic/scholarly publication.
—BLDSC (3120.258450); Genuine Article. **CCC.**
  Former titles (until 1994): Ceskoslovenska Neurologie a Neurochirurgie (ISSN 0301-0597); Neurologie a Psychiatrie Ceskoslovenska.

616.8 **XR**
CESKO-SLOVENSKA PSYCHIATRIE. (Text in Czech; summaries in Czech, English, Russian) 1904. 6/yr. $48.60. (Ceska Lekarska Spolecnost J.E. Purkyne - Czech Medical Society) Nakladatelske Stredisko C L S J.E. Purkyne, Sokolska 31, 120 26 Prague 2, Czech Republic. FAX 42-0-2-202788. (Dist. by: Artia, Ve Smeckach 30, 111 27 Prague 1, Czech Republic) (Co-sponsor: Cesko-Slovenska Psychiatricka Spolecnost) Ed. Dr. M. Zapletalek. bk.rev.; abstr. **Indexed:** C.I.S. Abstr., Excerp.Med., Ind.Med., Psychol.Abstr. (1959-). **Document type:** academic/scholarly publication.
—BLDSC (3122.490000). **CCC.**
  Formerly (until 1993): Ceskoslovenska Psychiatrie (ISSN 0069-2336).

CHILD AND ADOLESCENT PSYCHIATRIC CLINICS OF NORTH AMERICA. see *MEDICAL SCIENCES — Pediatrics*

CHILD BEHAVIOR AND DEVELOPMENT. see *MEDICAL SCIENCES — Pediatrics*

CHILD NEUROPSYCHOLOGY; a journal on normal and abnormal development in childhood and adolescence. see *PSYCHOLOGY*

616.89 **US** **ISSN 0009-398X**
RJ499.A1 CODEN: CPHDA3
CHILD PSYCHIATRY AND HUMAN DEVELOPMENT. 1970. q. $255 (foreign $300) (effective 1996). (American Association of Psychiatric Services for Children) Human Sciences Press, Inc. (Subsidiary of: Plenum Publishing Corp.), 233 Spring St., New York, NY 10013-1578. TEL 212-620-8000. FAX 212-463-0742. TELEX 23-421139. Ed. Dr. Jack C. Westman. adv.; bibl.; index. (also avail. in microform from UMI; back issues avail.; reprint service avail. from ISI,UMI) **Indexed:** Abstr.Crim.& Pen., Adol.Ment.Hlth.Abstr., Bibl.Dev.Med.& Child Neur., Biol.Abstr., C.I.J.E., Child Devel.Abstr., Curr.Cont., Educ.Ind., Except.Child.Educ.Abstr., Excerp.Med., IMFL, Ind.Med., Nutr.Abstr., Psychol.Abstr. (1970-), Psycscan D.P., Risk Abstr., Soc.Work Res.& Abstr., SSCI, Wom.Stud.Abstr. **Document type:** academic/scholarly publication.
—BLDSC (3172.945000); Faxon; Genuine Article; SWETS; UMI; UnCover. **CCC.**
  Description: Serves allied professional groups of specialists in child psychiatry, social science, pediatrics, psychology, and human development.
  Refereed Serial

618.92 612 **GW** **ISSN 0256-7040**
CODEN: CNSYE9
CHILD'S NERVOUS SYSTEM. (Text in English) 1972. 12/yr. DM.1458($1059) (effective 1996). (International Society for Pediatric Neurosurgery) Springer-Verlag, Heidelberger Platz 3, 14197 Berlin, Germany. TEL 030-8207-0. FAX 030-8214091. E-mail: orders@springer.de. (Subscr. in N. America to: Springer-Verlag New York, Inc., 44 Hartz Way, Secaucus, NJ 07096-2491. TEL 201-348-4033. FAX 201-348-4505) Ed. Anthony J. Raimondi. adv.; bibl.; charts; illus. circ. 1,125. (also avail. in microform from RPI; reprint service avail. from ISI) **Indexed:** Bibl.Dev.Med.& Child Neur., Biol.Abstr., Curr.Adv.Ecol.Sci., Curr.Cont., Dent.Ind., Excerp.Med., Helminthol.Abstr., Ind.Med., Nutr.Abstr., Protozool.Abstr., Sci.Cit.Ind. **Document type:** academic/scholarly publication.
—BLDSC (3172.993080); Genuine Article; SWETS; UMI; UnCover. **CCC.**
  Superseded in part (in 1985): Child's Brain (ISSN 0302-2803)
  Description: Encompasses all aspects of the pediatric neurosciences including development and growth, trauma, degenerative disorders, hereditary diseases, neurophysiology, neurology and neurosurgery.
  Refereed Serial

616.8 617 **BN** **ISSN 0353-6203**
CODEN: CNERE
CHIRURGIA NEUROLOGICA. (Text in English) s-a. $40. University Medical Centre, Department of Neurosurgery, Mose Pijade 25, 71000 Sarajevo, Bosnia Hercegovina. TEL 071-275993. FAX 071-513813. Ed. Faruk Konjhodzic. **Indexed:** Excerp.Med. (1992-). **Document type:** academic/scholarly publication.
—BLDSC (3181.250000).
  Description: Mainly devoted to neurosurgery and associated sciences.

616.8 **IT** **ISSN 0390-0088**
CLINICA NEUROPSICHIATRICA. (Text in Italian; summaries in English, French, German, Italian) 1965. irreg. Ospedale Neuropsichiatrico, Teramo, Italy.

616.804 **US** **ISSN 0009-9155**
CODEN: CEEGA
CLINICAL ELECTROENCEPHALOGRAPHY. 1970. q. $50 (Canada $55; elsewhere $59). American Medical Electroencephalographic Association, 850 Elm Grove Rd., Ste. 11, Elm Grove, WI 53122. TEL 414-797-7800. adv.; bk.rev.; charts; illus. circ. 2,424. (also avail. in microform from UMI; reprint service avail. from UMI,ISI) **Indexed:** Bibl.Dev.Med.& Child Neur., Biol.Abstr., Curr.Cont., Excerp.Med., Ind.Med., Ind.Sci.Rev., Sci.Cit.Ind.
—BLDSC (3286.274000); Faxon; SWETS; UMI; UnCover.
  Refereed Serial

616.8 **US** **ISSN 0749-8047**
CLINICAL JOURNAL OF PAIN. 1985. q. $96 to individuals; institutions $155 (effective 1995). (American Academy of Pain Medicine) Lippincott - Raven Press, 227 E. Washington Sq., Philadelphia, PA 19106. TEL 215-238-4200. Ed. Peter R. Wilson. adv. contact: Phyllis Noyes. bk.rev.; charts; illus.; index. circ. 2,500. (back issues avail.; reprint service avail. from UMI) **Indexed:** Behav.Med.Abstr., Excerp.Med., Ind.Med. (1992-). **Document type:** academic/scholarly publication.
—BLDSC (3286.294200); Faxon; Genuine Article; SWETS; UMI; UnCover. **CCC.**
  Description: Explores all aspects of pain and pain management, including diagnostic procedures, therapeutic modalities, psychosocial dimensions, and ethical problems.
  Refereed Serial

420 616.8 **UK** **ISSN 0269-9206**
RC423.A1
CLINICAL LINGUISTICS & PHONETICS. 1987. q. £121($199) (effective 1996). Taylor & Francis Ltd., Rankine Rd., Basingstoke, Hants RG24 8PR, England. TEL 44-1256-840366. FAX 44-1256-479438. TELEX 858540. E-mail: info@tandf.co.uk. (Subscr. in N. America to: Taylor & Francis Inc., 1900 Frost Rd., Ste. 101, Bristol, PA 19007-1598. TEL 800-821-8312. FAX 215-785-5515) Ed. Martin J. Ball. bk.rev. **Indexed:** Bibl.Ling., Excerp.Med., Lang.& Lang.Behav.Abstr. (1987-), Ling.Abstr. **Document type:** academic/scholarly publication.
—BLDSC (3286.297800); Faxon; Genuine Article; SWETS; UnCover. **CCC.**
  Description: Presents articles ranging from theoretical discussions to extremely practical tutorial reviews. Language development and other psycho- or neurolinguistic areas are included where they shed light on normative behavior against which to judge the non-normal.
  Refereed Serial

616.8 617 **NE** **ISSN 0303-8467**
CODEN: CNNSBV
CLINICAL NEUROLOGY AND NEUROSURGERY; an international journal publishing papers and reports on the clinical aspects of neurology and neurosurgery. (Text in English) 1975. q. fl.385 ($235) (effective 1996). Elsevier Science B.V., P.O. Box 211, 1000 AE Amsterdam, Netherlands. TEL 31-20-4853911. FAX 31-20-4853598. TELEX 18582 ESPA NL. E-mail: nlinfo-f@elsevier.nl; usinfo-f@elsevier.com; forinfo-kyf04035@niftyserve.or.jp; Site addr.: http://www.elsevier.nl/. (Subscr. in U.S. and Canada to: Elsevier Science Inc., Box 882, Madison Sq. Sta., New York, NY 10159. TEL 212-989-5800. FAX 212-633-3990) Ed. G.W. Bruyn. adv.; bk.rev. (also avail. in microform from UMI) **Indexed:** Bibl.Dev.Med.& Child Neur., Biol.Abstr., Curr.Adv.Cancer Res., Curr.Cont., Excerp.Med., Ind.Med., Psychol.Abstr. (1992-), Rev.Med.& Vet.Mycol. **Document type:** academic/scholarly publication.
—BLDSC (3286.310100); Faxon; Genuine Article; SWETS; UnCover. **CCC.**
  Description: Covers developments in the field of clinical neurology and neurosurgery, including invited reviews, original research, brief case histories of unusual clinical syndromes or diseases.
  Refereed Serial

616.8 **GW** **ISSN 0722-5091**
CODEN: CLNPDA
CLINICAL NEUROPATHOLOGY. (Text in English) 1982. bi-m. DM.245($143) Dustri-Verlag Dr. Karl Feistle, Bahnhofstr. 9, 82041 Deisenhofen, Germany. TEL 089-613861-0. FAX 089-6135412. Eds. Dr. W. Schlote, Dr. F. St. Vogel. **Indexed:** Curr.Adv.Ecol.Sci., Dent.Ind., Excerp.Med., Ind.Med., Ind.Sci.Rev., Sci.Cit.Ind. **Document type:** academic/scholarly publication.
—BLDSC (3286.310400); Genuine Article; SWETS; UnCover. **CCC.**

CLINICAL NEUROPHARMACOLOGY. see *PHARMACY AND PHARMACOLOGY*

MEDICAL SCIENCES — PSYCHIATRY AND NEUROLOGY

616.8   NE   ISSN 0923-084X
CLINICAL NEUROPHYSIOLOGY UPDATES. (Text in English) 1989. irreg., vol.3, 1990. price varies. Elsevier Science B.V., Books Division, P.O. Box 211, 1000 AE Amsterdam, Netherlands. TEL 31-20-4853911. FAX 31-20-4853705. TELEX 18582 ESPA NL. E-mail: nlinfo-f@elsevier.nl; usinfo-f@elsevier.com; forinfo-kyf04035@niftyserve.or.jp; Site addr.: http://www.elsevier.nl/. (Susbcr. in U.S. and Canada to: Elsevier Science Inc., Box 882, Madison Sq. Sta., New York, NY 10159. TEL 212-989-5800) Ed. J. Desmedt. (back issues avail.) **Document type:** monographic series.
Refereed Serial

THE CLINICAL NEUROPSYCHOLOGIST. see *PSYCHOLOGY*

616.8   US   ISSN 1065-6766
RC321   CODEN: CINUE5
CLINICAL NEUROSCIENCE. 1993. bi-m. $240 (foreign $333) (effective 1996). John Wiley & Sons, Inc., Journals, 605 Third Ave., New York, NY 10158. TEL 212-850-6645. FAX 212-850-6021. TELEX 12-7063. E-mail: SUBINFO@JWILEY.COM. (Subscr. outside the Americas to: John Wiley & Sons Ltd., Baffins Ln., Chichester, W. Sussex PO19 1UD, England. TEL 44-1243-779777. FAX 44-1243-776128) Ed.Bd. (also avail. in microform from UMI; back issues avail.) **Document type:** academic/scholarly publication.
—BLDSC (3286.310900); Genuine Article.
Refereed Serial

617.48   US   ISSN 0069-4827
RD593.A1   CODEN: CLNEA8
CLINICAL NEUROSURGERY: PROCEEDINGS. 1953. a. price varies. Congress of Neurological Surgeons, c/o Dr. Thomas G. Saul, 506 Oak St., OH 45219. TEL 513-872-2657. FAX 513-872-2597. **Indexed:** Ind.Med., INIS Atomind. **Document type:** proceedings.
—BLDSC (3286.311000); CASDDS; SWETS; UnCover. **CCC.**

616.89   US   ISSN 0270-6644
CLINICAL PSYCHIATRY NEWS. 1973. m. $60. International Medical News Group (Subsidiary of: Capital Cities- ABC Inc.), 12230 Wilkins Ave., Rockville, MD 20852. TEL 301-816-8700. Ed. Richard Camer. adv.; bk.rev. circ. 32,300. (tabloid format; also avail. in microform from UMI) **Document type:** newspaper.
—UMI.

CLINICS IN DEVELOPMENTAL MEDICINE. see *MEDICAL SCIENCES — Pediatrics*

616.8   NE   ISSN 0926-6410
QP360.5   CODEN: CBRREZ
COGNITIVE BRAIN RESEARCH. (Text in English) 1992. q. fl.452($276) (effective 1996). Elsevier Science B.V., P.O. Box 211, 1000 AE Amsterdam, Netherlands. TEL 31-20-4853911. FAX 31-20-4853598. TELEX 18582 ESPA NL. E-mail: nlinfo-f@elsevier.nl; usinfo-f@elsevier.com; forinfo-kyf04035@niftyserve.or.jp; Site addr.: http://www.elsevier.nl/. (Subscr. in U.S. and Canada to: Elsevier Science Inc., Box 882, Madison Sq. Sta., New York, NY 10159. TEL 212-989-5800. FAX 212-633-3990) Ed. D.P. Purpura. adv.; bk.rev. (also avail. in microform from UMI; back issues avail.) **Indexed:** Excerp.Med. (1993-), Psychol.Abstr. (1992-). **Document type:** academic/scholarly publication.
—BLDSC (3292.874000); ADONIS; CASDDS; Faxon; Genuine Article; SWETS; UnCover. **CCC.**
Description: Publishes original reports of research in computational neuroscience, including neural networks, brain mechanisms subserving cognition, and applications of chaos theory to the analysis of brain functions and aberrant neurobehavioral processes.
Refereed Serial

616.8   CN
COMMUNIQUE (VANCOUVER). 1986. bi-m. membership. Amyotrophic Lateral Sclerosis Society of B.C., 411 Dunsmuir St., 2nd Fl., Vancouver, BC V6B 1X4, Canada. TEL 604-685-0737. FAX 604-685-0725. Ed. Rhelda Evans. adv. contact: Judy Bonds. circ. 875. (looseleaf format; also avail. in diskette format; back issues avail.) **Document type:** newsletter.
Description: Studies ALS research, fundraising and coping mechanisms and services for families with the disease.

COMMUNITY MENTAL HEALTH JOURNAL. see *SOCIAL SERVICES AND WELFARE*

616.8   II
COMMUNITY PSYCHIATRY JOURNAL. Institute of Community Psychiatry and Mental Health, Department of Psychiatry, J. J. Group of Hospitals, Byculla, Bombay 400008, India.

616.89   US   ISSN 0010-440X
RC321   CODEN: COPYAV
COMPREHENSIVE PSYCHIATRY. 1960. bi-m. $225 (foreign $251) (effective 1996). (American Psychopathological Association) W.B. Saunders Co. (Subsidiary of: Harcourt Brace & Company), Curtis Center, 3rd Fl., Independence Sq. W., Philadelphia, PA 19106-3399. TEL 215-238-7800. FAX 215-238-6445. (Subscr. to: Periodicals Fulfillment, W.B. Saunders Co., 6277 Sea Harbor Dr., 4th Fl., Orlando, FL 32891-4800. TEL 800-654-2452. FAX 800-874-6418) Ed. Dr. Ralph A. O'Connell; Pub. Joan W. Blumberg. adv.: B&W page $580, color page $1380; 7 x 10; adv. contact: Steve Gray. bk.rev.; abstr.; bibl.; charts; illus.; index. circ. 1,262. **Indexed:** Adol.Ment.Hlth.Abstr., Biol.Abstr., Chem.Abstr., Curr.Cont., Dent.Ind., Excerp.Med., Ind.Med., Ind.Sci.Rev., Mid.East: Abstr.& Ind., NRN, Psychol.Abstr. (1960-), Sci.Cit.Ind., SSCI. **Document type:** academic/scholarly publication.
● Also available online.
—BLDSC (3366.390000); Faxon; Genuine Article; SWETS; UMI; UnCover. **CCC.**
Description: Covers developments in clinical and basic investigations, as well as new diagnostic and therapeutic practices.
Refereed Serial

616.8   SZ   ISSN 0251-2068
   CODEN: COPNDZ
CONCEPTS IN PEDIATRIC NEUROSURGERY. (Text in English) 1981. irreg. price varies. (American Society for Pediatric Neurosurgery) S. Karger AG, Allschwilerstr. 10, P.O. Box, CH-4009 Basel, Switzerland. TEL 061-3061111. FAX 061-3061234. E-mail: Karger@Karger.ch. **Indexed:** Biol.Abstr. **Document type:** academic/scholarly publication.
—BLDSC (3399.413700); Faxon. **CCC.**
Refereed Serial

616.6   IT   ISSN 1122-0279
CONFINIA CEPHALALGICA. 1992. q. L.71000($99) (effective 1994). Masson S.p.A., Divisione Periodici, Via Statuto 2-4, 20121 Milan, Italy. TEL 02-6367-1. FAX 02-6367211. Ed. Gian Camillo Manzoni. adv.: B&W page L.2300000, color page L.3300000. circ. 2,500. **Indexed:** Excerp.Med. (1993-). **Document type:** academic/scholarly publication.
—BLDSC (3410.634500).

616.8   US   ISSN 0069-9446
   CODEN: CNRSAG
CONTEMPORARY NEUROLOGY SERIES. 1966. irreg., vol.42, 1993. price varies. F.A. Davis Company, 1915 Arch St., Philadelphia, PA 19103. TEL 800-523-4049. TELEX 83-4837. Ed. Sid Gilman. **Indexed:** Chem.Abstr., Ind.Med. **Document type:** monographic series.
—BLDSC (3425.193000); CASDDS.
Refereed Serial

CONTEMPORARY NEUROSURGERY. see *MEDICAL SCIENCES — Surgery*

362.2 616.85   US   ISSN 1075-7082
▼**CONTINUUM (SAN FRANCISCO)**; developments in ambulatory mental health care. 1994. q. (American Association for Partial Hospitalization) Jossey-Bass Inc., Publishers, 350 Sansome St., 5th Fl., San Francisco, CA 94104. TEL 415-433-1767. FAX 415-433-0499. Ed. Dr. Lawrence L. Kennedy. **Document type:** trade publication.
Description: Dedicated to helping mental health professionals evaluate developments in ambulatory care in mental health services.

CONTRIBUICOES EM PSICOLOGIA, PSIQUIATRIA E PSICANALISE. see *PSYCHOLOGY*

616.8   US   ISSN 0749-8055
   CODEN: COTHE4
CONVULSIVE THERAPY. 1985. q. $118 to individuals; institutions $210 (effective 1995). Lippincott - Raven Press, 227 E. Washington Sq., Philadelphia, PA 19106. TEL 215-238-4200. Ed. Charles Horn Kellner. adv. contact: Phyllis Noyes. bk.rev.; charts; illus.; index. circ. 1,000. (back issues avail.; reprint service avail. from UMI) **Indexed:** Excerp.Med., Ind.Med. (1994-), Psychol.Abstr. (1988-). **Document type:** academic/scholarly publication.
—BLDSC (3463.679300); Faxon; Genuine Article; SWETS; UMI. **CCC.**
Description: Reports on major clinical and research advances worldwide on the the effects of electroconvulsive therapy, mode of seizure induction, and ethical issues.
Refereed Serial

CORRECTIVE AND SOCIAL PSYCHIATRY AND JOURNAL OF BEHAVIORAL TECHNOLOGY METHODS AND THERAPY. see *PSYCHOLOGY*

616.8   US   ISSN 1042-0398
RC346
CORRELATIVE NEUROANATOMY. 1952. triennial. Appleton & Lange (Subsidiary of: Simon & Schuster), 25 Van Zant St., East Norwalk, CT 06855.
Supersedes (in 1988): Correlative Neuroanatomy and Functional Neurology (ISSN 0892-1237)

616.8   IT   ISSN 0010-9452
CORTEX; journal devoted to study of the nervous system and behavior. (Text in English) 1964. q. L.120000($141) to individuals; institutions L.237000($262) (effective 1994). (Associazione per lo Sviluppo delle Ricerche Neuropsicologiche) Masson S.p.A., Divisione Periodici, Via Statuto 2-4, 20121 Milan, Italy. TEL 02-6367-1. FAX 02-6367211. Ed. Ennio De Renzi. adv.: B&W page L.1150000, color page L.1900000; trim 170 x 260. bk.rev.; charts; index. circ. 1,500. (also avail. in microform from SWZ,UMI; reprint service avail. from SWZ) **Indexed:** Bibl.Dev.Med.& Child Neur., Biol.Abstr., Curr.Adv.Ecol.Sci., Curr.Cont., Dent.Ind., Ergon.Abstr., Excerp.Med., Ind.Med., Ind.Sci.Rev., Psychol.Abstr. (1964-), Sci.Cit.Ind., Yrbk.Assoc.Educ.& Rehab.Blind. **Document type:** academic/scholarly publication.
—BLDSC (3477.150000); Faxon; Genuine Article; SWETS; UMI; UnCover.

COUNSELLING PSYCHOLOGY QUARTERLY. see *PSYCHOLOGY*

616.8 364   UK   ISSN 0957-9664
   CODEN: CBMHEE
CRIMINAL BEHAVIOUR AND MENTAL HEALTH. 1991. 4/yr. £52($140) to individuals; institutions £88 (effective 1996). Whurr Publishers Ltd., 19b Compton Terrace, London N1 2UN, England. TEL 0171-359-5979. FAX 0171-226-5290. (Subscr. to: Turpin Distribution Services Ltd., Blackhorse Rd., Letchworth, Herts. SG6 1HN, England. TEL 01462-672555. FAX 01462-480947; Subscr. in N. America to: Whurr Publishers Ltd., Box 1897, Lawrence, KS 66044-8897. TEL 913-843-1221. FAX 913-843-1274) Ed.Bd. adv.: page £195; adv. contact: Sarah Vicary. bk.rev.; charts; illus.; stat.; index. **Indexed:** Abstr.Crim.& Pen., Excerp.Med. (1993-), Psychol.Abstr. (1991-). **Document type:** academic/scholarly publication.
—BLDSC (3487.346200); ADONIS.

616.8   US   ISSN 0892-0915
RC321   CODEN: CCNBE8
CRITICAL REVIEWS IN NEUROBIOLOGY. 1985. q. $84 to individuals; institutions $265 (effective 1996). Begell House Inc., 79 Madison Ave., Ste. 1201, New York, NY 10016-7892. TEL 212-725-1999. FAX 212-213-8368. E-mail: 74353.2052@compuserve.com. Ed. James S. Nelson. **Indexed:** Excerp.Med. **Document type:** academic/scholarly publication.
—BLDSC (3487.478500); CASDDS; Genuine Article; UnCover. **CCC.**
Formerly: Critical Reviews in Clinical Neurobiology.
Description: Presents comprehensive reviews, analyses, and integration of recently developed substansive observations and information which influence the understanding of normal or disturbed processes involving nervous system.

CRITICAL REVIEWS IN NEUROSURGERY. see *MEDICAL SCIENCES — Surgery*

MEDICAL SCIENCES — PSYCHIATRY AND NEUROLOGY

CULTURE, MEDICINE AND PSYCHIATRY; an international journal of comparative cross-cultural research. see ANTHROPOLOGY

CURRENT ADVANCES IN NEUROSCIENCE. see MEDICAL SCIENCES — Abstracting, Bibliographies, Statistics

616.8 NE
▼**CURRENT ISSUES IN NEURODEGENERATIVE DISEASES.** (Text in English) 1994. irreg., vol.7, 1995. (Vrije Universiteit Amsterdam, Research Institute Neurosciences) I C G Publications, P.O. Box 509, 3300 AM Dordrecht, Netherlands. TEL 31-78-510454. FAX 31-78-510972. Eds. Erik Ch. Wolters, Philip Scheltens. **Document type:** monographic series.
  Description: Covers progress in basic science and clinical research in the fields of neurodegeneration, behavioral neurology and biological psychiatry.

616.0472 NE ISSN 0923-2354
  CODEN: CMPAEH
CURRENT MANAGEMENT OF PAIN. (Text in English) 1988. irreg. price varies. Kluwer Academic Publishers, Postbus 17, 3300 AA Dordrecht, Netherlands. TEL 31-78-392392. FAX 31-78-392254. TELEX 29245 KAPG NL. (Dist. by: Kluwer Academic Publishers Group, P.O. Box 322, 3300 AH Dordrecht, Netherlands. TEL 31-78-392392. FAX 31-78-546474; N. America dist. addr.: Box 358, Accord Sta., Hingham, MA 02018-0358. TEL 617-871-6600. FAX 617-871-6528) **Document type:** monographic series.
  Refereed Serial

616.8 US ISSN 0161-780X
RC321 CODEN: CNEUDS
CURRENT NEUROLOGY. 1980. a. $77.95 (residents $40) (effective 1996). Mosby - Year Book, Inc. (Chicago) (Subsidiary of: Times Mirror Company), 200 N. LaSalle St., Chicago, IL 60601-1080. TEL 312-726-9733. FAX 312-726-6075. TELEX 206155. (Subscr. to: 11830 Westline Industrial Dr., St. Louis, MO 63146. TEL 800-325-4177) Ed. Stanley H. Appel, M.D. illus. **Indexed:** Chem.Abstr.
  —BLDSC (3500.630000); CASDDS; Faxon. **CCC.**
  Description: Presents reviews of the pertinent literature combined with original papers in neurology.

CURRENT OPINION IN NEUROBIOLOGY. see BIOLOGY — Abstracting, Bibliographies, Statistics

CURRENT OPINION IN NEUROLOGY. see MEDICAL SCIENCES — Abstracting, Bibliographies, Statistics

CURRENT OPINION IN PSYCHIATRY. see MEDICAL SCIENCES — Abstracting, Bibliographies, Statistics

616 US ISSN 1069-5850
▼**CURRENT REVIEW OF PAIN.** 1994. irreg. $99.95. Current Medicine, 20 N. Third St., Philadelphia, PA 19106. TEL 215-574-2266; 800-552-5866. FAX 215-574-2270. (In UK: 34-42 Cleveland St., London W1P 5FB, England. TEL 44-71-323-0323. FAX 44-71-5801938) Ed. P. Prithvi Raj. bibl.; illus.
  —BLDSC (3502.480000).

616.4 US ISSN 0723-1229
  CODEN: CTNEEY
CURRENT TOPICS IN NEUROENDOCRINOLOGY. 1982. irreg. price varies. Springer-Verlag, 175 Fifth Ave., New York, NY 10010. TEL 212-460-1500. FAX 212-473-6272. (Also: Berlin, Heidelberg, Tokyo and Vienna) **Indexed:** Chem.Abstr. **Document type:** monographic series.
  —BLDSC (3504.893500); CASDDS; Faxon.

616.8 GW
D G S P RUNDBRIEF. 1977. q. DM.40. Deutsche Gesellschaft fuer Soziale Psychiatrie e.V., Stuppstr. 14, 50823 Cologne, Germany. TEL 221-511002. adv.; bk.rev. circ. 3,000. (back issues avail.)

616.89 SZ ISSN 0254-6221
  CODEN: DABAD9
DASEINSANALYSE; phaenomenologische Antropologie und Psychiatrie. 1984. 4/yr. 60 SFr.($46) to individuals; institutions 120 SFr.($92) (effective 1996). S. Karger AG, Allswilerstr. 10, P.O. Box, CH-4009 Basel, Switzerland. TEL 061-3061111. FAX 061-3061234. E-mail: Karger@Karger.ch. Eds. G. Condrau, A. Hicklin. adv.; bk.rev.; illus.; index. circ. 850. (also avail. in microform from UMI; back issues avail.) **Document type:** academic/scholarly publication.
  —CCC.
  Refereed Serial

616.8 SZ ISSN 1013-7424
  CODEN: DEMNEU
DEMENTIA. (Text in English) 1990. bi-m. 146.20 SFr.($112.40) to individuals; institutions 731 SFr.($562) (effective 1996). S. Karger AG, Allschwilerstr. 10, P.O. Box, CH-4009 Basel, Switzerland. TEL 061-3061111. FAX 061-3061234. E-mail: Karger@Karger.ch. (US and Canada subscr. to: S. Karger Publishers, Inc., 26 W. Avon Rd., Farmington, CT 06085) Ed. V. Chan-Palay. bibl.; charts; stat. (also avail. in microform from UMI) **Indexed:** Excerp.Med., Ind.Med. (1993-), Psychol.Abstr. (1990-). **Document type:** monographic series.
  —BLDSC (3550.524000); Genuine Article; SWETS. **CCC.**
  Description: Examines the neural bases of cognitive dysfunction. Concentrates on neuro-degenerative diseases such as Alzheimer's and Parkinson's diseases, as well as Huntington's chorea. Covers topics of interest to professional in neurobiology, pharmacology, genetics, gerontology, and psychiatry.
  Refereed Serial

618 323.4 US ISSN 1073-7138
DENDRON NEWS. 1988. q. $25. 454 Willamette St., Ste. 216, Box 11284, Eugene, OR 97440-3484. TEL 503-341-0100. E-mail: chrp@efn.org. Ed. David Oaks. adv.: page $250; adv. contact: David Oaks. bk.rev.; video rev. circ. 6,000. (also avail. in diskette format) **Document type:** newspaper.
  ●Also available online.
  Description: Covers human rights issues relating to psychiatric liberation and psychiatric system.

616.8 GW ISSN 0941-0406
DEUTSCHE ARBEITSGEMEINSCHAFT FUER KLINISCHE NEPHROLOGIE. MITTEILUNGEN. a. DM.66. (Deutsche Arbeitsgemeinschaft fuer Klinische Nephrologie e.V.) Vandenhoeck und Ruprecht, Robert-Bosch-Breite 6, 37079 Goettingen, Germany. TEL 0551-6959-0. FAX 0551-695917. (Subscr. to: 37070 Goettingen, Germany) Ed. E. Quellhorst. **Document type:** academic/scholarly publication.
  Formerly (until 1993): Arbeitsgemeinschaft fuer Klinische Nephrologie. Mitteilungen (ISSN 0172-7311)

362 618.92 GW ISSN 0939-4702
DEUTSCHE BEHINDERTENZEITSCHRIFT. Abbreviated title: D B Z. 1964. bi-m. DM.29. Reha-Verlag GmbH, Roonstr. 30, 53175 Bonn, Germany. TEL 0228-352328. FAX 0228-359569. Ed. L. Sparty. adv.: B&W page DM.1500; trim 210 x 297. bk.rev. circ. 10,000. **Document type:** bulletin.
  —CCC.
  Former titles: Behindertenzeitschrift (ISSN 0175-5854); Behinderte Kind (ISSN 0005-7991)

DEVELOPMENT AND PSYCHOPATHOLOGY. see PSYCHOLOGY

616.858 CN ISSN 1184-0412
DEVELOPMENTAL DISABILITIES BULLETIN. 1972. s-a. Can.$19.25 to individuals (foreign $15); institutions Can.$32.10 (foreign $25). University of Alberta, Developmental Disabilities Centre, 6-123D Education North, Edmonton, AB T6G 2G5, Canada. TEL 403-492-4505. FAX 403-492-1318. E-mail: henny_degroot@psych.educ.ualberta.ca. Ed. Jack Goldberg. adv. contact: Henny de Groot. bk.rev. circ. 250. **Indexed:** Psychol.Abstr. (1972-), Yrbk.Assoc.Educ.& Rehab.Blind. **Document type:** academic/scholarly publication, bulletin.
  —BLDSC (3579.054450). **CCC.**
  Formerly: Mental Retardation and Learning Disability Bulletin (ISSN 0822-4277)
  Description: Articles with both research and direct application to the education of, and provision of services for persons with mental retardation, learning disability and multiple handicaps.
  Refereed Serial

616.8 SZ ISSN 1019-5815
  CODEN: DBDYEV
DEVELOPMENTAL BRAIN DYSFUNCTION. (Text in English) 1988. 6/yr. 149.80 SFr.($115.15) to institutions; individuals 428 SFr.($329) (effective 1996). S. Karger AG, Allschwilerstr. 10, P.O. Box, CH-4009 Basel, Switzerland. TEL 061-3061111. FAX 061-3061234. E-mail: Karger@Karger.ch. Ed. R. Ferri. (also avail. in microfiche; microfilm; microform from UMI) **Indexed:** Excerp.Med., Psychol.Abstr. (1988-). **Document type:** academic/scholarly publication.
  —BLDSC (3579.054100); Genuine Article. **CCC.**
  Formerly: Brain Dysfunction (ISSN 0259-1278)
  Refereed Serial

616.8 NE ISSN 0165-3806
QP376 CODEN: DBRRDB
DEVELOPMENTAL BRAIN RESEARCH. (Section of: Brain Research (ISSN 0006-8993)) 1981. 14/yr. fl.3031($1848) (effective 1996). Elsevier Science B.V., P.O. Box 211, 1000 AE Amsterdam, Netherlands. TEL 31-20-4853911. FAX 31-20-4853598. TELEX 18582 ESPA NL. E-mail: nlinfo-f@elsevier.nl; usinfo-f@elsevier.com; forinfo-kyf04035@niftyserve.or.jp; Site addr.: http://www.elsevier.nl/. (Subscr. in U.S. and Canada to: Elsevier Science Inc., Box 882, Madison Sq. Sta., New York, NY 10159-0882. TEL 212-989-5800. FAX 212-633-3990) Ed. D.P. Purpura. (reprint service avail. from ISI) **Indexed:** Bibl.Dev.Med.& Child Neur., Biol.Abstr., Chem.Abstr., Curr.Adv.Biochem., Curr.Adv.Ecol.Sci., Curr.Cont., Excerp.Med., Ind.Sci.Rev., Psychol.Abstr. (1981-), Sci.Cit.Ind., Sport Fish.Abstr., Wild.Rev. **Document type:** academic/scholarly publication.
  —BLDSC (3579.054200); ADONIS; CASDDS; Faxon; Genuine Article; SWETS; UnCover. **CCC.**
  Description: Provides a medium for prompt publication of vitro and in vivo developmental studies concerned with the mechanism of neurogenesis, neuro migration, cell death, neuronal differentiation, synaptogenesis, myelination, the establishment of neuroglia relations and the development of various brain-barrier mechanisms.

DEVELOPMENTAL MEDICINE AND CHILD NEUROLOGY. see MEDICAL SCIENCES — Pediatrics

616.8 SZ ISSN 0378-5866
  CODEN: DENED7
DEVELOPMENTAL NEUROSCIENCE. 1979. bi-m. 245.35 SFr.($188.65) to individuals; institutions 701 SFr.($539) (effective 1996). S. Karger AG, Allschwilerstr. 10, P.O. Box, CH-4009 Basel, Switzerland. TEL 061-3061111. FAX 061-3061234. E-mail: Karger@Karger.ch. Ed. A.T. Campagnoni. adv.; illus.; index. circ. 800. (also avail. in microform from UMI) **Indexed:** ASCA, Biol.Abstr., Chem.Abstr., Curr.Adv.Biochem., Curr.Adv.Cell & Devel.Biol., Curr.Adv.Ecol.Sci., Curr.Cont., Excerp.Med., Helminthol.Abstr., Ind.Med., Ind.Sci.Rev., Sci.Cit.Ind. **Document type:** academic/scholarly publication.
  —BLDSC (3579.057500); CASDDS; Faxon; Genuine Article; SWETS. **CCC.**
  Refereed Serial

MEDICAL SCIENCES — PSYCHIATRY AND NEUROLOGY

616.8 NE ISSN 0165-7003
CODEN: DNEUD5
DEVELOPMENTS IN NEUROSCIENCE. 1977. irreg., vol.18, 1984. price varies. Elsevier Science B.V., Books Division, P.O. Box 211, 1000 AE Amsterdam, Netherlands. TEL 31-20-4853911.
FAX 31-20-4853705. TELEX 18582 ESPA NL.
E-mail: nlinfo-f@elsevier.nl; usinfo-f@elsevier.com; forinfo-kyf04035@niftyserve.or.jp; Site addr.: http://www.elsevier.nl/. (Subscr. in U.S. and Canada to: Elsevier Science Inc., Box 882, Madison Sq. Sta., New York, NY 10159. TEL 212-989-5800)
Indexed: Chem.Abstr., Ind.Sci.Rev., Sci.Cit.Ind.
Document type: monographic series.
—CASDDS.
Refereed Serial

616.8 NE ISSN 0166-2481
CODEN: DPSYDX
DEVELOPMENTS IN PSYCHIATRY. (Text in English) 1979. irreg., vol.9, 1992. Elsevier Science B.V., Books Division, P.O. Box 211, 1000 AE Amsterdam, Netherlands. TEL 31-20-4853911.
FAX 31-20-4853705. TELEX 18582 ESPA NL.
E-mail: nlinfo-f@elsevier.nl; usinfo-f@elsevier.com; forinfo-kyf04035@niftyserve.or.jp; Site addr.: http://www.elsevier.nl/. (Subscr. in U.S. and Canada to: Elsevier Science Inc., Box 882, Madison Sq. Sta., New York, NY 10159. TEL 212-989-5800) illus. (back issues avail.) **Indexed:** Chem.Abstr. **Document type:** monographic series.
—BLDSC (3579.087700); CASDDS.
Refereed Serial

616.891 615.1 US
DI CYAN BULLETIN. 1950. m. Erwin Di Cyan, Ed. & Pub., 1486 E. 33rd St., Brooklyn, NY 11234.
TEL 718-252-8844. bk.rev. **Document type:** bulletin.
Formerly: Di Cyan and Brown Bulletin (ISSN 0012-1754)

DIALECT. see SOCIAL SERVICES AND WELFARE

616.891 US ISSN 0891-3870
DIRECTIONS IN PSYCHIATRY. 1981. fortn. $257. Hatherleigh Company Ltd., 420 E. 51st St., New York, NY 10022. TEL 212-355-0882;
800-367-2550. FAX 212-308-7930. Ed. Dr. Fredric F. Flach. index. (looseleaf format; back issues avail.; reprint service avail.) **Document type:** academic/scholarly publication.
Description: Publishes scholarly, jargon-free articles on developments in psychiatry. Continuing Medical Education credits are available.

DIRECTORY OF GRADUATE TRAINING IN BEHAVIOR THERAPY. see EDUCATION — Guides To Schools And Colleges

DIRECTORY OF SUICIDE PREVENTION AND CRISIS INTERVENTION CENTERS. see PSYCHOLOGY

616.8 NE ISSN 0254-8852
CODEN: DISNEK
DISCUSSIONS IN NEUROSCIENCE. (Text and summaries in English) 1984. 4/yr. fl.77($42) (effective 1995). (Fondation pour l'Etude du Systeme Nerveux Central et Peripherique, SZ) Elsevier Science B.V., P.O. Box 211, 1000 AE Amsterdam, Netherlands.
TEL 31-20-4853911. FAX 31-20-4853598.
TELEX 18582 ESPA NL.
E-mail: nlinfo-f@elsevier.nl; usinfo-f@elsevier.com; forinfo-kyf04035@niftyserve.or.jp; Site addr.: http://www.elsevier.nl/. (Subscr. in U.S. and Canada to: Elsevier Science Inc., Box 882, Madison Sq. Sta., New York, NY 10159. TEL 212-989-5800. FAX 212-633-3990) Ed. P.J. Magistretti. adv.; bk.rev. (reprint service avail. from ISI) **Indexed:** Excerp.Med. (1993-). **Document type:** academic/scholarly publication.
—BLDSC (3597.053700); ADONIS; Faxon; Genuine Article; SWETS; UnCover. **CCC.**
Description: Publishes monographs and proceedings on various areas in neurosience.
Refereed Serial

616.748 IT ISSN 0012-4087
DISTROFIA MUSCOLARE. 1962. q. free. Unione Italiana Lotta alla Distrofia Muscolare, Via P.P. Vergerio 17, 35126 Padua, Italy. TEL 39-49-757361.
FAX 39-49-757033. Ed. Stefano Borgato. adv. contact: Franco Bompresi. bk.rev.; bibl.; charts; illus. circ. 43,000.
Description: Presents research papers from various doctors interested in the field of muscular dystrophy. Also features articles on how to deal with victims of this illness as well as how to make their lives easier and more autonomous.

616.858 371.9 US ISSN 0161-0716
DOWN SYNDROME NEWS. 1976. 10/yr. $20 membership (effective 1994). National Down Syndrome Congress, 1605 Chantilly Dr., NE, Ste 250, Atlanta, GA 30324-3269. Ed. Kathleen Morofino. bk.rev.; film rev.; video rev.; bibl.; index. circ. 5,000. **Document type:** newsletter.
Description: Parent-oriented information on Down syndrome, including medical research, education issues, resources, articles by and for parents.

616.858 UK ISSN 0968-7912
DOWN'S SYNDROME: RESEARCH AND PRACTICE. 1993. 3/yr. £15 to individuals; institutions £25. University of Portmouth, Sarah Duffen Centre, Belmont St., Southsea, Hants. PO5 1NA, England.
TEL 01705-824261. FAX 01705-824265. E-mail: BUCKLEYS2CSOVAX.PORTSMOUTH.AC.UK. Ed. Sue Buckley. **Document type:** academic/scholarly publication.
—BLDSC (3620.077000).
Refereed Serial

DREAMING. see BIOLOGY — Physiology

616.89 NE ISSN 0929-483X
THE DUTCH ANNUAL OF PSYCHOANALYSIS. 1993. a. fl.63.70. Swets & Zeitlinger bv, Heereweg 347, 2161 CA Lisse, Netherlands. TEL 31-2521-35111. FAX 31-2521-15888. TELEX 41325 SZLIS NL. (Dist. in N. America by: Swets & Zeitlinger, 440 Creamery Way, Ste. A, Exton, PA 19341. TEL 800-447-9387. FAX 610-524-5366) **Document type:** academic/scholarly publication.

616.85 371.94 UK ISSN 1076-9242
▼**DYSLEXIA.** 1995. 3/yr. $95 (foreign $95) (effective 1996). (British Dyslexia Association) John Wiley & Sons Ltd., Journals, Baffins Ln., Chichester, W. Sussex PO19 1UD, England. TEL 01243-779777. FAX 01243-776128. E-mail: subinfo@jwiley.com. (Subscr. in the Americas to: John Wiley & Sons, Inc., 605 Third Ave., New York, NY 10158. TEL 212-850-6645. FAX 212-850-6021) adv. contact: Michael Levermore. (also avail. in microform from UMI; back issues avail.) **Document type:** academic/scholarly publication.
—BLDSC (3637.234000).
Refereed Serial

621.3 GW ISSN 0012-7590
CODEN: EEGEAE
E E G - E M G; Zeitschrift fuer Elektroenzephalographie, Elektromyographie und verwandte Gebiete. 1970. q. DM.254. Georg Thieme Verlag, Ruedigerstr. 14, 70469 Stuttgart, Germany. TEL 0711-8931-0.
FAX 0711-8931298. (Subscr. to: Postfach 104853, 70042 Stuttgart, Germany) Ed.Bd. adv.; bk.rev.; abstr.; bibl.; charts; illus.; stat.; index. circ. 1,200. (also avail. in microform from UMI; reprint service avail. from UMI) **Indexed:** Curr.Cont., Excerp.Med., Ind.Med. (until 1992). **Document type:** academic/scholarly publication.
—BLDSC (3663.394000); Faxon; Genuine Article; SWETS; UMI. **CCC.**

EDUCATION AND TRAINING IN MENTAL RETARDATION AND DEVELOPMENTAL DISABILITIES. see
EDUCATION — Special Education And Rehabilitation

616.8 IE ISSN 0921-884X
RC321 CODEN: ECNEAZ
ELECTROENCEPHALOGRAPHY AND CLINICAL NEUROPHYSIOLOGY INCLUDING EVOKED POTENTIALS AND ELECTROMYOGRAPHY AND MOTOR CONTROL.
Variant title: E E G Journal. (Supplements and Proceedings Supplements avail.) (Text in English and French) 1949. 24/yr. I£302; $477 (effective 1996). (International Federation of Clinical Neurophysiology) Elsevier Science Ireland Ltd., P.O. Box 85, Limerick, Ireland. TEL 353-61-471944.
FAX 353-61-472144. (Subscr. in U.S. and Canada to: Elsevier Science Inc., Box 882, Madison Sq. Sta., New York, NY 10159. TEL 212-989-5800. FAX 212-633-3990) Ed.Bd. adv.; bk.rev.; abstr.; charts; illus.; index. (also avail. in microform from UMI)
Indexed: Bibl.Dev.Med.& Child Neur., Biol.Abstr., C.I.S. Abstr., Chem.Abstr., Curr.Adv.Ecol.Sci., Curr.Cont., Dent.Ind., Ergon.Abstr., Excerp.Med., Ind.Med., Ind.Sci.Rev., INSPEC (1985-), Int.Abstr.Biol.Sci., Psychol.Abstr. (1950-). **Document type:** academic/scholarly publication.
—BLDSC (3699.000000); ADONIS; Faxon; Genuine Article; SWETS. **CCC.**
Supersedes: Electroencephalography and Clinical Neurophysiology (ISSN 0013-4694); Which incorporates: Index to Current E E G Literature (ISSN 0019-3976)
Description: Provides comprehensive coverage of research into the electrical activity in the central nervous system.
Refereed Serial

616.8 NE ISSN 0424-8155
CODEN: EECSB3
ELECTROENCEPHALOGRAPHY AND CLINICAL NEUROPHYSIOLOGY. SUPPLEMENTS. (Text in English) 1950. irreg., vol.43, 1991. price varies. (International Federation of Clinical Neurophysiology) Elsevier Science B.V., Books Division, P.O. Box 211, 1000 AE Amsterdam, Netherlands.
TEL 31-20-4853911. FAX 31-20-4853705.
TELEX 18582 ESPA NL.
E-mail: nlinfo-f@elsevier.nl; usinfo-f@elsevier.com; forinfo-kyf04035@niftyserve.or.jp; Site addr.: http://www.elsevier.nl/. (Subscr. in U.S. and Canada to: Elsevier Science Inc., Box 882, Madison Sq. Sta., New York, NY 10159. TEL 212-989-5800. FAX 212-633-3990) Ed.Bd. **Document type:** monographic series.
—BLDSC (3699.020000); CASDDS; Faxon.
Refereed Serial

616.8 IE ISSN 0924-980X
ELECTROMYOGRAPHY AND MOTOR CONTROL. (Section of: Electroencephalography and Clinical Neurophysiology (ISSN 0921-884X)) 1991. bi-m. I£90($142) (effective 1996). (International Federation of Clinical Neurophysiology) Elsevier Science Ireland Ltd., P.O. Box 85, Limerick, Ireland. TEL 353-61-471944. FAX 353-61-472144.
(Subscr. in U.S. and Canada to: Elsevier Science Inc., Box 882, Madison Sq. Sta., New York, NY 10159.
TEL 212-989-5800. FAX 212-633-3990) Eds. F. Maugiere, G.G. Celesis. **Indexed:** Excerp.Med. (1992-), Psychol.Abstr. (1991-). **Document type:** academic/scholarly publication.
—ADONIS; SWETS. **CCC.**
Description: Covers all clinical applications of EMG, reflexology, premotor evoked potentials and brain stimulation as well as experimental studies of human motor physiology.
Refereed Serial

616.8 US ISSN 0734-9890
CODEN: EBMOEN
EMOTIONS AND BEHAVIOR. MONOGRAPH. irreg. price varies. (Chicago Institute for Psychoanalysis) International Universities Press, Inc., 59 Boston Post Rd., Box 1524, Madison, CT 06443-1524.
TEL 203-245-4000. Ed. George H. Pollock. **Indexed:** Psychol.Abstr. **Document type:** monographic series.
Refereed Serial

ENCOUNTERER. see PSYCHOLOGY

616.8 574.192 YU ISSN 0351-2665
ENGRAMI. (Text in Serbo-Croatian; summaries in English and Russian) 1979. q. 4000 din. Institut za Psihijatriju, University Clinical Center, Pasterova br. 2, 11000 Belgrade, Yugoslavia. (Co-sponsor: Yugoslav Psychiatric Association) Ed. Dimitrije Milovanovic. circ. 500.

MEDICAL SCIENCES — PSYCHIATRY AND NEUROLOGY

616.853 362.196　DK　ISSN 0107-2668
EPILEPSI. 1966. q. DKK 75. Dansk Epilepsiforening, Dr. Sellsvej 28, DK-4293 Dianalund, Denmark. TEL 45-58-26-44-66. FAX 45-58-26-44-51. Ed. Knud K. Brander. adv.; bk.rev.; illus. circ. 10,000. **Document type:** newsletter, consumer publication.
Formerly: Tidsskrift for Epilepsi.
Description: Publishes medical and general information about epilepsy and epileptics.

616.853　　　　US　ISSN 0013-9580
RC395　　　　　　CODEN: EPILAK
EPILEPSIA. 1959. m. $252 to individuals (foreign $286); institutions $424 (foreign $498) (effective 1996); newsstand price: $43. (International League against Epilepsy) Lippincott - Raven Publishers, 227 E. Washington Sq., Philadelphia, PA 19106. TEL 215-238-4200. Ed. Timothy A. Pedley. adv. contact: Phyllis Noyes. bk.rev.; charts; illus. circ. 4,000. (reprint service avail. from KTO) **Indexed:** Bibl.Dev.Med.& Child Neur., Biol.Abstr., Chem.Abstr., Curr.Adv.Ecol.Sci., Curr.Cont., Dent.Ind., Excerp.Med., Helminthol.Abstr., Ind.Med., Ind.Sci.Rev., Psychol.Abstr., Sci.Cit.Ind. **Document type:** academic/scholarly publication.
—BLDSC (3793.700000); CASDDS; Faxon; Genuine Article; SWETS; UMI; UnCover. **CCC.**
Description: Provides current clinical and research results on all aspects of epilepsy.
Refereed Serial

616.853 362.1　FI　ISSN 0780-0150
EPILEPSIA-LEHTI. (Text in Finnish; summaries in English and Swedish) 1968. q. FIM 100 (effective 1996). Epilepsialiitto - Finnish Epilepsy Association, Kalevankatu 61, FIN-00180 Helsinki, Finland. TEL 358-0-6948433. FAX 358-0-6949927. Ed. Minna Kurikka. adv.; bk.rev. circ. 10,000.
Formerly (until 1983): Epilepsia (ISSN 0356-598X)

616.853　　　　　　SZ
EPILEPSIE. (Text and summaries in French, German and Italian) 1983. 2/yr. 20 SFr. Schweizerische Liga gegen Epilepsie, Feldeggstr. 71, Postfach 1332, CH-8032 Zurich, Switzerland. TEL 01-3835455. Ed. A. Hagmann-Albrecht. adv. contact: Esther Hobi-Schaerer. bk.rev. circ. 800. **Document type:** academic/scholarly publication.
Description: Covers medical and social aspects, featuring research in treatment, diagnosis, therapy, and heredity, as well as social and educational problems of different age groups. Includes list of events.

616.853　　　　FR　ISSN 1149-6576
EPILEPSIES. 4/yr. 280 F. to individuals; institutions 510 F. (effective 1995). (Ligue Francaise Contre l'Epilepsie) John Libbey Eurotext, 127 av de la Republique, 92120 Montrouge, France. TEL 1-46-73-06-60. FAX 1-40-84-09-99. (Subscr. to: A T E I, 23-25 rue Fernand Combette, 93100 Montreuil sous Bois, France. TEL 48-59-58-11. FAX 48-59-57-99) Eds. Michelle Bureau, Pierre Genton. **Document type:** academic/scholarly publication.
—BLDSC (3793.740000).
Description: Provides a forum for neurologists, specialised institutions, general practitioners, nurses, technicians and electroencephalographers.

616.853　　　　NE　ISSN 0920-1211
　　　　　　　　　　CODEN: EPIRE8
EPILEPSY RESEARCH. (Supplement avail.) (Text in English) 1987. 9/yr. fl.1728($1054) (effective 1996). Elsevier Science B.V., P.O. Box 211, 1000 AE Amsterdam, Netherlands. TEL 31-20-4853911. FAX 31-20-4853598. TELEX 18582 ESPA NL. E-mail: nlinfo-f@elsevier.nl; usinfo-f@elsevier.com; forinfo-kyf04035@niftyserve.or.jp; Site addr.: http://www.elsevier.nl/. (Subscr. in U.S. and Canada to: Elsevier Science Inc., Box 882, Madison Sq. Sta., New York, NY 10159. TEL 212-989-5800. FAX 2121-633-3990) Ed.Bd. adv.; bk.rev.; index. circ. 850. (also avail. in microform from UMI; back issues avail.; reprint service avail. from ISI) **Indexed:** Excerp.Med. **Document type:** academic/scholarly publication.
—BLDSC (3793.805000); CASDDS; Genuine Article; SWETS; UnCover. **CCC.**
Description: Provides for rapid publication of high quality articles in both experimental and clinical epileptology, where the principal emphasis of the research is concerned with brain mechanisms in epilepsy.
Refereed Serial

616.853　　　　NE　ISSN 0922-9833
　　　　　　　　　　CODEN: ERSUED
EPILEPSY RESEARCH SUPPLEMENTS. (Supplement to: Epilepsy Research (ISSN 0920-1211)) (Text in English) 1988. irreg., vol.10, 1993. price varies. Elsevier Science B.V., Books Division, P.O. Box 211, 1000 AE Amsterdam, Netherlands. TEL 31-20-4853911. FAX 31-20-4853705. TELEX 18582 ESPA NL.
E-mail: nlinfo-f@elsevier.nl; usinfo-f@elsevier.com; forinfo-kyf04035@niftyserve.or.jp; Site addr.: http://www.elsevier.nl/. (Subscr. in U.S. and Canada to: Elsevier Science Inc., Box 882, Madison Sq. Sta., New York, NY 10159-0882. TEL 212-989-5800. FAX 212-633-3990) Ed.Bd. (also avail. in microform; back issues avail.) **Document type:** monographic series.
—BLDSC (3793.806000); CASDDS. **CCC.**
Refereed Serial

616.853　　　　UK　ISSN 0958-496X
EPILEPSY TODAY. 1976. q. £8 membership (foreign £15). British Epilepsy Association, Anstey House, 40 Hanover Sq., Leeds, England. TEL 01532-439393. FAX 01532-428804. Ed. Sue Cooper. adv.; bk.rev. circ. 18,000. **Indexed:** Sp.Ed.Needs Abstr. **Document type:** newsletter.
Former titles (until 1987): Epilepsy Now! (ISSN 0262-5474); (until 1981): Epilepsy News (ISSN 0308-9703); Candle (ISSN 0008-5502)

616.853　　　　US　ISSN 1060-9369
EPILEPSY U S A. vol.5, 1972. 8/yr. $20. Epilepsy Foundation of America, 4351 Garden City Dr., Ste. 406, Landover, MD 20785. TEL 301-459-3700. FAX 301-577-2684. Ed. Karina Barrentine. bk.rev. circ. 30,000. (tabloid format) **Indexed:** Rehabil.Lit. **Document type:** consumer publication.
Formerly (until 1991): National Spokesman (ISSN 0091-2387)
Description: Covers medical, legal, and legislative news and features for people with epilepsy.

EPILETTER. see *SOCIAL SERVICES AND WELFARE*

616.8　　　　　GW　ISSN 0940-1334
　　　　　　　　　　CODEN: EAPNES
EUROPEAN ARCHIVES OF PSYCHIATRY AND CLINICAL NEUROSCIENCES. (Vereinigt mit Zeitschrift fuer die Gesamte Neurologie und Psychiatrie) (Text in English) 1868. 6/yr. DM.968($703) (effective 1996). (Gesamtverband Deutscher Nervenaerzte) Springer-Verlag, Heidelberger Platz 3, 14197 Berlin, Germany. TEL 030-8207-0. FAX 030-8214091. E-mail: orders@springer.de. (Subscr. in N. America to: Springer-Verlag New York, Inc., 44 Hartz Way, Secaucus, NJ 07096-2491. TEL 201-348-4033. FAX 201-348-4505) Ed.Bd. adv.; bibl.; charts; illus. (also avail. in microform from UMI; microfiche from BHP; back issues avail.; reprint service avail. from ISI) **Indexed:** ASCA, Biol.Abstr., Chem.Abstr., Curr.Adv.Ecol.Sci., Curr.Adv.Genetics & Molec.Biol., Curr.Cont., Excerp.Med., Ger.J.Psych., Ind.Med., Psychol.Abstr. (1971-), Risk Abstr., Sci.Cit.Ind. **Document type:** academic/scholarly publication.
—BLDSC (3829.488545); Faxon; Genuine Article; SWETS; UMI; UnCover. **CCC.**
Former titles: European Archives of Psychiatry and Neurological Sciences (ISSN 0175-758X); (until 1984): Archiv fuer Psychiatrie und Nervenkrankheiten (ISSN 0003-9373)
Description: Covers clinical psychiatry, psychopathology, and epidemiology, as well as neuropathological, neurophysiological, and neurochemical studies of psychiatric disorders.

616.8　　　　　US　ISSN 1018-8827
EUROPEAN CHILD & ADOLESCENT PSYCHIATRY. 1992. 4/yr. $86. (European Society for Child and Adolescent Psychiatry) Hogrefe & Huber Publishers, Box 2487, Kirkland, WA 98083. TEL 206-820-1500. FAX 206-823-8324. Ed. C. Gillberg. bk.rev. **Indexed:** Excerp.Med. (1994-), Psychol.Abstr. (1992-). **Document type:** academic/scholarly publication.
—BLDSC (3829.600600).
Description: Aims to promote the growth of empirically based clinical child and adolescent psychiatry, not only in Europe but throughout the world.
Refereed Serial

616.8　　　　　UK　ISSN 1351-5101
▼**EUROPEAN JOURNAL OF NEUROLOGY.** 1994. bi-m. £195($330) to institutions (effective 1995). Rapid Communications of Oxford Ltd., The Old Malthouse, Paradise St., Oxford OX1 1LD, England. TEL 01865-790447. FAX 01865-244012. E-mail: rapidcom@vax.oxford.ac.uk. (Subscr. in N. America to: 115 Fifth Ave., 4th Fl., New York, NY 10003. TEL 212-780-6234) Eds. Francois Boller, Soelberg Sorensen. adv. contact: Mark Butler. **Indexed:** Int.Abstr.Biol.Sci. **Document type:** academic/scholarly publication.
●Also available on CD-ROM.
—BLDSC (3829.731680); ADONIS.
Description: Provides a forum on the major diseases of large clinical and socioeconomic importance.
Refereed Serial

616.8　　　　　UK　ISSN 0953-816X
　　　　　　　　　　CODEN: EJONEI
EUROPEAN JOURNAL OF NEUROSCIENCE. (Supplement avail.) 1989. m. £440($730) (effective 1996). Oxford University Press, Oxford Journals, Walton St., Oxford OX2 6DP, England. TEL 01865-267907. FAX 01865-267773. TELEX 837330-OXPRES-G. E-mail: jnlorders@oup.co.uk. (U.S. subscr. to: Oxford University Press Inc., 2001 Evans Rd., Cary, NC 27513. TEL 919-677-0977. FAX 919-677-1714) Ed. M. Cuenod. adv. circ. 600. **Indexed:** Biol.Abstr., Curr.Cont., Excerp.Med., Ind.Med. (1993-), Sci.Cit.Ind. **Document type:** academic/scholarly publication.
—BLDSC (3829.731700); Faxon; Genuine Article; SWETS; UMI; UnCover. **CCC.**
Description: Presents a broad scope of neuroscience, ranging from the behavioral to the molecular, with a European focus and a worldwide orientation.

616.89　　　　SP　ISSN 0213-6163
RC321　　　　　　CODEN: EJOPEO
EUROPEAN JOURNAL OF PSYCHIATRY. (Text in English) 1986. q. 10600 ptas.($90) to individuals; institutions 13500 ptas. ($115) (effective 1995). University of Zaragoza, P.O. Box 6029, Avda. S. Juan Bosco 15, 50009 Zaragoza. TEL 76-559795. Ed. A. Seva. adv.; bk.rev. **Indexed:** Curr.Cont., Excerp.Med., Psychol.Abstr. (1987-), Sociol.Abstr. **Document type:** academic/scholarly publication.
—BLDSC (3829.737700); Genuine Article; SWETS.
Description: Reports the scientific activity of European psychiatrists.
Refereed Serial

616.8　　　　　SZ　ISSN 0014-3022
　　　　　　　　　　CODEN: EUNEOM
EUROPEAN NEUROLOGY. (Text in English) 1968. bi-m. 402.60 SFr.($309.60) to individuals; institutions 671 SFr.($516) (effective 1996). S. Karger AG, Allschwilerstr. 10, P.O. Box, CH-4009 Basel, Switzerland. TEL 061-3061111. FAX 061-3061234. E-mail: Karger@Karger.ch. Ed. J. Bogousslavsky. index. circ. 1,050. (also avail. in microform) **Indexed:** Bibl.Dev.Med.& Child Neur., Biol.Abstr., Chem.Abstr., Curr.Adv.Ecol.Sci., Curr.Cont., Dent.Ind., Excerp.Med., Helminthol.Abstr., Ind.Med., Ind.Sci.Rev., Nutr.Abstr., Protozool.Abstr., Psychol.Abstr. (1990-), Sci.Cit.Ind. **Document type:** academic/scholarly publication.
—BLDSC (3829.765000); CASDDS; Faxon; Genuine Article; SWETS; UnCover. **CCC.**
Formerly (until 1968): Psychiatria et Neurologia.
Refereed Serial

MEDICAL SCIENCES — PSYCHIATRY AND NEUROLOGY

616.8 615.1   NE   ISSN 0924-977X
                        CODEN: EURNE8
EUROPEAN NEUROPSYCHOPHARMACOLOGY. (Text in English) 1990. q. fl.578($352) (effective 1996). (European College of Neuropsychopharmacology) Elsevier Science B.V., P.O. Box 211, 1000 AE Amsterdam, Netherlands. TEL 31-20-4853911. FAX 31-20-4853598. TELEX 18582 ESPA NL. E-mail: nlinfo-f@elsevier.nl; usinfo-f@elsevier.com; forinfo-kyf04035@niftyserve.or.jp; Site addr.: http://www.elsevier.nl/. (Subscr. in U.S. and Canada to: Elsevier Science Inc., Box 882, Madison Sq. Sta., New York, NY 10159. TEL 212-989-5800. FAX 212-633-3990) Eds. J.M. van Ree, S.A. Montgomery. adv.; bk.rev. (also avail. in microform from UMI; back issues avail.) **Indexed:** Excerp.Med. (1993-), Ind.Med. (1992-), Psychol.Abstr. (1991-). **Document type:** academic/scholarly publication.
—BLDSC (3829.765350); CASDDS; Genuine Article; UnCover. **CCC.**
   Description: Publishes clinical and basic research articles in the field of neuropsychopharmacology, with particular focus on the effects of centrally acting agents.
   Refereed Serial

616.8   FR   ISSN 0924-9338
EUROPEAN PSYCHIATRY. (Text in English; summaries in English, French) 1986. 8/yr. 1885 F. in France; foreign 2115 F.($413) (effective 1996). (Association of European Psychiatrists) Editions Scientifiques Elsevier, 141 rue de Javel, 75747 Paris, France. TEL 33-1-45589063. (Subscr. in U.S. and Canada to: Elsevier Science Inc., Box 882, Madison Sq. Sta., New York, NY 10159. TEL 212-989-5800) Ed.Bd. adv.; bk.rev. circ. 3,000. (also avail. in microform from UMI; back issues avail.) **Indexed:** Biol.Abstr., Excerp.Med., Psychol.Abstr. (1986-). **Document type:** academic/scholarly publication.
—BLDSC (3829.842700); Genuine Article; SWETS; UnCover. **CCC.**
   Formerly: Psychiatry and Psychobiology (ISSN 0767-399X)
   Description: Presents original research in psychopathology, nosography, chemotherapy, psychotherapy, clinical methodology, biological disorders and mental pathology, psychophysiology, neuropsychology, and animal behavior.
   Refereed Serial

EUROPEAN SPINE JOURNAL. see *MEDICAL SCIENCES — Surgery*

616.8   IE   ISSN 0168-5597
                        CODEN: ECNEAZ
EVOKED POTENTIALS. (Section of: Electroencephalography and Clinical Neurophysiology (ISSN 0921-884X)) 1984. bi-m. I£109($172) (effective 1996). (International Federation of Clinical Neurophysiology) Elsevier Science Ireland Ltd., P.O. Box 85, Limerick, Ireland. TEL 353-61-471944. FAX 353-61-472144. (Subscr. in U.S. and Canada to: Elsevier Science Inc., Box 882, Madison Sq. Sta., New York, NY 10159. TEL 212-989-5800. FAX 212-633-3990) Eds. F. Mauguiere, G.G. Celesia. **Indexed:** Biol.Abstr., Curr.Cont., Excerp.Med., Psychol.Abstr. (1990-). **Document type:** academic/scholarly publication.
—ADONIS; CASDDS; SWETS. **CCC.**
   Description: Covers anaesthesiology, clinical medicine, neurology, neuro-physiology, neurosurgery, psychiatry, psychology.
   Refereed Serial

616.89   FR   ISSN 0014-3855
                        CODEN: EVPSAG
EVOLUTION PSYCHIATRIQUE. 1925. q. 640 F. Dunod, 15 rue Gossin, 92543 Montrouge Cedex, France. TEL 33-1-40-92-65-00. FAX 33-1-40-92-65-97. TELEX 634 916 F. (Subscr. to: Centrale des Revues, 11 rue Gossin, 92543 Montrouge Cedex, France. TEL 33-1-46-56-52-66) Ed. Y. Thoret. adv.; bibl. **Indexed:** Biol.Abstr., Excerp.Med., Ind.Med., Lang.& Lang.Behav.Abstr., Psychol.Abstr. (1929-).
—BLDSC (3834.320000); Faxon; SWETS. **CCC.**
   Description: Exposes psychiatry to the different currents in scientific and philosophical thought, and in clinical research and critical reflection, as they develop both in this field and in related areas.

616.8   AU
EXISTENZANALYSE. 1984. q. S.150. Gesellschaft fuer Logotherapie und Existenzanalyse, Ed.-Suess-Gasse 10, A-1150 Vienna, Austria. TEL 0222-9859566. FAX 0222-9824845. bk.rev.; circ. 2,100. **Document type:** academic/scholarly publication.
   Formerly: Gesellschaft fuer Logotherapie und Existenzanalyse. Bulletin (ISSN 0258-5383)

616.8   US   ISSN 0272-6408
                        CODEN: ECPSDM
EXPERIMENTAL AND CLINICAL PSYCHIATRY. 1979. irreg., vol.8, 1983. price varies. Marcel Dekker, Inc., 270 Madison Ave., New York, NY 10016. TEL 212-696-9000. FAX 212-685-4540. TELEX 421419. Ed. Van Praag. **Indexed:** Psychol.Abstr.
—CASDDS.
   Refereed Serial

616.8   GW   ISSN 0014-4819
                        CODEN: EXBRAP
EXPERIMENTAL BRAIN RESEARCH. (Supplements avail.) (Text in English) 1965. 15/yr. (in 5 vols., 3 nos./vol.). DM.4900($3561) (effective 1996). (International Brain Research Organization) Springer-Verlag, Heidelberger Platz 3, 14197 Berlin, Germany. TEL 030-8207-0. FAX 030-8214091. E-mail: orders@springer.de. (Subscr. in N. America to: Springer-Verlag New York, Inc., 44 Hartz Way, Secaucus, NJ 07096-2491. TEL 201-348-4033. FAX 201-348-4505) Ed.Bd. adv.; bibl.; charts; illus.; index. (also avail. in microform from UMI; back issues avail.; reprint service avail. from ISI) **Indexed:** Apic.Abstr., Bibl.Dev.Med.& Child Neur., Biol.Abstr., Chem.Abstr., Curr.Adv.Ecol.Sci., Curr.Cont., Dairy Sci.Abstr., Dent.Ind., Excerp.Med., Ind.Med., INIS Atomind., Nutr.Abstr., Psychol.Abstr., Sci.Cit.Ind., Sport Fish.Abstr., Wild.Rev., Zoo.Rec. **Document type:** academic/scholarly publication.
—BLDSC (3838.800000); ADONIS; CASDDS; Faxon; Genuine Article; SWETS; UMI; UnCover. **CCC.**
   Description: Interdisciplinary approach to the study of the central and peripheral nervous systems. Covers the fields of morphology, physiology, behavior, neurochemistry, developmental neurobiology, and experimental pathology relevant to general problems of brain function.

616.8   US   ISSN 0172-9039
                        CODEN: EBRSDP
EXPERIMENTAL BRAIN RESEARCH. SUPPLEMENTA. 1976. irreg. price varies. Springer-Verlag, 175 Fifth Ave., New York, NY 10010. TEL 212-460-1500. FAX 212-473-6272. (Also: Berlin, Heidelberg, Tokyo and Vienna) (reprint service avail. from ISI) **Indexed:** Chem.Abstr., Ind.Sci.Rev. **Document type:** academic/scholarly publication.
—CASDDS.

616.8   US   ISSN 0014-4886
RC321   CODEN: EXNEAC
EXPERIMENTAL NEUROLOGY. 1959. m. $999 (foreign $1233) (effective 1996). Academic Press, Inc., Journal Division, 525 B St., Ste. 1900, San Diego, CA 92101-4495. TEL 619-230-1840. FAX 619-699-6800. (Subscr. to: Box 620000, Orlando, FL 32891-8340. TEL 800-543-9534) Ed. John R. Sladek, Jr. index. (back issues avail.) **Indexed:** Bibl.Dev.Med.& Child Neur., Biol.Abstr., Chem.Abstr., Curr.Adv.Biochem., Curr.Adv.Cell & Devel.Biol., Curr.Adv.Ecol.Sci., Curr.Cont., Curr.Ref.Fish Res., Dairy Sci.Abstr., Dent.Ind., Excerp.Med., Helminthol.Abstr., Ind.Med., Ind.Sci.Rev., INIS Atomind., Int.Aerosp.Abstr., Nutr.Abstr., Psychol.Abstr., Sci.Cit.Ind. **Document type:** academic/scholarly publication.
—BLDSC (3839.850000); ADONIS; CASDDS; Faxon; Genuine Article; SWETS; UnCover. **CCC.**
   Description: Publishes the results and conclusions of original research in neuroscience with emphasis on novel findings in neural development, regeneration, plasticity, and transplantation.
   Refereed Serial

EXPERIMENTELLE UND KLINISCHE HYPNOSE. see *MEDICAL SCIENCES — Hypnosis*

616.89   CN   ISSN 0834-129X
EXPRESS (MONTREAL). (Text in English, French) 1983. q. Can.$25 to families; professionals Can.$35; students Can.$15. Quebec Society for Autism - Societe Quebecoise de l'Autisme, 2300 bd. Rene Levesque ouest, Montreal, PQ H3H 2R5, Canada. TEL 514-931-2215. FAX 514-931-2397. bk.rev.
   Formerly (until 1986): Express de la Montagne (ISSN 0821-669X)

616.8   SP   ISSN 0213-7429
FACULTAD DE MEDICINA DE BARCELONA. REVISTA DE PSIQUIATRIA. (Supplement avail.) (Text in Spanish; summaries in English and Spanish) 1973. bi-m. 5500 ptas.($108) (effective 1995). (Facultad de Medicina de Barcelona, Departamento de Psiquiatria y Psicologia Medica del Hospital Clinico y Provincial de Barcelona) Editorial Rocas, Muntaner 393, pral. 4, 08021 Barcelona, Spain. TEL 39-3-2001389. FAX 39-3-2021958. Dir. Carlos Ballus Pascual. adv.; bk.rev.; illus.; charts; stat.; index. circ. 2,000. (back issues avail.) **Indexed:** Excerp.Med., Psychol.Abstr. (1979-). **Document type:** trade publication.
—BLDSC (7870.220000).
   Formerly: Facultad de Medicina de Barcelona. Departamento de Psiquiatria. Revista (ISSN 0210-1793)
   Description: Original research articles on various topics in psychiatry, medicine and psychology.

FAMILY SUPPORT BULLETIN. see *HANDICAPPED — Physically Impaired*

616.8   US   ISSN 0091-6544
RC488.5.A1   CODEN: FATHD6
FAMILY THERAPY. 1972. 3/yr. $62 to individuals; institutions $70. (California Graduate School of Family Psychology) Libra Publishers, Inc., 3089C Clairemont Dr., Ste. 383, San Diego, CA 92117. TEL 619-571-1414. Ed. Dr. Martin G. Blinder. adv. contact: Betty Kroll. index, cum.index. circ. 1,500. (also avail. in microform from UMI; back issues avail.; reprint service avail. from ISI,UMI) **Indexed:** Adol.Ment.Hlth.Abstr., ASSIA, IMFL, Mid.East: Abstr.& Ind., Psychol.Abstr. (1972-), Psycscan D.P., Sage Fam.Stud.Abstr., Sage Urb.Stud.Abstr., Soc.Work Res.& Abstr., Sp.Ed.Needs Abstr. **Document type:** academic/scholarly publication.
●Also available on CD-ROM.
—BLDSC (3865.576350); Faxon; SWETS; UMI; UnCover. **CCC.**

FLASH-INFORMATIONS. see *MEDICAL SCIENCES — Orthopedics And Traumatology*

616.8 371.9   US
RJ506.A9
FOCUS ON AUTISTIC AND OTHER DEVELOPMENTAL DISABILITIES. 1986. q. $39 to individuals; institutions $85 (foreign $95) (effective 1996). Pro-Ed Inc., 8700 Shoal Creek Blvd., Austin, TX 78757-6897. TEL 512-451-3246. FAX 512-451-8542. E-mail: proed1@aol.com. Ed. Richard Simpson; Pub. Donald D. Hammill. bibl. circ. 2,000. (looseleaf format; also avail. in microform from UMI; back issues avail.) **Indexed:** Psychol.Abstr. (1988-). **Document type:** academic/scholarly publication.
—BLDSC (3964.203820); UMI.
   Formerly: Focus on Autistic Behavior (ISSN 0887-1566)
   Description: Practitioner oriented articles for professionals involved in the education and treatment of children and youth with autism and pervasive developmental disorders.
   Refereed Serial

616.891 360   NO   ISSN 0332-5415
FOKUS PAA FAMILIEN; tidsskrift for familiebehandling. (Text in Scandinavian languages) 1972. q. NOK 440 in Nordic countries; elsewhere $84 (effective 1996). Scandinavian University Press, P.O. Box 2959 Toeyen, N-0608 Oslo, Norway. TEL 47-22-57-54-00. FAX 47-22-57-53-53. (U.S. addr.: Scandinavian University Press, 200 Meacham Ave., Elmont, NY 11003. TEL 516-352-7300) Eds. Sissel Gran, Haakon Haartveit. circ. 2,200. **Document type:** academic/scholarly publication, trade publication.
—**CCC.**
   Description: Covers a wide range of topics, both theoretical and practical, in family therapy and related fields including family sociology, family education and family politics.

MEDICAL SCIENCES — PSYCHIATRY AND NEUROLOGY

616.8   PL   CODEN: NUPOBT
FOLIA NEUROPATHOLOGICA. (Text in English; summaries in English, Polish) 1963. q. $70. Stowarzyszenie Neuropatologow Polskish - Association of Polish Neuropathologists, Ul. Dworkowa 3, 00-784 Warsaw, Poland. TEL 48-22-496793. FAX 48-22-496973. Ed. Maria Dambska. bk.rev.; bibl.; illus.; index, cum.index. **Indexed:** Biol.Abstr., Chem.Abstr., Excerp.Med., Ind.Med. **Document type:** academic/scholarly publication.
—CASDDS; EMDOCS.
    Formerly (until vol.32, 1994): Neuropatologia Polska (ISSN 0028-3894)
    Description: Papers devoted to achievements in experimental and clinical neuropathology.
Refereed Serial

616.8   SP   ISSN 0211-2558
FOLIA NEUROPSIQUIATRICA DEL SUR DE ESPANA. 1966. 3/yr. 1800 ptas. (effective 1995). Universidad de Granada, Servicio de Publicaciones, Antiguo Colegio Maximo, Campus de Cartuja, 18071 Granada, Spain. TEL 34-58-243930. FAX 34-58-242827. Ed. Rafael Navarro. **Indexed:** Biol.Abstr., Excerp.Med., Ind.Med.Esp., Psychol.Abstr. (1992-).
—BLDSC (3971.640000); Genuine Article.

FOLIA PHONIATRICA ET LOGOPAEDICA; international journal of phoniatrics, speech therapy and communication pathology. see *MEDICAL SCIENCES — Otorhinolaryngology*

616.8   GW
FORTSCHRITTE DER NEUROLOGIE, PSYCHIATRIE. (Supplement avail.: Neurochirurgia) 1931. m. DM.276. Georg Thieme Verlag, Ruedigerstr. 14, 70469 Stuttgart, Germany. TEL 0711-8931-0. FAX 0711-8931298. (Subscr. to: Postfach 104853, 70042 Stuttgart, Germany) Ed.Bd. adv.; bk.rev.; bibl.; charts; illus.; stat.; index. circ. 2,200. (reprint service avail. from UMI) **Indexed:** Biol.Abstr., Chem.Abstr., Curr.Cont., Dent.Ind., Excerp.Med., Ger.J.Psych., Ind.Med., Ind.Sci.Rev., INIS Atomind., Psychol.Abstr. (1972-), Sci.Cit.Ind. **Document type:** academic/scholarly publication.
—BLDSC (4022.380000); Genuine Article; SWETS; UMI. **CCC.**
    Former titles: Fortschritte der Neurologie, Psychiatrie und ihrer Grenzgebiete; Fortschritte der Neurologie - Psychiatrie (ISSN 0720-4299); (until 1980): Fortschritte der Neurologie, Psychiatrie und Ihrer Grenzgebiete (ISSN 0015-8194)

616.8   GW   ISSN 0071-8025
FORUM DER PSYCHIATRIE. 1961. NS 1977. irreg., vol.33, 1992. price varies. Ferdinand Enke Verlag, Postfach 300366, 70443 Stuttgart, Germany. TEL 0711-135798-0. FAX 0711-135798-30. TELEX 07252275-GTV-D. Ed.Bd. (reprint service avail. from IRC) **Document type:** monographic series.

617.48   NE   ISSN 0922-4386
FOUNDATIONS OF NEUROLOGICAL SURGERY. (Text in English) 1988. irreg. price varies. Kluwer Academic Publishers, Postbus 17, 3300 AA Dordrecht, Netherlands. TEL 31-78-392392. FAX 31-78-392254. TELEX 29245 KAPG NL. (Dist. by: Kluwer Academic Publishers Group, P.O. Box 322, 3300 AH Dordrecht, Netherlands. TEL 31-78-392392. FAX 31-78-546474; N. America dist. addr.: Box 358, Accord Sta., Hingham, MA 02018-0358. TEL 617-871-6600. FAX 617-871-6528) **Document type:** monographic series.
Refereed Serial

616.89   NE   ISSN 0924-8935
FOUNDATIONS OF NEUROLOGY. (Text in English) 1990. irreg. price varies. Kluwer Academic Publishers, Postbus 17, 3300 AA Dordrecht, Netherlands. TEL 31-78-392392. FAX 31-78-392254. TELEX 29245 KAPG NL. (Dist. by: Kluwer Academic Publishers Group, P.O. Box 322, 3300 AH Dordrecht, Netherlands. TEL 31-78-392392. FAX 31-78-546474; N. America dist. addr.: Box 358, Accord Sta., Hingham, MA 02018-0358. TEL 617-871-6600. FAX 617-871-6528) **Document type:** monographic series.
—BLDSC (4025.388000).
Refereed Serial

616.89   NE   ISSN 0924-0179
FOUNDATIONS OF NEUROPSYCHOLOGY. (Text in English) 1989. irreg. price varies. Kluwer Academic Publishers, Postbus 17, 3300 AA Dordrecht, Netherlands. TEL 31-78-392392. FAX 31-78-392254. TELEX 29245 KAPG NL. (Dist. by: Kluwer Academic Publishers Group, P.O. Box 322, 3300 AH Dordrecht, Netherlands. TEL 31-78-392392. FAX 31-78-546474; N. America dist. addr.: Box 358, Accord Sta., Hingham, MA 02018-0358. TEL 617-871-6600. FAX 617-871-6528) **Document type:** monographic series.
Refereed Serial

616.858 618.92   GW   ISSN 0721-9121
FRUEHFOERDERUNG INTERDISZIPLINAER; Zeitschrift fuer Praxis und Theorie der fruehen Hilfe fuer behinderte und entwicklungsauffaellige Kinder. 1982. q. DM.54 (students DM.43.20). Ernst Reinhardt Verlag, Kemnatenstr. 46, 80639 Munich, Germany. TEL 089-1783005. FAX 089-1781827. Ed.Bd. adv. contact: Sofie Bittlinger. bk.rev.; index. circ. 1,600. (back issues avail.) **Indexed:** Psychol.Abstr. **Document type:** academic/scholarly publication.
—BLDSC (4042.578000). **CCC.**

616.8   IT   ISSN 0393-5264
FUNCTIONAL NEUROLOGY; new trends in adaptive and behavioral disorders. (Text in English) 1986. bi-m. L.80000($80) (effective 1993). C I C Edizioni Internazionali s.r.l., Via L. Spallanzani, 11, 00161 Rome, Italy. TEL 06-8412673. FAX 06-8845590. Ed. Giuseppe Nappi. adv.; bk.rev. (back issues avail.) **Indexed:** Curr.Adv.Neurosci., Excerp.Med., Ind.Med.
—BLDSC (4055.619500); Faxon; Genuine Article; SWETS; UnCover. **CCC.**
    Description: Publishes scientific contributions dealing with all aspects of functional neurology. Focuses on the interaction of the nervous system with the environment, including neurochemistry, physiology and more.

616.8   GW   ISSN 0931-0428
FUNDAMENTA PSYCHIATRICA; Psychiatrie und Psychotherapie in Theorie und Praxis. 1987. 4/yr. DM.178($130.60) F.K. Schattauer Verlagsgesellschaft mbH, Lenzhalde 3, 70192 Stuttgart, Germany. TEL 0711-22987-0. FAX 0711-22987-50. Ed. E. Lungershausen. adv.; index. circ. 2,000. **Document type:** academic/scholarly publication.
—**CCC.**

616.8   IC   ISSN 1022-4920
GEDVERND; arsrit Gedverndarfelags Islands. 1966. a. membership. Gedverndarfelag Islands, Hatuni 10, 105 Reykjavik, Iceland. TEL 354-552-5508. Ed. Eirikur Oern Arnarson.

616.8   US   ISSN 0163-8343
                     CODEN: GHPSDB
GENERAL HOSPITAL PSYCHIATRY; psychiatry, medicine and primary care. 1979. bi-m. $335 to institutions (effective 1996). Elsevier Science Inc., 655 Ave. of the Americas, New York, NY 10010. TEL 212-989-5800. FAX 212-633-3990. TELEX 420643 AEP UI. (Subscr. to: Box 882, Madison Sq. Sta., New York, NY 10159-0882) Ed. Don R. Lipsitt. (also avail. in microform from UMI) **Indexed:** Abstr.Health Care Manage.Stud., Behav.Med.Abstr., Biol.Abstr., CINAHL, Curr.Cont., Excerp.Med., Ind.Med., INIS Atomind., Psychol.Abstr. (1980-), Soc.Work Res.& Abstr., SSCI. **Document type:** academic/scholarly publication.
—BLDSC (4104.344000); Faxon; Genuine Article; SWETS; UnCover. **CCC.**
    Description: Emphasizes a biopsychosocial approach to illness and health, and provides a forum for communication among professionals with clinical, academic, and research interests in psychiatry.
Refereed Serial

616.8   US
GENERATIONS (WAYZATA). 1957. s-a. $15. National Ataxia Foundation, 750 Twelve Oaks Center, 15500 Wayzata Blvd., Wayzata, MN 55391. TEL 612-473-7666. FAX 612-473-9289. Ed. Donna Gruetzmacher. bk.rev.; circ. 9,000 (controlled). (back issues avail.) **Indexed:** Hlth.Ind. **Document type:** newsletter.
●Also available on CD-ROM.
    Description: Covers meetings, current research, events and activities and other Foundation news relating to hereditary ataxias.

155   ISSN 0195-5594
GENESIS OF BEHAVIOR. 1978. irreg., vol.6, 1991. price varies. Plenum Publishing Corp., 233 Spring St., New York, NY 10013-1578. TEL 212-620-8000. FAX 212-463-0742. TELEX 23-421139. Eds. Michael Lewis, Leonard A. Rosenblum. (back issues avail.) **Document type:** monographic series.
—BLDSC (4111.840000).
Refereed Serial

616.8   AU   ISSN 0258-5391
GESELLSCHAFT FUER LOGOTHERAPIE UND EXISTENZANALYSE. TAGUNGSBERICHTE. 1985. a. S.140. Gesellschaft fuer Logotherapie und Existenzanalyse, Ed.-Suess-Gasse 10, A-1150 Vienna, Austria. TEL 0222-9859566. FAX 0222-9824845. adv.; circ. 1,000. (back issues avail.) **Document type:** academic/scholarly publication.

GESTALT JOURNAL. see *PSYCHOLOGY*

616.8   IT   ISSN 0392-4483
GIORNALE DI NEUROPSICHIATRIA DELL'ETA EVOLUTIVA. 1980. q. L.86000($115) (effective 1994). (Societa Italiana di Neuropsichiatria Infantile) Masson S.p.A., Divisione Periodici, Via Statuto 2-4, 20121 Milan, Italy. TEL 02-6367-1. FAX 02-6367211. Ed. Fabio Canziani. adv.: B&W page L.2100000, color page L.3100000; trim 170 x 240. circ. 2,000. **Indexed:** Excerp.Med., Psychol.Abstr. (1992-). **Document type:** academic/scholarly publication.
—BLDSC (4178.470000); Genuine Article.

616   IT   ISSN 0391-9048
GIORNALE DI NEUROPSICOFARMACOLOGIA. bi-m. L.60000($60) C I C Edizioni Internazionali s.r.l., Via Lazzaro Spallanzani, 11, 00161 Rome, Italy. TEL 06-8412673. FAX 06-44242033. TELEX 622099 CIC. Dir. C. Fieschi. **Indexed:** Psychol.Abstr. (1989-).
—BLDSC (4178.475000); Genuine Article. **CCC.**

616.834   YU   ISSN 0353-5746
GLASILO M S. (Text in Serbo-Croatian) 1974. q. 1000 din.($20) (typically set in Jan.). Savez Drustava Multiple Skleroze S F R J - Yugoslav Multiple Sclerosis Society, Bulevar AVNOJ-a 104, 11000 Belgrade, Yugoslavia. TEL 199-292. FAX 195-244. (Co-sponsor: Federal Executive Council of SFRJ) Ed. Dr. Miso Tiganjevic. adv.; bk.rev. circ. 50,000. (back issues avail.)

616.8   US   ISSN 0894-1491
QP363.2   CODEN: GLIAEJ
GLIA. 1988. m. $888 (foreign $1074) (effective 1996). John Wiley & Sons, Inc., Journals, 605 Third Ave, New York, NY 10158. TEL 212-850-6645. FAX 212-850-6021. TELEX 12-7063. E-mail: SUBINFO JWILEY.COM. (Subscr. outside the Americas to: John Wiley & Sons Ltd., Baffins Ln., Chichester, W. Sussex PO19 1UD, England. TEL 44-1243-779777. FAX 44-1243-776128) Eds. Bruce R. Ransom, Helmut Hettenmann. (also avail. in microform from UMI; back issues avail.) **Document type:** academic/scholarly publication.
—BLDSC (4195.208000); Faxon; Genuine Article; SWETS; UnCover. **CCC.**
    Description: Devoted to the study of the form and fucntion of neuroglial cells in health and disease.
Refereed Serial

616.89   US   ISSN 0888-3394
RC321   CODEN: GPSRB9
GROUP FOR THE ADVANCEMENT OF PSYCHIATRY. REPORT. 1947. irreg., approx. 10 in 3 yrs. price varies. American Psychiatric Press, Inc., Journals Division, 1400 K St., N.W., Ste. 1101, Washington, DC 20005. TEL 202-682-6130. FAX 202-789-2648. (UK addr.: 17 Belgrave Sq., London SW1X 8PG, England) cum.index. **Indexed:** Ind.Med., Psychol.Abstr.
—BLDSC (7495.400000); Faxon.
    Formerly (until 1984): Group for the Advancement of Psychiatry. Publication (ISSN 0149-2640); Supersedes (in 1977, vol.9): Group for the Advancement of Psychiatry. Report (ISSN 0072-775X); Group for the Advancement of Psychiatry. Symposium.
    Description: Reports from the Group for the Advancement of Psychiatry representing the latest thinking of the field on diverse and socially relevant topics.

GRUPPENANALYSE; Zeitschrift fuer gruppenanalytische Psychotherapie, Beratung und Supervision. see *PSYCHOLOGY*

MEDICAL SCIENCES — PSYCHIATRY AND NEUROLOGY

616.89   GW   ISSN 0017-4947
GRUPPENPSYCHOTHERAPIE UND GRUPPENDYNAMIK.
(Text in German; summaries in English and German) 1968. irreg. (4 nos. per vol.). DM.116. Vandenhoeck und Ruprecht, Robert-Bosch-Breite 6, 37079 Goettingen, Germany. TEL 0551-6959-26. FAX 0551-695917. (Subscr. to: 37070 Goettingen, Germany) Ed. Dr. Annelise Heigl-Evers. circ. 1,050. **Indexed:** Curr.Cont., Excerp.Med., Ger.J.Psych., SSCI. **Document type:** monographic series.
—BLDSC (4223.460000); Genuine Article. **CCC**.

616.858 371.9   US   ISSN 1057-3291
THE HABILITATIVE MENTAL HEALTHCARE NEWSLETTER.
1982. bi-m. $49 to individuals (foreign $66); institutions $63 (foreign $85). Psych-Media, Inc., Box 57, Bear Creek, NC 27207-0057. TEL 910-581-3700. FAX 910-581-3766. Eds. Dr. Robert Sovner, Anne DesNoyers Hurely. adv.; bk.rev.; bibl.; index; circ. 2,000 (paid). (tabloid format; back issues avail.) **Indexed:** Psychol.Abstr. **Document type:** newsletter.
—BLDSC (4237.337200). **CCC**.
Former titles (until vol.8, 1989): Psychiatric Aspects of Mental Retardation Reviews; (until 1983): Psychiatric Aspects of Mental Retardation Newsletter (ISSN 0278-9493)
Description: Provides clinicians and habilitative care givers with information regarding the diagnosis and treatment of neuropsychiatric disorders and therapeutic interventions that can improve the quality of psychosocial functioning of persons with developmental disabilities.

616.891   JA   ISSN 0916-3662
HAKONIWA RYOHOGAKU KENKYU/ARCHIVES OF SANDPLAY THERAPY. (Text in English, Japanese; summaries in English) 1988. a. 2300 Yen. Nihon Hakoniwa Ryoho Gakkai - Japan Association of Sandplay Therapy, Kyoto Daigaku Kyoikugakubu, Rinsho Shinrigaku Kyoshitsu, Yoshida Honmachi, Sakyo-ku, Kyoto 606, Japan.

HANDBOOK OF ANXIETY. see *PSYCHOLOGY*

618   US   ISSN 0194-0880
     CODEN: HBNEEV
HANDBOOK OF BEHAVIORAL NEUROBIOLOGY. 1978. irreg., vol.11, 1992. price varies. Plenum Publishing Corp., 233 Spring St., New York, NY 10013-1578. TEL 212-620-8000. FAX 212-463-0742. TELEX 23-421139. Ed. Norman T. Adler. (back issues avail.) **Document type:** monographic series.
—BLDSC (4250.340000); Faxon.
Refereed Serial

616.8 540   NE   ISSN 0924-8196
HANDBOOK OF CHEMICAL NEUROANATOMY. (Text in English) 1983. irreg., vol.11, 1992. price varies. Elsevier Science B.V., Books Division, P.O. Box 211, 1000 AE Amsterdam, Netherlands. TEL 31-20-4853911. FAX 31-20-4853705. TELEX 18582 ESPA NL. E-mail: nlinfo-f@elsevier.nl; usinfo-f@elsevier.com; forinfo-kyf04035@niftyserve.or.jp; Site addr.: http://www.elsevier.nl/. (Subscr. in U.S. and Canada to: Elsevier Science Inc., Box 882, Madison Sq. Sta, New York, NY 10159. TEL 212-989-5800) Eds. A. Bjorklund, T. Hokfelt. **Document type:** monographic series.
—BLDSC (4250.397000).
Refereed Serial

616.8   NE   ISSN 0072-9752
     CODEN: HACNEU
HANDBOOK OF CLINICAL NEUROLOGY; revised series. (Text in English) 1969; N.S. 1985. irreg., vol.19, 1993. price varies. Elsevier Science B.V., Books Division, P.O. Box 211, 1000 AE Amsterdam, Netherlands. TEL 31-20-4853911. FAX 31-20-4853705. TELEX 18582 ESPA NL. E-mail: nlinfo-f@elsevier.nl; usinfo-f@elsevier.com; forinfo-kyf04035@niftyserve.or.jp; Site addr.: http://www.elsevier.nl/. (Subscr. in U.S. and Canada to: Elsevier Science Inc., Box 882, Madison Sq. Sta, New York, NY 10159. TEL 212-989-5800) Ed.Bd. cum.index: vols.1-43 in vol.44, 1982. (back issues avail.) **Document type:** monographic series.
—BLDSC (4250.405000).
Refereed Serial

616.8   NE   ISSN 0304-4645
HANDBOOK OF ELECTROENCEPHALOGRAPHY AND CLINICAL NEUROPHYSIOLOGY; revised series. (Text in English) 1971; N.S. 1987. irreg., vol.4, 1990. price varies. Elsevier Science B.V., Books Division, P.O. Box 211, 1000 AE Amsterdam, Netherlands. TEL 31-20-4853911. FAX 31-20-4853705. TELEX 18582 ESPA NL. E-mail: nlinfo-f@elsevier.nl; usinfo-f@elsevier.com; forinfo-kyf04035@niftyserve.or.jp; Site addr.: http://www.elsevier.nl/. (Subscr. in U.S. and Canada to: Elsevier Science Inc., Box 882, Madison Sq. Sta., New York, NY 10159. TEL 212-989-5800) Ed. A. Remond. (back issues avail.) **Document type:** monographic series.
Refereed Serial

616.8   NE
HANDBOOK OF NEUROPSYCHOLOGY. (Text in English) 1988. irreg., vol.8, 1993. price varies. Elsevier Science B.V., Books Division, P.O. Box 211, 1000 AE Amsterdam, Netherlands. TEL 31-20-4853911. FAX 31-20-4853705. TELEX 18582 ESPA NL. E-mail: nlinfo-f@elsevier.nl; usinfo-f@elsevier.com; forinfo-kyf04035@niftyserve.or.jp; Site addr.: http://www.elsevier.nl/. (Subscr. in U.S. and Canada to: Elsevier Science Inc., Box 882, Madison Sq. Sta., New York, NY 10159. TEL 212-989-5800) Eds. F. Boller, J. Grafman. (back issues avail.) **Document type:** monographic series.
Refereed Serial

616.89   NE   ISSN 0924-8188
     CODEN: HASCE9
HANDBOOK OF SCHIZOPHRENIA. (Text in English) 1986. irreg., vol.5, 1991. price varies. Elsevier Science B.V., Books Division, P.O. Box 211, 1000 AE Amsterdam, Netherlands. TEL 31-20-4853911. FAX 31-20-4853705. TELEX 18582 ESPA NL. E-mail: nlinfo-f@elsevier.nl; usinfo-f@elsevier.com; forinfo-kyf04035@niftyserve.or.jp; Site addr.: http://www.elsevier.nl/. (Subscr. in U.S. and Canada to: Elsevier Science Inc., Box 882, Madison Sq. Sta., New York, NY 10159. TEL 212-989-5800) (back issues avail.) **Document type:** monographic series.
Refereed Serial

616.834   SW   ISSN 0348-8071
HANDIKAPP - REFLEX. 1954. bi-m. SEK 125. Neurologiskt Handikappades Riksfoerbund - Swedish Association of Neurologically Disabled, P.O. Box 3284, S-103 65 Stockholm, Sweden. Ed. Anne Thelander. adv.; bk.rev.; illus.; stat. circ. 13,500. (also avail. in audio cassette)
Formerly: M S-Brevet (ISSN 0345-8199)
Description: Deals with subjects concerned with neurological disease and disability.

616.8   US   ISSN 0884-3783
HARVARD MENTAL HEALTH LETTER. 1984. m. $48 (Canada $54; elsewhere $63). (Harvard College, Harvard Medical School) Harvard Health Publications Group, 164 Longwood Ave., Boston, MA 02115. FAX 617-432-1506. E-mail: jrudin@warren.med.edu. (Subscr. to: Box 420448, Palm Coast, FL 32142-0448. TEL 800-829-5379) Ed. Dr. Lester Grinspoon. circ. 65,000 (paid). **Indexed:** CINAHL. **Document type:** newsletter.
●Also available online. Vendor(s): Information Access Co..
Description: Interprets timely mental health information for both professionals and laypeople.

616.89   US   ISSN 1067-3229
     CODEN: HRPSEP
HARVARD REVIEW OF PSYCHIATRY. 1993. bi-m. $80 to individuals (Canada $109.14; elsewhere $102); institutions $108 (Canada $139.10; elsewhere $130); students, residents $44 (Canada $70.62; elsewhere $66); newsstand price: $14.50. Mosby, Journal Subscription Services (Subsidiary of: Times Mirror Company), 11830 Westline Industrial Dr., St. Louis, MO 63146-3318. TEL 314-453-4351; 800-325-4177. FAX 314-432-1158. Eds. Joseph T. Coyle, Steven M. Mirin. adv.; B&W page $670, color page $1265; trim 8 1/4 x 11. bk.rev. circ. 1,702. **Indexed:** Biol.Abstr., Excerp.Med. **Document type:** academic/scholarly publication.
—BLDSC (4270.020000); Genuine Article; UMI. **CCC**.
Incorporates (1976-1993): McLean Hospital Journal.
Description: Examines a wide variety of subjects, emphasizing the integration of research findings with clinical care. Articles cover the diagnosis and treatment of a full range of psychiatric disorders
Refereed Serial

616.857   US   ISSN 0017-8748
RC392   CODEN: HEADAE
HEADACHE; the journal of head and face pain. 1961. 10/yr. $95 (foreign $110) (effective 1996). American Association for the Study of Headache, 875 Kings Hwy., Ste. 200, Woodbury, NJ 08096. TEL 609-845-0322. FAX 609-384-5811. (Subscr. to: Allen Press, Box 1827, Lawrence, KS 66044. TEL 913-843-1221. FAX 913-843-1274) Ed. Dr. Keith Campbell. adv.: B&W page $499; trim 8 1/16 x 11 1/4; adv. contact: Linda McGillicuddy. bk.rev.; abstr.; charts; illus.; stat.; cum.index. circ. 2,150. (also avail. in microform from UMI; diskette format; magnetic tape; reprint service avail. from UMI) **Indexed:** Behav.Med.Abstr., Bibl.Dev.Med.& Child Neur., Biol.Abstr., Chem.Abstr., Curr.Adv.Ecol.Sci., Curr.Cont., Curr.Tit.Dent., Dent.Ind., Excerp.Med., Ind.Med., Ind.Sci.Rev., NRN, Psychol.Abstr. (1983-), Sci.Cit.Ind. **Document type:** academic/scholarly publication.
—BLDSC (4274.640000); CASDDS; Genuine Article; SWETS; UnCover.
Description: Publishes original manuscripts (clinical studies, case reports, base research), and other scientific materials concerned with the diagnosis and treatment of headache, in its many aspects, and head and face pain.

616.89   CN   ISSN 1199-7699
HEALTH AND NUTRITION UPDATE. 1974. q. $30 (foreign $35)(effective 1993). Canadian Schizophrenia Foundation, 16 Florence Ave., Toronto, ON M2N 1E9, Canada. TEL 416-733-2117. FAX 416-733-2352. (Co-sponsor: Huxley Institute for Biosocial Research) Ed. Steven Carter. bk.rev. circ. 1,000. (reprint service avail. from UMI) **Indexed:** Excerp.Med.
Former titles (unti 1993): Health and Nutrition Update (ISSN 0831-8530); Huxley Institute - C S F Newsletter (ISSN 0318-8272); **Incorporates:** Schizophrenics Anonymous International. Bulletin (ISSN 0048-9360)

616.858 371.9   GW   ISSN 0017-9647
HEILPAEDAGOGISCHE FORSCHUNG; Zeitschrift fuer Paedagogik und Psychologie Behinderter. 1964. 4./yr. DM.96. Wissenschaftsverlag Volker Spiess GmbH, Postfach 303046, 10730 Berlin, Germany. TEL 030-2165061. FAX 030-2165064. Ed.Bd. bk.rev. **Indexed:** SSCI. **Document type:** academic/scholarly publication.
—BLDSC (4284.195800). **CCC**.

616.858   US
HILL TOPIC. 1954. 3/yr. free. Glenwood State Hospital-School, 711 Vine, Glenwood, IA 51534. TEL 712-527-4811. Ed. Stephanie Gaskill. circ. 1,750.
Description: Highlights work with the mentally retarded.

616.8   UK   ISSN 0957-154X
HISTORY OF PSYCHIATRY. 1990. q. £68 (U.S. & Japan $140; elsewhere £70). Alpha Academic (Subsidiary of: Richard Sadler Ltd.), Halfpenny Furze, Mill Ln., Chalfont St. Giles, Bucks. HP8 4NR, England. TEL 01494-872509. (back issues avail.) **Indexed:** Psychol.Abstr. (1990-). **Document type:** academic/scholarly publication.
—BLDSC (4318.408000); SWETS.
Description: Aims to publish research articles, analysis, information, and reviews across the entire field of the history of mental illness and the forms of medicine, cultural response, and social policy that have evolved to understand and treat it.

MEDICAL SCIENCES — PSYCHIATRY AND NEUROLOGY

616.8 XR ISSN 0960-7560
QP351.S65 CODEN: HOMOEB
HOMEOSTASIS; integrative brain functions in health and disease. (Text in English) 1959. 6/yr. £105($190) (effective 1992). Collegium Internationale Activitatis Nervosae Superioris, c/o Institute of Hygiene and Epidemiology, Srobarova 48, 10042 Prague 10, Czech Republic. Ed. Milan Horvath. adv.; bk.rev.; illus.; index. **Indexed:** ASCA, Biol.Abstr., C.I.S. Abstr., Chem.Abstr., Curr.Adv.Ecol.Sci., Curr.Cont., Excerp.Med., Ind.Med. (until 1992), Ind.Sci.Rev., Nutr.Abstr., Psychol.Abstr. (1959-), Psychopharmacol.Abstr., Sci.Cit.Ind. **Document type:** academic/scholarly publication.
—BLDSC (4326.176430); CASDDS; Faxon; Genuine Article. **CCC**.
Formerly (until vol.33, 1991): Activitas Nervosa Superior (ISSN 0001-7604)
Description: Devoted to understanding regulatory mechanisms ranging from molecular to systemic processes in health and disease, with emphasis on integrative functions in homeostatic control and their adaptation to environmental conditions and behavioral needs.
Refereed Serial

616.8 CN ISSN 0827-7605
HORIZON (CAMBRIDGE). 1973. q. Can.$15 membership. Huntington Society of Canada - Societe Huntington du Canada, 13 Water St. N., Cambridge, ON N1R 7G6, Canada. TEL 519-622-1002. FAX 519-622-7370. Ed. Isla Horvath. circ. 7,500. (back issues avail.) **Document type:** newsletter.
Description: Relays items of interest about Huntington's disease and the Society to families, supporters and health care professionals.

616.89 CU ISSN 0138-7103
RC440
HOSPITAL PSIQUIATRICO DE LA HABANA. REVISTA. (Text in Spanish; summaries in English) 1959. s-a. $26 in S. America; N. America $28; elsewhere $30. Hospital Psiquiatrico de la Habana, Avenida de la Independencia No. 26520, Mazorra, Havana, Cuba. TEL 45-16-73. (Dist. by: Ediciones Cubanas, Obispo No. 527, Apdo. 605, Havana, Cuba) Ed. Dr. Edmundo Gutierrez Agramonte. adv.; abstr.; bibl.; illus.; stat. circ. 8,000. (back issues avail.) **Indexed:** Psychol.Abstr. **Document type:** academic/scholarly publication.
—BLDSC (7815.900000).

612 US ISSN 1065-9471
RC386.6.B7 CODEN: HBMAEE
HUMAN BRAIN MAPPING. 1993. q. $190 (foreign $252) (effective 1996). John Wiley & Sons, Inc., Journals, 605 Third Ave., New York, NY 10158. TEL 212-850-6645. FAX 212-850-6021. TELEX 12-7063. E-mail: SUBINFO@JWILEY.COM. (Subscr. outside the Americas to: John Wiley & Sons Ltd., Baffins Ln., Chichester, W. Sussex PO19 1UD, England. TEL 44-1243-779777. FAX 44-1243-776128) (also avail. in microform from UMI; back issues avail.) **Document type:** academic/scholarly publication.
—BLDSC (4336.031000).
Refereed Serial

616.8 615 UK ISSN 0885-6222
CODEN: HUPSEC
HUMAN PSYCHOPHARMACOLOGY: CLINICAL AND EXPERIMENTAL. 1986. bi-m. $455 (foreign $455) (effective 1996). John Wiley & Sons Ltd., Journals, Baffins Ln., Chichester, W. Sussex PO19 1UD, England. TEL 01243-779777.
FAX 01243-776128. TELEX 86290 WIBOOK G. (Subscr. in the Americas to: John Wiley & Sons, 605 Third Ave., New York, NY 10158. TEL 212-850-6645. FAX 212-850-6021) Ed. Guy Edwards. adv. circ. 171. (also avail. in microform from UMI; back issues avail.; reprint service avail. from SWZ) **Indexed:** Chem.Abstr., Curr.Cont., Excerp.Med., Psychol.Abstr. (1986-). **Document type:** academic/scholarly publication.
—BLDSC (4336.380000); ADONIS; CASDDS; Faxon; Genuine Article; SWETS; UMI; UnCover. **CCC**.
Description: Communicates the results of clinical and experimental studies relevant to the understanding of new and established psychotropic drugs.
Refereed Serial

616.8 371.4 US
HYDROCEPHALUS NEWS & NOTES. 1982. q. $30. National Hydrocephalus Foundation Organization, 1670 Green Oak Circle, Lawrewnceville, GA 30243. TEL 404-995-8982. Ed. Ann Marie Liakos. bk.rev.; tr.lit.; circ. 400 (paid). (looseleaf format; back issues avail.) **Document type:** newsletter.
Former titles (until 1995): Life-Line (ISSN 1059-6593); National Hydro Cephalus Foundation Newsletter.
Description: Information relating to hydrocephalus and associated problems of a medical, developmental, social and educational nature, including letters from family members.

I A S T E D. INTERNATIONAL CONFERENCE PROCEEDINGS. (International Association of Science and Technology for Development) see COMPUTERS — Artificial Intelligence

616.8 AU ISSN 0539-0230
I E S A INFORMATION. (Editions in English) 1967. irreg. (3-4/yr.). membership. International Society for Electrosleep and Electroanaesthesia, Chirurgische Universitaetsklinik, A-8036 Graz, Austria. Ed.Bd. adv.; bk.rev.; abstr.; bibl.; charts; illus. circ. 300. (processed)

I L S M H NEWS. (International League of Societies for Persons with Mental Handicap) see PSYCHOLOGY

616.8 US
I T F NEWSLETTER. 1988. q. $25. International Tremor Foundation, 833 W. Washington Blvd., Chicago, IL 60607-2316. TEL 312-664-2344. Ed. Judy Rosner. bk.rev.; circ. 26,000 (paid). (back issues avail.) **Document type:** newsletter.
Description: Reports recent advances in research in layman's terms for patient and family education.

616.891 US ISSN 0899-403X
I U P STRESS AND HEALTH SERIES. irreg. price varies. International Universities Press, Inc., 59 Boston Post Rd., Box 1524, Madison, CT 06443-1524. TEL 203-245-4000. Ed. Leo Goldberger.
Refereed Serial

616.89 150.19 AG ISSN 0325-4569
IMAGO; revista de psicoanalisis, psiquiatria y psicologia. 1974. q. Letra Viva, Coronel Diaz 1837, Buenos Aires, Argentina. (reprint service avail. from SCH)

616.8 618.92 IT
IMAGO; giornale italiano de psicopatologia e psichiatria dell'infanzia e dell'adolescenza. 3/yr. L.120000($180) (effective 1995). Casa Editrice Idelson, Via A. de Gasperi 55, 80133 Naples, Italy. TEL 39-81-5524733. FAX 39-81-5518295. Eds. A. Condini, M. Bertolini.

616.8 614.58 US
IMPACT (AUSTIN). 1971. 3/yr. free. Department of Mental Health and Mental Retardation, Public Information Office, Box 12668, Austin, TX 78711. TEL 512-465-4540. FAX 512-206-4711. Ed. Wendy Hazelwood. bk.rev.; charts; illus.; pat.; stat.; circ. 30,000 (controlled). **Document type:** government publication.
Description: Informs, educates, and provides recognition to employees and friends of the agency.

INDEPENDENT LIVING. see SOCIAL SERVICES AND WELFARE

362.3 II ISSN 0019-5375
HV3004
INDIAN JOURNAL OF MENTAL RETARDATION. 1968. s-a. Rs.50($10) All India Association of Mental Retardation, c/o Dr. K. G. Agrawal, Ed., National Labour Institute, AB-6 Skfdarjang Enclave, New Delhi 110029, India. adv.; bk.rev.; abstr. **Indexed:** Psychol.Abstr.

616.89 II ISSN 0019-5545
CODEN: IJRPAB
INDIAN JOURNAL OF PSYCHIATRY. (Text in English) 1959. q. $50 to individuals; institutions $50. Indian Psychiatric Society, K.G.'s Medical College, B 104-2 Niralanagar, Lucknow 226 020, India. TEL 91-416-22603. FAX 91-416-22788. TELEX 405-202 CMCH IN. Ed. K. Kuruvilla. adv.: page Rs.3000. bk.rev.; charts; illus.; stat.; index. circ. 1,800. **Indexed:** Chem.Abstr., Excerp.Med. (until 19??), ExtraMED, Psychol.Abstr. **Document type:** academic/scholarly publication.
● Also available on CD-ROM.
—BLDSC (4420.280000); CASDDS; Faxon; UnCover.
Description: Publishes original papers and review articles in psychiatry and related disciplines.

616.8 II ISSN 0253-7176
CODEN: IJPMEU
INDIAN JOURNAL OF PSYCHOLOGICAL MEDICINE. (Text in English) 1956. s-a. $15. Indian Psychiatric Society, South Zone, c/o Dr. Palaniappun M.D., Ed., D.P.M., Mnams 4A, V.P. Extension, Ayanavaran, Madras 23, India. TEL 5340. adv.; bk.rev.; abstr.; bibl.; charts; illus.; stat. circ. 600. (reprint service avail.) **Indexed:** Biol.Abstr., Curr.Adv.Ecol.Sci., Indian Psychol.Abstr., Indian Sci.Abstr., Lang.& Lang.Behav.Abstr., Psychol.Abstr.
—BLDSC (4420.290000); UMI.
Formerly (until 1978): Indian Journal of Psychology (ISSN 0019-5553)
Description: Research and review articles, and conference papers in various areas of psychiatry and related subjects.

INFANT SCREENING. see MEDICAL SCIENCES — Pediatrics

616.8 CN ISSN 0715-3120
INFO A L S. 1980. a. free. Amyotrophic Lateral Sclerosis Society of Canada, B101 - 90 Adelaide St. E., Toronto, ON M5C 2R4, Canada. TEL 416-362-0269. FAX 416-362-0414. Ed. Dr. Michael Sribney. abstr.
Description: Conveys latest research discoveries on the cause and cure of the A L S disease.

616.8 BL ISSN 0101-4331
INFORMACAO PSIQUIATRICA. (Text in Portuguese; summaries in English and Portuguese) 1980-1983 (vol.4, no.4); resumed 198? q. $60. Editora Cientifica Nacional Ltda., Rua da Gloria, 366 3o andar, 20241-180 Rio de Janeiro RJ, Brazil. TEL 55-21-2213235. FAX 55-21-252-1691. Ed. Jorge Alberto Costa e Silva. adv.; bk.rev.; index, cum.index. circ. 5,000. (back issues avail.)

616.8 FR ISSN 0020-0204
INFORMATION PSYCHIATRIQUE. 1947. m. (10/yr.). 805 F. (foreign 1510 F.). P D G Communication, 30 rue d'Armaille, 75017 Paris, France. TEL 40-55-05-95. FAX 45-74-65-67. Ed. Patrick de Gavre. **Indexed:** Excerp.Med., Psychol.Abstr.
—BLDSC (4493.920000); Faxon.

616.834 301 US ISSN 0739-9774
INSIDE M S; a magazine of the National Multiple Sclerosis Society. 1983. 3/yr. $20 membership. National Multiple Sclerosis Society, 733 Third Ave., New York, NY 10017-3288. TEL 212-986-3240. FAX 212-986-7981. Ed. Martha King. adv.; bk.rev.; illus. circ. 250,000. (also avail. in microform from UMI; also avail. in large print) **Indexed:** Hlth.Ind., Rehabil.Lit. **Document type:** consumer publication.
—UMI.
Incorporating (in 1983): Focus on Research; M S Messenger; National Multiple Sclerosis Society. Annual Report; Patient Service News.
Description: For people with MS and their families, health professionals, counselors and others interested in solving the problems of living with the chronic disease. Also covers disability rights and reports on current research in the field.

616.834 US
INSIDE M S BULLETIN. 1993. 3/yr. $20 membership. National Multiple Sclerosis Society, 733 Third Ave., New York, NY 10017-3288. TEL 212-986-3240. FAX 212-986-7981. Ed. Martha King. circ. 204,000. **Document type:** newsletter.
Description: Brief review of news of the society and its initiatives in employment, research funding, health care reform and other social issues.

INSIGHTS (BELLE MEAD). see HOSPITALS

INSTITUTE FOR ORGONOMIC SCIENCE. ANNALS. see
BIOLOGY — Physiology

616.89 150.19 302 SW ISSN 1102-6138
INTEGRAL PSYKOANALYS; psykoterapi, sociologi, filosofi. 1992. irreg. (1-2/yr.). SEK 100 membership. Svenska Saellskapet foer Analytisk Trilogi, Stockholmsv. 22, S-122 62 Enskede, Sweden. TEL 46-08-39-51-87. Ed. S.K. Simula. adv. circ. 5,000.

616.8 US ISSN 0735-3847
RC321 CODEN: IPSYDK
INTEGRATIVE PSYCHIATRY; an international journal for the synthesis of medicine and psychiatry. 1983. 4/yr. $57 to individuals (foreign $137); institutions $113 (foreign $137). (Academia Medicina Psychiatria) International Universities Press, Inc., 59 Boston Post Rd., Box 1523, CT 06443-1524. TEL 203-245-4000. FAX 203-245-0775. Eds. Drs. Alfred M. Freedman, Turan M. Itil. abstr.; bibl. **Indexed:** Excerp.Med., Psychol.Abstr. (1983-). —BLDSC (4531.816600); SWETS. CCC.
  Description: Covers psychiatry, neurology, medicine, biology, and relevant advances in the behavioral and social sciences.
  Refereed Serial

616.8 US ISSN 1071-0752
RJ503
INTERNATIONAL ANNALS OF ADOLESCENT PSYCHIATRY. 1988. irreg. (approx. a.). price varies. (International Society for Adolescent Psychiatry) University of Chicago Press, Journals Division, 5720 S. Woodlawn Ave., Chicago, IL 60637. TEL 312-753-3347. FAX 312-753-0811. (Orders to: Box 37005, Chicago, IL 60637) Ed. Allan Z. Schwartzberg. **Document type:** academic/scholarly publication.
  Description: Explores the issues and problems concerning adolescents and the professionals who serve them. Provides a forum for international and interdisciplinary research in adolescent psychiatry.
  Refereed Serial

616.89 UK ISSN 0085-2007
INTERNATIONAL ASSOCIATION FOR SCIENTIFIC STUDY OF MENTAL DEFICIENCY. PROCEEDINGS OF INTERNATIONAL CONGRESS. 1967. triennial, 8th, 1988, Dublin. £40. (International Association for Scientific Study of Mental Deficiency) Routledge, 11 New Fetter Ln., London EC4P 4EE, England. TEL 071-583-9855. FAX 071-583-0701. Ed. J. Berg. circ. 4,000. **Document type:** proceedings.

616.855 SZ ISSN 0074-1655
INTERNATIONAL ASSOCIATION OF LOGOPEDICS AND PHONIATRICS. REPORTS OF CONGRESS. 1947. triennial, 22nd, 1992, Hannover. $30. International Association of Logopedics and Phoniatrics, c/o Dr. A. Muller, Pres., Av. de la Gare 6, CH-1003 Lausanne, Switzerland. TEL 021-3124333. FAX 021-3112025. adv.; bk.rev. **Document type:** proceedings.

610 US ISSN 0361-0462
CODEN: IBRSDZ
INTERNATIONAL BRAIN RESEARCH ORGANIZATION MONOGRAPH SERIES. Short title: I B R O Monograph Series. 1975. irreg., latest vol.11. price varies. Raven Press (Subsidiary of: Wolters Kluwer N.V.), 1185 Ave. of the Americas, New York, NY 10036. TEL 212-930-9500. FAX 212-869-3495. (reprint service avail. from UMI) **Indexed:** Biol.Abstr., Chem.Abstr., Curr.Cont., Sci.Cit.Ind. **Document type:** monographic series.
  —CASDDS.

616.8 IE ISSN 0074-3631
INTERNATIONAL CONGRESS OF ELECTROENCEPHALOGRAPHY AND CLINICAL NEUROPHYSIOLOGY (PROCEEDINGS). (Supplement to: Electroencephalography and Clinical Neurophysiology (ISSN 0921-884X)) irreg., 1990, 12th, Rio de Janeiro. (International Federation of Clinical Neurophysiology) Elsevier Science Ireland Ltd., P.O. Box 85, Limerick, Ireland. TEL 353-61-471944. FAX 353-61-472144. (Subscr. in U.S. and Canada to: Elsevier Science Inc., Box 882, Madison Sq. Sta., New York, NY 10159. TEL 212-989-5800. FAX 212-633-3990) **Indexed:** Ind.Med., INSPEC. **Document type:** proceedings.

618 US ISSN 0020-6571
INTERNATIONAL DRUG THERAPY NEWSLETTER. 1966. m. (Sep.-Jun.). $45. Ayd Medical Communications, 1130 E. Cold Spring Ln., Baltimore, MD 21239. TEL 410-433-9220. FAX 410-532-5419. Ed. Frank J. Ayd, Jr., M.D. bk.rev. circ. 7,000. **Indexed:** I.P.A. **Document type:** newsletter.
  —BLDSC (4539.749000).
  Description: Psychoactive drug therapy.

616.8 SZ
INTERNATIONAL FEDERATION FOR PSYCHOTHERAPY. CONGRESS REPORTS. 1972. triennial, 16th, 1994, Seoul, S. Korea. International Federation for Psychotherapy, c/o Dr. Edgar Heim, Pres., Tannackerstr. 3, CH-3653 Oberhofen, Switzerland. TEL 033-431195. **Document type:** proceedings.
  Formerly: International Federation for Medical Psychotherapy. Congress Reports (ISSN 0074-5847)

616.8 UK ISSN 0736-5748
QP363.5 CODEN: IJDND6
INTERNATIONAL JOURNAL OF DEVELOPMENTAL NEUROSCIENCE. 1983. 8/yr. £561($892) (effective 1996). (International Society for Developmental Neuroscience) Elsevier Science Ltd., Pergamon, P.O. Box 800, Kidlington, Oxford OX5 1DX, England. TEL 44-1865-843000. FAX 44-1865-843010. E-mail: nlinfo-f@elsevier.nl; usinfo-f@elsevier.com; forinfo-kyf04035@niftyserve.or.jp; Site addr.: http://www.elsevier.nl/. (Subscr. in U.S. and Canada to: Elsevier Science, 660 White Plains Rd., Tarrytown, NY 10591-5153. TEL 914-524-9200. FAX 914-333-2444) Ed. J. Regino Perez-Polo. (also avail. in microform from UMI) **Indexed:** ASCA, Curr.Adv.Biochem., Curr.Adv.Ecol.Sci., Curr.Adv.Genetics & Molec.Biol., Excerp.Med., Ind.Sci.Rev., Psychol.Abstr. (1983-), Sci.Cit.Ind. **Document type:** academic/scholarly publication.
  —BLDSC (4542.185100); CASDDS; Faxon; Genuine Article; SWETS; UMI; UnCover. CCC.
  Description: Publishes research on basic and clinical aspects of the developing nervous system.
  Refereed Serial

INTERNATIONAL JOURNAL OF GERIATRIC PSYCHIATRY. see GERONTOLOGY AND GERIATRICS

INTERNATIONAL JOURNAL OF GROUP PSYCHOTHERAPY. see PSYCHOLOGY

INTERNATIONAL JOURNAL OF LAW AND PSYCHIATRY. see LAW

616.8 UK ISSN 1049-8931
RC337 CODEN: IPSREY
INTERNATIONAL JOURNAL OF METHODS IN PSYCHIATRIC RESEARCH. 1991. q. $275 (foreign $275) (effective 1996). John Wiley & Sons Ltd., Journals, Baffins Ln., Chichester, W. Sussex PO19 1UD, England. TEL 01243-779777. FAX 01243-776128. TELEX 86290 WIBOOK G. (Subscr. in the Americas to: John Wiley & Sons, Inc., 605 Third Ave., New York, NY 10158. TEL 212-850-6645. FAX 212-850-6021) Ed. Chris Thompson. bk.rev.; abstr. circ. 95. (also avail. in microform from UMI; back issues avail.) **Indexed:** Psychol.Abstr. (1993-). **Document type:** academic/scholarly publication.
  —BLDSC (4542.352300); Genuine Article; UMI.
  Description: Contains articles pertaining to important issues in the methods of psychiatric research, the measurement of psychiatric phenomena and related biological variables.
  Refereed Serial

616.8 UY ISSN 0020-7446
CODEN: IJONAO
INTERNATIONAL JOURNAL OF NEUROLOGY. (Editions in English, French, German and Spanish) 1960. q. $260 to individuals; institutions $320 (effective 1995). Fulton Society, Calle Buenos Aires 363, Montevideo, Uruguay. TEL 5982-95-61-07. Ed. Victor Soriano. adv.; bk.rev.; bibl.; charts; illus. **Indexed:** Biol.Abstr., Chem.Abstr., Curr.Adv.Ecol.Sci., Excerp.Med., Ind.Med. **Document type:** academic/scholarly publication, monographic series.
  —CASDDS.
  Description: Focuses on specific topics in neurology, with additional sections on teaching neurology and the history of medicine.

616.8 US ISSN 0020-7454
QP351 CODEN: IJNUB7
INTERNATIONAL JOURNAL OF NEUROSCIENCE. 1970. 24/yr. (in 6 vols., 4 nos./vol.). 291 ECU per vol. (effective 1996). Gordon and Breach Science Publishers, c/o International Publishers Distributor, 820 Town Center Dr., Langhorne, PA 19047. TEL 215-750-2642. FAX 215-750-6343. (Subscr. to: International Publishers Distributor, P.O. Box 90, Reading, Berkshire RG1 8JL, England. TEL 44-173-456-8316) Ed. Dr. Sidney Weinstein. adv.; bk.rev.; index. (also avail. in microform) **Indexed:** Biol.Abstr., Chem.Abstr., Curr.Adv.Ecol.Sci., Curr.Cont., Dent.Ind., Excerp.Med., Ind.Med., Ind.Sci.Rev., Psychol.Abstr. (1983-). **Document type:** academic/scholarly publication.
  —BLDSC (4542.386000); CASDDS; Faxon; SWETS; UnCover. CCC.
  Refereed Serial

INTERNATIONAL JOURNAL OF OFFENDER THERAPY AND COMPARATIVE CRIMINOLOGY. see CRIMINOLOGY AND LAW ENFORCEMENT

616.8 UK ISSN 0968-0624
▼**INTERNATIONAL JOURNAL OF PSYCHIATRIC NURSING RESEARCH.** 1994. q. University of Southampton, Psychiatric Nursing Research Unit, C Level, West Wing, Southampton General Hospital, Southampton, Hants. SO9 4XY, England. Ed. William Whitfield. **Document type:** academic/scholarly publication.
  —BLDSC (4542.490000).

616.89 US ISSN 0091-2174
RC321 CODEN: IJMEDO
INTERNATIONAL JOURNAL OF PSYCHIATRY IN MEDICINE; an international journal of medical psychology and psychiatry in the general hospital. 1970. q. $127 (effective 1996). Baywood Publishing Co., Inc., 26 Austin Ave., Box 337, Amityville, NY 11701. TEL 516-691-1270. FAX 516-691-1770. Ed. Dr. Daniel S.P. Schubert. bk.rev.; bibl.; charts; illus.; stat.; index. (back issues avail.) **Indexed:** Abstr.Health Care Manage.Stud., Behav.Med.Abstr., Biol.Abstr., Curr.Cont., Excerp.Med., Ind.Med., Mid.East: Abstr.& Ind., Nutr.Abstr., Psychol.Abstr. (1973-), Soc.Work Res.& Abstr., SSCI. **Document type:** academic/scholarly publication.
  —BLDSC (4542.495000); EMDOCS; Faxon; SWETS; UnCover.
  Formerly: Psychiatry in Medicine (ISSN 0033-278X)
  Description: Contains articles which apply the methods of psychiatry and psychology to the further understanding of disorders which are primarily psychiatric in nature.
  Refereed Serial

616.89 UK ISSN 1356-9082
▼**INTERNATIONAL JOURNAL OF PSYCHOTHERAPY.** Announced for publication in 1996. a. £12 to individuals; institutions £28 (effective 1996). Carfax Publishing Co., P.O. Box 25, Abingdon, Oxon. OX14 3UE, England. TEL 44-1235-555335. FAX 44-1235-553559. (N. American subscr. to: Carfax Publishing Co., 875-81 Massachusetts Ave., Cambridge, MA 02139) **Document type:** academic/scholarly publication.

616.89 UK ISSN 0020-7640
RC321
INTERNATIONAL JOURNAL OF SOCIAL PSYCHIATRY. 1955. q. £32 to individuals (foreign $120); institutions £52 (foreign $160) (effective 1996). Avenue Publishing Co., 55 Woodstock Ave., London NW11 9RG, England. TEL 0181-455-2940. Ed. Frank Holloway. adv.; bk.rev.; illus.; stat.; index. circ. 1,000. **Indexed:** Abstr.Health Care Manage.Stud., Adol.Ment.Hlth.Abstr., ASSIA, Curr.Cont., Excerp.Med., Ind.Med., Lang.& Lang.Behav.Abstr., Mid.East: Abstr.& Ind., Psychol.Abstr. (1955-), Soc.Sci.Ind., SSCI. **Document type:** academic/scholarly publication.
  ●Also available online. Vendor(s): University Microfilms International.
  —BLDSC (4542.560000); EMDOCS; Faxon; SWETS; UMI; UnCover.
  Description: Publishes articles on psychiatric problems, strategies for survival, drug abuse, psychiatry, social psychiatry, and psychotherapy.

MEDICAL SCIENCES — PSYCHIATRY AND NEUROLOGY

616.8 UK ISSN 1355-6177
CODEN: JINSF9
▼**INTERNATIONAL NEUROPSYCHOLOGICAL SOCIETY. JOURNAL.** Short title: J I N S. 1995. bi-m. £112($160) (effective 1996). Cambridge University Press, Edinburgh Bldg., Shaftesbury Rd., Cambridge CB2 2RU, England. TEL 01223-312393. FAX 01223-315052. TELEX 851817256. E-mail: jins@uscd.edu. (N. American addr.: Cambridge University Press, Journals Dept., 40 W. 20th St., New York, NY 10011. TEL 212-924-3900. FAX 212-691-3239) Ed. Igor Grant. adv.; bk.rev. **Document type:** academic/scholarly publication.
—BLDSC (4802.325000). **CCC.**
Description: Covers all areas of neuropsychology and related topics, including behavioral neurology, neuropsychiatry, neuroimaging, and electrophysiology
Refereed Serial

616.8 US ISSN 1041-6102
CODEN: INPSE8
INTERNATIONAL PSYCHOGERIATRICS. 1989. q. $52 to individuals (foreign $58); institutions $100 (foreign $110) (effective 1996). (International Psychogeriatric Association) Springer Publishing Company, 536 Broadway, New York, NY 10012-3955. TEL 212-431-4370. FAX 212-941-7842. Ed. Gene D. Cohen. adv.; bk.rev. **Indexed:** Abstr.Soc.Geront., Excerp.Med. (1993-), Ind.Med., Psychol.Abstr. (1989-), Psychol.Abstr., Sage Fam.Stud.Abstr., Sage Urb.Stud.Abstr., Sociol.Abstr. **Document type:** trade publication.
—BLDSC (4545.345000); UMI. **CCC.**
Description: Serves as an international forum for advances in practice, research, service development and education.
Refereed Serial

616.8 618.92 US ISSN 0899-3653
INTERNATIONAL REVIEW OF CHILD NEUROLOGY SERIES. 1982. irreg., latest 1995. price varies. Raven Press (Subsidiary of: Wolters Kluwer N.V.), 1185 Ave. of the Americas, New York, NY 10036. TEL 212-930-9500. FAX 212-869-3495. (reprint service avail. from UMI) **Document type:** monographic series.
Refereed Serial

616.8 US ISSN 0074-7742
RC341 CODEN: IRNEAE
INTERNATIONAL REVIEW OF NEUROBIOLOGY. 1959. irreg., vol.36, 1993. Academic Press, Inc., 525 B St., Ste. 1900, San Diego, CA 92101-4495. TEL 619-231-0926. FAX 619-699-6715. (Subscr. to: Order Dept., 6277 Sea Harbor Dr., 4th Fl., Orlando, FL 32887. TEL 800-321-5068) Eds. Carl C. Pfeiffer, John R. Smythies. index. (back issues avail. from ISI) **Indexed:** Biol.Abstr., Chem.Abstr., Dent.Ind., Excerp.Med., Ind.Med., Ind.Sci.Rev., Sci.Cit.Ind. **Document type:** academic/scholarly publication.
—BLDSC (4547.400000); CASDDS; EMDOCS; Faxon; UnCover. **CCC.**
Refereed Serial

616.8 UK ISSN 0954-0261
CODEN: IRPSE2
INTERNATIONAL REVIEW OF PSYCHIATRY. 1989. q. £78 to individuals; institutions £236 (effective 1996). Carfax Publishing Co., P.O. Box 25, Abingdon, Oxon. OX14 3UE, England. TEL 01235-555335. FAX 01235-553559. (U.S. subscr. to: Carfax Publishing Co., 875-81 Massachusetts Ave., Cambridge, MA 02139) Ed. Paul Bebbington. adv.; bk.rev. (also avail. in microfiche) **Indexed:** Excerp.Med. (1992-), Mult.Ed.Abstr., Psychol.Abstr. (1989-), Sp.Ed.Needs Abstr. **Document type:** academic/scholarly publication.
—BLDSC (4547.515000); SWETS; UMI. **CCC.**
Description: Publishes undergraduate-level reviews of topics in psychiatry.
Refereed Serial

157 **616.858** US ISSN 0074-7750
RC570
INTERNATIONAL REVIEW OF RESEARCH IN MENTAL RETARDATION. 1966. irreg., vol.19, 1993. Academic Press, Inc., 525 B St., Ste. 1900, San Diego, CA 92101-4495. TEL 619-231-0926. FAX 619-699-6715. (Subscr. to: Order Dept., 6277 Sea Harbor Dr., 4th Fl., Orlando, FL 32887. TEL 800-321-5068) Eds. Norman R. Ellis, Norman W. Bray. (back issues avail. from ISI) **Indexed:** SSCI.
—Faxon; UnCover. **CCC.**
Refereed Serial

INTUITION; a magazine for the higher potential of the mind. see *NEW AGE PUBLICATIONS*

616.8 IE ISSN 0790-1186
IRISH JOURNAL OF PSYCHIATRY. s-a. £2. Irish Institute of Psychiatry, 73 Lower Baggot St., Dublin 2, Ireland. Ed. Dermot Walsh. **Indexed:** Psychol.Abstr. (1986-).
—BLDSC (4572.170000).

616.89 IE ISSN 0790-9667
CODEN: IPMEEX
IRISH JOURNAL OF PSYCHOLOGICAL MEDICINE. 1982. q. I£43($96) (foreign I£53). (Irish Institute of Psychological Medicine) MedMedia Ltd., P.O. Box 86, Blackrock, Co. Dublin, Ireland. TEL 01-2803967. FAX 01-2807076. (Subscr. to: Royal Society of Medicine Services Ltd., 1 Wimpole St., London W1M 8AE, England. TEL 0171-290-2927. FAX 0171-290-2929; Alt. addr: MedMedia Ltd., Media House, 99 Upper George's St., Dun Laoghaire, Co. Dublin, Ireland) Ed. Dr. Brian Lawlor. adv.: B&W page I£790, color page I£1080. bk.rev.; charts. circ. 3,200. (also avail. in microform from UMI; reprint service avail. from UMI) **Indexed:** Biol.Abstr., CINAHL, Excerp.Med., I.P.A., Lang.& Lang.Behav.Abstr., Nutr.Abstr., Psychol.Abstr. (1982-), Ref.Zh., Soc.Work Res.& Abstr., Sociol.Abstr., SOPODA. **Document type:** academic/scholarly publication.
—BLDSC (4572.180000); ADONIS; UMI; UnCover. **CCC.**
Former titles: Irish Journal of Psychotherapy and Psychosomatic Medicine (ISSN 0790-0848); Irish Journal of Psychotherapy.
Description: Publishes original scientific contributions in psychiatry, psychological medicine, and related basic sciences (neurosciences, biological, psychological and social sciences).
Refereed Serial

ISSUES IN MENTAL HEALTH NURSING. see *MEDICAL SCIENCES — Nurses And Nursing*

ISSUES IN PSYCHOANALYTIC PSYCHOLOGY. see *PSYCHOLOGY*

616.858 371.9 IT ISSN 1123-7708
ITALIAN JOURNAL OF INTELLECTIVE IMPAIRMENT/RIVISTA ITALIANA DEL DISTURBO INTELLETTIVO. (Text in English or Italian) 1988. s-a. L.35000 (foreign L.65000) (effective 1995 & 1996). (Gruppo Italiano per lo Studio Scientifico e Terapia dell'Insufficienza Mentale, Mongolismo e Autismo Infantili) GISSTIMMAI Editore, Via Liberta 21, 61039 S. Costanza, Italy. TEL 39-721-950234. E-mail: mc7057@mclink.it. (Subscr. to: Via Liberta 21, 61039 San Costanzo, Italy. TEL 39-721-950234) Ed. Dr. Renato Cocchi. bk.rev. circ. 150. **Indexed:** Psychol.Abstr. (1988-). **Document type:** newspaper.
Refereed Serial

610 IT ISSN 0392-0461
CODEN: IJNSD3
ITALIAN JOURNAL OF NEUROLOGICAL SCIENCES. (Text in English) 1980. m. (9/yr.). L.149000($160) (effective 1994). (Società Italiana di Neurologia) Masson S.p.A., Divisione Periodici, Via Statuto 2-4, 20121 Milan, Italy. TEL 02-6367-1. FAX 02-6367-211. Ed. Giuliano Avanzini. adv.: B&W page L.2600000, color page L.4300000; trim 170 x 240. circ. 1,500. **Indexed:** Curr.Cont., Excerp.Med., Psychol.Abstr. (1989-). **Document type:** academic/scholarly publication.
—BLDSC (4588.340700); CASDDS; Faxon; Genuine Article; UMI; UnCover.

616.8 IT ISSN 1122-2247
ITALIAN JOURNAL OF PSYCHIATRY AND BEHAVIOURAL SCIENCES. (Text in English) 1991. q. L.90000($150) (effective 1995). (Società Italiana di Psichiatria) Casa Editrice Idelson, Via A. De Gasperi 55, 80133 Naples, Italy. TEL 39-81-5524733. FAX 39-81-5518295. Ed. Carlo Lorenzo Cazzullo.
Description: Publishes and diffuses the contributions of Italian researchers.

616.8 615.53 US ISSN 1067-8239
J N M S: JOURNAL OF THE NEUROMUSCULOSKELETAL SYSTEM. 1993. q. $58 to individuals; institutions $118 (effective 1995; typically set in Oct.). (American Chiropractic Association) Data Trace Chiropractic Publishers, Inc., 110 West Rd., Ste. 227, Baltimore, MD 21204-2316. TEL 410-494-4994. FAX 410-494-0515. Ed. Scott Haldeman. adv. circ. 12,014. **Document type:** academic/scholarly publication.
—BLDSC (4669.470800). **CCC.**
Description: Covers all areas reflecting the manifestations of neuromusculoskeletal function and dysfunction, including biomechanics, adjustive and manipulative therapy, neurology, nutrition, orthopedics, radiology and imaging, and physical therapy.
Refereed Serial

JAMES ARTHUR LECTURE ON THE EVOLUTION OF THE HUMAN BRAIN. see *BIOLOGY — Genetics*

616.89 JA ISSN 0289-0968
JAPANESE JOURNAL OF CHILD & ADOLESCENT PSYCHIATRY/JIDO SEINEN SEISHIN IGAKU TO SONO KINSETSU RYOIKI. (Text in Japanese; summaries in English) 1960. 5/yr. $30. Japanese Society of Child and Adolescent Psychiatry, c/o Department of Neuropsychiatry, School of Medicine, Kyoto University, Sakyo-ku, Kyoto 606, Japan. (Subscr. to: Maruzen Co. Ltd., Export Dept., Box 605, Tokyo Central, Tokyo, Japan) Ed. Dr. Kiyoyuki Koike. adv.; bk.rev.; abstr.; charts; index. circ. 2,000. (back issues avail.) **Indexed:** Child Devel.Abstr., Curr.Cont., Psychol.Abstr. (1960-), SSCI. **Document type:** academic/scholarly publication.
—BLDSC (4651.358000); UnCover.
Formerly: Japanese Journal of Child Psychiatry (ISSN 0021-4957)
Description: Addresses problems, issues, treatments, trends, and syndromes unique to child and adolescent psychology.

616.8 JA ISSN 0912-2036
CODEN: JJPNEA
JAPANESE JOURNAL OF PSYCHIATRY AND NEUROLOGY. (Text in English) 1933. q. $140. Folia Publishing Society, Academic Societies Bldg., 2-4-16 Yayoi, Bunkyo-ku, Tokyo 113, Japan. (Dist. by: Business Center for Academic Societies Japan, 5-16-9 Honkomagome, Bunkyo-ku, Tokyo 113, Japan. TEL 03-5814-5811) Ed. Teruo Okuma. adv.; abstr. **Indexed:** Biol.Abstr., Chem.Abstr., Curr.Cont., Excerp.Med., Ind.Med., INIS Atomind., Psychol.Abstr.
—CASDDS; SWETS; UnCover.
Formerly: Folia Psychiatrica et Neurologica Japonica (ISSN 0015-5721)

616.8 GW ISSN 0944-4068
JATROS NEUROLOGIE PSYCHIATRIE UND PSYCHOTHERAPIE. 1985. 12/yr. DM.90. P M I Verlagsgruppe GmbH, August-Schanz-Str. 21, 60433 Frankfurt a.M., Germany. TEL 069-5480000. FAX 069-54800077. Ed. Peter Hoffmann. circ. 4,500. (back issues avail.) **Document type:** academic/scholarly publication.
Formerly: Jatros Neurologie - Psychiatrie (ISSN 0178-7535)
Description: Seminar papers containing brief summaries of original articles, interviews and congress reports.

MEDICAL SCIENCES — PSYCHIATRY AND NEUROLOGY

616.89   BL   ISSN 0047-2085
CODEN: JBPSAX
JORNAL BRASILEIRO DE PSIQUIATRIA. (Text in Portuguese; summaries in English and Portuguese) 1942. m. Cr.$13($80) or exchange basis (effective 1995). (Universidade Federal do Rio de Janeiro, Instituto de Psiquiatria) Editora Cientifica Nacional Ltda., Rua da Gloria, 366, 3o andar, 20241-180 Rio de Janeiro, RJ, Brazil. TEL 55-21-221-3235. FAX 55-21-252-1691. Ed. Joao Romildo Bueno. adv. contact: Maria Luiza Carvalho Doneda. bk.rev.; bibl.; charts; illus.; stat.; index, cum.index. circ. 5,000. (also avail. in microform from UMI; back issues avail.) **Indexed:** Biol.Abstr., Chem.Abstr., Excerp.Med., Ind.Med., Psychol.Abstr. (1964-). **Document type:** academic/scholarly publication.
—BLDSC (4674.680000); EMDOCS; UMI.
Description: Studies in clinical psychiatry.

616.89   FR   ISSN 1155-1704
JOURNAL DE THERAPIE COMPORTAMENTALE ET COGNITIVE. (Text in English, French) q. 536 F. (foreign 637 F.) to individuals; institutions 651 F. (foreign 773 F.) (effective 1996). (Association Francaise de Therapie Comportementale et Cognitive) Masson - Periodiques, Villa Laromiguiere, 75005 Paris, France. TEL 1-40-46-62-00. FAX 1-40-46-62-01. Ed. J. Cottraux. adv. contact: Frederique Baudouin. bk.rev. circ. 1,500. **Document type:** academic/scholarly publication.
—BLDSC (5069.079500).
Description: Contains a clinical section with a didactical aspect as well as international reports on advances in behavioural science and cognition.

616.8   NE   ISSN 0165-0327
CODEN: JADID7
JOURNAL OF AFFECTIVE DISORDERS. 1979. 15/yr. fl.2400($1464) (effective 1996). Elsevier Science B.V., P.O. Box 211, 1000 AE Amsterdam, Netherlands. TEL 31-20-4853911. FAX 31-20-4853598. TELEX 18582 ESPA NL. E-mail: nlinfo-f@elsevier.nl; usinfo-f@elsevier.com; forinfo-kyf04035@niftyserve.or.jp; Site addr.: http://www.elsevier.nl/. (Subscr. in U.S. and Canada to: Elsevier Science Inc., Box 882, Madison Sq. Sta., New York, NY 10159. TEL 212-989-5800. FAX 212-633-3990) Eds. E.S. Paykel, G. Winokur. illus. (also avail. in microform from UMI; reprint service avail. ISI) **Indexed:** Adol.Ment.Hlth.Abstr., Biol.Abstr., Chem.Abstr., Curr.Cont., Excerp.Med., Ind.Med., Ind.Sci.Rev., Psychol.Abstr. (1979-), Sci.Cit.Ind. **Document type:** academic/scholarly publication.
—BLDSC (4919.986000); ADONIS; CASDDS; Faxon; Genuine Article; SWETS; UMI; UnCover. **CCC.**
Description: Publishes papers concerned with affective disorders in the widest sense: depression, mania and anxiety.
Refereed Serial

JOURNAL OF ANXIETY DISORDERS. see *PSYCHOLOGY*

616.89 371.94   US   ISSN 0162-3257
RJ499   CODEN: JADDDQ
JOURNAL OF AUTISM AND DEVELOPMENTAL DISORDERS. 1971. bi-m. $325 (foreign $380) (effective 1996). Plenum Publishing Corp., 233 Spring St., New York, NY 10013-1578. TEL 212-620-8000. FAX 212-463-0742. TELEX 23-421139. Ed. Eric Schopler. adv.; bk.rev.; abstr.; charts; illus.; stat.; index. (also avail. in microfilm from JSC; back issues avail.) **Indexed:** ASSIA, Bibl.Dev.Med.& Child Neur., Biol.Abstr., C.I.J.E., Chem.Abstr., Child Devel.Abstr., Curr.Cont., Educ.Ind., Except.Child.Educ.Abstr., Excerp.Med., IMFL, Ind.Med., INIS Atomind., Mid.East: Abstr.& Ind., Psychol.Abstr. (1971-), Psyscan D.P., Risk Abstr., Soc.Work Res.& Abstr., SSCI. **Document type:** academic/scholarly publication.
—BLDSC (4949.552000); Faxon; Genuine Article; SWETS; UMI; UnCover. **CCC.**
Formerly (until 1979): Journal of Autism and Childhood Schizophrenia (ISSN 0021-9185)
Refereed Serial

616.89   UK   ISSN 0005-7916
RC489.B4   CODEN: JBTEAB
JOURNAL OF BEHAVIOR THERAPY AND EXPERIMENTAL PSYCHIATRY; an interdisciplinary journal. 1970. q. £239($381) (effective 1996). (Behavior Therapy and Research Society) Elsevier Science Ltd., Pergamon, P.O. Box 800, Kidlington, Oxford OX5 1DX, England. TEL 44-1865-843000. FAX 44-1865-843010. E-mail: nlinfo-f@elsevier.nl; usinfo-f@elsevier.com; forinfo-kyf04035@niftyserve.or.jp; Site addr.: http://www.elsevier.nl/. (Subscr. in U.S. and Canada to: Elsevier Science, 660 White Plains Rd., Tarrytown, NY 10591-5153. TEL 914-524-9200. FAX 914-333-2444) Ed. Joseph Wolpe. adv.: B&W page $550, color page $1350. bk.rev.; index. circ. 3,100. (also avail. in microfilm from UMI; back issues avail.) **Indexed:** Abstr.Crim.& Pen., Adol.Ment.Hlth Abstr., ASCA, ASSIA, Behav.Med.Abstr., Biol.Abstr., Child Devel.Abstr., CINAHL, Curr.Cont., Excerp.Med., Ind.Med., Mid.East: Abstr.& Ind., Psychol.Abstr. (1970-), SSCI. **Document type:** academic/scholarly publication.
—BLDSC (4951.250000); Faxon; Genuine Article; SWETS; UMI; UnCover. **CCC.**
Description: Covers all aspects of behavior therapy and its applications in clinical psychiatry.
Refereed Serial

616.8   US   ISSN 0160-7715
R726.5   CODEN: JBMEDD
JOURNAL OF BEHAVIORAL MEDICINE. 1978. bi-m. $325 (foreign $380) (effective 1996). Plenum Publishing Corp., 233 Spring St., New York, NY 10013-1578. TEL 212-620-8000. FAX 212-463-0742. TELEX 23-421139. Ed. W. Doyle Gentry. adv.; bk.rev. (also avail. in microform from JSC; back issues avail.) **Indexed:** Adol.Ment.Hlth.Abstr., Behav.Med.Abstr., Biol.Abstr., CINAHL, Curr.Cont., Dent.Ind., Excerp.Med., IMFL, Ind.Med., Lang.& Lang.Behav.Abstr., Mult.Ed.Abstr., NRN, Psychol.Abstr. (1979-), Psyscan C.P., Ref.Zh., Soc.Work Res.& Abstr., Sociol.Abstr., SSCI. **Document type:** academic/scholarly publication.
—BLDSC (4951.262000); Faxon; Genuine Article; SWETS; UMI; UnCover. **CCC.**
Refereed Serial

616.8   US   ISSN 0748-7304
QH527   CODEN: JBRHEE
JOURNAL OF BIOLOGICAL RHYTHMS. Abbreviated title: J B R. 1985. q. $79 to individuals; institutions $178 (effective 1996). (Society for Research on Biological Rhythms) Sage Publications, Inc., Sage Science Press, 2455 Teller Rd., Thousand Oaks, CA 91320. TEL 805-499-0721. FAX 805-499-0871. Ed. Fred W. Turek. adv.; bibl.; charts; illus.; index. (back issues avail.; reprint service avail. from ISI,UMI) **Indexed:** Biol.Abstr., Curr.Cont., Ind.Med., Psychol.Abstr. (1986-). **Document type:** academic/scholarly publication.
—BLDSC (4953.260000); Faxon; Genuine Article; SWETS; UMI; UnCover.
Description: Reports on nature and functions of biological rhythms, using genetic, biochemical, physiological behavioral, and modeling approaches.
Refereed Serial

616.8 574   GW   ISSN 0944-8160
JOURNAL OF BRAIN RESEARCH. (Text in English) 1953. 4/yr. DM.848 (foreign DM.862). Akademie Verlag GmbH, Muehlenstr. 33-34, 13187 Berlin, Germany. TEL 030-47889348. FAX 030-47889357. Ed. E. Winkelmann. abstr.; charts; illus.; mkt.; index. **Indexed:** Curr.Cont., Excerp.Med., Ind.Med., Ind.Vet., INIS Atomind., Sci.Cit.Ind., Vet.Bull. **Document type:** academic/scholarly publication.
—BLDSC (4954.290000); EMDOCS; Faxon; Genuine Article; SWETS; UnCover.
Formerly: Journal fuer Hirnforschung (ISSN 0021-8359)

616.8 612.015   US   ISSN 0271-678X
QP108.5.C4   CODEN: JCBMDN
JOURNAL OF CEREBRAL BLOOD FLOW AND METABOLISM. 1981. bi-m. $333 to individuals (foreign $389); institutions $525 (foreign $603) (effective 1996); newsstand price: $103. (International Society of Cerebral Blood Flow and Metabolism) Lippincott - Raven Publishers, 276 Washington Sq., Philadelphia, PA 19106. TEL 215-238-4200. Ed. Dr. Myron Ginsberg. adv. contact: Phyllis Noyes. bk.rev.; charts; illus.; index. circ. 2,000. (back issues avail.; reprint service avail. from UMI) **Indexed:** Biol.Abstr., Chem.Abstr., Curr.Cont., Excerp.Med., Ind.Med., Ind.Sci.Rev., INIS Atomind., Sci.Cit.Ind. **Document type:** academic/scholarly publication.
—BLDSC (4955.110000); CASDDS; Faxon; Genuine Article; SWETS; UMI; UnCover. **CCC.**
Description: Gathers experimental, theoretical, and clinical information on brain circulation and metabolism.
Refereed Serial

616.8   NE   ISSN 0891-0618
CODEN: JCNAEE
JOURNAL OF CHEMICAL NEUROANATOMY. 1988. 8/yr. fl.1156($705) (effective 1996). Elsevier Science B.V., P.O. Box 211, 1000 AE Amsterdam, Netherlands. TEL 31-20-4853911. FAX 31-20-4853598. E-mail: nlinfo-f@elsevier.nl; usinfo-f@elsevier.com; forinfo-kyf04035@niftyserve.or.jp; Site addr.: http://www.elsevier.nl/. (Subscr. in U.S. and Canada to: Elsevier Science Inc., Box 882, Madison Sq. Sta., New York, NY 10159-0882. TEL 212-989-5800. FAX 212-633-3990) Eds. H.W.M. Steinbusch, A. Claudio Cuello. (also avail. in microform from UMI; reprint service avail. from SWZ) **Indexed:** Chem.Abstr., Curr.Adv.Cell & Devel.Biol., Excerp.Med., Ind.Med. **Document type:** academic/scholarly publication.
—BLDSC (4956.850000); CASDDS; Faxon; Genuine Article; SWETS; UMI; UnCover. **CCC.**
Description: Publishes scientific reports relating to the functional and biochemical aspects of the nervous system, with emphasis on microanatomical organization.
Refereed Serial

616.8 618.92   US   ISSN 1053-0800
RJ505.G7   CODEN: JAGTEM
JOURNAL OF CHILD AND ADOLESCENT GROUP THERAPY. 1991. q. $145 (foreign $170) (effective 1996). Human Sciences Press, Inc. (Subsidiary of: Plenum Publishing Corp.), 233 Spring St., New York, NY 10013. TEL 212-620-8000. FAX 212-463-0742. TELEX 23-421139. Ed. Edward S. Soo. adv. **Indexed:** IMFL, Psychol.Abstr. (1991-). **Document type:** academic/scholarly publication.
—BLDSC (4957.421000); Faxon; UnCover. **CCC.**
Description: Covers issues in child, adolescent and parent group therapy. Includes clinical reports and articles on new developments, theoretical issues, applications of group therapy and group methods, and the group process.
Refereed Serial

JOURNAL OF CHILD AND ADOLESCENT PSYCHIATRIC NURSING. see *MEDICAL SCIENCES — Nurses And Nursing*

616.8   US   ISSN 1044-5463
CODEN: JADPET
JOURNAL OF CHILD AND ADOLESCENT PSYCHOPHARMACOLOGY. 1990. q. $105 (foreign $138). Mary Ann Liebert, Inc. Publishers, 2 Madison Ave., Larchmont, NY 10538. TEL 914-834-3100. FAX 914-834-3688. E-mail: Liebert@pipeline.com. Eds. Dr. Charles W. Popper. **Indexed:** Excerp.Med. (1994-), Psychol.Abstr. (1990-). **Document type:** academic/scholarly publication.
—BLDSC (4957.424000); Genuine Article.
Description: Emphasizes the clinical aspects of psychotropic therapy. Includes depression, hyperactivity, attention deficit disorder, bulimia and anorexia, obsessive-compulsive disorder, phobias, retardation, and psychotic disorders.

MEDICAL SCIENCES — PSYCHIATRY AND NEUROLOGY

616.8 618.92 CN ISSN 0883-0738
CODEN: JOCNEE
JOURNAL OF CHILD NEUROLOGY. 1985. q. $140 to individuals (outside US & Canada $170); institutions $180 (outside US & Canada $215) (effective 1996). Decker Periodicals, P.O. Box 620, LCD1, Hamilton, ON L8N 3K7, Canada. TEL 905-522-7017; 800-568-7281. FAX 905-522-7839. E-mail: decker@io.org. Ed. Roger A. Brumback. circ. 900. **Indexed:** Excerp.Med., INIS Atomind., Psychol.Abstr. (1986-). **Document type:** academic/scholarly publication.
—BLDSC (4957.625000); Genuine Article; SWETS; UMI; UnCover. **CCC.**
Description: Covers all aspects of nervous system disorders in children, including medical, surgical, pathological, and psychological perspectives.
Refereed Serial

JOURNAL OF CHILD PSYCHOLOGY & PSYCHIATRY & ALLIED DISCIPLINES. see *PSYCHOLOGY*

616.8 US ISSN 0736-0258
JOURNAL OF CLINICAL NEUROPHYSIOLOGY. 1984. bi-m. $158 to individuals (foreign $214); institutions $286 (foreign $343) (effective 1996); newsstand price: $59. (American Electroencephalographic Society) Lippincott - Raven Publishers, 276 E. Washington Sq., Philadelphia, PA 19106. TEL 215-238-4200. Ed. Hans Otto Luders. adv. contact: Phyllis Noyes. bk.rev.; charts; illus.; index. circ. 2,500. (reprint service avail. from UMI) **Indexed:** ASCA, Bibl.Dev.Med.& Child Neur., Excerp.Med., Ind.Med., Ind.Sci.Rev., Psychol.Abstr., Sci.Cit.Ind. **Document type:** academic/scholarly publication.
—BLDSC (4958.578000); Faxon; Genuine Article; SWETS; UMI; UnCover. **CCC.**
Description: Covers clinical neurology, neurosurgery, psychiatry, electroencephalography and evoked potentials, and experimental research of the central nervous system.
Refereed Serial

616.8 AT
QP351 CODEN: PANUBL
JOURNAL OF CLINICAL NEUROSCIENCE. 1963. a. $125 to individuals; institutions $174. Australian Association of Neurologists, c/o Prof. Andrew Kaye, Ed., Dept. of Neurosurgery, Royal Melbourne Hospital, Prkville, Vic. 3050, Australia. TEL 03-429-2204. FAX 03-428-5375. adv.; bk.rev. circ. 300. (also avail. in microfilm from UMI) **Indexed:** Chem.Abstr., Excerp.Med., Ind.Med.
—BLDSC (3286.251700); CASDDS; SWETS.
Former titles (until vol.31, 1994): Clinical and Experimental Naurology (ISSN 0196-6383); Australian Association of Neurologists Proceedings (ISSN 0084-7224)

616.8 US ISSN 0160-6689
RC321 CODEN: JCLPDE
JOURNAL OF CLINICAL PSYCHIATRY. (Supplement avail.: Proceedings from Scientific Symposia). 1940. m. $66 (foreign $110). Physicians Postgraduate Press, Inc., Box 240008, Memphis, TN 38124. TEL 901-682-1001. FAX 901-682-6992. Ed. Dr. Alan Gelenberg; Irving R. Shelton. adv. contact: John S. Shelton. bk.rev.; charts; illus.; stat.; index. circ. 32,000. (also avail. in microfilm from UMI) back issues avail.; reprint service avail. from UMI) **Indexed:** Adol.Ment.Hlth.Abstr., ASSIA, Behav.Med.Abstr., Biol.Abstr., Biotech.Abstr., C.I.J.E., Chem.Abstr., CINAHL, Curr.Cont., Curr.Lit.Fam.Plan., Dent.Ind., Excerp.Med., HRIS, IMFL, Ind.Med., Ind.Sci.Rev., Int.Nurs.Ind., Lang.& Lang.Behav.Abstr., Nutr.Abstr., Psychol.Abstr. (1940-), Risk Abstr., Sci.Cit.Ind, SSCI. **Document type:** academic/scholarly publication, proceedings.
—BLDSC (4958.688000); CASDDS; Faxon; Genuine Article; SWETS; UMI; UnCover.
Formerly (until 1978): Diseases of the Nervous System (ISSN 0012-3714)
Description: Presents original material in the psychiatric, behavioral, and neural sciences, with special emphasis on papers dealing with practical and clinical subjects.
Refereed Serial

616.8 US ISSN 0898-929X
QP360 CODEN: JCONEO
JOURNAL OF COGNITIVE NEUROSCIENCE. 1989. q. $58 to individuals (foreign $74); institutions $156 (foreign $172); students $40 (foreign $56). (Cognitive Neuroscience Institute) M I T Press, 55 Hayward St., Cambridge, MA 02142. TEL 617-253-2889. FAX 617-258-6779. E-mail: journals-orders@mit.edu. (Editorial addr.: Center for Neuroscience, University of California at Davis, Davis, CA 95616) Ed. Michael S. Gazzaniga. circ. 1,200. (back issues avail.; reprint service avail. from UMI) **Indexed:** A.I.Abstr., Psychol.Abstr. (1989-). **Document type:** academic/scholarly publication.
—BLDSC (4958.798500); Ei; Faxon; Genuine Article; SWETS; UMI; UnCover. **CCC.**
Description: Provides a forum for research involving the interaction of brain and behavior. Devoted to the field of cognitive neuroscience.
Refereed Serial

JOURNAL OF COMMUNICATION DISORDERS. see *PSYCHOLOGY*

616.8 US ISSN 0021-9967
QL1 CODEN: JCNEAM
THE JOURNAL OF COMPARATIVE NEUROLOGY. 1891. 52/yr. $9568 (foreign $10374) (effective 1996). John Wiley & Sons, Inc., Journals, 605 Third Ave., New York, NY 10158. TEL 212-850-6645. FAX 212-850-6021. TELEX 12-7063. E-mail: SUBINFO@JWILEY.COM. (Subscr. outside the Americas to: John Wiley & Sons Ltd., Baffins Ln., Chichester, W. Sussex PO19 1UD, England. TEL 44-1243-779777. FAX 44-1243-776128) Ed. Sanford L. Palay. adv.; abstr.; bibl.; charts; illus.; index. (also avail. in microfiche from BHP,SWZ,PMC; microform from UMI; back issues avail.; reprint service avail. from SWZ) **Indexed:** Apic.Abstr., Biol.Abstr., Chem.Abstr., Curr.Adv.Cell & Devel.Biol., Curr.Cont., Curr.Ref.Fish Res., Dent.Ind., Excerp.Med., Helminthol.Abstr., Ind.Med., Ind.Sci.Rev., Ind.Vet., INIS Atomind., Poult.Abstr., Sci.Cit.Ind., Small Anim.Abstr., Sport Fish.Abstr., Vet.Bull., Wild.Rev., Zoo.Rec. **Document type:** academic/scholarly publication.
—BLDSC (4962.000000); CASDDS; EMDOCS; Faxon; Genuine Article; SWETS; UMI; UnCover. **CCC.**
Description: Presents original articles about the anatomy and physiology of the nervous system, especially with regard to its structure, growth and function.
Refereed Serial

616.89 006 NE ISSN 0929-5313
▼**JOURNAL OF COMPUTATIONAL NEUROSCIENCE.** (Text in English) 1994. q. fl.503 to institutions; $322 to institutions in U.S. (effective 1996). Kluwer Academic Publishers, Postbus 17, 3300 AA Dordrecht, Netherlands. TEL 31-78-392392. FAX 31-78-392254. E-mail: SERVICES@WKAP.NL. (Dist. by: Kluwer Academic Publishers Group, P.O. Box 322, 3300 AH Dordrecht, Netherlands. TEL 31-78-392392. FAX 31-78-546474; N. America dist. addr.: Box 358, Accord Sta., Hingham, MA 02018-0358. TEL 617-871-6600. FAX 617-871-6528) Ed. James M. Bower. adv. (back issues avail.) **Document type:** academic/scholarly publication.
—BLDSC (4963.490000). **CCC.**
Description: Publishes original papers describing theoretical and experimental work relevant to computations in the brain and nervous system.
Refereed Serial

JOURNAL OF CONSULTING AND CLINICAL PSYCHOLOGY. see *PSYCHOLOGY*

JOURNAL OF CONTEMPORARY PSYCHOTHERAPY. see *PSYCHOLOGY*

616.8 US ISSN 1063-4266
RJ499.A1
JOURNAL OF EMOTIONAL AND BEHAVIORAL DISORDERS. Short title: J E B D. 1993. q. $39 to individuals; institutions $85 (foreign $95) (effective 1996). Pro-Ed Inc., 8700 Shoal Creek Blvd., Austin, TX 78757-6897. TEL 512-451-3246. FAX 512-451-8542. E-mail: proed1@aol.com. Eds. Michael H. Epstein, Douglas Cullinan; Pub. Donald E. Hammill. adv. contact: Melissa Tullos. bibl.; illus. circ. 2,000. (also avail. in microfilm from UMI) **Indexed:** Psychol.Abstr. (1993-). **Document type:** academic/scholarly publication.
—BLDSC (4977.470000); Genuine Article; UMI. **CCC.**
Description: Covers the diagnosis and treatment of emotional and behavioral disorders of young people, from the research and practice perspectives.
Refereed Serial

616.8 US ISSN 0896-6974
CODEN: JOEPEU
JOURNAL OF EPILEPSY. 1988. q. $215 to institutions (effective 1996). Butterworth - Heinemann, Part of the Reed Elsevier group, 313 Washington St., Newton, MA 02158. TEL 617-928-2500; 800-366-2665. FAX 617-928-2610. TELEX 880052. (Subscr. to: Elsevier Science Inc., Box 882, Madison Sq. Sta., New York, NY 10159-0882. TEL 212-989-5800. FAX 212-633-3990) Ed. Allen R. Wyler. (also avail. in microform from UMI; back issues avail.) **Indexed:** Psychol.Abstr. (1988-). **Document type:** academic/scholarly publication.
—BLDSC (4979.477000); Genuine Article; SWETS; UMI. **CCC.**
Refereed Serial

JOURNAL OF ESTHETIC DENTISTRY. see *MEDICAL SCIENCES — Dentistry*

JOURNAL OF FAMILY PSYCHOTHERAPY; the quarterly journal of case studies, treatment reports, and strategies in clinical practice. see *PSYCHOLOGY*

616.8 150 301.1 UK ISSN 0163-4445
RC488.5
JOURNAL OF FAMILY THERAPY. 1979. q. £83($148) (foreign £92) (effective 1996). (Association of Family Therapy) Basil Blackwell Ltd., 108 Cowley Rd., Oxford OX4 1JF, England. TEL 01865-791100. (Subscr. addr.: c/o Marston Book Services, P.O. Box 87, Oxford OX2 0DT, England) Eds. John Carpenter, Bebe Speed. adv.; bk.rev.; index. circ. 2,500. (back issues avail.) **Indexed:** ASSIA, C.I.J.E., Curr.Cont., IMFL, Lang.& Lang.Behav.Abstr., Psychol.Abstr. (1980-), SSCI.
—BLDSC (4983.740000); Faxon; Genuine Article; SWETS; UMI; UnCover. **CCC.**

618 UK ISSN 0958-5184
JOURNAL OF FORENSIC PSYCHIATRY. 1990. 3/yr. £44 (U.S. and Canada $65; rest of world £46) to individuals; institutions £85 (U.S. and Canada $125; rest of world £90). Routledge, 11 New Fetter Ln., London EC4P 4EE, England. TEL 0171-583-9855. FAX 0171-842-2298. TELEX 263398-ROUT-G. E-mail: sample.journals@routledge.com. (Subscr. to: ITPS Ltd., Dept. J, Cheriton House, North Way, Andover, Hants SP10 5BE, England. TEL 01264-342919. FAX 01264-342807) Ed. Paul Bowden. adv.: page £175; trim 115 x 190. circ. 800. **Document type:** academic/scholarly publication.
—BLDSC (4984.597000). **CCC.**
Description: Forum for professionals working with the legal aspects of psychiatry and psychology.

616.8 306.4 US ISSN 1050-5350
RC569.5.G35 CODEN: JGSTEM
JOURNAL OF GAMBLING STUDIES. 1985. q. $215 (foreign $250) (effective 1995). (National Council on Problem Gambling) Human Sciences Press, Inc. (Subsidiary of: Plenum Publishing Corp.), 233 Spring St., New York, NY 10013-1578. TEL 212-620-8000. FAX 212-463-0742. TELEX 23-421139. Ed. Henry R. Lesieur. adv. (reprint service avail. from UMI) **Indexed:** Hospit.Ind., IMFL, Psychol.Abstr. (1985-), Soc.Work Res.& Abstr. **Document type:** academic/scholarly publication.
—BLDSC (4987.180000); UMI; UnCover. **CCC.**
Formerly: Journal of Gambling Behavior (ISSN 0742-0714)
Description: Covers social and pathological gambling research by professionals in all disciplines, including law, psychiatry, sociology, history, and counseling.
Refereed Serial

MEDICAL SCIENCES — PSYCHIATRY AND NEUROLOGY 4557

JOURNAL OF GAY & LESBIAN PSYCHOTHERAPY. see *HOMOSEXUALITY*

616.89 US ISSN 0022-1414
RC451.4.A5 CODEN: JGPSBZ
JOURNAL OF GERIATRIC PSYCHIATRY. 1967. s-a. $51.50 to individuals (foreign $90); institutions $73.50 (foreign $118.50). (Boston Society for Gerontologic Psychiatry, Inc.) International Universities Press, Inc., 59 Boston Post Rd., Box 1524, Madison, CT 06443-1524. TEL 203-245-4000. FAX 203-245-0775. Eds. Drs. David Blau, Ralph J. Kahana. bk.rev. (back issues avail.) **Indexed:** Biol.Abstr., CINAHL, CLOA, Curr.Cont., Excerp.Med., IMFL, Ind.Med., Mid.East: Abstr.& Ind., Psychol.Abstr. (1973-), Sage Fam.Stud.Abstr., SSCI. **Document type:** academic/scholarly publication.
—BLDSC (4995.080000); EMDOCS; Faxon; Genuine Article; SWETS; UnCover.
   Description: Presents current ideas and recent findings in the field of geriatric psychiatry. Also contains articles on Alzheimer's Disease.
   Refereed Serial

JOURNAL OF GERIATRIC PSYCHIATRY AND NEUROLOGY; an interdisciplinary forum for clinicians and scientists. see *GERONTOLOGY AND GERIATRICS*

JOURNAL OF INTEGRATIVE AND ECLECTIC PSYCHOTHERAPY. see *PSYCHOLOGY*

157.8 616.8 UK ISSN 0964-2633
RC321 CODEN: JIDREN
JOURNAL OF INTELLECTUAL DISABILITY RESEARCH. 1957. bi-m. £48 to individuals in Europe; elsewhere £53($85); institutions in Europe £158; elsewhere £174($280) (effective 1996). (Royal Society for Mentally Handicapped Children & Adults) Blackwell Science Ltd., Osney Mead, Oxford OX2 0EL, England. TEL 01865-240201. FAX 01865-721205. TELEX 83355 MEDBOK G. Ed. Dr. W.I. Fraser. adv.; bk.rev.; abstr.; bibl.; charts; illus.; index. circ. 1,000. (also avail. in microform from UMI; back issues avail.: reprint service avail. from SWZ,UMI) **Indexed:** Adol.Ment.Hlth.Abstr., ASCA, ASSIA, Bibl.Dev.Med.& Child Neur., Biol.Abstr., Br.Educ.Ind., C.I.J.E., Chem.Abstr., Child Devel.Abstr., Curr.Adv.Ecol.Sci., Curr.Cont., Dent.Ind., Except.Child.Educ.Abstr., Excerp.Med., Ind.Med., Ind.Sci.Rev., Lang.& Lang.Behav.Abstr., Mid.East: Abstr.& Ind., Nutr.Abstr., Psychol.Abstr. (1960-), Sci.Cit.Ind., Sp.Ed.Needs Abstr., SSCI. **Document type:** academic/scholarly publication.
—BLDSC (5007.538440); Faxon; Genuine Article; SWETS; UMI; UnCover. **CCC.**
   Formerly (until 1991): Journal of Mental Deficiency Research (ISSN 0022-264X)
   Refereed Serial

JOURNAL OF INTERPROFESSIONAL CARE. see *MEDICAL SCIENCES*

616.8 UK ISSN 0963-8237
JOURNAL OF MENTAL HEALTH. Online edition (ISSN 1360-0567) 1992. 5/yr. £56 to individuals; institutions £188 (effective 1996). Carfax Publishing Co., P.O. Box 25, Abingdon, Oxon. OX14 3UE, England. TEL 01235-555335. FAX 01235-553559. (Subscr. in N. America to: Carfax Publishing Co., 875-81 Massachusetts Ave., Cambridge, MA 02139) Ed. Ian Hughes. (also avail. in microfiche; back issues avail.) **Indexed:** Excerp.Med. (1995-), Psychol.Abstr. (1992-). **Document type:** academic/scholarly publication.
●Also available online.
—BLDSC (5017.670000); UMI. **CCC.**
   Description: Presents papers of direct relevance to clinical practice including all aspects of mental health work, elderly care, and addiction. Includes topics concerning work with offenders, learning difficulties, psychiatric rehabilitation, and primary care.
   Refereed Serial

616.8 US ISSN 0895-8696
QP356.2 CODEN: JMNEES
JOURNAL OF MOLECULAR NEUROSCIENCE. 1989. 4/yr. $195 (foreign $220) (effective 1996). Humana Press Inc., 999 Riverview Dr., Ste. 208, Totowa, NJ 07512. TEL 201-256-1699. FAX 201-256-8341. (Dist. in Japan by: Maruzen Co. Ltd., Journals Div., P.O. Box 5050, Tokyo 100-31, Japan. TEL 03-32758591. FAX 03-32781937) Ed. Colin J. Barnstable. bk.rev.; illus.; index. **Document type:** academic/scholarly publication.
—BLDSC (5020.717000); CASDDS; Genuine Article; SWETS. **CCC.**
   Description: Covers a broad rangeof subjects for molecular studies of neural genes through actions of the gene products to diseases caused by defects in particular genes.
   Refereed Serial

616.8 US ISSN 0022-3018
RC321 CODEN: JNMDAN
JOURNAL OF NERVOUS AND MENTAL DISEASE; an educational journal of neuropsychiatry. 1874. m. $98 to individuals; institutions $175 (effective 1995). Williams & Wilkins, 428 E. Preston St., Baltimore, MD 21202. TEL 410-528-4000; 800-638-6423. FAX 410-528-4312. Ed. Eugene B. Brody. adv.; bk.rev.; bibl.; illus.; index. circ. 2,350. (also avail. in microfilm from WWS) **Indexed:** Abstr.Crim.& Pen., Abstr.Health Care Manage.Stud., AIM, ASSIA, Biol.Abstr., Biotech.Abstr., Chem.Abstr., Chic.Per.Ind., Child Devel.Abstr., Curr.Adv.Ecol.Sci., Curr.Cont., Curr.Lit.Fam.Plan., Dent.Ind., Dok.Arbeitsmed., Except.Child.Educ.Abstr., Excerp.Med., I.P.A., Ind.Med., Ind.Sci.Rev., INIS Atomind., Int.Nurs.Ind., M.L.A., Nutr.Abstr., Psychol.Abstr. (1929-), Psycscan C.P., Risk Abstr., SSCI. **Document type:** academic/scholarly publication.
—BLDSC (5021.400000); EMDOCS; Faxon; Genuine Article; SWETS; UnCover. **CCC.**
   Description: Publishes studies in the social, behavioral and neurological sciences relevant to clinical psychiatry.
   Refereed Serial

616.8 AU ISSN 0303-6995
CODEN: JNTSD4
JOURNAL OF NEURAL TRANSMISSION. SUPPLEMENT. no.11, 1974. irreg., no.33, 1991. Springer-Verlag, Sachsenplatz 4-6, Postfach 89, A-1201 Vienna, Austria. TEL 0222-3302415. FAX 0222-3302426. (N. American subscr. to: Journal Fulfillment Services, Box 2485, Secaucus, NJ 07096-2491. TEL 800-777-4643. FAX 201-348-4505) (also avail. in microform from UMI; reprint service avail. from ISI) **Indexed:** Chem.Abstr., Excerp.Med. (1992-), Ind.Med. **Document type:** academic/scholarly publication.
—BLDSC (5021.425000); ADONIS; CASDDS; Faxon; SWETS; UMI; UnCover. **CCC.**
   Formerly: Journal of Neuro-Visceral Relations. Supplement (ISSN 0075-4323); Continues: Acta Neurovegetativa. Supplement.

616.8 AU
QP364.5
JOURNAL OF NEURAL TRANSMISSION - BASIC NEUROSCIENCES - NEUROLOGY SECTION - PSYCHIATRY SECTION. (Text in English, French and German) 1950. m. DM.1876($1363) (effective 1996). Springer-Verlag, Sachsenplatz 4-6, Postfach 89, A-1201 Vienna, Austria. TEL 0222-3302415. FAX 0222-3302426. (Subscr. in N. America to: Springer-Verlag New York, Inc., 44 Hartz Way, Secaucus, NJ 07096-2491. TEL 201-348-4033. FAX 201-348-4505) Ed. A. Carlsson. adv.; charts; illus.; index. (also avail. in microform from UMI; reprint service avail. from ISI) **Indexed:** Biol.Abstr., Biotech.Abstr., Chem.Abstr., Curr.Adv.Ecol.Sci., Curr.Cont., Dairy Sci.Abstr., Excerp.Med., Ind.Med., Ind.Sci.Rev., INIS Atomind., Sport Fish.Abstr., Wild.Rev., Zoo.Rec. **Document type:** academic/scholarly publication.
—BLDSC (5021.421000); ADONIS; CASDDS; Faxon; Genuine Article; SWETS; UMI; UnCover. **CCC.**
   Formed by the merger of: Journal of Neural Transmission. General Section (ISSN 0300-9564) & Journal of Neural Transmission. Parkinson's Disease and Dementia Section (ISSN 0936-3076); Formerly: Journal of Neuro-Visceral Relations (ISSN 0022-3026)

616.8 UK ISSN 0792-8483
JOURNAL OF NEURAL TRANSPLANTATION & PLASTICITY. q. $270 (effective 1996). Freund Publishing House Ltd., Ste. 500, Chesham House, 150 Regent St., London W1R 5FA, England. (And: P.O. Box 35010, Tel Aviv, Israel. TEL 972-2-5628540. FAX 972-3-5628538) Ed. W.J. Freed. **Indexed:** Excerp.Med., Psychol.Abstr. **Document type:** academic/scholarly publication.
—BLDSC (5021.435000).
   Formerly (until 1991): Journal of Neural Transplantation.

616.8 US ISSN 1069-7438
▼**JOURNAL OF NEURO-AIDS.** Announced for publication in 1996. q. $75 (foreign $105) (effective 1996). Haworth Press, Inc., 10 Alice St., Binghamton, NY 13904. TEL 607-722-5857; 800-342-9678. FAX 609-722-1424.
—Haworth.
   Refereed Serial

JOURNAL OF NEURO-OPHTHALMOLOGY. see *MEDICAL SCIENCES — Ophthalmology And Optometry*

JOURNAL OF NEUROBIOLOGY; an international journal. see *BIOLOGY — Physiology*

JOURNAL OF NEUROCHEMISTRY. see *BIOLOGY — Biological Chemistry*

616.8 616.4 UK ISSN 0953-8194
CODEN: JOUNE2
JOURNAL OF NEUROENDOCRINOLOGY. 1989. m. £396 in Europe; elsewhere £435($699) (effective 1996). Blackwell Science Ltd., Osney Mead, Oxford OX2 0EL, England. TEL 01865-206206. FAX 01865-206219. TELEX 83355 MEDBOK G. Ed. Stafford Lightman. adv.; bk.rev.; bibl.; illus.; index. circ. 450. (also avail. in microform from UMI; back issues avail.) **Indexed:** Excerp.Med., Ind.Med. (1993-). **Document type:** academic/scholarly publication.
—BLDSC (5021.543000); CASDDS; Faxon; Genuine Article; SWETS; UMI; UnCover. **CCC.**
   Description: Integrates the fields of endocrinology and neuroscience. Covers nonvertebrate, vertebrate and clinical endocrinology.
   Refereed Serial

616.8 US ISSN 0167-7063
QP356.22 CODEN: JLNEDK
JOURNAL OF NEUROGENETICS. 1983-1987. 8/yr. (in 2 vols., 4 nos./vol.). 131 ECU per vol. (effective 1996). Harwood Academic Publishers, c/o International Publishers Distributor, 820 Town Center Dr., Langhorne, PA 19047. TEL 215-750-2642. FAX 215-750-6343. (Subscr. to: International Publishers Distributor, PO Box 90, Reading, Berkshire, RG1 8JL England. TEL 44-173-456-8316) Ed. Jeffrey C. Hall. (also avail. in microform) **Indexed:** Chem.Abstr., Curr.Adv.Cell & Devel.Biol., Curr.Adv.Ecol.Sci., Curr.Adv.Genetics & Molec.Biol., Excerp.Med. **Document type:** academic/scholarly publication.
—BLDSC (5021.545000); CASDDS; Faxon; UnCover. **CCC.**
   Refereed Serial

616.8 615.842 US ISSN 1051-2284
CODEN: JNERET
JOURNAL OF NEUROIMAGING. 1991. q. $131 to individuals (foreign $169); institutions $309 (foreign $252); residents $65 (foreign $99) (effective Nov. 1994). (American Society of Neuroimaging) Little, Brown and Company, Medical Journals, 34 Beacon St., Boston, MA 02108. TEL 617-859-5500. FAX 617-859-0629. Ed. Dr. Leon Prockop. adv.; B&W page $645; trim 8 1/4 × 11. bk.rev.; abstr.; charts; illus.; stat.; index. circ. 1,819. (also avail. in microform from UMI; reprint service avail. from UMI; back issues avail.) **Indexed:** Excerp.Med. (1992-), Ind.Med. (1993-). **Document type:** academic/scholarly publication.
—BLDSC (5021.548000); Genuine Article; SWETS; UMI. **CCC.**
   Description: Includes coverage of MRI, CT, SPECT, PET, neurosonology, transcranial doppler, and carotid ultrasound, for specialists who rely on neuroimaging.
   Refereed Serial

MEDICAL SCIENCES — PSYCHIATRY AND NEUROLOGY

616.8 616.97 NE ISSN 0165-5728
CODEN: JNRIDW
JOURNAL OF NEUROIMMUNOLOGY. (Text in English) 1981. 16/yr. fl.4024($2454) (effective 1996). (International Society for Neuroimmunology) Elsevier Science B.V., P.O. Box 211, 1000 AE Amsterdam, Netherlands. TEL 31-20-4853911. FAX 31-20-4853598. TELEX 18582 ESPA NL. E-mail: nlinfo-f@elsevier.nl; usinfo-f@elsevier.com; forinfo-kyf04035@niftyserve.or.jp; Site addr.: http://www.elsevier.nl/. (Subscr. in U.S. and Canada to: Elsevier Science Inc., Box 882, Madison Sq. Sta., New York, NY 10159. TEL 212-989-5800. FAX 212-633-3990) Ed. Cedric S. Raine. adv.; charts; illus. (also avail. in microform from UMI; back issues avail.; reprint service avail. from ISI,SWZ) **Indexed:** Biol.Abstr., Chem.Abstr., Curr.Adv.Cell & Devel.Biol., Curr.Adv.Ecol.Sci., Curr.Adv.Genetics & Molec.Biol., Curr.Cont., Excerp.Med., Ind.Med., Ind.Sci.Rev., Protozool.Abstr., Psychol.Abstr. (1981-). **Document type:** academic/scholarly publication.
—BLDSC (5021.550000); CASDDS; Faxon; Genuine Article; SWETS. **CCC.**
Description: Publishes both basic research and clinical problems in neuroimmunology and related neuroscientific disciplines.
Refereed Serial

616.8 UK ISSN 0911-6044
JOURNAL OF NEUROLINGUISTICS. 1985. q. £193($307) (effective 1996). Elsevier Science Ltd., Pergamon, P.O. Box 800, Kidlington, Oxford OX5 1DX, England. TEL 44-1865-843000. FAX 44-1865-843010.
E-mail: nlinfo-f@elsevier.nl; usinfo-f@elsevier.com; forinfo-kyf04035@niftyserve.or.jp; Site addr.: http://www.elsevier.nl/. (Subscr. in U.S. and Canada to: Elsevier Science, 660 White Plains Rd., Tarrytown, NY 10591-5153. TEL 914-524-9200. FAX 914-333-2444) Ed. John Marshall. (also avail. in microfilm from UMI; back issues avail.) **Indexed:** Bibl.Ling., Lang.& Lang.Behav.Abstr. (1985-), Ling.Abstr. **Document type:** academic/scholarly publication.
—BLDSC (5021.553000); Genuine Article; SWETS; UMI. **CCC.**
Refereed Serial

616.8 US ISSN 0888-4390
JOURNAL OF NEUROLOGIC REHABILITATION. 1987. q. $95 to individuals (foreign $115); institutions and libraries $135 (foreign $155). Demos Publications, Inc., 386 Park Ave. S., Ste. 201, New York, NY 10016-8804. TEL 212-683-0072. FAX 212-683-0118. Ed. Fletcher McDowell. **Indexed:** Psychol.Abstr. (1988-). **Document type:** academic/scholarly publication.
—BLDSC (5021.553500); SWETS; UnCover.

616.8 GW ISSN 0340-5354
CODEN: JNRYA9
JOURNAL OF NEUROLOGY/ZEITSCHRIFT FUER NEUROLOGIE. (Supplement avail. (ISSN 0939-1517) (Text in English) 1891. 10/yr. DM.1698($1234) (effective 1996). (European Neurological Society) Springer-Verlag, Heidelberger Platz 3, 14197 Berlin, Germany. TEL 030-8207-0. FAX 030-8214091. E-mail: orders@springer.de. (Subscr. in N. America to: Springer-Verlag New York, Inc., 44 Hartz Way, Secaucus, NJ 07096-2491. TEL 201-348-4033. FAX 201-348-4505) (Co-sponsor: Deutsche Gesellschaft fuer Neurochirurgie) Eds. K. Poeck, A. Compston. adv.; bibl.; charts; illus.; index. (also avail. in microform from UMI; back issues avail.) reprint service avail. from ISI) **Indexed:** ASCA, Biol.Abstr., Chem.Abstr., Curr.Adv.Cancer Res., Curr.Cont., Dent.Ind., Excerp.Med., Ind.Med., INIS Atomind. **Document type:** academic/scholarly publication.
—BLDSC (5021.584000); CASDDS; Faxon; Genuine Article; SWETS; UMI; UnCover. **CCC.**
Former titles: Zeitschrift fuer Neurologie (ISSN 0012-1037); Deutsche Zeitschrift fuer Nervenheilkunde.
Description: Original investigations in clinical neurology, and related basic research.

616.8 GW ISSN 0939-1517
CODEN: JNSUE
JOURNAL OF NEUROLOGY. SUPPLEMENT. irreg. Springer-Verlag, Heidelberger Platz 3, 14197 Berlin, Germany. TEL 030-8207-0. FAX 030-8214091. **Indexed:** Excerp.Med. (1992-). **Document type:** monographic series.

616.8 UK ISSN 0022-3050
RC321 CODEN: JNNPAV
JOURNAL OF NEUROLOGY, NEUROSURGERY AND PSYCHIATRY. 1920. m. £187($324) (subscr. includes Society of British Neurological Surgeons & the Association of British Neurologists proceedings). B M J Publishing Group, B.M.A. House, Tavistock Sq., London WC1H 9JR, England. TEL 0171-383-6270. FAX 0171-383-6402. (N. American subscr. to: Box 480, Franklin, MA 02038. TEL 800-2-FON-BMJ. FAX 800-2-FAX-BMJ) Ed. R.A.C. Hughes. adv. contact: Sheila Rowe. bk.rev.; abstr.; bibl.; illus.; index. (also avail. in microform from UMI; reprint service avail. from UMI) **Indexed:** ASCA, Behav.Med.Abstr., Bibl.Dev.Med.& Child Neur., Biol.Abstr., Chem.Abstr., Curr.Adv.Ecol.Sci., Curr.Cont., Dent.Ind., Diab.Cont., Dok.Arbeitsmed., Excerp.Med., Ind.Med., Ind.Sci.Rev., INIS Atomind., Nutr.Abstr., Protozool.Abstr., Psychol.Abstr. (1950-), Rev.Med.& Vet.Mycol., Risk Abstr. **Document type:** academic/scholarly publication.
●Also available online. Vendor(s): Ovid Technologies.
—BLDSC (5021.600000); CASDDS; EMDOCS; Faxon; Genuine Article; SWETS; UMI; UnCover. **CCC.**
Description: Focuses on clinical neurology, neurosurgery, neuropsychology, neuropsychiatry, and closely related experimental work.
Refereed Serial

616.8 US ISSN 0022-3069
RC321 CODEN: JNENAD
JOURNAL OF NEUROPATHOLOGY AND EXPERIMENTAL NEUROLOGY. 1942. bi-m. $60 to individuals (foreign $72); institutions $80 (foreign $92). American Association of Neuropathologists, Inc., c/o Dr. Michael N. Hart, Ed., Division of Neuropathology, University of Iowa, College of Medicine, Rm. 148A ML, Iowa City, IA 52242-1181. TEL 319-335-8273. FAX 319-335-6510. adv.; bk.rev.; abstr.; bibl.; charts; illus.; index, cum.index: vol. 1-15 (1942-1956); vol. 16-25 (1957-1966). circ. 1,800. (also avail. in microform from UMI; reprint service avail. from UMI) **Indexed:** Bibl.Dev.Med.& Child Neur., Biol.Abstr., Chem.Abstr., Curr.Adv.Cell & Devel.Biol., Curr.Adv.Ecol.Sci., Curr.Cont., Excerp.Med., Ind.Med., Ind.Sci.Rev., Ind.Vet., INIS Atomind., Nutr.Abstr., Poult.Abstr., Protozool.Abstr., Vet.Bull. **Document type:** academic/scholarly publication.
—BLDSC (5021.700000); CASDDS; EMDOCS; Faxon; Genuine Article; SWETS; UMI; UnCover. **CCC.**
Refereed Serial

JOURNAL OF NEUROPHYSIOLOGY. see *BIOLOGY — Physiology*

616.8 US ISSN 0895-0172
RC321 CODEN: JNCNE7
JOURNAL OF NEUROPSYCHIATRY AND CLINICAL NEUROSCIENCES. (Supplement avail.) 1989. q. $135 (foreign $150) (effective 1996). (American Neuropsychiatric Association) American Psychiatric Press, Inc., Journals Division, 1400 K St. N.W., Ste., 1101, Washington, DC 20005. TEL 202-682-6240. FAX 202-682-6341. (UK addr.: 17 Belgrave Sq., London SW1X 8PG, England) Ed. Dr. Stuart Yudofsky. adv.; bk.rev.; abstr.; bibl.; charts; illus.; stat.; index. circ. 1,700. (also avail. in microform from UMI) **Indexed:** Ind.Med. (1992-), Psychol.Abstr. (1989-), Soc.Work Res.& Abstr. **Document type:** consumer publication.
—BLDSC (5022.040000); Genuine Article; SWETS; UMI; UnCover.
Description: Devoted to the relationships between the original research in psychiatry and neurology.
Refereed Serial

616.8 US ISSN 0270-6474
QP351 CODEN: JNRSDS
JOURNAL OF NEUROSCIENCE. 1981. m. $880 (foreign $995) (effective 1995). (Society for Neuroscience) Oxford University Press, Journals, 2001 Evans Rd., Cary, NC 27513. TEL 919-677-0977; 800-852-7323. FAX 919-677-1714. E-mail: jnlorders@oup-usa.org. (Subscr. outside N. America to: Oxford University Press, Journals, Walton St., Oxford OX2 6DP, England. TEL 44-1865-56767. FAX 44-1865-267773) Ed. David C. Van Essen. circ. 4,100. (also avail. in microfilm from WWS; microfiche from WWS; back issues avail.) **Indexed:** Chem.Abstr., Comput.Abstr., Curr.Adv.Biochem., Curr.Adv.Cell & Devel.Biol., Curr.Adv.Ecol.Sci., Curr.Adv.Genetics & Molec.Biol., Curr.Cont., Curr.Ref.Fish Res., Dent.Ind., Excerp.Med., Ind.Med., Ind.Sci.Rev., Psychol.Abstr. (1993-). **Document type:** academic/scholarly publication.
—BLDSC (5022.075000); CASDDS; Faxon; Genuine Article; SWETS; UMI; UnCover. **CCC.**
Refereed Serial

616.8 NE ISSN 0165-0270
CODEN: JNMEDT
JOURNAL OF NEUROSCIENCE METHODS. (Text in English) 1979. 14/yr. fl.3360($2049) (effective 1996). Elsevier Science B.V., P.O. Box 211, 1000 AE Amsterdam, Netherlands. TEL 31-20-4853911. FAX 31-20-4853598. TELEX 18582 ESPA NL. E-mail: nlinfo-f@elsevier.nl; usinfo-f@elsevier.com; forinfo-kyf04035@niftyserve.or.jp; Site addr.: http://www.elsevier.nl/. (Subscr. in U.S. and Canada to: Elsevier Science Inc., Box 882, Madison Sq. Sta., New York, NY 10159. TEL 212-989-5800. FAX 212-633-3990) Ed. J.S. Kelly. adv.; charts; abstr.; bibl.; illus. (also avail. in microform from UMI; back issues avail.; reprint service avail. from ISI) **Indexed:** Biol.Abstr., Chem.Abstr., Curr.Adv.Cell & Devel.Biol., Curr.Adv.Ecol.Sci., Curr.Cont., Excerp.Med., Ind.Med., Ind.Sci.Rev., INSPEC, Mass Spectr.Bull. **Document type:** academic/scholarly publication.
—BLDSC (5022.080000); CASDDS; Faxon; Genuine Article; SWETS; UnCover. **CCC.**
Description: Publishes research papers and critical reviews addressing new methods or significant developments of recognized methods.
Refereed Serial

616.8 US ISSN 0360-4012
QP351 CODEN: JNREDK
JOURNAL OF NEUROSCIENCE RESEARCH. 1975. 24/yr. $2904 (foreign $3276) (effective 1996). John Wiley & Sons, Inc., Journals, 605 Third Ave., New York, NY 10158. TEL 212-850-6645. FAX 212-850-6021. TELEX 12-7063. E-mail: SUBINFO@JWILEY.COM. (Subscr. outside the Americas to: John Wiley & Sons Ltd., Baffins Ln., Chichester, W. Sussex PO19 1UD, England. TEL 44-1243-779777. FAX 44-1243-776128) Ed. Bernard Haber. adv.; bk.rev.; charts; illus.; index. (also avail. in microform from UMI; back issues avail.; reprint service avail. from ISI) **Indexed:** Biol.Abstr., Chem.Abstr., Curr.Adv.Ecol.Sci., Curr.Cont., Excerp.Med., Ind.Med., Ind.Sci.Rev., INIS Atomind., Sport Fish.Abstr., Wild.Rev., Zoo.Rec. **Document type:** academic/scholarly publication.
—BLDSC (5022.090000); CASDDS; Faxon; Genuine Article; SWETS; UnCover. **CCC.**
Description: Concerned with basic research reports on molecular, cellular, and subcellular aspects of the neurosciences.
Refereed Serial

616.8 US ISSN 0022-3085
RD1 CODEN: JONSAC
JOURNAL OF NEUROSURGERY. 1944. m. $125. American Association of Neurological Surgeons, 1224 W. Main St., Ste. 450, Charlottesville, VA 22903. TEL 804-924-5503. FAX 804-924-2702. (Subscr. to: Fulco, Box 3000, Denville, NJ 07843. TEL 800-875-2997. FAX 201-627-5872) Ed. Dr. John A. Jane. adv.; bk.rev.; bibl.; charts; illus.; cum.index covering 50 vols. circ. 12,500. (also avail. in microform from UMI,WWS) **Indexed:** AIM, Biol.Abstr., Chem.Abstr., Curr.Adv.Cancer Res., Curr.Cont., Dent.Ind., Excerp.Med., Helminthol.Abstr., Ind.Med., Ind.Sci.Rev., INIS Atomind., Rev.Med.& Vet.Mycol., Rev.Plant Path. **Document type:** academic/scholarly publication.
—BLDSC (5022.100000); CASDDS; EMDOCS; Faxon; Genuine Article; SWETS; UMI; UnCover.
Description: Presents medical articles relating to neurosurgery and allied specialties.
Refereed Serial

JOURNAL OF NEUROSURGICAL SCIENCES. see *MEDICAL SCIENCES — Surgery*

JOURNAL OF NEUROTRAUMA. see *MEDICAL SCIENCES — Orthopedics And Traumatology*

616.8   UK   ISSN 1355-0284
                      CODEN: JNVIFK
▼**JOURNAL OF NEUROVIROLOGY.** 1995. bi-m. £65($99) to individuals; institutions in E.U. £135(elsewhere £145). Stockton Press (Subsidiary of: Macmillan Press Ltd.), Houndsmills, Basingstoke, Hants RG21 2XS, England. TEL 01256-817245. FAX 01256-28339. Ed. R.L. Knobler; Pub. Jayne Marks. adv. contact: Michael Rowley. **Document type:** academic/scholarly publication.
—CASDDS. **CCC.**
   Description: Studies neurotropic viruses and viral infections of the nervous system.

616.8   US   ISSN 0022-3298
RZ460
JOURNAL OF ORGONOMY. 1967. s-a. $40 (foreign $45; air mail $55) (effective 1995). (American College of Orgonomy) Orgonomic Publications, Box 490, Princeton, NJ 08542. TEL 908-821-1144. FAX 908-821-0174. Ed. Dr. Charles Konia; Pub. Dr. Peter Crist. bk.rev.; bibl.; charts; illus.; stat.; index, cum.index: 1967-1992. circ. 2,000. (also avail. in microfilm from UMI; back issues avail.; reprint service avail. from UMI) **Document type:** academic/scholarly publication.
—BLDSC (5027.150000); UMI.
   Description: Devoted to the study of orgone energy functions in living and nonliving nature, based on the discoveries of Wilhelm Reich.
   Refereed Serial

616.89   CN   ISSN 0834-4825
                      CODEN: JORMEI
JOURNAL OF ORTHOMOLECULAR MEDICINE. 1967. q. $85 to individuals (foreign $100); institutions $95 (foreign $110) (effective 1995). Canadian Schizophrenia Foundation, 16 Florence Ave., Toronto, ON M2N 1E9, Canada. TEL 416-733-2117. FAX 416-733-2352. Ed. A. Hoffer. adv.; bk.rev.; bibl.; charts; illus. circ. 1,400. (also avail. in microfilm from UMI; back issues avail.; reprint service avail. from UMI) **Indexed:** Biol.Abstr., Chem.Abstr., Curr.Adv.Biochem., Curr.Cont., Excerp.Med., Mid.East: Abstr.& Ind., Nutr.Abstr., Psychol.Abstr. (1975-), SSCI.
—BLDSC (5027.600000); CASDDS; Faxon; UMI; UnCover.
   Former titles: Journal of Orthomolecular Psychiatry (ISSN 0317-0209); (until 1973): Orthomolecular Psychiatry; (until 1972): Schizophrenia (ISSN 0036-6129); (until 1969): Journal of Schizophrenia (ISSN 0449-3109)

616.8   DK   ISSN 0742-3098
QP188.P55   CODEN: JPRSE9
JOURNAL OF PINEAL RESEARCH. (Text in English) 8/yr. DKK 4500 (effective 1996). Munksgaard International Publishers Ltd., P.O. Box 2148, DK-1016 Copenhagen K, Denmark. TEL 45-33-12-70-30. FAX 45-33-12-70-30. (U.S. addr.: 234 Main Street, Cambridge, MA 02142-9740) Ed. Russel J. Reiter. adv.; charts; illus. circ. 250. (reprint service avail.) **Indexed:** Anim.Breed.Abstr., Biol.Abstr., Chem.Abstr., Curr.Adv.Cancer Res., Curr.Adv.Ecol.Sci., Curr.Cont., Excerp.Med., Ind.Med., Pig News & Info., Poult.Abstr. **Document type:** academic/scholarly publication.
●Also available online.
—BLDSC (5040.329000); CASDDS; Faxon; Genuine Article; SWETS. **CCC.**
   Refereed Serial

JOURNAL OF POLYMORPHOUS PERVERSITY. see *PSYCHOLOGY*

616.8   UK   ISSN 1351-0126
                      CODEN: JPMNE3
▼**JOURNAL OF PSYCHIATRIC AND MENTAL HEALTH NURSING.** 1994. bi-m. £37 to individuals (outside Europe £40.50($60)); institutions £110 (outside Europe £121($177)) (effective 1996). Blackwell Science Ltd., Osney Mead, Oxford OX2 0EL, England. TEL 01865-240201. FAX 01865-721205. TELEX 83355 MEDBOK G. Ed. B. Lemmer. adv.; bk.rev.; bibl.; illus.; index. (also avail. in microfilm from UMI) **Document type:** academic/scholarly publication.
—BLDSC (5043.140000). **CCC.**
   Refereed Serial

616.89   UK   ISSN 0022-3956
RC321   CODEN: JPYRA3
JOURNAL OF PSYCHIATRIC RESEARCH. 1961. bi-m. £299($476) (effective 1996). Elsevier Science Ltd., Pergamon, P.O. Box 800, Kidlington, Oxford OX5 1DX, England. TEL 44-1865-843000. FAX 44-1865-843010. (Subscr. in U.S. and Canada to: Elsevier Science, 660 White Plains Rd., Tarrytown, NY 10591-5153. TEL 914-524-9200. FAX 914-333-2444) Eds. Merton Sandler, Joseph J. Schildkraut. adv.: B&W page $550, color page $1350. bk.rev.; charts; illus.; index. circ. 1,250. (also avail. in microfilm from UMI; back issues avail.) **Indexed:** Biol.Abstr., Chem.Abstr., Curr.Adv.Ecol.Sci., Curr.Cont., Dent.Ind., Excerp.Med., Hosp.Lit.Ind., Ind.Med., Ind.Sci.Rev., Lang.& Lang.Behav.Abstr., Mid.East: Abstr.& Ind., Psychol.Abstr. (1961-), Sci.Cit.Ind., SSCI. **Document type:** academic/scholarly publication.
—BLDSC (5043.250000); CASDDS; EMDOCS; Faxon; Genuine Article; SWETS; UMI; UnCover. **CCC.**
   Description: Covers the latest developments in psychiatry and cognate disciplines.
   Refereed Serial

JOURNAL OF PSYCHIATRY AND LAW. see *LAW*

616.8   CN   ISSN 1180-4882
RC321   CODEN: JPNEEF
JOURNAL OF PSYCHIATRY AND NEUROSCIENCE. (Text in English, French) 1976. 5/yr. Can.$71 to individuals; institutions Can.$90. Canadian Psychiatric Association, 200 - 237 Argyle Ave., Ottawa, ON K2P 1B8, Canada. TEL 613-234-2815. FAX 613-234-9857. Ed. Dr. Y.D. Lapierre. adv.: B&W page Can.$840, color page Can.$1790; trim 8 1/8 x 10 7/8; adv. contact: Kim Arial. bk.rev.; index. circ. 2,434. **Indexed:** Biol.Abstr., Child Devel.Abstr., Curr.Cont., Excerp.Med., Ind.Med., Psychol.Abstr. (1976-), Sociol.Abstr. **Document type:** academic/scholarly publication.
—BLDSC (5043.261000); Faxon; Genuine Article; UnCover. **CCC.**
   Formerly: Psychiatric Journal of the University of Ottawa (ISSN 0702-8466)
   Description: Publishes original research articles and review papers in clinical psychiatry and neuroscience which relate to major psychiatric disorders, particularly schizophrenia, affective disorders and neurodegenerative diseases.

JOURNAL OF PSYCHOACTIVE DRUGS; a multidisciplinary forum. see *DRUG ABUSE AND ALCOHOLISM*

JOURNAL OF PSYCHOPHYSIOLOGY. see *PSYCHOLOGY*

JOURNAL OF PSYCHOSOMATIC OBSTETRICS AND GYNAECOLOGY. see *MEDICAL SCIENCES — Obstetrics And Gynecology*

616.08   UK   ISSN 0022-3999
RC52   CODEN: JPCRAT
JOURNAL OF PSYCHOSOMATIC RESEARCH. 1956. m. $885 to institutions (effective 1996). Elsevier Science Ltd., Pergamon, P.O. Box 800, Kidlington, Oxford OX5 1DX, England. TEL 44-1865-843000. FAX 44-1865-843010.
E-mail: nlinfo-f@elsevier.nl; usinfo-f@elsevier.com; forinfo-kyf04035@niftyserve.or.jp; Site addr.: http://www.elsevier.nl/. (Subscr. in U.S. and Canada to: Elsevier Science, 660 White Plains Rd., Tarrytown, NY 10591-5153. TEL 914-524-9200. FAX 914-333-2444) Ed. Geoffrey Lloyd. adv.: B&W page $550, color page $1350. bk.rev.; bibl.; charts; index. circ. 1,600. (also avail. in microfilm from UMI) **Indexed:** Adol.Ment.Hlth.Abstr., ASSIA, Behav.Med.Abstr., Bibl.Dev.Med.& Child Neur., Biol.Abstr., Chem.Abstr., Curr.Adv.Ecol.Sci., Curr.Cont., Dent.Ind., Dok.Arbeitsmed., Excerp.Med., Ind.Med., Ind.Sci.Rev., Mid.East: Abstr.& Ind., Nutr.Abstr., Psychol.Abstr. (1956-), Risk Abstr., SSCI, Stud.Wom.Abstr. **Document type:** academic/scholarly publication.
—BLDSC (5043.480000); CASDDS; EMDOCS; Faxon; Genuine Article; SWETS; UMI; UnCover. **CCC.**
   Description: Reflects current research in the psychosomatic approach from both clinical and experimental perspectives, including scientific examination of theoretical topics.
   Refereed Serial

616.891   US   ISSN 1053-0479
RC475   CODEN: JPINEH
JOURNAL OF PSYCHOTHERAPY INTEGRATION. 1991. q. $145 (foreign $170) (effective 1996). Plenum Publishing Corp., 233 Spring St., New York, NY 10013-1578. TEL 212-620-8000. FAX 212-463-0742. TELEX 23-421139. Ed. Hal Arkowitz. (back issues avail.) **Indexed:** Psychol.Abstr. (1991-). **Document type:** academic/scholarly publication.
—BLDSC (5043.483300); Faxon; Genuine Article. **CCC.**
   Refereed Serial

616.8   US   ISSN 1055-050X
RC475   CODEN: JPYRE7
JOURNAL OF PSYCHOTHERAPY PRACTICE AND RESEARCH. 1992. q. $135 (foreign $150) (effective 1996). American Psychiatric Press, Inc., Journals Division, 1400 K St., N.W., Ste. 1101, Washington, DC 20005. TEL 202-682-6240. FAX 202-789-6341. (UK addr.: 17 Belgrave Sq., London SW1X 8PG, England) Ed. Dr. Jerald Kay. adv.; bk.rev.; abstr.; bibl.; charts; illus.; stat.; index. (also avail. in microfilm from UMI) **Indexed:** Excerp.Med. (1994-), Psychol.Abstr. (1992-). **Document type:** academic/scholarly publication.
—BLDSC (5043.483400); UMI.
   Description: Aims to advance the professional understanding of human behavior and to enhance the psychotherapeutic treatment of mental disorders.

616.8 612.3   US   ISSN 0887-8250
TX546   CODEN: JSSDEO
JOURNAL OF SENSORY STUDIES. 1986. q. $120. Food & Nutrition Press, Inc., 2 Corporate Dr., Box 374, Trumbull, CT 06611. TEL 203-261-8587. FAX 203-261-9724. Ed. M.C. Gacula, Jr. **Indexed:** Dairy Sci.Abstr. **Document type:** academic/scholarly publication.
—BLDSC (5063.600000); CASDDS; Faxon; SWETS; UnCover.
   Description: Promotes the technical and practical advancement of sensory science, publishing a broad spectrum of papers, including observational and experimental studies in the application of sensory evaluation to the food, medical, agricultural, biological, pharmaceutical, cosmetic, consumer, and materials industries.

JOURNAL OF SPINAL CORD MEDICINE. see *MEDICAL SCIENCES — Physical Medicine And Rehabilitation*

JOURNAL OF SYSTEMIC THERAPIES. see *PSYCHOLOGY*

616.8   NE   ISSN 0165-1838
                      CODEN: JASYDS
JOURNAL OF THE AUTONOMIC NERVOUS SYSTEM. (Text in English) 1979. 18/yr. fl.2754($1679) (effective 1996). Elsevier Science B.V., P.O. Box 211, 1000 AE Amsterdam, Netherlands. TEL 31-20-4853911. FAX 31-20-4853598. TELEX 18582 ESPA NL. E-mail: nlinfo-f@elsevier.nl; usinfo-f@elsevier.com; forinfo-kyf04035@niftyserve.or.jp; Site addr.: http://www.elsevier.nl/. (Subscr. in U.S. and Canada to: Elsevier Science Inc., Box 882, Madison Sq. Sta., New York, NY 10159. TEL 212-989-5800. FAX 212-633-3990) Ed. G. Burnstock. adv.; bk.rev.; charts; illus. (also avail. in microfilm from UMI; back issues avail.; reprint service avail. from ISI,SWZ) **Indexed:** Biol.Abstr., Chem.Abstr., Curr.Cont., Dent.Ind., Excerp.Med., Ind.Med., Ind.Sci.Rev. **Document type:** academic/scholarly publication.
—BLDSC (4949.750000); CASDDS; Faxon; Genuine Article; SWETS; UnCover. **CCC.**
   Description: Presents papers that deal with any aspect of the autonomic nervous system, including structure, physiology, pharmacology, biochemistry, development, evolution, ageing, behavioural aspects, integrative role and influence on emotional and physical states of the body.
   Refereed Serial

616.8   UK   ISSN 0964-704X
JOURNAL OF THE HISTORY OF THE NEUROSCIENCES. 1992. q. £37($74) to individuals; institutions £49($98). Smith-Gordon and Co. Ltd., 16 Gunter Grove, No. 1, London SW10 0UJ, England. TEL 071-351-7042. FAX 071-351-1250. Ed. F. Clifford Rose. **Document type:** academic/scholarly publication.
—BLDSC (5001.050000).

MEDICAL SCIENCES — PSYCHIATRY AND NEUROLOGY

616.8   NE   ISSN 0022-510X
RC321   CODEN: JNSCAG
JOURNAL OF THE NEUROLOGICAL SCIENCES. (Text and summaries in English, French, German, Spanish) 1964. 16/yr. fl.3096($1888) (effective 1996). (World Federation of Neurology) Elsevier Science B.V., P.O. Box 211, 1000 AE Amsterdam, Netherlands. TEL 31-20-4853911. FAX 31-20-4853598. TELEX 18582 ESPA NL. E-mail: nlinfo-f@elsevier.nl; usinfo-f@elsevier.com; forinfo-kyf04035@niftyserve.or.jp; Site addr.: http://www.elsevier.nl/. (Subscr. in U.S. and Canada to: Elsevier Science Inc., Box 882, Madison Sq. Sta., New York, NY 10159-0882. TEL 212-989-5800. FAX 212-633-3990) Ed. J.F. Toole. adv.: bk.rev.; bibl.; charts; illus.; index. (also avail. in microform from UMI; reprint service avail. from ISI,SWZ) **Indexed:** Bibl.Dev.Med.& Child Neur., Biol.Abstr., Chem.Abstr., Curr.Adv.Ecol.Sci., Curr.Cont., Excerp.Med., Helminthol.Abstr., Ind.Med., Ind.Sci.Rev., Ind.Vet., Nutr.Abstr., Psychol.Abstr., Vet.Bull. **Document type:** academic/scholarly publication.
—BLDSC (5021.560000); CASDDS; EMDOCS; Faxon; Genuine Article; SWETS; UnCover. **CCC.**
Description: Provides a medium for the publication of studies on the interface between clinical neurology and the basic sciences.
Refereed Serial

JUNG AT HEART; studies in Jungian psychology by Jungian analysts. see **PSYCHOLOGY**

616.8 617   JA   ISSN 0918-1172
KAGAWA NO SHINKEI GEKA DANWAKAI KAISHI/KAGAWA COLLOQUIUM ON NEUROSURGERY. JOURNAL. (Text in Japanese) 1985. a. Kagawa No Shinkei Geka Danwakai, Kagawa Ika Daigaku No Shinkei Gekagaku Kyoshitsu, 1750-1, Ikedo, Mikicho, Kida-gun, Kagawa-ken 761-07, Japan.

616.8   JA   ISSN 0288-9617
KANAGAWA-KEN SEISHIN IGAKKAISHI/KANAGAWA ASSOCIATION OF PSYCHIATRY. JOURNAL. (Text in Japanese) 1959. a. 3000 Yen. Kanagawa Association of Psychiatry, c/o Department of Psychiatry, Yokohama City University School of Medicine, 3-9, Fukuura, Kanagawa-ku, Yoakohama 236, Japan. TEL 81-045-787-2667. FAX 81-045-783-2540. Ed. Kenji Kosaka. adv. contact: Eizo Iseki. circ. 2,000. (back issues avail.) **Document type:** academic/scholarly publication.
Refereed Serial

616.8 617   US   ISSN 0886-8018
KEY NEUROLOGY AND NEUROSURGERY. 1985. q. $75 to individuals (foreign $89); institutions $112.50 (foreign $126.50); students $47.25 (foreign $61.25). Mosby - Year Book, Inc. (Subsidiary of: Times Mirror Company), 11830 Westline Industrial Dr., St. Louis, MO 63146. TEL 314-872-8370; 800-325-4177. FAX 314-432-1380. TELEX 44-2402. Ed. Walter G. Bradley.
—**CCC.**
Description: Provides surveys, with commentary, of key medical literature in neurology and neurosurgery.

616.8   JA
KINOTEKI NO SHINKEI GEKA/FUNCTIONAL NEUROSURGERY. (Text in English, Japanese) 1987. a. 5150 Yen. Nihon Teii No Shujutsu Kenkyukai - Japanese Society for Stereotactic and Functional Neurosurgery, Nihon Daigaku Igakubu No Shinkei Geka, 30-1, Oyaguchi Kamicho, Itabashi-ku, Tokyo 173, Japan.

KLINISCHE NEURORADIOLOGIE. see **MEDICAL SCIENCES — Radiology And Nuclear Medicine**

616.853   SZ
KONTAKTE; Zeitung fuer Epilepsie-Betroffene. 1986. 2/yr. 15 SFr. Schweizerische Liga gegen Epilepsie, Feldeggstr. 71, Postfach 1332, CH-8032 Zurich, Switzerland. TEL 01-3835455. FAX 01-3833049. Ed. Angie Hagmann-Albrecht. adv. contact: Esther Hobi-Schaerer. bk.rev. circ. 900. **Document type:** consumer publication.

616.8   KO   ISSN 1015-4817
QP351
KOREAN NEUROPSYCHIATRIC ASSOCIATION. JOURNAL.
Key Title: Taehan Sin'gyong Chongsin Uihak Hoeji. (Text in Korean; summaries in English) 1962. bi-m. free. Korean Neuropsychiatric Association, RN.403 Osung Bd. 13-5, Youido-dong, Yungdungpo-gu, Seoul, S. Korea. TEL 02-786-3355. Ed. Dr. Kwang-lel Kim; Pub. Jae-Ho Seok. adv. **Document type:** academic/scholarly publication.
—BLDSC (4812.340900).
Formerly: Neuro-Psychiatry.

616.89   JA   ISSN 0023-6144
CODEN: KSSIAC
KYUSHU NEURO-PSYCHIATRY/KYUSHU SHINKEI SEISHIN IGAKU. (Text in Japanese; summaries in English) 1954. q. 5000 Yen. Kyushu Association of Neuro-Psychiatry - Kyushu Shinkei Seishin Igaku, c/o Department of Neuro-Psychiatry, Faculty of Medicine, Kyushu University 60, Maidashi, Higashi-ku, Fukuoka 812, Japan. FAX 092-632-3558. Ed. N. Tashiro. adv.: bk.rev.; bibl.; charts; stat.; index; circ. 690 (controlled). (processed; also avail. in microform from UMI) **Indexed:** Chem.Abstr., Psychol.Abstr.
—CASDDS; UMI.

616.8   GW   ISSN 0944-405X
RC423.A1   CODEN: LOINEW
▼**L.O.G.O.S. INTERDISZIPLINAER.** 1994. q. DM.120 (foreign DM.124). Gustav Fischer Verlag, Wollgrasweg 49, 70599 Stuttgart, Germany. TEL 0711-458030. FAX 0711-4580334. TELEX 7111488-FIBUCH. (US subscr. to: VCH Publishers, Inc., 303 N.W. 12th Ave., Deerfield Beach, FL 33442-1788) Ed.Bd. **Document type:** academic/scholarly publication.
—BLDSC (5292.406500).

616.8   UK   ISSN 1357-650X
▼**LATERALITY.** Announced for publication in 1996. q. £25($52.50) to individuals (outside the E.U. £35); institutions £50 (outside the E.U. £60 ($90)) (effective 1996). Lawrence Erlbaum Associates Ltd., 27 Palmyra Mansions, Church Rd., Hove, E. Sussex BN3 2FA, England. TEL 01273-207411. FAX 01273-205613. (Subscr. to: Turpin Distribution Services Ltd., Blackhorse Rd., Letchworth, Herts. SG6 1HN, England. TEL 01462-672555. FAX 01462-480947) **Document type:** academic/scholarly publication.

616.8   IT   ISSN 0023-9097
LAVORO NEUROPSICHIATRICO. (Supplement avail.) (Text in Italian; summaries in English, French, German and Italian) 1947. bi-m. L.8000. Amministrazione Provinciale, Piazza S. Maria della Pieta 5, 00135 Rome, Italy. Ed. Giovanni Bonfiglio. bk.rev.; bibl.; charts; illus.; index. circ. 1,200. **Indexed:** Chem.Abstr., Excerp.Med., Psychol.Abstr.

616.8 155.67   UK   ISSN 0143-7534
LEARNING AND MEMORY. m. £80 (effective 1995). S U B I S, Mansion House, 19 Kingfield Rd., Sheffield S11 9AS, England. TEL 0114-2554433. FAX 0114-2554626. E-mail: admin@sheffac.demon.co.uk. (looseleaf format; back issues avail.) **Document type:** abstracting/indexing.
—**CCC.**
Description: Current awareness service for researchers in clinical and life sciences.

616.8 155.67   US   ISSN 1072-0502
QP406
▼**LEARNING & MEMORY.** 1994. bi-m. $85 to individuals; institutions $190. Cold Spring Harbor Laboratory Press, Publications Department, Box 100, Cold Spring Harbor, NY 11724. TEL 516-367-8492; 800-843-4388. FAX 516-349-1946. Ed. Judy Cuddihy. adv. contact: Deborah Dufton. **Document type:** academic/scholarly publication.
—BLDSC (5179.325895); Genuine Article; SWETS. **CCC.**
Description: Publishes experimental studies in humans and animals on cognition behavior, development, neuropsychology, neurophysiology, biochemistry, cell biology and genetics.

616.858   UK
LEARNING DISABILITIES BULLETIN. q. £21($45) to individuals; institutions £27 ($59). (British Institute of Learning Disabilities) B I L D Publications, Frankfurt Lodge, Clevedon Hall, Victoria Rd., Clevedon, Avon BS21 7SJ, England. TEL 01275-876519. FAX 01275-343096. Ed. Linda Averill. adv. circ. 1,000. **Document type:** academic/scholarly publication, bulletin.
—BLDSC (2415.050000).
Formerly (until 1993): Mental Handicap Bulletin (ISSN 0260-1222)

616.853   IT   ISSN 0394-560X
LEGA ITALIANA CONTRO L'EPILESSIA. 1973. q. L.250000 to non-members (effective 1995). Lega Italiana contro l'Epilessia, Via Fogazzaro 37, 20135 Milan, Italy. TEL 39-2-5468820. FAX 39-2-8910198. Ed. Raffaele Canger. adv.; bk.rev. **Indexed:** Excerp.Med.
—BLDSC (2227.150000).

616.89 340
LEGAL RESOURCES FOR THE MENTALLY DISABLED: A DIRECTORY OF LAWYERS AND OTHER SPECIALISTS. 1982. a. $5. American Bar Association, 1800 M St., N.W., Washington, DC 20036. TEL 202-331-2258. Ed. John Parry. **Document type:** directory.
Formerly: Mental and Developmental Disabilities Directory of Legal Advocates.

616.8   FR   ISSN 0223-9434
LETTRE DU PSYCHIATRE; psychiatrie et medicaments. 1979. 10/yr. 286 F. (foreign 400 F.) (effective 1996). Masson - Periodiques, Villa Laromiguiere, 75005 Paris, France. TEL 1-40-46-62-00. FAX 1-40-46-62-01. Ed. H. Ollat. circ. 600. (also avail. in microform from UMI) **Document type:** bulletin.
—UMI. **CCC.**
Description: Informs on new developments of therapeutics in psychiatry.

616.8   US   ISSN 0103-3212
CODEN: JLBEE
LIGA BRASILEIRA DE EPILEPSIA. q. Liga Brasileira de Epilepsia, Av. Ipiranga 6690, Sala 322, Porto Alegre 90610, Brazil. TEL 51-224-3092. **Indexed:** Excerp.Med.
—EMDOCS.

616.8 610.73   US
LINK (WOODLAND HILLS). 1987. bi-m. free. Amyotrophic Lateral Sclerosis Association, 21021 Ventura Blvd., Ste. 321, Woodland Hills, CA 91364. TEL 818-340-7500. FAX 818-340-2060. Ed.Bd. bk.rev. circ. 80,000. (tabloid format; back issues avail.)

616.8   US
LINKAGE (BALTIMORE). 1991. q. Department of Health and Mental Hygiene, 201 Preston St., Rm. 416A, Baltimore, MD 21201. TEL 410-225-6611. FAX 410-333-5402. Ed. Jean Smith. circ. 11,000. **Document type:** newsletter.
Description: Keeps mental health professionals, consumers and state employees up-to-date on specific mental health issues within the state system and on general mental health issues.

616.89   NE   ISSN 0024-8576
M G V. (Maandblad Geestelijke Volksgezondheid) 1946. 11/yr. fl.83.50 (foreign fl.96.50). Nederlands Centrum Geestelijke Volksgezondheid, Postbus 5103, 3502 JC Utrecht, Netherlands. TEL 31-2154-82211. Ed. A.J. Heerma van Voss. adv.; bk.rev.; index. circ. 7,300. **Document type:** academic/scholarly publication, trade publication.
—BLDSC (5318.930000); SWETS.
Refereed Serial

616.8   II
MADRAS INSTITUTE OF NEUROLOGY. PROCEEDINGS. (Text in English) vol. 2, 1972. 3/yr. $4. Wardha Press, 541 Swami Naichen St., Madras 600002, India. Ed. B. Ramamurthi. bk.rev.; bibl.; index. circ. 1,000. **Indexed:** Excerp.Med. **Document type:** proceedings.

MEDICAL SCIENCES — PSYCHIATRY AND NEUROLOGY

616.8 US ISSN 0301-5602
MAJOR PROBLEMS IN NEUROLOGY. 1973. irreg., vol.26. price varies. W.B. Saunders Co. (Subsidiary of: Harcourt Brace & Company), Curtis Center, 3rd Fl., Independence Sq. W., Philadelphia, PA 19106-3399. TEL 215-238-7800. FAX 215-238-6445. (Orders to: Periodicals Fulfillment, W.B. Saunders Co., 6277 Sea Harbor Dr., 4th Fl., Orlando, FL 32891-4800. TEL 800-654-2452. FAX 800-874-6418) **Document type:** monographic series.
—BLDSC (5353.670000).
Description: Explores clinical issues in treating neurological conditions and disorders.

MANAB MON; a journal depicting the modern trends in psychology, biology, and sociology. see *PSYCHOLOGY*

616.8 US ISSN 0882-3634
MARKER. 1967. q. free. Huntington's Disease Society of America, 140 W. 22nd St., 6th Fl., New York, NY 10011. TEL 212-242-1968. FAX 212-243-2443. Ed. Andrew J. McInnes. bk.rev. circ. 40,000. (back issues avail.)
Formerly: Committee to Combat Huntington's Disease Newsletter (ISSN 0882-3642)
Description: Covers national and local news and events relevant to Huntington's Disease patients and their families. Includes medical and scientific research updates.

MEDICAL HYPNOANALYSIS JOURNAL. see *MEDICAL SCIENCES — Hypnosis*

MEDICAL MALPRACTICE: PSYCHIATRIC CARE. see *LAW — Civil Law*

616.8 US ISSN 1054-4712
MEDICAL PSYCHIATRIC PRACTICE. 1991. irreg. American Psychiatric Press, Inc., Journals Division, 1400 K St., N.W., Ste. 1101, Washington, DC 20005. **Document type:** academic/scholarly publication.
—BLDSC (5531.360000).

618.89 US ISSN 1082-7579
▼**MEDICAL UPDATE FOR PSYCHIATRISTS.** Announced for publication in 1996. bi-m. $136 to institutions (effective 1996). Elsevier Science Inc., 655 Ave. of the Americas, New York, NY 10010. TEL 212-633-3650. FAX 212-633-3764. (Subscr. to: Box 882, Madison Sq. Sta., New York, NY 10159-0882)

616.8 150.5 IT ISSN 0394-1531
MEDICINA E PSICHE/MEDICINE AND MIND; semestrale di psicologia medica e di filosofia della medicina - semi-annual journal of philosophy of medicine and medical psychology. (Text in language of author; summaries in English, Italian) 1983. s-a. L.100000 (Europe L.100000; elsewhere $100) (effective 1994). Centro Italiano Studi di Psicologia Medica, Viale Romagna 51, 20133 Milan, Italy. TEL 02-236-1226. FAX 02-2361226. (Subscr. to: Swets Subscription Service, LACP Dept., Helen de Jongh, PO Box 84, 216 SZ Lisse, Netherlands) Ed. Giuseppe R. Brera. adv.; bk.rev. circ. 500. **Document type:** academic/scholarly publication.
Refereed Serial

616.89 IT ISSN 0025-7893
CODEN: MDPSAC
MEDICINA PSICOSOMATICA; rivista di medicina psicosomatica, psicologia clinica e psicoterapia. (Text in Italian; summaries in English, French, Italian) 1956. q. L.60000 (foreign L.120000). Societa Editrice Universo, Via G. B. Morgagni 1, 00161 Rome, Italy. Ed. Ferruccio Antonelli. adv.; bk.rev.; abstr.; bibl.; charts; index. Indexed: Biol.Abstr., Curr.Adv.Ecol.Sci., Excerp.Med., Psychol.Abstr. (1972-). **Document type:** academic/scholarly publication.
—BLDSC (5533.650000).

616.8 US
MEDICINE AND SOCIETY. 1988. irreg., vol.5, 1992. price varies. University of California Press, 2120 Berkeley Way, Berkeley, CA 94720. TEL 510-642-4247. FAX 510-643-7127. (Orders to: California-Princeton Fulfillment Services, 1445 Lower Ferry Rd., Ewing, NJ 08618. TEL 800-777-4726. FAX 800-999-1958) Ed. Andrew Scull. (back issues avail.) **Document type:** academic/scholarly publication.
Description: Discusses psychotherapy past and present in the U.S. and Europe.
Refereed Serial

616.89 616.89 US ISSN 0025-9284
RC321 CODEN: BMCLA4
MENNINGER CLINIC. BULLETIN; a journal for the mental health professions. 1936. q. $85 (foreign $95) (effective 1996). Menninger Foundation, Box 829, Topeka, KS 66601-0829. TEL 913-273-7500. FAX 913-273-8625. Ed. Dr. Jon G. Allen. adv. contact: Mary Ann Clifft. bk.rev.; bibl.; charts; illus.; index. circ. 2,200. (also avail. in microform from UMI; reprint service avail. from UMI) Indexed: Abstr.Crim.& Pen., Biol.Abstr., Chicago Psychoanal.Lit.Ind., Curr.Cont., Excerp.Med., Hosp.Lit.Ind., IMFL, Ind.Med., Int.Nurs.Ind., Lang.& Lang.Behav.Abstr., Mid.East: Abstr.& Ind., Psychoanal.Abstr., Psychol.Abstr. (1936-), Soc.Work Res.& Abstr., SOPODA, SSCI. **Document type:** academic/scholarly publication, abstracting/indexing.
—BLDSC (2612.200000); EMDOCS; Faxon; Genuine Article; SWETS; UMI; UnCover. CCC.
Description: Contains articles on psychiatry, psychology, psychoanalysis, child psychiatry, neuropsychology, clinical research, and related subjects, as well as clinical reports and brief communications.
Refereed Serial

THE MENNINGER LETTER; your national resource for mental health. see *PSYCHOLOGY*

616.89 616.89 US ISSN 0025-9292
RC321 CODEN: MNPVB
MENNINGER PERSPECTIVE. 1970. q. Menninger Foundation, Box 829, Topeka, KS 66601-0829. TEL 913-273-7500. Ed. Judith Craig. illus. circ. 24,500. (also avail. in microform from UMI; reprint service avail. from UMI) Indexed: Intl.Mgmt.Info, Psychol.Abstr. **Document type:** consumer publication.
—UMI; UnCover.
Formerly: Menninger Quarterly.
Description: Articles related to mental health, mental illness, and Menninger programs.

MENTAL AND PHYSICAL DISABILITY LAW REPORTER; covers all aspects of handicapped law. see *LAW — Civil Law*

616.858 UK ISSN 0952-9608
MENTAL HANDICAP RESEARCH. 1987. q. £29($62) to individuals; institutions £62 ($135). B I L D Publications, Frankfurt Lodge, Clevedon Hall, Victoria Rd., Clevedon, Avon BS21 7SJ, England. TEL 01275-876519. FAX 01275-343096. Eds. G. Murphy, D. Felce. circ. 2,000. Indexed: Psychol.Abstr. (1988-), Sp.Ed.Needs Abstr.
—BLDSC (5678.567000).
Description: Applied research in learning disabilities undertaken in the U.K. and overseas from all professional disciplines.

616.8 AT ISSN 0025-9667
MENTAL HEALTH IN AUSTRALIA. 1964. s-a. Aus.$25 (effective thru 1996). Australian National Association for Mental Health, c/o Secretariat, Mental Health Education and Resource Centre, Tweedie Place, Richmond, Vic. 3121, Australia. TEL 61-3-4270373. FAX 61-3-4271294. Ed. G.D. Burrows. adv.; bk.rev. circ. 1,000. (back issues avail.) Indexed: Aus.P.A.I.S., Psychol.Abstr. (1974-). **Document type:** academic/scholarly publication.
Description: Contains articles for debate and learned papers covering advocacy, discrimination, illness prevention, health promotion and social justice issues.

MENTAL HEALTH IN CHILDREN. see *PSYCHOLOGY*

616.8 AT
MENTAL HEALTH MATTERS. 1974. bi-m. Aus.$28 individual membership. New South Wales Association for Mental Health, 62 Victoria Rd., Gladesville, N.S.W. 2111, Australia. TEL 02-816-1611. FAX 02-816-4056. Ed. Jonine Penrose-Wall. bk.rev. circ. 350. (back issues avail.) **Document type:** newsletter.
Supersedes (in 1993): N S W A M H News; **Formerly:** New South Wales Association for Mental Health. Newsletter (ISSN 0813-1724)

616.8 UK ISSN 1353-0283
MENTAL HEALTH NURSING JOURNAL. bi-m. £47.50 to non-members (outside Europe £56.50) (effective Jan. 1996). Community Psychiatric Nurses Association, 44 Dartford Rd., Sevenoaks, Kent TN13 3TQ, England. TEL 01732-455244. FAX 01732-457542. (Subscr. to: C P N A Membership, 13 Redwood Dr., Rawtenstall, Lancs. BB4 6DR, England) Eds. Catherine Jackson, Nick Robin. adv. contact: Graham Watt. bk.rev.; video rev. circ. 1,500. **Document type:** academic/scholarly publication.
—BLDSC (5678.583720).
Supersedes (until 1994): Community Psychiatric Nursing Journal (ISSN 0265-7007); **Formerly (until 1984):** C P N A Journal (ISSN 0264-5483); (until 1978): C P N A Newsletter.
Description: Contains news of interest to CPNs, feature articles, research papers, conference reports, events listings, and association news.
Refereed Serial

MENTAL HEALTH REPORT. see *SOCIAL SERVICES AND WELFARE*

MENTAL RETARDATION. see *EDUCATION — Special Education And Rehabilitation*

618.9 US ISSN 0091-6315
RC570 CODEN: MRDDD8
MENTAL RETARDATION AND DEVELOPMENTAL DISABILITIES (NEW YORK, 1970). 1970. irreg., vol.13, 1984. Plenum Publishing Corp., 233 Spring St., New York, NY 10013-1578. TEL 212-620-8000. FAX 212-463-0742. TELEX 23-421139. Ed. J. Wortis. Indexed: Adol.Ment.Hlth.Abstr., Biol.Abstr., Except.Child.Educ.Abstr., Mid.East: Abstr.& Ind., Rehabil.Lit., Soc.Work Res.& Abstr., SSCI. **Document type:** monographic series.
Supersedes: Mental Retardation.
Refereed Serial

616.858 US ISSN 1080-4013
▼**MENTAL RETARDATION AND DEVELOPMENTAL DISABILITIES (NEW YORK, 1995).** 1995. q. $95 to institutions (Canada and Mexico $135; elsewhere $157) (effective 1996). John Wiley & Sons, Inc., Journals, 605 Third Ave., New York, NY 10158. TEL 212-850-6645. FAX 212-850-6021. TELEX 12-7063. E-mail: SUBINFO@JWILEY.COM. (Subscr. outside the Americas to: John Wiley & Sons Ltd., Baffins Ln., Chichester, W. Sussex PO19 1UD, England. TEL 44-1243-779777. FAX 44-1243-776128) (also avail. in microform from UMI; back issues avail.) **Document type:** academic/scholarly publication.
Refereed Serial

616.8 US ISSN 1043-9471
QP351 CODEN: MENEE5
METHODS IN NEUROSCIENCES. 1990. irreg., vol.14, 1993. Academic Press, Inc., 525 B St., Ste. 1900, San Diego, CA 92101-4495. TEL 619-231-6616. FAX 619-699-6715. (Subscr. to: Order Dept., 6277 Sea Harbor Dr., 4th Fl., Orlando, FL 32887. TEL 800-321-5068) Ed. P. Michael Conn.
—BLDSC (5748.202800); CASDDS; UnCover. CCC.

MEDICAL SCIENCES — PSYCHIATRY AND NEUROLOGY

616.857 UK ISSN 0544-1153
MIGRAINE NEWS. 1967. 3/yr. membership donation. Migraine Trust, 45 Great Ormond St., London WC1N 3HZ, England. TEL 0171-278-2676. FAX 0171-831-5174. adv.; bk.rev. circ. 12,000. (tabloid format) **Document type:** newsletter.

616.8 CN ISSN 1195-1990
▼**MIND - BODY MEDICINE.** 1995. q. $85 to individuals (outside N. America $115); institutions $130 (outside N. America $150) (effective 1996). (Society of Behavioral Medicine) Decker Periodicals, P.O. Box 620, LCD 1, Hamilton, ON L8N 3K7, Canada. TEL 905-522-7017; 800-568-7281. FAX 905-522-7839. E-mail: decker@io.org. (U.S. addr.: Box 785, Lewiston, NY 14092-0785) **Document type:** academic/scholarly publication.
—BLDSC (5775.555220).

616.8 IT ISSN 0374-9320
MINERVA PSICHIATRICA. (Text in Italian; summaries in English and Italian) 1960. q. $90 to individuals; institutions $140 (effective 1995). (Societa Italiana di Psichiatria Sociale) Edizioni Minerva Medica, Corso Bramante 83-85, 10126 Turin, Italy. TEL 39-11-678282. FAX 39-11-3121736. Ed. M. De Vanna; Pub. Alberto Oliaro. adv.: B&W page $1100, color page $1900; trim 190 x 270; adv. contact: F. Filippo. bk.rev.; bibl.; charts; illus.; index; circ. 2,000 (paid). (also avail. in microform from UMI) **Indexed:** Biol.Abstr., Excerp.Med., Ind.Med., Lang.& Lang.Behav.Abstr., Psychol.Abstr. (1992-). **Document type:** academic/scholarly publication.
Formerly (until 1972): Minerva Psichiatrica e Psicologica.
Description: Covers clinical psychiatry, clinical psychology, social psychiatry, neuropsychiatry, and psychopharmacology.
Refereed Serial

616.8 GW ISSN 0946-7211
CODEN: MINUE
MINIMALLY INVASIVE NEUROSURGERY. (Suppl. to: Fortschritte der Neurologie und Psychiatrie) (Text in German; summaries in English, French, German and Spanish) 1958. 4/yr. DM.255. (German Society of Neurosurgery) Georg Thieme Verlag, Ruedigerstr. 14, 70469 Stuttgart, Germany. TEL 0711-8931-0. FAX 0711-8931298. (Dist. in N. and S. America by: Thieme Medical Publishers, Inc., 381 Park Ave. S., New York, NY 10157-0208; Subscr. to: Postfach 104853, 70042 Stuttgart, Germany) Ed. Dr. Axel Perneczky. adv.; bk.rev.; charts; illus. circ. 1,000. (also avail. in microform from UMI; reprint service avail. from UMI) **Indexed:** Bibl.Dev.Med.& Child Neur., Biol.Abstr., Curr.Cont., Dent.Ind., Excerp.Med., Helminthol.Abstr., Ind.Med., Ind.Sci.Rev., Sci.Cit.Ind. **Document type:** academic/scholarly publication.
—BLDSC (5797.711000); EMDOCS; Genuine Article; UMI; UnCover. **CCC.**
Formerly (until 1994): Neurochirurgia (ISSN 0028-3819)

616.8 SZ ISSN 0077-0094
RC483 CODEN: MPPPBK
MODERN PROBLEMS OF PHARMACOPSYCHIATRY. (Text in English) 1968. irreg. price varies. S. Karger AG, Allschwilerstr. 10, P.O. Box, CH-4009 Basel, Switzerland. TEL 061-3061111. FAX 061-3061234. E-mail: Karger@Karger.ch. Eds. H.J. Freyberger, R.D. Stieglitz. (reprint service avail. from ISI) **Indexed:** Biol.Abstr., Chem.Abstr., Curr.Cont., Ind.Med., Psychol.Abstr. **Document type:** academic/scholarly publication.
—CASDDS; Faxon; UnCover. **CCC.**
Description: Information on the development, evaluation and use of drugs and selected therapeutic interventions in psychiatric practice and research.
Refereed Serial

616.8 US ISSN 1044-7431
QP356.2 CODEN: MOCNED
MOLECULAR AND CELLULAR NEUROSCIENCES. 1990. m. $395 (effective 1996). Academic Press, Inc., Journal Division, 525 B St., Ste. 1900, San Diego, CA 92101-4495. TEL 619-230-1840. FAX 619-699-6800. (Subscr. to: Box 620000, Orlando, FL 32891-8340. TEL 800-543-9534) Ed. P. Michael Conn. (back issues avail.) **Indexed:** Excerp.Med. (1992-), Ind.Med. (1994-). **Document type:** academic/scholarly publication.
—BLDSC (5900.760700); CASDDS; Faxon; Genuine Article; SWETS; UnCover. **CCC.**
Description: Describes novel and original results in the areas of neurobiology, neuropharmacology, neuroendocrinology, neurochemistry, and neuroanatomy at the molecular, cellular, and tissue levels.
Refereed Serial

616.8 US ISSN 1044-7393
CODEN: MCHNEM
MOLECULAR AND CHEMICAL NEUROPATHOLOGY. 1983. 9/yr. $385 (foreign $420) (effective 1996). Humana Press Inc., 999 Riverview Dr., Ste. 208, Totowa, NJ 07512. TEL 201-256-1699. FAX 201-256-8341. (Dist. in Japan by: Maruzen Co. Ltd., Journals Div., P.O. Box 5050, Tokyo 100-31, Japan. TEL 03-32758591. FAX 03-32781937) Eds. Lloyd A. Horrocks, Allan J. Yates. bk.rev.; abstr.; bibl.; charts; illus. **Indexed:** Biol.Abstr., Chem.Abstr., Curr.Adv.Ecol.Sci., Curr.Cont., Excerp.Med., Ind.Med. **Document type:** academic/scholarly publication.
—BLDSC (5900.762000); CASDDS; Faxon; Genuine Article; SWETS; UnCover. **CCC.**
Formerly (until 1989): Neurochemical Pathology (ISSN 0734-600X)
Description: Focuses on the biochemical pathology of central and peripheral nervous system tissue and fluids, as well as muscles, sense organs, CSF, blood and neurological tissues.
Refereed Serial

616.8 547.88 NE ISSN 0169-328X
QP356.2 CODEN: MBREE4
MOLECULAR BRAIN RESEARCH. (Section of: Brain Research (ISSN 0006-8993)) (Text in English) 1986. 16/yr. fl.3616($2205) (effective 1996). Elsevier Science B.V., P.O. Box 211, 1000 AE Amsterdam, Netherlands. TEL 31-20-4853911. FAX 31-20-4853598. TELEX 18582 ESPA NL. E-mail: nlinfo-f@elsevier.nl; usinfo-f@elsevier.com; forinfo-kyf04035@niftyserve.or.jp; Site addr.: http://www.elsevier.nl/. (Subscr. in U.S. and Canada to: Elsevier Science Inc., Box 882, Madison Sq. Sta., New York, NY 10159. TEL 212-989-5800. FAX 212-633-3990) Ed. D.P. Purpura. bibl.; index. (also avail. in microform from UMI; back issues avail.; reprint service avail. from ISI) **Indexed:** Anim.Breed.Abstr., Biol.Abstr., Chem.Abstr., Curr.Adv.Biochem., Curr.Adv.Cell & Devel.Biol., Curr.Adv.Genetics & Molec.Biol., Curr.Cont., Excerp.Med., Ind.Med. **Document type:** academic/scholarly publication.
—BLDSC (5900.799000); ADONIS; CASDDS; Faxon; Genuine Article; SWETS; UnCover. **CCC.**
Description: Provides a medium for the prompt publications of studies of molecular mechanisms of neuronal synaptic and related processes that underline the structure and funcion of the brain.

616.8 573.21 US ISSN 0893-7648
QP365.2 CODEN: MONBEW
MOLECULAR NEUROBIOLOGY; a review journal. 1987. bi-m. $325 (foreign $355) (effective 1996). Humana Press Inc., 999 Riverview Dr., Ste. 208, Totowa, NJ 07512. TEL 201-256-1699. FAX 201-256-8341. (Dist. in Japan by: Maruzen Co. Ltd., Journals Div., P.O. Box 5050, Tokyo 100-31, Japan. TEL 03-32758591. FAX 03-32781937) Eds. Nicolas Bazan, Jacques Mallet. adv. contact: Thomas B. Lanigan, Jr. bk.rev.; abstr.; bibl.; charts; illus.; index. (back issues avail.) **Indexed:** Biol.Abstr., Chem.Abstr., Curr.Cont., Excerp.Med., Ind.Med., Sci.Cit.Ind. **Document type:** academic/scholarly publication.
—BLDSC (5900.817980); CASDDS; Faxon; Genuine Article; SWETS; UnCover. **CCC.**
Description: For neuroscientists needing to keep abreast of current experimental and clinical brain research at the molecular level.
Refereed Serial

616.89 SP ISSN 0214-4220
CODEN: MONDE4
MONOGRAFIAS DE PSIQUIATRIA. 1989. 6/yr. Grupo Aula Medica, S.A., C.I. Venecia 2, Alfa III, Oficina 93, Isabel Colbrana s-n, 28050 Madrid, Spain. TEL 34-1-3588657. FAX 34-1-3589067. **Document type:** academic/scholarly publication.

616.894 US ISSN 0077-0620
MONOGRAPH SERIES ON SCHIZOPHRENIA. 1950. irreg., no.8, 1969. price varies. International Universities Press, Inc., 59 Boston Post Rd., Box 1524, Madison, CT 06443-1524. TEL 203-245-4000. **Document type:** monographic series.
Refereed Serial

616.8 US ISSN 0077-0671
CODEN: MGGPBE
MONOGRAPHIEN AUS DEM GESAMTGEBIETE DER PSYCHIATRIE - PSYCHIATRY SERIES. (Text in English and German) 1970. irreg. price varies. Springer-Verlag, 175 Fifth Ave., New York, NY 10010. TEL 212-460-1500. FAX 212-473-6272. (Also: Berlin, Heidelberg, Tokyo and Vienna) (reprint service avail. from ISI) **Indexed:** Ind.Med. (until 1992), Psychol.Abstr. **Document type:** monographic series.
—CASDDS.
Supersedes in part: Monographien aus dem Gesamtgebiete der Neurologie und Psychiatrie.

616.8 SZ ISSN 0300-5186
CODEN: MNUSB6
MONOGRAPHS IN NEURAL SCIENCES. (Text in English) 1972. irreg. price varies. S. Karger AG, Allschwilerstr. 10, P.O. Box, CH-4009 Basel, Switzerland. TEL 061-3061111. FAX 061-3061234. E-mail: Karger@Karger.ch. Ed. A. Korczyn. (reprint service avail. from ISI) **Indexed:** Biol.Abstr., Chem.Abstr., Curr.Cont., Ind.Med. (until 1992). **Document type:** monographic series. **CCC.**
Formerly: Monographs in Basic Neurology.
Description: Provides a broad, interdisciplinary approach to the neural sciences, advancing current information vital for the management of various neurological diseases.
Refereed Serial

616.8 US ISSN 0737-3953
MONOGRAPHS IN NEUROSCIENCE. 1984. irreg., latest vol.5. price varies. Gordon & Breach Science Publishers, c/o International Publishers Distributor, 820 Town Center Dr., Langhorne, PA 19047. TEL 215-750-2642. FAX 215-750-6343. (Subscr. to: International Publishers Distributor, P.O. Box 90, Reading, Berkshire RG1 8JL, England. TEL 44-173-456-8316) Ed. S. Weinstein. **Document type:** monographic series.
—BLDSC (5915.593000).
Refereed Serial

616.8 FR ISSN 0245-5919
MOTRICITE CEREBRALE, READAPTATION, NEUROLOGIE DU DEVELOPPEMENT. 1980. q. 348 f. Masson - Periodiques, Villa Laromiguere, 75005 Paris, France. TEL 1-40-46-62-00. FAX 1-40-46-62-01. Ed. M. le Metayer. circ. 1,800. (also avail. in microform from UMI) **Indexed:** Excerp.Med. **Document type:** academic/scholarly publication.
—BLDSC (5978.710000); UMI. **CCC.**
Description: Deals with the physiopathologic aspects of the neurology of development, and with motor or cerebral handicapped people.

616.8 US ISSN 0885-3185
CODEN: MOVDEA
MOVEMENT DISORDERS. 1986. bi-m. $289 to individuals (foreign $383); institutions $390 (foreign $500) (effective 1996) (incl. 2 videocassettes); newsstand price: $84. (Movement Disorder Society) Lippincott - Raven Publishers, 227 Washington Sq., Philadelphia, PA 19106. TEL 215-238-4200. Eds. Dr. Stanley Fahn, Dr. David Marsden. adv. contact: Phyllis Noyes. bk.rev.; video rev.; charts; illus.; index. circ. 1,500. (back issues avail.; reprint service avail. from UMI) **Indexed:** Excerp.Med., Ind.Med. **Document type:** academic/scholarly publication.
—BLDSC (5980.317200); Faxon; Genuine Article; SWETS; UMI; UnCover. **CCC.**
Description: Publishes articles on all aspects of movement disorders, their etiology, and management.
Refereed Serial

MEDICAL SCIENCES — PSYCHIATRY AND NEUROLOGY

616.8   UK   ISSN 1352-4585
CODEN: MUSCFZ
▼**MULTIPLE SCLEROSIS.** 1995. bi-m. £65($99) to individuals; institutions in E.U. £135(elsewhere £145). Stockton Press (Subsidiary of: Macmillan Press Ltd.), Houndsmills, Basingstoke, Hants RG21 2XS, England. TEL 01256-817245. FAX 01256-28339. Ed. Ingrid Allen; Pub. Jayne Marks. adv. contact: Michael Rowley. **Document type:** academic/scholarly publication.
—CASDDS. **CCC.**
Description: Covers the aetiology and pathogenesis of demyelinating and inflammatory diseases of the central nervous system.

MUSIK-, TANZ- UND KUNSTTHERAPIE. see *MEDICAL SCIENCES*

616.8   UK
N A C R O POLICY PAPER. irreg., no.3, 1994. National Association for the Care and Resettlement of Offenders, 169 Clapham Rd., London SW9 0PU, England. TEL 0171-582-6500. FAX 0171-735-4666. **Document type:** bulletin.

616.858   US
N A M I ADVOCATE. 1979. 6/yr. $25. National Alliance for the Mentally Ill, 200 N. Glebe Rd., no. 1015, Arlington, VA 22203-3754. TEL 703-524-9094. Ed. James A. Buie. adv.; bk.rev. circ. 68. **Document type:** newsletter.
Formerly: N A M I News.

616.8   II   ISSN 0254-0886
N I M H A N S JOURNAL. (Text in English) 1983. s-a. Rs.100($30) National Institute of Mental Health & Neuro Sciences, Bangalore 560 029, India. FAX 0812-641256. TELEX 0845-2186 NIMH IN. Ed. S.M. Channabasavanna. adv.; bk.rev. circ. 700. **Indexed:** Excerp.Med., Psychol.Abstr. (1986-).
—BLDSC (6113.182000); Genuine Article.
Description: Disseminates the institute's research results.

618 544   US
N K I REPORT. 1983. a. free. Nathan S. Kline Institute for Psychiatric Research, Old Orangeburg Rd., Orangeburg, NY 10962. TEL 914-365-2000. FAX 914-359-7029. Ed. Marilyn D. Cohen. circ. 1,000. **Document type:** newsletter.
Description: Discusses the etiology, treatment and prevention of chronic, severe mental illness.

616.8   US   ISSN 1040-3671
N S T A NEWSLETTER. 1984. q. $20. National Spasmodic Torticollis Association, Box 873, Royal Oak, MI 48068-0873. TEL 313-647-2280. Ed. Phyllis Jones. circ. 800.
Formerly (until 1986): National Spasmodic Torticollis Association Newsletter.
Description: Provides information for patients on the treatment of spasmodic torticollis, a neurological condition.

616.8   UK
NARCOLEPSY ASSOCIATION REPORT. irreg. £6 membership. Narcolepsy Association (U.K.), South Hall, High St., Farningham, Kent DA4 0DE, England. TEL 01322-863056. **Document type:** monographic series.
Description: Aims to promote awareness of narcolepsy and provide authoritative information to narcoleptics, to the medical profession, and to the public.

616.8 362.2   US   ISSN 0738-9159
NATIONAL COUNCIL NEWS. 1977. m. $25. National Community Mental Healthcare Council, 12300 Twinbrook Parkway, Ste. 320, Rockville, MD 20852. TEL 301-984-6200. Ed. Joanne Petro. adv.; bk.rev. circ. 2,600. (tabloid format) **Document type:** newsletter.
Description: Covers issues of interest to mental health care professionals and reports Council activities.

616.857   US
NATIONAL HEADACHE FOUNDATION HEAD LINES. 1970. q. $15. National Headache Foundation, 5252 N. Western Ave., Chicago, IL 60625. TEL 312-878-7715; 800-843-2256. FAX 312-907-6278. bk.rev.; circ. 45,000 (paid). (tabloid format; back issues avail.) **Document type:** newsletter.
Former titles: National Headache Foundation Newsletter; National Migraine Foundation Newsletter.
Description: Research and information on headache causes and treatments.

NEIROFIZIOLOGIYA/NEUROPHYSIOLOGY;
nauchno-teoreticheskii zhurnal. see *BIOLOGY — Physiology*

616.8   GW   ISSN 0028-2804
CODEN: NERVAF
DER NERVENARZT; Monatsschrift fuer alle Gebiete nervenaerztlicher Forschung und Praxis. (Includes: Deutsche Gesellschaft fuer Neurologie. Mitteilungsblatt and Gesellschaft Oesterreichischer Nervenaertze und Psychiater) 1928. 12/yr. DM.410($297) (effective 1996). (Deutschen Gesellschaft fuer Psychiatrie und Nervenheilkunde) Springer-Verlag, Heidelberger Platz 3, 14197 Berlin, Germany. TEL 030-8207-0. FAX 030-8214091. E-mail: orders@springer.de. (Subscr. in N. America to: Springer-Verlag New York, Inc., 44 Hartz Way, Secaucus, NJ 07096-2491. TEL 201-348-4033. FAX 201-348-4505) Ed. T. Brandt. adv.; bk.rev.; charts; illus.; index. (also avail. in microform from UMI; back issues avail.; reprint service avail. from ISI) **Indexed:** Biol.Abstr., Biotech.Abstr., Chem.Abstr., Curr.Adv.Ecol.Sci., Curr.Cont., Excerp.Med., Ger.J.Psych., Ind.Med., Nutr.Abstr., Psychol.Abstr. (1929-). **Document type:** academic/scholarly publication.
—BLDSC (6076.500000); EMDOCS; Faxon; Genuine Article; SWETS; UMI. **CCC.**
Description: Covers neurology, psychiatry, neurosurgery, and psychotherapy.

616.8   GW   ISSN 0722-1541
NERVENHEILKUNDE; Zeitschrift fuer interdisziplinaere Fortbildung. 1982. 8/yr. DM.158($118) F.K. Schattauer Verlagsgesellschaft mbH, Lenzhalde 3, 70192 Stuttgart, Germany. TEL 0711-22987-0. FAX 0711-22987-50. Eds. D. Soyka, E. Lungershausen. circ. 37,000. **Document type:** academic/scholarly publication.
—BLDSC (6076.520000); Genuine Article. **CCC.**

NEURAL COMPUTATION. see *COMPUTERS — Artificial Intelligence*

NEURAL NETWORK WORLD. see *COMPUTERS — Artificial Intelligence*

NEURAL NETWORKS. see *COMPUTERS — Artificial Intelligence*

NEURAL PROCESSING LETTERS. see *COMPUTERS — Artificial Intelligence*

NEURO-CHIRURGIE. see *MEDICAL SCIENCES — Surgery*

NEURO-FIBROMA-TOSIS. see *BIOLOGY — Genetics*

NEURO-FIBROMA-TOSIS RESEARCH NEWSLETTER. see *BIOLOGY — Genetics*

NEURO-ORTHOPEDICS. see *MEDICAL SCIENCES — Orthopedics And Traumatology*

616.8   BL   ISSN 0028-3800
RC321   CODEN: NURBAX
NEUROBIOLOGIA; revista de neurologia psiquiatria e neurocirurgia. (Text and summaries in English and Portuguese) 1938. q. $55 (effective 1995). (Sociedade de Neurologia, Psiquiatria e Higiene Mental do Brasil, Hospital das Clinicas Pedro II) Sociedade Editora da Revista Neurobiologia, Caixa Postal 651, 50001-970 Recife PE, Brazil. TEL 55-81-268-5495. (Affiliate: Sociedade de Medicina de Pernambuco. Departamento de Neurologia e Neurocirurgia) Ed. A. Codeceira Jr. adv.; bk.rev.; abstr.; bibl.; charts; illus.; index. circ. 700. (also avail. in talking book; back issues avail.) **Indexed:** Biol.Abstr., Excerp.Med., Psychol.Abstr. **Document type:** academic/scholarly publication.
—BLDSC (6081.300000).

NEUROBIOLOGY OF AGING; experimental and clinical research. see *BIOLOGY — Physiology*

616.8 156   US   ISSN 1074-7427
CODEN: NLMEFR
NEUROBIOLOGY OF LEARNING AND MEMORY. 1968. bi-m. $439 (foreign $531) (effective 1996). Academic Press, Inc., Journal Division, 525 B. St., Ste. 1900, San Diego, CA 92101-4495. TEL 619-230-1840. FAX 619-699-6800. (Subscr. to: Box 620000, Orlando, FL 32891-8340. TEL 800-543-9534) Eds. James L. McGaugh, William T. Greenough. adv.; abstr.; charts; illus.; stat.; index. (back issues avail.) **Indexed:** Abstr.Anthropol., Anim.Breed.Abstr., Biol.Abstr., Biol.& Agr.Ind., Chem.Abstr., Curr.Adv.Ecol.Sci., Curr.Cont., Dairy Sci.Abstr., Dent.Ind., Excerp.Med., Ind.Med., Ind.Sci.Rev., Ind.Vet., Nutr.Abstr., Poult.Abstr., Psychol.Abstr. (1972-), Sport Fish.Abstr., Vet.Bull., Wild.Rev., Zoo.Rec. **Document type:** academic/scholarly publication.
—BLDSC (6081.311300); CASDDS; Faxon; Genuine Article; SWETS; UnCover. **CCC.**
Former titles (until 1994): Behavioral and Neural Biology (ISSN 0163-1047); (until 1979): Behavioral Biology (ISSN 0091-6773); Communications in Behavioral Biology (ISSN 0010-3608)
Description: Publishes high-quality papers in all areas of neurally oriented behavioral research and emphasizes the areas of neural plasticity and of mechanisms of learning and memory.
Refereed Serial

616.8   UK   ISSN 1355-4794
▼**NEUROCASE.** 1995. bi-m. £220($350) (effective 1996). Oxford University Press, Oxford Journals, Walton St., Oxford OX2 6DP, England. TEL 01865-267907. FAX 01865-267773. E-mail: jnlorders@oup.co.uk. (Subscr. in U.S. to: Oxford University Press Inc., 2001 Evans Rd., Cary, NC 27513. TEL 919-677-0977. FAX 919-677-1714) Eds. Ian H. Robertson, H. Branch Coslett. (back issues avail.) **Document type:** academic/scholarly publication.
●Also available on CD-ROM.
—BLDSC (6081.311400).

619   US   ISSN 0364-3190
QP356.3   CODEN: NEREDZ
NEUROCHEMICAL RESEARCH. 1976. m. $825 (foreign $965) (effective 1996). Plenum Publishing Corp., 233 Spring St., New York, NY 10013-1578. TEL 212-620-8000. FAX 212-463-0742. TELEX 23-421139. Ed. Abel Lathja. adv. (also avail. in microfilm from JSC; back issues avail.) **Indexed:** Biol.Abstr., Chem.Abstr., Curr.Adv.Biochem., Curr.Adv.Cell & Devel.Biol., Curr.Adv.Ecol.Sci., Curr.Cont., Dent.Ind., Excerp.Med., Ind.Med., Ind.Sci.Rev. **Document type:** academic/scholarly publication.
—BLDSC (6081.312000); CASDDS; Faxon; Genuine Article; SWETS; UMI; UnCover. **CCC.**
Refereed Serial

NEUROCHEMISTRY. see *BIOLOGY — Biological Chemistry*

616.8 540   UK   ISSN 0197-0186
QP356.3   CODEN: NEUIDS
NEUROCHEMISTRY INTERNATIONAL; the international journal for the rapid publication of critical reviews, original and rapid research communications in neurochemistry. 1980. m. £489($778) (effective 1996). Elsevier Science Ltd., Pergamon, P.O. Box 800, Kidlington, Oxford OX5 1DX, England. TEL 44-1865-843000. FAX 44-1865-843010. E-mail: nlinfo-f@elsevier.nl; usinfo-f@elsevier.com; forinfo-kyf04035@niftyserve.or.jp; Site addr.: http://www.elsevier.nl/. (Subscr. in U.S. and Canada to: Elsevier Science, 660 White Plains Rd., Tarrytown, NY 10591-5153. TEL 914-524-9200. FAX 914-333-2444) Eds. N. Osborne, W. Lovenberg. (also avail. in microfilm from UMI) **Indexed:** Apic.Abstr., Biol.Abstr., Chem.Abstr., Curr.Adv.Ecol.Sci., Curr.Cont., Excerp.Med., Ind.Med. (1992-), Ind.Sci.Rev., Int.Aerosp.Abstr., Psychol.Abstr. (1984-). **Document type:** academic/scholarly publication.
—BLDSC (6081.317000); CASDDS; Faxon; Genuine Article; SWETS; UMI; UnCover. **CCC.**
Description: Publishes papers concerned with the metabolism and function of the nervous system.
Refereed Serial

MEDICAL SCIENCES — PSYCHIATRY AND NEUROLOGY

616.8 UK ISSN 1055-8330
NEURODEGENERATION. 1992. q. £200 (effective 1996). Academic Press Ltd. (Subsidiary of: Harcourt Brace & Company Ltd.), 24-28 Oval Rd., London NW1 7DX, England. TEL 44-171-267-4466. FAX 44-171-482-2293. TELEX 25775 ACPRES G. (Subscr. to: Harcourt Brace & Company Ltd., Foots Cray High St., Sidcup, Kent DA14 5HP, England. TEL 44-181-300-3322. FAX 44-181-309-0807) Eds. J.W. Langston, D. Mann. (back issues avail.) **Indexed:** Excerp.Med. (1995-). **Document type:** academic/scholarly publication.
—BLDSC (6081.365500); Genuine Article. **CCC.**
Description: Publishes papers in all fields relating to neurodegenerative disorders, including neurochemistry, neuropharmacology, neurotoxicology, and neuroprotection.

616.8 US ISSN 0047-942X
NEUROELECTRIC NEWS. 1970. 3/yr. $25. Neuroelectric Society, Inc., c/o Anthony Sances, Jr., Ed., Medical College of Wisconsin, 8700 W. Wisconsin Ave., Milwaukee, WI 53226. bk.rev.; abstr.; bibl. circ. 200. (also avail. in microform from UMI; reprint service avail. from UMI)
—UMI.
Description: Emphasizes theory and clinical applications of electroneurophysiology.

616.8 US ISSN 0168-0617
QP356.4 CODEN: NEPEEQ
NEUROENDOCRINE PERSPECTIVES. 1982. irreg., vol.9, 1991. price varies. Springer-Verlag, 175 Fifth Ave., New York, NY 10010. TEL 212-460-1500. FAX 212-473-6272. (Also: Berlin, Heidelberg, Tokyo and Vienna) Eds. E.E. Mueller, R.M. Macleod. **Indexed:** Biol.Abstr., Chem.Abstr. **Document type:** monographic series.
—BLDSC (6081.369000); CASDDS; Faxon.
Refereed Serial

NEUROENDOCRINOLOGY; international journal for basic and clinical studies on neuroendocrine relationships. see *MEDICAL SCIENCES — Endocrinology*

616.8 UK ISSN 0172-780X
CODEN: NLETDU
NEUROENDOCRINOLOGY LETTERS. 1979. bi-m. Brain Research Promotion, 10 Deena Close, Queen's Drive, London W3 0HR, England. adv.; bk.rev.; illus. (reprint service avail. from ISI) **Indexed:** Chem.Abstr., Curr.Adv.Biochem., Curr.Adv.Ecol.Sci., Dairy Sci.Abstr., Excerp.Med., Ind.Sci.Rev. **Document type:** academic/scholarly publication.
—BLDSC (6081.371000); CASDDS; Faxon; Genuine Article; SWETS. **CCC.**

616.8 US
NEUROENDOSCOPY ANNUAL. 1992. a. $35 (foreign $50). Mary Ann Liebert, Inc. Publishers, 2 Madison Ave., Larchmont, NY 10538. TEL 914-834-3100. FAX 914-834-3688. E-mail: Liebert@pipeline.com. Eds. Drs. Kerry R. Crone, Kim H. Manwarning.
Description: Reports on the various equipment applications in therapeutic endoscopy.

616.8 SZ ISSN 0251-5350
CODEN: NLEEPD3
NEUROEPIDEMIOLOGY. (Text in English) 1982. bi-m. 275.40 SFr.($211.80) to individuals; institutions 459 SFr.($353) (effective 1996). S. Karger AG, Allschwilerstr. 10, P.O. Box, CH-4009 Basel, Switzerland. TEL 061-3061111. FAX 061-3061234. E-mail: Karger@Karger.ch. (Or: S. Karger Publishers, Inc., 79 Fifth Ave., New York, NY 10011 U.S.A.) Ed. M. Alter. adv.; illus.; index. circ. 800. (also avail. in microform from UMI) **Indexed:** Biol.Abstr., Excerp.Med., Psychol.Abstr. (1992-). **Document type:** academic/scholarly publication.
—BLDSC (6081.371200); Faxon; Genuine Article; SWETS; UnCover. **CCC.**
Refereed Serial

616.8 US ISSN 1053-8119
CODEN: NEIMEF
NEUROIMAGE. 1992. bi-m. $300 (foreign $332) (effective 1996). Academic Press, Inc., Journal Division, 525 B St., Ste. 1900, San Diego, CA 92101-4495. TEL 619-230-1840. FAX 619-699-6800. (Subscr. to: Box 620000, Orlando, FL 32891-8340. TEL 800-543-9534) Ed. Arthur W. Toga. index. (back issues avail.) **Indexed:** Chem.Abstr., Excerp.Med. (1994-). **Document type:** academic/scholarly publication.
—BLDSC (6081.372200); Genuine Article; UnCover. **CCC.**
Description: Focuses on the visualization of all neuroscientific data.
Refereed Serial

NEUROIMMUNOMODULATION. see *MEDICAL SCIENCES — Allergology And Immunology*

616.8 SP ISSN 0213-4853
CODEN: NERLEN
NEUROLOGIA. (Text in Spanish; summaries in English) 1986. m. (10/yr.) 6900 ptas.($57) to non-members. (Sociedad Espanola de Neurologia) Ediciones Doyma, S.A., Travesera de Gracia, 17-21, 08021 Barcelona, Spain. TEL 34-1-200-07-11. FAX 34-1-209-11-36. TELEX 51695 INK-E. Ed. E. Tolosa Sarro. adv.: page 180000 ptas.; trim 210 x 280; adv. contact: Marte Vidal. circ. 2,000. (reprint service avail. from UMI) **Indexed:** Ind.Med.Esp.
—BLDSC (6081.374900); SWETS.
Description: Covers the investigative research of the Society and accredited clinics throughout the country.

616.8 CK ISSN 0120-1034
NEUROLOGIA COLOMBIA. (Text and summaries in English and Spanish) 1977. 3/yr. Col.$1000($25) Fundacion Instituto Neurologico de Colombia, Apdo. Aereo 90303, Bogota 8, Colombia. Ed. Edwin Ruiz-Alarcon, M.D. adv.; bk.rev.; bibl.; charts; illus.; stat.; index. circ. 3,000. **Indexed:** Ind.Med.

616.89 CI ISSN 0353-8842
CODEN: NRLGDY
NEUROLOGIA CROATICA; journal of neurology and its related fields. (Text in English; summaries in Croatian) 1953. q. DM.15 to individuals (foreign $25); institutions DM.45 (foreign $40). University Hospital, Department of Neurology, Kispaticeva 12, 41000 Zagreb, Croatia. TEL 385-41-222706. (Co-sponsor: Department of Neuropathology) Ed.Bd. adv.; bk.rev.; illus. circ. 1,000. (also avail. in microform from UMI; reprint service avail. from UMI) **Indexed:** Biol.Abstr., Dent.Ind., Excerp.Med., Ind.Med. (until 1992), Psychol.Abstr.
—BLDSC (6081.377000); CASDDS; Genuine Article; UMI.
Supersedes (in 1991): Neurologija (ISSN 0350-9559); (in 1977): Neuropsihijatrija (ISSN 0047-9438)

616.8 PL ISSN 0028-3843
CODEN: NNPOBE
NEUROLOGIA I NEUROCHIRURGIA POLSKA. (Text in Polish; summaries in English and Russian) 1951. bi-m. $102. Polskie Towarzystwo Neurologiczne - Polish Neurological Society, Ul. Kopcinskiego 22, 90-153 Lodz, Poland. (Dist. by: Ars Polona- Ruch, Krakowskie Przedmiescie 7, 00-068 Warsaw, Poland) (Co-sponsor: Polskie Towarzystwo Neurochirurgow - Polish Neurosurgeons' Society) Ed. Dr. Jerzy Kulczycki. adv.; bk.rev.; bibl.; illus.; stat.; index, cum.index. circ. 1,800. **Indexed:** Biol.Abstr., Chem.Abstr., Dent.Ind., Dok.Arbeitsmed., Excerp.Med., Ind.Med., Ref.Zh.
—BLDSC (6081.380000); CASDDS.

616.8 JA ISSN 0387-2572
NEUROLOGIA MEDICO-CHIRURGICA. Japanese edition: Shinkei Geka (ISSN 0470-8105) (Text in English) m. 16800 Yen. Japan Neurosurgical Society, 7-3-1 Hongo, Bunkyo-ku, Tokyo 113, Japan. (Dist. by: Business Center for Academic Societies Japan, 5-16-9 Honkomagome, Bunkyo-ku, Tokyo 113, Japan. TEL 03-5814-5811)
—BLDSC (6081.390000).

616.8 US ISSN 0733-8619
RC321
NEUROLOGIC CLINICS. 1983. q. $130 (foreign $155) (effective 1996). W.B. Saunders Co. (Subsidiary of: Harcourt Brace & Company), Curtis Center, 3rd Fl., Independence Sq. W., Philadelphia, PA 19106. TEL 215-238-7800. FAX 215-238-6445. (Subscr. to: Periodicals Fulfillment, W.B. Saunders Co., 6277 Sea Harbor Dr., 4th Fl., Orlando, FL 32891-4800. TEL 800-654-2452. FAX 800-874-6418) Ed. Lesley Day. adv. (also avail. in microform from UMI) **Indexed:** Ind.Med., Psychol.Abstr. (1987-). **Document type:** academic/scholarly publication.
—BLDSC (6081.441000); Faxon; Genuine Article; SWETS; UMI; UnCover. **CCC.**
Description: Each issue covers a neurologic disease in detail.

616.8 US ISSN 1058-7535
CODEN: NDTHEE
NEUROLOGICAL DISEASES AND THERAPY. 1987. irreg., vol.38, 1995. price varies. Marcel Dekker, Inc., 270 Madison Ave., New York, NY 10016. TEL 212-696-9000. FAX 212-685-4540. TELEX 421419. **Document type:** monographic series.
—BLDSC (6081.441400); CASDDS. **CCC.**

616.8 JA
NEUROLOGICAL INSTITUTE. BULLETIN. (Text in English, Japanese) 1964. a. free. Kyushu Daigaku, Igakubu, Fuzoku No Shinkeibyo Kenkyu Shisetsu - Kyushu University, Faculty of Medicine, Neurological Institute, 1-1, Maidashi 3-chome, Higashi-ku, Fukuoka-shi, Fukuoka-ken 812-82, Japan. TEL 81-92-641-1151. FAX 81-92-633-4306. E-mail: kato@neurophy.med.kyushu.ac.jp. circ. (controlled). **Document type:** bulletin.

616.8 US ISSN 0161-6412
RC321 CODEN: NRESDZ
NEUROLOGICAL RESEARCH;* a journal of progress in neurosurgery, neurology and neurosciences. 1979. bi-m. $95 to individuals; institutions $465 (effective 1994). Forefront Publishing Group, 5 River Rd., Ste. 113, Wilton, CT 06897-4069. TEL 203-761-0786. FAX 508-443-0221. (UK addr.: Celtic House, 33 John's Mews, London WC1N 2QL, England. TEL 44-483-472602) Ed.Bd. adv.; bk.rev.; abstr.; illus.; index. (also avail. in microfilm from UMI; back issues avail.; reprint service avail. from ISI,UMI) **Indexed:** Chem.Abstr., Curr.Adv.Ecol.Sci., Excerp.Med., Ind.Med., Ref.Zh., Telegen. **Document type:** academic/scholarly publication.
—BLDSC (6081.442000); CASDDS; Faxon; Genuine Article; SWETS; UMI; UnCover. **CCC.**
Description: Covers clinical neurosurgery, neuroanatomy, neuroradiology and other aspects of neurological research.
Refereed Serial

618 617 JA ISSN 0301-2603
CODEN: NOKGB6
NEUROLOGICAL SURGERY/NO SHINKEI GEKA. (Text in Japanese; summaries in English) 1973. m. 2100 Yen per no. Igaku Shoin Ltd., 24-3 Hongo 5-chome, Bunkyo-ku, Tokyo 113-91, Japan. TEL 03-817-5702. adv.; bk.rev. circ. 6,000. **Indexed:** Biol.Abstr., Chem.Abstr., Dent.Ind., Excerp.Med., Ind.Med.
●Also available online. Vendor(s): JICST.
—BLDSC (6081.445000); CASDDS.

616.8 US ISSN 0028-3878
RC321 CODEN: NEURAI
NEUROLOGY. 1950. m. $190 (foreign $240). Advanstar Communications, Inc., 7500 Old Oak Blvd., Cleveland, OH 44130. TEL 216-826-2839. FAX 216-891-2726. (Subscr. to: 131 W. First St., Duluth, MN 55802. TEL 800-346-0085) Ed. Peter G. Studer. adv.; bk.rev.; bibl.; charts; illus.; index. circ. 16,239. (also avail. in microform from UMI) **Indexed:** AIM, Behav.Med.Abstr., Bibl.Dev.Med.& Child Neur., Biol.Abstr., Chem.Abstr., Curr.Adv.Cancer Res., Curr.Adv.Ecol.Sci., Curr.Cont., Dent.Ind., Diab.Cont., Excerp.Med., Helminthol.Abstr., Ind.Med., Ind.Sci.Rev., Lang.& Lang.Behav.Abstr., Nutr.Abstr., Psychol.Abstr. (1951-), Yrbk.Assoc.Educ.& Rehab.Blind. **Document type:** trade publication.
●Also available online. Vendor(s): Ovid Technologies.
—BLDSC (6081.500000); CASDDS; EMDOCS; Faxon; Genuine Article; SWETS; UMI; UnCover. **CCC.**
Description: Reports, discussions, case findings and clinical findings on current research and developments in neurology. Covers neurological symptoms of diseases, diagnostic methods and treatments.
Refereed Serial

MEDICAL SCIENCES — PSYCHIATRY AND NEUROLOGY

616.8 US ISSN 0741-4234
NEUROLOGY ALERT. 1982. m. $128. American Health Consultants, Inc., Six Piedmont Center, Ste. 400, Atlanta, GA 30305. TEL 404-262-7436; 800-688-2421. FAX 800-284-3291. Ed. Dr. Fred Plum. index. circ. 2,600. (also avail. in audio cassette; reprint service avail.) **Document type:** newsletter.

616.8 US ISSN 0736-4563
CODEN: NEUND9
NEUROLOGY AND NEUROBIOLOGY. 1982. irreg., vol.60, 1990. price varies. A.R. Liss (Subsidiary of: John Wiley & Sons, Inc.), 605 Third Ave., New York, NY 10158. TEL 212-475-7700. **Indexed:** Biol.Abstr., Chem.Abstr. **Document type:** monographic series.
—BLDSC (6081.500150); CASDDS. CCC.

616.8 II ISSN 0028-3886
NEUROLOGY INDIA. (Text in English) 1952. q. Rs.750($110) Neurological Society of India, Dept. of Neurology, Post-graduate Institute of Medical Education & Research, Chandigarh 160 012, India. TEL 0172-541032. Ed. J.S. Chopra. adv.; bk.rev.; cum.index. circ. 1,300. (reprint service avail. from IRC) **Indexed:** Biol.Abstr., Chem.Abstr., Curr.Cont., Excerp.Med. (until 1990; 1995-), ExtraMED, Ind.Med. **Document type:** academic/scholarly publication.
●Also available on CD-ROM.
—EMDOCS; Genuine Article; UnCover.

616.8 UK ISSN 0261-4812
NEUROMUSCULAR DISEASES. m. £80 (effective 1995). S U B I S, Mansion House, 19 Kingfield Rd., Sheffield S11 9AS, England. TEL 0114-2554433. FAX 0114-2554626. E-mail: admin@sheffac.demon.co.uk. **Document type:** abstracting/indexing.
—CCC.
Description: Current awareness service for researchers in clinical and life sciences.

616.8 UK ISSN 0960-8966
CODEN: NEDIEC
NEUROMUSCULAR DISORDERS. 1991. bi-m. £273($435) (effective 1996). Elsevier Science Ltd., Pergamon, P.O. Box 800, Kidlington, Oxford OX5 1DX, England. TEL 44-1865-843000. FAX 44-1865-843010. E-mail: nlinfo-f@elsevier.nl; usinfo-f@elsevier.com; forinfo-kyf04035@niftyserve.or.jp; Site addr.: http://www.elsevier.nl/. (Subscr. in U.S. and Canada to: Elsevier Science, 660 White Plains Rd., Tarrytown, NY 10591-5153. TEL 914-524-9200. FAX 914-333-2444) Ed. Victor Dubowitz. index. (also avail. in microfilm from UMI; back issues avail.) **Indexed:** Excerp.Med. (1992-), Ind.Med. (1992-). **Document type:** academic/scholarly publication.
—BLDSC (6081.504850); Genuine Article; UMI; UnCover. CCC.
Description: Covers all aspects of neuromuscular disorders in childhood and adult life.
Refereed Serial

616.8 US ISSN 0896-6273
QP356.2 CODEN: NERNET
NEURON. 1988. m. $99 to individuals (foreign $165); institutions $350 (foreign $415). Cell Press, 50 Church St., Cambridge, MA 02138. TEL 617-661-7060. FAX 617-661-7061. adv.; bk.rev. **Indexed:** Sport Fish.Abstr., Wild.Rev., Zoo.Rec. **Document type:** academic/scholarly publication.
—BLDSC (6081.504900); CASDDS; Faxon; SWETS; UnCover.

NEUROORTHOPAEDIE. see *MEDICAL SCIENCES — Orthopedics And Traumatology*

616.8 AT ISSN 0919-6544
NEUROPATHOLOGY. 1980. q. Aus.$331($345) (22000 Yen) (effective 1996). (Japanese Society of Neuropathology) Blackwell Science Pty Ltd, P.O. Box 378, Carlton South, Vic. 3053, Australia. TEL 61-3-93470300. FAX 61-3-93493016. (back issues avail.) **Document type:** academic/scholarly publication.
Supersedes in part (in 1993): Shinkei Byorigaku (ISSN 0286-3626)

616.8 UK ISSN 0305-1846
CODEN: NANEDL
NEUROPATHOLOGY AND APPLIED NEUROBIOLOGY. 1975. bi-m. £440 in Europe; elsewhere £484($779) (effective 1996). (British Neuropathological Society) Blackwell Science Ltd., Osney Mead, Oxford OX2 0EL, England. TEL 01865-206206. FAX 01865-206219. TELEX 83355 MEDBOK G. Ed. R.O. Weller. adv.; bk.rev.; bibl.; charts; illus.; index. circ. 550. (also avail. in microform from UMI; back issues avail.; reprint service avail. from ISI) **Indexed:** ASCA, Biol.Abstr., Chem.Abstr., Curr.Adv.Cell & Devel.Biol., Curr.Adv.Ecol.Sci., Curr.Cont., Excerp.Med., Ind.Med., Ind.Sci.Rev., Ind.Vet., Sci.Cit.Ind., Small Anim.Abstr., Vet.Bull. **Document type:** academic/scholarly publication.
—BLDSC (6081.514000); CASDDS; Faxon; Genuine Article; SWETS; UMI; UnCover. CCC.
Refereed Serial

NEUROPEDIATRICS; journal of pediatric neurobiology, neurology and neurosurgery. see *MEDICAL SCIENCES — Pediatrics*

NEUROPHARMACOLOGY. see *PHARMACY AND PHARMACOLOGY*

616.8 FR ISSN 0987-7053
CODEN: NCLIE4
NEUROPHYSIOLOGIE CLINIQUE/CLINICAL NEUROPHYSIOLOGY; exploration fonctionnelle du systeme nerveux. (Text in French; summaries in English, French) 1970. bi-m. 1295 F. in France; foreign 1500 F.($293) (effective 1996). (Societe d'E E G et de Neurophysiologie Clinique de Langue Francaise) Editions Scientifiques Elsevier, 141 rue de Javel, 75747 Paris, France. TEL 33-1-45589063. (Subscr. in U.S. and Canada to: Elsevier Science Inc., Box 882, Madison Sq. Sta., New York, NY 10159. TEL 212-989-5800) Ed. A. Autret. adv.; bk.rev.; illus.; index. circ. 3,000. (also avail. in microform from UMI; reprint service avail. from ISI) **Indexed:** Bibl.Dev.Med.& Child Neur., Biol.Abstr., Bull.Signal., Curr.Cont., Excerp.Med., Ind.Med. **Document type:** academic/scholarly publication.
—BLDSC (6081.517800); Faxon; Genuine Article; SWETS. CCC.
Formerly: Revue d'Electroencephalographie et de Neurophysiologie Clinique (ISSN 0370-4475)
Description: Covers the field of neurophysiology, electroencephalography, electromyography, evoked potentials and other investigative approaches in neurology and psychiatry.
Refereed Serial

NEUROPHYSIOLOGY. see *BIOLOGY — Physiology*

616.8 US ISSN 0090-2977
CODEN: NPHYBI
NEUROPHYSIOLOGY. English translation of: Neirofiziologiya. 1969. bi-m. $1245 (foreign $1455) (effective 1996). Plenum Publishing Corp., Consultants Bureau, 233 Spring St., New York, NY 10013-1578. TEL 212-620-8468. FAX 212-463-0742. TELEX 23-421139. Eds. V.I. Skok, P.G. Kostyuk. (back issues avail.) **Indexed:** Biol.Abstr., Excerp.Med., Ind.Med., Int.Abstr.Biol.Sci., Psychol.Abstr. **Document type:** academic/scholarly publication.
—BLDSC (0416.260000); Faxon; Genuine Article; SWETS; UMI. CCC.
Refereed Serial

616.8 615 IT ISSN 0394-9540
NEUROPSICOFARMACOLOGIA DEL COMPORTAMENTO. (Text in Italian; summaries in English) 1988. q. L.40000($40) (Club Internazionale di Neuropsicofarmacologia del Comportamento) C I C Edizioni Internazionali s.r.l., Via L. Spallanzani, 11, 00161 Rome, Italy. TEL 06-8412673. FAX 06-44242033. TELEX 622099 CIC I. Dir. P. Pancheri.

616.8 GW
NEUROPSYCHIATRIE. 1985. q. DM.125($96) per vol. Dustri-Verlag Dr. Karl Feistle, Bahnhofstr. 9, 82041 Deisenhofen, Germany. TEL 089-613861-0. FAX 089-6135412. Ed. Dr. F. Gerstenbrand. **Indexed:** Excerp.Med. (1995-). **Document type:** academic/scholarly publication.

NEUROPSYCHIATRIE DE L'ENFANCE ET DE L'ADOLESCENCE. see *MEDICAL SCIENCES — Pediatrics*

616.8 US ISSN 0894-878X
CODEN: NNNEEB
NEUROPSYCHIATRY, NEUROPSYCHOLOGY AND BEHAVIORAL NEUROLOGY. 1989. q. $128 to individuals (foreign $171); institutions $186 (foreign $227) (effective 1996); newsstand price: $58. (Behavioral Neurology Society) Lippincott - Raven Publishers, 227 E. Washington Sq., Philadelphia, PA 19106. TEL 215-238-4200. Eds. Michael Alan Taylor, Elliott D. Ross. adv. contact: Phyllis Noyes. charts; illus. circ. 1,000. (reprint service avail. from UMI) **Indexed:** Excerp.Med., Psychol.Abstr. (1988-). **Document type:** academic/scholarly publication.
—BLDSC (6081.543000); Genuine Article; SWETS; UMI; UnCover. CCC.
Description: Presents original research articles on basic brain processes; includes critical review articles, case reports, and brief reports on preliminary studies and pertinent clinical issues.
Refereed Serial

616.8 612 SZ ISSN 0302-282X
CODEN: NPBYAL
NEUROPSYCHOBIOLOGY; international journal of experimental and clinical research in biological psychiatry, pharmacopsychiatry, biological psychology, pharmacopsychology and pharmacoelectroencephalography. (Text in English) 8/yr. (in 2 vols.). 477.60 SFr.($367.20) to individuals; institutions 796 SFr.($612) (effective 1996). (International Pharmaco-EEG Group) S. Karger AG, Allschwilerstr. 10, P.O. Box, CH-4009 Basel, Switzerland. TEL 061-3061111. FAX 061-3061234. E-mail: Karger@Karger.ch. Ed.Bd. bk.rev.; abstr.; index. circ. 1,000. (also avail. in microform from UMI) **Indexed:** Biol.Abstr., Biotech.Abstr., Chem.Abstr., Curr.Adv.Ecol.Sci., Curr.Cont., Dent.Ind., Excerp.Med., Ind.Med., Ind.Sci.Rev., Nutr.Abstr., Psychol.Abstr. (1975-). **Document type:** academic/scholarly publication.
—BLDSC (6081.545000); CASDDS; Faxon; Genuine Article; SWETS; UnCover. CCC.
Incorporates: International Pharmacopsychiatry (ISSN 0020-8272)
Refereed Serial

616.8 UK ISSN 0028-3932
RC321 CODEN: NUPSA6
NEUROPSYCHOLOGIA; an international journal in behavioural neuroscience. (Text in English, French or German; summaries in French, German) 1963. m. £853($1357) (effective 1996). Elsevier Science Ltd., Pergamon, P.O. Box 800, Kidlington, Oxford OX5 1DX, England. TEL 44-1865-843010. E-mail: nlinfo-f@elsevier.nl; usinfo-f@elsevier.com; forinfo-kyf04035@niftyserve.or.jp; Site addr.: http://www.elsevier.nl/. (Subscr. in U.S. and Canada to: Elsevier Science, 660 White Plains Rd., Tarrytown, NY 10591-5153. TEL 914-524-9200. FAX 914-333-2444) Ed. M. Jeeves. adv.: B&W page $550, color page $1350. bk.rev.; charts; illus.; index. circ. 1,950. (also avail. in microfilm from UMI; reprint service avail. from UMI) **Indexed:** Behav.Med.Abstr., Bibl.Dev.Med.& Child Neur., Biol.Abstr., Curr.Adv.Ecol.Sci., Curr.Cont., Dent.Ind., Excerp.Med., Ind.Med., Ind.Sci.Rev., Psychol.Abstr. (1967-), Yrbk.Assoc.Educ.& Rehab.Blind. **Document type:** academic/scholarly publication.
—BLDSC (6081.550000); EMDOCS; Faxon; Genuine Article; SWETS; UMI; UnCover. CCC.
Description: Promotes the study of human behavior from a neurological point of view, and integrates clinical, general, and experimental contributions to the field.
Refereed Serial

MEDICAL SCIENCES — PSYCHIATRY AND NEUROLOGY

616.8 UK ISSN 0960-2011
CODEN: NREHE3
NEUROPSYCHOLOGICAL REHABILITATION; an international journal. 1991. q. £32.50($60) to individuals (outside the E.U. £37.50); institutions £75 (outside the E.U. £80 ($135)) (effective 1996). Lawrence Erlbaum Associates Ltd., 27 Palmeira Mansions, Church Rd., Hove, E. Sussex, BN3 2FA, England. TEL 01273-207411. FAX 01273-205612. (Subscr. to: Turpin Distribution Services Ltd., Blackhorse Rd., Letchworth, Herts. SG6 1HN, England. TEL 01462-672555. FAX 01462-480947) Ed. Barbara A. Wilson. adv.: page £175; 110 x 190. **Indexed:** Excerp.Med. (1993-), Psychol.Abstr. (1991-). **Document type:** academic/scholarly publication.
—BLDSC (6081.551000).
Description: Provides an international forum for the publication of well-designed and properly evaluated intervention strategies, surveys, and observational procedures that are clinically relevent and may also back up theoretical arguments or models.

616.8 US ISSN 0893-133X
CODEN: NEROEW
NEUROPSYCHOPHARMACOLOGY. 1987. m. $580 to institutions (effective 1996). (American College of Neuropsychopharmacology) Elsevier Science Inc., 655 Ave. of the Americas, New York, NY 10010. TEL 212-989-5800. FAX 212-633-3990. TELEX 420643 AEP UI. (Subscr. to: Box 882, Madison Sq. Sta., New York, NY10159-0882) Ed. Dr. J. Christian Gillin. (back issues avail.) **Indexed:** Chem.Abstr., Curr.Cont., Excerp.Med., Psychol.Abstr. (1987-), Sci.Cit.Ind. **Document type:** academic/scholarly publication.
—BLDSC (6081.555500); ADONIS; CASDDS; Faxon; Genuine Article; SWETS; UnCover. **CCC.**
Description: Focuses on clinical and basic science contributions to the field of neuropsychopharmacology.
Refereed Serial

616.8 US ISSN 0097-0549
RC331 CODEN: NBHPBT
NEUROSCIENCE AND BEHAVIORAL PHYSIOLOGY. 1967. bi-m. $645 (foreign $755) (effective 1996). (Federation of American Societies for Experimental Biology) Plenum Publishing Corp., Consultants Bureau, 233 Spring St., New York, NY 10013-1578. TEL 212-620-8468. FAX 212-463-0742. TELEX 23-421139. Ed.Bd. (also avail. in microform from UMI,PMC; microfilm from JSC; reprint service avail. from UMI) **Indexed:** Biol.Abstr., Chem.Abstr., Curr.Cont., Excerp.Med., Psychol.Abstr. (1973-). **Document type:** academic/scholarly publication.
—BLDSC (6081.560000); Faxon; SWETS; UMI; UnCover. **CCC.**
Formerly (until vol.5, 1972): Neuroscience Translations (ISSN 0028-3959)
Description: Translation of selected articles from Russian neurology journals.
Refereed Serial

616.8 150 US ISSN 0894-4105
CODEN: NEUPEG
NEUROPSYCHOLOGY. 1987. q. $50 to non-members (foreign $65); members $30 (foreign $38); institutions $87 (foreign $117). American Psychological Association, 750 First St., N.E., Washington, DC 20002-4242. TEL 202-336-5600. FAX 202-336-5568. Ed. Nelson Butters. circ. 5,800. **Indexed:** Excerp.Med. (1995-), Psychol.Abstr. (1987-). **Document type:** academic/scholarly publication.
—BLDSC (6081.553000); SWETS; UMI; UnCover. **CCC.**
Description: Features interdisciplinary contributions on assessment, treatment, and rehabilitation in clinical neuropsychology, focusing on neuropsychological measurement techniques and psychosocial adjustment of the impaired patient.
Refereed Serial

616.8 IE ISSN 1053-8135
NEUROREHABILITATION; an interdisciplinary journal. 1991. bi-m. I£130($205) (effective 1996). Elsevier Science Ireland Ltd., P.O. Box 85, Limerick, Ireland. FAX 353-61-472144. (Subscr. in U.S. and Canada to: Elsevier Science, P.O. Box 882, Madison Sq. Sta., New York, NY 10159-0882. TEL 212-989-5800. FAX 212-633-3990) Eds. Jeffrey Kreutzer, Nathan Zasler. bk.rev. (also avail. in microform from UMI; back issues avail.) **Document type:** academic/scholarly publication.
—BLDSC (6081.558400); UMI. **CCC.**
Description: Provides multidisciplinary rehabilitation teams with current clinical information for treating patients who are cognitively or physically challenged due to acquired or congenital neurologic disability.
Refereed Serial

616.8 UK ISSN 0149-7634
QP360 CODEN: NBREDE
NEUROSCIENCE AND BIOBEHAVIORAL REVIEWS. 1977. q. £394($627) (effective 1996). Elsevier Science Ltd., Pergamon, P.O. Box 800, Kidlington, Oxford OX5 1DX, England. TEL 44-1865-843010. FAX 44-1865-843010.
E-mail: nlinfo-f@elsevier.nl; usinfo-f@elsevier.com; forinfo-kyf04035@niftyserve.or.jp; Site addr.: http://www.elsevier.nl/. (Subscr. in U.S. and Canada to: Elsevier Science, 660 White Plains Rd., Tarrytown, NY 10591-5153. TEL 914-524-9200. FAX 914-333-2444) Ed. Matthew J. Wayner. bk.rev.; index. (also avail. in microform from UMI; reprint service avail. from UMI,ISI) **Indexed:** Biol.Abstr., Chem.Abstr., Curr.Adv.Ecol.Sci., Curr.Cont., Dent.Ind., Excerp.Med., Ind.Med., Ind.Sci.Rev., Psychol.Abstr. (1977-), Sci.Cit.Ind. **Document type:** academic/scholarly publication.
—BLDSC (6081.561000); CASDDS; Faxon; Genuine Article; SWETS; UMI; UnCover. **CCC.**
Formerly: Biobehavioral Reviews.
Description: Articles on anatomy, biochemistry, embryology, endocrinology, genetics, pharmacology, physiology and all aspects of biological sciences related to the problems of the nervous system.
Refereed Serial

153.4 616.8 NE ISSN 0927-0116
NEUROPSYCHOLOGY AND COGNITION. (Text in English) 1989. irreg., vol.5, 1994. price varies. Kluwer Academic Publishers, Postbus 17, 3300 AA Dordrecht, Netherlands. TEL 31-78-392392. FAX 31-78-392254. TELEX 29245 KAPG NL. (Dist. by: Kluwer Academic Publishers Group, P.O. Box 322, 3300 AH Dordrecht, Netherlands. TEL 31-78-392392. FAX 31-78-546474; N. America dist. addr.: Box 358, Accord Sta., Hingham, MA 02018-0358. TEL 617-871-6600. FAX 617-871-6528) (back issues avail.) **Document type:** monographic series.
—BLDSC (6081.553300).
Refereed Serial

616.8 UK ISSN 0959-4965
CODEN: NERPEZ
NEUROREPORT. 1990. 18/yr. £735($1250) to institutions (effective 1995). Rapid Communications of Oxford Ltd., The Old Malthouse, Paradise St., Oxford OX1 1LD, England. TEL 01865-790447. FAX 01865-244012. E-mail: rapidcom@vax.oxford.ac.uk. Ed. David Ottoson. adv. contact: Julie Gribben. **Indexed:** Curr.Cont., Excerp.Med. (1992-), Ind.Med., Psychol.Abstr. (1990-), Sci.Cit.Ind. **Document type:** academic/scholarly publication.
●Also available on CD-ROM.
—BLDSC (6081.558500); ADONIS; CASDDS; Genuine Article; SWETS; UnCover. **CCC.**
Description: Encompasses all the major fields of neuroscience while still reflecting the specialization in each given field.

NEUROPSYCHOLOGY, DEVELOPMENT AND COGNITION. SECTION A: JOURNAL OF CLINICAL AND EXPERIMENTAL NEUROPSYCHOLOGY. see *PSYCHOLOGY*

616.8 UK ISSN 0306-4522
QP351 CODEN: NRSCDN
NEUROSCIENCE; an international journal. 1976. 24/yr. £2516($4001) (effective 1996). (International Brain Research Organization) Elsevier Science Ltd., Pergamon, P.O. Box 800, Kidlington, Oxford OX5 1DX, England. TEL 44-1865-843010. FAX 44-1865-843010.
E-mail: nlinfo-f@elsevier.nl; usinfo-f@elsevier.com; forinfo-kyf04035@niftyserve.or.jp; Site addr.: http://www.elsevier.nl/. (Subscr. in U.S. and Canada to: Elsevier Science, 660 White Plains Rd., Tarrytown, NY 10591-5153. TEL 914-524-9200. FAX 914-333-2444) Ed.Bd. adv.; bk.rev.; illus.; stat.; index. circ. 1,500. (also avail. in microform from UMI) **Indexed:** Apic.Abstr., Biol.Abstr., Curr.Adv.Ecol.Sci., Curr.Cont., Curr.Ref.Fish Res., Dairy Sci.Abstr., Dent.Ind., Excerp.Med., Ind.Med., Ind.Sci.Rev., Telegen. **Document type:** academic/scholarly publication.
—BLDSC (6081.559000); ADONIS; CASDDS; Faxon; Genuine Article; SWETS; UMI; UnCover. **CCC.**
Description: Original research on any aspect of the scientific study of the nervous system.
Refereed Serial

616.8 IE ISSN 0304-3940
QP351 CODEN: NELED5
NEUROSCIENCE LETTERS; an international multidisciplinary journal devoted to the rapid publication of basic research in neurosciences. 1975. 57/yr. I£2375($3753) (effective 1996). Elsevier Science Ireland Ltd., P.O. Box 85, Limerick, Ireland. TEL 353-61-471944.
FAX 353-61-472144. (Subscr. in U.S. and Canada to: Elsevier Science Inc., Box 882, Madison Sq. Sta., New York, NY 10159. TEL 212-989-5800. FAX 212-633-3990) Ed. M. Zimmermann. bibl.; charts; illus. (also avail. in microform from UMI; reprint service avail. from SWZ) **Indexed:** Apic.Abstr., Biol.Abstr., Chem.Abstr., Curr.Adv.Biochem., Curr.Adv.Cell & Devel.Biol., Curr.Adv.Ecol.Sci., Curr.Cont., Dairy Sci.Abstr., Dent.Ind., Excerp.Med., Ind.Med., Ind.Sci.Rev., Ind.Vet., Sci.Cit.Ind., Vet.Bull. **Document type:** academic/scholarly publication.
—BLDSC (6081.562000); ADONIS; CASDDS; Faxon; Genuine Article; SWETS; UMI; UnCover. **CCC.**
Refereed Serial

616.8 US ISSN 1040-7308
QP360 CODEN: NERVEJ
NEUROPSYCHOLOGY REVIEW. 1989. q. $150 (foreign $175) (effective 1996). Plenum Publishing Corp., 233 Spring St., New York, NY 10013-1578. TEL 212-620-8000. FAX 212-463-0742. TELEX 23-421139. Eds. Gerald Goldstein, Antonio E. Puente. adv. (also avail. in microform from JSC; back issues avail.) **Indexed:** Excerp.Med., Ind.Med. (1993-), Psychol.Abstr. (1990-), Soc.Work Res.& Abstr. **Document type:** academic/scholarly publication.
—BLDSC (6081.553600); Genuine Article; UMI; UnCover. **CCC.**
Description: Integrates and interprets topics of interest to clinical or research neuropsychologists and behavioral neurologists.
Refereed Serial

616.8 US ISSN 0278-3738
NEUROSCIENCE NEWSLETTER. 1970. bi-m. $50 membership. Society for Neuroscience, 11 Dupont Circle, N.W., Ste. 500, Washington, DC 20036. TEL 202-462-6688. adv. circ. 23,500. (back issues avail.) **Document type:** newsletter.

MEDICAL SCIENCES — PSYCHIATRY AND NEUROLOGY

616.8 IE ISSN 0168-0102
RC337 CODEN: NERADN
NEUROSCIENCE RESEARCH. (Text and summaries in English) 1984. m. I£492($777) (effective 1996). (Japan Neuroscience Society, JA) Elsevier Science Ireland Ltd., P.O. Box 85, Limerick, Ireland. TEL 353-61-471944. FAX 353-61-472144. (Subscr. in U.S. and Canada to: Elsevier Science Inc., Box 882, Madison Sq. Sta., New York, NY 10159. TEL 212-989-5800. FAX 212-633-3990) Ed. Masao Ito. index. (also avail. in microform from UMI; back issues avail.) **Indexed:** Apic.Abstr., Biol.Abstr., Chem.Abstr., Curr.Cont., Excerp.Med., Ind.Med., Psychol.Abstr. (1984-). **Document type:** academic/scholarly publication.
—BLDSC (6081.563600); CASDDS; Genuine Article; SWETS; UnCover. **CCC.**
Description: Covers all fields of neuroscience, from the molecular to behavioral levels.
Refereed Serial

616.8 UK ISSN 0893-6609
RC346 CODEN: NRCOEE
NEUROSCIENCE RESEARCH COMMUNICATONS. 1987. bi-m. $475 (foreign $475) (effective 1996). John Wiley & Sons Ltd., Journals, Baffins Ln., Chichester, W. Sussex PO19 1UD, England. TEL 01243-779777. FAX 01243-776128. TELEX 86290 WIBOOK G. (Subscr. in the Americas to: John Wiley & Sons, Inc., 605 Third Ave., New York, NY 10158. TEL 212-850-6645. FAX 212-850-6021) Ed. W.H. Gispen. (also avail. in microform from UMI; back issues avail.; reprint service avail. from SWZ) **Indexed:** A.I.Abstr., Chem.Abstr., Curr.Cont., Excerp.Med., Telegen. **Document type:** academic/scholarly publication.
—BLDSC (6081.563800); CASDDS; Faxon; Genuine Article; SWETS; UMI; UnCover. **CCC.**
Description: Contains international and multidisciplinary original contributions to the neurosciences.
Refereed Serial

616.8 JA ISSN 0388-7448
CODEN: NUOCDO
NEUROSCIENCES. Variant title: No Kenkyukai Kaishi. (Text in English and Japanese) 1975. q. 10000 Yen. (Japan Neurosciences Research Association - No Kenkyukai) Kinokuniya Shoten - Kinokuniya Co., Ltd., Yokohama Office, Ryoko Shin-Takashimadai Bldg., 7th Fl., 102 Sawatari, Kanagawa-ku, Yokohama-shi 221, Japan. FAX 0862-23-3569. (Editorial and subscr. addr.: Dept. of Neurochemistry, Institute for Neurobiology, Okayama University Medical School, 5-1, Shikata-cho 2-chome, Okayama 700, Japan) Ed. Akitane Mori. adv. circ. 800. (back issues avail.) **Indexed:** Biol.Abstr.
—CASDDS; Genuine Article.
Formerly: Joken Hansha (ISSN 0368-2803)
Description: Promotes integrated, interdisciplinary studies of the interaction between the neural system and the behavior and homeostasis of the living body, as well as the mental activity of the human being.

616.8 US ISSN 0148-396X
RD593
NEUROSURGERY (BALTIMORE). 1977. m. $145 to individuals; institutions $200 (effective 1995). (Congress of Neurological Surgeons) Williams & Wilkins, 428 E. Preston St., Baltimore, MD 21202. TEL 410-528-4000; 800-638-6423. FAX 410-528-4312. TELEX 87669. Ed. Dr. Michael L.J. Apuzzo. adv.; bk.rev.; abstr.; bibl.; charts; illus.; index. circ. 9,011. (also avail. in microform from WWS; back issues avail.) **Indexed:** Bibl.Dev.Med.& Child Neur., Curr.Adv.Cancer Res., Curr.Cont., Dent.Ind., Excerp.Med., Ind.Med., Ind.Sci.Rev., Rev.Med.& Vet.Mycol. **Document type:** academic/scholarly publication.
—BLDSC (6081.582000); Faxon; Genuine Article; SWETS; UnCover. **CCC.**
Description: Explains techniques and devices, plus pertinent research in neuroscience.
Refereed Serial

NEUROSURGERY CLINICS OF NORTH AMERICA. see *MEDICAL SCIENCES — Surgery*

NEUROSURGICAL REVIEW. see *MEDICAL SCIENCES — Surgery*

616.8 US ISSN 0161-813X
RC321 CODEN: NRTXDN
NEUROTOXICOLOGY (LITTLE ROCK); an international journal. Variant title: Journal of Neurotoxicology. (Supplement avail.) 1979. q. $129 (foreign $155) (effective 1995). Intox Press, Inc., 13924 Rivercrest Dr., Little Rock, AR 72212. TEL 501-227-8622. FAX 501-224-1947. (Subscr. to: Box 24865, Little Rock, AR 72221-4865) adv.; bk.rev.; abstr.; bibl.; charts; illus.; index. circ. 2,000. (back issues avail.) **Indexed:** Biol.Abstr., Chem.Abstr., Curr.Cont., Excerp.Med., Ind.Med. **Document type:** academic/scholarly publication.
—BLDSC (6081.585800); CASDDS; Faxon; Genuine Article; SWETS; UnCover.
Description: Publishes original research reports and brief communications relating to neurotoxicology.

616.8 UK ISSN 0892-0362
CODEN: NETEEC
NEUROTOXICOLOGY AND TERATOLOGY. 1979. bi-m. $745 to institutions (effective 1996). (Behavioral Toxicology Society) Elsevier Science Ltd., Pergamon, P.O. Box 800, Kidlington, Oxford OX5 1DX, England. TEL 44-1865-843000. FAX 44-1865-843010. E-mail: nlinfo-f@elsevier.nl; usinfo-f@elsevier.com; forinfo-kyf04035@niftyserve.or.jp; Site addr.: http://www.elsevier.nl/. (Subscr. in U.S. and Canada to: Elsevier Science, 660 White Plains Rd., Tarrytown, NY 10591-5153. TEL 914-524-9200. FAX 914-333-2444) (Co-sponsor: Neurobehavioral Teratology Society) Ed. Donald E. Hutchings. adv.; illus.; index. (also avail. in microfilm from UMI; reprint service avail. from ISI,UMI) **Indexed:** Biol.Abstr., Chem.Abstr., Curr.Adv.Ecol.Sci., Curr.Cont., Dairy Sci.Abstr., Dent.Ind., Environ.Abstr., Excerp.Med., Ind.Med., Ind.Sci.Rev., Psychol.Abstr. (1981-), Sci.Cit.Ind. **Document type:** academic/scholarly publication.
—BLDSC (6081.586500); ADONIS; CASDDS; Faxon; Genuine Article; SWETS; UMI; UnCover. **CCC.**
Former titles: Neurobehavioral Toxicology and Teratology (ISSN 0275-1380); Neurobehavioral Toxicology (ISSN 0191-3581)
Refereed Serial

616.8 BU ISSN 0548-3794
CODEN: NPNMAB
NEVROLOGIA, PSIHIATRIJA I NEVROHIRURGIJA. (Text in Bulgarian; summaries in Russian and English) 1962. bi-m. 16 lv.($7) (Ministerstvo na Narodnoto Zdrave) Izdatelstvo Meditsina i Fizkultura, 11, Pl. Slaveikov, Sofia, Bulgaria. (Dist. by: Hemus, 6, Rouski Blvd., 1000 Sofia, Bulgaria) (Co-sponsor: Nauchno Druzhestvo po Nevrologija, Psihiatrija i Nevrohirurgija) Ed. V. Ivanov. circ. 1,360. **Indexed:** Abstr.Bulg.Sci.Med.Lit., Chem.Abstr., Excerp.Med. (until 1993).
—CASDDS.

188 US ISSN 0193-9416
RA790.A1 CODEN: NMHSEG
NEW DIRECTIONS FOR MENTAL HEALTH SERVICES. 1979. q. $54 to individuals; institutions $75. Jossey-Bass Inc., Publishers, 350 Sansome St., 5th Fl., San Francisco, CA 94104. TEL 415-433-1767. FAX 415-433-0499. Ed. H. Richard Lamb. circ. 1,350. (back issues avail.) **Indexed:** Educ.Ind., Ind.Med., PSI, Psychol.Abstr. **Document type:** monographic series.
—BLDSC (6083.396000); UMI; UnCover.
Description: Gives practical descriptions of new treatment techniques, models and approaches. Also presents guidelines for planning and implementing effective services.

616.8 GW ISSN 1012-9871
NEW ISSUES IN NEUROSCIENCES. 1988. 3/yr. DM.162. Georg Thieme Verlag, Ruedigerstr. 14, 70469 Stuttgart, Germany. TEL 0711-89310. FAX 0711-8931298. TELEX 07252275-GTV-D. (Subscr. to: Postfach 104853, 70042 Stuttgart, Germany) Ed.Bd. **Document type:** academic/scholarly publication.
Description: Provides new perspectives on particular neurological diseases and related topics.

NEW TRENDS IN NEUROPHARMACOLOGY. see *PHARMACY AND PHARMACOLOGY*

NEW YORK (STATE). COMMISSION ON QUALITY OF CARE FOR THE MENTALLY DISABLED. ANNUAL REPORT. see *HOSPITALS*

616.8 UK ISSN 0959-8391
NEWS IN HEADACHE. 1990. q. (International Headache Society) Cambridge Medical Publications Ltd., Wicker House, High St., Worthing, W. Sussex BN11 1DJ, England. TEL 01903-205884.
FAX 01903-234862. TELEX 878372 PPSLTD G. Ed.Bd. circ. (controlled). **Document type:** newsletter.
—BLDSC (6104.430000).

NEWSLINK (DENVER). see *PSYCHOLOGY*

NIHON NO SHINKEI GEKA GAKKAI SOKAI SHOROKUSHU/JAPAN NEUROSURGICAL SOCIETY. ABSTRACTS OF THE ANNUAL MEETING. see *MEDICAL SCIENCES — Abstracting, Bibliographies, Statistics*

618.8 617 JA ISSN 0285-7936
NIHON NO SHINKEI GEKA KONGURESU KOENROKU/NEUROSURGEONS. (Text in English, Japanese; summaries in English) 1981. a. 10000 Yen. Nihon No Shinkei Geka Konguresu - Japanese Congress of Neurological Surgeons, Juntendo Daigakuu Igakubu No Shinkei Geka Kyoshitsu, 1-1, Hongo 2-chome, Bunkyo-ku, Tokyo 113, Japan.

NIHON PARAPUREJIA IGAKKAI ZASSHI/JAPAN SOCIETY OF PARAPLEGIA. JOURNAL. see *MEDICAL SCIENCES — Orthopedics And Traumatology*

618 617.3 JA ISSN 0917-1495
NO SHINKEI GEKA SOKUHO/NEUROSURGERY LETTERS. (Text in Japanese) 1990. m. 1200 Yen per no. Medika Shuppan - Medicus Publishing Inc., 18-24, Hiroshibacho, Suita-shi, Osaka 564, Japan.

618 617.3 JA ISSN 0914-5508
NO SOTCHU NO GEKA/SURGERY FOR CEREBRAL STROKE. (Text in Japanese; summaries in English) 1973. q. 2200 Yen per no. (Nihon No Sotchu no Geka Kenkyukai - Japanese Conference on Surgery of Cerebral Stroke) Nyuronsha - Neuron Publishing Co., 21-19-305, Higashigotanda 5-chome, Shinagawa-ku, Tokyo 141, Japan.

616.8 JA
CODEN: NTHAA7
NO TO HATTATSU. English edition: Brain and Development (ISSN 0387-7604) (Text in Japanese; summaries in English) 1969. bi-m. 8000 Yen($60) Japanese Society of Child Neurology - Nihon Shoni Shinkei Gakkai, Kenwado Bldg. 2F, 6-13 Wakamatsu-cho, Shinjuku-ku, Tokyo 162, Japan. Ed. Dr. Masataka Arima. adv.; bk.rev.; abstr.; index. circ. 3,000. **Indexed:** Adol.Ment.Hlth.Abstr., Bibl.Dev.Med.& Child Neur., Biol.Abstr., Chem.Abstr., Curr.Adv.Ecol.Sci., Dent.Ind., Excerp.Med., Ind.Med., Ind.Sci.Rev., Nutr.Abstr., Risk Abstr., Sci.Cit.Ind.
—BLDSC (6113.969000); CASDDS; EMDOCS.
Supersedes in part (in 1979): Brain and Development - No to Hattatsu (ISSN 0029-0831)

616.89 NO ISSN 0803-9488
NORDIC JOURNAL OF PSYCHIATRY. (Supplement avail. (ISSN 0803-9496)) (Text in English and Scandinavian languages; summaries in English) 1946. bi-m. NOK 620 in the Nordic countries; elsewhere NOK 715. Scandinavian University Press, P.O. Box 2959 Toeyen, N-0608 Oslo, Norway. TEL 47-22-57-54-00. FAX 47-22-57-53-53. (U.S. addr.: Scandinavian University Press, 200 Meacham Ave., Elmont, NY 11003. TEL 516-352-7300) Ed. Lars von Knorring. adv.; bk.rev.; index. circ. 4,000. **Indexed:** Biol.Abstr., Curr.Adv.Ecol.Sci., Excerp.Med., Psychol.Abstr. (1972-). **Document type:** academic/scholarly publication.
—BLDSC (6117.927050); Genuine Article. **CCC.**
Formerly: Nordisk Psykiatrisk Tidsskrift (ISSN 0029-1455)
Description: Addressed to clinical psychiatrists and their co-workers as well as reserchers.

616.89 NO
NORDIC JOURNAL OF PSYCHIATRY. SUPPLEMENT. 1974. irreg. Scandinavian University Press, P.O. Box 2959 Toeyen, N-0608 Oslo, Norway. TEL 47-22-57-54-00. FAX 47-22-57-53-53. **Indexed:** Excerp.Med.
Formerly: Nordisk Pyskiatrisk Tidsskrift. Supplement (ISSN 0346-8852)

MEDICAL SCIENCES — PSYCHIATRY AND NEUROLOGY

616.89   TU   ISSN 1300-0667
CODEN: NOPAB
NOROPSIKIYATRI ARSIVI/ARCHIVES OF NEUROPSYCHIATRY. 1964. q. Turk Noropsikiyatri Dernegi, Istanbul Universitesi, Istanbul Tip Fakultesi, 34390 Topkapi - Istanbul, Turkey. **Indexed:** Excerp.Med. (1994-). **Document type:** academic/scholarly publication.

616.8 301.15   FR   ISSN 0762-6819
NOUVELLE REVUE D'ETHNOPSYCHIATRIE. (Text in French; summaries in English) 1978. 4/yr. 330 F. to individuals (foreign 360 F.); institutions 450 F. (foreign 460 F.). Pensee Sauvage Editions, B.P. 141, 38002 Grenoble, France. TEL 76-87-13-03. FAX 76-46-27-25. Ed. Marie Rose Noro. **Indexed:** Anthropol.Lit.
Formerly: Ethnopsychiatrica (ISSN 0151-9808)

616.8   IT   ISSN 1122-035X
NUOVA RIVISTA DI NEUROLOGIA. (Text in English and Italian) 1931. bi-m. L.247500($150) (effective 1996). Pensieri Scientifico Editore s.r.l., Via Bradano 3-C, 00199 Rome, Italy. TEL 06-86207158. FAX 06-86207160. Eds. Vincenzo Floris, Cristoforo Norocutti. adv.; bk.rev.; bibl.; charts; illus. circ. 1,200. **Indexed:** Biol.Abstr., Chem.Abstr., Dent.Ind., Excerp.Med., Ind.Med. (until 1992). **Document type:** academic/scholarly publication.
—BLDSC (6184.909100); Faxon; SWETS.
Formerly (until 1990): Rivista di Neurologia (ISSN 0035-6344)

616.858   AT
O C D - THE HIDDEN DISORDER. 1992. q. Obsessive Compulsive Disorder Support Groups of New South Wales, 60 Victoria Rd., Gladesville, N.S.W. 2111, Australia. TEL 02-816-5688. (Co-sponsor: New South Wales Association for Mental Health) circ. 500.

150 361.3 610   US   ISSN 0164-212X
RC487   CODEN: OTMHDX
OCCUPATIONAL THERAPY IN MENTAL HEALTH; a journal of psychosocial practice and research. 1980. q. $175 (foreign $245) (effective 1996). Haworth Press, Inc., 10 Alice St., Binghamton, NY 13904. TEL 607-722-5857; 800-342-9678. FAX 607-722-1424. TELEX 4932599. Ed. Mary Louise Blount. adv.; bk.rev.; bibl. circ. 670. (also avail. in microfiche from UMI; back issues avail.; reprint service avail. from HAW) **Indexed:** Abstr.Health Care Manage.Stud., Adol.Ment.Hlth.Abstr., Behav.Abstr., Biol.Abstr., Bull.Signal., Chicago Psychoanal.Lit.Ind., Child Devel.Abstr., CINAHL, Excerp.Med., IMFL, Past.Care & Couns.Abstr., Psychol.Abstr., Rehabil.Lit., Soc.Work Res.& Abstr.
—BLDSC (6231.260000); Haworth; UnCover.
Description: Provides current material specifically for occupational therapists in mental health clinics, psychiatric hospitals, mental health programs, hospitals, and other settings.
Refereed Serial

616.89 150   DK   ISSN 0105-0621
ODENSE UNIVERSITY STUDIES IN PSYCHIATRY AND MEDICAL PSYCHOLOGY. (Text in Danish and English) 1973. irreg. price varies. Odense University Press, Campusvej 55, DK-5230 Odense M, Denmark. TEL 66-157999. FAX 66-158126. (back issues avail.) **Indexed:** Excerp.Med. **Document type:** monographic series, academic/scholarly publication.
Description: Biographies of important historical figures and how they influenced psychiatric medical history.

616.8   US   ISSN 0000-1570
RC335
OFFICIAL AMERICAN BOARD OF MEDICAL SPECIALTIES (A B M S) DIRECTORY OF BOARD CERTIFIED NEUROLOGISTS. 1985. biennial. $119.95. Marquis Who's Who, A Reed Reference Publishing company, 121 Chanlon Rd., New Providence, NJ 07974. TEL 908-464-6800. FAX 908-665-2898. (Subscr. to: Order Dept., Box 31, New Providence, NJ 07974-9903. TEL 800-521-8110) Ed. Roy Crego. **Document type:** directory.
Formerly: A B M S Directory of Certified Neurologists (ISSN 0884-1500)
Description: Biographical sketches of U.S. certified medical specialists sorted geographically with alpha index.

616.89   US   ISSN 0000-1651
RC335
OFFICIAL AMERICAN BOARD OF MEDICAL SPECIALTIES (A B M S) DIRECTORY OF BOARD CERTIFIED PSYCHIATRISTS. 1985. biennial. $99.95. Marquis Who's Who, A Reed Reference Publishing company, 121 Chanlon Rd., New Providence, NJ 07974. TEL 908-464-6800. FAX 908-665-2898. (Subscr. to: Order Dept., Box 31, New Providence, NJ 07974-9903. TEL 800-521-8110) Ed. Roy Crego. **Document type:** directory.
Formerly: A B M S Directory of Certified Psychiatrists (ISSN 0884-1519)
Description: Biographical sketches of U.S. certified medical specialists sorted geographically with alpha index.

616.83 362.2   UK   ISSN 0265-511X
OPEN MIND; the mental health magazine. 1983. bi-m. £15 to individuals; institutions £19; foreign £25. Mind, National Association for Mental Health, Granta House, 15-19 Broadway, Stratford, London E15 4BQ, England. TEL 0181-519-2122. FAX 0181-522-1725. Ed. Helen Imam. adv.; bk.rev.; film rev.; play rev.; illus.; tr.lit.; index. circ. 5,000. (back issues avail.) **Document type:** academic/scholarly publication.
—BLDSC (6266.325000).

150.198 615.856   US   ISSN 1054-075X
ORGONOMIC FUNCTIONALISM. 1989. a. $18.95 (effective 1995). Wilhelm Reich Infant Trust, Orgonon, Box 687, Rangeley, ME 04970. TEL 207-864-3443. Eds. Drs. Mary Boyd Higgins, Chester M. Raphael. circ. 200.
Description: Devoted to the writings of Wilhelm Reich.

616.835   IT   ISSN 0030-5618
ORIZZONTI APERTI; la voce dei poliomielitici. vol.4, 1970. irreg. (3-5/yr.). free. Associazione Nazionale Invalidi Esiti Poliomielite, Via Colttelli 7-D, 40124 Bologna, Italy. Ed. Gianni Selleri. circ. 16,000.
Description: Concerns poliomyelitis.

ORTHOMOLEKULAR; Fachzeitschrift fuer Ernaehrung, Gesundheit und Umwelt. *see* NUTRITION AND DIETETICS

616.8   US
OXFORD NEUROLOGICAL MONOGRAPHS. irreg. price varies. Oxford University Press, 200 Madison Ave., New York, NY 10016. TEL 212-679-7300. Ed. W. Ritchie Russell.
Refereed Serial

616.89   UK
OXFORD PSYCHIATRY SERIES. irreg., no.2, 1994. Oxford University Press, Oxford Journals, Walton St., Oxford OX2 6DP, England. TEL 01865-267907. FAX 01865-267773. TELEX 837330-OXPRES-G. E-mail: jnlorders@oup.co.uk. (US subscr. to: Oxford University Press Inc., 2001 Evans Rd., Cary, NC 27513. TEL 919-677-0977. FAX 919-677-1714) **Document type:** monographic series.

P A S C A L E 78: NEUROLOGIE. *see* MEDICAL SCIENCES — Abstracting, Bibliographies, Statistics

616.8   US
P.M. NEWS. 1972. bi-m. $15. White Plains Hospital Center, Anxiety and Phobia Clinic, Davis Ave. at Post Rd., White Plains, NY 10601. TEL 914-681-1038. FAX 914-681-2284. Ed. Judy Chessa. bk.rev. circ. 850. (back issues avail.) **Document type:** newsletter.
Description: Discusses the psychiatric specialties of anxieties, panic attacks, phobias, health anxiety, and obsessive-compulsive disorders.

616.89   GW   ISSN 0937-2032
P P M P. (Psychotherapie Psychosomatik Medizinische Psychologie) (Text in German; summaries in English) 1951. m. DM.222. (Allgemeine Aerztliche Gesellschaft fuer Psychotherapie) Georg Thieme Verlag, Ruedigerstr. 14, 70469 Stuttgart, Germany. TEL 0711-8931-0. FAX 0711-8931298. (Subscr. to: Postfach 104853, 70042 Stuttgart, Germany) (Co-sponsor: Oesterreichische Aerzte-Gesellschaft fuer Psychotherapie) Ed.Bd. adv.; bk.rev.; abstr.; bibl.; charts; illus.; index. circ. 1,900. (also avail. in microform from UMI; reprint service avail. from UMI) **Indexed:** Biol.Abstr., Curr.Cont., Excerp.Med., Ger.J.Psych., Ind.Med., Psychol.Abstr. (1951-), Risk Abstr., SSCI. **Document type:** academic/scholarly publication.
—BLDSC (6946.558250); Faxon; Genuine Article; SWETS; UMI. **CCC**.
Former titles (until 1988): Psychotherapie Psychosomatik Medizinische Psychologie (ISSN 0173-7937); Psychotherapie und Medizinische Psychologie (ISSN 0302-8984); Zeitschrift fuer Psychotherapie und Medizinische Psychologie (ISSN 0044-3417)

616.835   DK   ISSN 0901-7798
P T U NYT. 1985. bi-m. DKK 150. Landsforeningen af Polio-, Trafik og Ulykkesskadede, P.O. Box 64, Tuborgvej 5, DK-2900 Hellerup, Denmark. TEL 45-31-62-90-00. FAX 45-31-62-54-39. Ed. Hanne Birgitte Pedersen. adv. circ. 10,500.
Formerly: Polio-Nyt (ISSN 0900-5587)

616.8   NE   ISSN 0304-3959
RB127   CODEN: PAINDB
PAIN. 1975. m. fl.1292($788) (effective 1996). (International Association for the Study of Pain) Elsevier Science B.V., P.O. Box 211, 1000 AE Amsterdam, Netherlands. TEL 31-20-4853911. FAX 31-20-4853598. TELEX 18582 ESPA NL. E-mail: nlinfo-f@elsevier.nl; usinfo-f@elsevier.com; forinfo-kyf04035@niftyserve.or.jp; Site addr.: http"//www.elsevier.nl/. (Subscr. in U.S. and Canada to: Elsevier Science Inc., Box 882, Madison Sq. Sta., New York, NY 10159. TEL 212-989-5800. FAX 212-633-3990) Eds. P.D. Wall, R. Dubner. adv.; bk.rev.; abstr. circ. 5,000. (also avail. in microform from UMI; reprint service avail. from ISI,SWZ) **Indexed:** Behav.Med.Abstr., Biol.Abstr., Biotech.Abstr., Chem.Abstr., CINAHL, Curr.Adv.Cancer Res., Curr.Adv.Ecol.Sci., Curr.Cont., Dent.Ind., Excerp.Med., Ind.Med., Psychol.Abstr. (1976-). **Document type:** academic/scholarly publication.
—BLDSC (6333.795000); ADONIS; CASDDS; Faxon; Genuine Article; SWETS; UnCover. **CCC**.
Description: Provides a forum for information about the nature, mechanism and treatment of pain.
Refereed Serial

616.8   SZ   ISSN 0255-3910
CODEN: RCSHA8
PAIN AND HEADACHE. (Text in English) 1967. irreg. price varies. S. Karger AG, Allschwilerstr. 10, P.O. Box, CH-4009 Basel, Switzerland. TEL 061-3061111. FAX 061-3061234. E-mail: Karger@Karger.ch. Ed. P.L. Gildenberg. (reprint service avail. from ISI) **Indexed:** Biol.Abstr., Chem.Abstr., Curr.Cont., Ind.Med. (until 1992). **Document type:** academic/scholarly publication.
—BLDSC (6333.798500); CASDDS. **CCC**.
Formerly: Research and Clinical Studies in Headache (ISSN 0080-1453)
Description: The latest in understanding and controlling pain.
Refereed Serial

THE PAIN CLINIC. *see* MEDICAL SCIENCES — Anaesthesiology

THE PAIN CLINIC (PROCEEDINGS). *see* MEDICAL SCIENCES — Anaesthesiology

MEDICAL SCIENCES — PSYCHIATRY AND NEUROLOGY 4569

616 US
RB127
PAIN FORUM. 1992. q. $109 to individuals (foreign $131); institutions $149 (foreign $171). (American Pain Society) Churchill Livingstone International, 650 Ave. of the Americas, New York, NY 10011. TEL 212-206-5040. FAX 212-727-7808. **Indexed:** Excerp.Med. (1993-). **Document type:** academic/scholarly publication.
—BLDSC (6333.799500); Genuine Article. **CCC.**
Formerly (until 1995): A P S Journal (ISSN 1058-9139)
Description: Features scholarly discussion of issues of interest to practitioners and researchers in the field of pain management. Publishes hypotheses on basic scientific and clinical topics and critiques of those hypotheses.
Refereed Serial

PAIN MEDICINE JOURNAL CLUB JOURNAL. see *MEDICAL SCIENCES — Abstracting, Bibliographies, Statistics*

PARAGRAPHIC. see *HANDICAPPED*

616.837 617.3 UK ISSN 0031-1758
CODEN: PRPLBL
PARAPLEGIA. (Text in English; summaries in French and German) 1963. m. £180 to E.C.; elsewhere £200. (International Medical Society of Paraplegia) Stockton Press (Subsidiary of: Macmillan Press Ltd.), Houndmills, Basingstoke, Hants RG21 2XS, England. TEL 01256-817245. FAX 01256-28339. Ed. P. Harris. adv. contact: Michael Rowley. bk.rev.; abstr.; charts; illus.; stat.; index. (also avail. in microform from UMI) **Indexed:** Curr.Adv.Ecol.Sci., Curr.Cont., Excerp.Med., Ind.Med. **Document type:** academic/scholarly publication.
—BLDSC (6404.900000); EMDOCS; Faxon; Genuine Article; SWETS; UnCover. **CCC.**

PARAPLEGIA NEWS. see *HANDICAPPED — Physically Impaired*

016.8 SW ISSN 1104-2435
PARKINSON - JOURNALEN. 1993. q. Svenska Parkinsonfoerbundet, Karlagatan 23, S-416 61 Goeteborg, Sweden.

616.8 CN ISSN 0824-7315
PARKINSON NETWORK. French edition (ISSN 0845-4299) (Text in English) q. Can.$25 membership. Parkinson Foundation of Canada, 710-390 Bay St., Toronto, ON M5H 2Y2, Canada. TEL 416-366-0099; 800-565-3000. FAX 416-366-9190. Ed. Trevor Williams. adv. contact: Kennedy Coles. circ. 13,000 (paid). (back issues avail.) **Document type:** newsletter.
Formerly (until 1984): Parkinson Foundation of Canada. Bulletin (ISSN 0711-236X)
Description: Advises readers of events, new chapters and support groups, where to get help.

616.8 US
PARKINSON REPORT. 1957. q. membership. National Parkinson Foundation, Inc., 1501 N.W. Ninth Ave. - Bob Hope Rd., Miami, FL 33136-9990. TEL 305-547-6666; 800-327-4545. FAX 305-548-4403. Ed. Dr. Juan Sanchez-Ramos. charts; illus. **Document type:** newsletter.
Formerly: National Parkinson Foundation. Newsletter.
Description: Written for people affected by Parkinson's disease and explores various areas of the research.

616.89 US
PARKINSONIAN SPEAK-OUT. 1987. q. $72. 55 Merrick St., Rumford, RI 02916-2520. TEL 401-435-3179. Ed. R. Bernen. **Document type:** newsletter.

616.8 UK ISSN 1353-8020
▼**PARKINSONISM AND RELATED DISORDERS.** 1995. bi-m. £125($199) (effective 1996). Butterworth - Heinemann, Part of the Reed Elsevier group, Linacre House, Jordan Hill, Oxford OX2 8DP, England. TEL 01865-310366. FAX 01865-310898. TELEX 83111 BHPOXF G. (Subscr. to: Elsevier Science Ltd., P.O. Box 800, Kidlington, Oxford OX5 1DX, England. TEL 44-1865-843000. FAX 44-1865-843010; Subscr. in the U.S. and Canada to: Elsevier Science, 660 White Plains Rd., Tarrytown, NY 10591-5153. TEL 914-524-9200. FAX 914-333-2444) (also avail. in microform from UMI; back issues avail.) **Document type:** academic/scholarly publication.
—**CCC.**
Refereed Serial

616.8 US ISSN 0885-4807
PARKINSON'S DISEASE UPDATE. (Text in English and French) 1983. m. $40. Medical Publishing Co., Inc., 3917 Bluebird Rd., Huntingdon Valley, PA 19006. TEL 215-947-6648. FAX 215-947-6638. (Subscr. to: Box 24622, Philadelphia, PA 19111) Ed. Dr. Stuart Isaacson. bk.rev.; index. circ. 15,000. (back issues avail.) **Document type:** newsletter.

150 616.8 US
PATHWAYS (NEW YORK). q. free. Postgraduate Center for Mental Health, 124 E. 28th St., New York, NY 10016. TEL 212-689-7700. FAX 212-576-4198. Ed. Dawn Frost. circ. 1,500.

PEDIATRIC NEUROLOGY. see *MEDICAL SCIENCES — Pediatrics*

616.8 SZ ISSN 1016-2291
CODEN: PDNEEV
PEDIATRIC NEUROSURGERY. (Text in English) m. 459 SFr.($353) to individuals; institutions 918 SFr.($706) (effective 1996). (International Society for Paediatric Neurosurgery) S. Karger AG, Allschwilerstr. 10, P.O. Box, CH-4009 Basel, Switzerland. TEL 061-3061111. FAX 061-3061234. E-mail: Karger@Karger.ch. Ed. F. Epstein. (also avail. in microform from UMI) **Indexed:** Excerp.Med. **Document type:** academic/scholarly publication.
—BLDSC (6417.604700); CASDDS; Genuine Article; SWETS; UnCover. **CCC.**
Formerly (until 1991): Pediatric Neuroscience (ISSN 0255-7975); Which supersedes in part (in 1985): Child's Brain (ISSN 0302-2803)
Refereed Serial

PENNSYLVANIA MESSAGE. see *EDUCATION — Special Education And Rehabilitation*

616.8 IT
PERSONALITA - DIPENDENZE. 3/yr. L.70000 (foreign L.90000) (effective 1996). Mucchi Editore s.r.l., Via Emilia Est 1527, 41100 Modena, Italy. (Co-sponsors: Federazione Italiana Operatori Tossicodipendenze; Societa di Studio per i Disturbi di Personalita)

616.8 410 US
PERSPECTIVES IN NEUROLINGUISTICS, NEUROPSYCHOLOGY, AND PSYCHOLINGUISTICS; a series of monographs and treatises. 1976. irreg. Academic Press, Inc., 525 B St., Ste. 1900, San Diego, CA 92101-4495. TEL 619-231-6616. FAX 619-699-6715. (Subscr. to: Order Dept., 6277 Sea Harbor Dr., 4th Fl., Orlando, FL 32887. TEL 800-321-5068) Ed. Harry A. Whitaker. **Document type:** monographic series.
Refereed Serial

PERSPECTIVES IN NEUROLOGICAL SURGERY. see *MEDICAL SCIENCES — Surgery*

PERSPECTIVES IN PSYCHIATRIC CARE. see *MEDICAL SCIENCES — Nurses And Nursing*

591 US ISSN 1064-0517
QP363.5 CODEN: PDENED
PERSPECTIVES ON DEVELOPMENTAL NEUROBIOLOGY. 1989. q. 81 ECU (effective 1996). Gordon & Breach Science Publishers, c/o International Publishers Distributor, 280 Town Center Dr., Langhorne, PA 19047. TEL 215-750-2642. FAX 215-750-6343. (Subscr. to: Intern Publishers Distributor, P.O. Box 90, Reading, Berkshire RG1 8JL, England. TEL 44-173-456-8316) (also avail. in microform) **Indexed:** Ind.Med. (1994-).
—BLDSC (6428.141510); CASDDS. **CCC.**
Formerly (until 1992): Comments on Modern Biology. Part D, Comments on Developmental Neurology (ISSN 0896-5099)

616.89 371.9 US
PERSPECTIVES ON DYSLEXIA. q. $55 membership. Orton Dyslexia Society, 8600 LaSalle Rd., Ste. 382, Baltimore, MD 21204-6020. TEL 301-296-0232. circ. 12,000. **Document type:** newsletter.

616.89 FR ISSN 0031-6032
PERSPECTIVES PSYCHIATRIQUES. 1963. 5/yr. 370 F. to individuals; students 290 F. (foreign 440 F.). (Groupe d'Etudes de Psychiatrie Psychologie et Sciences Sociales) Galliena Promotion, 58 A, Rue du Dessous des Berges, 75013 Paris, France. TEL 45-84-97-66. FAX 45-84-92-56. Ed. Dr. Jacques Fortineau. adv.; bk.rev. circ. 2,500. **Indexed:** Psychol.Abstr.
—BLDSC (6428.161000).

616.89 GW ISSN 0176-3679
RM315 CODEN: PHRMEZ
PHARMACOPSYCHIATRY; clinical pharmacology, psychiatry, psychology, neurophysiology advances in theoretical and clinical research. (Text and summaries in English and German) 1968. bi-m. DM.297 (members of the Arbeitsgemeinschaft fuer Neuropsychopharmakologie DM.222.75). Georg Thieme Verlag, Ruedigerstr. 14, 70469 Stuttgart, Germany. TEL 0711-8931-0. FAX 0711-8931298. (Subscr. to: Postfach 104853, 70042 Stuttgart, Germany) Ed. B. Muller-Oerlinghausen. adv.; bibl.; charts; illus.; stat.; index. circ. 1,000. (also avail. in microform from UMI; microfiche; reprint service avail. from UMI) **Indexed:** Biol.Abstr., Biotech.Abstr., Chem.Abstr., Curr.Adv.Ecol.Sci., Curr.Cont., Dent.Ind., Excerp.Med., Ger.J.Psych., Ind.Med., Psychol.Abstr. (1989-), Sci.Cit.Ind. **Document type:** academic/scholarly publication.
—BLDSC (6447.087950); ADONIS; CASDDS; Faxon; Genuine Article; SWETS; UMI; UnCover. **CCC.**
Former titles: Pharmacopsychiatria (ISSN 0720-4280); (until 1980): Pharmakopsychiatrie - Neuro-Psychopharmakologie (ISSN 0031-7098)

616.89 GW ISSN 0936-9589
PHARMACOPSYCHIATRY. SUPPLEMENT. irreg. Georg Thieme Verlag, Ruedigerstr. 14, 70469 Stuttgart, Germany. TEL 0711-8931-0. FAX 0711-8931298. **Document type:** monographic series.

616.8 SP ISSN 0210-3931
PHRONESIS. 6/yr. Matematico Pedrayes 20, 1o, 33005 Oviedo, Spain. TEL 85-23-68-47. Ed. Dr. F. Bueno Martinez. circ. 50,000.

616.89 110 US ISSN 0361-0802
BF204.5 CODEN: PILGDR
PILGRIMAGE; reflections on the human journey. 1972. 5/yr. $39 (effective through 1996). Pilgrimage Press, Inc., RR1 Box 188M, Highlands, NC 28741-9707. TEL 704-526-3151. Ed. David Barstow. bk.rev.; circ. 1,000 (paid). (also avail. in microform from UMI; back issues avail.) **Document type:** academic/scholarly publication.
—UMI.
Description: Seeks to understand and celebrate the human journey through personal and experiential writing.

362.3 US ISSN 0031-9856
PINE CONE. 1966. q. free. Pinecrest State School, Box 191, Pineville, LA 71360. TEL 318-640-0754. illus. circ. 1,600. (processed)
Description: Articles related to mental retardation.

616.8 GW ISSN 0933-3851
PRAKTISCHE PSYCHIATRIE. 1988. irreg., vol.3, 1991. DM.39.80. W. Zuckschwerdt Verlag GmbH, Industriestr. 17, 82110 Germering, Germany. TEL 089-894349-0. FAX 089-89434950. Eds. R. Schuettler, R.M. Schulte. **Document type:** academic/scholarly publication.

616.89 150 GW ISSN 0032-7034
CODEN: PKIKAZ
PRAXIS DER KINDERPSYCOLOGIE UND KINDERPSYCHIATRIE. (Text in German; summaries in English and German) 1952. 10/yr. DM.95. Vandenhoeck und Ruprecht, Robert-Bosch-Breite 6, 37079 Goettingen, Germany. TEL 0551-6959-26. FAX 0551-695917. (Subscr. to: 37027 Goettingen, Germany) Eds. Annemarie Duehrssen, Rudolf Adam. adv.; bk.rev.; abstr.; illus.; stat.; index. circ. 2,900. **Indexed:** Biol.Abstr., Curr.Cont., Excerp.Med., Ger.J.Psych., Ind.Med., Psychol.Abstr. (1952-), SSCI. **Document type:** academic/scholarly publication.
—BLDSC (6603.171400); Faxon; Genuine Article; SWETS. **CCC.**

PRAXIS DER KINDERPSYCOLOGIE UND KINDERPSYCHIATRIE. BEIHEFTE. see *PSYCHOLOGY*

MEDICAL SCIENCES — PSYCHIATRY AND NEUROLOGY

616.858   CI   ISSN 0032-7301
PREGLED PROBLEMA MENTALNO RETARDIRANIH OSOBA. (Text in Serbo-Croatian) 1965. bi-m. Savjet Organizacija za Pomoc Mentalno Retardiranim Osobama u SFRJ, Prilaz JNA 43-III, Zagreb, Croatia. Ed. Sulejman Masovic. adv.; bk.rev. **Indexed:** Biol.Abstr.
Description: Concerns mental retardation.

616.89 362.2   UK   ISSN 1355-2570
▼**PRIMARY CARE PSYCHIATRY.** 1995. q. £75($125) to individuals; institutions £150($255). Rapid Communications of Oxford Ltd., The Old Malthouse, Paradise St., Oxford OX1 1LD, England. TEL 01865-790447. FAX 01865-244012. E-mail: rapidcom@vax.oxford.ac.uk. (Subscr. to: ITPS, Cheriton House, North Way, Andover, Hampshire SP10 5BE, England. TEL 01264-342919; Subscr. in US to: Rapid Communications of Oxford, One Penn Plaza, 41st Fl., New York, NY 10119) **Document type:** academic/scholarly publication.
—BLDSC (6612.908430). **CCC.**
Description: Provides comprehensive information on all aspects of the management of psychiatric illness throughout the primary care structure.

616.8 612   NE   ISSN 0929-9637
▼**PRIMARY SENSORY NEURON;** the international interdisciplinary journal reporting basic and clinical research on sensory receptors and primary afferent neurons. (Text in English) 1995. q. DM.320 (effective 1996). V S P, P.O. Box 346, 3700 AH Zeist, Netherlands. TEL 31-30-6925790. FAX 31-30-6932081. E-mail: 100341.2372@compuserve.com. Ed. G.N. Akoev. (back issues avail.) **Document type:** academic/scholarly publication.
Refereed Serial

PRINCIPLES AND TECHNIQUES IN SPINE SURGERY SERIES. see *MEDICAL SCIENCES — Orthopedics And Traumatology*

PROBLEMS OF INDUSTRIAL PSYCHIATRIC MEDICINE SERIES. see *PSYCHOLOGY*

616.8 612.821   NE   ISSN 0079-6123
QP376   CODEN: PBRRA4
PROGRESS IN BRAIN RESEARCH. 1963. irreg., vol. 101, 1994. price varies. Elsevier Science B.V., Books Division, P.O. Box 211, 1000 AE Amsterdam, Netherlands. TEL 31-20-4853911. FAX 31-20-4853705. TELEX 18582 ESPA NL. E-mail: nlinfo-f@elsevier.nl; usinfo-f@elsevier.com; forinfo-kyf04035@niftyserve.or.jp; Site addr.: http://www.elsevier.nl/. (Subscr. in U.S. and Canada to: Elsevier Science Inc., Box 882, Madison Sq. Sta., New York, NY 10159. TEL 212-989-5800) (back issues avail.) **Indexed:** Biol.Abstr., Chem.Abstr., Dent.Ind., Excerp.Med., Ind.Med., Ind.Sci.Rev., Sport Fish.Abstr., Wild.Rev., Zoo.Rec. **Document type:** monographic series.
—BLDSC (6866.400000); CASDDS; EMDOCS; Faxon; Genuine Article; SWETS; UnCover. **CCC.**
Refereed Serial

PROGRESS IN NEURAL NETWORKS. see *COMPUTERS — Artificial Intelligence*

PROGRESS IN NEURO-PSYCHOPHARMACOLOGY AND BIOLOGICAL PSYCHIATRY. see *PHARMACY AND PHARMACOLOGY*

PROGRESS IN NEUROBIOLOGY; an international review journal. see *BIOLOGY*

617.48   SZ   ISSN 0079-6492
PROGRESS IN NEUROLOGICAL SURGERY. (Text in English) 1966. irreg. (approx. a.). price varies. S. Karger AG, Allschwilerstr. 10, P.O. Box, CH-4009 Basel, Switzerland. TEL 061-3061111. FAX 061-3061234. E-mail: Karger@Karger.ch. (reprint service avail. from ISI) **Indexed:** Biol.Abstr., Chem.Abstr., Curr.Cont., Ind.Med. **Document type:** academic/scholarly publication.
—Faxon. **CCC.**
Refereed Serial

616.8   US   ISSN 0099-9016
RC347   CODEN: PRNPAM
PROGRESS IN NEUROPATHOLOGY. 1971. irreg., latest vol.7. price varies. Raven Press (Subsidiary of: Wolters Kluwer N.V.), 1185 Ave. of the Americas, New York, NY 10036. TEL 212-930-9500. FAX 212-869-3495. Ed. Dr. H.M. Zimmerman. (reprint service avail. from UMI) **Indexed:** Biol.Abstr. **Document type:** proceedings.
—BLDSC (6870.355000).
Refereed Serial

616.8   IT   ISSN 1120-3781
PROSPETTIVE PSICOANALITICHE NEL LAVORO ISTITUZIONALE. 1983. 3/yr. L.165000($100) (effective 1996). Pensiero Scientifico Editore s.r.l., Via Bradano 3-C, 00199 Rome, Italy. TEL 06-86207158. FAX 06-86207160. Ed. Massimo Ammaniti. bibl.; index. circ. 1,000. **Document type:** academic/scholarly publication.

616.89   IT   ISSN 0393-361X
PSICHIATRIA DELL'INFANZIA E DELL'ADOLESCENZA. (Text in Italian; summaries in English) 1907. bi-m. $54 to individuals (foreign $100); institutions $70 (foreign $120) (effective 1993). Universita di Roma, Istituto di Neuropsichiatria Infantile, Via dei Sabelli 108, 00185 Rome, Italy. TEL 4952233. FAX 4957857. Ed. Giovanni Bollea. adv.; bk.rev.; charts; illus.; stat.; tr.lit.; index, cum.index. circ. 3,000. **Indexed:** Biol.Abstr., Bull.Signal., Excerp.Med., Lang.& Lang.Behav.Abstr., Psychol.Abstr. (1993-). **Document type:** academic/scholarly publication.
—BLDSC (6945.843000).
Former titles (until 1983): Neuropsichiatria Infantile (ISSN 0028-3924); (until 1969): Infanzia Anormale.
Description: Encompasses all branches of psychiatry, from neonatal age to late adolescence. Comprises original research, synthetic reviews, case histories, field research, magazine reviews and more.

616.8 150.19   IT   ISSN 0393-9774
PSICHIATRIA E PSICOTERAPIA ANALITICA/ANALYTIC PSYCHOTHERAPY AND PSYCHOPATHOLOGY. (Text in English, Italian) 1984. q. L.60000($70) to individuals; institutions L.80000 (effective 1995-1996). Universita degli Studi di Roma II, Cattedra di Clinica Psichiatrica, Via Trionfale 11224, 00135 Rome, Italy. TEL 39-6-30818097. Ed. Maria Ilena Marozza; Pub. Giovanni Fioriti. adv. contact: Anna Amgelucci. bk.rev.; charts; illus.; stat. circ. 6,000. **Indexed:** Excerp.Med., Psychol.Abstr. (1986-), Ref.Zh. **Document type:** academic/scholarly publication.
—BLDSC (6945.841000).
Description: Features research papers by doctors worldwide in the field of analytical psychotherapy and psychopathology. Includes articles on mental health and psychopathology of infants, group psychotherapy and biological psychotherapy.
Refereed Serial

616.8   IT   ISSN 0555-5299
PSICHIATRIA GENERALE E DELL'ETA EVOLUTIVA. q. L.120000 includes supplement (effective 1995). Tipografia Editrice la Garangola, Via Montona, 4, 35137 Padua, Italy. FAX 39-49-8751743. **Indexed:** Psychol.Abstr.

616.8 150.5   AG   ISSN 0325-0695
PSICOLOGIA MEDICA; revista argentina de psicologia medica, psicoterapia y ciencias afines. 1973. s-a. (Fundacion Argentina para la Salud Mental (FASAM)) Carril Impresores, Avda. Salvado Maria del Caril 2639-41, Buenos Aires, Argentina. TEL 821-6887. Ed. Andres Magaz. **Indexed:** Psychol.Abstr.

616.891 001.3   IT
PSICOTERAPIA E SCIENZE UMANE. 1967. q. L.75000 (foreign L.95000) (effective 1993). Franco Angeli Editore, Viale Monza, 106, Casella Postale 17175, 20100 Milan, Italy. TEL 02-2895762. Ed.Bd.

131.3   YU   ISSN 0350-2538
   CODEN: AZMZB7
PSIHIJATRIJA DANAS/PSYCHIATRY TODAY. (Text in Serbo-Croatian; summaries in English) 1969. q. 250 din.($50) to individuals; institutions 500 din.($100). Institut za Mentalno Zdravlje - Institute for Mental Health, Palmoticeva 37, 11000 Belgrade, Yugoslavia. FAX 331-333. Ed. Predrag Kalicanin. adv.; bk.rev. circ. 700. **Indexed:** Excerp.Med., Psychol.Abstr. (1969-), Yrbk.Assoc.Educ.& Rehab.Blind.
—BLDSC (6945.870000).
Formerly: Zavod za Mentalno Zdravlje. Anali (ISSN 0350-1442)

616.89   SP   ISSN 0213-8972
PSIQUIATRIA PUBLICA. (Text in Spanish; summaries in English, French, Italian, Spanish) 1987. bi-m. 3900 ptas. Jarpyo Editores, S.A., Antonio Lopez Aguado 4, 28029 Madrid, Spain. TEL 34-1-3144338. FAX 34-1-3144499. Ed. Manuel Delviat. adv.; bk.rev. circ. 3,000. **Document type:** trade publication.
Description: Includes reviews, original research work, clinical cases, debates, and continuous education material.
Refereed Serial

616.8 614.58   SP   ISSN 0210-8348
PSIQUIS; revista de psiquiatria, psicologia y psicosomatica. 1979. 10/yr. 7500 ptas.($120) (Europe $80). Alpe Editores, S.A., Pedro Rico, 27, 28029 Madrid, Spain. TEL 34-1-7338811. FAX 34-1-3159652. Dir. Dr. J.L. Gonzalez de Rivera; Pub. A. Alvarez. adv.; color page 160000 ptas.; trim 210 x 280; adv. contact: C. Alvarez. charts; circc. 6,000 (controlled). **Indexed:** Curr.Cont., Excerp.Med. (1993-), Ind.Med.Esp., Psychol.Abstr. (1981-), SSCI.
—BLDSC (6945.935500).

616.8   GW   ISSN 0721-0949
PSYCHE UND SOMA. 1978. q. (Schuerholz Arzneimittel GmbH) P M I Verlagsgruppe GmbH, August-Schanz-Str. 21, 60433 Frankfurt a.M., Germany. TEL 069-5480000. FAX 069-548000-77. circ. 20,000. (tabloid format) **Document type:** academic/scholarly publication.

616.89   CI   ISSN 0353-5053
   CODEN: PSYDE
PSYCHIATRIA DANUBINA. 1989. 4/yr. (University of Zagreb, Danube Symposium of Psychiatry) Medicinska Naklada Co., Vlaska 69, 4100 Zagreb, Croatia. TEL 041-447255. **Indexed:** Excerp.Med., Psychol.Abstr. (1991-). **Document type:** academic/scholarly publication.

616.8   JA   ISSN 0033-2658
   CODEN: SSHZAS
PSYCHIATRIA ET NEUROLOGIA JAPONICA/SEISHIN SHINKEIGAKU ZASSHI. (Text in Japanese; summaries in English, Japanese) 1962. m. Japanese Society of Psychiatry and Neurology - Nihon Seishin Shinkei Gakkai, 38-11, Hongo 3-chome, Bunkyo-ku, Tokyo 113, Japan. adv.; bibl.; charts; illus.; index. **Indexed:** Biol.Abstr., Chem.Abstr., Ind.Med., INIS Atomind.
—BLDSC (6946.130000).

616.8   FI   ISSN 0079-7227
RC321   CODEN: PSFNBI
PSYCHIATRIA FENNICA. (Text mainly in English) 1970. a. FIM 145. (Foundation for Psychiatric Research in Finland) Psychiatria Fennica, Arkadiankatu 21 B 20, 00100 Helsinki 10, Finland. FAX 358-0-409663. adv.; bk.rev. circ. 1,500. **Indexed:** Biol.Abstr., CINAHL, Excerp.Med., Psychol.Abstr. (1972-).
—BLDSC (6946.160000).

616.8   FI   ISSN 0355-7707
   CODEN: MPFEE8
PSYCHIATRIA FENNICA. MONOGRAFIASARJA/PSYCHIATRIA FENNICA. MONOGRAPHS. (Text in English and Finnish) 1970. irreg. price varies. Psychiatria Fennica, Arkadiankatu 21 B207, 00100 Helsinki 10, Finland. FAX 358-0-409663. circ. 900. **Indexed:** Excerp.Med., Psychol.Abstr.

MEDICAL SCIENCES — PSYCHIATRY AND NEUROLOGY

616.8 FI
PSYCHIATRIA FENNICA. REPORTS. 1970. irreg. price varies. (Foundation for Psychiatric Research in Finland) Psychiatria Fennica, Arkadiankatu 21 B 20, 00100 Helsinki 10, Finland. FAX 358-0-409663. Ed. J.K. Loennqvist. circ. 150-300. **Indexed:** Excerp.Med., Psychol.Abstr.
Former titles: Psychiatria Fennica. Julkaisusarja (ISSN 0355-7693); Helsingin Yliopisto Keskussairaala. Psykiatrian Kliniikka. Julkaisusarja (ISSN 0073-1730)

616.89 PL ISSN 0033-2674
CODEN: PSPOB3
PSYCHIATRIA POLSKA. (Annual supplement in English avail.) (Text in Polish; summaries in English, Russian) 1923. bi-m. $102. Polskie Towarzystwo Psychiatryczne, Ul. Nowowiejska 27, 00-665 Warsaw, Poland. TEL 48-22-251236. FAX 48-22-215695. (Editorial and distribution addr.: Psychiatria Polska, Uniwersytet Jagielloski, Wydzial Psychoterapii, ul. Lenartowicza 14, 31-138 Krakow, Poland. TEL 48-22-331203. FAX 48-12-333869) Ed. Jerzy W. Aleksandrowicz. adv.; bk.rev. **Indexed:** Biol.Abstr., Chem.Abstr., Excerp.Med., Ind.Med., Psychol.Abstr. **Document type:** academic/scholarly publication.
—BLDSC (6946.210000); EMDOCS.
Formerly (until 1967): Rocznik Psychiatryczny.
Refereed Serial

616.89 US ISSN 0048-5713
RC321 CODEN: PSANCS
PSYCHIATRIC ANNALS. 1971. m. $85 to individuals; institutions $95. Slack, Inc., 6900 Grove Rd., Thorofare, NJ 08086. TEL 609-848-1000. FAX 609-853-5991. Ed. Dr. Howard P. Rome. adv.; B&W page $1650. bk.rev.; illus.; index. circ. 30,035. (also avail. in microform from UMI; reprint service avail. from UMI,ISI) **Indexed:** Adol.Ment.Hlth.Abstr., Biol.Abstr., Curr.Cont., Excerp.Med., Mid.East: Abstr.& Ind., Psychol.Abstr. (1971-), Soc.Sci.Ind., SSCI.
—BLDSC (6946.212000); Faxon; Genuine Article; SWETS; UMI; UnCover. **CCC.**

616.8 UK ISSN 0955-6036
CODEN: PBULE5
PSYCHIATRIC BULLETIN. 1971. m. £40($60) Royal College of Psychiatrists, 17 Belgrave Sq., London SW1X 8PG, England. TEL 0171-235-8857. FAX 0171-245-1231. (Subscr. to: Royal Society of Medicine Services Ltd., 1 Wimpole St., London W1M 8AE, England. TEL 0171-290-2928. FAX 0171-290-2929) Ed. Alan Kerr. bk.rev. circ. 8,000. **Indexed:** Abstr.Crim.& Pen., Excerp.Med. (1995-). **Document type:** academic/scholarly publication.
—BLDSC (6946.212400); SWETS.
Formerly: Royal College of Psychiatrists. Bulletin (ISSN 0140-0789)
Refereed Serial

616.89 UK ISSN 1352-9579
▼**PSYCHIATRIC CARE.** 1994. bi-m. £30 (Europe £40; rest of world £45). (Forensic Psychiatric Nurses Association) Mosby Europe Journals Ltd., Lynton House, 7-12 Tavistock Sq., London WC1H 9LB, England. TEL 0171-388-7676. FAX 0171-411-3118. (Subscr. to: Stonehart, Hainault Rd., Little Heath, Romford RM6 5NP, England. TEL 0181-597-7335) Ed. David Sallah. adv. contact: Clare Duley. **Document type:** academic/scholarly publication.
—BLDSC (6946.212450).
Description: Research-based journal for all professionals concerned with the care of people with mental illness in hospital, forensic and community settings.

616.8 US ISSN 1068-3178
▼**PSYCHIATRIC CLINICS: ANNUAL OF DRUG THERAPY.** 1994. 1/yr. $45 (foreign $53) (effective 1996). W.B. Saunders Co. (Subsidiary of: Harcourt Brace & Company), Curtis Center, 3rd Fl., Independence Sq. W., Philadelphia, PA 19106-3399. TEL 215-238-7800. FAX 215-238-6445. (Subscr. to: Periodicals Fulfillment, W.B. Saunders Co., 6277 Sea Harbor Dr., 4th Fl., Orlando, FL 32891-4800. TEL 800-654-2452. FAX 800-874-6418) Eds. Drs. James W. Jefferson, John H. Greist. **Indexed:** Adol.Ment.Hlth.Abstr., Curr.Adv.Ecol.Sci., Curr.Cont., Ind.Med., Psychol.Abstr., SSCI. **Document type:** academic/scholarly publication.
Description: Summarizes the year's developments in the pharmaceutical treatment of psychiatric disorders.

616.89 US ISSN 0193-953X
RC321
PSYCHIATRIC CLINICS OF NORTH AMERICA. 1978. q. $129 (foreign $152) (effective 1996). W.B. Saunders Co. (Subsidiary of: Harcourt Brace & Company), Curtis Center, 3rd Fl., Independence Sq. W., Philadelphia, PA 19106. TEL 215-238-7800. FAX 215-238-6445. (Subscr. to: Periodicals Fulfillment, W.B. Saunders Co., 6277 Sea Harbor Dr., 4th Fl., Orlando, FL 32891-4800. TEL 800-654-2452. FAX 800-874-6418) Ed. Lesley Day. bibl.; illus.; index, cum.index. (reprint service avail. from UMI) **Indexed:** Adol.Ment.Hlth.Abstr., CINAHL, Curr.Adv.Ecol.Sci., Curr.Cont., Ind.Med., Psychol.Abstr. (1982-), SSCI. **Document type:** academic/scholarly publication.
—BLDSC (6946.212500); Faxon; Genuine Article; SWETS; UMI; UnCover. **CCC.**

616.89 US ISSN 0033-2690
RC321 CODEN: PSYFAK
PSYCHIATRIC FORUM. 1969. s-a. free. Department of Mental Health, William S. Hall Psychiatric Institute, Box 202, Columbia, SC 29202. TEL 803-734-7154. FAX 803-734-0791. E-mail: SRL97. Ed. Dr. Lucius C. Pressley. bk.rev.; circ. 4,000 (controlled). **Indexed:** Adol.Ment.Hlth.Abstr., Chicago Psychoanal.Lit.Ind., CINAHL, Curr.Cont., Psychol.Abstr. (1971-), SSCI. **Document type:** academic/scholarly publication.
—BLDSC (6946.214000).
Description: Contains original articles related to mental health.

PSYCHIATRIC GENETICS. see *BIOLOGY — Genetics*

616.8 US
PSYCHIATRIC LENGTH OF STAY SERIES. (Editions avail.: United States Northcentral Region, Northeastern Region, Southern Region, Western Region) 1985. a. H C I A Inc., 300 E. Lombard St., Baltimore, MD 21202. TEL 800-568-3280. FAX 410-539-5220. **Indexed:** SRI.

616.8 US ISSN 0732-0868
CODEN: PSMDEQ
PSYCHIATRIC MEDICINE.* 1983. q. $55 to individuals; institutions $75. S P Medical & Scientific Books, Inc. (Subsidiary of: Spectrum Publications, Inc.), c/o Fisher, 200 Park Ave. S., New York, NY 10003-1503. Ed. Dr. Richard C.W. Hall. circ. 500. (back issues avail.) **Indexed:** Chem.Abstr., Psychol.Abstr.
—Faxon.

616.89 US ISSN 0033-2704
RC321
PSYCHIATRIC NEWS. 1966. fortn. $40 to individuals (foreign $60); institutions $60 (foreign $80). American Psychiatric Association, 1400 K St., N.W., Washington, DC 20005. TEL 202-682-6210. FAX 202-682-6114. Ed. Dr. Robert Campbell. adv.; B&W page $3570, color page $4820. bk.rev.; stat. circ. 37,000. (also avail. in microform from UMI; reprint service avail. from UMI) **Indexed:** Abstr.Crim.& Pen., Soc.Work Res.& Abstr.
—BLDSC (6946.215000); SWETS; UMI.
Formerly: American Psychiatric Association. Newsletter.
Description: Delivers current information on everything from legislative activities to the latest developments in the drug and therapy fields.

616.89 US ISSN 0033-2720
CODEN: PSQUAP
PSYCHIATRIC QUARTERLY. 1927. q. $275 (foreign $320) (effective 1996). (New York School of Psychiatry) Human Sciences Press, Inc. (Subsidiary of: Plenum Publishing Corp.), 233 Spring St., New York, NY 10013-1578. TEL 212-620-8000. FAX 212-463-0742. TELEX 23-421139. Ed. Dr. Stephen Rachlin. adv. (also avail. in microform from UMI; reprint service avail. from ISI,UMI) **Indexed:** Abstr.Hosp.Manage.Stud., Adol.Ment.Hlth.Abstr., ASCA, Biol.Abstr., CINAHL, Community Ment.Health Rev., Curr.Cont., Excerp.Med., Hosp.Lit.Ind., Ind.Med., Psychol.Abstr. (1977-), Sociol.Abstr., SSCI. **Document type:** academic/scholarly publication.
—BLDSC (6946.240000); Faxon; SWETS; UMI; UnCover. **CCC.**
Description: Includes articles on the social, clinical, administrative, legal, political, and ethical aspects of mental illness care. Presents pertinent scientific and delivery system data.
Refereed Serial

616.8 US
PSYCHIATRIC RESIDENT. 1992. bi-m. Slack, Inc., 6900 Grove Rd., Thorofare, NJ 08086. TEL 609-848-1000. FAX 609-853-5991. Ed. Laura Ronge. adv. circ. 6,323.
Description: Covers career, lifestyle and business issues facing residents.

616.89 US ISSN 1075-2730
RC443.A1 CODEN: PSSEFQ
PSYCHIATRIC SERVICES. 1950. m. $40 to individuals (foreign $60); institutions $60 (foreign $80). American Psychiatric Association, 1400 K St., N.W., Washington, DC 20005. TEL 202-682-6070. FAX 202-682-6114. Ed. Dr. John A. Talbott. adv.: B&W page $1700, color page $2650. bk.rev.; film rev.; charts; illus.; stat.; index. circ. 21,000. (also avail. in microform from MIM,UMI; reprint service avail. from UMI) **Indexed:** Abstr.Health Care Manage.Stud., Biol.Abstr., C.I.N.L., Chic.Per.Ind., Crim.Just.Abstr., Curr.Cont., Curr.Lit.Fam.Plan., Excerp.Med., Hosp.Lit.Ind., Ind.Med., Int.Nurs.Ind., Media Rev.Dig., Past.Care & Couns.Abstr., Psychol.Abstr. (1960-), Risk Abstr., Soc.Work Res.& Abstr., SSCI.
—BLDSC (6946.242300); EMDOCS; Faxon; Genuine Article; SWETS; UMI; UnCover.
Former titles (until 1995): Hospital and Community Psychiatry (ISSN 0022-1597); Mental Hospitals (ISSN 0096-5502)
Description: Interdisciplinary approach to issues related to the delivery of mental health services in organized settings.
Refereed Serial

616.89 US ISSN 0893-2905
PSYCHIATRIC TIMES. 1985. m. $120 (foreign $200). C M E Inc., 1924 E. Deere Ave., Santa Ana, CA 92705-5723. TEL 800-447-4474. FAX 714-250-1245. E-mail: psychtimes@aol.com. Ed. Dr. John L. Schwartz; Pub. David DeNinno. adv.: B&W page $4515, color page $5710; adv. contact: Frank Naley. bk.rev.; circ. 42,445 (controlled). **Document type:** newspaper, trade publication.
Description: Psychiatric news journal of interest to psychiatrists, mental health professionals and others in healthcare professions.
Refereed Serial

PSYCHIATRIE DE L'ENFANT. see *MEDICAL SCIENCES — Pediatrics*

616.8 GW ISSN 0303-4259
PSYCHIATRISCHE PRAXIS. (Supplement avail. (ISSN 0934-3008)) 1974. bi-m. DM.162. Georg Thieme Verlag, Ruedigerstr. 14, 70469 Stuttgart, Germany. TEL 0711-8931-0. FAX 0711-8931298. (Subscr. to: Postfach 104853, 70042 Stuttgart, Germany) Ed.Bd. adv.; bk.rev.; bibl.; charts; illus.; index. circ. 1,600. (reprint service avail. from UMI) **Indexed:** Biol.Abstr., Curr.Cont., Excerp.Med., Ger.J.Psych., Ind.Med., Risk Abstr., SSCI. **Document type:** academic/scholarly publication.
—BLDSC (6946.258000); Faxon; Genuine Article; SWETS; UMI. **CCC.**

616.8 GW ISSN 0934-3008
PSYCHIATRISCHE PRAXIS. SUPPLEMENT. irreg. price varies. Georg Thieme Verlag, Ruedigerstr. 14, 70469 Stuttgart, Germany. TEL 0711-8931-0. FAX 0711-8931298. (Subscr. to: Postfach 104853, 700042 Stuttgart, Germany) (back issues avail.) **Indexed:** Excerp.Med. (1994-). **Document type:** monographic series.

MEDICAL SCIENCES — PSYCHIATRY AND NEUROLOGY

616.89 US ISSN 0033-2747
RC321 CODEN: PSYCAB
PSYCHIATRY; interpersonal and biological processes. 1937. q. $37.50 to individuals (foreign $57.50); institutions $115 (foreign $135) (effective 1995). (Washington School of Psychiatry) Guilford Publications, Inc., 72 Spring St., 4th Fl., New York, NY 10012. TEL 212-431-9800. FAX 212-966-6708. Ed. Dr. David Reiss; Pub. Robert Matloff. adv. contact: Marian Robinson. bk.rev.; index, cum.index: 1938-1967, 1968-1977. circ. 2,200. (also avail. in microform from MIM,UMI; back issues avail.; reprint service avail. from ISI,UMI) **Indexed:** Abstr.Anthropol., Abstr.Crim.& Pen., Adol.Ment.Hlth.Abstr., Amer.Hist.& Life, ASSIA, Biol.Abstr., Child Devel.Abstr., Curr.Cont., Excerp.Med., Hist.Abstr., Hosp.Lit.Ind., Ind.Med., Int.Nurs.Ind., Mid.East: Abstr.& Ind., Psychol.Abstr. (1938-), Sage Fam.Stud.Abstr., Sage Urb.Stud.Abstr., Soc.Sci.Ind., SSCI. **Document type:** academic/scholarly publication.
—BLDSC (6946.260000); EMDOCS; Faxon; Genuine Article; SWETS; UMI; UnCover. **CCC.**
Description: New and controversial issues in psychiatry and related social and biological science disciplines.
Refereed Serial

616.8 CN ISSN 0838-7982
PSYCHIATRY. 1987. 4/yr. M P I Publishing Inc., 14 Ronan Ave., Toronto, Ont. M4N 2X9, Canada. TEL 416-481-6384. Ed. Dr. Vivian Rakoff. circ. 14,123.

PSYCHIATRY DRUG ALERTS. see *PHARMACY AND PHARMACOLOGY*

616.8 UK ISSN 0262-5377
PSYCHIATRY IN PRACTICE. Abbreviated title: P I P. 1981-198?; N.S. 1990. q. £31 (overseas £35) (effective 1994). Hayward Medical Communications Ltd., 44 Earlham St., Covent Garden, London WC2H 9LA, England. TEL 44-171-240-4493. FAX 44-171-240-4479. (Subscr. to: Essex House, Cromwell Park, Chipping Norton, Oxon. OX7 5SR, England. TEL 44-1608-645564. FAX 44-1608-645645) Ed. Dr. George Beaumont. adv.; bk.rev. circ. 21,000. **Document type:** academic/scholarly publication.
—BLDSC (6946.263600).

616.8 IE
PSYCHIATRY - IRELAND. 6/yr. 38 Albert College Park, Glasnevin, Dublin 9, Ireland. TEL 374447. Ed. Patrick O'Sullivan. circ. 2,000.

616.8 JO
PSYCHIATRY JOURNAL/MAJALLAT AL-SIHHAH AL-NAFSIYYAH.* (Text in Arabic) 1972. bi-m. Psychiatry Association, Box 1317, Amman, Jordan. Ed. Samir Liddawi.

616.8 340.6 AT ISSN 1321-8719
CODEN: PPLAFQ
PSYCHIATRY PSYCHOLOGY AND LAW. s-a. Aus.$75 to individuals in Australia & New Zealand (elsewhere Aus.$90); institutions Aus.$100 (elsewhere Aus.$125). Australian Academic Press Pty. Ltd., 32 Jeays St., Bowen Hills, Qld. 4006, Australia. TEL 61-7-2571176. **Indexed:** Excerp.Med. (1995-). **Document type:** academic/scholarly publication.
Description: Presents articles on topics relevant to forensic issues in psychiatry and psychology.
Refereed Serial

616.8 IE ISSN 0165-1781
CODEN: PSRSDR
PSYCHIATRY RESEARCH; an international journal for rapid communication. (Text in English) 1979. 15/yr. i£980($1548); with Neuroimaging Section I£810($1280) (effective 1996). Elsevier Science Ireland Ltd., P.O. Box 85, Limerick, Ireland. TEL 353-61-471944. FAX 353-61-472144. (Subscr. in U.S. and Canada to: Elsevier Science Publishing Co., Inc., Box 882, Madison Sq. Sta., New York, NY 10159. TEL 212-989-5800. FAX 212-633-3990) Eds. Monte S. Buchsbaum, Frederick K. Goodwin. illus. (also avail. in microform from UMI; back issues avail.; reprint service avail. from SWZ) **Indexed:** Biol.Abstr., Biotech.Abstr., Chem.Abstr., Curr.Cont., Excerp.Med., Ind.Med., Psychol.Abstr. (1979-). **Document type:** academic/scholarly publication.
—BLDSC (6946.263700); ADONIS; CASDDS; Faxon; Genuine Article; SWETS; UnCover. **CCC.**
Description: Publishes research in biochemical, physiological, genetic, psychological and social determinants of behavior, assessment of subjective states, evaluations of somatic and non-somatic psychiatric treatments, and relevant clinically related basic studies from fields such as neuropharmacology and neurochemistry.
Refereed Serial

616.8 IE ISSN 0925-4927
PSYCHIATRY RESEARCH: NEUROIMAGING SECTION. 1990. bi-m. I£258($408) (effective 1996). Elsevier Science Ireland Ltd., P.O. Box 85, Limerick, Ireland. TEL 353-61-471944. FAX 353-61-472144. (Subscr. in U.S. and Canada to: Elsevier Science Inc., Box 882, Madison Sq. Sta., New York, NY 10159. TEL 212-989-5800. FAX 212-633-3990) Ed. M.S. Buchsbaum. (back issues avail.) **Indexed:** Biol.Abstr., Chem.Abstr., Curr.Cont., Excerp.Med., Ind.Med., Psychol.Abstr. (1990-). **Document type:** academic/scholarly publication.
—ADONIS; Genuine Article; SWETS; UnCover. **CCC.**
Description: Publishes manuscripts on positron emission tomography, MRI, computerized electroencephalographic topography and other imaging techniques, results in psychiatric disorders, dementias, and the effects of behavioral tasks and pharmacological treatments.
Refereed Serial

616.8 GW ISSN 0340-7845
PSYCHO; Psychiatrie, Neurologie und Psychotherapie. 1975. m. DM.75 (effective 1996). Perimed - Spitta Medizinische Verlagsgesellschaft mbH, Ammonitenstr. 1, 72336 Balingen, Germany. TEL 07433-952-0. FAX 07433-952185. adv.; bk.rev.; abstr. circ. 6,500. **Indexed:** Excerp.Med. **Document type:** academic/scholarly publication.

616.89 SA ISSN 1023-0548
PSYCHO-ANALYTIC PSYCHOTHERAPY IN SOUTH AFRICA. 1992. 2/yr. R.60 for 3 copies to individuals (£20 in UK; elsewhere $30); institutions R.70 (£25 in UK; elsewhere $50) (effective 1995 & 1996). P.O. Box 16115, Vlaeberg 8018, South Africa. TEL 27-21-232550. FAX 27-21-232550. Ed. Trevor Lubbe. adv.; bk.rev. (back issues avail.) **Document type:** academic/scholarly publication.
Description: Publishes articles of interest to psychotherapists working psycho-analytically in South Africa.

PSYCHO-ONCOLOGY; journal of the psychological, social and behavioral dimensions of cancer. see *MEDICAL SCIENCES — Oncology*

PSYCHOANALYSE EN CULTUUR. see *PSYCHOLOGY*

616.9 US ISSN 0161-5289
RC500 CODEN: PCTHDS
PSYCHOANALYSIS AND CONTEMPORARY THOUGHT; a quarterly of integrative and interdisciplinary studies. 1978. q. $67 to individuals (foreign $109); institutions $113 (foreign $148). (Psychoanalysis and Contemporary Science, Inc.) International Universities Press, Inc., 59 Boston Post Rd., Box 1524, Madison, CT 06443-1524. TEL 203-245-4000. FAX 203-245-0775. Ed. Dr. Leo Goldberger. bk.rev.; index. (back issues avail.) **Indexed:** Biol.Abstr., Excerp.Med., Lang.& Lang.Behav.Abstr., Psychoanal.Abstr., Psychol.Abstr. (1978-). **Document type:** academic/scholarly publication.
—BLDSC (6946.264700); SWETS; UnCover.
Incorporates (1972-1976): Psychoanalysis and Contemporary Science (ISSN 0092-864X)
Description: Aimed at broadening the scientific and intellectual horizon of psychoanalysis. Includes original clinical, theoretical and experimental contributions intergrating psychoanalysis with social, biological and behaviorial sciences.
Refereed Serial

PSYCHOANALYSIS AND CULTURE. see *PSYCHOLOGY*

PSYCHOANALYSIS AND PSYCHOTHERAPY. see *PSYCHOLOGY*

PSYCHOANALYTIC BOOKS; a quarterly journal of reviews. see *PSYCHOLOGY*

PSYCHOANALYTIC PSYCHOLOGY. see *PSYCHOLOGY*

616.8 GW
▼**PSYCHOANALYTISCHE BLAETTER ZU KLINIK, FORSCHUNG, ZEITGESCHEHEN.** 1994. 2/yr. DM.59. Vandenhoeck und Ruprecht, Robert-Bosch-Breite 6, 37079 Goettingen, Germany. TEL 0551-6959-0. FAX 0551-695917. (Subscr. to: 37070 Goettingen, Germany) Ed.Bd. circ. 1,600. **Document type:** monographic series.

616.8 GW ISSN 0478-6866
PSYCHOBIOLOGIE. 1952. s-a. DM.16. Psychobiologische Gesellschaft, Freundhofweg 5, 45479 Muelheim, Germany.

616.8 UK ISSN 1353-3339
▼**PSYCHODYNAMIC COUNSELLING.** 1994. 4/yr. £22 (U.S. and Canada $30; rest of world £24) to individuals; institutions £60 (U.S. and Canada $85; rest of world £65). Routledge, 11 New Fetter Ln., London EC4P 4EE, England. TEL 0171-583-9855. FAX 0171-842-2298. E-mail: sample.journals@routledge.com. (Subscr. to: ITPS Ltd., Cheriton House, North Way, Andover, Hants SP10 5BE, England. TEL 01264-342919. FAX 01264-342807) Eds. John Lees, Diana Bass. adv.: page £175; trim 115 x 190. circ. 2,000. **Document type:** academic/scholarly publication.
—BLDSC (6946.277150).
Description: Explores the application of psychodynamic ideas through different occupational settings, techniques and theories.

616.89 UK ISSN 0033-2917
RC321 CODEN: PSMDCO
PSYCHOLOGICAL MEDICINE. 1970. bi-m. £185($339) (effective 1996). Cambridge University Press, Edinburgh Bldg., Shaftesbury Rd., Cambridge CB2 2RU, England. TEL 01223-312393. FAX 01223-315052. TELEX 851817256. (N. American addr.: Cambridge University Press, Journals Dept., 40 W. 20th St., New York, NY 10011. TEL 212-924-3900. FAX 212-691-3239) Ed. Eugene Paykel. adv.; bk.rev.; charts; illus.; index. (also avail. in microfilm from UMI; back issues avail.; reprint service avail. from SWZ) **Indexed:** Abstr.Health Care Manage.Stud., Adol.Ment.Hlth.Abstr., ASSIA, Behav.Med.Abstr., Chem.Abstr., CINAHL, Curr.Adv.Ecol.Sci., Curr.Cont., Dok.Arbeitsmed., Excerp.Med., IMFL, Ind.Med., Mid.East: Abstr.& Ind., Nutr.Abstr., Psychol.Abstr. (1970-), Res.High.Educ.Abstr., Risk Abstr., SSCI. **Document type:** academic/scholarly publication.
—BLDSC (6946.450000); CASDDS; EMDOCS; Faxon; Genuine Article; SWETS; UMI; UnCover. **CCC.**
Description: Contains original research in clinical psychiatry and the basic sciences relating to it.

MEDICAL SCIENCES — PSYCHIATRY AND NEUROLOGY

616.89   FR   ISSN 0048-5756
PSYCHOLOGIE MEDICALE. (Text in French, summaries in English, French) 1969. 14/yr. 700 F. (foreign 1000 F.). Societe de Presse Medicale, 14 rue Drouot, 75009 Paris, France. TEL 48-24-96-93. FAX 47-70-02-73. TELEX OTRASPE 660484 F. Ed. E.J. Caille. adv.; bk.rev.; index. circ. 7,500. **Indexed:** Biol.Abstr., Excerp.Med., Psychol.Abstr. (1970-).
—BLDSC (6946.532300); EMDOCS; SWETS.
    Description: Covers a number of case studies in psychiatry and psychological medicine coming out of France, Switzerland, Canada and Argentina.
    Refereed Serial

616.8 616.4   UK   ISSN 0306-4530
                             CODEN: PSYCDE
PSYCHONEUROENDOCRINOLOGY. 1976. 8/yr. £473($753) (effective 1996). (International Society of Psychoneuroendocrinology) Elsevier Science Ltd., Pergamon, P.O. Box 800, Kidlington, Oxford OX5 1DX, England. TEL 44-1865-843000. FAX 44-1865-843010.
E-mail: nlinfo-f@elsevier.nl; usinfo-f@elsevier.com; forinfo-kyf04035@niftyserve.or.jp; Site addr.: http://www.elsevier.nl/. (Subscr. in U.S. and Canada to: Elsevier Science, 660 White Plains Rd., Tarrytown, NY 10591-5153. TEL 914-524-9200. FAX 914-333-2444) Ed. Robert T. Rubin. adv.; B&W page $550, color page $1350. bk.rev.; charts; illus.; stat.; index. circ. 1,000. (also avail. in microfilm from UMI) **Indexed:** Biol.Abstr., Biotech.Abstr., Curr.Adv.Ecol.Sci., Curr.Cont., Dairy Sci.Abstr., Excerp.Med., Ind.Med., Nutr.Abstr., Psychol.Abstr. (1975-). **Document type:** academic/scholarly publication.
—BLDSC (6946.540300); ADONIS; CASDDS; Faxon; Genuine Article; SWETS; UMI; UnCover. **CCC.**
    Description: Multidisciplinary journal addressing issues in psychiatry, psychology, neurology and endocrinology.
    Refereed Serial

616.89   SG   ISSN 0033-314X
                             CODEN: PSAFB3
PSYCHOPATHOLOGIE AFRICAINE; sciences sociales et psychiatrie en Afrique. (Text and summaries in English and French) 1965. 3/yr. 7500 Fr.CFA to individuals; institutions 12000 Fr.CFA. Societe de Psychopathologie et d'Hygiene Mentale de Dakar, B.P. 5097, Dakar-Fann, Senegal. Dir. Babacar Diop. adv.; bk.rev.; charts; index. circ. 11,250. (also avail. in microfiche) **Indexed:** Biol.Abstr., Curr.Cont., Documentatieblad, ExtraMED, Psychol.Abstr., SSCI. **Document type:** academic/scholarly publication.
●Also available on CD-ROM.
—BLDSC (6946.543500).
    Description: Seeks to collect and make known works related to psychiatry, psychopathology and mental health in sub-Saharan Africa.

616.89   SZ   ISSN 0254-4962
                             CODEN: PSYHEU
PSYCHOPATHOLOGY. (Text in English) 1968. 6/yr. 248.40 SFrs.($190.80) to individuals; institutions 414 SFrs.($318) (effective 1996). S. Karger AG, Allschwilerstr. 10, P.O. Box, CH-4009 Basel, Switzerland. TEL 061-3061111. FAX 061-3061234. E-mail: Karger@Karger.ch. Eds. P. Berner, E. Gabriel. adv.; bk.rev.; index. circ. 800. (also avail. in microform) **Indexed:** ASCA, Biol.Abstr., Curr.Cont., Dent.Ind., Excerp.Med., Ind.Med., Psychol.Abstr. (1968-), SSCI. **Document type:** academic/scholarly publication.
—BLDSC (6946.543700); CASDDS; Faxon; Genuine Article; SWETS; UnCover. **CCC.**
    Formerly (until vol.17, 1984): Psychiatria Clinica (ISSN 0033-264X)
    Refereed Serial

PSYCHOPHARMACOLOGY. see *PHARMACY AND PHARMACOLOGY*

PSYCHOPHARMACOLOGY BULLETIN. see *PHARMACY AND PHARMACOLOGY*

PSYCHOPHARMACOLOGY UPDATE. see *PHARMACY AND PHARMACOLOGY*

616.89   US   ISSN 0033-3174
RC49   CODEN: PSMEAP
PSYCHOSOMATIC MEDICINE. 1939. bi-m. $128 to individuals; institutions $259. (American Psychosomatic Society) Williams & Wilkins, 428 E. Preston St., Baltimore, MD 21202. TEL 410-528-4000. FAX 410-528-4312. Ed. Dr. J. Dimsdale. adv.; bk.rev.; index. circ. 2,300. (also avail. in microform from RPI,WWS; reprint service avail. from KTO) **Indexed:** Behav.Med.Abstr., Biol.Abstr., Chem.Abstr., Curr.Cont., Excerp.Med., Ind.Med., Med.& Surg.Dermat., Psychol.Abstr. (1939-), Sociol.Abstr., SSCI.
—BLDSC (6946.555000); CASDDS; EMDOCS; Faxon; Genuine Article; SWETS; UnCover. **CCC.**
    Description: Presents research and clinical studies concerning psychosomatic disorders. Examines many disciplines including psychiatry, psychology, and social sciences.
    Refereed Serial

616.89   US   ISSN 0033-3182
RC49   CODEN: PSYCBC
PSYCHOSOMATICS; the journal of consultation and liaison psychiatry. 1960. bi-m. $149 (foreign $164) Effective 1996). (Academy of Psychosomatic Medicine) American Psychiatric Press, Inc., Journals Division, 1400 K St., N.W., Ste. 1101, Washington, DC 20005. TEL 202-682-6240. FAX 202-682-6341. (UK addr.: 17 Belgrave Sq., London SW1X 8PG, England) Ed. Dr. Thomas Wise. adv.; bk.rev.; abstr.; bibl.; charts; illus.; stat.; index. circ. 2,500. (also avail. in microform from UMI; reprint service avail. from UMI) **Indexed:** Adol.Ment.Hlth.Abstr., Biol.Abstr., Chem.Abstr., CINAHL, Curr.Cont., Excerp.Med., Ind.Med., Nutr.Abstr., Psychol.Abstr. (1966-), Soc.Work Res.& Abstr., SSCI.
—BLDSC (6946.557000); EMDOCS; Faxon; Genuine Article; SWETS; UMI; UnCover.
    Description: Devoted to the relationship between medical and psychiatric phenomena.
    Refereed Serial

616.8   SZ   ISSN 0555-5841
PSYCHOSOMATISCHE MEDIZIN. q. Policlinique Medicale, Rue Cesar Roux 19, CH-1005 Lausanne, Switzerland. Ed. Dr. Decrey Hedi. circ. 800.

616.8 360   GW   ISSN 0930-4177
PSYCHOSOZIALE UMSCHAU. 1985. q. DM.36 (foreign DM.44). (Dachverband Psychosoziale Hilfsvereinigungen) Psychiatrie Verlag GmbH, Thomas-Mann-Str. 49a, 53111 Bonn, Germany. TEL 0228-695540. FAX 0228-695595. **Document type:** academic/scholarly publication.

616.89   GW   ISSN 0935-6185
DER PSYCHOTHERAPEUT. (Text in German) 1956. 6/yr. DM.198($143) (effective 1996). (Deutsche Kollegiums fuer Psychosomatische Medizin) Springer-Verlag, Heidelberger Platz 3, 14197 Berlin, Germany. TEL 030-8207-0. FAX 030-8214091. E-mail: orders@springer.de. (Subscr. in N. America to: Springer-Verlag New York, Inc., 44 Hartz Way, Secaucus, NJ 07096-2491. TEL 201-348-4033. FAX 201-348-4505) (Co-sponsor: Deutsche Gesellschaft fuer Psychosomatische Geburtshilfe und Gynaekologie) Ed. M. Cierpka. adv.; bk.rev.; bibl.; charts; illus. (tabloid format; also avail. in microform from UMI; back issues avail.; reprint service avail. from ISI) **Indexed:** Biol.Abstr., Chem.Abstr., Curr.Cont., Excerp.Med., Psychol.Abstr. (1959-), SSCI. **Document type:** academic/scholarly publication.
—BLDSC (6946.558210); Genuine Article; SWETS; UMI. **CCC.**
    Former titles: Praxis der Psychotherapie und Psychosomatik (ISSN 0171-791X); Praxis der Psychotherapie (ISSN 0032-7077)

616.89   US   ISSN 0033-3204
                             CODEN: PSYOAD
PSYCHOTHERAPY. Variant title: Psychotherapy: Theory, Research and Practice. 1963. q. $70 to individuals (foreign $85); institutions $90 (foreign $100) (effective 1995). American Psychological Association, Division of Psychotherapy, 3900 E. Camelback Rd., Ste. 200, Phoenix, AZ 85018. TEL 602-912-5329. Ed. Wade . Silverman. adv.; bk.rev.; charts; index. circ. 6,000. (reprint service avail. from UMI,ISI) **Indexed:** Adol.Ment.Hlth.Abstr., Biol.Abstr., Excerp.Med., Psychol.Abstr. (1963-), Psycscan C.P., SSCI. **Document type:** academic/scholarly publication.
—BLDSC (6946.558530); EMDOCS; Genuine Article; SWETS; UMI; UnCover.
    Refereed Serial

616.89   SZ   ISSN 0033-3190
RC49   CODEN: PSPSBF
PSYCHOTHERAPY AND PSYCHOSOMATICS. (Text in English) 1953. 8/yr. (2 vols.). 203.35 SFrr.($156.45) to individuals; institutions 581 SFr.($447) (effective 1996). (International Federation for Medical Psychotherapy) S. Karger AG, Allschwilerstr. 10, P.O. Box, CH-4009 Basel, Switzerland. TEL 061-3061111. FAX 061-3061234. E-mail: Karger@Karger.ch. Ed. G. Fava. adv.; bk.rev.; charts; illus.; bibl.; index. circ. 1,000. (also avail. in microform; back issues avail.) **Indexed:** Adol.Ment.Hlth.Abstr., Biol.Abstr., Chem.Abstr., Curr.Cont., Dent.Ind., Excerp.Med., Ind.Med., Nutr.Abstr., Psychol.Abstr. (1953-), SSCI, Stud.Wom.Abstr. **Document type:** academic/scholarly publication.
—BLDSC (6946.559000); EMDOCS; Faxon; Genuine Article; SWETS; UnCover. **CCC.**
    Refereed Serial

PSYCHOTHERAPY, RECOVERY AND PERSONAL GROWTH UPDATE. see *PSYCHOLOGY*

616.8   AT   ISSN 1039-1568
PSYCHOTROPIC GUIDELINES. 1989. irreg. (every 2-3 years). Aus.$18. Victorian Medical Postgraduate Foundation Inc., Therapeutics Committee, Chelsea House, Level 3, 55 Flemington Rd., N. Melbourne, Vic. 3051, Australia. TEL 03-329-1566. FAX 03-326-5632. (Co-sponsor: Victorian Drug Usage Advisory Committee) bk.rev. circ. 5,000. **Document type:** academic/scholarly publication.
    Description: Gives concrete recommendations for rational therapy of psychotropic disease and where necessary justifies the choice.

PSYSCSCAN: NEUROPSYCHOLOGY. see *MEDICAL SCIENCES — Abstracting, Bibliographies, Statistics*

PSYKISK HAELSA/MENTAL HEALTH. see *PSYCHOLOGY*

616.8 664.06   US
PURE FACTS. 1978. 10/yr. $25 (membership $45). Feingold Association of the United States, Box 6550, Alexandria, VA 22306. TEL 703-768-3287. Ed. Jane Hersey. circ. 6,000. (back issues avail.)
    Description: Non-profit support group helping children with learning or behavior problems and chemically-sensitive adults.

616.8   IT   ISSN 0393-0645
QUADERNI ITALIANI DI PSICHIATRIA. 1981. bi-m. L.105000($145) (effective 1994). Masson S.p.A., Divisione Periodici, Via Statuto 2-4, 20121 Milan, Italy. TEL 02-6367-1. FAX 02-6367211. Eds. Vittorino Andreoli, Giovanni B. Cassano. adv.; B&W page L.2000000, color page L.3100000; trim 170 x 240. circ. 1,000. **Document type:** academic/scholarly publication.

QUADRANT; the journal of contemporary Jungian thought. see *PSYCHOLOGY*

616.8 610.73 371.9   US
QUALITY OF CARE. 1980. bi-m. Commission on Quality of Care for the Mentally Disabled, 99 Washington Ave., Ste. 1002, Albany, NY 12210. TEL 518-473-6304. FAX 518-473-6302. Ed. Marcus A. Gigliotti. bk.rev.; circ. 11,000 (controlled). **Document type:** government publication.

616.89   US
QUEST (TUCSON). 1950. q. free. Muscular Dystrophy Association, Inc., 3300 E. Sunrise Dr., Tucson, AZ 85718-3208. TEL 602-529-2000. FAX 602-529-5300. Ed. Bob Mackle. illus. circ. 85,000. **Indexed:** CHNI, Rehabil.Lit. **Document type:** consumer publication.
    Former titles: M D A Reports (ISSN 1061-4370); (until 1992): M D A Newsmagazine (ISSN 8750-2321); M D A News - Muscular Dystrophy Association (ISSN 0279-0742); Muscular Dystrophy News (ISSN 0027-3759)
    Description: Presents patient profiles, instructive articles, research and association news, resource listings, and helpful articles of special interest to those with neuromuscular diseases and their families.

MEDICAL SCIENCES — PSYCHIATRY AND NEUROLOGY

616.89   IT   ISSN 0033-9636
CODEN: RSPSA
RASSEGNA DI STUDI PSICHIATRICI. (Text in Italian; summaries in English, French and Italian) 1911. q. Unita Sanitaria Locale no. 30, USL 30 Area Senese, Via Roma 56, 53100 Siena, Italy.
TEL 577-299023. adv.; bk.rev.; charts. **Indexed:** Chem.Abstr., Excerp.Med.
—BLDSC (7294.940000); EMDOCS.

READING AND WRITING; an interdisciplinary journal. see *LINGUISTICS*

150 028   US   ISSN 0886-3784
READINGS; a journal of reviews and commentary in mental health. 1986. q. $25 to individuals; institutions $35. American Orthopsychiatric Association, Inc., 330 Seventh Ave., 18th Fl., New York, NY 10001. TEL 212-564-5930. FAX 212-564-6180. (Subscr. to: 49 Sheridan Ave., Albany, NY 12201-1413) Ed. Ernest Herman. adv. contact: Jean Arbeiter. bk.rev. circ. 11,000. (also avail. in microfiche; back issues avail.) **Indexed:** Bk.Rev.Ind. (1990-), Child.Bk.Rev.Ind. (1990-). **Document type:** academic/scholarly publication.
Description: Four to six essay reviews and 30-40 brief reviews of books interesting to the mental health professional.

616.8   SZ   ISSN 1013-7467
RECENT ACHIEVEMENTS IN RESTORATIVE NEUROLOGY. (Text in English) 1985. irreg., vol.3, 1990. price varies. S. Karger AG, Allschwilerstr. 10, P.O. Box, CH-4009 Basel, Switzerland. TEL 061-3061111. FAX 061-3061234. E-mail: Karger@Karger.ch. Ed. M.R. Dimitrijevic. **Indexed:** Biol.Abstr., Curr.Cont., Ind.Med. **Document type:** academic/scholarly publication.
—BLDSC (7303.650000).
Description: Looks at new procedures for restoring or improving functions of the impaired nervous system.
Refereed Serial

616.853   UK   ISSN 0264-7400
RC372.A1
RECENT ADVANCES IN EPILEPSY. 1983. irreg., vol.6, 1995. price varies. Churchill Livingstone Medical Journals, Robert Stevenson House, 1-3 Baxter's Pl., Leith Walk, Edinburgh EH1 3AF, Scotland. TEL 0131-556-2424. FAX 0131-459-1177. (Orders to: Pearson Professional Ltd., Journals Subscription Department, P.O. Box 77, Fourth Ave., Harlow, Essex CM19 5AA, England; U.S. subscr. to: Churchill Livingstone, 650 Ave. of the Americas, New York, NY 10011. TEL 212-206-5000) Eds. Timothy A. Pedley, Brian S. Meldrum. circ. 850. **Document type:** monographic series.
—BLDSC (7303.831000).
Description: Publishes up-to-date reviews on topics of current interest. Highlights key points for clinical practice.
Refereed Serial

RECHT & PSYCHIATRIE. see *PSYCHOLOGY*

REFERATOVY VYBER Z NEUROLOGIE/ABSTRACTS OF NEUROLOGY. see *MEDICAL SCIENCES — Abstracting, Bibliographies, Statistics*

REHABILITATION COUNSELING BULLETIN. see *HANDICAPPED*

RESEARCH COMMUNICATIONS IN PSYCHOLOGY, PSYCHIATRY AND BEHAVIOR. see *PSYCHOLOGY*

616.8   UK   ISSN 0891-4222
HV1570.5.U65   CODEN: RDDIEF
RESEARCH IN DEVELOPMENTAL DISABILITIES; a multidisciplinary journal. 1981. bi-m. £188($299) (effective 1996). Elsevier Science Ltd., Pergamon, P.O. Box 800, Kidlington, Oxford OX5 1DX, England. TEL 44-1865-843000. FAX 44-1865-843010. E-mail: nlinfo-f@elsevier.nl; usinfo-f@elsevier.com; forinfo-kyf04035@niftyserve.or.jp; Site addr.: http://www.elsevier.nl/. (Subscr. in U.S. and Canada to: Elsevier Science, 660 White Plains Rd., Tarrytown, NY 10591-5153. TEL 914-524-9200. FAX 914-333-2444) Ed. Johnny L. Matson. adv.: B&W page $550, color page $1350. (also avail. in microfilm from UMI) **Indexed:** Biol.Abstr., C.I.J.E., Chic.Per.Ind., Curr.Adv.Ecol.Sci., Curr.Cont., Dent.Ind., Ind.Med., Psychol.Abstr. (1987-), SSCI, Yrbk.Assoc.Educ.& Rehab.Blind. **Document type:** academic/scholarly publication.
—BLDSC (7738.450000); Faxon; Genuine Article; SWETS; UMI; UnCover. **CCC.**
Formed by the 1987 merger of: Applied Research in Mental Retardation (ISSN 0270-3092); Analysis and Intervention in Developmental Disabilities (ISSN 0270-4684)
Description: Devoted to original behavioral research and theory of severe and pervasive developmental disabilities.
Refereed Serial

RESEARCH METHODS IN NEUROCHEMISTRY. see *BIOLOGY — Biological Chemistry*

616.8   NE   ISSN 0169-0833
CODEN: RETNEF
RESTORATIVE NEUROLOGY. (Text in English) 1985. irreg., vol.6, 1993. price varies. Elsevier Science B.V., Books Division, P.O. Box 211, 1000 AE Amsterdam, Netherlands. TEL 31-20-4853911. FAX 31-20-4853705.
E-mail: nlinfo-f@elsevier.nl; usinfo-f@elsevier.com; forinfo-kyf04035@niftyserve.or.jp; Site addr.: http://www.elsevier.nl/. (Subscr. in U.S. and Canada to: Elsevier Science Inc., Box 882, Madison Sq. Sta., New York, NY 10159-0882. TEL 212-989-5800. FAX 212-633-3680) **Document type:** monographic series.
—BLDSC (7777.865000); CASDDS.

616.8   IE   ISSN 0922-6028
CODEN: RNNEEL
RESTORATIVE NEUROLOGY AND NEUROSCIENCE. (Text in English) 1989. 8/yr. I£454($717) (effective 1996). Elsevier Science Ireland Ltd., P.O. Box 85, Limerick, Ireland. TEL 353-61-471944. FAX 353-61-472144. (Subscr. in U.S. and Canada to: Elsevier Science Inc., Box 882, Madison Sq. Sta., New York, NY 10159. TEL 212-989-5800. FAX 212-633-3990) Ed. D.G. Stein. bk.rev. (also avail. in microform from UMI; back issues avail.) **Indexed:** Curr.Cont., Excerp.Med. **Document type:** academic/scholarly publication.
—BLDSC (7777.865100); CASDDS; Faxon; Genuine Article. **CCC.**
Description: Interdisciplinary journal; contains papers on plasticity and response of the nervous system to accidental or experimental injuries, or transplantation.
Refereed Serial

616.89 362.2   SW   ISSN 0283-7587
REVANSCH!; klientperspektivet i psykiatrin. 1980. s-m. SEK 100. R S M H - Riksfoerbundet foer Social och Mental Haelsa, P.O. Box 15094, S-104 65 Stockholm, Sweden. TEL 46-8-772-33-60. FAX 46-8-772-33-61. Ed. Tommy Engman. **Document type:** bulletin.
Formerly (until 1985): R S M H - Information - Revansch! (ISSN 0280-0187)

REVIEW OF CLINICAL PSYCHIATRY AND THE LAW. see *LAW*

616.8   UK   ISSN 0334-1763
CODEN: RNEUEO
REVIEWS IN THE NEUROSCIENCES. (Text in English) 1986. q. $250 (effective 1996). Freund Publishing House Ltd., Ste. 500, Chesham House, 150 Regent St., London W1R 5FA, England. (And: P.O. Box 35010, Tel Aviv, Israel. TEL 972-3-5628540. FAX 972-3-5628538) Ed. J.P. Huston. adv. circ. 1,000. (back issues avail.) **Indexed:** Curr.Adv.Ecol.Sci., Excerp.Med., Ind.Med. (1993-). **Document type:** academic/scholarly publication.
—BLDSC (7793.571000); CASDDS; Faxon; UnCover.

REVIEWS OF OCULOMOTOR RESEARCH. see *MEDICAL SCIENCES — Ophthalmology And Optometry*

616.8   BL   ISSN 0101-8469
REVISTA BRASILEIRA DE NEUROLOGIA. (Text in Portuguese; summaries in English and Portuguese) 1949. bi-m. Cr.$19($80) (effective 1995). (Universidade Federal do Rio de Janeiro, Instituto de Neurologia) Editora Cientifica Nacional Ltda., Rua da Gloria 366, 3o andar, 20241-180 Rio de Janeiro, RJ, Brazil. TEL 55-21-2213235.
FAX 55-21-2521691. Ed. Helcio Alvarenga. adv. contact: Maria Luiza Carvalho Doneda. charts; illus. **Indexed:** Chem.Abstr., Excerp.Med., Ind.Med. **Document type:** academic/scholarly publication.
—EMDOCS; UMI.
Formerly: Jornal Brasileiro de Neurologia (ISSN 0021-7514)

616.8   CL   ISSN 0034-7388
REVISTA CHILENA DE NEUROPSIQUIATRIA. vol.16, 1978. q. $30. Sociedad Chilena de Neurologia, Psiquiatria y Neurocirugia, Av. Presidente Riesco 6007, Las Condes Clasificados, Correo, 27, Santiago, Chile. FAX 56-2-212-1521. Ed. Dr. Otto Dorr Zegers. adv.; bk.rev.; abstr.; bibl.; charts; illus.; stat. circ. 1,000. (reprint service avail. from IRC) **Indexed:** Chem.Abstr., Excerp.Med., Ind.Med., Psychol.Abstr.
—BLDSC (7848.900000).

616.89   CK   ISSN 0034-7450
CODEN: RCPSBR
REVISTA COLOMBIANA DE PSIQUIATRIA. 1964. q. $40. Sociedad Colombiana de Psiquiatria, Carrera 18, No. 8487, Apdo. 203, Bogota, Colombia. TEL 57-1-2561148. Ed. Roberto Chaskel. adv.; bk.rev.; abstr.; charts; illus.; index. circ. 1,500. **Indexed:** Excerp.Med., Psychol.Abstr. **Document type:** academic/scholarly publication.

616.8 616.5   RM   ISSN 0377-497X
CODEN: RMNPDC
REVISTA DE MEDICINA INTERNA, NEUROLOGIE, PSIHIATRIE, NEURO-CHIRURGIE, DERMATO-VENEROLOGIE. SERIES NEUROLOGIE, PSIHIATRIE, NEUROCHIRUGIE. (Text in Rumanian; summaries in English, French, German and Russian) 1956. 4/yr. $25. Uniunea Societatilor de Stiinte Medicale din Republica Socialista Rumania, Str. Progresului No. 8, R-70754 Bucharest, Rumania. (Subscr. to: ILEXIM, Str. 13 Decembrie Nr. 3, P.O. Box 136-137, Bucharest, Rumania) Ed.Bd. adv.; bk.rev.; abstr.; charts; illus. **Indexed:** Biol.Abstr., Chem.Abstr., Excerp.Med. (until 1993), Ind.Med. (until 1992), Psychol.Abstr.
—CASDDS.
Supersedes: Neurologie, Psihiatrie, Neurochirurgie (ISSN 0028-386X); Dermato-Venerologie (ISSN 0011-9024)

616.8   PE   ISSN 0034-8597
REVISTA DE NEURO-PSIQUIATRIA. (Text in Spanish; summaries in English, French and German) 1938. q. $50. Talleres Graficos P.L. Villanueva S.A., Casilla 1589, Lima 100, Peru. Eds. Javier Mariategui, Luis Trelles. adv.; bk.rev.; abstr.; charts; illus.; index. circ. 1,000. **Indexed:** Biol.Abstr., Excerp.Med., Ind.Med., Psychol.Abstr. **Document type:** academic/scholarly publication.

616.8 618.92   SP   ISSN 1130-9512
REVISTA DE PSIQUIATRIA INFANTO-JUVENIL. 1983. q. 5900 ptas.($65) (effective 1995). Editorial Garsi, S.A., Juan Bravo 46, 28006 Madrid, Spain. TEL 34-1-4021212. FAX 34-1-4020954.
Former titles (until 1990): Revista de Neuropsiquiatria Infanto-Juvenil (ISSN 0214-6428); (until 1987): Revista de Neuropsiquiatria Infantil (ISSN 0213-4985)

616.8   EC   ISSN 1019-8113
REVISTA ECUATORIANA DE NEUROLOGIA. 1992. s-a. $50 (effective 1995 & 1996). Sociedad Ecuatoriana de Neurologia, P.O. Box (09-01) 3734, Guayaquil, Ecuador. FAX 593-4285790. Ed. Dr. Oscar H. Del Brutto. adv. circ. 1,000. **Indexed:** Excerp.Med. (1993-). **Document type:** academic/scholarly publication.
—BLDSC (7852.810000); Genuine Article.

616.853   SP   ISSN 0213-4241
REVISTA ESPANOLA DE EPILEPSIA. 1986. q. Saned, S.A., Paseo de la Habana 202-bis, 28036 Madrid, Spain. TEL 1-3594092. Ed. Imes Picornell. **Indexed:** Excerp.Med. (1993-1994).

MEDICAL SCIENCES — PSYCHIATRY AND NEUROLOGY

616.8 SP ISSN 0213-4233
CODEN: RESNEA
REVISTA ESPANOLA DE NEUROLOGIA. 1986. 6/yr. Saned, S.A., Paseo de la Haban 202-bis, 28036 Madrid, Spain. TEL 1-3594092. Ed. Dr. A. Gimeno Alava. circ. 9,500. **Indexed:** Excerp.Med.
—BLDSC (7854.117000).

616.89 FR ISSN 0298-3850
REVUE DE MEDECINE PSYCHOSOMATIQUE. (Text in French; summaries in English) 1959. q. 350 F. to individuals (foreign 360 F.); institutions 450 F. (foreign 460 F.). (Societe Francaise de Medecine Psychosomatique) Pensee Sauvage Editions, B.P. 141, 38002 Grenoble, France. TEL 76-87-13-03. FAX 76-46-27-25. Eds. Dr. L. Chertok, Dr. M. Sapir. **Indexed:** Excerp.Med., Ind.Med., Psychol.Abstr.

616.8 FR ISSN 0035-161X
REVUE DE NEUROPSYCHIATRIE DE L'OUEST. 1963. q. 130 F. Societe de Neuro-Psychiatrie de l'Ouest, B.P. 226, Rennes, France.

616.8 FR ISSN 1155-4452
CODEN: RNURER
REVUE DE NEUROPSYCHOLOGIE. 1991. 4/yr. 550 F. to individuals; institutions 500 F. (effective 1996). Association pour la Diffusion des Recherches en Sciences Cognitives de Langue Francaise, IBHOP, Traverse Charles Susini, 13388 Marseille Cedex 13, France. TEL 91-66-00-69. FAX 91-61-14-20. Ed. Michel Habib. adv. contact: Francoise Joubaud. bk.rev. **Indexed:** Psychol.Abstr. (1991-). **Document type:** academic/scholarly publication.
—BLDSC (7937.880000).

REVUE EUROPEENE DE PSYCHOLOGIE APPLIQUEE/EUROPEAN REVIEW OF APPLIED PSYCHOLOGY. see PSYCHOLOGY

616.89 FR ISSN 1150-6652
REVUE INTERNATIONALE DE PSYCHOPATHOLOGIE. 1990. q. 510 F. (foreign 570 F.) (effective 1996). Presses Universitaires de France, Departement des Revues, 14 av. du Bois-de-l'Epine, B.P. 90, 91003 Evry Cedex, France. TEL 1-60-77-82-05. FAX 1-60-79-20-45. TELEX PUF 600 474 F. Eds. Daniel Widlocher, Pierre Fedida.
—BLDSC (7925.263000).

616.8 FR ISSN 0035-3787
CODEN: RENEAM
REVUE NEUROLOGIQUE. (Text in French; summaries in English) 1893. 10/yr. 1098 F. (foreign 1398 F.) (effective 1996). (Societe Francaise de Neurologie) Masson - Periodiques, Villa Laromiguiere, 75005 Paris, France. TEL 1-40-46-62-00. FAX 1-40-46-62-01. Ed. J.M. Leger. adv.; bk.rev.; abstr.; illus.; index. circ. 3,000. (also avail. in microform from UMI,BHP; reprint service avail. from ISI) **Indexed:** Bibl.Dev.Med.& Child Neur., Biol.Abstr., C.I.S. Abstr., Chem.Abstr., Curr.Adv.Biochem., Curr.Adv.Cancer Res., Curr.Adv.Cell & Devel.Biol., Curr.Adv.Ecol.Sci., Curr.Cont., Excerp.Med., Helminthol.Abstr., Ind.Med., Protozool.Abstr., Psychol.Abstr. (1992-). **Document type:** academic/scholarly publication.
—BLDSC (7937.750000); EMDOCS; Genuine Article; SWETS; UMI. **CCC.**
Description: Publishes the works of the society, and French and foreign articles.

616.8 RM ISSN 1017-5644
CODEN: RRNPEE
REVUE ROUMAINE DE NEUROLOGIE ET PSYCHIATRIE/ROMANIAN JOURNAL OF NEUROLOGY AND PSYCHIATRY. (Text in English, French, German and Russian; summaries in English) 1964. q. 200 lei($55) (Academia de Stiinte Medicale) Editura Academiei Romane, Calea Victoriei 125, 79717 Bucharest, Rumania. (Dist. by: Rompresfilatelia, Calea Grivitei 64-66, P.O. Box 12-201, 78104 Bucharest, Rumania) Ed. Vlad Voiculescu. bk.rev.; charts; illus.; index. circ. 700. **Indexed:** Biol.Abstr., Excerp.Med., Ind.Med., Psychol.Abstr. (1979-). **Document type:** academic/scholarly publication.
—BLDSC (8019.638500); EMDOCS.
Formerly (until 1990): Revue Roumaine de Medecine. Neurologie et Psychiatrie (ISSN 0259-6326); **Supersedes in part (in 1975):** Revue Roumaine de Medecine (ISSN 0303-822X); Which was formed by the 1974 merger of: Revue Roumaine de Medecine Interne (ISSN 0035-3973); Revue Roumaine d'Endocrinologie (ISSN 0035-4015); Revue Roumaine de Neurologie et de Psychiatrie (ISSN 0301-7303); Which was (until 1973): Revue Roumaine de Neurologie (ISSN 0035 3981).

616.8 JA ISSN 0009-918X
RINSHO SHINKEIGAKU/CLINICAL NEUROLOGY. (Text in Japanese; summaries in English) 1960. m. 13000 Yen. Japanese Society of Neurology - Nihon Shinkei Gakkai, Ichimaru Bldg., 2-31-21 Yushima, Bunkyo-ku, Tokyo 113, Japan. TEL 03-3815-1080. FAX 03-3815-1931. Ed. Toru Mannen. adv.; charts; illus.; index. circ. 6,895. **Indexed:** Biol.Abstr., Dent.Ind., Excerp.Med., Ind.Med.
—BLDSC (3286.309000); Faxon; SWETS.

616.8 IT ISSN 0035-6336
CODEN: RNBLAC
RIVISTA DI NEUROBIOLOGIA. (Text in Italian; summaries in English) 1955. q. Ospedale Neuropsichiatrico Provinciale, 52100 Arezzo, Italy. Ed. Marino Benvenuti. adv.; bibl.; charts; illus.; index. circ. 300. **Indexed:** Biol.Abstr., Chem.Abstr., Dent.Ind., Excerp.Med., Ind.Med.
—EMDOCS.

616.8 IT ISSN 0035-6352
RIVISTA DI NEUROPSICHIATRIA E SCIENZE AFFINI. (Text in Italian; summaries in English) 1955. q. L.60000 (foreign L.120000) (effective 1994). Casa Editrice Maccari, Via Trento 53, 43100 Parma, Italy. FAX 039-521-771268. Ed.Bd. adv.; bk.rev. circ. 1,600. **Indexed:** Chem.Abstr., Excerp.Med.
—BLDSC (7991.420000); UMI.

RIVISTA DI NEURORADIOLOGIA; periodico quadrimestrale scientifico indipendente. see MEDICAL SCIENCES — Radiology And Nuclear Medicine

616.89 IT ISSN 0035-6484
CODEN: RPSID3
RIVISTA DI PSICHIATRIA. (Text in Italian; abstracts in English) 1966. bi-m. L.412500($250) (effective 1996). Pensiero Scientifico Editore s.r.l., Via Bradano 3-C, 00199 Rome, Italy. TEL 06-86207158. FAX 06-86207160. Eds. G.C. Reda, P. Pancheri. adv.; bk.rev.; charts; illus.; index. circ. 1,000. **Indexed:** Excerp.Med., Psychol.Abstr. (1966-). **Document type:** academic/scholarly publication.
—BLDSC (7992.731000); EMDOCS; Faxon.

616.8 IT ISSN 1122-2263
RIVISTA DI RIABILITAZIONE PSICHIATRICA E PSICOSOCIALE. (Supplement avail. (ISSN 1122-2298)) (Text in English, Italian) 1992. 3/yr. L.60000($100) (effective 1995). Casa Editrice Idelson, Via A. De Gasperi 55, 80133 Naples, Italy. TEL 39-81-5524733. FAX 39-81-5518295. Ed. Massimo Casacchia. **Document type:** academic/scholarly publication.

616.8 IT ISSN 0035-7057
CODEN: RSFMA
RIVISTA SPERIMENTALE DI FRENIATRIA; medicina legale delle alienazioni mentali. (Text in Italian; summaries in English and French) 1875. bi-m. L.80000 (foreign L.100000) (effective 1995). (Istituti Ospedalieri Neuropsichiatrici di San Lazzaro) Artigianato Grafico Editoriale s.n.c., Via Casorati, 29, 42100 Reggio Emilia, Italy. Ed. Piero Benassi. adv.; bk.rev. **Indexed:** Biol.Abstr., Chem.Abstr., Excerp.Med., Ind.Med., Psychol.Abstr.
—EMDOCS.

616.8 JA ISSN 0914-7691
RONENKICHIHO/JOURNAL OF SENILE DEMENTIA. (Text in Japanese) 1987. 4/yr. 1545 Yen per no. Medikaru Rebyusha - Medical Review Co., Ltd., 7-3, Hiranomachi 1-chome, Chuo-ku, Osaka 541, Japan.

616.8 UK
ROYAL COLLEGE OF PSYCHIATRISTS. COUNCIL REPORTS. irreg., no.35, 1995. Royal College of Psychiatrists, 17 Belgrave Sq., London SW1X 8PG, England. TEL 0171-235-8857. FAX 0171-245-1231. **Document type:** monographic series.

S A M I K S A. see PSYCHOLOGY

S T K. see MEDICAL SCIENCES

616.8 371.9 IT ISSN 0390-5179
SAGGI; neuropsicologia infantile psicopedagogia riabilitazione. (Supplements avail.) (Text in Italian; summaries in English) 1975. s-a. L.45000 (foreign L.55000) (typically set in Jan.). (Scientific Institute "Eugenio Medea" - Bosisio Parini) Masson S.p.A., Divisione Periodici, Via Statuto 2-4, 20121 Milan, Italy. TEL 39-2-63671. FAX 39-2-6367211. Ed. Giaele Spreafico. adv.; bk.rev.; cum.index: 1975-1994; circ. 800 (controlled). **Indexed:** Psychol.Abstr. (1993-). **Document type:** academic/scholarly publication, monographic series.
—Genuine Article.
Description: Covers infant neuropsychology and psychopedagogic rehabilitation.
Refereed Serial

616.8 617 JA ISSN 0385-0943
SAITAMAKEN NO SHINKEI GEKAIKAI KAIHO/SAITAMA NEUROSURGICAL ASSOCIATION. BULLETIN. (Text in Japanese) 1974. s-a. 4000 Yen membership. Saitamaken No Shinkei Geka Ikai, 5-1, Nakacho 3-chome, Urawa-shi, Saitama-ken 336, Japan. Eds. Takao Ishibashi, Fujio Mizoguchi. **Document type:** bulletin.

616.89 MX ISSN 0185-3325
SALUD MENTAL. (Text in Spanish; summaries in English) 1978. q. Mex.$170($55) to individuals; institutions $70 (effective 1995). Instituto Mexicana de Psiquiatria, Calz. Mexico-Xochimilco, No. 101, Col. San L. Huipulco, Del. Tlalpan, 14370 Mexico DF, Mexico. TEL 525-655-28-11 ext. 144. FAX 525-655-4292. Ed. Hector Perez-Rincon. adv.; bk.rev.; bibl.; illus.; cum.index. circ. 3,000. (back issues avail.) **Indexed:** Curr.Cont., Excerp.Med. (1995-), Ind.Med., Psychol.Abstr. (1979-), SSCI. **Document type:** academic/scholarly publication.
●Also available on CD-ROM.
—BLDSC (8071.770000); Genuine Article.
Description: Covers research in neurosciences, clinical psychiatry, epidemiology, mental health, psychopharmacology, history of psychiatry and problems of ethics.
Refereed Serial

616.891 DK ISSN 0106-2301
RC500
SCANDINAVIAN PSYCHOANALYTIC REVIEW. (Text in English) 1978. s-a. DKK 380 (effective 1996). (Psycho-Analytical Societies in Denmark, Finland, Norway and Sweden) Munksgaard International Publishers Ltd., 35 Noerre Soegade, P.O. Box 2148, DK-1016 Copenhagen K, Denmark. TEL 33-127030. FAX 33-129387. Ed. Anders Zachrisson. bk.rev. circ. 900. (reprint service avail. from ISI) **Indexed:** ASCA, Curr.Cont., IMFL, Psychoanal.Abstr., Psychol.Abstr. (1978-), SSCI.
—BLDSC (8087.572800); UnCover. **CCC.**
Refereed Serial

MEDICAL SCIENCES — PSYCHIATRY AND NEUROLOGY

618 150   US   ISSN 0586-7614
RC514   CODEN: SCZBB3
SCHIZOPHRENIA BULLETIN. 1969. q. $17 (foreign $21.50). U.S. Public Health Service, National Institute of Mental Health, 5600 Fishers Ln., Rockville, MD 20857. TEL 301-443-9772. (Subscr. to: Superintendent of Documents, U.S. Government Printing Office, Box 371954, Pittsburgh, PA 15250-7954. TEL 202-512-1800. FAX 202-512-2250) Ed. Dr. David Shore. abstr.; bibl. circ. 7,000. (also avail. in microform from MIM,UMI; back issues avail.; reprint service avail. from UMI) **Indexed:** Adol.Ment.Hlth.Abstr., ASCA, Biol.Abstr., CINAHL, Curr.Adv.Ecol.Sci., Curr.Cont., Except.Child.Educ.Abstr., Excerp.Med., Ind.Med., Ind.U.S.Gov.Per., MEDOC, Psychol.Abstr. (1969-), SSCI. **Document type:** government publication, bulletin.
●Also available online.
—BLDSC (8089.400000); Faxon; Genuine Article; SWETS; UMI; UnCover.
Refereed Serial

616.8   NE   ISSN 0920-9964
CODEN: SCRSEH
SCHIZOPHRENIA RESEARCH; an international multidisciplinary journal. (Text in English) 1988. 15/yr. fl.2730($1665) (effective 1996). Elsevier Science B.V., P.O. Box 211, 1000 AE Amsterdam, Netherlands. TEL 31-20-4853911. FAX 31-20-4853598. TELEX 18582 ESPA NL. E-mail: nlinfo-f@elsevier.nl; usinfo-f@elsevier.com; forinfo-kyf04035@niftyserve.or.jp; Site addr.: http://www.elsevier.nl/. (Subscr. in U.S. and Canada to: Elsevier Science Inc., Box 882, Madison Sq. Sta., New York, NY 10159-0882. TEL 212-989-5800. FAX 212-633-3990) Eds. H.A. Nasrallah, L.E. DeLisi. circ. 800. (also avail. in microform from UMI; reprint service avail. from ISI) **Indexed:** Curr.Cont., Excerp.Med., Psychol.Abstr. (1988-). **Document type:** academic/scholarly publication.
—BLDSC (8089.440000); Faxon; Genuine Article; SWETS; UnCover. **CCC.**
Description: Presents new international research that contributes to the understanding of schizophrenic disorders.
Refereed Serial

616.8   US   ISSN 0080-715X
SCHRIFTENREIHE NEUROLOGIE - NEUROLOGY SERIES. (Text in German; occasionally in English) 1959. irreg. price varies. Springer-Verlag, 175 Fifth Ave., New York, NY 10010. TEL 212-460-1500. FAX 212-473-6272. (Also: Berlin, Heidelberg, Tokyo and Vienna) (reprint service avail. from ISI) **Indexed:** Biol.Abstr., Ind.Med. **Document type:** monographic series.
Supersedes in part: Monographien aus dem Gesamtgebiete der Neurologie und Psychiatrie.

616.89   SZ
CODEN: SANNAW
SCHWEIZER ARCHIV FUER NEUROLOGIE UND PSYCHIATRIE. (Text and title in English, French, German and Italian) 1917. 6/yr. 255 SFr. (Europe 235 SFr.; overseas 241.10 SFr.). (Schweizerische Neurologische Gesellschaft) Verlag Baebler, Postfach 109, CH-3000 Bern 21, Switzerland. TEL 031-3714552. FAX 01-9285520. (Subscr. to: Zuerichsee Zeitschriftenverlag, Seestr. 86, CH-8712 Staefa, Switzerland. TEL 01-9285616) (Co-sponsor: Schweizerische Gesellschaft fuer Psychiatrie) Ed. Jacques Baebler. adv.; bk.rev.; charts; illus.; index per vol. circ. 750. (also avail. in microform from UMI; reprint service avail. from UMI) **Indexed:** Biol.Abstr., Chem.Abstr., Curr.Cont., Excerp.Med., Ind.Med., Ind.Vet., Nutr.Abstr., Psychol.Abstr. (1970-), Vet.Bull. **Document type:** academic/scholarly publication.
—CASDDS; UMI. **CCC.**
Formerly: Schweizer Archiv fuer Neurologie, Neurochirurgie und Psychiatrie (ISSN 0036-7273)

SCRIPT. see *PSYCHOLOGY*

616.8   JA   ISSN 0488-1281
SEISHIN IGAKU/CLINICAL PSYCHIATRY. (Text in Japanese; summaries in English) 1959. m. 22320 Yen($172) Igaku-Shoin Ltd., 5-24-3 Hongo, Bunkyo-ku, Tokyo 113-91, Japan. TEL 03-817-5711. Ed.Bd. circ. 6,000.
●Also available online. Vendor(s): JICST.
—BLDSC (3286.340000).

616.8   JA   ISSN 0080-8547
SEISHIN IGAKU KENKYUJO, TOKYO. GYOSEKISHU/SEISHIN IGAKU INSTITUTE OF PSYCHIATRY, TOKYO. BULLETIN. (Text in Japanese; table of contents and summaries in English) 1954. a. free. Seishin Igaku Institute of Psychiatry - Seishin Igaku Kenkyujo, 11-11 Komone 4-chome, Itabashi-ku, Tokyo 173, Japan. FAX 03-956-9644. (reprint service avail.) **Indexed:** Biol.Abstr., Excerp.Med.

616.891   JA   ISSN 0916-8710
SEISHIN RYOHO/JAPANESE JOURNAL OF PSYCHOTHERAPY. (Text in Japanese) 1975. bi-m. 1850 Yen per no. Kongo Shuppan, 5-16, Suido 1-chome, Bunkyo-ku, Tokyo 112, Japan.
Formerly (until 1992): Kikan Seishin Ryoho (ISSN 0386-9660)

616.8   UK   ISSN 1059-1311
CODEN: SEIZE7
SEIZURE. 1992. 4/yr. £50 in Europe (rest of world $90) to individuals; institutions £99 in Europe (rest of world $178). W.B. Saunders Co. Ltd. (Subsidiary of: Harcourt Brace & Company Ltd.), 24-28 Oval Rd., London NW1 7DX, England. TEL 0171-267-4466. FAX 0171-482-2293. TELEX 25775-ACPRES-G. (Subscr. to: Harcourt Brace & Company Ltd., Foots Cray High St., Sidcup, Kent DA14 5HP, England. TEL 0181-300-3322. FAX 0181-309-0807; Subscr. in N. America to: W.B. Saunders Co., Journals Subscription Fulfillment, 6277 Sea Harbor Dr., 4th Fl., Orlando, FL 32887-4800. TEL 800-654-2452. FAX 800-874-6418) Ed. T. Betts. (back issues avail.) **Indexed:** Excerp.Med. (1994-), Ind.Med. (1994-). **Document type:** academic/scholarly publication.
—BLDSC (8229.100000); Genuine Article. **CCC.**
Description: Provides an interdisciplinary forum for original research in all aspects of epilepsy, including the basic sciences, diagnosis and epidemiology of seizures, treatment and management of epilepsy, and related social issues.
Refereed Serial

SEMINARS IN NEUROLOGICAL SURGERY. see *MEDICAL SCIENCES — Surgery*

616.8   US   ISSN 0271-8235
CODEN: SEMNEP
SEMINARS IN NEUROLOGY. 1980. q. $89 to individuals (foreign $114); institutions $125 (foreign $150). Thieme Medical Publishers, Inc., 381 Park Ave. S., Ste. 1501, New York, NY 10016. TEL 212-683-5088. FAX 212-779-9020. Ed. Dr. David Goldblatt. adv.; abstr.; bibl.; charts; illus.; stat.; index. circ. 2,300. (also avail. in microform from UMI) **Indexed:** Curr.Adv.Ecol.Sci., Curr.Cont. **Document type:** academic/scholarly publication.
●Also available online. Vendor(s): Ovid Technologies.
—BLDSC (8239.455550); Faxon; Genuine Article; SWETS; UMI; UnCover. **CCC.**

616.8 618.92   US   ISSN 1071-9091
▼**SEMINARS IN PEDIATRIC NEUROLOGY.** 1994 (Sep.). q. $118 (foreign $142) (effective 1996). W.B. Saunders Co. (Subsidiary of: Harcourt Brace & Company), Curtis Center, Independence Sq. W., Philadelphia, PA 19106-3399. TEL 215-238-7800. FAX 215-238-6445. (Subscr. to: Periodicals Fulfillment, W.B. Saunders Co., 6277 Sea Harbor Dr., 4th Fl., Orlando, FL 32891-4800. TEL 800-654-2452. FAX 800-874-6418) Ed. Dr. John B. Bodensteiner; Pub. Joan W. Blumberg. adv.; B&W page $565, color page $1390; 7 x 10; adv. contact: Steve Gray. circ. 1,500. **Document type:** academic/scholarly publication.
—UMI.
Description: Covers topics of current importance in the field of pediatric neurology.

616.8   UK   ISSN 1044-5765
RC321   CODEN: SNEUEZ
SEMINARS IN THE NEUROSCIENCES. 1989. bi-m. £115 (effective 1996). Academic Press Ltd. (Subsidiary of: Harcourt Brace & Company Ltd.), 24-28 Oval Rd., London NW1 7DX, England. TEL 44-171-267-4466. FAX 44-171-482-2293. TELEX 25775 ACPRES G. (Subscr. to: Harcourt Brace & Company Ltd., Foots Cray High St., Sidcup, Kent DA14 5HP, England. TEL 44-181-300-3322. FAX 44-181-309-0807) Ed. Dr. Johannes Velterop. **Indexed:** Excerp.Med. (1993-). **Document type:** academic/scholarly publication.
—BLDSC (8239.455580); CASDDS; Genuine Article; SWETS; UnCover. **CCC.**
Description: For scientists in the neurological sciences and the life sciences.

616.89   CC   ISSN 1002-0829
SHANGHAI JINGSHEN YIXUE/SHANGHAI ARCHIVES OF PSYCHIATRY. (Text in Chinese) 1989. q. $13. Shanghai Shi Jingshen Weisheng Zhongxin - Shanghai Mental Health Centre, 600 Wanping Nanlu, Shanghai 200030, People's Republic of China. TEL 4387250. FAX 4387986. Ed. Wenwei Yan. adv.: page $900; adv. contact: Keliang Zhan. circ. 5,300.
Description: Provides up-to-date coverage of psychiatry in China and around the world.

616.8 617.7   JA   ISSN 0389-5610
SHINKEI GAISHO/NEUROTRAUMATOLOGY. Variant title: Nihon Shinkei Gaisho Kenkyukai Koenshu. (Text in Japanese; summaries in English) 1979. a. 5000 Yen. Japanese Society of Neurotraumatology - Nihon Shinkei Gaisho Kenkyukai, Tokyo Jikei University School of Medicine, Department of Neurosurgery, 3-25-8, Nishi-Shinbashi, Minato-ku, Tokyo 105, Japan. circ. 1,000. (back issues avail.)

SHINKEI GANKA/NEURO-OPHTHALMOLOGY JAPAN. see *MEDICAL SCIENCES — Ophthalmology And Optometry*

618   JA   ISSN 0470-8105
CODEN: NMCHBN
SHINKEI GEKA. English edition: Neurologia Medico-Chirurgica (ISSN 0387-2572) (Text in Japanese; summaries in English) 1959. m. Japan Neurosurgical Society - Nihon Noshinkei Geka Gakkai, Department of Neurosurgery, Faculty of Medicine, University of Tokyo, 7-3-1 Hongo, Bunkyo-ku, Tokyo 113, Japan. **Indexed:** Biol.Abstr., Dent.Ind., Excerp.Med., Ind.Med.
—**CCC.**

616.8   JA   ISSN 0037-3796
SHINKEI KAGAKU/JAPANESE NEUROCHEMICAL SOCIETY. BULLETIN. (Text in Japanese) 1962. s-a. price varies. Japanese Neurochemical Society - Nihon Shinkei Kagakkai, Nihon Gakkai Jimu Senta, 16-9 Honkomagome 5-chome, Bunkyo-ku, Tokyo 113, Japan. Ed. Yasuo Kakimoto. adv.; bk.rev.; bibl. circ. 1,500. (processed) **Indexed:** Biol.Abstr., Chem.Abstr.
—BLDSC (2593.910000).
Formerly: Nerve Chemistry.

616.8   JA   ISSN 0001-8724
CODEN: SKNSAF
SHINKEI KENKYU NO SHINPO/ADVANCES IN NEUROLOGICAL SCIENCES. (Text in Japanese; summaries in European languages) 1966. bi-m. 29100 Yen($224) Igaku-Shoin Ltd., 5-24-3 Hongo, Bunkyo-ku, Tokyo 113-91, Japan. TEL 03-817-5702. Ed.Bd. circ. 3,000. **Indexed:** Apic.Abstr., Biol.Abstr., Chem.Abstr., Excerp.Med., Ind.Med.
—BLDSC (0709.480000); CASDDS.

616.8   JA   ISSN 0385-0307
CODEN: SHIGD4
SHINSHIN-IGAKU/JAPANESE JOURNAL OF PSYCHOSOMATIC MEDICINE. (Text in Japanese; summaries in English) 1976. 7/yr. 10990 Yen($85) (Japanese Society of Psychosomatic Medicine) Igaku-Shoin Ltd., 5-24-3 Hongo, Bunkyo-ku, Tokyo 113-91, Japan. TEL 03-817-5711. Ed.Bd. circ. 4,500.
●Also available online. Vendor(s): JICST.
—BLDSC (4658.340000).

MEDICAL SCIENCES — PSYCHIATRY AND NEUROLOGY

616.8   JA   ISSN 0285-9513
SHITSUGOSHO KENKYU/HIGHER BRAIN FUNCTION RESEARCH. (Text in Japanese; summaries in English, Japanese) 1981. q. 2000 Yen per no. Nihon Shitsugosho Gakkai - Japanese Society of Aphasiology, Izu Nirayama Onsen Byoin, 234, Chujo, Nirayama-cho, Tagata-gun, Shizuoka-ken 410-21, Japan.

SIGNAL'NAYA INFORMATSIYA. NEIROPEPTIDY. see MEDICAL SCIENCES — Abstracting, Bibliographies, Statistics

616.8   US   ISSN 0161-8105
QP425   CODEN: SLEED6
SLEEP. 1978. 10/yr. $129 to individuals (foreign $159); institutions $180. American Sleep Disorders Association, c/o Allen Press, Box 1897, Lawrence, KS 66044. TEL 913-843-1234. FAX 913-843-1274. (And: 1610 14th St., N.W., Ste. 300, Rochester, MN 55901-0246) (Co-publisher: Sleep Research Society) (Co-sponsors: European Sleep Research Society, Latin American Sleep Research Society, Japanese Sleep Research Society) Ed. Christian Guilleminault. adv.; bk.rev.; index. circ. 3,000. (back issues avail.) **Indexed:** ASCA, Bibl.Dev.Med.& Child Neur., Dent.Ind., Excerp.Med., Ind.Med., Psychol.Abstr. (1979-), Risk Abstr. **Document type:** trade publication.
—BLDSC (8309.440000); CASDDS; Faxon; SWETS; UnCover. **CCC.**
   Description: Focuses on medicine and sleep research.

616.8   US   ISSN 0093-0407
SLEEP RESEARCH. 1972. a. $92 (effective 1994). Brain Research Institute, Brain Information Service, B R I Publications Office, No. 43-367 CHS, University of California at Los Angeless Medical Center, CA 90024-1761. TEL 310-825-3417. FAX 310-206-3499. Ed.Bd. bk.rev.; abstr.; bibl. circ. 2,000. (back issues avail.) **Document type:** academic/scholarly publication.
—BLDSC (8309.460000); SWETS.
   Description: Current claims and abstracts from the annual meeting of the Association of Professional Sleep Societies.

616.89   GW   ISSN 0933-7954
RC321   CODEN: SPPEEM
SOCIAL PSYCHIATRY AND PSYCHIATRIC EPIDEMIOLOGY. (Text in English) 1966. 6/yr. DM.698($507) (effective 1996). Springer-Verlag, Heidelberger Platz 3, 14197 Berlin, Germany. TEL 030-8207-0. FAX 030-8214091. E-mail: orders@springer.de. (Subcr. in N. America to: Springer-Verlag New York, Inc., 44 Hartz Way, Secaucus, NJ 07096-2491. TEL 201-348-4033. FAX 201-348-4505) Ed. P. Bebbington. adv.; charts; illus.; index. (also avail. in microform from UMI; reprint service avail. from ISI) **Indexed:** Biol.Abstr., Curr.Cont., Excerp.Med., Psychol.Abstr. (1985-), SSCI, Trop.Dis.Bull. **Document type:** academic/scholarly publication.
—BLDSC (8318.145700); Faxon; Genuine Article; SWETS; UMI; UnCover. **CCC.**
   Formerly: Social Psychiatry (ISSN 0037-7813)
   Description: Concerned with the effects of social conditions on behavior, and the relationship between psychiatric disorders and the social environment.

SOCIOLOGY OF HEALTH AND ILLNESS. see SOCIOLOGY

616.8   IT   ISSN 1121-0664
SOGNO DELLA FARFALLA; journal of psychiatry and psychotherapy. 1992. q. L.60000($60) (effective 1994). Wichtig Editore s.r.l., Via Friuli 71-74, 20135 Milan, Italy. TEL 02-5452306. FAX 02-5451843.

SOINS - PSYCHIATRIE. see MEDICAL SCIENCES — Nurses And Nursing

606.89   US   ISSN 1047-6334
SOUTHERN CALIFORNIA PSYCHIATRIST.* 1955. m. (11/yr.). $25. Southern California Psychiatric Society, 2999 Overland Ave., Ste. 116, Los Angeles, CA 90404-4243. Ed. Dr. Don Rockwell. adv.; bk.rev.; film rev.; play rev. circ. 1,900.
   Formerly (until Aug. 1988): Southern California Psychiatric Society. Newsletter.

SOZIALPSYCHIATRISCHE INFORMATIONEN. see PSYCHOLOGY

616.8   GW   ISSN 0341-9738
SPEKTRUM DER PSYCHIATRIE UND NERVENHEILKUNDE. 1971. bi-m. DM.36 (students DM.27). Deutscher Aerzte-Verlag GmbH, Postfach 400265, 50832 Cologne, Germany. TEL 02234-7011-0. FAX 02234-7011444. adv. circ. 6,300. **Document type:** trade publication.
   Description: Clinical and scientific information for psychiatrists and neurologists.

SPRINGER SERIES ON BEHAVIOR THERAPY AND BEHAVIORAL MEDICINE. see PSYCHOLOGY

616.8   US   ISSN 0740-4212
SPRINGER SERIES ON PSYCHIATRY. 1982. irreg., latest 1994. price varies. Springer Publishing Company, 536 Broadway, New York, NY 10012-3955. TEL 212-431-4370. FAX 212-941-7842. Ed. Dr. Carl Eisdorfer. **Document type:** monographic series.
—BLDSC (8424.772000).
   Description: Explores issues in experimental and clinical psychiatry.

616.85   NE   ISSN 0924-7025
STEM-, SPRAAK- EN TAALPATHOLOGIE. 1992. 4/yr. fl.96.20 to individuals; institutions fl.116.60 (effective 1994). Swets & Zeitlinger bv, Heereweg 347, 2161 CA Lisse, Netherlands. TEL 31-2521-35111. FAX 31-2521-15888. TELEX 41325 SZLIS NL. (Dist. in N. America by: Swets & Zeitlinger, 440 Creamery Way, Ste. A, Exton, PA 19341. TEL 800-447-9387) Ed.Bd. (back issues avail.) **Document type:** academic/scholarly publication.
   Description: Publishes empirical studies and review articles on the theory, diagnosis and clinical care of speech and language disorders.

STEREOTACTIC AND FUNCTIONAL NEUROSURGERY. see MEDICAL SCIENCES — Surgery

STRABISMUS. see MEDICAL SCIENCES — Ophthalmology And Optometry

616.8   UK   ISSN 0748-8386
CODEN: STMEEZ
STRESS MEDICINE. 1985. q. $545 (foreign $545) (effective 1996). John Wiley & Sons Ltd., Journals, Baffins Ln., Chichester, W. Sussex PO19 1UD, England. TEL 01243-779777. FAX 01243-776128. TELEX 86290 WIBOOK G. (Subscr. in the Americas to: John Wiley & Sons, Inc., 605 Third Ave., New York, NY 10158. TEL 212-850-6645. FAX 212-850-6021) Ed. David Wheatley. adv.; bk.rev. circ. 180. (also avail. in microform from UMI; reprint service avail. from SWZ) **Indexed:** Behav.Med.Abstr., Curr.Adv.Ecol.Sci., Curr.Cont., Excerp.Med., Psychol.Abstr. (1987-), Risk Abstr. **Document type:** academic/scholarly publication.
—BLDSC (8474.129500); Genuine Article; SWETS; UMI; UnCover. **CCC.**
   Description: Provides a forum for the discussion of all aspects of stress that affect the individual in both health and disease.
   Refereed Serial

STRESSFORSKNINGSRAPPORTER. see PSYCHOLOGY

616.8   UK   ISSN 1351-8194
CODEN: SNRSEQ
STUDIES IN NEUROSCIENCE. 1985. irreg. price varies. Elsevier Science Ltd., Books Division, P.O. Box 800, Kidlington, Oxford OX5 1DK, England. TEL 44-1865-843000. FAX 44-1865-843010. E-mail: nlinfo-f@elsevier.nl; usinfo-f@elsevier.com; forinfo-kyf04035@niftyserve.or.jp; Site addr.: http://www.elsevier.nl/. (And: Elsevier Science, 660 White Plains Rd., Tarrytown, NY 10591-5153. TEL 914-524-9200. FAX 914-333-2444) Ed. W. Winlow. **Document type:** monographic series.
—CASDDS.

616.85   NE   ISSN 0927-1813
STUDIES IN SPEECH PATHOLOGY AND CLINICAL LINGUISTICS. (Text in English) 1991. irreg., vol.5, 1995. price varies. John Benjamins Publishing Co., Amsteldijk 44, P.O. Box 75577, 1070 AN Amsterdam, Netherlands. TEL 31-20-6738156. FAX 31-20-6792956. (In N. America: Box 27519, Philadelphia, PA 19118-0519. TEL 215-836-1200. FAX 215-836-1204) Eds. Martin J. Ball, Raymond D. Kent. **Document type:** monographic series.
—BLDSC (8491.747000).
   Description: Forum for academic research in speech disorders integrating research from the related fields of speech pathology and clinical linguistics.
   Refereed Serial

152.1 006.4   NE   ISSN 0926-907X
STUDIES IN VISUAL INFORMATION PROCESSING. (Text in English) 1990. irreg., vol.4, 1993. price varies. Elsevier Science B.V., Books Division, P.O. Box 211, 1000 AE Amsterdam, Netherlands. TEL 31-20-4853911. FAX 31-20-4853705. TELEX 18582 ESPA NL. E-mail: nlinfo-f@elsevier.nl; usinfo-f@elsevier.com; forinfo-kyf04035@niftyserve.or.jp; Site addr.: http://www.elsevier.nl/. (Subscr. in U.S. and Canada to: Elsevier Science Inc., Box 882, Madison Sq. Sta., New York, NY 10159. TEL 212-989-5800) Eds. Rudolf Groner, Gery d'Yderwalle. (back issues avail.) **Document type:** monographic series.
—BLDSC (8491.846600).
   Refereed Serial

SUICIDE AND LIFE-THREATENING BEHAVIOR. see PSYCHOLOGY

616.8 360   GW   ISSN 0173-458X
SUIZIDPROPHYLAXE. 1973. q. DM.64. (German Association of Suicide Prevention) S. Roderer Verlag, Postfach 110506, 93018 Regensburg, Germany. TEL 0941-795124. FAX 0941-795198. Eds. Michel Heinrich, Hans Wedler. adv.; bk.rev. circ. 1,000. (back issues avail.) **Document type:** academic/scholarly publication.

SURGICAL NEUROLOGY. see MEDICAL SCIENCES — Surgery

616.8   US   ISSN 0887-4476
QP364   CODEN: SYNAET
SYNAPSE (NEW YORK). m. $1116 (foreign $1302) (effective 1996). John Wiley & Sons, Inc., Journals, 605 Third Ave., New York, NY 10158. TEL 212-850-6645. FAX 212-850-6021. TELEX 12-7063. E-mail: SUBINFO@JWILEY.COM. (Subscr. outside the Americas to: John Wiley & Sons Ltd., Baffins Ln., Chichester, W. Sussex PO19 1UD, England. TEL 44-1243-779777. FAX 44-1243-776128) Ed. John E. Johnson, Jr. adv. circ. 166. (also avail. in microform from UMI; back issues avail.) **Document type:** academic/scholarly publication.
—BLDSC (8585.880200); CASDDS; Faxon; Genuine Article; SWETS; UnCover. **CCC.**
   Description: Embraces new basic and clinical research pertaining to all aspects of synaptic structure and function, including attention to practical clinical consideration.
   Refereed Serial

616.8   GW   ISSN 0933-3053
SYSTEM FAMILIE; Forschung und Therapie. 4/yr. DM.158($114) (effective 1996). Springer-Verlag, Heidelberger Platz 3, 14197 Berlin, Germany. TEL 030-8207-0. FAX 030-8214091. E-mail: orders@springer.de. (Subscr. in N. America to: Springer-Verlag New York, Inc., 44 Hartz Way, Secaucus, NJ 07096-2491. TEL 201-348-4033. FAX 201-348-4505) **Document type:** academic/scholarly publication.
—Genuine Article; SWETS; UMI. **CCC.**

SYSTEM UBW; Zeitschrift fuer klassische Psychoanalyse. see PSYCHOLOGY

616.8   GW   ISSN 0935-3224
CODEN: TWNPE3
T W NEUROLOGIE - PSYCHIATRIE. 1987. 10/yr. DM.108 (foreign DM.145). Verlag G. Braun GmbH, Karl-Friedrich-Str. 14-18, 76133 Karlsruhe, Germany. TEL 0721-165-0. FAX 0721-165191. **Indexed:** Excerp.Med. **Document type:** trade publication.
—BLDSC (9076.749500).

MEDICAL SCIENCES — PSYCHIATRY AND NEUROLOGY

TECHNIQUES IN NEUROSURGERY. see *MEDICAL SCIENCES — Surgery*

616.8 NE ISSN 0921-0709
CODEN: TBSCEC
TECHNIQUES IN THE BEHAVIORAL AND NEURAL SCIENCES. (Text in English) 1987. irreg., vol.11, 1993. Elsevier Science B.V., Books Division, P.O. Box 211, 1000 AE Amsterdam, Netherlands. TEL 31-20-4853911. FAX 31-20-4853705. TELEX 18582 ESPA NL.
E-mail: nlinfo-f@elsevier.nl; usinfo-f@elsevier.com; forinfo-kyf04035@niftyserve.or.jp; Site addr.: http://www.elsevier.nl/. (Subscr. in U.S. and Canada to: Elsevier Science Inc., Box 882, Madison Sq. Sta., New York, NY 10159. TEL 212-989-5800) (back issues avail.) **Document type:** monographic series.
—BLDSC (8743.720000); CASDDS. **CCC.**
Refereed Serial

616.8 SZ ISSN 0250-4952
THERAPIE FAMILIALE. (Text in French) 1980. q. 67 SFr. to individuals; institutions 134 SFr. Editions Medecine et Hygiene, Case Postale 456, CH-1211 Geneva 4, Switzerland. TEL 022-3469355. FAX 022-3475610. Ed.Bd. **Indexed:** Psychol.Abstr. (1991-). **Document type:** academic/scholarly publication.
—BLDSC (8814.754000). **CCC.**

THERMOLOGY. see *BIOLOGY — Physiology*

616.89 NE ISSN 0303-7339
CODEN: TPSYB3
TIJDSCHRIFT VOOR PSYCHIATRIE. Variant title: Psychiatrie. (Supplement avail. (ISSN 0922-0712)) (Text in Dutch, summaries in English) vol.15, 1973. 10/yr. fl.83.25 (effective 1994). (Nederlandse Vereniging voor Psychiatrie) Uitgeverij Boom, P.O. Box 400, 7940 AK Meppel, Netherlands. TEL 31-5220-57012. FAX 31-5220-53864. (Co-sponsor: Vereniging van Vlaamse Zenuwartsen) Ed. Dr. P.J. Jongerius. adv.; bk.rev.; illus.; index. circ. 3,600. **Indexed:** Abstr.Crim.& Pen., Excerp.Med., Nutr.Abstr., Psychol.Abstr. (1985-). **Document type:** academic/scholarly publication.
—BLDSC (8844.180000); SWETS.
Formerly: Nederlands Tijdschrift voor Psychiatrie (ISSN 0028-2197)

616.89 NE ISSN 0922-0712
TIJDSCHRIFT VOOR PSYCHIATRIE. BOEKEN. 1983. irreg. Uitgeverij Boom, P.O. Box 400, 7940 AK Meppel. TEL 31-5220-57012. FAX 31-5220-53864. **Document type:** monographic series.

616.89 NE ISSN 0165-1188
TIJDSCHRIFT VOOR PSYCHOTHERAPIE. 6/yr. fl.122.50. Bohn Stafleu van Loghum B.V. (Subsidiary of: Wolters Kluwer B.V.), Postbus 246, 3990 GA Houten, Netherlands. TEL 31-3403-95711. FAX 31-3403-50903. adv. **Indexed:** Psychol.Abstr. (1977-). **Document type:** trade publication.
—BLDSC (8844.250000); SWETS.

616.8 JA
TOKYO-TO SHINKEI KAGAKU SOGO KENKYUJO NENPO/TOKYO METROPOLITAN INSTITUTE OF NEUROSCIENCES. ANNUAL REPORT. (Text in Japanese) 1972. a. Tokyo-to Shinkei Kagaku Sogo Kenkyujo - Tokyo Metropolitan Institute of Neurosciences, 2-6 Musashidai, Fuchu-shi, Tokyo 183, Japan.

616.8 NE
TOPICS IN NEUROLOGY. (Text in English) irreg. price varies. Kluwer Academic Publishers, Postbus 17, 3300 AA Dordrecht, Netherlands. TEL 31-78-392392. FAX 31-78-392254. TELEX 29245 KAPG NL. (Dist. by: Kluwer Academic Publishers Group, P.O. Box 322, 3300 AH Dordrecht, Netherlands. TEL 31-78-392392. FAX 31-78-546474; N. America dist. addr.: Box 358, Accord Sta., Hingham, MA 02018-0358. TEL 617-871-6600. FAX 617-871-6528) **Document type:** monographic series.
Refereed Serial

617.48 NE ISSN 0924-6169
TOPICS IN NEUROSURGERY. (Text in English) 1988. irreg. price varies. Kluwer Academic Publishers, Postbus 17, 3300 AA Dordrecht, Netherlands. TEL 31-78-392392. FAX 31-78-392254. TELEX 29245 KAPG NL. (Dist. by: Kluwer Academic Publishers Group, P.O. Box 322, 3300 AH Dordrecht, Netherlands. TEL 31-78-392392. FAX 31-78-546474; N. America dist. addr.: Box 358, Accord Sta., Hingham, MA 02018-0358. TEL 617-871-6600. FAX 617-871-6528) **Document type:** monographic series.
Refereed Serial

616.8 NE ISSN 0897-3946
TOPICS IN THE NEUROSCIENCES. (Text in English) 1986. irreg. price varies. Kluwer Academic Publishers, Postbus 17, 3300 AA Dordrecht, Netherlands. TEL 31-78-392392. FAX 31-78-392254. TELEX 29245 KAPG NL. (Dist. by: Kluwer Academic Publishers Group, P.O. Box 322, 3300 AH Dordrecht, Netherlands. TEL 31-78-392392. FAX 31-78-546474; N. America dist. addr.: Box 358, Accord Sta., Hingham, MA 02018-0358. TEL 617-871-6600. FAX 617-871-6528) **Document type:** monographic series.
Refereed Serial

616.89 FR ISSN 0040-9375
BF173.A2
TOPIQUE - REVUE FREUDIENNE. 1969. 2/yr. 300 F. Dunod, 15 rue Gossin, 92543 Montrouge Cedex, France. TEL 33-1-40-92-65-00. FAX 33-1-40-92-65-97. TELEX 634 916 F. (Subscr. to: Centrale des Revues, 11 rue Gossin, 92543 Montrouge Cedex, France. TEL 33-1-46-56-52-66) Ed. S. De Mijolla-Mellor. **Indexed:** Psychoanal.Abstr., Psychol.Abstr. (1983-). —SWETS. **CCC.**
Description: Scope is to offer a place where theoretical reflection and clinical experience in psychoanalysis may enrich each other and confront their conflictual borders.

TRANSACTIONAL ANALYSIS JOURNAL. see *PSYCHOLOGY*

616.89 CN ISSN 0041-1108
TRANSCULTURAL PSYCHIATRIC RESEARCH REVIEW. (Text in English) 1956. q. Can.$36 to individuals; institutions Can.$56. McGill University, Department of Psychiatry, Division of Social and Transcultural Psychiatry, 1033 Pine Ave. W., Montreal, PQ H3A 1A1, Canada. TEL 514-398-7302. FAX 514-398-4370. Ed. L.J. Kirmayer. adv.; bk.rev.; abstr.; bibl.; charts; index, cum.index: 1956-1972; circ. 600 (controlled). (also avail. in microfilm from UMI; reprint service avail. from UMI) **Indexed:** Excerp.Med., Ind.Med., Psychol.Abstr. (1987-). **Document type:** academic/scholarly publication.
—BLDSC (9020.580500); Faxon; UMI; UnCover.
Formerly: Transcultural Psychiatric Research Review and Newsletter.
Description: Publishes critical reviews and peer commentary on current research in culture and psychiatry.
Refereed Serial

TRANSMITTERS, RECEPTORS & SYNAPSES. see *PHARMACY AND PHARMACOLOGY*

616.8 US
TRAUMATIC STRESS POINTS NEWSLETTER. 1985. q. $90. (International Society of Traumatic Stress Studies) Sherwood Group, Inc., 60 Revere Dr., Ste. 500, Northbrook, IL 60062. TEL 708-480-9028. FAX 708-480-9282. Ed. Dr. Mary Harvey. adv. contact: Angelo Artemakis. bk.rev.; circ. 1,800 (paid). **Document type:** newsletter.
Description: Provides a forum for information and news on the worldwide study and treatment of traumatic stress.

616.8 UK ISSN 0166-2236
QP351 CODEN: TNSCDR
TRENDS IN NEUROSCIENCES. Library compendium: Trends in Neurosciences (Reference Edition) (ISSN 0378-5912) (Text in English) 1978. m. £386 to institutions; $614 to institutions (effective 1996). Elsevier Science Ltd., P.O. Box 800, Kidlington, Oxford OX5 1DX, England. TEL 44-1865-843000. FAX 44-1865-843010.
E-mail: nlinfo-f@elsevier.nl; usinfo-f@elsevier.com; forinfo-kyf04035@niftyserve.or.jp; Site addr.: http://www.elsevier.nl/. (Subscr. in U.S. and Canada to: Elsevier Science, 660 White Plains Rd., Tarrytown, NY 10591-5153. TEL 914-524-9200. FAX 914-333-2444) Ed. Gavin Swanson. adv.; bk.rev.; illus.; index. circ. 6,000. (also avail. in microform from UMI; back issues avail.) **Indexed:** ASCA, Biol.Abstr., Chem.Abstr., Curr.Adv.Biochem., Curr.Adv.Cell & Devel.Biol., Curr.Adv.Ecol.Sci., Curr.Adv.Genetics & Molec.Biol., Curr.Cont., Excerp.Med., Ind.Sci.Rev., Psychol.Abstr. (1979-), Sci.Cit.Ind., Telegen. **Document type:** academic/scholarly publication.
—BLDSC (9049.667000); ADONIS; CASDDS; Faxon; Genuine Article; SWETS; UnCover. **CCC.**
Description: For research workers, teachers and students concerned with the structure and function of the brain and with the biological substrates of behavior.
Refereed Serial

616.8 UK ISSN 0378-5912
QP351
TRENDS IN NEUROSCIENCES (REFERENCE EDITION). 1978. a. £345($514) includes m. Trends in Neurosciences (effective 1995). Elsevier Science Ltd., P.O. Box 800, Kidlington, Oxford OX5 1DX, England. TEL 44-1865-843000. FAX 44-1865-843010.
E-mail: nlinfo-f@elsevier.nl; usinfo-f@elsevier.com; forinfo-kyf04035@niftyserve.or.jp; Site addr.: http://www.elsevier.nl/. (Subscr. in U.S. and Canada to: Elsevier Science, 660 White Plains Rd., Tarrytown, NY 10591-5153. TEL 914-524-9200. FAX 914-333-2444) Ed. Gavin Swanson. (back issues avail.; reprint service avail. from SWZ) **Document type:** academic/scholarly publication.
—BLDSC (9049.668000). **CCC.**
Description: Compendium of archival material from Trends in Neurosciences.
Refereed Serial

616.8 TU ISSN 1019-5149
CODEN: TUNEE
TURKISH NEUROSURGERY. Turkish edition: Turk Norosirurji Dergisi (ISSN 1019-5157) (Text in English) 1990. q. $40 to individuals in Europe and Middle East (elsewhere $50); institutions in Europe and Middle East $50 (elsewhere $60). Turkish Neurological Society, Buklum Sokak 82-3, Kavaklidere 06700 - Ankara, Turkey. TEL 90-312-4266764. FAX 90-312-4268811. Ed.Bd. **Indexed:** Excerp.Med. **Document type:** academic/scholarly publication.
—BLDSC (9072.570000).

616.8 US
U P F NEWSLETTER.* 1968. q. $25. United Parkinson Foundation, 833 W. Washington Blvd., Chicago, IL 60607-2316. TEL 312-664-2344. Ed. Judy Rosner. bk.rev. circ. 38,000.

UNDERSTANDING STRESS, ANXIETY AND DEPRESSION. see *PSYCHOLOGY*

616.835 US
U.S. CENTERS FOR DISEASE CONTROL. NEUROTROPIC VIRAL DISEASES SURVEILLANCE: POLIOMYELITIS. a. free. U.S. Centers for Disease Control, 1600 Clifton Rd., Atlanta, GA 30333. TEL 404-639-3311. **Document type:** government publication.

616.858 US
U.S. CONGRESS: MENTAL HEALTH;* legal updates, children & youth updates, federal agencies, state reports, studies on state mental health systems. vol.11, 1972. irreg. (several times a month). $350. National Association of State Mental Health Program Directors, 66 Canal Center Plz. No. 302, Alexandria, VA 22314-1591. Ed. Harry Schnibbe. circ. 135.
Formerly: U.S. Congress: Mental Health, Mental Retardation.

MEDICAL SCIENCES — PSYCHIATRY AND NEUROLOGY

616.8   **US**
U.S. OFFICE OF TECHNOLOGY ASSESSMENT. REPORTS. BIOLOGICAL AND BEHAVIORAL SCIENCES PROGRAM. irreg. price varies. U.S. Office of Technology Assessment, Publication Distribution, U.S. Congress, 600 Pennsylvania Ave., S.E., Washington, DC 20510-8025. TEL 202-224-8996. FAX 202-228-6098. E-mail: PUBSREQUEST@OTA.GOV. (Dist. by: Superintendent of Documents, U.S. Government Printing Office, Box 371954, Pittsburgh, PA 15250-7954. TEL 202-783-3238. FAX 202-512-2250; And: National Technical Information Service, 5285 Port Royal Rd., Springfield, VA 22161. TEL 703-487-4650. FAX 703-321-8547) (also avail. in microfiche from CIS; back issues avail.; reprint service avail. from CIS) **Document type:** monographic series, government publication.
    Formerly: U.S. Office of Technology Assessment. Reports. Biological Applications Program.
    Description: Reports provide technical information on a wide variety of medical issues, especially in the neurosciences.

616.6 617.7 616.6   **US**   **ISSN 1066-4130**
V H L FAMILY FORUM. (Von Hippel-Lindau Disease) (Text in English; summaries avail. in Italian, Spanish) 1993. q. $25 (effective 1995-1996). V H L Family Alliance, 171 Clinton Rd., Brookline, MA 02146. TEL 617-232-5946; 800-767-4VHL. FAX 617-734-8233. E-mail: vhl.pipeline.com; Site addr.: http://www.neurosurgery.mgh.harvard.edu:80/vhl-fa. Ed. Joyce Wilcox Graff. adv.; circ. Pub. Joyce Wilcox Graff. (also avail. in audio cassette) **Document type:** newsletter, consumer publication.
    ●Also available online.
    Description: Enables physicians, patients and family members to exchange information on all aspects of the disease.
    Refereed Serial

616.8   **SZ**   **ISSN 1016-6262**
VERHALTENSTHERAPIE. (Text in German) 1991. q. 118 SFr.($91) to individuals; institutions 118 SFr.($91) (effective 1996). S. Karger AG, Allschwilerstr. 10, P.O. Box, CH-4009 Basel, Switzerland. TEL 061-3061111. FAX 061-3061234. E-mail: Karger@Karger.ch. Eds. I. Hand, H.-U. Wittchen. (also avail. in microform from UMI) **Indexed:** Psychol.Abstr. (1991-). **Document type:** academic/scholarly publication.
—BLDSC (9156.600000); Genuine Article.
    Refereed Serial

616.858 362.3   **UK**   **ISSN 1358-6076**
VIEWPOINT (LONDON, 1995). 1990. 10/yr. £10 (Europe £12; America, Africa and Middle East £24.45; elsewhere £28.85). Royal Society for Mentally Handicapped Children and Adults, Mencap Centre, 123 Golden Lane, London EC1Y 0RT, England. TEL 0171-454-0454. FAX 0171-696-5554. Ed. Steve Billington. adv.; bk.rev.; illus. circ. 30,000. (reprint service avail. from UMI) **Indexed:** ASSIA, Except.Child.Educ.Abstr. **Document type:** trade publication, consumer publication.
—BLDSC (5678.439200).
    Former titles (until 1995): Mencap News (ISSN 0963-7117); (until 1992): Mencap News and Parents Voice; Incorporates: Parents Voice (ISSN 0031-1936)
    Description: Publishes features, news items and reports on services and campaigns about issues concerning people with learning disabilities. Aimed at parents, carers and health professionals.

616.8   **UK**   **ISSN 0952-5238**
QP474   **CODEN: VNEUEY**
VISUAL NEUROSCIENCE. 1988. bi-m. £258($399) (effective 1996). Cambridge University Press, Edinburgh House, Shaftesbury Rd., Cambridge CB2 2RU, England. TEL 01223-312393. FAX 01223-315052. TELEX 851817256. (N. American addr.: Cambridge University Press, Journals Dept., 40 W. 20th St., New York, NY 10011. TEL 212-924-3900. FAX 212-691-3239) Ed. Dr. James T. McIlwain. adv.; bk.rev. (back issues avail.) **Indexed:** Apic.Abstr., Curr.Cont., Psychol.Abstr. (1988-), Sci.Cit.Ind.
—BLDSC (9241.296000); Genuine Article; SWETS; UMI; UnCover. CCC.
    Description: Theoretical and research-based articles on visual neuroscience, with primary emphasis on retinal and brain mechanisms underlying visually guided behavior and visual perception.

VOPROSY NEIROKHIRURGII/JOURNAL OF NEUROSURGINAL PROBLEMS. see *MEDICAL SCIENCES — Surgery*

WORD FROM WASHINGTON. see *HANDICAPPED*

616.89   **AU**   **ISSN 0084-1609**
WORLD CONGRESS OF PSYCHIATRY. PROCEEDINGS. 1950. irreg., 5th, 1971, Mexico. $100. World Psychiatric Association, c/o Prof. P. Berner, Psychiatrische Universitaetsklinik, Lazarettg. 14, A-1097 Vienna, Austria. (Proceedings of 5th, 1971 avail. from: Excerpta Medica, Box 211, Amsterdam, Netherlands) Ed.Bd.

616.89   **US**   **ISSN 0043-860X**
RC475
WORLD JOURNAL OF PSYCHOSYNTHESIS. 1969. biennial. $20. (Michigan Institute of Psychosynthesis) World Journal Press, Box 859, E. Lansing, MI 48823. TEL 517-372-4660. FAX 517-372-9959. Ed. Dr. H.C. Tien. adv.; bk.rev.; bibl.; charts; illus.; stat.; index. circ. 1,000. (also avail. in microfilm from UMI; reprint service avail. from UMI)
—UMI.
    Refereed Serial

616.8 617   **US**   **ISSN 0513-5117**
RC329
YEAR BOOK OF NEUROLOGY & NEUROSURGERY. 1902. a. $69.95 (residents $35) (effective 1996). Mosby - Year Book, Inc., Continuity Division, 200 N. LaSalle, Chicago, IL 60601. TEL 312-726-9733. FAX 312-726-6075. TELEX 206155. Eds. Drs. Walter G. Bradley, Robert M. Crowell. (reprint service avail.) **Indexed:** Curr.Adv.Ecol.Sci.
    ●Also available online. Vendor(s): Ovid Technologies.
    —Faxon.

YEAR BOOK OF NEURORADIOLOGY. see *MEDICAL SCIENCES — Radiology And Nuclear Medicine*

616.89   **US**   **ISSN 0084-3970**
RC329
YEAR BOOK OF PSYCHIATRY AND APPLIED MENTAL HEALTH. 1970. a. $66.95 (residents $35) (effective 1996). Mosby - Year Book, Inc., Continuity Division, 200 N. LaSalle, Chicago, IL 60601. TEL 312-726-9733. FAX 312-726-6075. TELEX 206155. Ed. Dr. John A. Talbott. (reprint service avail.)
    ●Also available online. Vendor(s): Ovid Technologies.
    —BLDSC (9415.700000); Faxon.

616.8   **GW**
Z N S - ZENTRALES NERVENSYSTEM. 1987. irreg., vol.2, 1988. DM.48. W. Zuckschwerdt Verlag GmbH, Industriestr. 17, 82110 Germering, Germany. TEL 089-894349-0. FAX 089-89434950. Ed. M. Schirmer. **Document type:** academic/scholarly publication.

150   **PL**   **ISSN 0324-8526**
ZAGADNIENIA WYCHOWAWCZE A ZDROWIE PSYCHICZNE. (Text in Polish; summaries in English, Russian) 1968. bi-m. $15. Polskie Towarzystwo Higieny Psychicznej, Ul. Targowa 59-16, 03-729 Warsaw, Poland. TEL 48-22-186599. (Dist. by: Ars Polona-Ruch, Krakowskie Przedmiescie 7, Warsaw, Poland) bibl.
    Formerly (until 1973): Zagadnienia Wychowawcze w Aspekcie Zdrowia Psychicznego (ISSN 0324-8690)

614.58   **PL**   **ISSN 0044-2003**
ZDROWIE PSYCHICZNE. (Text in Polish; summaries in English, Russian) 1961. q. Polskie Towarzystwo Higieny Psychicznej - Polish Mental Hygiene Society, Ul. Targowa 59-16, 03-729 Warsaw, Poland. TEL 48-22-186599. bk.rev.; bibl.; index.

ZEITSCHRIFT FUER GERONTOPSYCHOLOGIE UND PSYCHIATRIE. see *GERONTOLOGY AND GERIATRICS*

616.89   **SZ**   **ISSN 0301-6811**
ZEITSCHRIFT FUER KINDER- UND JUGENDPSYCHIATRIE. 1973. q. 109 SFr. Verlag Hans Huber, Laenggassstr. 76, Postfach, CH-3000 Bern 9, Switzerland. TEL 031-3004500. FAX 031-3004590. Ed. H. Remschmidt. circ. 1,300. **Indexed:** Biol.Abstr., Curr.Cont., Excerp.Med., Psychol.Abstr. (1976-), SSCI. **Document type:** academic/scholarly publication.
—BLDSC (9467.480000); Genuine Article. CCC.

616.8   **GW**   **ISSN 0300-869X**
     CODEN: ZKPPAP
ZEITSCHRIFT FUER KLINISCHE PSYCHOLOGIE UND PSYCHOTHERAPIE. 1951. q. DM.58. (Goerres-Gesellschaft) Karl Alber GmbH, Hermann-Herder-Str. 4, 79104 Freiburg, Germany. Ed.Bd. adv.; bk.rev.; index. circ. 1,000. **Indexed:** Biol.Abstr., Excerp.Med., Ger.J.Psych., Ind.Med., Lang.& Lang.Behav.Abstr., Psychol.Abstr. (1971-).
    Formerly: Jahrbuch fuer Psychologie, Psychotherapie, und Medizinische Anthropologie (ISSN 0021-4000)

616.89   **GW**   **ISSN 0340-5613**
     CODEN: ZPPSB2
ZEITSCHRIFT FUER PSYCHOSOMATISCHE MEDIZIN UND PSYCHOANALYSE. (Text in German; summaries in English and German) 1954. q. DM.137. Vandenhoeck und Ruprecht, Robert-Bosch-Breite 6, 37079 Goettingen, Germany. TEL 0551-6959-26. FAX 0551-695917. (Subscr. to: 37070 Goettingen, Germany) Eds. Annemarie Duehrssen, Rudolf Adam. adv.; bk.rev.; abstr.; index. circ. 1,100. **Indexed:** Biol.Abstr., CERDIC, Curr.Cont., Ger.J.Psych., Ind.Med., Nutr.Abstr., Psychoanal.Abstr., Psychol.Abstr. (1956-), Risk Abstr., SSCI. **Document type:** academic/scholarly publication.
—BLDSC (9485.270000); Genuine Article. CCC.
    Formerly: Zeitschrift fuer Psycho-Somatische Medizin.

150 616.89   **GW**   **ISSN 0085-8412**
ZEITSCHRIFT FUER PSYCHOSOMATISCHE MEDIZIN UND PSYCHOANALYSE. BEIHEFTE. 1970. irreg. price varies. Vandenhoeck und Ruprecht, Robert-Bosch-Breite 6, 37079 Goettingen, Germany. TEL 0551-6959-0. FAX 0551-695917. (Subscr. to: 37070 Goettingen, Germany) **Indexed:** Psychol.Abstr., SSCI. **Document type:** monographic series.

616.8   **GW**   **ISSN 0044-4251**
ZENTRALBLATT FUER NEUROCHIRURGIE. (Text and summaries in English and German) 1936. 4/yr. DM.265 (foreign DM.270). Johann Ambrosius Barth, Postfach 102869, 69018 Heidelberg, Germany. TEL 06221-489281. FAX 06221-489205. Ed. W.J. Bock. adv.: B&W page DM.750; trim 210 x 275; adv. contact: Petra Schoene. bk.rev.; abstr.; illus.; index per vol. **Indexed:** Biol.Abstr., Dent.Ind., Excerp.Med., Ind.Med. **Document type:** academic/scholarly publication.
—BLDSC (9511.300000); EMDOCS; Genuine Article; SWETS.
    Description: Covers all areas of neurosurgical research and clinical practice.

ZENTRALBLATT NEUROLOGIE - PSYCHIATRIE/NEUROLOGY - PSYCHIATRY. see *MEDICAL SCIENCES — Abstracting, Bibliographies, Statistics*

616.8   **CC**   **ISSN 0412-4057**
     CODEN: CHSCA
ZHONGHUA SHENJING-JINGSHENKE ZAZHI/CHINESE JOURNAL OF NEUROLOGY AND PSYCHIATRY. (Text in Chinese) bi-m. $3 per no. Chinese Medical Association - Zhonghua Yixuehui, P.O. Box 2258, 42 Dongsi Xidajie, Beijing 100710, People's Republic of China. TEL 1-550394. **Indexed:** Excerp.Med. (1993-), ExtraMED, Ind.Med. **Document type:** academic/scholarly publication.
    ●Also available on CD-ROM.
    —BLDSC (3180.436000).

616.8   **CC**   **ISSN 1001-2346**
ZHONGHUA SHENJING WAIKE ZAZHI/CHINESE JOURNAL OF NEUROSURGERY. (Text in Chinese; summaries in English) 1985. bi-m. Y11($2) per no. Beijing Neurosurgical Institute, No.6, Tiantan Xili, Beijing, People's Republic of China. TEL 86-1-5113169. FAX 86-1-7018349. (Co-sponsor: Chinese Medical Association) Eds. Wang Chungcheng, Li Li. adv.; bk.rev.; index. circ. 10,000. (back issues avail.) **Indexed:** ExtraMED. **Document type:** academic/scholarly publication.
    ●Also available on CD-ROM.
    —BLDSC (3180.436500).

ZHURNAL VYSSHEI NERVNOI DEYATEL'NOSTI. see *BIOLOGY — Physiology*

MEDICAL SCIENCES — Radiology And Nuclear Medicine

615.842 **CN** **ISSN 0833-3106**
A A M R T JOURNAL. vol.18, 1982. 3/yr. Can.$7. Alberta Association of Medical Radiation Technologists, Red Deer Regional Hospital Centre, P.O. Bag 5030, Red Deer, AB T4N 6N2, Canada. Ed. Pat Kehoe. adv. circ. 1,500.

615.842 **US** **ISSN 0098-6070**
A C R BULLETIN. 1942. m. $60 to non-members. American College of Radiology, 1891 Preston White Dr., Reston, VA 22091. TEL 703-264-2443. FAX 703-264-2443. E-mail: bulletin@acr.org. Ed. Marion Dinitz. illus. circ. 30,000. Indexed: Med.Care Rev. **Document type:** bulletin, newsletter, trade publication.
Former titles (until 1968): American College of Radiology. Bulletin (ISSN 0002-8037); (until 1958): American College of Radiology. Monthly Newsletter.
Description: Provides organization news and member information, and examines current socio-economic issues in radiology.

615.842 **US**
A H R A LINK. 1982. m. membership. American Healthcare Radiology Administrators, 111 Boston Post Rd., Box 334, Sudbury, MA 01776. TEL 508-443-7591. Ed. Teresa V. Cryan. circ. 3,500. (back issues avail.)
Formerly: A H R A Announcement.

616.075 618 **US**
A I U M REPORTER. 1985. m. $20. American Institute of Ultrasound in Medicine, Attn.: James Packer, Ph.D., 14750 Sweitzer Ln., Ste. 100, Laurel, MD 20707-5906. TEL 301-498-4100. FAX 301-498-4450. Ed. Frederick W. Kremkau. adv. contact: Kathleen Wilson. bk.rev.; circ. 13,000 (paid). (back issues avail.) **Document type:** newsletter.
Description: Keeps members and ultrasound professionals up-to-date on A.I.U.M. activities, as well as on news and legislation that can affect the field. Provides educational opportunities to practitioners.

615.842 **US** **ISSN 0195-6108**
RC349.R3
A J N R (American Journal of Neuroradiology) 1980. bi-m. $210 (foreign $265) (effective 1996). American Society of Neuroradiology, 2210 Midwest Rd., Ste. 207, Oak Brook, IL 60521. TEL 708-574-0220. FAX 708-574-0661. (Subscr. to: Fulco, Box 3000, Denville, NJ 07843. TEL 800-875-2997. FAX 201-627-5872) Ed. Michael I. Huckman. adv.; bk.rev. circ. 5,460. (also avail. in microfilm from WWS; back issues avail.) Indexed: Curr.Cont., Dent.Ind., Excerp.Med., Helminthol.Abstr., Ind.Med., Ind.Sci.Rev., INIS Atomind., Rev.Med.& Vet.Mycol., Sci.Cit.Ind. **Document type:** academic/scholarly publication.
—BLDSC (0828.400000); Faxon; Genuine Article; SWETS; UnCover.
Description: Publishes original clinical articles on imaging diagnosis of the central nervous system, including the spine, for radiologists, neuroradiologists, neurosurgeons, and neurologists
Refereed Serial

615.842 **US** **ISSN 0361-803X**
RM845 **CODEN: AJROAM**
A J R. (American Journal of Roentgenology) 1906. m. $125 to individuals; institutions $135. American Roentgen Ray Society, Attn.: Haley Walsh, 1891 Preston White Dr., VA 22091. TEL 301-528-4000. FAX 301-528-4312. (Subscr. to: Fulco, Box 3000, Denville, NJ 07843. TEL 800-875-2997. FAX 201-627-5872) (Co-sponsor: American Radium Society) Ed. Dr. Robert N. Berk. adv.; bk.rev.; abstr.; bibl.; illus.; index, cum.index every 5 yrs. circ. 22,500. (also avail. in microform; microfilm from WWS) Indexed: AIM, Bibl.Dev.Med.& Child Neur., Biol.Abstr., Biotech.Abstr., C.I.S. Abstr., Chem.Abstr., Curr.Adv.Cancer Res., Curr.Adv.Ecol.Sci., Curr.Cont., Dent.Ind., Excerp.Med., Helminthol.Abstr., I.P.A., Ind.Med., Ind.Sci.Rev., INIS Atomind., Kidney, Med.& Surg.Dermat., Nutr.Abstr., Rev.Plant Path., Risk Abstr., Sci.Cit.Ind. **Document type:** academic/scholarly publication.
●Also available online.
—BLDSC (0836.980000); Faxon; Genuine Article; SWETS; UnCover. CCC.
Former titles (1952-1976): American Journal of Roentgenology, Radium Therapy and Nuclear Medicine (ISSN 0002-9580); (1923-1951): American Journal of Roentgenology and Radium Therapy (ISSN 0092-5632)
Description: Original articles on all aspects of general and diagnostic radiology, covering all current modalities, including MRI.
Refereed Serial

ABDOMINAL IMAGING; a journal of diagnostic imaging. see *MEDICAL SCIENCES — Gastroenterology*

615.842 **DK** **ISSN 0284-1851**
CODEN: ACRAE3
ACTA RADIOLOGICA. (Supplement avail.: Acta Radiologica. Supplementum (ISSN 0365-5954)) (Text in English) 1921. bi-m. DKK 990 (incl. supplements) (effective 1996). (Scandinavian Society of Radiology, SW) Munksgaard International Publishers Ltd., 35 Noerre Soegade, P.O. Box 2148, DK-1016 Copenhagen K, Denmark. TEL 33-127030. FAX 33-129387. Ed. Anders Hemmingsson. adv.; bk.rev.; bibl.; charts; illus.; index, cum.index. circ. 3,400. (also avail. in microfilm from UMI; reprint service avail.) Indexed: ASCA, Biol.Abstr., Biotech.Abstr., Chem.Abstr., Curr.Adv.Cell & Devel.Biol., Curr.Adv.Ecol.Sci., Curr.Cont., Dent.Ind., Excerp.Med., Helminthol.Abstr., Ind.Med., Ind.Sci.Rev., INSPEC (1987-1992), Kidney, Met.Abstr., Nutr.Abstr., Sci.Cit.Ind.
—BLDSC (0662.000000); CASDDS; Faxon; Genuine Article; SWETS; UMI. CCC.
Formerly (until 1986): Acta Radiologica. Diagnosis (ISSN 0567-8056); Which superseded in part (in 1962): Acta Radiologica (ISSN 0001-6926).
Refereed Serial

615.847 **DK** **ISSN 0365-5954**
CODEN: ARASA5
ACTA RADIOLOGICA. SUPPLEMENTUM. (Supplement to: Acta Radiologica (ISSN 0365-5954)) (Text in English) 1921. irreg. free to subscr. of Acta Radiologica. (Scandinavian Society of Radiology, SW) Munksgaard International Publishers Ltd., 35 Noerre Soegade, P.O. Box 2148, DK-1016 Copenhagen K, Denmark. TEL 45-33-12-70-30. FAX 45-33-12-93-87. Ed. Anders Hemmingsson.
—BLDSC (0662.005000); Ei; SWETS; UnCover. CCC.

615.842 658 **US** **ISSN 0738-6974**
RA975.5.R3
ADMINISTRATIVE RADIOLOGY; the journal of medical imaging administration & management. 1981. m. $42 (Canada $72; elsewhere $96) (effective 1995). Glendale Publishing Corp., 1305 Glenoaks Blvd., Glendale, CA 91201. TEL 818-500-1872. Ed. Cynthia Stout. adv. contact: Louis Martinez. bk.rev.; illus.; tr.lit.; index, cum.index; circ. 13,500 (paid). (also avail. in microform from UMI; back issues avail.; reprint service avail. from UMI) **Document type:** academic/scholarly publication, trade publication.
—BLDSC (1583.209500); UMI.
Description: Healthcare management publication serving healthcare executives in people, business and administrative management relative to medical imaging and radiation sciences.
Refereed Serial

615.842 616.07 **US**
ADVANCE FOR ADMINISTRATORS IN RADIOLOGY. 1991. m. free to qualified personnel. Merion Publications, 650 Park Ave., Box 61556, King of Prussia, PA 19406. TEL 610-265-8971. FAX 610-265-8971. E-mail: blammey@merion.com. Ed. Richard A. Leonowitz. adv.: B&W page $1764; trim 8 1/2 x 11. circ. 21,500. **Document type:** trade publication.

616 **US** **ISSN 1074-231X**
ADVANCE FOR RADIOLOGIC SCIENCE PROFESSIONALS. w. Merion Publications, 650 Park Ave., Box 61556, King of Prussia, PA 19406. TEL 610-265-7812. FAX 61-265-8971. Ed. Jeanette Sabatini. adv.: B&W page $1654, color page $2354; trim 10 x 13 1/4. circ. 69,500. **Document type:** trade publication.

ADVANCES IN ECHO-CONTRAST; ultrasound imaging innovations, echo-enhancing agents, clinical impact. see *MEDICAL SCIENCES — Computer Applications*

616.075 **NE** **ISSN 0925-9848**
ADVANCES IN M R I - CONTRAST. (Magnetic Resonance Imaging); MRI innovations, contrast-enhancing agents, clinical impact. (Text in English) 1991. q. fl.131 to institutions; $ 84 to institutions in U.S. (effective 1996). (Schering AG, GW) Kluwer Academic Publishers, Postbus 17, 3300 AA Dordrecht, Netherlands. TEL 31-78-392392. FAX 31-78-392254. TELEX 29245 KAPG NL. E-mail: SERVICES@WKAP.NL. (Dist. by: Kluwer Academic Publishers Group, P.O. Box 322, 3300 AH Dordrecht, Netherlands. TEL 31-78-392392. FAX 31-78-546474; N. America dist. addr.: Box 358, Accord Sta., Hingham, MA 02018-0358. TEL 617-871-6600. FAX 617-871-6528) Ed.Bd. (also avail. in microform from UMI; back issues avail.) Indexed: Excerp.Med. (1995-). **Document type:** academic/scholarly publication.
—BLDSC (0709.453600). CCC.
Refereed Serial

ADVANCES IN X-RAY ANALYSIS. see *METALLURGY*

616.07 **NE** **ISSN 0928-1509**
ADVANCES IN X-RAY CONTRAST; x-ray enhancing agents, clinical impact and clinical research. (Text in English) 1993. q. fl.148 to institutions; $ 95 to institutions in U.S. (effective 1996). (Schering AG, GW) Kluwer Academic Publishers, Postbus 17, 3300 AA Dordrecht, Netherlands. TEL 31-78-392392. FAX 31-78-392254. TELEX 29245 KAPG NL. E-mail: SERVICES@WKAP.NL. (Dist. by: Kluwer Academic Publishers Group, P.O. Box 322, 3300 AH Dordrecht, Netherlands. TEL 31-78-392392. FAX 31-78-546474; N. America dist. addr.: Box 358, Accord St., Hingham, MA 02018-0358. TEL 617-871-6600. FAX 617-871-6528) Ed.Bd. (back issues avail.) **Document type:** academic/scholarly publication.
—BLDSC (0712.206000). CCC.
Description: Covers recent developments in iodinated contrast media and issues such as renal tolerance, blood clotting and pharmacokinetics, within a clinically relevant framework.

619 **GW** **ISSN 0939-267X**
RC78 **CODEN: AKRAEP**
AKTUELLE RADIOLOGIE. 1948. bi-m. DM.192. Georg Thieme Verlag, Ruedigerstr. 14, 70469 Stuttgart, Germany. TEL 0711-8931-0. FAX 0711-8931298. (Subscr. to: Postfach 104853, 70042 Stuttgart, Germany) Ed.Bd. adv.; index. circ. 2,200. (also avail. in microfilm from UMI; reprint service avail. from UMI) Indexed: Biol.Abstr., Dent.Ind., Excerp.Med., Ind.Med. **Document type:** academic/scholarly publication.
—BLDSC (0785.865000); SWETS; UMI. CCC.
Formed by the 1991 merger of: Roentgen Blaetter (ISSN 0300-8592) & Digitale Bilddiagnostik (ISSN 0724-7591)

615.842 **US** **ISSN 1073-0214**
AMERICAN BOARD OF NUCLEAR MEDICINE. INFORMATION POLICIES AND PROCEDURES. 1975. a. American Board of Nuclear Medicine, 900 Veteran Ave., Los Angeles, CA 90024. TEL 310-825-6787. FAX 310-825-9433. circ. 1,500.
Description: Information on requirements for certifying examination in nuclear medicine.

MEDICAL SCIENCES — RADIOLOGY AND NUCLEAR MEDICINE 4581

616 US
AMERICAN INSTITUTE OF ULTRASOUND IN MEDICINE. ANNUAL SCIENTIFIC CONFERENCE. PROCEEDINGS. a. membership. American Institute of Ultrasound in Medicine, Attn. James Packer, Ph.D., 14750 Swietzer Lane, Ste. 100, Laurel, MD 20707-5906. TEL 301-881-2486. FAX 301-881-7303. adv.; bk.rev. circ. 3,000. **Document type:** proceedings.
Formerly: American Institute of Ultrasound in Medicine. Annual Scientific Conference. Program (ISSN 0065-8871)

AMERICAN JOURNAL OF CARDIAC IMAGING. see MEDICAL SCIENCES — Cardiovascular Diseases

615.842 UN ISSN 1011-2529
ANIMAL PRODUCTION AND HEALTH NEWSLETTER. (Text in English) 1976. s-a. free. International Atomic Energy Agency, Wagramerstr. 5, P.O. Box 100, A-1400 Vienna, Austria. TEL 43-1-209-2360. FAX 43-1-209-5302. E-mail: fossett@adp01.iaea.or.at. Ed. (Co-sponsor: Food and Agriculture Organization) circ. 230. **Indexed:** Nutr.Abstr. **Document type:** newsletter.

615.842 FR ISSN 0003-4185
CODEN: ANLRAT
ANNALES DE RADIOLOGIE; radiologie clinique, radiobiologie. (Text in English and French) 1958. 7/yr. 1370 F. to individuals (foreign 1910 F.); students 685 F. (foreign 1030 F.). (Semaine des Hopitaux) Expansion Scientifique, 31 bd. de la Tour Maubourg, 75007 Paris, France. TEL 40-62-64-00. FAX 45-55-69-20. adv.; bk.rev.; abstr.; charts; illus.; index. **Indexed:** Biol.Abstr., C.I.S. Abstr., Chem.Abstr., Curr.Cont., Excerp.Med., Helminthol.Abstr., Ind.Med., Ind.Sci.Rev., INIS Atomind., Sci.Cit.Ind.
—BLDSC (0995.100000); Faxon; Genuine Article; SWETS. **CCC.**

616.07 JA ISSN 0914-7187
CODEN: ANMEEX
ANNALS OF NUCLEAR MEDICINE. (Text in English) 1987. q. 1500 Yen per no. Japanese Society of Nuclear Medicine - Nihon Kaku Igakkai, Nihon Aisotopu Kyokai, 28-45 Honkomagome 2-chome, Bunkyo-ku, Tokyo 113, Japan. **Indexed:** Chem.Abstr., Excerp.Med., Ind.Med., INIS Atomind.
—BLDSC (1043.175000); CASDDS.

APPLIED RADIATION AND ISOTOPES; including data, instrumentation and methods for use in agriculture, industry and medicine. see PHYSICS — Nuclear Physics

615.842 US ISSN 0160-9963
RM845
APPLIED RADIOLOGY; the journal of practical medical imaging and management. 1972. m. $75 (foreign $95). Anderson Publishing, Ltd., 80 Shore Rd., Port Washington, NY 11050. TEL 516-883-0164. FAX 516-883-0171. Ed. Theodore Keats. adv.; charts; illus.; tr.lit.; cum.index. circ. 36,559. **Indexed:** Biol.Abstr., CINAHL, Excerp.Med., Hosp.Lit.Ind. **Document type:** academic/scholarly publication.
—BLDSC (1576.570000); Faxon; SWETS; UnCover.
Former titles: Applied Radiology and Nuclear Medicine (ISSN 0099-2364); Applied Radiology (ISSN 0044-8451)

615.842 AT ISSN 0004-8461
CODEN: AURDAW
AUSTRALASIAN RADIOLOGY. 1966. 4/yr. Aus.$175 (foreign Aus.$246) (effective 1996). (Royal Australasian College of Radiologists) Blackwell Science Pty Ltd, P.O. Box 378, Carlton, Vic. 3053, Australia. TEL 61-3-93470300. FAX 61-3-93493016. Ed. F.J. Palmer. adv.: B&W page $720, color page $1510; trim 296 x 210. bk.rev.; charts; illus.; index, cum.index. circ. 2,000. (also avail. in microform from UMI) **Indexed:** Biol.Abstr., Chem.Abstr., Curr.Cont., Dent.Ind., Excerp.Med., Ind.Med., INIS Atomind.
—BLDSC (1796.300000); ADONIS; Faxon; SWETS; UMI; UnCover. **CCC.**

616.842 UK ISSN 0966-1905
B M U S BULLETIN. 1975. q. £30 (effective 1995). British Medical Ultrasound Society, 36 Portland Pl., London W1N 3DG, England. TEL 0171-636-3714. FAX 0171-323-2175. Ed. Dr. P. Twinning. adv. contact: J. Pedersen. bk.rev.; bibl.; charts; illus.; stat.; tr.lit.; circ. 1,800 (paid). **Document type:** bulletin.
—BLDSC (2116.243000).
Description: Analyzes current developments in ultrasound for members.

615.842 SZ ISSN 1012-5655
CODEN: BILDEZ
BILDGEBUNG/IMAGING. (Text in English, German) 1933. q. 153 SFr.($118) to individuals; institutions 153 SFr.($118) (effective 1996). S. Karger AG, Allschwilerstr. 10, P.O. Box, CH-4009 Basel, Switzerland. TEL 061-3061111. FAX 061-3061234. E-mail: Karger@Karger.ch. Ed. W.G. Zoller. (also avail. in microform from UMI) **Document type:** academic/scholarly publication.
—BLDSC (2058.988000); Genuine Article.
Refereed Serial

BIOELECTROMAGNETICS. see BIOLOGY — Biophysics

616.82 UK
BRITISH INSTITUTE OF RADIOLOGY REPORTS. irreg., no. 22, 1991. price varies. British Institute of Radiology, 36 Portland Pl., London W1N 4AT, England. TEL 071-580-4189. FAX 071-255-3201. (Dist. by: Vine House Distribution, Waldenbury, N. Common, Chailey, E. Sussex BN8 4DR, England. TEL 0825-723398. FAX 0825-724188; U.S. subscr. to: Professional & Scientific Publications, Box 560B, Kennebunkport, ME 04046) (back issues avail.) **Document type:** monographic series.
Description: Covers major topics in radiation therapy and research.

615.842 UK ISSN 0007-1285
QC1 CODEN: BJRAAP
BRITISH JOURNAL OF RADIOLOGY. (Supplements avail.) 1896. m. £204 in E.C. nations; elsewhere £224 (includes a. supplement) (effective 1994). British Institute of Radiology, 36 Portland Pl., Londonn W1N 4AT, England. TEL 071-580-4085. FAX 071-255-3209. (Back issues from: Vine House Distribution, Waldenbury, North Common, Chailey, E. Sussex BN8 4DR, England. TEL 0825-723398; Subscr. to: P S P Subscriptions Direct, P.O. Box 299, London WC1H 9TD, England. TEL 0825-724188. FAX 071-383-6668; U.S. subscr. to: Professional & Scientific Publications, Box 560B, Kennebunkport, ME 04046) Eds. J.T. Patton, N.J. McNally. adv.; bk.rev.; abstr.; charts; illus.; stat.; index. circ. 4,600. (back issues avail.) **Indexed:** AIM, Biol.Abstr., Biotech.Abstr., C.I.S. Abstr., Chem.Abstr., Curr.Adv.Cancer Res., Curr.Adv.Ecol.Sci., Curr.Cont., Dairy Sci.Abstr., Dent.Ind., Dok.Arbeitsmed., Excerp.Med., Helminthol.Abstr., Ind.Med., Ind.Sci.Rev., INIS Atomind., INSPEC, Nutr.Abstr., Protozool.Abstr., Rev.Med.& Vet.Mycol., Risk Abstr., Sci.Cit.Ind. **Document type:** academic/scholarly publication.
—BLDSC (2323.000000); CASDDS; Faxon; Genuine Article; SWETS; UMI; UnCover.
Description: Presents research covering the spectrum of radiological disciplines, including radio-diagnosis and therapy, nuclear medicine, ultrasound, NMR, radiobiology, radiation protection, and hyperthermia.

BULLETIN DU CANCER - RADIOTHERAPIE. see MEDICAL SCIENCES — Oncology

615.842 CN ISSN 0008-2902
CANADIAN ASSOCIATION OF RADIOLOGISTS. JOURNAL/ASSOCIATION CANADIENNE DES RADIOLOGISTES. JOURNAL. (Text and title in English, French) 1959. bi-m. Can.$120($120) Canadian Medical Association, P.O. Box 8650, Ottawa, ON K1G 0G8, Canada. TEL 613-731-9331. FAX 613-523-0937. Ed. Dr. Michel Azouz. adv.: B&W page Can. $745, color page Can. $1525; trim 8 3/8 X 10 7/8. bk.rev.; illus.; index. circ. 2,400. (also avail. in microform from UMI; reprint service avail. from UMI) **Indexed:** Biol.Abstr., Chem.Abstr., Curr.Adv.Cancer Res., Curr.Cont., Excerp.Med., Ind.Med., INIS Atomind. **Document type:** academic/scholarly publication.
—BLDSC (4722.500000); Genuine Article; SWETS; UMI. **CCC.**
Description: Reports on the most recent advances in the field of radiology, including equipment, technique and procedures.
Refereed Serial

615.842 CN ISSN 0820-5930
CANADIAN JOURNAL OF MEDICAL RADIATION TECHNOLOGY/JOURNAL CANADIEN DES TECHNIQUES EN RADIATION MEDICALE. (Text in English, French) 1943. q. Can.$25($30) Canadian Association of Medical Radiation Technologists - Association Canadienne des Technologues en Radiation Medicale, Ste. 601, 294 Albert St., Ottawa, ON K1P 6E6, Canada. TEL 613-234-0012. FAX 613-234-1097. Ed. S. Brasier. adv.; bk.rev.; charts; illus.; stat.; index, cum.index. circ. 10,468. (also avail. in microform from UMI; reprint service avail. from UMI) **Indexed:** Biol.Abstr., CINAHL. **Document type:** academic/scholarly publication, trade publication.
—BLDSC (3032.300000); UMI.
Former titles: Canadian Journal of Radiography, Radiation Therapy, Nuclear Medicine (ISSN 0382-6333); (until 1987): Canadian Journal of Radiography, Radiotherapy, Nuclear Medicine (ISSN 0319-4434); Canadian Journal of Radiography, Radiotherapy, Nucleography (ISSN 0015-4938); (until 1970): Focal Spot.

615.84 XR ISSN 1210-7883
CESKA RADIOLOGIE. (Text in Czech or Slovak; summaries in English and Russian) 1946. 6/yr. $48.60. (Ceska Lekarska Spolecnost J.E.Purkyne - Czech Medical Society) Nakladetelske Stredisko C L S J.E. Purkyne, Sokolska 31, 120 26 Prague 2, Czech Republic. FAX 42-0-2-202788. (Dist. by: Artia, Ve Smeckach 30, 111 27 Prague 1, Czech Republic) (Co-sponsor: Ceska Radiologicka Spolecnost) Ed. Dr. J. Kolar. bk.rev. circ. 1,000. **Indexed:** Curr.Adv.Ecol.Sci., Dent.Ind., Excerp.Med., Ind.Med., INIS Atomind.
—BLDSC (3120.318000); EMDOCS. **CCC.**
Former titles: Ceskoslovenska Radiologie (ISSN 0069-2344); Ceskoslovenska Roentgenologie.

CHEMICAL SOCIETY OF JAPAN. SYMPOSIUM ON PHYSICAL AND CHEMICAL ASPECTS OF ULTRASOUND. PROCEEDINGS/ONPA NO BUSSEI TO KAGAKU TORONKAI KOEN RONBUNSHU. see CHEMISTRY

616.075 JA ISSN 0287-0592
CHOONPA IGAKU/JAPANESE JOURNAL OF MEDICAL ULTRASONICS. (Text in Japanese; summaries in English) 1974. m. 2060 Yen per no. Nihon Choonpa Igakkai - Japan Society of Ultrasonics in Medicine, Hongo 3-23-1, Crosevia Hongo 3F, Bunkyo-ku, Tokyo 113, Japan. TEL 03-3813-5540. FAX 03-3816-7644. Ed. Kouichi Itoh. circ. 15,000. **Indexed:** Excerp.Med. **Document type:** academic/scholarly publication.
—BLDSC (4656.448500).
Refereed Serial

616.075 JA
CHOONPA KENSA GIJUTSU/JAPAN SOCIETY OF SONOGRAPHERS. JOURNAL. (Text in Japanese) 1976. q. Nihon Choonpa Igau Kensa Kenkyukai - Japan Society of Sonographers, Mitsui Kinen Byoin Chuo Kensabu, 1 Kanda Izumicho, Chiyoda-ku, Tokyo 101, Japan.

616.842 US
CLINICAL DIAGNOSTIC IMAGING SERIES. 1988. irreg., latest 1992. price varies. Raven Press (Subsidiary of: Wolters Kluwer N.V.), 1185 Ave. of the Americas, New York, NY 10036. TEL 212-930-9500. FAX 212-869-3495. Ed. Morrie E. Kricun. **Document type:** monographic series.

MEDICAL SCIENCES — RADIOLOGY AND NUCLEAR MEDICINE

615.8 US ISSN 0899-7071
RC78.T6 CODEN: CLIMEB
CLINICAL IMAGING. 1977. q. $325 to institutions (effective 1996). Elsevier Science Inc., 655 Ave. of the Americas, New York, NY 10010. TEL 212-989-5800. FAX 212-633-3990. TELEX 420643 AEP UI. (Subscr. to: Box 882, Madison Sq. Sta., New York, NY 10159-0882) Ed. Dr. Joseph P. Whalen. adv.; bk.rev.; abstr.; charts; illus.; index. circ. 2,200. (also avail. in microform from UMI; back issues avail.; reprint service avail. from ISI) **Indexed:** Biol.Abstr., Comput.Cont., Curr.Cont., Excerp.Med., Ind.Med., INIS Atomind., Sci.Cit.Ind. **Document type:** academic/scholarly publication.
—BLDSC (3286.290600); Ei; Faxon; Genuine Article; SWETS; UnCover. CCC.
Former titles: C T: The Journal of Computed Tomography (ISSN 0149-936X); Journal of Computed Tomography; Computed Axial Tomography (ISSN 0145-7616)
Description: Provides information for radiologists, radiology residents, and radiologic technologists. Covers new technology, new applications, and important issues concerning all diagnostic imaging methods.
Refereed Serial

615.842 US ISSN 0363-9762
R895.A1 CODEN: CNMEDK
CLINICAL NUCLEAR MEDICINE. 1976. m. $135 to individuals (foreign $178); institutions $216 (foreign $251) (effective 1996). Lippincott - Raven Publishers, 227 E. Washington Sq., Philadelphia, PA 19106. TEL 215-238-4200. Ed. Dr. Sheldon Baum. adv.; illus.; index. circ. 2,813. (also avail. in microform from UMI) **Indexed:** Biol.Abstr., Curr.Adv.Cancer Res., Curr.Cont., Dent.Ind., Excerp.Med. (1993-), Ind.Med., Ind.Sci.Rev., INIS Atomind., Protozool.Abstr., Rev.Med.& Vet.Mycol., Sci.Cit.Ind., SSCI.
—BLDSC (3286.314000); Faxon; Genuine Article; SWETS; UMI; UnCover. CCC.
Refereed Serial

615.842 616.99 UK ISSN 0009-9260
CODEN: CLRAAG
CLINICAL RADIOLOGY. 1949. m. £162 in Europe; elsewhere £178($287) (effective 1996). (Royal College of Radiologists) Blackwell Science Ltd., Osney Mead, Oxford OX2 OEL, England. TEL 01865-206206. FAX 01865-206219. TELEX 83355 MEDBOK G. Ed. P. Armstrong. adv.; bk.rev.; index, cum.index: 1970-1979. circ. 4,500. (also avail. in microform from UMI; back issues avail) **Indexed:** Biol.Abstr., C.I.S. Abstr., Curr.Adv.Cancer Res., Curr.Adv.Ecol.Sci., Curr.Cont., Dent.Ind., Excerp.Med., Helminthol.Abstr., Ind.Med., INIS Atomind., Rev.Med.& Vet.Mycol., Sci.Cit.Ind. **Document type:** academic/scholarly publication.
—BLDSC (3286.350000); Faxon; Genuine Article; SWETS; UMI; UnCover. CCC.
Refereed Serial

615.842 US ISSN 0172-4843
COMPREHENSIVE MANUALS IN RADIOLOGY. 1978. irreg. price varies. Springer-Verlag, 175 Fifth Ave., New York, NY 10010. TEL 212-460-1500. FAX 212-473-6272. (Also: Berlin, Heidelberg, Tokyo, Vienna) (reprint service avail. from ISI) **Document type:** monographic series.

COMPUTERIZED MEDICAL IMAGING AND GRAPHICS; the international journal on imaging and image archiving in all medical specialties. see *MEDICAL SCIENCES — Computer Applications*

538.36 US ISSN 1043-7347
QC762 CODEN: CMAEEM
CONCEPTS IN MAGNETIC RESONANCE; an educational quarterly. 1989. q. $99 to individuals; institutions $198. John Wiley & Sons, Inc., Journals, 605 Third Ave., New York, NY 10158-0012. TEL 212-850-6347. FAX 212-850-6021. E-mail: subinfo@jwiley.com. Ed. Daniel D. Traficante. bk.rev.; charts; index, cum.index every 5 yrs. circ. 750. (back issues avail.) **Indexed:** Anal.Abstr., Chem.Abstr. **Document type:** academic/scholarly publication.
—BLDSC (3399.413400); CASDDS; Ei; Faxon; Genuine Article; SWETS; UnCover. CCC.
Description: Covers magnetic resonance in the areas of medicine and chemistry for educational purposes.
Refereed Serial

616.07 US ISSN 0149-9009
CODEN: CDRAEW
CONTEMPORARY DIAGNOSTIC RADIOLOGY. 1977. bi-w. $247 unscored; scored $297 (effective 1995). Williams & Wilkins, 428 E. Preston St., Baltimore, MD 21202. TEL 410-528-4000; 800-638-6423. FAX 410-528-4312. Ed. Dr. Robert E. Campbell. circ. 2,800. (also avail. in microfilm from WWS) **Document type:** academic/scholarly publication.
—CCC.
Description: Features original articles on current topics in neurosurgery with optional Category or C.M.E. credits.

615.842 US ISSN 1040-8371
RC78.A1 CODEN: CRDIDF
CRITICAL REVIEWS IN DIAGNOSTIC IMAGING. 1970. bi-m. $90 to individuals; institutions $420. C R C Press, Inc., 2000 Corporate Blvd., N.W., Boca Raton, FL 33431. TEL 407-994-0555; 800-272-7737. FAX 407-998-9784. TELEX 568689-CRC PRESS. Ed. Yen Wang. bibl.; charts; illus. circ. 340. (back issues avail.) **Indexed:** Biol.Abstr., Ind.Med., Ind.Sci.Rev., Sci.Cit.Ind.
—BLDSC (3487.474000); Faxon; Genuine Article; SWETS. CCC.
Former titles: C R C Critical Reviews in Diagnostic Imaging (ISSN 0147-6750); C R C Critical Reviews in Clinical Radiology and Nuclear Medicine (ISSN 0091-6536); C R C Critical Reviews in Radiological Sciences and Nuclear Medicine (ISSN 0007-9014)
Description: Includes critical surveys of specific topics contributed by authors. Each author provides a review of the most significant papers from the current literature and the latest technology being used.
Refereed Serial

615.842 US ISSN 0363-0188
CODEN: CPDRDS
CURRENT PROBLEMS IN DIAGNOSTIC RADIOLOGY. Short title: C P D R. 1972. bi-m. $65 to individuals (foreign $71); institutions $90 (foreign $96); students $40; (foreign $46) (effective Jan. 1994). Mosby - Year Book, Inc. (Subsidiary of: Times Mirror Company), 11830 Westline Industrial Dr., St. Louis, MO 63146. TEL 314-872-8370; 800-325-4177. FAX 314-432-1380. Ed. Theodore E. Keats. bibl.; illus.; cum.index. circ. 3,000. (also avail. in microform from UMI) **Indexed:** Biol.Abstr., Excerp.Med., Ind.Med. **Document type:** monographic series.
—BLDSC (3501.380000); SWETS; UMI; UnCover. CCC.
Formerly: Current Problems in Radiology (ISSN 0045-9399)
Description: Provides monographic clinical reviews written by and intended for practitioners.

615.8 JA ISSN 0914-8663
DANSO EIZO KENKYUKAI ZASSHI/JAPANESE JOURNAL OF TOMOGRAPHY. (Text in Japanese; summaries in English) 1973. a. Danso Eizo Kenkyukai - Japanese Association of Tomography, Fukushima Kenritsu Ika Daigaku Hoshasenka, 1 Hiharigaoka, Fukushima-shi, Fukushima-ken 960-12, Japan. **Indexed:** INIS Atomind.

615.842 UK ISSN 0250-832X
DENTO-MAXILLO-FACIAL RADIOLOGY. (Supplement avail. (ISSN 0349-490X)) 1971. 5/yr. £165($263) (effective 1996). (International Association of Dento-Maxillo-Facial Radiology) Butterworth - Heinemann, Part of the Reed Elsevier group, Linacre House, Jordan Hill, Oxford OX2 8DP, England. TEL 0865-310366. FAX 0865-310898. TELEX 83111 BHPOXF G. (Subscr. to: Elsevier Science Ltd., P.O. Box 800, Kidlington, Oxford OX5 1DX, England. TEL 44-865-843000. FAX 44-865-843010; Subscr. in U.S. and Canada to: Elsevier Science, 660 White Plains Rd., Tarrytown, NY 10591-5153. TEL 914-524-9200. FAX 914-333-2444) Ed. P.N. Hirschmann. adv. (also avail. in microform from UMI; back issues avail.) **Document type:** academic/scholarly publication.
—BLDSC (3553.561000); Genuine Article; SWETS; UMI; UnCover. CCC.
Description: Contains research papers on radiology of the "lower third," together with clinical reports that illustrate specific uses of diagnostic imaging.
Refereed Serial

615.849 NE ISSN 0167-9074
CODEN: DNMDDS
DEVELOPMENTS IN NUCLEAR MEDICINE. (Text in English) 1981. irreg., vol.18, 1991. price varies. Kluwer Academic Publishers, Postbus 17, 3300 AA Dordrecht, Netherlands. TEL 31-78-392392. FAX 31-78-392254. TELEX 29245 KAPG NL. (Dist. by: Kluwer Academic Publishers Group, P.O. Box 322, 3300 AH Dordrecht, Netherlands. TEL 31-78-392392. FAX 31-78-546474; N. America dist. addr.: Box 358, Accord Sta., Hingham, MA 02018-0358. TEL 617-871-6600. FAX 617-871-6528) **Document type:** monographic series.
—BLDSC (3579.085430); CASDDS; Faxon.
Refereed Serial

615.842 US ISSN 0194-2514
RC78.7.D53
DIAGNOSTIC IMAGING. 1979. m. $105 (free to qualified personnel). Miller Freeman, Inc. (Subsidiary of: United Newspapers), 600 Harrison St., San Francisco, CA 94107. TEL 415-905-2200. FAX 415-905-2233. TELEX 278273. Ed. Peter Ogle. adv.; bk.rev. circ. 30,000. (also avail. in microform from UMI; back issues avail.; reprint service avail. from UMI) **Indexed:** Dent.Ind., Ind.Sci.Rev.
—BLDSC (3579.658050); Faxon; SWETS; UMI. CCC.

615.842 US
DIAGNOSTIC IMAGING & RADIOLOGY PRODUCT COMPARISON SYSTEM. m. $695. (Emergency Care Research Institute) E C R I, 5200 Butler Pike, Plymouth Meeting, PA 19462. TEL 610-825-6000. FAX 610-834-1275. Ed. Garrett Hayner. (looseleaf format)
●Also available on CD-ROM. Producer(s): Knight-Ridder, Inc..
Description: Covers hospital-based or freestanding radiology facilities, from MRI units to ultrasonic scanners and cardiac catheterization systems.
Refereed Serial

615.842 US ISSN 0898-2473
DIAGNOSTIC IMAGING INTERNATIONAL. 1985. 8/yr. $65. Miller Freeman, Inc. (Subsidiary of: United Newspapers), 600 Harrison St., San Francisco, CA 94107. TEL 415-905-2200. FAX 415-905-2233. TELEX 278273. Ed. Philip Ward. circ. 9,000.
—UMI.

615.842 US ISSN 0742-8383
CODEN: DRSEDL
DIAGNOSTIC RADIOLOGY SERIES. 1983. irreg., vol.2, 1983. price varies. Marcel Dekker, Inc., 270 Madison Ave., New York, NY 10016. TEL 212-696-9000. FAX 212-685-4540. TELEX 421419. **Indexed:** Biol.Abstr.
Refereed Serial

615.84 FR ISSN 0298-3834
E R Q. (Electro-Radiologiste Qualifie) 1947. 4/yr. Federation Nationale des Medecins Electroradiologistes Qualifies, 25 rue Pigalle, 75009 Paris, France. TEL 42-85-17-67. FAX 40-16-16-29. Ed. Pierre Lebert. circ. 3,500.
Former titles (until 1985): Medecin Electro-Radiologiste Qualifie de France (ISSN 0076-5813); (until 1962): Syndicat National des Medecins Electro-Radiologistes Qualifies. Bulletin (ISSN 0988-9728).

615.842 539.2 UA ISSN 1110-0303
EGYPTIAN JOURNAL OF RADIATION SCIENCES & APPLICATIONS. (Text in Arabic, English) 1984. 2/yr. $57 (effective 1996). (National Centre for Radiation Research & Technology) National Information and Documentation Centre (NIDOC), Tahrir St., Dokki, Awqaf P.O., Cairo, Egypt. TEL 20-2-701696. Ed. H.M. Roushdy. charts; illus.; stat. circ. 1,000. (reprint service avail. from IRC) **Document type:** academic/scholarly publication.

616.07 IT ISSN 1121-8800
EIDO ELECTA; Mediterranean journal of radiology and imaging. (Text in English, Italian; summaries in English, French, Italian) 1989. q. L.80000($150) (effective 1995). Casa Editrice Idelson, Via A. De Gasperi 55, 80133 Naples, Italy. TEL 39-81-5524733. FAX 39-81-5518295. Ed. Elio Adelfio Cardinale.
Description: Covers radiotherapy, radiobiology, and nuclear medicine.

MEDICAL SCIENCES — RADIOLOGY AND NUCLEAR MEDICINE

616.842 US ISSN 1070-3004
▼**EMERGENCY RADIOLOGY**; a journal of practical imaging. 1994. bi-m. $84 to non-member individuals; institutions $119. (American Society of Emergency Radiology) Williams & Wilkins, 428 E. Preston St., Baltimore, MD 21202-3993. TEL 410-528-8555; 800-638-6423. FAX 410-528-8596. (Subscr. in Japan to: Igaku-Shoin M.Y.W. Ltd., 3-23-14 Hongo, Bunkyo-ku, Tokyo 113, Japan. TEL 03-5689-5400. FAX 03-5689-5402) Ed. Dr. Theodore E. Keats; Pub. Timothy Grayson. adv. contact: Sherry Reed. bk.rev.; circ. 1,700 (paid). (also avail. in microfilm; microfiche) **Indexed:** Excerp.Med. (1995-). **Document type:** academic/scholarly publication.
—BLDSC (3733.197500).
Description: Original articles for radiologists and emergency medicine physicians treating acutely ill and injured patients.
Refereed Serial

618 619 GW ISSN 0340-6997
CODEN: EJNMD9
EUROPEAN JOURNAL OF NUCLEAR MEDICINE. (Text in English) 1976. 12/yr. DM.1298($943) (effective 1996). (European Association of Nuclear Medicine) Springer-Verlag, Heidelberger Platz 3, 14197 Berlin, Germany. TEL 030-8207-0. FAX 030-8214091. E-mail: orders@springer.de. (Subscr. in N. America to: Springer-Verlag New York, Inc., 44 Hartz Way, Secaucus, NJ 07096-2491. TEL 201-348-4033. FAX 201-348-4505) Ed. P.J. Ell. (also avail. in microfiche from UMI; reprint service avail. from ISI) **Indexed:** Chem.Abstr., Curr.Adv.Cancer Res., Curr.Adv.Ecol.Sci., Curr.Cont., Excerp.Med., Ind.Med., Ind.Sci.Rev., INIS Atomind., INSPEC, Kidney, Rev.Med.& Vet.Mycol., Sci.Cit.Ind. **Document type:** academic/scholarly publication.
—BLDSC (3829.731800); CASDDS; Faxon; Genuine Article; SWETS; UMI; UnCover. **CCC.**
Description: Covers developments in nuclear medicine, including original articles on diagnosis, therapy with 'open' radionuclides, in-vitro radiobiological and radiation protection.

615.842 IE ISSN 0720-048X
CODEN: EJRADR
EUROPEAN JOURNAL OF RADIOLOGY. 1980. bi-m. I£332($525) (effective 1996). (European Association of Radiology) Elsevier Science Ireland Ltd., P.O. Box 85, Limerick, Ireland. TEL 353-61-471944. FAX 353-61-472144. (Subscr. in U.S. and Canada to: Elsevier Science Inc., Box 882, Madison Sq. Sta., New York, NY 10159. TEL 212-989-5800. FAX 212-633-3990) Ed. H.E. Schutte. adv.; bk.rev.; charts; illus.; index. circ. 1,500. (reprint service avail. from UMI) **Indexed:** Chem.Abstr., Curr.Cont., Dent.Ind., Excerp.Med., Ind.Med., INIS Atomind., Rev.Med.& Vet.Mycol. **Document type:** academic/scholarly publication.
—BLDSC (3829.738050); CASDDS; Ei; Genuine Article; SWETS; UMI; UnCover. **CCC.**
Incorporates (1987-1989): Journal of Medical Imaging (ISSN 0920-5497)
Description: Provides information on the use of radiological and allied medical imaging techniques in clinical diagnosis and practice and of interventional techniques.
Refereed Serial

616.075 IE ISSN 0929-8266
▼**EUROPEAN JOURNAL OF ULTRASOUND**. 1994. bi-m. I£188($297) (effective 1996). (European Federation of Societies for Ultrasound in Medicine and Biology) Elsevier Science Ireland Ltd., P.O. Box 85, Limerick, Ireland. TEL 353-61-471944. FAX 353-61-472144. (Subscr. in U.S. and Canada to: Elsevier Science Inc., Box 889, Madison Sq. Sta., New York, NY 10159. TEL 212-989-5800. FAX 212-633-3990) Ed. J.M. Thijssen. (back issues avail.) **Indexed:** Bioeng.Abstr., Excerp.Med. (1995-). **Document type:** academic/scholarly publication.
—BLDSC (3829.747100). **Ei; CCC.**
Description: Serves as a forum for the European scientific and clinical community working with ultrasound in the fields of medicine and biology.
Refereed Serial

615.842 GW ISSN 0938-7994
CODEN: EURAE3
EUROPEAN RADIOLOGY. (Text in English) 1991. 6/yr. DM.498($361) (effective 1996). (European Association of Radiology) Springer-Verlag, Heidelberger Platz 3, 14197 Berlin, Germany. TEL 030-8207-0. FAX 030-8214091. E-mail: orders@springer.de. (Subscr. in N. America to: Springer-Verlag New York, Inc., 44 Hartz Way, Secaucus, NJ 07096-2491. TEL 201-348-4033. FAX 201-348-4505) Ed.Bd. **Document type:** academic/scholarly publication.
—BLDSC (3829.847300); Genuine Article; SWETS; UMI. **CCC.**
Incorporates (1989-1992): Diagnostic and Interventional Radiology (ISSN 0998-433X)
Description: Covers all aspects of diagnostic and interventional radiology.

616.842 JA ISSN 0914-790X
FACIAL NERVE RESEARCH. (Text in various languages) 1981. a. Japan Society of Facial Nerve Research, Dept. of Otorhinolaryngology, School of Medicine, Nihon University, 30-1 Kami-machi Oyaguchi, Itabashi-ku, Tokyo 173, Japan. TEL 03-972-8111. Ed. Jin Kanzaki.

615.8 FR ISSN 0181-9801
FEUILLETS DE RADIOLOGIE. 1961. bi-m. 784 F. (foreign 941 F.) (effective 1996). Masson - Periodiques, Villa Laromiguiere, 75005 Paris, France. TEL 1-40-46-62-00. FAX 1-40-46-62-01. Eds. V. Bismuth, M. Blery. circ. 4,000. (also avail. in microform from UMI; reprint service avail. from UMI) **Indexed:** Excerp.Med., INIS Atomind. **Document type:** academic/scholarly publication.
—UMI. **CCC.**
Description: For help in the preparation of university examinations and the competitive exams of French radiology hospitals.

615.842 US ISSN 0722-7035
FRONTIERS IN EUROPEAN RADIOLOGY. 1982. irreg. price varies. Springer-Verlag, 175 Fifth Ave., New York, NY 10010. TEL 212-460-1500. FAX 212-473-6272. (Also: Berlin, Heidelberg, Tokyo, Vienna) (reprint service avail. from ISI) **Document type:** academic/scholarly publication.
—BLDSC (4042.014000).

615 616.9 SZ ISSN 0071-9676
CODEN: FRTOA7
FRONTIERS OF RADIATION THERAPY AND ONCOLOGY. (Text in English) 1967. irreg. (approx. 1/yr.) price varies. S. Karger AG, Allschwilerstr. 10, P.O. Box, CH-4009 Basel, Switzerland. TEL 061-3061111. FAX 061-3061234. E-mail: Karger@Karger.ch. Ed. J.L. Meyer. (reprint service avail. from ISI) **Indexed:** Biol.Abstr., Chem.Abstr., Curr.Cont., Dent.Ind., Ind.Med. **Document type:** academic/scholarly publication.
—BLDSC (4042.060000); CASDDS; Faxon; Genuine Article; SWETS; UnCover. **CCC.**
Description: Covers developments in the treatment of cancer with radiation therapy.
Refereed Serial

616.07 JA
FUKUOKAKEN HOSHASEN GISHIKAISHI/FUKUOKA ASSOCIATION OF RADIOLOGICAL TECHNOLOGISTS. JOURNAL. (Text in Japanese) bi-m. Fukuokaken Hoshasen Gishika, Fukuoka-ken Kangoto Kenkyu Kenshu Senta, 14-5, Akasaka 1-chome, Fukuoka-shi, Fukuoka-ken 810, Japan.

616.07 615 JA ISSN 0911-2855
GAIKOKU BUNKEN DAIJESUTO. KAKU IGAKU/FOREIGN LITERATURE DIGEST. NUCLEAR MEDICINE. (Text in Japanese) 1971. bi-m. Daiichi Rajio Aisotopu Kenkyujo - Daiichi Radioisotope Laboratories, Ltd., 19-8, Kyobashi 1-chome, Chuo-ku, Tokyo 104, Japan.

615.842 NE ISSN 0016-4380
CODEN: GAMMDV
GAMMA. 1950. m. membership. Nederlandse Vereniging van Radiologisch Laboranten, Catharijnesingel 73, 3511 GM Utrecht, Netherlands. Ed. G.J.R. Bos. adv.; bk.rev. circ. 3,000. **Indexed:** Chem.Abstr.

615.842 IT ISSN 1120-3846
GIORNALE ITALIANO DI ULTRASONOLOGIA. 1990. 4/yr. L.80000($90) to individuals; institutions L.130000 ($140) (effective 1995). (Societa Italiana di Ultrasonologia in Medicina e Biologia) International University Press, Via Monte delle Gioie 22, 00199 Rome, Italy. TEL 39-6-86211027. FAX 39-6-86211026. Eds. Luigi Buscarini, Lorenzo Derchi. adv.: B&W page $1600, color page $2550; trim 179 x 235; adv. contact: Isabella Leonardo. circ. 3,000. (reprint service avail.) **Indexed:** Excerp.Med. (1993-). **Document type:** academic/scholarly publication.
—BLDSC (4178.252000).
Description: Disseminates the results of clinical research and stimulates scientific cooperation within the field.

615.842 CC ISSN 1001-1021
GUOWAI YIXUE (LINCHUANG FANGSHEXUE FENCE)/FOREIGN MEDICAL SCIENCES (CLINICAL RADIOLOGY). (Text in Chinese) 1978. bi-m. Tianjin Fangshe Zhenliao Yanjiu Peixun Zhongxin, 123, Anshan Dao, Tianjin 300052, People's Republic of China. TEL 705960. Ed. Wu Enhui.

612.014 US ISSN 0073-1498
HEALTH PHYSICS SOCIETY. NEWSLETTER.* 1959. m. membership. Health Physics Society, 1313 Dolley Madison Blvd., Ste. 402, McLean, VA 22101-3926. TEL 507-362-8958. FAX 507-362-4513. Ed. Genevieve S. Roessler. adv. circ. 7,000. **Document type:** newsletter.

612.014 JA
HIROSHIMA UNIVERSITY. RESEARCH INSTITUTE FOR RADIATION BIOLOGY AND MEDICINE. PROCEEDINGS. (Text in English and Japanese) 1960. a. Hiroshima University, Research Institute for Radiation Biology and Medicine - Hiroshima Daigaku Genbaku Hoshano Kenkyujo, Kasumi, Hiroshima 734, Japan. Ed. Yukio Satow. circ. 450 (controlled). **Indexed:** INIS Atomind. **Document type:** proceedings.
—BLDSC (6789.310000).
Formerly: Hiroshima University. Research Institute for Nuclear Medicine and Biology. Proceedings (ISSN 0073-232X)

615.842 JA
HOIKEN SHINPOJUMU SHIRIZU/N I R S SYMPOSIUM. PROCEEDINGS. (Text in Japanese; summaries in English) 1962. a. Science and Technology Agency, National Institute of Radiological Sciences - Kagaku Gijutsucho Hoshasen Igaku Sogo Kenkyujo, 9-1, Anagawa 4-chome, Inage-ku, Chiba-shi, Chiba-ken 263, Japan. **Document type:** proceedings.

615.842 JA ISSN 0912-0327
HOKKAIDO HOSHASEN GIJUTSU ZASSHI/JOURNAL OF HOKKAIDO RADIOLOGICAL TECHNOLOGY. (Text in Japanese) 1945. a. 1500 Yen. Nihon Hoshasen Gijutsu Gakkai, Hokkaido Bukai - Japanese Society of Radiological Technology, Hokkaido Branch, 427-26, Nishi 29-chome, Kita 3-jo, Chuo-ku, Sapporo-shi, Hokkaido 060, Japan. TEL 011-643-2713. FAX 011-614-7918. Ed. Motomichi Sakata; Pub. Takayuki Shibata. adv. contact: Junicki Suzuki. circ. 1,500. **Document type:** academic/scholarly publication.

615.842 NO ISSN 0332-9410
HOLD PUSTEN. 1974. 11/yr. NOK 210. Norsk Radiografforbund, Lakkegt. 19-21, N-0187 Oslo, Norway. FAX 47-22-17-52-04. Eds. Per Zaring, Knut Nordlid. adv.; circ. 1,276 (controlled). **Document type:** trade publication.
—CCC.

615.842 JA
HOSHANO CHOSA KENKYU HOKOKUSHO/NATIONAL INSTITUTE OF RADIOLOGICAL SCIENCES. SURVEY REPORT. (Text in Japanese) a. Kagaku Gijutsucho, Hoshasen Igaku Sogo Kenkyujo - Science and Technology Agency, National Institute of Radiological Sciences, 9-1, Anagawa 4-chome, Inage-ku, Chiba 263, Japan. **Document type:** government publication.

HOSHASEN EIKYO KENKYUJO HAPPYO RONBUN MOKUROKU/RADIATION EFFECTS RESEARCH FOUNDATION. BIBLIOGRAPHY OF PUBLISHED PAPERS.
see *MEDICAL SCIENCES — Abstracting, Bibliographies, Statistics*

MEDICAL SCIENCES — RADIOLOGY AND NUCLEAR MEDICINE

616.07 JA ISSN 0441-2540
CODEN: HOKAAN
HOSHASEN KAGAKU/RADIOLOGICAL SCIENCES.* (Text in Japanese) 1958. m. 550 Yen per no. Kagaku Gijutsucho, Hoshasen Igaku Sogo Kenkyujo - Science and Technology Agency, National Institute of Radiological Sciences, 1-3-1 Kasumigaseki, Chiyoda-ku, Tokyo 100, Japan.
—CASDDS.

616.842 JA
HOSHASEN RIYO KENKYUKAI HOKOKUSHO, IGAKU RIYO GURUPU/RESEARCH REPORT OF UTILIZATION OF RADIATION BY MEDICAL USER'S GROUP. (Text in Japanese) a. Nihon Genshiryoku Sangyo Kaigi - Japan Atomic Industrial Forum, 1-13, Shinbashi 1-chome, Minato-ku, Tokyo 105, Japan.

HYPERTHERMIA AND ONCOLOGY. see *MEDICAL SCIENCES* — *Oncology*

615.842 US ISSN 0278-0062
RC78.A1 CODEN: ITMID4
I E E E TRANSACTIONS ON MEDICAL IMAGING. 1982. q. $200 to non-members (effective 1996). Institute of Electrical and Electronics Engineers, Inc., 345 E. 47th St., New York, NY 10017-2394. TEL 908-981-0060. FAX 908-981-9667. (Subscr. to: Box 1331, 445 Hoes Lane, Piscataway, NJ 08855-1331) (Co-sponsors: I E E E Acoustics, Speech, and Signal Processing Society; Engineering in Medicine and Biology Society; Nuclear and Plasma Sciences Society; Ultrasonics, Ferroelectrics and Frequency Control Society) Ed. Gabor Herman. (also avail. in microform) **Indexed:** Bioeng.Abstr., Ergon.Abstr., INSPEC.
—BLDSC (4363.204500); Ei; Faxon; Genuine Article; SWETS; UMI. **CCC**.
Description: Explores ultrasonics, x-ray imaging and tomography, image processing by computers, microwave and nuclear magnetic resonance imaging.

616.842 JA ISSN 0915-308X
IBARAKI KAKU IGAKU/IBARAKI JOURNAL OF NUCLEAR MEDICINE. (Text in Japanese) 1989. s-a. Ibarakiken Rinsho Kaku Igaku Kenkyukai - Ibaraki Association of Clinical Nuclear Medicine, Tsukuba Daigaku Fuzoku Byoin Kaku Igakushitsu, 1-1, Amakubo 2-chome, Tsukuba-shi, Ibaraki-ken 305, Japan.

616.075 UK ISSN 0965-6812
CODEN: IAGIEC
IMAGING; an international journal of clinico-radiological practice. 1989. q. £135($230) to institutions (effective 1995). Rapid Communications of Oxford Ltd., The Old Malthouse, Paradise St., Oxford OX1 1LD, England. TEL 01865-790447. FAX 01865-244012. E-mail: rapidcom@vax.oxford.ac.uk. Ed. Dr. Philip Owen. **Indexed:** Excerp.Med., Info.Media & Tech. **Document type:** academic/scholarly publication.
●Also available on CD-ROM.
—BLDSC (4368.996447). **CCC**.
Formerly (until 1992): Current Imaging (ISSN 0952-0619)
Description: Provides the latest information on the integrated role of imaging modalities in diagnostic problem solving.

616 US
IMAGING DECISIONS. 1987. q. $36 (Canada $44; elsewhere $61). (Berlex Laboratories) P W Communications Group, Box 1505, Secaucus, NJ 07096-1505. TEL 201-865-7500. FAX 201-865-0753. Ed. Elaine D. Gomez; Pub. Ray Thibodeau. adv.; illus. **Document type:** trade publication.
Formerly (until 1994): M R I Decisions (ISSN 0896-0704)
Description: Impartially presents pros and cons of current state-of-the-art clinical information on magnetic resonance imaging and other imaging modalities.
Refereed Serial

615.842 AT
IMAGING GUIDELINES. irreg., 2nd ed., 1993. Aus.$20. Victorian Medical Postgraduate Foundation Inc., P.O. Box 27, Parkville, Vic. 3052, Australia. TEL 61-3-93479633. FAX 61-3-93474547. circ. 5,000.
Description: Assisting medical practitioners to make the best possible use of available imaging facilities.

615.842 II ISSN 0970-2016
CODEN: IJRAAY
INDIAN JOURNAL OF RADIOLOGY & IMAGING. (Text in English) 1946. q. Rs.450($13) Indian Radiological & Imaging Association, 13 Bheemanna Mudali Garden St., Madras 600018, India. TEL 91-22-412-1521. FAX 91-22-382-9595. Eds. Dr. M.G. Varadarajan, Dr. R. Ganapathi. adv.; bk.rev.; abstr.; bibl.; charts; illus.; stat.; index. circ. 1,500. **Indexed:** Biol.Abstr., Excerp.Med., ExtraMED. **Document type:** academic/scholarly publication.
●Also available on CD-ROM.
—BLDSC (4421.010000).
Formerly (until 1984): Indian Journal of Radiology (ISSN 0019-560X)

574.191 PL ISSN 0074-0640
INSTYTUT BADAN JADROWYCH. ZAKLAD RADIOBIOLOGII I OCHRONY ZDROWIA. PRACE DOSWIADCZALNE. (Text in English, French, German or Polish; summaries in English) 1960. irreg., vol.4, 1973. free. Osrodek Informacji o Energii Jadrowej, Palac Kultury i Nauki, Warsaw, Poland. Ed. Maria Kopec. author index.

613.6 UK ISSN 0146-6453
RA1231.R2 CODEN: ANICD6
INTERNATIONAL COMMISSION ON RADIOLOGICAL PROTECTION. ANNALS. Key Title: Annals of the I C R P. 1960. q. £143($228) (effective 1996). Elsevier Science Ltd., Pergamon, P.O. Box 800, Kidlington, Oxford OX5 1DX, England. TEL 44-1865-843000. FAX 44-1865-843010.
E-mail: nlinfo-f@elsevier.nl; usinfo-f@elsevier.com; forinfo-kyf04035@niftyserve.or.jp; Site addr.: http://www.elsevier.nl/. (Subscr. in U.S. and Canada to: Elsevier Science, 660 White Plains Rd., Tarrytown, NY 10591-5153. TEL 914-524-9200. FAX 914-333-2444) Ed. H. Smith. (also avail. in microfilm from UMI) **Indexed:** Abstr.Hyg., AESIS, Biol.Abstr., C.I.S. Abstr., Curr.Adv.Ecol.Sci., Energy Ind., Energy Info.Abstr., Excerp.Med., Ind.Med., Trop.Dis.Bull. **Document type:** academic/scholarly publication.
—Ei; SWETS; UMI. **CCC**.
Formerly: Advances in Radiological Protection.
Description: Covers topics in the field of radiation protection for members of the medical professions and other interested groups.
Refereed Serial

615.84 612.014 FI ISSN 0074-3933
INTERNATIONAL CONGRESS OF RADIOLOGY. (REPORTS). quadrennial; 17th, 1989, Paris; 18th, 1994, Singapore. International Society of Radiology, c/o Prof. Dr. C.G. Standertskjoeld, Department of Radiology, Helsinki University Central Hospital, 00290 Helsinki, Finland. FAX 0471-4404. **Indexed:** Excerp.Med.

615.8 US ISSN 1079-8110
▼**INTERNATIONAL JOURNAL OF NEURORADIOLOGY.** 1995. bi-m. $160 to individuals (foreign 175); institutions $175 (foreign $199) (effective 1996); newsstand price: $35. Lippincott - Raven Publishers, 227 E. Washington Sq., Philadelphia, PA 19106. TEL 215-238-4200. Eds. Dr. Thomas P. Nacich, Dr. Anne G. Osborn.
Refereed Serial

INTERNATIONAL JOURNAL OF RADIATION: ONCOLOGY - BIOLOGY - PHYSICS. see *PHYSICS* — *Nuclear Physics*

616.07 US ISSN 1079-3240
▼**INTERNATIONAL MEDICAL IMAGE REGISTRY.** 1995. bi-m. $75 to individuals; institutions $100 (effective 1995). Lippincott - Raven Press, 227 E. Washington Sq., Philadelphia, PA 19106. TEL 215-238-4200. Ed. Dr. J. Randy Jinkins. **Document type:** academic/scholarly publication.
Description: Succinct case presentations of diagnostic images describing rare disorders and classic teaching examples.

615.842 US ISSN 0020-9996
RC78 CODEN: INVRAV
INVESTIGATIVE RADIOLOGY. 1966. m. $175 to individuals (foreign $235); institutions $250 (foeign $320) (effective 1996); newsstand price: $28. Lippincot - Raven Publishers, 227 E. Washington Sq., Philadelphia, PA 19106. TEL 215-238-4200. Ed. Dr. Val M. Runge; Pub. Marcia E. Serepy. adv. contact: Jennifer Bass. illus.; index. circ. 2,670. (also avail. in microform from UMI; reprint service avail. from UMI) **Indexed:** Biol.Abstr., Biotech.Abstr., Chem.Abstr., Curr.Adv.Cancer Res., Curr.Cont., Excerp.Med., Hosp.Lit.Ind., Ind.Med., Ind.Sci.Rev., INIS Atomind., Sci.Cit.Ind., SSCI.
—BLDSC (4560.350000); CASDDS; EMDOCS; Faxon; Genuine Article; SWETS; UMI; UnCover. **CCC**.
Refereed Serial

616.07 JA ISSN 0917-3056
IRYO HOSHASEN BOGO NEWSLETTER/NEWSLETTER ON RADIOLOGICAL PROTECTION IN MEDICINE. (Text in Japanese) 1991. 3/yr. Iryo Hoshasen Bogo Renraku Kyogikai - Japan Association on Radiological Protection in Medicine, Nihon Aisotopu Kyokai, 28-45, Honkomagome 2-chome, Bunkyo-ku, Tokyo 113, Japan.

615.842 UA ISSN 0021-1907
CODEN: ISRRAC
ISOTOPE AND RADIATION RESEARCH.* (Text in English; summaries in Arabic) 1968. s-a. $20. Middle Eastern Regional Radioisotope Centre for the Arab Countries, Sh. Malaeb el Gamaa, Cairo 11321, Egypt. TELEX 2098-94381 PBDKIUN. adv.; bk.rev. circ. 500. **Indexed:** Chem.Abstr., Excerp.Med. (until 1992), INSPEC (1987-), Soils & Fert.
—BLDSC (4583.325000); CASDDS.

615.842 IT ISSN 0394-1574
ITALIAN CURRENT RADIOLOGY; trimestrale di tomografia computerizzata, ultrasuoni e nuove diagnostiche per immagini. 1982. q. L.90000($150) (effective 1995). Casa Editrice Idelson, Via A. De Gasperi 55, 80133 Naples, Italy. TEL 39-81-5524733. FAX 39-81-5518295. Ed. Enrico Del Vecchio. circ. 4,000.
—BLDSC (4588.332800).

615 JA ISSN 0910-1543
IYO GAZO JOHO GAKKAI ZASSHI/JAPANESE JOURNAL OF MEDICAL IMAGING AND INFORMATION SCIENCES. (Text in English, Japanese; summaries in English) 3/yr. Iyo Gazo Joho Gakkai - Japan Society of Medical Imaging and Information Sciences, Kyoto Kogei Sen'i Daigaku, Kogeigakubu Denki Kogakka, Matsugasaki Goshokaidocho, Sakyo-ku, Kyoto 606, Japan.

IZOTOPTECHNIKA, DIAGNOSZTIKA/ISOTOPE TECHNICS, DIAGNOSTICS. see *CHEMISTRY*

616 JA ISSN 0918-399X
J A S T R O NEWSLETTER. (Text in Japanese) 1988. q. Japanese Society for Therapeutic Radiology and Oncology - Nihon Hoshasen Shuyo Gakkai, c/o Nihon Hosha Kiki Kogyokai, 6-2, Yushima 1-chome, Bunkyo-ku, Tokyo 113, Japan. **Document type:** newsletter.

615.842 JA
JIKI KYOMEI IGAKKAI PUROGURAMU/SOCIETY OF MAGNETIC RESONANCE IN MEDICINE. PROCEEDINGS OF ANNUAL CONFERENCE. (Text in Japanese; summaries in English) a. Jiki Kyomei Igakkai, 465, Kajichiicho, Hirokoji Agaru, Kawaramachi Dori, Kamigyo-ku, Kyoto 602, Japan.

615.842 JA
JIKI KYOMEI TO IGAKU/MAGNETIC RESONANCE IN MEDICINE. (Text in Japanese; summaries in English) 1990. a. 5150 Yen. Nihon Igakukan, 9-6-505, Otsuka 3-chome, Bunkyo-ku, Tokyo 112, Japan. TEL 03-3942-7631. FAX 03-3942-2086. Ed. Toshiaki Kikuzawa.

615.842 BE ISSN 0021-7646
CODEN: JBRAAN
JOURNAL BELGE DE RADIOLOGIE. (Text in Dutch and French; summaries in Dutch, English, French and German) 1907. 6/yr. Societe Royale Belge de Radiologie, Ave. des Eglantines, 10, 1150 Brussels, Belgium. TEL 32-2-7716868. adv.; charts; illus.; stat.; index. **Indexed:** Biol.Abstr., Chem.Abstr., Excerp.Med., Helminthol.Abstr., Ind.Med., INSPEC (1973-1986), Sci.Cit.Ind.
—EMDOCS; SWETS.

MEDICAL SCIENCES — RADIOLOGY AND NUCLEAR MEDICINE

616.842   FR   ISSN 0245-5552
CODEN: JEMUEF
JOURNAL D'ECHOGRAPHIE ET DE MEDECINE PAR ULTRASONS. 1980. bi-m. 684 F. (foreign 838 F.) (effective 1996). Masson - Periodiques, Villa Laromiguiere, 75005 Paris, France. TEL 1-40-46-62-00. FAX 1-40-46-62-01. Ed. J.M. de Bray. circ. 2,000. (also avail. in microform from UMI) **Indexed:** Excerp.Med., INIS Atomind. **Document type:** academic/scholarly publication.
—BLDSC (4663.550000); UMI. **CCC.**
   Description: Publishes essentially practical articles dealing with the main fields of ultrasonic medicine.

615.842   FR   ISSN 0221-0363
JOURNAL DE RADIOLOGIE. (Text in French; summaries in English) 1914. 12/yr. 1200 F. (foreign 1650 F.) (effective 1996). (Societe Francaise de Radiologie) Editions Francaises de Radiologie, Villa Laromiguiere, 75005 Paris, France. TEL 1-40-46-62-00. FAX 1-40-46-62-01. Eds. J.F. Moreau, Y. Menu. adv.; bk.rev.; abstr.; illus.; index. circ. 5,000. (also avail. in microform from UMI; reprint service avail. from ISI) **Indexed:** Biol.Abstr., Chem.Abstr., Dent.Ind., Excerp.Med., Helminthol.Abstr., Ind.Med., INIS Atomind., Rev.Med.& Vet.Mycol. **Document type:** academic/scholarly publication.
—BLDSC (5043.972000); Genuine Article; SWETS; UMI.
   Formerly: Journal de Radiologie d'Electrologie et de Medecine Nucleaire (ISSN 0021-7964)
   Description: Discusses radiodiagnosis and new methods of investigation. Reports on international congresses of radiology and on the section meetings of the society

615.842   US   ISSN 1044-5471
CODEN: JCLSEO
JOURNAL OF CLINICAL LASER MEDICINE & SURGERY. 1983. bi-m. $140 (foreign $180). (International Society for Laser Surgery and Medicine) Mary Ann Liebert, Inc. Publishers, 2 Madison, Larchmont, NY 10538. TEL 914-834-3100. FAX 914-834-3688. E-mail: Liebert@pipeline.com. Ed. Dr. Eugene W. Friedman. adv. **Indexed:** Excerp.Med. (1993-), Med.& Surg.Dermat. **Document type:** academic/scholarly publication.
—BLDSC (4958.540000); Ei; Faxon.
   Former titles: Laser Medicine and Surgery News and Advances; Laser Medicine and Surgery News (ISSN 0736-9417)
   Description: Covers advances and expanded applications and procedures, significant clinical and basic research, safety programs, and new instrumentation. Includes profiles of laser institutes, companies, and physicians.

JOURNAL OF CLINICAL ONCOLOGY. see *MEDICAL SCIENCES — Oncology*

616.07   US   ISSN 0091-2751
RM862.7   CODEN: JCULDD
JOURNAL OF CLINICAL ULTRASOUND. 1973. 9/yr. $396 (foreign $535.50) (effective 1996). John Wiley & Sons, Inc., Journals, 605 Third Ave., New York, NY 10158. TEL 212-850-6645. FAX 212-850-6021. TELEX 12-7063. E-mail: SUBINFO@JWILEY.COM. (Subscr. outside the Americas to: John Wiley & Sons Ltd., Baffins Ln., Chichester, W. Sussex PO19 1UD, England. TEL 44-1243-779777. FAX 44-1243-776128) Ed. Russell L. Deter. adv.; bk.rev.; abstr.; charts; illus.; stat.; index. circ. 5,000. (also avail. in microform from UMI; back issues avail.; reprint service avail. from UMI) **Indexed:** Bibl.Dev.Med.& Child Neur., Biol.Abstr., Curr.Adv.Cancer Res., Curr.Cont., Dent.Ind., Dok.Arbeitsmed., Excerp.Med., Helminthol.Abstr., Ind.Med., Ind.Sci.Rev., INIS Atomind., INSPEC, Sci.Cit.Ind.
—BLDSC (4958.791000); EMDOCS; Faxon; Genuine Article; SWETS; UMI; UnCover. **CCC.**
   Description: Covers current uses of ultrasound in evaluating disorders affecting the central nervous system, fetus and placenta, gastrointestinal system, reproductive system, urinary system.
   Refereed Serial

615.842   US   ISSN 0363-8715
RC78.7.T6   CODEN: JCATD5
JOURNAL OF COMPUTER ASSISTED TOMOGRAPHY; a radiological journal dedicated to the basic and clinical aspects of reconstructive tomography. 1977. bi-m. $150 to individuals (foreign $195); institutions $365 (foreign $410) (effective 1996); newsstand price: $70. Lippincott - Raven Press, 276 Washington Sq., Philadelphia, PA 19106. TEL 215-237-4200. Ed. Dr. Giovanni Di Chiro. adv. contact: Phyllis Noyes. bk.rev.; index. circ. 6,000. (also avail. in microform from UMI; back issues avail.; reprint service avail. from UMI) **Indexed:** Bibl.Dev.Med.& Child Neur., Biol.Abstr., Curr.Cont., Dent.Ind., Excerp.Med., Helminthol.Abstr., Ind.Med., Ind.Sci.Rev., INIS Atomind., INSPEC, Kidney, Nutr.Abstr., Rev.Med.& Vet.Mycol., Sci.Cit.Ind. **Document type:** academic/scholarly publication.
—BLDSC (4963.650000); Faxon; Genuine Article; SWETS; UMI; UnCover. **CCC.**
   Description: Articles and reports on technological advances in radiology.
   Refereed Serial

616.07   US   ISSN 8756-4793
JOURNAL OF DIAGNOSTIC MEDICAL SONOGRAPHY. 1985. bi-m. $79 to individuals (foreign $110); institutions $120 (foreign $140) (effective 1996); newsstand price: $25. (Society of Diagnostic Medical Sonographers) Lippincott - Raven Publishers, 227 E. Washington Sq., Philadelphia, PA 19105. TEL 215-238-4200. Ed. Jean Lea Spitz; Pub. Lisa R. Marshall. adv. contact: Kathleen Phelan. illus.; index. circ. 12,268. (also avail. in microform) **Indexed:** Excerp.Med.
—Faxon; Genuine Article; SWETS; UMI. **CCC.**
   Refereed Serial

616.842   US   ISSN 0897-1889
CODEN: JDIMEW
JOURNAL OF DIGITAL IMAGING. 1988 (Nov.). q. $243 (foreign $291) (effective 1996). (Society for Computer Applications in Radiology) W.B. Saunders Co. (Subsidiary of: Harcourt Brace & Company), The Curtis Center, 3rd Fl., Independence Sq. W., Philadelphia, PA 19106-3399. TEL 215-238-7800. FAX 215-238-6445. (Subscr. to: Periodicals Fulfillment, W.B. Saunders Co., 6277 Sea Harbor Dr., 4th Fl., Orlando, FL 32887-4800. TEL 800-654-2452. FAX 800-874-6418) Ed. Dr. Roger A. Bauman; Pub. Joan W. Blumberg. adv.: B&W page $600, color page $1600; 7 x 10. index. circ. 703. (back issues avail.) **Document type:** academic/scholarly publication.
—BLDSC (4969.610000); Ei; UMI. **CCC.**
   Description: Presents the practicing radiologist with information to enhance in the understanding, selection, and use of computer applications in everyday practice.
   Refereed Serial

615.842   UK   ISSN 0268-0882
CODEN: JIRAE8
JOURNAL OF INTERVENTIONAL RADIOLOGY. q. £95($157) to individuals; institutions £127 ($209) (effective 1995). (B S I R) Churchill Livingstone Journals (Subsidiary of: Pearson Professional), Robert Stevenson House, 1-3 Baxter's Pl., Leith Walk, Edinburgh EH1 3AF, Scotland. TEL 0131-556-2424. FAX 0131-459-1177. (Subscr. to: Pearson Professional Ltd., P.O. Box 77, Fourth Ave., Harlow, Essex CM19 5AA, England. TEL 01279-623760; U.S. subscr. to: Churchill Livingstone, 650 Ave. of the Americas, New York, NY 10011. TEL 212-206-5000) adv. contact: David Dunnachie. circ. 570. **Document type:** academic/scholarly publication.
—BLDSC (5007.697000); Faxon; Genuine Article; SWETS. **CCC.**
   Description: Publishes original and commissioned articles. Emphasis is on the practical aspects of interventional radiology.

616.07   HK   ISSN 0929-6441
CODEN: JMEUEV
JOURNAL OF MEDICAL ULTRASOUND. (Text in English) 4/yr. Excerpta Medica Asia Ltd., Eight Commercial Tower, 19th Fl., 8 Sun Yip St., Chai Wan, Hong Kong. TEL 852-9651300. **Indexed:** Excerp.Med. (1994-). **Document type:** academic/scholarly publication.

JOURNAL OF NEUROIMAGING. see *MEDICAL SCIENCES — Psychiatry And Neurology*

615.842   FR   ISSN 0150-9861
CODEN: JNEUD3
JOURNAL OF NEURORADIOLOGY/JOURNAL DE NEURORADIOLOGIE. (Text in English, French) 1974. q. 1088 F.($242) (foreign 1357 F.) (effective 1996). (Societe Francaise de Neuroradiologie) Masson - Periodiques, Villa Laromiguiere, 75005 Paris, France. TEL 1-40-46-62-00. FAX 1-40-46-62-01. Ed. L. Picard. adv.; bk.rev.; illus. circ. 1,000. (also avail. in microform from UMI; reprint service avail. from ISI) **Indexed:** Bibl.Dev.Med.& Child Neur., Biol.Abstr., Curr.Cont., Excerp.Med., Ind.Med. **Document type:** academic/scholarly publication.
—BLDSC (5022.072000); Faxon; Genuine Article; SWETS; UMI. **CCC.**
   Formerly (until Mar. 1978): Journal de Neuroradiologie (ISSN 0335-0800)
   Description: Covers all subjects common to neurology, neurosurgery, and general radiology.

616.1   US   ISSN 1071-3581
CODEN: JNCAE2
▼**JOURNAL OF NUCLEAR CARDIOLOGY.** (Supplements avail.) 1994. bi-m. $105 to individuals (Canada $144.45; elsewhere $135); institutions $133 (Canada $174.41; elsewhere $163); students, residents $50 (Canada $85.60; elsewhere $80) (effective 1996); newsstand price: $12. (American Society of Nuclear Cardiology (ASNC)) Mosby - Year Book, Inc. (Subsidiary of: Times Mirror Company), 11830 Westline Industrial Dr., St. Louis, MO 63146-3318. TEL 314-872-8370. FAX 314-432-1380. Ed. Dr. Barry L. Zaret. adv.: B&W page $880, color page $17170; trim 8 1/4 x 11. circ. 2,571. **Indexed:** Excerp.Med. (1995-). **Document type:** academic/scholarly publication.
—BLDSC (5022.870000); UMI. **CCC.**
   Description: Addresses all aspects of nuclear cardiology, including interpretation, diagnosis, radio-pharmaceuticals, and imaging equipment. Keeps readers up-to-date on legislative and regulatory issues, as well as upcoming events, activities and continuing education.
   Refereed Serial

615.842   US   ISSN 0161-5505
RM845   CODEN: JNMEAQ
JOURNAL OF NUCLEAR MEDICINE.* 1960. m. $140 (foreign $185) (effective 1996). Society of Nuclear Medicine, 1850 Samuel Morse Dr., Reston, VA 22090-5316. TEL 212-889-0717. FAX 212-545-0221. Ed. Dr. Stanley J. Goldsmith. adv.; bk.rev.; abstr.; bibl.; charts; illus.; index. circ. 14,000. (also avail. in microform from UMI; back issues avail.; reprint service avail. from UMI) **Indexed:** Biol.Abstr., Chem.Abstr., Curr.Adv.Biochem., Curr.Adv.Cancer Res., Curr.Adv.Ecol.Sci., Curr.Cont., Dairy Sci.Abstr., Dent.Ind., Excerp.Med., Helminthol.Abstr., I.P.A., Ind.Med., Ind.Sci.Rev., Ind.Vet., INIS Atomind., INSPEC, Kidney, Nutr.Abstr., Vet.Bull. **Document type:** academic/scholarly publication.
—BLDSC (5023.300000); CASDDS; Faxon; Genuine Article; SWETS; UMI; UnCover. **CCC.**
   Incorporates: S N M Newsline; **Former titles:** J N M (ISSN 0097-9031); Journal of Nuclear Medicine (ISSN 0022-3123)
   Refereed Serial

615.8   US   ISSN 0091-4916
R895.A1   CODEN: JNMTB4
JOURNAL OF NUCLEAR MEDICINE TECHNOLOGY.* 1973. q. $60 (foreign $70). Society of Nuclear Medicine, 1850 Samuel Morse Dr., Reston, VA 22090-5316. TEL 212-889-0717. FAX 212-545-0221. Ed. Susan C. Weiss. adv.; bk.rev.; charts; illus.; index. circ. 5,500. (also avail. in microform from UMI; back issues avail.; reprint service avail. from UMI) **Indexed:** Biol.Abstr., Chem.Abstr., Excerp.Med. (1993-), I.P.A., INIS Atomind., INSPEC. **Document type:** academic/scholarly publication.
●Also available online.
—BLDSC (5023.340000); CASDDS; EMDOCS; Faxon; SWETS; UMI; UnCover. **CCC.**
   Refereed Serial

MEDICAL SCIENCES — RADIOLOGY AND NUCLEAR MEDICINE

615 JA ISSN 0449-3060
QH652.A1 CODEN: JRARAX
JOURNAL OF RADIATION RESEARCH. (Text in English) 1960. q. 8000 Yen($95) membership. Japan Radiation Research Society, 4-9-1 Anagawa, Inage-ku, Chiba-shi 263, Japan. (Dist. by: Business Center for Academic Societies Japan, 5-16-9 Honkomagome, Bunkyo-ku, Tokyo 113, Japan. TEL 03-5814-5811) Ed. Hiraku Takebe. adv.; bk.rev. circ. 1,500. **Indexed:** Biol.Abstr., Biwk.Pap.Rad.Chem.& Photochem., Chem.Abstr., Curr.Adv.Ecol.Sci., Curr.Cont., Dairy Sci.Abstr., Deep Sea Res.& Oceanogr.Abstr., Dent.Ind., Excerp.Med., Ind.Med., Ind.Sci.Rev., INIS Atomind., INSPEC, Pollut.Abstr. **Document type:** academic/scholarly publication.
—BLDSC (5043.800000); CASDDS; Ei; Faxon; Genuine Article; SWETS.
Formerly: Japan Radiation Research Society. Journal.

JOURNAL OF RADIOLOGICAL PROTECTION. see ENERGY — Nuclear Energy

616 US ISSN 0883-5993
CODEN: JTIME8
JOURNAL OF THORACIC IMAGING. 1985. q. $150 to individuals (foreign $191); institutions $185 (foreign $218) (effective 1996); newsstand price: $56. (Society of Thoracic Radiology) Lippincott - Raven Publishers, 276 E. Washington Sq., Philadelphia, PA 19106. TEL 215-238-4200. Ed. Sanford A. Rubin. adv. contact: Phyllis Noyes. illus.; index. (also avail. in microform; back issues avail.) **Indexed:** Curr.Adv.Cancer Res., Excerp.Med., Ind.Med., INIS Atomind. **Document type:** academic/scholarly publication.
—BLDSC (5069.120000); Genuine Article; SWETS; UMI; UnCover. **CCC.**
Description: Discusses all aspects of the diagnosis of chest disease using imaging techniques.
Refereed Serial

616.07 534 US ISSN 0278-4297
CODEN: JUMEDA
JOURNAL OF ULTRASOUND IN MEDICINE. 1982. m. $132 (foreign $166) (effective 1996). American Institute for Ultrasound in Medicine, 14750 Sweitzer Ln., Ste. 100, Laurel, MD 20707-5906. TEL 301-498-4100. FAX 301-498-4450. Ed. Dr. George R. Leopold. adv. contact: Marti Boyer. bk.rev.; abstr.; bibl.; charts; illus.; index; circ. 13,000 (paid). (also avail. in microform from UMI; reprint service avail. from UMI) **Indexed:** Curr.Cont., Dent.Ind., Excerp.Med., Ind.Med., Ind.Sci.Rev., Sci.Cit.Ind. **Document type:** academic/scholarly publication.
—BLDSC (5071.455000); Ei; Faxon; Genuine Article; SWETS; UMI; UnCover. **CCC.**
Description: Contains original articles on basic and clinical aspects of ultrasound, advances in the field, techniques, and equipment modifications.
Refereed Serial

615.842 US ISSN 1051-0443
CODEN: JVIRE3
JOURNAL OF VASCULAR AND INTERVENTIONAL RADIOLOGY. 1990. bi-m. $125 (foreign $150). Radiological Society of North America, Inc., 2021 Spring Rd., Ste. 600, Oak Brook, IL 60521. TEL 708-571-7819. FAX 708-571-7837. (Co-publisher: Society of Cardiovascular and Interventional Radiology) Ed. Dr. Gary J. Becker. adv. contact: Tom Shimala. circ. 1,691. (also avail. in microform from UMI) **Indexed:** Ind.Med. (1992-). **Document type:** academic/scholarly publication.
●Also available online. Vendor(s): National Library of Medicine.
—BLDSC (5072.263000); Genuine Article; SWETS.
Description: Covers clinical and laboratory studies in the field of interventional radiology.
Refereed Serial

616.07 JA ISSN 0075-4579
JUNTENDO UNIVERSITY. MEDICAL ULTRASONICS RESEARCH CENTER. ANNUAL REPORT.⁑ (Text in English) a. Juntendo University, School of Medicine, Medical Ultrasonics Research Center, 2-1-2 Hongo, Bunkyo-ku, Tokyo 113, Japan.

615.842 CN ISSN 0022-7439
K V P NEWS. 1964. q. membership. Manitoba Association of Medical Radiation Technologists Inc., 215-819 Sargent Ave., Winnipeg, MB R3E 0B9, Canada. TEL 204-774-5346. Ed. L Wills. adv.; charts; illus. circ. 800. (processed) **Document type:** newsletter.

615.8 JA ISSN 0022-7854
CODEN: KAIGBZ
KAKU IGAKU/JAPANESE JOURNAL OF NUCLEAR MEDICINE. Variant title: Nihon Kaku Igakkai Kikanshi. (Text in Japanese; summaries in English, Japanese) 1964. 12/yr. 1500 Yen per no. Nihon Kaku Igakkai - Japanese Society of Nuclear Medicine, Nihon Aisotopu Kyokai, 2-28-45 Honkomagome, Bunkyo-ku, Tokyo 113, Japan. Ed. Dr. S. Hashimoto. adv.; abstr.; charts; illus.; index. **Indexed:** Biol.Abstr., Chem.Abstr., Excerp.Med., Ind.Med., INIS Atomind., JTA.
—BLDSC (4656.650000); CASDDS; EMDOCS.

615.842 JA ISSN 0912-4195
KAKU IGAKU GAZO SHINDAN/IMAGING DIAGNOSIS IN NUCLEAR MEDICINE. (Text in Japanese) 1986. 3/yr. Hokuriku Kaku Igaku Kanfarensu - Hokuriku Nuclear Medicine Conference, Kanazawa Daigaku Igakubu Kaku Igaku Kyoshitsu, 13-1, Takaramachi, Kanazawa-shi, Ishikawa-ken 920, Japan.

615.8 JA ISSN 0289-100X
CODEN: KIGIEM
KAKU IGAKU GIJUTSU/JAPANESE JOURNAL OF NUCLEAR MEDICINE TECHNOLOGY. (Text in Japanese) 1981. q. Nihon Kaku Igaku Gijutsu Gakkai - Japanese Society of Nuclear Medicine Technology, Sumitomo Byoin Aisotopu Kensabu, 2-2, Nakanoshima 5-chome, Kita-ku, Osaka 530, Japan. **Indexed:** Chem.Abstr.
—CASDDS.

615.8 JA ISSN 0912-6104
KAKU IGAKU SEMINA SHOREISHU/TOKAI SEMINAR IN NUCLEAR MEDICINE. (Text in Japanese) 1985. a. (Kaku Igaku Semina Shoreishu Kenkyujo - Tokai Seminar in Nuclear Medicine) Daiichi Rajio Aisotopu Kenkyujo - Daiichi Radioisotope Laboratories, Ltd., 19-8, Kyobashi 1-chome, Chuo-ku, Tokyo 104, Japan.

615.8 JA ISSN 0910-2213
KAKU IGAKU SHOREI KENTOKAI SHOREISHU/PROCEEDINGS OF MEETING ON CASE OF NUCLEAR MEDICINE. (Text in Japanese) 1979. q. Nihon Mejifijikkusu K.K. - Japan Mediphysics Co., Ltd., 9-8, Rokutanjicho, Nishinomiya-shi, Hyogo-ken 662, Japan.

615.8 JA ISSN 0461-5956
CODEN: KASHAJ
KANKO SHIKISO/MEDICAL RESEARCHES FOR PHOTOSENSITIZING DYES. (Text in Japanese; summaries in English, Japanese) 1950. irreg. Kanko Shikiso Kenkyukai - Research Society for Photosensitizing Dyes, c/o Kyoto Daigaku Igakubu Byorigaku Kyoshitsu, Yoshida Konoecho, Sakyo-ku, Kyoto 606, Japan.
—CASDDS.

615.8 KZ ISSN 0075-529X
KAZAKHSKII NAUCHNO-ISSLEDOVATEL'SKII INSTITUT ONKOLOGII I RADIOLOGII. TRUDY. (Text in Russian; summaries in English) 1965. a. price varies. Kazakhskii Nauchno-Issledovatel'skii Institut Onkologii i Radiologii, Alma-Ata, Kazakhstan. (Co-producer: Ministerstvo Zdravokhraneniya Kazakhskoi S.S.R.) Eds. O.K. Kabiev, S.B. Balmukhanov. circ. 400. **Indexed:** Biol.Abstr.

616.075 JA
KISO GIJUTSU KENKYU BUKAI SHIRYO/BASIC TECHNOLOGY RESEARCH COMMITTEE. MATERIALS. (Text in English, Japanese) 1986. irreg. Nihon Choopa Igakkai - Japan Society of Ultrasonics in Medicine, 23-1, Hongo 3-chome, Bunkyo-ku, Tokyo 113, Japan.

616.842 JA ISSN 0915-0919
KITA NIHON KAKU IGAKU DANWAKAI/NORTH JAPANESE JOURNAL OF NUCLEAR MEDICINE. (Text in Japanese) 1988. 2/yr. Kita Nihon Kaku Igaku Danwakai - North Japanese Society of Nuclear Medicine, c/o Mr. Mamoru Nakamura, Kokuritsu Sendai Byoin Hoshasenka, 8-8, Miyagino 2-chome, Miyagino-ku, Sendai-shi, Miyagi-ken 983, Japan.

615.842 GW ISSN 0939-7116
KLINISCHE NEURORADIOLOGIE. 1991. q. DM.262($190) (effective 1996). (Deutsche, Oesterreichische und Schweizerische Gesellschaft fuer Neuroradiologie) Urban und Vogel, Lindwurmstr. 95, 80337 Munich, Germany. TEL 089-53292-0. FAX 089-53292100. TELEX 7252275-GTV-D. (Subscr. to: Postfach 152209, 80052 Munich, Germany) Ed. Dr. M. Nadjmi. circ. 1,100. **Document type:** academic/scholarly publication.
—BLDSC (5099.455000); Genuine Article.

616.07 JA ISSN 0914-871X
KONIKA X REI SHASHIN KENKYU/KONICA X-RAY PHOTOGRAPHIC REVIEW. (Text in Japanese) bi-m. Konica Corp., 26-2, Nishishinjuku 1-chome, Shinjuku-ku, Tokyo 163, Japan.

616.07 JA ISSN 0911-9701
KYOKKO X-RAY/KASEI OPTONIX LTD. JOURNAL. (Text in Japanese) a. Kasei Oputonikusu K.K., 12-7, Shiba Daimon 2-chome, Minato-ku, Tokyo 105, Japan.

616.075 FR ISSN 1169-3827
L U S. (Litterature Ultra-Sonore.) m. 1970 F. (effective 1996). Faculte de Medecine de Montpellier - Nimes, Antenne de Nimes, Av. Kennedy, 30000 Nimes, France. TEL 66-27-31-77. Ed. J.M. Bourgeois. bk.rev. circ. 2,500. **Document type:** bulletin.
Formerly (until 1992): Journal Francais d'Echographie.

615.842 JA
M R NYUMON KOZA TEKISUTO/BEGINNER'S TEXTBOOK OF MAGNETIC RESONANCE IN MEDICINE. (Magnetic Resonance) (Text in Japanese) 1972. 2/yr. 15000 Yen. Nihon Jiki Kyomei Igakkai - Japanese Society of Magnetic Resonance in Medicine, 2-4, Hongo 7-chome, Bunkyo-ku, Tokyo 113, Japan.

615.842 JA
M R RINSHO KOZA TEKISUTO/TEXTBOOK OF CLINICAL MEDICINE ON MAGNETIC RESONANCE. (Magnetic Resonance) (Text in Japanese) 1989. 2/yr. 4000 Yen per no. Nihon Jiki Kyomei Igakkai - Japanese Society of Magnetic Resonance in Medicine, 2-4, Hongo 7-chome, Bunkyo-ku, Tokyo 113, Japan.

615.842 UK ISSN 0730-725X
RC78.7.N83 CODEN: MRIMDQ
MAGNETIC RESONANCE IMAGING; an international journal of basic research & clinical applications. 1982. 10/yr. $715 to institutions (effective 1996). (Society for Magnetic Resonance Imaging) Elsevier Science Ltd., Pergamon, P.O. Box 800, Kidlington, Oxford OX5 1DX, England. TEL 44-1865-843000. FAX 44-1865-843010. E-mail: nlinfo-f@elsevier.nl; usinfo-f@elsevier.com; forinfo-kyf04035@niftyserve.or.jp; Site addr.: http://www.elsevier.nl/. (Subscr. in U.S. and Canada to: Elsevier Science, 660 White Plains Rd., Tarrytown, NY 10591-5153. TEL 914-524-9200. FAX 914-333-2444) Eds. John Gore, Francis W. Smith. adv.; bk.rev. circ. 2,000. (also avail. in microfilm from UMI; back issues avail.) **Indexed:** Biol.Abstr., Chem.Abstr., Curr.Adv.Cancer Res., Curr.Adv.Ecol.Sci., Curr.Cont., INIS Atomind., INSPEC. **Document type:** academic/scholarly publication.
—BLDSC (5337.795000); CASDDS; Faxon; Genuine Article; SWETS; UMI; UnCover. **CCC.**
Incorporates (1986-1992): Reviews of Magnetic Resonance in Medicine (ISSN 0883-8291)
Description: Covers clinical, physical and life science investigations relating to the development and use of magnetic resonance methods and instrumentation as well as applications of imaging and spectroscopic techniques.
Refereed Serial

616.842 US ISSN 1064-9689
MAGNETIC RESONANCE IMAGING CLINICS. 1993. q. $132 (foreign $158) (effective 1996). W.B. Saunders Co. (Subsidiary of: Harcourt Brace & Company), Curtis Center, 3rd Fl., Independence Sq. W., Philadelphia, PA 19106-3399. TEL 215-238-7800. FAX 215-238-6445. (Subscr. to: Periodicals Fulfillment, W.B. Saunders Co., 6277 Sea Harbor Dr., Orlando, FL 32891-4800. TEL 800-654-2452. FAX 800-874-6418) Ed. Dr. Jeffrey Weinreb. (also avail. in microform from UMI) **Document type:** academic/scholarly publication.
—BLDSC (5337.796000); UMI.
Description: Emphasizes the conduct of examinations, interpretation of data, differential diagnosis, and pitfalls encountered in MRI practices.

615.842　　　US　　ISSN 0740-3194
RC78.7.N83　　　　　CODEN: MRMEEN
MAGNETIC RESONANCE IN MEDICINE. 1984. m. $394 to individuals (foreign $479); institutions $527 (foreign 612) (effective 1995). Williams & Wilkins, 428 E. Preston St., Baltimore, MD 21202-3993. TEL 410-528-4000; 800-638-6423. FAX 410-528-4312. TELEX 87669. Ed. Felix W. Wehrli. adv.; index. circ. 2,967. (back issues avail.) **Indexed:** Curr.Adv.Cancer Res., INSPEC (1989-). **Document type:** academic/scholarly publication.
—BLDSC (5337.798000); CASDDS; Faxon; Genuine Article; SWETS; UnCover. **CCC.**
Description: Publishes original investigations concerned with all aspects of the development and use of nuclear magnetic resonance and electron paramagnetic resonance techniques for medical applications.
Refereed Serial

MAGNETIC RESONANCE MATERIALS IN PHYSICS, BIOLOGY AND MEDICINE. see *PHYSICS — Nuclear Physics*

615　　　US　　ISSN 0899-9422
RC78.7.N83　　　　　CODEN: MRQUEN
MAGNETIC RESONANCE QUARTERLY. 1989. q. $104 to individuals; institutions $135 (effective 1994). Lippincott - Raven Publishers, 227 E. Washington Sq., Philadelphia, PA 19106. TEL 215-238-4200. Eds. Robert R. Edelman, Michael Brant-Zawadski. adv. contact: Phyllis Noyes. illus.; index. circ. 1,900. (back issues avail.; reprint service avail. from UMI) **Indexed:** Excerp.Med., Ind.Med., INSPEC (1991-). **Document type:** academic/scholarly publication.
—BLDSC (5337.799000); Faxon; Genuine Article; SWETS; UMI; UnCover. **CCC.**
Supersedes (in 1989): Magnetic Resonance Annual.
Description: Presents international advances in MRI that affect daily practice.
Refereed Serial

¹ 574.191 615.842　　FR　　ISSN 0928-1258
　　　　　　　　　　　　CODEN: JBMND6
MEDECINE NUCLEAIRE; imagerie fonctionelle et metabolique. (Text in French, summaries in English and French) 1967. 9/yr. 1015 F. in France; foreign 1135 F.($222) (effective 1996). (Societe Francaise de Biophysique et de Medecine Nucleaire) Editions Scientifiques Elsevier, 141 rue de Javel, 75747 Paris, France. TEL 33-1-45586093. (Subscr. in U.S. and Canada to: Elsevier Science Inc., Box 882, Madison Sq. Sta., New York, NY 10159. TEL 212-989-5800. FAX 212-633-3990) Ed. A. Desgrez. adv. circ. 700. (also avail. in microform from UMI; reprint service avail. from UMI) **Indexed:** Bull.Signal., Chem.Abstr., Curr.Cont., Excerp.Med., Ind.Sci.Rev., INSPEC, Sci.Cit.Ind. **Document type:** academic/scholarly publication.
—BLDSC (5487.920000); CASDDS; Genuine Article. **CCC.**
Former titles (until 1993): Journal de Medecine Nucleaire et Biophysique (ISSN 0992-3039); (until 1988): Journal de Biophysique et de Biomecanique (ISSN 0766-5717); (until 1985): Journal de Biophysique et Medecine Nucleaire (ISSN 0243-3354); (until 1980): Journal Francais de Biophysique et Medecine Nucleaire (ISSN 0399-0435); Annales de Physique Biologique et Medicale (ISSN 0029-0793)
Description: Emphasizes current nuclear medicine practices, in vivo as well as in vitro, including clinical practice, methodology and instrumentation, signal processing, and fundamental and applied biophysics.
Refereed Serial

MEDICAL AND RADIOLOGICAL DEVICES GUIDANCE MANUAL. see *PUBLIC HEALTH AND SAFETY*

615　　　US　　ISSN 0958-3947
MEDICAL DOSIMETRY. vol.15, 1990. q. $195 to institutions (effective 1996). (American Association of Medical Dosimetrists) Elsevier Science Inc., 655 Ave. of the Americas, New York, NY 10011. TEL 212-989-5800. FAX 212-633-3990. E-mail: nlinfo@elsevier.nl; usinfo-f@elsevier.com; forinfo-kyf04035@niftyserve.or.jp; Site addr.: http://www.elsevier.nl/. Ed. Ray Garcia. (also avail. in microform from UMI; back issues avail.) **Indexed:** Curr.Adv.Cancer Res. **Document type:** academic/scholarly publication.
—BLDSC (5527.130000); SWETS; UnCover. **CCC.**
Formerly: American Association of Medical Dosimetrists. Journal (ISSN 0739-0211)
Refereed Serial

615　　　JA　　ISSN 0288-450X
MEDICAL IMAGING TECHNOLOGY. (Text in English, Japanese) 1983. 6/yr. 2000 Yen per no. (Nihon Iyo Gazo Kogakkai - Japanese Society of Medical Imaging Technology) Shinohara Shuppan K.K., 11-7, Hongo 2-chome, Bunkyo-ku, Tokyo 113, Japan. FAX 03-3816-5314. Ed. Mikio Yamamoto. **Indexed:** INIS Atomind.
—BLDSC (5527.542000).

615.842　　　US　　ISSN 0942-5373
　　　　　　　　　　　CODEN: MERAED
MEDICAL RADIOLOGY. 1963? irreg. price varies. Springer-Verlag, 175 Fifth Ave., New York, NY 10010. TEL 212-460-1500. FAX 212-473-6272. (Also: Berlin, Heidelberg, Tokyo and Vienna) (reprint service avail. from ISI) **Document type:** academic/scholarly publication.
Formerly (until 1985): Handbuch der Medizinischen Radiologie (ISSN 0085-1396)

616.07　　　US　　ISSN 1081-1915
▼**MEDICAL ULTRASOUND TECHNOLOGY.** 1995. m. Quest Publishing Co., Inc., A Division of Raven Press Ltd. (Subsidiary of: Wolters Kluwer N.V.), 1351 Titan Way, Brea, CA 92621. TEL 714-738-6400. FAX 714-525-6258. (Subscr. to: Raven Press, 1185 Ave. of the Americas, New York, NY 10036. TEL 212-930-9500. FAX 212-869-3495) Pub. Mary Waltham. **Document type:** newsletter.

615.842　　　NE　　ISSN 0025-7664
　　　　　　　　　　　CODEN: MEMUAA
MEDICAMUNDI. (Text in English; summaries in French, German, Spanish) 1955. q. free to qualified personnel. Philips Medical Systems International, P.O. Box 10000, 5680 DA Best, Netherlands. FAX 31-40-762499. (U.S. addr.: c/o Janet Collins, Advertising Manager, Philips Medical Systems, Inc., 710 Bridgeport Ave., Shelton, CT 06484) Ed. Dr. L.C.J. Baghuis. adv.; charts; illus.; stat.; index; circ. 14,000 (controlled). **Indexed:** Biol.Abstr., Chem.Abstr., Excerp.Med., Ind.Med., INSPEC (1968-). **Document type:** academic/scholarly publication.
—BLDSC (5532.300000); CASDDS; EMDOCS.

MEN'EKI KAKU IGAKU/IMMUNONUCLEAR MEDICINE. see *MEDICAL SCIENCES — Allergology And Immunology*

616.842　　　US　　ISSN 1051-1369
　　　　　　　　　　　CODEN: MONEE7
MODERN NEURORADIOLOGY SERIES. 1983. irreg., latest vol.4. price varies. Raven Press (Subsidiary of: Wolters Kluwer N.V.), 1185 Ave. of the Americas, New York, NY 10036. TEL 212-930-9500. FAX 212-869-3495. Ed. Thomas H. Newton. (reprint service avail. from UMI) **Document type:** monographic series.
Refereed Serial

615.842　　　SP
MONOGRAFIAS DE DIAGNOSTICO POR IMAGEN. Short title: M.D.I. 3/yr. 13197 ptas. (effective 1990). Interamericana de Espana, S.A., Manuel Ferrero, 13, 28036 Madrid, Spain. TEL 315-0340. FAX 733-6627. Ed. R. Casanova.

615.842　　　US
N C R P STATEMENTS. 1954. irreg. free. National Council on Radiation Protection and Measurements, 7910 Woodmont Ave., Ste. 800, Bethesda, MD 20814. TEL 301-657-2652. Ed. W. Roger Ney.

615.842　　　UK　　ISSN 0952-3480
　　　　　　　　　　　CODEN: NMRBEF
N M R IN BIOMEDICINE. (Nuclear Magnetic Resonance) 1988. 8/yr. $675 (foreign $675) (effective 1996). John Wiley & Sons Ltd., Journals, Baffins Ln., Chichester, W. Sussex PO19 1UD, England. TEL 01243-779777. FAX 01243-776128. TELEX 86290 WIBOOK G. (Subscr. in the Americas to: John Wiley & Sons, Inc., 605 Third Ave., New York, NY 10158. TEL 212-850-6645. FAX 212-850-6021) Ed. John R. Griffiths. adv. circ. 219. (also avail. in microform from UMI; back issues avail.; reprint service avail. from SWZ) **Document type:** academic/scholarly publication.
—BLDSC (6113.931000); CASDDS; Ei; Faxon; Genuine Article; SWETS; UMI. **CCC.**
Description: Presents original papers in which nuclear magnetic resonance spectroscopy is used for investigating basic biochemical and clinical problems.
Refereed Serial

615.842　　　JA　　ISSN 0439-5956
R895.A1　　　　　　CODEN: HISKBI
NATIONAL INSTITUTE OF RADIOLOGICAL SCIENCES. ANNUAL REPORT. (Text in English) 1961. a. Science and Technology Agency, National Institute of Radiological Sciences - Kagaku Gijutsucho Hoshasen Igaku Sogo Kenkyujo, 9-1 Anagawa 4-chome, Inage-ku, Chiba-shi, Chiba-ken 263, Japan. TEL 0472-51-2111. FAX 0472-56-9616. TELEX 03722205-NIRS-J. Ed. T. Iwakura. circ. 1,400.
—BLDSC (1364.740000).

616.842　　　US　　ISSN 1052-5149
　　　　　　　　　　　CODEN: NCNAEO
NEUROIMAGING CLINICS OF NORTH AMERICA. 1991. q. $130 (foreign $155) (effective 1996). W.B. Saunders Co. (Subsidiary of: Harcourt Brace & Company), The Curtis Center, 3rd Fl., Ed. Dr. Burton P. Drayer, Philadelphia, PA 19106-3399. TEL 215-238-7800. FAX 215-238-6445. (Subscr. to: Periodicals Fulfillment, W.B. Saunders Co., 6277 Sea Harbor Dr., 4th Fl., Orlando, FL 32887-4800. TEL 800-654-2452. FAX 800-874-6418) adv.; index. (also avail. in microform from UMI; back issues avail.) **Indexed:** Excerp.Med. (1993-), Ind.Med. (1994-). **Document type:** academic/scholarly publication.
—BLDSC (6081.372400); UMI.
Description: Covers a single topic in the field in each issue.

615.842　　　GW　　ISSN 0028-3940
RC349.R3
NEURORADIOLOGY; a journal devoted to neuroimaging and interventional neuroradiology. (Text in English) 1970. 8/yr. DM.898($652) (effective 1996). (European Society of Neuroradiology) Springer-Verlag, Heidelberger Platz 3, 14197 Berlin, Germany. TEL 030-8207-0. FAX 030-8214091. E-mail: orders@springer.de. (Subscr. in N. America to: Springer-Verlag New York, Inc., 44 Hartz Way, Secaucus, NJ 07096-2491. TEL 201-348-4033. FAX 201-348-4505) (Co-sponsor: Japanese Neuroradiological Society) Ed.Bd. adv.; charts. (also avail. in microform from UMI; back issues avail.; reprint service avail. from ISI) **Indexed:** Bibl.Dev.Med.& Child Neur., Curr.Adv.Cancer Res., Curr.Adv.Ecol.Sci., Curr.Cont., Dent.Ind., Excerp.Med., Helminthol.Abstr., Ind.Med., Ind.Sci.Rev., Kidney, Rev.Med.& Vet.Mycol. **Document type:** academic/scholarly publication.
—BLDSC (6081.558000); EMDOCS; Faxon; Genuine Article; SWETS; UMI; UnCover. **CCC.**
Description: Covers the diagnosis and treatment of the central nervous system using plain x-rays, computed tomography, angiography, pneumoencephalography and isotope studies, spinal radiographs, myelography, and spinal vascular studies.

616.07　　　NE
NEW CLINICAL APPLICATIONS IN RADIOLOGY. (Text in English) irreg. price varies. Kluwer Academic Publishers, Postbus 17, 3300 AA Dordrecht, Netherlands. TEL 31-78-392392. FAX 31-78-392254. TELEX 29245 KAPG NL. (Dist. by: Kluwer Academic Publishers Group, P.O. Box 322, 3300 AH Dordrecht, Netherlands. TEL 31-78-392392. FAX 31-78-546474; N. America dist. addr.: Box 358, Accord Sta., Hingham, MA 02018-0358. TEL 617-871-6600. FAX 617-871-6528) **Document type:** monographic series.
Refereed Serial

616.07　　　JA
NIHON HOSHASEN GIJUTSU GAKKAI BUNKENSHU. (Text in Japanese) 1974. irreg. Nihon Hoshasen Gijutsu Gakkai - Japanese Society of Radiological Technology, Nijo Puraza, 88, Nishinokyo Kitatsubocho, Nakagyo-ku, Kyoto 604, Japan.

NIHON SEIKEI GEKA CHOONPA KENKYUKAI KAISHI/JAPANESE SOCIETY OF ORTHOPEDIC ULTRASONICS. JOURNAL. see *MEDICAL SCIENCES — Orthopedics And Traumatology*

MEDICAL SCIENCES — RADIOLOGY AND NUCLEAR MEDICINE

615.8   JA   ISSN 0048-0428
                        CODEN: NHGZAR
NIPPON ACTA RADIOLOGICA/NIPPON IGAKU HOSHASEN GAKKAI ZASSHI. (Text in Japanese; table of contents and summaries in English) 1940. m. 12000 Yen. Nippon Societas Radiologica - Japan Radiological Society, Rm. 301 Akamon Habitation, 5-29-13 Hongo, Bunkyo-ku, Tokyo 113, Japan. FAX 03-5684-4075. Ed. Takahiro Kozuka. adv.; bk.rev.; illus. circ. 6,000. **Indexed:** Biol.Abstr., Chem.Abstr., Excerp.Med., Ind.Med., JTA. **Document type:** academic/scholarly publication.
—BLDSC (6113.254000); CASDDS.

612.014   UK   ISSN 0969-8051
R895.A1   CODEN: NMBIEO
NUCLEAR MEDICINE AND BIOLOGY. 1973. 8/yr. $740 to institutions (effective 1996). Elsevier Science Ltd., Pergamon, P.O. Box 800, Kidlington, Oxford OX5 1DX, England. TEL 44-1865-843000. FAX 44-1865-843010. E-mail: nlinfo-f@elsevier.nl; usinfo-f@elsevier.com; forinfo-kyf04035@niftyserve.or.jp; Site addr.: http://www.elsevier.nl/. (Subscr. in U.S. and Canada to: Elsevier Science, 660 White Plains Rd., Tarrytown, NY 10591-5153. TEL 914-524-9200. FAX 914-333-2444) Ed. W.C. Eckelman. adv. circ. 1,200. (also avail. in microfilm from UMI; reprint service avail. from UMI) **Indexed:** Biol.Abstr., Chem.Abstr., Curr.Adv.Ecol.Sci., Curr.Cont., Excerp.Med., Ind.Med., Ind.Sci.Rev., INSPEC, Nutr.Abstr., Sci.Cit.Ind. **Document type:** academic/scholarly publication.
—BLDSC (6180.920500); ADONIS; CASDDS; Faxon; Genuine Article; SWETS; UMI. **CCC.**
Former titles (until 1993): International Journal of Radiation Applications and Instrumentation. Part B: Nuclear Medicine and Biology (ISSN 0883-2897); (until 1985): International Journal of Nuclear Medicine and Biology (ISSN 0047-0740)
Description: Publishes papers examining and proposing new diagnostic and therapeutic procedures as well as new data obtained using established nuclear medical procedures.
Refereed Serial

615.842   US   ISSN 0272-0108
R895.A1   CODEN: NMANDX
NUCLEAR MEDICINE ANNUAL. a. price varies. Raven Press (Subsidiary of: Wolters Kluwer N.V.), 1185 Ave. of the Americas, New York, NY 10036. TEL 212-930-9500. FAX 212-869-3495. Ed. Leonard M. Freeman. (reprint service avail. from UMI) **Indexed:** Biol.Abstr., Chem.Abstr. **Document type:** monographic series.
—BLDSC (6180.921000); CASDDS; Faxon.
Refereed Serial

615.8   UK   ISSN 0143-3636
                        CODEN: NMCODC
NUCLEAR MEDICINE COMMUNICATIONS. 1980. m. £140($259) to individuals; institutions in the E.U. £390 (N. America $670; elsewhere £425) (effective 1995). Chapman & Hall, Journals Department (Subsidiary of: International Thomson Publishing Group), 2-6 Boundary Row, London SE1 8HN, England. TEL 0171-865-0066. FAX 0171-522-9623. TELEX 290164 CHAPMA G. E-mail: journal@chall.mhs.compuserve.com. (Dist. by: International Thomson Publishing Services Ltd., Cheriton House, North Way, Andover, Hants. SP10 5BE, England. TEL 01264-342713. FAX 01264-642807; N. American subsr. to: Chapman & Hall, Journals Promotion Department, One Penn Plaza, 41st Fl., New York, NY 10119. TEL 212-564-1060. FAX 212-564-1505) Ed.Bd. bk.rev.; index. (reprint service avail. from UMI) **Indexed:** Biol.Abstr., Chem.Abstr., Curr.Adv.Cancer Res., Curr.Adv.Ecol.Sci., Curr.Cont., Excerp.Med., Ind.Med. **Document type:** academic/scholarly publication.
—BLDSC (6180.923000); ADONIS; CASDDS; Faxon; Genuine Article; SWETS; UMI. **CCC.**
Description: Describes worldwide research and clinical work in nuclear medicine.
Refereed Serial

NUCLEUS. see *ENERGY — Nuclear Energy*

615.8   GW   ISSN 0029-5566
R895.A1   CODEN: NMIMAX
NUKLEARMEDIZIN/NUCLEAR MEDICINE. (Text in English and German) 1961. 6/yr. DM.238($175) to individuals; institutions DM.328($234). (German Society of Nuclear Medicine) F. K. Schattauer Verlagsgesellschaft mbH, Lenzhalde 3, 70192 Stuttgart, Germany. TEL 0711-22987-0. FAX 0711-22987-50. adv.; bk.rev.; abstr.; bibl.; charts; illus.; index. circ. 1,600. **Indexed:** Biol.Abstr., Chem.Abstr., Curr.Cont., Excerp.Med., Ind.Med., Risk Abstr. **Document type:** academic/scholarly publication.
—BLDSC (6184.453000); CASDDS; EMDOCS; Faxon; Genuine Article; SWETS. **CCC.**
Description: Original material covering experimental and clinical research with radionuclides, radionuclide imaging, new concepts of functional imaging, case reports.

615.842   GW   ISSN 0723-7065
                        CODEN: NKLZD8
DER NUKLEARMEDIZINER. (Text in German; summaries in English) 1977. 5/yr. DM.180. (Berufsverband Deutscher Nuklearmediziner) Demeter Verlag GmbH und Co. KG, Bussardstr. 5, 82166 Graefelfing, Germany. TEL 089-85463-0. FAX 089-8543347. Ed. Dr. D.W. Nitz. circ. 1,800. **Document type:** academic/scholarly publication.
—BLDSC (6184.485000); CASDDS; Genuine Article.

616.842   AU
OE R G MITTEILUNGEN. q. (Oesterreichische Roentgengesellschaft) Blackwell Wissenschafts-Verlag GmbH, Feldgasse 13, A-1238 Vienna, Austria. TEL 0222-8893646. FAX 0222-8893647. Ed. G. Mostbeck. **Document type:** academic/scholarly publication.

615.842   US   ISSN 0000-1457
R895.A4
OFFICIAL AMERICAN BOARD OF MEDICAL SPECIALTIES (A B M S) DIRECTORY OF BOARD CERTIFIED NUCLEAR MEDICINE SPECIALISTS. 1984. biennial. $119.95. Marquis Who's Who, A Reed Reference Publishing company, 121 Chanlon Rd., New Providence, NJ 07974. TEL 908-464-6800. FAX 908-665-2898. Ed. Roy Crego. **Document type:** directory.
Formerly (until 1992): A B M S Directory of Certified Nuclear Medicine Specialists (ISSN 0884-1454)
Description: Biographical sketches of U.S. certified medical specialists sorted alphabetically with a geographical index.

615.842   US   ISSN 0000-166X
R895.A4
OFFICIAL AMERICAN BOARD OF MEDICAL SPECIALTIES (A B M S) DIRECTORY OF BOARD CERTIFIED RADIOLOGISTS AND RADIOLOGICAL PHYSICISTS. 1985. biennial. $119.95. Marquis Who's Who, A Reed Reference Publishing company, 121 Chanlon Rd., New Providence, NJ 07974-9903. TEL 908-464-6800. FAX 908-665-2898. (Subscr. to: Order Dept., Box 31, New Providence, NJ 07974-9903. TEL 800-521-8110) Ed. Roy Crego. **Document type:** directory.
Formerly: A B M S Directory of Certified Radiologists (ISSN 0883-1238)
Description: Biographical sketches of U.S. certified medical specialists sorted alphabetically with a geographical index.

ORAL RADIOLOGY. see *MEDICAL SCIENCES — Dentistry*

PEDIATRIC RADIOLOGY; roentgenology, nuclear medicine, ultrasonics, CT, MRI. see *MEDICAL SCIENCES — Pediatrics*

615.842   US   ISSN 0273-0278
                        CODEN: PORADD
POSTGRADUATE RADIOLOGY; a journal of continuing education. 1981. q. $83 to individuals (foreign $90); institutions $109 (foreign $116); students $49 (foreign $56). Mosby - Year Book, Inc. (Subsidiary of: Times Mirror Company), 11830 Westline Industrial Dr., St. Louis, MO 63146. TEL 314-872-8370; 800-325-4177. FAX 314-432-1380. TELEX 44-2402. Ed. Dr. Herbert L. Abrams. adv.; bk.rev.; abstr.; index. circ. 1,500. (back issues avail.) **Indexed:** Excerp.Med.
—BLDSC (6563.906500); UMI; UnCover. **CCC.**
Description: Provides timely review articles and abstracts of current literature.

PROGRESS IN NUCLEAR MAGNETIC RESONANCE SPECTROSCOPY. see *CHEMISTRY — Analytical Chemistry*

612.014   IT
R61   CODEN: JNMSD3
QUARTERLY JOURNAL OF NUCLEAR MEDICINE. (Text and summaries in English) 1957. q. L.80000($90) to individuals; institutions $140 (effective 1995). (Italian Association of Nuclear Medicine) Edizioni Minerva Medica, Corso Bramante 83-85, 10126 Turin, Italy. TEL 39-11-678282. FAX 39-11-3121736. (Co-sponsor: International Association of Radiopharmacology) Ed. G. Lucignani; Pub. Alberto Oliaro. adv.: B&W page $1100, color page $1900; trim 215 x 280; adv. contact: F. Filippo. bk.rev.; bibl.; charts; illus.; index; circ. 3,000 (paid). (also avail. in microform from UMI; reprint service avail. from UMI) **Indexed:** C.I.S. Abstr., Chem.Abstr., Curr.Adv.Ecol.Sci., Curr.Cont., Dairy Sci.Abstr., Excerp.Med., Ind.Med., Ind.Sci.Rev., INIS Atomind., INSPEC, Nutr.Abstr. **Document type:** academic/scholarly publication.
—CASDDS; Faxon; SWETS; UMI; UnCover.
Former titles (until 1995): Journal of Nuclear Biology and Medicine (ISSN 1121-1075); (until 1991): Journal of Nuclear Medicine and Allied Sciences (ISSN 0392-0208); Minerva Mediconucleare (ISSN 0026-4857); Minerva Nuclear Medical Section.
Refereed Serial

615.842   US
R B M A BULLETIN; progress through sharing. vol.23, no.11, 1988. m. $100 to non-members (foreign $110). Radiology Business Management Association, 2755 Bristol St., No. 110, Costa Mesa, CA 92626. TEL 714-833-1651. Ed. Sharon Urch. adv.; bk.rev. **Document type:** bulletin.

616.07   JA
R E R F UPDATE. (Text in English) q. Radiation Effects Research Foundation, 5-2 Hijiyama Koen, Minami-ku, Hiroshima-shi, Hiroshima-ken 732, Japan. FAX 81-82-263-7279. E-mail: magura@rerf.or.jp. Ed. S. Abrahamson. **Document type:** newsletter.

615.842   US
R R S NEWS. q. membership. Radiation Research Society, 2021 Spring Rd., Ste. 600, Oak Brook, IL 60564. TEL 708-571-2881. Ed. R.J.M. Fry. circ. 1,500. (looseleaf format) **Document type:** newsletter.

615.842   US   ISSN 1041-2182
R T IMAGE. (Radiologic Technology) 1988. bi-w. $13 (free to radiology department managers). Valley Forge Press, 1288 Valley Forge Rd., Box 1135, Valley Forge, PA 19482. TEL 610-935-3302; 800-9VF-PRES. FAX 610-935-3072. E-mail: vpfedit@aol.com. Ed. Beverly Hamill. bk.rev.; charts; illus. circ. 65,000.
Description: Contains items of interest to radiology managers and radiologic science professionals in all modalities and in hospitals, free-standing centers, and schools.

615.842   UK   ISSN 0264-6412
RAD FOR RADIOGRAPHERS, RADIOLOGISTS AND RADIOTHERAPISTS. 1975. m. £54 (Europe £63). Kingsmoor Publications Ltd., P.O. Box 3, Harlow, Essex CM19 4RF, England. TEL 01279-429731. FAX 01279-441038. Eds. D.G. Messer, D.J. Roberts. adv.: page £1095; trim 419 x 297; adv. contact: D.J. Roberts. bk.rev.; software rev.; video rev. circ. 15,000. (tabloid format) **Document type:** trade publication.
Incorporates: Consultant Radiologist and Radiotherapist.

616.07   JA
RADIATION EFFECTS RESEARCH FOUNDATION. ANNUAL REPORT. (Text in English) a. Radiation Effects Research Foundation - Hoshasen Eikyo Kenkyujo, 5-2 Hijiyama Koen, Minami-ku, Hiroshima-shi, Hiroshima-ken 732, Japan.

616.07   JA
RADIATION EFFECTS RESEARCH FOUNDATION. COMMENTARY AND REVIEW SERIES. (Text in English; summaries in English, Japanese) 1989. irreg. Radiation Effects Research Foundation - Hoshasen Eikyo Kenkyujo, 5-2 Hijiyama Koen, Minami-ku, Hiroshima-shi, Hiroshima-ken 732, Japan.

MEDICAL SCIENCES — RADIOLOGY AND NUCLEAR MEDICINE

616.07   JA
RADIATION EFFECTS RESEARCH FOUNDATION. TECHNICAL REPORT/HOSHASEN EIKYO KENKYUJO GYOSEKI HOKOKUSHO. (Text in English, Japanese) 1975. irreg. Radiation Effects Research Foundation - Hoshasen Eikyo Kenkyujo, 5-2, Hijiyama Koen, Minami-ku, Hiroshima-shi, Hiroshima-ken 732, Japan.

616.07   JA
RADIATION EFFECTS RESEARCH FOUNDATION NEWSLETTER/HOEIKEN NYUZU RETA. (Text in Japanese) 1975. m. Radiation Effects Research Foundation - Hoshasen Eikyo Kenkyujo, 5-2, Hijiyama Koen, Minami-ku, Hiroshima-shi, Hiroshima-ken 732, Japan. **Document type:** newsletter.

615.842 616.99   JA   ISSN 0288-2043
CODEN: RAMEER
RADIATION MEDICINE; medical imaging and radiation oncology. 1983. bi-m. 12000 Yen($80) Radiation Medicine Association, University of Tokyo, Faculty of Medicine, Department of Radiology, 7-3-1 Hongo, Bunkyo-ku, Tokyo 113, Japan. (Subscr. to: Igaku-Shoin Medical Publishers Inc., 1140 Ave. of the Americas, New York, N.Y. 10036, U.S.A.. TEL 212-944-7540) Ed. Masahiro Iio. adv. circ. 1,500. **Indexed:** Excerp.Med., Ind.Med.
—BLDSC (7227.975000); CASDDS; Faxon; SWETS; UnCover.

615.842   US
RADIATION ONCOLOGY NEWS. 1986. 4/yr. $50 (foreign $60). Society for Radiation Oncology Administrators, 2021 Spring Rd., Ste. 600, Oak Brook, IL 60521. FAX 708-571-7837. Ed. Rita Cipollo. bibl.; tr.lit. circ. 275. (back issues avail.)
Formerly (until vol.4, 1990): S R O A Newsletter.

615.842   US
RADIATION THERAPIST. 1992. s-a. $25. American Society of Radiologic Technologists, 15000 Central Ave., S.E., Albuquerque, NM 87123. TEL 505-298-4500. FAX 505-298-5063. Ed. Ceela McElveny. adv. circ. 13,000. **Document type:** academic/scholarly publication.

615.832   RU   ISSN 0869-8031
CODEN: RBIRE
RADIATSIONNAYA BIOLOGIYA, RADIOEKOLOGIYA. 1961. bi-m. 33.30 Rub.($125) (Rossiiskaya Akademiya Nauk, Otdelenie Biokhimii, Biofiziki i Khimii Fiziologicheski Aktivnykh Soedinenii) Izdatel'stvo Nauka, 90 Profsoyuznaya ul., 117864 Moscow, Russia. TEL 095-336-0266. FAX 095-420-2220. (Dist. in U.S. by: Victor Kamkin Inc., 4956 Boiling Brook Pkwy., Rockville, MD 20852. TEL 301-881-5973. FAX 301-881-1637) Ed. E.B. Burlakova. bk.rev.; index. (tabloid format) **Indexed:** Biol.Abstr., Chem.Abstr., Excerp.Med., Ind.Med., INSPEC (1981-), Int.Aerosp.Abstr. **Document type:** academic/scholarly publication.
—BLDSC (0136.620000); CASDDS; EMDOCS. CCC.
Formerly (until no.4, 1993): Radiobiologiya (ISSN 0033-8192)

615.842   AT   ISSN 0033-8273
CODEN: RDGRAJ
RADIOGRAPHER. 1948. q. Aus.$45. Australian Institute of Radiography, Attn: E.M. Hughes, Sec., P.O. Box 1169, Collingwood, Vic. 3066, Australia. TEL 61-3-419-3336. FAX 61-3-416-0783. Ed. E.M. Hughes. adv.; bk.rev.; abstr.; illus.; index. circ. 2,900. **Indexed:** Chem.Abstr., INSPEC.
—BLDSC (7236.850000); CASDDS; UnCover.

615.842   US   ISSN 0271-5333
RC78.A1
RADIOGRAPHICS. 1981. bi-m. $90 (foreign $100). Radiological Society of North America, Inc., 2021 Spring Rd., Ste. 600, Oak Brook, IL 60521-1860. TEL 708-571-2670. FAX 708-571-7837. (Subscr. to: 1991 Northampton St., Easton, PA 18042-3189. TEL 215-250-7277) Ed. William W. Olmsted. adv. contact: Tom Shimala. circ. 26,089. (also avail. in microform from UMI) **Indexed:** Curr.Cont., Ind.Med. **Document type:** academic/scholarly publication.
—BLDSC (7236.900000); Faxon; Genuine Article; SWETS; UMI; UnCover. CCC.

615.842   UK   ISSN 1078-8174
CODEN: RATOEO
RADIOGRAPHY; an international journal of diagnostic imaging and radiation therapy. 1935. q. £56 to individuals (outside Europe $100); institutions £112 (outside Europe $200) (effective 1996). (College of Radiographers) W.B. Saunders Co. Ltd. (Subsidiary of: Harcourt Brace & Company Ltd.), 24-28 Oval Rd., London NW1 7DX, England. TEL 0171-267-4466. FAX 0171-482-2293. Ed. H. Brian Bentley. adv.: half page £200; adv. contact: Greg Holt. bk.rev.; charts; illus.; index. circ. 2,000. (reprint service avail.) **Indexed:** Biol.Abstr., CINAHL, Curr.Adv.Ecol.Sci., Ind.Med. **Document type:** academic/scholarly publication.
—BLDSC (7237.037000); SWETS; UnCover.
Formerly (until 1995): Radiography Today (ISSN 0954-8211); Formed by the 1988 merger of: Radiography (ISSN 0033-8281); Radiography News (ISSN 0144-5510)
Description: Reports original clinical and scientific research in all aspects of the field.
Refereed Serial

RADIOKHIMIYA. see CHEMISTRY — Physical Chemistry

616.842   GW
RADIOLIT; radiologische Literatur. 1992. a. DM.99. Georg Thieme Verlag, Ruedigerstr. 14, 70469 Stuttgart, Germany. TEL 0711-8931-0. FAX 0711-8931298. (Subscr. to: Postfach 104853, 70042 Stuttgart, Germany) (diskette format)

615.842   GW   ISSN 0033-832X
CODEN: RDLGBC
DER RADIOLOGE; die Fachzeitschrift fuer bildgebende Verfahren, Radioonkologie und Nuklearmedizin. (Text in German; summaries in English) 1961. m. DM.520($377) (effective 1996). Springer-Verlag, Heidelberger Platz 3, 14197 Berlin, Germany. TEL 030-8207-0. FAX 030-8214091. E-mail: orders@springer.de. (Subscr. in N. America to: Springer-Verlag New York, Inc., 44 Hartz Way, Secaucus, NJ 07096-2491. TEL 201-348-4033. FAX 201-348-4505) Ed.Bd. adv.; bk.rev.; charts; illus.; index. (also avail. in microform from UMI; back issues avail.; reprint service avail. from ISI) **Indexed:** Biol.Abstr., Curr.Cont., Dent.Ind., Excerp.Med., Helminthol.Abstr., Ind.Med., INIS Atomind., Rev.Med.& Vet.Mycol. **Document type:** academic/scholarly publication.
●Also available online. Vendor(s): FIZ Technik.
—BLDSC (7237.700000); EMDOCS; Faxon; Genuine Article; SWETS; UMI. CCC.
Description: Discusses diagnostic techniques in the field.

615.842   SP   ISSN 0033-8338
RADIOLOGIA. 1958. m. (9/yr.). 10300 ptas.($105) (effective 1995). (Sociedad Espanola de Radiologia y Electrologia Medicas y de Medicina Nuclear) Editorial Garsi, S.A., Juan Bravo 46, 28006 Madrid, Spain. TEL 34-1-4021212. FAX 34-1-4020954. Dir. Dr. L. Ramos Gonzalez. adv.; bk.rev.; abstr.; bibl.; charts; illus.; stat.; index. circ. 3,000. **Indexed:** Biol.Abstr., Curr.Cont., Excerp.Med., Helminthol.Abstr., Ind.Med.Esp.
—BLDSC (7237.730000); EMDOCS.

615.842   BL   ISSN 0100-3984
RADIOLOGIA BRASILEIRA. 1958. 6/yr. $50. Colegio Brasileiro de Radiologia, Departamento da Associacao Medica Brasileira, Av. Paulista, 491, 13a andar, 01311-909 Sao Paulo, Brazil. TEL 55-11-285-4022. Ed. Dr. Giovanni Guido Cerri. circ. 3,000. **Document type:** newspaper.
Description: Publishes original works in radiology, ultrasonography, nuclear medicine, radiotherapy, magnetic resonance and tomography.

615.842   IT   ISSN 0033-8362
RADIOLOGIA MEDICA. (Text in Italian; summaries in English, Italian) 1914. m. $130 to individuals; institutions $160 (effective 1995). (Societa Italiana di Radiologia Medica) Edizioni Minerva Medica, Corso Bramante 83-85, 10126 Turin, Italy. TEL 39-11-678282. FAX 39-11-3121736. Ed. L. DiGuglielmo; Pub. Alberto Oliaro. adv.: B&W page $1400, color page $2300; trim 215 x 280; adv. contact: F. Filippo. bk.rev.; bibl.; charts; illus.; index. circ. 6,500. (also avail. in microform from UMI; reprint service avail. from UMI) **Indexed:** Biol.Abstr., Chem.Abstr., Dent.Ind., Excerp.Med., Ind.Med. **Document type:** academic/scholarly publication.
—BLDSC (7237.800000); EMDOCS; Faxon; SWETS; UMI.
Formerly: Minerva Radiologica (ISSN 0026-4962)
Description: Covers imaging diagnostics and radiotherapy.
Refereed Serial

615.842   US   ISSN 0033-8389
RM846   CODEN: RCNAAU
RADIOLOGIC CLINICS OF NORTH AMERICA. 1963. bi-m. $149 (foreign $185) (effective 1996). W.B. Saunders Co. (Subsidiary of: Harcourt Brace & Company), Curtis Center, 3rd Fl., Independence Sq. W., Philadelphia, PA 19106-3399. TEL 215-238-7800. FAX 215-238-6445. (Subscr. to: Periodicals Fulfillment, W.B. Saunders Co., 6277 Sea Harbor Dr., 4th Fl., Orlando, FL 32891-4800. TEL 800-654-2452. FAX 800-874-6418) Ed. Melissa Mitchell. illus. (also avail. in microform from MIM,UMI; reprint service avail. from UMI) **Indexed:** AIM, Biol.Abstr., Curr.Adv.Ecol.Sci., Curr.Cont., Dent.Ind., Excerp.Med., Ind.Med. **Document type:** academic/scholarly publication.
●Also available online. Vendor(s): Ovid Technologies.
—BLDSC (7237.830000); EMDOCS; Faxon; Genuine Article; SWETS; UMI; UnCover. CCC.

615.842   US   ISSN 0033-8397
CODEN: RATIB3
RADIOLOGIC TECHNOLOGY. 1929. bi-m. $49 (foreign $75). American Society of Radiologic Technologists, 15000 Central Ave. S.E., Albuquerque, NM 87123-3917. TEL 505-298-4500. FAX 505-298-5063. Ed. Ceela McElveny. adv.; bk.rev.; bibl.; charts; illus.; index, cum.index: vols.26-35; circ. 40,000 (paid). (also avail. in microform from MIM,WWS) **Indexed:** Biol.Abstr., Chem.Abstr., CINAHL, Excerp.Med., Hosp.Lit.Ind., Ind.Med. **Document type:** academic/scholarly publication.
—BLDSC (7237.850000); Faxon; SWETS; UnCover.
Refereed Serial

616.842   US   ISSN 0888-8086
RADIOLOGICAL HEALTH BULLETIN. 1967. m. U.S. Food and Drug Administration, Center for Devices and Radiological Health, 5600 Fishers Ln., Rockville, MD 20857. TEL 301-443-5860. FAX 301-227-6834. (Subscr. to: National Technical Information Service, 5285 Port Royal Rd., Springfield, VA 22161. TEL 703-487-4630. FAX 703-321-8547) Ed. Mickie Kivel. circ. 4,000. **Document type:** bulletin, government publication.
●Also available online.

616.842   GW   ISSN 0935-1779
RADIOLOGIE ASSISTENT. 4/yr. DM.26. Schmidt-Roemhild Verlag, Mengstr. 16, 23552 Luebeck, Germany. TEL 0451-1605-0. FAX 0451-1605253. **Document type:** trade publication.

615.842   US
RADIOLOGISCHE KLINIK. 1983. irreg. price varies. Springer-Verlag, 175 Fifth Ave., New York, NY 10010. TEL 212-460-1500. FAX 212-473-6272. (Also: Berlin, Heidelberg, Tokyo and Vienna) **Document type:** academic/scholarly publication.

616.07   US   ISSN 1069-1286
CODEN: RIOLEC
▼**THE RADIOLOGIST.** 1994. bi-m. Williams & Wilkins, 428 E. Preston St., Baltimore, MD 21202. TEL 410-528-4000; 800-638-6423. FAX 410-528-4312. **Indexed:** Excerp.Med. (1995-). **Document type:** academic/scholarly publication.
—BLDSC (7237.996000).

MEDICAL SCIENCES — RADIOLOGY AND NUCLEAR MEDICINE

615.842 US ISSN 0033-8419
RC78 CODEN: RADLAX
RADIOLOGY; a monthly journal devoted to clinical radiology and allied sciences. 1915. m. $195 (foreign $235). Radiological Society of North America, Inc., 2021 Spring Rd., Ste. 600, Oak Brook, IL 60521-1860. TEL 708-571-2670. FAX 708-571-7837. (Subscr. to: 1991 Northampton St., Easton, PA 18042-3189. TEL 610-250-7277) Ed. Dr. Stanley S. Siegelman. adv. contact: Tom Shimala. bk.rev.; abstr.; charts; illus.; index, cum.index every 3 yrs. circ. 35,684. (also avail. in microform from UMI; reprint service avail. from UMI) **Indexed:** AIM, Bibl.Dev.Med.& Child Neur., Biol.Abstr., Biotech.Abstr., C.I.S. Abstr., Cadscan, Chem.Abstr., Curr.Adv.Cancer Res., Curr.Adv.Ecol.Sci., Curr.Adv.Genetics & Molec.Biol., Curr.Cont., Dairy Sci.Abstr., Dent.Ind., Excerp.Med., Helminthol.Abstr., I.P.A., Ind.Med., INSPEC (1980-), Int.Nurs.Ind., Kidney, Lead Abstr., Med.& Surg.Dermat., Rev.Med.& Vet.Mycol., Rev.Plant Path., Zincscan. **Document type:** academic/scholarly publication.
●Also available online.
—BLDSC (7238.000000); CASDDS; EMDOCS; Faxon; Genuine Article; SWETS; UMI; UnCover. **CCC**.

615.842 US ISSN 0741-160X
RADIOLOGY AND IMAGING LETTER. 1981. s-m. (m. in Jan. & Aug.). $274 (foreign $315). Quest Publishing Co., Inc., A Division of Raven Press Ltd. (Subsidiary of: Wolters Kluwer N.V.), 1351 Titan Way, Brea, CA 92621. TEL 714-738-6400. FAX 714-525-6528. (Subscr. to: Raven Press, 1185 Ave. of the Americas, New York, NY 10036. TEL 212-930-9500. FAX 212-869-3495) Pub. Mary Waltham. bk.rev.; charts; illus.; tr.lit.; index. (looseleaf format; back issues avail.) **Document type:** newsletter.
—UMI. **CCC**.
Formerly (until 1984): Radiology Letter (ISSN 0273-4958)
Description: For clinical professionals. Covers latest advances in all areas of diagnostic imaging, radiation therapy and nuclear medicine, as well as safety hazards, recalls, legislation, products, legal issues and education.

615.842 XV ISSN 1318-2099
CODEN: RDIUA4
RADIOLOGY AND ONCOLOGY. (Text in English) 1964. q. $50 to individuals; institutions $100. Onkoloski Institut - Institute of Oncology, Vrazov trg 4, 61000 Ljubljana, Slovenia. TEL 386-61-1320068. FAX 386-61-1314180. (Co-sponsor: Assembly of the Research Community of Slovenia) Ed. Dr. Tomaz Benulic. adv.; bk.rev.; abstr.; illus. circ. 1,500. (reprint service avail. from IRC) **Indexed:** Chem.Abstr., Excerp.Med.
—BLDSC (7238.120000); CASDDS.
Formerly (until vol.25, 1991): Radiologia Iugoslavica (ISSN 0485-893X)
Description: Covers radiology, radiotherapy, oncology, nuclear medicine, radiophysics, radiobiology and radiation protection.

RADIOLOGY MANAGEMENT. see HOSPITALS

615.842 US
RADIOLOGY OF IATROGENIC DISORDERS. 1981. irreg. price varies. Springer-Verlag, 175 Fifth Ave., New York, NY 10010. TEL 212-460-1500. FAX 212-473-6272. (Also: Berlin, Heidelberg, Tokyo and Vienna) (reprint service avail. from ISI) **Document type:** academic/scholarly publication.

RADIOLOGY ONCOLOGY INVESTIGATIONS. see MEDICAL SCIENCES — Oncology

615.842 US ISSN 1063-8563
RADIOLOGY RESIDENT. 1992. bi-m. $44. Slack, Inc., 6900 Grove Rd., Thorofare, NJ 08086. TEL 609-848-1000. FAX 609-853-5991. adv.: B&W page $2000, color page $3000; trim 8 1/8 x 10 7/8. circ. 6,172.

615.842 US
RADIOLOGY TODAY (NEW YORK). 1981. irreg. price varies. Springer-Verlag, 175 Fifth Ave., New York, NY 10010. TEL 212-460-1500. FAX 212-473-6272. (Also: Berlin, Heidelberg, Tokyo and Vienna) (reprint service avail. from ISI) **Document type:** academic/scholarly publication.

615.842 US ISSN 0893-1054
RADIOLOGY TODAY (THOROFARE). 1983. m. $110 to individuals; institutions $120. Slack, Inc., 6900 Grove Rd., Thorofare, NJ 08086. TEL 609-848-1000. FAX 609-853-5991. Ed. Dr. Jack G. Rabinowitz. adv. circ. 27,000. (reprint service avail.)
—**CCC**.

616.6 US
▼**RADIONUCLIDES IN NEPHROUROLOGY.** Announced for publication in 1996. q. $125 to individuals; institutions $170 (effective 1996). Field & Wood, Medical Periodicals, Inc., Box 975, Blue Bell, PA 19422. TEL 610-828-4010. FAX 215-482-0226. Ed. Dr. O'Reilly. **Document type:** academic/scholarly publication.
Refereed Serial

615.842 IE ISSN 0167-8140
CODEN: RAONDT
RADIOTHERAPY AND ONCOLOGY. (Text in English) m. I£788($1245) (effective 1996). (European Society for Therapeutic Radiology and Oncology) Elsevier Science Ireland Ltd., P.O. Box 85, Limerick, Ireland. TEL 353-61-471944. FAX 353-61-472144. (Subscr. in U.S. and Canada to: Elsevier Science Inc., Box 882, Madison Sq. Sta., New York, NY 10159. TEL 212-989-5800. FAX 212-633-3990) Eds. H. Bartelink, J. Overgaard. adv.; index. (also avail. in microform from UMI; back issues avail.; reprint service avail. from SWZ) **Indexed:** ASCA, Chem.Abstr., Curr.Adv.Cancer Res., Curr.Adv.Ecol.Sci., Curr.Cont., Excerp.Med., Ind.Med., Med.& Surg.Dermat. **Document type:** academic/scholarly publication.
—BLDSC (7240.790000); ADONIS; CASDDS; Faxon; Genuine Article; SWETS; UnCover. **CCC**.
Description: Covers areas of interest relating to radiation oncology.
Refereed Serial

615.8 IT ISSN 0390-7740
CODEN: RAYSDQ
RAYS; international journal of radiological sciences. (Text in English; summaries in Italian) 1976. 4/yr. L.264000($160) (effective 1996). (Universita Cattolica del Sacro Cuore, Istituto di Radiologia) Pensiero Scientifico Editore s.r.l., Via Bradano 3-C, 00199 Rome, Italy. TEL 39-6-86207158. FAX 39-6-86207160. Ed. Pasquale Marano. adv.: B&W page L.990000, color page L.1550000; trim 160 x 230. abstr.; charts; illus.; stat. circ. 1,000. **Indexed:** Biol.Abstr., Chem.Abstr., Excerp.Med.
—BLDSC (7298.087000); CASDDS.
Description: Provides an internation forum for the discussion of physical, biological, clinical, and technical problems involved in the use of radiation in medicine.

REFERATOVY VYBER Z RADIODIAGNOSTIKY/ABSTRACTS OF RADIOLOGY. see MEDICAL SCIENCES — Abstracting, Bibliographies, Statistics

616 615 BU ISSN 0486-400X
CODEN: RENRAR
RENTGENOLOGIJA I RADIOLOGIJA. (Text in Bulgarian; summaries in Russian and English) 1962. q. 16 lv.($5) (Ministerstvo na Narodnoto Zdrave) Izdatelstvo Meditsina i Fizkultura, 11, Pl. Slaveikov, Sofia, Bulgaria. (Dist. by: Hemus, 6, Rouski Blvd., 1000 Sofia, Bulgaria) (Co-sponsor: Nauchno Druzhestvo po Rentgenologija i Radiologija) Ed. J.V. Nikolov. circ. 620. **Indexed:** Abstr.Bulg.Sci.Med.Lit., Chem.Abstr., Excerp.Med. (until 1993).
—CASDDS.

616.842 BL ISSN 0100-9699
REVISTA DA IMAGEM. (Text in Portuguese; summaries in English, Portuguese) 1978. q. $40 (effective July 1992). Sociedade Paulista de Radiologia, Av. Paulista, 491, 4o andar, 01311-909 Sao Paulo, SP, Brazil. TEL 11-284-3988. FAX 11-284-3152. Ed. Antonio S. Clemente Filho. circ. 3,000.
Description: Covers imaging methods for medical diagnosis, research, and clinical applications.

615.842 RM ISSN 0481-6684
CODEN: ROORD
REVISTA DE CHIRURGIE, ONCOLOGIE, RADIOLOGIE, O.R.L, OFTALMOLOGIE, STOMATOLOGIE. RADIOLOGIE. (Text in Rumanian; summaries in English, French, German, Russian) 1956. 4/yr. $20. Uniunea Societatilor de Stiinte Medicale din Republica Socialista Rumania, Str. Progresului No. 8-10, Sectorul 1, R-70754 Bucharest, Rumania. (Subscr. to: ILEXIM, Str. 13 Decembrie Nr. 3, P.O. Box 136-137, Bucharest, Rumania) Ed.Bd. adv.; bk.rev. **Indexed:** Excerp.Med. (until 1993).
Supersedes in part: Oncologia si Radiologia (ISSN 0030-2406)

615.842 SP ISSN 0212-6982
REVISTA ESPANOLA DE MEDICINA NUCLEAR. (Supplement avail.: Revista Espanola de Medicina Nuclear. Supplemento (ISSN 0213-814X)) 1982. bi-m. 6900 ptas.($75) (effective 1995). (Sociedad Espanola de Medicina Nuclear) Editorial Garsi, S.A., Juan Bravo 46, 28006 Madrid, Spain. TEL 34-1-4021212. FAX 34-1-4020954. Ed. A. Gomez Embuena. circ. 1,000. **Indexed:** Excerp.Med. (1992-).

615.842 JA ISSN 0009-9252
CODEN: JJCRA
RINSHO HOSHASEN/JAPANESE JOURNAL OF CLINICAL RADIOLOGY. Variant title: Clinical Radiology. (Text in Japanese; summaries in English) 1956. m. 1900 Yen per no. Kanehara Shuppan Co. Ltd., P.O. Box 1, Hongo Post Office, Tokyo 113-91, Japan. TEL 03-3811-7163. Ed. Dr. Katsutoshi Yoshimura. abstr.; charts; illus.; index. circ. 4,700. **Indexed:** Dent.Ind., Excerp.Med., Ind.Med., Ind.Sci.Rev. **Document type:** academic/scholarly publication.
—BLDSC (4651.430000).

615.842 616.8 IT ISSN 1120-9976
RIVISTA DI NEURORADIOLOGIA; periodico quadrimestrale scientifico indipendente. (Text in Italian; summaries in English) 1988. q. L.200000. (Societa Italiana di Neuroradiologia) Edizioni del Cantauro, Via Cosattini 32, 33100 Udine, Italy. TEL 39-337-532604. FAX 39-432-59901109. Ed. Marco Leonardi. adv.: page L.5000000. bk.rev. circ. 1,900. **Indexed:** Excerp.Med., Ref.Zh.
—BLDSC (7991.435000); Genuine Article.
Refereed Serial

615.842 GW ISSN 0936-6652
CODEN: RFGVEF
ROEFO. FORTSCHRITTE AUF DEM GEBIETE DER ROENTGENSTRAHLEN UND DER NEUEN BILDGEBENDEN VERFAHREN. (Summaries in English, French, German and Spanish) 1897. m. DM.594. (Deutsche Roentgengesellschaft) Georg Thieme Verlag, Ruedigerstr. 14, 70469 Stuttgart, Germany. TEL 0711-8931-0. FAX 0711-8931298. (Subscr. to: Postfach 104853, 70042 Stuttgart, Germany) (Co-sponsor: Oesterreichische Roentgengesellschaft) Ed.Bd. adv.; bk.rev.; abstr.; bibl.; charts; illus.; stat.; index. circ. 3,100. (also avail. in microform from UMI; reprint service avail. from UMI) **Indexed:** Biol.Abstr., C.I.S. Abstr., Chem.Abstr., Curr.Cont., Dairy Sci.Abstr., Dent.Ind., Excerp.Med., Helminthol.Abstr., Ind.Med., Ind.Sci.Rev., Rev.Med.& Vet.Mycol., Sci.Cit.Ind. **Document type:** academic/scholarly publication.
—BLDSC (8019.170000); CASDDS; Faxon; Genuine Article; SWETS; UMI. **CCC**.
Former titles: RoeFo. Fortschritte auf dem Gebiete der Roentgenstrahlen und der Nuklearmedizin (ISSN 0340-1618); Fortschritte auf dem Gebiete der Roentgenstrahlen und der Nuklearmedizin (ISSN 0015-8151)

615.842 II ISSN 0303-2590
ROENTGEN TECHNOLOGY. (Text in English) 1974. s-a. Rs.10($3) Indian Association of Radiological Technologists, Postgraduate Institute of Medical Education and Research, Dept. of Radiology, Chandigarh, India.

MEDICAL SCIENCES — RADIOLOGY AND NUCLEAR MEDICINE

615.842   GW   ISSN 0035-7820
CODEN: RGPXB2
ROENTGENPRAXIS; Bildgebende Diagnostik, Strahlentherapie, Nuklearmedizin. 1947. m. DM.231. S. Hirzel Verlag, Postfach 101061, 70009 Stuttgart, Germany. TEL 0711-2582-0. FAX 0711-2582290. Ed. Dr. Paul Gerhardt. adv.; bk.rev.; charts; illus.; index. circ. 3,200. Indexed: Chem.Abstr., Dent.Ind., Excerp.Med., Ind.Med. Document type: academic/scholarly publication.
—BLDSC (8021.700000); EMDOCS; SWETS. **CCC**.
   Description: Examines the various aspects of radiology and nuclear medicine.

612   US   ISSN 0739-9529
CODEN: SIRAE5
SEMINARS IN INTERVENTIONAL RADIOLOGY. 1984. q. $95 to individuals (foreign $120); institutions $132 (foreign $157). Thieme Medical Publishers, Inc., 381 Park Ave. S., Ste. 1501, New York, NY 10016. TEL 212-683-5088. FAX 212-779-9020. Ed. Peter Mueller. adv.; abstr.; bibl; illus. circ. 2,100. Document type: academic/scholarly publication.
—BLDSC (8239.453000); Faxon; Genuine Article; UMI; UnCover. **CCC**.

615.842   US   ISSN 0001-2998
CODEN: SMNMAB
SEMINARS IN NUCLEAR MEDICINE. 1971. q. $160 (foreign $200) (effective 1996). W.B. Saunders Co. (Subsidiary of: Harcourt Brace & Company), Curtis Center, 3rd Fl., Independence Sq. W., Philadelphia, PA 19106-3399. TEL 215-238-7800. FAX 215-238-6445. (Subscr. to: Periodicals Fulfillment, W.B. Saunders Co., 6277 Sea Harbor Dr., 4th Fl., Orlando, FL 32891-4800. TEL 800-654-2452. FAX 800-874-6418) Eds. Drs. M. Donald Blaufox, Leonard Freeman; Pub. Joan W. Blumberg. adv.: B&W page $950, color page $1950; 7 x 10. abstr.; bibl.; charts; illus. circ. 4,897. Indexed: ASCA, Biol.Abstr., Chem.Abstr., Curr.Adv.Ecol.Sci., Curr.Cont., Excerp.Med., Ind.Med., INSPEC, Sci.Cit.Ind. Document type: academic/scholarly publication.
—BLDSC (8239.456000); CASDDS; Faxon; Genuine Article; SWETS; UMI; UnCover. **CCC**.
   Description: Discusses new concepts and techniques developed in nuclear medicine.

SEMINARS IN ONCOLOGY NURSING. see *MEDICAL SCIENCES — Nurses And Nursing*

SEMINARS IN RADIATION ONCOLOGY. see *MEDICAL SCIENCES — Oncology*

616.842   US   ISSN 1070-535X
SEMINARS IN RADIOLOGIC TECHNOLOGY. 1993. q. $109 (foreign $139) (effective 1996). W.B. Saunders Co. (Subsidiary of: Harcourt Brace & Company), Curtis Center, 3rd Fl., Independence Sq. W., Philadelphia, PA 19106-3399. TEL 215-238-7800. FAX 215-238-6445. (Subscr. to: Periodicals Fulfillment, W.B. Saunders Co., 6277 Sea Harbor Dr., 4th Fl., Orlando, FL 32891-4800. TEL 800-654-2452. FAX 800-874-6418) Eds. Richard R. Carlton, Arlene Adler; Pub. Joan W. Blumberg. adv.: B&W page $515, color page $1315; 7 x 10. circ. 2,000. Document type: academic/scholarly publication.
—BLDSC (8239.457350). **CCC**.
   Description: Each issue covers a development in or new application of a radiologic technology.

SEMINARS IN RESPIRATORY INFECTIONS. see *MEDICAL SCIENCES — Respiratory Diseases*

615.842   US   ISSN 0037-198X
RC78   CODEN: SEROAF
SEMINARS IN ROENTGENOLOGY. 1966. q. $163 (foreign $196) (effective 1996). W.B. Saunders Co. (Subsidiary of: Harcourt Brace & Company), Curtis Center, 3rd Fl., Independence Sq. W., Philadelphia, PA 19106-3399. TEL 215-238-7800. FAX 215-238-6445. (Subscr. to: Periodicals Fulfillment, W.B. Saunders Co., 6277 Sea Harbor Dr., 4th Fl., Orlando, FL 32891-4800. TEL 800-654-2452. FAX 800-874-6418) Ed. Dr. Wallace T. Miller; Pub. Joan W. Blumberg. adv.: B&W page $915, color page $1915; 7 x 10. bibl.; charts; illus. circ. 5,518. Indexed: ASCA, Bibl.Dev.Med.& Child Neur., Biol.Abstr., Curr.Cont., Dent.Ind., Excerp.Med., Ind.Med., Sci.Cit.Ind. Document type: academic/scholarly publication.
●Also available online.
—BLDSC (8239.460000); EMDOCS; Faxon; Genuine Article; SWETS; UnCover. **CCC**.

615.842   US   ISSN 0887-2171
CODEN: SEULDO
SEMINARS IN ULTRASOUND, C T AND M R. (Computerized Tomography and Magnetic Resonance) Variant title: Seminars in Ultrasound, C T and M R I. 1980. bi-m. $155 (foreign $199) (effective 1996). W.B. Saunders Co. (Subsidiary of: Harcourt Brace & Company), Curtis Center, 3rd Fl., Independence Sq. W., Philadelphia, PA 19106-3399. TEL 215-238-7800. FAX 215-238-6445. (Subscr. to: Periodicals Fulfillment, W.B. Saunders Co., 6277 Sea Harbor Dr., 4th Fl., Orlando, FL 32891-4800. TEL 800-654-2452. FAX 800-874-6418) Ed.Bd; Pub. Joan W. Blumberg. adv.: B&W page $815; color page $1815. bibl.; charts; illus.; index. circ. 5,768. (back issues avail.) Indexed: ASCA, Biol.Abstr. Document type: academic/scholarly publication.
●Also available online.
—BLDSC (8239.485505); Faxon; Genuine Article; SWETS; UnCover. **CCC**.
   Formerly (until 1984): Seminars in Ultrasound (ISSN 0194-1720)

616.842   NE   ISSN 0167-465X
SERIES IN RADIOLOGY. (Text in English) 1979. irreg., vol.22, 1991. price varies. Kluwer Academic Publishers, Postbus 17, 3300 AA Dordrecht, Netherlands. TEL 31-78-392392. FAX 31-78-392254. TELEX 29245 KAPG NL. (Dist. by: Kluwer Academic Publishers Group, P.O. Box 322, 3300 AH Dordrecht, Netherlands. TEL 31-78-392392. FAX 31-78-546474; N. America dist. addr.: Box 358, Accord Sta., Hingham, MA 02018-0358. TEL 617-871-6600. FAX 617-871-6528) Document type: monographic series.
—BLDSC (8250.200500).
   Refereed Serial

615.842   NZ   ISSN 1170-9758
SHADOWS; journal of the New Zealand Institute of Medical Radiation Technology. 1958. q. NZ.$60. New Zealand Institute of Medical Radiation Technology, Radiology Dept., Princess Margaret Hospital, Christchurch 2, New Zealand. TEL 03-337-7200. FAX 03-337-7214. Ed. Jan Palmer. adv.; bk.rev. circ. 800.

SHIKA HOSHASEN. see *MEDICAL SCIENCES — Dentistry*

618   GW   ISSN 0364-2348
SKELETAL RADIOLOGY; journal of radiology, pathology and orthopaedics. (Text in English) 1976. 8/yr. DM.728($529) (effective 1996). (International Skeletal Society) Springer-Verlag, Heidelberger Platz 3, 14197 Berlin, Germany. TEL 030-8207-0. FAX 030-8214091. E-mail: orders@springer.de. (Subscr. in N. America to: Springer-Verlag New York, Inc., 44 Hartz Way, Secaucus, NJ 07096-2491. TEL 201-348-4033. FAX 201-348-4505) Ed.Bd. adv.; bk.rev.; charts, illus.; index. (also avail. in microfilm from UMI; reprint service avail. from ISI) Indexed: ASCA, Bibl.Dev.Med.& Child Neur., Curr.Adv.Cancer Res., Curr.Cont., Dent.Ind., Excerp.Med., Ind.Med., Rev.Med.& Vet.Mycol. Document type: academic/scholarly publication.
—BLDSC (8295.200000); Faxon; Genuine Article; SWETS; UMI; UnCover. **CCC**.
   Description: Covers the anatomical, pathological, physiological, clinical, metabolic, and epidemiological aspects of the many entities affecting the skeleton.

SOLID STATE NUCLEAR MAGNETIC RESONANCE; an international journal. see *CHEMISTRY — Analytical Chemistry*

615.842   GW   ISSN 0179-7158
STRAHLENTHERAPIE UND ONKOLOGIE; Zeitschrift fuer Radiologie, Strahlenbiologie, Strahlenphysik. (Text and summaries in English and German) 1912. m. DM.672($488) (effective 1996). (Deutsche Roentgengesellschaft) Urban und Vogel, Lindwurmstr. 95, 80337 Munich, Germany. TEL 089-53292-0. FAX 089-53292-100. (Subscr. to: Postfach 152209, 80052 Munich, Germany) (Co-sponsors: Gesellschaft fuer Medizinische Radiologie, Strahlenbiologie und Nuklearmedizin; Deutsche Gesellschaft fuer Medizinische Physik; Arbeitsgemeinschaft Radioonkologie (ARO) der Deutschen Krebsgesellschaft) Ed. Dr. R. Sauer. adv.; bk.rev.; bibl.; charts; illus.; index, cum.index: vols.1-125 (in 5 vols.). circ. 1,600. (also avail. in microform from PMC) Indexed: ASCA, Biol.Abstr., Chem.Abstr., Curr.Adv.Cancer Res., Curr.Cont., Dent.Ind., Excerp.Med., Ind.Med., Nutr.Abstr. Document type: academic/scholarly publication.
—BLDSC (8470.010000); CASDDS; SWETS; UMI. **CCC**.
   Formerly: Strahlentherapie; Zeitschrift fuer Radiologie und Onkologie (ISSN 0039-2073)

SURGICAL AND RADIOLOGIC ANATOMY. see *BIOLOGY — Physiology*

THERMOLOGY. see *BIOLOGY — Physiology*

THYROBULLETIN. see *MEDICAL SCIENCES — Endocrinology*

616.842   US
TOPICS IN DIAGNOSTIC RADIOLOGY AND ADVANCED IMAGING.* 1993. q. $100 to non-members; members $75. Council on Diagnostic Imaging, Box 25, Palatine, IL 60078-0025. FAX 708-705-1178. Ed. Dr. Robert Hacker. circ. 2,500 (paid).
   Formerly: Roentgenological Briefs.
   Description: Contains articles on diagnostic imaging (radiology and thermology) to educate chiropractic physicians (radiologists) and others.

616   US   ISSN 0899-3459
CODEN: TMRIEY
TOPICS IN MAGNETIC RESONANCE IMAGING. 1988. 4/yr. $134 to individuals; institutions $145 (effective 1995). Lippincott - Raven Press, 227 Washington Sq., Philadelphia, PA 19106. TEL 215-238-4200. Ed. Joseph K.T. Lee. adv. contact: Phyllis Noyes. illus.; index. (also avail. in microform; back issues avail.) Indexed: Excerp.Med., Ind.Med. Document type: academic/scholarly publication.
—BLDSC (8867.459300); Genuine Article; SWETS. **CCC**.
   Description: Discusses practical clinical applications of MRI to the entire body, including the brain, spine, extracranial organs, and the musculo-skeletal system.
   Refereed Serial

615.842   US   ISSN 1073-0206
TRACERS. 1985. a. American Board of Nuclear Medicine, 900 Veteran Ave., Los Angeles, CA 90024. TEL 310-825-6787. FAX 310-825-9433. Ed. J.F. Ross. circ. 3,900. (back issues avail.) Document type: newsletter.
   Description: Information regarding specialty of nuclear medicine and certification.

616.07 500   US   ISSN 0161-7346
RC78.7.U4   CODEN: ULIMD4
ULTRASONIC IMAGING; an international journal. 1979. q. $168 (foreign $218) (effective 1996). Academic Press, Inc., Journal Division, 525 B St., Ste. 1900, San Diego, CA 92101-4495. TEL 619-230-1840. FAX 619-699-6800. (Subscr. to: Box 620000, Orlando, FL 32891-8340. TEL 800-543-9534) Ed. Melvin Linzer. adv.; index. (back issues avail.) Indexed: Curr.Cont., Ind.Med., INSPEC. Document type: academic/scholarly publication.
—BLDSC (9082.787000); Faxon; Genuine Article; SWETS; UnCover. **CCC**.
   Description: Covers the development and application of ultrasonic techniques, with emphasis on medical diagnosis.

MEDICAL SCIENCES — RESPIRATORY DISEASES

616.07   PL   ISSN 0867-3845
ULTRASONOGRAFIA POLSKA; czasopismo polskiego srodowiska ultrasonograficznego. 1991. irreg. Akademia Medyczna w Warszawie, Drugi Wydzial Lekarski, Zaklad Diagnostyki Obrazowej, Ul. Kondratowicza 8, 03-285 Warsaw, Poland. TEL 48-22-116977. Ed. Wieslaw Jakubovski.
—BLDSC (9082.810100).

ULTRASOUND IN OBSTETRICS & GYNECOLOGY. see *MEDICAL SCIENCES — Obstetrics And Gynecology*

615.842   US   ISSN 0894-8771
RC78.7.U4   CODEN: ULQUEZ
ULTRASOUND QUARTERLY. 1983. q. $119 to individuals (foreign $152); institutions $160 (foreign 186) (effective 1996); newsstand price: $48. Lippincott - Raven Press, 227 Washington Sq., Philadelphia, PA 19106. TEL 215-238-4200. Ed. Roger C. Sanders. adv. contact: Phyllis Noyes. charts; illus. circ. 2,000. (reprint service avail. from UMI) **Document type:** academic/scholarly publication.
—BLDSC (9082.815550); UMI. **CCC.**
Formerly (until 1989): Ultrasound Annual (ISSN 0888-8264)
Description: Publishes original articles on diagnostic information obtained by recent technological advances, and discussions of fundamental or controversial subjects.
Refereed Serial

615.8   NE   ISSN 0921-2574
     CODEN: VNGTD6
VANGNET. 1978. bi-m. fl.90. Vereniging voor Medisch Nucleair Werkers, c/o V.A.N.G., P.J., Graan voor Visch 14509, 2132 VE Hoofddorp, Netherlands. adv.; bk.rev. circ. 350.
—CASDDS.

615.842 618   US   ISSN 1052-2182
VIDEO JOURNAL OF COLOR FLOW IMAGING. (Includes 4 video cassettes.) 1987. q. $250 (Canada $270; elsewhere $290) (effective 1994). Dynamedia, Inc., 2 Fulham Court, Silver Spring, MD 20902-3016. TEL 301-649-6886. FAX 301-649-3447. Eds. C.R.B. Merritt, D.E. Strandness. adv. circ. 1,000. (back issues avail.)
—**CCC.**
Supersedes in part (in 1991): Dynamic Cardiovascular Imaging (ISSN 0891-9313)
Description: Covers ultrasound imaging. Consists of tutorials, reviews, case reports and original research.
Refereed Serial

615.84 612.014   US
VIEWBOX. 4/yr. American Osteopathic College of Radiology, 1402 Cottage Lane, Kirksville, MO 63501. TEL 816-626-2121. circ. 400.
Formerly: American Osteopathic College of Radiology. Newsletter. (ISSN 0065-9576)

618 574   RU   ISSN 0302-556X
VOPROSY RADIOBIOLOGII I BIOLOGICHESKOGO DEISTVIYA TSITOSTATICHESKIKH PREPARATOV. 1969. irreg. (Tomskii Meditsinskii Institut, Tsentral'naya Nauchno-Issledovatel'skaya Laboratoriya) Izdatel'svo Tomskii Universitet, Prospekt Lenina, 36, Tomsk-10, Russia. bibl.; illus.

615.84   US   ISSN 0098-1672
RC78   CODEN: YBDRE3
YEAR BOOK OF DIAGNOSTIC RADIOLOGY. 1932. a. $68.95 (residents $35) (effective 1996). Mosby - Year Book, Inc., Continuity Division, 200 N. LaSalle, Chicago, IL 60601. TEL 312-726-9733. FAX 312-726-6075. TELEX 206155. Ed. Dr. Michael P. Federle. (reprint service avail.) **Indexed:** Curr.Adv.Ecol.Sci.
●Also available online. Vendor(s): Ovid Technologies.
—BLDSC (9411.629000); Faxon.
Formerly (until 1975): Year Book of Radiology (ISSN 0084-3989)

615.842 616.8   US   ISSN 1062-337X
YEAR BOOK OF NEURORADIOLOGY. 1992. a. $84.95 (residents $35) (effective 1996). Mosby - Year Book, Inc. (Chicago) (Subsidiary of: Times Mirror Company), 200 N. LaSalle St., Chicago, IL 60601. TEL 312-726-9733. Ed. Dr. Anne Osborn.
●Also available online. Vendor(s): Ovid Technologies.

615.8   US   ISSN 0084-3903
RC93.A1   CODEN: YNUMAH
YEAR BOOK OF NUCLEAR MEDICINE. 1966. a. $74.95 (residents $35) (effective 1996). Mosby - Year Book, Inc., Continuity Division, 200 N. LaSalle, Chicago, IL 60601. TEL 312-726-9733. FAX 312-726-6075. TELEX 206155. Ed. Dr. F. Gottschallk. illus. (reprint service avail.) **Indexed:** Curr.Adv.Ecol.Sci.
●Also available online. Vendor(s): Ovid Technologies.
—BLDSC (9414.645000); SWETS.

615.842 534   US   ISSN 1050-4443
RC78.7.U4
YEAR BOOK OF ULTRASOUND. 1991. a. $82.95 (residents $35) (effective 1996). Mosby - Year Book, Inc. (Chicago) (Subsidiary of: Times Mirror Company), 200 N. LaSalle St., Chicago, IL 60601-1080. TEL 312-726-9733. FAX 312-726-6075. TELEX 206155. Ed. Dr. Christopher R.B. Merritt. illus.
●Also available online. Vendor(s): Ovid Technologies.

615.842   CC   ISSN 1001-6384
YINGXIANG YIXUE/MEDICAL IMAGING. (Text in Chinese) 1988. s-a. $10. Tianjin Di'er Yixueyuan - Tianjin No. 2 Medical Academy, 1 Guangdong Lu, Tianjin 300203, People's Republic of China. TEL 395086. (Co-sponsor: Japan Association of Radiological Technologists) Ed. Wu Enhui. adv.; bk.rev.

615.842   GW   ISSN 0722-5067
ZEITSCHRIFT FUER CHEMOTHERAPIE. 1980. 6/yr. DM.42. c/o Prof. H. Lode, Eichenallee 36a, 14050 Berlin, Germany. TEL 030-3125059. Ed. Dr. R. Stahlmann. (back issues avail.) **Document type:** academic/scholarly publication.

615.842   CC   ISSN 1003-3289
ZHONGGUO YIXUE YINGXIANG JISHU/CHINESE JOURNAL OF MEDICAL IMAGING TECHNOLOGY. (Text in Chinese) 1985. q. Y12.80 (effective Jan. 1994). (Zhongguo Kexueyuan, Kejian Gongsi) Zhongguo Yixue Yingxiang Jishu Bianjibu, P.O. Box 2712, Beijing 100080, People's Republic of China. TEL 86-1-2554038. Ed. Zhang Xingfu. adv. (back issues avail.) **Document type:** academic/scholarly publication.
Description: Contains research papers on the new developments of medical equipments in the field of medical imaging technology.

MEDICAL SCIENCES — Respiratory Diseases

616.2   US   ISSN 0893-8520
     CODEN: AATIEN
A A R C TIMES. 1977. m. $50. (American Association for Respiratory Care) Daedalus Enterprises, Inc., 11030 Ables Ln., Dallas, TX 75229. TEL 214-243-2272. FAX 214-484-6010. Ed. Marsha Cathcart. adv. circ. 37,000. (also avail. in microfilm from UMI; reprint service avail.) **Indexed:** CINAHL.
—BLDSC (0537.535500); Faxon; SWETS; UMI. **CCC.**
Formerly: A A R Times (ISSN 0195-1777)
Description: Presents news and features for the cardiorespiratory care profession.

A S D A NEWS. (American Sleep Disorders Association) see *MEDICAL SCIENCES — Psychiatry And Neurology*

616.2   US   ISSN 0892-8916
A T S NEWS. 1975. m. membership. American Thoracic Society, 1740 Broadway, New York, NY 10019-4374. TEL 212-315-8808. FAX 212-315-8808. Ed. Graham M. Nelan. cum.index. circ. 11,000.

615   US   ISSN 1074-2301
ADVANCE FOR RESPIRATORY CARE PRACTITIONERS. w. Merion Publications, 650 Park Ave., Box 61556, King of Prussia, PA 19406. TEL 610-265-7812. FAX 610-265-8971. Ed. Vern Enge. adv.: B&W page $1575, color page $2075; trim 10 x 13 1/4. circ. 47,000. **Document type:** trade publication.

616.2   CN   ISSN 1187-9106
AIRWAVE.* 1974. 3/yr. free. (Manitoba Lung Association) Idea Marketing Group, 207 - 110 Osborne St. S., Winnipeg, MB R3L 1Y5, Canada. TEL 204-774-5501. FAX 204-772-5083. (Subscr. to: M.L.A., 629 McDermot Ave., Winnipeg, MB R3A 1P6, Canada. TEL 204-744-5501) Ed. Linda Sawchuk. adv.; stat. circ. 5,000. (back issues avail.) **Document type:** newsletter.
Formerly (until 1989): Easy Breathing (ISSN 0315-2421)
Description: Keeps MLA program users, donors and volunteers up-to-date regarding organization activities.

AMERICAN JOURNAL OF ASTHMA & ALLERGY FOR PEDIATRICIANS. see *MEDICAL SCIENCES — Allergology And Immunology*

616.2   US   ISSN 1073-449X
RC306   CODEN: AJCMED
AMERICAN JOURNAL OF RESPIRATORY AND CRITICAL CARE MEDICINE. 1917. m. $130 to individuals (foreign $170); institutions $220 (foreign $260) (effective 1994). (American Thoracic Society) American Lung Association, 1740 Broadway, New York, NY 10019-4374. TEL 212-315-8700. Ed. Robert A. Klocke. adv.; bk.rev.; abstr.; bibl.; charts; illus.; stat.; index, cum.index. circ. 14,500. (also avail. in microform from UMI,PMC; reprint service avail. from UMI) **Indexed:** Abstr.Hyg., Abstr.Inter.Med., AIM, Behav.Med.Abstr., Biol.Abstr., Biol.Dig., Biotech.Abstr., C.I.S.Abstr., Chem.Abstr., CINAHL, Curr.Adv.Cell & Devel.Biol., Curr.Adv.Ecol.Sci., Curr.Adv.Genetics & Molec.Biol., Curr.Cont., Dairy Sci.Abstr., Dent.Ind., Energy Ind., Energy Info.Abstr., Excerp.Med., Helminthol.Abstr., Hosp.Lit.Ind., Ind.Med., Ind.Sci.Rev., Ind.Vet., INIS Atomind., Lab.Haz.Bull., Ocean.Abstr., Pollut.Abstr., Protozool.Abstr., Rev.Med.& Vet.Mycol., Rev.Plant Path., Risk Abstr., Sci.Cit.Ind., Trop.Dis.Bull., Vet.Bull.
—BLDSC (0836.590000); CASDDS; Faxon; Genuine Article; SWETS; UMI; UnCover. **CCC.**
Former titles (until 1994): American Review of Respiratory Disease (ISSN 0003-0805); (until 1959): American Review of Tuberculosis and Pulmonary Diseases (ISSN 0096-039X); (until 1955): American Review of Tuberculosis (ISSN 0096-0381)
Refereed Serial

616.2   US   ISSN 1044-1549
QP121.A1   CODEN: AJRBEL
AMERICAN JOURNAL OF RESPIRATORY CELL AND MOLECULAR BIOLOGY. 1989. m. $95 (foreign $115). (American Thoracic Society) American Lung Association, 1740 Broadway, New York, NY 10019-4374. TEL 212-315-8700.
—BLDSC (0836.600000); ADONIS; CASDDS; Faxon; Genuine Article; SWETS; UMI; UnCover. **CCC.**

616.2   JA
ANNUAL REVIEW KOKYUKI/ANNUAL REVIEW. RESPIRATORY ORGAN. (Text in Japanese) 1988. a. 9064 Yen. Chugai Igakusha, 62, Yaraicho, Shinjuku-ku, Tokyo 162, Japan.

616.2   AG   ISSN 0004-0509
ARCHIVOS ARGENTINOS DE TISIOLOGIA Y NEUMONOLOGIA. 1924. q. Hospital Municipal Dr. Enrique Tornu, Sociedad de Tisiologia y Neumologia, Hospital Tornu, Buenos Aires, Argentina. **Indexed:** Biol.Abstr., Chem.Abstr.
Formerly: Archivos de Tisiologia.

616.2   SP   ISSN 0300-2896
     CODEN: ARBRDA
ARCHIVOS DE BRONCONEUMOLOGIA. (Text in Spanish; summaries in English) m. (10/yr.). 6900 ptas.($53) to non-members. (Sociedad Espanola de Neumologia y Cirugia Toracica) Ediciones Doyma, S.A., Travesera de Gracia 17-21, 08021 Barcelona, Spain. TEL 34-1-200-07-11. FAX 34-1-209-11-36. TELEX 51964 INK-E. Ed. J. Ruiz Manzano. adv.: page 180000 ptas.; trim 210 x 280; adv. contact: Anna Pahissa. bk.rev. circ. 3,100. (reprint service avail. from UMI) **Indexed:** Excerp.Med., Ind.Med. (1994-), Ind.Med.Esp.
—BLDSC (1654.890000); UMI.
Description: Covers broncho-pneumology, respiratory immunology, biochemical studies of secretions, and pulmonary surgery.

ARERUGIA. see *MEDICAL SCIENCES — Allergology And Immunology*

MEDICAL SCIENCES — RESPIRATORY DISEASES

616.246 BL ISSN 0004-2765
ARQUIVOS BRASILEIROS DE TUBERCULOSE E DOENCAS DO TORAX. (Summaries in English) 1938-1982; resumed 1987. q. gift or exchange basis. Instituto Brasileiro para Investigacao do Torax, Caixa Postal 635, Salvador, Bahia, Brazil. Ed. Jose Silveira. adv.; bk.rev.; bibl.; charts; illus. circ. 1,000. **Indexed:** Biol.Abstr., Chem.Abstr.
Formerly: I B I T Arquivos.

ASTHMA AND ALLERGY ADVOCATE. see *MEDICAL SCIENCES — Allergology And Immunology*

616.23 US ISSN 1050-5253
CODEN: ASMAFN
ASTHMA MANAGEMENT. 1991. q. $128 (foreign $178). Mary Ann Liebert, Inc.Publishers, 2 Madison Ave., Larchmont, NY 10538. TEL 914-834-3100. FAX 914-834-3688. E-mail: Liebert@pipeline.com. **Document type:** trade publication.
Description: Covers current management techniques for clinicians and other health care professionals who treat patients with asthma. Includes current therapies, new treatment modalities, and sources for information.

616.23 AT ISSN 0044-9776
ASTHMA WELFARER. 1964. irreg. (2-3/yr.) Aus.$12.50. Asthma Foundation of New South Wales, Unit 1, 82-86 Pacific Hwy., St. Leonards, N.S.W 2065, Australia. TEL 02-906-3233. FAX 02-906-4493. Ed. Clair Isbister. adv.; bk.rev. circ. 5,000.
Description: Journal of the Asthma Foundation of N.S.W., a voluntary organisation involved in research, welfare and education to assist asthma sufferers.

616.2 GW ISSN 0341-3055
CODEN: ATLUDF
ATEMWEGS- UND LUNGENKRANKHEITEN. 1975. m. DM.228($172) Dustri-Verlag Dr. Karl Feistle, Bahnhofstr. 9, 82041 Deisenhofen, Germany. TEL 089-613861-0. FAX 089-6135412. Ed. Dr. E. Krieger. **Indexed:** Biol.Abstr., Chem.Abstr., Curr.Adv.Ecol.Sci., Curr.Cont., Dok.Arbeitsmed., Excerp.Med., Ind.Sci.Rev., Sci.Cit.Ind. **Document type:** academic/scholarly publication.
—BLDSC (1765.856000); CASDDS. **CCC.**

616.2 US ISSN 0005-6367
BATTING THE BREEZE.* 1965. bi-m. $15. Emphysema Anonymous, Inc., Box 2644, Clearwater, FL 34617-2644. TEL 813-391-9977. Ed. William E. Jaeckle. adv., 3,500.
Description: Educational articles for patients with emphysema and other respiratory diseases.

616.2 US
BRONCHIAL MUCOLOGY SERIES. 1988. irreg., latest 1990. price varies. Raven Press (Subsidiary of: Wolters Kluwer N.V.), 1185 Ave. of the Americas, New York, NY 10036. TEL 212-930-9500. FAX 212-869-3495. (reprint service avail. from UMI) **Document type:** monographic series.
Refereed Serial

615.64 CN
CANADIAN RESPIRATORY JOURNAL. 4/yr. Can.$61 to individuals; institutions Can.$84. (Canadian Thoracic Society - Societe Canadienne de Thoracologie) Pulsus Group Inc., 2902 S. Sheridan Way, Oakville, ON L6J 7L6, Canada. TEL 905-829-4770. FAX 905-829-4799. Ed. Dr. Norman Jones; Pub. Robert B. Kalina. adv.; B&W page Can.$2165; color page Can.$3815. bk.rev. circ. 15,500. **Document type:** academic/scholarly publication.
Description: Publishes original research in all areas of respiratory research and therapy, reviews, case reports, letters to the editor, industry news, meeting announcements and reports.
Refereed Serial

616.2 PE ISSN 0069-2166
CENTRO DE SALUD "MAX ARIAS SCHREIBER", LIMA. CONGRESO NACIONAL DE TUBERCULOSIS Y ENFERMEDADES RESPIRATORIAS.* irreg., 1970, 9th. Dispensario Antituberculoso "Max Arias Schreiber", Raymondi 2da Cuadra (La Victoria), Lima, Peru.

616.246 PK ISSN 0528-7944
THE CHALLENGE. (Text in English) 1959. q. Rs.60($16) Pakistan Anti-Tuberculosis Association, Block No. 55, Rm. 8, Pakistan Secretariat, Karachi, Pakistan. TEL 92-21-5688011. Ed. Dr. Al-Haj Syed Amjed Ali Jafri. adv. contact: M.Z Baig. bk.rev.; charts; stat.; bibl.; illus. circ. 2,000. **Indexed:** Acad.Ind., ExtraMED, Ind.Med. **Document type:** academic/scholarly publication.
●Also available on CD-ROM.
—BLDSC (3129.070000).
Description: Covers news, views and new methods relating to global TB control.
Refereed Serial

616.2 616.12 US ISSN 0012-3692
RC705 CODEN: CHETBF
CHEST; the cardiopulmonary and critical care journal. 1935. m. $108 to individuals; institutions $144. American College of Chest Physicians, 3300 Dundee Rd., Northbrook, IL 60062. FAX 708-498-5460. Ed. Dr. A. Jay Block. adv.; bk.rev.; bibl.; illus.; s-a. index. circ. 23,000. (also avail. in microform from UMI; reprint service avail.) **Indexed:** Abstr.Inter.Med., AIM, Behav.Med.Abstr., Biol.Abstr., C.I.S. Abstr., Chem.Abstr., CINAHL, Curr.Adv.Ecol.Sci., Curr.Cont., Dent.Ind., Dok.Arbeitsmed., Excerp.Med., Helminthol.Abstr., Ind.Med., Ind.Sci.Rev., Ind.Vet., INIS Atomind., Int.Nurs.Ind., Kidney, Nutr.Abstr., Protozool.Abstr., Rev.Med.& Vet.Mycol., Rev.Plant Path., Risk Abstr., Sci.Cit.Ind., Small Anim.Abstr. **Document type:** academic/scholarly publication.
●Also available online.
—BLDSC (3172.530000); ADONIS; CASDDS; Faxon; Genuine Article; SWETS; UMI; UnCover. **CCC.**
Formerly: Diseases of the Chest.
Refereed Serial

616.2 US ISSN 1068-0640
▼**CLINICAL PULMONARY MEDICINE.** 1994. bi-m. $84 to individuals (foreign $109); institutions $119 (foreign $144) (effective 1995). Williams & Wilkins, 428 E. Preston St., Baltimore, MD 21202-3993. TEL 410-528-4000; 800-638-6423. FAX 410-528-4312. Ed. Dr. Michael S. Niederman; Pub. Nancy Collins. adv. circ. 2,000. **Indexed:** Excerp.Med. (1995-). **Document type:** academic/scholarly publication.
—BLDSC (3286.347000).
Description: Disseminates research on the diagnosis and treatment of lung diseases.

616.2 US ISSN 0272-5231
RC941
CLINICS IN CHEST MEDICINE. 1980. q. $129 (foreign $155) (effective 1996). W.B. Saunders Co. (Subsidiary of: Harcourt Brace & Company), Curtis Center, 3rd Fl., Independence Sq. W., Philadelphia, PA 19106-3399. TEL 215-238-7800. FAX 215-238-6445. (Subscr. to: Periodicals Fulfillment, W.B. Saunders Co., 6277 Sea Harbor Dr., 4th Fl., Orlando, FL 32891-4800. TEL 800-654-2452. FAX 800-874-6418) Ed. Livia Berardi. **Indexed:** CINAHL, Dok.Arbeitsmed., Excerp.Med., Ind.Med., Ind.Sci.Rev., Sci.Cit.Ind. **Document type:** academic/scholarly publication.
—BLDSC (3286.545000); Faxon; Genuine Article; SWETS; UMI; UnCover. **CCC.**

616.7 US ISSN 1078-1641
▼**CURRENT OPINION IN PULMONARY MEDICINE.** 1995. bi-m. $129.95 to individuals; institutions $259.95; residents $55. Current Science, 500 Market St., Ste. 700, Philadelphia, PA 19106. TEL 215-574-2210; 800-552-5866. FAX 215-574-3533. (And: Current Science Ltd., 34-42 Cleveland St., London W1P 6LB, England. TEL 0171-323-0323. FAX 0171-639-6911) Ed. R.C. Bone. adv.; bibl.; illus. (also avail. in diskette format) **Indexed:** Excerp.Med. **Document type:** academic/scholarly publication, abstracting/indexing.
●Also available online. Vendor(s): OCLC.
Also available on CD-ROM.
Description: Keeps readers abreast of clinical and research advances in the field.

616.2 US ISSN 0163-7800
RC756 CODEN: CUPUDU
CURRENT PULMONOLOGY. 1977. a. $72.95 (residents $40) (effective 1996). Mosby - Year Book, Inc. (Chicago) (Subsidiary of: Times Mirror Company), 200 N. LaSalle St., Chicago, IL 60601-1080. TEL 312-726-9733. FAX 312-726-6075. TELEX 206155. (Subscr. to: 11830 Westline Industrial Dr., St. Louis, MO 63146. TEL 800-325-1380) Ed. Dr. Donald F. Tierney. illus.
—BLDSC (3501.850000); CASDDS; Faxon. **CCC.**
Description: Survey developments in the field through a synopsis of the past twelve months of medical literature. Contains original papers in pulmonology.

CURRENT TOPICS IN PULMONARY PHARMACOLOGY AND TOXICOLOGY. see *PHARMACY AND PHARMACOLOGY*

616.2 DK ISSN 0903-1936
CODEN: ERJOEI
EUROPEAN RESPIRATORY JOURNAL. (Supplement avail. (ISSN 0904-1850)) (Text in English; summaries in French) 1924. 12/yr. DKK 2500 (incl. supplements) (effective 1996). (European Respiratory Society) Munksgaard International Publishers Ltd., 35 Noerre Soegade, P.O. Box 2148, DK-1016 Copenhagen K, Denmark. TEL 33-127030. FAX 33-129387. Ed. P. Vermiere. adv.; bk.rev.; illus.; index. circ. 4,500. (reprint service avail. from ISI) **Indexed:** Abstr.Hyg., Agri.Eng.Abstr., Biol.Abstr., Biotech.Abstr., C.I.S. Abstr., Chem.Abstr., CINAHL, Curr.Adv.Ecol.Sci., Curr.Cont., Dent.Ind., Dok.Arbeitsmed., Excerp.Med., Helminthol.Abstr., Ind.Med., Ind.Vet., Pig News & Info., Rev.Med.& Vet.Mycol., Rev.Plant Path., Sci.Cit.Ind., Triticale Abstr., Trop.Dis.Bull., Vet.Bull.
—BLDSC (3829.924200); CASDDS; Faxon; Genuine Article; SWETS; UnCover. **CCC.**
Formed by the merger of: European Journal of Respiratory Diseases (ISSN 0106-4339); Which was formerly: Acta Tuberculosa et Pneumologica Belgica (ISSN 0001-7078) & Clinical Respiratory Physiology (ISSN 0271-9983); Which was formerly: Bulletin Europeen de Physiopathologie Respiratoire (ISSN 0395-3890)
Refereed Serial

616.2 DK ISSN 0904-1850
CODEN: ERJSEU
EUROPEAN RESPIRATORY JOURNAL. SUPPLEMENT. (Text in English) 1934. irreg. free to subscribers. (European Respiratory Society) Munksgaard International Publishers Ltd., P.O. Box 2148, DK-1016 Copenhagen K, Denmark. TEL 45-33-12-70-30. FAX 45-33-12-93-87. Ed. E. Berglund. adv. (reprint service avail. from ISI) **Indexed:** Biol.Abstr., Curr.Adv.Ecol.Sci., Curr.Cont., Excerp.Med. (1992-), Ind.Med., Ind.Sci.Rev.
—CASDDS; Faxon. **CCC.**
Former titles (until 1987): European Journal of Respiratory Diseases. Supplementum (ISSN 0106-4347); (until 1979): Scandinavian Journal of Respiratory Diseases. Supplementum (ISSN 0080-6730); (until 1965): Acta Tuberculosea et Pneumologica Scandinavica, Supplementum (ISSN 0365-7612); (until 1961): Acta Tuberculosea Scandinavica. Supplementum (ISSN 0365-7604)

616.2 DK ISSN 0905-9180
CODEN: EREWEH
EUROPEAN RESPIRATORY REVIEW. (Text in English) 1991. irreg.(5-6/yr.). DKK 850 (effective 1996). (European Respiratory Society) Munksgaard International Publishers Ltd., 35 Noerre Soegade, P.O. Box 2148, DK-2148 Copenhagen K, Denmark. TEL 45-33-12-70-30. FAX 45-33-12-93-87. Ed. Jean Claud Yernault. adv.; bk.rev. circ. 2,500. (reprint service avail.) **Indexed:** Excerp.Med. (1992-). **Document type:** academic/scholarly publication.
—BLDSC (3829.924400); SWETS. **CCC.**
Refereed Serial

MEDICAL SCIENCES — RESPIRATORY DISEASES

616.2   US   ISSN 0190-2148
QP121.A1   CODEN: EXLRDA
EXPERIMENTAL LUNG RESEARCH. 1979. bi-m. £291($480) (effective 1996). Taylor & Francis Inc., 1900 Frost Rd., Ste. 101, Bristol, PA 19007-1598. TEL 215-785-5800; 800-821-8312. FAX 215-785-5515. (Subscr. in Europe to: Taylor & Francis Ltd., Rankine Rd., Basingstoke, Hants. RG24 8PR, England. TEL 44-1256-840366. FAX 44-1256-479438) Ed. Paul Nettesheim. adv. circ. 400. (back issues avail.; reprint service avail. from UMI) **Indexed:** Biol.Abstr., Chem.Abstr., Curr.Adv.Cell & Devel.Biol., Curr.Adv.Ecol.Sci., Curr.Cont., Excerp.Med., Ind.Med., Ind.Sci.Rev., Ind.Vet., INIS Atomind., Sci.Cit.Ind., Vet.Bull. **Document type:** academic/scholarly publication.
—BLDSC (3839.440000); ADONIS; CASDDS; Faxon; Genuine Article; SWETS; UnCover. **CCC.**
Description: Explores mechanisms of pulmonary biology and pathobiology, investigated at biochemical, subcellular, cellular, and tissue levels.
Refereed Serial

FOCUS ON PULMONARY PHARMACOLOGY AND TOXICOLOGY. see ENVIRONMENTAL STUDIES — *Toxicology And Environmental Safety*

616.2   CC   ISSN 1001-1064
GUOWAI YIXUE (HUXI XITONG FENCE)/FOREIGN MEDICAL SCIENCES (RESPIRATORY DISEASES). (Text in Chinese) 1981. q. Hebei Yixueyuan - Hebei Medical Institute, 5, Chang'an Xilu, Shijiazhuang, Hebei 050017, People's Republic of China. TEL 44121. Ed. Sun Yiyu.

H L B NEWSLETTER; reporting on heart, lung and blood disease research program, policy development. see MEDICAL SCIENCES — *Experimental Medicine, Laboratory Technique*

HJAERT-LUNGFONDEN; Kvartalsskrift. see MEDICAL SCIENCES — *Cardiovascular Diseases*

616.2   JA
HOKKAIDO UNIVERSITY. INSTITUTE OF IMMUNOLOGICAL SCIENCE. BULLETIN. (Text in Japanese; summaries in English and Japanese) 1953. a. exchange basis. Hokkaido University, Institute of Immunological Science, North 15, West 7, Sapporo 060, Japan. Ed. Ken-Ichi Yamamoto. circ. 300. **Indexed:** Biol.Abstr.
Formerly (until 1975): Kekkaku No Kenkyu (ISSN 0075-5354)

616.2   US   ISSN 0046-8762
IN-SHORT. 1971. m. free. American Lung Association of Brooklyn, 165 Cadman Plaza E., Brooklyn, NY 11201-1484. TEL 718-624-8531. Ed.Bd. bk.rev.; charts; illus. circ. 2,300.
Formerly: Life and Breath of Brooklyn - Fresh Air News.

616.2   II   ISSN 0019-5707
                   CODEN: IJTBAD
INDIAN JOURNAL OF TUBERCULOSIS. (Text in English) 1953. q. Rs.150($40) Tuberculosis Association of India, 3 Red Cross Rd., New Delhi 110 001, India. TEL 381303. Ed. D.R. Nagpaul. adv.; bk.rev.; abstr.; bibl.; charts; illus.; stat.; index, cum.index. circ. 3,000. **Indexed:** Abstr.Hyg., Biol.Abstr., Chem.Abstr., Excerp.Med., Trop.Dis.Bull. **Document type:** academic/scholarly publication.
—BLDSC (4421.700000); EMDOCS; Faxon.
Description: Contains original papers, review articles, case reports in all aspects of tuberculosis and other chest diseases.

616.2   MX   ISSN 0187-7585
INSTITUTO NACIONAL DE ENFERMEDADES RESPIRATORIAS. REVISTA. Short title: Revista I N E R. (Text in Spanish; summaries in English, Spanish) 1988. q. $40. Obsidiana Editores, S.A., Czda. de Tlalpan 2365, Col. Ciudad Jardin, 04370 Mexico DF, Mexico. TEL 6899133. FAX 6896545. Ed. Dr. Celso Garcia Espinosa; Pub. Jorge Godoy. circ. 3,000. **Document type:** academic/scholarly publication.
●Also available on CD-ROM.
Description: Contains original articles, research reports, review articles, clinical cases and notices related to the pathology of the respiratory tract.

616.2 613.62   US   ISSN 0892-6298
INTERNATIONAL SOCIETY FOR RESPIRATORY PROTECTION. JOURNAL. Abbreviated title: J I S R P. q. International Society for Respiratory Protection, 2090 Eola Dr., N.W., Salem, OR 97304-4443. TEL 503-588-1382. (Subscr. to: Bradley S. Squibb, Aerojet Ordnance, Box 158, Jonesborough, TN 37659. TEL 615-753-1388. FAX 615-753-8645) Ed. Darrel D. Douglas.
—BLDSC (4802.508000).
Description: A forum for open and responsible discussion in the field of respiratory protection.
Refereed Serial

616.246   FR
INTERNATIONAL UNION AGAINST TUBERCULOSIS AND LUNG DISEASE. CONFERENCE PROCEEDINGS. quadrennial, 27th, 1990, Boston. International Union Against Tuberculosis and Lung Disease - Union Internationale contre la Tuberculose et les Maladies Respiratoires, 68 bd Saint-Michel, 75006 Paris, France. TEL 33-1-46330830. FAX 33-1-43299087. Dir. Dr. Nils E. Billo. **Document type:** proceedings.
Supersedes: International Union Against Tuberculosis. Conference Proceedings (ISSN 0074-9257)

615.64   JA   ISSN 0910-9927
JINKO KOKYU/ARTIFICIAL VENTILATION. (Text in English, Japanese) 1984. s-a. 2000 Yen per no. Nihon Jinko Kokyu Gakkai - Japan Society of Respiratory Care, Fukushima Kenritsu Ika Daigaku Masuikagaku Kenkyushitsu, 1, Hikarigaoka, Fukushima-shi, Fukushima-ken 960-12, Japan.

616.2   BL   ISSN 0102-3586
JORNAL DE PNEUMOLOGIA. (Text in English, Portuguese, Spanish; summaries in English, Portuguese) 1974. q. Esc.1700($30) (Sociedade Brasileira de Pneumologia e Tisiologia) Ponto Cardeal Publicacoes Ltda., Rua Sete de Abril, 261 cj 512, 01043 Sao Paulo, Brazil. TEL 255-7340. Ed. Dr. Miguel Bogossian. circ. 2,200.
—EMDOCS.

616.2   US   ISSN 0894-2684
                   CODEN: JAEMEP
JOURNAL OF AEROSOL MEDICINE; deposition, clearance, and effects in the lung. q. $139 (foreign $179). Mary Ann Liebert, Inc. Publishers, 2 Madison Ave., Larchmont, NY 10538. TEL 914-834-3100. FAX 914-834-3688. E-mail: Liebert@pipeline.com. Ed. Dr. Gerald C. Smaldone. **Indexed:** Excerp.Med. (1993-). **Document type:** academic/scholarly publication.
—BLDSC (4919.054000); Genuine Article; SWETS; UnCover.
Description: Contains original articles and reviews that apply aerosols to the delivery of medication and the investigation for physiologic, pharmacologic, and toxicologic phenomena in the lung.

616.97   US   ISSN 0277-0903
RC591   CODEN: JOUADU
JOURNAL OF ASTHMA (NEW YORK). 1963. 6/yr. $65 to individuals; institutions $550. (Association for the Care of Asthma) Marcel Dekker Journals, 270 Madison Ave., New York, NY 10016. FAX 212-685-4540. TELEX 421419. (Subscr. to: Box 5017, Monticello, NY 12701) Ed. David Tinkelman. adv.; bk.rev.; bibl.; charts; illus.; stat.; index, cum. index: 1963-1965. (also avail. in microfilm; reprint service avail.) **Indexed:** Biol.Abstr., Chem.Abstr., Curr.Cont., Dent.Ind., Excerp.Med., Ind.Med., INIS Atomind., NRN, Psychol.Abstr. (1963-), Ref.Zh. **Document type:** academic/scholarly publication.
—BLDSC (4947.295000); ADONIS; CASDDS; Genuine Article; SWETS; UMI; UnCover. **CCC.**
Formerly (until vol.18, 1981): Journal of Asthma Research (ISSN 0021-9134)
Refereed Serial

616.2   US   ISSN 1070-8030
▼**JOURNAL OF BRONCHOLOGY.** 1994. q. $98 to individuals (foreign $120); institutions $128 (foreign $146) (effective 1996); newsstand price: $38. (World Association for Bronchology) Lippincott - Raven Publishers, 227 E. Washington Sq., Philadelphia, PA 19106. TEL 215-238-4200. (Co-sponsor: American Association for Bronchology) Ed. Udaya B.S. Prakash. adv. contact: Phyllis Noyes. charts; illus. circ. 1,000. **Document type:** academic/scholarly publication.
—BLDSC (4954.552500). **CCC.**
Description: Examines all aspects of the prevention, diagnosis and treatment of disorders affecting the respiratory system.
Refereed Serial

JOURNAL OF CHEMOTHERAPY. see MEDICAL SCIENCES — *Oncology*

616.2   US   ISSN 0194-259X
RC705   CODEN: JRDIFQ
JOURNAL OF RESPIRATORY DISEASES. 1979. m. $70. Cliggott Publishing Co., 55 Holly Hill Ln., Box 4010, Greenwich, CT 06830. TEL 203-661-0600. Ed. Craig R. Borders; Pub. Molly K. Sawyer. adv. contact: Amy Birnbach. circ. 86,000. (reprint service avail.) **Document type:** academic/scholarly publication.
—BLDSC (5052.038200); Faxon. **CCC.**
Description: Provides practical information about diagnosis and treatment pertaining to the respiratory system, both as the site of primary disease and as a complication of other clinical problems.
Refereed Serial

616.246   JA   ISSN 0022-9776
                   CODEN: KEKKAG
KEKKAKU/TUBERCULOSIS. (Text in Japanese; summaries in English) 1923. m. 15000 Yen. Japanese Society for Tuberculosis, c/o Research Institute of Tuberculosis, Matsuyama 3-chome, Kiyose-shi, Tokyo 204, Japan. TEL 81-424-92-2091. FAX 81-424-91-8315. (Subscr. to: Tonggang Shudian, Export Dept., Rm. 106 NKB Azeria Bldg., 7-7 Shin-Ogawachou, Shinjuku-ku, Tokyo 162 Japan. TEL 81-3-3269-2131. FAX 81-3-3269-8655) Ed. Keichi Nagao. adv.; abstr.; bibl.; charts; illus.; index. circ. 3,000. **Indexed:** Biol.Abstr., Chem.Abstr., Excerp.Med., Ind.Med., INIS Atomind. **Document type:** academic/scholarly publication.
—BLDSC (5089.250000); CASDDS; EMDOCS; UMI.
Description: Publishes original studies, reviews and case reports in the field of tuberculosis.

616.2   JA   ISSN 0452-3458
                   CODEN: KOJUA9
KOKYU TO JUNKAN/RESPIRATION AND CIRCULATION. (Text in Japanese; summaries in English) 1953. m. 2100 Yen per no. Igaku Shoin Ltd., 5-24-3 Hongo, Bunkyo-ku, Tokyo 113-91, Japan. TEL 03-817-5703. Ed.Bd. circ. 4,500. **Indexed:** Biol.Abstr., Chem.Abstr., Excerp.Med., Ind.Med., INIS Atomind.
●Also available online. Vendor(s): JICST.
—BLDSC (7777.630000); CASDDS.

KOKYUKI GEKA/JAPANESE ASSOCIATION FOR CHEST SURGERY. JOURNAL. see MEDICAL SCIENCES — *Surgery*

KOSANKINBYO KENKYUSHO ZASSHI. see MEDICAL SCIENCES — *Communicable Diseases*

LIVEWELL. see PHYSICAL FITNESS AND HYGIENE

616.2   IT   ISSN 0368-7546
                   CODEN: LCTMAU
LOTTA CONTRO LA TUBERCOLOSI E LE MALATTIE POLMONARI SOCIALI. (Text in Italian) 1930. q. L.60000. Federazione Italiana contro la Tubercolosi e le Malattie Polmonari Sociali, Via Giovanni da Procida 7-D, 00162 Rome, Italy. TEL 39-6-44240682. adv.; bk.rev.; bibl.; charts; illus.; stat.; index, cum. index: 1943-1944. circ. 3,000. **Indexed:** Abstr.Hyg., Biol.Abstr., C.I.S. Abstr., Chem.Abstr., Excerp.Med., Ind.Med., Trop.Dis.Bull. **Document type:** academic/scholarly publication, bulletin.
—BLDSC (5294.890000).
Formerly (until 1972): Lotta contro la Tubercolosi (ISSN 0024-6638)
Description: Covers the study and research of tuberculosis and respiratory diseases.

MEDICAL SCIENCES — RESPIRATORY DISEASES

616.2   US   ISSN 0341-2040
CODEN: LUNGD9
LUNG; an international journal on lungs, airways and breathing. (Text in English or German) 1903. bi-m. $247 (effective 1996). (Deutsche Gesellschaft fuer Lungen- und Atmungsforschung, GW) Springer-Verlag, Journals, 175 Fifth Ave., New York, NY 10010. TEL 212-460-1500.
FAX 212-473-6272. (N. American subscr. to: Journal Fulfillment Services, Box 2485, Secaucus, NJ 07096-2491. TEL 800-777-4643. FAX 201-348-4505; Elsewhere: Heidelberger Platz 3, 1000 Berlin 33, Germany. TEL 030-8207-1. FAX 030-8214091) Ed.Bd. adv.; bibl.; illus. (also avail. in microform from UMI; back issues avail.; reprint service avail. from ISI) **Indexed:** Biol.Abstr., Biotech.Abstr., C.I.S. Abstr., Chem.Abstr., Curr.Adv.Ecol.Sci., Curr.Cont., Excerp.Med., Ind.Med., Ind.Sci.Rev., Ind.Vet., INIS Atomind., Rev.Med.& Vet.Mycol., Vet.Bull. **Document type:** academic/scholarly publication.
—BLDSC (5307.160000); ADONIS; CASDDS; Faxon; Genuine Article; SWETS; UMI; UnCover. **CCC.**
Former titles: Pneumonologie - Pneumonology (ISSN 0033-4073); Beitraege zur Klinik und Erforschung der Tuberkulose und der Lungenkrankheiten.
Description: Contains original articles on all aspects of basic and clinical research dealing with the lungs, airways, and breathing, including developmental, environmental, and genetic aspects.
Refereed Serial

616.2   GW   ISSN 0176-1749
LUNG AND RESPIRATION; diseases of lung and respiratory tract. 1984. q. P M I Verlagsgruppe GmbH, August-Schanz-Str. 21, 60433 Frankfurt a.M., Germany. TEL 069-548000-0.
FAX 069-548000-77. TELEX 412952-PMI-D. Ed. Peter Hoffmann. circ. 5,000. (back issues avail.) **Document type:** academic/scholarly publication.

616.2   US   ISSN 0362-3181
CODEN: LBHDD7
LUNG BIOLOGY IN HEALTH AND DISEASE. 1976. irreg., vol.80, 1995. price varies. Marcel Dekker, Inc., 270 Madison Ave., New York, NY 10016.
TEL 212-696-9000. FAX 212-685-4540. TELEX 421419. **Indexed:** Biol.Abstr., Chem.Abstr.
—BLDSC (5307.240000); CASDDS. **CCC.**
Refereed Serial

616.2   US
LUNG LINE LETTER. 1986. q. free. National Jewish Center for Immunology and Respiratory Medicine, 1400 Jackson St., Denver, CO 80206.
TEL 303-398-1080. FAX 303-398-1125. Ed. Janet Bronk. circ. 130,000. **Document type:** newsletter.
Description: Assistance for patients coping with respiratory and immune system problems.

616.2   JA   ISSN 0919-5742
CODEN: LUPEFF
THE LUNG PERSPECTIVES. (Text in Japanese) 1993. 4/yr. 1600 Yen per no. Medikaru Rebyusha - Medical Review Co., Ltd., 7-3, Hiranomachi 1-chome, Chuo-ku, Osaka 541, Japan.

616.2   GW   ISSN 0720-0706
LUNGE UND ATMUNG. 1975. bi-m. DM.40. P M I Verlagsgruppe GmbH, August-Schanz-Str. 21, 60433 Frankfurt a.M., Germany.
TEL 069-548000-0. FAX 069-548000-77. TELEX 412952-PMI-D. (Co-sponsor: Dr. Karl Thomae GmbH) Ed. Peter Hoffmann. circ. 24,500. (back issues avail.) **Document type:** academic/scholarly publication.
Description: Seminar paper journal containing summaries of pneumologic articles and interviews.

616.2   JA   ISSN 0917-1363
MAKUGATA HAI/MEMBRANE OXYGENATOR. (Text in English, Japanese) 1978. a. Makugata Jinko Hai Kenkyukai Jimukyoku, c/o Okayama Daigaku Dai 2 Geka, 2-51, Shikatacho, Okayama-shi, Okayama-ken 700, Japan.

616.2   JA
MEDICAL CONFERENCE SERIES. 1961. a. Japan Anti-Tuberculosis Association - Kekkaku Yobokai, 3-12, Misakicho 1-chome, Chiyoda-ku, Tokyo 101, Japan. FAX 03-3292-9208. Ed. Masakazu Aoki. circ. 20,000.

616.2   US
MEDICAL SCIENTIFIC UPDATE. 1982. m. free. National Jewish Center for Immunology and Respiratory Medicine, 1400 Jackson St., Denver, CO 80206.
TEL 303-388-4461. FAX 303-398-1125. Ed. Adele Gelfand. circ. 26,000 (controlled).
Description: Informs physicians about clinical programs and research activities conducted at the center.

616.2   IT   ISSN 0393-8506
MEDICINA TORACICA; rassegna di fisiopatologia, clinica e riabilitazione cardiorespiratoria. 1978. q. L.85500($99) (Societa Italiana di Fisiopatologia Respiratoria) Masson S.p.A., Divisione Periodici, Via Statuto 2-4, 20121 Milan, Italy. TEL 02-6367-1.
FAX 02-6367211. (Co-sponsor: Fondazione pro Clinica del Lavoro di Pavia) Ed. Carlo Grassi. adv.; B&W page L.2100000, color page L.3300000; trim 170 x 235. circ. 1,000. **Document type:** academic/scholarly publication.
Refereed Serial

616.2   US   ISSN 0047-7060
MICHIGAN SOCIETY FOR RESPIRATORY THERAPY.
JOURNAL. 1965. s-a. membership. Michigan Society for Respiratory Therapy, Box 950, 120 W. Saginaw St., E. Lansing, MI 48823. Ed. John Darin. adv.; bk.rev.; abstr. circ. 2,000. (tabloid format) **Indexed:** CINAHL.
Formerly (until spring 1975): Michigan Airway.

616.2   IT   ISSN 0026-4954
MINERVA PNEUMOLOGICA; rivista trimestrale di fisiopatologia e clinica delle malattie dell'apparato respiratorio. (Text in Italian; summaries in English and Italian) 1962. q. $90 to individuals; institutions $140 (effective 1995). (Societa Italiana di Pneumologia) Edizioni Minerva Medica, Corso Bramante 83-85, 10126 Turin, Italy.
TEL 39-11-678282. FAX 39-11-3121736. Ed. O. Orlandi; Pub. Alberto Oliaro. adv.; B&W page $1100, color page $1900; trim 190 x 270; adv. contact: F. Filippo. bibl.; charts; illus.; index; circ. 2,000 (paid). (also avail. in microform from UMI) **Indexed:** Biol.Abstr., Excerp.Med.
—BLDSC (5794.450000); EMDOCS; UMI.
Description: Covers pathophysiology and clinical medicine of the diseases of the respiratory system.
Refereed Serial

616.2   IT   ISSN 1122-0643
CODEN: MACDE
MONALDI ARCHIVES FOR CHEST DISEASE. (Text in Italian; summaries in English, French) 1945. bi-m. L.70000($100) (effective 1993). PI-ME Tipografia Editrice s.r.l., Viale Sardegna 24, 27100 Pavia, Italy. adv. **Indexed:** Biol.Abstr., Chem.Abstr., Dent.Ind., Excerp.Med., Ind.Med. **Document type:** academic/scholarly publication.
—BLDSC (5901.590800); CASDDS.
Former titles (until 1994): Archivio Monaldi per le Malattie del Torace (ISSN 1120-0391); (until 1987): Archivio di Tisiologia e delle Malattie dell'Aparato Respiratorio (ISSN 0004-0185)
Description: Publishes original works, editorials, and reviews on matters of the pathology of the upper respiratory system.

MUCOSAL IMMUNOLOGY UPDATE. see *MEDICAL SCIENCES — Allergology And Immunology*

616.246 614   II
N T I BULLETIN. (Text in English) 1964. q. free. National Tuberculosis Institute, No. 8 Bellary Rd., Bangalore 560003, India. TEL 361192-93. Ed.Bd. bk.rev.; abstr.; bibl.; illus. circ. 1,000. **Document type:** bulletin.
Formerly (until vol.29, 1993): N T I Newsletter (ISSN 0047-9136)
Description: Contains original research articles, field reports, TB programmes, and discussions on current problems in the field.

NATIONAL CENTRE FOR OCCUPATIONAL HEALTH. ANNUAL REPORT. see *OCCUPATIONAL HEALTH AND SAFETY*

616.2   NE   ISSN 0925-1944
NEDERLANDSE CYSTIC FIBROSIS STICHTING. C F NIEUWS. 1969. q. fl.2.10. Nederlandse Cystic Fibrosis Stichting, Lt. Gen. van Heutszlaan 6, 3743 JN Baarn, Netherlands. Ed. H. Wevers. circ. 2,000.
Formerly: Nederlandse Cystic Fibrosis Stichting. Bericht.

616.2   JA   ISSN 0029-0645
NIHON KIKAN SHOKUDOKA GAKKAI KAIHO/JAPAN BRONCHO-ESOPHAGOLOGICAL SOCIETY. JOURNAL.
(Text in Japanese; summaries in English) 1949. bi-m. 13000 Yen. Nihon Kikan Shokudoka Gakkai - Japan Broncho-Esophagological Society, Hakuo Bldg., 2-3-10 Koraku, Bunkyo-ku, Tokyo 112, Japan. FAX 03-3815-2810. Ed. Seiji Niimi. adv.; bk.rev.; abstr.; cum.index. circ. 3,850. **Indexed:** Biol.Abstr., Excerp.Med. **Document type:** academic/scholarly publication.

613   US
NOVA REPORT ON LUNG HEALTH AND WELLNESS. 1964. bi-m. free. American Lung Association of Northern Virginia, 9735 Main St., Fairfax, VA 22031. TEL 703-591-4131. Ed. Kurt Gregory Erickson. film rev.; stat. circ. 6,000. (processed)
Former titles (until 1983): Potomac View on Lung Health; Potomac View (ISSN 0032-5643)

616.2   CN
ONTARIO THORACIC REVIEWS. 1985. 3/yr. free to members. Ontario Thoracic Society, 573 King St. E., Toronto, ON M5A 4L3, Canada.
TEL 416-864-9911. FAX 416-864-9916. Ed. Dr. Robert Hyland. adv. circ. 6,000. **Document type:** trade publication.
Description: Covers advances in treatment and prevention of respiratory disease.

616.2   SP   ISSN 0212-1522
P A R. (Patologia del Aparato Respiratorio) 1980. 12/yr. Luz, Virgen de la Alegria 9, 28027 Madrid, Spain. TEL 1-405-15-95. FAX 1-403-49-07. Ed. J.M. Monturiol.

PEDIATRIC PULMONOLOGY. see *MEDICAL SCIENCES — Pediatrics*

PERSPECTIVES IN RESPIRATORY NURSING. see *MEDICAL SCIENCES — Nurses And Nursing*

616.2   US
PNEUMOGRAM.* 1980. q. free. California Society of Respiratory Care, c/o Equicor Health Plan, 505 N. Brand Blvd. 300, Glendale, CA 91203-1925.
TEL 818-995-7338. FAX 818-995-0878. Ed. Chuck Swanson. adv. circ. 2,623.

616.2   BU   ISSN 0324-1491
CODEN: PNFTD3
PNEUMOLOGIA I FTIZIATRIA. (Text in Bulgarian; summaries in English, Russian) 1964. q. 240 lv.($70) Tsentar za Informatsiia po Meditsina, 1, Sv. Georgi Sofiiski St., 1431 Sofia, Bulgaria. TEL 359-2-522342. (Co-sponsor: Nauchno Druzhestvo po Pneumologia i Ftiziatria) Ed. P. Dobrev. circ. 603. **Indexed:** Abstr.Bulg.Sci.Med.Lit., C.I.S. Abstr., Excerp.Med. (until 1993). **Document type:** academic/scholarly publication.
Formerly: Ftiziatria.
Description: Publishes original articles on lung diseases with emphasis on tuberculosis.

616.2   GW   ISSN 0934-8387
CODEN: PNEMEC
PNEUMOLOGIE. (Text in German; summaries in English, French, German, Spanish) 1945. m. DM.270. (Deutsches Zentralkommittee zur Bekaempfung der Tuberkulose) Georg Thieme Verlag, Ruedigerstr. 14, 70469 Stuttgart, Germany. TEL 0711-8931-0. FAX 0711-8931298. (Subscr. to: Postfach 104853, 70042 Stuttgart, Germany) (Co-sponsor: Deutsche Gesellschaft fuer Lungenkrankheiten und Tuberkulose) Ed. R. Ferlinz. adv.; bk.rev.; charts; illus.; stat.; index. circ. 2,500. (also avail. in microfilm from UMI; reprint service avail. from UMI) **Indexed:** Biol.Abstr., C.I.S. Abstr., Chem.Abstr., Curr.Cont., Dent.Ind., Ind.Med., Ind.Vet., Sci.Cit.Ind., Vet.Bull. **Document type:** academic/scholarly publication.
—BLDSC (6541.113200); ADONIS; SWETS; UMI. **CCC.**
Former titles: Praxis und Klinik der Pneumologie (ISSN 0342-7498); Praxis der Pneumologie (ISSN 0032-7069); Incorporates: Tuberkulosearzt.

MEDICAL SCIENCES — RESPIRATORY DISEASES

616.2   PL   ISSN 0867-7077
CODEN: PAPKE4
PNEUMONOLOGIA I ALERGOLOGIA POLSKA. (Text and abstracts in English and Polish) 1926. bi-m. $168. Institute of Tuberculosis and Pulmonary Deseases, Ul. Plocka 26, 01-138 Warsaw, Poland. TEL 48-22-324451. (Co-sponsors: Polish Society of Allergology; Polish Society of Phtysiopneunomology) Ed. Tadeusz Plusa. adv.; bk.rev.; abstr.; illus.; stat. circ. 1,500. **Indexed:** Chem.Abstr., Dok.Arbeitsmed., Excerp.Med., Ind.Med. **Document type:** academic/scholarly publication.
—BLDSC (6541.112200); CASDDS.
Former titles (until 1991): Pneumonologia Polska (ISSN 0376-4761); Gruzlica i Choroby Pluc (ISSN 0017-4955)
Description: Discusses diseases of the lungs, epidemiology, physiology of respiration and clinical pneumonology, allergic diseases of the respiratory system.

616.246   RU   ISSN 0032-9533
CODEN: PRTUAX
PROBLEMY TUBERKULEZA/PROBLEMS OF TUBERCULOSIS. (Text in Russian; summaries in English) 1923. bi-m. $79. (Nauchnoe Obshchestvo Ftiziatrov) Izdatel'stvo Meditsina, Petroverigskii pereulok 6-8, 101000 Moscow, Russia. (Dist. by: Mezhdunarodnaya Kniga, B. Yakimanka 39, 117049 Moscow, Russian. TEL 7-095-2384600. FAX 7-095-2384634) (Co-sponsor: Ministerstvo Zdravookhraneniya) Ed. A.G. Khomenko. adv. contact: A.G. Khomenko. bk.rev.; index. **Indexed:** Biol.Abstr., Chem.Abstr., Dent.Ind., Dok.Arbeitsmed., Excerp.Med., Ind.Med., Ind.Vet., Vet.Bull.
—BLDSC (0133.840000); CASDDS; EMDOCS. **CCC.**
Description: Deals with problems of epidemiology and organization of tuberculosis control, as well as prophylaxis, clinical diagnosis and treatment of tuberculosis. Includes data on the theoretical and practical achievements in phthisis and pulmonology.

616.2   SZ   ISSN 0079-6751
QP121.A1   CODEN: PGRRB6
PROGRESS IN RESPIRATION RESEARCH. (Text in English) 1963. irreg. (approx. 1/yr.). price varies. S. Karger AG, Allschwilerstr. 10, P.O. Box, CH-4009 Basel, Switzerland. TEL 061-3061111. FAX 061-3061234. E-mail: Karger@Karger.ch. Ed. H. Herzog. (reprint service avail. from ISI) **Indexed:** Biol.Abstr., Chem.Abstr., Curr.Adv.Ecol.Sci., Curr.Cont., Ind.Med. **Document type:** academic/scholarly publication.
—BLDSC (6924.525500); CASDDS; Faxon. **CCC.**
Description: Surveys of new knowledge on normal and impaired respiratory function.
Refereed Serial

616.2   US
PULMONARY PERSPECTIVES. q. American College of Chest Physicians, 3300 Dundee Rd., Northbrook, IL 60062. TEL 708-498-1400. FAX 708-498-5460. Ed. Deborah Shure. circ. 16,000. **Document type:** academic/scholarly publication.
Description: Contains brief articles with editorial commentary for practicing physicians in the chest disciplines.
Refereed Serial

616.2   UK   ISSN 0952-0600
CODEN: PUPHEX
PULMONARY PHARMACOLOGY (LONDON). 1988. bi-m. £210 (effective 1996). Academic Press Ltd. (Subsidiary of: Harcourt Brace & Company Ltd.), 24-28 Oval Rd., London, NW1 7DX, England. TEL 44-171-267-4466. FAX 44-171-482-2293. TELEX 25775 ACPRES G. (Subscr. to: Harcourt Brace & Company Ltd., Foots Cray High St., Sidcup, Kent DA14 5HP, England. TEL 44-181-300-3322. FAX 44-181-309-0807) Eds. P.J. Barnes, J. Douglas. **Indexed:** Biol.Abstr., Chem.Abstr., Curr.Cont., Excerp.Med., Ind.Med. (1992-). **Document type:** academic/scholarly publication.
—BLDSC (7156.975000); ADONIS; CASDDS; Genuine Article; SWETS. **CCC.**
Description: Presents articles on all aspects of lung pharmacology.

615.64   CN   ISSN 0831-2478
R R T: THE CANADIAN JOURNAL OF RESPIRATORY THERAPY. 1965. q. (plus suppl.). Can.$30($30) Canadian Medical Association, P.O. Box 8650, Ottawa, ON K1G 0G8, Canada. TEL 613-731-9331. FAX 613-523-0937. Ed. Cliff Seville. adv.; bk.rev.; charts; illus.; stat.; bibl. circ. 3,000. (back issues avail.) **Indexed:** C.I.N.L. **Document type:** academic/scholarly publication.
Former titles: Respiratory Technology; Canadian Inhalation Therapy (ISSN 0008-3852)
Description: Official publication of Canadian Society of Respiratory Therapists. Contains feature articles, new product news, history, editorials and abstracts.
Refereed Serial

616.2   US   ISSN 1040-6050
R T; the journal for respiratory care practitioners. 1988. bi-m. free to qualified personnel. Allied Healthcare Publications, 4676 Admiralty Way, Ste. 202, Marina Del Rey, CA 90292. TEL 310-306-2206. FAX 310-301-8101. Ed. Peri Caylor. adv. contact: Michelle Lee. circ. 20,000. (controlled). **Document type:** trade publication.
Description: Features literature reviews of clinical topics, articles on respiratory care department management, legislative and regulatory news, case reports, profiles of outstanding facilities and practitioners, and departments containing news, industry news, and new product information.

616.2   US
R T MAGAZINE. (Respiratory Therapy) 1988. bi-m. Curant Communications, Inc., 4676 Admiralty Way., Ste. 202, Marina Del Rey, CA 90292-6603. TEL 213-479-1769. FAX 213-301-3329. Ed. Sandra Todd.

616.2   IT   ISSN 0033-9563
RASSEGNA DI PATOLOGIA DELL'APPARATO RESPIRATORIO. 1951. bi-m. L.100000 (foreign L.130000) (effective 1995). (Associazione Italiana Pneumologi Ospedalieri) Pacini Editore s.r.l., Via A. Gherardesca 1, 56121 Ospedaletto (Pisa), Italy. TEL 39-50-982439. FAX 39-50-983906. Ed. Benito Leoncini. adv.; bk.rev.; bibl.; charts; illus.; index. circ. 1,000. **Indexed:** Chem.Abstr., Excerp.Med.

616.2   JA   ISSN 0016-2531
RED DOUBLE-BARRED CROSS/FUKUJUJI. (Text in Japanese) 1955. bi-m. free. Japan Anti-Tuberculosis Association - Kekkaku Yobokai, 1-3-12 Misaki-cho, Chiyoda-ku, Tokyo 101, Japan. FAX 03-3292-9208. Ed. Tetsuo Kawakami. adv.; bk.rev.; charts; illus.; stat. circ. 20,000.

REFERATOVY VYBER Z PNEUMOLOGIE A TUBERKULOSY/ABSTRACTS OF PNEUMOLOGY AND TUBERCULOSIS. see *MEDICAL SCIENCES — Abstracting, Bibliographies, Statistics*

616.2   AG   ISSN 0326-9116
RESPIRACION; revista de enfermedades respiratorias y tuberculosis. 1986. q. Fundacion Ayuda al Enfermo Respiratorio, Av. Velez Sarsfield 405, 1281 Buenos Aires, Argentina. Ed. Luis Julio Gonzalez Montaner.

617.54 616.995   SZ   ISSN 0025-7931
RC705   CODEN: RESPBD
RESPIRATION; international review of thoracic diseases. (Text in English, French and German; summaries in English) 1944. bi-m. 366.60 SFr.($282.) to individuals; institutions 611 SFr.($470) (effective 1996). S. Karger AG, Allschwilerstr. 10, P.O. Box, CH-4009 Basel, Switzerland. TEL 061-3061111. FAX 061-3061234. E-mail: Karger@Karger.ch. Ed. H. Herzog. adv.; charts; illus. circ. 1,200. (also avail. in microform) **Indexed:** Biol.Abstr., C.I.S. Abstr., Chem.Abstr., Curr.Adv.Ecol.Sci., Curr.Cont., Dok.Arbeitsmed., Excerp.Med., Helminthol.Abstr., Ind.Med., Rev.Plant Path. **Document type:** academic/scholarly publication.
—BLDSC (7777.620000); CASDDS; EMDOCS; Faxon; Genuine Article; SWETS; UnCover. **CCC.**
Formerly: Medicina Thoracalis.
Refereed Serial

615.64   US   ISSN 0730-8418
RESPIRATORY CARE; a monthly science journal. 1956. m. $50. (American Association for Respiratory Care) Daedalus Enterprises, Inc., 11030 Ables Lane, Dallas, TX 75229. TEL 214-243-2272. FAX 214-484-6010. Ed. Pat Brougher. adv.; bk.rev.; abstr.; charts; illus.; index. circ. 38,000. (also avail. in microform from UMI; reprint service avail.) **Indexed:** Biol.Abstr., C.I.N.L., CINAHL, Excerp.Med., Hosp.Lit.Ind., Nurs.Abstr.
—BLDSC (7777.660000); EMDOCS; Faxon; SWETS; UMI; UnCover. **CCC.**
Former titles (until 1979): R C Respiratory Care (ISSN 0098-9142); (until 1973): Respiratory Care (ISSN 0020-1324); (until 1970): Inhalation Therapy.

615.64   US   ISSN 1078-5337
▼**RESPIRATORY CARE CLINICS.** 1995. q. $65 (foreign $90) (effective 1996). W.B. Saunders Co. (Subsidiary of: Harcourt Brace & Company), Curtis Center, 3rd Fl., Philadelphia, PA 19106-3399. TEL 215-238-7800. FAX 215-238-6445. (Subscr. to: Periodicals Fulfillment, W.B. Saunders Co., 6277 Sea Harbor Dr., 4th Fl., Orlando, FL 32891-4800. TEL 800-654-2452. FAX 800-874-6418) Eds. Richard D. Branson, Dr. Neil MacIntyre. **Document type:** academic/scholarly publication.
Description: Contains clinical and experimental reviews aimed primarily at respiratory therapists, as well as physicians and nurses involved in this area of care.

616.2 658   US   ISSN 1076-6030
RESPIRATORY CARE MANAGER. 1992. m. $127. Opus Communications, Box 1168, Marblehead, MA 01945. TEL 617-639-1872. FAX 617-639-2982. (looseleaf format) **Document type:** newsletter.
Description: Provides information and guidance for managers in respiratory care, including coverage of regulatory issues, quality improvement, patient-focused care, budget and staff management techniques.

616.2   UK   ISSN 0262-7043
RESPIRATORY DISEASE IN PRACTICE. Abbreviated title: R D I P. 1982. q. £331 (overseas £35) (effective 1995). Hayward Medical Communications Ltd., 44 Earlham St., Covent Garden, London WC2H 9LA, England. TEL 44-171-240-4493. FAX 44-171-240-4479. (Subscr. to: Essex House, Cromwell Park, Chipping Norton, Oxon. OX7 5SR, England. TEL 44-1608-645564. FAX 44-1608-645645) Ed. Dr. Martyn Partridge. adv.; bk.rev. circ. 21,000. **Document type:** academic/scholarly publication.
—BLDSC (7777.661000).

616.2   NE   ISSN 0923-7240
RESPIRATORY DISEASES DIGEST. 8/yr. fl.60.50. Uitgeverij Promedia B.V., De Steiger 180, 1351 AT Almere, Netherlands. Ed. Hans Weill. adv. circ. 400.

616.246   KE
RESPIRATORY DISEASES RESEARCH CENTRE. ANNUAL REPORT. (Text in English) 1974. a. free. Kenya Medical Research Institute, Kenya Tuberculosis & Respiratory Diseases Research Centre, P.O. Box 47855, Nairobi, Kenya. circ. 200. (back issues avail.) **Indexed:** Biol.Abstr.
Former titles: Kenya Tuberculosis and Respiratory Diseases Research Center. Annual Report; Kenya Tuberculosis Investigation Centre. Annual Report; Supersedes in part: East African Tuberculosis Investigation Centre. Annual Report.

MEDICAL SCIENCES — RESPIRATORY DISEASES

616.2   UK   ISSN 0954-6111
CODEN: RMEDEY
RESPIRATORY MEDICINE. 1907. 10/yr. £101 in Europe (rest of world $186) to individuals; institutions £142 in Europe (rest of world $256). W.B. Saunders Co. Ltd. (Subsidiary of: Harcourt Brace & Company Ltd.), 24-28 Oval Rd., London NW1 7DX, England. TEL 0171-267-4466. FAX 0171-482-2293. TELEX 25775-ACPRES-G. (Subscr. to: Harcourt Brace & Company Ltd., Foots Cray High St., Sidcup, Kent DA14 5HP, England. TEL 0181-300-3322. FAX 0181-309-0807; US, Canadian, and Mexican subscr. to: W.B. Saunders Co., Journals Subscription Fulfillment, 6277 Sea Harbor Dr., 4th Fl., Orlando, FL 32887-4800) Ed R. Davies. adv.; bk.rev.; charts; illus.; stat.; index. (also avail. in microform from UMI; back issues avail.) **Indexed:** Abstr.Hyg., Biol.Abstr., Biotech.Abstr., C.I.S. Abstr., Chem.Abstr., Curr.Adv.Ecol.Sci., Curr.Cont., Excerp.Med., Helminthol.Abstr., Ind.Med., Ind.Sci.Rev., Protozool.Abstr., Rev.Plant Path., Trop.Dis.Bull. **Document type:** academic/scholarly publication.
●Also available online. Vendor(s): Ovid Technologies.
—BLDSC (7777.661900); Faxon; Genuine Article; SWETS; UMI; UnCover. **CCC.**
Formerly: British Journal of Diseases of the Chest (ISSN 0007-0971)
Description: Provides an international forum for people involved in the various disciplines concerned with all aspects of respiratory tract diseases.

RESPIRATORY PHARMACOLOGY AND PHARMACOTHERAPY. see *PHARMACY AND PHARMACOLOGY*

616.2   US   ISSN 0895-0881
RESPIRATORY PRACTITIONER.* 1986. q. $25. Reliable Multi-Media Productions, 5705 Sepulveda Blvd., Culver City, CA 90230-6405. Eds. James B. Fink, Stephan W. Ruesh. adv. circ. 20,000.
Description: For individuals and institutions involved in the services and technologies of respiratory care and its associated diseases.

RESPIRATORY SYSTEM. see *BIOLOGY — Physiology*

616.2   AT   ISSN 1323-7799
▼**RESPIROLOGY.** Announced for publication in 1996. q. Aus.$282($200) (effective 1996). Blackwell Science Pty Ltd, P.O. Box 378, Carlton South, Vic. 3053, Australia. TEL 61-3-93470300. FAX 61-3-93493016. **Document type:** academic/scholarly publication.

616.2 615.8   IE   ISSN 0300-9572
CODEN: RSUSBS
RESUSCITATION; an interdisciplinary journal for the dissemination of clinical and basic science research relating to acute care medicine and cardiopulmonary resuscitation. 1972. bi-m. I£308($487) (effective 1996). (European Resuscitation Council) Elsevier Science Ireland Ltd., P.O. Box 85, Limerick, Ireland. TEL 353-61-471944. FAX 353-61-472144. (Subscr. in U.S. and Canada to: Elsevier Science Inc., Box 882, Madison Sq. Sta., New York, NY 10159. TEL 212-989-5800. FAX 212-633-3990) Eds. D. Chamberlain, J. Ornato. adv.; bk.rev.; charts; illus.; index. (also avail. in microform from UMI) **Indexed:** Biol.Abstr., Bull.Signal., Chem.Abstr., Curr.Adv.Ecol.Sci., Curr.Cont., Excerp.Med., Ind.Med. **Document type:** academic/scholarly publication.
—BLDSC (7785.420000); CASDDS; Faxon; Genuine Article; SWETS; UnCover. **CCC.**
Description: Covers etiology, pathophysiology, diagnosis and treatment of acute diseases.
Refereed Serial

616.995 616.2   RM
REVISTA DE IGIENA, BACTERIOLOGIE, VIRUSOLOGIE, PARAZITOLOGIE, PNEUMOFTIZIOLOGIE. (Text in Rumanian; summaries in English, French, German, Russian) 1952. 4/yr. $20. Uniunea Societatilor de Stiinte Medicale din Republica Socialista Rumania, Str. Progresului No. 8, Sect. 1, Bucharest, Rumania. TEL 13-89-73. (Subscr. to: ILEXIM, Str. 13 Decembrie Nr. 3, P.O. Box 136-137, Bucharest, Rumania) Ed.Bd. adv.; bk.rev.; abstr.; charts; illus. **Indexed:** Biol.Abstr., Chem.Abstr., Ind.Med.
Formerly: Ftiziologia (ISSN 0016-2329)

616.2 616.1   FR   ISSN 0761-8417
CODEN: RPCLEZ
REVUE DE PNEUMOLOGIE CLINIQUE; le poumon et le coeur. (Text in French; summaries in English) 1945. bi-m. 808 F. (foreign 1007 F.) (effective 1996). Masson - Periodiques, Villa Laromiguiere, 75005 Paris, France. TEL 1-40-46-62-00. FAX 1-40-46-62-01. Eds. C. Mayaud, M. Milleron. adv.; bk.rev.; abstr.; bibl.; charts; illus.; stat.; index. circ. 1,500. (also avail. in microform from UMI; reprint service avail. from ISI,UMI) **Indexed:** Biol.Abstr., C.I.S. Abstr., Chem.Abstr., Dent.Ind., Dok.Arbeitsmed., Excerp.Med., Ind.Med., Rev.Med.& Vet.Mycol., Rev.Plant Path. **Document type:** academic/scholarly publication.
—BLDSC (7942.535000); CASDDS; EMDOCS; Faxon; SWETS; UMI. **CCC.**
Formerly: Poumon et le Coeur (ISSN 0032-5821)
Description: Devoted to the pathology and therapy of afflictions of the respiratory tract.

616.2   FR   ISSN 0761-8425
CODEN: RMREEY
REVUE DES MALADIES RESPIRATOIRES. 1893. bi-m. 840 F. (foreign 1161 F.) (effective 1996). (Societe Francaise de Tuberculose) Masson - Periodiques, Villa Laromiguiere, 75005 Paris, France. TEL 1-40-46-62-00. FAX 1-40-46-62-01. (Co-sponsor: Comite National de Defense Contre la Tuberculose) Ed. B. Housset. adv.; bk.rev.; abstr.; illus.; index. circ. 3,000. (also avail. in microfilm; reprint service avail. from ISI) **Indexed:** ASCA, Biol.Abstr., C.I.S. Abstr., Chem.Abstr., Curr.Adv.Ecol.Sci., Curr.Cont., Dok.Arbeitsmed., Excerp.Med., Helminthol.Abstr., Ind.Med., Rev.Plant Path. **Document type:** academic/scholarly publication.
—BLDSC (7926.824000); CASDDS; Faxon; Genuine Article; SWETS. **CCC.**
Former titles (until 1983): Revue Francaise des Maladies Respiratoires (ISSN 0301-0279); (until 1973): Revue de Tuberculose et de Pneumologie (ISSN 0035-1792)
Description: Publishes original articles on clinical and laboratory work in the field of respiratory diseases.

616.2   JA   ISSN 0911-1182
RINSHO KOKYU SEIRI/JOURNAL OF CLINICAL RESPIRATORY PHYSIOLOGY. (Text in Japanese) 1968. s-a. 2000 Yen per no. (Rinsho Kokyu Seiri Kenkyukai - Society of Clinical Respiratory Physiology) Faiza Seiyaku K.K. - Pfizer Pharmaceuticals, Inc., 1-1, Nishishinju-ku 2-chome, Shinjuku-ku, Tokyo 160, Japan.

616.2   IT   ISSN 0302-4717
RIVISTA DI PATOLOGIA E CLINICA DELLA TUBERCOLOSI E DI PNEUMOLOGIA. (Text in Italian; summaries in English, French) 1927. bi-m. L.40000($70) Associazione Emilia Romagna Contro la Tubercolosi e le Malatie Polmonari Sociali, Via Brugnoli 5, 40122 Bologna, Italy. Ed. Enrico Fasano. adv.; bk.rev.; abstr.; index, cum.index. circ. 1,000. **Indexed:** Biol.Abstr., Excerp.Med. (until 1993).
Formerly: Rivista di Patologia e Clinica della Tubercolosi (ISSN 0035-6425)

616.2   SA   ISSN 0081-2501
S A N T A ANNUAL REPORT. (Text in English) 1949. a. free. South African National Tuberculosis Association - Suid-Afrikaanse Nasionale Tuberkulose Vereniging, P.O. Box 10501, Johannesburg 2000, South Africa. TEL 27-11-3369636. FAX 27-11-333-9057. Ed. Heather Basson. circ. 2,000. **Document type:** corporate report.
Description: Features SANTA's financial statements, review of the year's activities, history of investments made, as well as the present status of TB containment.

616.246   SA
S.A.N.T.A. T B AND HEALTH NEWS. (Text in English) 1953. m. donation. South African National Tuberculosis Association - Suid-Afrikaanse Nasionale Tuberkulose Vereniging, P.O. Box 10501, Johannesburg 2000, South Africa. TEL 27-11-3369636. FAX 27-11-333-9057. Ed. Heather Basson. adv.; illus.; stat. circ. 10,500. **Document type:** newsletter.
Formerly (until vol.33, no.9, 1994): S.A.N.T.A. T B News (ISSN 0036-8972)
Description: Informs readers of news and events involving the association, and discusses issues relating to tuberculosis in South Africa.

616.2   US   ISSN 1069-3424
CODEN: SRCCEX
SEMINARS IN RESPIRATORY AND CRITICAL CARE MEDICINE. 1979. bi-m. $99 to individuals (foreign $124); institutions $135 (foreign $160). Thieme Medical Publishers, Inc., 381 Park Ave. S., Ste. 1501, New York, NY 10016. TEL 212-683-5088. FAX 212-779-9020. (Overseas subscr. to: Georg Thieme Verlag, Postfach 30 11 20, 70451 Stuttgart 10, Germany) Eds. T.L. Petty, R.M. Cherniack. adv.; index. circ. 2,700. (also avail. in microform from UMI; reprint service avail. from UMI) **Indexed:** ASCA, Curr.Adv.Ecol.Sci., Excerp.Med., Rev.Med.& Vet.Mycol. **Document type:** academic/scholarly publication.
●Also available online. Vendor(s): Ovid Technologies.
—BLDSC (8239.457750); Faxon; Genuine Article; SWETS; UMI; UnCover. **CCC.**
Formerly (until 1994): Seminars in Respiratory Medicine (ISSN 0192-9755)
Description: Contains clinical articles written by pulmonary clinicians providing an overview of principles and practice of modern respiratory care.

616.2   US   ISSN 0882-0546
CODEN: SRINES
SEMINARS IN RESPIRATORY INFECTIONS. (Translated into Spanish) 1986 (Mar.). q. $135 (foreign $169) (effective 1996). W.B. Saunders Co. (Subsidiary of: Harcourt Brace & Company), Curtis Center, 3rd Fl., Independence Sq. W., Philadelphia, PA 19106-3399. TEL 215-238-7800. FAX 215-238-644. (Subscr. to: Periodicals Fulfillment, W.B. Saunders Co., 6277 Sea Harbor Dr., 4th Fl., Orlando, FL 32891-4800. TEL 800-654-2452. FAX 800-874-6418) Ed. Dr. George A. Sarosi; Pub. Joan W. Blumberg. adv.: B&W page 700, color page $1650, 7 x 10. abstr.; bibl.; charts; illus.; index. circ. 875. **Document type:** academic/scholarly publication.
—BLDSC (8239.457800); Faxon; SWETS; UnCover. **CCC.**
Description: Each issue treats a type of infection relative to lung disorders in depth.

616.2   US   ISSN 8756-8616
TECHNOLOGY FOR RESPIRATORY THERAPY. m. $95. (Emergency Care Research Institute) E C R I, 5200 Butler Pike, Plymouth Meeting, PA 19462. TEL 610-825-6000. FAX 610-834-1275. Ed. Michele Moscarella. **Document type:** newsletter.
—**CCC.**
Formerly: Health Devices Update: Respiratory Therapy.
Description: Contains technology-related information for respiratory specialists.
Refereed Serial

616.2   NE   ISSN 0040-2125
TEGEN DE TUBERCULOSE. 1904. q. free. Koninklijke Nederlandse Centrale Vereniging tot Bestrijding der Tuberculose, P.O. Box 146, 2501 CC The Hague, Netherlands. Ed.Bd. adv.; bk.rev.; illus. circ. 5,500.

616.2   UY   ISSN 0049-4143
TORAX. (Text in Spanish; summaries in English) 1952. q. Urg.$15($20) Sociedad de Tisiologia y Enfermedades del Torax de Uruguay, Avda. 18 de Julio 2175, Casilla de Correo 10724, Montevideo, Uruguay. (Co-sponsor: Sociedad de Cardiologia) Ed. Dante Tomalino. adv.; bibl.; charts; illus.; index. **Indexed:** Biol.Abstr., Excerp.Med., Ind.Med.
Supersedes: Revista de Tuberculosis del Uruguay.

MEDICAL SCIENCES — RHEUMATOLOGY

616.246 UK ISSN 0962-8479
CODEN: TLDIEP
TUBERCLE AND LUNG DISEASE. 1991. bi-m. £220($352) to institutions (effective 1995). (International Union against Tuberculosis and Lung Disease) Churchill Livingstone Medical Journals (Subsidiary of: Pearson Professional), Robert Stevenson House, 1-3 Baxter's Pl., Leith Walk, Edinburgh EH1 3AF, Scotland. TEL 0131-556-2424. FAX 0131-459-1177. (Subscr. to: Pearson Professional Ltd., P.O. Box 77, Fourth Ave., Harlow, Essex CM19 5AA, England. TEL 01279-623760; U.S. subscr. to: Churchill Livingstone, 650 Ave. of the Americas, New York, NY 10011. TEL 212-206-5000) Ed. M.D. Iseman. adv. contact: David Dunnachie. bk.rev.; abstr.; bibl.; illus.; index. circ. 2,300. Indexed: Abstr.Hyg., Biol.Abstr., Biotech.Abstr., Chem.Abstr., Curr.Adv.Ecol.Sci., Curr.Cont., Excerp.Med., Ind.Med., Ind.Vet., Rev.Med.& Vet.Mycol., Trop.Dis.Bull., Vet.Bull. **Document type:** academic/scholarly publication.
—BLDSC (9068.105000); ADONIS; Faxon; Genuine Article; SWETS; UnCover. **CCC.**
Formed by the merger of (1919-1992): Tubercle (ISSN 0041-3879) & International Union against Tuberculosis and Lung Disease. Bulletin; Which was formerly (1924-1986): International Union against Tuberculosis. Bulletin (ISSN 0074-9249)
Description: Publishes primary articles and commissioned reviews on both research and clinical work in tuberculosis and other lung diseases, with particular emphasis on community health.
Refereed Serial

616.246 614 US
RC313
U.S. CENTERS FOR DISEASE CONTROL. TUBERCULOSIS STATISTICS IN THE UNITED STATES. 1974. irreg., latest 1991. free. U.S. Centers for Disease Control, Division of Tuberculosis Elimination, 1600 Clifton Rd., N.E., Atlanta, GA 30333. TEL 404-634-2512. charts; illus. circ. 7,000. **Document type:** government publication.
Formed by the merger of: U.S. Centers for Disease Control. Tuberculosis in the United States (ISSN 0149-2616); U.S. Centers for Disease Control. Tuberculosis Statistics: States and Cities; Which was formerly: U.S. Centers for Disease Control. Tuberculosis: States and Cities; Which was formed by the merger of: U.S. Centers for Disease Control. Reported Tuberculosis Data; U.S. Centers for Disease Control. Tuberculosis Program Reports.

616.995 AG ISSN 0301-8911
UNIVERSIDAD DE BUENOS AIRES. CATEDRA DE PATOLOGIA Y CLINICA DE LA TUBERCULOSIS. ANALES. vol.29, 1970. irreg. Universidad de Buenos Aires, Catedra de Patologia y Clinica de la Tuberculosis, Avda. Velez Sarsfield 405, Buenos Aires, Argentina. **Indexed:** Biol.Abstr.

616.2 US
VOICE FOUNDATION. NEWSLETTER. 3/yr. $50. Voice Foundation, 1721 Pine St., Philadelphia, PA 19103. Ed. Charlotte Cathcart. **Document type:** newsletter.

616.2 US ISSN 8756-3452
RC705
YEAR BOOK OF PULMONARY DISEASE. 1986. a. $72.95 (residents $35) (effective 1996). Mosby - Year Book, Inc., Continuity Division, 200 N. LaSalle, Chicago, IL 60601. TEL 312-726-9746. FAX 312-726-6075. TELEX 206155. Ed. Dr. Roger C. Bone. illus. (reprint service avail.)
●Also available online. Vendor(s): Ovid Technologies.
—BLDSC (9415.850000).

616.2 CN ISSN 0044-104X
YOUR HEALTH. 1918. s-a. free. British Columbia Lung Association, 2675 Oak St., Vancouver, BC V6H 2K2, Canada. TEL 604-731-5864. FAX 604-731-5810. Ed. Jerry Miller. bk.rev.; charts; illus.; circ. 19,500 (controlled).

616.2 ZA ISSN 0084-5000
ZAMBIA. PNEUMOCONIOSIS MEDICAL AND RESEARCH BUREAU AND PNEUMOCONIOSIS COMPENSATION BOARD. ANNUAL REPORT. 1964. a. K.100. Zambia Government Printing Department, P.O. Box 30136, Lusaka, Zambia. **Document type:** government publication.

616.2 GW ISSN 0303-657X
CODEN: ZEATAM
ZEITSCHRIFT FUER ERKRANKUNGEN DER ATMUNGSORGANE.* 1900. 3/yr. DM.66 per vol. Johann Ambrosius Barth, Postfach 102869, 69018 Heidelberg, Germany. TEL 06221-489281. FAX 06221-489205. (Co-sponsor: International Society for Aerosols in Medicine) Ed. W. Schilling. adv.; bk.rev.; abstr.; bibl.; charts; illus.; index. circ. 1,600. **Indexed:** Biol.Abstr., C.I.S. Abstr., Chem.Abstr., Excerp.Med. (until 1993), Ind.Med. (until 1992). **Document type:** academic/scholarly publication.
—CASDDS. **CCC.**
Incorporates: Folia Bronchologica; Former titles: Zeitschrift fuer Tuberkulose und Erkrankungen der Thoraxorgane; Zeitschrift fuer Erkrankungen der Atmungsorgane mit Folia Bronchologica; Absorbs: Monatsschrift fuer Lungenkrankheiten und Tuberkulosebekaempfung.

616.23 JA ISSN 0914-7683
ZENSOKU/ASTHMA. (Text in Japanese) 1988. 4/yr. 1545 Yen per no. Medikaru Rebyusha - Medical Review Co., Ltd., 7-3, Hiranomachi 1-chome, Chuo-ku, Osaka 541, Japan.

MEDICAL SCIENCES — Rheumatology

616.7 US
A H P A PERSPECTIVE. 1965. q. membership. (Arthritis Health Professions Association) Arthritis Foundation, 1314 Spring St., N.W., Atlanta, GA 30309. TEL 404-872-7100. FAX 404-872-8694. Ed. Dr. Gail Davis.

616.742 PO ISSN 0303-464X
CODEN: ARUPB
ACTA REUMATOLOGICA PORTUGUESA. (Text in Portuguese; summaries in Portuguese, English, French) 1973. q. free. Sociedade Portuguesa de Reumatologia, Rua de Dona Estefania, 187-189, Lisbon 1, Portugal. TEL 01-572326. adv.; bk.rev.; abstr.; bibl.; charts; illus.; stat. circ. 1,000. **Indexed:** Excerp.Med. (1994-). **Document type:** academic/scholarly publication.

616.742 FR ISSN 0065-1818
ACTUALITE RHUMATOLOGIQUE PRESENTEE AU PRATICIEN; cahier annuel d'informations et de renseignements. a. price varies. Expansion Scientifique, 31 bd. de la Tour Maubourg, 75007 Paris, France. TEL 40-62-64-00. FAX 45-55-69-20.
—**CCC.**

616.7 US
RC933
ADVISORY BOARD FOR ARTHRITIS AND MUSCULOSKELETAL AND SKIN DISEASES. ANNUAL REPORT. 1977. a. free. Advisory Board for Arthritis and Musculoskeletal and Skin Diseases, National Institute of Arthritis and Musculoskeletal and Skin Diseases, 1801 Rockville Pike, Ste. 500, Rockville, MD 20852. circ. 1,000.
Formerly: U.S. National Arthritis Advisory Board. Annual Report (ISSN 0190-5422)

616.72 GW ISSN 0341-051X
CODEN: AKRHDB
AKTUELLE RHEUMATOLOGIE. 1976. bi-m. DM.183. Georg Thieme Verlag, Ruedigerstr. 14, 70469 Stuttgart, Germany. TEL 0711-8931-0. FAX 0711-8931298. (Subscr. to: Postfach 104853, 70042 Stuttgart, Germany) Ed.Bd. index. circ. 4,200. (reprint service avail. from UMI) **Indexed:** Curr.Adv.Ecol.Sci., Curr.Cont., Excerp.Med., INIS Atomind. **Document type:** academic/scholarly publication.
—BLDSC (0785.873000); Genuine Article. **CCC.**

616.7 UK ISSN 1350-6129
CODEN: AIJIET
▼**AMYLOID;** international journal of experimental and clinical investigation. 1994. q. £88($130) to individuals; institutions £130($190) (effective 1996). (International Society of Amyloidosis) Parthenon Publishing Group, Casterton Hall, Carnforth, Lancs LA6 2LA, England. TEL 015242-72084. FAX 015242-71587. (In U.S.: Box 1564, Pearl River, NY 10965. TEL 914-735-9363. FAX 914-735-1585) Ed. Dr. Alan S. Cohen. (back issues avail.) **Indexed:** ASCA, Curr.Cont., Int.Abstr.Biol.Sci. **Document type:** academic/scholarly publication.
—BLDSC (0859.841173); CASDDS.
Refereed Serial

616.742 UK ISSN 0003-4967
CODEN: ARDIAO
ANNALS OF THE RHEUMATIC DISEASES. 1939. m. £233($368) B M J Publishing Group, B.M.A. House, Tavistock Sq., London WC1H 9JR, England. TEL 0171-383-6270. FAX 0171-383-6402. (N. American subscr. to: Box 408, Franklin, MA 02038. TEL 800-2-FON-BMJ. FAX 800-2-FAX-BMJ) Ed. M. Doherty. adv. contact: Sheila Rowe. bk.rev.; charts; illus.; index. (also avail. in microform from UMI; reprint service avail. from UMI) **Indexed:** Abstr.Inter.Med., Behav.Med.Abstr., Biol.Abstr., C.I.S. Abstr., Chem.Abstr., CINAHL, Curr.Cont., Dent.Ind., Excerp.Med., Helminthol.Abstr., Ind.Med., Ind.Sci.Rev., INIS Atomind., Kidney, Med.& Surg.Dermat., Nutr.Abstr., Sci.Cit.Ind. **Document type:** academic/scholarly publication.
●Also available online. Vendor(s): Ovid Technologies.
—BLDSC (1043.800000); ADONIS; CASDDS; Faxon; Genuine Article; SWETS; UMI; UnCover. **CCC.**
Description: Contains work on all aspects of rheumatology and disorders of connective tissue.
Refereed Serial

616.7 SP ISSN 0213-0645
APARATO LOCOMOTOR. Spanish edition of: Rheumatology and Traumatology. 1976. q. 5000 ptas. (foreign $50). Editores Medicos, S.A., C. Gabriela Mistral 2, 28035 Madrid, Spain. TEL 34-1-3860033. FAX 34-1-3739907. circ. 10,000.
Formerly (until 1984): Cuadernos de Reumatologia (ISSN 0210-2986)

ARCHIVIO DI ORTOPEDIA E REUMATOLOGIA. see MEDICAL SCIENCES — Orthopedics And Traumatology

616.742 US ISSN 0004-3591
RC927.A1 CODEN: ARHEAW
ARTHRITIS AND RHEUMATISM. 1958. m. $135 to individuals (foreign $190); institutions $210 (foreign $235) (effective 1996). (American College of Rheumatology) Lippincott - Raven Publishers, 227 E. Washington Sq., Philadelphia, PA 19106. TEL 215-238-4200. FAX 215-238-4227. Ed. Dr. William P. Arend. adv.; bk.rev.; bibl.charts; illus. circ. 8,982. (also avail. in microform from UMI; back issues avail.) **Indexed:** AIM, Behav.Med.Abstr., Biol.Abstr., Biotech.Abstr., C.I.S. Abstr., Chem.Abstr., CINAHL, Curr.Adv.Ecol.Sci., Curr.Cont., Dent.Ind., Excerp.Med., Helminthol.Abstr., I.P.A., Ind.Med., Ind.Sci.Rev., INIS Atomind., Kidney, Med.& Surg.Dermat., Sci.Cit.Ind.
●Also available online. Vendor(s): Lexis-Nexis, Ovid Technologies.
—BLDSC (1733.800000); CASDDS; Faxon; Genuine Article; SWETS; UMI; UnCover. **CCC.**
Refereed Serial

616.7 US ISSN 0893-7524
RC933.A1 CODEN: ARCREG
ARTHRITIS CARE AND RESEARCH. 1988. 4/yr. $115 (foreign $139) (effective 1996). Arthritis Health Professions Association, 1314 Spring St., N.W., Atlanta, GA 30309. TEL 404-872-7100. Ed. Dr. Graciela Alarcon. **Indexed:** Behav.Med.Abstr., CINAHL, Psychol.Abstr. (1988-). **Document type:** academic/scholarly publication.
—BLDSC (1733.840000); SWETS; UnCover.
Description: Offers papers on rheumatology and rheumatology-related issues.
Refereed Serial

616.7 US ISSN 0191-2836
ARTHRITIS FOUNDATION ANNUAL REPORT. 1948. a. Arthritis Foundation, 1314 Spring St., N.W., Atlanta, GA 30309. TEL 404-872-7100. FAX 404-872-0457.

616.7 UK ISSN 0144-6339
ARTHRITIS NEWS; the quarterly paper for people with arthritis. 1950. 4/yr. £4 (foreign £15). Arthritis Care, 18 Stephenson Way, London NW1 2HO, England. TEL 44-71-916-1500. FAX 44-71-916-1505. Ed. James Pollard. adv.; bk.rev.; illus. circ. 100,000. (tabloid format) **Indexed:** Rehabil.Lit. **Document type:** consumer publication.
Formerly (until Jan-Feb 1980): B R A Review (ISSN 0005-3279)
Description: A paper for people with arthritis and how it affects their lives personally, professionally, and socially.

MEDICAL SCIENCES — RHEUMATOLOGY

616.742   CN   ISSN 0820-9006
ARTHRITIS NEWS. 1979. q. $10. Arthritis Society, 250 Bloor St., E., Ste. 401, Toronto, ON M4W 3P2, Canada. TEL 416-967-1414. FAX 416-967-7171. Ed. Dennis Jeanes. bk.rev. circ. 20,000.
   Formerly: C.A.R. Scope (ISSN 0068-8258)
   Description: Provides articles on arthritis, its treatment, the latest research and coping strategies.

616.742   UK   ISSN 0969-7039
ARTHRITIS TODAY. 1965. 3/yr. $25. Arthritis and Rheumatism Council, P.O. Box 177, Chesterfield, Derbys. S41 7TQ, England. TEL 01264-558033. FAX 01264-558007. charts; illus. circ. 140,000. **Document type:** consumer publication.
—BLDSC (1733.878000).
   Formerly (until 1992): Arthritis Research Today (ISSN 0960-4499)
   Description: Offers the general reader reviews of ARC-funded research and its progress, along with advice for coping with arthritis day to day.

616.7   US   ISSN 0890-1120
RC933.A1
ARTHRITIS TODAY; the magazine for help and hope. 1980. bi-m. $20 includes membership. Arthritis Foundation, 1314 Spring St., N.W., Atlanta, GA 30309. TEL 404-872-7100. FAX 404-872-9559. Ed. Cindy McDaniel. circ. 500,000. **Indexed:** Hlth.Ind.
—BLDSC (1733.877900).
   Formerly (until 1987): National Arthritis News (ISSN 0882-9705)

ARTHROSCOPY. see *MEDICAL SCIENCES — Orthopedics And Traumatology*

AUTOIMMUNE DISEASES. see *MEDICAL SCIENCES — Allergology And Immunology*

616.7   UK   ISSN 0950-3579
RC925.A1   CODEN: CRHDDK
BAILLIERE'S CLINICAL RHEUMATOLOGY. 1975. q. £76 institutions £87. Bailliere Tindall - W.B. Saunders Co. Ltd. (Subsidiary of Harcourt Brace & Company Ltd.), 24-28 Oval Rd., London NW1 7DX, England. TEL 0171-267-4466. FAX 0171-482-2293. TELEX 25775 ACPRES G. (Subscr. to: Journals Subscription Fulfillment, Foots Cray High St., Sidcup, Kent DA14 5HP, England. TEL 0181-300-3322. FAX 0181-309-0807; Subscr. in N. America to: W.B. Saunders Co., Journal Subscription Fulfillment, 6277 Sea Harbor Dr., 4th Fl., Orlando, FL 32887-4800. TEL 800-874-6418) **Indexed:** Biol.Abstr., Curr.Adv.Ecol.Sci., Excerp.Med., Ind.Med., Ind.Sci.Rev., Sci.Cit.Ind. **Document type:** academic/scholarly publication.
—BLDSC (1856.727000); CASDDS; Genuine Article; SWETS; UMI; UnCover. CCC.
   Supersedes in part (in 1986): Clinics in Rheumatic Diseases (ISSN 0307-742X)
   Refereed Serial

616.7   GW
BECHTEREW-BRIEF. 1980. q. DM.48 membership. Deutsche Vereinigung Morbus Bechterew, Metzgergasse 16, 97421 Schweinfurt, Germany. TEL 09721-22033. FAX 09721-22955. Ed. Ernst Feldtkeller. adv.; bk.rev.; charts; illus.; index. (back issues avail.) **Document type:** newsletter.

616.7   NO
BERTINE KOPERBERG CONFERENCE (PROCEEDINGS). (Supplement to: Scandinavian Journal of Rheumatology) 2nd, 1978. irreg. $28.50. Scandinavian University Press, P.O. Box 2959 Toeyen, N-0608 Oslo, Norway.
TEL 47-22-57-54-00. FAX 47-22-57-53-53. Ed. T.W. Feltkamp. illus.

616.742   UK   ISSN 0263-7103
    CODEN: BJRHDF
BRITISH JOURNAL OF RHEUMATOLOGY. (Supplements avail.: Abstracts from B S R Scientific Meetings) 1952. m. £205($355) (effective 1996). (British Society of Rheumatology) Oxford University Press, Oxford Journals, Walton St., Oxford OX2 6DP, England. TEL 01865-267907.
FAX 01865-267773. TELEX 837330-OXPRES-G. E-mail: jnlorders@oup.co.uk. (US subscr. to: Oxford University Press Inc., 2001 Evans Rd., Cary, NC 27513. TEL 919-677-0977. FAX 919-677-1714) Ed. Howard Bird. adv.; bk.rev.; bibl.; illus.; index. (also avail. in microform from UMI; reprint service avail. from UMI) **Indexed:** Abstr.Inter.Med., AIM, Behav.Med.Abstr., Biol.Abstr., Biotech.Abstr., Chem.Abstr., CINAHL, Curr.Adv.Ecol.Sci., Curr.Adv.Ecol.Sci., Curr.Cont., Dent.Ind., Excerp.Med., Ind.Med., Ind.Sci.Rev., Med.& Surg.Dermat., Sci.Cit.Ind. **Document type:** academic/scholarly publication.
●Also available online. Vendor(s): Ovid Technologies.
—BLDSC (2324.320000); Faxon; Genuine Article; SWETS; UMI; UnCover. CCC.
   Former titles: Rheumatology and Rehabilitation (ISSN 0300-3396); Rheumatology and Physical Medicine (ISSN 0003-4908)
   Description: Devoted to clinical and laboratory rheumatology worldwide.
   Refereed Serial

616.742   US   ISSN 0007-5248
RC927   CODEN: BRDIAZ
BULLETIN ON THE RHEUMATIC DISEASES. 1950. bi-m. $15 (free in US). Arthritis Foundation, 1314 Spring St., N.W., Atlanta, GA 30309. TEL 404-872-7100. FAX 404-872-0457. Ed. Dr. John S. Sergent. bibl.; cum.index.every 4 yrs. circ. 45,000. (also avail. in microform from UMI; reprint service avail. from UMI) **Indexed:** Biol.Abstr., Chem.Abstr., Curr.Cont., Excerp.Med., Ind.Med., Ind.Sci.Rev., Sci.Cit.Ind.
●Also available online. Vendor(s): Lexis-Nexis.
—BLDSC (2885.200000); CASDDS; Genuine Article; UMI. CCC.

617.6   SP   ISSN 1134-3613
▼**CADERA.** 1994. q. 4500 ptas.($108) (effective 1995). (Fundacion Maurice Muller) Editorial Rocas, Muntaner 393, Pral. 2a, 08021 Barcelona, Spain. TEL 39-3-20001389. FAX 39-3-2021958. **Document type:** trade publication.

616.7   IT   ISSN 0392-856X
    CODEN: CERHDP
CLINICAL AND EXPERIMENTAL RHEUMATOLOGY. (Text in English) 1983. bi-m. L.105000 (foreign $135) to individuals; institutions L.140000 (foreign $155) (effective 1996). Pacini Editore s.r.l., Via A. Gherardesca 1, 56121 Ospedaletto (Pisa), Italy. TEL 39-50-982439. FAX 39-50-983905. (Subscr. to: Via Santa Maria 31, 56126 Pisa, Italy. TEL 39-50-40124. FAX 39-50-502299) (back issues avail.) **Indexed:** Kidney, Med.& Surg.Dermat.
—BLDSC (3286.252700); CASDDS; Faxon; Genuine Article; SWETS; UnCover.

616.742   BE   ISSN 0770-3198
    CODEN: CLRHD6
CLINICAL RHEUMATOLOGY. (Supplements avail.) 1946. 4/yr. 3200 Fr. (foreign 3300 Fr.). Association des Societes Scientifiques Medicales Belges - Vereiniging van de Belgische Medische Wetenschappelijke Genootschappen, Av. Circulaire 138A, B-1180 Brussels, Belgium. TEL 02-374-5158. Ed. J. Dequeker. adv.; abstr.; illus. **Indexed:** Biol.Abstr., Chem.Abstr., Excerp.Med., Ind.Med.
—BLDSC (3286.374600); CASDDS; Faxon; Genuine Article; SWETS; UnCover.
   Formerly: Journal Belge de Rhumatologie et de Medecine Physique (ISSN 0021-7654)

616.748   CN   ISSN 0828-301X
CONNECTIONS. French edition: Connexions. 1984. q. free. Muscular Dystrophy Association of Canada, 2345 Yonge St., 9th Fl., Toronto, ON M4P 2E5, Canada. TEL 416-488-0030. FAX 416-488-7523. Ed. M.W. Thompson. bk.rev.; illus.; circ. 16,000 (controlled). (back issues avail.) **Document type:** newsletter.
   Description: Covers research news, fund raising, lient profiles and disability issues.

616.7   IT   ISSN 0394-0748
CONNECTIVE TISSUE DISEASES/MALATTIE DEL TESSUTO CONNETTIVO. (Text in English, Italian) 1981. s-a. L.50000($70) (effective 1995). (Societa Neopolitana Mario Giordano) Casa Editrece Idelson, Via A. De Gasperi 55, 80133 Naples, Italy.
TEL 39-81-5524733. FAX 39-81-5518295. Ed. Giuseppe Tirri. stat.
   Description: Presents research papers on the study of connective tissue diseases.

CURRENT OPINION IN RHEUMATOLOGY. see *MEDICAL SCIENCES — Abstracting, Bibliographies, Statistics*

616.7   NO
    CODEN: EJEREE
EUROPEAN JOURNAL OF EXPERIMENTAL MUSCULOSKELETAL RESEARCH. (Text in English) 1991. q. NOK 805 in Nordic countries; elsewhere $138 (effective 1996). Scandinavian University Press, P.O. Box 2959 Toeyen, N-0608 Oslo, Norway. TEL 47-22-57-54-00.
FAX 47-22-57-53-53. Ed. John Sevastik. index. **Indexed:** Excerp.Med. (1993-). **Document type:** academic/scholarly publication.
—BLDSC (3829.728950); CASDDS.
   Formerly: European Journal of Musculoskeletal Research (ISSN 0803-5288)
   Description: Publishes original papers, short communications and review articles on experimental research concerning the physiology and pathology of the locomotor system.

FORTSCHRITTE IN DER ARTHROSKOPIE. see *MEDICAL SCIENCES*

616.7   SZ
FORUM R. (Text in French, German, Italian) q. Schweizer Rheumaliga, Renggerstr. 71, CH-8038 Zurich, Switzerland. TEL 01-4825600.
FAX 01-4826439. Ed. Gisela Dalvit. circ. 30,000. **Document type:** newsletter.

DIE FUNKTIONSKRANKHEITEN DES BEWEGUNGSAPPARATES; Zeitschrift fuer interdisziplinaere Diagnostik und Therapie. see *MEDICAL SCIENCES — Orthopedics And Traumatology*

GASTROENTEROLOGY IN PRACTICE. see *MEDICAL SCIENCES — Gastroenterology*

616.7   US   ISSN 0887-168X
HELIOGRAM (BRIDGEPORT). 1986. 4/yr. $10. Lupus Network, Inc., 230 Ranch Dr., Bridgeport, CT 06606. TEL 203-372-5795. Ed. Linda Rosinsky. bk.rev. **Document type:** newsletter.
   Description: Educational information on lupus for patients and professionals.

616.7   NE   ISSN 0169-1163
JAPANESE JOURNAL OF RHEUMATOLOGY. (Text in English) 1986. q. DM.280 (effective 1996). V S P, P.O. Box 346, 3700 AH Zeist, Netherlands. TEL 31-30-6925790. FAX 31-30-6932081. E-mail: 100341.2372@compuserve.com. Ed. T. Azuma. adv. (back issues avail.) **Document type:** academic/scholarly publication.
—BLDSC (4658.680000).
   Description: Current Japanese research in rheumatology and associated areas (pathology, physiology, clinical immunology).

JOURNAL OF MUSCULOSKELETAL MEDICINE. see *MEDICAL SCIENCES — Orthopedics And Traumatology*

JOURNAL OF MUSCULOSKELETAL PAIN. see *MEDICAL SCIENCES — Orthopedics And Traumatology*

616.7 617.3   UK   ISSN 0951-9580
    CODEN: JORHE3
JOURNAL OF ORTHOPAEDIC RHEUMATOLOGY. 1988. q. £165($275) to institutions (effective 1995). Rapid Communications of Oxford Ltd., The Old Malthouse, Paradise St., Oxford OX1 1LD, England.
TEL 01865-790447. FAX 01865-244012. E-mail: rapidcom@vax.oxford.ac.uk. Ed. Dr. J. Moll. (reprint service avail. from UMI) **Indexed:** Excerp.Med. **Document type:** academic/scholarly publication.
●Also available on CD-ROM.
—BLDSC (5027.664000); ADONIS; Genuine Article. CCC.
   Description: Covers techniques and evaluation of reconstructive surgery in arthritis patients, investigation and treatment of spinal problems, soft tissues disorders, and sports injuries.

MEDICAL SCIENCES — RHEUMATOLOGY

616.742　　　　　CN　　ISSN 0315-162X
　　　　　　　　　　　　　　　CODEN: JRHUA9
JOURNAL OF RHEUMATOLOGY. 1974. m. Can.$170($190) to individuals; institutions Can.$190 ($180) (effective 1996). Journal of Rheumatology Publishing Co. Ltd., 920 Yonge St., Ste. 115, Toronto, ON M4W 3C7, Canada. TEL 416-967-5155. FAX 416-967-7556. Ed. D.A. Gordon. adv. contact: Michelle Garneau. bk.rev.; index. circ. 3,400. (also avail. in microform from UMI; reprint service avail. from UMI) **Indexed:** Behav.Med.Abstr., Biol.Abstr., Chem.Abstr., Chic.Per.Ind., Curr.Adv.Cancer Res., Curr.Adv.Ecol.Sci., Curr.Adv.Genetics & Molec.Biol., Curr.Cont., Dent.Ind., Dok.Arbeitsmed., Excerp.Med., Ind.Med., Ind.Sci.Rev., INIS Atomind., Kidney, Med.& Surg.Dermat., Nutr.Abstr., Protozool.Abstr., Rev.Med.& Vet.Mycol. **Document type:** academic/scholarly publication.
—BLDSC (5052.070000); CASDDS; Faxon; Genuine Article; SWETS; UMI; UnCover. **CCC.**

616.99105 615.82　　TU　　ISSN 1300-0691
JOURNAL OF RHEUMATOLOGY AND MEDICAL REHABILITATION. Key Title: Romatoloji ve Tibbi Rehabilitasyon Dergisi. 1990. a. $10. Society of Rehabilitation Medicine, Hacettepe Universitesi, Tip Fakultesi, 06100 Hacettepe - Ankara, Turkey. TEL 90-312-3105769. FAX 90-312-3105769. Ed. Dr. Ridvan Ozker. adv. contact: Dr. Zafer Hascelit. bk.rev. circ. 600. **Indexed:** Excerp.Med. (1994-). **Document type:** academic/scholarly publication.
Refereed Serial

616.7 617.3　　　　JA　　ISSN 0915-1125
KOTSU KANSETSU JINTAI/JOURNAL OF MUSCULOSKELETAL SYSTEM. (Text in Japanese) m. 2400 Yen per no. Kokusai Isho Shuppan, 42-4, Hongo 3-chome, Bunkyo-ku, Tokyo 113, Japan.

616.7　　　　　　　　US
L.E. BEACON. (Lupus Erythematosus) 1984. bi-m. $20 in U.S.: Mexico and Canada $23; elsewhere $25. L.E. Support Group, 8039 Nova Court, N. Charleston, SC 29420. TEL 803-764-1769. Ed. Harriet B. Mesic. bk.rev. circ. 1,500. (back issues avail.) **Document type:** newsletter.
Description: Educational and medical news for patients with Systemic Lupus Erythematosus.
Refereed Serial

616.7　　　　　　　UK　　ISSN 0961-2033
　　　　　　　　　　　　　　　CODEN: LUPUES
LUPUS. 1991. bi-m. £65 to individuals; institutions £130. Stockton Press (Subsidiary of: Macmillan Press Ltd.), Houndmills, Basingstoke, Hants RG21 2XS, England. TEL 01256-817245. FAX 01256-28339. Ed. Graham Hughes; Pub. Marija Vukovojac. adv. contact: Michael Rowley. **Indexed:** Excerp.Med. (1993-), Ind.Med. (1993-). **Document type:** academic/scholarly publication.
—BLDSC (5307.422000); CASDDS; Genuine Article; SWETS. **CCC.**
Description: Comprehensive information on all aspects of lupus care and research.

616.7　　　　　　　AT　　ISSN 1033-2480
LUPUS ASSOCIATION OF NEW SOUTH WALES. NEWSLETTER. 1979. 5/yr. Aus.$20. Lupus Association of New South Wales Inc., P.O. Box 89, North Ryde, N.S.W. 2113, Australia. TEL 61-2-878-6055. Ed. Leslie McAllister. bk.rev. circ. 1,000. (back issues avail.) **Document type:** newsletter.
Description: News from the Association, a self-help organization for sufferers of systemic Lupus Erythematosus and related diseases.

616.7　　　　　　　US　　ISSN 0277-1748
LUPUS TODAY. 1978. q. $12 individual membership; professional membership $100. American Lupus Society, 260 Maple Ct., Ste. 123, Ventura, CA 93003-3512. TEL 805-339-0443; 800-331-1802. FAX 805-339-0467. Ed. Vernon S. White. circ. 10,000. (back issues avail.) **Document type:** newsletter.
Description: Contains medical, patient and chapter articles of interest to lupus patients.

616.742　　　　　UK
MATHILDA AND TERENCE KENNEDY INSTITUTE OF RHEUMATOLOGY. ANNUAL REPORT. 1967. a. free. Mathilda and Terence Kennedy Institute of Rheumatology, 6 Bute Gardens, Hammersmith, London W6 7DW, England. TEL 0181-748-9966. FAX 0181-748-5090. circ. 1,000 (controlled). **Document type:** corporate report.

616.7　　　　　　　BL
MEDISOM: RHEUMATOLOGY. 1981. bi-m. $90. Editora Medisom, Ltda., Rua Sao Paulino 224, Caixa Postal 7650, 01064-970 Sao Paulo, Brazil.
FAX 55-11-572-5957. Ed. Dr. Philip Querido. adv. (audio cassette)

616.7　　　　　　　GW　　ISSN 0939-219X
MIT RHEUMA LEBEN. 1991. q. DM.20. Verlag fuer Medizin Dr. Ewald Fischer GmbH, Fritz-Frey-Str. 21, 69121 Heidelberg, Germany. TEL 06221-4062-0. FAX 06221-400727. TELEX 461683-HVVFM. Ed. Arndt Kroedel. adv.; bk.rev.; illus. **Document type:** academic/scholarly publication.

616.7　　　　　　　NE　　ISSN 0924-4506
NEW CLINICAL APPLICATIONS. RHEUMATOLOGY. (Text in English) 1989. irreg. price varies. Kluwer Academic Publishers, Postbus 17, 3300 AA Dordrecht, Netherlands. TEL 31-78-392392. FAX 31-78-392254. TELEX 29245 KAPG NL. (Dist. by: Kluwer Academic Publishers Group, P.O. Box 322, 3300 AH Dordrecht, Netherlands. TEL 31-78-392392. FAX 31-78-546474; N. America dist. addr.: Box 358, Accord Sta., Hingham, MA 02018-0358. TEL 617-871-6600. FAX 617-871-6528) **Document type:** monographic series.

616.7　　　　　　　JA　　ISSN 0287-3214
NIHON RYUMACHI KANSETSU GEKA GAKKAI ZASSHI/JAPANESE JOURNAL OF RHEUMATISM AND JOINT SURGERY. (Text in English, Japanese) 1982. q. Nihon Ryumachi Kansetsu Geka Gakkai, Shiga Ika Daigaku Seikei Gekagakku Kyoshitsu, Seta Tsukiwacho, Otsu-shi, Shiga-ken 520-21, Japan.

616.7　　　　　　　JA
NIHON RYUMACHI KANSETSU GEKA GEKKAI/JAPANESE SOCIETY OF RHEUMATISM AND JOINT SURGERY. CONGRESS. (Text in English, Japanese) 1984. a. Nihon Ryumachi Kansetsu Geka Gakkai, Shiga Ika Daigaku Seikei Gekagakku Kyoshitsu, Seta Tsukiwacho, Otsu-shi, Shiga-ken 520-21, Japan.

NIHON SEKITSUI GEKA GAKKAI DAYORI/JAPAN SPINE RESEARCH SOCIETY. NEWS. see *MEDICAL SCIENCES — Orthopedics And Traumatology*

NIHON SEKITSUI GEKA GAKKAI ZASSHI/JAPAN SPINE RESEARCH SOCIETY. JOURNAL. see *MEDICAL SCIENCES — Orthopedics And Traumatology*

616.742　　　　　DK　　ISSN 0108-2841
NYT OM GIGT. 1982. q. DKK 20. Gigtforeningen, Hauchsvej 14, DK-1825 Frederiksberg C, Denmark. illus.

616.7　　　　　　　AT
ON THE MOVE (ASHFORD). 1983. q. Aus.$10. Arthritis Foundation of South Australia, 99 Anzac Hwy., Ashford, S.A. 5035, Australia. TEL 08-297-2488. FAX 08-293-1177. Ed. Gillian Leach. adv.; bk.rev. circ. 8,000. (back issues avail.) **Document type:** newsletter.
Former titles: Arthritis Action; Arthritis News.
Description: News of foundation activities, information on self-help courses, researches on arthritis and treatments.

616.7　　　　　　　UK　　ISSN 1063-4584
　　　　　　　　　　　　　　　CODEN: OSCAEO
OSTEOARTHRITIS AND CARTILAGE. 1993. q. £64 in Europe (rest of world $117) to individuals; institutions £96 in Europe (rest of world $172). (Osteoarthritis Research Society) W.B. Saunders Ltd. (Subsidiary of: Harcourt Brace & Company Ltd.), 24-28 Oval Rd., London NW1 7DX, England. TEL 0171-267-4466. FAX 0171-282-2293. TELEX 25775-ACPRES-G. (Subscr. to: Harcourt Brace & Company Ltd., Foots Cray High St., Sidcup DA14 5HP, England. TEL 0181-300-3322. FAX 0181-309-0807; US, Canadian, and Mexican subscr. to: W.B. Saunders Co., Journal Subscription Fulfillment, 6277 Sea Harbor Dr., 4th Fl., Orlando, FL 32887-4800. TEL 800-654-2452. FAX 800-874-6418) Ed. R.D. Altman. (back issues avail.) **Indexed:** Excerp.Med. (1994-). **Document type:** academic/scholarly publication.
—BLDSC (6303.858870).
Description: Publishes original articles on clinical, laboratory, and therapeutic research in osteoarthritis and related concerns, including cartilage, collagen, and orthopedics.

PRACTICAL GASTROENTEROLOGY; for the busy internist. see *MEDICAL SCIENCES — Gastroenterology*

616.7 617.3　　　FR　　ISSN 0997-7503
RACHIS; revue de pathologie vertebrale. 1989. bi-m. 700 F. Edimedica, 146 bd Voltaire, 92600 Asnieres, France. TEL 47-93-56-03. FAX 47-93-40-52. Ed. F. Vidal. adv.; bk.rev.; charts; illus.; index. circ. 4,000.

REFERATOVY VYBER Z REVMATOLOGIE/ABSTRACTS OF RHEUMATOLOGY. see *MEDICAL SCIENCES — Abstracting, Bibliographies, Statistics*

616.742　　　　　　XR
REHABILITACE A FYZIKALNI LEKARSTVI. (Text in Czech; summaries in Czech, English, Russian) 1923. q. $48.60. (Ceska Lekarska Spolecnost J.E. Purkyne - Czech Medical Society) Nakladatelske Stredisko C L S J.E. Purkyne, Sokolska 31, 120 26 Prague 2, Czech Republic. TEL 42-2-530640. (Dist. by: Artia, Ve Smeckach 30, 111 27 Prague 1, Czech Republic) (Co-sponsor: Ceska Fysiatricka Spolecnost) Ed. Dr. V. Rauser. bk.rev. **Indexed:** Biol.Abstr., Excerp.Med., Ind.Med.
—BLDSC (3120.319000); EMDOCS. **CCC.**
Former titles (until 1994): Ceska Revmatologie (ISSN 1210-7905); (until 1993): Fysiatricky a Reumatologicky Vestnik (ISSN 0072-0038); Supersedes: Fysiatricky Vestnik.

616.742　　　　　UK　　ISSN 1351-4873
REPORTS ON RHEUMATIC DISEASES. PRACTICAL PROBLEMS (SERIES 3). N.S. 1985; N.S. 1993. 3/yr. free. Arthritis and Rheumatism Council, P.O. Box 177, Chesterfield, Derbys. S41 7TQ, England. TEL 02146-558033. FAX 01246-558007. circ. 40,000. **Document type:** academic/scholarly publication.
—BLDSC (7669.507000).
Supersedes (in Sep. 1993): Reports on Rheumatic Diseases. Practical Problems (Series 2) (ISSN 1351-3060)
Description: Offers advice on the diagnosis and treatment of common problems, topical research findings, and theories. Aimed at physicians and other health care professionals.

616.742　　　　　UK　　ISSN 0957-0381
　　　　　　　　　　　　　　　CODEN: RRDPEW
REPORTS ON RHEUMATIC DISEASES (SERIES 2). 1959-1983; N.S. 1985. 3/yr. free. Arthritis and Rheumatism Council, P.O. Box 177, Chesterfield, Derbys. S41 7TQ, England. TEL 01246-558033. FAX 01246-558007. circ. 40,000. **Indexed:** Biol.Abstr., Ind.Med. **Document type:** academic/scholarly publication.
Supersedes (in 1985): Reports on Rheumatic Diseases (First Series) (ISSN 0048-7279)
Description: Offers advice on the diagnosis and treatment of common problems, topical research findings, and theories. Aimed at physicians and other health care professionals.

616.742　　　　　UK　　ISSN 1351-4881
REPORTS ON RHEUMATIC DISEASES. TOPICAL REVIEWS (SERIES 3). N.S. 1985; N.S. 1993. 3/yr. free. Arthritis and Rheumatism Council, P.O. Box 177, Chesterfield, Derbys. S41 7TD, England. TEL 01246-558033. FAX 01246-558007. **Document type:** academic/scholarly publication.
—BLDSC (7669.508000).
Supersedes (in Sep. 1993): Reports on Rheumatic Diseases. Topical Reviews (Series 2) (ISSN 1351-3508)
Description: Offers advice on the diagnosis and treatment of common problems, topical research findings, and theories. Aimed at physicians and other health care professionals.

616.742　　　　　NE　　ISSN 0034-6217
REUMA BULLETIN. q. fl.10. Nationaal Reumafonds, Statenlaan 128, 2582 GW The Hague, Netherlands.

616.742　　　　　SW　　ISSN 1104-0696
REUMATIKERTIDNINGEN. 1949. bi-m. SEK 120 membership (effective 1994). Riksforbundet mot Reumatism - Swedish National Association Against Rheumatism, P.O. Box 12851, Alstroemergatan 39, S-112 98 Stockholm, Sweden.
TEL 46-8-653-21-00. FAX 46-8-650-64-15. Ed. Anders Arhammar. adv. circ. 53,000. (also avail. in audio cassette)
Formerly (until 1994): Reuma (ISSN 0034-6209)

MEDICAL SCIENCES — RHEUMATOLOGY

616.7   IT   ISSN 0048-7449
REUMATISMO. (Supplements avail.) 1949. 4/yr. $115 to non-members (effective 1994). Societa Italiana di Reumatologia (S.I.R.), C.so Plebisciti 9, 20129 Milano, Italy. TEL 39-2-7382330. FAX 39-2-7385763. TELEX 33215 BOFFIS I. Ed. Claudio Cervini. adv.: B&W page L.1550000, color page L.2800000; trim 135 x 230. bk.rev.; illus. circ. 2,500. (back issues avail.) **Indexed:** Biol.Abstr., Chem.Abstr., Excerp.Med., Ind.Med. **Document type:** bulletin.
—BLDSC (7785.544100); EMDOCS.
Refereed Serial

616.7   CI   ISSN 0374-1338
REUMATIZAM. (Text in Croatian; summaries in English) 1954. bi-m. Croatian League Against Rheumatism, Lovcenska 100, 41000 Zagreb, Croatia. TEL 041-572-440. (Subscr. to: Jurjevska 25-I, 41000 Zagreb, Croatia) Ed. Ivo Jajic. adv.; bk.rev.; index. circ. 1,000. (back issues avail.) **Indexed:** Biol.Abstr., Ind.Med.

616.742   PL   ISSN 0034-6233
CODEN: RMTOA2
REUMATOLOGIA. (Text in Polish; summaries in English) 1963. q. $140 (effective 1995 & 1996). Instytut Reumatologiczny, Spartanska 1, 02-637 Warsaw, Poland. TEL 48-22-444241. TELEX 816458 REUM. (Co-sponsor: Polskie Towarzystwo Reumatologiczne) Ed. Jacek Pazdur. adv.; bk.rev.; bibl.; illus.; index; circ. 1,000 (paid). **Indexed:** Biol.Abstr., Chem.Abstr., Dent.Ind., Excerp.Med., Ind.Med., Ind.Rheum. **Document type:** academic/scholarly publication.
—BLDSC (7785.548000); CASDDS; EMDOCS.

616.7   IT   ISSN 0391-8963
REUMATOLOGO. (Text in Italian; summaries in English) 1980. bi-m. L.25000($25) C I C Edizioni Internazionali s.r.l., Via L. Spallanzani, 11, 00161 Rome, Italy. TEL 06-8412673. FAX 06-44242033. TELEX 622099 CIC I. Dir. C. Cervini.

616.7   SP   ISSN 0304-4815
REVISTA ESPANOLA DE REUMATOLOGIA. (Text in Spanish; summaries in English, Spanish) 1974. 10/yr. 6600 ptas.($57) to non-members. (Sociedad Espanola de Reumatologia) Ediciones Doyma, S.A., Travesera de Gracia, 17-21, 08021 Barcelona, Spain. TEL 34-1-200-07-11. FAX 34-1-209-11-36. TELEX 51964 INK-E. Ed. M. Figueroa Pedrosa. adv.: page 180000 ptas.; trim 210 x 280; adv. contact: Julio Esteva. charts; illus.; stat.; index. circ. 2,000. (reprint service avail. from UMI) **Indexed:** Excerp.Med., Ind.Med.Esp.
—BLDSC (7854.310000); UMI.
Description: Contains investigative work in the field of rheumatology done in Spain. Serves to continue the education of internists and physicians.

616.742   FR   ISSN 1169-8330
CODEN: RRMOA2
REVUE DU RHUMATISME (EDITION FRANCAISE). 1933. 10/yr. 1000 F. to individuals (foreign 1250 F.); students 500 F. (foreign 680 F.). (Societe Francaise de Rhumatologie) Expansion Scientifique, 31 bd. de la Tour Maubourg, 75007 Paris, France. TEL 40-62-64-00. FAX 45-55-69-20. Ed. Stanislas De Seze. adv.; bk.rev.; abstr.; bibl.; charts; illus.; index. circ. 4,000. (also avail. in microform from UMI; reprint service avail. from UMI) **Indexed:** Biol.Abstr., C.I.S. Abstr., Chem.Abstr., Curr.Cont., Excerp.Med. (until 1994), Helminthol.Abstr., Ind.Med. (until 1994), Nutr.Abstr. **Document type:** academic/scholarly publication.
—CASDDS; EMDOCS; Faxon; Genuine Article; SWETS; UMI. **CCC.**
Supersedes in part (in 1993): Revue du Rhumatisme et des Maladies Osteoarticulaires (ISSN 0035-2659); Which was formerly (until 1946): Revue du Rhumatisme (ISSN 0301-8474)

616.742   FR   ISSN 1169-8446
CODEN: RRHUE
REVUE DU RHUMATISME (ENGLISH EDITION). 1933. 10/yr. $250 to individuals; students $125. (Societe Francaise de Rhumatologie) Expansion Scientifique, 31 bd. de la Tour Maubourg, 75007 Paris, France. TEL 40-62-64-00. FAX 15-55-69-20. Ed. Stanislas De Seze. **Indexed:** Excerp.Med. (1994-), Ind.Med. (1994-). **Document type:** academic/scholarly publication.
—BLDSC (7945.595000); CASDDS; EMDOCS; Faxon; Genuine Article; SWETS; UMI. **CCC.**
Supersedes in part (in 1993): Revue du Rhumatisme et des Maladies Osteoarticulaires (ISSN 0035-2659); Which was formerly (until 1946): Revue du Rhumatisme (ISSN 0301-8474)

616.7   SP   ISSN 0211-7274
RHEUMA. 6/yr. 6000 ptas. Antonio Lopez Aguado 4, 28029 Madrid, Spain. TEL 1-314-43-38. FAX 1-314-44-99. circ. 2,096.

616.7   GW
RHEUMA JOURNAL. 4/yr. DM.18. P. Keppler Verlag GmbH und Co. KG, Industriestr. 2, 63150 Heusenstamm, Germany. TEL 06104-6060. FAX 06104-606145. **Document type:** academic/scholarly publication.

616.7   US   ISSN 0889-857X
RC927   CODEN: RDCAEK
RHEUMATIC DISEASES CLINICS OF NORTH AMERICA. 1987. q. $131 (foreign $157) (effective 1996). W.B. Saunders Co. (Subsidiary of: Harcourt Brace & Company), The Curtis Center, 3rd Fl., Independence Sq. W., Philadelphia, PA 19106-3399. TEL 215-238-7800. FAX 215-238-6445. (Subscr. to: Periodicals Fulfillment, W.B. Saunders Co., 6277 Sea Harbor Dr., 4th Fl., Orlando, FL 32887-4800. TEL 800-654-2452. FAX 800-874-6418) Ed. Barton Dudlick. index. (back issues avail.) **Document type:** academic/scholarly publication.
—BLDSC (7960.618000); CASDDS; Faxon; Genuine Article; SWETS; UMI; UnCover. **CCC.**
Supersedes in part (in 1986): Clinics in Rheumatic Diseases (ISSN 0307-742X)
Description: Discusses topics in the diagnosis and treatment of rheumatic conditions.

616.742   II   ISSN 0035-4546
RHEUMATISM. (Text and summaries in English and Hindi) 1965. q. Rs.32($12) (£10). M M L Centre for Rheumatic Diseases, Sanskriti Bhawan, Jhandewalan, New Delhi 110055, India. TEL 011-3313306. Ed. Kaviraj A. Majumdar. adv.; bk.rev.; abstr.; charts; illus.; index. circ. 200. **Indexed:** Biol.Abstr.

616.7   XO   ISSN 1210-1931
CODEN: RHEUE
RHEUMATOLOGIA. 1987. 4/yr. Obzor, Spitalska ul. 35, 815 85 Bratislava, Slovakia. **Indexed:** Excerp.Med. (1994-).

616.742   SZ   ISSN 0080-2727
RC927.A1   CODEN: RHEUBD
RHEUMATOLOGY; the interdisciplinary concept. (Text in English) 1966. irreg. (approx. 1/yr.). price varies. S. Karger AG, Allschwilerstr. 10, P.O. Box, CH-4009 Basel, Switzerland. TEL 061-3061111. FAX 061-3061234. E-mail: Karger@Karger.ch. (reprint service avail. from ISI) **Indexed:** Biol.Abstr., Chem.Abstr., Curr.Cont., Ind.Med. **Document type:** academic/scholarly publication.
—BLDSC (7960.730000); CASDDS; Faxon; SWETS. **CCC.**
Refereed Serial

616.7   SZ   ISSN 1021-8564
RHEUMATOLOGY IN EUROPE; journal for education and information in rheumatology. German edition (ISSN 1021-8580); French edition (ISSN 1021-8572) 1972. q. 117 SFr. (European League Against Rheumatism) E U L A R Publishers, P.O. Box, CH-4012 Basel, Switzerland. TEL 061-2646465. FAX 061-2646470. Ed. Dr. Colin Barnes. adv. contact: R. Reinhardt. bk.rev. circ. 19,000. **Document type:** academic/scholarly publication, newsletter.
—BLDSC (7960.738100).
Formerly (until 1993): E U L A R Bulletin (ISSN 0379-1041)

616.7   UK
RHEUMATOLOGY IN PRACTICE. 1990. 5/yr. £38 (overseas £42) (effective 1995). Hayward Medical Communications Ltd., 44 Earlham St., Covent Garden, London WC2H 9LA, England. TEL 44-171-240-4493. FAX 44-171-240-4479. (Subscr. to: Essex House Cromwell Park, Chipping Norton, Oxon. OX7 5SR, England. TEL 44-1608-645564. FAX 44-1608-645645) **Document type:** academic/scholarly publication.
Supersedes in part (in 1993): Gastroenterology and Rheumatology in Practice (ISSN 0959-3314); Which was formed by the merger of (1981-1990): Rheumatology in Practice (ISSN 0262-5512); (1983-1990): Gastroenterology in Practice (ISSN 0264-7478)

616.7   GW   ISSN 0172-8172
CODEN: RHINDE
RHEUMATOLOGY INTERNATIONAL; clinical and experimental investigations. (Text in English) 1981. 6/yr. DM.568($412) (effective 1996). Springer-Verlag, Heidelberger Platz 3, 14197 Berlin, Germany. TEL 030-8207-0. FAX 030-8214091. E-mail: orders@springer.de. (Subscr. in N. America to: Springer-Verlag New York, Inc., 44 Hartz Way, Secaucus, NJ 07096-2491. TEL 201-348-4033. FAX 201-348-4505) Ed.Bd. adv. (also avail. in microform from UMI; reprint service avail. from ISI) **Indexed:** Chem.Abstr., Curr.Adv.Ecol.Sci., Curr.Cont., Dent.Ind., Excerp.Med., Ind.Med. **Document type:** academic/scholarly publication.
—BLDSC (7960.738300); CASDDS; Faxon; Genuine Article; SWETS; UMI. **CCC.**
Description: Reflects world-wide progress in the research, diagnosis, and treatment of various rheumatic diseases.

616.7   FR   ISSN 0249-7581
RHUMATOLOGIE.* 1949. m. 320 Fr. (Societe Aixoise de Documentation Medicale et d'Edition) Publications Periodiques Specialisees, 17 Place Bellecour, 69002, France. TEL 43-31-57-27. FAX 45-35-33-76. Ed. J.J. Herbert. adv.; bk.rev. circ. 2,000. **Indexed:** Biol.Abstr.
—BLDSC (7963.400000).

616.7   FR   ISSN 0295-5261
RHUMATOLOGIE PRATIQUE. 1986. bi-m. (20/yr.). 250 F. L.E.N. Medical, 48 bis, av. Kleber, 75016 Paris, France. TEL 47-55-06-06. FAX 47-55-69-41. TELEX 640 748. Ed. Dr. Gerald Ratzbaum. circ. 3,850.

616.742   NO   ISSN 0300-9742
RC927   CODEN: SJRHAT
SCANDINAVIAN JOURNAL OF RHEUMATOLOGY. (Supplement avail. (ISSN 0301-3847)) 6/yr. NOK 955 in Nordic countries; elsewhere $175 (incl. supplements) (effective 1996). (Scandinavian Society for Rheumatology) Scandinavian University Press, P.O. Box 2959 Toeyen, N-0608 Oslo, Norway. TEL 47-22-57-54-00. FAX 47-22-57-53-53. (U.S. addr.: Scandinavian University Press, 200 Meacham Ave., Elmont, NY 11003. TEL 516-352-7300) Ed. Gunnar Husby. adv. circ. 1,800. **Indexed:** ASCA, Behav.Med.Abstr., Biol.Abstr., Biotech.Abstr., Chem.Abstr., Curr.Adv.Ecol.Sci., Curr.Cont., Dent.Ind., Energy Res.Abstr., Excerp.Med., Ind.Med., Med.& Surg.Dermat. **Document type:** academic/scholarly publication.
—BLDSC (8087.546000); ADONIS; CASDDS; Faxon; Genuine Article; SWETS; UnCover. **CCC.**
Formerly: Acta Rheumatologica Scandinavica (ISSN 0001-6934)
Description: Covers clinical and experimental aspects of rheumatic diseases.

617.742   NO   ISSN 0301-3847
CODEN: SJRSAS
SCANDINAVIAN JOURNAL OF RHEUMATOLOGY. SUPPLEMENT. (Text in English) 1958. irreg. (Scandinavian Society for Rheumatology) Scandinavian University Press, P.O. Box 2959 Toeyen, N-0608 Oslo, Norway. TEL 47-22-57-54-00. FAX 47-22-57-53-53. (US addr.: Scandinavian University Press, 200 Meacham Ave., Elmont, NY 11003. TEL 516-352-7300) **Indexed:** Excerp.Med., Ind.Med. **Document type:** academic/scholarly publication.
—BLDSC (8087.546300); CASDDS; SWETS.
Formerly (until 1973): Acta Rheumatologica Scandinavica. Supplementum (ISSN 0065-163X)

MEDICAL SCIENCES — SPORTS MEDICINE

616.7 574.192 US ISSN 0049-0172
RC933.A1 CODEN: SAHRBF
SEMINARS IN ARTHRITIS & RHEUMATISM. 1971. bi-m. $189 (foreign $233) (effective 1996). W.B. Saunders Co. (Subsidiary of: Harcourt Brace & Company), Curtis Center, 3rd Fl., Independence Sq. W., Philadelphia, PA 19106-3399. TEL 215-238-7800. FAX 215-238-6445. (Subscr. to: Periodicals Fulfillment, W.B. Saunders Co., 6277 Sea Harbor Dr., 4th Fl., Orlando, FL 32891-4800. TEL 800-654-2452. FAX 800-874-6418) Ed.Bd; Pub. Joan W. Blumberg. adv.: B&W page $995, color page $1915; 7 x 10; adv. contact: Steve Gray. bibl.; charts; illus.; index. circ. 4,242. **Indexed:** ASCA, Behav.Med.Abstr., Biol.Abstr., Chem.Abstr., Curr.Adv.Ecol.Sci., Curr.Cont., Dent.Ind., Excerp.Med., Ind.Med., Med.& Surg.Dermat., Nutr.Abstr., Protozool.Abstr., Sci.Cit.Ind. **Document type:** academic/scholarly publication.
—BLDSC (8239.448000); CASDDS; EMDOCS; Faxon; Genuine Article; SWETS; UMI; UnCover. **CCC**.
Description: Provides clinical expositions of topics of current importance to practicing physicians, including inflammatory and degenerative disorders of bone, joints, and connective tissue; arthritis; gout; and collegen diseases.
Refereed Serial

616.742 PO
SOCIEDADE PORTUGUESA DE REUMATOLOGIA. BOLETIM INFORMATIVO. 1972. q. free. Sociedade Portuguesa de Reumatologia, Rua de Dona Estefania 187-189, Lisbon 1, Portugal. Dir. Joao Figueirinhas. adv.; bibl.; illus.; stat. circ. 1,000.

VATRECHNI BOLESTI. see *MEDICAL SCIENCES — Endocrinology*

616.7 US ISSN 1070-5406
▼**YEAR BOOK OF RHEUMATOLOGY.** 1994. a. $79.95 (residents $35) (effective 1996). Mosby - Year Book, Inc. (Chicago) (Subsidiary of: Times Mirror Company), 200 N. LaSalle St., Chicago, IL 60601-1080. TEL 312-726-9733. FAX 312-726-6075. TELEX 206155. Ed. John S. Sergent.
—BLDSC (9416.155000).

616.742 GW ISSN 0340-1855
CODEN: ZRHMBQ
ZEITSCHRIFT FUER RHEUMATOLOGIE. (Text and summaries in English, German) 1938. bi-m. DM.368($267) (effective 1996). Dr. Dietrich Steinkopff Verlag, Saalbaustr. 12, 64283 Darmstadt, Germany. TEL 06151-1745-0. FAX 06151-174510. (Subscr. to: Postfach 111442, 64229 Darmstadt, Germany.) (Co-sponsors: Deutsche Gesellschaft fuer Rheumatologie; Oesterreichische Rheumaliga; Schweizerische Gesellschaft fuer Rheumatologie; Berufsverband Deutscher Rheumatologen) Ed.Bd. adv.; bk.rev.; bibl.; charts; illus.; pat. circ. 1,500. (also avail. in microform from UMI) **Indexed:** Biol.Abstr., Biotech.Abstr., Chem.Abstr., Curr.Adv.Ecol.Sci., Curr.Cont., Dent.Ind., Ind.Med. **Document type:** academic/scholarly publication.
—BLDSC (9485.455000); ADONIS; CASDDS; Genuine Article; SWETS; UMI. **CCC**.
Formerly: Zeitschrift fuer Rheumaforschung (ISSN 0044-345X)

MEDICAL SCIENCES — Sports Medicine

A S M A NEWS. (American Sports Medecine Association) see *SPORTS AND GAMES*

ABILITY BALLROOM DANCE JOURNAL. see *DANCE*

617.1 FR ISSN 1151-3195
ACTUALITES SPORT ET MEDECINE. 1979. 10/yr. 120 F. (foreign 150 F.). M P H Editions, 8 bis, av. des Vagues, B.P. 521, 17211 Royan Cedex, France. TEL 46-38-42-67. FAX 46-38-34-16. Ed. Dr. Ph. Most. circ. 12,000.
Former titles (until 1990): Sport Medicine Actualites (ISSN 0753-2814); (until 1985): Sport Medicine (ISSN 0245-5021)
Description: Contains sports medicine information for the general practitioner.

617.1 US
AMERICAN ACADEMY OF PODIATRIC SPORTS MEDICINE NEWSLETTER. 1982. q. $30. American Academy of Podiatric Sports Medicine, 1729 Glastonberry Rd., Potomac, MD 20854. TEL 301-424-7440. Ed. Larry Shane. adv. circ. 8,000. **Indexed:** Sportsearch (1988-). **Document type:** newsletter.
Formerly: American Academy of Podiatric Sports Medicine Journal.

617.1 US ISSN 1060-4219
AMERICAN COLLEGE OF SPORTS MEDICINE. CAREER SERVICES BULLETIN. m. $20 to non-members; members $10. American College of Sports Medicine, Box 1440, Indianapolis, IN 46206-1440. TEL 317-637-9200. FAX 317-634-7817. (Street addr.: 401 W. Michigan St., Indianapolis, IN 46202-3233) Ed. Anne Brown. circ. 1,200. (looseleaf format; back issues avail.) **Document type:** bulletin, consumer publication.
Description: Lists current exercise science and sports medicine positions available in a variety of fields across the nation for both members and non-members of A C S M.

617.1 US ISSN 1056-9677
AMERICAN COLLEGE OF SPORTS MEDICINE. CERTIFIED NEWS. 3/yr. American College of Sports Medicine, Certification Committee, Box 1440, Indianapolis, IN 46206-1440. TEL 317-637-9200. FAX 317-634-7817. (Alt addr.: 401 W. Michigan St., Indianapolis, IN 46202-3233) **Document type:** academic/scholarly publication.
Description: Provides continuing education credits (CECs) and information to those certified by ACSM.

AMERICAN JOURNAL OF KNEE SURGERY. see *MEDICAL SCIENCES — Surgery*

617 US ISSN 0363-5465
RC1200 CODEN: AJSMDO
AMERICAN JOURNAL OF SPORTS MEDICINE. 1972. bi-m. $85 to individuals (foreign $100); institutions $100 (foreign $105) (effective 1996). American Orthopaedic Society for Sports Medicine, 230 Calvary St., Waltham, MA 02154. TEL 617-736-0707. FAX 617-736-0607. (Subscr. to: Box 830259, Birmingham, AL 35283-0259. TEL 205-995-1567) Ed. Dr. Robert E. Leach. adv.; illus.; cum.index: 1972-1989; circ. 11,000 (paid). (also avail. in microform; microfilm from WWS; reprint service from UMI) **Indexed:** Abstr.Anthropol., Behav.Med.Abstr., CINAHL, Curr.Cont., Educ.Ind., Excerp.Med., Hlth.Ind., Ind.Med., NRN, Phys.Ed.Ind., Sportsearch (1976-). **Document type:** trade publication.
●Also available online. Vendor(s): University Microfilms International.
—BLDSC (0838.400000); Faxon; Genuine Article; SWETS; UMI; UnCover. **CCC**.
Formerly (until 1976): Journal of Sports Medicine (ISSN 0090-4201)
Refereed Serial

615.8 FR ISSN 0302-427X
ANNALES DE KINESITHERAPIE. 1974. 8/yr. 530 F. (foreign 711 F.) (effective 1996). (Societe de Kinesitherapie) Masson - Periodiques, Villa Laromiguiere, 75005 Paris, France. TEL 1-40-46-62-00. FAX 1-40-46-62-01. Ed. E. Viel. adv.; bk.rev.; charts; illus. circ. 3,500. (also avail. in microform from UMI; reprint service avail. from ISI) **Indexed:** Biol.Abstr., Curr.Cont., Sportsearch (1974-). **Document type:** academic/scholarly publication.
—BLDSC (0981.040000); SWETS. **CCC**.
Formed by the merger of: Revue de Kinesitherapie (ISSN 0035-1172); Journal de Kinesitherapie (ISSN 0021-7751)
Description: Focuses on physical therapy and rehabilitation. Contains original articles, new developments, practical suggestions and technical articles.

617.1 JA ISSN 0918-0257
AOMORIKEN SUPOTSU IGAKU KENKYUKAISHI/AOMORI SOCIETY OF SPORTS MEDICINE. JOURNAL. (Text in Japanese) s-a. Aomoriken Supotsu Igaku Kenkyukai - Aomori Society of Sports Medicine, c/o Mr. Yoshihisa Okamura, Hirosaki Daigaku Igakubu Seikei Geka Kyoshitsu, 5, Zaifucho, Hirosaki-shi, Aomori-ken 036, Japan.
Formerly: Aomoriken Supotsu Igaku Kenkyukai Koenshu.

617.3 SP ISSN 0212-4009
APUNTS; medicina de l'esport. (Text in Catalan, Spanish) 1963. q. Centro d'Estudis de l'Alt Rendiment Esportiu, Direccio General de l'Esport, Av. Paisos Catalan, 12, 08950 Esplugas de Llobregat, Barcelona, Spain. TEL 371-90-11. FAX 372-01-84. TELEX 54845 GCDE. (Dist. by: Les Punxes, Calle Escornalbou, 12, Barcelona, Spain) Ed.Bd. adv.; bibl.; illus.; index. circ. 2,000. (back issues avail.) **Indexed:** Ind.Med.Esp.
Formerly: Apuntes de Medicina Deportiva.

610 AT ISSN 0813-6289
AUSTRALIAN JOURNAL OF SCIENCE AND MEDICINE IN SPORT. 1961. q. Aus.$25 (foreign Aus.$35). Australian Sports Medicine Federation, P.O. Box 897, Belconnen, A.C.T. 2616, Australia. TEL 61-6-2516944. FAX 61-6-2531489. TELEX AUSIS 62400. Ed. Bruce Abernethy. adv.; bk.rev.; charts; illus.; stat. circ. 3,500. (back issues avail.) **Indexed:** Ergon.Abstr., Excerp.Med., Geotech.Abstr., Phys.Ed.Ind., Sportsearch (1984-). **Document type:** academic/scholarly publication.
—BLDSC (1812.250000); UnCover.
Formerly: Australian Journal of Sports Medicine (ISSN 0045-0650)
Description: Focuses on sports science and medicine.
Refereed Serial

BARIATRICIAN. see *NUTRITION AND DIETETICS*

617.1 SZ
BEHINDERTENSPORT/SPORT-HANDICAP. (Text and summaries in French, German) 1962. bi-m. 31 SFr. Schweizerischer Verband fuer Behindertensport, Chriesbaumstr. 6, CH-8604 Volketswil, Switzerland. TEL 01-9460860. FAX 01-9460870. Ed. Elvira Jaeger. adv.; bk.rev. circ. 8,500. **Document type:** bulletin.
Formerly: Invalidensport (ISSN 0020-9880)

617 UK ISSN 0306-3674
CODEN: BJSMDZ
BRITISH JOURNAL OF SPORTS MEDICINE. 1968. 6/yr. £145($217) (effective 1995). (British Association of Sport and Medicine) Butterworth - Heinemann, Part of the Reed Elsevier group, Linacre House, Jordan Hill, Oxford OX2 8DP, England. TEL 0865-310366. FAX 0865-310898. TELEX 83111 BHPOXF G. (Subscr. to: Elsevier Science Ltd., P.O. Box 800, Kidlington, Oxford OX5 1DX, England. TEL 44-865-843000. FAX 44-865-843010; Subscr. in U.S. and Canada to: Elsevier Science, 660 White Plains Rd., Tarrytown, NY 10591-5153. TEL 914-524-9200. FAX 914-333-2444) Eds. Drs. Adrianne Hardman, Wendy Dodds. adv.; bk.rev.; illus.; stat. (also avail. in microform from UMI; back issues avail.) **Indexed:** CINAHL, Curr.Adv.Ecol.Sci., Ergon.Abstr., Ind.Med., NRN, Phys.Ed.Ind., Sportsearch (1975-). **Document type:** academic/scholarly publication.
—BLDSC (2324.900000); CASDDS; Faxon; Genuine Article; SWETS; UMI; UnCover. **CCC**.
Incorporates: British Association of Sport and Medicine. Bulletin.
Description: Covers management of injuries and physiotherapy, physiological evaluations of sports performance, psychology, nutrition, and the role of medical personnel.
Refereed Serial

CAHIERS DE KINESITHERAPIE; revue d'enseignement post-scolaire et de documentation technique. see *MEDICAL SCIENCES — Physical Medicine And Rehabilitation*

CANADIAN JOURNAL OF APPLIED PHYSIOLOGY/REVUE CANADIENNE DE PHYSIOLOGIE APPLIQUEE. see *SPORTS AND GAMES*

CARDIOVASCULAR PHYSIOLOGY. see *BIOLOGY — Physiology*

CHIROPRACTIC SPORTS MEDICINE. see *MEDICAL SCIENCES — Chiropractic, Homeopathy, Osteopathy*

610   FR   ISSN 0009-7209
CINESIOLOGIE; la revue internationale des medecins du sport. (Text in French, summaries in English, French) 1962. 6/yr. 450 F. (foreign 550 F.). Syndicat National des Medecins du Sport, 1, rue d'Alsace, 49100 Angers, France. TEL 41-88-35-35. FAX 33-41-88-13-55. Ed. Dr. Andre Monroche. adv.: B&W page 6900 F., color page 9200 F.; trim 21 x 27; adv. contact: Dr. Jacques Baudoux. bk.rev. **Indexed:** Sportsearch (1975-).
—BLDSC (3198.645000). **CCC.**
Description: Practical and scientific review of sport medicine and stress.
Refereed Serial

617.1   US   ISSN 1050-642X
RC1200   CODEN: CJSMED
CLINICAL JOURNAL OF SPORT MEDICINE. 1975. q. $112 to individuals (foreign $125); institutions $160 (foreign $191) (effective 1996). (Canadian Academy of Sport Medicine, CN) Lippincott - Raven Publishers, 227 E. Washington Sq., Philadelphia, PA 19106. TEL 215-238-4200. FAX 212-869-3495. (Canadian Academy membership addr.: 1600 James Naismith Dr., Ste. 502, Gloucester, Ont. K1B 5N4, Canada. TEL 613-748-5671) (Co-sponsor: American Medical Society for Sports Medicine) Ed. Dr. Gordon O. Matheson. adv. contact: Phyllis Noyes. bk.rev.; charts; illus. circ. 2,000. (reprint service avail. from UMI) **Indexed:** Excerp.Med. (1993-), Sportsearch (1991-). **Document type:** academic/scholarly publication.
—BLDSC (3286.294300); Genuine Article; UMI; UnCover. **CCC.**
Former titles (until 1990): Canadian Academy of Sport Medicine Review (ISSN 0831-2893); Canadian Academy of Sport Medicine Newsletter.
Description: Features original research articles, clinical reviews, case reports, new techniques and procedures in physical examination, exercise testing, diagnostic imaging, and other developments relevent to the clinical practice of sports medicine.
Refereed Serial

617.1   SP
CLINICAS DE MEDICINA DEPORTIVA DE NORTEAMERICA. 4/yr. 15900 ptas. (effective 1990). Interamericana de Espana, S.A., Division de Ciencias de la Salud de McGraw-Hill, Manuel Ferrero, 13, 28036 Madrid, Spain. TEL 315-0340. FAX 733-6627.

617   US   ISSN 0278-5919
CLINICS IN SPORTS MEDICINE. 1982. q. $125 (foreign $149) (effective 1996). W.B. Saunders Co. (Subsidiary of: Harcourt Brace & Company), Curtis Center, 3rd Fl., Independence Sq. W., Philadelphia, PA 19106-3399. TEL 215-238-7800. FAX 215-238-6445. (Subscr. to: Periodicals Fulfillment, W.B. Saunders Co., 6277 Sea Harbor Dr., 4th Fl., Orlando, FL 32891-4800. TEL 800-654-2452. FAX 800-874-6418) Ed. Barton Dudlick. (also avail. in microform from UMI) **Indexed:** ASCA, CINAHL, Dent.Ind., Excerp.Med., Ind.Med., Sportsearch (1982-). **Document type:** academic/scholarly publication.
—BLDSC (3286.595500); Faxon; Genuine Article; SWETS; UMI; UnCover. **CCC.**

617.102   GW   ISSN 0344-5925
                         CODEN: DZSPD8
DEUTSCHE ZEITSCHRIFT FUER SPORTMEDIZIN. 1949. m. DM.93.20. Deutscher Aerzte-Verlag GmbH, Postfach 400265, 50832 Cologne, Germany. TEL 02234-7011-0. FAX 02234-7011444. Ed. Dr. Urte Kuenstlinger. adv. circ. 14,867. **Indexed:** Chem.Abstr., Nutr.Abstr., Sportsearch (1978-). **Document type:** trade publication.
—CASDDS; SWETS.
Formerly: Sportarzt und Sportmedizin.

616.07 612.7   US   ISSN 1077-5552
QP301
▼**EXERCISE IMMUNOLOGY REVIEW.** 1995. a. $18 to individuals; institutions $30; students $12. Human Kinetics Publishers, Inc., Box 5076, 1607 N. Market St., Champaign, IL 61825-5076. TEL 217-351-5076. FAX 217-351-2674. Ed. Roy Shepherd; Pub. Rainer Martens. adv. contact: Pamela Anderson. (back issues avail.; reprint service avail.) **Document type:** trade publication.
—**CCC.**
Description: Committed to developing and enriching knowledge in all aspects of immunology that relate to sport, exercise, and regular physical activity.

EXERCISE STANDARDS AND MALPRACTICE REPORTER. see *LAW*

FIT FOR THE NATION. see *PHYSICAL FITNESS AND HYGIENE*

613.707   US   ISSN 1068-5952
GV201
FITNESS & SPORTS REVIEW INTERNATIONAL; specializing in track and field, weightlifting (weight training) and sports medicine. 1966. q. $40 (foreign $47) (effective 1995-1996). Sports Training, Inc., Box 460429, Escondido, CA 92046. TEL 619-480-0558. FAX 619-480-1277. Ed. Michael Yessis. bk.rev.; illus.; circ. 900 (paid). (back issues avail.) **Indexed:** Educ.Ind., Phys.Ed.Ind., R.G., Sportsearch (1979-). **Document type:** academic/scholarly publication.
—BLDSC (3948.227880); Faxon; SWETS; UnCover.
Incorporates (in 1992): Soviet Sports Review (ISSN 0275-598X); Which was formerly: Yessis Review of Soviet Physical Education and Sports (ISSN 0513-5389)

FOOT & ANKLE INTERNATIONAL. see *MEDICAL SCIENCES — Orthopedics And Traumatology*

FUJIAN TIYU KEJI/FUJIAN SPORTS SCIENCE AND TECHNOLOGY. see *SPORTS AND GAMES*

610 613   NE   ISSN 0016-6448
                         CODEN: GESPBS
GENEESKUNDE EN SPORT. 1968. 6/yr. fl.67.50 (foreign fl.79.50) (effective 1994). (Vereniging voor Sportgeneeskunde) Uitgeverij De Tijdstroom b.v., Postbus 19135, 3501 DC Utrecht, Netherlands. TEL 31-30-586900. FAX 31-30-586950. adv.; bk.rev.; illus.; stat. circ. 4,000. **Indexed:** Biol.Abstr.
—BLDSC (4096.443000); SWETS.

GOAL POST. see *PHYSICAL FITNESS AND HYGIENE*

INTERNATIONAL JOURNAL OF SPORT NUTRITION. see *NUTRITION AND DIETETICS*

616.8   IT   ISSN 0047-0767
GV706.4   CODEN: ISPYAN
INTERNATIONAL JOURNAL OF SPORT PSYCHOLOGY. (Text in English and French) 1970. q. L.110000($100) (International Society of Sports Psychology) Edizioni Luigi Pozzi s.r.l., Via Panama 68, 00198 Rome, Italy. TEL 39-6-8553548. FAX 39-6-8554105. Eds. A. Cei, J.H. Salmela. adv.; bk.rev. circ. 1,500. (also avail. in microform from SWZ; reprint service avail. from SWZ) **Indexed:** Curr.Cont., Phys.Ed.Ind., Psychol.Abstr. (1970-), Sportsearch (1974-), SSCI.
—BLDSC (4542.681000); Faxon; SWETS; UnCover.
Description: Covers sports medicine.

610   GW   ISSN 0172-4622
                         CODEN: IJSMDA
INTERNATIONAL JOURNAL OF SPORTS MEDICINE. (Text in English) 1980. 8/yr. DM.334. (German Society of Sports Medicine) Georg Thieme Verlag, Ruedigerstr. 14, 70469 Stuttgart, Germany. TEL 0711-8931-0. FAX 0711-8931298. (Subscr. to: Postfach 104853, 70042 Stuttgart, Germany; US addr.: Thieme-Stratton Inc., 381 Park Ave., S., New York, NY 10016) Ed.Bd. adv.; bk.rev.; abstr.; bibl.; charts; illus. circ. 1,500. **Indexed:** Chem.Abstr., Dok.Arbeitsmed., Excerp.Med., Ind.Med., Ind.Sci.Rev., NRN, Sci.Cit.Ind., Sportsearch (1980-), Sugar Ind.Abstr. **Document type:** academic/scholarly publication.
—BLDSC (4542.681300); ADONIS; CASDDS; Faxon; Genuine Article; SWETS; UMI; UnCover. **CCC.**

617 613   IE   ISSN 0959-3020
                         CODEN: IESCEE
ISOKINETICS AND EXERCISE SCIENCE. 1991. q. I£110($174) (effective 1996). Elsevier Science Ireland Ltd., P.O. Box 85, Limerick, Ireland. TEL 353-61-471944. FAX 353-61-472144. (Subscr. in U.S. and Canada to: Elsevier Science, Box 882, Madison Sq. Sta., New York, NY 10159-0882. TEL 212-989-5800. FAX 212-633-3990) Ed.Bd. illus. (also avail. in microform from UMI; back issues avail.) **Document type:** academic/scholarly publication.
—BLDSC (4583.269000); Genuine Article; UMI. **CCC.**
Description: Meets the needs of the contemporary exercise scientist and medical practitioner through a consolidated focus on the field of isokinetics.

JAPANESE JOURNAL OF PHYSICAL FITNESS AND SPORTS MEDICINE. see *PHYSICAL FITNESS AND HYGIENE*

617.1   FR   ISSN 0762-915X
JOURNAL DE TRAUMATOLOGIE DU SPORT. 1983. q. 501 F. (foreign 658 F.) (effective 1996). Masson - Periodiques, Villa Laromiguiere, 75005 Paris, France. TEL 1-40-46-62-00. FAX 1-40-46-62-01. Eds. J. Rodineau, G. Saillant. circ. 2,100. **Document type:** academic/scholarly publication.
—BLDSC (5070.525100). **CCC.**
Description: For all specialists concerned with bone, visceral, urological, and neurological traumatology, and reconstructive surgery, and for intensive care anaethesists.

617.1 612   US   ISSN 1065-8483
RC1235
JOURNAL OF APPLIED BIOMECHANICS. Abbreviated title: J A B. 1985. q. $40 to individuals (foreign $44); institutions $90 (foreign $94); students $24 (foreign $28). (International Society of Biomechanics) Human Kinetics Publishers, Inc., Box 5076, Champaign, IL 61825-5076. TEL 217-351-5076. FAX 217-351-2674. (Co-sponsor: International Society for the Biomechanics of Sport) Ed. Robert J. Gregor; Pub. Rainer Martens. adv. contact: Pamela Anderson. bk.rev.; bibl.; charts; stat.; index. circ. 980. (back issues avail.) **Indexed:** Curr.Cont., Excerp.Med. (1995-), Phys.Ed.Ind., Sportsearch (1985-). **Document type:** academic/scholarly publication.
—BLDSC (4940.653000); Faxon; Genuine Article; SWETS; UnCover. **CCC.**
Formerly (until 1992): International Journal of Sport Biomechanics (ISSN 0740-2082)
Description: Designed to stimulate and communicate research and theory on the forces affecting human movement in sport exercise and rehabilitation.
Refereed Serial

617.1   US   ISSN 1041-3200
GV706.4
JOURNAL OF APPLIED SPORT PSYCHOLOGY. 1989. s-a. $50 (foreign $60). Association for the Advancement of Applied Sport Psychology, c/o Joan L. Duda, Editor, Dept. of HKLS, Lambert 113, Purdue University, West Lafayette, IN 47907. TEL 317-494-5827. FAX 317-496-1239. adv. circ. 1,000. **Indexed:** Mark.Res.Abstr. (1963-), Psychol.Abstr. (1989-). **Document type:** academic/scholarly publication.
—BLDSC (4947.105000); UnCover.
Description: Promotes quality research in the field of sport psychology.
Refereed Serial

796   US   ISSN 1062-6050
RC1200   CODEN: JATTEJ
JOURNAL OF ATHLETIC TRAINING. 1956. q. $32 (foreign $40). National Athletic Trainers Association, Inc., 2952 N. Stemmons Fwy., Dallas, TX 75247-6117. TEL 800-879-6282. FAX 214-637-2206. Ed. Ken Knight. adv. contact: Paula Jacobs. bk.rev.; bibl.; illus.; index, cum.index; circ. 19,000 (controlled). (also avail. in microform from UMI; avail. on records; reprint service avail. from UMI) **Indexed:** Excerp.Med., Phys.Ed.Ind., Sports Per.Ind., Sportsearch (1974-). **Document type:** academic/scholarly publication.
—BLDSC (4947.850000); Faxon; SWETS; UMI; UnCover.
Former titles (until 1992): Athletic Training (ISSN 0160-8320); National Athletic Trainers Association. Journal (ISSN 0027-8718)
Refereed Serial

JOURNAL OF BACK AND MUSCULOSKELETAL REHABILITATION. see *MEDICAL SCIENCES — Orthopedics And Traumatology*

JOURNAL OF MUSCLE RESEARCH AND CELL MOTILITY. see *MEDICAL SCIENCES*

JOURNAL OF MUSCULOSKELETAL MEDICINE. see *MEDICAL SCIENCES — Orthopedics And Traumatology*

MEDICAL SCIENCES — SPORTS MEDICINE

617 615.82 US ISSN 0190-6011
RD701 CODEN: JOSPDV
JOURNAL OF ORTHOPAEDIC AND SPORTS PHYSICAL THERAPY. 1979. m. $80 to individuals; institutions $130 (effective 1995). (American Physical Therapy Association, Orthopaedic and Sports Physical Therapy Sections) Williams & Wilkins, 428 E. Preston St., Baltimore, MD 21202. TEL 410-528-4000; 800-638-6423. FAX 410-528-4312. Ed. Gary L. Smidt. circ. 19,807. (also avail. in microfilm from WWS) **Indexed:** Behav.Med.Abstr., CINAHL, Excerp.Med., Ind.Med. (1993-), Phys.Ed.Ind., Rehabil.Lit., Sportsearch (1980-). **Document type:** academic/scholarly publication.
—BLDSC (5027.660000); Faxon; Genuine Article; SWETS; UnCover. **CCC.**
Description: Clinical developments in sports medicine for practicing PT's, athletic trainers and orthopedic surgeons.
Refereed Serial

JOURNAL OF SMOOTH MUSCLE RESEARCH/NIHON HEIKATSUKIN GAKKAI KIKANSHI. see *MEDICAL SCIENCES*

JOURNAL OF SPORT AND EXERCISE PSYCHOLOGY. see *PSYCHOLOGY*

617.1 US ISSN 1056-6716
RD97 CODEN: JSRHEV
JOURNAL OF SPORT REHABILITATION. Short title: J S R. 1992. q. $36 to individuals (foreign $40); institutions $80 (foreign $84); students $24 (foreign $28). Human Kinetics Publishers, Inc., Box 5076, Champaign, IL 61825-5076. TEL 217-351-5076. FAX 217-351-2674. Ed. Dr. David H. Perrin. adv. contact: Pamela Anderson. bk.rev.; abstr.; bibl.; charts; stat.; index. circ. 525. (back issues avail.) **Indexed:** Excerp.Med. (1993-). **Document type:** academic/scholarly publication.
—BLDSC (5066.189000); Genuine Article; UnCover. **CCC.**
Description: Investigates the process of rehabilitation of sport and exercise injuries regardless of age, gender, athletic ability, level of fitness or health status of the participant.
Refereed Serial

610 613.7 IT ISSN 0022-4707
CODEN: JMPFA3
JOURNAL OF SPORTS MEDICINE AND PHYSICAL FITNESS. (Text in English) 1961. q. L.80000($90) to individuals; institutions $140 (effective 1995). Edizioni Minerva Medica, Corso Bramante 83-85, 10126 Turin, Italy. TEL 011-678282. FAX 011-3121736. Eds. A. Del Monte, G. Tuccimei; Pub. Alberto Oliaro. adv.: B&W page $1100, color page $1900; trim 215 x 280; adv. contact: F. Filippo. bk.rev.; bibl.; charts; illus.; index; circ. 5,000 (paid). (also avail. in microform from SWZ; back issues avail. from SWZ) **Indexed:** Chem.Abstr., CINAHL, Curr.Cont., Excerp.Med., Ind.Med., Mid.East: Abstr.& Ind., Nutr.Abstr., Phys.Ed.Ind., Sportsearch (1975-). **Document type:** academic/scholarly publication.
—BLDSC (5066.200000); CASDDS; EMDOCS; Faxon; Genuine Article; SWETS; UnCover.
Description: Covers applied physiology, preventive medicine, sports medicine and traumatology, and sports psychology.
Refereed Serial

JOURNAL OF SPORTS SCIENCES. see *SPORTS AND GAMES*

617 IT ISSN 1120-3137
JOURNAL OF SPORTS TRAUMATOLOGY AND RELATED RESEARCH. (Text and summaries in English, Italian) 1979. q. L.80000($80) Editrice Kurtis s.r.l., Via L. Zoja, 30, 20153 Milan, Italy. TEL 39-2-48202740. FAX 39-2-48201219. Ed. Paolo Aglietti. adv.: B&W page L.1900000, color page L.2350000; trim 200 x 260. bk.rev. circ. 5,000. **Indexed:** Excerp.Med., Sportsearch (1989-).
—BLDSC (5066.400000); Genuine Article.
Formerly: Italian Journal of Sports Traumatology (ISSN 0391-4089)
Description: Contains original studies on experimental and clinical research. Includes case reports, short communications, interviews and conferences.

617.1 US ISSN 1064-8011
GV711
JOURNAL OF STRENGTH AND CONDITIONING RESEARCH. 1987. q. $32 to individuals (foreign $36); institutions $64 (foreign $68); students $20 (foreign $24). (National Strength and Conditioning Association) Human Kinetics Publishers, Inc., Box 5076, Champaign, IL 61825-5076. TEL 217-351-5076. FAX 217-351-2674. Ed. William J. Kraemer. adv. contact: Pamela Anderson. abstr.; bibl.; charts; stat. circ. 8,205. **Indexed:** Sportsearch (1987-). **Document type:** academic/scholarly publication.
—BLDSC (5066.873700); Faxon; Genuine Article; UnCover. **CCC.**
Formerly: Journal of Applied Sports Research.
Description: Publishes original research dealing with strength and conditioning in sports and exercise.
Refereed Serial

617.1 GW ISSN 0942-2056
KNEE SURGERY, SPORTS TRAUMATOLOGY, ARTHROSCOPY. (Text in English) 1993. 4/yr. DM.298($216) (effective 1996). (European Society of Sports Traumatology, Knee Surgery and Arthroscopy) Springer-Verlag, Heidelberger Platz 3, 14197 Berlin, Germany. TEL 030-8207-0. FAX 030-8214091. E-mail: orders@springer.de. (Subscr. in N. America to: Springer-Verlag New York, Inc., 44 Hartz Way, Secaucus, NJ 07096-2491. TEL 201-348-4033. FAX 201-348-4505) Ed. E. Eriksson. (also avail. in microform from UMI) **Document type:** academic/scholarly publication.
—UMI. **CCC.**

617.1 AT ISSN 1035-5715
M I M S DRUGS AND SPORT. 1990. a. Aus.$25.50. M I M S Australia, 48 Albany St., Crows Nest, N.S.W. 2065, Australia. Ed. Linda H. Badewitz-Dodd. circ. 18,000.
Description: Listing of banned and permitted prescription and non-prescription drugs available in Australia.

617.1 615.9 SA ISSN 1019-7753
M I M S DRUGS AND SPORT. 1991. irreg. M I M S, Division of Times Media Limited, P.O. Box 2059, Pretoria 0001, South Africa. TEL 27-12-3485010. FAX 27-12-477716. Ed. D. Brandt. adv.; circ. 3,000 (paid).
Description: Lists banned and permitted medicines according to the International Olympic Committee.

MASSAGE THERAPY JOURNAL. see *PHYSICAL FITNESS AND HYGIENE*

610 613.7 FR ISSN 0025-6722
CODEN: MNSPBL
MEDECINE DU SPORT. (Text in French; summaries in English, German) 1925. bi-m. 500 F. Galliena Promotion, 58 A rue du Dessous des Berges, 75012 Paris, France. TEL 45-84-97-66. FAX 45-84-92-56. Ed. Dr. F. Commandre; Pub. B. Mennier. adv.; bk.rev.; abstr.; bibl.; charts; illus.; stat.; index. circ. 1,500. **Indexed:** Biol.Abstr., Sportsearch (1971-).
—**CCC.**
Formerly: Medecine Education Physique et Sport.

617.102 IT ISSN 0025-7826
MEDICINA DELLO SPORT. (Text and summaries in English, Italian, Spanish) 1947. q. L.80000($90) to individuals; institutions $140 (effective 1995). (Federazione Medico-Sportiva Italiana) Edizioni Minerva Medica, Corso Bramante 83-85, 10126 Turin, Italy. TEL 39-11-678282. FAX 39-11-3121736. Eds. T. Lubich, G. Tuccimei; Pub. Alberto Oliaro. adv.: B&W page $1100, color page $1900; trim 190 x 270; adv. contact: F. Filippo. bk.rev.; bibl.; charts; illus.; index. circ. 6,000. **Indexed:** Biol.Abstr., Chem.Abstr., Excerp.Med., Ind.Med., Sportsearch (1974-). **Document type:** academic/scholarly publication.
—BLDSC (5533.700000); Genuine Article; UMI.
Refereed Serial

617.102 796 BL ISSN 0100-0780
CODEN: MEESDZ
MEDICINA DO ESPORTE. (Text in Portuguese; summaries in English, French, Spanish) 1973. q. Cr.$160($10) Federacao Brasileira de Medicina Desportiva, Centro de Documentacao e Informacao em Ciencias do Esporte, Av. Sen. Salgado Filho, 135 - 6, 90000 Porto Alegre, R.S., Brazil. abstr.; bibl.; illus.; index, cum.index; circ. 1,000 (controlled). **Indexed:** Biol.Abstr., Excerp.Med.
—CASDDS.

617.1 SP
MEDICINA Y DEPORTE. 1986. q. Asociacion Asturiana de Medicina de la Educacion Fisica y el Deporte, Calle Catedratico Gimeno, Oviedo, Spain. bibl.; illus.

617.102 US ISSN 0195-9131
RC1200 CODEN: MSPEDA
MEDICINE AND SCIENCE IN SPORTS AND EXERCISE. 1969. m. $109 to non-members; institutions $192; students $55 (effective 1995). American College of Sports Medicine, Box 1440, Indianapolis, IN 46206-1440. TEL 317-637-9200. FAX 317-634-7817. TELEX 87669. (Subscr. to: Williams & Wilkins, Box 64380, Baltimore, MD 21264-4380. TEL 800-638-6423) Ed. Peter B. Raven. adv.; bk.rev.; abstr.; bibl.; charts; illus.; index. circ. 13,148. (also avail. in microfilm from UMI,WWS; back issues avail.) **Indexed:** Abstr.Anthropol., Biol.Abstr., Chem.Abstr., CINAHL, Curr.Adv.Biochem., Curr.Adv.Ecol.Sci., Curr.Cont., Excerp.Med., Ind.Med., Ind.Sci.Rev., INIS Atomind., Int.Aerosp.Abstr., Nucl.Sci.Abstr., Phys.Ed.Ind., Psychol.Abstr. (1983-), Sci.Cit.Ind., Sportsearch (1980-), Sugar Ind.Abstr., Wom.Stud.Abstr. **Document type:** academic/scholarly publication.
—BLDSC (5534.006700); CASDDS; Faxon; Genuine Article; SWETS; UMI; UnCover. **CCC.**
Formerly: Medicine and Science in Sports (ISSN 0025-7990)
Description: Research in sports medicine topics for exercise physiologists, physiatrists, physical therpists and athletic trainers.
Refereed Serial

617.102 SZ ISSN 0254-5020
CODEN: MSPOB4
MEDICINE AND SPORT SCIENCE. (Text in English) 1966. irreg. price varies. S. Karger AG, Allschwilerstr. 10, P.O. Box, CH-4009 Basel, Switzerland. TEL 061-3061111. FAX 061-3061234. E-mail: Karger@Karger.ch. Eds. M. Hebbelinck, R.J. Shephard. (reprint service avail. from ISI; back issues avail.) **Indexed:** Biol.Abstr., Chem.Abstr., Curr.Cont., Ind.Med. **Document type:** academic/scholarly publication.
—BLDSC (5534.007300); CASDDS; Faxon. **CCC.**
Formerly: Medicine and Sport (ISSN 0076-6070)
Description: Provides information on the development of sports medicine as a dynamic scientific discipline.
Refereed Serial

MOVIMENTO. see *MEDICAL SCIENCES*

NEWS FROM A S B P. (American Society of Bariatric Physicians) see *NUTRITION AND DIETETICS*

NIHON SEIKEI GEKA SUPOTSU IGAKKAISHI/JAPANESE JOURNAL OF ORTHOPEDIC SPORTS MEDICINE. see *MEDICAL SCIENCES — Orthopedics And Traumatology*

617.1 US ISSN 1060-1872
OPERATIVE TECHNIQUES IN SPORTS MEDICINE. 1993. q. $159 (foreign $205) (effective 1996). W.B. Saunders Co. (Subsidiary of: Harcourt Brace & Company), Curtis Center, 3rd Fl., Independence Sq. W., Philadelphia, PA 19106-3399. TEL 215-238-7800. FAX 215-238-6445. (Subscr. to: Periodicals Fulfillment, W.B. Saunders Co., 6277 Sea Harbor Dr., 4th Fl., Orlando, FL 32891-4800. TEL 800-654-2452. FAX 800-874-6418) Eds. Drs. David Drez, Jr., Jesse C. DeLee; Joan W. Blumberg. adv.: B&W page $580, color page $1380; 7 3/4 x 11; adv. contact: Cindy Gray. circ. 2,269. **Document type:** academic/scholarly publication.
—BLDSC (6269.382500). **CCC.**
Description: Discussses a new clinical condition or surgical procedure in each issue.

ORTHOPAEDIC AND TRAUMATIC SURGERY/SEKEI SAIGAI GEKA. see *MEDICAL SCIENCES — Orthopedics And Traumatology*

MEDICAL SCIENCES — SPORTS MEDICINE

PEDIATRIC EXERCISE SCIENCE. see *MEDICAL SCIENCES — Pediatrics*

PERSONAL FITNESS. see *PHYSICAL FITNESS AND HYGIENE*

610 617.102 US ISSN 0091-3847
RC1200
PHYSICIAN AND SPORTSMEDICINE. 1973. m. $46 (Canada $61; elsewhere $100) (free to qualified personnel). McGraw-Hill, Inc., 1221 Ave. of the Americas, New York, NY 10020. TEL 212-512-2000. (Subscr. to: 4530 W. 77th St., Minneapolis, MN 55435. TEL 612-835-3222) Ed. Richard M. Strauss. adv.; bk.rev.; cum.index: 1973-1986. circ. 104,228. (also avail. in microform from UMI; reprint service avail. from UMI) Indexed: Bus.Ind., C.I.J.E, CINAHL, Excerp.Med., Gen.Sci.Ind., Hlth.Ind., Phys.Ed.Ind., Sportsearch (1974-), Tr.& Indus.Ind.
●Also available online. Vendor(s): Knight-Ridder, Inc., Dow Jones News Retrieval, NewsNet (ME05).
—BLDSC (6476.357000); EMDOCS; Faxon; Genuine Article; SWETS; UMI; UnCover. **CCC.**
Description: Serves healthcare professionals' interests in the medical aspects of sports, exercise and fitness.

617.1 GW ISSN 0177-0438
PRAKTISCHE SPORT-TRAUMATOLOGIE UND SPORTMEDIZIN. q. DM.45. W. Zuckschwerdt Verlag GmbH, Industriestr. 17, 82110 Germering, Germany. TEL 089-894349-0. FAX 089-89434950. Ed. P. Bernett. **Document type:** academic/scholarly publication.

PSYCHOLOGY AND SOCIOLOGY OF SPORT: CURRENT SELECTED RESEARCH. see *PSYCHOLOGY*

QUEST (CHAMPAIGN). see *EDUCATION — Teaching Methods And Curriculum*

REFERATOVY VYBER ZE SPORTOVNI MEDICINY A LECEBNE REHABILITACE/ABSTRACTS OF SPORTS MEDICINE AND REHABILITATION. see *MEDICAL SCIENCES — Abstracting, Bibliographies, Statistics*

617.1 613.7 FR
S T A P S. (Sciences et Techniques des Activites Physiques et Sportives) (Text in French; summaries in English, French) 1980. 3/yr. 180 F. to individuals (foreign 200 F.); institutions 250 F. (Association Francophone pour la Recherche en Activites Physiques et Sportives) Presses Universitaires de Grenoble, B.P. 47, 38040 Grenoble Cedex 9, France. TEL 76-82-56-51. FAX 76-82-56-54. Ed. Pierre Chifflet.

617.1 DK ISSN 0905-7188
RC1200 CODEN: SMSSEO
SCANDINAVIAN JOURNAL OF MEDICINE & SCIENCE IN SPORTS. (Text in English) 1979. 6/yr. DKK 1000 (effective 1996). (Scandinavian Foundation of Medical Science in Sports) Munksgaard International Publishers Ltd., P.O. Box 2148, DK-1016 Copenhagen K, Denmark. TEL 45-33-12-70-30. FAX 45-33-12-93-87. (U.S. addr.: 238 Main Street, Cambridge, MA 02142-9740) Ed. Bengt Saltin. circ. 4,000. Indexed: Sportsearch (1979-).
—BLDSC (8087.517400); Genuine Article; SWETS; UnCover. **CCC.**
Formerly (until 1990): Scandinavian Journal of Sports Sciences (ISSN 0357-5632)
Description: Publishes original articles in the fields of traumatology and orthopedics, physiology, biomechanics, and cardiology, as well as sociological, pedagogic, historical and philosophical contributions to the study of sports.
Refereed Serial

617.102 SZ ISSN 1022-6699
RC1200
SCHWEIZERISCHE ZEITSCHRIFT FUER SPORTMEDIZIN UND SPORTTRAUMATOLOGIE/REVUE SUISSE POUR MEDECINE ET TRAUMATOLOGIE DE SPORTS/REVISTA SVIZZERA PER MEDICINA E TRAUMATOLOGIA DELLO SPORT. (Text in French, German and Italian; summaries in English and French) 1963. 4/yr. 53 SFr. (Schweizerische Gesellschaft fuer Sportmedizin) Paul Haupt AG, Falkenplatz 14, CH-3001 Bern, Switzerland. TEL 031-3012345. FAX 031-3015469. Ed. H. Howald. adv.; bk.rev.; bibl.; charts; illus.; index. Indexed: Biol.Abstr., Chem.Abstr., Excerp.Med., Ind.Med., Sportsearch. **Document type:** academic/scholarly publication.
—BLDSC (8123.485000); EMDOCS. **CCC.**
Formerly (until 1993): Schweizerische Zeitschrift fuer Sportmedizin (ISSN 0036-7885)

617.1 FR ISSN 0765-1597
CODEN: SCSPED
SCIENCE ET SPORTS; journal de la medecine, des sciences et des techniques. (Text in French; summaries in English, French) 1986. q. 895 F. in France; foreign 1025 F.($200) (effective 1996). (Societe Francaise de Medecine du Sport) Editions Scientifiques Elsevier, 141 rue de Javel, 75747 Paris, France. TEL 33-1-45589063. (Subscr. in U.S. and Canada to: Elsevier Science Inc., Box 882, Madison Sq. Sta., New York, NY 10159. TEL 212-989-5800) Ed. Pierre Pesquies. circ. 2,000. (back issues avail.) Indexed: Biol.Abstr., Excerp.Med. **Document type:** academic/scholarly publication.
—BLDSC (8142.998000); CASDDS; Genuine Article; UnCover. **CCC.**
Description: Covers central topics related to sports medicine, connected with internal medicine, traumatology, psychology, physiology, biochemistry, biomechanics or technology. Includes original articles, letters to the editor and technical notes.
Refereed Serial

617.1 SP ISSN 0214-8927
SELECCION. 1990. 4/yr. 4000 ptas.($80) (Europe $50). (Asociacion Espanola de Escuelas de Medicina de la Educacion Fisica y el Deporte) Alpe Editores, S.A., Pedro Rico, 27, 28029 Madrid, Spain. TEL 34-1-7338811. FAX 34-1-3159652. Dir. Jose Ma. Villalon; Pub. A. Alvarez. adv.: B&W page 95000 ptas., color page 160000 ptas.; trim 210 x 280; adv. contact: C. Alvarez. circ. 5,500 (controlled).

SOCIOLOGY OF SPORT JOURNAL. see *SOCIOLOGY*

SOMATICS; magazine-journal of the mind body arts and sciences. see *PHYSICAL FITNESS AND HYGIENE*

617.102 TU ISSN 1300-0551
SPOR HEKIMLIGI DERGISI/TURKISH JOURNAL OF SPORTS MEDICINE. (Text in Turkish, summaries in English) 1966. q. $20. (Ege University, Medical Faculty, Division of Sports Medicine) Ege University Press, Bornova, Izmir, Turkey. TEL 90-232-881097. Eds. Necati Akgun, Dr. Fikret Durusoy. adv.; bk.rev.; abstr. Indexed: Sportsearch (1979-). **Document type:** academic/scholarly publication.
—BLDSC (9072.496000).

617.1 IT ISSN 0392-9647
SPORT & MEDICINA. 1984. bi-m. L.30000 (foreign L.60000). Edi. Ermes, Viale Forlanini 65, 20134 Milan, Italy. TEL 02-70209911. FAX 02-70209919. Ed. Raffaele Grandi. adv.; bk.rev.; cum.index. circ. 18,000. (back issues avail.; reprint service avail.)
Description: Features articles in fields of sports and medicine. Includes articles on pharmaceutical aids and physical fitness.

617.1 AT ISSN 1032-5662
SPORT HEALTH. 1983. q. Aus.$25 (foreign Aus.$35). Australian Sports Medicine Federation, P.O. Box 897, Belconnen, A.C.T 2616, Australia. TEL 61-6-2516944. FAX 61-6-2531489. TELEX AUSUS 62400. Ed. Peter Brukner. bk.rev.; video rev.; charts; illus.; stat.; index. (back issues avail.) Indexed: Sportsearch (1983-).
Description: Education and news in sports medicine and science.

617.1 FR ISSN 0993-1252
SPORT MED. 1988. 10/yr. 390 F. (foreign 600 F.). Meditions Carline, 1 rue du Depart, 75014 Paris, France. TEL 40-64-00-75. FAX 43-22-26-99. Ed. Patrick Borg; Pub. Christian de Vaublanc. adv. contact: Sonzyk Brault. bk.rev. circ. 16,000.

617.1 US ISSN 1056-6724
GV557 CODEN: SSREFK
SPORT SCIENCE REVIEW. Short title: S S R. 1992. s-a. $26 to individuals (foreign $29); institutions $52 (foreign $55). (International Council of Sport Science and Physical Education) Human Kinetics Publishers, Inc., Box 5076, Champaign, IL 61825-5076. TEL 217-351-5076. FAX 217-351-3674. adv. contact: Pamela Anderson. abstr.; bibl.; charts; stat. circ. 325. (back issues avail.) Indexed: Psychol.Abstr. (1992-). **Document type:** academic/scholarly publication.
—BLDSC (8419.643000); Genuine Article; SWETS; UnCover. **CCC.**
Description: Provides an international review of new developments in various areas of sport science.
Refereed Serial

617.1 SP ISSN 1130-0183
SPORT & MEDICINA. 6/yr. Ediciones Eseuve, S.A., Batalla del Saldo 34, 28045 Madrid, Spain. TEL 1-539-01-03. FAX 1-528-87-59. Ed. Alberto Munoz Soler. circ. 21,000.

617.1 UK ISSN 1353-2693
▼**SPORTCARE;** the journal for professionals in sport. 1994. bi-m. £32 (foreign £47). (National Sports Medicine Institute of the United Kingdom) Quintessence Publishing Co. Ltd., 2 Blagdon Rd., New Malden, Surrey KT3 4AD, England. TEL 0181-949-6087. FAX 0181-336-1484. (Subscr. in Americas to: Quintessence Publishing Co. Inc., 551 N. Kimberly Dr., Carol Stream, IL 60188. TEL 708-682-3223. FAX 708-682-3288) Ed. Lee Willis. **Document type:** trade publication.
—BLDSC (8419.801500).

617.102 GW ISSN 0075-8655
SPORTMEDIZINISCHE SCHRIFTENREIHE. 1967. irreg., vol.29, 1993. price varies. Johann Ambrosius Barth, Postfach 102869, 69108 Heidelberg, Germany. TEL 06221-489281. FAX 06221-489205. Ed. K. Tittel. (back issues avail.) **Document type:** monographic series.

SPORTS AND RECREATIONAL INJURIES. see *LAW*

617.3 UK ISSN 1351-0029
CODEN: SEINF6
▼**SPORTS, EXERCISE AND INJURY.** 1994. q. £78($122) to individuals; institutions £123 ($192) (effective 1995). (European Federation of Orthopaedic Sports Traumatology) Churchill Livingstone Journals (Subsidiary of: Pearson Professional), Robert Stevenson House, 1-3 Baxter's Pl., Leith Walk, Edinburgh EH1 3AF, Scotland. TEL 0131-556-2424. FAX 0131-459-1177. (Subscr. to: Pearson Professional Ltd. P.O. Box 77, Fourth Ave., Harlow, Essex CM19 5AA, England. TEL 01279-623760; U.S. subscr. to: Churchill Livingstone, 650 Ave. of the Americas, New York, NY 10011. TEL 212-206-5000) Eds. G. McLatchie, H.H. Paessler. adv. contact: David Dunnachie. bk.rev. **Document type:** academic/scholarly publication.
—BLDSC (8419.834270).
Description: Publishes original and commissioned reviews, mini-symposia, and clinical reports on all aspects of clinical sports medicine.

610 NZ ISSN 0112-1642
CODEN: SPMEE7
SPORTS MEDICINE; an international review of applied medicine and science in sport and exercise. 1984. m. $395 (effective 1996). Adis International Limited, Private Bag 65901, Mairangi Bay, Auckland 10, New Zealand. TEL 64-9-479-8100. FAX 64-9-479-8145. E-mail: pcl@topgun.adis.co.nz. (Subscr. addr. in US: Adis International Inc., Attn. Subscriptions Dept., Ste. F-10, 940 Town Center Dr., Langhorne, PA 19047. TEL 215-741-5229. FAX 215-741-5251) Ed. Jeremy N. Shanahan. abstr.; bibl.; illus. Indexed: Curr.Adv.Ecol.Sci., Curr.Cont., Excerp.Med., Ind.Med., Sci.Cit.Ind., Sportsearch (1984-). **Document type:** academic/scholarly publication.
—BLDSC (8419.837340); CASDDS; Faxon; Genuine Article; SWETS; UnCover. **CCC.**
Description: Source of comprehensive reviews of the latest research in applied medicine and science in sport and exercise.

SPORTS MEDICINE AND ARTHROSCOPY REVIEW. see *MEDICAL SCIENCES — Orthopedics And Traumatology*

MEDICAL SCIENCES — SURGERY

617.1 613.7 US ISSN 0746-9306
SPORTS MEDICINE BULLETIN. 1966. q. membership only. American College of Sports Medicine, Box 1440, Indianapolis, IN 46206-1440. TEL 317-637-9200. FAX 317-634-7817. (Street addr.: 401 W. Michigan St., Indianapolis, IN 46202-3233) Ed. Julia Cullison. circ. 15,000.
Document type: bulletin.
 Description: Newsmagazine to inform members about ACSM issues, upcoming events, future plans and member news.

617.102 US ISSN 0731-9770
RC1200
SPORTS MEDICINE DIGEST. Key Title: Sportsmedicine Digest. 1979. m. $49 (foreign $75) (effective 1995). Quest Publishing Co., Inc., A Division of Raven Press Ltd. (Subsidiary of: Wolters Kluwer N.V.), 1351 Titan Way, Brea, CA 92621. TEL 714-738-6400. FAX 714-525-6258. (Subscr. to: Raven Press, 1185 Ave. of the Americas, New York, NY 10036. TEL 212-930-9500. FAX 212-869-3495) Ed. Dr. James C. Puffer; Pub. Mary Waltham. bk.rev. circ. 1,017. (back issues avail.) **Indexed:** Sportsearch (1980-). **Document type:** newsletter.
—BLDSC (8419.837530). **CCC.**

617.1 618.92 US
SPORTS MEDICINE: HEALTH CARE FOR YOUNG ATHLETES. 1983. irreg., 2nd ed., 1991. $41.95. American Academy of Pediatrics, 141 Northwest Point Blvd., Box 927, Elk Grove Village, IL 60009-0927. TEL 708-228-5005; 800-433-9016. FAX 708-228-1281. **Document type:** monographic series.

617.1 US
SPORTS MEDICINE IN PRIMARY CARE. 1992. m. $157 (Canada $177; elsewhere $197) (effective 1996). Phys Ed Fitness Ltd., Box 717, Decatur, GA 30031-0717. TEL 404-377-0300. FAX 404-377-0604. Pub. Elizabeth Medley Wilson. adv. **Document type:** newsletter.
 Formerly (until 1995): Phys Ed. Journal of Sports Medicine (ISSN 1062-9297)
 Description: Helps physicians keep up with developments in sports medicine, recent research studies, and related issues, including medicolegal updates.
 Refereed Serial

SPORTS MEDICINE STANDARDS & MALPRACTICE REPORTER. see *LAW*

617.1 US ISSN 1057-8315
 CODEN: SMTJE2
SPORTS MEDICINE, TRAINING AND REHABILITATION; an international journal. 1988. 4/yr. 119 ECU (effective 1996). Harwood Academic Publishers, c/o International Publishers Distributor, 820 Town Center Dr., Langhorne, PA 19047. TEL 215-750-2642. FAX 215-750-6343. (Subscr. to: International Publishers Distributor, P.O. Box 90, Reading, Berkshire RG1 8JL, England. TEL 44-173-456-8316) Ed. Eric Banister. (also avail. in microform) **Indexed:** Excerp.Med. (1993-).
—BLDSC (8419.837568); UnCover. **CCC.**
 Formerly: Sports Training, Medicine and Rehabilitation (ISSN 0893-102X)
 Refereed Serial

SPORTS PHYSIOLOGY AND MEDICINE. see *MEDICAL SCIENCES — Abstracting, Bibliographies, Statistics*

SPORTSVISION QUARTERLY. see *MEDICAL SCIENCES — Ophthalmology And Optometry*

STRATEGIES (RESTON); a journal for physical and sport educators. see *EDUCATION — Teaching Methods And Curriculum*

SUID-AFRIKAANSE TYDSKRIF VIR NAVORSING IN SPORT, LIGGAAMLIKE OPVOEDKUNDE EN ONTSPANNING/SOUTH AFRICAN JOURNAL FOR RESEARCH IN SPORT, PHYSICAL EDUCATION AND RECREATION. see *PHYSICAL FITNESS AND HYGIENE*

617.1 GW ISSN 0937-0854
T W SPORT UND MEDIZIN. 1989. bi-m. DM.74 (foreign DM.100). Verlag G. Braun GmbH, Karl-Friedrich-Str. 14-18, 76133 Karlsruhe, Germany. TEL 0721-165-0. FAX 0721-165191. **Document type:** trade publication.

TENNISPRO. see *SPORTS AND GAMES — Ball Games*

610 613.7 JA ISSN 0914-4285
TOKYO JIKEIKAI IKA DAIGAKU TAIRYOKU IGAKU KENKYUSHITSU NENPO/JIKEI UNIVERSITY. SCHOOL OF MEDICINE. ANNUAL REPORT OF LABORATORY SPORTS MEDICINE. (Text in English, Japanese) irreg. Tokyo Jikeikai Ika Daigaku, Tairyoku Igaku Kenkyushitsu, 3-1, Kokuryocho 8-chome, Chofu-shi, Tokyo 182, Japan.

DER UNFALLCHIRURG. see *MEDICAL SCIENCES — Orthopedics And Traumatology*

617.1 796.552 UK ISSN 1080-6032
RC1200.M6
WILDERNESS AND ENVIRONMENTAL MEDICINE. 1990. q. £75($80) to individuals; institutions £140 (N. America $175) (effective 1995). (Wilderness Medical Society) Chapman & Hall, Journals Department (Subsidiary of: International Thomson Publishing Group), 2-6 Boundary Row, London SE1 8HN, England. TEL 0171-865-0066. FAX 0171-522-9623. TELEX 290164 CHAPMA G. E-mail: journal@chall.mhs.compuserve.com. (Dist. by: International Thomson Publishing Services Ltd., Cheriton House, North Way, Andover, Hants. SP10 5BE, England. TEL 01264-342713. FAX 01264-342807; N. American subscr. to: Chapman & Hall, Journals Promotion Department, One Penn Plaza, 41st Fl., New York, NY 10019. TEL 212-564-1060. FAX 212-564-1505) Eds. Paul S. Auerback, Oswald Oelz. (reprint service avail.) **Indexed:** Curr.Cont., Energy Rev., Environ.Per.Bibl. (1991-), Excerp.Med. **Document type:** academic/scholarly publication.
—BLDSC (9317.236000); ADONIS; Genuine Article. **CCC.**
 Formerly (until 1995): Journal of Wilderness Medicine (ISSN 0953-9859)
 Description: Publishes research on all aspects of medicine in hostile, natural environments.
 Refereed Serial

617.1 US ISSN 0162-0908
RC1200
YEAR BOOK OF SPORTS MEDICINE. 1979. a. $68.95 (residents $35) (effective 1996). (American College of Sports Medicine) Mosby - Year Book, Inc., Continuity Division, 200 N. LaSalle, Chicago, IL 60601. TEL 312-726-9733. FAX 312-726-6075. TELEX 206155. Ed. Dr. Roy J. Shephard. illus. (reprint service avail.)
—BLDSC (9416.417000); SWETS.

617.1 CC ISSN 1000-6710
ZHONGGUO YUNDONG YIXUE ZAZHI/CHINESE JOURNAL OF SPORTS MEDICAL SCIENCE. (Text in Chinese) q. (Zhongguo Tiyu Kexue Xuehui - China Sports Science Society) Renmin Tiyu Chubanshe - People's Sports Publishing House, 8 Tiyuguan Lu, Chongwen Qu, Beijing 100061, People's Republic of China. TEL 5112466. FAX 7016129. (Co-sponsor: Yundong Yixue Xuehui - Sports Medical Science Association) Ed. Lu Shaozhong.

MEDICAL SCIENCES — Surgery

617.95 US ISSN 1066-8128
A A A A P S F NEWSLETTER. 1992. s-a. membership only. American Association for Accreditation of Ambulatory Plastic Surgery Facilities, 1202 Allanson Rd., Mundelein, IL 60060. TEL 708-949-6058. Ed. Dr. Ron Iverson. adv. contact: Edward Stygar. circ. 500 (controlled). (back issues avail.) **Document type:** newsletter.
 Description: Covers topics of interest to member plastic surgeons, specifically concerning ambulatory surgery facilities.

617 US
A C O M S REVIEW. 1975. q. American College of Oral & Maxillofacial Surgeons, 1100 N.W. Loop 410, Ste. 520, San Antonio, TX 78213-2266. TEL 210-344-5674. FAX 210-344-9754. Ed. Dr. John R. Westine. circ. 6,000. (back issues avail.; reprint service avail.) **Document type:** academic/scholarly publication.

617 US ISSN 0001-0790
A C O S NEWS. 1962. m. members only. American College of Osteopathic Surgeons, 123 N. Henry St., Alexandria, VA 22314. TEL 703-684-0416. Ed. Sharon H. Cool. adv.; abstr. circ. 1,450. **Document type:** newsletter.

ACOUSTIC NEUROMA ASSOCIATION NOTES. see *MEDICAL SCIENCES — Otorhinolaryngology*

617.95 XR ISSN 0001-5423
ACTA CHIRURGIAE PLASTICAE; international journal of plastic surgery. (Editions in English and Russian; English edition has summaries in English, French, German, Spanish) 1959. q. 109 Fr.($40) (Ceska Lekarska Spolecnost J.E. Purkyne - Czech Medical Society) Nakladatelske Stredisko C L S J.E. Purkyne, Sokolska 31, 120 26 Prague 2, Czech Republic. FAX 42-0-202788. (Dist. in Western countries by: Karger Libri A G, Petersgraben 31, 4001 Basel, Switzerland) (Co-sponsor: Association of Czech Plastic Surgeons) Ed. Machaela Malinova. adv.; bk.rev.; charts; illus.; index. circ. 200. **Indexed:** Biol.Abstr., Dent.Ind., Excerp.Med., Ind.Med.
—SWETS.

617 GW ISSN 0001-544X
 CODEN: ACAUB9
ACTA CHIRURGICA AUSTRIACA. (Text in German or English; summaries in English) 1968. 6/yr. DM.332. (Oesterreichische Gesellschaft fuer Chirurgie) Blackwell Wissenschafts-Verlag GmbH, Kurfuerstendamm 57, 10707 Berlin, Germany. TEL 030-327906-0. FAX 030-32790610. (Co-sponsor: Ukrainian Society of Surgeons) Ed. Dr. B. Niederle. circ. 1,500. (reprint service avail. from ISI) **Indexed:** ASCA, Biol.Abstr., Curr.Cont., Excerp.Med. (until 1992; 1994-). **Document type:** academic/scholarly publication.
—BLDSC (0611.128000); ADONIS; UMI. **CCC.**

617 BE ISSN 0001-5458
 CODEN: ACBEAX
ACTA CHIRURGICA BELGICA. (Supplements avail.) (Text in French; summaries in English) 1901. 6/yr. 1950 Fr. (foreign 2200 Fr.). Association des Societes Scientifiques Medicales Belges - Vereiniging van de Belgische Medische Wetenschappelijke Genootschappen, Av. Circulaire 138A, B-1180 Brussels, Belgium. TEL 02-374-5158. adv.; bk.rev.; charts; illus.; index. **Indexed:** ASCA, Biol.Abstr., C.I.S. Abstr., Chem.Abstr., Curr.Cont., Dent.Ind., Excerp.Med., Ind.Med.
—BLDSC (0611.130000); Genuine Article; SWETS; UnCover.

617 HU ISSN 0231-4614
 CODEN: ACAHA3
ACTA CHIRURGICA HUNGARICA. (Text in English; summaries in German, Russian) 1960. q. $76 (effective 1992). (Magyar Tudomanyos Akademia) Akademiai Kiado, Publishing House of the Hungarian Academy of Sciences, P.O. Box 245, H-1519 Budapest, Hungary. TEL 181-2134. FAX 166-6466. TELEX 22-6228 AKNYO H. Ed. Mihaly Ihasz. adv.; bk.rev.; bibl.; charts; illus.; index. **Indexed:** Biol.Abstr., Chem.Abstr., Curr.Adv.Ecol.Sci., Curr.Cont., Excerp.Med., Ind.Med., INIS Atomind.
—BLDSC (0611.138000); CASDDS. **CCC.**
 Formerly (until 1982): Academia Scientiarum Hungarica. Acta Chirurgica (ISSN 0001-5431)
 Description: Provides a forum for papers in surgery, including surgical aspects of gynecology, urology, otolaryngology, orthopedics, opthalmology, neural surgery, pulmonary surgery, oral surgery and heart and blood vessel surgery.

617 IT ISSN 0001-5466
 CODEN: ACHIA7
ACTA CHIRURGICA ITALICA. (Text in Italian; summaries in English) 1944. bi-m. L.120000 includes supplements (effective 1995). Tipografia Editrice la Garangola, Via Montona 4, 35137 Padua, Italy. FAX 39-49-8751743. Ed. R. Vecchioni. bk.rev.; index. (back issues avail.) **Indexed:** Biol.Abstr., Chem.Abstr., Dent.Ind., Excerp.Med., Ind.Med.
—BLDSC (0611.140000); Faxon; Genuine Article.

617 YU ISSN 0001-5474
ACTA CHIRURGICA JUGOSLAVICA. (Text in English, German, Serbo-Croatian) 1954. q. $50. Udruzenje Hirurga Jugoslavije - Association of Yugoslav Surgeons, Univerzitetski Klinicki Centar, Institut za Bolesti Digestivnog Sistema, Ul. Koste Todorivica 6, 11000 Belgrade, Yugoslavia. TEL 011-643-070. FAX 011-646-988. TELEX 011-12099 CLI CTRYU. Ed. Dr. Zoran Gerzic. adv.; bk.rev. circ. 2,000. **Indexed:** Ind.Med.
—BLDSC (0611.150000).

MEDICAL SCIENCES — SURGERY

617   IT   ISSN 0393-6376
ACTA CHIRURGICA MEDITERRANEA. (Text in English, Italian) 1960. bi-m. L.40000($40) Carbone Editore, Via G. Daita, 29, 90139 Palermo, Italy. TEL 091-321273. FAX 091-321782. adv.; abstr.; bibl.; illus.; stat.; index. circ. 6,000.
Formerly: Archivio Siciliano di Medicina e Chirurgia (Sezione Chirurgica).
Description: Clinical cases in the surgical field are reviewed and discussed.

616   AU   ISSN 0001-6268
CODEN: ACNUA5
ACTA NEUROCHIRURGICA. (Supplement avail.: Acta Neurochirurgica. Supplementum (ISSN 0065-1419)) 1950. 24/yr. (in 6 vols., 4 nos./vol.). DM.2182($1585) (effective 1996). (European Association of Neurosurgical Societies) Springer-Verlag, Sachsenplatz 4-6, Postfach 89, A-1201 Vienna, Austria. TEL 0222-330-2415. FAX 0222-330-2426. (Subscr. in N. America to: Springer-Verlag New York, Inc., 44 Hartz Way, Secaucus, NJ 07096-2491. TEL 201-348-4033. FAX 201-348-4505) Ed E. F. Loew. adv. (also avail. in microfilm from UMI; reprint service avail. from ISI) **Indexed:** ASCA, Bibl.Dev.Med.& Child Neur., Curr.Adv.Cancer Res., Curr.Adv.Ecol.Sci., Curr.Cont., Excerp.Med., Ind.Med., Ind.Sci.Rev., INIS Atomind., Sci.Cit.Ind. **Document type:** academic/scholarly publication.
—BLDSC (0639.850000); ADONIS; Faxon; Genuine Article; SWETS; UMI; UnCover. **CCC.**

ACTA NEUROCHIRURGICA. SUPPLEMENTUM. see *MEDICAL SCIENCES — Psychiatry And Neurology*

617   IT   ISSN 0392-3088
ACTA PHONIATRICA LATINA. 1978. q. L.120000 includes supplements (effective 1995). Tipografia Editrice la Garangola, Via Montona 4, 35137 Padua, Italy. FAX 39-49-8751743. (back issues avail.) **Indexed:** Excerp.Med., NBA.
—BLDSC (0648.600000).

ADVANCES AND TECHNICAL STANDARDS IN NEUROSURGERY. see *MEDICAL SCIENCES — Psychiatry And Neurology*

ADVANCES IN CARDIAC SURGERY. see *MEDICAL SCIENCES — Cardiovascular Diseases*

ADVANCES IN NEUROSURGERY. see *MEDICAL SCIENCES — Psychiatry And Neurology*

ADVANCES IN NEUROTRAUMA RESEARCH. see *MEDICAL SCIENCES — Psychiatry And Neurology*

ADVANCES IN OTOLARYNGOLOGY - HEAD AND NECK SURGERY. see *MEDICAL SCIENCES — Otorhinolaryngology*

617.95   US   ISSN 0748-5212
RD118.A1
ADVANCES IN PLASTIC AND RECONSTRUCTIVE SURGERY. 1984. a. $77.95 (residents $40) (effective 1996). Mosby - Year Book, Inc. (Chicago) (Subsidiary of: Times Mirror Company), 200 N. LaSalle St., Chicago, IL 60601-1080. TEL 312-726-9733. FAX 312-726-6075. TELEX 206155. (Subscr. to: 11830 Westline Industrial Dr., St. Louis, MO 63146. TEL 800-325-4177) Eds. Drs. Mutaz B. Habal, William D. Morain. illus.
—BLDSC (0710.235000). **CCC.**
Description: Presents a collection of original, fully-referenced review articles written by experts in plastic and reconstructive surgery.

ADVANCES IN RENAL REPLACEMENT THERAPY. see *MEDICAL SCIENCES — Urology And Nephrology*

617.082   US   ISSN 0065-3411
RD1
ADVANCES IN SURGERY. 1966. a. $64.95 (residents $40) (effective 1996). Mosby - Year Book, Inc. (Chicago) (Subsidiary of: Times Mirror Company), 200 N. LaSalle St., Chicago, IL 60601-1080. TEL 312-726-9733. FAX 312-726-6075. TELEX 206155. (Subscr. to: 11830 Westline Dr., St. Louis, MO 63146. TEL 800-325-4177) Ed. Dr. John L. Cameron. illus. (also avail. in microfilm from UMI; reprint service avail. from UMI) **Indexed:** Ind.Med.
—BLDSC (0711.595000); SWETS; UMI. **CCC.**
Description: Presents a collection of original, fully-referenced review articles in selected clinical topics important in the field of surgery.

617.4   US   ISSN 1069-7292
ADVANCES IN VASCULAR SURGERY. 1993. a. $72.95 (residents $40) (effective 1996). Mosby - Year Book, Inc. (Chicago) (Subsidiary of: Times Mirror Company), 200 N. LaSalle St., Chicago, IL 60601-1080. TEL 312-726-9733. FAX 312-726-6075. TELEX 206155. Ed. Dr. Charles Whittemore.
Description: Presents original, fully referenced review articles on selected clinical topics in the field of vascular surgery.

617.95   US   ISSN 0364-216X
RD119
AESTHETIC PLASTIC SURGERY. 1976. q. $285 (effective 1996). (International Society of Aesthetic Plastic Surgery) Springer-Verlag, Journals, 175 Fifth Ave., New York, NY 10010. TEL 212-460-1500. FAX 212-473-6272. (N. American subscr. to: Journal Fulfillment Services, Box 2485, Secaucus, NJ 07096-4643. TEL 800-777-4643. FAX 201-348-4505; Subscr. outside N. America to: Heidelberger Platz 3, 1000 Berlin 33, Germany. TEL 030-8207-1. FAX 030-8214091) Ed. Blair O. Rogers. adv. (also avail. in microform from UMI; reprint service avail.) **Indexed:** Curr.Cont., Excerp.Med., Med.& Surg.Dermat. **Document type:** academic/scholarly publication.
—BLDSC (0730.380000); Faxon; Genuine Article; SWETS; UMI; UnCover. **CCC.**
Description: Devoted to the aesthetic surgery of the entire body surface, including facial surgery, body surgery, and extremity surgery.
Refereed Serial

617   GW   ISSN 0001-785X
AKTUELLE CHIRURGIE. 1966. bi-m. DM.288. Georg Thieme Verlag, Ruedigerstr. 14, 70469 Stuttgart, Germany. TEL 0711-8931-0. FAX 0711-8931298. (Subscr. to: Postfach 104853, 70042 Stuttgart, Germany) Ed. H.D. Roeher. adv.; bibl.; charts; illus.; stat.; index. circ. 2,000. (reprint service avail. from UMI) **Indexed:** Excerp.Med. **Document type:** academic/scholarly publication.
—BLDSC (0785.729500); UMI. **CCC.**

617   UK   ISSN 0966-6532
AMBULATORY SURGERY. 1993. q. £132($210) (effective 1996). Butterworth - Heinemann, Part of the Reed Elsevier group, Linacre House, Jordan Hill, Oxford OX2 8DP, England. TEL 0865-310366. FAX 0865-310898. (Subscr. to: Elsevier Science Ltd., P.O. Box 800, Kidlington, Oxford OX5 1DX, England. TEL 44-865-843000. FAX 44-865-843010; Subscr. in U.S. and Canada to: Elsevier Science, 660 White Plains Rd., Tarrytown, NY 10591-5153. TEL 914-524-9200. FAX 914-333-2444) (also avail. in microfilm from UMI; back issues avail.) **Document type:** academic/scholarly publication.
—BLDSC (0809.215700); UMI.
Refereed Serial

617.585   US
AMERICAN COLLEGE OF FOOT SPECIALISTS. ANNUAL YEARBOOK. 1958. a. American College of Foot Specialists, 1801 Vauxhall Rd., Box 54, Union, NJ 02083. circ. 2,000.
Formerly (until 1980): American Association of Foot Specialists. Program Journal (ISSN 0065-7190)

617   US   ISSN 0002-8045
RD1
AMERICAN COLLEGE OF SURGEONS. BULLETIN. 1916. m. American College of Surgeons, Communications Department, 55 E. Erie St., Chicago, IL 60611-2797. TEL 312-664-4050. FAX 312-440-7014. Ed. Stephen J. Regnier. charts; illus.; index; circ. 67,257 (controlled). (also avail. in microform from UMI; reprint service avail. from UMI) **Indexed:** Chem.Abstr., Med.Care Rev. **Document type:** bulletin.
—BLDSC (2386.540000); Faxon; UMI; UnCover.

617   US   ISSN 1072-7515
RD1   CODEN: JACSEX
AMERICAN COLLEGE OF SURGEONS. JOURNAL. Key Title: Journal of the American College of Surgeons. 1905. m. (2 vols./yr., 6 nos./vol.). $70 to individuals (foreign $80) (effective 1995). American College of Surgeons, Publishing Department, 54 E. Erie St., Chicago, IL 60611. TEL 312-787-9282. FAX 312-440-7360. Ed. Dr. Samuel A. Wells, Jr; Pub. Sean Griskenas. adv.; bk.rev.; bibl.; charts; illus.; s-a. index. circ. 19,370. (also avail. in microform from UMI,PMC; reprint service avail. from UMI) **Indexed:** AIM, ASCA, Biol.Abstr., Chem.Abstr., Curr.Adv.Ecol.Sci., Curr.Cont., Dent.Ind., Excerp.Med., Helminthol.Abstr., Hosp.Lit.Ind., Ind.Med., Ind.Vet., Kidney, Med.& Surg.Dermat., Nutr.Abstr., Rev.Plant Path., Vet.Bull. **Document type:** academic/scholarly publication.
●Also available online. Vendor(s): Lexis-Nexis.
—BLDSC (4685.784000); CASDDS; EMDOCS; Faxon; Genuine Article; SWETS; UMI; UnCover. **CCC.**
Formerly (until 1994): Surgery, Gynecology and Obstetrics (ISSN 0039-6087)
Description: Publishes original papers on topics in general surgery.
Refereed Serial

617.95   US   ISSN 0748-8068
AMERICAN JOURNAL OF COSMETIC SURGERY. 1984. q. $85 (foreign $100) (effective 1996). American Academy of Cosmetic Surgery, Inc., 401 N. Michigan Ave., Chicago, IL 60611-4212. TEL 312-527-6713. FAX 312-644-1815. Ed. Dr. Melvin A. Shiffman. adv.; B&W page $900, color page $1725. bk.rev. circ. 8,500. (reprint service avail.) **Document type:** academic/scholarly publication.
Description: Covers thought, experience, opinion, technique, research, legal aspects, patient relations, office protocol and any other subject relating to cosmetic surgery.

617   US   ISSN 0899-7403
AMERICAN JOURNAL OF KNEE SURGERY. Abbreviated title: A J K S. 1988. q. $85 to individuals; institutions $100; foreign $124. Slack, Inc., 6900 Grove Rd., Thorofare, NJ 08086-9447. TEL 609-848-1000. FAX 609-853-5991. TELEX 517108. Ed. Dr. Kelly Vince. adv. circ. 1,500. (also avail. in microform from UMI).
—BLDSC (0826.870000); UMI.
Description: Geared towards knee specialists and sports trainers, including articles on surgery and rehabilitation.
Refereed Serial

617   US   ISSN 0002-9610
RD1   CODEN: AJSUAB
AMERICAN JOURNAL OF SURGERY. 1891. m. $215 to institutions outside the Americas; $135 to institutions in U.S (effective 1996). Excerpta Medica, Inc. (Subsidiary of: Reed Elsevier Medical group), 105 Raider Blvd., Belle Mead, NJ 08502. TEL 908-874-8550. FAX 908-874-8419. (Subscr. to: Box 3085, Princeton, NJ 08543-3085. TEL 800-662-7776) Eds. Hiram C. Polk, Monica Schmidt. adv.; bk.rev.; bibl.; charts; illus. circ. 15,131. (also avail. in microform from RPI,PMC; reprint service avail. from UMI) **Indexed:** Abstr.Inter.Med., AIM, Biol.Abstr., C.I.S.Abstr., Chem.Abstr., Curr.Adv.Cancer Res., Curr.Adv.Ecol.Sci., Curr.Cont., Dairy Sci.Abstr., Dent.Ind., Excerp.Med., Helminthol.Abstr., I.P.A., Ind.Med., Ind.Sci.Rev., INIS Atomind., Kidney, Med.& Surg.Dermat., Nutr.Abstr., Rev.Med.& Vet.Mycol., Rev.Plant Path., Risk Abstr., Sci.Cit.Ind. **Document type:** academic/scholarly publication.
●Also available online. Vendor(s): Ovid Technologies, Lexis-Nexis.
—BLDSC (0838.500000); ADONIS; CASDDS; Faxon; Genuine Article; SWETS; UMI; UnCover. **CCC.**
Description: Specializes in clinical papers on general surgery, including latest operative techniques and procedures. The official publication of record of eight major surgical associations in the US.
Refereed Serial

AMERICAN JOURNAL OF SURGICAL PATHOLOGY. see *MEDICAL SCIENCES*

MEDICAL SCIENCES — SURGERY

617 US ISSN 0003-1348
RD1 CODEN: AMSUAW
AMERICAN SURGEON. 1935. m. $89 to individuals (foreign $114); institutions $149 (foreign $174). (Southeastern Surgical Congress) Waverly Press, Inc. (Subsidiary of: Williams & Wilkins), 428 Preston St., Box 60425, Baltimore, MD 21202. TEL 410-528-4000. FAX 410-528-4412. (Subscr. to: Fulco, Box 3000, Denville, NJ 07843. TEL 800-875-2997. FAX 201-627-5872; Or: Southeastern Surgical Congress, 1776 Peachtree St., Ste 410N, Atlanta, GA 30309. TEL 404-607-8958. FAX 404-607-8972) (Co-sponsors: Midwest Surgical Association; Association of Clinical Anatomists; Society of American Gastrointestinal and Endoscopic Surgeons) Ed. Dr. Talmadge A. Bowden, Jr. adv.; illus.; index. circ. 5,530. (also avail. in microform from UMI; reprint service avail. from UMI) **Indexed:** Biol.Abstr., Chem.Abstr., Curr.Cont., Excerp.Med., Hosp.Lit.Ind., Ind.Med., Ind.Sci.Rev., Ind.Vet., INIS Atomind., Med.& Surg.Dermat., Rev.Med.& Vet.Mycol., Sci.Cit.Ind., Small Anim.Abstr., SSCI.
—BLDSC (0857.750000); Faxon; Genuine Article; SWETS; UMI; UnCover. **CCC.**
Refereed Serial

617 617 BL ISSN 0003-245X
ANAIS PAULISTAS DE MEDICINA E CIRURGIA. 1913. q. Cr.$5000($30) Real e Benerita Sociedade Portuguesa de Sao Paulo, Rua Maestro Cardim, 769, 01323 Sao Paulo, Brazil. Ed. Abrahao Kerzner. adv.; bk.rev.; bibl.; illus.; index. circ. 2,000. **Indexed:** Biol.Abstr., Chem.Abstr., Excerp.Med., Ind.Med.
—BLDSC (0869.130000); Faxon; UMI.

617 AG ISSN 0066-1465
ANALES DE CIRUGIA. 1935. irreg. Calle Paraguay 40, Rosario, Prov. de Santa Fe, Argentina. **Indexed:** Biol.Abstr., Excerp.Med.

ANALES DE CIRUGIA CARDIACA Y CIRUGIA VASCULAR. see *MEDICAL SCIENCES — Cardiovascular Diseases*

ANESTEZIOLOGIYA I REANIMATOLOGIYA/ANESTHESIOLOGY AND REANIMATOLOGY. see *MEDICAL SCIENCES — Anaesthesiology*

617 618.1 FI ISSN 0355-9521
CODEN: ACGYDJ
ANNALES CHIRURGIAE ET GYNAECOLOGIAE. (Text in English) 1946. q. FIM 600 in Finland; Europe FIM 950; elsewhere FIM 1050 (effective 1996); newsstand price: FIM 100. Finnish Surgical Society, Maekelaekatu 2 A, SF-00500 Helsinki, Finland. TEL 358-0-393-0768. FAX 358-0-393-0801. Ed. J. Niinikoski. adv. contact: Anja Maaskola. bibl.; charts; illus. circ. 2,000. (also avail. in microform from UMI; back issues avail.) **Indexed:** Biol.Abstr., Chem.Abstr., Curr.Adv.Ecol.Sci., Curr.Cont., Excerp.Med., Ind.Med., INIS Atomind. **Document type:** academic/scholarly publication.
—BLDSC (0970.510000); CASDDS; Faxon; SWETS; UMI; UnCover.
Formerly (until vol.65, no.1): Annales Chirurgiae et Gynaecologiae Fenniae (ISSN 0003-3855)

617 FR ISSN 0003-3944
ANNALES DE CHIRURGIE. 1947. 10/yr. 1000 F. to individuals (foreign 1430 F.); students 500 F. (foreign 715 F.). (Semaine des Hopitaux) Expansion Scientifique, 31 bd. de la Tour Maubourg, 75007 Paris, France. TEL 40-62-64-00. FAX 45-55-69-20. Ed. M. Edelmann. **Indexed:** Biol.Abstr., Chem.Abstr., Curr.Adv.Cancer Res., Curr.Cont., Excerp.Med., Ind.Med.
—BLDSC (0970.532000); Genuine Article; SWETS. **CCC.**

617 FR ISSN 1153-2424
CODEN: AMSPEL
ANNALES DE CHIRURGIE DE LA MAIN ET DU MEMBRE SUPERIEUR/ANNALS OF HAND AND UPPER LIMB SURGERY. (Text in English and French) 5/yr. 1060 F. to individuals (foreign 1300 F.); students 1470 F. (foreign 1830 F.); students 730 F. (foreign 1020 F.). (Societes de Chirurgie de la Main) Expansion Scientifique, 31 bd. de la Tour Maubourg, 75007 Paris, France. TEL 40-62-64-00. FAX 45-55-69-20. (Co-sponsors: Societe Belge de Chirurgie de la Main; Groupe d'Etude de la Main; Societe Francaise de Chirurgie de la Main) **Indexed:** Biol.Abstr., Excerp.Med.
—BLDSC (0970.539000); Faxon; SWETS. **CCC.**
Formerly: Annales de Chirurgie de la Main (ISSN 0753-9053)

617.95 FR ISSN 0294-1260
CODEN: ACESE
ANNALES DE CHIRURGIE PLASTIQUE ET ESTHETIQUE. (Text in French; summaries in English) 1956. 6/yr. 1320 F. to individuals (foreign 1540 F.); students 660 F. (foreign 770 F.). (Semaine des Hopitaux) Expansion Scientifique, 31 bd. de la Tour Maubourg, 75007 Paris, France. TEL 40-62-64-00. FAX 45-55-69-20. Ed. J.T. Lalardrie. adv.; abstr.; charts; illus. **Indexed:** Biol.Abstr., Chem.Abstr., Curr.Cont., Excerp.Med., Ind.Med., Med.& Surg.Dermat.
—BLDSC (0970.541000); Faxon; Genuine Article; SWETS. **CCC.**
Formerly: Annales de Chirurgie Plastique (ISSN 0003-3960)

ANNALES DE CHIRURGIE THORACIQUE ET CARDIO-VASCULAIRE. see *MEDICAL SCIENCES — Cardiovascular Diseases*

617 IT ISSN 0003-469X
CODEN: AICHAL
ANNALI ITALIANI DI CHIRURGIA. 1922. 6/yr. L.80000($100) Nuova Casa Editrice Licinio Cappelli di G.E.M. s.r.l., Via Farini, 14, 40126 Bologna, Italy. TEL 39-51-239060. FAX 39-51-239286. Ed. N. Picardi. adv.; bk.rev.; charts; illus. circ. 3,000. **Indexed:** Biol.Abstr., Chem.Abstr., Dent.Ind., Excerp.Med., Ind.Med.
—BLDSC (1014.300000); Faxon.

617.95 US ISSN 0148-7043
RD118.AI CODEN: APCSD4
ANNALS OF PLASTIC SURGERY. 1978. m. $161 to individuals (foreign $245); institutions $235 (foreign $323); residents $95 (foreign $145) (effective Oct. 1994). Little, Brown and Company, Medical Journals, 34 Beacon St., Boston, MA 02108. TEL 617-859-5500. FAX 617-859-0629. Ed. Dr. William D. Morain. adv.; B&W page $785; trim 8 1/4 x 11. bk.rev.; abstr.; charts; illus.; stat.; index. circ. 3,998. (also avail. in microform from UMI; reprint service avail. from UMI; back issues avail.) **Indexed:** Biol.Abstr., CINAHL, Curr.Cont., Dent.Ind., Excerp.Med., Ind.Med., Ind.Sci.Rev., INIS Atomind., Med.& Surg.Dermat., Sci.Cit.Ind. **Document type:** academic/scholarly publication.
●Also available online. Vendor(s): Lexis-Nexis.
—BLDSC (1043.525000); Genuine Article; SWETS; UMI; UnCover. **CCC.**
Description: Forum for the latest in surgical techniques, interesting cases, and practical briefs on surgical devices. Includes articles, case reports, hypotheses, and letters to the editor.
Refereed Serial

617 US ISSN 0003-4932
RD1 CODEN: ANSUA5
ANNALS OF SURGERY. 1885. m. $105 to individuals (foreign $180); institutions $205 (foreign $260) (effective 1996). Lippincott - Raven Publishers, 227 E. Washington Sq., Philadelphia, PA 19106. TEL 215-238-4200. (Co-sponsors: Southern Surgical Association; Philadelphia Academy of Surgery; New York Surgical Society; American Surgical Association) Ed. David C. Sabiston, Jr., M.D. adv.; illus.; index. circ. 14,765. (also avail. in microform from UMI,PMC; reprint service avail. from UMI) **Indexed:** Abstr.Health Care Manage.Stud., Abstr.Inter.Med., AIM, Biol.Abstr., Chem.Abstr., Curr.Adv.Cancer Res., Curr.Adv.Ecol.Sci., Curr.Cont., Excerp.Med., Helminthol.Abstr., Hosp.Lit.Ind., Ind.Med., Ind.Sci.Rev., INIS Atomind., Kidney, Med.& Surg.Dermat., Risk Abstr., Sci.Cit.Ind., SSCI.
●Also available online. Vendor(s): Lexis-Nexis, Ovid Technologies.
—BLDSC (1044.500000); CASDDS; Faxon; Genuine Article; SWETS; UMI; UnCover. **CCC.**
Refereed Serial

617 US ISSN 1068-9265
▼**ANNALS OF SURGICAL ONCOLOGY.** 1994. bi-m. $136 to individuals (foreign $160); institutions $198 (foreign $223) (effective 1996). (Society of Surgical Oncology) Lippincott - Raven Press, 227 E. Washington Sq., Philadelphia, PA 19106. TEL 215-238-4200. Ed. Charles M. Balch. adv. contact: Phyllis Noyes. charts; illus. circ. 2,000. (also avail. in microform from UMI) **Document type:** academic/scholarly publication.
—BLDSC (1044.550000); Genuine Article; UMI. **CCC.**
Description: Presents significant developments involving multidisciplinary cancer care and research, for practicing surgeons in all specialties.
Refereed Serial

617.54 JA
ANNALS OF THORACIC AND CARDIOVASCULAR SURGERY. (Text in English) 1981. bi-m. 15000 Yen to individuals; institutions 20000 Yen. Axel Springer Japan Publishing, Inc., 2-1 Nibancho, Chiyoda-ku, Tokyo 102, Japan. FAX 81-3-3239-9388. Ed. Yukiyasu Sezai.
Formerly (until 1995): Rinsho Kyobu Geka - Japanese Annals of Thoracic Surgery (ISSN 0389-7893)

617.54 US ISSN 0003-4975
RD536 CODEN: ATHSAK
ANNALS OF THORACIC SURGERY. 1965. m. $250 to institutions in U.S.; $295 to institutions outside the Americas; $340 to institutions in Europe; $363 to institutions in Japan (effective 1996). (Society of Thoracic Surgeons) Elsevier Science Inc., 655 Ave. of the Americas, New York, NY 10010. TEL 212-989-5800. FAX 212-633-3990. TELEX 420643 AEP UI. (Subscr. to: Box 882, Madison Sq. Sta., New York, NY 10159-0882) (Co-sponsor: Southern Thoracic Surgical Association) Ed. Dr. Thomas Ferguson. adv.; bk.rev.; charts; illus.; index. circ. 8,100. (also avail. in microform from UMI; back issues avail.) **Indexed:** Abstr.Inter.Med., AIM, Biol.Abstr., CINAHL, Curr.Adv.Cancer Res., Curr.Cont., Excerp.Med., Helminthol.Abstr., Ind.Med., Ind.Sci.Rev., INIS Atomind., Kidney, Nutr.Abstr., Rev.Med.& Vet.Mycol., Sci.Cit.Ind. **Document type:** academic/scholarly publication.
●Also available online. Vendor(s): Lexis-Nexis.
—BLDSC (1044.750000); ADONIS; Faxon; Genuine Article; SWETS; UnCover. **CCC.**
Description: Presents original papers on topics in thoracic and cardiovascular surgery, featuring case reports, "how-to-do-it" articles, classics in thoracic surgery, collective and current reviews, and correspondence.
Refereed Serial

617 616.1 US ISSN 0890-5096
CODEN: AVSUEV
ANNALS OF VASCULAR SURGERY; international journal of vascular surgery. 1986. bi-m. $75 to individuals (Canada & Mexico $85; elsewhere $110); institutions $135 (Canada & Mexico $150; elsewhere $175). Quality Medical Publishing, Inc., 11970 Borman Dr., Ste. 222, St. Louis, MO 63146. TEL 314-878-7808; 800-348-7808. FAX 314-878-9937. Eds. Dr. Ramon Berguer, Dr. Edouard Kieffer. **Indexed:** Excerp.Med. **Document type:** academic/scholarly publication.
—BLDSC (1045.350000); Faxon; SWETS; UMI; UnCover. **CCC.**
Description: Worldwide coverage of all clinical or research-oriented work going on today in vascular surgery.

ANNUAL OF CARDIAC SURGERY. see *MEDICAL SCIENCES — Abstracting, Bibliographies, Statistics*

617 FR ISSN 0003-5394
ANTENNE MEDICALE. (Includes supplements) 1964. m. 150 F. Service de Radiologie Adulte, c/o Doctuer G. Pelissier, 439 rue Paradise, 13008 Marseille, France. Ed.Bd. adv.; bk.rev.; bibl, illus.

617 II ISSN 0003-5998
R97
THE ANTISEPTIC; monthly journal of medicine and surgery. (Text in English) 1904. m. Rs.240 (foreign Rs.1440) (effective 1995). Professional Publications Ltd., P.O. Box 2, Satya Sai Nagar, Madurai 625 003, Tamil Nadu, India. TEL 0452-600001. FAX 0452-601602. Ed.Bd. adv.; bk.rev.; abstr.; bibl.; illus.; index. circ. 22,563. (reprint service avail. from UMI) **Indexed:** Chem.Abstr., Excerp.Med., Ind.Med. **Document type:** trade publication.
—BLDSC (1552.000000).

617 JA ISSN 0003-9152
CODEN: NIGHAE
ARCHIV FUER JAPANISCHE CHIRURGIE/NIHON GEKA HOKAN. (Text in various languages) 1924. bi-m. 6000 Yen or exchange basis. Kyoto University, Faculty of Medicine, Department of Surgery, 54 Shogoin Kawara-cho, Sakyo-ku, Kyoto 606, Japan. Ed. Kazae Ozawa. abstr.; charts; illus.; index. circ. 1,000. **Indexed:** Biol.Abstr., Chem.Abstr., Curr.Cont., Excerp.Med., Ind.Med.
—BLDSC (1615.400000); CASDDS.

MEDICAL SCIENCES — SURGERY

617   US   ISSN 0004-0010
CODEN: ARSUAX
ARCHIVES OF SURGERY. 1920. m. $100 (foreign $140). American Medical Association, 515 N. State St., Chicago, IL 60610. TEL 312-464-5000; 800-262-2350. FAX 312-464-4184. Ed. Dr. Claude H. Organ. adv.; bk.rev.; charts; illus.; index. circ. 39,000. (also avail. in microform from UMI,PMC) **Indexed:** Abstr.Inter.Med., AIM, Biol.Abstr., C.I.S. Abstr., Chem.Abstr., CINAHL, Curr.Adv.Cancer Res., Curr.Adv.Cell & Devel.Biol., Curr.Adv.Ecol.Sci., Dairy Sci.Abstr., Dent.Ind., Excerp.Med., Helminthol.Abstr., Ind.Med., Ind.Sci.Rev., INIS Atomind., Int.Nurs.Ind., Med.& Surg.Dermat., Nutr.Abstr., Protozool.Abstr., Rev.Med.& Vet.Mycol., Risk Abstr., Sci.Cit.Ind. **Document type:** academic/scholarly publication.
●Also available online. Vendor(s): Lexis-Nexis.
—BLDSC (1643.200000); CASDDS; Faxon; Genuine Article; SWETS; UMI; UnCover. **CCC.**
Refereed Serial

617.54 616.1   IT   ISSN 0391-7029
ARCHIVIO DI CHIRURGIA TORACICA E CARDIOVASCOLARE. (Text in English and Italian) 1979. bi-m. $120. (Italian Society of Cardiovascular Surgery) Edizioni Luigi Pozzi s.r.l., Via Panama 68, 00198 Rome, Italy. TEL 39-6-8553548. FAX 39-6-8554105. Ed. B. Marino. adv.; bk.rev. circ. 1,200.
Description: Articles on thoracic and cardiovascular surgery.

617   IT   ISSN 0066-670X
ARCHIVIO PUTTI DI CHIRURGIA DEGLI ORGANI DI MOVIMENTO. (Text in Italian; summaries in English, Italian) 1951. a. $70. Aulo Gaggi Editore, Via Andrea Costa 131-5, 40134 Bologna, Italy. TEL 0222-5339614. FAX 0222-638158. Ed. O. Scaglietti. bk.rev. circ. 1,500. **Indexed:** Dent.Ind., Excerp.Med., Ind.Med.
—BLDSC (1647.900000).

617   BL   ISSN 0066-7846
ARQUIVOS DE CIRURGIA CLINICA E EXPERIMENTAL.★ (Supplements accompany some issues) (Some summaries in English) 1937. irreg. $35. Universidade de Sao Paulo, Hospital das Clinicas, Caixa Postal 8091, Sao Paulo, Brazil. Ed Ruy G. Bevilacqua. index, cum.index. circ. 10,000. **Indexed:** Biol.Abstr.

617   PO   ISSN 0872-2226
ARQUIVOS PORTUGUESES DE CIRURGIA. (Text in English and Portuguese) 1990. q. Esc.2000. A E F M U P, Alameda Prof. H. Monteiro, Piso 1, Apdo. 4514, 4008 Porto Codex, Portugal. TEL 351-2-524901. FAX 351-2-5509096. (Co-sponsors: Hospital de S. Joao, Faculdade de Medicina do Porto) Ed. Amarante Junior. adv.: B&W page Esc.150000; adv. contact: Fernando Araujo. circ. 2,500. **Document type:** academic/scholarly publication.

ARTHROSCOPY; journal of arthroscopic and related surgery. see *MEDICAL SCIENCES — Orthopedics And Traumatology*

ARTHROSCOPY. see *MEDICAL SCIENCES — Orthopedics And Traumatology*

ARTIFICIAL ORGANS. see *MEDICAL SCIENCES — Experimental Medicine, Laboratory Technique*

ASIAN JOURNAL OF ORAL AND MAXILLOFACIAL SURGERY. see *MEDICAL SCIENCES — Dentistry*

617   HK   ISSN 1015-9584
CODEN: AJSUEF
ASIAN JOURNAL OF SURGERY. (Text in English) 1978. 4/yr. $80. Asian Surgical Association, Queen Mary Hospital, Hong Kong. TEL 852-2855-4080. FAX 852-2855-9950. Ed. Edward C.S. Lai. adv.: B&W page $2000, color page $4000. circ. 1,800 (controlled). **Indexed:** Excerp.Med. **Document type:** academic/scholarly publication.
—BLDSC (1742.578000).
Formerly (until 1989): Southeast Asian Journal of Surgery (ISSN 0258-3186)

ATLAS OF THE ORAL AND MAXILLOFACIAL SURGERY CLINICS OF NORTH AMERICA. see *MEDICAL SCIENCES — Dentistry*

616.21   US   ISSN 1047-6954
AUDIO-DIGEST GENERAL SURGERY. 1954. s-m. $168. Audio-Digest Foundation (Subsidiary of: California Medical Association), 1577 E. Chevy Chase Dr., Glendale, CA 91206. TEL 213-245-8505. FAX 818-240-7379. Ed. Claron L. Oakley. (audio cassette)
Formerly: Audio-Digest Surgery (ISSN 0271-1273)
Refereed Serial

617   AT   ISSN 0004-8682
CODEN: ANZJA7
AUSTRALIAN AND NEW ZEALAND JOURNAL OF SURGERY. 1931. m. Aus.$320 (foreign Aus.$620) (effective 1996). (Royal Australasian College of Surgeons) Blackwell Science Pty Ltd, P.O. Box 378, Carlton, Vic. 3053, Australia. TEL 61-3-93470300. FAX 61-3-93493016. Eds. G.J.A. Clunie, J. Ludbrook. adv.: B&W page $720, color page $1510. bk.rev.; bibl.; illus.; index. circ. 5,400. (also avail. in microform from UMI; back issues avail.; reprint service avail. from UMI) **Indexed:** Biol.Abstr., Curr.Adv.Cancer Res., Curr.Cont., Dent.Ind., Excerp.Med., Ind.Med., Nutr.Abstr., Rev.Med.& Vet.Mycol., Sci.Cit.Ind. **Document type:** academic/scholarly publication.
—BLDSC (1796.900000); ADONIS; Faxon; Genuine Article; SWETS; UMI. **CCC.**
Description: Covers original contributions related to clinical practice and research in all fields of surgery and related disciplines.

AUSTRALIAN JOURNAL OF EMERGENCY CARE. see *MEDICAL SCIENCES — Orthopedics And Traumatology*

616   AT   ISSN 0157-5821
AUSTRALIAN SURGEON. 1977. bi-m. membership only. Australian Association of Surgeons, Ste. 1, 2A Mona Rd., Darling Point, n.S.W. 2027, Australia. FAX 61-2-363-5001. Ed. Christopher Thomas. adv. circ. 2,000. **Document type:** academic/scholarly publication, bulletin.
—UnCover.

617   SP
BARCELONA QUIRURGICA. 1957. 6/yr. 4500 ptas.($108) (effective 1995). Editorial Rocas, Muntaner 393, pral. 4, 08021 Barcelona, Spain. TEL 39-3-2001389. FAX 39-3-2021958. Ed. G. Gili Cirera. bk.rev. circ. 18,000. **Document type:** trade publication.
Description: Covers all the specialties of surgery.

617   SZ   ISSN 1013-7459
CODEN: BBCHEL
BASELER BEITRAEGE ZUR CHIRURGIE; Aktuelle Entwicklungen und neue Verfahren aus der chirurgischen Praxis kompakt vermittelt. (Text in German) 1989. irreg. varies. (University of Basel, Department of Surgery) Schwabe und Co. AG, Steinentorstr. 13, CH-4010 Basel, Switzerland. TEL 061-2725523. FAX 061-2725593. TELEX CH-962652. Eds. U. Laffer, M. Duerig. abstr.; bibl.; charts. **Document type:** academic/scholarly publication.
Description: Discusses developments in surgery and its techniques.

617   US
▼**BODY CONTOURING SURGERY.** Announced for publication in 1996. q. $195 to individuals; institutions $245 (effective 1996). Field & Wood, Medical Periodicals, Inc., Box 975, Blue Bell, PA 19422. TEL 610-828-4010. FAX 215-482-0226. Ed. Dr. Ricardo Baroudi. **Document type:** academic/scholarly publication.
Refereed Serial

617.6   UK   ISSN 1356-3807
BRITISH DENTAL NURSES' JOURNAL. vol.32, 1973. q. £30. British Association of Dental Nurses, 38 Meadowhead Dr., Sheffield, Yorks. S8 7TQ, England. TEL 01253-778631. FAX 01253-777268. Ed. Pamela A. Swain. adv.; bk.rev.; illus. circ. 3,500. **Indexed:** Dent.Ind. **Document type:** academic/scholarly publication.
—BLDSC (2299.050000).
Formerly (until 1994): British Dental Surgery Assistant (ISSN 0007-0629)

617   UK   ISSN 0268-8697
CODEN: BJNEEL
BRITISH JOURNAL OF NEUROSURGERY. Online edition (ISSN 1360-046X) 1987. bi-m. £96 to individuals; institutions £266 (effective 1996). Carfax Publishing Co., P.O. Box 25, Abingdon, Oxon. OX14 3UE, England. TEL 01235-555335. FAX 01235-553559. (Subscr. in N. America to: Carfax Publishing Co., 875-81 Massachusetts Ave., Cambridge, MA 02139) Ed. Robert Maurice-Williams. adv.; B&W page £250; adv. contact: Mark Butler. bk.rev.; index. (also avail. in microfiche; back issues avail.) **Indexed:** Excerp.Med. **Document type:** academic/scholarly publication.
●Also available online.
—BLDSC (2311.940000); Faxon; Genuine Article; SWETS; UMI; UnCover. **CCC.**
Refereed Serial

BRITISH JOURNAL OF ORAL AND MAXILLOFACIAL SURGERY. see *MEDICAL SCIENCES — Dentistry*

617.95   UK   ISSN 0007-1226
CODEN: BJPSAZ
BRITISH JOURNAL OF PLASTIC SURGERY. 1948. 8/yr. £119($169) (effective 1995). (British Association of Plastic Surgeons) Churchill Livingstone Journals (Subsidiary of: Pearson Professional), Robert Stevenson House, 1-3 Baxter's Pl., Leith Walk, Edinburgh EH1 3AF, Scotland. TEL 0131-556-2424. FAX 0131-459-1177. TELEX 727511. (Subscr. to: Pearson Professional Ltd., P.O. Box 77, Fourth Ave., Harlow, Essex CM19 5AA, England. TEL 01279-623760; U.S. subscr. to: Churchill Livingstone, 650 Ave. of the Americas, New York, NY 10011. TEL 212-206-5000) Ed. M.J. Timmons. adv. contact: David Dunnachie. bk.rev.; abstr.; illus.; index. circ. 4,800. (also avail. in microform from UMI; back issues avail.; reprint service avail. from SWZ) **Indexed:** Biol.Abstr., Chem.Abstr., Curr.Adv.Ecol.Sci., Curr.Cont., Dent.Ind., Excerp.Med., Ind.Med., Ind.Sci.Rev., Med.& Surg.Dermat., Sci.Cit.Ind. **Document type:** academic/scholarly publication.
—BLDSC (2319.500000); Faxon; Genuine Article; SWETS; UnCover. **CCC.**
Description: Discusses techniques and developments in plastic surgery.

617   UK   ISSN 0007-1323
CODEN: BJSUAM
BRITISH JOURNAL OF SURGERY. 1913. m. £74.50 to individuals (outside Europe £84($135)); institutions £114.50 (outside Europe £128.50($179)) (effective 1996). (Surgery Society Ltd.) Blackwell Science Ltd., Osney Mead, Oxford OX2 OEL, England. TEL 01865-240201. FAX 01865-721205. TELEX 83355 MEDBOK G. Ed. R.C.N. Williamson. adv.; bk.rev.; abstr.; illus.; index. circ. 6,600. (also avail. in microform from UMI; back issues avail.) **Indexed:** Abstr.Inter.Med., AIM, Biol.Abstr., Biotech.Abstr., Chem.Abstr., Curr.Adv.Ecol.Sci., Curr.Cont., Dent.Ind., Dok.Arbeitsmed., Excerp.Med., Helminthol.Abstr., Ind.Med., Ind.Sci.Rev., Ind.Vet., INIS Atomind., Int.Nurs.Ind., Kidney, Med.& Surg.Dermat., Nutr.Abstr., Pig News & Info., Protozool.Abstr., Rev.Med.& Vet.Mycol., Risk Abstr., Sci.Cit.Ind., Small Anim.Abstr., Sugar Ind.Abstr., Vet.Bull. **Document type:** academic/scholarly publication.
●Also available online. Vendor(s): Lexis-Nexis, Ovid Technologies.
—BLDSC (2325.000000); ADONIS; Faxon; Genuine Article; SWETS; UMI; UnCover. **CCC.**
Description: Publishes original papers and reviews covering the latest techniques, treatment, and advances in surgery. Includes abstracts of the Surgical Research and the Vascular Societies.
Refereed Serial

617   SP   ISSN 0214-2376
BRITISH JOURNAL OF SURGERY (EDICION ESPANOLA). 1974. m. 12500 ptas.($112) (free to qualified personnel). Ediciones Doyma S.A., Travesera de Gracia 17-21, 08021 Barcelona, Spain. TEL 34-1-200-07-11. FAX 34-1-209-11-36. TELEX 51694 INK-E. (Co-sponsors: Association of Surgeons of Great Britain and Ireland, Surgical Research Society, UK) Ed. C. Pera Blanco-Morales. adv.: page 190000 ptas.; trim 210 x 280; adv. contact: Anna Pahissa. circ. 2,700. **Indexed:** Ind.Med.Esp.
—UMI.
Supersedes (in Jan. 1989): Revista Quirurgica Espanola (ISSN 0210-2196)
Description: Covers all areas of surgery as translated from the English edition.

4610 MEDICAL SCIENCES — SURGERY

BRITISH JOURNAL OF THEATRE NURSING. see *MEDICAL SCIENCES — Nurses And Nursing*

C A E T JOURNAL. (Canadian Association for Enterostomal Therapy) see *MEDICAL SCIENCES — Gastroenterology*

C I N N REPORT. (Chicago Institute of Neurosurgery and Neuroresearch) see *MEDICAL SCIENCES — Psychiatry And Neurology*

617   FR   ISSN 0301-0791
CAHIERS DE CHIRURGIE. 1972. 4/yr. 550 F. (foreign 600 F.) to non-members; members 270 F. (foreign 300 F.). College National des Chirurgiens Francais, 7 Avenue Theophile Gautier, 75016 Paris, France. TEL 46-47-71-04. FAX 45-27-15-39. Ed. Dr. J. Meurette. adv.: B&W page 3900 F., color page 9800 F.; 21 x 29.7. bk.rev. circ. 4,000. **Indexed:** Biol.Abstr.
—BLDSC (2948.797000).

CANADIAN JOURNAL OF CARDIOLOGY. see *MEDICAL SCIENCES — Cardiovascular Diseases*

617.95   CN   ISSN 1195-2199
CANADIAN JOURNAL OF PLASTIC SURGERY. 1993. 4/yr. Pulsus Group Inc., 2902 S. Sheridan Way, Oakville, ON L6J 7L6, Canada. TEL 905-829-4770. FAX 905-829-4799. Ed. Dr. Peter Wyshynski; Pub. Robert B. Kalina. adv.: B&W page Can.$940, color page Can.$1560; trim 8 1/8 x 10 7/8. circ. 4,000. **Document type:** academic/scholarly publication.
—BLDSC (3034.520000).

617   CN   ISSN 0008-428X
                              CODEN: CJSUAX
CANADIAN JOURNAL OF SURGERY/JOURNAL CANADIEN DE CHIRURGIE. (Text in English and French) 1957. bi-m. Can.$63($68) (effective 1996). Canadian Medical Association, Box 8650, Ottawa, ON K1G 0G8, Canada. TEL 613-731-9331. FAX 613-523-0937. adv.: B&W page Can. $1300, color page Can. $2725; trim 8 1/8 x 10 7/8. bk.rev.; bibl.; charts; illus.; index. circ. 3,500. (also avail. in microform from UMI; reprint service avail. from UMI) **Indexed:** Biol.Abstr., Chem.Abstr., Curr.Cont., Dent.Ind., Excerp.Med., Helminthol.Abstr., Ind.Med., Ind.Sci.Rev., NRN, Nutr.Abstr., Sci.Cit.Ind. **Document type:** academic/scholarly publication.
—BLDSC (3035.800000); Faxon; Genuine Article; SWETS; UMI; UnCover. **CCC.**
Description: Contributes to the effective continuing medical education of Canadian surgical specialists, using innovative techniques when feasible. Provides a vehicle for the dissemination of observations in clinical research.

CANADIAN OPERATING ROOM NURSING JOURNAL. see *MEDICAL SCIENCES — Nurses And Nursing*

CARDIOTHORACIC SURGERY SERIES. see *MEDICAL SCIENCES — Cardiovascular Diseases*

CARDIOVASCULAR SURGERY. see *MEDICAL SCIENCES — Cardiovascular Diseases*

CARDIOVASCULAR SURGERY. see *MEDICAL SCIENCES — Cardiovascular Diseases*

CESKA A SLOVENSKA NEUROLOGIE A NEUROCHIRURGIE. see *MEDICAL SCIENCES — Psychiatry And Neurology*

617   US   ISSN 1052-3359
                              CODEN: CSCAFT
CHEST SURGERY CLINICS OF NORTH AMERICA. 1991. q. $115 (foreign $145) (effective 1996). W.B. Saunders Co. (Subsidiary of: Harcourt Brace & Company), The Curtis Center, 3rd Fl., Independence Sq. W., Philadelphia, PA 19106-3399. TEL 215-238-7800. FAX 215-238-6445. (Subscr. to: W.B. Saunders Co., Periodicals Fulfillment, 6277 Sea Harbor Dr., 4th Fl., Orlando, FL 32891-4800. TEL 800-654-2452. FAX 800-874-6418) Ed. Dr. L. Penfield Faber. index. (also avail. in microform from UMI; back issues avail.) **Indexed:** Excerp.Med. (1995-), Ind.Med. (1994-). **Document type:** academic/scholarly publication.
—BLDSC (3172.604300); UMI.
Description: Covers a single specific topic in the diagnosis or surgical treatment of lung, heart, and throat diseases in each issue.

615.534   UK   ISSN 0009-4714
CHIROPODY REVIEW. 1939. bi-m. £12 (foreign £15). Institute of Chiropodists, 27 Wright St., Southport, Merseyside PR9 0TL, England. TEL 01704-546141. FAX 01704-500477. Ed. P.G.F. Bashary. adv. contact: A.D. Vines. bk.rev. circ. 1,500. **Document type:** trade publication, academic/scholarly publication.
Description: Features innovations in the field of podiatry.

617   BU   ISSN 0450-2167
                              CODEN: KHIGAF
CHIRURGIA. (Text in Bulgarian; summaries in English, Russian) 1948. bi-m. 24 lv.($11) (Ministerstvo na Narodnoto Zdrave) Izdatelstvo Meditsina i Fizkultura, 11, Pl. Slaveikov, Sofia, Bulgaria. (Co-sponsor: Nauchno Druzhestvo po Chirurgia) Ed. N. Vasilev. circ. 1,200. **Indexed:** Chem.Abstr., Dent.Ind., Excerp.Med., Helminthol.Abstr., Ind.Med.
—BLDSC (0394.790000); CASDDS.

617   IT   ISSN 0394-9508
CHIRURGIA. (Text in Italian; summaries in English) 1988. bi-m. $130 to individuals; institutions $160 (effective 1995). (Societa Italiana di Chirurgia) Edizioni Minerva Medica, Corso Bramante 83-85, 10126 Turin, Italy. TEL 39-11-3121736. FAX 39-11-3121736. Ed. Prof. Pezzuoli; Pub. Alberto Oliaro. adv.: B&W page $1400, color page $2300; trim 215 x 280; adv. contact: F. Filippo. bk.rev.; bibl.; charts; illus.; circ. 5,000 (paid). (back issues avail.) **Indexed:** Excerp.Med. **Document type:** academic/scholarly publication.
—BLDSC (3181.183000).
Description: Original articles on clinical and experimental surgery.
Refereed Serial

617   IT   ISSN 0009-4749
                              CODEN: CHOMA9
CHIRURGIA DEGLI ORGANI DI MOVIMENTO. (Text in Italian, English) 1917. q. L.80000($100) Nuova Casa Editrice Licinio Cappelli di G.E.M. s.r.l., Via Farini, 14, 40126 Bologna, Italy. TEL 39-51-239060. FAX 39-51-239286. Ed. M. Campanacci. adv.; bk.rev.; abstr.; bibl.; illus. circ. 3,000. **Indexed:** Biol.Abstr., Chem.Abstr., Dent.Ind., Excerp.Med., Ind.Med.
—BLDSC (3181.300000); Faxon; SWETS.

616   IT   ISSN 0392-0771
CHIRURGIA DEL PIEDE/FOOT SURGERY. (Text and summaries in English, Italian) 1977. bi-m. $95 to individuals; institutions $145 (effective 1995). (Societa Italiana di Medicina e Chirugia del Piede) Edizioni Minerva Medica, Corso Bramante 83-85, Turin 10126, Italy. TEL 39-11-678282. FAX 39-11-3121736. Dir. Giacomo Pisani; Pub. Alberto Oliaro. adv.: B&W page $1100, color page $1900; trim 215 x 280; adv. contact: F. Filippo. circ. 2,000 (paid). **Indexed:** Excerp.Med. **Document type:** academic/scholarly publication.
—BLDSC (3181.360000).
Formerly: Rivista di Chirurgia del Piede.
Description: Covers the anatomy, physiology, pathology and clinical medicine of the foot.
Refereed Serial

617   IT   ISSN 0394-9079
CHIRURGIA DELLA TESTA E DEL COLLO. 1983. s-a. L.60000 includes supplement (effective 1995). Tipografia Editrice la Garangola, Via Montona, 4, 35137 Padua, Italy. FAX 39-49-8751743.

617   IT   ISSN 0009-4757
CHIRURGIA E PATOLOGIA SPERIMENTALE. vol. 18, 1970. a. L.47000($59) Universita Cattolica del Sacro Cuore, Clinica Chirurgica, Via della Pineta Sacchetti N. 526, 00168 Rome, Italy. Dir. Gian Carlo Castiglioni. adv. circ. 500. **Indexed:** Biol.Abstr., Chem.Abstr., Dent.Ind., Excerp.Med., Ind.Med.

CHIRURGIA GASTROENTEROLOGICA (ITALIAN EDITION); rassegna trimestrale di chirurgia dell'apparato digerente e degli organi addominali. see *MEDICAL SCIENCES — Gastroenterology*

617   IT   ISSN 0009-4773
CHIRURGIA ITALIANA. (Text in Italian, summaries in English) 1947. bi-m. L.240000 (foreign L.300000). Bi & Gi Editori, Via Ca di Cozzi 41, 37124 Verona, Italy. TEL 045-8300968. FAX 045-8300970. Ed.Bd. adv.; bk.rev.; index, cum.index. **Indexed:** Biol.Abstr., Chem.Abstr., Excerp.Med., Ind.Med.
—BLDSC (3181.187000); Faxon.

617.95   CI   ISSN 0009-4781
                              CODEN: CMXPAU
CHIRURGIA MAXILLOFACIALIS ET PLASTICA/MAXILLOFACIAL AND PLASTIC SURGERY. (Text in Croatian or English; abstracts in English) 1957. 3/yr. $30. Hrvatski Lijecnicki Zbor, Drustvo za Maksilofacijalnu i Plasticnu Kirurgiju - Croatian Medical Association, Society for Maxillofacial and Plastic Surgery, Subiceva 9, Zagreb. TEL 385-41-420-470. FAX 385-41-425-629. Ed. Darco Mocan. adv.; bk.rev. circ. 500. (reprint service avail. from IRC) **Indexed:** Dent.Ind., Excerp.Med., Ind.Med., Ref.Zh.
●Also available online.
Description: Publishes articles on maxillofacial, plastic and reconstructive surgery, as well as related disciplines.

CHIRURGIA NEUROLOGICA. see *MEDICAL SCIENCES — Psychiatry And Neurology*

617   IT   ISSN 0009-4811
CHIRURGIA TRIVENETA. (Text in Italian; summaries in English) 1960. q. L.100000 (effective Jan. 1994). Ospedale Civile Maggiore, I Divisione Chirurgia Generale, Piazzale Stefani 1, 37126 Verona, Italy. TEL 045-8072410. FAX 045-8072057. Ed. G. Fattovich. adv.; bk.rev.; charts; illus. circ. 150.
Refereed Serial

617   FR   ISSN 0001-4001
CHIRURGIE. 1851. 10/yr. 1264 F. (foreign 1550 F.) (effective 1996). (Academie de Chirurgie) Masson - Periodiques, Villa Laromiguiere, 75005 Paris, France. TEL 1-40-46-62-00. FAX 1-40-46-62-01. Ed. Ph. Boutelier. adv.; bk.rev.; illus.; index. circ. 2,000. (also avail. in microform from UMI; reprint service avail. from ISI) **Indexed:** Chem.Abstr., Curr.Cont., Dent.Ind., Excerp.Med., Ind.Med., Ind.Sci.Rev., Sci.Cit.Ind. **Document type:** academic/scholarly publication.
—BLDSC (3181.462000); Faxon; SWETS; UMI. **CCC.**
Description: Offers articles on the practice and science of surgery written by top French and foreign surgeons.
Refereed Serial

617   GW   ISSN 0009-4846
                              CODEN: CHPXBE
CHIRURGISCHE PRAXIS; taegliche Praxis der gesamten Chirurgie. 1957. 4/yr. DM.280. Hans Marseille Verlag GmbH, Buerkleinstr. 12, 80538 Munich, Germany. TEL 089-227988. FAX 089-2904643. Ed.Bd. bk.rev.; abstr.; charts; illus.; index, cum.index every 5 yrs. circ. 5,000. (also avail. in microfilm from UMI) **Indexed:** Biol.Abstr., Excerp.Med. **Document type:** academic/scholarly publication.
—BLDSC (3181.472000); SWETS; UMI. **CCC.**
Description: Articles about orthopedic, internal and plastic surgery, featuring new techniques. Includes questions and answers, detailed photographs.

617   JA
CHUBU GEKA GAKKAI SOKAIGO/CHUBU SURGICAL SOCIETY. PROCEEDINGS OF ANNUAL MEETING. (Text in Japanese) 1965. a. Chubu Geka Gakkai, Nagoya Daigaku Igakubu Dai 1 Gekagaku Kyoshitsu, 65, Tsurumaicho, Showa-ku, Nagoya-shi, Aichi-ken 466, Japan. **Document type:** proceedings.

617   SP   ISSN 0213-5353
CIRUGIA DE URGENCIA. 1986. 10/yr. Antonio Lopez Aguado 4, 28029 Madrid, Spain. TEL 1-314-43-38. FAX 1-314-44-99. circ. 5,184.

617   UY   ISSN 0009-7381
                              CODEN: CRGUAT
CIRUGIA DEL URUGUAY. Abbreviated title: C U. (Table of contents in English, Spanish) 1920. bi-m. (with supplements). Urg.$50000($25) to non-members. Sociedad de Cirugia del Uruguay, Hospital de Clinicas "Dr. Manuel Quintela", C.C. 10.972, Piso 4, Montevideo, Uruguay. (Co-sponsor: Congresos Uruguayos de Cirugia) Ed. Dr. Gustavo Bogliaccini. adv.; abstr.; bibl.; illus.; index; circ. 1,000 (controlled). **Indexed:** Biol.Abstr., Excerp.Med.
—BLDSC (3267.623000).
Formerly (1965-1969): Revista de Cirugia del Uruguay; Supersedes (1930-1964): Sociedad de Cirugia del Uruguay. Boletines.

MEDICAL SCIENCES — SURGERY 4611

617 SP ISSN 0009-739X
CODEN: CRESAD
CIRUGIA ESPANOLA. (Text in English, French and Spanish; abstracts in English) 1946. m. 9200 ptas.($75) (Asociacion Espanola de Cirujanos) Ediciones Doyma S.A., Traversa de Gracia, 17-21, 08021 Barcelona, Spain. TEL 34-1-200-07-11. FAX 34-1-209-11-36. TELEX 51964 INK E. Ed. A Gomez Alonso. adv.: page 180000 ptas.; trim 210 x 180; adv. contact: Julio Esteva. bk.rev.; abstr.; bibl.; illus.; charts; index. circ. 2,500. **Indexed:** Biol.Abstr., Chem.Abstr., Excerp.Med., Helminthol.Abstr., Ind.Med.Esp.
—BLDSC (3267.550000); CASDDS.
Formerly (until 1969): Cirugia, Ginecologia y Urologia (ISSN 0412-5878)

617.95 SP ISSN 0376-7892
CIRUGIA PLASTICA IBERO LATINOMERICANA. (Text in Spanish; summaries in English & Spanish) 1975. q. $54 (effective 1995). Sociedad Espanola de Cirurgia Plastica, Casilla 10059, 28080 Madrid, Spain. TEL 34-1-4454934. FAX 34-1-4454939. (Co-sponsor: Federacion Ibero Latinoamericana de Cirurgia Plastica) Ed. F. Rodriguez Duran. adv. contact: Juan Quetglas. bk.rev.; charts; illus. circ. 1,500. (also avail. in microform from UMI; reprint service avail. from UMI) **Indexed:** Biol.Abstr., Excerp.Med., Ind.Med.Esp. **Document type:** academic/scholarly publication.
—BLDSC (3267.610000).
Formed by the merger of: Revista Latinamericana de Cirugia Plastica (ISSN 0034-9755); (1968-1974): Revista Espanola de Cirugia Plastica (ISSN 0034-9364)

617.95 UY ISSN 0009-7403
CIRUGIA PLASTICA URUGUAYA.* (Text in Spanish; summaries in English and Spanish) 1960. q. (Sociedad de Cirugia Plastica del Uruguay) Hospital de Clinicas "Dr. Manuel Quintela", Piso 4, Montevideo, Uruguay.
Formerly: Cirugia Plastica del Uruguay.

617 MX ISSN 0009-7411
CIRUGIA Y CIRUJANOS. 1933. bi-m. $100 (effective 1995). Academia Mexicana de Cirugia - Mexican Academy of Surgery, Col. Centro, Deleg. Cuauhtemoc, Apdo. Postal 7994, 06080 Mexico, D.F., Mexico. TEL 52-5-588-0458. FAX 52-5-761-2581. Ed. Dr. Humberto Hurtado. adv. contact: Francisco Tenorio Gonzalez. bk.rev.; abstr.; bibl.; illus. circ. 3,000. **Indexed:** Biol.Abstr., Chem.Abstr., Excerp.Med., Ind.Med. **Document type:** academic/scholarly publication.
Description: Publishes surgical and medical aarticles.

617.522 CN ISSN 1055-6656
RD525 CODEN: CPJOEG
CLEFT PALATE - CRANIOFACIAL JOURNAL; an international journal of craniofacial anomalies. 1964. bi-m. $115 to individuals (outside US & Canada); institutions $158 (outside US & Canada $190) (effective 1996). (American Cleft Palate - Craniofacial Association) Decker Periodicals, P.O. Box 620, LCD 1, Hamilton, ON L8N 3K7, Canada. TEL 416-522-7017; 800-568-7281. FAX 416-522-7839. (U.S. addr.: Box 785, Lewiston, NY 14092) Ed. Stewart R. Rood. adv.; bk.rev.; abstr.; charts; illus.; stat.; cum.index: 1964-1988. circ. 3,500. (also avail. in microform from MIM,WWS; back issues avail.; reprint service avail. from UMI) **Indexed:** Chic.Per.Ind., Child Devel.Abstr., Curr.Adv.Ecol.Sci., Curr.Cont., Dent.Ind., Excerp.Med., Ind.Med., Ind.Sci.Rev., Rehabil.Lit., Sci.Cit.Ind. **Document type:** academic/scholarly publication.
—BLDSC (3278.559800); Faxon; Genuine Article; SWETS; UnCover. **CCC**.
Formerly: Cleft Palate Journal (ISSN 0009-8701)
Description: International interdisciplinary professional journal on clinical and research activities in cleft palate and other craniofacial anomalies.
Refereed Serial

616 IT ISSN 0393-7577
CLINICA CHIRURGICA DEL NORD AMERICA. bi-m. L.180000($180) Piccin Editore, Via Altinate 107, 35100 Padua, Italy. TEL 049-655566. FAX 049-8750693. (reprint service avail. from UMI)

617 US ISSN 0746-469X
CLINICAL LASER MONTHLY. 1983. m. $279. American Health Consultants, Inc., Six Piedmont Center, Ste. 400, Atlanta, GA 30305. TEL 800-688-2421. FAX 800-284-3291. Ed. Becky Whidden. circ. 1,335. (back issues avail.; reprint service avail.) **Indexed:** CINAHL. **Document type:** newsletter.
●Also available online. Vendor(s): Lexis-Nexis.
—**CCC**.

CLINICAL NEUROLOGY AND NEUROSURGERY; an international journal publishing papers and reports on the clinical aspects of neurology and neurosurgery. *see MEDICAL SCIENCES — Psychiatry And Neurology*

CLINICAL NEUROSURGERY: PROCEEDINGS. *see MEDICAL SCIENCES — Psychiatry And Neurology*

617 DK ISSN 0902-0063
CODEN: CLTRED
CLINICAL TRANSPLANTATION. (Text in English) 1987. 6/yr. DKK 1400 (effective 1996). Munksgaard International Publishers Ltd., 35 Noerre Soegade, P.O. Box 2148, DK-1016 Copenhagen K, Denmark. TEL 33-12-70-30. FAX 33-12-93-87. Eds. John S. Najarian, R.L. Simmons. bk.rev. circ. 1,000. (reprint service avail. from ISI) **Indexed:** Excerp.Med., Ind.Med. (1993-). **Document type:** academic/scholarly publication.
—BLDSC (3286.399780); Faxon; Genuine Article; SWETS; UnCover. **CCC**.
Refereed Serial

617 SP
CLINICAS QUIRURGICAS DE NORTEAMERICA. Spanish translation of: Surgical Clinics of North America. 1961. 6/yr. 20670 ptas.($150) (effective 1990). Interamericana de Espana, S.A., Division de Ciencias de la Salud de McGraw-Hill, Calle Manuel Ferrero, 13, 28036 Madrid, Spain. TEL 315-0340. FAX 733-6627. charts; illus.; index.

617 US ISSN 0094-1298
CLINICS IN PLASTIC SURGERY. 1974. q. $170 (foreign $200) (effective 1996). W.B. Saunders Co. (Subsidiary of: Harcourt Brace & Company), Curtis Center, 3rd Fl., Independence Sq. W., Philadelphia, PA 19106-3399. TEL 215-238-7800. FAX 215-238-6445. (Subscr. to: Periodicals Fulfillment, W.B. Saunders Co., 6277 Sea Harbor Dr., 4th Fl., Orlando, FL 32891-4800. TEL 800-654-2452. FAX 800-874-6418) Ed. Susan Short. (also avail. in microform; reprint service avail. from ISI,UMI) **Indexed:** Dent.Ind., Excerp.Med., Ind.Med., Ind.Sci.Rev., INIS Atomind., Med.& Surg.Dermat., Sci.Cit.Ind. **Document type:** academic/scholarly publication.
—BLDSC (3286.590000); EMDOCS; Faxon; Genuine Article; SWETS; UMI; UnCover. **CCC**.

617 BL ISSN 0100-6991
COLEGIO BRASILEIRO DE CIRURGIOES. REVISTA. (Text in Portuguese; abstracts in English) 1944. bi-m. Cr.$140 to members; non-members Cr.$40. Colegio Brasileiro de Cirurgioes, R. Visconde de Silva, 52, 3o andar, 22271-090 Botafogo, RJ, Brazil. TEL 021-286-3795. FAX 021-286-2595. Ed. Dr. Merisa M. Garrido. adv.; bk.rev. circ. 7,000. (back issues avail.) **Document type:** academic/scholarly publication.
Description: Includes reports of original investigations, review papers, editorials, case reports, letters to the editor and proceedings of meetings.
Refereed Serial

617 US ISSN 0894-8062
COLON AND RECTAL SURGERY OUTLOOK. 1988. 9/yr. free to subscribers of Perspective in Colon & Rectal Surgery. Quality Medical Publishing, Inc., 11970 Borman Dr., Ste. 222, St. Louis, MO 63146. TEL 314-878-7808; 800-348-7808. FAX 314-878-9937. Ed. Dr. Theodore R. Schrock. **Document type:** newsletter.

617 US ISSN 1053-749X
CODEN: CSURE
COMPLICATIONS IN SURGERY. 1982. m. $50 to individuals; residents and students $30. S C P Communications, Inc., 134 W. 29th St., New York, NY 10001-5304. TEL 212-714-1740. Ed. Katherine Rice. adv. **Indexed:** Excerp.Med.
—BLDSC (3364.588000); Genuine Article. **CCC**.
Formerly (until 1991): Infections in Surgery (ISSN 0277-7746)

617 US ISSN 0172-4827
COMPREHENSIVE MANUALS OF SURGICAL SPECIALITIES. 1975. irreg. price varies. Springer-Verlag, 175 Fifth Ave., New York, NY 10010. TEL 212-460-1500. FAX 212-473-6272. (Also: Berlin, Heidelberg, Tokyo and Vienna) Ed. R.H. Egdahl. (reprint service avail. from ISI) **Document type:** monographic series.

617 616.8 US ISSN 0163-2108
CODEN: CNEUET
CONTEMPORARY NEUROSURGERY. 1978. bi-w. $257 unscored; scored $298 (effective 1995). Williams & Wilkins, 428 E. Preston St., Baltimore, MD 21202. TEL 410-528-4000; 800-638-6423. FAX 410-528-4312. Ed. Dr. George T. Tindall. circ. 1,400. (also avail. in microfilm from WWS) **Document type:** academic/scholarly publication.
—BLDSC (3425.195300). **CCC**.
Description: Features original articles on current topics in neurosurgery with optional Category or C.M.E. credits.

617 US ISSN 0045-8341
RD1 CODEN: CSGYA
CONTEMPORARY SURGERY. 1972. m. $53 (Canada $63; elsewhere $80). Bobit Publishing Company, 2512 Artesia Blvd., Redondo Beach, CA 90278-3210. TEL 310-376-8788. FAX 310-376-9043. Ed. Seymour Schwartz. bk.rev.; bibl.; charts; illus.; index; circ. 50,000 (controlled). (also avail. in microform from UMI; reprint service avail. from UMI) **Indexed:** Biol.Abstr., Excerp.Med. **Document type:** academic/scholarly publication.
—UMI; UnCover.
Description: Original clinical information covering the latest developments and techniques in surgery.
Refereed Serial

617.4 616.8 GW ISSN 0939-0146
CODEN: CRRNEX
CRITICAL REVIEWS IN NEUROSURGERY. (Text in English) 1991. bi-m. DM.524($380) (effective 1996). Springer-Verlag, Heidelberger Platz 3, 14197 Berlin, Germany. TEL 030-8207-0. FAX 030-8214091. E-mail: orders@springer.de. (Subscr. in N. America to: Springer-Verlag New York, Inc., 44 Hartz Way, Secaucus, NJ 07096-2491. TEL 201-348-4033. FAX 201-348-4505) **Document type:** academic/scholarly publication.
—BLDSC (3487.478600); Genuine Article; UMI.

617.4 US ISSN 1052-4436
RD598.5
CURRENT CRITICAL PROBLEMS IN VASCULAR SURGERY. 1989. a. Quality Medical Publishing, Inc., 11970 Borman Dr., Ste. 222, St. Louis, MO 63146. TEL 314-878-7808; 800-348-7808. FAX 314-878-9937.

CURRENT OPINION IN OTOLARYNGOLOGY & HEAD AND NECK SURGERY. *see MEDICAL SCIENCES — Otorhinolaryngology*

617 616.9 US ISSN 0969-8868
▼**CURRENT OPINION IN SURGICAL INFECTIONS.** 1993. q. $109.95 to individuals; institutions $219.95; residents $55. Current Science, 400 Market St., Ste. 700, Philadelphia, PA 19106. TEL 215-574-2210; 800-552-5866. FAX 215-574-3533. (And: 34-42 Cleveland St., London W1P 6LB, England. TEL 0171-323-0323. FAX 0171-636-6911) Ed. A.V. Pollock. (back issues avail.) **Indexed:** Excerp.Med. (1995-). **Document type:** academic/scholarly publication.
●Also available online. Vendor(s): OCLC.
Also available on CD-ROM.
—BLDSC (3500.779100); ADONIS.

MEDICAL SCIENCES — SURGERY

617 UK ISSN 0952-0627
CODEN: CRPSE4
CURRENT PRACTICE IN SURGERY. q. £55($87) to individuals; institutions £125 ($194) (effective 1995). Churchill Livingstone Journals (Subsidiary of: Pearson Professional), Robert Stevenson House, 1-3 Baxter's Pl., Leith Walk, Edinburgh EH1 3AF, Scotland. TEL 0131-556-2424. FAX 0131-459-1177. (Subscr. to: Pearson Professional Ltd., P.O. Box 77, Fourth Ave., Harlow, Essex CM19 5AA, England. TEL 01279-623760; U.S. subscr. to: Churchill Livingstone, 650 Ave. of the Americas, New York, NY 10011. TEL 212-206-5000) Ed. W.E.G. Thomas. adv. contact: David Dunnachie. circ. 560. **Document type:** academic/scholarly publication.
—BLDSC (3501.315500). **CCC.**
Description: International review journal covering all the disciplines of general surgery.

617 US ISSN 0011-3840
RD1 CODEN: CPSUA
CURRENT PROBLEMS IN SURGERY. Short title: C P S. 1964. m. $78 to individuals (foreign $87); institutions $100 (foreign $109); students $45 (foreign $54) (effective Jan. 1994). Mosby - Year Book, Inc. (Subsidiary of: Times Mirror Company), 11830 Westline Industrial Dr., St. Louis, MO 63146. TEL 314-872-8370; 800-325-4177. FAX 314-432-1380. Ed. Dr. Samuel A. Wells. charts; illus.; cum.index. circ. 6,600. (also avail. in microfilm from UMI; back issues avail.; reprint service avail. from UMI) **Indexed:** AIM, Curr.Cont., Dent.Ind., Excerp.Med., Ind.Med., Ind.Sci.Rev.
—BLDSC (3501.450000); Faxon; Genuine Article; SWETS; UMI; UnCover. **CCC.**
Description: Written by recognized surgical experts. CPS is a monographic journal which provides current fully referenced information to practicing surgeons.

617 US ISSN 0149-7944
RD1 CODEN: CUSUDB
CURRENT SURGERY. 1933. 9/yr. $80 to individuals (foreign $120); institutions $105 (foreign $145) (effective 1995). (Association of Program Directors in Surgery) Williams & Wilkins, 428 E. Preston St., Baltimore, MD 21202. TEL 410-528-4000; 800-638-6423. FAX 410-528-4312. Ed. Dr. Walter J. Pories. adv. contact: Gayle Miller. illus.; index. circ. 1,583. (also avail. in microfilm from UMI) **Indexed:** Biol.Abstr., Chem.Abstr., Dent.Ind., Ind.Med. **Document type:** academic/scholarly publication.
—BLDSC (3504.047000); CASDDS; Faxon; Genuine Article; SWETS; UMI; UnCover. **CCC.**
Formerly: Review of Surgery (ISSN 0034-6780)
Description: Surveys and reports on significant articles on general surgery, surgical subspecialties and nonsurgical medicine.
Refereed Serial

617 US ISSN 0894-2277
CURRENT SURGICAL DIAGNOSIS & TREATMENT. 1980. irreg., 9th ed., 1990. $39.95. Appleton & Lange (Subsidiary of: Simon & Schuster Company), 25 Van Zant St., Box 5630, Norwalk, CT 06856. TEL 203-838-4400. Ed. Lawrence W. Way.
●Also available online. Vendor(s): Lexis-Nexis.
—BLDSC (3504.049000). **CCC.**

617 UK ISSN 0141-3368
CURRENT SURGICAL PRACTICE. 1976. irreg. Arnold (Subsidiary of: Hodder Headline plc.), 338 Euston Rd., London NW1 3BH, England. TEL 0171-873-6000. FAX 0171-783-6325. **Document type:** monographic series.
—BLDSC (3504.052000).

617.54 NE ISSN 1063-2581
CURRENT TOPICS IN GENERAL THORACIC SURGERY. 1985; N.S. 1991. irreg., vol.3, 1995. Elsevier Science B.V., Books Division, P.O. Box 211, 1000 AE Amsterdam, Netherlands. TEL 31-20-4853911. FAX 31-20-4853705. E-mail: nlinfo-f@elsevier.nl; usinfo-f@elsevier.com; forinfo-kyf04035@niftyserve.or.jp; Site addr.: http://www.elsevier.nl/. (Subscr. in U.S. and Canada to: Elsevier Science Inc., Box 882, Madison Sq. Sta, New York, NY 10159-0882. TEL 212-989-5800. FAX 212-633-3680) **Document type:** monographic series.
—CCC.
Supersedes (in 1991): International Trends in General Thoracic Surgery (ISSN 0891-3382)
Refereed Serial

617 DK ISSN 0900-4041
DANSK KIRURGISK SELSKAB. NYHEDSBREV. 1982. q. Dansk Kirurgisk Selskab - Danish Surgical Society, Kirurgisk Afd. D, Amtssygehuset, Gentofte, Denmark. TEL 45-31-65-12-00. Ed. Dr. Anders Fischer. adv.; bk.rev. **Document type:** newsletter.

DENTO-MAXILLO-FACIAL RADIOLOGY. see *MEDICAL SCIENCES — Radiology And Nuclear Medicine*

617 US ISSN 1076-0512
RD520 CODEN: DESUFE
DERMATOLOGIC SURGERY. 1975. m. $195 to institutions (effective 1996). (American Society for Dermatologic Surgery) Elsevier Science Inc., 655 Ave. of the Americas, New York, NY 10010. TEL 212-989-5800. FAX 212-633-3990. TELEX 420643 AEP UI. (Co-sponsors: American College of Mohs Micrographic Surgery and Cutaneous Oncology; International Society for Dermatologic Surgery; North American Society of Phlebology) Ed. C. William Hanke. adv.; bk.rev.; index. circ. 13,015. (also avail. in microform from UMI) **Indexed:** Biol.Abstr., Curr.Adv.Cancer Res., Curr.Cont., Dent.Ind., Excerp.Med., Helminthol.Abstr., Ind.Med., Ind.Sci.Rev., INIS Atomind., Med.& Surg.Dermat., Rev.Med.& Vet.Mycol., Sci.Cit.Ind. **Document type:** academic/scholarly publication.
—BLDSC (3555.140000); Faxon; Genuine Article; SWETS; UnCover. **CCC.**
Former titles (until 1995): Journal of Dermatologic Surgery and Oncology (ISSN 0148-0812); (until 1976): Journal of Dermatologic Surgery (ISSN 0097-9716)
Description: Publishes information on new research, methods and instruments used in performing all types of cutaneous surgery.
Refereed Serial

617 NE ISSN 0167-5079
DEVELOPMENTS IN SURGERY. (Text in English) 1979. irreg. price varies. Kluwer Academic Publishers, Postbus 17, 3300 AA Dordrecht, Netherlands. TEL 31-78-392392. FAX 31-78-392254. TELEX 29245 KAPG NL. (Dist. by: Kluwer Academic Publishers Group, P.O. Box 322, 3300 AH Dordrecht, Netherlands. TEL 31-78-392392. FAX 31-78-546474; N. America dist. addr.: Box 358, Accord Sta., Hingham, MA 02018-0358. TEL 617-871-6600. FAX 617-871-6528) **Document type:** monographic series.
—BLDSC (3579.095270).
Refereed Serial

617 SZ ISSN 0253-4886
DIGESTIVE SURGERY. (Text in English) 1984. bi-m. 335.50 SFr.($258) to individuals; institutions 671 SFr.($516) (effective 1996). S. Karger AG, Allschwilerstr. 10, P.O. Box, CH-4009 Basel, Switzerland. TEL 061-3061111. FAX 061-3061234. E-mail: Karger@Karger.ch. Ed. E.H. Farthmann. adv.; illus.; index. circ. 1,000. (also avail. in microform from UMI) **Indexed:** Curr.Cont., Excerp.Med. **Document type:** academic/scholarly publication.
—BLDSC (3588.346900); Faxon; Genuine Article; SWETS. **CCC.**
Incorporates: Surgical Gastroenterology.
Refereed Serial

617 UK
DIRECTORY OF OPERATING THEATRES AND DEPARTMENTS OF SURGERY (YEAR). a? £45. C M A Medical Data Ltd., Cambridge Research Laboratories, 181A Huntingdon Rd., Cambridge CB3 0DJ, England. TEL 0223-277709. FAX 0223-276444.
Description: Contains detailed information on operating theatres and Departments of Surgery in NHS and independent hospitals throughout the U.K.

617 US ISSN 0012-3706
CODEN: DICRAG
DISEASES OF THE COLON AND RECTUM. 1958. m. $125 to individuals; institutions $188 (effective 1995). (American Society of Colon and Rectal Surgeons) Williams & Wilkins, 428 E. Preston St., Baltimore, MD 21202. TEL 410-528-4000; 800-638-6423. FAX 410-528-4312. Ed. Dr. Robert W. Beart, Jr. adv.; illus.; index. circ. 5,8,672. (also avail. in microfilm from UMI) **Indexed:** Behav.Med.Abstr., Biol.Abstr., Chem.Abstr., Curr.Adv.Cancer Res., Curr.Adv.Ecol.Sci., Curr.Cont., Dent.Ind., Excerp.Med., Hosp.Lit.Ind., Ind.Med., Ind.Sci.Rev., INIS Atomind., NRN, Protozool.Abstr., Rev.Med.& Vet.Mycol., Sci.Cit.Ind., SSCI. **Document type:** academic/scholarly publication.
●Also available online. Vendor(s): Lexis-Nexis.
—BLDSC (3598.200000); Genuine Article; SWETS; UMI; UnCover. **CCC.**
Description: Contains original articles on the surgical management of lower gastrointestinal tract disorders.
Refereed Serial

617.4 ZA
EAST AND CENTRAL AFRICAN JOURNAL OF SURGERY. (Text and summaries in English) 1978. a. £5. Association of Surgeons of East Africa, P.O. Box 320159, Woodlands, Lusaka, Zambia. TEL 260-1-230710. FAX 260-1-250753. E-mail: jjellis@unza.gn.apc.org. Ed. John E. Jellis. adv.; bk.rev.; cum.index. circ. 800. (back issues avail.) **Document type:** academic/scholarly publication.
Supersedes (in 1994): Association of Surgeons of East Africa. Proceedings (ISSN 0253-8466)
Description: Publishes origrnal papers on surgery with special relevance for Africa.
Refereed Serial

617 UA ISSN 0013-2454
EGYPTIAN SURGICAL SOCIETY QUARTERLY REVIEW. (Text in English) 1966. q. £E1. Egyptian Surgical Society, Dar el Hekma, 42 Kasr el-Aini St., Cairo, Egypt. Ed. Ahmed Abu-Zikry. adv.; bk.rev.; bibl.; charts; illus.

617 CN
EMERGENCY PRODUCT BUYER. 1986. 6/yr. $35 (foreign Can.$45). C M E Communications, Inc., 20854 Dalton Rd., P.O. Box 507, Sutton W., ON L0E 1L0, Canada. TEL 416-722-9839. FAX 416-722-9687. Ed. Michael Roschette. adv. contact: John W. Moir. bk.rev.; abstr.; charts; illus.; stat.; tr.lit. circ. 6,200. (back issues avail.)
Former titles: Emergency Prehospital Medicine (ISSN 0836-7272); (until 1987): Canadian Journal of Prehospital Medicine (ISSN 0829-5603)
Description: Provides a source of continuing medical, business education and professional news for ambulance officers, paramedics, emergency physicians and nurses, and EMS management and training officers in Canada.
Refereed Serial

617 GW ISSN 0942-6027
ENDOSCOPIC SURGERY AND ALLIED TECHNOLOGIES. 1993. bi-m. DM.288. Georg Thieme Verlag, Ruedigerstr. 14, 70469 Stuttgart, Germany. TEL 0711-8931-0. FAX 0711-8931298. Ed. A. Melzer. adv. contact: M. Lechelt. circ. 2,100. **Indexed:** Ind.Med. (1994-). **Document type:** academic/scholarly publication.
—BLDSC (3743.580000).

617 IT ISSN 1122-8695
ENDOSURGERY. (Text in English) 1993. 3/yr. L.85000($90) to individuals; institutions L.115000 ($140) (effective 1995). (Italian Society of Endoscopic Surgery) Edizioni Minerva Medica, Corso Bramante 83-85, 10126 Turin, Italy. TEL 39-11-678282. FAX 39-11-31217364. Ed.Bd; Pub. Alberto Oliaro. adv.: B&W page $1100, color page $1900; trim 215 x 280; adv. contact: F. Filippo. circ. 4,900 (paid). **Document type:** academic/scholarly publication.
—BLDSC (3743.640000).
Description: Covers laparoscopy, thoracoscopy, surgical endoscopy and minimally invasive surgery.
Refereed Serial

MEDICAL SCIENCES — SURGERY

617   GW   ISSN 0939-7248
CODEN: EPSUEX
EUROPEAN JOURNAL OF PEDIATRIC SURGERY.
(Supplement avail. (ISSN 0939-6764)) 1960. bi-m. 1558 F. in France; elsewhere 1643 F. Hippokrates Verlag GmbH, Postfach 300504, 70445 Stuttgart, Germany. TEL 0711-8931-0. FAX 0711-8931453. (Co-publisher: Masson - Periodiques, FR) Eds. A.M. Holschneider, Y. Revillon. adv.; bk.rev.; abstr.; charts; illus.; index. circ. 2,000. (also avail. in microform from UMI; reprint service avail. from ISI) **Indexed:** Bibl.Dev.Med.& Child Neur., Biol.Abstr., Curr.Adv.Cell & Devel.Biol., Curr.Adv.Ecol.Sci., Curr.Cont., Dent.Ind., Excerp.Med., Helminthol.Abstr., Ind.Med., Nutr.Abstr., Sci.Cit.Ind. **Document type:** academic/scholarly publication.
—BLDSC (3829.733450); Genuine Article; SWETS; UMI. **CCC.**
    Formed by the 1991 merger of: Zeitschrift fuer Kinderchirurgie (ISSN 0174-3082); Which was formerly (until 1981): Zeitschrift fuer Kinderchirurgie und Grenzgebiete (ISSN 0044-2909); Chirurgie Pediatrique (ISSN 0180-5738); Which was formerly (until vol.18, 1977): Annales de Chirurgie Infantile (ISSN 0003-3952)
    Description: Aims to integrate and coordinate all endeavors in pediatric surgery and related disciplines in accordance with European standards, to widen the scope and variety of published papers in the specialty and to provide a European forum for pediatric surgery and specialties.

617   GW   ISSN 0939-6764
EUROPEAN JOURNAL OF PEDIATRIC SURGERY. SUPPLEMENT. 1966. irreg. Hippokrates Verlag GmbH, Postfach 300504, 70445 Stuttgart, Germany. TEL 0711-8931-0. FAX 0711-891453. (Co-publisher: Masson) Ed. Guenther Buck. **Indexed:** Excerp.Med. (1993-). **Document type:** academic/scholarly publication.
    Former titles (until 1991): Zeitschrift fuer Kinderchirurgie. Supplement (ISSN 0932-5654); (until 1981): Zeitschrift fuer Kinderchirurgie und Grenzgebiete (ISSN 0932-5638)

617.95   GW   ISSN 0930-343X
EUROPEAN JOURNAL OF PLASTIC SURGERY. (Text in English) 1971. 6/yr. DM.528($383) (effective 1996). (European Society of Plastic Surgeons) Springer-Verlag, Heidelberger Platz 3, 14197 Berlin, Germany. TEL 030-8207-0. FAX 030-8214091. E-mail: orders@springer.de. (Subscr. in N. America to: Springer-Verlag New York, Inc., 44 Hartz Way, Secaucus, NJ 07096-2491. TEL 201-348-4033. FAX 201-348-4505) Ed. I.T. Jackson. (also avail. in microform from UMI; reprint service avail. from ISI) **Indexed:** Biol.Abstr., Curr.Adv.Cancer Res., Excerp.Med., Med.& Surg.Dermat., Sci.Cit.Ind. **Document type:** academic/scholarly publication.
—BLDSC (3829.736300); Faxon; Genuine Article; SWETS; UMI; UnCover. **CCC.**
    Formerly: Chirurgia Plastica (ISSN 0340-5664)
    Description: Covers developments in microsurgery, tissue expansion, craniofacial surgery, and the spin-offs of these techniques into the areas of trauma, the treatment of malignancy, and aesthetic surgery.

617   NO   ISSN 1102-4151
CODEN: ACHIEB
EUROPEAN JOURNAL OF SURGERY. (Supplement avail.) (Text in English) 1869. 12/yr. NOK 1480 in Nordic countries; elsewhere $258 (effective 1996). Scandinavian University Press, P.O. Box 2959 Toeyen, N-0608 Oslo, Norway. TEL 47-22-57-54-00. FAX 47-22-57-53-53. (U.S. addr.: Scandinavian University Press, 200 Meacham Ave., Elmont, NY 11003. TEL 516-352-7300) Ed. Sten Lennquist. adv.; index, cum.index every 10-15 yrs. circ. 2,400. **Indexed:** ASCA, Biol.Abstr., Chem.Abstr., Curr.Adv.Ecol.Sci., Curr.Cont., Energy.Res.Abstr., Excerp.Med., Helminthol.Abstr., Ind.Med., Ind.Sci.Rev., Nucl.Sci.Abstr., Nutr.Abstr., Protozool.Abstr., Sci.Cit.Ind, Sportsearch. **Document type:** academic/scholarly publication.
—BLDSC (3829.745300); ADONIS; CASDDS; Faxon; Genuine Article; SWETS; UnCover. **CCC.**
    Former titles (until 1992): Acta Chirurgica (ISSN 1102-1101); (until 1991) Acta Chirurgica Scandinavica (ISSN 0001-5482); Incorporates (in 1992): Netherlands Journal of Surgery (ISSN 0167-2487); Which was formerly (1949-1979): Archivum Chirurgicum Neerlandicum (ISSN 0004-0657)
    Description: Focuses on promoting clinical progress, research and the exchange of research information within the field of surgery.

617   NO   ISSN 1102-416X
CODEN: ACSSAO
EUROPEAN JOURNAL OF SURGERY. SUPPLEMENT. (Text in English) 1922. irreg. Scandinavian University Press, P.O. Box 2959 Toeyen, N-0608 Oslo, Norway. TEL 47-22-57-54-00. FAX 47-22-57-53-53. (U.S. addr.: Scandinavian University Press, 200 Meacham Ave., Elmont, NY 11003. TEL 516-352-7300) **Indexed:** Excerp.Med. (1992-). **Document type:** monographic series.
—BLDSC (3829.745320); ADONIS; CASDDS; Faxon.
    Former titles (until 1992): Acta Chirurgica. Supplement (ISSN 1102-3309); (until 1991): Acta Chirurgica Scandinavica. Supplement (ISSN 0301-1860)

EUROPEAN JOURNAL OF VASCULAR AND ENDOVASCULAR SURGERY. see *MEDICAL SCIENCES — Cardiovascular Diseases*

617   GW   ISSN 0940-6719
EUROPEAN SPINE JOURNAL. (Text in English) 1992. 6/yr. DM.498($361) (effective 1996). Springer-Verlag, Heidelberger Platz 3, 14197 Berlin, Germany. TEL 030-8207-0. FAX 030-8214091. E-mail: orders@springer.de. (Subscr. in N. America to: Springer-Verlag New York, Inc., 44 Hartz Way, Secaucus, NJ 07096-2491. TEL 201-348-4033. FAX 201-348-4505) Eds. M. Aebi, S. Nazarian. **Indexed:** Excerp.Med. (1993-). **Document type:** academic/scholarly publication.
—BLDSC (3830.232200); ADONIS; UMI.
    Description: Devoted to spine surgery and all related disciplines, including functional and surgical anatomy, biomechanics and pathophysiology, neurology, as well as basic sciences, diagnostic procedures and alternative methods.
Refereed Serial

617   SZ   ISSN 0014-312X
CODEN: EUSRBM
EUROPEAN SURGICAL RESEARCH; clinical and experimental surgery. (Text in English) 1969. bi-m. 312.60 SFr.($240.60) ti individuals; institutions 521 SFr.($401) (effective 1996). S. Karger AG, Allschwilerstr. 10, P.O. Box, CH-4009 Basel, Switzerland. TEL 061-3061111. FAX 061-3061234. E-mail: Karger@Karger.ch. Ed. K. Messmer. adv. circ. 800. (also avail. in microform; back issues avail.) **Indexed:** Biol.Abstr., Chem.Abstr., Curr.Adv.Ecol.Sci., Curr.Cont., Excerp.Med., Ind.Med., Ind.Sci.Rev., Ind.Vet., Sci.Cit.Ind., Vet.Bull. **Document type:** academic/scholarly publication.
—BLDSC (3830.235000); CASDDS; Faxon; Genuine Article; SWETS; UnCover. **CCC.**
Refereed Serial

EXTRACTA DERMATOLOGICA; weltweit Auserlesen. see *MEDICAL SCIENCES — Abstracting, Bibliographies, Statistics*

EXTRACTA ORTHOPAEDICA; Weltweit Auserlesen. see *MEDICAL SCIENCES — Abstracting, Bibliographies, Statistics*

617.95   US   ISSN 0736-6825
CODEN: FPSUEA
FACIAL PLASTIC SURGERY. 1983. q. $105 to individuals (foreign $130); institutions $145 (foreign $170). Thieme Medical Publishers, Inc., 381 Park Ave., S., Ste. 1501, New York, NY 10016. TEL 212-683-5088. FAX 212-779-9020. circ. 2,400. (also avail. in microfilm) **Indexed:** Excerp.Med. **Document type:** academic/scholarly publication.
—BLDSC (3863.421000); Faxon; UMI; UnCover. **CCC.**
    Formerly: Seminars in Facial Plastic Surgery.

617.5   US   ISSN 1064-7406
FACIAL PLASTIC SURGERY CLINICS OF NORTH AMERICA. 1993. q. $137 (foreign $165) (effective 1996). W.B. Saunders Co. (Subsidiary of: Harcourt Brace & Company), Curtis Center, 3rd Fl., Independence Sq. W., Philadelphia, PA 19106-3399. TEL 215-238-7800. FAX 215-238-6445. (Subscr. to: Periodicals Fulfillment, W.B. Saunders Co., 6277 Sea Harbor Dr., 4th Fl., Orlando, FL 32891-4800. TEL 800-654-2452. FAX 800-874-6418) Eds. Drs. Wayne F. Larrabee, Jr., J. Regan Thomas. illus. (also avail. in microform from UMI; back issues avail.) **Document type:** academic/scholarly publication.
—BLDSC (3863.421700); UMI.
    Description: Reviews a single topic in the field in each issue, with emphasis on techniques and procedures.

FIBRIN SEALING IN SURGICAL AND NONSURGICAL FIELDS. see *MEDICAL SCIENCES*

617   GW   ISSN 0930-8245
FORTSCHRITTE IN DER CHIRURGIE. 1986. irreg., vol.9, 1992. DM.48. W. Zuckschwerdt Verlag GmbH, Industriestr. 17, 82110 Germering, Germany. TEL 089-894349-0. FAX 089-89434950. Eds. F.P. Gall, P. Hermanek. **Document type:** academic/scholarly publication.

617   US   ISSN 0071-8041
CODEN: SUFOAX
FORUM ON FUNDAMENTAL SURGICAL PROBLEMS. Variant title: Surgical Forum. 1950. a. $25. American College of Surgeons, Communications Department, 55 E. Erie St., Chicago, IL 60611-2797. TEL 312-664-4050. FAX 312-440-7014. Ed. Kevin Oliver. circ. 3,500. (also avail. in microform from UMI; reprint service avail. from UMI) **Indexed:** ASCA, Biol.Abstr., Curr.Adv.Ecol.Sci., Curr.Cont., Excerp.Med. (until 1993).
—BLDSC (8548.220000); CASDDS; Genuine Article; SWETS; UMI.

FOUNDATIONS OF NEUROLOGICAL SURGERY. see *MEDICAL SCIENCES — Psychiatry And Neurology*

617   JA
FUKUOKAKEN RINSHO GEKA IGAKKAI KAISHI/FUKUOKA SOCIETY FOR CLINICAL SURGERY. JOURNAL. (Text in Japanese) 1976. a. membership. Fukuokaken Rinsho Geka Igakkai, 9-30, Hakataeki Minami 2-chome, Hakata-ku, Fukuoka-shi, Fukuoka-ken 812, Japan.

617.585   GW   ISSN 0427-7783
DER FUSS. 1948. m. DM.72 (foreign DM.80). (Zentralverband der Fusspfleger Deutschlands e.V.) Verlag Neuer Merkur GmbH, Ingolstaedter Str. 63a, 80939 Munich, Germany. TEL 089-318905-0. FAX 089-31890553. adv.; bk.rev.; charts; illus.; index. circ. 6,633. **Document type:** academic/scholarly publication.

617   IT   ISSN 0016-5662
GAZZETTA INTERNAZIONALE DI MEDICINA E CHIRURGIA.* vol.76, 1971. s-m. L.12320. Edizioni Mediche e Scientifiche, Largo A.Ravizza 17, Rome, Italy. Eds. C. Bazzicalupo, G. Marcozzi. **Indexed:** Chem.Abstr.

617   GW   ISSN 0948-7034
▼**GEFASSCHIRURGIE;** Zeitschrift fuer vaskulaere und endovaskulaere Chirurgie. Announced for publication in 1996. q. DM.248($180) (effective 1996). Springer-Verlag, Heidelberger Platz 3, 14197 Berlin, Germany. TEL 030-8207-0. FAX 030-8214091. (Subscr. in N. America to: Springer-Verlag New York, Inc., 44 Hartz Way, Secaucus, NJ 07096-2491. TEL 201-348-4033. FAX 201-348-4505) **Document type:** academic/scholarly publication.

MEDICAL SCIENCES — SURGERY

617   JA   ISSN 0433-2644
CODEN: GECYA8
GEKA CHIRYO/SURGICAL THERAPY. (Text in Japanese) 1959. m. $350. Nagai Shoten Co., Ltd., 21-15, Fukushima 8-chome, Fukushima-ku, Osaka 553, Japan. **Indexed:** INIS Atomind.
—CASDDS.

617   JA   ISSN 0433-2679
GEKA SHINRYO/SURGICAL DIAGNOSIS AND TREATMENT. (Text in Japanese) 1959. m. 1500 Yen per no. Shindan to Chiryosha, 4-1, Marunouchi 2-chome, Chiyoda-ku, Tokyo 100, Japan. **Indexed:** INIS Atomind.
—BLDSC (4096.275000).

GEKA SHUDANKAI SHOROKUSHU/TOKYO SURGICAL SOCIETY. ABSTRACTS. see *MEDICAL SCIENCES — Abstracting, Bibliographies, Statistics*

617   JA   ISSN 0389-5564
CODEN: GTEIDA
GEKA TO TAISHA EIYO/JAPANESE JOURNAL OF SURGICAL METABOLISM AND NUTRITION. (Text in Japanese; summaries in English, Japanese) 1968. 5/yr. 2000 Yen per no. Nihon Geka Taisha Eiyo Gakkai - Japanese Academy of Surgical Metabolism and Nutrition, Nihon Gakkai Jimu Senta, 16-9, Hongkomagome 5-chome, Bunkyo-ku, Tokyo 113, Japan. **Indexed:** Chem.Abstr.
—CASDDS.

617   US
GENERAL SURGERY NEWS. m. McMahon Group, 148 W. 24th St., 8th Fl., New York, NY 10011-1916. TEL 212-620-4600. FAX 212-620-5928. Ed. Cornelia Kean. circ. 36,862.

616   IT   ISSN 0391-9005
IL GIORNALE DI CHIRURGIA. (Text in Italian; summaries in English) 1980. 10/yr. L.90000($90) (Societa Italiana di Ricerche in Chirurgia) C I C Edizioni Internazionali s.r.l., Via L. Spallanzani 11, 00161 Rome, Italy. TEL 06-8412673. FAX 06-44242033. TELEX 622099 CIC. Dir. G. Di Matteo. adv. **Indexed:** Excerp.Med.
—BLDSC (4177.350000).

617.95   IT   ISSN 1120-0405
GIORNALE DI CHIRURGIA PLASTICA RICOSTRUTTIVA ED ESTETICA. (Text in English, Italian, Spanish, Swedish) 1985. 3/yr. L.70000($85) (effective 1995). Casa Editrice Idelson, Via A. DeGasperi, 55, 80133 Naples, Italy. TEL 39-81-5524733. FAX 39-81-5518295. Ed. Nicolo Scuderi.
Description: Covers one specific area of plastic surgery in each issue.

617   IT   ISSN 0017-0453
GIORNALE ITALIANO DI CHIRURGIA. (Text in Italian; summaries in English) 1945. w. L.80000. Casa Editrice l' Antologia, Via G. Tropeano 48, 80131 Naples, Italy. TEL 39-81-7701302. Ed. Roberto Ruggiero. adv.; charts; illus. **Indexed:** Chem.Abstr., Excerp.Med., Ind.Med.
—BLDSC (4178.203000).

617   IT   ISSN 1122-8679
▼**GIORNALE ITALIANO DI CHIRURGIA VASCOLARE.** (Text in English, Italian) 1994. q. $90 to individuals; institutions $140 (effective 1995). Edizioni Minerva Medica, Corso Bramante 83-85, 10126 Turin, Italy. TEL 011-678282. FAX 011-3121736. Ed. M. D'Addato; Pub. A. Oliaro. adv.: B&W page $1400, color page $2300; trim 215 x 280; adv. contact: F. Filippo. circ. 2,900 (paid). **Document type:** academic/scholarly publication.
—BLDSC (4178.206000).
Refereed Serial

617   RU   ISSN 0236-2791
CODEN: GSKHEV
GRUDNAYA I SERDECHNOSOSUDISTAYA KHIRURGIYA/CHEST AND CARDIOVASCULAR SURGERY. (Text in Russian; summaries in English) 1959. q. $70 (effective 1996). (Akademiya meditsinskikh Nauk Rossii, Institut Serdecho-sosudistoi Khirurgii) Izdatel'stvo Meditsina, Petroverigskii pereulok 6-8, 101000 Moscow, Russia. FAX 7-095-2384634. (Dist. by: Mezhdunarodnaya Kniga, B. Yakimanka 39, 117049 Moscow, Russia. TEL 7-095-2384600) (Co-sponsor: Ministerstvo Zdravookhraneniya) Ed. V.S. Saveliev. adv. contact: T.V. Ivanova. bk.rev.; bibl.; index. **Indexed:** Biol.Abstr., Excerp.Med., Ind.Med.
—BLDSC (0052.008900).
Formerly: Grudnaya Khirurgiya (ISSN 0017-4866)
Description: Deals with theoretical and organization problems of chest surgery and with problems of allied fields.

GYNAECOLOGICAL ENDOSCOPY. see *MEDICAL SCIENCES — Obstetrics And Gynecology*

GYNECOLOGIC LASER AND ADVANCED TECHNOLOGY SOCIETY. MEMBERSHIP NEWSLETTER. see *MEDICAL SCIENCES — Obstetrics And Gynecology*

617   US   ISSN 0894-8569
CODEN: HPBSE9
H P B SURGERY; a world journal of hepatic, pancreatic, and biliary surgery. 8/yr. (in 2 vols., 4 nos./vol.). 116 ECU per vol. (effective 1996). Harwood Academic Publishers, 820 Town Center Dr., Langhorne, PA 19047. TEL 215-750-2642. FAX 215-750-6343. (UK subscr. to: P.O. Box 90, Reading, Berkshire RG1 8JL, England. TEL 0734-560-080) Ed. Stig Bengmark. (also avail. in microform) **Document type:** academic/scholarly publication.
—BLDSC (4335.262350); SWETS. **CCC.**
Refereed Serial

HAMAMATSU SEIKEI GEKA KIYO/HAMAMATSU UNIVERSITY. ANNUAL OF ORTHOPAEDIC SURGERY. see *MEDICAL SCIENCES — Orthopedics And Traumatology*

617   GW   ISSN 0046-6794
HANDCHIRURGIE. 1969. q. DM.75. (Deutschsprachige Arbeitsgemeinschaft fuer Handchirurgie) V L E Verlags-GmbH, Wasserturmstr. 8, 91054 Erlangen, Germany. Ed.Bd. bk.rev.; illus. circ. 1,600. **Indexed:** Excerp.Med., Ind.Med.

617.95   GW   ISSN 0722-1819
CODEN: HMPCD9
HANDCHIRURGIE - MIKROCHIRURGIE - PLASTISCHE CHIRURGIE. 1969. bi-m. DM.288. Hippokrates Verlag GmbH, Postfach 300504, 70445 Stuttgart, Germany. TEL 0711-8931-0. FAX 0711-8931453. (Co-sponsors: Deutschsprachige Arbeitsgemeinschaft fuer Handchirurgie; Deutschsprachige Arbeitsgemeinschaft fuer Mikrochirurgie der Peripheren Nerven; Verein der Deutschen Plastischen Chirurgie; Deutsche Gesellschaft fuer Handchirurgie; Oesterreichischen Gesellschaft fuer Handchirurgie) Ed.Bd. circ. 1,600. **Indexed:** Biol.Abstr., Dent.Ind., Excerp.Med., Ind.Med. **Document type:** academic/scholarly publication.
—BLDSC (4254.577000); Faxon; SWETS. **CCC.**
Formerly: Zeitschrift fuer Plastische Chirurgie (ISSN 0342-7978)

617   US   ISSN 1043-3074
RD523   CODEN: HEANEE
HEAD & NECK. 1978. bi-m. $396 to instutions (foreign $489) (effective 1996). John Wiley & Sons, Inc., Journals, 605 Third Ave., New York, NY 10158. TEL 212-692-6645. FAX 212-850-6021. TELEX 12-7063. E-mail: SUBINFO@JWILEY.COM. (Subscr. outside the Americas to: John Wiley & Sons Ltd., Baffins Ln., Chichester, W. Sussex PO19 1UD, England. TEL 44-1243-779777. FAX 44-1243-776128) Ed. Dr. Helmuth Goepfert. adv. contact: Roberta Frederick. bk.rev.; abstr.; charts; illus.; stat.; index. circ. 2,500. (also avail. in microform from UMI; back issues avail.; reprint service avail. from UMI) **Indexed:** Curr.Cont., Excerp.Med., Ind.Med., Ind.Sci.Rev., Sci.Cit.Ind. **Document type:** academic/scholarly publication.
—BLDSC (4274.608500); Faxon; Genuine Article; SWETS; UMI; UnCover. **CCC.**
Formerly (until 1989): Head and Neck Surgery (ISSN 0148-6403)
Description: Examines the management and prevention of all diseases in the head and neck area, including benign and malignant tumors, congenital deformities, and trauma.
Refereed Serial

617   JA   ISSN 0288-7509
HOKKAIDO GEKA ZASSHI/HOKKAIDO JOURNAL OF SURGERY. (Text in Japanese; summaries in English, Japanese) 1952. s-a. Hokkaido Geka Gakkai - Hokkaido Surgical Society, Hokkaido Daigaku Igakubu, Nishi 7-chome, Kita 5-jo, Kita-ku, Sapporo-shi, Hokkaido 060, Japan. **Indexed:** INIS Atomind.

617   JA   ISSN 0913-7629
HOKURIKU GEKA GAKKAI ZASSHI/HOKURIKU JOURNAL OF SURGERY. (Text in Japanese; summaries in English) 1982. a. Hokuriku Geka Gakkai - Hokuriku Surgical Society, Kanazawa Daigaku Igakubu Dai 1 Gekagaku Kyoshitsu, 13-1, Takaramachi, Kanazawa-shi, Ishikawa-ken 920, Japan.

617   US   ISSN 0362-0727
RD701
HOSPITAL FOR SPECIAL SURGERY. JOURNAL. 1975. irreg. Hospital for Special Surgery, Public Relations Department, 535 E. 70th St., New York, NY 10021.

617   JA   ISSN 0385-5325
HYOGOKEN ZENGEKAIKAI KAISHI/HYOGO ASSOCIATION OF SURGEONS. JOURNAL. (Text in Japanese) 1962. irreg. Hyogoken Zengeka Ikai, 1-30, Nakayamate Dori 6-chome, Chuo-ku, Kobe-shi, Hyogo-ken 650, Japan.

617   JA   ISSN 0917-9070
ICHIGE/JUNTENDO UNIVERSITY. CLINICAL SURGERY SOCIETY. JOURNAL. (Text in Japanese) 2/yr. Juntendo Daigaku, Igakubu, Daiichi Geka Rinsho Kenkyukai, 1-1, Hongo 2-chome, Bunkyo-ku, Tokyo 113, Japan.

INDIAN JOURNAL OF COLO-PROCTOLOGY. see *MEDICAL SCIENCES — Gastroenterology*

617.95   II   ISSN 0970-0358
INDIAN JOURNAL OF PLASTIC SURGERY. 1968. s-a. Rs.400 (effective 1995). Association of Plastic Surgeons of India, Ganga Hospital, Swarnambika Layout, Coimbatore 641 009, India. TEL 91-422-32050. FAX 91-422-438433. Ed. Dr. S. Raja Sabapathy. adv.; bk.rev. circ. 750. (reprint service avail. from IRC) **Document type:** academic/scholarly publication.
Refereed Serial

617   II   ISSN 0019-5650
RD1   CODEN: IJSUAV
INDIAN JOURNAL OF SURGERY. (Text in English) vol. 32, 1970. bi-m. Rs.50.($15.) (Association of Surgeons in India) Popular Prakashan Pvt. Ltd., 35-C Tardeo Rd., Bombay 400034, India. Ed. Dr. R.K. Gandhi. adv.; bk.rev.; charts; illus. circ. 2,400. **Indexed:** Biol.Abstr., Chem.Abstr., Excerp.Med., INIS Atomind.
—BLDSC (4421.350000).

MEDICAL SCIENCES — SURGERY

617   II   ISSN 0019-5863
CODEN: IMGAAY
INDIAN MEDICAL GAZETTE.* (Text in English) 1961. m. Rs.150. Martin & Harris Private Ltd., Savory Chambers, Wallace St., Bombay 400001, India. Ed. L.K. Pandeya. bk.rev.; abstr.; bibl.; illus. circ. 27,689. **Indexed:** Chem.Abstr., Excerp.Med., Nutr.Abstr.
—CASDDS.
Description: Promotes the development of modern medicine and surgery in India.

617   US
INSIDE SURGERY. 1993. m. $486. Medical Data International, 2 Park Plaza, Ste. 750, Irvine, CA 92714. TEL 714-251-2780. FAX 714-251-2781. Ed. Sharon O'Reilley. **Document type:** newsletter.

INTERNATIONAL JOURNAL OF ADULT ORTHODONTICS AND ORTHOGNATHIC SURGERY. see *MEDICAL SCIENCES — Dentistry*

INTERNATIONAL JOURNAL OF ANGIOLOGY. see *MEDICAL SCIENCES — Cardiovascular Diseases*

617   GW   ISSN 0179-1958
CODEN: IJCDE6
INTERNATIONAL JOURNAL OF COLORECTAL DISEASE. (Text in English) 1986. 4/yr. DM.398($289) (effective 1996). Springer-Verlag, Heidelberger Platz 3, 14197 Berlin, Germany. TEL 030-8207-0. FAX 030-8214091. E-mail: orders@springer.de. (Subscr. in N. America to: Springer-Verlag New York, Inc., 44 Hartz Way, Secaucus, NJ 07096-2491. TEL 201-348-4033. FAX 201-348-4505) Ed. R.J. Nicholls. **Indexed:** Excerp.Med. **Document type:** academic/scholarly publication.
—BLDSC (4542.172400); Faxon; Genuine Article; SWETS; UMI. **CCC.**
Description: Includes clinical and laboratory research in the field with sections devoted to symposia and reviews of subjects of topical interest.

INTERNATIONAL JOURNAL OF ORAL & MAXILLOFACIAL SURGERY. see *MEDICAL SCIENCES — Dentistry*

INTERNATIONAL JOURNAL OF PERIODONTICS & RESTORATIVE DENTISTRY. see *MEDICAL SCIENCES — Dentistry*

617   US   ISSN 1066-8969
INTERNATIONAL JOURNAL OF SURGICAL PATHOLOGY. 1993. q. $104 to individuals (foreign $129); institutions $138 (foreign $163). (International Academy of Pathology, Australasian, Hong Kong, Spanish, Korean Divisions) Churchill Livingstone International, 650 Ave. of the Americas, New York, NY 10011. TEL 212-206-5040. FAX 212-727-7808. (Subscr. to: Fulfillment Center, 5S 250 Frontenac Rd., Naperville, IL 60563-1711. TEL 800-553-5426) Ed. John S.J. Brooks. adv.; bk.rev. (also avail. in microfilm from UMI; microfiche from UMI) **Indexed:** Excerp.Med. (1995-). **Document type:** academic/scholarly publication.
—BLDSC (4542.685300). **CCC.**
Description: Forum for the communication of scientific information in the field of surgical pathology. Includes studies that emphasize diagnostic and prognostic features involving human tissue.
Refereed Serial

INTERNATIONAL SOCIETY OF CARDIO-THORACIC SURGEONS. ANNUAL MEETING. see *MEDICAL SCIENCES — Cardiovascular Diseases*

617   IT   ISSN 0020-8868
CODEN: INTSAO
INTERNATIONAL SURGERY. (Text in English) 1913. q. $90 to individuals; institutions $140 (effective 1995). (International College of Surgeons) Edizioni Minerva Medica, Corso Bramante 83-85, 10126 Turin, Italy. TEL 39-11-678282. FAX 39-11-3121736. Ed. Dr. Giuseppe Pezzuoli; Pub. Alberto Oliaro. adv.: B&W page $1100, color page $1900; trim 215 x 280; adv. contact: F. Filippo. bk.rev.; abstr.; illus.; index. circ. 10,000. (also avail. in microform from JAI,UMI; reprint service avail. from UMI) **Indexed:** Biol.Abstr., Chem.Abstr., Curr.Cont., Excerp.Med., Hosp.Lit.Ind., Ind.Med., INIS Atomind., Sci.Cit.Ind. **Document type:** academic/scholarly publication.
—BLDSC (4550.020000); EMDOCS; Genuine Article; SWETS; UMI; UnCover.
Formerly: International College of Surgeons. Journal.
Description: Publishes original scientific articles covering important clinical observations, surgical techniques, experimental surgery and research.
Refereed Serial

617   US
INTERNATIONAL U S SURGEON. 1940. q. membership. International College of Surgeons, United States Section, 1516 N. Lake Shore Dr., Chicago, IL 60610-1694. TEL 312-787-6274. FAX 312-787-9289. circ. 6,000. (tabloid format)
Former titles: News and Notes (Chicago); U S News and Notes.

INTERVENTIONAL CARDIOLOGY NEWSLETTER. see *MEDICAL SCIENCES — Cardiovascular Diseases*

617   GW   ISSN 0935-6517
JAHRBUCH DER CHIRURGIE. (Text in German; summaries in English, German) 1988. a. DM.126.40. Biermann Verlag GmbH, Nideggenerstr. 18, 53909 Zuelpich, Germany. TEL 02252-9410-0. FAX 02252-941015. Eds. H. Buente, T. Junginger. (back issues avail.) **Document type:** academic/scholarly publication.

JAPANESE JOURNAL OF INTERVENTIONAL CARDIOLOGY. see *MEDICAL SCIENCES — Cardiovascular Diseases*

617.95   JA   ISSN 0021-5228
JAPANESE JOURNAL OF PLASTIC & RECONSTRUCTIVE SURGERY/KEISEI GEKA. (Text mainly in Japanese, occasionally in English) q. 32000 Yen. Kokuseido Publishing Co., Ltd., 3-23-5, 202 Hongo, Bunkyo-ku, Tokyo 113, Japan. TEL 03-3811-0995. FAX 03-3813-1866. Ed. Akira Imai. adv.; bk.rev.; charts; illus.; index. circ. 3,500. **Indexed:** Biol.Abstr., Excerp.Med., INIS Atomind. **Document type:** academic/scholarly publication.
—BLDSC (4658.100000); EMDOCS.

617.54   JA   ISSN 0021-5252
JAPANESE JOURNAL OF THORACIC SURGERY/KYOBU GEKA. (Text in Japanese; contents page and summaries in English) 1948. m. 29100 Yen (foreign 45000 Yen). Nankodo Co., Ltd., 42-6, Hongo 3-chome, Bunkyo-ku, Tokyo 113, Japan. TEL 03-3811-7239. FAX 03-3811-7230. Eds. Akira Furuse, Shigefumi Fujimura. adv.; charts; illus.; index. circ. 3,000. **Indexed:** Curr.Cont., Excerp.Med., Ind.Med., INIS Atomind.
—BLDSC (4658.900000).

617   GW   ISSN 0941-7346
JATROS CHIRURGIE MIT INFEKTIONSKLINIK UND ONKOLOGISCHE KLINIK. 1992. m. DM.90. P M I Verlagsgruppe GmbH, August-Schanz-Str. 21, 60433 Frankfurt a.M., Germany. TEL 069-5480000. FAX 069-54800077. Ed. Peter Hoffmann. circ. 4,700. **Document type:** academic/scholarly publication.

617   JA   ISSN 0915-9118
JIN ISHOKU KEKKAN GEKA/RENAL TRANSPLANTATION, VASCULAR SURGERY. (Text in English, Japanese) 1989. 2/yr. Jin Ishoku Kekkan Geka Kenkyukai - Japanese Society of Renal Transplantation and Vascular Surgery, Tokyo Daigaku Igakubu, Hinyokikagaku Kyoshitu, 3-1, Hongo 7-chome, Bunkyo-ku, Tokyo 113, Japan.

617   FR   ISSN 0021-7697
CODEN: JOCHAQ
JOURNAL DE CHIRURGIE. 1908. 10/yr. 1130 F. (foreign 1418 F.) (effective 1996). Masson - Periodiques, Villa Laromiguiere, 75005 Paris, France. TEL 1-40-46-62-00. FAX 1-40-46-62-01. Ed. Ph. Detrie. adv.; bk.rev.; abstr.; bibl.; illus.; index. circ. 3,500. (also avail. in microform from UMI; reprint service avail. from UMI) **Indexed:** Biol.Abstr., C.I.S. Abstr., Excerp.Med., Helminthol.Abstr., Ind.Med., Ind.Sci.Rev., Rev.Med.& Vet.Mycol., Sci.Cit.Ind. **Document type:** academic/scholarly publication.
—BLDSC (4958.200000); EMDOCS; Genuine Article; SWETS; UMI. **CCC.**
Description: Provides original articles, and clinical cases on the main surgical specialities. Includes a regular section on experimental surgery and a review of the international publications in surgery.

617   FR   ISSN 0021-7913
JOURNAL DE MEDECINE ET DE CHIRURGIE PRATIQUES.* 1830. s-m. 250 F. Association des Amis de Just Lucas Championniere, c/o Expansion Scientifique, 15 rue St-Benoit, 75278 Paris Cedex 06, France. **Indexed:** Excerp.Med.

617   US   ISSN 0021-8421
JOURNAL OF ABDOMINAL SURGERY. Variant title: Abdominal Surgery. 1959. m. $15. American Society of Abdominal Surgeons, 675 Main St., Melrose, MA 02176. TEL 617-665-6102. Eds. John M. Langone, Dr. Meyer O. Cantor. adv.; bk.rev.; abstr.; charts; illus.; stat.; index. circ. 13,900. **Indexed:** Biol.Abstr., Excerp.Med.
Refereed Serial

617   UK   ISSN 1351-0622
CODEN: JEMMEP
JOURNAL OF ACCIDENT AND EMERGENCY MEDICINE. 1984. q. (British Association for Accident and Emergency Medicine) B M J Publishing Group, B.M.A. House, Tavistock Sq., London WC1H 9JR, England. TEL 44-171-3836270. FAX 44-171-3836402. (N. American subscr. to: Box 408, Franklin, MA 02038. TEL 800-2-FON-BMJ) Ed. S. Mason. adv.; bk.rev.; abstr.; bibl.; illus.; index. (also avail. in microform from UMI; back issues avail.) **Indexed:** ASCA, Excerp.Med. **Document type:** academic/scholarly publication.
—BLDSC (4918.859800); Faxon; Genuine Article; UMI; UnCover. **CCC.**
Formerly (until 1993): Archives of Emergency Medicine (ISSN 0264-4924)
Description: Publishes articles on all aspects of emergency medicine.
Refereed Serial

JOURNAL OF BONE AND JOINT SURGERY: BRITISH VOLUME. see *MEDICAL SCIENCES — Orthopedics And Traumatology*

JOURNAL OF CARDIOVASCULAR SURGERY. see *MEDICAL SCIENCES — Cardiovascular Diseases*

JOURNAL OF CLINICAL LASER MEDICINE & SURGERY. see *MEDICAL SCIENCES — Radiology And Nuclear Medicine*

617   UK   ISSN 1010-5182
CODEN: JCMSET
JOURNAL OF CRANIO-MAXILLO-FACIAL SURGERY. 1973. bi-m. £105($167) (overseas £106) (effective 1995). (European Association for Cranio Maxillo-Facial Surgery) Churchill Livingstone Journals (Subsidiary of: Pearson Professional), Robert Stevenson House, 1-3 Baxter's Pl., Leith Walk, Edinburgh EH1 3AF, Scotland. TEL 0131-556-2424. FAX 0131-459-1177. (Subscr. to: Pearson Professional Ltd., P.O. Box 77, Fourth Ave., Harlow, Essex CM19 5AA, England. TEL 01279-623760; U.S. subscr. to: Churchill Livingstone, 650 Ave. of the Americas, New York, NY 10011. TEL 212-206-5000) Ed. E.W. Steinhauser. adv. contact: David Dunnachie. illus.; index. circ. 1,775. (also avail. in microform from UMI; reprint service avail. from UMI) **Indexed:** Biol.Abstr., Curr.Adv.Cancer Res., Curr.Cont., Curr.Tit.Dent., Dent.Ind., Excerp.Med., Ind.Med., Ind.Sci.Rev., Rev.Med.& Vet.Mycol., Sci.Cit.Ind. **Document type:** academic/scholarly publication.
—BLDSC (4965.482000); Faxon; Genuine Article; SWETS; UMI; UnCover. **CCC.**
Former titles: Journal of Cranio and Maxillofacial Surgery; Journal of Maxillofacial Surgery (ISSN 0301-0503)

MEDICAL SCIENCES — SURGERY

617.95 US ISSN 1049-2275
CODEN: JSURE8
JOURNAL OF CRANIOFACIAL SURGERY. 1990. bi-m. $240 to individuals (foreign $280); institutions $335 (foreign $377); residents $240 (foreign $280); (effective Oct. 1994). (American Association of Pediatric Plastic Surgeons) Little, Brown and Company, Medical Journals, 34 Beacon St., Boston, MA 02108. TEL 617-859-5500.
FAX 617-859-0629. (Co-sponsor: International Society of Craniofacial Surgery) Ed. Dr. Mutaz B. Habal. bk.rev.; abstr.; charts; illus.; stat.; index. circ. 555. (also avail. in microform from UMI; back issues avail.; reprint service avail. from UMI) **Indexed:** Curr.Tit.Dent., Excerp.Med. (1993-). **Document type:** academic/scholarly publication.
—BLDSC (4965.476000); Faxon; SWETS; UnCover. **CCC.**
 Description: Covers all areas of craniofacial surgery, including treatment of congenital malformation, repair of post-traumatic deformation, treatment of oncological deformities, and resection of tumors in the skull base.
 Refereed Serial

617 IT ISSN 1120-8708
JOURNAL OF EMERGENCY SURGERY AND INTENSIVE CARE. (Multilingual text) 1978. q. L.79000($98) (effective 1994). (Societa Italiana di Chirurgia d'Urgenza) Masson S.p.A., Divisione Periodici, Via Statuto 2-4, 20121 Milan, Italy. TEL 02-6367-1. FAX 02-6367-211. (Co-sponsors: Comitato Permanente per i Congresi Internazionali di Chirugia di Urgenza; Gruppo Aperto di Terapia Intensiva Chirurgica) Eds. Vittorio Staudacher, Louis F. Hollender. adv.: B&W page L.1850000, color page L.3000000; trim 210 x 275. circ. 1,500. **Document type:** academic/scholarly publication.
—BLDSC (4977.450000).
 Formerly: Urgentis Chirurgiae Commentaria.

617.4 616.1 US ISSN 1074-6218
CODEN: JESUFC
▼**JOURNAL OF ENDOVASCULAR SURGERY.** 1994. q. $70 (foreign $90) (effective 1995). Futura Publishing Company, Inc., 135 Bedford Rd., Box 418, Armonk, NY 10504-0418.
TEL 914-273-1014; 800-877-8761.
FAX 914-273-1015. Eds. Drs. Edward B. Diethrich, Thomas J. Fogarty. adv.: B&W page $765, color page $1700; trim 8 1/4 x 10 7/8; adv. contact: suzanne Fath. bk.rev.; charts; illus. circ. 1,800. **Document type:** academic/scholarly publication.
—ADONIS.
 Supersedes (in 1995): Vascular Surgery (Armonk) (ISSN 1067-5051)
 Description: Presents interesting, difficult or unusual case reports.
 Refereed Serial

617 US ISSN 1067-2516
CODEN: JFSUEI
JOURNAL OF FOOT AND ANKLE SURGERY. 1963. bi-m. $109 to individuals; institutions $139 (effective 1995). (American College of Foot and Ankle Surgeons) Williams & Wilkins, 428 E. Preston St., Baltimore, MD 21202. TEL 410-528-4000; 800-638-6423. FAX 410-528-4312. Ed. Dr. Richard Reinherz. circ. 6,553. (also avail. in microform from WWS) **Indexed:** Excerp.Med., Ind.Med., INIS Atomind. **Document type:** academic/scholarly publication.
—BLDSC (4984.572000); SWETS; UnCover. **CCC.**
 Former titles (until 1993): Journal of Foot Surgery (ISSN 0449-2544); (until 1967): American College of Foot Surgeons. Journal (ISSN 0517-0591)
 Description: Clinical advances in foot surgery for podiatrists and orthopedic foot surgeons.
 Refereed Serial

JOURNAL OF GYNECOLOGIC SURGERY. see *MEDICAL SCIENCES — Obstetrics And Gynecology*

616 US ISSN 0363-5023
RD559 CODEN: JHSUDV
JOURNAL OF HAND SURGERY: AMERICAN VOLUME. 1976. bi-m. $85 to individuals (foreign $127); institutions $149 (foreign $191). (American Society for Surgery of the Hand) Churchill Livingstone International (Subsidiary of: Pearson Professional), 650 Ave. of the Americas, New York, NY 10011. TEL 212-206-5040. FAX 212-727-7808. TELEX 662266. Ed. Dr. F. William Bora, Jr; Pub. Jane Grochowski. adv.; bk.rev.; charts; illus.; index. circ. 7,900. (also avail. in microform from UMI; reprint service avail. from UMI) **Indexed:** ASCA, Bibl.Dev.Med.& Child Neur., Biol.Abstr., Curr.Adv.Ecol.Sci., Curr.Cont., Dok.Arbeitsmed., Excerp.Med., Ind.Med., INIS Atomind., Rev.Med.& Vet.Mycol. **Document type:** academic/scholarly publication.
—BLDSC (4996.620000); Faxon; Genuine Article; SWETS; UMI; UnCover. **CCC.**
 Description: Edited for hand, orthopedic, plastic and reconstructive, and general surgeons who seek to restore function to the hand and upper extremity.
 Refereed Serial

617 UK ISSN 0266-7681
JOURNAL OF HAND SURGERY: BRITISH AND EUROPEAN VOLUME. 1969. bi-m. £145($237) (effective 1995). (British Society for Surgery of the Hand) Churchill Livingstone Journals (Subsidiary of: Pearson Professional), Robert Stevenson House, 1-3 Baxter's Pl., Leith Walk, Edinburgh EH1 3AF, Scotland. TEL 0131-556-2424.
FAX 0131-459-1177. (Subscr. to: Pearson Professional Ltd., P.O. Box 77, Fourth Ave., Harlow, Essex CM19 5AA, England. TEL 01279-623790; U.S. subscr. to: Churchill Livingstone, 650 Ave. of the Americas, New York, NY 10011. TEL 212-206-5000) Ed. David Evans. adv. contact: David Dunnachie. circ. 3,100. (also avail. in microform from UMI; back issues avail.) **Indexed:** ASCA, Curr.Cont., Excerp.Med., Ind.Med., Rev.Med.& Vet.Mycol. **Document type:** academic/scholarly publication.
—BLDSC (4996.623000); Genuine Article; SWETS. **CCC.**
 Formerly: Hand (ISSN 0072-968X)

617 US ISSN 1053-2498
RD598 CODEN: JHLTES
JOURNAL OF HEART AND LUNG TRANSPLANTATION. 1981. bi-m. $90 to individuals (Canada $135.89; elsewhere $127); institutions $137 (Canada $186.18; elsewhere 174); students, residents $42 (Canada $84.53; elsewhere $79) (effective 1996); newsstand price: $16. (International Society for Heart Transplantation) Mosby - Year Book, Inc. (Subsidiary of: Times Mirror Company), 11830 Westline Industrial Dr., St. Louis, MO 63146-3318. TEL 314-872-8370; 800-325-4177.
FAX 314-432-1380. TELEX 44-2402. Ed. Dr. Michael P. Kaye. adv.: B&W page $780, color page $2435; trim 8 1/4 x 11. charts; illus.; index. circ. 3,543. (also avail. in microfilm from UMI; back issues avail.; reprint service avail. from UMI) **Indexed:** Curr.Cont., Excerp.Med., Ind.Med., INIS Atomind.
—BLDSC (4996.874000); Faxon; Genuine Article; SWETS; UMI; UnCover. **CCC.**
 Former titles (until Jan.1991): Journal of Heart Transplantation (ISSN 0887-2570); Heart Transplantation.
 Description: Latest information on heart and heart-lung transplantation.
 Refereed Serial

617 GW ISSN 0944-1166
JOURNAL OF HEPATO - BILIARY - PANCREATIC SURGERY. (Text in English) 1993. 4/yr. DM.260($188) (effective 1996). (Japanese Society of Hepato-Biliary-Pancreatic Surgery) Springer-Verlag, Heidelberger Platz 3, 14197 Berlin, Germany. TEL 030-8207-0. FAX 030-8214091. E-mail: orders@springer.de. (Subscr. in N. America to: Springer-Verlag New York, Inc., 44 Hartz Way, Secaucus, NJ 07096-2491. TEL 201-348-4033. FAX 201-348-4505) Eds. T. Suzuki, T. Takada. **Document type:** academic/scholarly publication.
—BLDSC (4997.670000).
 Description: Deals with clinical investigations of and basic research on all aspects of the field of hepatic, biliary, and pancreatic surgery. Also presents case studies and descriptions of surgical techniques.

617 US ISSN 1078-7844
▼**JOURNAL OF IMAGE GUIDED SURGERY.** 1995. bi-m. $245 (effective 1996). John Wiley & Sons, Inc., Journals, 605 Third Ave., New York, NY 10158-0012. TEL 212-850-6645.
FAX 212-850-6021. E-mail: subinfo@jwiley.com. (Subscr. outside the Americas to: John Wiley & Sons Ltd., Baffins Ln., Chcichester, W. Sussex PO19 1UD, England. TEL 44-1243-779777. FAX 44-1243-776128) Ed. Richard Bucholz. (back issues avail.) **Document type:** academic/scholarly publication.

617 US ISSN 0894-1939
CODEN: JISUE5
JOURNAL OF INVESTIGATIVE SURGERY. 1988. bi-m. £148($245) (effective 1996). Taylor & Francis Inc., 1900 Frost Rd., Ste. 101, Bristol, PA 19007.
TEL 215-785-5800; 800-821-8312.
FAX 215-785-5515. (Subscr. in Europe to: Taylor & Francis Ltd., Rankine Rd., Basingstoke, Hants. RG24 8PR, England. TEL 44-1256-840366. FAX 44-1256-479438) Ed. Andreas F. von Recum. **Document type:** academic/scholarly publication.
—BLDSC (5008.020000); SWETS. **CCC.**
 Description: Discusses the development of novel surgical concepts and the development of surgical models, devices, and instruments.
 Refereed Serial

617 US ISSN 1052-3901
CODEN: JLSUEQ
JOURNAL OF LAPAROENDOSCOPIC SURGERY. 1990. bi-m. $168 (foreign $208). Mary Ann Liebert Inc. Publishers, 2 Madison Ave., Larchmont, NY 10538. TEL 914-834-3100. FAX 914-834-3688. E-mail: Siebert@pipeline.com. Ed. David R. Nahrwold. **Indexed:** Excerp.Med. (1992-), Ind.Med. (1992-). **Document type:** academic/scholarly publication.
—BLDSC (5010.099000); Genuine Article; SWETS; UnCover.
 Description: Central forum for disseminating information on the surgical techniques that encompass laparoscopy and endoscopy.

627 US ISSN 0191-3239
RD33.6 CODEN: JMICDU
JOURNAL OF MICROSURGERY.* 1979. q. $45. Le Jacq Communications, 777 W Putnam St., Greenwich, CT 06830-5014. TEL 212-766-4300. Ed. Dr. R.M. Peardon Donaghy. adv.
—CCC.

617 JA ISSN 0917-7728
JOURNAL OF MICROWAVE SURGERY. (Text in English, Japanese) 1988. a. 1500 Yen. Medikaru Rebyusha - Medical Review Co., Ltd., 7-3, Hiranomachi 1-chome, Chuo-ku, Osaka 541, Japan. Ed. Hatsuoka Jabuse.
 Formerly (until 1991): Maikurowebu Sajeri (ISSN 0917-1231)

JOURNAL OF NEUROLOGY, NEUROSURGERY AND PSYCHIATRY. see *MEDICAL SCIENCES — Psychiatry And Neurology*

JOURNAL OF NEUROSURGERY. see *MEDICAL SCIENCES — Psychiatry And Neurology*

JOURNAL OF NEUROSURGICAL ANESTHESIOLOGY. see *MEDICAL SCIENCES — Anaesthesiology*

617 616.8 IT ISSN 0390-5616
JOURNAL OF NEUROSURGICAL SCIENCES. (Text in English) 1957. q. $90 to individuals; institutions $140 (effective 1995). (Societa Italiana di Neurochirurgia - Italian Society for Neurosurgery) Edizioni Minerva Medica, Corso Bramante 83-85, 10126 Turin, Italy. TEL 39-11-678282.
FAX 39-11-3121736. Ed. R.M. Villani; Pub. Alberto Oliaro. adv.: B&W page $1100, color page $1900; trim 190 x 270; adv. contact: F. Filippo. bk.rev.; bibl.; charts; illus.; index; circ. 3,000 (paid). (also avail. in microform from RPI,UMI) **Indexed:** Bibl.Dev.Med.& Child Neur., Biol.Abstr., Curr.Adv.Cancer Res., Curr.Adv.Genetics & Molec.Biol., Curr.Cont., Excerp.Med., Ind.Med., Ind.Vet., Nutr.Abstr. **Document type:** academic/scholarly publication.
—BLDSC (5022.250000); EMDOCS; Faxon; SWETS; UMI; UnCover.
 Incorporates: Journal of Pediatric Neurosciences; **Formerly (until 1973):** Minerva Neurochirurgica (ISSN 0026-4881)
 Refereed Serial

MEDICAL SCIENCES — SURGERY

617   UK   ISSN 0963-5386
THE JOURNAL OF ONE-DAY SURGERY. 1991. q. £14 (foreign £16). (British Association of Day Surgery) Newton Mann Ltd., Stretton Rd., Tansley, Matlock, Derbyshire DE4 5GE, England. TEL 01629-583941. FAX 01629-580479. Ed. H.T. Davenport. adv.: B&W page £345, color page £595; trim 297 x 210; adv. contact: Tim Blake. bk.rev.; abstr. (back issues avail.) **Document type:** academic/scholarly publication.
—BLDSC (5026.314600).
Refereed Serial

JOURNAL OF ORAL AND MAXILLOFACIAL SURGERY. see MEDICAL SCIENCES — Dentistry

617.3   UK   ISSN 0334-0326
CODEN: JOSTEA
JOURNAL OF ORTHOPEDIC SURGICAL TECHNIQUES. 1985. q. $85 to individuals; institutions $145. Medical Advance of Technique & Research Ltd., 48 Aylestone Ave., London NW6 7AA, England. FAX 0181-960-8901. Ed. Dan Herness. adv.; bk.rev. circ. 1,000. **Indexed:** Curr.Adv.Ecol.Sci., Excerp.Med. **Document type:** academic/scholarly publication.
Description: International forum dealing mainly with the techniques of orthopedic surgery, operative and conservative, and with clinical basic research on the techniques themselves.

617   US   ISSN 0022-3468
RD137.A1   CODEN: JPDSA3
JOURNAL OF PEDIATRIC SURGERY. 1966 (Feb.). m. $283 (foreign $337) (effective 1996). (American Academy of Pediatrics, Surgical Section) W.B. Saunders Co. (Subsidiary of: Harcourt Brace & Company), Curtis Center, Independence Sq. W., Philadelphia, PA 19106-3399. TEL 215-238-7800. FAX 215-238-6445. (Subscr. to: Periodicals Fulfillment, W.B. Saunders Co., 6277 Sea Harbor Dr., 4th Fl., Orlando, FL 32891-4800. TEL 800-654-2452. FAX 800-874-6418) (Co-sponsors: British Association of Paediatric Surgeons; American Pediatric Surgical Association; Canadian Association of Paediatric Surgeons; Pacific Association of Paediatric Surgeons) Ed.Bd; Pub. Joan W. Blumberg. adv.: B&W page $880, color page $1830; 7 x 10. bk.rev.; abstr.; bibl.; charts; illus.; index. circ. 4,229. **Indexed:** Bibl.Dev.Med.& Child Neur., Biol.Abstr., C.C.I.P., Curr.Adv.Cancer Res., Curr.Adv.Genetics & Molec.Biol., Curr.Cont., Dent.Ind., Excerp.Med., Ind.Med., Ind.Sci.Rev., INIS Atomind., Nutr.Abstr., Protozool.Abstr., Sci.Cit.Ind. **Document type:** academic/scholarly publication.
●Also available online. Vendor(s): Lexis-Nexis.
—BLDSC (5030.275000); EMDOCS; Faxon; Genuine Article; SWETS; UMI; UnCover. **CCC.**
Description: Disseminates original articles that address the need to improve the surgical care of infants and children, through advances in physiology and pathology, as well as surgical techniques.
Refereed Serial

617.5   US   ISSN 1077-2847
▼**JOURNAL OF PELVIC SURGERY.** 1995. bi-m. $95 to individuals (foreign $150); institutions $140 (foreign $180) (effective 1996); newsstand price: $32. Lippincott - Raven Publishers, 277 E. Washington Sq., Philadelphia, PA 19106. TEL 215-238-4200. Ed. Dr. Raymond A. Lee. circ. 1,000.
Refereed Serial

616   US   ISSN 0743-684X
CODEN: JRMIE2
JOURNAL OF RECONSTRUCTIVE MICROSURGERY. 1984. bi-m. $135 to individuals (foreign $160); institutions $153 (foreign $194). Thieme Medical Publishers, Inc., 381 Park Ave. S., Ste. 1501, New York, NY 10016. TEL 212-683-5088. FAX 212-779-9020. Ed. Berish Strauch. adv. circ. 1,200. (also avail. in microfilm) **Document type:** academic/scholarly publication.
—BLDSC (5048.157000); Faxon; Genuine Article; SWETS; UMI; UnCover. **CCC.**

617.57   US   ISSN 1058-2746
JOURNAL OF SHOULDER AND ELBOW SURGERY. 1992. bi-m. $98 to individuals (Canada $132.68; elsewhere $124); institutions $118 (Canada $154.08; elsewhere $144); students, residents $49 (Canada $80.25; elsewhere $75); (effective 1996); newsstand price: 18. (American Shoulder and Elbow Surgeons) Mosby - Year Book, Inc. (Subsidiary of: Times Mirror Company), 11830 Westline Industrial Dr., St. Louis, MO 63146-3318. TEL 314-872-8370. FAX 314-432-1380. Ed. Dr. Robert H. Cofield. adv.: B&W page $860, color page $1620; trim $8 1/4 x 11. circ. 2,883. **Document type:** academic/scholarly publication.
—BLDSC (5064.435000); SWETS; UMI. **CCC.**
Description: For orthopaedic surgeons who seek to restore form and function of the shoulder girdle, arm, and elbow by medical and surgical means. Provides and international forum for the exchange of information on new techniques, instruments, and materials.
Refereed Serial

JOURNAL OF SPINAL DISORDERS. see MEDICAL SCIENCES — Orthopedics And Traumatology

617 616.994   US   ISSN 0022-4790
RD651   CODEN: JSONAU
JOURNAL OF SURGICAL ONCOLOGY. 1969. m. $1092 (foreign $1278) (effective 1996). John Wiley & Sons, Inc., Journals, 605 Third Ave., New York, NY 10158. TEL 212-850-6645. FAX 212-850-6021. TELEX 12-7063. E-mail: SUBINFO@JWILEY.DOC. (Subscr. outside the Americas to: John Wiley & Sons Ltd., Baffins Ln., Chichester, W. Sussex PO19 1UD, England. TEL 44-1243-779777. FAX 44-1243-776128) Ed. Gerald P. Murphy. adv.; charts; illus.; stat.; index. (also avail. in microform from ISI) **Indexed:** Biol.Abstr., Chem.Abstr., Curr.Adv.Cancer Res., Curr.Adv.Ecol.Sci., Curr.Cont., Dent.Ind., Excerp.Med., Ind.Med., INIS Atomind., Med.& Surg.Dermat.
●Also available online.
—BLDSC (5067.380000); CASDDS; EMDOCS; Faxon; Genuine Article; SWETS; UnCover. **CCC.**
Description: Encompasses surgical approaches and presents studies of related topics such as radiotherapy, chemotherapy, and immunotherapy.
Refereed Serial

JOURNAL OF SURGICAL PATHOLOGY. see MEDICAL SCIENCES

617   US   ISSN 0161-9721
RD1
JOURNAL OF SURGICAL PRACTICE.* 1972. bi-m. McMahon Publishing Co., 83 Peaceable St., West Redding, CT 06896. Ed. Kenneth J. Zeserson. adv. circ. 90,000.
Formerly: Surgical Team (ISSN 0091-6277)

617   US   ISSN 0022-4804
RD1   CODEN: JSGRA2
JOURNAL OF SURGICAL RESEARCH; clinical and laboratory investigation. 1961. 14/yr. $598 (foreign $726) (effective 1996). (Association for Academic Surgery) Academic Press, Inc., Journal Division, 525 B St., Ste. 1900, San Diego, CA 92101-4495. TEL 619-230-1840. FAX 619-699-6800. (Subscr. to: Box 620000, Orlando, FL 32891-8340. TEL 800-543-9534) Eds. Bruce L. Gerwertz, Christopher K. Zarins. adv.; bk.rev.; charts; illus.; index. (back issues avail.) **Indexed:** Biol.Abstr., Chem.Abstr., Curr.Cont., Excerp.Med., Ind.Med., Ind.Sci.Rev., Ind.Vet., INIS Atomind., Med.& Surg.Dermat., Nutr.Abstr., Vet.Bull. **Document type:** academic/scholarly publication.
—BLDSC (5067.400000); CASDDS; EMDOCS; Faxon; Genuine Article; SWETS; UnCover. **CCC.**
Description: Publishes original articles concerned with clinical and laboratory investigations relevant to surgical practice and teaching.
Refereed Serial

617   US   ISSN 0022-5223
RD536   CODEN: JTCSAQ
JOURNAL OF THORACIC AND CARDIOVASCULAR SURGERY. 1931. m. $143 to individuals (Canada $189.39; elsewhere $177); institutions $247 (Canada $300.67; elsewhere $281); students, residents $67 (Canada $108.07; elsewhere $101) (effective 1996); newsstand price: $13.50. (American Association for Thoracic Surgery) Mosby - Year Book, Inc. (Subsidiary of: Times Mirror Company), 11830 Westline Industrial Dr., St. Louis, MO 63146-3318. TEL 314-872-8370; 800-325-4177. FAX 314-432-1380. TELEX 44-2402. (Co-sponsor: Western Thoracic Surgical Association) Ed. Dr. John A. Waldhausen. adv.: B&W page $875, color page $1900; trim 8 1/8 x 10 7/8. bibl.; illus.; s-a. index. circ. 10,167. (also avail. in microfilm from UMI; reprint service avail. from UMI) **Indexed:** AIM, ASCA, Biol.Abstr., Chem.Abstr., Curr.Adv.Cancer Res., Curr.Cont., Excerp.Med., Helminthol.Abstr., Ind.Med., Ind.Sci.Rev., INIS Atomind., Nutr.Abstr., Rev.Med.& Vet.Mycol., Rev.Plant Path., Sci.Cit.Ind.
—BLDSC (5069.100000); EMDOCS; Faxon; Genuine Article; SWETS; UMI; UnCover. **CCC.**
Formerly: Journal of Thoracic Surgery.
Description: Devoted to conditions of the heart, lungs, chest and great vessels where surgical intervention is indicated.
Refereed Serial

617.4   DK   ISSN 0905-9199
RD129.5   CODEN: JTCOEI
JOURNAL OF TRANSPLANT COORDINATION.* (Text in English) 1991. 3/yr. DKK 395. (North American Transplant Coordinators Organization) Munksgaard International Publishers Ltd., 35 Noerre Soegade, P.O. Box 2148, DK-1016 Copenhagen K, Denmark. TEL 45-33-12-70-30. FAX 45-33-12-93-87. Ed. Barbara A. Elick. adv.; illus. circ. 2,000. (reprint service avail.) **Indexed:** Excerp.Med. (1993-). **Document type:** academic/scholarly publication.
—BLDSC (5069.880000). **CCC.**
Refereed Serial

617.4   US   ISSN 0741-5214
RD598.5
JOURNAL OF VASCULAR SURGERY. 1984. m. $127 to individuals (Canada $169.06; elsewhere $158); institutions $238 (Canada $287.83; elsewhere $269); students, residents $55 (Canada 92.02; elsewhere 86) (effective 1996); newsstand price: $12.50. (Society for Vascular Surgery) Mosby - Year Book, Inc. (Subsidiary of: Times Mirror Company), 11830 Westline Industrial Dr., St. Louis, MO 63146-3318. TEL 314-872-8370; 800-325-4177. FAX 314-432-1380. TELEX 44-2402. (Co-sponsor: International Society for Cardiovascular Surgery, North American Chapter) Eds. Drs. Calvin B. Ernst, James C. Stanley. adv.: B&W page $1170, color page $2160; trim 8 1/4 x 11. bk.rev.; s-a. index. circ. 7,463. (also avail. in microfilm from UMI; reprint service avail. from UMI) **Indexed:** ASCA, Curr.Adv.Cancer Res., Curr.Cont., Ind.Med., INIS Atomind., Rev.Med.& Vet.Mycol., Sci.Cit.Ind.
—BLDSC (5072.270000); Faxon; Genuine Article; SWETS; UMI; UnCover. **CCC.**
Description: Presentation of the latest advances in the knowledge of the peripheral vascular system and vascular surgery.
Refereed Serial

MEDICAL SCIENCES — SURGERY

617.554
RD540.6
US   ISSN 1071-5754
JOURNAL OF WOUND, OSTOMY AND CONTINENCE NURSING. 1974. bi-m. $52 to individuals (Canada $70.62; elsewhere $66); institutions $133 (Canada $157.29; elsewhere $147); students $29 (Canada $46.01; elsewhere $430) (effective 1996); newsstand price: $10. (Wound, Ostomy and Continence Nurses Society) Mosby - Year Book, Inc. (Subsidiary of: Times Mirror Company), 11830 Westline Industrial Dr., St. Louis, MO 63146-3318. TEL 314-872-8370; 800-325-4177. FAX 314-432-1380. TELEX 44-2402. Ed. Mikel Gray. adv.: B&W page $985; trim 8 1/4 x 11. charts; illus.; stat.; index. circ. 4,870. (also avail. in microfilm from UMI; reprint service avail. from UMI) **Indexed:** CINAHL, Int.Nurs.Ind., Nurs.Abstr.
—BLDSC (5072.632700); SWETS; UMI. **CCC.**
Former titles: Journal of E T Nursing (ISSN 1055-3045); (until 1991): Journal of Enterostomal Therapy (ISSN 0270-1170); (until 1979): E T Journal (ISSN 0195-9883)
Description: Serves enterostomal therapy practitioners with data relating to the care of persons with stomas, draining wounds, fistulas, dermal ulcers and incontinence.
Refereed Serial

KAGAWA NO SHINKEI GEKA DANWAKAI KAISHI/KAGAWA COLLOQUIUM ON NEUROSURGERY. JOURNAL. see *MEDICAL SCIENCES — Psychiatry And Neurology*

617   JA   ISSN 0913-459X
KAGOSHIMAKEN RINSHO GEKA IKAISHI/KAGOSHIMA SOCIETY FOR CLINICAL SURGERY. JOURNAL. (Text in Japanese) 1985. a. Kagoshimaken Rinsho Geka Ikai, 8-1, Chuocho, Kagoshima-shi, Kagoshima-ken 890, Japan.

617   JA   ISSN 0912-0904
KANAGAWA KANSETSU GEKA KENKYUKAISHI/JOINT. (Text in English, Japanese) 1986. s-a. Kanagawa Kansetsu Geka Kenkyukai - Kanagawa Society of Joint Surgery, Showa Daigaku Igakubu, Fuzoku Fujigaoka Byoin Seikei Geka, 1-30, Fujigaoka, Midori-ku, Yokohama-shi, Kanagawaken 227, Japan.

KANSAI KANSETSUKYO HIZA KENKYUKAISHI/JOURNAL OF KANSAI ARTHROSCOPY AND KNEE. see *MEDICAL SCIENCES — Orthopedics And Traumatology*

KEY NEUROLOGY AND NEUROSURGERY. see *MEDICAL SCIENCES — Psychiatry And Neurology*

617   RU   ISSN 0023-1207
CODEN: KHIRAE
KHIRURGIYA/SURGERY. (Text in Russian; summaries in English) 1925. bi-m. $122 (effective 1996). (Assotsiatsiya Khirurgov im. N.I. Pirogova) Izdatel'stvo Meditsina, Petroverigskii pereulok 6-8, 101000 Moscow, Russia. TEL 7-095-2948785. (Dist. by: Mezhdunarodnaya Kniga, B. Yakimanka 39, 117049 Moscow, Russia. TEL 7-095-2384600. FAX 7-095-2384634) (Co-sponsors: Assotsiatsiya "Soyuz Inter-Med"; Ministerstvo Zdravookhraneniya) Ed. N.N. Malinovskii. adv. contact: T.A. Roshe. bk.rev.; index. **Indexed:** Biol.Abstr., Chem.Abstr., Curr.Cont., Dent.Ind., Excerp.Med., Helminthol.Abstr., Ind.Med., Nutr.Abstr.
—BLDSC (0394.785000); EMDOCS; Genuine Article; SWETS. **CCC.**
Description: Discusses general and abdominal surgery, oncology, traumatology, endocrinology, pediatric surgery, problems of chest surgery and anesthesiology.

KIKAN GANKA SHUJUTSU/JAPANESE SOCIETY OF OPHTHALMIC SURGEONS. JOURNAL. see *MEDICAL SCIENCES — Ophthalmology And Optometry*

617   KR   ISSN 0023-2130
CODEN: KLKHAM
KLINICHESKAYA KHIRURGIYA. 1961. m. $131 (effective 1996). (Akademiya Nauk Ukrainy) Izdatel'stvo Zdorovya - Health Publishing House, Ul. Chkalova 65, 252054 Kiev, Ukraine. TEL 044-216-89-08. bk.rev.; bibl.; index. **Indexed:** Biol.Abstr., Chem.Abstr., Dent.Ind., Excerp.Med., Ind.Med., INIS Atomind.
—BLDSC (0089.250000); CASDDS; Genuine Article. **CCC.**

KNEE SURGERY, SPORTS TRAUMATOLOGY, ARTHROSCOPY. see *MEDICAL SCIENCES — Sports Medicine*

617   JA
KOKYUKI GEKA/JAPANESE ASSOCIATION FOR CHEST SURGERY. JOURNAL. (Text in English, Japanese) 1987. bi-m. Nihon Kokyuki Geka Gakkai, Kyoto Daigaku Kyobu Shikkan Kenkyujo Kyobu Geka, 53, Shogoin Kawaracho, Sakyo-ku, Kyoto 606, Japan.

617   JA   ISSN 0914-4463
KOTSU TO IRYO/TRAFFIC ACCIDENTS AND MEDICAL CARE. (Text in Japanese) 1987. bi-m. 1000 Yen per no. Nihon Kotsu Iryo Kyogikai - Japan Traffic Accidents Litigation's Medical Expert Association, 20-go 3-ban 5-chome Toranomon, Minato-ku, Tokyo 105, Japan. TEL 03-5473-8883. Ed. Mitsutaka Matsuo.

617   GW   ISSN 0023-8236
CODEN: LAACBS
LANGENBECKS ARCHIV FUER CHIRURGIE. (Text in German; summaries in English, German) 1860. 6/yr. DM.748($543) (effective 1996). (Deutsche Gesellschaft fuer Chirurgie) Springer-Verlag, Heidelberger Platz 3, 14197 Berlin, Germany. TEL 030-8207-0. FAX 030-8214091. E-mail: orders@springer.de. (Subscr. in N. America to: Springer-Verlag New York, Inc., 44 Hartz Way, Secaucus, NJ 07096-2491. TEL 201-348-4033. FAX 201-348-4505) Ed.Bd. (also avail. in microform from UMI; back issues avail.; reprint service avail. from ISI) **Indexed:** Biol.Abstr., Chem.Abstr., Curr.Cont., Dent.Ind., Excerp.Med., Ind.Med., Ind.Sci.Rev., INIS Atomind. **Document type:** academic/scholarly publication.
—BLDSC (5155.675000); EMDOCS; Genuine Article; SWETS; UMI. **CCC.**
Incorporated (in 1975): Bruns' Beitraege fuer Klinische Chirurgie (ISSN 0007-2680)

617   GW   ISSN 0944-226X
LAPARO-ENDOSKOPISCHE CHIRURGIE. (Supplement to: Chirurgische Praxis (ISSN 0009-4846)) 1992. irreg. Hans Marseille Verlag GmbH, Buerkleinstr. 12, 80538 Munich, Germany. TEL 089-227988. FAX 089-2904643. Ed. Paul Kaiser. **Document type:** academic/scholarly publication.
—SWETS.

617.5 618   CN   ISSN 1188-0252
LAPAROSCOPIC SURGERY. 1992. 3/yr. $135 to individuals (outside US & Canada $160); institutions $180 (outside US & Canada $210) (effective 1995). Decker Periodicals, P.O. Box 620, L.C.D. 1, Hamilton, ON L8N 3K7, Canada. TEL 905-522-7017; 800-568-7281. FAX 905-522-7839. E-mail: decker@io.org. (U.S. addr.: Box 785, Lewistin, NY 14092-0785) **Document type:** academic/scholarly publication.
—BLDSC (5155.834500).

617 535.58   US   ISSN 0196-8092
CODEN: LSMEDI
LASERS IN SURGERY AND MEDICINE. 1980. 9/yr. $621 (foreign $760.50) (effective 1996). John Wiley & Sons, Inc., Journals, 605 Third Ave., New York, NY 10158. TEL 212-850-6645. FAX 212-850-6021. TELEX 12-7063. E-mail: SUBINFO@JWILEY.COM. (Subscr. outside the Americas to: John Wiley & Sons Ltd., Baffins Ln., Chichester, W. Sussex PO19 1UD, England. TEL 44-1243-779777. FAX 44-1243-776128) Ed. Carmen A. Puliafito. adv.; abstr.; bibl.; charts; illus.; index. (also avail. in microform from UMI; back issues avail.; reprint service avail. from ISI) **Indexed:** Curr.Cont., Dent.Ind., Excerp.Med., Ind.Med., Med.& Surg.Dermat. **Document type:** academic/scholarly publication.
—BLDSC (5156.683000); CASDDS; Faxon; Genuine Article; SWETS; UnCover. **CCC.**
Description: Covers clinical and experimental applications of various types of lasers.
Refereed Serial

617   FR   ISSN 0024-3493
CODEN: LICHA6
LILLE CHIRURGICAL.* 1945. q. 160 F. (Societe de Chirurgie de Lille) Editions Morel et Corduant, 11 Rue des Bouchers, 59000 Lille, France. adv.; bk.rev.; illus.; index. circ. 1,000. **Indexed:** Biol.Abstr., Excerp.Med., Ind.Med.

LIVER TRANSPLANTATION AND SURGERY. see *MEDICAL SCIENCES — Gastroenterology*

617   FR   ISSN 0024-7782
LYON CHIRURGICAL. (Text in French; summaries in English) 1908. bi-m. 450 F. (foreign 500 F.) (effective 1995-1996). Hotel Dieu, 69288 Lyon Cedex 02, France. TEL 72-41-31-88. FAX 72-41-31-36. Ed. Ph. Berard. adv.; bk.rev.; bibl.; charts; illus.; index. circ. 2,050. (also avail. in microform from UMI; reprint service avail. from ISI) **Indexed:** Biol.Abstr., Chem.Abstr., Curr.Cont., Excerp.Med. (1993-), Helminthol.Abstr., Ind.Med., Nutr.Abstr. **Document type:** academic/scholarly publication.
—BLDSC (5311.900000); EMDOCS; Faxon; Genuine Article; UMI. **CCC.**

MALPRACTICE REPORTER. SURGEON'S. see *LAW*

617   US
MANAGEMENT AND AVOIDANCE OF COMPLICATIONS IN EYELID SURGERY. 1993. 3/yr. $295 to individuals; institutions $355 (effective 1996). Field & Wood, Medical Periodicals, Inc., Box 975, Blue Bell, PA 19422. TEL 610-828-4010. FAX 215-482-0226. Ed. Dr. Joseph A. Mauriello, Jr. **Document type:** academic/scholarly publication.
Refereed Serial

MANAGEMENT & AVOIDANCE OF COMPLICATIONS OF LACRIMAL SURGERY. see *MEDICAL SCIENCES — Ophthalmology And Optometry*

617   US
MASTER SERIES IN SURGERY. 1993. irreg. price varies. World Medical Press, 7 Ridgedale Ave., Cedar Knolls, NJ 07927. Ed. Dana K. Andersen. **Document type:** monographic series.

MEDECINE ET CHIRURGIE DIGESTIVES. see *MEDICAL SCIENCES — Gastroenterology*

617   FR   ISSN 0759-2280
MEDECINE ET CHIRURGIE DU PIED. 1984. 4/yr. 835 F. to individuals (foreign 1035 F.); students 575 F. (foreign 745 F.). (Societe Francaise de Medecine et Chirurgie du Pied) Expansion Scientifique, 31 bd. de la Tour Maubourg, 75007 Paris, France. TEL 40-62-64-00. FAX 45-55-69-20.
—BLDSC (5487.729300). **CCC.**

617   US   ISSN 0744-4206
RD27.42
MEDICAL ECONOMICS FOR SURGEONS. 1982. m. $64 (foreign $109). Medical Economics Publishing Co., Inc., Five Paragon Dr., Montvale, NJ 07645. TEL 201-358-7200. FAX 201-573-1045. Ed. Stephen K. Murata. adv. circ. 48,000. (also avail. in microform from RPI,UMI) **Indexed:** Ind.Med. **Document type:** trade publication.
—UMI.
Description: Covers non-clinical aspects of a surgeon's practice, including investments, taxes, office management and family spending.

617   CR   ISSN 0377-1253
MEDICINA Y CIRUGIA. (Text in Spanish; summaries in English, Spanish) 1974. Colegio de Medicos y Cirujanos, Apartado 4054, San Jose, Costa Rica. **Indexed:** Biol.Abstr.

617   US
MEDSURG NURSING. 1992. bi-m. $24 to individuals (foreign $37); institutions $32 (foreign $45). Jannetti Publications, Inc., East Holly Ave., Box 56, Pitman, NJ 08071-0056. TEL 609-589-2319. FAX 609-589-7463. Ed.Bd.
Refereed Serial

MEDICAL SCIENCES — SURGERY

617 681 US ISSN 0738-1085
RD33.6
MICROSURGERY. 1979. m. $456 (foreign $642) (effective 1996). John Wiley & Sons, Inc., Journals, 605 Third Ave., New York, NY 10158. TEL 212-850-6645. FAX 212-850-6021. TELEX 12-7063. E-mail: SUBINFO@JWILEY.COM. (Subscr. outside the Americas to: John Wiley & Sons Ltd., Baffins Ln., Chichester, W. Sussex PO19 1UD, England. TEL 44-1243-779777. FAX 44-1243-776128] Ed. John S. Gould. adv.; bibl.; charts; illus.; index. (also avail. in microform from UMI; back issues avail.; reprint service avail. from ISI) **Indexed:** Biol.Abstr., Excerp.Med., Ind.Med. **Document type:** academic/scholarly publication.
—BLDSC (5760.770000); Faxon; Genuine Article; SWETS; UnCover. **CCC.**
Description: Acts as a multidisciplinary forum for original ideas regarding the use of the operating microscope in a variety of areas.
Refereed Serial

617 IT ISSN 0026-4733
MINERVA CHIRURGICA. (Supplement avail.: Notiziario Chirugico (ISSN 0392-3584)) (Text in Italian; summaries in English and Italian) 1946. m. $130 to individuals; institutions $160 (effective 1995). Edizioni Minerva Medica, Corso Bramante 83-85, 10126 Turin, Italy. TEL 39-11-678282. FAX 39-11-3121736. Ed. P.A. Giudice; Pub. Alberto Oliaro. adv.: B&W page $1100, color page $1900; trim 190 x 270; adv. contact: F. Filippo. bk.rev.; bibl.; charts; illus.; index; circ. 5,000 (paid). (also avail. in microform from UMI) **Indexed:** Biol.Abstr., Chem.Abstr., Dent.Ind., Excerp.Med., Ind.Med., Nutr.Abstr. **Document type:** academic/scholarly publication.
—BLDSC (5794.100000); EMDOCS; Faxon; Genuine Article; SWETS; UMI.
Refereed Serial

617 GW
MINIMAL INVASIVE CHIRURGIE. q. DM.100. W. Zuckschwerdt Verlag GmbH, Industriestr. 17, 82110 Germering, Germany. TEL 089-894349-0. FAX 089-89434950. Eds. E.P. Gall, F. Koeckerling. **Document type:** academic/scholarly publication.

617 GW ISSN 0942-9042
MINIMAL INVASIVE MEDIZIN. (Text in English, German) 1990. q. DM.82 to individuals; institutions DM.132. Ecomed Verlagsgesellschaft AG & Co. KG, Rudolf-Diesel-Str. 3, 86899 Landsberg, Germany. TEL 08191-125500. FAX 08191-125513. Ed. Almut Heinrich. adv.: page DM.2960; trim 176 x 238; adv. contact: Ruile Luitgard. bk.rev. circ. 1,500. (back issues avail.) **Document type:** academic/scholarly publication.
Formerly (until 1992): MedTech (ISSN 0938-8435)

MINIMALLY INVASIVE NEUROSURGERY. see *MEDICAL SCIENCES — Psychiatry And Neurology*

616 US ISSN 0723-0990
MODERN NEUROSURGERY. (Consists of selected papers from the Congress of the World Federation of Neurosurgical Societies) 1982. quadrennial. price varies. Springer-Verlag, 175 Fifth Ave., New York, NY 10010. TEL 212-460-1500. FAX 212-473-6272. (Also: Berlin, Heidelberg, Tokyo and Vienna) Ed. M. Brock. **Document type:** proceedings.

NAIBUNPI GEKA/ENDOCRINE SURGERY. see *MEDICAL SCIENCES — Endocrinology*

617 616.8 FR ISSN 0028-3770
CODEN: NUREB9
NEURO-CHIRURGIE. 1955. 7/yr. 1412 F. (foreign 1676 F.) (effective 1996). (Societe de Neuro-Chirurgie de Langue Francaise) Masson - Periodiques, Villa Laromiguiere, 75005 Paris, France. TEL 1-40-46-62-00. FAX 1-40-46-62-01. Ed. P.M. Hurth. adv.; bk.rev.; illus.; index. circ. 1,500. (also avail. in microform from UMI; reprint service avail. from ISI) **Indexed:** Biol.Abstr., Excerp.Med., Ind.Med., Ind.Sci.Rev. **Document type:** academic/scholarly publication.
—BLDSC (6081.350000); EMDOCS; Faxon; Genuine Article; SWETS; UMI. **CCC.**
Description: The scope goes beyond neurosurgery into neuro-anaesthesiology, neuroradiology, electro-encephalography, gamma-encephalography, echo-encephalography, neuro-ophthalmology, oto-neurology, neuro-endocrinology and more.

NEURO-ORTHOPEDICS. see *MEDICAL SCIENCES — Orthopedics And Traumatology*

NEUROBIOLOGIA; revista de neurologia psiquiatria e neurocirurgia. see *MEDICAL SCIENCES — Psychiatry And Neurology*

NEUROLOGIA I NEUROCHIRURGIA POLSKA. see *MEDICAL SCIENCES — Psychiatry And Neurology*

NEUROLOGICAL RESEARCH; a journal of progress in neurosurgery, neurology and neurosciences. see *MEDICAL SCIENCES — Psychiatry And Neurology*

NEUROLOGICAL SURGERY/NO SHINKEI GEKA. see *MEDICAL SCIENCES — Psychiatry And Neurology*

NEUROPEDIATRICS; journal of pediatric neurobiology, neurology and neurosurgery. see *MEDICAL SCIENCES — Pediatrics*

NEUROSURGERY (BALTIMORE). see *MEDICAL SCIENCES — Psychiatry And Neurology*

617 616.8 US ISSN 1042-3680
CODEN: NCNAFP
NEUROSURGERY CLINICS OF NORTH AMERICA. 1989. q. $145 (foreign $173) (effective 1996). W.B. Saunders Co. (Subsidiary of: Harcourt Brace & Company), Curtis Center, 3rd Fl., Independence Sq. W., Philadelphia, PA 19106-3399. TEL 215-238-7800. FAX 215-238-6445. (Subscr. to: Periodicals Fulfillment, W.B. Saunders Co., 6277 Sea Harbor Dr., 4th Fl., Orlando, FL 32891-4800. TEL 800-654-2452. FAX 800-874-6418) Eds. Dr. H. Richard Winn, Dr. Mark R. Mayberg. adv. (also avail. in microform from UMI) **Indexed:** Excerp.Med. (1995-), Ind.Med. (1992-). **Document type:** academic/scholarly publication.
—BLDSC (6081.582500); UMI; UnCover.
Description: Each issue addresses a single topic in the diagnosis and therapy of patients with neurological disorders.

617 US ISSN 1050-6438
CODEN: NEQUEB
NEUROSURGERY QUARTERLY. 1991. q. $118 to individuals (foreign $154); institutions $154 (foreign $180) (effective 1996); newsstand price: $45. Lippincott - Raven Press, 227 E. Washington Sq., Philadelphia, PA 19106. TEL 215-238-4200. Ed. Donlin M. Long. adv. contact: Phyllis Noyes. charts; illus. circ. 1,000. (reprint service avail. from UMI) **Indexed:** Excerp.Med. (1992-). **Document type:** academic/scholarly publication.
—BLDSC (6081.582800); Genuine Article; UMI. **CCC.**
Description: Presents comprehensive reviews by international authorities on the surgical management and treatment of neurological disorders.
Refereed Serial

616 GW ISSN 0344-5607
CODEN: NSREDV
NEUROSURGICAL REVIEW. 1978. 4/yr. DM.460. Walter de Gruyter und Co., Genthinerstr. 13, 10785 Berlin, Germany. TEL 030-26005-0. FAX 030-26005251. TELEX 184027. (U.S. addr.: Walter de Gruyter, Inc., 200 Saw Mill River Rd., Hawthorne, NY 10532. TEL 914-747-0110) Eds. D. Voth, K. Sano. **Indexed:** Curr.Adv.Ecol.Sci., Dent.Ind., Excerp.Med., Ind.Med. **Document type:** academic/scholarly publication.
—BLDSC (6081.585000); Faxon; Genuine Article; SWETS; UnCover. **CCC.**

NEVROLOGIA, PSIHIATRIJA I NEVROHIRURGIJA. see *MEDICAL SCIENCES — Psychiatry And Neurology*

617 JA ISSN 0914-9058
NIHON ASHI NO GEKA KENKYUKAI ZASSHI/JAPAN SOCIETY FOR SURGERY OF THE FOOT. JOURNAL. (Text in Japanese) 1980. a. Nihon Ashi no Geka Kenkyukai, Sei Marianna Ika Daigaku Seikei Gekagaku Kyoshitsu, 16-1, Sugao 2-chome, Miyamae-ku, Kawasaki-shi, Kanagawa-ken 213, Japan.

617.95 JA ISSN 0288-2027
NIHON BIYO GEKA GAKKAI KAIHO/JAPAN SOCIETY OF AESTHETIC PLASTIC SURGERY. JOURNAL. (Text in Japanese; summaries in English) 1979. q. Nihon Biyo Geka Gakkai, Nihon Gakkai Jimu Senta, 16-9, Honkomagome 5-chome, Bunkyo-ku, Tokyo 113, Japan.

617 JA
NIHON GEKA KANSENSHO KENKYU/SURGICAL INFECTION SOCIETY OF JAPAN. JOURNAL. (Text in Japanese; summaries in English, Japanese) 1989. a. 6700 Yen. (Nihon Geka Kansensho Kenkyukai) Igaku Janarusha - Medical Journal Co., Ltd., 12-3, Minamisenba 1-chome, Chuo-ku, Osaka 542, Japan. Ed. Kosaku Maeda; Pub. Jaka Akagi. adv. contact: Ichihiko Akagi.

NIHON GEKAKEI RENGO GAKKAI GAKUJUTSU SHUKAI SHOROKUGO/JAPANESE COLLEGE OF SURGEONS. ABSTRACTS OF MEETING. see *MEDICAL SCIENCES — Abstracting, Bibliographies, Statistics*

NIHON GEKAKEI RENGO GAKKAISHI/JAPANESE COLLEGE OF SURGEONS. JOURNAL. see *MEDICAL SCIENCES — Abstracting, Bibliographies, Statistics*

617.95 JA
NIHON KEISEI GEKA GAKKAI GAKUJUTSU SHUKAI/JAPAN SOCIETY OF PLASTIC AND RECONSTRUCTIVE SURGERY. ANNUAL MEETING. (Text in English, Japanese) a. Nihon Keisei Geka Gakkai, Nihon Gakkai Jimu Senta, 16-9, Honkomagome 5-chome, Bunkyo-ku, Tokyo 113, Japan.

617.95 JA ISSN 0389-4703
CODEN: NKGKE7
NIHON KEISEI GEKA GAKKAI KAISHI/JAPAN SOCIETY OF PLASTIC AND RECONSTRUCTIVE SURGERY. JOURNAL. (Text in Japanese; summaries in English) 1981. m. 3000 Yen per no. Nihon Keisei Geka Gakkai, Nihon Gakkai Jimu Senta, 16-9, Hongkomagome 5-chome, Bunkyo-ku, Tokyo 113, Japan.
—BLDSC (4808.060000).

617.54 JA ISSN 0369-4739
CODEN: NKZAAY
NIHON KYOBU GEKA GAKKAI ZASSHI/JAPANESE ASSOCIATION FOR THORACIC SURGERY. JOURNAL. (Text in Japanese; summaries in English, Japanese) 1953. m. 1000 Yen per no. Nihon Kyobu Geka Gakkai, 3-10, Koraku 2-chome, Bunkyo-ku, Tokyo 112, Japan. **Indexed:** Biol.Abstr., Excerp.Med., Ind.Med., INIS Atomind.
—BLDSC (4809.100000); Genuine Article.

616 JA ISSN 0916-4936
NIHON MAIKURO SAJARI GAKKAI KAISHI/JAPANESE SOCIETY OF RECONSTRUCTIVE MICROSURGERY. JOURNAL. (Text in Japanese; summaries in English) 1988. s-a. Nihon Maikuro Sajari Gakkai, Keio Daigaku Igakubu Maikuro Sajarishitsu, 35, Shinanomachi, Shinjiku-ku, Tokyo 160, Japan.

NIHON NO SHINKEI GEKA GAKKAI SOKAI SHOROKUSHU/JAPAN NEUROSURGICAL SOCIETY. ABSTRACTS OF THE ANNUAL MEETING. see *MEDICAL SCIENCES — Abstracting, Bibliographies, Statistics*

NIHON NO SHINKEI GEKA KONGURESU KOENROKU/NEUROSURGEONS. see *MEDICAL SCIENCES — Psychiatry And Neurology*

617 JA ISSN 0386-9776
NIHON RINSHO GEKA IGAKKAI ZASSHI/JAPANESE SOCIETY FOR CLINICAL SURGERY. JOURNAL. (Text in English, Japanese) 1937. m. 1000 Yen per no. Nihon Rinsho Geka Igakkai, Eregansu Iidabashi 402, 4-3, Iidabashi 3-chome, Chiyoda-ku, Tokyo 102, Japan. Ed. Junichi Ishii. circ. 16,000. **Indexed:** INIS Atomind. **Document type:** academic/scholarly publication.

NIHON RYUMACHI KANSETSU GEKA GAKKAI ZASSHI/JAPANESE JOURNAL OF RHEUMATISM AND JOINT SURGERY. see *MEDICAL SCIENCES — Rheumatology*

NIHON RYUMACHI KANSETSU GEKA GAKKAI/JAPANESE SOCIETY OF RHEUMATISM AND JOINT SURGERY. CONGRESS. see *MEDICAL SCIENCES — Rheumatology*

NIHON SHINZO KEKKAN GEKA GAKKAI GAKUJUTSU SOKAI NITTEI TO ENDAI SHOROKUSHU/JAPANESE SOCIETY FOR CARDIOVASCULAR SURGERY. ABSTRACTS OF MEETING. see *MEDICAL SCIENCES — Abstracting, Bibliographies, Statistics*

MEDICAL SCIENCES — SURGERY

617   JA   ISSN 0285-1474
NIHON SHINZO KEKKAN GEKA GAKKAI ZASSHI/JAPANESE JOURNAL OF CARDIOVASCULAR SURGERY. (Text in Japanese; summaries in English, Japanese) 1972. bi-m. Nihon Shinzo Kekkan Geka Gakkai - Japanese Society for Cardiovascular Surgery, c/o Tokyo Daigaku Igakubu Kyobu Geka Kyoshitsu, 3-1, Hongo 7-chome, Bunkyo-ku, Tokyo 113, Japan.

NIHON SHONI GEKA GAKKAI ZASSHI/JAPANESE SOCIETY OF PEDIATRIC SURGEONS. JOURNAL. see MEDICAL SCIENCES — Pediatrics

617   JA   ISSN 0914-4498
NIHON SHUJUTSUBU IGAKKAISHI/JAPANESE ASSOCIATION FOR OPERATING ROOM TECHNOLOGY. JOURNAL. (Text in Japanese; summaries in English) 1980. 5/yr. Nihon Shujutsubu Igakkai, c/o Tokyo Daigaku Igakubu Fuzoku Byoin Chuo Shujutsubu, 3-1, Hongo 7-chome, Bunkyo-ku, Tokyo 113, Japan.

617   JA   ISSN 0914-594X
NIHON TOGAI GAKU GANMEN GEKA GAKKAISHI/JAPAN SOCIETY OF CRANIO-MAXILLO-FACIAL SURGERY. JOURNAL. (Text in Japanese; summaries in English, Japanese) 1984. a. Nihon Togai Gaku Ganmen Geka Gakkai, c/o Nagasaki Daigaku Igakubu Fuzoku Byoin Keisei Geka, 7-1, Sakamotomachi, Nagasaki-shi, Nagasaki-ken 852, Japan. **Indexed:** INIS Atomind.

617.95   JA   ISSN 0387-9194
NIPPON BIYO GEKA GAKKAISHI/JAPAN SOCIETY OF AESTHETIC SURGERY. JOURNAL. (Text in Japanese; summaries in English, Japanese) 1962. q. $50. Nippon Biyo Geka Gakkai, 12-5, Shinbashi 1-chome, Minato-ku, Tokyo 105, Japan. TEL 03-3573-2111. FAX 03-3573-2114. Ed. Takashi Akamatsu; Pub. Fumihiko Umezawa. adv.: page 30000Yen. circ. 700 (paid); 400 (controlled).
Description: Publishes scientific papers relating to medicine and aesthetic/cosmetic surgery.

617   JA   ISSN 0301-4894
                     CODEN: NGGZAK
NIPPON GEKA GAKKAI ZASSHI/JAPAN SURGICAL SOCIETY. JOURNAL. (Text in Japanese; summaries in English, Japanese) 1899. m. 700 Yen per no. Nihon Geka Gakkai, Hakuoh Bldg., 3-10, Koraku 2-chome, Bunkyo-ku, Tokyo 112, Japan. **Indexed:** Chem.Abstr., Ind.Med., INIS Atomind.
—BLDSC (4808.350000); CASDDS.
Formerly (until 1907): Nippon Geka Gakkaishi (ISSN 0301-4886)

NO SHINKEI GEKA JANARU/JAPANESE JOURNAL OF NEUROSURGERY. see PSYCHOLOGY

NO SHINKEI GEKA SOKUHO/NEUROSURGERY LETTERS. see MEDICAL SCIENCES — Psychiatry And Neurology

NO SOTCHU NO GEKA/SURGERY FOR CEREBRAL STROKE. see MEDICAL SCIENCES — Psychiatry And Neurology

617   IT   ISSN 0392-3584
NOTIZIARIO CHIRURGICO. (Supplement to: Minerva Chirurgica (ISSN 0026-4733)) 1980. q. included with Minerva Chirurgica. Edizioni Minerva Medica, Corso Bramante 83-85, 10126 Turin, Italy. TEL 39-11-678282. FAX 39-11-3121736. Pub. A. Oliaro. adv.: B&W page $1100; color page $1900; trim 190 x 270; adv. contact: F. Filippo. **Indexed:** Excerp.Med., Ind.Med. **Document type:** academic/scholarly publication.
—BLDSC (6174.285000); Faxon.

617   GW   ISSN 0178-1715
O P JOURNAL; wissenschaftlich - medizinische informationen fuer das O P personal. 1985. 3/yr. DM.72. Georg Thieme Verlag, Ruedigerstr. 14, 70469 Stuttgart, Germany. TEL 0711-8931-0. FAX 0711-8931298. TELEX 7252275-GTV-D. (Subscr. to: Postfach 104853, 70042 Stuttgart, Germany) Eds. M. Hansis, J.E. Mueller. **Document type:** academic/scholarly publication.

O R REPORTS. see HOSPITALS — Abstracting, Bibliographies, Statistics

617   UK   ISSN 0960-8923
                     CODEN: OBSUEB
OBESITY SURGERY. 1991. q. £150($255) to institutions (effective 1995). Rapid Communications of Oxford Ltd., The Old Malthouse, Paradise St., Oxford OX1 1LD, England. TEL 01865-790447. FAX 01865-244012. E-mail: rapidcom@vax.oxford.ac.uk. (Co-sponsors: American Society for Bariatric Surgery, Obesity Surgery Society of Australia and New Zealand, Obesity Surgery Section of the British Surgical Stapling Group) Ed. Mervyn Deitel. adv. contact: Julie Gribben. (reprint service avail.) **Indexed:** Excerp.Med. (1992-). **Document type:** academic/scholarly publication.
—BLDSC (6196.953000); ADONIS; Genuine Article; UnCover. CCC.
Description: Aims to provide a new international and interdisciplinary opportunity for publishing and communicating important research and techniques in bariatric surgery.

617.7   US   ISSN 8750-3085
OCULAR SURGERY NEWS. s-m. $150 to individuals; institutions $160. Slack, Inc., 6900 Grove Rd., Thorofare, NJ 08086. TEL 609-848-1000. FAX 609-853-5991. Ed. Dr. Donald R. Sanders. adv. (tabloid format)
—BLDSC (6235.154600).
Formerly: I O L and Ocular Surgery News.

617.7   US   ISSN 1047-9120
OCULAR SURGERY NEWS INTERNATIONAL EDITION. Abbreviated title: O S N I E. 1990. m. $100 to individuals; institutions $115. Slack, Inc., 6900 Grove Rd., Thorofare, NJ 08086-9447. TEL 609-848-1000. FAX 609-853-5991. Ed. Dr. Donald R. Sanders. circ. 17,000.

617   US   ISSN 0000-1473
RD10.U6
OFFICIAL AMERICAN BOARD OF MEDICAL SPECIALTIES (A B M S) DIRECTORY OF BOARD CERTIFIED PLASTIC SURGEONS. 1983. biennial. $99.95. Marquis Who's Who, A Reed Reference Publishing company, 121 Chanlon Rd., New Providence, NJ 07974. TEL 908-464-6800. FAX 908-665-3898. (Subscr. to: Order Dept., Box 31, New Providence, NJ 07974-9903. TEL 800-521-8110) Ed. Roy Crego. **Document type:** directory.
Formerly (until 1992): A B M S Directory of Certified Plastic Surgeons (ISSN 0749-839X)
Description: Biographical sketches of U.S. certified medical specialists sorted alphabetically with a geographical index.

617   US   ISSN 0000-1678
RD10.U6
OFFICIAL AMERICAN BOARD OF MEDICAL SPECIALTIES (A B M S) DIRECTORY OF BOARD CERTIFIED SURGEONS. 1985. biennial. $119.95. Marquis Who's Who, A Reed Reference Publishing company, 121 Chanlon Rd., New Providencs, NJ 07974. TEL 908-464-6800. FAX 908-665-2898. (Subscr. to: Order Dept., Box 31, New Providence, NJ 07974-9903. TEL 800-521-8110) Ed. Roy Crego. **Document type:** directory.
Formerly: A B M S Directory of Certified Surgeons (ISSN 0884-1527)
Description: Biographical sketches of U.S. certified medical specialists sorted geographically with alpha index.

OFFICIAL AMERICAN BOARD OF MEDICAL SPECIALTIES (A B M S) DIRECTORY OF BOARD CERTIFIED THORACIC SURGEONS. see MEDICAL SCIENCES

ONGOING CURRENT BIBLIOGRAPHY OF PLASTIC & RECONSTRUCTIVE SURGERY. see MEDICAL SCIENCES — Abstracting, Bibliographies, Statistics

617   US
OPERATING ROOM RISK MANAGEMENT. bi-m. $365. (Emergency Care Research Institute) E C R I, 5200 Butler Pike, Plymouth Meeting, PA 19462. TEL 610-825-6000. FAX 610-834-1275. Ed. Sharon Baeless. **Document type:** trade publication.
Description: Covers operating room risk management and quality assurance issues. Refereed Serial

OPERATIVE TECHNIQUES IN OTOLARYNGOLOGY - HEAD AND NECK SURGERY. see MEDICAL SCIENCES — Otorhinolaryngology

617   US   ISSN 1071-0949
▼**OPERATIVE TECHNIQUES IN PLASTIC AND RECONSTRUCTIVE SURGERY.** 1994. q. $151 (foreign $175) (effective 1996). W.B. Saunders Co. (Subsidiary of: Harcourt Brace & Company), Curtis Center, 3rd Fl., Independence Sq. W., Philadelphia, PA 19106-3399. TEL 215-238-7800. FAX 215-238-6445. (Subscr. to: Periodicals Fulfillment, W.B. Saunders Co, 6277 Sea Harbor Dr., 4th Fl., Orlando, FL 32891-4800. TEL 800-654-5452. FAX 800-874-6418) Eds. Drs. Maurice J. Jurkiewicz, John H. Culbertson, Jr; Pub. Joan W. Blumberg. adv.: B&W page 565; color page $1390; 7 3/4 x 11; adv. contact: Cindy Gray. illus. circ. 2,000. **Document type:** academic/scholarly publication.
—BLDSC (6269.382300); UMI.
Description: Each issue focuses on a particular restorative surgical procedure or clinical condition. Refereed Serial

OPHTHALMIC PLASTIC AND RECONSTRUCTIVE SURGERY. see MEDICAL SCIENCES — Ophthalmology And Optometry

617.7   US   ISSN 0022-023X
RE80   CODEN: OPSGAT
OPHTHALMIC SURGERY. 1968. m. $47 to individuals; institutions $70. Slack, Inc., 6900 Grove Rd., Thorofare, NJ 08086. TEL 609-848-1000. FAX 609-853-5991. Ed. Dr. George L. Spaeth. adv.; bk.rev.; charts; illus. circ. 4,300. (also avail. in microform from UMI; back issues avail.; reprint service avail. from UMI) **Indexed:** Biol.Abstr., Curr.Cont., Dent.Ind., Excerp.Med., Ind.Med., Med.& Surg.Dermat.
—BLDSC (6271.500000); EMDOCS; Genuine Article; SWETS; UMI; UnCover.
Supersedes: Journal of Cryosurgery.
Description: Articles of clinical interest for the ophthalmic surgeon.

OPPORTUNITIES FOR THEATRE STAFF & OTHER SPECIALISTS. see MEDICAL SCIENCES — Nurses And Nursing

617.6   US   ISSN 1042-3699
ORAL AND MAXILLOFACIAL SURGERY CLINICS OF NORTH AMERICA. 1989. q. $122 (foreign $147) (effective 1996). W.B. Saunders Co. (Subsidiary of: Harcourt Brace & Company), Curtis Center, 3rd Fl., Independence Sq. W., Philadelphia, PA 19106-3399. TEL 215-238-7800. FAX 215-238-6445. (Subscr. to: Periodicals Fulfillment, W.B. Saunders Co, 6277 Sea Harbor Dr., 4th Fl., Orlando, FL 32891-4800. TEL 800-654-2452. FAX 800-874-6418) Ed. Livia Berardi. (also avail. in microform from UMI) **Document type:** academic/scholarly publication.
—BLDSC (6277.442000); SWETS; UMI.
Description: Aimed at oral maxillofacial surgeons and discusses surgical procedures, including orthroscopy, cosmetic oral, maxillofacial surgery, and surgery of cleft palette.

ORBIT; an international journal on orbital disorders, oculoplastic and lacrimal surgery. see MEDICAL SCIENCES — Ophthalmology And Optometry

617   IT   ISSN 0394-0756
ORIZZONTI DI CHIRURGIA; trimestrale di scienze chirurgiche e branche affini. (Text in Italian; summaries in English) 1981. q. L.50000($85) (effective 1995). (Societa Italiana di Chirurgia Oncologica) Casa Editrice Idelson, Via A. De Gasperi 55, 80133 Naples, Italy. TEL 39-81-5524733. FAX 39-81-5518295. (Co-sponsor: Societa Italiana di Patologia dell'Apparato Digerente) Ed. Francesco Mazzeo.
Description: Presents research papers on the science of surgery focusing on oncology. Includes diagrams and statistical data.

ORTHOPAEDIC AND TRAUMATIC SURGERY/SEKEI SAIGAI GEKA. see MEDICAL SCIENCES — Orthopedics And Traumatology

617   IT   ISSN 0030-6266
OSPEDALI D'ITALIA - CHIRURGIA. (Summaries in English) 1959. bi-m. L.100000. Editrice Sedicesimo, Via Mannelli 29r, 50136 Florence, Italy. TEL 055-2476781. FAX 055-2478568. Ed. Carlo Massimo. adv.; bk.rev.; abstr.; bibl.; charts; illus.; index. circ. 3,000. **Indexed:** Biol.Abstr., Excerp.Med. (until 1995), Ind.Med.
—BLDSC (6301.750000); EMDOCS.

OSTOMY - WOUND MANAGEMENT; the journal of extended patient care management. see MEDICAL SCIENCES — Orthopedics And Traumatology

OTOLARYNGOLOGY - HEAD AND NECK SURGERY. see MEDICAL SCIENCES — Otorhinolaryngology

PEDIATRIA OGGI MEDICA E CHIRURGICA. see MEDICAL SCIENCES — Pediatrics

PEDIATRIC CARDIOLOGY. see MEDICAL SCIENCES — Cardiovascular Diseases

617 618.92   GW   ISSN 0179-0358
CODEN: PSUIED
PEDIATRIC SURGERY INTERNATIONAL. (Text in English) 8/yr. DM.625($454) (effective 1996). Springer-Verlag, Heidelberger Platz 3, 14197 Berlin, Germany. TEL 030-8207-0. FAX 030-8214091. E-mail: orders@springer.de. (Subscr. in N. America to: Springer-Verlag New York, Inc., 44 Hartz Way, Secaucus, NJ 07096-2491. TEL 201-348-4033. FAX 201-348-4505) Ed. A.F. Schaerli. (also avail. in microform from UMI) **Indexed:** Curr.Cont. **Document type:** academic/scholarly publication.
—BLDSC (6417.628000); Faxon; Genuine Article; SWETS; UMI. **CCC.**
  Description: Devoted to publishing new and important information from the spectrum of pediatric surgery.

PEDIATRIK CERRAHI DERGISI. see MEDICAL SCIENCES — Pediatrics

617   US   ISSN 0894-8054
PERSPECTIVES IN COLON & RECTAL SURGERY. 1988. 2/yr. $145 to individuals (Canada $151; elsewhere $194.50); institutions $224 (Canada$250; elsewhere $281.50) (includes Colon & Rectal Surgery Outlook). Quality Medical Publishing, Inc., 11970 Borman Dr., Ste. 222, St. Louis, MO 63146. TEL 314-878-7808; 800-348-7808. FAX 314-878-9937. Ed. Dr. Theodore R. Schrock. **Document type:** academic/scholarly publication.
—**CCC.**

617   US   ISSN 1045-3733
PERSPECTIVES IN NEUROLOGICAL SURGERY. 1990. 2/yr. $85 to individuals (Canada $91; elsewhere $123.50); institutions $112.25 (Canada $118.25; elsewhere $153.50). Quality Medical Publishing, Inc., 11970 Borman Dr., Ste. 222, St. Louis, MO 63146. TEL 314-878-7808; 800-348-7808. FAX 314-878-9937. Ed. Dr. Marrk N. Hadley. **Document type:** academic/scholarly publication.
—BLDSC (6428.145800).

617   US   ISSN 0892-3957
RD118.A1   CODEN: PPSUEI
PERSPECTIVES IN PLASTIC SURGERY. 1987. 2/yr. $185 to individuals (Canada $191; elsewhere $238.50); institutions $244 (Canada $250; elsewhere $303.50) (includes Plastic Surgery Outlook). Quality Medical Publishing, Inc., 11970 Borman Dr., Ste. 222, St. Louis, MO 63146. TEL 314-878-7808; 800-348-7808. FAX 314-878-9937. Ed.Bd. cum.index: vols.1-5. **Document type:** academic/scholarly publication.
—**CCC.**

617   US   ISSN 0894-8046
RD598.5
PERSPECTIVES IN VASCULAR SURGERY. 1988. 2/yr. $165 to individuals (Canada $171; elsewhere $216.50); institutions $244 (Canada $250; elsewhere $303.50) (includes Vascular Surgery Outlook). Quality Medical Publishing, Inc., 11970 Borman Dr., Ste. 222, St. Louis, MO 63146. TEL 800-423-6865. FAX 314-878-9937. Ed. Dr. Jerry Goldstone. (back issues avail.) **Document type:** academic/scholarly publication.
—**CCC.**

617   PH   ISSN 0031-7691
PHILIPPINE JOURNAL OF SURGICAL SPECIALTIES.* vol.25, 1970. q. P.50($20) to non-members; members P.40. Philippine College of Surgeons, c/o Philippine Medical Association, PMA Bldg., North Ave., Quezon City, Philippine. Ed. Enrique T. Ona. adv.; charts; illus.; stat. circ. 1,000. **Indexed:** Biol.Abstr., Chem.Abstr., ExtraMED, Ind.Med (until 19??).
  ●Also available on CD-ROM.
  Formerly: Philippine Journal of Surgery and Surgery Specialties.

617.95   US   ISSN 0032-1052
CODEN: PRSUAS
PLASTIC AND RECONSTRUCTIVE SURGERY. 1946. 14/yr. $193 to individuals; institutions $226 (effective 1995). (American Society of Plastic & Reconstructive Surgeons) Williams & Wilkins, 428 E. Preston St., Baltimore, MD 21202. TEL 410-528-4000; 800-638-6423. FAX 410-528-4312. TELEX 87669. Ed. Dr. Robert M. Goldwyn. adv.; bk.rev.; abstr.; charts; illus.; index, cum.index vols.59-72, 1985. circ. 13,400. (also avail. in microfilm from WWS) **Indexed:** AIM, Biol.Abstr., Chem.Abstr., Curr.Adv.Cancer Res., Curr.Adv.Cell & Devel.Biol., Curr.Cont., Dent.Ind., Excerp.Med., Ind.Med., Med.& Surg.Dermat., Rev.Med.& Vet.Mycol. **Document type:** academic/scholarly publication.
—BLDSC (6528.924000); EMDOCS; Faxon; Genuine Article; SWETS; UnCover. **CCC.**
  Description: Examines plastic and reconstructive surgery techniques.
  Refereed Serial

617.95   US   ISSN 1043-4119
PLASTIC SURGERY NEWS. 1989. m. $75. American Society of Plastic and Reconstructive Surgeons, 444 E. Algonquin Rd., Arlington Heights, IL 60005-4664. TEL 708-228-9900. FAX 708-229-9131. Ed. Lori Lovett. adv. contact: Sheila Carter. circ. 5,200. **Document type:** trade publication.

617   US   ISSN 0892-3965
PLASTIC SURGERY OUTLOOK. 1987. 9/yr. $185 (free to subscribers to Perspectives in Plastic Surgery). Quality Medical Publishing, Inc., 11970 Borman Dr., Ste. 222, St. Louis, MO 63146. TEL 314-878-7808; 800-348-7808. FAX 314-878-9937. Ed.Bd. index; circ. 1,050 (paid). (looseleaf format) **Document type:** newsletter.

617.95   US
PLASTIC SURGERY PRODUCTS. 1991. bi-m. $12 (foreign $30) (free to qualified personnel). Novicom, Inc., 20000 Mariner Ave., Ste. 480, Torrance, CA 90503. TEL 310-793-4141. FAX 310-793-4138. adv.: B&W page $1040, color page $1640; trim 8 3/8 x 10 7/8. circ. 18,000. **Document type:** trade publication.
  Description: Contains new product and services news and applications.

PLASTIC SURGICAL NURSING. see MEDICAL SCIENCES — Nurses And Nursing

617   IT   ISSN 0032-2636
POLICLINICO. SEZIONE CHIRURGICA. (Text in Italian; summaries in English) 1897. bi-m. $120. (Societa di Ricerche in Chirurgia) Edizioni Luigi Pozzi s.r.l., Via Panama 68, 00198 Rome, Italy. TEL 39-6-8553548. FAX 39-6-8554105. Eds. G.F. Fegiz, S. Stipa. adv.; charts; illus.; stat. circ. 2,250. **Indexed:** Chem.Abstr., Excerp.Med., Ind.Med. —BLDSC (6543.300000); EMDOCS.

617   PL   ISSN 0032-373X
POLSKI PRZEGLAD CHIRURGICZNY. (Text in Polish; summaries in English and Russian) 1922. m. $192. Towarzystwo Chirurgow Polskich, Ul. M. Sklodowskiej-Curie 66, 50-368 Wroclaw, Poland. TEL 223379. Ed. S. Szyszko. bk.rev.; index. circ. 2,100. **Indexed:** Biol.Abstr., Chem.Abstr., Dent.Ind., Ind.Med.

POST ANESTHESIA AND AMBULATORY SURGERY NURSING UPDATE. see MEDICAL SCIENCES — Nurses And Nursing

617.0956   UK   ISSN 0959-6674
POSTGRADUATE SURGERY: MIDDLE EAST. 1990. q. £20 (outside Europe £30) (effective 1996). Barker Publications Ltd., Barker House, 539 London Rd., Isleworth, Mddx. TW7 4DA, England. TEL 44-181-847-1774. FAX 44-181-568-2766. Ed. Christopher Wastell. adv.; bk.rev.; charts; illus. circ. 6,200. **Document type:** academic/scholarly publication.
  Description: Contains specially commissioned review articles written at the postgraduate level on surgical and anaesthetic techniques for specialists in the Middle East.

617.96   GW   ISSN 0079-4899
PRAKTISCHE CHIRURGIE. 1936. irreg., no.103, 1991. price varies. Ferdinand Enke Verlag, Postfach 300366, 70443 Stuttgart, Germany. TEL 0711-135798-0. FAX 0711-135798-30. TELEX 07252275-GTV-D. Eds. K. Kremer, A. Encke. (reprint service avail. from IRC) **Document type:** monographic series.
  Supersedes: Vortraege aus der Praktischen Chirurgie (ISSN 0083-6931)

616   US
PRAXIS DER CHIRURGIE. 1982. irreg. price varies. Springer-Verlag, 175 Fifth Ave., New York, NY 10010. TEL 212-460-1500. FAX 212-473-6272. (Also: Berlin, Heidelberg, Tokyo and Vienna) **Document type:** academic/scholarly publication.

617   GW
PRAXIS NAH. 1970. m. DM.106. (Berufsverband der Arzthelferinnen) Verlag Johann August Koch, Postfach 1829, 35007 Marburg, Germany. circ. 32,000. (back issues avail.)
  Formerly: Arzthelferin Aktuell (ISSN 0176-1897)

PRINCIPLES AND TECHNIQUES IN GYNECOLOGIC SURGERY SERIES. see MEDICAL SCIENCES — Obstetrics And Gynecology

PRINCIPLES OF PEDIATRIC NEUROSURGERY. see MEDICAL SCIENCES — Pediatrics

617   US   ISSN 0739-8328
RD98
PROBLEMS IN GENERAL SURGERY. 1984. q. $102 to individuals (foreign $140); institutions $143 (foreign $177) (effective 1966); newsstand price: $48. Lippincott - Raven Publishers, 227 E. Washington Sq., Philadelphia, PA 19106. TEL 215-238-4200. Ed. Dr. Nathaniel J. Soper. illus. circ. 4,000. (also avail. in microform from UMI) **Indexed:** Excerp.Med. (1993-). **Document type:** academic/scholarly publication.
—BLDSC (6617.885000); Genuine Article; SWETS; UMI. **CCC.**
  Refereed Serial

PROGRESS IN NEUROLOGICAL SURGERY. see MEDICAL SCIENCES — Psychiatry And Neurology

PROGRESS IN PEDIATRIC SURGERY. see MEDICAL SCIENCES — Pediatrics

617   SZ   ISSN 0079-6824
RD11   CODEN: PSURA2
PROGRESS IN SURGERY. (Text in English) 1961. irreg. (approx. 1/yr.) price varies. S. Karger AG, Allschwilerstr. 10, P.O. Box, CH-4009 Basel, Switzerland. TEL 061-3061111. FAX 061-3061234. E-mail: Karger@Karger.ch. Ed. E.H. Farthmann. (reprint service avail. from ISI) **Indexed:** Biol.Abstr., Chem.Abstr., Curr.Cont., Ind.Med. **Document type:** academic/scholarly publication.
—BLDSC (6924.580000). **CCC.**
  Refereed Serial

PROGRESS IN SURGICAL PATHOLOGY. see MEDICAL SCIENCES

617   IT   ISSN 0393-764X
PROGRESSI CLINICI: CHIRURGIA. 1985. bi-m. L.180000($180) Piccin Editore, Via Altinate 107, 35100 Padua, Italy. TEL 049-655566. FAX 049-8750693. Eds. M. Lise, D. Nitti. circ. 3,000.

QUADERNI DI MEDICINA E CHIRURGIA. see MEDICAL SCIENCES

617   II   ISSN 0033-5657
CODEN: QJSSAB
QUARTERLY JOURNAL OF SURGICAL SCIENCES. (Text in English) 1965. q. Rs.40($10) Banaras Hindu University, Institute of Medical Sciences, Surgical Research Laboratory, Varanasi 221 005, India. Ed. K.N. Udupa. charts; illus.; stat. circ. 1,200. (also avail. in microform from UMI; reprint service avail. from UMI) **Indexed:** Chem.Abstr., Ind.Med.
—CASDDS.

MEDICAL SCIENCES — SURGERY

617   IT   ISSN 0033-9776
CODEN: RMSAAN
RASSEGNA MEDICA SARDA. (Text in Italian; summaries in English) 1882. bi-m. L.30000. Universita degli Studi di Cagliari, Facolta di Medicina Chirurgia, Casella Postale 287, 09100 Cagliari, Italy. Ed. A. Cabitza. adv.; bk.rev.; charts; illus.; index, cum.index. circ. 550. **Indexed:** Biol.Abstr., C.I.S. Abstr., Chem.Abstr., Excerp.Med., Rev.Plant Path.
—BLDSC (7294.410000); CASDDS.

617.95   SZ   ISSN 0080-0260
RECONSTRUCTION SURGERY AND TRAUMATOLOGY. (Text in English) 1953. irreg. (approx. 1/yr.) price varies. S. Karger AG, Allschwilerstr. 10, P.O. Box, CH-4009 Basel, Switzerland. TEL 061-3061111. FAX 061-3061234. E-mail: Karger@Karger.ch. Eds. R. DeRoche, N. Luescher. (reprint service avail. from ISI) **Indexed:** Biol.Abstr., Chem.Abstr., Curr.Cont., Ind.Med. **Document type:** academic/scholarly publication.
—CCC.
Description: New techniques and procedures described by the surgeons responsible for their development.
Refereed Serial

617.7   US   ISSN 1042-962X
CODEN: RCSUEH
REFRACTIVE & CORNEAL SURGERY. Cover title: Journal of Refractive and Corneal Surgery. 1983. bi-m. $110 to non-member individuals (foreign $146); institutions $113 (foreign $159); residents $52.50 (foreign $88.50) (effective 1994). (International Society of Refractive Keratoplasty) SLACK, Inc., 6900 Grove Rd., Thorofare, NJ 08068. TEL 609-848-1000. FAX 609-853-5991. (Co-sponsor: European Refractive Surgery Society) Ed. Patricia A. Perry; Pub. Richard N. Roash. adv. contact: Theresa Dempsey. bk.rev.; abstr.; charts; illus.; stat.; tr.lit.; index. circ. 2,000. (back issues avail.; reprint service avail.) **Indexed:** Curr.Cont., Ind.Med., Ophthal.Lit. **Document type:** academic/scholarly publication.
—BLDSC (5048.290000); Faxon; Genuine Article; SWETS; UnCover.
Formerly (until 1989): Journal of Refractive Surgery (ISSN 0883-0444)
Description: Presents research, articles on industry trends, case studies, and opinion on corneal and refractive surgery.
Refereed Serial

617   SP   ISSN 0214-5987
CODEN: RSURES
RESEARCH IN SURGERY. 1989. 3/yr. Spanish Society for Surgical Research, Hospital General Universitario de Valencia, Avda. Tres Cruces s-n, 46018 Valencia, Spain. Ed. Jose Miguel Lloris-Carsi. **Indexed:** Excerp.Med. **Document type:** academic/scholarly publication.
—BLDSC (7773.703530).

RESPIRATION; international review of thoracic diseases. see *MEDICAL SCIENCES — Respiratory Diseases*

617   BL   ISSN 0034-7124
CODEN: RBCHAN
REVISTA BRASILEIRA DE CIRURGIA. (Text in Portuguese; summaries in English and Portuguese) 1932. bi-m. $180. Cidade - Editora Cientifica Ltda., Rua Mexico 90-2 Andar, 20031 Rio de Janeiro RJ, Brazil. Ed. Fernando Moyses. adv.; bk.rev.; charts; illus.; index. circ. 7,000. **Indexed:** Biol.Abstr., Chem.Abstr., Excerp.Med., Ind.Med.
—BLDSC (7844.150000); Faxon.

617   CU   ISSN 0034-7493
REVISTA CUBANA DE CIRUGIA. (Text in Spanish; summaries in English, Spanish) 1962. s-a. $28 in S. America; N. America $30; elsewhere $34. Ministerio de Salud Publica, Centro Nacional de Informacion de Ciencias Medicas, Calle E No. 452, e-19 y 21, Plaza de la Revolucion, Apdo. 6520, Havana, Cuba. TEL 809-32-5338. (Dist. by: Ediciones Cubanas, Obispo No. 527, Apdo. 605, Havana, Cuba) Ed. Ulises Barnet. bibl.; charts; illus.; index. circ. 1,500. **Indexed:** Biol.Abstr., Chem.Abstr., Excerp.Med., Ind.Med.

617   RM   ISSN 0377-5003
CODEN: RCOCDA
REVISTA DE CHIRURGIE, ONCOLOGIE, RADIOLOGIE, O.R.L, OFTALMOLOGIE, STOMATOLOGIE, CHIRURGIA. (Text in Rumanian; summaries in English, French, German, Russian) 1952. bi-m. $25. Uniunea Societatilor de Stiinte Medicale din Republica Socialista Rumania, Str. Progresului No. 8-10, Sectorul 1, Bucharest 70754, Rumania. (Subscr. to: ILEXIM, Str. 13 Decembrie Nr. 3, P.O. Box 136-137, Bucharest, Rumania) Ed.Bd. adv.; bk.rev.; abstr.; charts; illus. **Indexed:** Biol.Abstr., Chem.Abstr., Excerp.Med., Ind.Med.
Formerly (until 1975): Chirurgia (ISSN 0009-4730)

REVISTA MEDICO-CHIRURGICALA. see *MEDICAL SCIENCES*

REVISTA PORTUGUESA DE ESTOMATOLOGIA E CIRURGIA MAXILO-FACIAL. see *MEDICAL SCIENCES — Dentistry*

617   FR   ISSN 0336-7525
REVUE DE CHIRURGIE ESTHETIQUE DE LANGUE FRANCAISE. (Text in French; summaries in English, French) 1975. q. 800 F. (foreign 950 F.) (effective 1996). Societe Francaise de Chirurgie Esthetique, 54 av. Lefevre, 94420 le Plessis-Trevise, France. TEL 1-45-94-16-64. FAX 45-72-91-12. Ed. Dr. Jacques Bassot. adv.; bk.rev.; bibl.

617.6   FR   ISSN 0035-1768
CODEN: RSCMAL
REVUE DE STOMATOLOGIE ET DE CHIRURGIE MAXILLO-FACIALE. 1894. bi-m. 1342 F. (foreign 1585 F.) (effective 1996). (Societe de Stomatologie et de Chirurgie Maxillo-Faciale de France) Masson - Periodiques, Villa Laromiguiere, 75005 Paris, France. TEL 1-40-46-62-00. FAX 1-40-46-62-01. Ed. M. Grellet. adv.; bk.rev.; illus.; index. circ. 1,600. (also avail. in microform from UMI; reprint service avail. from ISI) **Indexed:** Biol.Abstr., Chem.Abstr., Curr.Adv.Ecol.Sci., Curr.Cancer Res., Curr.Adv.Ecol.Sci., Curr.Cont., Curr.Tit.Dent., Dent.Ind., Excerp.Med., Ind.Med. **Document type:** academic/scholarly publication.
—BLDSC (7953.325000); Faxon; SWETS; UMI. CCC.
Formerly: Revue de Stomatologie.
Description: Presents general reviews on topical subjects, original articles concerning maxillofacial pathology and surgery, and practical notes concerning topical therapeutics or techniques.

617   JA   ISSN 0386-9857
CODEN: RIGEBG
RINSHO GEKA/JOURNAL OF CLINICAL SURGERY. (Text in Japanese) 1946. m. 2000 Yen per no. Igaku Shoin Ltd., 24-3, Hongo 5-chome, Bunkyo-ku, Tokyo 113-91, Japan.
—CASDDS.

617 615.82   IT
RIVISTA DI CHIRURGIA E RIABILITAZIONE DELLA MANO E DELL'ARTO SUPERIORE. 1962. 3/yr. L.80000($110) (Societa Italiana di Chirurgia della Mano) Piccin Editore, Via Altinate 107, 35100 Padua, Italy. TEL 049-655566. FAX 049-8750693. Ed. Renzo Mantero. adv.: color page L.2000000; trim 175 x 250. illus.; index, cum.index. circ. 1,500. (also avail. in microform)
Formerly: Rivista di Chirurgia della Mano (ISSN 0080-3243)

RIVISTA DI MEDICINA E CHIRURGIA. see *MEDICAL SCIENCES*

617   IT   ISSN 0035-6689
RIVISTA GENERALE ITALIANA DI CHIRURGIA. (Text in Italian; summaries in English) 1950. bi-m. L.60000 (foreign L.120000) (effective 1994). Casa Editrice Maccari, Via Trento 53, 43100 Parma, Italy. FAX 039-521-771268. Ed. F. Morino. adv.; bk.rev. circ. 1,400. **Indexed:** Excerp.Med., Psychol.Abstr.
—BLDSC (7986.400000); UMI.

617   IT   ISSN 0393-9715
RIVISTA INTERNAZIONALE DI CHIRURGIA VERTEBRALE E DEI NERVI PERIFERICI; mensile di chirurgia e branche affini. (Text in Italian; summaries in English) 1986. m. L.20000. Casa Editrice I' Antologia, Via G. Tropeano 48, 80131 Naples, Italy. TEL 39-81-7701302. Ed. Alfredo Tedeschi. bk.rev.

617.95   IT   ISSN 0391-2221
RIVISTA ITALIANA DI CHIRURGIA PLASTICA. 1968. q. L.150000 includes supplement (effective 1995). (Societa Italiana di Chirurgia Plastica) Tipografia Editrice la Garangola, Via Montona 4, 35137 Padua, Italy. FAX 39-49-8751743. (back issues avail.) **Indexed:** Excerp.Med.
—Faxon.

617   UK   ISSN 0035-8835
CODEN: JRCSAC
ROYAL COLLEGE OF SURGEONS OF EDINBURGH. JOURNAL. 1955. bi-m. £124 in Europe; elsewhere £137($220) (effective 1996). Blackwell Science Ltd., Osney Mead, Oxford OX2 OEL, England. TEL 01865-240201. FAX 01865-721205. TELEX 83355 MEDBOK G. Ed. A. Cuschieri. adv.; bk.rev.; charts; illus.; index, cum.index every 5 yrs. circ. 9,500. (also avail. in microform from UMI; back issues avail.) **Indexed:** Biol.Abstr., CINAHL, Curr.Adv.Ecol.Sci., Dent.Ind., Excerp.Med., Helminthol.Abstr., Ind.Med., Nutr.Abstr., Rev.Med.& Vet.Mycol. **Document type:** academic/scholarly publication.
—BLDSC (4856.200000); EMDOCS; Faxon; SWETS; UMI; UnCover. CCC.
Refereed Serial

617   UK   ISSN 0035-8843
CODEN: ARCSAF
ROYAL COLLEGE OF SURGEONS OF ENGLAND. ANNALS. 1947. bi-m. £95 (foreign £105). Royal College of Surgeons of England, 35-43 Lincolns Inn Fields, London WC2A 3PN, England. TEL 071-405-3474. FAX 071-831-9438. TELEX 936573-RCSENG. Ed. Barry Jackson. adv.; bk.rev.; charts; illus.; index, cum.index every 10 yrs. (also avail. in microform from UMI) **Indexed:** Biol.Abstr., Chem.Abstr., Curr.Adv.Ecol.Sci., Dent.Ind., Excerp.Med., Helminthol.Abstr., Ind.Med., Nutr.Abstr., Sci.Cit.Ind. **Document type:** academic/scholarly publication.
—BLDSC (1031.550000); EMDOCS; SWETS; UnCover.
Description: Scientific journal covering aspects of surgery and dental surgery.

617   XR   ISSN 0035-9351
ROZHLEDY V CHIRURGII. (Text in Czech; summaries in Czech, English, Russian) 1922. 12/yr. $79.90. (Ceska Lekarska Spolecnost J.E. Purkyne - Czech Medical Society) Nakladatelske Stredisko C L S J.E. Purkyne, Sokolska 31, 120 26 Prague 2, Czech Republic. FAX 42-0-2-202788. (Dist. by: Artia, Ve Smeckach 30, 111 27 Prague 1, Czech Republic) (Co-sponsor: Ceska Chirurgicka Spolecnost) Ed. B. Spacek. bk.rev. **Indexed:** Curr.Adv.Ecol.Sci., Ind.Med.
—BLDSC (8033.480000). CCC.

617 368   US
ST. ANTHONY'S CODING FOR GENERAL SURGERY REIMBURSEMENT.* m. $129. St. Anthony's Publishing, Inc., 11410 Isaac Newton Sq., Ste. 200, Reston, VA 22090-5004. TEL 800-632-0123. Ed. Kimberly Fullmer.
Description: Focuses on day-to-day coding and reimbursement issues faced by general surgery practitioners.

SAITAMAKEN NO SHINKEI GEKAIKAI KAIHO/SAITAMA NEUROSURGICAL ASSOCIATION. BULLETIN. see *MEDICAL SCIENCES — Psychiatry And Neurology*

658   US   ISSN 0190-5066
SAME-DAY SURGERY. 1977. m. $299. American Health Consultants, Inc., Six Piedmont Center, Ste. 400, Atlanta, GA 30305. TEL 404-262-7436; 800-688-2421. FAX 800-284-3291. Ed. Joy Daughtery. bk.rev. circ. 1,960. (also avail. in microfilm from UMI; back issues avail.; reprint service avail.) **Indexed:** CINAHL. **Document type:** newsletter.
●Also available online. Vendor(s): Lexis-Nexis.
—BLDSC (8071.966000); Genuine Article; UMI. CCC.

617   BL   ISSN 0036-4258
SANATORIO SAO LUCAS. BOLETIM.* 1939. bi-m. free. Fundacao para o Progresso da Cirurgia, Rua Pirapitingui 80, Sao Paulo, Brazil. Ed. R. Ney Penteado De Castro. adv.; bk.rev.; illus.; index; circ. 2,000 (controlled). (also avail. in microform from UMI) **Indexed:** Excerp.Med., Ind.Med.

SANFUJINKA MAIKURO SAJARI GAKKAI ZASSHI/JAPANESE JOURNAL OF GYNECOLOGICAL MICROSURGERY. see *MEDICAL SCIENCES — Obstetrics And Gynecology*

SANFUJINKA SHUJUTSU/GYNECOLOGIC AND OBSTETRIC SURGERY. see *MEDICAL SCIENCES — Obstetrics And Gynecology*

617.95   NO   ISSN 0284-4311
CODEN: SJPSEM
SCANDINAVIAN JOURNAL OF PLASTIC AND RECONSTRUCTIVE SURGERY AND HAND SURGERY. (Supplement avail. (ISSN 1235-662X)) (Text in English) 1967. 4/yr. NOK 920 in Nordic countries; elsewhere $157 (effective 1996). (Scandinavian Association of Plastic Surgeons) Scandinavian University Press, P.O. Box 2959 Toeyen, N-0608 Oslo, Norway. TEL 47-22-57-54-00. FAX 47-57-53-53. (U.S. addr.: Scandinavian University Press, 200 Meacham Ave., Elmont, NY 11003. TEL 516-352-7300) Ed. Jan Lilja. **Indexed:** ASCA, Biol.Abstr., Curr.Adv.Cell & Devel.Biol., Curr.Cont., Dent.Ind., Excerp.Med., Ind.Med., Med.& Surg.Dermat., Nutr.Abstr. **Document type:** academic/scholarly publication.
—BLDSC (8087.518500); ADONIS; CASDDS; Faxon; Genuine Article; SWETS; UnCover. **CCC**.
Formerly (until 1987): Scandinavian Journal of Plastic and Reconstructive Surgery (ISSN 0036-5556)
Description: Intended to serve as a forum for plastic surgery, hand surgery and related research in Scandinavia. Interest is focused on original articles on basic research and clinical evaluation.

617.95   NO   ISSN 1235-662X
SCANDINAVIAN JOURNAL OF PLASTIC AND RECONSTRUCTIVE SURGERY AND HAND SURGERY. SUPPLEMENT. (Text in English) 1967. irreg. (Scandinavian Hand Surgery Foundation) Scandinavian University Press, P.O. Box 2959 Toeyen, N-0608 Oslo, Norway. TEL 47-22-57-54-00. FAX 47-22-57-53-53. **Indexed:** Excerp.Med. (1993-). **Document type:** academic/scholarly publication.
—BLDSC (8087.519000); SWETS.
Supersedes (1967-1984): Scandinavian Journal of Plastic and Reconstructive Surgery. Supplementum (ISSN 0581-9474)

617.54 617.41   NO   ISSN 0036-5580
RD536   CODEN: SJTCAO
SCANDINAVIAN JOURNAL OF THORACIC AND CARDIOVASCULAR SURGERY. (Supplements avail. (ISSN 0586-9587)) (Text in English) 1967. 4/yr. NOK 895 in Nordic countries; elsewhere $151 (effective 1996). (Scandinavian Association for Thoracic and Cardiovascular Surgery) Scandinavian University Press, P.O. Box 2959 Toeyen, N-0608 Oslo, Norway. TEL 47-22-57-54-00. FAX 47-22-57-53-53. (U.S. addr.: Scandinavian University Press, 200 Meacham Ave., Elmont, NY 11003. TEL 516-352-7300) Ed. Axel Henze. adv. circ. 2,600. **Indexed:** ASCA, Biol.Abstr., Curr.Cont., Excerp.Med., Ind.Med. **Document type:** academic/scholarly publication.
—BLDSC (8087.550000); EMDOCS; Faxon; Genuine Article; SWETS; UnCover. **CCC**.

617.54 617.41   NO   ISSN 0586-9587
CODEN: STCSBO
SCANDINAVIAN JOURNAL OF THORACIC AND CARDIOVASCULAR SURGERY. SUPPLEMENTUM. (Text in English) 1969. irreg. (Scandinavian Association for Thoracic and Cardiovascular Surgery) Scandinavian University Press, P.O. Box 2959 Toeyen, N-0608 Oslo, Norway. TEL 47-22-57-54-00. FAX 47-22-57-53-53. (U.S. addr.: Scandinavian University Press, 200 Meacham Ave., Elmont, NY 11003. TEL 516-352-7300) **Indexed:** Ind.Med. **Document type:** monographic series.
—BLDSC (8087.555000); SWETS.

SCHWEIZER ARCHIV FUER NEUROLOGIE UND PSYCHIATRIE. see *MEDICAL SCIENCES — Psychiatry And Neurology*

617.585   SZ
SCHWEIZER PODOLOGE.* (Text in French & German) 1943. m. Schweizerischer Podologenverband, Grundstr. 14, Postfach 212, CH-6343 Rotkreuz, Switzerland. Ed. Wilhelm Heiz. adv. circ. 600.
Formerly (until 1980): Schweizer Pedicure (ISSN 0036-7435)

617   US   ISSN 0731-1680
CODEN: SCSUDR
SCIENCE AND PRACTICE OF SURGERY SERIES. 1980. irreg., vol.15, 1988. price varies. Marcel Dekker, Inc., 270 Madison Ave., New York, NY 10016. TEL 212-696-9000. FAX 212-685-4540. TELEX 421419. **Document type:** monographic series.
—CASDDS.
Refereed Serial

617   US
SCIENTIFIC AMERICAN SURGERY. 1988. base vol. (plus q. updates). $247.50 to individuals; institutions $310 (includes supplements). Scientific American, Inc., 415 Madison Ave., New York, NY 10017. TEL 212-754-0550. Ed. Douglas Wilmore. adv. circ. 10,000. (looseleaf format) **Document type:** academic/scholarly publication.
Formerly (until 1995): Care of the Surgical Patient.
Description: Contains current information for surgeons on all aspects of perioperative care.

617.6   US   ISSN 1044-7032
SELECTED READINGS IN ORAL AND MAXILLOFACIAL SURGERY. 1988. bi-m. $185 (foreign $210) per 8-issue vol. University of Texas at Dallas, Southwestern Medical Center at Dallas, 5323 Harry Hines Blvd., Dallas, TX 75235-9109. TEL 214-648-3548. FAX 214-648-2918. Ed. Dr. Douglas P. Sinn; Pub. Dr. Douglas P. Sinn. circ. 1,000. **Document type:** academic/scholarly publication.
—BLDSC (8234.855000).

617.95   US   ISSN 0739-5523
SELECTED READINGS IN PLASTIC SURGERY. 1980. 20/yr. $190 (foreign $210) for print edition; audio cassette $250 (foreign $290) (effective 1995-1996). 411 N. Washington Ave., Ste. 6900, Dallas, TX 75246. TEL 214-824-0154. FAX 214-824-0463. Ed. Dr. Fritz E. Barton, Jr. bibl.; circ. 1,800 (controlled). (also avail. in audio cassette) **Document type:** monographic series.

SEMINARS IN ANESTHESIA. see *MEDICAL SCIENCES — Anaesthesiology*

616.3   US   ISSN 1043-1489
SEMINARS IN COLON AND RECTAL SURGERY. 1990 (Mar.). q. $130 (foreign $164) (effective 1996). W.B. Saunders Co. (Subsidiary of: Harcourt Brace & Company), Curtis Center, Independence Sq. W., Philadelphia, PA 19106-3399. TEL 215-238-2800. FAX 215-238-6445. (Subscr. to: Periodicals Fulfillment, W.B. Saunders Co., 6277 Sea Harbor Dr., 4th Fl., Orlando, FL 32891-4800. TEL 800-654-2452. FAX 800-874-6418) Ed. Dr. Malcolm C. Veidenheimer; Ed. Joan W. Blumberg. adv.: B&W page $655, color page $1605; 7 x 10. circ. 1,112. **Document type:** academic/scholarly publication.
—BLDSC (8239.448400); Faxon; UMI. **CCC**.
Description: Each issue focuses on a single topic on the surgical treatment of patients with disorders of the colon or rectum.

617 618   US   ISSN 1071-5517
▼**SEMINARS IN LAPAROSCOPIC SURGERY.** 1994 (Mar.). q. $107 (foreign $142) (effective 1996). W.B. Saunders Co. (Subsidiary of: Harcourt Brace & Company), Curtis Center, 3rd Fl., Independence Sq. W., Philadelphia, PA 19106-3399. TEL 215-238-7800; 800-654-2452. FAX 215-238-6445. (Subscr. to: Periodicals Fulfillment, W.B. Saunders Co., 6277 Sea Harbor Dr., 4th Fl., Orlando, FL 32891-4800. TEL 800-654-2452. FAX 800-874-6418) Eds. Drs. Alfred Cuschieri, Bruce V. MacFayden, Jr; Pub. Joan W. Blumberg. adv.: B&W page $620, color page $1470; 7 x 10. illus. circ. 1,000. (back issues avail.) **Document type:** academic/scholarly publication.
—UMI. **CCC**.
Description: Each issue focuses on a current application of this minimally invasive surgery; also covers surgical techniques and technological advances.

SEMINARS IN NEPHROLOGY. see *MEDICAL SCIENCES — Urology And Nephrology*

616   US   ISSN 0160-2489
SEMINARS IN NEUROLOGICAL SURGERY. 1978. irreg., latest 1985. Raven Press (Subsidiary of: Wolters Kluwer N.V.), 1185 Ave. of the Americas, New York, NY 10036. TEL 212-930-9500. FAX 212-869-3495. (reprint service avail. from UMI) **Indexed:** ASCA, Excerp.Med. **Document type:** monographic series.
Refereed Serial

SEMINARS IN OPHTHALMOLOGY. see *MEDICAL SCIENCES — Ophthalmology And Optometry*

618.92   US   ISSN 1055-8586
CODEN: SPSUEH
SEMINARS IN PEDIATRIC SURGERY. 1992 (Feb.). q. $139 (foreign $185) (effective 1996). W.B. Saunders Co. (Subsidiary of: Harcourt Brace & Company), The Curtis Center, 3rd Fl., Independence Sq. W., Philadelphia, PA 19106-3399. TEL 215-238-7800. FAX 215-238-6445. (Subscr. to: Periodicals Fulfillment, W.B. Saunders Co. 6277 Sea Harbor Dr., 4th Fl., Orlando FL 32887-4800. TEL 800-654-2452. FAX 800-874-6418) Eds. Drs. Stephen L. Gans, Jay L. Grosfeld; Pub. Joan W. Blumberg. adv.: B&W page $540, color page $1290; 7 x 10. circ. 1,110. (back issues avail.) **Indexed:** Excerp.Med. (1994-), Ind.Med. (1994-). **Document type:** academic/scholarly publication.
—BLDSC (8239.456790); SWETS; UMI. **CCC**.
Description: Addresses a single topic of the specialty in each issue.

SEMINARS IN PERINATOLOGY. see *MEDICAL SCIENCES — Pediatrics*

SEMINARS IN PERIOPERATIVE NURSING. see *MEDICAL SCIENCES — Nurses And Nursing*

SEMINARS IN SPINE SURGERY. see *MEDICAL SCIENCES — Orthopedics And Traumatology*

SEMINARS IN SURGICAL ONCOLOGY. see *MEDICAL SCIENCES — Oncology*

617.54 616.1   US   ISSN 1043-0679
SEMINARS IN THORACIC AND CARDIOVASCULAR SURGERY. 1989. q. $141 (foreign $178) (effective 1996). W.B. Saunders Co. (Subsidiary of: Harcourt Brace & Company), Curtis Center, 3rd Fl., Independence Sq. W., Philadelphia, PA 19106-3399. TEL 215-238-7800. FAX 215-238-6445. (Subscr. to: Periodicals Fulfillment, W.B. Saunders Co., 6277 Sea Harbor Dr., 4th Fl., Orlando, FL 32891-4800. TEL 800-654-2452. FAX 800-874-6418) Ed. Dr. Floyd D. Loop; Pub. Joan W. Blumberg. adv.: B&W page $625, color page $1575; 7 x 10. circ. 1,877. **Document type:** academic/scholarly publication.
—BLDSC (8239.475000).
Description: Offers original articles that provide a current perspective on a relevant new topic in thoracic and cardiovascular surgery.

616   US   ISSN 0895-7967
CODEN: SVSUEP
SEMINARS IN VASCULAR SURGERY. 1988. q. $152 (foreign $184) (effective 1996). W.B. Saunders Co. (Subsidiary of: Harcourt Brace & Company), Curtis Center, 3rd Fl., Independence Sq. W., Philadelphia, PA 19106-3399. TEL 215-238-7800. FAX 215-238-6445. (Subscr. to: Periodicals Fulfillment, W.B. Saunders Co., 6277 Sea Harbor Dr., 4th Fl., Orlando, FL 32891-4800. TEL 800-654-2452. FAX 800-874-6418) Ed. Dr. Robert B. Rutherford; Pub. Joan W. Blumberg. adv.: B&W page $650, color page $1600; 7 x 10. circ. 2,040. (back issues avail.) **Indexed:** Excerp.Med., Ind.Med. (1993-). **Document type:** academic/scholarly publication.
—BLDSC (8239.486500); UMI; UnCover. **CCC**.
Description: Provides clinical information to keep specialists in the field up to date.

SHINKEI GEKA. see *MEDICAL SCIENCES — Psychiatry And Neurology*

617   JA   ISSN 0917-7175
SHINSHU TO MEN'EKI/SURGICAL TRAUMA & IMMUNOLOGICAL RESPONSES. (Text in Japanese) 1991. q. 2060 Yen per no. Medical View Co., Ltd. - Mejikaru Byusha, 2-30, Ichigaya Honmuracho, Shinjuku-ku, Tokyo 162, Japan.

MEDICAL SCIENCES — SURGERY

617 CC ISSN 1001-0831
SHIYONG WAIKE ZAZHI/JOURNAL OF PRACTICAL SURGERY. (Text in Chinese; abstracts in English) 1981. m. $60. Shiyong Yixue Zazhishe - Applied Medical Science Journal Publishing House, 44-1, Jixian St., Heping District, Shenyang, Liaoning 110005, People's Republic of China. TEL 364398. Ed. He Sanguang. circ. 55,000. **Document type:** academic/scholarly publication.
Description: Features new developments and methods of practical diagnosis, treatment, and prevention of surgical diseases.
Refereed Serial

617 JA ISSN 0385-6313
SHONI GEKA/JAPANESE JOURNAL OF PEDIATRIC SURGERY. (Text in Japanese; summaries in English) 1969. m. 2300 Yen per no. Tokyo Igakusha Ltd., 35-4, Hongo 3-chome, Bunkyo-ku, Tokyo 113, Japan.

617 JA ISSN 0037-4423
SHUJUTSU/OPERATION. (Text in Japanese) 1947. m. 1750 Yen per no. Kanehara & Co., Ltd., 2-31-14 Yushima, Bunkyo-ku, Tokyo 113, Japan. Ed. Dr. Tokuji Ichikawa. bk.rev.; cum.index. circ. 9,500. **Indexed:** Ind.Med.

617 US ISSN 1052-1453
CODEN: SBSUEL
SKULL BASE SURGERY. 1991. q. $109 to individuals (foreign $134); institutions $149 (foreign $174). Thieme Medical Publishers, Inc., 381 Park Ave. S., Ste. 1501, New York, NY 10016. TEL 212-683-5088. FAX 212-779-9020. Eds. Douglas Mattox, Madjid Samii. circ. 1,100. **Indexed:** Excerp.Med. (1993-). **Document type:** academic/scholarly publication.
—BLDSC (8308.850000); Genuine Article; SWETS; UMI.
Description: Takes a multidisciplinary approach, using original research articles.

617 VE
SOCIEDAD VENEZOLANA DE CIRUGIA BOLETIN.* vol. 29, 1975. Bs.13.50. Sociedad Venezolana de Cirugia, Torre del Colegio 150, Of. A, Avde. Jose Maria Vargas, Urb. Santa Fe, Caracas 1080, Venezuela.

617 BL
SOCIEDADE DE MEDICINA E CIRURGIA DE SAO JOSE DO RIO PRETO. REVISTA. (Text and summaries in English and Portuguese) 1968. q. Cr.$100($15) Sociedade de Medicina e Cirurgia de Sao Jose do Rio Preto, Rua Spinola s-n, Sao Jose da Rio Preto 15100, Brazil. Ed. Dr. Jorge Paulete. adv.; bk.rev.; illus.; index; circ. controlled. (also avail. in microform) **Indexed:** Biol.Abstr.

617 IT ISSN 1121-1342
SOCIETA MEDICO-CHIRURGICA DELLA PROVINCIA DI CREMONA. BOLLETTINO. (Text in Italian; summaries in English) 1946. s-a. L.30000($20) Societa Medico-Chirurgica di Cremona, Ordine dei Medici, Via Palestro 66, 26100 Cremona, Italy. TEL 0372-35224. Ed. Luciano Boari. adv.; abstr.; bibl.; charts; illus.; index. circ. 400. **Indexed:** Biol.Abstr., Ind.Med.
Former titles (until 1982): Societa Medico-Chirurigica e Ospedali Provincia de Cremona. Bollettino (ISSN 0391-5999); (until 1975): Societa Medico-Chirurgica di Cremona. Bollettino (ISSN 0037-8852)

616 IT
SOCIETA MEDICO-CHIRURGICA DI MODENA. BOLLETTINO. (Text in Italian; summaries in English) vol. 82, 1982. fortn. L.10000($7) Societa Medico-Chirurgica di Modena, Policlinico, Via del Pozzo, 41100 Modena, Italy. circ. 500. **Indexed:** Biol.Abstr.

617 FR ISSN 0037-9492
SOCIETE MEDICO-CHIRURGICALE DES HOPITAUX ET FORMATIONS SANITAIRES DES ARMEES. BULLETIN. 1969. 10/yr. 20 F. Societe Medico-Chirurgicale des Hopitaux et Formations Sanitaires des Armees, Val-De-Grace, 277 bis rue Saint Jacques, 75005 Paris, France. adv.; bibl.; charts; illus.; index. **Indexed:** Biol.Abstr.

SOINS - CHIRURGIE. see *MEDICAL SCIENCES — Nurses And Nursing*

617 SA ISSN 0038-2361
CODEN: SAJSBS
SOUTH AFRICAN JOURNAL OF SURGERY/SUID-AFRIKAANSE TYDSKRIF VIR CHIRURGIE. (Text in Afrikaans and English) 1963. q. R.72 (foreign R.110($35) (effective 1995). (Association of Surgeons of South Africa) M A S A Publications, Private Bag X1, Pinelands 7430, South Africa. TEL 27-21-531-3081. FAX 27-21-531-4126. Ed. Cedric Bremner. adv.; bk.rev.; bibl.; charts; illus.; index. circ. 1,200. (also avail. in microform from UMI; reprint service avail. from ISI,UMI) **Indexed:** Abstr.Hyg., ASCA, Biol.Abstr., Curr.Cont., Excerp.Med., Helminthol.Abstr., Ind.Med., Ind.S.A.Per., Trop.Dis.Bull. **Document type:** academic/scholarly publication.
—BLDSC (8340.300000); EMDOCS; Genuine Article; SWETS; UMI; UnCover.

617 US
SOUTHERN SURGICAL ASSOCIATION. TRANSACTIONS. 1991. a. Lippincott - Raven Publishers, 227 E. Washington Sq., Philadelphia, PA 19106. TEL 215-238-4200. (also avail. in microform from UMI)

SPOR HEKIMLIGI DERGISI/TURKISH JOURNAL OF SPORTS MEDICINE. see *MEDICAL SCIENCES — Sports Medicine*

617 SZ ISSN 1011-6125
CODEN: SFUNE4
STEREOTACTIC AND FUNCTIONAL NEUROSURGERY. (Text in English) 1938. 8/yr (in 2 vols.). 297.60 SFr.($229.20) to individuals; institutions 496 SFr.($382) (effective 1996). (World Society for Stereotactic and Functional Neurosurgery) S. Karger AG, Allschwilerstr. 10, P.O. Box, CH-4009 Basel, Switzerland. TEL 061-3061111. FAX 061-3061234. E-mail: Karger@Karger.ch. Ed. P.L Gildenberg. adv.; bibl.; illus.; charts; index. circ. 1,000. (also avail. in microform from RPI; back issues avail.) **Indexed:** Bibl.Dev.Med.& Child Neur., Biol.Abstr., Chem.Abstr., Curr.Adv.Ecol.Sci., Curr.Cont., Dent.Ind., Excerp.Med., Helminthol.Abstr., Ind.Med., Ind.Sci.Rev., Psychol.Abstr., Sci.Cit.Ind. **Document type:** academic/scholarly publication.
—BLDSC (8464.368000); CASDDS; Faxon; Genuine Article; SWETS; UnCover. **CCC.**
Former titles: Applied Neurophysiology (ISSN 0302-2773); Confinia Neurologia (ISSN 0010-5678)
Refereed Serial

617 JA ISSN 0016-593X
SURGERY/GEKA. (Text in Japanese) 1937. m. 29500 Yen (foreign 44000 Yen). Nankodo Co., Ltd., 42-6, Hongo 3-chome, Bunkyo-ku, Tokyo 113, Japan. TEL 03-3811-7239. FAX 03-3811-7230. Ed. Kenji Sakurai. adv.; charts; illus.; index. circ. 6,000. **Indexed:** INIS Atomind.

617.05 US ISSN 0039-6060
RD1 CODEN: SURGAZ
SURGERY; devoted to the art and science of surgery. 1937. m. $116 to individuals (Canada $153.01; elsewhere $143); institutions $236 (Canada $281.41; elsewhere $263); students, residents $53 (Canada $85.60; elsewhere $80) (effective 1996); newsstand price: $10.50. (Society of University Surgeons) Mosby - Year Book, Inc. (Subsidiary of: Times Mirror Company), 11830 Westline Industrial Dr., St. Louis, MO 63146-3318. TEL 314-872-8370; 800-325-4177. FAX 314-432-1380. TELEX 44-2402. (Co-sponsors: American Association of Endocrine Surgeons; Central Surgical Association) Eds. Drs. Walter F. Ballinger, George D. Zuidema. adv.: B&W page $1075, color page $1945; trim 8 1/8 x 10 7/8. illus.; s-a. index. circ. 8,513. (also avail. in microfilm from UMI,PMC; reprint service avail. from UMI) **Indexed:** Abstr.Health Care Manage.Stud., AIM, ASCA, Biol.Abstr., Chem.Abstr., Curr.Adv.Cancer Res., Curr.Adv.Ecol.Sci., Curr.Adv.Genetics & Molec.Biol., Curr.Cont., Dairy Sci.Abstr., Excerp.Med., Helminthol.Abstr., Ind.Med., Kidney, Med.& Surg.Dermat., Nutr.Abstr., Rev.Med.& Vet.Mycol., Risk Abstr., Sci.Cit.Ind.
—BLDSC (8548.125000); ADONIS; CASDDS; EMDOCS; Faxon; Genuine Article; SWETS; UMI; UnCover. **CCC.**
Description: Developments in clinical and experimental surgery.
Refereed Serial

617 UK ISSN 0263-9319
SURGERY. m. £64.20 (foreign £72). The Medicine Group (Journals) Ltd., Publishing House, 62 Stert St., Abingdon, Oxon. OX14 3UQ, England. TEL 01235-555770. FAX 01235-554691. Eds. John Lumley, John Craven. adv. contact: Christian Benzing. **Document type:** academic/scholarly publication.
—BLDSC (8548.123600).

617 US ISSN 0748-1942
SURGERY ALERT. 1984. m. $113. American Health Consultants, Inc., Six Piedmont Center, Ste. 400, Atlanta, GA 30305. TEL 404-262-7436; 800-688-2421. FAX 800-284-3291. Ed. Dr. Leonard Schultz. index. circ. 1,255. (also avail. in audio cassette; reprint service avail.) **Document type:** newsletter.

616 US ISSN 0081-9638
RD9 CODEN: SURABI
SURGERY ANNUAL. 1969. s-a. $75 per vol. Appleton & Lange (Subsidiary of: Simon & Schuster Company), 25 Van Zant St., Box 5630, Norwalk, CT 06856. TEL 203-838-4400. Ed. Dr. Lloyd Nyhus. **Indexed:** Biol.Abstr., Dent.Ind., Excerp.Med., Ind.Med.
—BLDSC (8548.135000); Faxon; SWETS. **CCC.**
Description: Selection of original articles on latest surgical advances.

617 JA ISSN 1340-5594
▼**SURGERY FRONTIER.** (Text in Japanese) 1994. 4/yr. 2000 Yen per no. Medikaru Rebyusha - Medical Review Co., Ltd., 7-3, Hiranomachi 1-chome, Chuo-ku, Osaka 541, Japan.

617 JA ISSN 0941-1291
CODEN: SUTOE
SURGERY TODAY. (Text in English) 1899. 12/yr. DM.810($588) (effective 1996). (Japan Surgical Society - Nihon Geka Gakkai) Springer-Verlag Tokyo, 3-13 Hongo 3-chome, Bunkyo-ku, Tokyo 113, Japan. TEL 03-3812-0617. FAX 03-3812-4699. (Subscr. in N. America to: Springer-Verlag New York Inc., Service Center Secaucus 44, Hartz Way, Secaucus, NJ 07096-2491. TEL 201-348-4033) Ed. Yoshio Mishima. bk.rev. circ. 1,200. **Indexed:** Biol.Abstr., Chem.Abstr., Curr.Cont., Excerp.Med., Ind.Med., INIS Atomind., So.Pac.Per.Ind. **Document type:** academic/scholarly publication.
—BLDSC (8548.164500); ADONIS; CASDDS; Faxon; Genuine Article; SWETS; UnCover.
Formerly (until 1993): Japanese Journal of Surgery (ISSN 0047-1909)

SURGICAL AND RADIOLOGIC ANATOMY. see *BIOLOGY — Physiology*

617 US ISSN 0039-6109
RD34 CODEN: SCNAA7
SURGICAL CLINICS OF NORTH AMERICA. 1912. bi-m. $135 (foreign $163) (effective 1996). W.B. Saunders Co. (Subsidiary of: Harcourt Brace & Company), Curtis Center, 3rd Fl., Independence Sq. W., Philadelphia, PA 19106-3399. TEL 215-238-7800. FAX 215-238-6445. (Subscr. to: Periodicals Fulfillment, W.B. Saunders Co., 6277 Sea Harbor Dr., 4th Fl., Orlando, FL 32891-4800. TEL 800-654-2452. FAX 800-874-6418) Ed. Livia Berardi; Pub. Joan W. Blumberg. adv.; bibl.; illus.; index, cum.index every 3 yrs. (also avail. in microform from UMI; reprint service avail. from UMI, ISI) **Indexed:** AIM, ASCA, Biol.Abstr., Chem.Abstr., Curr.Adv.Ecol.Sci., Curr.Cont., Excerp.Med., Helminthol.Abstr., Ind.Med., Int.Nurs.Ind., Nutr.Abstr. **Document type:** academic/scholarly publication.
—BLDSC (8548.200000); CASDDS; EMDOCS; Faxon; Genuine Article; SWETS; UMI; UnCover. **CCC.**
Description: Discusses various surgical techniques and procedures.

MEDICAL SCIENCES — SURGERY

617 US ISSN 0930-2794
CODEN: SUREEX
SURGICAL ENDOSCOPY; ultrasound and interventional techniques. 1987. bi-m. $261 (effective 1996). Springer-Verlag, Journals, 175 Fifth Ave., New York, NY 10010. TEL 212-460-1500. FAX 212-473-6272. (N. American subscr. to: Journal Fulfillment Services, Box 2485, Secaucus, NJ 07096-2491. TEL 800-777-4643. FAX 201-348-4505; Elsewhere: Heidelberger Platz 3, 1000 Berlin 33, Germany. TEL 030-8207-1. FAX 030-821-4091) (Co-sponsors: Society of American Gastrointestinal Endoscopic Surgeons; European Association for Endoscopic Surgery) Eds. K.A. Forde, A. Cuschieri. circ. 3,000. (also avail. in microform from UMI; reprint service avail.) **Indexed:** Biol.Abstr., Curr.Cont. **Document type:** academic/scholarly publication.
—BLDSC (8548.215000); Faxon; Genuine Article; SWETS; UMI. **CCC.**
Description: Represents the surgical aspects of interventional endoscopy, ultrasound and other techniques in the fields of gastroenterology, obstetrics, gynecology, and urology.
Refereed Serial

617 616.3 618 US ISSN 1051-7200
CODEN: SLENEY
SURGICAL LAPAROSCOPY AND ENDOSCOPY. 1991. bi-m. $120 to individuals (foreign $144); institutions $189 (foreign $214) (effective 1996); newsstand price: $37. Lippincott - Raven Publishers, 227 Washington Sq., Philadelphia, PA 19106. TEL 215-238-4200. Ed. Karl A. Zucker. adv. contact: Phyllis Noyes. charts; illus. circ. 7,000. (also avail. in microform from UMI; reprint service avail. from UMI) **Indexed:** Excerp.Med. (1992-), Ind.Med. (1993-). **Document type:** academic/scholarly publication.
—BLDSC (8548.234000); Genuine Article; SWETS; UMI. **CCC.**
Description: Publishes reports on major developments in laparoscopic and endoscopic techniques and procedures, current clinical and basic science research, patient management, surgical complications, and new developments in instrumentation and technology.
Refereed Serial

617 616.8 US ISSN 0090-3019
RD593 CODEN: SGNRAI
SURGICAL NEUROLOGY. 1973. m. $415 to institutions (effective 1996). Elsevier Science Inc., 655 Ave. of the Americas, New York, NY 10010. TEL 212-989-5800. FAX 212-633-3990. TELEX 420643 AEP UI. (Subscr. to: Box 882, Madison Sq. Sta., New York, NY 10159-0882) Ed. Eben Alexander, Jr. adv.; bk.rev.; index. circ. 4,300. (also avail. in microform from UMI; back issues avail.) **Indexed:** ASCA, Bibl.Dev.Med.& Child Neur., Biol.Abstr., Curr.Adv.Cancer Res., Curr.Adv.Ecol.Sci., Curr.Cont., Dent.Ind., Excerp.Med., Helminthol.Abstr., Ind.Med., Rev.Med.& Vet.Mycol., Sci.Cit.Ind. **Document type:** academic/scholarly publication.
—BLDSC (8548.240000); EMDOCS; Faxon; Genuine Article; SWETS; UnCover. **CCC.**
Description: Presents original papers on clinical and research advances in neurosurgery.
Refereed Serial

SURGICAL NURSE. see *MEDICAL SCIENCES — Nurses And Nursing*

SURGICAL ONCOLOGY CLINICS OF NORTH AMERICA. see *MEDICAL SCIENCES — Oncology*

SURGICAL PATHOLOGY. see *MEDICAL SCIENCES*

610 US ISSN 0273-7655
SURGICAL PRACTICE NEWS. 1981. m. $28. McMahon Publishing Co., 83 Peaceable St., West Redding, CT 06896. TEL 203-944-9343. (Subscr. to: 121 S. Gertrude Ave., Paramus, NJ 07652) Ed. Hank Rogers. (tabloid format; back issues avail.)
Refereed Serial

617 US
SURGICAL PRODUCT COMPARISON SYSTEM. m. $370. (Emergency Care Research Institute) E C R I, 5200 Butler Pike, Plymouth Meeting, PA 19462. TEL 610-825-6000. FAX 610-834-1275. Ed. Garrett Hayner. (looseleaf format) **Document type:** trade publication.
●Also available on CD-ROM. Producer(s): Knight-Ridder, Inc.
Description: Covers ambulatory surgery facilities, from arthroscopes to operating tables.

617 US ISSN 0882-9233
CODEN: SRCOEZ
SURGICAL RESEARCH COMMUNICATIONS. 1986. 4/yr. 101 ECU (effective 1996). Harwood Academic Publishers, c/o International Publishers Distributor, 820 Town Center Dr., Langhorne, PA 19047. TEL 215-750-2642. FAX 215-750-6343. (Subscr. to: International Publishers Distributor, P.O. Box 90, Reading, Berkshire RG1 8JL, England. TEL 44-173-456-8316) Ed. D.J. Leaper. (also avail. in microform)
—BLDSC (8548.247000); SWETS. **CCC.**
Refereed Serial

617 US ISSN 1063-8547
SURGICAL RESIDENT. 1992. bi-m. $44. Slack, Inc., 6900 Grove Rd., Thorofare, NJ 08086. TEL 609-848-1000. FAX 609-853-5991. adv.: B&W page $1900, color page $3100; trim 8 1/8 x 10 7/8. circ. 12,085.

616 US ISSN 0161-1372
RD1
SURGICAL ROUNDS. 1978. m. $50 (foreign $92). Romaine Pierson Publishers, Inc., 80 Shore Rd., Port Washington, NY 11050. TEL 516-883-6350. FAX 516-883-6609. Ed. Dr. Bernard M. Jaffe; Pub. O. Oliver Anderson. adv. contact: Ann Hussey. circ. 53,530. (also avail. in microform from UMI; back issues avail.) **Indexed:** CINAHL.
—BLDSC (8548.249000); Faxon; UMI. **CCC.**

617 US ISSN 0164-4238
SURGICAL TECHNOLOGIST. 1972. m. $36 (effective 1993). Association of Surgical Technologists, Inc., 7108-C S. Alton Way, Englewood, CO 80112-2106. TEL 303-694-9130. FAX 303-694-9164. Ed. Sharon Pellowe. adv.; bk.rev.; illus. circ. 17,000. **Indexed:** CINAHL, Hosp.Lit.Ind. **Document type:** trade publication.
—BLDSC (8548.259000).
Formerly (until 1978): O R Tech.
Description: Emphasis is given to surgical procedures and equipment, legislative-regulatory issues, aseptic techniques and professional development.

617 UK ISSN 0039-6125
SURGO. 1933. 3/yr. £5. University of Glasgow, Medico-Chirurgical Society, University Union, 32 University Ave., Glasgow, G12 8LX, Scotland. Ed. Paul Jarrett. adv.; bk.rev.; bibl.; charts; illus. circ. 1,000.

617 US
SUTURELINE.* q. membership. American Association of Surgeon Assistants, 11250 Roger Bacon Dr., Ste. 8, Restont, VA 22090-5202. TEL 703-525-1191. FAX 703-276-8196. adv. circ. 500.

617 SZ ISSN 1023-9332
▼**SWISS SURGERY/SCHWEIZER CHIRURGIE/CHIRURGIE SUISSE.** (Text in English, French, German) 1995. bi-m. 158 SFr. (foreign 180 SFr.). Verlag Hans Huber, Laenggassstr. 76, CH-3000 Bern 9, Switzerland. FAX 031-3004500. Ed. Dr. P. Matter. circ. 2,000. **Document type:** academic/scholarly publication.
—BLDSC (8576.790000).
Refereed Serial

617 SA ISSN 1077-2855
▼**TECHNIQUES IN NEUROSURGERY.** 1995. q. $99 to individuals (foreign $111); institutions $126 (foreign $140) (effective 1996); newsstand price: $36. Lippincott - Raven Publishers, 227 Washington Sq., Philadelphia, PA 19106. TEL 215-238-4200. Eds. Dr. Christopher M. Loftus, Dr. H. Hunt Batjer. (back issues avail.) **Document type:** academic/scholarly publication.
—BLDSC (8745.260000). **CCC.**
Description: Provides complete reviews of neurosurgical procedures, relevant instrumentation and anatomy.

617 GW ISSN 0171-6425
CODEN: TCSUD4
THORACIC AND CARDIOVASCULAR SURGEON. (Text in English) 1952. bi-m. DM.294. (Deutsche Gesellschaft fuer Thorax-, Herz- und Gefaesschirurgie - German Society for Thoracic and Cardiovascular Surgery) Georg Thieme Verlag, Ruedigerstr. 14, 70469 Stuttgart, Germany. TEL 0711-8931-0. FAX 0711-8931298. (U.S. subscr. to: Thieme Medical Publishers, Inc., 381 Park Ave. S., New York, NY 10016) Ed. K. Stapenhorst. adv.; bk.rev.; abstr.; bibl.; charts; illus.; stat.; index. circ. 1,500. (reprint service avail. from UMI) **Indexed:** ASCA, Chem.Abstr., Curr.Cont., Excerp.Med., Ind.Med., Sci.Cit.Ind. **Document type:** academic/scholarly publication.
—BLDSC (8820.240000); CASDDS; Genuine Article; SWETS; UMI; UnCover. **CCC.**
Formerly (until 1979): Thoraxchirurgie - Vaskulaere Chirurgie (ISSN 0040-6384)

TOPICS IN NEUROSURGERY. see *MEDICAL SCIENCES — Psychiatry And Neurology*

TRANSPLANT CHRONICLES. see *MEDICAL SCIENCES — Urology And Nephrology*

617 US ISSN 0041-1337
QP89 CODEN: TRPLAU
TRANSPLANTATION. 1963. s-m. $260 to individuals; institutions $415 (effective 1995). (Transplantation Society) Williams & Wilkins, 428 E. Preston St., Baltimore, MD 21202. TEL 410-528-4000; 800-638-6423. FAX 410-528-4312. TELEX 87669. Ed. Dr. A.P. Monaco. adv.; bk.rev.; illus.; index. circ. 4,011. (also avail. in microfilm from WWS; back issues avail.) **Indexed:** Anim.Breed.Abstr., ASCA, Biol.Abstr., Chem.Abstr., Curr.Adv.Cancer Res., Curr.Adv.Ecol.Sci., Curr.Cont., Dairy Sci.Abstr., Diab.Cont., Excerp.Med., Ind.Med., Ind.Vet., Kidney, Med.& Surg.Dermat., Poult.Abstr., Protozool.Abstr., Rev.Med.& Vet.Mycol., Risk Abstr., Telegen, Vet.Bull. **Document type:** academic/scholarly publication.
—BLDSC (9024.990000); ADONIS; CASDDS; EMDOCS; Faxon; Genuine Article; SWETS; UnCover. **CCC.**
Description: Publishes original papers and abstracts from pertinent specialties: immunology, hematology, endocrinology and embryology.
Refereed Serial

617 US ISSN 0041-1345
RD120.7 CODEN: TRPPA8
TRANSPLANTATION PROCEEDINGS. 1969. bi-m. $180 to individuals (Canada $210, elsewhere $243); institutions $305 (Canada $325, elsewhere $355); students $138 (Canada $161, elsewhere $185). (Transplantation Society) Appleton & Lange, Journal Division (Subsidiary of: Simon & Schuster Company), 25 Van Zant St., Box 5630, Norwalk, CT 06856. TEL 203-838-4400. (Subscr. to: Appleton & Lange, Box 318, Pearl River, NY 10965-0118) Ed. Dr. Felix T. Rapaport. adv.; bibl.; charts; illus.; index. circ. 2,600. (also avail. in microform from UMI; back issues avail.; reprint service avail.) **Indexed:** Anim.Breed.Abstr., ASCA, Biol.Abstr., Chem.Abstr., Curr.Adv.Cancer Res., Curr.Adv.Ecol.Sci., Curr.Cont., Excerp.Med., Ind.Med., Ind.Vet., Med.& Surg.Dermat., Sci.Cit.Ind. **Document type:** academic/scholarly publication, proceedings.
●Also available online.
—BLDSC (9025.100000); CASDDS; EMDOCS; Faxon; Genuine Article; SWETS; UMI; UnCover. **CCC.**
Description: Includes reviews and original reports in current problems in transplantation biology and medicine.
Refereed Serial

617 US ISSN 0955-470X
TRANSPLANTATION REVIEWS. q. $162 (foreign $189) (effective 1996). W.B. Saunders Co. (Subsidiary of: Harcourt Brace & Co.), Curtis Center, 3rd Fl., Independence Sq. W., Philadelphia, PA 19106-3399. TEL 215-238-7800. FAX 215-238-6445. (Subscr. to: W.B. Saunders Co., Periodicals Dept., 6277 Sea Harbor Dr., 4th Fl., Orlando, FL 32891. TEL 800-654-2452. FAX 800-874-6418) Eds. Peter J. Morris, Dr. Nicholas J. Tilney; Pub. Joan W. Blumberg. adv.: B&W page $565, color page $1415; 7 x 10. circ. 1,006. (back issues avail.) **Document type:** academic/scholarly publication.
Description: Contains review articles on the latest developments in both clinical and experimental transplantation surgery.
Refereed Serial

MEDICAL SCIENCES — SURGERY

617   GW   ISSN 0946-9648
TRANSPLANTATIONSMEDIZIN. (Text and summaries in English, German) 1989. q. DM.64 (foreign DM.70). (Deutsche Transplantationsgesellschaft) Pabst Science Publishers, Am Eichengrund 28, 49525 Lengerich, Germany. TEL 05484-308. FAX 05484-550. Ed. A.-E. Lison. adv.; bk.rev. circ. 1,600. Indexed: Excerp.Med. (1994-). Document type: academic/scholarly publication.
 Formerly (until 1994): Zeitschrift fuer Transplantationsmedizin (ISSN 0935-1965)
 Description: Original articles and case reports on transplantation in surgery, immunology, internal medicine, urology, nephrology.

617   SP   ISSN 1134-315X
CODEN: TANSE
TRANSPLANTOLOGY; journal of cell and organ transplantation. 1989. q. Aran Ediciones, S.A., Avda. General Peron 20, 5 dcha, 28020 Madrid, Spain. TEL 34-1-5332525. FAX 34-1-5332123. Indexed: Excerp.Med. Document type: academic/scholarly publication.
 Formerly (until 1992): Transplant of Organs and Tissues (ISSN 0214-820X)

617.3   US   ISSN 0743-6637
CODEN: TRAUEK
TRAUMA QUARTERLY. 1984-1993; resumed 1996. q. V S P, P.O. Box 346, 3700 AH Zeist. TEL 31-30-6935790. FAX 31-30-6932081. adv.; illus.; index. (also avail. in microform; back issues avail.) Indexed: Hlth.Ind. Document type: academic/scholarly publication.
 —CASDDS; UMI; UnCover. CCC.
 Description: Surgically oriented discussion of clinical care in the trauma care setting.
 Refereed Serial

617   JA   ISSN 0917-0197
TRENDS & TOPICS IN TRANSPLANTATION. (Text in Japanese) 1992. q. Standard McIntyre - Sutandado Makkintaiya, 3-7, Irifune 2-chome, Chuo-ku, Tokyo 104, Japan.

617   TU
CODEN: UCDEE
TURKISH JOURNAL OF SURGERY. q.? Turkish Surgical Society, Guzelbahce Sok. Tugrul Apt. No. 35-7, Nisantasi, 80200 Istanbul, Turkey. TEL 90-212-2475295. Indexed: Excerp.Med. (1994-).

TURKISH NEUROSURGERY. see *MEDICAL SCIENCES — Psychiatry And Neurology*

617   IT   ISSN 0014-648X
UNIVERSITA DEGLI STUDI DI PERUGIA. FACOLTA DI MEDICINA E CHIRURGIA. ANNALI. (Includes: Accademia Anatomico Chirurgica. Atti) 1885. q. L.30000. Universita degli Studi di Perugia, Facolta di Medicina e Chirugia, Perugia, Italy. Ed. Giovanni Bolis. circ. 500. Indexed: Apic.Abstr., Chem.Abstr., Excerp.Med.

616   US   ISSN 0042-2835
RD598   CODEN: VASUA9
VASCULAR SURGERY (GLEN HEAD). 1967. bi-m. $125 to individuals (overseas $135); institutions $160 (overseas $170) (effective 1996). Westminster Publications, Inc., 708 Glen Cove Ave., Glen Head, NY 11545. TEL 516-759-0025. FAX 516-759-5524. adv. circ. 4,249. Indexed: Biol.Abstr., Curr.Adv.Cancer Res., Excerp.Med. Document type: academic/scholarly publication.
 —BLDSC (9148.900000); EMDOCS; Faxon; Genuine Article; SWETS; UnCover. CCC.
 Description: Contains original papers relating to any phase of vascular diseases, operative procedures, clinical or laboratory research and case reports.

617 616.1   US   ISSN 0894-8038
VASCULAR SURGERY OUTLOOK. 1988. 9/yr. free to subscribers to Perspectives in Vascular Surgery. Quality Medical Publishing, Inc., 1970 Borman Dr., Ste. 222, St. Louis, MO 63146. TEL 314-878-7808; 800-348-7808. FAX 314-878-9937. Ed. Dr. Jerry Goldstein. Document type: newsletter.

617   RU   ISSN 0042-4625
CODEN: VKHGAG
VESTNIK KHIRURGII IM. I.I. GREKOVA/I.I. GREKOV ANNALS OF SURGERY. (Text in Russian; summaries in English) 1885. m. $114 (effective 1996). (Khirurgicheskoe Obshchestvo im. Pirogova) Izdatel'stvo Meditsina, Peterburgskoe Ordelenie, Park Lenina, 5a, 197046 St. Petersburg, Russia. (Co-sponsor: Ministerstvo Zdravookhraneniya S.S.S.R.) Ed. F.G. Uglov. bk.rev.; illus.; index. Indexed: Biol.Abstr., Chem.Abstr., Dent.Ind., Dok.Arbeitsmed., Excerp.Med., Ind.Med.
 —BLDSC (0036.700000); EMDOCS; Genuine Article. CCC.
 Description: Carries articles touching on various problems of clinical and experimental surgery, anesthesiology and reanimatology.

VIDEO JOURNAL OF CATARACT & REFRACTIVE SURGERY. see *MEDICAL SCIENCES — Ophthalmology And Optometry*

617   SP   ISSN 0212-7695
VIDEO REVISTA DE CIRUGIA/VIDEO REVIEW OF SURGERY. (Text, video in English, French, Italian, Spanish) 1984. 6/yr. 21000 ptas. to individuals; institutions 30000 ptas. (Portugal 21000 ptas.; Italy L.450000; France 1890 Fr.; other European $410; elsewhere $500). (Asociacion Europea de Video Cirugia - European Association of Video Surgery) Video Medica, S.L., Badal 102 Bis. Loc. 1, 08014 Barcelona, Spain. TEL 34-3-4319666. FAX 34-3-4219942. Ed. Carlos Ballesta Lopez. adv. contact: G. Gozzetti. circ. 5,000. (video cassette; plus text) Document type: trade publication.

616.89   RU   ISSN 0042-8817
CODEN: ZVNBDJ
VOPROSY NEIROKHIRURGII/JOURNAL OF NEUROSURGINAL PROBLEMS. Varian title: Zhurnal Voprosy Neirokhirurgii im. N.N. Burdenko. (Text in Russian; summaries in English) 1937. q. $62 (effective 1996). (N I I Neirokhirurgii im. N.N. Burdenko) Izdatel'stvo Meditsina, Petroverigskii pereulok 6-8, 101000 Moscow, Russia. (Dist. by: Mezhdunarodnaya Kniga, B. Yakimanka 39, 117049 Moscow, Russian. TEL 7-095-2384600. FAX 7-095-2384634) (Co-sponsor: Ministerstvo Zdravookhraneniya) Ed. A.N. Konovalov. adv. contact: V.K. Ivannikova. bk.rev.; index. Indexed: Biol.Abstr., Chem.Abstr., Excerp.Med., Ind.Med., Int.Aerosp.Abstr.
 —BLDSC (0060.630000); EMDOCS.
 Description: Discusses theoretical, practical and organization problems of modern neurosurgery. Informs of the advances in the treatment of neurosurgical diseases of the central, peripheral and vegetative nervous system.

617   US   ISSN 0364-2313
CODEN: WJSUDI
WORLD JOURNAL OF SURGERY. 1936. bi-m. $298 (effective 1996). (Societe Internationale de Chirurgie, BE) Springer-Verlag, Journals, 175 Fifth Ave., New York, NY 10010. TEL 212-460-1500. FAX 212-473-6272. (N. American subscr. to: Journal Fulfillment Services, Box 2485, Secaucus, NJ 07096-2491. TEL 800-777-4643. FAX 201-348-4505; Elsewhere: Heidelberger Platz 3, 1000 Berlin 33, Germany. TEL 030-8207-1. FAX 030-821-4091) (Co-sponsors: Collegium Internationale Chirurgie Digestivae; International Association of Endocrine Surgeons) Ed. Ronald D. Tomkins. adv.; bk.rev.; illus. (also avail. in microform from UMI; reprint service avail. from ISI) Indexed: Biol.Abstr., Chem.Abstr., Curr.Cont., Excerp.Med., Ind.Med. Document type: academic/scholarly publication.
 —BLDSC (9356.074300); CASDDS; Faxon; Genuine Article; SWETS; UMI; UnCover. CCC.
 Supersedes (until 1976): Societe Internationale de Chirurgie. Bulletin (ISSN 0037-945X); Formerly: Journal International de Chirurgie.
 Description: Provides in-depth coverage of recent surgical developments.
 Refereed Serial

617   US   ISSN 1075-3931
▼**WORLDPLAST;** the world journal of plastic surgery. 1995. q. $165 to individuals; institutions $210 (effective 1996). Field & Wood, Medical Periodicals, Inc., Box 975, Blue Bell, PA 19422. TEL 610-828-4010. FAX 215-482-0226. Ed. Dr. Jose Guerrerosantos. Document type: academic/scholarly publication.
 —BLDSC (9360.485000).
 Refereed Serial

617.95   DK
▼**XENOTRANSPLANTATION.** 1994. q. DKK 1200 (effective 1996). Munksgaard International Publishers Ltd., 35 Noerre Soegade, P.O. Box 2148, DK-1016 Copenhagen, Denmark. TEL 45-33-12-70-30. FAX 45-33-12-93-87.

YEAR BOOK OF DERMATOLOGIC SURGERY. see *MEDICAL SCIENCES — Dermatology And Venereology*

617   US   ISSN 0739-5949
RD559   CODEN: YBHSEQ
YEAR BOOK OF HAND SURGERY. 1985. a. $72.95 (residents $35) (effective 1996). Mosby - Year Book, Inc., Continuity Division, 200 N. LaSalle St., Chicago, IL 60601-1080. TEL 312-726-9733. FAX 312-726-6075. TELEX 206155. Ed. Dr. Peter C. Amadio. illus. (reprint service avail.)
 ●Also available online. Vendor(s): Ovid Technologies.
 —BLDSC (9412.860000).

YEAR BOOK OF NEUROLOGY & NEUROSURGERY. see *MEDICAL SCIENCES — Psychiatry And Neurology*

617.95   US   ISSN 1040-175X
RD118.A1   CODEN: YPRSA
YEAR BOOK OF PLASTIC, RECONSTRUCTIVE, AND AESTHETIC SURGERY. 1970. a. $72.95 (residents $35) (effective 1996). Mosby - Year Book, Inc., Continuity Division, 200 N. LaSalle, Chicago, IL 60601. TEL 312-726-9733. FAX 312-726-6075. TELEX 206155. Ed. Stephen Miller. illus. (reprint service avail.)
 ●Also available online. Vendor(s): Ovid Technologies.
 —BLDSC (9415.520000).
 Formerly: Year Book of Plastic and Reconstructive Surgery (ISSN 0084-3962)

YEAR BOOK OF PODIATRIC MEDICINE AND SURGERY. see *MEDICAL SCIENCES — Orthopedics And Traumatology*

617.005   US   ISSN 0090-3671
RD9
YEAR BOOK OF SURGERY. 1901. a. $67.95 (residents $35) (effective 1996). Mosby - Year Book, Inc., Continuity Division, 200 N. LaSalle, Chicago, IL 60601. TEL 312-726-9733. FAX 312-726-6075. TELEX 206155. Ed. Dr. Edward M. Copeland. illus. (reprint service avail.)
 ●Also available online. Vendor(s): Ovid Technologies.
 —BLDSC (9416.450000).
 Formerly: Year Book of General Surgery.

617   US   ISSN 1060-2968
RD120.7
YEAR BOOK OF TRANSPLANTATION. 1992. a. $80.95 (residents $35) (effective 1996). Mosby - Year Book, Inc. (Chicago) (Subsidiary of: Times Mirror Company), 200 N. LaSalle St., Chicago, IL 60601. TEL 312-726-9733. Ed. Dr. Hans W. Sollinger.
 ●Also available online. Vendor(s): Ovid Technologies.
 —BLDSC (9416.825000).

YEAR BOOK OF VASCULAR SURGERY. see *MEDICAL SCIENCES — Cardiovascular Diseases*

617   GW   ISSN 0930-9225
ZEITSCHRIFT FUER HERZ, THORAX- UND GEFAESSCHIRURGIE. (Summaries in English) 1987. 4/yr. DM.240($174) (effective 1996). Dr. Dietrich Steinkopff Verlag, Saalbaustr. 12, 64283 Darmstadt, Germany. TEL 06151-1745-0. FAX 06151-174510. (Subscr. to: Postfach 111442, 64229 Darmstadt, Germany) Ed.Bd. (also avail. in microform from UMI) Document type: academic/scholarly publication.
 —BLDSC (9464.530000); UMI. CCC.

617   GW   ISSN 0044-409X
CODEN: ZECHAU
ZENTRALBLATT FUER CHIRURGIE. 1874. m. DM.306 (foreign DM.322). (Vereinigung Mittelrheinischer Chirurgen) Johann Ambrosius Barth, Postfach 102869, 69018 Heidelberg, Germany. TEL 06221-489281. FAX 06221-489205. (Co-sponsors: Thueringische Gesellschaft fuer Chirurgie, Saechsische Chirurgenvereinigung) Ed.Bd. adv.: B&W page DM.2500; trim 210 x 275; adv. contact: Petra Schoene. bk.rev.; abstr.; charts; illus.; index. circ. 2,500. (also avail. in microform from BHP) Indexed: Chem.Abstr., Curr.Cont., Dent.Ind., Excerp.Med., Ind.Med., Nutr.Abstr., Rev.Med.& Vet.Mycol. Document type: academic/scholarly publication.
 —BLDSC (9504.700000); EMDOCS; Faxon; Genuine Article; SWETS; UMI.

MEDICAL SCIENCES — UROLOGY AND NEPHROLOGY

617 GW ISSN 0940-9599
ZENTRALBLATT FUER KINDERCHIRURGIE. 1992. q. DM.175 (foreign DM.180). Johann Ambrosius Barth, Postfach 102869, 69018 Heidelberg, Germany. TEL 06221-489281. FAX 06221-489205. Ed. S. Hofmann v. Kap-herr. circ. 800. **Document type:** academic/scholarly publication.
—BLDSC (9508.770000).

ZENTRALBLATT FUER NEUROCHIRURGIE. see *MEDICAL SCIENCES — Psychiatry And Neurology*

ZENTRALORGAN CHIRURGIE/SURGERY. see *MEDICAL SCIENCES — Abstracting, Bibliographies, Statistics*

ZHONGHUA SHENJING WAIKE ZAZHI/CHINESE JOURNAL OF NEUROSURGERY. see *MEDICAL SCIENCES — Psychiatry And Neurology*

313 CC
ZHONGHUA WAIKE ZAZHI/CHINESE JOURNAL OF SURGERY. (Text in Chinese) m. $3 per no. Guoji Shudian, Qikan Bu - China International Book Trading Corp., Chegongzhuang Xilu 21, P.O. Box 399, Beijing 100044, People's Republic of China. **Indexed:** ExtraMED, Ind.Med. **Document type:** academic/scholarly publication.
●Also available on CD-ROM.

617.95 CC ISSN 1000-7806
CODEN: ZZSZE9
ZHONGHUA ZHENGXING SHAOSHANG WAIKE ZAZHI/CHINESE JOURNAL OF PLASTIC SURGERY AND BURNS. (Text in Chinese; summaries in English) 1985. bi-m. Y12($40) Chinese Academy of Medical Sciences (CAMS), Plastic Surgery Hospital, Institute of Plastic Surgery - Zhongguo Yixue Kexueyuan Zhengxing Waike Yiyuan, Ba-Da-Chu Rd., Beijing 100041, People's Republic of China. TEL 86-1-8862233. FAX 86-1-8864137. (Dist. overseas by: China International Book Trading Corp., P.O. Box 399, Beijing 100044, P.R. China) (Co-sponsor: Chinese Medical Association of Plastic Surgeons) Ed. Xu Xiangmin. adv.; bk.rev. circ. 6,200. (back issues avail.) **Indexed:** ExtraMED. **Document type:** academic/scholarly publication.
●Also available on CD-ROM.
—BLDSC (3180.558000).

MEDICAL SCIENCES — Urology And Nephrology

616.6 US
A K F NEPHROLOGY LETTER. 1984. q. free. American Kidney Fund, 6110 Executive Blvd., Ste. 1010, Rockville, MD 20852-3903. TEL 800-638-8299. FAX 301-881-0898. Eds. Drs. Serafino Garella, William D. Mattern. circ. 10,000. (back issues avail.) **Document type:** newsletter.
Description: Each issue contains a review of a clinical topic emphasizing recent scientific advances, descriptions of new technology, notices of upcoming meetings, and legislative developments of interest to the nephrology community.

616.6 US
A K F NEWS. 1973. q. free. American Kidney Fund, 6110 Executive Blvd., Ste. 1010, Rockville, MD 20852-3903. TEL 301-881-3052. FAX 301-881-0898. Ed. Anna E. Monsef. illus. circ. 3,000. **Document type:** newsletter.
Formerly (until 1990): Torchbearer.
Description: Features articles on patients who have benefited from AKF programs. Provides the general public with information on AKF activities.

A N N A JOURNAL. (American Nephrology Nurses' Association) see *MEDICAL SCIENCES — Nurses And Nursing*

616.6 US ISSN 1046-1051
A U A TODAY; urology's clinical, research, and socioeconomic newspaper. 1987. m. $109 to individuals; institutions $129 (effective 1995). (American Urological Association) Williams & Wilkins, 428 E. Preston St., Baltimore, MD 21202. TEL 410-528-4000; 800-638-6423. FAX 410-528-4312. Ed. Dr. Abraham T.K. Cockett. circ. 11,221. **Document type:** newspaper.
—CCC.
Description: Issues news and developments in urology, including clinical information, case studies, and reports on economic policies and legislation.

616.6 BE ISSN 0001-7183
CODEN: AUBEAN
ACTA UROLOGICA BELGICA. (Text in English, French) 1927. 4/yr. 2800 Fr. (foreign 3800 Fr.). Association des Societes Scientifiques Medicales Belges - Vereiniging van de Belgische Medische Wetenschappelijke Genootschappen, Av. Circulaire 138A, B-1180 Brussels, Belgium. TEL 02-374-5158. Ed. Ch. Bouffioux. adv.; bk.rev.; abstr.; bibl.; charts; illus.; index. **Indexed:** Biol.Abstr., Chem.Abstr., Excerp.Med., Ind.Med.
—BLDSC (0670.415000); SWETS.

616.6 IT ISSN 0394-2511
CODEN: AUITE5
ACTA UROLOGICA ITALICA. 1986. bi-m. L.105000 (effective 1992). (Italian Society of Urology) Editoriale Poligrafica s.r.l., Acta Medica Edizioni e Congresi, Via Gian Giacomo Porro 5, 00197 Rome, Italy. TEL 6-4820432. FAX 6-48903487. adv.; bk.rev.
—BLDSC (0670.419000).

616.6 JA ISSN 0018-1994
CODEN: HIKYAJ
ACTA UROLOGICA JAPONICA/HINYOKIKA KIYO. (Text in Japanese; summaries in English) 1955. m. 10000 Yen($50) Kyoto University, Faculty of Medicine, Department of Urology - Kyoto Daigaku Igakubu Hinyokikagaku Kyoshitsu, 54 Shogoin Kawara-cho, Sakyo-ku, Kyoto 606, Japan. TEL 075-751-3326. FAX 075-761-3441. Ed. Osamu Yoshida. adv.; index. circ. 2,500. **Indexed:** Biol.Abstr., Excerp.Med., Ind.Med., INIS Atomind.
—BLDSC (0670.420000); SWETS.

616.6 FR ISSN 0073-3326
ACTUALITES NEPHROLOGIQUES. 1960. a. price varies. (Hopital Necker, Clinique Nephrologique) Flammarion Medecine Sciences, 4 rue Casimir Delavigne, 75006 Paris, France. (U.S. subscr. address: S.F.P.A., c/o Mr. Benech, 14 E. 60th St., New York, NY 10022) Ed. J.P. Grunfeld. cum.index: 1960-69. **Indexed:** Chem.Abstr., Excerp.Med.
—CCC.

616.6 US
CODEN: ANGYBQ
ADVANCES IN NEPHROLOGY. 1971. a. $80.95 (residents $40) (effective 1996). Mosby - Year Book, Inc. (Chicago) (Subsidiary of: Times Mirror Company), 200 N. LaSalle St., Chicago, IL 60601-1080. TEL 312-726-9733. FAX 312-726-6075. TELEX 206155. (Subscr. to: 11830 Westline Industrial Dr., St. Louis, MO 63146. TEL 800-325-4177) Ed. Dr. Jean-Pierre Grunfeld. (also avail. in microfilm from UMI; reprint service avail. from UMI) **Indexed:** Chem.Abstr., Biol.Abstr., Ind.Med.
—BLDSC (0709.470000); CASDDS; UMI; UnCover. CCC.
Formerly: Advances in Nephrology from the Necker Hospital (ISSN 0084-5957)
Description: Presents original topical review articles of importance in nephrology.

616.6 617 US ISSN 1073-4449
▼**ADVANCES IN RENAL REPLACEMENT THERAPY.** 1994. q. $123 (foreign $144) (effective 1996). (National Kidney Foundation) W.B. Saunders Co. (Subsidiary of: Harcourt Brace & Co.), Curtis Center, 3rd Fl., Indpendence Sq. W., Philadelphia, PA 19106-3399. TEL 215-238-7800. FAX 215-238-6445. (Subscr. to: Periodicals Fulfillment, W.B. /Saunders Co., 6277 Sea Harbor Dr., 4th Fl., Orlando, FL 32891-4800. TEL 800-654-2452. FAX 800-874-6418) Ed. Dr. Allen R. Nissenson; Pub. Joan W. Blumberg. adv.: B&W page $600, color $1475; 7 x 10. circ. 1,100. (reprint service avail.) **Document type:** academic/scholarly publication.
—BLDSC (0711.318000); UMI.
Description: Reports on advancements in the treatment and care of patients with kidney failure. Contains material also of interest to medical technicians, nurses, and social workers.

ADVANCES IN REPRODUCTIVE HEALTH CARE. see *MEDICAL SCIENCES — Obstetrics And Gynecology*

616.6 US ISSN 0894-4385
RC870
ADVANCES IN UROLOGY. 1988. a. $79.95 (residents $40) (effective 1996). Mosby - Year Book, Inc. (Chicago) (Subsidiary of: Times Mirror Company), 200 N. LaSalle St., Chicago, IL 60601-1080. TEL 312-726-9733. FAX 312-726-6075. TELEX 206155. (Subscr. to: 11830 Westline Industrial Dr., St. Louis, MO 63146) Ed. Dr. Edward J. McGuire.
—CCC.
Description: Presents a collection of original, fully-referenced review articles on selected clinical topics in the field of urology.

616.6 GW ISSN 0001-7868
CODEN: ZURNAV
AKTUELLE UROLOGIE. (Text in German; summaries in English) 1970. bi-m. DM.306. Georg Thieme Verlag, Ruedigerstr. 14, 70469 Stuttgart, Germany. TEL 0711-8931-0. FAX 0711-8931298. (Subscr. to: Postfach 104853, 70042 Stuttgart, Germany) Ed.Bd. adv.; bk.rev.; abstr.; bibl.; charts; illus.; stat.; index. circ. 2,600. (reprint service avail. from UMI) **Indexed:** Biol.Abstr., Chem.Abstr., Curr.Adv.Cancer Res., Curr.Cont., Excerp.Med. (until 1992), Ind.Med., INIS Atomind., Sci.Cit.Ind. **Document type:** academic/scholarly publication.
—BLDSC (0785.887000); CASDDS; Genuine Article; SWETS; UMI. CCC.
Incorporates (1907-1991): Zeitschrift fuer Urologie und Nephrologie (ISSN 0044-3611)

616.6 574.8 US ISSN 0272-6386
CODEN: AJKDDP
AMERICAN JOURNAL OF KIDNEY DISEASES. 1981 (Jul.). m. $347 (foreign $395) (effective 1996). (National Kidney Foundation) W.B. Saunders Co. (Subsidiary of: Harcourt Brace & Company), Curtis Center, 3rd Fl., Independence Sq. W., Philadelphia, PA 19106-3399. TEL 215-238-7800. FAX 215-238-6445. (Subscr. to: Periodicals Fulfillment, W.B. Saunders Co., 6277 Sea Harbor Dr., 4th Fl., Orlando, FL 32891-4800. TEL 800-654-2452. FAX 800-874-6418) Ed. Dr. Saulo Klahr; Pub. Joan W. Blumberg. adv.: B&W page $855, color page $1855; 7 x 10; adv. contact: Valerie Marvin. bk.rev.; abstr.; index. circ. 6,318. **Indexed:** Abstr.Inter.Med., Curr.Adv.Ecol.Sci., Curr.Cont., Excerp.Med., Ind.Med., Kidney, Rev.Med.& Vet.Mycol., Sci.Cit.Ind. **Document type:** academic/scholarly publication.
●Also available online.
—BLDSC (0826.860000); CASDDS; Faxon; Genuine Article; SWETS; UMI; UnCover. CCC.
Description: Covers a wide range of kidney-related topics in investigations, in-depth reviews, abstracts, news items, and editorials.
Refereed Serial

616.6 SZ ISSN 0250-8095
CODEN: AJNED9
AMERICAN JOURNAL OF NEPHROLOGY. (Text in English) 1981. 6/yr. 196.50 SFr.($151.20) to individuals; institutions 655 SFr.($504) (effective 1996). S. Karger AG, Allschwilerstr. 10, P.O. Box, CH-4009 Basel, Switzerland. TEL 061-3061111. FAX 061-3061234. E-mail: Karger@Karger.ch. Ed. S.G. Massry. adv.; illus.; index. circ. 2,900. (also avail. in microform from UMI) **Indexed:** Biol.Abstr., Chem.Abstr., Curr.Adv.Ecol.Sci., Curr.Cont., Dent.Ind., Excerp.Med., Ind.Med., Kidney, Protozool.Abstr. **Document type:** academic/scholarly publication.
—BLDSC (0828.370000); CASDDS; Faxon; Genuine Article; SWETS; UnCover. CCC.
Refereed Serial

616.6 US
AMERICAN KIDNEY FUND. ANNUAL REPORT. 1971. a. free. American Kidney Fund, 6110 Executive Blvd., Ste. 1010, Rockville, MD 20852-3903. TEL 301-881-3052. FAX 301-881-0898. circ. 1,000. **Document type:** corporate report.

MEDICAL SCIENCES — UROLOGY AND NEPHROLOGY

616.6 — US — ISSN 1046-6673 — CODEN: JASNEU
AMERICAN SOCIETY OF NEPHROLOGY. JOURNAL. Abbreviated title: J A S N. 1990. m. $130 to individuals; institutions $185 (effective 1995). Williams & Wilkins, 428 E. Preston St., Baltimore, MD 21202. TEL 410-528-4000; 800-638-6423. FAX 410-528-4312. Ed. Dr. Jared J. Grantham. circ. 6,267. **Indexed:** Excerp.Med. (1995-), Ind.Med., Kidney. **Document type:** academic/scholarly publication.
—BLDSC (4693.005000); CASDDS; Genuine Article; SWETS; UnCover. **CCC.**
Description: Contains original articles for nephrologists and other specialists who study kidney function and renal diseases.
Refereed Serial

616.6 — FR — ISSN 0003-4401 — CODEN: AUROAV
ANNALES D'UROLOGIE. (Text in French; summaries in English) 1967. 7/yr. 1270 F. to individuals (foreign 1790 F.); students 635 F. (foreign 895 F.). (Semaine des Hopitaux) Expansion Scientifique, 31 bd. de la Tour Maubourg, 75007 Paris, France. TEL 40-62-64-00. FAX 45-55-69-20. Ed. A. Steg. bk.rev. **Indexed:** Biol.Abstr., Curr.Cont., Excerp.Med., Helminthol.Abstr., Ind.Med., Ind.Sci.Rev., Sci.Cit.Ind.
—BLDSC (1003.500000); CASDDS; Faxon; Genuine Article; SWETS. **CCC.**

616.6 — JA
ANNUAL REVIEW JINZO/ANNUAL REVIEW. KIDNEY. (Text in Japanese) 1988. a. 8446 Yen. Chugai Igakusha, 62, Yaraicho, Shinjuku-ku, Tokyo 162, Japan.

616.6 — IT
ARCHIVIO ITALIANO DI UROLOGIA I ANDROLOGIA. (Text in English, Italian; summaries in English, French) 1924. 5/yr. L.83000($103) (effective 1994). (Universita di Milano, Istituto di Urologia) Masson S.p.A., Divisione Periodici, Via Statuto 2-4, 20121 Milan, Italy. TEL 02-6367-1. FAX 02-6367211. (Co-sponsors: Associazione per la Ricerca in Urologia; Societa Italiana di Ecografia Urologica e Nefrologica) Ed. E. Pisani. adv.: B&W page L.2200000, color page L.3200000; trim 140 x 210. bk.rev.; charts; illus. circ. 2,000. (back issues avail.) **Indexed:** Biol.Abstr., Excerp.Med., Ind.Med. **Document type:** proceedings.
Former titles: Archivio Italiano di Urologia e Nefrologia, Andrologia (ISSN 1120-8538); Archivio Italiano di Dermatologia, Sifilografia, Venereologia e Sessuologia; Archivio Italiano di Urologia e Nefrologia (ISSN 0004-0460)

616.6 — SP — ISSN 0004-0614
ARCHIVOS ESPANOLES DE UROLOGIA. (Text in Spanish; summaries in English) 1944. m. 12000 ptas. to individuals; institutions 16000 ptas.; Europe $145; elsewhere $165 (effective 1996). B O K, S.A. Ediciones, C. San Gregorio 8, 3o Pta. 4, 28004 Madrid, Spain. TEL 34-1-3196001. FAX 34-1-3197768. Ed. Dr. E. Perez-Castro Ellendt. adv. contact: Concha Martin. bk.rev.; bibl.; charts; illus.; stat.; tr.lit.; index. circ. 1,500. **Indexed:** Biol.Abstr., Chem.Abstr., Excerp.Med., Ind.Med.Esp., Ind.Med. **Document type:** academic/scholarly publication.
—BLDSC (1654.960000); SWETS. **CCC.**
Refereed Serial

616.6 — US — ISSN 1063-5777
ATLAS OF THE UROLOGIC CLINICS OF NORTH AMERICA. 1993. bi-a. $70 to subscribers of Urologic Clinics of North America (foreign $90); nonsubscribers $90 (foreign $110) (effective 1994). W.B. Saunders Co. (Subsidiary of: Harcourt Brace & Company), Curtis Center, 3rd Fl., Independence Sq. W., Philadelphia, PA 19106-3399. TEL 215-238-7800. FAX 215-238-6445. (Subscr. to: Periodicals Fulfillment, W.B. Saunders Co., 6277 Sea Harbor Dr., 4th Fl., Orlando, FL 32891-4800. TEL 800-654-2452. FAX 800-874-6418) Ed. Dr. Martin I. Resnik. illus. (also avail. in microform from UMI; back issues avail.) **Document type:** academic/scholarly publication.
—BLDSC (1767.087500); UMI.
Description: Contains line drawings and photographs, along with articles, on a specific urologic surgical technique or problem.

616.6 — US — ISSN 0271-1338
AUDIO-DIGEST UROLOGY. 1978. m. $84. Audio-Digest Foundation (Subsidiary of: California Medical Association), 1577 E. Chevy Chase Dr., Glendale, CA 91206. TEL 213-245-8505. FAX 818-240-7379. Ed. Claron L. Oakley. circ. controlled. (audio cassette)
Refereed Serial

616.6 — IT
AULA MEDICA; sezione uro-nefrologia. 1988. q. L.80000 (effective 1992). Editoriale Poligrafica s.r.l., Acta Medica Edizioni e Congressi, Via Gian Giacomo Porro 5, 00197 Rome, Italy. TEL 6-4820432. FAX 6-48903487. adv.

616.602 — SZ — ISSN 0250-3212 — CODEN: BEURDP
BEITRAEGE ZUR UROLOGIE. (Text in German) 1979. irreg. S. Karger AG, Allschwilerstr. 10, P.O. Box, CH-4009 Basel, Switzerland. TEL 061-3061111. FAX 061-3061234. E-mail: Karger@Karger.ch. Ed. H. Melchior. charts; illus. (back issues avail.) **Indexed:** Biol.Abstr., Curr.Cont. **Document type:** academic/scholarly publication.
—CCC.
Refereed Serial

616.6 — UK — ISSN 0007-1331 — CODEN: BJURAN
BRITISH JOURNAL OF UROLOGY. 1929. 12/yr. £172 in Europe; elsewhere £190.50($307) (effective 1996). (British Association of Urological Surgeons) Blackwell Science Ltd., Osney Mead, Oxford OX2 0EL, England. TEL 44-1865-206206. FAX 44-1865-721205. TELEX 83355-MEDBOK-G. Ed.Bd. adv.; bk.rev.; abstr.; bibl.; illus.; index, cum.index. circ. 6,000. (also avail. in microform from UMI; back issues avail.) **Indexed:** Biol.Abstr., Chem.Abstr., Curr.Adv.Cancer Res., Curr.Adv.Ecol.Sci., Curr.Cont., Excerp.Med., Helminthol.Abstr., Ind.Med., Ind.Sci.Rev., Ind.Vet., INIS Atomind., NRN, Nutr.Abstr., Rev.Med.& Vet.Mycol., Rev.Plant Path., Sci.Cit.Ind., Small Anim.Abstr. **Document type:** academic/scholarly publication.
●Also available online. Vendor(s): Ovid Technologies.
—BLDSC (2326.100000); ADONIS; CASDDS; Faxon; Genuine Article; SWETS; UnCover. **CCC.**
Refereed Serial

C A N N T JOURNAL/JOURNAL C A N N T. (Canadian Association of Nephrology Nurses and Technicians) see MEDICAL SCIENCES — Nurses And Nursing

616.6 — US
C N N T NEWSLETTER. q. $55. National Kidney Foundation, Council of Nephrology Nurses & Technicians, 30 E. 33rd St., New York, NY 10016. TEL 212-889-2210. FAX 212-689-9261. Ed. Maggie Holloway. circ. 400. **Document type:** newsletter.
Formerly: Renal Nursing and Technology Today.

616.6 360 — US — ISSN 0164-7032
C N S W NEWSLETTER. 1977. q. membership. National Kidney Foundation, Council of Nephrology Social Workers, 30 E. 33rd St., New York, NY 10016. TEL 212-889-2210. FAX 212-689-9261. Ed. Julie Loftin. bibl. circ. 600. (looseleaf format) **Document type:** newsletter.
Description: Covers professional, legislative and regional issues of concern to social workers who specialize in working with renal patients.

616.6 360 — US
C N S W PERSPECTIVES. 1977. a. membership. National Kidney Foundation, Council of Nephrology Social Workers, 30 E. 33rd St., New York, NY 10016. TEL 212-889-2210. circ. 1,000. **Document type:** academic/scholarly publication.
Description: Compilation of significant original and recently published articles relating to the practice of nephrology social work.

616.6 — CN — ISSN 1195-9479
▼**CANADIAN JOURNAL OF UROLOGY.** 1994. q. Rodar Publishing Inc., 8102 Trans Canada Hwy., St. Laurent, PQ H4S 1Z4, Canada. TEL 514-333-5350.

616.6 — GW — ISSN 0301-0430 — CODEN: CLNHBI
CLINICAL NEPHROLOGY. (Text in English) 1973. m. DM.340($172) Dustri-Verlag Dr. Karl Feistle, Bahnhofstr. 9, 82041 Deisenhofen, Germany. TEL 089-613861-0. FAX 089-613-5412. Ed. Dr. K.M. Koch. (reprint service avail. from SWZ) **Indexed:** Biol.Abstr., Chem.Abstr., Curr.Adv.Ecol.Sci., Curr.Cont., Excerp.Med., Ind.Med., Ind.Sci.Rev., INIS Atomind., Kidney, Nutr.Abstr., Rev.Plant Path., Sci.Cit.Ind. **Document type:** academic/scholarly publication.
—BLDSC (3286.307100); CASDDS; Genuine Article; SWETS; UnCover. **CCC.**

616.1 — US — ISSN 0177-8994
CLINICAL PRACTICE IN UROLOGY. 1982. irreg. price varies. Springer-Verlag, 175 Fifth Ave., New York, NY 10010. TEL 212-460-1500. FAX 212-473-6272. Ed. G.D. Chisholm. **Document type:** monographic series.

616.6 — US
CLINICAL STRATEGIES: A K F NEWSLETTER FOR NEPHROLOGY PROFESSIONALS. 1984. 2/yr. free. American Kidney Fund, 6110 Executive Blvd., Ste. 1010, Rockville, MD 20852-3903. TEL 800-638-8299. FAX 301-881-0898. index. circ. 12,000. (back issues avail.)
Formerly (until 1993): A K F Newsletter for Health Professionals.
Description: Offers current information to health professionals in the renal community. Reports on developments in the renal field as well as the AKF services and programs.

616.6 — US — ISSN 0899-837X
CONTEMPORARY DIALYSIS & NEPHROLOGY; the news and issues journal of the renal care field. 1980. m. $42. Contemporary Dialysis, Inc., 6300 Variel Ave., I, Woodland Hills, CA 91367-2513. TEL 818-704-5555. FAX 818-704-6500. TELEX 181545 CDLA. Ed. Gordon Lore. adv.: B&W page $2284. bk.rev.; charts; illus.; stat.; index. circ. 16,000. (back issues avail.) **Indexed:** Chem.Abstr. **Document type:** trade publication.
—BLDSC (3425.178410); UnCover. **CCC.**
Formerly: Contemporary Dialysis (ISSN 0273-6535)

616.6 — US — ISSN 0278-1700 — CODEN: CONHD7
CONTEMPORARY NEPHROLOGY. 1981. biennial, vol.5, 1989. price varies. Plenum Publishing Corp., 233 Spring St., New York, NY 10013-1578. TEL 212-620-8000. FAX 212-463-0742. TELEX 23-421139. Eds. Saulo Klahr, Shaul G. Massry. (back issues avail.) **Document type:** monographic series.
—BLDSC (3425.192500); CASDDS. **CCC.**
Refereed Serial

616.6 — US — ISSN 1042-2250
CONTEMPORARY UROLOGY. 1989. m. $89 (foreign $109). Medical Economics, Five Paragon Dr., Montvale, NJ 07645. TEL 201-358-7200. FAX 201-573-8979. Ed. Judith Orvos. adv.; charts; illus.; index. circ. 9,075. (also avail. in microform from UMI; reprint service avail.) **Document type:** trade publication.
—BLDSC (3425.314500); UMI.
Description: For office and hospital-based urologists. Includes news and features on solving clinical problems.

616.6 — SZ — ISSN 0302-5144 — CODEN: CNEPDD
CONTRIBUTIONS TO NEPHROLOGY. (Text in English) 1975. irreg. price varies. S. Karger AG, Allschwilerstr. 10, P.O. Box, CH-4009 Basel, Switzerland. TEL 061-3061111. FAX 061-3061234. E-mail: Karger@Karger.ch. Eds. G.M. Berlyne, S. Giovannetti. (reprint service avail. from ISI) **Indexed:** Biol.Abstr., Chem.Abstr., CINAHL, Curr.Cont., Ind.Med. **Document type:** academic/scholarly publication.
—BLDSC (3461.035000); CASDDS; Faxon; Genuine Article; SWETS. **CCC.**
Refereed Serial

MEDICAL SCIENCES — UROLOGY AND NEPHROLOGY

616.6 US ISSN 0148-4265
RC902.A1 CODEN: CUNED6
CURRENT NEPHROLOGY. 1977. a. $84.95 (residents $40) (effective 1996). Mosby - Year Book, Inc. (Chicago) (Subsidiary of: Times Mirror Company), 200 N. LaSalle St., Chicago, IL 60601-1080. TEL 312-726-9733. FAX 312-726-6075. TELEX 206155. (Subscr. to: 11830 Westline Industrial Dr., St. Louis, MO 63146. TEL 800-325-4177) Ed. Dr. Harvey C. Gonick. illus. **Indexed:** Biol.Abstr., Chem.Abstr.
—BLDSC (3500.620000); CASDDS; Faxon; UnCover. **CCC.**
Description: Surveys developments in the field through a synopsis of the medical literature from the past twelve months.

CURRENT OPINION IN NEPHROLOGY & HYPERTENSION. see *MEDICAL SCIENCES — Abstracting, Bibliographies, Statistics*

CURRENT OPINION IN UROLOGY. see *MEDICAL SCIENCES — Abstracting, Bibliographies, Statistics*

616.6 GW ISSN 0178-4625
DEUTSCHE GESELLSCHAFT FUER UROLOGIE. MITTEILUNGEN. 1985. q. DM.96. Demeter Verlag GmbH und Co. KG, Bussardstr. 5, 82166 Graefelfing, Germany. TEL 089-85463-0. FAX 089-8543347. circ. 4,400. **Document type:** academic/scholarly publication.
—BLDSC (3567.990000).

616.6 US
DEUTSCHE GESELLSCHAFT FUER UROLOGIE. VERHANDLUNGEN. 19th Session, 1962. irreg. price varies. Springer-Verlag, 175 Fifth Ave., New York, NY 10010. TEL 212-460-1500. FAX 212-473-6272. (Also: Berlin, Heidelberg, Tokyo and Vienna) (reprint service avail. from ISI) **Document type:** monographic series.
Formerly: Deutsche Gesellschaft fuer Urologie. Verhandlungsbericht (ISSN 0070-413X)

616.6 NE ISSN 0167-8205
CODEN: DNEPDO
DEVELOPMENTS IN NEPHROLOGY. (Text in English) 1981. irreg., vol.34, 1993. price varies. Kluwer Academic Publishers, Postbus 17, 3300 AA Dordrecht, Netherlands. TEL 31-78-392392. FAX 31-78-392254. TELEX 29245 KAPG NL. (Dist. by: Kluwer Academic Publishers Group, P.O. Box 322, 3300 AH Dordrecht, Netherlands. TEL 31-78-392392. FAX 31-78-546474; N. America dist. addr.: Box 358, Accord Sta., Hingham, MA 02018-0358. TEL 617-871-6600. FAX 617-871-6528) (back issues avail.) **Document type:** monographic series.
—BLDSC (3579.085360); CASDDS.
Refereed Serial

616.6 610.73 SW ISSN 1104-4616
DIALAESEN; tidningen foer Svenska dialysskoeterskor. 1986. q. SEK 100 membership. (Svenska Dialysskoeterkefoereningen - S D F) Dialaesen, c/o K. Johansson, Helsingoersg. 51, S-164 44 Kista, Sweden.

DIALOGUES IN PEDIATRIC UROLOGY. see *MEDICAL SCIENCES — Pediatrics*

616.6 GW ISSN 0932-190X
DIALYSE JOURNAL. (Text in German; summaries in English, German) 1983. q. DM.20($15) Pabst Science Publishers, Am Eichengrund 28, 49525 Lengerich, Germany. TEL 05484-308. FAX 05484-550. Ed. Petra Reinke. adv.: bk.rev. circ. 6,400. **Document type:** academic/scholarly publication.

616.6 GW ISSN 0724-0252
DER DIALYSEPATIENT; Zeitschrift fuer chronisch Nierenkranke. 1976. q. DM.36. (Dialysepatienten Deutschlands e.V.) Verlag Kirchheim und Co., Kaiserstr. 41, 55116 Mainz, Germany. TEL 06131-96070-0. FAX 06131-9607070. Ed. Alexander Schulz. adv. contact: Andreas Goerner. bk.rev. circ. 20,000. **Document type:** academic/scholarly publication.
Description: Covers nephrology in the areas of medicine, law, social services and welfare for doctors, patients and medical personnel.

616.61 US ISSN 0090-2934
CODEN: DITRD2
DIALYSIS & TRANSPLANTATION. 1972. m. $35. Creative Age Publications, 7628 Densmore Ave., Van Nuys, CA 91406-2088. TEL 818-782-7328. FAX 818-782-7450. Ed. Joe Herman. adv.: B&W page $2621, color page $3471. charts; illus. circ. 17,559. **Indexed:** Biol.Abstr., Curr.Adv.Ecol.Sci., Curr.Cont., Excerp.Med., Nutr.Abstr. **Document type:** trade publication.
—BLDSC (3579.785000); CASDDS; EMDOCS; Faxon; Genuine Article; SWETS; UnCover.
Description: For nephrology professionals; publishes clinical articles on new techniques and technologies, as well as coverage of pertinent legislative and economic issues.
Refereed Serial

616.6 GW ISSN 0940-5623
DIATRA JOURNAL. 1991. q. DM.35. Diatra Verlag GmbH, Balduinstr. 2, Postfach 1230, 6228 Eltville a.R. 1, Germany. TEL 6123-1007. FAX 6123-1220. Ed. S.K. Hammers-Kaplan. adv.: B&W page DM.1636; trim 260 x 170. bk.rev. circ. 19,000.
Description: Covers nephrology and transplantation in the areas of medicine, law and social welfare.

616.6 SZ ISSN 1019-083X
E D T N A - E R C A JOURNAL (ENGLISH EDITION). Dutch edition (ISSN 1019-0864); French edition (ISSN 1019-0848); German edition (ISSN 1019-0856); Italian edition (ISSN 1019-0880); Spanish edition (ISSN 1019-0872) 1983. q. European Dialysis and Transplant Nurses Association, European Renal Care Association, P.O. Box 3052, CH-6002 Luzern, Switzerland. **Indexed:** Excerp.Med. (1994-). **Document type:** academic/scholarly publication.
—BLDSC (3661.116725).
Formerly (until 1985): E D T N A Journal (English Edition) (ISSN 0265-3133)

616.6 NO
EUROPEAN COLLOQUIUM ON RENAL PHYSIOLOGY (PROCEEDINGS). (Supplement to: Uppsala Journal of Medical Sciences) 3rd, 1979. irreg. price varies. Scandinavian University Press, P.O. Box 2959 Toeyen, N-0608 Oslo, Norway. TEL 47-22-57-54-00. FAX 47-22-57-53-53. Ed. Hans R. Ulfendahl. **Document type:** proceedings.

616.6 SZ ISSN 0302-2838
CODEN: EUURAV
EUROPEAN UROLOGY. (Text in English) 8/yr. (in 2 vols.) 550.80 SFr.($423.60) to individuals; institutions 918 SFr.($706) (effective 1996). (European Association of Urology) S. Karger AG, Allschwilerstr. 10, P.O. Box, CH-4009 Basel, Switzerland. TEL 061-3061111. FAX 061-3061234. E-mail: Karger@Karger.ch. Ed. C.C. Schulman. abstr.; index. circ. 3,200. (also avail. in microform) **Indexed:** Biol.Abstr., Chem.Abstr., Curr.Adv.Cell & Devel.Biol., Curr.Adv.Ecol.Sci., Curr.Cont., Excerp.Med., Helminthol.Abstr., Ind.Med., Ind.Sci.Rev., NRN, Sci.Cit.Ind. **Document type:** academic/scholarly publication.
—BLDSC (3830.370500); CASDDS; Faxon; Genuine Article; SWETS; UnCover. **CCC.**
Refereed Serial

616.6 NE ISSN 0968-7645
EUROPEAN UROLOGY UPDATE SERIES. 1992. bi-m. European Board of Urology, Education Committee - Office of Education, P.O. Box 25285, 3001 HG Rotterdam, Netherlands. TEL 31-10-4366665. FAX 31-10-4366669. Ed. H.N. Whitfield. **Document type:** academic/scholarly publication.
—BLDSC (3830.370550).

616.6 SZ ISSN 1018-7782
CODEN: EXNEEG
EXPERIMENTAL NEPHROLOGY. (Text in English) 1993. 6/yr. 229.25 SFr.($176.40) to individuals; institutions 655 SFr.($504) (effective 1996). S. Karger AG, Allschwilerstr. 10, P.O. Box, CH-4009 Basel, Switzerland. TEL 061-3061111. FAX 061-3061235. E-mail: Karger@Karger.ch. Ed. L.G. Fine. (also avail. in microform from UMI) **Indexed:** Excerp.Med. (1994-), Ind.Med. (1994-). **Document type:** academic/scholarly publication.
—BLDSC (3839.830000); CASDDS; Genuine Article. **CCC.**
Description: Devoted to the biology of the kidney, including developmental, cellular and molecular aspects, and to the scientific basis of renal diseases.
Refereed Serial

616.6 GW ISSN 0344-5038
EXTRACTA UROLOGICA. 1978. bi-m. DM.99. Selecta Verlagsgesellschaft mbH, Postfach 4240, 65032 Wiesbaden, Germany. TEL 0611-17050. FAX 0611-1705379. Ed. Dr. Juergen Boedeker. circ. 2,400. (back issues avail.) **Document type:** academic/scholarly publication.

616.6 US
FAMILY FOCUS. q. free. National Kidney Foundation, 30 E. 33rd St., New York, NY 10016. TEL 212-889-2210. circ. 100,000. **Document type:** newsletter.
Description: Information for dialysis and transplant patients and their families.

616.6 US
FOR PATIENTS ONLY. 1988. bi-m. $17. Contemporary Dialysis, Inc., 6300 Variel Ave., I, Woodland, CA 91367-2513. TEL 818-704-6500. FAX 818-704-6500. adv.: B&W page $1800, color page $2625; trim 8 1/4 x 11 1/8. circ. 16,000. **Document type:** trade publication.
Description: Brings professional understanding to patients living with chronic kidney disease. Covers patient-caregiver relationships, psychological issues, homecare and rehabilitation.

616.6 360 US
FOR THOSE WHO GIVE AND GRIEVE; a quarterly newsletter for donor families. 1991. q. free. National Kidney Foundation, 30 E. 33rd St., New York, NY 10016. TEL 212-889-2210. FAX 212-689-9261. Ed. Maggie Coolican. circ. 20,000. (looseleaf format) **Document type:** newsletter.
Description: Discusses grief among families of kidney donors, advances in kidney transplant techniques and support organizations to assist families.

616.6 NE ISSN 0924-8455
CODEN: GNURE8
GERIATRIC NEPHROLOGY AND UROLOGY. (Text in English) 1991. 3/yr. fl.262 to institutions; $168 to institutions in U.S. (effective 1996). Kluwer Academic Publishers, Postbus 17, 3300 AA Dordrecht, Netherlands. TEL 31-78-392392. FAX 31-78-392254. TELEX 29245 KAPG NL. E-mail: SERVICES@WKAP.NL. (Dist. by: Kluwer Academic Publishers, P.O. Box 322, 3300 AH Dordrecht, Netherlands. TEL 31-78-392392. FAX 31-78-546474; N. America dist. addr.: Box 358, Accord Sta., Hingham, MA 02018-0358. TEL 617-871-6600. FAX 617-871-6528) Ed. Dimitros G. Oreopoulos. (also avail. in microform from UMI; back issues avail.; reprint service avail. from SWZ) **Document type:** academic/scholarly publication.
—BLDSC (4161.697000); UMI; UnCover. **CCC.**
Description: Publishes articles concerning the diagnosis and therapy of nephrological and urological disorders in elderly patients.
Refereed Serial

616.6 IT ISSN 0394-9362
GIORNALE DI TECNICHE NEFROLOGICHE E DIALITICHE. 1989. q. L.90000($90) (effective 1994). Wichtig Editore s.r.l., Via Friuli, 72-74, 20135 Milan, Italy. TEL 02-5452306. FAX 02-5451843.

616.6 IT ISSN 0393-5590
GIORNALE ITALIANO DI NEFROLOGIA. (Text in Italian; summaries in English) 1984? bi-m. L.140000($140) (effective 1994). Wichtig Editore s.r.l., Via Friuli, 72-74, 20135 Milan, Italy. TEL 02-5452306. FAX 02-5451843.
—BLDSC (4178.233000).

616.6 GW ISSN 0935-8234
HAEUSLICHE PFLEGE; Organisieren - Betreuen - Kompetent beraten. 1992. m. DM.92.40 (foreign DM.102). Vincentz Verlag, Schiffgraben 43, 30175 Hannover, Germany. TEL 0511-9909847. FAX 0511-9909871. (Subscr. to: Postfach 6247, 30062 Hannover, Germany) Ed. Stefan Neumann. circ. 8,565. **Document type:** academic/scholarly publication.

616.6 360 AT
HARICOT; newsletter for the renal patients of Australia. 1983. q. free. P.O. Box 3, Diamond Creek, Vic. 3089, Australia. Eds. J. Coleman, S. Evans. bk.rev. circ. 1,500. (back issues avail.)

HOKKAIDO TOSEKI RYOHO GAKKAI PUROGURAMU ENDAI SHOROKU/HOKKAIDO SOCIETY FOR DIALYSIS THERAPY. PROGRAM AND ABSTRACTS. see *MEDICAL SCIENCES — Abstracting, Bibliographies, Statistics*

MEDICAL SCIENCES — UROLOGY AND NEPHROLOGY

616.6 JA
HOKKAIDO TOSEKI RYOHO GAKKAI SHINPOJUMU/HOKKAIDO SOCIETY FOR DIALYSIS THERAPY. PROCEEDINGS OF SYMPOSIUM. (Text in Japanese) 1988. a. Hokkaido Toseki Ryoho Gakkai, 3, Nishi 7-chome, Kita 1-jo, Chuo-ku, Sapporo-shi, Hokkaido 090, Japan. **Document type:** proceedings.

616.6 US
I C A UPDATE. 4/yr. $35 membership. Interstitial Cystitus Association, Box 1553, Madison Square Sta., New York, NY 10159. TEL 212-979-6057. Ed. Debra Slade. **Document type:** newsletter.
Description: Creates public awareness and provides information about IC research and ICA activities to patients and the medical community.

616.65 UK ISSN 0105-6263
CODEN: IJANDP
INTERNATIONAL JOURNAL OF ANDROLOGY. (Text in English) bi-m. £168($270) (effective 1996). (European Academy of Andrology) Blackwell Science Ltd., Osney Mead, Oxford OX2 OEL, England. TEL 01865-206206. FAX 01865-206219. TELEX 83355 MEDBOK G. Ed. R. Sharpe. adv.; bk.rev.; abstr.; bibl.; illus.; index. circ. 600. (also avail. in microform from UMI; back issues avail.) **Indexed:** Anim.Breed.Abstr., Biol.Abstr., Chem.Abstr., Curr.Adv.Ecol.Sci., Dent.Ind., Excerp.Med., Ind.Med., Ind.Vet., Protozool.Abstr., Sci.Cit.Ind., Small Anim.Abstr., Vet.Bull. **Document type:** academic/scholarly publication.
—BLDSC (4542.080000); CASDDS; Faxon; Genuine Article; SWETS; UMI; UnCover. **CCC.**
Refereed Serial

616.65 UK ISSN 0106-1607
CODEN: IJSPDJ
INTERNATIONAL JOURNAL OF ANDROLOGY. SUPPLEMENT. 1978. irreg. price varies. Blackwell Science Ltd., Osney Mead, Oxford OX2 OEL, England. TEL 01865-240201. FAX 01865-721205. TELEX 83355 MEDBOK G. illus. **Indexed:** Biol.Abstr., Chem.Abstr. **Document type:** academic/scholarly publication.
—CASDDS.

616.6 UK
INTERNATIONAL JOURNAL OF IMPOTENCE RESEARCH. 1989. 4/yr. £40($73) to individuals; institutions £68($123). Smith-Gordon and Co. Ltd., 16 Gunter Grove, No. 1, London SW10 OUJ, England. TEL 0171-351-7042. FAX 0171-351-1250. (Subscr. to: Royal Society of Medicine Press Ltd., 1 Wimpole St., London W1M 8AE, England. TEL 0171-290-2900. FAX 0171-290-2929) **Indexed:** Ind.Med. (1993-). **Document type:** academic/scholarly publication.

616.6 JA ISSN 0919-8172
▼**INTERNATIONAL JOURNAL OF UROLOGY.** (Text in English) 1994. bi-m. $120 to individuals; institutions $200 (effective 1996). (Japanese Urological Association) Churchill Livingstone Japan, Churchill Bldg., 2-8-16 Yutenji, Meguro-ku, Tokyo 153, Japan. TEL 81-3-5721-0442. FAX 81-3-5721-0415. E-mail: kyj04632@niftyserv.or.jp. Ed. Osamu Yoshida. circ. 4,000 (paid).
—BLDSC (4542.697100); ADONIS.

616.6 GR
INTERNATIONAL SATELLITE SYMPOSIUM ON ACUTE RENAL FAILURE. PROCEEDINGS. 1960. biennial. $100 effective 1995-1996. International Society of Nephrology, Commission on Acute Renal Failure, Hippokration General Hospital, 50 Papanastasiou St., 543 42 Thessaloniki, Greece. TEL 30-31-835955. FAX 30-31-861111. (Co-sponsors: Hellenic Society of Nephrology; Ministry of Macedonia - Thrace; Aristotelian University) Ed. Menelaos Papadimitriou. **Indexed:** Chem.Abstr. **Document type:** academic/scholarly publication, proceedings.
Formerly: International Congress of Nephrology. Abstracts of Reports and Communications (ISSN 0074-3771)
Refereed Serial

616.6 FR ISSN 0074-8579
INTERNATIONAL SOCIETY OF UROLOGY. REPORTS OF CONGRESS. (Reports published in host country) irreg., 17th, 1975, Madrid. International Society of Urology, c/o Prof. Rene Kuess, 63 Ave. Niel, 75017 Paris, France.

INTERNATIONAL UROGYNECOLOGY JOURNAL. see *MEDICAL SCIENCES — Obstetrics And Gynecology*

616.6 HU ISSN 0301-1623
CODEN: IURNAE
INTERNATIONAL UROLOGY AND NEPHROLOGY. (Text in English) 1969. bi-m. DM.640 (effective 1996). (Magyar Tudomanyos Akademia) Akademiai Kiado, Publishing House of the Hungarian Academy of Sciences, P.O. Box 245, H-1519 Budapest, Hungary. TEL 181-2134. FAX 166-6466. TELEX 22-6228 AKNYO H. (Co-publisher and distributor: V S P, P.O. Box 346, 3700 AH Zeist, Netherlands. TEL 31-30-6925790. FAX 31-30-6932081) Eds. D. Frang, J. Kondas. adv.; bk.rev. **Indexed:** Biol.Abstr., Chem.Abstr., Curr.Cont., Excerp.Med., Ind.Med., INIS Atomind. **Document type:** academic/scholarly publication.
—BLDSC (4551.568000); CASDDS; Faxon; SWETS; UnCover. **CCC.**
Formerly: Urology and Nephrology (ISSN 0042-1162)
Description: Publishes original papers, preliminary reports and reviews which contribute to progress in urological surgery, nephrology and andrology.
Refereed Serial

616.6 GW ISSN 0921-9862
RC902.A1
INTERNATIONAL YEARBOOK OF NEPHROLOGY. (Text in English) 1989. a., latest 1993. $219 (effective 1994). Springer-Verlag, Heidelberger Platz 3, 14197 Berlin, Germany. TEL 030-8207-1. FAX 030-8214091. (Subscr. in N. America to: Springer-Verlag New York, Inc., 44 Hartz Way, Secaucus, NJ 07096-2491. TEL 201-348-4033) (back issues avail.) **Document type:** academic/scholarly publication.
—BLDSC (4552.334000); Genuine Article.

616.6 IT ISSN 1121-8428
J N: JOURNAL OF NEPHROLOGY. 1988. q. L.160000($160) (effective 1994). Wichtig Editore s.r.l., Via Friuli 72-74, 20135 Milan, Italy. TEL 02-5452306. FAX 02-5451843. **Indexed:** Excerp.Med. (1994-), Kidney.
—BLDSC (5021.399400). **CCC.**
Formerly (until 1992): Journal of Nephrology (ISSN 1120-3625)

616.6 GW ISSN 0932-1624
JAHRBUCH DER UROLOGIE (YEAR). 1986. a. Med. Hochschule Hannover, Klinik und Poliklinik fuer Urologie, Konstant-Gutschow-Str. 8, 30625 Hannover, Germany. Ed. M. Truss. **Document type:** academic/scholarly publication.
—BLDSC (4632.650120).

616.6 JA ISSN 0914-6180
JAPANESE JOURNAL OF UROLOGICAL SURGERY. 1988. m. Igaku Tosho Shuppan Co. Ltd., 2-28-1 Tohgane Bldg., Hongo Bunkyo-ku, Tokyo 113, Japan.

616.6 JA ISSN 0021-5287
CODEN: NGKZA6
THE JAPANESE JOURNAL OF UROLOGY/NIHON HINYOKIKA GAKKAI ZASSHI. (Text in Japanese; summaries in English) 1911. m. 20000 Yen. Japanese Urological Association, Faculty of Medicine - Nihon Hinyokika Gakkai, Taisei Bldg., 3-14-10 Hongo, Bunkyo-ku, Tokyo 113, Japan. FAX 03-3814-4117. Ed. Osamu Yoshida. adv. circ. 5,500. (also avail. in microform from UMI; reprint service avail. from UMI) **Indexed:** C.I.S. Abstr., Curr.Cont., Excerp.Med., Ind.Med.
—BLDSC (4659.050000); CASDDS; EMDOCS; Genuine Article; UMI.

616.6 GW ISSN 0941-4789
JATROS UROLOGIE. 1986. 12/yr. DM.90. P M I Verlagsgruppe GmbH, August-Schanz-Str. 21, 60433 Frankfurt a.M., Germany. TEL 069-5480000. FAX 069-54800077. Ed. Peter Hoffmann. circ. 2,500. (back issues avail.) **Document type:** academic/scholarly publication.
Description: A seminar paper journal with summaries of original articles, interviews and congress reports.

JIN TO TOSEKI/KIDNEY AND DIALYSIS. see *MEDICAL SCIENCES*

616.6 FR ISSN 0248-0018
CODEN: JOURDD
JOURNAL D'UROLOGIE. 1912. bi-m. 938 F. (foreign 1174 F.) (effective 1996). (Association Francaise d'Urologie) Masson - Periodiques, Villa Laromiguiere, 75005 Paris, France. TEL 1-40-46-62-00. FAX 1-40-46-62-01. Ed. B. Debre. adv.; bk.rev.; abstr.; illus.; index. circ. 2,100. (also avail. in microform from UMI; reprint service avail. from ISI) **Indexed:** Chem.Abstr., Curr.Adv.Cancer Res., Excerp.Med., Helminthol.Abstr., Ind.Med., Ind.Sci.Rev., Nutr.Abstr., Sci.Cit.Ind. **Document type:** academic/scholarly publication.
—BLDSC (5071.799950); Faxon; Genuine Article; SWETS; UMI. **CCC.**
Formerly: Journal d'Urologie et de Nephrologie (ISSN 0021-8200)
Description: Publishes original articles, topical outlines, clinical and therapeutic data and meeting reports.

616.6 GW
JOURNAL FUER DAS NEPHROLOGISCHE TEAM. (Text in German; summaries in English and German) 1983. q. DM.20($15) Pabst Science Publishers, Am Eichengrund 28, 49525 Lengerich, Germany. TEL 05484-308. FAX 05484-550. Ed. Wolfgang Pabst. adv.; bk.rev. circ. 11,600. (back issues avail.) **Document type:** academic/scholarly publication.
Formerly: Nierenpatient (ISSN 0176-5183)
Description: Original articles and case reports on nephrology and dialysis.

JOURNAL OF ANDROLOGY. see *MEDICAL SCIENCES*

616.1 US ISSN 0733-2459
CODEN: JCAPES
JOURNAL OF CLINICAL APHERESIS. 1982. q. $312 (foreign $374) (effective 1996). (American Society for Apheresis) John Wiley & Sons, Inc., Journals, 605 Third Ave., New York, NY 10158. TEL 212-850-6645. FAX 212-850-6021. TELEX 12-7063. E-mail: SUBINFO@JWILEY.COM. (Subscr. outside the Americas to: John Wiley & Sons Ltd., Baffins Ln., Chichester, W. Sussex PO19 1UD, England. TEL 44-1243-779777. FAX 44-1243-776128) Ed.Bd. (also avail. in microform from UMI; back issues avail.) **Indexed:** Excerp.Med., Ind.Med. **Document type:** academic/scholarly publication.
—BLDSC (4958.381500); Faxon; Genuine Article; SWETS; UnCover. **CCC.**
Description: Examines research articles on all topics relating to apheresis: plasmapheresis, lymphoplasmapheresis, and ctyapheresis, including experimental and technical developments.
Refereed Serial

616.6 US ISSN 0892-7790
CODEN: JENDE3
JOURNAL OF ENDOUROLOGY. q. $160 (foreign $195). (Endourological Society) Mary Ann Liebert, Inc. Publishers, 2 Madison Ave., Larchmont, NY 10538. TEL 914-834-3100. FAX 914-83402688. E-mail: Liebert@pipeline.com. Eds. Drs. Ralph V. Clayman, Arthur D. Smith. **Indexed:** Excerp.Med. (1993-), Ind.Med. (1993-). **Document type:** academic/scholarly publication.
—BLDSC (4978.210000); Genuine Article; SWETS; UnCover.
Description: Covers topics including percutaneous renal and ureteral procedures, ureteroscopy for diagnostic and therapeutic indications, endoscopic use of lasers, and extracorporeal lithotripsy of renal and ureteral stones.
Refereed Serial

JOURNAL OF RENAL NUTRITION. see *NUTRITION AND DIETETICS*

616.6 US ISSN 1054-8734
CODEN: JUPAEE
JOURNAL OF UROGENITAL PATHOLOGY. 1991. q. $125 to individuals; institutions $155 (effective 1993). Field & Wood, Medical Periodicals, Inc., Box 975, Blue Bell, PA 19422. TEL 610-828-4010. FAX 215-482-0226. Ed. Dr. Ivan Damjanov. bk.rev. **Indexed:** Excerp.Med. (1993-). **Document type:** academic/scholarly publication.
—BLDSC (5071.700000).
Refereed Serial

MEDICAL SCIENCES — UROLOGY AND NEPHROLOGY

616.6 US ISSN 1067-1919
JOURNAL OF UROLOGIC PATHOLOGY. 1993. q. $285 (foreign $310) (effective 1996). (International Society of Urological Pathology) Humana Press Inc., 999 Riverview Dr., Ste. 208, Totowa, NJ 07512. TEL 201-256-1699. FAX 201-256-8341. (Dist. in Japan by: Maruzen Co. Ltd., Journals Div., P.O. Box 5050, Tokyo 100-31, Japan. TEL 03-32758591. FAX 03-32781937) Ed. Dr. David G. Bostwick. bk.rev.; illus.; index. **Indexed:** Curr.Cont., Excerp.Med., Sci.Cit.Ind. **Document type:** academic/scholarly publication.
—BLDSC (5071.730000). **CCC.**
 Description: Provides the latest information on pathology of the genitourinary tract. The primary emphasis is on diseases that clinically fall under the domain of urologists, urologic oncologists, and andrologists.
 Refereed Serial

616.6 US ISSN 0022-5347
RC870 CODEN: JOURAA
JOURNAL OF UROLOGY. 1917. m. $229 to individuals; institutions $255 (effective 1995). (American Urological Association) Williams & Wilkins, 428 E. Preston St., Baltimore, MD 21202. TEL 410-528-4000; 800-638-6423. FAX 410-528-4312. TELEX 87669. Ed. Dr. Jay T. Gillenwater. adv.; abstr.; bibl.; illus.; index. circ. 19,706. (also avail. in microform from WWS) **Indexed:** AIM, Biol.Abstr., Biotech.Abstr., C.I.S. Abstr., Chem.Abstr., Curr.Adv.Cancer Res., Curr.Adv.Cell & Devel.Biol., Curr.Adv.Ecol.Sci., Curr.Adv.Genetics & Molec.Biol., Curr.Cont., Excerp.Med., Helminthol.Abstr., Ind.Med., Ind.Sci.Rev., INIS Atomind., Int.Nurs.Ind., Kidney, Med.& Surg.Dermat., Nutr.Abstr., Rev.Med.& Vet.Mycol., Rev.Plant Path. **Document type:** academic/scholarly publication.
—BLDSC (5071.900000); ADONIS; CASDDS; EMDOCS; Faxon; Genuine Article; SWETS; UnCover. **CCC.**
 Incorporates (in Jan. 1982): Investigation Urology (ISSN 0021-0005); Urological Survey (ISSN 0042-1146).
 Description: Publishes clinical papers, commentary, research and new techniques for the urologist.
 Refereed Serial

616.6 US ISSN 0023-1304
CODEN: KIDNA
THE KIDNEY (NEW YORK, 1968). 1968. bi-m. membership. National Kidney Foundation, 30 East 33rd St., New York, NY 10016. TEL 212-889-2210. Ed. Dr. H. David Humes. charts; illus. circ. 8,000. (looseleaf format) **Indexed:** Biol.Abstr., Excerp.Med. **Document type:** newsletter.
—BLDSC (5094.200000); EMDOCS.
 Refereed Serial

KIDNEY (NEW YORK, 1992); a current survey of world literature. see *MEDICAL SCIENCES — Abstracting, Bibliographies, Statistics*

616.6 US
KIDNEY (YEAR). vol.8, 1991. q. membership. National Kidney Foundation, 30 E. 33rd St., New York, NY 10016. TEL 212-889-2210. FAX 212-689-9261.
 Description: News for patients and members about foundation activities and devlopments affecting kidney disease and treatment, including transplant issues.

616.6 US ISSN 0270-062X
CODEN: KIDID6
KIDNEY DISEASES. 1979. irreg., vol.10, 1992. price varies. Marcel Dekker, Inc., 270 Madison Ave., New York, NY 10016. TEL 212-696-9000. FAX 212-685-4540. TELEX 421419. **Indexed:** Chem.Abstr.
—BLDSC (5094.230000); CASDDS.
 Refereed Serial

616.6 US ISSN 0085-2538
RC902.A1 CODEN: KDYIA5
KIDNEY INTERNATIONAL. (Supplement avail. (ISSN 0098-6577)) 1972. 12/yr. (in 2 vols., 6 nos./vol.). $440 to individuals; institutions $725 (effective 1996). (International Society of Nephrology) Blackwell Science Inc., 238 Main St., Cambridge, MA 02142-1413. TEL 617-876-7022. FAX 617-492-5263. Ed. Dr. Thomas E. Andreoli. adv. circ. 9,000. (also avail. in microform from UMI; reprint service avail. from ISI) **Indexed:** Biol.Abstr., Chem.Abstr., Curr.Adv.Ecol.Sci., Curr.Cont., Dairy Sci.Abstr., Diab.Cont., Excerp.Med., Ind.Med., Ind.Sci.Rev., Kidney, Nutr.Abstr., Rev.Med.& Vet.Mycol. **Document type:** academic/scholarly publication.
—BLDSC (5094.300000); ADONIS; CASDDS; EMDOCS; Faxon; Genuine Article; SWETS; UMI; UnCover. **CCC.**
 Description: Provides current information on renal physiology, biochemistry, pathology, immunology and morphology.

616.6 US ISSN 0098-6577
CODEN: KISUDF
KIDNEY INTERNATIONAL. SUPPLEMENT. 1974. irreg., vol.40, 1991. price varies (free to subscribers of Kidney International). (International Society of Nephrology) Blackwell Scientific Publications, Inc., 3 Cambridge Center, Ste. 208, Cambridge, MA 02142-1413. TEL 617-876-7000. (reprint service avail. from ISI) **Indexed:** Biol.Abstr., Chem.Abstr., Excerp.Med. (1993-), Ind.Med., Nutr.Abstr.
—BLDSC (5094.301000); ADONIS; CASDDS; EMDOCS; SWETS; UnCover. **CCC.**

616.6 UK
KIDNEY RESEARCH NEWS. 1974. s-a. free. National Kidney Research Fund, 184b Station Rd., Harrow, London HA1 2RH, England. Ed. John F. Ringrose. circ. 9,000.
 Formerly: Kidney Research Fund Newsletter.

616.6 GW ISSN 0174-2752
CODEN: KEURDM
KLINISCHE UND EXPERIMENTELLE UROLOGIE. (Each edition has distinctive title) 1980. irreg., vol.24, 1992. DM.59.80. W. Zuckschwerdt Verlag GmbH, Industriestr. 17, 82110 Germering, Germany. TEL 089-894349-0. FAX 089-89434950. Eds. A. Hofstetter, M. Kriegmair. circ. 1,500. (back issues avail.) **Document type:** academic/scholarly publication.
—BLDSC (5099.490000); CASDDS.

616.6 JA ISSN 0919-5491
KONYOUSANKESSHO TO TSUFU/HYPERURICEMIA AND GOUT. (Text in English) 1993. 2/yr. 1600 Yen per no. Medikaru Rebyusha - Medical Review Co., Ltd., 7-3, Hiranomachi 1-chome, Chuo-ku, Osaka 541, Japan.

616.6 HU ISSN 0864-8921
MAGYAR UROLOGIA. 1974. 4/yr. Society of Hungarian Urological Surgeons, P.O. Box 29, Nagyerdei krt. 98, 4012 Debrecen, Hungary. **Indexed:** Excerp.Med. **Document type:** academic/scholarly publication.
—BLDSC (5351.015000).
 Formerly (until 1989): Urologiai es Nephrologiai Szemle (ISSN 0133-3127)

MEN'S CONFIDENTIAL NEWSLETTER; health, sex and fitness news for men. see *MEN'S HEALTH*

616.6 IT ISSN 0393-2249
CODEN: MINEAT
MINERVA UROLOGICA E NEFROLOGICA; rivista trimestrale di fisiopatologia e clinica delle malattie renali e di urologia medica e chirurgica. (Text in Italian; summaries in English, Italian) 1949. q. $90 to individuals; institutions $140 (effective 1995). Edizioni Minerva Medica, Corso Bramante 83-85, 10126 Turin, Italy. TEL 39-11-678282. FAX 39-11-3121736. Eds. A. Tizzani, P. Stratta; Pub. Alberto Oliaro. adv.: B&W page $1100, color page $1900; trim 190 x 270; adv. contact: F. Filippo. bk.rev.; bibl.; charts; illus.; index; circ. 3,000 (paid). (also avail. in microform from UMI) **Indexed:** Biol.Abstr., Chem.Abstr., Excerp.Med., Ind.Med.
—BLDSC (5794.720000); CASDDS; Faxon; UMI.
 Formed by the merger of (1949-1983): Minerva Urologica (ISSN 0026-4989); (1954-1983): Minerva Nefrologica (ISSN 0026-4873)
 Description: Covers pathophysiology and clinical medicine of renal disease and medical and surgical urology.
 Refereed Serial

616.6 JA ISSN 0910-2329
NAGANOKEN JINKO TOSEKI KENKYUKAISHI/NAGANO PREFECTURAL SOCIETY OF DIALYSIS THERAPY. JOURNAL. (Text in English, Japanese; summaries in English) 1978. a. Naganoken Jinko Toseki Kenkyukai, Koseiren Saku Sogo Byoin, 197, Usuda, Usudamachi, Minamisaku-gun, Nakano-shi, Nagano-ken 384-03, Japan.

616.6 US ISSN 0077-5096
NATIONAL KIDNEY FOUNDATION. ANNUAL REPORT. 1957. a. free. National Kidney Foundation, 30 E. 33rd St., New York, NY 10016. TEL 212-889-2210.

616.6 US
NATIONAL KIDNEY FOUNDATION. PROGRAMS AND ABSTRACTS BOOK. a. free to qualified personnel. National Kidney Foundation, 30 E. 33rd St., New York, NY 10016. TEL 212-889-2210. **Document type:** proceedings.
 Description: Contains the agenda of all sessions of the NKF annual meeting, including scientific council programs, and summaries of papers submitted for presentation.

616.6 US
NATIONAL KIDNEY FOUNDATION. RESEARCH PROGRAM. a. free. National Kidney Foundation, 30 E. 33rd St., New York, NY 10016. TEL 212-889-2210. **Document type:** directory.
 Description: Lists information on research projects supported by the NKF, with biographies of investigators and summaries of research reports.

616.6 NE ISSN 0929-0184
CODEN: NTURE
NEDERLANDS TIJDSCHRIFT VOOR UROLOGIE. 1993. q. (Nederlandse Vereniging voor Urologie - Dutch Association of Urology) Reed HealthCare (Subsidiary of: Reed Elsevier plc), P.O. Box 1126, 1000 BC Amsterdam, Netherlands. TEL 31-20-5153350. Ed. M.T.W.T. Lock. adv. contact: G.J.M. van den Akker. circ. 750. **Indexed:** Excerp.Med. (1995-). **Document type:** academic/scholarly publication.
 Description: For urologists and urologists in training.
 Refereed Serial

616.6 SP ISSN 0211-6995
NEFROLOGIA. 6/yr. Grupo Aula Medica, S.A., C.I. Venecia 2, Alfa III, Oficina 93, Isabel Colbrana s-n, 28050 Madrid, Spain. TEL 1-3588657. Ed. Dr. Rafael Matesanz. **Indexed:** Excerp.Med.
—BLDSC (6075.150500); Genuine Article.

616.6 SZ ISSN 0250-4960
CODEN: NEPHDY
NEPHROLOGIE. (Text in French) 1980. 6/yr. 105 SFr. to individuals; institutions 155 SFr. (effective 1996). Editions Medecine et Hygiene, Case Postale 456, CH-1211 Geneva 4, Switzerland. TEL 022-3469355. FAX 022-3475610. adv.; bk.rev. circ. 1,100. **Indexed:** Biol.Abstr., Excerp.Med., Ind.Med. **Document type:** academic/scholarly publication.
—BLDSC (6075.677000); CASDDS; Genuine Article; SWETS. **CCC.**

616.6 AT ISSN 1320-5358
▼**NEPHROLOGY.** 1995. bi-m. Aus.$394($280) (effective 1996). Blackwell Science Pty Ltd, P.O. Box 378, Carlton South, Vic. 3053, Australia. TEL 61-3-93470300. FAX 61-3-93493016. (back issues avail.) **Document type:** academic/scholarly publication.

616.6 UK ISSN 0931-0509
CODEN: NDTREA
NEPHROLOGY, DIALYSIS AND TRANSPLANTATION. 1986. m. £260($480) (effective 1996). (European Dialysis and Transplant Association) Oxford University Press, Oxford Journals, Walton St., Oxford OX2 6DP, England. TEL 01865-267907. FAX 01865-267773. TELEX 837330-OXPRES-G. E-mail: jnlorders@oup.co.uk. (U.S. subscr. to: Oxford University Press Inc., 2001 Evans Rd., Cary, NC 27513. TEL 919-677-0977. FAX 919-677-1714) (Co-sponsor: European Renal Association) Eds. Alex Davison, E. Ritz. circ. 3,800. **Indexed:** Curr.Cont., Excerp.Med., Ind.Med., Kidney, Sci.Cit.Ind. **Document type:** academic/scholarly publication.
—BLDSC (6075.685300); Faxon; Genuine Article; SWETS; UMI; UnCover. **CCC.**

MEDICAL SCIENCES — UROLOGY AND NEPHROLOGY

616.6   US   ISSN 0896-1263
                         CODEN: NNISES
NEPHROLOGY NEWS & ISSUES. 1987. m. $50. Nephrology News & Issues, Inc., 15150 N. Hayden Rd., Ste. 101, Scottsdale, AZ 85260-2514. TEL 602-443-4635. FAX 602-443-4528. Ed. Cynthia Lefton; Pub. Lawrence R. Coutts. adv.: B&W page $2485, color page $3335; trim 8 1/4 x 11. bk.rev.; illus.; stat.; circ. 2,700 (paid); 13,100 (controlled). **Document type:** trade publication.
—BLDSC (6075.685600).
     Description: Serves the nephrology and renal care community, including nephrologists, surgeons, nurses, technicians and administrators in transplant centers, private practice, in-hospital and free standing clinics. Reports news and information on new techniques, issues, products, government actions and other developments.
Refereed Serial

616.6   US
NEPHROLOGY NEWS & ISSUES - EUROPE. 1993. q. $35. Nephrology News & Issues, Inc., 15150 N. Hayden Rd., Ste. 101, Scottsdale, AZ 85260-2514. TEL 602-443-4635. FAX 602-443-4528. Ed. Mark E. Neumann; Pub. Lawrence R. Coutts. adv.: B&W page $1070, color page $1970; trim 8 1/4 x 11 1/4. illus.; stat.; circ. 5,000 (controlled). **Document type:** trade publication.
     Description: Serves the European and Asia-Pacific nephrology and renal care community, including nephrologists, surgeons, nurses, technicians and administrators in transplant centers, private practice, in-hospital and free-standing clinics. Reports news and information on new techniques, issues, products, government actions and other developments.
Refereed Serial

616.6   SZ   ISSN 0028-2766
                         CODEN: NPRNAY
NEPHRON. (Text in English) 1964. m. (3 vols./yr.) 691.20 SFr.($531) to individuals; institutions 1152 SFr.($885) (effective 1996). S. Karger AG, Allschwilerstr. 10, P.O. Box, CH-4009 Basel, Switzerland. TEL 061-3061111.
FAX 061-3061234. E-mail: Karger@Karger.ch. Eds. G.M. Berlyne, S. Giovannetti. adv.; charts; illus.; index. circ. 3,000. (also avail. in microform from RPI) **Indexed:** Biol.Abstr., Chem.Abstr., Curr.Adv.Cancer Res., Curr.Adv.Ecol.Sci., Curr.Cont., Dent.Ind., Diab.Cont., Excerp.Med., Helminthol.Abstr., Ind.Med., Ind.Sci.Rev., Kidney, Nutr.Abstr. **Document type:** academic/scholarly publication.
—BLDSC (6075.690000); CASDDS; EMDOCS; Faxon; Genuine Article; SWETS; UnCover. **CCC.**
Refereed Serial

616.1   US   ISSN 0733-2467
                         CODEN: NEUREM
NEUROUROLOGY AND URODYNAMICS. 1982. bi-m. $558 (foreign $651) (effective 1996). John Wiley & Sons, Inc., Journals, 605 Third Ave., New York, NY 10158. TEL 212-850-6645.
FAX 212-850-6021. TELEX 12-7063. E-mail: SUBINFO@JWILEY.COM. (Subscr. outside the Americas to: John Wiley & Sons Ltd., Baffins Ln., Chichester, W. Sussex PO19 1UD, England. TEL 44-1243-779777. FAX 44-1243-776128) Ed. Jerry G. Blaivas. bk.rev. (also avail. in microform from RPI; back issues avail.) **Indexed:** Biol.Abstr., Chem.Abstr., Curr.Adv.Ecol.Sci., Curr.Cont., Excerp.Med., Ind.Med. (1993-). **Document type:** academic/scholarly publication.
—BLDSC (6081.589000); CASDDS; Genuine Article; SWETS; UnCover. **CCC.**
     Description: Provides multidisciplinary coverage of recent developments in the study of the urinary tract function.
Refereed Serial

616.6   NE   ISSN 0924-4999
NEW CLINICAL APPLICATIONS. DERMATOLOGY. (Text in English) 1986. irreg. price varies. Kluwer Academic Publishers, Postbus 17, 3300 AA Dordrecht, Netherlands. TEL 31-78-392392.
FAX 31-78-392254. TELEX 29245 KAPG NL. (Dist. by: Kluwer Academic Publishers Group, P.O. Box 322, 3300 AH Dordrecht, Netherlands. TEL 31-78-392392. FAX 31-78-546474; N. America dist. addr.: Box 358, Accord Sta., Hingham, MA 02018-0358. TEL 617-871-6600. FAX 617-871-6528) **Document type:** monographic series.
Refereed Serial

616.6   NE   ISSN 0924-4514
NEW CLINICAL APPLICATIONS. NEPHROLOGY. (Text in English) 1988. irreg. price varies. Kluwer Academic Publishers, Postbus 17, 3300 AA Dordrecht, Netherlands. TEL 31-78-392392.
FAX 31-78-392254. TELEX 29245 KAPG NL. (Dist. by: Kluwer Academic Publishers Group, P.O. Box 322, 3300 AH Dordrecht, Netherlands. TEL 31-78-392392. FAX 31-78-546474; N. America dist. addr.: Box 358, Accord Sta., Hingham, MA 02018-0358. TEL 617-871-6600. FAX 617-871-6528) **Document type:** monographic series.
Refereed Serial

616.61   JA   ISSN 0914-7136
NIHON TOSEKI IKAI ZASSHI/JOURNAL OF JAPAN CLINICAL DIALYSIS. (Text in Japanese) 1985. irreg. Nihon Toseki Ikai, 15-2, Kanda Sudacho 1-chome, Chiyoda-ku, Tokyo 101, Japan.

616.61   JA   ISSN 0911-5889
NIHON TOSEKI RYOHO GAKKAI ZASSHI/JAPANESE SOCIETY OF DIALYSIS THERAPY. JOURNAL. (Text in English, Japanese) 1968. m. 1000 Yen per no. Nihon Toseki Ryoho Gakkai, 38-11, Hongo 3-chome, Bunkyo-ku, Tokyo 113, Japan.

616.6   JA   ISSN 0029-0726
NISHINIHON JOURNAL OF UROLOGY/NISHI NIHON HINYOKIKA. (Text in Japanese; summaries in English) 1969. m. 10000 Yen. Kyushu University, Faculty of Medicine, Department of Urology, Maidashi 3-1-1, Higashi-ku, Fukuoka 812, Japan. TEL 81-92-641-1151. FAX 81-92-651-0165. Ed. Joichi Kumazawa. adv.: bk.rev. circ. 3,000. **Indexed:** Biol.Abstr., Excerp.Med. **Document type:** academic/scholarly publication.
—BLDSC (6113.604000); EMDOCS.
     Supersedes in part: Dermatology and Urology - Hifu to Hinyo (ISSN 0011-9091)

616.6   US
NUTRITION AND BLOOD PRESSURE REVIEWS. q. membership. National Kidney Foundation, Scientific Advisory Board, 30 E. 33rd St., New York, NY 10016. TEL 212-889-2210. circ. 6,000. **Document type:** newsletter.
     Description: Provides critical abstracts of recent publications related to nutrition, blood pressure and nephrology.

616.61060489   DK   ISSN 0108-2388
NYRENYT; medlemsblad. 1981. 6/yr. DKK 75. Nyreforeningen - Danish Kidney Association, Valbyvej 20, 2630 Taastrup, Denmark. TEL 4252 4252. FAX 43-71-00-96. Ed. Poul B. Joergensen. adv.; bk.rev.; illus. circ. 4,000. **Document type:** bulletin.
     Formerly: Dialyse og Transplantation (ISSN 0108-2779)

616.6   US   ISSN 0000-149X
RC870
OFFICIAL AMERICAN BOARD OF MEDICAL SPECIALTIES (A B M S) DIRECTORY OF BOARD CERTIFIED UROLOGISTS. 1983. biennial. $119.95. Marquis Who's Who, A Reed Reference Publishing company, 121 Chanlon Rd., New Providence, NJ 07974. TEL 908-464-6800. FAX 908-665-2898. (Subscr. to: Order Dept., Box 31, New Providence, NJ 07974-9903. TEL 800-521-8110) Ed. Roy Crego. **Document type:** directory.
     Formerly (until 1992): A B M S Directory of Certified Urologists (ISSN 0742-0374)
     Description: Biographical sketches of U.S. certified medical specialists sorted alphabetically with a geographical index.

616.61   JA   ISSN 0912-6937
OSAKA TOSEKI KENKYUKAI KAISHI/OSAKA SOCIETY FOR DIALYSIS THERAPY. JOURNAL. (Text in Japanese) 1983. s-a. Osaka Toseki Kenkyukai, Osaka Shiritsu Daigaku Igakubu Hinyokika Kyoshitsu, 5-7, Asahimachi 1-chome, Abeno-ku, Osaka 545, Japan.

P A S C A L E 77: NEPHROLOGIE. VOIES URINAIRES. see *MEDICAL SCIENCES — Abstracting, Bibliographies, Statistics*

616.6   US
▼**PAN AMERICAN JOURNAL OF DIALYSIS & TRANSPLANTATION.** Announced for publication in 1996. q. $99 to individuals; institutions $145 (effective 1996). (Pan American Society for Dialysis & Transplantation) Field & Wood, Medical Periodicals, Inc., Box 975, Blue Bell, PA 19422. TEL 610-828-4010. FAX 215-482-0226. Ed. Dr. Alejandro Trevino-Beccera. **Document type:** academic/scholarly publication.
Refereed Serial

616.6   GW   ISSN 0931-041X
                         CODEN: PEDNEF
PEDIATRIC NEPHROLOGY. (Text in English) 1987. 6/yr. DM.1198($870) (effective 1996). (International Pediatric Nephrology Association) Springer-Verlag, Heidelberger Platz 3, 14197 Berlin, Germany. TEL 030-8207-0. FAX 030-8214091. E-mail: orders@springer.de. (Subscr. in N. America to: Springer-Verlag New York, Inc., 44 Hartz Way, Secaucus, NJ 07096-2491. TEL 201-348-4033. FAX 201-348-4505) Ed. A.M. Robson. **Indexed:** Kidney. **Document type:** academic/scholarly publication.
—BLDSC (6417.603000); CASDDS; Faxon; Genuine Article; SWETS; UMI; UnCover. **CCC.**
     Description: Laboratory and clinical research of acute and chronic diseases that affect renal function in children.

PERITONEAL DIALYSIS INTERNATIONAL. see *MEDICAL SCIENCES*

616.6   FR   ISSN 1166-7087
PROGRES EN UROLOGIE. 1991. bi-m. (Association Francaise d'Urologie) Progres en Urologie S.A.R.L., 7 bd. Flandrin, 75116 Paris, France.
TEL 45-03-31-96. FAX 45-04-72-89. (Co-sponsors: Societe Francaise d'Urologie; Association des Urologues du Quebec) Ed. B. Gattegno. **Indexed:** Ind.Med. (1993-).
—BLDSC (6864.938800).

RADIONUCLIDES IN NEPHROUROLOGY. see *MEDICAL SCIENCES — Radiology And Nuclear Medicine*

616.6   US   ISSN 0886-022X
RC918.R4   CODEN: REFAE8
RENAL FAILURE. 1977. 6/yr. $262.50 to individuals; institutions $525. Marcel Dekker Journals, 270 Madison Ave., New York, NY 10016.
TEL 212-696-9000. FAX 212-685-4540. TELEX 421419 MARDEEK. (Subscr. to: Box 5017, Monticello, NY 12701) Ed. William F. Finn. (also avail. in microform from RPI) **Indexed:** Biol.Abstr., Chem.Abstr., Curr.Cont., Excerp.Med., Ind.Med., Ind.Sci.Rev., INIS Atomind., Sci.Cit.Ind. **Document type:** academic/scholarly publication.
—BLDSC (7356.869800); CASDDS; Faxon; Genuine Article; SWETS; UMI. **CCC.**
     Former titles: Uremia Investigation; Clinical and Experimental Dialysis and Apheresis (ISSN 0276-5497); (until 1981): Journal of Dialysis (ISSN 0362-8558)
Refereed Serial

612   UK   ISSN 0300-3434
RENAL PHYSIOLOGY. 1970. s-m. (diskette m.) £110 (diskette £115; both £175) (effective 1995). S U B I S, Mansion House, 19 Kingfield Rd., Sheffield S11 9AS, England. TEL 0114-255-4433.
FAX 0114-255-4626. E-mail: admin@sheffac.demon.co.uk. (also avail. in diskette format) **Indexed:** Biol.Abstr., Chem.Abstr., Ind.Med. **Document type:** abstracting/indexing.
—CCC.
     Description: Current awareness service for researchers. Covers the structure and function of kidneys, immunology, toxicology, pharmacology.

MEDICAL SCIENCES — UROLOGY AND NEPHROLOGY

616.6   SZ   ISSN 1011-6524
CODEN: RPBIEL
RENAL PHYSIOLOGY AND BIOCHEMISTRY; international journal of experimental renal physiology, pathophysiology, biochemistry and pharmacology. 1979. bi-m. 275.40 SFr.($211.80) to individuals; institutions 459 SFr.($353) (effective 1996). S. Karger AG, Allschwilerstr. 10, P.O. Box, CH-4009 Basel, Switzerland. TEL 061-3061111. FAX 061-3061234. E-mail: Karger@Karger.ch. Eds. G.M. Berlyne, F. Lang. adv.; illus.; index. circ. 800. (also avail. in microfilm; microform from UMI; back issues avail.) **Indexed:** Biol.Abstr., Curr.Adv.Ecol.Sci., Curr.Cont., Excerp.Med. **Document type:** academic/scholarly publication.
—BLDSC (7356.880500); CASDDS; Faxon; Genuine Article; SWETS; UnCover. **CCC.**
Formerly (until 1989): Renal Physiology (ISSN 0378-5858)
Refereed Serial

616.6   UK   ISSN 0142-8357
RENAL TRANSPLANTATION AND DIALYSIS. 1971. m. £75 (effective 1995). S U B I S, Mansion House, 19 Kingfield Rd., Sheffield S11 9AS, England. TEL 0114-255-4433. FAX 0114-255-4626. E-mail: admin@sheffac.demon.co.uk. **Document type:** abstracting/indexing.
—CCC.
Description: Current awareness service for researchers. Studies dialysis, artificial kidneys and peritoneal dialysis.

616.6   BO   ISSN 1018-5321
REVISTA BOLIVIANA DE NEFROLOGIA. 1990. s-a. free. Sociedad Boliviana de Nefrologia, Casilla Correo 6, Sucre, Bolivia. TEL 591-064-23282. FAX 591-064-25559. Ed. Antonio Dubravcic L. adv.; charts; illus.; stat. circ. 500.

616.6   JA   ISSN 0385-2393
RINSHO HINYOKIKA/JAPANESE JOURNAL OF CLINICAL UROLOGY. (Text in Japanese; summaries in English) 1967. m. 24720 Yen($190) Igaku-Shoin Ltd., 5-25-3 Hongo, Bunkyo-ku, Tokyo 113-91, Japan. TEL 03-817-5709. Ed. Bd. circ. 4,000.
—BLDSC (4651.450000).

616.61   JA   ISSN 0910-5808
RINSHO TOSEKI/JAPANESE JOURNAL OF CLINICAL DIALYSIS. (Text in Japanese) 1985. m. 1960 Yen per no. Nihon Medikaru Senta - Japan Medical Center Inc., 1-64, Kanda Jinbocho, Chiyoda-ku, Tokyo 101, Japan.

616.6   NO   ISSN 0036-5599
CODEN: SJUNAS
SCANDINAVIAN JOURNAL OF UROLOGY AND NEPHROLOGY. (Supplements avail.) (Text in English) 1967. 4/yr. NOK 1065 in Nordic countries; elsewhere $184 (incl. supplements) (effective 1996). (Scandinavian Association of Urology) Scandinavian University Press, P.O. Box 2959 Toeyen, N-0608 Oslo, Norway. TEL 47-22-57-54-00. FAX 47-22-57-53-53. (U.S. addr.: Scandinavian University Press, 200 Meacham Ave., Elmont, NY 11003. TEL 516-352-7300) Ed. Stig Colleen. adv.; charts; illus. circ. 2,600. **Indexed:** ASCA, Biol.Abstr., Biotech.Abstr., Chem.Abstr., Curr.Adv.Ecol.Sci., Curr.Cont., Excerp.Med., Ind.Med., Nutr.Abstr.
—BLDSC (8087.560000); ADONIS; CASDDS; EMDOCS; Faxon; Genuine Article; SWETS; UnCover. **CCC.**
Description: Focuses on basic and clinical research work in the two fields of medicine within the five Nordic countries.

616.6   NO   ISSN 0300-8886
CODEN: SJUNBT
SCANDINAVIAN JOURNAL OF UROLOGY AND NEPHROLOGY. SUPPLEMENT. (Text in English) 1968. irreg. Scandinavian University Press, P.O. Box 2959 Toeyen, N-0608 Oslo, Norway. TEL 47-22-57-54-00. FAX 47-22-57-53-53. (U.S. addr.: Scandinavian University Press, 200 Meacham Ave., Elmont, NY 11003. TEL 516-352-7300) **Indexed:** Chem.Abstr., Excerp.Med. (1993-), Ind.Med.
—BLDSC (8087.565000); ADONIS; CASDDS; Faxon; SWETS.

616.6   US   ISSN 0894-0959
SEMINARS IN DIALYSIS. 1988. bi-w. $145 (foreign $175) (effective 1996). Blackwell Science Inc., 238 Main St., Cambridge, MA 02142-1413. TEL 617-876-7022. FAX 617-492-5263. Ed. Dr. Richard Sherman. circ. 3,000. (back issues avail.)
—BLDSC (8239.448930); Genuine Article; SWETS. **CCC.**
Description: Clinical journal devoted to research and practice of dialysis.
Refereed Serial

616.6   US   ISSN 0270-9295
CODEN: SNEPDJ
SEMINARS IN NEPHROLOGY. 1981 (Mar.). bi-m. $188 (foreign $232) (effective 1996). W.B. Saunders Co. (Subsidiary of: Harcourt Brace & Company), Curtis Center, 3rd Fl., Independence Sq. W., Philadelphia, PA 19106-3399. FAX 215-238-6445. (Subscr. to: Periodicals Fulfillment, W.B. Saunders Co., 6277 Sea Harbor Dr., 4th Fl., Orlando, FL 32891-4800. TEL 800-654-2452. FAX 800-874-6418) Ed. Dr. Neil A. Kurtzman; Pub. Joan W. Blumberg. adv.; B&W page $790, color page $1740; 7 x 10. bibl.; charts; illus.; index. circ. 2,565. **Indexed:** ASCA, Chem.Abstr., Curr.Cont., Sci.Cit.Ind. **Document type:** academic/scholarly publication.
•Also available online.
—BLDSC (8239.455200); CASDDS; Genuine Article; SWETS; UMI; UnCover. **CCC.**
Description: Each issue covers new concepts and original research into one particular kidney disorder.

SEMINARS IN UROLOGIC ONCOLOGY. see *MEDICAL SCIENCES — Oncology*

616.6   GW   ISSN 0936-2002
CODEN: TWUNE
T W UROLOGIE, NEPHROLOGIE. 1989. 6/yr. DM.74 (foreign DM.100). Verlag G. Braun GmbH, Karl-Friedrich-Str. 14-18, 76133 Karlsruhe, Germany. TEL 0721-165-0. FAX 0721-165191. **Indexed:** Excerp.Med. **Document type:** trade publication.
—BLDSC (9076.749700).

616.6   US   ISSN 1079-3259
▼**TECHNIQUES IN UROLOGY.** 1995. q. $89 to individuals (foreign $96); institutions $128 (foreign $141) (effective 1996); newsstand price: 35. Lippincott - Raven Press, 227 E. Washington Sq., Philadelphia, PA 19106. TEL 215-238-4200. Eds. Dr. David Albala, Dr. Leonard Gomella. **Document type:** academic/scholarly publication.
—BLDSC (8745.405000).
Description: Provides expert knowledge and guidance on the most advanced procedures for the treatment of urologic disorders.

616.6   JA
TOHSEKI FRONTIER/QUARTERLY JOURNAL OF DIALYSIS. (Text in Japanese) 1990. 4/yr. 380 Yen per no. Medikaru Rebyusha - Medical Review Co., Ltd., 7-3, Hiranomachi 1-chome, Chuo-ku, Osaka 541, Japan.

616.6   NE   ISSN 0924-6177
TOPICS IN RENAL MEDICINE. (Text in English) 1986. irreg. price varies. Kluwer Academic Publishers, Postbus 17, 3300 AA Dordrecht, Netherlands. TEL 31-78-392392. FAX 31-78-392254. TELEX 29245 KAPG NL. (Dist. by: Kluwer Academic Publishers Group, P.O. Box 322, 3300 AH Dordrecht, Netherlands. TEL 31-78-392392. FAX 31-78-546474; N. America dist. addr.: Box 358, Accord Sta., Hingham, MA 02018-0358. TEL 617-871-6600. FAX 617-871-6528) Ed. Vittorio E. Andreucci. **Document type:** monographic series.
Refereed Serial

616.6   JA
TOSEKI/DIALYSIS. (Text in Japanese) 1972. a. 4000 Yen. Nihon Toseki Ryoho Gakkai - Japanese Society of Dialysis Therapy, 38-11, Hongo 3-chome, Bunkyo-ku, Tokyo 113, Japan.

616.6   JA   ISSN 0917-2114
TOSEKI FURONTIA/QUARTERLY JOURNAL OF DIALYSIS. (Text in Japanese) 1991. q. Fuso Yakuhin Kogyo K.K. - Fuso Pharmaceutical Industries, Ltd., 3-11, Morinomiya 2-chome, Joto-ku, Osaka 536, Japan.

616.6   JA
TOSEKI RAIFU/DIALYSIS LIFE. (Text in Japanese) 1981. q. (Pharma International, Inc.) Terumo Corp., 44-1, Hatagaya 2-chome, Shibuya-ku, Tokyo 151, Japan.

616.6 617   US
TRANSPLANT CHRONICLES. q. free. National Kidney Foundation, 30 E. 33rd St., New York, NY 10016. TEL 212-889-2210. circ. 25,000. **Document type:** newsletter.
Description: News and information for transplant patients and their families.

616.6   US   ISSN 1074-8687
URO-GRAM. 1976. bi-m. $40 membership. Society of Urologic Nurses and Associates, Box 56, Pitman, NJ 08071-0056. Eds. Marie Wilson, Glenda Wilkinson. bk.rev. circ. 2,500. **Document type:** newsletter.
Description: Provides Urology health care workers with information, news and events of the Association as well as items affecting urologic practice in general.

616.6   IT   ISSN 1120-5989
URODINAMICA, NEUROUROLOGY, URODYNAMICS AND CONTINENCE. (Text in English) 1991. q. L.80000($80) Editrice Kurtis s.r.l., Via L. Zoja, 30, 20153 Milan, Italy. TEL 39-2-48202740. FAX 39-2-48201219. Ed. W. Artibani. adv.; B&W page L.2500000, color page L.3150000; 200 x 260.
—BLDSC (9124.395500).
Description: Publishes original articles on urodynamics and related research.

UROGYNAECOLOGIA INTERNATIONAL JOURNAL. see *MEDICAL SCIENCES — Obstetrics And Gynecology*

616.6   GW   ISSN 0340-2592
CODEN: URGABW
DER UROLOGE. SECTION A; Zeitschrift fuer klinische und praktische Urologie. Key Title: Urologe (Ausgabe A). (Text in German; summaries in English, German) 1962. 6/yr. DM.498($361) (effective 1996). (Deutsche Gesellschaft fuer Urologie) Springer-Verlag, Heidelberger Platz 3, 14197 Berlin, Germany. TEL 030-8207-0. FAX 030-8214091. E-mail: orders@springer.de. (Subscr. in N. America to: Springer-Verlag New York, Inc., 44 Hartz Way, Secaucus, NJ 07096-2491. TEL 201-348-4033. FAX 201-348-4505) Ed. R. Hautmann. adv.; bk.rev.; abstr.; charts; illus.; index, cum.index: 1962-1969. (also avail. in microfilm from UMI; back issues avail.; reprint service avail. from ISI) **Indexed:** Curr.Cont., Excerp.Med., Helminthol.Abstr., Ind.Med. **Document type:** academic/scholarly publication.
—BLDSC (9124.410000); Faxon; Genuine Article; SWETS; UMI. **CCC.**
Formerly (until 1970): Urologe (ISSN 0375-4685)

616.6   GW   ISSN 0042-1111
DER UROLOGE. SECTION B. Key Title: Urologe. Ausgabe B. 1961. 6/yr. DM.544($395) (effective 1996). (Berufsverband der Deutschen Urologen) Springer-Verlag, Heidelberger Platz 3, 14197 Berlin, Germany. TEL 030-8207-0. FAX 030-8214091. E-mail: orders@springer.de. (Subscr. in N. America to: Springer-Verlag New York, Inc., 44 Hartz Way, Secaucus, NJ 07096-2491. TEL 201-348-4033. FAX 201-348-4505) Ed.Bd. adv.; charts; illus.; index. (also avail. in microfilm from UMI; back issues avail.; reprint service avail. from ISI) **Indexed:** Curr.Cont., Excerp.Med., Helminthol.Abstr. **Document type:** academic/scholarly publication.
—BLDSC (9124.420000); EMDOCS; SWETS; UMI. **CCC.**
Formerly (until 1970): Urologische Facharzt (ISSN 0301-1410)

616.6   IT   ISSN 0391-5603
UROLOGIA/UROLOGY; rivista internazionale di cultura urologica. (Supplements avail.) (Text in English, Italian) 1934. q. $150 in Europe; elsewhere $170. (Society of Urology of Northern Italy) Libreria Editrice Canova, Viale della Liberazione 40, 31030 Dosson di Casier (Treviso), Italy. TEL 39-422-322393. FAX 39-422-322305. Ed. Giuseppe Anselmo. adv.; bk.rev.; charts; illus.; index; circ. 1,300 (controlled). (back issues avail.) **Indexed:** Biol.Abstr., Chem.Abstr., Excerp.Med. **Document type:** academic/scholarly publication.
—BLDSC (9124.460000).

616.6 SZ ISSN 0042-1138
CODEN: URINAC
UROLOGIA INTERNATIONALIS. (Text in English) 1955. 8/yr (in 2 vols.). 625.20 SFr.($481.20) to individuals; institutions 1042 SFr.($802) (effective 1996). S. Karger AG, Allschwilerstr. 10, P.O. Box, CH-4009 Basel, Switzerland. TEL 061-3061111. FAX 061-3061234. E-mail: Karger@Karger.ch. Ed. D. Hauri. adv.; bk.rev.; bibl.; charts; illus.; index. circ. 1,000. (also avail. in microform) **Indexed:** Biol.Abstr., Chem.Abstr., Curr.Cont., Excerp.Med., Helminthol.Abstr., Ind.Med. **Document type:** academic/scholarly publication.
—BLDSC (9124.480000); CASDDS; EMDOCS; Faxon; Genuine Article; SWETS; UMI; UnCover. **CCC.**
Refereed Serial

616.6 US ISSN 0094-0143
CODEN: UCNADW
UROLOGIC CLINICS OF NORTH AMERICA. 1974. q. $140 (foreign $166) (effective 1996). W.B. Saunders Co. (Subsidiary of: Harcourt Brace & Co.), Curtis Center, Independence Sq. W., Philadelphia, PA 19106-3399. TEL 215-238-7800. FAX 215-238-6445. (Subscr. to: Periodicals Fulfillment, W.B. Saunders Co., 6277 Sea Harbor Dr., 4th Fl., Orlando, FL 32891-4800. TEL 800-654-2452. FAX 800-874-6418) Ed. Livia Berardi. (also avail. in microform from UMI; reprint service avail. from UMI,ISI) **Indexed:** AIM, Biol.Abstr., Curr.Cont., Dent.Ind., Excerp.Med., Ind.Med. **Document type:** academic/scholarly publication.
—BLDSC (9124.620000); EMDOCS; Faxon; Genuine Article; SWETS; UMI; UnCover. **CCC.**

616.6 610.736 US ISSN 1053-816X
CODEN: URNUES
UROLOGIC NURSING. 1980. q. $42 to individuals (Canada $55.64; elsewhere $52); institutions $66 (Canada $81.32; elsewhere $76); students $21 (Canada $33.17; elsewhere $31) (effective 1996); newsstand price: $12.50. (Society of Urologic Nurses and Associates, Inc. (SUNA)) Mosby - Year Book, Inc. (Subsidiary of: Times Mirror Company), 11830 Westline Industrial Dr., St. Louis, MO 63146-3318. TEL 314-872-8370. FAX 314-432-1380. (Co-sponsor: rology Nurses of Canada (UNC)) Ed. Patricia Bates. adv.; B&W page $925, color page $1660; trim 8 1/4 x 11. circ. 3,316. **Indexed:** CINAHL.
—BLDSC (9124.625000); Faxon; UMI. **CCC.**
Formerly (until 1989): A U A A Journal (ISSN 0882-9594)
Description: For nurses, technicians, and allied health care professionals.

UROLOGIC ONCOLOGY. see *MEDICAL SCIENCES — Oncology*

616.6 GW ISSN 0300-5623
CODEN: URLRA5
UROLOGICAL RESEARCH; journal of clinical and laboratory investigation. (Text and summaries in English) 1973. 6/yr. DM.698($507) (effective 1996). Springer-Verlag, Heidelberger Platz 3, 14197 Berlin, Germany. TEL 030-8207-0. FAX 030-8214091. E-mail: orders@springer.de. (Subscr. in N. America to: Springer-Verlag New York, Inc., 44 Hartz Way, Secaucus, NJ 07096-2491. TEL 201-348-4033. FAX 201-348-4505) Ed.Bd. adv.; charts; index. (also avail. in microform from UMI; reprint service avail. from ISI) **Indexed:** Chem.Abstr., Curr.Adv.Cancer Res., Curr.Cont., Excerp.Med., Ind.Med., Kidney, Rev.Med.& Vet.Mycol. **Document type:** academic/scholarly publication.
—BLDSC (9124.650000); CASDDS; Faxon; Genuine Article; SWETS; UMI; UnCover. **CCC.**
Description: Covers research in the fields of clinical medicine, animal experimentation, and laboratory techniques. Contributions are designed to increase understanding of the functions of the genitourinary system in normal and diseased states.

UROLOGIST'S SPORTSLIFE. see *SPORTS AND GAMES*

616.6 RU ISSN 0042-1154
CODEN: URNEAA
UROLOGIYA I NEFROLOGIYA/UROLOGY AND NEPHROLOGY. (Text in Russian; summaries in English) 1923. bi-m. $67 (effective 1996). (Vsesoyuznoe Nauchnoe Obshchestvo Urologov) Izdatel'stvo Meditsina, Petroverigskii pereulok 6-8, 101000 Moscow, Russia. (Dist. by: Mezhdunarodnaya Kniga, B. Yakimanka 39, 117049 Moscow, Russia. TEL 7-095-2384600. FAX 7-095-2384634) (Co-sponsor: Ministerstvo Zdravookhraneniya) Ed. N.A. Lopatkin. adv. contact: Z.Ya. Sladkova. bk.rev.; bibl. **Indexed:** Biol.Abstr., Chem.Abstr., Excerp.Med., Ind.Med.
—BLDSC (0385.120000); CASDDS; EMDOCS. **CCC.**
Description: Reports on the advances of Soviet and foreign medicine in the domain of urology and nephrology.

616.6 US ISSN 0090-4295
RC870 CODEN: URGYA
UROLOGY. 1973. m. $235 to institutions outside the Americas; $160 to institutions in U.S (effective 1996). Excerpta Medica, Inc. (Subsidiary of: Reed Elsevier Medical group), 105 Raider Blvd., Belle Meade, NJ 08502. TEL 908-874-8550. FAX 908-874-8419. (Subscr. to: Box 3085, Princeton, NJ 08543-3085) Eds. Dr. Joseph E. Oesterling, Mary Politano. adv.; bk.rev.; abstr.; bibl.; charts; stat. circ. 7,500. (also avail. in microform; reprint service avail. from UMI, ISI) **Indexed:** Biol.Abstr., Curr.Adv.Cancer Res., Curr.Adv.Ecol.Sci., Curr.Cont., Dent.Ind., Excerp.Med., Ind.Med., Nutr.Abstr., Rev.Med.& Vet.Mycol., Rev.Plant Path. **Document type:** academic/scholarly publication.
—BLDSC (9124.703000); EMDOCS; Faxon; Genuine Article; SWETS; UMI; UnCover. **CCC.**
Description: For hospital based and private practice physicians. Contains original scientific reports, case reports and review updates.
Refereed Serial

616.6 US ISSN 0889-6283
RC870
UROLOGY ANNUAL. 1987. a. $75. Appleton & Lange (Subsidiary of: Simon & Schuster Company), 25 Van Zant St., Box 5630, Norwalk, CT 06856. TEL 203-838-4400. Ed. Dr. Stephen N. Rous.
—**CCC.**

616.6 UK ISSN 1352-9544
▼**UROLOGY INTERNATIONAL.** 1994. q. free. (SmithKline Beecham Pharmaceuticals) Complete Medical Communications Ltd., C M C House, 19 King Edward St., Macclesfield, Ches. SK10 1AQ, England. TEL 01625-619855. FAX 01625-619812. Ed. Dr. Mark Soloway. circ. 24,000. **Document type:** academic/scholarly publication.
—BLDSC (9124.707100).
Description: Provides practising urologists with information on techniques and therapies and provides case studies.

616.6 US ISSN 0093-9722
UROLOGY TIMES. 1973. m. $75 (Canada $125; elsewhere $175). Advanstar Communications, Inc., 7500 Old Oak Blvd., Cleveland, OH 44130. TEL 216-826-2839. FAX 216-891-2726. (Subscr. to: 131 W. First St., Duluth, MN 55802. TEL 800-346-0085) Ed. Michael Malley. circ. 9,152. (also avail. in microform from UMI) **Document type:** trade publication.
●Also available online. Vendor(s): Knight-Ridder, Inc.
—UMI. **CCC.**
Description: News for office-based and hospital-based urologists and osteopathic urologists.

616.6 CN
UROLOGY TIMES OF CANADA. (Text in English, French) 1993. 6/yr. Can.$60 (foreign Can.$100). C T C Communications Corp., Toronto Star Bldg., 1 Yonge St., Ste. 1801, Toronto, ON M5E 1W7, Canada. TEL 416-869-3862. FAX 416-368-0515. Ed. R. Allan Ryan; Pub. Mitchell Shannon. adv.; B&W page Can.$1690; trim 11 x 16. (tabloid format)

V H L FAMILY FORUM. (Von Hippel-Lindau Disease) see *MEDICAL SCIENCES — Psychiatry And Neurology*

616.6 GW ISSN 0724-4983
WORLD JOURNAL OF UROLOGY. (Text in English) 1983. 6/yr. DM.498($361) (effective 1996). Springer-Verlag, Heidelberger Platz 3, 14197 Berlin, Germany. TEL 030-8207-0. FAX 030-8214091. E-mail: orders@springer.de. (Subscr. in N. America to: Springer-Verlag New York, Inc., 44 Hartz Way, Secaucus, NJ 07096-2491. TEL 201-348-4033. FAX 201-348-4505) Eds. U. Jonas, R.J. Krane. adv.; bk.rev.; charts; illus. (also avail. in microform from UMI; reprint service avail. from ISI) **Indexed:** Curr.Adv.Ecol.Sci., Curr.Cont., Ind.Med. (1993-). **Document type:** academic/scholarly publication.
—BLDSC (9356.074500); Faxon; Genuine Article; SWETS; UMI; UnCover. **CCC.**
Description: Conveys the essential results of urological research and their practical and clinical relevance.

616.6 US ISSN 1046-6266
RC902.A1
YEAR BOOK OF NEPHROLOGY. 1991. a. $74.95 (residents $35) (effective 1996). Mosby - Year Book, Inc. (Chicago) (Subsidiary of: Times Mirror Company), 200 N. LaSalle St., Chicago, IL 60601-1080. TEL 312-726-9733. FAX 312-726-6075. TELEX 206155. Ed. Dr. Fredric L. Coe. illus.
●Also available online. Vendor(s): Ovid Technologies.

616.6 US ISSN 0084-4071
YEAR BOOK OF UROLOGY. 1933. a. $72.95 (residents $35) (effective 1996). Mosby - Year Book, Inc., Continuity Division, 200 N. LaSalle, Chicago, IL 60601. TEL 312-726-9733. FAX 312-726-6075. Ed. Dr. K. Kekernion. illus. (reprint service avail.) **Indexed:** Curr.Adv.Ecol.Sci.
●Also available online. Vendor(s): Ovid Technologies.

MEETINGS AND CONGRESSES

578 011 US ISSN 0569-2628
SF97 CODEN: OPFMAG
A A F M PROCEEDINGS OF ANNUAL MEETING. 1952. a. $25. American Association of Feed Microscopists, c/o Marjorie McCutcheon, Box 5246, Charleston, WV 25361. TEL 304-558-2208. FAX 304-338-3594. Ed. Wynne Landgraf. circ. 300. **Document type:** proceedings.

A C J S PROGRAM BOOK. (Academy of Criminal Justice Sciences) see *EDUCATION — Higher Education*

A C O M MODATE QUARTERLY. (Association for Convention Operations Management) see *BUSINESS AND ECONOMICS — Management*

A P S A NEWSLETTER. (Australasian Political Studies Association) see *POLITICAL SCIENCE*

A S D A NEWS. (American Sleep Disorders Association) see *MEDICAL SCIENCES — Psychiatry And Neurology*

A U M A HANDBOOK INTERNATIONAL. (Ausstellungs und Messe-Ausschuss der Deutschen Wirtschaft e.V.) see *BUSINESS AND ECONOMICS — Marketing And Purchasing*

A U M A HANDBOOK REGIONAL. (Ausstellungs und Messe-Ausschuss der Deutschen Wirtschaft e.V.) see *BUSINESS AND ECONOMICS — Marketing And Purchasing*

A U M A INFOBLAETTER; Daten und Fakten ueber Messen und Ausstellungen im In- und Ausland. (Ausstellungs- und Messe-Ausschuss der Deutschen Wirtschaft e.V.) see *ADVERTISING AND PUBLIC RELATIONS*

ADVANCE BAND MAGAZINE; the international voice of adult bands. see *MUSIC*

AERZTE ZEITUNG; die Tagesinformation fuer den Arzt. see *MEDICAL SCIENCES*

ALLESTIRE; politica-tecnica-economia per mostre fiere congressi vetrine negozi stand. see *BUSINESS AND ECONOMICS*

AMERICAN LIBRARY ASSOCIATION. ANNUAL CONFERENCE PROGRAM. see *LIBRARY AND INFORMATION SCIENCES*

MEETINGS AND CONGRESSES

011   US
ANNUAL GUIDE TO EXPOSITION SERVICE. a. Exposition Service Contractors Association, Union Sta., 400 S. Houston St., Ste. 210, Dallas, TX 75202. TEL 214-742-9217. FAX 214-741-2519. **Document type:** directory.

011   HK   ISSN 1015-3128
ASIAN MEETINGS AND INCENTIVES. Short title: A M I. (Text in English) 1988. m. free to qualified personnel. (Convention and Visitors Bureaus) Travel & Trade Publishing (Asia) Ltd., 16-F, Capitol Centre, 5-19 Jardine's Bazaar, Causeway Bay, Hong Kong. TEL 890-3067. FAX 895-2378. TELEX 76591-TPAL-HX. Ed. Sue Girdwood. adv.; circ. 12,000 (controlled).
   Formerly (until Jan. 1989): M I C E Asia.
   Description: For meetings and exhibitions industry executives around the world.

011   659.1   CN
ASSOCIATION. 1974. bi-m. August Communications, 200-388 Donald St., Winnipeg, MB R3B 2J4, Canada. TEL 204-957-0265. FAX 204-957-0217. Ed. Andrea Kuch. adv. contact: Gladwyn Nickel. circ. 3,500. **Indexed:** Can.B.P.I.

ASSOCIATION FOR CONVENTION OPERATIONS MANAGEMENT. CONVENTION PROCEEDINGS. see *BUSINESS AND ECONOMICS — Management*

011   US   ISSN 1042-3141
AS6
ASSOCIATION MEETINGS; conventions, conferences, and exhibitions. 1984. bi-m. $42. Adams-Laux Company, Inc., 63 Great Rd., Maynard, MA 01754. TEL 508-897-5552. FAX 508-897-6824. Ed. Betsy Bair. adv.; charts; illus. circ. 21,000.
   —UnCover. CCC.
   Formerly (until 1989): Convention World (ISSN 8750-1686); Incorporates (1916-198?): World Convention Dates (ISSN 0043-8383)

011   UK   ISSN 0958-0271
ASSOCIATION MEETINGS INTERNATIONAL. 1989. bi-m. £20($75) Conference and Travel Publications Ltd., Media House, The Square, Forest Row, E. Sussex RH18 5EP, England. TEL 44-342-824044. FAX 44-342-824030. adv.; B&W page £4360 or £1785, color page £6560 or £2625; trim 210 x 297. circ. 10,000.

ASSOCIATION OF HUMAN RESOURCE SYSTEMS PROFESSIONALS. CONFERENCE HIGHLIGHTS. see *BUSINESS AND ECONOMICS — Personnel Management*

011   US
ASSOCIATION OF INTERNATIONAL MEETING PLANNERS. NEWSLETTER. m. Association of International Meeting Planners, 1811 Monroe St., Dearborn, MI 48124. TEL 313-563-0360. FAX 713-563-0360. Ed. Stephen R. Caster. **Document type:** academic/scholarly publication.

ASSOCIATIONS REPORT. see *BUSINESS AND ECONOMICS — Management*

011   IT
AZIENDE IN FIERA; la guida professionale per fiere, congresi e convegni. s.a. Protogesco s.r.l., Via Molino 1, 25010 Pozzolengo (BS), Italy. TEL 030-914260. FAX 030-918454. adv.; B&W page L.1800000, color page L.3200000; trim 185 x 260. circ. 5,955.

011   US
B O M A INTERNATIONAL CONVENTION DIRECTORY. 1908. a. Building Owners and Managers Association International, 1201 New York Ave., N.W., Ste. 300, Washington, DC 20005. TEL 202-408-2662. FAX 202-321-0181. Ed. Patricia Areno. adv. contact: 5,000. **Document type:** directory.

011   GW   ISSN 0940-533X
BERLINER KONGRESSKALENDER. 1991. m. DM.60. Infoexpert Verlag GmbH, Koepenickerstr. 80-82, 1020 Berlin, Germany. TEL 030-2344282. FAX 030-2793996.

060   US
BLACK CONVENTION MAGAZINE. 1991. m. $30 (free to qualified personnel). A & E Publishing, Inc., 11631 Victory Blvd., Ste. 201, N. Hollywood, CA 91606. TEL 818-753-9198. Ed. Solomon Herbert. **Document type:** trade publication.
   Description: News of the Black tourism and convention market for meeting planners, vendors and suppliers.

011   BS
BOTSWANA INTERNATIONAL TRADE FAIR. ANNUAL EXHIBITORS' CATALOGUE. Abbreviated title: B I T F Annual Exhibitors' Catalogue. (Former name of issuing body: Gaborone International Fair) 1968. a. free. Ministry of Commerce and Industry, Minstry of Commerce and Industry, Private Bag 00367, Gaborone, Botswana. TEL 267-351790. FAX 267-305375. TELEX 2674 TRADE BD. Ed.Bd. adv. circ. 10,000. **Document type:** catalog, government publication.
   Description: Profiles exhibitors and their products, both national and international.

011   IT   ISSN 1121-2977
BUSINESS CONGRESS. 1990. 8/yr. Foro Bonaparte 74, 20121 Milani, Italy. TEL 2-72-00-34-51. FAX 2-720-03-505. Ed. Renato Andreoletti.

658   338   UK   ISSN 0955-4483
BUSINESS RATIO REPORT: EXHIBITION AND CONFERENCE ORGANISERS; an industry sector analysis. 1988. a. I C C Business Ratios Ltd., Freepost, Field House, Hampton TW12 1BR, England. TEL 081-783-0977. FAX 081-783-1940. charts; stat. **Document type:** trade publication.
   —BLDSC (3836.249450).

011   330   US
C L C LEGAL INFORMATION REVIEW. q. $65. Convention Liaison Council, 1575 Eye St., N.E., Ste. 1190, Washington, DC 20005. TEL 202-626-2839. Ed. Jeffrey W. King. **Document type:** newsletter.
   Description: Provides up-to-date legal information, including court cases in the meetings industry.

610   011   SZ   ISSN 0301-2891
CALENDAR OF CONGRESSES OF MEDICAL SCIENCES. (Text in English and French) 1949. a. 10 SFr.($5.50) Council for International Organizations of Medical Sciences - Conseil des Organisations Internationales des Sciences Medicales, c/o World Health Organization, 20 Ave. Appia, CH-1211 Geneva 27, Switzerland. FAX 022-7910746. TELEX 415416. Ed. Dr. Zbigniew Bankowski. adv. circ. 2,000. **Document type:** proceedings.
   Formed by the merger of, and continuing the numbering of: Calendar of International Congresses of Medical Sciences (ISSN 0589-915X); Calendar of Regional Congresses of Medical Sciences (ISSN 0574-248X)

340   US   ISSN 0364-0558
J47
CALENDARS OF THE UNITED STATES HOUSE OF REPRESENTATIVES AND HISTORY OF LEGISLATION. 1986. w. $247 (U.S. subscr. only). U.S. House of Representatives, The Capitol, Washington, DC 20515. (Subscr. to: Superintendent of Documents, U.S. Government Printing Office, Box 371954, Pittsburgh, PA 15250-7954. TEL 202-512-1800. FAX 202-512-2250) **Document type:** government publication.

011   658   CN
CANADIAN ASSOCIATION OF EXPOSITION MANAGERS. COMMUNIQUE. 8/yr. Canadian Association of Exposition Managers - Association Canadienne des Directeurs d'Expositions, 6900 Airport Rd., Ste. 239 A, Box 82, Mississauga, ON L4V 1E8, Canada. TEL 905-678-9377. FAX 905-678-9578. Ed. Carol Ann Burrell. adv.; page Can.$525; adv. contact: Pat Haight. circ. 400. **Document type:** newsletter.

011   610   CN   ISSN 1193-6452
CANADIAN DIRECTORY OF HEALTH CARE CONFERENCES/REPERTOIRE CANADIEN DES CONFERENCES DE SOINS DE SANTE. 1991. a. Can.$20. Canadian Nurses Association - Association des Infirmieres et Infirmiers du Canada, 50 Driveway, Ottawa, ON K2P 1E2, Canada. TEL 613-237-2133. FAX 613-237-3520. **Document type:** directory.
   Description: Lists all Canadian health care conferences currently scheduled to the year 2000. Listings are organized by month and year and include location, theme, sponsoring organization and contact person.

M

011   US
CENTER LINES.* q. International Association of Conference Centers, 243 N. Lindbergh Blvd., St. Louis, MO 63141. TEL 314-349-5576. FAX 314-349-5578. **Document type:** newsletter.

323.4   US
CIVIL LIBERTIES ALERT. 1977. a. free. American Civil Liberties Union (Washington, DC), 122 Maryland Ave., N.E., Washington, DC 20002. TEL 202-544-1681. FAX 202-546-0738. (National Headquarters addr.: 132 W. 43rd St., New York, NY 10036) Ed. Rachel Fischer Alberts. circ. 5,000. **Document type:** newsletter.
   Description: National legislative report includes Congressional voting records on selected votes and information about important legislation in the Congress concerning civil liberties.

CLINICAL CONGRESS NEWS. see *MEDICAL SCIENCES*

011   001.6   HK
COMPUTER EXPO (YEAR): EXHIBITION GUIDE. 1985. a. $25. Business & International Trade Fairs, 18-F First Pacific Bank Centre, 51 Gloucester Rd., Wanchai, Hong Kong. TEL 852-865-2633. FAX 852-866-1770. adv.
   Formerly: Hong Kong Computer Expo (Year).
   Description: Directory of exhibitors with address and brief description.

011   US
CONFERENCE & EXHIBITION FACT FINDER. 1985. m. £30.60 (overseas £45). Batiste Publications Ltd., Pembroke House, Campsbourne Rd., Hornsey, London N8 7PE, England. TEL 0181-340-3291. FAX 0181-341-4840. Ed. William Benjarun. adv. circ. 6,000. (back issues avail.) **Document type:** directory, trade publication.
   Description: Provides an overview of the conference and exhibition industries, including destinations, venues, services, and related areas.

011   UK   ISSN 0260-2431
THE CONFERENCE BLUE BOOK; your guaranteed guide to conference venues in the British Isles. 1978. a. £65 (overseas £90) (includes Green Book). Miller Freeman Information Services (Subsidiary of: United News & Media), Riverbank House, Angel Ln., Tonbridge, Kent TN9 1SE, England. TEL 01732-362666. FAX 01732-367301. TELEX 957829. Ed. Gwen Young. adv. contact: Elaine Soni. illus.; charts. circ. 8,000. **Document type:** directory.
   —BLDSC (3409.030000).
   Description: Directed to all technically oriented meeting organizers, from large conferences to small training seminars. Provides a regionalized list of more than 4,500 U.K. venues indexed alphabetically with contacts.

011   US
CONFERENCE CHRONICLES. s-a. General Merchandise Distributors Council, 1275 Lake Ave., Colorado Springs, CO 80906. TEL 303-576-4260.

MEETINGS AND CONGRESSES

011   UK   ISSN 0260-2199
THE CONFERENCE GREEN BOOK; guide to conference venues in the British Isles offering sports, leisure, and "special interest" facilities. 1980. a. £65 (foreign £90) (includes Blue Book). Miller Freeman Information Services (Subsidiary of: United News & Media), Riverbank House, Angel Ln., Tonbridge, Kent TN9 1SE, England. TEL 01732-362666. FAX 01732-367301. TELEX 957829. Ed. Gwen Young. adv. contact: Elaine Soni. charts; illus. circ. 8,000. **Document type:** directory.
—BLDSC (3409.538000).
Description: Directed to special-interest and leisure-oriented meeting organizers, from large conferences to small training seminars. Provides a regionalized list of more than 4,500 United Kingdom venues indexed alphabetically with contact names.

CONFERENCE PAPERS ANNUAL INDEX. see *MEETINGS AND CONGRESSES — Abstracting, Bibliographies, Statistics*

CONFERENCE PAPERS INDEX. see *MEETINGS AND CONGRESSES — Abstracting, Bibliographies, Statistics*

011   UK   ISSN 0143-7895
CONFERENCE WORLD. 1972. bi-m. £12 to non-members. Association of Conference Executives, Riverside House, High St., Huntingdon, Cambs. PE18 6SG, England. adv.; bk.rev. circ. 4,500. **Indexed:** Build.Manage.Abstr., Fluidex.
Formerly (until Jan. 1978): A C E News.

011   CN   ISSN 0841-968X
CONGRES MENSUEL, BULLETIN DE NOUVELLES. English edition: Meetings Monthly, News Bulletin (ISSN 0841-9663) 1988. m. $40 (effective Jan. 1991). Publicom Inc., C.P. 365, Place d'Armes, Montreal, PQ H2Y 3H1, Canada. TEL 514-274-0004. FAX 514-274-5884. Ed. Guy Jonkman. adv. contact: Guy Jonkman. circ. 6,341. **Document type:** trade publication.
Formerly (until 1988): Congres Mensuel (ISSN 0841-9671)
Description: A trade publication for meeting planners.

011   SP   ISSN 0214-8056
CONGRESOS CONVENCIONES E INCENTIVOS. 1983. 9/yr. 20000 ptas. Princesa 1, Torre de Madrid, planta 27-1, 28008 Madrid, Spain. TEL 91-548-09-73. FAX 91-5479813. TELEX 41037 GOSA E. Ed. J.L. Gonzalez Salgado. adv.; bk.rev. circ. 12,000. **Document type:** trade publication.

711   UK
CONGRESS IN PARK AND RECREATION ADMINISTRATION. PROGRAMME. triennial. International Federation of Park and Recreation Administration, General Secretary, The Grotto, Lower Basildon, Reading, Berks. RG8 9NE, England. TEL 0491-874222. FAX 0491-874059.
Formerly: World Congress in Public Park Administration. Programme (ISSN 0510-8233)

910.09   IT
CONGRESS TODAY E INCENTIVE TRAVEL. 1991. bi-m. L.60000. Centro Italiano Pubblicita s.r.l., Via G. Bruzzesi 35, 20146 Milan, Italy. TEL 39-2-472122. FAX 39-2-48951269. Ed. Bruno Bonisolli. adv.; B&W page L.3000000, color page L.4500000. **Document type:** consumer publication.
Formerly (until 1994): Congress Today (ISSN 1121-3051)

CONGRESVISIE; vakblad voor congressen en zakelijke evenementen. see *BUSINESS AND ECONOMICS — International Commerce*

CONTROLLED RELEASE NEWSLETTER. see *CHEMISTRY — Organic Chemistry*

011   IT
CONVEGNI; e comunicazione. (Text in English, Italian) 1987. 11/yr. L.190000 (foreign L.360000). Convegni s.r.l., Viale Lombardia 20, 20131 Milan, Italy. TEL 2-706-000-58. FAX 2-706-00-740. Ed. Vittore Castellazzi. adv.; B&W page L.3500000; adv. contact: Anna Bravil. bk.rev. circ. 10,000. **Document type:** trade publication, consumer publication.

CONVENE. see *BUSINESS AND ECONOMICS — Management*

011   AT   ISSN 1039-1029
CONVENTION & INCENTIVE MARKETING. 1974. m. Aus.$60. Rank Publishing Co., 66 Chandos St., St. Leonards, N.S.W. 2065, Australia. TEL 02-438-2300. FAX 612-438-5962. Ed. Julia Newbould. adv. circ. 15,145.
Formerly (until 1988): Convention (ISSN 0312-0821)
Description: Discusses conferences, exhibitions and incentives throughout Australia, New Zealand and Asia.

011 330   US
CONVENTION LIAISON COUNCIL. LEGAL REVIEW. q. Convention Liaison Council, 1575 Eye St., N.W., Ste. 1200, Washington, DC 20005. TEL 202-626-2764. FAX 202-371-8825.

011   US
CONVENTION NEWS. q. Netherlands Convention Bureau, 355 Lexington Ave., 21st Fl., New York, NY 10017. TEL 213-370-7360. FAX 212-370-9507.

011   AT   ISSN 0156-0166
CONVENTION ROSTRUM. 1976. 2/yr. Aus.$60. Rank Publishing Company, 66 Chandos St., St. Leonards, N.S.W. 2065, Australia. TEL 02-438-2300. FAX 02-438-5962. Ed. Sandra Yeomans. adv.; bk.rev.; stat. circ. 9,263. (back issues avail.) **Document type:** directory.
Description: Covers Australasian Pacific venues and services register.

011   CN   ISSN 0226-8922
CONVENTIONS & MEETINGS CANADA. 1971. a. Can.$43. Effective Communications Ltd., 5762 Highway 7, Ste. 207, Markham, ON L3P 1A8, Canada. TEL 905-471-1550. FAX 905-471-1552. Ed. James Nuttall. adv.; circ. 10,416 (controlled). (back issues avail.) **Document type:** trade publication.
Description: Includes information on hotels, motor inns, convention centers and other meeting facilities across Canada.

011   US   ISSN 1074-0627
CONVENTIONSOUTH. 1982. m. $15. Covey Communications Corp., Box 2267, Gulf Shores, AL 36547. TEL 334-968-5300. FAX 334-968-4532. Ed. J. Talty O'Connor. adv.; circ. 10,000 (controlled). **Document type:** trade publication, directory.
Description: For people who plan meetings, conferences and conventions that are held in the South. Covers 13 southeastern states. Articles include how-to features, meeting site profiles, and related news items.

011   UK
CORPORATE EVENT SERVICES. 1990. a. £30 (foreign £37). Showcase Publications Ltd., 12 Felix Ave., London N8 9TL, England. TEL 0181-348-2332. FAX 0181-340-3750. Ed. Kay Chestnutt. adv.; B&W page £1000, color page £1600. circ. 12,000. **Document type:** directory.

910.09   US   ISSN 0745-1636
HD5260
CORPORATE MEETINGS & INCENTIVES. 1980. m. $60. Adams-Laux Company, Inc., 63 Great Rd., Maynard, MA 01754. TEL 508-897-5552. Ed. Connie Goldstein. circ. 36,000.
—CCC.
Description: Articles for senior-level corporate executives and travel agents responsible for selecting sites and destinations for meetings and incentive travel programs.

011   US
COUNCIL OF PROTOCOL EXECUTIVES. NEWSLETTER. 1989. q. $41. Council of Protocol Executives, 101 W. 12th St., Ste. PHH, New York, NY 10011. TEL 212-633-6934. circ. 5,000 (paid). **Document type:** newsletter.

D W J - INFO; Mitteilungen des Bundesverbandes. (Deutsche Waldjugend) see *FORESTS AND FORESTRY*

DAWSONS VENUE DIRECTORY. see *TRAVEL AND TOURISM*

011   UK   ISSN 0954-7134
DELEGATES. 1986. bi-m. £39.50 (overseas £59.50). Blenheim Business Publications, Blenheim House, 630 Chiswick High Rd., London W4 5BG, England. TEL 0181-742-2828. FAX 0181-742-0387. Ed. Robin Anderson; Pub. Georgina Faux. adv. contact: Ophelia Smith. circ. 18,363 (controlled). **Document type:** trade publication.
Description: Covers conferences, incentives, meetings, exhibitions and seminars, and product launches worldwide.

011   GW   ISSN 0933-9760
DEMETER KONGRESS KALENDER MEDIZIN. 1961. a. DM.43. Demeter Verlag GmbH und Co. KG, Bussardstr. 5, 82166 Graefelfing, Germany. TEL 089-85463-0. FAX 089-8543347. **Document type:** catalog.

617.6 011   CN
DENTAL GUIDE (SCARBOROUGH); the CE planner for the dental profession. 1993. q. Can.$35 (foreign Can.$55). Thomson Healthcare Communications, 1120 Birchmount Rd., Ste. 200, Scarborough, ON M1K 5G4, Canada. TEL 416-750-8900. FAX 416-751-8126. Ed. Heather Howie. adv.: B&W page Can.$1595, color page Can.$2685; trim 8 1/8 x 10 3/4; adv. contact: Peter Greenhough. circ. 16,000.
Description: Lists dental conferences, meetings and seminars around the world, with a focus on travel combined with dental education.

011 617.6   GW
DEUTSCHER KONGRESS KALENDER ZAHNMEDIZINER. 1980. a. DM.25. Demeter Verlag GmbH und Co. KG, Bussardstr. 5, 82166 Graefelfing, Germany. TEL 089-85463-0. FAX 089-8543347. **Document type:** catalog.

610 011   SP   ISSN 0210-5578
DIARIO DE CONGRESOS MEDICOS. 1972. irreg. (40/yr.). free to qualified personnel. Ediciones Doyma S.A., Travesera de Gracia 17-21, 80821 Barcelona, Spain. TEL 34-1-200-07-11. FAX 34-1-209-11-36. TELEX 51964 INK-E. Ed. Pedro Espinosa Bravo. adv.: page 260000 ptas.; trim 305 x 420. circ. 3,000. (reprint service avail. from UMI)
—CCC.
Description: Publishes the best and most interesting papers from national and international medical conferences.

011   US
DIRECTORY OF ASSOCIATION MEETING PLANNERS & CONFERENCE - CONVENTION DIRECTORS. a. $237. Salesman's Guide, A Reed Reference Publishing Company, Part of the Reed Elsevier group, 121 Chanlon Rd., New Providence, NJ 07974. TEL 908-464-6800. FAX 908-665-2894. TELEX 138 755. (Subscr. to: Order Dept., Box 1009, Summit, NJ 07902. TEL 800-521-8110) Ed. Dorrell Buono; Pub. Randy Mysel. (also avail. in magnetic tape) **Document type:** directory.
Formerly (until 1992): Nationwide Directory of Association Meeting Planners and Conference - Convention Directors.
Description: Lists approximately 13,000 convention planners for 8,400 national associations that have off-site meetings and, or conventions. Includes separate information on conventions and meetings.

DOMOVA POKLADNICA. see *LITERATURE*

011   GW
DORTMUNDER MESSEBRIEF. s-a. Westfalenhallen Dortmund GmbH, Rheinlanddamm 200, 44139 Dortmund, Germany. TEL 0231-1204521. FAX 0231-1204678. Ed. Peter Weber. adv.; bk.rev.; illus. **Document type:** directory.

011   US
E S C A VOICE. q. Exposition Service Contractors Association, Union Sta., 400 S. Houston St., Ste. 210, Dallas, TX 75202. TEL 214-742-9217. FAX 214-741-2519. **Document type:** newsletter.

ENERGY MEETINGS, CONFERENCES AND SYMPOSIA. see *ENERGY — Abstracting, Bibliographies, Statistics*

EVENT ORGANISER. see *BUSINESS AND ECONOMICS — Marketing And Purchasing*

MEETINGS AND CONGRESSES   4637

011   UK   ISSN 0014-4649
EXHIBITION BULLETIN. 1948. m. £54 (Europe £58; overseas £60). London Bureau, 266-272 Kirkdale, London SE26 4RZ, England. TEL 0181-778-2288. FAX 0181-659-8495. Ed. Peter Cole. adv. contact: Lydia Cole. charts; illus.; index. circ. 4,950. **Indexed:** Key to Econ.Sci. **Document type:** directory, trade publication.
—BLDSC (3836.250000).
  Description: Advance listings of fairs and shows throughout the world.

011   UK   ISSN 0965-3457
EXHIBITION MANAGEMENT. bi-m. £34.55($57.40) (foreign £35.85). Argus Businesss Media Ltd., Fuel and Metals Journals (Subsidiary of: Argus Press Group), Queensway House, 2 Queensway, Redhill, Surrey RH1 1QS, England. TEL 01737-768611. FAX 01737-761685. TELEX 948669 TOPJNL G. Ed. Carol Boxall. **Document type:** trade publication.
  Description: Aimed at the professional exhibition organizer. Covers news, opinions, and the latest products in the exhibition industry.

338.025   CH   ISSN 1019-0996
EXHIBITIONS ROUND THE WORLD. (Text in English) a. $80. Trade Winds, Inc., No.7, Lane 75, Yungkang St., Taipei, Taiwan 10602, Republic of China. TEL 886-2-3913251. FAX 886-2-3964022. **Document type:** directory.
  Description: Contains dates, locations, and all other essential data on over 4,000 of the world's major trade exhibitions.

011   SZ
EXPODATA. 10/yr. Kunzler-Bachmann AG, Geltenwilenstr. 8a, CH-9001 St. Gallen, Switzerland. TEL 071-235555. FAX 071-236745. Ed. Urs Seiler. circ. 5,500. **Document type:** trade publication.

EXPOVISIE. see *BUSINESS AND ECONOMICS — International Commerce*

011   US   ISSN 1043-3740
FAIR NEWS. 1968. bi-m. $17 (Canada $20; elsewhere $30). World's Fair Collectors Society, Inc., Box 20806, Sarasota, FL 34276-3806. TEL 813-923-2590. Ed. Michael R. Pender; Pub. Michael Pender. adv.: page $35; 8 1/2 x 11; adv. contact: Fran Pender. bk.rev./ circ. 5,000 (paid). (looseleaf format; back issues avail.) **Document type:** newsletter.

011   US   ISSN 0194-4649
FAIRS AND EXPOSITIONS. 10/yr. $30 to non-members. International Association of Fairs and Expositions, Box 985, Springfield, MO 65801. TEL 417-862-5771. FAX 417-862-0156. adv. circ. 3,500.

FEDERAZIONE DELLE SOCIETA MEDICO-SCIENTIFICHE ITALIANE. CONGRESSI (YEAR). see *MEDICAL SCIENCES*

FIERA DEL LIBRO. see *PUBLISHING AND BOOK TRADE*

381 690   IT   ISSN 0393-8050
FIERE; rassegna periodica tecnica di documentazione e informazione. 1969. bi-m. L.60000 (foreign L.80000). Casa Editrice la Fiaccola (Milan), Via Carlo Ravizza 62, 20149 Milan, Italy. TEL 02-4814355. FAX 02-4814834. TELEX 335512 COSTRU I. Ed. Giuseppe Saronni. adv.; charts; index. circ. 7,500. (back issues avail.)
  Formerly: Edilizia alle Fiere (ISSN 0013-0877)

500 600 011   UK   ISSN 0046-4686
FORTHCOMING INTERNATIONAL SCIENTIFIC AND TECHNICAL CONFERENCES. no.48, 1971. q. £75($160) to non-members; members £60. Aslib, Association for Information Management, Publications Department, Information House, 20-24 Old St., London EC1V 9AP, England. TEL 071-253-4488. FAX 071-430-0514. (Dist. in N. America by: Learned Information, Inc., 143 Old Marlton Pike, Medford, NJ 08055-8750. TEL 609-654-6266) Ed. Caroline Gulliver. adv. **Indexed:** Fluidex, J.of Ferroc.
—BLDSC (4018.000000). **CCC.**
  Description: Covers forthcoming international conferences in science, technology and medicine.

FRANCE. INSTITUT NATIONAL DE LA SANTE ET DE LA RECHERCHE MEDICALE. COLLOQUES. see *MEDICAL SCIENCES*

011   US
GENERAL MERCHANDISE DISTRIBUTORS COUNCIL. MARKETING CONFERENCE TRANSCRIPTS. s-a. General Merchandise Distributors Council, 1275 Lake Ave., Colorado Springs, CO 80906. TEL 303-576-4260.

GENETICS SOCIETY OF CANADA BULLETIN. see *BIOLOGY — Genetics*

GIORNALE DEI CONGRESSI MEDICI. see *MEDICAL SCIENCES*

011   US
GLOBAL CONNECTIONS. 1978. q. membership. International Society of Meeting Planners, 8383 E. Evans Rd., Scottsdale, AZ 85260. TEL 602-483-0000. FAX 602-998-8022. Ed. Troy E. Johnson. adv. contact: Troy E. Johnson. circ. 5,000. **Document type:** newsletter.
  Description: Aimed at registered meeting planners, certified destination specialists and certified event planners.

011   AG   ISSN 0301-7567
Q101
GUIA DE REUNIONES CIENTIFICAS Y TECNICAS EN LA ARGENTINA. 1959. a. free. (Secretaria de Estado de Ciencia y Tecnologia, Ministerio de Cultura y Educacion) Fundacion para la Educacion la Ciencia y la Cultura, Moreno 431 (Guia de Reuniones) 1091, Buenos Aires, Argentina. adv. circ. 4,000.
—BLDSC (4224.836020).

011   CN   ISSN 1193-7076
GUIDE ANNUEL (YEAR) SALONS EXPOSITIONS CONGRES.* 1990. a. Can.$85. Business Event Guide, 714 Chemin du Golfe, Nun's Island, Quebec, H3E 1A8, Canada. TEL 514-766-1000. FAX 514-766-7667. Ed. Marie Bois Vert. adv. circ. 10,000.

610 011   US
H C E A EXHIBITORS ADVISORY COUNCIL'S ACTION MEMO. s-a. free to members. Healthcare Convention & Exhibitors Association, 5775 Peachtree-Dunwoody Rd., Ste. 500 G, Atlanta, GA 30342. TEL 404-252-3663. FAX 404-252-0774. Ed.Bd. circ. 1,800. (back issues avail.)
  Description: Promotes the use of exhibitors advisory councils in the healthcare convention and exhibition industry.

060 610   US
H C E A HANDBOOK; a directory of healthcare meetings and conventions. 2/yr. $168 to non-members. Healthcare Convention & Exhibitors Association, 5775 Peachtree-Dunwoody Rd., Ste. 500 G, Atlanta, GA 30342. TEL 404-252-3663. FAX 404-252-0774. circ. 1,000 (paid).
  Description: Lists more than 1500 healthcare meetings.

011   US
I A F E DIRECTORY. a. $85 to non-members. International Association of Fairs and Expositions, Box 985, Springfield, MO 65801. TEL 417-862-5771. FAX 417-862-0156. adv. circ. 3,000. **Document type:** directory.

011   IT
IN FIERA. (Text in English, Italian) 1989. 9/yr. Ente Autonomo Fiera Milano, Palazzo Cisi, 20131 Milan, Italy. TEL 1-499-298. FAX 2-481-3072. TELEX 331360 EAFM I. Ed. Gino Colombo. adv.; charts; illus. circ. 35,000.

INCENTIVE JOURNAL; magazine for motivation and sales promotion. see *BUSINESS AND ECONOMICS — Marketing And Purchasing*

INNOVATION AND TECHNOLOGY TRANSFER. see *LIBRARY AND INFORMATION SCIENCES*

610 011   US
INSIGHT (ATLANTA). 3/yr. free to members. Healthcare Convention & Exhibitors Association, 5775 Peachtree-Dunwoody Rd., Ste. 500 G, Atlanta, GA 30342. TEL 404-252-3663. FAX 404-252-0774. Ed.Bd. circ. 1,350. (back issues avail.)

011   US   ISSN 0193-0516
INSURANCE CONFERENCE PLANNER. 1965. bi-m. $42. Adams-Laux Company, Inc., 63 Great Rd., Maynard, MA 01754. TEL 508-897-5552. FAX 508-897-6824. Ed. Susan Hatch. adv. circ. 7,300.
—UnCover. **CCC.**
  Formerly: Insurance Magazine's Green Book of Convention Planning.

011   US
INSURANCE MEETINGS AND INCENTIVE TRAVEL. 1992. bi-m. $20. Coastal Communications Corporation, 2600 N. Military Trail, Boca Raton, FL 33431. TEL 407-989-0600. FAX 407-989-9509. Ed. Harvey Golden. circ. 2,418. **Document type:** trade publication.
  Formerly (until Nov. 1994): Insurance Conventions and Incentive Travel (ISSN 1068-9435)
  Description: Contains articles and relevant information about convention destinations, industry activities, motivation and incentive programs, platform speakers, studies on convention practices and related topics.

011 910.202   US
INTERNATIONAL ASSOCIATION OF CONVENTION AND VISITOR BUREAUS. NEWSLETTER. m. International Association of Convention and Visitor Bureaus, 2000 L St., N.W., Ste. 702, Washington, DC 20036-4990. TEL 202-296-7888. FAX 202-296-7889. TELEX 910-245-0151. Ed. Gina Barrett. adv. contact: Emily Cates. circ. 1,600. **Document type:** newsletter.

011   BE   ISSN 0538-6349
INTERNATIONAL CONGRESS CALENDAR. (Text in English) 1961. q. $395 (effective 1995). Union of International Associations, Rue Washington 40, 1050 Brussels, Belgium. TEL 32-2-6401808. FAX 32-2-6460525. Ed. G. de Coninck. adv.; index, cum.index. **Document type:** directory.
—BLDSC (4539.057000).
  Description: Provides current information on over 7,000 international events scheduled for the next 12 to 15 months.

011   BE   ISSN 0538-6772
INTERNATIONAL CONGRESS SCIENCE SERIES. 1961. irreg., latest vol.12. price varies. Union of International Associations, Rue Washington 40, 1050 Brussels, Belgium. TEL 32-2-6401808. FAX 32-2-6460525.

INTERNATIONAL CONGRESS SERIES. see *SCIENCES: COMPREHENSIVE WORKS*

011   PH   ISSN 0074-588X
INTERNATIONAL FEDERATION OF ASIAN AND WESTERN PACIFIC CONTRACTORS' ASSOCIATIONS. PROCEEDINGS OF THE ANNUAL CONVENTION. (Proceedings published by organizing committee) irreg. International Federation of Asian and Western Pacific Contractors Associations, Padilla Building, 3rd Fl., Ortigas Commercial Center, Emerald Ave., Pasig, Metro Manila, Philippines. FAX 632-631-2789. TELEX 29083 IFAWPCA PH. **Document type:** proceedings.

INTERNATIONAL SOCIETY OF CITRICULTURE. PROCEEDINGS. see *AGRICULTURE*

INTERNATIONAL THIRD WORLD STUDIES - JOURNAL AND REVIEW. see *POLITICAL SCIENCE — International Relations*

INTERNATIONAL TRADESHOW DIRECTORY. see *BUSINESS AND ECONOMICS — Trade And Industrial Directories*

INTERNATIONAL UPDATE. see *BUSINESS AND ECONOMICS — International Commerce*

011 323.4   GW
JULI-MAGAZIN. 1984. q. DM.24. Junge Liberale NRW e.V., Luisenstr. 7, 40215 Dusseldorf, Germany. TEL 0211-378085. Ed. Oliver Kroehl. adv.; bk.rev.; bibl.; stat. circ. 3,000. (back issues avail.)

KALENDAR ODBORARA. see *LABOR UNIONS*

MEETINGS AND CONGRESSES

011 UK
KEY NOTE REPORT: EXHIBITIONS AND CONFERENCE ORGANISERS. irreg., vol.2, 1994. £185. Key Note Publications Ltd., Field House, 72 Oldfield Rd., Hampton, Middlesex TW12 2HQ, England. TEL 0181-783-0755. FAX 0181-783-1720. Ed. Richard Caines. **Document type:** monographic series.
●Also available online.
Also available on CD-ROM.

910.09 GW
KOELNER KONGRESS REPORT. English edition: Cologne Convention. 1970. s-a. free. Cologne Tourist Office, Convention Department, Unter Fettenhennen 19, 50667 Cologne, Germany. FAX 0221-2213320. Eds. Erhard Schlieter, Elke Reiff. adv. contact: Erhard Schlieter. circ. 6,000. **Document type:** consumer publication.

011 NE ISSN 0942-0568
KONCIZE. (Text in Esperanto) 1975. bi-m. European Esperanto Youth, Jan Luykenlaan 102, NL-7412 NS Deventer, Netherlands. Ed. Klaas Dijkstra. adv.; bk.rev. circ. 2,000. **Document type:** bulletin. **Description:** Information on Esperanto meetings, travel.

499.992 NE ISSN 0083-3851
PM8201
KONGRESA LIBRO. (Text in Esperanto) 1905. a. fl.12($7) Universala Esperanto-Asocio, Nieuwe Binnenweg 176, 3015 BJ Rotterdam, Netherlands. TEL 31-10-4361044. FAX 31-10-4361751. E-mail: uea@inter.nl.net. Ed. Nikola Rasic. adv.: B&W page fl.970; adv. contact: Nikola Rasic. circ. 2,500. **Document type:** proceedings. **Description:** Contains program information, background articles and lists of participants.

057.87 XO
KULTURNOPOLITICKY KALENDAR. a. Obzor, Spitalska 35, 815 85 Bratislava, Slovakia. illus.

L I N K LINE. (Library and Information Network) see *BIRTH CONTROL*

LEADER IN ACTION. see *EDUCATION*

L5 SPACE DEVELOPMENT CONFERENCE. PROCEEDINGS. see *AERONAUTICS AND SPACE FLIGHT*

011 IT
M & C. (Meeting & Congressi) 1973. 10/yr. L.210000. Ediman s.r.l., Corso San Gottardo, 39, 20136 Milan, Italy. TEL 39-2-58103791. FAX 39-2-58103789. adv.: B&W page L.4100000, color page L.6200000. circ. 19,000.

011 US
M E & I T NEWSLETTER.* (Meetings, Expositions & Incentive Travel); the weekly about meetings, expositions & incentive travel. 1981. w. $199. Aviation - Space Writers Association, 6540 50th St., N., Oakdale, MN 55128-1708. Ed. William F. Kaiser. bk.rev. circ. 2,100. (looseleaf format)

M UND A - MESSEPLANER INTERNATIONAL; schedule for fairs and exhibitions worldwide. see *BUSINESS AND ECONOMICS — Trade And Industrial Directories*

M UND A REPORT; Messen und Marketing Events. see *ADVERTISING AND PUBLIC RELATIONS*

MADISON AREA'S GAY - LESBIAN CALENDAR AND GUIDE. see *HOMOSEXUALITY*

MEDICAL EXPRESS REPORTS. see *MEDICAL SCIENCES*

MEDICAL FORUM REPORTER. see *MEDICAL SCIENCES*

011 US ISSN 0093-1314
MEDICAL MEETINGS. 1973. 8/yr. $56 (foreign $105). 63 Great Rd., Maynard, MA 01754. TEL 508-897-5552. FAX 508-897-6824. Ed. David Erickson; Pub. Peter Huestis. adv.; circ. 14,000. **Indexed:** Rehabil.Lit. **Document type:** trade publication.
—BLDSC (5529.972000); UnCover. **CCC.**

011 GW ISSN 0175-3053
MEDIZINISCHE KONGRESSE; national - international. 1957. a. DM.30. M K und K Verlagsgesellschaft mbH, Mitteldicker Weg 1, 63263 Neu-Isenburg, Germany. TEL 069-69500845. FAX 069-69500850. adv. circ. 40,000. (back issues avail.) **Document type:** directory.

011 AU
MEETING. (Text in English, German) m. S.300. Johann L. Bondi und Sohn, Industriestr. 2, A-2380 Perchtoldsdorf, Austria. TEL 01-864921. FAX 01-86492144. circ. 10,500. **Document type:** trade publication.

350 US ISSN 1080-7489
MEETING & CONFERENCE EXECUTIVES. 1984. m. $94.50 (foreign $107.50). Mather Communications Inc., Box 990024, Boston, MA 02199-0024. TEL 617-523-2123. FAX 617-523-2575. Ed. Joan Mather. bk.rev.; index. circ. 1,000. (looseleaf format; back issues avail.) **Document type:** newsletter.
Formerly: Meeting Planners Alert (ISSN 0743-3832)

001 910.09 UK ISSN 0953-2803
MEETING AND INCENTIVE TRAVEL. 1986. 10/yr. £50($150) Conference and Travel Publications Ltd., Media House, The Square, Forest Row, E. Sussex RH18 5EP, England. TEL 44-342-824044. FAX 44-342-824030. adv.: B&W page £4360 or £1785, color page £6560 or £2625; trim 297 x 210. circ. 12,245.
—BLDSC (5536.222490).
Formerly (until 1987): Venue (ISSN 0267-7490)

011 910 CN ISSN 1188-1739
MEETING COMMUNICATIONS.* (Text in French) 1991. 4/yr. Can.$3.95 per no. Business Event Guide, 714 Chemin du Golfe, Nun's Island, Quebec, H3E 1A8, Canada. TEL 514-766-7667. FAX 514-766-7667. Ed. Marie Bois Vert. adv. circ. 10,000.

011 US ISSN 8750-7218
MEETING MANAGER. 1981. m. $35. Meeting Planners International, 1950 Stemmons Freeway, Ste. 5018, Dallas, TX 75207-3109. TEL 214-712-7735. FAX 214-712-7770. TELEX 535109 MPI. Ed. Tina Berres Filipski. adv.: B&W page $3750, color page $5040; trim 7 x 10; adv. contact: Bridget McGlynn. bk.rev. circ. 12,500. (back issues avail.)
—UnCover.
Formerly (until 1984): Meeting Place.
Description: Focuses on educating readers on all aspects of meeting planning, including site selection and negotiation, food and beverage tips, special event ideas, budgeting, and general meeting management.

658.4 US ISSN 0145-630X
MEETING NEWS; news, information & ideas for better meetings. (Supplement avail.: V I P) 1977. 18/yr. $65. Miller Freeman Inc. (New York) (Subsidiary of: United Newspapers Group), 1515 Broadway, New York, NY 10036. TEL 212-869-1300; 800-447-0138. FAX 212-302-6273. Ed. Laura Rowleyer. adv.; circ. 75,000 (controlled). **Indexed:** Hospit.Ind. **Document type:** trade publication.
—CCC.
Description: Methods and ideas for meeting planners and convention managers.

350 US ISSN 0886-2214
MEETING PLANNERS GUIDEBOOK. CALIFORNIA & NEVADA EDITION. 1982. a. $12.95. M P G Productions, 6 Morton Court, Ste. C, Mill Valley, CA 94941. TEL 415-388-1140. FAX 415-388-0804. adv. circ. 50,000.
Formerly (until 1986): Meeting Planners Guidebook. San Francisco Bay Area and Northern California Edition (ISSN 8755-7495)
Description: Lists information on sites and services in western US.

011 US ISSN 0025-8652
AS6
MEETINGS AND CONVENTIONS; the meeting & incentive planner's resource. Abbreviated title: M & C. 1969. m. $70 (Canada $102; Mexico $95; elsewhere $120). Reed Travel Group, Part of the Reed Elsevier group (Subsidiary of: Reed Telepublishing), 500 Plaza Dr., Secaucus, NJ 07096. TEL 201-902-1700. FAX 201-319-1796. (Subscr. to: Box 173327, Denver, CO 80217-9421. TEL 303-388-4511) Ed. Lori Cioffi; Pub. Mort Silverman. adv.: B&W page $12265, color page $15925; trim 7 1/8 x 10 7/8; adv. contact: Peg Haw. bk.rev.; illus.; tr.lit. circ. 80,141. **Indexed:** Bus.Ind., Tr.& Dev.Alert, Tr.& Indus.Ind.
—BLDSC (5312.920000); UMI; UnCover.
Incorporates: Incentive World.

011 US
MEETINGS AND CONVENTIONS ASIA PACIFIC. 1993. q. Reed Travel Group, Part of the Reed Elsevier group (Subsidiary of: Reed Telepublishing), 500 Plaza Dr., Secaucus, NJ 07096. TEL 201-902-1700. (Subscr. to: 44 Cook St., Denver, CO 80206) Ed. Lori Cioffi. adv.: page $5530; adv. contact: Mort Silverman. circ. 12,059 (controlled). (back issues avail.) **Document type:** trade publication.
Description: Covers issues related to planning meetings, conventions and exhibitions for key decision-makers in 12 Asia Pacific countries.

011 US
MEETINGS AND CONVENTIONS GAVEL; international guide to facilities and services. 1969. a. Reed Travel Group, Part of the Reed Elsevier group (Subsidiary of: Reed Telepublishing), 500 Plaza Dr., Secaucus, NJ 07096. TEL 201-902-2000. FAX 201-902-7900. (Subscr. to: Box 173327, Denver, CO 80217-9421. TEL 303-388-4511) adv.: B&W page $12025, color $15540; trim 7 7/8 x 10 7/8. circ. 80,141.

MEETINGS & EXPOSITIONS. see *BUSINESS AND ECONOMICS — Management*

011 CN ISSN 0318-1049
MEETINGS & INCENTIVE TRAVEL. 1972. 7/yr. Can.$36. Maclean-Hunter Ltd., Maclean-Hunter Bldg., 777 Bay St., Toronto, ON M5W 1A7, Canada. TEL 416-596-2697. FAX 416-596-5810. Ed. Lori Bak. adv. circ. 12,300. **Indexed:** Can.B.P.I.
Formerly: Canadian Sales Meetings and Conventions.
Description: News, trends and technologies for corporate and association meeting, convention and incentive travel planners.

011 CN ISSN 0841-9663
MEETINGS MONTHLY, NEWS BULLETIN; for Canadian meeting planners. French edition: Congres Mensuel, Bulletin de Nouvelles (ISSN 0841-968X) 1988. m. $40. (Association of Meeting Organizers) Publicom Inc., C.P. 365, Place d'Armes, Montreal, PQ H2Y 3H1, Canada. TEL 514-274-0004. FAX 514-274-5884. TELEX 055-61866. Ed. Guy Jonkman. adv.; bk.rev.; circ. 12,703 (controlled). (back issues avail.) **Document type:** trade publication.
Formerly: Meetings Monthly (ISSN 0841-9655)

333.792 UN ISSN 0047-6641
QC770
MEETINGS ON ATOMIC ENERGY. (Text in English) 1969. q. S.720. International Atomic Energy Agency, Wagramerstr. 5, P.O. Box 100, A-1400 Vienna, Austria. TEL 43-1-209-2360. FAX 43-1-209-5302. E-mail: fossett@adp01.iaea.or.at. (Dist. in U.S. by: Unipub, 4611-F Assembly Dr., Lanham, MD 20706-4391) Ed. Sandra Salvini-Plawen. index; circ. 2,150 (paid). **Document type:** proceedings.

011 352 GW
▼**MESSAGE.** (Text in English, German) 1995. q. free. Congress Centrum Mainz GmbH, Rheinstr. 66, 55116 Mainz, Germany. TEL 06131-242100. FAX 06131-242105. Ed. Martin Brunwinkel. adv. contact: Heidrun Dietze. circ. 25,000. **Document type:** government publication.

011 AU
MESSE MARKT INTERNATIONAL. bi-m. Jenullgasse 4, A-1141 Vienna, Austria. TEL 01-8946452. FAX 01-8946523. TELEX 133832. Ed. Karin Repp. circ. 21,000. **Document type:** bulletin.

011 AU
MESSEMARKT. 1981. bi-m. S.180 (foreign S.250). Carl Gerold und Sohn Verlagsbuchhandlung, Koenigstetterstr. 132, A-3430 Tulln, Austria. TEL 01-8946449. FAX 01-894644960. Ed. Karin Repp. adv.; bk.rev. circ. 21,000. **Document type:** trade publication.

011 II
N A S S D O C RESEARCH INFORMATION SERIES. CONFERENCE ALERT; quarterly calendar. (Text in English) q. Rs.40. Indian Council of Social Science Research, National Social Science Documentation Centre, 35 Ferozshah Rd., New Delhi 110 001, India. TEL 91-11-388342. FAX 91-11-388037. TELEX 31-61083 ISSR IN. Ed. Indira Kaul. circ. 100. **Description:** Quarterly list of conferences, seminars and training courses in social sciences, and library and information sciences.

011 US
**NATIONAL COALITION OF BLACK MEETING PLANNERS.
NEWSLETTER.** q. membership. National Coalition of Black Meeting Planners, 8630 Fenton St., Ste. 328, Silver Spring, MD 20910-3803. circ. 2,000. **Document type:** newsletter.

011 020 US ISSN 0739-1471
QA76.55 CODEN: PNOMDR
NATIONAL ONLINE MEETING. PROCEEDINGS. 1980. a. $55. Learned Information, Inc., 143 Old Marlton Pike, Medford, NJ 08055-8750.
TEL 609-654-6266. FAX 609-654-4309. Eds. Martha Williams, Thomas H. Hogan. (back issues avail.) **Indexed:** INSPEC. **Document type:** proceedings.
—BLDSC (6027.839000); Ei. **CCC.**
Formerly (until 1980): National Online Information Meeting. Proceedings.
Description: Examines changes and challenges that will face the online industry as it reaches the 21st century.

011 US ISSN 0735-4444
HD2743
NATIONWIDE DIRECTORY OF CORPORATE MEETING PLANNERS. a. $345. Salesman's Guide, A Reed Reference Publishing Company, Part of the Reed Elsevier group, 121 Chanlon Rd., New Providence, NJ 07974. TEL 908-464-6800.
FAX 908-665-2894. TELEX 138 755. (Subscr. to: Salesman's Guide, Order Dept., Box 1009, Summit, NJ 07902. TEL 800-521-8110) Ed. Dorrell Buono; Pub. Randy Mysel. **Document type:** directory.
Description: Lists over 17,000 corporate meeting planners who plan off-site meetings for over 11,000 corporations. Arranged alphabetically by state and city, information includes: type of business, addresses and telephone numbers, FAX numbers, number of meetings per year, number of attendees, basic geographic destination (including outside USA), and months meetings are held.

011 YU ISSN 0350-011X
NAUCNI I STRUCNI SKUPOVI U JUGOSLAVII I U INOSTRANSTVU/SCIENTIFIC AND PROFESSIONAL MEETINGS IN YUGOSLAVIA AND FOREIGN COUNTRIES. (Text in English and Serbo-Croatian) 1975. s-a. $102. Jugoslovenski Centar za Tehniku i Naucnu Dokumentaciju - Yugoslav Center for Technical and Scientific Documentation (YCTSD), Slobodana Penezica-Krcuna 29-31, Belgrade, Yugoslavia. Ed. Ljiljana Kojic-Bogdanovic.
Formerly: Naunci Skupovi u SFRJ i u Inostranstvu (ISSN 0028-1220)

011 US
NETWORK - INK. 7/yr. National Association of Exposition Managers, c/o I A E M Foundation, Box 802425, Dallas, TX 75380-2425.
FAX 317-687-0017.

NEWSMETER. see ADVERTISING AND PUBLIC RELATIONS

011 JA ISSN 0913-3437
NIKKEI EVENTS. (Text in Japanese) 1987. m. 21000 Yen. Nikkei Business Publications, Inc. (Subsidiary of: Nihon Keizai Shimbun, Inc.), 2-7-6 Hirakawa-cho, Chiyoda-ku, Tokyo 102, Japan. TEL 03-5210-8502. FAX 03-5210-8119. Ed. Hiroshi Nagai; Pub. Ryoji Migiya. adv. contact: Masahiko Miyauchi. circ. 14,553. **Document type:** trade publication.
Description: For planners of events, meetings, and conventions. Provides news on exhibitions, conventions, conferences and seminars, including guidelines for the planning of corporate events.

O S A ANNUAL MEETING DIGEST. (Optical Society of America, Inc.) see PHYSICS — Optics

647 US ISSN 1070-4515
TX907 CODEN: OMFGDE
OFFICIAL MEETING FACILITIES GUIDE. NORTH AMERICA. 1974. s-a. $60. Reed Travel Group, Part of the Reed Elsevier group (Subsidiary of: Reed Telepublishing), 500 Plaza Dr., Secaucus, NJ 07096. TEL 201-902-2000. FAX 201-902-2053. Ed. Virginia Nonnenman. illus. circ. 18,500. —CASDDS.
Formerly (until 1992): Official Meeting Facilities Guide (ISSN 0094-5242)

647 US ISSN 1054-3309
TX907.5.E85
OFFICIAL MEETING FACILITIES GUIDE EUROPE. 1990. s-a. $100. Reed Travel Group, Part of the Reed Elsevier group (Subsidiary of: Reed Telepublishing), 500 Plaza Dr., Secaucus, NJ 07096. TEL 201-902-2000. FAX 201-902-2053. (Subscr. to: P.O. Box 9000, 2130 OB Hootdorf, Netherlands) Ed. Virginia Nonnenman. circ. 10,300.

OFFICIEL DES CONGRES ET DU TOURISME D'AFFAIRES. see TRAVEL AND TOURISM

PEN IN HAND. see JOURNALISM

PHILATELIC EXHIBITOR. see PHILATELY

PHYSICIANS' TRAVEL & MEETING GUIDE. see TRAVEL AND TOURISM

POLITICA MERIDIONALISTA; rivista mensile di cultura, economia e informazione. see BUSINESS AND ECONOMICS — Economic Situation And Conditions

011 AT ISSN 0811-594X
QUORUM. 1982. bi-m. Aus.$30 (foreign Aus.$60). Braynart Group Pty.Ltd., 1 Waterloo Rd., Macquarie Park, N.S.W. 2113, Australia. TEL 02-875-3700.
FAX 02-878-8016. Ed. David Latta. adv. contact: Michael Bleakley. circ. 8,500. **Document type:** trade publication.
Description: Provides information on services, products and destinations relating to conferences, conventions, meetings and incentives.

R C M A INSIGHTS. (Religious Conference Management Association) see RELIGIONS AND THEOLOGY

RAHNAMA-YI SIMINARHA-YI IRAN/DIRECTORY OF SCIENTIFIC MEETINGS HELD IN IRAN. see SCIENCES: COMPREHENSIVE WORKS

RELIGIOUS CONFERENCE MANAGER. see RELIGIONS AND THEOLOGY

RESOURCES IN AGING; an international newsletter featuring new developments in aging. see GERONTOLOGY AND GERIATRICS

S C A L A C S. (American Chemical Society) see CHEMISTRY

S C M P NEWSLETTER. (Society of Corporate Meeting Professionals) see BUSINESS AND ECONOMICS

011 US
SCIENCE FICTION CONVENTION REGISTER. 1974. 3/yr. $12. Erwin S. "Filthy Pierre" Strauss, Ed. & Pub., 101 S. Whiting, Ste. 700, Fairfax, VA 22038-3343. TEL 703-461-8645. circ. 400 (paid). **Document type:** directory.

500 011 US ISSN 0487-8965
Q101 CODEN: SMETAL
SCIENTIFIC MEETINGS. 1957. q. $70 (rates typically set in Jan.). Scientific Meetings Publications, Box 81662, San Diego, CA 92138. TEL 619-270-2910. FAX 619-270-2910. Ed. Marian Holleman; Pub. Irving Wasserberg. circ. 1,200 (paid). (also avail. in microform from UMI; back issues avail.) reprint service avail. from UMI) **Indexed:** Fluidex. **Document type:** directory.
—CASDDS; UMI.
Description: Directory of forthcoming scientific, technical, medical, engineering and management meetings and international conferences.

011 UK
SCOTLAND: CONFERENCE AND INCENTIVE BROCHURE. irreg. free. Scottish Tourist Board, 23 Ravelston Terrace, Edinburgh EH4 3EU, Scotland. TEL 0131-332-2433. FAX 0131-343-1513. **Document type:** directory.
Formerly: Scotland: Conferences, Meetings, Seminars.

SHOW MEETING. see COMMUNICATIONS

MEETINGS AND CONGRESSES 4639

011 338 CN ISSN 0845-8448
SHOWS AND EXHIBITIONS. 1964. a. (plus 3 updates). Can.$107.50. Maclean-Hunter Ltd., Business Publication Division, Maclean-Hunter Bldg., 777 Bay St., Toronto, ON M5W 1A7, Canada.
TEL 416-867-9500. FAX 416-867-1505. Ed. Nancy Remnant.
Formerly (until 1989): Canadian Industry Shows and Exhibitions (ISSN 0068-8967)
Description: Describes major shows and exhibitions held each year in Canada, along with selected American shows, in addition to major European and Asian exhibitions. Complete listings of location, dates, products displayed, personnel, and exhibition rates.

381.1 SI
SINGAPORE CONVENTION & EXHIBITION DIRECTORY (YEAR). (Text in English) a. $40. Times Trade Directories Pte. Ltd., Times Centre, 1 New Industrial Rd., Singapore 1953, Singapore. TEL 2848844. FAX 2881186. TELEX RS 25713 TIMES. **Document type:** directory.
Description: Guide to the convention and exhibition facilities and the relevant supporting services available in Singapore.

011 US
SOCIETY OF GOVERNMENT MEETING PLANNERS. NEWSLETTER. m. Society of Government Meeting Planners, 219 E. Main St., Mechanicsburg, PA 17055. TEL 717-795-7467.

616.07 SA
SOUTH AFRICAN SOCIETY OF PATHOLOGISTS. CONGRESS BROCHURE. (Text in Afrikaans and English) a. free. South Africa Society of Pathologists, P.O. Box 2034, Pretoria 0001, South Africa. TEL 27-12-3283600. adv. circ. 300. **Document type:** proceedings.
Refereed Serial

SUCCESSFUL MEETINGS; the authority on meetings and incentive travel management. see BUSINESS AND ECONOMICS — Marketing And Purchasing

011 GW ISSN 0342-7951
T W/CONVENTION INDUSTRY. (Tagungs-Wirtschaft); international magazine for meeting and incentive professionals. (Text in English, German) 1977. 8/yr. DM.109.14 (foreign DM.115). M und A Verlag fuer Messen, Ausstellungen und Kongresse GmbH, Postfach 101528, 60015 Frankfurt a.M., Germany. TEL 069-759502. FAX 069-75951280. Ed. Klaus Goschmann. adv.: B&W page DM.5400, color page DM.6600; trim 186 x 255; adv. contact: Britta Schlenker-Witt. tr.lit. circ. 20,500. (back issues avail.) **Indexed:** Art.Hosp.& Tour. **Document type:** trade publication.
—BLDSC (9076.748500).
Description: International trade magazine for meeting and incentive professionals.

011 GW
T W TAGUNGSREGIONEN. 1983. a. DM.50. T W Tagungswirtschaft GmbH, M und A Verlag fuer Messen, Ausstellungen und Kongresse GmbH, Mainzer Landstr. 251, 60326 Frankfurt a.M., Germany. TEL 069-759502. FAX 069-75951909. Ed. Klaus Goschmann. adv.: B&W page DM.5400, color page DM.6600; trim 255 x 184. circ. 13,500. **Document type:** trade publication.
—CCC.
Former titles (until 1993): T W Veranstaltungsplaner; M und A Tagungsplaner; M und A Tagungsplaner Europa (ISSN 0343-0545)
Refereed Serial

011 JA
TRADE FAIRS IN JAPAN (YEAR); a guide to trade fairs designed for specific products and industries. 1990. a. $76. Japan External Trade Organization, Publications Department, 2-5 Toranomon 2-chome, Minato-ku, Tokyo 105, Japan. TEL 03-3582-3518. FAX 03-3587-2485.
Description: Basic source for information on trade exhibition centers and overseas representatives of exhibitions.

MEETINGS AND CONGRESSES — ABSTRACTING, BIBLIOGRAPHIES, STATISTICS

381.1 US ISSN 1046-4395
T394
TRADE SHOWS WORLDWIDE; an international directory of events, facilities and suppliers. irreg., 7th ed., 1992. $195. Gale Research Inc., 835 Penobscot Bldg., Detroit, MI 48266. TEL 313-961-2242. FAX 313-961-6083. Eds. Martin Connors, Charity Anne Dorgan. (also avail. in magnetic tape; diskette format) **Document type:** directory.
Formerly: Trade Shows and Professional Exhibits Directory (ISSN 0886-1439)
Description: Contains detailed entries for over 5900 scheduled exhibitions, trade shows, association conventions, and similar events.

TRADESHOW & CONVENTION GUIDE. see *TRAVEL AND TOURISM*

TRADESHOW DIRECTORY. see *BUSINESS AND ECONOMICS* — *Trade And Industrial Directories*

616.994 011 SZ
U I C C INTERNATIONAL CALENDAR OF MEETINGS ON CANCER. biennial. free. Union Internationale Contre le Cancer - International Union Against Cancer, 3 rue de Conseil-General, CH-1205 Geneva, Switzerland. TEL 022-3201811. FAX 022-3201810. E-mail: uicc@atge.automail.com. **Document type:** proceedings.
Formerly: U I C C Calendar of International Meetings on Cancer.

U N CHRONICLE. see *POLITICAL SCIENCE — International Relations*

UNITY: UNITED NEWSLETTER. see *HOMOSEXUALITY*

011 658 AT
UNIVERSAL DIRECTORY - CONFERENCES - EXHIBITIONS - FUNCTIONS. 1988. a. Aus.$50. Universal Press Pty. Ltd., 64 Talavera Rd., Macquarie Park, N.S.W. 2113, Australia. TEL 02-8881877. FAX 02-8889850. adv. circ. 20,000.
Description: Contains information on venues, guest speakers, conference organizers and all the support companies you might need to organize a meeting in N.S.W. and A.C.T.

VIRGATS. see *ETHNIC INTERESTS*

VOYAGES ET STRATEGIE; le magazine de la stimulation et du tourisme d'affaires. see *TRAVEL AND TOURISM*

011 US
▼**WASHINGTON CRIME NEWS SERVICES CALENDAR OF EVENTS;** seminars, workshops, conferences, etc. 1995. q. with subscr. to any Washington Crime News Services newsletter. Washington Crime News Services, 3918 Prosperity Ave., Ste. 318, Fairfax, VA 22031-3304. TEL 703-573-1600; 800-422-9267. FAX 703-573-1604. Ed. Nancy J. Weaver; Pub. Richard J. O'Connell. circ. (controlled). **Document type:** bulletin.
Description: Lists conferences, seminars, and workshops of interest to criminal justice professionals.

WELLA AKTIENGESELLSCHAFT. REPORT; Mitarbeitermagazin fuer Mitarbeiter und Pensionaere der weltweiten Wella-Unternehmen. see *BUSINESS AND ECONOMICS*

WOLFENBUETTELER BIBLIOTHEKS - INFORMATIONEN. see *HISTORY*

380 011 UK
WORLD DIRECTORY OF EXHIBITIONS AND TRADE FAIRS. 1993. irreg. £195($390) (effective 1996). Euromonitor, 60-61 Britton St., London EC1M 5QU, England. TEL 0171-251-8024. FAX 0171-608-3149. (N. American addr.: Euromonitor International, 122 S. Michigan Ave., Ste. 1200, Chicago, IL 60603. TEL 312-922-1115. FAX 312-922-1157) **Document type:** directory.
Description: Covers in detail all the major trade fairs and exhibitions in more than 50 countries.

669 011 US
WORLD MATERIALS CALENDAR; comprehensive international coverage of forthcoming events in metallurgy and materials science. 1965. q. $165 (effective 1996). (Institute of Metals, UK) A S M International, Materials Information, Materials Park, OH 44073. TEL 216-338-5151. FAX 216-338-4634. TELEX 980-619. E-mail: DBarthel@po.ASM-Intl.org. (UK addr.: Institute of Materials, Materials Information, 1 Carlton House Terr., London SW1Y 5DB, England. TEL 071-839-4071) Ed.Bd.
—BLDSC (9352.973500).
Former titles: World Calendar (ISSN 0263-7987); (until 1976): World Calendar of Forthcoming Meetings: Metallurgical and Related Fields (ISSN 0043-8294)
Description: Lists forthcoming meetings in metals and materials.

011 610 US ISSN 0161-2875
CODEN: WMMEDT
WORLD MEETINGS: MEDICINE. 1978. q. $165. Macmillan Publishing Company, Macmillan Reference, 866 Third Ave., New York, NY 10022. TEL 212-702-4301. FAX 212-605-9368. Ed. Peter J. Jaskowiak.
—BLDSC (9356.655750).

011 US ISSN 0043-8677
Q101 CODEN: WMUCBR
WORLD MEETINGS: OUTSIDE UNITED STATES AND CANADA. 1968. q. $185. Macmillan Publishing Company, Macmillan Reference, 866 Third Ave., New York, NY 10022. TEL 212-702-4301. FAX 212-605-9368. Ed. Peter J. Jaskowiak. **Indexed:** BMT, Fluidex.
—BLDSC (9356.655900); CASDDS.

300 650 011 US ISSN 0194-6161
AS8
WORLD MEETINGS: SOCIAL & BEHAVIORAL SCIENCES, HUMAN SERVICES AND MANAGEMENT. 1971. q. $170. Macmillan Publishing Company, Macmillan Reference, 866 Third Ave., New York, NY 10022. TEL 212-702-4301. FAX 212-605-9368. Ed. Peter J. Jaskowiak.
—BLDSC (9356.655840).
Formerly: World Meetings: Social and Behavioral Sciences, Education and Management (ISSN 0043-8685)

011 US ISSN 0043-8693
Q11 CODEN: WMUCAQ
WORLD MEETINGS: UNITED STATES AND CANADA. 1963. q. $185. Macmillan Publishing Company, Macmillan Reference, 866 Third Ave., New York, NY 10022. TEL 212-702-4301. FAX 212-605-9368. Ed. Peter J. Jaskowiak. **Indexed:** BMT.
—BLDSC (9356.657000); CASDDS.

1 X 1 IHR PARTNER. see *AGRICULTURE*

MEETINGS AND CONGRESSES — Abstracting, Bibliographies, Statistics

016 UK ISSN 0959-4906
Z7403
BRITISH LIBRARY. DOCUMENT SUPPLY CENTRE. INDEX OF CONFERENCE PROCEEDINGS. 1964. m. (plus a. cumulation). £99 (foreign £104); cumulation £70 (foreign £75) (effective 1996). British Library, Document Supply Centre, Boston Spa, Wetherby, W. Yorks. LS23 7BQ, England. TEL 01937-546080. FAX 01937-546286. TELEX 557381. (Subscr. to: Turpin Distribution Services Ltd., Blackhorse Rd., Letchworth, Herts. SG6 1HN,England. TEL 01462-672555. FAX 01462-480947) cum.index: 1964-1988. (back issues avail.) **Indexed:** AESIS, Dairy Sci.Abstr., Rev.Appl.Entomol., Rev.Plant Path. **Document type:** abstracting/indexing, proceedings.
●Also available online.
—BLDSC (4377.416600).
Formerly: British Library. Lending Division. Index of Conference Proceedings Received (ISSN 0305-5183)

011 600 500 US ISSN 0194-0546
Z7403
CONFERENCE PAPERS ANNUAL INDEX. a. $475 (foreign $595). Cambridge Scientific Abstracts, 7200 Wisconsin Ave., 6th Fl., Bethesda, MD 20814. TEL 301-961-6750. FAX 301-961-6720. E-mail: market@csa.com. Ed. C. Droffner; Pub. Ted Caris. **Document type:** abstracting/indexing.
●Also available online. Vendor(s): Knight-Ridder, Inc. (File no. 77), STN International (CONFSCI).
Formerly: Current Programs Annual Index.

600 500 011 US ISSN 0162-704X
Z7403
CONFERENCE PAPERS INDEX. 1973. bi-m. $965 (foreign $995); with annual index $985 (foreign $995); annual index only $475 (foreign $595). Cambridge Scientific Abstracts, 7200 Wisconsin Ave., 6th Fl., Bethesda, MD 20814. TEL 301-961-6750. FAX 301-961-6720. E-mail: market@csa.com. Pub. Ted Caris. index. (also avail. in magnetic tape; back issues avail.) **Indexed:** Cal.Tiss.Abstr., Chemorec.Abstr., Comput.& Info.Sys., Oncol.Abstr., Pollut.Abstr. **Document type:** abstracting/indexing.
●Also available online. Vendor(s): Knight-Ridder, Inc. (File no.77), STN International (CONFSCI).
—BLDSC (3409.745300).
Formerly (until 1977): World Meetings Information Center. Current Programs (ISSN 0091-0139)
Description: Lists authors and titles of papers presented at scientific conferences worldwide.

DIRECTORY OF PUBLISHED PROCEEDINGS. SERIES P C E: POLLUTION CONTROL & ECOLOGY. see *ENVIRONMENTAL STUDIES — Abstracting, Bibliographies, Statistics*

DIRECTORY OF PUBLISHED PROCEEDINGS. SERIES S E M T - SCIENCE, ENGINEERING, MEDICINE AND TECHNOLOGY. see *SCIENCES: COMPREHENSIVE WORKS — Abstracting, Bibliographies, Statistics*

DIRECTORY OF PUBLISHED PROCEEDINGS. SERIES S S H - SOCIAL SCIENCES - HUMANITIES. see *HUMANITIES: COMPREHENSIVE WORKS — Abstracting, Bibliographies, Statistics*

015.595 MY ISSN 0127-4880
INDEX TO MALAYSIAN CONFERENCES/INDEKS PERSIDANGAN MALAYSIA. (Text in Bahasa Malaysia, Chinese, English, Tamil) 1976. a. M.$50 (foreign M.$60). National Library of Malaysia, Technical Services Division, Ground Fl., East Block, 232 Jalan Tun Razak, 50572 Kuala Lumpur, Malaysia. TEL 03-2943488. FAX 03-2927899. (Subscr. to: University of Malaya Co-operative Bookshop Ltd., Library Bldg., University of Malaya, 59100 Kuala Lumpur, Malaysia) Ed. Noraini Noran Abdullah. circ. 120. **Document type:** abstracting/indexing.
—BLDSC (4382.310000).
Description: Covers working papers of conferences, seminars, workshops held in Malaysia.

016 GW ISSN 0933-1905
INTERNATIONALE JAHRESBIBLIOGRAPHIE DER KONGRESSBERICHTE/INTERNATIONAL ANNUAL BIBLIOGRAPHY OF CONGRESS PROCEEDINGS. Short title: I J B K. 1987. 3 vols./yr. DM.1200. Zeller Verlag GmbH, Postfach 1949, 49009 Osnabrueck, Germany. TEL 0541-4045914. FAX 0541-41255. **Document type:** bibliography.

016 US ISSN 0032-9568
Z5063.A2 CODEN: PPRNA
PROCEEDINGS IN PRINT. 1964. bi-m. $615 (foreign $680); cum.index $300 (foreign $310). Proceedings in Print, Inc., Box 369, Halifax, MA 02338-0369. Ed. Barbara A. Spence. index. (back issues avail.) **Document type:** abstracting/indexing.
—BLDSC (6848.850000).
Description: Lists proceedings and indexes of conferences, symposia in all subject areas, and in all languages.

MEN'S HEALTH

AMERICAN INSTITUTE OF STRESS. NEWSLETTER. see *MEDICAL SCIENCES*

BACK TO HEALTH MAGAZINE; your guide to relief recovery and well-being. see *PHYSICAL FITNESS AND HYGIENE*

EXECUTIVE EDGE. see *PHYSICAL FITNESS AND HYGIENE*

MEN'S INTERESTS

EXERCISE FOR MEN ONLY. see PHYSICAL FITNESS AND HYGIENE

HEALTH & FITNESS; magazine for healthy, sound living. see PHYSICAL FITNESS AND HYGIENE

HEALTH EDUCATION JOURNAL. see PHYSICAL FITNESS AND HYGIENE

HEALTH NOW. see NUTRITION AND DIETETICS

JOE WEIDER'S MEN'S FITNESS. see PHYSICAL FITNESS AND HYGIENE

JOURNAL OF SPIRITUAL HEALTH. see ALTERNATIVE MEDICINE

MAENNER AKTUELL. see HOMOSEXUALITY

MASSAGE THERAPY JOURNAL. see PHYSICAL FITNESS AND HYGIENE

613.7 US ISSN 1066-5706
MEN'S CONFIDENTIAL NEWSLETTER; health, sex and fitness news for men. 1985. m. $48. Rodale Press, Inc., 33 E. Minor St., Emmaus, PA 18098. TEL 610-967-7627. FAX 610-967-7725. (Subscr. to: Box 7315, Red Oak, IA 51591-0315. TEL 800-666-2106) Ed. Michael Lafavore; Pub. John Griffin. bk.rev.; charts; illus.; index; circ. 110,000 (paid). (back issues avail.) Document type: newsletter, consumer publication.
Formerly (until 1993): Men's Health Newsletter (ISSN 0747-8461)
Description: Delivers current medical advice on health subjects unique to men with ways to improve health, "slow down" the aging process, reduce stress, plus information on nutrition.

610 US ISSN 1054-4836
RA777.8 CODEN: MEHEE9
MEN'S HEALTH. 1986. 10/yr. $19.97. Rodale Press, Inc., 33 E. Minor St., Emmaus, PA 18098. TEL 610-967-5171; 800-666-2303. TELEX 847338. circ. 575,000. Indexed: Hlth.Ind. Document type: consumer publication.
●Also available online. Vendor(s): University Microfilms International.
—UMI; UnCover.
Description: Tells you how to look good, live better - and longer.

MENSTUFF, THE NATIONAL MEN'S RESOURCE. see MEN'S STUDIES

NIKKEI WELLNESS. see WOMEN'S HEALTH

OUTLOOK (SEATTLE); drug regulation and reproductive health. see PUBLIC HEALTH AND SAFETY

PRIME FITNESS & HEALTH. see PHYSICAL FITNESS AND HYGIENE

613.081 155 US ISSN 0277-3422
SPRINGER SERIES: FOCUS ON MEN. 1981. irreg., latest 1995. price varies. Springer Publishing Company, 536 Broadway, New York, NY 10012-3955. TEL 212-431-4370. FAX 212-941-4370. Ed. Daniel Jay Sonkin. Document type: monographic series.
—BLDSC (8424.763200).
Description: Focuses on men's issues from a psychological perspective.

MEN'S INTERESTS

051 US
A A G INTERNATIONAL.* (Adult Action Guide) 9/yr. $4.95 per no. Eton Publishing, 1775 Broadway, Ste. 604, New York, NY 10019-1903. TEL 212-213-8620. FAX 212-532-1309.

054.1 FR ISSN 0221-4784
ABSOUS. 1974. m. 140 F. Societe Francaise des Revues, 9 rue Diderot, 93100 Montreuil, France. Ed. Michel Buh. adv. circ. 110,000.
Former titles (until 1979): Le Novel Absolu (ISSN 0397-0841); (until 1976): Absolu (ISSN 0397-0833)

051 US ISSN 0001-8007
HQ450
ADAM; the man's home companion. 1956. m. $4.95 per no. Knight Publishing Corp., 8060 Melrose Ave., Los Angeles, CA 90046. TEL 213-653-8060. Ed. Jared Rutter. adv. contact: Douglas Johnson. bk.rev. circ. 150,000. Document type: consumer publication.

051 US
ADAM EROTOMIC. q. $5.95 per no. Knight Publishing Corp., 8060 Melrose Ave., Los Angeles, CA 90046. TEL 213-653-8060. FAX 213-655-9452. Ed. Tim Connelly. adv. contact: Douglas Johnson. Document type: consumer publication.

051 US
ADAM GIRLS INTERNATIONAL. bi-m. $5.95. Knight Publishing Corp., 8060 Melrose Ave., Los Angeles, CA 90046. TEL 213-653-8060. FAX 213-655-9452.

051 US ISSN 0277-2914
ADULT CINEMA REVIEW.* 9/yr. $4.95 per no. Adult Movie Review, Inc., c/o Scott Magazines Dist. Co., 28 W. 25th St., New York, NY 10010-2705. TEL 212-967-6262.

051 US ISSN 1066-2294
ADVOCATE CLASSIFIEDS. 1992. 26/yr. $24.95. Liberation Publications, Inc., Box 4371, Los Angeles, CA 90078. TEL 213-871-1225. FAX 213-467-0173.

051 US ISSN 0742-4701
TR681.M4
ADVOCATE MEN. m. $39.98. Liberation Publications, Inc., Box 4371, Los Angeles, CA 90078. TEL 213-871-1225. FAX 213-467-0173.

051 US ISSN 0986-9182
ALL MAN. 1987. bi-m. $24.95. Bruce Publications, Ltd. (Subsidiary of: Mavety Media Group Ltd.), 462 Broadway, Ste. 4000, New York, NY 10013. TEL 212-966-8400. (Dist. by: Flynt Distributing Co., 9171 Wilshire Blvd., Ste. 300, Beverly Hills, CA 90210) Ed. Jason Fairchild. illus.
Formerly: All Male.

AMERICAN SENIOR. see GERONTOLOGY AND GERIATRICS

ANDERSCHUME - KONTIKI; das Schweizer Magazin fuer den schwulen Mann. see HOMOSEXUALITY

ANTHEM. see MUSIC

070.4834 917.306 US
AQUI (RIVER EDGE).* (Text in Spanish) 1988. m. $33. Aqui Publications Inc., c/o Faces Magazines, Inc., 210 E. Ste. Rt. 4, Ste. 401, Paramus, NJ 07652-5103. TEL 201-487-3255. Ed. Fernando Moreno. circ. 100,000.
Description: Includes articles on lifestyle, sports, humor and pictorials of nude women geared towards Spanish men between the ages of 18-49.

052 UK ISSN 0955-0046
ARENA (LONDON). 1986. bi-m. £15($35) Wagadon Ltd., 3rd Fl. Block A, Exmouth House, Pine St., London EC1R OJL, England. TEL 0171-837-7270. FAX 0171-837-3906. (Subscr. to: P.O. Box 500, Leicester LE99 OAA, England) Ed. Kathryn Flett. adv. contact: Rod Sopp. bk.rev.; film rev.; rec.rev. circ. 92,000. Document type: consumer publication.

052 AT ISSN 0158-0655
AUSTRALIAN PENTHOUSE; Australian men's magazine. 1979. m. Aus.$74. P H Editorial Services Pty. Ltd., P.O. Box 42, Cammeray, N.S.W. 2062, Australia. Ed. Phil Abraham. circ. 132,000. (back issues avail.)

052 AT ISSN 0156-8892
AUSTRALIAN PLAYBOY. 1979. m. Aus.$69.50. Mason Stewart Publishing Pty. Ltd., P.O. Box 746, Darlinghurst, N.S.W. 2010, Australia. TEL 61-2-331-5006. FAX 61-2-360-5367. Ed. Andrew Cowell. adv.: B&W page $1764, color page $2521. circ. 43,000. Document type: consumer publication.

051 US
BABBLE MAGAZINE. 1992. w. newsstand price: $1. 3223 N. Sheffield, Chicago, IL 60657. TEL 312-248-4542. FAX 312-477-6382. E-mail: babblemag@aol.com. Ed. Jim Pickett; Pub. Malone Sizelove. adv. contact: Nancy A. Reiff. bk.rev. circ. 18,000. Document type: newspaper.
Formerly (until 1993): Gag.

051 301.4157 US
BEAU. 1989. 8/yr. $17.69; newsstand price: $3.95. Sportomatic Ltd., Box 470, Port Chester, NY 10573. TEL 914-939-2111. Ed. Dan Maxwell. adv.; bk.rev.; film rev. circ. 75,000. (back issues avail.) Document type: consumer publication.
Description: Covers sexual relations between gay men.

051 US
BEELINE BOOKS. m. Carlyle Communications, Ltd. (Subsidiary of: Mavety Media Group Ltd.), 462 Broadway, Ste. 4000, New York, NY 10013. TEL 212-966-8400. (Dist. by: Kable News Co., 11 W. 42nd St, 28th Fl., New York, NY 10036. TEL 212-768-1000) Indexed: Apic.Abstr.

051 US
BEST OF CLUB SPECIALS. Cover title: Club Specials. 10/yr. $4.95 per no. Paragon Publishing Inc., Box 380, Sandy Hook, CT 06482-0380. TEL 203-426-6533. FAX 203-426-9533. Document type: consumer publication.
Formerly: Best of Club.

051 US
BEST OF GENESIS.* 13/yr. $35. Jakel Corp., 110 E. 9th St., 31st Fl., New York, NY 10022-1304. TEL 212-265-3500. FAX 212-265-8087.

051 US
BEST OF REAL LETTERS. s-a. $3.50 per no. Vanity Publications, 1775 Broadway, Ste. 604, New York, NY 10019-1903. TEL 212-213-8620. FAX 212-532-1302.

051 US
BEST OF SENSUOUS LETTERS.* s-a. $3.50 per no. Vanity Publications, 1775 Broadway, Ste. 604, New York, NY 10019-1903. TEL 212-213-8620. FAX 212-532-1302. Document type: consumer publication.

051 US
BI-LIFESTYLES; devoted to the sensual interests of bisexual gay males, females and couples. q. $45 (foreign $60) (effective 1996). Continental Spectator, Box 278, Canal St. Sta., New York, NY 10013. TEL 800-325-4122. Ed. Linda Lee. adv.

BIG APPLE PARENTS' PAPER. see CHILDREN AND YOUTH — About

051 US
BIG BUTT. bi-m. $14.95. Heat Wave Publications, Inc. (Subsidiary of: Mavety Media Group Ltd.), 462 Broadway, Ste. 4000, New York, NY 10013. TEL 212-966-8400. (Dist. by: Flynt Distributing Co., 9171 Wilshire Blvd., Ste. 300, Beverly Hills, CA 90210)

051 US
BIKINI. 1993. bi-m. $19.97 (effective 1994). Ray Gun Publishing, 807 Navy St., Santa Monica, CA 90405. TEL 310-452-6222. Ed. Marvin Jarrett. adv.; illus. Document type: consumer publication.
Description: Fashion and life-style magazine for hip young men.

306.84 CN
BIMBOX. q. $5 per no. 282 Parliament St., No. 68, Toronto, Ont. M5A 3A4, Canada. Ed. Johnny Noxzema.

BIRTH OF TRAGEDY MAGAZINE; the fear issue, the God issue, the power issue, the love issue, the sex issue. see LITERARY AND POLITICAL REVIEWS

051 US
BLACK TAIL. 1989. 9/yr. $19.95. Tux Magazine, Inc. (Subsidiary of: Mavety Media Group Ltd.), 462 Broadway, Ste. 4000, New York, NY 10013. TEL 212-966-8400. (Dist. by: Flynt Distributing Co., 9171 Wilshire Blvd., Ste. 300, Beverly Hills, CA 90210) illus.
Formerly (until 1991): Mocha.

MEN'S INTERESTS

051 US
BLUE BOY. 9/yr. newsstand price: $4.99. Leemar Publishing, 28 W. 25th St., New York, NY 10010. TEL 212-647-0222. FAX 212-966-9366. **Document type:** consumer publication.

BODY PLAY AND MODERN PRIMITIVES QUARTERLY. see *NEW AGE PUBLICATIONS*

BOLD GAY LIFE STYLE. see *HOMOSEXUALITY*

BRAUT UND BRAEUTIGAM; wissenwertes ueber heiraten und wohnen. see *WOMEN'S INTERESTS*

BRIDE AND GROOM. see *MATRIMONY*

BRITISH G Q. see *CLOTHING TRADE — Fashions*

070.48346 JA
BRUTUS. (Text in Japanese) 1980. bi-w. newsstand price: 430Yen. Magazine House, 3-13-10, Ginza, Chuo-ku, Tokyo 104, Japan. TEL 03-3545-7170. FAX 03-3544-1463. Ed. Koichi Tezuka. circ. 250,000.

CADET. see *CONSUMER EDUCATION AND PROTECTION*

051 US
CELEBRITY CONFIDENTIAL. bi-m. Fast Lane Publishing, Inc., 462 Broadway, Ste. 4000, New York, NY 10013. TEL 212-966-8400. (Dist. by: Flynt Distributing Co., 9171 Wilshire Blvd., Ste. 300, Beverly Hills, CA 90210)

051 US
CELEBRITY SKIN. 8/yr. $19.95. Man's World Publications Inc., 801 Second Ave., New York, NY 10017. TEL 212-661-7878.

051 US
CELEBRITY SLEUTH. vol.2, no.4, 1989. 9/yr. $4.95 per no. Broadcast Communications, Inc. (Subsidiary of: Mavety Media Group Ltd.), 462 Broadway, Ste. 4000, New York, NY 10013. TEL 212-966-8400. (Dist. by: Flynt Distributing Co., 9171 Wilshire Blvd., Ste. 300, Beverly Hills, CA 90210) illus.

CHALLENGE (CONVENT STATION). see *HOMOSEXUALITY*

051 US ISSN 1059-7131
CHERI; the all-true sex news magazine. 13/yr. $47.95. Cheri Magazine, Inc., 801 Second Ave., New York, NY 10017. TEL 212-661-7878. Ed. Ken Kimmec.

051 US
CHERI PILLOW TALK. bi-m. $2.95 per no. Cheri Magazine, Inc., 801 Second Ave., New York, NY 10017. TEL 212-661-7878. FAX 212-883-1244.

070.48346 808.87 US
CHERRY. 2/yr. $6 per no. Last Gasp of San Francisco, 777 Floida St., San Francisco, CA 94110. TEL 415-824-6636. FAX 415-824-1836. Ed. Larry Welz. circ. 40,000. (back issues avail.) **Description:** Adult cartoon satire.

051 US
CHIC LETTERS. 9/yr. $2.95 per no. Larry Flynt Publications, Inc., 9171 Wilshire Blvd., Ste.300, Beverly Hills, CA 90210. TEL 213-858-7100. FAX 213-274-7985. **Document type:** consumer publication.

646.32 US ISSN 0194-648X
CHIC MAGAZINE. 1976. m. $39.95. H G Publications, Inc., 9171 Wilshire Blvd., Ste. 300, Beverly Hills, CA 90210-5530. TEL 310-858-7100. FAX 310-275-3857. Ed. Doug Oliver. adv.

CHILD CARE ACTION NEWS. see *CHILDREN AND YOUTH — About*

CHIRON RISING; entertainment for mature men and admirers. see *HOMOSEXUALITY*

CHROME - DOME. see *BIOLOGY — Physiology*

CIGAR AFICIONADO. see *TOBACCO*

051 US ISSN 0743-8389
CINEMA BLUE. vol.6, no.4, 1989. 9/yr. $32.95. Hudson Communications, Inc. (Subsidiary of: Mavety Media Group Ltd.), 462 Broadway, Ste. 4000, New York, NY 10013. TEL 212-966-8400. (Dist. by: Flynt Distributing Co., 9171 Wilshire Blvd., Ste. 300, Beverly Hills, CA 90210) Ed. Felicia Freedom. **Description:** Reviews of x-rated video cassettes.

051 US
CINEMA BLUE PRESENTS EROTIC STARS. 1989. bi-m. $19.95. Galaxy Publications, Inc. (Subsidiary of: Mavety Media Group Ltd.), 462 Broadway, Ste. 4000, New York, NY 10013. TEL 212-966-8400. (Dist. by: Flynt Distributing Co., 9171 Wilshire Blvd., Ste. 300, Beverly Hills, CA 90210) illus.

051 US
CINEMA BLUE PRESENTS RED-HOT COUPLES. 1989. bi-m. $19.95. Heartland Publications, Inc. (Subsidiary of: Mavety Media Group Ltd.), 462 Broadway, Ste. 4000, New York, NY 10013. TEL 212-966-8400. (Dist. by: Flynt Distributing Co., 9171 Wilshire Blvd., Ste. 300, Beverly Hills, CA 90210) illus.

051 US
CLIMAX. 8/yr. Man's World Publications Inc., 801 Second Ave., New York, NY 10017. TEL 212-661-7878. FAX 212-883-1244.

051 US
CLOSE SHAVE. 1989. 9/yr. $32.95. Vista Publications, Inc. (Subsidiary of: Mavety Media Group Ltd.), 462 Broadway, Ste. 4000, New York, NY 10013. TEL 212-966-8400. (Dist. by: Flynt Distributing Co., 9171 Wilshire Blvd., Ste. 300, Beverly Hills, CA 90210) illus.

051 US ISSN 1072-8066
CLUB CONFIDENTIAL. m. $49. Paragon Publishing Inc., Box 380, Sandy Hook, CT 06482-0380. TEL 203-426-6533. FAX 203-426-9533. Ed. Nigel Franks. adv. contact: Susan Freeman. illus. **Document type:** consumer publication.
Formerly: Best of Club International (ISSN 0956-0319)

051 US ISSN 0747-0819
CLUB INTERNATIONAL. 13/yr. $49. Paragon Publishing Inc., Box 380, Sandy Hook, CT 06482-0380. TEL 203-426-6533. FAX 203-426-9533. Ed. Simon Belter. adv. contact: Carolyn James.

051 US ISSN 0747-0827
CLUB MAGAZINE. 1954. m. $49.99. Paragon Publishing Inc., Box 200, Sandy Hook, CT 06482. TEL 203-426-6533. FAX 203-426-9533. Ed. Nigel Franks. adv. contact: Susan Freeman. circ. 648,717. (back issues avail.) **Description:** Contains erotically entertaining articles and cartoons and pictorials featuring popular models.

051 US
COLT STUDIO PUBLICATIONS. m. $12.50 per no. Colt Studio, Box 4371, Los Angeles, CA 90078. TEL 213-871-1225. FAX 213-467-6805.

COMPETITION ANGLER. see *SPORTS AND GAMES — Outdoor Life*

CONSCIENCE (WASHINGTON); a news journal of prochoice Catholic opinion. see *RELIGIONS AND THEOLOGY — Roman Catholic*

CONTINENTAL SPECTATOR. see *SINGLES' INTERESTS AND LIFESTYLES*

070.483 GW ISSN 0935-7475
COUPE. 1985. m. Klaus Helbert Verlagsgesellschaft mbH, Gustav-Stresemann-Ring 1, 65026 Wiesbaden, Germany. TEL 0611-7633-0. FAX 0611-7633139. Ed. Peter Rensch; Pub. Klaus Helbert. adv. contact: Michael Wesp. circ. 627,114. **Document type:** consumer publication.

051 US
COUPLES ONLY.* bi-m. $2.95 per no. Vanity Publications, 1775 Broadway, Ste. 604, New York, NY 10019-1903. TEL 212-213-8620. FAX 212-532-1302. **Document type:** consumer publication.

CROSS-TALK; transgender community news & information monthly. see *SOCIOLOGY*

DETAILS. see *GENERAL INTEREST PERIODICALS — United States*

051 US
DIVERSIONS.* bi-m. $3.95 per no. Vanity Publications, 1775 Broadway, Ste. 604, New York, NY 10019-1903. TEL 212-213-8620. FAX 212-532-1302. **Document type:** consumer publication.

DOMINANTLY YOURS. see *SINGLES' INTERESTS AND LIFESTYLES*

051 US
DOMINATRIX CROSS ROADS. no.119, 1991. 12/yr. $29. R S Connections, Box 97077-DM, Las Vegas, NV 89193.

051 US
E F G HIGHLIGHTS.* bi-m. $4.95 per no. Eton Publishing, 1775 Broadway, Ste. 604, New York, NY 10019-1903. TEL 212-213-8620. FAX 212-532-1302.

054.1 FR
ECHO DES SAVANES. m. (11/yr.). 220 F. (foreign 325 F.) (effective 1995). Publications Filipacchi, 63 Champs-Elysees, 75008 Paris, France. TEL 40-74-74-55. FAX 40-74-74-91. (Subscr. to: 99 rue d'Amsterdam, 75008 Paris, France. TEL 42-80-68-55. FAX 45-26-24-80) **Document type:** consumer publication.

056.1 MX
EL.* 1971. m. Mex.$400($43) Corporacion Editorial, S.A., Lucio Blanco 435, Col. San Juan Tlihuaca, 02400 Mexico D.F., Mexico. Ed. Javier Ortiz Camorlinga. adv. circ. 120,000.

ELE E ELA; uma revista para ler a dois. see *WOMEN'S INTERESTS*

L'ELEGANTE UOMO SUD. see *CLOTHING TRADE — Fashions*

053.1 GW
ER. bi-m. Konrad A. Holtz AG, Gutenberstr. 1, 95512 Neudrossenfeld, Germany. TEL 09203-600-0. Ed. Siegfried Kohl. adv. circ. 80,000. **Document type:** consumer publication.

EROTIC WRITER'S AND COLLECTOR'S MARKET. see *PUBLISHING AND BOOK TRADE*

051 US
EROTIC X-FILM GUIDE. m. $4.95 per no. Eton Publishing, 475 Park Ave. S., New York, NY 10016. TEL 212-213-8620. FAX 212-532-1309.

051 US ISSN 0194-9535 AP2
ESQUIRE; the magazine for men. 1933. m. $15.94; newsstand price: 3. Hearst Corporation, Esquire, 250 W. 55th St., New York, NY 10019. TEL 212-649-2000. FAX 212-977-3158. (Subscr. to: C.D.S., 1901 Bell Ave., Des Moines, IA 50315. TEL 800-888-5400) Ed. Terry McDonell. adv.; bk.rev.; film rev.; rec.rev.; illus. circ. 702,611. (also avail. in microform from UMI; reprint service avail. from UMI) **Indexed:** Abstr.Engl.Stud., Acad.Ind., Bibl.Engl.Lang.& Lit., Bk.Rev.Ind. (1965-), Child.Bk.Rev.Ind. (1965-), Curr.Lit.Fam.Plan., Film Lit.Ind. (1973-), Hlth.Ind., Mag.Ind., PMR, R.G. **Document type:** consumer publication.
—BLDSC (3811.662500); Faxon; UnCover.
Former titles (until 1979): Esquire Fortnightly (ISSN 0884-5220); *(until 1978):* Esquire (ISSN 0014-0791)
Description: Features interviews and the latest in contemporary fiction and non-fiction writing; also includes information about popular culture with takes on fashion, travel, and more.

052 UK ISSN 0960-5150
ESQUIRE. 1991. m. £20. National Magazine Co. Ltd., 72 Broadwick St., London W1V 2BP, England. TEL 0171-439-5000. FAX 0171-439-5067. Ed. Rosie Boycott. circ. 110,583. **Document type:** consumer publication.

ESQUIRE GENTLEMAN. see *CLOTHING TRADE — Fashions*

MEN'S INTERESTS

051   HD28   US   ISSN 1072-4818
EXEC. 1992. s-a. newsstand price: $3.50. Rodale Press, Inc., 33 Minor St., Emmaus, PA 18098. TEL 610-967-5171. FAX 610-967-8693. Ed. Mark Bricklin. adv.; illus. circ. 200,000. **Document type:** consumer publication.
   Formerly (until 1993): Young Executive (ISSN 1060-2119)
   Description: Covers life-style and career advancement issues for career-oriented men 25-40.

EXERCISE FOR MEN ONLY. see PHYSICAL FITNESS AND HYGIENE

EXPRESSMALE. see OCCUPATIONS AND CAREERS

EZERMESTER HOBBI. see HOW-TO AND DO-IT-YOURSELF

070.48   UK   ISSN 0958-0980
F H M. (For Him Magazine) 1985. m. £30. E M A P Metro, Mappin House, 4 Winsley St., London W1N 7AR, England. TEL 0171-436-1515. FAX 0171-312-8191. (Subscr. to: Select Subscriptions, Northbridge Rd., Berkhamstead, Herts. HP4 1ST, England. TEL 01442-876661. FAX 01442-872279) Ed. Mike Soutar; Pub. Steve Newbold. adv. contact: James Carter. bk.rev.; circ. 81,104 (paid). Indexed: DAAI. **Document type:** consumer publication.
   Description: Contains life-style articles for image-conscious men.

808   US
FAMILY AFFAIRS. 1980. m. $43.97. Letters Magazines, Inc., 310 Cedar Lane, Teaneck, NJ 07666. TEL 201-836-9177. FAX 201-836-5055. Eds. Jackie Lewis, Lisa Rosen; Pub. Louis Rosen. adv. contact: Allison Reynolds. circ. 80,000. (back issues avail.) **Document type:** consumer publication.
   Description: Erotic literature.

051   US
FAMILY HEAT. bi-m. $15.95. Mountainside Press, Inc. (Subsidiary of: Mavety Media Group Ltd.), 462 Broadway, Ste. 4000, New York, NY 10013. TEL 212-966-8400. (Dist. by: Flynt Distributing Co., 9171 Wilshire Blvd., Ste. 300, Beverly Hills, CA 90210)

051   US
FAMILY LETTERS. m. $43.97. Piccolo Publications, Inc., 310 Cedar Lane, Teaneck, NJ 07666. TEL 201-836-9177. FAX 201-836-5055. Eds. Jackie Lewis, Lisa Rosen; Pub. Louis Rosen. adv. contact: Allison Reynolds. **Document type:** consumer publication.

059.927   LE
AL-FARES. (Text in Arabic) m. $135. Dar Assayad S.A.L., P.O. Box 1038, Hazmieh, Beirut, Lebanon. FAX 961-1-3456373. (U.K. addr.: c/o Contact PR & Mgt. (UK) Ltd., 3 Park Pl., 12 Lawn Ln., Vauxhall, London SW8 1UA, England. TEL 44-71-582-2220) adv. contact: Salim Zreik. illus. circ. 68,400. **Document type:** consumer publication.

056.1   US
FASCINACION.* (Avail. in editions for Central America, Colombia, Mexico, Puerto Rico, Venezuela) (Text in Spanish) 1974. m. De Armas Publications, c/o Saral Publications, 780 Third Ave., 10th Fl., New York, NY 10017-2024. adv. circ. 70,000.

FERRARI ITALIAN STYLE; periodico internazionale d'immagine, automobilismo e cultura. see TRANSPORTATION — Automobiles

500 051   US
FETISH & FANTASY MAGAZINE. q.? $40. Slave Productions, Box 356, Ronkonkoma, NY 11779-0356. adv.; illus.
   Description: Presents stories and photographs of erotic, forbidden, sensual swinging experiences.

051   US
FETISH LETTERS. bi-m. $15.95. Domino Press, Inc. (Subsidiary of: Mavety Media Group Ltd.), 462 Broadway, Ste. 4000, New York, NY 10013. TEL 212-966-8400. (Dist. by: Flynt Distributing Co., 9171 Wilshire Blvd., Ste. 300, Beverly Hills, CA 90210)

052   UK   ISSN 0265-1270
FIESTA. 1965. m. £19($60) Galaxy Publications Ltd., P.O. Box 312, Witham, Essex CM8 3SZ, England. FAX 0376-510680. TELEX 98431. Ed. Ross Gilfillam. adv. contact: Pam Askew. bk.rev. circ. 327,998.

052   SA   ISSN 1022-3088
FIRST BITE; the adults' choice. (Text in English) 1993. bi-m. R.24; newsstand price: R.5.20. Viclen Promotions, P.O. Box 354, Mondeor 2110, South Africa. illus. **Document type:** consumer publication.

FOCUS (BURLINGTON). see RELIGIONS AND THEOLOGY — Protestant

051   US
FORBIDDEN LETTERS.* bi-m. $4.50 per no. Vanity Publications, 1775 Broadway, Ste. 604, New York, NY 10019-1903. TEL 212-213-8620. FAX 212-532-1302. **Document type:** consumer publication.

FORMALWORDS. see CLOTHING TRADE — Fashions

051   US
FORUM SPECIALS. q. newsstand price: $5. Penthouse International, Ltd. (Subsidiary of: General Media Publishing Group), 277 Park Ave. 4th Fl., New York, NY 10172-0003. TEL 212-702-6000. FAX 212-702-6282. **Document type:** consumer publication.

051   US   ISSN 1041-9470
FOX MAGAZINE. 1984. 13/yr. $39. Montcalm Publishing Corp., 401 Park Ave. S., New York, NY 10016-8802. TEL 212-779-8900. Ed. Barry Jaroff. adv.; bk.rev.; film rev.; illus. circ. 150,000.

053.1   GW
FREITAG (BADEN-BADEN); die Monatszeitschrift fuer freie Tage. 1975. s-m. DM.4 per no. Sonnenverlag GmbH, Bismarckstr. 4, Postfach 720, 76530 Baden-Baden, Germany. Ed. Helmut Eilers. adv.

051   US   ISSN 1060-5266
FRESHMEN. m. $39.99. Liberation Publications, Inc., Box 4371, Los Angeles, CA 90078. TEL 213-871-1225. FAX 213-467-0173.

051   US
FRICTION. m. $36. Momentum Publishing, Inc. (Subsidiary of: Mavety Media Group Ltd.), 462 Broadway, Ste. 4000, New York, NY 10013. TEL 212-966-8400. (Dist. by: Flynt Distributing Co., 9171 Wilshire Blvd., Ste. 300, Beverly Hills, CA 90210)

FRONT PAGE. see HOMOSEXUALITY

301   US   ISSN 1055-2367
FULL-TIME DADS; the magazine for caring fathers. 1993. bi-m. $26 (foreign $35). Stephen Harris, Ed. & Pub., Box 577, Cumberland, ME 04021. TEL 207-829-5260. E-mail: fulltdad@aol.com. adv.: B&W page $150; 7 x 10. bk.rev.; illus.; circ. 375 (paid). **Document type:** consumer publication.
   Description: Contains articles and features of interest and important to fathers involved with their children. Promotes support, encouragement, and open exchange of ideas, to help us become better parents.

FUTURE SEX. see SINGLES' INTERESTS AND LIFESTYLES

G Q. (Gentlemen's Quarterly) see CLOTHING TRADE — Fashions

051   US   ISSN 0195-072X
GALLERY. 1972. 13/yr. $25. Montcalm Publishing Corp., 401 Park Ave. S., New York, NY 10016-8802. TEL 212-779-8900. Ed. Barry Janoff. adv.; bk.rev.; film rev.; illus.; circ. 400,000 (paid).

051   US
GALLERY SPECIALS. 14/yr. newsstand price: $5.95. Montcalm Publishing Corp., 401 Park Ave. S., New York, NY 10016-8802. TEL 212-779-8900.

051   US   ISSN 1052-8555
GENESIS (NEW YORK).* 1973. 13/yr. $34.95 (Canada $41; elsewhere $56). Jakel Corp., 110 E. 59th St., New York, NY 10022-1304. TEL 212-644-8800. FAX 212-644-9212. Ed. Michael Banka. adv.; bk.rev.; illus. circ. 400,000.

051   US
GENESIS INTERNATIONAL.* 1993. m. newsstand price: $5. Jakel Corp., 110 E. 59th St., 31st Fl., New York, NY 10022-1304. TEL 212-265-3500. FAX 212-265-8087. **Document type:** consumer publication.
   Description: Features photographs of attractive women from all over the world.

051   US   ISSN 1074-5246
GENRE MAGAZINE. 1991. 10/yr. $19.95; newsstand price: $3.95. 7080 Hollywood Blvd., Ste. 1104, Hollywood, CA 90028. TEL 213-467-8300. FAX 213-467-8365. E-mail: GENRE@enews.com. Ed. Ron/Kraft; Pub. Richard Settles. adv. contact: James Kelly. circ. 50,000 (paid); 20,000 (controlled). **Document type:** consumer publication. ●Also available online.
   Description: Profiles gay men's lives in a positive, informative, and upbeat way. Includes travel features, articles on current events, and celebrity interviews.

070.38   US   ISSN 1063-8229
GENT; home of the D-cups. 1959. m. $30. Dugent Publishing Corp., 2600 Douglas Rd., Ste. 600, Coral Gables, FL 33134. TEL 305-443-2378. (Subscr. to: Box 141, Mt. Morris, IL 61054) Ed. Bruce Arthur. film rev.; illus. circ. 100,000.

051   US
GET KINKY. 1982. bi-m. $29.95. Contact Advertising, 2010 St. Lucie Blvd., Ft. Pierce, FL 34946. TEL 407-464-5447. FAX 407-466-7294. (Subscr. to: Modern Products, 976 Murfreesboro Rd., Ste. 155, Nashville, TN 37217. TEL 800-637-5779) Ed. Holly Adams. adv. contact: Fonda Nietzche. circ. 30,000 (controlled).
   Description: National lifestyles information magazine for singles and couples into or interested in fetishes.

051   US
GIRLS - GIRLS.* 13/yr. $35. Jakel Corp., 110 E. 59th St., 31st Fl., New York, NY 10022-1304. TEL 212-265-3500. FAX 212-265-8087.

051   US   ISSN 1060-1422
GIRLS OF OUTLAW BIKER. 1990. q. Outlaw Biker Enterprises, Inc., 450 Seventh Ave., Ste. 2305, New York, NY 10123. TEL 212-564-0112. FAX 212-465-8350. adv.; illus. **Document type:** consumer publication.

051   US   ISSN 0031-4935
GIRLS OF PENTHOUSE. 1969. 10/yr. Penthouse International, Ltd. (Subsidiary of: General Media Publishing Group), 277 Park Ave., 4th Fl., New York, NY 10172. TEL 212-702-6000. FAX 212-702-6282. (Subscr. to: Box 420235, Palm Coast, FL 32142-0235) Ed. Don Myrus. adv.; illus. circ. 3,172,898. (back issues avail.) Indexed: Access, Film Lit.Ind., Mag.Ind., PMR. **Document type:** consumer publication.
   Description: Erotic literature.

051   MX   ISSN 0187-8999
GOLDEN PENTHOUSE; para el hombre internacional. 1987. m. Mex.$12 per issue. Corporacion Editorial, S.A. de C.V., Lucio Blanco 435, Col. San Juan Tlihuaca, 02400 Mexico D.F., Mexico. TEL 352-6056. Ed. Javier Ortiz. adv.; bk.rev. circ. 40,000. (back issues avail.)

GREEN MAN; a magazine for pagan men. see PARAPSYCHOLOGY AND OCCULTISM

GUIDE MAGAZINE (SEATTLE). see HOMOSEXUALITY

H A C TECHLINE. (Historical Aircraft Corporation) see AERONAUTICS AND SPACE FLIGHT

305.2   US
HARVEY FOR LOVING PEOPLE. 1979. m. $34.95. Harvey Shapiro, Ed. & Pub. (New York), 450 Seventh Ave., Ste. 2305, New York, NY 10001. TEL 212-564-0112. adv. circ. 200,000.

051   US   ISSN 1075-0797
HAWK. 1991. 10/yr. $24.95. Killer Joe Productions, Inc., 801 Second Ave., New York, NY 10017. TEL 212-986-5100. Ed. Richard Dobbins. adv.: B&W page $2000; adv. contact: Colleen Ireland. circ. 250,000. **Document type:** consumer publication.
   Description: Targets men in their 20s and 30s, with editorial on fashion, fitness, and music.

MEN'S INTERESTS

305.3 301.412 US
HE - SHE DIRECTORY. a. $14. Continental Spectator, Box 278, Canal St. Sta., New York, NY 10013. TEL 800-325-4122. Ed. Linda Lee. **Document type:** directory.
 Description: Devoted to the interest of transvestites, transexuals, cross-dressers, female impersonators, and people who want to contact these people.

070.48 US
HEARTLAND U S A. bi-m. $12. U S T Publishing, 418 N. River St., Box 925, Hailey, ID 83333. TEL 208-788-4500. FAX 208-788-5098. Ed. Brad Pearson. adv.; bk.rev. circ. 1,000,000. **Document type:** consumer publication.
 Description: General-interest publication for mainstream America.

051 US
HEAT. vol.2, 1989. 9/yr. $32.95 (foreign $39.95). Heat Publications, Inc. (Subsidiary of: Mavety Media Group Ltd.), 462 Broadway, Ste. 4000, New York, NY 10013. TEL 212-966-8400. FAX 212-966-9366. (Dist. by: Flynt Distributing Co., 9171 Wilshire Blvd., Ste. 300, Beverly Hills, CA 90210) Ed. Chuck Love. illus.

070.48346 US ISSN 1075-0800
HIGH SOCIETY. 1976. m. (13/yr.) $29.95. Crescent Publishing Group, 801 Second Ave., New York, NY 10017. TEL 212-661-7878. (Subscr. to: High Society, Box 316, Mt. Morris, IL 61054. TEL 800-877-5389) Ed. Stephen Loshiavo. adv.; illus. circ. 294,952.

053.1 GW
HIGH SOCIETY. 13/yr. Verlag Grafinter Edicions, Lorenzstr. 21, 81737 Munich, Germany. TEL 089-5420873. FAX 089-5420837. Ed. Rainer Schilling. **Document type:** consumer publication.

301.412 US
HIGH SOCIETY'S PRIVATE LETTERS. bi-m. $2.95 per no. Crescent Publishing Group, 801 Second Ave., New York, NY 10017. TEL 212-661-7878.

305.3 056.1 US
HOMBRE. (Editions avail. for Central America, Chile, Columbia, Ecuador, Mexico, Peru, Puerto Rico, U.S., Venezuela, Argentina) (Text in Spanish) 1976. m. $22.50. Editorial America, S.A., Vanidades Continental Bldg., 6355 N.W. 36th St., Virginia Gardens, FL 33166. TEL 305-871-6400. FAX 305-871-8769. Ed. Franco Caputi. adv. circ. 67,000.
 Formerly: Hombre de Mundo.

051 US
HOMESTYLE AFFAIRS.* bi-m. $2.95 per no. Vanity Publications, 1775 Broadway, Ste. 604, New York, NY 10019-1903. TEL 212-213-8620. FAX 212-532-1302. **Document type:** consumer publication.

051 US
HOMO XTRA; the totally biased politically incorrect party paper. 1991. w. 129.95; newsstand price: $1.50. Two Queens, Inc., 19 W. 21st St., Ste. 504, New York, NY 10010. TEL 212-627-0747. FAX 212-627-5280. Eds. Austin Downey; Pub. Matthew Bank. adv. contact: Gary Lacinski. circ. 30,000. **Document type:** consumer publication.

051 US ISSN 0733-5865
HONCHO. vol.12, no.5, 1989. m. $59.95 (foreign $79.95). Modernismo Publications, Ltd., 462 Broadway, Ste. 4000, New York, NY 10013. TEL 212-966-8400. FAX 212-966-9366. (Dist. by: Flynt Distributing Co., 8484 Wilshire Blvd., Beverly Hills, CA 90211) Ed. Douglas McClemont. **Document type:** consumer publication.
 Description: Contains male erotica, stories, and nonfiction articles.

051 US
HOOTERS. q. $14.95. Leisure Plus Publications, Inc. (Subsidiary of: Mavety Media Group Ltd.), 462 Broadway, Ste. 4000, New York, NY 10013. TEL 212-966-8400. (Dist. by: Flynt Distributing Co., 9171 Wilshire Blvd., Ste. 300, Beverly Hills, CA 90210)

070.48 JA
HOT DOG PRESS. (Text in Japanese) 1979. s-m. Kodansha Ltd., 12-21 Otowa 2-chome, Bunkyo-ku, Tokyo 112, Japan. TEL 03-5395-3472. FAX 03-3944-5489. TELEX J34509 KODANSHA. Ed. Atsuhide Kokubo. circ. 700,000. **Document type:** consumer publication.
 Description: Variety magazine for young men.

808 US
HOT FAMILY LETTERS. 1980. 10/yr. $39.97. Piccolo Publications, Inc., 310 Cedar Lane, Teaneck, NJ 07666. TEL 201-836-9177. FAX 201-836-5055. Eds. Jackie Lewis. Lisa Rosen; Pub. Louis Rosen. adv. contact: Allison Reynolds. circ. 65,900. (back issues avail.)
 Formerly: Hot Letters.
 Description: Erotic literature.

051 US ISSN 0898-1086
HOT TALK. 10/yr. newsstand price: $4.95. Hot Talk Publications, Ltd. (Subsidiary of: General Media Publishing Group), 277 Park Ave., 4th Fl., New York, NY 10172. TEL 212-702-6000. FAX 212-702-6282. **Document type:** consumer publication.

301.412 US ISSN 0149-4635 AP2
HUSTLER. 1974. 13/yr. $39.95. H G Publications, Inc., 9171 Wilshire Blvd., Ste. 300, Beverly Hills, CA 90210. TEL 310-858-7100. FAX 310-275-3857. Ed. Allan McDonell. adv.; bk.rev.; film rev.; play rev. circ. 500,000. (back issues avail.)

052 SA ISSN 1021-707X
HUSTLER. Variant title: Hustler S.A. (Text in English) 1993. m. R.89.99. J T Publishing, P.O. Box 17134, Doornfontein 2028, South Africa. adv.; illus. **Document type:** consumer publication.

051 US ISSN 1059-6798
HUSTLER BUSTY BEAUTIES. 1988. m. $39.95. H G Publications, Inc., 9171 Wilshire Blvd., Ste. 300, Beverly Hills, CA 90210. TEL 213-858-7100. Ed. N. Morgen Hagen. circ. 180,000. (back issues avail.)

052 SA ISSN 1022-0046
HUSTLER CLASSICS. (Text in English) 1993. q. R.19.99 per no. J T Publishing, P.O. Box 17134, Doornfontein 2028, South Africa. illus. (cards) **Document type:** consumer publication.

051 US ISSN 1059-9703
HUSTLER EROTIC VIDEO GUIDE. 1985. m. $39.95. H G Publications, Inc., 9171 Wilshire Blvd., Ste. 300, Beverly Hills, CA 90210. TEL 310-858-7100. FAX 310-275-3857. (Subscr. to: Box 16507, N. Hollywood, CA 91615) Ed. Mal O'Ree. film rev. (back issues avail.)
 Description: Reviews of and behind-the-scene looks at erotic video, the performers and producers, plus interviews.

301.412 US ISSN 0884-4348
HUSTLER FANTASIES. m. $31.95. H G Publications, Inc., 9171 Wilshire Blvd., Ste. 300, Beverly Hills, CA 90210. TEL 310-858-7100. FAX 310-275-3857.

301.412 US ISSN 0199-5405
HUSTLER HUMOR. m. $33.95. Larry Flynt Publications, Inc., 9171 Wilshire Blvd., Ste. 300, Beverly Hills, CA 90210. TEL 310-858-7100. FAX 310-274-7985. Ed. Minette Watkins. **Document type:** consumer publication.

052 SA ISSN 1021-9765
HUSTLER HUMOR. (Text in English) 1993. m. R.39.99 for 6 issues. J T Publishing, P.O. Box 17134, Doornfontein 2028, South Africa. adv.; illus. **Document type:** consumer publication.

305.3 FR ISSN 0183-5122
IL; magazine de l'homme cosmopolite. m. 150 Fr. 30 bis rue Spontini, 75016 Paris, France. Ed. S. Slama.

IMAGE (STUDIO CITY); empowering the man of color image. see ETHNIC INTERESTS

IMPETUS. see ART

051 US ISSN 8756-6338
INCHES. vol.5, no.4, 1989. m. $59.95 (foreign $79.95). Inches, Inc., 462 Broadway, Ste. 4000, New York, NY 10013. TEL 212-966-8400. FAX 212-966-9366. (Dist. by: Flynt Distributing Co., 8484 Wilshire Blvd., Beverly Hills, CA 90211) Ed. Douglas McClemont. illus. **Document type:** consumer publication.

051 US
INCITING DESIRE; the zine of desire without boundaries. 1990. irreg. $4.50 per issue. 343 Soquel Ave., Ste. 151, Santa Cruz, CA 95062. TEL 408-425-3397. adv.: B&W page $150; adv. contact: Rhonda Oxley. bk.rev. **Document type:** consumer publication.

305.31 US ISSN 1064-7597
INSIDE EDGE.* 1993. 10/yr. $14.95 (Canada $26.95; elsewhere $44.95). S.H. Eliot Publishing Co., Inc., 258 Harvard St., Ste. 329, Brookline, MA 02146-2904. TEL 617-497-5621. FAX 617-497-5623. (Subscr. to: Box 712, Cambridge, MA 02238. TEL 800-55-EDGE-1) Ed. J. Hsu. adv.; bk.rev.; film rev.; illus. circ. 125,000. (back issues avail.) **Document type:** consumer publication.
 Description: Lifestyle magazine for young men covering sports, entertainment, relationship advice, and style tips.

JIATING/FAMILY. see HOME ECONOMICS

JOCK. see HOMOSEXUALITY

JOURNAL OF COUPLES THERAPY; studies in the enhancement of intimacy and bonding for the clinical practitioner. see PSYCHOLOGY

305.3 US ISSN 1061-8538 HQ1090.3
JOURNEYMEN. 1991. q. $18 (Canada $24). 513 Chester Turnpike, Candia, NH 03034. TEL 603-483-8029. (Dist. by: Bookpeople, 7900 Edgewater Dr., Oakland, CA 94621. TEL 800-999-4650) Ed. Paul S. Boynton. adv.: B&W page $155; trim 7 1/2 x 10. bk.rev.; illus.
 Description: Presents a wide variety of subject matter, as it relates to the male experience.

051 US ISSN 0734-4309
JUGGS. vol.8, no.8, 1989. m. $39.95 (foreign $55.95). M M Publications, Ltd. (Subsidiary of: Mavety Media Group Ltd.), 462 Broadway, Ste. 4000, New York, NY 10013. TEL 212-966-8400. (Dist. by: Flynt Distributing Co., 9171 Wilshire Blvd., Ste. 300, Beverly Hills, CA 90210) Ed. Dian Hanson. illus.

KING. see CLOTHING TRADE — Fashions

051 US
KINKY FETISHES. 1993. 8/yr. $17.69; newsstand price: $3.95. A J A Publishing, Box 70, Port Chester, NY 10573. TEL 914-939-2111. Ed. Julie Silver. adv. circ. 75,000. **Document type:** consumer publication.

052 UK ISSN 0265-1289
KNAVE. 1968. m. £40($70) Galaxy Publications Ltd., P.O. Box 312, Witham, Essex CM8 3SZ, England. Ed. Ross Gilfillam. adv. contact: Pam Askew. bk.rev. circ. 154,735.

051 US
LATIN MEN. 3/yr. Heat Publications, Inc. (Subsidiary of: Mavety Media Group Ltd.), 462 Broadway, Ste. 4000, New York, NY 10013. TEL 212-966-8400. (Dist. by: Flynt Distributing Co., 9171 Wilshire Blvd., Ste. 300, Beverly Hills, CA 90210)

051 US
LATIN WOMEN. q. Leisure Plus Publications, Inc. (Subsidiary of: Mavety Media Group Ltd.), 462 Broadway, Ste. 4000, New York, NY 10013. TEL 212-966-8400. (Dist. by: Flynt Distributing Co., 9171 Wilshire Blvd., Ste. 300, Beverly Hills, CA 90210)

051 US ISSN 0734-4295
LEG SHOW. vol.7, no.2, 1989. m. $39.95 (foreign $55.95). Leg Glamour, Inc. (Subsidiary of: Mavety Media Group Ltd.), 462 Broadway, Ste. 4000, New York, NY 10013. TEL 212-966-8400. (Dist. by: Flynt Distributing Co., 9171 Wilshire Blvd., Ste. 300, Beverly Hills, CA 90210) Ed. Dian Hanson. illus.

MEN'S INTERESTS 4645

051 US
LEG SHOW PRESENTS HIGH-HEELED WOMEN. vol.2, no.2, 1989. q. $14.95. Leg Glamour, Inc. (Subsidiary of: Mavety Media Group Ltd.), 462 Broadway, Ste. 4000, New York, NY 10013. TEL 212-966-8400. (Dist. by: Flynt Distributing Co., 2029 Century Park E., Ste. 3800, Los Angeles, CA 90067) illus.

LEGEND OF JENNIE LEE. see CLUBS

808 US ISSN 0279-1250
LETTERS MAGAZINE (TEANECK). 1979. m. $32. Letters, Magazine, Inc., 310 Cedar Lane, Box 1314, Teaneck, NJ 07666. TEL 201-836-9177. FAX 201-836-5055. Eds. Jackie Lewis, Lisa Rosen; Pub. Louis Rosen. adv. contact: Allison Reynolds. circ. 97,535. (back issues avail.) **Document type:** consumer publication.
 Description: Erotic literature.

051 US
LIPS (NEW YORK). 1989. m. $39.95. Leisure Plus Publications, Inc. (Subsidiary of: Mavety Media Group Ltd.), 462 Broadway, Ste. 4000, New York, NY 10013. TEL 212-966-8400. (Dist. by: Flynt Distributing Co., 9171 Wilshire Blvd., Ste. 300, Beverly Hills, CA 90210) illus.

051 US ISSN 1074-844X
LIVE GIRLS. 10/yr. $33. Live Periodicals, Inc., 801 Second Ave., New York, NY 10017. TEL 212-661-7878. FAX 212-883-1244.
 Formerly: Live! (New York) (ISSN 1060-1139)

051 US
LIVERPOOL LIBRARY - CLASSIC. m. Liverpool International, Ltd. (Subsidiary of: Mavety Media Group Ltd.), 462 Broadway, Ste. 4000, New York, NY 10013. TEL 212-966-8400. (Dist. by: Kable News Co., 11 W. 42nd St., 28th Fl., New York, NY 10036. TEL 212-768-1000)

LONG ISLAND PARENTING NEWS. see CHILDREN AND YOUTH — About

LOVING MORE. see SOCIOLOGY

070.48346 GW
LUI. 1977. m. DM.99. RedMag Gesellschaft fuer Redaktionelle Dienstleistungen, Buttermelchstr. 16, 80469 Munich, Germany. TEL 089-2025200. (Subscr. to: I P V Presse Vertrieb GmbH, Wendenstr. 27-29, D-2000 Hamburg 1, Germany) Ed. Heinz van Nouhuys. circ. 303,200. (back issues avail.)

051 US
LUSTY LETTERS. m. newsstand price: $3.76. Sportomatic Ltd. USA, Box 470, Port Chester, NY 10573. TEL 914-939-5138. adv. **Document type:** consumer publication.

M G F. (Mens's Guide to Fashion) see CLOTHING TRADE — Fashions

M R (NORWALK). (Menswear Retailing) see CLOTHING TRADE

MAENNER VOGUE. see CLOTHING TRADE — Fashions

051 US
MALE INSIDER. Short title: M I. vol.3, no.6, 1989. q. $14.95 (foreign $34.95). Macho Publications, Inc. (Subsidiary of: Mavety Media Group Ltd.), 462 Broadway, Ste. 4000, New York, NY 10013. TEL 212-966-8400. (Dist. by: Flynt Distributing Co., 9171 Wilshire Blvd., Ste. 300, Beverly Hills, CA 90210) Ed. Joe Mauro. illus.

MALEBOX. see HOMOSEXUALITY

301 NE ISSN 0165-4578
MAN. 1972. 10/yr. fl.87.50 (foreign fl.189.50) (effective 1995). B.V. Uitgeversmaatschappij Bonaventura (Subsidiary of: Elsevier N.V.), Postbus 2158, 1000 CD Amsterdam, Netherlands. TEL 31-20-6914111. FAX 31-20-5674398. Ed. Rupert V. Woerkom. adv.; illus. **Document type:** consumer publication.

070.48346 SI ISSN 0217-9288
MAN - LIFE & STYLE. (Text in English) 1986. bi-m. 322A Jalan Besar, SLS Bldg., Singapore 0820, Singapore. TEL 2968178. FAX 2968319. TELEX 24200. Ed. Michael Chiang. circ. 20,000.

305.31 US ISSN 1078-5388
▼MANZINE. 1994. q. $20; newsstand price: 6. Source Publications, Box 654, Monroe, CT 06468. E-mail: fhwallis. Ed. Frank Wallis. film rev.; video rev.; illus. (back issues avail.)
 Description: Investigates all areas of sexuality to a primarily heterosexual adult male audience, including homosexuality, lesbianism, bisexuality, and sadomasochism. Examines popular sexual opinion and how it is expressed in erotic art, photography, and cinema.

THE MASTER'S WAY. see SINGLES' INTERESTS AND LIFESTYLES

070.483 059.992
790.1 IO ISSN 0215-1715
MATRA; Majalan Trend Pria. (Text in Indonesian) 1986. m. $26. Yayasan Bapora, Jl. Warung Buncit Raya, Perumahan, Buncit Raya Permai Kav. 1, Jakarta 12550, Indonesia. TEL 021-780-3510. FAX 021-780-1660. TELEX 62797-IA. (Singapore addr.: Media Link, 1 Sophia Rd., No. 04-26, Peace Centre, Singapore 0922. TEL 65-3361725; Japan addr.: Raira Enterprise Co., Ltd., 1-6-8-402, Shimoochiai, Shinjuku-ku, Tokyo 161, Japan. TEL 03-3360-9171) Ed. Fikri Jufri. adv.: B&W page $1316, color page $2632; trim 190 X 257. circ. 95,000.
 Description: Leisure magazine for men.

051 US ISSN 8756-7644
MAX. vol.4, no.3, 1989. 9/yr. $37.95 (foreign $47.95). Max Magazine, Inc. (Subsidiary of: Mavety Media Group Ltd.), 462 Broadway, Ste. 4000, New York, NY 10013. TEL 212-966-8400. (Dist. by: Kable News Co., 11 W. 42nd St., 28th Fl., New York, NY 10036. TEL 212-768-1000) Ed. Dian Hanson. illus.

070.48346 UK ISSN 0025-6161
MAYFAIR. 1966. 13/yr. £33 (foreign £39). Paul Raymond Publications Ltd., 2 Archer St., London W1V 7HF, England. Ed. Robert Swift. adv.; bk.rev. **Document type:** consumer publication.

051 US
MEN (BOSTON).* 1990. bi-m. $14.95. Norris Publishing, Inc., 7 Worcester Sq., Boston, MA 02118-2701. TEL 203-259-7015. Ed. Peter Kaplan. circ. 140,000.
 Description: For men in their early thirties who are starting to make major lifestyle decisions. Covers clothing, food, travel, sports, health, money, home repair and women.

305.31 US
MEN OF ACTION. 1992. q. free. Promise Keepers, Box 18376, Boulder, CO 80308. Ed. Pete Richardson. circ. 85,000. **Document type:** newsletter.

052 UK ISSN 0025-9217
MEN ONLY. m. 50s.($9) Paul Raymond Publications Ltd., 2 Archer St., London W1, England. Ed. Tony Power. bk.rev.; film rev. circ. 150,000.

MEN'S CONFIDENTIAL NEWSLETTER; health, sex and fitness news for men. see MEN'S HEALTH

051 US ISSN 1063-4657
GV191.2
MEN'S JOURNAL. 1992. 10/yr. newsstand price: $3. Straight Arrow Publishers Company, L.P., 1290 Ave. of the Americas, New York, NY 10104. TEL 212-484-1616. (Subscr. to: Box 57055, Boulder, CO 80322-7055) Ed. John Rasmus. adv. circ. 100,000. **Indexed:** Access (1993-). **Document type:** consumer publication.
 Description: Active men's journal with articles featuring travel and adventure.

MENSTUFF, THE NATIONAL MEN'S RESOURCE. see MEN'S STUDIES

MISS MOM - MISTER MOM. see CHILDREN AND YOUTH — About

056.1 808 CU
MUJERES Y MUCHACHA. m. $48. (Federacion de Mujeres Cubanas) Ediciones Cubanas, Departamento de Exportacion, Obispo No. 461, Apdo. 605, Havana, Cuba. illus.
 Formerly: Romances.

MUSCLE & HEALTH. see PHYSICAL FITNESS AND HYGIENE

N S MAN. see MILITARY

070.483 US
NANZI HAN/MANLINESS. (Text in Chinese) bi-m. $20.70. China Books & Periodicals, Inc., 2929 24th St., San Francisco, CA 94110. TEL 415-282-2994. FAX 415-282-0994.

051 US
NASTY LETTERS. bi-m. $15.95. Starlight Press, Inc. (Subsidiary of: Mavety Media Group Ltd.), 462 Broadway, Ste. 4000, New York, NY 10013. TEL 212-966-8400. (Dist. by: Flynt Distributing Co., 9171 Wilshire Blvd., Ste. 300, Beverly Hills, CA 90210)

051 US
NASTY PHOTOS. q. $14.95. Leisure Plus Publications, Inc. (Subsidiary of: Mavety Media Group Ltd.), 462 Broadway, Ste. 4000, New York, NY 10013. TEL 212-966-8400. (Dist. by: Flynt Distributing Co., 9171 Wilshire Blvd., Ste. 300, Beverly Hills, CA 90210)

NATURAL BODYBUILDING AND FITNESS. see PHYSICAL FITNESS AND HYGIENE

053.1 GW
NEW MAG. m. DM.99.60 (foreign DM.108). New Magazines Verlagsgesellschaft mbH, Buttermelcherstr. 16, 80469 Munich, Germany. TEL 089-202520-0. FAX 089-20252020. Ed. Peter Herzberg. adv. contact: Dieter Petri. circ. 51,088. **Document type:** consumer publication.

NEW MAN. see RELIGIONS AND THEOLOGY

051 US ISSN 1063-8237
NUGGET. 9/yr. newsstand price: $5.95. Dugent Publishing Corp., 2600 Douglas Rd., Ste. 600, Coral Gables, FL 33134. TEL 305-443-2378. adv. **Document type:** consumer publication.

051 US ISSN 0279-3725
NUMBERS. q. newsstand price: $4.95. Leemar Publishing, 28 W. 25th St., New York, NY 10010. TEL 212-647-0222. FAX 212-647-0236. adv. **Document type:** consumer publication.

051 US
OFF-BEAT LETTERS. bi-m. $15.95. Opal Press, Inc. (Subsidiary of: Mavety Media Group Ltd.), 462 Broadway, Ste. 4000, New York, NY 10013. TEL 212-966-8400. (Dist. by: Flynt Distributing Co., 9171 Wilshire Blvd., Ste. 300, Beverly Hills, CA 90210)

ONTARIO WRESTLER MAGAZINE. see SPORTS AND GAMES

OPTIONS (PORT CHESTER). see HOMOSEXUALITY

051 US
ORALRAMA!. 1989. q. $4.95 per no. Leisure Plus Publications, Inc. (Subsidiary of: Mavety Media Group Ltd.), 462 Broadway, Ste. 4000, New York, NY 10013. TEL 212-966-8400. (Dist. by: Flynt Distributing Co., 9171 Wilshire Blvd., Ste. 300, Beverly Hills, CA 90210) illus.

051 US
ORIENTAL DOLLS. 9/yr. $19.95. Fast Lane Publishing, Inc. (Subsidiary of: Mavety Media Group Ltd.), 462 Broadway, Ste. 4000, New York, NY 10013. TEL 212-966-8400. (Dist. by: Flynt Distributing Co., 9171 Wilshire Blvd., Ste. 300, Beverly Hills, CA 90210)

OSTENTATIOUS MIND. see LITERATURE — Poetry

OUT. see HOMOSEXUALITY

070.48346
OUTRAGEOUS LETTERS.* bi-m. $18. Vanity Publications, 1775 Broadway, Ste. 604, New York, NY 10019-1903. Ed. Sybil Norfolk. **Document type:** consumer publication.
 Description: Contains erotica.

051 US
OVER 40. vol.2, no.2, 1989. m. $39.95. Midlife Publications, Inc. (Subsidiary of: Mavety Media Group Ltd.), 462 Broadway, Ste. 4000, New York, NY 10013. TEL 212-966-8400. (Dist. by: Flynt Distributing Co., 2029 Century Park E., Ste. 3800, Los Angeles, CA 90067) illus.

MEN'S INTERESTS

051 US
OVER 50. q. $14.95. Midlife Publications, Inc. (Subsidiary of: Mavety Media Group Ltd.), 462 Broadway, Ste. 4000, New York, NY 10013. TEL 212-966-8400. (Dist. by: Flynt Distributing Co., 9171 Wilshire Blvd., Ste. 300, Beverly Hills, CA 90210)

051 US
PARADISE MAGAZINE; for the 90's male. 1993. m. newsstand price: $3.95. Paradise Entertainment, Box 2116, New York, NY 10116-2116. TEL 212-630-0242. Ed. J. Walters. adv.; illus. **Document type:** consumer publication.

PARENTS EXPRESS; the newspaper for Philadelphia area parents. see EDUCATION — Teaching Methods And Curriculum

070.48346 UK ISSN 0955-1824
PAUL RAYMOND'S MODEL DIRECTORY. 1980. 13/yr. £33($39) Paul Raymond Publications Ltd., 2 Archer St., London W1V 7HF, England. Ed. Cara Harrison. (back issues avail.) **Document type:** consumer publication.

052 UK ISSN 0950-0685
PENTHOUSE. 1965. m. £19. Northern & Shell Publications, Northern & Shell Tower, City Harbour, London E14 9GL, England. TEL 44-171-987-5090. adv.; circ. 113,000 (paid). **Document type:** consumer publication.

363.47 HK
PENTHOUSE. (Text in Chinese) 1985. m. Yongder Hall Ltd., G-F, Cheung Kong Bldg., 661 Kings Road, Quarry Bay, Hong Kong, Hong Kong. TEL 565-1313. FAX 565-8217. Eds. Alan Zie Yongder, Andrew Ho. adv.; film rev. circ. 51,684.

051 US ISSN 0090-2020
AP2
PENTHOUSE; the international magazine for men. 1969. m. $36. Penthouse International, Ltd. (Subsidiary of: General Media Publishing Group), 277 Park Ave., 4th Fl., New York, NY 10172. TEL 212-702-6000. FAX 212-702-6282. (Subscr. to: Box 420235, Palm Coast, FL 32142-0235) Ed. Peter Bloch. adv. contact: Peter Johnsmeyer. circ. 1,304,709. Indexed: Access (1975-). **Document type:** consumer publication.
—UMI.

054.1 FR ISSN 0762-5006
PENTHOUSE. 1985. m. 300 F. (foreign 420 F.) (effective 1995). Publications Filipacchi, 63-65 Champs Elysees, 75008 Paris, France. TEL 40-74-70-00. (Subscr. to: 99 rue d'Amsterdam, 75008 Paris, France. TEL 42-80-68-55) **Document type:** consumer publication.

053.1 GW
PENTHOUSE. m. DM.99.60 (foreign DM.108). New Magazines Verlagsgesellschaft mbH, Buttermelcherstr. 16, 80469 Munich, Germany. TEL 089-202520-0. FAX 089-20252020. Ed. Rudolf Hajduk. adv. contact: Dieter Petri. circ. 203,290. **Document type:** consumer publication.

305.31 SP
PENTHOUSE. 1978. m. $40. Blue Sky Ediciones S.A., Londres 2-4, Esc. A, 1o 4e, 08029 Barcelona, Spain. TEL 419-02-41. FAX 419-35-24. Ed. Pedro Balart Codina. adv. contact: Julian Poveda. circ. 98,000. **Document type:** consumer publication.

053.931 NE ISSN 0920-8305
PENTHOUSE. (Text in Dutch) 1986. m. fl.84; newsstand price: fl.8. Magasell, Pr. Hendriklaan 26, 1075 BD Amsterdam, Netherlands. TEL 31-20-6643016. FAX 31-20-6626236. adv.; circ. 78,500 (paid). **Document type:** consumer publication.

051 US ISSN 1043-0210
HQ1
PENTHOUSE FORUM; the international journal of human relations. 1976. m. (13/yr.). $30 (effective 1995). Penthouse International, Ltd. (Subsidiary of: General Media Publishing Group), 277 Park Ave., 4th Fl., New York, NY 10172. TEL 212-702-6000. FAX 212-702-6282. (Subscr. to: Box 420235, Palm Coast, FL 32142-0235. TEL 800-333-0012) Ed. V.K. McCarty. bk.rev.; index. (back issues avail.) **Document type:** consumer publication.
—UMI.
Formerly (until 1988): Forum (ISSN 0160-2195)
Description: Allows men and women to share experiences and fantasies. Provides data and entertainment concerning sex and sexuality.

051 US ISSN 0883-8798
PENTHOUSE LETTERS; the magazine of sexual marvels. 1979. m. $28. Penthouse Letters International, Ltd. (Subsidiary of: General Media Publishing Group), 277 Park Ave., 4th Fl., New York, NY 10172. TEL 212-702-6000. FAX 212-702-6282. (Subscr. to: Box 420235, Palm Coast, FL 32142-0235) Ed. Don Myrus. adv.; bk.rev. circ. 550,000. (back issues avail.) **Document type:** consumer publication.

051 US ISSN 0274-5143
PENTHOUSE VARIATIONS; for liberated lovers. 1978. m. (13/yr.). $30. Penthouse International, Ltd. (Subsidiary of: General Media Publishing Group), 277 Park Ave., 4th Fl., New York, NY 10172. TEL 212-702-6000. FAX 212-702-6282. (Subscr. to: Box 420235, Palm Coast, FL 32142-0235. TEL 800-333-0012) Ed. V.K. McCarty. **Document type:** consumer publication.
Description: Provides interpersonal portraits of America's couples. Offers sexual fact and fiction for entertainment and education.

051 US
PERSUASION. bi-m. Domino Press, Inc., 462 Broadway, Ste. 4000, New York, NY 10013. TEL 212-966-8400. (Dist. by: Flynt Distributing Co., 9171 Wilshire Blvd., Ste. 300, Beverly Hills, CA 90210)

051 US
PILLOW TALK; adult erotica. 1977. bi-m. $3.25 per no. Crescent Publishing Group, 801 Second Ave., New York, NY 10017. TEL 212-661-7878. FAX 212-692-9297. Ed. Asia Fraser. video rev. **Document type:** consumer publication.

051 US
PLATINUM MAGAZINE. 1993. m. $25.95 (effective 1995). Platinum Publications, 122 E. 42nd St., Ste. 1700, New York, NY 10168. TEL 212-551-1147. FAX 212-551-1001. Ed. David Rafael. adv.; B&W page $5100, color page $6800; adv. contact: Ira Isserson. illus.; circ. 150,000 (paid). **Document type:** consumer publication.

051 US ISSN 0032-1478
AP2
PLAYBOY. (Also published in 14 overseas editions) 1953. m. $29.97 (foreign $45; Canada $47.05) (effective 1994). Playboy Enterprises, Inc., 680 N. Lake Shore Dr., Chicago, IL 60611. TEL 312-751-8000. FAX 312-751-2818. (Subscr. to: Box 2007, Harlan, IA 51537-4007. TEL 800-999-4438) Ed. Arthur Kretchmer; Pub. Hugh Hefner. adv.: B&W page $60630, color page $84900. bk.rev.; film rev.; rec.rev.; illus.; index, cum.index: 1953-68, 1969-73, 1974-78, 1979-83, 1984-88; circ. 3,402,617 (paid). (also avail. in microform from UMI,BHP; reprint service avail. from UMI) Indexed: Access (1975-), Bibl.Engl.Lang.& Lit., Film Lit.Ind. (1973-), Mag.Ind., Media Rev.Dig., PMR. **Document type:** consumer publication.
—Faxon; UMI; UnCover.

056.9 BL ISSN 0104-1746
PLAYBOY. 1975. m. $130. Editora Abril, S.A., R. Geraldo Flausino Gomes, 61, 04573-900 Sao Paulo SP, Brazil. TEL 55-11-534-5582. FAX 55-11-534-5396. (Subscr. to: Rua do Curtume, 769, 05065-900 Sao Paulo SP, Brazil. TEL 011-823-9100) Ed. Ricardo Setti. adv.: B&W page $16374, color page $18815. bk.rev.; film rev.; music rev.; play rev.; video rev.; charts; illus. circ. 251,000. **Document type:** consumer publication.
Formerly: Homen.
Description: Presents the most beautiful and famous women of Brazil and the world.

053.1 GW ISSN 0939-8546
PLAYBOY. 1972. m. $80. Heinrich Bauer Verlag (Muenchen), Charles-de-Gaulle-Str. 8, 81737 Munich, Germany. TEL 089-6786-400. FAX 089-672981. (Dist. in U.S. by: G L P International, Inc., 153 S. Dean St., Englewood, NJ 07631-3513. TEL 201-871-1010. FAX 201-871-0870) Ed. Nikolas Marten. adv.: B&W page $13424, color page $24852. circ. 225,000. **Document type:** consumer publication.

056.1 SP
PLAYBOY. 1978. m. $90. R.B.A. Revistas, S.A., C. Perez Galdos, 36 bis, 08012 Barcelona, Spain. TEL 34-3-415-7374. FAX 34-3-217-7378. Ed. Jose Luis Cordoba. adv.: B&W page $5256, color page $5484. bk.rev.; illus. circ. 70,000. **Document type:** consumer publication.

056.1 MX
PLAYBOY. 1976. m. Editorial Caballero, Maricopa No. 57, Col. Napoles, 03810 Mexico, D.F., Mexico. TEL 52-5-687-6638. FAX 52-5-682-0534. Ed. Perla Carreto. adv.: B&W page $4376, color page $6612. bk.rev.; illus. circ. 100,000. **Document type:** consumer publication.

059.956 JA
PLAYBOY. (Text in Japanese) 1975. m. Shueisha Inc., 2-5-10 Hititsubashi, Chiyoda-ku, Tokyo 101-50, Japan. TEL 81-3-3230-6032. FAX 81-3-3264-6575. Ed. Suzuhito Imai. adv.: B&W page $10638, color page $14730. bk.rev.; illus. circ. 450,000. **Document type:** consumer publication.

055.1 IT
PLAYBOY. 1972. m. L.97000($120) Edizioni Lancio S.p.A., Via Roccagiovine, 267, 00156 Rome, Italy. TEL 39-6-411-2651. FAX 39-6-674-8185. Ed. Alvaro Zerboni. adv.: B&W page $5053, color page $8296. bk.rev.; illus. circ. 75,000. **Document type:** consumer publication.

059.8 GR
PLAYBOY. (Text in Greek) 1985. m. Dr.8000($92) Hachette-Rizzoli Magazines Ltd., 20-22 Hersifronos Str., 116 36 Athens, Greece. TEL 30-1-902-5150. FAX 30-1-902-4683. Ed. Anteos Chrystostomides. adv.: B&W page $2804, color page $3506; adv. contact: Yiannis Matsades. bk.rev.; illus. circ. 45,000. **Document type:** consumer publication.

053.1 AG
PLAYBOY. 1985. m. Editorial Perfil, Sarmiento 1113, Piso 2, 1041 Buenos Aires, Argentina. TEL 54-1-352-046. FAX 54-1-353-462. Ed. Edgardo Martolio. adv.: B&W page $7490, color page $11660. bk.rev.; illus. circ. 70,000. **Document type:** consumer publication.

057.8 XR ISSN 0862-9374
PLAYBOY.* 1991. m. V I Press Publishing Limited Prague, Charkovska 24, 100 00 Prague 10, Czech Republic. TEL 42-2-264-298. Ed. Jaroslav Koran. adv.: B&W page $3000, color page $4032. illus. circ. 45,000. **Document type:** consumer publication.

052 SA ISSN 1022-2200
PLAYBOY; entertainment for men. (Text in English) 1993. m. R.54. Playboy South Africa (Subsidiary of: Times Media Limited), P.O. Box 1138, Johannesburg 2000, South Africa. adv.; bk.rev.; illus. **Document type:** consumer publication.

059.9511 HU ISSN 0865-350X
PLAYBOY (MAGYAR KIADAS). 1989. m. V I Press, Kassak Lajos u. 78, 1134 Budapest, Hungary. TEL 36-1-140-8927. FAX 36-1-140-8929. Ed. Peter Bakonyi. adv.: B&W page $2972, color page $3692. bk.rev.; illus. circ. 40,000. **Document type:** consumer publication.

057.85 PL ISSN 1230-2724
PLAYBOY (POLSKA EDYCJA). 1992. m. $1.70 per no. VIPress Poland, Sieroszewskiego 16a, 81-376 Gdynia, Poland. TEL 48-58-208376. Ed. Tomasz Raczek; Pub. Beata Milewska. adv.: B&W page $2300, color page $4000; adv. contact: Halszka Ciolkowska. bk.rev.; illus. circ. 75,000. **Document type:** consumer publication.

MEN'S INTERESTS 4647

059.951   CH
PLAYBOY (TAIWAN EDITION). 1990. m. P B I Publications (Taiwan) Ltd., 5F-4, 137, Fu-Shing S. Rd., Sec. 1, Taipei, Taiwan, Republic of China. TEL 886-2-771-8876. FAX 886-2-752-1432. Ed. Ann Wang. adv.: B&W page $3157, color page $4341. bk.rev.; illus. circ. 32,000. **Document type:** consumer publication.

059.943   TU
PLAYBOY (TURKISH EDITION). 1985. m. Karacan Yayinlari A.S., Koyalti Mevkii, Orus Reis Sok No. 10, Yeni Bosna, Istanbul, Turkey. TEL 90-1-551-3571. FAX 90-1-551-3526. Ed. Dogan Sener. adv.: B&W page $2291, color page $2619. bk.rev.; illus. circ. 35,000. **Document type:** consumer publication.

PLAYBOY ENTERPRISES. ANNUAL REPORT. see *BUSINESS AND ECONOMICS — Abstracting, Bibliographies, Statistics*

051 746.92   US   ISSN 0744-4885
PLAYBOY FASHION. q. Playboy Enterprises, Inc., 680 N. Lakeshore Dr., Chicago, IL 60611. TEL 312-751-8000. FAX 312-751-2818. Pub. Hugh Hefner. **Document type:** consumer publication.
    Formerly: Playboy Guide Fashion for Men (ISSN 0279-7755)

053.931   NE   ISSN 0168-1184
PLAYBOY NEDERLAND. 1983. m. fl.87($55); newsstand price: fl.7.95. Uitgeverij Spaarnestad B.V., Ceylonpoort 5-25, Postbus 1, 2000 MA Haarlem (Schalwijk), Netherlands. TEL 31-23-304304. FAX 31-23-337293. Ed. Jan Heemskerk; Pub. Meinard Carper. adv.: B&W page $7935, color page $11337; trim 210 x 280; adv. contact: Anouk Boering. bk.rev.; circ. 135,000 (paid). **Document type:** consumer publication.

051   US   ISSN 1062-225X
PLAYBOY NUDES. 1990. a. Playboy Enterprises, Inc., 680 N. Lake Shore Dr., Chicago, IL 60611. TEL 312-751-8000. FAX 312-751-2818. Pub. Hugh Hefner. **Document type:** consumer publication.
    Description: Features erotic photographs portraying nude women.

051   US   ISSN 1062-2284
PLAYBOY PRESENTS INTERNATIONAL PLAYMATES. 1992. a. Playboy Enterprises, Inc., 680 N. Lake Shore Dr., Chicago, IL 60611. TEL 312-751-8000. FAX 312-751-2818. Pub. Hugh Hefner. **Document type:** consumer publication.
    Description: Presents women from all over the world in erotic poses.

051   US   ISSN 1069-1251
PLAYBOY PRESENTS PLAYBOY'S VIDEO PLAYMATES. 1993. a. Playboy Enterprises, Inc., 680 N. Lake Shore Dr., Chicago, IL 60611. TEL 312-751-8000. FAX 312-751-2818. Pub. Hugh Hefner. **Document type:** consumer publication.
    Description: Features women who have appeared in Playboy's erotic videotapes.

051   US   ISSN 1062-2276
PLAYBOY'S BATHING BEAUTIES. 1989. a. Playboy Enterprises, Inc., 680 N. Lake Shore Dr., Chicago, IL 60611. TEL 312-751-8000. FAX 312-751-2818. Pub. Hugh Hefner. **Document type:** consumer publication.
    Description: Presents attractive women in swimsuits.

051   US   ISSN 1066-5129
PLAYBOY'S BLONDES, BRUNETTES, REDHEADS. 1985. a. Playboy Enterprises, Inc., 680 N. Lakeshore Dr., Chicago, IL 60611. TEL 312-751-8000. FAX 312-751-2818. Pub. Hugh Hefner. **Document type:** consumer publication.
    Description: Presents attractive women in erotic poses.

051 746.92   US
PLAYBOY'S BOOK OF LINGERIE. bi-m. newsstand price: $5.95. Playboy Enterprises, Inc., 680 N. Lake Shore Dr., Chicago, IL 60611. TEL 312-751-8000. FAX 312-751-2818. Pub. Hugh Hefner. **Document type:** consumer publication.
    Description: Contains erotic photographs of women wearing lingerie.

051   US   ISSN 1063-9616
PLAYBOY'S CALENDAR PLAYMATES. 1992. a. Playboy Enterprises, Inc., 680 N. Lake Shore Dr., Chicago, IL 60611. TEL 312-751-8000. FAX 312-751-2818. Pub. Hugh Hefner. **Document type:** consumer publication.
    Description: Presents Playboy centerfold models who have appeared in calendars.

051   US   ISSN 1061-9070
PLAYBOY'S CAREER GIRLS. 1992. a. Playboy Enterprises, Inc., 680 N. Lake Shore Dr., Chicago, IL 60611. TEL 312-751-8000. FAX 312-751-2818. Pub. Hugh Hefner. **Document type:** consumer publication.
    Description: Presents career women in erotic poses.

051   US   ISSN 1062-2268
PLAYBOY'S COLLEGE GIRLS. 1983. a. Playboy Enterprises, Inc., 680 N. Lake Shore Dr., Chicago, IL 60611. TEL 312-751-8000. FAX 312-751-2818. Pub. Hugh Hefner. **Document type:** consumer publication.
    Description: Presents college women in erotic poses.

051   US   ISSN 1062-0494
PLAYBOY'S GIRLS OF SUMMER. 1983. a. Playboy Enterprises, Inc., 680 N. Lake Shore Dr., Chicago, IL 60611. TEL 312-751-8000. FAX 312-751-2818. Pub. Hugh Hefner. **Document type:** consumer publication.
    Description: Features erotic photographs of attractive women.

051   US   ISSN 1061-9089
PLAYBOY'S GIRLS OF THE WORLD. 1992. a. Playboy Enterprises, Inc., 680 N. Lakeshore Dr., Chicago, IL 60611. TEL 312-751-8000. FAX 312-751-2818. Pub. Hugh Hefner. **Document type:** consumer publication.
    Description: Features erotic photographs of attractive women from all over the world.

051   US   ISSN 1068-2295
PLAYBOY'S GIRLS OF WINTER. 1984. a. Playboy Enterprises, Inc., 680 N. Lake Shore Dr., Chicago, IL 60611. TEL 312-751-8000. FAX 312-751-2818. Pub. Hugh Hefner. **Document type:** consumer publication.
    Description: Features erotic photographs of attractive women.

051   US   ISSN 1069-224X
PLAYBOY'S GREAT PLAYMATE HUNT. 1989. a. Playboy Enterprises, Inc., 680 N. Lake Shore Dr., Chicago, IL 60611. TEL 312-751-8000. FAX 312-751-2818. Pub. Hugh Hefner. **Document type:** consumer publication.

051   US   ISSN 1061-6640
PLAYBOY'S PLAYMATE REVIEW. 1985. a. Playboy Enterprises, Inc., 680 N. Lake Shore Dr., Chicago, IL 60611. TEL 312-751-8000. FAX 312-751-2818. Pub. Hugh Hefner. **Document type:** consumer publication.
    Description: Presents women who have appeared in Playboy centerfolds.

051   US   ISSN 1066-5137
PLAYBOY'S WET & WILD WOMEN. 1987. a. Playboy Enterprises, Inc., 680 N. Lakeshore Dr., Chicago, IL 60611. TEL 312-751-8000. FAX 312-751-2818. Pub. Hugh Hefner. **Document type:** consumer publication.
    Description: Presents women in erotic poses.

051   US   ISSN 0733-5695
PLAYGUY. vol.13, 1989. m. $59.95 (foreign $79.95). Playguy Publications, Ltd., 462 Broadway, Ste. 4000, New York, NY 10013. TEL 212-966-8400. FAX 212-966-9366. (Dist. by: Flynt Distributing Co., 8484 Wilshire Blvd., Beverly Hills, CA 90211) Ed. Douglas McClemont. adv.; bk.rev.; film rev.; play rev.; illus. circ. 75,000. (back issues avail.) **Document type:** consumer publication.

070.4834   IT   ISSN 0032-1532
PLAYMEN; mensile di cultura, attualita, politica e costume. 1967. m. L.100000 (foreign L.110000) (effective 1990). Periodici Tattilo s.r.l., Via del Casale Piombino, 30, 00135 Rome, Italy. TEL 06-305-26-41. FAX 06-30-52-506. Ed. Roberto Balsamo. adv.: B&W page L.6600000, color page L.11850000; 212 x 274. bk.rev.; illus. circ. 29,092.

051   US
PLUMPERS AND BIG WOMEN. bi-m. newsstand price: $4.95. Dugent Publishing Corp., 2600 Douglas Rd., Ste. 600, Coral Gables, FL 33134. TEL 305-443-2378. adv. **Document type:** consumer publication.

051   US
POCKETFOX. q. newsstand price: $3.50. Montcalm Publishing Corp., 401 Park Ave. S., New York, NY 10016-8802. TEL 212-779-8900. **Document type:** consumer publication.

051   US
PORTFOLIO.* bi-m. newsstand price: $3.95. Magna Publishing, 210 E. State St., Rte. 4, Ste. 401, Paramus, NJ 07652-5103. TEL 201-487-6124. FAX 201-487-9360. **Document type:** consumer publication.

051   US
PRIVATE LETTERS. bi-m. Crescent Publishing Group, 801 Second Ave., New York, NY 10017. TEL 212-661-7878. FAX 212-692-9297. Ed. Asia Fraser.

051   US
PRIVATE MOMENTS. bi-m. Mountainside Press, Inc., 462 Broadway, Ste. 4000, New York, NY 10013. TEL 212-966-8400. (Dist. by: Flynt Distributing Co., 9171 Wilshire Blvd., Ste. 300, Beverly Hills, CA 90210)

059.927   UK   ISSN 1319-089X
AL-RAJUL. Key Title: Al-Ragul (Guddat). (Text in Arabic) 1992. m. $154 (effective 1994). Saudi Research and Marketing, Arab Press House, 184 High Holborn, London WC1V 7AP, England. TEL 44-171-831-8181. FAX 44-171-404-6311. (And: P.O. Box 4556, Jeddah 21441, Saudi Arabia. TEL 966-2-6691888. FAX 966-2-6671650; Subscr. in U.S. to: Attache International, 3050 Broadway, Ste. 300, Boulder, CO 80304-3154. TEL 303-442-8900. FAX 303-442-7979) Ed. Abdul Rahman Al-Rashid. adv.: B&W page $2400, color page $4000; trim 220 x 285. illus.; circ. 23,349 (paid). **Document type:** consumer publication.
    Description: Upscale lifestyle features and topics.

052 305.31   DK
RAPPORT. 1972. m. DKK 426. Forlaget Rapport A-S, Marienlundvej 46 D, DK-2730 Herlev, Denmark. TEL 45-33-13-60-60. FAX 45-44-94-04-06. (Subscr. to: Allers Press, Vigerslev Alle, DK-2500 Valby, Denmark. TEL 45-36-30-33-33) Ed. Jan Nielsen. adv.: B&W page DKK 6500, color page DKK 9900; trim 196 x 297. circ. 70,000.

RELATIONSHIPS TODAY. see *WOMEN'S INTERESTS*

RODINA. see *WOMEN'S INTERESTS*

305.3 301.412   US
SANDMUTOPIA GUARDIAN & DUNGEON JOURNAL.* 1988. q. $24. A S W G T Inc., Box 1146, New York, NY 10156. Ed. Marcus - Jay Wonacott. adv.; bk.rev.; film rev.; play rev.; illus. circ. 14,000. (back issues avail.)

052   SA   ISSN 0036-9012
SCOPE. 1966. fortn. R.124.04 (overseas R.188.82) (effective 1993). Republican Press (Pty) Ltd., P.O. Box 32083, Mobeni 4060, Natal, South Africa. TEL 27-31-422041. FAX 27-31-921231. Ed. David Mullany. bk.rev.; film rev. circ. 120,000. **Document type:** consumer publication.
    Description: Features glamour, sensationalism, adventure, humour, and escapism.

301.412   US   ISSN 1073-2438
SCORE (MIAMI). 1992. m. $52. Quad International, Inc., 13360 S.W. 128th St., Miami, FL 33186. TEL 305-238-5040. FAX 305-238-6716. Ed. John C. Fox; Pub. Sam Lessner. adv.: color page $3225; trim 8 x 10 7/8; adv. contact: Jack Dailey. circ. 187,221 (paid). **Document type:** consumer publication.

SCREW. see *LITERARY AND POLITICAL REVIEWS*

SENSATIONS. see *LITERATURE*

070.48346   US
SENSUOUS LETTERS.* bi-m. $18. Vanity Publications, 1775 Broadway, Ste. 604, New York, NY 10019-1903. **Document type:** consumer publication.

MEN'S STUDIES

SER PADRES/BEING PARENTS. see *WOMEN'S INTERESTS*

SERVANT LEADER. see *RELIGIONS AND THEOLOGY — Protestant*

051 US
SEXUAL CONFESSIONS. bi-m. newsstand price: $3.95. Mavety Media Group, 462 Broadway, New York, NY 10013. TEL 212-966-8400. FAX 212-966-9366. adv. **Document type:** consumer publication.

051 US ISSN 1072-7590
SLIPPERY WHEN WET; bisexual, penetration-positive, queer. 1991. q. $19.50. More! Productions, Box 3101, Berkeley, CA 94703. Ed. Sunah Cherwin. adv.; bk.rev.; film rev.; illus.; circ. 2,000 (paid). (back issues avail.) **Document type:** consumer publication.
   Formerly (until 1993): Logomotive.

051 US
SPECIAL EDITION; personal letters; uncensored letters; confidential letters. 1981. bi-m. A J A Publishing Corp., Box 470, Port Chester, NY 10573. Ed. Josh Piano. adv. circ. 75,000. **Document type:** consumer publication.
   Description: Letters from readers on a variety of sexual topics.

052 SA ISSN 1022-3096
STAG SEXUAL FORUM. 1993. m. R.5.50 per no. Viclen Promotions, P.O. Box 354, Mondeor 2110, South Africa. adv.; illus. **Document type:** consumer publication.

051 US
STARS. 9/yr. newsstand price: $5.95. G T Publishing, 28 W. 25th St., New York, NY 10010. TEL 212-647-0222. FAX 212-647-0236. adv. **Indexed:** Int.Ind.Film Per. **Document type:** consumer publication.

STEAM; a quarterly journal for men. see *HOMOSEXUALITY*

STEPFAMILIES & BEYOND; America's first independent newsletter about remarriage for stepparents and professionals. see *CHILDREN AND YOUTH — About*

051 US
SUGAH. bi-m. newsstand price: $4.95. Dugent Publishing Corp., 2600 Douglas Rd., Ste. 600, Coral Gables, FL 33134. TEL 305-443-2378. adv. **Document type:** consumer publication.

051 US ISSN 1069-1723
SWANK. 1956. m. $52. G C R Publishing Group, Inc., 1700 Broadway, 34th Fl., New York, NY 10019. TEL 212-541-7100. Ed. Michael Wilde. adv. circ. 200,000.

051 US
SWANK'S D-CUP.* s-a. newsstand price: $5.99. Magna Publishing, 210 E. State St., Rte. 4, Ste. 401, Paramus, NJ 07652-5103. TEL 201-487-6124. FAX 201-487-9360. **Document type:** consumer publication.

051 US
SWANK'S LEG ACTION.* m. newsstand price: $5.99. Magna Publishing, 210 E. State St., Rte. 4, Ste. 401, Paramus, NJ 07652-5103. TEL 201-487-6124. FAX 201-487-9360. **Document type:** consumer publication.

051 790.1 US
SWANK'S LEISURE.* 8/yr. newsstand price: $5.95. Magna Publishing, 210 E. State St., Rte. 4, Ste. 401, Paramus, NJ 07652-5103. TEL 201-487-6124. FAX 201-487-9360. adv. **Document type:** consumer publication.

051 US
SWINGER'S TODAY. 1985. bi-m. $24.95. Contact Advertising, 2010 St. Lucie Blvd., Ft. Pierce, FL 34946. TEL 407-464-5447. FAX 407-466-7294. (Subscr. to: Modern Products, 976 Murfreesboro Rd., Ste. 155, Nashville, TN 37217. TEL 800-637-5779) Ed. Holly Adams. adv. contact: Fonda Nietzche. circ. 15,000 (controlled).
   Description: Nationwide contact magazine for the travelling swinger.

051 US
SWINGERS UPDATE. 1980. bi-m. $29.95. Contact Advertising, 2010 St. Lucie Blvd., Ft. Pierce, FL 34946. TEL 407-464-5447. FAX 407-466-7294. (Subscr. to: Box 3431, Ft. Pierce, FL 34948. TEL 800-637-5779) Ed. Holly Adams. adv. contact: Fonda Nietzche. film rev.; circ. 22,000 (controlled). **Document type:** consumer publication.
   Description: Contains life-styles information for couples and clubs in the national swinging community.

051 US
SWINGING TIMES. 1982. m. $19.95. Contact Advertising, 2010 St. Lucie Blvd., Ft. Pierce, FL 34946. TEL 407-464-5447. FAX 407-466-7294. (Subscr. to: Box 3431, Ft. Pierce, FL 34948. TEL 800-637-5779) Ed. Holly Adams. adv. contact: Fonda Nietzche. film rev.; circ. 50,000 (controlled). (tabloid format)
   Description: National lifestyles publication for singles and couples interested in the swinging lifestyle.

051 US
TAIL ENDS. 1989. m. $39.95. Leisure Plus Publications, Inc. (Subsidiary of: Mavety Media Group Ltd.), 462 Broadway, Ste. 4000, New York, NY 10013. TEL 212-966-8400. (Dist. by: Flynt Distributing Co., 9171 Wilshire Blvd., Ste. 300, Beverly Hills, CA 90210) illus.

TASTE OF LATEX; entertainment for the sexually disenfranchised. see *LITERATURE*

051 US
THIGH HIGH. q. Drake Publishers, 801 Second Ave., New York, NY 10017. TEL 212-661-7878. FAX 212-883-1244.

TORCHLIGHT. see *RELIGIONS AND THEOLOGY — Judaic*

051 US ISSN 0733-5873
TORSO. 1981. m. $59.95 (foreign $79.95). Varsity Communications, Ltd., 462 Broadway, Ste. 4000, New York, NY 10013. TEL 212-966-8400. FAX 212-966-9366. (Dist. by: Flynt Distributing Co., 8484 Wilshire Blvd., Beverly Hills, CA 90211) Ed. Douglas McClemont. adv.; bk.rev. circ. 100,000. (back issues avail.) **Document type:** consumer publication.

051 US
TURN-ONS. 1980. 5/yr. A J A Publishing Corp., Box 470, Port Chester, NY 10573. Ed. John Velvel. adv. circ. 75,000. **Document type:** consumer publication.
   Description: Letters from readers on a variety of sexual topics.

051 301.412 US
UNCENSORED AMATEUR SWINGER. s-a. $13.95 per no. Continental Spectator, Box 278, Canal St. Sta., New York, NY 10013. TEL 800-325-4122. Ed. Linda Lee.
   Formerly: Unsensored Swinger.

051 US
UNCUT; the magazine of the natural man. vol.3, no.6, 1989. s-a. $10.95. Crete International, Inc. (Subsidiary of: Mavety Media Group Ltd.), 462 Broadway, Ste. 4000, New York, NY 10013. TEL 212-966-8400. (Dist. by: Flynt Distributing Co., 2029 Century Park E., Ste. 3800, Los Angeles, CA 90067) Ed. John W. Rowberry. illus.

051 US
THE VEGAS CONNECTION. 1989. q. $19.95. Contact Advertising, 2010 St. Lucie Blvd., Ft. Pierce, FL 34946. FAX 407-464-5447. (Subscr. to: Contact, 860 E. Twain, Ste. 128-547, Las Vegas, NV 89109. TEL 800-637-5779) Ed. Holly Adams. circ. 6,000 (controlled). **Document type:** consumer publication.
   Description: Contains life-styles information for singles and couples in the swinging community in Nevada, Arizona and California.

051 US ISSN 0194-6935
VELVET.* 13/yr. newsstand price: $5.99. Magna Publishing, 210 E. State St., Rte. 4, Ste. 401, Paramus, NJ 07652-5103. TEL 201-487-6124. FAX 201-487-9360. adv. **Document type:** consumer publication.

058.82 NO ISSN 0042-4951
VI MENN. 1951. w. NOK 1248. Hjemmet Mortensens Forlag AS, Soerkedalsveien 10 A, N-0369 Oslo, Norway. TEL 47-2-961-500. FAX 47-2-961-382. Ed. Ola Nissen. adv.: B&W page NOK 17900, color page NOK 29900; adv. contact: Paal Oeverby. illus. circ. 118,000. **Document type:** consumer publication. —CCC.

VIDEO RESERVED COLLECTION. see *COMMUNICATIONS — Video*

VIVE LA DIFFERENCE. see *SOCIOLOGY*

054.1 659.152 FR ISSN 0750-3725
VOGUE HOMMES. (Text in English and French) 1976. 10/yr. 200 F. (N. America 625 F.). Conde Nast S.A., 73 rue Vaugirard, 75006 Paris, France. TEL 40-62-01-01. FAX 45-55-49-36. (Subscr. to: 60732 Sainte-Genevieve Cedex, France. TEL 16-44-89-55-00; In U.S. subscr. to: International Subscriptions Inc., 30 Montgomery St., 7th Fl., Jersey City, NJ 07302. TEL 201-451-9420) Ed. Bernard Chapuis. circ. 55,112. (back issues avail.) **Document type:** consumer publication.

051 US
WANTED. bi-m. Metal Hammer Communications, Inc., 462 Broadway, Ste. 4000, New York, NY 10013. TEL 212-966-8400. (Dist. by: Flynt Distributing Co., 9171 Wilshire Blvd., Ste. 300, Beverly Hills, CA 90210)

WHITE CRANE NEWSLETTER. see *HOMOSEXUALITY*

WILDE. see *HOMOSEXUALITY*

WILDFOWL; the magazine for duck & goose hunters. see *SPORTS AND GAMES — Outdoor Life*

808
X FAMILY LETTERS. 1980. 10/yr. $39.97. Piccolo Publications, Inc., 310 Cedar Lane, Teaneck, NJ 07666. TEL 201-836-9177. FAX 201-836-5055. Eds. Jackie Lewis, Lisa Rosen; Pub. Louis Rosen. adv. contact: Allison Reynolds. circ. 66,000. (back issues avail.)
   Formerly: X Letters.
   Description: Erotic literature.

070.48346 UK
ZIPPER. 1976. bi-m. £24.95 (effective June 1993). Millivres Ltd., 116-134 Bayham St., London NW1 OBA, England. TEL 0171-482-2576. FAX 0171-284-0329. Ed. Nigel Hatton. adv. circ. 16,500. (back issues avail.)

MEN'S STUDIES

305.31 US
ACTIVIST MEN'S JOURNAL. 1987. 6/yr. $20. Box 85541, Seattle, WA 98145. Ed.Bd. circ. 90. **Document type:** bulletin.

305.31 US ISSN 1070-6836
ALADDIN'S WINDOW; the vision of awakened men. 1991. q. $30 (effective thru 1996). J.R. Molloy, Box 333, Palo Cedro, CA 96073. TEL 916-474-1385. Ed. Chrom Blackstone. adv. contact: J.R. Molloy. bk.rev.; film rev.; circ. 200 (paid). (also avail. in magnetic tape; back issues avail.) **Document type:** monographic series.
   Description: Covers men's issues as they relate to psychology of evolution and awareness.

301 US ISSN 0889-7174
HQ1090.3
CHANGING MEN; issues in gender, sex and politics. 1979. 2/yr. $24 to individuals; institutions $40 for 4 nos. Feminist Men's Publications, P.O. Box 3121, Kansas City, KS 66103-0121. TEL 816-374-5969. Eds. Paul Matalucci, Rick Cote; Pub. Frank Mauro. adv.; bk.rev.; illus. circ. 7,000. **Indexed:** Alt.Press Ind. **Document type:** consumer publication.
   Formerly (until Apr. 1985): M: Gentle Men for Gender Justice.
   Description: Covers men's psychology, health, relationships, the men's movement, ending violence, rape, fathering and sexuality.

305.31 UK
CRITICAL STUDIES ON MEN AND MASCULINITIES. irreg. Unwin Hyman Ltd., 15-17 Broadwick St., London W1V 1FP, England. Eds. Jeff Hearn, David Morgan. **Document type:** academic/scholarly publication.

305.31 808 US
FATHERS, BROTHERS, SONS. 1993. 4/yr. $9.95. 1346 Joan Dr., Southampton, PA 18966. TEL 215-322-1346. Ed. Mark McLaughlin. circ. 1,000.

305.31 US
FATHERS' JOURNAL. m. membership. Fathers for Equal Rights of America, Box 2272, Southfield, MI 48037. TEL 313-354-3080.
 Description: Dedicated to preserving the rights of fathers.

GENDER AND EDUCATION. see EDUCATION

GENDER AND HISTORY. see HISTORY

GENDER AND SOCIETY. see SOCIOLOGY

305.31 US ISSN 1063-4460
E185.86
JOURNAL OF AFRICAN AMERICAN MALE STUDIES. 1993. 2/yr. $40 (foreign $48). c/o Institute for Black Leadership Development & Research, 1028 Dole Human Development Center, University of Kansas, Lawrence, KS 66045. TEL 913-864-3990. FAX 913-864-5323. Ed. Courtland Lee. **Document type:** academic/scholarly publication.
 Description: Publishes Black male studies that can enhance our knowledge of Black males and their families in American society. To research, develop, and disseminate data and information on the status of Blacks in the region.

JOURNAL OF GENDER STUDIES. see WOMEN'S STUDIES

305.31 US ISSN 1060-8265
HQ1088
JOURNAL OF MEN'S STUDIES. 1972. q. $30 to individuals; institutions $40. Box 32, Harriman, TN 37748-0032. Ed. James Doyle. circ. 500. **Document type:** academic/scholarly publication.

KIND UND VATER. see CHILDREN AND YOUTH — About

305.3 340 US ISSN 1040-3760
LIBERATOR; male call. 1968. m. $24. Men's Defense Association, 17854 Lyons St., Forest Lake, MN 55025. TEL 612-464-7663. Ed. Richard F. Doyle. adv.; bk.rev. circ. 2,000. (back issues avail.) **Document type:** newsletter.
 Formerly: Legal Beagle.
 Description: Supports equal treatment for men in gender issues, divorce, employment, crime and punishment, and image.

305.31 US
M.E.N. MAGAZINE. 1981. m. $20 (effective 1995). 7552 31st Ave., N.E., Seattle, WA 98115. TEL 206-522-9701. E-mail: menmag@wln.com. Ed. Bert H. Hoff; Pub. Susi Henderson. adv.; page $180; adv. contact: Carl Merner. bk.rev. circ. 5,000. **Document type:** consumer publication.
 •Also available online.
 Formerly: Seattle M.E.N. Newsletter.
 Description: Focuses on men's issues, especially "inner work" and personal growth.

305.31 US ISSN 1072-8538
HQ1088 CODEN: MSCUES
MASCULINITIES. 1984. q. $30 to individuals (foreign $45); institutions $65 (foreign $80). Guilford Publications, Inc., 72 Spring St., New York, NY 10012. TEL 212-431-9800; 800-365-7006. FAX 212-966-6708. (Editorial addr.: 827 Delaware St., Berkeley, CA 94710) (Co-sponsors: Men's Studies Association; National Organization for Men Against Sexism) Ed. Michael Kimmel; Pub. Robert Matloff. adv. contact: Marian Robinson. bk.rev. circ. 400. (also avail. in microform from UMI) **Indexed:** IMFL. **Document type:** academic/scholarly publication. —UMI.
 Formerly (until 1993): Men's Studies Review.
 Description: Features empirical and theoretical articles that explore the construction of masculinities, male-female relationships, sexual behavior and sexual identities, representations of gender, issues of diversity among men and other topics.

305.31 US
MEN (SEATTLE). no.4, 1989. irreg. $3. Rational Island Publishers, Box 2081, Main Office Sta., Seattle, WA 98111. TEL 206-284-0311.
 Description: Drafts policy statement on the liberation of males and on U.S. veterans' oppression; includes section on men's oppression, counseling men, men and women as allies, and war and violence.

305.31 US
MEN'S COUNCIL JOURNAL. 1988. q. $15 to individuals; institutions $30. Box 385, Boulder, CO 80306. circ. 10,000. **Document type:** bulletin.

MEN'S JOURNAL. see MEN'S INTERESTS

305.31 613.081 US ISSN 1074-7842
MENSTUFF, THE NATIONAL MEN'S RESOURCE. 1985. q. $10 (foreign $20). National Men's Resource Center, Box 800, San Anselmo, CA 94979-0800. TEL 415-453-2839. Ed. Gordon Clay. bk.rev.; illus.; circ. 750 (paid). **Document type:** newsletter.
 Formerly: National Men's Resource Calendar.
 Description: Publishes information, events listings, resources and reviews concerning a positive change in male roles and relationships.

STUDIES IN GENDER AND CULTURE. see SOCIOLOGY

TODAY'S DADS; taking the needs of children to heart. see LAW — Family And Matrimonial Law

305.31 US ISSN 0886-862X
TRANSITIONS (MANHASSET). 1981. bi-m. $30. National Coalition of Free Men, Box 129, Manhasset, NY 11030. TEL 516-482-6378. E-mail: 76104.3424@compuserve.com. Ed. Hugh Nations. **Document type:** newsletter.
 Description: Looks at the ways sex discrimination affects men.

155.362 305.3 US
WINGSPAN: JOURNAL OF THE MALE SPIRIT. 1986. q. donation. Box 23550, Brightmoor Sta., Detroit, MI 48223. TEL 617-876-1999. Ed. Christopher Harding. circ. 150,000 (controlled).
 Description: Covers issues pertaining to male psychology and spirituality, with think pieces from leaders of the men's movement, workshop profiles and extensive listings of nationwide men's events.

METALLURGY

see also Metallurgy–Welding

669 BL ISSN 0104-0898
TN4 CODEN: MABMA5
A B M METALURGIA E MATERIAIS. 1965. m. (foreign $155) (effective 1995). Associacao Brasileira de Metalurgia e Materiais, Rua Antonio Comparato 218, C.P. 42081, 04605-030 Sao Paulo, Brazil. TEL 55-11-5364333. FAX 55-11-2404273. E-mail: abmet@fpsp.fapesp.br. Ed. Maria Da Luz Calegari. adv. contact: Fernando Cosme Rizzo Assuncao. bk.rev.; abstr.; charts; illus.; stat.; index, cum.index every 10 yrs. circ. 6,000. (also avail. in microform from UMI) **Indexed:** Chem.Abstr., Met.Abstr. **Document type:** academic/scholarly publication. —BLDSC (5699.870000); CASDDS; Ei; UMI.
 Formerly (until Apr. 1992): Metalurgia A B M (ISSN 0026-0983); Which was formed by the merger of: A B M Boletim; A B M Noticiario.

669 US
A I S E YEARBOOK. 1907. a. $60 to non-members; members $45. Association of Iron and Steel Engineers, Three Gateway Center, Ste. 2350, Pittsburgh, PA 15222. TEL 412-281-6323. Ed. Dennis J. Fuga. index. circ. 400.
 Formerly: Association of Iron and Steel Engineers. A I S E Proceedings.

669 US ISSN 0044-7889
A S M NEWS (MATERIALS PARK). 1929. m. membership only. (American Society for Metals) A S M International, Materials Information, Materials Park, OH 44073-0002. TEL 216-338-5151. FAX 216-338-4634. TELEX 98-0619 ASMINT. Ed. Sarina Pastoric. adv.; illus.; stat. circ. 52,000.
 Description: Covers materials technology with news from professional, political, industrial and public sectors.

METALLURGY 4649

669.1 IT ISSN 0001-4567
L'ACCIAIO INOSSIDABILE. 1933. q. free. Edizioni Avesta Sheffield S.p.A., Viale Lancetti 3, 20158 Milan, Italy. TEL 39-2-69651. FAX 39-2-6965325. TELEX 330398 ASPA I. Ed. Alessandro Amoroso. bk.rev.; bibl.; charts; illus.; stat.; index. circ. 2,000. (also avail. in microform from UMI) **Indexed:** Chem.Abstr., Met.Abstr., World Alum.Abstr. **Document type:** bulletin.
 Description: Features technical articles on the different uses of stainless steel, both in engineering and in art.

ACIER DANS LE MONDE. see BUILDING AND CONSTRUCTION

669.6 FR
ACIERS POUR EMBALLAGE EN FRANCE ET DANS LE MONDE. 1956. a. free. Chambre Syndicale des Aciers pour Emballage, Immeuble La Pacific TSA 20002, 92070 Paris La Defense Cedex, France. FAX 41-25-87-55. charts; stat. circ. 800.
 Formerly: Fer-Blanc en France et dans le Monde (ISSN 0085-0519)

669 UK ISSN 1359-6454
ACTA MATERIALIA. (Text in English, French, German) 1953. 12/yr. £714($1135) (effective 1996). (Acta Metallurgica, Inc.) Elsevier Science Ltd., Pergamon, P.O. Box 800, Kidlington, Oxford OX5 1DX, England. TEL 44-1865-843000. FAX 44-1865-843010. E-mail: nlinfo-f@elsevier.nl; usinfo-f@elsevier.com; forinfo-kyf04035@niftyserve.or.jp; Site addr.: http://www.elsevier.nl/. (Subscr. in U.S. and Canada to: Elsevier Science, 660 White Plains Rd., Tarrytown, NY 10591-5153. TEL 914-524-9200. FAX 914-333-2444) Ed. M.F. Ashby. adv.; bk.rev.; charts; illus.; index. circ. 2,300. (also avail. in microform from UMI) **Indexed:** Appl.Mech.Rev., ASCA, Bibl.& Ind.Geol., Cadscan, Chem.Abstr., Curr.Cont., Eng.Ind., Fuel & Energy Abstr., Ind.Sci.Rev., INIS Atomind., INSPEC (1968-), Int.Aerosp.Abstr., Lead Abstr., Met.Abstr., Phys.Ber., Sci.Cit.Ind., World Alum.Abstr., Zincscan. **Document type:** academic/scholarly publication. —BLDSC (0637.100000); CASDDS; Ei; Faxon; Genuine Article; SWETS; UMI; UnCover. **CCC.**
 Former titles (until vol.44): Acta Metallurgica et Materialia (ISSN 0956-7151); (until 1990): Acta Metallurgica (ISSN 0001-6160)
 Description: Publishes papers on the structure of solids and their properties, on the thermodynamics, kinetics and mechanics of solids, and recent advances in engineering materials.
 Refereed Serial

669 CC ISSN 1006-7191
TN689
ACTA METALLURGICA SINICA. (Publication interrupted twice and resumed in 1974) (Text in English) 1956. bi-m. $120. Chinese Society for Metals, 46 Dongsi Xidajie, Beijing 100711, People's Republic of China. TEL 86-1-5133925. FAX 86-1-5124122. (Dist. by: Allerton Press, Inc., 150 Fifth Ave., New York, NY 10011, USA. TEL 212-924-3950) Ed. Shi Changxu. circ. 400. (back issues avail.) **Indexed:** Chem.Abstr., Corros.Abstr., Eng.Ind., Met.Abstr. **Document type:** academic/scholarly publication. —CCC.
 Formed by the 1994 merger of: Acta Metallurgica Sinica. Series A: Physical Metallurgy and Material Science (ISSN 1000-9442); Acta Metallurgica Sinica. Series B: Process Metallurgy and Miscellaneous (ISSN 1000-9450)
 Description: Covers research on physical metallurgy and materials science. Includes original research papers, critical reviews, notes, letters, discussions and academic activities.

ACTA POLYTECHNICA SCANDINAVICA. CHEMICAL TECHNOLOGY AND METALLURGY SERIES. see CHEMISTRY

669 BE ISSN 0365-7302
 CODEN: ATBMA6
ACTA TECHNICA BELGICA METALLURGIE. Key Title: A T B Metallurgie. 1956. q. 540 Fr. (Societe Benelouxienne de Metallurgie) Union des Revues Techniques Belges, Hotel de Societes Scientifiques, Rue des Champs-Elysees 43, 1050 Brussels, Belgium. Ed. Rene Winand. adv.; charts; illus. circ. 1,500. (also avail. in microform from UMI) **Indexed:** Art & Archaeol.Tech.Abstr., Bull.Signal., Chem.Abstr., Copper Abstr., Eng.Ind., Met.Abstr., W.R.C.Inf., World Alum.Abstr.
 —CASDDS.

METALLURGY

669   FR   ISSN 0044-6165
ACTUALITES INDUSTRIELLES LORRAINES. 1949. bi-m. 85 F. Maisonneuve S.A., 386 Route de Verdun a Sainte Ruffine, 57160 Moulin-les-Mets, France. Ed. Louis Labbez. adv.; bk.rev.; charts; illus. circ. 29,000.

669   KR   ISSN 0136-1732
TA401   CODEN: ARPMDV
ADGEZIYA RASPLAVOV I PAIKA MATERIALOV; respublikanskii mezhvedomstvennyi sbornik nauchnykh trudov. (Text in Russian) 1976. s-a. (Akademiya Nauk Ukrainy, Institut Problem Materialovedeniya) Vidavnitstvo Naukova Dumka, Vul. Tereshchenkivska 3, 252601 Kiev, Ukraine. TEL 044-224-4068. FAX 044-224-7060. (Dist. by: Mezhdunarodnaya Kniga, B. Yakimanka 39, 117049 Moscow, Russia) Ed. Yu.V. Naidich. **Indexed:** Chem.Abstr.
—BLDSC (0005.278000); CASDDS.

ADVANCED COMPOSITES BULLETIN; an international newsletter. see *PLASTICS*

671.3705 669   US   ISSN 1065-5824
TN695   CODEN: APMME3
ADVANCES IN POWDER METALLURGY & PARTICULATE MATERIALS. 1989. a. price varies. Metal Powder Industries Federation, 105 College Rd. E., Princeton, NJ 08540. TEL 609-452-7700. FAX 609-987-8523. **Document type:** proceedings.
—BLDSC (0710.635000); CASDDS; Ei. **CCC.**
Formerly (until 1994): Advances in Powder Metallurgy (ISSN 1042-8860)

671.732   UK   ISSN 0267-4009
TN681
ADVANCES IN SPECIAL ELECTROMETALLURGY. English translation of: Problemy Spetsial'noi Elektrometallurgii (UR ISSN 0131-1611) 1985. q. £75($124) Riecansky Science Publishing Co., 7 Meadow Walk, Great Abington, Cambridge CB1 6AZ, England. TEL 0223 893295. FAX 0223-893295. Ed. V.E. Riecansky.
—BLDSC (0404.613000); Faxon.

669 620.1   US   ISSN 0069-8490
ADVANCES IN X-RAY ANALYSIS. Represents: Annual Conference on Applications of X-Ray Analysis. Proceedings. 1960. a., vol.37, 1994. price varies. (University of Denver, Denver Research Institute) Plenum Publishing Corp., 233 Spring St., New York, NY 10013-1578. TEL 212-620-8000. FAX 212-463-0742. TELEX 23-421139. Ed.Bd. **Indexed:** Biol.Abstr., Br.Ceram.Abstr., Chem.Abstr., GeoRef., INSPEC. **Document type:** proceedings.
Refereed Serial

669   PL   ISSN 0137-6535
TN4   CODEN: MEODD6
AKADEMIA GORNICZO-HUTNICZA IM. STANISLAWA STASZICA. ZESZYTY NAUKOWE. METALURGIA I ODLEWNICTWO. KWARTALNIK. (Text in English, Polish; summaries in Polish) 1975. q. 5 Zl. per issue (effective 1995). Wydawnictwo A G H, Al. Mickiewicza 30, 30-059 Krakow, Poland. TEL 48-12-364038. TELEX 322203 AGH PL. (Dist. by: Ars Polona, Krakowskie Przedmiescie 7, 00-068 Warsaw, Poland) Ed. Z. Kleczek. bibl.; charts. circ. 300. **Indexed:** Chem.Abstr., Met.Abstr., World Alum.Abstr. **Document type:** academic/scholarly publication.
—BLDSC (9512.150175); CASDDS; UnCover.

669   KZ
AKADEMIYA NAUK KAZAKHSTANA. INSTITUT METALLURGII I OBOGASHCHENIYA. TRUDY. vol.52, 1977. irreg. 1.80 Rub. per no. Gylym, Ul. Pushkina 111-113, 480100 Alma-Ata, Kazakhstan. TEL 3272-611877. Ed. A. Kunaev. abstr.; bibl.; illus. circ. 1,000. **Indexed:** Chem.Abstr.
Formerly: Akademiya Nauk Kazakhskoi S.S.R. Institut Metallurgii i Obogashcheniya.

669.722   IT   ISSN 1122-1429
AL - ALLUMINIO E LEGHE. (Text in English and Italian) m. (11/yr.). L.120000 (foreign L.200000) (effective 1995). Edimet S.p.A., Via Corfu, 102, 25124 Brescia, Italy. TEL 030-2421043. FAX 030-223802. Ed. Mario Comserva. adv.; B&W page L.1900000, color page L.2300000; trim 210 x 297; adv. contact: Anna Brescianini. circ. 5,000. **Document type:** newspaper.
—BLDSC (0796.040000).

ALAMBRE; revista tecnica international para la industria del alambre y del cable y para todos los sectores de la elaboracion de alambres metalicos. see *ENGINEERING — Electrical Engineering*

620   GW
ALCAN INFORMIERT. 1970. q. free. Alcan Deutschland GmbH, Postfach 5149, 65726 Eschborn, Germany. TEL 06196-407-0. Ed. R. Wypior. illus. circ. 8,000. (back issues avail.) **Document type:** trade publication.

669   US   ISSN 0002-614X
ALLOY DIGEST. 1952. m. $180 (effective 1995). Alloy Digest, Inc., 27 Canfield St., Orange, NJ 07050. TEL 201-677-9161. Ed. Dennis Rahoi. abstr.; charts; index, cum.index: 1952-1986. circ. 1,000. (looseleaf format; back issues avail.) **Indexed:** Met.Abstr., World Alum.Abstr.

669.722   IT   ISSN 0365-3927
    CODEN: ALLUAO
ALLUMINIO. 1932. bi-m. L.65000 (foreign L.110000). Tecnomedia s.r.l., Via Sansovino 28, 20133 Milan, Italy. TEL 2-70602276. FAX 2-266-80-468. Ed. Arrigo Perrone. adv.; B&W page L.1240000, color page L.1520000; trim 185 x 272. bk.rev.; abstr.; bibl.; charts; illus.; mkt.; stat.; index. circ. 3,000. **Indexed:** Chem.Abstr., Eng.Ind., Met.Abstr., World Alum.Abstr.
—BLDSC (0796.070000); CASDDS.
Formerly: Alluminio e Nuova Metallurgia (ISSN 0002-6212)

669.722   JA
ALUMI-AGE. (Text in Japanese) 1964. q. free. Japan Aluminum Federation, Nihonbashi Asahiseimei Bldg., 1-3 Nihonbashi, 2-chome, Chuo-ku, Tokyo 103, Japan. TEL 03-274-4551. FAX 03-274-3179. TELEX 02223074-JALF-J. Ed.Bd. adv. circ. 10,000.
Description: Aims to educate the public about aluminum.

ALUMINIUM INDUSTRY. see *ENGINEERING*

669.722   GW   ISSN 0934-3938
ALUMINIUM INTERN: ALUMINIUM UND AUTOMOBIL. irreg. (approx. 3/yr.). DM.75. Aluminium-Zentrale e.V., Postfach 101262, 40003 Duesseldorf, Germany. TEL 0211-4796-0. FAX 0211-4796410. **Indexed:** Int.Packag.Abstr. **Document type:** consumer publication.

669.722   UK   ISSN 0955-8209
    CODEN: ALTOEG
ALUMINIUM TODAY; the international journal of aluminium production and processing. 1989. q. £134.65($234.40) (foreign £146.50). Argus Business Media Ltd., Fuel and Metals Jourals (Subsidiary of: Argus Press Group), Queensway House, 2 Queensway, Redhill, Surrey RH1 1QS, England. TEL 01737-768611. FAX 01737-761685. TELEX 948669 TOPJNL G. Ed. Ken Stanford. **Document type:** trade publication.
—BLDSC (0806.166000); Ei.

669.722   GW   ISSN 0002-6689
    CODEN: ALUMAB
ALUMINUM. (Text in English and German) 1919. m. DM.386($276) (Aluminum-Zentrale e.V.) Giesel Verlag fuer Publizitaet GmbH, Auf der Heide 20, 30916 Isernhagen, Germany. TEL 0511-7304-0. FAX 0511-7304157. adv.; bk.rev.; abstr.; bibl.; charts; illus.; stat.; index. circ. 3,300. **Indexed:** Chem.Abstr., Eng.Ind., Excerp.Med., INIS Atomind., Int.Packag.Abstr., Met.Abstr., Packag.Sci.Tech., PROMT, World Alum.Abstr. **Document type:** academic/scholarly publication.
—BLDSC (0804.050000); CASDDS; Ei; Faxon; SWETS. **CCC.**

669.722   US
ALUMINUM SITUATION. m. free. Aluminum Association, Inc., 900 19th St., N.W., Ste. 300, Washington, DC 20006. TEL 202-862-5100. FAX 202-862-5164. TELEX 710-822-1129. (also avail. in microfiche from CIS) **Indexed:** SRI.

673   US   ISSN 0065-6658
TA480.A6
ALUMINUM STANDARDS AND DATA. 1968. biennial. $25. Aluminum Association, Inc., 900 19th St., N.W., Ste. 300, Washington, DC 20006. TEL 202-862-5100. FAX 202-862-5164. TELEX 710-822-1129. circ. 40,000.

673   US
ALUMINUM STANDARDS AND DATA-METRIC. biennial. $12. Aluminum Association, Inc., 900 19th St., N.W., Ste. 300, Washington, DC 20006. TEL 202-862-5100. circ. 40,000.

673 338.4   US   ISSN 0065-6666
ALUMINUM STATISTICAL REVIEW. (Title varies: Aluminum Industry Annual Statistical Review) 1962. a. $50. Aluminum Association, Inc., 900 19th St., N.W., Ste. 300, Washington, DC 20006. TEL 202-862-5100. FAX 202-862-5164. TELEX 710-822-1129. circ. 15,000. (also avail. in microfiche from CIS) **Indexed:** SRI.

669   US
AMERICAN COPPER COUNCIL. NEWSLETTER. q. membership. American Copper Council, 2 South End Ave., No. 4C, New York, NY 10280. TEL 212-945-4990. **Document type:** newsletter.

669.028 671.2   US   ISSN 0065-8375
TS200   CODEN: TAFOA6
AMERICAN FOUNDRYMEN'S SOCIETY. TRANSACTIONS. 1896. a. $200 to non-members. American Foundrymen's Society, Inc., 505 State St., Des Plaines, IL 60016. TEL 708-824-0181. cum.index every 10 yrs. (also avail. in microform from PMC,UMI; reprint service avail. from UMI) **Indexed:** B.C.I.R.A., Chem.Abstr. **Document type:** proceedings, academic/scholarly publication.
—BLDSC (8887.000000); CASDDS; Ei; Faxon; SWETS. **CCC.**

AMERICAN METAL MARKET. see *BUSINESS AND ECONOMICS — Marketing And Purchasing*

ANALYTICA. see *CHEMISTRY — Analytical Chemistry*

ANNUAL BOOK OF A S T M STANDARDS. VOLUME 01.01. STEEL-PIPING, TUBING, FITTINGS. (American Society for Testing and Materials) see *ENGINEERING — Engineering Mechanics And Materials*

ANNUAL BOOK OF A S T M STANDARDS. VOLUME 01.02. FERROUS CASTINGS, FERRO ALLOYS. see *ENGINEERING — Engineering Mechanics And Materials*

ANNUAL BOOK OF A S T M STANDARDS. VOLUME 01.03. STEEL PLATE, SHEET, STRIP WIRE. see *ENGINEERING — Engineering Mechanics And Materials*

ANNUAL BOOK OF A S T M STANDARDS. VOLUME 01.04. STEEL-STRUCTURAL, REINFORCING, PRESSURE VESSEL; RAILWAY. see *ENGINEERING — Engineering Mechanics And Materials*

ANNUAL BOOK OF A S T M STANDARDS. VOLUME 01.05. STEEL-BARS, BEARINGS, FORGINGS, CHAIN, SPRINGS. see *ENGINEERING — Engineering Mechanics And Materials*

ANNUAL BOOK OF A S T M STANDARDS. VOLUME 01.06. COATED STEEL PRODUCTS. see *ENGINEERING — Engineering Mechanics And Materials*

ANNUAL BOOK OF A S T M STANDARDS. VOLUME 01.07. SHIPBUILDING. see *ENGINEERING — Engineering Mechanics And Materials*

ANNUAL BOOK OF A S T M STANDARDS. VOLUME 02.01. COPPER AND COPPER ALLOYS. see *ENGINEERING — Engineering Mechanics And Materials*

ANNUAL BOOK OF A S T M STANDARDS. VOLUME 02.02. DIE-CAST METALS; ALUMINUM AND MAGNESIUM ALLOYS. see *ENGINEERING — Engineering Mechanics And Materials*

ANNUAL BOOK OF A S T M STANDARDS. VOLUME 02.04. NONFERROUS METALS-NICKEL, LEAD, TIN ALLOYS, PRECIOUS, PRIMARY, REACTIVE METALS. see *ENGINEERING — Engineering Mechanics And Materials*

ANNUAL BOOK OF A S T M STANDARDS. VOLUME 02.05. METALLIC AND INORGANIC COATINGS; METAL POWDERS, SINTERED P-M STRUCTURAL PARTS. see *ENGINEERING — Engineering Mechanics And Materials*

METALLURGY 4651

ANNUAL BOOK OF A S T M STANDARDS. VOLUME 03.01. METALS - MECHANICAL TESTING; ELEVATED AND LOW-TEMPERATURE TESTS METALLOGRAPHY. see ENGINEERING — Engineering Mechanics And Materials

ANNUAL BOOK OF A S T M STANDARDS. VOLUME 03.02. WEAR AND EROSION; METAL CORROSION. see ENGINEERING — Engineering Mechanics And Materials

ANNUAL BOOK OF A S T M STANDARDS. VOLUME 03.03. NONDESTRUCTIVE TESTS. see ENGINEERING — Engineering Mechanics And Materials

ANNUAL BOOK OF A S T M STANDARDS. VOLUME 03.05. CHEMICAL ANALYSIS OF METALS; METAL BEARING ORES. see ENGINEERING — Engineering Mechanics And Materials

338.4 JA
ANNUAL STATISTICS OF MATERIALS PROCESS INDUSTRIES, JAPAN. (Editions in English, Japanese) 1984. a. newsstand price: 4500Yen. Materials Process Technology Center - Sokeizai Senta, 5-8, Shiba Koen 3-chome, Minato-ku, Tokyo 105, Japan.
Formerly: Foundry Statistics of Japan.

669 UK ISSN 0959-6054
ANTI-CORROSION HANDBOOK & DIRECTORY. a. free with Anti-Corrosion Methods and Materials. Sawell Publications Ltd., 127 Stanstead Rd., London SE23 1JE, England. Ed. J.E. Bean. circ. 2,880. **Document type:** directory.

620.162 UK ISSN 0003-5599
TA462 CODEN: ACMEBL
ANTI-CORROSION METHODS AND MATERIALS; the first British journal of corrosion control, prevention, engineering and research. 1954. m. £139($199) (effective 1996). M C B University Press Ltd., 60-62 Toller Ln., Bradford, W. Yorks BD8 9BY, England. TEL 01274-777700. FAX 01274-785201. Ed. T.R. Savage. adv.; bk.rev.; abstr.; bibl.; charts; illus.; tr.lit.; index. circ. 2,880. **Indexed:** AESIS, API Abstr., API Catal., API Hlth.& Environ., API Oil., API Pet.Ref., API Pet.Subst., API Transport., BMT, Br.Tech.Ind., Cadscan, Chem.Abstr., Chem.Eng.Abstr., Eng.Ind., Fluidex, Fuel & Energy Abstr., Gas Abstr., HRIS, INIS Atomind., Lead Abstr., Met.Abstr., Petrol.Abstr., RAPRA, W.R.C.Inf., World Surf.Coat., Zincscan.
—BLDSC (1547.450000); CASDDS; Ei; Faxon; Genuine Article; SWETS.
Formerly: Corrosion Technology.

ANUARIO METAL; guia especializada de compras del sector metalurgico y metalmecanico. see BUSINESS AND ECONOMICS — Trade And Industrial Directories

669 US ISSN 1059-2997
ANVIL MAGAZINE. 1975. m. $49.50 (Canada $55.50; elsewhere $69.50). Rob Edwards, Ed. & Pub., 2776 Sourdough Flat, Box 1810, Georgetown, CA 95634-1810. TEL 916-333-2142. FAX 916-333-2906. adv.; bk.rev. circ. 5,000. (back issues avail.) **Document type:** consumer publication.
Formerly (until 1992): Anvil (ISSN 0890-2534)
Description: Trade magazine for farriers and blacksmiths.

AOMORI PREFECTURE TECHNICAL INFORMATION: MACHINERY AND METAL. see MACHINERY

669 541.37 NE ISSN 0169-4332
TA418.7 CODEN: ASUSEE
APPLIED SURFACE SCIENCE; a journal devoted to the properties of interfaces in relation to the synthesis and behaviour of materials. (Text in English) 1978. 48/yr. fl.5160($3147) (effective 1996). North-Holland (Subsidiary of: Elsevier Science B.V.), P.O. Box 211, 1000 AE Amsterdam, Netherlands. TEL 31-20-4853911. FAX 31-20-4853598. TELEX 18582 ESPA NL. (Subscr. in U.S. and Canada to: Elsevier Science Inc., Box 882, Madison Sq. Sta., New York, NY 10159. TEL 212-989-5800. FAX 212-633-3990) Eds. L.C. Feldman, W.F. van der Weg. cum.index: vols.11-20, 1986. (also avail. in microform from UMI; back issues avail.) **Indexed:** Cadscan, Chem.Abstr., Ind.Sci.Rev., INIS Atomind., INSPEC (1985-), Lead Abstr., Mass Spectr.Bull., Met.Abstr., Sci.Cit.Ind., Soils & Fert., World Alum.Abstr., Zincscan. **Document type:** academic/scholarly publication.
—BLDSC (1580.082000); CASDDS; Ei; Faxon; Genuine Article; SWETS; UnCover. **CCC.**
Formerly: Applications of Surface Science (ISSN 0378-5963)
Description: Concerned with the microscopic understanding of the synthesis and behaviour of surfaces and interfaces.
Refereed Serial

669 PL ISSN 0860-7052
TN4.P57 CODEN: ARMEER
ARCHIVES OF METALLURGY. (Text in English) 1956. q. $80. (Polska Akademia Nauk, Komitet Metalurgii) Wydawnictwo Naukowe P W N, Miodowa 10, 00-251 Warsaw, Poland. Ed. Zbigniew Moser. abstr.; charts; illus. circ. 510. **Indexed:** Chem.Abstr., Copper Abstr., Eng.Ind., INIS Atomind., INSPEC (1987-), Met.Abstr., World Alum.Abstr.
—BLDSC (1637.934000); CASDDS; Ei.
Formerly (until 1987): Archiwum Hutnictwa (ISSN 0004-0770)

ARCHIWUM NAUKI O MATERIALACH. see ENGINEERING — Engineering Mechanics And Materials

669 FR ISSN 0220-3332
ARGUS DES METAUX. d. 5090 F. (foreign 5300 F.). Societe d' Information et de Documentation, Bureau d'Informations Professionnelles, 142 rue Montmartre, 75002 Paris, France. TEL 40-26-83-21. FAX 40-39-97-52. TELEX 220 528 BIP.

669 621.9 US
ASSOCIATION OF FRENCH MECHANICAL INDUSTRIES. BULLETIN D'INFORMATION. (Text in French) q. Association of French Mechanical Industries, 401 N. Michigan Ave., Ste. 1760, Chicago, IL 60611. TEL 312-222-1238. FAX 312-222-1237.

669.142 US
ASSOCIATION OF STEEL DISTRIBUTORS. NEWS AND VIEWS. m. membership. Association of Steel Distributors, 401 N. Michigan Ave., Chicago, IL 60611-4267. TEL 312-644-6610. FAX 312-321-6869. circ. 200 (controlled).

ASU O KIZUKU/CONSTRUCTION TOMORROW. see ENGINEERING — Civil Engineering

AUS I M M PROCEEDINGS. (Australasian Institute of Mining and Metallurgy) see MINES AND MINING INDUSTRY

AUSTRALASIAN INSTITUTE OF MINING AND METALLURGY CONFERENCE SERIES. see MINES AND MINING INDUSTRY

AUSTRALASIAN INSTITUTE OF MINING AND METALLURGY MONOGRAPH SERIES. see MINES AND MINING INDUSTRY

B H M. (Berg- und Huettenmaennische Monatshefte) see MINES AND MINING INDUSTRY

669.1 II ISSN 0005-3325
B S P MAGAZINE/ISPAT VIHANGAM. (Editions in English and Hindi) 1959. q. free. Steel Authority of India Ltd., Bhilai Steel Plant, Bhilai 490001 (M.P.), India. Ed. A.K. Bhatt. circ. 10,000.

669 GW ISSN 0005-3848
CODEN: BBROAB
BAENDER, BLECHE, ROHRE; Fachzeitschrift fuer Walzwerkstechnik, Blechbearbeitung, gezogene und geschweisste Rohre. 1959. m. DM.210. Vogel Verlag und Druck GmbH & Co. KG, Max-Planck-Str. 7-9, 97082 Wuerzburg, Germany. TEL 0931-4182145. FAX 0931-4182640. (Subscr. to: Vogel Verlag, 97064 Wuerzburg, Germany; Dist. in U.S. by: Vogel Europublishing, Inc., 19927 Gibbs Dr., Sonora, CA 95370. TEL 209-533-3555. FAX 209-533-9555) Ed. Hasso Reschenberg. adv.: B&W page DM.4300, color page DM.6080; trim 270 x 190; adv. contact: Helmut Sieber. bk.rev.; charts; illus.; index; circ. 11,166 (controlled). **Indexed:** C.I.S. Abstr., Cadscan, Chem.Abstr., INIS Atomind., Lead Abstr., Met.Abstr., World Alum.Abstr., Zincscan. **Document type:** trade publication.
—BLDSC (1861.580000); CASDDS; Ei; SWETS. **CCC.**

669 II ISSN 0366-1210
BANARAS METALLURGIST. (Text in English and Hindi) 1968. a. free. Banaras Hindu University, Institute of Technology, Department of Metallurgical Engineering, Varanasi 221 005, Uttar Pradesh, India. TELEX 0545-208. Ed. J.S. Kachhawaha. adv.; bk.rev. circ. 500. **Indexed:** Met.Abstr.

669 HU ISSN 0522-3512
TN4 CODEN: BKLBB6
BANYASZATI ES KOHASZATI LAPOK - BANYASZAT. (Text in Hungarian; summaries in English, German, and Russian) 1868. m. (Orszagos Magyar Banyaszati es Kohaszati Egyesulet) Lapkiado Vallalat, Lenin korut 9-11, 1073 Budapest 7, Hungary. TEL 222-408. (Subscr. to: Kultura, Box 149, 1389 Budapest, Hungary)
—BLDSC (1862.830000); CASDDS.
Formerly (until 1968): Banyaszati Lapok (ISSN 0365-9003); Which supersedes in part (in 1951): Banyaszati es Kohaszati Lapok (ISSN 0365-9011)

669 HU ISSN 0005-5670
TN4 CODEN: BKLKBX
BANYASZATI ES KOHASZATI LAPOK - KOHASZAT. (Text in Hungarian; summaries in English, German and Russian) 1868. m. $52. (Orszagos Magyar Banyaszati es Kohaszati Egyesulet) Lapkiado Vallalat, Lenin korut 9-11, 1073 Budapest 7, Hungary. TEL 222-408. (Subscr. to: Kultura, Box 149, H-1389 Budapest, Hungary) Ed. Antal Ovari. adv.; bk.rev.; charts; illus.; pat.; tr.mk.; index. circ. 3,450. **Indexed:** Appl.Mech.Rev., Bibl.& Ind.Geol., Chem.Abstr., INIS Atomind., Met.Abstr., Petrol.Abstr., World Alum.Abstr.
—BLDSC (1862.860000); CASDDS.
Formerly (until 1968): Kohaszati Lapok (ISSN 0368-6469); Which supersedes in part (in 1951): Banyaszati es Kohaszati Lapok (ISSN 0365-9011)

669 HU ISSN 0572-6034
TN860 CODEN: BKKFAC
BANYASZATI ES KOHASZATI LAPOK - KOOLAJ ES FOLDGAZ. (Text in Hungarian; summaries in English, German, and Russian) 1966. m. (Orszagos Magyar Banyaszati es Kohaszati Egyesulet) Lapkiado Vallalat, Lenin korut 9-11, 1073 Budapest 7, Hungary. TEL 222-408. (Subscr. to: Kultura, Box 149, 1389 Budapest, Hungary) **Indexed:** Chem.Abstr.
—BLDSC (1862.870000); CASDDS.
Formerly (until 1968): Koolaj es Foldgaz (ISSN 0324-5357)

669 HU ISSN 0375-9504
CODEN: BKLOAA
BANYASZATI ES KOHASZATI LAPOK - ONTODE. (Text in Hungarian; summaries in English, German and Russian) 1950. m. $25. (Orszagos Magyar Banyaszati es Kohaszati Egyesulet) Lapkiado Vallalat, Lenin korut 9-11, 1073 Budapest 7, Hungary. TEL 222-408. (Subscr. to: Kultura, Box 149, H-1389 Budapest, Hungary) Ed. Dr. Lajos Pilissy. adv.; bk.rev.; charts; pat.; index. circ. 500. **Indexed:** B.C.I.R.A., Chem.Abstr., Met.Abstr., World Alum.Abstr.
—CASDDS.
Continues: Ontode (ISSN 0030-3143)

METALLURGY

669 UK ISSN 0964-7686
BASE METALS MONTHLY. 1991. m. $1020. Metal Bulletin plc, Park House, Park Terrace, Worcester Park, Surrey KT4 7HY, England. TEL 0171-827-9977. FAX 0181-337-8943. (U.S. subscr. to: Metal Bulletin Inc., 220 Fifth Ave., New York, NY 10001-7781. TEL 212-213-6202. FAX 212-213-1870) Ed. Neil Buxton. **Document type:** trade publication.

620.12 UK ISSN 0142-6834
BASIC METALLURGY FOR NON-DESTRUCTIVE TESTING. 1974. irreg. British Institute of Non-Destructive Testing, 1 Spencer Parade, Northampton NN1 5AA, England. TEL 01604-30124. FAX 01604-231489. Ed. David J. Gilbert; Pub. Matt E. Gallagher. **Document type:** academic/scholarly publication.

BAYERN METALL. see ENGINEERING — Mechanical Engineering

669.1 CC ISSN 0476-0255
BEIJING UNIVERSITY OF IRON AND STEEL TECHNOLOGY. JOURNAL/BEIJING GANGTIE JISHU DAXUE XUEBAO. 1955. q. $25. Beijing Gangtie Jishu Daxue - Beijing University of Iron and Steel Technology, 30 Xueyuan Lu, Haidian Qu, Beijing, People's Republic of China. (reprint service avail.)

BERGSMANNEN. see MINES AND MINING INDUSTRY

BERGVERKS-NYTT; the Scandinavian journal of mining and quarrying. see MINES AND MINING INDUSTRY

669 375 GW ISSN 0343-2386
BETRIEBLICHE AUSBILDUNGSPRAXIS; Merkblaetter fuer Ausbilder in der Eisen- und Metallindustrie. 1955. bi-m. DM.14. (Wirtschaftsvereinigung Eisen- und Stahlindustrie) Verlag und Vertriebsgesellschaft mbH, Breite Str. 69, Postfach 8232, 40211 Duesseldorf, Germany. (Co-sponsors: Arbeitgeberverband Eisen- und Stahlindustrie e.V.; Verband der Metallindustrie Nordrhein-Westfalens e.V.) Ed.Bd. adv.; bk.rev.; charts; illus.; stat.; tr.lit.; circ. 1,800 (controlled). (also avail. in microform; back issues avail.)

660 UK ISSN 0269-7572 CODEN: BRECEQ
BIORECOVERY; an international journal of biotechnology applied to materials recovery and handling. 4/yr. £89($179) A B Academic Publishers, P.O. Box 42, Bicester, Oxon. OX6 7NW, England. TEL 0869-320949. Ed. Robert Edyvean. adv.; bk.rev. (back issues avail.) **Indexed:** Biodet.Abstr., Energy Info.Abstr. (until 1994), Environ.Abstr., Environ.Per.Bibl. (1989-). **Document type:** academic/scholarly publication.
—BLDSC (2089.477000); CASDDS; UnCover.
Description: Use of living organisms and their products in extraction recovery of minerals, oils and other materials.

669 537.5 BE ISSN 0379-0401 CODEN: BBIBDW
BISMUTH INSTITUTE. BULLETIN. (Text in English) 1973. irreg. (3-4/yr.). free. Bismuth Institute - Information Centre, 301 Borgstraat, B-1850 Grimbergen, Belgium. TEL 32-2-252-4747. FAX 32-2-252-2775. Ed. Yves Palmieri. bk.rev.; pat.; tr.lit.; cum.index: 1973-1992. circ. 2,000. (back issues avail.) **Indexed:** Energy Info.Abstr. **Document type:** bulletin.
—BLDSC (2411.710000); CASDDS.
Description: Technical publication reporting advances of permanent interest in metallurgy, electronics, chemistry, medicine, and cosmetics.

669 GW ISSN 0006-4688 CODEN: BRPFBJ
BLECH-ROHRE-PROFILE; internationale Fachzeitschrift fuer die Herstellung und Verarbeitung von Band, Blech, Rohren und Profilen. 1953. m. (11/yr.). DM.185 (foreign DM.204) (effective 1995). Meisenbach GmbH, Hainstr. 18, 96047 Bamberg, Germany. TEL 0951-861-0. FAX 0951-861-161. (Subscr. to: Postfach 2069, 96011 Bamberg, Germany) Ed. Arnt Hannewald; Pub. Meinhard Meisenbach. adv.: B&W page DM.4312, color page DM.6122; trim 297 x 210; adv. contact: Oskar Ohler. bk.rev.; charts; illus.; mkt.; pat.; tr.lit. circ. 12,000. (also avail. in microfilm from UMI) **Indexed:** Appl.Mech.Rev., Chem.Abstr., Eng.Ind., Excerpt.Med., INIS Atomind., Met.Abstr., World Alum.Abstr. **Document type:** trade publication.
—BLDSC (2110.630000); CASDDS; SWETS; UMI.
Formerly: Blech.

BOUWEN MET STAAL. see BUILDING AND CONSTRUCTION

620.162 UK ISSN 0007-0599
TA462 CODEN: BCRJA3
BRITISH CORROSION JOURNAL. 1965. q. £152($296) to non-members; members £85 ($170). Institute of Materials, 1 Carlton House Terrace, London SW1Y 5DB, England. TEL 071-839-4071. FAX 071-839-2078. TELEX 8814813-METSOC-G. Ed. A.D. Mercer. adv.; bk.rev.; charts; illus.; index. circ. 950. (back issues avail.) **Indexed:** ABTICS, AESIS, API Abstr., API Catal., API Hlth.& Environ., API Oil., API Pet.Ref., API Pet.Subst., API Transport., Art & Archaeol.Tech.Abstr., B.C.I.R.A., Br.Tech.Ind., Cadscan, Chem.Abstr., Chem.Eng.Abstr., Corros.Abstr., Curr.Cont., Eng.Ind., Excerp.Med., Fluidex, Ind.Sci.Rev., INIS Atomind., INSPEC (1968-), ISMEC, Lead Abstr., Met.Abstr., Petrol.Abstr., Sci.Cit.Ind., T.C.E.A., W.R.C.Inf, World Alum.Abstr., World Surf.Coat., Zincscan. **Document type:** academic/scholarly publication.
—BLDSC (2298.400000); CASDDS; Ei; Faxon; Genuine Article; SWETS; UMI; UnCover.
Description: Covers all aspects of the theory and practice of corrosion processes and control.

669 UK
BRITISH INDEPENDENT STEEL COMPANIES AND THEIR PRODUCTS. 1969. irreg. free. British Iron and Steel Producers Association (B.I.S.P.A.), c/o G.I.Peddar, 5 Cromwell Rd., London SW7 2HX, England. circ. 5,000. **Document type:** trade publication.

669 UK
BRITISH STEEL. ANNUAL REPORT AND ACCOUNTS. 1969. a. £1. British Steel plc., 9 Albert Embankment, London SE1 7SN, England. TEL 071-735-7654. FAX 071-587-1142. TELEX 916061. illus. **Document type:** corporate report.
Formerly (until 1989): British Steel Corporation. Annual Report and Accounts (ISSN 0068-2586)
Description: Discusses the firm's activities and the applications of its products in the U.K. market.

669.1 FR ISSN 1144-0678
BULLETIN STATISTIQUE ACIER. SERIE BLEUE. COMMERCE EXTERIEUR. a. 480.33 F. (includes Serie Rouge - Production). Centre Professionnel des Statistiques de l'Acier, 1, Rue Paul Cezanne, B.P. 710-08, 75008 Paris, France. TEL 49-53-70-00. FAX 49-53-71-00. TELEX FRASIA 280172F.
Former titles: Comptoir Francais des Produits Siderurgiques. Bulletin Statistique. Serie Bleue. Commerce Exterieur; Chambre Syndicale de la Siderurgie Francaise. Bulletin Statistique. Serie Bleue. Commerce Exterieur.

669.1 FR ISSN 1144-066X
BULLETIN STATISTIQUE ACIER. SERIE ROUGE. PRODUCTION. a. 480.33 F. (includes Serie Bleue - Commerce Exterieur). Centre Professionnel des Statistiques de l'Acier, 1, Rue Paul Cezanne, 75008 Paris, France. TEL 49-53-70-00. FAX 49-53-71-00.
Former titles: Comptoir Francais des Produits Siderurgiques. Bulletin Statistique. Serie Rouge. Production; Chambre Syndicale de la Siderurgie Francaise. Bulletin Statistique. Serie Rouge. Production (ISSN 0755-2025)

671.2 658.8 UK ISSN 0951-2527
BUSINESS RATIO REPORT: DIE AND MOULD MANUFACTURERS AND DISTRIBUTORS.; an industry sector analysis. 1987. a. I C C Business Ratios Ltd., Freepost, Field House, Hampton, Mddx. TW12 1BR, England. TEL 081-783-0977. FAX 081-783-1940. charts; stat. **Document type:** trade publication.
—BLDSC (3580.396800).

671.2 UK ISSN 0261-7838
BUSINESS RATIO REPORT: DROP FORGERS; an industry sector analysis. 1979. a. I C C Business Ratios Ltd., Freepost, Field House, Hampton, Mddx. TW12 1BR, England. TEL 081-783-0977. FAX 081-783-1940. charts; stat. **Document type:** trade publication.

671.2 658.8 UK ISSN 0261-8559
BUSINESS RATIO REPORT: IRON FOUNDERS; an industry sector analysis. 1976. a. I C C Business Ratios Ltd., Freepost, Field House, Hampton, Mddx. TW12 1BR, England. TEL 081-783-0977. FAX 081-783-1940. charts; stat. **Document type:** trade publication.
—BLDSC (4580.406250).

669.1 658.8 UK ISSN 0261-9083
BUSINESS RATIO REPORT: METAL FINISHERS; an industry sector analysis. 1980. a. I C C Business Ratios Ltd., Freepost, Field House, Hampton, Mddx. TW12 1BR, England. TEL 081-783-0977. FAX 081-783-1940. charts; stat. **Document type:** trade publication.
—BLDSC (5683.990000).

671.2 658.8 UK ISSN 0261-9164
BUSINESS RATIO REPORT: NON-FERROUS FOUNDERS; an industry sector analysis. 1978. a. I C C Business Ratios Ltd., Freepost, Field House, Hampton, Mddx. TW12 1BR, England. TEL 081-783-0977. FAX 081-783-1940. charts; stat. **Document type:** trade publication.
—BLDSC (6117.016000).

671.2 UK ISSN 0267-2731
BUSINESS RATIO REPORT: NON-FERROUS METAL STOCKHOLDERS; an industry sector analysis. 1974. a. I C C Business Ratios Ltd., Freepost, Field House, Hampton, Mddx. TW12 1BR, England. TEL 081-783-0977. FAX 081-783-1940. charts; stat. **Document type:** trade publication.
—BLDSC (6117.059800).
Supersedes (in 1985): Business Ratio Reports: Metal Stockholders (ISSN 0261-9091)

669.1 US
C B I NEWS. 1914. s-m. free. C B I Industries, Inc., Public Relations Department, 800 Jorie Blvd., Oak Brook, IL 60521. TEL 312-654-7305. Ed. Jerry Patterson. circ. 22,000. **Indexed:** Acid Rain Abstr., Acid Rain Ind.
Former titles: Water Tower; C B I Water Tower News.

669.3 US
C B S A CAPSULES. 1951. m. $25. Copper & Brass Servicenter Association, Adams Bldg., Ste. 109, 251 W. Dekalb Pike, King of Prussia, PA 19406. TEL 610-265-6658. FAX 610-265-3419. Ed. R. Franklin Brown, Jr. charts; illus.; stat.; tr.lit. circ. 165. (back issues avail.) **Document type:** newsletter.
Description: Includes legislative and regulatory news related to metal industry, management and business news, and news about members.

C I M DIRECTORY. (Canadian Institute of Mining, Metallurgy & Petroleum) see MINES AND MINING INDUSTRY

669 GW ISSN 0935-7262
C P & T INTERNATIONAL. (Casting Plant and Technology) 1985. q. DM.130. (Verein Deutscher Giessereifachleute) Giesserei-Verlag GmbH, Postfach 102532, 40016 Duesseldorf, Germany. TEL 0211-6707-0. circ. 7,830. **Document type:** trade publication.
—CCC.
Formerly: C P and T (ISSN 0177-1469)

C S N D T JOURNAL. (Canadian Society for Nondestructive Testing, Inc.) see ENGINEERING — Engineering Mechanics And Materials

669 CC ISSN 1000-8500 CODEN: CKJIEV
CAILIAO KEXUE JINZHAN/ADVANCES IN MATERIAL SCIENCE. (Text in Chinese) bi-m. Zhongguo Kexueyuan, Jinshu Yanjiusuo - Chinese Academy of Sciences, Institute of Metallurgy, 72, Wenhua Lu, Shenyang, Liaoning 110015, People's Republic of China. TEL 483125. Ed. Li De.
—CASDDS.

669.1 MX
CAMARA NACIONAL DE LA INDUSTRIA DEL HIERRO Y DEL ACERO. INFORME DEL PRESIDENTE. a. $5. Camara Nacional de la Industria del Hierro y del Acero, Amores 338, Apdo. Postal 12783, Mexico 12, D.F., Mexico.

669 CN ISSN 0835-0116
HD9539.A3
CANADA. STATISTICS CANADA. PRIMARY METAL INDUSTRIES. (Catalogue 41-250) (Text in English and French) 1927. a. Can.$20($42) (foreign $49). Statistics Canada, Publications Sales and Services, Ottawa, ON K1A 0T6, Canada. TEL 613-951-7277. FAX 613-951-1584. (also avail. in microform from MML) **Document type:** government publication.
Supersedes (in 1985): Canada. Statistics Canada. Smelting and Refining (ISSN 0384-4935)
Description: Annual census of manufactures.

| 669.3 | CN | ISSN 0008-3291 |

CANADIAN COPPER/CUIVRE CANADIEN. (Text in English, French) 1960. q. free. Canadian Copper and Brass Development Association, 10 Gateway Blvd., Ste. 375, Don Mills, ON M3C 3A1, Canada. TEL 416-421-0788. FAX 416-421-8092. Ed. R. John Catterall. illus. circ. 14,000. **Indexed:** Copper Abstr., Met.Abstr. **Document type:** trade publication. —BLDSC (3019.495000).
   Formerly: Canadian Coppermetals.
   Description: Articles promoting and developing the uses of copper, its alloys and compounds.

CANADIAN MACHINERY & METALWORKING. see *MACHINERY*

| 669 | UK | ISSN 0008-4433 |
| | | CODEN: CAMQAU |

CANADIAN METALLURGICAL QUARTERLY. 1977. 5/yr. £334($530) (effective 1996). (Canadian Institute of Mining & Metallurgy, Metallurgical Society, CN) Elsevier Science Ltd., Pergamon, P.O. Box 800, Kidlington, Oxford OX5 1DX, England. TEL 44-1865-843000. FAX 44-1865-843010. E-mail: nlinfo-f@elsevier.nl; usinfo-f@elsevier.com; forinfo-ky04035@niftyserve.or.jp; Site addr.: http://www.elsevier.nl/. (Subscr. in U.S. and Canada to: Elsevier Science, 660 White Plains Rd., Tarrytown, NY 10591-5153. TEL 914-524-9200. FAX 914-333-2444) Ed. H. Henein. adv. circ. 1,200. (also avail. in microfilm from UMI; back issues avail.; reprint service avail. from UMI) **Indexed:** AESIS, B.C.I.R.A., Cadscan, Chem.Abstr., Curr.Cont., Ind.Sci.Rev., INIS Atomind., INSPEC (1985-), Lead Abstr., Met.Abstr., Sci.Cit.Ind., World Alum.Abstr., Zincscan. **Document type:** academic/scholarly publication.
   —BLDSC (3038.800000); CASDDS; Ei; Faxon; Genuine Article; SWETS; UMI; UnCover. **CCC.**
   Description: Devoted to the science, practice and technology of metallurgy, including mineral processing, extractive metallurgy, alloy development and metal working.
   Refereed Serial

| 669 | US | ISSN 1051-1237 |

CASTING DESIGN & APPLICATION; the magazine for designers and buyers of castings. q. $20 (free to qualified personnel). Penton Publishing (Subsidiary of: Pittway Company), 1100 Superior Ave., Cleveland, OH 44114. TEL 216-696-7000. Ed. Bob Rodgers. circ. 22,000 (controlled).
   Description: Devoted to the interests of OEM designers and buyers of engineered cast parts. Covers casting design, including the sourcing of qualified producers of all types of castings.

| 671.2 | JA | ISSN 0019-2813 |

CASTING DIGEST/IMONO DAIJESUTO. (Text in Japanese) 1949. m. 1200 Yen. Nihon Cast Iron Foundry Association - Nihon Imono Kogyokai, 501 Kikai Shinko Kaikan, 3-5-8 Shiba Koen, Minato-ku, Tokyo 105, Japan. Ed. G. Kunitomo.

| 669 | US | |

CASTING DIGEST. 1976. m. $160 to non-members (foreign $180); members $130 (foreign $145) (effective 1996). A S M International, Materials Information, Materials Park, OH 44073. TEL 216-338-5151. FAX 216-338-4634. TELEX 980-619. E-mail: DBartherl@po.ASM-Intl.org. (UK addr.: Institute of Materials, Materials Information, 1 Carlton House Terr., London SW1Y 5DB, England. TEL 071-839-4071) **Indexed:** Met.Abstr. **Document type:** abstracting/indexing.

| 669 | UK | ISSN 0964-3281 |

CASTING PROCESSES. English translation of: Protsessy Lit'ya. 1992. 4/yr. (Academy of the Sciences of the Ukraine, Institute of Casting, KR) Riecansky Science Publishing Co., 7 Meadow Walk, Great Abington, Cambridge CB1 6AZ, England. TEL 0223-893295. Ed. V.A. Efimov. **Document type:** trade publication.
   —BLDSC (0409.870000).

CASTING SOURCE DIRECTORY. see *BUSINESS AND ECONOMICS — Trade And Industrial Directories*

| 671.2 | US | ISSN 0887-9060 |
| TS200 | | CODEN: CEFWDA |

CASTING WORLD. 1969. q. $20. Continental Communications Inc., Box 1919, Bridgeport, CT 06601-1919. Ed. W. Troland. adv.; bk.rev.; illus. circ. 76,000. **Indexed:** B.C.I.R.A., Cadscan, Lead Abstr., Met.Abstr., World Alum.Abstr., Zincscan. —CASDDS.
   Formerly: Casting Engineering and Foundry World (ISSN 0273-9607); Formed by the merger of: Casting Engineering (ISSN 0008-7513) & Foundry World (ISSN 0191-1767)

| 669 | UK | |

CASTINGS BUYER. 1987. 3/yr. free. Argus Business Media Ltd., Fuel and Metals Journals (Subsidiary of: Argus Press Group), Queensway House, 2 Queensway, Redhill, Surrey RH1 1QS, England. TEL 01737-768611. FAX 01737-761685. TELEX 948669 TOPJNL G. adv.: B&W page £1690, color page £2265; trim 280 x 405; adv. contact: Colin Robinson. circ. 20,000. **Document type:** trade publication.

| 669.1 | SP | |

CATALOGO EXPOFERRO. 1986. a. 3500 ptas. Tecnipublicaciones, S.A., C. Albacete 5, 28027 Madrid, Spain. TEL 34-1-3261440. FAX 34-1-3262341. Ed. Juan M. Fernandez. adv. circ. 10,000.

| 669.1 | SP | |

CATALOGO SIDERURGICO. 1987. a. 4850 ptas. Tecnipublicaciones, S.A., C. Albacete 5, 28027 Madrid, Spain. TEL 34-1-3261440. FAX 34-1-3262407.

CENTRAL SOUTH UNIVERSITY OF TECHNOLOGY. JOURNAL. see *MINES AND MINING INDUSTRY*

| 669 | SP | |

CENTRE METAL.LURGIC. 4/yr. Centre Metal.lurgic, Tres Creus 66, 08020 Sabadell (Barcelona), Spain. TEL 3-725-75-77. FAX 3-726-09-95. Ed. Pere Font Grasa. circ. 1,500.

CHEMPRESS; onafhankelijk financieel-economisch en technisch nieuwsblad voor de chemie in de Benelux. see *ENGINEERING — Chemical Engineering*

CHIBA KIKINSHI NYUSU. see *MACHINERY*

CHIBAKEN KIKAI KINZOKU SHIKENJO. JIGYO GAIYO/MACHINERY AND METALLURGY RESEARCH INSTITUTE OF CHIBA PREFECTURE. REPORT. see *MACHINERY*

| 669.142 | CH | ISSN 1015-6070 |

CHINA STEEL TECHNICAL REPORT/CHUNG KANG CHI PAO. Key Title: C S C China Steel Technical Report - Zhonggang Jibao. (Text in English) 1987. a. China Steel Corporation, R & D Department, No. 1 Chungkang Rd., Lin Hai Industrial District, Hsiaokang, Kaohsiung, Taiwan, Republic of China. TEL 07-8021111. FAX 07-8022432. TELEX 71108-STLMILL. Ed. Rung-Jin Hung. **Document type:** bulletin.
   —BLDSC (3180.234639).
   Description: Covers steelmaking, new materials and technology. Highlights current technical activities at China Steel, and serves to exchange information with foreign and domestic steelmakers.
   Refereed Serial

| 669 | CC | |

CHINA'S REFRACTORIES. (Text in English) 1992. bi-m. $76. Yejin Bu, Luoyang Naihuo Cailiao Yanjiusuo, No. 43, Xiyuan Lu, Jianxi-qu, Luoyang, Henan 471039, People's Republic of China. TEL 86-379-4913501. FAX 86-379-4913630. TELEX 473053 LIRR CN. adv.; bk.rev.
   Description: Provides important news and statistical data on the Chinese refractories market as well as technical and academic discussions.

METALLURGY

| 669 | CH | ISSN 0379-6906 |
| | | CODEN: TLKHAJ |

CHINESE JOURNAL OF MATERIALS SCIENCE. Key Title: Cailiao Kexue. Variant title: Materials Science Quarterly. (Text in Chinese and English) 1969. q. $22 (foreign $36). Chinese Society for Materials Science, 195-5 Chung-Hsing Rd. Sec. 4, Chutung, Hsinchu, Taiwan 31015, Republic of China. TEL 035-916836. FAX 035-820237. TELEX 34684-MRL. Ed. Sing-Tien Wu; Pub. Li-Chung Lee. circ. 1,500. (reprint service avail. from NTIS) **Document type:** academic/scholarly publication.
   —BLDSC (3180.370000); CASDDS; Ei. **CCC.**

| 669 | CC | |

CHINESE JOURNAL OF METALLURGY/ZHONGGUO JINSHU KEXUE JISHU ZAZHI. (Text in English) bi-m. Zhongguo Kexueyuan, Jinshu Yanjiusuo - Chinese Academy of Sciences, Institute of Metallurgy, 72, Wenhua Lu, Shenyang, Liaoning 110015, People's Republic of China. TEL 483125. Ed. Shi Changxu.

CHINESE JOURNAL OF REACTIVE POLYMERS. see *ENGINEERING — Chemical Engineering*

| 669 | CH | ISSN 1011-6761 |

CHUKUNG; journal of Chinese Foundrymen's Association. Key Title: Zhugong (Gaoxiong). (Text in Chinese) 1969. q. NT.$800($70) Chinese Foundrymen's Association, 1001 Kaonan Highway, Kaohsiung, Taiwan, Republic of China. TEL 07-353-4791. FAX 07-352-4989. Ed. M.H. Hung. adv. contact: Ingeborg Ouyang. bk.rev. circ. 650. **Document type:** academic/scholarly publication, proceedings.
   —BLDSC (3189.654500).

| 671.2 | JA | ISSN 0387-0502 |
| | | CODEN: CTONDV |

CHUTANZO, NETSUSHORI/CASTING, FORGING & HEAT TREATMENTS. (Text in Japanese) 1947. m. 8500 Yen($49.25) Nihon Chutanzo Kyokai - Japan Casting & Forging Society, 3-13 Urashima Bldg., Kyobashi, Higashi-ku, Osaka-shi, Osaka-fu 540, Japan. Ed. Jun Dodo. adv.; bk.rev.; abstr.; bibl.; charts; illus.; mkt.; pat.; stat.; index. circ. 20,000. **Indexed:** Chem.Abstr.
   —CASDDS.
   Formerly (until Aug. 1978): Casting and Forging (ISSN 0009-6652)

| 669 | SP | ISSN 1132-8592 |
| | | CODEN: TMEBAC |

CIENCIA Y TECNOLOGIA DE LOS MATERIALES. 1945-1990; resumed 1992. bi-m. Universidad Politecnica de Catalunya, Departamento de Ciencia de los Materiales, Barcelona, Spain. TEL 3-257-12-20. **Document type:** academic/scholarly publication.
   —CASDDS.
   Formerly (until 1990): Tecnica Metalurgica (ISSN 0371-9537).

COKE OVEN MANAGERS' ASSOCIATION. YEAR BOOK. see *MINES AND MINING INDUSTRY*

| 669.142 | US | |

COLD FINISHED STEEL BAR INSTITUTE. MONTHLY IMPORT ANALYSIS. m. membership. Cold Finished Steel Bar Institute, 700 14th St., N.W., Ste. 900, Washington, DC 20005. TEL 202-508-1030.

| 669 | CL | ISSN 0589-2813 |
| HD9524.L3 | | CODEN: CLSMBO |

CONGRESO LATINAMERICANO DE SIDERURGIA. MEMORIA TECNICA. 1961. irreg. Instituto Latinoamericano del Fierro y el Acero, Secretaria General, Moneda 1140, Casilla Postal 13810, Santiago, Chile. **Indexed:** Chem.Abstr. —CASDDS.

CONNECTION (ARLINGTON). see *BUILDING AND CONSTRUCTION*

CONSTRUCT IN STEEL. see *BUILDING AND CONSTRUCTION*

| 669.3 621 | US | ISSN 0730-8299 |

COPPER TOPICS. 1968. q. free. Copper Development Association Inc., 260 Madison Ave., New York, NY 10016-2401. TEL 212-251-7200. FAX 203-251-7234. Ed. Ken Geremia. circ. 35,000 (controlled). (back issues avail.) **Document type:** newspaper.
   Description: Cites newsworthy applications of copper, brass and bronze products in the USA.

METALLURGY

CORROSION; journal of science and engineering. see ENGINEERING — Mechanical Engineering

CORROSION AND COATINGS. see PAINTS AND PROTECTIVE COATINGS

669 541.37   US   ISSN 0892-4228
TA418.74
CORROSION ENGINEERING. English translation of: Zairyo to Kankyo (JA ISSN 0917-0480) 1987. m. $740 (effective 1996). (Japan Society of Corrosion Engineering, JA) Allerton Press, Inc., 150 Fifth Ave., New York, NY 10011. TEL 212-924-3950. FAX 212-463-9684. Ed. Isao Sekine. **Document type:** academic/scholarly publication.
—BLDSC (3473.585000); Ei; Faxon; SWETS. **CCC.**

CORROSION MANAGEMENT. see ENGINEERING — Engineering Mechanics And Materials

620.112   UK   ISSN 0010-9371
TA462   CODEN: CRPCAK
CORROSION PREVENTION AND CONTROL. 1954. bi-m. $150. Scientific Surveys Ltd., Box 21, Beaconsfield, Bucks. HP9 1NS, England. TEL 01494-675139. FAX 01494-670155. Ed. J. Tiratsoo. adv.; bk.rev.; illus.; pat.; tr.lit.; index. **Indexed:** Abstr.Bull.Inst.Pap.Chem., Agri.Eng.Abstr., API Abstr., API Catal., API Hlth.& Environ., API Oil., API Pet.Ref., API Pet.Subst., API Transport., BMT, Br.Tech.Ind., Cadscan, Chem.Abstr., Copper Abstr., Corros.Abstr., E&P Hlth. (1993-), Eng.Ind., Fluidex, Gas Process.& Ppl. (1993-), INIS Atomind., Lead Abstr., Met.Abstr., Off.Tech. (1993-), Petrol.Abstr. (1961-64, 1970-), W.R.C.Inf., World Alum.Abstr., World Surf.Coat., Zincscan. **Document type:** trade publication.
—BLDSC (3475.000000); CASDDS; Ei; Faxon; Genuine Article; PADDS; SWETS; UnCover.
Description: Technical journal concerning corrosion prevention research.

620.112   US
TA462
CORROSION PREVENTION TECHNOLOGY. 1976. m. $160 to non-members (foreign $180); members $130 (foreign $145) (effective 1996). A S M International, Materials Information, Materials Park, OH 44073. TEL 216-338-5151. FAX 216-338-4634. TELEX 980-619. E-mail: DBarthel@po.ASM-Intl.org. (UK addr.: Institute of Materials, Materials Information, 1 Carlton House Terr., London SW1Y 5DB, England. TEL 071-839-4071) **Indexed:** Abstr.Bull.Inst.Pap.Chem., Met.Abstr. **Document type:** abstracting/indexing.
Formerly: Corrosion Prevention - Inhibition Digest (ISSN 0364-3301)

669 016   UK   ISSN 0334-6005
                         CODEN: CORVE2
CORROSION REVIEWS. 1972. q. $230 (effective 1996). Freund Publishing House Ltd., Ste. 500, Chesham House, 150 Regent St., London W1R 5FA, England. (And: P.O. Box 35010, Tel Aviv, Israel. TEL 972-3-5628540. FAX 972-3-5628538) Ed. M. Schorr. adv.; bk.rev.; index. circ. 1,000. (back issues avail.) **Indexed:** Chem.Abstr., Corros.Abstr., Excerp.Med., Met.Abstr., World Alum.Abstr. **Document type:** academic/scholarly publication.
—CASDDS; Faxon.
Formerly: Reviews on Coatings and Corrosion (ISSN 0048-7538)

620.112   UK   ISSN 0010-938X
TA462   CODEN: CRRSAA
CORROSION SCIENCE; journal on environmental degradation of materials and its control. 1961. m. £975($1551) (effective 1995). (Institute of Corrosion) Elsevier Science Ltd., Pergamon, P.O. Box 800, Kidlington, Oxford OX5 1DX, England. TEL 44-1865-843000. FAX 44-1865-843010. E-mail: nlinfo-f@elsevier.nl; usinfo-f@elsevier.com; forinfo-kyf04035@niftyserve.or.jp; Site addr.: http://www.elsevier.nl/. (Subscr. in U.S. and Canada to: Elsevier Science, 660 White Plains Rd., Tarrytown, NY 10591-5153. TEL 914-524-9200. FAX 914-333-2444) Ed. J.C. Scully. adv.; charts; illus.; index. circ. 1,800. (also avail. in microfilm from UMI) **Indexed:** A.S.& T.Ind., Abstr.Bull.Inst.Pap.Chem., API Abstr., API Catal., API Hlth.& Environ., API Oil., API Pet.Ref., API Pet.Subst., API Transport., Appl.Mech.Rev., Art & Archaeol.Tech.Abstr., BMT, Br.Tech.Ind., Cadscan, Chem.Abstr., Chem.Eng.Abstr., Chem.Infd., Copper Abstr., Corros.Abstr., Curr.Cont., Deep Sea Res.& Oceanogr.Abstr., Energy Rev., Eng.Ind., Environ.Per.Bibl., Excerp.Med., Fuel & Energy Abstr., Geo.Abstr., Geol.Abstr., Ind.Sci.Rev., INIS Atomind., INSPEC, Int.Aerosp.Abstr., ISMEC, Lead Abstr., Mass Spectr.Bull., Met.Abstr., Petrol.Abstr., Sci.Cit.Ind., T.C.E.A., W.R.C.Inf., World Alum.Abstr., World Surf.Coat., Zincscan. **Document type:** academic/scholarly publication.
—BLDSC (3476.500000); CASDDS; Ei; Faxon; Genuine Article; SWETS; UMI; UnCover. **CCC.**
Description: Covers topics including high temperature oxidation, passivity, anodic oxidation, biochemical corrosion, stress corrosion cracking, and corrosion control.
Refereed Serial

CURRENT BIBLIOGRAPHIES ON SCIENCE AND TECHNOLOGY: METALLURGY, NATURAL RESOURCES & ENERGY. see METALLURGY — Abstracting, Bibliographies, Statistics

671.5   US   ISSN 1078-6902
D D I N INTERNATIONAL MACHINERY. 1986. q. $40 in U.S.; Canada $49; elsewhere $55. Larson Associates, 95 Mt. Blue St., Norwell, MA 02061. TEL 617-659-2115. FAX 617-659-2411. Ed. Robert Larson. adv. contact: Susan Conway. circ. 6,000. **Document type:** trade publication.
Former titles (until 1993): D D I N North America (ISSN 1073-760X); Diemaking Diecutting Intelligence Newsletter.
Description: Focuses on the complete diecutting process to include flat, multi-contour and rotary diecutting and diemaking.

669.142   US
D R I - MCGRAW-HILL STEEL INDUSTRY REVIEW. 1978. q. D R I - McGraw-Hill, 24 Hartwell Ave., Lexington, MA 02173. TEL 617-863-5100. FAX 617-860-6332. TELEX 200 284. illus.
Formerly: Data Resources Steel Industry Review (ISSN 0163-206X)

682   DK   ISSN 0011-6483
DANSK SMEDE-TIDENDE. 1909. 25/yr. DKK 425 membership. Danmarks Smedemesterforening - Danish Blacksmith Association, Magnoliavej 2, DK-5250 Odense SV, Denmark.
TEL 45-66-17-33-12. FAX 45-66-17-36-12. Ed. Ulrik Schroeder. adv.; bk.rev.; abstr.; illus.; tr.lit.; circ. 3,700 (controlled). **Document type:** trade publication.
Description: Oriented towards the metallic industries, heating, ventilation, sanitary installations, as well as being a member magazine for the Association.

669   SZ   ISSN 1012-0386
                   CODEN: DDAFE7
DEFECT AND DIFFUSION FORUM. 12/yr. $1056. Scitec Publications Ltd., Untermuehleweg 11, CH-6300 Zug, Switzerland. FAX 062-741058. E-mail: ddd@scitec.ch. Ed. G.E. Murch. **Document type:** academic/scholarly publication.
—BLDSC (3584.254000); CASDDS; Ei; Faxon; SWETS.

669   SP   ISSN 0210-685X
DEFORMACION METALICA; revista de las tecnicas de fabricacion, acabado y transformacion del fleje, de la chapa, de tubos, perfiles y alambre. 1974. 7/yr. 18500 ptas.($160) (effective 1995). Elsevier Prensa S.A., Avda Paral.lel, 180, Apdo. No. 350 F.D., 08015 Barcelona, Spain. TEL 34-3-3255350. FAX 34-3-4252880. Ed. Pere Molera Sola. adv. contact: Manuel Fernandez de Liencres. charts; illus. circ. 4,000. **Indexed:** Art & Archaeol.Tech.Abstr., Ind.SST, Met.Abstr., World Alum.Abstr. **Document type:** trade publication.
—BLDSC (3546.292230).
Description: Covers manufacturing techniques, finishing and transformation of sheet iron, pipes and tubing, profiles, wires and cables.

DENNITSA. see COLLEGE AND ALUMNI

669 620   UK   ISSN 0263-1628
DIAL METALS, METALWORKING, MECHANICAL ENGINEERING, SHIPBUILDING, AEROSPACE, MARINE AND VEHICLE INDUSTRIES. a. Dial Industry Publications (Subsidiary of: Reed Information Services), Windsor Ct., East Grinstead House, E. Grinstead, W. Sussex RH19 1XA, England. TEL 01342-326972. FAX 01342-335612. TELEX 95127 INSFER G. **Document type:** trade publication.

DIE CASTING BUYERS GUIDE. see MACHINERY

DIE CASTING ENGINEER. see ENGINEERING — Engineering Mechanics And Materials

669   US   ISSN 0745-449X
TS239
DIE CASTING MANAGEMENT. 1983. bi-m. $35 (foreign $84). C-K Publishing, Inc., Box 247, Wonder Lake, IL 60097-0247. TEL 815-728-0912. Ed. Larry Teeman; Pub. Robert Crofts. adv. circ. 4,200. **Indexed:** Cadscan, Lead Abstr., Met.Abstr., World Alum.Abstr., Zincscan. **Document type:** trade publication.
—BLDSC (3580.483000); Ei.

669   SZ   ISSN 0377-6883
QD543   CODEN: DDDAD6
DIFFUSION AND DEFECT DATA; reviews and original contributions in solid state physics. (Consists of two parts: A (Defect and Diffusion Forum) & B (Solid State Phenomena)) 1967. 18/yr. $1584. Scitec Publications Ltd., Untermuehleweg 11, CH-6300 Zug, Switzerland. FAX 062-741058. E-mail: ddd@scitec.ch. Ed. G.E. Murch. bk.rev.; bibl.; charts; index, cum.index. circ. 700. **Indexed:** Chem.Abstr., INSPEC (1969-1971, 1983-), Met.Abstr., Nucl.Sci.Abstr. **Document type:** academic/scholarly publication.
—CASDDS; UnCover.
Formerly: Diffusion Data (ISSN 0012-267X)

671   US
DIRECT FROM MIDREX. 1974. q. free. (Midrex International B.V.) Midrex Direct Reduction Corporation, Charlotte Plaza, Charlotte, NC 28244. TEL 704-373-1600. FAX 704-373-1611. TELEX 6827031 MIDRX UW. Ed. David F. Wood. charts; illus.; circ. 2,000 (controlled). **Indexed:** Met.Abstr., World Alum.Abstr. **Document type:** bulletin.
Description: News, features, and announcements pertaining to direct reduction of iron ore.

669   US   ISSN 0070-5039
DIRECTORY IRON AND STEEL PLANTS. 1917. a. $60. Association of Iron and Steel Engineers, Three Gateway Center, Ste. 2350, Pittsburgh, PA 15222. TEL 412-281-6323. Ed. Paul Rozmus. adv. circ. 4,000. **Document type:** directory.

DIRECTORY OF METALLURGICAL CONSULTANTS & TRANSLATORS. see BUSINESS AND ECONOMICS — Trade And Industrial Directories

DIRECTORY OF STEEL FOUNDRIES IN THE UNITED STATES, CANADA AND MEXICO. see BUSINESS AND ECONOMICS — Trade And Industrial Directories

669   US
DISCOVER F M A. bi-m. membership. Fabricators and Manufacturers Association International, 833 Featherstone Rd., Rockford, IL 61107. TEL 815-399-8700. FAX 815-399-7279. **Document type:** newsletter.
Formerly (until July 1993): F M A News.

METALLURGY 4655

671.84 GW ISSN 0012-5911
CODEN: DRAHA5
DRAHT; internationale Fachzeitschrift fuer die Draht- und Kabelindustrie und alle Bereiche der Drahtverarbeitung. English edition: Wire (ISSN 0043-5996) Italian edition: Filo Metallico (ISSN 0430-4578); Spanish edition: Alambre (ISSN 0002-4406) 1950. m. (10/yr.). DM.185 (foreign DM.204) (effective 1995). Meisenbach GmbH, Hainstr. 18, 96047 Bamberg, Germany. TEL 0951-861-135. FAX 0951-861-158. (Subscr. to: Postfach 2069, 96011 Bamberg, Germany) Ed. Arnt Hannewald; Pub. Meinhard Meisenbach. adv.: B&W page DM.3540, color page DM.5325; trim 260 x 184; adv. contact: Oskar Ohler. bk.rev.; illus.; pat. circ. 7,200. (also avail. in microfilm from UMI) **Indexed:** Cadscan, Chem.Abstr., Eng.Ind., Excerp.Med., INIS Atomind., Lead Abstr., Met.Abstr., Zincscan. **Document type:** trade publication.
—CASDDS; SWETS; UMI. **CCC.**
Incorporates (1907-1995): Drahtwelt (ISSN 0012-592X)

669 GW ISSN 0940-2691
DRAHT UND KABEL PANORAMA; internationale Fachzeitschrift fuer alle Gebiete in der Draht-, Kabel- und verwandten Industrie. English edition: Wire and Cable Panorama. 1984. 4/yr. DM.80($50) D K S Fachverlag GmbH, Im Wiesengrund 21, 53539 Kelberg, Germany. TEL 02692-1071. FAX 02692-1073. Ed. Juergen Hendricks. adv.; bk.rev.; bibl.; illus.; tr.lit. circ. 7,100. (back issues avail.)

DUN'S INDUSTRIAL GUIDE - THE METALWORKING DIRECTORY. see *BUSINESS AND ECONOMICS — Trade And Industrial Directories*

669.6 UK
E E C - TIN IN TINPLATE. (European Economic Community) 1981. irreg. £15. International Tin Council, 1 Oxendon St., London SW1Y 4EQ, England. **Description:** Surveys tinplate manufacturing, can making and canning in the EEC.

E R A TECHNOLOGY NEWS. (Electrical Research Association) see *BUSINESS AND ECONOMICS — Marketing And Purchasing*

669 GW
DIE EISEN, BLECH UND METALL VERARBEITENDE INDUSTRIE, STAHLVERFORMUNG UND IHRE HELFER. 1952. a. $51. Industrieschau-Verlagsgesellschaft mbH, Berliner Allee 8, 64295 Darmstadt, Germany. TEL 06151-38920. FAX 06151-33164. (U.S. subscr. to: Western Hemisphere Publishing Corp., Box 847, Hillsboro, OR 97123-0847. TEL 503-640-3736. FAX 503-640-2748) Ed. Margit Selka. circ. 10,000. **Document type:** directory.
●Also available online.
Also available on CD-ROM.

669 GW
DIE EISEN-, STAHL- UND N E METALL-INDUSTRIE UND IHRE HELFER/IRON, STEEL AND NON-FERROUS METAL INDUSTRIES AND THEIR SUPPLIERS. 1952. a. $51. Industrieschau-Verlagsgesellschaft mbH, Berliner Allee 8, 64295 Darmstadt, Germany. TEL 06151-38920. FAX 06151-33164. (U.S. subscr. to: Western Hemisphere Publishing Corp., Box 847, Hillsboro, OR 97123-0847. TEL 503-640-3736. FAX 503-640-2748) Ed. Margit Selka. circ. 3,000. **Document type:** directory.
●Also available online.
Also available on CD-ROM.

669.1 US ISSN 0096-0128
TN750 CODEN: EFCPAY
ELECTRIC FURNACE CONFERENCE PROCEEDINGS. 1943. a., 52nd ed., 1994. $90 to non-members; members $45. Iron & Steel Society, 410 Commonwealth Dr., Warrendale, PA 15086-7512. TEL 412-776-9535. FAX 412-776-0430. (also avail. in microfilm from UMI; back issues avail.) **Document type:** proceedings.
—BLDSC (3671.558000); CASDDS.
Description: For iron and steelmakers.

669.142 JA ISSN 0011-8389
CODEN: DESEAT
ELECTRIC FURNACE STEEL/DENKI SEIKO. (Text in Japanese; summaries in English) 1925. q. 2000 Yen. (Electric Furnace Steel Research Association - Denki Seiko Kenkyukai) Daido Steel Co., Ltd., 2-30 Daido-cho, Minami-ku, Nagoya 457, Japan. TEL 052-611-9414. FAX 052-614-5812. Ed. Yuzo Ohtakara. bk.rev.; charts; illus. circ. 1,700. (processed) **Indexed:** Chem.Abstr., Met.Abstr., World Alum.Abstr. **Document type:** academic/scholarly publication.
—CASDDS.

ENGINEERED MATERIALS DIRECTORY OF CONSULTANTS & TRANSLATORS. see *BUSINESS AND ECONOMICS — Trade And Industrial Directories*

669 622 GW ISSN 0044-2658
TN3 CODEN: ERZMAK
ERZMETALL; journal for exploration, mining and metallurgy. (Text in German; summaries in English) 1912. m. DM.525 (foreign DM.540). Gesellschaft Deutscher Metallhuetten und Bergleute e.V., Paul-Ernst-Str. 10, 38678 Clausthal-Zellerfeld, Germany. Ed. D. Dornbusch. adv.; bk.rev.; abstr.; charts; illus.; mkt.; pat.; stat.; index. circ. 2,600. (reprint service avail. from ISI) **Indexed:** C.I.S. Abstr., Cadscan, Chem.Abstr., Copper Abstr., Eng.Ind., Excerp.Med., Fuel & Energy Abstr., GeoRef., INIS Atomind., Lead Abstr., Met.Abstr., World Alum.Abstr., Zincscan. **Document type:** trade publication.
—BLDSC (3810.920000); CASDDS; Ei; Faxon; SWETS. **CCC.**
Formerly (until 1945): Metall und Erz.
Description: Journal for exploration, mining, processing, recycling and environmental technology.

669 UK ISSN 0264-9047
EUROPEAN ADHESIVES & SEALANTS. 1983. q. £82.80($155) (foreign £96.85). Argus Business Media Ltd., Fuel and Metals Journals (Subsidiary of: Argus Press Group), Queensway House, 2 Queensway, Redhill, Surrey RH1 1QS, England. TEL 01737-768611. FAX 01737-761685. TELEX 948669 TOPJNL G. Ed. Tom Mulligan. **Indexed:** Intl.Polym.Sci.& Tech., RAPRA, World Surf.Coat. **Document type:** trade publication.
—BLDSC (3829.482950); Ei; SWETS.

669.142 UK
EUROPEAN STAINLESS STEEL DIRECTORY. 1975. biennial. £35.50. Modern Metals Publications Ltd., 5 Pond St., Hampstead, London NW3 2PN, England. Ed. F.W.S. Russell. adv. circ. 700. **Document type:** directory.
Former titles: Stainless Steel Directory; Directory of the Stainless Steel Industry.

669 US ISSN 0888-0301
THE FABRICATOR. 1971. 10/yr. $30 (Canada and Mexico $50; elsewhere $125); free to qualified personnel. Croydon Group, Ltd. (Subsidiary of: Fabricators & Manufacturers Association, International), 833 Featherstone Rd., Rockford, IL 61107-6203. TEL 815-399-8700. FAX 815-399-7279. Ed. Theresa Olmsted; Pub. John Nandzik. adv.; B&W page $4260; trim 10 3/4 x 14 3/4; adv. contact: Jack Broughton. bk.rev. circ. 54,120. (tabloid format) **Indexed:** BMT, CAD CAM Abstr., Met.Abstr., World Alum.Abstr. **Document type:** trade publication.
—BLDSC (3863.147000).
Formerly: F M A's Journal of the Fabricator (ISSN 0192-8066)
Description: Disseminates practical design, engineering, and manufacturing technical information about modern metal forming and fabricating techniques, machinery, tooling, and management concepts, emphasizing the fabrication of sheet, coil, tube, pipe, plate, and structural shapes.

669 BE ISSN 0377-9084
FABRIMETAL MAGAZINE. (Editions in Dutch and French) 1946. m. (9/yr.). 1378 BEF to non-members (foreign 1500 BEF); members 795 BEF. (Federation des Entreprises de l'Industrie des Fabrications Metalliques, Mecaniques, Electriques, Electroniques et de la Transformation des Matieres Plastiques) Fabrimetal A.S.B.L., 21 rue des Drapiers, 1050 Brussels, Belgium. TEL 32-2-510-2311. FAX 32-2-510-2301. Ed. Luc Lambrecht. adv.; bk.rev.; charts; illus.; mkt.; index. circ. 7,700 (3,700 Dutch ed.; 4,000 French ed.). **Indexed:** Key to Econ.Sci. **Document type:** trade publication.
Supersedes: Federation des Entreprises de l'Industrie des Fabrications Metalliques, Mecaniques, Electriques et de la Transformation des Matieres Plastiques. Revue Mensuelle; Which was formerly: Federation des Entreprises de l'Industrie des Fabrications Metalliques, Mecaniques, Electriques et de la Transformation des Matieres Plastiques. Bulletin d'Information Mensuel (ISSN 0014-9330)
Refereed Serial

669 GW ISSN 0014-6854
DER FAHRZEUG- UND METALL-LACKIERER; das Lackiererhandwerk. 1956. m. DM.80 (foreign DM.88). Audin Verlag GmbH, Maximilianstr. 29, 80539 Munich, Germany. TEL 089-29160240. FAX 089-29160247. Ed. Wolfgang Auer. adv.; bk.rev.; abstr.; charts; illus.; mkt.; pat.; stat.; tr.lit.; index. circ. 4,500. **Indexed:** World Surf.Coat. **Document type:** trade publication.

674.84 US
FASTENER INDUSTRY NEWS. 1979. bi-w. $200 (foreign $250) (effective 1995-96). 2009 N.E. 16th Ave., Portland, OR 97212-4430. TEL 503-335-0183. FAX 503-335-3451. Ed. John Wolz; Pubs. John Wolz, Ann Bisgyer. adv. contact: Ann Bisgyer. bk.rev. (back issues avail.) **Document type:** newsletter.
Description: Focuses on management, mergers, buyouts, current events in manufacturing and distribution segments of the industry.

FEDERATIE GOUD EN ZILVER. VADEMECUM. see *JEWELRY, CLOCKS AND WATCHES*

669 GW ISSN 0940-2675
FEDERN - KETTEN - BIEGETEILE; internationale Fachzeitschrift fuer die Herstellung, Behandlung und Pruefung von Federn, Ketten sowie Biege- und Stanzteilen aus Draht und Bandmaterial. English edition: Springs - Chains - Formed Parts. 1988. 2/yr. DM.40($25) D K S Fachverlag GmbH, Im Wiesengrund 21, 53539 Kelberg, Germany. TEL 02692-1071. FAX 02692-1073. Ed. Juergen Hendricks. adv.; bk.rev.; bibl.; illus.; tr.lit. circ. 3,500. (back issues avail.)

669 VE
FERRETARIA/HARDWARE. 1973. m. Camara Ferreteria Nacional - National Hardware Chamber, Av. Este 2, No. 215, Edif. Camara de Comercio, Piso 5, Los Caobos, Caracas, Venezuela. TEL 571-16-12. Dir. Andreina Salazar. adv.: B&W page $750, color page $1000. circ. 6,000. **Document type:** trade publication.
Description: Covers information on management and marketing that is of interest to the industrial and trade sector.

669 MX
FERRETECNIC - F Y T; la revista de la industria ferretera. 1963. m. free. Publitecnic S.A., Calle 4, no. 188, Apdo. Postal 74-290, C.P. 09070, Mexico 13, D.F., Mexico. TEL 685-28-19. FAX 6706318. Ed. Fernando Ulacia Esteve. adv.; bk.rev.; circ. 10,000 (controlled). (back issues avail.) **Document type:** trade publication.

669 US ISSN 0953-721X
FERRO ALLOY DIRECTORY AND DATABOOK. 1984. irreg., 3rd ed., 1992. $223. Metal Bulletin Inc., 220 Fifth Ave., New York, NY 10001. TEL 212-213-6202. FAX 212-213-1870. adv. **Document type:** directory.
—CCC.
Supersedes: Ferro Alloy Directory (ISSN 0266-3198)
Description: Lists ferro alloy producers and traders with product guides.

METALLURGY

669 330   UK   ISSN 0967-8204
FERRO ALLOYS MONTHLY. 1992. m. $1235. Metal Bulletin plc, Park House, Park Terrace, Worcester Park, Surrey KT4 7HY, England.
TEL 0171-827-9977. FAX 0181-337-8943. (U.S. subscr. to: Metal Bulletin Inc., 220 Fifth Ave., New York, NY 10001-7781. TEL 212-213-6202. FAX 212-213-1870) Ed. Neil Buxton. **Document type:** trade publication.

669.1   SZ
FERRUM; Nachrichten aus der Eisenbibliothek. 1954. a. free. Eisenbibliothek, Klostergut Paradies, CH-8246 Langwiesen, Switzerland. TEL 053-293810. FAX 053-291666. Ed. Annette Bouheiry. bk.rev. (back issues avail.) **Document type:** academic/scholarly publication.
Description: Examines the history of technology, in particular iron and steel manufacturing.

669   UK
FINANCIAL SURVEY. COMPANY DATA FOR SUCCESS: NON-FERROUS METAL FOUNDERS. a. I C C Financial Surveys Ltd., Field House, 72 Oldfield Rd., Hampton, Mddx. TW12 2HQ, England. TEL 081-783-0977. FAX 081-783-1940. charts; stat. **Document type:** trade publication.
Former titles (until 1986): Financial Survey. Company Data for Success: Metal Founders. Non-Ferrous (ISSN 0952-0120); I C C Financial Survey and Directory: Metal Founders - Non-Ferrous.

669 739.27   US
FINE METAL GAZETTE. m. Institute of Metal Repair, 1558 S. Redwood St., Escondido, CA 92025.
TEL 619-747-5978. adv. **Document type:** newsletter.

671.732   US   ISSN 0015-2358
FINISHERS' MANAGEMENT. 1957. m. (10/yr.). $28. Publications Management, Inc., 4350 DiPaolo Center, Dearlove Rd., Glenview, IL 60025.
TEL 708-699-1700. FAX 708-699-1703. Ed. Hugh Morgan. adv.: B&W page $1790, color page $2960; adv. contact: John McConnell. bk.rev.; charts; illus.; mkt. circ. 11,200. (also avail. in microfilm from UMI; reprint service avail. from UMI) **Indexed:** Met.Abstr., World Alum.Abstr. **Document type:** trade publication.
—BLDSC (3928.170000); UMI.
Formerly: Plating Management and Metal Finishers Management.
Description: Management magazine for job shop owners and captive shop managers in the surface finishing market.

671   UK   ISSN 0071-5182
FINISHING HANDBOOK AND DIRECTORY. 1950. a. free to subscribers to Product Finishing. Sawell Publications Ltd., 127 Stanstead Rd., London SE23 1JE, England. Ed. J.E. Bean. adv. circ. 4,500.

669   RU   ISSN 0015-3230
TN690   CODEN: FMMTAK
FIZIKA METALLOV I METALLOVEDENIE. English edition: Physics of Metals and Metallography (ISSN 0031-918X) 1955. m. 77.40 Rub. (Rossiiskaya Akademiya Nauk, Ural'skoe Otdelenie) Interperiodica, Ul. Profsoyuznaya 90, 117864 Moscow, Russia. TEL 7-095-3360066. FAX 7-096-3360666. Ed. S.V. Vonsovski. index. (tabloid format) **Indexed:** Cadscan, Chem.Abstr., Copper Abstr., Curr.Cont., Eng.Ind., Ind.Sci.Rev., INIS Atomind., INSPEC, Int.Aerosp.Abstr., Lead Abstr., Met.Abstr., Phys.Ber., Sci.Cit.Ind., World Alum.Abstr., Zincscan. **Document type:** academic/scholarly publication.
—BLDSC (0389.800000); CASDDS; Genuine Article. CCC.

FLUID PHASE EQUILIBRIA. see *CHEMISTRY — Physical Chemistry*

671.2   IT   ISSN 0015-6078
TS200   CODEN: FNDAAR
FONDERIA.✶ 1951. bi-m. L.75000. E T M, S.r.l., Via Principe Eugenio 3, 20155 Milan, Italy.
TEL 02-48010095. FAX 02-48010011. Dir. Antonio Urti. adv.; bk.rev.; charts; illus.; tr.lit.; index. circ. 3,500. **Indexed:** B.C.I.R.A., Chem.Abstr., Met.Abstr., World Alum.Abstr.
—CASDDS.
Description: Technical review of Italian foundry industry. Covers metals, metallurgy, casting processes, treatments, foundry items and equipment.

671.2   IT
▼**FONDERIA OGGI.** 1994. bi-m. L.80000 (foreign L.120000). Gruppo Editoriale Rossini s.r.l., Via Cola di Rienzo 26, 20144 Milan, Italy.
TEL 39-2-425201. FAX 39-2-425498. adv.: B&W page L.1900000, color page L.2800000; adv. contact: Contino Lillo. **Document type:** trade publication.

671.2   FR   ISSN 0249-3136
TS200   CODEN: FFAUDJ
FONDERIE, FONDEUR D'AUJOURD'HUI. (Text in French; summaries in English, French, German) 1981. m. 710 F. (effective Jan. 1994). Editions Techniques des Industries de la Fonderie, 44 av. de la Division Leclerc, 92310 Sevres, France. FAX 45-34-14-34. TELEX 634 104 CTIFSE. Ed. Chantal Couvret. adv.; bk.rev.; abstr.; bibl.; charts; illus.; index, cum.index. circ. 1,953. **Indexed:** B.C.I.R.A., Cadscan, Chem.Abstr., Eng.Ind., INSPEC, Lead Abstr., Met.Abstr., Zincscan.
—BLDSC (3976.050000); CASDDS; Ei; UMI.
Incorporates (in 1981): Fondeur d'Aujourd'hui (ISSN 0015-6116)
Description: Publishes results of studies of CTIF. Features original works of French as well as foreign engineers, practical advice, industrial projects, information on the professional life of engineers, etc.

671.2   FR   ISSN 1260-3120
FONDERIE SOUS PRESSION. q. 279.14 F. (foreign 375 F.) (effective 1996). Revue Francaise des Metallurgistes, 32 rue Saint-Marc, 75002 Paris, France. TEL 42-60-31-51. FAX 42-60-38-42. **Document type:** trade publication.
Description: Covers techniques and technologies in diecasting.

671.2   UK   ISSN 0955-5293
FORGE (YEAR). 1908. bi-m. £2.50($40) (National Association Farriers, Blacksmiths and Agricultural Engineers) Farriers' Journal Publishing Co. Ltd., Ave. R., 7th St., N.A.C. Stoneleigh, Warks. CV8 2LG, England. TEL 01203-696595.
FAX 01203-696708. Ed. Jackie A. Webb. adv. contact: Jackie A. Webb. bk.rev.; bibl.; stat.; tr.lit. circ. 4,200. **Document type:** trade publication.
Formerly: Farriers Journal.
Description: News about farriery and blacksmithing.

671.2   US   ISSN 1054-1756
FORGING. 1990. q. $20 (free to qualified personnel). Penton Publishing (Subsidiary of: Pittway Company), 1100 Superior Ave., Cleveland, OH 44114-2534. TEL 216-696-7000. FAX 216-696-7658. Ed. Wallace D. Huskonen. adv.; illus.; tr.lit.; circ. 5,000 (controlled).
—UMI.

FORSCHUNGSGEMEINSCHAFT EISENHUETTENSCHLACKEN. SCHRIFTENREIHE. see *ENVIRONMENTAL STUDIES — Waste Management*

699   US
FOUNDRY DATABOOK & CATALOG FILE. 1970. a. $10 (free to qualified personnel). Penton Publishing (Subsidiary of: Pittway Company), 1100 Superior Ave., Cleveland, OH 44114-2543.
TEL 216-696-7000. FAX 216-696-8765. (Subscr. to: Box 95759, Cleveland, OH 44101) adv.; circ. 24,000 (controlled). (reprint service avail. from UMI)
Formerly: Foundry Catalog File (ISSN 0533-005X)

669   UK   ISSN 0071-8130
FOUNDRY DIRECTORY AND REGISTER OF FORGES. 1959. biennial. $167. Metal Bulletin plc, Park House, Park Terrace, Worcester Park, Surrey KT4 7HY, England. TEL 0171-827-9977.
FAX 0181-337-8943. (U.S. subscr. to: Metal Bulletin Inc., 220 Fifth Ave., New York, NY 10001-7781. TEL 212-213-6202. FAX 212-213-1870) **Document type:** directory.
Description: List of iron and non-ferrous founders in Europe.

671.2   UK
FOUNDRY INTERNATIONAL. 1978. q.
£93.40($181.55) (foreign £113.45). Argus Business Media Ltd., Fuel and Metals Journals (Subsidiary of: Argus Press Group), Queensway House, 2 Queensway, Redhill, Surrey RH1 1QS, England. TEL 01737-768611.
FAX 01737-761685. TELEX 948669 TOPJNL G. Ed. J. Mitchell. **Indexed:** Art & Archaeol.Tech.Abstr., B.C.I.R.A., Met.Abstr., World Alum.Abstr. **Document type:** trade publication.
—BLDSC (4026.550000); Ei.
Formerly: Foundry Trade Journal International (ISSN 0143-6902)
Description: Reviews the worldwide foundry industry.

671.2   US   ISSN 0360-8999
TS200   CODEN: FNMTBS
FOUNDRY MANAGEMENT & TECHNOLOGY. 1892. m. $45 (free to qualified personnel). Penton Publishing (Subsidiary of: Pittway Company), 1100 Superior Ave., Cleveland, OH 44114-2543.
TEL 216-696-7000. FAX 216-696-8765. (Subscr. to: Box 95759, Cleveland, OH, 44101) Ed. Robert C. Rodgers. adv.; bk.rev.; illus.; stat.; tr.lit.; circ. 22,000 (controlled). (also avail. in microfilm from UMI; reprint service avail. from UMI) **Indexed:** A.S.& T.Ind., B.C.I.R.A., Bus.Ind., Ceram.Abstr., Ergon.Abstr., Excerp.Med., ISMEC, Met.Abstr., PROMT, SRI, Tr.& Indus.Ind., World Alum.Abstr.
●Also available online. Vendor(s): Knight-Ridder, Inc.
—BLDSC (4026.600000); Ei; Faxon; SWETS; UMI; UnCover. CCC.
Formerly: Foundry (ISSN 0015-9034)
Description: Includes technical developments, foundry management problems and operating practices.

671.2   UK   ISSN 0015-9042
TS200   CODEN: FUTJAD
FOUNDRY TRADE JOURNAL. 1902. m.
£128.60($277.55) (foreign £173.45). (National Society of Master Patternmakers) Argus Business Media Ltd., Fuel and Metals Journals (Subsidiary of: Argus Press Group), Queensway House, 2 Queensway, Redhill, Surrey RH1 1QS, England. TEL 01737-768611. FAX 01737-761685. TELEX 948669 TOPJNL G. (Co-sponsors: Diecasting Society, B.I.C.T.A., L.M.F.A.) Ed. John Lawrenson. adv.; bk.rev.; film rev.; abstr.; charts; illus.; mkt.; pat.; stat.; tr.lit.; s-a. index. (also avail. in microfilm from UMI; reprint service avail. from UMI) **Indexed:** Art & Archaeol.Tech.Abstr., B.C.I.R.A., Br.Tech.Ind., C.I.S. Abstr., Cadscan, Chem.Abstr., Copper Abstr., Eng.Ind., Ergon.Abstr., Excerp.Med., Fuel & Energy Abstr., ISMEC, Lead Abstr., Met.Abstr., World Alum.Abstr., Zincscan. **Document type:** trade publication.
—BLDSC (4028.000000); CASDDS; Ei; SWETS; UMI.
Incorporates: Iron and Steel Trades Journal and Iron Trade Circular.
Description: Reports on trade and technical matters in the foundry industry.

FOUNDRY YEAR BOOK AND CASTING BUYERS' DIRECTORY. see *BUSINESS AND ECONOMICS — Trade And Industrial Directories*

671.2   UK   ISSN 0953-6035
   CODEN: BRFOAT
FOUNDRYMAN. 1956. m. £65 (foreign £79). (Institute of British Foundrymen) I B F Publications, Bordsley Hall, The Holloway, Alvechurch, Birmingham B48 7QA, England. TEL 0527-596101.
FAX 0527-596102. (Subscr. to: 6 Bourne Enterprise Centre, Wrotham Rd., Borough Green, Kent TN15 8DG, England) Ed. L.M. Postle. adv.; B&W page £505; adv. contact: Les Rivers. bk.rev.; abstr.; bibl.; charts; illus.; index. circ. 2,813. (also avail. in microform from UMI; reprint service avail. from UMI) **Indexed:** Art & Archaeol.Tech.Abstr., B.C.I.R.A., Br.Tech.Ind., C.I.S. Abstr., Chem.Abstr., Eng.Ind., Ergon.Abstr., Excerp.Med., ISMEC, Met.Abstr., World Alum.Abstr.
—BLDSC (4028.024000); CASDDS; Ei; SWETS; UMI.
Formerly: British Foundryman (ISSN 0007-0718)

METALLURGY

671.2   PO
FUNDICAO. (Text in Portuguese; summaries in English, French and Portuguese) 1964. 4/yr. Esc.12000($80) Associacao Portuguesa de Fundicao, Rua do Campo Alegre 672, 4100 Porto, Portugal. TEL 351-2-6090675. FAX 351-2-6000764. TELEX 27180 APFP. Ed. Mr. Malheiro. adv.; bk.rev.; film rev.; stat.; tr.lit.; index. circ. 1,000. (tabloid format) **Indexed:** Met.Abstr., World Alum.Abstr. **Document type:** directory.

669   BL
FUNDICAO E SERVICOS. 1990. bi-m. $80. Aranda Editora Ltda., Rua Dona Elisa 167, 01155-900 Sao Paulo SP, Brazil. TEL 55-11-826-4511. FAX 55-11-66-9585. Ed. Maria C. Bottura. circ. 8,000. (back issues avail.)

669   AG   ISSN 0429-8950
CODEN: FUNDBY
FUNDIDOR. 1957. 3/yr. free. Camara de Industriales Fundidores, Alsina 1607, 1088 Buenos Aires, Argentina. TEL 541-406840. FAX 541-8144407. adv.; B&W page Arg.$450; 160 x 230. bk.rev. circ. 3,000. **Indexed:** B.C.I.R.A., Chem.Abstr., Met.Abstr., World Alum.Abstr. **Document type:** trade publication.
—CASDDS.

669   SP   ISSN 1132-0362
FUNDIDORES. 1989. m. 12900 ptas.($149) Deltacad, Alcala 93, 4M, 28009 Madrid, Spain. TEL 341-576-5609. FAX 341-578-2924. adv. contact: Perez de Camino. circ. 2,500 (paid). **Document type:** trade publication.

669   AT
GALVANIZE. 1981. q. free. Galvanizers Association of Australia, 124 Exhibition St., Melbourne, Vic. 3000, Australia. TEL 613-654-1266. FAX 613-654-1136. Ed. G. Thomson. bk.rev. circ. 8,500.
Formerly (until 1981): Galvanizing Report.
Description: Data sheet on uses and performance of hot-dip galvanizing.

671.732   FR   ISSN 0982-7870
CODEN: GAOREN
GALVANO-ORGANO - TRAITEMENTS DE SURFACE. (Text in French; summaries in English) 1932. 10/yr. 525 F. (Societe Galvano) S.A.R.L. Galvano, 22-24 rue du President Wilson, 92532 Levallois-Perret Cedex, France. TEL 47-39-34-81. FAX 47-39-34-79. Ed. Isabelle Clin. adv.; bk.rev.; abstr.; bibl.; charts; illus.; index. circ. 4,500. **Indexed:** Art & Archaeol.Tech.Abstr., Cadscan, Chem.Abstr., Excerp.Med., INIS Atomind., Lead Abstr., Met.Abstr., W.R.C.Inf., World Alum.Abstr., Zincscan.
—BLDSC (4068.040000); CASDDS; SWETS.
Formed by the 1980 merger of: Galvano-Organo (ISSN 0302-6477); Which was formerly (until 1973): Galvano (ISSN 0016-4224); Traitements de Surface.

671.732   GW   ISSN 0016-4232
CODEN: GVTKAY
GALVANOTECHNIK. 1902. m. DM.60. Eugen G. Leuze Verlag, Karlstr. 4, 88348 Saulgau, Germany. TEL 07581-7617. FAX 07851-1756. Ed. Heinz Leuze. adv.; bk.rev.; abstr.; charts;illus.; pat.; stat.; index. **Indexed:** Chem.Abstr., Curr.Cont., Eng.Ind., Excerp.Med., INIS Atomind., INSPEC, Met.Abstr., World Alum.Abstr.
—BLDSC (4068.080000); CASDDS; Ei; SWETS. CCC.

671.732   IT   ISSN 1120-6454
CODEN: GNFIE8
GALVANOTECNICA E NUOVE FINITURE. 1950. bi-m. L.110000. Associazione Italiana Finiture dei Metalli, Via R. Fucini, 6, 20133 Milan, Italy. TEL 0332-312707. Ed. Eugenio Bertorelle. adv.; bk.rev.; abstr.; bibl.; illus.; index, cum.index: 1953-1987. circ. 25,000. **Indexed:** Chem.Abstr., Met.Abstr., World Alum.Abstr.
—CASDDS.
Former titles: Galvanotecnica e Processi al Plasma and Galvanotecnica; Galvanotecnica (ISSN 0016-4240)
Description: Electroplating, ion plating and new finishing.

669   CC   ISSN 0449-749X
TS300   CODEN: KATIAR
GANGTIE/IRON AND STEEL. (Text in Chinese) m. Yejin Gongye Chubanshe, 39 Songzhuyuan Beixiang, Shatan, Beijing 100009, People's Republic of China. TEL 4015782. Ed. Lu Da.
—BLDSC (4577.900000); CASDDS.

GEOLOGICAL, MINING AND METALLURGICAL SOCIETY OF INDIA. BULLETIN. see **EARTH SCIENCES — Geology**

GEOLOGY AND WORLD DEPOSITS. see **EARTH SCIENCES — Geology**

671.2   GW   ISSN 0016-9765
TS200   CODEN: GIESAS
GIESSEREI; Zeitschrift fuer das gesamte Giessereiwesen. (Contents page in English and French) 1914. s-m. DM.298. (Verein Deutscher Giessereifachleute e.V.) Giesserei-Verlag GmbH, Postfach 102532, 40016 Duesseldorf, Germany. TEL 0211-6707-0. adv.; bk.rev.; bibl.; charts; illus.; mkt.; pat.; index. circ. 4,300. (also avail. in microfilm from PMC) **Indexed:** B.C.I.R.A., C.I.S. Abstr., Chem.Abstr., Excerp.Med., INIS Atomind., ISMEC, Met.Abstr., Numis.Lit., PROMT, World Alum.Abstr. **Document type:** trade publication.
—BLDSC (4174.000000); CASDDS; Ei; Faxon; SWETS. CCC.

671.2   GW   ISSN 0016-9773
GIESSEREI - ERFAHRUNGSAUSTAUSCH. 1957. m. DM.26. Fachverlag Giesserei-Erfahrungsaustausch, Kleiststr. 10, 68542 Heddesheim, Germany. Ed. Max Schied. adv.; bk.rev. **Indexed:** Met.Abstr., World Alum.Abstr.

669   GW
DIE GIESSEREI-INDUSTRIE UND IHRE HELFER/FOUNDRY INDUSTRY AND ITS SUPPLIERS. 1952. a. $51. Industrieschau-Verlagsgesellschaft mbH, Berliner Allee 8, 64295 Darmstadt, Germany. TEL 06151-38920. FAX 06151-33164. (U.S. subscr. to: Western Hemisphere Publishing Corp., Box 847, Hillsboro, OR 97123-0847. TEL 503-640-3736. FAX 503-640-2748) Ed. Margit Selka. circ. 4,000. **Document type:** directory.
●Also available online.
Also available on CD-ROM.

669   GW   ISSN 0340-8175
GIESSEREI-KALENDER. 1954. a. (Verein Deutscher Giessereifachleute) Giesserei-Verlag GmbH, Postfach 102532, 40016 Duesseldorf, Germany. TEL 0211-6707-0. **Document type:** trade publication.

671.2   GW   ISSN 0016-9781
CODEN: GIPXAU
GIESSEREI-PRAXIS. 1950. s-m. DM.174. Fachverlag Schiele und Schoen GmbH, Markgrafenstr. 11, 10969 Berlin, Germany. TEL 030-253752-0. FAX 030-2517248. Ed. Dr. Roehrig. adv.; bk.rev.; abstr.; charts; illus.; mkt.; tr.lit.; index. circ. 4,000. **Indexed:** B.C.I.R.A., C.I.S. Abstr., Cadscan, Chem.Abstr., Eng.Ind., INIS Atomind., Lead Abstr., Met.Abstr., World Alum.Abstr., Zincscan. **Document type:** trade publication.
—CASDDS. CCC.

671.2   AU   ISSN 0016-979X
CODEN: GIERBQ
GIESSEREI RUNDSCHAU. 1954. 6/yr. S.612. (Verein Oesterreichischer Giessereifachleute) Verlag Lorenz, Ebendorferstr. 10, A-1010 Vienna, Austria. TEL 0222-426695. FAX 0222-438693. (Co-sponsor: Fachverband der Giessereiindustrie und des Oesterreichischen Giesserei Institutes) Ed. G. Kosicek. adv.; bk.rev.; bibl.; illus.; pat.; stat.; tr.lit. circ. 1,000. (tabloid format) **Indexed:** B.C.I.R.A., Chem.Abstr. **Document type:** trade publication.
—BLDSC (4175.050000); CASDDS.

671.2   GW   ISSN 0046-5933
CODEN: GSFGBY
GIESSEREIFORSCHUNG. (Text in German; contents page in English, French, and German) 1949. q. DM.308. (Verein Deutscher Giessereifachleute e.V.) Giesserei-Verlag GmbH, Postfach 102532, 40016 Duesseldorf, Germany. TEL 0211-6707-0. adv. **Indexed:** B.C.I.R.A., Chem.Abstr., Eng.Ind., INIS Atomind., Met.Abstr. **Document type:** trade publication.
—BLDSC (4175.090000); CASDDS; Ei; SWETS. CCC.

669   NE   ISSN 0167-9066
GIETWERK PERSPEKTIEF. Key Title: G P. Gietwerk Perspektief. 1967. bi-m. fl.110. (Dutch Foundry Organization (NVvGT)) Technische Uitgeverij de Vey Mestdagh BV, Markt 51, 4331 LK Middelburg, Netherlands. TEL 31-1180-81240. FAX 31-1180-81215. Ed. H. Nieswaag. adv. contact: W. van den Broek. bk.rev.; charts; illus.; circ. 1,000. (paid) **Indexed:** B.C.I.R.A., Chem.Abstr., Excerp.Med. **Document type:** trade publication.
—SWETS.
Former titles (until 1980): Gieterij (ISSN 0016-982X); Metalen en Andere Constructiematerialen (ISSN 0921-1586); Supersedes: Gieterijcentrumberichten.

GIJUTSU JOHO MIE. KIKAI KINZOKU HEN/TECHNICAL INFORMATION IN MIE PREFECTURE: MACHINE AND METAL SERIES. see **MACHINERY**

GIORNALE DEL FABBRO E DEL SERRAMENTISTA. see **CRIMINOLOGY AND LAW ENFORCEMENT — Security**

669   IT   ISSN 0392-3622
IL GIORNALE DELLA SUBFORNITURA. 1980. m. (11/yr.). L.75000 (foreign L.150000) (effective 1995). Stammer S.p.A., Via della Liberazione 1, 20068 Peschiera Borromeo (MI), Italy. TEL 02-55302606. FAX 02-55302700. Ed. Girolamo Bellina. adv.: B&W page L.1850000, color page L.2960000; trim 185 x 267. circ. 30,000.

GOLD NEWS/NOUVELLES DE L'OR. see **MINES AND MINING INDUSTRY**

669   US
GUIDE TO PRODUCTS AND SERVICES OF MEMBER COMPANIES. 1985. a. Titanium Development Association, 4141 Arapahoe Ave., Ste.100, Boulder, CO 80303. TEL 303-443-7515. FAX 303-443-4406. Ed. John Mousees. adv. circ. 1,500.
Formerly: Titanium Development Association. (Year) Buyer's Guide.
Description: Covers titanium companies, products, services.

669   CC   ISSN 1000-7563
GUOWAI NAIHUO CAILIAO. (Text in Chinese) m. Anshan Jiaohua Nanhuo Cailiao Sheji Yanjiuyuan, Qingbao Shi, 27, Shengli Lu, Anshan, Liaoning 114002, People's Republic of China. TEL 29738. Ed. Wang Jing'er.

669   GW   ISSN 0341-101X
CODEN: HTMMD5
HAERTEREI-TECHNISCHE MITTEILUNGEN; Zeitschrift fuer Waermebehandlung und Werkstofftechnik. Short title: H T M. 1941. bi-m. DM.389.40. (Arbeitsgemeinschaft Waermebehandlung und Werkstoff-Technik e.V.) Carl Hanser Verlag, Kolbergerstr. 22, 81679 Munich, Germany. TEL 089-998300. FAX 089-984809. (Subscr. to: Postfach 860420, 81631 Munich, Germany) Eds. Johann Grosch, Rudi Jonck. adv.; bibl.; charts; illus.; index. circ. 1,550. **Indexed:** Chem.Abstr., Eng.Ind., Met.Abstr., World Alum.Abstr. **Document type:** trade publication.
—BLDSC (4265.000000); CASDDS; Ei. CCC.

669.1 530   NE
HANDBOOK ON FERROMAGNETIC MATERIALS. Variant title: Handbook of Magnetic Materials. 1980. irreg., vol.7, 1993. price varies. Elsevier Science B.V., Books Division, P.O. Box 211, 1000 AE Amsterdam, Netherlands. TEL 31-20-4853911. FAX 31-20-4853705. TELEX 18582 ESPA NL. E-mail: nlinfo-f@elsevier.nl; usinfo-f@elsevier.com; forinfo-kyf04035@niftyserve.or.jp; Site addr.: http://www.elsevier.nl/. (Subscr. in U.S. and Canada to: Elsevier Science Inc., Box 882, Madison Sq. Sta., New York, NY 10159. TEL 212-989-5800) Eds. E.P. Wohlfarth, K.H.J. Buschow. **Document type:** monographic series.
Refereed Serial

HANDBOOK ON THE PHYSICS AND CHEMISTRY OF RARE EARTHS. see **PHYSICS**

METALLURGY

669 US
HEAT PROCESSING DIGEST. 1974. m. $175 to non-members (foreign $195); members $145 (foreign $160). A S M International, Materials Information, Materials Park, OH 44073. TEL 216-338-5151. FAX 216-338-4634. TELEX 980-619. (UK addr.: Institute of Materials, Materials Information, 1 Carlton House Terrace, London SW1Y 5DB, England. TEL 071-839-4071) Eds. M. Stephen Chang, Michael P. Finical. (reprint service avail. from UMI) **Indexed:** Met.Abstr. **Document type:** abstracting/indexing.
Description: Digest of materials information for heat processing.

669 US
HEAT TREATERS CERTIFICATION MANUAL. a. $69. Metal Treating Institute, 302 Third St., Ste. 1, Neptune Beach, FL 32266. TEL 904-249-0448. FAX 904-249-0459.

669 UK **ISSN 0305-4829**
TN672 **CODEN: HTRMBS**
HEAT TREATMENT OF METALS. 1974. q. £85.50 (foreign £93) to individuals; educational institutions £73(foreign £78). Wolfson Heat Treatment Centre, Aston University, Aston Triangle, Birmingham B4 7ET, England. TEL 0121-359-3611. FAX 0121-359-8910. E-mail: wolfson_heat_treatment_centre@aston.ac.uk. Ed. A.J. Hick. adv. contact: Derek Close. bk.rev.; index. circ. 1,000. (back issues avail.) **Indexed:** B.C.I.R.A., Cadscan, Chem.Abstr., Curr.Cont., INSPEC, Lead Abstr., Met.Abstr., Risk Abstr., World Alum.Abstr., Zincscan. **Document type:** trade publication.
—BLDSC (4276.370000); CASDDS; Ei; Faxon; Genuine Article; SWETS.
Description: Devoted to industrial heat treatment practice and innovation.

HEPHAISTOS; internationale Zeitschrift fuer Metallgestalter. see *ART*

HIGH - TC UPDATE. see *PHYSICS*

669 UK **ISSN 0142-3304**
CODEN: HIMED6
HISTORICAL METALLURGY. 1963. s-a. £15. Historical Metallurgy Society Ltd., Rock House, Bowens Hill, Coleford, Glos. GL16 8DH, England. TEL 01594-833778. Eds. Justine Bayley. adv.; bk.rev.; cum.index: vols.1-7, vols.8-18. circ. 500. **Indexed:** Art & Archaeol.Tech.Abstr., B.C.I.R.A., Br.Archaeol.Abstr., Chem.Abstr., Met.Abstr., Numis.Lit., World Alum.Abstr. **Document type:** academic/scholarly publication.
—BLDSC (4758.360000); CASDDS; Faxon; UnCover.
Formerly: Historical Metallurgy Group. Bulletin.
Description: Covers metallurgy from prehistoric times to the present.
Refereed Serial

669 UK
HISTORICAL METALLURGY SOCIETY. NEWSLETTER. 3/yr. Historical Metallurgy Society Ltd., Rock House, Bowens Hill, Coleford, Glos. GL16 8DH, England. TEL 01594-833778. E-mail: j.bayley@eng-h.gov.uk. Ed. Justine Bayley. **Document type:** newsletter.

HOME SHOP MACHINIST; dedicated to precision metalworking. see *MACHINERY*

671.2 FR **ISSN 0018-4357**
CODEN: HFONDM
HOMMES ET FONDERIE. 1970. m. (10/yr.). 520 F. (foreign 640 F.) (effective 1996). (Association Technique de Fonderie) P Y C Edition, B.P. 105, 5, av. de Verdun, 94208 Ivry sur Seine Cedex, France. TEL 1-49-60-86-36. FAX 1-46-72-41-85. Ed. Regis Fouques-Duparc. adv.; illus. circ. 3,139. **Indexed:** B.C.I.R.A., Met.Abstr., World Alum.Abstr.
—BLDSC (4326.265000); CASDDS. CCC.
Formed by the merger of: Technicien de Fonderie & Association Technique de Fonderie. Bulletin Mensuel d'Information.

HOOGOVENS GROEP BULLETIN. see *ENGINEERING*

HUAGONG YEJIN/JOURNAL OF ENGINEERING CHEMISTRY AND METALLURGY. see *ENGINEERING — Chemical Engineering*

669 XR **ISSN 0018-8069**
TN4 **CODEN: HUTLA7**
HUTNICKE LISTY. English translation: Metallurgical Journal (UK ISSN 0951-0869) (Text in Czech; summaries in English, French, German, Russian) 1945. m. $65.70. Ocelot, spol. s r.o., Politickych Veznu 14, P.O. Box 751, 111 21 Prague 1, Czech Republic. (Dist. by: Artia, Ve Smeckach 30, 111 27 Prague 1, Czech Republic) Ed. Pavel Haase. adv.; bk.rev.; charts; illus.; pat.; tr.lit.; index. circ. 2,900. **Indexed:** Anal.Abstr., Art & Archaeol.Tech.Abstr., C.I.S. Abstr., Cadscan, Chem.Abstr., Eng.Ind., INIS Atomind., Lead Abstr., Met.Abstr., World Alum.Abstr., Zincscan.
—BLDSC (4338.000000); CASDDS.
Incorporates (1950-1991): Hutnik (ISSN 0438-2757)

671.2 PL **ISSN 1230-3534**
TS200 **CODEN: HWHUEQ**
HUTNIK - WIADOMOSCI HUTNICZE. (Text in Polish; summaries in English, German, Russian) 1992. m. $82. (Stowarzyszenie Inzynierow i Technikow Przemyslu Hutniczego w Polsce) Wydawnictwo Czasopism i Ksiazek Technicznych SIGMA - NOT, Ul. Ratuszowa 11, P.O. Box 1004, 00-950 Warsaw, Poland. TEL 48-22-180918. FAX 48-22-192187. TELEX 814550 SIGMA PL. (Dist. by: Zaklad Kolportazu SIGMA-NOT, ul. Bartycka 20, 00-950 Warsaw, Poland) Ed. Remigiusz Sosnowski. adv.; B&W page $1000. bk.rev.; abstr.; illus.; index. circ. 500. **Indexed:** Ceram.Abstr., Chem.Abstr., Eng.Ind., Met.Abstr., World Alum.Abstr.
—CASDDS; SWETS.
Formed by the merger of (1929-1992): Hutnik (ISSN 0018-8077); (1945-1992): Wiadomosci Hutnicze (ISSN 0043-5139)
Description: Covers steel production.

669 NE **ISSN 0304-386X**
TN688 **CODEN: HYDRDA**
HYDROMETALLURGY; international journal devoted to all aspects of the aqueous processing of metals. (Text in English) 1975. 9/yr. fl.1650($1006) (effective 1996). Elsevier Science B.V., P.O. Box 211, 1000 AE Amsterdam, Netherlands. TEL 31-20-4853911. FAX 31-20-4853598. TELEX 18582 ESPA NL. E-mail: nlinfo-f@elsevier.nl; usinfo-f@elsevier.com; forinfo-kyf04035@niftyserve.or.jp; Site addr.: http://www.elsevier.nl/. (Subscr. in U.S. and Canada to: Elsevier Science Inc., Box 882, Madison Sq. Sta., New York, NY 10159. TEL 212-989-5800. FAX 212-633-3990) Eds. G.M. Ritcey, M.J. Slater. adv.; bk.rev.; charts; illus.; index. (also avail. in microform from UMI) **Indexed:** AESIS, Cadscan, Chem.Abstr., Chem.Eng.Abstr., Copper Abstr., Curr.Cont., Eng.Ind., Ind.Sci.Rev., Lead Abstr., Met.Abstr., Sci.Cit.Ind., Soils & Fert., T.C.E.A., World Alum.Abstr., Zincscan. **Document type:** academic/scholarly publication.
—BLDSC (4352.153000); CASDDS; Ei; Faxon; Genuine Article; SWETS; UnCover. CCC.
Description: Brings together studies on novel processes, process design, chemistry, modelling, control, economics and interfaces between unit operations, and provides a forum for discussions on case histories and operational difficulties.
Refereed Serial

671.3 SZ
I M F NEWS. 1972. fortn. free. International Metalworkers Federation, 54 bis, Rte. des Acacias, CH-1227 Geneva, Switzerland. FAX 022-3431510. TELEX 423298-METL-CH.

I M I MONITOR. see *BUSINESS AND ECONOMICS — Labor And Industrial Relations*

669 739.27 US
I M R SOURCEBOOK UPDATE. q. Institute of Metal Repair, 1558 S. Redwood St., Escondido, CA 92025. TEL 619-747-5978. adv. **Document type:** newsletter.

669.1 JA **ISSN 0915-1559**
TS300 **CODEN: IINTEY**
I S I J INTERNATIONAL. (Text in English) 1961. m. 52000 Yen to non-members (effective 1995). Iron and Steel Institute of Japan - Nippon Tekko Kyokai, Keidanren Kaikan, 3rd Fl., 9-4, Otemachi 1-chome, Chiyoda-ku, Tokyo 100, Japan. TEL 03-3279-6021. FAX 03-3245-1355. TELEX 02228153-ISIJTK-J. Ed. Nobuo Sano. adv.; abstr.; bibl.; charts; illus.; stat.; index, cum.index. circ. 5,000. (also avail. in microfilm; back issues avail.) **Indexed:** Chem.Abstr., Corros.Abstr., Curr.Cont., Eng.Ind., JCT, JTA, Met.Abstr., World Alum.Abstr. **Document type:** academic/scholarly publication.
—BLDSC (4582.963000); CASDDS; Ei; Faxon; Genuine Article; SWETS. CCC.
Formerly: Iron and Steel Institute of Japan. Transactions (ISSN 0021-1583); *Supersedes:* Tetsu-To-Hagane Overseas.
Description: Provides the core subject matter of iron and steel worldwide. Intended for those concerned with the processing, structure, property, and application of engineering materials.

669.142 690 UK
I S T C PHOENIX. Short title: Phoenix. 1980. 4/yr. free. Iron and Steel Trades Confederation, Swinton House, 324 Gray's Inn Rd., London WC1 8DD, England. FAX 01-278-8378. Ed. Len Powell. adv.; illus. circ. 40,000.
Former titles: I S T C Banner (ISSN 0260-0625); Steelworker's Banner.

IBARAKIKEN KOGYO GIJUTSU JOHO. KIKAI KENZOKU HEN/IBARAKI PREFECTURE INDUSTRIAL RESEARCH INFORMATION: MACHINE AND METAL SECTION. see *MACHINERY*

671.2 II **ISSN 0379-5446**
CODEN: IFOJAI
INDIAN FOUNDRY JOURNAL. (Text in English) 1956. m. $50 for Bangladesh, Nepal & Maldives; elsewhere $80 (effective Jan. 1995). Institute of Indian Foundrymen, Middleton Court, 1st Floor, 4-2 Middleton St., Calcutta 700071, W. Bengal, India. TEL 91-33-403210. FAX 91-33-406498. TELEX 021-5166-IIF-IN. Ed. P.N. Chakraborty. adv.; bk.rev.; film rev.; abstr.; bibl.; charts; illus.; pat.; stat. circ. 3,500. **Indexed:** B.C.I.R.A., Cadscan, Chem.Abstr., Lead Abstr., Met.Abstr., World Alum.Abstr., Zincscan.
—BLDSC (4409.300000); CASDDS.

669 II
INDIAN INSTITUTE OF METALS. PROCEEDINGS. irreg. Indian Institute of Metals, A-1 Flat, 15th Fl. Chatterjee International Centre, 33A Chowringhee Rd., Calcutta 700 071, India. Ed. P. Rodriguez. circ. 5,000. **Indexed:** Chem.Abstr. **Document type:** proceedings.

669 II **ISSN 0019-493X**
TN4 **CODEN: TIIMA3**
INDIAN INSTITUTE OF METALS. TRANSACTIONS. (Text in English) 1946. bi-m. Rs.150. Indian Institute of Metals, 2 Sambhunath Pandit St., Calcutta 700020, India. Ed. P. Rodriguez. adv.; bk.rev.; charts; illus.; index, cum.index covering 5 yrs. circ. 4,000. **Indexed:** Art & Archaeol.Tech.Abstr., Curr.Cont., Energy Ind., Energy Info.Abstr., Eng.Ind., Fuel & Energy Abstr., INSPEC (1981-), Met.Abstr., World Alum.Abstr.
—BLDSC (8939.000000); CASDDS; Ei; Faxon; Genuine Article; UMI.

INDIAN JOURNAL OF GEOLOGY. see *EARTH SCIENCES — Geology*

669.1 MX **ISSN 0188-4301**
INDUSTRIA SIDERURGICA EN MEXICO. 1981. a. Mex.$5($11) Instituto Nacional de Estadistica, Geografia e Informatica, Secretaria de Programacion y Presupuesto, Prol. Heroe de Nacozari, 2301, Sur, Puerta 11, Acceso, 20270 Aguascalientes, Ags., Mexico. TEL 91-49-18-19-48. FAX 91-491-80739. circ. 2,000.

INDUSTRIAL HEATING. see *ENGINEERING — Industrial Engineering*

669 US
INFOMET. (Supplement to: World Industrial Reporter) (Editions in English, Spanish) 6/yr. Keller International Publishing Corporation, 150 Great Neck Rd., Great Neck, NY 11021. TEL 516-829-9210. FAX 516-829-5414. TELEX 221547 KELLE. circ. 60,061 (30,041 English ed.; 30,020 Spanish ed.). **Document type:** trade publication.

669.722 CN ISSN 0707-8013
INGOT. (Text in French) 1936. fortn. free. Alcan Smelters and Chemicals Ltd., Box 1370, Jonquiere, Que. G7S 4K9, Canada. TEL 418-548-1121. Ed. Raymond Arcand. circ. 15,000. (tabloid format) **Indexed:** Met.Abstr., World Alum.Abstr.
 Formerly: Kitimat-Kemano Ingot.

INORGANIC MATERIALS. see *CHEMISTRY — Inorganic Chemistry*

620.112 UK ISSN 1354-2575
TA417.2 CODEN: ITMOEN
INSIGHT (NORTHAMPTON); non-destructive testing and condition monitoring. m. £80 (rest of Europe £105 ($185); elsewhere £155 ($260)) (effective 1995). British Institute of Non-Destructive Testing, 1 Spencer Parade, Northampton NN1 5AA, England. TEL 01604-30124. FAX 01604-231489. Ed. David E. Gilbert; Pub. Matt E. Gallagher. adv. contact: David E. Gilbert. bk.rev.; bibl.; charts; illus.; index. circ. 3,000. (also avail. in microform from UMI; back issues avail.; reprint service avail. from UMI) **Indexed:** Appl.Mech.Rev., B.C.I.R.A., Br.Tech.Ind., Chem.Abstr., Eng.Ind., Fuel & Energy Abstr., INIS Atomind., INSPEC (1968-), ISMEC, Met.Abstr., World Alum.Abstr. **Document type:** academic/scholarly publication.
 —BLDSC (4518.176100); CASDDS; Ei; Faxon; Genuine Article; SWETS; UMI; UnCover.
 Formed by the merger of (1959-1994): British Journal of Non-Destructive Testing (ISSN 0007-1137); (1991-1994): European Journal of Non-Destructive Testing (ISSN 0957-767X)
 Refereed Serial

669 UK ISSN 0020-2967
CODEN: TIMFA2
INSTITUTE OF METAL FINISHING. TRANSACTIONS. 1951. bi-m. £136 (foreign £139) (effective 1996). Institute of Metal Finishing, Exeter House, 48 Holloway Head, Birmingham B1 1NQ, England. TEL 0121-622-7387. FAX 0121-666-6316. Ed. Peter Farr. adv. contact: Clive Larson. bk.rev.; abstr.; charts; illus. circ. 2,250. **Indexed:** C.I.S. Abstr., Chem.Abstr., Copper Abstr., Excerp.Med., INSPEC, Met.Abstr., World Alum.Abstr., World Surf.Coat. **Document type:** academic/scholarly publication.
 —BLDSC (8941.000000); CASDDS; Ei; Faxon; Genuine Article; SWETS; UnCover.
 Refereed Serial

669 AT
INSTITUTE OF METALS AND MATERIALS AUSTRALASIA. PROCEEDINGS. 1947. a. price varies. Institute of Metals and Materials Australasia Ltd., P.O. Box 19, Parkville, Vic. 3052, Australia. TEL 03-347-2544. FAX 03-348-1208. Ed. R. Nethercott. bibl.; charts; illus. circ. 300. **Indexed:** Met.Abstr. **Document type:** proceedings.
 Former titles: Australasian Institute of Metals. Proceedings of the Annual Conference; Australian Institute of Metals. Proceedings of the Annual Conference.

669 SW ISSN 0015-7953
INSTITUTET FOER METALLFORSKNING. FORSKNINGSVERKSAMHETEN. 1952. a. free. Institutet foer Metallforskning - Swedish Institute for Metals Research, Drottning Kristinas Vaeg 48, S-114 28 Stockholm, Sweden. FAX 46-8-723-0423. Ed. Rune Lagneborg. bibl.; illus. circ. 2,400. **Document type:** corporate report.

669 II ISSN 0257-4411
TN1 CODEN: JIMDEQ
INSTITUTION OF ENGINEERS (INDIA). METALLURGY & MATERIAL SCIENCE DIVISION. JOURNAL. (Text in English) 1983. s-a. Rs.40($5) Institution of Engineers (India), Metallurgy & Material Science Division, 8 Gokhale Rd., Calcutta 700 020, India. TEL 033-288334. FAX 033-288345. TELEX 0217885 IEIC IN. Ed. S.P. Misra. adv.; charts; illus.; index. circ. 3,500. **Indexed:** INSPEC (1985-). **Document type:** academic/scholarly publication.
 —BLDSC (4794.039500); CASDDS; Ei.

INSTITUTION OF ENGINEERS (INDIA). MINING ENGINEERING DIVISION. JOURNAL. see *MINES AND MINING INDUSTRY*

INSTITUTION OF MINING AND METALLURGY. TRANSACTIONS. SECTION A: MINING INDUSTRY. see *MINES AND MINING INDUSTRY*

INSTITUTION OF MINING AND METALLURGY. TRANSACTIONS. SECTION B: APPLIED EARTH SCIENCE. see *MINES AND MINING INDUSTRY*

INSTITUTION OF MINING AND METALLURGY. TRANSACTIONS. SECTION C: MINERAL PROCESSING & EXTRACTIVE METALLURGY. see *MINES AND MINING INDUSTRY*

669 US ISSN 0361-3070
TN153 CODEN: IMIDBK
INSTRUMENTATION IN THE MINING AND METALLURGY INDUSTRIES. 1975. irreg. price varies. Instrument Society of America, 67 Alexander Dr., Box 12277, Research Triangle Park, NC 27709. TEL 919-549-8411. FAX 919-549-8288. TELEX 802540 ISA DURM. (reprint service avail. from ISI,UMI) **Indexed:** Chem.Abstr., INIS Atomind., INSPEC. **Document type:** proceedings.
 —CASDDS. CCC.
 Formerly: I S A Mining and Metallurgy Instrumentation Symposium. Proceedings.
 Refereed Serial

669 PL ISSN 0137-9941
TN4 CODEN: PIMZDL
INSTYTUT METALURGII ZELAZA. PRACE/INSTITUTE OF FERROUS METALLURGY. TRANSACTIONS. (Text in Polish; summaries in English and Russian) 1949. q. $120 (effective 1995 & 1996). Instytut Metalurgii Zelaza, Ul. K. Miarki 12, 44-100 Gliwice, Poland. TEL 48-32-314051. FAX 48-32-313594. TELEX 036363 IMZ PL. E-mail: inmetzel@zeus.polsl.gliwicw.pl. Ed. Edward Barszcz. circ. 400. **Indexed:** Chem.Abstr., Met.Abstr., Ref.Zh. **Document type:** academic/scholarly publication.
 —CASDDS; Ei.
 Description: Covers production of iron and steel and further processing of steel.
 Refereed Serial

540 620.1 UK ISSN 0966-9795
TN689 CODEN: IERME5
INTERMETALLICS. 1993. 8/yr. £390($621) (effective 1996). Elsevier Science Ltd., P.O. Box 800, Kidlington, Oxford OX5 1DX, England. TEL 44-1865-843000. FAX 44-1865-843010. E-mail: nlinfo-f@elsevier.nl; usinfo-f@elsevier.com; forinfo-kyf04035@niftyserve.or.jp; Site addr.: http://www.elsevier.nl/. (Subscr. in U.S. and Canada to: Elsevier Science, 660 White Plains Rd., Tarrytown, NY 10591-5153. TEL 914-524-9200. FAX 914-333-2444) Ed.Bd. adv.; bk.rev.; abstr.; index. (also avail. in microform from UMI; back issues avail.) **Document type:** academic/scholarly publication.
 —BLDSC (4534.562000); CASDDS; Faxon; Genuine Article; SWETS. CCC.
 Description: Covers all aspects of ordered chemical compounds between two or more metals, including fundamental chemistry, microstructure, dynamics and stress as well as applications in processing and synthesis, multiphase intermetallic alloys in dentistry, and applications of hard magnetic materials incorporating rare earth metals.
 Refereed Serial

669.4 UK ISSN 0074-316X
TA480.L4 CODEN: ICLPAY
INTERNATIONAL CONFERENCE ON LEAD. PROCEEDINGS. 1962. triennial, 11th, 1993, Venice. Lead Development Association, 42 Weymouth St., London W1N 3LQ, England. TEL 01-499-8422. FAX 01-493-1555. Ed. D.N. Wilson. circ. 1,000. **Document type:** proceedings.
 —CASDDS.

620.112 CN ISSN 0074-4123
INTERNATIONAL CONGRESS ON METALLIC CORROSION. (PROCEEDINGS). (Proceedings published by host country) 1961. triennial, 10th, 1987. DM.250. (International Corrosion Council) National Research Council of Canada, Publication Sales and Distribution, Ottawa, Ontario K1A 0R6, Canada.
 —CCC.

669 692.1 US ISSN 0074-6118
INTERNATIONAL FOUNDRY CONGRESS. PAPERS AND COMMUNICATIONS. (Papers published in host countries) a. price varies. c/o American Foundrymen's Society, 505 State St., Des Plaines, IL 60016. TEL 708-824-0181. FAX 708-824-7848. **Indexed:** Chem.Abstr.
 Formerly: World Foundry Congress.

338.2 672 BE ISSN 0074-6630
INTERNATIONAL IRON AND STEEL INSTITUTE. REPORT OF CONFERENCE PROCEEDINGS. 1967. a. 2000 BEF. International Iron and Steel Institute, Rue Colonel Bourg 120, B-1140 Brussels, Belgium. TEL 32-2-7265095. FAX 32-2-7264012. TELEX 22639. charts; illus.; stat. **Document type:** proceedings.
 Description: Includes a verbatim record of the proceedings as well as the question and answer periods of the annual conference.

INTERNATIONAL JOURNAL OF MINERAL PROCESSING. see *MINES AND MINING INDUSTRY*

669 US ISSN 0888-7462
TN695 CODEN: IPMTEA
INTERNATIONAL JOURNAL OF POWDER METALLURGY. 1965. q. $150 (foreign $170) (effective 1996). American Powder Metallurgy Institute, 105 College Rd. E., Princeton, NJ 08540. TEL 609-452-7700. FAX 609-987-8523. Ed. Dr. Alan Lawley. adv.; bk.rev.; abstr.; charts; stat.; index. circ. 3,300. (also avail. in microform from UMI; reprint service avail. from UMI) **Indexed:** A.S.& T.Ind., Cadscan, Chem.Abstr., Copper Abstr., Curr.Cont.; Ind.Sci.Rev., Int.Aerosp.Abstr., Lead Abstr., Met.Abstr., Sci.Cit.Ind., World Alum.Abstr., Zincscan. **Document type:** academic/scholarly publication.
 —BLDSC (4542.477000); CASDDS; Ei; Faxon; Genuine Article; SWETS; UMI; UnCover. CCC.
 Former titles: International Journal of Powder Metallurgy and Powder Technology (ISSN 0361-3488); International Journal of Powder Metallurgy (ISSN 0020-7535)

669 621 UK ISSN 0265-0916
CODEN: IJRSEO
INTERNATIONAL JOURNAL OF RAPID SOLIDIFICATION. 1984. 4/yr. £109($198) A B Academic Publishers, P.O. Box 42, Bicester, Oxon. OX6 7NW, England. TEL 0869-320949. Ed. Howard Jones. **Indexed:** INSPEC (1985-). **Document type:** academic/scholarly publication.
 —BLDSC (4542.525200); CASDDS; Ei; Faxon; SWETS; UnCover.
 Description: Covers science and technology of rapid solidification and allied processes and the formation, structure, properties, and application of its products.

669 UK ISSN 0958-0611
CODEN: IRMME3
INTERNATIONAL JOURNAL OF REFRACTORY METALS AND HARD MATERIALS. 1982. bi-m. £250($398) (effective 1996). (International Plansee Society for Powder Metallurgy) Elsevier Science Ltd., P.O. Box 800, Kidlington, Oxford OX5 1DX, England. TEL 44-1865-843000. FAX 44-1865-843010. E-mail: nlinfo-f@elsevier.nl; usinfo-f@elsevier.com; forinfo-kyf04035@niftyserve.or.jp; Site addr.: http://www.elsevier.nl/. (Subscr. in U.S. and Canada to: Elsevier Science, 660 White Plains Rd., Tarrytown, NY 10591-5153. TEL 914-524-9200. FAX 914-333-2444) Ed. B. Lux. adv. (also avail. in microform from UMI) **Indexed:** Chem.Abstr., INSPEC, Int.Aerosp.Abstr., Met.Abstr., World Alum.Abstr. **Document type:** academic/scholarly publication.
 —BLDSC (4542.525420); CASDDS; Ei; Faxon; Genuine Article; SWETS. CCC.
 Formerly (until 1989): International Journal of Refractory and Hard Metals (ISSN 0263-4368)
 Refereed Serial

INTERNATIONAL JOURNAL OF SELF-PROPAGATING HIGH-TEMPERATURE SYNTHESIS. see *PHYSICS — Heat*

INTERNATIONAL JOURNAL OF SURFACE MINING, RECLAMATION AND ENVIRONMENT. see *MINES AND MINING INDUSTRY*

METALLURGY

671 US ISSN 0161-5769
TN799.M2
INTERNATIONAL MAGNESIUM ASSOCIATION. WORLD MAGNESIUM CONFERENCE. PROCEEDINGS. 1943. a. $80. International Magnesium Association, 1303 Vincent Pl., No. 1, McLean, VA 22101-2615. TEL 703-442-8888. FAX 703-821-1824. TELEX 710-733-0313. circ. 500. (back issues avail.) **Document type:** proceedings.

669 US
INTERNATIONAL MAGNESIUM ASSOCIATION BUYERS GUIDE. 1990. biennial. $40. International Magnesium Association, 1303 Vincent Pl., No. 1, McLean, VA 22101. TEL 703-442-8888. FAX 703-821-1824. circ. 500. **Document type:** directory.
Description: Lists companies offering metallic magnesium products and services.

669 US ISSN 0950-6608
TN1 CODEN: INMREO
INTERNATIONAL MATERIALS REVIEW. 1956. 6/yr. £198($397) to non-members; members £97 ($178). A S M International, Materials Information, Materials Park, OH 44073-0002. FAX 216-338-4634. TELEX 98-0619 ASMINT. Ed. Mary Chim. bk.rev.; charts; illus.; cum.index: 1976-1986. circ. 1,200. (back issues avail.) **Indexed:** ABTICS, B.C.I.R.A., Deep Sea Res.& Oceanogr.Abstr., Excerp.Med., Ind.Sci.Rev., INSPEC, Int.Aerosp.Abstr., Met.Abstr., World Alum.Abstr. **Document type:** academic/scholarly publication.
—BLDSC (4543.995000); CASDDS; Ei; Faxon; Genuine Article; SWETS. **CCC.**
Former titles (until 1987): International Metals Review (ISSN 0308-4590); International Metallurgical Reviews; Metallurgical Reviews (ISSN 0076-6690)
Description: Critical reviews on specific topics covering all aspects of metals and alloys.

671.3 SZ ISSN 0074-6983
INTERNATIONAL METALWORKERS' CONGRESS. REPORTS. quadrennial, 27th, 1989, Copenhagen, Denmark. $10. International Metalworkers' Federation, 54 bis, Rte. des Acacias, 1227 Geneva, Switzerland. FAX 022-3431510. TELEX 423298-METL-CH.

INTERNATIONAL PRESS CUTTING SERVICE: MACHINE TOOL AND IRON STEEL INDUSTRY. see *MACHINERY*

669.722 II ISSN 0047-1011
INTERNATIONAL PRESS CUTTING SERVICE: NON-FERROUS METALS - ALUMINIUM. 1967. w. $65. International Press Cutting Service, Box 63, Allahabad 211001, India. Ed. N. Khanna. bk.rev.; index. circ. 1,200. (processed)

669 US
INTERNATIONAL SCRAP DIRECTORY. 1976. irreg. $199. Metal Bulletin Inc., 220 Fifth Ave., New York, NY 10001-7781. TEL 212-213-6202. FAX 212-213-1870. Ed.Bd. **Document type:** directory.
Supersedes: European and North American Scrap Directory (ISSN 0261-426X); **Formerly:** European Scrap Directory (ISSN 0308-7786)
Description: International directory of companies engaged in trading and physical processing of iron and steel and non-ferrous scrap metals.

669.6 UK
INTERNATIONAL TIN COUNCIL. MONTHLY STATISTICAL SUMMARY. m. £4 per no. International Tin Council, 1 Oxendon St., London SW1Y 4EQ, England.
Description: Covers the production and consumption of tin.

669.6 UK
INTERNATIONAL TIN RESEARCH INSTITUTE. ANNUAL REPORT. 1938. a. free. International Tin Research Institute, Kingston Lane, Uxbridge, Mddsx. UB8 3PJ, England. TEL 0895-272406. (Subscr. in U.S.: Tin Information Center of North America, 1353 Perry St., Columbus, OH 43201. TEL 614-424-6200) circ. 5,000. **Indexed:** IIS, Met.Abstr., World Alum.Abstr.
—BLDSC (1311.920000).
Formerly: International Tin Research Council. Annual Report (ISSN 0074-9125)

699.1 US ISSN 0897-4365
HD9506.U6
IRON AGE; the management magazine for metal producers. 1867-1993. m. $55. Hitchcock Publishing (Subsidiary of: Capital Cities - A B C, Inc.), 191 S. Gary Ave., Carol Stream, IL 60188. TEL 708-462-4641. FAX 708-462-2205. (Subscr. to: Box 3038, Southeastern, PA 19398-9862) Ed. Anne Armel. adv.; circ. 24,000 (controlled). (also avail. in microform from PMC; reprint service avail. from UMI) **Indexed:** A.S.& T.Ind., ABI Inform., Met.Abstr., SRI (until 1993), Tr.& Indus.Ind.
●Also available online. Vendor(s): Knight-Ridder, Inc.
—Ei; Faxon; SWETS; UMI; UnCover. **CCC.**
Former titles (until 1987): Iron Age. Metals Producers (ISSN 0893-9616); (until 1986): Chilton's Iron Age: Metals Producer (ISSN 0747-6329); Which superseded in part (in 1984) and continued numbering of: Chilton's Iron Age (ISSN 0164-5137); Which was formerly (until 1976): Iron Age (ISSN 0021-1508).

669.1 US ISSN 0021-1559
TS300 CODEN: IRSEA5
IRON AND STEEL ENGINEER. 1924. m. $50. Association of Iron and Steel Engineers, Three Gateway Center, Ste. 2350, Pittsburgh, PA 15222. TEL 412-281-6323. Ed. Dennis J. Fuga. adv.; bk.rev.; charts; illus.; tr.lit.; index. circ. 12,000. (also avail. in microform from UMI; reprint service avail. from UMI) **Indexed:** A.S.& T.Ind., Appl.Mech.Rev., Br.Ceram.Abstr., Cadscan, Chem.Abstr., Eng.Ind., Excerp.Med., Fuel & Energy Abstr., Ind.Sci.Rev., INSPEC, ISMEC, Lead Abstr., Met.Abstr., World Alum.Abstr., Zincscan.
—BLDSC (4580.000000); CASDDS; Ei; Faxon; SWETS; UMI; UnCover.

669 UK
IRON AND STEEL INTERNATIONAL (REDHILL). a. (issued Mar.). £78.90($126.25) Argus Business Media Ltd., Fuel and Metals Journals (Subsidiary of: Argus Press Group), Queensway House, 2 Queensway, Redhill, Surrey RH1 1QS, England. TEL 01737-768611. FAX 01737-761685. TELEX 948669 TOPJNL G. **Document type:** directory.
Description: Contains reference information for iron- and steelmakers worldwide, in addition to a listing of plants and services.

669.1 II ISSN 0021-1613
TS304.I4
IRON & STEEL JOURNAL OF INDIA. (Text in English) 1957. m. $50. Wadhera Publications, General Assurance Bldg., 232 Dr. D.N. Rd., Bombay 400 001, India. Ed. Roshanlal Wadhera. adv.; bk.rev.; illus.; pat.; stat.; tr.lit. circ. 7,800.
Former titles: Iron; Steel; Hardware Journal of India.

669.1 US ISSN 1075-878X
CODEN: MWSPEJ
IRON & STEEL SOCIETY. MECHANICAL WORKING AND STEEL PROCESSING CONFERENCE PROCEEDINGS. 1964. a., 32nd ed., 1994. $110 to non-members; members $55. Iron & Steel Society, 410 Commonwealth Dr., Warrendale, PA 15086-7512. TEL 412-776-9535. FAX 412-776-0430. (also avail. in microform from UMI; back issues avail.) **Document type:** proceedings.
—BLDSC (5420.500000); CASDDS; Ei.
Formerly: Mechanical Working and Steel Processing (ISSN 0147-7781)

669.1 US ISSN 1075-8607
TN701.5 CODEN: PTECEO
IRON & STEEL SOCIETY. PROCESS TECHNOLOGY CONFERENCE PROCEEDINGS. 1981. a., 12th ed., 1993. $90 to non-members; members $45. Iron & Steel Society, 410 Commonwealth Dr., Warrendale, PA 15086-7512. TEL 412-776-9535. FAX 412-776-0430. (also avail. in microform from UMI; back issues avail.) **Document type:** proceedings.
—CASDDS.
Description: For iron and steel makers.

669.1 US ISSN 1051-0508
TS300 CODEN: TISSE7
IRON & STEEL SOCIETY. TRANSACTIONS. 1982. a., 16th ed., 1995. $55 to non-members; members $30. Iron and Steel Society, 410 Commonwealth Dr., Warrendale, PA 15086-7512. TEL 412-776-9535. FAX 412-776-0430. (back issues avail.) **Document type:** academic/scholarly publication.
—BLDSC (8973.470000); CASDDS; Ei; UnCover.
Formerly (until 1984): Iron and Steel Society of the A I M E. Transactions (ISSN 0737-0059)
Description: For iron and steel workers.

669.1 US ISSN 0075-0875
IRON AND STEEL WORKS OF THE WORLD. 1952. quadrennial, 11th ed., 1994. $322. Metal Bulletin Inc., 220 Fifth Ave., New York, NY 10001-7781. TEL 212-213-6202. FAX 212-213-1870. Ed.Bd. adv. **Document type:** directory.
—BLDSC (4580.405700).
Description: Information on major iron and steel producers.

672 622 US ISSN 0275-8687
TS300 CODEN: IRSTDJ
IRON & STEELMAKER. 1974. m. $55 (outside N. America $65). Iron & Steel Society, 410 Commonwealth Dr., Warrendale, PA 15086-7512. TEL 412-776-9535. FAX 412-776-0430. Ed. Thomas P. McAloon; Pub. Charles E. Slater. adv.: B&W page $1348, color page $1994; adv. contact: Peg Simanaitis. bk.rev.; charts; illus.; tr.lit.; index. circ. 8,572. (back issues avail.) **Indexed:** Cadscan, Chem.Abstr., Lead Abstr., Met.Abstr., World Alum.Abstr., Zincscan. **Document type:** trade publication.
—BLDSC (4580.406100); CASDDS; Ei; Faxon; SWETS; UnCover.
Formerly: I and S M (ISSN 0097-8388)
Description: Professional journal for the iron and steel industry.

669.1 UK ISSN 0301-9233
TS300 CODEN: IMKSB7
IRONMAKING AND STEELMAKING. 1974. bi-m. £184($420) to non-members; members £90 ($180). Institute of Materials, 1 Carlton House Terrace, London SW1Y 5DB, England. TEL 071-839-4071. FAX 071-839-2078. TELEX 8814813-METSOC-G. Ed. Mary Chim. adv.; bk.rev.; charts; illus. circ. 1,220. (back issues avail.) **Indexed:** ABTICS, Br.Tech.Ind., Cadscan, Chem.Abstr., Ergon.Abstr., Fuel & Energy Abstr., Ind.Sci.Rev., INIS Atomind., Lead Abstr., Met.Abstr., Sci.Cit.Ind., World Alum.Abstr., Zincscan. **Document type:** trade publication.
—BLDSC (4580.440000); CASDDS; Ei; Faxon; Genuine Article; SWETS; UMI; UnCover. **CCC.**
Description: Covers all aspects of the ironmaking and steelmaking industry, including the rolling and application of ferrous products.

669.1 US ISSN 0099-6874
CODEN: PIRCB9
IRONMAKING CONFERENCE PROCEEDINGS. 1943. a., 53rd ed., 1994. $90 to non-members; members $45. Iron & Steel Society, 410 Commonwealth Dr., Warrendale, PA 15086-7512. TEL 412-776-9535. FAX 412-776-0430. (also avail. in microform from UMI; back issues avail.) **Document type:** proceedings.
—BLDSC (4580.470000); CASDDS.
Formerly: Iron & Steel Society. Ironmaking Proceedings.
Description: For iron and steelmakers.

IRONWORKER. see *LABOR UNIONS*

669.1 SA ISSN 0019-0594
ISCOR NEWS/YSKORNUUS. (Text and summaries in Afrikaans, English) 1936. bi-m. free. Iscor Limited - Yscor Beperk, H.Q. Bldg., Roger Dyason Rd., Box 450, Pretoria 0001, South Africa. TEL 012-298-1111. FAX 021-26-4721. TELEX 32-2007 SA. Ed.Bd. illus. circ. 28,000. **Indexed:** Ind.S.A.Per., Met.Abstr., World Alum.Abstr.
Description: Covers the latest techniques, productivity improvements and developments in metallurgy, as well as other corporate activities.

669.142 BG
ISPAT (CHITTAGONG). (Text in Bengali or English) 1973. a. free. Chittagong Steel Mills Ltd., Box 429, Chittagong, Bangladesh. Ed.Bd. adv. circ. 2,500.

620.112　　　　　RU　　ISSN 0202-7976
　　　　　　　　　　CODEN: IKZKA9
ITOGI NAUKI I TEKHNIKI: KORROZIYA I ZASHCHITA OT KORROZII. irreg., vol.15, 1989. 8 Rub. Vsesoyuznyi Institut Nauchno-Tekhnicheskoi Informatsii (VINITI), Ul. Baltiiskaya 14, Moscow A-219, Russia. (Subscr. to: Mezhdunarodnaya Kniga, Dimitrova ul. 39, 113095 Moscow, Russia) **Indexed:** Chem.Abstr.
—BLDSC (0092.460000); CASDDS.

669　　　　　　　RU　　ISSN 0202-7739
　　　　　　　　　　CODEN: IMTOA5
ITOGI NAUKI I TEKHNIKI: METALLOVEDENIE I TERMICHESKAYA OBRABOTKA. irreg., vol.23, 1989. 6.60 Rub. Vsesoyuznyi Institut Nauchno-Tekhnicheskoi Informatsii (VINITI), Ul. Baltiiskaya 14, Moscow A-219, Russia. (Subscr. to: Mezhdunarodnaya Kniga, Dimitrova ul. 39, 113095 Moscow, Russia) **Indexed:** Chem.Abstr.
—BLDSC (0108.190000); CASDDS.

669　　　　　　　RU　　ISSN 0202-7755
TN4　　　　　　　　　CODEN: IMTKAR
ITOGI NAUKI I TEKHNIKI: METALLURGICHESKAYA TEPLOTEKHNIKA; oborudovanie, izmerenie, kontrol' i avtomatizatsiya v metallurgicheskom proizvodstve. irreg., vol.8, 1989. price varies. Vsesoyuznyi Institut Nauchno-Tekhnicheskoi Informatsii (VINITI), Ul. Baltiiskaya 14, Moscow A-219, Russia. (Subscr. to: Mezhdunarodnaya Kniga, Dimitrova ul. 39, 113095 Moscow, Russia) **Indexed:** Chem.Abstr.
—BLDSC (0109.071500).

669　　　　　　　RU　　ISSN 0202-7747
TN758　　　　　　　　CODEN: ITMRAS
ITOGI NAUKI I TEKHNIKI: METALLURGIYA TSVETNYKH METALLOV. irreg., vol.19, 1989. 4.20 Rub. Vsesoyuznyi Institut Nauchno-Tekhnicheskoi Informatsii (VINITI), Ul. Baltiiskaya 14, Moscow A-219, Russia. (Subscr. to: Mezhdunarodnaya Kniga, Dimitrova ul. 39, 113095 Moscow, Russia) **Indexed:** Chem.Abstr.
—BLDSC (0109.160000); CASDDS.

669　　　　　　　RU　　ISSN 0202-7798
ITOGI NAUKI I TEKHNIKI: TEORIYA METALLURGICHESKIKH PROTSESSOV. irreg., vol.7, 1987. price varies. Vsesoyuznyi Institut Nauchno-Tekhnicheskoi Informatsii (VINITI), Ul. Usievicha 20-A, 125219 Moscow A-219, Russian. (Subscr. to: Mezhdunarodnaya Kniga, Moscow 121200, Russian) **Indexed:** Chem.Abstr.
—BLDSC (0178.220000).

669　　　　　　　US　　ISSN 1047-4838
TN1　　　　　　　　　CODEN: JOMMER
J O M. 1949. m. $121 (foreign $141) (effective 1996). Minerals, Metals and Materials Society, 420 Commonwealth Dr., Warrendale, PA 15086. TEL 412-776-9080. adv.; bk.rev.; charts; illus.; index. circ. 14,000. (also avail. in microform from UMI; reprint service avail. from UMI) **Indexed:** A.S.& T.Ind., AESIS, B.C.I.R.A., Cadscan, Chem.Abstr., Corros.Abstr., Curr.Cont., Eng.Ind., Fuel & Energy Abstr., GeoRef., Ind.Sci.Rev., INSPEC (1989-), Int.Aerosp.Abstr., Lead Abstr., Met.Abstr., PROMT, World Alum.Abstr., Zincscan.
—BLDSC (4673.254500); CASDDS; Ei; Faxon; Genuine Article; SWETS; UMI; UnCover. **CCC.**
　Former titles (until 1989): Journal of Metals (ISSN 0148-6608); (until 1977): JOM (ISSN 0098-4558)

J O T. (Journal fuer Oberflaechentechnik) see
MACHINERY

669　　　　　　　GW　　ISSN 0075-2819
TS670　　　　　　　　CODEN: JBOFAN
JAHRBUCH OBERFLAECHENTECHNIK (YEAR). a. DM.188. Huethig GmbH, Postfach 102869, 69018 Heidelberg, Germany. TEL 06221-489-0. FAX 06221-489482. Ed.Bd. adv. **Indexed:** Cadscan, Chem.Abstr., Lead Abstr., Zincscan. **Document type:** trade publication.
—BLDSC (4631.900000); CASDDS.

JAHRBUCH SCHWEISSTECHNIK. see TECHNOLOGY: COMPREHENSIVE WORKS

672　　　　　　　GW　　ISSN 0724-8482
HD9523.1
JAHRBUCH STAHL. 1951. a. DM.44. (Verein Deutscher Eisenhuettenleute) Verlag Stahleisen mbH, Sohnstr. 65, 40237 Duesseldorf, Germany. TEL 0211-6707-0. FAX 0211-6707517. **Document type:** trade publication.
—BLDSC (4632.355000).
　Former titles: Stahleisen Kalender (ISSN 0081-4180); Taschenbuch fuer die Stahlindustrie.

671.2　　　　　　 JA　　ISSN 0021-4396
WMLC 93-4304　　　　CODEN: IMNOA9
JAPAN FOUNDRYMEN'S SOCIETY. JOURNAL/IMONO. (Text in Japanese) 1929. m. 12000 Yen. Japan Foundrymen's Society - Nippon Imono Kyokai, 8-12-13 Ginza, Chuo-ku, Tokyo 104, Japan. TEL 03-3541-2758. FAX 03-3541-2750. Ed. Tohru Namai. adv.; bk.rev. **Indexed:** B.C.I.R.A., Chem.Abstr., INIS Atomind., Met.Abstr., World Alum.Abstr. **Document type:** academic/scholarly publication.
—CASDDS; Ei.

371.2　　　　　　 JA　　ISSN 0287-041X
WMLC 93-4304　　　　CODEN: TJFSEH
JAPAN FOUNDRYMEN'S SOCIETY. TRANSACTIONS. (Text in English) 1982. a. Japan Foundrymen's Society - Nippon Imono Kyokai, 8-12-13 Ginza, Chuo-ku, Tokyo 104, Japan. TEL 03-3541-2758. FAX 03-3541-2750. **Indexed:** Chem.Abstr.
—BLDSC (8973.670000).

669　　　　　　　JA　　ISSN 0021-4426
　　　　　　　　　　CODEN: NKZKAU
JAPAN INSTITUTE OF METALS. BULLETIN/NIHON KINZOKU GAKKAI KAIHO. (Text in Japanese) 1962. m. 14400 Yen. Japan Institute of Metals - Nihon Kinzoku Gakkai, Aoba Aramaki, Aoba-ku, Sendai 980, Japan. TEL 022-223-3685. FAX 8-22-223-6312. Ed. Hiroshi Oikawa. adv.; charts. circ. 10,000. **Indexed:** JTA, Met.Abstr., World Alum.Abstr.
—CASDDS.

669　　　　　　　JA　　ISSN 0021-4876
　　　　　　　　　　CODEN: NIKGAV
JAPAN INSTITUTE OF METALS. JOURNAL/NIPPON KINZOKU GAKKAISHI. (Text in Japanese; title, contents page and summaries in English) 1937. m. 14400 Yen. Japan Institute of Metals - Nihon Kinzoku Gakkai, Aoba Aramaki, Aoba-ku, Sendai 980, Japan. TEL 022-223-3685. FAX 8-22-223-6312. Ed. Koji Sumino. adv.; index. circ. 5,000. **Indexed:** Cadscan, Chem.Abstr., Curr.Cont., INSPEC, Int.Aerosp.Abstr., JCT, JTA, Lead Abstr., Met.Abstr., Phys.Ber., World Alum.Abstr., Zincscan.
—BLDSC (4805.250000); CASDDS; Ei; Genuine Article; SWETS. **CCC.**

669　　　　　　　JA　　ISSN 0021-4523
JAPAN METAL BULLETIN. (Text in English) 1953. w. $680 in Asia; N. America $690; elsewhere $700. Nalk Corporation, Rm. 615, Grand Palace Tamachi, 4-9-18 Shibaura, Minato-ku, Tokyo 108, Japan. TEL 03-3456-4416. FAX 03-3456-4417. Ed. Isao Nakada. adv.; bk.rev.; mkt.; stat. circ. 10,000. (looseleaf format) **Document type:** bulletin.
　Description: Covers imports, exports and production of Japanese metal industry.

669　　　　　　　JA　　ISSN 0368-444X
　　　　　　　　　　CODEN: JSWTAK
JAPAN STEEL WORKS TECHNICAL NEWS. (Text in European languages) 1961. irreg. exchange basis. Nihon Seikosho - Japan Steel Works, Ltd., 1-12 Yuraku-cho, Chiyoda-ku, Tokyo 100, Japan.

669.6　　　　　　 UK
JAPAN - TIN IN TINPLATE. 1984. irreg. £15. International Tin Council, 1 Oxendon St., London SW1Y 4EQ, England.
　Description: Surveys tinplate manufacturing, can making and canning in Japan.

JAPANESE SOCIETY FOR NON-DESTRUCTIVE INSPECTION. TRANSACTIONS. see ENGINEERING — Engineering Mechanics And Materials

METALLURGY　　4661

669.2　　　　　　 JA　　ISSN 0075-3475
HD9526.J3
JAPAN'S IRON AND STEEL INDUSTRY. (Text in English) 1951. a. 4000 Yen (foreign $60). Kawata Publicity Inc. - Kawata Paburishiti K.K., Rm. 605, Otawa House, 3-1, Otsuka 2-chome, Bunkyo-ku, Tokyo 112, Japan. TEL 81-3-3945-3878. FAX 81-3-3945-4870. Ed. Sukeyuki Kawata. adv. contact: Toshiyuki Uehara. circ. 3,000 (paid). **Document type:** trade publication.
　Description: Covers Japanese steel industry.

671　　　　　　　DK　　ISSN 0109-9418
JERN- OG MASKININDUSTRIEN. 1970. s-m. DKK 250($16.50) T-Press, Falkoner Alle, DK-2000 Frederiksberg, Denmark. TEL 45-33-140010. FAX 45-33-123137. TELEX 21317 T-PRESS. Ed. Jan Paustian. adv. circ. 25,000. (tabloid format; back issues avail.)
　Formerly (until 1972): Jern- og Metalindustrien.

669　　　　　　　CC　　ISSN 1006-4451
JIANGXI TONGYE GONGCHENG/JIANGXI COPPER ENGINEERING. (Text in Chinese) 1984. q. $12. Jiangxi Tongye Gongcheng Bianjibu, Jiangxi Tongye Gongsi, Keyan Shejisuo Nei, Guixi, Jiangxi 335400, People's Republic of China. TEL 86-7032-771308. (Dist. by: Zhongguo Chuban Duiwai Maoyi Zonggongsi, P.O. Box 782, Beijing, P.R China) Ed. Zhang Shanjing. adv. contact: Liu Weige. circ. 1,600. **Document type:** academic/scholarly publication.
　Description: Covers scientific experiments, applications of new technology relating to copper producation.

669　　　　　　　CC　　ISSN 1001-0181
JINSHU KEXUE YU GONGYI/MATERIAL SCIENCE AND TECHNOLOGY. (Text in Chinese) 1982. q. Y12.80 (effective 1996). Harbin Gongye Daxue - Harbin Institute of Technology, 166, Dazhi Jie, Harbin, Heilongjiang 150001, People's Republic of China. TEL 0451-3621000. FAX 0451-321048. TELEX 87217 HIT CN. Ed. Li Cao. circ. 2,500. **Document type:** academic/scholarly publication.
　Description: Covers metal materials and hot working as well as ceramic materials, semi-conduct materials, polymer and composites materials.
　Refereed Serial

JINSHU RECHULI/HEAT TREATMENT OF METALS. see ENGINEERING — Engineering Mechanics And Materials

669　　　　　　　CC　　ISSN 0412-1961
TN4　　　　　　　　　CODEN: CHSPA4
JINSHU XUEBAO/ACTA METALLURGICA SINICA. English edition: Journal of Metallurgy, Part A & B. (Text in Chinese; abstracts in English) 1956. m. $240. (Chinese Academy of Sciences, Institute of Metallurgy) Science Press, Marketing and Sales Department, 16 Donghuangchenggen North St., Beijing 100707, People's Republic of China. TEL 4010642. FAX 4012180. TELEX 210247 SPBJ CN. Eds. Shi Changxu, Xing Zhongshu. (back issues avail.) **Indexed:** INSPEC (1974-). **Document type:** academic/scholarly publication.
—BLDSC (0637.500000); CASDDS.
　Description: Covers research on physical metallurgy, process metallurgy and materials science in China, including mining and ore dressing, oxidation and corrosion, metal working, testing methods and refractories.

METALLURGY

669   SZ   ISSN 0925-8388
TN1   CODEN: JALCEU
JOURNAL OF ALLOYS AND COMPOUNDS; an interdisciplinary journal of materials science and solid-state chemistry and physics. (Text in English, French and German) 1959. 32/yr. 7200 SFr.($5902) (effective 1996). Elsevier Science S.A., P.O. Box 564, CH-1001 Lausanne 1, Switzerland. TEL 41-21-3207381. FAX 41-21-3235444. TELEX 450620-ELSA-CH. (Subscr. in U.S. and Canada to: Elsevier Science Inc., Box 882, Madison Sq. Sta., New York, NY 10159. TEL 212-989-5800. FAX 212-633-3990) Ed.Bd. adv.; bk.rev.; bibl.; illus.; index. (also avail. in microform from UMI; back issues avail.) **Indexed**: Br.Ceram.Abstr., Cadscan, Chem.Abstr., Chem.Infd., Curr.Cont., Eng.Ind., GeoRef., Ind.Sci.Rev., INIS Atomind., INSPEC, Lead Abstr., Mass Spectr.Bull., Met.Abstr., Phys.Ber., Sci.Cit.Ind., Soils & Fert., World Alum.Abstr., Zincscan. **Document type**: academic/scholarly publication.
—BLDSC (4927.180000); CASDDS; Ei; Faxon; Genuine Article; SWETS; UnCover. **CCC**.
  Formerly (until 1991): Journal of the Less-Common Metals (ISSN 0022-5088)
  Description: Provides an international forum where materials scientists, chemists and physicists can present their results both to workers in their own fields and to others active in related areas.
  Refereed Serial

JOURNAL OF MATERIALS ENGINEERING AND PERFORMANCE. see ENGINEERING — Engineering Mechanics And Materials

669   CC   ISSN 1005-0302
CODEN: JSCTEQ
JOURNAL OF MATERIALS SCIENCE & TECHNOLOGY; an international journal in the field of materials science. (Text in English) 1985. bi-m. $325 (foreign $415) (effective 1996). Chinese Society for Metals, 72 Wenhua Rd., Shenyang 110015, People's Republic of China. TEL 86-024-3843531. FAX 86-024-3891320. (Dist. by: Allerton Press, Inc., 150 Fifth Ave., New York, NY 10011, USA. TEL 212-924-3950) (Co-sponsors: Chinese Materials Research Society; Chinese Academy of Sciences, International Centre for Materials Physics) Ed. Shi Changxu. abstr. **Document type**: academic/scholarly publication.
—BLDSC (5012.252000); CASDDS; Ei; Faxon. **CCC**.
  Formerly (until 1993): Chinese Journal of Metal Science and Technology (ISSN 1000-3029)
  Description: Covers metals, inorganic nonmetallic materials, organic polymer materials and composite materials.
  Refereed Serial

JOURNAL OF MINES, METALS AND FUELS. see MINES AND MINING INDUSTRY

669   US   ISSN 1054-9714
TN689   CODEN: JPEQE6
JOURNAL OF PHASE EQUILIBRIA. 1979. bi-m. $447. A S M International, Materials Information, Materials Park, OH 44073-0002. TEL 216-338-5151. FAX 216-338-4634. TELEX 98-0619 ASMINT. Ed. Jack F. Smith. adv.; bk.rev. circ. 450. (also avail. in microform from UMI; reprint service avail.) **Indexed**: Chem.Abstr., Copper Abstr., Met.Abstr., World Alum.Abstr.
—BLDSC (5034.060000); CASDDS; Ei; Faxon; SWETS; UMI; UnCover. **CCC**.
  Formerly: Bulletin of Alloy Phase Diagrams (ISSN 0197-0216)
  Description: Features articles using revised alloy phase diagram data in applications.
  Refereed Serial

669   II   ISSN 0257-4993
JOURNAL OF POTASSIUM RESEARCH. (Text in English) 1985. q. Rs.65($40) Potash Research Institute of India, Sector 19, Dundahera, Gurgaon 122 001 (Haryana), India. TEL 0124-340185. Ed. Janardan Singh. bk.rev. circ. 700. (reprint service avail.)
—BLDSC (5041.170000).
  Description: Covers soil science, agronomy, mineralogy, plant physiology, and related topics.
  Refereed Serial

669 016   UK   ISSN 0334-8938
TA417.6   CODEN: JMBMEQ
JOURNAL OF THE MECHANICAL BEHAVIOR OF MATERIALS. 1972. q. $230. Freund Publishing House Ltd., Ste. 500, Chesham House, 150 Regent St., London W1R 5FA, England. (And: P.O. Box 35010, Tel Aviv, Israel. TEL 972-3-5628540. FAX 972-3-5628538) Ed. B-Z Weiss. adv.; bk.rev. circ. 1,000. (back issues avail.) **Indexed**: Geo.Abstr., Met.Abstr. **Document type**: academic/scholarly publication.
—BLDSC (5015.810000); CASDDS.
  Formerly (until 1989): Reviews on Deformation Behaviour of Materials (ISSN 0048-7589)

671   GW   ISSN 0936-062X
DER JUNGE METALL-FACHARBEITER. 1955. m. DM.70.80. Frankfurter Fachverlag, Emil-Sulzbach-Str. 12, 60486 Frankfurt a.M., Germany. FAX 069-702003. Ed. Heinz Kirsch. bk.rev.; illus.; index. circ. 35,000. (also avail. in microform from UMI; reprint service avail. from UMI) **Document type**: trade publication.
—SWETS; UMI. **CCC**.
  Formerly (until 1988): Junge Metallhandwerker (ISSN 0022-6335)

669   JA   ISSN 0285-7030
TN207   CODEN: KHKKD6
KAGAKU GIJYUTSUCHO KINZOKU ZAIRYO GIJYUTSU KENKYUJO. KENKYU HOKOKUSHU. (Text in Japanese) 1958. a. National Research Institute for Metals - Kagaku Gijutsucho Kinzoku Zairyo Gijutsu Kenkyujo, Planning Section of Administration Division, 2-3-12, Nakameguro, Meguro-ku, Tokyo 153, Japan. TEL 81-3-3719-2271. FAX 81-3-3792-3337.
—BLDSC (5097.305000); CASDDS.
  Formerly (until 1980): Kinzoku Zairyo Gijutsu Kenkyujo Kenkyu Hokoku (ISSN 0450-2922)

669   JA
KATAYAMA GIHO/KATAYAMA TECHNICAL REPORT. (Text in Japanese) 1981. a. Katayama Tekkojo - Katayama Iron Works, Ltd., 2-21, Minamiokajima 6-chome, Taisho-ku, Osaka-shi, Osaka 551, Japan.

669   JA   ISSN 0916-6211
KAWASAKI STEEL BULLETIN. (Text in English) 1979. bi-m. free. Kawasaki Steel Corporation, Public Relations Section, Hibiya Kokusai Bldg., 2-2-3 Uchisaiwai-cho, Chiyoda-ku, Tokyo 100, Japan. FAX 03-3597-3160.
  Description: Publishes economic and technical reports of Kawasaki Steel Corporation.

669   JA   ISSN 0388-9475
TS300   CODEN: KSTRDD
KAWASAKI STEEL TECHNICAL REPORT. (Text in English) 1980. s-a. free. Kawasaki Steel Corporation, Public Relations Section, Hibiya Kokusai Bldg., 2-2-3 Uchisaiwai-cho, Chiyoda-ku, Tokyo 100, Japan. FAX 03-3597-4868. illus. circ. 1,600. **Indexed**: Chem.Abstr., Corros.Abstr., Met.Abstr.
—BLDSC (5088.103500); CASDDS; Ei; Faxon.
  Description: Technical reports on the latest developments of Kawasaki Steel.

669 666   SZ   ISSN 1013-9826
TA401   CODEN: KEMAEY
KEY ENGINEERING MATERIALS. 1975. 12/yr. $1036. Trans Tech Publications, Trottenstr. 20, CH-8037 Zurich, Switzerland. FAX 01-2721092. Ed. F.H. Wohlbier. bk.rev.; abstr.; bibl.; charts; illus.; cum.index. **Indexed**: INSPEC (1986-), Int.Aerosp.Abstr., Met.Abstr., World Alum.Abstr. **Document type**: academic/scholarly publication.
—BLDSC (5091.822720); CASDDS; Ei; UnCover.
  Formerly: Mechanical and Corrosion Properties. Series A. Key Engineering Materials (ISSN 0252-1059); Which superseded in part: Mechanical and Corrosion Properties (ISSN 0250-9784); Which was formerly (until Jan. 1979): Mechanical Properties (ISSN 0361-2821)

669   UK   ISSN 1357-8359
KEY NOTE REPORT: SCRAP METAL PROCESSING. irreg., vol.8, 1995. Key Note Publications Ltd., Field House, 72 Oldfield Rd., Hampton, Mddx. TW12 2HQ, England. TEL 0181-783-0755. FAX 0181-783-1940. Ed. Richard Caines. **Document type**: monographic series.
  ●Also available online.
  Also available on CD-ROM.
  Formerly: Key Note Report: Scrap Metal (ISSN 0954-4402)

669   JA   ISSN 0910-2205
CODEN: KIDOEP
KIDORUI/RARE EARTHS. (Text in English, Japanese; summaries in English) 1982. s-a. Nihon Kidorui Gakkai - Rare Earth Society of Japan, Osaka Daigaku Kogakubu Oyo Kagakka, 2-1, Yamadaoka, Suita-shi, Osaka 565, Japan. TEL 81-6-879-7352. FAX 81-6-877-4728. Ed. Gin-ya Adachi. **Document type**: academic/scholarly publication.
—CASDDS. **CCC**.

669   JA
KISHO KINZOKU KOBUTSU SHIGEN NO FUZON JOKYO CHOSA HOKOKUSHO/INVESTIGATION OF UNDERGROUND RARE METALS. (Text in Japanese) irreg. Shigen Enerugicho - Agency of Natural Resources and Energy, 3-1, Kasumigaseki 1-chome, Chiyoda-ku, Tokyo 100, Japan. **Document type**: government publication.

KJEMI. see CHEMISTRY

669.142 621   GW   ISSN 0937-6186
KLOECKNER WERKE HEUTE; Maschinenbau, Kunststoff Verarbeitung. 1952. q. (Kloeckner-Werke AG) Kloeckner Werke AG, Kloecknerstr. 29, 47057 Duisburg, Germany. TEL 0203-396-1. FAX 0203-343695. bk.rev. circ. 15,000. **Document type**: consumer publication.
  Formerly: K W Heute.
  Description: Staff magazine of Kloeckner-Werke.

KOMPASS PROFESSIONNEL. PRODUITS DU METAL. see BUSINESS AND ECONOMICS — Trade And Industrial Directories

KOMPASS PROFESSIONNEL. SIDERURGIE, METALLURGIE, FONDERIE. see BUSINESS AND ECONOMICS — Trade And Industrial Directories

671.025489   DK   ISSN 0106-1194
KOMPASS SELECT EXPORT. METAL PRODUCTS. Cover title: Euro Kompass Denmark. Metal. (Text in Danish, English, French, German and Spanish) 1980. a. DKK 300 (listed companies DKK 100). Oeveroedvej 5, DK-2840 Holte, Denmark. TEL 45-45-41-21-00. FAX 45-45-41-06-65. illus. **Document type**: directory.
  ●Also available on CD-ROM.
  Formerly: Kompass Select Denmark. Metal.

669   KO
CODEN: TKHCDJ
KOREAN INSTITUTE OF METALS AND MATERIALS. JOURNAL. (Text in English, Korean) 1963. m. membership. (Korean Science Foundation) Korean Institute of Metals and Materials, Rm. 605, Keoyang Bldg., 51-8 Susong-dong, Chong Ro-ku, Seoul 110-140, S. Korea. TEL 02-734-0595. FAX 02-734-0596. Ed. Chong Sool Choi. adv.; film rev.; software rev.; bibl.; illus. circ. 2,500. **Indexed**: Corros.Abstr., INIS Atomind., INSPEC (1992-), Soils & Fert. **Document type**: academic/scholarly publication.
—CASDDS.
  Formerly (until 1991, vol.29, no.5): Korean Institute of Metals. Journal (ISSN 0253-3847)
  Description: Original papers covering metallurgy and materials science.
  Refereed Serial

620.112   NO   ISSN 0047-3634
KORROSJONS NYTT.* 1971. bi-m. Kr.52. Studiegruppen for Korrosjonsproblemer, Box 1041, 5001 Bergen, Norway. Ed. Reidar Thomassen. adv.; bk.rev.; charts; illus. circ. 3,200. **Indexed**: Chem.Abstr.

669   XO   ISSN 0023-432X
CODEN: KOMAAW
KOVOVE MATERIALY/METAL MATERIALS. (Text in Slovak; summaries in English, German and Russian) 1952. bi-m. $34. Slovenska Akademia Vied, Ustav Materialov a Mechaniky Strojov, Racianska 75, P.O. Box 95, 830 08 Bratislava, Slovakia. (Dist. by: Slovart, Nam. Slobody 6, 817 64 Bratislava, Slovakia) Ed. Premysl Rys. bk.rev.; charts; illus.; index. circ. 900. **Indexed**: Cadscan, Chem.Abstr., Curr.Cont., Eng.Ind., INIS Atomind., INSPEC, Int.Aerosp.Abstr., Lead Abstr., Met.Abstr., World Alum.Abstr., Zincscan.
—BLDSC (5115.120000); CASDDS; Genuine Article.
  Description: Publishes original works from research of metal structure and structure of metal alloys as well as the results of basic research in physical metallurgy and metallurgical processes of iron and non-iron metals.

METALLURGY

669 UK ISSN 0208-9386
TS228.9 CODEN: KMSTD6
KRZEPNIECIE METALI I STOPOW. (Text in Polish; summaries in English, Russian) irreg., vol.11, 1987. price varies. (Polish Academy of Sciences, Katowice Section, Commission on Founding) Ossolineum, Publishing House of the Polish Academy of Sciences, Rynek 9, 50-106 Wroclaw, Poland. TEL 386-25. (Dist. by: Ars Polona, Krakowskie Przedmiescie 7, 00-068 Warsaw, Poland) Ed. Waclaw Sakwa.
—CASDDS.
Description: Original papers on different questions of iron and non-iron metallurgy.

669 551 CC ISSN 1001-5663
KUANGCHAN YU DIZHI/MINERALS AND GEOLOGY. (Text in Chinese) q. Zhongguo Youse Jinshu Gongye Zonggongsi, Kuangshan Dizhi Yanjiuyuan, Sanlidian, Guilin, Guangxi 541004, People's Republic of China. TEL 443865. Ed. Li Jiazhen.

671 RU ISSN 0201-7296
CODEN: KSPRAO
KUZNECHNO-SHTAMPOVOCHNOE PROIZVODSTVO. 1959. m. $158 (effective 1996). Izdatel'stvo Mashinostroenie, 4, Stromynsky per. 5, 107076 Moscow, Russia. Ed. A.P. Vailiev. adv.: page DM.4000. index. circ. 8,000. **Indexed:** Chem.Abstr., INIS Atomind., Met.Abstr., World Alum.Abstr. **Document type:** academic/scholarly publication.
—BLDSC (0093.850000).
Description: Publishes the latest development of research institutes, carries articles on novel metal forming technology, including precision stamping under superductility conditions.

LALU. see *MACHINERY*

669 IT ISSN 0391-5891
CODEN: LAMID6
LAMIERA. 1964. 11/yr. L.85000 (foreign L.210000) (effective 1995). Tecniche Nuove s.p.a., Via C. Menotti 14, 20129 Milan, Italy. TEL 02-75701. FAX 02-7610351. Ed. G. Nardella. adv.: B&W page L.2360000, color page L.3180000; trim 185 x 266. illus. circ. 9,000. **Indexed:** Chem.Abstr.
—BLDSC (5144.200000); CASDDS.
Description: Information on the pressing, deformation, cut finishing and assembling of cut metal.

669 FR ISSN 0181-1223
LETTRE D'INFORMATION METAUX. (Text in French) 1959. w. 1020 F. Societe d' Information et de Documentation, Bureau d'Informations Professionnelles, 142 rue Montmartre, 75002 Paris, France. TEL 40-26-83-21. FAX 40-39-97-52. TELEX 220 528 BIP. Ed. Philippe Dommanget.

669 FR ISSN 1146-0113
LIAISON DES UTILISATEURS. 10/yr. L A L U, 2 av. d'Estiennes-d'Ornes, 94700 Maisons Alfort, France. TEL 43-96-51-57. FAX 48-59-49-22. TELEX 233 765 LALU. Ed. M. Schuster. circ. 20,000.

669.1 CC ISSN 1001-1471
LIANTIE/IRONMAKING. (Text in Chinese) 1982. bi-m. Yejin Gongyebu, Wuhan Gangtie Sheji Yanjiuyuan, 12 Yejin Dadao, Qingshan District, Wuhan, Hubei 430080, People's Republic of China. (Dist. overseas by: China International Book Trading Corp., P.O. Box 399, Beijing, P.R. China) Ed. Zheng Zhixing. **Document type:** trade publication.
—BLDSC (4580.438000).

669 US ISSN 0024-3345
TN1 CODEN: LMAGAL
LIGHT METAL AGE. 1943. bi-m. $35. Fellom Publishing, 170 S. Spruce Ave., Ste. 120, S. San Francisco, CA 94080. TEL 415-588-8832. FAX 415-588-0901. Ed. Wanda Fellom; Pub. Ann Marie Fellon. adv.; bk.rev.; abstr.; bibl.; illus.; pat.; index. circ. 5,210. **Indexed:** A.S.& T.Ind., B.C.I.R.A., Chem.Abstr., Eng.Ind., Ind.Sci.Rev., Met.Abstr., PROMT, World Alum.Abstr. **Document type:** trade publication.
—BLDSC (5210.500000); CASDDS; Ei; Faxon; SWETS; UnCover.

671.2 RU ISSN 0024-449X
T4 CODEN: LIPRAX
LITEINOE PROIZVODSTVO. English translation: Russian Castings Technology (US ISSN 1068-3690) (Text in Russian; contents page in English) 1930. m. $81. (Ministerstvo Avtomobil'noi Promyshlennosti) Izdatel'stvo Mashinostroenie, 4, Stromynsky per., 107076 Moscow, Russia. TEL 095-269-7141. FAX 095-269-4897. Ed. I.A. Yaskevich. adv.: page DM.4000. bk.rev.; abstr.; bibl.; charts; illus.; stat.; index. circ. 5,700. **Indexed:** B.C.I.R.A., Chem.Abstr., INIS Atomind., Met.Abstr., World Alum.Abstr. **Document type:** academic/scholarly publication.
—BLDSC (0098.000000); CASDDS. **CCC.**
Description: Covers the experience of advanced plants in technical renovation of operating foundries and deals with the use of low-waste and energy-saving technologies.

669 RU ISSN 0302-9069
TS200
LITEINOE PROIZVODSTVO, METALLOVEDENIE I OBRABOTKA METALLOV DAVLENIEM. irreg. 0.47 Rub. (Krasnoyarskii Institut Tsvetnykh Metallov) Krasnoyarskoe Knizhnoe Izdatel'stvo, Prospekt Mira, 89, Krasnoyarsk, Russia. illus. **Indexed:** Chem.Abstr.

669 GW ISSN 0933-8934
LITERATURSCHAU "STAHL UND EISEN". s-m. DM.2330. Fachinformationszentrum Technik e.V., Ostbahnhofstr. 13, 60314 Frankfurt a.M., Germany. TEL 069-4308234. (Dist. by: Verlag Stahleisen mbH, Sohnstr. 65, 40237 Duesseldorf, Germany. TEL 0211-6707-0. FAX 0211-6707517) **Document type:** abstracting/indexing.
—CCC.
Formerly: Zeitschriften- und Buecherschau "Stahl und Eisen" (ISSN 0340-4951)

671.2 XV ISSN 0024-5135
TS200 CODEN: LIVVA7
LIVARSKI VESTNIK. (Text in Slovenian; summaries in English) 1953. bi-m. 600 SLT($12) Drustvo Livarjev Slovenije, Lepi Pot 6, Ljubljana, Slovenia. TEL 061 222-488. Ed. Milan Trbizan. adv.; bk.rev.; abstr.; bibl.; charts; illus.; index. circ. 2,500. **Indexed:** Chem.Abstr.
—CASDDS.

671.2 YU ISSN 0352-8936
TS228.99
LIVARSTVO. 1986. q. 45000 din.($20) Savez Organizacija Livaca Jugoslavije, Bulevar Avnoja 86, 11000 Belgrade, Yugoslavia. TEL 011 141-092. (Subscr. to: Savez Gevaca Hrvatske, Forudeova 9, 41020 Novi Zagreb, Yugoslavia) Eds. Miroslav Vranesic, Mile Galic. circ. 2,250.
Description: For theory and application in foundry.

LOCAL 1010 STEELWORKER. see *LABOR UNIONS*

M & T - METALLHANDWERK & TECHNIK. see *BUILDING AND CONSTRUCTION*

M I T E. (Manufacturing Ideas for Today's Engineers) see *ENGINEERING — Mechanical Engineering*

669 JA
M M I J INTERNATIONAL CONFERENCES. PROCEEDINGS. 1985. irreg., no.7, 1991. price varies. Mining and Materials Processing Institute of Japan - Shigen, Sozai Gakkai, Nogizaka Bldg., 9-6-41 Akasaka, Minato-ku, Tokyo 107, Japan. TEL 03-3402-0541. FAX 03-3403-1776. **Document type:** proceedings.

669 GW ISSN 0933-8810
M - MODERNE METALLTECHNIK; das Magazin fuer Ausbildung und Beruf. 1987. m. Verlag Moderne Metalltechnik GmbH, Am Spargelhof 2, 23554 Luebeck, Germany. TEL 0451-478311. Ed. Jean-Herbert Wahl.

669 600 GW ISSN 0026-0797
TS200 CODEN: MOFEAV
M O - METALLOBERFLAECHE; Beschichten von Metall und Kunststoff. 1946. m. DM.139.80. Carl Hanser Verlag, Kolbergerstr. 22, 81679 Munich, Germany. TEL 089-998300. FAX 089-984809. (Subscr. to: Postfach 860420, 81631 Munich, Germany) Ed. W. Jantsch. adv.; bk.rev.; abstr.; illus. circ. 5,250. **Indexed:** Art & Archaeol.Tech.Abstr., Cadscan, Chem.Abstr., Corros.Abstr., Eng.Ind., Excerp.Med., INIS Atomind., Lead Abstr., Met.Abstr., Packag.Sci.Tech., World Alum.Abstr., World Surf.Coat., Zincscan. **Document type:** trade publication.
—BLDSC (5693.000000); CASDDS; Ei; SWETS. **CCC.**

669 GW ISSN 0935-7254
TN600 CODEN: MMTIEZ
M P T - METALLURGICAL PLANT AND TECHNOLOGY INTERNATIONAL. (Text and summaries in English) 1978. bi-m. DM.215. Verlag Stahleisen mbH, Sohnstr. 65, 40237 Duesseldorf, Germany. TEL 0211-6707-0. FAX 0211-6707-517. Ed.Bd. circ. 10,500. **Indexed:** Met.Abstr. **Document type:** trade publication.
—BLDSC (5698.453100); CASDDS; Ei; SWETS; UnCover. **CCC.**
Formerly: M P T - Metallurgical Plant and Technology (ISSN 0171-4511)

M T I A ANNUAL REPORT. (Metal Trades Industry Association of Australia) see *BUSINESS AND ECONOMICS — Labor And Industrial Relations*

M T I A INPUT. (Metal Trades Industry Association of Australia) see *BUSINESS AND ECONOMICS — Labor And Industrial Relations*

M T I A METAL & ENGINEERING INDUSTRY YEARBOOK AND BUYERS GUIDE. (Metal Trades Industry Association of Australia) see *BUSINESS AND ECONOMICS — Labor And Industrial Relations*

671 382 AT
M T I A'S ENGINEERING EXPORTER. 1969. fortn. Aus.$150. Metal Trades Industry Association, National Export Council, National Office, 214 Northbourne Ave., Canberra, A.C.T. 2600, Australia. Ed. B.H. Trevanion. adv. circ. 1,000.
Former titles: M T I A N E G's Export Note Pad; Australian Metal Trades Export Group's Export Note Pad.

669 SA
MACHINE TOOL BUYERS GUIDE FOR SOUTHERN AFRICA. (Text in English) 1988. a. R.110. George Warman Publications (Pty.) Ltd., P.O. Box 3847, Cape Town 8000, South Africa. TEL 27-21-24-5320. FAX 27-21-261-332. Ed. Paddy Atwell. **Document type:** trade publication.
Description: Intended for users of metalworking machinery.

MACHINERY AND STEEL. see *MACHINERY*

669 US ISSN 0047-5491
MAGNESIUM MONTHLY REVIEW. 1971. m. $60. 106 Spring Forest Rd., Greenville, SC 29615-2241. TEL 803-244-5718. Ed. David C. Brown; Pub. Robert Brown. bk.rev.; index. circ. 527. **Indexed:** Met.Abstr., World Alum.Abstr. **Document type:** newsletter.
Description: Updates on and predictions for this structural metal industry, covering production, markets, techniques, and foreign developments.

669 US ISSN 0891-6942
MAGNESIUM NEWSLETTER. 1944. 9/yr. $90. International Magnesium Association, 1303 Vincent Pl., No. 1, McLean, VA 22101-3615. TEL 703-442-8888. FAX 703-821-1824. Ed. Felicia Garber. circ. 300. (looseleaf format) **Document type:** newsletter.

METALLURGY

669.723 615.328   UK   ISSN 0953-1424
CODEN: MAGREF
MAGNESIUM RESEARCH. (Text in English; summaries in French) 1988. 4/yr. £45 to individuals; institutions £85. (International Development of Research on Magnesium) John Libbey & Company Ltd., 13 Smiths Yard, Summerley St., London SW18 4HR, England. TEL 0181-947-2777.
FAX 0181-947-2664. E-mail: libbey@earlsfield.win-uk.net. Ed. Jean Durlach. Document type: academic/scholarly publication.
—BLDSC (5334.930000); CASDDS; Genuine Article.

669.722   HU   ISSN 0025-0058
HD9539.A63   CODEN: MAGABT
MAGYAR ALUMINIUM/HUNGARIAN ALUMINUM. (Text in Hungarian; table of contents in English, German and Russian; summaries in English) 1964. m. $41.50. Lapkiado Vallalat, Lenin korut 9-11, 1073 Budapest 7, Hungary. TEL 222-408. (Subscr. to: Kultura, Box 149, H-1389 Budapest, Hungary) Ed. Dr. Andras Domony. adv.; bk.rev.; illus. Indexed: Chem.Abstr., Hung.Build.Bull., INIS Atomind., Met.Abstr., World Alum.Abstr.
—CASDDS.

669 540   UK   ISSN 0792-1241
QD1   CODEN: MGMCE8
MAIN GROUP METAL CHEMISTRY. 1972. m. $410 (effective 1996). Freund Publishing House Ltd., Ste. 500, Chesham House, 150 Regent St., London W1R 5FA, England. (And: P.O. Box 35010, Tel Aviv, Israel. TEL 972-3-5628540. FAX 972-3-5628538) Ed. M. Gielen, F. Spielvogel. adv.; bk.rev.; index. circ. 1,000. (back issues avail.) Indexed: Chem.Abstr., Met.Abstr., World Alum.Abstr. Document type: academic/scholarly publication.
—BLDSC (5351.850000); CASDDS; Faxon; UnCover.
Former titles (until 1987): Silicon, Germanium, Tin and Lead Compounds (ISSN 0334-7575); (until 1986): Reviews on Silicon, Germanium, Tin and Lead Compounds (ISSN 0048-7570)

669   US
MANUFACTURING & MANAGEMENT MAGAZINE.* Short title: M & M Magazine. 1965. 6/yr. $20 (foreign $60); free to qualfied personnel. Rimol Associates, Inc., Box 9, Francestown, NH 03043-0009. TEL 201-383-7080. FAX 201-383-8090. Ed. Andrew J. Rimol. adv.; bk.rev. circ. 11,410. Document type: trade publication.
Formerly (until 1991): Tool and Die Magazine.
Description: Covers aspects of tool, die and manufacturing operations for management personnel.

MAQUINAS & METAIS. see MACHINERY

MAQUINAS E METAIS. see MACHINERY

669   DK   ISSN 0905-2151
MASKIN - AKTUELT. 1950. 15/yr. DKK 310. Teknisk Forlag A-S, Skelbaekgade 4, DK-1717 Copenhagen V, Denmark. TEL 45-31-21-68-01.
FAX 45-31-21-04-01. Ed. Peter Friis. adv.: B&W page DKK 10930, color page DKK 15910; trim 277 x 191. bk.rev.; bibl.; illus.; circ. 20,430 (controlled). (tabloid format) Indexed: ASCA.
Former titles (until 1989): S M E A (ISSN 0105-8711); S M E A Maskin - Industrien (ISSN 0036-164X)
Description: Focuses on people and companies in the iron, metal and engineering industry. Provides information on the products and services which form the basis of production, as well as on the political and economic conditions in the industry.

620.112   GW   ISSN 0947-5117
TA401
MATERIALS AND CORROSION/WERKSTOFFE UND KORROSION; with international corrosion abstracts. (Text in English and German) 1925. m. DM.948($660) (Arbeitsgemeinschaft Korrosion - DECHEMA) V C H Verlagsgesellschaft mbH, Postfach 101161, 69451 Weinheim, Germany.
TEL 06201-606-147. FAX 06201-606117. TELEX 465516-VCHWH-D. (U.S. addr.: V C H Publishers Inc., 220 E. 23rd St., New York, NY 10010-4606. TEL 212-683-8333) Ed. B. Isecke. adv.; bk.rev.; abstr.; charts; illus.; pat.; tr.lit.; index. circ. 1,250. (also avail. in microfilm from VCI; reprint service avail. from ISI) Indexed: API Catal., API Hlth.& Environ., API Oil., API Pet.Ref., API Pet.Subst., API Transport., Appl.Mech.Rev., Art & Archaeol.Tech.Abstr., BMT, Chem.Abstr., Copper Abstr., Curr.Cont., Dok.Arbeitsmed., Eng.Ind., Excerp.Med., INSPEC (1983-), Met.Abstr., Petrol.Abstr. Document type: academic/scholarly publication.
—BLDSC (9298.000000); CASDDS; Ei; Faxon; Genuine Article; SWETS. CCC.
Former titles: Werkstoffe und Korrosion (ISSN 0043-2822); (until 1949): Archiv fuer Metallkunde (ISSN 0365-4303); (until 1946): Korrosion und Metallschutz (ISSN 0368-6191)
Refereed Serial

MATERIALS AND MANUFACTURE. see ENGINEERING — Mechanical Engineering

MATERIALS AT HIGH TEMPERATURES; materials generation applications. see ENGINEERING — Engineering Mechanics And Materials

669   AT   ISSN 1037-7107
TA401   CODEN: MAUSEK
MATERIALS AUSTRALIA;* the magazine of engineering materials technology. 1969. 10/yr. Aus.$90 (foreign Aus.$130). Institute of Metals and Materials Australasia Ltd., P.O. Box 19, Parkville, Vic. 3052, Australia. TEL 61-3-347-2544.
FAX 61-3-348-1208. Ed.Bd. adv.: B&W page Aus.$650, color page Aus$.1040; trim 250 x 185; adv. contact: Angela Krepcik. bk.rev. circ. 2,500. Indexed: Chem.Abstr., INIS Atomind., Met.Abstr., World Alum.Abstr.
—BLDSC (5394.105800); CASDDS.
Former titles (until 1991): Materials Australasia (ISSN 0818-3597); (until 1986): Materials Australasia (ISSN 0156-174X); (until 1977): Metals Australia (ISSN 0047-6897)
Description: Offers news on the latest technological developments, case studies, company profiles, news on the people who make up the industry, new products and processes; includes a conference diary featuring an extensive list of Australian and overseas conferences.

669.95   US   ISSN 1044-5803
TN690   CODEN: MACHEX
MATERIALS CHARACTERIZATION; an international journal on materials structure and behavior. 1968. 10/yr. $510 to institutions (effective 1996). (International Metallographic Society Inc.) Elsevier Science Inc., 655 Ave. of the Americas, New York, NY 10010. TEL 212-989-5800.
FAX 212-633-3990. TELEX 420643 AEP UI. (Subscr. to: Box 882, Madison Square Sta., New York, NY 10159-0882) Ed. Chris Bagnall. adv.; bk.rev.; bibl.; charts; illus.; index. (also avail. in microform from UMI) Indexed: Appl.Mech.Rev., Cadscan, Chem.Abstr., Curr.Cont., Eng.Ind., INIS Atomind., INSPEC (1969-), Lead Abstr., Met.Abstr., Nucl.Sci.Abstr., Phys.Ber., Ref.Zh., Sci.Cit.Ind., Zincscan. Document type: academic/scholarly publication.
—BLDSC (5394.106500); CASDDS; Ei; Faxon; Genuine Article; SWETS; UnCover. CCC.
Formerly (until 1990): Metallography (ISSN 0026-0800)
Description: Covers technical knowledge, advances in materials structure and behavior.
Refereed Serial

669   AT   ISSN 0883-2900
TN1   CODEN: MFOREM
MATERIALS FORUM.* 1955. q. Aus.$250($250) (effective 1993). (Institution of Engineers, Australia) Engineers Australia Pty. Ltd., Crows Nest Centre, 2 Ernest St., Crows News, N.S.W. 2065, Australia. (Co-sponsor: Institute of Metals and Materials) Ed. B.C. Muddle. adv.; bk.rev.; bibl.; charts; illus.; index. circ. 1,800. (also avail. in microform from UMI) Indexed: B.C.I.R.A., Cadscan, Chem.Abstr., Curr.Cont., Eng.Ind., Eng.Mat.Abstr., Ind.Sci.Rev., INIS Atomind., INSPEC, ISMEC, Lead Abstr., Met.Abstr., World Alum.Abstr., Zincscan. Document type: academic/scholarly publication.
—BLDSC (5394.320000); CASDDS; Ei; Faxon; Genuine Article; UMI. CCC.
Formerly (until 1986): Metals Forum (ISSN 0160-7952); Supersedes (in 1977): Australasian Institute of Metals. Journal; Which was formerly: Australian Institute of Metals. Journal (ISSN 0004-9352)
Description: Structure and properties of engineering materials: metals, ceramics, polymers, composites.

669 671.52   UK
MATERIALS INFORMATION DIGEST SERIES. 1975. m. £95($175) to non-members; members £80 ($145). Institute of Materials, 1 Carlton House Terrace, London SW1Y 5DB, England.
TEL 071-839-4071. FAX 071-839-2078. TELEX 8814813-METSOC-G. Ed. M. Furneaux. Indexed: Met.Abstr. Document type: monographic series.
Formerly: Metals Society. Digest Series.

669   UK
MATERIALS INFORMATION TRANSLATIONS SERVICE. Short title: M I T S. 1957. m. £20($20) Institute of Materials, 1 Carlton House Terrace, London SW1Y 5DB, England. TEL 071-839-4071.
FAX 071-839-2289. TELEX 8814813-METSOC-G. (also avail. in microfiche) Indexed: Cadscan, Corros.Abstr., Lead Abstr., Zincscan. Document type: academic/scholarly publication.
•Also available online. Vendor(s): Knight-Ridder, Inc.
Formerly: British Industrial and Scientific International Translations Service.
Description: Contains articles about metals and materials translated into English.

669 628.44   UK   ISSN 1354-8522
MATERIALS RECYCLING WEEK. Abbreviated title: M R W. 1912. w. £54 (rest of Europe £73; elsewhere £98) (effective 1995); newsstand price: £1.20. E M A P Business Communications, P.O. Box, Maclaren House, 19 Scarbrook Rd., Croydon CR9 1QH, England. TEL 0181-688-7788.
FAX 0181-688-8375. (Subscr. to: Readerlink Ltd., Audit House, 260 Field End Rd., Ruislip, Mddx. HA4 9LT, England. TEL 0181-868-9050) Ed. Steve Eminton; Pub. Jim Hay. adv. contact: Kevin Boyce. bk.rev.; charts; illus.; mkt.; tr.lit. circ. 5,100. (also avail. in microform from UMI) Indexed: Excerp.Med., Int.Packag.Abstr., Intl.Polym.Sci.& Tech., Key to Econ.Sci., Paper & Bd.Abstr., RAPRA. Document type: trade publication.
—BLDSC (5396.300500). CCC.
Former titles (until 1994): Materials Reclamation Weekly (ISSN 0025-5386); Waste Trade World and Iron and Steel Scrap Review.
Description: Presents information on metallic materials reclamation.

669   US
MATERIALS RESEARCH AND ENGINEERING/REINE UND ANGEWANDTE METALLKUNDE. 1980. irreg. price varies. Springer-Verlag, 175 Fifth Ave., New York, NY 10010. TEL 212-460-1500.
FAX 212-473-6272. (Also: Berlin, Heidelberg, Tokyo and Vienna) Ed. B. Ilschner. (reprint service avail. from ISI) Indexed: INSPEC. Document type: monographic series.
Supersedes (1948-1976): Reine und Angewandte Metallkunde in Einzeldarstellungen (ISSN 0080-0791)

METALLURGY

669   UK   ISSN 0267-0836
TA401   CODEN: MSCTEP
MATERIALS SCIENCE AND TECHNOLOGY. 1985. m. £438($837) to non-members; members £175 ($333). Institute of Materials, 1 Carlton House Terrace, London SW1Y 5DB, England. TEL 071-839-4071. FAX 071-839-2078. TELEX 8814813-METSOC-G. Ed. Mary Chim. bk.rev.; charts; illus. circ. 1,600. (also avail. in microfilm from PMC; back issues avail.) **Indexed:** A.S.& T.Ind., B.C.I.R.A., Br.Tech.Ind., Cadscan, INSPEC (1985-), Lead Abstr., Met.Abstr., Zincscan. **Document type:** trade publication.
—BLDSC (5396.434400); CASDDS; Ei; Faxon; SWETS; UMI; UnCover.
   Incorporates: Metals Science & Metals Technology.
   Description: Covers metals alloys and nonmetallic materials (e.g., engineering ceramics, cements and concrete, polymers, adhesives, composites and electronic materials).

669   US   ISSN 1066-7857
                       CODEN: MATTEI
MATERIALS TECHNOLOGY. 1986. bi-m. Elsevier Science Inc., 655 Ave. of the Americas, New York, NY 10010. TEL 212-989-5800. FAX 212-633-3990. TELEX 420643 AEP UI. (Subscr. to: Box 882, Madison Square Sta., New York, NY 10159-0882) Ed. Renee G. Ford. index. circ. 350. (also avail. in microform from UMI; back issues avail.; reprint service avail. from UMI) **Indexed:** INSPEC (1993-), Met.Abstr. **Document type:** academic/scholarly publication.
—BLDSC (5396.444180); Ei; SWETS. **CCC.**
   Formerly (until 1993): Materials and Processing Report (ISSN 0887-1949)
   Description: Publishes news, articles, and announcements pertaining to technological advancements and research in the fields of metallurgy, ceramics, polymers, fibers, and composites.
   Refereed Serial

669   JA   ISSN 0916-1821
TN4   CODEN: MTJIEY
MATERIALS TRANSACTIONS, J I M. (Text in English) 1960. m. 24000 Yen. Japan Institute of Metals - Nihon Kinzoku Gakkai, Aoba Aramaki, Aoba-ku, Sendai 980, Japan. TEL 022-223-3685. FAX 8-22-223-6312. Ed. Yasuo Omori. circ. 2,000. **Indexed:** Chem.Abstr., Corros.Abstr., Curr.Cont., Eng.Ind., GeoRef., INSPEC, Int.Aerosp.Abstr., JCT, JTA, Met.Abstr., World Alum.Abstr.
—BLDSC (5396.520000); CASDDS; Ei; Faxon; Genuine Article; SWETS; UnCover. **CCC.**
   Formerly (until 1989): Japan Institute of Metals. Transactions (ISSN 0021-4434)

669   UK   ISSN 0967-8638
TN1   CODEN: MORLEE
MATERIALS WORLD. 1967-1981 (Dec.); resumed 1985. m. £136($283) to non-members. Institute of Materials, 1 Carlton House Terrace, London SW1Y 5DB, England. TEL 0171-839-4071. FAX 0171-839-2078. TELEX 8814813 METSOC G. Ed. Nuna Staniaszek. adv.; bk.rev.; charts; illus.; tr.lit.; index. circ. 13,000. (also avail. in microform from UMI) **Indexed:** ABTICS, Art & Archaeol.Tech.Abstr., B.C.I.R.A., Br.Ceram.Abstr., Br.Tech.Ind., Cadscan, Chem.Abstr., Copper Abstr., Curr.Pack.Abstr., Eng.Ind., Excerp.Med., High.Educ.Curr.Aware.Bull., INSPEC, Intl.Polym.Sci.& Tech., ISMEC, Lead Abstr., Met.Abstr., Packag.Sci.Tech., RAPRA, Text.Tech.Dig., Zincscan. **Document type:** trade publication.
—BLDSC (5396.550000); CASDDS; Ei; Faxon; Genuine Article; SWETS; UMI; UnCover. **CCC.**
   Incorporates (in 1993): British Ceramic Journal; (1976-1993): Plastics and Rubber International; Which was formerly: Plastics and Rubber (ISSN 0309-4561); Plastics and Polymers (ISSN 0300-3582); Former titles (until 1993): Metals and Materials (ISSN 0266-7185); Which supersedes (in 1985): Metallurgist and Materials Technologist (ISSN 0306-526X); Metals Society World (ISSN 0265-2722); Metals and Metallurgist (ISSN 0026-0940).
   Description: Covers the science, manufacturing technology and use of metals and other engineering materials.

669   GW   ISSN 0933-5137
TA401   CODEN: MATWER
MATERIALWISSENSCHAFT UND WERKSTOFFTECHNIK. (Text in English, German) 1970. m. DM.1028($773) (effective 1996). V C H Verlagsgesellschaft mbH, Postfach 101161, 69451 Weinheim, Germany. TEL 06201-606-147. FAX 06201-606117. TELEX 465516-VCHWH-D. (U.S. addr.: V C H Publishers Inc., 220 E. 23rd St., New York, NY 10010-4606. TEL 212-683-8333) (Co-sponsors: Verein Deutscher Eisenhuettenleute; Deutsche Gesellschaft fuer Chemisches Apparatewesen (DECHEMA); Deutsche Gesellschaft fur Materialkunde) Eds. E. Broszeit, H. Speckhardt. bk.rev.; index. circ. 700. (also avail. in microfilm from VCI; reprint service avail. from ISI) **Indexed:** B.C.I.R.A., Chem.Abstr., Copper Abstr., INSPEC, Int.Aerosp.Abstr., Met.Abstr., World Alum.Abstr. **Document type:** academic/scholarly publication.
—BLDSC (5396.640000); CASDDS; Ei; Genuine Article; SWETS. **CCC.**
   Formerly: Zeitschrift fuer Werkstofftechnik (ISSN 0049-8688)

669   GW
MAX-PLANCK-INSTITUT FUER METALLFORSCHUNG. MITTEILUNGEN. (Text in English and German) 1966. 3/yr. Max-Planck-Institut fuer Metallforschung, Seestr. 92, 70174 Stuttgart, Germany. TEL 0711-2095-1. FAX 0711-2265722. (back issues avail.) **Document type:** academic/scholarly publication.

MEILLEURES ADRESSES DE LA FONDERIE (YEAR). see *BUSINESS AND ECONOMICS — Trade And Industrial Directories*

MEILLEURES ADRESSES DU TRAITEMENT DE SURFACE. see *BUSINESS AND ECONOMICS — Trade And Industrial Directories*

MEILLEURES ADRESSES DU TRAITEMENT THERMIQUE. see *BUSINESS AND ECONOMICS — Trade And Industrial Directories*

669   IT   ISSN 0025-9829
MERCATO METALSIDERURGICO. 1954. 2/m. L.50000. Assofermet, Corso Venezia 47-49, 20121 Milan, Italy. TEL 39-2-76008824. FAX 39-2-781027. Ed. Eugenio Turchetti. adv.; B&W page L.800000; 305 x 440. bk.rev. circ. 1,800. (tabloid format) **Document type:** trade publication.
   Description: Review of markets for and prices of major steel products and non-ferrous metals, ferrous and non-ferrous scrap and hardware.

671   NE   ISSN 0026-0479
METAAL & TECHNIEK; vakblad voor de metaalnijverheid. Short title: M & T. 1955. m. fl.139.50. Misset (Subsidiary of: Reed Elsevier plc), Postbus 4, 7000 BA Doetinchem, Netherlands. TEL 31-8340-49911. FAX 31-8340-63638. (Co-sponsor: Metaalunie) Ed. F.A. Wolters. adv.; B&W page fl.2627, color page fl.4917; trim 215 x 285; adv. contact: Cor van Nek. stat. circ. 8,670. **Indexed:** Key to Econ.Sci., Met.Abstr., World Alum.Abstr. **Document type:** trade publication.
   Description: Follows the latest developments in methods of production and new products. Also discusses organizational, marketing and economic aspects of the metallurgical industry.

METAL. see *LABOR UNIONS*

METAL ARCHITECTURE. see *ARCHITECTURE*

669   AT
METAL ASIA. q. Aus.$116($80) Rala Information Service Pty. Ltd., 203-205 Darling St., Balmain, N.S.W. 2041, Australia. TEL 61-2-5551944. FAX 61-2-551496.

METAL BUILDING REVIEW. see *BUILDING AND CONSTRUCTION*

669   UK   ISSN 0026-0533
TN1   CODEN: MTBLAX
METAL BULLETIN. 1913. s-w. $949. Metal Bulletin plc, Park House, Park Terrace, Worcester Park, Surrey KT4 7HY, England. TEL 0171-827-9977. FAX 0181-337-8943. (U.S. subscr. to: Metal Bulletin Inc., 220 Fifth Ave., New York, NY 10001-7781. TEL 212-213-6202. FAX 212-213-1870) Eds. H. Cooke, A-M. Moreno. adv.; mkt.; stat.; tr.lit.; index. circ. 11,000. **Indexed:** AESIS, Art & Archaeol.Tech.Abstr., Cadscan, Chem.Abstr, Copper Abstr., Key to Econ.Sci., Lead Abstr., PROMT, World Alum.Abstr., Zincscan. **Document type:** bulletin.
—CASDDS. **CCC.**

669   US   ISSN 0373-4064
METAL BULLETIN MONTHLY. 1972. m. $345. Metal Bulletin Inc., 220 Fifth Ave., 19th Fl., New York. TEL 800-638-2525. FAX 212-213-6273. Ed. P. Millbank. adv.; bk.rev.; tr.lit.; index. circ. 10,000. **Indexed:** AESIS, Art & Archaeol.Tech.Abstr., Cadscan, Copper Abstr., Key to Econ.Sci., Lead Abstr., Met.Abstr., PROMT, World Alum.Abstr., Zincscan.
—BLDSC (5683.770000); Ei; Faxon; SWETS; UnCover. **CCC.**

669 338.2   UK   ISSN 0269-1698
HD9506.4
METAL BULLETIN PRICES & DATA BOOK. 1968. a. $97. Metal Bulletin plc, Park House, Park Terrace, Worcester Park, Surrey KT4 7HY, England. TEL 0171-827-9977. FAX 0181-337-8943. (U.S. subscr. to: Metal Bulletin Inc., 220 Fifth Ave., New York, NY 1001-7781. TEL 212-213-6202. FAX 212-213-1870) Ed. R. Serjeantson. adv. (back issues avail.) **Document type:** trade publication.
—BLDSC (5683.777000).
   Formerly (until 1986): Metal Bulletin Handbook (ISSN 0262-6454); Supersedes: Quin's Metal Handbook.
   Description: National and international prices, key international statistical information and data for the steel and non-ferrous metals and minerals industries.

671.2   AT
TS200
METAL CASTING AND SURFACE FINISHING; a journal for the foundryman metal finishers, diecasters and general metals industry. 1955. bi-m. Aus.$66. (Australian Foundry Institute) Rala Information Service Pty. Ltd., 203-205 Darling St., Balmain, N.S.W. 2041, Australia. TEL 02-555-1944. FAX 02-555-1496. Ed. Danielle Tibbles. adv.; bk.rev.; illus.; pat.; stat.; index. circ. 2,550. (also avail. in microform from UMI; back issues avail.) **Indexed:** AESIS, B.C.I.R.A., C.I.S. Abstr., Chem.Abstr., Met.Abstr., World Alum.Abstr.
—UMI.
   Former titles: Metals and Castings Australasia; Castings (ISSN 0008-7521)

669   US   ISSN 0539-4511
METAL CENTER NEWS. 1961. m. $55. Hitchcock Publishing (Subsidiary of: Capital Cities - A B C, Inc.), 191 S. Gary Ave., Carol Stream, IL 60188. TEL 708-665-1000. FAX 708-462-2225. TELEX 72-0404. Ed. Joseph C. Marino. adv.; bk.rev.; charts; illus.; stat.; circ. 12,600 (controlled).
—UMI. **CCC.**

METAL CONSTRUCTION NEWS. see *BUILDING AND CONSTRUCTION*

381   US   ISSN 0098-2210
HD9506.U6
METAL DISTRIBUTION. 1975. a. $15. Hitchcock Publishing (Subsidiary of: Capital Cities - A B C, Inc.), 191 S. Gary Ave., Carol Stream, IL 60188. TEL 708-665-1000. FAX 708-462-2225. Ed. Joseph C. Marino. adv.; illus. circ. 11,800.

669   US   ISSN 0026-055X
METAL FABRICATING NEWS. vol.8, 1970. q. free. W.A. Witney Co., 650 Race St., Rockford, IL 61105. TEL 815-965-4031. FAX 815-964-3175. Ed. Ronald L. Fowler. adv.; B&W page $1858; 7 x 10; adv. contact: Bonnie Fisher. bk.rev.; charts; illus.; tr.lit. circ. 37,000. **Indexed:** Met.Abstr., World Alum.Abstr. **Document type:** trade publication.

METALLURGY

669 US ISSN 0026-0576
TS550 CODEN: MEFIA7
METAL FINISHING; devoted exclusively to metallic surface treatments. (Includes annual: Metal Finishing Guidebook & Directory) 1903. m. $48 to institutions in U.S.; $71 to institutions in Canada & Mexico; $123 to institutions outside the Americas (effective 1996). Elsevier Science Inc., 655 Ave. of the Americas, New York, NY 10010. TEL 212-989-5800. FAX 212-633-3990. TELEX 420643 AEP Ul. (Subscr. to: Box 882, Madison Sq. Sta., New York, NY 10159-0882) adv.; bk.rev.; abstr.; illus.; mkt.; pat.; tr.lit.; index. circ. 11,293. (also avail. in microfilm from UMI; reprint service avail. from UMI) **Indexed:** A.S.& T.Ind., Cadscan, Chem.Abstr., Eng.Ind., Excerp.Med., Ind.Sci.Rev., INSPEC, Int.Packag.Abstr., Lead Abstr., Met.Abstr., PROMT, W.R.C.Inf., World Alum.Abstr., World Surf.Coat., Zincscan. **Document type:** trade publication.
—BLDSC (5684.000000); CASDDS; Ei; Faxon; SWETS; UnCover. CCC.
Former titles: Metal Industry (New York) (ISSN 0360-5159); Aluminum World and Brass and Copper Industries; Brass Founder and Finisher and Electro-Platers' Review; Copper and Brass; Platers' Guide.
Description: Covers technical and practical aspects of finishing metal and plastic products, including waste treatment and pollution control.
Refereed Serial

671 US ISSN 1040-967X
TS200
METAL FORMING. 1967. m. $25 (foreign $175) (free to qualified personnel). Precision Metal Forming Association, 27027 Chardon Rd., Richmond Hts., OH 44143. TEL 216-585-8800. FAX 216-585-2126. Ed. Donald B. Dobbins. adv.; charts; illus.; stat.; tr.lit.; circ. 60,000 (controlled). (back issues avail.) **Indexed:** Excerp.Med., Met.Abstr., World Alum.Abstr. **Document type:** trade publication.
—BLDSC (5685.230000); Ei; SWETS.
Formerly: Metal Stamping (ISSN 0026-069X)
Description: Covers industry news and trends, new technologies, equipment and materials in the metal forming and fabricating industries.

METAL MARKETING CORPORATION OF ZAMBIA. ANNUAL REPORT. see *BUSINESS AND ECONOMICS — Marketing And Purchasing*

669 II
METAL NEWS. bi-m. Indian Institute of Metals, A-1 Flat, 15th Fl., Chatterjee International Centre, 33A Chowringhee Rd., Calcutta 700 071, India. **Indexed:** Met.Abstr.

671 US ISSN 0026-0673
TN4 CODEN: MHTRAN
METAL SCIENCE AND HEAT TREATMENT. English translation of: Metallovedenie i Termicheskaya Obrabotka Metallov (RU ISSN 0026-0819) 1959. m. $1395 (foreign $1630) (effective 1996). (Ministerstvo Moshinostroeniya i Aiborostroeniya, Tsentral'nyi Sovet Nauchno-Tekhnicheskogo Obshchestva po Mashinostroeniyi, RU) Plenum Publishing Corp., Consultants Bureau, 233 Spring St., New York, NY 10013-1578. TEL 212-620-8468. FAX 212-463-0742. TELEX 23-421139. Ed. A.P. Gulyaev. (also avail. in microfilm from JSC; back issues avail.) **Indexed:** Cadscan, Chem.Titles, Curr.Cont., Energy Res.Abstr., Eng.Ind., Ind.Sci.Rev., INIS Atomind., INSPEC, ISMEC, Lead Abstr., Solid St.Abstr., Zincscan. **Document type:** academic/scholarly publication.
—BLDSC (0415.895000); Ei; Faxon; Genuine Article; SWETS; UMI; UnCover. CCC.
Refereed Serial

669 671 US ISSN 0076-6658
HD9506.U6
METAL STATISTICS. 1908. a. $153 (softcover $63). Capital Cities - A B C, Inc., Diversified Publishing Group, 825 Seventh Ave., New York, NY 10019. TEL 212-887-8532. FAX 212-887-8358. Ed. Jess Espinosa. adv. circ. 13,000. **Indexed:** AESIS.
Description: Contains historical data on production, consumption, import, export, inventories and prices of more than 25 metals, plus minor metals. Year-end review for each metal group, top 50 North American Metals companies, listing of major trade and industry associations, nonferrous and ferrous scrap definitions.

669 UK ISSN 0143-7607
HD9506.A1
METAL TRADERS OF THE WORLD. 1980. irreg., 5th ed., 1994. $221. Metal Bulletin plc, Park House, Park Terrace, Worcester Park, Surrey KT4 7HY, England. TEL 0171-827-9977. FAX 0181-337-8943. (U.S. subscr. to: Metal Bulletin Inc., 220 Fifth Ave., New York, NY 10001-7781. TEL 212-213-6202. FAX 212-213-1870) Ed. R. Serjeantson. adv. **Document type:** directory.
Description: Directory of metal traders worldwide; includes trading personnel, ownership, products handled and an ore classification guide.

669 AT ISSN 1039-9917
METAL WORKING AUSTRALIA. 1986. bi-m. Aus.$29. Thomson Business Publishing, 47 Chippen St., Chippendale, N.S.W. 2008, Australia. TEL 02-699-2411. FAX 02-698-3920. Ed. Graham Smith. adv. circ. 6,794.
Formerly (until 1993): Sheet Metal Australia (ISSN 0818-1764)

METALCASTER. see *BUSINESS AND ECONOMICS — Management*

669 621.9 SP
METALES Y METALURGIA. 1959. w. 30500 ptas. (foreign 42700 ptas.). Tecnipublicaciones, S.A., C. Albacete 5, 28027 Madrid, Spain. TEL 34-1-3261440. FAX 34-1-3262407. Ed. Jesus Heras. adv.; bk.rev.; illus.; stat.; circ. 5,000 (controlled).
Formerly (until 1984): Metales y Maquinas (ISSN 0210-055X)

METALETTER. see *LABOR UNIONS*

669 US
METALFORMING DIGEST. m. $160 to non-members (foreign $180); members $130 (foreign $145) (effective 1996). A S M International, Materials Information, Materials Park, OH 44073. TEL 216-338-5151. FAX 216-338-4634. TELEX 980-619. E-mail: DBarther@po.ASM-Intl.org. (UK addr.: Institute of Materials, Materials Information, 1 Carlton House Terr., London SW1Y 5DB, England. TEL 071-839-4071) (Co-sponsor: Institute of Materials) (reprint service avail. from UMI) **Document type:** abstracting/indexing.
Description: For metalforming professionals.

669 GW ISSN 0026-0746
TN3 CODEN: MTLLAF
METALL; internationale Zeitschrift fuer Handel, Wirtschaft, Technik und Wissenschaft. (Text in German; summaries in English) 1946. 11/yr. DM.427.50 (foreign DM.444). Huethig GmbH, Postfach 102869, 69018 Heidelberg, Germany. TEL 06221-489-0. FAX 06221-489482. Ed.Bd. adv.; bk.rev.; abstr.; charts; illus.; mkt.; pat.; tr.lit.; index, cum.index. circ. 2,827. **Indexed:** Art & Archaeol.Tech.Abstr., Chem.Abstr., Copper Abstr., Eng.Ind., Excerp.Med., INIS Atomind., Int.Aerosp.Abstr., Key to Econ.Sci., Met.Abstr., PROMT, World Alum.Abstr. **Document type:** academic/scholarly publication.
—BLDSC (5692.000000); CASDDS; Ei; Faxon; Genuine Article; SWETS. CCC.

669 AU
METALL; Fachblatt fuer die Metallverarbeitende Wirtschaft. m. S.596. (Wiener Innung der Schlosser) Oesterreichischer Wirtschaftsverlag, Nikolsdorfer Gasse 7-11, A-1051 Vienna, Austria. TEL 0222-555585. TELEX 1-11669. Ed. Wolfgang Biedermann. adv.; bk.rev.; illus. circ. 8,600. **Indexed:** Met.Abstr., PROMT, World Alum.Abstr.

669 SZ
METALL. 12/yr. Zuerichsee Medien AG, Seestr. 86, CH-7612 Staefa, Switzerland. TEL 01-9285611. FAX 01-9285600. Ed. Fridolin Kretz. circ. 5,000. **Document type:** trade publication.

669 331.8 SW ISSN 0026-0754
METALLARBETAREN. 1890. 11/yr. SEK 200 (effective 1990). Svenska Metallindustriarbetarefoerbundet, S-105 52 Stockholm, Sweden. TEL 46-8-786-81-73. Ed. Per Aahlstroem. adv.; bk.rev.; charts; stat.; index. circ. 450,192. (also avail. in microfilm) **Document type:** trade publication.
Formerly (until 1914): Jaernarbetaren.

669 GW ISSN 0938-7579
METALLBAU; die Fachzeitschrift fuer den Erfolg ihres Unternehmens. 1990. m. DM.151.20 (students DM.123.60). Callwey Verlag, Postfach 800409, 81604 Munich, Germany. TEL 089-436005-0. FAX 089-43600513. **Document type:** trade publication.

669 AU ISSN 0026-0762
METALLE. 1950. 5/w. S.1150 per month. Austria Presse Agentur (APA), Gunoldstrasse 14, A-1199 Vienna, Austria. Ed. H. Jaros. (processed) **Indexed:** Cadscan, Lead Abstr., Zincscan.

669 GW ISSN 0369-2345
METALLGESELLSCHAFT AKTIENGESELLSCHAFT. REVIEW OF THE ACTIVITIES. (Text in English and German) 1929; N.S. 1959. a. free. Metallgesellschaft AG, Reuterweg 14, 60271 Frankfurt a.M., Germany. TEL 069-159-2635. FAX 069-159-2107. TELEX 412250-MGF-D. Eds. Hans Schreiber, Sylvia Noske. bk.rev.; bibl.; charts; illus. circ. 7,000. **Indexed:** Chem.Abstr., Eng.Ind., Met.Abstr. **Document type:** trade publication.

669 IT ISSN 1122-1410
METALLI. m. (11/yr.) L.200000 (effective 1995). Edimet S.p.A., Via Corfu 102, 25124 Brescia, Italy. TEL 030-2421043. FAX 030-223802. Ed. Mario Comserva. adv.; B&W page L.3500000, color page L.4500000; trim 254 x 390; adv. contact: Anna Brescianini. circ. 4,500 (paid).
Description: Covers the global aluminium market from an Italian perspective.

671 FI ISSN 1237-6663
TJ4
METALLI TEKNIIKKA; Finnish journal of metalworking production. 1947. 11/yr. FIM 378. (Metalliteollisuusyhd Keskusliitto - Federation of Finnish Metal, Engineering and Electrotechnical Industries) Oy Talentum Ab, Ratavartijankatu 2, 00520 Helsinki, Finland. FAX 358-0-14422232. Ed. Tapani Luojus. adv.; B&W page FIM 12300, color page FIM 17600; trim 175 x 260; adv. contact: Raija Palomaki. bk.rev.; abstr.; bibl.; charts; illus. circ. 5,387. **Indexed:** B.C.I.R.A. **Document type:** trade publication.
Formerly (until 1995): Konepajamies (ISSN 0023-3277)
Description: For metallurgy professionals in Finland.

METALLIC MATERIALS. see *ENGINEERING — Engineering Mechanics And Materials*

669 KR
TN689 CODEN: MANFDD
METALLOFIZIKA I NOVEISHIE TEKHNOLOGII; nauchno-teoreticheskii zhurnal. English translation: Physics of Metals (UK ISSN 0275-9144) (Text in Russian) 1968. bi-m. $161. Akademiya Nauk Ukrainy, Institut Metallofiziki, Prosp. Vernadskogo, 36, 252142 Kiev, Ukraine. TEL 044-244-4068. FAX 044-224-7060. (Dist. by: Mezhdunarodnaya Kniga, B. Yakimanka 39, 117049 Moscow, Russia; Dist. in U.S. by: Victor Kamkin Inc., 4956 Boiling Brook Pkwy., Rockville, MD 20852. TEL 801-881-5973. FAX 301-881-1637) Ed. V.V. Nemoshkalenko. **Indexed:** Chem.Abstr., INIS Atomind., INSPEC, Int.Aerosp.Abstr., Met.Abstr., Phys.Ber., World Alum.Abstr.
—CASDDS. CCC.
Formerly (until 1994): Metallofizika (ISSN 0204-3580)

669 RU ISSN 0026-0819
CODEN: MTOBD3
METALLOVEDENIE I TERMICHESKAYA OBRABOTKA METALLOV. English translation: Metal Science and Heat Treatment (US ISSN 0026-0673) 1955. m. $93.60. Izdatel'stvo Mashinostroenie, 4, Stromynsky per., 107076 Moscow, Russia. TEL 095-269-7141. FAX 095-269-4897. E.d A.P. Gulyaev. adv.; page DM.4000. bk.rev.; bibl.; index. circ. 6,000. **Indexed:** Chem.Abstr., Eng.Ind., INIS Atomind., INSPEC, ISMEC, Met.Abstr., World Alum.Abstr. **Document type:** academic/scholarly publication.
—BLDSC (0108.300000); CASDDS. CCC.
Description: Covers the state-of-the-art developments of advanced science and engineering in the area of physical metalurgy and metal heat treatment.

METALLURGY

671.2   RU   ISSN 0026-0827
TS300   CODEN: METGA3
METALLURG. English translation: Metallurgist (US ISSN 0026-0894) 1956. m. $101 (effective 1996). (Mezhdunarodnyi Soyuz Metallurgov, Komitet R F po Metallurgii) Izdatel'stvo Metallurgiya, 2-i Obydenskii Per., 14, Moscow G-34, Russia. TEL 7-095-202-5747. FAX 7-095-202-5707. (Dist. by: Mezhdunarodnaya Kniga, B. Yakimanka 39, 117049 Moscow, Russia) Ed. A.G. Belikov. adv.: page $300. bk.rev.; bibl.; charts; illus.; stat.; index. circ. 1,500. **Indexed:** Chem.Abstr., Eng.Ind., INIS Atomind., ISMEC, Met.Abstr., World Alum.Abstr.
—CASDDS. **CCC.**

669   IT   ISSN 0026-0843
TN4   CODEN: MITLAC
LA METALLURGIA ITALIANA. 1909. m. L.100000 (foreign L.150000) (effective 1993). (Associazione Italiana di Metallurgia) Franco Angeli Editore, Viale Monza, 106, 20127 Milan, Italy. TEL 02-2895762. Dir. Aurelio Molaroni. adv.; bk.rev.; illus.; index. circ. 3,500. **Indexed:** Anal.Abstr., Appl.Mech.Rev., Cadscan, Chem.Abstr., Copper Abstr., Eng.Ind., INIS Atomind., Met.Abstr., World Alum.Abstr., Zincscan.
—BLDSC (5697.000000); CASDDS; Ei. **CCC.**

669   UK   ISSN 0141-8602
TN1   CODEN: MEMFAX
METALLURGIA: THE JOURNAL OF METALS TECHNOLOGY, METAL FORMING AND THERMAL PROCESSING. 1929. m. £104.55($200.80) (foreign £125.50). (British Forging Industry Association) Argus Business Publications Ltd. (Subsidiary of: Argus Press Group), Queensway House, 2 Queensway, Redhill, Surrey RH1 1QS, England. TEL 01737-768611. FAX 01737-761685. TELEX 948669 TOPJNL G. (Co-sponsors: British Industrial Furnace Constructors Association; British Cold Forging Group) Ed. K. Stanford. (also avail. in microform from UMI) **Indexed:** A.S.& T.Ind., Anal.Abstr., Appl.Mech.Rev., BMT, Br.Ceram.Abstr., Br.Tech.Ind., Cadscan, Chem.Abstr., Copper Abstr., Curr.Cont., Eng.Ind., Excerp.Med., ISMEC, Lead Abstr., Met.Abstr., PROMT, Zincscan. **Document type:** trade publication.
—BLDSC (5695.000000); CASDDS; Ei; Faxon; SWETS; UMI; UnCover.
Former titles (until 1978): Metallurgia and Metal Forming (ISSN 0368-945X); Which was formed by the merger of: Metallurgia (ISSN 0026-0835); And: Metal Forming (ISSN 0026-0622)
Description: Serves the thermal processing and forming sectors of the metals industry, with news, technical articles, and features covering forging, stamping, extrusion, casting, and powder forming.

669   US   ISSN 1073-5623
TN1   CODEN: MMTAEB
METALLURGICAL AND MATERIALS TRANSACTIONS A - PHYSICAL METALLURGY AND MATERIALS SCIENCE. 1970. m. $820 (effective 1996). A S M International, Materials Information, Materials Park, OH 44073-0002. TEL 216-338-5151. FAX 216-338-4634. TELEX 98-0619 ASMINT. (Co-sponsor: Minerals, Metals, and Materials Society) Ed. David E. Laughlin. charts; illus.; stat.; index. circ. 3,425. (also avail. in microform from UMI,PMC; reprint service avail. from UMI) **Indexed:** Agri.Eng.Abstr., B.C.I.R.A., Br.Ceram.Abstr., Cadscan, Chem.Abstr., Deep Sea Res.& Oceanogr.Abstr., Eng.Ind., Ind.Sci.Rev., INIS Atomind., INSPEC, Int.Aerosp.Abstr., Lead Abstr., Mass Spectr.Bull., Met.Abstr., Phys.Ber., World Alum.Abstr., Zincscan. **Document type:** academic/scholarly publication.
—BLDSC (5698.110000); CASDDS; Ei; Faxon; Genuine Article; SWETS; UMI; UnCover. **CCC.**
Former titles (until 1994): Metallurgical Transactions A - Physical Metallurgy and Materials Science (ISSN 0360-2133); Which supersedes in part: Metallurgical Transactions (ISSN 0026-086X); Which was formed by the merger of: American Society for Metals. Transactions Quarterly; T M S Transactions.
Description: Written to transfer basic research in physical metallurgy and materials science from the laboratory into the shop.
Refereed Serial

669   UK   ISSN 0951-0869
METALLURGICAL JOURNAL. English translation of: Hutnicke Listy (CS ISSN 0018-8069) 1987. m. £120($200) Riecansky Science Publishing Co., 7 Meadow Walk, Great Abingdon, Cambridge CB1 6AZ, England. TEL 0223 893295. FAX 0223-893295. **Indexed:** Eng.Ind., Met.Abstr.

669   UK   ISSN 0308-7794
METALLURGICAL PLANTMAKERS OF THE WORLD. 1973. irreg., latest 1988. $167. Metal Bulletin plc, Park House, Park Terrace, Worcester Park, Surrey KT4 7HY, England. TEL 0171-827-9977. FAX 0181-337-8943. (U.S. aubscr. to: Metal Bulletin Inc., 220 Fifth Ave., New York, NY 10001-7781. TEL 212-213-6202. FAX 212-213-1870) Ed. R. Serjeantson. adv. **Document type:** directory.
Description: International guide to ferrous and non-ferrous plant and equipment designers.

669   US   ISSN 0360-2141
CODEN: MTTBCR
METALLURGICAL TRANSACTIONS B - PROCESS METALLURGY. 1975. bi-m. $589 (effective 1996). A S M International, Materials Information, Materials Park, OH 44073-0002. TEL 216-338-5151. FAX 216-338-4634. TELEX 98-0619 ASMINT. (Co-sponsor: The Minerals, Metals, and Materials Society, Metallurgical) Ed. David E. Laughlin. bk.rev.; charts; illus.; stat.; index. circ. 1,570. (also avail. in microform from UMI; reprint service avail.) **Indexed:** AESIS, Agri.Eng.Abstr., Cadscan, Chem.Abstr., Deep Sea Res.& Oceanogr.Abstr., Eng.Ind., INIS Atomind., INSPEC, Lead Abstr., Mass Spectr.Bull., Met.Abstr., Phys.Ber., Soils & Fert., Zincscan. **Document type:** academic/scholarly publication.
—CASDDS; Faxon; Genuine Article; UMI; UnCover. **CCC.**
Supersedes in part: Metallurgy Transactions.
Description: Articles on extractive and process metallurgy.
Refereed Serial

669   US   ISSN 0026-0894
TS300   CODEN: MTLUA8
METALLURGIST. English translation of: Metallurg (RU ISSN 0026-0827) 1959. m. $1195 (foreign $1400) (effective 1996). (Ministerstvo Chernoi Metallurgii, RU) Plenum Publishing Corp., Consultants Bureau, 233 Spring St., New York, NY 10013-1578. TEL 212-620-8468. FAX 212-463-0742. TELEX 23-421139. Ed. A.G. Belikov. (also avail. in microfilm from JSC; back issues avail.) **Indexed:** Cadscan, Curr.Cont., Eng.Ind., INIS Atomind., ISMEC, Lead Abstr., Met.Abstr., Solid St.Abstr., Zincscan. **Document type:** academic/scholarly publication.
—BLDSC (0416.000000); Ei; Faxon; Genuine Article; UMI. **CCC.**
Refereed Serial

669   US   ISSN 0094-5447
TN675.3
METALLURGY - MATERIALS EDUCATION YEARBOOK. 1961. a. $35 to non-members; members $15. A S M International, Student Outreach, Materials Park, OH 44073-0002. TEL 216-338-5151. FAX 216-338-4634. TELEX 98-0619 ASMINT. **Document type:** directory.
Description: Reference source of metallurgy-materials science and engineering for four-year and graduate college programs. Includes U.S. and international programs. Lists faculty members in those departments.

669   GW   ISSN 0026-0908
CODEN: MLVBAD
METALLVERARBEITUNG; Fachzeitschrift fuer das Metallhandwerk in den oestlichen Bundeslaendern. 1947. bi-m. DM.80. Charles Coleman Verlag GmbH & Co. KG, Wahmstr. 56, 23552 Luebeck, Germany. TEL 0451-79933-0. FAX 0451-7993399. Ed. Dietrich Muhs. adv.: B&W page DM.3270; trim 190 x 263; adv. contact: Ulrich Claussen. bk.rev.; bibl.; charts; illus.; pat.; index, cum.index. circ. 6,700. **Indexed:** Art & Archaeol.Tech.Abstr., Chem.Abstr., Excerp.Med., Met.Abstr., Numis.Lit., World Alum.Abstr. **Document type:** trade publication.
—CASDDS.
Description: Technical journal dealing with traditional production methods; aimed at skilled workers from all branches of metals processing.

669   US
METALMECHANICS: LATIN AMERICAN INDUSTRIAL REPORT. (Avail. for each of 22 Latin American countries) 1985. a. $435 per country report. Aquino Productions, Box 15760, Stamford, CT 06901. TEL 203-325-3138. Ed. Andres C. Aquino.

METALS ALERT. see *MINES AND MINING INDUSTRY*

METALS AND MINERALS REVIEW. see *MINES AND MINING INDUSTRY*

669   UK   ISSN 0265-8321
METALS INDUSTRY NEWS. 1984. q. £35 (foreign £48). Argus Business Media Ltd., Fuel and Metals Journals (Subsidiary of: Argus Press Group), Queensway House, 2 Queensway, Redhill, Surrey RH1 1QS, England. TEL 01737-768611. FAX 01737-761685. TELEX 948669 TOPJNL G. Ed. Ken Stanford. adv.: B&W page £2060, color page £3095; trim 280 x 405. circ. 40,000. **Document type:** trade publication.
—BLDSC (5699.375300); Ei; SWETS.
Description: Features reports on various aspects of the metal industry worldwide.

669   II   ISSN 0970-423X
CODEN: MEMPEX
METALS MATERIALS AND PROCESSES. (Text in English) 1989. q. Rs.1500($125) Meshap Science Publishers, 75, 4th Floor, Lakshmi Building, Sir P.M. Road, Fort, Bombay 400 001, India. (Subscr. to: Meshap Science Publishers, Circulation Department, P.O. Box 8319, T.F. Deonar, Bombay 400 088, India) Ed. C.V. Sundaram. bk.rev.
—BLDSC (5699.388000); CASDDS.
Description: Covers the broad spectrum of materials systems including alloys, amorphous materials, ceramics, composites, metals, and polymers.

METALS WEEK. see *MINES AND MINING INDUSTRY*

METALS WEEK PRICE NOTIFICATION SERVICE. see *MINES AND MINING INDUSTRY*

METALSMITH. see *ARTS AND HANDICRAFTS*

669   AG
METALURGIA.* Asociacion de Industriales Metalurgicos, Alsina 1607 1 Piso, Buenos Aires, Argentina. **Indexed:** Chem.Abstr.

669   AG   ISSN 0325-0202
METALURGIA MODERNA. (Text in Spanish; summaries in English and Spanish) 1959. biennial. Sociedad Argentina de Metales, Santa Fe 1145, 1059 Buenos Aires, Argentina. adv. circ. 1,000.
Description: Covers the structure and behavior of metals.

669   SP   ISSN 0026-0991
T4   CODEN: MYELAF
METALURGIA Y ELECTRICIDAD. 1937. m. 8500 ptas. Antonio Gonzalez Porras., 35 2o, Apdo. 756, 28019 Madrid, Spain. TEL 34-1-469-04-20. FAX 34-1-4690304. Ed. Antonio Recio Cuevas. adv.: B&W page 93000 ptas., color page 106000 ptas.; 210 x 297. bk.rev.; abstr.; bibl.; charts; illus.; tr.lit.; index. circ. 55,000. **Indexed:** Chem.Abstr., Copper Abstr., Ind.SST, INSPEC, Met.Abstr., World Alum.Abstr.
—BLDSC (5700.000000); CASDDS; Ei.

669 643   CI   ISSN 0543-5846
CODEN: METABK
METALURGIJA. 1962. q. Faculty of Metallurgy, Aleja Narodnih Heroja 3, 44103 Sisak, Croatia. TEL 044 35226. FAX 044-30284. TELEX 23617. Ed. Ilija Mamuzic. adv. circ. 600. **Indexed:** Chem.Abstr., Met.Abstr., Ref.Zh. **Document type:** academic/scholarly publication.
—BLDSC (5700.120000); CASDDS; Ei.
Description: Presents scientific and professional papers.

671.3   US   ISSN 0026-1009
METALWORKING DIGEST. 1968. 12/yr. (includes end-of-year Metalworking Digest Literature Review). $48 (Canada $57.78; Mexico $ 54; elsewhere $72) (effective 1996). Gordon Publications, Inc., Part of Cahners Publishing Company, Division of Reed Elsevier Inc., 301 Gibraltar Dr., Box 650, Morris Plains, NJ 07950-0650. TEL 201-292-5100. FAX 201-898-9281. Ed. Richard Stevancsez. adv.; illus. circ. 115,000. (tabloid format)
—CCC.
Description: Focuses on metalworking plants manufacturing end-products by means of cutting and-or forming-type machine tools and allied equipment.

4668 METALLURGY

669 US ISSN 0197-2774
CODEN: MEIND6
METALWORKING INTERFACES;* bimonthly international report on lubrication and roles of interfaces in metalworking. 1976. bi-m. $55. Mk Infotech Company, 98 Schiller Ln., Lake Zurich, IL 60047. Ed. Mark Mrozek. abstr.; pat. circ. 1,000. **Indexed:** Chem.Abstr., Met.Abstr.
—CASDDS.

669 UK ISSN 0026-1033
METALWORKING PRODUCTION. 1900. m. Morgan-Grampian (Publishers) Ltd. (Subsidiary of: Morgan-Grampian plc), Morgan-Grampian House, 30 Calderwood St., London SE18 6QH, England. TEL 081-855-7777. FAX 081-854-7476. Ed. Andy Sandford. adv.; charts; illus.; tr.lit.; index. circ. 17,025. (also avail. in microform from UMI) **Indexed:** BMT, Br.Tech.Ind., INSPEC, ISMEC, Key to Econ.Sci., Met.Abstr., World Alum.Abstr., World Text.Abstr. **Document type:** trade publication.
—BLDSC (5700.250000); Ei; Faxon; SWETS. **CCC.**
Description: For production executives and engineers responsible for purchase of production machine tools and auxilliary equipment.

669 CN ISSN 0383-090X
METALWORKING PRODUCTION & PURCHASING; Canadian publication for production, purchasing & management in metalworking. 1974. 6/yr. Can.$34($55) Action Communications Inc., 135 Spy Court, Markham, ON L3R 5H6, Canada. TEL 905-477-3222. FAX 905-477-4320. Ed. M. Holtham. adv.; circ. 20,000 (controlled).
—UMI.

669 UK ISSN 0965-335X
METALWORKING TECHNOLOGY EUROPE. a. £60. Sterling Publications Ltd. (Subsidiary of: Sterling Publishing Group PLC), 86-88 Edgware Rd., London W2 2YW, England. TEL 071-258-0066. Ed. Peter Dempsey. **Document type:** trade publication.
—BLDSC (5700.350000).
Formerly: Manufacturing Technology International. Europe.

620.112 FR ISSN 0026-1084
TA462 CODEN: MTUXAS
METAUX; corrosion-industries. 1925. m. (11/yr.). 1700 F. Editions Metaux, 32 rue du Marechal-Joffre, 78100 Saint-Germain-en-Laye, France. TEL 34-51-62-11. FAX 30-61-49-57. TELEX 695 679. Ed. Dir. Jose Delville. adv.; bk.rev.; bibl.; charts; illus.; index. circ. 4,000. **Indexed:** Chem.Abstr., Eng.Ind., Met.Abstr.
—CASDDS.
Formed by the merger of (1950-1951): Metaux et Industries (ISSN 0461-9625); (1937-1951): Metaux et Corrosion (ISSN 0369-2930); Which was formerly (until 1937): Metaux (ISSN 1160-7262); (until 1934): Aciers Speciaux, Metaux et Alliages (ISSN 0365-7094); (until 1928): Aciers Speciaux et leurs Emplois (ISSN 0365-6683)

METAUX DEFORMATION. see *MACHINERY*

669 US ISSN 0026-1297
METLFAX. 1956. m. $45 (foreign $85; Canada $65). Huebcore Communications, Inc., 29100 Aurora Rd., Ste. 200, Solon, OH 44139. TEL 216-248-1125. FAX 612-686-0214. (Subscr. to: Box 21640, Eagan, MN 55121-0640. TEL 612-686-0303) Ed. James A. Masar. adv.; bk.rev.; charts; illus.; tr.lit. circ. 102,000.
—CCC.

MINERACAO METALURGIA. see *MINES AND MINING INDUSTRY*

669 531.64 US ISSN 0882-7508
TN496 CODEN: MPERE8
MINERAL PROCESSING AND EXTRACTIVE METALLURGY REVIEW. 1982. 8/yr. (in 2 vols., 4 nos./vol.). 265 ECU per vol. (effective 1994). Gordon and Breach Science Publishers, c/o International Publishers Distributor, 820 Town Center Dr., Langhorne, PA 19047. TEL 215-750-2642. FAX 215-750-6343. (Subscr. to: International Publishers Distributor, P.O. Box 90, Reading, Berkshire RG1 8JL, England. TEL 44-173-456-8316) Eds. Fiona Doyle, Kenneth N. Han. (also avail. in microform)
—BLDSC (5779.681500); CASDDS; Faxon; SWETS. **CCC.**
Former titles: Mineral Processing and Technology Review; Extractive and Process Metallurgy (ISSN 0273-3706)
Refereed Serial

MINERALES. see *MINES AND MINING INDUSTRY*

MINERALS INDUSTRY INTERNATIONAL. see *MINES AND MINING INDUSTRY*

MINERIA CHILENA. see *MINES AND MINING INDUSTRY*

669 JA ISSN 0289-6214
CODEN: MRMMED
MINING AND MATERIALS PROCESSING INSTITUTE OF JAPAN. METALLURGICAL REVIEW. (Text in English) s-a. $20. Mining and Materials Processing Institute of Japan - Shigen, Sozai Gakkai, Nogizaka Bldg., 9-6-41 Akasaka, Minato-ku, Tokyo 107, Japan. TEL 03-3402-0541. FAX 03-3402-1776. **Document type:** bulletin.
—BLDSC (5698.497000); CASDDS; Ei.

MINING, GEOLOGICAL AND METALLURGICAL INSTITUTE OF INDIA. TRANSACTIONS. see *MINES AND MINING INDUSTRY*

669 JA ISSN 0914-5958
MIYAJI GIHO/MIYAJI TECHNICAL REPORT. (Text in Japanese; summaries in English) 1985. a. Miyaji Tekkojo - Miyaji Iron Works Co., Ltd., 15-18, Nihonbashi Kodenma-cho, Chuo-ku, Tokyo 103, Japan.

671 US ISSN 0277-9951
MODERN APPLICATIONS NEWS; the metalworking idea magazine. Short title: M A N. 1967. 12/yr. $93 (foreign $110). Nelson Publishing Co., 2504 N. Tamiami Trail, Nokomis, FL 34275-3476. TEL 813-966-9521. FAX 813-966-2590. Ed. A. Verner Nelson. adv.; illus.; tr.lit. circ. 72,677. (reprint service avail. from UMI) **Document type:** trade publication.
—CCC.
Former titles: Modern Applications News for Design and Manufacturing (ISSN 0026-7473); Materials Application News for Design and Manufacturing.

671.2 US ISSN 0026-7562
TS200 CODEN: MOCAB5
MODERN CASTING. 1938. m. $45 (foreign $55). American Foundrymen's Society, Inc., 505 State St., Des Plaines, IL 60016. TEL 708-824-0181. Ed. David P. Kanicki. adv.; bk.rev.; charts; illus.; tr.lit. circ. 24,000. (also avail. in microform; reprint service avail. from UMI) **Indexed:** A.S.& T.Ind., AESIS, B.C.I.R.A., Chem.Abstr., Eng.Ind., Excerp.Med., Ind.Sci.Rev., Met.Abstr., PROMT, World Alum.Abstr. **Document type:** trade publication.
—BLDSC (5884.800000); CASDDS; Ei; Faxon; SWETS; UMI; UnCover. **CCC.**

671 US ISSN 0026-8127
TS200 CODEN: MOMLAJ
MODERN METALS.* 1945. m. $50. Trend Publishing Inc., 625 N. Michigan Ave., Ste. 2500, Chicago, IL 60611. TEL 312-222-2000. FAX 312-222-2026. Ed. Victor Cassidy. adv.; charts; illus.; mkt.; tr.lit. circ. 32,170. **Indexed:** A.S.& T.Ind., Chem.Abstr., Copper Abstr., Eng.Ind., Excerp.Med., Ind.Sci.Rev., Met.Abstr., Packag.Sci.Tech., World Alum.Abstr. **Document type:** trade publication.
—BLDSC (5890.000000); Ei; Faxon; SWETS; UnCover.

MODERN STEEL CONSTRUCTION. see *BUILDING AND CONSTRUCTION*

669 SP ISSN 1132-0354
MOLDES. 1989. 4/yr. $149 (effective 1994). Deltacad, Alcala 93, 4o M, 28009 Madrid, Spain. TEL 1-576-56-09. FAX 1-578-29-24. Ed. A. Perez de Camino. adv. circ. 3,500. **Document type:** trade publication.

669 US ISSN 1061-6071
CODEN: MMSEEI
MONOGRAPHS IN P - M SERIES. (Powder Metallurgy) 1992. irreg., no.2, 1992. price varies. Metal Powder Industries Federation, 105 College Rd. E., Princeton, NJ 08540. TEL 609-452-7700. FAX 609-987-8523. **Document type:** monographic series.
—BLDSC (5915.954000).
Description: Supplies a detailed tutorial of the technologies of powder metallurgy and particulate materials, emphasizing both scientific principles and commercial applications.

672 RU ISSN 0131-5145
TN730 CODEN: NTMSDL
MOSKOVSKII INSTITUT STALI I SPLAVOV. NAUCHNYE TRUDY. 1972. irreg. 0.85 Rub. Izdatel'stvo Metallurgiya, 2-i Obydenskii Per., 14, Moscow G-34, Russia. illus. **Indexed:** Chem.Abstr.
—BLDSC (0123.078000); CASDDS.

N A D C A INTERNATIONAL DIE CASTING CONGRESS. TRANSACTIONS. (North American Die Casting Association) see *ENGINEERING — Engineering Mechanics And Materials*

669 658.5 US ISSN 0077-3379
N A M F MANAGEMENT MANUAL. 1960. irreg., latest 1990. $100 to non-members; members $50. National Association of Metal Finishers, 401 N. Michigan Ave., Chicago, IL 60611-4267. TEL 312-644-6610. Ed. Brad Parcells. index.

669 658.5 US
N A M F REGULATORY COMPLIANCE MANUAL. irreg., updates approx. 3/yr. $250 to non-members; members $50. National Association of Metal Finishers, 401 N. Michigan Ave., Chicago, IL 60611-4267. TEL 312-644-6610. (looseleaf format)

669 GW
N C FERTIGUNG; Fachmagazin fuer Metallbearbeitung und Automation. 1980. 8/yr. DM.120. N C Technologie Verlags GmbH, Katernbergerstr. 55, Postfach 101169, 5600 Wuppertal 1, Germany. TEL 0202-389050. Ed. Juergen Kromberg.

669 II ISSN 0027-6839
TN1 CODEN: NLMJA3
N M L TECHNICAL JOURNAL. (Text in English) 1959. q. Rs.15($9) (effective 1990). National Metallurgical Laboratory, P.O. Burmamines, Jamshedpur 831 007, Bihar, India. TEL 26091. FAX 0657-27356. TELEX 0626-210. (Affiliate: Council of Scientific and Industrial Research) Ed. O.N. Mohanty. bk.rev.; charts; illus.; mkt.; pat. circ. 1,000. **Indexed:** Chem.Abstr., Eng.Ind., Met.Abstr., World Alum.Abstr.
—BLDSC (6113.900000); CASDDS.

669 US
N O M M A NEWSLETTER. bi-m. National Ornamental & Miscellaneous Metals Association, 804-10 Main St., Ste. E, Forest Park, GA 30050. TEL 404-363-4009. FAX 404-366-1852. **Document type:** newsletter.

669 JA ISSN 0918-4597
TN4
N R I M RESEARCH ACTIVITIES. (Text in English) 1959. a. exchange basis. National Research Institute for Metals - Kagaku Gijutsucho Kinzoku Zairyo Gijutsu Kenkyujo, Planning Section of Administration Division, 2-3-12 Nakameguro, Meguro-ku, Tokyo 153, Japan. TEL 81-3-3719-2271. FAX 81-3-3792-3337. circ. 660. **Indexed:** Curr.Cont., INSPEC (1968-), Met.Abstr., World Alum.Abstr.
—BLDSC (6180.548840); Ei; UnCover.
Formerly (until 1991): National Research Institute for Metals. Transactions (ISSN 0453-9222)
Description: Contains up-to-date research activities in NRIM and other information such as its organization and budget.

N T TECNICA E TECNOLOGIA. see *ENGINEERING — Mechanical Engineering*

METALLURGY 4669

669   CC   ISSN 1001-1935
CODEN: NACAEN
NAIHUO CAILIAO. (Text in Chinese) 1966. bi-m. $90. Yejin Bu, Luoyang Naihuo Cailiao Yanjiusuo, No. 43, Xiyuan Lu, Jianxi-qu, Luoyang, Henan 471039, People's Republic of China. TEL 86-379-413501. FAX 86-379-413630. TELEX 473053 LIRR CN. Ed. Liu Jiehua. adv.; bk.rev. circ. 8,500. **Document type:** academic/scholarly publication.
—CASDDS.
Description: Reports new achievements and experiences in the research, production, and application of refractories in China.

669.2   JA   ISSN 0027-772X
NAMARI TO AEN/LEAD AND ZINC. (Text in Japanese) 1964. bi-m. 1000 Yen (effective 1996). Japan Lead Zinc Development Association - Nihon Namari Aen Juyo Kenkyukai, New Hibiya Bldg., 1-3-6 Uchisaiwai-cho, Chiyoda-ku, Tokyo 100, Japan. FAX 03-591-9841. Ed. Hiroshi Tokunaga. adv.; bk.rev.; abstr.; charts; illus.; stat.; cum.index. circ. 1,900. Indexed: JTA, Met.Abstr., World Alum.Abstr.

669.722   US
NATIONAL ASSOCIATION OF ALUMINUM DISTRIBUTORS. TOPICS. 6/yr. free to qualified personnel. National Association of Aluminum Distributors, 1900 Arch St., Philadelphia, PA 19103-1498. TEL 215-564-3484. FAX 215-963-9785. Ed. Shannon Coghlan. circ. 1,000. **Document type:** newsletter.

669   JA   ISSN 0918-5119
NATIONAL RESEARCH INSTITUTE FOR METALS. ANNUAL REPORT/KINZOKU ZAIRYO GIJUTSU KENKYUJO NENPO. (Text in Japanese) 1985. a. National Research Institute for Metals, Planning Section of Administration Division, 2-3-12, Nakameguro, Meguro-ku, Tokyo 153, Japan. TEL 81-3-3719-2271. FAX 81-3-3792-3337. **Document type:** corporate report.

669 600   JA   ISSN 0288-0490
CODEN: NESHDF
NETSU SHORI/JAPAN SOCIETY FOR HEAT TREATMENT. JOURNAL. 1960. bi-m. 6600 Yen. Japan Society for Heat Treatment, Shinsen Bldg., 8-2, Shinsen-cho, Shibuya-ku, Tokyo 150, Japan. TEL 03-461-7116. FAX 03-461-0750. Ed. Suzuki Tomoo. adv.; bk.rev. circ. 5,000. Indexed: Chem.Abstr.
—BLDSC (4807.500000); CASDDS.

671.3705   US   ISSN 0146-9711
CODEN: NPPMDO
NEW PERSPECTIVES IN POWDER METALLURGY. 1966. irreg., vol.11, 1993. price varies. Metal Powder Industries Federation, 105 College Rd. E., Princeton, NJ 08540. TEL 609-452-7700. FAX 609-987-8523. circ. 1,000.
—CASDDS; Faxon. **CCC**.
Formerly: Perspectives in Powder Metallurgy (ISSN 0079-1032)
Description: Collection of papers on one specific topic from various sources.

669.1   JA   ISSN 0911-8764
NEWS FROM NISSHIN STEEL. (Text in English) m. Nisshin Steel Co., Ltd., 4-1 Marunouchi 3-chome, Chiyoda-ku, Tokyo 100, Japan. TEL 03-216-5511. FAX 03-214-1895. TELEX 222-2788. illus.
Description: Contains news and articles about the company.

669   CN   ISSN 0829-8351
NICKEL. 1985. q. free. Nickel Development Institute (NiDI), 214 King St. W., Ste. 510, Toronto, ON M5H 3S6, Canada. TEL 416-591-7999. FAX 416-591-7987. TELEX 06-218656. Ed. James S. Borland. bk.rev. circ. 35,000. **Document type:** trade publication.
Description: Devoted to nickel and its applications.

669   JA   ISSN 0546-126X
NIHON SEIKOSHO GIHO/JAPAN STEEL WORKS TECHNICAL REVIEW. (Text in English and Japanese) 1959. s-a. Nihon Seikosho - Japan Steel Works, Ltd., 1-12 Yuraku-cho, Chiyoda-ku, Tokyo 100, Japan. Indexed: Met.Abstr., World Alum.Abstr.

669.1   JA
NIPPON STEEL FORUM. s-a. free. Nippon Steel Corporation, Public Relations Dept., Corporate Secretariat Div., 6-3 Ote-machi 2-chome, Chiyoda-ku, Tokyo 100-71, Japan. TEL 03-242-4111. (US addr.: 345 Park Ave. S., 41st Fl., New York, NY 10154. TEL 212-486-7150) charts; illus.
Description: Aims to survey the company's full range of activities in the context of the economic environment in which it operates. Also attempts to present the current trends in Japan's industry and economy. Cultural factors affecting the economy are examined.

669.1   JA   ISSN 0048-0452
NIPPON STEEL NEWS. (Text in English) 1970. m. free. Nippon Steel Corporation, 6-3 Ote-machi 2-chome, Chiyoda-ku, Tokyo 100-71, Japan. TEL 03-242-4111. FAX 03-275-9607. TELEX J-22291. (US addr.: 345 Park Ave., 41st Fl., New York, NY 10154. TEL 212-486-7150) illus. Indexed: Br.Ceram.Abstr., Met.Abstr., World Alum.Abstr.
Description: Focuses on technological innovations, new companies and mergers.

669.1   JA
NIPPON STEEL REPORT. a. Nippon Steel Corporation, 6-3 Ote-machi 2-chome, Chiyoda-ku, Tokyo 100-71, Japan. TEL 03-242-4111. FAX 03-275-5607. TELEX J-22291. (US addr.: 345 Park Ave., 41st Fl., New York, NY 10154. TEL 212-486-7150)
Description: Presents financial information on the company. Explores business developments, electronics information, new materials, sales, revenue and future management risks.

672.05   JA   ISSN 0300-306X
TS300
NIPPON STEEL TECHNICAL REPORT. English translation of: Seitetsu Kenkyu. 1972. s-a. free. Nippon Steel Corporation, 2-6-3 Otemachi, Chiyoda-ku, Tokyo 100, Japan. TEL 03-242-4111. (U.S. addr.: 345 Park Ave, 41st Fl., New York, NY 10154. TEL 212-486-7150) illus. Indexed: Br.Ceram.Abstr., Corros.Abstr., J.of Ferroc., JCT, JTA, Met.Abstr., World Alum.Abstr.
—BLDSC (6113.557000); Ei; Faxon; UnCover.
Formerly: Nippon Steel Technical Report. Overseas.

669.1   JA
NISSHIN. (Text in Japanese) no.434, Apr. 1990. m. Nisshin Steel Co., Inc., 4-1 Marunouchi 3-chome, Chiyoda-ku, Tokyo 100, Japan. TEL 03-216-5511. FAX 03-214-1895. TELEX 222-2788. **Document type:** newsletter.
Description: In-house magazine for company employees.

669.1   JA
NISSHIN STEEL. ANNUAL REPORT. (Text in English) a. Nisshin Steel Co., Ltd., General Administrattion Department, 4-1 Marunouchi 3-chome, Chiyoda-ku, Tokyo 100, Japan. TEL 03-216-5511. FAX 03-214-1895. TELEX 222-2788. (Or: 16 Raffles Quay, No.20-01, Hong Leong Bldg., Singapore 0104, Singapore; Nisshin USA, Inc., 375 Park Ave., New York, NY 10152; Immermannstr. 45, D-4000 Dusseldorf 1, Germany; Changfugong Center Office Bldg., 5F, Jianguomenwai Dajie 26, Chaoyang Qu, Beijing, People's Republic of China) charts; illus.; stat.

NON-DESTRUCTIVE TESTING - AUSTRALIA; a journal of measurement control & testing. see ENGINEERING — Engineering Mechanics And Materials

669   US   ISSN 0360-9553
HD9506.U6
NON-FERROUS METAL DATA (YEAR). 1920. a. $350. American Bureau of Metal Statistics Inc., Box 1405, Plaza Sta., 400 Plaza Dr., Secaucus, NJ 07094-0405. TEL 201-863-6900. FAX 201-863-6050. Ed. John Barna. cum.index. circ. 3,000. Indexed: SRI.
Formerly (until 1974): American Bureau of Metal Statistics. Year Book (ISSN 0065-7611)
Description: Provides statistical industry data of mine, smelter and refined production, consumption, inventories, imports, exports and metal statistics for ABMS members, industry, government agencies and subscribers.
Refereed Serial

673   UK   ISSN 0078-0987
HD9539.A1
NON-FERROUS METAL WORKS OF THE WORLD. 1967. irreg., latest 1993. $309. Metal Bulletin plc, Park House, Park Terrace, Worcester Park, Surrey KT4 7HY, England. TEL 0171-827-9977. FAX 0181-337-8943. (Dist. in U.S. by: Metal Bulletin Inc., 220 Fifth Ave., New York, NY 10001-7781. TEL 212-213-6202. FAX 212-213-1870) Ed. R. Serjeantson. adv. **Document type:** directory.
Description: Definitive guide to the world's nonferrous metal smelters, refiners, semi-fabricators and secondary ingot makers.

669 622   CC   ISSN 1003-6326
CODEN: TNMCEW
NONFERROUS METALS SOCIETY OF CHINA. TRANSACTIONS. Chinese edition: Zhongguo Youse Jinshu Xuebao (ISSN 1004-0609) (Text in English) 4/yr. $245 (foreign $260) (effective 1996). Zhongguo Youse Jinshu Gongye Zonggongsi - China Nonferrous Metals Industrial Company, 1 Wenxingjie, Xiwai, Beijing 100044, People's Republic of China. TEL 86-1-8322211. FAX 86-1-8321362. TELEX 222589 GRIMM CN. (Subscr. to: Zhongguo Youse Jinshu Xuebao Bianjibu, Zhongnan Gongye Daxue, Changsha, Hunan 410083, P.R. China; Dist. outside of P.R. China by: Alerton Press, Inc. 150 Fifth Ave., New York, NY 10011. TEL 212-924-3950. FAX 212-463-9684) (Co-sponsor: Zhongguo Youse Jinshu Xuehui - Nonferrous Metals Society of China) Ed. He Jishan. **Document type:** academic/scholarly publication.
—CASDDS; Ei; UnCover. **CCC**.
Description: Publishes research papers on the latest developments in the fields of nonferrous metals and mining technology.

NORTH CAROLINA METALWORKING DIRECTORY. see BUSINESS AND ECONOMICS — Trade And Industrial Directories

669.6   UK   ISSN 0029-4098
NOTES ON TIN. 1956. m. £24. International Tin Council, Haymarket House, 1 Oxendon St., London SW1Y 4EQ, England. stat. circ. 500. (processed)
Description: World press digest on tin prospecting, mining, smelting, recycling, tin-using industry, trade, prices, market, government legislation and taxes.

669   RU
NOVYE ISSLEDOVANIYA V KHIMII, METALLURGII I OBOGASHCHENII. (Subseries of: Nauchnye Trudy) irreg. 0.75 Rub. Sankt-Peterburgskii Gornyi Institut - St. Petersburg Mining Institute, 21-ya Liniya 2, Vasilevskii Ostrov, 199026 St. Petersburg, Russia. TEL 7-812-2136078. FAX 7-812-2132613. TELEX 121494. illus.

338.47 672   FR   ISSN 0474-5973
O E C D IRON AND STEEL INDUSTRY. (Text in English, French) 1953. a. price varies. Organization for Economic Cooperation and Development, 2 rue Andre-Pascal, 75775 Paris Cedex 16, France. (U.S. orders to: O.E.C.D. Publications and Information Center, 2001 L St., N.W., Ste. 700, Washington, DC 20036-4910. TEL 202-785-6323) (also avail. in microfiche from OEC,CIS) Indexed: IIS.

669   PL   ISSN 0867-2628
CODEN: OBPLAX
OBROBKA PLASTYCZNA METALI/METAL FORMING. 1959. 5/yr. 65 Zl. (effective 1996). Instytut Obrobki Plastycznej, Ul. Zamenhofa 4, 61-120 Poznan, Poland. TEL 48-61-771081. FAX 48-61-791682. TELEX 0413480 INOP PL. Ed. Boleslaw Kwasniewski. adv. circ. 300. **Document type:** monographic series.
—BLDSC (6197.450100); CASDDS.
Formerly (until 1990): Obrobka Plastyczna (ISSN 0472-4313)
Description: Publishes articles about metal forming technology, machines, tools and scientific investigations.

671   RU
OCHISTKA VODNOGO I VOZDUSHNOGO BASSEINOV NA PREDPRIYATIYAKH CHERNOI METALLURGII. irreg. 1.12 Rub.($18.60) Izdatel'stvo Metallurgiya, 2-i Obydenskii Per., 14, Moscow G-34, Russia. (Co-sponsor: Ministerstvo Chernoi Metallurgii) illus. Indexed: Chem.Abstr.

METALLURGY

669   PL   ISSN 1230-7408
CODEN: OCPOAF
OCHRONA POWIETRZA I PROBLEMY ODPADOW. 1967. bi-m. $20.50. (Stowarzyszenie Inzynierow i Technikow Przemyslu Hutniczego) Wydawnictwo Czasopism i Ksiazek Technicznych SIGMA - NOT, Ul. Ratuszowa 11, P.O. Box 1004, 00-950 Warsaw, Poland. TEL 48-22-180918. FAX 48-22-192187. TELEX 814550 SIGMA PL. (Dist. by: SIGMA NOT Ltd., Ul. Bartycka 20, 00-716 Warsaw, Poland) Ed. Janusz Lutynski. circ. 2,150. **Indexed:** Met.Abstr., World Alum.Abstr.
—BLDSC (6235.081000); CASDDS.
Formerly (until 1993): Ochrona Powietrza (ISSN 0137-3714)

669   GW   ISSN 0078-3420
CODEN: ORSMAR
OERLIKON SCHWEISSMITTEILUNGEN. 1955. irreg. free. Oerlikon Schweisstechnik GmbH, 67304 Eisenberg-Pfalz, Germany. FAX 06351-76335. Ed. K. Weigel. adv. contact: H. Bilarski. circ. 5,000. **Indexed:** BMT, Chem.Abstr. **Document type:** bulletin.
—CASDDS.
Description: Technical and scientific information on welding and related fields.

669   NE
ONDERNEMINGSANALYSES METAAL- EN ELEKTRO-INDUSTRIE. a. fl.89.50. Delwel Uitgeverij B.V., Postbus 19110, 2500 CC The Hague, Netherlands. TEL 31-70-3624800. FAX 31-70-3605606.
Description: Financial and economic information on the metals and electronics industries in the Netherlands.

669   UK   ISSN 0969-9929
ORACLE TECHNICAL SUPPLEMENT. 1989. m. £32 to non-members. Institute of Sheet Metal Engineering, Exeter House, 48 Holloway Head, Birmingham B1 1NQ, England. TEL 0121-622-7387. FAX 0121-666-6316. Ed. M.A. Ruston. adv.; bk.rev.; abstr. **Document type:** academic/scholarly publication, newsletter.
Description: Contains technical articles on metallurgy and informs members of coming events and conferences.

669   US   ISSN 0474-6392
ORGANOMETALLIC SYNTHESES. 1965. irreg., vol.2, 1982. Academic Press, Inc., 525 B St., Ste. 1900, San Diego, CA 92101-4495. TEL 619-231-0926. FAX 619-699-6715. (Subscr. to: Order Dept., 6277 Sea Harbor Dr., 4th Fl., Orlando, FL 32887. TEL 800-321-5068) Eds. John J. Eisch, R. Bruce King. (reprint service avail. from ISI)
Refereed Serial

669   US   ISSN 0191-5940
ORNAMENTAL - MISCELLANEOUS METAL FABRICATOR. 1959. bi-mo. $15. National Ornamental & Miscellaneous Metals Association, 804-10 Main St., Ste. E, Forest Park, GA 30050. TEL 404-237-5334. FAX 404-366-1852. Ed. Todd Daniel. adv. contact: Todd Daniel. bk.rev.; index. circ. 8,000. **Document type:** trade publication.
Formerly (until 1977): Ornamental Metal Fabricator.

OXIDATION OF METALS; an international journal of the science of gas-solid reactions. see CHEMISTRY — Physical Chemistry

671   US   ISSN 0146-972X
P - M TECHNOLOGY NEWSLETTER. (Powder Metallurgy) 1960. m. $70 to individuals; institutions $145. American Powder Metallurgy Institute, 105 College Rd. E., Princeton, NJ 08540. TEL 609-452-7700. FAX 609-987-8523. Ed. Peter K. Johnson. bk.rev.; charts; illus.; stat.; tr.lit. circ. 3,000. (reprint service avail. from UMI) **Document type:** newsletter.
Description: Covers international developments in metal powder industry and technology; R & D reports, company and industry news, meetings, and new products.

PARTICULATE SCIENCE AND TECHNOLOGY; an international journal. see ENGINEERING — Chemical Engineering

PHOENIX: VOICE OF THE SCRAP RECYCLING INDUSTRIES. see ENVIRONMENTAL STUDIES

669 530   US   ISSN 0275-9144
TN689   CODEN: PMTSDT
PHYSICS OF METALS. English translation of: Metallofizika i Noveishie Tekhnologii. vol.3, 1982. 6/yr. (in 1 vol.; 6 nos./vol.). 424 ECU (effective 1996). (Akademiya Nauk Ukrainy, Institut Metallofiziki, KR) Gordon and Breach Science Publishers, c/o International Publishers Distributor, 820 Town Center Dr., Langhorne, PA 19046. TEL 215-750-2642. FAX 215-750-6343. (Subscr. to: International Publishers Distributor, P.O. Box 90, Reading, Berkshire RG1 8JL, England. TEL 44-173-456-8316) Ed. V. Baryakhtar. adv. (also avail. in microform; back issues avail.) **Indexed:** INSPEC, Met.Abstr., World Alum.Abstr.
—BLDSC (0416.855000). CCC.
Refereed Serial

620.1 669   RU   ISSN 0031-918X
TN690   CODEN: PHMMA6
PHYSICS OF METALS AND METALLOGRAPHY. Russian edition: Fizika Metallov i Metallovedenie (ISSN 0015-3230) 1957. 12/yr. (in 2 vols., 6 nos./vol.). $1550 in U.S. & Canada (elsewhere $1692) (effective 1995). Interperiodica, Ul. Profsoyuznaya 90, Moscow 117864, Russia. TEL 7-095-3360066. FAX 7-095-3360666. (Subscr. to: Interperiodica, Box 1831, Birmingham, AL 35201-1831. TEL 205-995-1567. FAX 205-995-1588) adv.; bk.rev.; bibl.; charts; illus. circ. 900. (also avail. in microfilm from UMI; back issues avail.) **Indexed:** Eng.Ind., INSPEC, Met.Abstr., Phys.Ber., World Alum.Abstr. **Document type:** academic/scholarly publication.
—BLDSC (0416.860000); Ei; Faxon; SWETS; UMI; UnCover. CCC.
Description: Contains investigations of the physical properties of metals and alloys, and studies of phenomena occuring during all phases of manufacture.
Refereed Serial

671.732   US   ISSN 0360-3164
TS670   CODEN: PSFMDH
PLATING AND SURFACE FINISHING; electroplating, finishing of metals, organic finishing. 1909. m. $60 to non-members; members $16. American Electroplaters and Surface Finishers Society, Inc. (AESF), 12644 Research Pkwy., Orlando, FL 32826-3298. TEL 407-281-6441. FAX 407-281-6446. TELEX 510-601-6246. Ed. Sylvia L. Baxley; Pub. Ted Witt. adv. contact: Steve Rigo. bk.rev.; abstr.; bibl.; charts; illus.; pat.; tr.lit.; index. circ. 10,975. (also avail. in microform from UMI; reprint service avail. from UMI) **Indexed:** A.S.& T.Ind., Cadscan, Chem.Abstr., Copper Abstr., Curr.Cont., Eng.Ind., Excerp.Med., INSPEC, Lead Abstr., Met.Abstr., Risk Abstr., World Alum.Abstr., Zincscan. **Document type:** trade publication.
—BLDSC (6538.050000); CASDDS; Ei; Faxon; SWETS; UMI; UnCover.
Supersedes: Plating (ISSN 0032-1397)

669.2   UK   ISSN 0032-1400
TN799.P7   CODEN: PTMRA3
PLATINUM METALS REVIEW. 1957. q. free. Johnson Matthey PLC, 78 Hatton Garden, London EC1N 8JP, England. TEL 0171-269-8000. FAX 0171-269-8389. Ed. S.V. Ashton. bk.rev.; abstr.; illus.; pat.; index. circ. 10,000. **Indexed:** AESIS, Art & Archaeol.Tech.Abstr., Br.Ceram.Abstr., C.R.I.Abstr., C.R.I.Curr.Cont., Chem.Abstr., Energy Info.Abstr., Eng.Ind., Environ.Abstr., Excerp.Med., Met.Abstr., Soils & Fert., World Alum.Abstr., World Text.Abstr. **Document type:** trade publication.
—BLDSC (6538.300000); CASDDS; CIS; Ei; Faxon; UnCover.
Description: Survey of research on the platinum metals (platinum, palladium, rhodium, iridium, osmium, rutherium) and developments in their application in industry.

669   PL   ISSN 0324-802X
TN600   CODEN: ZNPHBN
POLITECHNIKA SLASKA. ZESZYTY NAUKOWE. HUTNICTWO. (Text in Polish; summaries in English and Russian) 1971. irreg. price varies. Politechnika Slaska, Katowicka 7, 44-100 Gliwice, Poland. FAX 371655. TELEX 036304. (Dist. by: Ars Polona, Krakowskie Przedmiescie 7, 00-068 Warsaw, Poland) Ed. Stanislaw Serkowski. circ. 205. **Indexed:** Chem.Abstr., Met.Abstr.
—BLDSC (9512.327300); CASDDS.

669   PL   ISSN 0079-3345
TN607   CODEN: POPMB3
POLSKA AKADEMIA NAUK. ODDZIAL W KRAKOWIE. KOMISJA METALURGICZNO-ODLEWNICZA. PRACE: METALURGIA. (Text in English and Polish; summaries in English and Russian) 1965. irreg., no.41, 1991. price varies. Polska Akademia Nauk, Oddzial w Krakowie, Komisja Metalurgiczno-Odlewnicza, Ul. Slawkowska 17, 31-016 Krakow, Poland. TEL 48-12-224853. FAX 48-12-222791. Ed. Czeslaw Podrzucki. circ. 500. **Indexed:** Chem.Abstr., Eng.Ind. **Document type:** monographic series.
—BLDSC (6588.010000); CASDDS.
Formerly: Polska Akademia Nauk. Komisja Metalurgii i Odlewnictwa. Metalurgia.

666   KR   ISSN 0032-4795
TN695   CODEN: PMANAI
POROSHKOVAYA METALLURGIYA; vsesoyznyi nauchno-tekhnicheskii zhurnal. English translation: Powder Metallurgy and Metal Ceramics (US ISSN 1068-1302) (Text in Russian; summaries in English and Russian) 1961. bi-m. $99 (effective 1996). (Akademiya Nauk Ukrainy, Institut Problem Materialovedeniya) Vidavnitstvo Naukova Dumka, Vul. Tereshchenkivska 3, 252601 Kiev, Ukraine. TEL 044-224-40-68. FAX 044-224-70-60. Ed. V.I. Trefilov. bk.rev.; illus. circ. 1,300. **Indexed:** Chem.Abstr., Copper Abstr., Eng.Ind., INSPEC, Int.Aerosp.Abstr., ISMEC, Met.Abstr., World Alum.Abstr.
—BLDSC (0130.280000); CASDDS. CCC.

671   UK   ISSN 0032-5899
TN695   CODEN: PWMTAU
POWDER METALLURGY. 1958. q. £152($331) to non-members; members £85 ($170). Institute of Materials, 1 Carlton House Terrace, London SW1Y 5DB, England. TEL 071-839-4071. FAX 071-839-2078. TELEX 8814813-METSOC-G. Ed. Mary Chim. adv.; index. circ. 850. **Indexed:** ABTICS, Br.Ceram.Abstr., Br.Tech.Ind., Cadscan, Chem.Abstr., Copper Abstr., Curr.Cont., Eng.Ind., INSPEC, Int.Aerosp.Abstr., Lead Abstr., Met.Abstr., World Alum.Abstr., Zincscan. **Document type:** academic/scholarly publication.
—BLDSC (6571.950000); CASDDS; Ei; Faxon; SWETS; UMI; UnCover.
Description: Provides international coverage of the science and practice of powder metallurgy.

671.37   US   ISSN 1068-1302
TN695   CODEN: PMMCEF
POWDER METALLURGY AND METAL CERAMICS. English translation of: Poroshkovaya Metallurgiya (KR ISSN 0032-4795) 1962. m. $1395 (foreign $1630) (effective 1996). (Ukrainian Academy of Sciences, KR) Plenum Publishing Corp., Consultants Bureau, 233 Spring St., New York, NY 10013-1578. TEL 212-620-8468. FAX 212-463-0742. TELEX 23-421139. Ed. V.I. Trefilov. (also avail. in microfilm from JSC; back issues avail.) **Indexed:** Chem.Titles, Curr.Cont., Energy Res.Abstr., Eng.Ind., INSPEC, ISMEC, Met.Abstr., Solid St.Abstr. **Document type:** academic/scholarly publication.
—BLDSC (0416.906000); Faxon; Genuine Article; SWETS; UMI; UnCover. CCC.
Formerly (until 1994): Soviet Powder Metallurgy and Metal Ceramics (ISSN 0038-5735)

669   II   ISSN 0971-0728
CODEN: PMSTES
POWDER METALLURGY SCIENCE & TECHNOLOGY. (Text in English) 1989. q. Rs.500 (foreign $50). Powder Metallurgy Development Centre Pvt. Ltd., P-26 Laxminagar, Saidabad, Hyderabad 500 659, India. TEL 91-40-4065951. FAX 91-40-4069587. TELEX 425 2184 PSL IN. Ed. N.T. George. adv. contact: K. Damodar Rao. bk.rev. circ. 1,200. **Document type:** academic/scholarly publication.
—BLDSC (6572.290000); CASDDS; Ei.

METALLURGY

669 PL ISSN 0137-3846
TA418.76 CODEN: PLOCAE
POWLOKI OCHRONNE. (Text in Polish; summaries in English, German, and Russian) 1973. bi-m. 490000 Zl.($51.60) (effective 1994). Instytut Mechaniki Precyzyjnej, Duchnicka 3, 00-967 Warsaw, Poland. TEL 48-2-6634313. FAX 48-2-6634332. TELEX 813555 PL. (Dist. by: Ars Polona- Ruch, Krakowskie Przedmiescie 7, Warsaw, Poland) Ed. Henryk Andrzejewski. bk.rev. circ. 400. **Indexed:** Chem.Abstr., Copper Abstr., Met.Abstr., World Alum.Abstr.
—BLDSC (6579.010000); CASDDS.
Description: Covers corrosion, and protection of metals, electroplating, chemical and mechanical surface treatment, conversion coatings, etc.

669 GW ISSN 0032-678X
TN690 CODEN: PMTLA5
PRAKTISCHE METALLOGRAPHIE. (Text in English and German) 1964. m. DM.182.40. Carl Hanser Verlag, Kolbergerstr. 22, 81679 Munich, Germany. TEL 089-998300. FAX 089-984809. (Subscr. to: Postfach 860420, 81631 Munich, Germany) Ed. G. Petzow. adv.; bk.rev.; abstr.; charts; illus.; mkt.; index. circ. 2,000. **Indexed:** Ceram.Abstr., Chem.Abstr., Eng.Ind., INSPEC (1971-), Met.Abstr., World Alum.Abstr. **Document type:** trade publication.
—BLDSC (6595.060000); CASDDS; Ei; Faxon; SWETS. **CCC**.

PRECIOUS METALS NEWS AND REVIEW. see *JEWELRY, CLOCKS AND WATCHES*

669 UK ISSN 0264-4703
PRECISION TOOLMAKER. 1983. bi-m. £68($173) (overseas £94). Argus Business Media Ltd., International Trade Publications (Subsidiary of: Argus Press Group), Queensway House, 2 Queensway, Redhill, Surrey RH1 1QS, England. TEL 01737-768611. FAX 01737-773993. TELEX 948669 TOPJNL G. Ed. D. Tellett. circ. 5,000. **Document type:** trade publication.
—BLDSC (6604.015000); Ei; SWETS.
Incorporates (vol.3, 1985): Tooling and Machining.

PREVISIONS GLISSANTES DETAILLEES EN PERSPECTIVES SECTORIELLES (VOL.9): FONDERIE ET TRANSFORMATION DES METAUX. see *BUSINESS AND ECONOMICS — Economic Situation And Conditions*

PREVISIONS GLISSANTES DETAILLEES EN PERSPECTIVES SECTORIELLES (VOL.18): SIDERUGIE ET PREMIERE TRANSFORMATION DE L'ACIER. see *BUSINESS AND ECONOMICS — Economic Situation And Conditions*

PREVISIONS GLISSANTES DETAILLEES EN PERSPECTIVES SECTORIELLES (VOL.19): INDUSTRIE DES NON-FERREUX. see *BUSINESS AND ECONOMICS — Economic Situation And Conditions*

660 546 PL
PROBLEMY PROJEKTOWE PRZEMYSLU I BUDOWNICTWA; czasopismo naukowo-techniczne. 1953. q. 40 Zl.($20) (effective 1996). Przedsiebiorstwo Inzynierskie "Biprohut", Sp. z o.o., Ul. Dubois 16, 44-100 Gliwice, Poland. TEL 48-32-316011. FAX 48-32-312435. TELEX 036227 PL. Ed. Ryszard Gorczynski. adv.: color page $1000; trim 200 x 290. bk.rev.; index. circ. 1,800. (back issues avail.) **Document type:** consumer publication, trade publication.
Former titles: Problemy Projektowe (ISSN 0239-7404); (until 1982): Problemy Projektowe Hutnictwa i Przemyslu Maszynowego oraz Biur Projektujacych Zaklady Produkcyjne (ISSN 0239-2089); Which was formed by the merger of (1960-1981): Problemy Projektowe Hutnictwa i Przemyslu Maszynowego (ISSN 0137-8449) & (1965-1981): Problemy Projekowe Biur Projektujacych Zaklady Produkcyjne (ISSN 0208-6921).
Description: For engineers, technicians, engineering designers, constructors, and investment institutions.

669 KR ISSN 0233-7681
TN681 CODEN: PSELEA
PROBLEMY SPETSIAL'NOI ELEKTROMETALLURGII; respublikanskii mezhvedomstvennyi sbornik nauchnykh trudov. (Text in Ukrainian) 1975. q. $61 (effective 1996). (Akademiiya Nauk Ukrainy) Izdatel'stvo Naukova Dumka, Vul. Tereshchenkivska 3, Kiev 252601, Ukraine. (Subscr. to: Mezhdunarodnaya Kniga, B. Yakimanka 39, 117049 Moscow, Russia) Ed. B.E. Paton. **Indexed:** Met.Abstr., World Alum.Abstr.
—BLDSC (0133.774900); CASDDS.

669 NE
PROCESS METALLURGY. 1978. irreg., vol.8, 1992. price varies. Elsevier Science B.V., Books Division, P.O. Box 211, 1000 AE Amsterdam, Netherlands. TEL 31-20-4853911. FAX 31-20-4853705. TELEX 18582 ESPA NL. E-mail: nlinfo-f@elsevier.nl; usinfo-f@elsevier.com; forinfo-kyf04035@niftyserve.or.jp; Site addr.: http://www.elsevier.nl/. (Subscr. in U.S. and Canada to: Elsevier Science Inc., Box 882, Madison Sq. Sta., New York, NY 10159. TEL 212-989-5800) Eds. G.M. Ritcey, A.W. Ashbrook. **Document type:** monographic series.
Refereed Serial

PRODUKTIONS NYT. LEVERANDOERREGISTER. see *MACHINERY*

669 RU ISSN 0033-1732
TA462 CODEN: PTNMAR
PROTECTION OF METALS. English translation of: Zashchita Metallov (RU ISSN 0044-1856) 1964. bi-m. $1345 (foreign $1575) (effective 1996). (Russian Academy of Sciences) Interperiodica, Ul. Profsoyuznaya 90, Moscow 117864, Russia. TEL 7-095-231-2164. FAX 7-095-233-5590. (Dist. by: Plenum Publishing Corp., 233 Spring St., New York, NY 10013-1578. TEL 212-620-8468. FAX 212-463-0742) (Co-publisher: Maik Nauka) Ed. Yu.M. Polukarov. (also avail. in microfilm from JSC; back issues avail.) **Indexed:** Chem.Titles, Corros.Abstr., Energy Res.Abstr., Eng.Ind., ISMEC. **Document type:** academic/scholarly publication.
—BLDSC (0420.520000); CASDDS; Faxon; Genuine Article; SWETS; UMI. **CCC**.
Refereed Serial

671.2 PL ISSN 0033-2275
TS200 CODEN: PRZOAB
PRZEGLAD ODLEWNICTWA. (Text in Polish; summaries in English, German and Russian) 1951. m. $35.50. Wydawnictwo Czasopism i Ksiazek Technicznych SIGMA - NOT, Ul. Ratuszowa 11, P.O. Box 1004, 00-950 Warsaw, Poland. TEL 48-22-180918. FAX 48-22-102187. TELEX 814550 SIGMA PL. (Dist. by: Zaklad Kolportazu SIGMA-NOT, ul. Bartycka 20, P.O. Box 1004, 00-950 Warsaw, Poland) adv.; bk.rev.; abstr.; charts; illus.; pat.; index. circ. 1,000. **Indexed:** B.C.I.R.A., C.I.S. Abstr., Chem.Abstr., Met.Abstr., World Alum.Abstr.
—CASDDS; SWETS.

R & I BLUE BOOK. (Recognition & Identification) see *BUSINESS AND ECONOMICS — Trade And Industrial Directories*

669 FR ISSN 0988-629X
R F M. 1965. 10/yr. 602.35 F. (foreign 975 F.) (effective 1996). Revue Francaise des Metallurgistes, 32 rue Saint-Marc, 75002 Paris, France. TEL 42-60-31-51. FAX 42-60-38-42. Ed. A. Willemetz. adv.; bk.rev. circ. 15,000. **Indexed:** Chem.Abstr., Met.Abstr., World Alum.Abstr.
Incorporates: Metaux Deformations.

669 622 US
R I C INSIGHT. 1988. m. $300. Rare-earth Information Center, Institute for Physical Research and Technology, Iowa State University, 255 Spedding Hall, Ames, IA 50011-3020. TEL 515-294-2272. FAX 515-294-3709. TELEX 283 359. E-mail: RIC@ameslab.gov. Ed. Karl A. Gschneidner, Jr. circ. 250. **Document type:** newsletter.
Description: Covers current developments and trends in the science and technology of rare earth minerals, with emphasis on applications and commercialization of these materials.

669 622 US
R I C NEWS. 1966. q. free. Rare-earth Information Center, Institute for Physical Research and Technology, Iowa State University, 255 Spedding Hall, Ames, IA 50011-3020. TEL 515-294-2272. FAX 515-294-3709. TELEX 283 359. E-mail: RIC@ameslab.gov. Ed. Karl A. Gschneidner, Jr. bk.rev.; bibl.; illus. circ. 13,000. **Document type:** newsletter.
●Also available online.
Description: Emphasizes research and business news in the areas of metallurgy and physics of rare earth metals, alloys, and compounds.

669 UK ISSN 0143-4861
R L J: ROSKILL'S LETTER FROM JAPAN. 1976. m. £140($250) Roskill Information Services Ltd., 2 Clapham Rd., London SW9 OJA, England. TEL 0171-582-5155. FAX 0171-793-0008. index. circ. 75. (back issues avail.) **Document type:** newsletter.

669 US
RADIUS (ROCKFORD). bi-m. membership. Fabricators and Manufacturers Association International, 833 Featherstone Rd., Rockford, IL 61107. TEL 815-399-8700. FAX 815-399-7279. **Document type:** newsletter.
Formerly (until Apr. 1995): A T A News.
Description: Covers the tube- and pipe-producing and fabricating industries.

669 UK ISSN 0307-8531
QD172.R2
RARE EARTH BULLETIN. 1973. bi-m. £151 U.K. and Europe; rest of world £163. Multi-Science Publishing Co. Ltd., 107 High St., Brentwood, Essex CM14 4RX, England. TEL 01277-224632. FAX 01277-223453. (U.S. subscr. to: Box 176, Avenel, NJ 07001) Ed. Carolyn Kirby. index. (back issues avail.) **Document type:** bulletin.
—CCC.
Description: Covers work on the lanthanides, yttrium and scandium.

669 JA
RARE METAL NEWS. (Text in Japanese) 1955. w. 50000 Yen($350) Arumu Shuppansha, 5-6, 2-chome, Hongo, Bunkyo-ku, Tokyo 113, Japan. TEL 03-814-1009. Ed. Megumi Hiramatsu. circ. 5,000.

669 CC ISSN 1001-0521
TA479.3 CODEN: RARME8
RARE METALS. Chinese edition: Xiyou Jinshu (ISSN 0258-7076) (Text in English) 1982. q. $60 (effective 1995). Zhongguo Youse Jinshu Xuehui - Chinese Society of Nonferrous Metal, 2 Xinjiekouwai Dajie, Room 603, Beijing 100088, People's Republic of China. TEL 2014488. FAX 2015019. TELEX 222204 GRINM CN. Ed. Wan Qun. adv. circ. 300. **Document type:** academic/scholarly research.
—BLDSC (7291.829850); CASDDS.
Description: Devoted to experimental and theoretical developments in metallurgy, characterization and applications of rare metals and alloys, with particular emphasis on semiconductor applications.

669 UK ISSN 0950-8198
RAW MATERIALS FOR THE REFRACTORIES INDUSTRY. irreg., latest ed. 1993. $147. Metal Bulletin plc, Park House, Park Terrace, Worcester Park, Surrey KT4 7HY, England. TEL 0171-827-9977. FAX 0181-337-8943. (U.S. subscr. to: Metal Bulletin Inc., 220 Fifth Ave., New York, NY 10001-7781. TEL 212-213-6202. FAX 212-213-1870) Eds. B.M. Coope, E.M. Dickson. **Document type:** trade publication.
Description: Comprised of twenty-one review articles on the world's metallurgy industries and the major minerals used.

REACTIVE AND FUNCTIONAL POLYMERS. see *ENGINEERING — Chemical Engineering*

669 SP
RECUPERACION. 12/yr. 9000 ptas. (foreign 13000 ptas.). Tecnipublicaciones S.A., C. Albacete 5, 28027 Madrid, Spain. TEL 34-1-3261440. FAX 34-1-3262407.

RECYCLING MANAGER FAX. see *ENVIRONMENTAL STUDIES — Waste Management*

RECYCLING TODAY. see *ENVIRONMENTAL STUDIES — Waste Management*

METALLURGY

669.6 546   BE   ISSN 1021-0180
REGARDS SUR L'ETAIN. English edition: Focus on Tin. 1953. q. free to qualified personnel. (International Tin Research Institute) Centre d'Information de l'Etain, 44 rue d'Arenberg, Ste. 33, B-1000 Brussels, Belgium. FAX 32-2-5145518. Ed. N. Andre. bk.rev. circ. 2,500.
    Formerly (until 1992): L'Etain et ses Usages (ISSN 0014-1631)

REPAIRING METALWARE. see *JEWELRY, CLOCKS AND WATCHES*

REPERTORIO SIDERURGICO LATINOAMERICANO. see *BUSINESS AND ECONOMICS — Trade And Industrial Directories*

671.3705   US   ISSN 1063-5750
TN695   CODEN: RPRMEB
REVIEWS IN PARTICULATE MATERIALS. 1993. irreg., latest no. 2, 1994. $75 (foreign $85). Metal Powder Industries Federation, 105 College Rd. E., Princeton, NJ 08540. TEL 609-987-8523. FAX 609-987-8523. Ed.Bd. Document type: academic/scholarly publication.
—BLDSC (7793.846300); CASDDS; Ei; Genuine Article. **CCC.**
    Description: Serves as an international forum for comprehensive reviews on all aspects of particulate materials technology, encompassing powder metallurgy, ceramics, intermetallics, and composites.
    Refereed Serial

669   SP   ISSN 0034-8570
TN600   CODEN: RMTGAC
REVISTA DE METALURGIA. (Text in English, Spanish; summaries in English) 1965. bi-m. 12000 ptas. (effective 1995). Centro Nacional de Investigaciones Metalurgicas, Avda. Gregorio del Amo, 8, 28040 Madrid, Spain. FAX 341-5347425. Ed. J. Fernandez. adv.; bk.rev.; abstr.; index. circ. 2,500. (also avail. in microfilm; back issues avail.) Indexed: Anal.Abstr., Cadscan, Chem.Abstr., Chem.Eng.Abstr., Ind.SST, Int.Aerosp.Abstr., Lead Abstr., Met.Abstr., T.C.E.A., World Alum.Abstr., Zincscan. Document type: academic/scholarly publication, trade publication.
—BLDSC (7865.800000); CASDDS; Ei; Genuine Article; SWETS.

620.112   SP   ISSN 0210-6604
    CODEN: RCPRDQ
REVISTA IBEROAMERICANA DE CORROSION Y PROTECCION. (Text in English, Portuguese, Spanish) 1970. bi-m. 12000 ptas. (Europe $110; America $120). Instituto de Corrosion y Proteccion, Claudio Coello, 20, 5o Izq., 28001 Madrid, Spain. FAX 91-4313291. Ed. Miguel A. Guillen Rodrigo. adv.; bk.rev.; bibl.; charts; illus. circ. 8,000. Indexed: Met.Abstr., Sugar Ind.Abstr., World Alum.Abstr. Document type: academic/scholarly publication.
—CASDDS.
    Formerly: Corrosion y Proteccion (ISSN 0045-8678)

669   CU
REVISTA TECNOLOGIA: MINERIA Y METALURGIA. s-a. $12. (Ministerio de la Industria Basica) Ediciones Cubanas, Obispo No. 461, Apdo. 605, Havana, Cuba. TEL 32-5556-60.

669   FR
TN2   CODEN: CITMDA
REVUE DE METALLURGIE. CAHIERS D'INFORMATION TECHNIQUES. (Text in French; summaries in English) 1904. 11/yr. Revue de Metallurgie, Elysees la Defense, 19 le Parvis Cedex 35, 92072 Paris La Defense, France. TEL 47-67-87-11. FAX 47-67-85-77. TELEX 611672 SISYNDL. adv.; bk.rev.; abstr.; bibl.; charts; pat.; index. circ. 2,800. (also avail. in microform from PMC) Indexed: Appl.Mech.Rev., Cadscan, Chem.Abstr., Curr.Cont., Eng.Ind., Ergon.Abstr., Excerp.Med., Fuel & Energy Abstr., INIS Atomind., Lead Abstr., Met.Abstr., World Alum.Abstr., Zincscan. Document type: academic/scholarly publication.
—BLDSC (7933.100000); CASDDS; Ei; Genuine Article; SWETS. **CCC.**
    Formerly: Revue de Metallurgie (ISSN 0035-1563); Incorporates: Centre de Documentation Siderurgique. Circulaire d'Informations (ISSN 0008-963X)

669   FR   ISSN 0245-8292
TN2   CODEN: MESMDJ
REVUE DE METALLURGIE. MEMOIRES ET ETUDES SCIENTIFIQUES. Title varies: Memoires et Etudes Scientifiques de la Revue de Metallurgie. (Text in French; summaries in English, French, German, Spanish) 1904. 11/yr. Revue de Metallurgie, Elysees la Defense 19, le Parvis Cedex 35, 92072 Paris la Defense, France. TEL 47-67-87-10. FAX 47-67-85-77. TELEX 611 672 SISYNDI. adv.; bk.rev.; abstr.; bibl.; charts; illus.; index. circ. 1,200. Indexed: Appl.Mech.Rev., Art & Archaeol.Tech.Abstr., Cadscan, Chem.Abstr., Eng.Ind., Ind.Sci.Rev., INSPEC, Int.Aerosp.Abstr., Lead Abstr., Met.Abstr., World Alum.Abstr., Zincscan.
—CASDDS; Genuine Article; UMI. **CCC.**
    Formerly: Revue de Metallurgie. Memoires Scientifiques (ISSN 0025-9128)

051   US   ISSN 0192-9569
REYNOLDS REVIEW. q. Reynolds Metals Company, 6601 W. Broad St., Richmond, VA 23230. TEL 804-281-2468. Ed. Anne F. Waring. circ. 30,750. (back issues avail.) Document type: newsletter.

620.11   DK   ISSN 0907-0079
RISOE INTERNATIONAL SYMPOSIUM ON MATERIALS SCIENCE. PROCEEDINGS. 1980. a. price varies. Risoe National Laboratory, P.O. Box 49, DK-4000 Roskilde, Denmark. Document type: proceedings.
    Formerly (until 1991): Risoe International Symposium on Metallurgy and Materials Science. Proceedings (ISSN 0108-8599)

671.3   IT   ISSN 0391-4631
RIVISTA DI MECCANICA INTERNATIONAL EDITION. (Text in English) bi-m. L.62000 (foreign L.114000). Gruppo Editorial Jackson S.p.A., Via Gorki 69, 20092 Cinisello B. (MI), Italy. TEL 39-2-66034205. FAX 39-2-66034238. Ed. Sergio Oltolini. adv.: B&W page L.2910000, color page L.3790000; trim 181 x 270.
    Formerly: I.M.E.
    Description: Italian suppliers to the metalworking industry in the world.

669   UK   ISSN 0965-7711
ROSKILL'S LITHIUM DIGEST. 1992. q. £100($200) Roskill Information Services Ltd., 2 Clapham Rd., London SW9 0JA, England. TEL 0171-582-5155. FAX 0171-793-0008.

RUDARSKO-METALURSKI ZBORNIK/MINING AND METALLURGY QUARTERLY. see *MINES AND MINING INDUSTRY*

669 622   YU   ISSN 0350-2627
RUDARSTVO - GEOLOGIJA - METALURGIJA. (Supplement to: Tehnika) (Text in Serbo-Croatian; summaries in English, Russian) vol.27, 1976. m. $50. Savez Inzenjera i Tehnicara Jugoslavije, Kneza Milosa 9, Box 187, 11000 Belgrade, Yugoslavia. Ed. Dejan Milovanovic. Indexed: Met.Abstr.

669   PL   ISSN 0035-9696
    CODEN: RMNZA5
RUDY I METALE NIEZELAZNE. (Text in Polish; summaries in English, French, German, Russian) 1956. m. $162. (Instytut Metali Niezelaznych) Wydawnictwa Czasopism i Ksiazek Technicznych SIGMA - NOT, Ul. Ratuszkowa 11, P.O. Box 1004, 00-950 Watrsaw, Poland. (Dist. by: Ars Polona-Ruch, Krakowskie Przedmiescie 7, Warsaw, Poland) Ed. Zbigniew Misiolek. adv.: B&W page $1000. bk.rev.; abstr.; charts; illus.; mkt.; index. circ. 500. Indexed: Ceram.Abstr., Chem.Abstr., Copper Abstr., Met.Abstr., World Alum.Abstr.
—CASDDS.
    Description: Explores mining, ore geology and dressing, metallurgy of nonferrous metals (mainly Zn, Pb, Cu, Ag, Al) and roll mills.

669   US   ISSN 1068-3690
TS200
RUSSIAN CASTINGS TECHNOLOGY. English translation of: Liteinoe Proizvodstvo (UR ISSN 0024-449X) 1986. m. $755 (effective 1996). (Russian Machine Tool Industry and Scientific - Technical Society for the Engineering Industry, RU) Allerton Press, Inc., 150 Fifth Ave., New York, NY 10011. TEL 212-924-3950. FAX 212-463-9684. Ed. I.A. Yaskevich. Document type: academic/scholarly publication.
—CCC.
    Formerly: Soviet Castings Technology (ISSN 0891-0316)

669   US   ISSN 1067-8212
TN758
RUSSIAN JOURNAL OF NON-FERROUS METALS. English translation of: Tsvetnye Metally (RU ISSN 0372-2929) 1960. m. $470 (effective 1996). (Ministerstvo Tsvetnoi Metallurgii, RU) Allerton Press, Inc., 150 Fifth Ave., New York, NY 10011. TEL 212-924-3950. FAX 212-463-9684. Ed. V.A. Generalov. charts; illus.; index. Indexed: Met.Abstr., World Alum.Abstr. Document type: academic/scholarly publication.
—BLDSC (0420.761900); UnCover. **CCC.**
    Formerly (until 1993): Soviet Journal of Non-Ferrous Metals (ISSN 0038-5484)
    Description: Covers theoretical and applied aspects of production and treatment of heavy non-ferrous metals.

669   US   ISSN 0036-0295
    CODEN: RMLYAQ
RUSSIAN METALLURGY (METALLY). English translation of: Rossiiskaya Akademiya Nauk. Metally. 1962. bi-m. $1165 (effective 1996). Allerton Press, Inc., 150 Fifth Ave., New York, NY 10011. TEL 212-924-3950. FAX 212-463-9684. Ed. O.A. Bannykh. charts; illus.; index. Indexed: Cadscan, Curr.Cont., Excerp.Med., INSPEC, Lead Abstr., Met.Abstr., World Alum.Abstr., Zincscan. Document type: academic/scholarly publication.
—BLDSC (0420.769000); Ei; Faxon; Genuine Article; UnCover. **CCC.**
    Former titles: Russian Metallurgy and Fuels; Russian Metallurgy and Mining.

669.1   MY   ISSN 0129-5721
TS300   CODEN: SEQUDV
S E A I S I QUARTERLY JOURNAL. (Text in English) 1972. q. $85. South East Asia Iron and Steel Institute, P.O. Box 7094, 40702 Snah Alam, Selangor, Malaysia. TEL 60-3-559-1102. FAX 60-3-559-1159. Ed. Keel Chung Sou. circ. 2,000. (back issues avail.) Indexed: B.C.I.R.A., Chem.Abstr., Corros.Abstr., Met.Abstr., World Alum.Abstr. Document type: academic/scholarly publication.
—BLDSC (8213.725000); CASDDS; Ei.

669   SZ
S M U V ZEITUNG. vol.72, 1973. w. 50 SFr. Gewerkschaft Industrie, Gewerbe, Dienstleistungen SMUV - Syndicat de l'Industrie, de la Construction et des Services FTMH, Postfach 272, CH-3000 Bern 15, Switzerland. TEL 031-3502345. FAX 031-3502211. adv. contact: Doris Jossen. bk.rev.; charts; illus. circ. 57,906. Document type: newspaper.

S N A G NEWSLETTER. (Society of North American Goldsmiths) see *ARTS AND HANDICRAFTS*

669   DK   ISSN 0371-0459
TN1   CODEN: SJMLAG
SCANDINAVIAN JOURNAL OF METALLURGY; processes and materials engineering. (Text in English) 1971. 6/yr. DKK 1300 (effective 1996). (Swedish Institute for Metals Research) Munksgaard International Publishers Ltd., 35 Noerre Soegade, P.O. Box 2148, DK-1016 Copenhagen K, Denmark. TEL 33-127030. FAX 33-129387. Ed. J.O. Edstroem. adv.; bk.rev. circ. 500. (illus.) Indexed: Soils & Fert.
—BLDSC (8087.517500); CASDDS; Ei; Faxon; Genuine Article; SWETS; UnCover. **CCC.**
    Supersedes in part (in 1977): Jernkontorets Annaler (ISSN 0021-5902)
    Refereed Serial

669   GW   ISSN 0933-8330
SCHMIEDE JOURNAL. 1988. s-a. DM.40. Industrieverband Deutscher Schmieden e.V., Informationsstelle Schmiedestueck-Verwendung, Goldene Pforte 1, 58093 Hagen, Germany. TEL 02331-958828. FAX 02331-51046. Ed. Werner Adlof. adv.: B&W page DM.3290, color page DM.5180; trim 270 x 186. bk.rev. circ. 5,000. Document type: trade publication.

METALLURGY

669 666 YU ISSN 0350-820X
TN695 CODEN: SCSNB4
SCIENCE OF SINTERING. (Text in English; summaries in Russian, Serbo-Croatian) 1969. 3/yr. $83 (effective Jan. 1991). Committee for Etan, Kneza Milosa 9, 11000 Belgrade, Yugoslavia. TEL 637-239. FAX 182825. TELEX 72593 SANY JU. (Subscr. to: Jugoslovenska Knjiga, Export Dept., Trg Repulike 5-VIII, 11000 Belgrade, Yugoslavia) (Co-sponsor: Serbian Academy of Sciences and Arts) Ed. M.M. Ristic. adv.; bk.rev. circ. 700. (back issues avail.) **Indexed:** Br.Ceram.Abstr., Chem.Abstr., Eng.Ind., INSPEC, Met.Abstr., Nucl.Sci.Abstr., World Alum.Abstr.
—BLDSC (8164.278000); CASDDS; Ei; Faxon; SWETS.
   Formerly: Physics of Sintering (ISSN 0031-9198)
   Description: Provides a suitable medium for the publication of papers on theoretical and experimental studies.

669 US
SCRAP PRICE BULLETIN; the weekly newsletter for secondary materials prices. Cover title: Iron Age Scrap Price Bulletin. w. $195 in US & Canada (fax $360); elsewhere $400. Chilton Publications (Subsidiary of: Capital Cities - A B C Publishing Group), 191 S. Gary Ave., Carol Stream, IL 60188. TEL 708-665-1000. FAX 708-462-2862. (Subscr. to: Box 7695, Riverton, NJ 08077-7695) Ed. El Hoeffer. (avail. via fax) **Document type:** bulletin, trade publication.

SCRAP PROCESSING AND RECYCLING. see *CONSERVATION*

669 UK ISSN 1359-6462
TN1
SCRIPTA MATERIALIA. 1967. 24/yr. (in 2 vols.). £431($685) (effective 1996). (Acta Metallurgica, Inc.) Elsevier Science Ltd., Pergamon, P.O. Box 800, Kidlington, Oxford OX5 1DX, England. TEL 44-1865-843000. FAX 44-1865-843010. E-mail: nlinfo-f@elsevier.nl; usinfo-f@elsevier.com; forinfo-kyf04035@niftyserve.or.jp; Site addr.: http://www.elsevier.nl/. (Subscr. in U.S. and Canada to: Elsevier Science, 660 White Plains Rd., Tarrytown, NY 10591-5153. TEL 914-524-9200. FAX 914-333-2444) Ed. John P. Hirth. adv.: B&W page $550, color page $1350. bk.rev.; bibl.; charts; illus.; stat. circ. 1,600. (also avail. in microfilm from UMI; back issues avail.) **Indexed:** ASCA, Biol.Abstr., Cadscan, Chem.Abstr., Curr.Cont., Eng.Ind., INSPEC, Int.Aerosp.Abstr., Lead Abstr., Met.Abstr., Phys.Ber., World Alum.Abstr., Zincscan. **Document type:** academic/scholarly publication.
—BLDSC (8213.151000); CASDDS; Ei; Faxon; Genuine Article; SWETS; UMI; UnCover. **CCC.**
   Former titles (until vol.34): Scripta Metallurgica et Materialia (ISSN 0956-716X); (until 1990): Scripta Metallurgica (ISSN 0036-9748)
   Description: Publishes papers advancing the understanding of the physical properties of materials, including metals, alloys, ceramics, polymers, and glasses.
   Refereed Serial

SEARCHER. see *LABOR UNIONS*

669.722 GW
SECONDARY ALUMINUM EUROPE JAPAN USA. (Text in English) 1965. a. DM.25. Organisation of European Aluminum Smelters, Postfach 200840, 40105 Duesseldorf, Germany. TEL 0211-451933. FAX 0211-431009. Ed. Guenter Kirchner. circ. 2,000. **Document type:** trade publication.

661.072 BE
SELENIUM - TELLURIUM DEVELOPMENT ASSOCIATION. BULLETIN. irreg. (3-4/yr.). free. Selenium - Tellurium Development Association, 301 Borgstraat, B-1850 Grimbergen, Belgium. TEL 32-2-252-1490. FAX 32-2-252-2775. Ed. Yves Palmieri. circ. 2,000. **Document type:** bulletin.
   Description: Promote knowledge about applications of selenium and tellurium in metallurgy, pharmaceuticals, feed additives, pigments, chemicals and electronics.

669 CC ISSN 0253-2344
CODEN: JINSD7
SHANGHAI JINSHU/SHANGHAI METALS. (Text in Chinese) 1979. bi-m. Shanghai Jinshu Xuehui - Shanghai Society of Metals, 1118 Dingsi Rd., Shanghai 200050, People's Republic of China. TEL 021-2400928. FAX 021-2401044. Ed. Gu Deji. adv.: B&W page $500, color page $800; trim 180 x 260. **Document type:** academic/scholarly publication.
—CASDDS.

669 CC ISSN 1001-2125
SHANGHAI JINSHU (YOUSE FENCE). (Text in Chinese) 1979. bi-m. Shanghai Youse Jinshu Xiehui - Shanghai Nonferrous Metal Society, P.O. Box 600-402, Shanghai 201600, People's Republic of China. TEL 86-21-7822880. FAX 86-21-325739. (Dist. overseas by: China International Book Trading Corp., P.O. Box 399, Beijing, P.R. China) Ed. Guan Dagao. adv.: B&W page $350, color page $600. **Document type:** academic/scholarly publication.
   Formerly (until 1981): Shanghai Yejin.
   Description: Publishes original papers on the properties of nonferrous metals and alloys, as well as material producing and measuring techniques.

669 JA ISSN 0918-0699
SHEET METAL/SHITO METARU; comprehensive news. (Text in Japanese) 1991. m. $150. Machinist Publishing Co., Ltd. - Mashinisuto Shuppan K.K., 1-11-5-111 Tamazutsumi, Setagaya-ku, Tokyo 158, Japan. TEL 81-3-3703-1730. FAX 81-3-3703-4402. Ed. Norio Ishikawa. adv.: B&W page $1100, color page $2900; trim 728 x 100; adv. contact: Hiroshi Tozuka. circ. 28,000. **Document type:** bulletin.
   Former titles (until 1992): Machinist - Mashinisuto (ISSN 0911-7903); (until 1958): World Progress of Production Engineering - Kaigai Kikai Shiryo (ISSN 0911-789X)

SHEET METAL INDUSTRIES YEARBOOK. see *METALLURGY — Welding*

SHIGEN SOZAI/MINING AND MATERIALS PROCESSING INSTITUTE OF JAPAN. JOURNAL. see *MINES AND MINING INDUSTRY*

669 JA
SHITO METARU SUKURU/SHEET METAL SCHOOL. (Text in Japanese) bi-m. 1500 Yen per no. Amada Sukuru - Amada School, 1500, Ishida, Isehara-shi, Kanagawa-ken 259-11, Japan. **Document type:** academic/scholarly publication.

669.142 BL
SIDERURGIA BRASILEIRA. RELATORIO DE DIRETORIA. (Text in English) 1973. a. free. Siderurgia Brasileira S.A., Setor de Autarquias sul, Quadra 2, Bloco E, 70070 Brazil. FAX 061-226-5844. TELEX 061-1542. stat. circ. 5,000.

669 CL ISSN 0379-7759
TS300 CODEN: SILAD8
SIDERURGIA LATINOAMERICANA. (Text in Portuguese and Spanish; summaries in English) 1960. m. $56. Instituto Latinoamericano del Fierro y el Acero, Casilla 16065, Santiago 9, Chile. Ed. Jorge Ramirez. adv.; bk.rev.; bibl.; charts; illus.; index. circ. 6,000. (also avail. in microform from UMI; reprint service avail. from UMI) **Indexed:** Chem.Abstr., Met.Abstr., World Alum.Abstr.
—BLDSC (8271.750000); CASDDS; SWETS; UMI.
   Former titles: Revista Latinoamericana de Siderurgia (ISSN 0034-9798); (until 1962): Instituto Latinoamericana del Fierro y Acero. Boletin Informativo.

669.1 620 VE
SIDOR HOY INTERNACIONAL. (Text in English or Spanish; summaries in English, Spanish) 1978. q. free to qualified personnel. C.V.G. Siderurgica del Orinoco C.A. (Sidor), Vicepresidencia de Tecnologia Siderurgica, Matanzas - Edo. Bolivar, Venezuela. TEL 58-86-937143. FAX 58-86-225938. (Subscr. to: Sidor, Gerencia Corporativa de Asuntos Publicos, Edif. General, Avda. la Estancia, Piso 9, Chuao, Apdo. Postal 5638, Caracas, Venezuela) Ed. Federico Genolet; Pub. Socorro Baron. adv. contact: Gastion Montiel. bibl.; stat.; index. circ. 3,500. (also avail. in microfiche; back issues avail.) **Indexed:** Met.Abstr. **Document type:** trade publication.
   Formerly (until 1993): Sidor Hoy (ISSN 0798-1163)
   Description: Informs on the technologies, processes and products that have been modified or innovated by the company. Includes information on improvements made by specialists in steel plants worldwide.
   Refereed Serial

SILVER INSTITUTE LETTER; information on silver for industry. see *MINES AND MINING INDUSTRY*

669.23 336 US ISSN 0066-4332
SILVER MARKET.* 1916. a. free. Handy and Harman, 555 Theodore Fremd Ave., Ste. A, Rye, NY 10580-1437. TEL 212-752-3400. FAX 212-207-2614. Ed. Stephen Mudd. circ. 10,000. (also avail. in microfiche from CIS) **Indexed:** SRI.

SINDACATO MODERNO. see *LABOR UNIONS*

669 XR ISSN 0037-6825
CODEN: SLEVAK
SLEVARENSTVI/FOUNDRY INDUSTRY; casopis pro slevarensky prumysl. (Text in Czech; summaries in English, French, German, Russian) 1953. m. $56.70. (Ministerstvo Hutnictva, Strojarstva a Elektrotechniky, XO) Svaz Slevaren, Brnenska 17, 617 00 Brno, Czech Republic. (Dist. by: Artia, Ve Smeckach 30, 111 27 Prague 1, Czech Republic) Ed. Radovan Koplik. abstr.; bibl.; charts; illus. circ. 2,900. **Indexed:** B.C.I.R.A., C.I.S. Abstr., Chem.Abstr., Met.Abstr., World Alum.Abstr.
—BLDSC (8309.500000); CASDDS.

669 SZ ISSN 1012-0394
CODEN: DDBPE8
SOLID STATE PHENOMENA. 6/yr. $528. Scitec Publications Ltd., Untermuehleweg 11, CH-6300 Zug, Switzerland. FAX 062-741058. E-mail: ddd@scitec.ch. Ed. G.E. Murch. **Indexed:** INSPEC (1993-). **Document type:** academic/scholarly publication.
—BLDSC (3584.255000); CASDDS; Faxon; SWETS.

669 US ISSN 0968-1043
SOURCE JOURNALS IN METALS AND MATERIALS. 1981. biennial. $90 in US, Canada, Mexico; elsewhere $100 (effective 1995). (Institute of Materials, UK) A S M International, Materials Information, Materials Park, OH 44073. TEL 216-338-5151. FAX 216-338-4634. TELEX 980-619. (UK addr.: Institute of Materials, Materials Information, 1 Carlton House Terr., London SW1Y 5DB, England. TEL 071-839-4071) **Document type:** directory.
—BLDSC (8330.581500).
   Formerly: Source Journals in Metallurgy.

669 US
SOURCES (RICHMOND HEIGHTS). 1962. a. $35. Precision Metal Forming Association, 27027 Chardon Rd., Richmond Heights, OH 44143. TEL 216-585-8800. adv. circ. 12,000. **Document type:** trade publication, directory.
   Former titles: Sources for Stamping; (until 1979): Metal Stamping Buyer's Guide.

METALLURGY

669 622   SA   ISSN 0038-223X
CODEN: JSAMAP
SOUTH AFRICAN INSTITUTE OF MINING AND METALLURGY. JOURNAL. 1894. bi-m. $120. South African Institute of Mining and Metallurgy, P.O. Box 61127, Marshalltown 2107, South Africa. TEL 27-11-834-1273. FAX 27-11-838-5923. Ed. H. Glen. adv.; bk.rev.; bibl.; charts; illus.; index, cum.index: vols. 35-54 (July 1935-June 1954). circ. 3,800. (also avail. in microform from UMI,PMC; reprint service avail. from UMI) **Indexed:** AESIS, Anal.Abstr., Appl.Mech.Rev., C.I.S. Abstr., Cadscan, Chem.Abstr., Chem.Eng.Abstr., Curr.Cont., Energy Info.Abstr., Eng.Ind., Ergon.Abstr., GeoRef., HRIS, Ind.S.A.Per., INIS Atomind., Lead Abstr., Met.Abstr., T.C.E.A., W.R.C.Inf., World Alum.Abstr., Zincscan.
—BLDSC (4901.500000); CASDDS; Ei; Faxon; Genuine Article; SWETS; UMI; UnCover. **CCC**.
Refereed Serial

669 622   SA
SOUTH AFRICAN INSTITUTE OF MINING AND METALLURGY. MONOGRAPH SERIES. 1978. irreg. price varies. South African Institute of Mining and Metallurgy, P.O. Box 61127, Marshallton 2107, South Africa. TEL 27-11-834-1273. FAX 27-11-838-5923. **Indexed:** GeoRef. **Document type:** monographic series.

669   II
SPOTLIGHT/PARIKRAMA. (Editions in English, Hindi) fortn. free. Steel Authority of India Ltd., Bhilai Steel Plant, Bhilai 490001 (M.P.), India. Ed. A.K. Bhatt. circ. 15,000.

672   GW   ISSN 0941-0821
CODEN: STAHEI
STAHL. 1992. 6/yr. DM.95. Verlag Stahleisen mbH, Sohnstr. 65, 40237 Duesseldorf, Germany. TEL 0211-6707-0. FAX 0211-6707517. Ed.Bd. circ. 10,000. **Document type:** trade publication.
—BLDSC (8426.800000); CASDDS.

669.1   GW   ISSN 0340-4803
TS300   CODEN: STEIA3
STAHL UND EISEN; Zeitschrift fuer die Herstellung und Verarbeitung von Eisen und Stahl. (Text in German; contents page in English) 1881. 12/yr. DM.380. (Verein Deutscher Eisenhuettenleute) Verlag Stahleisen mbH, Sohnstr. 65, 40237 Duesseldorf, Germany. TEL 0211-6707-0. FAX 0211-6707517. Ed. D. Springorum. adv.; bk.rev.; bibl.; charts; illus.; mkt.; pat.; stat.; tr.lit.; index. circ. 7,000. (also avail. in microform from PMC) **Indexed:** Appl.Mech.Rev., ASCA, B.C.I.R.A., C.I.S. Abstr., Ceram.Abstr., Chem.Abstr., Corros.Abstr., Curr.Cont., ELLIS, Eng.Ind., Excerp.Med., INSPEC (1984-1986), ISMEC, Key to Econ.Sci., Met.Abstr., Risk Abstr., World Alum.Abstr. **Document type:** trade publication.
—BLDSC (8427.000000); CASDDS; Ei; Faxon; Genuine Article; SWETS. **CCC**.

STAHLBAU - NACHRICHTEN. see *BUILDING AND CONSTRUCTION*

STAHLBAU - RUNDSCHAU - MITTEILUNGEN. see *BUILDING AND CONSTRUCTION*

669   GW   ISSN 0138-1679
CODEN: STAHDH
STAHLBERATUNG. 1976. 5/yr. DM.48. Ministerium fuer Erzbau, Metallurgie und Kali Stahlberatungsstelle, Agricolastr. 24, 09599 Freiberg, Germany. **Indexed:** Chem.Abstr.
—CASDDS.

669.142   GW   ISSN 0178-6571
STAHLMARKT; Informationen ueber Erzeugnisse aus Stahl und anderen Werkstoffen. 1951. m. DM.143 (foreign DM.155). Montan- und Wirtschaftsverlag GmbH, Postfach 105164, 40042 Duesseldorf, Germany. TEL 0211-6707-0. FAX 0211-6707517. Ed. Hans-Heinrich Eichler. adv. contact: H.-G. Puelz. bk.rev.; illus.; stat.; index. circ. 7,900. **Indexed:** ELLIS, Key to Econ.Sci., Met.Abstr., World Alum.Abstr. **Document type:** trade publication.
Former titles: Contintentaler Stahlmarkt (ISSN 0010-7743); Continentaler Eisenhandel.

669.1   SA   ISSN 0038-917X
STAINLESS STEEL. (Text in English) 1965. bi-m. free. Southern Africa Stainless Steel Development Association, P.O. Box 4479, Rivonia 2128, South Africa. TEL 27-11-803-5610. FAX 27-11-803-2011. Ed. Jan Lancaster. adv.; bk.rev.; charts; illus.; circ. 7,623 (controlled). **Document type:** trade publication.
Description: Includes technical articles, association news, company profiles, new products.

669.1   SA
STAINLESS STEEL BUYER'S GUIDE (YEAR). (Text in English) a. free. Southern Africa Stainless Steel Development Association, P.O. Box 4479, Rivonia 2128, South Africa. TEL 27-11-803-5610. FAX 27-11-803-2011. Ed. Jan Lancaster. adv.; circ. 3,010 (controlled). **Document type:** trade publication, directory.
Description: Provides list of members, and information on products supplied, with company profiles and technical data for the stainless steel industry.

669   US   ISSN 0953-7228
STAINLESS STEEL DATABOOK. 1957. irreg., latest 1991. $144. Metal Bulletin plc, Park House, Park Terrace, Worcester Park, Surrey KT4 7HY, England. TEL 071-827-9977. FAX 081-337-8943. (U.S. subscr. to: Metal Bulletin Inc., 220 Fifth Ave., New York, NY 10001-7781. TEL 212-213-6202. FAX 212-213-1870) Eds. Henry Cooke, Richard Serjeantson. adv. **Document type:** directory.
Supersedes: Stainless Steel: An International Survey and Directory; *Formerly:* Stainless Steel: An International Directory (ISSN 0143-5442)
Description: Directory of international stainless steel producers, processors and traders with data on world refining plants.

669.142   UK   ISSN 0306-2988
CODEN: SSTID6
STAINLESS STEEL INDUSTRY. 1973. bi-m. £36. Modern Metals Publications Ltd., 5 Pond St., Hampstead, London NW3 2PN, England. Ed. F.W.S. Russell. adv.; bk.rev. circ. 4,000. (back issues avail.) **Indexed:** Chem.Abstr., Met.Abstr., World Alum.Abstr. **Document type:** trade publication.
—BLDSC (8430.120000); CASDDS.

669.142   US   ISSN 0730-8140
STAINLESS STEELS DIGEST. 1976. m. $160 to non-members (foreign $180); members $130 (foreign $145) (effective 1996). A S M International, Materials Information, Materials Park, OH 44073. TEL 216-338-5151. FAX 216-338-4634. TELEX 980-619. E-mail: DBartherl@po.ASM-Intl.org. (UK addr.: Institute of Materials, Materials Information, 1 Carlton House Terr., London SW1Y 5DB, England. TEL 071-839-4071) Eds. M. Stephen Chang, Michael B. Finical. **Indexed:** Met.Abstr. **Document type:** abstracting/indexing.
Description: Covers austenitic, martensitic and ferritic stainless steels.

669.1   RU   ISSN 0038-920X
TS300   CODEN: STALAQ
STAL'. (Text in Russian) 1931. m. 6000 Rub.($104) (Mezhdunarodnyi Soyuz Metallurgov - International Metallurgists' Union) Izdatel'stvo Metallurgiya, 2-i Obydenskii Per., 14, 119857 Moscow, Russia. TEL 7-095-2025532. FAX 7-095-2025752. (Dist. by: Mezhdunarodnaya Kniga, B. Yakimanka 39, 117049 Moscow, Russia) (Co-sponsor: Komitet Rossiiskoi Federatsii po Metallurgii) Ed. S.V. Kolpakov. adv.; bk.rev.; charts; illus.; index. circ. 1,350. **Indexed:** Chem.Abstr., Eng.Ind., Met.Abstr., Ref.Zh.
—BLDSC (0166.740000); CASDDS; Faxon. **CCC**.

669 621   US   ISSN 1043-5093
STAMPING QUARTERLY. 1989. q. $15 (Canada and Mexico $25; elsewhere $45); free to qualified personnel. Croydon Group, Ltd. (Subsidiary of: Fabricators & Manufacturers Association, International), 833 Featherstone Rd., Rockford, IL 61107-6301. TEL 815-399-8700. FAX 815-399-7279. Ed. Theresa Olmsted; Pub. John Nandzik. adv.: B&W page $2380; trim 8 1/4 x 10 3/4; adv. contact: Jack Broughton. circ. 35,377. **Document type:** trade publication.
—BLDSC (8430.235400); Faxon.
Description: Disseminates news and information relating to the metal stamping industry. Contains articles and news releases designed to assist owners, managers, manufacturing engineers, supervisors and foremen in the evaluation of new methods and techniques.

671.732 621.9   GW   ISSN 0941-388X
CODEN: FACHDN
STEEL AND MATERIALS TECHNOLOGY. (Text in German; summaries in English) 1963. bi-m. DM.360. Sprechsaal Publishing Group, Mauer 2, 96450 Coburg, Germany. TEL 09561-76773. FAX 09561-90009. TELEX 663226. Ed. Christoph Mueller. adv.; bk.rev.; abstr.; bibl.; charts; illus.; tr.lit.; index. circ. 12,000. **Indexed:** Chem.Abstr., INIS Atomind. **Document type:** trade publication.
—CASDDS.
Former titles (until 1990): Fachberichte International Steel and Metals Magazine (ISSN 0934-5965); (until 1987): Fachberichte Huettenpraxis Metallweiterverarbeitung (ISSN 0340-8043); Fachberichte fuer Oberflaechentechnik (ISSN 0014-6323)

669.1   II
STEEL BULLETIN - PANORAMA. Hindi edition: Steel Bulletin - Bhilai Darshan. (English and Hindi editions alternate, each published once a month.) (Text in English) s-m. free. Steel Authority of India Ltd., Bhilai Steel Plant, Bhilai 490001 (M.P.), India. Ed. Pradip Singh. **Document type:** bulletin.

STEEL CONSTRUCTION. see *BUILDING AND CONSTRUCTION*

STEEL CONSTRUCTION. see *BUILDING AND CONSTRUCTION*

669   US
STEEL DIGEST. 1983. bi-m. free. Intersteel Technology, Inc., 8301 University Exec. Park, Ste. 130, Charlotte, NC 28262. TEL 704-549-4177. FAX 704-549-4178. Ed. John A. Vallomy. circ. 550. (back issues avail.) **Document type:** newsletter.
Description: Examines continuous steelmaking process; reports on development and new technologies in international steelmaking industry.

669.1   US   ISSN 0967-0912
TS300   CODEN: STETE6
STEEL IN TRANSLATION. (Selective article translation from the Russian journals: Stal' (ISSN 0038-920X) and Izvestiya Vysshikh Uchebnykh Zavedenii. Chernaya Matallurgiya (ISSN 0021-3438)) 1971. m. $980 (effective 1996). Allerton Press Inc., 150 Fifth Ave., New York, NY 10011. TEL 212-924-3950. FAX 212-463-9684. Eds. S.V. Kolpakov, V.A. Grigoryan. bibl.; charts; illus.; index. circ. 300. **Indexed:** ASCA, Ceram.Abstr., Chem.Abstr., Curr.Cont., Eng.Ind., Ergon.Abstr., Excerp.Med., Met.Abstr., World Alum.Abstr.
—BLDSC (0425.890050); Ei; Faxon; SWETS.
Formerly (until 1992): Steel in the U S S R (ISSN 0038-9218); *Supersedes (in 1971):* Stal' in English (ISSN 0585-0282)
Description: Covers technical and scientific developments in ferrous metallurgy.

669   II   ISSN 0970-1311
CODEN: STINE8
STEEL INDIA. (Text in English) 1978. s-a. free. Steel Authority of India Ltd., R & D Centre for Iron & Steel, Ranchi 834 002, India. FAX 0651-300023. TELEX 0625-267. Ed. Sanak Mishra. abstr.; bibl.; charts; illus.; stat.; index. circ. 1,000. **Document type:** trade publication.
—BLDSC (8463.550000); CASDDS.
Description: Technical journal covering the iron and steel industry in India. Provides a forum for exchange of knowledge between academicians and professionals.
Refereed Serial

METALLURGY 4675

669.1   UN   ISSN 0497-9478
HD9510.1
STEEL MARKET. French edition: Marche de l'Acier (ISSN 0497-9486); Russian edition: Rynok Produktsii Chernoi Metallurgii (ISSN 0255-5069) 1953. a. price varies. (Economic Commission for Europe (ECE)) United Nations Publications, Room DC2-0853, New York, NY 10017. TEL 212-963-8302; 212-963-3489; 800-253-9646. (Or: Distribution and Sales Section, Palais des Nations, 1211 Geneva 10, Switzerland) (also avail. in microfiche from CIS) **Indexed:** IIS.
   Description: Provides trade information on iron and steel industry in Europe.

669   UK   ISSN 0964-7694
STEEL MARKETS MONTHLY. 1991. m. $1235. Metal Bulletin plc, Park House, Park Terrace, Worcester Park, Surrey KT4 7HY, England. TEL 0171-827-9977. FAX 0181-337-8943. (U.S. subscr. to: Metal Bulletins Inc., 220 Fifth Ave., New York, NY 10001-7781. TEL 212-213-6202. FAX 212-213-1870) Ed. Tony Murray. **Document type:** trade publication.

669   UK
STEEL NEWS (LONDON). 11/yr. 9 Albert Embankment, London SE1 7SN, England. TEL 44-71-735-7654. TELEX 916061. Ed. Brian Richards. circ. 53,000.

669   UK
STEEL NEWS (NEWPORT). 10/yr. British Steel Strip Products, P.O. Box 10, Llawern Works, Newport, Gwent NP9 0XN, Wales. TEL 0633-290022. Ed. D. Danter.

369   UK
STEEL NEWS (SCUNTHORPE EDITION). 11/yr. British Steel General Steels (Scunthorpe), P.O. Box 1, Scunthorpe, S. Humberside DN16 1BP, England. TEL 0724-280280. TELEX 52601-BRISTEEL-G. Ed. S. Pearcy. circ. 11,000.

669   UK
STEEL NEWS (TEESSIDE EDITION). m. British Steel Section Plates & Commercial Steels, Teesside Works, Steel House, Redcar, Cleveland TS10 5QW, England. TEL 0642-474111. FAX 0642-489466. TELEX 587401. Ed. D. Adamson. adv.; bk.rev. circ. 11,000.

669   US
STEEL PLATE JOURNAL.* q. Steel Plate Fabricators Association, 3158 Des Plains Ave., Ste. 209, Des Plains, IL 60018-4222. TEL 708-562-8750. FAX 708-562-8436. circ. 500. **Document type:** newsletter.

669.1   GW   ISSN 0177-4832
TS300   CODEN: STRSEY
STEEL RESEARCH. 1927. m. DM.480. (Verein Deutscher Eisenhuettenleute) Verlag Stahleisen mbH, Sohnstr. 65, 40237 Duesseldorf, Germany. TEL 0211-6707-0. FAX 0211-6707517. (Co-sponsor: Max-Planck-Institut fuer Eisenforschung) adv.; charts; illus.; index. circ. 900. **Indexed:** Anal.Abstr., Appl.Mech.Rev., Chem.Abstr., Curr.Cont., Eng.Ind., Excerp.Med., GeoRef., INSPEC, Met.Abstr., Sci.Cit.Ind., World Alum.Abstr. **Document type:** trade publication.
—BLDSC (8464.090400); CASDDS; Ei; Faxon; Genuine Article; SWETS; UnCover. **CCC**
   Former titles: Steel Research - Archiv fuer das Eisenhuettenwesen; (until 1985): Archiv fuer das Eisenhuettenwesen (ISSN 0003-8962)

669.142   UK   ISSN 0953-2412
TS300   CODEN: STTIEE
STEEL TECHNOLOGY INTERNATIONAL. a. Sterling Publications Ltd. (Subsidiary of: Sterling Publishing Group PLC), 86-88 Edgware Road, London W2 2YW, England. TEL 01-258-0066. Ed. Peter H. Scholes.
—BLDSC (8464.103500); Ei.

669.1   UK   ISSN 0039-095X
TN1   CODEN: STLTA3
STEEL TIMES. 1866. m. £105.15($232.40) (foreign £145.25). Argus Business Media Ltd., Fuel and Metals Journals (Subsidiary of: Argus Press Group), Queensway House, 2 Queensway, Redhill, Surrey RH1 1QS, England. TEL 01737-768611. FAX 01737-761685. TELEX 948669 TOPJNL G. Ed. Tim Smith. bk.rev. (also avail. in microform from UMI; reprint service avail. from UMI) **Indexed:** Br.Ceram.Abstr., Br.Tech.Ind., C.I.S. Abstr., Ceram.Abstr., Chem.Abstr., Eng.Ind., Excerp.Med., Fuel & Energy Abstr., Key to Econ.Sci., Met.Abstr., World Alum.Abstr. **Document type:** trade publication.
—BLDSC (8464.104000); CASDDS; Ei; SWETS; UMI; UnCover.
   Incorporates in part: Steel and Coal (ISSN 0371-3628); Iron & Coal (ISSN 0140-5101)
   Description: Covers the production cycle from ore processing, through ironmaking, steelmaking, casting and rolling, to finishing and stockholding.

669.1 338.4   UK   ISSN 0143-7798
TN730   CODEN: STTIDD
STEEL TIMES INTERNATIONAL. bi-m. £88.35($183.60) (foreign £114.60). Argus Business Media Ltd., Fuel and Metals Journals (Subsidiary of: Argus Press Group), Queensway House, 2 Queensway, Redhill, Surrey RH1 1QS, England. TEL 01737-768611. FAX 01737-761685. TELEX 948669 TOPJNL G. Ed. B. Cooper. **Indexed:** C.I.S. Abstr., Cadscan, Chem.Abstr., ISMEC, Lead Abstr., Met.Abstr., World Alum.Abstr., Zincscan. **Document type:** trade publication.
—BLDSC (8464.105300); CASDDS; Ei; Faxon; SWETS.
   Description: Covers the iron- and steelmaking industries worldwide.

669   JA
STEEL TODAY AND TOMORROW. (Text in English) 1973. 5/yr. free. Japan Iron and Steel Exporter's Association - Nihon Tekko Yushutsu Kumiai, c/o Tekko Kaikan, 3-2-10 Nihonbashi Kayaba-cho, Chuo-ku, Tokyo 103, Japan. Ed. Soichiro Yoshimura. **Indexed:** Met.Abstr., World Alum.Abstr.

669   UK   ISSN 0308-8006
STEEL TRADERS OF THE WORLD. 1976. quadrennial, 6th ed., 1993. $221. Metal Bulletin plc, Park House, Park Terrace, Worcester Park, Surrey KT4 7HY, England. TEL 0171-827-9977. FAX 0181-337-8943. (U.S. subscr. to: Metal Bulletin Inc., 220 Fifth Ave., New York, NY 10001-7781. TEL 212-213-6202. FAX 212-213-1870) Ed. Dick Serjeantson. adv. **Document type:** directory.
   Description: World listing of steel traders and products handled.

STEELABOR. see *LABOR UNIONS*

669.1 622 665.5   US   ISSN 0896-0429
TN701.5   CODEN: STCPDH
STEELMAKING CONFERENCE: PROCEEDINGS. 1928. a., 77th ed., 1994. $90 to non-members; members $45. Iron and Steel Society, 410 Commonwealth Dr., Warrendale, PA 15086-7512. TEL 412-776-9535. FAX 412-776-0430. (also avail. in microfilm from UMI; back issues avail.) **Indexed:** Iron & Steel Indus.Pr. **Document type:** proceedings.
—BLDSC (8464.106800); CASDDS.
   Former titles: Steelmaking Proceedings; American Institute of Mining, Metallurgical and Petroleum Engineers. National Open Hearth and Basic Oxygen Steel Division. Proceedings of the Conference.
   Description: For iron and steel makers.

671.2   DK
STOEBRIET. m. DKK 30. Danmarks Stoeberitekniske Foreninger, Chr. Winthersvej 88, DK-4700 Naestved, Denmark.

671.2   NO   ISSN 0039-1824
   CODEN: STOEA7
STOEPERITIDENDE. 1935. 6/yr. NOK 170. Norges Stoeperitekniske Forening - Norwegian Foundry Technical Association, Box 7117 H, N-0307 Oslo 3, Norway. adv.; bk.rev.; abstr.; bibl.; charts; illus. circ. 800. **Indexed:** B.C.I.R.A., Met.Abstr., World Alum.Abstr. **Document type:** trade publication.
—BLDSC (8466.310000); CASDDS.

STUDIES OF HIGH TEMPERATURE SUPERCONDUCTORS. see *CHEMISTRY — Electrochemistry*

669   JA   ISSN 0039-4963
   CODEN: SKEGA2
SUMITOMO KEIKINZOKU GIHO/SUMITOMO LIGHT METAL TECHNICAL REPORTS. (Text in English and Japanese) 1960. q. exchange basis. Sumitomo Light Metal Industries, Ltd., Technical Research Labratories - Sumitomo Keikinzoku Kogyo K. K., 3-1-12 Chitose, Minato-ku, Nagoya 455, Japan. TEL 052-651-2100. FAX 052-651-8117. Ed. Koji Nagata. adv.; charts; illus.; index. circ. 1,750. **Indexed:** Chem.Abstr., Copper Abstr., Curr.Cont., Eng.Ind., Met.Abstr., World Alum.Abstr. **Document type:** academic/scholarly publication.
—BLDSC (8517.985000); CASDDS.

669   UK   ISSN 0267-0844
TA418.7   CODEN: SUENET
SURFACE ENGINEERING. 1985. q. £165($328) to non-members; members £88 ($176). Institute of Materials, 1 Carlton House Terrace, London SW1Y 5DB, England. TEL 071-839-4071. FAX 071-839-2078. TELEX 8144813-METSOC-G. Ed. Tom Bell. circ. 600. **Indexed:** B.C.I.R.A., INSPEC (1985-). **Document type:** academic/scholarly publication.
—BLDSC (8547.850000); CASDDS; Ei; Faxon; SWETS; UnCover.
   Incorporates: Surfacing Journal International (ISSN 0269-2848); Which superseded (1972-1986): Surfacing Journal (ISSN 0307-7365)
   Description: Covers developments in processes and techniques of surface engineering and their industrial applications.

669   US
SURFACE FINISHING TECHNOLOGY. 1974. m. $160 to non-members (foreign $180); members $130 (foreign $145) (effective 1996). A S M International, Materials Information, Materials Park, OH 44073. TEL 216-338-5151. FAX 216-338-4634. TELEX 980-619. E-mail: DBarthel@po.ASM-Intl.org. (UK adnl.: Institute of Materials, Materials Information, 1 Carlton House Terr., London SW1Y 5DB, England. TEL 071-839-4071) **Indexed:** Met.Abstr. **Document type:** abstracting/indexing.
   Formerly: Cleaning - Finishing - Coating Digest.

669.1   SW
SWEDISH STEEL MANUAL. (Text in English; list of various mills and their product lines in English, French, German and Spanish) 1962. irreg. SEK 135. Jernkontoret - Swedish Steel Producers Association, P.O. Box 1721, S-111 87 Stockholm, Sweden. TEL 46-8-679-1700. FAX 46-8-611-2089. Ed. Hans von Delwig.
   Description: Accounts for the origin and development of the Swedish steel industry, present structure, exports, research and development of new products. The main institutions in the industry are also indicated. The various companies are presented with all pertinent data.

669   FR   ISSN 0151-0568
SYNDICAT GENERAL DES FONDEURS DE FRANCE ET INDUSTRIES CONNEXES. ANNUAIRE. 1925. a. 748.81 F. (foreign 1010 F.) (effective 1996). Revue Francaise des Metallurgistes, 32 rue Saint-Marc, 75002 Paris, France. TEL 42-60-31-51. FAX 42-60-38-42. **Document type:** trade publication.
   Formerly (until 1949): Syndicat General des Fondeurs de France. Annuaire (ISSN 0562-9888)

669.1   II   ISSN 0039-8411
T I S C O TECHNICAL JOURNAL. (Text in English) 1954. q. Rs.12($3) Tata Iron and Steel Co. Ltd., Jamshedpur 831001, Bihar, India. Ed. K. Banerjee. adv.; charts; illus.; index. circ. 1,500. **Indexed:** ABTICS, Chem.Abstr., Eng.Ind., Met.Abstr.

669   JA   ISSN 0039-8993
   CODEN: TAKOAV
TAIKABUTSU/REFRACTORIES. (Text in Japanese) 1949. m. 15000 Yen (effective 1996). Technical Association of Refractories - Taikabutsu Gijutsu Kyokai, c/o New Ginza Bldg., 7-3-13 Ginza, Chuo-ku, Tokyo 104, Japan. FAX 81-33572-0175. Ed. Yoshio Hattori. adv. contact: Youko Yoshii. charts; illus.; stat. info. circ. 2,500. **Indexed:** Br.Ceram.Abstr., Ceram.Abstr., Chem.Abstr., JTA. **Document type:** bulletin.
—BLDSC (8598.515000); CASDDS.

METALLURGY

669   JA   ISSN 0285-0028
TN677.5   CODEN: TAOVD7
TAIKABUTSU OVERSEAS/REFRACTORIES OVERSEAS. (Text in English) 1981. q. 40000 Yen (effective 1996). Technical Association of Refractories - Taikabutsu Gijutsu Kyokai, c/o New Ginza Bldg., 7-3-13 Ginza, Chuo-ku, Tokyo 104, Japan. FAX 81-33572-0175. Ed. Kazunori Kijima. adv. contact: Youko Yoshii. illus.; charts; stat. circ. 600. **Document type:** bulletin.
—BLDSC (8598.516000); CASDDS.

669   BE   ISSN 1019-2026
TANTALUM-NIOBIUM INTERNATIONAL STUDY CENTER. QUARTERLY BULLETIN. 1974. q. free. Tantalum-Niobium International Study Center, 40 rue Washington, B-1050 Brussels, Belgium. TEL 32-2-649-5158. FAX 32-2-649-6447. TELEX 65080 INAC B. circ. 1,000. (back issues avail.) **Document type:** newsletter.
—BLDSC (2772.350000).

669   GW   ISSN 0082-1772
TASCHENBUCH DER GIESSEREI-PRAXIS. 1952. a. DM.64. Fachverlag Schiele und Schoen GmbH, Markgrafenstr. 11, 10969 Berlin, Germany. TEL 030-253752-0. FAX 030-3517248. adv. circ. 5,000. **Document type:** trade publication.

669   GW
TASCHENBUCH DES METALLHANDELS. irreg. DM.182. Huethig GmbH, Postfach 102869, 69018 Heidelberg, Germany. TEL 06221-489-0. FAX 06221-489482. **Document type:** trade publication.

669   HU   ISSN 0324-4679
TN600   CODEN: PTUBDW
TECHNICAL UNIVERSITY FOR HEAVY INDUSTRY. PUBLICATIONS. SERIES B, METALLURGY. (Text in English, German, Russian) irreg., vol.37, no.3, 1989. Nehezipari Muszaki Egyetem, Miskolc, Hungary. TEL 46-6511. FAX 46-69554. TELEX 62223-NMEMIS. Ed.Bd. bibl.; index. circ. 300. **Indexed:** C.R.I.Abstr., C.R.I.Curr.Cont., Met.Abstr.
—BLDSC (7113.412000); CASDDS.

TECHNISCHE MITTEILUNGEN KRUPP. see
TECHNOLOGY: COMPREHENSIVE WORKS

TECNOLOGIA DELLA DEFORMAZIONE. see *MACHINERY*

669.1   PO   ISSN 0871-5742
TECNOLOGIA QUALIDADE. 1981. q. Esc.2420 (Europe Esc.3850; elsewhere Esc.4950) (effective 1994). Instituto de Soldadura e Qualidade, Estrada Nacional 249, km 3, Apdo. 119, 2781 Oeiras Codex, Portugal. TEL 351-4211307. FAX 351-4211471. Ed. Mario Figueira. adv.: B&W page Esc.110000, color page Esc.120000; trim 180 x 268; adv. contact: J.M. Dias Miranda. bk.rev.; abstr.; bibl. circ. 4,000. **Indexed:** Met.Abstr. **Document type:** trade publication.
Formerly (until 1988): Soldadura e Construcao Metalica (ISSN 0870-0710)

669   IT   ISSN 0392-7954
TECNOLOGIE DEL FILO. 1983. bi-m. L.48000 (foreign L.135000) (effective 1995). Tecniche Nuove s.p.a., Via C. Menotti 14, 20129 Milan, Italy. TEL 02-75701. FAX 02-7610351. Ed. Mario Palmisano. adv.: B&W page L.1790000, color page L.2610000; trim 185 x 266. circ. 5,000.
Description: Technical information on wire, steel wire and new ferrous wire work.

669 621   IT   ISSN 0391-1683
TECNOLOGIE MECCANICHE; sistemi per produrre. 1970. m. L.110000 (foreign-L.220000) (effective 1995). Stammer S.p.A., Via della Liberazione 1, 20068 Peschiera Borromeo (MI), Italy. TEL 02-55302606. FAX 02-55302700. Ed. Girolamo Bellina. adv.: B&W page L.1850000, color page L.2470000; trim 185 x 267. circ. 15,500.

669.1   JA   ISSN 0040-2273
TEKKO RODO EISEI/JOURNAL OF LABOR HYGIENE IN IRON AND STEEL INDUSTRY. (Text in Japanese; table of contents in English) 1950. 2/yr. free. Japan Iron and Steel Federation, Hygiene Committee - Nihon Tekko Renmei, Eisei Iinkai, Keidanren Kaikan, 9-4, 1-chome, Ote-machi, Chiyoda-ku, Tokyo 100, Japan. TEL 03-3279-3611. FAX 03-3245-0144. TELEX 222-4210. bk.rev. circ. 500. **Indexed:** C.I.S. Abstr.

TEKKOTSU/STEEL FRAME. see *BUILDING AND CONSTRUCTION*

669   US
TESTING TECHNOLOGY. 1976. m. $160 to non-members (foreign $180); members $130 (foreign $145) (effective 1996). A S M International, Materials Information, Materials Park, OH 44073. TEL 216-338-5151. FAX 216-338-4634. TELEX 980-619. E-mail: DBarthel@po.ASM-Intl.org. (UK addr.: Institute of Metals, Materials Information, 1 Carlton House Terr., London SW1Y 5DB, England. TEL 071-839-4071) **Indexed:** Met.Abstr. **Document type:** abstracting/indexing.
Former titles: Metallography and Testing Digest & Testing and Control Digest.

669.1   JA   ISSN 0021-1575
     CODEN: TEHAA2
TETSU-TO-HAGANE. (Text in Japanese; summaries in English) 1915. m. 52000 Yen to non-members (effective 1995). Iron and Steel Institute of Japan - Nippon Tekko Kyokai, Keidanren Kaikan, 3rd Fl., 9-4, Otemachi, 1-chome, Chiyoda-ku, Tokyo 100, Japan. TEL 03-3279-6021. FAX 03-3245-1355. TELEX 02228153-ISIJTK-J. Ed. Jin Shimada. adv.; index. circ. 11,000. **Indexed:** ASCA, Br.Ceram.Abstr., Ceram.Abstr., Chem.Abstr., JTA, Met.Abstr., World Alum.Abstr. **Document type:** academic/scholarly publication.
—BLDSC (4803.045000); CASDDS; Ei; Genuine Article; SWETS. **CCC.**

669   US   ISSN 1052-7877
Z695.1.M55
THESAURUS OF METALLURGICAL TERMS. 1968. biennial. $80 in US, Canada, Mexico; elsewhere $90. A S M International, Materials Information, Materials Park, OH 44073. TEL 216-338-5151. FAX 216-338-4634. TELEX 980-619. (UK addr.: Institute of Materials, Materials Information, 1 Carlton House Terr., London SW1Y 5DB, England. TEL 071-839-4071)
Description: Controlled vocabulary for effective searching of Materials Information Metadex database.

669   NE   ISSN 0923-1722
     CODEN: TOCOEP
TIJDSCHRIFT VOOR OPPERVLAKTETECHNIEKEN EN CORROSIEBESTRIJDING. 1957. m. fl.118.50. (Vereniging voor Oppervlaktetechnieken van Materialen) Tijl Tijdschriften B.V., P.B. 9943, 1006 AP Amsterdam, Netherlands. FAX 030-287674. Ed. R.I. de Jong. adv.; bk.rev. circ. 2,200. **Indexed:** C.I.S. Abstr., Chem.Abstr., Excerp.Med.
—BLDSC (8843.850000); CASDDS; SWETS.
Former titles (until 1988): Belgisch-Nederlands Tijdschrift voor Oppervlaktetechnieken van Metalen (ISSN 0366-144X); Tijdschrift voor Oppervlaktetechnieken van Materialen (ISSN 0040-7569)

669.6 688   UK   ISSN 0040-795X
TN793.A1
TIN INTERNATIONAL. 1928. m. £144 (effective 1996). M I I D A Ltd., P.O. Box 2137, London NW10 6TN, England. TEL 0181-961-7407. FAX 0181-961-7487. Ed. R. Amlot. adv.; bk.rev.; charts; illus.; mkt.; stat.; index. circ. 7,200. (also avail. in microfilm reprint; reprint service avail. from UMI) **Indexed:** Art & Archaeol.Tech.Abstr., Br.Tech.Ind., Curr.Pack.Abstr., Int.Packag.Abstr., Key to Econ.Sci., Met.Abstr., PROMT, World Alum.Abstr. **Document type:** trade publication, newsletter.
●Also available online. Vendor(s): Knight-Ridder, Inc.
—BLDSC (8856.500000); UMI; UnCover.
Incorporates: Tin Printer and Box Maker (ISSN 0040-7976); Canning and Packing (ISSN 0008-5588)

669.6   UK
TIN PRODUCTION AND INVESTMENT. 1979. irreg. £40. International Tin Council, 1 Oxendon St., London SW1Y 4EQ, England.
Description: Designed to assess the economics of investment in new tin mining ventures.

669   US   ISSN 0364-7943
     CODEN: MTITDR
TITANIUM (YEAR): A STATISTICAL REVIEW. 1989. a. $50. Titanium Development Association, 4141 Arapahoe Ave., Ste. 100, Boulder, CO 80303. TEL 303-443-7515. FAX 303-443-4406. (back issues avail.) **Document type:** trade publication.
—CASDDS; UMI.
Description: Compiles titanium statistics obtained from government and trade organization data. Includes industry statistics on Japanese imports and exports.

669   US
TITANIUM DEVELOPMENT ASSOCIATION. INTERNATIONAL CONFERENCE ON TITANIUM PRODUCTS AND APPLICATIONS. PROCEEDINGS. a. price varies. Titanium Development Association, 4141 Arapahoe Ave., Ste. 100, Boulder, CO 80303. TEL 303-443-7515. FAX 303-443-4406. **Document type:** proceedings.
Description: Covers the mining, processing, and applications of titanium.

669   US
TITANIUM DIGEST. 1976. m. $160 to non-members (foreign $180); members $130 (foreign $145) (effective 1996). A S M International, Materials Information, Materials Park, OH 44073. TEL 216-338-5151. FAX 216-338-4634. TELEX 980-619. E-mail: DBartherl@po.ASM-Intl.org. (UK addr.: Institute of Materials, Materials Information, 1 Carlton House Terr., London SW1Y 5DB, England. TEL 071-839-4071) **Indexed:** Met.Abstr. **Document type:** abstracting/indexing.

669 622   JA   ISSN 0919-4827
     CODEN: TDSSA2
TOHOKU DAIGAKU SOZAI KOGAKU KENKYUJO IHO/TOHOKU UNIVERSITY. INSTITUTE FOR ADVANCED MATERIALS PROCESSING. BULLETIN. (Text in Japanese; summaries in English) 1942. s-a. exchange basis. Tohoku Daigaku, Sozai Kogaku Kenkyujo - Tohoku University, Institute for Advanced Materials Processing, 1-1 Katahira 2-chome, Aoba-ku, Sendai 980, Japan. TEL 81-22-227-6200. FAX 81-22-261-0938. TELEX 0852-233 SENKEN J. Ed. Yoshio Waseda. charts; illus.; stat.; circ. controlled. **Indexed:** Chem.Abstr., JTA, Met.Abstr. **Document type:** academic/scholarly publication.
—BLDSC (2577.810000); CASDDS.
Formerly (until 1993): Tohoku Daigaku Senko Seiren Kenkyujo Iho - Tohoku University, Research Institute of Mineral Dressing and Metallurgy. Bulletin (ISSN 0040-876X)
Description: Covers the field of metallurgical, environmental and nuclear chemistry and materials science.

TOHOKU UNIVERSITY. SCIENCE REPORTS OF THE RESEARCH INSTITUTES. SERIES A: PHYSICS, CHEMISTRY, AND METALLURGY/TOHOKU DAIGAKU KENKYUJO HOKOKU. A-SHU: BUTSURIGAKU, KAGAKU, YAKINGAKU. see *PHYSICS*

669   FR   ISSN 0985-5637
TOLERIE; le magazine du materiel et de la technologie du travail des metaux en feuille. 1987. 10/yr. 950 F. (foreign 1195 F.). Marlau Editions, 16 allee de la Source, 77340 Pontault-Combault, France. TEL 60-28-05-33. FAX 60-28-77-30. Ed. Laurence Renoult. circ. 7,000.
Description: Contains information about new products and thematic information on technology used in sheet metal working, such as punching machines, bending machines, lasers, shearing machines.

TOMOEGUMI TEKKOJO GIHO/TOMOEGUMI IRON WORKS TECHNICAL REPORT. see *BUILDING AND CONSTRUCTION*

669   II   ISSN 0377-9408
     CODEN: TASTDL
TOOL AND ALLOY STEELS. 1967. m. Rs.500($75) Alloy Steel Producers Association of India, 1, Nazir Wadi, Juhu Beach, Bombay 400 049, India. TEL 4110364. Ed. K.S. Mathew. adv.; bk.rev.; tr.lit. circ. 5,000. **Indexed:** Chem.Abstr., Met.Abstr., World Alum.Abstr. **Document type:** trade publication.
—CASDDS.

669   JA
TOTAN GIHO/TOKYO TUNGSTEN TECHNICAL REVIEW. (Text in Japanese; summaries in English) 1989. a. Tokyo Tungsten Co., Ltd., 6-1, Kajicho 2-chome, Chiyoda-ku, Tokyo 101, Japan. TEL 03-3258-5325.

METALLURGY 4677

671 FR ISSN 0041-0950
TN672 CODEN: TRTHA4
TRAITEMENT THERMIQUE/HEAT TREATMENT. 1963. 9/yr. 720 F. (foreign 980 F.) (effective 1996). P Y C Editions, 5 ave de Verdun, B.P. 105, 94280 Ivry sur Seine Cedex, France. TEL 1-49-60-86-36. FAX 1-46-72-41-85. TELEX 263 424. Ed. Rene Caule. adv.: B&W page 6130 F., color page 12680 F.; trim 190 X 260; adv. contact: Pierre Pagnard. bk.rev.; charts; illus.; index. circ. 2,700. **Indexed:** Chem.Abstr., Met.Abstr., World Alum.Abstr.
—BLDSC (8883.800000); CASDDS; Ei. **CCC.**
   Description: Technical review for engineers and technicians of heat treatment.

TRANSACTIONS OF THE MONUMENTAL BRASS SOCIETY. see *ARCHAEOLOGY*

669 FR ISSN 1143-3760
TRANSFIL EUROPE. 1987. q. S T Diffusion, 29-31 av. des Champs Elysees, 75008 Paris, France. TEL 45-63-85-94. FAX 42-89-32-77. Ed. P. Caudebec. circ. 5,000.

669 UK ISSN 0340-4285
  CODEN: TMCHDN
TRANSITION METAL CHEMISTRY; an international journal. bi-m. £410 to institutions in the E.U. (N. America $695; elsewhere £440) (effective 1995). Chapman & Hall, Journals Department (Subsidiary of: International Thomson Publishing Group), 2-6 Boundary Row, London SE1 8HN, England. TEL 0171-865-0066. FAX 0171-522-9623. TELEX 290164 CHAPMA G. E-mail: journal@chall.mhs.compuserve.com. (Dist. by: International Thomson Publishing Services Ltd., Cheriton House, North Way, Andover, Hants. SP10 5BE, England. TEL 01264-342713; Subscr. in N. America to: Chapman & Hall, Journals Promotion Department, One Penn Plaza, 41st Fl., New York, NY 10019. TEL 212-564-1060. FAX 212-564-1505) Ed. D.R.M. Walton. adv. (also avail. in microfilm from VCI; reprint service avail. from ISI) **Indexed:** ASCA, Chem.Abstr., Curr.Cont., Sci.Cit.Ind. **Document type:** academic/scholarly publication.
—BLDSC (9020.860000); CASDDS; Ei; Faxon; Genuine Article; SWETS; UMI. **CCC.**
   Description: Publishes preliminary communications and full-length research papers on the chemistry of the f-group metals.
   Refereed Serial

669 536 SP ISSN 1132-0346
TRATAMIENTOS TERMICOS. 1991. 12/yr. Deltacad, Alcala 93, 4o, 28009 Madrid, Spain. TEL 1-576-56-09. FAX 1-578-29-24. Ed. J.M. Palacios. circ. 2,500.

TRATTAMENTI E FINITURE; rivista tecnica dei trattamenti, processi, finiture delle superfici. see *PAINTS AND PROTECTIVE COATINGS*

669 RU ISSN 0372-2929
TN4 CODEN: TVMTAX
TSVETNYE METALLY. English translation: Russian Journal of Non-Ferrous Metals (US ISSN 1067-8212) (Text in Russian) 1926. m. $140 (effective 1996). Izdatel'stvo Metallurgiya, 2-i Obydenskii Per., 14, Moscow G-34, Russia. (Dist. by: Mezhdunarodnaya Kniga, B. Yakimanka 39, 117049 Moscow, Russia) (Co-sponsor: Komitet Rossiiskoi Federatsii po Metallurgii) Ed. V.A. Generalov. adv.: page $500. bibl.; illus.; index. circ. 5,400. **Indexed:** Chem.Abstr., Eng.Ind., Met.Abstr., World Alum.Abstr.
—BLDSC (0396.450000); CASDDS; SWETS. **CCC.**

669 621 US ISSN 1051-4120
TS280
TUBE & PIPE QUARTERLY. Abbreviated title: T P Q. 1990. q. $15 (Canada and Mexico $25; elsewhere $45); free to qualified personnel. Croydon Group, Ltd. (Subsidiary of: Fabricators & Manufacturers Association, International), 833 Featherstone Rd., Rockford, IL 61107-6301. TEL 815-399-8700. FAX 815-399-7279. Ed. Kathy Velasco; Pub. John Nandzik. adv.: B&W page $2380; trim 8 1/4 x 10 3/4; adv. contact: Jack Broughton. circ. 30,328. **Document type:** trade publication.
—Faxon.
   Description: Contains news and information relating to the metal tube and pipe industry. Includes articles and news releases to assist owners, managers, manufacturing engineers, supervisors, and foremen in the evaluation of new methods and techniques.

671.8 UK ISSN 0263-6794
TUBE INTERNATIONAL. 1982. bi-m. free. Publex International Ltd., 110 Station Rd. E., Oxted, Surrey RH8 0QA, England. TEL 01883-717755. FAX 01883-714554. Ed. Adam Schulman. circ. 7,977. **Indexed:** Met.Abstr., World Alum.Abstr. **Document type:** trade publication.
—BLDSC (9068.070000).

669 UK
U E S STEELS NEWS. m. U E S Steels (Subsidiary of: United Engineering Steels Ltd.), Stocksbridge, Sheffield S30 5JA, England. TEL 0742-882361. FAX 0742-885033. Ed. T.J. Lodge. circ. 9,000. **Document type:** newsletter.
   Formed by the 1993 merger of: Rotherham & Wolverhampton Review & Stocksbridge Gazette.

669 UK
U K EXPORTS OF IRON AND STEEL (YEAR). a. £250 (outside Europe £280) (effective 1995). (Iron and Steel Statistics Bureau) I S S B Ltd., 2 Sydenham Rd., Croydon, Surrey CR9 2LZ, England. TEL 0181-686-9050. FAX 0181-680-8616. charts; stat. **Document type:** trade publication.
   Description: Compiles monthly statistics of U.K. exports of iron and steel products to more than 100 countries.

669 UK
U K IMPORTS OF IRON AND STEEL (YEAR). a. £250 (outside Europe £280) (effective 1995). (Iron and Steel Statistics Bureau) I S S B Ltd., 2 Sydenham Rd., Croydon, Surrey CR9 2LA. TEL 0181-686-9050. FAX 0181-680-8616. charts; stat. **Document type:** trade publication.
   Description: Compiles statistics of U.K. imports of iron and steel, by month, from more than 36 nations.

671.2 US ISSN 0041-8048
U S PIPER. 1928. q. free. United States Pipe and Foundry Company, Box 10406, Birmingham, AL 35202. TEL 205-254-7442. FAX 205-254-7494. Ed. George J. Bogs. illus. circ. 8,500. **Indexed:** Met.Abstr. **Document type:** trade publication.

671 621.9 668.4 GW ISSN 0300-3167
UMFORMTECHNIK. 1967. 4/yr. DM.114 (effective 1995). Meisenbach GmbH, Hainstr. 18, 96047 Bamberg, Germany. TEL 0951-861-0. FAX 0951-861-161. (Subscr. to: Postfach 2069, 96011 Bamberg, Germany) Ed. Arnt Hannewald; Pub. Meinhard Meisenbach. adv.: B&W page DM.3200, color page DM.5075; trim 260 x 184; adv. contact: Oskar Ohler. charts; illus.; index. circ. 5,100. **Indexed:** Excerp.Med., Met.Abstr., World Alum.Abstr. **Document type:** trade publication.
   Description: Methods, machines and tooling for sheet-metal forming, forging and rolling processes, parting techniques as well as plastics processing.

669.6 UK
UNITED KINGDOM - TIN IN TINPLATE. 1981. irreg. £10. International Tin Council, 1 Oxendon St., London SW1Y 4EQ, England.
   Description: Surveys tinplate manufacturing, can making and canning in the UK.

669.6 UK
UNITED STATES OF AMERICA - TIN IN TINPLATE. 1983. irreg. £15. International Tin Council, 1 Oxendon St., London SW1Y 4EQ, England. **Indexed:** Refug.Abstr.
   Description: Surveys tinplate manufacturing, can making, and canning in the United States.

UNITED STEELWORKERS OF AMERICA. INFORMATION. see *LABOR UNIONS*

UNIVERSIDAD AUTONOMA DE SAN LUIS POTOSI. INSTITUTO DE GEOLOGIA. FOLLETO TECNICO. see *EARTH SCIENCES* — Geology

UNIVERSITATEA POLITEHNICA BUCURESTI. BULETIN STIINTIFIC. CHIMIE SI STIINTA MATERIALELOR/POLYTECHNICAL UNIVERSITY OF BUCHAREST. SCIENTIFIC BULLETIN. CHEMISTRY AND MATERIALS SCIENCE. see *CHEMISTRY*

669 PL ISSN 0208-578X
UNIWERSYTET SLASKI W KATOWICACH. PRACE NAUKOWE. FIZYKA I CHEMIA METALI. (Text in Polish; summaries in English, Polish) 1976. irreg. price varies. Wydawnictwo Uniwersytetu Slaskiego, Ul. Bankowa 12B, 40-007 Katowice, Poland. TEL 48-32-596-915. FAX 48-32-599-605. TELEX 0315584 USKPL. (Dist. by: CHZ Ars Polona, P.O. Box 1001, 00-950 Warsaw, Poland) **Document type:** academic/scholarly publication.
   Description: Covers metalselectrodeposition of alloys, texture, epitaxie, electrocrystallization of metals and alloys, structure investigation method, underpotential effects, electrooxidation processes, martensit transformation, sharp memory effect.

V W D - N E - METALLE. see *BUSINESS AND ECONOMICS* — Investments

V W D - STAHL. see *BUSINESS AND ECONOMICS* — Investments

669 AU
  CODEN: RAXRAF
VEITSCH-RADEX RUNDSCHAU. 1946. s-a. Veitsch-Radex AG fuer Feuerfeste Erzeugnisse, Mommsengasse 35, Postfach 143, A-1011 Vienna, Austria. Ed. Karl Hajek. **Document type:** bulletin.
—CASDDS; Ei.
   Formerly (until 1994): Radex Rundschau (ISSN 0370-3657)

VUORITEOLLISUS/BERGSHANTERINGEN. see *MINES AND MINING INDUSTRY*

669 XR ISSN 0474-8484
TN4 CODEN: SRAHAY
VYSOKA SKOLA BANSKA. SBORNIK VEDECKYCH PRACI: RADA HUTNICKA/INSTITUTE OF MINING AND METALLURGY. TRANSACTIONS: METALLURGICAL SERIES. (Text in Czech; summaries in English, German, Russian) 1955. irreg. (2-8/yr.) 25 Kc.($1) per issue. Vysoka Skola Banska - Technical University of Mining and Metallurgy, Trida 17 Listopadu 15, 708 33 Ostrava, Czech Republic. bk.rev.; abstr.; bibl.; charts; illus.; stat.; index. **Indexed:** Copper Abstr., Fuel & Energy Abstr., Geo.Abstr., Met.Abstr., World Alum.Abstr.
—BLDSC (8087.400200); CASDDS.

671.84 GW ISSN 0043-5996
WIRE; international technical journal for the wire and cable industry and all areas of wire processing. German edition: Draht (ISSN 0012-5911); Italian edition: Filo Metallico (ISSN 0430-4578); Spanish edition: Alambre (ISSN 0002-4406) (Text in English) 1951. bi-m. DM.135 (effective 1995). Meisenbach GmbH, Hainstr. 18, 96047 Bamberg, Germany. TEL 0951-861-135. FAX 0951-861-161. (Subscr. to: Postfach 2069, 96011 Bamberg, Germany) Ed. Arnt Hannewald; Pub. Meinhard Meisenbach. adv.: B&W page DM.3980, color page DM.6005; trim 260 x 184; adv. contact: Oskar Ohler. bk.rev.; charts; illus. circ. 9,000. (also avail. in microfilm from UMI) **Indexed:** Chem.Abstr., Copper Abstr., Eng.Ind., Met.Abstr. **Document type:** trade publication.
—BLDSC (9320.350000); Ei; Faxon; UMI. **CCC.**
   Incorporates (1959-1995): Wireworld (ISSN 0934-5906)

671.84 UK ISSN 0043-6011
  CODEN: WIRIAZ
WIRE INDUSTRY; international monthly journal. 1934. m. $132. Publex International Ltd., 110 Station Rd. E., Oxted, Surrey RH8 0QA, England. TEL 01883-717755. FAX 01883-714554. Ed. Adam Schulman. adv.; bk.rev.; bibl.; charts; illus.; pat.; index. circ. 8,770. **Indexed:** Br.Tech.Ind., Chem.Abstr., Copper Abstr., Eng.Ind., Excerp.Med., Met.Abstr., World Alum.Abstr. **Document type:** trade publication.
—BLDSC (9321.000000); Ei; Faxon; SWETS; UnCover.

674.84 US
WIRE INDUSTRY NEWS. 1973. bi-w. $250 (foreign $300). C R U International, 7500 Greenway Center Dr., Ste. 480, Greenbelt, MD 20770. TEL 301-441-8997. FAX 301-441-9091. Ed. Karen Chasez. **Document type:** newsletter.
   Description: Focuses on management, mergers, buy-outs, current events in the industry, promotions and business conditions.

ULRICH'S INTERNATIONAL PERIODICALS DIRECTORY 1996

METALLURGY

671.8 UK ISSN 0084-0424
WIRE INDUSTRY YEARBOOK; international buyers guide. (Text in English, French, German, Italian and Spanish) 1951. a. $115.50. Publex International Ltd., 110 Station Rd. E., Oxted, Surrey RH8 0QA, England. TEL 01883-717755.
FAX 01883-714554. Ed. B.J. Mitchell. adv. circ. 9,500. **Document type:** trade publication.

WIRE ROPE NEWS AND SLING TECHNOLOGY. see *PACKAGING*

669 658.8 UK ISSN 0144-5960
WOLFF'S GUIDE TO THE LONDON METAL EXCHANGE.
1976. irreg., latest 1991. $91. Metal Bulletin plc, Park House, Park Terrace, Worcester Park, Surrey KT4 7HY, England. TEL 0171-827-9977.
FAX 0181-337-8943. (Subscr. to: Metal Bulletin Inc., 220 Fifth Ave., New York, NY 10001-7781. TEL 212-213-6202. FAX 212-213-1870)
(Co-publisher: Rudolf Wolff and Co. Ltd.) **Document type:** directory.
Description: Covers market operations together with historical background and individual chapters devoted to each product traded.

669 UK
HD9539.A6
WORLD ALUMINIUM DATABOOK. 1954. irreg., latest 1990. $171.60. Metal Bulletin plc, Park House, Park Terrace, Worcester Park, Surrey KT4 7HY, England. TEL 0171-827-9977.
FAX 0181-337-8943. (U.S. subscr. to: Metal Bulletin Inc., 220 Fifth Ave., New York, NY 10001-7781. TEL 212-213-6202. FAX 212-213-1870) Ed. Richard Serjeantson. adv. **Document type:** directory.
—BLDSC (9352.910500).
Former titles: World Aluminium (ISSN 0951-2233); (until 1987): World Aluminum Databook.
Description: Divided into producers and products directories; lists alphabetically by country and product.

669.6 UK
WORLD CONFERENCE ON TIN. PROCEEDINGS. irreg., 4th, 1974 Kuala Lumpur. £36. International Tin Council, Haymarket House, 1 Oxendon St., London SW1Y 4EQ, England. **Document type:** proceedings.
Description: Papers on tin resources, prospecting and mining, processing and smelting, and marketing and consumption.

WORLD MATERIALS CALENDAR; comprehensive international coverage of forthcoming events in metallurgy and materials science. see *MEETINGS AND CONGRESSES*

669 UK ISSN 0266-7355
HD9539.A1
WORLD METAL STATISTICS. YEARBOOK. 1984. a. £250. World Bureau of Metal Statistics, 27a High St., Ware, Herts SG12 9BA, England. TEL 01920-461274.
FAX 01920-464258. **Indexed:** Copper Abstr. **Document type:** corporate report.
—BLDSC (9356.670300).

669 UK ISSN 0965-0830
WORLD NICKEL STATISTICS. 1991. m. $330. (World Bureau of Metal Statistics) Metal Bulletin plc, Park House, Park Terrace, Worcester Park, Surrey KT4 7HY, England. TEL 0171-827-9977.
FAX 0181-337-8943. (U.S. subscr. to: Metal Bulletin Inc., 220 Fifth Ave., New York, NY 10001-7781. TEL 212-213-6202. FAX 212-213-1870) **Document type:** trade publication.

669 GW ISSN 0943-3511
WORLD OF METALS. (Text in English, German) 1993. irreg. DM.185($140) Metallgesellschaft AG, Reuterweg 14, 60271 Frankfurt a.M., Germany. TEL 069-1592741. FAX 069-1592107. TELEX 412250-MGF-D. Eds. Hans Schreiber, Sylvia Narke. **Document type:** trade publication.

669 UK
WORLD PRECIOUS METALS DATABOOK. 1982. irreg. $144. Metal Bulletin plc, Park House, Park Terrace, Worcester Park, Surrey KT4 7HY, England. TEL 0171-827-9977. FAX 0181-337-8943. (U.S. subscr. to: Metal Bulletin Inc., 220 Fifth Ave., New York, NY 10001-7781. TEL 212-213-6202. FAX 212-213-1870) adv. **Document type:** directory.
Formerly: World Precious Metals Survey (ISSN 0263-9661)

669.6 UK
WORLD - TIN IN TINPLATE. 1986. irreg. £25. International Tin Council, 1 Oxendon St., London SW1Y 4EQ, England.
Description: Survey of world tinplate manufacturing, can making and canning.

669 UK
WORLD TIN MINING OPERATIONS, EXPLORATION AND DEVELOPMENTS. irreg. £20. International Tin Council, 1 Oxendon St., London SW1Y 4EQ, England.
Description: Inventory of tin mining operations in 40 countries giving production details and planned developments.

669 CC ISSN 1001-1587
WUJIN KEJI. (Text in Chinese) 1973. bi-m. Y3 per no. (China Hardware Association) Shenyang Light Industry Research and Design Institute, 7, Ningshan Donglu, Huanggu-qu, Shenyang, Liaoning 110032, People's Republic of China. TEL 465196.
(Co-sponsor: Quanguo Riyong Wujin Gongye Keji Qingbaozhan) Ed. Hou Zhiguang. circ. 10,000.
Description: Covers research, technology, management in the field of daily use hardware.

669 CC ISSN 1001-1617
YEJIN NENGYUAN/ENERGY FOR METALLURGICAL INDUSTRY. (Text in Chinese) 1982. bi-m. Yejin Bu, Anshan Reneng Yanjiusuo - Ministry of Metallurgical Industry, Anshan Research Institute of Thermo-Energy, 43 Luhua St., Tiedong-qu, Anshan, Liaoning 114004, People's Republic of China. TEL 0412-536495. Ed. Huang Renxiang. **Document type:** trade publication.
Description: Covers energy economics and management, systematic energy saving techniques, waste heat and energy recovery techniques, and energy conversion technology.

669 CC ISSN 1001-1269
YEJIN SHEBEI/METALLURGICAL EQUIPMENT. (Text in Chinese) bi-m. Beijing Yejin Shebei Yanjiusuo - Beijing Institute of Metallurgical Equipment, P.O. Box 2430, Beijing 100081, People's Republic of China. TEL 892531. Ed. Chen Zhongming.

669 CC ISSN 1001-0211
CODEN: YSCSAE
YOUSE JINSHU/CHINESE JOURNAL OF NONFERROUS METAL. (Text in Chinese) 1980. q. $23.86 (effective 1996). Zhongguo Youse Jinshu Gongye Zonggongsi - China Nonferrous Metal Industrial Company, 1 Wenxingjie, Xiwai, Beijing 100044, People's Republic of China. TEL 861-8322211. FAX 861-8321362. TELEX 222589 GRIMM CN. (Co-sponsor: Nonferrous Metals Society of China) Ed. Huang Digong. adv.: B&W page $1200, color page $1800. bk.rev. circ. 12,000. **Document type:** academic/scholarly publication.
—BLDSC (6117.069000).
Description: Covers the fields of geology, mining, mineral processing, metallurgy, materials science and engineering.

620.11 SW ISSN 0349-4470
YTFORUM. 1980. 8/yr. SEK 375 (foreign SEK 425); newsstand price: SEK 60. Ytforum Foerlags AB, P.O. Box 462, S-581 05 Linkoeping, Sweden. TEL 46-13-11-41-75. FAX 46-13-14-38-49. Ed. Goeran Ekstroem. adv.: B&W page SEK 7400; trim 185 x 265; adv. contact: Goeran Ekstroem. circ. 3,500. cols./p.: 3.

669 943.7 XR ISSN 0139-9810
Z DEJIN HUTNICTVI. (Text in Czech; summaries in English and German) 1972. irreg. exchange basis. Narodni Technicke Muzeum, Kostelni 42, 170 78 Prague 7, Czech Republic. illus.; bibl.

671.2 JA ISSN 0919-8423
CODEN: ZAIKFC
ZAIKEN/WASEDA UNIVERSITY. KAGAMI MEMORIAL LABORATORY FOR MATERIALS SCIENCE AND TECHNOLOGY. (Text in English) 1950. a. free. Waseda University, Kagami Memorials Laboratory for Materials Science and Technology, 2-8-26 Nishiwaseda, Shinjuku-ku, Tokyo 169, Japan. TEL 03-3203-4782. FAX 03-3205-1353. Ed. M. Nagumo. adv. contact: M. Uda. circ. 500. **Indexed:** Chem.Abstr., Met.Abstr. **Document type:** academic/scholarly publication.
—BLDSC (9425.920330); CASDDS.
Former titles (until 1993): Waseda University. Report of Materials Science and Technology (ISSN 0916-6521); (until 1989): Waseda University. Report of Castings Research Laboratory (ISSN 0511-1927)

620.112 JA ISSN 0917-0480
TA418.74 CODEN: ZAKAEP
ZAIRYO TO KANKYO. English translation: Corrosion Engineering (US ISSN 0892-4228) (Text in Japanese, summaries in English) 1951. m. 27640 Yen (members 9000 Yen). Japan Society of Corrosion Engineering, Koyasu Buil, 1-12-5 Yushima, Bunkyo-ku, Tokyo 113, Japan. TEL 03-5818-6765. FAX 03-5818-8726. Ed. Koji Hashimoto. adv. contact: Shiro Haruyama. bk.rev.; charts; illus.; pat.; index. circ. 1,200. **Indexed:** Chem.Abstr., Corros.Abstr., INIS Atomind., JTA, Met.Abstr., World Alum.Abstr. **Document type:** academic/scholarly publication.
—BLDSC (3473.600000); CASDDS; Ei. **CCC.**
Formerly (until vol.40, no.1, 1991): Boshoku Gijutsu (ISSN 0010-9355)

ZAMBIA CONSOLIDATED COPPER MINES LTD. ANNUAL REPORT AND ACCOUNTS. see *MINES AND MINING INDUSTRY*

620.1 RU ISSN 0044-1856
TA467 CODEN: ZAMEA9
ZASHCHITA METALLOV. English translation: Protection of Metals (US ISSN 0033-1732) 1965. bi-m. $134 (effective 1996). (Rossiiskaya Akademiya Nauk) Izdatel'stvo Nauka, 90 Profsoyuznaya ul., 117864 Moscow, Russia. TEL 234-05-84. (Dist. in U.S. by: Victor Kamkin Inc., 4956 Boiling Brook Pkwy, Rockville, MD 20852. TEL 301-881-5973) Ed. Ya.U. Kolotyrkin. index. circ. 3,175. (tabloid format) **Indexed:** Art & Archaeol.Tech.Abstr., Chem.Abstr., ISMEC, Met.Abstr., World Alum.Abstr., World Surf.Coat.
—BLDSC (0070.930000); CASDDS.

663 KR ISSN 0130-1519
ZASHCHITNYE POKRYTIYA NA METALLAKH; respublikanskii mezhvedomstvennyi sbornik nauchnykh trudov. (Text in Russian) 1967. a. (Akademiya Nauk Ukrainy, Institut Problem Materialovedeniya) Vidavnitstvo Naukova Dumka, Vul. Tereshchenkivska 3, 252601 Kiev, Ukraine. TEL 044-224-4068. FAX 044-224-7060. (Dist. by: Mezhdunarodnaya Kniga, B. Yakimanka 39, 117049 Moscow, Russia) Ed. J.M. Fedorchenko. **Indexed:** Chem.Abstr.
—BLDSC (0071.010000).

ZBORNIK RADOVA MUZEJA RUDARSTVA I METALURGIJE BOR. see *ARCHAEOLOGY*

669 GW ISSN 0044-3093
CODEN: ZEMTAE
ZEITSCHRIFT FUER METALLKUNDE. (Text in German; summaries in English) 1911. m. DM.418.20. (Deutsche Gesellschaft fuer Materialkunde e.V.) Carl Hanser Verlag, Kolbergerstr. 22, 81679 Munich, Germany. TEL 089-998300. FAX 089-984809. (Subscr. to: Postfach 860420, 81631 Munich, Germany) adv.; bk.rev.; charts; illus.; pat.; index. circ. 2,000. (also avail. in microform from PMC) **Indexed:** Appl.Mech.Rev., Chem.Abstr., Chem.Infd., Copper Abstr., Curr.Cont., Eng.Ind., GeoRef., INSPEC, Int.Aerosp.Abstr., Met.Abstr., World Alum.Abstr. **Document type:** trade publication.
—BLDSC (9471.000000); CASDDS; Ei; Faxon; Genuine Article; SWETS; UnCover. **CCC.**

METALLURGY — ABSTRACTING, BIBLIOGRAPHIES, STATISTICS

669 604.6   CC   ISSN 1004-0986
ZHONGGUO WUZI ZAISHENG/CHINESE NATIONAL RESOURCES RECYCLING. (Text in Chinese) 1982. m. Y40. Guonei Maoyi Bu, Huanghe Nanlu Xiduan, Xuzhou, Jiangsu 221006, People's Republic of China. TEL 0516-5736600. FAX 0516-5736119. Ed. Chen Lizhu; Pub. Zei Xin. adv. contact: Zhou Ming.
    Formerly (until 1992): Jishu Zaisheng (ISSN 1001-4446)

669 622   CC   ISSN 1004-0609
ZHONGGUO YOUSE JINSHU XUEBAO. English edition: Nonferrous Metals Society of China. Transactions (ISSN 1003-6326) (Text in Chinese) 1990. q. $10. Zhongguo Youse Jinshu Gongye Zonggongsi - China Nonferrous Metals Industrial Company, 12 Fuxinglu Yi, Beijing 100814, People's Republic of China. TEL 86-1-8322211. FAX 0731-8851136. TELEX 222589 GRIMM CN. (Subscr. to: Zhongguo Youse Jinshu Xuebao Bianjibu, Zhongnan Gongye Daxue, Changsha, Hunan 410083, P.R. China; Dist. overseas by: Allerton Press, Inc., 150 Fifth Ave., New York, NY 10011) (Co-sponsor: Zhongguo Youse Jinshu Xuehui - Nonferrous Metals Society of China) Ed. He Jishan. **Document type:** academic/scholarly publication.
    —BLDSC (8989.490000).
    Description: Publishes research papers on the latest developments in the fields of nonferrous metals and mining technology.

ZHONGNAN GONGYE DAXUE XUEBAO. see *MINES AND MINING INDUSTRY*

669   US   ISSN 0149-1210
TS300   CODEN: THMMAG
33 METAL PRODUCING. 20000. 1963. m. $50 (free to qualified personnel). Penton Publishing (Subsidiary of: Pittway Company), 1100 Superior Ave., Cleveland, OH 44114. TEL 216-696-7000. FAX 216-696-8765. Ed. Wally Huskonen. adv.; charts; illus.; pat.; stat.; tr.lit.; circ. 22,000 (controlled). (also avail. in microform from UMI; back issues avail.) **Indexed:** Br.Ceram.Abstr., Met.Abstr., SRI.
    —BLDSC (9725.806000); Faxon; SWETS; UMI. CCC.
    Former titles: 33 Magazine (ISSN 0563-4725); Magazine of Metals Producing (ISSN 0040-6155)
    Description: Covers metal smelting through processing and distribution of both ferrous and nonferrous metals.

METALLURGY — Abstracting, Bibliographies, Statistics

669 016   US   ISSN 0094-8233
Z6679.A4
ALLOYS INDEX. (Auxiliary publication to Metals Abstracts and Metals Abstracts Index) 1974. m. (plus a. cummulation). $425 (with a. cum. $760); foreign $495 (with a. cum. $855) (effective 1996). A S M International, Materials Information, Materials Park, OH 44073. TEL 216-338-5151. FAX 216-338-4634. TELEX 980-619. E-mail: DBarthel@po.ASM-Intl.org. (UK addr.: Institute of Materials, Materials Information, 1 Carlton House Terr., London SW1Y 5DB, England. TEL 071-839-4071) (Co-sponsor: Institute of Materials, London) Ed. Mark Furneaux. **Document type:** abstracting/indexing.
    ●Also available online. Vendor(s): CEDOCAR, CISTI, Data-Star (META), European Space Agency (File no.3), FIZ Technik (META), Knight-Ridder, Inc. (File no.32/METADEX), Orbit Search Service (MDEX), STN International.
    Also available on CD-ROM. Producer(s): Knight-Ridder, Inc.
    —CCC.
    Description: Monthly information and updates on alloys.

669.722 016   US   ISSN 1066-0623
Z6679.A47
ALUMINIUM INDUSTRY ABSTRACTS; a monthly review of the world's technical literature on aluminum. (Text in English) 1968. m. $595 (effective 1996). Aluminum Association, Inc., Materials Park, OH 44073. TEL 216-338-5151. FAX 216-338-4634. TELEX 980-619. E-mail: DBarthel@po.ASM-Intl.org. (UK addr.: Institute of Materials, Materials Information, 1 Carlton House Terr., London SW1Y 5DB, England. TEL 071-839-4071) (Co-sponsors: European Aluminum Association; Japan Light Metal Association; Aluminum Development Council) abstr.; index. circ. 1,100. (magnetic tape; also avail. in microfiche from UMI) **Indexed:** Chem.Abstr. **Document type:** abstracting/indexing.
    ●Also available online. Vendor(s): European Space Agency (File no.9/ALUMINUM), Knight-Ridder, Inc. (File no.33).
    Formerly (until 1991): World Aluminium Abstracts (ISSN 0002-6697).
    Description: Compendium of information on aluminium and its alloys derived from the business and technical literature published worldwide.

016.67152   US
AMERICAN WELDING SOCIETY ANNUAL MEETING. ABSTRACTS OF PAPERS. a. American Welding Society, Box 351040, Miami, FL 33135. TEL 305-443-9353. **Document type:** abstracting/indexing.

669.142 310   UN   ISSN 0250-9903
ANNUAL BULLETIN OF STEEL STATISTICS FOR EUROPE. (Text in English, French and Russian) 1973. a. price varies. Economic Commission for Europe (ECE), Palais des Nations, 1211 Geneva 10, Switzerland. TEL 022-917-1234. FAX 022-917-0123. TELEX 412962. (Orders in N. America to: United Nations Publications, Rd. DC2-853, New York, NY 10017. TEL 212-963-8302. FAX 212-963-3489; Or: Unipub, 4611-F Assembly Dr., Lanham, MD 20706. TEL 301-459-7666. FAX 301-459-0056) (also avail. in microfiche from CIS) **Indexed:** IIS, PROMT. **Document type:** government publication, bulletin.
    Description: Contains statistics on steel production, along with imports and exports, raw materials trade, and steel consumption.

669   AT   ISSN 0818-3422
AUSTRALIA. BUREAU OF STATISTICS. PRICE INDEXES OF COPPER MATERIALS, AUSTRALIA. 1972. m. Aus.$10 per no. Australian Bureau of Statistics, P.O. Box 10, Belconnen, A.C.T. 2616, Australia. **Document type:** government publication.
    Formerly: Price Indexes of Metallic Materials, Australia.
    Description: Measures price movements in copper materials used in the manufacture of electrical equipment.

AVANCE DE INFORMACION ECONOMICA. INDUSTRIA MINEROMETALURGICA. see *MINES AND MINING INDUSTRY — Abstracting, Bibliographies, Statistics*

669 016   UK   ISSN 0268-3393
Z7914.F7
B C I R A ABSTRACTS OF INTERNATIONAL LITERATURE ON METAL CASTINGS PRODUCTION. (British Cast Iron Research Association) 1969. bi-m. £110 (effective 1995). B C I R A, Membership Services, Alvechurch, Birmingham B48 7QB, England. TEL 01527-66414. FAX 01527-585070. bk.rev.; abstr. circ. 250. **Document type:** abstracting/indexing.
    Former titles: B C I R A Abstracts of International Foundry Literature (ISSN 0141-2930); (until 1978): B C I R A Abstracts of Foundry Literature (ISSN 0005-2868)
    Description: Presents information on cast metals technology. Abstracts contain full bibliographical information, together with details of references, tables, figures.

BEIKOKU TOKKYO SHOROKU. MUKI KAGAKU, KINZOKU, BUKI DAN'YAKU HEN/U.S. PATENT ABSTRACTS. INORGANIC CHEMISTRY, METALS, ARMAMENT AND AMMUNITION. see *PATENTS, TRADEMARKS AND COPYRIGHTS — Abstracting, Bibliographies, Statistics*

669 016   YU   ISSN 0006-2642
BILTEN DOKUMENTACIJE. METALURGIJA/BULLETIN OF DOCUMENTATION. METALLURGY. 1950. bi-m. $264. Jugoslovenski Centar za Tehnicku i Naucnu Dokumentaciju - Yugoslav Center for Technical and Scientific Documentation (YCTSD), SI. Penezica-Krcuna 29-31, Box 724, 11000 Belgrade, Yugoslavia. Ed. Ljiljana Kojic-Bogdanovic. (also avail. in microfilm)

C A SELECTS. INORGANIC & ORGANOMETALLIC REACTION SYSTEMS. see *CHEMISTRY — Abstracting, Bibliographies, Statistics*

C A SELECTS. METALLO ENZYMES & METALLO COENZYMES. see *CHEMISTRY — Abstracting, Bibliographies, Statistics*

669.7 016   US   ISSN 0749-7350
                         CODEN: CSSCEC
C A SELECTS. SELENIUM & TELLURIUM CHEMISTRY. 1984. s-w. $220 to non-members; members $65 (effective 1996). Chemical Abstracts Service (Subsidiary of: American Chemical Society), 2540 Olentangy River Rd., Box 3012, Columbus, OH 43210-0012. TEL 614-447-3600. FAX 614-447-3713. TELEX 6842086. abstr.; index. circ. 800. (looseleaf format) **Document type:** abstracting/indexing.
    Incorporates: Selenium and Tellurium Abstracts (ISSN 0037-1467)
    Description: Covers all aspects of selenium and tellurium chemistry.

669   US   ISSN 0148-2440
                         CODEN: CSCMDT
C A SELECTS. SILVER CHEMISTRY. s-w. $220 to non-members; members $65 (effective 1996). Chemical Abstracts Service (Subsidiary of: American Chemical Society), 2540 Olentangy River Rd., Box 3012, Columbus, OH 43210-0012. TEL 614-447-3600. FAX 614-447-3713. TELEX 6842086. **Document type:** abstracting/indexing.
    Description: Covers the chemistry and chemical technology of silver and silver-containing compounds.

669   UK   ISSN 0950-1576
CADSCAN. 1977. q. £50. Cadmium Association, 42 Weymouth St., London W1N 3LQ, England. Ed. C. Larson. adv.; bk.rev.; index. circ. 400. (back issues avail.) **Indexed:** AESIS, Br.Ceram.Abstr., Corros.Abstr., World Surf.Coat.
    —UMI.
    Formerly (until Oct. 1986): Cadmium Abstracts (ISSN 0309-1139)

338.4   CN   ISSN 0835-0124
HD9506.C2
CANADA. STATISTICS CANADA. FABRICATED METAL PRODUCTS INDUSTRIES. (Catalogue 41-251) (Text in English and French) 1960. a. Can.$20($42) (foreign $49). Statistics Canada, Publications Sales and Services, Ottawa, Ont. K1A 0T6, Canada. TEL 613-951-7277. FAX 613-951-1584. (also avail. in microform from MML) **Document type:** government publication.
    Supersedes: Canada. Statistics Canada. Wire and Wire Products Industries (ISSN 0828-9913); Canada. Statistics Canada. Ornamental and Architectural Metal Products Industry (ISSN 0828-9921); Which was formerly: Canada. Statistics Canada. Ornamental and Architectural Metal Industry (ISSN 0527-5997)

669.1   CN   ISSN 0380-7851
HD9524.C2
CANADA. STATISTICS CANADA. PRIMARY IRON AND STEEL. (Catalogue 41-001) (Text in English and French) 1946. m. Can.$50($60) (foreign $70). Statistics Canada, Publications Sales and Services, Ottawa, Ont. K1A 0T6, Canada. TEL 613-951-7277. FAX 613-951-1584. **Document type:** government publication.
    Description: Provides current data on the Canadian iron and steel industry.

669   FR
CHAMBRE SYNDICALE DES ACIERS POUR EMBALLAGE. RAPPORT STATISTIQUES ANNUEL. a. free. Chambre Syndicale des Aciers Pour Emballage, Immeuble La Pacific TSA 20002, 92070 Paris La Defense Cedex, France. TEL 41-25-92-87. FAX 41-25-87-55.
    Formerly: Chambre Syndicale des Producteurs de Fer-blanc. Rapport Statistiques Annuel.

METALLURGY — ABSTRACTING, BIBLIOGRAPHIES, STATISTICS

CORROSION ABSTRACTS; abstracts of the world's literature on corrosion and corrosion mitigation. see ENGINEERING — Abstracting, Bibliographies, Statistics

016 621.9 669   KO
CURRENT BIBLIOGRAPHIES ON SCIENCE AND TECHNOLOGY: MECHANICAL ENGINEERING & CONSTRUCTION ENGINEERING. 1962. m. $92. Korea Institute for Economics and Technology, P.O.Box 250, Seoul, S. Korea. circ. 300. (reprint service avail. from UMI) **Document type:** bibliography.
    Formerly: Current Index to Journals in Science and Technology: Mechanical, Metallurgical, Natural Resources and Construction Engineering; Supersedes in part: Current Bibliography on Science and Technology.

011 669   KO
CURRENT BIBLIOGRAPHIES ON SCIENCE AND TECHNOLOGY: METALLURGY, NATURAL RESOURCES & ENERGY. m. $92. Institute for Economics and Technology, P.O. Box 205, Seoul, S. Korea. circ. 300. **Document type:** bibliography.

CURRENT BIBLIOGRAPHY ON SCIENCE AND TECHNOLOGY: EARTH SCIENCE, MINING AND METALLURGY/KAGAKU GIJUTSU BUNKEN SOKUHO. KINZOKU KOGAKU, KOZAN KOGAKU, CHIKYU NO KAGAKU-HEN. see EARTH SCIENCES — Abstracting, Bibliographies, Statistics

669.7 310   US   ISSN 0146-5678
HD9539.5.C383   CODEN: CINCDI
CURRENT INDUSTRIAL REPORTS: NONFERROUS CASTINGS. (Series MA33E) a. price varies. U.S. Bureau of the Census, Data User Services Division, Washington, DC 20233. TEL 301-457-4100. (also avail. in microfiche from CIS; reprint service avail. from CIS) **Indexed:** Amer.Stat.Ind. (1975-), Chem.Abstr. **Document type:** government publication.
    ●Also available online.

669   US   ISSN 1049-1384
C2C ABSTRACTS: JAPAN - METALS.* 1990. m. $200. Scan C2C, 1001 Pennsylvania Ave., N.W., No.1300, Washington, DC 20024-2505. TEL 800-525-3865. FAX 202-863-3855. **Document type:** abstracting/indexing.
    ●Also available online. **Vendor(s):** Data-Star (JPTC), Knight-Ridder, Inc. (File no.582), European Space Agency (File no.241), Orbit Search Service (JTEC). Also available on CD-ROM. **Producer(s):** Knight-Ridder, Inc.
    Description: Contains abstracts of articles from Japanese scientific, business, and technical journals. Lists title, author, author affiliation, journal title, volume and number, date, page numbers, abstract, number of bibliographic references, and language.

669.1   GW
EISEN UND STAHL. 1958. m. DM.84. Statistisches Bundesamt, 65180 Wiesbaden, Germany. TEL 0611-75-1. FAX 0611-724000. TELEX 61186-STBA-D. adv.; bk.rev. circ. 350. **Document type:** government publication.

620.1 016   RU   ISSN 0131-0232
EKSPRESS-INFORMATSIYA. KORROZIYA I ZASHCHITA METALLOV. 1959. 48/yr. $184 (effective 1996). Vsesoyuznyi Institut Nauchno-Tekhnicheskoi Informatsii (VINITI), Baltiiskaya ul., 14, Moscow A-219, Russia. (Subscr. to: Mezhdunarodnaya Kniga, Dimitrova ul. 39, 113095 Moscow, Russia)

669 016   UK
ELBASE; metal finishing database software. 1989. bi-m. £180($324) M F I S Ltd., P.O. Box 70, Stevenage, Herts. SG1 4DF, England. TEL 01438-745115. FAX 01438-364536. Ed. A.T. Kuhn. (diskette format) **Document type:** abstracting/indexing.
    Description: Summarizes articles from major journals covering electroplating, electroless plating, electroforming, anodizing, conversion coating, etching, and other surface-finishing processes, including P.C.B. processing and effluent treatment.

ESTADISTICAS DEL COBRE Y OTROS MINERALES ANUARIO. see MINES AND MINING INDUSTRY — Abstracting, Bibliographies, Statistics

669   FR
FRANCE. SERVICE D'ETUDE DES STRATEGIES ET DES STATISTIQUES INDUSTRIELLES. RESULTATS MENSUELS DES ENQUETES DE BRANCHE. TRAVAIL DES METAUX. m. 260 F. (foreign 310 F.)(effective 1991). Service d'Etude des Strategies et des Statistiques Industrielles (SESSI), 85 Bd. du Montparnasse, 75270 Paris Cedex 06, France. TEL 45-56-42-34. FAX 45-56-40-71. stat. **Document type:** government publication.
    Description: Follows developments in the metalworking industry through the performance of selected indicators.

669   FR
FRANCE. SERVICE D'ETUDE DES STRATEGIES ET DES STATISTIQUES INDUSTRIELLES. RESULTATS TRIMESTRIELS DES ENQUETES DE BRANCHE. TRAVAIL DES METAUX. q. 180 F. (foreign 210 F.)(effective 1991). Service d'Etude des Strategies et des Statistiques Industrielles (SESSI), 85 Bd. du Montparnasse, 75270 Paris Cedex 06, France. TEL 45-56-42-34. FAX 45-56-40-71. stat. **Document type:** government publication.
    Description: Provides detailed industry-wide performance statistics for comparative evaluations.

669 620   GW   ISSN 0344-2241
GALVANO-REFERATE. (Supplement to: Galvanotechnik (ISSN 0016-4232)) 1954. m. Eugen G. Leuze Verlag, Karlstr. 4, 88348 Saulgau, Germany. TEL 07581-7617. FAX 07581-1756. **Document type:** abstracting/indexing.
    Formerly (until 1959): Archiv fuer Metall-Finisching (ISSN 0176-1935)

669 016   GW   ISSN 0721-9679
GIESSEREI-LITERATURSCHAU. 1982. m. DM.310. Verein Deutscher Giessereifachleute, Sohnstr. 70, 40237 Duesseldorf, Germany. TEL 0211-6871-254. FAX 0211-6871333. Ed.Bd. bk.rev. circ. 200. **Document type:** abstracting/indexing, trade publication.
    Description: Comprehensive information about new publications in the field of foundry technology, including related issues such as environmental protection, energy industry, and industrial safety.

669.22 016   SZ   ISSN 0017-1557
QD181.A9   CODEN: GLDBBS
GOLD BULLETIN; research on gold and its applications in industry. 1968. q. free. World Gold Council, 1 rue de la Rotisserie, CH-1204 Geneva, Switzerland. TEL 022-3119666. FAX 022-3108160. Ed. Dr. Paern Taimsalu. bk.rev.; abstr.; illus.; circ. 5,500 (controlled). (tabloid format) **Indexed:** AESIS, Art & Archaeol.Tech.Abstr., Br.Archaeol.Abstr., Br.Ceram.Abstr., Bull.Signal., Chem.Abstr., Corros.Abstr., Eng.Ind., Ind.S.A.Per., INIS Atomind., Met.Abstr., World Alum.Abstr., World Text.Abstr. **Document type:** academic/scholarly publication.
    —BLDSC (4201.141700); CASDDS; UnCover.
    Incorporates: Gold Patent Digest (ISSN 0258-7262)

669.142   UK
GUIDE TO THE CLASSIFICATION OF STEEL INDUSTRY PRODUCTS IN THE U.K. CUSTOMS TARIFF AND COMBINED NOMENCLATURE OF THE EUROPEAN UNION (YEAR). a. £40 (outside Europe £45) (effective 1995). (Iron and Steel Statistics Bureau) I S S B Ltd., Canterbury House, 2 Sydenham Rd., Croydon CR9 2LZ, England. TEL 0181-686-9050. FAX 0181-680-8616. **Document type:** directory.
    Former titles (until 1994): Guide to the Classification of Steel Industry Products in the U.K. Customs Tariff and E E C Combined Nomenclature; (until 1993): Guide to the Classification of Steel Industry Products in the Customs Tariff of the European Communities; Guide to the Classification of Steel Industry Products in the U K Customs Tariff.

I M M ABSTRACTS AND INDEX; a survey of world literature on the economic geology and mining of all minerals (except coal), mineral processing and non-ferrous extraction metallurgy. (Institution of Mining and Metallurgy) see MINES AND MINING INDUSTRY — Abstracting, Bibliographies, Statistics

INSTYTUT OBROBKI SKRAWANIEM. PRZEGLAD DOKUMENTACYJNY. see ENGINEERING — Abstracting, Bibliographies, Statistics

669.1   UK   ISSN 0952-5831
INTERNATIONAL STEEL STATISTICS - AUSTRALIA. (Part of: International Steel Statistics Country Books Series) 1970. a. £100 (outside Europe £105); complete set of 23 countries £1500 (effective 1995). (Iron & Steel Statistics Bureau) I S S B Ltd., Canterbury House, 2 Sydenham Rd., Croydon, Surrey CR9 2LZ, England. TEL 0181-686-9050. FAX 0181-680-8616. **Document type:** trade publication.
    Formerly: International Steel Statistics - Australia and New Zealand.
    Description: Covers the production, consumption, and import and export of iron and steel products by quality and market in Australia.

669.1   UK   ISSN 0952-584X
INTERNATIONAL STEEL STATISTICS - AUSTRIA. (Part of: International Steel Statistics Country Books Series) 1970. a. £100 (outside Europe £105); complete set of 23 countries £1500 (effective 1995). (Iron & Steel Statistics Bureau) I S S B Ltd., Canterbury House, 2 Sydenham Rd., Croydon, Surrey CR9 2LZ, England. TEL 0181-686-9050. FAX 0181-680-8616. **Document type:** trade publication.
    —BLDSC (4549.702000).
    Description: Provides information on the production, consumption, import and export of iron and steel products by quality and market in Austria.

669.1   UK   ISSN 0952-5858
INTERNATIONAL STEEL STATISTICS - BELGIUM, LUXEMBOURG. (Part of: International Steel Statistics Country Books Series) 1979. a. £100 (outside Europe £105); complete set of 23 countries £1500 (effective 1995). (Iron & Steel Statistics Bureau) I S S B Ltd., Canterbury House, 2 Sydenham Rd., Croydon, Surrey CR9 2LZ, England. TEL 0181-686-9050. FAX 0181-680-8616. **Document type:** trade publication.
    —BLDSC (4549.702500).
    Description: Provides information on the consumption, production, and export and import of steel products by quality and market in Belgium and Luxemburg.

669.1   UK   ISSN 0952-5866
INTERNATIONAL STEEL STATISTICS - BRAZIL. (Part of: International Steel Statistics Country Books Series) 1970. a. £100 (outside Europe £105); complete set of 23 nations £1500 (effective 1995). (Iron & Steel Statistics Bureau) I S S B Ltd., Canterbury House, 2 Sydenham Rd., Croydon, Surrey CR9 2LZ, England. TEL 0181-686-9050. FAX 0181-680-8616. **Document type:** trade publication.
    —BLDSC (4549.703000).
    Description: Covers the production, consumption, and import and export of iron and steel products by quality and market in Brazil.

669.1   UK   ISSN 0952-5874
INTERNATIONAL STEEL STATISTICS - CANADA. (Part of: International Steel Statistics Country Books Series) 1970. a. £100 (outside Europe £105); complete set of 23 countries £1500 (effective 1995). (Iron & Steel Statistics Bureau) I S S B Ltd., Canterbury House, 2 Sydenham Rd., Croydon, Surrey CR9 2LZ, England. TEL 0181-686-9050. FAX 0181-680-8616. **Document type:** trade publication.
    —BLDSC (4549.704000).
    Description: Provides information on the production, consumption, and import and export of iron and steel products by quality and market in Canada.

669.1   UK   ISSN 0960-2372
INTERNATIONAL STEEL STATISTICS - DENMARK. (Part of: International Steel Statistics Country Books Series) 1979. a. £100 (outside Europe £105); compelete set of 23 countries £1500 (effective 1995). (Iron & Steel Statistics Bureau) I S S B Ltd., Canterbury House, 2 Sydenham Rd., Croydon, Surrey CR9 2LZ, England. TEL 0181-686-9050. FAX 0181-680-8616. **Document type:** trade publication.
    —BLDSC (4549.704500).
    Formerly: International Steel Statistics - Denmark and Greece (ISSN 0952-5882)
    Description: Provides information on the production, consumption, and import and export of iron and steel products by quality and market in Denmark.

METALLURGY — ABSTRACTING, BIBLIOGRAPHIES, STATISTICS

669.1 UK ISSN 0952-5890
INTERNATIONAL STEEL STATISTICS - FINLAND. (Part of: International Steel Statistics Country Books) 1970. a. £100 (outside Europe £105); complete set of 23 countries £1550 (effective 1995). (Iron & Steel Statistics Bureau) I S S B Ltd., Canterbury House, 2 Sydenham Rd., Croydon, Surrey CR9 2LZ, England. TEL 0181-686-9050. FAX 0181-680-8616. **Document type:** trade publication.
—BLDSC (4549.706500).
 Description: Covers the production, consumption, and import and export of iron and steel products by quality and market in Finland.

669.1 UK ISSN 0952-5904
INTERNATIONAL STEEL STATISTICS - FRANCE. (Part of: International Steel Statistics Country Books) 1970. a. £100 (outside Europe £105); complete set of 23 nations £1500 (effective 1995). (Iron & Steel Statistics Bureau) I S S B Ltd., Canterbury House, 2 Sydenham Rd., Croydon, Surrey CR9 2LZ, England. TEL 0181-686-9050. FAX 0181-680-8616. **Document type:** trade publication.
—BLDSC (4549.707000).
 Description: Provides information on the production, consumption, and import and export of iron and steel products by quality and market in France.

669.1 UK ISSN 0952-5912
INTERNATIONAL STEEL STATISTICS - GERMANY, FEDERAL REPUBLIC. (Part of: International Steel Statistics Country Books) 1970. a. £100 (outside Europe £105) (effective 1995). (Iron & Steel Statistics Bureau) I S S B Ltd., Canterbury House, 2 Sydenham Rd., Croydon, Surrey CR9 2LZ, England. TEL 0181-686-9050. FAX 0181-680-8616. **Document type:** trade publication.
—BLDSC (4549.706000).
 Description: Provides information on the consumption, production, and export and import of iron and steel products by quality and market in Germany.

669.1 UK ISSN 0960-2380
INTERNATIONAL STEEL STATISTICS - GREECE. (Part of: International Steel Statistics Country Book Series) a. £100 (outside Europe £105); complete set of 23 nations £1500 (effective 1995). (Iron & Steel Statistics Bureau) I S S B Ltd., Canterbury House, 2 Sydenham Rd., Croydon, Surrey CR9 2LZ, England. TEL 0181-686-9050. FAX 0181-680-8616. **Document type:** trade publication.
—BLDSC (4549.707400).
 Description: Provides information on the consumption, production, and export and import of iron and steel products by quality and markets in Greece.

669.1 UK ISSN 0952-5920
INTERNATIONAL STEEL STATISTICS - IRISH REPUBLIC. (Part of: International Steel Statistics Country Books Series) 1970. a. £100 (outside Europe £105); complete set of 23 countries £1500 (effective 1995). (Iron & Steel Statistics Bureau) I S S B Ltd., Canterbury House, 2 Sydenham Rd., Croydon, Surrey CR9 2LZ, England. TEL 0181-686-9050. FAX 0181-680-8616. **Document type:** trade publication.
—BLDSC (4549.707700).
 Description: Covers the production, consumption, and import and export of iron and steel products by quality and market in Ireland.

669.1 UK ISSN 0952-5939
INTERNATIONAL STEEL STATISTICS - ITALY. (Part of: International Steel Statistics Country Books Series) 1970. a. £100. a. £100 (outside Europe £105); complete set of 23 countries £1550 (effective 1995). (Iron & Steel Statistics Bureau) I S S B Ltd., Canterbury House, 2 Sydenham Rd., Croydon, Surrey CR9 2LZ, England. TEL 0181-686-9050. FAX 0181-680-8616. **Document type:** trade publication.
—BLDSC (4549.709000).
 Description: Provides information on the production, consumption, and import and export of iron and steel products by quality and market in Italy.

669.1 UK ISSN 0952-5947
INTERNATIONAL STEEL STATISTICS - JAPAN. (Part of: International Steel Statistics Country Books) 1970. a. £100 (outside Europe £105); complete set of 23 countries £1500 (effective 1995). (Iron & Steel Statistics Bureau) I S S B Ltd., Canterbury House, 2 Sydenham Rd., Croydon, Surrey CR9 2LZ, England. TEL 0181-686-9050. FAX 0181-680-8616. **Document type:** trade publication.
—BLDSC (4549.709500).
 Description: Covers the production, consumption, and import and export of iron and steel products by quality and market in Japan.

669.1 UK ISSN 0952-603X
INTERNATIONAL STEEL STATISTICS - KOREA (SOUTH). (Part of: International Steel Statistics Country Books Series) 1970. a. £100 (outside Europe £105); complete set of 23 countries £1500 (effective 1995). (Iron & Steel Statistics Bureau) I S S B Ltd., Canterbury House, 2 Sydenham Rd., Croydon, Surrey CR9 2LZ, England. TEL 0181-686-9050. FAX 0181-680-8616. **Document type:** trade publication.
—BLDSC (4549.713000).
 Description: Provides information on the production, consumption, and import and export of iron and steel products by quality and market in South Korea.

669.1 UK ISSN 0952-6005
INTERNATIONAL STEEL STATISTICS - NETHERLANDS. (Part of: International Steel Statistics Country Books Series) 1970. a. £100 (outside Europe £105); complete set of 23 countries £1500 (effective 1995). (Iron & Steel Statistics Bureau) I S S B Ltd., Canterbury House, 2 Sydenham Rd., Croydon, Surrey CR9 2LZ, England. TEL 0181-686-9050. FAX 0181-680-8616. **Document type:** trade publication.
—BLDSC (4549.710500).
 Description: Supplies information on the consumption and production, and import and export of iron and steel products by quality and market in the Netherlands.

669.1 UK ISSN 0952-6013
INTERNATIONAL STEEL STATISTICS - NORWAY. (Part of: International Steel Statistics Country Books Series) 1970. a. £100 (outside Europe £1500); complete set of 23 countries £1500 (effective 1995). (Iron & Steel Statistics Bureau) I S S B Ltd., Canterbury House, 2 Sydenham Rd., Croydon, Surrey CR9 2LZ, England. TEL 0181-686-9050. FAX 0181-680-8616. **Document type:** trade publication.
—BLDSC (4549.710700).
 Description: Covers the production, consumption, and import and export of iron and steel products by quality and market in Norway.

669.1 UK ISSN 0958-4951
INTERNATIONAL STEEL STATISTICS - PORTUGAL. (Part of: International Steel Statistics Country Book Series) a. £100 (outside Europe £105); complete set of 23 countries £1500 (effective 1995). (Iron & Steel Statistics Bureau) I S S B Ltd., Canterbury House, 2 Sydenham Rd., Croydon, Surrey CR9 2LZ, England. TEL 0181-686-9050. FAX 0181-680-8616. **Document type:** trade publication.
—BLDSC (4549.710900).
 Description: Provides information on the consumption, production, and export and import of iron and steel products by quality and markets in Portugal.

669.1 UK ISSN 0952-6102
INTERNATIONAL STEEL STATISTICS - SELECTED CENTRAL AND SOUTH AMERICAN COUNTRIES. (Part of: International Steel Statistics Country Books Series) 1970. a. £100 (foreign £105). (Iron & Steel Statistics Bureau) I S S B Ltd., Canterbury House, 2 Sydenham Rd., Croydon, Surrey CR9 2LZ, England. TEL 0181-686-9050. FAX 0181-680-8616. **Document type:** trade publication.
—BLDSC (4549.711500).
 Description: Covers the production, consumption, and import and export of iron and steel products by quality and market.

669.1 UK ISSN 0958-4943
INTERNATIONAL STEEL STATISTICS - SPAIN. (Part of: International Steel Statistics Country Books Series) 1970. a. £100 (outside Europe £105); complete set of 23 countries £1500 (effective 1995). (Iron & Steel Statistics Bureau) I S S B Ltd., Canterbury House, 2 Sydenham Rd., Croydon, Surrey CR9 2LZ, England. TEL 0181-686-9050. FAX 0181-680-8616. **Document type:** trade publication.
—BLDSC (4549.713500).
 Formerly: International Steel Statistics - Spain and Portugal (ISSN 0952-6129)
 Description: Covers the production, consumption, and import and export of iron and steel products by quality and market in Spain.

310 671 UK ISSN 0952-6803
INTERNATIONAL STEEL STATISTICS - SUMMARY TABLES. 1970. a. £200 per title (outside Europe £205) (effective 1995). (Iron & Steel Statistics Bureau) I S S B Ltd., Canterbury House, 2 Sydenham Rd., Croydon, Surrey CR9 2LZ, England. TEL 0181-686-9050. FAX 0181-680-8616. **Document type:** trade publication.
—BLDSC (4549.714000).
 Description: Sets out summary tables for the countries in the International Steel Statistics Country Books Series. Covers production iron and crude steel, imports and exports of finished steel products.

669.1 UK ISSN 0952-6048
INTERNATIONAL STEEL STATISTICS - SWEDEN. (Part of: International Steel Statistics Country Books Series) 1970. a. £100 (outside Europe £105); complete set of 23 countries £1500 (effective 1995). (Iron & Steel Statistics Bureau) I S S B Ltd., Canterbury House, 2 Sydenham Rd., Croydon, Surrey CR9 2LZ, England. TEL 0181-686-9050. FAX 0181-680-8616. **Document type:** trade publication.
—BLDSC (4549.714500).
 Description: Provides information on the production, consumption, and import and export of iron and steel products by quality and market in Sweden.

669.1 UK ISSN 0952-6099
INTERNATIONAL STEEL STATISTICS - SWITZERLAND. (Part of: International Steel Statistics Country Books Series) 1970. a. £100 (outside Europe £105); complete set of 23 countries £1500 (effective 1995). (Iron & Steel Statistics Bureau) I S S B Ltd., Canterbury House, 2 Sydenham Rd., Croydon, Surrey CR9 2LZ, England. TEL 0181-686-9050. FAX 0181-680-8616. **Document type:** trade publication.
—BLDSC (4549.715000).
 Description: Provides information on the consumption, production, and export and import of iron and steel products by quality and markets in Switzerland.

669.1 UK
INTERNATIONAL STEEL STATISTICS - TAIWAN. (Part of: International Steel Statistics Country Books Series) a. £100 (outside Europe £105); complete set of 23 countries £1500 (effective 1995). (Iron & Steel Statistics Bureau) I S S B Ltd., Canterbury House, 2 Sydenham Rd., Croydon, Surrey CR9 2LZ, England. TEL 0181-686-9050. FAX 0181-680-8616. **Document type:** trade publication.
 Description: Provides information on the production, consumption, and import and export of iron and steel products by quality and market in Taiwan.

669.1 UK ISSN 0952-6811
INTERNATIONAL STEEL STATISTICS - U S A. (Part of: International Steel Statistics Country Books Series) 1970. a. £100 (outside Europe £105); complete set of 23 countries £1500 (effective 1995). (Iron & Steel Statistics Bureau) I S S B Ltd., Canterbury House, 2 Sydenham Rd., Croydon, Surrey CR9 2LZ, England. TEL 0181-686-9050. FAX 0181-680-8616. **Document type:** trade publication.
—BLDSC (4549.716000).
 Description: Provides information on the production, consumption, and import and export of iron and steel products by quality and market in the U.S.

METALLURGY — ABSTRACTING, BIBLIOGRAPHIES, STATISTICS

669.1 UK ISSN 0307-7608
HD9521.4
INTERNATIONAL STEEL STATISTICS - UNITED KINGDOM. (Part of: International Steel Statistics Country Books Series) 1970. a. £100 (outside Europe £105); complete set of 23 countries £1500 (effective 1995). (Iron & Steel Statistics Bureau) I S S B Ltd., Canterbury House, 2 Sydenham Rd., Croydon, Surrey CR9 2LZ, England. TEL 0181-686-9050. FAX 0181-680-8616. **Document type:** trade publication.
—BLDSC (4549.715500).
Description: Covers the production, consumption, and import and export of iron and steel products by quality and market in the U.K.

INTERNATIONAL TIN COUNCIL. MONTHLY STATISTICAL SUMMARY. see *METALLURGY*

669 UK
INTERNATIONAL TIN COUNCIL. QUARTERLY STATISTICAL BULLETIN. 1948. q. £60 (includes 8 monthly statistical summaries). International Tin Council, 1 Oxendon St., London SW1Y 4EQ, England. (also avail. in microform from UMI; reprint service avail. from UMI) **Indexed:** Cadscan, IIS, Lead Abstr., Zincscan.
Formerly (1974-1983): International Tin Council. Monthly Statistical Bulletin.
Description: Tables of data on mine and smelter production and tin metal consumption.

IRON & MANGANESE ORE DATABOOK. see *MINES AND MINING INDUSTRY — Abstracting, Bibliographies, Statistics*

314 669 EI
IRON AND STEEL YEARLY STATISTICS. (Text in English) 1977. a. $35. (Statistical Office of the European Communities) Office for Official Publications of the European Communities, L-2985 Luxembourg, Luxembourg. (Dist. in the U.S. by: Unipub, 4611-F Assembly Dr., Lanham, MD 20706-4391. TEL 800-274-4888. FAX 301-459-0056) Ed.Bd. (also avail. in microfiche from CIS) **Indexed:** IIS.
Former titles: Iron and Steel Statistical Yearbook; Statistical Office of the European Communities. Iron and Steel. Yearbook.

JOURNAL OF MATERIALS SCIENCE & TECHNOLOGY; an international journal in the field of materials science. see *METALLURGY*

669 JA ISSN 0451-6001
KEIKINZOKU KOGYO TOKEI NENPO/LIGHT METAL STATISTICS IN JAPAN. Variant title: Light Metal Statistics in Japan. Annual Report. (Text in English, Japanese) 1950. a. 15000 Yen. Japan Aluminium Federation, Nihonbashi Asahi Seimei Bldg., 1-3 Nihonbashi 2-chome, Chuo-ku, Tokyo 103, Japan. FAX 03-3274-3179. TELEX 02223074-JALF-J. Ed. K. Nagakubo. bk.rev.; stat. circ. 1,200. **Document type:** trade publication.

669 016 HU ISSN 0231-0708
KOHASZATI ES ONTESZETI SZAKIRODALMI TAJEKOZTATO/METALLURGY AND FOUNDRY ABSTRACTS. 1949. m. 9700 Ft. Orszagos Muszaki Informacios Kozpont es Konyvtar (O.M.I.K.K.) - National Technical Information Centre and Library, Muzeum u. 17, Box 12, 1428 Budapest, Hungary. (Subscr. to: Kultura, Box 149, 1389 Budapest, Hungary) Ed. Gabor Libertiny. abstr.; index. circ. 330.
Supersedes (in 1982): Muszaki Lapszemle. Kohaszat, Onteszet - Technical Abstracts. Metallurgy, Foundry (ISSN 0027-5034)

669.2 UN ISSN 0023-9577
LEAD AND ZINC STATISTICS. (Suppl. avail: Advance Data Service) (Text in English and French) 1961. m. £135($220) for bulletin; m. Advance Data Service £40 ($75). International Lead and Zinc Study Group, Metro House, 58 St. James's St., London SW1A 1LD, England. TEL 0171-499-9373. FAX 0171-493-3725. TELEX 299819 ILZSG G. mkt.; stat.; charts. circ. 700. (also avail. in microfiche from CIS) **Indexed:** IIS, P.A.I.S., PROMT. **Document type:** bulletin.
●Also available online.
Description: Provides long-term historical coverage of world production and consumption of lead and zinc since 1960, combining detailed annual tables with quarterly and monthly series.

669 016 UK ISSN 0950-1584
LEADSCAN; a review of recent technical literature on the uses of lead and its products. 1958. 4/yr. £55. (Zinc-Lead Library and Abstracts Service) Lead Development Association, 42 Weymouth St., London W1X 3LQ, England. Ed. C. Larson. bk.rev.; abstr.; index. circ. 1,300. (also avail. in microform from UMI) **Indexed:** AESIS, Br.Ceram.Abstr., Corros.Abstr., Lead Abstr., World Surf.Coat.
—UMI.
Formerly: Lead Abstracts (ISSN 0023-9569)

669 UK
MATERIALS BUSINESS INFORMATION. 1985. m. price avail. to applicable subscribers. Institute of Materials, 1 Carlton House Terrace, London SW1Y 5DB, England. TEL 071-839-4071. FAX 071-839-2078. TELEX 8814813-METSOC-G. (N. American addr.: Materials Information, A S M International, Meterials Park, OH 44073) **Document type:** abstracting/indexing.
●Also available online. Vendor(s): Knight-Ridder, Inc. (File no.269).
Formerly: Materials Business Abstracts.
Description: Discusses steel, nonferrous metals, polymers, ceramics and composites.

MATERIALS INFORMATION ENGINEERED MATERIALS SEARCH-IN-PRINT SERIES. see *ENGINEERING — Abstracting, Bibliographies, Statistics*

669 016 US
MATERIALS INFORMATION METALLURGICAL SEARCH-IN-PRINT SERIES. (248 topics avail.) 1967. a. $105 per topic to non-members; members $95 (effective 1995). A S M International, Materials Information, Materials Park, OH 44073. TEL 216-338-5151. FAX 216-338-4634. TELEX 980-619. (UK addr.: Institute of Materialsterials Information, 1 Carlton House Terr., London SW1Y 5DB, England. TEL 071-839-4071) **Document type:** abstracting/indexing, bibliography.
Former titles: Materials Information Metallurgical Published Search Series; Materials Information Metallurgical Bibliography Series; A S M Bibliography Series (ISSN 0001-2556)

669 016 UK ISSN 0026-0657
TN695
METAL POWDER REPORT. 1946. m. £121($193) (effective 1996). Elsevier Science Ltd., P.O. Box 800, Kidlington, Oxford OX5 1DX, England. TEL 44-1865-843000. FAX 44-1865-843010. E-mail: nlinfo-f@elsevier.nl; usinfo-f@elsevier.com; forinfo-kyf04035@niftyserve.or.jp; Site addr.: http://www.elsevier.nl/. (Subscr. in U.S. and Canada to: Elsevier Science, 660 White Plains Rd., Tarrytown, NY 10591-5153. TEL 914-524-9200. FAX 914-333-2444) Ed. A. Weaver. adv.; bk.rev.; abstr.; charts; pat.; tr.lit.; index. circ. 1,200. **Indexed:** Br.Ceram.Abstr., Cadscan, Copper Abstr., Lead Abstr., Met.Abstr., World Alum.Abstr., Zincscan. **Document type:** trade publication.
—BLDSC (5687.825000); Ei; Faxon; SWETS. **CCC.**
Description: Reports the latest developments in worldwide powder production, consolidation, sintering and new powder metallurgy products and their applications.

310 669 GW ISSN 0076-6682
HD9539.A1
METALL STATISTIK. (Text in English, German) 1893. a. DM.200($150) Metallgesellschaft AG, Reuterweg 14, 60271 Frankfurt a.M., Germany. TEL 069-1592390. FAX 069-1592125. TELEX 0412250-MGF-D. Ed. Michael Hergenhahn. **Document type:** trade publication.
—BLDSC (5694.800000).
Formerly: Metal Statistics (ISSN 0170-9933)

880 016 US ISSN 0026-0924
TN1
METALS ABSTRACTS. 1968. m. $2195 (foreign $2450) (effective 1996). A S M International, Materials Information, Materials Park, OH 44073. TEL 216-338-5151. FAX 216-338-4634. TELEX 980-619. E-mail: DBarthel@po.ASM-Intl.org. (UK addr.: Institute of Materials, Materials Information, 1 Carlton House Terr., London SW1Y 5DB, England. TEL 071-839-4071) (Co-sponsor: Institute of Materials, London) circ. 1,500. **Indexed:** AESIS, Br.Ceram.Abstr. **Document type:** abstracting/indexing.
●Also available online. Vendor(s): CEDOCAR, CISTI, Data-Star (META), European Space Agency (File no.3/METADEX), FIZ Technik (META), Knight-Ridder, Inc. (File no.32/METADEX), Orbit Search Service (MDEX), STN International (METADEX).
Also available on CD-ROM. Producer(s): Knight-Ridder, Inc.
—BLDSC (5699.250000).
Formed by the merger of: Review of Metal Literature; Metallurgical Abstracts.
Description: Monitors international literature on all aspects of metallurgical science and technology.

669 016 US ISSN 0026-0932
METALS ABSTRACTS INDEX. 1968. m. $960 (foreign $1074) (effective 1996). A S M International, Materials Information, Materials Park, OH 44073. TEL 216-338-5151. FAX 216-338-4634. TELEX 980-619. E-mail: DBarthel@po.ASM-Intl.org. (UK addr.: Institute of Materials, Materials Information, 1 Carlton House Terr., London SW1Y 5DB, England. TEL 071-839-4071) (Co-sponsor: Institute of Materials, London) cum.index. **Document type:** abstracting/indexing.
●Also available online. Vendor(s): CEDOCAR, CISTI, Data-Star (META), European Space Agency (File no.3/METADEX), FIZ Technik (META), Knight-Ridder, Inc. (File no.32/METADEX), Orbit Search Service (MDEX), STN International (METADEX).
Also available on CD-ROM. Producer(s): Knight-Ridder, Inc.
—BLDSC (5699.260000).
Description: Companion publication of Metals Abstract containing subject, author and corporate author indexes.

669.1 JA ISSN 0497-1140
MONTHLY REPORT OF THE IRON AND STEEL STATISTICS. (Text in English and Japanese) vol.20, 1977. m. 6000 Yen. Japan Iron and Steel Federation, Economic Research and Statistics Department - Nihon Tekko Renmei, Keidanren Kaikan, 9-4, 1-chome, Ote-machi, Chiyoda-ku, Tokyo 100, Japan. TEL 03-3279-3611. FAX 03-3245-0144. TELEX 222-4210. stat.

669 338 US
NONFERROUS METALS ALERT. (Part of: Materials Business Information Series) 1985. m. $325 (foreign $350); Metal Abstracts subscribers $210 (foreign $230). A S M International, Materials Information, Materials Park, OH 44073. TEL 216-338-5151. FAX 216-338-4634. TELEX 980-619. E-mail: DBarthel@po.ASM-Intl.org. (UK addr.: Institute of Materials, Materials Information, 1 Carlton House Terr., London SW1Y 5DB, England. TEL 071-839-4071) Ed.Bd. **Document type:** abstracting/indexing.
●Also available online. Vendor(s): CEDOCAR, CISTI, Data-Star (MBUS), European Space Agency (File no.111), Knight-Ridder, Inc. (File no.269), Orbit Search Service (MABU), STN International (MATBUS).
Also available on CD-ROM. Producer(s): Knight-Ridder, Inc.
Formerly: Nonferrous Alert.
Description: International coverage of business developments for the nonferrous metals industry.

O E C D STEEL MARKET IN (YEAR) AND OUTLOOK FOR (YEAR). (Organization for Economic Cooperation and Development) see *BUSINESS AND ECONOMICS — Abstracting, Bibliographies, Statistics*

METALLURGY — ABSTRACTING, BIBLIOGRAPHIES, STATISTICS

669 016   **FR**   **ISSN 1146-5069**
P A S C A L T 240: METAUX - METALLURGIE. (Printed format ceased Jan. 1995) (Text in English, French) 1984. 10/yr. Centre National de la Recherche Scientifique, Institut de l'Information Scientifique et Technique, 2 allee du Parc de Brabois, 54514 Vandoeuvre-Les-Nancy Cedex, France.
TEL 83-50-46-00. FAX 83-50-46-50. adv. contact: Veronique Guinvarc'h. abstr.; index, cum.index. (also avail. in microfiche) **Indexed:** World Alum.Abstr. **Document type:** bibliography.
●Also available online. Vendor(s): European Space Agency (File no.14), Knight-Ridder, Inc. (File no.144), Telesystemes - Questel.
Also available on CD-ROM.
   Former titles: P A S C A L Thema. T 240: Metaux. Metallurgie (ISSN 0761-1684); P A S C A L Thema. Part 240: Metaux. Metallurgie; Which superseded (1969-1984): Bulletin Signaletique. Part 740: Metaux. Metallurgie (ISSN 0007-5655)

PROGRESS IN COAL STEEL AND RELATED SOCIAL RESEARCH; a European journal. see MINES AND MINING INDUSTRY — Abstracting, Bibliographies, Statistics

671.52 016   **GW**   **ISSN 0944-9396**
REFERATE: SCHWEISSEN UND VERWANDTE VERFAHREN/BULLETIN OF ABSTRACTS: WELDING AND ALLIED PROCESSES. 1956. 10/yr. DM.315. Bundesanstalt fuer Materialforschung und -pruefung, Unter den Eichen 87, 12205 Berlin, Germany. TEL 030-8104-1645. FAX 030-8121013. (Co-sponsors: Deutscher Verband fuer Schweisstechnik (DVS); Fachinformationszentrum Technik e.V.) bk.rev.; abstr.; charts; illus.; cumulative author and keyword index. circ. 400. (back issues avail.) **Document type:** government publication.
●Also available online.
   Former titles: Referateorgan Schweissen und Verwandte Verfahren (ISSN 0340-4749); Formerly: Selective Abstracting Service: Welding and Allied Processes (ISSN 0037-1432)
   Description: Features developments in welding, metallurgy, engineering weldability of materials, equipment, application, failures, testing, etc.

620.1 016   **RU**   **ISSN 0131-3533**
Z6679.C7   **CODEN: RKZKA6**
REFERATIVNYI ZHURNAL. KORROZIYA I ZASHCHITA OT KORROZII. English translation: Corrosion Control Abstracts (UK ISSN 0010-9347) 1968. m. $321 (effective 1996). Vsesoyuznyi Institut Nauchno-Tekhnicheskoi Informatsii (VINITI), Baltiiskaya ul., 14, Moscow A-219, Russia. (Subscr. to: Mezhdunarodnaya Kniga, Dimitrova ul. 39, 113095 Moscow, Russia) **Indexed:** Chem.Abstr., Met.Abstr., World Alum.Abstr. **Document type:** abstracting/indexing.
—CASDDS.

669 016   **RU**   **ISSN 0034-2491**
        CODEN: RZMTA5
REFERATIVNYI ZHURNAL. METALLURGIYA. 1961. m. $1210 (effective 1996). Vsesoyuznyi Institut Nauchno-Tekhnicheskoi Informatsii (VINITI), Baltiiskaya ul., 14, Moscow A-219, Russia. (Subscr. to: Mezhdunarodnaya Kniga, Dimitrova ul. 39, 113095 Moscow, Russia) abstr.; bibl.; pat. circ. 1,649. **Indexed:** Chem.Abstr., Met.Abstr., World Alum.Abstr. **Document type:** abstracting/indexing.
—CASDDS. CCC.

671.52 316   **RU**   **ISSN 0131-3525**
REFERATIVNYI ZHURNAL. SVARKA. 1965. m. $293 (effective 1996). Vsesoyuznyi Institut Nauchno-Tekhnicheskoi Informatsii (VINITI), Baltiiskaya ul., 14, Moscow A-219, Russia. (Subscr. to: Mezhdunarodnaya Kniga, Dimitrova ul. 39, 113095 Moscow, Russia) **Document type:** abstracting/indexing.
—BLDSC (0148.460000).

669 016   **RU**   **ISSN 0135-0935**
SIGNAL'NAYA INFORMATSIYA. KOMPOZITSIONNYE MATERIALY. 1976. m. 8.40 Rub. Vsesoyuznyi Institut Nauchno-Tekhnicheskoi Informatsii (VINITI), Baltiiskaya ul. 14, Moscow A-219, Russia. (Subscr. to: Mezhdunarodnaya Kniga, Dimitrova ul. 39, 113095 Moscow, Russia) **Document type:** abstracting/indexing.

620.112 016   **RU**   **ISSN 0202-8670**
SIGNAL'NAYA INFORMATSIYA. KORROZIYA I ZASHCHITA OT KORROZII. 1970. s-m. 30.40 Rub. Vsesoyuznyi Institut Nauchno-Tekhnicheskoi Informatsii (VINITI), Baltiiskaya ul. 14, Moscow A-219, Russia. (Subscr. to: Mezhdunarodnaya Kniga, Dimitrova ul. 39, 113095 Moscow, Russia) **Document type:** abstracting/indexing.

SOURCE JOURNALS IN METALS AND MATERIALS. see METALLURGY

338.4 316.8   **SA**
SOUTH AFRICA. CENTRAL STATISTICAL SERVICE. STATISTICAL RELEASE. STOCK OF PRIMARY STEEL PRODUCTS ON HAND. (No. P3044) m. free. Central Statistical Service - Sentrale Statistiekdiens, Private Bag X44, Pretoria 0001, South Africa.
TEL 27-12-310-8911. FAX 27-12-310-8500. **Document type:** government publication.

669.1 310   **II**   **ISSN 0081-511X**
HD9526.I6
STATISTICS FOR IRON AND STEEL INDUSTRY IN INDIA. (Text in English) 1964. biennial. price varies. Steel Authority of India Ltd., Ispat Bhavan, Lodi Rd., New Delhi 110003, India. FAX 4694015. TELEX 031-62689. Ed. M. Usman. index. circ. 600.

669.142 310   **UN**   **ISSN 0501-3062**
HD9510.4
STATISTICS OF WORLD TRADE IN STEEL. 1961. a. price varies. Economic Commission for Europe (ECE), Palais des Nations, 1211 Geneva 10, Switzerland. TEL 022-917-1234. FAX 022-917-0036. TELEX 412962. (Subscr. in N. America to: United Nations Publications, Rm. DC2-853, New York, NY 10017. TEL 212-963-8302. FAX 212-963-3489; Or: Unipub, 4611-F Assembly Dr., Lanham, MD 20707. TEL 310-459-7666. FAX 310-459-0056) charts. (also avail. in microfiche) **Indexed:** IIS. **Document type:** government publication.
   Description: Summarizes the exports of finished and semifinished steel products.

669 310   **GW**   **ISSN 0081-5365**
STATISTISCHES JAHRBUCH DER EISEN- UND STAHLINDUSTRIE. 1929. a. DM.49. (Wirtschaftsvereinigung Eisen- und Stahlindustrie) Verlag Stahleisen mbH, Sohnstr. 65, 40237 Duesseldorf, Germany. TEL 0211-6707-0. FAX 0211-6707517. **Document type:** trade publication.

669.1   **BE**   **ISSN 0771-2871**
HD9510.1
STEEL STATISTICAL YEARBOOK (YEAR). (Text in English) a. 3000 BEF (diskette 3500 BEF). International Iron and Steel Institute, Rue Colonel Bourg 120, B-1040 Brussels, Belgium. TEL 32-2-7359075.
FAX 32-2-7358012. TELEX 22639. charts; illus.; stat. (also avail. in diskette format)
   Description: Presents statistics and information, by country, on crude steel production, casting development, trade figures, consumption, and raw materials.

669 338   **US**   **ISSN 1048-0307**
STEELS ALERT. (Part of: Materials Business Information Series) 1983. m. $325 (foreign $350); Metals Abstracts subscribers $210 (foreign $230) (effective 1996). A S M International, Materials Information, Materials Park, OH 44073.
TEL 216-338-5151. FAX 216-338-4634. TELEX 980-619. E-mail: DBarthel@po.ASM-Int.org. (UK addr.: Institute of Materials, Materials Information, 1 Carlton House Terr., London SW1Y 4DB, England. TEL 071-839-4071) Ed.Bd. circ. 180. **Document type:** abstracting/indexing.
●Also available online. Vendor(s): CISTI, CREDOC, Data-Star (MBUS), European Space Agency (File no.111), Knight-Ridder, Inc. (File no.269), Orbit Search Service (MABU), STN International (MATBUS).
Also available on CD-ROM. Producer(s): Knight-Ridder, Inc.
   Formerly (until 1985): Materials Business Abstracts: Steels Supplement to Metals Abstracts.
   Description: International coverage of business developments for the steel industry.

669 016   **UK**   **ISSN 0950-5199**
SURFACE TREATMENT TECHNOLOGY ABSTRACTS. CD-ROM edition: Surface Finishing C D. 1959. bi-m. £395($840) (CD-ROM £400($750)). Finishing Publications Ltd., 105 Whitney Dr., Stevenage, Herts. SG1 4DF, England. TEL 01438-745115.
FAX 01438-364536. Ed. R. Pinner. adv.; bk.rev.; abstr.; pat.; index. circ. 1,000. **Indexed:** Art & Archaeol.Tech.Abstr., Corros.Abstr., World Surf.Coat. **Document type:** abstracting/indexing.
●Also available on CD-ROM.
—CCC.
   Formerly: Metal Finishing Abstracts (ISSN 0026-0584); Incorporates (1985-1995): Printed Circuits and Electronics Coatings Abstracts (ISSN 0953-0509)
   Description: Details, patents, reports, standards and translations from industrial countries of the world.

669 310   **UK**   **ISSN 0256-8187**
TIN STATISTICS. 1973. a. £25. International Tin Council, Haymarket House, 1 Oxendon St., London SW1Y 4EQ, England. TEL 0171-930 0451. **Indexed:** IIS.
   Supersedes in part: International Tin Council. Statistical Yearbook (ISSN 0074-9117); International Tin Council. Statistical Supplement. Tin, Tinplate Canning (ISSN 0074-9109)
   Description: Statistical profile of tin productions, consumption, trade, stocks, tin prices and price indices of nonferrous metals.

669   **US**
TITANIUM DEVELOPMENT ASSOCIATION. INTERNATIONAL CONFERENCE ON TITANIUM PRODUCTS AND APPLICATIONS. a. price varies. Titanium Development Association, 4141 Arapahoe Ave., Ste. 100, Boulder, CO 80303.
TEL 303-443-7515. FAX 303-443-4406. **Document type:** abstracting/indexing.
   Description: Abstracts papers presented at the T D A annual conference.

669   **US**   **ISSN 0278-4238**
Z6678
TRANSLATIONS INDEX; a quarterly source and author index to the available translations into English of technical papers in metals and materials. 1977. q. $145. A S M International, Materials Information, Materials Park, OH 44073. TEL 216-338-5151.
FAX 216-338-4634. TELEX 980-619. (UK addr.: Institute of Materials, Materials Information, 1 Carlton Terr., London SW1Y 5DB, England. TEL 071-839-4071)
   Formerly: A S M Translations Index (ISSN 0263-2659)

669 310   **UN**   **ISSN 0049-4828**
HD9539.T8
TUNGSTEN STATISTICS. 1967. q. $25 per no. (United Nations Conference on Trade and Development (UNCTAD)) United Nations Publications, Room DC2-853, New York, NY 10017.
TEL 212-963-8302; 212-063-3489; 800-253-9646. (Or: Palais des Nations, CH-1211 Geneva 10, Switzerland) (also avail. in microfiche from CIS) **Indexed:** IIS.

669.1 338.4   **UK**   **ISSN 0952-5505**
U K IRON AND STEEL INDUSTRY. ANNUAL STATISTICS. 1918. a. £125 (outside Europe £130) (effective 1995). (Iron & Steel Statistics Bureau) I S S B Ltd., Canterbury House, 2 Sydenham Rd., Croydon, Surrey CR9 2LZ, England. TEL 0181-686-9050.
FAX 0181-680-8616. stat. circ. 600. (back issues avail.) **Document type:** trade publication.
   Formerly: Iron and Steel. Annual Statistics for the United Kingdom (ISSN 0075-0867)
   Description: Provides U.K. iron and steel industry with historical comparisons and detailed trade information.

669 016   **NE**
VERENIGING VOOR OPPERVLAKTETECHNIEKEN VAN MATERIALEN. DOCUMENTATIESERVICE. (Text in Dutch; summaries in various languages) 1957. m. fl.340. Vereniging voor Oppervlaktetechnieken van Materialen - Association for Surface Finishing Techniques, P.O. Box 120, 3720 AC Bilthoven, Netherlands. FAX 31-30-287674. Ed. T. van der Klis. abstr. circ. 95.
   Formerly: Vereniging voor Oppervlaktetechnieken van Metalen. Documentatieservice (ISSN 0042-3882)

METALLURGY — WELDING

671.52 016 UK
WELDALERT; selective dissemination of information. 12/yr. £200. T W I - The Welding Institute, Abington Hall, Abington, Cambridge CB1 6AL, England. TEL 01223-891162. FAX 01223-892588. **Document type:** abstracting/indexing.
   Description: Provides selections according to a subscriber's specific information need of current abstracts from the Weldasearch database covering all aspects of welding technology.

671.52 UK ISSN 0952-0287
TS227.A1
WELDING ABSTRACTS. 1988. 12/yr. £390 (effective 1993). T W I - The Welding Institute, Abington Hall, Abington, Cambridge CB1 6AL. TEL 01223-891162. FAX 01223-892588. Ed. Peter Adams. (also avail. in microfilm from UMI; back issues avail.) **Document type:** abstracting/indexing.
   ●Also available online. Vendor(s): Orbit Search Service.
   Description: Covers all aspects of research into joining and welding, including relevant developments in adhesives and automation.

669 UK
WORLD BUREAU OF METAL STATISTICS. ANNUAL REPORT. a. World Bureau of Metal Statistics, 27a High St., Ware, Herts SG12 9BA, England. TEL 01920-461274. FAX 01920-464258. **Document type:** corporate report.

669 UK ISSN 0043-8758
HD9539.A1
WORLD METAL STATISTICS. 1948. m. £885 (Europe £935). World Bureau of Metal Statistics, 27a High St., Ware, Herts SG12 9BA, England. TEL 01920-461274. FAX 01920-464258. Ed. J.L.T. Davies. adv.; stat. circ. 520. (also avail. in microfilm) **Indexed:** P.A.I.S. **Document type:** bulletin.
   —BLDSC (9356.670000). **CCC.**
   Formerly: World Non-Ferrous Metal Statistics.

WORLD METAL STATISTICS. YEARBOOK. see METALLURGY

669.23 338.2 US ISSN 1044-7482
HD9536.A1
WORLD MINE PRODUCTION OF SILVER. Variant title: Mine Production of Silver. 1973. a. $40. Silver Institute, 1112 16th St., N.W., Ste. 240, Washington, DC 20036-4823. TEL 202-835-0185. FAX 202-835-0155. Ed. John H. Lutley. stat. (back issues avail.) **Indexed:** SRI.
   Description: Covers silver production in 58 countries.

669.142 UK ISSN 0141-0806
WORLD STAINLESS STEEL STATISTICS. 1972. a. £250. World Bureau of Metal Statistics, 27a High St., Ware, Herts SG12 9BA, England. TEL 01920-461274. FAX 01920-464258. (Subscr. to: Metal Bulletin PLC, Park House, Park Terrace, Worcester Park, Surrey KT4 7HY, England) Ed. J.L.T. Davies. **Document type:** bulletin.

669 UK
WORLD STEEL EXPORTS. 1970. q.(quantities); a.(values). £300 (outside Europe £320) (effective 1995). (Iron & Steel Statistics Bureau) I S S B Ltd., Canterbury House, 2 Sydenham Rd., Croydon CR9 2LZ, England. TEL 0181-686-9050. FAX 0181-680-8616. circ. 200. **Document type:** trade publication.
   Formerly: World Trade Steel (ISSN 0952-5734)
   Description: Takes a cumulative (quarterly) book detailing the export trade of 16 major steel-producing countries collectively accounting for more than 85% of world exports. Covers 28 product groups and 100 export markets.

669.142 UK
WORLD STEEL EXPORTS - STAINLESS, HIGH SPEED & OTHER ALLOY. 1979. q.(quantities); a.(values). £500 (outside Europe £520) (effective 1995). (Iron & Steel Statistics Bureau) I S S B Ltd., Canterbury House, 2 Sydenham Rd., Croydon, Surrey CR9 2LZ, England. TEL 0181-686-9050. FAX 0181-680-8616. **Document type:** trade publication.
   Formerly: World Trade - Stainless, High Speed & Other Alloy Steel (ISSN 0952-5742)
   Description: Takes a cumulative (quarterly) look at the export trade of major steel-producing countries in selected alloy products.

669.1 BE
WORLD STEEL IN FIGURES (YEAR). (Text in English) a. single copy free. International Iron and Steel Institute, Rue Colonel Bourg 120, B-1040 Brussels, Belgium. TEL 32-2-7359075. FAX 32-2-7358012. TELEX 22639. charts; illus.; stat.
   Description: Contains facts on employment, capital investment expenditure, iron ore production, scrap consumption and the geographic distribution of production and consumption.

669 UK ISSN 0965-0822
WORLD TIN STATISTICS. 1988. m. $330. (World Bureau of Metal Statistics) Metal Bulletin plc, Park House, Park Terrace, Worcester Park, Surrey KT4 7HY, England. TEL 0171-827-9977. FAX 0181-337-8943. (U.S. subscr. to: Metal Bulletin Inc., 220 Fifth Ave., New York, NY 10001-7781. TEL 212-213-6202. FAX 212-213-1870) **Document type:** trade publication.

669.142 UK ISSN 0266-7347
WORLD WROUGHT COPPER STATISTICS. 1985. a. £175. World Bureau of Metal Statistics, 27a High St., Ware, Herts SG12 9BA, England. TEL 01920-461274. FAX 01920-464258. Ed. J.L.T. Davies. **Indexed:** Copper Abstr. **Document type:** bulletin.

METALLURGY — Welding

AMERICAN WELDING SOCIETY ANNUAL MEETING. ABSTRACTS OF PAPERS. see METALLURGY — Abstracting, Bibliographies, Statistics

671.52 AT ISSN 1039-0642
   CODEN: AUWJA7
AUSTRALASIAN WELDING JOURNAL. 1957. q. Aus.$45. (Welding Technology Institute of Australia) Thomson Business Publishing, 47 Chippen St., Chippendale, N.S.W. 2008, Australia. TEL 02-699-2411. FAX 02-690-1961. Ed. Graeme Smith. adv.; illus. circ. 20,500.
   —BLDSC (1796.405000); CASDDS; UnCover.
   Former titles (until 1967): Welding Fabrication and Design (ISSN 0372-7246); (until 1960): Australian Welding Journal (ISSN 0005-0431)
   Description: Disseminates information about welding developments, techniques, processes and equipment for the Australian industry.

669 KR ISSN 0005-111X
TK4660.A1 CODEN: AVSVAU
AVTOMATICHESKAYA SVARKA; vsesoyuznyi nauchno-tekhnicheskii i proizvodstvennyi zhurnal. 1948. m. 10.80 Rub.($39) (Akademiya Nauk Ukrainy, Institut Elektrosvarki im. E.O. Patona) 3, 252601 Kiev, Ukraine. TEL 044-224-40-68. FAX 044-224-70-60. (Subscr. to: Mezhdunarodnaya Kniga, Moscow, G-200, Russia) Ed. B.E. Paton. adv.; bk.rev.; charts; illus.; index. circ. 6,000. **Indexed:** Chem.Abstr., INIS Atomind., INSPEC (1968-1986), Met.Abstr.
   —BLDSC (0002.000000); CASDDS.

671.52 FR ISSN 0153-9965
CAHIERS DE LA FONDERIE; bulletin economique mensual. 1963. m. 280 F. Groupement d'Achats des Fondeurs de France, 2 rue de Bassano, 75783 Paris Cedex 16, France. TELEX 620617. Ed. G. Cornet. bk.rev.; stat.; index. circ. 1,400.

671.52 UK
CONNECT. m. T W I - The Welding Institute, Abington Hall, Abington, Cambridge CB1 6AL, England. TEL 01223-891162. FAX 01223-892588. **Document type:** newsletter.

671.52 UK ISSN 0306-0217
FAB GUIDE; guide to the UK welding & welding fabrication industry. a. Argus Business Media Ltd., International Trade Publications (Subsidiary of: Argus Press Group), Queensway House, 2 Queensway, Redhill, Surrey RH1 1QS, England. TEL 01737-768611. FAX 01737-761989. TELEX 948669 TOPJNL G. Ed. Ken Murrell. **Document type:** trade publication.
   —BLDSC (3863.070000).

FACTS. see ENGINEERING

671.52 SA ISSN 1022-8187
   CODEN: FWPJA7
FOUNDRY & HEAT TREATMENT S A. 1961. bi-m. (South African Institutes of Foundrymen, Welding and Production Engineers) George Warman Publications (Pty.) Ltd., P.O. Box 3487, Cape Town 8000, South Africa. TEL 27-21-245320. FAX 27-21-261332. adv.; bk.rev.; charts; illus.; tr.lit.; index, cum.index: 1961-1963. circ. 3,500. (also avail. in microform from UMI; reprint service avail. from UMI) **Indexed:** B.C.I.R.A., Br.Ceram.Abstr., Chem.Abstr., Eng.Ind., Excerp.Med., Ind.S.A.Per., INIS Atomind., ISMEC, Met.Abstr., World Alum.Abstr. **Document type:** trade publication.
   —CASDDS; Ei; UMI.
   Former titles (until 1993): F W P Materials Engineering Journal (ISSN 1021-5999); Founding, Welding, Production Engineering Journal; (until vol.17, no.3, 1977): F.W.P. Journal (ISSN 0015-9026)

671.52 US ISSN 1079-3909
TS227
THE GASES & WELDING DISTRIBUTOR. 1921. bi-m. $40 (free to qualified personnel). Penton Publishing (Subsidiary of: Pittway Company), 1100 Superior Ave., Cleveland, OH 44114-2543. TEL 216-696-7000. FAX 216-696-7658. (Subscr. to: Box 95759, Cleveland, OH 44101) Ed. Ronald Welter; Pub. Rosalie Brosilow. circ. 11,000. (reprint service avail. from UMI) **Document type:** trade publication.
   —UMI. **CCC.**
   Formerly (until Sep. 1994): Welding Distributor (ISSN 0192-7671)
   Description: Informs on management, market statistics, selling techniques, merchandizing methods and case histories.

671.52 CC ISSN 1001-1382
TS227.A1
HANJIE/WELDING. (Text in Chinese) m. Jixie Dianzi Gongye Bu, Harbin Hanjie Yanjiusuo - Ministry of Engineering and Electronic Industry, Harbin Welding Research Institute, 65, Hexing Lu, Harbin, Heilongjiang 150080, People's Republic of China. TEL 36695. Ed. Ren Dacheng.

671.52 CC ISSN 0253-360X
TS227.A1 CODEN: HHPAD2
HANJIE XUEBAO/CHINA WELDING INSTITUTION. TRANSACTIONS. (Text in Chinese; abstracts in English) 1980. q. $20. (Zhongguo Jixie Gongcheng Xuehui - Chinese Society of Mechanical Engineering) Harbin Hanjie Yanjiusuo - Harbin Research Institute of Welding, 111 Hexing Lu, Harbin, Heilongjiang 150080, People's Republic of China. TEL 6336695. (Dist. overseas by: China International Book Trading Corp., P.O. Box 399, Beijing, P.R. China) Ed. Li Zhaoshan. adv.: page $2000. circ. 12,000. **Document type:** academic/scholarly publication, proceedings.
   —BLDSC (8912.450000); CASDDS.

671.52 US
HAYNES ALLOYS DIGEST. 1950. q. free. Haynes International, Inc., 1020 W. Park Ave., Box 9013, Kokomo, IN 46904-9013. TEL 317-456-6000. FAX 317-456-6905. TELEX 27-2280. circ. 11,000 (controlled). (back issues avail.) **Document type:** bulletin.
   Former titles: Haynes High Performance Alloys Digest; Cabot High Performance Alloys Digest.
   Description: Solutions to problems caused by deterioration of equipment from heat and corrosion.

671.52 FI
HITSAUSTEKNIIKKA - SVETSTEKNIK. 1949. 6/yr. FIM 240 (outside Scandinavia FIM 270). Suomen Hitsausteknillinen Yhdistys - Welding Society of Finland, Makelankatu 36A, 00510 Helsinki, Finland. TEL 358-773-21-99. FAX 358-773-26-66. Ed. Juha Lukkari. adv.: B&W page FIM 6500; trim 178 x 266. circ. 5,500 (controlled). **Indexed:** Met.Abstr.
   Description: Aims to provide professionally high quality theoretical and practical information concerning welding technology and its related trades for specialists and non-specialists alike.

METALLURGY — WELDING

671.52   II   ISSN 0046-9092
CODEN: IWLJAK
INDIAN WELDING JOURNAL. 1969. 4/yr. Rs.80. Indian Institute of Welding, 3A Loudon St., Calcutta 700 017, India. TEL 91-33-401350. Ed. A.K. Mitra. adv.; bk.rev.; abstr.; bibl.; charts; illus. circ. 2,500. **Indexed:** Chem.Abstr., Met.Abstr., World Alum.Abstr.
—BLDSC (4431.070000); CASDDS.
Description: Promotes knowledge and technology of joining materials.

671.52   II   ISSN 0377-7391
TS227.A1
INDUSTRIAL WELDER. (Text in English) 1971. m. Rs.36. Industrial Welder Publications, Zita Villa, 212, Kalina, Santa Cruz E., Bombay 400029, India. Ed. Felix K. Soans. adv.; bk.rev.; illus. circ. 3,700.

671.5   DK   ISSN 0905-6866
INTERNATIONAL JOURNAL FOR JOINING OF MATERIALS. Variant title: J O M. (Text in English) 1989. 3/yr. DKK 1000. J O M Institute, Ingenioerhoejskolen Helsingoer Teknikum, Rasmus Knudsens Vej 50, DK-3000 Helsingoer, Denmark. TEL 45-46-46-222-85-97. FAX 45-46-46-222-45-29. Ed. Gunnar S. Bolmsjoe. index. circ. 200. (back issues avail.) **Document type:** academic/scholarly publication.
—BLDSC (4542.311800); Ei.
Description: Provides an international forum for the multidisciplinary subjects within joining of materials. Encourages development of important work in the field.
Refereed Serial

671.52   US
INTERNATIONAL THERMAL SPRAYING CONFERENCE. PREPRINT OF PAPERS. irreg., 9th, 1980. $25. American Welding Society, Box 351040, Miami, FL 33135. TEL 305-443-9353.

671.52   GW   ISSN 0930-9241
INTERNATIONAL WELDING ENGINEERING. (Text in Chinese) 1987. a. free in the Peoples Republic of China. Deutscher Verlag fuer Schweisstechnik, Postfach 101965, 40010 Duesseldorf, Germany. TEL 0211-1591-0. FAX 0211-1591-200. TELEX 8582583. circ. 7,000. (back issues avail.) **Document type:** trade publication.

671.52   RU   ISSN 0202-778X
CODEN: INTSBP
ITOGI NAUKI I TEKHNIKI: SVARKA. (Text in Russian) 1967. irreg., vol.20, 1989. 5.40 Rub. Vsesoyuznyi Institut Nauchno-Tekhnicheskoi Informatsii (VINITI), Ul. Baltiiskaya 14, Moscow A-219, Russia. (Subscr. to: Mezhdunarodnaya Kniga, Dimitrova ul. 39, 113095 Moscow, Russia) **Indexed:** Chem.Abstr.
—BLDSC (0160.800000); CASDDS.

671.52   JA   ISSN 0021-4787
TS227.A1   CODEN: YOGAAK
JAPAN WELDING SOCIETY. JOURNAL/YOSETSU GAKKAISHI. (Text in English or Japanese) 1926. q. 12000 Yen. Japan Welding Society - Yosetsu Gakkai, 1-11 Kanda Sakumo-cho, Chiyoda-ku, Tokyo 101, Japan. FAX 03-3253-3059. Ed. Masabumi Buzaki. adv.; bk.rev.; bibl.; charts; illus. **Indexed:** Chem.Abstr., JTA, Met.Abstr., World Alum.Abstr.
—CASDDS.

671.52   NE   ISSN 0023-8694
CODEN: LASTAW
LASTECHNIEK. 1934. m. fl.160. (Nederlands Instituut voor Lastechniek - Dutch Welding Institute) Wyt Uitgeefgroep B.V., P.O. Box 268, Rotterdam, Netherlands. adv.; index. circ. 3,800. **Indexed:** C.I.S. Abstr., Excerp.Med., Met.Abstr., World Alum.Abstr. **Document type:** trade publication.
—BLDSC (5157.000000); CASDDS; SWETS.

671.52   NE   ISSN 0927-751X
LINCOLN SMITWELD REPORTAGE. (Editions in Dutch, English and German) 1962. q. free. Lincoln Smitweld B.V., Box 253, Nieuwe Dukenburgseweg 20, Nijmegen, Netherlands. TEL 080-522204. FAX 080-522670. TELEX 48129. Ed. A. Schreuder. bk.rev.; charts; illus.; stat.; index. circ. 13,000.
Former titles (until 1991): Smitweld Reportage (ISSN 0166-6703); (until 1971): Smit-las (ISSN 0037-7287)

M E M C O NEWS. 1950. q. free to qualified personnel. Miller Electric Manufacturing Co., 1635 W. Spencer, Box 1079, Appleton, WI 54911. TEL 414-735-4249. FAX 414-735-4013. Ed. R.F. Metko. circ. 44,000 (controlled). **Indexed:** Met.Abstr., World Alum.Abstr.
Description: News, features, and photography on contemporary applications of arc welding equipment.

MATERIALS AND MANUFACTURE. see *ENGINEERING — Mechanical Engineering*

MATERIALS INFORMATION DIGEST SERIES. see *METALLURGY*

METALLIC MATERIALS. see *ENGINEERING — Engineering Mechanics And Materials*

671.52   CC   ISSN 1001-4934
MO JU. (Text in Chinese) bi-m. Shanghai Moju Jishu Yanjiusuo, Jiaotong Daxue Nei, No. 1954, Huashan Lu, Shanghai 200030, People's Republic of China. TEL 4310310.

671.52   GW   ISSN 0554-9965
DER PRAKTIKER; Schweissen und Schneiden. 1948. m. DM.142 (foreign DM.147) (effective 1996). Deutscher Verlag fuer Schweisstechnik, Postfach 101965, 40010 Duesseldorf, Germany. TEL 0211-1591-159. FAX 0211-1591-200. TELEX 8582583. Ed. M. Weinreich. circ. 18,000. **Indexed:** Met.Abstr., World Alum.Abstr. **Document type:** trade publication.
—SWETS. **CCC.**

671.52   PL   ISSN 0033-2364
CODEN: PRZAA3
PRZEGLAD SPAWALNICTWA. 1949. m. $90. (Stowarzyszenie Inzynierow i Technikow Mechanikow Polskich - Association of Polish Mechanical Engineers and Technicians) Oficyna Wydawnicza SIMP Press, Ltd., Swietokrzyska 14A, 00-050 Warsaw, Poland. TEL 48-22-272542. (Dist. by: Ars Polona-Ruch, Krakowskie Przedmiescie 7, Warsaw, Poland) Ed. Jan Pilarczyk. adv.: B&W page $1010. bk.rev.; bibl.; charts; illus.; index. circ. 1,100. (also avail. in microfilm) **Indexed:** C.I.S. Abstr., Chem.Abstr., Met.Abstr., World Alum.Abstr.
—CASDDS.

671.52   US
R & D FOCUS. 1986. 3/yr. free. International Lead Zinc Research Organization, Inc. Box 12036, Research Triangle Park, NC 27709-2036. TEL 919-361-4647. FAX 919-361-1957. TELEX 261513. Ed. John A. Sharpe III. charts; illus. circ. 1,100.
Description: Covers ongoing cooperative research and development in zinc and lead.

671.52   SP   ISSN 0048-7759
CODEN: RSLDB6
REVISTA DE SOLDADURA. 1971. q. 8500 ptas. (effective 1995). Centro Nacional de Investigaciones Metalurgicas, Avda. Gregorio De Amo, 8, 28040 Madrid, Spain. FAX 341-5347425. Ed. J. Fernandez. adv.; bk.rev.; bibl.; charts; illus. circ. 1,800. **Indexed:** Chem.Abstr., Ind.SST, Met.Abstr., World Alum.Abstr. **Document type:** academic/scholarly publication, trade publication.
—CASDDS; Ei; SWETS.

671.52   BE   ISSN 0035-127X
TS227   CODEN: RSOUA3
REVUE DE LA SOUDURE/LASTIJDSCHRIFT. (Text in Dutch, English, French) 1945. q. 2000 BEF (effective 1995). (Institut Belge de la Soudure - Belgisch Instituut voor Lastechniek) Business & Management Editions Brussels s.p.r.l., Rue Stephanie, 17, 1020 Brussels, Belgium. TEL 32-2-4266115. FAX 32-2-4258226. adv.; bk.rev.; abstr.; charts; illus.; tr.lit.; index. circ. 10,000. **Indexed:** Chem.Abstr., Met.Abstr., World Alum.Abstr. **Document type:** trade publication.
—BLDSC (7952.000000); CASDDS.
Incorporates (in 1976): Pratique du Soudage (ISSN 0032-6909)
Description: Covers technical and scientific developments and news affecting the welding and surface treatment industries

671.52   IT   ISSN 0035-6794
TS227   CODEN: RISAAT
RIVISTA ITALIANA DELLA SALDATURA. 1949. bi-m. L.220000. Istituto Italiano della Saldatura, Lungobisagno Istria 15, 16141 Genoa, Italy. TEL 39-10-83411. FAX 39-10-8367780. Ed. Sergio Giorgi; Pub. Giulio Costa. adv.; bk.rev.; bibl.; charts; illus.; pat.; index. circ. 3,200. **Indexed:** Bull.Signal., C.I.S. Abstr., Chem.Abstr., Met.Abstr., World Alum.Abstr.
—BLDSC (7987.600000); CASDDS.

671.52   GW   ISSN 0036-7184
TS227   CODEN: SCSCA4
SCHWEISSEN UND SCHNEIDEN. 1948. m. DM.265 (Switzerland & Austria DM.270; elsewhere DM.378) (effective 1996). Deutscher Verlag fuer Schweisstechnik, Postfach 101965, 40010 Duesseldorf, Germany. TEL 0211-1591-159. FAX 0211-1591-200. TELEX 8582583. Ed. M. Weinreich. adv.: B&W page DM.4400; trim 253 x 176. bk.rev.; bibl.; charts; illus.; pat.; index. circ. 14,000. (also avail. in microform from UMI; reprint service avail. from UMI) **Indexed:** Appl.Mech.Rev., BMT, C.I.S. Abstr., Chem.Abstr., Copper Abstr., Dok.Arbeitsmed., Eng.Ind., Excerp.Med., Met.Abstr., World Alum.Abstr. **Document type:** trade publication.
—BLDSC (8106.000000); CASDDS; Ei; Faxon; SWETS; UMI. **CCC.**
Incorporates: Schweisstechnik (ISSN 0036-7192)

671.52   SZ   ISSN 0036-7206
SCHWEISSTECHNIK/SOUDURE. (Supplement to: Technica) (Text in French and German) 1911. m. (Schweizerischer Verein fuer Schweisstechnik) Industrie-Verlag AG, Muehlebachstr. 43, CH-8032 Zurich, Switzerland. Ed.Bd. adv.; charts; illus.; pat. circ. 3,330. **Indexed:** C.I.S. Abstr., Chem.Abstr., Eng.Ind., Excerp.Med., Met.Abstr. **Document type:** trade publication.

671.52   AU   ISSN 0253-5262
CODEN: SWTEAJ
SCHWEISSTECHNIK. 1946. m. S.770 (foreign S.790). Oesterreichische Gesellschaft fuer Schweisstechnik, A-1030 Vienna, Austria. TEL 01-7982168. FAX 01-798216815. Ed. G. Czesany. bk.rev. circ. 1,100. **Document type:** trade publication.
—CASDDS.

671   UK   ISSN 0037-3435
TS250   CODEN: SHMIAR
SHEET METAL INDUSTRIES. 1927. m. £114($222) (overseas £142) (includes Yearbook). Argus Business Media Ltd., International Trade Publications (Subsidiary of: Argus Press Group), Queensway House, 2 Queensway, Redhill, Surrey RH1 1QS. TEL 01737-768611. TELEX 948669 TOPJNL G. Ed. R. Pendrous. adv.; bk.rev.; charts; illus.; tr.lit.; index. (also avail. in microform from UMI) **Indexed:** Br.Tech.Ind., C.I.S. Abstr., Chem.Abstr., Eng.Ind., Excerp.Med., Int.Packag.Abstr., ISMEC, Met.Abstr., World Alum.Abstr. **Document type:** trade publication.
—BLDSC (8255.000000); CASDDS; Ei; SWETS; UMI.

669   UK   ISSN 0305-7798
TS250
SHEET METAL INDUSTRIES YEARBOOK. a. (free with subscr. to Sheet Metal Industries). International Trade Publications (Subsidiary of: Argus Press Group), Queensway House, 2 Queensway, Redhill, Surrey RH1 1QS, England. TEL 01737-768611. FAX 01737-761989. TELEX 948669 TOPJNL G. Ed. G. Lloyd. adv.; bibl.; index. **Document type:** trade publication.

671.52   SP   ISSN 1130-0280
SOLDADURA Y TECNOLOGIAS DE UNION. 1990. 6/yr. 11500 ptas.($104) (effective 1995). Elsevier Prensa S.A., Av. Parallel 180, 08015 Barcelona, Spain. TEL 34-3-3255350. FAX 34-3-4252880. adv. contact: Manuel Fernandez de Liencres. circ. 3,500. **Document type:** trade publication.
Description: Covers soldering and welding techniques, equipment and installations.

METALLURGY — WELDING

671.52
TS610
UK ISSN 0954-0911
CODEN: SSMOEO
SOLDERING & SURFACE MOUNT TECHNOLOGY. 1981. 3/yr. £38.50($77) (Surface Mount and Related Technologies (SMART) Group) Wela Publications Ltd., Asahi House, 10 Church Rd., Port Erin IM99 8HD, Isle of Man. TEL 01624-836044. FAX 01624-835400. Ed. William Goldie. charts; illus. **Indexed:** Cadscan, Chem.Abstr., INSPEC (1994-), Lead Abstr., Met.Abstr., World Alum.Abstr., Zincscan. **Document type:** academic/scholarly publication.
—BLDSC (8327.242650); CASDDS; Ei; SWETS; UMI. **CCC.**
Formerly (until 1989): Brazing and Soldering (ISSN 0263-0060)

STROJNISKI VESTNIK/MECHANICAL ENGINEERING JOURNAL. see ENGINEERING — Mechanical Engineering

671
RU ISSN 0491-6441
CODEN: SVAPAI
SVAROCHNOE PROIZVODSTVO. 1930. m. $123 (effective 1996). Izdatel'stvo Mashinostroenie, 4, Stromynsky per., 107076 Moscow, Russia. TEL 095-269-7141. FAX 095-269-4897. Ed. V.F. Tyurin. adv.: page DM.4000. bk.rev.; abstr.; bibl.; charts; illus.; index. circ. 9,400. **Indexed:** C.I.S. Abstr., Chem.Abstr., INSPEC, Met.Abstr., World Alum.Abstr. **Document type:** academic/scholarly publication.
—BLDSC (0160.860000); CASDDS.
Description: Carries articles on the following major processes: welding, resurfacing, brazing, thermal cutting, spraying and application of metal coating.

671.52
SW ISSN 0039-7083
SVETSAREN; a welding review. (Text in English) 1936. 2/yr. free. Esab AB, Marketing Communications, P.O. Box 8804, S-402 77 Goeteborg, Sweden. FAX 46-31-509-390. Ed. Lennart Lundberg. charts; illus. circ. 15,000. **Indexed:** Appl.Mech.Rev., Chem.Abstr., INSPEC (1970-), Met.Abstr., World Alum.Abstr. **Document type:** trade publication.
Formerly: Kjelberg och E S A B Schriften (ISSN 0075-6261)
Description: Focuses on technical developments and new applications in welding and cutting as well as presenting new technology and products.8

671.52
SW ISSN 0039-7091
CODEN: SVTNA5
SVETSEN. (Text in Scandinavian languages) 1942. bi-m. SEK 360 (effective 1993). (Svetstekniska Foereningen) Svetsen Foerlags AB, I V A, P.O. Box 5073, 102 42 Stockholm, Sweden. TEL 791-29-00. FAX 08-679-9404. Ed. Hans Wickstroem. adv.; bk.rev.; charts; illus. circ. 3,800. **Indexed:** Chem.Abstr., Met.Abstr.
—CASDDS.

671.52
UK
T W I BULLETIN. 1968. bi-m. membership only. T W I - The Welding Institute, Abington Hall, Abington, Cambridge CB1 6AH, England. TEL 01223-891162. FAX 01223-892588. Eds. John Dadson, Catherine Condie. **Document type:** bulletin.
Former titles: Welding Institute Research Bulletin; B W R A Bulletin.

671.52
UK ISSN 0963-6927
CODEN: TWJOEE
T W I JOURNAL. 1992. q. £175 in Europe; America £295; elsewhere £185 (effective 1996). (T W I - The Welding Institute) Woodhead Publishing Ltd., Abington Hall, Abington, Cambridge CB1 6AH, England. TEL 01223-891358. FAX 01223-893694. (Subscr. to Turpin Distribution Services Ltd., Blackhorse Rd. Letchworth, Herts. SG6 1HN, England. TEL 01462-672555. FAX 01462-480947) Pub. Martin Woodhead. **Document type:** academic/scholarly publication.
—BLDSC (9076.953800); CASDDS.
Description: Contains research papers from the engineers and scientists at TWI.

671.52
UK
TECHNICAL DIAGNOSTICS AND NONDESTRUCTIVE TESTING. English translation of: Tekhnicheskaya Diagnostika i Nerazrushayushchii Kontrol' 1989. q. £79($130) (E.O. Paton Welding Institute, UR) Riecansky Science Publishing Co., 7 Meadow Walk, Great Abington, Cambridge CB1 6AZ, England. TEL 0223-893295. FAX 0223-893295. Ed. B.E. Paton.
—BLDSC (0425.899000); UnCover.
Formerly: Technical Diagnostics and Nondestructive Testing in Welding (ISSN 0955-3835)
Description: Presents the latest achievements in the field of technical diagnostics and nondestructive testing in welding.

671.52
US
W R C PROGRESS REPORTS. 6/yr. $1100 includes Welding Research Abroad, W R C Bulletins, W R C News and Welding Journal. Welding Research Council, United Engineering Center, 345 E. 47th St., New York, NY 10017. TEL 212-705-7956. **Indexed:** Met.Abstr., World Alum.Abstr.

671.52
II ISSN 0970-4477
W R I JOURNAL. (Text in English) 1977. q. Rs.300($36) Bharat Heavy Electricals Ltd., Welding Research Institute, Tiruchirapalli 620 014, Tamil Nadu, India. TEL 0431-53448. FAX 91-0431-52710. TELEX 0455-211 BHTP IN. Ed. B. Pullat. adv. circ. 300. (back issues avail.) **Indexed:** Eng.Ind. **Document type:** newspaper.
Formerly (until 1989): W R I Keywords.

WELDALERT; selective dissemination of information. see METALLURGY — Abstracting, Bibliographies, Statistics

671.52
UK ISSN 0043-2237
TK1
WELDER. 1929. q. free. Boc-Murex, Hertford Rd., Waltham Cross, Herts., England. Ed. A.S. Ailes. adv.; bk.rev.; charts; illus.; index every 3 yrs; circ. 15,500 (controlled). **Indexed:** Br.Tech.Ind., Chem.Abstr., Eng.Ind., Met.Abstr.

WELDING ABSTRACTS. see METALLURGY — Abstracting, Bibliographies, Statistics

671.5
US ISSN 0278-7067
TS227
WELDING AND FABRICATING DATA BOOK. 1958. biennial. $30. Penton Publishing, 1100 Superior Ave., Cleveland, OH 44114-2543. TEL 216-696-7000. FAX 216-696-8765. (Subscr. to: Box 95759, Cleveland, OH 44101) Ed. Rosalie Brosilow. adv.; charts; illus. circ. 24,000. (reprint service avail. from UMI)
—UMI.
Formerly: Welding Data Book (ISSN 0511-4365)

671.52
UK ISSN 0043-2245
TS227
CODEN: WLMFAM
WELDING AND METAL FABRICATION. 1933. 10/yr. £101($213) in the U.K.; overseas £116 (effective 1994). Argus Business Media Ltd., International Trade Publications (Subsidiary of: Argus Press Group), Queensway House, 2 Queensway, Redhill, Surrey RH1 1QS, England. TEL 01737-768611. FAX 01737-761989. TELEX 948669 TOPJNL G. Ed. Roderick Robinson. adv.; bk.rev.; charts; illus.; index. (also avail. in microfiche; reprint service avail. from ISI) **Indexed:** BMT, Br.Tech.Ind., C.I.S. Abstr., Chem.Abstr., Eng.Ind., Fuel & Energy Abstr., INSPEC, ISMEC, Met.Abstr., Robomat., World Alum.Abstr. **Document type:** trade publication.
—BLDSC (9290.000000); CASDDS; Ei; Faxon; SWETS; UnCover.
Description: For welding engineers, supervisors, distributors, sales and purchasing personnel, as well as welders.

671.52
US ISSN 1073-4511
TS227.A1
WELDING AND SURFACING REVIEWS. 1989. q. 151 ECU (effective 1996). (Ukrainian Academy of Sciences, E.O. Paton Electric Welding Institute, KR) Harwood Academic Publishers, c/o International Publishers Distributor, 820 Town Center Dr., Langhorne, PA 19047. TEL 215-750-2642. FAX 215-750-6343. (Subscr. to: International Publishers Distributor, P.O. Box 90, Reading, Berkshire RG1 8JL, England. TEL 44-173-456-8316) Ed. B.E. Paton. (also avail. in microform)
—BLDSC (9290.060000). **CCC.**
Former titles: Soviet Technology Reviews. Section C: Welding and Surfacing Reviews (ISSN 1040-7073); Soviet Technology Reviews. Section C: Welding Reviews.
Description: Deals with new developments in the fields of welding surfacing and of producation of high quality metallic materials using special electrometallurgy processes.
Refereed Serial

671.52
US ISSN 0043-2253
TS227
CODEN: WDEFAS
WELDING DESIGN AND FABRICATION. 1930. m. $50 (free to qualified personnel). Penton Publishing (Subsidiary of: Pittway Company), 1100 Superior Ave., Cleveland, OH 44114-2543. TEL 216-696-7000. FAX 216-696-8765. (Subscr. to: Box 95759, Cleveland, OH 44101) Ed. Rosalie Brosilow. adv.; bk.rev.; charts; illus.; index; circ. 40,000 (controlled). (also avail. in microform from UMI,PMC; reprint service avail. from UMI) **Indexed:** A.I.Abstr. (until 1992), A.S.& T.Ind., CAD CAM Abstr. (until 1992), Chem.Abstr., Eng.Ind., Excerp.Med., INSPEC (1975-), ISMEC, Met.Abstr., Robomat. (until 1992), World Alum.Abstr.
—BLDSC (9290.200000); Ei; Faxon; SWETS; UMI; UnCover. **CCC.**
Incorporates (in 1975): Welding Engineer (ISSN 0043-227X)
Description: Welding processes and equipment, fabrication of weldments, structural projects and maintenance.

671.52
JA
WELDING ENGINEER.* (Text in Japanese) 1971. q. 2600 Yen. Sanpo Shuppan K.K. - Sanpo Publications, Inc., 2, Kanda Hirakawa-cho, Chiyoda-ku, Tokyo 101, Japan. Ed. Hiroshi Morita.

671.52
UK ISSN 0043-2288
TS227
CODEN: WDWRAI
WELDING IN THE WORLD/SOUDAGE DANS LE MONDE. (Text in English and French) 1963. 7/yr. £210($334) (effective 1996). (International Institute of Welding - Institut International de la Soudure) Elsevier Science Ltd., Pergamon, P.O. Box 800, Kidlington, Oxford OX5 1DX, England. TEL 44-1865-843000. FAX 44-1865-843010. E-mail: nlinfo-f@elsevier.nl; usinfo-f@elsevier.com; forinfo-kyf04035@niftyserve.or.jp; Site addr.: http://www.elsevier.nl/. (Subscr. in U.S. and Canada to: Elsevier Science, 660 White Plains Rd., Tarrytown, NY 10591-5153. TEL 914-524-9200. FAX 914-333-2444) Eds. J.G. Hicks, M. Bramat. adv.; abstr.; charts; illus. circ. 900. (also avail. in microfilm from UMI; back issues avail.) **Indexed:** BMT, Br.Tech.Ind., C.I.S. Abstr., Chem.Abstr., Curr.Cont., Eng.Ind., ISMEC, Met.Abstr., World Alum.Abstr. **Document type:** academic/scholarly publication.
—BLDSC (9293.200000); CASDDS; Ei; Faxon; SWETS; UMI. **CCC.**
Description: Contains reports, recommendations, addresses and draft standards emanating from commissioned reports and surveys of the IIW, including coverage of processes, metallurgy, testing and inspection, health and safety issues.
Refereed Serial

671.52
WELDING INNOVATION QUARTERLY. q. James F. Lincoln Arc Welding Foundation, Box 17035, Cleveland, OH 44117-0035. TEL 216-481-4300. Ed. Richard Smith. circ. 60,000.

671.52 UK ISSN 0950-7116
TS227.A1 CODEN: WEINEF
WELDING INTERNATIONAL. 1987. m. £745 in Europe; America £1295; elsewhere £765 (effective 1996). (T W I - The Welding Institute) Woodhead Publishing Ltd., Abington Hall, Abington, Cambridge CB1 6AH, England. TEL 01223-891358. FAX 01223-893694. (Subscr. to: Turpin Distribution Services Ltd., Blackhorse Rd. Letchworth, Herts. SG6 1HN, England. TEL 01462-672555. FAX 01462-480947) Pub. Martin Woodhead. bibl.; charts; illus.; index. **Indexed:** Excerp.Med. **Document type:** abstracting/indexing.
—BLDSC (9290.670000); Ei; Faxon; SWETS.
Description: Provides translations of complete articles selected from major welding journals of the world.

671.52 US ISSN 0043-2296
TS227 CODEN: WEJUA3
WELDING JOURNAL. 1922. m. $30. American Welding Society, Box 351040, Miami, FL 33135. TEL 305-443-9353. Ed. Jeff Weber. adv.; bk.rev.; illus.; pat.; tr.lit.; index. circ. 40,000. (also avail. in microform from UMI,PMC) **Indexed:** A.S.& T.Ind., AESIS, Appl.Mech.Rev., BMT, CAD CAM Abstr. (until 1992), Chem.Abstr., Curr.Cont., Eng.Ind., Ergon.Abstr., Excerp.Med., Int.Aerosp.Abstr., ISMEC, Met.Abstr., Robomat. (until 1992), World Alum.Abstr. **Document type:** trade publication.
—BLDSC (9291.000000); CASDDS; Ei; Faxon; Genuine Article; SWETS; UMI; UnCover. **CCC.**

671.52 US ISSN 0043-2318
TS227
WELDING RESEARCH ABROAD. 1954. 10/yr. $1100 includes Progress Reports, W R C Bulletins, W R C News and Welding Journal. Welding Research Council, 345 E. 47th St., New York, NY 10017. TEL 212-705-7956. Ed. C.R. Felmley, Jr. charts; illus.; stat.; index; circ. 800 (controlled). **Indexed:** Met.Abstr., World Alum.Abstr.
—BLDSC (9291.500000); SWETS; UnCover.

671.52 US ISSN 0043-2326
TS227 CODEN: WRCBA2
WELDING RESEARCH COUNCIL BULLETIN. 1949. 10/yr. $1100 includes Welding Research Abroad, Progress Reports, W R C News and Welding Journal. Welding Research Council, 345 E. 47th St., New York, NY 10017. TEL 212-705-7956. Ed. C.R. Felmley, Jr. charts; illus.; circ. 900 (controlled). **Indexed:** Chem.Abstr., Curr.Cont., Eng.Ind., Int.Aerosp.Abstr., Met.Abstr., World Alum.Abstr.
—BLDSC (9364.585000); CASDDS; UnCover.

671.52 US ISSN 0743-1929
WELDING RESEARCH COUNCIL YEARBOOK. 1936. a. membership. Welding Research Council, United Engineering Center, 345 E. 47th St., New York, NY 10017. TEL 212-705-7956. circ. 700.

671.52 US ISSN 0511-4381
CODEN: WERNA
WELDING RESEARCH NEWS. 4/yr. $1100 includes Welding Research Abroad, Progress Reports, W R C Bulletins and Welding Journal. Welding Research Council, 345 E. 47th St., New York, NY 10017. TEL 212-705-7956.
Description: Highlights articles and items on current developments in welding research.

671.52 UK
CODEN: WELRD7
WELDING REVIEW INTERNATIONAL. 1982. q. £73($178) (overseas £96) (effective 1995). Argus Business Media Ltd., International Trade Publications (Subsidiary of: Argus Press Group), Queensway House, 2 Queensway, Redhill, Surrey RH1 1QS, England. TEL 01737-768611. FAX 01737-761989. TELEX 948669 TOPJNL G. Ed. Richard Southgate. adv. contact: David Hendry. bk.rev. circ. 5,000. **Indexed:** BMT, Chem.Abstr., Met.Abstr., World Alum.Abstr. **Document type:** trade publication.
—CASDDS; Ei; SWETS.
Formerly: Welding Review (ISSN 0262-642X)

671.52 US ISSN
TS227.A1
WELDING TECHNOLOGY. m. $160 to non-members (foreign $180); members $130 (foreign $145) (effective 1996). A S M International, Materials Information, Materials Park, OH 44073. TEL 216-338-5151. FAX 216-338-4634. TELEX 980-619. E-mail: DBarthel@po.ASM-Intl.org. (UK addr.: Institute of Materials, Materials Information, 1 Carlton House Terr., London SW1Y 5DB, England. TEL 071-839-4071) Eds. M. Stephen Chang, Michael P. Finical. circ. 100. **Indexed:** Met.Abstr. **Document type:** abstracting/indexing.
—CCC.
Former titles: Welding - Brazing - Soldering Digest (ISSN 1050-3013); Welding and Joining Digest (ISSN 0361-3747)
Description: Covers brazing, soldering, hard facing, adhesive-diffusion bonding, riveting and welding processes.

671.52 CN ISSN 1191-9833
WHAT'S NEW IN WELDING. 1988. 6/yr. Maclean-Hunter Ltd., Maclean-Hunter Bldg., 777 Bay St., Toronto, ON M5W 1A7, Canada. TEL 416-596-5713. FAX 416-593-3193. TELEX 06-219547.
Formerly: Welding Quarterly (ISSN 0845-812X)

671.52 CI ISSN 0044-1902
CODEN: ZAVAA8
ZAVARIVANJE. (Text in Croatian; summaries and content pages in English and German) 1958. bi-m. $70. Drustvo za Tehniku Zavarivanja Hrvatske, Dure Salaja 1, 41000 Zagreb, Croatia. TELEX 22648 FSB YU. Ed. Goran Vrucimic. adv.; bk.rev.; index. circ. 2,000. **Indexed:** Bull.Signal., Chem.Abstr., Eng.Ind., Met.Abstr., Ref.Zh., World Alum.Abstr.
—BLDSC (9428.260000); CASDDS.

671.52 XO ISSN 0044-5525
CODEN: ZVARAX
ZVARANIE/WELDING. (Text in Czech or Slovak; summaries in English, German, Russian) 1952. m. $33. Vyskumny Ustav Zvaracky, Racianska 71, 832 59 Bratislava, Slovakia. TEL 33-14-41. FAX 42-7-594-43. (Dist. by: Slovart, nam. Slobody 6, 817 64 Bratislava, Slovakia) adv.; bk.rev.; charts; illus.; pat. circ. 3,000. **Indexed:** C.I.S. Abstr., Chem.Abstr., Met.Abstr., World Alum.Abstr. **Document type:** trade publication.
—CASDDS.

METEOROLOGY

551.5 US ISSN 0730-2029
A M S NEWSLETTER (BOSTON). 1980. m. $100 (foreign $120). American Meteorological Society, 45 Beacon St., Boston, MA 02108-3693. TEL 617-227-2425. FAX 617-742-8718. Ed. Roland D. Paine. circ. 610. **Document type:** newsletter.
Description: Contains news briefs, dates, notes on people, information on grants, and contracts for meteorologists, oceanographers, and hydrologists.

551.5 US
A R M OUTREACH. (Atmospheric Radiation Measurement) 1992. irreg. (1-2/yr.) free. (U.S. Department of Energy) Carbon Dioxide Information Analysis Center, Oak Ridge National Laboratory, Box 2008 (MS-6335), Oak Ridge, TN 37831-6335. TEL 615-574-0390. FAX 615-574-2232. Ed. Marv Dickerson. **Document type:** government publication, newsletter.
Description: Provides news of ARM Program activities and research initiatives.

ACTA GEOGRAPHICA AC GEOLOGICA ET METEOROLOGICA DEBRECINA. see GEOGRAPHY

551.5 CC ISSN 0894-0525
QC851 CODEN: AMTSEZ
ACTA METEOROLOGICA SINICA. Chinese edition: Qixiang Xuebao (ISSN 0577-6619) (Text in English) 1987. 4/yr. $250 (effective 1995). (Zhongguo Qixiang Xuehui - Chinese Meteorological Society) China Meteorological Press, 46 Baishiqiao Rd., West Suburb, Beijing 100081, People's Republic of China. TEL 86-1-8331337. FAX 81-1-8331377. Ed. Zhou Shijian. **Indexed:** Cadscan, Chem.Abstr., Corros.Abstr., Environ.Per.Bibl. (1991-), Geo.Abstr., IDA, INSPEC (1981-), Int.Aerosp.Abstr., Lead Abstr., Met.Abstr., Meteor.& Geoastrophys.Abstr., Phys.Ber., Zincscan. **Document type:** academic/scholarly publication.
—BLDSC (0637.710000); Faxon; UMI.
Description: Carries research papers and review articles on the advance of atmospheric sciences.
Refereed Serial

551.6 HU ISSN 0563-0614
ACTA UNIVERSITATIS DE ATTILA JOZSEF NOMINATAE. ACTA CLIMATOLOGICA. (Text in English) 1959. biennial. exchange basis. Attila Jozsef University, c/o E. Szabo, Exchange Librarian, Dugonics ter 13, P.O.B. 393, Szeged H-6701, Hungary. (Subscr. to: Kultura, P.O. Box 149, H-1389 Budapest, Hungary) Ed. Gyorgy Koppany. charts; illus. circ. 400.
Description: Focus on general climatology, bio- and agrometeorology.

551.5 CC ISSN 0256-1530
ADVANCES IN ATMOSPHERIC SCIENCES. Chinese Edition: Daqi Kexue Jinzhan. (Editions in Chinese, English) 1984. q. $249 (effective 1996). (Chinese Committee of Meteorology and Atmospheric Physics) China Ocean Press, International Department, Haimao Dalou, 1 Fuxingmenwai Dajie, Beijing 100860, People's Republic of China. TEL 8032211. FAX 8033515. Eds. Tao Shiyan, Ruan Zhongjia. circ. 1,000. (also avail. in microform from UMI; reprint service avail. from ISI) **Document type:** academic/scholarly publication.
—BLDSC (0699.600000); Faxon; UnCover. **CCC.**
Description: Covers the latest achievements and developments in atmospheric sciences, including marine meteorology, meteorology-associated geophysics, and theoretical and practical aspects of these disciplines.
Refereed Serial

551.5 613.1 GW ISSN 0942-5225
QH543 CODEN: ADVBEX
ADVANCES IN BIOCLIMATOLOGY. (Text in English) 1992. irreg. Springer-Verlag, Heidelberger Platz 3, 14197 Berlin, Germany. TEL 030-8207-0. FAX 030-8207300. E-mail: orders@springer.de. **Document type:** monographic series.
—BLDSC (0699.937000).

ADVANCES IN NATURAL AND TECHNOLOGICAL HAZARDS RESEARCH. see PUBLIC HEALTH AND SAFETY

551.65 JA ISSN 0448-3723
AEROLOGICAL DATA OF JAPAN/KOSO GEPPO. (Text in English) 1947. m. Kishocho - Japan Meteorological Agency, 3-4, Otemachi 1-chome, Chiyoda-ku, Tokyo 100, Japan. stat.; circ. controlled. (processed)

551 JA ISSN 0448-3723
AEROLOGICAL DATA OF JAPAN: 5-YEAR PERIOD AVERAGES. (Text in English, Japanese) 1958. every 5 yrs. Kishocho, Kansokubu - Japan Meteorological Agency, Observation Department, 3-4, Otemachi 1-chome, Chiyoda-ku, Tokyo 100, Japan. **Document type:** government publication.

551.5 SG ISSN 0065-4248
AGENCE POUR LA SECURITE DE LA NAVIGATION AERIENNE EN AFRIQUE ET A MADAGASCAR. DIRECTION DE L'EXPLOITATION METEOROLOGIQUE. PUBLICATIONS. SERIE 1. 1966. irreg. price varies. Agence pour la Securite de la Navigation Aerienne en Afrique et a Madagascar, Direction de l'Exploitation Meteorologique, B.P. 3144, Dakar, Senegal.

551.5 SG ISSN 0084-6015
AGENCE POUR LA SECURITE DE LA NAVIGATION AERIENNE EN AFRIQUE ET A MADAGASCAR. DIRECTION DE L'EXPLOITATION METEOROLOGIQUE. PUBLICATIONS. SERIE 2. 1965. irreg. price varies. Agence pour la Securite de la Navigation Aerienne en Afrique et a Madagascar, Direction de l'Exploitation Meteorologique, B.P. 3144, Dakar, Senegal.

METEOROLOGY

AGRARMETEOROLOGISCHER WOCHENBERICHT FUER NORDRHEIN - WESTFALEN. see *AGRICULTURE*

AGRARMETEOROLOGISCHER WOCHENHINWEIS FUER DAS GEBIET BUNDESREPUBLIK DEUTSCHLAND. see *AGRICULTURE*

551.5 630   NE   ISSN 0168-1923
AGRICULTURAL AND FOREST METEOROLOGY; an international journal. (Text in English, French and German) 1964. 20/yr. fl.2400($1464) (effective 1996). Elsevier Science B.V., P.O. Box 211, 1000 AE Amsterdam, Netherlands. TEL 31-20-4853911. FAX 31-20-4853598. TELEX 18582 ESPA NL. E-mail: nlinfo-f@elsevier.nl; usinfo-f@elsevier.com; forinfo-kyf04035@niftyserve.or.jp; Site addr.: http://www.elsevier.nl/. (Subscr. in U.S. and Canada to: Elsevier Science Inc., Box 882, Madison Sq. Sta., New York, NY 10159-0882. TEL 212-989-5800. FAX 212-633-3990) Ed. W.E. Reifsnyder. adv.; bk.rev.; abstr.; bibl.; charts; illus.; index. (also avail. in microform from UMI; reprint service avail. from SWZ) **Indexed:** Agri.Eng.Abstr., Agroforest.Abstr., Anim.Breed.Abstr., ASCA, Biol.Abstr., Cott.& Trop.Fibr.Abstr., Crop Physiol.Abstr., Curr.Cont., Dairy Sci.Abstr., Ecol.Abstr., Environ.Abstr., Environ.Per.Bibl. (1990-), Excerp.Med., Field Crop Abstr., Forest.Abstr., Forest Prod.Abstr., Geo.Abstr., Helminthol.Abstr., Herb.Abstr., Hort.Abstr., IDA, Ind.Sci.Rev., Int.Abstr.Oper.Res., Irr.& Drain.Abstr., Maize Abstr., Meteor.& Geoastrophys.Abstr., Ornam.Hort., Rev.Plant Path., Rice Abstr., Sci.Cit.Ind., Seed Abstr., Sel.Water Res.Abstr., Soils & Fert., Sorghum & Millets Abstr., Soyabean Abstr., Triticale Abstr., Vet.Bull., VITIS, W.R.C.Inf., Weed Abstr., 03962544dEcol.Sci. **Document type:** academic/scholarly publication.
—BLDSC (0742.890000); Ei; Faxon; Genuine Article; SWETS; UnCover. **CCC.**
Formerly (until 1984): Agricultural Meteorology (ISSN 0002-1571)
Description: Publishes articles and reviews in the interdisciplinary fields of meteorology and climatology applied to agriculture and forestry.
Refereed Serial

551.5   TH   ISSN 0857-2410
AGROMETEOROLOGICAL REPORT. (Text in Thai) 1968. m. free. Ministry of Transport and Communications, Meteorological Department, 4353 Sukhumvit Road, Bangna, Bangkok 10260, Thailand. TEL 399-2322. FAX 393-9409. TELEX 72004 DEPMETE TH. Ed.Bd. circ. 250. **Document type:** government publication.

551.5   XV   ISSN 0352-1818
AGROMETEOROLOSKO POROCILO. (ISSN 0352-180X for 3/m.) (Text in Slovenian) 1955. m. (Dec.-Feb.); 3/m. (Mar.-Nov.) $80 (effective 1992). Hidrometeoroloski Zavod SR Slovenije, Oddelek za Agrometeorologijo, Vojkova ul. 1-b, 61000 Ljubljana, Slovenia. TEL 3861 327 461. FAX 3861-320466. TELEX 31620. Ed. Janko Pristov. abstr. circ. 120.
Description: Textual tabular, graphical and cartographical survey of climatological data, the influence of weather elements on crops and day to day operations of plant growing.

551.63   JA   ISSN 0916-5053
AICHIKEN KISHO GEPPO/AICHI PREFECTURE. MONTHLY REPORT OF METEOROLOGY. (Text in Japanese) 1926. m. Kishocho, Nagoya Chiho Kishodai - Japan Meteorological Agency, Nagoya Local Meteorological Observatory, 2-18, Hiyoricho, Chikusa-ku, Nagoya-shi, Aichi-ken 464, Japan.

551.5   US   ISSN 0002-2616
AIR WEATHER SERVICE OBSERVER. Short title: A W S Observer. 1954. m. qualified personnel only. U.S. Air Force, Air Weather Service, Headquarters AWS-PA, 102 W. Losey St., Rm.105, Scott AFB, IL 62225-5206. TEL 618-256-2065. Ed. Sgt. w. Rhodes. circ. 1,100. (tabloid format)

551.5   US   ISSN 0003-0007
QC851   CODEN: BAMIAT
AMERICAN METEOROLOGICAL SOCIETY. BULLETIN. 1920. m. $80 (foreign $110) (effective 1996). American Meteorological Society, 45 Beacon St., Boston, MA 02108-3693. TEL 617-227-2425. FAX 618-742-8718. Ed. Richard E. Hallgren. adv.; bk.rev.; abstr.; bibl.; charts; illus.; stat.; index. circ. 11,528. (also avail. in microfilm from PMC; back issues avail.) **Indexed:** A.S.& T.Ind., Acid Pre.Dig., Appl.Mech.Rev., Biol.Abstr., Chem.Abstr., Curr.Adv.Ecol.Sci., Curr.Cont., Deep Sea Res.& Oceanogr.Abstr., Environ.Abstr., Excerp.Med., Fluidex, Geo.Abstr., Geol.Abstr., GeoRef, INIS Atomind., INSPEC (1968-), Meteor.& Geoastrophys.Abstr., Ocean.Abstr., Pollut.Abstr., Risk Abstr., Rural Recreat.Tour.Abstr., Sci.Cit.Ind., Sel.Water Res.Abstr., World Agri.Econ.& Rural Sociol.Abstr. **Document type:** bulletin.
—BLDSC (2388.000000); Ei; Faxon; Genuine Article; SWETS; UnCover. **CCC.**
Description: Contains survey articles, professional and membership news, announcements and society activities.
Refereed Serial

551.6   US
AMERICAN METEOROLOGICAL SOCIETY. HISTORICAL MONOGRAPH SERIES. 1963. irreg., latest 1989. price varies. American Meteorological Society, 45 Beacon St., Boston, MA 02108-3693. TEL 617-227-2425. FAX 617-742-8718. Ed. Ronald C. Taylor. **Document type:** monographic series.
Description: Covers the history of weather, weather forecasting, and the science of meteorology from its inception through the present day, with special emphasis on US weather.
Refereed Serial

551.5   US   ISSN 0065-9401
CODEN: MMONAL
AMERICAN METEOROLOGICAL SOCIETY. METEOROLOGICAL MONOGRAPHS. 1947. irreg., latest vol.21, no.47. price varies. American Meteorological Society, 45 Beacon St., Boston, MA 02108-3693. TEL 617-227-2425. FAX 617-742-8718. Ed. Donald R. Johnson. **Indexed:** Biol.Abstr., Chem.Abstr., INSPEC, Meteor.& Geoastrophys.Abstr. **Document type:** monographic series.
—BLDSC (5709.000000). **CCC.**
Description: Collections of scientific papers devoted to individual research topics of concern to meteorologists, oceanographers, and hydrologists.
Refereed Serial

551.5   US   ISSN 8755-9552
AMERICAN WEATHER OBSERVER. 1984. m. $16.95. Belvidere Daily Republican Company, 401 Whitney Blvd., Box 455, Belvidere, IL 61008. TEL 815-544-5665. FAX 815-544-6334. Ed. Steven D. Steinke. adv.; index. circ. 2,000. (tabloid format; back issues avail.) **Document type:** newspaper.
Description: For amateur or professional weather observers, weather enthusiasts, or school weather clubs.

555.1   PH   ISSN 0115-5032
ANG TAGAMASID. (Text in English, Filipino) 1973. bi-m. free. Philippine Atmospheric, Geophysical and Astronomical Services Administration (PAGASA), Public Information and International Affairs Staff, PAGASA Central Office, 1424 Quezon Ave., Quezon City, Philippines. TELEX 42021-PAGASA-PM. Ed. Juanito E. Lucas. circ. 1,000.

551.5   GW   ISSN 0072-4122
QC851   CODEN: ANMTA6
ANNALEN DER METEOROLOGIE. NEUE FOLGE. 1948; N.S. 1963. irreg., no.30, 1994. DM.72. Deutscher Wetterdienst, Bibliothek, Postfach 100465, 63004 Offenbach a.M., Germany. **Indexed:** Deep Sea Res.& Oceanogr.Abstr., Geo.Abstr., Meteor.& Geoastrophys.Abstr. **Document type:** government publication, monographic series.
—CASDDS. **CCC.**

551.6   BD
ANNUAIRE PLUVIOMETRIQUE. a., latest 1990. Institut Geographique du Burundi, Departement de l'Hydrometeorologie, B.P. 34, Gitega, Burundi.

551   JA
ANTARCTIC METEOROLOGICAL DATA. (Text in English) 1963. a. Kishocho - Japan Meteorological Agency, 3-4, Otemachi 1-chome, Chiyoda-ku, Tokyo 100, Japan.

551.5   PO   ISSN 0870-2950
ANUARIO CLIMATOLOGICO. (Since 1977 issued in 3 parts: A: Continente (ISSN 0870-6360); B: Acores (ISSN 0870-6379); C: Madeira (ISSN 0870-6387)) 1947. a. (Part A, Esc.5250; Part B, Esc.2100; Part C, Esc.2100) (effective Jan. 1995). Instituto de Meteorologia, Rua C do Aeroporto, 1700 Lisbon, Portugal. TEL 351-1-8472880. FAX 351-1-802370. TELEX 12742 DIRMET P. stat. circ. 500.

551.5   JA   ISSN 0029-7399
AOMORIKEN KISHO GEPPO/AOMORI PREFECTURE. MONTHLY REPORT OF METEOROLOGY. (Text in Japanese) 1951. m. free. Kishocho, Aomori Chiho Kishodai - Japan Meteorological Agency, Aomori Local Meteorological Observatory, 255 14 Tsukuda, Aomori-shi, Aomori-ken 030, Japan. bk.rev.; charts; stat.; circ. 340 (controlled).

551.5   JA   ISSN 0003-6323
AOMORIKEN NOGYO KISHO JUNPO. (Text in Japanese) 1963. 3/m. free to qualified personnel. Kishodai, Aomori Chiho Kishodai - Japan Meteorological Agency, Aomori Local Meteorological Observatory, 255-14 Tsukuda, Aomori-shi, Aomori-ken 030, Japan. bk.rev.; charts; stat.; circ. 180 (controlled). (processed)

551.63 630   JA
AOMORIKEN NOGYO KISHO SAIGAI SOKUHO/AOMORI PREFECTURE. NEWS OF DISASTER ON AGRICULTURAL METEOROLOGY. (Text in Japanese) 1986. irreg. Kishocho, Aomori Chiho Kishodai - Japan Meteorological Agency, Aomori Local Meteorological Observatory, 255-14, Tsukuda, Aomori-shi, Aomori-ken 030, Japan.

551.6   FR   ISSN 0242-4002
ASSOCIATION NATIONALE D'ETUDE ET DE LUTTE CONTRE LES FLEAUX ATMOSPHERIQUES. RAPPORT DE CAMPAGNE. 1951. a. free. Association Nationale de Lutte Contre les Fleaux Atmospheriques, 52 rue Alfred-Dumeril, 31400 Toulouse, France. TEL 61-52-05-65. FAX 62-26-71-24. bk.rev.; charts; illus.; stat. circ. 1,000. **Indexed:** Meteor.& Geoastrophys.Abstr.
Formerly: Association Nationale de Lutte Contre les Fleaux Atmospheriques. Rapport de Campagne (ISSN 0373-7349); Continues the Rapport sur la Campagne issued by the association under its earlier name: Association d'Etudes des Moyens de Lutte Contre les Fleaux Atmospheriques.
Description: Presents research conducted in the control and relief of natural disasters.

551.5   CN   ISSN 0705-5900
QC851   CODEN: ATOCDA
ATMOSPHERE - OCEAN. (Text in English and French) 1963. q. Can.$30 to members; institutions and non-members Can.$85. Canadian Meteorological and Oceanographic Society - Societe Canadienne de Meteorologie et d'Oceanographie, Ste. 903, 151 Slater St., Ottawa, ON K1P 5H3, Canada. TEL 613-237-3393. FAX 613-238-1677. Eds. C.A. Lin, P.C. Smith. charts; illus.; stat.; index. circ. 700. (processed; back issues avail.) **Indexed:** Deep Sea Res.& Oceanogr.Abstr., Environ.Per.Bibl., Geo.Abstr., Meteor. & Geoastrophys.Abstr., Sel.Water Res.Abstr. **Document type:** academic/scholarly publication.
—BLDSC (1767.117000); Ei; Faxon; Genuine Article; SWETS; UnCover. **CCC.**
Supersedes (with vol. 16, 1978): Atmosphere (ISSN 0004-6973)
Description: Contains scientific articles on all aspects of meteorology, oceanography, hydrology, and relevant notes, correspondence.
Refereed Serial

METEOROLOGY

551.5   NE   ISSN 0169-8095
CODEN: ATREEW
ATMOSPHERIC RESEARCH; clouds - precipitation - aerosols - radiation - weather modification. (Text in English and French) 1963. 16/yr. fl.1740($1061) (effective 1996). Elsevier Science B.V., P.O. Box 211, 1000 AE Amsterdam, Netherlands. TEL 31-20-4853911. FAX 31-20-4853598. TELEX 18582 ESPA NL.
E-mail: nlinfo-f@elsevier.nl; usinfo-f@elsevier.com; forinfo-kyf04035@niftyserve.or.jp; Site addr.: http://www.elsevier.nl/. (Subscr. in U.S. and Canada to: Elsevier Science Inc., Box 882, Madison Sq. Sta., New York, NY 10159-0882. TEL 212-989-5800. FAX 212-633-3990) Eds. J. Dessens, A.W. Hogan. bk.rev.; abstr.; bibl.; charts; illus.; index. circ. 350. **Indexed**: Bull.Signal., Chem.Abstr., Energy Rev., Environ.Abstr., Environ.Per.Bibl. (1987-), Geo.Abstr., GeoRef., INIS Atomind., INSPEC (1986-), Meteor.& Geoastrophys.Abstr., Ocean.Abstr., Phys.Ber., Pollut.Abstr. **Document type**: academic/scholarly publication.
—BLDSC (1767.470000); CASDDS; Ei; Faxon; SWETS; UMI; UnCover. **CCC**.
  Formerly (until 1986): Journal de Recherches Atmospheriques (ISSN 0021-7972)
  Description: Publishes scientific papers dealing with the part of the atmosphere where meteorological events occur.
  Refereed Serial

551.5   AT   ISSN 0067-1312
AUSTRALIA. BUREAU OF METEOROLOGY. BULLETIN. 1908. irreg., no.53, 1995. price varies. Australian Government Publishing Service, G.P.O. Box 84, Canberra, A.C.T., Australia. TEL 61-6-295-4612. FAX 61-6-295-4500. **Indexed**: Meteor.& Geoastrophys.Abstr. **Document type**: government publication, bulletin.
—CCC.

551.5   AT   ISSN 1035-6576
AUSTRALIAN METEOROLOGICAL AND OCEANOGRAPHIC SOCIETY. BULLETIN. 1988. bi-m. Aus.$45 to individuals; institutions Aus.$90. Australian Meteorological and Oceanographic Society, G.P.O. Box 654 E, Melbourne, Vic. 3001, Australia. TEL 61-3-669-4506. FAX 61-3-669-4695. Ed. Allyson Williams. adv. contact: W. Wright. bk.rev. circ. 400. (back issues avail.) **Document type**: bulletin.
  Formerly (until 1991): Australian Meteorological and Oceanographic Society. Newsletter.
  Description: For all readers with an interest in the meteorology or the oceanography of the southern hemisphere.

551.5   AT   ISSN 0004-9743
QC851
AUSTRALIAN METEOROLOGICAL MAGAZINE. 1952. q. Aus.$30 (Asia Aus.$39; N. America Aus.$46.50; Europe Aus.$52). (Australian Bureau of Meteorology) Australian Government Publishing Service, G.P.O. Box 84, Canberra, A.C.T. 2601, Australia. TEL 61-6-295-4411.
FAX 61-6-295-4455. TELEX AA62013. (Co-sponsor: Australian Meteorological and Oceanographic Society) Ed. Mike Manton. abstr.; charts; illus.; index. **Indexed**: Chem.Abstr., Curr.Tit.Ocean, Deep Sea Res.& Oceanogr.Abstr., Geo.Abstr., INSPEC (1984-), Meteor.& Geoastrophys.Abstr., Ocean.Abstr., Pollut.Abstr., Sel.Water Res.Abstr. **Document type**: academic/scholarly publication.
—Faxon; Genuine Article; UnCover. **CCC**.
  Description: Covers meteorology, oceanography, hydrology and related fields with emphasis on the Southern Hemisphere.

551.5 551   AU   ISSN 0067-2351
AUSTRIA. ZENTRALANSTALT FUER METEOROLOGIE UND GEODYNAMIK. JAHRBUCH. 1864. irreg. price varies. Zentralanstalt fuer Meteorologie und Geodynamik, Hohe Warte 38, A-1190 Vienna, Austria. circ. 500. **Indexed**: GeoRef. **Document type**: government publication.

AVALANCHE REVIEW. see *EARTH SCIENCES*

551.5   IO   ISSN 0126-0561
QC925.8 .I5
BADAN METEOROLOGI DAN GEOFISIKA. LAPORAN EVALUASI HUJAN DAN PERKIRAAN HUJAN. 1976. m. Meteorological and Geophysical Institute, Jalan Arief Rakhman Hakim 3, Jakarta, Indonesia.
  Formerly: Pusat Meteorologi dan Geofisika. Laporan Evaluasi Hujan dan Perkiraan Hujan.

551.63   JA
BAIU TO TAIFU NO YOSO/BAIU AND TYPHOON PREDICTION. (Text in Japanese) a. Kishocho, Fukuoka Kanku Kishodai - Japan Meteorological Agency, Fukuoka District Meteorological Observatory, 2-36, Ohori 1-chome, Chuo-ku, Fukuoka-shi, Fukuoka-ken 810, Japan.

551.63   US   ISSN 0749-3584
BIBLE OF WEATHER FORECASTING. 1984. bi-m. $28. Singer Press, 1540 Rollins Dr., Box 63302, Los Angeles, CA 90063. TEL 213-263-2640. Ed. Oscar Singer; Pub. Oscar Singer. bk.rev. circ. 150. **Document type**: academic/scholarly publication.
  Formerly: Lock.

574   CN
BIOMETEOROLOGY; proceedings of the International Congress of Biometeorology. triennial, 13th, 1993, Calgary. Can.$95. International Society of Biometeorology, c/o N.N. Barthakur, Dept. of Natural Resource Sciences, Universite McGill-Campus MacDonald, 21 111 Lakeshore Dr., Ste. Anne de Bellevue, PQ H9X 3V9, Canada. circ. 1,200. **Indexed**: Biol.Abstr., Curr.Cont. **Document type**: proceedings.
  Formerly: International Biometeorology Congress. Summaries and Reports Presented to the Congress (ISSN 0074-2082)

574   CN   ISSN 1022-9205
BIOMETEOROLOGY BULLETIN. irreg. membership. International Society of Biometeorology, c/o N.N. Barthakur, Ed., Dept. of Natural Resource Science, Universite McGill-MacDonald Campus, 21,111 Lakeshore Rd., Ste. Anne de Bellevue, PQ H9X 3V9, Canada. circ. controlled.

551.5   CN   ISSN 0067-8902
QH543   CODEN: BMTLAL
BIOMETEOROLOGY PROCEEDINGS. Represents: International Biometeorological Congress. Proceedings. triennial, 13th, 1993, Calgary. price varies. International Society of Biometeorology, c/o Prof. N.N. Barthakur, McGill University, Campus MacDonald, Lakeshore Rd. 21, Ste. Anne de Bellevue, PQ H9X 3V9, Canada. **Indexed**: Biol.Abstr., Chem.Abstr. **Document type**: proceedings.

551.5   PO   ISSN 0870-4740
BOLETIM ACTINOMETRICO DE PORTUGAL. 1955. m. Esc.1900 (effective Jan. 1993). Instituto de Meteorologia, Rua C do Aeroporto, 1700 Lisbon, Portugal. TEL 351-1-8472880.
FAX 351-1-802370. TELEX 12742 DIRMET P. stat. **Document type**: bulletin.
  Formerly: Boletim Actinometrico (ISSN 0477-7166)
  Description: Information on global and diffuse radiation.

551.5   BL   ISSN 0067-9585
BOLETIM CLIMATOLOGICO. 1960. irreg., no.5, 1984. price varies or avail. on exchange. Universidade de Sao Paulo, Instituto Oceanografico, Cidade Universitaria, Butanta, 05508 Sao Paulo, SP, Brazil. circ. 100.

551.5   PO   ISSN 0870-4686
BOLETIM METEOROLOGICO. 1948. d. Esc.51870. Instituto de Meteorologia, Rua C do Aeroporto, 1700 Lisbon, Portugal. TEL 351-1-8472880.
FAX 351-1-802370. TELEX 12742 DIRMET P. charts; stat. **Document type**: bulletin.
  Description: Charts of isobaric surfaces.

551.5 630   PO   ISSN 0870-4694
BOLETIM METEOROLOGICO PARA A AGRICULTURA. 1951-1958; resumed. 3/m. Esc.7120. Instituto de Meteorologia, Rua C do Aeroporto, 1700 Lisbon, Portugal. TEL 351-1-8472880.
FAX 351-1-802370. TELEX 12742 DIRMET P. charts; illus.; stat. **Document type**: bulletin.
  Description: Meteorological information and its impact on agriculture.

551.5   GW   ISSN 0006-7156
BONNER METEOROLOGISCHE ABHANDLUNGEN. (Text in English and German) 1962. irreg. price varies. (Universitaet Bonn, Meteorologisches Institut) Ferd. Duemmlers Verlag, Kaiserstr. 31-37, 53113 Bonn, Germany. (Subscr. to: Postfach 1480, 53004 Bonn, Germany) Ed. Michael Hantel. abstr.; charts; illus. **Indexed**: Geo.Abstr., Meteor.& Geoastrophys.Abstr.

551.5 574   NE   ISSN 0006-8314
QC880   CODEN: BLMEBR
BOUNDARY-LAYER METEOROLOGY; an international journal of physical and biological processes in the atmospheric boundary layer. (Text in English) 1970. 20/yr. fl.2510 to institutions; $1531 to institutions in U.S. (effective 1996). Kluwer Academic Publishers, Postbus 17, 3300 AA Dordrecht, Netherlands. TEL 31-78-392392.
FAX 31-78-392254. TELEX 29245 KAPG NL. (Dist. by: Kluwer Academic Publishers Group, P.O. Box 322, 3300 AH Dordrecht, Netherlands. TEL 31-78-392392. FAX 31-78-546474; N. America dist. addr.: Box 358, Accord Sta., Hingham, MA 02018-0358. TEL 617-871-6600. FAX 617-871-6528) Ed. R.E. Munn. adv.; bk.rev.; illus.; index. (also avail. in microform from UMI; reprint service avail. from SWZ) **Indexed**: Acid Pre.Dig., Appl.Mech.Rev., Biol.Abstr., Curr.Adv.Ecol.Sci., Curr.Cont., Curr.Tit.Ocean, Deep Sea Res.& Oceanogr.Abstr., Energy Rev., Environ.Per.Bibl. (1979-), Excerpt.Med., Fluidex, Forest.Abstr., Geo.Abstr., GeoRef., Herb.Abstr., Ind.Sci.Rev., INSPEC (1970-), Int.Aerosp.Abstr., Meteor.& Geoastrophys.Abstr., Ocean.Abstr., Phys.Ber., Pollut.Abstr., Sci.Cit.Ind., Sel.Water Res.Abstr., Soils & Fert. **Document type**: academic/scholarly publication.
—BLDSC (2264.270000); Ei; Faxon; Genuine Article; SWETS; UMI; UnCover. **CCC**.
  Description: Publishes papers on the physical and biological processes occurring in the lowest 1000 meters of the Earth's atmosphere.
  Refereed Serial

551.579   CN   ISSN 0045-303X
QC929.S7
BRITISH COLUMBIA SNOW SURVEY BULLETIN. 1940. 6/yr. free. Ministry of the Environment, Water Investigation Branch, Parliament Bldgs., Victoria, B.C. V8V 1X5, Canada. TEL 604-387-5162. Ed. C.H. Coulson. circ. 1,200.

332.6   US   ISSN 0896-3045
BROWNING NEWSLETTER. vol.5, 1981. m. $225. Fraser Management Associates, Inc., 309 S. Willard St., Box 494, Burlington, VT 05402.
TEL 802-658-0322. FAX 802-658-0260. Ed. Evelyn Browning Garriss. charts; stat.
  Description: Based on the proposition that the Earth's climate has entered a period of sharp change and that this change in climate is the driving force behind human history. Extensive studies of physical data and phenomena (named for Dr. Iben Browning, a climatologist).

551.6   JA   ISSN 0913-4190
GB2401
BULLETIN OF GLACIER RESEARCH.* (Text in English) 1987. a. Nihon Seppyo Gakkai - Japanese Society of Snow and Ice, Rm.207, Belvedere - Kudan, Fujimi 2-15-5, Chiyoda-ku, Tokyo 102, Japan.

551.5   US   ISSN 1053-1106
QD181.C1   CODEN: CDCOEX
C D I A C COMMUNICATIONS. 3/yr. free. (U.S. Department of Energy) Carbon Dioxide Information Analysis Center, Oak Ridge National Laboratory, Box 2008, (MS-6335), Oak Ridge, TN 37831-6335. TEL 615-574-0390. FAX 615-574-2232. Ed. Frederick M. O'Hara, Jr. bk.rev.; charts; illus. circ. 10,000. **Document type**: newsletter, government publication.
  Description: Communicates information relevant to research and information management in global environmental change, including climate change and global warming.

551.6   CN   ISSN 1195-8898
C M O S BULLETIN S C M O. (Text in English, occasionally French) 1972. bi-m. Can.$45. Canadian Meteorological & Oceanographic Society - Societe Canadienne de Meteorologie et d'Oceanographie, Ste. 903, 151 Slater St., Ottawa, ON K1P 5H3, Canada. TEL 613-237-3393. FAX 613-238-1677. Ed. J.P. Blanchet. adv.; bk.rev.; charts; illus. circ. 860. (back issues avail.) **Document type**: newsletter.
  Supersedes (in 1994): Canadian Meteorological and Oceanographic Society. Newsletter (ISSN 0827-0384)
  Description: News of the activities of the Society and of meteorology and oceanography in Canada and around the world. Also includes technical articles and views on applied climatology, operational meteorology and oceanography.

METEOROLOGY

CALIFORNIA. AGRICULTURAL STATISTICS SERVICE. CROP WEATHER REPORT. see *AGRICULTURE — Abstracting, Bibliographies, Statistics*

551.5   CN   ISSN 0705-5919
CANADIAN METEOROLOGICAL AND OCEANOGRAPHIC SOCIETY. ANNUAL CONGRESS. 1967. a. Can.$25 (typically set in Jun.). Canadian Meteorological and Oceanographic Society - Societe Canadienne de Meteorologie et d'Oceanographie, Ste. 903, 151 Slater St., Ottawa, ON K1P 5H3, Canada. TEL 613-237-3393. FAX 613-238-1677. adv.; circ. 850 (controlled). (back issues avail.) **Indexed:** Meteor.& Geoastrophys.Abstr. **Document type:** academic/scholarly publication.
—BLDSC (1083.085000).
 Formerly: Canadian Meteorological Society. Annual Congress (ISSN 0068-9254)
 Description: Program for, and abstracts of, papers on all aspects of meteorology and oceanography, presented at yearly CMOS congresses.

551.6   CN   ISSN 1181-6163
CANADIAN METEOROLOGICAL AND OCEANOGRAPHIC SOCIETY. ANNUAL REVIEW (YEAR). (Text in English, French) 1983. a. free to members. Canadian Meteorological and Oceanographic Society - Societe Canadienne de Meteorologie et d'Oceanographie, Ste. 903, 151 Slater St., Ottawa, ON K1P 5H3, Canada. TEL 613-237-3393. FAX 613-238-1677. Ed. E.J. Truhlar. adv. circ. 860. (back issues avail.) **Document type:** academic/scholarly publication.
 Description: Reports on the Society's activities including budget, financial reports and auditor's reports for the previous fiscal period.

551.5 613.1   US
CARBON DIOXIDE AND CLIMATE. a. free. U.S. Department of Energy, Carbon Dioxide Research Program, Washington, DC 20585. (Dist. by: U.S. National Technical Information Service, 5285 Port Royal Rd., Springfield, VA 22161. TEL 703-487-4630. FAX 703-321-8547) **Document type:** government publication, newsletter.

551.65   JA   ISSN 0009-3467
CHIBAKEN KISHO GEPPO/CHIBA PREFECTURE. MONTHLY REPORT OF METEOROLOGY. (Text in Japanese) 1933. m. 5200 Yen. Kishocho, Choshi Chiho Kishodai - Japan Meteorological Agency, Choshi Local Meteorological Observatory, 2-6431, Kawaguchicho, Choshi-shi, Chiba-ken 288, Japan. charts; stat. (processed)

551.5   US   ISSN 0891-3862
QC851   CODEN: TKHSDX
CHINESE JOURNAL OF ATMOSPHERIC SCIENCES. English translation of: Daqi Kexue (CC ISSN 0254-0002) 1987. q. $505 (effective 1996). (Academia Sinica (Chinese Academy of Sciences), Institute of Atmospheric Physics, CC - Zhongguo Kexueyuan Daqi Wuli Yanjiusuo) Allerton Press, Inc., 150 Fifth Ave., New York, NY 10011. TEL 212-924-3950. FAX 212-463-9684. Ed. Zhou Xiaoping. **Document type:** academic/scholarly publication.
 Description: Covers meteorological research in mainland China, including climate changes and prediction, and acid rain.
 Refereed Serial

551.6 537   JA
CHUGOKU CHIHO DENRYOKU KISHO GAIHO/CHUGOKU DISTRICT. REPORT OF THE POWER AND WEATHER. (Text in Japanese) 1942. a. Kishocho, Hiroshima Chiho Kishodai - Japan Meteorological Agency, Hiroshima Local Meteorological Observatory, 6-30, Kamihatchobori, Naka-ku, Hiroshima-shi, Hiroshima-ken 730, Japan.

551.63 630   JA   ISSN 0917-7868
CHUGOKU SHIKOKU NO NOGYO KISHO/AGRICULTURAL METEOROLOGY OF CHUGOKU AND SHIKOKU. (Text in Japanese) 1988. a. 1800 Yen. Nihon Nogyo Kisho Gakkai, Chugoku Shikoku Shibu - Society of Agricultural Meteorology of Japan, Chugoku-Shikoku Chapter, Ehime Daigaku Nogakubu, 5-7, Tarumicho 3-chome, Matsuyama-shi, Ehime-ken 790, Japan. TEL 086-434-1239. FAX 086-421-0699. E-mail: stanakam@rib.okayama-u.ac.jp. Ed. Yoshitaka Fukuoka. **Document type:** bulletin.
 Refereed Serial

CIEL ET TERRE. see *ASTRONOMY*

551.6   US   ISSN 1071-3271
CLIMATE ALERT. 1988. 6/yr. $95. Climate Institute, 324 Fourth St., N.E., Washington, DC 20002. TEL 202-547-0104. FAX 202-547-0111. Ed. Nancy Wilson. circ. 1,500 (paid). **Document type:** newsletter.
 Description: International publication on climate change: sea level rise, drought, stratospheric ozone depletion. Emphasis on developing countries.

551.5 613.1   CN   ISSN 0835-3980
CLIMATE CHANGE DIGEST. 1984. irreg. free. Canadian Climate Centre, 4905 Dufferin St., Downsview, ON M3H 5T4, Canada. **Document type:** monographic series.

551.6   GW   ISSN 0930-7575
QC981.7.D94   CODEN: CLDYEM
CLIMATE DYNAMICS; observational, theoretical and computational research on the climate system. (Text in English) 1986. 8/yr. DM.1450($1053) (effective 1996). Springer-Verlag, Heidelberger Platz 3, 14197 Berlin, Germany. TEL 030-8207-0. FAX 030-8214091. E-mail: orders@springer.de. (Subscr. in N. America to: Springer-Verlag New York, Inc., 44 Hartz Way, Secaucus, NJ 07096-2491. TEL 201-348-4033. FAX 201-348-4505) Ed.Bd. **Indexed:** Geo.Abstr., Geol.Abstr. **Document type:** academic/scholarly publication.
—BLDSC (3279.108000); Ei; Faxon; Genuine Article; SWETS; UMI; UnCover. **CCC.**
 Description: Focuses on the dynamics of the entire climate system, including atmosphere, ocean, cryosphere, surface biomass and lithosphere.

551.6   UK   ISSN 0140-458X
CLIMATE MONITOR. vol.5, 1976. 5/yr. £14 to individuals; institutions £20. University of East Anglia, Climatic Research Unit, School of Environmental Sciences, Norwich NR4 7TJ, England. TEL 01603-592088. FAX 01603-507784. Ed. Don MacKinlay. adv. contact: S. Boland. circ. 250. **Indexed:** Deep Sea Res.& Oceanogr.Abstr., Meteor.& Geoastrophys.Abstr. **Document type:** academic/scholarly publication.
—BLDSC (3279.150000).
 Description: Contains summaries of global climatic conditions and articles of general interest on climatology.

551.6   GW   ISSN 0936-577X
QC851   CODEN: CLREEW
CLIMATE RESEARCH. 1990. 6/yr. (2 vols., 3 nos./vol.). DM.570 (effective 1996). Inter-Research, Nordbuente 23, 21385 Oldendorf, Germany. TEL 04132-7127. FAX 04132-8883. E-mail: 100327.535@compuserve.com. **Indexed:** Ecol.Abstr., Environ.Abstr., Environ.Per.Bibl. (1990-), Geo.Abstr., IDA. **Document type:** academic/scholarly publication.
—BLDSC (3279.180000); UnCover.

551.5   US
CLIMATE WATCH. 1992. 4/yr. Global Climate Coalition, 1331 Pennsylvania Ave., N.W., Ste. 1500, North Tower, Washington, DC 20004-1703. **Document type:** newsletter.

551.5   NE   ISSN 0165-0009
QC981.8.C5   CODEN: CLCHDX
CLIMATIC CHANGE; an interdisciplinary, international journal devoted to the description, causes and implications of climatic change. (Text in English) 1977. m. fl.1584 to institutions; $967 to institutions in U.S. (effective 1996). Kluwer Academic Publishers, P.O. Box 17, 3300 AA Dordrecht, Netherlands. TEL 31-78-392392. FAX 31-78-392254. TELEX 29245 KAPG NL. E-mail: SERVICES@WKAP.NL. (Dist. by: Kluwer Academic Publishers Group, P.O. Box 322, 3300 AH Dordrecht, Netherlands. TEL 31-78-392392. FAX 31-78-546474; N. America dist. addr.: Box 358, Accord Sta., Hingham, MA 02018-0358. TEL 617-871-6600. FAX 617-871-6528) Ed. Stephen H. Schneider. adv.; bk.rev.; illus.; index. (also avail. in microform from UMI; reprint service avail. from SWZ) **Indexed:** Astron.& Astrophys.Abstr., Biol.Abstr., Bull.Signal., Chem.Abstr., Curr.Adv.Ecol.Sci., Curr.Cont., Deep Sea Res.& Oceanogr.Abstr., Energy Ind., Energy Info.Abstr., Energy Rev., Eng.Ind., Environ.Abstr., Environ.Abstr., Environ.Ind., Environ.Per.Bibl. (1978-), Excerp.Med., Field Crop Abstr., Geo.Abstr., GeoRef., Herb.Abstr., Ind.Sci.Rev., INSPEC (1977-), Meteor.& Geoastrophys.Abstr., Sci.Cit.Ind., Soils & Fert. **Document type:** academic/scholarly publication.
—BLDSC (3279.250000); CASDDS; CIS; Ei; Faxon; Genuine Article; SWETS; UMI; UnCover. **CCC**.
 Refereed Serial

551.6   JA
CLIMATIC TABLE OF JAPAN. (Text in Japanese) 1918. every 10 yrs. 28000 Yen. (Japan Meteorological Agency) Japan Weather Association, 2-9-2, Kanda-nishikicho, Chiyoda-ku, Tokyo 101, Japan. TEL 81-3-3295-1525. FAX 81-3-3295-1097. circ. 1,472.

551.5   US   ISSN 0009-8949
CLIMATOLOGICAL DATA. (Issued separately in: 42 states, 6 New England states, Maryland-Delaware, Puerto Rico, Virgin Islands and Pacific Islands) 1897. m. (plus a. update). $30 per region. U.S. National Climatic Data Center, National Oceanic and Atmospheric Administration, U.S. Department of Commerce, Federal Bldg., Rm. 120, 151 Patton Ave., Asheville, NC 28801-5001. TEL 704-271-4756. FAX 704-271-4876. TELEX 6502643731. E-mail: orders@ncdc.noaa.gov. circ. 23,000. (also avail. in microfiche; magnetic tape; back issues avail.) **Indexed:** Abstr.Bull.Inst.Pap.Chem. **Document type:** government publication.

551.5   IO   ISSN 0009-8957
CLIMATOLOGICAL DATA FOR JAKARTA OBSERVATORY. (Text in English) 1956. a. exchange basis. Meteorological and Geophysical Institute - Badan Meteorologi dan Geofisika, Jalan Arief Rakhman Hakim 3, Jakarta, Indonesia.

551.6   JA   ISSN 0388-0206
CLIMATOLOGICAL NOTES. (Text in English) 1969. irreg. Tsukuba Daigaku, Chikyu Kagakukei - University of Tsukuba, Institute of Geoscience, 1-1, Tennodai 1-chome, Tsukuba-shi, Ibaraki-ken 305, Japan.
—BLDSC (3284.560000).

551.51   AT   ISSN 0159-0219
QC869.4.A8
COMMONWEALTH SCIENTIFIC AND INDUSTRIAL RESEARCH ORGANIZATION. DIVISION OF ATMOSPHERIC RESEARCH. RESEARCH REPORT. biennial. Aus.$3 free. C.S.I.R.O., Division of Atmospheric Research, Station St., Aspendale, Vic. 3195, Australia. TEL 61-3-5867666. FAX 61-3-5867600. E-mail: chief@dar.csiro.au. illus.
 Formerly: Commonwealth Scientific and Industrial Research Organization. Division of Atmospheric Physics. Annual Report (ISSN 0310-1908)

551.51   AT   ISSN 1038-2186
COMMONWEALTH SCIENTIFIC AND INDUSTRIAL RESEARCH ORGANIZATION. DIVISION OF ATMOSPHERIC RESEARCH. TECHNICAL PAPER. 1983. irreg. (approx. 1-3/yr.) price varies. C.S.I.R.O., Division of Atmospheric Research, Station St., Aspendale, Vic. 3195, Australia. TEL 61-3-5867666. FAX 61-3-5867600. E-mail: chief@dar.csiro.au. circ. 750. **Indexed:** Biol.Abstr., Deep Sea Res.& Oceanogr.Abstr., Meteor.& Geoastrophys.Abstr.
 Formerly: Commonwealth Scientific and Industrial Research Organization. Division of Atmospheric Physics. Technical Paper.

METEOROLOGY 4691

551.5   UN   ISSN 0250-9288
COMPOSITION OF THE W M O. q. price varies. World Meteorological Organization, 41 av. Giuseppe Motta, CH-1211 Geneva 2, Switzerland. TEL 730-8111. (Dist. in U.S. by: American Meteorogical Society, 45 Beacon St., Boston, MA 02108. TEL 617-227-2425) **Document type:** directory.
Description: Lists members of the WMO and the composition of W.M.O. constituent bodies, panels, committees and working groups.

551.5   GW   ISSN 0005-8173
CODEN: BPYAAY
CONTRIBUTIONS TO ATMOSPHERIC PHYSICS/BEITRAEGE ZUR PHYSIK DER ATMOSPHAERE. (Text in English; summaries in English, French and German) 1957. q. DM.312($212) (effective 1996). Friedr. Vieweg und Sohn Verlagsgesellschaft mbH, Postfach 1546, 65005 Wiesbaden, Germany. TEL 0611-534389. FAX 0611-534430. Ed. D. Etling. bk.rev.; bibl.; charts; illus. **Indexed:** Chem.Abstr., Deep Sea Res.& Oceanogr.Abstr., Geo.Abstr., INIS Atomind., INSPEC, Int.Aerosp.Abstr., Meteor.& Geoastrophys.Abstr., Phys.Ber. **Document type:** academic/scholarly publication.
—BLDSC (3458.265000); SWETS; UnCover. CCC.
Description: Presents information on all atmospheric processes, with a major emphasis on those parts of the atmosphere where meteorological events occur.

551.5 630   CU   ISSN 0138-6190
CUBA. MINISTERIO DE LA AGRICULTURA. CENTRO DE INFORMACION Y DOCUMENTACION AGROPECUARIO. NOTICIERO AGROPECUARIO. SUPLEMENTO AGROMETEOROLOGICO. irreg. Ministerio de la Agricultura, Centro de Informacion y Documentacion Agropecuario, Calle 11 No. 1057, Vedado, Havana, Cuba. **Document type:** government publication.

551.5 370   US
CURRICULA IN THE ATMOSPHERIC, OCEANIC, HYDROLOGIC AND RELATED SCIENCES. 1963. biennial. $40. American Meteorological Society, 45 Beacon St., Boston, MA 02108. TEL 617-227-2425. FAX 617-742-8718. (Co-sponsor: University Corporation for Atmospheric Research) **Document type:** monographic series.
Former titles: Curricula in the Atmospheric, Oceanic and Related Sciences; Curricula in the Atmospheric and Oceanographic Sciences.
Description: Contains description of the curricula in atmospheric, oceanic and related sciences at the major colleges and universities in the U.S., Canada and Puerto Rico.

D M I NEWS. (Danish Maritime Institute) see TRANSPORTATION — Ships And Shipping

551.5   US
D O E RESEARCH SUMMARY. 1992. irreg. (10-12/yr.). free. (U.S. Department of Energy) Carbon Dioxide Information Analysis Center, Oak Ridge National Laboratory, Box 2008 (MS-6335), Oak Ridge, TN 37831-6335. TEL 615-574-0390. FAX 615-574-2232. E-mail: CDIAC@ornl.gov. Ed. Robert M. Cushman. charts; illus. **Document type:** newsletter, government publication.
Description: Each issue provides a 4-page description of an ongoing U.S. Department of Energy research project.

DAIKIKYU SHINPOJUMU. see ASTRONOMY

551.5   US
DAILY WEATHER MAPS (WEEKLY SERIES). 1967. w. $60. U.S. National Climatic Data Center, National Oceanic and Atmospheric Administration, U.S. Department of Commerce, Federal Bldg., Rm. 120, 151 Patton Ave., Asheville, NC 28801-5001. TEL 704-271-4756. FAX 704-271-4876. illus. circ. 3,400. **Document type:** government publication.

551.5   CC   ISSN 0254-0002
QC851   CODEN: TKHSDX
DAQI KEXUE/SCIENTIA ATMOSPHERICA SINICA. English translation: Chinese Journal of Atmospheric Sciences (US ISSN 0891-3862) (Text in Chinese; summaries in English) 1976. q. $81.80. (Chinese Academy of Sciences, Institute of Atmospheric Physics) Science Press, Marketing and Sales Department, 16 Donghuangchenggen North St., Beijing 100717, People's Republic of China. TEL 4010642. FAX 4019810. adv. circ. 6,000. **Indexed:** Chem.Abstr., INSPEC (1978-), Math.R., Meteor.& Geoastrophys.Abstr.
—BLDSC (8169.600000); CASDDS; Faxon; UnCover. CCC.
Description: Covers meteorological research in mainland China, including weather modification and prediction, atmospheric turbulence and diffusion, climatology, and acid rain.
Refereed Serial

551.5   IO   ISSN 0303-1969
DATA-DATA IKLIM DI INDONESIA. (Text in English and Indonesian) 1971. a. Meteorological and Geophysical Institute - Badan Meteorologi dan Geofisika, Jalan Arif Rachman Hakim 3, Jakarta, Indonesia.

551.6 537   JA   ISSN 0286-0937
DENRYOKU TO KISHO/POWER AND WEATHER COORDINATING COMMITTEE. ANNUAL REPORT. (Text in Japanese) 1953. biennial. 3090 Yen. Denryoku Kisho Renrakukai - Power and Weather Coordination Committee, Nihon Kisho Kyokai, Nanbu Bldg., 2-7 Nishiki-cho, Kanda, Chiyoda-ku, Tokyo 101, Japan. TEL 81-3-3295-1521. FAX 81-3-3295-7835.
Refereed Serial

551.5   GW   ISSN 0072-4130
QC857.G3
DEUTSCHER WETTERDIENST. BERICHTE. 1953. irreg., no.193, 1995. price varies. Deutscher Wetterdienst, Bibliothek, Postfach 100465, 63004 Offenbach a.M., Germany. **Indexed:** Deep Sea Res.& Oceanogr.Abstr. **Document type:** government publication, monographic series.

551.5   GW   ISSN 0433-8251
QC989
DEUTSCHER WETTERDIENST. JAHRESBERICHT. 1953. a. DM.15. Deutscher Wetterdienst, Bibliothek, Postfach 100465, 63004 Offenbach a.M., Germany. TEL 069-80622271. FAX 069-80622486. circ. 1,000. **Document type:** government publication.

551.65   GW   ISSN 0435-7965
DEUTSCHER WETTERDIENST. MONATLICHER WITTERUNGSBERICHT. (Includes "Jahresuebersicht") 1953. m. DM.100. Deutscher Wetterdienst, Bibliothek, Postfach 100465, 63004 Offenbach a.M., Germany. TEL 069-80622225. FAX 069-80622486. **Document type:** government publication.

551.5   GW   ISSN 0072-1603
DEUTSCHER WETTERDIENST. SEEWETTERAMT. EINZELVEROEFFENTLICHUNGEN. 1953. irreg., no.117, 1990. price varies. Deutscher Wetterdienst, Seewetteramt, Postfach 301190, 20304 Hamburg, Germany. bk.rev. circ. 250. **Indexed:** Meteor.& Geoastrophys.Abstr. **Document type:** monographic series.
Description: Different meteorological topics, mainly on the marine climatological sector.

551.63   GW   ISSN 0724-7125
QC989.G3
DEUTSCHES METEOROLOGISCHES JAHRBUCH, BUNDESREPUBLIK DEUTSCHLAND. 1953. a. DM.300. Deutscher Wetterdienst, Bibliothek, Postfach 100465, 63004 Offenbach a.M., Germany. TEL 069-80622225. FAX 069-80622486. **Document type:** government publication.

551.5   NE   ISSN 0167-5117
CODEN: DASCDW
DEVELOPMENTS IN ATMOSPHERIC SCIENCE. (Text in English) 1974. irreg., vol.20, 1992. price varies. Elsevier Science B.V., Books Division, P.O. Box 211, 1000 AE Amsterdam, Netherlands. TEL 31-20-4853911. FAX 31-20-4853705. TELEX 18582 ESPA NL. E-mail: nlinfo-f@elsevier.nl; usinfo-f@elsevier.com; forinfo-kyf04035@niftyserve.or.jp; Site addr.: http://www.elsevier.nl/. (Subscr. in U.S. and Canada to: Elsevier Science Inc., Box 882, Madison Sq. Sta., New York, NY 10159. TEL 212-989-5800) (back issues avail.) **Indexed:** INSPEC. **Document type:** monographic series.
—BLDSC (3579.065000); CASDDS; Faxon.
Refereed Serial

DISASTERS; the journal of disaster relief and management. see EARTH SCIENCES — Geophysics

551.5 551.46   NE   ISSN 0377-0265
GC190.2   CODEN: DAOCDC
DYNAMICS OF ATMOSPHERES AND OCEANS; planetary fluids, climatic and biogeochemical systems. (Text mainly in English; occasionally French and German) 1977. 8/yr. fl.1040($634) (effective 1996). Elsevier Science B.V., P.O. Box 211, 1000 AE Amsterdam, Netherlands. TEL 31-20-4853911. FAX 31-20-4853598. TELEX 18582 ESPA NL. E-mail: nlinfo-f@elsevier.nl; usinfo-f@elsevier.com; forinfo-kyf04035@niftyserve.or.jp; Site addr.: http://www.elsevier.nl/. (Subscr. in U.S. and Canada to: Elsevier Science Inc., Box 882, Madison Sq. Sta., New York, NY 10159-0882. TEL 212-989-5800. FAX 212-633-3990) Ed. A.R. Robinson. adv.; bk.rev. (also avail. in microform from UMI; reprint service avail. from SWZ) **Indexed:** Appl.Mech.Rev., Curr.Cont., Deep Sea Res.& Oceanogr.Abstr., Environ.Abstr., Environ.Per.Bibl. (1991-), Fluidex, Geo.Abstr., Ind.Sci.Rev., INSPEC, Mar.Sci.Cont.Tab., Meteor.& Geoastrophys.Abstr., Ocean.Abstr., Phys.Ber., Sci.Cit.Ind. **Document type:** academic/scholarly publication.
—BLDSC (3637.143300); Faxon; Genuine Article; SWETS; UnCover. CCC.
Description: Publishes theoretical, numerical, observational and laboratory studies on the fluid dynamics of atmospheres and oceans and their interactions, on related basic dynamical processes, and on climatic and biogeochemical problems in which fluid dynamics play an essential role.
Refereed Serial

551.5   EC
ECUADOR. INSTITUTO NACIONAL DE METEOROLOGIA E HIDROLOGIA. ANUARIO METEOROLOGICO. 1959. a. exchange basis. Instituto Nacional de Meteorologia e Hidrologia, Paris 270 y Gaspar de Villarroel, Quito, Ecuador. index. **Document type:** government publication.
Supersedes: Ecuador. Servicio Nacional de Meteorologia e Hidrologia. Anuario Meteorologico (ISSN 0070-8941)

551.6   EC
ECUADOR. INSTITUTO NACIONAL DE METEOROLOGIA E HIDROLOGIA. BOLETIN CLIMATOLOGICO. 1962. m. Instituto Nacional de Meteorologia e Hidrologia, Paris 270 y Gaspar de Villarroel, Quito, Ecuador. **Document type:** government publication, bulletin.
Supersedes: Ecuador. Servicio Nacional de Meteorologia e Hidrologia. Boletin Climatologico.

551.5   UA
EGYPT. METEOROLOGICAL AUTHORITY. ANNUAL METEOROLOGICAL REPORT. a. $1.50. Meteorological Authority, Kubri-el-Qubbeh, Cairo, Egypt.

551.5   UA
EGYPT. METEOROLOGICAL AUTHORITY. METEOROLOGICAL RESEARCH BULLETIN. (Text in English; summaries in Arabic) 1969. s-a. $4.50. Meteorological Authority, Koubri-el-Qubbeh, Cairo, Egypt. charts.

550   UA
EGYPT. METEOROLOGICAL AUTHORITY. MONTHLY WEATHER REPORT. (Text in English) 1909. m. $18. Meteorological Authority, Kubri-el-Qubbeh, Cairo, Egypt. charts; stat.

METEOROLOGY

551   JA   ISSN 0916-5061
EHIMEKEN KISHO GEPPO/EHIME PREFECTURE. MONTHLY REPORT OF METEOROLOGY. (Text in Japanese) 1903. m. Kishocho, Matsuyama Chiho Kishodai - Japan Meteorological Agency, Matsuyama Local Meteorological Observatory, 102, Kitamochidacho, Matsuyama-shi, Ehime-ken 790, Japan.

551.5 318   PN
ESTADISTICA PANAMENA. SITUACION FISICA. SECCION 121. METEOROLOGIA. 1952. a. Bl.0.75 (foreign Bl.2) (effective 1995). Direccion de Estadistica y Censo, Contraloria General, Apartado 5213, Panama 5, Panama. FAX 507-69-7494. circ. 500. **Document type:** government publication, bulletin.
Former titles: Estadistica Panamena. Situacion Fisica. Seccion 121. Clima - Meteorologia (ISSN 0378-6757); Estadistica Panamena. Serie L. Meteorologia (ISSN 0078-8953).
Description: Offers a complete list of meteorological stations in Panama. Presents data on rainfall, temperature, humidity, atmospheric pressure, wind, solar radiation and other data.

551.65   GW   ISSN 0341-2970
EUROPAEISCHER WETTERBERICHT. 1976. d. DM.456. Deutscher Wetterdienst, Bibliothek, Postfach 100465, 63004 Offenbach a.M., Germany. charts; stat. **Document type:** government publication.
Formerly (1876-1975): Taeglicher Wetterbericht (ISSN 0039-8926)

551.5 614.7   FI   ISSN 0782-6079
FINNISH METEOROLOGICAL INSTITUTE. REPORTS. (Text in various languages) 1986. irreg. Ilmatieteen Laitos, P.O. Box 503, SF-0101 Helsinki, Finland. E-mail: kirjasto@fmi.fi. **Document type:** government publication.

550   KR   ISSN 0367-1631
QC882   CODEN: FADSAO
FIZIKA AERODISPERSNYKH SISTEM. (Text in Russian; summaries in English) 1969. irreg. Izdatel'stvo Kievskii Universitet, Bul'var Tarasa Shevchenko, 14, Kiev, Ukraine. TEL 23-62-93. (Dist. by: Mezhdunarodnaya Kniga, ul. Dimitrova D.39, 113095 Moscow, Russia) Ed. D.J. Polyschuk. illus. **Indexed:** Chem.Abstr.
—CASDDS.

550   RU
FIZIKA NIZHNEI ATMOSFERY. (Subseries of: Institut Eksperimental'noi Meteorologii. Trudy) 1972. irreg. (Institut Eksperimental'noi Meteorologii) Gidrometeoizdat, Ul. Beringa, d.38, St. Petersburg, Russia. illus.

551.5   AT   ISSN 0159-9372
FLINDERS INSTITUTE FOR ATMOSPHERIC AND MARINE SCIENCES. COMPUTING REPORTS. 1972. irreg., no.11, 1978. Aus.$30 per no. Flinders Institute for Atmospheric and Marine Sciences, Flinders University of South Australia, P.O. Box 2100, Adelaide, S.A. 5001, Australia. Ed. Jorg Hacker. circ. 150.

551.5   AT   ISSN 0159-9364
FLINDERS INSTITUTE FOR ATMOSPHERIC AND MARINE SCIENCES. RESEARCH REPORTS. 1972. irreg., no.33, 1980. Flinders Institute for Atmospheric and Marine Sciences, Flinders University of South Australia, P.O. Box 2100, Adelaide, S.A. 5001, Australia. Ed. Jorg Hacker. circ. 200.

551.5   AT   ISSN 0158-9776
FLINDERS INSTITUTE FOR ATMOSPHERIC AND MARINE SCIENCES. TECHNICAL REPORTS. 1973. irreg., no.4, 1980. Aus.$30. Flinders Institute for Atmospheric and Marine Sciences, Flinders University of South Australia, G.P.O. Box 2100, Adelaide, S.A. 5001, Australia. Ed. Jorg Hacker. circ. 150.

551   JA   ISSN 0912-5639
FUKUI DAIGAKU SEKISETSU KENKYUSHITSU HOKOKU/FUKUI UNIVERSITY. LABORATORY OF SNOW AND ICE. RESEARCH REPORT. (Text in Japanese; summaries in English) 1970. a. Fukui Daigaku, Sekisetsu Kenkyushitsu - Fukui University, Laboratory of Snow and Ice, 9-1, Bunkyo 3-chome, Fukui-shi, Fukui-ken 910, Japan.

551   JA
FUKUIKEN KISHO GEPPO/FUKUI PREFECTURE. MONTHLY REPORT OF METEOROLOGY. (Text in Japanese) 1968. m. Kishocho, Fukui Chiho Kishodai - Japan Meteorological Agency, Fukui Local Meteorological Observatory, 5-2, Toyoshima 2-chome, Fukui-shi, Fukui-ken 910, Japan.

551.5   JA   ISSN 0016-2558
FUKUOKA DISTRICT METEOROLOGICAL OBSERVATORY. UNUSUAL METEOROLOGICAL REPORT/FUKUOKA KANKU KISHODAI IJO KISHO HOKOKU. (Text in Japanese) 1961. q. free. Fukuoka District Meteorological Observatory - Fukuoka Kanku Kishodai, 1-2-36 Ohori, Chuo-ku, Fukuoka 810, Japan. circ. 200.

551   JA
FUKUOKA KANKU KISHO KENKYUKAISHI/FUKUOKA DISTRICT MEETING FOR THE STUDY OF METEOROLOGY. PROCEEDINGS. (Text in Japanese) 1947. a. Kishocho, Fukuoka Kanku Kishodai - Japan Meteorological Agency, Fukuoka District Meteorological Observatory, 2-36, Ohori 1-chome, Chuo-ku, Fukuoka-shi, Fukuoka-ken 810, Japan. **Document type:** proceedings.

551.5   JA   ISSN 0016-2566
FUKUOKA KANKU KISHODAI GIJUTSU TSUSHIN/FUKUOKA DISTRICT METEOROLOGICAL OBSERVATORY. TECHNICAL TIMES. (Text in Japanese) 1955. m. free. Kishocho, Fukuoka Kanku Kishodai - Japan Meteorological Agency, Fukuoka District Meteorological Observatory, 1-2-36 Ohori, Chuo-ku, Fukuoka-shi, Fukuoka-ken 810, Japan. bk.rev. circ. 170.

551.6   JA
FUKUOKA KANKU KISHODAI YOHO/FUKUOKA METEOROLOGICAL OBSERVATORY. MEMOIRS. (Text in Japanese) 1941. a. Kishocho, Fukuoka Kanku Kishodai - Japan Meteorological Agency, Fukuoka District Meteorological Observatory, 2-36, Ohori 1-chome, Chuo-ku, Fukuoka-shi, Fukuoka-ken 810, Japan.

551.65   JA   ISSN 0016-2574
FUKUOKAKEN KISHO GEPPO/FUKUOKA PREFECTURE. MONTHLY REPORT OF METEOROLOGY. (Text in Japanese) 1890. m. 1600 Yen. Kishocho, Fukuoka Kanku Kishodai - Japan Meteorological Agency, Fukuoka District Meteorological Observatory, 2-36 Ohori 1-chome, Chuo-ku, Fukuoka-shi, Fukuoka-ken 810, Japan. circ. 140.

551   ISSN 0916-5371
FUKUSHIMAKEN KISHO GEPPO/FUKUSHIMA PREFECTURE. MONTHLY REPORT OF METEOROLOGY. (Text in Japanese) 1951. m. Kishocho, Fukushima Chiho Kishodai - Japan Meteorological Agency, Fukushima Local Meteorological Observatory, 1-9, Matsukicho, Fukushima-shi, Fukushima-ken 960, Japan.

551.6   JA   ISSN 0429-9000
FUNE TO KAIJO KISHO/SHIP AND MARITIME METEOROLOGY. (Text in Japanese) 1957. q. Kishocho - Japan Meteorological Agency, 3-4, Otemachi 1-chome, Chiyoda-ku, Tokyo 100, Japan. **Indexed:** Jap.Per.Ind.

551.6   JA   ISSN 0912-3164
FUNE TO KISHO/VESSELS AND WEATHER. (Text in Japanese) irreg. free to qualified personnel. Nihon Kisho Kyokai, Senpaku Bunkai - Japan Weather Association, Section of Vessels, 9-2, Kanda Nishikicho 2-chome, Chiyoda-ku, Tokyo 102, Japan. TEL 81-3-3295-1525. FAX 81-3-3295-1097. Ed. Seiichi Shinoki. circ. (controlled).

551.5 630   GH
GHANA. METEOROLOGICAL DEPARTMENT. AGROMETEOROLOGICAL BULLETIN. 1965. m. Meteorological Department, Box 87, Legon, Accra, Ghana. stat. **Document type:** government publication, bulletin.

551.5   GH
GHANA. METEOROLOGICAL DEPARTMENT. CLIMATOLOGICAL NOTES. irreg., latest no.5. price varies. Meteorological Department, Box 87, Legon, Accra, Ghana. **Document type:** government publication, academic/scholarly publication.

551.5   GH
GHANA. METEOROLOGICAL DEPARTMENT. MONTHLY SUMMARY OF EVAPORATION. 1961. m. NC.500. Meteorological Department, Box 87, Legon, Accra, Ghana. **Document type:** government publication, academic/scholarly publication.

551.5   GH   ISSN 0431-8315
GHANA. METEOROLOGICAL DEPARTMENT. MONTHLY SUMMARY OF RAINFALL. 1952. m. NC.500. Meteorological Department, Box 87, Legon, Accra, Ghana. **Document type:** government publication, academic/scholarly publication.

551.5   GH   ISSN 0431-8323
GHANA. METEOROLOGICAL DEPARTMENT. MONTHLY WEATHER REPORT. 1949. m. NC.500. Meteorological Department, Box 87, Legon, Accra, Ghana. **Document type:** government publication, academic/scholarly publication.

551.5   GH
GHANA. METEOROLOGICAL DEPARTMENT. PROFESSIONAL NOTES. irreg., latest no.23. price varies. Meteorological Department, Box 87, Legon, Accra, Ghana. **Document type:** government publication, academic/scholarly publication.

551.5   GH
GHANA. METEOROLOGICAL DEPARTMENT. SUN AND MOON TABLES FOR GHANA. Short title: Sun and Moon Tables for Ghana. 1954. a. NC.500. Meteorological Department, Box 87, Legon, Accra, Ghana. **Document type:** government publication.

551   JA   ISSN 0916-507X
GIFUKEN KISHO GEPPO/GIFU PREFECTURE. MONTHLY REPORT OF METEOROLOGY. (Text in Japanese) 1952. m. Kishocho, Gifu Chiho Kishodai - Japan Meteorological Agency, Gifu Local Meteorological Observatory, 6, Ninomaru, Kano, Gifu-shi, Gifu-ken 500, Japan.

551.5   US   ISSN 1023-6732
▼**THE GLOBAL ATMOSPHERE - OCEAN SYSTEM.** 1994. 4/yr. Gordon and Breach Science Publishers, c/o International Publishers Distributor, 820 Town Center Dr., Langhorne, PA 19047. TEL 215-750-2642; 800-545-8398. FAX 215-750-6343. (Subscr. to: International Publishers Distributor, P.O. Box 90, Reading, Berkshire RG1 8JL, England. TEL 44-173-456-8316. FAX 44-173-456-8316) (back issues avail.) **Document type:** academic/scholarly publication.
—BLDSC (4195.350150).

GLOBAL VOLCANISM NETWORK. BULLETIN. see EARTH SCIENCES — Geology

551.5   UK   ISSN 0027-0636
GREAT BRITAIN. METEOROLOGICAL OFFICE. MONTHLY WEATHER REPORT. 1884-1970; resumed 1984. m. £36.75 (includes a. summary) (effective 1993). H.M.S.O., 51 Nine Elms Ln., London SW8 5DR, England. TEL 071-873-0011. FAX 071-873-8463. (Subscr. to: H.M.S.O. Publications Centre, P.O. Box 276, London SW8 5DT, England. TEL 071-873-9090. FAX 071-873-8200) charts. circ. 1,250. (reprint service avail. from UMI) **Document type:** government publication.
—BLDSC (5962.400000); UMI. **CCC**.

551.65   GW   ISSN 0017-4645
QC880.4.A8
GROSSWETTERLAGEN EUROPAS. 1962. m. DM.59. Deutscher Wetterdienst, Bibliothek, Postfach 100465, 63004 Offenbach a.M., Germany. TEL 069-80622225. FAX 069-80622486. charts. **Document type:** government publication.
Formerly: Grosswetterlagen Mitteleuropas.

551   JA   ISSN 0916-5088
GUNMAKEN KISHO GEPPO/GUNMA PREFECTURE. MONTHLY REPORT OF METEOROLOGY. (Text in Japanese) 1900. m. Kishocho, Maebashi Chiho Kishodai - Japan Meteorological Agency, Maebashi Local Meteorological Observatory, 20-12, Showamachi 3-chome, Maebashi-shi, Gunma-ken 371, Japan.

METEOROLOGY 4693

551.63 630   JA
GUNMAKEN NOGYO KISHO SAIGAI SOKUHO/GUNMA PREFECTURE. NEWS OF AGRICULTURAL METEOROLOGY DISASTER. (Text in Japanese) 1987. irreg. Gunmaken Prefectural Government, 1-1, Otemachi 1-chome, Maebashi-shi, Gunma-ken 371, Japan. **Document type:** government publication.

GUOWAI NONGXUE - NONGYE QIXIANG/FOREIGN AGRICULTURE - AGRICULTURAL METEOROLOGY. see *AGRICULTURE*

551.6   GY
GUYANA. HYDROMETEOROLOGICAL SERVICE. ANNUAL CLIMATOLOGICAL DATA SUMMARY. (Subseries of: Guyana. Hydrometeorological Service) 1973. a. G.$1000 (typically set in Dec.). Ministry of Agriculture, Hydrometeorological Service, 18 Brickdam, Stabroek, Georgetown, Guyana. TEL 592-2-72463. Ed. Simon Kemp. illus. circ. 200. **Document type:** government publication.

551 639.2   JA   ISSN 0912-3156
GYOGYO TO KISHO/FISHERY AND METEOROLOGY. (Text in Japanese) a. Kanto Tokai Gyogyo Kisho Renrakukai - Panel Meteorological Service for Fishing, Nihon Kisho Kyokai, 4-5, Kojimachi, Chiyoda-ku, Tokyo 102, Japan.

551.5   IT
HABITAT - CALABRIA. 1965. m. free. Habitat-Calabria s.r.l., Via Parco Fiamma, 8, I-89100 Reggio Calabria, Italy. TEL 0039 965 92183. Ed.Bd. circ. 400. (back issues avail.)

551.63   JA   ISSN 0440-1077
QC994.6
HAKODATE KAIYO KISHODAI. KAIJO KISHO HOKOKU/HAKODATE MARINE OBSERVATORY. MARINE METEOROLOGICAL REPORT. (Text in Japanese) 1957. a. Kishocho, Hakodate Kaiyo Kishodai - Japan Meteorological Agency, Hakodate Marine Observatory, 4-4, Mihara 3-chome, Hakodate-shi, Hokkaido 041, Japan.

551   JA   ISSN 0438-4172
HAKODATE KAIYO KISHODAI. YOHO/HAKODATE MARINE OBSERVATORY. BULLETIN. (Text in English, Japanese) 1944. irreg. Kishocho, Hakodate Kaiyo Kishodai - Japan Meteorological Agency, Hakodate Marine Observatory, 4-4, Mihara 3-chome, Hakodate-shi, Hokkaido 041, Japan.

551.63 631   US
HAWAII WEEKLY WEATHER & CROP BULLETIN. 1955. w. $15 (foreign $60). Agricultural Service, National Agricultural Statistics Service, Box 22159, Honolulu, HI 96823-2159. TEL 808-973-9588. stat. circ. 500. (processed) **Document type:** government publication.

551.6   JA   ISSN 0916-2038
HIROSAKI DAIGAKU RIGAKUBU KANCHI KISHO JIKKENSHITSU HOKOKU/HIROSAKI UNIVERSITY. FACULTY OF SCIENCE. LABORATORY OF COLD REGIONS METEOROLOGY. ANNUAL REPORT. (Text in Japanese) 1989. a. Hirosaki Daigaku, Rigakubu, Kanchi Kisho Jikkenshitsu - Hirosaki University, Faculty of Science. Laboratory of Cold Regions Meteorology, 3, Bunkyo-cho, Hirosaki-shi, Aomori-ken 036, Japan.

551.6   JA   ISSN 0285-6840
HIROSAKI DAIGAKU RIGAKUBU SETSUGAI KANSOKUJO HOKOKU/HIRASAKI UNIVERSITY. SNOW AND ICE OBSERVATORY. SCIENCE REPORTS. (Text in English, Japanese) 1981. irreg. Hirosaki Daigaku, Rigakubu, Setsugai Kansokujo - Hirosaki University, Faculty of Science, Snow and Ice Observatory, 3, Bunkyo-cho, Hirosaki-shi, Aomori-ken 036, Japan.

551   JA   ISSN 0385-7158
HIROSHIMAKEN KISHO GEPPO/HIROSHIMA PREFECTURE. MONTHLY REPORT OF METEOROLOGY. (Text in Japanese) m. Kishocho, Hiroshima Chiho Kishodai - Japan Meteorological Agency, Hiroshima Local Meteorological Observatory, 6-30, Kamihatchobori, Naka-ku, Hiroshima-shi, Hiroshima-ken 730, Japan.

551.5   US
HISTORICAL CLIMATOLOGY SERIES 1. HEATING DEGREE DAYS. m. $24. U.S. National Climatic Data Center, National Oceanic and Atmospheric Administration, U.S. Department of Commerce, Federal Bldg., Rm. 120, 151 Patton Ave., Asheville, NC 28801-5001. TEL 704-271-4756. FAX 704-271-4876. TELEX 6502643731. E-mail: orders@ncdc.noaa.gov. stat. **Document type:** government publication.

551.5   US
HISTORICAL CLIMATOLOGY SERIES 2: COOLING DEGREE DAYS. m. $24. U.S. National Climatic Data Center, National Oceanic and Atmospheric Administration, U.S. Department of Commerce, Federal Bldg., Rm. 120, 151 Patton Ave., Asheville, NC 28801-5001. TEL 704-271-4756. FAX 704-271-4876. TELEX 6502643731. E-mail: orders@ncdc.noaa.gov. stat. **Document type:** government publication.

551   JA   ISSN 0916-5096
HOKKAIDO KISHO GEPPO/HOKKAIDO MONTHLY REPORT OF METEOROLOGY. (Text in Japanese) 1865. m. Kishocho, Sapporo Kanku Kishodai - Japan Meteorological Agency, Sapporo District Meteorological Observatory, 2, Nishi 18-chome, Kita 2-jo, Chuo-ku, Sapporo-shi, Hokkaido 060.

551 630   JA   ISSN 0915-6062
HOKKAIDO NO NOGYO KISHO/HOKKAIDO JOURNAL OF AGRICULTURAL METEOROLOGY. (Text in Japanese) 1964. a. Nihon Nogyo Kisho Gakkai, Hokkaido Shibu - Society of Agricultural Meteorology of Japan, Hokkaido Branch, Hokkaido Daigaku Nogakubu, Nogyo Butsurigaku Kenkyushitsu, Nishi 9-chome, Kita 9-jo, Sapporo-shi, Hokkaido 060, Japan.

551   JA
HOKKAIDO NO SEPPYO/SNOW AND ICE IN HOKKAIDO. (Text in Japanese) 1982. a. membership. Nihon Seppyo Gakkai, Hokkaido Shibu - Japanese Society of Snow and Ice, Hokkaido Branch, Hokkaido Daigaku Teion Kagaku Kenkyujo, Nishi 8-chome, Kita 19-jo, Kita-ku, Sapporo-shi, Hokkaido 060, Japan.

551.5   HK
HONG KONG. ROYAL OBSERVATORY. A SUMMARY OF RADIOSONDE - RADIOWIND ASCENTS MADE IN (YEAR). 1987. a., latest 1991. price varies. Royal Observatory, 134A Nathan Rd., Kowloon, Hong Kong.

551.5   HK
HONG KONG. ROYAL OBSERVATORY. DAILY WEATHER CHART. (Text in English) 1934. d. price varies. Royal Observatory, 134 A Nathan Rd., Kowloon, Hong Kong. Ed.Bd. charts; stat.

551.5   HK
HONG KONG. ROYAL OBSERVATORY. HISTORICAL PUBLICATIONS. (Text in English) 1884. irreg. price varies. Royal Observatory, 134A Nathan Rd., Kowloon, Hong Kong. Ed.Bd.

551.5   HK
HONG KONG. ROYAL OBSERVATORY. MARINE CLIMATOLOGICAL SUMMARY CHARTS FOR THE SOUTH CHINA SEA. 1971. a., latest 1988. price varies. Royal Observatory, 134A Nathan Rd., Kowloon, Hong Kong.

551.5   HK
HONG KONG. ROYAL OBSERVATORY. MONTHLY WEATHER SUMMARY. 1976. m. Royal Observatory, 134A Nathan Rd., Kowloon, Hong Kong.

551.5   HK   ISSN 1012-4497
HONG KONG. ROYAL OBSERVATORY. OCCASIONAL PAPER. 1950. irreg., no. 63, 1989. Royal Observatory, 134 A Nathan Rd., Kowloon, Hong Kong.

551.5   HK
HONG KONG. ROYAL OBSERVATORY. RAINFALL CHART. (Text in English) 1952. a. price varies. Royal Observatory, 134A Nathan Rd., Kowloon, Hong Kong. Ed.Bd. charts; stat.

551.5   HK
HONG KONG. ROYAL OBSERVATORY. SURFACE OBSERVATIONS IN HONG KONG (YEAR). 1987. a., latest 1991. price varies. Royal Observatory, 134A Nathan Rd., Kowloon, Hong Kong.

551.5   HK
HONG KONG. ROYAL OBSERVATORY. TECHNICAL MEMOIRS. (Text in English) 1948. irreg., latest 1974. price varies. Royal Observatory, 134A Nathan Rd., Kowloon, Hong Kong. Ed.Bd. **Document type:** monographic series.

551.5   HK
HONG KONG. ROYAL OBSERVATORY. TECHNICAL NOTE. 1949. irreg., no.84, 1991. price varies. Royal Observatory, 134A Nathan Rd., Kowloon, Hong Kong. **Indexed:** Meteor.& Geoastrophys.Abstr.
Formerly: Hong Kong. Royal Observatory. Climatological Note.

551.5   HK
HONG KONG. ROYAL OBSERVATORY. TECHNICAL NOTES (LOCAL). (Text in English) 1961. irreg., latest 1986. price varies. Royal Observatory, 134 A Nathan Rd., Kowloon, Hong Kong. Ed.Bd.

551.5   HK
HONG KONG TIDE TABLES. 1987. a. price varies. Royal Observatory, 134A Nathan Rd., Kowloon, Hong Kong.

551.5   US   ISSN 0364-6076
HOURLY PRECIPITATION DATA. ALABAMA. 1965. m. $45. U.S. National Climatic Data Center, National Oceanic and Atmospheric Administration, U.S. Department of Commerce, Federal Bldg., Rm. 120, 151 Patton Ave., Asheville, NC 28801-5001. TEL 704-271-4756. FAX 704-271-4876. TELEX 6502643731. E-mail: orders@ncdc.noaa.gov. (also avail. in microfiche; magnetic tape; back issues avail.) **Document type:** government publication.

551.5   US   ISSN 0364-6084
HOURLY PRECIPITATION DATA. ARIZONA. 1965. m. $45. U.S. National Climatic Data Center, National Oceanic and Atmospheric Administration, U.S. Department of Commerce, Federal Bldg., Rm. 120, 151 Patton Ave., Asheville, NC 28801-5001. TEL 704-271-4756. FAX 704-271-4876. TELEX 6502643731. E-mail: orders@ncdc.noaa.gov. (also avail. in microfiche; magnetic tape; back issues avail.) **Document type:** government publication.

551.5   US   ISSN 0090-2683
HOURLY PRECIPITATION DATA. ARKANSAS. 1951. m. $45. U.S. National Climatic Data Center, National Oceanic and Atmospheric Administration, U.S. Department of Commerce, Federal Bldg., Rm. 120, 151 Patton Ave., Asheville, NC 28801-5001. TEL 704-271-4756. FAX 704-271-4876. TELEX 6502643731. E-mail: orders@ncdc.noaa.gov. (also avail. in microfiche; magnetic tape; back issues avail.) **Document type:** government publication.

551.5   US   ISSN 0364-6092
HOURLY PRECIPITATION DATA. CALIFORNIA. 1965. m. $45. U.S. National Climatic Data Center, National Oceanic and Atmospheric Administration, U.S. Department of Commerce, Federal Bldg., 37 Battery Park Ave., Asheville, NC 28801-5001. TEL 704-271-4756. FAX 704-271-4786. TELEX 6502643731. E-mail: orders@ncdc.noaa.gov. (also avail. in microfiche; magnetic tape; back issues avail.) **Document type:** government publication.

551.5   US   ISSN 0364-6106
HOURLY PRECIPITATION DATA. COLORADO. 1965. m. $45. U.S. National Climatic Data Center, National Oceanic and Atmospheric Administration, U.S. Department of Commerce, Federal Bldg., Rm. 120, 151 Patton Ave., Asheville, NC 28801-5001. TEL 704-271-4756. FAX 704-271-4876. TELEX 6502643731. E-mail: orders@ncdc.noaa.gov. (also avail. in microfiche; magnetic tape; back issues avail.) **Document type:** government publication.

551.5   US   ISSN 0364-6114
HOURLY PRECIPITATION DATA. FLORIDA. 1965. m. $45. U.S. National Climatic Data Center, National Oceanic and Atmospheric Administration, U.S. Department of Commerce, Federal Bldg., Rm. 120, 151 Patton Ave., Asheville, NC 28801-5001. TEL 704-271-4756. FAX 704-271-4876. TELEX 6502643731. E-mail: orders@ncdc.noaa.gov. (also avail. in microfiche; magnetic tape; back issues avail.) **Document type:** government publication.

METEOROLOGY

551.5   US   ISSN 0364-6122
HOURLY PRECIPITATION DATA. GEORGIA. 1965. m. $45. U.S. National Climatic Data Center, National Oceanic and Atmospheric Administration, U.S. Department of Commerce, Federal Bldg., Rm. 120, 151 Patton Ave., Asheville, NC 28801-5001. TEL 704-271-4756. FAX 704-271-4876. TELEX 6502643731. E-mail: orders@ncdc.noaa.gov. (also avail. in microfiche; magnetic tape; back issues avail.) **Document type:** government publication.

551.5   US   ISSN 0364-6149
HOURLY PRECIPITATION DATA. IDAHO. 1965. m. $45. U.S. National Climatic Data Center, National Oceanic and Atmospheric Administration, U.S. Department of Commerce, Federal Bldg., Rm. 120, 151 Patton Ave., Asheville, NC 28801-5001. TEL 704-271-4756. FAX 704-271-4876. TELEX 6502643731. E-mail: orders@ncdc.noaa.gov. (also avail. in microfiche; magnetic tape; back issues avail.) **Document type:** government publication.

551.5   US   ISSN 0364-6157
HOURLY PRECIPITATION DATA. ILLINOIS. 1951. m. $45. U.S. National Climatic Data Center, National Oceanic and Atmospheric Administration, U.S. Department of Commerce, Federal Bldg., Rm. 120, 151 Patton Ave., Asheville, NC 28801-5001. TEL 704-271-4756. FAX 704-271-4876. TELEX 6502643731. E-mail: orders@ncdc.noaa.gov. (also avail. in microfiche; magnetic tape; back issues avail.) **Document type:** government publication.

551.5   US   ISSN 0364-6165
HOURLY PRECIPITATION DATA. INDIANA. 1951. m. $45. U.S. National Climatic Data Center, National Oceanic and Atmospheric Administration, U.S. Department of Commerce, Federal Bldg., Rm. 120, 151 Patton Ave., Asheville, NC 28801-2696. TEL 704-271-4756. FAX 704-257-4876. TELEX 6502643731. E-mail: orders@ncdc.noaa.gov. (also avail. in microfiche; magnetic tape; back issues avail.) **Document type:** government publication.

551.5   US   ISSN 0364-6173
HOURLY PRECIPITATION DATA. IOWA. 1951. m. $45. U.S. National Climatic Data Center, National Oceanic and Atmospheric Administration, U.S. Department of Commerce, Federal Bldg., Rm. 120, 151 Patton Ave., Asheville, NC 28801-5001. TEL 704-271-4756. FAX 704-271-4876. TELEX 6502643731. E-mail: orders@ncdc.noaa.gov. (also avail. in microfiche; magnetic tape; back issues avail.) **Document type:** government publication.

551.5   US   ISSN 0364-6181
HOURLY PRECIPITATION DATA. KANSAS. 1951. m. $45. U.S. National Climatic Data Center, National Oceanic and Atmospheric Administration, U.S. Department of Commerce, Federal Bldg., Rm. 120, 151 Patton Ave., Asheville, NC 28801-5001. TEL 704-271-4756. FAX 704-271-4876. TELEX 6502643731. E-mail: orders@ncdc.noaa.gov. (also avail. in microfiche; magnetic tape; back issues avail.) **Document type:** government publication.

551.5   US   ISSN 0364-5401
HOURLY PRECIPITATION DATA. KENTUCKY. 1951. m. $45. U.S. National Climatic Data Center, National Oceanic and Atmospheric Administration, U.S. Department of Commerce, Federal Bldg., Rm. 120, 151 Patton Ave., Asheville, NC 28801-5001. TEL 704-271-4756. FAX 704-271-4876. TELEX 6502643731. E-mail: orders@ncdc.noaa.gov. (also avail. in microfiche; magnetic tape; back issues avail.) **Document type:** government publication.

551.5   US   ISSN 0364-5398
HOURLY PRECIPITATION DATA. LOUISIANA. 1951. m. $45. U.S. National Climatic Data Center, National Oceanic and Atmospheric Administration, U.S. Department of Commerce, Federal Bldg., Rm. 120, 151 Patton Ave., Asheville, NC 28801-5001. TEL 704-271-4756. FAX 704-271-4876. TELEX 6502643731. E-mail: orders@ncdc.noaa.gov. (also avail. in microfiche; magnetic tape; back issues avail.) **Document type:** government publication.

551.5   US   ISSN 0364-538X
HOURLY PRECIPITATION DATA. MARYLAND & DELAWARE. 1951. m. $45. U.S. National Climatic Data Center, National Oceanic and Atmospheric Administration, U.S. Department of Commerce, Federal Bldg., Rm. 120, 151 Patton Ave., Asheville, NC 28801-5001. TEL 704-271-4756. FAX 704-271-4876. TELEX 6502643731. E-mail: orders@ncdc.noaa.gov. (also avail. in microfiche; magnetic tape; back issues avail.) **Document type:** government publication.

551.5   US   ISSN 0364-6203
HOURLY PRECIPITATION DATA. MICHIGAN. 1951. m. $45. U.S. National Climatic Data Center, National Oceanic and Atmospheric Administration, U.S. Department of Commerce, Federal Bldg., Rm. 120, 151 Patton Ave., Asheville, NC 28801-5001. TEL 704-271-4756. FAX 704-271-4876. TELEX 6502643731. E-mail: orders@ncdc.noaa.gov. (also avail. in microfiche; magnetic tape; back issues avail.) **Document type:** government publication.

551.5   US   ISSN 0364-6211
HOURLY PRECIPITATION DATA. MINNESOTA. 1951. m. $45. U.S. National Climatic Data Center, Federal Bldg., Rm. 120, 151 Patton Ave., Asheville, NC 28801-2696. TEL 704-271-4756. FAX 704-271-4876. TELEX 6502643731. E-mail: orders@ncdc.noaa.gov. (also avail. in microfiche; magnetic tape; back issues avail.) **Document type:** government publication.

551.5   US   ISSN 0364-622X
HOURLY PRECIPITATION DATA. MISSISSIPPI. 1951. m. $45. U.S. National Climatic Data Center, National Oceanic and Atmospheric Administration, U.S. Department of Commerce, Federal Bldg., Rm. 120, 151 Patton Ave., Asheville, NC 28801-5001. TEL 704-271-4756. FAX 704-271-4876. TELEX 6502643731. E-mail: orders@ncdc.noaa.gov. (also avail. in microfiche; magnetic tape; back issues avail.) **Document type:** government publication.

551.5   US   ISSN 0364-6238
HOURLY PRECIPITATION DATA. MISSOURI. 1951. m. $45. U.S. National Climatic Data Center, National Oceanic and Atmospheric Administration, U.S. Department of Commerce, Federal Bldg., Rm. 120, 151 Patton Ave., Asheville, NC 28801-5001. TEL 704-271-4756. FAX 704-271-4876. TELEX 6502643731. E-mail: orders@ncdc.noaa.gov. (also avail. in microfiche; magnetic tape; back issues avail.) **Document type:** government publication.

551.5   US   ISSN 0364-6246
HOURLY PRECIPITATION DATA. MONTANA. 1951. m. $45. U.S. National Climatic Data Center, National Oceanic and Atmospheric Administration, U.S. Department of Commerce, Federal Bldg., Rm. 120, 151 Patton Ave., Asheville, NC 28801-5001. TEL 704-271-4756. FAX 704-271-4876. TELEX 6502643731. E-mail: orders@ncdc.noaa.gov. (also avail. in microfiche; magnetic tape; back issues avail.) **Document type:** government publication.

551.5   US   ISSN 0364-6254
HOURLY PRECIPITATION DATA. NEBRASKA. 1951. m. $45. U.S. National Climatic Data Center, National Oceanic and Atmospheric Administration, U.S. Department of Commerce, Federal Bldg., Rm. 120, 151 Patton Ave., Asheville, NC 28801-5001. TEL 704-271-4756. FAX 704-271-4756. TELEX 6502643731. E-mail: orders@ncdc.noaa.gov. (also avail. in microfiche; magnetic tape; back issues avail.) **Document type:** government publication.

551.5   US   ISSN 0364-6262
HOURLY PRECIPITATION DATA. NEVADA. 1951. m. $45. U.S. National Climatic Data Center, National Oceanic and Atmospheric Administration, U.S. Department of Commerce, Federal Bldg., Rm. 120, 151 Patton Ave., Asheville, NC 28801-5001. TEL 704-271-4756. FAX 704-257-4876. TELEX 6502643731. E-mail: orders@ncdc.noaa.gov. (also avail. in microfiche; magnetic tape; back issues avail.) **Document type:** government publication.

551.5   US   ISSN 0364-6270
HOURLY PRECIPITATION DATA. NEW ENGLAND. 1951. m. $45. U.S. National Climatic Data Center, National Oceanic and Atmospheric Administration, U.S. Department of Commerce, Federal Bldg., Rm. 120, 151 Patton Ave., Asheville, NC 28801-5001. TEL 704-271-4756. FAX 704-271-4876. TELEX 6502643731. E-mail: orders@ncdc.noaa.gov. (also avail. in microfiche; magnetic tape; back issues avail.) **Document type:** government publication.

551.5   US   ISSN 0364-6289
HOURLY PRECIPITATION DATA. NEW JERSEY. 1951. m. $45. U.S. National Climatic Data Center, National Oceanic and Atmospheric Administration, U.S. Department of Commerce, Federal Bldg., Rm. 120, 151 Patton Ave., Asheville, NC 28801-5001. TEL 704-271-4756. FAX 704-271-4876. TELEX 6502643731. E-mail: orders@ncdc.noaa.gov. (also avail. in microfiche; magnetic tape; back issues avail.) **Document type:** government publication.

551.5   US   ISSN 0364-6297
HOURLY PRECIPITATION DATA. NEW MEXICO. 1951. m. $45. U.S. National Climatic Data Center, National Oceanic and Atmospheric Administration, U.S. Department of Commerce, Federal Bldg., Rm. 120, 151 Patton Ave., Asheville, NC 28801-5001. TEL 704-257-4756. FAX 704-271-4876. TELEX 6502643731. E-mail: orders@ncdc.noaa.gov. (also avail. in microfiche; magnetic tape; back issues avail.) **Document type:** government publication.

551.5   US   ISSN 0364-6300
HOURLY PRECIPITATION DATA. NEW YORK. 1951. m. $45. U.S. National Climatic Data Center, National Oceanic and Atmospheric Administration, U.S. Department of Commerce, Federal Bldg., Rm. 120, 151 Patton Ave., Asheville, NC 28801-5001. TEL 704-271-4756. FAX 704-271-4876. TELEX 6502643731. E-mail: orders@ncdc.noaa.gov. (also avail. in microfiche; magnetic tape; back issues avail.) **Document type:** government publication.

551.5   US   ISSN 0364-6319
HOURLY PRECIPITATION DATA. NORTH CAROLINA. 1951. m. $45. U.S. National Climatic Data Center, National Oceanic and Atmospheric Administration, U.S. Department of Commerce, Federal Bldg., Rm. 120, 151 Patton Ave., Asheville, NC 28801-5001. TEL 704-271-4756. FAX 704-271-4876. TELEX 6502643731. E-mail: orders@ncdc.noaa.gov. (also avail. in microfiche; magnetic tape; back issues avail.) **Document type:** government publication.

551.5   US   ISSN 0364-6327
HOURLY PRECIPITATION DATA. NORTH DAKOTA. 1951. m. $45. U.S. National Climatic Data Center, National Oceanic and Atmospheric Administration, U.S. Department of Commerce, Federal Bldg., Rm. 120, 151 Patton Ave., Asheville, NC 28801-5001. TEL 704-271-4756. FAX 704-271-4876. TELEX 6502643731. E-mail: orders@ncdc.noaa.gov. (also avail. in microfiche; magnetic tape; back issues avail.) **Document type:** government publication.

551.5   US   ISSN 0364-6335
HOURLY PRECIPITATION DATA. OHIO. 1951. m. $45. U.S. National Climatic Data Center, National Oceanic and Atmospheric Administration, U.S. Department of Commerce, Federal Bldg., Rm. 120, 151 Patton Ave., Asheville, NC 28801-5001. TEL 704-271-4756. FAX 704-271-4876. TELEX 6502643731. E-mail: orders@ncdc.noaa.gov. (also avail. in microfiche; magnetic tape; back issues avail.) **Document type:** government publication.

551.5   US   ISSN 0364-6343
HOURLY PRECIPITATION DATA. OKLAHOMA. 1951. m. $45. U.S. National Climatic Data Center, National Oceanic and Atmospheric Administration, U.S. Department of Commerce, Federal Bldg., Rm. 120, 151 Patton Ave., Asheville, NC 28801-5001. TEL 704-271-4756. FAX 704-271-4876. TELEX 6502643731. E-mail: orders@ncdc.noaa.gov. (also avail. in microfiche; magnetic tape; back issues avail.) **Document type:** government publication.

551.5 US ISSN 0364-6351
HOURLY PRECIPITATION DATA. OREGON. 1951. m. $45. U.S. National Climatic Data Center, National Oceanic and Atmospheric Administration, U.S. Department of Commerce, Federal Bldg., Rm. 120, 151 Patton Ave., Asheville, NC 28801-5001. TEL 704-271-4756. FAX 704-271-4876. TELEX 6502643731. E-mail: orders@ncdc.noaa.gov. (also avail. in microfiche; magnetic tape; back issues avail.) **Document type:** government publication.

551.5 US ISSN 0364-619X
HOURLY PRECIPITATION DATA. PENNSYLVANIA. 1951. m. $45. U.S. National Climatic Data Center, National Oceanic and Atmospheric Administration, U.S. Department of Commerce, Federal Bldg., Rm. 120, 151 Patton Ave., Asheville, NC 28801-5001. TEL 704-271-4756. FAX 704-271-4876. TELEX 6502643731. E-mail: orders@ncdc.noaa.gov. (also avail. in microfiche; magnetic tape; back issues avail.) **Document type:** government publication.

551.5 US ISSN 1058-5079
HOURLY PRECIPITATION DATA. PUERTO RICO & VIRGIN ISLANDS. 1971. m. $45. U.S. National Climatic Data Center, National Oceanic and Atmospheric Administration, U.S. Department of Commerce, Federal Bldg., Rm. 120, 151 Patton Ave., Asheville, NC 28801-5001. TEL 704-271-4756. FAX 704-271-4876. TELEX 6502643731. E-mail: orders@ncdc.noaa.gov. (also avail. in microfiche; magnetic tape; back issues avail.) **Document type:** government publication.
   Formerly (until 1978): Hourly Precipitation Data. Puerto Rico (ISSN 0090-2691)

551.5 US ISSN 0364-636X
HOURLY PRECIPITATION DATA. SOUTH CAROLINA. 1951. m. $45. U.S. National Climatic Data Center, National Oceanic and Atmospheric Administration, U.S. Department of Commerce, Federal Bldg., Rm. 120, 151 Patton Ave., Asheville, NC 28801-5001. TEL 704-271-4756. FAX 704-271-4876. TELEX 6502643731. E-mail: orders@ncdc.noaa.gov. (also avail. in microfiche; magnetic tape; back issues avail.) **Document type:** government publication.

551.5 US ISSN 0364-6378
HOURLY PRECIPITATION DATA. SOUTH DAKOTA. 1951. m. $45. U.S. National Climatic Data Center, National Oceanic and Atmospheric Administration, U.S. Department of Commerce, Federal Bldg., Rm. 120, 151 Patton Ave., Asheville, NC 28801-5001. TEL 704-271-4756. FAX 704-271-4876. TELEX 6502643731. E-mail: orders@ncdc.noaa.gov. (also avail. in microfiche; magnetic tape; back issues avail.) **Document type:** government publication.

551.5 US ISSN 0364-6386
HOURLY PRECIPITATION DATA. TENNESSEE. 1951. m. $45. U.S. National Climatic Data Center, National Oceanic and Atmospheric Administration, U.S. Department of Commerce, Federal Bldg., Rm. 120, 151 Patton Ave., Asheville, NC 28801-5001. TEL 704-271-4756. FAX 704-271-4876. TELEX 6502643731. E-mail: orders@ncdc.noaa.gov. (also avail. in microfiche; magnetic tape; back issues avail.) **Document type:** government publication.

551.5 US ISSN 0364-6882
HOURLY PRECIPITATION DATA. TEXAS. 1951. m. $45. U.S. National Climatic Data Center, National Oceanic and Atmospheric Administration, U.S. Department of Commerce, Federal Bldg., Rm. 120, 151 Patton Ave., Asheville, NC 28801-5001. TEL 704-271-1756. FAX 704-271-4876. TELEX 6502643731. E-mail: orders@ncdc.noaa.gov. (also avail. in microfiche; magnetic tape; back issues avail.) **Document type:** government publication.

551.5 US ISSN 0364-6920
HOURLY PRECIPITATION DATA. UTAH. 1951. m. $45. U.S. National Climatic Data Center, National Oceanic and Atmospheric Administration, U.S. Department of Commerce, Federal Bldg., 37 Battery Park Ave., Asheville, NC 28801-2696. TEL 704-259-0682. FAX 704-259-0876. TELEX 6502643731. E-mail: orders@ncdc.noaa.gov. (also avail. in microfiche; magnetic tape; back issues avail.) **Document type:** government publication.

551.5 US ISSN 0364-6874
HOURLY PRECIPITATION DATA. VIRGINIA. 1951. m. $45. U.S. National Climatic Data Center, National Oceanic and Atmospheric Administration, U.S. Department of Commerce, Federal Bldg., Rm. 120, 151 Patton Ave., Asheville, NC 28801-5001. TEL 704-271-4756. FAX 704-271-4876. TELEX 6502643731. E-mail: orders@ncdc.noaa.gov. (also avail. in microfiche; magnetic tape; back issues avail.) **Document type:** government publication.

551.5 US ISSN 0364-6912
HOURLY PRECIPITATION DATA. WASHINGTON. 1951. m. $45. U.S. National Climatic Data Center, National Oceanic and Atmospheric Administration, U.S. Department of Commerce, Federal Bldg., Rm. 120, 151 Patton Ave., Asheville, NC 28801-5001. TEL 704-271-4756. FAX 704-271-4876. TELEX 6502643731. E-mail: orders@ncdc.noaa.gov. (also avail. in microfiche; magnetic tape; back issues avail.) **Document type:** government publication.

551.5 US ISSN 0364-6904
HOURLY PRECIPITATION DATA. WEST VIRGINIA. 1951. m. $45. U.S. National Climatic Data Center, National Oceanic and Atmospheric Administration, U.S. Department of Commerce, Federal Bldg., Rm. 120, 151 Patton Ave., Asheville, NC 28801-5001. TEL 704-271-4756. FAX 704-271-4876. TELEX 6502643731. E-mail: orders@ncdc.noaa.gov. (also avail. in microfiche; magnetic tape; back issues avail.) **Document type:** government publication.

551.5 US ISSN 0364-6939
HOURLY PRECIPITATION DATA. WISCONSIN. 1951. m. $45. U.S. National Climatic Data Center, National Oceanic and Atmospheric Administration, U.S. Department of Commerce, Federal Bldg., Rm. 120, 151 Patton Ave., Asheville, NC 28801-5001. TEL 704-271-4756. FAX 704-271-4876. TELEX 6502643731. E-mail: orders ncdc.noaa.gov. (also avail. in microfiche; magnetic tape; back issues avail.) **Document type:** government publication.

551.1 US ISSN 0364-6890
HOURLY PRECIPITATION DATA. WYOMING. 1951. m. $45. U.S. National Climatic Data Center, National Oceanic and Atmospheric Administration, U.S. Department of Commerce, Federal Bldg., Rm. 120, 151 Patton Ave., Asheville, NC 28801-5001. TEL 704-271-4756. FAX 704-271-4876. TELEX 6502643731. E-mail: orders@ncdc.noaa.gov. (also avail. in microfiche; magnetic tape; back issues avail.) **Document type:** government publication.

551.5 BU ISSN 0018-1331
HYDROLOGY AND METEOROLOGY/HIDROLOGIJA I METEOROLOGIJA. (Summaries in various languages) 1964. irreg. price varies. Publishing House of the Bulgarian Academy of Sciences, Acad. G. Bonchev St., Bldg. 6, 1113 Sofia, Bulgaria. (Dist. by: Hemus, 6, Rouski Blvd., 1000 Sofia, Bulgaria) Ed. I. Marinov. circ. 500. (reprint service avail. from IRC) **Indexed:** BSL Geo. **Document type:** academic/scholarly publication.
   Formerly: Bulgarska Akademiia na Naukite. Institut po Khidrologiia i Meteorologiia. Izvestiia (ISSN 0068-3876)

551.57 XO ISSN 0139-8318
GB651
HYDROMETEOROLOGICKY USTAV, BRATISLAVA. ZBORNIK PRAC. (Text in Russian; summaries in Czech or Slovak, and in German) 1972. irreg. (approx. biennial). Alfa, Hubanovo nam. 3, 815 89 Bratislava, Slovakia. illus.

551 JA ISSN 0916-5037
HYOGOKEN KISHO GEPPO/HYOGO PREFECTURE. MONTHLY REPORT OF METEOROLOGY. (Text in Japanese) m. Kishocho, Kobe Kaiyo Kishodai - Japan Meteorological Agency, Kobe Marine Observatory, 14-1, Nakayamate Dori 7-chome, Chuo-ku, Kobe-shi, Hyogo-ken 650. Ed. Tuyoshi Nakai.

I C R R ANNUAL REPORT. (Institute for Cosmic Ray Research) see *ASTRONOMY*

551 JA ISSN 0916-5304
IBARAKIKEN KISHO GEPPO/IBARAKI PREFECTURE. MONTHLY REPORT OF METEOROLOGY. (Text in Japanese) 1897. m. Kishocho, Mito Chiho Kishodai - Japan Meteorological Agency, Mito Local Meteorological Observatory, 4-6, Kanamachi 1-chome, Mito-shi, Ibaraki-ken 310, Japan.

METEOROLOGY 4695

551.5 FI ISSN 0782-6109
ILMATIETEEN LAITOS. METEOROLOGISIA JULKAISUJA/FINNISH METEOROLOGICAL INSTITUTE. PUBLICATIONS. irreg. Ilmatieteen Laitos - Finnish Meteorological Institute, P.O. Box 503, SF-00101 Helsinki, Finland. FAX 1929218. TELEX 124436 EFKL SF. E-mail: kirjasto@fmi.fi. **Indexed:** Meteor.& Geoastrophys.Abstr.

551.5 II
INDIA. METEOROLOGICAL DEPARTMENT. MEMOIRS. (Text in English) irreg. price varies. Meteorological Department, Lodi Rd., New Delhi 110003, India. (Dist. by: Controller of Publications, Government of India, Civil Lines, Delhi 110 054, India) **Document type:** government publication.

551.5 II ISSN 0250-6017
INDIAN INSTITUTE OF TROPICAL METEOROLOGY. ANNUAL REPORT. 1971. a. free. Indian Institute of Tropical Meteorology, Dr. Homi Bhabha Rd., Pashan, Pune 411 008, India. circ. controlled.

551.5 II ISSN 0252-1075
INDIAN INSTITUTE OF TROPICAL METEOROLOGY. CONTRIBUTIONS. Key Title: Contributions from the Indian Institute of Tropical Meteorology. 1980. irreg. Indian Institute of Tropical Meteorology, Dr. Homi Bhabha Rd., Pashan, Pune 411 008, India. circ. controlled.
   Supersedes (1971-1980): Indian Institute of Tropical Meteorology. Research Report (ISSN 0250-6009)

INDIAN JOURNAL OF RADIO & SPACE PHYSICS. see *ASTRONOMY*

551.5 RU ISSN 0131-4823
INSTITUT EKSPERIMENTAL'NOI METEOROLOGII. TRUDY. vol.16, 1977. irreg. price varies. Gidrometeoizdat, Ul. Beringa, d.38, 199397 St. Petersburg, Russia. abstr. circ. 400. **Indexed:** Chem.Abstr.
—BLDSC (0296.150000).

INSTITUT ROYAL METEOROLOGIQUE DE BELGIQUE. ANNUAIRE: MAGNETISME TERRESTRE/KONINKLIJK METEOROLOGISCH INSTITUUT VAN BELGIE. JAARBOEK: AARDMAGNETISME. see *EARTH SCIENCES — Geology*

551.6 BE ISSN 0029-7682
QC989.B8
INSTITUT ROYAL METEOROLOGIQUE DE BELGIQUE. BULLETIN MENSUEL: OBSERVATIONS CLIMATOLOGIQUES/KONINKLIJKE METEOROLOGISCH INSTITUUT VAN BELGIE. MAANDBULLETIN: KLIMATOLOGISCHE WAARNEMINGEN. Key Title: Bulletin Mensuel: Observations Climatologiques - Maandbulletin: Klimatologische Waarnemingen. (Text in Dutch, French) 1928. m. 2500 BEF (effective 1994). Institut Royal Meteorologique de Belgique - Koninklijke Meteorologisch Instituut van Belgie, Ave. Circulaire 3, 1180 Brussels, Belgium. TEL 32-2-3730502. FAX 32-2-3751259. TELEX 21315 METEOBRU. charts; stat. circ. 540. **Document type:** bulletin.
—BLDSC (2870.980000).
   Former titles (until 1965): Institut Royal Meteorologique de Belgique. Bulletin Mensuel: Climatologie, Rayonnement, Radioactivite, Declinaison Magnetique (ISSN 0772-358X; (until 1959): Institut Royal Meteorologique de Belgique. Bulletin Mensuel: Apercu Climatologique (ISSN 0772-3598).

551.514 523.01 BE ISSN 0020-2533
INSTITUT ROYAL METEOROLOGIQUE DE BELGIQUE. BULLETIN MENSUEL: OBSERVATIONS IONOSPHERIQUES ET DU RAYONNEMENT COSMIQUE/KONINKLIJK METEOROLOGISCH INSTITUUT VAN BELGIE. MAANDBULLETIN: WAARNEMINGEN VAN DE IONOSFEER EN DE KOSMISCHE STRALING. Key Title: Bulletin Mensuel: Observations Ionospheriques et du Rayonnement Cosmique - Maandbulletin van de Ionosfeer en de Kosmische Straling. (Text in Dutch, French) 1961. m. 2500 BEF. Institut Royal Meteorologique de Belgique - Koninklijk Meteorologisch Instituut van Belgie, Ave. Circulaire 3, 1180 Brussels, Belgium. TEL 32-2-3730502. FAX 32-2-3751259. TELEX 21315 METEOBRU. charts; stat. circ. 320. **Indexed:** Ocean.Abstr., Pollut.Abstr. **Document type:** bulletin.

METEOROLOGY

529 BE ISSN 0007-5280
INSTITUT ROYAL METEOROLOGIQUE DE BELGIQUE. BULLETIN QUOTIDIEN DU TEMPS/KONINKLIJK METEOROLOGISCH INSTITUUT VAN BELGIE. DAGELIJKS WEERBULLETIN. Cover title: Bulletin Quotidien du Temps - Dagelijks Weerbulletin. (Text in Dutch, French) d. 9000 BEF (effective 1994). Institut Royal Meteorologique de Belgique - Koninklijk Meteorologisch Instituut van Belgie, Ave. Circulaire 3, 1180 Brussels, Belgium. TEL 32-2-3730502. FAX 32-2-3751259. TELEX 21315 METEOBRU. charts; stat. circ. 300. **Document type:** bulletin.

551.514 BE ISSN 0770-0164
INSTITUT ROYAL METEOROLOGIQUE DE BELGIQUE. BULLETIN TRIMESTRIEL: OBSERVATIONS D'OZONE/KONINKLIJK METEOROLOGISCH INSTITUUT VAN BELGIE. DRIEMAANDELIJKS BULLETIN: OZON WAARNEMINGEN. Key Title: Bulletin Trimestriel: Observations d'Ozone - Driemaandelijks Bulletin: Ozon Waarnemingen. (Text in Dutch, French) 1965. q. 1100 BEF (effective 1994). Institut Royal Meteorologique de Belgique - Koninklijk Meteorologisch Instituut van Belgie, Ave. Circulaire 3, 1180 Brussels, Belgium. TEL 32-2-3730502. FAX 32-2-3751259. charts. circ. 190. **Indexed:** INSPEC (1976-). **Document type:** bulletin.

551.5 PL ISSN 0208-4325
INSTYTUT METEOROLOGII I GOSPODARKI WODNEJ. GAZETA OBSERWATORA/JOURNAL OF I M W M OBSERVER. Key Title: Gazeta Obserwatora I M G W. 1948. 6/yr. $36. Instytut Meteorologii i Gospodarki Wodnej - Institute of Meteorology and Water Management, 61 Podlesna St., 01-673 Warsaw, Poland. FAX 48-22-345466. TELEX 814331. Ed. Stefan Chojnowski. charts, illus.; cum.index. circ. 3,600.
—BLDSC (4092.300000).
Formerly (until 1973): Gazeta Obserwatora P I H M (ISSN 0208-4341)
Description: Articles on meteorology, hydrology, oceanography, water management, hydrotechnics, water quality, methodic, measurements, and instruments.

551.5 PL ISSN 0239-6262
INSTYTUT METEOROLOGII I GOSPODARKI WODNEJ. MATERIALY BADAWCZE. SERIA: METEOROLOGIA/INSTITUTE OF METEOROLOGY AND WATER MANAGEMENT. RESEARCH PAPERS SERIES: METEOROLOGY. (Text in Polish; summaries in English and Russian) 1974. irregr. $15. Instytut Meteorologii i Gospodarki Wodnej - Institute of Meteorology and Water Management, 61 Podlesna St., 01-673 Warsaw, Poland. FAX 48-22-345466. TELEX 814331. circ. 200.
Description: Articles on meteorology, meteorological elements, observational data, forecastings, measurements, instruments, research works.

551.5 PL ISSN 0208-6263
QC869.4.P63 CODEN: WIMWDL
INSTYTUT METEOROLOGII I GOSPODARKI WODNEJ. WIADOMOSCI/INSTITUTE OF METEOROLOGY AND WATER MANAGEMENT. REPORTS. Cover title: Wiadomosci Instytutu Meteorologii i Gospodarki Wodnej. (Text in Polish; summaries in English and Russian) 1947. q. $80. Instytut Meteorologii i Gospodarki Wodnej - Institute of Meteorology and Water Management, 61 Podlesna St., 01-673 Warsaw, Poland. FAX 48-22-345466. TELEX 814331. Ed. Wlodzimierz Meyer. abstr.; bibl.; charts; illus.; stat.; cum.index. circ. 450. **Indexed:** Deep Sea Res.& Oceanogr.Abstr., Meteor.& Geoastrophys.Abstr.
—CASDDS.
Former titles (until 1978): Wiadomosci Meteorologii i Gospodarki Wodnej (ISSN 0137-2653); (until 1974): Wiadomosci Sluzby Hydrologicznej i Meteorologicznej (ISSN 0043-5171)
Description: Articles on meteorology, hydrology, oceanography, water management, water quality, forecastings, methodics measurements.

551.5 AU ISSN 0074-1663
INTERNATIONAL ASSOCIATION OF METEOROLOGY AND ATMOSPHERIC PHYSICS. REPORT OF PROCEEDINGS OF GENERAL ASSEMBLY. 1924. biennial. $20. International Association of Meteorology and Atmospheric Physics, c/o Prof. M. Kuhn, Institut fuer Met. und Geophys., Univ. Innsbruck, Innrain 52, A-6020 Innsbruck, Austria. TEL 512-5072183. FAX 512-5072170. circ. controlled.

551.576 CN ISSN 0074-3011
INTERNATIONAL CONFERENCE ON CLOUD PHYSICS. PROCEEDINGS. (Proceedings published in host countries) 1968. irreg., 8th, 1982, Aubiere, France. Can.$20. (International Association of Meteorology and Atmospheric Physics) International Commission on Cloud Physics, c/o Prof. R. List, University of Toronto, Toronto, Ont. M5S 1A6, Canada. adv. circ. 1,500.

551.5 574 GW ISSN 0020-7128
QH543 CODEN: IJBMAO
INTERNATIONAL JOURNAL OF BIOMETEOROLOGY. (Text in English) 1957. 4/yr. DM.468($340) (effective 1996). (International Society of Biometeorology) Springer-Verlag, Heidelberger Platz 3, 14197 Berlin, Germany. TEL 030-8207-0. FAX 030-8214091. E-mail: orders@springer.de. (Subscr. in N. America to: Springer-Verlag New York, Inc., 44 Hartz Way, Secaucus, NJ 07096-2491. TEL 201-348-4033. FAX 201-348-4505) Ed. H. Lieth. abstr.; bibl.; charts; illus.; index. circ. 1,300. **Indexed:** Anim.Breed.Abstr., Biol.Abstr., Chem.Abstr., Curr.Adv.Ecol.Sci., Curr.Cont., Dairy Sci.Abstr., Excerp.Med., Geo.Abstr., Helminthol.Abstr., Herb.Abstr., Ind.Med., Ind.Sci.Rev., Ind.Vet., Meteor.& Geoastrophys.Abstr., Pig News & Info., Sci.Cit.Ind., Sel.Water Res.Abstr., Sport Fish.Abstr., Vet.Bull., Wild.Rev., Zoo.Rec. **Document type:** academic/scholarly publication.
—BLDSC (4542.154000); CASDDS; Faxon; Genuine Article; SWETS; UMI; UnCover. **CCC.**
Description: Covers research in plant, animal, human and general biometeorology in the areas of plant-weather interaction, ecological modelling, animal-weather interaction, and the effects of electric, magnetic and electromagnetic fields on biological functions.

551.5 UK ISSN 0899-8418
QC980 CODEN: IJCLEU
INTERNATIONAL JOURNAL OF CLIMATOLOGY. 1981. m. $895 (foreign $895) (effective 1996). (Royal Meteorological Society) John Wiley & Sons Ltd., Journals, Baffins Ln., Chichester, W. Sussex PO19 1UD, England. TEL 01243-779777. FAX 01243-776128. TELEX 86290 WIBOOK G. (Subscr. in the Americas to: John Wiley & Sons, Inc., 605 Third Ave., New York, NY 10158. TEL 212-850-6645. FAX 212-850-6021) Ed. B.D. Giles. adv.; bk.rev.; charts; illus.; maps; index. circ. 578. (also avail. in microform from UMI; back issues avail.; reprint service avail. from SWZ,UMI) **Indexed:** Acid Pre.Dig., Curr.Cont., Deep Sea Res.& Oceanogr.Abstr., Energy Rev., Geo.Abstr., IDA, Ind.Sci.Rev., INSPEC, Meteor.& Geoastrophys.Abstr., Sci.Cit.Ind., Sel.Water Res.Abstr. **Document type:** academic/scholarly publication.
—BLDSC (4542.168000); Ei; Faxon; Genuine Article; SWETS; UMI; UnCover. **CCC.**
Formerly: Journal of Climatology (ISSN 0196-1748)
Description: Spans the field of climatology, encompassing regional and global studies, local and microclimatological investigations, changes in climate, and applications.

551.5 SW ISSN 0349-0068
QC851.I53
INTERNATIONAL METEOROLOGICAL INSTITUTE IN STOCKHOLM. ANNUAL REPORT. (Report year ends June 30) 1973. a. free. International Meteorological Institute in Stockholm, Arrhenius Laboratory, S-106 91 Stockholm, Sweden. FAX 8-157185. Ed. Henning Rodhe. circ. 400. **Document type:** corporate report.

550 JA ISSN 0389-8237
IONOSPHERIC DATA AT SHOWA STATION (ANTARCTICA). s-a. Ministry of Posts and Telecommunications, Communications Research Laboratory - Yuseisho Tsushinsogo Kenkyujo, 2-1 Nukui Kita-machi 4-chome, Koganei-shi, Tokyo 184, Japan. TEL 0423-21-1211. TELEX 2832611-DEMPA-J. stat. **Document type:** government publication.

551.514 JA ISSN 0021-0382
IONOSPHERIC DATA IN JAPAN/DENRISO GEPPO. (Text in English) 1950. m. free. Ministry of Posts and Telecommunications, Communications Research Laboratory, Upper Atmosphere Section - Yuseisho Tsushinsogo Kenkyujo, 2-1, Nukui Kita-machi 4-chome, Koganei-shi, Tokyo 184, Japan. TEL 0423-21-1211. FAX 0423-27-7606. TELEX 2832611 DEMPA J. charts; stat. circ. 250. **Document type:** government publication.

551.5 IS ISSN 0333-7936
ISRAEL. METEOROLOGICAL SERVICE. MONTHLY AGROCLIMATOLOGICAL REPORT. (Headings in English and Hebrew) 1975. m. Meteorological Service, Box 25, Bet Dagan, Israel. **Document type:** government publication.
Former titles: Israel. Meteorological Service. Monthly Agroclimatological Bulletin; Israel. Meteorological Service. Agro-Meteorological Bulletin (ISSN 0002-1806)

551.5 333.91 IS
ISRAEL. METEOROLOGICAL SERVICE. RAINFALL SEASON. (Text in English and Hebrew) a. Meteorological Service, P.O. Box 25, Beit Dagan 50 200, Israel. TEL 03-625231. **Document type:** government publication.

551.5 IS ISSN 0075-126X
ISRAEL. METEOROLOGICAL SERVICE. SERIES B: OBSERVATIONAL DATA. ANNUAL RAINFALL SUMMARY. (Text in Hebrew, summaries in English and Hebrew) 1947. a. Meteorological Service, Box 25, Bet Dagan, Israel. **Document type:** government publication.

551.5 IS ISSN 0075-1286
ISRAEL. METEOROLOGICAL SERVICE. SERIES B: OBSERVATIONAL DATA. ANNUAL WEATHER REPORT. (Text in Hebrew; summaries in English, Hebrew) 1948. a. Meteorological Service, Box 25, Bet Dagan, Israel. **Document type:** government publication.

551.5 IS ISSN 0021-2261
ISRAEL. METEOROLOGICAL SERVICE. SERIES B: OBSERVATIONAL DATA. MONTHLY WEATHER REPORT. (Text and summaries in English, Hebrew) 1947. m. $0.20. Meteorological Service, Box 25, Bet Dagan, Israel. **Document type:** government publication.

551.5 IS ISSN 0026-1122
ISRAEL. METEOROLOGICAL SOCIETY. METEOROLOGIA BE-ISRAEL. (Text in Hebrew) 1963. irreg. $5. Meteorological Society, Box 25, Bet-Dagan, Israel. Ed.Bd. bk.rev.; charts; illus. circ. 300. (processed) **Indexed:** Meteor. & Geoastrophys.Abstr.

551.51 IT ISSN 0075-191X
ISTITUTO DI FISICA DELL'ATMOSFERA, ROME. CONTRIBUTI SCIENTIFICI: PUBBLICAZIONI DI FISICA DELL'ATMOSFERA E DI METEOROLOGIA. (Contributions in English, German and Italian) 1964. irreg. Istituto di Fisica dell'Atmosfera, Piazzale Luigi Sturzo 31, 00144 Rome, Italy. TEL 06-59-10-941. FAX 06-59-15-790. **Indexed:** Meteor.& Geoastrophys.Abstr.

551.51 IT ISSN 0075-1928
ISTITUTO DI FISICA DELL'ATMOSFERA, ROME. PUBBLICAZIONI DIDATTICHE. 1962. irreg. $10. Istituto di Fisica dell'Atmosfera, Piazzale Luigi Sturzo 31, 00144 Rome, Italy. TEL 06-59-10-941. FAX 06-59-15-790. **Indexed:** Meteor.& Geoastrophys.Abstr. **Document type:** monographic series.

551.51 IT ISSN 0075-1936
ISTITUTO DI FISICA DELL'ATMOSFERA, ROME. PUBBLICAZIONI SCIENTIFICHE. (Contributions in English and Italian) 1962. irreg. Istituto di Fisica dell'Atmosfera, Piazzale Luigi Sturzo 31, 00144 Rome, Italy. TEL 06-59-10-941. FAX 06-59-15-790. **Indexed:** Meteor.& Geoastrophys.Abstr. **Document type:** monographic series.

551.51 IT ISSN 0075-1944
ISTITUTO DI FISICA DELL'ATMOSFERA, ROME. PUBBLICAZIONI VARIE.. (Contributions in English and Italian) 1962. irreg. Istituto di Fisica dell'Atmosfera, Piazzale Luigi Sturzo 31, 00144 Rome, Italy. TEL 06-59-10-941. FAX 06-59-15-790. **Indexed:** Meteor.& Geoastrophys.Abstr. **Document type:** monographic series.

551.51 IT ISSN 0075-1952
ISTITUTO DI FISICA DELL'ATMOSFERA, ROME. RAPPORTI INTERNI PROVVISORI ADIFFUSIONE LIMITATA. (Contributions in English and Italian) 1966. irreg. Istituto di Fisica dell'Atmosfera, Piazzale Luigi Sturzo 31, 00144 Rome, Italy. TEL 39-6-59-10-941. FAX 39-6-59-15-790. **Indexed:** Meteor.& Geoastrophys.Abstr. **Document type:** monographic series.

METEOROLOGY 4697

551.51   IT   ISSN 0075-1960
ISTITUTO DI FISICA DELL'ATMOSFERA, ROME. RAPPORTI SCIENTIFICI. (Contributions in English and Italian) 1962. irreg. Istituto di Fisica dell'Atmosfera, Piazzale Luigi Sturzo 31, 00144 Rome, Italy. TEL 39-6-59-10-941. FAX 39-6-59-15-790. **Indexed:** Meteor.& Geostrophys.Abstr. **Document type:** monographic series.

551.51   IT   ISSN 0075-1979
ISTITUTO DI FISICA DELL'ATMOSFERA, ROME. RAPPORTI TECNICI. (Contributions in English, French and Italian) 1961. irreg. Istituto di Fisica dell'Atmosfera, Piazzale Luigi Sturzo 31, 00144 Rome, Italy. TEL 39-6-59-10-941. FAX 39-6-59-15-790. **Indexed:** Meteor.& Geostrophys.Abstr. **Document type:** monographic series.

551   JA   ISSN 0916-5355
IWATEKEN KISHO GEPPO/IWATE PREFECTURE. MONTHLY REPORT OF METEOROLOGY. (Text in Japanese) 1951. m. Kishocho, Morioka Chiho Kishodai - Japan Meteorological Agency, Morioka Local Meteorological Observatory, 7-60, Sannocho, Morioka-shi, Iwate-ken 020, Japan.

551.5   US   ISSN 0148-0227
QC811   CODEN: JGREA2
J G R: JOURNAL OF GEOPHYSICAL RESEARCH. 1896. m. $3510 (foreign $3718). American Geophysical Union, 2000 Florida Ave., N.W., Washington, DC 20009. TEL 202-462-6900. FAX 202-328-0566. TELEX 710-822-9300. (also avail. in microform from AGU) **Indexed:** Environ.Abstr., Geo.Abstr., Geol.Abstr., INIS Atomind., Meteor.& Geostrophys.Abstr.
—BLDSC (4995.000000); CASDDS; Ei; Faxon; Genuine Article; PADDS; SWETS; UnCover. **CCC**.
Formerly (until 1974): Journal of Geophysical Research (ISSN 0022-1406)
Description: Original contributions on the physics and chemistry of the Earth, its environment, and the solar system.
Refereed Serial

551.5
J G R: JOURNAL OF GEOPHYSICAL RESEARCH: ATMOSPHERE. 1896. m. $2460 to non-members (includes J G T: Oceans) (foreign $2550); members $135 (foreign $188); students $65 (foreign $118). American Geophysical Union, 2000 Florida Ave., N.W., Washington, DC 20009. TEL 202-462-6900. FAX 202-328-0566. TELEX 710-822-9300. (also avail. in microform from AGU)
Description: Covers the physics and chemistry of the atmosphere, as well as the atmospheric, biospheric, lithospheric, and hydrospheric interface.

551.65   JA   ISSN 0448-3758
JAPAN METEOROLOGICAL AGENCY. ANNUAL REPORT/KISHOCHO NENPO ZENKOKU KISHOHYO. (Issued in two parts) (Text in English, Japanese) 1887. a. 2163 Yen. Kishocho - Japan Meteorological Agency, 3-4, Otemachi 1-chome, Chiyoda-ku, Tokyo 100, Japan. circ. 724. **Indexed:** Meteor.& Geostrophys.Abstr. **Document type:** government publication.

551.6   JA   ISSN 0075-3467
JAPANESE PROGRESS IN CLIMATOLOGY/NIPPON NO KIKOGAKU NO SHINPO. (Text in English) 1964. a. $20 also available on exchange. Japanese Climatological Seminar - Kikogaku Danwakai, Hosei Daigaku Bungakubu Chirigaku Kyoshitsu, 17-1, Fujimi 2-chome, Chiyoda-ku, Tokyo 102, Japan. TEL 03-3264-9457. Ed. Norihito Satou. circ. 1,050. **Indexed:** Deep Sea Res.& Oceanogr.Abstr., Geo.Abstr., GeoRef. **Document type:** academic/scholarly publication.

551.5 630   JA   ISSN 0021-8588
JOURNAL OF AGRICULTURAL METEOROLOGY/NOGYO KISHO. (Text in English, Japanese; summaries in English) 1943. q. 2060 Yen per no. Society of Agricultural Meteorology of Japan - Nihon Nogyo Kisho Gakkai, University of Tokyo, Department of Agricultural Engineering, Yayoi, Bunkyo, Tokyo 113, Japan. FAX 81-3-3813-2437. Ed. Taichi Maki. adv.; bk.rev.; abstr.; charts; index. circ. 1,100. **Indexed:** Agrindex, Biol.Abstr., Chem.Abstr., Excerp.Med., Field Crop Abstr., Fluidex, Herb.Abstr., Hort.Abstr., Meteor.& Geostrophys.Abstr., Ornam.Hort., Plant Breed.Abstr., Rice Abstr.
—BLDSC (4922.000000).

551.5   US   ISSN 0894-8763
QC851   CODEN: JOAMEZ
JOURNAL OF APPLIED METEOROLOGY. 1962. m. $235 (foreign $265) (effective 1996). American Meteorological Society, 45 Beacon St., Boston, MA 02108-3693. TEL 617-227-2425. FAX 617-742-8718. Ed. Steven R. Hanna. abstr.; bibl.; charts; illus.; stat.; index. circ. 1,978. (back issues avail.; reprint service avail.) **Indexed:** A.S.& T.Ind., Acid Pre.Dig., Appl.Mech.Rev., Biol.Abstr., Biol.& Agr.Ind., Chem.Abstr., Curr.Cont., Deep Sea Res.& Oceanogr.Abstr., Eng.Ind., Environ.Per.Bibl., Excerp.Med., Field Crop Abstr., Fluidex, Forest.Abstr., Geo.Abstr., GeoRef., Herb.Abstr., Hort.Abstr., Ind.Sci.Rev., INIS Atomind., INSPEC, Int.Aerosp.Abstr., Meteor.& Geostrophys.Abstr., Ocean.Abstr., Pollut.Abstr., Sci.Cit.Ind., Sel.Water Res.Abstr., So.Pac.Per.Ind., Soils & Fert. **Document type:** academic/scholarly publication.
—BLDSC (4943.050000); CASDDS; Ei; Faxon; Genuine Article; SWETS; UnCover. **CCC**.
Supersedes in part (in 1988): Journal of Climate and Applied Meteorology (ISSN 0733-3021); **Formerly (until 1983):** Journal of Applied Meteorology (ISSN 0021-8952)
Description: Publishes applied research related to physical meteorology, weather modification, cloud physics, satellite meteorology, air pollution.
Refereed Serial

551.5   US   ISSN 0739-0572
CODEN: JAOTES
JOURNAL OF ATMOSPHERIC AND OCEANIC TECHNOLOGY. 1984. bi-m. $155 (foreign $175 effective 1996). American Meteorological Society, 45 Beacon St., Boston, MA 02108-3693. TEL 617-227-2425. FAX 617-742-8718. Eds. William A. Cooper, Thomas Sanford. abstr.; bibl.; charts; illus.; stat.; index. circ. 798. (back issues avail.; reprint service avail.) **Indexed:** Chem.Abstr., Deep Sea Res.& Oceanogr.Abstr., Geo.Abstr., INSPEC (1984-), Meteor.& Geostrophys.Abstr., Ocean.Abstr., Sel.Water Res.Abstr. **Document type:** trade publication.
—BLDSC (4947.900000); Ei; Faxon; Genuine Article; SWETS; UnCover. **CCC**.
Description: Presents information related to the state-of-the-art development of technical support to the atmospheric and oceanic science.
Refereed Serial

JOURNAL OF ATMOSPHERIC CHEMISTRY. see *CHEMISTRY*

551.5   US   ISSN 0894-8755
QC851   CODEN: JLCLEL
JOURNAL OF CLIMATE. 1986. m. $255 (foreign $285) (effective 1996). American Meteorological Society, 45 Beacon St., Boston, MA 02108-3693. TEL 617-227-2425. FAX 617-742-8718. Ed. Peter J. Lamb. abstr.; bibl.; charts; illus.; stat.; index. circ. 1,689. (back issues avail.; reprint service avail.) **Indexed:** Environ.Per.Bibl., Geo.Abstr., Geol.Abstr., INSPEC (1988-), Meteor.& Geostrophys. Abstr., Sel.Water Res.Abstr. **Document type:** academic/scholarly publication.
—BLDSC (4958.369730); CASDDS; Ei; Faxon; Genuine Article; SWETS; UnCover. **CCC**.
Supersedes in part (in 1988): Journal of Climate and Applied Meteorology (ISSN 0733-3021); **Formerly (until 1983):** Journal of Applied Meteorology (ISSN 0021-8952)
Description: Provides a focus for articles on climate research and impact analysis.
Refereed Serial

551.1   JA   ISSN 0368-5942
JOURNAL OF METEOROLOGICAL RESEARCH/KISHOCHO KENKYU JIHO. (Text in Japanese; summaries in English) 1891. bi-m. Kishocho - Japan Meteorological Agency, 3-4, Otemachi 1-chome, Chiyoda-ku, Tokyo 100, Japan. circ. 879. **Indexed:** INIS Atomind., Jap.Per.Ind., Meteor.& Geostrophys.Abstr.
—BLDSC (5018.800000).

551.5   UK   ISSN 0307-5966
JOURNAL OF METEOROLOGY. 1975. 10/yr. $180 (effective 1995-1996). (Tornado & Storm Research Organisation) Artetech Publishing Co., 54 Frome Rd., Bradford-on-Avon, Wilts. BA15 1LD, England. TEL 01225-862482. FAX 01225-86560. Ed. G.T. Meaden. adv.; bk.rev.; index. **Indexed:** Deep Sea Res.& Oceanogr.Abstr., Ecol.Abstr., Geo.Abstr., W.R.C.Inf. **Document type:** academic/scholarly publication.
—BLDSC (5019.020000); Ei; Faxon; SWETS; UMI; UnCover.
Description: Aimed at those interested in climate and the weather, and man's effect on them.
Refereed Serial

551.5   US   ISSN 0022-4928
QC851   CODEN: JATSDF
JOURNAL OF THE ATMOSPHERIC SCIENCES. 1944. s-m. $390 (foreign $430) (effective 1996). American Meteorological Society, 45 Beacon St., Boston, MA 02108-3693. TEL 617-227-2425. FAX 617-742-8718. Eds. Robert L. Gall, G. Brant Foote. abstr.; bibl.; charts; illus.; stat.; index. circ. 2,136. (back issues avail.; reprint service avail.) **Indexed:** A.S.& T.Ind., Acid Pre.Dig., Chem.Abstr., Excerp.Med., Gen.Sci.Ind., Geo.Abstr., GeoRef., Ind.Sci.Rev., INIS Atomind., INSPEC, Int.Aerosp.Abstr., Math.R., Meteor.& Geostrophys.Abstr., Sel.Water Res.Abstr., So.Pac.Per.Ind. **Document type:** academic/scholarly publication.
—BLDSC (4949.200000); CASDDS; Ei; Faxon; Genuine Article; SWETS; UnCover. **CCC**.
Description: Publishes basic research related to the physics and dynamics of the atmosphere of the earth and other planets, with emphasis on the quantitative and deductive aspects of the subject.
Refereed Serial

551.63   US   ISSN 0739-1781
CODEN: JWMOEL
JOURNAL OF WEATHER MODIFICATION. 1969. a. $50. Weather Modification Association, Box 8116, Fresno, CA 93747. TEL 209-434-3486. FAX 209-434-3486. Ed. James A. Miller. adv. contact: Hilda Duckering. cum.index: 1969-1991. circ. 500. (back issues avail.) **Indexed:** INSPEC (1987-). **Document type:** academic/scholarly publication.
—UnCover.

551   JA   ISSN 0916-5126
KAGAWAKEN KISHO GEPPO/KAGAWA PREFECTURE. MONTHLY REPORT OF METEOROLOGY. (Text in Japanese) 1946. m. Kishocho, Takamatsu Chiho Kishodai - Japan Meteorological Agency, Takamatsu Local Meteorological Observatory, 1277-1, Fuseishicho, Takamatsu-shi, Kagawa-ken 761, Japan.

551.65 630   JA   ISSN 0022-7706
KAGOSHIMAKEN NOGYO KISHO GEPPO/KAGOSHIMA PREFECTURE. MONTHLY REPORT OF METEOROLOGY. (Text in Japanese) 1923. m. Kishocho, Kagoshima Chiho Kishoda - Japan Meteorological Agency, Kagoshima Local Meteorological Observatory, 24-13, Arata 1-chome, Kagoshima-shi, Kagoshima-ken 890, Japan. charts; stat.

551.6   JA
KAIJO KISHO GAIHO/MARINE METEOROLOGICAL REPORT. (Text in Japanese) 1954. m. Kishocho, Maizuru Kaiyo Kishodai - Japan Meteorological Agency, Maizuru Marine Observatory, 901, Shimofukui, Maizuru-shi, Kyoto 624, Japan.

942 551.5   JA
KAISHO NENPO/ANNUAL REPORT OF MARITIME METEOROLOGY. (Text in Japanese) 1979. a. Kensetsusho, Kasenkyoku - Ministry of Construction, River Bureau, 1-3, Kasumigaseki 2-chome, Chiyoda-ku, Tokyo 100, Japan.

KAISHO TO KISHO/OCEANOGRAPHY AND METEOROLOGY. see *EARTH SCIENCES — Oceanography*

551   JA   ISSN 0449-7392
KANAGAWAKEN KISHO GEPPO/KANAGAWA PREFECTURE. MONTHLY REPORT OF METEOROLOGY. (Text in Japanese) 1950. m. Kishocho, Yokohama Chiho Kishodai - Japan Meteorological Agency, Yokohama Local Meteorological Observatory, 99 Yamatecho, Naka-ku, Yokohama-shi, Kanagawa-ken 231, Japan.

METEOROLOGY

551.5   JA
KANSOKUJO KISHO NENPO/ANNUAL REPORT OF CLIMATOLOGICAL STATIONS. (Text in Japanese) 1968. a. 3800 Yen. (Japan Meteorological Agency) Japan Weather Association, 2-9-2, Kanda-nishikicho, Chiyoda-ku, Tokyo 101, Japan. TEL 81-3-3295-1525. FAX 81-3-3295-1097. circ. 542. **Indexed:** Meteor.& Geoastrophys.Abstr. **Document type:** government publication.

551.5   RU
KATALOG RADIATSIONNYKH DANNYKH/CATALOGUE OF SOLAR RADIATION DATA. 1987. a. $15 (effective 1994). Glavnaya Geofizicheskaya Observatoriya im. A.I. Voeikova, Mirovoi Tsentr Radiatsionnykh Dannykh - Voeikov Main Geophysical Observatory, World Radiation Data Centre, Ul. Karbysheva 7, St. Petersburg 194018, Russia. TEL 812-247-01-03. FAX 812-247-86-61. Dir. E.P. Borisenkov.

551.5   JA
KAZE NI KANSURU SHINPOJUMU KOEN YOSHISHU/PROCEEDINGS OF THE WIND SYMPOSIUM. (Text in Japanese) a. Jishin Gakkai - Seismological Society of Japan, Tokyo Daigaku Jishin Kenkyujo, 1-1, Yayoi 1-chome, Bunkyo-ku, Tokyo 113, Japan.

551.656   KE
KENYA METEOROLOGICAL DEPARTMENT. ANNUAL REPORT. 1929. a. Meteorological Department, P.O. Box 30259, Dagoretti Corner, Ngong Rd., Nairobi, Kenya. circ. 1,200.
   Supersedes in part: East African Community. East African Meteorological Department. Annual Report.

551   JA   ISSN 0916-474X
KIKO EIKYO RIYO KENKYUKAI KAIHO/JAPANESE STUDY GROUP FOR THE W C I P AND W C A P NEWSLETTER. (Text in Japanese) 1984. a. Kiko Eikyo Riyo Kenkyukai - Japanese Study Group for the W C I P and W C A P, c/o Yoshino Kenkyushitsu, Tsukuba Daigaku Chikyu Kagakukei, 1-1, Tennodai 1-chome, Tsukuba-shi, Ibaraki-ken 305, Japan. **Document type:** newsletter.

551.6   JA   ISSN 0916-166X
KIKOGAKU KISHOGAKU KENKYU HOKOKU/RESEARCH REPORT OF METEOROLOGY AND CLIMATOLOGY. (Text in Japanese) a.? University of Tsukuba, Institute of Geoscience - Tsukuba Daigaku Chikyu Kagakukei, 1-1, Tennodai 1-chome, Tsukuba-shi, Ibaraki-ken 305, Japan.

551.636   JA   ISSN 0916-927X
KIKOKEI KANSHI HOKOKU/MONTHLY REPORT ON CLIMATE SYSTEM. (Text in English, Japanese) 1960. m. 13390 Yen. Kishocho, Yohobu - Japan Meteorological Agency, Forecast Department, 3-4, Otemachi 1-chome, Chiyoda-ku, Tokyo 100, Japan. stat. circ. 624.
   Formerly (until 1987): Japan Meteorological Agency. Mean Maps. Long Range Weather Forecasting.

551   JA
KINNEN NI OKERU SEKAI NO IJO KISHO TO KIKO HENDO/REPORT OF UNUSUAL METEOROLOGY AND CLIMATIC VARIATION IN RECENT YEARS. (Text in Japanese) 1974. every 5 yrs. 1400 Yen per no. (Kishocho - Japan Meteorological Agency) Okurasho Insatsukyoku - Ministry of Finance, Printing Bureau, 2-4, Toranomon 2-chome, Minato-ku, Tokyo 105, Japan. **Document type:** government publication.

551   JA   ISSN 0450-3325
KISHO/JAPAN WEATHER ASSOCIATION. WEATHER. (Text in Japanese) 1952. m. 500 Yen per no. Japan Weather Association - Nihon Kisho Kyokai, 9-2, Kanda Nishikicho 2-chome, Chiyoda-ku, Tokyo 101, Japan. TEL 81-3-3295-1525. FAX 81-3-3295-1097.

551.6 629.1   JA   ISSN 0388-9653
KISHO EISEI SENTA GIJUTSU HOKOKU/METEOROLOGICAL SATELLITE CENTER TECHNICAL NOTE. (Text in English, Japanese) 1980. s-a. Kishocho, Kisho Eisei Senta - Japan Meteorological Agency, Meteorological Satellite Center, 3-235, Nakakiyoto, Kiyose-shi, Tokyo 204, Japan.

551 629.1   JA   ISSN 0287-9247
KISHO EISEI SENTA NYUSU/METEOROLOGICAL SATELLITE CENTER NEWS. (Text in Japanese) 1983. q. Kishocho, Kisho Eisei Senta - Japan Meteorological Agency, Meteorological Satellite Center, 3-235, Nakakiyoto, Kiyose-shi, Tokyo 204, Japan.

551   JA
KISHO GYOMU HOKOKU CHOSA SHUKEISHO/ANNUAL REPORT OF METEOROLOGICAL SERVICE. (Text in Japanese) a. Kishocho, Somubu - Japan Meteorological Agency, General Administration Division, 3-4, Otemachi 1-chome, Chiyoda-ku, Tokyo 100, Japan.

551   JA
KISHO KAISHO YORAN/REVIEW ON METEOROLOGY AND MARITIME METEOROLOGY. (Text in Japanese) a. 15000 Yen. Japan Weather Association - Nihon Kisho Kyokai, 9-2, Kanda Nishikicho 2-chome, Chiyoda-ku, Tokyo 101, Japan. TEL 81-3-3295-1525. FAX 81-3-3295-1097.

551   JA
KISHO KANSOKUKYO TETTO KANSOKU SHIRYO/REPORT OF OBSERVATION AT THE METEOROLOGICAL OBSERVATION TOWER. (Text in English, Japanese) 1982. triennial. Kishocho, Kisho Kenkyujo - Japan Meteorological Agency, Meteorological Research Institute, 1-1, Nagamine, Tsukuba-shi, Ibaraki-ken 305, Japan.

551   JA   ISSN 0386-4049
KISHO KENKYUJO GIJUTSU HOKOKU/METEOROLOGICAL RESEARCH INSTITUTE. TECHNICAL REPORTS. (Text in Japanese; summaries in English, Japanese) 1978. irreg. Kishocho, Kisho Kenkyujo - Japan Meteorological Agency, Meteorological Research Institute, 1-1, Nagamine, Tsukuba-shi, Ibaraki-ken 305, Japan. **Indexed:** Jap.Per.Ind.

551   JA
KISHO KENKYUJO NYUSU/METEOROLOGICAL RESEARCH INSTITUTE NEWS. (Text in Japanese) 1965. m. Kishocho, Kisho Kenkyujo - Japan Meteorological Agency, Meteorological Research Institute, 1-1, Nagamine, Tsukuba-shi, Ibaraki-ken 305, Japan.

551   JA
KISHO NENKAN/YEARBOOK OF METEOROLOGY. (Text in Japanese) a. 3100 Yen. Japan Weather Association - Nihon Kisho Kyokai, 9-1, Kanda Nishikicho 2-chome, Chiyoda-ku, Tokyo 101, Japan. TEL 81-3-3295-1525. FAX 81-3-3295-1097.

551.6   JA   ISSN 0917-494X
KISHO RIYO KENKYU/APPLIED CLIMATE RESOURCES RESEARCH. (Text in Japanese) 1988. a. 2000 Yen. Kisho Riyo Kenkyukai - Applied Climate Resources Research Association, Kyushu Daigaku Nogakubu Nogyo Kishogaku Kyoshitsu, 10-1, Hakozaki 6-chome, Higashi-ku, Fukuoka-shi, Fukuoka-ken 812, Japan. TEL 81-92-641-1101. FAX 81-92-641-2928. Ed. T. Takemasa. adv. contact: T. Kobayashi. bk.rev. circ. 280. **Document type:** academic/scholarly publication.
   Description: Contains reports, opinions, lectures, interpretations and reviews on applied meteorology and climate resources.
   Refereed Serial

551 630   JA
KISHO TO NOSAGYO/METEOROLOGY AND AGRICULTURE. (Text in Japanese) 1967. m. Kishocho, Kumamoto Chiho Kishodai - Japan Meteorological Agency, Kumamoto Local Meteorological Observatory, 12-2-, Kymachi 2-chome, Kumamoto-shi, Kumamoto-ken 860, Japan.

551.65   JA   ISSN 0448-374X
KISHOCHO GEPPO ZENKOKU KISHOHYO/JAPAN METEOROLOGICAL AGENCY. MONTHLY REPORT. METEOROLOGICAL OBSERVATIONS. (Text in Japanese, English) 1892. m. $227. Kishocho - Japan Meteorological Agency, 3-4, Otemachi 1-chome, Chiyoda-ku, Tokyo 100, Japan.

551   JA
KISHOCHO KAIYO JUNPO/TEN-DAY MARINE REPORT. (Text in English, Japanese) 1946. 3/m. Kishocho, Kaiyo Kishobu - Japan Meteorological Agency, Marine Department, 3-4, Otemachi 1-chome, Chiyoda-ku, Tokyo 100, Japan.

551.5   JA
KISHOCHO KANSOKU GIJUTSU SHIRYO/JAPAN METEOROLOGICAL AGENCY. TECHNICAL DATA SERIES. (Text in English, Japanese) 1956. a. 2000 Yen. Kishocho - Japan Meteorological Agency, 3-4, Otemachi 1-chome, Chiyoda-ku, Tokyo 100, Japan. circ. 461.

551   JA
KISHOCHO KISHO KENKYUJO KENKYU HOKOKUSHO/METEOROLOGICAL RESEARCH INSTITUTE. ANNUAL RESEARCH REPORT. (Text in Japanese) 1966. a. Kishocho, Kisho Kenkyujo - Japan Meteorological Agency, Meteorological Research Institute, 1-1, Nagamine, Tsukuba-shi, Ibaraki-ken 305, Japan.

551.5   JA   ISSN 0387-5369
                       CODEN: KNOTDR
KISHOU KENKYUU NOTE/METEOROLOGICAL STUDY NOTE. (Text in Japanese) irreg., latest No.175. price varies. Meteorological Society of Japan - Nihon Kisho Gakkai, c/o Japan Meteorological Agency, 1-3-4 Ote-machi, Chiyoda-ku, Tokyo 100, Japan. TEL 03-3212-8341. FAX 03-3216-4401. —CASDDS.

551.6   GW
KLIMA-EILINFORMATION. 1972. m. DM.20. Deutscher Wetterdienst, Bibliothek, Postfach 100465, 63004 Offenbach a.M., Germany. TEL 069-8062-2271. FAX 069-80622486. **Document type:** government publication.
   Description: Updates on the weather in Germany.

551.5   RU
KLIMAT I GIDROGRAFIYA ZABAIKAL'YA. 1972. irreg. 0.40 Rub. Geograficheskoe Obshchestvo S.S.S.R., Zabaikal'skii Filial, Chita, Russia. illus.

551.6   GW
KLIMATOLOGISCHE WERTE. 1968. m. DM.20. Deutscher Wetterdienst, Bibliothek, Postfach 100465, 63004 Offenbach a.M., Germany. TEL 069-8062-2271. FAX 069-80622486. **Document type:** government publication.

KOBE KAIYO KISHODAI. IHO/KOBE MARINE OBSERVATORY. BULLETIN. see *EARTH SCIENCES — Oceanography*

551   JA
KOCHIKEN KISHO GEPPO/KOCHI PREFECTURE. MONTHLY REPORT OF METEOROLOGY. (Text in Japanese) 1904. m. Kishocho, Kochi Chiho Kishodai - Japan Meteorological Agency, Kochi Local Meteorological Observatory, 3-41, Honmachi 4-chome, Kochi-shi, Kochi-ken 780, Japan.

551   JA
KOKUSETSU RISETSU GIJUTSU KENKYU/STUDY ON CONQUEST AND UTILIZATION OF SNOW.* (Text in Japanese) 1986. a. 8000 Yen. Nihon Shisutemu Kaihatsu Kenkyujo - Systems Research and Development Institute of Japan, c/o Nihon Seppyo Gakkai, Rm. 207, Belvedere-Kudan, Fujimi 2-15-5, Chiyoda-ku, Tokyo 102, Japan.

551.6 630   JA
KONGETSU NO TENKO TO NORIN SAGYO/MONTHLY NEWS OF WEATHER, AGRICULTURE AND FORESTRY. (Text in Japanese) 1967. m. Kishocho, Matsue Chiho Kishodai - Japan Meteorological Agency, Matsue Local Meteorological Observatory, 1-11, Nishitsuda 7-chome, Matsue-shi, Shimane-ken 690, Japan.

551.5   KO
KOREA (REPUBLIC). KOREA METEOROLOGICAL SERVICE. ANNUAL REPORT.* a. 1900 Won($2) Korea Meteorological Service, c/o Ministry of Public Information, 82 Sejong-no, Chongno-ku, Seoul 110050, S. Korea.
   Formerly: Korea (Republic). Central Meteorological Office. Annual Report.

551.5   KO
KOREA (REPUBLIC). KOREA METEOROLOGICAL SERVICE. MONTHLY WEATHER REPORT.* (Text in English, Korean) 1974. m. free. Korea Meteorological Service, c/o Ministry of Public Information, 82 Sejong-no, Chongno-ku, Seoul 110050, S. Korea. charts; stat.
   Formerly: Korea (Republic). Central Meteorological Office. Monthly Weather Report (ISSN 1012-702X)

METEOROLOGY

551 JA ISSN 0373-5842
KOSO KISHODAI IHO/AEROLOGICAL OBSERVATORY AT TATENO. JOURNAL. (Text in Japanese; summaries in English, Japanese) 1923. a. Kishocho, Koso Kishodai - Japan Meteorological Agency, Aerological Observatory, 1-2, Nagamine, Tsukuba-shi, Ibaraki-ken 305, Japan. Indexed: Jap.Per.Ind.

551.5 JA
KUMAMOTO PREFECTURE. MONTHLY REPORT. 1953. m. Kumamoto Prefecture, 12-20, Kyo-machi 2-chome, Kumamoto-shi, Kumamoto-ken 860, Japan. circ. 100.

551 JA
KUMAMOTOKEN KISHO GEPPO/KUMAMOTO PREFECTURE. MONTHLY REPORT OF METEOROLOGY. (Text in Japanese) 1951. m. Kishocho, Kumamoto Chiho Kishodai - Japan Meteorological Agency, Kumamoto Local Meteorological Observatory, 12-20, Kyomachi 2-chome, Kumamoto-shi, Kumamoto-ken 860, Japan.

551.5 FI ISSN 0303-2485
QC989.F3
KUUKAUSIKATSAUS SUOMEN ILMASTOON/MAANADSOEVERSIKT OEVER FINLANDS KLIMAT. (Text and summaries in Finnish and Swedish) 1907. m. FIM 140 in Scandinavia; in Europe FIM 270; elsewhere FIM 290. Painatuskeskus Oy, P.O. Box 516, FIN-00101 Helsinki, Finland. Ed. Veikko A. Helminen. (back issues avail.) Document type: government publication.
  Description: Examines climatological and meteorological data.

551 JA ISSN 0916-5169
KYOTOFU KISHO GEPPO/KYOTO PREFECTURE. MONTHLY REPORT OF METEOROLOGY. (Text in Japanese) 1951. m. Kishocho, Kyoto Chiho Kishodai - Japan Meteorological Agency, Kyoto Local Meteorological Observatory, 38, Nishinokyo Kasadonomachi, Nakagyo-ku, Kyoto-shi, Kyoto 604, Japan.

551.5 US
LOCAL CLIMATOLOGICAL DATA. (Published separately in: 274 cities) 1897. m. (plus a. update). $22 per city. U.S. National Climatic Data Center, National Oceanic and Atmospheric Administration, U.S. Department of Commerce, Federal Bldg., Rm. 120, 151 Patton Ave., Asheville, NC 28801-5001. TEL 704-271-4756. FAX 704-271-4876. TELEX 6502643731. E-mail: orders@ncdc.noaa.gov. circ. 33,000. (also avail. in microfiche; back issues avail.) Document type: government publication.
  Former titles (until 1951): Monthly Climatological Summary; (until 1947): Monthly Meteorological Summary.

551.6 CN ISSN 0076-1931
QC851
MCGILL UNIVERSITY, MONTREAL. DEPARTMENT OF GEOGRAPHY. CLIMATOLOGICAL RESEARCH SERIES. 1966. irreg. price varies. McGill University, Department of Geography, 805 Sherbrooke St. W., Montreal, Que. H3A 2R6, Canada. TEL 514-392-5700. Eds. T. Moore, J. Lewis.

551.63 JA ISSN 0460-7317
MAIZURU KAIYO KISHODAI YOHO/MAIZURU MARINE OBSERVATORY. BULLETIN. (Text in English, Japanese) 1950. irreg. Kishocho, Maizuru Kaiyo Kishodai - Japan Meteorological Agency, Maizuru Marine Observatory, 901, Shimofukui, Maizuru-shi, Kyoto 624, Japan.

551.5 MW
MALAWI. METEOROLOGICAL DEPARTMENT. MONTHLY SUMMARIES. (Text in English) 1969. m. free. Meteorological Department, Box 2, Chileka, Malawi. TELEX 44611. circ. 100.
  Formerly: Malawi. Meteorological Services. Monthly Summaries.

551.5 MW
MALAWI. METEOROLOGICAL DEPARTMENT. TOTALS OF MONTHLY AND ANNUAL RAINFALL. (Text and summaries in English) 1969. a. K.1. Meteorological Department, Box 2, Chileka, Malawi. TELEX 44611. stat.
  Formerly: Malawi. Meteorological Services. Totals of Monthly and Annual Rainfall.

551.5 MY
MALAYSIAN METEOROLOGICAL SERVICE. ANNUAL SUMMARY OF METEOROLOGICAL OBSERVATIONS. (Text and summaries in English) 1930. a. M.30. Malaysian Meteorological Service - Perkhidmatan Kajicuaca Malaysia, Jalan Sultan, Petaling Jaya 46667, Selangor, Malaysia. FAX 6-03-7550964. TELEX MA 37245. circ. 210. Indexed: Meteor.& Geostrophys.Abstr.
  Former titles: Malaysian Meteorological Service. Summary of Observations for Malaysia (ISSN 0126-8864); Malaysia. Meteorological Service. Summary of Observations for Malaya, Sabah and Sarawak.

551 UK ISSN 0025-3251
QC851
MARINE OBSERVER; a quarterly journal of maritime meteorology. 1924. q. £19 (effective 1994). H.M.S.O., 51 Nine Elms Ln., London SW8 5DR, England. TEL 071-873-0011. FAX 071-873-8463. (Subscr. to: H.M.S.O., Publications Centre, P.O. Box 276, London SW8 5DT, England. TEL 071-873-9090. FAX 071-873-8200) adv.; bk.rev.; charts; illus.; maps; index. (also avail. in microform from UMI; reprint service avail. from UMI) Indexed: Chem.Abstr., Deep Sea Res.& Oceanogr.Abstr., Geo.Abstr., Meteor.& Geostrophys.Abstr., Ocean.Abstr., Pollut.Abstr. Document type: government publication, academic/scholarly publication.
—BLDSC (5377.000000); UMI; UnCover.

551 US ISSN 0025-3367
QC994
MARINERS WEATHER LOG; a climatic review of North Atlantic and North Pacific Ocean and Great Lake areas. 1957. q. $12 (foreign $15). U.S. National Oceanographic Data Center, NOAA-NESDIS, E-OC2, Universal Bldg. 1, Rm. 415, 1825 Connecticut Ave., N.W., Washington, DC 20235. TEL 202-606-4561. (Subscr. to: Superintendent of Documents, U.S. Government Printing Office, Box 371954, Pittsburgh, PA 15250-7950. TEL 202-512-1800. FAX 202-512-2250) Ed. Richard De Angelis. charts; illus.; stat.; index. circ. 7,500. (also avail. in microform from MIM,UMI; microfiche from CIS; back issues avail; reprint service avail. from CIS) Indexed: Amer.Stat.Ind. (1975-), Deep Sea Res.& Oceanogr.Abstr., Ind.U.S.Gov.Per., Meteor.& Geostrophys.Abstr., Ocean.Abstr., Pollut.Abstr., So.Pac.Per.Ind. Document type: government publication.
—Faxon; UMI; UnCover.
  Description: Furnishes information on the weather affecting marine commerce.

551.5 MF ISSN 0076-5511
MAURITIUS. METEOROLOGICAL SERVICES. REPORT. a. price varies. Government Printing Office, Elizabeth II Ave., Port Louis, Mauritius.

551.5 II ISSN 0252-9416
QC851 CODEN: MAUSDJ
MAUSAM. (Text in English and Hindi) 1950. q. Rs.200($72) Meteorological Department, Lodi Rd., New Delhi 110 003, India. (Dist. by: Department of Publication, Government of India, Civil Lines, Delhi 110 054, India) Ed. N. Sen Roy. adv.; bk.rev.; abstr.; charts; illus.; index. circ. 850. Indexed: Chem.Abstr., Deep Sea Res.& Oceanogr.Abstr., GeoRef., INSPEC, Meteor.& Geostrophys.Abstr., Rice Abstr., Sel.Water Res.Abstr. Document type: government publication.
—BLDSC (5413.279550); UnCover.
  Former titles: Indian Journal of Meteorology, Hydrology and Geophysics (ISSN 0376-4796); Indian Journal of Meteorology and Geophysics (ISSN 0019-5383).

551 JA
MEIKEN KISHO GEPPO/MIE PREFECTURE. MONTHLY REPORT OF METEOROLOGY. (Text in Japanese) 1956. m. Kishocho, Tsu Chiho Kishodai - Japan Meteorological Agency, Tsu Local Meteorological Observatory, Tsu Dai 2 Chiho Godo Chosha, 327-2, Shimazakicho, Tsu-shi, Mie-ken 514, Japan.

551.5 UK ISSN 1350-4827
▼**METEOROLOGICAL APPLICATIONS.** 1994. q. £106($188) (effective 1996). (Royal Meteorological Society) Cambridge University Press, The Edinburgh Bldg., Shaftesbury Rd., Cambridge DB2 2RU, England. TEL 01223-312393. FAX 01223-315052. TELEX 851817256. (N. American addr.: Cambridge University Press, Journals Division, 40 W. 20th St., New York, NY 10011. TEL 212-924-3900. FAX 212-691-3239) Ed. R.W. Riddaway. adv.; bk.rev. (back issues avail.; reprint service avail. from ISI) Document type: academic/scholarly publication.
—BLDSC (5705.280000); UMI. CCC.
  Description: Covers the analysis and prediction of weather events and the tools, models and methods used.

551.65 JA ISSN 0018-3423
METEOROLOGICAL DATA OF HOKKAIDO/HOKKAIDO NO KISHO. (Text in Japanese) 1957. m. (plus special issue). 5500 Yen. Japan Weather Association, Administration Division, Kita 4-jo Nish 23-1-18, Chuo-ku, Sapporo-shi, Hokkaido 064, Japan. TEL 011-622-2230. FAX 011-640-2383. Ed. Jigyo Bu. bk.rev.; illus.; stat.; index.

551.5 UK ISSN 0026-1149
QC851 CODEN: MTMGA5
METEOROLOGICAL MAGAZINE. 1866. m. £40 (effective 1994). H.M.S.O., 51 Nine Elms Ln., London SW8 5DR, England. TEL 071-873-0011. FAX 071-873-8463. (Subscr. to: H.M.S.O. Publications Centre, P.O. Box 276, London SW8 5DT, England. TEL 071-873-9090. FAX 071-873-8200) Ed. R.P.W. Lewis. adv.; bk.rev.; abstr.; bibl.; charts; illus.; index. circ. 1,950. (also avail. in microfiche from BHP; reprint service avail. from UMI) Indexed: Chem.Abstr., Curr.Adv.Ecol.Sci., Curr.Cont., Deep Sea Res.& Oceanogr.Abstr., Geo.Abstr., Hort.Abstr., INSPEC, Meteor.& Geostrophys.Abstr., Sci.Cit.Ind., Sel.Water Res.Abstr., So.Pac.Per.Ind., Soils & Fert. Document type: government publication, academic/scholarly publication.
—Faxon; Genuine Article; UMI; UnCover. CCC.

551 629.1 JA ISSN 0387-4028
METEOROLOGICAL SATELLITE CENTER. MONTHLY REPORT. (Text in English) 1978. m. Kishocho, Kisho Eisei Senta - Japan Meteorological Agency, Meteorological Satellite Center, 3-235, Nakakiyoto, Kiyose-shi, Tokyo 204, Japan.

551.5 JA ISSN 0026-1165
QC851 CODEN: JMSJAU
METEOROLOGICAL SOCIETY OF JAPAN. JOURNAL/KISHO SHUSHI. (Text in English) 1882. bi-m. 6600 Yen to individuals; institutions 10200Yen. Meteorological Society of Japan - Nihon Kisho Gakkai, c/o Japan Meteorological Agency, 1-3-4 Ote-machi, Chiyoda-ku, Tokyo 100, Japan. TEL 03-3212-8341. FAX 03-3216-4401. Ed. M. Murakami. circ. 2,000. Indexed: Chem.Abstr., Deep Sea Res.& Oceanogr.Abstr., Geo.Abstr., INIS Atomind., JTA, Meteor.& Geostrophys.Abstr., Sel.Water Res.Abstr.
—BLDSC (4825.000000); CASDDS; Faxon; Genuine Article; UnCover. CCC.

551 JA
METEOROLOGICAL SOCIETY OF JAPAN. PREPRINTS OF MEETING/NIHON KISHO GAKKAI TAIKAI KOEN YOKOSHU. (Text in English, Japanese) s-a. Meteorological Society of Japan - Nihon Kisho Gakkai, Kishocho, 3-4 Otemachi 1-chome, Chiyoda-ku, Tokyo 100, Japan.

METEOROLOGY

551.5   **FI**   ISSN 1235-0419
QC989.R5
METEOROLOGICAL YEARBOOK OF FINLAND. (Text in English, Finnish) 1991. a. price varies. Ilmatieteen Laitos - Finnish Meteorological Institute, P.O. Box 503, SF-00101 Helsinki, Finland. FAX 1929218. TELEX 124436 EFKL SF. E-mail: kirjasto@fmi.fi.
Formed by the merger of (1981-1991): Meteorological Yearbook of Finland. Part 1. Climatological Data (ISSN 0076-6747); (1960-1991): Meteorological Yearbook of Finland. Part 2. Precipitation and Snow Cover Data (ISSN 0076-6755); (1984-1991): Meteorological Yearbook of Finland. Part 3. Statistics of Radiosonde Observations (Years) (ISSN 0780-7295); (1982-1991): Meteorological Yearbook of Finland. Part 4.1. Measurements of Solar Radiation (ISSN 0783-103X) & Meteorological Yearbook of Finland. Part 4.2. Measurements of Sunshine Duration (ISSN 0783-0556)
Description: Review of climatological data in Finland.

551.5   **XR**   ISSN 0026-1173
QC851   CODEN: MEZPAQ
METEOROLOGICKE ZPRAVY. (Text in Czech or Slovak; summaries in English, German, Russian) 1948. bi-m. $27.70. Cesky Hydrometeorologicky Ustav, Na Sabatce 17, 143 06 Prague 4, Czech Republic. (Subscr. to: Artia, Ve Smeckach 30, 111 27 Prague 1, Czech Republic) (Co-sponsor: Slovensky Hydrometeorologicky Ustav (XO)) Ed. O. Sebek. adv.; bk.rev.; bibl.; charts; illus.; maps; stat.; index. **Indexed:** Chem.Abstr., Field Crop Abstr., Herb.Abstr., Meteor.& Geoastrophys.Abstr., Ref.Zh.
—BLDSC (5739.400000).

551.5   **GW**   ISSN 0026-1203
QC851
METEOROLOGISCHE ABHANDLUNGEN. (Text in English or German) 1950. irreg. price varies. (Freie Universitaet Berlin, Institut fuer Meteorologie) Dietrich Reimer Verlag, Unter den Eichen 57, 12203 Berlin, Germany. TEL 030-8314081. FAX 030-8313873. charts; illus.; index. **Document type:** bulletin.

551.5   **GW**   ISSN 0941-2948
                   CODEN: MEZEEV
METEOROLOGISCHE ZEITSCHRIFT. (Text and summaries in English and German) 1948. 6/yr. $301 (effective 1996). (Deutsche Meteorologische Gesellschaft) Gebrueder Borntraeger Verlagsbuchhandlung, Johannesstr. 3A, 70176 Stuttgart, Germany. TEL 0711-625001. FAX 0711-625005. Ed.Bd. adv.; bk.rev.; bibl.; charts; illus.; index. (back issues avail.) **Indexed:** Appl.Mech.Rev., Bibl.Cart., Chem.Abstr., Curr.Cont., Deep Sea Res.& Oceanogr.Abstr., Excerp.Med., Ind.Sci.Rev., INSPEC, Int.Aerosp.Abstr., Meteor.& Geoastrophys.Abstr. **Document type:** academic/scholarly publication.
—BLDSC (5742.180000); Faxon; UMI. **CCC.**
Formerly: Meteorologische Rundschau (ISSN 0026-1211)

551.5   **NO**   ISSN 0373-4463
METEOROLOGISKE ANNALER. (Text in English) vol.6, 1974. m. Norske Meteorologiske Institutt, Blindern, Oslo 3, Norway. Ed. O. Haug. charts.

551.5   **RU**   ISSN 0130-2906
QC851   CODEN: MEGIAC
METEOROLOGIYA I GIDROLOGIYA. English translation: Russian Meteorology and Hydrology (US ISSN 1068-3739) 1935. m. $88 (effective 1996). Gidrometeoizdat, Ul. Beringa, d.38, 199397 St. Petersburg, Russia. (Subscr. to: Mezhdunarodnaya Kniga, B. Yakimanka 39, 117049 Moscow, Russia) Ed. Yu.S. Sedunov. bk.rev.; charts; illus. circ. 4,000. **Indexed:** Biol.Abstr., Chem.Abstr., Deep Sea Res.& Oceanogr.Abstr., Ecol.Abstr., Field Crop Abstr., Geo.Abstr., GeoRef, Herb.Abstr., INSPEC, Int.Aerosp.Abstr., Meteor.& Geoastrophys.Abstr., Ocean.Abstr., Pollut.Abstr.
—BLDSC (0110.000000); CASDDS.

551.5   **AU**   ISSN 0177-7971
                   CODEN: MAPHEU
METEOROLOGY AND ATMOSPHERIC PHYSICS. (Text in English and German) 1949. 12/yr. DM.1680($1220) (effective 1996). Springer-Verlag, Sachsenplatz 4-6, Postfach 89, A-1201 Vienna, Austria. TEL 0222-3302415. FAX 0222-3302426. (Subscr. in N. America to: Springer-Verlag New York, Inc., 44 Hartz Way, Secaucus, NJ 07096-2491. TEL 201-348-4033. FAX 201-348-4505) Ed. E.R. Reiter. (also avail. in microform from UMI) **Indexed:** ASCA, Curr.Adv.Ecol.Sci., Curr.Cont., Deep Sea Res.& Oceanogr.Abstr., Environ.Per.Bibl. (1992-), Geo.Abstr., Ind.Sci.Rev., INIS Atomind., INSPEC (1984-), Meteor.& Geoastrophys.Abstr., Sci.Cit.Ind. **Document type:** academic/scholarly publication.
—BLDSC (5744.045000); Ei; Faxon; Genuine Article; SWETS; UMI; UnCover. **CCC.**
Formerly (until 1986): Archives for Meteorology, Geophysics, and Bioclimatology. Series A: Meteorology and Geophysics - Archiv fuer Meteorologie, Geophysik und Bioklimatologie. Series A. (ISSN 0066-6416)
Description: Discusses physical and chemical processes in all atmospheric conditions, including radiation, optical and electrical effects, precipitation and cloud microphysics.

551.65   **US**
MINNESOTA WEATHERGUIDE CALENDAR. Short title: Weatherguide. 1975. a. $11. Freshwater Foundation, 725 County Rd. 6, Wayzata, MN 55391. TEL 612-449-0092. FAX 612-449-0592. E-mail: frshwtr@freshwater.org. Ed. Tom Cousins. circ. 32,000.
Former titles: Weather Guide Calendar (ISSN 0270-9031); Weather Guide Calendar Almanac; (until 1977): Minnesota and Environs Weather Almanac (ISSN 0095-7348)

551   **JA**   ISSN 0916-5398
MIYAGIKEN KISHO GEPPO/MIYAGI PREFECTURE. MONTHLY REPORT OF METEOROLOGY. (Text in Japanese) 1964. m. Kishocho, Sendai Kanku Kishodai - Japan Meteorological Agency, Sendai District Meteorological Observatory, 3-15, Gorin 1-chome, Migagino-ku, Sendai-shi, Miyagi-ken 983, Japan.

551   **JA**   ISSN 0916-5290
MIYAZAKIKEN KISHO GEPPO/MIYAZAKI PREFECTURE. MONTHLY REPORT OF METEOROLOGY. (Text in Japanese) m. Kishocho, Miyazaki Chiho Kishodai - Japan Meteorological Agency, Miyazaki Local Meteorological Observatory, 1-14, Wachikawaracho, Miyazaki-shi, Miyazaki-ken 880, Japan.

551.6   **US**   ISSN 0027-0296
QC982
MONTHLY CLIMATIC DATA FOR THE WORLD. 1948. m. $41. U.S. National Climatic Data Center, National Oceanic and Atmospheric Administration, U.S. Department of Commerce, Federal Bldg., Rm. 120, 151 Patton Ave., Asheville, NC 28801-5001. TEL 704-271-4756. FAX 704-271-4876. TELEX 6502643731. E-mail: orders@ncdc.noaa.gov. (Co-sponsor: World Meteorological Organization) charts. circ. 500. (also avail. in microfiche from CIS; back issues avail.; reprint service avail. from CIS) **Indexed:** Amer.Stat.Ind. (1973-). **Document type:** government publication.

551.5   **AT**   ISSN 0819-3592
MONTHLY RAINFALL REVIEW - AUSTRALIA. 1966. m. price varies. Bureau of Meteorology, 150 Lonsdale St, Melbourne, Vic. 3000, Australia. FAX 03-669-4699. TELEX AA 30664. Ed. Zoya Krawczenko. (back issues avail.) **Document type:** government publication.

551.5   **US**   ISSN 0027-0644
QC983   CODEN: MWREAB
MONTHLY WEATHER REVIEW. 1872. m. $365 (foreign $395) (effective 1996). American Meteorological Society, 45 Beacon St., Boston, MA 02108-3693. TEL 617-227-2425. FAX 617-742-8718. Eds. T.N. Krishamurti, Peter S. Ray. abstr.; bibl.; charts; illus.; stat.; index. circ. 2,327. (also avail. in microform from PMC; back issues avail.; reprint service avail.) **Indexed:** A.S.& T.Ind., Chem.Abstr., Curr.Cont., Excerpt.Med., Fluidex, Geo.Abstr., GeoRef., Ind.Sci.Rev., INSPEC, Int.Aerosp.Abstr., Meteor.& Geoastrophys.Abstr., Ocean.Abstr., Pollut.Abstr., Sel.Water Res.Abstr., So.Pac.Per.Ind. **Document type:** bulletin.
—BLDSC (5965.000000); Ei; Faxon; Genuine Article; SWETS; UnCover. **CCC.**
Description: Publishes research related to weather analysis and forecasting, observed and modelled circulations including techniques development and verification studies.

551.5   **US**   ISSN 0027-2523
QC875
MOUNT WASHINGTON OBSERVATORY NEWS BULLETIN. 1937. q. $25 to individuals; families $45. Mount Washington Observatory, Box 2310, Main St., North Conway, NH 03860. TEL 603-356-8345. FAX 603-356-3060. E-mail: compuserve 74653. Ed. Margaret Dillon. adv.; bk.rev.; charts; illus.; stat.; cum.index: 1937-1960. circ. 3,500. **Document type:** bulletin.

551.5   **MZ**
MOZAMBIQUE. INSTITUTO NACIONAL DE METEOROLOGIA. BOLETIM METEOROLOGICO PARA AGRICULTURA. 1963. 3/m. 50000 mt($17) (effective 1992). Instituto Nacional de Geologia, C.P. 256, Maputo, Mozambique. TEL 491061-3. TELEX SMMMP 6-259. stat. (processed) **Document type:** bulletin.
Formerly: Mozambique. Servico Meteorologico. Boletim Meteorologico para a Agricultura (ISSN 0006-6044)

551   **JA**   ISSN 0916-5185
NAGANOKEN KISHO GEPPO/NAGANO PREFECTURE. MONTHLY REPORT METEOROLOGY. (Text in Japanese) 1950. m. Kishocho, Nagano Chiho Kishodai - Japan Meteorological Agency, Nagano Local Meteorological Observatory, 2417, Hakoshimizu, Nagano-shi, Nagano-ken 380, Japan.

551   **JA**   ISSN 0916-5312
NAGASAKIKEN KISHO GEPPO/NAGASAKI PREFECTURE. MONTHLY REPORT OF METEOROLOGY. (Text in Japanese) 1952. m. Kishocho, Nagasaki Kaiyo Kishodai - Japan Meteorological Agency, Nagasaki Marine Observatory, 11-51, Minamiyamatecho, Nagasaki-shi, Nagasaki-ken 850, Japan.

551.6 629.1   **JA**
NAGOYA KOKU KISHOHYO/NAGOYA DATA OF AERONAUTICAL METEOROLOGY. (Text in Japanese) m. Kishocho, Nagoya Koku Sokkojo - Japan Meteorological Agency, Nagoya Aeronautical Meteorological Station, Nakashinden, Toyoba, Toyoyamacho, Nishikasugai-gun, Aichi-ken 480-02, Japan.

551   **JA**
NARAKEN KISHO GEPPO/NARA PREFECTURE. MONTHLY REPORT OF METEOROLOGY. (Text in Japanese) 1965. m. Kishocho, Nara Chiho Kishodai - Japan Meteorological Agency, Nara Local Meteorological Observatory, 7, Handabirakicho, Nara-shi, Nara-ken 630, Japan.

551.5   **JA**
NATIONAL INSTITUTE OF POLAR RESEARCH. MEMOIRS. SERIES A: UPPER ATMOSPHERE PHYSICS. (Text and summaries in English) 1963. irreg., no.19, 1989. exchange basis. National Institute of Polar Research - Kokuritsu Kyokuchi Kenkyujo, Library, 9-10, Kaga 1-chome, Itabashi-ku, Tokyo 173, Japan. TEL 03-3962-2214. FAX 03-3962-2225. TELEX 272-3525 POLRSCJ. Ed. Takeo Hirasawa. circ. 1,000. **Indexed:** Int.Aerosp.Abstr., Meteor.& Geoastrophys.Abstr. **Document type:** monographic series.
—BLDSC (5626.700000).
Former titles: National Institute of Polar Research. Memoirs. Series A: Aeronomy (ISSN 0386-5517); Japanese Antarctic Research Expedition Scientific Reports. Series A: Aeronomy (ISSN 0075-3351)

METEOROLOGY

551.65   JA   ISSN 0386-5525
NATIONAL INSTITUTE OF POLAR RESEARCH. MEMOIRS. SERIES B: METEOROLOGY. (Text and summaries in English) 1969. irreg., no.2, 1974. exchange basis. National Institute of Polar Research - Kokuritsu Kyokuchi Kenkyujo, Library, 9-10, Kaga 1-chome, Itabashi-ku, Tokyo 173, Japan. TEL 03-3962-2214. FAX 03-3962-2225. Ed. Takeo Hirasawa. circ. 1,000. **Document type:** monographic series.
Supersedes: Japanese Antarctic Research Expedition, 1956-1962. Scientific Reports. Series B: Meteorology (ISSN 0075-336X)

551.63   US   ISSN 0271-1044
NATIONAL WEATHER ASSOCIATION NEWSLETTER. (Supplement to: National Weather Digest) 1976. m. $18. National Weather Association, 6704 Wolke Ct., Montgomery, AL 36116-2134. TEL 205-213-0388. Eds. Eli Jacks, Larrry Burch. circ. 2,400. **Document type:** newsletter.
Description: Details association news and provides meeting and job announcements for members. Also covers new equipment and techniques.

551.63   US   ISSN 0271-1052
QC983
NATIONAL WEATHER DIGEST. 1976. q. $29. National Weather Association, 6704 Wolke Ct., Montgomery, AL 36116-2134. TEL 205-213-0388. Eds. Richard McNulty, Peter Roohr. adv.; bk.rev.; bibl. circ. 2,400. (back issues avail.) Indexed: Meteor. & Geoastrophys.Abstr.
—BLDSC (6033.330500); Faxon; UnCover.

551.6   NR   ISSN 0545-9923
NIGERIA. METEOROLOGICAL SERVICE. AGROMETEOROLOGICAL BULLETIN. 1965. m. K.50 per no. Meteorological Service, Department Headquarters, Strachan St., Near Tafawa Balewa Square, Lagos, Nigeria. Ed. L.E. Akeh. stat.

551.5 620   JA   ISSN 0389-1313
NIHON SEIKISHO GAKKAI ZASSHI/JAPANESE JOURNAL OF BIOMETEOROLOGY. (Text and summaries in English or Japanese) 1966. 4/yr. 5000 Yen($40) (Japanese Society of Biometeorology - Nihon Seikisho Gakkai) I P E C, Inc., 1-2-3 Sugamo, Toshima-ku, Tokyo 170, Japan. TEL 03-5978-4067. FAX 03-5978-4068. (Subscr. to: Kanazawa University School of Medicine, Department of Physiology - Kanazawa Daigaku Igakubu Seirigaku Kyoshitsu, 13-1 Takara-machi, Kanazawa-shi, Ishikawa-ken 920, Japan) Ed. Yutaka Inaba. adv.; bk.rev. circ. 600. (back issues avail.) **Document type:** academic/scholarly publication.
Description: Covers the effects of climate, weather, season and temperature on homes, physiology, pathology of man, animals and plants.

NIHON SHASHIN SOKURYO GAKKAI. GAKUJUTSU KOENKAI HAPPYO RONBUNSHU. see *GEOGRAPHY*

551 537   JA
NIHON TAIKI DENKI GAKKAI KAIHO/SOCIETY OF ATMOSPHERIC ELECTRICITY OF JAPAN. JOURNAL. (Text in Japanese) 1969. s-a. Nihon Taiki Denki Gakkai - Society of Atmospheric Electricity of Japan, Osaka Daigaku Kogakubu Denkikogakka, 2-1, Yamadaoka, Suita-shi, Osaka 565, Japan.

551   JA
NIIGATAKEN KISHO GEPPO/NIIGATA PREFECTURE. MONTHLY REPORT OF METEOROLOGY. (Text in Japanese) 1970. m. Kishocho, Niigata Chiho Kishodai - Japan Meteorological Agency, Niigata Local Meteorological Observatory, 4-1, Saiwaini-shi 4-chome, Niigata-shi, Niigata-ken 950, Japan.

551.5   IT   ISSN 1122-4339
NIMBUS. (Text in Italian; table of contents in French and Italian) 1993. q. L.40000 to non-members; members L.30000. Societa Meteorologica Subalpina, V. Gioberti 88, 10128 Turin, Italy. TEL 39-11-591145. FAX 39-11-5683190.
—BLDSC (6113.179830).

551   JA
NISHINHON KAIKYO JUNPO/TEN-DAY MARINE REPORT OF THE EAST CHINA SEA. (Text in Japanese) 1948. 3/m. Kishocho, Nagasaki Kaiyo Kishodai - Japan Meteorological Agency, Nagasaki Marine Observatory, 11-51, Minamiyamatecho, Nagasaki-shi, Nagasaki-ken 850, Japan.

551 630   JA   ISSN 0287-9824
NOGYO KISHO KENKYU SHUROKU/COLLECTED PAPERS OF AGRICULTURAL METEOROLOGY. (Text in English, Japanese) 1953. a. Norin Suisansho, Nogyo Kankyo Gijutsu Kenkyujo, Kankyo Shigenbu Kisho Kanrika - Ministry of Agriculture, Forestry and Fisheries, National Institute of Agro-Environmental Sciences, Department of Natural Resources, Division of Agrometeorology, 1-1 Kannondai 3-chome, Tsukuba-shi, Ibaraki-ken 305, Japan. TEL 81-298-38-8237. FAX 81-298-38-8199. circ. 230.

551.5 630   JA
NOGYO KISHO NENPO/ANNUAL REPORT OF AGRICULTURAL METEOROLOGY. (Text in Japanese) 1950. a. membership. Kishocho - Japan Meterological Agency, 3-4, Otemachi 1-chome, Chiyoda-ku, Tokyo 100, Japan. circ. 383. **Document type:** government publication.

551 630   JA
NOGYO KISHO SHIRYO/DATA OF AGRICULTURAL METEOROLOGY. (Text in Japanese) 1980. a. Norin Suisansho - Ministry of Agriculture, Forestry and Fisheries, 2-1, Kasumigaseki 1-chome, Chiyoda-ku, Tokyo 100, Japan.

551   JA
NYUZU RETA SEPPYO HOKUSHIN'ETSU/JAPANESE SOCIETY OF SNOW AND ICE. HOKUSHIN'ETSU BRANCH. NEWSLETTER. (Text in Japanese) bi-m. Nihon Seppyo Gakkai, Hokushin'etsu Shibu - Japanese Society of Snow and Ice, Hokushin'etsu Branch, c/o Prof. Norio Hayakawa, Nagaoka Gijyutsu Kagaku Daigaku, 1603-1, Jamitomiokacho, Nagaoka-shi, Niigta-ken 940-21, Japan. **Document type:** newsletter.

551.5   GW
OESTERREICHISCHE BEITRAEGE ZU METEOROLOGIE UND GEOPHYSIK. (Text in English, German) 1989. irreg. Zentralanstalt fuer Meteorologie und Geodynamik, Hohe Warte 38, A-1191 Vienna, Austria. TEL 43-1-364453. FAX 43-1-3691233. TELEX 43-1-131837-METW. Ed. Peter Steinhauser. circ. 350.

551.5   JA   ISSN 0916-5320
OITAKEN KISHO GEPPO/OITA PREFECTURE. MONTHLY REPORT OF METEOROLOGY. (Text in Japanese) 1956. m. Kishocho, Oita Chiho Kishodai - Japan Meteorological Agency, Oita Local Meteorological Observatory, 1-38, Nagahamacho 3-chome, Oita-shi, Oita-ken 870, Japan. FAX 0975-36-0091. circ. 100.
Description: Circulated only in the domestic government and municipal office.

551   JA   ISSN 0916-5045
OKAYAMAKEN KISHO GEPPO/OKAYAMA PREFECTURE. MONTHLY REPORT OF METEOROLOGY. (Text in Japanese) 1936. m. Kishocho, Okayama Chiho Kishodai - Japan Meteorological Agency, Okayama Local Meteorological Observatory, 1-36, Kuwadacho, Okayama-shi, Okayama-ken 700, Japan.

551   JA   ISSN 0387-8341
OKINAWA GIJUTSU NOTO/OKINAWA METEOROLOGICAL OBSERVATORY. TECHNICAL NOTE. (Text in Japanese) 1972. s-a. Kishocho, Okinawa Kishodai - Japan Meteorological Agency, Okinawa Meteorological Observatory, 15-15, Higawa 1-chome, Naha-shi, Okinawa-ken 900, Japan. Indexed: Jap.Per.Ind.

551.6
OKINAWA KANNAI IJO KISHO HOKOKU/OKINAWA METEOROLOGICAL OBSERVATORY. UNUSUAL METEOROLOGICAL REPORT. (Text in Japanese) 1972. a. Kishocho, Okinawa Kishodai - Japan Meteorological Agency, Okinawa Meteorological Observatory, 15-15, Higawa 1-chome, Naha-shi, Okinawa-ken 900, Japan.

551   JA   ISSN 0386-2380
OKINAWA KANNAI KISHO KENKYUKAISHI/OKINAWA METEOROLOGICAL OBSERVATORY. COLLECTED PAPERS. (Text in Japanese) 1973. a. Kishocho, Okinawa Kishodai - Japan Meteorological Agency, Okinawa Meteorological Observatory, 15-15, Higwa 1-chome, Naha-shi, Okinawa-ken 900, Japan.

551   JA   ISSN 0916-5339
OKINAWAKEN KISHO GEPPO/OKINAWA PREFECTURE. MONTHLY REPORT OF METEOROLOGY. (Text in Japanese) 1974. m. Kishocho, Okinawa Kishodai - Japan Meteorological Agency, Okinawa Meteorological Observatory, 15-15, Higawa 1-chome, Naha-shi, Okinawa-ken 900, Japan.

551   JA
OSAKA KANKU FUKEN KISHO KENKYUKAISHI/OSAKA DISTRICT METEOROLOGICAL SOCIETY. JOURNAL. (Text in Japanese) 1975. a. Kishocho, Osaka Kanku Kishodai - Japan Meteorological Agency, Osaka District Meteorological Observatory, 1-67, Otemachi 4-chome, Chuo-ku, Osaka 540, Japan.

551   JA
OSAKA KANKU IJO KISHO HOKOKU/OSAKA DISTRICT METEOROLOGICAL OBSERVATORY. UNUSUAL METEOROLOGICAL REPORT. (Text in Japanese) 1953. a. Kishocho, Osaka Kanku Kishodai - Japan Meteorological Agency, Osaka District Meteorological Observatory, 1-67, Otemachi 4-chome, Chuo-ku, Osaka 540, Japan.

551   JA
OSAKA KANKU KISHODAI GIJUTSU JOHO/OSAKA DISTRICT METEOROLOGICAL OBSERVATORY. TECHNICAL REPORT. (Text in Japanese) 3/yr. Kishocho, Osaka Kanku Kishodai - Japan Meteorological Agency, Osaka District Meteorological Observatory, 1-67, Otemachi 4-chome, Chuo-ku, Osaka 540, Japan.

551.65   JA   ISSN 0030-6088
OSAKAFU KISHO GEPPO/OSAKA PREFECTURE. MONTHLY REPORT OF METEOROLOGY. (Text in Japanese) 1965. m. Kishocho, Osaka Kanku Kishodai - Japan Meteorological Agency, Osaka District Meteorological Observatory, 1-67, Otemachi 4-chome, Chuo-ku, Osaka 540, Japan. stat. circ. 120.

551.5   JA
OSHIMA-HIYAMA CHIHO NOGYO KISHO SOKUHO/MONTHLY REPORT OF AGRICULTURAL METEOROLOGY. (Text in Japanese) 1979. m. Kishocho, Hakodate Kaiyo Kishodai - Japan Meteorological Agency, Hakodate Marine Observatory, 3-4-4 Mihar, Hakodate-shi, Hokkaido 041, Japan. circ. 100.

551.5   US
OXFORD MONOGRAPHS ON METEOROLOGY AND PHYSICAL OCEANOGRAPHY. irreg. price varies. Oxford University Press, 200 Madison Ave., New York, NY 10016. TEL 212-679-7300. Ed. P.A. Sheppard.
Formerly: Oxford Monographs on Meteorology. *Refereed Serial*

551.6   SP   ISSN 0212-9221
OXYMURA; revista sobre las zonas humedas. 1984. a. free. Asociacion Amigos de la Malvasia, Apdo. 3059, 14080 Cordoba, Spain. circ. 1,000.

OZONE NEWS. see *ENVIRONMENTAL STUDIES — Pollution*

551.6 551   US   ISSN 1063-7176
PALAEOCLIMATES: DATA AND MODELLING. 1993. q. 70 ECU (effective 1996). Harwood Academic Publishers, c/o International Publishers Distributor, 820 Town Center Dr., Langhorne, PA 19047. TEL 215-750-2642. FAX 215-750-6343. (Subscr. to: International Publishers Distributor, PO Box 90, Reading, Berkshire, RG1 8JL, England. TEL 44-173-456-8316) (also avail. in microform)
—CCC.
Description: Publishes on both the geological and climatological aspects of palaeoclimate research.

THE PALEOCLIMATE DATA RECORD. see *PALEONTOLOGY*

PALEOCLIMATE PUBLICATIONS SERIES. see *PALEONTOLOGY*

551.5 551　　　　JA　　ISSN 0031-126X
QC851　　　　　　　　CODEN: PMGTAW
PAPERS IN METEOROLOGY AND GEOPHYSICS. (Text in English, Japanese) 1950. q. 6180 Yen (or on exchange basis). Japan Meteorological Agency, Meteorological Research Institute - Kishocho Kisho Kenkyujo, Office of Planning, 1-1 Nagamine, Tukuba-shi, Ibaraki-ken 305, Japan. Ed. Kenji Okada. charts; illus. **Indexed:** Appl.Mech.Rev., Chem.Abstr., Curr.Cont., Deep Sea Res.& Oceanogr.Abstr., JTA, Sci.Cit.Ind. **Document type:** academic/scholarly publication.
—CASDDS; Faxon; UnCover.

PHYSICAL GEOGRAPHY. see *EARTH SCIENCES*

PROBLEMY FIZIKI ATMOSFERY. see *PHYSICS*

610 551.5　　　　NE　　ISSN 0923-0688
　　　　　　　　　　　　CODEN: PRBIED
PROGRESS IN BIOMETEOROLOGY. (Text in English) 1972. irreg. price varies. S P B Academic Publishing b.v., P.O. Box 11188, 1001 GD Amsterdam, Netherlands. circ. 300. **Indexed:** Biol.Abstr., Chem.Abstr. **Document type:** monographic series.
—BLDSC (6865.992700); Faxon.

036　　　　　　PO　　ISSN 0870-4724
PROJECTO I2 DO PIDDAC. BOLETIM. 1978. a. Esc.1500 (effective Jan. 1993). Instituto de Meteorologia, Rua C do Aeroporto, 1700 Lisbon, Portugal. TEL 351-1-8472880. FAX 351-1-802370. TELEX 12742 DIRMET P. stat. circ. 150. **Document type:** bulletin.

551.5　　　　　GW　　ISSN 0340-4552
PROMET; meteorologische Fortbildung. 1971. q. DM.44. Deutscher Wetterdienst, Bibliothek, Postfach 100465, 63004 Offenbach a.M., Germany. TEL 069-80622283. FAX 069-30622486. **Document type:** government publication.

PROTECTION OF ATMOSPHERE AGAINST POLLUTION; determination of atmospheric background pollution in South Prebaltic. see *ENVIRONMENTAL STUDIES — Pollution*

551.6　　　　　US　　ISSN 0160-9599
QC981　　　　　　　　CODEN: PCTLD6
PUBLICATIONS IN CLIMATOLOGY. 1948. a. (3 or 4 nos./vol.). price varies. (Laboratory of Climatology) C.W. Thornthwaite Associates, Rt. 1, Box 412, Elmer, NJ 08318. TEL 609-358-2350. Ed. John R. Mather. circ. 500. **Indexed:** GeoRef.
—BLDSC (7126.990000).

551.5　　　　　CC　　ISSN 1000-0526
QIXIANG/METEOROLOGICAL MONTHLY. (Text in Chinese) 1975. m. Y21.60($54) (Zhongguo Qixiangju - China Meteorological Administration) China Meteorological Press, 46 Baishiqiao Road, West Suburb, Beijing 100081, People's Republic of China. TEL 8332277-3336. TELEX 22094 FD SMA CN. (Dist. by: China International Book Trading Corporation, P.O. Box 2820, Beijing, P.R.C.) Ed. Li Xiaodong. charts; stat.; index. circ. 6,000. (back issues avail.) **Indexed:** Meteor.& Geoastrophys.Abstr. **Document type:** academic/scholarly publication.
　Description: Middle-level journal for academic exchange. Covers all aspects of atmospheric science, especially synoptic meteorology, climatology, atmospheric physics, and atmospheric sounding.

551.5　　　　　CC　　ISSN 0577-6619
QC851　　　　　　　　CODEN: CHIHAW
QIXIANG XUEBAO. English edition: Acta Meteorologica Sinica (ISSN 0894-0525) (Text in Chinese) 1941. q. $20. (Zhongguo Qixiang Xuehui - Chinese Meteorological Society) China Meteorological Press, 46 Baishiqiao Road, Xijiao (West Suburb), Beijing 100081, People's Republic of China. TEL 8312277-2942. Ed. Hu Shengchang. **Document type:** academic/scholarly publication.
　Refereed Serial

551.63　　　　　JA
R S M C TOKYO - TYPHOON CENTER. ANNUAL ACTIVITY REPORT. (Text in English) a. Kishocho - Japan Meteorological Agency, 3-4, Otemachi 1-chome, Chiyoda-ku, Tokyo 100, Japan.

551.527　　　　NO　　ISSN 0027-0490
RADIATION OBSERVATIONS IN BERGEN; radiation yearbook. 1965. a. free. Universitetet i Bergen - University of Bergen, Geofysisk Institutt, Bergen, Norway. FAX 47-55-960566. Ed. Arvid Skartveit. circ. 300.
　Description: Presentation of different radiation parameters: global radiation, diffuse radiation, solar and ultraviolet radiation and duration of sunshine.

551.6　　　　　CC　　ISSN 1004-4965
REDAI QIXIANG XUEBAO/JOURNAL OF TROPICAL METEOROLOGY. (Text in Chinese; abstracts in English) 1984. q. $40. Guangdong Redai Haiyang Qixiang Yanjiusuo - Guangzhou Institute of Tropical and Oceanic Meteorology, No. 6, Fujin Rd., Dongshan District, Guangzhou, Guangdong 510080, People's Republic of China. TEL 020-7775231. FAX 020-7765281. (Dist. overseas by: China International Book Trading Corp., P.O. Box 399, Beijing, P.R. China) Ed. Lin Yuanbi. adv. contact: Cao Chaoxiong. circ. 1,000. **Document type:** academic/scholarly publication.
　Formerly (until 1993): Redai Qixiang (ISSN 1000-4068)
　Description: Covers the latest research achievements in tropical atmospheric science.
　Refereed Serial

551 537　　　　JA　　ISSN 0286-6188
QC960.5　　　　　　　　CODEN: RLAEEA
RESEARCH LETTERS ON ATMOSPHERIC ELECTRICITY. (Text in English, Japanese; summaries in English) 1981. s-a. Nihon Taiki Denki Gakkai - Society of Atmospheric Electricity of Japan, Osaka Daigaku Kogakubu Denkikogakka, 2-1 Yamadaoka, Suita-shi, Osaka 565, Japan. **Indexed:** Chem.Abstr.
—CASDDS.

551.5　　　　　MH　　ISSN 0460-3060
RESULTADOS DAS OBSERVACOES METEOROLOGICAS DE MACAU. (Text in Chinese, English, Portuguese) 1952. m. (plus a. issue). free. Servicos Meteorologicos e Geofisicos de Macau, Caixa Postal 93, Macao. TEL 333995. FAX 308601. TELEX 88523-METEO. Ed.Bd. charts; stat. circ. 120. **Document type:** government publication.
　Description: Contains meteorological results.

551.5　　　　　SP　　ISSN 0214-4387
REVISTA DE METEOROLOGIA. 1982. s-a. free. Asociacion Meteorologica Espanola, Apdo. 285, 28080 Madrid, Spain.
　Formerly (until 1983): Asociacion Meteorologica Espanola. Boletin (ISSN 0211-3635)

551.5　　　　　RM　　ISSN 1223-1118
▼**ROMANIAN JOURNAL OF METEOROLOGY.** 1994. s-a. exchange basis. National Institute of Meteorology and Hydrology, 97 Bucuresti-Ploiesti Hwy., 71581 Bucharest, Rumania. TEL 40-1-6793240. FAX 40-1-3129843. TELEX 10460 IMH R. E-mail: inmh01@roearn.ici.ro. Ed. Sergiu Tumanov. circ. 250 (controlled). **Document type:** academic/scholarly publication.
　●Also available online.
—BLDSC (8019.636050).

551.5　　　　　RU
QC851　　　　　　　　CODEN: IFAOAV
ROSSIISKAYA AKADEMIYA NAUK. IZVESTIYA. SERIYA FIZIKA ATMOSFERY I OKEANA. English translation: Russian Academy of Sciences. Izvestiya. Atmospheric and Oceanic Physics. (Text in Russian; summaries in English and Russian) 1965. m. 53.40 Rub. Izdatel'stvo Nauka, 90 Profsoyuznaya ul., 117864 Moscow, Russia. (Dist. by: Mezhdunarodnaya Kniga, B. Yakimanka 39, 117049 Moscow, Russia) Ed. A.M. Oboukhov. adv.; bk.rev.; charts; illus.; index. circ. 1,000. **Indexed:** Bibl.Cart., Chem.Abstr., INIS Atomind., INSPEC (1992-), Math.R., Meteor.& Geoastrophys.Abstr., Phys.Ber.
—CASDDS; Genuine Article. CCC.
　Formerly: Akademiya Nauk S.S.S.R. Izvestiya. Seriya Fizika Atmosfery I Okeana (ISSN 0002-3515)

ROYAL ASTRONOMICAL SOCIETY. MONTHLY NOTICES. see *ASTRONOMY*

551.5　　　　　UK　　ISSN 0035-9009
QC851　　　　　　　　CODEN: QJRMAM
ROYAL METEOROLOGICAL SOCIETY. QUARTERLY JOURNAL. 1871. 8/yr. $283. Royal Meteorological Society, 104 Oxford Rd., Reading, Berks RG1 7LJ, England. TEL 01734-568500. FAX 01734-568571. Ed. P.W. White. adv.; bk.rev.; charts; index. circ. 1,600. **Indexed:** Biol.Abstr., Curr.Adv.Ecol.Sci., Curr.Cont., Curr.Tit.Ocean, Deep Sea Res.& Oceanogr.Abstr., Excerp.Med., Field Crop Abstr., Fluidex, Geo.Abstr., GeoRef., Herb.Abstr., Hort.Abstr., INSPEC, Int.Aerosp.Abstr., Meteor.& Geoastrophys.Abstr, Soils & Fert. **Document type:** academic/scholarly publication.
—BLDSC (7186.000000); CASDDS; Ei; Faxon; Genuine Article; SWETS; UnCover.
　Description: Includes some oceanographic aspects of meteorology.

551.5　　　　　　HK
ROYAL OBSERVATORY ALMANAC. 1984. a. price varies. Royal Observatory, 134A Nathan Rd., Kowloon, Hong Kong.

551　　　　　US　　ISSN 0001-4338
QC851　　　　　　　　CODEN: IRAPEK
RUSSIAN ACADEMY OF SCIENCES. IZVESTIYA. ATMOSPHERIC AND OCEAN PHYSICS. Key Title: Izvestiya. Atmospheric and Oceanic Physics. English translation of: Rossiiskaya Akademiya Nauk. Izvestiya. Seriya Fizika Atmosfery i Okeana. 1965. 6/yr. $550 to non-members (foreign $562); members $440 (foreign $452). (Russian Academy of Sciences, RU) American Geophysical Union, 2000 Florida Ave., N.W., Washington, DC 20009. TEL 202-462-6900. FAX 202-328-0566. TELEX 710-822-9300. (Germany addr.: Postfach 49, 37189 Katlenburg-Lindau, Germany. TEL 49-5556-1440) bibl.; charts; illus.; index. (reprint service avail. from ISI) **Indexed:** INSPEC, Math.R., Ocean.Abstr. **Document type:** academic/scholarly publication.
—BLDSC (4593.510000); Faxon; SWETS; UnCover. CCC.
　Formerly: Academy of Sciences of the U S S R. Izvestiya. Atmospheric and Oceanic Physics.

551.5 551.4　　US　　ISSN 1068-3739
QC851　　　　　　　　CODEN: RMHYEA
RUSSIAN METEOROLOGY AND HYDROLOGY. English translation of: Meteorologiya i Gidrologiya (RU ISSN 0130-2906) 1976. m. $1055 (effective 1996). (Gidrometeoizdat, RU) Allerton Press, Inc., 150 Fifth Ave., New York, NY 10011. TEL 212-924-3950. FAX 212-463-9684. Ed. Yu.A. Izrael. bibl.; charts; illus.; stat.; index. **Indexed:** Agri.Eng.Abstr., Deep Sea Res.& Oceanogr.Abstr., Excerp.Med., Field Crop Abstr., Forest.Abstr., Herb.Abstr., INSPEC, Irr.& Drain.Abstr., Seed Abstr., Soils & Fert., Triticale Abstr., W.R.C.Inf. **Document type:** academic/scholarly publication.
—BLDSC (0420.772200); Faxon; SWETS; UnCover. CCC.
　Formerly: Soviet Meteorology and Hydrology (ISSN 0146-4108)

551.527　　　　FR
S B A R M O BULLETIN. (Text in English) vol.6, 1974. 4/yr. 130 F.($20) Scientific Ballooning and Radiations Monitoring Organization, Observatoire de Parc Saint-Marie, 4 av. Neptune, 94 Saint-Maur des Fosses, France. bibl.; charts.

551.5　　　　　JA
SAGAKEN KISHO GEPPO/SAGA PREFECTURE. MONTHLY REPORT OF METEOROLOGY. (Text in Japanese) 1957. m. Kishocho, Saga Chiho Kishoda - Japan Meteorological Agency, Saga Local Meteorological Observatory, 8-14 Jonai 2-chome, Saga-shi, Saga-ken 840, Japan. circ. 100.

551.656　　　　MG
SAISON CYCLONIQUE A MADAGASCAR. (Text in French) 1973. a. Service de la Meteorologie Nationale, B.P. 1254, Antananarivo, Madagascar.
　Description: Presents meteorological readings in Madagascar for the year.

551　　　　　　JA
SAITAMAKEN KISHO GEPPO/SAITAMA PREFECTURE. MONTHLY REPORT OF METEOROLOGY. (Text in Japanese) 1897. m. Kishocho, Kumagaya Chiho Kishodai - Japan Meteorological Agency, Kumagaya Local Meteorological Observatory, 6010, Sakuracho 1-chome, Kumagaya-shi, Saitama-ken 360, Japan.

METEOROLOGY

551 JA
SAITAMAKEN NO KISHO SAIGAI/METEOROLOGICAL DISASTER IN SAITAMA PREFECTURE. (Text in Japanese) triennial. (Kishocho, Kumagaya Chiho Kishodai - Japan Meteorological Agency, Kumagaya Local Meteorological Observatory) Saitama Prefectural Government, 15-1, Takasago 3-chome, Urawa-shi, Saitama-ken 336, Japan.

551 JA
SAPPORO KANKU KISHO KENKYUKAISHI/SAPPORO DISTRICT METEOROLOGICAL OBSERVATORY. JOURNAL. (Text in Japanese) a. Kishocho, Sapporo Kanku Kishodai - Japan Meteorological Agency, Sapporo District Meteorological Observatory, 2 Nisho 18-chome, Kita 2-jo, Chuo-ku, Sapporo-shi, Hokkaido 060, Japan.

551 JA
SAPPORO KANKU KISHODAI GIJUTSU JIHO/SAPPORO DISTRICT METEOROLOGICAL OBSERVATORY. TECHNICAL REPORT. (Text in Japanese) s-a. Kishocho, Sapporo Kanku Kishodai - Japan Meteorological Agency, Sapporo District Meteorological Observatory, 2, Nishi 18-chome, Kita 2-jo, Chuo-ku, Sapporo-shi, Hokkaido 060, Japan.

551.6 CN ISSN 0821-0284
SASKATCHEWAN RESEARCH COUNCIL. CLIMATOLOGICAL REFERENCE STATION. ANNUAL SUMMARY. 1975. a. Can.$35. Saskatchewan Research Council, Environment Division, 15 Innovation Blvd., Saskatoon, SK S7N 2X8, Canada. TEL 306-933-8179. FAX 306-933-7446. E-mail: wheaton@sask.usask.ca. Ed. Elaine Wheaton. circ. 350. **Document type:** academic/scholarly publication.
Former titles: Saskatoon S.R.C. Climatological Reference Station. Annual Summary (ISSN 0848-6964); Saskatchewan Research Council. Physics Division. Annual Climatic Summary (ISSN 0706-9391)

551 JA
SENDAI KANKU CHOSA KENKYUKAI SHIRYO/SENDAI DISTRICT METEOROLOGICAL OBSERVATORY. PROCEEDINGS OF THE MEETING. (Text in Japanese) a. Kishocho, Sendai Kanku Kishodai - Japan Meteorological Agency, Sendai District Meteorological Observatory, 3-15, Gorin 1-chome, Migagino-ku, Sendai-shi, Miyagi-ken 983, Japan. **Document type:** proceedings.

551 JA
SENDAI KANKU GIJUTSU SHIRYO/SENDAI DISTRICT METEOROLOGICAL OBSERVATORY. TECHNICAL DATA. (Text in Japanese) 1969. irreg. Kishocho, Sendai Kanku Kishodai - Japan Meteorological Agency, Sendai District Meteorological Observatory, 3-15, Gorin 1-chome, Migagino-ku, Sendai-shi, Miyagi-ken 983, Japan.

551 JA
SENDAI KANKU IJO KISHO HOKOKU/SENDAI DISTRICT METEOROLOGICAL OBSERVATORY. UNUSUAL METEOROLOGICAL REPORT. (Text in Japanese) 1964. a. Kishocho, Sendai Kanku Kishodai - Japan Meteorological Agency, Sendai District Meteorological Observatory, 3-15, Gorin 1-chome, Migagino-ku, Sendai-shi, Miyagi-ken 983.

551.6 JA ISSN 0918-1474
SEPPYO HOKUSHIN'ETSU/JAPANESE SOCIETY OF SNOW AND ICE. HOKUSHIN'ETSU BRANCH. JOURNAL. (Text in Japanese) 1988. s-a. Nihon Seppyo Gakkai, Hokushin'etsu Shibu - Japanese Society of Snow and Ice, Hokushin'etsu Branch, c/o Prof. Norio Hayakawa, Nagoaka Gijutsu Kagaku Daigaku, 1603-1, Kamitomiokacho, Nagaoka-shi, Niigata-ken 940-21, Japan. **Document type:** academic/scholarly publication.

551.6 CC
SHANXI QIXIANG/SHANXI METEOROLOGY. (Text in Chinese) q. Shanxi Sheng Qixiang Ju - Shanxi Provincial Bureau of Meteorology, 28, Xinjian Lu, Taiyuan, Shanxin 030002, People's Republic of China. TEL 220713. Ed. Zhou Yihe.

551 JA
SHIGAKEN KISHO GEPPO/SHIGA PREFECTURE. MONTHLY REPORT OF METEOROLOGY. (Text in Japanese) 1900. m. Kishocho, Hikone Chiho Kishodai - Japan Meteorological Agency, Hikone Local Meteorological Observatory, 5-25, Shiromachi 2-chome, Hikone-shi, Shiga-ken 522, Japan.

551 JA
SHIKOKU URYO GEPPO/MONTHLY PRECIPITATION REPORT IN SHIKOKU DISTRICT. (Text in Japanese) 1957. m. Nihon Kisho Kyokai, Taimatsu Shibu - Japan Weather Association, Takamatsu Branch, 1277-1 Fuseishicho, Takamatsu-shi, Kagawa-ken 761, Japan.

551 JA ISSN 0916-538X
SHIMANEKEN KISHO GEPPO/SHIMANE PREFECTURE. MONTHLY REPORT OF METEOROLOGY. (Text in Japanese) 1967. m. Kishocho, Matsue Chiho Kishodai - Japan Meteorological Agency, Matsue Local Meteorological Observatory, 1-11, Nishitsuda 7-chome, Matsue-shi, Shimane-ken 690, Japan. **Document type:** academic/scholarly publication.

551 JA ISSN 0916-5002
SHIZUOKAKEN KISHO GEPPO/SHIZUOKA PREFECTURE. MONTHLY REPORT OF METEOROLOGY. (Text in Japanese) 1950. m. Kishocho, Shizuoka Chiho Kishodai - Japan Meteorological Agency, Shizuoka Local Meteorologcial Observatory, 1-11, Nishitsudda 7-chome, Matsue-shi, Shizuoka-ken 422, Japan.

551.5 XO ISSN 0231-9004
QC851 CODEN: CGIMD9
SLOVAK ACADEMY OF SCIENCES. GEOPHYSICAL INSTITUTE. CONTRIBUTIONS. SERIES OF METEOROLOGY. (Text in English, German, Russian) 1974. a. exchange basis. Veda, Publishing House of the Slovak Academy of Sciences, Klemensova 19, 814 67 Bratislava, Slovakia. (Subscr. addr.: Slovak Academy of Sciences, Geophysical Institute, Dept. of Physics of the Atmosphere, Dubravska cesta 9, 842 28 Bratislava, Slovakia) Ed. Eva Zavodska. circ. 600. **Indexed:** Meteor.& Geoastrophys.Abstr. **Document type:** academic/scholarly publication.
—BLDSC (3443.571000).
Description: Presents new research results in the field of atmospheric sciences, applied meteorology, climatology and air pollution meteorology.

551.5 JA
SOKKO JIHO/WEATHER SERVICE BULLETIN. 1930. bi-m. 7800 Yen. Kishocho - Japan Meteorological Agency, 3-4, Otemachi 1-chome, Chiyoda-ku, Tokyo 100, Japan. index. circ. 914. **Document type:** bulletin.

551.5 SA
SOUTH AFRICA. WEATHER BUREAU. CLIMATE SUMMARY FOR SOUTHERN AFRICA. (Text in Afrikaans, English) 1990. m. R.50 (effective Apr. 1995 - Mar. 1996). Weather Bureau, Department of Environment Affairs, Private Bag X97, Pretoria 0001, South Africa. TEL 27-12-2908025. FAX 27-12-2902958. E-mail: climenq@cirrus.sawb.gov.za. circ. 300. **Document type:** government publication.

551.65 SA ISSN 0011-5517
SOUTH AFRICA. WEATHER BUREAU. DAILY WEATHER BULLETIN. (Text in Afrikaans, English) 1950. m. R.80 (effective Apr. 1995 - Mar. 1996). Weather Bureau, Department of Environment Affairs, Private Bag X97, Pretoria 0001, South Africa. TEL 27-12-2908025. FAX 27-12-2902958. E-mail: climenq@cirrus.sawb.gov.za. bibl. circ. 400. **Document type:** government publication.

551.6 SA ISSN 0032-7948
SOUTH AFRICA. WEATHER BUREAU. NEWSLETTER. (Text in Afrikaans, English) 1949. m. R.80 (effective Apr. 1995 - Mar. 1996). Weather Bureau, Department of Environment Affairs, Private Bag X97, Pretoria 0001, South Africa. TEL 27-12-2908025. FAX 27-12-2902958. E-mail: climenq@cirrus.sawb.gov.za. charts; stat.; index. circ. 400. **Document type:** government publication, newsletter.

551.6 SA ISSN 0379-6736
SOUTH AFRICA. WEATHER BUREAU. TECHNICAL PAPER. 1974. irreg., no.27, 1995. R.25 per no. (effective Apr. 1995 - Mar. 1996). Weather Bureau, Department of Environment Affairs, Private Bag X97, Pretoria 0001, South Africa. TEL 27-12-2908025. FAX 27-12-2902958. E-mail: climenq@cirrus.sawb.gov.za. **Document type:** government publication.

551.578 SA
SOUTH AFRICA. WEATHER BUREAU. TEN DAILY RAINFALL REPORT. 3/m. Weather Bureau, Department of Environment Affairs, Private Bag X97, Pretoria 0001, South Africa. TEL 27-12-2908025. FAX 27-12-2902958. E-mail: climenq@cirrus.sawb.gov.za. **Document type:** government publication.

551.5 SA ISSN 0081-2331
SOUTH AFRICA. WEATHER BUREAU. W.B. SERIES. 1971. irreg., no.41, 1990. R.30 per no. (effective Apr. 1995 - Mar. 1996). Weather Bureau, Department of Environment Affairs, Private Bag X97, Pretoria 0001, South Africa. TEL 27-12-2908025. FAX 27-12-2902958. E-mail: climenq@cirrus.sawb.gov.za. circ. 1,500. **Document type:** government publication.

551.65 SA
SOUTH AFRICA. WEATHER BUREAU. YEARLY WEATHER REPORT. (Text and summaries in Afrikaans, English) 1936. a. R.50 per no. (effective Apr. 1995 - Mar. 1996). Weather Bureau, Department of Environment Affairs, Private Bag X97, Pretoria 0001, South Africa. TEL 27-12-2908025. FAX 27-12-2902958. E-mail: climenq@cirrus.sawb.gov.za. stat. circ. 400. **Document type:** government publication.
Supersedes (in 1990): South Africa. Weather Bureau. Monthly Weather Report (ISSN 0038-1942)

551.5 CE
SRI LANKA METEOROLOGICAL SOCIETY. JOURNAL. (Text in English) 1972. q. Sri Lanka Meteorological Society, 26 Clifford Place, Colombo 4, Sri Lanka. adv.; bibl.; charts; stat. circ. 150-200.

551.6 PL
STACJA ARCTOWSKIEGO. ROCZNIK METEOROLOGICZNY. (Text in Polish or English) 1978. irreg. $200. Instytut Meteorologii i Gospodarki Wodnej, Oddzial Morski w Gdyni - Institute of Meteorology and Water Management, Maritime Branch in Gdynia, 42 Waszyngtona St., 81-342 Gdynia, Poland. TEL 4858-203532. FAX 4858-201641. TELEX 54216 PL. Eds. Danuta Wielbinska, Miroslaw Mietus. circ. 120. (tabloid format)
Description: Covers meteorology and observation results at the subantarctic meteorological research station.

551.6 PL
STACJA HORNSUND. ROCZNIK METEOROLOGICZNY. (Text in Polish or English) 1979. irreg. $200. Instytut Meteorologii i Gospodarki Wodnej, Oddzial Morski w Gdyni - Institute of Meteorology and Water Management, Maritime Branch in Gdynia, 42 Waszyngtona St., 81-342 Gdynia, Poland. TEL 4858-203532. FAX 4858-201641. TELEX 54216 PL. Eds. Danuta Wielbinska, Miroslaw Mietus. circ. 120. (tabloid format)
Description: Covers meteorology and observation results at the polar meteorological research station.

STATIONS RADIOMETEOROLOGIQUES. see *TRANSPORTATION — Ships And Shipping*

551.55 US ISSN 0039-1972
QC943.5.U6
STORM DATA. 1922. m. $51. U.S. National Climatic Data Center, National Oceanic and Atmospheric Administration, U.S. Department of Commerce, Federal Bldg., Rm. 120, 151 Patton Ave., Asheville, NC 28801-5001. TEL 704-271-4756. FAX 704-271-4876. TELEX 6502643731. E-mail: orders@ncdc.noaa.gov. circ. 1,500. (also avail. in microfiche from CIS; back issues avail.; reprint service avail. from CIS) **Indexed:** Amer.Stat.Ind. (1974-). **Document type:** government publication.

551.5 US
STORMTRACK. 1977. bi-m. $14. 1336 Brazos Blvd., Lewisville, TX 75067. TEL 214-317-7910. FAX 214-484-1821. Ed. Tim Marshall. adv.: B&W page $250; trim 7 1/2 x 10; adv. contact: Tim Marshall. charts; illus.; circ. 600 (paid). (back issues avail.) **Document type:** newsletter.
Description: Caters to the scientist and amateur alike who share an avid interest in the acquisition and advancement of knowledge concerning severe storms.

STUDIA GEOPHYSICA ET GEODAETICA; a journal of geophysics, geodesy, meteorology and climatology. see *EARTH SCIENCES — Geophysics*

551.5　　　　　　JA　ISSN 0916-1295
SYMPOSIUM ON ATMOSPHERE/TAIKIKEN SHINPOJUMU. (Text in English, Japanese) 1986. a. Institute of Space and Astronautical Science - Uchu Kagaku Kenkyujo, 1-1, Yoshindodai 3-chome, Sagamihara-shi, Kanagawa-ken 229, Japan.

551.5 620　　　　　　JA
SYMPOSIUM ON WIND ENGINEERING. PROCEEDINGS. (Text in Japanese; summaries in English) 1970. biennial. price varies. Nihon Gakujutsu Kaigi, Meteorological Society of Japan - Science Council of Japan, c/o Japan Meteorological Agency, 1-3 Ote-machi, Chiyoda-ku, Tokyo 100, Japan. **Document type:** proceedings.
 Former titles: Symposium on Wind Effects on Structures in Japan. Proceedings; National Symposium on Wind Engineering. Proceedings.

551　　　　　　JA　ISSN 0286-3405
TAIKI DENKI KENKYU/SOCIETY OF ATMOSPHERIC ELECTRICITY OF JAPAN. PROCEEDINGS. (Text in English, Japanese) 1969. a. Nihon Taiki Denki Gakkai - Society of Atmospheric Electricity of Japan, Osaka Daigaku Kogakubu Denkikogakka, 2-1 Yamadaoka, Suita-shi, Osaka 565, Japan. **Document type:** proceedings.

551 539.2　　　　　　JA　ISSN 0447-3884
TAIKI HOSHANO KANSOKU SEISEKI/BULLETIN OF ATMOSPHERIC RADIOACTIVITY. (Text in English, Japanese) 1955. a. Kishocho - Japan Meteorological Agency, 3-4, Otemachi 1-chome, Chiyoda-ku, Tokyo 100, Japan. **Indexed:** INIS Atomind.
 —BLDSC (2834.100000).

551.5　　　　　　JA　ISSN 0546-0921
**　　　　　　　　CODEN: TENKBT**
TENKI/METEOROLOGICAL SOCIETY OF JAPAN. WEATHER. (Text in Japanese) 12/yr. 6900 Yen to individuals; institutions 9000 Yen. Nihon Kisho Gakkai - Meteorological Society of Japan, c/o Japan Meteorological Agency, 1-3-4 Ote-machi, Chiyoda-ku, Tokyo 100, Japan. TEL 03-3212-8341. FAX 03-3216-4401. **Indexed:** INIS Atomind., Jap.Per.Ind.
 —CASDDS.

551.5　　　　　　JA
TENKIZU/DAILY WEATHER MAPS. (Text in English, Japanese) 1940. m. 180000 Yen. Kishocho - Japan Meteorological Agency, 3-4 Otemachi 1-chome, Chiyoda-ku, Tokyo 100, Japan. circ. 501.
 Incorporates (in 1989): Taifu Keirozu.

551.5　　　　　　AU　ISSN 0177-798X
**　　　　　　　　CODEN: TACLEK**
THEORETICAL AND APPLIED CLIMATOLOGY. (Text in English and German) 1949. 8/yr. (in 2 vols., 4 nos./vol.). DM.1260($915) (effective 1996). Springer-Verlag, Sachsenplatz 4-6, Postfach 89, A-1201 Vienna, Austria. TEL 0222-330-2415. FAX 0222-330-2426. (Subscr. in N. America to: Springer-Verlag New York, Inc., 44 Hartz Way, Secaucus, NJ 07096-2491. TEL 201-348-4033. FAX 201-348-4505; Elsewhere: Heidelberger Platz 3, 14197 Berlin, Germany. TEL 030-8207-1. FAX 030-8214091) Ed. I. Dirmhirn. (also avail. in microform from UMI) **Indexed:** ASCA, Curr.Adv.Ecol.Sci., Deep Sea Res.& Oceanogr.Abstr., Environ.Per.Bibl., Forest.Abstr., Geo.Abstr., Ind.Sci.Rev., INSPEC, Meteor.& Geoastrophys.Abstr., Sci.Cit.Ind., Soils & Fert. **Document type:** academic/scholarly publication.
 —BLDSC (8814.551500); Faxon; Genuine Article; SWETS; UMI; UnCover. **CCC.**
 Formerly (until 1985): Archives for Meteorology, Geophysics, and Bioclimatology. Series B: Climatology, Environmental Meteorology, Radiation Research - Archiv fuer Meteorologie, Geophysik und Bioklimatologie. Series B (ISSN 0066-6424)
 Description: Discusses climate and climatic change modeling, applied meteorology, micrometeorology and atmospheric radiation problems, air pollution, and techniques and technologies to measure climatic phenomena.

551　　　　　　JA　ISSN 0916-5010
TOCHIGIKEN KISHO GEPPO/TOCHIGI PREFECTURE. MONTHLY REPORT OF METEOROLOGY. (Text in Japanese) 1900. m. Kishocho, Utsunomiya Chiho Kishodai - Japan Meteorological Agency, Utsunomiya Local Meteorological Observatory, 1-7, Akebonocho, Utsunomiya-shi, Tochigi-ken 320, Japan. **Document type:** academic/scholarly publication.

551.5　　　　　　TG
TOGO. DIRECTION DE LA METEOROLOGIE NATIONALE. RESUME ANNUEL DU TEMPS. a. Direction de la Meteorologie Nationale, B.P. 1505, Lome, Togo.

551.5　　　　　　TG
TOGO. DIRECTION DE LA METEOROLOGIE NATIONALE. RESUME MENSUEL DU TEMPS. m. Direction de la Meteorologie Nationale, B.P. 1505, Lome, Togo.

551.63
TOHOKU CHIHO CHOKI YOHO SOKUHO/BULLETIN OF LONG RANGE WEATHER FORECASTING OF TOHOKU DISTRICT. (Text in Japanese) 1942. 3/yr. Kishocho, Sendai Kanku Kishodai - Japan Meteorological Agency, Sendai District Meteorological Observatory, 3-15, Gorin 1-chome, Migagino-ku, Sendai-shi, Miyagi-ken 983, Japan.

551　　　　　　JA　ISSN 0563-6493
TOHOKU CHIHO KISHO KENKYUKAISHI/JOURNAL OF METEOROLOGICAL RESEARCH OF TOHOKU DISTRICT. (Text in English, Japanese) triennial. Kishocho, Sendai Kanku Kishodai - Japan Meteorological Agency, Sendai District Meteorological Observatory, 3-15, Gorin 1-chome, Migagino-ke, Sendai-shi, Miyagi-ken 983, Japan.

551　　　　　　JA　ISSN 0289-3126
QC851
TOHOKU GIJUTSU DAYORI/TOHOKU DISTRICT METEOROLOGICAL OBSERVATORY. TECHNICAL NEWS. (Text in Japanese) 1962. bi-m. Kishocho, Sendai Kanku Kishodai - Japan Meteorological Agency, Sendai District Meteorological Observatory, 3-15 Gorin 1-chome, Migagino-ku, Sendai-shi, Miyagi-ken 983, Japan.

551 630　　　　　　JA　ISSN 0287-1173
TOHOKU NO NOGYO KISHO/BULLETIN OF THE AGRICULTURAL METEOROLOGY OF TOHOKU DISTRICT. (Text in Japanese) 1956. a. 2000 Yen. Nihon Nogyo Kisho Gakkai, Tohoku Shibu - Society of Agricultural Meteorology of Japan, Tohoku Branch, Norin Suisansho Tohoku Nogyo Shikenjo, 4 Akahira, Shimokuriyagawa, Morioka-shi, Iwate-ken 020-01, Japan. TEL 81-196-43-3461. FAX 81-196-41-7794. E-mail: Kanno@tnaes.affrc.go.jp. Ed. Takashi Ozawa. adv. contact: Kimio Enoue. **Document type:** bulletin.
 Refereed Serial

551　　　　　　JA　ISSN 0385-0625
TOKAN GIJUTSU NYUSU/TOKYO DISTRICT METEOROLOGICAL OBSERVATORY. TECHNICAL INFORMATION NEWS. (Text in Japanese) 1968. 4/yr. Kishocho, Tokyo Kanku Kishodai - Japan Meteorological Agency, Tokyo District Meteorological Observatory, 3-4, Otemachi 1-chome, Chiyoda-ku, Tokyo 100, Japan.

551　　　　　　JA　ISSN 0916-5231
TOKUSHIMA-KEN KISHO GEPPO/TOKUSHIMA PREFECTURE. MONTHLY REPORT OF METEOROLOGY. (Text in Japanese) 1954. m. Kishocho, Tokushima Chiho Kishodai - Japan Meteorological Agency, Tokushima Local Meteorological Observatory, 3-36 Yamatocho 2-chome, Tokushima-shi, Tokushima-ken 770, Japan.
 Formerly (until 1965): Tokushima no Kisho.

551　　　　　　JA　ISSN 0289-310X
TOKYO KANKU CHIHO KISHO KENKYUKAISHI/TOKYO DISTRICT METEOROLOGICAL OBSERVATORY. GEOPHYSICAL NOTES. (Text in Japanese) 1968. a. Kishocho, Tokyo Kanku Kishodai - Japan Meteorological Agency, Tokyo District Meteorological Observatory, 3-4, Otemachi 1-chome, Chiyoda-ku, Tokyo 100, Japan.

551.6　　　　　　JA
TOKYO KANKU IJO KISHO HOKOKU/TOKYO DISTRICT METEOROLOGICAL OBSERVATORY. UNUSUAL METEOROLOGICAL REPORT. (Text in Japanese) 1960. a. Kishocho, Tokyo Kanku Kishodai - Japan Meteorological Agency, Tokyo District Meteorological Observatory, 3-4 Otemachi 1-chome, Chiyoda-ku, Tokyo 100, Japan.

551　　　　　　JA　ISSN 0916-524X
TOKYOTO KISHO GEPPO/TOKYO METROPOLIS. MONTHLY REPORT OF METEOROLOGY. (Text in Japanese) 1951. m. Kishocho, Tokyo Kanku Kishodai - Japan Meteorological Agency, Tokyo District Meteorological Observatory, 3-4, Otemachi 1-chome, Chiyoda-ku, Tokyo 100, Japan.

TOPICS IN ATMOSPHERIC AND OCEANOGRAPHIC SCIENCES. see *EARTH SCIENCES — Oceanography*

551.5　　　　　　UK
TORNADOES AND STORMS; Oxford conference proceedings. 1985. biennial. $25. (Tornado & Storm Research Organisation) Artetech Publishing Co., 54 Frome Rd., Bradford-on-Avon, Wilts. BA15 1LD, England. TEL 01225-862482. FAX 01225-865601. Ed. G.T. Meaden. circ. 1,000. (back issues avail.) **Document type:** academic/scholarly publication, proceedings.
 Description: Discusses tornadoes, waterspouts, whirlwinds, damaging hail, ball lightning and thunderstorms.

551　　　　　　JA　ISSN 0916-5258
TOTTORIKEN KISHO GEPPO/TOTTORI PREFECTURE. MONTHLY REPORT OF METEOROLOGY. (Text in Japanese) 1950. m. Kishocho, Tottori Chiho Kishodai - Japan Meteorological Agency, Tottori Local Meteorological Observatory, c/o Tottori Dai 3 Chiho Godo Chosha, 109 Yoshikata, Tottori-shi, Tottori-ken 680, Japan.

551.5　　　　　　JA　ISSN 0916-5614
TOTTORIKEN KISHO NENPO/TOTTORI PREFECTURE. ANNUAL REPORT OF METEOROLOGY. (Text in Japanese) a. Kishocho, Tottori Chicho Kishodai - Japan Meteorological Agency, Tottori Local Meteorological Observatory, c/o Tottori Dai 3 Chiho Goda Chosha, 109 Yoshikata, Tottori-shi, Tottori-ken 680, Japan.

551.5　　　　　　JA　ISSN 0916-5266
TOYAMAKEN KISHO GEPPO/TOYAMA PREFECTURE. MONTHLY REPORT OF METEOROLOGY. (Text in Japanese) 1951. m. Kishocho, Toyama Chiho Kishodai - Japan Meteorological Agency, Toyama Local Meteorological Observatory, 2415 Ishizaka, Toyama-shi, Toyama-ken 930, Japan.

551.5　　　　　　JA　ISSN 0916-5630
TOYAMAKEN KISHO NENPO/TOYAMA PREFECTURE. ANNUAL REPORT OF METEOROLOGY. (Text in Japanese) a. Kishocho, Toyama Chiho Kishodai - Japan Meteorological Society, Toyama Local Meteorological Observatory, 2415 Ishizaka, Toyama-shi, Toyama-ken 930, Japan.

551.5 613.1　　　　　　US
TRENDS (YEAR); a compendium of data on global change. 1990. biennial. free. U.S. Department of Energy, Carbon Dioxide Information Analysis Center, Oak Ridge National Laboratory, Box 2008, MS-6335, Oak Ridge, TN 37831-6335. TEL 615-574-0390. FAX 615-574-2332. E-mail: CDIAC@ORNL.gov. Ed.Bd. circ. 12,000. **Document type:** newsletter, government publication.

551.5 613.1　　　　　　US
TRENDS: A COMPENDIUM OF DATA ON GLOBAL CHANGE. irreg. free. (U.S. Department of Energy) Carbon Dioxide Information Analysis Center, Oak Ridge National Laboratory, Box 2008 (MS-6335), Oak Ridge, TN 37831-6335. TEL 615-574-0390. FAX 615-574-2332. E-mail: cdiaC@ornl.gov. Ed. Thomas A. Boden. **Document type:** monographic series, government publication.
 Formerly: C02 Technical Report.
 Description: Provides synopses of critical data related to global environmental change: atmospheric carbon dioxide, atmospheric methane, other trace gases and derosols, carbon dioxide emissions, temperature, and precipitation.

551.5
THE TRIPOD. 1988. s-a. University of Nebraska at Lincoln, High Plains Climate Center, 237 L.W. Chase Hall, Box 830728, Lincoln, NE 68583-0728. TEL 402-472-6706. FAX 402-472-6614. TELEX UNL COMM LCN 484340. Dir. Kenneth G. Hubbard. circ. 320. **Document type:** newsletter.
 Description: Covers the operation of weather stations in an automated environment, measurement and calibration of sensors, programming techniques for dataloggers, data retrieval, storage quality control and dissemination mechanism.

551.5　　　　　　HK
TROPICAL CYCLONES (YEAR); tropical cyclone summaries. (Text in English) 1968. a. price varies. Royal Observatory, 134A Nathan Rd., Kowloon, Hong Kong. Ed.Bd.
 Formerly (until 1987): Hong Kong. Royal Observatory. Meteorological Results - Part III.

TYDSKRIF VIR SKOONLUG/CLEAN AIR JOURNAL. see ENVIRONMENTAL STUDIES — Pollution

551.5 US ISSN 0273-0707
U C A R QUARTERLY. 1977. q. free. University Corporation for Atmospheric Research, Box 3000, Boulder, CO 80307. TEL 303-497-8611. FAX 303-497-8610. E-mail: gopher@ncar.ucar.edu or lcarroll@ncar.ucar.edu. Ed. Louise Carroll. index. circ. 4,000. (back issues avail.) Document type: newsletter.
●Also available online.
Description: Covers meteorology, climate studies, earth sciences, oceanography, and "global change."

551 JA ISSN 0287-5276
UMI NO KISHO/MARINE METEOROLOGY. (Text in Japanese) 1955. bi-m. Kaiyo Kisho Gakkai - Marine Meteorological Society, Kobe Kaiyo Kishodai, 14-1 Nakayamate Dori 7-chome, Chuo-ku, Kobe-shi, Hyogo-ken 650, Japan.

551 JA ISSN 0503-1567
UMI TO SORA/SEA AND SKY. (Text in English, Japanese) 1921. irreg. Kaiyo Kisho Gakkai - Marine Meteorological Society, Kobe Kaiyo Kishodai, 14-1 Nakayamate Dori 7-chome, Chuo-ku, Kobe-shi, Hyogo-ken 650, Japan. Indexed: Jap.Per.Ind.

551.6 US ISSN 0192-8759
QC980
U.S. NATIONAL OCEANIC AND ATMOSPHERIC ADMINISTRATION. ANNUAL CLIMATE DIAGNOSTICS WORKSHOP. PROCEEDINGS. 1976. a. U.S. National Oceanic and Atmospheric Administration, 6010 Executive Blvd., Rockville, MD 20852. TEL 301-655-4000. (Orders to: N T I S, U.S. Dept. of Commerce, Sills Bldg., 5285 Port Royal Rd., Springfield, VA 22161) Document type: proceedings.
—UnCover.

551.552 US ISSN 0092-2056
QC851
U.S. NATIONAL OCEANIC AND ATMOSPHERIC ADMINISTRATION. INTERDEPARTMENTAL COMMITTEE FOR METEOROLOGICAL SERVICES AND SUPPORTING RESEARCH. NATIONAL HURRICANE OPERATIONS PLAN.* Key Title: National Hurricane Operations Plan. (Formerly issued by: Office of Federal Coordinator for Meteorological Services and Supporting Research) 1962. irreg. U.S. National Oceanic and Atmospheric Administration, Interdepartmental Committee for Meteorological Services and Supporting Research, 1315 East-West Hwy., Silver Spring, MD 20910. TEL 301-655-4000. illus. circ. 1,000. Document type: government publication.

UNIVERSIDAD DE GUADALAJARA. INSTITUTO DE ASTRONOMIA Y METEOROLOGIA. INFORMACION. see ASTRONOMY

UNIVERSITAET ZU KOELN. INSTITUT FUER GEOPHYSIK UND METEOROLOGIE. MITTEILUNGEN. see EARTH SCIENCES — Geophysics

551.5 551 BE
UNIVERSITEIT TE GENT. STERRENKUNDIG OBSERVATORIUM. MEDEDELINGEN: METEOROLOGIE EN GEOFYSICA. (Text and summaries in Dutch, English) 1961. irreg. free. Universiteit te Gent, Sterrenkundig Observatorium, Krijgslaan 281, B-9000 Ghent, Belgium. TEL 32-9-2464798. FAX 32-9-2644989. Indexed: Apic.Abstr. Document type: academic/scholarly publication.
Formerly: Rijksuniversiteit te Gent. Sterrenkundig Observatorium. Mededelingen: Meteorologie en Geofysica (ISSN 0072-4440)

UNIVERSITY OF ALASKA. GEOPHYSICAL INSTITUTE. REPORT SERIES. see EARTH SCIENCES — Geophysics

551.6 UK ISSN 0306-1566
UNIVERSITY OF EAST ANGLIA. CLIMATIC RESEARCH UNIT. RESEARCH PUBLICATION. 1973. irreg. price varies. University of East Anglia, Climatic Research Unit, School of Environmental Sciences, Norwich NR4 7TJ, England. TEL 01603-592088. FAX 01603-507784. TELEX 975197. Indexed: Geo.Abstr. Document type: academic/scholarly publication.
—BLDSC (7759.149000).

551.5 PL
UNIWERSYTET WROCLAWSKI. INSTYTUT GEOGRAFICZNY. PRACE. SERIA C: METEOROLOGIA I KLIMATOLOGIA. (Subseries of: Acta Universitatis Wratislaviensis) 1971. irreg. price varies. Wydawnictwo Uniwersytetu Wroclawskiego, Pl. Uniwersytecki 9-13, 50-137 Wroclaw, Poland. (Dist. by: Ksiegarnia Uniwersytetu Wroclawskiego, Pl. Uniwersytecki 9-13, 50137 Wroclaw, Poland) Ed.Bd. Document type: academic/scholarly publication.
Formerly: Biuletyn Meteorologiczny.

V Z L U ZPRAVODAJ. (Vyzkumny a Zkusebni Letecky Ustav) see AERONAUTICS AND SPACE FLIGHT

551.5 NO ISSN 0803-3293
VAER OG KLIMA; populaervitenskapelig tidsskrift. 1977. q. NOK 230 in Nordic countries; elsewhere NOK 290 (effective 1995). (Norwegian Institute of Meteorology) Scandinavian University Press, P.O. Box 2050-Toeyen, N-0608 Oslo, Norway. TEL 47-22-57-54-00. FAX 47-22-57-53-53. (U.S. addr.: Scandinavian University Press, 200 Meacham Ave., Elmont, NY 11003. TEL 516-352-7300) Ed. Alf Sunde. circ. 2,000.
Formerly: Vaeret (ISSN 0332-5040)
Description: Covers meteorology and climate changes from a popular science angle.

551.5 II ISSN 0970-1397
VAYU MANDAL; science journal on the human environment. (Text in English) 1971. s-a. Rs.24($10) Indian Meteorological Society, The Observatory, Lodi Rd., New Delhi 3, India. Ed. S.K. Das. adv.; bk.rev.; charts; illus. circ. 1,000.

551.5 UN ISSN 0042-9767
QC851   CODEN: WMOBAR
W M O BULLETIN. Russian edition: Byulleten' V M O (ISSN 0250-6076); Spanish edition: Boletin de la O M M (ISSN 0250-6025); French edition: Bulletin de l'O M M (ISSN 0510-9019) 1952. q. $52. World Meteorological Organization, 41 av. Giuseppe Motta, Ch-1211 Geneva 2, Switzerland. TEL 730-8111. (Dist. in U.S. by: American Meteorological Society, 45 Beacon St., Boston, MA 02108. TEL 617-227-2425) Ed. R. Czelnai. adv.; bk.rev.; illus.; index. circ. 7,000. Indexed: Curr.Adv.Ecol.Sci., Field Crop Abstr., Geo.Abstr., Herb.Abstr., Meteor.& Geoastrophys.Abstr. Document type: bulletin.
—Faxon; SWETS; UnCover.
Description: Provides a summary of the work and developments in international meteorology and hydrology.

551.6 JA
W N O KAIYO KIKO GAIYO/MARINE CLIMATOLOGICAL SUMMARY. (Text in English) 1961. a. Kishocho - Japan Meteorological Agency, 3-4, Otemachi 1-chome, Chiyoda-ku, Tokyo 100, Japan.

551.65 JA ISSN 0910-4542
WAKAYAMA PREFECTURE. ANNUAL REPORT OF METEOROLOGY/WAKAYAMA-KEN KISHO NENPO. (Text in Japanese) a. Wakayama Local Meteorological Observatory - Wakayama Chiho Kishodai, 4 Onoshiba-cho, Wakayama 640, Japan. charts; stat.

551.65 JA ISSN 0043-0021
WAKAYAMAKEN KISHO GEPPO/WAKAYAMA PREFECTURE. MONTHLY REPORT OF METEOROLOGY. (Text in Japanese) 1917. m. Kishocho, Wakayama Chiho Kishodai - Japan Meteorological Agency, Wakayama Local Meteorological Observatory, 4-1 Onoshibacho, Wakayama-shi, Wakayama-ken 640, Japan. charts; illus.

551.6 UK ISSN 0043-1656
QC851   CODEN: WTHRAL
WEATHER. 1946. m. $51. Royal Meteorological Society, 104 Oxford Rd., Reading, Berks RG1 7LJ, England. TEL 01734-568500. FAX 01734-568571. Ed. R. Brugge. adv.; bk.rev.; illus.; index. circ. 4,800. Indexed: Agri.Eng.Abstr., Chem.Abstr., Curr.Adv.Ecol.Sci., Curr.Tit.Ocean, Deep Sea Res.& Oceanogr.Abstr., Forest.Abstr., Geo.Abstr., Hort.Abstr., INSPEC, Int.Aerosp.Abstr., Meteor.& Geoastrophys.Abstr., Mid.East: Abstr.& Ind., Ocean.Abstr., Pollut.Abstr., Sel.Water Res.Abstr., So.Pac.Per.Ind., Soils & Fert., W.R.C.Inf. Document type: academic/scholarly publication.
—BLDSC (9282.000000); Ei; Faxon; SWETS; UnCover.
Description: Articles on the science, technology, informational aspects, and broadcasting of meteorology and climatology, with announcements of conferences, seminars and meetings.

551.6 US ISSN 0731-5627
QC983
WEATHER ALMANAC. 1974. irreg., 6th ed., 1991. $120. Gale Research Inc., 835 Penobscot Bldg., Detroit, MI 48226. TEL 313-961-2242. FAX 313-961-6083. TELEX 810-221-7086. Eds. James A. Ruffner, Frank E. Bair.
Description: Provides information on weather in the U.S.

551.6 NZ ISSN 0111-5499
WEATHER AND CLIMATE. 1981. s-a. NZ.$75 to institutions; individual members NZ.$30. Meteorological Society of New Zealand, P.O. Box 6523, Te Aro, Wellington, New Zealand. TEL 64-9-373-7599. FAX 64-9-373-7434. Ed. Anthony Fowler. adv.; bk.rev. circ. 450. Indexed: Meteor.& Geoastrophys.Abstr. Document type: academic/scholarly publication.
—CCC.
Description: Deals with meteorological or climatological subject with preference given to contributions related to New Zealand and The Southwest Pacific.

551.6 US ISSN 0730-8256
WEATHER & CLIMATE REPORT. 1977. m. $95 (foreign $110) (effective 1996). Nautilus Press, Inc., 1201 National Press Bldg., Washington, DC 20045. TEL 202-347-6643. Ed. John R. Botzum, Jr. Document type: newsletter.
Description: Features federal actions impacting weather and climate research.

551.5 310 US ISSN 0882-8156
QC994.95 CODEN: WEFOE3
WEATHER AND FORECASTING. 1986. q. $110 (foreign $130) (effective 1996). American Meteorological Society, 45 Beacon St., Boston, MA 02108-3693. TEL 617-227-2427. FAX 617-742-8718. Ed. Bradley Colmam. abstr.; bibl.; charts; illus.; stat.; index. circ. 1,640. (back issues avail.) Indexed: Geo.Abstr., Meteor.& Geoastrophys.Abstr. Document type: trade publication.
—BLDSC (9282.600000); Ei; Faxon; Genuine Article; UnCover. CCC.
Description: Published operational forecasting techniques, applications of new analysis methods, forecasting verification studies, and meso-scale and synoptic-scale case studies that have direct applicability to forecasting.

551.5 US
WEATHER OF U S CITIES. quinquennial. $200. Gale Research Inc., 835 Penobscot Bldg., Detroit, MI 48266. TEL 313-961-2242. FAX 313-961-6083. Ed. Frank E. Blair.

551.6 US ISSN 0043-1672
QC851 CODEN: WTHWA2
WEATHERWISE; popular weather magazine. 1948. bi-m. $33 to individuals; institutions $57. (Helen Dwight Reid Educational Foundation) Heldref Publications, 1319 Eighteenth St., N.W., Washington, DC 20036-1802. TEL 202-296-6267. FAX 202-296-5149. Ed. Jeffrey Rosenfeld. adv. contact: Raymond Rallo. bk.rev.; charts; illus.; index, cum.index: vols.1-31. circ. 10,000. (also avail. in microform from UMI; reprint service avail.) Indexed: Acid Rain Abstr., Acid Rain Ind., Chem.Abstr., Curr.Tit.Ocean, Deep Sea Res.& Oceanogr.Abstr., Environ.Abstr., Gen.Sci.Ind., Geo.Abstr., GeoRef., INSPEC (1987-), Int.Aerosp.Abstr., Mag.Ind., Meteor.& Geoastrophys.Abstr., PMR, RG, Sel.Water Res.Abstr. Document type: consumer publication.
●Also available online. Vendor(s): University Microfilms International.
Also available on CD-ROM. Producer(s): University Microfilms International.
—BLDSC (9283.900000); Faxon; SWETS; UMI; UnCover. CCC.
Refereed Serial

551.5 AU ISSN 0043-4450
QH543 CODEN: WTLBAR
WETTER UND LEBEN; Zeitschrift fuer angewandte Meteorologie. (Summaries in English) 1948. q. S.500. Oesterreichische Gesellschaft fuer Meteorologie, Hohe Warte 38, A-1190 Vienna, Austria. FAX 3691233. TELEX 131837-METW. Ed. Hartwig Dobesch. adv.; bk.rev.; abstr.; illus.; index. circ. 600. Indexed: Chem.Abstr., Meteor.& Geoastrophys.Abstr., Ocean.Abstr., Pollut.Abstr.
—CASDDS.

METEOROLOGY

551.654   GW   ISSN 0936-5818
WETTERKARTE; Amtsblatt des Deutschen Wetterdienstes. 1973. d. Deutscher Wetterdienst, Bibliothek, Postfach 100465, 63004 Offenbach a.M. TEL 069-80622283. FAX 069-30622486. **Document type:** government publication.

551.5   GW   ISSN 0943-0504
DER WETTERLOTSE. 1949. m. DM.25. Deutscher Wetterdienst, Seewetteramt, Postfach 301190, 20304 Hamburg, Germany. index. circ. 1,000. (back issues avail.) **Indexed:** Meteor.& Geoastrophys.Abstr. **Document type:** bulletin.
Description: For weather observers on ships.

WHOLE EARTH FORECASTER. see *BUSINESS AND ECONOMICS — Investments*

551.65   AU   ISSN 0043-7077
WITTERUNG IN OESTERREICH. MONATSUEBERSICHT. 1946. m. price varies. Zentralanstalt fuer Meteorologie und Geodynamik, A-1190 Vienna, Austria. charts; stat. **Document type:** government publication.

551.6   GW   ISSN 0043-7085
WITTERUNG IN UEBERSEE. 1953. m. DM.80. Deutscher Wetterdienst, Seewetteramt, Postfach 301190, 20304 Hamburg, Germany. charts. circ. 300. **Document type:** bulletin.
Description: Monthly and annual global climate review of tropical storms, temperature, precipitation and sea level pressure (actual values and departures from normal).

551   JA
WORLD DATA CENTER C2 FOR AURORA. DATA CATALOGUE. (Text in English) 1985. irreg., no.5, 1995. exchange basis. National Institute of Polar Research - Kokuritsu Kyokuchi Kenkyujo, 9-10, Kaga 1-chome, Itabashi-ku, Tokyo 173, Japan. TEL 03-3962-2214. FAX 03-3962-2225. circ. 800. **Document type:** catalog.
Supersedes in part (in 1993): Data Catalogue in World Data Center C2 for Aurora.

551.5   UN   ISSN 0084-1935
WORLD METEOROLOGICAL CONGRESS. PROCEEDINGS. French edition: Organisation Meteorologique Mondiale. Congres. Proces - Verbaux (ISSN 0250-9237) 1952. quadrennial, latest 1991. World Meteorological Organization, 41 av. Giuseppe Motta, CH-1211 Geneva 2, Switzerland. TEL 730-8111. (Dist. in U.S. by: American Meteorological Society, 45 Beacon St., Boston, MA 02108. TEL 617-227-2425) **Document type:** proceedings.

551.5   UN
WORLD METEOROLOGICAL ORGANIZATION. ABRIDGED FINAL REPORTS OF SESSIONS OF TECHNICAL COMMISSIONS. irreg. price varies. World Meteorological Organization, 41 av. Giuseppe Motta, CH-1211 Geneva 2, Switzerland. TEL 730-8111. (Dist. in U.S. by: American Meteorological Society, 45 Beacon St., Boston, MA 02108. TEL 617-227-2425) **Document type:** monographic series.
Formerly: World Meteorological Association. Technical Commissions Abridged Final Reports (ISSN 0084-1919)

551.5   UN   ISSN 0084-1994
WORLD METEOROLOGICAL ORGANIZATION. ANNUAL REPORT. Russian edition: Vsemirnaya Meteorologicheskaya Organizatsiya. Godovoi Otchet (ISSN 0250-8893) 1953. a., latest 1993 (for 1992). price varies. World Meteorological Organization, 41 av. Giuseppe Motta, CH-1211 Geneva 2, Switzerland. TEL 730-8111. (Dist. in U.S. by: American Meteorological Society, 45 Beacon St., Boston, MA 02108. TEL 617-227-2425) **Indexed:** IIS. **Document type:** monographic series.
Description: Reports on the activities.

551.5   UN
WORLD METEOROLOGICAL ORGANIZATION. BASIC DOCUMENTS. (In 3 vols.) irreg. price varies. World Meteorological Organization, 41 av. Giuseppe Motta, CH-1211 Geneva 2, Switzerland. TEL 730-8111. (Dist. in U.S. by: American Meteorological Society, 45 Beacon St., Boston, MA 02108. TEL 617-227-2425)
Former titles: World Meteorological Organization. Basic Documents and Official Reports; World Meteorological Organization. Basic Documents, Records and Reports (ISSN 0084-1943)
Description: Contains regulations of the W.M.O. and agreements with the U.N. and the Swiss governments by which the W.M.O. operates.

551.3 387.7   UN   ISSN 0510-906X
QC851
WORLD METEOROLOGICAL ORGANIZATION. COMMISSION FOR AERONAUTICAL METEOROLOGY. ABRIDGED FINAL REPORT OF THE (NO.) SESSION. French edition: Organisation Meteorologique Mondiale. Commission de Meteorologie Aeronautique. Rapport Final Abrege de la (No.) Session (ISSN 0251-8899); Russian edition: Vsemirnaya Meteorologicheskaya Organizatsiya. Komissiya po Aviatsionnoi Meteorologii. Okonchatel'nyi Sokrashchennyi Otchet (No.) Sessii (ISSN 0251-8880); Spanish edition: Organizacion Meteorologica Mundial. Comision de Meteorologia Aeronautica. Informe Final Abreviado de la (No.) Reunion (ISSN 0251-8902) 1954. irreg., latest 1991. price varies. World Meteorological Organization, Commission for Aeronautical Meteorology, 41 av. Giuseppe-Motta, CH-1211 Geneva 20, Switzerland. TEL 730-8111. (Dist. in U.S. by: American Meteorological Society, 45 Beacon St., Boston, MA 02108, TEL 617-227-2425) **Document type:** monographic series.

551.3 630   UN   ISSN 0510-9078
QC851
WORLD METEOROLOGICAL ORGANIZATION. COMMISSION FOR AGRICULTURAL METEOROLOGY. ABRIDGED FINAL REPORT OF THE (NO.) SESSION. French edition: Organisation Meteorologique Mondiale. Commission de Meteorologie Agricole. Rapport Final Abrege de la (No.) Session (ISSN 0251-883X); Russian edition: Vsemirnaya Meteorologicheskaya Organizatsiya Komissiya po Sel'skokhozyaistvennoi Meteorologii. Okonchatel'nyi Sokrashchennyi Otchet (No.) Sessii (ISSN 0251-8848); Spanish edition: Organizacion Meteorologica Mundial. Comision de Meteorologia Agricola. Informe Final Abreviado de la (No.) Reunion (ISSN 0251-8821) 1953. irreg., latest 1992. price varies. World Meteorological Organization, Commission for Agricultural Meteorology, 41 av. Giuseppe-Motta, CH-1211 Geneva 20, Switzerland. TEL 730-8111. (Dist. in U.S. by: American Meteorological Society, 45 Beacon St., Boston, MA 02108. TEL 617-227-2425)

551.3   UN   ISSN 0250-9172
WORLD METEOROLOGICAL ORGANIZATION. COMMISSION FOR ATMOSPHERIC SCIENCES. ABRIDGED FINAL REPORT OF THE (NO.) SESSION. French edition: Organisation Meteorologique Mondiale. Commission des Sciences de l'Atmosphere. Rapport Final Abrege de la (No.) Session (ISSN 0250-9156); Russian edition: Vsemirnaya Meteorologicheskaya Organizatsiya. Komissiya po Atmosfernym Naukam. Okonchatel'nyi Sokrashchennyi Otchet (No.) Sessii. (ISSN 0250-9164); Spanish edition: Organizacion Meteorologica Mundial. Comision de Ciencias Atmosfericas. Informe Final Abreviado de la (No.) Reunion (ISSN 0250-9180) 1953-1965; N.S. 1970. irreg., latest 1994. price varies. World Meteorological Organization, Commission for Atmospheric Sciences, 41 av. Giuseppe-Motta, CH-1211 Geneva 20, Switzerland. TEL 730-8111. (Dist. in U.S. by: American Meteorological Society, 45 Beacon St., Boston, MA 02108. TEL 617-227-2425)
Formerly (until 1965): World Meteorological Organization. Commission of Aerology. Abridged Final Report of the (No.) Session (ISSN 1011-3223)

551.3   UN   ISSN 0251-8953
WORLD METEOROLOGICAL ORGANIZATION. COMMISSION FOR BASIC SYSTEMS. ABRIDGED FINAL REPORT OF THE (NO.) SESSION. French edition: Organisation Meteorologique Mondiale. Commission des Systems de Base. Rapport Final Abrege de la (No.) Session (ISSN 0251-8988); Russian edition: Vsemirnaya Meteorologicheskaya Organizatsiya. Komissiya po Osnovnym Sistemam. Okonchatel'nyi Sokrashchennyi Otchet (No.) Sessii (ISSN 0251-8961); Spanish edition: Meteorologica Mundial. Comision de Sistemas Basicos. Informe Final Abreviado de la (No.) Reunion (ISSN 0251-897X) 1953-1970; N.S. 1974. irreg., latest 1993. price varies. World Meteorological Organization, Commission for Basic Systems, 41 av. Giuseppe-Motta, CH-1211 Geneva 20, Switzerland. TEL 730-8111. (Dist. in U.S. by: American Meteorological Society, 45 Beacon St., Boston, MA 02108. TEL 617-227-2425)
Formerly (until 1970): World Meteorological Organization. Commission of Synoptic Meteorology. Abridged Final Report of the (No.) Session (ISSN 0510-9116)

551.3 551.46   UN   ISSN 0251-8775
WORLD METEOROLOGICAL ORGANIZATION. COMMISSION FOR HYDROLOGY. ABRIDGED FINAL REPORT OF THE (NO.) SESSION. French edition: Organisation Meteorologique Mondiale. Commission d'Hydrologie. Rapport Final Abrege de la (No.) Session (ISSN 0251-8740); Russian edition: Vsemirnaya Meteorologicheskaya Organizatsiya. Komissiya po Gidrologii. Okonchatel'nyi Sokrashchennyi Otchet (No.) Sessii (ISSN 0251-8767); Spanish edition: Organizacion Meteorologica Mundial. Comision de Hidrologia. Informe Final Abreviado de la (No.) Reunion (ISSN 0251-8759) 1972. irreg. latest 1993. price varies. World Meteorological Organization, Commission for Hydrology, 41 av. Giuseppe-Motta, CH-1211 Geneva 20, Switzerland. TEL 730-8111. (Dist. in the U.S. by: American Meteorological Society, 45 Beacon St., Boston, MA 02108. TEL 617-227-2425)

551.3   UN   ISSN 0251-8783
WORLD METEOROLOGICAL ORGANIZATION. COMMISSION FOR INSTRUMENTS AND METHODS OF OBSERVATION. ABRIDGED FINAL REPORT OF THE (NO.) SESSION. French edition: Organisation Meteorologique Mondiale. Commission des Instruments et des Methodes d'Observation. Rapport Final Abrege de la (No.) Session (ISSN 0251-8791); Russian edition: Vsemirnaya Meteorologicheskaya Organizatsiya. Komissiya po Priboram i Metodam Nablyudenii. Okonchatel'nyi Sokrashchennyi Otchet (No.) Sessii (ISSN 0251-8813); Spanish edition: Organizacion Meteorologica Mundial. Comision de Instrumentos y Metodos de Observacion. Informe Final Abreviado de la (No.) Reunion. 1953. quadrennial, latest 1994. price varies. World Meteorological Organization, Commission for Instruments and Methods of Observation, 41 av. Giuseppe-Motta, CH-1211 Geneva 20, Switzerland. TEL 730-8111. (Dist. in the U.S. by: American Meteorological Society, 45 Beacon St., Boston, MA 02108. TEL 617-227-2425)

551.3 387   UN   ISSN 1011-3207
WORLD METEOROLOGICAL ORGANIZATION. COMMISSION FOR MARINE METEOROLOGY. ABRIDGED FINAL REPORT OF THE (NO.) SESSION. French edition: Organisation Meteorologique Mondiale. Commission de Meteorologie Maritime. Rapport Final Abrege de la (No.) Session (ISSN 0251-8872); Russian edition: Vsemirnaya Meteorologicheskaya Organizatsiya. Komissiya po Morskoi Meteorologii. Okonchatel'nyi Sokrashchennyi Otchet (No.) Sessii (ISSN 0251-8856); Spanish edition: Organizacion Meteorologica Mundial. Comision de Meteorologia Marina. Informe Final Abreviado de la (No.) Reunion (ISSN 0251-8864) 1952. quadrennial. latest 1993. price varies. World Meteorological Organization, Commission for Marine Meteorology, 41 av. Giuseppe-Motta, CH-1211 Geneva 20, Switzerland. TEL 730-8111. (Dist. in U.S. by: American Meteorological Society, 45 Beacon St., Boston, MA 02108. TEL 617-227-2425)
Formerly (until 1968): World Meteorological Organization. Commission for Maritime Meteorology. Abridged Final Report of the (No.) Session (ISSN 0084-1951)

METEOROLOGY 4707

551.5 UN ISSN 0084-1927
WORLD METEOROLOGICAL ORGANIZATION. CONGRESS. ABRIDGED REPORT WITH RESOLUTIONS. French edition: Organisation Meteorologique Mondiale. Congres. Rapport Abrege et Resolutions (ISSN 0250-9261); Spanish edition: Organizacion Meteorologica Mundial. Congreso. Informe Abreviado y Resoluciones (ISSN 0250-9253); Russian edition: Vsemirnaya Meteorologicheskaya Organizatsiya. Kongress. Sokrashchennyi Otchet s Rezolyutsiyami (ISSN 0250-9245) 1951. quadrennial, latest 1994. price varies. World Meteorological Organization, 41 av. Giuseppe-Motta, CH-1211 Geneva 20, Switzerland. TEL 730-8111. (Dist. in U.S. by: American Meteorological Society, 45 Beacon St., Boston, MA 02108. TEL 617-227-2425)

551.5 UN ISSN 1011-3231
WORLD METEOROLOGICAL ORGANIZATION. EXECUTIVE COUNCIL SESSION. ABRIDGED FINAL REPORTS WITH RESOLUTIONS. French edition: Organisation Meteorologique Mondiale. Session du Conseil Executif. Rapport Abrege et Resolutions (ISSN 1011-3592); Spanish edition: Organizacion Meteorologica Mundial. Reunion del Consejo Ejecutivo. Informe Abreviado y Resoluciones (ISSN 1011-3576); Russian edition: Vsemirnaya Meteorologicheskaya Organizatsiya. Sessiya Ispolnitel'nogo Soveta. Sokrashchennyi Otchet s Rezolyutsiyami (ISSN 1011-3673) a. price varies. World Meteorological Organization, 41 av. Giuseppe Motta, CH-1211 Geneva 2, Switzerland. TEL 730-8111. (Dist. in U.S. by: American Meteorological Society, 45 Beacon St., Boston, MA 02108. TEL 617-227-2425)
Former titles: World Meteorological Organization. Executive Committee Reports. Abridged Final Reports with Resolutions; World Meteorological Organization. Executive Committee Sessions: Abridged Reports with Resolutions (ISSN 0084-196X)

551.656 UN ISSN 0510-9124
WORLD METEOROLOGICAL ORGANIZATION. REGIONAL ASSOCIATION I (AFRICA). ABRIDGED FINAL REPORT OF THE (NO.) SESSION. French edition: Organisation Meteorologique Mondiale. Association Regionale I (Afrique). Rapport Final Abrege de la (No.) Session (ISSN 0250-9059) irreg., latest 1991. price varies. World Meteorological Organization, 41 av. Giuseppe Motta, CH-1211 Geneva 20, Switzerland. TEL 730-8111. (Dist. in U.S. by: American Meteorological Society, 45 Beacon St., Boston, MA 02108. TEL 617-227-2425)

551.655 UN ISSN 0509-3007
WORLD METEOROLOGICAL ORGANIZATION. REGIONAL ASSOCIATION II (ASIA). ABRIDGED FINAL REPORT OF THE (NO.) SESSION. French edition: Organisation Meteorologique Mondiale. Association Regionale II (Asie). Rapport Final Abrege de la (No.) Session (ISSN 0250-9113); Russian edition: Vsemirnaya Meteorologicheskaya Organizatsiya. Regional'naya Assotsiatsiya II (Aziya). Okonchatel'nyi Sokrashchennyi Otchet (No.) Sessii (ISSN 0250-9105) 1955. irreg., latest 1992. price varies. World Meteorological Organization, 41 av. Giuseppe-Motta, CH-1211 Geneva 20, Switzerland. TEL 730-8111. (Dist. in U.S. by: American Meteorological Society, 45 Beacon St., Boston, MA 02108. TEL 617-227-2425)

551.658 UN ISSN 0510-9132
WORLD METEOROLOGICAL ORGANIZATION. REGIONAL ASSOCIATION III (SOUTH AMERICA). ABRIDGED FINAL REPORT OF THE (NO.) SESSION. Spanish edition: Organizacion Meteorologica Mundial. Asociacion Regional III (America del Sur). Informe Final Abreviado de la (No.) Reunion (ISSN 0250-9148) 1953. irreg, latest 1994. price varies. World Meteorological Organization, 41 av. Giuseppe-Motta, CH-1211 Geneva 20, Switzerland. TEL 730-8111. (Dist. in U.S. by: American Meteorological Society, 45 Beacon St., Boston, MA 02108. TEL 617-227-2425)

551.657 UN ISSN 0250-9121
WORLD METEOROLOGICAL ORGANIZATION. REGIONAL ASSOCIATION IV (NORTH AMERICA AND CENTRAL AMERICA). ABRIDGED FINAL REPORT OF THE (NO.) SESSION. Spanish edition: Organizacion Meteorologica Mundial. Asociacion Regional IV (America del Norte y America Central). Informe Final Abreviado de la (No.) Reunion (ISSN 0250-913X) 1953. irreg., latest 1993. price varies. World Meteorological Organization, 41 av. Giuseppe-Motta, CH-1211 Geneva 20, Switzerland. TEL 730-8111. (Dist. in U.S. by: American Meteorological Society, 45 Beacon St., Boston, MA 02108. TEL 617-227-2425)

551.659 UN ISSN 0250-9040
WORLD METEOROLOGICAL ORGANIZATION. REGIONAL ASSOCIATION V (SOUTH WEST PACIFIC). ABRIDGED FINAL REPORT OF THE (NO.) SESSION. French edition: Organisation Meteorologique Mondiale. Association Regionale V (Pacifique Sud-Ouest). Rapport Final Abrege de la (No.) Session (ISSN 0250-9032) 1954. quadrennial., latest 1990. price varies. World Meteorological Organization, 41 av. Giuseppe-Motta, CH-1211 Geneva 2, Switzerland. TEL 730-8111. (Dist. in U.S. by: American Meteorological Society, 45 Beacon St., Boston, MA 02108. TEL 617-227-2425)

WORLD METEOROLOGICAL ORGANIZATION. SPECIAL ENVIRONMENTAL REPORTS. see *ENVIRONMENTAL STUDIES*

551.5 UN ISSN 0084-201X
QC851 CODEN: WMOTAD
WORLD METEOROLOGICAL ORGANIZATION. TECHNICAL NOTES. 1954. irreg., latest no.196. price varies. World Meteorological Organization, 41 av. Giuseppe Motta, CH-1211 Geneva 2, Switzerland. TEL 730-8111. (Dist. in U.S. by: American Meteorological Society, 45 Beacon St., Boston, MA 02108. TEL 617-227-2425) **Indexed:** Biol.Abstr., GeoRef., Rural Recreat.Tour.Abstr., World Agri.Econ.& Rural Sociol.Abstr.

551.632 UN ISSN 0250-9393
WORLD METEOROLOGICAL ORGANIZATION. WEATHER REPORTING. VOLUME A: OBSERVING STATIONS. (Catalogue W M O No. 9) 1952. base vol. plus s-a updates. $154 for updates; base vol. $100. World Meteorological Organization, 41 Av. Giuseppe Motta, CH-1211 Geneva 2, Switzerland. TEL 730-8111. (Dist. in U.S. by: American Meteorological Society, 45 Beacon St., Boston, MA 02108. TEL 617-227-2425) (looseleaf format)
Description: Contains information on stations providing synoptic meteorological reports.

551.632 UN ISSN 0250-9415
WORLD METEOROLOGICAL ORGANIZATION. WEATHER REPORTING. VOLUME C: TRANSMISSIONS. (Catalogue W M O No. 9) 1952. base vol. plus bi-m. updates. $164 for updates; base vol. $152. World Meteorological Organization, 41 av. Giuseppe Motta, CH-1211 Geneva 2, Switzerland. TEL 730-8111. (Dist. in U.S. by: American Meteorological Society, 45 Beacon St., Boston, MA 02108. TEL 617-227-2425) (looseleaf format)
Description: Contains schedules of broadcasts and point-to-point transmission of coded meteorological information.

551.632 UN ISSN 0250-9423
WORLD METEOROLOGICAL ORGANIZATION. WEATHER REPORTING. VOLUME D: INFORMATION FOR SHIPPING. (Catalogue W M O No.9) 1952. base vol. plus bi-m. updates. $96 for updates; base vol. $183. World Meteorological Organization, 41 av. Giuseppe Motta, CH-1211 Geneva 2, Switzerland. TEL 730-8111. (Dist. in U.S. by: American Meteorological Society, 45 Beacon St., Boston, MA 02108. TEL 671-227-2425) (looseleaf format)
Description: Information about meteorological forecasts and warnings to shipping and on the collection of ships' weather reports.

551.5 RU
WORLD RADIATION DATA CENTRE. QUARTERLY REPORT. (Semi-annual supplement avail.) (Text in English, Russian) 1964. q. $92. Glavnaya Geofizicheskaya Observatoriya im. A.I. Voeikova, Mirovoi Tsentr Radiatsionnykh Dannykh - Voeikov Main Geophysical Observatory, World Radiation Data Centre, Ul. Karbysheva, 7, St. Petersburg 194018, Russia. TEL 812-247-01-03. FAX 812-247-86-61. (Co-sponsor: World Meteorological Organization) Dir. E.P. Borisenkov. stat.
Formerly (until 1994): Solnechnaya Radiatsiya i Radiatsionnyi Balans. Mirovaya Set' - Solar Radiation and Radiation Balance Data. The World Network (ISSN 0235-4519)
Description: Provides the users with data on solar radiation, radiation balance and sunshine duration.

551.58 NE ISSN 0168-6321
WORLD SURVEY OF CLIMATOLOGY. (Text in English) 1969. irreg., vol.1B, 1986. price varies. Elsevier Science B.V., Books Division, P.O. Box 211, 1000 AE Amsterdam, Netherlands. TEL 31-20-4853911. FAX 31-20-4853705. TELEX 18582 ESPA NL. E-mail: nlinfo-f@elsevier.nl; usinfo-f@elsevier.com; forinfo-kyf04035@niftyserve.or.jp; Site addr.: http://www.elsevier.nl/. (Subscr. in U.S. and Canada to: Elsevier Science Inc., Box 882, Madison Sq. Sta., New York, NY 10159. TEL 212-989-5800) (back issues avail.) **Indexed:** INSPEC. **Document type:** monographic series.
Refereed Serial

551.63 UN ISSN 0084-2451
WORLD WEATHER WATCH PLANNING REPORTS. 1966. irreg., latest 1983. price varies. World Meteorological Organization, 41 av. Giuseppe Motta, CH-1211 Geneva 2, Switzerland. TEL 730-8111. (Dist. in U.S. by: American Meteorological Society, 45 Beacon St., Boston, MA 02108)

551 JA ISSN 0916-5274
YAMAGUCHIKEN KISHO GEPPO/YAMAGUCHI PREFECTURE. MONTHLY REPORT OF METEOROLOGY. (Text in Japanese) 1947. m. Kishocho, Shimonoseki Chiho Kishodai - Japan Meteorological Agency, Shimonoseki Local Meteorological Observatory, 6-1, Takezakicho 4-chome, Shimonoseki-shi, Yamaguchi-ken 750, Japan.

551 JA ISSN 0916-5282
YAMANASHIKEN KISHO GEPPO/YAMANASHI PREFECTURE. MONTHLY REPORT OF METEOROLOGY. (Text in Japanese) 1900. m. Kishocho, Kofu Chiho Kishodai - Japan Meteorological Agency, Kofu Local Meteorological Observatory, 7-29 Iidacho 4-chome, Kofu-shi, Yamanashi-ken 400, Japan.

551.6 CC ISSN 1001-7313
YINGYONG QIXIANG XUEBAO/JOURNAL OF APPLIED METEOROLOGY. (Text in Chinese) 1986. q. $184 (effective 1996). (Zhongguo Qixiang Kexueyuan - Chinese Academy of Meteorology) China Meteorological Press, 46, Baishiqiao Lu, Beijing 100081, People's Republic of China. TEL 86-1-8312277. FAX 86-1-8327390. Ed. Zhang Wanpei. **Document type:** academic/scholarly publication.

551 JA
YUKIGUNI JOHO SHIRYOSHU/INFORMATION MATERIALS FOR HEAVY SNOW AREA.* (Text in Japanese) 1986. a. Nihon Shisutemu Kaihatsu Kenkyujo - Systems Research and Development Institute of Japan, c/o Nihon Seppyo Gakkai, Rm. 207, Belvedere-Kudan, Fujimi 2-15-5, Chiyoda-ku, Tokyo 102, Japan.

551.5 ZA ISSN 0302-5047
ZAMBIA. METEOROLOGICAL DEPARTMENT. TOTALS OF MONTHLY AND ANNUAL RAINFALL; for selected stations in Zambia. (Former name of issuing body: Department of Meteorology) a. Meteorological Department, P.O. Box 30200, Lusaka, Zambia. TEL 260-1-228939. TELEX ZA 41450. **Document type:** government publication.
Description: Lists rainfall of the entire Zambian rainfall network catchment by catchment, including an annual map and its percentage to normal rainfall.

METEOROLOGY — ABSTRACTING, BIBLIOGRAPHIES, STATISTICS

551.6   ZA
ZAMBIAN CLIMATOLOGICAL SUMMARY; SURFACE AND UPPER AIR DATA. (Former name of issuing body: Department of Meteorology) m. Meteorological Department, P.O. Box 30200, 10101 Lusaka, Zambia. TEL 260-1-228939. TELEX ZA 41450. **Document type:** government publication.
Description: Lists hourly, daily and monthly values of weather elements.

551.5   CC   ISSN 1000-6362
ZHONGGUO NONGYE QIXIANG/CHINESE AGRICULTURAL METEOROLOGY. (Text in Chinese) q. Zhongguo Nongye Kexueyuan - Chinese Academy of Agriculture, 30 Baishiqiao Lu, Beijing 100081, People's Republic of China. TEL 8314433. Ed. Min Jinru.
Refereed Serial

551.5   RH   ISSN 0085-5707
QC875.Z55
ZIMBABWE. DEPARTMENT OF METEOROLOGICAL SERVICES. REPORT OF THE DIRECTOR. a. Department of Meteorological Services, P.O. Box B 150, Belvedere, Harare, Zimbabwe. TEL 704955. TELEX 4460 ZW. circ. 80. (back issues avail.) **Document type:** government publication.

METEOROLOGY — Abstracting, Bibliographies, Statistics

AGRARMETEOROLOGISCHE BIBLIOGRAPHIE. see *AGRICULTURE — Abstracting, Bibliographies, Statistics*

551.5   US
ALASKA BASIN OUTLOOK REPORT. irreg. U.S. Natural Resources Conservation Service (Anchorage), 949 E. 36th Ave., Ste. 400, Anchorage, AK 99508-4362. charts. **Document type:** government publication.
Description: Provides statistics on the precipitation and other meteorological data for the state of Alaska.

ALASKA WEEKLY CROP WEATHER. see *AGRICULTURE — Abstracting, Bibliographies, Statistics*

551.5   PL   ISSN 0239-6270
BIBLIOGRAFIA METEOROLOGII/BIBLIOGRAPHY OF METEOROLOGY. (Text in English, French, German, Polish and Russian) 1963. irreg. $75. Instytut Meteorologii i Gospodarki Wodnej - Institute of Meteorology and Water Management, 61 Podlesna St., 01-673 Warsaw, Poland. FAX 48-22-345466. TELEX 814331. circ. 150. **Document type:** bibliography.
Description: Articles on meteorology, climatology, hydrometeorology, meteorological elements, meteorological instruments, biometeorology, agrometeorology, atmospheric phenomena, weather forecasting, and dynamical meteorology.

551.5 016   GW   ISSN 0072-4149
Z6681
DEUTSCHER WETTERDIENST. BIBLIOGRAPHIEN. 1955. irreg., no.50, 1993. DM.100. Deutscher Wetterdienst, Bibliothek, Postfach 100465, 63004 Offenbach a.M., Germany. **Document type:** government publication, monographic series.

IOWA CROPS & WEATHER. see *AGRICULTURE — Abstracting, Bibliographies, Statistics*

551.5 016   IT   ISSN 0075-1901
ISTITUTO DI FISICA DELL'ATMOSFERA, ROME. BIBLIOGRAFIA GENERALE. (Text in Italian; occasional English or French editions avail.) 1963. irreg. Istituto di Fisica dell'Atmosfera, Piazzale Luigi Sturzo 31, 00144 Rome, Italy. TEL 06-59-10-941. FAX 06-59-15-790. **Indexed:** Meteor.& Geostrophys.Abstr. **Document type:** academic/scholarly publication, bibliography.

551.65   IT
QC851
ITALY. ISTITUTO NAZIONALE DI STATISTICA. STATISTICHE METEOROLOGICHE. 1959. a. L.15800 (effective 1991). Istituto Nazionale di Statistica, Via Cesare Balbo 16, 00100 Rome, Italy. FAX 06-46735198. circ. 1,200.
Formerly: Italy. Istituto Centrale di Statistica. Annuario di Statistiche Meteorologiche (ISSN 0075-1731)

551.6 629.1   JA   ISSN 0289-3118
KOKU KISHO NOTO/ABSTRACTS IN AVIATION METEOROLOGY. (Text in Japanese) 1970. s-a. Kishocho - Japan Meteorological Agency, 3-4, Otemachi 1-chome, Chiyoda-ku, Tokyo 100, Japan. **Document type:** abstracting/indexing.

551.5   LU
LUXEMBOURG. SERVICE CENTRAL DE LA STATISTIQUE ET DES ETUDES ECONOMIQUES. INDICATEURS RAPIDES. SERIE M: METEOROLOGIE. m. Service Central de la Statistique et des Etudes Economiques, 6 bd. Royal, B.P. 304, 2013 Luxembourg, Luxembourg. TEL 478-4268. FAX 46-42-89. (looseleaf format) **Document type:** government publication.
Description: Covers temperature, atmospheric pressure, precipitation, and sunshine.

551.5 523.01 016   US   ISSN 0026-1130
QC851   CODEN: MGEAAQ
METEOROLOGICAL AND GEOASTROPHYSICAL ABSTRACTS. 1950. m. $985 (CD-ROM $5100) (effective 1996). American Meteorological Society, c/o Inforonics, Inc., 550 Newtown Rd., Littleton, MA 01460. TEL 508-486-8976. FAX 508-486-0027. E-mail: mga@infor.com. bk.rev.; abstr.; index. circ. 334. (also avail. in microform from PMC; back issues avail.; reprint service avail.) **Indexed:** Chem.Abstr., INSPEC. **Document type:** abstracting/indexing.
●Also available online. Vendor(s): Knight-Ridder, Inc. (File no.29).
Also available on CD-ROM.
—BLDSC (5705.200000). CCC.
Description: Presents current abstracts of books, reports, research papers, and miscellaneous literature published worldwide in the areas of environmental sciences, meteorology, astrophysics, hydrology, glaciology, and physical oceanography.
Refereed Serial

551.5   MY   ISSN 0126-8872
MONTHLY ABSTRACT OF METEOROLOGICAL OBSERVATIONS OF MALAYSIA. (Text and summaries in English) 1950. m. M.$12. Malaysian Meteorological Service - Perkhidmatan Kajicuaca Malaysia, Jalan Sultan, Petaling Jaya 46667, Selangor, Malaysia. FAX 6-03-7550964. TELEX MA37243. circ. 160.

551.5 011   FR   ISSN 1164-5997
P A S C A L E 49: METEOROLOGIE, GLACIOLOGIE, PHYSIQUE DES OCEANS. (Printed format ceased Jan. 1995) (Text in English, French) 1985. 10/yr. Centre National de la Recherche Scientifique, Institut de l'Information Scientifique et Technique, 2 allee du Parc de Brabois, 54514 Vandoeuvre-Les-Nancy Cedex, France. TEL 83-50-46-00. FAX 83-50-46-50. adv. contact: Veronique Guinvarc'h. (also avail. in microfiche) **Document type:** bibliography.
●Also available online. Vendor(s): European Space Agency (File no.14), Knight-Ridder, Inc. (File no.144), Telesystemes - Questel.
Also available on CD-ROM.
Former titles (until 1992): P A S C A L Explore. E 49: Meterologie (ISSN 0761-2117); P A S C A L Explore. Part 49: Meteorologie; Which superseded in part: Bulletin Signaletique. Part 120: Astronomie - Physique Spatiale - Geophysique (ISSN 0240-849X)

551.5   JA
REKISHO NENPYO. (Text in Japanese) 1946. a. free. University of Tokyo, National Astronomical Observatory, 21-1, Osawa 2-chome, Mitaka-shi, Tokyo 181, Japan. TEL 81-422-34-3621. FAX 81-422-34-3793. charts; stat.
Description: Publishes astronomical data.

551.5   JA   ISSN 0388-3515
SEIKEI KISHO KANSOKUJO HOKOKU. (Text in Japanese) 1958. a. free. (Seikei Kisho Kansokujo - Seikei Meteorological Observatory) Seikei Gakuen Integrated Educational Institute, 3-1, Kichijoji Kita-machi 3-chome, Musashino-shi, Tokyo 180, Japan. FAX 0422-37-3863. E-mail: KHF02211@niltyserveorjp. Ed. Atsushi Miyashita. stat.; circ. controlled. **Document type:** academic/scholarly publication.

SOLAR TERRESTRIAL ACTIVITY CHART. see *ASTRONOMY — Abstracting, Bibliographies, Statistics*

METROLOGY AND STANDARDIZATION

620.1 389   US   ISSN 0038-9676
T59.A1
A N S I REPORTER. 1967. m. $100 includes Standards Action. American National Standards Institute, Inc., 11 W. 42nd St., 13th Fl., New York, NY 10036. TEL 212-642-4900. FAX 212-302-1286. circ. 8,000. (also avail. in microform from UMI; reprint service avail.)
—UMI.
Formerly: Standards Institute Reporter.

620.1 389   US   ISSN 0090-1210
TA368   CODEN: STDNA
A S T M STANDARDIZATION NEWS. 1973. m. $18. American Society for Testing and Materials, 1916 Race St., Philadelphia, PA 19103. TEL 215-299-5400. FAX 215-977-9679. Ed. K. Riley. charts; illus.; index. circ. 32,000. (also avail. in microform from MIM,UMI,PMC; reprint service avail. from UMI) **Indexed:** A.S.& T.Ind., Abstr.Bull.Inst.Pap.Chem., AESIS, Appl.Mech.Rev., BMT, Br.Ceram.Abstr., C.R.I.Abstr., C.R.I.Curr.Cont., Cadscan, Chem.Abstr., Copper Abstr., Deep Sea Res.& Oceanogr.Abstr., Eng.Ind., Ergon.Abstr., Excerp.Med., GeoRef., INIS Atomind., INSPEC (1973-1985), Intl.Civil Eng.Abstr., J.of Ferroc., Lead Abstr., Met.Abstr., RAPRA, Soft.Abstr.Eng., Text.Tech.Dig., W.R.C.Inf., World Alum.Abstr., World Surf.Coat., World Text.Abstr., Zincscan. **Document type:** trade publication.
—BLDSC (1747.091000); Ei; Faxon; SWETS; UMI; UnCover. CCC.
Supersedes: Materials Research and Standards - MIRS (ISSN 0025-5394)

A 2 L A (YEAR) ANNUAL REPORT. (American Association for Laboratory Accreditation) see *BUSINESS AND ECONOMICS — Trade And Industrial Directories*

A 2 L A (YEAR) DIRECTORY OF ACCREDITED LABORATORIES. see *BUSINESS AND ECONOMICS — Trade And Industrial Directories*

A 2 L A NEWS. (American Association for Laboratory Accreditation) see *BUSINESS AND ECONOMICS — Trade And Industrial Directories*

681 389   HU   ISSN 0237-028X
ACTA I M E K O. 1958. triennial, 13th, 1994, Italy. International Measurement Confederation (IMEKO), P.O. Box 457, 1371 Budapest, Hungary. FAX 361-153-1406. TELEX 225792. Ed.Bd. circ. 500. **Indexed:** Chem.Abstr. **Document type:** proceedings.
—BLDSC (0627.820000).
Formerly: International Measurement Conference. Proceedings. Acta IMEKO (ISSN 0074-6916)

389 658.5   US   ISSN 1067-7267
TP149   CODEN: AQATAZ
AMERICAN SOCIETY FOR QUALITY CONTROL. ANNUAL QUALITY CONGRESS TRANSACTIONS. 1947. a. American Society for Quality Control, 611 E. Wisconsin Ave., Box 3005, Milwaukee, WI 53201-3005. TEL 414-272-8575. index by category, author and title. circ. 5,500. (also avail. in microfiche from UMI) **Indexed:** Curr.Ind.Stat., Eng.Ind. **Document type:** proceedings.
—CCC.
Former titles: American Society for Quality Control. Annual Technical Conference Transactions (ISSN 0360-6929); American Society for Quality Control. Transactions of Annual Technical Conferences (ISSN 0066-0159)

389   AT   ISSN 0158-3999
AUSTRALIAN STANDARD. 1980. m. membership. Standards Australia, Standards House, 80 Arthur St., N. Sydney, N.S.W. 2059, Australia. FAX 02-959-3896. TELEX 26514. Ed. J. Moncrieff. adv.; bibl. circ. 10,700. **Indexed:** Dairy Sci.Abstr., Food Sci.& Tech.Abstr.
—CCC.
Supersedes (in Jan.1980): S A A Monthly Information Sheet.

389   AU
AUSTRIA. BUNDESAMT FUER EICH- UND VERMESSUNGSWESEN. AMTSBLATT FUER DAS EICHWESEN. 1952. 8/yr. S.885. Kommissionsverlag der Oesterreichischen Staatsdruckerei, Rennweg 12a, A-1037 Vienna, Austria. TEL 01-79789294. FAX 01-79789419. index. circ. 450. **Document type:** government publication.

METROLOGY AND STANDARDIZATION 4709

620.1 389   UK   ISSN 0005-3309
T59   CODEN: BSINAE
B S I NEWS. 1956. m. British Standards Institution, Linford Wood, Milton Keynes, Bucks. MK14 6LE, England. TEL 01908-220022.
FAX 01908-320856. TELEX 825777. Ed. C. Boffey. circ. 41,000. **Indexed:** Agri.Eng.Abstr., BMT, Br.Ceram.Abstr., Build.Manage.Abstr., Cadscan, Copper Abstr., Dairy Sci.Abstr., Ergon.Abstr., Fluidex, Int.Packag.Abstr., Intl.Polym.Sci.& Tech., Lead Abstr., Met.Abstr., Paper & Bd.Abstr., RAPRA, World Alum.Abstr., World Surf.Coat., World Text.Abstr., Zincscan. **Document type:** trade publication.
—BLDSC (2354.200000).
    Incorporates (in Feb. 1995): International News on Standards and Exporting - I N S T E P (ISSN 0969-3696); Which was formed by the 1993 merger of: Bibliotech; And: Technical Export News (ISSN 0140-4474); Which was formerly (1971-1995): Technical Help to Exporters Quarterly Bulletin (ISSN 0308-907X)

389   UK   ISSN 0953-0339
B S I STANDARDS CATALOGUE. 1959. a. £36 to non-members. British Standards Institution, Linford Wood, Milton Keynes, Bucks. MK14 6LE, England. TEL 01908-220022. FAX 01908-320856. TELEX 825777. circ. 34,000. **Document type:** catalog.
●Also available on CD-ROM.
—BLDSC (2354.227000).
    Formerly (until 1983): British Standards Yearbook (ISSN 0068-2578)

BEIKOKU TOKKYO SHOROKU. SOKUTEI, SEIMITSU KIKI, INSATSU, ONKYO, KYOIKU HEN/U.S. PATENT ABSTRACTS. MEASURING, PRECISION INSTRUMENT, PRINTING, SOUND RECORDING, EDUCATION. see **PATENTS, TRADEMARKS AND COPYRIGHTS — Abstracting, Bibliographies, Statistics**

BENCHMARK. see **ENGINEERING**

389.6   UK   ISSN 0524-675X
BRITISH STANDARDS INSTITUTION. ANNUAL REVIEW. Issued with: B S I News (ISSN 0005-3309) a. British Standards Institution, Linford Wood, Milton Keynes, Bucks. MK14 6LE, England. TEL 01908-220022. FAX 01908-320856. TELEX 825777. **Document type:** corporate report.
    Formerly (until 1992): British Standards Institution. Annual Report.

640.73   CN   ISSN 0011-2313
C S A AND THE CONSUMER. (Editions in English and French) 1970. q. free. Canadian Standards Association, 178 Rexdale Blvd., Toronto (Rexdale), Ont. M9W 1R3, Canada. TEL 416-747-4129. FAX 416-747-4149. illus. circ. 600,000 (500,000 English ed.; 100,000 French ed.). **Indexed:** Sportsearch.

389.6   GW   ISSN 1131-6047
CALIDAD, GESTION Y TECNICA. (Text in Spanish) 1991. q. 4500 ptas.($72) (effective 1993). Carl Hanser Verlag, Kolbergerstr. 22, 81679 Munich, Germany. TEL 089-998300. FAX 089-984809. (Subscr. to: Postfach 860420, 81631 Munich, Germany; In Spain: Gran Via Corts Catalanes, 322-324, 08004 Barcelona, Spain. TEL 3-425-45-44) Ed. Daniel Crespo. adv.; bk.rev.; bibl.; charts; illus. circ. 4,000.

389.6   CN
CANADIAN STANDARDS ASSOCIATION. ANNUAL REPORT. (Editions in English and French) 1919. a. free. Canadian Standards Association, Public Affairs, 178 Rexdale Blvd., Toronto (Rexdale), Ont. M9W 1R3, Canada. TEL 416-747-4129. FAX 416-747-4149. Ed.Bd. circ. 10,000.

389.6   CN   ISSN 0829-0873
CANADIAN STANDARDS ASSOCIATION. CATALOGUE. 1930. a. free. Canadian Standards Association, Standards Sales, 178 Rexdale Blvd., Rexdale (Toronto), ON M9W 1R3, Canada. TEL 416-747-4044. FAX 416-747-2475. TELEX 06-989344. Ed.Bd. circ. 50,000. **Document type:** catalog.
    Supersedes: Canadian Standards Association. Standards Catalogue; Canadian Standards Association. List of Publications.

389.6   CN   ISSN 1182-0187
CANADIAN STANDARDS ASSOCIATION. INFO UPDATE. 1981. 8/yr. Can.$59.50($71) Canadian Standards Association, 178 Rexdale Blvd., Etobicoke, ON M9W 1R3, Canada. TEL 416-747-4116. FAX 416-747-2473. circ. 3,500.
    Formerly: C S A Information Update (ISSN 0702-7583)

389.6 621.3   CN
CANADIAN STANDARDS ASSOCIATION E - CODE, ELECTRICAL SAFETY STANDARDS. 1992. 4/yr. Can.$1900. Canadian Standards Association, 178 Rexdale Blvd., Toronto, ON M9W 1R3, Canada. TEL 416-747-4044. FAX 416-747-2475.
●Also available on CD-ROM.
    Description: Includes CSA's collection of Electrical Product Safety Standards (wiring, industrial, environmental, consumer and commercial products), outside wiring standards, electrical installation rules and related information.

389   US   ISSN 1043-7002
Z7914.A22
CATALOG OF AMERICAN NATIONAL STANDARDS. 1977. a. American National Standards Institute, Inc., 11 W. 42nd St., 13th Fl., New York, NY 10036. TEL 212-642-4900. FAX 212-302-1286.

389   FR   ISSN 0750-7046
TA368
CATALOGUE AFNOR (NORMES FRANCAISES). vol.32, 1976. a. 349.87 F. Association Francaise de Normalisation, Tour Europe, 92049 Paris La Defense, Cedex, France. TEL 42-91-55-55. FAX 42-91-56-56. TELEX 611974F. Ed. Luc Lemiere. adv. circ. 11,000.
●Also available online. Vendor(s): Telesystemes - Questel.
Also available on CD-ROM.
    Formerly: Catalogue des Normes Francaises.

389.6   FR   ISSN 1016-3778
COMITE CONSULTATIF POUR LA MASSE ET LES GRANDEURS APPARENTES. 1981. irreg., 5th session, 1993. 177 F. Bureau International des Poids et Mesures, Pavillon de Breteuil, 92312 Sevres, France. FAX 45-34-20-21. TELEX BIPM 631 351. circ. 500. **Document type:** proceedings.

621.3   FR   ISSN 0069-6455
COMITE INTERNATIONAL DES POIDS ET MESURES. COMITE CONSULTATIF D'ELECTRICITE. (RAPPORT ET ANNEXES). (Travaux d'sessions 1-8 (1928-57) issued in Proces-Verbaux du Comite International des Poids et Mesures) 1961, 9th. irreg., 19th session, 1992. 150 F. Bureau International des Poids et Mesures, Pavillon de Breteuil, 92312 Sevres Cedex, France. TEL 42-91-55-55. FAX 45-34-20-21. TELEX BIPM 631 351. **Document type:** proceedings.

535   FR
COMITE INTERNATIONAL DES POIDS ET MESURES. COMITE CONSULTATIF DE PHOTOMETRIE ET RADIOMETRIE. (RAPPORT ET ANNEXES). (Sessions 1-4, 1937-1957 issued in Proces-Verbaux du Comite International des Poids et Mesures)) irreg., 12th session, 1990. 105 F. Bureau International des Poids et Mesures, Pavillon de Breteuil, 92312 Sevres, France. FAX 45-34-20-21. TELEX BIPM 631 351. charts; illus. **Document type:** proceedings.
    Formerly: Comite International des Poids et Mesures. Comite Consultatif de Photometrie. (Rapport et Annexes) (ISSN 0588-621X); Supersedes: Comite International des Poids et Mesures. Comite Consultatif de Photometrie. Travaux (ISSN 0069-6447)

536.5   FR   ISSN 0069-6463
    CODEN: CCTMCZ
COMITE INTERNATIONAL DES POIDS ET MESURES. COMITE CONSULTATIF DE THERMOMETRIE. RAPPORTS ET ANNEXES. (Sessions 1-5 (1939-1958) issued in Proces-Verbaux du Comite International des Poids et Mesures) 1950. irreg., 18th session, 1993. 100 F. Bureau International des Poids et Mesures, Pavillon de Breteuil, 92312 Sevres Cedex, France. FAX 45-34-20-21. TELEX BIPM 631 351. bibl.; charts; stat. **Document type:** proceedings.
—CASDDS.

389   FR   ISSN 0373-3181
COMITE INTERNATIONAL DES POIDS ET MESURES. COMITE CONSULTATIF DES UNITES (RAPPORT ET ANNEXES). (Editions in English, French) 1967. irreg., 10th session, 1990. 80 F. Bureau International des Poids et Mesures, Pavillon de Breteuil, 92312 Sevres Cedex, France. FAX 45-34-20-21. TELEX BIPM 631 351. **Document type:** proceedings.

389   FR   ISSN 0588-6228
COMITE INTERNATIONAL DES POIDS ET MESURES. COMITE CONSULTATIF POUR LA DEFINITION DE LA SECONDE. (RAPPORT ET ANNEXES). (First session issued in Proces-Verbaux du Comite International des Poids et Mesures) 1957. irreg., 12th session, 1992. 171 F. Bureau International des Poids et Mesures, Pavillon de Breteuil, 92310 Sevres Cedex, France. FAX 45-34-20-21. TELEX BIPM 631 351. **Document type:** proceedings.

389   FR   ISSN 0253-2182
COMITE INTERNATIONAL DES POIDS ET MESURES. COMITE CONSULTATIF POUR LA DEFINITION DU METRE (RAPPORT ET ANNEXES). (Sessions 1-2 (1953-1957) Issued in Proces-Verbaux du Comite International des Poids et Mesures) (Editions in English and French) 3rd, 1962. irreg., 8th session, 1992. Bureau International des Poids et Mesures, Pavillon de Breteuil, 92312 Sevres Cedex, France. FAX 45-34-20-21. TELEX BIPM 631 351. **Document type:** proceedings.

389   FR   ISSN 0255-3147
COMITE INTERNATIONAL DES POIDS ET MESURES. COMITE CONSULTATIF POUR LES ETALONS DES MESURE DES RAYONNEMENTS IONISANTS (RAPPORT ET ANNEXES). (First session issued in Proces-Verbaux du Comite International des Poids et Mesures) (Editions in English, French) 1959. irreg., 13th session, 1994. 205 F. Bureau International des Poids et Mesures, Pavillon de Breteuil, 92312 Sevres, France. FAX 45-34-20-21. TELEX BIPM 631 351. **Document type:** proceedings.
    Formerly: Comite International des Poids et Mesures. Comite Consultatif pour les Etalons des Mesure des Radiations Ionisantes (Rapport et Annexes) (ISSN 0588-6244)

389   FR   ISSN 0370-2596
    CODEN: PVSPA7
COMITE INTERNATIONAL DES POIDS ET MESURES. PROCES-VERBAUX DES SEANCES. 1875. a., 81st session, 1992. 405 F. Bureau International des Poids et Mesures - International Bureau of Weights and Measures, Pavillon de Breteuil, 92312 Sevres Cedex, France. FAX 45-34-20-21. TELEX BIPM 631 351. charts; illus.; stat.; index. circ. 650. **Document type:** proceedings.

389   FR
COMITE INTERNATIONAL DES POIDS ET MESURES. SYSTEME INTERNATIONAL D'UNITES. 1970. irreg., 6th ed., 1991. 120 F. Bureau International des Poids et Mesures, Pavillon de Breteuil, F-92312 Sevres, France. FAX 45-34-20-21. TELEX BIPM 631 351. **Document type:** proceedings.

389.6   FR   ISSN 1016-5983
CONFERENCE GENERALE DES POIDS ET MESURES. COMPTES RENDUS DES SEANCES. 1889. every 4 yrs., 19th, 1991. 235 F. Bureau International des Poids et Mesures, 92312 Sevres Cedex, France. FAX 45-34-20-21. TELEX BIPM 631 351. **Document type:** proceedings.

389.6   MX
CONGRESO MEXICANO DE CONTROL DE CALIDAD. ANNUAL PROCEEDINGS. (In 2 vols.) 1973. a. $30. Instituto Mexicano de Control de Calidad, Thiers 251-Col. Anzures, 11590 Mexico, D.F., Mexico. Ed. Patricia Gonzalez Prado. adv.; bk.rev. circ. 3,000.

389.6   CN   ISSN 0380-1314
CONSENSUS (OTTAWA). (Editions in English, French) 1974. q. Can.$12 (foreign Can.$20). Standards Council of Canada, 1200 - 45 O'Connor St., Ottawa, ON K1P 6N7, Canada. TEL 613-238-3222. FAX 613-995-4564. TELEX 053-4403. Ed. Steven Brasier. adv.; bk.rev. circ. 10,000. **Document type:** trade publication.
    Description: Provides insight into the use of standards as tools for achieving quality, accuracy and efficiency. Studies technology and trade as they relate to manufacturing, information technology, communications and distribution.

METROLOGY AND STANDARDIZATION

389.6   XR
CZECH REPUBLIC. URAD PRO TECHNICKOU NORMALIZACI, METROLOGII A STATNI ZKUSEBNICTVI. VESTNIK. (Text in Czech or Slovak) 1962. m. 42 Kc. (Urad pro Technickou Normalizaci, Metrologii a Statni Zkusebnictvi) Vydavatestvi Norem, Hornomecholupska 40, 102 04 Prague 10, Czech Republic. (Dist. by: SEVT, Trziste 9, 118 16 Prague 1, Czech Republic) (Co-sponsor: Cesky Normalizacni Institut) Ed. Marie Bartunkova. adv.; charts. circ. 12,000. (looseleaf format)
   Former titles (until 1993): Czech Republic. Federalni Urad pro Technickou Normalizaci a Mereni. Vestnik (ISSN 1210-2857); (until 1990): Czechoslovakia. Urad pro Normalizaci a Mereni. Vestnik ISSN 0042-4714)

389.1   GW
D I N CATALOGUE OF TECHNICAL RULES. SUPPLEMENT. 1978. a. DM.58. (Deutsches Institut fuer Normung e.V. (D I N)) Beuth Verlag GmbH, Burggrafenstr. 6, 10787 Berlin, Germany. TEL 030-2601-0. FAX 030-26011260. TELEX 183622-BVB-D. (Dist in U.S. by: Global Engineering Documents, 2805 McGaw Ave., Box 19539, Irvine, CA 92714) circ. 2,000. **Document type:** catalog.
   Former titles: Catalogue: English Translations of German Standards (ISSN 0174-3805); English Translations of German Standards (ISSN 0071-0660)

389.1   GW   ISSN 0722-7337
D I N - HANDBOOKS. 1982. irreg. price varies. (Deutsches Institut fuer Normung e.V. (D I N)) Beuth Verlag GmbH, Burggrafenstr. 6, 10787 Berlin, Germany. TEL 030-2601-0. FAX 030-26011260. TELEX 183622-BVB-D. (Dist. in U.S. by: Global Engineering Documents, 2805 McGaw Ave., Box 19539, Irvine, CA 92714) **Document type:** trade publication.

620.1 389   GW   ISSN 0722-2912
D I N MITTEILUNGEN & ELEKTRONORM. 1918. m. DM.535.41. (Deutsches Institut fuer Normung e.V. (D I N)) Beuth Verlag GmbH, Burggrafenstr. 6, 10787 Berlin, Germany. TEL 030-2601-0. FAX 030-26011260. TELEX 183633-BVB-D. (Dist. in U.S. by: Global Engineering Documents, 2805 McGaw Ave., Box 19539, Irvine, CA 92714) bk.rev.; charts; illus.; index. circ. 7,650. **Indexed:** C.I.S. Abstr., INIS Atomind. **Document type:** trade publication.
—SWETS. **CCC.**
   Formed by the merger of: D I N Mitteilungen (ISSN 0011-4952); (1947-1977): Elektronorm (ISSN 0013-5747); **Formerly** (1961-198?): Schiffbau-Normung (ISSN 0036-6048)

389.1   GW   ISSN 0342-801X
D I N - TASCHENBUECHER. 1963. irreg. price varies. (Deutsches Institut fuer Normung e.V. (D I N)) Beuth Verlag GmbH, Burggrafenstr. 6, 10787 Berlin, Germany. TEL 030-2601-0. FAX 030-26011260. TELEX 183622-BVB-D. (Dist. in U.S. by: Global Engineering Documents, 2805 McGaw Ave., Box 19539, Irvine, CA 92714) **Document type:** trade publication.

389.1   GW
D I T R INFO; Informationen fuer Kunden der D I T R Datenbank. q. Deutsches Institut fuer Normung e.V., Deutsches Informationszentrum fuer Technische Regeln, Burggrafenstr. 6, 10787 Berlin, Germany. TEL 030-26012493. FAX 030-2628125. Ed. Daniela Schlicht. **Document type:** bulletin.

389.602   DK   ISSN 0900-5145
D S - KATALOG. (Text in Danish, English) 1972. a. (plus m. updates). DKK 490. Dansk Standard - Danish Standards Association, Baunegaardsvej 73, DK-2900 Hellerup, Denmark. TEL 45-39-77-01-01. FAX 45-39-77-02-02. E-mail: ds.dk. circ. 5,000. **Document type:** catalog.
   Description: Contains a survey of about 3800 Danish standards.

389.6   DK   ISSN 0908-0783
DANSK STANDARD. 1958. bi-m. DKK 500. Dansk Standard - Danish Standards Association, Baunegaardsvej 73, DK-2900 Hellerup, Denmark. TEL 45-39-77-01-01. FAX 45-39-77-02-02. E-mail: ds.dk. Ed. Mogens Winther. bk.rev. circ. 1,800.
   Formerly: Standardnyt (ISSN 0107-2870)
   Description: Contains information on standards and draft standards, relevant information concerning standardization and certification.

621.38   US   ISSN 0900-5579
   CODEN: DAINEG
DANTEC INFORMATION. (Text in English; summaries in English, French and German) 1965. a. free. Dantec Measurement Technology Inc., 777 Corporate Dr., Mahwah, NJ 07430. TEL 201-512-0037. FAX 201-512-0120. circ. 21,000. **Indexed:** BMT, Fluidex, INSPEC, Int.Aerosp.Abstr., Met.Abstr., W.R.C.Inf., World Alum.Abstr. **Document type:** academic/scholarly publication.
—BLDSC (3533.151000).
   Former titles: D I S A Information. Measurement and Analysis (ISSN 0070-6639); D I S A Information. Electronic Measurement of Mechanic Events.
   Description: Measurement and analysis of fluid, surface, and particle dynamics research programs.

389.6 574   SZ   ISSN 0301-5149
RS189   CODEN: DVBSA3
DEVELOPMENTS IN BIOLOGICAL STANDARDIZATION. (Text in English) 1964. a. price varies. (International Association of Biological Standardization) S. Karger AG, Allschwilerstr. 10, P.O. Box, CH-4009 Basel, Switzerland. TEL 061-3061111. FAX 061-3061234. E-mail: Karger@karger.ch. (reprint service avail. from ISI; back issues avail.) **Indexed:** Biol.Abstr., Chem.Abstr., Curr.Cont., Dairy Sci.Abstr., Excerp.Med., Ind.Med., Ind.Sci.Rev., Ind.Vet., Rev.Plant Path., Sci.Cit.Ind., Vet.Bull. **Document type:** academic/scholarly publication.
—BLDSC (3579.067000); CASDDS; Faxon; Genuine Article; SWETS; UnCover. **CCC.**
   Supersedes: Progress in Immunobiological Standardization (ISSN 0079-6344); Symposia Series in Immunobiological Standardization (ISSN 0082-0768)
   Description: Reports on the development and use of standardized biologicals.
   Refereed Serial

ELEKTRICHESKIE STANTSII. see *ENGINEERING — Electrical Engineering*

620.1 389   FR   ISSN 0223-4866
ENJEUX. 1981. m. 820 F. (foreign 1150 F.). Association Francaise de Normalisation, Tour Europe, 92049 Paris La Defense Cedex, France. TEL 42-91-55-55. FAX 42-91-56-56. TELEX 611 974F. Ed. Claude Fouquet. adv.; bk.rev.; abstr.; bibl.; charts; illus.; stat. circ. 10,300. **Indexed:** Biol.Abstr., C.I.S. Abstr., Chem.Abstr., ELLIS, Excerp.Med.
—BLDSC (3775.480000).
   Supersedes: Bulletin Mensuel de la Normalisation Francaise (ISSN 0300-1164); Courrier de la Normalisation (ISSN 0011-0485)

F D C CONTROL NEWSLETTER. (Food, Drug, and Cosmetics) see *FOOD AND FOOD INDUSTRIES*

F UND M, FEINWERKTECHNIK MIKROTECHNIK MESSTECHNIK; Zeitschrift fuer Elektronik, Optik, Feinmechanik und Mikrotechnik in Geraetebau und Messtechnik. see *ENGINEERING*

389   US
   CODEN: FIPPAT
FEDERAL INFORMATION PROCESSING STANDARDS PUBLICATION. Abbreviated title: F I P S Publication. m. updates. price varies (updates for individual categories also avail.). U.S. National Institute of Standards and Technology, Gaithersburg, MD 20899. TEL 301-975-3058. (Subscr. to: National Technical Information Service, 5285 Port Royal Rd., Springfield, VA 22161. TEL 703-487-4630. FAX 703-321-8547) **Document type:** government publication.
   Formerly: U.S. National Bureau of Standards. Federal Information Processing Standards (ISSN 0083-1816)
   Description: Provides updates on all official U.S. government information processing standards.
   Refereed Serial

FLOW MEASUREMENT AND INSTRUMENTATION. see *INSTRUMENTS*

620.1 389   CN   ISSN 0831-4888
FOCUS. (Editions in English and French) 1970. q. free. Canadian Standards Association, Public Affairs, 178 Rexdale Blvd., Toronto (Rexdale), ON M9W 1R3, Canada. TEL 416-747-4129. FAX 416-747-4149. illus. circ. 30,000. **Indexed:** Can.B.P.I.
   Formerly: Standards - Canada (ISSN 0038-965X)

HOSTILE ENVIRONMENTS AND HIGH TEMPERATURE MEASUREMENTS. see *ENGINEERING — Mechanical Engineering*

I E C BULLETIN. (International Electrotechnical Commission) see *ENGINEERING — Electrical Engineering*

I E E E INSTRUMENTATION AND MEASUREMENT TECHNOLOGY CONFERENCE. PROCEEDINGS. see *INSTRUMENTS*

389   US   ISSN 0896-1425
   CODEN: ISBEEX
I E E E STANDARDS BEARER. German edition: I E E E Normen Nachrichten (ISSN 1050-6187); French edition: I E E E Nouvelle des Normes (ISSN 1050-6195); Italian edition: Notiziario degli Standard I E E E (ISSN 1050-6179); British edition (ISSN 1050-6209) 1986. q. free. Institute of Electrical and Electronics Engineers, Inc., 345 E. 47th St., New York, NY 10017. TEL 908-562-3830. FAX 908-562-1571. (Subscr. to: Box 1331, 445 Hoes La., Piscataway, NJ 08855-1331) Ed. Kristin M. Dittmann. (back issues avail.) **Document type:** newsletter.
—CASDDS.
   Formerly (until 1987): Standards Bearer of the I E E E (ISSN 0895-7614)
   Description: Aimed primarily at standards users and developers. Topics include IEEE standards, information and news, general topics related to standards, legal issues.

621.37   US   ISSN 0018-9456
   CODEN: IEIMAO
I E E E TRANSACTIONS ON INSTRUMENTATION AND MEASUREMENT. 1952. bi-m. $190 to non-members (effective 1996). (I E E E, Instrumentation and Measurement Society) Institute of Electrical and Electronics Engineers, Inc., 345 E. 47th St., New York, NY 10017-2394. TEL 908-981-0060. FAX 908-981-9667. (Subscr. to: Box 1331, 445 Hoes Lane, Piscataway, NJ 08855-1331) Ed. Stephen Dyer. bk.rev.; abstr.; illus.; index. (also avail. in microform) **Indexed:** A.S.& T.Ind., Appl.Mech.Rev., Chem.Abstr., Comput.Abstr., Comput.Cont., Curr.Cont., Deep Sea Res.& Oceanogr.Abstr., Eng.Ind., Excerp.Med., Ind.Sci.Rev., INSPEC, Int.Aerosp.Abstr., Math.R., Sci.Cit.Ind., Sh.& Vib.Dig.
—BLDSC (4363.199100); CASDDS; Ei; Faxon; Genuine Article; SWETS; UMI; UnCover. **CCC.**

389.6   IR
I S I R I YEARBOOK. (Text in English) 1975. a. free. Institute of Standards and Industrial Research of Iran, P.O. Box 15875-4618, Teheran, Iran. FAX 98-26130664. Ed. M. Seifi. circ. 1,000.

658.7   SZ   ISSN 0303-805X
T59.A1
I S O BULLETIN (ENGLISH EDITION). French edition (ISSN 0303-8009) 1970. m. International Organization for Standardization, 1 rue de Varembe, CH-1211 Geneva 20, Switzerland. TEL 022-7490111. FAX 022-7333430. TELEX 412205-ISO-CH. (Dist. in the U.S. by: American National Standards Institute, 11 W. 42nd St., 13th Fl., New York, NY 10036) illus. circ. 8,600. **Indexed:** Cadscan, Lead Abstr., Zincscan. **Document type:** bulletin.
—SWETS.
   Description: Includes standardization news, calendar of ISO meetings, list of new draft standards and newly published standards.

389.6   SZ   ISSN 0303-3309
Z7914.A22   CODEN: ISCADP
I S O CATALOGUE. (Supplement avail.: I S O Catalogue. Supplement (ISSN 1018-5968)) (Editions in English, French) a. International Organization for Standardization, 1 rue de Varembe, CH-1211 Geneva 20, Switzerland. TEL 022-7490111. FAX 022-7333430. TELEX 412205-ISO-CH. (Dist. in US by: American National Standards Institute, 11 W. 42nd St., 13th Fl., New York, NY 10036) **Document type:** catalog.
—BLDSC (4583.261000); CASDDS.
   Description: Lists all published ISO standards.

METROLOGY AND STANDARDIZATION

389.6 SZ ISSN 1018-5968
I S O CATALOGUE. SUPPLEMENT. (Supplement to: I S O Catalogue (ISSN 0303-3309)) q. International Organization for Standardization, 1 rue de Varembe, CH-1211 Geneva 20, Switzerland. TEL 022-7490111. FAX 022-7333430. TELEX 412205-ISO-CH. (Dist. in U.S. by: American National Standards Institute, 11 W. 42nd St., 13th Fl., New York, NY 10036) **Document type:** catalog.
—BLDSC (4583.261200).

389 SZ ISSN 0536-2067
I S O MEMENTO. (Text in English and French) a. International Organization for Standardization, 1 rue de Varembe, CH-1211 Geneva 20, Switzerland. TEL 022-7490111. FAX 022-7333430. TELEX 412205-ISO-CH. (Dist. in the U.S. by: American National Standards Institute, 11 W. 42nd St., 13th Fl., New York, NY 10036) **Document type:** directory.
—BLDSC (4583.264000).
Description: Gives the scope of responsibility, organizational structure and secretariats for each technical committee.

658.7 SZ
I S O TECHNICAL PROGRAMME. 1985. 2/yr. International Organization for Standardization, 1 rue de Varembe, Case Postale 56, CH-1211 Geneva 20, Switzerland. TEL 022-7490111. FAX 022-7333430. TELEX 412205-ISO-CH. E-mail: central@isocs.iso.ch. **Document type:** bulletin.
—BLDSC (8704.659000).

389.6 SZ ISSN 1018-6638
I S O 9000 NEWS. French edition (ISSN 1018-6646) (Text in English) 1992. bi-m. International Organization for Standardization, 1 rue de Varembe, CH-1211 Geneva 20, Switzerland. FAX 022-7333430. TELEX 412205-ISO-CH. (Dist. in U.S. by: American National Standards Institute, 11 W. 42nd St., 13th Fl., New York, NY 10036) **Document type:** newsletter.
Description: News and information on ISO quality assurance standards and activities.

I T STANDARDNYT. see COMPUTERS

389 US
INDEX AND DIRECTORY OF INDUSTRY STANDARDS. (In 7 vols.) 1983. a. price varies. Information Handling Services, 15 Inverness Way. E., Box 1154, Englewood, CO 80150. TEL 800-841-7179. FAX 303-799-4085. TELEX 4322083 IHS UI. (Subscr. to: Global Engineering, 2805 McGaw Ave., Irvine, CA 92714. TEL 714-261-1455) Ed. Liz Maynard Prigge. circ. 500. **Document type:** directory.
Formerly: Index and Directory of U.S. Industry Standards.
Description: Provides access to subject and numeric international and domestic standards documents of professional societies.

389.6 US ISSN 0198-9138
JK1679
INDEX OF FEDERAL SPECIFICATIONS, STANDARDS AND COMMERCIAL ITEM DESCRIPTIONS. 1952. a. $27. U.S. Federal Supply Service, General Services Administration, 1941 Jefferson Davis Hwy., Washington, DC 20406. TEL 202-655-4000. (Subscr. to: Supt. of Documents, Washington, DC 20402. TEL 202-783-3238)
Former titles: Index of Federal Specifications, Standards, and Handbooks (ISSN 0364-1414); Index of Federal Specifications and Standards.
Description: Provides alphabetic, numeric and Federal Supply Classification listings of specifications, lists and descriptions in general use throughout the Federal Government.

INSTITUTE OF MEASUREMENT AND CONTROL. TRANSACTIONS. see INSTRUMENTS

INSTRUMENT ENGINEER'S YEARBOOK; manufacturers'-users' guide to instrumentation & control. see INSTRUMENTS

389.6 US
INTERNATIONAL SOCIETY OF WEIGHING AND MEASUREMENT. MEMBERSHIP DIRECTORY & PRODUCT GUIDE. a. $50 to non-members. International Society of Weighing and Measurement, 2299 Brockett Rd., Tucker, GA 30084. TEL 404-939-2200. FAX 404-939-7924. Ed. Mimi Harlan. adv.; circ. 1,400 (controlled). **Document type:** directory.

389.6 UK ISSN 0968-347X
QC270
ISOTECH JOURNAL OF THERMOMETRY. s-a. £15($25) Isothermal Technology Inc., Southport PR9 9AG, England. (U.S. addr.: 2307 Whitley Dr., Durham, NC 27707. TEL 919-490-323) circ. 600. (back issues avail.) **Document type:** academic/scholarly publication.
Description: Devoted to the art and science of temperature measurement in the laboratory, technical workplace, and the environment.

389.6 RU ISSN 0202-7585
ITOGI NAUKI I TEKHNIKI: METROLOGIYA I IZMERITEL'NAYA TEKHNIKA. irreg., vol.8, 1991. price varies. Vsesoyuznyi Institut Nauchno-Tekhnicheskoi Informatsii (VINITI), Ul. Usievicha 20-A, 125219 Moscow A-219, Russia. (Subscr. to: Mezhdunarodnaya Kniga, Moscow 121200, Russia)
—BLDSC (0110.730000).

389.6 JA
J I S YEARBOOK (YEAR). a. 4100 Yen. Japanese Standards Association, 1-24 Akasaka 4-chome, Minato-ku, Tokyo 107, Japan.

JOURNAL OF DYNAMIC SYSTEMS, MEASUREMENT AND CONTROL. see ENGINEERING — Engineering Mechanics And Materials

389.6 658.5 JA ISSN 0453-4662
KEISOKU TO SEIGYO/SOCIETY OF INSTRUMENT AND CONTROL ENGINEERS. JOURNAL.* (Text in Japanese) vol.12,1973. m. Keisoku Jido Seigyo Gakkai - Society of Instrument and Control Engineers, 35-28-303, Hongo 1-chome, Bunkyo-ku, Tokyo 113, Japan, Japan. Ed.Bd. adv.; bk.rev.; charts; illus.; tr.lit. **Indexed:** Agri.Eng.Abstr., INIS Atomind., INSPEC, JCT, JTA.
—BLDSC (4889.250000). **CCC.**

KOMPASS PROFESSIONNEL. PRECISION. see BUSINESS AND ECONOMICS — Trade And Industrial Directories

350.821 US
LAB DATA. 1969. q. $6 (foreign $7.50). Underwriters Laboratories Inc., Corporate Communications, 333 Pfingsten Rd., Northbrook, IL 60062. TEL 708-272-8800. FAX 708-272-8129. TELEX 6502543343. Ed. Ward Wilson.
Description: Emphasizes the underlying philosophy of Underwriters Laboratories requirements and safety issues.

389 XR ISSN 0862-7932
T59.2.C95 CODEN: MACSEW
MAGAZIN C S N; odborny casopis pro technickou normalizaci, zkusebnictvi, certifikaci a jakost. (Text in Czech or Slovak; summaries in English and Czech) 1976. m. (Urad pro Technickou Normalizaci, Metrologii a Statni Zkusebnictvi) Vydavatelstvi Norem, Hornomecholupska 40, 102 04 Prague 10, Czech Republic. Distr. by: PNS-UED, ul. Kafkova 19, 160 00 Pragje 6, Czech Republic) Ed. Pavel Cerny. charts; illus. circ. 3,000. **Indexed:** INIS Atomind.
Formerly (until 1991): Ceskoslovenska Standardizace (ISSN 0139-5890); Which was formed by the merger of (1962-1976): Merova Technika (ISSN 0026-0142); (1953-1976): Normalizace (ISSN 0029-1781)
Description: Deals with standardization, quality control, testing and metrology.

389.6 MW
MALAWI. MALAWI BUREAU OF STANDARDS. ANNUAL REPORT AND STATEMENT OF ACCOUNTS. (Text in English) a. Malawi Bureau of Standards, PO Box 946, Blantyre, Malawi.

MARINE STANDARDIZATION IN JAPAN. see TRANSPORTATION — Ships And Shipping

620.1 389 IS ISSN 0025-5912
TA368
MATI. (Text in Hebrew; summaries in English) 1968. q. free. Standards Institution of Israel, 42 Chaim Levanon St., Tel Aviv 69977, Israel. TEL 972-3-6465154. FAX 972-3-6419683. TELEX 35508-SIIT-IL. Ed. Adina Caspi. circ. 7,000. **Indexed:** Ind.Heb.Per.

350.821 MF
MAURITIUS STANDARDS BUREAU. ANNUAL REPORT. (Text in English) a., latest 1978. Government Printing Office, Elizabeth II Ave., Port Louis, Mauritius.

389.6 621 530 NE ISSN 0263-2241
MEASUREMENT. 1983. m. fl.969($591) (effective 1996). (International Measurement Confederation) Elsevier Science B.V., P.O. Box 211, 1000 AE Amsterdam, Netherlands. TEL 31-20-4853911. FAX 31-20-4853598. TELEX 18582 ESPA NL. E-mail: nlinfo-f@elsevier; usinfo-f@elsevier.com; forinfo-kyf04035@niftyserve.or.jp; Site addr.: http://www.elsevier.nl/. (Subscr. in U.S. and Canada to: Elsevier Science Inc., Box 882, Madison Sq. Sta., New York, NY 10159. TEL 212-989-5800. FAX 212-633-3990) Ed. L. Finkelstein. adv.; charts; illus. circ. 200. (also avail. in microform from UMI; back issues avail.) **Indexed:** Environ.Abstr., INSPEC (1993-). **Document type:** academic/scholarly publication.
—BLDSC (5413.544700); Ei; Faxon; SWETS. **CCC.**
Incorporates (1990-1992): Industrial Metrology (ISSN 0921-5956)
Description: Gives a worldwide report on the state and progress of the science and technology of measurement.
Refereed Serial

MEASUREMENT AND CONTROL. see INSTRUMENTS

389.6 US
MEASUREMENT METHODS FOR THE SOCIAL SCIENCES SERIES. irreg., no.4, 1994. price varies. Sage Publications, Inc., 2455 Teller Rd., Thousand Oaks, CA 91320. TEL 805-499-0721. FAX 805-499-0871. E-mail: libraries@sagepub.com. (Overseas subscr. to: Sage Publications Ltd., 6 Bonhill St., London EC2A 4PU, England; Sage Publications India Pvt. Ltd./B-42, Panchsheel Enclave, P.O. Box 4125, New Delhi 110 048, India) Ed. Richard M. Jaeger. **Document type:** monographic series.
Description: Provides professionals and students in the social sciences with succinct information on methodology.

389.6 US ISSN 0543-1972
TJ1313 CODEN: MSTCAL
MEASUREMENT TECHNIQUES. English translation of: Izmeritel'naya Tekhnika (RU ISSN 0368-1025) 1958. m. $1395 (foreign $1630) (effective 1996). (Komitet po Delam Standartov Mer i Izmeritel'noy Tekhniki, RU) Plenum Publishing Corp., Consultants Bureau, 233 Spring St., New York, NY 10013-1578. TEL 212-620-8468. FAX 212-463-0742. TELEX 23-421139. Ed. L.K. Isaev. (also avail. in microform from JSC; back issues avail.) **Indexed:** Appl.Mech.Rev., Curr.Cont., Electron.& Communic.Abstr.J., Energy Res.Abstr., Eng.Ind., Ind.Sci.Rev., INIS Atomind., INSPEC, ISMEC, Solid St.Abstr. **Document type:** academic/scholarly publication.
—BLDSC (0415.830000); Ei; Faxon; Genuine Article; SWETS; UMI; UnCover. **CCC.**
Refereed Serial

389 HU ISSN 0025-9993
CODEN: MEAUAI
MERES ES AUTOMATIKA. (Summaries in English, German and Russian) 1952. m. $47. (Merestechnikai es Automatizalasi Tudomanyos Egyesulet) Lapkiado Vallalat, Lenin korut 9-11, 1073 Budapest 7, Hungary. TEL 222-408. (Subscr. to: Kultura, P.O. Box 149, H-1389 Budapest, Hungary) Ed. Telkes Bela. adv.; bk.rev.; charts; illus. circ. 1,500. **Indexed:** Appl.Mech.Rev., Chem.Abstr., Eng.Ind., Fluidex, INSPEC, Met.Abstr., World Alum.Abstr.
—BLDSC (5680.500000); CASDDS.
Description: Contains articles on all aspects of automation technology. Covers a broad range of pertinent topics - from semiconductor optoelectronic sensors to operation of and developments in automation devices and systems.

389 HU ISSN 0026-0002
MERESUGYI KOZLEMENYEK. 1959. q. $24.50. (Orszagos Meresugyi Hivatal) Lapkiado Vallalat, Lenin korut 9-11, 1073 Budapest 7, Hungary. TEL 222-408. (Subscr. to: Kultura, P.O. Box 149, H-1389 Budapest, Hungary) charts. **Indexed:** INIS Atomind.

389.6 CN ISSN 0383-9184
METRIC FACT SHEETS. 1973. irreg. $5. Canadian Metric Association, P.O. Box 35, Fonthill, ON L0S 1E0, Canada. TEL 416-892-3800. Ed. Albert J. Mettler. adv. circ. 1,000. **Document type:** academic/scholarly publication.
Description: Presents various aspects of metrication and international standardization.

METROLOGY AND STANDARDIZATION

389 US
METRIC REPORTER. 1973. bi-m. $100 membership. American National Metric Council, 4330 East-West Hwy., Ste. 1117, Bethesda, MD 20814. TEL 301-718-6508. FAX 301-656-0989. Ed. Ruth E. Thaler-Carter. bk.rev. circ. 5,000. **Document type:** newsletter.

389.6 US ISSN 1050-5628
METRIC TODAY. 1966. bi-m. $30 membership to individuals (foreign $35); institutions $150. U S Metric Association, Inc., 10245 Andasol Ave., Northridge, CA 91325. TEL 818-368-7443. Ed. Valerie Antoine. bk.rev.; illus.; tr.lit.; cum.index. circ. 2,500. (looseleaf format; back issues avail.) **Document type:** newsletter.
Former titles (until Mar. 1990): U S M A Newsletter (ISSN 0271-2555); U S Metric Association Newsletter; Metric Association Newsletter (ISSN 0300-7308)
Description: Provides information on the progress of the U.S. government's congressionally directed changeover to use only metric system measurements in conducting its business by 1992 (except where inefficiencies can be proven).

389 FR ISSN 0026-1394
QC81 CODEN: MTRGAU
METROLOGIA; international journal of scientific metrology. (Text in English, French or German) 1965. 6/yr. $310. Bureau International des Poids et Mesures, Pavillon de Breteuil, 92312 Sevres Cedex, France. FAX 45-34-20-21. Ed. David A. Blackburn. adv.; charts; illus.; index. (also avail. in microform from UMI; back issues avail.; reprint service avail. from ISI) **Indexed:** Chem.Abstr., Curr.Cont., Eng.Ind., INSPEC, Phys.Ber. **Document type:** proceedings.
—BLDSC (5748.800000); CASDDS; Ei; Faxon; Genuine Article; SWETS; UMI; UnCover. **CCC.**
Description: Disseminates new and fundamental knowledge in all areas of scientific metrology.

389 US
CODEN: NIHAE2
N I S T HANDBOOK. irreg. $22. U.S. National Institute of Standards and Technology, Gaithersburg, MD 20899. TEL 301-975-3058. (Orders to: National Technical Information Service, 5285 Port Royal Rd., Springfield, VA 22161. TEL 703-487-4650. FAX 703-321-8547; Or: Bernan, 4611-F Assembly Dr., Lanham, MD 20706. TEL 800-274-4447. FAX 301-459-0056) **Document type:** government publication.
Formerly (until 1989): N B S Handbook (ISSN 0083-1824)
Refereed Serial

389 US
QC100 CODEN: NBSMA6
N I S T MONOGRAPH. 1959. irreg. price varies. U.S. National Institute of Standards and Technology, Gaithersburg, MD 20899. TEL 301-975-3058. (Orders to: National Technical Information Service, 5285 Port Royal Rd., Springfield, VA 22161. TEL 703-487-4650. FAX 703-321-8547; Or: Bernan, 4611-F Assembly Dr., Lanham, MD 20706. TEL 800-274-4447. FAX 301-459-0056) **Indexed:** GeoRef. **Document type:** government publication, monographic series.
—CASDDS.
Formerly (until 1988): U.S. National Bureau of Standards. Monograph (ISSN 0083-1832)
Refereed Serial

389 US ISSN 1048-776X
QC100 CODEN: NSPUE2
N I S T SPECIAL PUBLICATION. (Subseries avail.: Standards Activities of Organizations in the U.S.; National Conference on Weights and Measures. Report (ISSN 0077-3964) irreg. price varies. U.S. National Institute of Standards and Technology, Gaithersburg, MD 20899. TEL 301-975-3058. (Orders to: National Technical Information Service, 5285 Port Royal Rd., Springfield, VA 22161. TEL 703-487-4650. FAX 703-321-8547; Or: Bernan, 4611-F Assembly Dr., Lanham, MD 20706. TEL 800-274-4447. FAX 301-459-0056) **Document type:** government publication.
—BLDSC (6113.655200); CASDDS.
Formerly (until 1988): N B S Special Publication (ISSN 0083-1883)
Refereed Serial

389 US ISSN 1054-013X
QC100 CODEN: NTNOEF
N I S T TECHNICAL NOTES. 1959. irreg. price varies. U.S. National Institute of Standards and Technology, Gaithersburg, MD 20899. TEL 301-975-3058. (Orders to: National Technical Information Service, 5285 Port Royal Rd., Springfield, VA 22161. TEL 703-487-4650. FAX 703-321-8547; Or: Bernan, 4611-F Assembly Dr., Lanham, MD 20706. TEL 800-274-4447. FAX 301-459-0056) **Indexed:** Chem.Abstr., INSPEC. **Document type:** government publication.
—BLDSC (6113.655300); CASDDS.
Formerly (until 1988): U.S. National Bureau of Standards. Technical Notes (ISSN 0083-1913)
Refereed Serial

389.6 UK
N P L REPORT D Q M. 1967. irreg., no.98, 1994. National Physical Laboratory, Division of Quantum Metrology, Teddington, Middx. TW11 0LW, England. TEL 081-943-6055. FAX 081-943-2155. **Document type:** monographic series.
Formerly (until 1993): N P L Report Q U (ISSN 0309-3050)

389 US ISSN 0097-0395
QC100 CODEN: NSRDAP
N S R D S - N B S: NATIONAL STANDARD REFERENCE DATA SERIES. irreg. price varies. U.S. National Institute of Standards and Technology, Gaithersburg, MD 20899. TEL 301-975-3058. (Avail. from: National Technical Information Service, 5285 Port Royal Rd., Springfield, VA 22161. TEL 703-487-4650. FAX 703-321-8547) **Document type:** government publication.
—CASDDS.
Formerly: U.S. National Bureau of Standards. National Standard Reference Data Series (ISSN 0083-1840)
Description: Compiles quantitative data on physical and chemical properties of materials; compiled from world literature and critically evaluated.
Refereed Serial

389 JA ISSN 0916-1546
NAGARE NO KEISOKU/ASSOCIATION FOR THE STUDY OF FLOW MEASUREMENTS OF JAPAN. JOURNAL. (Text in Japanese) 1983. a. Nagare no Keisoku Kondankai - Association for the Study of Flow Measurements of Japan, Nihon Kagaku Kogyo K.K., 2-1, Shimizu, Suita-shi, Osaka 565, Japan.

389 JA
NAGARE NO KEISOKU OSAKA SHINPOJUMU KOEN YOSHISHU/PROCEEDINGS OF THE OSAKA SYMPOSIUM ON FLOW MEASURING TECHNIQUES. (Text in English, Japanese) 1983. a. Nagare no Keisoku Kondankai - Association for the Study of Flow Measurements of Japan, Nihon Kagaku Kogyo K.K., 2-1, Shimizu, Suita-shi, Osaka 565, Japan. **Document type:** proceedings.

NATIONAL CONFERENCE OF STANDARDS LABORATORIES. DIRECTORY OF STANDARDS LABS.
see *BUSINESS AND ECONOMICS — Trade And Industrial Directories*

389.6 US ISSN 0194-5149
NATIONAL CONFERENCE OF STANDARDS LABORATORIES. NEWSLETTER. vol.12, 1972. q. $15. National Conference of Standards Laboratories, 1800 30th St., Ste. 305B, Boulder, CO 80301. TEL 303-440-3339. FAX 303-440-3384. Ed. John Minck. circ. 2,000. (processed) **Document type:** newsletter.

389.6 US
NATIONAL CONFERENCE OF STANDARDS LABORATORIES. TRAINING INFORMATION DIRECTORY. a. $10. National Conference of Standards Laboratories, 1800 30th St., Ste. 305B, Boulder, CO 80301. TEL 303-440-3339. FAX 303-440-3384. **Document type:** directory.

389.6 US
NATIONAL CONFERENCE OF STANDARDS LABORATORIES. WORKSHOP & SYMPOSIUM PROCEEDINGS. 1962? a. $30 (effective 1993). National Conference of Standards Laboratories, 1800 30th St., Ste. 305B, Boulder, CO 80301. TEL 303-440-3339. FAX 303-440-3384. **Document type:** proceedings.
Supersedes: National Conference of Standards Laboratories. Proceedings (ISSN 0081-4318)

389.1 US ISSN 0077-3964
QC100
NATIONAL CONFERENCE ON WEIGHTS AND MEASURES. REPORT. (Subseries of: NIST Special Publication (ISSN 1048-776X)) 1905. a. price varies. U.S. National Institute of Standards and Technology, Gaithersburg, MD 20899. TEL 301-975-3058. (Orders to: National Technical Information Service, 5285 Port Royal Rd., Springfield, VA 22161. TEL 703-487-4650. FAX 703-321-8547; Or: Bernan, 4611-F Assembly Dr., Lanham, MD 20706. TEL 800-274-4447. FAX 301-459-0056) cum.index: 1905-60. **Document type:** government publication.
Refereed Serial

500 600 US ISSN 1044-677X
QC100.U6 CODEN: JRITEF
NATIONAL INSTITUTE OF STANDARDS AND TECHNOLOGY. JOURNAL OF RESEARCH. 1928. bi-m. $25 (foreign $31.25). U.S. National Institute of Standards and Technology, U.S. Department of Commerce, Gaithersburg, MD 20899. TEL 301-975-3069. (Subscr. to: Superintendent of Documents, U.S. Government Printing Office, Box 317954, Pittsburgh, PA 15250-7954. TEL 202-512-1800. FAX 202-512-2250) Ed. Barry Taylor. illus.; index. circ. 2,000. (also avail. in microform from UMI; reprint service avail. from UMI) **Indexed:** A.S.& T.Ind., Anal.Abstr., Appl.Mech.Rev., Biol.Abstr., Br.Ceram.Abstr., Chem.Abstr., Deep Sea Res.& Oceanogr.Abstr., Eng.Ind., Ind.U.S.Gov.Per., INIS Atomind., INSPEC, Mass Spectr.Bull., Math.R., Met.Abstr., RAPRA, Sci.Cit.Ind., World Text.Abstr. **Document type:** government publication.
—BLDSC (5050.600000); CASDDS; Faxon; Genuine Article; SWETS; UMI; UnCover.
Former titles (until 1988): U.S. National Bureau of Standards. Journal of Research (ISSN 0160-1741); Formed by the 1977 merger of: U.S. National Bureau of Standards. Journal of Research. Section A. Physics and Chemistry (ISSN 0022-4332); U.S. National Bureau of Standards. Journal of Research. Section B. Mathematical Sciences (ISSN 0098-8979); Which was formerly (until 1967): U.S. National Bureau of Standards. Journal of Research. Section B. Mathematics and Mathematical Physics (ISSN 0022-4340); Which superseded in part (in 1959): U.S. National Bureau of Standards. Journal of Research (ISSN 0091-0635).
Description: Reports on research conducted in the fields of the physical and engineering sciences.
Refereed Serial

681 JA ISSN 0451-6109
CODEN: BNLMAP
NATIONAL RESEARCH LABORATORY OF METROLOGY. BULLETIN. (Text in English, Japanese) 1955. s-a. exchange basis. National Research Laboratory of Metrology - Tsusho Sangyosho Kogyo Gijutsu-in Keiryo Kenkyujo, 1-1-4 Umezono, Tsukuba, Ibaraki-ken 305, Japan. FAX 0298-54-4135. TELEX 3652570-AIST-J. E-mail: nagai@nrlm.go.jp. Ed. Satoshi Nagai. circ. 700. **Indexed:** Fluidex, INSPEC (1984-), JCT, Met.Abstr., World Alum.Abstr. **Document type:** government publication, bulletin.
—BLDSC (2643.400000).

389.6 NE ISSN 0929-2985
NORMALISATIE-NIEUWS. 1924. 10/yr. fl.60 (effective 1995). Nederlands Normalisatie-instituut, Kalfjeslaan 2, 2623 AA Delft, Netherlands. TEL 31-15-690302. FAX 31-15-690232. TELEX 38144 NNI NL. Ed. Eugene van der Put. adv.; bk.rev.; illus.; index. circ. 4,000. **Indexed:** C.I.S. Abstr., Excerp.Med., Key to Econ.Sci. **Document type:** newsletter.
Formerly (until July 1993): Normalisatie Magazine (ISSN 0921-8211)
Description: Includes news from the NNI, European and international standards organizations, and articles on standardization and related issues.

NORMALIZACJA. see *ENGINEERING*

NUCLEAR STANDARDS NEWS. see *ENERGY — Nuclear Energy*

METROLOGY AND STANDARDIZATION

530 GW
CODEN: PTBMAZ
P T B - MITTEILUNGEN FORSCHEN UND PRUEFEN. 1890. bi-m. DM.233 (effective 1996). (Physikalisch-Technische Bundesanstalt) Friedr. Vieweg und Sohn Verlagsgesellschaft mbH, Postfach 1546, 65005 Wiesbaden, Germany. TEL 0611-534389. FAX 0611-534430. Eds. W. Hauser, E. Seiler. adv.; bk.rev. **Indexed:** C.I.S. Abstr., Cadscan, Chem.Abstr., Curr.Cont., Excerp.Med., Lead Abstr., Phys.Ber., Zincscan. **Document type:** trade publication.
—BLDSC (6946.570000); CASDDS; Genuine Article; SWETS. **CCC.**
Formerly: P T B Mitteilungen (ISSN 0030-834X)

POLITECHNIKA WROCLAWSKA. INSTYTUT METROLOGII ELEKTRYCZNEJ. PRACE NAUKOWE. KONFERENCJE. see ENGINEERING — Electrical Engineering

POLITECHNIKA WROCLAWSKA. INSTYTUT METROLOGII ELEKTRYCZNEJ. PRACE NAUKOWE. MONOGRAFIE. see ENGINEERING — Electrical Engineering

POLITECHNIKA WROCLAWSKA. INSTYTUT METROLOGII ELEKTRYCZNEJ. PRACE NAUKOWE. STUDIA I MATERIALY. see ENGINEERING — Electrical Engineering

658 PL ISSN 0137-8651
PROBLEMY JAKOSCI; dwumiesiecznik naukowo-techniczny. (Text in Polish; summaries in various languages) 1968. bi-m. $25. Wydawnictwo Czasopism i Ksiazek Technicznych SIGMA - NOT, Ul. Ratuszowa 11, P.O. Box 1004, 00-950 Warsaw, Poland. TEL 48-22-180918. FAX 48-22-192187. TELEX 814550 SIGMA PL. (Dist. by: SIGMA - NOT Ltd., Ul. Bartycka 20, 00-716 Warsaw, Poland) Ed. H. Chojecki. adv.; bk.rev. circ. 1,600. (microform)

389.6 NE ISSN 0924-3089
TJ212 CODEN: PCQUEJ
PROCESS CONTROL AND QUALITY. (Text in English) 1990. 3/yr. fl.570($348) (effective 1996). Elsevier Science B.V., P.O. Box 211, Amsterdam, Netherlands. TEL 31-20-4853911.
FAX 31-20-4853598. TELEX 18582 ESPA NL. E-mail: nlinfo-f@elsevier.nl; usinfo-f@elsevier.com; forinfo-kyf04035@niftyserve.or.jp; Site addr.: http://www.elsevier.nl/. (Subscr. in U.S. and Canada to: Elsevier Science Inc., Box 882, Madison Sq. Sta., New York, NY 10159-0882. TEL 212-989-5800. FAX 212-363-3990) Ed. K.J. Clevett. adv.; bk.rev.; cum.index. (also avail. in microform from UMI; back issues avail.) **Indexed:** Anal.Abstr., Chem.Abstr., INSPEC (1990-). **Document type:** academic/scholarly publication.
—BLDSC (6849.985020); CASDDS; Ei; Faxon; SWETS. **CCC.**
Description: Covers the science and technology of process quality measurement systems, with emphasis on the practical application of in-process analyzer technology for process control and product quality measurement.
Refereed Serial

PROTECTION OF ATMOSPHERE AGAINST POLLUTION; determination of atmospheric background pollution in South Prebaltic. see ENVIRONMENTAL STUDIES — Pollution

620.1 US
Q A QUEST. 1981. m. membership only. Quality Assurance Institute, 7575 Dr. Phillips Blvd., Ste. 350, Orlando, FL 32819. TEL 407-363-1111. FAX 407-363-1112. Ed William E. Perry. bk.rev. circ. 1,000. (back issues avail.) **Document type:** newsletter.

620 IT
QUALITA. vol.4, 1974. q. L.50000. Associazione Italiana per la Qualita, Piazza Diaz 2, 20121 Milan, Italy. TEL 02-72023476. FAX 02-72023085. Ed. Giovanni Frigerio. adv.; bk.rev. circ. 2,200.

658.5 GW
QUALITAET UND ZUVERLAESSIGKEIT; Zeitschrift fuer industrielles Qualitaetsmanagement. 1956. m. DM.157.20. (Deutsche Gesellschaft fuer Qualitaet) Carl Hanser Verlag, Kolbergerstr. 22, 81679 Munich, Germany. TEL 089-998300. FAX 089-984809. (Subscr. to: Postfach 860420, 81631 Munich, Germany) adv.; bk.rev.; bibl.; charts; illus.; index. circ. 14,000. **Indexed:** Excerp.Med., INSPEC, Oper.Res.Manage.Sci., Qual.Contr.Appl.Stat. **Document type:** trade publication.
—BLDSC (7168.124000); SWETS. **CCC.**
Former titles: Q Z Qualitaet und Zuverlaessigkeit (ISSN 0720-1214); Qualitaet und Zuverlaessigkeit (ISSN 0033-5126); (until 1969): Qualitaetskontrolle.

620.1 FR ISSN 1162-1982
QUALITE EN MOUVEMENT. 1960. 5/yr. 622.30 F. to non-members (foreign 700 F.); members 510.50 F. (foreign 550 F.). Mouvement Francais pour la Qualite, 5 esplanade Charles de Gaulle, 92733 Nanterre Cedex, France. TEL 47-29-09-29. FAX 47-25-32-21. adv.; bk.rev.; bibl.; charts; illus. circ. 1,500. **Document type:** bulletin.
Former titles: Qualite Magazine (ISSN 0768-858X); A F C I Q Bulletin (ISSN 0033-4782)

620.1 UK ISSN 0959-3756
QUALITY NEWS. 1973. m. membership. Institute of Quality Assurance, P.O. Box 712, 61 Southwark St., London SE1 1SB, England. TEL 071-401-7227. adv.; bk.rev. circ. 12,444. **Document type:** trade publication.
Former titles (until 1990): Q A News; Quality Assurance News.

620.1 389 UK ISSN 0956-733X
QUALITY TESTING TODAY. 1969. 11/yr. £71 (foreign £88). Nexus Media Ltd., Warwick House, Azalea Dr., Swanley, Kent BR8 8HY, England.
TEL 01322-660070. FAX 01322-667633. Ed. Brendan Coyne. circ. 4,700. **Indexed:** B.C.I.R.A., BMT, Br.Ceram.Abstr., Br.Rail.Bd., Br.Tech.Ind., Fluidex, ISMEC, Met.Abstr., World Alum.Abstr. **Document type:** trade publication.
—BLDSC (7168.175000); SWETS.
Former titles (until 1985): Quality Today (ISSN 0264-2344); (until 1983): Measurement and Inspection Technology (ISSN 0143-4020); (until 1979): Metrology and Inspection (ISSN 0026-1408)

620.1 389.9 UK ISSN 1352-8769
TS156.A1 CODEN: QUWOEW
QUALITY WORLD; for the quality professional. 1935; N.S. 1975. q. £30. Institute of Quality Assurance, P.O. Box 712, 61 Southwark St., London SE1 1SB, England. TEL 071-401-7227. Ed. Teresa Harris. charts; illus.; stat. circ. 13,474. (reprint service avail. from UMI) **Indexed:** Account.& Data Proc.Abstr., BMT, Br.Tech.Ind., Eng.Ind., Ergon.Abstr., INSPEC (1972-), ISMEC, Oper.Res.Manage.Sci., Qual.Contr.Appl.Stat. **Document type:** academic/scholarly publication.
—BLDSC (7168.181500); Ei; Faxon; UMI.
Former titles (until 1994): Quality Forum (ISSN 0959-3268); (until 1990): Quality Assurance (ISSN 0306-2856); (until 1975): Quality Engineer (ISSN 0033-5215)

389.6 CU ISSN 0138-8118
REVISTA DE NORMALIZACION. (Text in Spanish; summaries in English) 1971. s-a. C.$2 ($24 in S. America; $26 in N. America; elsewhere $30) (effective 1995). Oficina Nacional de Normalizacion, Instituto de Investigaciones en Normalizacion, Reina 359 e. Escobar y Lealtad, Habana Vieja 2, Havana C.P. 10200, Cuba. FAX 537-627-657. TELEX 512245 ONN CU. (Dist. by: Ediciones Cubanas, Obispo No. 461, Apdo. 605, Havana, Cuba) Ed. Rosario Fernandez Jaimerena. adv. contact: Josefa Gonzalez Lopez. circ. 1,000.
Description: Deals with standardization, metrology and quality assurance subjects in Cuba.

620.1 389 341 FR ISSN 1161-4951
QC81
REVUE DE METROLOGIE PRATIQUE ET LEGALE; poids et mesures. 1923. m. 800 F. (foreign 1017 F.) (effective 1995). (Service des Instruments de Mesure) Editions de Genie Moderne S.a.r.l., 102 rue de la Tour, 75116 Paris, France. TEL 45-04-80-11. FAX 45-03-29-32. Ed. Paul Rey; Pub. Paul Rey. adv.: B&W page 6250 F., color page 10400 F.; 260 x 190; adv. contact: Paul Rey. charts; illus.; cum.index. 1957-1995. circ. 1,500. **Indexed:** C.I.S. Abstr. **Document type:** bulletin, catalog.
—BLDSC (7933.400000).
Description: Contains scientific information, including official and legal metrology agreements and certifications.

389.6 FR ISSN 0766-5210
REVUE PRATIQUE DE CONTROLE INDUSTRIEL. 1962. 8/yr. 400 F. (foreign 520 F.) (effective May 1995); newsstand price: 52 F. Editions Ampere, Groupe C.E.P.P., 25, rue Dagorno, 75012 Paris, France. TEL 43-47-30-20. FAX 43-47-30-80. Ed. C. Guedes. adv.; bk.rev.; abstr.; bibl.; charts; illus.; stat.; index, cum.index. circ. 5,000. **Indexed:** C.I.S. Abstr., Met.Abstr., World Alum.Abstr.
—**CCC.**
Formerly (until 1984): Qualite (ISSN 0033-5142); (until 1967): Revue Pratique de Controle Industriel (ISSN 0373-8809)
Description: Covers quality control, material testing, and N.D.T. testing in industry.

389 SA ISSN 1018-4295
TA368
S A B S CATALOGUE/S A B S KATALOGUS. (Text in Afrikaans, English) 1963. a. price varies. South African Bureau of Standards, Information and Publications, Private Bag X191, Pretoria 0001, South Africa. TEL 27-12-428-7911.
FAX 27-12-344-1568. TELEX 321308. Ed. E. Fourie. circ. 2,000 (controlled). **Document type:** catalog.
Supersedes: S A B S Katalogus (Afrikaans Edition) (ISSN 0259-3610); S A B S Catalogue (English Edition) (ISSN 0259-3602); Formerly: S A B S Yearbook (ISSN 0081-2137)

389.6 620 FI
S F S CATALOGUE; catalogue of Finnish national standards. (Supplement avail. (ISSN 0780-766X)) (Text and summaries in English and Finnish) 1924. a. plus s-a. updates. FIM 100 (FIM 210 with supplements). Suomen Standardisoimisliitto - Finnish Standards Association, P.O. Box 116, Maistraatinportti 2, FIN-00241 Helsinki, Finland. TEL 358-0-149-9331. FAX 358-0-146-4914. circ. 2,000.

389.6 US
S M A WEIGHLOG.* q. Scale Manufacturers Association, 9384D Forestwood Ln., Manassas, VA 22110-4702. **Document type:** trade publication.

389.6 620 SZ
S N V BULLETIN. (Text in English, French, German) 1952. m. 60 SFr. Schweizerische Normen-Vereinigung, Muehlebachstr. 54, CH-8008 Zurich, Switzerland. TEL 01-2545454. FAX 01-2545474. adv.: page 1000 SFr.; adv. contact: Heinz Kull. index; circ. 1,200. (back issues avail.) **Document type:** bulletin.

658.5 SZ
SCHWEIZERISCHE ARBEITSGEMEINSCHAFT FUER QUALITAETSFOERDERUNG. BULLETIN. (Text in French and German) 1965. m. (10/yr.). 140 SFr. Schweizerische Arbeitsgemeinschaft fuer Qualitaetsfoerderung, Postfach, CH-4603 Olten, Switzerland. TEL 062-329329. FAX 062-329330. adv.; bk.rev. circ. 3,000. **Document type:** bulletin.

658 MX
SISTEMAS DE CALIDAD. 1973. bi-m. $15. Instituto Mexicano de Control de Calidad, Division de Divulgacion - Mexican Institute for Quality Control, Thiers No. 251-Penthouse, Mexico 5, D.F., Mexico. FAX 525-2547390. TELEX 1763190 IMECME. Ed. Patricia Gonzalez Prado. adv.; bk.rev.; index. circ. 5,000.

METROLOGY AND STANDARDIZATION

316.8   SA
SOUTH AFRICA. CENTRAL STATISTICAL SERVICE. STANDARD CODE LIST FOR STATISTICAL REGIONS, MAGISTERIAL DISTRICTS, CITIES, TOWNS, AND NON-URBAN AREAS. (Report No. 09-90-03) irreg., 11th ed., 1993. free. Central Statistical Service - Sentrale Statistiekdiens, Private Bag X44, Pretoria 0001, South Africa. TEL 27-12-310-8911. FAX 27-12-310-8500. **Document type:** government publication.

338.4 316.8   SA
SOUTH AFRICA. CENTRAL STATISTICAL SERVICE. STANDARD INDUSTRIAL CLASSIFICATION OF ALL ECONOMIC ACTIVITIES. (Report No. 09-90-02) irreg., 5th ed., 1993. free. Central Statistical Service - Sentrale Statistiekdiens, Private Bag X44, Pretoria 0001, South Afrcia. TEL 27-12-310-8911. FAX 27-12-310-8500. **Document type:** government publication.
Description: Statistical classifications of type of activity applied to South African industries, businesses and services, with all divisions, groups, and sub-groups.

620.1 389   SA   ISSN 0038-2698
SOUTH AFRICAN BUREAU OF STANDARDS. BULLETIN. (Text in Afrikaans and English) 1947. bi-m. free. South African Bureau of Standards, Private Bag X191, Pretoria 0001, South Africa. FAX 27-12-344-1568. TELEX 3-21308 SA. Ed. C.M. Meyer. illus. circ. 5,500. **Indexed:** Ind.S.A.Per. **Document type:** bulletin.

620
TE200   US   ISSN 0360-6902
STANDARD SPECIFICATIONS FOR TRANSPORTATION MATERIALS AND METHODS OF SAMPLING AND TESTING. (In 2 vols.) 1931. a. $222. American Association of State Highway and Transportation Officials, 444 N. Capital St., N.W., Ste. 249, Washington, DC 20001. TEL 202-624-5800. FAX 202-624-5806. **Document type:** bulletin.
Formerly (until 1935): Tentative Specifications for Highway Materials and Methods of Sampling and Testing.

389   NO   ISSN 0038-9625
STANDARDISERING. 1964. bi-m. NOK 250. Norges Standardiseringsforbund - Norwegian Standards Association, P.O. Box 7020, N-0306 Oslo 3, Norway. TEL 22-46-60-94. FAX 22-46-44-57. TELEX 19050-NSF-N. Ed. J. Johan Bing. adv.; bk.rev.; charts; illus. circ. 1,900. **Document type:** bulletin.

389   US
STANDARDS ACTIVITIES OF ORGANIZATIONS IN THE U.S. (Subseries of: NIST Special Publication (ISSN 1048-776X)) irreg. $31. U.S. National Institute of Standards and Technology, Gaithersburg, MD 20899. TEL 301-975-3058. (Subscr. to: Superintendent of Documents, U.S. Government Printing Office, Box 317954, Pittsburgh, PA 15250-7954. TEL 202-783-3238. FAX 202-512-2233) **Document type:** government publication.
Formerly: Directory of United States Standardization Activities (ISSN 0070-6558)
Refereed Serial

STANDARDS AND TECHNOLOGY UPDATE. see ENGINEERING — Mechanical Engineering

620.1
T59   US   ISSN 0038-9668
STANDARDS ENGINEERING. 1948. bi-m. $40 (foreign $60) (effective 1995-1996). Standards Engineering Society, 1706 Darst Ave., Dayton, OH 45403-3104. TEL 513-258-1955. FAX 513-256-9919. (Subscr. to: Box 184, Dayton, OH 45402-0184) Ed. John Rolleston. adv.; bk.rev.; bibl.; charts; illus.; stat. circ. 600. **Document type:** newsletter.
—Faxon.

620.1 389   II   ISSN 0970-2628
T59.2.I4   CODEN: STNDE3
STANDARDS INDIA. (Text in English) 1949. m. $70. Bureau of Indian Standards, Manak Bhavan, 9 Bahadur Shah Zafar Marg, New Delhi 110 002, India. Ed. R.B. Mathur. adv.; bk.rev.; charts; illus.; index. circ. 4,000. **Indexed:** Chem.Abstr., Food Sci.& Tech.Abstr., INSPEC.
Formerly (until 1987): Indian Standards Institution Bulletin (ISSN 0019-0632)

620.1 389   II   ISSN 0038-9684
STANDARDS: MONTHLY ADDITIONS. (Text in English) 1960. m. free. Bureau of Indian Standards, Manak Bhavan, 9 Bahadur Shah Zafar Marg, New Delhi 110 002, India. Ed. R.B. Mathur. circ. 2,000.
Formerly (until 1987): I S I Standards: Monthly Additions (Indian Standards Institution).

350.821   CE
STANDARDS NEWS. (Text in English) 1975. s-a. free. Bureau of Ceylon Standards, 53 Dharmapala Mawatha, Colombo 3, Sri Lanka. Ed. S.G. Weragoda. adv. circ. 1,000. **Indexed:** Sri Lanka Sci.Ind.

620.1 389   RU   ISSN 0038-9692
     CODEN: STKABA
STANDARTY I KACHESTVO. 1927. m. $145 (effective 1996). Izdatel'stvo Kniga, 125047 Moscow, Russia. **Indexed:** Chem.Abstr.
—BLDSC (0167.600000); CASDDS.

620.1   TZ   ISSN 0856-0374
TANZANIA. BUREAU OF STANDARDS. ANNOUNCER. 1979. q. Bureau of Standards, P.O. Box 9524, Dar es Salaam, Tanzania. TEL 255-51-48051. TELEX 41667 TBS TZ. Ed. N.N. Maingu. circ. 830. (back issues avail.)

620.1   TZ   ISSN 0856-2539
TANZANIA. BUREAU OF STANDARDS. DIRECTOR'S ANNUAL REPORT. 1976. a. Bureau of Standards, P.O. Box 9524, Dar es Salaam, Tanzania. TEL 255-51-48051. TELEX 416677 TBS TZ. Ed. N.N. Maingu. circ. controlled.

TERMINOLOGY; international journal of theoretical and applied issues in specialized communication. see LINGUISTICS

TEST & MEASUREMENT WORLD BUYER'S GUIDE. see ENGINEERING — Electrical Engineering

530.7 389.6   JA   ISSN 0040-8689
     CODEN: TDKKA6
TOHOKU DAIGAKU KAGAKU KEISOKU KENKYUJO HOKOKU/TOHOKU UNIVERSITY. RESEARCH INSTITUTE FOR SCIENTIFIC MEASUREMENTS. BULLETIN. (Text in Japanese; summaries in English) 1951. 3/yr. exchange basis only. Tohoku Daigaku, Kagaku Keisoku Kenkyujo - Tohoku University, Research Institute for Scientific Measurements, 1-1, Katahira 2-chome, Aoba-ku, Sendai-shi, Miyagi-ken 980, Japan. Ed. Shigenori Nawata. charts; illus. (also avail. in microfilm) **Indexed:** Chem.Abstr., INIS Atomind., INSPEC (1972-), Jap.Per.Ind., JTA.
—BLDSC (2696.130000).

389   JA
TOHOKU DAIGAKU KAGAKU KEISOKU KENKYUJO KENKYU HOKOKU/TOHOKU UNIVERSITY. RESEARCH INSTITUTE FOR SCIENTIFIC MEASUREMENTS. ANNUAL REPORT. (Text in English, Japanese) a. Tohoku Daigaku, Kagaku Keisoku Kenkyujo - Tohoku University, Research Institute for Scientific Measurements, 1-1, Katahira 2-chome, Aoba-ku, Sendai-shi, Miyagi-ken 980, Japan.

389.6   PL   ISSN 0860-7222
TA357.5.T87
TURBULENCE. (Text and summaries in English) 1989. irreg. price varies. (Politechnika Czestochowska) Wydawnictwo Politechniki Czestochowskiej, Ul. Dabrowskiego 69, 42-200 Czestochowa, Poland. TEL 48-34-250974. FAX 48-34-612385. E-mail: ppam@d.polczest.us.edu.pl. (Dist. by: Ars Polona-Ruch, Krakowskie Przedmiescie 7, Warsaw, Poland) Ed. Janusz Elsner. circ. 500 (controlled). **Document type:** academic/scholarly publication.
Description: Theoretical and experimental approach to the phenomena of turbulence.
Refereed Serial

350.821   SP   ISSN 0213-9510
U N E. (Former name of issuing body: Instituto Nacional de Racionalizacion y Normalizacion) 1978. m. 10500 ptas. (effective 1995 & 1996). Asociacion Espanola de Normalizacion y Certificacion, Fernandez de la Hoz, 52, 28010 Madrid, Spain. TEL 34-1-3104851. FAX 34-1-3104976. Ed. Victor Reig; Pub. Ana Maria Lopez. adv.; bk.rev.; illus. circ. 8,000. **Document type:** bulletin.
Formerly (until 1980): Boletin de la Normalizacion Espanola (ISSN 0210-2315); Which was formed by the merger of (1975-1977): Iranor (ISSN 0211-3813); (1973-1977): Boletin Informativo Iranor (ISSN 0211-3694); Which was formerly: I y E - Innovacion y Empresa (ISSN 0211-3783)
Description: Informs on all topics related to quality, standardization and certification.

350.821   US
UNDERWRITERS LABORATORIES. ANNUAL PRODUCT DIRECTORIES.. a. Underwriters Laboratories Inc., 333 Pfingsten Rd., Northbrook, Chicago, IL 60062. TEL 708-272-8800. FAX 708-272-8129. TELEX 6502543343.
Formerly: Underwriters Laboratories. Annual Product Directories. Semi-Annual Supplement.
Description: Lists the manufacturers who have demonstrated the ability to produce items, devices or systems that comply with UL safety requirements.

389.6   US   ISSN 0363-8464
UC263
U.S. DEPARTMENT OF DEFENSE. INDEX OF SPECIFICATIONS AND STANDARDS. (In 3 parts) 1952. bi-m. $40 for pts. 1 & 2; $60 for all 3 pts. U.S. Naval Publications and Forms Center, 5801 Tabor Ave., Philadelphia, PA 19111. TEL 215-697-2000. (Subscr. to: Supt. of Documents, Washington, DC 20402) circ. 8,200. (also avail. in microfiche)

350.821 355.6   US
U.S. DEPARTMENT OF DEFENSE. INDEX OF SPECIFICATIONS AND STANDARDS: PART 1, ALPHABETICAL LISTING. base vol. plus irreg. updates. $126 (foreign $157.50). (U.S. Department of Defense) U.S. Government Printing Office, Washington, DC 20402. (Subscr. to: Superintendent of Documents, U.S. Government Printing Office, Box 371954, Pittsburgh, PA 15250-9754. TEL 202-512-1800. FAX 202-512-2250) **Document type:** government publication.
Description: Lists all current standardization documents in order by the document, as well as all standardization documents cancelled since the last basic DODISS.

350.821 355.6   US
U.S. DEPARTMENT OF DEFENSE. INDEX OF SPECIFICATIONS AND STANDARDS: PART 2, NUMERIC LISTING. irreg. $126 (foreign $157.50). (U.S. Department of Defense) U.S. Government Printing Office, Washington, DC 20402. (Subscr. to: Superintendent of Documents, U.S. Government Printing Office, Box 371954, Pittsburgh, PA 15250-7954. TEL 202-512-1800. FAX 202-512-2250) **Document type:** government publication.
Description: Provides a numerical listing of current standardization documents cancelled since the last DODISS.

350.821 355.6   US
U.S. DEPARTMENT OF DEFENSE. INDEX OF SPECIFICATIONS AND STANDARDS: PART 3, FEDERAL SUPPLY CLASS LISTING. base vol. plus irreg. updates. $57 (foreign $71.25). (U.S. Department of Defense) U.S. Government Printing Office, Washington, DC 20402. (Subscr. to: Superintendent of Documents, U.S. Government Printing Office, Box 371954, Pittsburgh, PA 15250-7954. TEL 202-512-1800. FAX 202-512-2250) (looseleaf format) **Document type:** government publication.
Description: Lists all current standardization documents in alphabetical order within each FSC, as well as all standardization documents cancelled since the last basic DODISS.

350.821 355.6   US
U.S. DEPARTMENT OF DEFENSE. INDEX OF SPECIFICATIONS AND STANDARDS: PART 4, NUMERICAL LISTING OF CANCELLED DOCUMENTS. triennial. $126 (foreign $157.50). (U.S. Department of Defense) U.S. Government Printing Office, Washington, DC 20402. (Subscr. to: Superintendent of Documents, U.S. Government Printing Office, Box 371954, Pittsburgh, PA 15250-7954. TEL 202-512-1800. FAX 202-512-2250) Document type: government publication.
 Description: Provides a cumulative numerical listing of all standardization documents cancelled since 1964.

389.6   GW   ISSN 0342-5916
WAEGEN UND DOSIEREN. 1969. bi-m. DM.93. Verlagsgesellschaft Keppler-Kirchheim mbH, Kaiserstr. 41, 55116 Mainz, Germany. TEL 06131-96070-0. FAX 06131-9607070. Ed.Bd. adv.: B&W page DM.4130; trim 250 x 178. bk.rev.; charts; illus. circ. 7,800. Document type: trade publication.
—SWETS. CCC.
 Description: Devoted to the technology of weights, measures, and testing. Includes new developments and research results, new materials for construction, and current information, both national and international.

389.6 389   US
WEEKLY STANDARDS AND SPECIFICATIONS BULLETIN. 1964. w. $95 (includes cumulative Update). Global Engineering Documents, 1990 M St., N.W., Ste. 400, Washington, DC 20036. TEL 301-590-2300.
 Formerly: Standards and Specifications Information Bulletin (ISSN 0038-9641)

389.6   US   ISSN 0095-537X
TS410
WEIGHING & MEASUREMENT. 1914. bi-m. $30. Key Markets Publishing Co., Box 5867, Rockford, IL 61125-0867. TEL 815-636-7739. FAX 815-636-7741. Ed. David M. Mathieu. adv.; bk.rev.; charts; illus.; tr.lit. circ. 14,500. Indexed: Br.Ceram.Abstr. Document type: trade publication.
 Formerly: Scale Journal.

389.6   ZA
Z B S REVIEW. (Zambia Bureau of Standards) (Text in English) 1988. q. $15. Bureau of Standards, P.O. Box RW 50259, Lusaka, Zambia. TEL 260-1-227171. Ed. Dennis Mukukaku. adv.; bk.rev.; circ. 500 (controlled). Document type: government publication.
 Formerly: Zambian Standards Reporter.
 Description: Reports on standards activities carried out by Bureau staff.

METROLOGY AND STANDARDIZATION — Abstracting, Bibliographies, Statistics

621.3 389.6 016   UK   ISSN 0950-4818
QC39
KEY ABSTRACTS - MEASUREMENTS IN PHYSICS. 1976. m. £110 (effective 1996). INSPEC, I.E.E., Michael Faraday House, Six Hills Way, Stevenage, Herts. SG1 2AY, England. TEL 01438-313311. FAX 01438-742840. TELEX 825578 IEESTV G. E-mail: inspec@iee.org.uk. (Subscr. to: Publication Sales Dept., P.O. Box 96, Stevenage, Herts. SG1 2SD, England; U.S. addr.: INSPEC/IEEE, Box 1331, 445 Hoes Ln., Piscataway, NJ 08855-1331. TEL 908-562-5549. FAX 908-562-8737) index.
Indexed: Agri.Eng.Abstr., Excerp.Med. Document type: abstracting/indexing.
 Formerly (until 1987): Key Abstracts - Physical Measurements and Instrumentation (ISSN 0307-7969)
 Description: Covers radiation detectors and measurement, mass spectrometry, plasma diagnostics, measurements and instrumentation in mechanics, heat, optics, fluid dynamics, and the environment.

389.6   MW
MALAWI. MALAWI BUREAU OF STANDARDS. LIBRARY. ADDITIONS TO THE LIBRARY. (Text in English) 1978. m. Malawi Bureau of Standards, Library, P.O. Box 946, Blantyre, Malawi.

389.6   FR   ISSN 1146-5409
P A S C A L E 32: METROLOGIE ET APPAREILLAGE EN PHYSIQUE ET PHYSICOCHIMIE. (Printed format ceased Jan. 1995) (Text in English, French) 1984. 10/yr. Centre National de la Recherche Scientifique, Institut de l'Information Scientifique et Technique, 2 allee du Parc de Brabois, 54514 Vandoeuvre-Les-Nancy Cedex, France. TEL 83-50-46-00. FAX 83-50-46-50. adv. contact: Veronique Guinvarc'h. (also avail. in microfiche) Document type: bibliography.
●Also available online. Vendor(s): European Space Agency (File no.14), Knight-Ridder, Inc. (File no.144), Telesystemes - Questel.
Also available on CD-ROM.
 Former titles: P A S C A L Explore. E 32: Metrologie et Appareillage en Physique et Physicochimie (ISSN 0761-2044); P A S C A L Explore. Part 32: Metrologie et Appareillage en Physique et Physicochimie; Which superseded in part (1961-1984): Bulletin Signaletique. Part 130: Physique Mathematique, Optique, Acoustique, Mecanique, Chaleur (ISSN 0397-7757)

389 016   RU   ISSN 0034-2505
REFERATIVNYI ZHURNAL. METROLOGIYA I IZMERITEL'NAYA TEKHNIKA. 1963. m. $1026 (effective 1996). Vsesoyuznyi Institut Nauchno-Tekhnicheskoi Informatsii (VINITI), Baltiiskaya ul., 14, Moscow A-219, Russia. (Dist. by: Mezhdunarodnaya Kniga, Dimitrova ul. 39, 113095 Moscow, Russia) Indexed: Chem.Abstr. Document type: abstracting/indexing.

600 016   US   ISSN 0038-9633
T59.A1
STANDARDS ACTION. 1970. fortn. $100 includes A N S I Reporter. American National Standards Institute, Inc., 11 W. 42nd St., 13th Fl., New York, NY 10036. TEL 212-642-4900. FAX 212-302-1286. circ. 8,000. (also avail. in microform from UMI) —UMI.

MICROBIOLOGY

see Biology–Microbiology

MICROCOMPUTERS

see Computers–Microcomputers

MICROSCOPY

see Biology–Microscopy

MILITARY

see also Civil Defense

A A M U C FOOTLOCKER. (Association of American Military Uniforms Collectors) see HOBBIES

A C R O N Y M BOOKLET SERIES. see POLITICAL SCIENCE — International Relations

355 384.554   GW
A F N - T V GUIDE. 1965. m. DM.80($50) (American Forces Network) Miltrends Verlags GmbH, Bruchkoebeler Landstr. 39, 63452 Hanau, Germany. adv. circ. 70,000.
 Description: Provides radio and television program listings. Includes features on travel, shopping, military news, homemaking, health and beauty, sports and photography.

A G A R D BULLETIN. (Advisory Group for Aerospace Research and Development) see AERONAUTICS AND SPACE FLIGHT

A G A R D HIGHLIGHTS. see AERONAUTICS AND SPACE FLIGHT

A G A R D REPORTS. see AERONAUTICS AND SPACE FLIGHT

A G A R D TECHNICAL PROGRAMME. see AERONAUTICS AND SPACE FLIGHT

355 658   US   ISSN 0741-076X
UC263
A L A WORLDWIDE DIRECTORY AND FACT BOOK. 1982. a. $75 per no. American Logistics Association, 1133 15th St., N.W., Ste. 640, Washington, DC 20005. TEL 202-466-2520. FAX 202-296-4419. Ed. Herman Marshall. adv. circ. 10,000. (also avail. in microfiche from CIS; back issues avail.) Indexed: SRI. Document type: directory.
 Description: Military resale directory.

A M S STUDIES IN THE EMBLEM. see GENEALOGY AND HERALDRY

355   SZ
A O G MITTEILUNGEN. 4/yr. A O G, Sekretariat, Postfach 849, CH-8021 Zurich, Switzerland. TEL 01-2420230. Ed. B. Wicki.

355.155   US   ISSN 0001-2874
A V C BULLETIN. 1946. irreg. (2-4/yr.). $5. American Veterans Committee, Inc., 6309 Bannockburn Dr., Bethesda, MD 20817-5403. TEL 301-320-6490. Ed. June A. Willenz. bk.rev.; illus. circ. 15,000. Document type: newsletter.

355   PE   ISSN 0001-3811
ACADEMIA MILITAR DE CHORRILLOS. REVISTA.* 1926. q. Academia Militar de Chorrillos, Chorrillos, Peru.

355.6   US
ACQUISITION REVIEW QUARTERLY. q. $12 (foreign $15). U.S. Department of Defense, Under Secretary for Acquisition, Rm. 3E933, The Pentagon, Washington, DC 20301. TEL 703-695-2381. (Subscr. to: Superintendent of Documents, U.S. Government Printing Office, Box 371954, Pittsburgh, PA 15250-7954. TEL 202-512-1800. FAX 202-512-2250) (back issues avail.) Document type: government publication.

355 790.1   CN   ISSN 0705-0992
ADSUM. (Text in French) 1972. w. Fonds Non-Publics, Bldg. 534, BFC Valcartier, PQ G0A 1R0, Canada. TEL 418-844-5000. FAX 418-844-6055. Ed. Caroline Charest. adv.; bk.rev.; index, cum.index. circ. 5,000. (tabloid format; back issues avail.) Document type: newspaper.

358.4   UK   ISSN 0262-8791
AEROMILITARIA; Air-Britain military aviation historical journal. 1975. q. £14. Air-Britain (Historians) Ltd., 1 East St., Tonbridge, Kent TN9 1HP, England. (Subscr. to: c/o 15 Mallory Close, St. Athan, S. Glamorgan CF6 9JJ, Wales).

AEROPHILE. see HOBBIES

355   AF
AFGHAN MILITARY REVIEW. (Text in Persian or Pushto) vol.56, 1976. m. $15. Military Press, Urdoo Moojella, Kabul 23208, Afghanistan.

355   SA
U1
AFRICAN ARMED FORCES; a monthly journal devoted to defence matters. 1975. m. $25. Military Publications Pty. Ltd., P.O. Box 23022, Joubert Park 2044, Johannesburg, South Africa. TEL 011-725-2701. FAX 011-725-2703. Ed. S.J. McIntosh. adv.; bk.rev. circ. 10,000. (back issues avail.) Indexed: Abstr.Mil.Bibl., Ind.S.A.Per., PROMT.
 Formerly (until July 1994): Armed Forces (ISSN 0379-6477)

355   SA   ISSN 1022-6745
AFRICAN DEFENCE REVIEW; a working paper series. 1992. 8/yr. R.57. Institute for Defence Policy, P.O. Box 4167, Halfway House 1685, South Africa. Document type: monographic series.
 Formerly (until no.14, 1994): South African Defence Review (ISSN 1018-9335)

355 940   UK   ISSN 0306-154X
AFTER THE BATTLE. 1973. q. $26. Battle of Britain Prints International Ltd., Church House, Church St., Stratford, London E15 3JA, England. (Dist. in U.S. by: Sky Books International Inc., 48 E. 50th St., New York, NY 10022) Ed. Winston G. Ramsey.
—BLDSC (0735.620000).
 Description: Explores twentieth century British history.

MILITARY

355.31 FR ISSN 1154-3264
AGENDA DES ARMEES, TERRE, AIR, MER, GENDARMERIE. a. 82 F. per no. Editions Charles Lavauzelle, Le Prouet, B.P. 8, 87350 Panazol, France. FAX 55-31-24-20. TELEX 580 995 F.
  Formed by the 1978 merger of: Agenda de la Gendarmerie (ISSN 1154-3213); Agenda des Armees (ISSN 1154-3256); Which was formerly (until 1976): Agenda des Armees, Terre, Air (ISSN 0376-6284)

AGENT ORANGE REVIEW; for veterans who served in Vietnam. see *LAW*

358.4 FR ISSN 0002-2152
AIR ACTUALITES; le magazine de l'Armee de l'air. 1968. 10/yr. 170 F. (foreign 210 F.) (effective 1996). (Service d'Information de Recrutement et de Presse de l'Armee de l'Air) Association pour le Developpement et la Diffusion de l'Information Militaire, 6 rue Saint Charles, 75015 Paris, France. TEL 45-77-03-76. FAX 45-73-53-73. Ed. Lcl Blanchard. adv. contact: Didier Contoux. bk.rev. circ. 35,000.
  Supersedes: France. Secretariat d'Etat aux Forces Armees "Air". Bulletin d'Information.
  Description: Provides editorials, news, reviews of aircraft.

358.4 US ISSN 0044-6955
AIR COMBAT. 9/yr. $19.95. Challenge Publications, Inc., 7950 Deering Ave., Canoga Park, CA 91304. TEL 818-887-0550. FAX 818-883-1343. Ed. Michael O'Leary. **Document type:** consumer publication.

358.4 US ISSN 0740-803X
AIR DEFENSE ARTILLERY. 1969-199?; resumed 1995. bi-m. $14 (foreign $17.50). U.S. Army Air Defense School, Ft. Bliss, TX 79916. (Subscr. to: Superintendent of Documents, U.S. Government Printing Office, Box 371954, Pittsburgh, PA 15250-7954. TEL 202-512-1800. FAX 202-512-2250) bk.rev.; illus. circ. 12,000. (back issues avail.) **Indexed:** Abstr.Mil.Bibl., Air Un.Lib.Ind., DM&T, Ind.U.S.Gov.Per. **Document type:** government publication.
  Former titles (until 1983): Air Defense Magazine (ISSN 0192-964X); (until 1976): Air Defense Trends (ISSN 0091-9225)

358.4 FR ISSN 0223-0038
AIR FAN; mensuel de l'aeronautique militaire. 1978. m. 350 F. (foreign 420 F.). Edimat, 48 bd. des Batignolles, 75017 Paris, France. TEL 42-93-67-24. FAX 42-94-25-40. Ed. Olivier Cabiac. adv.; bk.rev.; charts; illus. circ. 24,000.

THE AIR FORCE CIVIL ENGINEER. see *ENGINEERING — Civil Engineering*

358.4 US ISSN 0002-2365
UG633 CODEN: AFCTB3
AIR FORCE COMPTROLLER. 1967. q. $7 (foreign $8.75). U.S. Air Force, Financial Management & Comptroller Department, The Pentagon, Washington, DC 20330-1000. TEL 703-275-3054. (Subscr. to: Superintendent of Documents, U.S. Government Printing Office, Box 371954, Pittsburgh, PA 15250-7954. TEL 202-512-1800. FAX 202-512-2250) bk.rev.; charts; illus. circ. 4,500. (also avail. in microfiche from CIS; back issues avail.; reprint service avail. from CIS) **Indexed:** Air Un.Lib.Ind., Amer.Stat.Ind. (1977-), BPIA, Bus.Ind., Ind.U.S.Gov.Per., Tr.& Indus.Ind. **Document type:** government publication.
  —BLDSC (0776.072000); UMI; UnCover.
  Description: Provides timely information to Air Force Comptroller personnel relating to accomplishing objectives, solving problems and improving operation efficiency, and communicating developments and new techniques.

358.4 US ISSN 0270-403X
UG1123
AIR FORCE JOURNAL OF LOGISTICS. 1976. q. $7.50 (foreign $9.40). U.S. Air Force, Logistics Management Agency, Maxwell A.F.B., Gunter Annex, AL 36114-3236. TEL 205-416-4087. FAX 205-596-4638. (Subscr. to: Superintendent of Documents, U.S. Government Printing Office, Box 371954, Pittsburgh, PA 15250-7954. TEL 202-512-1800. FAX 202-512-2250) Ed. Lt. Col. Bruce A. Newell. bk.rev.; circ. 9,600 (paid). (also avail. in microfiche; back issues avail.) **Indexed:** Air Un.Lib.Ind., Ind.U.S.Gov.Per., PROMT. **Document type:** government publication, academic/scholarly publication.
  —UnCover.
  Formerly: Pipeline.
  Description: Provides a forum for the presentation of issues, ideas, research, and information of concern to logisticians who plan, acquire, maintain, supply, transport, and provide supporting engineering and services for military aerospace forces.
  Refereed Serial

AIR FORCE LAW REVIEW. see *LAW — Military Law*

358.4 UK ISSN 0266-8610
AIR FORCE LIST. 1949. a. price varies. H.M.S.O., P.O. Box 276, London SW8 5DT, England. circ. 3,400.
  Document type: government publication.
  —BLDSC (0776.072800).

358.4 US ISSN 0730-6784
UG633
AIR FORCE MAGAZINE. 1942. m. $25 (foreign $50). Air Force Association, 1501 Lee Hwy., Arlington, VA 22209-1198. TEL 703-247-5800. FAX 703-247-5855. Ed. John T. Correll. adv.: B&W page $5673. bk.rev.; charts; illus.; tr.lit. circ. 172,000. (also avail. in microform from UMI) **Indexed:** Abstr.Mil.Bibl., Air Un.Lib.Ind., Amer.Bibl.Slavic. & E.Eur.Stud., Amer.Hist.& Life, DM & T, Hist.Abstr., Int.Aerosp.Abstr.
  —BLDSC (0776.073000); Ei; Faxon; SWETS; UMI; UnCover.
  Formerly: Air Force and Space Digest (ISSN 0002-2349)

358.4 US ISSN 0002-2403
AIR FORCE TIMES. (In three eds.: Domestic, European, Pacific) 1947. w. $52. Army Times Publishing Co., 6883 Commercial Dr., Springfield, VA 22159. TEL 703-750-8646. FAX 703-750-8622. Ed. Tom Breen. adv. contact: Nat Kornfeld. bk.rev.; charts; illus.; stat.; circ. 90,000 (paid). (tabloid format; also avail. in microform from UMI; reprint service avail. from UMI) **Indexed:** Air Un.Lib.Ind. **Document type:** newspaper.
  —UMI. CCC.
  Description: Serving all air force personnel and their families.

358.4 UK ISSN 0955-7091
AIR FORCES MONTHLY. 1988. m. £29($60) (foreign £33). Key Publishing Ltd., P.O. Box 100, Stamford, Lincs. PE9 1XQ, England. TEL 01780-55131. FAX 01780-57261. TELEX 265871-MONREF-G. Ed. David Oliver. adv.; bk.rev.; bibl.; illus. circ. 31,134. (back issues avail.) **Document type:** bulletin.

358.4 US ISSN 0002-2756
UG 633.A1
AIRMAN; official magazine of the U.S. Air Force. 1957. m. $19 (foreign $23.75). U.S. Air Force, Air Force News Agency, Kelly AFB, TX 78241-6105. TEL 210-925-7757. FAX 210-925-7219. (Subscr. to: Superintendent of Documents, Box 371954, Pittsburgh, PA 15250-7954. TEL 202-512-1800. FAX 202-512-2250) Ed. Jerry R. Stringer. bk.rev.; illus. circ. 900,000. (also avail. in microform from MIM,UMI; back issues avail.; reprint service avail. from UMI) **Indexed:** Air Un.Lib.Ind., Ind.U.S.Gov.Per., Mid.East: Abstr.& Ind. **Document type:** newsletter, government publication.
  —Faxon; UMI; UnCover.
  Description: Covers Air Force events, missions, operations, and human-interest stories.

AIRPOWER; the story of combat aviation. see *AERONAUTICS AND SPACE FLIGHT*

358.4 US ISSN 0897-0823
UG633
AIRPOWER JOURNAL. (Semi-annual editions in Spanish and Portuguese) 1947. q. $14 (foreign $17.50) (effective 1995). U.S. Air Force, Air University, Maxwell Air Force Base, AL 36112. TEL 205-953-5322. FAX 205-953-6739. E-mail: spencerjames%arj%cadre@chicago.afwc.af.mil. (Subscr. to: Superintendent of Documents, Box 371954, Pittsburgh, PA 15250-7954. TEL 202-512-1800. FAX 202-512-2250) Ed. Lt. Col. James W. Spencer. bk.rev.; charts; illus.; stat. circ. 20,000. (also avail. in microform from UMI; back issues avail.) **Indexed:** Abstr.Mil.Bibl., Air Un.Lib.Ind., Amer.Bibl.Slavic & E.Eur.Stud., Amer.Hist.& Life, DM& T, Eng.Ind., Hist.Abstr., Ind.U.S.Gov.Per., Mid.East: Abstr.& Ind., P.A.I.S., PROMT. **Document type:** academic/scholarly publication.
  —BLDSC (0785.090000); Faxon; SWETS; UMI; UnCover.
  Formerly (until 1987): Air University Review (ISSN 0002-2594)
  Description: Provides an open forum for the discussion of operational-level, as well as strategy and policy issues, with an emphasis on the uses of aerospace power.
  Refereed Serial

358.4 US
AIRTIDES. 1949. w. Burlington County Times, 2901 Falcon Ln., McGuire Air Force Base, Trenton, NJ 08641. TEL 609-724-4091. FAX 609-724-6999. Ed. SSgt. Mary McHale. adv. (tabloid format) **Document type:** newspaper.
  Description: News and features pertaining to Air Force members and their families, military retirees and their families, and government civilian employees.

355 YU ISSN 0350-0527
AKADEMAC. 1969. m. free. Vojna Akademija Rodova Kopnene Vojske i Intendantske Sluzbe, Veljka Lukica-Kurjaka 33, Belgrade, Serbia, Yugoslavia. Ed. Djordje Zirojevic.

355 IT
ALERE FLAMMAM; bollettino d'informazione della Scuola di Guerra. 1952. bi-m. qualified personnel only. Comando Scuola di Guerra, 00053 Civitavecchia, Italy. TEL 0766-30051. FAX 0766-500680. bk.rev.; bibl.; illus.; circ. 900 (controlled). **Document type:** bulletin.

359 US ISSN 0002-5577
ALL HANDS; magazine of the United States Navy. 1922. m. $21 (foreign $26.25) (effective 1995). (U.S. Navy) Naval Media Center, Publishing Division, Naval Sta. Anacostia, Bldg. 168, 2701 S. Capitol St., S.W., Washington, DC 20374-5080. TEL 202-433-4171. FAX 202-433-4747. (Subscr. to: Superintendent of Documents, U.S. Government Printing Office, Pittsburgh, PA 15250-7954. TEL 202-512-1706. FAX 202-512-2250) Ed. M.G. Johnston. bk.rev.; illus. circ. 87,000. (back issues avail.) **Indexed:** Abstr.Mil.Bibl., Air Un.Lib.Ind, Ind.U.S.Gov.Per. **Document type:** government publication, consumer publication.
  —UMI; UnCover.
  Description: Features general-interest articles about the U.S. Navy and its operations.

359.96 NE ISSN 0002-5674
VA530
ALLE HENS. 1947. m. fl.29.50. Ministerie van Defensie, Directie Voorlichting, Postbus 20701, 2500 ES The Hague, Netherlands. FAX 31-70-3188426. Ed. Bert van Elk. adv.; bk.rev.; charts; illus. circ. 36,000. **Indexed:** Abstr.Mil.Bibl. **Document type:** government publication.
  —SWETS.

355 SZ ISSN 0002-5925
ALLGEMEINE SCHWEIZERISCHE MILITAERZEITSCHRIFT. Short title: A S M Z. 1855. m. 65 SFr. (foreign 85 SFr.). (Schweizerische Offiziersgesellschaft) Huber und Co. AG, Promenadenstr. 16, CH-8501 Frauenfeld, Switzerland. TEL 054-271111. Ed. Charles Ott. adv.; bk.rev.; abstr.; bibl.; charts; illus.; maps; index. circ. 33,806. **Document type:** consumer publication.
  —BLDSC (0791.942000); SWETS.
  Description: Covers all aspects of the Swiss military, including training, equipment, information, international news, new publications and positions available.

MILITARY

355   SZ
ALLGEMEINEN OFFIZIERSGESELLSCHAFT. MITTEILUNGEN. q. Sihl AG, CH-8004 Zurich, Switzerland. TEL 01-2423200. circ. 5,000.

359   US   ISSN 0736-3559
V1
ALMANAC OF SEAPOWER. (Special issue of: Sea Power) a. $14.95 to non-members (hardbound $24.95) (effective 1992). Navy League of the United States, 2300 Wilson Blvd., Arlington, VA 22201-3308. TEL 703-528-1775. FAX 703-528-2333. Ed. Vincent C. Thomas, Jr.
—UMI. **CCC**.

355.155   IT
ALPIN JO, MAME! 1967. q. free. Alpino National Association (A.N.A.), Via S. Agostino 8-A, 33100 Udine, Italy. Ed. Claudio Cojutti. circ. 16,000. (tabloid format)

355   GW   ISSN 0401-5436
ALTE KAMERADEN. 1953. m. DM.64.80 (foreign DM.74.80). (Arbeitsgemeinschaft fuer Kameradenwerke und Traditionsverbaende) Verlag Harald Thomas, Ostmerheimerstr. 259, 51109 Cologne, Germany. Ed. W. Probst. circ. 16,000.

ALTOS ESTUDIOS. see *POLITICAL SCIENCE*

355   US
ALWAYS HOME; the magazine of today's USO. 1991. m. Times Mirror Magazines, Inc., Sports Marketing Group, 2 Park Ave., 5th Fl., New York, NY 10016. Ed. Dewey Blanton.

AMERICAN COUNCIL ON EDUCATION. CENTER FOR ADULT LEARNING AND EDUCATIONAL CREDENTIALS UPDATE. see *EDUCATION — Higher Education*

355   US   ISSN 0882-1038
UA23.A1
AMERICAN DEFENSE ANNUAL (YEAR). 1985. a. price varies. (Ohio State University, Mershon Center) Lexington Books, 866 Third Ave., New York, NY 10022. TEL 212-702-2102. FAX 212-605-4872. Ed. Joseph J. Kruzel.
—BLDSC (0812.736000); UnCover.
   Description: Presents essays by leading security experts who offer a wide-ranging, provocative overview of contemporary U.S. security issues.

355   US   ISSN 0883-072X
AMERICAN INTELLIGENCE JOURNAL. 1977. irreg. (2-3/yr.) $25 (foreign $55). National Military Intelligence Association, Pentagon Station, Box 46583, Washington, DC 20050-6583. TEL 301-840-6642. FAX 301-840-8502. (Editorial addr.: Box 6712, Falls Church, VA 22040. TEL 703-824-3211) Ed. Roy K. Jonkers. adv.; bk.rev.; circ. 2,500 (paid).
   Description: Contains articles of professional government/industry and academic interest in the areas of intelligence and counter-intelligence.

AMERICAN LEGION MAGAZINE. see *CLUBS*

AMERICA'S CIVIL WAR. see *HISTORY — History Of North And South America*

366   FR
AMICALES REGIMENTAIRES. 1925. q. 15 F. Federation des Amicales Regimentaires et d'Anciens Combattants, 28 bd. de Strasbourg, 75010 Paris, France.

355.115   FR   ISSN 0044-815X
AMPUTE DE GUERRE. 1932. m. 25 F. Federation des Amputes de Guerre de France, 74 bd. Haussmann, 75008 Paris, France. TEL 43-87-41-00. Ed. Maurice Desmier. adv.; bk.rev. circ. 11,500.

355   GR
AMYNA & TEKNOLOGIA. m. Velos Ltd., Alexandras Ave. 9, 11473 Athens, Greece. TEL 01-6439641. FAX 01-6461361. (Subscr. to: Moench Verlagsgesellschaft mbH, Postfach 140261, 53057 Bonn, Germany. TEL 0228-6483-0. FAX 0228-6483109) Ed. Sotiris Poulopoulos. adv.; B&W page $3500, color page $6500; trim 255 x 175; adv. contact: Ute Steuer. circ. 15,526. **Document type:** trade publication.

359 975   US
ANCHOR WATCH. 1983. q. $10. (Historic Naval Ships Association of North America) U S Naval Institute, c/o US Naval Academy Museum, 118 Maryland Ave., Annapolis, MD 21402-5035. TEL 410-293-2109. Ed. Fred H. Rainbow; Pub. James Barber. circ. 100. (looseleaf format; back issues avail.) **Document type:** trade publication.
   Description: Information on historic ships. Includes news clips, announcements, calendar of events, and member information.

320   GW   ISSN 0342-5789
ANTIMILITARISMUS INFORMATION. 1971. m. DM.40. (Gesellschaft buergerlichen Rechts) A M I Verlag G b R, Elssholzstr. 11, 10781 Berlin, Germany. TEL 030-2151035. Ed.Bd. adv.; bk.rev. circ. 3,800. **Document type:** newsletter.

355   RM
APARAREA PATRIEI. 1945. w. Ministry of National Defense, Str. Izvor 137, Bucharest, Rumania. Ed. Col. Radu Olaru. circ. 75,000.

APPROACH; the naval aviation safety review. see *AERONAUTICS AND SPACE FLIGHT*

355   GW
ARAB DEFENCE AND AEROSPACE BUSINESS. (Text in Arabic, English) bi-m. Moench Verlagsgesellschaft mbH, Postfach 140261, 53057 Bonn, Germany. TEL 0228-6483-0. FAX 0228-6483109. (Co-publisher: Al-Iktissad Wal-Aamal) Ed. Raouf Abou Zaki. adv.; B&W page $3200, color page $5405; trim 9 7/16 x 7 5/16; adv. contact: Ute Steuer. circ. 33,349. **Document type:** trade publication.

355   BE
ARES. (Text in Dutch, French) 1935. q. 250 BEF. (Union Royale Nationale des Officiers de Reserve (URNOR) - National Association of Reserve Officers (KNVRO)) F. Lepeer, Ed. & Pub., 110 Ave. de Heyn, B-1090 Brussels, Belgium. bk.rev. circ. 9,000.
Indexed: Int.Polit.Sci.Abstr.
   Formerly: Officier de Reserve (ISSN 0030-0551)

359   AG   ISSN 0066-703X
ARGENTINA. DEPARTAMENTO DE ESTUDIOS HISTORICOS NAVALES. SERIE A: CULTURA NAUTICA.* 1961. irreg. Departamento de Estudios Historicos Navales, Av. Almirante Brown 401, 1155 Buenos Aires, Argentina.

359   AG   ISSN 0066-7048
ARGENTINA. DEPARTAMENTO DE ESTUDIOS HISTORICOS NAVALES. SERIE B: HISTORIA NAVAL ARGENTINA.* 1960. irreg., no.18, 1975. price varies. Departamento de Estudios Historicos Navales, Av. Almirante Brown 401, 1155 Buenos Aires, Argentina.

359 920   AG   ISSN 0066-7056
ARGENTINA. DEPARTAMENTO DE ESTUDIOS HISTORICOS NAVALES. SERIE C: BIOGRAFIAS NAVALES ARGENTINAS.* irreg. Departamento de Estudios Historicos Navales, Av. Almirante Brown 401, 1155 Buenos Aires, Argentina.

359 980   AG
ARGENTINA. DEPARTAMENTO DE ESTUDIOS HISTORICOS NAVALES. SERIE E: DOCUMENTOS.* 1977. irreg. Departamento de Estudios Historicos Navales, Av. Almirante Brown 401, 1155 Buenos Aires, Argentina.

359 860   AG   ISSN 0066-7064
ARGENTINA. DEPARTAMENTO DE ESTUDIOS HISTORICOS NAVALES. SERIE G: CUENTOS, POEMAS Y NARRACIONES MARINERAS.* 1969. irreg. Departamento de Estudios Historicos Navales, Av. Almirante Brown 401, 1155 Buenos Aires, Argentina.

359   AG   ISSN 0066-7072
ARGENTINA. DEPARTAMENTO DE ESTUDIOS HISTORICOS NAVALES. SERIE H: ICONOGRAFIA.* irreg. Departamento de Estudios Historicos Navales, Av. Almirante Brown 401, 1155 Buenos Aires, Argentina.

ARGENTINA. ESCUELA DE DEFENSA NACIONAL. REVISTA. see *POLITICAL SCIENCE — International Relations*

ARGENTINA. SECRETARIA DE GUERRA. DIRECCION DE ESTUDIOS HISTORICOS. BOLETIN BIBLIOGRAFICO. see *HISTORY — History Of North And South America*

ARMADA INTERNATIONAL. see *AERONAUTICS AND SPACE FLIGHT*

355 949.2   NE   ISSN 0168-1672
ARMAMENTARIA. 1966. a. fl.35. Kon. Nederlands Leger- en Wapenmuseum "Generaal Hoefer", Korte Geer 1, 2611 CA Delft, Netherlands. TEL 31-15-150558. circ. 1,500. **Document type:** bulletin.
   Description: Covers Dutch military history; history of arms and uniforms.

355 799.202   SP
ARMAS. 1982. 12/yr. 6600 ptas. (Europe 9636 ptas.; elsewhere 10920 ptas.) (effective 1995). Hobby Press, S.A., C. de los Ciruelos, 4, 28700 S. Sebastian de los Reyes (Madrid), Spain. TEL 1-654-81-99. FAX 1-654-86-92. Ed. Luis Perez de Leon. adv. contact: Jose Orcasitas. circ. 35,000. **Document type:** consumer publication.
   Description: Covers guns.

ARMAS Y MUNICIONES. see *SPORTS AND GAMES*

ARMED CONFLICTS REPORT. see *POLITICAL SCIENCE*

355 320 301   US   ISSN 0095-327X
U21.5
ARMED FORCES AND SOCIETY; an interdisciplinary journal on military institutions, civil-military relations, arms control and peacekeeping, and conflict management. 1972. q. $62 to individuals (foreign $94); institutions $124 (foreign $156) (effective Aug. 1995). (Inter-University Seminar on Armed Forces & Society) Transaction Publishers, Transaction Periodicals Consortium, Department 3092, Rutgers University, New Brunswick, NJ 08903. TEL 908-445-2280. FAX 908-445-3138. Ed. Jay Stanley. adv.; bk.rev.; charts; illus.; index. circ. 2,000. (also avail. in microfilm from UMI; back issues avail.) **Indexed:** A.B.C.Pol.Sci., Abstr.Mil.Bibl., Air Un.Lib.Ind., Amer.Bibl.Slavic & E.Eur.Stud., Amer.Hist.& Life, Bk.Rev.Ind. (1991-), Chic.Per.Ind., Child.Bk.Rev.Ind. (1991-), Curr.Cont., Hist.Abstr., Int.Polit.Sci.Abstr., Mid.East: Abstr.& Ind., P.A.I.S., Peace Res.Abstr., Polit.Sci.Abstr., Psychol.Abstr., Soc.Sci.Ind., Sociol.Abstr., SSCI. **Document type:** academic/scholarly publication.
●Also available online. Vendor(s): University Microfilms International.
—BLDSC (1682.970000); Ei; Faxon; Genuine Article; SWETS; UMI; UnCover. **CCC**.
   Description: Provides an international forum for a wide range of topics, including war, revolution, recruitment and conscription policies, arms control, peacekeeping, military history, economics of defense, and strategic issues.
   Refereed Serial

355   US   ISSN 0004-2188
UC20
ARMED FORCES COMPTROLLER. 1956. q. $10 to non-members (foreign $13). American Society of Military Comptrollers, 225 Reinekers Ln., Ste. 250, Alexandria, VA 22314-2875. TEL 703-549-0360. FAX 703-549-3181. Ed. Ltg. James F. McCall. adv.; bk.rev.; charts. circ. 20,000. (also avail. in microfilm from UMI) **Indexed:** Account.Ind. (1974-), Air Un.Lib.Ind., BPIA, Bus.Ind., Manage.Abstr., Manage.Cont., Tr.& Indus.Ind. **Document type:** trade publication.
●Also available online. Vendor(s): University Microfilms International.
—BLDSC (1683.005000); UMI.

355   US   ISSN 0196-3597
U1   CODEN: AFJIE8
ARMED FORCES JOURNAL INTERNATIONAL. 1863. m. $35. Armed Forces Journal International, Inc., 2000 L St., N.W., Ste. 520, Washington, DC 20036. TEL 202-296-0450. FAX 202-296-5727. Ed. John G. Roos; Pub. Donald L. Freuhling. adv. contact: A. Wiley Loughran. bk.rev. circ. 45,000. (also avail. in microform from UMI; reprint service avail. from UMI) **Indexed:** Abstr.Mil.Bibl., Air Un.Lib.Ind., DM & T, Mid.East: Abstr.& Ind., Polit.Sci.Abstr., PROMT. **Document type:** trade publication.
—BLDSC (1683.007200); Ei; Faxon; SWETS; UMI; UnCover.
   Formerly: Armed Forces Journal (ISSN 0004-220X)
   Description: Contains defense news for career military officers, government officials, and industry executives involved in defense.

MILITARY

355   **GH**
ARMED FORCES NEWS. 1966. q. $50. General Headquarters, Directorate of Public Relations, Burma Camp, Accra, Ghana. TEL 77611. Ed. A. Hoffman. circ. 8,000. **Document type:** newspaper.
    Description: Provides military information to Ghanaian troops.

355   **UV**
ARMEE DU PEUPLE. 1982. m. Ouagadougou, Burkina Faso. Ed. Seydou Niang.
    Description: Presents armed forces and defense information.

356   **FR**   **ISSN 0004-2242**
ARMEE ET DEFENSE; revue d'informations et de liaison. 1928. bi-m. 115 F. Editions de l'Aulne, 27 rue du Dessous des Berges, 75013 Paris, France. TEL 43-47-40-16. FAX 49-28-02-87. Ed. Claude Patanchon. adv.; bk.rev.; illus. circ. 18,000.
    Formerly: Officier de Reserve.

355   **SZ**   **ISSN 0004-2269**
ARMEE-MOTOR. (Text in French and German) 1956. m. 32 SFr. Weka Verlag AG, Hermetschloostr. 77, CH-8010 Zurich, Switzerland. TEL 01-4320456. FAX 01-4329436. Ed. Col. Furrer. adv. circ. 4,300. **Document type:** bulletin.

355   **FR**   **ISSN 0338-3520**
ARMEES D'AUJOURD'HUI. 1962. 10/yr. 160 F. (foreign 220 F.) (effective 1996). (Service d'Information et de Relations Publiques des Armees) Association pour le Developpement et la Diffusion de l'Information Militaire, 6 rue Saint-Charles, 75015 Paris, France. TEL 45-77-03-76. FAX 45-79-53-73. Ed. Capitaine de Corvette Weber. adv. contact: Didier Contoux. bk.rev.; index. circ. 150,000. **Indexed:** Abstr.Mil.Bibl., Amer.Hist.& Life, Hist.Abstr.
    Supersedes: Forces Armees Francaises (ISSN 0338-3512); Armee (ISSN 0004-2234)
    Description: Provides editorials, news, reviews of defense and French forces.

355   **FR**   **ISSN 0243-6019**
ARMEMENT. 1969. 5/yr. 320 F. (foreign 360 F.) (effective 1996). Association pour le Developpement et la Diffusion de l'Information Militaire, 6 rue St. Charles, 75015 Paris, France. TEL 45-77-03-76. FAX 45-79-53-73. Ed. Ingenieur General Legrand. circ. 12,000.
    Description: News of the Delegation Generale pour l'Armement for members and the public, technical studies about the arms industry and engineering.

ARMEMUSEUM - MEDDELANDE. see *MUSEUMS AND ART GALLERIES*

356   **SW**   **ISSN 0004-2404**
ARMENYTT. 1949. 6/yr. SEK 20 (foreign SEK 40) (effective 1996). Foersvarsmakten, H K V - Info, Armenytt, Prenumeration, S-107 85 Stockholm, Sweden. TEL 46-788-85-54. FAX 46-8-788-88-66. TELEX 19633. Ed. Sven-Aake Haglund; Pub. Carol Paraniak. adv.; bk.rev.; illus. circ. 140,000. **Document type:** academic/scholarly publication, government publication.

355   **NE**   **ISSN 0922-2979**
ARMEX; defensiemagazine. 1919. m. fl.40($20) Koninklijke Nederlandse Vereniging "Ons Leger" - Royal Netherlands Army Association, Postbus 11586, 2502 AN The Hague, Netherlands. TEL 070-3186841. FAX 070-3659599. Ed. A.W. Schulte. adv.; bk.rev.; illus. circ. 10,000.
    Formerly (until Apr. 1988): Ons Leger (ISSN 0030-2724)
    Description: Discusses peace, security, arms control, military technology and history, defense policies, and current developments affecting the Netherlands Armed Forces, independent from the Ministry of Defense.

355   **US**   **ISSN 0004-2420**
UE1
ARMOR; the magazine of mobile warfare. 1888. bi-m. $16 to members; non-members $20. U.S. Army Armor Center, Attn.: ATZK-ARM 141, Ft. Knox, KY 40121. TEL 502-624-2249. FAX 502-942-6219. (Subscr. to: U.S. Armor Association, Box 607, Ft. Knox, KY 40121. TEL 502-942-8624) Ed. Maj. James D. Brewer. bk.rev.; illus.; charts; index, cum.index: 1888-1968. circ. 20,500. (also avail. in microfilm) **Indexed:** Abstr.Mil.Bibl., Air Un.Lib.Ind., Amer.Bibl.Slavic & E.Eur.Stud., DM & T, Ind.U.S.Gov.Per., Mid.East: Abstr.& Ind. **Document type:** government publication.
    —BLDSC (1683.040000); Faxon; UMI; UnCover.

ARMS CONTROL REPORTER. see *POLITICAL SCIENCE — International Relations*

355   **AT**   **ISSN 0729-5685**
ARMY; the soldiers newspaper. 1959. s-m. Aus.$20. Department of Defence, Army Newspaper Unit, P.O. Box E33, QVT, Canberra, A.C.T. 2600, Australia. TEL 61-6-2665419. FAX 61-6-2665137. Ed. W.E. Pickering. adv.: B&W page Aus.$1610, color page Aus.$2500; trim 276 x 206. bk.rev. circ. 42,000. (tabloid format) **Document type:** newspaper.
    Formerly (until 1980): Australian Army (ISSN 0729-5677)

355.31   **US**   **ISSN 0004-2455**
U1
ARMY. 1950. m. $25. Association of the U.S. Army, 2425 Wilson Blvd., Arlington, VA 22201-3385. TEL 703-841-4300; 800-336-4570. FAX 703-525-9039. E-mail: ausaarmag@ad.com. Ed. Mary Blake French. adv.: B&W page $4030, color page $4980; trim 7 x 10; adv. contact: James Burke. bk.rev.; circ. 106,675 (paid). **Indexed:** Air Un.Lib.Ind.
    —Faxon; UMI; UnCover.

358.4   **UK**   **ISSN 0307-0069**
THE ARMY AIR CORPS JOURNAL. 1959. a. £6. Headquarters Director, Army Aviation, Middle Wallop, Stockbridge, Hants. SO20 8DY, England. TEL 01980-674426. FAX 01980-674163. Ed. Maj. T.M. Deane. adv. contact: Maj. T.C. Morley. bk.rev. circ. 4,000. (back issues avail.)
    Description: Gives both serving and retired members of the Army Air Corps news about the Corps history, operational accounts, honors, awards, promotions, appointments, and other association-related matters. Includes sporting and adventurous expedition accounts

355   **UK**   **ISSN 0004-2463**
ARMY, AIR FORCE & NAVAL AIR STATISTICAL RECORD. bi-m. $675 (with Weekly Report $1400; with Weekly Profile $1200). Aviation Studies International, Sussex House, Parkside, Wimbledon, London SW19 5NB, England. TEL 0181-946-5082. **Document type:** directory, trade publication.
    Description: Compiles data on aircraft, helicopters, nuclear weapons, missiles, guns, ships, personnel, funds: Air Force, Navy, Army, Marines, Coast Guard, Customs, Police, DOT, and CRAF/airline assets for 200 territories.

358.4   **US**   **ISSN 0004-248X**
ARMY AVIATION. 1953. m. $25. Army Aviation Publications Inc., 49 Richmondville Ave., Westport, CT 06880. TEL 203-226-8184. FAX 203-222-9863. Ed. William R. Harris, Jr; Pub. Lynn Codkley. adv. contact: Peter M. Stern. circ. 16,100.

355.347   **US**
UH23
ARMY CHAPLAINCY. 1972. q. free to qualified personnel. U.S. Army Chaplain Center and School, ATSC-CMT-PAO, Ft. Monmouth, NJ 07703-5612. TEL 908-532-4534. FAX 908-532-0114. Ed. Nella Hartog. bk.rev.; circ. 6,000 (controlled). **Indexed:** Ind.U.S.Gov.Per. **Document type:** government publication.
    —UnCover.
    Formerly (until 1992): Military Chaplains' Review (ISSN 0360-9693)
    Description: Seeks to support and strengthen Army chaplains and chaplain assistants.

355.27 621.38   **US**   **ISSN 0362-5745**
UA943
ARMY COMMUNICATOR; voice of the Signal Corps. 1976. q. $9 (foreign $11.25). U.S. Army Signal Center, Ft. Gordon, GA 30905-5301. TEL 404-791-7204. (Subscr. to: Superintendent of Documents, U.S. Government Printing Office, Box 371954, Pittsburgh, PA 15250-7954. TEL 202-512-1800. FAX 202-512-2250) (Co-sponsor: Ft. Gordon Signal Towers) Ed. Richard Davis, Jr. bk.rev. circ. 10,000. (also avail. in microform from UMI; back issues avail.) **Indexed:** Abstr.Mil.Bibl., Ind.U.S.Gov.Per. **Document type:** government publication.
    —BLDSC (1683.151000); UMI; UnCover.
    Description: Promotes the professional development of Army communicators by disseminating doctrinal and technical information and presenting new ideas concerning communications and electronics.

358.4   **US**
ARMY FLIER. w. Box 1140, Enterprise, AL 36331. TEL 205-347-9533. FAX 205-347-0825. Pub. Mark J. Cullen. adv. circ. 10,000. **Document type:** government publication, newspaper.

355.31   **UK**   **ISSN 0965-9544**
ARMY LIST. (Supplement avail. (ISSN 0965-9552)) 1845. a. price varies. H.M.S.O., P.O. Box 276, London SW8 5DT, England. **Document type:** government publication.
    —BLDSC (1683.157000).

355   **US**
ARMY LOGISTICIAN; the professional bulletin of United States Army logistics. 1969. bi-m. $9.50 (foreign $11.90). U.S. Army Logistics Management College, Ft. Lee, VA 23801-6044. TEL 804-734-6400. FAX 804-734-6401. E-mail: tspeigh@almc-lee.army.mil. (Subscr. to: Superintendent of Documents, U.S. Government Printing Office, Box 371954, Pittsburgh, PA 15250-7954. TEL 202-512-1800. FAX 202-512-2250) Ed. Terry R. Speights. bk.rev.; bibl.; charts; illus. circ. 55,000. (also avail. in microform from MIM,UMI; back issues avail.) **Indexed:** Abstr.Mil.Bibl., Air Un.Lib.Ind., DM & T, Ind.U.S.Gov.Per., PROMT. **Document type:** government publication.
    —BLDSC (1683.160000); SWETS; UMI; UnCover.
    Former titles: Alog Magazine; (until 1984): Army Logistician (ISSN 0004-2528)

355   **AT**   **ISSN 1034-3695**
ARMY MAGAZINE. 1988. q. Aus.$12. (Australian Army Personnel Division) Army Newspaper Unit, NBH - Annex - 66, P.O. Box E33, QVT, ACT 2600, Australia. TEL 61-6-266-5419. FAX 61-6-266-5137. Ed. Rod Horan. adv. contact: brian Lockley. bk.rev. circ. 30,000. (back issues avail.) **Document type:** consumer publication.

355.31   **US**
ARMY MASTER DATA FILE: ARMY RETRIEVAL MICROFORM SYSTEMS AND INTERC. Short title: A M D F: A R M S and Interc. m. $1050 per no. in N. America; elsewhere $2100. (Department of the Army) U.S. National Technical Information Service, 5825 Port Royal Rd., Springfield, VA 22161. TEL 703-487-4630. (magnetic tape)
    Description: Provides commonly used supply management data required to perform logistics functions, relating them to their mission responsibilities.

610.6 610.6   **UK**
ARMY MEDICAL SERVICES MAGAZINE. 1927. 3/yr. £3.30. R A M C Historial Museum, Keogh Barracks, Ash Vale, Aldershot, Hants. GU12 5RQ, England. TEL 01252-340212. FAX 01252-340209. Ed. Capt. P.H. Starling. adv. circ. 2,500. **Document type:** government publication, newsletter.

ARMY MOTORS. see *HOBBIES*

MILITARY

355 U1   UK   ISSN 0004-2552
ARMY QUARTERLY AND DEFENCE JOURNAL. 1829. q. £49.80($98.60) (effective 1995). AQ & DJ Publications, One West St., Tavistock, Devon PL19 8DS, England. TEL 01822-613577. FAX 01822-612785. Ed. T.D. Bridge; Pub. T.D. Bridge. adv. contact: M. Lindsay-Browne. bk.rev.; charts; illus.; index. circ. 21,000. (also avail. in microform from RPI; reprint service avail.) **Indexed:** Air Un.Lib.Ind., Amer.Hist.& Life, Hist.Abstr., P.A.I.S., PROMT. **Document type:** academic/scholarly publication, trade publication.
—BLDSC (1683.180000); SWETS; UnCover.
    Description: Contains coverage of current and historical international defense subjects.

356 U393   US   ISSN 0892-8657
ARMY R D & A BULLETIN. (Research, Development and Acquisition) 1960. bi-m. $11 13.75. U.S. Department of the Army, Office of Chief, Research and Development, Washington, DC 20310-1508. TEL 202-545-6700. (Subscr. to: Superintendent of Documents, U.S. Government Printing Office, Box 371954, Pittsburgh, PA 15250-7954. TEL 202-512-1800. FAX 202-512-2250) (Published in coordination with DARCOM Information Office, Office of Chief of Engineers. Office of Surgeon General's Medical R & D Command, and Office of Deputy Chief of Staff for Research, Development and Acquisition. HQ. Dept. of the Army) circ. 42,000. (also avail. in microform from MIM,UMI; back issues avail.) **Indexed:** Ind.U.S.Gov.Per. **Document type:** government publication.
—BLDSC (1683.193300); UMI; UnCover.
Former titles: Army R D and A Magazine (ISSN 0895-111X); Army R D and A (ISSN 0162-7082); Army Research and Development (ISSN 0004-2560)
    Description: Reports on U.S. Army research, development and acquisition.

355 UA23.A1   US   ISSN 0004-2579
ARMY RESERVE MAGAZINE. 1954. 4/yr. $5.50 (foreign $6.90) (effective 1995). U.S. Army Reserve, 1815 N. Ft. Myer Dr., Rm. 203, Arlington, VA 22209-1805. TEL 703-696-6212. FAX 703-696-5300. TELEX 703-696-3962. (Subscr. to: Superintendent of Documents, U.S. Government Printing Office, Box 371954, Pittsburgh, PA 15250-7954. TEL 202-512-1800. FAX 202-512-2250) Ed. Lt. Col. James Nielsen. bk.rev.; charts; illus.; index; circ. 665,000 (controlled). **Indexed:** Air Un.Lib.Ind, Ind.U.S.Gov.Per. **Document type:** government publication.
—UMI; UnCover.
Formerly: Army Reservist.

355   US   ISSN 0004-2595
ARMY TIMES. (In three eds.: Domestic, European, Pacific) 1940. w. $52. Army Times Publishing Co., 6883 Commercial Dr., Springfield, VA 22159. TEL 800-368-5718. FAX 703-750-8612. Ed. Donna Peterson. adv.: B&W page $9100; adv. contact: Martin Stein. bk.rev.; charts; illus.; circ. 108,000 (paid). (tabloid format; also avail. in microform from UMI; reprint service avail. from UMI) **Document type:** newspaper.
—UMI. **CCC.**
    Description: Serving all army personnel and their families.

355.31 U408.3   US   ISSN 0731-3144
ARMY TRAINER. 1981. q. $9 (foreign $11.25). U.S. Department of the Army, The Pentagon, Washington, DC 20301-1155. (Subscr. to: Superintendent of Documents, U.S. Government Printing Office, Box 371954, Pittsburgh, PA 15250-7954. TEL 202-512-1800. FAX 202-512-2250) **Indexed:** Abstr.Mil.Bibl.
    Description: Provides timely information on training plans, policies, and developments and promotes an exchange of firsthand knowledge and experiences among Active and Reserve components, as well as Department of the Army civilians responsible for training.

355   IT   ISSN 0004-3745
ARTIGLIERE; voce di tutti gli artiglieri. 1935. m. L.6500. Associazione Nazionale Artiglieri d'Italia, Via Aureliana 25, 00187 Rome, Italy. TEL 06/4814046. Ed. Alberto Raimondi. adv.; bk.rev.; bibl.; charts; illus.; stat. circ. 2,000.

356   SW   ISSN 0004-3788
ARTILLERI-TIDSKRIFT. 1872. 4/yr. SEK 100 in Sweden; other Nordic countries SEK 120; elsewhere SEK 140 (effective 1996). Artilleriklubben, Drakenbergsgatan 45, S-117 41 Stockholm, Sweden. Ed. Jan Anshelm. adv.; bk.rev.; charts; illus.; index, cum.index every 4 yrs. circ. 700.

356   SZ   ISSN 0004-3796
ARTILLERIE, ARMEE & TECHNIK.* m. Verband Schweizerischer Artillerie-Vereine, Berne, Switzerland.
Formerly: Schweizer Artillerist.

355   II   ISSN 0004-3826
ARTILLERY JOURNAL. 1948. a. Rs.20 (members Rs.14). Artillery Association, Nasik Road Camp, Deolali, India. Ed. Lt.Col. A.K. Sakhuja. adv.; bk.rev. circ. 6,300.
    Description: Articles on tactical and technical doctrines, primarily with a gunner military application.

355 UA870   AT   ISSN 1037-1427
ASIA - PACIFIC DEFENCE REPORTER. 1974. bi-m. $60. Peter Isaacson Publications Pty. Ltd., 45-50 Porter St., Prahran, Vic. 3181, Australia. TEL 03-245-7777. FAX 03-245-7606. **Indexed:** Abstr.Mil.Bibl., Air Un.Lib.Ind., Aus.P.A.I.S., DM & T, PROMT.
—BLDSC (1742.260150); UnCover. **CCC.**
Formerly: Pacific Defence Reporter (ISSN 0311-385X)

355   US
ASIA - PACIFIC DEFENSE FORUM. 1976. q. free to qualified foreign military personnel. U.S. Pacific Command (USCINCPAC), Box 64013, Camp H.M. Smith, HI 96861-4013. TEL 808-477-0760. FAX 808-477-6247. Ed. Paul R. Stankiewicz. circ. 30,200. (back issues avail.) **Document type:** government publication.
    Description: International forum for military personnel of the Asian and Pacific areas.

355 UA830   MY   ISSN 0126-6403
ASIAN DEFENCE JOURNAL. (Text in English) 1971. m. $200. Syed Hussain Publications (Sdn) Bhd., 61A & B Jalan Dato, Haji Eusoff Damai Complex, Box 10836, 50726 Kuala Lumpur, Malaysia. TEL 603-442-0852. FAX 603-442-7840. TELEX ADE MA 31147. Ed. Syed Hussain B. adv.; bk.rev.; charts; illus. circ. 20,000. (back issues avail.) **Indexed:** Abstr.Mil.Bibl., Air Un.Lib.Ind., PROMT.
—BLDSC (1742.407700); Ei; Faxon; SWETS; UMI; UnCover.
    Description: Covers military, geopolitical affairs and all spheres of defence activities and industries from an Asia-Pacific perspective.

ASSEMBLY (WEST POINT). see **EDUCATION — Higher Education**

355   GU
ASSIGNMENT GUAM. 1976. a. free. Glimpses of Guam, Inc., P.O. Box 3191, Agana, Guam 96910. TEL 618-477-7606. Ed. Jonathan Needham.

ASSOCIATION FOR EDUCATORS AND COUNSELORS IN GOVERNMENT NEWSLETTER. see **EDUCATION — Higher Education**

355.15   IT   ISSN 0004-5993
ASSOCIAZIONE NAZIONALE MUTILATI E INVALIDI DI GUERRA. SEZIONE DI ROMA. NOTIZIARIO.* 1950. m. L.400. Associazione Nazionale Mutilati e Invalidi di Guerra, Sezione di Roma, Lungotevere Castello N.2, 00193 Rome, Italy.

335   AT   ISSN 1039-1738
AUSTRALIAN AND NEW ZEALAND INDUSTRY DEFENCE EQUIPMENT AND CAPABILITY CATALOGUE. 1974. a. $45. (Department of Defence Support) Peter Isaacson Publications Pty. Ltd., 45-50 Porter St., Prahran, Vic. 3181, Australia. TEL 03-245-7777. FAX 03-245-7606. adv.; illus. **Document type:** catalog.
Former titles: Australian and New Zealand Defence Equipment Catalogue; Australian Defence Equipment Catalogue.

355 900 U1   AT   ISSN 1320-2545
AUSTRALIAN DEFENCE FORCE JOURNAL; journal of Australian profession of arms. 1976. bi-m. free. Department of Defence, Board of Management, Canberra A.C.T. 2600, Australia. FAX 06-2651099. Ed. Irene Coombes. adv.: B&W page Aus.$1950, color page Aus.$2500; trim 210 x 150; adv. contact: Irene Coombes. bk.rev.; charts; illus.; index; circ. 17,500 (controlled). (back issues avail.) **Indexed:** Abstr.Mil.Bibl., DM & T, PROMT. **Document type:** government publication.
—BLDSC (1798.390000); UnCover.
Former titles (until 1991): Defence Force Journal (ISSN 0314-1039); Army Journal (ISSN 0004-251X); Australian Army Journal.

355   AT   ISSN 0312-5807
AUSTRALIAN NAVAL INSTITUTE. JOURNAL. 1975. q. Aus.$30. Australian Naval Institute, P.O. Box 80, Campbell, ACT 2601, Australia. TEL 61-6-2688454. FAX 61-6-2688440. Ed. Alan Hinge. adv.; bk.rev.; charts; illus.; stat.; cum.index: 1975-1985. circ. 800. **Indexed:** Aus.P.A.I.S. **Document type:** academic/scholarly publication.
—UnCover.

355 VA710   AT   ISSN 1035-6088
AUSTRALIA'S NAVY (YEAR). 1990. a. price varies. (Department of Defence, Chief of Naval Staff) Australian Government Publishing Service, G.P.O. Box 84, Canberra, A.C.T. 2601, Australia. TEL 61-6-295-4411. FAX 61-6-295-4455. TELEX AA62013. **Document type:** government publication.
    Description: Offers insight into a wide range of navy activities since the Gulf War.

355 388   GW
AUTO MAGAZINE. (Text in English) 1982. bi-m. Miltrends Verlags GmbH, Bruchkoebeler Landstr. 39, 63452 Hanau, Germany. Ed. Bill Munn. adv.; bk.rev. circ. 50,000. **Document type:** consumer publication.

355   US   ISSN 0888-1081
AVALON HILL GENERAL. 1964. bi-m. $18. Avalon Hill Game Co. (Subsidiary of: Monarch Avalon, Inc.), 4517 Harford Rd., Baltimore, MD 21214. TEL 301-254-5300. FAX 301-254-0991. Ed. Donald J. Hawthorne. charts; illus. circ. 15,000. (tabloid format) **Document type:** consumer publication, trade publication.
    Description: Devoted to the strategy and play of the company's line of simulation games, with emphasis on military, political and economic history.

355   CU
AVANTE. a. Ministerio de las Fuerzas Armadas Revolucionarias, Ave. del Puerto esq. a, Obrapia, Habana Vieja, Havana, Cuba.

358.4   PE   ISSN 0005-2078
AVIACION. 1936. m. Fuerza Aerea, Edificio Ministerio de Aeronautica, 28 de Julio, Campo de Marte, Lima, Peru.
    Description: Discusses Peruvian Air Force.

AVIASTRO; international aerospace & defence monthly. see **AERONAUTICS AND SPACE FLIGHT**

B G S. (Bundesgrenzschutz) see **POLITICAL SCIENCE — International Relations**

621.3   US   ISSN 1069-8175
B M D MONITOR. (Ballistic Missile Defense) 1986. fortn. $787 (foreign $802). Pasha Publications Inc., 1616 N. Ft. Myer Dr., Ste. 1000, Arlington, VA 22209-3107. TEL 703-528-1244. FAX 703-528-1253. Ed. Ann Roosevelt. **Indexed:** CAD CAM Abstr. **Document type:** newsletter.
●Also available online. Vendor(s): NewsNet (DE05).
—CCC.
Formerly (until 1993): S D I Monitor (Strategic Defense Initiative) (ISSN 0886-7607)
    Description: Follows technical, political and policy aspects of the ballistic missile defense programs.

355.115   US   ISSN 0005-3767
BADGER LEGIONNAIRE. vol.48, 1970. m. $5 to non-members. Wisconsin American Legion, 812 E. State St., Milwaukee, WI 53202. TEL 414-271-1940. Ed. Rick Barnett. adv. circ. 96,000. (tabloid format) **Document type:** newspaper.
    Description: Contains articles of interest to veterans.

MILITARY

355   IS
BAMACHANE. (Text in Hebrew) 1948. w. Defense Department, Military P.O. Box 01013, Israel. Ed. Avi Lavski. adv. circ. 70,000.

355   GW   ISSN 0930-7974
BARETT; internationales Militaermagazin. 1986. bi-m. DM.36 (foreign DM.42). Barett Verlag GmbH, Opladenerstr. 11, 40591 Duesseldorf, Germany. TEL 0211-764180. FAX 0211-764147. adv.; bk.rev. circ. 22,000. (back issues avail.) **Document type:** bulletin.

355   NE   ISSN 0005-6146
BASIS. vol.17, 1975. s-m. fl.25. Stichting Geestelijke Weerbaarheid, Zomerstraat 1, Heerlen, Netherlands. Ed. M.G. Haringman. adv.; bk.rev.; illus. circ. 4,000. **Indexed:** E.I.

355   977   US
BATTLE CALL. 1963. m. $20. Army of Tennessee, C S A - U S A, Box 91, Rosedale, IN 47874. TEL 317-548-2594. Ed. Ruby I. Walker. adv. contact: Kimberly A. Walker. bk.rev. circ. 350. **Document type:** newsletter.
     Description: Presents articles on the Civil War, including military uniform and battle information.

335   331.88   NO   ISSN 0332-9097
BEFALSBLADET. 1895. 8/yr. Norges Offisersforbund, Moellergatan 10, Oslo, Norway. TEL 47-2-40-15-74. adv.: B&W page NOK 8000, color page NOK 12000. circ. 7,400.
     Formerly (until 1930): Underofficersbladet (ISSN 0333-3272)

355.115   369.11   US   ISSN 0894-9964
BENNIES. 1989. m. $15. Vietnam Veterans of Hawaii, 1155 Ft. St. Mall, Honolulu, HI 96813. TEL 808-538-3402. (Subscr. to: Box 1301, Honolulu, HI 96807) Ed. Gabby Makuakane; Pub. Martin E. Diamond. adv.: page $1400; adv. contact: Steve Trigonis. bk.rev. circ. 22,000.

355   GW   ISSN 0171-922X
BERNARD UND GRAEFE AKTUELL.* 1967. irreg. price varies. (Arbeitskreis fuer Wehrforschung) Bernard und Graefe Verlag, Karl-Mand-Str. 2, Postfach 2060, 5400 Koblenz, Germany.
     Formed by the 1979 merger of: Wehrwissenschaftliche Berichte (ISSN 0083-7822); Wehrforschung Aktuell (ISSN 0171-9203); Beitraege zur Wehrforschung (ISSN 0067-5253)

BITAON HEYL HA-AVIR/ISRAEL AIR FORCE MAGAZINE. see *AERONAUTICS AND SPACE FLIGHT*

359.96   GW   ISSN 0936-3971
BLAUE JUNGS; Magazin der Marine. m. DM.56. A. Bernecker Verlag, Unter dem Schoeneberg 1, 34212 Melsungen, Germany. TEL 05661-731-0. FAX 05661-73189. Ed. Holger Hoffmann. adv.; bk.rev. circ. 9,800.

355   SW   ISSN 0347-299X
BOCKEN. 1938. a. SEK 75 membership (effective 1990). Haelsinge Regementes Kamratfoerening, I 14/Fo 21, P.O. Box 614, S-801 26 Gaevle, Sweden.

BOEI DAIGAKKO RIKOGAKU KENKYU HOKOKU/NATIONAL DEFENSE ACADEMY. SCIENTIFIC AND ENGINEERING REPORTS. see *ENGINEERING*

355   620   JA   ISSN 0285-0893
UA10
BOEI GIJUTSU/DEFENSE TECHNOLOGY JOURNAL. (Text in Japanese; summaries in English, Japanese) 1981. m. Boei Gijutsu Kyokai - Defense Technology Foundation, 8-10, Ebisu Nishi 1-chome, Shibuya-ku, Tokyo 150, Japan. **Document type:** academic/scholarly publication.

359   PY   ISSN 0006-646X
BOLETIN NAVAL.* 1944. bi-m. Armada Nacional, Asuncion, Paraguay.

355   GW
DER BOTE AUS DEM WEHRGESCHICHTLICHEN MUSEUM. 1977. s-a. DM.40($25) Vereinigung der Freunde des Wehrgeschichtlichen Museums Schloss Rastatt e.V., Postfach 1633, 76401 Rastatt, Germany. TEL 07222-34244. Ed. Sabina Hermes. cum.index every 15 nos. circ. 1,000. (back issues avail.) **Document type:** bulletin.

355   US
BOW HOOK. 1960. w. free. Community Press, Inc., Box 12110, Charleston, SC 29422. TEL 803-849-1778. FAX 803-849-0214. Ed. Betsy Overcamp Smith. circ. 12,500. **Document type:** newspaper.

355.058   UK
V10
BRASSEY'S DEFENCE YEARBOOK. 1890. a. $58. Brassey's (UK) Ltd., 33 John St., London WC1N 2AT, England. TEL 0171-753-7777. FAX 0171-753-7794. (Subscr. to: Turpin Distribution Services, Blackhorse Rd., Letchworth, Herts. SG1 1HN, England. TEL 01462-672555. FAX 01462-480947; Subscr. in the U.S. to: Brassey's Inc., Marketing Department, 1313 Dolly Madison Blvd., Ste. 401, McLean, VA 22102-3101. TEL 703-442-4535. FAX 703-442-9848) **Indexed:** Int.Polit.Sci.Abstr.
     Former titles: R U S I and Brassey's Defence Yearbook (Royal United Services Institute) (ISSN 0305-6155); Brassey's Annual - the Armed Forces Year-Book (ISSN 0068-0702)

BRIGADIER. see *COLLEGE AND ALUMNI*

355   UK   ISSN 0272-4782
UA647
BRITISH DEFENCE DIRECTORY. 1982. q. £180 to members; institutions £267 ($495) (effective 1996). Brassey's (UK) Ltd., 33 John St., London WC1N 2AT, England. TEL 0171-753-7777. FAX 0171-753-7794. (Subscr. to: Turpin Distribution Services, Blackhorse Rd., Letchworth, Herts. SG4 1HN, England. TEL 01462-372555. FAX 01462-483011; Dist. in the U.S. by: Brassey's Inc., Marketing Department, 1313 Dolly Madison Blvd., Ste. 401, McLean, VA 22101. TEL 703-442-4535. FAX 703-442-9848) Ed. D.C. Lycett-Gregson.
     —BLDSC (2298.762000); UMI. CCC.
     Incorporating: Defence Attache.
     Description: Lists senior service and civilian personnel in the U.K. Ministry of Defence, Royal Navy, Army, Royal Air Force, N.A.T.O. and the diplomatic corps.

DER BUECHSENMACHER - MESSER UND SCHERE. see *HOBBIES*

355   BU
BULGARSKI VOENEN KNIGOPIS. 1955. bi-m. free. (Institut po Voena Istoriia) Voenno Izdatelstvo na M O, 12, Ul. Ivan Vazov, Sofia, Bulgaria. Ed. L. Ilieva. bibl. circ. 835.

355   GW   ISSN 0007-5949
DIE BUNDESWEHR. 1956. m. DM.36. Deutscher Bundeswehr-Verband e.V, Suedstr. 123, 53175 Bonn, Germany. TEL 0228-3823212. FAX 0228-3823219. Ed. Wilfried Stolze. adv. contact: Wilhelm Koester. bk.rev.; illus.; index. circ. 205,000. (tabloid format) **Document type:** bulletin.

BUNDESWEHRVERWALTUNG; Fachzeitschrift fuer Administration. see *LAW*

355   658.8   UK   ISSN 0261-7781
BUSINESS RATIO REPORT: DEFENCE EQUIPMENT MANUFACTURERS; an industry sector analysis. 1979. a. I C C Business Ratios Ltd., Freepost, Field House, Hampton, Mddx. TW12 1BR, England. TEL 081-783-0977. FAX 081-783-1940. charts; stat. **Document type:** trade publication.
     —BLDSC (3541.610500).

C A A T NEWSLETTER. (Campaign Against Arms Trade) see *POLITICAL SCIENCE*

355   323.4   US
C C C O ACTION ALERT. 1993. m.? Central Committee for Conscientious Objectors, 1515 Cherry St., Philadelphia, PA 19102-1403. TEL 215-545-4626. FAX 215-545-4628.

355   327   CN
C F B CALGARY. 1967. bi-w. free to qualified personnel. North Hill News, 4000 19 St. N.E., Calgary, AB T2E 6P8, Canada. TEL 403-250-6633. FAX 403-291-0502. Ed. 2Lt. P.J. Lindsay. adv. contact: Mickey Dumont. (tabloid format) **Document type:** newspaper.

355   CN   ISSN 0045-8872
C F B COLD LAKE COURIER. 1967. w. Can.$20. Canadian Forces Base, Cold Lake, PO Box 3190, Medley, AB T0A 2M0, Canada. TEL 403-594-5206. FAX 403-594-2139. Ed. Debbie Lawrence. adv. contact: Laura Saueracker. bk.rev. circ. 4,000. **Document type:** newspaper.

355   CN
C F B COMOX TOTEM TIMES. (Text in English, French) 1960. fortn. Can.$20($40) (effective 1995-1996). C F B Comox Totem Times, Lazo, BC V0R 2K0, Canada. TEL 604-339-2541. FAX 604-339-5209. Ed. Norm Blondel; Pub. Col. T.B. Rogers. adv.: page Can.$300; adv. contact: Norm Blondel. bk.rev.; circ. 2,600 (controlled). (tabloid format) **Document type:** newspaper.
     Description: Provides a mix of military news, community, sports, health, history, music for serving and retired members of the local military community.

C H I DISPATCH. (Confederate Historical Institute) see *HISTORY — History Of North And South America*

C M L ARMY CHEMICAL REVIEW. see *CHEMISTRY — Analytical Chemistry*

355.309489   DK   ISSN 0902-3488
C S BLADET.* 1966. m. DKK 36. Centralforeningen for Stampersonel, Farvergade 10, 4, DK-1463 Copenhagen K, Denmark. circ. controlled. (tabloid format)
     Former titles (until 1986): Stampersonel (ISSN 0105-3000); (until 1976): Fagbladet Stampersonel (ISSN 0105-2993); (until 1973): Fagblad for Seniorsergenter of Stampersonel (ISSN 0902-1701); Supersedes (in 1971): S F O Bladet (ISSN 0036-1356)

355.27   US   ISSN 0749-4408
C 3 I NEWS. 1985. m. $195 (foreign $206) (effective 1995). Washington Defense Reports, Inc., 5112 52nd St., N.W., Washington, DC 20016. TEL 703-560-8045. Ed. Clay Wick. bk.rev. (back issues avail.)
     Description: Confidential Washington report on new research, development, and marketing opportunities in the fields of command, control, communications and intelligence.

355   629.13   US   ISSN 1071-1317
HD9744.E433
C 4 I NEWS. 1993. bi-w. $595 (foreign $630) (effective 1995). Phillips Business Information, Inc., 1201 Seven Locks Rd., Potomac, MD 20854. TEL 301-424-3338. FAX 301-309-3847. E-mail: pbi@phillips.com. Ed. Lurdes da Maia. (back issues avail.) **Document type:** newsletter.
     —CCC.

CAL - VET INSURANCE PLANS. ANNUAL REPORT. see *INSURANCE*

355.115   US
CALIFORNIA LEGIONNAIRE. 1930. m. $3. American Legion, Department of California, 117 War Memorial Bldg., San Francisco, CA 94102. TEL 415-431-2400. Ed. Norman H. Bowman. adv.; bk.rev.; tr.lit. circ. 161,200. (tabloid format; back issues avail.)

355.115   US   ISSN 1069-8477
CALIFORNIA VETERAN. 1954. m. Veterans of Foreign Wars of the United States, 7111 Governors Circle, Sacramento, CA 95823. TEL 916-424-1684. Ed. Oren D. Robinson. adv. circ. 120,500.
     Description: Provides news on legislation, benefits, rights, and other veteran-related information.

355   US   ISSN 1055-2790
CAMP CHASE GAZETTE; the voice of Civil War reenacting. 1972. 10/yr. $24. Camp Chase Publishing Company, Inc., Box 707, Marietta, OH 45750. TEL 614-373-1865. FAX 614-374-5710. adv.
     Description: Source of information for those individuals and organizations that participate in Civil War Reenacting. Each issue contains a complete national calendar of events, articles on topics of interest to Civil War Reenactors, event reports, and letters to the editor.

CAMPAIGN; journal of strategy gaming. see *HOBBIES*

MILITARY

354 CN ISSN 0383-4638
UA600
CANADA. DEPARTMENT OF NATIONAL DEFENCE. DEFENCE (YEAR). (Catalog no. D3-6-1992) (Text in English and French) 1970. a. free. Canada Communication Group, Publishing Division, Ottawa, Ont. K1A 0S9, Canada. TEL 613-951-7277. illus. circ. 25,000.

355 CN
CANADA. DEPARTMENT OF NATIONAL DEFENCE. DIRECTORATE OF HISTORY. MONOGRAPH SERIES. (Catalog D63-1-1992) 1976. irreg. price varies. Canada Communication Group, Publishing Division, Ottawa, Ont. K1A 0S9, Canada. TEL 613-951-7277. **Document type:** monographic series.
 Supersedes (in 1983): Canada. Department of National Defence. Directorate of History. Occasional Paper.

359 CN ISSN 0820-5078
CANADA'S NAVY ANNUAL. 1986. a. Can.$15. Corvus Publishing Group Ltd., 158 1224 Aviation Park N.E., Calgary, AB T2E 7E2, Canada. TEL 403-275-9457. FAX 403-275-3925. Ed. Richard Donaldson. adv. contact: Paul J. Skinner. circ. 15,000. (back issues avail.) **Document type:** trade publication.
 Description: Covers Canadian naval and military subjects of the past, present and future.

355 CN ISSN 0315-3495
UA600
CANADIAN DEFENCE QUARTERLY/REVUE CANADIENNE DE DEFENSE. (Text in English, French) 1969. bi-m. Can.$36.11 (foreign $45). Baxter Publishing Co., 310 Dupont St., Toronto, ON M5R 1V9, Canada. TEL 416-968-7252. FAX 416-968-2377. Ed. David McClung. adv. contact: Marlene Schwengers. bk.rev. circ. 10,000. (also avail. in microfiche from MML) **Indexed:** Abstr.Mil.Bibl., Air Un.Lib.Ind., Can.B.P.I., DM & T, Polit.Sci.Abstr., PROMT. **Document type:** academic/scholarly publication.
 —BLDSC (3020.450000). **CCC.**
 Description: Provides informed coverage of defense policy and strategic issues, as well as military technology, operational concepts, tactics and military history.

355 CN
CANADIAN FORCES NEWS UPDATE. (Text in English, French) 1993. m. Armed Forces Advertising Agency, 52 Chadburn Cres., Aurora, ON L4G 4V7, Canada. TEL 416-464-3246. FAX 416-727-2228. adv.: B&W page Can.$6000, color page Can.$6400. circ. 105,000. (tabloid format) **Document type:** newspaper.

358 CN ISSN 0068-8843
CANADIAN GUNNER. 1965. a. Can.$15. (Royal Regiment of Canadian Artillery) Leech Printing Ltd., 18th and Park, Brandon, MB R7A 5B8, Canada. TEL 204-728-3037. FAX 204-727-3338. (back issues avail.)

355 CN ISSN 1195-8472
CANADIAN MILITARY HISTORY. 1992. s-a. Can.$15 (foreign $19). Wilfrid Laurier University, Center for Military, Strategic and Disarmament Studies, Waterloo, ON N2L 3C5, Canada. TEL 519-884-1970. FAX 519-746-7908. E-mail: mbechtho@mach1.wlu.ca. Ed. Terry Copp. adv. contact: Michael Bechthold. **Indexed:** Amer.Hist.& Life (1993-), Hist.Abstr. (1993-). **Document type:** academic/scholarly publication.
 Description: Explores all aspects of Canada's military history.

359 CN ISSN 0008-4972
CANADIAN SAILOR. (Text in English, French) 1950. m. Can.$15. Seafarers International Union of Canada, 1333 rue St-Jacques, Montreal, Que. H3C 4K2, Canada. FAX 514-931-3667. Ed. Andrew Boyle. circ. 5,000 (controlled).

355 CN ISSN 0701-0427
CANADIAN SOCIETY OF MILITARY MEDALS AND INSIGNIA. JOURNAL. 1965. q. Can.$15 (typically set in Jan.). Canadian Society of Military Medals and Insignia, 34 Blue Spruce Cres., Winnipeg, MB R2M 4C2, Canada. TEL 204-255-8537. (Subscr. to: 1531 Bayview Ave., Box 43536, Toronto, ON M4G 4G8, Canada) Ed. Ian C. Steingaszner. adv. contact: Geoff Todd. bk.rev.; index. circ. 700. **Document type:** academic/scholarly publication, monographic series.
 Description: Aims to advance the study of military orders, decorations, medals and related insignia along educational and historical lines.

355 371.42 US
CAREERS UNLIMITED. 1990. a. Target Marketing, Inc., 5 Victory Lane, Ste. 101, Liberty, MO 64068. TEL 816-781-7557. FAX 816-792-3892. adv.: B&W page $14081, color page $15953; trim 7 7/8 x 10 3/4. circ. 200,000.

CASS SERIES ON THE SOVIET STUDY OF WAR. see HISTORY — History Of Europe

355 387 US
CENTER FOR NAVAL ANALYSES. BIENNIAL REPORT. biennial. Center for Naval Analyses, 4401 Ford Ave., Box 16268, Alexandria, VA 22302-0268.

CENTRAL EURASIA SERIAL REPORTS: FOREIGN MILITARY REVIEW. see POLITICAL SCIENCE — International Relations

CENTRAL INTELLIGENCE AGENCY. MONOGRAPHS. see POLITICAL SCIENCE

CENTRAL INTELLIGENCE AGENCY. MONOGRAPHS. ALL COMMUNIST COUNTRIES REPORTS. see POLITICAL SCIENCE

CENTRAL INTELLIGENCE AGENCY. MONOGRAPHS. ALL COUNTRIES REPORTS. see POLITICAL SCIENCE

CENTRAL INTELLIGENCE AGENCY. MONOGRAPHS. ALL INTERNATIONAL COUNTRIES REPORTS. see POLITICAL SCIENCE

CENTRAL INTELLIGENCE AGENCY. MONOGRAPHS. CHINA REPORTS. see POLITICAL SCIENCE

CENTRAL INTELLIGENCE AGENCY. MONOGRAPHS. COMMONWEALTH OF INDEPENDENT STATES REPORT. see POLITICAL SCIENCE

CENTRAL INTELLIGENCE AGENCY. MONOGRAPHS. MAPS ONLY. see POLITICAL SCIENCE

359 AG ISSN 0009-0123
CENTRO NAVAL. BOLETIN. (Text in Spanish; abstracts in English, Spanish) 1882. q. $50 (effective 1995). Centro Naval Argentina, Florida 826, 1St, 1005 Buenos Aires, Argentina. TEL 54-1-311-0041. FAX 54-1-322-5791. Dir. Rodolfo Remotti. adv.; bk.rev.; bibl.; index. circ. 5,000. (also avail. in microform) **Indexed:** Abstr.Mil.Bibl., INIS Atomind. **Document type:** bulletin.

355 II ISSN 0069-2654
CHANAKYA DEFENCE ANNUAL. (Text in English) 1969. a. $10. Chanakya Publishing House, 3 Thornhill Rd., Allahabad 1, India. Ed. Ravi Kaul. adv.; bk.rev. circ. 5,200. (back issues avail.)

CHINA REPORT: POLITICAL, SOCIOLOGICAL, AND MILITARY AFFAIRS. see POLITICAL SCIENCE

CHINA'S MILITARY: P L A IN (YEAR). (Chinese Council of Advanced Policy Studies) see HISTORY — History Of Asia

CIVIL AIR PATROL NEWS. see AERONAUTICS AND SPACE FLIGHT

355 028.1 II
CIVIL AND MILITARY REVIEW. m. Rs.10. Deep & Deep Publications, D-1-24, Rajouri Garden, New Delhi 110 027, India. TEL 5435369. Ed. G.S. Bhatia.

355 US ISSN 0897-6015
E461
CIVIL WAR. 1983. bi-m. $19.97. (Civil War Society) Outlook Inc., 24 N. Buckmarsh St., Box 770, Berryville, VA 22611-0770. TEL 703-955-1176. FAX 703-955-1297. Ed. William Miller; Pub. Christopher M. Curran. adv. contact: Vincent Kiczales. bk.rev. circ. 60,000. (back issues avail.) **Document type:** consumer publication.
 Description: Covers the events, personalities and lessons of the American Civil War; features news about the society.

CIVIL WAR CHRONICLES. see HISTORY — History Of North And South America

CIVIL WAR COLLECTORS' DEALER DIRECTORY. see ANTIQUES

355 US
THE CIVIL WAR LADY; women studies, living history, historical information, research, clothing. 1991. bi-m. $20 (foreign $30). 622 Third Ave., S.W., Dept. I, Pipestone, MN 56164. TEL 507-825-3182. Ed. Joy Melcher. adv.; bk.rev. **Document type:** consumer publication.

CIVILIAN-BASED DEFENSE. see POLITICAL SCIENCE — International Relations

CIVILIAN CONGRESS; includes a directory of persons holding executive branch-military office in Congress contrary to constitutional prohibition (Art.1, Sec.6, Cl.2) of concurrent office-holding. see LAW

355 UK
CLASSIC ARMS AND MILITARIA. bi-m. £36 (foreign £43). Peterson Publications Ltd., Peterson House, Northbank, Berryhill Industrial Estate, Droitwich, Worcs. WR9 9BL, England. TEL 0905-795564. FAX 0905-795905. **Document type:** consumer publication.

355 BL ISSN 0101-6547
CLUBE MILITAR. REVISTA. 1926. 6/yr. free. Clube Militar, Av. Rio Branco 251 9, CEP 20040, Rio de Janeiro, RJ, Brazil. TEL (021) 220-9076. TELEX (21) 38 848 TPPG. Ed. Luiz Paulo Macedo Carvalho. adv.; bk.rev. circ. 40,000.
 Description: Covers the history, economics, politics, and strategy of soldiering.

359 BL ISSN 0102-0382
CLUBE NAVAL REVISTA. 1888. 4/yr. free to qualified personnel. Clube Naval, Departamento Cultural, Av. Rio Branco, 180, 5o andar, 20040 Rio de Janeiro RJ, Brazil. TEL 021-282-1273 ext. 225. FAX 021-220-8681. adv.; bk.rev. circ. 9,700.
 Supersedes (in 1975): Mar (ISSN 0025-2727); Which was formerly (until 1966): Clube Naval. Boletim, Proceedings.

COLLEGE ALUMNI AND MILITARY PUBLICATIONS. see COLLEGE AND ALUMNI

355 CK ISSN 0010-1389
COLOMBIA. MINISTERIO DE DEFENSA. BOLETIN.* 1926. bi-m. Ministerio de Defensa, Bogota D.E., Colombia.

355 US
COLORADO LEGIONNAIRE. 1967. m. $1 to non-members. American Legion, Department of Colorado, 3003 Tejon, Denver, CO 80211. TEL 303-477-1655. Ed. E. Dean Hunter. adv. circ. 27,000. (tabloid format)

355 FR ISSN 0010-1834
COLS BLEUS. 1945. w. 415 F. (foreign 540 F.) (effective 1996). (Service d'Information et des Relations Publiques de la Marine) Association pour le Developpement et la Diffusion de l'Information Militaire, 6 rue Saint Charles, 75015 Paris, France. TEL 45-77-03-76. FAX 45-79-53-73. Ed. C.V. de Drezigue. adv. contact: Didier Contoux. bk.rev.; play rev.; film rev.; charts; illus.; stat. circ. 24,000. (tabloid format)
 —SWETS.
 Description: Provides news of the French navy.

668 UK ISSN 0955-9841
COMBAT & SURVIVAL MAGAZINE. m. £21($45) 45. M A I Publications, Revenue Chambers, St. Peter's St., Huddersfield, W. Yorks HD1 1EL, England. TEL 01484-435011. FAX 01484-422177. Ed. Tim Ripley. adv.: B&W page £275, color page £550; trim 297 x 210; adv. contact: Moira Spencer. circ. 28,500. **Document type:** consumer publication.

MILITARY

358.4 US ISSN 0010-213X
UG633
COMBAT CREW. 1950. m. $30 (foreign $37.50). U.S. Air Force Strategic Air Command, c/o Superintendent of Documents, Washington, DC 20402-9341. TEL 202-512-1710. FAX 202-512-1656. (Subscr. to: Superintendent of Documents, U.S Governement Printing Office, Box 371854, Pittsburgh, PA 15250-7954. TEL 202-512-1800. FAX 202-512-2250) circ. controlled. **Indexed:** Air Un.Lib.Ind., DM & T, PROMT. **Document type:** government publication.
Supersedes: Professional Pilot.
Description: Publishes articles for the purpose of promoting safety.

COMBAT EDGE. see *AERONAUTICS AND SPACE FLIGHT*

355 CU
COMBATIENTE. w. Ministerio de las Fuerzas Armadas Revolucionarias, Hermanos Villasana No. 70, Santiago de Cuba, Cuba.

355 UK
COMMAND. 1992. q. £25($50) Diplomatist Associates Ltd., 58 Theolbald's Rd., London WC1X 8SF, England. TEL 0171-405-4903. FAX 0171-831-0667. **Document type:** trade publication.
Description: Contains articles for officers and senior noncommissioned officers in the U.K. armed forces throughout the world.

355 US ISSN 1059-5651
COMMAND MAGAZINE; military history, strategy & analysis. 1989. bi-m. $25.95 (foreign $43.95). X T R Corp., 3547-D South Higuera, San Luis Obispo, CA 93401. TEL 805-546-9596; 800-488-2249. FAX 805-546-0570. (Subscr. to: Box 4017, San Luis Obispo, CA 93403) Ed. Ty Bomba. adv. contact: Chris Perello.

355 CU
CON LA GUARDIA EN ALTO. 1961. m. Ministerio de las Fuerzas Armadas Revolucionarias, Ave. Salvador Allende No. 601, La Habana 3, Havana, Cuba. TEL 7-79-4443. Dir. Omelia Guerra Perez. circ. 60,000.
Description: For members of the Committees for the Defense of the Revolution.

CONCISE; aerospace news from the commonwealth of independent states. see *AERONAUTICS AND SPACE FLIGHT*

CONFIDENCE BUILDING MATTERS. see *POLITICAL SCIENCE — International Relations*

909 US ISSN 0883-6884
CONTRIBUTIONS IN MILITARY STUDIES. 1969. irreg., no.128, 1992. price varies. Greenwood Press, Inc. (Subsidiary of: Greenwood Publishing Group Inc.), 88 Post Rd. W., Box 5007, Westport, CT 06881-5007. TEL 203-226-3571. FAX 203-222-1502. Eds. Thomas E. Griess, Jay Luvass.
—BLDSC (3460.805000).
Formerly: Contributions in Military History (ISSN 0084-9251)

355 IE ISSN 0010-9460
AN COSANTOIR; Irish defence forces magazine. 1940. 10/yr. £10 (foreign £26). Defence Forces, Defence Forces Headquarters, Parkgate, Dublin 8, Ireland. TEL 01-8379911. FAX 01-6779018. Ed. Ray Slattery. adv.: B&W page I£700, color page I£850; trim 255 x 175; adv. contact: Tom O'Callaghan. bk.rev.; illus.; index. circ. 8,000. (also avail. in microform from UMI; back issues avail., reprint service avail. from UMI) **Document type:** newsletter. —BLDSC (3477.169000).
Description: For troops; chronicles the Irish Defence Forces involvement with United Nations Peacekeeping Missions.

614.7 531.64 US
COUNCIL FOR A LIVABLE WORLD. NEWSLETTER. 12/yr. Council for a Livable World, 110 Maryland Ave., N.E., Washington, DC 20002. TEL 202-543-4100. **Document type:** newsletter.

COUNCIL ON AMERICA'S MILITARY PAST. PERIODICAL. see *HISTORY — History Of North And South America*

327 US ISSN 1076-8645
COVERT INTELLIGENCE LETTER. 1974. bi-m. $14 for 12 nos. to individuals (foreign $18); institutions $20. Horizone, Box 67, St. Charles, MO 63302. TEL 314-731-0993. Ed. W. Waltzer. bk.rev. circ. 300. **Document type:** newsletter.

358.4 UK
CROSS & COCKADE INTERNATIONAL. 1970. q. £17($30) (effective 1995). First World War Aviation Historical Society, Cragg Cottage, The Cragg, Bramham, Wetherby, W. Yorks. LS23 6QB, England. Ed. Paul Stuart Leaman. adv.; bk.rev. circ. 1,400. (back issues avail.)

355 CI ISSN 0011-4200
CUVAR JADRANA. 1947. s-m. Savezniсka Obala 18, Split, Croatia. Ed. Dusan Vesic.

355 IS
CYCLONE; digest of military literature. (Supplement to: Maarachot) (Text in Hebrew) 1939. q. P.O. Box 7026, Tel Aviv 61070, Israel. TEL 972-3-5694343. (Subscr. to: 29 El' azar St., Tel Aviv, Israel) Eds. Rachel Rojansky, Eviathar Ben-Zedeff. (back issues avail.) **Indexed:** Ind.Heb.Per.

355.115 US ISSN 0011-474X
D A V MAGAZINE. 1960. m. $4 to non-members. Disabled American Veterans, 807 Maine Ave., S.W., Washington, DC 20024. TEL 202-554-3501. FAX 202-554-3581. Ed. David Autry. circ. 1,300,000. (also avail. in audio cassette)
Description: Covers issues affecting disabled veterans and their families.

D C A A CONTRACT AUDIT MANUAL. (U.S. Defense Contract Audit Agency) see *BUSINESS AND ECONOMICS — Public Finance, Taxation*

355 GW
D I Z SCHRIFTEN. 1989. 2/yr. DM.22. (Dokumentations und Informations Zentrum Emslandlager) Edition Temmen, Hohenlohestr. 21, 28209 Bremen, Germany. TEL 0421-344280. FAX 0421-348094. Ed. Horst Temmen. **Document type:** academic/scholarly publication.

363.35 629.13 US
D M S MARKET INTELLIGENCE REPORTS: AEROSPACE COMPANIES. (Defense Market Services) m. updated suppl. $1200. Forecast International Inc. - D M S, 22 Commerce Rd., Newtown, CT 06470. TEL 203-426-0800. FAX 203-426-1964. TELEX 467615. (looseleaf format; back issues avail.)
Description: Presents studies of forecast sales volume by division for major defense programs, including merger, acquisition, and divestiture news, and provides data on aerospace and defense teaming, competition, and joint ventures. More than 100 top U.S. aerospace defense contractors are analyzed.

355 US
D M S MARKET INTELLIGENCE REPORTS: "AN" EQUIPMENT. (Defense Market Services) m. updated suppl. $1200. Forecast International Inc. - D M S, 22 Commerce Rd., Newtown, CT 06470. TEL 203-426-0800. FAX 203-426-1964. TELEX 467615. (looseleaf format; back issues avail.)
Description: Identifies 5,500 AN system with descriptions, applications, contractors, contract values, and major components. More than 260 major AN equipment programs procured by the Air Force, Navy, Army, and defense agencies are covered.

355 629.13 US
D M S MARKET INTELLIGENCE REPORTS: ANTI-SUBMARINE WARFARE. m. updated suppl. $1200. Forecast International Inc. - D M S, 22 Commerce Rd., Newtown, CT 06470. TEL 203-426-0800. FAX 203-426-1964. TELEX 467615. (looseleaf format; back issues avail.)
Description: Presents a guide to more than 130 western ASW programs detailing status and outlook, development, funding and contract history, and program analysis. It includes information on sonobuoys, torpedoes and ASW missile-rocket systems, submarine and helicopter-borne sonars.

355 629.13 363.35 US
D M S MARKET INTELLIGENCE REPORTS: C 3 I. (Command, Control, Communications & Intelligence) m. updated suppl. $1200. Forecast International Inc. - D M S, 22 Commerce Rd., Newtown, CT 06470. TEL 203-426-0800. FAX 203-426-1964. TELEX 467615. (looseleaf format; back issues avail.)
Description: Presents an analysis of 150 C3I projects worldwide, in five mission areas: Strategic, Theater and Tactical, Special Warfare, Intelligence and Information, and Communications. Also contained are marked overviews of RDT & E and procurement budget trends.

D M S MARKET INTELLIGENCE REPORTS: CIVIL AIRCRAFT. see *AERONAUTICS AND SPACE FLIGHT*

629.13 355 363.35 US
D M S MARKET INTELLIGENCE REPORTS: DEFENSE MARKET. (Defense Market Services) m. updated suppl. $1200. Forecast International Inc. - D M S, 22 Commerce Rd., Newtown, CT 06470. TEL 203-426-0800. FAX 203-426-1964. TELEX 467615. (looseleaf format)
Description: Current examination of the U.S. congressional review of RDT & E and Procurement portions of the Department of Defense budget.

629.13 355 US
D M S MARKET INTELLIGENCE REPORTS: ELECTRONIC SYSTEMS. m. updated suppl. $1200. Forecast International Inc. - D M S, 22 Commerce Rd., Newtown, CT 06470. TEL 203-426-0800. FAX 203-426-1964. TELEX 467615. (looseleaf format; back issues avail.)
Description: Reviews of the major U.S. electronic systems developed and procured by the Army, Navy, Air Force, defense agencies, and the FAA. Emphasis is placed on multifaceted electronics that can incorporate C3I, EW, radar, and other technologies into a comprehensive program.

355 US
D M S MARKET INTELLIGENCE REPORTS: ELECTRONIC WARFARE. m. updated suppl. $1200. Forecast International Inc. - D M S, 22 Commerce Rd., Newtown, CT 06470. TEL 203-426-0800. FAX 203-426-1964. TELEX 467615. (looseleaf format; back issues avail.)
Description: Covers research and development, procurement, and major production efforts. Over 125 EW programs (funded by the U.S. Department of Defense) are examined in full detail, according to sea-based, and airborne systems.

355 US
D M S MARKET INTELLIGENCE REPORTS: LATIN AMERICA & AUSTRALASIA. m. updated suppl. $1200. Forecast International Inc. - D M S, 22 Commerce Rd., Newtown, CT 06470. TEL 203-426-0800. FAX 203-426-1964. TELEX 467615. (looseleaf format)
Description: Analysis of the military requirements and market opportunities in the South American and Australasian regions. Details of each country's military equipment inventories are discussed.

355 US
D M S MARKET INTELLIGENCE REPORTS: MIDDLE EAST - AFRICA. m. updated suppl. $1200. Forecast International Inc. - D M S, 22 Commerce Rd., Newtown, CT 06470. TEL 203-426-0800. FAX 203-426-1964. TELEX 467615. (looseleaf format)
Description: Details the region's military budget, military posture, manufacturing capability, and future requirements. Detailed inventories of each country's aircraft, warships, missiles, electronics, ordnance, and vehicles are supplied.

355 629.13 US
D M S MARKET INTELLIGENCE REPORTS: MILITARY AIRCRAFT. m. updated suppl. $1200. Forecast International Inc. - D M S, 22 Commerce Rd., Newtown, CT 06470. TEL 203-426-0800. FAX 203-426-1964. TELEX 467615. (looseleaf format)
Description: Over 100 military aircraft programs are covered, from concept through retirement, excluding Warsaw Pact nations. Contains information on performance, historical data, milestones and budget for U.S. platforms, price range, procurement, and budget forecast.

MILITARY

255   US
D M S MARKET INTELLIGENCE REPORTS: MILITARY VEHICLES. m. updated suppl. $1200. Forecast International Inc. - D M S, 22 Commerce Rd., Newtown, CT 06470. TEL 203-426-0800. FAX 203-426-1964. TELEX 467615. (looseleaf format; back issues avail.)
    Description: Over 150 U.S. and international military vehicle programs are examined, covering tanks, self-propelled tactical vehicles, trucks, and APCs.

355 629.13   US
D M S MARKET INTELLIGENCE REPORTS: MISSILES. m. updated suppl. $1200. Forecast International Inc. - D M S, 22 Commerce Rd., Newtown, CT 06470. TEL 203-426-0800. FAX 203-426-1964. TELEX 467615. (looseleaf format; back issues avail.)
    Description: Covers the development and manufacture of tactical and strategic missiles worldwide. Includes an examination of the characteristics, background, funding, current status, and contracting activity of more than 100 U.S. and international missile programs.

355 629.13   US
D M S MARKET INTELLIGENCE REPORTS: NATO & EUROPE. m. updated suppl. $1200. Forecast International Inc. - D M S, 22 Commerce Rd., Newtown, CT 06470. TEL 203-426-0800. FAX 203-426-1964. TELEX 467615. (looseleaf format; back issues avail.)
    Description: Country-by-country examination of the military capabilities, equipment requirements, and current inventories for 15 NATO and 6 other European countries. Discusses manufacturing capabilities, military budgets, recent transactions, and future requirements.

355   US
D M S MARKET INTELLIGENCE REPORTS: ORDNANCE. m. updated suppl. $1200. Forecast International Inc. - D M S, 22 Commerce Rd., Newtown, CT 06470. TEL 203-426-0800. FAX 203-426-1964. TELEX 467615. (looseleaf format; back issues avail.)
    Description: Examines U.S. and European ordnance programs, provides information on project history, funding, mission requirements, modification programs, development and replacement plans. Covers air defense guns, mine neutralization, tank guns, howitzers, bombs, mortars, light and anti-tank weapons, and ammunition.

355 629.13   US
D M S MARKET INTELLIGENCE REPORTS: RADAR. m. updated suppl. $1200. Forecast International Inc. - D M S, 22 Commerce Rd., Newtown, CT 06470. TEL 203-426-0800. FAX 203-426-1964. TELEX 467615. (looseleaf format; back issues avail.)
    Description: Analysis of sea-based, airborne, land-based, and space-based radar systems in the U.S., NATO alliance, and other major western military powers. Details over 160 radar programs in R&D, modification, and procurement.

355 629.13   US
D M S MARKET INTELLIGENCE REPORTS: SPACE SYSTEMS. m. updated suppl. $1200. Forecast International Inc. - D M S, 22 Commerce Rd., Newtown, CT 06470. TEL 203-426-0800. FAX 203-426-1964. TELEX 467615. (looseleaf format)
    Description: Details business opportunities associated with major spacecraft and satellite programs worldwide. Every major R&D, modification, and procurement effort is evaluated, with information on missions, manufacturers, price range, timetable, funding recent activity, and characteristics.

355   US
D M S MARKET INTELLIGENCE REPORTS: WARSHIPS. m. updated suppl. $1200. Forecast International Inc. - D M S, 22 Commerce Rd., Newtown, CT 06470. TEL 203-426-0800. FAX 203-426-1964. TELEX 467615. (looseleaf format; back issues avail.)
    Description: Guide to warships, weapons, and subsystems worldwide, including aircraft carriers, frigates, nuclear and conventional attack submarines, naval radar, and naval EW systems. Analyzes major warship development and overhaul.

355   US   ISSN 1042-1041
D M S - PRECISION GUIDED MUNITIONS MARKET STUDY. 1986. a. $1495. Forecast International Inc. - D M S, 22 Commerce Rd., Newtown, CT 06470. TEL 203-426-0800. FAX 203-426-1964. TELEX 467615.
    Formerly (until 1989): Precision Guided Munitions (ISSN 1040-922X)
    Description: Presents comprehensive study of more than 125 U.S. and international PGM programs, covering a broad range of new anti-armor weapons such as short-range, direct-fire systems and indirect fire PGMs.

355   DK   ISSN 0011-6203
DANSK ARTILLERI-TIDSSKRIFT. 1914. 6/yr. DKK 170. Artilleriofficersforeningen - Artillery Officers Association, Postbox 182, DK-6800 Varde, Denmark. Ed. Lt.Col. K.D. Yttesen. adv.; bk.rev.; abstr.; charts; illus.; index. circ. 700.

355   UK
DAVENPORT LINK. bi-m. Media Services, Devonport Royal Dockyard, Bldg. S104, Plymouth PL1 4SG, England. TEL 0752-605665. FAX 0752-552807. TELEX 45228-DEVDYD-G. Ed. H. Purser. circ. 9,000.

355   US
DAWK. 1959. a. $25. American Model Soldier Society, 1390 El Camino, San Carlos, CA 94070. TEL 415-591-8289. FAX 415-592-1203. bk.rev.

355 338   US   ISSN 1024-2694
HC79.D4
DEFENCE AND PEACE ECONOMICS. 1989. 4/yr. (in 1 vol.). 91 ECU (effective 1996). Harwood Academic Publishers, c/o International Publishers Distributor, 820 Town Center Dr., Langhorne, PA 19047. TEL 215-750-2642; 800-545-8398. FAX 215-750-6343. (Subscr. to: International Publishers Distributor, PO Box 90, Reading, Berkshire, RG1 8JL, England. TEL 44-1733-456-8316. FAX 44-173-456-8316) Ed. Keith Hartley. (also avail. in microform) **Document type:** academic/scholarly publication.
    —Faxon; UnCover. **CCC.**
    Formerly (until 1994): Defence Economics (ISSN 1043-0717)

355   SI   ISSN 1011-2200
UA830
DEFENCE ASIA - PACIFIC. Key Title: Mao yu Dun. (Text in Chinese and English) 1985. m. S.100($50) (foreign $80). Darti Publications, c/o World Journal Bookstore, 141-07 20 Ave., Whitestone, NY 11357. TEL 779-1702. FAX 779-1703. (US addr.: Gemini Consultants, Box 6186, Los Osos, CA 93412. TEL 212-226-5131) Ed. D. Gan. adv.; bk.rev.; charts; illus.; index. circ. 22,500. (back issues avail.)
    Description: Dedicated to international defense news and issues: military sales and aid, weapon systems, technology.

623   UK   ISSN 0957-9532
DEFENCE DOCUMENTS MICROFILE. Key Title: Defense Documents Microfilm Index. Short title: DEFDOCS Microfile. q. Technical Indexes Ltd., Willoughby Rd., Bracknell, Berks. RG12 8DW, England. TEL 01344-426311. FAX 01344-424971. **Document type:** abstracting/indexing.

DEFENCE HELICOPTER. see **AERONAUTICS AND SPACE FLIGHT**

DEFENCE INDUSTRY DIGEST. see **BUSINESS AND ECONOMICS**

335   PK   ISSN 0257-2141
DEFENCE JOURNAL. (Text in English) 1975. m. $30 in Asia, Africa, Europe; N. America $40; Australia and S. America $45). 16-B 7th Central St., Defence Housing Society, Karachi 75500, Pakistan. TEL 21-541911. FAX 21-571710. TELEX 23625 EMMAY PK. Ed. A.R. Siddiqi. adv.; bk.rev.; bibl. circ. 10,000. **Indexed:** Abstr.Mil.Bibl.

355   II
DEFENCE MANAGEMENT. (Text in English) 1974. s-a. Rs.42. College of Defence Management, Bolarum P.O., Secunderabad 500010, India. TEL 862251. Ed. R. Prabhakar. bk.rev.; bibl.; charts. circ. 800.
    Formerly: Defence Manager.

356   PK
DEFENCE REVIEW. (Text in English) 1989. 2/yr. $8. Inspector General Training & Evaluation Branch, Training Publications & Information Directorate, General Staff Branch, General Headquarters, Rawalpindi, Pakistan. TELEX 32854 GHQ PK. Ed. Syed Ishfaq Ali. circ. 3,500.

355   II   ISSN 0011-748X
U395.I5   **CODEN: DSJOAA**
DEFENCE SCIENCE JOURNAL. (Text in English) 1949. q. Rs.50 to individuals (foreign $24); institutions Rs.100 (foreign $40). (Ministry of Defence, Defence Research & Development Organization) Defence Scientific Information & Documentation Centre (DESIDOC), Metcalfe House, New Delhi 110 054, India. TEL 011-239975. FAX 011-2919151. E-mail: pub@desidoc.ernet.in. Ed. S.S. Murthy. charts; illus.; index. circ. 500. **Indexed:** Appl.Mech.Rev., Biol.Abstr., Chem.Abstr., Corros.Abstr., Eng.Ind., INIS Atomind., INSPEC, Int.Abstr.Biol.Sci., Int.Aerosp.Abstr., Math.R., Nutr.Abstr., Plast.Abstr. **Document type:** government publication.
    —BLDSC (3546.200000); CASDDS; Ei.
    Description: Covers engineering and technology, including applied physics, chemical technology, biomedical engineering, computer science and electronics.
    Refereed Serial

355   UK   ISSN 0953-4970
DEFENCE SYSTEMS MODERNISATION. 1988. m. Janes Information Group, Sentinel House, 163 Brighton Rd., Coulsdon, Surrey CR5 2NH, England. TEL 081-763-1030. FAX 081-763-1006. E-mail: http://www.janes.com/janes.html. Ed. S. Cassy. Pub. Simon Kay. **Document type:** trade publication.

355   SP   ISSN 0211-3732
DEFENSA; revista internacional de ejercitos, armamento y tecnologia. 1978. m. 7300 ptas. (Europe 14800 ptas.; America 13600 ptas.) (effective 1995). Edefa, S.A., Editorial de Publicaciones, Jorge Juan, 98-2, 28009 Madrid, Spain. TEL 577-49-57. FAX 577-46-70. Ed. Vicente Talon. adv.: B&W page 365000 ptas., color page 578000 ptas.; trim 186 x 275. bk.rev.; index. circ. 22,000. (back issues avail.)
    Description: Covers armies, weapons, and industries.

335   US   ISSN 0273-2491
UA10
DEFENSE. (Subseries of: S I R S Social Issues (ISSN 0740-3127)) 1979. a. price varies; a. supplement $17. Social Issues Resources Series, Box 2348, Boca Raton, FL 33427-2348. TEL 407-994-0079; 800-232-7477. FAX 407-994-4704. (looseleaf format; also avail. in microfiche; back issues avail.)
    Description: Reprints articles examining the role of the military.

355.6   US
DEFENSE (WASHINGTON). bi-m. $9.50 (foreign $11.90). (U.S. Department of Defense) U.S. Government Printing Office, Washington, DC 20402. (Subscr. to: Superintendent of Documents, U.S. Government Printing Office, Box 371954, Pittsburgh, PA 15250-7954. TEL 202-512-1800. FAX 202-512-2250) **Document type:** government publication.
    Description: Provides official and professional information on Department of Defense policies, programs, and interests for commanders and key personnel to promote a better understanding and teamwork within the department.

355   US   ISSN 0737-1217
UA23.A1
DEFENSE (YEAR). 1980. bi-m. $23. (U.S. Department of Defense) American Forces Information Service, 601 N. Fairfax St., No.310, Alexandria, VA 22314-2007. TEL 703-274-4849. FAX 703-274-4865. (Subscr. to: Supt. of Documents, Washington, DC 20402) Ed. S. Hara. circ. 80,000. **Indexed:** Abstr.Mil.Bibl., Air Un.Lib.Ind., Ind.U.S.Gov.Per.
    —Faxon; UMI; UnCover.

MILITARY

355 US ISSN 1072-2386
DEFENSE ACQUISITION REPORT; twice-monthly letter on contracting opportunities and legislative initiatives for military procurement, acquisition, and research, development, test & evaluation. 1958. s-m. $190. Callahan Publications, Box 1173, McLean, VA 22101. TEL 703-356-1925. FAX 703-356-9614. Ed. Vincent F. Callahan, Jr. bk.rev.; charts; stat. (processed) **Document type:** newsletter.
  Incorporates (1960-1993): Military Research Letter (ISSN 0026-413X); (1958-1993): Missile - Ordnance Letter (ISSN 0026-5993)

327 UK ISSN 0743-0175
UA11
DEFENSE ANALYSIS. 1985. 3/yr. 30($55) to individuals; institutions £89 ($160) (effective 1996). Brassey's (UK) Ltd., 33 John St., London WC1N 2AT, England. TEL 0171-753-7777. FAX 0171-753-7794. (Subscr. to Turpin Distribution Services, Blackhorse Rd., Letchworth, Herts. SG6 1HN, England. TEL 01462-672555. FAX 01462-480947) Ed. Martin Edmonds. adv. (also avail. in microfilm from MIM,UMI) **Indexed:** Curr.Cont., Int.Polit.Sci.Abstr., Polit.Sci.Abstr. **Document type:** academic/scholarly publication. —BLDSC (3546.212600); Faxon; SWETS; UMI; UnCover. **CCC.**
  Description: Analyzes defense and intelligence policies.

355 629.1 US
DEFENSE AND AEROSPACE MARKETS. a. $1495. Forecast International Inc. - D M S, 22 Commerce Rd., Newtown, CT 06470. TEL 203-426-0800. FAX 203-426-1964. TELEX 467615.
  Description: Worldwide business opportunities (excluding the U.S.) are identified and analyzed in the following markets: military aircraft, civil aircraft, missiles, warships, ordnance, space systems, SDI, C3I, electronic warfare, military laser and EO, military vehicles, radar, and ASW.

DEFENSE AND AEROSPACE NOTES. see BUSINESS AND ECONOMICS

350.71 US
UA10
DEFENSE & ECONOMY WORLD REPORT. 1969. m. $330. Government Business Worldwide Reports, Box 5997, Washington, DC 20016. TEL 202-244-7050. FAX 202-244-5410. Ed. J.H. Wagner. bk.rev.; bibl.; charts; illus.; stat.; index. (looseleaf format; back issues avail.) **Document type:** newsletter.
  Former titles: Defense and Economy World Report and Survey; Defense Business (ISSN 0364-9008); (until 1976): International Defense Business (ISSN 0360-8417)
  Description: Presents information on international, defense affairs, with emphasis on defense plans and requirements, force changes, procurement, arms transfer, defense budget and industry.

DEFENSE & FOREIGN AFFAIRS STRATEGIC POLICY; the international journal of national management and national security management. see POLITICAL SCIENCE

355 US ISSN 1062-0613
DEFENSE CONTRACT AWARDS. 22/yr. $510 in U.S., Canada & Mexico; elsewhere $800. 1057-B National Press Bldg., Washington, DC 20045. (Subscr. to: Pentagon Sta., Box 47036, Washington DC 20050-7036) Ed. Murray Felsher. **Document type:** newsletter.
  Description: Monitors and tracks all contracts let by the various agencies of the U.S. Department of Defense. Directed to industrial companies and consultants doing business with the Department of Defense.

DEFENSE DAILY. see AERONAUTICS AND SPACE FLIGHT

DEFENSE DES GRADES DE LA POLICE NATIONALE. see LABOR UNIONS

355.6 US
DEFENSE F A R SUPPLEMENT. (Federal Acquisition Regulation) (Supplement to: Federal Acquisition Regulation) base vol. plus irreg. updates. $120 (foreign $150). (U.S. Department of Defense) U.S. Government Printing Office, Washington, DC 20402. (Subscr. to: Superintendent of Documents, U.S. Government Printing Office, Box 371954, Pittsburgh, PA 15250-7954) (looseleaf format) **Document type:** government publication.
  Description: Contains guidelines on the provisions, clauses, and cost principles authorized for Department of Defense contracts, as well as the procedure actions necessary for awarding and administering contracts.

355 327 UK ISSN 0160-5836
UA10
DEFENSE FOREIGN AFFAIRS HANDBOOK; political, economic & defense data on every country in the world. 1976. a. $257. International Media Corporation Ltd., 175 Piccadilly, Ste. 1A, London W1V 9DB, England. TEL 071-409-2044. FAX 071-409-1923. Ed. Gregory Copley. adv. circ. 4,000. (back issues avail.) **Document type:** trade publication.

355 352.7 US ISSN 1047-6504
DEFENSE HOUSING. 1986. bi-m. $50 to non-members; members $15. (Professional Housing Management Association) Stratton Publishing and Marketing Inc., 2800 Shirlington Rd., Ste. 706, Arlington, VA 22206. TEL 703-998-2534. FAX 703-379-4561. Ed. Sharon Bonar. adv. contact: Alison Basnian Victoroff. circ. 3,000. **Document type:** trade publication.
  Description: For military and civilian managers of on- and off-base military housing.

355 AT ISSN 1033-2898
DEFENSE INDUSTRY & AEROSPACE REPORT. 1981. fortn. Aus.$325. Business Communications Group, P.O. Box 250, Mawson, A.C.T. 2607, Australia. TEL 06-286-4605. FAX 06-286-3441. Ed. Trevor Thomas. adv.: B&W page Aus.$1200, color page Aus.$1500. circ. 6,000 (controlled).
  Formerly: Defense Industry.

355 380.1 US
DEFENSE INDUSTRY SERVICE. base vol. (plus updates every 90 days). $785. Carroll Publishing, 1058 Thomas Jefferson St., N.W., Washington, DC 20007. TEL 202-333-8620. FAX 202-337-7020. (looseleaf format)
  Formerly: Defense Organization Service - Industry.
  Description: Organization charts for 115 of the major aerospace, electronics, military Department of Defense contractors, and contact information for over 9,000 personnel in more than 900 top US defence contractors.

DEFENSE INTEGRATED DATA SYSTEM TOTAL ITEM RECORD: SEGMENT V. see MILITARY — Abstracting, Bibliographies, Statistics

355 US
DEFENSE MANUFACTURERS & SUPPLIERS ASSOCIATION OF AMERICA NEWSLETTER; providing service and support to the defense community. 1991. m. $57. D M S A Corporation, P.O. Box 421057, Plymouth, MN 55442-0057. TEL 612-595-0244. FAX 612-595-0229. bk.rev. circ. 9,200. **Document type:** newsletter.

355 US ISSN 0893-0619
DEFENSE MEDIA REVIEW; a survey of the National Security Press with analysis and commentary. 1987. m. $60. Boston University, Center for Defense Journalism, 67 Bay State Rd., Boston, MA 02215. TEL 617-353-6186. FAX 617-353-8707. Ed. H. Joachim Maitre. circ. 600.
  Description: Tracks media coverage of defense issues and policies.

355 US ISSN 0195-6450
UA23.A1
DEFENSE MONITOR. 1972. 10/yr. $35. Center for Defense Information, 1500 Massachusetts Ave., N.W., Washington, DC 20005. FAX 202-862-0708. TELEX 904059 WSH (CDI). E-mail: cdi@igc.apc.org. illus. circ. 50,000. (reprint service avail.) **Indexed:** Air Un.Lib.Ind., DM & T, HR Rep. **Document type:** newsletter.
  —BLDSC (3546.225500).

355 FR ISSN 0336-1489
D410
DEFENSE NATIONALE; etudes politiques, economiques, scientifiques, militaires. 1939. m. 430 F. (foreign 650 F.). Comite d'Etudes de Defense Nationale, c/o Dir.Gen. M. Paul-Marie de La Gorce, 1, place Joffre, 75700 Paris, France. TEL 44-42-31-92. FAX 44-42-31-89. Ed. J. Hugon. adv.: B&W page 9000 F., color page 14000 F.; trim 195 x 116; adv. contact: Francois Estrangin. bk.rev.; bibl. circ. 8,000. (back issues avail.) **Indexed:** Abstr.Mil.Bibl., Amer.Hist.& Life, ELLIS, Hist.Abstr., INIS Atomind., Int.Polit.Sci.Abstr., P.A.I.S.For.Lang.Ind., PROMT. —BLDSC (3546.226100); Faxon; SWETS.
  Formerly (until 1973): Revue de Defense Nationale (ISSN 0035-1075)
  Description: Discusses political, strategic, economical, scientific and military studies.

355 US ISSN 0884-139X
DEFENSE NEWS. 1986. 50/yr. $99 (Canada $139; elsewhere $169) (effective Mar. 1995). Army Times Publishing Co., 6883 Commercial Dr., Springfield, VA 22159. TEL 703-750-8137. FAX 703-642-7352. Ed. Sharon Denny. adv.; charts; stat. circ. 42,000. (tabloid format; also avail. in microform; reprint service avail. from UMI) **Document type:** newspaper.
  —BLDSC (3546.227000); SWETS; UMI. **CCC.**
  Description: Covers the international politics and business of the defense community.

355 JA
DEFENSE OF JAPAN (YEAR); the white paper on defense. 1989. a. 5150 Yen. (Defense Agency) Japan Times Ltd., 4-5-4 Shibaura, Minato-ku, Tokyo 108, Japan. TEL 03-3453-2013. FAX 03-3453-8023.
  Description: Gives a full account of Japan's defense policy and the current state of the Japanese "self-defense" forces. Includes reference material and statistical data related to Japan's defense.

355 350 US
DEFENSE ORGANIZATION SERVICE. base vol. (plus updates every 6 w.). $1010. Carroll Publishing, 1058 Thomas Jefferson St., N.W., Washington, DC 20007. TEL 202-333-8620. FAX 202-337-7020. (looseleaf format)
  Formerly: Federal Organization Service - Military.
  Description: Organization charts covering key officials in more than 2,400 military departments and offices.

355 US
DEFENSE PROGRAMS SERVICE. 1989. base vol. (plus irreg. updates). $960. Carroll Publishing, 1058 Thomas Jefferson St., N.W., Washington, DC 20007. TEL 202-333-8620. FAX 202-337-7020. (looseleaf format)
  Incorporates (in 1990): Defense Programs Service - R D T and E (Research, Development, Test and Evaluation) & Defense Program Service - Procurement.
  Description: Details information about nearly 1,600 key programs in the procurement and research, development, test, and evaluation stages of the United States defense budget.

355 IS ISSN 0931-7317
DEFENSE UPDATE; international. Hebrew edition: Romach (ISSN 0334-8466) (Text in English) 1978. m. $42. Eshel-Drahmit Publishing, P.O.B. 115, Hod Hasharon, Israel. TEL 052-31357. FAX 972-3-285456. TELEX 35770-COIN-IL. (U.S. adress: 4350 DiPaulo Center-Dearlove Road, Glenview, IL 60025) Ed. Tamir Eshel. adv.; bk.rev.; index. circ. 50,000. **Indexed:** Air Un.Lib.Ind.
  Formerly: Born in Battle.

355 US ISSN 0273-3188
DEFENSE WEEK. 1980. w. $1099. King Publishing Group, Inc., 627 National Press Bldg., Washington, DC 20045. TEL 202-638-4260. FAX 202-662-9744. Eds. Tony Capaccio, Eric Rosenberg. adv. contact: Julie Lee. bk.rev. **Document type:** newsletter.
  ●Also available online. Vendor(s): Lexis-Nexis, NewsNet (DE16).
  —BLDSC (3546.255000). **CCC.**
  Description: Covers all areas of the U.S. military establishment and defense industry. Reports on defense policy, the DoD budget, congressional priorities and alliances, acquisition issues, weapon research and development.

MILITARY

355   BL   ISSN 0011-7641
DEFESA NACIONAL;[*] revista de assuntos militares e estudo de problemas brasileiros. 1913. bi-m. $30. Ministerio da Guerra, Esplanada dos Ministerios, Bloco 4, 70042 Brasilia D.F., Brazil. Dir. Carlos A. Gigante de Castro. adv.; bk.rev. circ. 10,000.
Indexed: Abstr.Mil.Bibl.

355.0330489   DK   ISSN 0109-5757
UA691
DENMARK. FORSVARSMINISTERIET. AARLIGE REDEGOERELSE. 1982. a. free. Forsvarsministeriet - Ministry of Defense, Holmens Kanal 42, DK-1060 Copenhagen K, Denmark. TELEX DK-33-32-06-55. illus. circ. 6,000. **Document type:** government publication.
Formerly: Denmark. Forsvarsministeriet. Forsvarsministerens Aarlige Redegoerelse (ISSN 0108-7193)

355   US   ISSN 1048-7557
U24
DEPARTMENT OF DEFENSE DICTIONARY OF MILITARY AND ASSOCIATED TERMS. 1972. irreg. $22. (U.S. Department of Defense) U.S. Government Printing Office, Washington, DC 20402. (Orders to: Superindendent of Documents, U.S. Printing Office, Box 371954, Pittsburgh, PA 15250-7954. TEL 202-512-1800. FAX 202-512-2250; Or: Bernan, 4611-F Assembly Dr., Lanham, MD 20706. TEL 301-459-7666. FAX 301-459-0056)
Formerly: Dictionary of United States Military Terms for Joint Usage (ISSN 0193-7839)

355   US
DESERT AIRMAN. 1942. w. $12 (to qualified military personnel only). Territorial Newspapers, Box 35250, Tucson, AZ 85740. TEL 602-297-1107. FAX 602-297-6253. Ed. SSSgt. Dawn McKee. adv.; circ. 11,500 (controlled). (tabloid format) **Document type:** newsletter.

355   AT   ISSN 0046-0079
DESPATCH. 1966. bi-m. Aus.$30. New South Wales Military Historical Society, c/o Hon.Secr., Mrs. M. Taplin, 397 Willarong Rd., Caringbah, N.S.W. 2229, Australia. Ed. R. Sutton. adv.; bk.rev. circ. 200.

355   GW   ISSN 0417-3635
DEUTSCHES SOLDATENJAHRBUCH. 1953. a. DM.68. Schild-Verlag GmbH, Henschelstr. 7, 81249 Munich, Germany. TEL 089-8641189. FAX 089-8632310. Ed. Otto Krumm. adv.; bk.rev.; bibl.; charts; illus.; stat.; circ. 7,000 (controlled). **Document type:** bulletin.

DEUTSCHLAND-MAGAZIN. see *POLITICAL SCIENCE*

355   LE
AL-DIFA' AL-ARABI/ARAB DEFENSE JOURNAL. (Text in Arabic) 1976. m. $150. Dar Assayad S.A.L., P.O. Box 1038, Hazmieh, Beirut, Lebanon. FAX 961-1-456373. TELEX 44224 SAYYAD LE. (UK addr.: c/o Contact PR & Mgt. (UK) Ltd., 3 Park Pl., 12 Lawn Ln., London SW8, England. TEL 071-582-2220) Ed. Maj.Gen. Wadih Gebrane. adv. contact: Salim Zreik. circ. 22,120. **Indexed:** PROMT.

355   IT   ISSN 1120-1657
DIFESA OGGI. (Includes a. directory: La Difesa in Italia) 1977. 9/yr. $108 (effective 1995). Publi & Consult S.P.A., Via Tagliamento 29, 00198 Rome, Italy. TEL 39-6-8543603. FAX 39-6-85350021. Ed. Paolo F. Bancale. adv.; B&W page 3070 ptas., color page 5600 ptas.; trim 185 x 275; adv. contact: Laura Gigli. illus. circ. 17,400. **Document type:** trade publication.
Description: Covers the defense industry and technology and operational aspects.

DIPLOMAT; the review of the diplomatic and consular world. see *POLITICAL SCIENCE* — International Relations

355   US
DIRECTOR OF SELECTIVE SERVICE. ANNUAL REPORT. 1967. a. free. U.S. Selective Service System, 1515 Wilson Blvd., Arlington, VA 22209. TEL 703-235-2053. (Orders to: Superindendent of Documents, U.S. Government Printing Office, Box 371954, Pittsburgh, PA 15250-7954. TEL 202-512-1800. FAX 202-512-2250) Ed. Lewis C. Brodsky. charts; stat.; circ. controlled. **Document type:** government publication.

DIRECTORY OF D C A A OFFICES. see *BUSINESS AND ECONOMICS* — Public Finance, Taxation

DIR'U AL-ISLAM. see *RELIGIONS AND THEOLOGY* — Islamic

355   TS
DIR'U AL-WATAN. 1971. m. General Command for the Armed Forces, Public Relations Administration, P.O. Box 4224, Abu Dhabi, United Arab Emirates. TEL 447999. circ. 1,000.
Description: Covers military issues.

327.174   UN   ISSN 0251-9518
JX1974   CODEN: DISAEF
DISARMAMENT; a periodic review by the United Nations. Arabic edition: Naz' al-silah (ISSN 0251-950X); Chinese edition: Caijun (ISSN 0251-9496); French edition: Desarmement (ISSN 0251-9542); Russian edition: Razoruzhenie (ISSN 0251-9526); Spanish edition: Desarme (ISSN 0251-9534) 1978. irreg. (2-3/yr.) latest vol.13, no.3. $15 per no. United Nations Publications, Subscription Office, Box 361, Birmingham, AL 35201-0361. bibl.; charts. **Indexed:** Amer.Bibl.Slavic & E.Eur.Stud., Int.Polit.Sci.Abstr., P.A.I.S., Polit.Sci.Abstr. **Document type:** academic/scholarly publication.
—BLDSC (3595.439500); Faxon; UnCover.

THE DISPATCH (MIDLAND); American airpower a proud heritage. see *AERONAUTICS AND SPACE FLIGHT*

355   SZ
DIVISIONS KURIER. 4/yr. Juchstr. 21, CH-8192 Glattfelden, Switzerland. TEL 01-8368283. FAX 01-8367414. Ed. Christoph Hagedorn. circ. 25,000.

355.31 320   AE
AL-DJEICH; revue de l'Armee Nationale Populaire. (Text in Arabic, French) 1963. m. Office de l'Armee Nationale Populaire, 3 Chemin de Gascogne, Algiers, Algeria. film rev.; illus. circ. 10,000.

355   SZ
DRUE-BLATT. 3/yr. Postfach 246, CH-3097 Liebefeld, Switzerland. circ. 25,000.

EA WARUDO/AIR WORLD. see *AERONAUTICS AND SPACE FLIGHT*

355   US
EAGLE (NEW YORK). 1981. bi-m. $3.95 per no. Command Publications, Inc., 1115 Broadway, New York, NY 10010. Ed. Harry Kane. adv.; bk.rev. circ. 75,000.
Formerly: Eagle: For the American Fighting Man.

355   GW
EICHENBLATT. 1954. q. Kameradschaftsbund Erste Panzerdivision, Ludwigsteinstr. 63, 37214 Witzenhausen, Germany. TEL 05542-3028. circ. 850.

355   SP   ISSN 0013-2918
EJERCITO; revista de las armas y servicios. 1940. m. 2060 ptas. Ministerio de Defensa, Estado Mayor del Ejercito, Servicio de Publicaciones, Alcala 18 4o, Apdo. 317, 28014 Madrid, Spain. TEL 34-1-5225254. Ed. Alberto Perez Moreno; Pub. Oliverio Celemin Pena. adv. contact: Carmelo Metrano Salto. bk.rev.; bibl.; charts; illus.; index. circ. 180,000. **Indexed:** Amer.Hist.& Life, Hist.Abstr. **Document type:** government publication.

355   CU
EJERCITO. w. Ministerio de las Fuerzas Armadas Revolucionarias, Calzada de Managua No. 1829, Claverio, Havana, Cuba.

355   US   ISSN 0884-4828
ELECTRONIC WARFARE DIGEST. 1977. m. $195 (foreign $206) (effective 1996). Washington National News Reports, Inc., 3918 Prosperity Ave., Ste. 318, Fairfax, VA 22031-3334. TEL 703-573-1600. FAX 703-573-1604. Ed. Brian Thomas; Pub. Richard J. O'Connell. circ. 500 (paid). (looseleaf format; back issues avail.) **Document type:** newsletter.

355   CU
EN GUARDIA.[*] m. (Ministerio de las Fuerzas Armadas Revolucionarias, Ejercito Central) Ediciones Cubanas, Obispo 527, Apdo. 605, Havana, Cuba.

ENGINEER (FORT LEONARD WOOD); professional bulletin. see *ENGINEERING*

355   UK   ISSN 0013-8401
ENGLISH WESTERNERS' BRAND BOOK. 1954. s-a. £10.75($17.50) English Westerners' Society, 15 Hurstwood Dr., Bromley, Kent BR1 2JE, England. Ed. T. Wanless. bk.rev.; bibl.; cum.index. circ. 350. **Document type:** monographic series.

355   UK   ISSN 0013-841X
ENGLISH WESTERNERS' TALLY SHEET. 1958. 3/yr. $17.50. English Westerners Society, 15 Hurstwood Dr., Bromley, Kent BR1 2JE, England. Ed. T. Wanlesss. bk.rev.; bibl.; cum.index. circ. 300. **Indexed:** A.I.C.P. **Document type:** newsletter.

355   GR
EPITHEORISIS ETHNIKIS AMYNIS/NATIONAL DEFENSE REVUE. q. $8. Hellenic Army General Staff, 10 Pittakou, Athens, Greece. **Document type:** government publication.

355 320   AG   ISSN 0327-6961
ESCUELA NACIONAL DE INTELIGENCIA. REVISTA. 1992. 3/yr. exchange basis. Escuela Nacional de Inteligencia, C. Libertad 1235, 1012 Buenos Aires, Argentina. TEL 5411-812-4930. FAX 54-1-812-9230. Alberto Ramon Varela. circ. 3,500. **Document type:** academic/scholarly publication.

355 327   US   ISSN 1043-1667
THE ESTIMATE;[*] political and security intelligence analysis of North Africa, the Middle East, South Asia, East Asia, & the Pacific. 1989. fortn. $295 (foreign $330). The International Estimate, Inc., 3030 S. Abington St., Arlington, VA 22206-1605. TEL 202-332-0849. Eds. Julia A. Ackerman, Michael C. Dunn. bk.rev.; index. circ. 100. (back issues avail.)
Description: Political and security intelligence and risk analysis.

355   GW
EUROPAEISCHE SICHERHEIT. 1983. m. DM.114. (Clausewitz-Gesellschaft Arbeitskreis fuer Wehrforschung, Gesellschaft fuer Wehr- und Sicherheitspolitik e.V.) E.S. Mittler und Sohn GmbH, Striepenweg 31, 21147 Hamburg, Germany. TEL 040-79713322. FAX 040-79713324. Ed. Franz Mendel. adv.; bk.rev.; illus. circ. 8,500.
—BLDSC (3829.361650).
Incorporates (in 1994): Europaeische Sicherheit. Ausgabe "A": Kampftruppen; **Formerly (until 1990):** Europaeische Wehrkunde, Wehrwissenschaftliche Rundschau (ISSN 0723-9432); Which was formed by the 1983 merger of: Wehrwissenschaftliche Rundschau (ISSN 0342-4847); Europaeische Wehrkunde (ISSN 0343-6373); Which was formerly (1952-1976): Wehrkunde (ISSN 0043-213X)

EUROPEAN DEFENCE AND STRATEGIC STUDIES ANNUAL (YEAR). see *POLITICAL SCIENCE*

355   GW
EUROPEAN STARS & STRIPES. 1942. d. $10 per mo. European Stars & Stripes, Postfach 111437, 64278 Darmstadt, Germany. TEL 06155-601214. FAX 06155-601395. (APO addr.: Unit 29480, APO AE 09211-4211) Ed. Bernhard Zovistoski; Pub. Col. Steven Hoffman. adv. contact: David Weikal. bk.rev. circ. 50,000. **Document type:** newspaper.

355.15   US   ISSN 0014-388X
D769.A15
EX - C B I ROUNDUP. (China - Burma - India Veterans Association) 1946. m. (except Aug.-Sep.). $13. Dwight O. King, Ed. & Pub., Box 2665, La Habra, CA 90631. TEL 310-947-2007. adv.; bk.rev. circ. 6,185.

355   US   ISSN 0161-7451
EX - P O W BULLETIN. 1949. m. $13. American Ex-Prisoners of War, c/o Clydie J. Morgan, 3201 E. Pioneer Pkwy., Ste. 40, Arlington, TX 76010. TEL 817-649-2979. Ed. Susan Langseth. adv.; bk.rev. circ. 23,000. (back issues avail.)

355   US   ISSN 0014-4452
EXCHANGE & COMMISSARY NEWS. 1962. m. $40. Executive Business Media, Inc., Box 1500, 825 Old Country Rd., Westbury, NY 11590. TEL 516-334-3030. Ed. Robert Moran. adv. circ. 10,200. (tabloid format)

MILITARY

355 BL ISSN 0102-3608
EXPEDICIONARIO. m. (Associacao Nacional dos Veteranos da FEB) Editora Expedicionario, Rua Leandro Martins, 20, Grupos 504, 505, 506, Rio de Janeiro CEP 20080, Brazil. (Co-sponsor: Associacao dos Ex-Combatentes do Brazil)

355 SW ISSN 0005-7797
F B U - BEFAEL. (Frivilliga Befaelsutbildningsroerelsen) 1918. 6/yr. SEK 30 (effective 1992). Centralfoerbundet Foer Befaelsutbildning (CFB), P.O. Box 5034, 102 41 Stockholm, Sweden. TEL 00946-8-670-8200. FAX 00946-8-667-2731. Ed. Bert-Olof Lax. adv.; bk.rev. circ. 37,000.
Former titles (until vol.4, 1971): Befael; (until 1947): Befael, Landstormsmannen; (until 1946): Landstormsmannen.

355 SW ISSN 0429-9531
F O A TIDNINGEN. 1963. 6/yr. SEK 200 (effective 1994). F O A Info, S172 90 Stockholm, Sweden. ED. Jan-Ivar Askelin. Document type: corporate report.
Formerly (until 1964): F O A: Tidning foer Foersvarets Forskningsanstalt.

F X O REPORT. see ENGINEERING — Electrical Engineering

F-5 TECHNICAL DIGEST. see AERONAUTICS AND SPACE FLIGHT

355.31 DK ISSN 0107-7716
FAGLIGT FORSVAR.* 1982. m. DKK 60. Haerens Konstabel- og Korporalforening, Trommesalen 3, 1614 Copenhagen V, Denmark. illus.

358.4 US
FALCON FLYER. 1960. w. $45 (effective Sep. 1992). Gowdy Printcraft Press, Inc., 22 N. Sierra Madre, Colorado Springs, CO 80903. TEL 719-634-1593. FAX 719-632-0762. Ed. Doug Roth; Pub. John Bernheim. adv. contact: Michael Murt. bk.rev. circ. 7,500. (tabloid format) Document type: newspaper.
Description: Covers student activities, military news, sports and current events in government for cadets at the U.S. Air Force Academy.

355 UK ISSN 0956-2400
FALLING LEAF. 1958. q. £8($12) Psywar Society, c/o R. Oakland, 21 Metchley Ln., Harborne, Birmingham B17 0HT, England. Ed. R.G. Auckland. adv.; bk.rev.; illus. circ. 150. Document type: bulletin.
Description: Primarily concerns the dissemination and effects of aerial propaganda leaflets in wars and conflicts.

355 US
FAMILY (NEW YORK); the magazine for military wives. 1958. m. free. Military Forces Features, 169 Lexington Ave., New York, NY 10016-7305. TEL 212-545-9740. FAX 212-779-3080. Ed. Liz DeFranco; Pub. Joseph Mugnai, Sr. adv. contact: Joseph Mugnai, Jr. bk.rev.; illus. circ. 500,000.
Formerly: Stateside Family.

358.4 355.6 343.01 US ISSN 1068-7041
KF844.7
FEDERAL ACQUISITION REGULATION. Abbreviated title: F A R. base vol. plus irreg. supplements. $92 (foreign $115). (U.S. Air Force) Commerce Clearing House, Inc., 4025 W. Paterson Ave., Chicago, IL 60646. TEL 312-583-8500. (Subscr. also to: Superintendent of Documents, U.S. Government Printing Office, Box 371954, Pittsburgh, PA 15250-7954. TEL 202-512-1800. FAX 202-512-2250) (looseleaf format) Document type: government publication.
Description: Provides information on acquiring supplies and services for the U.S. Air Force.

FEDERAL BENEFITS FOR VETERANS AND DEPENDENTS. see INSURANCE

355.11 368.4 US
FEDERAL BENEFITS FOR VETERANS AND DEPENDENTS, IS-1 FACT SHEET. 1961. a. $2.25. U.S. Department of Veterans Affairs, 810 Vermont Ave., N.W., Washington, DC 20420. TEL 202-233-3557. (Subscr. to: Superintendent of Documents, U.S. Government Printing Office, Box 371954, Pittsburgh, PA 15250. TEL 202-512-1800. FAX 202-512-2250) Document type: government publication.
●Also available online.
Formerly: U.S. Veterans Administration. V A Fact Sheets (ISSN 0083-3576)

335 SZ ISSN 0046-3620
FELDPOST/POSTE DE CAMPAGNE/POSTA DE CAMPO.* (Text in French, German and Italian) 1937. q. Schweizerischer Feldpostverein, Bernstr. 115, CH-3072 Ostermundigen, Switzerland. Ed. Stierli Karl. charts; stat.

355 SZ ISSN 0014-9780
FELDWEBEL/SERGENT-MAJOR/SERGENTE MAGGIORE. (Text in French and German) vol.12, 1970. m. 48 SFr. (Schweizerischer Feldwebelverband) Huber und Co. AG, Promenadenstr. 16, CH-8501 Frauenfeld, Switzerland. TEL 054-271111. Ed. P. Roethlin. adv.; charts; illus. Document type: bulletin.
Description: Covers association news and information, training, technical information. Includes reports and calendar of events.

355 US ISSN 0899-2525
UF1
FIELD ARTILLERY; the journal of fire support. 1911. bi-m. $18. U.S. Army Field Artillery School, Box 33311, Fort Sill, OK 73503. TEL 405-442-5121. FAX 405-442-5127. bk.rev.; illus. circ. 15,000. (also avail. in microform from UMI; reprint service avail. from UMI) Indexed: Abstr.Mil.Bibl., Air Un.Lib.Ind., Amer.Bibl.Slavic & E.Eur.Stud., Amer.Hist.& Life, DM & T, Hist.Abstr., Mid.East: Abstr.& Ind., PROMT. Document type: government publication.
—BLDSC (3919.340000); UMI; UnCover.
Former titles: Field Artillery Journal (ISSN 0191-975X); Artillery Trends.

FIVE-YEAR INFORMATION RESOURCES MANAGEMENT PROGRAM. see LIBRARY AND INFORMATION SCIENCES

359 SW ISSN 0015-4431
FLOTTANS MAEN; kamratskap, oerlogstradition, sjoefoersvar. 1935. q. SEK 50. Foereningen Flottans Maen, Teatergatan 3, 111 48 Stockholm, Sweden. Eds. Christer Hammarberg, Emanuel Fornander. adv.; bk.rev.; illus. circ. 3,000. Indexed: Abstr.Mil.Bibl.

358.4 SW ISSN 0015-4792
FLYGVAPENNYTT. 1948. irreg. (4-5/yr.). SEK 50 (effective 1996). Foersvarsmakten, H K V - Info, Flygvapennytt, Prenumeration, S-107 85 Stockholm, Sweden. TEL 46-8-788-75-69. FAX 46-8-788-88-66. Ed. Jahn Charleville. bk.rev.; illus. circ. 35,500.
Former titles (until 1970): Flygvapen-Nytt med Vaardkasen; (until vol.2, 1967): Flygvapen-Nytt; (until 1960): Ufl - Underraettelser Fraan Flygledningen.

FLYING M. see AERONAUTICS AND SPACE FLIGHT

FLYING SAFETY. see AERONAUTICS AND SPACE FLIGHT

355 SW ISSN 0015-5225
FOERBUNDET SVENSKA FINLANDSFRIVILLIGA. TIDNING. 1941. q. SEK 40 (effective 1995). Foerbundet Svenska Finlandsfrivilliga - Association of Swedish Volunteers in the Finnish Wars, PO Box 4043, 181 04 Lidingoe, Sweden. Ed. Gunnar Nordloef. adv.; bk.rev. circ. 1,100. (processed) Document type: bulletin.
Formerly (until 1949): Foerbundet Svenska Frivilligkaaren. Tidning.

355 SW ISSN 0046-4643
FOERSVAR I NUTID. 1965. bi-m. SEK 180. Centralfoerbundet Folk och Foersvar, Sibyllegatan 9, S-114 42 Stockholm, Sweden. TEL 46-8-23-18-25. FAX 46-8-660-63-55. Ed. Jonas Landahl. bk.rev.; charts; illus.; stat. circ. 1,600.

355 SW ISSN 0347-7576
FOERSVARETS FOERFATTNINGSSAMLING. 1977. 40/yr. SEK 370 (effective 1990). Foersvarets Materielverk, T D Redaktionen, S-115 82 Stockholm, Sweden.
Supersedes in part: Tjaenstemeddelanden fraan Foersvarsmakten.

355 SW ISSN 1100-8245
FOERSVARETS FORUM. 1989. 8/yr. SEK 100 (effective 1996). Foersvarsmakten, H K V - Info - Swedish Armed Forces, Information Department, Foersvarets Forum, Prenumeration, S-107 85 Stockholm, Sweden. TEL 46-8-788-87-57. FAX 46-8-788-88-66. bk.rev.
Description: Focuses on relevant topics of interest to the Swedish armed forces and others with an interest in Swedish defense and national security.

355 363.35 SW ISSN 0345-3529
FOLK OCH FOERSVAR. 1941-1952; resumed 1958. q. free. Centralfoerbundet Folk och Foersvar, Sibylleg. 9, S-114 42 Stockholm, Sweden.
Formerly (until vol.14, 1941): Folk och Foersvar, Paa Vakt; Supersedes: Paa Vakt.

355 US ISSN 0738-4203
FOR YOUR EYES ONLY; an open intelligence summary of current military affairs. Short title: F.Y.E.O. 1980. fortn. $65 in U.S. and Canada (effective Oct. 1993 - Sep. 1995). Tiger Publications, Box 8759, Amarillo, TX 79114-8759. TEL 806-655-2009. Ed. Stephen V. Cole. bk.rev.; charts; illus.; stat. circ. 1,000. (back issues avail.)
●Also available online. Vendor(s): NewsNet (DE15).
—CCC.

355 UK
FORCES WEEKLY ECHO. 1980. w. £55. Combined Service Publications, P.O. Box 4, Farnborough, Hants GU14 7LR, England. TEL 0252-515891. FAX 0252-517918. Ed. D.D. Crossley. adv. circ. 25,000. (tabloid format)

FOREIGN INTELLIGENCE LITERARY SCENE. see LITERATURE

355.3 NO ISSN 0332-9062
FORSVARETS FORUM. 1945. fortn. (25/yr.). NOK 150($30) Forsvarets Rekrutterings- og Mediasenter, Oslo MIL-Akershus, Oslo 1, Norway. TEL 47-22-40-34-53. FAX 47-22-40-35-10. Ed. Tor Eigil Stordahl. adv.; bk.rev.; illus. circ. 95,000.
—CCC.
Supersedes: Mannskapsavisa (ISSN 0025-2352); Militaer Orientering.

355 900 UK ISSN 0261-586X
FORT; the international journal of fortification and military architecture. 1976. a. £15($34) (outside Europe £20). Fortress Study Group, c/o Athanassios Migos, Ed., Nearchos, 9 Rock Park, Rock Ferry, Wirral L42 1PJ, England. TEL 44-151-644-0761. FAX 44-151-707-2953. Ed. Anthanassios Migos. bk.rev.; circ. 700 (paid). (also avail. in microfiche) Indexed: Avery Ind.Archit.Per., Br.Archaeol.Abstr., RILA. Document type: academic/scholarly publication.
—BLDSC (4014.820000).
Description: Devoted to the history and development of military architecture, fortification theory and practice, and related military history throughout the ages.
Refereed Serial

FORT CONCHO GUIDON. see MUSEUMS AND ART GALLERIES

355 974 US ISSN 0015-8070
E199
FORT TICONDEROGA MUSEUM. BULLETIN. 1927. a. $10 per no. (effective 1991). Fort Ticonderoga Association Inc., Fort Ticonderoga Museum, Ticonderoga, NY 12883. TEL 518-585-2821. FAX 518-585-2210. Ed. Nicholas Westbrook. bk.rev.; illus.; index. circ. 750. Indexed: Amer.Hist.& Life, Hist.Abstr. Document type: academic/scholarly publication.
Description: Covers military history from 1609 to 1781.

355 SZ
FORTERESSE. 11/yr. 7 rue de Geneve, CH-1002 Lausanne, Switzerland. TEL 021-505901. circ. 1,400.

359.96 US ISSN 0362-9910
VE23.A1
FORTITUDINE; newsletter of the Marine Corps historical program. 1970. q. $7 (foreign $8.75) (effective 1995). U.S. Marine Corps, History and Museums Division, Director of Marine Corps History and Museums, Headquarters, Washington, DC 20380. TEL 202-433-3840. (Subscr. to: Superintendent of Documents, U.S. Government Printing Office, Box 371954, Pittsburgh, PA 15250-7954. TEL 202-512-1800. FAX 202-512-2250) bibl.; charts; illus. circ. 18,000. (back issues avail.) Indexed: Ind.U.S.Gov.Per.
Formerly: Harumfrodite.
Description: Seeks to educate and train Marines on active duty in the uses of military and Marine Corps history.

FORTRESS; the castles and fortifications quarterly. see ARCHITECTURE

MILITARY

355 CN ISSN 0843-5995
FORUM. 1985. q. $72 (foreign $80). Synergistic Enterprises, 132 Adrian Cres., Markham, Ont. L3P 7B3, Canada. TEL 416-472-2801. FAX 416-472-3091. Ed. Peter A. Kitchen. adv. circ. 12,000. (back issues avail.)
  Description: Independent publication whose mandate is to write about issues and events concerning Canada's defense community.

355 BE ISSN 0015-8488
FORUM DE LA FORCE TERRESTRE. Dutch edition: Forum Landmacht. (Text in French) 1970. bi-m. 250 BEF. Forum A.S.B.L., Rue d'Evere Quartier Reine Elisabeth, 1140 Brussels, Belgium. FAX 3222433550. Ed. Jacobs Marcel. adv.; bk.rev.; charts; illus. circ. 20,000.

355 SZ ISSN 0015-914X
FOURIER. 1928. m. 28 SFr.($23) Schweizerischer Fourierverband, Postfach 2840, CH-6002 Luzern, Switzerland. FAX 041-237122. Ed. Schuler Meinrad. adv.; bk.rev. circ. 10,736. Document type: bulletin.

355 SZ ISSN 1022-8217
FOURRIER SUISSE. (Text in French) 1922. 10/yr. 30 SFr. Association Romande des Fourriers Suisses, Case Postale 2570, CH-1211 Geneva 2, Switzerland. TEL 022-7324550. FAX 022-7384738. Ed. Andrew Young. adv.; bk.rev. circ. 2,000. Document type: bulletin.

355 FR ISSN 0015-9719
FRANCE. MINISTERE DE LA DEFENSE NATIONALE. BULLETIN D'INFORMATION TECHNIQUE ET SCIENTIFIQUE. 12/yr. 220 F. (foreign 240 F.). Ministere de la Defense Nationale, 14 rue Saint Dominique, 75007 Paris, France.

355 FR ISSN 0015-9727
FRANCE. MINISTERE DE LA DEFENSE NATIONALE. BULLETIN OFFICIEL. 1947. w. Ministere de la Defense Nationale, 14 rue Saint Dominique, 75007 Paris, France.

351.06 FR
FRANCE. MINISTERE DES ARMEES. BULLETIN OFFICIEL DES ARMEES. (Supplement to: Armee Francaise. Journal Officiel) w. 3132 F. Editions Charles Lavauzelle, Le Prouet, B.P. 8, 87350 Panazol, France. FAX 55-58-45-25. TELEX 580 995 F.

351.06 FR ISSN 0755-2289
FRANCE. MINISTERE DES ARMEES. BULLETIN OFFICIEL DES ARMEES. EDITION CHRONOLOGIQUE. w. 1850 F. Editions Charles Lavauzelle, Le Prouet, B.P. 8, 87350 Panazol, France. TEL 55-58-45-45. FAX 55-58-45-25. (back issues avail.) Document type: government publication.

351.06 FR ISSN 0755-2270
FRANCE. MINISTERE DES ARMEES. BULLETIN OFFICIEL DES ARMEES. EDITION CHRONOLOGIQUE. PARTIE PRINCIPALE. w. 1887 F. Editions Charles Lavauzelle, Le Prouet, B.P. 8, 87350 Panazol, France. TEL 55-58-45-45. FAX 55-58-45-25. (back issues avail.) Document type: government publication.

355 GW ISSN 0016-092X
DER FREIWILLIGE. 1955. m. DM.66. (Bundesverband der Soldaten der ehemaligen Waffen-SS e.V.) Munin Verlag GmbH, Postfach 3023, 49020 Osnabrueck, Germany. TEL 0541-589746. FAX 0541-572278. Ed. K.H. Ruehl. adv.; bk.rev. circ. 9,000. Document type: newsletter.

355 FR ISSN 0016-1144
FRERES D'ARMES; organe de Liaison des Forces Armees Francaises, Africaines et Malgaches. 1963. bi-m. 85 F. (foreign 125 F.) (effective 1996). Association pour le Developpement et la Diffusion de l'Information Militaire, 6, rue Saint-Charles, 75015 Paris, France. TEL 45-77-03-76. adv. contact: Didier Contoux. bk.rev.; bibl.; illus. circ. 10,000.
  Description: News of French military cooperation with Africa.

FRITT MILITAERT FORUM. see CIVIL DEFENSE

355 973 US ISSN 0071-9641
FRONTIER MILITARY SERIES. 1951. irreg. price varies. Arthur H. Clark Co., Box 14707, Spokane, WA 99214. index. Document type: monographic series.

358.4 CL ISSN 0716-4866
FUERZA AEREA. 1941. q. $60. Editorial Fuerza Aerea, Av. B. O'Higgins 1316 of 63, Santiago, Chile. adv. circ. 15,000.
  Formerly: Revista de la Fuerza Aerea.

G M V. (Government and Military Video) see COMMUNICATIONS — Video

355 CN ISSN 1193-7467
GARRISON.* 1991. 8/yr. Land Force Central Area, 6 Adelaide St., E., Ste. 1010, Toronto, ON M5C 1H6, Canada. TEL 416-971-3368. FAX 416-971-7521. Ed. Col. B.M. Archibald; Pub. D. Brian Hay. adv.: B&W page Can.$850; adv. contact: Michele Pelyhe.

DAS GELTENDE SEEVOELKERRECHT IN EINZELDARSTELLUNGEN. see LAW — International Law

363.2 FR ISSN 1161-1715
GEND INFO. 1990. 11/yr. 135 F. (foreign 170 F.) (effective 1996). Association pour le Developpement et la Diffusion de l'Information Militaire, 6 rue St. Charles, 75015 Paris, France. TEL 45-77-06-76. FAX 45-79-53-73. Ed. Lieutenant-Colonel Dedeban. illus. circ. 98,000.
  Description: Offers a look at the lives of police officials.

355.331 US ISSN 1058-0131
UB412
GENERAL - FLAG OFFICER WORLDWIDE ROSTER. 1985. q. $10 (foreign $12.50) (effective 1995). U.S. Department of Defense, Washington Headquarters Services, Directorate for Information Operations and Reports, The Pentagon, Washington, DC 20301-1155. TEL 703-545-6700. (Subscr. to: Superintendent of Documents, U.S. Government Printing Office, Box 371954, Pittsburgh, PA 15250-7954. TEL 202-512-1800. FAX 202-512-2250) Document type: directory, government publication.

355 614.85 CN ISSN 0707-0403
GENERAL SAFETY DIGEST/DIGEST DE SECURITE GENERALE. (Text in English, French) 1973. 4/yr. Can.$11($13.40) Department of National Defence, Directorate of General Safety, National Defense Headquarters, Major - General George Pearkes Bldg., 101 Colonel By Drive, Ottawa, ON K1A 0K2, Canada. (Dist. by: Canada Communication Group, Publishing Division, Ottawa, ON K1A 0S9, Canada) Ed. Bob Britton. illus. circ. 13,000. Document type: government publication.

GEORGE C. MARSHALL FOUNDATION. TOPICS. see HISTORY — History Of North And South America

355 IT
GIORNALE DEI MILITARI. 1952. w. L.25000 (foreign L.50000). Giormil s.r.l., Via Tacito 74, 00193 Rome, Italy. TEL 39-6-3222284. Ed. Giorgio Castellano. adv.: B&W page L.3400000. circ. 60,000.

GLADIUS; etudes sur les armes anciennes, l'armement, l'art militaire et la vie culturelle en Orient et Occident. see ANTIQUES

355 US ISSN 1075-4644
UA10
GLOBAL SURVEY. 1969. m. $335. Government Business Worldwide Reports, Box 5997, Washington, DC 20016. TEL 202-244-7050. FAX 202-244-5410. Ed. J.H. Wagner. charts; stat. Document type: monographic series.
  Formerly: Defense Reference Reports.
  Description: Information on international, government and defense affairs.

359.96 UK ISSN 0017-1204
GLOBE AND LAUREL. 1892. 6/yr. £8.40 (foreign £11.40). Royal Marines, HMS Excellent, Whale Island, Portsmouth, Hants PO2 8ER, England. TEL 01705-651305. FAX 01705-547207. Ed. Captain A.G. Newing. adv.; bk.rev.; charts; illus.; index. circ. 12,000. Document type: bulletin.

355 US
GOODFELLOW MONITOR. 1958. w. free. (17th Training Wing) San Angelo Standard - Times, 30 W. Harris, San Angelo, TX 76903. TEL 915-653-1221. Ed. Sheri Foley. adv.: page 4498; trim 10 1/4 x 13; adv. contact: John Nebling. charts; illus.; maps; stat. circ. 4,500. (tabloid format; back issues avail.) Document type: newspaper.
  Description: Provides news and information concerning all aspects of Goodfellow Air Force Base, Texas, along with news from all branches of the Department of Defense for all persons in San Angelo affiliated with the U.S. military.

369.11 US
GOPHER OVERSEA'R. 1929. 6/yr. $2 to non-members. Veterans of Foreign Wars of the United States, Department of Minnesota, Veterans Service Bldg., St. Paul, MN 55155. TEL 612-291-1757. FAX 612-291-2753. Ed. Jim Hesselgrave. adv.; bk.rev.; circ. 85,000 (controlled). (tabloid format; back issues avail.)

355.115 FR ISSN 1162-5031
GRAND INVALIDE. 1924. bi-m. 145 F. Federation Nationale des Plus Grands Invalides de Guerre, 13 av. de La Motte-Picquet, 75007 Paris, France. TEL 45-51-33-72. FAX 44-18-93-60. Ed. Jean-Claude Gouellain. adv. circ. 5,000.

GREAT BATTLES. see HISTORY — History Of North And South America

359 UK
GREAT BRITAIN. MINISTRY OF DEFENCE. NAVY LIST. a. £17.50. (Ministry of Defence) H.M.S.O. Books, Publications Centre, 51 Nine Elms Ln., London SW8 5DR, England. TEL 071-873-0011. (Subscr. to: H.M.S.O. Books, P.O. Box 276, London SW8 5DT, England. TEL 071-873-9090. FAX 071-873-8200) circ. 900 (paid). Document type: government publication, directory.
  Description: Lists officers of the U.K. Royal Navy.

355.347 UK
GREAT BRITAIN. ROYAL ARMY CHAPLAINS' DEPARTMENT. JOURNAL. 1922. 2/yr. £10. Ministry of Defense (Army), Royal Army Chaplains' Department Centre, Bagshot Park, Bagshot, Surrey GU19 5PL, England. TEL 01276-471717. Ed. Rev. J. Andrews. adv.; bk.rev. circ. 800. Document type: bulletin.
  Formerly: Royal Army Chaplains Department. Quarterly Journal (ISSN 0035-8657)

355 SZ
GRENADIER. 10/yr. Case Postale 129, CH-1211 Geneva 9, Switzerland. TEL 022-201327. Ed. Jean-Louis Corbat. circ. 1,500.

355.351 SP ISSN 0210-5470
GUARDIA CIVIL. 1944. 12/yr. 275 ptas. per no. Guzman el Bueno 110, 28003 Madrid, Spain. TEL 534-20-00. FAX 533-47-48. Ed. Miguel Lopez Corral. adv.: B&W page 125000 ptas. ($1154); trim 210 x 290. circ. 480,000. Document type: trade publication.

355 UK ISSN 0017-503X
GUARDS MAGAZINE. 1862. q. £12. B P C C Paulton Books Ltd., H Q Household Division, Horse Guards, Whitehall, London SW1A 2AX, England. Ed. Maj. H.W. Schofield. adv.; bk.rev.; illus. circ. 4,000.
  Formerly: Household Brigade Magazine.

355 US
GUERRE E PACE. m. (10/yr.) L.30000 (foreign L.60000). Comitato Golfo, Via Fiesta del Perdono 6, 20122 Milan, Italy. TEL 02-58315437. FAX 02-28302611. Ed. Walter Peruzzi.

GUIDE TO GOVERNMENT-LOAN FILMS. see MOTION PICTURES

355 SP ISSN 0017-5455
GUION;* revista ilustrada de los mandos subalternos. 1942. m. 1500 ptas. Ministerio de Defensa, Estado Mayor del Ejercito, Servicio de Publicaciones, Alcala 18, p.4, 28014 Madrid, Spain. Ed. Enrique Jarnes Bergua. adv. circ. 168,000. Indexed: Amer.Hist.& Life, Hist.Abstr.

GULHANE ASKERI TIP AKADEMISI BULTEN/GULHANE MILITARY MEDICAL ACADEMY. BULLETIN. see MEDICAL SCIENCES

MILITARY

GUN DIGEST. see *HOBBIES*

H B S A NEWSLETTER. (Historical Breechloading Smallarms Association) see *ANTIQUES*

H S F K STANDPUNKTE - FRIEDENSFORSCHUNG AKTUELL. (Hessische Stiftung Friedens- und Konfliktforschung) see *POLITICAL SCIENCE*

H V W P IN ACTION. (Hospitalized Veterans Writing Project, Inc.) see *LITERATURE*

355   HU   ISSN 0017-6540
DB925.5
HADTORTENELMI KOZLEMENYEK. 1954. q. $10 (effective 1993). Kultura, P.O. Box 149, 1389 Budapest 62, Hungary. TEL 361-250-01-94. FAX 361-250-02-33. TELEX 20-2855 KULT H. **Indexed:** Amer.Hist.& Life, Hist.Abstr.

623   FI   ISSN 0017-6796
HAKKU; Pioneerien lehti. 1923. q. FIM 60. Pioneeriaselajin Liitto r.y., PL 919, SF-00101 Helsinki 10, Finland. FAX 90-161-2556. Ed. Kari Melleri. adv.; bk.rev.; charts; illus. circ. 3,500.

HANDGUNS (YEAR). see *HOBBIES*

HANDLOADER'S DIGEST. see *HOBBIES*

AL-HARAS AL-WATANI/NATIONAL GUARD MAGAZINE. see *GENERAL INTEREST PERIODICALS — Saudi Arabia*

355   US
HARRISON POST. 1965. w. 7962 Pendleton Park, Lawrence, KS 46226. TEL 317-542-8149. circ. 10,000.

358.4   UK
THE HAWK; the independent journal of the Royal Air Force Staff College. 1953. a. £3 (foreign £4). Royal Air Force Staff College, Bracknell, Berkshire RG12 3DD, England. TEL 01344-54593. adv.; bk.rev. circ. 3,000. **Indexed:** Air Un.Lib.Ind. **Document type:** academic/scholarly publication.
—BLDSC (4274.127000).

HEADQUARTERS HELIOGRAM; military history - historic preservation. see *HISTORY — History Of North And South America*

355.31   GW   ISSN 0342-3867
HEER. m. DM.56. A. Bernecker Verlag, Unter dem Schoeneberg 1, 3508 Melsungen, Germany. TEL 05661-731-0. FAX 05661-73189. adv.; bk.rev. circ. 81,000.

355 620   JA
HEIKI TO GIJUTSU/ORDNANCE AND TECHNOLOGY. (Text in Japanese) 1952. m. Nihon Boei Sobi Kogyokai - Japan Association of Defence Industry, 21-3, Akasaka 2-chome, Minato-ku, Tokyo 107, Japan.

355   NO   ISSN 0017-985X
HEIMEVERNSBLADET. 1946. 8/yr. NOK 50 free to members of the Home Guard. (Norwegian Armed Forces) AS Naper, P.O. Box 53, 3771 Krageroe, Norway. TEL 008 25 91053. FAX 02-49-83-12. Ed. Lars Reiermark. bk.rev.; index. circ. 87,500.
—CCC.

HELICOPTER INTERNATIONAL MAGAZINE. see *AERONAUTICS AND SPACE FLIGHT*

363.35   SW   ISSN 0018-0351
HEMVAERNET; tidskrift foer allmaenna hemvaernet och driftvaernet. 1941. 6/yr. SEK 100 (effective 1995). Rikshemvaernsraadet (RiksHvr), S-107 87 Stockholm, Sweden. TEL 46-8-788-97-19. FAX 46-8-664-57-90. Ed. Stig Wallin. adv.; bk.rev.; circ. 130,000 (controlled).
Incorporates (in 1978): Hemvaernsbefael.

623   US   ISSN 0899-8531
UG485
HIGH RELIABILITY ELECTRONIC COMPONENTS. (Subseries of: D.A.T.A. Digest Electronic Information Series) 1985. q. $225. D.A.T.A. Business Publishing (Subsidiary of: Information Handling Services), 15 Inverness Way E., Box 6510, Englewood, CO 80155-6510. TEL 800-447-4666. FAX 303-799-4082. TELEX 4322083 IHS UI. adv. contact: Kevin Asbjorson.
Formerly (until 1988): Military Electronic Devices Guide. Microcircuits and Semiconductors (ISSN 0887-0063)
Description: Reference guide covering up to 20 technical parameters on over 39,000 high reliability devices from more than 150 manufacturers.

355 944   FR   ISSN 0765-0531
HISTOIRE ET DEFENSE.* 1986. 2/yr. Universite de Montpellier III (Universite Paul Valery), Centre d'Histoire Militaire et d'Etudes de Defense Nationale, Montpellier, France. TEL 67-14-20-00.
Formerly (until 1986): Cahiers de Montpellier (ISSN 0298-7996)

HISTOIRE ET MAQUETTISME. see *HOBBIES*

HISTORIA MILITAR DEL PARAGUAY. see *HISTORY — History Of North And South America*

335 909   FR
HISTORICA. (Supplement to: 39 - 45 Magazine (ISSN 0761-7348)) 6/yr. 470 F. Editions Heimdal, Chateau de Damigny, 14400 Bayeux, France.
Formerly (until 1990): 39 - 45 Magazine. Guerres Contemporaines (ISSN 1167-962X)

355   UK   ISSN 0305-0440
HISTORICAL BREECHLOADING SMALLARMS ASSOCIATION. JOURNAL. 1973. a. £7. Historical Breechloading Smallarms Association, c/o Imperial War Museum, Lambeth Road, London SE1 6HZ, England. Ed. B. Bergman-Field. bk.rev.; bibl.; charts; illus. circ. 2,000.
Description: Gives a history of both military & civilian firearms & ammunition from 1800-1945.

355 900   XR   ISSN 0018-2583
DB2070
HISTORIE A VOJENSTVI. (Text in Czech; summaries in English) 1953. bi-m. $26.40. (Ceskoslovenska Armada, Historicky Ustav) Vydavatelstvi Magnet Press, Vladislavova 26, Prague 1, Czech Republic. (Subscr. to: Artia, Ve Smeckach 30, 111 27 Prague 1, Czech Republic) **Indexed:** Amer.Hist.& Life, Hist.Abstr.

355   DK   ISSN 0906-8228
HJEMMEVAERNET. 1945. m. (10/yr.). free. Generalstab, 2100 Kastellet OE, Copenhagen, Denmark. Ed. Knud Damgaard. adv.; charts; illus. circ. 97,000.
Former titles (until 1991): Hjemmevaernsbladet (ISSN 0108-9978); (until 1975): Hjemmevaernet (ISSN 0018-2834)

355.115   SA
HOME FRONT. (Text in English) 1928. m. R.10 (free to war veterans). (Memorable Order of Tin Hats) Home Front - M O T H, P.O. Box 2549, Durban 4000, South Africa. TEL 27-31-3071574. FAX 27-31-3054148. Ed. Reg Sweet. adv.; bk.rev.; bibl.; illus.; stat. circ. 12,500. (back issues avail.)
Description: Contains articles and news relevant to war veterans.

355   CM   ISSN 0046-7855
HONNEUR ET FIDELITE; bulletin de liaison des forces armees. 1953. 6/yr. free. Bureau Information Presse de Forces Armees de la Republique, B.P. 1191, Yaounde, Cameroon. Ed. Lt. Mpeck Marius. adv.; film rev.; charts; illus. circ. 2,000.

355   UK   ISSN 0046-7863
HONOURABLE ARTILLERY COMPANY JOURNAL. 1923. s-a. £10 membership. Honourable Artillery Company, Armoury House, London, EC1Y 2BQ, England. FAX 0171-628-0949. Ed. Brig. M.R.N. Bray. adv.; bk.rev. circ. 2,800 (controlled).

355 369   US   ISSN 0736-9220
VG93
THE HOOK. 1977. q. $35. Tailhook Association, 9696 Businesspark Ave., San Diego, CA 92131-1643. TEL 619-689-9227. FAX 619-578-8839. E-mail: thookassn@aol.com. Ed. Stephen T. Millikin. adv.; bk.rev.; circ. 13,000 (paid). (back issues avail.) **Document type:** academic/scholarly publication.
Description: Covers U.S. Naval carrier aviation, past and present.

355.15   US   ISSN 0018-4772
HOOSIER LEGIONNAIRE. 1926. bi-m. $3. American Legion, Department of Indiana, 777 N. Meridian St., Indianapolis, IN 46204. TEL 317-635-8411. FAX 317-237-9891. Ed. Bruce D. Barnett. adv.; bk.rev.; illus. circ. 140,000. (tabloid format)
Description: Contains news, features and issues of interest to Indiana war time veterans and their families.

355   CU
I T C N. Variant title: Informacion Technico Cientifico Noval. 3/yr. Ministerio de las Fuerzas Armadas Revolucionarias, Ave. del Puerto No. 53, Habana Vieja, Havana, Cuba.

355.351   US
ILLINOIS GUARD CHRONICLE. 1985. 4/yr. membership. Illinois National Guard, Public Affairs Office, 1301 N. MacArthur Blvd., Springfield, IL 62702-2399. TEL 217-785-3569. FAX 217-785-3527. Ed. Capt. Brian E. DeLoche. circ. 18,000. **Document type:** newspaper, government publication.
Description: Informs Guard members on training and events.

IMPERIAL WAR MUSEUM REVIEW. see *HISTORY*

IMPLEMENTATION MATTERS. see *POLITICAL SCIENCE — International Relations*

IN PERSPECTIVE OF THE BLACK AMERICAN VETERAN. see *ETHNIC INTERESTS*

355   II   ISSN 0970-2512
INDIAN DEFENCE REVIEW. 1986. 4/yr. $100 (effective 1996). Lancer International, B-3 Gulmohar Park, New Delhi 110 049, India. TEL 655652. FAX 6862077. (Subscr. to: Spantech & Lancer, 3986 Ernst Rd., Hartford, WI 53027. FAX 414-673-9064) Ed. Maj Gen Afsir Karim; Pub. Capt. Bharar Verma. adv.; bk.rev. circ. 2,000. **Document type:** academic/scholarly publication.
Description: Examines a wide range of military-related matters concerning the Indian sub-continent.
Refereed Serial

355   US
INDIANA COMBAT VETERAN. 1947. m. $2. Indiana Veterans of Foreign Wars, 1402 N. Shadeland Ave., Indianapolis, IN 46219-3637. TEL 317-634-4331. Ed. Patrick Moran. circ. 63,400. **Document type:** newspaper.
Description: Publishes articles of interest to veterans.

355   IO   ISSN 0303-4992
UA853.I5
INDONESIA. LEMBAGA PERTAHANAN NASIONAL. KETAHANAN NASIONAL. 1965. bi-m. Rps.3500. Lembaga Pertahanan Nasional, Jalan Kebon Sirih 26, Jakarta, Indonesia. adv. circ. 10,000.

355   IO   ISSN 0216-3217
INDONESIA. LEMBAGA PERTAHANAN NASIONAL. NATIONAL RESILIENCE. q. Lembaga Pertahanan Nasional, Jalan Kebon Sirih 26, Jakarta, Indonesia.

356.1   PE   ISSN 0019-9524
INFANTERIA.* 1950. q. Ministerio de Guerra, Avda. Boulevar s-n, Lima, Peru.

356.1   US   ISSN 0019-9532
UD1
INFANTRY; a professional bulletin for the U.S. Army infantryman. 1921. bi-m. $12 (typically set in Oct.). U.S. Army Infantry School, Box 2005, Ft. Benning, GA 31995-2005. TEL 706-545-2350. Ed. Russell A. Eno. bk.rev. circ. 16,000. (also avail. in microform from UMI; reprint service avail. from UMI) **Indexed:** Abstr.Mil.Bibl., Air Un.Lib.Ind., DM & T, Ind.U.S.Gov.Per., PROMT. **Document type:** government publication.
—BLDSC (4478.280000); Faxon; UMI; UnCover.
Formerly: U.S. Army Infantry School Quarterly.

MILITARY

355 II ISSN 0019-9540
UD1
INFANTRY JOURNAL. 1949. s-a. Rs.20. Infantry School, Mhow, India. Ed. B.D. Dogra. bk.rev. circ. 3,500. (also avail. in microfilm from UMI; reprint service avail. from UMI)

355 FR
INFO D G A. (Delegation Generale pour l'Armement.) m. (10/yr.). 250 F. (foreign 350 F.) (effective 1996). Association pour le Developpement et la Diffusion de l'Information Militaire, 6 rue St. Charles, 75015 Paris, France. TEL 45-77-03-76. FAX 45-79-53-73. Ed. Simone Tricot-Jourand. circ. 58,000.
Description: News of the services of the Delegation Generale pour l'Armement.

355 GW
INFOPOST. 1977. q. free. Bundesministerium der Verteidigung, Informationsstab 2, Postfach 1328, 53003 Bonn, Germany. circ. 200,000. **Document type:** government publication.
Description: Discusses life in the Armed Forces; directed at teenagers.

355 GW ISSN 0443-1243
INFORMATION FUER DIE TRUPPE; innere Fuehrung. 1956. m. free. Bundesministerium der Verteidigung, Fue SI 3, Postfach 1328, 53003 Bonn, Germany. bk.rev.; circ. controlled. **Document type:** government publication.
Description: Covers defense policy in the NATO troops.

621.38 355.31 US
INSIDE DEFENSE ELECTRONICS. w. $590 (foreign $640). Inside Washington Publishers, Box 7167, Benjamin Franklin Sta., Washington, DC 20044. TEL 703-416-8500. FAX 703-416-8543. **Document type:** newsletter.
Former titles: Electronics Report; Electronic Combat Report.

355 US
INSIDE THE AIR FORCE. w. $580 (foreign $630). Inside Washington Publishers, Box 7167, Benjamin Franklin Sta., Washington, DC 20044. TEL 703-416-8500. FAX 703-416-8543. **Document type:** newsletter.

355 US
INSIDE THE ARMY. w. $580 (foreign $630). Inside Washington Publishers, Box 7167, Benjamin Franklin Sta., Washington, DC 20044. TEL 703-416-8500. FAX 703-416-8543. **Document type:** newsletter.

359 US
INSIDE THE NAVY. w. $590 (foreign $640). Inside Washington Publishers, Box 7167, Benjamin Franklin Sta., Washington, DC 20044. TEL 703-416-8500. FAX 703-416-8543. **Document type:** newsletter.

359 US
INSIDE THE PENTAGON. w. $745 (foreign $795). Inside Washington Publishers, Box 7167, Benjamin Franklin Sta., Washington, DC 20044. TEL 703-416-8500. FAX 703-416-8543. **Document type:** newsletter.

355 US
INSIDE THE TURRET. 1948. w. free. U.S. Army, Box 995, Fort Knox, KY 40121. TEL 502-624-1211. FAX 502-624-6074. Ed. Larry Barnes. adv. contact: Cindy Smith. circ. 20,000. **Document type:** newspaper.

INSTITUTE FOR DEFENCE STUDIES AND ANALYSES. STRATEGIC ANALYSIS. see POLITICAL SCIENCE — International Relations

INSTITUTE FOR DEFENCE STUDIES AND ANALYSES. STRATEGIC DIGEST. see CIVIL DEFENSE

INSTITUTO DE GEOGRAFIA E HISTORIA MILITAR DO BRASIL. REVISTA. see HISTORY — History Of North And South America

355 364 FR ISSN 0762-8374
INTELLIGENCE NEWSLETTER. French edition: Monde du Renseignement (ISSN 0765-9776) 1980. 24/yr. 3450 F.($635) Indigo Publications, 10, rue du Sentier, 75002 Paris, France. TEL 44-88-26-10. FAX 44-88-26-15. Ed. Maurice Botbol. **Document type:** newsletter.
Description: Processes intelligence data worldwide.

355 IT
INTERARMA MILITARY NEWS. (Text in Italian) 1969. s-m. L.260000 (Europe L.370000; America L.410000). Editoriale Aeronautica s.r.l., Via Prenestina 685, 00155 Rome, Italy. TEL 39-6-2280535. Ed. Oscar Dariz. adv.: B&W page L.1800000, color page L.3700000; adv. contact: Grazia Prunas. circ. 1,110. **Document type:** newsletter.

INTERNATIONAL ASSOCIATION OF MUSEUMS OF ARMS AND MILITARY HISTORY. CONGRESS REPORTS. see MUSEUMS AND ART GALLERIES

355 UK ISSN 0950-3714
INTERNATIONAL DEFENCE NEWSLETTER, Short title: I D N. 1986. m. (except Dec.). £220 (rest of Europe £235; N. America £250) (effective 1996). P.O. Box 28, Twickenham, Mddx. TW1 1EH, England. TEL 0181-892-7471. FAX 0181-744-2702. Ed. John Jayes. **Document type:** newsletter.
Description: Provides a concise independent news reports on developments in the defense industry worldwide.

355 US ISSN 1074-3472
UG485
INTERNATIONAL DEFENSE ELECTRONICS SYSTEMS HANDBOOK. 1975. a. $195. Cardiff Publishing Co., 6300 S. Syracuse Way, Ste. 650, Englewood, CO 80111-9912. TEL 303-220-0600. FAX 303-773-9716. adv.; bibl.; charts; illus.; stat. circ. 4,000. (back issues avail.; reprint service avail.) **Document type:** trade publication.
—Faxon. **CCC.**
Incorporates (in 1992): International Countermeasure Handbook (ISSN 0145-2584)
Description: Explores electronic warfare, technology and Soviet weapons systems.

355 UK ISSN 0020-6512
U1 CODEN: IDRVAL
INTERNATIONAL DEFENSE REVIEW. (Text in English) 1968. m. £104($180) Jane's Information Group, Sentinel House, 163 Brighton Rd., Coulsdon, Surrey CR3 2NX, England. TEL 0181-763-1030. FAX 0181-763-1006. TELEX 916907-JANES-G. E-mail: http://www.janes.com/janes.html. Ed. Rupert Pengelly. adv.; bk.rev.; abstr.; charts; illus.; stat.; index. (also avail. in microform from UMI; reprint service avail. from UMI) **Indexed:** Abstr.Mil.Bibl., Air Un.Lib.Ind., DM & T, PROMT. **Document type:** trade publication.
●Also available online. Vendor(s): Knight-Ridder, Inc., Lexis-Nexis.
—BLDSC (4539.510000); Ei; Faxon; SWETS; UnCover. **CCC.**
Description: Coverage on all aspects of defense affairs.

358.4 629.13 AT
▼**INTERNATIONAL DIRECTORY OF MILITARY AIRCRAFT.** 1995. biennial. $17.95. Aerospace Publications Pty. Ltd., Weston Creek, A.C.T., Australia. Eds. Gerard Frawley and Jim Thorn. illus. **Document type:** directory.
Description: Lists all military aircraft serving in the world's air forces, giving for each technical specifications and performance data.

355 US ISSN 1056-5728
U1
INTERNATIONAL MILITARY REVIEW. q. Challenge Publications, Inc., 7950 Deering Ave., Canoga Park, CA 91304. TEL 213-887-0550. FAX 213-883-3019.

355 US ISSN 1061-0324
UA10
INTERNATIONAL OBSERVER. 1992. m. $320. Government Business Worldwide Reports, Box 55997, Washington, DC 20016. TEL 202-244-7050. FAX 202-244-5410.
Description: Presents information on political, diplomatic and economic developments around the world, with emphasis on government changes, domestic conditions and policy.

INTERNATIONAL PEACEKEEPING. see POLITICAL SCIENCE — International Relations

INTERNATIONAL STUDIES ON TERRORISM. see POLITICAL SCIENCE — International Relations

355 658 US ISSN 0273-7485
INTERSERVICE. Key Title: I S. Inter Service. 1980. q. $20. American Logistics Association, 1133 15th St., N.W., Ste. 600, Washington, DC 20005. TEL 202-466-2520. FAX 202-296-4419. Ed. Herman Marshall. adv.; illus. circ. 10,000. (back issues avail.) **Indexed:** Abstr.Mil.Bibl., Air Un.Lib.Ind., SRI. **Document type:** trade publication.
—UnCover.
Supersedes (1921-1980): American Logistics Association Review (ISSN 0034-6322); Which was formerly: Quartermaster Review.

355.15 BE
INVALIDE BELGE. Dutch edition: Belgische Verminkte. (Text in French) 1917. m. 350 BEF (foreign 450 BEF). Place E. Flagey 7-4, B-1050 Brussels, Belgium. TEL 02-647-07-78. Ed. Roger Thysebaert. adv.; bk.rev. circ. 14,000 (5,000 Dutch ed.; 9,000 French ed.).

355 IE
IRISH DEFENCE FORCES MAGAZINE. 1940. 10/yr. I£10. Defence Forces Headquarters, Parkgate St., Dublin 8, Ireland. TEL 01-379911. FAX 01-6779018. Ed. Ray Slattery. adv. contact: Tom O'Callagman. bk.rev. circ. 7,000. **Document type:** bulletin.

355 IE ISSN 0021-1389
IRISH SWORD. 1949. 2/yr. I£25. Military History Society of Ireland, c/o University College Dublin, Newman House, 86 St. Stephen's Green, Dublin 2, Ireland. Ed. Harman Murtagh. bk.rev.; charts; illus.; index. circ. 2,500. **Indexed:** Amer.Hist.& Life, Br.Archaeol.Abstr., Hist.Abstr. **Document type:** academic/scholarly publication.
—BLDSC (4574.840000).

623 IT ISSN 0021-2555
ISTITUTO STORICO E DI CULTURA DELL'ARMA DEL GENIO. BOLLETTINO. 1935. s-a. L.5000($6.) Istituto Storico e di Cultura dell'Arma del Genio, Lungotevere della Vittoria 31, 00195 Rome, Italy. Dir. Roberto Scorza. adv.; bk.rev.; abstr.; charts; illus.; index. circ. 650. **Indexed:** Amer.Hist.& Life, Hist.Abstr.

ITALY. SCUOLA DI GUERRA. BIBLIOTECA. BOLLETTINO. see LIBRARY AND INFORMATION SCIENCES

358 623 GW ISSN 0075-2428
UF530
JAHRBUCH DER WEHRTECHNIK. 1966. a. DM.39.80. Bernard & Graefe Verlag, Karl-Mand-Strasse 2, 56070 Koblenz, Germany. TEL 0261-80706-0. FAX 0228-6483109. TELEX 862662-SPS-D. Ed. Wolfgang Flume. adv. circ. 5,000.
—CCC.

355 UK ISSN 0143-9952
UG446.5
JANE'S ARMOUR AND ARTILLERY. 1979. a. £185. Jane's Information Group, Sentinel House, 163 Brighton Rd., Coulsdon, Surrey CR5 2NH, England. TEL 0181-763-1030. FAX 0181-763-1006. TELEX 916907-JANES-G. (Orders in U.S. and Canada to: Dept. DSM, 1340 Braddock Pl., Ste. 300, Box 1436, Alexandria, VA 22314-1651) Ed. Christopher F. Foss. adv.; index. **Document type:** directory.
●Also available on CD-ROM.
—CCC.
Description: Covers development histories, detailed descriptions, lists of variants and modifications, full specifications, lists of user countries and manufacturer contact details for armoured fighting vehicles and artillery worldwide.

355 UK
JANE'S ARMOUR AND ARTILLERY INFORMATION PACKAGE. 1993. 11/yr. Jane's Information Group, Sentinel House, 163 Brighton Rd., Coulsdon, Surrey CR5 2NH, England. TEL 0181-763-1030. FAX 0181-763-1006. Ed. Christopher Foss. **Document type:** bulletin.
Formerly: Jane's Information Update. Armour and Artillery.

MILITARY

358.4 UK
JANE'S ARMOUR AND ARTILLERY UPGRADES. 1988. a. £175($255) Jane's Information Group, Sentinel House, 163 Brighton Rd., Coulsdon, Surrey CR5 2NH, England. TEL 0181-763-1030. FAX 0181-763-1006. TELEX 916907-JANES-G. (Orders in U.S. and Canada to: Dept. DSM, 1340 Braddock Pl., Ste. 300, Box 1436, Alexandria, VA 22314-1651) Ed. Christopher F. Foss. illus. **Document type:** trade publication.
● Also available on CD-ROM.
Former titles: Jane's A F V Retrofit Systems (ISSN 0954-383X); Jane's A F V Systems.
Description: Covers the key armoured fighting vehicle and artillery sub-systems available for installation in new and rebuilt vehicles, with development histories, descriptions, specifications, photographs, and supplier contact information for manufacturers worldwide.

355 629.13 UK   ISSN 0960-6211
JANE'S BATTLEFIELD SURVEILLANCE. a. £160($255) Jane's Information Group, Sentinel House, 163 Brighton Rd., Coulsdon, Surrey CR5 2NH, England. TEL 0181-763-1030. FAX 0181-763-1006. TELEX 916907-JANES-G. (Orders in U.S. and Canada to: Dept. DSM, 1340 Braddock Pl., Ste. 300, Box 1436, Alexandria, VA 22314-1651) Eds. T. Hooton, K. Munson. **Document type:** trade publication.
● Also available on CD-ROM.
—BLDSC (4646.660000). **CCC.**
Supersedes in part: Jane's Weapon Systems (ISSN 0075-3068)
Description: Analysis of airborne ground-based reconnaissance and surveillance systems used in the modern battle field.

355 629.13 UK
JANE'S C 4 I SYSTEMS. a. £160($255) Jane's Information Group, Sentinel House, 163 Brighton Rd., Coulsdon, Surrey CR5 2NH, England. TEL 0181-763-1030. FAX 0181-763-1006. TELEX 916907-JANES-G. (Subscr. in U.S. and Canada to: Dept. DSM, 1340 Braddock Pl., Ste. 300, Box 1436, Alexandria, VA 22314-1651) Ed. Peter Rackman. adv. contact: Sandie Palmer. **Document type:** directory.
● Also available on CD-ROM.
—CCC.
Former titles (until 1994): Jane's C 3 I Systems (ISSN 0961-0278); Jane's C 3 I; Which supersedes in part: Jane's Weapon Systems (ISSN 0075-3068)
Description: Guide to all "C4I" systems around the world, including command information systems, communications networks, and intelligence gathering systems.

355 UK
▼**JANE'S DEFENCE CONTRACTS.** (Supplement to: Jane's Defence Weekly) 1994. m. £75. Jane's Information Group, Sentinel House, 163 Brighton Rd., Coulsdon, Surrey CR5 2NH, England. TEL 0181-763-1030. FAX 0181-763-1006. E-mail: http://www.janes.com/janes.html. (Subscr. in N. America to: 1340 Braddock Pl., Ste. 300, Alexandria, VA 22314-1657. TEL 703-683-3700. FAX 703-836-5328) Ed. Peter Howard. **Document type:** trade publication.
Description: Provides information dealing with important defense contracts from around the world.

355 UK   ISSN 0265-3818
UF530
JANE'S DEFENCE WEEKLY. (Supplement avail: Jane's Defence Contracts) 1980. w. £167($187) Jane's Information Group, Sentinel House, 163 Brighton Rd., Coulsdon, Surrey CR5 2NH, England. TEL 0181-763-1030. FAX 0181-763-1006. E-mail: http://www.janes.com/janes.html. (Subscr. in N. America to: 1340 Braddock Pl., Ste. 300, Alexandria, VA 22314-1657. TEL 703-683-3700. FAX 703-836-5328) Ed. Peter Howard. **Indexed:** Abstr.Mil.Bibl., Air Un.Lib.Ind., DM & T. **Document type:** bulletin.
● Also available online. Vendor(s): Knight-Ridder, Inc.
—BLDSC (4646.840000); Faxon; SWETS; UnCover.
CCC.
Formerly (until 1984): Jane's Defence Review (ISSN 0144-0470)

359 UK   ISSN 0075-3025
VA40
JANE'S FIGHTING SHIPS. 1898. a. £185. Jane's Information Group, Sentinel House, 163 Brighton Rd., Coulsdon, Surrey CR5 2NH, England. TEL 0181-763-1030. FAX 0181-763-1006. TELEX 916907-JANES-G. E-mail: http://www.janes.com/janes.html. (Orders in U.S. and Canada to: Dept. DSM, 1430 Braddock Pl., Ste. 300, Box 1436, Alexandria, VA 22314-1651) Ed. Capt. Richard Sharpe. adv.; index. **Document type:** directory.
● Also available on CD-ROM.
—CCC.
Description: Survey of the fleets, equipment, structures, and personnel of the world's navy.

355 UK   ISSN 0306-3410
JANE'S INFANTRY WEAPONS. 1975. a. £160($255) Jane's Information Group, Sentinel House, 163 Brighton Rd., Coulsdon, Surrey CR5 2NH, England. TEL 081-763-1030. FAX 081-763-1006. TELEX 916907-JANES-G. (Orders in U.S. and Canada to: Dept. DSM, 1340 Braddock Pl., Ste. 300, Box 1436, Alexandria, VA 22314-1651) Ed. Ian V. Hogg. adv.; index. **Document type:** directory.
● Also available on CD-ROM.
Description: Describes and analyzes over 1500 weapons from every manufacturing country in the world. Also details national inventories.

359 UK
JANE'S INFORMATION UPDATE. FIGHTING SHIPS. 1993. 11/yr. Jane's Information Group, Sentinel House, 163 Brighton Rd., Coulsdon, Surrey CR5 2NH, England. TEL 0181-763-1030. FAX 0181-763-1006. Ed. Richard Sharpe. **Document type:** bulletin.

355 UK   ISSN 1350-6226
UA15   CODEN: JINRE5
JANE'S INTELLIGENCE REVIEW. 1989. 12/yr. £149($250) Jane's Information Group, Sentinel House, 163 Brighton Road, Couldsdon, Surrey CR3 2NH, England. TEL 0181-763-1030. FAX 0181-763-1006. TELEX 916907-JANES-G. E-mail: http://www.janes.com/james.html. (Subscr. in U.S. and Canada to: Dept. DSM, 1340 Braddock Pl., Ste. 300, Box 1436, Alexandria, VA 22313-2036) bk.rev. circ. 3,000. **Indexed:** Air Un.Lib.Ind. **Document type:** trade publication.
● Also available online. Vendor(s): Knight-Ridder, Inc.
—BLDSC (4647.071000); SWETS. **CCC.**
Formerly: Jane's Soviet Intelligence Review (ISSN 0955-1247)
Description: Intelligence briefing reports.

355 UK   ISSN 0256-7822
UC260
JANE'S INTERNATIONAL DEFENCE DIRECTORY. 1984. a. £275($425) Jane's Information Group, Sentinel House, 163 Brighton Rd., Coulsdon, Surrey CR5 2NH, England. TEL 0181-763-1030. FAX 0181-763-1006. TELEX 916907-JANES-G. E-mail: directories@janes.com.uk. Ed. Ian Tandy. adv. contact: Richard West. index. (back issues avail.) **Document type:** directory.
● Also available on CD-ROM.
—BLDSC (4539.509600).
Description: Lists defense companies, organisations worldwide. Includes company name, key personnel and product, service description.

355 UK   ISSN 0959-5821
JANE'S LAND-BASED AIR DEFENCE. 1988. a. £175. Jane's Information Group, Sentinel House, 163 Brighton Rd., Coulsdon, Surrey CR5 2NH, England. TEL 0181-763-1030. FAX 0181-763-1006. TELEX 916907-JANES-G. (Orders in U.S. and Canada to: Dept. DSM, 1340 Braddock Pl., Ste. 300, Box 1436, Alexandria, VA 22314-1651) Eds. C. Foss, T. Cullen. **Document type:** directory.
● Also available on CD-ROM.
—BLDSC (4647.073000).
Formerly (until 1988): Jane's Battlefield Air Defence (ISSN 0954-3821)
Description: Presents data on land-based air defence weapons, covering all types of static and mobile anti-aircraft, anti-helicopter and anti-missile systems in service or under development all over the world.

355 UK   ISSN 0144-0004
UG590
JANE'S MILITARY COMMUNICATIONS. 1979. a. £160($255) Jane's Information Group, Sentinel House, 163 Brighton Rd., Coulsdon, Surrey CR5 2NH, England. TEL 081-763-1030. FAX 081-763-1006. TELEX 916907-JANE-G. (Orders in U.S. and Canada to: Dept. DSM, 1340 Braddock Pl., Ste. 300, Box 1436, Alexandria, VA 22314-1651) Ed. John Williamson. adv.; index. **Document type:** trade publication.
● Also available on CD-ROM.
—CCC.
Description: Devoted to communication systems, equipment and ancillaries designed for, and used by, the world's armed forces. Includes sections devoted to test and maintenance, security, surveillance and signal analysis, direction finding and jamming.

355 UK   ISSN 0954-3805
JANE'S MILITARY TRAINING SYSTEMS. a. £160($255) Jane's Information Group, Sentinel House, 163 Brighton Rd., Coulsdon, Surrey CR5 2NH, England. TEL 081-763-1030. FAX 081-763-1006. TELEX 916907-JANES-G. (Orders in U.S. and Canada to: Dept. DSM, 1340 Braddock Pl., Ste. 300, Box 1436, Alexandria, VA 22314-1651) Ed. Terry Gander. **Document type:** directory.
● Also available on CD-ROM.
—BLDSC (4647.086500).
Description: Incorporates technical profiles of more than 400 items of land, sea, and air military training equipment from small arms ranges to full-scale aviation and ship-building simulators.

355 UK
JANE'S MILITARY VEHICLES AND LOGISTICS. 1978. a. £160($255) Jane's Information Group, Sentinel House, 163 Brighton Rd., Coulsdon, Surrey CR5 2NH, England. TEL 081-763-1030. FAX 081-763-1006. TELEX 916907-JANES-G. (Orders in U.S. and Canada to: Dept. DSM, 1340 Braddock Pl., Ste. 300, Box 1436, Alexandria, VA 22314-1651) Eds. Terry Gander, Christopher Foss. illus.; index. **Document type:** directory.
● Also available on CD-ROM.
Former titles: Jane's Military Logistics (ISSN 0954-4941); Jane's Military Vehicles and Ground Support Equipment (ISSN 0263-2594); Jane's Combat Support Equipment (ISSN 0143-1420)
Description: Worldwide survey using text, photographs, drawings and diagrams of logistic vehicles and associated equipment including materials handling equipment, personnel transport, bridging, land and mine warfare plus fuel and water supplies.

355 UK   ISSN 0954-3791
JANE'S N B C PROTECTION EQUIPMENT. a. £160($255) Jane's Information Group, Sentinel House, 163 Brighton Rd., Coulsdon, Surrey CR5 2NH, England. TEL 0181-763-1030. FAX 0181-763-1006. TELEX 916907-JANES-G. E-mail: http://www.janes.com/janes.html. (Orders in U.S. and Canada to: Dept. DSM, 1340 Braddock Pl., Ste. 300, Box 1436, Alexandria, VA 22314-1651) Ed. Terry Gander. **Document type:** directory.
● Also available on CD-ROM.
—BLDSC (4647.089700).
Description: Covers all types of NBC protection from respirators and clothing to new medical and life support equipment.

359 UK   ISSN 0960-4448
JANE'S NAVAL WEAPON SYSTEM. 1988. 3/yr. £290($360) Jane's Information Group, Sentinel House, 163 Brighton Rd., Coulsdon, Surrey CR5 2NH, England. TEL 0181-763-1030. FAX 0181-763-1006. TELEX 916907-JANES-G. E-mail: http://www.janes.com/janes.html. Ed. Edward Robert Hooton. (looseleaf format; back issues avail.) **Document type:** directory.
● Also available on CD-ROM.
—BLDSC (4647.089500).
Description: Examines naval weapon systems and associated equipment.

JANE'S POLICE AND SECURITY EQUIPMENT. see *CRIMINOLOGY AND LAW ENFORCEMENT — Security*

MILITARY   4731

621.38 355   UK   ISSN 0959-5759
JANE'S RADAR AND ELECTRONIC WARFARE SYSTEMS. 1989. a. £160($255) Jane's Information Group, Sentinel House, 163 Brighton Rd., Coulsdon, Surrey CR5 2NH, England. TEL 081-763-1030. FAX 081-763-1006. TELEX 916907-JANES-G. (Subscr. in U.S. and Canada to: Dept. DSM, 1340 Braddock Pl., Ste. 300, Box 1436, Alexandria, VA 22314-1651) Ed. Bernard Blake. **Document type:** directory.
● Also available on CD-ROM.
—BLDSC (4647.094000).
Formerly: Jane's Radar and E-W Systems.
Description: Covers international air-defence systems, land-based air defence radars, land, sea, space, and air-based surveillance radars, naval and airborne fire control radars, ATC systems and land, sea and air based COMINT, ELINT AND ECM systems.

355   UK   ISSN 0959-6283
JANE'S UNDERWATER WARFARE SYSTEMS. 1989. a. £175($265) Jane's Information Group, Sentinel House, 163 Brighton Rd., Coulsdon, Surrey CR5 2NH, England. TEL 0181-736-1030. FAX 0181-763-1006. TELEX 916907-JANES-G. (Orders in U.S. and Canada to: Dept. DSM, 1340 Braddock Pl., Ste. 300, Box 1436, Alexandria, VA 22314-1651) Ed. T. Watts. **Document type:** catalog.
● Also available on CD-ROM.
—BLDSC (4647.115000).
Description: Covers all aspects of the underwater warfare scene, including underwater weapons and their fire control systems, sonar, sonobuoys, MAD, underwater commmunications ranges and targets.

355 327   HK
JAPAN DEFENSE & SECURITY REPORT. (Text in English) 1993. m. $495. N & N International (Hong Kong) Ltd., G.P.O. Box 8926, Hong Kong. FAX 852-856-5648. Ed. Edward Neilan.
Description: Contains analysis and commentary on Japan's increasing defense establishment and security apparatus.

355.15 296.7   US   ISSN 0047-2018
DS101
JEWISH VETERAN; the patriotic voice of American Jewry. 1933. 5/yr. $10. Jewish War Veterans of the U.S.A., 1811 R St., N.W., Washington, DC 20009. TEL 202-265-6280. FAX 202-234-5662. Ed. Howard Metzger. adv.; bk.rev.; charts; illus. circ. 100,000. (also avail. in microfilm from AJP)
Description: Updates readers on issues of concern to veterans and Jews, including benefits, entitlement, veteran's health care, the Middle East, Israel, anti-Semitism and racism.

JIANCHUAN ZHISHI. see TRANSPORTATION — Ships And Shipping

355   US
JIEFANGJUN BAO/LIBERATION ARMY DAILY. (Text in Chinese). d. $329.80. (Zhongguo Renmin Jiefangjun, CC - Chinese People's Liberation Army) China Books & Periodicals, Inc., 2929 24th St., San Francisco, CA 94110. TEL 415-282-2994. FAX 415-282-0994. **Document type:** newspaper.

355.1   CC   ISSN 0009-3823
JIEFANGJUN HUABAO/P L A PICTORIAL. (Text in Chinese) 1951. m. Y43.20($108) (Zhongguo Renmin Jiefangjun, Zong Zhengzhibu - Chinese People's Liberation Army) Jiefangjun Huabao She, 40 Sanlihe Lu, Ganjiakou, Beijing 100037, People's Republic of China. TEL 831-1525. (Dist. outside China by: China International Book Trading Corp., P.O. Box 399, Beijing, P.R.C.; Dist. in US by: China Books & Periodicals, Inc., 2929 24th St., San Francisco, CA 94110. TEL 415-282-2994) Ed. Liu Tiesheng. illus. (tabloid format)

355   US
JING BAO JOURNAL. 1948. bi-m. membership only. Flying Tigers of the 14th Air Force Association, Inc., Box 285, Selden, NY 11784. TEL 516-698-1782. Ed. Milt Miller. bk.rev.; film rev.; play rev. circ. 4,070. **Document type:** newsletter.
Description: Covers association activities and tales of members during World War II in China.

355   II
JODESA. (Text in English) 1978. q. Rs.5. Defence Scientists Association, Metcalfe House, Delhi 110 054, India. FAX 11-2919151. TELEX 031-78030.

355   PO   ISSN 0447-8819
JORNAL DO EXERCITO. 1960. m. Esc.950. Estado Maior do Exercito, Largo da Graca 94, 1100 Lisbon, Portugal. TEL 870355. Ed. Maj. Jose Machado Diniz. adv.; bk.rev.; charts; illus.; index. circ. 8,000.

355   FR   ISSN 0021-8014
JOURNAL DES COMBATTANTS. 1916. w. 180 F. 80 rue des Prairies, 75020 Paris, France. Ed. Mrs. Daniel. adv.; bk.rev.; bibl.; illus.; stat. circ. 30,000.

355   US   ISSN 0897-0475
E487
JOURNAL OF CONFEDERATE HISTORY. 1988. q. $39.95. Southern Heritage Press, Box 347163, Atlanta, GA 30334. TEL 404-963-6776. Ed. J.H. Segars; Pub. John McGlone. adv.; bk.rev. (back issues avail.) **Document type:** academic/scholarly publication, monographic series.
Description: Publishes scholarly monographs on the Civil War.
Refereed Serial

355   US   ISSN 0192-429X
UG485   CODEN: JELDER
JOURNAL OF ELECTRONIC DEFENSE. 1978. m. $67 to non-members; foreign $120. (Association of Old Crows) Horizon - House - Publications, Inc., 685 Canton St., Norwood, MA 02062.
TEL 617-769-9750. FAX 617-762-9230. TELEX 951 659. Ed. Hal Gershanoff. adv. circ. 25,000. (reprint service avail.) **Indexed:** Abstr.Mil.Bibl., Air Un.Lib.Ind., DM & T, INSPEC (1989-), PROMT.
—BLDSC (4974.920000); Ei; Faxon; SWETS; UMI. CCC.
Description: Planning and procurement, technology and application of EW equipment and subsystems, EW system integration, performance and operations.

355   US   ISSN 0899-3718
E181
JOURNAL OF MILITARY HISTORY. 1937. q. $25 to individuals; institutions $45. Society for Military History, c/o Virginia Military Institute, Lexington, VA 24450. TEL 703-464-7468. FAX 703-464-5229. (Co-sponsors: George C. Marshall Foundation; Virginia Military Institute) Eds. Henry S. Bausum, Larry I. Bland. adv. contact: Frances Richardson. bk.rev.; bibl.; charts; illus.; index, cum.index: 1937-1995; circ. 2,700 (paid). (also avail. in microfilm from UMI) **Indexed:** Abstr.Mil.Bibl., Air Un.Lib.Ind., Amer.Bibl.Slavic & E.Eur.Stud., Amer.Hist.& Life, Arts & Hum.Cit.Ind., Curr.Cont., Hist.Abstr., Mid.East: Abstr.& Ind., So.Pac.Per.Ind. **Document type:** academic/scholarly publication.
● Also available online. Vendor(s): University Microfilms International.
—BLDSC (5019.945000); Faxon; UMI; UnCover.
Formerly: (until vol.52): Military Affairs (ISSN 0026-3931)
Description: Publishes scholarly articles and reviews on all aspects of military history.
Refereed Serial

JOURNAL OF MILITARY PREPARATORY SCHOOL EDUCATION. see EDUCATION

JOURNAL OF POLITICAL AND MILITARY SOCIOLOGY. see SOCIOLOGY

355   UK   ISSN 1351-8046
UA770   CODEN: JSMTE8
THE JOURNAL OF SLAVIC MILITARY STUDIES. 1988. q. £42($48) to individuals; institutions £130 ($195) (effective 1996). Frank Cass, Newbury House, 890-900 Eastern Ave., Newbury Park, Ilford, Essex 1G2 7HH, England. TEL 44-181-599-8866. FAX 44-181-599-0984. E-mail: 100067,1576@compuserve.com. Eds. Christopher Donnelly, David Glantz. adv.; B&W page £195 ($275); adv. contact: Anne Kidson. bk.rev.; index. (back issues avail.) **Indexed:** Air Un.Lib.Ind, Int.Polit.Sci.Abstr., Polit.Sci.Abstr. **Document type:** academic/scholarly publication.
—BLDSC (5064.675000). CCC.
Formerly: (until 1993): Journal of Soviet Military Studies (ISSN 0954-254X)
Description: Investigates all aspects of military affairs in the Slavic nations of Central and Eastern Europe in a historical and geopolitical context.
Refereed Serial

355 990 900   AT   ISSN 0729-6274
JOURNAL OF THE AUSTRALIAN WAR MEMORIAL. 1982. 2/yr. Aus.$25 (effective 1995). Australian War Memorial, G.P.O. Box 345, Canberra, A.C.T. 2601, Australia. TEL 61-6-2434345. FAX 61-6-2434325. E-mail: peter.londey@awn.gov.au. Ed. P. Londey. adv.; bk.rev.; illus. circ. 1,200. (back issues avail.) **Indexed:** Aus.P.A.I.S. **Document type:** academic/scholarly publication.
—UnCover.
Description: Articles on all aspects of Australian military history, notes on the Memorial's collection, and reviews of latest publications in the field.
Refereed Serial

355   UK   ISSN 0022-5134
JOURNAL OF THE ROYAL ARTILLERY. 1858. s-a. £6. Royal Artillery Institution, Artillery House, Front Parade, R.A. Barracks, Woolrich, London SE18 4BH, England. TEL 0181-781-3705. FAX 0181-781-3706. Ed. P.J.F. Painter. adv.; bk.rev.; illus.; maps; index every 10 yrs. circ. 4,000. **Indexed:** Air Un.Lib.Ind., DM & T. **Document type:** bulletin.
—BLDSC (4853.100000).

355.15   SA   ISSN 0022-5770
JUDEAN. (Text in Afrikaans and English) 1946. s-a. South African Jewish Ex-Service League, P.O. Box 7309, Johannesburg, South Africa. Ed. L.L. Spilg. adv.; bk.rev.; abstr.; bibl.; illus. circ. 3,000. (tabloid format)

355   MK
JUND OMAN. m. Ministry of Defence, P.O. Box 113, Muscat, Sultanate of Oman. TEL 613615. TELEX 5228. illus.

355   TS
AL-JUNDI. 1973. m. $82 (effective 1994). Ministry of Defence, Morale & Cultural Affairs Department - Wizarat al-Difa'a, P.O. Box 2838, Dubai, United Arab Emirates. TEL 971-4-451515. FAX 971-4-455033. TELEX 45554 MOD EM. Ed. Maj. Ismail Khamis Mubarak. adv.: color page $4000; adv. contact: LTC Khalid M. Al-Shaibah. circ. 4,000.
Description: Covers military affairs in the U.A.E., the Gulf region and worldwide, including the latest developments in weapons systems, as well as sports and cultural topics.

JUNDUI ZHUANYE GANBU. see BUSINESS AND ECONOMICS — Personnel Management

KAISERZEIT. see HISTORY — History Of Europe

355   AU   ISSN 0029-974X
KAMERADSCHAFT DER WIENER PANZER-DIVISION. MITTEILUNGSBLATT. 1961. q. Kameradschaft der Wiener Panzer-Division, Postfach 159, A-1061 Vienna, Austria. TEL 01-5866357. Ed. Franz Steinzer. adv.; bk.rev.; illus. circ. 4,000. **Document type:** newsletter.

355.115   GW
KAMERADSCHAFTSBUND SECHSTE PANZERDIVISION. NACHRICHTENBLATT. 1955. q. DM.18. Kameradschaftsbund Sechste Panzerdivision, Postfach 160126, 44331 Dortmund, Germany. TEL 0231-854058. **Document type:** newsletter.

KAVALLO; Zeitschrift fuer Pferdesport und Pferdezucht. see SPORTS AND GAMES — Horses And Horsemanship

355   DK   ISSN 0023-0057
KENTAUR. 1954. 5/yr. DKK 85. Kentaur, Haerens Kampskole, DK-6840 Oksboel, Denmark. TEL 45-75-27-12-00. FAX 45-75-27-25-63. Ed. Col. P. Hvidberg. adv.: B&W page DKK 1600, color page DKK 4100; adv. contact: S.E. Jensen. circ. 1,800.
Description: Deals with issues of primary interest to Army and Home Guard personnel.

970.04   US
KENTUCKY. ADJUTANT-GENERAL'S OFFICE. REPORT. Variant Title--Annual Report. a. Adjutant-General's Office, Frankfort, KY 40601. TEL 502-564-8558.

355   FR   ISSN 1141-524X
KEPI BLANC. 1947. m. 110 F. Service du moral et du foyer d'entraide de la Legion Etrangere, B.P. 78, 13673 Aubagne, France. Ed. Jean-Baptiste Chiaroni. adv.; bk.rev. circ. 12,000.

MILITARY

KESHER ELEKTRONIKA MACHSHAVIM. see *COMMUNICATIONS*

355   UK
KEY NOTE MARKET REVIEW: U K DEFENCE INDUSTRY. Variant title: U K Defence Industry. irreg. £375. Key Note Publications Ltd., Field House, 72 Oldfield Rd., Hampton, Middlesex TW12 2HQ, England. TEL 0181-783-0755. FAX 0181-783-1720. **Document type:** trade publication.
● Also available online.
Also available on CD-ROM.

355   UK
KEY NOTE REPORT: DEFENCE EQUIPMENT. irreg., vol.5, 1994. £185. Key Note Publications Ltd., Field House, 72 Oldfield Rd., Hampton, Middlesex TW12 2HQ, England. TEL 0181-783-0755. FAX 0181-783-1720. Ed. Kim Thomasson. **Document type:** monographic series.
● Also available online.
Also available on CD-ROM.

356   UK   ISSN 0140-0991
THE KINGSMAN. 1970. a. £3. The King's Regiment, Graeme House, Derby Sq., Liverpool L2 7SD, England. TEL 0151-236-6363. FAX 0151-236-6363. adv.; bk.rev.; charts; illus. circ. 1,500. **Document type:** bulletin.
Formerly: White Horse and Fleur de Lys (ISSN 0043-4930)
Description: Records the annual events and personalities in the King's Regiment, the British Army's City Regiment of Liverpool and Manchester.

355   IR
KITAB-I MUQAVAMAT. 1989. q. Rs.720 per no. Hawzah-i Hunari Sazman-i Tablighat-i Islami, 213 Summaiyah St., P.O. Box 1677-15815, Teheran, Iran. illus.

KOEHLERS FLOTTENKALENDER. JAHRBUCH FUER SCHIFFAHRT UND HAEFEN. see *TRANSPORTATION — Ships And Shipping*

355   KO   ISSN 1016-3271
THE KOREAN JOURNAL OF DEFENSE ANALYSIS. (Text in English) s-a. free. Korea Institute for Defense Analyses, Policy Planning Directorate, Chung Ryang P.O. Box 250, Seoul 130-650, Korea. TEL 82-2-9611-779. FAX 82-2-965-3295. TELEX HNMICK 23173. Ed. Young Koo Cha. **Indexed:** Int.Polit.Sci.Abstr., Polit.Sci.Abstr. **Document type:** academic/scholarly publication.
—BLDSC (5113.529000).
Description: Discusses all Asian security issues with a focus on the political, economic and military aspects of Northeast Asia.

355   JA   ISSN 0910-0423
KOWAN JIJO SOKUHO/PORT AND HARBOUR NEWS. (Text in Japanese) 1955. m. 1000 Yen per no. Kaijo Hoancho, Suirobu - Maritime Safety Agency, Hydrographic Department, 3-1, Tsukiji 5-chome, Chuo-ku, Tokyo 104, Japan. (Co-sponsor: Kaijo Hoan Kyokai - Maritime Safety Association)

355   GW   ISSN 0023-4648
KRIEGSGRAEBERFUERSORGE; Stimme und Weg. 1921. q. membership. Volksbund Deutsche Kriegsgraeberfuersorge e.V. - German War Graves Commission, Werner-Hilpert-Str. 2, 34112 Kassel, Germany. FAX 0561-7009211. Ed. Willi Kammerer. illus.; stat.; index. circ. 396,000. **Document type:** newsletter.
Description: For members of the German war graves commission.

358.4   YU   ISSN 0023-4672
KRILA ARMIJE. 1948. fortn. 50 din. per no. Ratno Vozduhoplovstvo i Protivvazdusne Odbrane, Marsala Tita 1, Zemun, Belgrade, Serbia, Yugoslavia. Ed. Predrag Pejcic.

KUN LUN/ARMY LITERATURE. see *LITERATURE*

355   SW   ISSN 0023-5369
U43.D4
KUNGLIGA KRIGSVETENSKAPSAKADEMIEN. HANDLINGAR OCH TIDSKRIFT. 1796. 6/yr. SEK 200 (includes Militaerhistorisk Tidskrift). Kungliga Krigsvetenskapsakademien - Royal Swedish Academy of Military Sciences, S-107 87 Stockholm, Sweden. TEL 46-8-788-94-43. FAX 46-8-788-99-11. Ed. Col. Bo Hugemark. adv.; bk.rev.; bibl.; charts; maps; index. circ. 1,500. **Indexed:** Amer.Hist.& Life, Hist.Abstr.
● Also available on CD-ROM.
—BLDSC (5125.500000).

355   US   ISSN 1044-8756
KF337.5.A7
L A M P LIGHTER. 1970. q. free. (American Bar Association, Standing Committee on Legal Assistance for Military Personnel) A B A Press, 750 N. Lake Shore Dr., Chicago, IL 60611. TEL 312-988-5760. FAX 312-988-5664. bk.rev.; charts. circ. 4,000. (back issues avail.) **Document type:** newsletter.
Former titles: Legal Assistance Newsletter; L A M P Occasional Newsletter (ISSN 0163-1373); American Bar Association. Standing Committee on Legal Assistance for Servicemen. Occasional Newsletter (ISSN 0065-7522)
Description: Information for legal assistance officers of the armed forces.

359.96   US   ISSN 0023-981X
D501
LEATHERNECK; magazine of the Marines. 1917. m. $18.75. Marine Corps Association, Box 1775, MCB, Quantico, VA 22134. TEL 800-336-0291. FAX 703-640-0823. Ed. Col. William White. adv.; bk.rev.; illus.; index. circ. 95,439. (also avail. in microfilm from UMI; reprint service avail. from UMI)
—UMI; UnCover.
Description: Information on what Marines do throughout the world.

356   NE   ISSN 0024-0389
LEGERKOERIER. 1951. m. fl.31. Ministerie van Defensie, Directie Voorlichting, Postbus 20701, 2500 ES The Hague, Netherlands. TEL 31-70-3188333. FAX 31-70-3188426. Ed. Wiebren J. Tabak. adv.; bk.rev.; film rev.; rec.rev. circ. 110,000. **Document type:** government publication.

355.115   CN   ISSN 0024-0435
LEGION MAGAZINE. 1926. 10/yr. Can.$10($15) Canvet Publications Ltd., Legion House, 359 Kent St., Ste. 407, Ottawa, ON K2P 0R6, Canada. TEL 613-235-8741. Ed. Mac Johnston. adv. contact: Jan Buchanan-Redden. charts; illus.; tr.lit.; circ. 488,792 (paid). (also avail. in microfilm from UMI) **Document type:** consumer publication.
—UMI.
Description: Of particular interest to veterans, serving and ex-serving personnel and their families.

354   LB
LIBERIA. MINISTRY OF NATIONAL DEFENSE. ANNUAL REPORT.* a. Ministry of National Defense, Monrovia, Liberia. **Document type:** government publication.

358.4   US
LIMELITE.* w. free. 42nd Bomb Wing, 6000 Georgia Rd., Information Office, Loring A.F.B., ME 04751. TEL 207-999-4235. FAX 207-999-2648. Ed. A. Lybargar. circ. 6,100. (tabloid format) **Document type:** newspaper.

LINCOLN MEMORIAL ASSOCIATION NEWSLETTER. see *HISTORY — History Of North And South America*

LINK (SAN ANTONIO). see *FOOD AND FOOD INDUSTRIES*

355.31   CY
LION. w. includes Services Sound & Vision Corp. Guide. (British Sovereign Base) Zavallis, British Forces Post Office 53, Nicosia, Cyprus. TEL 357-5-263926. FAX 357-5-363181. Ed. K. Fish. circ. 4,500. **Document type:** newspaper.

355   UK
LIONESS. 1945. 2/yr. £1.50 per issue to non-members. Women's Royal Army Corps Association, Block 10, A.G.C. Centre, Worthy Down, Winchester, Hants SO21 2RG, England. Ed. Lt. Col. (Retd.) David Dunn. adv.; bk.rev. circ. 6,000. **Document type:** newsletter.

355   UN
LITANI. (Text in English) m. (United Nations Interim Force in Lebanon) CMPIO - UNIFIL HQ, P.O. Box 75, Nahariya 22100, Israel. Ed. Lt.Col. S. Oduro-Kwarteng.

355.115   IS   ISSN 0334-357X
HALOCHAME. 1950. q. Organization of Disabled Veterans, Beit Halochame, P.O. Box 39262, Tel Aviv 61 392, Israel. FAX 03-421316. Ed. Gil Yudelevich. adv.; bk.rev. circ. 35,000.

LOGISTICS AND TRANSPORTATION REVIEW. see *TRANSPORTATION*

355   US
LOMPOC RECORD. 1957. d. (except Sat.) $67.92. 115 N. H St., Lompoc, CA 93436. TEL 805-736-2313. FAX 805-736-5554. Ed. Rita Henning. adv. contact: Dick Bausman. circ. 10,000. **Document type:** newspaper.
Formerly: Space and Missile Times.

327   UK   ISSN 0961-8422
U1
LONDON DEFENCE STUDIES. 1991. 10/yr. £70($233) (effective 1996). (Centre for Defence Studies) Brassey's (UK) Ltd., 33 John St., London WC1N 2AT, England. TEL 0171-753-7777. FAX 0171-753-7794. (Subscr. to: Turpin Distribution Services, Blackhorse Rd., Letchworth, Herts. SG1 1HN, England. TEL 01462-672555. FAX 01462-480947) (also avail. in microform) **Document type:** academic/scholarly publication.
—BLDSC (5293.208500).
Description: Reports on U.K. Department of Defence research.

355   CN   ISSN 0315-6389
LOOKOUT. 1955. w. Can.$26 (foreign Can.$76). Canadian Forces Base (CFB), Esquimalt F M O, Victoria, B.C. VOS 1B0, Canada. TEL 604-385-0313. FAX 604-361-3512. Ed. Corina DeGuire. adv.; bk.rev. circ. 5,000. **Document type:** newspaper.
Former titles: Maritime Command (Pacific) Lookout (ISSN 0315-6370); Naden Lookout.

355.351   NO
LOTTEBLADET. 1928. 6/yr. NOK 200 (membership). Norges Lotteforbund - Norwegian Women's Voluntary Defense League, Oslo Mil-Akershus, Oslo 1, Norway. Ed. Astrid Thon. adv.; bk.rev.; illus. circ. 4,000.

LOW INTENSITY CONFLICT & LAW ENFORCEMENT. see *POLITICAL SCIENCE — International Relations*

355.37   GW   ISSN 0343-0103
LOYAL; das Deutsche Wehrmagazin. 1960. m. DM.36. (Verband der Reservisten der Deutschen Bundeswehr e.V.) Moench Verlagsgesellschaft mbH, Postfach 140261, 53057 Bonn, Germany. TEL 0228-6483-0. FAX 0228-6483109. (Subs) adv.: B&W page $4600, color page $8500; trim 10 2/3 x 7 1/4. illus. circ. 156,000. (back issues avail.) **Document type:** trade publication.
Formerly: Reserve.

LUCIANO MANARA. see *HISTORY — History Of Europe*

358.4   GW   ISSN 0944-6826
LUFTWAFFEN-FORUM. 1987. bi-m. newsstand price: DM.9. (German Air Force) Vereinigte Motor-Verlage GmbH und Co. KG, Leuschnerstr. 1, 70162 Stuttgart, Germany. TEL 0711-1821226. FAX 0711-1821349. Ed. Wolfdietrich Hoeveler; Pub. Peter-Paul Pietsch. adv. contact: Reinhard Wittstamm. circ. 23,000. **Document type:** bulletin.
Description: News, events and features concerning military aviation for the German Armed Forces, as well as their NATO partners.

355   US   ISSN 0024-788X
UC333
M A C FLYER.* (Military Airlift Command) 1954. m. $19. U.S. Air Force, Military Airlift Command, Headquarters MAC-IGFE, Scott Air Force Base, IL 62225-5101. TEL 618-256-3534. (Orders to: Supt. of Documents, Washington, DC 20402) Ed. Maj. James M. Lee. bk.rev.; stat. circ. 12,000. (also avail. in microform from MIM,UMI; reprint service avail. from UMI) **Indexed:** Air Un.Lib.Ind., Ind.U.S.Gov.Per.
—UMI; UnCover.

M H Q: THE QUARTERLY JOURNAL OF MILITARY HISTORY. see *HISTORY — History Of North And South America*

M O D CONTRACTS BULLETIN. (Ministry of Defence) see *BUSINESS AND ECONOMICS*

M O D NEWS. (Ministry of Defence) see *BUSINESS AND ECONOMICS*

355   GW   ISSN 0937-6348
M S & T - MILITARY SIMULATION AND TRAINING. 1985. bi-m. DM.60. Moench Verlagsgesellschaft mbH, Postfach 140261, 53057 Bonn, Germany. TEL 0228-6483-0. FAX 0228-6483109. Ed. Trevor Nash. adv.: B&W page $3300, color page $6000; trim 10 1/6 x 7 5/16; adv. contact: Ute Steuer. circ. 18,872. **Document type:** trade publication.
—BLDSC (5980.840150); SWETS.
   Description: Provides reports and descriptions on training armed forces throughout the world, with an emphasis on targeting DODs, serving officers and training establishments.

355   IS   ISSN 0464-2147
MA'ARACHOT. (Supplement avail.: Cyclone) (Text and summaries in Hebrew) 1939. bi-m. Ministry of Defense Publishing House, 29 Elaazar St., P.O. Box 7026, Hakirya, Tel Aviv 61070, Israel. TEL 972-3-5694343. Eds. Rachel Rojansky, Eliavar Ben-Zedeff. bk.rev. (back issues avail.) **Indexed:** Ind.Heb.Per.

MANUAL OF AIR FORCE LAW - AMENDMENTS. see *LAW — Military Law*

MANUAL OF MILITARY LAW - AMENDMENTS. see *LAW — Military Law*

359.96   FR   ISSN 1151-1397
MARINE. 1951. q. 150 F. Association Centrale des Officiers de Reserve de l'Armee de Mer, 15 rue de LaBorde, B.P. 12, 00312 Armes, France. TEL 42-92-10-09. FAX 45-22-53-03. Eds. M. Paumier, H. Nguyen Tan. adv.; bk.rev. circ. 8,000.

359.96   US   ISSN 0025-3170
VE7
MARINE CORPS GAZETTE; the professional magazine for United States Marines. 1916. m. $18.75. Marine Corps Association, Box 1775, MCB, Quantico, VA 22134. TEL 800-336-0291. FAX 703-640-0823. Ed. Col. John E. Greenwood. adv.; bk.rev.; illus.; index. circ. 36,630. (also avail. in microfilm from UMI; reprint service avail. from UMI) **Indexed:** Abstr.Mil.Bibl., Air Un.Lib.Ind., Amer.Hist.& Life, DM & T, Hist.Abstr., PROMT, So.Pac.Per.Ind. **Document type:** trade publication.
—BLDSC (5373.765000); UMI; UnCover.
   Description: Professional Marines journal.

MARINE-RUNDSCHAU. see *TRANSPORTATION — Ships And Shipping*

359   NE   ISSN 0025-3340
V5
MARINEBLAD. 1887. m. (11/yr.) fl.72.50. Koninklijke Vereniging van Marine-Officieren, Wassenaarseweg 2b, 2596 CH The Hague, Netherlands. TEL 31-70-3839504. FAX 31-70-3835911. Ed. D.C.L. Schoonoord. adv.; bk.rev.; charts; illus. circ. 6,000. **Indexed:** Excerp.Med. **Document type:** trade publication.
—SWETS.

359.009   DK   ISSN 0106-5122
MARINEHISTORISK TIDSSKRIFT. 1967. 4/yr. DKK 55. Orlogsmuseet, Overgaden oven Vandet 58, DK-1415 Copenhagen K, Denmark. FAX 45-31-54-29-80. Ed. J.H. Barfod. bk.rev. circ. 2,500.

359.96   US   ISSN 1056-9073
MARINES. 1983. m. U.S. Marine Corps, Public Affairs, HQMC, Washington, DC 20380. TEL 202-694-1494.

359.1   SW   ISSN 0025-3375
V5
MARINNYTT. 1950. 8/yr. SEK 100 (effective 1996). Foersvarsmakten, H K V - Info, Marinnytt, Prenumeration, S-107 85 Stockholm, Sweden. TEL 46-8-788-84-58. FAX 46-8-788-88-66. Ed. Wyn Enqvist. charts; illus.; stat.

358.4   CN   ISSN 0025-3413
MARITIME COMMAND TRIDENT. (Text in English and French) 1966. s-m. Can.$20 (foreign $25). Trident Military Newspaper Ltd., P.O. Box 3308 S., Halifax, NS B3J 3J1, Canada. TEL 902-427-2347. FAX 902-427-2539. Ed. Capt. Darlene Blakeley. adv. contact: Joel Fournier. bk.rev. circ. 14,000. (tabloid format) **Document type:** newspaper.
   Description: Contains news of the maritime fleet, CFB Halifax, and the naval community at large.

359   UK   ISSN 0950-558X
V1
MARITIME DEFENCE; the journal of international naval technology. 1976. m. $70. Eldon Publications Ltd., 292-294 Walton Rd., E. Molesey, Surrey KT8 OHY, England. TEL 081-941-7510. FAX 081-941-7449. Ed. David Foxwell. adv.; illus.; stat. circ. 4,069. (also avail. in microform from UMI; back issues avail) **Indexed:** Abstr.Mil.Bibl., DM & T, PROMT.
—BLDSC (5381.352690); SWETS; UMI.
   Formerly: Maritime Defence International (ISSN 0308-5201)

355   BE
MARS ET MERCURE/MARS EN MERCURIUS. (Text in Dutch, English, French) 1926. q. 500 BEF. (Cercle Royal Mars et Mercure - Koninklijke Kring Mars en Mercurius) F. Lepeer, Ed. & Pub., 110 Ave. de Heyn, B-1090 Brussels, Belgium. TEL 32-2-4781050. FAX 32-2-4781050. adv.: B&W page 4000 BEF. bk.rev. circ. 1,500. **Document type:** bulletin.

355   NE   ISSN 0025-4029
MARS IN CATHEDRA. (Supplement to: Militaire Spectator) 1865. q. fl.40. Koninklijke Vereniging ter Beoefening van de Krijgswetenschap - Royal Society for Military Science, Karel Doormanlaan 274, 2283 BB Rijswijk, Netherlands. Ed. T. de Kruyf.

MEDAL NEWS. see *HOBBIES*

MEDICINE AND WAR. see *MEDICAL SCIENCES*

355 620   SP   ISSN 0211-4488
MEMORIAL DE INGENIERIA DE ARMAMENTO. 1965. q. 4000 ptas. Colegio Oficial de Ingenieros de Armamento, Conde de Ziquena, 13, 28004 Madrid, Spain.

MEXICAN WAR JOURNAL. see *HISTORY — History Of North And South America*

355   US   ISSN 1067-0661
MICHIGAN OVERSEAS VETERAN. 1923. m. $2. Michigan Veterans of Foreign Wars of the United States, 924 N. Washington Ave., Lansing, MI 48906-5136. TEL 313-722-4090. Ed. Elmer Wurster. adv. circ. 85,000. **Document type:** newspaper.
   Description: Covers veteran information & news in Michigan.

355   IS   ISSN 0334-5041
MIDDLE EAST MILITARY BALANCE (YEAR). (Text in English) 1983. irreg., approx. a. $49. (Tel Aviv University, Jaffee Center for Stategic Studies) Jerusalem Post, P.O. Box 81, Jerusalem 91000, Israel. TEL 972-2-551616. FAX 972-2-537527. (U.S. subscr. to: 221 E. 43rd St., Ste. 601, New York, NY 10017) circ. 2,000. (back issues avail.) **Document type:** academic/scholarly publication.
—BLDSC (5761.390020).

359.96   US
MIDWAY MIRROR; reflections of the past and present. 1941-1945; N.S. 1987. s-a. free. 6618 N. 46th Ave., Glendale, AZ 85301. TEL 602-931-1214. Ed. Albert J. Robinson. circ. 700. (looseleaf format) **Document type:** newsletter.
   Description: Covers life on Midway prior to and during World War II.

MIKROWELLEN AND H F - MAGAZIN; Telecommunications. see *ENGINEERING — Electrical Engineering*

355   SZ   ISSN 0026-3907
MILITAER-KUECHENCHEF. vol.15, 1971. bi-m. Verband Schweizerischer Militaerkuechenchefs, Muehleweg 10, CH-8135 Langnau-Gattikon, Switzerland. TEL 01-7201462. Ed. Major Qm Stampfli Pius. adv.; charts; illus.

355   SW   ISSN 0047-7354
MILITAER TEKNISK TIDSKRIFT. 1931. q. SEK 100 (typically set in Oct.). (Militaer Tekniska Foereningen) Dordius, Djurgaardslaetten 92, S-115 21 Stockholm, Sweden. TEL 46-8-662-1071. FAX 46-8-662-1071. Ed. Walter Wicklund; Pub. Aake Tison Loven. adv.: B&W page SEK 2850; trim 112 x 172. bk.rev. circ. 1,153. **Document type:** trade publication.

MILITAERGESCHICHTE. see *HISTORY — History Of Europe*

355   GW   ISSN 0026-3826
DD101
MILITAERGESCHICHTLICHE MITTEILUNGEN. (Supplement: War and Society. Newsletter.) 1967. s-a. DM.50 (students DM.35) (effective 1996). (Militaergeschichtliches Forschungsamt) R. Oldenbourg Verlag GmbH, Rosenheimerstr. 145, 81671 Munich, Germany. TEL 089-45051-0. FAX 089-45051207. (Subscr. to: Postfach 801360, 81613 Munich, Germany) Ed.Bd. adv.; bk.rev.; charts; illus.; stat.; cum.index: 1967-1971. (reprint service avail. from SCH) **Indexed:** Amer.Hist.& Life, Arts & Hum.Cit.Ind., Curr.Cont., Hist.Abstr. **Document type:** academic/scholarly publication.
—Faxon; SWETS.

MILITAERHISTORISK TIDSKRIFT. see *HISTORY — History Of Europe*

355   NO   ISSN 0801-8960
MILITAERPSYKOLOGISKE MEDDELELSER. 1955. irreg. free. Norwegian Armed Forces, Chief Psychologist, Oslo Mil, Huseby, K-Z, N-0016-Oslo, Norway. Dir. Ivar Hansen.

355.347   GW   ISSN 0047-7362
MILITAERSEELSORGE. (Supplements avail.) 1965. q. free. Katholisches Militaerbischofsamt, Postfach 190199, 53037 Bonn, Germany. TEL 0228-9121-0. FAX 0228-9121105. Ed. Ernst Niermann. bk.rev. **Document type:** bulletin.
   Description: Catholic publication with articles devoted to the spiritual care of people in the military.

355   DK   ISSN 0026-3850
MILITAERT TIDSSKRIFT. 1871. 6/yr. DKK 150 (effective 1995). Krigsvidenskabelige Selskab, Tvaerbygningen, Rigensgade 11, 2, DK-1316 Copenhagen K, Denmark. TEL 45-33-14-24-27. Ed. N.L. Fredenslund. adv.; bk.rev.; index. circ. 1,500. **Indexed:** Amer.Hist.& Life (until 1990), Hist.Abstr. (until 1990). **Document type:** proceedings.

355   NE   ISSN 0026-3869
MILITAIRE SPECTATOR. 1832. m. fl.30 (foreign fl.40). (Ministerie van Defensie) Koninklijke Vereniging ter Beoefening van de Krijgswetenschap, Karel Doormanlaan 274, 2283 BB Rijswijk, Netherlands. TEL 31-70-3984620. (Editorial addr.: Postbus 20701, 2500 ES The Hague, Netherlands. TEL 31-15-152700) adv.; bk.rev.; charts; illus.; index, cum.index. circ. 8,600. (back issues avail.)
—BLDSC (5767.900000); SWETS.

355   GW   ISSN 0724-3529
MILITARIA; Wissenschaftliches Organ fur Orden, Uniformen, Militar- und Zeitgeschicht. 1971. bi-m. DM.54 (foreign DM.60). Verlag Klaus Patzwall, Tangstedter Weg 52, 22851 Norderstedt, Germany. TEL 040-5249297. Ed. K.D. Patzwall. **Document type:** bulletin.

355   BE   ISSN 0776-7412
MILITARIA BELGICA; revue d'uniformologie et d'histoire militaire Belge. (Text in Dutch and French) 1977. q. 700 BEF includes Revue Belge d'Histoire Militaire. Societe Royale des Amis du Musee Royal de l'Armee et d'Histoire Militaire, Parc du Cinquantenaire 3, 1040 Brussels, Belgium. Ed. E.-A. Jacobs. circ. 1,000. (back issues avail.)
   Description: Highlights arms and armor.

355   US   ISSN 1046-2511
E840.4
MILITARY. 1985. 12/yr. $12. M H R Publishing Corp., 2122 28 St., Sacramento, CA 95818. TEL 916-457-8990. Ed. LTC Mike Mark. adv.; bk.rev. circ. 14,280.
   Formerly: Military History Review.
   Description: Covers World War II, Korea, Vietnam, and present military actions worldwide.

MILITARY

MILITARY ADVISOR; the publication for international military hobbyists and historians. see *HOBBIES*

MILITARY AIRCRAFT AND MISSILE DATA SHEETS. see *AERONAUTICS AND SPACE FLIGHT*

MILITARY & AEROSPACE ELECTRONICS. see *AERONAUTICS AND SPACE FLIGHT*

358 629.132   US   ISSN 0887-2465
MILITARY & COMMERCIAL FIBER BUSINESS.* 1987. fortn. $445 (foreign $480)(effective 1992). Phillips Publishing, Inc., Defense - Aviation Group, 1111 19th St., N., Ste. 503, Arlington, VA 22209-1704. TEL 703-522-8333. FAX 703-522-6448. Ed. Eric DeRitis.
●Also available online. Vendor(s): Data-Star, Knight-Ridder, Inc., NewsNet (DE06).
—CCC.
   Former titles: Military Fiber Optics News; Military Avionics (ISSN 0895-9242); Inside Military Aviation.
   Description: Covers all navigation, communications and weapons electronics systems aircraft.

355   UK   ISSN 0459-7222
UA15
THE MILITARY BALANCE. 1959. 1/yr. £40($65) (effective 1996). (International Institute for Strategic Studies) Oxford University Press, Walton St., Oxford OX2 6DP, England. TEL 44-1865-267907. FAX 44-1865-267773. E-mail: jnlorders@oup.co.uk. (Subscr. in U.S. to: Oxford University Press Inc., 2001 Evans Rd., Cary, NC 27513. TEL 919-677-0977. FAX 919-677-1714) charts; stat. circ. 22,000. **Document type:** academic/scholarly publication.
—BLDSC (5767.990000); Faxon; UMI. **CCC.**
   Description: Provides a quantitative assessment of military strength and defense spending of every country with armed forces.

262 355   US   ISSN 0026-3958
MILITARY CHAPLAIN. 1931. bi-m. $12 (foreign $15). Military Chaplains Association of the United States of America, Box 42660, Washington, DC 20015-0660. TEL 717-642-6792. FAX 717-642-6792. E-mail: CHAPLAINS@charitiesusa.com. Ed. G. William Dando. adv.; bk.rev.; illus. circ. 1,700. **Indexed:** Air Un.Lib.Ind. **Document type:** trade publication.
   Refereed Serial

MILITARY CLUB & HOSPITALITY. see *FOOD AND FOOD INDUSTRIES*

647   US   ISSN 0192-2718
MILITARY CLUBS & RECREATION. 1961. m. $10. Club Executive, Inc., Box 7088, Alexandria, VA 22307. TEL 703-765-3388. FAX 703-548-0095. Ed. Paul E. Reece. adv.; illus.; index. circ. 7,000. **Indexed:** Hospit.Ind. **Document type:** trade publication.
   Former titles: Club Executive (ISSN 0009-9554); Clubs and Recreation.

MILITARY COLLECTOR & HISTORIAN. see *ANTIQUES*

355   II   ISSN 0462-4874
MILITARY DIGEST. 1973. q. Director of Military Training, General Staff Branch MT4, Army Headquarters, DHQ P.O., New Delhi 110 011, India. bk.rev.; charts; illus.

MILITARY ENGINEER. see *ENGINEERING*

MILITARY FACILITIES LISTING. see *BUSINESS AND ECONOMICS — Trade And Industrial Directories*

355   US
MILITARY FUZES. a. $1495. Forecast International Inc. - D M S, 22 Commerce Rd., Newtown, CT 06470. TEL 203-426-0800. FAX 203-426-1964. TELEX 467615.
   Description: Features market overviews of major fuze market segments: artillery, missiles, bombs, mines, rockets, small arms, and submunitions. Reports on more than 350 U.S., European, and international fuze programs with 10-year production forecasts.

355   UK   ISSN 0026-4008
DA49
MILITARY HISTORICAL SOCIETY. BULLETIN. 1951. q. £10 (Europe £12; elsewhere £15). Military Historical Society, National Army Museum, Royal Hospital Rd., London SW3 4HT, England. adv. contact: David Hunter. bk.rev.; charts; illus.; cum.index every 5 yrs. circ. 1,400. **Indexed:** Amer.Hist.& Life, Hist.Abstr. **Document type:** bulletin.
   Description: Covers all aspects of British and Commonwealth Military History.

MILITARY HISTORY. see *HISTORY — History Of North And South America*

355   SA   ISSN 0026-4016
DT769
MILITARY HISTORY JOURNAL/KRYGSHISTORIESE TYDSKRIF. (Text and summaries in Afrikaans, English) 1967. s-a. R.35 (overseas R.50) (effective 1994). South African National Museum of Military History, P.O. Box 52090, Saxonwold 2132, South Africa. TEL 27-11-646-5513. FAX 27-11-646-5256. (Co-sponsor: South African Military History Society) Ed. S. Blendulf. bk.rev.; charts; illus.; cum.index. circ. 750. (back issues avail.) **Indexed:** Ind.S.A.Per. **Document type:** academic/scholarly publication.
—BLDSC (5768.080000); Faxon.
   Incorporates (1985-1991): South African National Museum of Military History. Review (ISSN 1016-2550)

MILITARY HISTORY OF THE WEST. see *HISTORY — History Of North And South America*

355 790.13   UK   ISSN 0953-0290
MILITARY HOBBIES. 1988. bi-m. £13 (foreign £15). Pireme Publishing Ltd., 34 Chatsworth Rd., Bournemouth, Dorset BH8 8SW, England. TEL 01202-512355. FAX 01202-512355. (Dist. by: S M Distribution, 6 Leigham Court Rd., Streatham, London SW16 2PG, England. TEL 081-677-8111; Subscr. in US to: Wise Owl Worldwide Publications, 4314 W. 238th St., Torrance, CA 90505-4509. TEL 310-375-6258. FAX 310-375-0548; Dist. in US by: Wargames Inc., Box 278, Rte. 40 E., Triadelphia, WV 26059-0278) Ed. Iain Dickie; Pub. Iain Dickie. adv. contact: Iain Dickie. bk.rev. circ. 6,000. (back issues avail.) **Document type:** consumer publication.
   Description: Covers military models, toy soldiers, and books and videos on military history.

355   US   ISSN 1040-4961
MILITARY IMAGES. 1979. bi-m. $24 (foreign $28). Harry Roach, Ed. & Pub., RD 1, Box 99A, Henryville, PA 18332. TEL 717-629-9152. adv.: B&W page $150; trim 8 1/2 x 11. bk.rev.; cum.index every 5 yrs.; circ. 2,000 (paid). (also avail. in microform from UMI; microfiche; back issues avail.; reprint service avail. from UMI)
—UnCover.
   Formerly: Military Images Magazine (ISSN 0193-9866)
   Description: Covers U.S. military history from 1839 to 1900, with particular emphasis on the Civil war, biographies of the common soldier, and original, unpublished photographs from private collections.

355   UK
MILITARY INTELLIGENCE CRITICAL ATTRIBUTES. 1981. irreg. $665. Aviation Studies International, Sussex House, Parkside, Wimbledon, London SW19 5NB, England. TEL 0181-946-5082. **Document type:** trade publication, directory.
   Description: For military intelligence planners and leaders. Covers organization, roles, missions, costs, staffing, NIE planning, and kinds of intelligence.

355   US
UB250
MILITARY INTELLIGENCE PROFESSIONAL BULLETIN. 1974. q. $8.50 (foreign $10.65) (effective 1995). U.S. Army, Intelligence Center and School, Attn.: ATZS-TDL-B, Ft. Huachuca, AZ 85613-6000. TEL 602-538-0797. FAX 602-533-6308. Ed. Capt. Stephen B. Leeder. bk.rev.; illus. circ. 5,000. (also avail. in microfiche) **Indexed:** Abstr.Mil.Bibl., Ind.U.S.Gov.Per., PROMT. **Document type:** government publication.
—UMI; UnCover.
   Formerly (until 1994): Military Intelligence (ISSN 0026-4024)
   Description: Enhances professional development in intelligence and to help formulate doctrine.

355   JO
MILITARY JOURNAL/AL-MAJALLAH AL-ASKARIYYAH.* (Text in Arabic) 1955. q. Armed Forces, Army Headquarters, Amman, Jordan.

640.73   US   ISSN 0740-5065
MILITARY LIVING. 1969. m. $12. Military Living Publications, Box 2347, Falls Church, VA 22042-0347. TEL 703-237-0203. Ed. William R. Crawford. **Document type:** consumer publication.
—CCC.
   Description: Military benefits, facilities, rest and recreation.

355   US   ISSN 0740-5073
MILITARY LIVING'S R & R REPORT; the voice of the military traveler. 1971. bi-m. $15. Military Living Publications, Box 2347, Falls Church, VA 22042-0347. TEL 703-237-0203. Ed. Ann Crawford. adv. (tabloid format; back issues avail.)
—CCC.
   Description: Military rest and recreation and travel.

355.621   US   ISSN 0026-4067
MILITARY MARKET; magazine for the military retail system. 1954. m. $84 (Special numbers: Buyers Guide; Almanac and Directory Number $10 ea.). Army Times Publishing Co., 6883 Commercial Dr., Springfield, VA 22159. TEL 703-750-8676. Ed. Roger Hyneman. adv. contact: Nat Kornfeld. charts; illus.; tr.lit.; circ. 12,000 (controlled). (also avail. in microform from UMI; microfiche from CIS; reprint service avail. from UMI) **Indexed:** SRI. **Document type:** trade publication.
   Description: Aimed at military officials and key civilians who buy for and operate base stores.

MILITARY MEDAL SOCIETY OF SOUTH AFRICA. JOURNAL. see *NUMISMATICS*

355   US   ISSN 0195-1467
U311
MILITARY MODELER. 1974. m. $27.95. Challenge Publications, Inc., 7950 Deering Ave., Canoga Park, CA 91304. TEL 818-887-0550. FAX 818-883-1343. Ed. Sydney P. Chivers. adv. circ. 20,039. **Document type:** consumer publication.

MILITARY MODELLING. see *HOBBIES*

355.4 003   US   ISSN 0275-5823
MILITARY OPERATIONS RESEARCH. 1981. irreg., vol.2, 1982. price varies. Gordon & Breach Science Publishers, c/o International Publishers Distributor, 820 Town Center Dr., Langhorne, PA 19047. TEL 215-750-2642. FAX 215-750-6343. (Subscr. to: International Publishers Distributor, P.O. Box 90, Reading, Berkshire RG1 8JL, England. TEL 44-173-456-8316) Ed. Stephen W. Leibholz. **Document type:** monographic series.
   Refereed Serial

343.01   US   ISSN 0895-4208
UB825.U54
MILITARY POLICE. 1951. s-a. $5 (foreign $6.25). U.S. Army Military Police School, Ft. McClellan, AL 36205. TEL 205-848-4326. FAX 205-848-5885. (Subscr. to: Superintendent of Documents, U.S. Government Printing Office, Box 371954, Pittsburgh, PA 15250-7954. TEL 202-512-1800. FAX 202-512-2250) Ed. Lois C. Perry. bk.rev.; illus.; index. circ. 11,000. (back issues avail.) **Indexed:** Air Un.Lib.Ind. **Document type:** government publication.
—UMI.
   Former titles (until 1987): Military Police Journal (ISSN 0884-0024); Military Police Law Enforcement Journal (ISSN 0199-7211)
   Description: Discusses the functions of military police in combat.

MILITARY PSYCHOLOGY. see *PSYCHOLOGY*

MILITARY   4735

355   US   ISSN 0026-4148
Z6723
MILITARY REVIEW. Portuguese edition (ISSN 0193-2985); Spanish edition (ISSN 0193-2977) 1922. m. (Spanish ed. q.; Portuguese ed. bi-m.) $24 (Spanish ed. $12; Portuguese ed. $8); (typically set in July). U.S. Army Command and General Staff College, Truesdell Hall, Ft. Leavenworth, KS 66027-6910. TEL 913-684-5642. FAX 913-684-4647. Ed. Ronald Mazzia. bk.rev.; abstr.; charts; illus.; maps; index. circ. 27,000. (also avail. in microfilm from UMI; back issues avail.) **Indexed:** Abstr.Mil.Bibl., Air Un.Lib.Ind., Amer.Bibl.Slavic & E.Eur.Stud, Amer.Hist.& Life, DM & T, Hist.Abstr., Ind.U.S.Gov.Per., Int.Polit.Sci.Abstr., P.A.I.S., PROMT. —BLDSC (5768.170000); Faxon; SWETS; UMI; UnCover.

MILITARY ROBOTICS NEWSLETTER; covering government and defense applications of robotics. see *COMPUTERS — Robotics*

621.3 629   US   ISSN 0743-7897
MILITARY SPACE. 1984. fortn. $552 (foreign $567). Pasha Publications Inc., 1616 N. Ft. Myer Dr., Ste. 1000, Arlington, VA 22209-3107. TEL 703-528-1244. FAX 703-528-1253. Ed. Frank Sietzen. **Document type:** newsletter.
●Also available online. Vendor(s): NewsNet (DE04). —CCC.
  Description: Reports on political issues, technological and international developments and opportunities in military space programs.

623   US
MILITARY SPECIFICATIONS AND STANDARDS SERVICES NUMERIC INDEX. (In 2 vols.) 1963. bi-m. $200. Information Handling Services, 15 Inverness Way East, Englewood, CO 80150. TEL 303-790-0600. FAX 303-799-4085. TELEX 4322083 IHS UI. Ed. Liz Maynard Prigge. adv. circ. 2,715.
●Also available online. Vendor(s): Knight-Ridder, Inc. Also available on CD-ROM.
  Formerly: Military Specifications and Standard Services Index.
  Description: Provides numeric access to military specifications and standards documents.

623   US
MILITARY TECHNOLOGY. m. $80. N & A Military Publishing Service Inc., 8 W. Madison St., Baltimore, MD 21201. **Indexed:** Air Un.Lib.Ind.

355   GW
MILITARY TECHNOLOGY: MILTECH. (Text in English) 1977. m. DM.115($85) Moench Verlagsgesellschaft mbH, Postfach 140261, 53057 Bonn, Germany. TEL 0228-6483-0. FAX 0228-6483109. TELEX 8869429-MVB-D. Ed. Ezio Bonsignore. adv.: B&W page $4100, color page $7400; trim 10 1/6 x 7 5/16; adv. contact: Ute Steuer. bk.rev. circ. 25,952. **Indexed:** DM & T, PROMT. **Document type:** trade publication. —BLDSC (5768.361000); Ei; SWETS. **CCC.**
  Formerly: Military Technology (ISSN 0722-3226)
  Description: Journal of defense technology and economics.

MILITARY TRAVEL GUIDE. see *TRAVEL AND TOURISM*

MILITARY TRAVEL NEWS. see *TRAVEL AND TOURISM*

355 388.3   US   ISSN 0893-3863
MILITARY VEHICLES. 1987. bi-m. $15. Eagle Press, Box 1748, Union, NJ 07083. TEL 908-688-6015. FAX 908-686-0358. Eds. R.G. Ivory, D.R. Spence. adv.; bk.rev.; circ. 8,500 (paid). (back issues avail.)
  Description: Features restoration of historic U.S. military vehicles (jeeps, trucks).

355   II   ISSN 0076-8782
U10.I5
MILITARY YEARBOOK. (Text in English) 1965. a. Rs.425($105.65) (£55.05). Guide Publications, P.O. Box 2525, New Delhi 110 005, India. TEL 91-11-5724832. TELEX 031-77174 GPUB IN. (Dist. in U.S. by: Taylor & Francis Inc, 242 Cherry St., Philadelphia, PA 19106) Ed. J. Baranwal. adv.; illus.; stat. circ. 5,800.
  Description: Covers organizational and technological aspects, global events affecting the security environment, and a complete equipment catalogue of army, navy, air force of India.

355.133 350   RU   ISSN 0869-558X
HV8224   CODEN: SOMIEC
MILITSIYA. 1922. m. $66. Ministerstvo Vnutrennikh Del, c/o A.G. Gorlov, Ed., Ul. Ivanovskaya 24, 127434 Moscow, Russia. TEL 216-87-19. (Dist. in U.S. by: Victor Kamkin Inc., 4956 Boiling Brook Pkwy, Rockville, MD 20852. TEL 301-881-5973) Ed. G.E. Mel'nik. circ. 107,200.
  Formerly: Sovetskaya Militsiya (ISSN 0320-2259)

MILIZ; das Magazin fuer Sicherheits- und Friedenspolitik. see *POLITICAL SCIENCE — International Relations*

301   US   ISSN 0736-718X
UB418.W65
MINERVA; quarterly report on women and the military. 1983. q. $50 to individuals; institutions $75; students $25. (Minerva Center) Linda Grant DePauw, Ed. & Pub., 20 Granada Rd., Pasadena, MD 21122-2708. TEL 410-437-5379. bk.rev.; film rev.; play rev.; bibl.; charts; illus.; cum.index: 1983-1984. circ. 800. (back issues avail.) **Indexed:** Amer.Hist.& Life, Hist.Abstr.
  Description: Contains articles relating to service women, military wives, and women veterans (both military and civilian) from all nations and all eras.

301   US   ISSN 0897-6104
UB418.W65
MINERVA'S BULLETIN BOARD. 1988. q. $25 to individuals; institutions $50; students $12.50. (Minerva Center) Linda Grant DePauw, Ed. & Pub., 20 Granada Rd., Pasadena, MD 21122-2708. TEL 410-437-5379.
  Description: Focuses on women and the military. Includes news briefs, short announcements and letters to the editors.

355 900   UK   ISSN 0266-3228
MINIATURE WARGAMES. 1983. m. £28 (foreign £32). Pireme Publishing Ltd., 34 Chatsworth Rd., Charminster, Bournemouth BH8 8SW, England. TEL 01202-512355. FAX 01202-512355. (Dist. in U.K. by: S M Distributor, 6 Leigham Court Rd., Streatham, London SW16 2PG, England. TEL 0181-677-8111; Dist. in U.S. by: Wargames Inc., Box 278, Rte. 40 E., Triadelphia, WV 26059-0278. TEL 304-547-0000) Ed. Iain Dickie; Pub. Iain Dickie. adv. contact: Iain Dickie. bk.rev. circ. 15,000. (back issues avail.) **Document type:** consumer publication.
  Description: Discusses the simulation of battles in miniature of all periods and theaters.

355   US   ISSN 0164-4270
MINNESOTA LEGIONNAIRE. 1922. m. $5. American Legion, Department of Minnesota, Veterans Service Bldg., St. Paul, MN 55155. TEL 612-291-1800. FAX 612-291-1057. Ed. Ron D. Johnson. adv.; B&W page $1215. bk.rev. circ. 137,000. (back issues avail.)

355.347 200   UK
MISSION TO MILITARY GARRISONS NEWS. 1971. 4/yr. free to supporters. Mission to Military Garrisons Inc., 23 Royal Exchange Sq., Glasgow G1 3AJ, Scotland. TEL 0141-221-3575. Ed. K.P. Green. circ. 1,600. **Document type:** newsletter.
  Former titles (until 1992): Mission to Military Garrisons Quarterly Record; Mission to Mediterranean Garrisons Quarterly Record.
  Description: Covers the activities at each of the centers operated by the Mission. Includes prayer topics.

MISSISSIPPI LEGION-AIRE. see *CLUBS*

MONTANA LEGIONNAIRE. see *CLUBS*

359   YU   ISSN 0027-1136
MORNARICKI GLASNIK/NAVY JOURNAL. 1951. bi-m. $20. (Ratna Mornarica) Vojnoizdavacki Zavod, Svetozara Markovica 70, 11002 Belgrade, Serbia, Yugoslavia. Ed. Malin Malivuk.

355   US
MOUNTAINEER (COLORADO SPRINGS). 1942. w. $50 (effective Dec. 1990). Fort Carson, Public Affairs Office, Bldg. 1544, Fort Carson, CO 80913-5000. TEL 719-579-4144. FAX 719-579-1021. Ed. Sam Sears. adv.; bk.rev. circ. 12,000. **Document type:** newspaper, government publication.

335.115   AT
MUFTI. 1934. q. Aus.$2. (Returned Services League of Australia, Victorian Branch) Newsprinters Pty. Ltd. Shepparton, Anzac House, 4 Collins St., Melbourne, Vic. 3000, Australia. Ed. P. O'Neil. adv.; bk.rev. circ. 65,000.

355   UK   ISSN 0027-5662
N A A F I NEWS. 1945. bi-m. Navy, Army & Air Force Institutes, HQ N A A F I, London Rd., Amesbury, Wilts SP4 7EN, England. TEL 0980-627043. FAX 0980-627155. Ed. Sarah Wintle. illus.; circ. 11,000 (controlled). **Document type:** newsletter.

355 327   BE
N A T O DATA. (Text in English, French) 1993. irreg. free. North Atlantic Treaty Organization, Integrated Data Service, Leopold III Laan, Brussels 1110, Belgium. TEL 32-2-7284599. FAX 32-2-7285229. E-mail: scheurwe@hq.nato.int. **Document type:** newsletter.
●Available only online.
  Description: Distributes NATO public information, and studies and reports in the field of international security.

N A T O'S SIXTEEN NATIONS. (North Atlantic Treaty Organization) see *POLITICAL SCIENCE — International Relations*

355.115   US   ISSN 0747-0150
THE N C O A JOURNAL. m. membership. Non-Commissioned Officers Association, Box 33610, San Antonio, TX 78265. TEL 512-653-6161. FAX 512-656-6225. Ed. Thomas F. Silk. adv.: B&W page $3245, color page $4989; trim 11 1/2 x 13 1/2; adv. contact: Tracey Campbell. circ. 175,000. (tabloid format) **Document type:** newspaper.
  Description: Covers news, legislation, association updates and other items of interest to active duty, veteran & Guard members of the NCOA in all five branches of the armed forces.

355   US   ISSN 0882-9667
N S I ADVISORY. 1985. m. $324. National Security Institute, 57 E. Main St., No. 217, Westborough, MA 01581-1464. TEL 508-366-5800. FAX 508-898-0132. Ed. David A. Marston. **Document type:** newsletter.
  Description: Provides news, analysis, and commentary on national security issues of concern to cleared U.S. defense contractors.

355.37 305.31   SI
N S MAN. (Text in English) 1973. bi-m. (Singapore Armed Forces Reservist Association) Singapore Press Holdings Ltd., Corporate Relations Department, 82 Genting Ln., News Centre, Singapore 1334, Singapore. TEL 743-8800. FAX 748-0747. (Subscr. to: Times Periodicals Pvt. Ltd., Times Industrial Bldg., 422 Thomson Rd., Singapore 1129, Singapore. TEL 255-0011. FAX 256-8016) Ed. Tan Wang Joo. adv.: B&W page S.$1500, color page S.$2300; 275 x 205; adv. contact: Anne Goh-Taylor. circ. 90,000. cols./p.: 3; pp./issue: 44. **Document type:** consumer publication.
  Formerly: Reservist.
  Description: Covers men's life-style topics for members of the Singapore Armed Forces.

356   YU   ISSN 0027-7908
U4
NARODNA ARMIJA; list jugoslavenske narodne armije. 1945. w. ($10.85) Narodna Armija, Proletarskih Brigada 13, Belgrade, Serbia, Yugoslavia. Ed. Ivo Tominic.

355   YU   ISSN 0027-7916
NARODNA ODBRANA. 1948. w. Korpus Narodne Odbrane, Kommanda, Belgrade, Yugoslavia.

356   BN   ISSN 0027-7959
NARODNI BORAC; list Sarajevske armijske oblasti. 1948. fortn. 24 din. per no. Narodna Armija Sarajevska Armijska Oblast, Box 01-25, Sarajevo, Bosnia Hercegovina. Ed. Petar Jankovic.

355.15   US   ISSN 0027-853X
NATIONAL AMVET. 1947. q. $10. American Veterans of World War II, Korea and Viet Nam (AMVETS), 4647 Forbes Blvd., Lanham, MD 20706. TEL 301-459-9600. FAX 301-459-7924. Ed. Richard W. Flanagan. adv.; bk.rev.; charts; illus.; stat. circ. 170,000. **Document type:** bulletin.

ULRICH'S INTERNATIONAL PERIODICALS DIRECTORY 1996

MILITARY

355 US ISSN 0092-1491
UF1 CODEN: NTDFA2
NATIONAL DEFENSE. 1920. 10/yr. $35 (foreign $40) (effective 1996). American Defense Preparedness Association, 2101 Wilson Blvd., Ste. 400, Arlington, VA 22201-3061. TEL 703-522-1820. FAX 703-522-1885. Ed. Robert Williams. adv. contact: Jerry Merna. bk.rev.; charts; illus.; stat.; index. circ. 35,000. (also avail. in microform from UMI; reprint service avail. from UMI) **Indexed:** Abstr.Mil.Bibl., Air Un.Lib.Ind., Chem.Abstr., DM & T, Eng.Ind., PROMT. **Document type:** trade publication.
—BLDSC (6021.869000); SWETS; UMI; UnCover.
Formerly: Ordnance (ISSN 0030-4557); Incorporates: American Defense Preparedness Association. Annual Directory. (ISSN 0092-7422); Defense Manager (ISSN 0011-7609); Which was formerly: A F M A Bulletin.
Description: Covers the issues influencing US defense policy and the defense industrial base.

NATIONAL DEFENSE ACADEMY. MEMOIRS. MATHEMATICS, PHYSICS, CHEMISTRY AND ENGINEERING/BOEI DAIGAKKO KIYO RIKOGAKU-HEN. see *SCIENCES: COMPREHENSIVE WORKS*

355 US ISSN 0163-3945
UA42
NATIONAL GUARD. 1947. m. $10 for non-members. National Guard Association of the United States, 1 Massachusetts Ave., N.W., Washington, DC 20001. TEL 202-789-0031. FAX 202-543-5692. Ed. Col. Reid K. Beveridge. adv.; bk.rev.; illus. circ. 70,000. (also avail. in microform from UMI; reprint service avail. from UMI) **Indexed:** Air Un.Lib.Ind.
—UMI.
Formerly (until 1979): National Guardsman (ISSN 0027-9412)

355 US ISSN 0363-8618
U9
NATIONAL GUARD ALMANAC. 1975. a. $5.95 (effective 1995). Uniformed Services Almanac, Inc., Box 4144, Falls Church, VA 22044. TEL 703-532-1631. FAX 703-532-1635. Ed. Lt. Col. Sol Gordon, U.S.A.F.-Ret. bk.rev. circ. 35,000. **Document type:** consumer publication.
Formerly: Uniformed Services Almanac. National Guard Edition (ISSN 0363-8588)
Description: Annual guide to pay, benefits, entitlements and subjects of interest to members of the National Guard and other military personnel, and their families.

355 CN ISSN 0316-1919
F1028
NATIONAL MUSEUM OF MAN. MERCURY SERIES. CANADIAN WAR MUSEUM. PAPERS/MUSEE NATIONAL DE L'HOMME. COLLECTION MERCURE. MUSEE CANADIEN DE LA GUERRE. DOSSIERS. (Text in English or French) 1972. irreg., no.9, 1978. free. National Museum of Man, c/o Canadian Museum of Civilization, 100 Laurier St., Hull, PQ J8X 4H2, Canada.

NATIONAL SECURITY REVIEW. see *POLITICAL SCIENCE*

355 947 BU ISSN 0324-0835
NATSIONALEN VOENNOISTORICHESKI MUZEI, SOFIA. IZVESTIYA. 1973. a. Voenno Izdatelstvo na M O, 12, Ul. Ivan Vazov, Sofia, Bulgaria. illus.

359 US ISSN 0028-1409
VA49
NAVAL AFFAIRS; in the interest of the enlisted active duty, reserve and retired personnel of the U.S. Navy, Marine Corps and Coast Guard. 1922. m. $7 to non-members. Fleet Reserve Association, 125 N. West St., Alexandria, VA 22314-2754. TEL 703-683-1400. Ed. Patricia J. Williamson; Pub. Norman E. Pearson. adv.; bk.rev.; illus. circ. 180,000.

NAVAL AVIATION NEWS. see *AERONAUTICS AND SPACE FLIGHT*

NAVAL ENGINEERS JOURNAL. see *ENGINEERING*

359 GW ISSN 0722-8880
V1
NAVAL FORCES. 1980. bi-m. DM.65. Moench Verlagsgesellschaft mbH, Postfach 140261, 53057 Bonn, Germany. TEL 0228-6483-0. FAX 0228-6483109. Ed. Antony Preston. adv.: B&W page $4200, color page $7500; trim 10 5/8 x 7 5/16; adv. contact: Ute Steuer. bk.rev. circ. 18,691. (back issues avail.) **Indexed:** Abstr.Mil.Bibl., Air Un.Lib.Ind., BMT, DM & T, PROMT. **Document type:** trade publication.
—BLDSC (6064.210000).
Description: Provides specialist naval reports and features.

359 975 US ISSN 1042-1920
V27
NAVAL HISTORY. 1987. bi-m. $20 to non-members; members $18. U S Naval Institute, 118 Maryland Ave., Annapolis, MD 21402-5035. TEL 410-293-2109. Ed. Fred Schultz. adv.; bk.rev.; illus.; index. circ. 35,000. **Document type:** academic/scholarly publication.
—UnCover.
Description: Covers naval history, including various areas, subjects and countries, and services branches.

359 US ISSN 1057-4581
VA40
NAVAL INSTITUTE GUIDE TO COMBAT FLEETS OF THE WORLD. (Text in English; French edition avail.) 1897. biennial, latest 1995. $145. (U.S. Naval Institute) Naval Institute Press, 118 Maryland Ave., Annapolis, MD 21402. TEL 410-268-6110. FAX 410-269-7940. (Orders to: Naval Insttitute Press, 2062 Generals Hwy., Annapolis, MD 21401. TEL 800-233-8764) Ed. A.D. Baker. (reprint service avail.)
—BLDSC (3324.650000).
Formerly: Combat Fleets of the World (ISSN 0364-3263)

359 US
NAVAL RESERVIST NEWS; news of the total force Navy for the Naval Reserve community. vol.11, 1987. m. free to qualified personnel. Commander, Naval Reserve Force, Public Affairs Office (Code 004), 4400 Dauphine St., New Orleans, LA 70146-5000. TEL 504-942-6058. FAX 504-948-5049. Ed. Nat Chesnut. illus. circ. 240,000. (tabloid format) **Document type:** government publication.

359 US ISSN 0077-6238
V10
NAVAL REVIEW; annual review of world seapower. (May issue of: U S Naval Institute, Proceedings) 1962. a. U S Naval Institute, 118 Maryland Ave., Annapolis, MD 21402-5035. TEL 410-268-6110. Ed. Fred H. Rainbow. adv. circ. 119,790. (back issues avail.)
Description: Covers the previous year's events in the naval-maritime field.

359 UK
NAVAL REVIEW. 1912. q. £15. Salthill Rd., Fishbourne, Chichester, W. Sussex PO19 3PY, England. TEL 01243-782553. FAX 01243-775285. Ed. Richard Hill. adv. contact: G.F. Liardet. bk.rev. circ. 3,000. **Document type:** academic/scholarly publication.

359 US ISSN 0028-1484
V1
NAVAL WAR COLLEGE REVIEW. 1948. q. free to qualified personnel. U.S. Naval War College, 686 Cushing Rd., Code 32, Newport, RI 02841-1207. TEL 401-841-2236. FAX 401-841-3579. E-mail: NWC-PRESS@NPT.NUWC.NAVY.MIL. Ed. Thomas B. Grassey. bk.rev.; index; circ. 9,500 (controlled). (also avail. in microform from MIM,UMI,BHP; reprint service avail. from UMI) **Indexed:** Abstr.Mil.Bibl., Air Un.Lib.Ind., Amer.Bibl.Slavic & E.Eur.Stud, Amer.Hist.& Life, DM& T, Hist.Abstr., Ind.U.S.Gov.Per., Int.Polit.Sci.Abstr., Mid.East Abstr.& Ind., Ocean.Abstr., Peace Res.Abstr, PROMT. **Document type:** government publication, academic/scholarly publication.
—Faxon; UMI; UnCover.

355 UK ISSN 0955-7261
NAVINT; the international naval newsletter. 1989. fortn. £320($530) Tileprint Ltd., 145A Putney High St., London SW15 1SU, England. TEL 0181-789-6627. FAX 0181-789-6628. Ed. Antony Preston. index; circ. 300 (paid). (back issues avail.) **Document type:** newsletter.

359.347 US
VG23
NAVY CHAPLAIN. 1955. q. free to qualified personnel. U.S. Navy, Bureau of Naval Personnel, Office of the Navy Chief of Chaplains, Washington, DC 20370. TEL 804-444-7665. FAX 804-445-1006. Eds. Capt. T.C. Carter, Cmdr. A.L. Hill. bk.rev.; circ. 4,200 (controlled). **Indexed:** CERDIC. **Document type:** trade publication, government publication.
Incorporates (in 1986): Navy Chaplains Bulletin (ISSN 0028-1654) & Porthole.
Refereed Serial

355 624 US ISSN 0096-9419
VG593
NAVY CIVIL ENGINEER. 1946. q. $6.50 (foreign $8.15). U.S. Naval Facilities Engineering Command, c/o Superintendent of Documents, Washington, DC 20402. TEL 202-512-1710. FAX 202-512-1656. (Subscr. to: Superintendent of Documents, U.S. Government Printing Office, Box 371594, Pittsburgh, PA 15250-7954. TEL 202-512-1800. FAX 202-512-2250) Ed. K. Fedele. bk.rev.; abstr.; charts; illus.; stat.; index, cum.index. circ. 15,400. (also avail. in microform from UMI) **Indexed:** Geotech.Abstr., Ind.U.S.Gov.Per. **Document type:** government publication.
—BLDSC (6067.560000); Faxon; UMI; UnCover.
Description: Features articles on the U.S. Navy's shore establishments throughout the world, along with technical articles on planning and designing, public works, construction and maintenance, utilities, transportation, and housing. Covers research and feature articles on the Civil Engineer Corps and the Seabees.

359 UK ISSN 0144-3194
V1
NAVY INTERNATIONAL. 1895. 6/yr. £47($94) Maritime World Ltd., 114 South St., Dorking, Surrey RH4 2EZ, England. TEL 0306-631442. FAX 0306-631226. Ed. Anthony Watts. adv.; bk.rev.; illus. circ. 2,500. **Indexed:** Abstr.Mil.Bibl., BMT, DM & T, PROMT. **Document type:** trade publication.
Incorporates: Combat Craft (ISSN 0264-4649); Which was formerly: Navy (ISSN 0028-1646)

355 UK
NAVY LIST OF RETIRED OFFICERS. a. price varies. H.M.S.O., P.O. Box 276, London SW8 5DT, England. **Document type:** government publication.

359 UK ISSN 0028-1670
NAVY NEWS. 1954. m. £12 (foreign £15.50). Navy News, H.M.S. Nelson, Portsmouth, Hants PO1 3HH, England. TEL 01705-826040. FAX 01705-830149. Ed. Jim Allaway. adv.: B&W page £1875; trim 370 x 273; adv. contact: Lesley Williams. illus.; circ. 90,000 (paid). **Document type:** newspaper.
Description: Directed to the navy and to naval enthusiasts.

359 US ISSN 0028-1662
NAVY NEWS. 1927. w. $29.95. Adcrafters of Virginia, 2429 Bowland Pkwy., Ste.118, Virginia Beach, VA 23454-5230. TEL 804-486-8000. FAX 804-486-8017. Ed. Nicole Ard. adv. contact: Tricia Odom. bk.rev.; charts; illus. circ. 46,000. (tabloid format) **Document type:** newspaper.
Description: Serves those in the Norfolk - Hampton - Virginia Beach - Chesapeake - Portsmouth - Newport News area. Blends news features and information of interest to service personnel and provides a communication link for better understanding between the armed service and civilian community.

359 551.46 US ISSN 8756-1700
NAVY NEWS & UNDERSEA TECHNOLOGY. 1984. w. $545 (foreign $575). Pasha Publications Inc., 1616 N. Ft. Myer Dr., Ste. 1000, Arlington, VA 22209-3107. TEL 703-528-1244. FAX 703-528-1253. Ed. Len Famiglietti. index. **Document type:** newsletter.
●Also available online. Vendor(s): NewsNet (DE18).
—BLDSC (6067.595900). CCC.
Description: Tracks naval aircraft, computers, electronics, shipbuilding and weapons programs as well as domestic and foreign policy.

MILITARY

359 US ISSN 0360-716X
VC35
NAVY SUPPLY CORPS NEWSLETTER. 1937. bi-m. U.S. Department of the Navy, Supply Systems Command, Navy Supply Corps, Washington, DC 20374. TEL 703-607-1301. FAX 703-607-2221. Ed. Nancy Dimond. circ. 15,000 (controlled).

359 US ISSN 0028-1697
V1
NAVY TIMES; Marine Corps, Navy, Coast Guard. (In 3 editions: Domestic, European, Pacific) 1951. w. $52. Army Times Publishing Co., 6883 Commercial Dr., Springfield, VA 22159. TEL 703-750-9000. Ed. Tobias Naegele. adv.; bk.rev.; charts; illus.; mkt.; stat.; circ. 82,000 (paid). (tabloid format; also avail. in microform from UMI; reprint service avail. from UMI) **Document type:** newspaper.
—UMI. **CCC.**
 Description: Serving all sea service personnel and their families.

NEDERLANDS MILITAIR GENEESKUNDIG TIJDSCHRIFT. see *MEDICAL SCIENCES*

355 US
NEW BREED. 1982. bi-m. $17. New Breed Publications, Inc., Box 428, Nanuet, NY 10954. Ed. Harry Belil. adv.; bk.rev. circ. 68,000.
 Description: Covers all areas of the military: history, law enforcement, weapons and intelligence.

353.9 US ISSN 0094-7326
UB358.N6
NEW MEXICO. VETERANS' SERVICE COMMISSION. REPORT. Key Title: Report of the New Mexico Veteran's Service Commission. a. free. Veterans' Service Commission, Bataan Memorial Building, 408 Galisteo St., Box 2324, Santa Fe, NM 87503. TEL 505-827-6300. FAX 505-827-6300. charts; stat. circ. 100. **Document type:** corporate report, government publication.

355.45 US
NEW YORK (STATE). ASSEMBLY. STANDING COMMITTEE ON VETERANS' AFFAIRS. ANNUAL REPORT. a. State Assembly, Rm. 841, Legislative Office Bldg., Albany, NY 12248. TEL 518-455-4178. **Document type:** government publication.

NEW ZEALAND R S A REVIEW. see *SOCIAL SERVICES AND WELFARE*

359 US
NEWPORT NAVALOG. 1901. w. free. Edward A. Sherman Publishing Co., 101 Malbone Rd., Box 420, Newport, RI 02840. FAX 401-849-3300. adv.; circ. 7,200 (controlled). **Document type:** newspaper.
 Description: Civilian enterprise newspaper published for the naval eduction and training center, Newport, Rhode Island.

355 US
NEWSLETTER OF THE S.L.A. MARSHALL MILITARY HISTORY COLLECTION. 1980. irreg., no.16, 1991. free. University of Texas at El Paso, University Library, El Paso, TX 79968-0582. TEL 915-747-5697. FAX 915-747-6717. Ed. Thomas F. Burdett. bk.rev. circ. 500. **Document type:** newsletter.
 Description: Presents news of developments in the collection. Distributed to military historians, active-duty and retired military officers, and libraries with an institutional interest in military history.

THE NONPROLIFERATION REVIEW. see *POLITICAL SCIENCE — International Relations*

355 NO ISSN 0029-1692
NORGES FORSVAR. (Includes annual report) 1951. 10/yr. NOK 110. Norges Forsvarsforening - Norwegian Defence Association, Sporveisgaten 29, 0354-Oslo 3, Norway. TEL 02-696500. FAX 02-4608. Ed. Bjoern Hoelseth. adv.; bk.rev.; illus.; index. circ. 11,500.
—CCC.

355 NO ISSN 0029-1854
NORSK ARTILLERI - TIDSSKRIFT. 1900. 4/yr. NOK 100. Artilleriets Offisersforening, Artilleriregimentet, N-2437 Haslemoen, Norway. TEL 47-62-42-92-01. FAX 47-62-42-90-14. Ed. K. Gillingsrud. adv.; bk.rev.; charts; illus.; index. circ. 600. **Document type:** academic/scholarly publication.

359 NO ISSN 0029-2222
V5
NORSK TIDSSKRIFT FOR SJOVESEN. 1882. 6/yr. NOK 90. Sjomilitaere Samfund, P.O. Box 105, 5078 Haakonsven, Norway. Ed. Svein C. Sivertsen. adv.; bk.rev.; illus.; index. circ. 2,300.

NORTH CAROLINA AMERICAN LEGION NEWS. see *CLUBS*

NORTHERN IRELAND NEWS SERVICE; NINS NewsBreak. see *POLITICAL SCIENCE*

355 SZ
NOTRE ARMEE DE MILICE. 10/yr. Postfach 501, CH-1400 Yverdon-les-Bains 1, Switzerland. TEL 024-217424. FAX 024-220939. Ed. J.-H. Schule. circ. 15,839.

355 US
NOW HEAR THIS U S S CALLAWAY NEWSLETTER. 1965. a. 5319 Manning Pl., N.W., Washington, DC 20013-5311. TEL 202-363-3663. Eds. Wallace & Dorothy Shipp. circ. 384 (controlled). **Document type:** newsletter.
 Description: News and items of interest to WWII veterans of USS Callaway and the U.S. Coast Guard.

355 UK
NUCLEAR WEAPONS DATA FILE. 1979. q. $726. Aviation Studies International, Sussex House, Parkside, Wimbledon, London SW19 5NB, England. TEL 0181-946-5082. **Document type:** directory, trade publication.
 Description: Compiles data on the weights, dimensions, explosive power, costs, and production of 50,000 nuclear weapons.

355 IT ISSN 0048-1122
NUOVA TRADOTTA. 1955. m. free. Associazione Nazionale Combattenti e Reduci, Via Bagutta 12, 20121 Milan, Italy. TEL 02-76001175. FAX 02-76001089. Ed. Franco Mattavelli. bibl.; illus. circ. 3,000. **Document type:** academic/scholarly publication.

355 629.4 US ISSN 1041-7478
O & M INTELLIGENCE. (Operation & Maintenance) w. $300. Forecast International Inc. - D M S, 22 Commerce Rd., Newtown, CT 06470. TEL 203-426-0800. FAX 203-426-1964. TELEX 467615. (back issues avail.)
●Also available online. Vendor(s): Knight-Ridder, Inc. (File no.587/DMS DEFENSE NEWSLETTERS).
 Description: Provides information on developments and trends in defense and aerospace O & M, including budget actions, congressional directives on contracting, major competition announcements and contract awards.

355 SZ
O G B MITTEILUNGEN. 8/yr. Fischer Druck AG, CH-3110 Muensingen, Switzerland. TEL 031-7212211. FAX 031-7211253. circ. 3,300.

355 976 US
O I W COMMUNIQUE. 1979. m. $20. Order of the Indian Wars, Box 7401, Little Rock, AR 72217. TEL 501-225-3996. Ed. Jerry L. Russell. circ. 550 (paid). **Document type:** newsletter.
 Description: Devoted to the study and historic preservation of Indian Wars sites.

359 US ISSN 0029-7356
OAK LEAF. vol.30, 1974. bi-m. free. Naval Surface Weapons Center, Public Affairs Office, Silver Spring, MD 20910. TEL 301-394-1796. Ed. Karen L. Pelham. charts; illus. circ. 4,500.

355 GW ISSN 0029-7402
DIE OASE. 1951. m. DM.39.60 (foreign DM.45). (Deutsches Afrika-Korps e.V.) Heinrich Poeppinghaus GmbH, Postfach 700209, 44884 Bochum, Germany. TEL 0234-287254. Ed. Erich Steinhilb. bk.rev.; illus. **Document type:** newsletter.
 Description: Publication of the German Africa Corps. Includes reports of events and activities, history, personal stories, travel stories and announcements of events.

358.4 YU ISSN 0029-8336
ODBRANA. 1949. bi-m. Savez Rezervnih Vojnih Staresina Beograda, Trg Bratstva i Jedinstva 9, Belgrade, Serbia, Yugoslavia.

ODBRANA I ZASTITA. see *CIVIL DEFENSE*

355 AU ISSN 0048-1440
U3
OESTERREICHISCHE MILITAERISCHE ZEITSCHRIFT. 1963. bi-m. S.160 (foreign S.200). (Ministry of Defense) Carl Ueberreuter, Alserstr. 24, A-1090 Vienna, Austria. TEL 0222-40444. Ed. Franz Freistetter. adv.; bk.rev.; charts; illus.; index. circ. 5,000. **Indexed:** Abstr.Mil.Bibl.
—SWETS.

355.12 US
OFF DUTY AMERICA. 1974. 7/yr. membership. Off Duty Enterprises, 3303 Harbor Blvd., Ste. C-2, Costa Mesa, CA 92626. TEL 714-549-7172. FAX 714-549-4222. Ed. Jim Shaw. adv.; bk.rev.; film rev.; tr.lit.; index; circ. 450,000 (controlled).
 Formerly: Off Duty West.
 Description: Written for service personnel in the U.S. and the Caribbean.

355 US
OFF DUTY - EUROPE. 1970. m. $10 (free to U.S. military personnel). Off Duty Enterprises, 3303 Harbor Blvd., Ste. C-2, Costa Mesa, CA 92626. TEL 714-549-7172. Ed. James Shaw. adv.; bk.rev.; film rev.; tr.lit.; index. circ. 95,000.
 Description: Information on U.S. military personnel and their families in Europe and the Middle East.

355.12 HK
OFF DUTY - PACIFIC. (Text in English) 1971. m. $18. Off Duty Publications Ltd., 14-F Park Commercial Centre, 8 Shelter St., Causeway Bay, Hong Kong. FAX 852-5-8901761. (U.S. addr.: Off Duty Enterprises, 3303 Harbor Blvd., Ste. C-2, Costa Mesa, CA 92626. TEL 714-549-7172) Ed. James Shaw. adv.; bk.rev.; film rev.; tr.lit.; index. circ. 80,000.
 Description: For U.S. military personnel and their families.

355 US ISSN 0030-0268
UA23.A1
OFFICER. 1924. m. $12. Reserve Officers Association of the United States, 1 Constitution Ave. N.E., Washington, DC 20002. TEL 202-479-2200. Ed. Norman S. Burzynski; Pub. Roger Sandler. adv. contact: Betsy Lauer. bk.rev.; illus. circ. 124,000. (also avail. in microform from UMI; reprint service avail. from UMI) **Indexed:** Air Un.Lib.Ind.
—UMI.
 Description: Covers active and reserve force activities of the Army, Navy, Air Force, Coast Guard, Public Health Service and National Oceanic and Atmospheric Administration, as well as congressional and administrative actions affecting the nation's uniformed services.

355 US ISSN 0736-7317
U56
OFFICER REVIEW. vol.14, 1976. 10/yr. $8. Military Order of the World Wars, 435 N. Lee St., Alexandria, VA 22314. TEL 703-683-4911. FAX 703-683-4501. Ed. John S. Guthrie, Jr. adv.; bk.rev.; charts; illus. circ. 17,000. **Indexed:** RILM. **Document type:** newsletter.

355 US ISSN 1040-029X
OFFICERS CALL. 1981. q. membership only. National Officers Association, Box 4975, Reston, VA 22090-1464. TEL 703-438-3060. FAX 703-438-3072. Ed. Monica Worth. adv.; bk.rev.; circ. 21,000 (controlled). (looseleaf format; back issues avail.) **Document type:** newsletter.
 Description: Focuses on benefits and entitlement programs for military personnel, as well as on issues relating to financial and second career management.

355 CU
EL OFICIAL. m. Ministerio de las Fuerzas Armadas Revolucionarias, Ave. 47, No. 1414th, 14 y 18 Playa, Marianao, Cuba.

355 US
OHIO LEGION NEWS. m. American Legion, Department of Ohio, Box 14348, Columbus, OH 43214. TEL 614-268-7072. circ. 148,000. **Document type:** newspaper.

355 US
OKINAWA TODAY. 1982. fortn. 825 Old Country Rd., Westbury, NY 11590. TEL 516-334-3030. Ed. Kari Valtaoja. adv. circ. 15,000.
 Description: Military consumer magazine.

OKLAHOMA LEGIONNAIRE. see *CLUBS*

MILITARY

355 323.4 US ISSN 1064-007X
ON GUARD. 1986. s-a. $10. Citizen Soldier, 175 Fifth Ave., Ste. 808, New York, NY 10010. TEL 212-777-3470. Eds. Thomas Ensign, Ken Cunningham. bk.rev. circ. 15,000. (looseleaf format; also avail. in microform from UMI; back issues avail.) **Indexed:** Alt.Press Ind.
Description: Covers human rights, civil rights, and liberties; issues for active-duty military personnel.

359 US ISSN 1047-1731
ON WATCH. 1988. bi-m. free. Fleet Reserve Association, 125 N. West St., Alexandria, VA 22314-2754. TEL 703-683-1400. FAX 703-549-6610. Ed. Heidi Schuller. circ. 200,000.
Description: For enlisted (active duty and reserve) members of the U.S. Navy, Marine Corps and Coast Guard.

355.133 NE ISSN 0030-2783
ONS WAPEN. 1954. bi-m. fl.10. Stichting Tijdschrift Ons Wapen, Raamweg 4, The Hague, Netherlands. adv.; bk.rev.; illus. circ. 5,000.

358.4 NE ISSN 0030-3208
ONZE LUCHTMACHT. 1948. bi-m. fl.40. Koninklijke Nederlandse Vereniging "Onze Luchtmacht", Dommeldaal 1, 5282 WB Boxtel, Netherlands. TEL 31-4116-78691. (Editorial addr.: Postbus 183, 5520 AD Eersel, Netherlands. TEL 31-4970-16789. FAX 31-4970-18272) adv.; bk.rev.; illus.; index. circ. 11,500.

940.53 NE ISSN 0925-2665
OORLOGSDOCUMENTATIE '40-'45. Variant title: Jaarboek van het Rijksinstituut voor Oorlogsdocumentatie. 1989. a. fl.39.50. (Rijksinstituut voor Oorlogsdocumentatie) Uitgeversmaatschappij Walburg Pers BV, Postbus 4159, 7200 BD Zutphen, Netherlands. TEL 31-5750-10522. FAX 31-5750-41025. **Document type:** academic/scholarly publication.

ORDERS AND MEDALS SOCIETY OF AMERICA. JOURNAL. see *HOBBIES*

355 GU
ORDERS GUAM. 1976. a. free to qualified personnel. Glimpses of Guam, Inc., P.O. Box 3191, Agana, Guam 96910. circ. 10,000.

360 IT
ORDRE SOUVERAIN MILITAIRE DE MALTA. REVUE INTERNATIONALE. (Editions in English, French and Italian) 1969. 3/yr. L.2500($3) Ordre Souverain Militaire de Malte, Palazzo Malta, 68 via Condotti, Rome, Italy. charts; illus. circ. 4,000.

355 US
OVERSEAS! m. Military Consumer Today, Inc., Box 1500, 825 Old Country Rd., Westbury, NY 11590. TEL 516-334-3030. FAX 516-334-3059. adv. circ. 82,300.
Description: Concerns leisure time for military men serving in Europe.

355 FR ISSN 0154-7313
P G - C A T M. vol.26, 1971. 11/yr. 60 F. Federation Nationale des Combattants Prisonniers de Guerre Combattants d'Algerie, Tunisie et Maroc, 46 rue Copernic, 75782 Paris Cedex 16, France. TEL 45-00-18-19. FAX 45-00-97-29. Ed. Jacques Goujat. bk.rev.; bibl.; charts; illus. circ. 270,000. **Document type:** newspaper.
Former titles: C A T M; P G - Prisonniers de Guerre (ISSN 0048-2595)

355 NE
P M T - NIEUWS. vol.82, 1971. 4/yr. free. Koninklijke Nederlandse Militaire Bond pro Rege, Nieuwegracht 90, 3512 LW Utrecht, Netherlands. TEL 31-30-311892. FAX 31-30-316578. adv.; bk.rev.; charts; illus. circ. 100,000.
Formerly: Nederlandse Krijgsman.

PACIFIC RESEARCH. see *POLITICAL SCIENCE — International Relations*

355 JA
PACIFIC STARS & STRIPES. d. Pacific Stars & Stripes, 23-17 Roppongi 7-chome, Minato-ku, Tokyo 106, Japan. TEL 81-3-3408-8936. FAX 81-3-3408-8936. (APO addr.: Unit 45002, APO AP 96337-0110) Ed. Robert Trounson. circ. 27,000. **Document type:** newspaper.

356 PK ISSN 0030-9656
PAKISTAN ARMY JOURNAL. 1956. q. Rs.90($8) Inspector General Training & Evaluation Branch, Training Publications & Information Directorate, General Staff Branch, General Headquarters, Rawalpindi, Pakistan. Ed. Lt. Col. Syed Ishia Ali. bk.rev. circ. 3,500.

355 IT ISSN 0394-3429
PANORAMA DIFESA. 1982. m. (11/yr.). L.65000 (foreign L.80000). Ed.A.I. s.r.l. (Edizioni Aeronautiche Italiane), V. Guinicelli 4, 50133 Florence, Italy. TEL 055-574774. FAX 055-570103. TELEX 580217 EDAI I. Ed. Ruggero Stanglini. adv.: B&W page L.3500000, color page L.5950000. circ. 31,600. **Document type:** consumer publication.
Description: Features a broad view of novelties in the following sectors: Air Force, Navy, space and civil defense.

355 US ISSN 0031-1723
U1
PARAMETERS (CARLISLE BARRACKS); United States Army War College. 1971. q. $11 (foreign $13.75) (effective 1995). U.S. Army War College, Carlisle Barracks, PA 17013-6050. TEL 717-245-4943. FAX 717-245-4721. E-mail: AWCA-Parameters@carlisle-emh2.army.mil (Internet). (Subscr. to: Superintendent of Documents, U.S. Government Printing Office, Box 371954, Pittsburgh, PA 15250-7954. TEL 202-512-1800. FAX 202-512-2250) Ed. Col. John J. Madigan III. bk.rev.; charts; illus. circ. 12,000. (also avail. in microfilm from UMI; microfiche from UMI) **Indexed:** A.B.C.Pol.Sci., Abstr.Mil.Bibl., Air Un.Lib.Ind., Amer.Hist.& Life, Bk.Rev.Ind. (1989-), Child.Bk.Rev.Ind. (1989-), Hist.Abstr., Ind.U.S.Gov.Per., Mid.East: Abstr.& Ind., P.A.I.S., PROMT, R.G. **Document type:** academic/scholarly publication, government publication.
—BLDSC (6404.837000); Faxon; UMI; UnCover.
Description: Provides a forum for the expression of mature, professional thought on the art and science of land warfare; national and international security affairs, military strategy, military leadership and management, military history; ethics and other topics of important and current interest to the U.S. Army, and the Department of Defense.
Refereed Serial

PEACE ACTION. see *POLITICAL SCIENCE — International Relations*

PEACE MAGAZINE. see *POLITICAL SCIENCE — International Relations*

358.4 UK ISSN 0031-4080
PEGASUS JOURNAL. 1946. s-a. £7 (foreign £9). Parachute Regiment and Airborne Forces, Browning Barracks, Aldershot, Hants. GU11 2BU, England. TEL 01252-349624. FAX 01252-349203. Ed. Col. K. Coates. adv.; bk.rev.; circ. 6,000 (controlled). **Document type:** newsletter.

355.115 UK ISSN 0048-3192
PENNANT. 1946. s-a. membership. Officers' Pensions Society Ltd., 68 S. Lambeth Rd., London SW1 1RL, England. TEL 0171-820-9988. FAX 0171-820-9948. Ed. Maj. Gen. Sir Laurence New. adv. contact: Alexandra Penncott. bk.rev. circ. 37,000. **Document type:** bulletin.

355.115 362 US
PERSIAN GULF REVIEW; information for veterans who served in Desert Storm. 1992. irreg. (approx. 4/yr.). free. U.S. Veterans Administration, Environmental Agents Service - 103A, V.A. Central Office, 810 Vermont Ave., N.W., Washington, DC 20420. TEL 800-827-1000. Ed. Donald J. Rosenblum. (back issues avail.) **Document type:** bulletin, government publication.
Description: Addresses the concerns of U.S. veterans of the Persian Gulf war, along with those of their families and others interested in the possible long-term health implications of exposure to various potential environmental hazards during their tour of duty. Describes the actions the Veterans Administration and other agencies are taking in response to these concerns.

355.4 US ISSN 0195-1920
PHALANX; bulletin of military operations research and related sciences. 1965. q. $30 for 2 yrs. Military Operations Research Society, Inc., Landmark Towers, 101 S. Whiting St., Ste. 202, Alexandria, VA 22304. TEL 703-751-7290. FAX 703-751-7290. (Co-sponsor: Operations Research Society of America) Ed. James Richmann; Pub. Natalie Addison. bk.rev. circ. 9,100. (back issues avail.) **Document type:** bulletin.

355 CN
PHARE/BEACON. m. Can.$15. C.P. 369, Alouette, PQ G0V 1A0, Canada. TEL 418-677-8160. FAX 418-677-8480. Ed. Capt. Leonard. adv. contact: Michel Aubin. circ. 3,000 (controlled). (tabloid format; also avail. in diskette format; back issues avail.) **Document type:** newspaper.

PHYLLIS SCHLAFLY REPORT. see *WOMEN'S INTERESTS*

PILOT UND FLUGZEUG. see *TRANSPORTATION — Air Transport*

355 SI ISSN 0048-4199
PIONEER; Singapore armed forces news. 1969. m. S.$0.50 per no. Ministry of Defense, Public Affairs Department, Tanglin Rd., Singapore 1024, Singapore. Ed. Francis Gomes. adv.; bk.rev.; charts; illus. circ. 120,000. **Indexed:** Abstr.Mil.Bibl.

355 SZ
PIONIER. m. Redaktion Pionier, H & W Wiesner, Stutzweg 23, 4434 Hoelstein, Switzerland.

POLITICA E ESTRATEGIA. see *POLITICAL SCIENCE — International Relations*

355 PL ISSN 0867-4523
POLSKA ZBROJNA. 1950. 5/w. (Ministerstvo Obrony Narodowej) Wydawnictwo Czasopisma Wojskowe, Ul. Grzybowska 77, Rembertow, Poland. TEL 48-22-204293. FAX 48-22-202127. Ed. Jerzy Slaski. circ. 100,000. **Document type:** newspaper.
Former titles: Zolnierz Rzeczypospolitej (ISSN 0867-4515); (until 1990): Zolnierz Wolnosci (ISSN 0137-9402)

355 PO
PORTUGAL. SERVICO DE ADMINISTRACAO MILITAR. REVISTA BIMESTRAL. bi-m. Esc.150. Servico de Administracao Militar, Rua Rodrigo da Fonseca, No. 180, Lisbon, Portugal. illus.
Supersedes: Portugal. Servico de Administracao Militar. Revista Mensal (ISSN 0037-2714)

355 CN
POST - GAZETTE. 1960. w. Can.$20. Canadian Forces Base Gagetown, Bldg. H-10, Oromocto, NB E0G 2P0, Canada. TEL 506-357-9813. FAX 506-357-5222. Ed. Ross Ingram. adv. contact: Caryle Hill. circ. 6,000. **Document type:** newspaper.
Formed by the 1993 merger of: C F B Gagetown Gazette (ISSN 0713-391X) & Oromocto Post.

355 949.7 YU ISSN 0351-3912
UA18.Y8
POZADINA. 1947. b-m. Savezni Sekretarijat za Narodnu Odbranu, 11002 Belgrade, Serbia, Yugoslavia. (Dist. by: Vojnoizdavacki i Novinski Centar, Svetozara Markovica 70, 11002 Belgrade, Serbia, Yugoslavia) Ed. Borisav Nedic. bk.rev.
Formerly (until 1980): Vojnoekonomski Pregled (ISSN 0350-0578)

PRESENZA: IL BOLLETTINO. see *SOCIAL SERVICES AND WELFARE*

355 NO ISSN 0032-910X
PRO PATRIA. 1922. m. NOK 140. Norske Reserveoffiserers Forbund - Norwegian Reserve Officers Federation, Oslo Mil-Akershus, N-0015 Oslo, Norway. TEL 47-22403238. FAX 47-22440338. Ed. Kjell A. Bratli. adv. contact: Arild Rovde. bk.rev.; bibl.; illus. circ. 16,100.

335 US ISSN 0145-112X
UA23.A1
PROFILE (NORFOLK). 1957. bi-m. free. (U.S. Department of the Navy, Office of Information) U.S. Department of Defense, High School News Service, 1877 Dillingham Blvd., Norfolk, VA 23511. TEL 804-444-2828. FAX 804-445-1092. Ed. E.H. Lundquist. circ. 30,000. **Indexed:** Ind.Free Per., Ind.U.S.Gov.Per.
—UnCover.
Formerly: High School News Service Report.

MILITARY 4739

PROGRAM MANAGER. see *COMPUTERS — Computer Systems*

355.8 341.7 US
PROLIFERATION WATCH. bi-m. U.S. Senate Committee on Governmental Affairs, SD-340, Washington, DC 20510-6250. TEL 202-224-4751. FAX 202-224-9682. Dir. Sen. John Glenn. **Document type:** government publication.
Description: Discusses all issues of nuclear weapons proliferation.

PROPEL; tidsskrift for flyvning og rumfart. see *AERONAUTICS AND SPACE FLIGHT*

355.133 UK ISSN 0033-1945
PROVOST PARADE. 1947. s-a. £1.20. (R.A.F. Provost Branch) Royal Air Force Police School, RAF Newton, Nottingham NG13 8HR, England. Ed. B. Hicks. adv.; bk.rev.; charts; illus. stat. circ. 2,000. (back issues avail.)

PRZYSPOSOBIENIE OBRONNE W SZKOLE. see *EDUCATION*

355 US
PUPUKAHI/HARMONIOUSLY UNITED. 1950. 4/yr. free. Department of Defense, 3949 Diamond Head Rd., Honolulu, HI 96816-4495. TEL 808-737-8839. FAX 808-734-8527. circ. 7,500.
Formerly (until 1973): Hawaii Guardsman (ISSN 0017-8578)

355.115 US ISSN 0279-0653
PURPLE HEART MAGAZINE. vol.43, 1980. bi-m. $5 to non-members. Military Order of the Purple Heart of the U.S.A., 5413-B Backlick Rd., Springfield, VA 22151. TEL 703-642-5360. FAX 203-662-0212. Ed. Evans Kerrigan. bk.rev. circ. 30,000.

355 IT
QUADRANTE; rivista per le forze armate italiane. 1947. m. L.15000. Ministero della Difesa, Via XX Settembre 8, Rome, Italy. TEL 39-6-4819450. adv.: B&W page L.1750000.

359 CH ISSN 1010-3228
QUANQIU FANGWEI ZAZHI/DEFENSE INTERNATIONAL. (Text in Chinese) 1984. m. Quanqiu Fangwei Zazhishe, 9F, 182-2 Sec. 1 Ho-Ping Rd., E., Taipei, Taiwan, Republic of China. TEL 02-362-7093. FAX 02-362-7016.

355.1 UK
QUEEN'S REGULATIONS FOR THE ARMY AMENDMENTS. irreg. price varies. H.M.S.O., P.O. Box 276, London SW8 5DT, England. **Document type:** government publication.

358.4 343.01 UK
QUEEN'S REGULATIONS FOR THE R.A.F. AMENDMENTS. irreg. price varies. H.M.S.O., P.O. Box 276, London SW8 5DT, England. **Document type:** government publication.

355 BA
AL-QUWWA. 1974. m. free. Bahrain Defence Forces, P.O. Box 245, Manama, Bahrain. TEL 973-665599. FAX 973-663923. TELEX 8429 DEFFA'A. Ed. Maj. Ahmad Muhammad as-Suwaidi. **Document type:** government publication.

358.4 TS
AL-QUWWAT AL-JAWWIYYAH/U A E AIR FORCE MAGAZINE. (Text in Arabic) 1984. bi-m. 120DH. (Europe 380DH.; N. America 460DH.). General Command for the Armed Forces, Air Force and Air Defence Command, P.O. Box 3231, Abu Dhabi, United Arab Emirates. TEL 2-478128. FAX 2-479585. TELEX 24345 AIRFORM EM. Ed. Ahmad Khamis al-Hamili. adv. circ. 22,000.
Description: Covers military aviation and air force and air defence matters.

358.4 UK ISSN 0035-8614
R A F NEWS. 1961. fortn. £0.20 per no. to service personnel; others £0.50. Royal Air Force, Rm. 1025, HQ PTC, RAF Innsworth, Gloucester GL3 1EZ, England. TEL 01452-712612. FAX 01452-510848. Ed. John Dalling. adv. contact: Tony Kidd. bk.rev.; illus. circ. 20,000. (tabloid format) **Document type:** newspaper.

R & D CONTRACTS MONTHLY; a continuously up-dated sales and R & D tool for all research organizations and manufacturers. (Research & Development) see *SCIENCES: COMPREHENSIVE WORKS*

355 US
R & R ENTERTAINMENT DIGEST. (Rest & Relaxation) 1982. m. 825 Old Country Rd., Westbury, NY 11590. TEL 516-334-3030. Ed. Tory Billard. adv. circ. 182,500.
Description: Military consumer magazine.

R & R SHOPPERS NEWS. (Rest & Relaxation) see *COMMUNICATIONS — Television And Cable*

355 UK
R U S I INTERNATIONAL SECURITY REVIEW BOOK. 1993. a. Royal United Services Institute for Defence Studies, Whitehall, London SW1A 2ET, England. TEL 0171-930-5854. FAX 0171-321-0943. **Document type:** bulletin.

355 UK ISSN 0307-1847
U1
R U S I JOURNAL. 1858. bi-m. £46($90) Royal United Services Institute for Defence Studies, Whitehall, London SW1A 2ET, England. TEL 0171-930-5854. FAX 0171-321-0943. Ed. Alex Citron. adv.; bk.rev.; bibl.; illus.; index. circ. 4,000. (also avail. in microform from UMI; reprint service avail. from UMI) **Indexed:** Abstr.Mil.Bibl., Air Un.Lib.Ind., Amer.Hist.& Life, Br.Hum.Ind., DM & T, Hist.Abstr., P.A.I.S. **Document type:** bulletin.
—BLDSC (8052.647530); Ei; SWETS; UMI; UnCover.
Formerly: Royal United Service Institution. Journal (ISSN 0035-9289)

355 UK ISSN 0268-2656
R U S I NEWSBRIEF. 1980. m. Royal United Services Institute for Defence Studies, Whitehall, London SW1A 2ET, England. TEL 0171-930-5854. FAX 0171-321-0943. Ed. Jonathan Eyal. circ. 1,000. (back issues avail.) **Document type:** newsletter.
—BLDSC (6106.244600).

355 UK ISSN 0963-1852
RAIDS. Terminal House, Sta. Approach, Shepperton, Middx TW17 8AS, England. TEL 0932-228950. FAX 0932-247520. Ed. R. Adshead.

355 FI ISSN 0483-9080
RAJAMME VARTIJAT. 1949. bi-m. (free to qualified personnel). Suomen Rajavartiolaitos, PL 3, FIN-00131 Helsinki, Finland. TEL 358-0-1616514. FAX 629552. Ed. Marja Naapuri. **Document type:** government publication.
Formerly (until 1962): Rajajaakari (ISSN 0481-7338)
Description: Deals with matters of particular interest to members of the border patrol.

355.347 UK ISSN 1358-0507
READY. 1912. 3/yr. £3. Soldiers' & Airmen's Scripture Readers Association, Havelock House, Barrack Rd., Aldershot, Hants. GU11 3NP, England. TEL 01252-310033. FAX 01252-311222. Ed. John Diaper. circ. 17,000. **Document type:** bulletin.
Description: Presents claims of Jesus Christ to members of Her Majesty's Armed Forces and their families.

355 SP
RECONQUISTA - FORMACION. 12/yr. Ronda Segoria 17 bajo A, 28005 Madrid, Spain. TEL 1-266-04-57.

355 US ISSN 1059-9878
REENACTOR'S JOURNAL; for Civil War military and civilian reenactors. 1990. 12/yr. $24 (effective 1994). Rick Keating, Ed. & Pub., Box 1864, Varna, IL 61375. TEL 309-463-2123. adv. contact: Patricia A. Keating. bk.rev. **Document type:** consumer publication.

REGULAR. see *BUSINESS AND ECONOMICS — Labor And Industrial Relations*

REPORTER (WASHINGTON). see *LAW — Military Law*

355.81 US ISSN 0198-0181
CODEN: ARYTDT
RESEARCH & DEVELOPMENT ASSOCIATES FOR MILITARY FOOD AND PACKAGING SYSTEMS. ACTIVITIES REPORT. Key Title: Activities Report of the R & D Associates. 1947. s-a. $50 (foreign $85) (effective 1996). Research and Development Associates for Military Food & Packaging Systems, Inc., 16607 Blanco Rd., Ste. 501, San Antonio, TX 78232. TEL 210-493-8024. FAX 210-493-8036. Ed. Anna May Schenck. circ. 800. (back issues avail.) **Indexed:** Biol.Abstr.
—BLDSC (0676.557000).
Former titles (until 1978): Research and Development Associates for Military Food and Packaging Systems (ISSN 0099-6335); U.S. Army Natick Laboratories. Activities Report (ISSN 0041-7505)

355 US ISSN 0899-0166
RESEARCH GUIDES IN MILITARY STUDIES. 1988. irreg. price varies. Greenwood Press, Inc. (Subsidiary of Greenwood Publishing Group Inc.), 88 Post Rd. W., Box 5007, Westport, CT 06881-5007. TEL 203-226-3571. FAX 203-222-1502. **Document type:** monographic series.

355.3 US ISSN 0363-860X
U9
RESERVE FORCES ALMANAC. 1975. a. $5.95 (effective 1995). Uniformed Services Almanac, Inc., Box 4144, Falls Church, VA 22044. TEL 703-532-1631. FAX 703-532-1635. Ed. Lt.Col. Sol Gordon, U.S.A.F.-Ret. bk.rev. circ. 35,000. **Document type:** consumer publication.
Formerly: Uniformed Services Almanac. Special Reserve Forces Edition (ISSN 0360-554X)
Description: Annual guide to pay, benefits, entitlements and subjects of interest to Reservists and other military personnel, and their families.

355.37 US
RESERVIST.* 1971. q. free to qualified personnel. Reserve Enlisted Association, 1020 St. Paul St., Baltimore, MD 21202. Ed. Donald Kohr. adv.; bk.rev.; charts; illus. circ. 100,000.

355 US ISSN 0149-7197
UB357
RETIRED MILITARY ALMANAC. 1978. a. $5.95 (effective 1995). Uniformed Services Almanac, Inc., Box 4144, Falls Church, VA 22044. TEL 703-532-1631. FAX 703-532-1635. Ed. Lt. Col. Sol Gordon, U.S.A.F.-Retired. bk.rev. circ. 50,000. **Document type:** consumer publication.
Description: Annual guide to retired pay, benefits, entitlements and other important subjects for active and retired military personnel.

355 US
▼**RETIRED MILITARY FAMILY.** 1994. m. free. Military Forces Features, 169 Lexington Ave., New York, NY 10016-7305. TEL 212-545-9740. FAX 212-779-3080. Ed. Liz DeFranco; Pub. Joseph Mugnai, Sr. adv. contact: Joseph Mugnai, Jr. bk.rev.; illus. **Document type:** consumer publication.
Description: Publishes material of interest to the wives of retired military personnel.

355.5 US ISSN 0034-6160
UB413
THE RETIRED OFFICER. 1945. m. $20. Retired Officers' Association, 201 N. Washington St., Alexandria, VA 22314-2539. TEL 703-838-8115. FAX 703-838-8179. Ed. Maj. Dale Robinson. adv. contact: Lt.Col. Brian M. Hacker. bk.rev.; circ. 385,290 (controlled). (also avail. in microfilm from UMI; reprint service avail. from UMI) **Document type:** consumer publication.
Description: For men and women who are or have been commissioned or warrant officers in any component of the seven uniformed services of the United States.

355.115 AT ISSN 0034-6306
REVEILLE; the voice of more than 126,000 ex-servicemen and women. 1927. bi-m. Aus.$6. Returned and Services League of Australia, New South Wales State Branch, Anzac House, 365 Kent St., Sydney, N.S.W. 2000, Australia. TEL 61-2-299-2671. FAX 61-2-290-2046. Ed. Tom Jackson. adv.; bk.rev. circ. 110,000.

4740 MILITARY

355   AG   ISSN 0326-6427
REVISTA ARGENTINA DE ESTUDIOS ESTRATEGICOS. 1969. q. $30. (Centro Argentino de Estudios Estrategicos y de las Relaciones Internacionales) Olcese Editores, Viamonte 494, 2o piso, Of. 8, 1053 Buenos Aires, Argentina. Ed. Haroldo Olcese. adv.; bk.rev. circ. 5,000. (also avail. in microfilm) **Indexed:** Abstr.Mil.Bibl., Hisp.Amer.Per.Ind. (1970-).
Formerly (until 1984): Estrategia (ISSN 0046-2578)

REVISTA CUBANA DE MEDICINA MILITAR. see *MEDICAL SCIENCES*

359   PO
REVISTA DA ARMADA. 11/yr. Pc. do Comercio 1188, Lisbon, Portugal. TEL 346-89-61. Ed. J. de Carvalho Alfonso. circ. 7,000.

355   CK   ISSN 0120-0631
REVISTA DE LAS FUERZAS ARMADAS. 1976. 6/yr. Escuela Superior de Guerra, Fuerzas Militares de Colombia, Avenida 81, No. 45a-40, Apdo. Aereo 4403, Bogota, D.E., Colombia. Dir. Miguel Rodriguez Casas. adv.; bibl.; charts; illus. circ. 6,800.

355   VE   ISSN 0034-8473
REVISTA DE LAS FUERZAS ARMADAS.* 1946. m. Ministerio de la Defenza, La Planicie, Caracas, Venezuela.

359   CL   ISSN 0034-8511
V5
REVISTA DE MARINA. 1885. bi-m. $75 (effective 1996). Armada de Chile, Casilla 220, Valparaiso, Chile. TEL 56-32-281222. FAX 56-32-281223. Dir. Claudio Collados Nunez. bk.rev.; index. circ. 3,000. **Indexed:** Amer.Hist.& Life, Hist.Abstr. **Document type:** government publication.

359   EC   ISSN 0034-852X
REVISTA DE MARINA.* vol.13, 1970. Comandancia General de Marina, Apdo. 2095, Quito, Ecuador. charts; illus.

359   PE   ISSN 0034-8538
REVISTA DE MARINA DEL PERU. 1916. q. $20 (effective 1992). Marina de Guerra del Peru, Direccion de Informacion, Av. Salaverry Cdra. 24 Jesus Maria, Lima 11, Peru. TEL 5114-634141. adv.

REVISTA DE MEDICINA MILITARA. see *MEDICAL SCIENCES*

359   MX   ISSN 0034-9046
REVISTA DEL EJERCITO. 1906. m. Mex.$35000. Secretaria de la Defensa Nacional, Estado Mayor del Ejercito, Mexico, D.F., Mexico. circ. 4,000.

355   PY   ISSN 0034-9054
REVISTA DEL EJERCITO Y ARMADA.* 1937. m. Centro Militar y Naval, Asuncion, Paraguay.

355   AG   ISSN 0327-6953
REVISTA DEL SUBOFICIAL. 1919. q. $6.80. Estado Mayor General del Ejercito, Azopardo 250, piso 9, 1328 Buenos Aires, Argentina. TEL 342121. FAX 3315139. adv.; B&W page $1000; 200 x 280; adv. contact: Victor Raul Lessler. circ. 26,000.
Description: Publishes contributions from officers and non-commissioned officers of the Argentine army.

355   BL   ISSN 0101-7284
U4
REVISTA DO EXERCITO BRASILEIRO. 1882. q. $50. Diretoria de Assuntos Culturais, Educacao Fisica e Desportos, Biblioteca do Exercito, Palacio Duque De Caxais, 25, Ala Marcilio Dias, 3 andar, Rio de Janeiro, RJ - 20455, Brazil. TEL (021) 233-1338. Ed. Davis Ribeiro de Sena. adv. circ. 2,000.
Formerly (until vol.119, 1982): Revista Militar Brasileira (ISSN 0035-0125); (1920-1923): Boletim do Estado Major do Exercito.

355   SP
REVISTA ESPANOLA DE DEFENSA. 1982? 11/yr. Paseo de la Castellana, 109, 28071 Madrid, Spain. TEL 1-555-50-00. FAX 1-597-35-40. Ed. Jesus Sanmiguel. circ. 30,000.

355   SP   ISSN 0034-9569
REVISTA GENERAL DE MARINA. 1877. m. (except Aug.-Sep.). 2400 ptas. Estado Mayor de la Armada, Montalban, 2, 28014 Madrid, Spain. Dir. Juan Genova. adv.; bk.rev. circ. 3,000. **Indexed:** Abstr.Mil.Bibl., Amer.Hist.& Life, Hist.Abstr., Ind.SST.
—BLDSC (7856.675000).

359   BL   ISSN 0034-9860
V5
REVISTA MARITIMA BRASILEIRA. 1851. q. $22. Ministerio da Marinha, Servico de Documentacao da Marinha, Rua Dom Manuel 15, 20010-090 Rio de Janeiro RJ, Brazil. TEL 55-21-2216696. FAX 55-21-2166716. Ed. Jose Geraldo da Costa Cardoso de Melo. adv.; bibl.; charts; illus.; index. circ. 4,000.

REVISTA MEDICA DA AERONAUTICA DO BRASIL. see *MEDICAL SCIENCES*

355   DR   ISSN 0035-0117
REVISTA MILITAR.* 1934. Ejercito Nacional, Ciudad Trujillo, Dominican Republic.

355   PO
REVISTA MILITAR. 1849. 12/yr. Esc.7000 (effective 1993). Lg. Anunciada 9 s-1E, Lisbon, Portugal. TEL 3421512. adv. contact: Maia da Silva Forte. circ. 1,000.

355   PE   ISSN 0035-0141
REVISTA MILITAR DEL PERU.* 1904. m. Ministerio de Guerra, Avda. Boulevar s-n, Lima, Peru.

355   CU
REVISTA TECNICA MILITAR. m. Ministerio de las Fuerzas Armadas Revolucionarias, Avda. 47 No. 1414th, 14 y 18, Playa, Havana, Cuba.

355   BE   ISSN 0035-0877
DH540
REVUE BELGE D'HISTOIRE MILITAIRE/BELGISCH TIJDSCHRIFT VOOR MILITAIRE GESCHIEDENIS. (Text in Dutch and French) 1924. q. 700 BEF includes Militaria Belgica. Societe Royale des Amis du Musee Royal de l'Armee et d'Histoire Militaire, Parc du Cinquantenaire 3, 1040 Brussels, Belgium. Ed. J. Lorette. bk.rev. circ. 1,000. (back issues avail.) **Indexed:** Numis.Lit.

355   FR   ISSN 0035-2306
REVUE D'ETUDES MILITAIRES, AERIENNES ET NAVALES. 1912. m. 270 F. Societe d'Etudes, 5 bd. Beaumarchais, 75180 Paris Cedex 04, France. TEL 42-72-23-39.

355.15   FR   ISSN 0035-1210
REVUE DE LA FRANCE LIBRE. 1945. q. 30 Fr. in Europe; elsewhere 40 F. per issue. Association des Francais Libres, 59 rue Vergniaud, 75013 Paris, France. TEL 45-88-72-52. Ed. Georges Caitucoli. adv.; bk.rev.; illus. circ. 9,500. **Document type:** bulletin.

909   FR   ISSN 0035-3299
UA700
REVUE HISTORIQUE DES ARMEES. q. 320 F. (foreign 520 F.) (effective 1996). Association pour le Developpement et la Diffusion de l'Information Militaire, 6 rue Saint Charles, 75015 Paris, France. TEL 45-77-03-76. FAX 45-79-53-73. Ed. General Paillart. circ. 4,000. **Indexed:** Amer.Hist.& Life, Hist.Abstr.
—Faxon.
Description: Covers the history of the French military forces.

355   BE   ISSN 0254-8186
D25
REVUE INTERNATIONALE D'HISTOIRE MILITAIRE. (Text in English, French, German, Italian, Russian and Spanish) 1939. irreg. price varies. Commission Internationale d'Histoire Militaire, c/o Secretary-General Dr. P. Lefeure, Musee Royal de l'Armee et d'Histoire Militaire, Parc du Cinquantenaire 3, 1040 Brussels, Belgium. FAX 32-2-734-54-21. Ed.Bd. circ. 1,500. **Indexed:** Amer.Hist.& Life, Hist.Abstr.
Description: Each volume devoted to the military history of a single country.

359   FR   ISSN 1146-2132
REVUE MARITIME. 1861. 4/yr. 180 F. (foreign 250 F.) (effective 1996). Institut Francais de la Mer, 9 av. du Dr. Gley, 75020 Paris, France. TEL 40-31-04-00. Ed. Claude Benoit. adv. circ. 7,000. **Document type:** academic/scholarly publication.
—BLDSC (7927.000000); SWETS.
Former titles: Nouvelle Revue Maritime; (until 1974): Institut de la Mer. Revue Maritime.

355   SZ   ISSN 0035-368X
REVUE MILITAIRE SUISSE.* 1856. m. 60 SFr. Association de la Revue Militaire Suisse, Case Postale 7, CH-1669 Albeuve, Switzerland. adv.; bk.rev.; abstr.; bibl.; charts; illus.; circ. 3,105 (controlled). **Indexed:** Abstr.Mil.Bibl.
—BLDSC (7933.620000).

RIVER CURRENTS. see *TRANSPORTATION — Ships And Shipping*

355   RM   ISSN 1220-5710
RIVISTA DE ISTORIE MILITARA. English edition (annual): Review of Military History. (Supplement to: Viata Armatei) (Text in Romanian, summaries in English, French, German, Rumanian, Russian, Spanish) 1984. bi-m. $40. Ministerul Apararii Nationale - Ministry of National Defense, Str. Stirbei Voda Nr. 79-81, 70736 Bucharest, Rumania. TEL 313044. TELEX 10376. (Subscr. to: Rodipet S.A., P.O. Box 33-57, Piata Presei Libere nr.1, Bucharest, Rumania) Ed. Ilie Manole. adv.; bk.rev.; illus.
Formerly (until 1990): Lupta Intregului Popor (ISSN 1220-5729)
Description: Covers archaeology, numismatics, heraldics, philately, and uniforms.

355   IT
RIVISTA ITALIANA DIFESA. Short title: R I D. 1982. m. L.70000($85) (foreign L.95000). Cooperativa Giornalistica Riviera s.r.l., Via Martiri Liberazione 79-3, 16043 Chiavari (GE), Italy. TEL 39-185-308606. FAX 39-185-309063. TELEX 270630 PP CHV. Ed. Andrea Nativi. adv.: B&W page $3000, color page $5700; trim 10 5/8 x 7 5/16. bk.rev.; index. circ. 30,746. (back issues avail.) **Document type:** trade publication.

359   IT   ISSN 0035-6964
V4
RIVISTA MARITTIMA. (Supplement avail.: Marina Militare Italiana Rapporto) 1868. m. L.58000. Stato Maggiore della Marina, Via Romeo Romei 5, 00136 Rome, Italy. FAX 39-6-39728182. TELEX 39-6-39728421. Ed. Roberto Cesaretti. bk.rev.; abstr.; charts; illus.; index, cum.index. circ. 5,500. (tabloid format) **Indexed:** Abstr.Mil.Bibl., Amer.Hist.& Life, Hist.Abstr.
—BLDSC (7989.000000); Faxon; SWETS.

355   IT   ISSN 0035-6980
U4
RIVISTA MILITARE. (English ed. ceased in 1991 with no.2) 1856. bi-m. L.22000 (foreign L.40000) (effective 1993). Stato Maggiore Esercito, Pza. Sisto V, 3, 00185 Rome, Italy. TEL 39-6-47357371. FAX 39-6-6794200. Ed. Pier G. Franzosi. adv.: B&W page L.2100000, color page L.4200000. bk.rev.; bibl.; charts; illus.; index. circ. 30,000. **Indexed:** Abstr.Mil.Bibl., Amer.Hist.& Life, Hist.Abstr., Int.Polit.Sci.Abstr.

355   SZ   ISSN 0035-6999
RIVISTA MILITARE DELLA SVIZZERA ITALIANA.* 1927. bi-m. 30 SFr. Via Rodari 10a, 6900 Lugano, Switzerland. adv.; charts; illus.

ROAD AND REC; the Air Force journal of driving and recreational safety. see *TRANSPORTATION*

355   IS   ISSN 0334-8466
U1
ROMACH. English edition: Defense Update (ISSN 0931-7317) 1986. 9/yr. $57. Eshel-Drahmit Publishing, P.O. Box 115, Hod Hasharon 45 100, Israel. TEL 052-31357. FAX 972-3-285456. TELEX 35770-COIN-IL. Ed. Tamir Eshel. adv.; bk.rev. circ. 6,500.

358.4   UK   ISSN 0035-8606
ROYAL AIR FORCE COLLEGE JOURNAL.* 1920. a. £1($5) Ministry of Defence, PR11 - RAF, Turnstile House, 98 High Holborn, London WC1V 6LL, England. Ed. Sgr. Ldr. Parker. adv.; bk.rev. circ. 1,800.
—CCC.

MILITARY 4741

358.4 UK
ROYAL AIR FORCE EDUCATION BULLETIN. 1964. a. free. Royal Air Force Training Development and Support Unit, Department of Educational and Training Technology Development, RAF Newton, Nottingham NG13 8HL, England. TEL 0949-20771. FAX 0949-21201. (Co-sponsor: Ministry of Defence) circ. 1,300 (controlled). (back issues avail.) **Indexed:** Cont.Pg.Educ., Educ.Tech.Abstr., Res.High.Educ.Abstr. **Document type:** bulletin.

358.4 UK ISSN 0954-092X
ROYAL AIR FORCE YEARBOOK. 1975. a. £3. Royal Air Force Benevolent Fund Enterprises, Building 15, RAF Fairford, Glos. GL7 4DL, England. TEL 01285-713300. FAX 01285-713268. Ed. Peter R. March. adv. circ. 100,000. **Document type:** corporate report.

355 UK
ROYAL BRITISH LEGION ANNUAL REPORT AND ACCOUNTS. 1921. a. free. Royal British Legion, 48 Pall Mall, London SW1Y 5JY, England. circ. 8,000. **Document type:** corporate report.

623 UK ISSN 0035-8878
UG1
ROYAL ENGINEERS JOURNAL. 1870. 3/yr. £17.47 (overseas £19.33) (effective 1991). Institution of Royal Engineers, Brompton Barracks, Chatham, Kent ME4 4UG, England. Ed. Lt. Col. R.I. Reive. adv.; bk.rev.; illus.; index. circ. 4,400. **Indexed:** Chem.Abstr., Eng.Ind., GeoRef. **Document type:** academic/scholarly publication.
—BLDSC (8030.000000); Faxon; UnCover.

355.133 UK ISSN 0035-9025
ROYAL MILITARY POLICE JOURNAL. 1950. 3/yr. £5.50. Royal Military Police, Regimental Headquarters, Ed. Lt.Col. P. Squier, Roussillon Barracks, Chichester, W. Sussex, England. TEL 01243-534237. FAX 01243-534288. adv.; bk.rev.; illus. circ. 2,900. **Document type:** newsletter.

355 327 AT ISSN 0728-1188
ROYAL UNITED SERVICES INSTITUTE OF AUSTRALIA. JOURNAL. 1977. a. Aus.$16 (foreign Aus.$21) (typically set in Sep.). Royal United Services Institute of Australia Inc., G.P.O. Box 590, Canberra, A.C.T. 2601, Australia. FAX 06-265-3105. Ed. J. Donovan. adv.; bk.rev. circ. 6,000. (back issues avail.) **Document type:** academic/scholarly publication.
—UnCover.
 Description: Aims to advance the study of strategy, national defence and related affairs.

355 310 US
RUSSIA & EURASIA ARMED FORCES REVIEW ANNUAL. Abbreviated title: R E A F R A. 1977. a. 75. Academic International Press, Box 1111, Gulf Breeze, FL 32562-1111. Ed. George M. Mellinger. bibl.; charts; illus.; stat. (back issues avail.) **Indexed:** Amer.Bibl.Slavic & E.Eur.Stud.
—BLDSC (8359.190000).
 Formerly: Soviet Armed Forces Review Annual (ISSN 0148-0928)

355 RW
RWANDA. MINISTERE DE LA DEFENSE NATIONALE. FORCES DE SECURITE AU SERVICE DE LA NATION. bi-m. Ministere de la Defense Nationale, B.P. 85, Kigali, Rwanda. **Document type:** government publication.

355 362.4 US
S.C. DISABLED AMERICAN VETERANS JOURNAL. q. $4. South Carolina Department of Disabled American Veterans, 1801 Assembly St., Columbia, SC 29201. TEL 803-796-9200. Ed. Marion Shoemake. adv. circ. 3,700.
 Description: Covers the D.A.V.'s opinion of legislative happenings, veteran affairs, treatment of disabled veterans at VA hospitals or out patient clinics, and suggestions for better veteran benefits.

355 UK
S C S I OCCASIONAL PAPERS. irreg., no.11, 1995. free. Strategic and Combat Studies Institute, Staff College, Camberley, Surrey GU15 4NP, England. TEL 01276-412653. FAX 01276-412718. Ed. Humphry Crum Ewing. **Document type:** monographic series.

355 US
S D I REPORT. (Strategic Defense Initiative) m. newsstand price: $2. Heritage Foundation, 214 Massachusetts Ave., N.E., Washington, DC 20002. TEL 202-546-4400. FAX 202-546-8328.
 Description: Keeps readers up to date on all SDI issues, including an insider's perspective on SDI-related developments in the White House, the Pentagon's SDI office and the Congress.

355 AG
S E R EN EL 2000. (Seguridad Estrategia Regional) 1992. 3/yr. $21. Hipolito Yrigoyen 1994, 2do. 4, 1089 Buenos Aires, Argentina. TEL 54-1-9510712. Ed. Marcela R. Donadio; Pub. Eduardo Pedro Vaca. adv. contact: Luis Tibiletti. bk.rev. circ. 1,000. **Document type:** academic/scholarly publication.

355 SZ
S M P V. m. Postfach 438, CH-3607 Thun, Switzerland. TEL 033-228316. circ. 4,600.

355 US
S S A M.* (Soldier, Sailor, Airman, Marine) 1978. m. $13. U.S. Department of Defense, The Pentagon, Washington, DC 20301. (Dist. by: Supt. of Documents, Washington, DC 20402) **Indexed:** Int.Polit.Sci.Abstr.

355 AT ISSN 0048-8933
SABRETACHE. 1958. q. Aus.$26. Military Historical Society of Australia, P.O. Box 30, Garran, A.C.T. 2605, Australia. E-mail: astaunto@pcug.arg.au. Ed. Elizabeth Topperwien. adv.; bk.rev.; index. circ. 420. **Indexed:** Aus.P.A.I.S. **Document type:** academic/scholarly publication, proceedings.
—UnCover.

355 US ISSN 0080-5335
UF526.3
SAGAMORE ARMY MATERIALS RESEARCH CONFERENCE. PROCEEDINGS. 1954. irreg., vol.31, 1986. price varies. Plenum Publishing Corp., 233 Spring St., New York, NY 10013-1578. TEL 212-620-8000. FAX 212-463-0742. TELEX 23-421139. **Indexed:** Chem.Abstr., INSPEC. **Document type:** proceedings.
—CCC.
 Refereed Serial

355 II ISSN 0036-2743
U4
SAINIK SAMACHAR; pictorial weekly of India's armed forces. (Editions in 12 languages) 1909. w. Rs.20 (foreign Rs. 90). Ministry of Defence, Directorate of Public Relations, Block L-1, Church Rd., New Delhi 110 011, India. TEL 3019668. Ed. Bibekananda Ray. adv.; bk.rev.; charts; illus. circ. 18,000.
 Incorporates: Fauji Akhbar.
 Description: Provides news and entertainment as well as education to those enrolled in Indian Armed Forces.

355 SA
SALUT. (Text in Afrikaans, English) 1949. m. R.66 (overseas R.80). South African Defence Force, Private Bag X158, Pretoria 0001, South Africa. TEL 27-12-4284234. FAX 27-12-4284274. Ed. Mrs. A. van der Westhuizen. adv.; bk.rev.; illus. circ. 70,000. **Indexed:** Abstr.Mil.Bibl., Ind.S.A.Per.
 Former titles (until 1994): Paratus (ISSN 0031-1839); Commando (ISSN 0010-2504)

SALVO. see HISTORY — History Of North And South America

255 US
SAN DIEGO NAVY DISPATCH. 1961. w. $60. Western States Weeklies, Inc., 6312 Riverdale St., Box 600600, San Diego, CA 92160-0600. TEL 619-280-2985. Ed. Carol Burke; Pub. Sarah E. Hagerty. adv. contact: Chris Blaisdale. circ. 25,000 (paid). (tabloid format; back issues avail.) **Document type:** newspaper.
 Description: Covers all base and local activities.

355 UK
THE SAPPER. bi-m. £5.40. Corps of Royal Engineers, Brompton Barracks, Chatham, Kent ME4 4UG, England. TEL 0634-822299. FAX 0634-822309. Ed. R.I. Reive. bk.rev. circ. 7,000. **Document type:** bulletin.

355 629.1 TU ISSN 1300-2082
SAVUNMA VE HAVACILIK; defence and aerospace. 1987. bi-m. $65. Monch Media Ltd., Ahmet Mithat Efendi Sk. 20-2, 06550 Cankaya Ankara, Turkey. TEL 90-312-439-1937. FAX 90-312-439-5724. (Subscr. to: Moench Verlagsgesellschaft mbH, Postfach 140261, 53057 Bonn, Germany. TEL 0228-6483-0. FAX 0228-6483109) Ed. Hakki Aris. adv.: B&W page $3500, color page $6500; trim 10 5/8 x 7 5/16; adv. contact: Ute Steuer. circ. 21,030. (back issues avail.) **Document type:** trade publication.
 Description: Covers technical issues in the defense and civilian sectors of the aviation and aerospace industries.

355 US ISSN 0036-5408
SCABBARD AND BLADE JOURNAL. 1913. 3/yr. $3. National Society of Scabbard and Blade, 205 Thatcher Hall, Oklahoma State University, Stillwater, OK 74078. TEL 405-624-5000. Ed. Max Rodgers. bk.rev.; illus. circ. 2,000.

355 SZ ISSN 0036-7451
SCHWEIZER SOLDAT UND M F D; Die Monatszeitschrift fuer Armee und Kader mit MFD-Zeitung. Key Title: Schweizer Soldat. 1925. m. 42 SFr. (foreign 64 SFr.). Huber und Co. AG, Promenadestr. 16, CH-8501 Frauenfeld, Switzerland. TEL 054-271111. Ed. Edwin Hofstetter. adv.; bk.rev. circ. 12,500. **Document type:** trade publication.
—SWETS.
 Incorporates: M F D-Zeitung (ISSN 0014-584X)
 Description: Covers current issues, news, information and new developments concerning the national and foreign military. Includes list of events, new publications and positions available.

355 SZ
SCHWEIZER WEHRSPORT. 11/yr. Endlikerstr. 79, CH-8400 Winterthur, Switzerland. TEL 052-296296. Ed. Heinz Koch. circ. 3,000.

355 SZ ISSN 0036-7591
SCHWEIZERISCHE GESELLSCHAFT DER OFFIZIERE DES MUNITIONSDIENSTES. BULLETIN.* (Text in French and German) 1960. m. Schweizerische Gesellschaft der Offiziere des Munitionsdienstes, Geissbergstr. 59, CH-5400 Ennetbaden, Switzerland. bk.rev. **Document type:** bulletin.

355 SZ
SCHWEIZERISCHE MILITAERPERSONAL ZEITUNG. m. Postfach 4, CH-8532 Warth, Switzerland. TEL 054-211464. circ. 9,000.

359 US
SCIPIO NEWSLETTER. 1979. m. membership. Scipio Society of Naval and Military History, Inc., Box 93, Cold Spring Harbor, NY 11724. TEL 516-271-7037. FAX 516-271-7137. Ed. Richard N. Handock. bk.rev. circ. 53. (back issues avail.) **Document type:** newsletter.
 Formerly (until 1992): Grenade (ISSN 0891-124X)

355.15 UK
SCOTTISH LEGION NEWS. 1950. 6/yr. £2.50 free to Legion clubs and branches in Scotland. Royal British Legion Scotland, New Haig House, Logie Green Rd., Edinburgh EH7 4HR, Scotland. TEL 0131-557-2782. FAX 0131-557-5819. Ed. Neil Griffiths. adv. contact: Tony Simpson. bk.rev.; illus. circ. 13,000. **Document type:** newsletter.
 Incorporates (in 1987): Claymore (ISSN 0009-8590)

335 US
SCREAMING EAGLE. 1945. bi-m. $20 membership. 101st Airborne Division Association, 101 E. Morris St., Box 586, Sweetwater, TN 37874-0586. TEL 615-337-4103. FAX 615-337-41-3. Ed. Ivan G. Worrell. adv.; bk.rev. circ. 6,200. **Document type:** newsletter.
 Description: News and features for all veterans of the 101st Airborne Division.

MILITARY

359   US   ISSN 0199-1337
VA49
SEA POWER. (Includes annual: Almanac of Seapower) 1958. m. $25 to non-members (effective 1992). Navy League of the United States, 2300 Wilson Blvd., Arlington, VA 22201-3308. TEL 703-528-1775. FAX 703-528-2333. Ed. James D. Hessman. adv.; bk.rev.; charts; illus.; index. circ. 74,000. (also avail. in microform from UMI) **Indexed:** Abstr.Mil.Bibl, Air Un.Lib.Ind., Amer.Bibl.Slavic & E.Eur.Stud, DM & T, Ocean.Abstr., Pollut.Abstr., PROMT.
—UMI; UnCover. **CCC.**
   Formerly: Navy - the Magazine of Sea Power (ISSN 0028-1689)

355   CN   ISSN 0048-9883
SEALANDAIR. 1969. fortn. Can.$10($20) Canadian Forces Base Edmonton, Lancaster Park, Edmonton, Alta. T0A 2H0, Canada. TEL 403-457-8481. adv.; charts; illus. circ. 3,000.

SECURITY INTELLIGENCE. see *POLITICAL SCIENCE*

SECURITY STUDIES. see *POLITICAL SCIENCE — International Relations*

355   VE
SEGURIDAD Y DEFENSA; revista plural sobre temas militares y geopolitica. q. Miracielos a Hospital, Edif. Sur 2, piso 8, Of. 812, Caracas 1010, Venezuela. TEL 4835853. Ed. Manuel Molina Penaloza.

355 359   JA
SEKAI NO KANSEN/SHIPS OF THE WORLD. (Text in Japanese) 1957. m. 980 Yen per no. Kaijinsha Co., Ltd., 9-8, Iidabashi 4-chome, Chiyoda-ku, Tokyo 102, Japan.

355   CN   ISSN 0037-2315
SENTINEL (OTTAWA); magazine of the Canadian Forces. French edition: Sentinelle (ISSN 0037-2358) 1965. 6/yr. Can.$15.50($18.60) Directorate Public Affairs, National Defence Headquarters, Ottawa, ON K1A 0K2, Canada. TEL 613-996-4418. FAX 613-992-6468. (Subscr. to: Supply and Services Canada, Ottawa, ON K1A 0S9, Canada. TEL 819-956-4802) Eds. Cpts. Rita LePage, Stephane Grenier. bk.rev.; charts; illus.; index. circ. 54,000 (40,000 English ed., 14,000 French ed.) **Document type:** government publication.
   Description: International information magazine of the Canadian Forces providing a wide view of its functions, objectives, accomplishments and activities.

355   CN
SERVIR. (Text in English, French) 1971. m. free. Canadian Forces Base Montreal, St. Hubert, PQ J3Y 5T4, Canada. TEL 514-462-8085. FAX 514-462-8938. Ed. Roger Gauthier. adv. contact: Roger Gauthier. bk.rev.; illus. circ. 4,500. **Document type:** newspaper.
   Formerly: Parapet (ISSN 0384-0417)

355 359   JA   ISSN 0286-6064
SHI PAWA/SEA POWER. (Text in Japanese) m. 12-8, Roppongi 4-chome, Minato-ku, Tokyo 106, Japan.

355   CN   ISSN 0037-3729
SHILO STAG. vol.9, 1970. s-m. Can.$12.50. Leech Printing Ltd., 18th and Park, Brandon, MB R7A 5B8, Canada. TEL 204-728-3037. FAX 204-727-3338. adv.; bibl.; charts; illus.; tr.lit.

355   JA   ISSN 0286-9241
SHI BOEI RONSHU/JOURNAL OF NATIONAL DEFENSE. (Text in Japanese; abstract in English) 1973. 4/yr. 4000 Yen (effective since 1995). (Boei Gakkai - National Defense Society) Boei Gakkai, Daini-Matsuda Bldg., 7-8-7, Roppongi, Minato-ku, Tokyo 106, Japan. TEL 81-3-3713-2469. FAX 81-3-3713-2723. E-mail: kyc04242@niftyserve.or.jp. Ed. Yasuto Fukushima. bk.rev. circ. 2,200. **Document type:** academic/scholarly publication.
   Description: Promotes society members' theoretical study on the defense issues.
   Refereed Serial

SHIPMATE. see *COLLEGE AND ALUMNI*

359   US   ISSN 0080-9292
VA61
SHIPS AND AIRCRAFT OF THE UNITED STATES FLEET. Running title: Naval Institute Guide ti Ships and Aircraft of the United States Fleet. 1939. irreg., 15th ed., 1992. $72.50. (U.S. Naval Institute) Naval Institute Press, 118 Maryland Ave., Annapolis, MD 21402. TEL 410-268-6110. FAX 410-269-7940. (Orders to: Naval Institute Press, 2062 Generals Hwy., Annapolis, MD 21401. TEL 800-233-8764) Ed. Norman Polmar. index. (reprint service avail.)

355 387   US   ISSN 1073-8258
SHIPYARD LOG. Cover title: Pearl Harbor Shipyard Log. 1946. s-m. free. Pearl Harbor Naval Shipyard, 401 Ave. E, Ste. 124, Pearl Harbor, HI 96860-5350. TEL 808-474-3214. FAX 808-471-1514. Ed. Marshall Fukuki. adv.; illus.; circ. 4,700 (controlled). (tabloid format) **Document type:** government publication, newspaper.

355.115   US   ISSN 0276-8135
DS557
SHORT-TIMER'S JOURNAL; * soldiering in Vietnam. 1981. 5/yr. $3 to veterans; non-veterans $15. Winter Soldier Archive, 2315 Oak St., Berkeley, CA 94708-1628. Ed. Clark C. Smith. circ. 1,000. (back issues avail.)

355.15   US   ISSN 0037-4334
SHOW-ME MISSOURI LEGIONNAIRE. 1934. m. $2.75. American Legion, Department of Missouri, Box 179, Jefferson City, MO 65102. TEL 314-893-2353. FAX 314-893-2980. Ed. L. Carey Bankhead. adv.; bk.rev. circ. 68,000.

355   US   ISSN 0733-0367
DD253.65
SIEGRUNEN; * the Waffen-SS in historical perspective. 1975. q. $20. Merriam Press, Box 6718, Brookings, OR 97415. Ed. Richard Landwehr. adv.; bk.rev. circ. 375. (back issues avail.)
   Description: Covers history of Waffen-SS and biographies of personalities, units, and battles.

355   CU
SIEMPRE ALERTA. w. Ministerio de las Fuerzas Armadas Revolucionarias, 84 No. 8401 esq. 19, Playa, Havana, Cuba.

351.06   GW   ISSN 0941-4959
SISTRA. 1986. irreg. DM.11 per issue. Sistra Verlag, Postfach 160163, 53060 Bonn, Germany. TEL 0228-281852. FAX 0228-285798. Ed. Michael Forster. circ. 300. (looseleaf format) **Document type:** trade publication.

SMALL WARS AND INSURGENCIES. see *POLITICAL SCIENCE — International Relations*

355   SZ
SOCIETE MILITAIRE DU CANTON DE GENEVE. BULLETIN. 10/yr. (Societe Militaire du Canton de Geneve) Bercher SA, Rue de l'Athenee 34, CH-1206 Geneva, Switzerland. TEL 022-3473388. FAX 022-3462047. circ. 1,300. **Document type:** bulletin.

355 900   UK   ISSN 0037-9700
DA49
SOCIETY FOR ARMY HISTORICAL RESEARCH. JOURNAL. 1921. q. £18. Society for Army Historical Research, National Army Museum, Royal Hospital Rd., London SW3 4HT, England. TEL 01425-621950. Ed. A. Harfield. adv.; bk.rev.; illus.; maps; cum.index. circ. 1,200. **Indexed:** Amer.Hist.& Life, Br.Hum.Ind., Hist.Abstr. **Document type:** academic/scholarly publication.
—BLDSC (4880.790000).

SOCIETY OF COLONIAL WARS. BULLETIN. see *HISTORY — History Of North And South America*

355   AU   ISSN 0038-0962
DER SOLDAT; Oesterreichische Soldaten-Zeitung. 1956. fortn. S.290. Der Soldat Zeitungs- und Zeitschriftenverlags-Gesellschaft mbH, Seidengasse 3-11, A-1070 Vienna, Austria. TEL 01-934713. FAX 01-5225832. adv.: B&W page S.67000; trim 267 x 400. charts; illus. circ. 15,000. (tabloid format) **Document type:** newspaper.

355   RU   ISSN 0869-4338
U1
SOLDAT. English edition: Soldier (ISSN 0869-432X) (Editions in Arabic, English, French, Russian, Spanish) m. $118 (effective 1996). Voenizdat, Ul. Zorge 1, 103160 Moscow, K-160, Russia. TEL 095-195-4595. (Dist. by: Mezhdunarodnaya Kniga, ul. Bolshya Yakimanka, 39, 117049 Moscow, Russia. TEL 095-238-4600; Dist. in U.S. by: Victor Kamkin Inc., 4956 Boiling Brook Pkwy., Rockville, MD 20852. TEL 301-881-5973) illus. (also avail. in microform) **Indexed:** Abstr.Mil.Bibl., Air Un.Lib.Ind., DM & T, PROMT.
   Former titles: Sovetsky Voin & Sovetskoe Voennoe Obozrenie (ISSN 0201-7741)

355   GW   ISSN 0038-0989
U3
SOLDAT UND TECHNIK. 1958. m. DM.122.40 (military personnel DM.102.60). (Bundesministerium der Verteidigung) Umschau Zeitschriftenverlag Breidenstein GmbH, Stuttgarter Str. 18-24, 60329 Frankfurt a.M., Germany. TEL 069-2600-0. FAX 069-2600-619. Ed. Gerhard Hubatschek. adv.: B&W page DM.6180, color page DM.10815; trim 176 x 257; adv. contact: Brigitte Benzing. bk.rev.; charts; illus.; stat.; index. circ. 29,148. **Indexed:** Bibl.Cart., DM & T, PROMT. **Document type:** trade publication.
—BLDSC (8327.240000). **CCC.**

355   UK   ISSN 0038-1004
SOLDIER. 1945. fortn. £19.30 (foreign £25.30). Ministry of Defence, Parson House, Ordnance Rd., Aldershot, Hants GU11 2DU, England. TEL 0252-347352. FAX 0252-347358. Ed. J.N. Elliott. adv.: B&W page £630, color page £765; trim 297 x 210. bk.rev. circ. 23,000. (back issues avail.) **Document type:** government publication.
—SWETS.
   Description: Official magazine of the British Army.

355   RU   ISSN 0869-432X
U1
SOLDIER. Russian edition: Soldat (ISSN 0869-4338) (Editions in English, French, Portuguese, Spanish, Russian) m. Voenizdat, Ul. Zorge 1, 103160 Moscow, K-160, Russia. TEL 095-195-4595. (Dist. by: Mezhdunarodnaya Kniga, B. Yakimanka 39, 117049 Moscow, Russia; Dist. in U.S. by: Victor Kamkin Inc., 4956 Boiling Brook Pkwy., Rockville, MD 20852. TEL 301-881-5973) Ed. Leonid Golovnov.
—UnCover.
   Former titles: Soviet Soldier (ISSN 0236-2104) & Soviet Military Review (ISSN 0038-5220)

355.115   II
SOLDIER IN NATIONAL SERVICE. 1982. q. All India Congress Committee, 24 Akbar Rd., New Delhi 110 011, India. Ed. Proash Shyan.

355   US   ISSN 0145-6784
G539
SOLDIER OF FORTUNE; the journal of professional adventurers. 1975. m. $26 (foreign $45.95). Omega Group Ltd., Box 693, Boulder, CO 80306. TEL 303-449-3750. Ed. Robert K. Brown. adv.; bk.rev.; tr.lit. circ. 104,593. (back issues avail.) **Indexed:** PMR.
—UnCover.
   Description: Reports on combat from front lines around the world.

355   US   ISSN 0093-8440
U1
SOLDIERS. 1946. m. $19 (foreign $23.75) (effective 1995). U.S. Department of the Army, Cameron Sta., Alexandria, VA 22304-5050. TEL 703-274-6671. FAX 703-274-1896. (Subscr. to: Superintendent of Documents, U.S. Government Printing Office, Box 371954, Pittsburgh, PA 15250-7954. TEL 202-512-1800. FAX 202-512-2250) Ed. Eileen M. Bratz. illus.; index; circ. 250,000 (controlled). (also avail. in microform from UMI; reprint service avail. from UMI) **Indexed:** Air Un.Lib.Ind., Ind.U.S.Gov.Per., P.A.I.S. **Document type:** government publication.
—Faxon; UMI; UnCover.
   Formerly: Army Digest (ISSN 0004-2498)
   Description: Discusses the operations and technical developments of the Army and its reserve components.

MILITARY

355
SOLDIERS TODAY.* 1991. q. $29.99. Publishing & Business Consultants, 101 W. 64th St., Unit 3, Inglewood, CA 90302-1255. TEL 213-732-3477. FAX 213-732-9123. (Subscr. to: Box 75392, Los Angeles, CA 90075) Ed. Andeson Napoleon Atia. **Document type:** consumer publication.

948 355   FI   ISSN 0357-816X
DL1037
SOTAHISTORIALLINEN AIKAKAUSKIRJA. (Text in Finnish, Swedish; summaries in English) 1948. a. FIM 70. Sotahistoriallinen Seura - Society for Military History, Maurinkatu 1, 00170 Helsinki 17, Finland. TEL 90-1616389. (Co-sponsor: Sotatieteen Laitos) Ed.Bd. circ. 1,000.

355   FI   ISSN 0038-1675
U4
SOTILASAIKAKAUSLEHTI/FINNISH MILITARY REVIEW. (Text in Finnish; contents page in English and Finnish) 1921. m. FIM 250. Upseeriliitto, Luotsikatu 7 A 2, FIN-00160 Helsinki, Finland. TEL 358-0-6689-4060. FAX 358-0-6689-4020. Ed. Erkki Nordberg. adv.; bk.rev.; charts; illus.; maps; stat.; index, cum.index; circ. 6,078 (controlled). **Document type:** academic/scholarly publication, corporate report.

355.03   SA
SOUTH AFRICA. DEPARTMENT OF DEFENSE. WHITE PAPER ON DEFENSE AND ARMAMENT PRODUCTION. (Text in Afrikaans and English) irreg. Department of Defense, Cape Town, South Africa. **Document type:** government publication.

SOZIALRECHT & PRAXIS; Fachzeitschrift des VdK Deutschland fuer Vertrauensleute der Behinderten und fuer Sozialpolitiker. see *SOCIAL SERVICES AND WELFARE*

358.4   US
SPACE OBSERVER. 1956. w. $45. Gowdy Printcraft Press, Inc., 22 N. Sierre Madre, Colorado Springs, CO 80903. TEL 719-634-1593. FAX 719-632-0762. Ed. Elton Price; Pub. John Bernheim. adv. contact: Michael Murt. bk.rev. circ. 7,500. (tabloid format) **Document type:** newspaper.

355   US
SPEARHEAD (MONETA). 1945. q. membership only. First Special Service Force Association, 262 Pine Knob, Moneta, VA 24121-2609. TEL 703-297-8308. Ed. Bill Story. circ. 1,300. **Document type:** newsletter.

355   US   ISSN 1058-0123
SPECIAL WARFARE. 1988. q. $8 (foreign $10) (effective 1995). John F. Kennedy Special Warfare Center and School, Attn.: AOJK-DTP-B, USAJFKSWCS, Ft. Bragg, NC 28307-5000. TEL 919-432-5703. (Subscr. to: Superintendent of Documents, U.S. Government Printing Office, Box 371954, Pittsburgh, PA 15250-7954. TEL 202-512-1800. FAX 202-512-2250) Ed. Jerry D. Steelman. bk.rev. circ. 9,200. **Indexed:** Air Un.Lib.Ind. **Document type:** government publication.
—BLDSC (8404.760300).

355   SA
SPRINGBOK. (Text in Afrikaans and English) 1922. 4/yr. R.10. South African Legion - Suid-Afrikaase Legioen, P.O. Box 8751, Johannesburg 2000, South Africa. Ed. L. van Rhynveldt. adv.; bk.rev.; charts; illus. circ. 4,750. **Document type:** newsletter.
Description: News of the activities of the legion, members' recollections of their experiences, and other items of interest to South African war veterans.

STAND TO!. see *HISTORY — History Of Europe*

STAR AND GARTER MAGAZINE. see *HOSPITALS*

355.15   CN   ISSN 0038-9889
STAR SERVICEMAN.* 1946. m. Can.$3. Media Public Relations Ltd., P.O. Box 2929, Vancouver 3, B.C., Canada. Ed. George S. Hobson. adv.; bk.rev.; charts; illus.; index. circ. 2,410.
Supersedes: New Veteran.

355.115   US   ISSN 0894-8542
STARS AND STRIPES. 1877. w. $19. National Tribune Corporation, Box 1803, Washington, DC 20013. TEL 202-829-3225. FAX 202-829-5657. Ed. Mark A. Peterson; Pub. Howard Haugerud. adv. contact: Scott Cohen. bk.rev. (tabloid format; also avail. in microfilm from BHP,KTO) **Document type:** newspaper.
Description: News and information concerning veterans and veterans affairs.

358.4   US   ISSN 1059-7468
STATIC LINE; your airborne lifeline. 1965. m. $25 (Canada and Mexico $30; elsewhere $35). Spearhead, Inc., Box 87518, College Park, GA 30337. TEL 404-478-5301. FAX 404-478-5301. Ed. Don Lassen. adv.; bk.rev.; illus.; circ. 20,000 (paid). cols./p.: 5; pp./issue: 40. (tabloid format) **Document type:** newspaper.
Description: Directed to former military paratroopers; perpetuates the camaraderie of military service.

341.1   AU   ISSN 0039-1085
STEIRISCHE KRIEGSOPFER ZEITUNG.* 1947. q. membership. Kriegsopferverband Steiermark, Muenzgrabenstr. 4-11, A-8011 Graz, Austria. Ed. Johann Pocsics. adv.; bk.rev.; bibl.; illus.; stat.; index. circ. 22,000. (tabloid format)

STRATEGIC AND DEFENCE STUDIES CENTRE NEWSLETTER. see *POLITICAL SCIENCE*

355   US   ISSN 0091-6846
U162
STRATEGIC REVIEW. 1973. q. $25 (foreign $37.50). United States Strategic Institute, Box 15618, Kenmore Sta., Boston, MA 02215. TEL 617-353-8700. FAX 617-353-7330. Ed. Mackubin T. Owens. bk.rev. circ. 3,500. (back issues avail.) **Indexed:** A.B.C.Pol.Sci., Abstr.Mil.Bibl., Air Un.Lib.Ind., Amer.Bibl.Slavic & E.Eur.Stud., Amer.Hist.& Life (until 1993), Chic.Per.Ind., Hist.Abstr. (until 1993), Int.Polit.Sci.Abstr., Mid.East: Abstr.& Ind., P.A.I.S., PROMT, Soc.Sci.Ind. **Document type:** academic/scholarly publication.
—BLDSC (8474.031700); Faxon; SWETS; UnCover.
Description: Provides a forum for the discussion of matters of current significance in the politico-military field.

STRATEGIC REVIEW FOR SOUTHERN AFRICA. see *POLITICAL SCIENCE — International Relations*

355   PK
STRATEGIC STUDIES. (Text in English) 1977. q. Rs.50($10) to individuals; students Rs. 30 per no. Institute of Strategic Studies, P.O. Box 1173, Islamabad, Pakistan. TEL 824658. Ed. Ross Masood Husain. adv.; bk.rev. circ. 1,000. **Indexed:** Abstr.Mil.Bibl.

355 320   FR   ISSN 0224-0424
U162
STRATEGIQUE. 1979. q. 295 F. Fondation pour les Etudes de Defense Nationale (F.E.D.N.), Hotel National des Invalides, 75007 Paris, France. circ. 1,500. (back issues avail.)

355   US   ISSN 1040-886X
STRATEGY AND TACTICS; the magazine of conflict simulation. (Special edition avail. s-a. (ISSN 0736-654X)) 1967. 6/yr. $59 (foreign $72). Decision Games, Box 4049, Lancaster, CA 93539-4049. TEL 805-723-2088. Ed. Joseph Miranda; Pub. Christopher Cummins. adv. contact: Callie Cummins. bk.rev.; charts; illus.; stat. circ. 6,000. (tabloid format) **Indexed:** Abstr.Mil.Bibl., Amer.Hist.& Life, Hist.Abstr.
Former titles (until 1988): Strategy and Tactics Magazine (ISSN 0736-6531); (until 1982): Stategy and Tactics (ISSN 0049-2310)
Description: Covers military history and analysis.

355   GR
STRATIOTIKI EPITHEORISIS/MILITARY REVUE. m. $25. Hellenic Army General Staff, 10 Pittakou St., Athens, Greece. **Indexed:** Abstr.Mil.Bibl.

355 069   PL   ISSN 0137-5733
STUDIA DO DZIEJOW DAWNEGO UZBROJENIA I UBIORU WOJSKOWEGO. (Text in Polish; summaries in English) 1963. irreg., nos.9-10, 1988. price varies. Muzeum Narodowe w Krakowie - National Museum in Cracow, Ul. J. Pilsudskiego 12, 31-109 Krakow, Poland. (Dist. by: Ars-Polona, Krakowskie Przedmiescie 7, Warsaw, Poland) (Co-sponsor: Association of Old Arms and Uniforms Amateurs) Ed. Elzbieta Hyzy. circ. 1,000. (also avail. in microfilm) **Document type:** academic/scholarly publication.

355 943.8   PL   ISSN 0562-2786
STUDIA I MATERIALY DO HISTORII WOJSKOWOSCI. 1954. a. price varies. (Polska Akademia Nauk, Komitet Nauk Historycznych) Ossolineum, Publishing House of the Polish Academy of Sciences, Rynek 9, 50-106 Wroclaw, Poland. TEL 48-71-386-25. FAX 48-71-448-103. TELEX 0712771 OSS PL. Ed. Benon Miskiewicz. **Document type:** academic/scholarly publication.
Formerly (until 1956): Studia i Materialy do Historii Sztuki Wojennej.
Description: History of Polish military science and arms.

355 320   US
STUDIES IN DEFENSE POLICY. 1971. irreg. price varies. Brookings Institution, 1775 Massachusetts Ave., N.W., Washington, DC 20036-2188. TEL 202-797-6255. FAX 202-797-6195. (Subscr. to: Box 037, Washington, DC 20042-0037. TEL 202-797-6255) **Document type:** academic/scholarly publication.

355   NE
STUDIES IN U S NATIONAL SECURITY. 1977. irreg. (U.S. Army War College, Strategic Studies Institute, US) Kluwer Academic Publishers, Postbus 17, 3300 AA Dordrecht, Netherlands. TEL 31-78-392392. FAX 31-78-392254. TELEX 29245 KAPG NL. (Dist. by: Kluwer Academic Publishers Group, P.O. Box 322, 3300 AH Dordrecht, Netherlands. TEL 31-78-392392. FAX 31-78-546474; N. America dist. addr.: Boc 358, Accord Sta., Hingham, MA 02018-0358. TEL 617-871-6600) Ed. James A. Kuhlman. **Document type:** monographic series. *Refereed Serial*

STUDY WAR NO MORE. see *POLITICAL SCIENCE*

355   US
SUBMARINE REVIEW. q. Naval Submarine League, Box 1146, Annandale, VA 22003. TEL 703-256-0891. Ed. Capt. James C. Hay. **Document type:** trade publication.

355   UK
SUPPLY LINE. bi-m. M O D, Room 39A, D Block, Ensleigh, Bath BA1 5AB, England. TEL 0225-467715. FAX 0225-68607. TELEX 44662-LDPENS-G. Ed. A. Weeks. circ. 15,500.

359   US   ISSN 0145-1073
V1
SURFACE WARFARE. 1976. bi-m. $9.50 (foreign $11.90). U.S. Navy, Chief of Naval Operations (N86AX), c/o Dir., Surface Warfare Division, 601 N. Fairfax St., Rm. 270, Alexandria, VA 22314. TEL 703-274-4535. FAX 703-274-0743. (Subscr. to: Superintendent of Documents, U.S. Government Printing Office, Box 371954, Pittsburgh, PA 15250-9574. TEL 202-512-1800. FAX 202-512-2250) bk.rev. circ. 39,000. **Indexed:** DM & T. **Document type:** government publication.
—BLDSC (8547.951800).

355.155   UK   ISSN 0491-6204
SURMACH. (Text in Ukrainian) 1955. a. £3. Association of Ukrainian Former Combatants in Great Britain, 49 Linden Gardens, London W2 4HG, England. TEL 0171-229-8392. Ed. S.M. Fostun. adv.; bk.rev. circ. 1,000. **Document type:** newspaper.
Description: Covers historical and military events of Ukraine and other nations with news of the activities of the Association of Ukrainian Former Combatants in Great Britain.

SURVEILLANT; acquisitions and commentary for intelligence and security professionals. see *POLITICAL SCIENCE — International Relations*

MILITARY

355   IO   ISSN 0215-4501
UA853.I5
T S M - TEKNOLOGI & STRATEGI MILITER. 1987. m. P.T. Sinar Cakra Sakti, Dewi Sartika 136, Jakarta, Indonesia. TEL 021-8096130. FAX 021-8091652. (Subscr. to: Moench Verlagsgesellschaft mbH, Postfach 140261, 53057 Bonn, Germany. TEL 0228-6483-0. FAX 0228-6483109) adv.: B&W page $3400, color page $6100; trim 240 x 190; adv. contact: Ute Steuer. circ. 21,000. **Document type:** trade publication.

355   629.1   US   ISSN 1059-0552
TACTICAL TECHNOLOGY. 1991. fortn. $545 (foreign $580) (effective 1995). Phillips Business Information, Inc., 1201 Seven Locks Rd., Potomac, MD 20854. TEL 301-424-3338. FAX 301-309-3847. E-mail: pbi@phillips.com. Ed. Eric DeRitis. (looseleaf format) **Document type:** newsletter.
●Also available online. Vendor(s): NewsNet (GT45).
—CCC.

356   UK   ISSN 0039-9418
TANK. 1919. q. £13. Royal Tank Regiment Publications Ltd., Regimental Headquarters Royal Tank Regiment, Bovington, Wareham, Dorset, England. TEL 01929-403444. FAX 01929-403218. Ed. Lt.Col. George Forty. adv.; bk.rev. circ. 2,200. **Document type:** newsletter.

TANKETTE. see HOBBIES

623   SZ
TECHNISCHE MITTEILUNGEN FUER SAPPEURE, PONTONIERE UND MINEURE. Abbreviated title: T M. (Text in French, German, Italian) 1936. q. 50 SFr. Gesellschaft fuer Militaerische Bautechnik, Auf der Mauer 2, CH-8001 Zurich, Switzerland. TEL 01-2526260. FAX 01-2521667. Ed. Simon Wiedemann. adv. contact: Peter Mettler. bk.rev.; charts; illus.; stat.; index. circ. 1,600. **Document type:** bulletin.

355   600   II   ISSN 0971-4413
TECHNOLOGY FOCUS. (Text in English) 1993. bi-m. (Ministry of Defense, Defence Scientific Information & Documentation Centre) Defence Research & Development Organization, Metcalfe House, New Delhi 110 054, India. TEL 011-2932252. FAX 011-2919151. TELEX 031-78030. E-mail: pubs@desidoc.ernet.in. Ed. S.S, Murthy. charts; illus.; circ. 2,500. (controlled). **Document type:** government publication.
Description: Covers military products, processes and technologies.

355   658   US   ISSN 1074-4363
TECHNOLOGY TRANSFER WEEK. 1989. bi-w. $695 (foreign $760) (effective 1995). Phillips Business Information, Inc., 1201 Seven Locks Rd., Potomac, MD 20854. TEL 301-424-3338. FAX 301-309-3847. E-mail: pbi@phillips.com. **Document type:** newsletter.
●Also available online. Vendor(s): Data-Star, Knight-Ridder, Inc., NewsNet (DE17).
—CCC.
Formerly (until 1994): Defense Marketing International (ISSN 1044-3975); Incorporates: Pac-Rim Defense Marketing (ISSN 1051-2497)

355   GW   ISSN 0722-2904
UA10
TECNOLOGIA MILITAR. (Text in Spanish) 1979. 6/yr. DM.45($30) Moench Verlagsgesellschaft mbH, Postfach 140261, 53057 Bonn, Germany. TEL 0228-6483-0. FAX 0228-6483109. TELEX 8869429-MVB-D. Ed. Ezio Bonsignore. adv.: B&W page $3700, color page $6700; trim 10 5/8 x 7 5/16; adv. contact: Ute Steuer. circ. 17,184. **Indexed:** Abstr.Mil.Bibl. **Document type:** trade publication.

355   DR
TEMAS SOBRE LA PROFESIONALIZACION MILITAR EN LA REPUBLICA DOMINICANA. 1983. m. Editora Corripio, C. Por A., Calle A esq. Central, Zona Industrial de Herrera, Santo Domingo, Dominican Republic.

355   FR   ISSN 0758-4083
TERRE INFORMATION. 1973. m. 60 F. (Service d'Information, Recrutement, Promotion de l'Armee de Terre) Association pour le Developpement et la Diffusion de l'Information Militaire, 6 rue St. Charles, 75015 Paris, France. TEL 45-77-03-76. FAX 45-79-53-73. Ed. Major Maxant. circ. 123,000.
Description: News for active, reserve and retired members of the army.

355   FR   ISSN 0995-6999
TERRE MAGAZINE. m. (10/yr.). 150 F. (foreign 210 F.) (effective 1996). (Service d'Information, Recrutement, Promotion de l'Armee de Terre) Association pour le Developpement et la Diffusion de l'Information Militaire, 6 rue St. Charles, 75015 Paris, France. TEL 45-77-03-76. FAX 45-79-53-73. illus. circ. 75,000.
Description: Covers news of the ground armies throughout the world.

TERRORISM AND POLITICAL VIOLENCE. see POLITICAL SCIENCE — International Relations

TEST BAN VERIFICATION MATTERS. see POLITICAL SCIENCE — International Relations

355.115   US
TEXAN VETERAN NEWS. q. Box 7440, Ft. Worth, TX 76111-0440. TEL 817-834-7573.

355.155   US
THUNDER FROM HEAVEN. 1954. 3/yr. $15 membership. 17th Airborne Division Association, 4 Cain Ct., Montville, NJ 07045-9151. TEL 201-263-2433. Ed. Joe Quade. adv. contact: Joe Quade. bk.rev.; circ. 6,500 (paid). **Document type:** newsletter.
Description: For military veterans of WW II who served in the 17th Airborne Division.

TICKET; tips and travel. see TRAVEL AND TOURISM

355   SW   ISSN 0040-683X
TIDSKRIFT FOER KUSTARTILLERIET. 1943. q. SEK 100. Kustartilleriklubben, P.O. Box 30202, S-104 50 Stockholm, Sweden. TEL 08-788-8291. Ed. Bengt Delang. adv.; bk.rev.; abstr.; illus.; cum.index. circ. 1,100.

TIDSKRIFT I FORTIFIKATION; foer fortifikationsofficerare och officerare ingenjoerer, vaeg- och vattenbyggradskaaren. see ENGINEERING — Civil Engineering

359   SW   ISSN 0040-6945
V5
TIDSKRIFT I SJOVASENDET. 1836. 4/yr. SEK 50 (foreign SEK 80). Kungl. Oerlogsmannasaellskapet, P.O. Box 10186, S-100 55 Stockholm, Sweden. Ed. Lars Wigert. adv.; bk.rev. circ. 1,000.
Description: Journal from Royal Swedish Naval Institute.

359.009489   DK   ISSN 0040-7186
V5
TIDSSKRIFT FOR SOEVAESEN. 1827. m. DKK 50. (Soe-Lieutenant-Selskabet) Erhvervenes Forlag, Overgangen over Vandet 62 B, DK-1415 Copenhagen K, Denmark. adv.; bk.rev.; bibl.; charts; illus.; maps; stat.; index; cum.index every 25 yrs. —BLDSC (8828.150000).
Former titles (until 1842): Archiv for Soevaernet (ISSN 0909-2471); (until 1856): Nyt Archiv for Soevaernet (ISSN 0909-248X)

355   US   ISSN 1040-9025
TOP 500 R D T & E CONTRACTORS. a. $1495. Forecast International Inc. - D M S, 22 Commerce Rd., Newtown, CT 06470. TEL 203-426-0800. FAX 203-426-1964. TELEX 467615.
Description: Examines each company according to the last two years' contracting by the U.S. Navy, Army, and Air Force, as well as by R & D category, and by performance.

369.271 355.15   CN   ISSN 1189-007X
THE TORCH (DARTMOUTH). 1989. q. Can.$8.56. (Royal Canadian Legion, Nova Scotia Command) Nationwide Promotion Limited, 12 Dawn Dr., Dartmouth, NS B3B 1H9, Canada. TEL 902-468-5709. FAX 902-468-4843. Ed. Harold Shea. adv.: page Can.$1595; adv. contact: Jack Ryan. circ. 28,000. (tabloid format) **Document type:** newspaper.

TRADING POST (GREENVILLE). see HOBBIES

TRANSLOG; journal of military transportation management. see TRANSPORTATION — Roads And Traffic

355   FR   ISSN 0036-2794
TRIOMPHE SAINT-CYR; plaquette annuelle des promotions de l'Ecole Special Militaire de St. Cyr et de l'Ecole Militaire Interarmes. 1949. a. 43 F. Ecole Speciale Militaire de Saint-Cyr, 56210 Coetquidan, France. (Co-sponsor: Ecole Militaire Interarmes) adv. circ. 1,000.
Formerly: Triomphe.

355   NE   ISSN 0925-6237
TRIVIZIER. 1990. m. V B M - L K V, Mesdagstraat 118, 2596 XZ The Hague, Netherlands. TEL 31-70-3242125. FAX 31-70-3282000. Ed. A.R.V. van Nierop. circ. 23,000 (controlled).
Description: Union publication for the Dutch armed forces.

355   AU   ISSN 0041-3658
TRUPPENDIENST; Zeitschrift fuer Fuehrung und Ausbildung im Bundesheer. 1962. bi-m. S.250. Herold Druck und Verlag GmbH, Faradaygasse 6, A-1032 Vienna, Austria. FAX 01-79594115. Ed. Horst Maeder. bk.rev.; bibl.; charts; illus.; stat.; index. circ. 12,000. **Document type:** bulletin.
—SWETS.

355   GW
TRUPPENPRAXIS - WEHRAUSBILDUNG. 1957. 12/yr. DM.108. (Bundesministerium der Verteidigung) Verlag Offene Worte, Striepenweg 31, 21147 Hamburg, Germany. TEL 040-79713322. FAX 040-79713324. adv.; bk.rev. circ. 33,000. **Document type:** government publication.
Formed by the 1994 merger of: Truppenpraxis (ISSN 0041-3666) & Wehrausbildung.

TRUST AND VERIFY. see POLITICAL SCIENCE — International Relations

355   629.1   US
TURBINE ENGINE OVERHAUL. a. $1495. Forecast International Inc. - D M S, 22 Commerce Rd., Newtown, CT 06470. TEL 203-426-0800. FAX 203-426-1964. TELEX 467615.
Description: Reports and analyzes worldwide business opportunities in the turbine overhaul and upgrading market. Identifies inventories of major military and commercial turbine engines with 10-year forecast of overhaul requirements.

355   629.1   TU   ISSN 1300-5030
TURKISH DEFENCE & AEROSPACE UPDATE. (Text in English) 1990. m. $220. Monch Media Ltd., Ahmet Mithat Efendi Sk. 20-2, 06550 Cankaya Ankara, Turkey. TEL 90-312-4391937. FAX 90-312-4395724. circ. 2,000. (back issues avail.)
Description: Covers economic and industry developments in military and civil aerospace and aviation.

U N I D I R NEWSLETTER/LETTRE DE L'U N I D I R. (United Nations Institute for Disarmament Research) see POLITICAL SCIENCE — International Relations

355   IT   ISSN 0041-5375
U N U C I. 1964. m. membership. Unione Nazionale Ufficiali in Congedo d'Italia, Via Nomentana 313, 00162 Rome, Italy. Ed. Giovanni Spadea. adv.; bk.rev.; illus.

358.4   US   ISSN 0274-6824
U S A F WEAPONS REVIEW. q. (to Department of Defense personnel only). U.S. Air Force, 57 T.R.S.S. - T.S.M., 4269 Tyndall Ave., Ste. 104, Nellis A.F.B., NV 89191-6074. **Indexed:** Air Un.Lib.Ind. **Document type:** government publication.

355   II   ISSN 0041-770X
U S I JOURNAL. (Text in English) 1870. q. Rs.120($26) (typically set in Oct.). United Service Institution of India, Kashmir House, Rajaji Marg, New Delhi 110011, India. TEL 301-5828. Ed. N.B. Singh. adv.; bk.rev.; illus. circ. 5,000. **Indexed:** Abstr.Mil.Bibl., Amer.Hist.& Life, Hist.Abstr., P.A.I.S. **Document type:** academic/scholarly publication.
—BLDSC (4910.650000).

MILITARY 4745

355.115 US
U S J. (Uniformed Services Journal) 1968. bi-m. $15 to non-members. National Association for Uniformed Services, 5535 Hempstead Way, Springfield, VA 22151. TEL 703-750-1342. FAX 703-354-4380. Ed. Sharon Barnes. adv.; bk.rev.; charts; illus. circ. 60,000.
Supersedes: N A U S Newsletter.

359 US ISSN 0041-798X
V1
U S NAVAL INSTITUTE. PROCEEDINGS. Key Title: Proceedings - United States Naval Institute. 1874. m. $35. U S Naval Institute, 118 Maryland Ave., Annapolis, MD 21402-5035. TEL 410-268-6110. Ed. Fred H. Rainbow. adv.; bk.rev.; charts; illus.; index. circ. 125,000. (also avail. in microform from UMI; reprint service avail. from UMI) **Indexed:** Air Un.Lib.Ind., Amer.Bibl.Slavic & E.Eur.Stud., Amer.Hist.& Life, BMT, Chem.Abstr., Deep Sea Res.& Oceanogr.Abstr., DM & T, Hist.Abstr., P.A.I.S., So.Pac.Per.Ind. **Document type:** proceedings.
—BLDSC (6829.000000); Faxon; SWETS; UMI; UnCover.
Description: Covers aspects of naval affairs for the U.S. Navy, Marines and Coast Guard. Examines foreign naval forces.

355 US
U S S HENRICO A P A -45 REUNION ASSOCIATION. NEWSLETTER. 1974. s-a. $20. U S S Henrico A P A - 45 Reunion Association, 15875 Interurban Rd., Platte City, MO 64079-9185. TEL 816-858-5411. FAX 816-858-5556. Ed. Don Soper; Pub. Gil Tarr. circ. 760 (paid). (looseleaf format) **Document type:** newsletter.
Description: Contains history of the ship, crew and officer muster roll 1943-1968, and reunion information.

385 359 US
U S S ST. LOUIS HUBBLE BUBBLE. 1942. m. $10 to non-members. U S S St. Louis CL 49 Association, Inc., 220 Otis Ave., Staten Island, NY 10306. TEL 718-351-4556. Ed. Harry Price. bk.rev. circ. 500. **Document type:** newsletter.

355 NO ISSN 0041-6584
UNDERVISNING OG VELFERD/EDUCATION AND WELFARE.* 1955. 10/yr. Undervisnings- og Velferdsoffiserenes Forening, Bergen, Norway.

355 US ISSN 0041-6592
UNDERWATER LETTER; twice-monthly letter on contracting opportunities, research and development, and legislation in underwater defense, offshore activities, and military and civilian oceanography. 1960. s-m. $190. Callahan Publications, Box 1173, McLean, VA 22101. TEL 703-356-1925. FAX 703-356-9614. Ed. Vincent F. Callahan, Jr. bk.rev.; charts; illus. (back issues avail.) **Indexed:** DM & T, PROMT. **Document type:** newsletter.
Formerly: Underwater Defense Letter.
Description: Non-technical report for businessmen and others who want to share in the nation's underwater-related budget. Provides contracting, marketing and development data in military, civilian government, private industry, and academic ocean-related programs.

355 US ISSN 0503-1982
U9
UNIFORMED SERVICES ALMANAC. 1959. a. $5.95 (effective 1995). Uniformed Services Almanac, Inc., Box 4144, Falls Church, VA 22044. TEL 703-532-1631. FAX 703-532-1635. Ed. Lt. Col. Sol Gordon, U.S.A.F.-Ret. bk.rev. circ. 55,000. **Document type:** consumer publication.
Description: Annual guide to pay, benefits, entitlements and other subjects of great interest to military personnel and their families.

UNION DES AVEUGLES DE GUERRE. BULLETIN BIMESTRIEL. see *HANDICAPPED* — *Visually Impaired*

UNITED ARAB EMIRATES. AL-QIYADAH AL-AAMAH LIL-QUWWAT AL-MUSALLIHAH. MAJALLAH AL-TIBBIYYAH/UNITED ARAB EMIRATES. GENERAL COMMAND FOR THE ARMED FORCES. MEDICAL JOURNAL. see *MEDICAL SCIENCES*

355 539.7 320 UN ISSN 0252-5607
UNITED NATIONS DISARMAMENT YEARBOOK. Spanish edition: Anuario de las Naciones Unidas sobre Desarme (ISSN 0252-5593); French edition: Nations Unies Annuaire de Desarmement (ISSN 0252-5615); Russian edition (ISSN 0252-5585) (Text in English) 1952. irreg., latest vol.14, 1989. $45. United Nations Publications, Rm. DC2-853, New York, NY 10017. TEL 212-965-8302; 800-253-9646. FAX 212-963-3489. (Or: Distribution and Sales Section, Palais des Nations, CH-1211 Geneva 10, Switzerland) (also avail. in microfiche)
—BLDSC (9096.972000).
Former titles: United Nations. Disarmament Commission. Yearbook; United Nations. Disarmament Commission. Official Records (ISSN 0082-8076)

355 539.7 320 UN ISSN 1014-2177
UNITED NATIONS ECONOMIC AND SOCIAL COUNCIL. DISARMAMENT STUDY SERIES. 1981. irreg., latest no.16. price varies. United Nations Publications, Room DC2-0853, New York, NY 10017. TEL 212-963-8302; 800-253-9646. FAX 212-963-3489. (Or: Distribution and Sales Section, Palais des Nations, 1211 Geneva 10, Switzerland)
—BLDSC (3595.453000).

358 600 US
U.S. AIR FORCE GEOPHYSICS LABORATORY. A F G L (SERIES). 1960? irreg. U.S. Air Force Geophysics Laboratory, Hanscom Air Force Base, MA 01731. TEL 617-861-4441. (Dist. by: National Technical Information Service, Springfield, VA 22151) (also avail. in microform) **Indexed:** Geo.Abstr., GeoRef.
Supersedes: U.S. Air Force Cambridge Research Laboratories. A F C R L (Series) (ISSN 0082-870X)

355 343 US ISSN 8755-7819
JX1974
U.S. ARMS CONTROL AND DISARMAMENT AGENCY. ANNUAL REPORT. 1961. a. U.S. Arms Control and Disarmament Agency, Department of State Bldg., Washington, DC 20451. TEL 202-632-8715. (Also avail. from: Superintendent of Documents, U.S. Government Printing Office, Box 371954, Pittsburgh, PA 15250-7954. TEL 202-783-3238. FAX 202-512-2250) **Document type:** government publication.
Former titles: Arms Control (ISSN 0275-0023); U.S. Arms Control and Disarmament Agency. Annual Report to Congress (ISSN 0082-8769)

355 US
U.S. ARMY MATERIEL COMMAND. ANNUAL HISTORICAL REVIEW. a. U.S. Army, Materiel Command (Headquarters), Historical Office (AMC-HO), 500 Eisenhower Ave., Alexandria, VA 22333-0001. TEL 703-274-3776. (Orders to: Superintendent of Documents, U.S. Government Printing Office, Box 371954, Pittsburgh, PA 15250-7954. TEL 202-512-1800. FAX 202-512-2250) **Document type:** government publication.
Description: Serves as a chronicle of the U.S. Army Materiel Command Headquarters, making the past a means for managing the present and projecting the future.

U.S. CIVIL AIR PATROL. QUARTERLY PUBLIC AFFAIRS. see *AERONAUTICS AND SPACE FLIGHT*

U.S. COAST GUARD MARINE SAFETY COUNCIL. PROCEEDINGS. see *TRANSPORTATION* — *Ships And Shipping*

U.S. DEFENSE LOGISTICS AGENCY. D O D HAZARDOUS MATERIALS INFORMATION SYSTEM: HAZARDOUS ITEM LISTING. see *PUBLIC HEALTH AND SAFETY*

355 US ISSN 0082-9862
U.S. DEPARTMENT OF DEFENSE. DEFENSE PROGRAM AND DEFENSE BUDGET.* (Also called: Defense Budget and Defense Program) a. U.S. Department of Defense, The Pentagon, Washington, DC 20301. TEL 202-545-6700. (Orders to: Supt. of Documents, Washington, DC 20402) **Indexed:** DM & T. **Document type:** government publication.

U.S. DEPARTMENT OF DEFENSE. INDEX OF SPECIFICATIONS AND STANDARDS. see *METROLOGY AND STANDARDIZATION*

U.S. DEPARTMENT OF DEFENSE. INDEX OF SPECIFICATIONS AND STANDARDS: PART 1, ALPHABETICAL LISTING. see *METROLOGY AND STANDARDIZATION*

U.S. DEPARTMENT OF DEFENSE. INDEX OF SPECIFICATIONS AND STANDARDS: PART 2, NUMERIC LISTING. see *METROLOGY AND STANDARDIZATION*

U.S. DEPARTMENT OF DEFENSE. INDEX OF SPECIFICATIONS AND STANDARDS: PART 3, FEDERAL SUPPLY CLASS LISTING. see *METROLOGY AND STANDARDIZATION*

U.S. DEPARTMENT OF DEFENSE. INDEX OF SPECIFICATIONS AND STANDARDS: PART 4, NUMERICAL LISTING OF CANCELLED DOCUMENTS. see *METROLOGY AND STANDARDIZATION*

355.6 US ISSN 0098-3888
UA23.2
U.S. DEPARTMENT OF DEFENSE. REPORT OF SECRETARY OF DEFENSE TO THE CONGRESS.* Key Title: Report of Secretary of Defense to the Congress. Cover title: Annual Defense Department Report. a. $9.50. U.S. Department of Defense, Office of the Secretary, The Pentagon, Rm. 3E933, Washington, DC 20301-1155. TEL 202-695-5261. (Also avail. from: Bernan, 4611-F Assembly Dr., Lanham, MD 20706. TEL 800-274-4447. FAX 301-459-0056) **Document type:** government publication.

U.S. DEPARTMENT OF VETERANS AFFAIRS. ANNUAL REPORT. see *INSURANCE*

355 US ISSN 0083-1328
U.S. INDUSTRIAL COLLEGE OF THE ARMED FORCES. MONOGRAPHS. R SERIES.* 1944. irreg. U.S. Industrial College of the Armed Forces., Ft. McNeir, Washington, DC 20319-6000. TEL 202-475-0717. **Document type:** monographic series.

359.07 US ISSN 0500-1951
V393
U.S. OFFICE OF NAVAL RESEARCH. ANNUAL TASK SUMMARY: CONTRACT RESEARCH PROGRAM. Key Title: Annual Task Summary, Contract Research Program. a. U.S. Office of Naval Research, Arlington, VA 22217. TEL 202-545-6200.

355 600 US
U.S. OFFICE OF TECHNOLOGY ASSESSMENT. REPORTS. INTERNATIONAL SECURITY AND COMMERCE PROGRAM. irreg. price varies. U.S. Office of Technology Assessment, Publication Distribution, U.S. Congress, 600 Pennsylvania Ave., S.E., Washington, DC 20510-8025. TEL 202-224-8713. FAX 202-228-6098. E-mail: PUBREQUEST@OTA.GOV. (Dist. by: Superintendent of Documents, U.S. Government Printing Office, Box 371954, Pittsburgh, PA 15250-7954. TEL 202-783-3238. FAX 202-512-2250; And: National Technical Information Service, 5285 Port Royal Rd., Springfield, VA 22161. TEL 703-487-4650. FAX 703-321-4630) (also avail. in microfiche from CIS; back issues avail.; reprint service avail. from CIS) **Document type:** monographic series, government publication.
Formerly: U.S. Office of Technology Assessment. Reports. National Security Program.
Description: Reports provide technical information on U.S. domestic and international security; military space technology and international treaties are also covered.

358.4 UK ISSN 0956-2826
UNITED STATES AIR FORCES EUROPE YEARBOOK. 1989. a. £2.95. Royal Air Force Benevolent Fund Enterprises, Building 15, RAF Fairford, Glos. GL7 4DL, England. TEL 01285-713300. FAX 01285-713268. Ed. Peter March. adv. contact: Clive Elliott. circ. 60,000. **Document type:** bulletin.

UNIVERSITY OF PRETORIA. INSTITUTE FOR STRATEGIC STUDIES. BULLETIN. see *POLITICAL SCIENCE* — *International Relations*

MILITARY

355   US   ISSN 0892-4023
CODEN: UNSYE3
UNMANNED SYSTEMS. 1975. q. $40 to non-members; institutions $100. Association for Unmanned Vehicle Systems International, 1735 N. Lynn St., Ste. 950, Arlington, VA 22209-2229. TEL 703-524-6646. FAX 703-524-2303. E-mail: 74260,3212@compuserve.com. Ed. Sarah M. Cook. adv.: B&W page $1245, color page $2145; trim 8 1/2 x 11; adv. contact: Sarah M. Cook. charts,illus. circ. 3,000. (back issues avail.) **Indexed:** DM& T, INSPEC (1986-). **Document type:** trade publication.
—BLDSC (9120.550000); Ei; Faxon.
Former titles: A U V S Magazine; Remotely Piloted Magazine.
Description: Highlights developments in unmanned vehicles and related systems with the intent to forsee what course the industry may take.

355   IT
UNUCI. m. L.1000 per no. Unione Nazionale Ufficiali in Congedo d'Italia, Via Nomentana 313, 00162 Rome, Italy. TEL 869-007. Ed. Alberto Scotti. illus.
Description: Covers the different types of Italian army activities that go on outside of Italy. It also describes each section of the Army and its responsibilities.

V D K ZEITUNG. (Verband der Kriegs- und Wehrdienstopfer, Behinderten und Rentner Deutschlands e.V. (VdK)) see *SOCIAL SERVICES AND WELFARE*

V E R T I C MATTERS. see *POLITICAL SCIENCE — International Relations*

V F W AUXILIARY. (Veterans of Foreign Wars of the United States) see *CLUBS*

355.115   US   ISSN 0042-1820
V F W MAGAZINE. 1912. m. $10 to non-members. Veterans of Foreign Wars of the United States, 406 W. 34th St., Kansas City, MO 64111. TEL 816-756-3390. Ed. Richard Kolb. adv.; bk.rev.; illus. circ. 2,100,000. (also avail. in microfilm from UMI)

355   SW   ISSN 0042-2800
VAART FOERSVAR. 1890. 6/yr. SEK 200. Allmaenna Foersvarsfoereningen, Riddargatan 13, S-114 51 Stockholm, Sweden. Ed. Bo Hugemark. adv.; bk.rev.; abstr.; illus. circ. 4,000.

355   NO   ISSN 0042-2037
VAART VERN. 1912. bi-m. NOK 150. Krigsskoleutdannede Offiserers Landsforening - Norwegian Academic Officers Association, P.O. Box 7207, Ho, N-0307 Oslo 3, Norway. TEL 02-52-15-46. FAX 02-69-56-08. Ed. Tore Hiorth Oppegaard. adv.; bk.rev.; circ. 2,000.
Description: Directed to political, military and academic leaders to promote Norwegian national defense.

355   DK   ISSN 0109-7172
VAERN OM DANMARK/NATIONAL DEFENSE SOCIETY. 1980. q. DKK 120. Vaern om Danmark, Trommesalen 1, 1614 Copenhagen V, Denmark. adv.; illus. circ. 4,000.
Formerly: Defenser.

VEILIG VLIEGEN; flight, ground and maintenance safety journal. see *AERONAUTICS AND SPACE FLIGHT*

VERIFICATION (YEAR). see *POLITICAL SCIENCE — International Relations*

VERIFICATION MATTERS BRIEFING PAPER. see *POLITICAL SCIENCE — International Relations*

355.133   RU
VERSIYA. 1990. m. 1 Rub. per issue. Mestnyi Komitet Gosudarstvennoi Bezopasnosti, Ul. Gor'kogo 32 "A", 664000 Irkutsk, Russia. Ed. Nina Voronina. circ. 60,000.

355.15   US   ISSN 0042-4765
VETERAN. (Text in Polish) 1921. m. $5. Polish Army Veterans Association of America, Inc., 17 Irving Place, New York, NY 10003. TEL 212-475-5585. Ed. Zbigniew A. Konikowski. adv.; bk.rev.; bibl. circ. 4,500. (tabloid format) **Indexed:** Alt.Press Ind.

355.115   BE
VETERAN BELGE. (Text in Dutch, French) 1922. q. 250 BEF. (Amicale des Officiers de Campagne) F. Lepeer, Ed. & Pub., 110 Av. de Heyn, B-1090 Brussels, Belgium. adv.; bk.rev. circ. 500.

355.115   US
VETERANS AFFAIRS IN WISCONSIN. 1983. s-a. free. Department of Veterans Affairs, 30 W. Mifflin St., Box 7843, Madison, WI 53707. TEL 608-266-1311. Ed. Steve L. Olson. circ. 4,000. **Document type:** government publication.

VETERANS' BULLETIN. see *CLUBS*

VETERANS FOR PEACE JOURNAL. see *POLITICAL SCIENCE — International Relations*

355.115   US
VETERAN'S OBSERVER. 1983. m. free. 7314 Deering Ave., Canoga Park, CA 91303. TEL 818-713-9447. FAX 818-713-8086. Pub. Richard A. Bivona, Sr. adv.; bk.rev. circ. 410,000. **Document type:** newspaper.

355.115   US
VETERANS OF THE VIETNAM WAR; the "Veteran Leader". 1980. q. $12. Veterans of the Vietnam War, Inc., 760 Jumper Rd., Wilkes-Barre, PA 18702. TEL 717-825-7215. FAX 717-825-8223. Ed. Michael Milne. circ. 10,000.

335.115   US   ISSN 1054-0962
UA23.A1
VETERAN'S VIEW. m. Central Newspaper, Inc., 8 South Michigan Ave., Chicago, IL 60603. TEL 312-263-5388. Ed. Michael Haddad.

255   US
VETS HELPING VETS. 1974. q. $1 per no. USVMI, Golden Triangle Sales, 3738 E. First St., Fort Worth, TX 76111. TEL 817-834-7573. Ed. Danea Cox. adv.; circ. 10,000 (controlled).
Description: Provides veterans and memorial stories, along with other information.

355.115   US
VETS' NEWS. 1945. bi-m. free. Department of Veterans' Affairs, 700 Summer St., N.E., Salem, OR 97310-1201. TEL 503-373-2385. FAX 503-373-2362. Ed. Sharon Robertson. circ. 48,000. **Document type:** government publication, newsletter.
Formerly: Vets' Newsletter.
Description: Informs veterans and dependants of available benefits, and discusses veteran-related activities.

355   RM   ISSN 1018-0400
U4
VIATA ARMATEI. 1947. m. 1680 lei($60) (effective Jan. 1993). Ministerul Apararii Nationale - Ministry of National Defense, Str. General Cristescu nr. 5, sector 1, 70764 Bucharest, Rumania. TEL 1-614-20-12. FAX 1-615-94-56. (Subscr. to: Rodipet S.A., P.O. Box 33-57, Piata Presei Libere nr. 1, Sect. 1, Bucharest 3, Rumania) Ed. Ion Jianu. bk.rev.; abstr.; charts; illus.
Former titles (until Dec. 1989): Viata Militara (ISSN 0042-5044); Imagini Militare.

VIET NAM GENERATION; a journal of recent history & contemporary issues. see *HISTORY — History Of North And South America*

355.115   US   ISSN 0743-2496
DS557
VIETNAM WAR NEWSLETTER. 1979. m. $24.95. Thomas W. Hebert, Ed. & Pub., Box 469, Collinsville, CT 06022. adv.; bk.rev.; film rev.; bibl. circ. 3,000. (looseleaf format; back issues avail.) **Document type:** newsletter.

355   BE
VIGILO. 1960. q. 300 BEF. (Cercle des Officiers de Reserve de Bruxelles - Kring der Reserveofficieren van Brussel) F. Lepeer, Ed. & Pub., 110 Ave. de Heyn, B-1090 Brussels, Belgium. adv.; bk.rev. circ. 1,500.

VITAL SIGNS (CAMBRIDGE). see *PUBLIC HEALTH AND SAFETY*

355   FR
VIVAT HUSSAR. 1966. a. 120 F. Association des Amis du Musee International des Hussards, Jardin Massey, 65000 Tarbes, France. Ed.Bd. adv.; bk.rev.; bibl.; illus. circ. 1,500. (back issues avail.)

355   BU   ISSN 0861-7392
VOENEN JOURNAL. 1888. bi-m. 35. Voenno Izdatelstvo na M O, 12, Ul. Ivan Vazov, Sofia, Bulgaria. Ed. Valery Rachev.

355   RU   ISSN 0236-2058
U4
VOENNAYA MYSL'. 1918. bi-m $79 (effective 1996). Ministerstvo Oborony S.S.S.R., c/o A.B. Bazhenov, Ed., Kropotinskaya ul. 19, 103160 Moscow K-160, Russia. TEL 293-52-01.

VOENNO ISTORICHESKI SBORNIK. see *HISTORY — History Of Europe*

355   RU   ISSN 0042-9058
VOENNO-ISTORICHESKII ZHURNAL. 1959. m. 22.20 Rub. Voenizdat, Ul. Zorge 1, 103160 Moscow, K-160, Russia. TEL 095-195-4595. (Co-sponsor: Ministerstvo Oborony) (also avail. in microform) **Indexed:** Amer.Hist.& Life, Hist.Abstr., Numis.Lit.

355   RU   ISSN 0134-8256
VOENNYE ZNANIYA/MILITARY REVIEW. 1925. m. $57 (effective 1996). Izdatel'stvo DOSAAF, Novo-Ryazanskaya ul. 26, 107066 Moscow, Russia. TEL 445-39-20. (Dist. by: Mezhdunarodnaya Kniga, B. Yakimanka 39, 117049 Moscow, Russia) Ed. S. Sinyutin.

355   RU   ISSN 0042-9066
VOENNYI VESTNIK. 1921. m. 17.40 Rub. Voenizdat, Ul. Zorge 1, 103160 Moscow, K-160, Russia. TEL 095-195-4595. (Co-sponsor: Ministerstvo Oborony) index. **Indexed:** Curr.Dig.Sov.Press.

355.115   FR
VOIX DU CHEMINOT ANCIEN COMBATTANT. 1927. q. 1.80 F. Federation Nationales des Anciens Combattants, Prisonniers, Deportes, Resistants et Victimes, 7 rue de Chateau-Landon, 75010 Paris, France. adv. circ. 15,000.

355   YU   ISSN 0042-840X
VOJNI GLASNIK; strucni casopis rodova vojske i sluzbi jna. (Text in Macedonian, Serbo-Croatian) 1947. bi-m. $20. Vojnoizdavacki Zavod, Svetozara Markovica 70, Belgrade, Yugoslavia. (Dist. by: Jugoslovenska Knjiga, P.O. Box 36, 11001 Belgrade, Yugoslavia) Ed. Sava Krstic.

355   YU   ISSN 0067-5660
U4.B37
VOJNI MUZEJ, BELGRADE. VESNIK/MILITARY MUSEUM, BELGRADE. BULLETIN. (Text in Serbo-Croatian; summaries in English, French) 1954. irreg. $1 per copy. Vojni Muzej, Kalemegdan bb, 11000 Belgrade, Yugoslavia. Ed. Marijan Mozgon. bk.rev. circ. 2,000. **Indexed:** Amer.Hist.& Life, Hist.Abstr.

355   YU   ISSN 0042-8426
VOJNO DELO; opstevojni teorijski casopis. 1949. bi-m. 300000 din.($5) per no. Savazni Sekretarijat za Narodnu Odbranu, Belgrade, Yugoslavia. TEL 011-681-565. (Dist. by: Vojnoizdavacki i Novinski Centar, Svetozava Markovica 70, 11002 Belgrade, Yugoslavia) Ed. Jovan Canak.

355   YU   ISSN 0042-8442
VOJNOISTORIJSKI GLASNIK. (Text in Serbo-Croatian; summaries in English, French) 1950. 3/yr. $49. Vojnoistorijski Institut - Military-Historical Institute, Bircaninova Br.5, Belgrade, Yugoslavia. (Subscr. to: Jugoslovanska Knjiga, Trg Republike 5-VIII, Belgrade, Yugoslavia) Ed. Slavko Vukcevic. bk.rev.; bibl.; charts; illus.; stat.; index, cum.index. circ. 1,000. **Indexed:** Amer.Hist.& Life, Hist.Abstr.

355   YU   ISSN 0042-8469
VOJNOTEHNICKI GLASNIK. (Text in Serbo-Croatian) 1953. bi-m. 70 din.($8.50) (Savezni Sekretarijat za Narodnu Odbranu) Vojnoizdavacki Zavod, Balkanska 53, 11002 Belgrade, Yugoslavia. Ed. Nikola Zoric.

MILITARY 4747

355   BE
VOX: HEBDOMADAIRE MILITAIRE. Dutch edition: Vox: Militair Weekblad. (Text in French) 1974. w. 1500 BEF (effective Jan. 1992). Ministere de la Defense Nationale, Service de l'Information, Publication Hebdomadaire Militaire VOX, Quartier Reine Elisabeth, Bloc 5, Rue d'Evere, B-1050 Brussels, Belgium. FAX 32-2-7013931. Eds. J. Reyniers, A. Vergeynst. bk.rev.; illus.; index. circ. 30,000.
     Formerly: F M (ISSN 0014-5963)

355   CN   ISSN 0300-3213
VOXAIR. 1952. s-m. Can.$4. Canadian Forces Base Winnipeg, Westwin, MB R3J 0T0, Canada. TEL 204-889-3963. FAX 204-885-4176. Ed. Capt. Tom Walls. adv. contact: Jim Holland. play rev.; circ. 4,000 (controlled). (tabloid format) **Document type:** newspaper.

W A M M NEWSLETTER. (Women Against Military Madness) see *WOMEN'S INTERESTS*

355   US
W M A 'NOUNCEMENTS. 1967. q. $15. (Women Marine Association) Marine Corps Association, Box 1775, MCB Quantico, VA 22134-0387. TEL 703-640-6161. (Subscr. to: Assistant Secretary, Box 387, MCB Quantico, VA 22134-0387) Ed. Virginia Allred. circ. 3,563. (back issues avail.)
     Formerly: Nouncements.
     Description: Includes items of interest, and Marine Corps and Veterans information for all WMA members.

355   GW
DAS WAFFEN-ARSENAL. 1973. q. Podzun-Pallas Publishing GmbH, Markt 9, 61169 Friedberg, Germany. FAX 06031-62969. Ed. Horst Scheibert. adv. circ. 12,000. (back issues avail.)

WAR AND SOCIETY. see *HISTORY*

WAR COMMUNIQUES. see *POLITICAL SCIENCE*

355.0209 909   UK   ISSN 0968-3445
▼**WAR IN HISTORY.** 1994. q. £31($50) to individuals; institutions £78 ($125) (effective 1996). Arnold (Subsidiary of: Hodder Headline plc.), 338 Euston Rd., London NW1 3BH, England. TEL 0171-873-6000. FAX 0171-873-6325. (Subscr. to: Turpin Distribution Services Ltd., Blackhorse Rd., Letchworth, Herts. SG6 1HN, England. TEL 01462-672555. FAX 01462-480947) Eds. Hew Strachan, Dennis E. Showalter. adv.: B&W page £250; trim 234 x 156; adv. contact: Mary Attree. bk.rev.; index. (back issues avail.) **Indexed:** Amer.Hist.& Life, Hist.Abstr. **Document type:** academic/scholarly publication.
     —BLDSC (9261.810700).
     Description: Explores the military as it is integrated into a broader definition of history. Deals with war in all its aspects: economic, social, and political for all periods.
     Refereed Serial

355   UK   ISSN 0308-0676
WARFARE. 1972. s-a. Ronald King, Ed. & Pub., 157 Vicarage Rd., London E10 5DU, England. TEL 0181-539-3876. bk.rev. **Document type:** academic/scholarly publication.

355   CN   ISSN 0707-8056
WARRIOR. 1974. fortn. Can.$20. P.O. Box 190, CFB Shearwater, Shearwater, NS B0J 3A0, Canada. TEL 902-460-1013. FAX 902-460-1796. Ed. John L. Houston. adv. contact: Ted Doiron. bk.rev.; illus. circ. 6,500. **Document type:** newspaper.
     Formerly: Shearwater Warrior (ISSN 0705-1980)

623.82   UK   ISSN 0142-6222
V765
WARSHIP. 1977. a. £26. Conway Maritime Press, 33 John St., London WC1N 2AT, England. TEL 0171-753-7777. FAX 0171-753-7794. (Subscr. to: Brassey's Mail Order Department, 33 John St., London WC1N 2AT, England. TEL 0171-753-7799. FAX 0171-753-7795) Ed. Robert Gardiner. adv.: bk.rev. **Document type:** consumer publication.
     —BLDSC (9261.868600).

623.82   US   ISSN 0043-0374
V750
WARSHIP INTERNATIONAL. 1964. q. $22 (foreign $25) (effective 1996). I N R O, Inc, (International Naval Research Organization), 5905 Reinwood Dr., Toledo, OH 43613-5605. TEL 419-472-1331. Ed. Christopher C. Wright. adv./ bk.rev.; charts; illus.; stat. circ. 4,000. (also avail. in microfilm from UMI; reprint service avail. from UMI) **Indexed:** Abstr.Mil.Bibl., Amer.Hist.& Life, Hist.Abstr.
     —BLDSC (9261.869000); UMI.
     Description: Concentrates on warships of various types, brief summaries of their careers and related subjects such as the armoring of ships, elements of ballistics needed for a full understanding of the ships designs.

359   UK
WARSHIP WORLD. 1984. q. £12 (foreign £14). Maritime Books, Lodge Hill, Liskeard, Cornwall PL14 4EL, England. TEL 01579-343663. FAX 01579-346747. Ed. M.A. Critchley. adv. contact: Roger May. bk.rev.; circ. 3,500 (paid). (back issues avail.) **Document type:** consumer publication.
     Description: Current information on ships and weapons in the Royal Navy.

355.115   US   ISSN 0195-5233
WASHINGTON ACTION REPORTER. 1976. m. Veterans of Foreign Wars of the United States, National Headquarters, Broadway at 34th St., Kansas City, MO 64111. TEL 816-756-3390. illus.

WEHRMEDIZIN UND WEHRPHARMAZIE. see *MEDICAL SCIENCES*

WEHRTECHNIK, VEREINIGT MIT WEHR UND WIRTSCHAFT; Monatsschrift fuer wirtschaftliche Fragen der Verteidigung, Luftfahrt und Industrie. see *AERONAUTICS AND SPACE FLIGHT*

350   GW
WEISSBUCH ZUR SICHERHEIT DER BUNDESREPUBLIK DEUTSCHLAND UND ZUR LAGE DER BUNDESWEHR. 1970. irreg. price varies. Bundesministerium der Verteidigung, Fue SI 3, Postfach 1328, 5330 Bonn 1, Germany. **Document type:** government publication.

369.1   US   ISSN 0745-2799
WEST VIRGINIA LEGIONNAIRE. m. $2 to non-members. (American Legion, Department of West Virginia) Record-Delta, Box 550, Buckhannon, WV 26201. TEL 304-747-2800. (Subscr. to: Box 3191, Charleston, WV 26201) Ed. Robert E. Vass. adv. circ. 27,000.

WEST'S VETERANS APPEALS REPORTER. see *LAW — Legal Aid*

355   GW   ISSN 0083-9078
WEYERS FLOTTENTASCHENBUCH/WARSHIPS OF THE WORLD. 1900. a. DM.98. Bernard and Graefe Verlag, Karl-Mand-Str. 2, 56070 Koblenz, Germany. TEL 0261-80706-0. TELEX 862662-SPS-D.
     Former titles: Taschenbuch der Kriegsflotten; Taschenbuch der Deutschen Kriegsflotten.

355.115   US   ISSN 0083-9108
WHAT EVERY VETERAN SHOULD KNOW. 1937. a. (plus m. supplements). $10 for a.; supplements $22; both $30 (efffective 1993). Veterans Information Service, Box 111, East Moline, IL 61244. Ed. Patrick L. Murphy.

WHEELS & TRACKS; international historical review of military vehicles. see *TRANSPORTATION — Automobiles*

355   UK   ISSN 0268-1307
WHITEHALL PAPERS. 1985. bi-m. £77($145) membership. Royal United Services Institute for Defence Studies, Whitehall, London SW1A 2ET, England. TEL 0171-930-5854. FAX 0171-321-0943. **Document type:** bulletin.
     —BLDSC (9311.023460).

355 975   US   ISSN 1046-4638
F596
WILD WEST.* 1988. bi-m. $16.95 (foreign $22.95). Empire Press, 741 Miller Dr., S.E., No. D-2, Leesburg, VA 22075-8920. TEL 703-771-9400. FAX 703-777-4627. (Subscr. to: Box 385, Mt. Morris, IL 61054-7943. TEL 815-734-1115) Ed. Harry G. Summers, Jr. circ. 238,000.
     —UMI; UnCover.
     Description: Explains the Vietnam War - from grand strategy to daily search-and destroy patrol. Covers personalities, weapons, battles, heroes, and perspectives of both North and South.

WINGS; world review of aviation & defence. see *AERONAUTICS AND SPACE FLIGHT*

WINGS (GRANADA HILLS). see *AERONAUTICS AND SPACE FLIGHT*

WINGS OF GOLD. see *AERONAUTICS AND SPACE FLIGHT*

355   US
WINGSPREAD RANDOLPH A F B.* w. 934 Coronado Blvd., Universal City, TX 78148-3227. TEL 512-658-7424.

355   PL   ISSN 0867-1400
WOJSKO I WYCHOWANIE. m. $33. Wydawnictwo Czasopisma Wojskowe, Grzybowska 77, Rembertow, 00-950 Warsaw, Poland. (Dist. by: Ars Polona-Ruch, Krakowskie Przedmiescie 7, 00-068 Warsaw, Poland) Ed. Zdzislaw Czerwinski.
     —BLDSC (9342.640000).
     Supersedes (in 1990): Wojsko Ludowe (ISSN 0043-7174)

355   PL   ISSN 0043-7182
DK417
WOJSKOWY PRZEGLAD HISTORYCZNY. q. 850 Zl. per no. (Wojskowy Instytut Historyczny) Wydawnictwo Czasopisma Wojskowe, Ul. Grzybowska 77, Rembertow, 00-950 Warsaw, Poland. Ed. Marek Tarczynski. bk.rev.; bibl. circ. 15,000. **Indexed:** Amer.Hist.& Life, Hist.Abstr.
     Description: Covers military history of Poland.

355   US   ISSN 1040-2888
UG446.5
WORLD ARMORED VEHICLE INVENTORY & FORECAST. a. $1700. Forecast International Inc. - D M S, 22 Commerce Rd., Newtown, CT 06470. TEL 203-426-0800. FAX 203-426-1964. TELEX 467615.
     Description: Examines the armored vehicle market: past, present, and future. Covers all active global AV programs - applications, characteristics, and manufacturers for six major component types.

355 629.133   US   ISSN 1050-8910
TL716.A1
WORLD HELICOPTER INVENTORY & FORECAST. a. $1700. Forecast International Inc. - D M S, 22 Commerce Rd., Newtown, CT 06470. TEL 203-426-0800. FAX 203-426-1964. TELEX 467615.
     Description: Over 100 active helicopter programs are covered from concept definition through retirement. Contains performance data, systems information, historical data, milestones, price range, and production forecast for the next 10 years.

355 629.1   US   ISSN 1040-2896
UG1240
WORLD MILITARY AIRCRAFT INVENTORY & FORECAST. a. $1700. Forecast International Inc. - D M S, 22 Commerce Rd., Newtown, CT 06470. TEL 203-426-0800. FAX 203-426-1964. TELEX 467615.
     Description: Identifies world requirements for all types of fixed wing military aircraft and details, by country, manufacturer, mission, unit cost, technical specifications, inventory, employment trends, and ten-year production and acquisition forecasts.

WORLD MILITARY AVIATION (YEAR). see *AERONAUTICS AND SPACE FLIGHT*

MILITARY — ABSTRACTING, BIBLIOGRAPHIES, STATISTICS

355 US ISSN 1040-290X
UG1420
WORLD MILITARY AVIONICS INVENTORY & FORECAST. a. $1700. Forecast International Inc. - D M S, 22 Commerce Rd., Newtown, CT 06470. TEL 203-426-0800. FAX 203-426-1964. TELEX 467615.
Description: Covers inventory and production forecast of avionics equipment used on every military aircraft, fixed and rotary wing, outside the Soviet bloc.

355 US ISSN 0897-4667
JX1974.A1
WORLD MILITARY EXPENDITURES AND ARMS TRANSFERS. a. U.S. Arms Control and Disarmament Agency, Bureau of Nuclear and Weapons Control, Defense Program and Analysis Division, Washington, DC 20451. TEL 202-632-8715. (Also avail. from: Supt. of Documents, Washington, DC 20402) Ed. Daniel Gallik.
—BLDSC (9356.674650).
Formerly: World Military Expenditures (ISSN 0363-7204); Which supersedes: World Military Expenditures and Related Data (ISSN 0082-8793)
Description: Provides information on military resources by country throughout the world.

355 US ISSN 1040-2918
UG1310
WORLD MISSILES INVENTORY & FORECAST. a. $1700. Forecast International Inc. - D M S, 22 Commerce Rd., Newtown, CT 06470. TEL 203-426-0800. FAX 203-426-1964. TELEX 467615.
Description: Examines the world market for strategic, cruise, anti-surface, anti-ship, air defense, air-to-air, and anti-tank missiles. Includes missile inventory and 10-year forecast for over 50 countries.

359 US
WORLD NAVAL WEAPONS SYSTEMS. Cover title: Naval Institute Guide to World Naval Weapons Systems. irreg., latest 1991-1992 ed. $145 (1994 update $49.95). (Naval Institute) Naval Institute Press, 118 Maryland Ave., Anapolis, MD 21402. TEL 410-268-6110. FAX 410-269-7940. (Orders to: Naval Institute Press, 2062 Generals Hwy., Annapolis, MD 21401. TEL 800-233-8764) Ed. Norman Friedman. illus.
Description: Covers worldwide naval fleets of ships, aircraft, and armament.

355 US ISSN 1050-8929
UF530
WORLD ORDNANCE INVENTORY & FORECAST. a. $1700. Forecast International Inc. - D M S, 22 Commerce Rd., Newtown, CT 06470. TEL 203-426-0800. FAX 203-426-1964. TELEX 467615.
Description: Covers over 100 countries, detailing current inventories of ordnance, force structure analysis, procurement histories, and future acquisitions. Includes towed and self-propelled artillery, armored vehicles, armaments, mortars, artillery ammunition, anti-tank weapons, automatic cannon, and rocket launchers.

WORLD WAR II. see HISTORY — History Of North And South America

355 900 UK ISSN 0964-6833
WORLD WAR II REVIEW. 1990. 6/yr. $20. Broadhead, Castleshaw, Delph, Oldham OL3 5L2, England. Ed. Jim Auld. **Document type:** newsletter.
Description: Publishes news, views and reviews of events and personalities connected with World War II.

355 320 US ISSN 1073-5097
UA15
WORLDWIDE DIRECTORY OF DEFENSE AUTHORITIES. a. (plus q. updates). $647 for annual; q. updates $897 (effective 1995). Worldwide Government Directories, Inc., 7979 Old Georgetown Rd., Ste. 900, Bethesda, MD 20814. TEL 301-718-8770. FAX 301-718-8494. **Document type:** directory.
Description: Examines national security apparatus in countries.

355 363.2 NP
WORLDWIDE MILITARY AND POLICE AWARD. 1980. a. $350. Siveast Consultants, Inc., USA, P.O. Box 8510, Kathmandu, Nepal.
Description: Lists distinguished military and police officers.

WORLDWIDE REPORT: ARMS CONTROL. see POLITICAL SCIENCE — International Relations

355 539.7 US
WORLDWIDE REPORT: NUCLEAR DEVELOPMENTS. irreg. (approx. 30/yr.) $7 per no. (foreign $14 per no.). U.S. Joint Publications Research Service, Box 12507, Arlington, VA 22209. TEL 703-487-4630. (Orders to: NTIS, Springfield, VA 22161)
Formerly: Worldwide Report: Nuclear Development and Proliferation.

WOUND BALLISTICS REVIEW. see MEDICAL SCIENCES — Forensic Sciences

355 CC ISSN 1000-7385
CODEN: XIBIE4
XIANDAI BINGQI/MODERN WEAPONRY. (Text in Chinese) 1979. m. $72 (effective 1996). Xiandai Bingqi Zazhishe, P.O. Box 2413-8, Beijing 100081, People's Republic of China. TEL 8414477. FAX 8413642. TELEX 22558 NISYI CN. Ed. Shen Liping. bk.rev.; circ. 150,000 (paid).
Description: Covers the development of modern defense technology, defense industries and manufacturers, military establishments and colleges. Refereed Serial

327.1 RU
▼**YADERNYI KONTROL'.** (Editions in English, Russian) 1994. m. free. (Tsentr Politicheskikh Issledovanii v Rossii) Yadernyi Kontrol', Tverskaya 16-2, No. 201, Moscow, Russia. TEL 7-95-229-1058. FAX 7-95-229-1650. E-mail: mosnex@sovamsu.sovusa.com. Ed. Vladimir A. Orlov.

355.14 GW ISSN 0044-2852
ZEITSCHRIFT FUER HEERESKUNDE. 1929. bi-m. DM.75. Deutsche Gesellschaft fuer Heereskunde e.V., Augustin-Wibbelt-Str. 8, 59269 Beckum, Germany. Ed. Georg Ortenburg. adv.; bk.rev.; bibl.; illus.; index. circ. 1,000. **Indexed:** Amer.Hist.& Life, Hist.Abstr.
—BLDSC (9464.330000).

355 IS
ZIKA. q. Defense Department, Miltary P.O. Box 01013, Tel Aviv, Israel. adv.

355 PL ISSN 0044-4979
ZOLNIERZ POLSKI. 1945. w. $56. Wydawnictwo Czasopisma Wojskowe, Grzybowska 77, Rembertow, 00-950 Warsaw, Poland. TEL 48-22-201261. (Dist. by: Ars Polona-Ruch, Krakowskia Przedmiescie 7, 00-068 Warsaw, Poland) Ed. Wieslaw Jan Wysocki. illus.

335 909 FR ISSN 0761-7348
39 - 45 MAGAZINE. (Supplement avail.: Historica (ISSN 1167-9638)) m. (11/yr.). 270 F. (foreign 280 F.). Editions Heimdal, Chateau de Damigny, 14400 Bayeux, France. (back issues avail.)
Description: Covers World War II.

355 US
43RD INFANTRY DIVISION VETERANS ASSOCIATION. BULLETIN. 1953. q. membership only. 43rd Infantry Division Veterans Association, 150 Lakedell Dr., E. Greenwich, RI 02818. TEL 401-884-7052. Ed. Howard F. Brown. circ. 1,900. **Document type:** bulletin.
Description: Contains personal anecdotes and veterans' information mainly of interest to veterans of the 43rd Infantry Division.

MILITARY — Abstracting, Bibliographies, Statistics

A G A R D INDEX TO PUBLICATIONS. see AERONAUTICS AND SPACE FLIGHT — Abstracting, Bibliographies, Statistics

355 016 AG
ABSTRACTS OF MILITARY BIBLIOGRAPHY. (Text in English) 1967. q. $70. Ruben A. Ramirez Mitchell, Ed. & Pub., Maipu 262, 1084 Buenos Aires, Argentina. adv.; bk.rev.; abstr.; tr.mk.; index, cum.index. circ. 2,000. **Document type:** abstracting/indexing, bibliography.
Former titles: Resumenes Analiticos sobre Defensa y Seguridad Nacional - Abstracts of Military Bibliography (ISSN 0034-5873); Resumenes Analiticos de Bibliografia Militar.

358.4 US
AIR FORCE INTERCHANGEABLE AND SUBSTITUTION REPORT. m. $4320 in U.S., Canada, Mexico; elsewhere $8640. (Department of the Air Force) U.S. National Technical Information Service, 5285 Port Royal Rd., Springfield, VA 22161. TEL 703-487-4630. (magnetic tape)

355 016 US ISSN 0002-2586
Z5063.A2
AIR UNIVERSITY LIBRARY INDEX TO MILITARY PERIODICALS. 1949. q. (plus a. cum. index). free to qualified personnel. U.S. Air Force, Air University Library, Maxwell AFB, AL 36112-6424. TEL 334-953-2504. Ed. Martha M. Stewart. bk.rev.; index, cum.index; circ. 1,500. (controlled). (also avail. in microform) **Document type:** abstracting/indexing, government publication.
●Also available on CD-ROM.
—BLDSC (0777.490000).

359 090 AG ISSN 0066-7080
ARGENTINA. DEPARTAMENTO DE ESTUDIOS HISTORICOS NAVALES. SERIE J: LIBROS Y IMPRESOS RAROS.* 1962. irreg., no.2, 1970. Departamento de Estudios Historicos Navales, Av. Almirante Brown 401, 1155 Buenos Aires, Argentina.

359 AG ISSN 0066-7331
ARGENTINA. SERVICIO DE INTELIGENCIA NAVAL. BIBLIOTECAS DE LA ARMADA. BOLETIN BIBLIOGRAFICO. 1943. a. Servicio de Inteligencia Naval, Bibliotecas de la Armada, Edificio Libertad, Comodoro Py y Corbeta Uruguay, Buenos Aires, Argentina. Ed. Juan A. Manon.

355.31 US
ARMY MANUALS AND REGULATIONS INDEX (CONSOLIDATED INDEX OF ARMY PUBLICATIONS). q. $15 in U.S., Canada, Mexico; elsewhere $30. (Department of the Army) U.S. National Technical Information Service, 5825 Port Royal Rd., Springfield, VA 22161. TEL 703-487-4630. (microfiche) **Document type:** abstracting/indexing.
Description: Comprised of technical and field manuals, Army regulations, lubrication orders, and technical bulletins. Provides cross-reference of national stock number to each publication.

BEIKOKU TOKKYO SHOROKU. MUKI KAGAKU, KINZOKU, BUKI DAN'YAKU HEN/U.S. PATENT ABSTRACTS. INORGANIC CHEMISTRY, METALS, ARMAMENT AND AMMUNITION. see PATENTS, TRADEMARKS AND COPYRIGHTS — Abstracting, Bibliographies, Statistics

355 US ISSN 1040-7995
BIBLIOGRAPHIES AND INDEXES IN MILITARY STUDIES. 1988. irreg. price varies. Greenwood Press, Inc. (Subsidiary of: Greenwood Publishing Group Inc.), 88 Post Rd. W., Box 5007, Westport, CT 06881-5007. TEL 203-226-3571. FAX 203-222-1502. **Document type:** monographic series.
—BLDSC (1993.097425).

355 US ISSN 1056-7410
BIBLIOGRAPHIES OF BATTLES AND LEADERS. 1990. irreg. price varies. Greenwood Press, Inc. (Subsidiary of: Greenwood Publishing Group Inc.), 88 Post Rd. W., Box 5007, Westport, CT 06881-5007. TEL 203-226-3571. FAX 203-222-1502. **Document type:** bibliography, monographic series.

355 JA ISSN 0523-8080
BOEI DAIGAKKO KYOKAN KENKYU YOROKU/NATIONAL DEFENSE ACADEMY. DIGEST OF RESEARCHES BY FACULTY MEMBERS. (Text in English and Japanese) 1956. a. Boei Daigakko - National Defense Academy, 10-20 Hashirimizu 1-chome, Yokosuka-shi, Kanagawa-ken 239, Japan.

327 355 015 UK ISSN 0954-3589
Z6725.G7
CURRENT MILITARY AND POLITICAL LITERATURE. 1983. bi-m. $324. Military Press Ltd., 92A Church Way, Iffley, Oxford OX4 4EF, England. TEL 0865-770144. FAX 0256-479438. Ed. Simon King. index. **Document type:** abstracting/indexing.
—BLDSC (3500.430000).
Formerly: Current Military Literature (ISSN 0264-1674)
Description: Presents abstracts and citations, with comment, of articles from journals and monographs about strategic and defence studies, military science, political science and international affairs.

D L A P S. (Defense Logistics Agency Publishing System) see PUBLIC ADMINISTRATION — Abstracting, Bibliographies, Statistics

335.27 US
DEFENSE INTEGRATED DATA SYSTEM TOTAL ITEM RECORD: MASTER REQUIREMENTS. Short title: D I D S - T I R: Master Requirements. q. $2360 for 1600 bpi in US, Canada, Mexico; elsewhere $4720. (Department of Defense, Defense Logistics Services) U.S. National Technical Information Service, 5825 Port Royal Rd., Springfield, VA 22161. TEL 703-487-4630. (magnetic tape)

335.27 US
DEFENSE INTEGRATED DATA SYSTEM TOTAL ITEM RECORD: SEGMENT V. q. $12000 for 1600 bpi in N. America; elsewhere $24000. (U.S. Department of Defense, Defense Logistics Services) U.S. National Technical Information Service, 5825 Port Royal Rd., Springfield, VA 22161. TEL 703-487-4630. (magnetic tape)
Description: Features coded item characteristics data.

335.27 US
DEFENSE INTEGRATED DATA SYSTEM TOTAL ITEM RECORD: SEGMENTS A, B, C. Short title: D I D S - T I R: Segments A, B, C. q. $20800 for 1600 bpi in US, Canada, Mexico; elsewhere $41600. (Department of Defense, Defense Logistics Services) U.S. National Technical Information Service, 5825 Port Royal Rd., Springfield, VA 22161. TEL 703-487-4630. (magnetic tape)
Description: Contains the following information--Segment A: identification data; Segment B: major organizational entity (MOE) rule data; Segment C: reference number data.

351.06 US
H4 - H8 COMMERCIAL AND GOVERNMENT ENTITY PUBLICATION, SECTION A: U.S. AND CANADA. Short title: H4 - H8 C A G E Publication, Sec. A: U.S. and Canada. 6/yr. $4260 for 1600 bpi in US, Canada, Mexico; elsewhere $8520. (Department of Defense, Defense Logistics Services) U.S. National Technical Information Service, 5825 Port Royal Rd., Springfield, VA 22161. TEL 703-487-4630. (magnetic tape)
Description: Lists international organizations which have contracts with the Department of Defense.

351.06 US
H4 - H8 COMMERCIAL AND GOVERNMENT ENTITY PUBLICATION, SECTION B: C A G E CODE. Short title: H4 - H8 C A G E Publication, Sec. B: C A G E Code. 6/yr. $4260 for 1600 bpi in US, Canada, Mexico; elsewhere $8520. (Department of Defense, Defense Logistics Services) U.S. National Technical Information Service, 5825 Port Royal Rd., Springfield, VA 22161. TEL 703-487-4630. (magnetic tape)

351.06 US
H4 - H8 COMMERCIAL AND GOVERNMENT ENTITY PUBLICATION, SECTION C: NATO MANUFACTURERS. Short title: H4 - H8 C A G E Publication, Sec. C: NATO Manufacturers. 6/yr. $1440 in US, Canada, Mexico; elsewhere $2880. (Department of Defense, Defense Logistics Service) U.S. National Technical Information Service, 5825 Port Royal Rd., Springfield, VA 22161. TEL 703-487-4630. (magnetic tape)
Description: Lists international contractors and suppliers of the Department of Defense.

351.06 US
H4 - H8 COMMERCIAL AND GOVERNMENT ENTITY PUBLICATION, SECTION D: NATO C A G E. Short title: H4 - H8 C A G E Publication, Sec. D: NATO C A G E. 6/yr. $1440 in US, Canada, Mexico; elsewhere $2880. (Department of Defense, Defense Logistics Services) U.S. National Technical Information Service, 5825 Port Royal Rd., Springfield, VA 22161. TEL 703-487-4630. (magnetic tape)
Description: Lists international contractors and suppliers to the Department of Defense.

355 UK
IMPERIAL WAR MUSEUM, LONDON. DEPARTMENT OF PRINTED BOOKS. ACCESSIONS LIST. 1970. irreg. free to libraries. Imperial War Museum, Department of Printed Books, Lambeth Rd., London SE1 6HZ, England. circ. 200. (processed) *Document type:* academic/scholarly publication.
Description: Covers the history of warfare since 1914.

JAPANESE MILITARY AIRCRAFT SERIALS. see AERONAUTICS AND SPACE FLIGHT — Abstracting, Bibliographies, Statistics

351.06 US
MANAGEMENT DATA LIST (ML): ML - MARINE CORPS. q. $75 in US, Canada, Mexico; elsewhere $150. (Department of Defense, Defense Logistics Services) U.S. National Technical Information Service, 5825 Port Royal Rd., Springfield, VA 22161. TEL 703-487-4630. (microfiche)
Description: Contains supply management data to assist in acquiring and accounting for items of supply.

351.06 US
MANAGEMENT DATA LIST (ML): ML - NAVY. q. $375 in US, Canada, Mexico; elsewhere $750. (Department of Defense, Defense Logistics Services) U.S. National Technical Information Service, 5825 Port Royal Rd., Springfield, VA 22161. TEL 703-487-4630. (microfiche)
Description: Contains supply management data to assist requisitioners in acquiring and accounting for items of supply.

351.06 US
MANAGEMENT DATA LIST CONSOLIDATED (ML-C). q. $3700 (foreign $3000). (Department of Defense, Defense Logistics Services) U.S. National Technical Information Service, 5825 Port Royal Rd., Springfield, VA 22161. TEL 703-487-4630. (magnetic tape; also avail. in microfiche)
Description: Provides supply management data on all national stock numbers recorded in DIDS Total Item Record.

355 UK ISSN 0960-2054
MILITARY SCIENCE INDEX. 1962. 6/yr. Royal Military College of Science Library, Shrivenham, Swindon, Wiltshire SN6 8LA, England. TEL 01793-785484. FAX 01793-785555. E-mail: howorth@rmcs.cranfield.ac.uk. Ed. J. Stephen Town. index. circ. 250. (back issues avail.) *Document type:* abstracting/indexing.
Description: Indexes key articles in the field of defense science and technology.

359 310 US ISSN 0894-069X
V179 CODEN: NRLOEP
NAVAL RESEARCH LOGISTICS: AN INTERNATIONAL JOURNAL. 1954. 8/yr. $560 (foreign $684) (effective 1996). John Wiley & Sons, Inc., Journals, 605 Third Ave., New York, NY 10158. TEL 212-850-6645. FAX 212-850-6021. TELEX 12-7063. E-mail: SUBINFO@WILEY.COM. (Subscr. outside the Americas to: John Wiley & Sons Ltd., Baffins Ln., Chichester, W. Sussex PO19 1UD, England. TEL 44-1243-779777. FAX 44-1243-776218) Ed. Richard Rosenthal. bk.rev.; bibl.; charts; index, cum.index. circ. 950. (also avail. in microform from UMI; back issues avail.; reprint service avail.) Indexed: Appl.Mech.Rev., Compumath, Curr.Cont., Curr.Ind.Stat., Cyb.Abstr., Eng.Ind., Ind.Sci.Rev., Ind.U.S.Gov.Per., INSPEC, Int.Abstr.Oper.Res., Int.Aerosp.Abstr., J.Cont.Quant.Meth., Math.R., Oper.Res.Manage.Sci., Qual.Contr.Appl.Stat., Risk Abstr., Sci.Cit.Ind., Stat.Theor.Meth.Abstr. *Document type:* academic/scholarly publication.
—BLDSC (6064.995000); Ei; Faxon; Genuine Article; SWETS; UMI; UnCover. **CCC**.
Formerly: Naval Research Logistics Quarterly (ISSN 0028-1441)
Description: Publishes articles on both theory and applications in key areas, including mathematical statistics, economics, tactics and strategy.
Refereed Serial

359 016 AG ISSN 0034-8775
REVISTA DE PUBLICACIONES NAVALES. 1901. 3/yr. free. Estado Mayor General de la Armada, Jefatura de Inteligencia, Buenos Aires, Argentina. Ed. Emilio J. Del Real. adv.; bk.rev. circ. 3,400. *Document type:* academic/scholarly publication, bibliography.

943 011 GW ISSN 0036-5920
SCHARNHORST AUSLESE. 1954. q. DM.12($12) Tuermer-Verlag, Postfach, D-8137 Berg 3, Germany. Ed. E. Vowinckel. adv.; bk.rev.; bibl.; illus. circ. 2,800.
Formerly: Scharnhorst Mitteilungen.

011 355 II ISSN 0970-3403
UNIVERSAL MILITARY ABSTRACTS. (Text in English) 1987. bi-m. $45. 10 A Astley Hall, Dehra Dun 248 001, India. TEL 25845. Ed. S.K. Arora. adv.; bk.rev.; abstr.; charts; illus.; index. *Document type:* abstracting/indexing.

355.115 310 US
WISCONSIN. DEPARTMENT OF VETERANS AFFAIRS. BIENNIAL REPORT. 1977. biennial. free. Department of Veterans Affairs, 30 W. Mifflin St., Box 7843, Madison, WI 53707. TEL 608-266-1311. Ed. Steve L. Olson. circ. 700. *Document type:* government publication.

MILITARY LAW

see Law–Military Law

MINES AND MINING INDUSTRY

see also Metallurgy

A M D E L BULLETIN. (Australia Mineral Development Laboratories) see EARTH SCIENCES — Geology

622 665.5 340 AT ISSN 1034-327X
A M P L A BULLETIN. 1982. q. Aus.$130. Australian Mining and Petroleum Law Association Ltd., 360 Little Bourke St., 4th Fl., Melbourne, Vic. 3000, Australia. TEL 61-3-9-670-2544. FAX 61-3-9-670-2616. Ed. Michael Crommelin. circ. 700. (back issues avail.) Indexed: AESIS. *Document type:* bulletin.
Description: Presents nationwide reports, articles and case notes on mining, oil and gas law.

622 665.5 340 AT ISSN 0812-857X
K1
A M P L A YEARBOOK. 1977. a. Aus.$185 (effective 1994). Australian Mining and Petroleum Law Association Ltd., 360 Little Bourke St., 4th Fl., Melbourne, Vic. 3000, Australia. TEL 613-670-2544. FAX 613-670-2616. Ed. M.Crommelin. bibl. circ. 600. (back issues avail.) Indexed: AESIS, C.L.I., L.R.I.
—BLDSC (1814.614000).
Formerly (until 1983): Australian Mining and Petroleum Law Journal (ISSN 0157-2083)
Description: Reference source on Australian resources industries law; contains up to 30 articles each year.

622 AT ISSN 0816-942X
A M R E P DATABASE BULLETIN. 1984. m. (10/yr.). Aus.$210($165) Australian Mineral Resource Politics Pty. Ltd., 10 Hampstead Hill Rd., Aldgate, S.A. 5154, Australia. TEL 8 339 2960. Ed. Antony C. Turner. circ. 50. (looseleaf format; back issues avail.)
●Also available online.
Description: Covers areas of political concern to the Australian mining and petroleum industry.

622.8 631.62 GW
A S VORORT. (Arbeit und Sicherheit); Zeitschrift fuer Unfallverhuetung und Grubensicherheitswesen. 1947. 10/yr. DM.30 (foreign DM.36). (Landesoberbergamt) Verlag Glueckauf GmbH, Postfach 185620, 45206 Essen, Germany. TEL 02054-92412023. FAX 02054-924129. adv.; circ. controlled. *Document type:* trade publication.
—CCC.
Former titles: Arbeit und Sicherheit (ISSN 0344-239X); Grubensicherheit (ISSN 0017-4858)

622 GW
A V INFORMATION. 1975. bi-m. Gewerkschaft Auguste Victoria, Victoriastr. 43, 45772 Marl, Germany. TEL 02365-402851. FAX 02365-402204. TELEX 0829886-AVMA-D. circ. 6,000. *Document type:* newsletter.

622 US
ABANDONED MINED LAND REPORTS. irreg. price varies. U.S. Bureau of Mines, Office of Surface Mining, 810 Seventh St., N.W., MS-9800, Washington, DC 20241-0001. TEL 202-501-9358. FAX 202-501-9958. (Orders to: U.S.B.M., Box 18070, Pittsburgh, PA 15236. TEL 202-512-1800. FAX 202-512-2250) *Document type:* government publication.

MINES AND MINING INDUSTRY

622 665.5   AT   ISSN 1032-8599
ACCESS (GLENSIDE); information and education for the mining and petroleum industry. (Supplement avail.: Syllabus) q. Australian Mineral Foundation, 63 Conyngham St., Glenside, S.A. 5065, Australia. TEL 61-8-379-0444. FAX 61-8-379-4634. TELEX AA87437.

549 665.5   HU   ISSN 0365-8066
                       CODEN: AUSEA6
ACTA UNIVERSITATIS DE ATTILA JOZSEF NOMINATAE. ACTA MINERALOGICA - PETROGRAPHICA. (Text in English) 1943. a. exchange basis. Attila Jozsef University, c/o E. Szabo, Exchange Librarian, Dugonics ter 13, P.O.B. 393, Szeged H-6701, Hungary. (Subscr. to: Kultura, P.O. Box 149, H-1389 Budapest, Hungary) Ed. Tibor Szederkenyi. bk.rev.; charts; illus. circ. 600. Indexed: Geol.Abstr., INIS Atomind., Met.Abstr.
—BLDSC (0638.700000); CASDDS.
Description: Discusses geochemistry, mineralogy and petrology with studies of Hungarian topics of global interest.

622   AG   ISSN 0326-6672
ACTIVIDAD MINERA. 1983. m. $24. Minera Piedra Libre S.R.L., Bolivar 187, 4 B, 1066 Buenos Aires, Argentina. TEL 343-6422. FAX 343-6138. Eds. Horacio Piccinini, Mariode Pablos. circ. 1,200.

622   CM   ISSN 0575-7258
ACTIVITES MINERES AU CAMEROUN. 1962. a., latest 1975. Direction des Mines et de la Geologie, Ministere des Mines et de l'Energie, Yaounde, Cameroon.

622   NE   ISSN 0921-8602
ADVANCES IN MINING SCIENCE AND TECHNOLOGY. (Text in English) 1987. irreg., vol.7, 1992. price varies. Elsevier Science B.V., Books Division, P.O. Box 211, 100 AE Amsterdam, Netherlands. TEL 31-20-4853911. FAX 31-20-4853705. TELEX 18582 ESPA NL.
E-mail: nlinfo-f@elsevier.nl; usinfo-f@elsevier.com; forinfo-kyf04035@niftyserve.or.jp; Site addr.: http://www.elsevier.nl/. (Subscr. in U.S. and Canada to: Elsevier Science Inc., Box 882, Madison Sq. Sta., New York, NY 10159. TEL 212-989-5800) (back issues avail.) Document type: monographic series.
—BLDSC (0709.432000).
Refereed Serial

AFRICA ENERGY AND MINING. see *PETROLEUM AND GAS*

622 531.64   FR
AFRIQUE INDUSTRIE. m. (11/yr.). 3210 F. (foreign 3400 F.). Moreux, 190, bd. Haussmann, 75008 Paris, France. TEL 45-63-11-55. FAX 42-89-08-72. adv.

622   PL   ISSN 0138-0990
TN4   CODEN: GORNDL
AKADEMIA GORNICZO-HUTNICZA IM. STANISLAWA STASZICA. ZESZYTY NAUKOWE. GORNICTWO. KWARTALNIK. (Text in English and Polish; summaries in English, Polish) 1977. q. 50 Zl. per issue (effective 1995). Wydawnictwo A G H, Al. Mickiewicza 30, 30-059 Krakow, Poland. TEL 48-12-334038. TELEX 322203 AGH PL. (Dist. by: Ars Polona, Krakowskie Przedmiescie 7, 00-068 Warsaw, Poland) Ed. Z. Kleczek. illus. circ. 460.
Document type: academic/scholarly publication.
—BLDSC (9512.150162); CASDDS; Ei.

ALBERTA OIL & GAS DIRECTORY. see *BUSINESS AND ECONOMICS — Trade And Industrial Directories*

622 330.9   US   ISSN 0253-7516
AMAX NEWS.* 1987. bi-m. free to qualified personnel. Amax Inc., 9100 W. Mineral Cir., Englewood, CO 80112-3401. TEL 212-856-4200. FAX 212-856-5986. Ed. Diane Hafter. circ. 7,500. (tabloid format) Document type: newsletter.
Formerly: Headquarters News.
Description: Focuses on company operations and employee issues.

549   US   ISSN 0003-004X
QE351   CODEN: AMMIAY
AMERICAN MINERALOGIST. 1916. bi-m. $295 (Canada & Mexico $300; elsewhere $305) (effective 1996). Mineralogical Society of America, 1130 17th St. N.W., Ste. 330, Washington, DC 20036. TEL 202-775-4344. FAX 202-775-0018. Eds. Steven Bohlen, Donald Peacor. adv.; bk.rev.; bibl.; illus. circ. 4,000. (also avail. in microfilm from PMC; back issues avail.; reprint service avail. from KTO) Indexed: A.S.& T.Ind., AESIS, Br.Ceram.Abstr., C.R.I.Abstr., Cadscan, Chem.Abstr., Curr.Cont., Deep Sea Res.& Oceanogr.Abstr., Eng.Ind., Geo.Abstr., Geol.Abstr., GeoRef., Ind.Sci.Rev., INIS Atomind., INSPEC (1971-), Lead Abstr., Met.Abstr., Petrol.Abstr., Photo.Abstr., Sci.Cit.Ind., Soils & Fert., Zincscan. Document type: academic/scholarly publication.
—BLDSC (0845.000000); CASDDS; Ei; Faxon; Genuine Article; SWETS; UnCover. **CCC.**
Description: Publishes the results of original scientific research in the general fields of mineralogy, crystallography, and petrology.

622   CN   ISSN 0840-8610
AMERICAN MINES HANDBOOK. 1989. a. Can.$41.50. Southam Magazine Group, 1450 Don Mills Rd., Don Mills, ON M3B 2X7, Canada. TEL 416-442-2004. FAX 416-442-2214. Ed. D. Giancola. adv.: B&W page Can.$1255. Document type: directory.
Description: Lists information on every mining company registered in the United States.

ANALYTICA. see *CHEMISTRY — Analytical Chemistry*

ANGOLA. DIRECCAO PROVINCIAL DOS SERVICOS DE GEOLOGIA E MINAS. BOLETIM. see *EARTH SCIENCES — Geology*

ANNUAL BOOK OF A S T M STANDARDS. VOLUME 05.05. GASEOUS FUELS; COAL AND COKE. see *ENGINEERING — Engineering Mechanics And Materials*

ANNUAL INSTITUTE ON MINERAL LAW. see *LAW*

338.7   II
ANNUAL REPORT OF THE WORKING AND AFFAIRS OF MYSORE MINERALS LIMITED. (Text in English) a. Mysore Minerals Ltd., Bangalore, Karnataka, India.

622 700   GW   ISSN 0003-5238
DER ANSCHNITT; Zeitschrift fuer Kunst und Kultur im Bergbau. 1949. 6/yr. DM.90. (Vereinigung der Freunde von Kunst und Kultur im Bergbau e.V.) Verlag Glueckauf GmbH, Postfach 185620, 45206 Essen, Germany. TEL 92954-92412023. FAX 02054-924129. bk.rev.; illus. Indexed: Art & Archaeol.Tech.Abstr. Document type: bulletin.
—CCC.

622 558   CL   ISSN 0066-5096
HD9506.C5
ANUARIO DE LA MINERIA DE CHILE. 1961. a. $25 (effective 1994) or exchange basis. Servicio Nacional de Geologia y Mineria, Casilla 10465, Santiago, Chile. TEL 56-2-7375050. FAX 56-2-7372026. Ed. Juan Williams. stat. circ. 1,000. Document type: government publication.
—BLDSC (1564.877000).

338.2   BL   ISSN 0100-9303
HD9506.B7   CODEN: AMBRD9
ANUARIO MINERAL BRASILEIRO. 1972. a. 3 BTN($3) Departamento Nacional da Producao Mineral, Setor Autarquias Norte, Quadra 1 Bloco B, 70040 Brasilia D.F., Brazil. TEL 061-061-224-2670. illus.; stat.

549   US   ISSN 0066-5487
APPLIED MINERALOGY - TECHNISCHE MINEROLOGIE. 1971. irreg., vol.12, 1981. price varies. Springer-Verlag, 175 Fifth Ave., New York, NY 10010. TEL 212-460-1500. FAX 212-473-6272. (Also Berlin, Heidelberg, Tokyo and Vienna) (reprint service avail. from ISI) Indexed: GeoRef. Document type: monographic series.

622   JO   ISSN 0250-9881
HD9506.A62
ARAB MINING JOURNAL. (Text in Arabic, English) 1980. q. free. Arab Mining Company, P.O. Box 20198, Amman, Jordon. TEL 663148. FAX 962-6-684114. TELEX 21489 ARMICO JO. Ed. Talal Sa'di. bk.rev.; bibl.; stat.; index. circ. 700.
Description: Covers issues pertaining to mining throughout the Arab world.

ARAB PETROLEUM. see *PETROLEUM AND GAS*

622   PL   ISSN 0860-7001
TN4   CODEN: AMNSE5
ARCHIVES OF MINING SCIENCES. (Text in various languages) 1956. q. $80. (Polska Akademia Nauk, Komitet Gornictwa) Wydawnictwo Naukowe P W N, Miodowa 10, Warsaw, Poland. Ed. Stanislaw Knothe. abstr.; bibl. circ. 480. Indexed: Appl.Mech.Rev., Chem.Abstr., Eng.Ind., GeoRef., Geotech.Abstr.
—BLDSC (1637.941300); CASDDS; UnCover.
Formerly (until 1987): Archiwum Gornictwa (ISSN 0004-0754)

622 551   BN   ISSN 0518-5327
TN4   CODEN: ARUTA6
ARHIV ZA RUDARSTVO I GEOLOGIJU. vol.17, 1979. q. $15. Radna Organizacija Rudarsko-Geolosk Institut i Fakultet Tuzla, Rudarska Ulica 400, Tuzla, Bosnia Hercegovina. Ed. Odgovorni Urednik. circ. 600.
—CASDDS.

622 690   US
ASBESTOS INFORMATION ASSOCIATION - NORTH AMERICA. NEWS AND NOTES. m. Asbestos Information Association - North America, 1745 Jefferson Davis Hwy., Ste. 509, Arlington, VA 22202. TEL 703-979-1150. FAX 703-979-1152. Document type: newsletter.

ASBESTOS PRODUCER/PRODUCTEUR D'AMIANTE. see *BUILDING AND CONSTRUCTION*

622   SP
ASOCIACION DE INVESTIGACION TECNOLOGIA DE EQUIPOS MINEROS. BOLETIN. irreg. free. Asociacion de Investigacion Tecnologia de Equipos Mineros, Alenza 1, 28003 Madrid, Spain.

622.33   FR
ASSOCIATION TECHNIQUE DE L'IMPORTATION CHARBONNIERE. ANNUAL REPORT. a. Association Technique de l'Importation Charbonniere, 149 rue de Longchamp, 75016 Paris, France. TEL 1-5032113.

549   UN   ISSN 1014-5451
ATLAS OF MINERAL RESOURCES OF THE E S C A P REGION. 1989. a. $25. United Nations Economic and Social Commission for Asia and the Pacific, United Nations Bldg., Rajdamnern Ave., Bangkok 10200, Thailand. (Orders to: United Nations Publications, Rm. DC2-0853, New York, NY 10017; Distribution and Sales Section, Palais des Nations, CH-1211 Geneva 10, Switzerland) maps. (back issues avail.)

664   GW   ISSN 0004-783X
                       CODEN: AUFTAK
AUFBEREITUNGS-TECHNIK - MINERAL PROCESSING. (Text in English, German; summaries in French, Spanish) 1960. m. DM.276 (foreign DM.316). A T Verlag fuer Aufbereitung GmbH, Postfach 5809, 65048 Wiesbaden, Germany. TEL 06123-700-0. FAX 06123-700122. Ed. Ing. Rolf Koehling. adv.; bk.rev. circ. 3,700. Indexed: C.R.I.Abstr., Cadscan, Chem.Abstr., Chem.Eng.Abstr., Eng.Ind., Excerp.Med., Fluidex, Fuel & Energy Abstr., INIS Atomind., Lead Abstr., Met.Abstr., PROMT, T.C.E.A., World Alum.Abstr., Zincscan. Document type: trade publication.
—BLDSC (1790.900000); CASDDS; Ei; SWETS. **CCC.**

MINES AND MINING INDUSTRY

622 AT ISSN 1034-6775
TN121 CODEN: AIBUEP
AUS I M M BULLETIN. 1983. 8/yr. Aus.$140 (foreign Aus.$200). Australasian Institute of Mining and Metallurgy, P.O. Box 660, Carcton South, Vic. 3053, Australia. TEL 61-3-347-3166. FAX 61-3-662-3662. Ed. Penelope Griffiths. adv. circ. 8,526. **Indexed:** AESIS, GeoRef., INIS Atomind., Met.Abstr., World Alum.Abstr. **Document type:** trade publication.
—BLDSC (1792.932000); CASDDS; Ei; Faxon; SWETS; UnCover. **CCC.**
Supersedes in part (in 1989): Aus I M M Bulletin and Proceedings (ISSN 0818-3848); Which was formerly (until 1986): A I M M Bulletin and Proceedings (ISSN 0817-2668); (until 1984): A I M M Bulletin (ISSN 0814-4346); Which was formed by the merger of (1978-1983): Aus.I.M.M. Bulletin (ISSN 0158-6602) & (1933-1983): Australasian Institute of Mining and Metallurgy. Proceedings (ISSN 0004-8364).
Description: To keep mineral industry abreast of latest developments, important news, personnel movements, current issues and product developments.

622.05 669 AT ISSN 1034-6783
TN1 CODEN: AIPREI
AUS I M M PROCEEDINGS. 1983. s-a. Australasian Institute of Mining and Metallurgy, P.O. Box 660, Carlton South, Vic. 3053, Australia. TEL 61-3-662-3166. FAX 61-3-662-3662. **Document type:** proceedings.
—BLDSC (1792.932130); CASDDS; Ei; UnCover. **CCC.**
Supersedes in part (in 1989): Aus I M M Bulletin and Proceedings (ISSN 0818-3848); Which was formerly (until 1986): A I M M Bulletin and Proceedings (ISSN 0817-2668); (until 1984): A I M M Bulletin (ISSN 0814-4346); Which was formed by the merger of (1978-1983): Aus.I.M.M. Bulletin (ISSN 0158-6602) & (1933-1983): Australasian Institute of Mining and Metallurgy. Proceedings (ISSN 0004-8364).

622.05 669 AT ISSN 0728-7178
CODEN: CSAMDJ
AUSTRALASIAN INSTITUTE OF MINING AND METALLURGY CONFERENCE SERIES. 1972. a. price varies. Australasian Institute of Mining and Metallurgy, P.O. Box 660, Carlton South, Vic. 3053, Australia. TEL 61-3-662-3166. FAX 61-3-662-3662.
—CASDDS; Ei. **CCC.**

622.05 669 AT ISSN 0155-3399
CODEN: MSAMDR
AUSTRALASIAN INSTITUTE OF MINING AND METALLURGY MONOGRAPH SERIES. 1962. irreg. price varies. Australasian Institute of Mining and Metallurgy, P.O. Box 660, Carlton South, Vic. 3053, Australia. TEL 61-3-622-3166. FAX 61-3-622-3662. **Document type:** monographic series.
—BLDSC (5916.210000); CASDDS; Ei.

622 550 AT
AUSTRALIA. BUREAU OF RESOURCE SCIENCES. MINERAL RESOURCE REPORT. 1987. irreg. price varies. Bureau of Resource Sciences, P.O. Box E11, Queen Victoria Terr., A.C.T. 2600, Australia. **Document type:** government publication.
Former titles: Australia. Bureau of Mineral Resources, Geology and Geophysics. Mineral Resource Report; Australia. Bureau of Mineral Resources, Geology and Geophysics. Resource Report (ISSN 0818-6278)

338.2 AT ISSN 0067-1762
TN811.A8
AUSTRALIAN COAL INDUSTRY RESEARCH LABORATORIES. ANNUAL REPORT. 1966. a. free. Australian Coal Industry Research Laboratories Ltd., P.O. Box 83, North Ryde, N.S.W. 2113, Australia. **Indexed:** AESIS, Chem.Abstr. **Document type:** corporate report.

333.8 AT ISSN 0157-4566
AUSTRALIAN COAL REPORT. 1979. m. $450 (effective 1994). J. Barlow Consultants Pty. Ltd., Level 9, 16 O'Connell St., Sydney, N.S.W. 2000, Australia. TEL 61-2-221-8440. FAX 61-2-221-8592. Ed. J.W. Barlow. bk.rev. circ. 500. (back issues avail.) **Indexed:** AESIS. **Document type:** newsletter, trade publication.
Description: Includes export coal prices, news, contract and industry information, shipping news, and freight rates.

AUSTRALIAN GEMMOLOGIST. see *JEWELRY, CLOCKS AND WATCHES*

622 620.1 AT ISSN 0705-5838
SH224.Q4
AUSTRALIAN GEOMECHANICS NEWS. 1980. 2/yr. Aus.$17($10.50) Institution of Engineers, Australia, 11 National Circuit, Barton, A.C.T. 2600, Australia. (Co-sponsor: Australasian Institute of Mining and Metallurgy) adv.; bk.rev. circ. 650. (back issues avail.) **Indexed:** GeoRef., HRIS, Intl.Civil Eng.Abstr., Soft.Abstr.Eng.
—BLDSC (1801.060000).
Formerly: Australian Geomechanics Journal.
Description: News journal of Australian Geomechanics Society with news and technical papers in the general field of geomechanics.

622 AT ISSN 0817-9646
AUSTRALIAN JOURNAL OF MINING; Australian, Asian and Pacific mining. 1986. m. Aus.$80($115) (effective Dec. 1990). G M C Studio Pty. Ltd., 8 Shelley St., Richmond North, Vic. 3121, Australia. TEL 03-429-5599. FAX 03-427-0332. Ed. Elizabeth Red. adv.; bk.rev. circ. 7,900. (back issues avail.)
—BLDSC (1810.500000).
Description: Covers all aspects of mining in Asia - Pacific Region including exploration, extraction, investment, marketing, trade and politics.

AUSTRALIAN MINERALOGIST. see *EARTH SCIENCES — Geology*

622 AT ISSN 0004-976X
TP1 CODEN: AUMNA3
AUSTRALIAN MINING. 1908. m. Aus.$69. Thomson Business Publishing, 47 Chippen St., Chippendale, N.S.W. 2008, Australia. TEL 02-6992411. FAX 02-698-3920. Ed. Mike Syddell. adv.; bk.rev.; illus.; mkt.; tr.lit.; index. circ. 7,180. (also avail. in microfilm from UMI,PMC) **Indexed:** AESIS, Aus.Rd.Ind., Chem.Abstr., Eng.Ind., Fuel & Energy Abstr., GeoRef., Met.Abstr., PROMT, World Alum.Abstr.
—BLDSC (1814.600000); Ei; Faxon; SWETS; UMI; UnCover.
Formerly: Mining and Chemical Engineering Review.

338.2 332.6 AT ISSN 1030-7915
AUSTRALIAN NUGGET JOURNAL. 1987. q. free. Goldcorp Australia, 300 Hay St., E. Perth, W.A. 6004, Australia. TEL 61-9-421-7222. FAX 61-9-221-3812. TELEX 197171. Ed. Ron Barry. bk.rev.; circ. 4,500 (controlled). (back issues avail.) **Document type:** trade publication.
Description: Provides regular reference information on precious metals generally, precious metals investment, the Australian gold mining industry and Australia's legal tender precious metal coinage.

622 AT
AUSTRALIA'S MINING MONTHLY. 1980. m. Aus.$55. P.O. Box 78, Leederville, W.A. 6902, Australia. TEL 61-9-3821800. FAX 61-9-3811847. Ed. Richard Roberts. adv.; B&W page Aus.$1705, color page Aus.$2425; 215 x 305. bk.rev.; charts. circ. 7,730. **Indexed:** AESIS. **Document type:** trade publication.
—UnCover.
Former titles: Mining Monthly (ISSN 0725-9131); (until 1981): Mining Quarterly; Which incorporated: Lodestone's Australian Oil and Gas Journal.

622 CN
B C MINE RESCUE MANUAL. base vol. (plus irreg. suppl.). Can.$18. Ministry of Energy, Mines and Petroleum Resources, Mineral Resources Division, 5th Fl., 1810 Blanshard St., Victoria, BC V8V 1X4, Canada. (Subscr. to: Crown Publications, 521 Fort St., Victoria, BC V8W 1E7, Canada. TEL 604-386-4636) Ed. Brian Grant. (looseleaf format) **Document type:** government publication.
Description: Provides basic training in the rescue procedures to be followed in the event of an accident at a surface or underground mining operation.

622 669 AU ISSN 0005-8912
CODEN: BHMMAM
B H M. (Berg- und Huettenmaennische Monatshefte) 1841. m. DM.292($212) (effective 1996). Springer-Verlag, Sachsenplatz 4-6, Postfach 89, A-1201 Vienna, Austria. TEL 0222-3302415. FAX 0222-3302426. (Subscr. in N. America to: Springer-Verlag New York, Inc., 44 Hartz Way, Secaucus, NJ 07096-2491. TEL 201-348-4033. FAX 201-348-4505) (Co-sponsors: Bergmaennischen Verbandes Oesterreich; Eisenhuette Oesterreich; Montanuniversitaet Leoben) Ed.Bd. adv.; bk.rev.; bibl.; charts; illus.; index. (reprint service avail. from ISI) **Indexed:** Chem.Abstr., Eng.Ind., GeoRef., INIS Atomind., INSPEC (1979-1982). **Document type:** bulletin.
—BLDSC (1909.000000); CASDDS; SWETS. **CCC.**
Incorporates: Montan-Berichte (ISSN 0026-9875); Montan-Rundschau (ISSN 0026-9883); Former titles (until 1962): Berg- und Huettenmaennische Monatshefte (ISSN 0170-0278); (until 1961): Berg- und Huettenmaennische Monatshefte der Montanistischen Hochschule in Leoben (ISSN 0365-9747)

622 BL ISSN 0101-2886
BALANCO MINERAL BRASILEIRO. 1978. triennial. 3 BTN($3) Departamento Nacional da Producao Mineral, Setor de Autarquias Norte, Quadra 1, Bloco B, 70040 Brasilia D.F., Brazil. TEL 061-224-2670.

622 XO ISSN 0231-6854
BANICKE LISTY/FOLIA MONTANA. (Text in Slovak; summaries in English, French and Russian) 1974. irreg. (Slovenska Akademia Vied, Banicky Ustav Sav) Veda, Publishing House of the Slovak Academy of Sciences, Klemensova 19, 814 30 Bratislava, Slovakia. (Dist. by: Slovart, Nam. Slobody 6, 817 64 Bratislava, Slovakia) illus.

BANYASZATI SZAKIRODALMI TAJEKOZTATO/MINING ABSTRACTS. see *MINES AND MINING INDUSTRY — Abstracting, Bibliographies, Statistics*

622 333.8 GW ISSN 0342-5681
TN3
BERGBAU; Zeitschrift fuer Bergbau und Energiewirtschaft. m. DM.127.80 (foreign DM.147.40). (Ring Deutscher Berginsgenieure e.V.) Makossa Druck und Medien GmbH, Pommernstr. 17, 45889 Gelsenkirchen, Germany. TEL 0209-980850. FAX 0209-9808585. Ed. Werner Makossa. adv. circ. 13,600. **Indexed:** INIS Atomind. **Document type:** trade publication.
—BLDSC (1910.000000).
Description: Covers all branches of the mining industry.

622 669 SW ISSN 0284-0448
HD9525.S85 CODEN: JJAND2
BERGSMANNEN. 1817. 7/yr. SEK 220($28) Moraberg Foerlags AB, P.O. Box 5, S-151 21 Soedertaelje, Sweden. FAX 46-8-550-856-00. Ed. Anders H. Almgren. adv.; bk.rev.; illus.; stat.; index. circ. 4,500. (back issues avail.) **Indexed:** Appl.Mech.Rev., Chem.Abstr., Curr.Cont., Eng.Ind., INIS Atomind., Met.Abstr., World Alum.Abstr.
—CASDDS; Ei.
Formerly: Bergsmannen med Jernkontorets Annaler (ISSN 0280-4239); Supersedes in part (in 1977): Jernkontorets Annaler (ISSN 0021-5902)

622 669 NO ISSN 0005-8971
BERGVERKS-NYTT; the Scandinavian journal of mining and quarrying. 1954. m. (except Jan., Jul., Dec.). NOK 250. Bergverks-Nytt, P.O. Box 1438 Strindheim, 7002 Trondheim, Norway. (Co-sponsors: Bergverkenes Landssammenslutning, Steinindustriens Landssammenslutning; Pukk- og Grusleverandorenes Landforening, Norsk Bergindustriforening) Ed. Stoerk Halstensen. adv.; bk.rev.; charts; illus.; mkt.; stat. circ. 2,000.
—**CCC.**

MINES AND MINING INDUSTRY

622   GW   ISSN 0935-123X
QE351
BERICHTE DER DEUTSCHEN MINERALOGISCHEN GESELLSCHAFT. (Supplement to: European Journal of Mineralogy (ISSN: 0935-1221)) 1989. s-a. price varies. E. Schweizerbart'sche Verlagsbuchhandlung, Johannesstr. 3A, 70176 Stuttgart, Germany. TEL 0711-625001. FAX 0711-625005. Ed. W.V. Maresch. **Document type:** academic/scholarly publication.
—SWETS. CCC.

BIBLIOGRAPHY OF ECONOMIC GEOLOGY. see *ENERGY*

622   AU
BOECKSTEINER MONTANA. irreg., no.9, 1991. varies. Verein Montandenkmal Altboeckstein, Postfach 78, A-8700 Leoben, Austria. TEL 932166. **Document type:** monographic series.

622   PO   ISSN 0006-5935
TN83   CODEN: PBMIBL
BOLETIM DE MINAS. (Summaries in French and English) 1912. q. free. Instituto Geologico e Mineiro, Rua Almirante Barroso 38, 1097 Lisbon, Portugal. TEL 351-1-3537596. charts; illus. circ. 1,100. **Indexed:** GeoRef, P.A.I.S.For.Lang.Ind. **Document type:** bulletin.
—BLDSC (2157.175000).

BOLETIN GEOLOGICO Y MINERO. see *EARTH SCIENCES — Geology*

BOLETIN GEOLOGICO Y MINERO. PUBLICACIONES ESPECIALES. see *EARTH SCIENCES — Geology*

622   BO   ISSN 0067-9852
BOLIVIA. SERVICIO GEOLOGICO. SERIE MINERALOGICA. CONTRIBUCIONE. 1968. irreg. Servicio Geologico, Casilla 2729, La Paz, Bolivia.

622   JA   ISSN 0385-0501
BONANZA. (Text in Japanese) Kinzoku Kogyo Jigyodan - Metal Mining Agency of Japan, 24-14, Toranomon 1-chome, Minato-ku, Tokyo 105, Japan. illus.

662   RU
BOR'BA S GAZOM V UGOL'NYKH SHAKHTAKH. irreg. 0.61 Rub. (Nauchno-Issledovatelskii Institut po Bezopasnosti Rabot v Gornoi Promyshlennosti, Makeevka) Izdatel'stvo Nedra, Pl. Belorusskogo Vokzala, 3, 125047 Moscow, Russia. TEL 250-52-55. illus.

622 662   GW   ISSN 0341-1060
TN831   CODEN: BRUKAO
BRAUNKOHLE; Zeitschrift fuer Tagebautechnik und Energieversorgung. 1902; N.S. 1949. m. DM.237 (foreign DM.269.40). Rheinische-Bergische Drueckerei- und Verlagsgesellschaft mbH, Postfach 1135, 4000 Duesseldorf 1, Germany. Ed. Dr.-Ing. Ernst-Pater Froehling. adv.; bk.rev.; abstr.; charts; maps; pat. circ. 1,900. **Indexed:** C.I.S. Abstr., Chem.Abstr., Excerp.Med., GeoRef, Geotech.Abstr., INIS Atomind.
—BLDSC (2275.998000); CASDDS; SWETS. CCC.
  Formerly: Braunkohle Waerme und Energie (ISSN 0006-9299)

622   BL   ISSN 0100-3577
    CODEN: BPMBAB
BRAZIL. DEPARTAMENTO NACIONAL DA PRODUCAO MINERAL. BOLETIM. 1972. irreg., no.60, 1986. 3 BTN($3) Departamento Nacional da Producao Mineral, Setor Autarquias Norte, Quadra 1, Bloco B, 70040 Brasilia, D.F., Brazil. TEL 061-224-2670. (back issues avail.) **Document type:** government publication, bulletin.

338.2   BL
BRAZIL. DEPARTAMENTO NACIONAL DA PRODUCAO MINERAL. BOLETIM DE PRECOS. 1974. 4/yr. free. Departamento Nacional da Producao Mineral, Setor Autacuia Norte, Quadra 1, Bloco B, 70040 Brasilia S.F., Brazil. TEL 061-224-4670. **Document type:** government publication.

622   BL
BRAZIL. DEPARTAMENTO NACIONAL DA PRODUCAO MINERAL. MONOGRAFIA. 1975. irreg., no.47, 1988. price varies. Departamento Nacional da Producao Mineral, Setor Autarquias Norte, Quadra 1, Bloco B, 70040 Brasilia, D.F., Brazil. TEL 061-224-2670. **Document type:** government publication, monographic series.

622   BL
BRAZIL. DEPARTAMENTO NACIONAL DA PRODUCAO MINERAL. RELATORIO ANUAL DE ATIVIDADES E PROGRAMACAO. (In 2 vols.: vol.1 Atividades, vol.2 Programacao) 1972. a. free. Departamento Nacional da Producao Mineral, Setor Autarquia Norte, Quadra 1, Bloco B, 70040-200 Brasilia D.F., Brazil. TEL 55-61-224-2670. FAX 55-61-2258274. circ. 150 (controlled). **Document type:** government publication.
  Description: Reports on all planned activities of the Department: geochemical and geophysical surveys, geological mapping and more.

622   BL   ISSN 0101-8159
BRAZIL. DEPARTAMENTO NACIONAL DE PRODUCAO MINERAL. SERIE TECNOLOGIA MINERAL. 1979. irreg., no.46, 1994. Departamento Nacional da Producao Mineral, Setor Autarquias Norte, Quadra 1, Bloco B, 70040-200 Brasilia, D.F., Brazil. TEL 55-61-2242670. FAX 55-61-2258274. **Document type:** government publication.

622 665.5   CN   ISSN 0365-9356
TN27.B9   CODEN: BCMAA
BRITISH COLUMBIA. MINISTRY OF ENERGY, MINES AND PETROLEUM RESOURCES. ANNUAL REPORT. a. Can.$10.70. Ministry of Energy, Mines and Petroleum Resources, Parliament Bldgs., Victoria, BC V8V 1X4, Canada. TEL 604-952-0152. (Subscr. to: Crown Publications, 521 Fort St., Victoria, BC V8W 1E7, Canada. TEL 604-386-4636) **Document type:** government publication.
  Description: Summary of ministry operations, including hydroelectric energy, mineral and petroleum and natural gas production statistics.

549   CN
BRITISH COLUMBIA. MINISTRY OF ENERGY, MINES AND PETROLEUM RESOURCES. MINERAL MARKET UPDATE. 3/yr. free. Ministry of Energy, Mines and Petroleum Resources, Parliament Bldgs., Victoria, BC V8V 1X4, Canada. TEL 604-952-0152. FAX 604-952-0151. **Document type:** government publication.
  Description: Information on mining in B.C. Includes value and volume of B.C.'s mineral products, mine output and employment, exploration project highlights, an update on projects in the mine development review process, and news on provincial initiatives of interest to the international investment and mining sectors.

622   CN   ISSN 0846-0051
TN27.B9
BRITISH COLUMBIA MINERAL EXPLORATION REVIEW. a. free. Ministry of Energy, Mines and Petroleum Resources, Mineral Resources Division, 5th Fl., 1810 Blanshard St., Victoria, BC V8V 1K8, Canada. illus. **Document type:** government publication.
  Formerly (until 1985): British Columbia Exploration Review (ISSN 0828-6094)

622   UK   ISSN 0308-2199
BRITISH MINING; memoirs and monographs. 1975. 2/yr. £18. Northern Mine Research Society, 38 Main St., Sutton in Craven, Keighley, Yorkshire BD20 7HD, England. TEL 0535-635388. Ed. Hazel Martell. circ. 700. **Indexed:** GeoRef. **Document type:** monographic series.
—BLDSC (2330.540000).

BULETINI I SHKENCAVE GJEOLOGJIKE. see *EARTH SCIENCES — Geology*

BULLETIN STATISTIQUE ACIER. SERIE BLEUE. COMMERCE EXTERIEUR. see *METALLURGY*

BULLETIN STATISTIQUE ACIER. SERIE ROUGE. PRODUCTION. see *METALLURGY*

338.2   UK   ISSN 0269-9117
BUSINESS RATIO REPORT: MINING & QUARRYING; an industry sector analysis. 1986. a. I C C Business Ratios Ltd., Freepost, Field House, Hampton, Mddx. TW12 1BR, England. TEL 081-783-0977. FAX 081-783-1940. charts; stat. **Document type:** trade publication.
—BLDSC (5799.279000).

621.9 358.8   UK   ISSN 0261-9105
BUSINESS RATIO REPORT: MINING EQUIPMENT MANUFACTURERS; an industry sector analysis. 1980. a. I C C Business Ratios Ltd., Freepost, Field House, Hampton, Mddx. TW12 1BR, England. TEL 081-783-0977. FAX 081-783-1940. charts; stat. **Document type:** trade publication.
—BLDSC (5803.150000).

622   CN   ISSN 0705-5196
    CODEN: CANRD7
C A N M E T REPORTS. 1974. irreg. price varies. Canada Centre for Mineral and Energy Technology, 555 Booth St., Ottawa, Ont. K1A 0G1, Canada. FAX 613-995-3192. TELEX 053-3395. Ed. R. Kamra. circ. 1,000. (also avail. in microfiche) **Indexed:** Chem.Abstr., Energy Ind., GeoRef.
—BLDSC (3047.275000); CASDDS; Ei.
  Incorporates (in 1977): C A N M E T Review.

622   II   ISSN 0376-7787
HD9556.I4
C C A I MONTHLY NEWS LETTER. (Text in English) 1972. m. $10. Coal Consumers Association of India, 4, India Exchange, 7th Fl., Calcutta 700 001, India. TEL 22-4488. Ed. S.S. Parikh. adv.; bk.rev.; charts. circ. 5,000. **Document type:** newsletter.
  Description: News and articles intended to create awareness among industrial coal consumers about the development of coal industry in India and international markets.

622   CN   ISSN 0317-0926
TN1   CODEN: CIBUBA
C I M BULLETIN. 1898. m. Can.$135 (foreign $150). Canadian Institute of Mining, Metallurgy & Petroleum, Xerox Tower, 3400 de Maisonneuve Blvd. W., Ste. 1210, Montreal, PQ H3Z 3B8, Canada. TEL 514-939-2710. FAX 514-939-2714. Ed. Perla Gantz. adv.; bk.rev.; bibl.; charts; illus.; index. circ. 11,000. (back issues avail.) **Indexed:** A.I.Abstr., A.S.& T.Ind., AESIS, Art & Archaeol.Tech.Abstr., CAD CAM Abstr., Cadscan, Can.B.P.I., Chem.Abstr., Chem.Eng.Abstr., Curr.Cont., Energy Info.Abstr., Environ.Abstr., Fluidex, Fuel & Energy Abstr., INIS Atomind., INSPEC, Lead Abstr., Sci.Cit.Ind., T.C.E.A., Zincscan. **Document type:** academic/scholarly publication.
—BLDSC (3198.243000); CASDDS; Ei; Faxon; SWETS; UnCover.
  Description: Technical data and information on mineral engineering subjects to promote the technological interests of people involved in the development of the industry in Canada.
  Refereed Serial

622 669   CN   ISSN 0068-9009
TN1
C I M DIRECTORY. 1967. a. Can.$100. Canadian Institute of Mining, Metallurgy & Petroleum, Xerox Tower, 3400 de Maisonneuve Blvd. W., Ste. 1210, Montreal, PQ H3Z 3B8, Canada. TEL 514-939-2710. FAX 514-939-2714. Ed. Perla Gantz. adv. circ. 12,750. **Document type:** directory.
  Description: Lists officers and members, as well as feature articles on a subject dealing with mining in Canada.

622   CN   ISSN 0701-0710
C I M REPORTER. 2/yr. Canadian Institute of Mining, Metallurgy & Petroleum, Ste. 1200, 3400 de Maisonneuve Blvd. W., Montreal, PQ H3Z 3B8, Canada. TEL 514-939-2710. FAX 514-939-2714. Ed. Perla Gantz. adv. circ. 10,119. **Indexed:** GeoRef. **Document type:** newspaper.
  Description: Composed of current mining and milling information.

622 340   US
C M A COMMUNICATOR. 1991. m. $60. Colorado Mining Association, 1600 Broadway, Ste. 1340, Denver, CO 80202. TEL 303-894-0536. FAX 303-894-8416. adv. circ. 1,300. **Document type:** newsletter.
  Description: Keeps members informed about mining regulations, laws and other activities.

622   II
C M R I ANNUAL REPORT. (Former name of issuing body: Central Mining Research Station) 1961. a. Central Mining Research Institute, Barwa Rd., Dhanbad 826001, Bihar, India. FAX 91-0326-202429. (Affiliate: Council of Scientific and Industrial Research) Ed. M.C. Chatterjee. circ. 500. **Document type:** academic/scholarly publication.
  Former titles: C M R S Annual Report; Central Mining Research Station, Dhanbad. Progress Research (ISSN 0070-4628)
  Description: Research and development activities carried out at the Research Institute.

MINES AND MINING INDUSTRY 4753

622 — II
C M R I NEWSLETTER. (Former name of issuing body: Central Mining Research Station) (Text in English) 1974. 4/m. Central Mining Research Institute, Barwa Rd., Dhanbad 826001, Bihar, India. FAX 91-0326-202429. (Affiliate: Council of Scientific and Industrial Research) Ed. S.K. Gupta. circ. 2,000. **Document type:** newsletter.
Former titles: C M R S Newsletter; (until 1992): C M R S Bulletin.

549 630 — US
C M S NEWS. q. $20. Clay Minerals Society, Box 4416, Boulder, CO 80306. TEL 303-444-6405. Ed. Patricia Jo Eberl. **Document type:** newsletter.

622 330 — CN — ISSN 0228-1821
C R S PERSPECTIVES. 1978. 4/yr. ffree. Centre for Resource Studies, Queen's University, 100 Barrie St., Kingston, ON K7L 3N6, Canada. TEL 613-545-2553. FAX 613-545-6651. Ed. Moira Jackson. bk.rev. circ. 3,000.
Description: Focuses on current mineral policy concerns in Canada.

CALIFORNIA. DIVISION OF MINES AND GEOLOGY. BULLETIN. see *EARTH SCIENCES — Geology*

CALIFORNIA. DIVISION OF MINES AND GEOLOGY. SPECIAL REPORT. see *EARTH SCIENCES — Geology*

338.2 — CN
CANADA. INDIAN AND NORTHERN AFFAIRS CANADA. MINES AND MINERAL ACTIVITIES (YEAR). (Text in English; summaries in French) 1967. a. free. Indian and Northern Affairs Canada, Mineral Resources Directorate, Rm. 603, Ottawa, ON K1A 0H4, Canada. TEL 819-994-6421. FAX 819-953-9066. Ed. T.W. Caine. circ. 2,200. **Document type:** government publication.
Formerly: Canada. Northern Natural Resources and Environment Branch. Mining Section. North of 60: Mines and Mineral Activities; **Supersedes:** Canada. Department of Indian Affairs and Northern Development. Mines and Minerals, Activities (ISSN 0590-580X)
Description: Summary of mining and mineral exploration activities in the Yukon and Northwest territories during the calendar year.
Refereed Serial

622 — CN
CANADA. NATURAL RESOURCES CANADA. MINING SECTOR. MINERAL BULLETINS. 1953. irreg. (approx. a.). price varies. Natural Resources Canada, Mining Sector, Publishing Division, 460 O'Connor, Ottawa, ON K1A 0E4, Canada. TEL 819-956-4802. FAX 819-994-1498. (Subscr. to: Supply and Services Canada, Canada Communications Group - Publishing, Ottawa, ON K1A 0S5, Canada) **Document type:** government publication.
Former titles: Canada. Natural Resources Canada. Mineral Policy Sector. Mineral Bulletins; Canada. Mineral Policy Sector. Mineral Information Bulletin; Canada. Mineral Development Sector. Mineral Information Bulletin; Canada. Mineral Resources Branch. Mineral Information Bulletin (ISSN 0068-7812)

CANADA A-Z; oil, gas, mining directory. see *BUSINESS AND ECONOMICS — Trade And Industrial Directories*

CANADIAN MINERALOGIST; crystallography, geochemistry, mineralogy, petrology, mineral deposits. see *EARTH SCIENCES — Geology*

622 — CN — ISSN 0068-9270
CANADIAN MINERALS YEARBOOK/ANNUAIRE DES MINERAUX DU CANADA. 1962. a. price varies. Energy, Mines and Resources Canada, Mineral Policy Sector, Publishing Division, 460 O'Connor, Ottawa, ON K1A 0E4, Canada. TEL 819-956-4802. FAX 819-994-1498. (Orders to: Supply and Services Canada, Canada Communication Group - Publishing, Ottawa, ON K1A 0S5, Canada) Ed. E. Godin. **Indexed:** AESIS. **Document type:** government publication.

622 — CN — ISSN 0068-9289
HG5159.M4
CANADIAN MINES HANDBOOK. 1931. a. Can.$50.95. Southam Magazine Group, 1450 Don Mills Rd., Don Mills, ON M3B 2X7, Canada. TEL 416-445-6641. FAX 416-442-2272. Ed. D. Giancola. adv.: B&W page Can.$2015. circ. 8,000. **Document type:** directory.
Description: Lists and supplies information on every mining company registered in Canada.

338.2 662 — CN — ISSN 0008-4492
CODEN: CAMJA9
CANADIAN MINING JOURNAL. 1879. bi-m. Can.$26.22($24.50) (foreign $46). Southam Magazine Gruop, 1450 Don Mills Rd., Don Mills, ON M3B 2X7, Canada. TEL 416-445-6641. FAX 416-442-2272. Ed. P. Whiteway. adv.: B&W page Can.$2350. illus.; mkt.; index. circ. 87,000. (also avail. in microfilm from PMC) **Indexed:** AESIS, C.I.S. Abstr., Cadscan, Can.B.P.I., Chem.Abstr., Curr.Cont., Eng.Ind., Environ.Per.Bibl., Excerp.Med., Fuel & Energy Abstr., GeoRef., INIS Atomind., Key to Econ.Sci., Lead Abstr., Met.Abstr., Petrol.Abstr., Zincscan. **Document type:** trade publication.
●Also available online. Vendor(s): Southam Electronic Publishing.
—BLDSC (3042.000000); CASDDS; Ei; Faxon; Genuine Article; SWETS; UMI; UnCover. **CCC**.
Incorporates: Mining in Canada (ISSN 0047-7494)
Description: Provides technical oriented information and on-site coverage of mine and mill operations.

624 621.9 — SP — ISSN 0008-5677
CANTERAS Y EXPLOTACIONES; revista tecnica de maquinaria para canteras, minas, cementos y obras hidraulicas. 1967. m. 7000 ptas. Pedeca Sociedad Cooperativa, Ltda., Maria Auxiliadora 5, 28040 Madrid, Spain. TEL 1-450-88-37. FAX 1-450-94-29. Ed. Ricardo J. Heranandez. circ. 10,273 (controlled). **Indexed:** Fluidex, Ind.SST.
—BLDSC (3049.900000). **CCC**.

622 — PE
CARTA MINERA Y PANORAMA PETROLERO. 1982. w. $290 includes annual directory. Andean Air Mail & Peruvian Times S.A., Pasaje Los Pinos, 156, Piso B, Of. 6, Miraflores, Lima, Peru. TEL 5114-453761. FAX 5114-467888. Ed. Maibi Montoya; Pub. Eleanor Zuniga. adv. contact: Luisa Perbuli. charts; stat. **Document type:** newsletter.
Description: Covers mining in Peru.

622 338.2 — US — ISSN 0082-9382
CENSUS OF MINERAL INDUSTRIES: FINAL REPORTS. (Issued in 3 series: Geographic Area Series, Industry Series, and Subject Series) 1840. quinquennial, latest 1992. $38 for Geographic Area Series (foreign $47.50); Industry Series $32 (foreign $40). U.S. Bureau of the Census, Data User Services Division, Washington, DC 20233. TEL 301-457-4100. FAX 301-457-4714. (Subscr. to: Superintendent of Documents, U.S. Government Printing Office, Box 317954, Pittsburgh, PA 15250-7954. TEL 202-512-1800. FAX 202-512-2250; Or: Bernan, 4611-F Assembly Dr., Lanham, MD 20706. TEL 301-459-7666. FAX 301-459-0056) **Document type:** government publication.
●Also available on CD-ROM.

622 — US
CENSUS OF MINERAL INDUSTRIES: PRELIMINARY REPORTS. quinquennial, latest 1992. $24 for Preliminary Industry Series (foreign $30); United States Summary Report $5. U.S. Bureau of the Census, Data User Services Division, Washington, DC 20233. TEL 301-457-4100. FAX 301-457-4714. (Subscr. to: Superintendent of Documents, U.S Government Printing Office, Box 371954, Pittsburgh, PA 15250-7954. TEL 202-512-1800. FAX 202-512-2250; Or: Bernan, 4611-F Assembly Dr., Lanham, MD 20706. TEL 301-274-4447. FAX 301-459-0056) **Document type:** government publication.
●Also available on CD-ROM.

622 — II
CENTRAL MINE PLANNING & DESIGN INSTITUTE. MANUALS. (Text in English) 1976. irreg. free. Central Mine Planning & Design Institute Ltd. (Subsidiary of: Coal India Limited), Publications Wing, Gondwana Place, Kanke Rd., Ranchi 834008, Bihar, India.

CENTRAL QUEENSLAND NEWS. see *AGRICULTURE*

622 — CC — ISSN 1005-9784
CODEN: JCSTFT
▼**CENTRAL SOUTH UNIVERSITY OF TECHNOLOGY. JOURNAL.** Chinese edition: Zhongnan Gongye Daxue Xuebao (ISSN 1005-9792) (Text in English) 1994. s-a. $15. Central South University of Technology, Institute of Mining and Metallurgy - Zhongnan Jishu Daxue Kuangye Xueyuan, Changsha, Human, People's Republic of China. FAX 4731-82817. (Dist. by: China International Book Trading Corp., P.O. Box 399, Beijing 100044, P.R. China) adv. circ. 500. **Document type:** academic/scholarly publication.
—CASDDS.

622 — CN — ISSN 0711-6039
CENTRE FOR RESOURCE STUDIES. PROCEEDINGS. 1978. irreg., latest 1993. price varies. Centre for Resource Studies, Queen's University, Kingston, ON K7L 3N6, Canada. TEL 613-545-2553. **Document type:** proceedings.
—BLDSC (6787.890000).

622 — CN
CENTRE FOR RESOURCE STUDIES. TECHNICAL PAPERS. 1981. irreg., latest 1994. price varies. Centre for Resource Studies, Queen's University, Kingston, ON K7L 3N6, Canada. TEL 613-545-2553. FAX 613-545-6651. (also avail. in microfiche).

622 — CN — ISSN 0226-7616
CENTRE FOR RESOURCES STUDIES. WORKING PAPERS. no.3, 1977. irreg., latest 1993. price varies. Centre for Resource Studies, Queen's University, Kingston, ON K7L 3N6, Canada. TEL 613-545-2553.

622 — RH — ISSN 0009-1162
TN119.R6 — CODEN: CHMJBP
CHAMBER OF MINES JOURNAL. 1959. m. Z.$64.80 (foreign Z.$82.20. (Chamber of Mines, Zimbabwe) Thomson Publications Zimbabwe (Pvt) Ltd., Thomson House, P.O. Box 1683, Harare, Zimbabwe. TEL 263-4-736835. FAX 263-4-752390. TELEX 24705 ZW. adv. **Document type:** trade publication.
Supersedes (in 1963): Rhodesia Mining and Engineering.

622 — SA
CHAMBER OF MINES' NEWSLETTER; serving South Africa's private sector mining industry. bi-m. free to qualified readers. Chamber of Mines of South Africa, P.O. Box 809, Johannesburg 2000, South Africa. TEL 27-11-4987100. FAX 27-11-8384251. TELEX 4-87057. Ed. Al Smit. charts; illus.; stat. **Indexed:** INIS Atomind. **Document type:** trade publication, newsletter.
Description: Presents articles on South Africa's mining industry and related issues.

338.2 — CM — ISSN 0069-2530
CHAMBRE DE COMMERCE, D'INDUSTRIE ET DES MINES DU CAMEROUN. RAPPORT ANNUEL. a. EAs.1000. Chambre de Commerce, d'Industrie et des Mines du Cameroun, B.P. 4011, Douala, Cameroon. FAX 42-55-96. TELEX 5616 KN. Ed. Saidou A. Bobboy. circ. 350. **Document type:** corporate report.

549 — FR — ISSN 0182-564X
TN260 — CODEN: CRMIDQ
CHRONIQUE DE LA RECHERCHE MINIERE/CHRONICLE OF MINERAL RESEARCH & EXPLORATION. (Text in English, French; summaries in English, French) 1977. q. 700 F. (Bureau de Recherches Geologiques et Minieres) Editions B R G M, B.P. 6009, 45060 Orleans Cedex, France. (Dist. by: Gauthier-Villars, Centrale des Revues, 11 rue Gossin, 92543 Montrouge Cedex, France. TEL 46-56-52-66) Ed. Philippe Lagny; Pub. G. Sustrac. index. **Indexed:** Bull.Signal., Chem.Abstr., Geo.Abstr., Geol.Abstr., GeoRef., INIS Atomind., Petrol.Abstr., Ref.Zh. **Document type:** bulletin, academic/scholarly publication.
—CASDDS; Ei; SWETS; UnCover. **CCC**.
Description: Features articles and reviews on mineral deposits, including descriptions of deposits, regional or thematic geologic reviews, metallogenic reviews and more.

4754 MINES AND MINING INDUSTRY

549 666 US ISSN 0009-8604
TN941 CODEN: CLCMAB
CLAYS AND CLAY MINERALS. 1968. bi-m. $165 (foreign $180) (effective 1996). Clay Minerals Society, Box 4416, Boulder, CO 80306. TEL 303-444-6405. Ed. Ray E. Ferrell, Jr. bk.rev.; bibl.; charts; illus. circ. 1,800. (also avail. in microform; reprint service avail. from ISI; back issues avail.) **Indexed:** AESIS, Anal.Abstr., Br.Ceram.Abstr., Chem.Abstr., Curr.Cont., Deep Sea Res.& Oceanogr.Abstr., E&P Hlth. (1993-), Eng.Ind., Excerp.Med., Gas Process.& Ppl. (1993-), Geo.Abstr., Geol.Abstr., Geotech.Abstr., Ind.Sci.Rev., Int.Aerosp.Abstr., Mineral.Abstr., Off.Tech. (1993-), Petrol.Abstr. (1970-), Sci.Cit.Ind., Sel.Water Res.Abstr., Soils & Fert. —BLDSC (3278.100000); CASDDS; Ei; Faxon; Genuine Article; PADDS; SWETS; UnCover.
Formerly: Clay Minerals Society. Annual Proceedings.

622 US ISSN 1040-7820
TN799.9 CODEN: COALEN
COAL. 1964. m. $36. Intertec Publishing Corp., 29 N. Wacker Dr., Chicago, IL 60606. TEL 312-726-2802. FAX 312-726-4103. Ed. Arthur P. Sanda. adv.; tr.lit.; index; circ. 18,623 (controlled). (also avail. in microfilm from UMI) **Indexed:** A.S.& T.Ind., Acid Rain Abstr., Acid Rain Ind., AESIS, C.I.S.Abstr., Energy Info.Abstr., Eng.Ind., Excerp.Med., Fuel & Energy Abstr., Gas Abstr., GeoRef., INIS Atomind., PROMT, SRI, Tr.& Indus.Ind. ●Also available online. Vendor(s): Lexis-Nexis. —BLDSC (3287.945000); CASDDS; Ei; Faxon; SWETS; UMI; UnCover. **CCC.**
Formed by the merger of (1911-1988): Coal Age (ISSN 0009-9910); Coal Mining (ISSN 0749-1948); Which was formerly (until 1984): Coal Mining and Processing (ISSN 0009-9961)
Description: Covers the exploration, development, underground and surface mining, preparation and distribution of anthracite, bituminous coal, and ignite.

622 US ISSN 0145-417X
HD9564
COAL DATA. a. $75 to individuals; non-profit institutions $50. National Coal Association, 1130 17th St., N.W., Washington, DC 20036. TEL 202-463-2640. **Indexed:** GeoRef., SRI.
Formerly: Bituminous Coal Data (ISSN 0067-897X)

338.2 622 US ISSN 0734-8908
COAL FACTS. Variant form of title: Facts about Coal. 1948. a. $15. National Coal Association, 1130 17th St. N.W., Washington, DC 20036. TEL 202-463-2640. Ed. Thomas B. Johnson. index.
Formerly (until 1972): Bituminous Coal Facts (ISSN 0067-8988)

622 UK ISSN 1357-6941
TN800 CODEN: CLGUAL
COAL INTERNATIONAL (REDHILL, 1994). 1858. bi-m. £111.30($211.70) (foreign £132.30). Argus Business Publications Ltd. (Subsidiary of: Argus Press Group), Queensway House, 2 Queensway, Redhill, Surrey RH1 1QS, England. TEL 01737-768611. FAX 01737-761685. TELEX 948669 TOPJNL G. Ed. J Wallis. **Indexed:** Br.Geol.Lit., Br.Tech.Ind., C.I.S. Abstr., Chem.Abstr., Eng.Ind., Excerp.Med., Fuel & Energy Abstr., GeoRef., RICS. **Document type:** trade publication. —Faxon; SWETS.
Formerly (until 1994): Colliery Guardian (Redhill, 1982); Which superseded in part (in 1982): Colliery Guardian Coal International (ISSN 0143-778X); Which was formerly (until 1979): Colliery Guardian (Redhill, 1942) (ISSN 0010-1281); Which superseded: Colliery Guardian and Journal of the Coal and Iron Trades (ISSN 0366-5917); And incorporated in part (in 1963): Steel & Coal (ISSN 0371-3628); Which was formerly (until 1962): Iron & Coal (ISSN 0140-5101); (1866-1961): Iron & Coal Trades Review (ISSN 0367-732X); Which incorporated: British Iron Trade Association Engineering Review. Bulletin.
Description: Explores coal mining and resources.

COAL MINING NEWSLETTER. see *OCCUPATIONAL HEALTH AND SAFETY*

622 US ISSN 0530-0037
HD9541
COAL NEWS. w. $100 to non-members (foreign $150). National Coal Association, 1130 17th St., N.W., Washington, DC 20036. TEL 202-463-2640. FAX 202-857-0135. Ed. Katherine Kirkpatrick. **Document type:** newsletter.

622.33 531.64 US ISSN 0162-2714
COAL OUTLOOK. 1975. w. $775 (foreign $795). Pasha Publications Inc., 1616 N. Ft. Myer Dr., Ste. 1000, Arlington, VA 22209-3107. TEL 703-528-1244. FAX 703-528-1253. Ed. Barry Cassell. **Indexed:** PROMT. **Document type:** newsletter. ●Also available online. Vendor(s): Information Access Co., NewsNet (EY30).
—CCC.
Description: Reports on coal market trends.

051 US ISSN 0748-6073
COAL PEOPLE. 1976. m. $25. Al Skinner Enterprises Inc., Box 6247, Charleston, WV 25302. TEL 304-342-4129. FAX 304-343-3124. Ed. Christina Karawan; Pub. Al Skinner. adv. contact: Alan Terranova. bk.rev. circ. 11,500. **Document type:** trade publication.

622.33 US ISSN 0734-9343
TN816.A1 CODEN: COAPDY
COAL PREPARATION; a multinational journal. 12/yr. (in 3 vols., 4 nos./vol.). 224 ECU per vol. (effective 1996). Gordon & Breach Science Publishers, c/o International Publishers Distributor, 820 Town Center Dr., Langhorne, PA 19047. TEL 215-750-2642. FAX 215-750-6343. (Subscr. to: International Publishers Distributor, P.O. Box 90, Reading, Berkshire RG1 8JL, England. TEL 44-173-456-8316) Ed. J. Laskowski. adv.; bk.rev (also avail. in microform) **Indexed:** AESIS. **Document type:** academic/scholarly publication. —BLDSC (3291.457000); CASDDS; Faxon. **CCC.**
Refereed Serial

622 FR ISSN 0258-6398
COAL PROSPECTS AND POLICIES IN I E A COUNTRIES. irreg. price varies. Organization for Economic Cooperation and Development, International Energy Agency, 2 rue Andre-Pascal, 75775 Paris Cedex 16, France. (U.S. orders to: O.E.C.D. Publications and Information Center, 2001 L St., N.W., Ste. 700, Washington, DC 20036-4910. TEL 202-785-6323) (also avail. in microfiche)

622 AT
COAL QUEENSLAND MAGAZINE. q. Aus.$24. (Queensland Department of Minerals and Energy) Magazine Publishing Compny, 4 Wandoo St., Fortitude Valley, Qld. 4006, Australia. TEL 61-7-3529677. FAX 61-7-32524667. Ed. Michael Holliday. adv.: B&W page Aus.$1485, color page Aus.$2356; adv. contact: Trevor Kirk. circ. 3,500. **Document type:** trade publication.
Description: Covers news and legislation pertaining to the mining industry specifically in relation to coal mining, exploration, scientific research, processing, etc.

622.33 681.3 NE ISSN 0167-9449
CODEN: CSTYEF
COAL SCIENCE AND TECHNOLOGY. (Text in English) 1981. irreg. vol.21, 1993. price varies. Elsevier Science B.V., Books Division, P.O. Box 211, 1000 AE Amsterdam, Netherlands. TEL 31-20-4853911. FAX 31-20-4853705. TELEX 18582 ESPA NL. E-mail: nlinfo-f@elsevier.nl; usinfo-f@elsevier.com; forinfo-kyf04035@niftyserve.or.jp; Site addr.: http://www.elsevier.nl/. (Subscr. in U.S. and Canada to: Elsevier Science Inc., Box 882, Madison Sq. Sta., New York, NY 10159. TEL 212-989-5800)
Document type: monographic series.
—BLDSC (3291.770000); CASDDS. **CCC.**
Refereed Serial

553 US ISSN 1046-9486
HE199.5.C6
COAL TRANSPORTATION STATISTICS. a. $35 (non-profit organizations $25). National Coal Association, 1130 17th St., N.W., Washington, DC 20036. TEL 202-463-2640. Ed. Leslie Coleman. **Indexed:** SRI.
Formerly: Coal Traffic Annual (ISSN 0069-4916)

622.33 US ISSN 1049-0574
HD9541
COAL VOICE; national magazine of coal and energy issues. 1978. bi-m. $25. National Coal Association, 1130 17th St., N.W., Washington, DC 20036. TEL 202-463-2640. Ed. Aundrea Cika. charts; illus. circ. 14,000. (back issues avail.)
—Faxon; UnCover.
Formerly (until Jan. 1990): LandMARC (ISSN 0199-1523)
Description: Provides information, comments and perspective on US coal, energy and environmental issues and trends.

622 US ISSN 0149-578X
COAL WEEK. 1975. w. $912 (foreign $946). McGraw-Hill, Inc., Energy & Business Newsletters, 1221 Ave. of the Americas, 36th Fl., New York, NY 10020. TEL 212-512-6410. Ed. John K. Higgins. adv.; charts; stat.; index. (looseleaf format; reprint service avail. from UMI) **Indexed:** Fuel & Energy Abstr.
●Also available online. Vendor(s): Knight-Ridder, Inc. (File no.624/McGRAW-HILL PUBLICATIONS ONLINE), Dow Jones News Retrieval (COW), Lexis-Nexis (COALWK), NewsNet (EY77). Also available on CD-ROM. Producer(s): SilverPlatter Information, Inc. (McGraw-Hill Energy Library).
Incorporates: Mine Regulation and Productivity Report (ISSN 0277-8696); Which was formerly: Mine Productivity Report (ISSN 0149-5283)

622 US ISSN 0272-0205
CODEN: CWIOEQ
COAL WEEK INTERNATIONAL. 1984. w. $1060 (foreign $1186). McGraw-Hill, Inc., Energy & Business Newsletters, 1221 Ave. of the Americas, 36th Fl., New York, NY 10020. TEL 212-512-6410. Ed. John Higgins. (reprint service avail. from UMI)
●Also available online. Vendor(s): Knight-Ridder, Inc. (File no.624/McGRAW-HILL PUBLICATIONS ONLINE), Dow Jones News Retrieval (CWI), Lexis-Nexis (COALIN), NewsNet (EY78). Also available on CD-ROM. Producer(s): SilverPlatter Information, Inc. (McGraw-Hill Energy Library).

553 UK ISSN 0069-4991
COKE OVEN MANAGERS' ASSOCIATION. YEAR BOOK. 1917. a. £30. Coke Oven Manager's Association, Waveney House, Adwick Rd., Mexborough, Yorks S64 0BS, England. Ed. J. Dartnell. adv. circ. 750. **Indexed:** Br.Ceram.Abstr.

622.33 GW ISSN 0937-9258
COKEMAKING INTERNATIONAL. (Text in English) 1990. 2/yr. DM.62. (Verein Deutscher Kokereifachleute) Verlag Stahleisen mbH, Sohnstr. 65, 40237 Duesseldorf, Germany. TEL 0211-6707-0. FAX 0211-6707517. **Document type:** trade publication.
—BLDSC (3293.500000).
Description: Provides information on the complete spectrum of coke production.

622 SA
COLIMPEX MINING EXECUPAD. (Text in Afrikaans and English) a. free to qualified personnel. Colimpex Africa (Pty.) Ltd., P.O. Box 5838, Johannesburg 2000, South Africa. adv.

622 550 560 US ISSN 0069-6056
CODEN: PCCOAT
COLORADO SCHOOL OF MINES. PROFESSIONAL CONTRIBUTIONS. 1965. irreg., no.11, 1983. $25. (Colorado School of Mines) Colorado School of Mines Press, Golden, CO 80401. TEL 303-273-3607. bibl.; charts; illus.; cum.index: 1953-1973. circ. 1,000. (reprint service avail. from UMI) **Indexed:** Chem.Abstr., GeoRef.
—BLDSC (6857.500000); CASDDS. **CCC.**

MINES AND MINING INDUSTRY

622 550 US ISSN 1068-2937
TN210 CODEN: CSEREL
COLORADO SCHOOL OF MINES QUARTERLY REVIEW OF ENGINEERING, SCIENCE, EDUCATION AND RESEARCH. 1905. q. $50. Colorado School of Mines Press, 1500 Illinois, Golden, CO 80401-1887. TEL 303-273-3000. FAX 303-273-3310. bibl.; charts; illus.; stat.; cum.index: 1953-1973. circ. 1,500. (also avail. in microform from UMI; back issues avail.) **Indexed:** AESIS, Appl.Mech.Rev., Chem.Abstr., E&P Hlth. (1993-), Energy Info.Abstr., Eng.Ind., Environ.Abstr., Fuel & Energy Abstr., Gas Process.& Ppl. (1993-), GeoRef., Geotech.Abstr., INIS Atomind., INSPEC, Off.Tech. (1993-), Petrol.Abstr. (1961-1969, 1979-). **Document type:** academic/scholarly publication.
—BLDSC (3490.293900); CASDDS; CIS; PADDS; UnCover. **CCC.**
Former titles (until 1992): Colorado School of Mines Quarterly (ISSN 0163-9153); (until 1979): Colorado School of Mines. Quarterly (ISSN 0010-1753)

COLORED STONE; the international reporter of the gemstone trade. see JEWELRY, CLOCKS AND WATCHES

COMIMEX. see BUILDING AND CONSTRUCTION

622.33 AT ISSN 0726-6510
COMMONWEALTH SCIENTIFIC AND INDUSTRIAL RESEARCH ORGANIZATION. DIVISION OF GEOMECHANICS. GEOMECHANICS OF COAL MINING REPORT. 1978. irreg. Aus.$5 per no. C.S.I.R.O., Division of Geomechanics, Box 54, Mt. Waverley, Vic. 3149, Australia. **Indexed:** AESIS. **Document type:** academic/scholarly publication.
Description: Documentation of the research results in a range of aspects related to the coal mining industry.

624.176 AT ISSN 0069-7249
COMMONWEALTH SCIENTIFIC AND INDUSTRIAL RESEARCH ORGANIZATION. DIVISION OF GEOMECHANICS. TECHNICAL REPORT. 1963. irreg. Aus.$5 per no. C.S.I.R.O., Division of Geomechanics, Box 54, Mt. Waverley, Vic. 3149, Australia. **Indexed:** AESIS, Biol.Abstr.
Formerly: Commonwealth Scientific and Industrial Research Organization. Division of Soil Mechanics. Technical Report.
Description: Descriptions of equipment and procedures developed during, or used in, geotechnical investigations; full details of data obtained in these investigations.

622 614.7 US
COMPACT. 1983. q. Interstate Mining Compact Commission, 459 Carlisle Dr. Ste. B, Herndon, VA 22070. TEL 703-709-8654. FAX 703-709-8655. Ed. Gregory E. Conrad. circ. 700. **Document type:** government publication.
Description: Information service for member states on mining laws, regulations and other related areas.

622 CL ISSN 0716-5153
COMPENDIO DE LA MINERIA CHILENA. 1985. a. $50. Editec Ltda., Matilde Salamanca 736, Santiago 09, Chile. TEL 56-2-209-8100. FAX 56-2-209-8101. (Subscr. to: P.O. Box 3074, Correo Central, Santiago, Chile) Eds. Ricardo Cortes, Roly Sollis. adv.; B&W page $2700, color page $3400; trim 10 7/8 x 8 1/8. bk.rev.; index. circ. 10,000. (back issues avail.)

622 US ISSN 0010-6577
CONSOL NEWS.* 1962. bi-m. free. Consolidation Coal Co., 1800 Washington Rd., Pittsburgh, PA 15241. charts; illus.; index. circ. 22,500.
Description: Reports on coal mining and resources.

CONSTRUCTION EQUIPMENT BUYERS' GUIDE. see BUILDING AND CONSTRUCTION

CONTRIBUTIONS TO MINERALOGY AND PETROLOGY. see EARTH SCIENCES — Geology

CURTIN UNIVERSITY OF TECHNOLOGY. MULGA RESEARCH CENTRE JOURNAL. see BIOLOGY

DAKOTA COUNSEL. see ENERGY

DEVELOPMENTS IN PETROLEUM ENGINEERING. see PETROLEUM AND GAS

338.2 UK ISSN 0070-6175
DIRECTORY OF QUARRIES AND PITS. 1929. biennial. £35. Quarry Managers' Journal Ltd., 7 Regent St., Nottingham NG1 5BY, England. TEL 0602-411315. FAX 0602-484035. adv. circ. 2,000. **Document type:** directory.

622 GW ISSN 0012-5857
CODEN: DRAEAU
DRAEGERHEFT/DRAEGER REVIEW. (Editions in English and German) 1912. q. free. Draegerwerk AG, Moislinger Allee 53, 23542 Luebeck, Germany. TEL 0451-8822185. FAX 0451-8822133. Ed. Burkard Dillig. charts; illus.; cum.index. circ. 13,000. **Indexed:** C.I.S. Abstr., Chem.Abstr. **Document type:** consumer publication.
—CASDDS. **CCC.**

622 340 FR ISSN 1148-7941
DROIT DU SOUS SOL. 2/yr. 953 F. (foreign 1111 F.) (includes subscr. to: Realites Industrielles, Gerer et Comprenre) (effective 1995). (Annales des Mines) Editions E S K A, 27 rue Dunois, 75013 Paris, France. TEL 44-00-80-42. FAX 44-24-06-94. Ed. Francois Baratin. **Document type:** academic/scholarly publication.
—Ei; Faxon; SWETS.
Description: Reports on development in the law of subterranean resources.

DYNA. see ENGINEERING

622 US
E & M J INTERNATIONAL DIRECTORY OF MINING. (Engineering & Mining Journal) 1973. a. $130 in US & Canada; elsewhere $155. Intertec, Mining Information Services, 29 N. Wacker Dr., Chicago, IL 60606. TEL 312-726-2802. FAX 312-726-2574. adv. contact: Daria Shahriari. **Indexed:** Tr.& Indus.Ind. **Document type:** directory.
Formerly: E & M J International Directory of Mining and Mineral Processing Operations.
Description: Lists major metal, non-metal, and coal mines and processing plants, as well as company headquarters throughout the world. Includes addresses, phone and fax numbers, minerals produced and key personnel names.

EARTH AND MINERAL SCIENCES. see EARTH SCIENCES

EASTERN MINERAL LAW FOUNDATION. CASE UPDATE. see LAW

EASTERN MINERAL LAW FOUNDATION NEWSLETTER. see LAW

622 US ISSN 0733-6365
TN859.U52
EASTERN OIL SHALE SYMPOSIUM. PROCEEDINGS. 1981. a. University of Kentucky, Institute for Mining and Minerals Research, Iron Works Pike, Box 1315, Lexington, KY 40583. (Co-sponsors: U.S. Department of Energy; Kentucky Department of Energy, Institute of Gas Technology, Stone and Webster Engineering Corporation) **Indexed:** GeoRef.

ECUADOR. MINISTERIO DE ENERGIA Y MINAS. INFORME DE LABORES. see ENERGY

333.79 621.042 SW ISSN 0348-9493
ENERGIMAGASINET. 1979. 7/yr. SEK 255 (effective 1994). Teknikfoerlaget Facktidnings T F A B, P.O. Box 104, S-301 04 Halmstad, Sweden. TEL 46-35-10-41-50. FAX 46-35-18-65-09. Ed. Kurt-Viktor Bengtsson. adv.; B&W page SEK 8200, color page SEK 10900; trim 180 x 260; adv. contact: Stig Hoffert. circ. 3,000. cols./p.: 4. **Document type:** trade publication.
—BLDSC (3746.250000).

ENERGY REPORT; energy policy and technology news bulletin. see ENERGY

622.33 CN
ENGINEERING AND INSPECTION ANNUAL REPORT. a. Can.$15. Ministry of Energy, Mines and Petroleum Resources, Mineral Resources Division, 5th Fl., 1810 Blansherd St., Victoria, BC V8V 1X4, Canada. (Subscr. to: Crown Publications, 521 Fort St., Victoria, BC V8W 1E7, Canada. TEL 604-386-4636) (back issues avail.) **Document type:** government publication.
Formerly: Mining in British Columbia (ISSN 0823-1265); Which supersedes in part: Geology, Exploration and Mining in British Columbia (ISSN 0085-1027); Which was formerly: Lode Metals in British Columbia.

622 620 US ISSN 0095-8948
TA1 CODEN: ENMJAK
ENGINEERING & MINING JOURNAL. Short title: E & M J. 1866. m. $69. Intertec Publishing Corp., 29 N. Wacker Dr., Chicago, IL 60606. TEL 312-726-2802. FAX 312-726-4103. TELEX 270258 EXP. Ed. Robert J.M. Wyllie. adv.; bk.rev.; tr.lit.; index; circ. 22,892 (controlled). (also avail. in microform from UMI) **Indexed:** A.S.& T.Ind., Acid Rain Abstr., Acid Rain Ind., AESIS, Br.Geol.Lit., Bus.Ind., C.I.S. Abstr., CAD CAM Abstr., Cadscan, Chem.Abstr., Copper Abstr., Curr.Cont., Energy Info.Abstr., Eng.Ind., Environ.Abstr., Environ.Per.Bibl., Excerp.Med., Geo.Abstr., GeoRef., Geotech.Abstr., Intl.Civil Eng.Abstr., Lead Abstr., Met.Abstr., Ocean.Abstr., Petrol.Abstr., Pollut.Abstr., PROMT, Soft.Abstr.Eng., Soils & Fert., SRI, Tr.& Indus.Ind., World Alum.Abstr., Zincscan.
●Also available online. Vendor(s): Lexis-Nexis.
—BLDSC (3755.000000); CIS; Ei; Faxon; Genuine Article; SWETS; UMI; UnCover. **CCC.**
Incorporates (in 1991): International Mining.
Description: Covers exploration, development, milling, smelting, refining, and other extrative processing of metals and nonmetallics, including coal.

622 II
ENGINEERING & PRODUCT NEWS. m. (Mining Engineers' Association of India) I M E Publications, Plot No. 1457, Laxmisagarpatna, Bhubaneswar 751-006, India. TEL 0674-51224. adv.

ENVIRONMENTAL GEOCHEMISTRY AND HEALTH. see ENVIRONMENTAL STUDIES

EQUIPMENT ECHOES. see BUILDING AND CONSTRUCTION

EROSION CONTROL; the journal for erosion & sediment control professionals. see CONSERVATION

ERZMETALL; journal for exploration, mining and metallurgy. see METALLURGY

622.8 SP
ESPANA SEGURIDAD MINERA. Abbreviated title: E S M. 4/yr. Grupo Staff de Ediciones S.L., Viaducto Marquina 6 bajo, 33004 Oviedo (Asturias), Spain. TEL 8-523-58-54. FAX 8-257-38-32. Ed. M. Munarriz Cellini. circ. 200,000.

338.2 BO ISSN 0014-1194
ESTANO. 1961. bi-m. free. Corporacion Minera de Bolivia, Departamento de Relaciones Publicas e Informacion, Avda. Mariscal Santa Cruz 1092, Casilla 349, La Paz, Bolivia. Ed. Dir. Felix R. Nieto. adv.; illus.

622 BE
EUROPA STAR DIAMOND INTELLIGENCE BRIEFS. (Text in English) 1985. 20/yr. $350. Miller Freeman Inc., 123 A Chausee de Charleroi, Bte. 5, 1060 Brussels, Belgium. TEL 32-2-5386040. FAX 32-2-5390809. bk.rev. **Document type:** trade publication.

549 GW ISSN 0935-1221
QE351 CODEN: EJMIER
EUROPEAN JOURNAL OF MINERALOGY. (Supplement avail.: Berichte der Deutschen Mineralogischen Gesellschaft (ISSN-0935-123X)) (Text in English, French, German and Italian) 1911. 6/yr. $308 (effective 1996). (Deutsche Mineralogische Gesellschaft) E. Schweizerbart'sche Verlagsbuchhandlung, Johannesstr. 3A, 70176 Stuttgart, Germany. TEL 0711-625001. FAX 0711-625005. (Co-sponsors: Societa Italiana di Mineralogia e Petrologia; Societe Francaise de Mineralogie et de Cristallographie) Ed.Bd. adv.; bibl.; charts; illus. **Indexed:** Bull.Signal., Chem.Abstr., Excerp.Med., Geo.Abstr., Geol.Abstr., INIS Atomind., INSPEC (1989-). **Document type:** academic/scholarly publication.
—BLDSC (3829.731630); CASDDS; Genuine Article; SWETS; UnCover. **CCC.**
Formed by 1988 merger of: Fortschritte der Mineralogie (ISSN 0015-8186); Rendiconti della Societa Italiana di Mineralogie e Petrologia (ISSN 0037-8828) & Bulletin de Mineralogie (ISSN 0180-9210).
Description: Contains original papers, review articles and short notes dealing with mineralogical sciences: mineralogy, petrology, geochemistry, crystallography, ore deposits, and related fields, including applied mineralogy.
Refereed Serial

MINES AND MINING INDUSTRY

EXPLORATION & MINING GEOLOGY. see *EARTH SCIENCES — Geology*

EXPLORATION IN BRITISH COLUMBIA. see *EARTH SCIENCES — Geology*

622   CN
EXTRA. 1980. w. INCO Limited, Manitoba Division, Public Affairs Dept., Thompson, MB. R8N 1P3, Canada. TEL 204-778-2289. FAX 204-778-2975. Ed. Mark Tessier. circ. 2,500. **Document type:** newsletter.
    Description: Newsletter for employees.

622   UK
EXTRACTION BRIEFING. 1976. 10/yr. £145. The Publicity Works, 7 Vallet Ave., Alcester, Warks B49 6AU, England. TEL 01789-400222. FAX 01789-763629. Ed. Paul Erlanger. adv.: B&W page £420; trim 280 x 180. bk.rev. circ. 7,000. (also avail. in microform from UMI; reprint service avail. from UMI) **Indexed:** Fluidex. **Document type:** trade publication.
—UMI.
    Former titles (until 1991): New Quarrying and Mining (ISSN 0950-110X); (until 1986): Quarry and Mining News (ISSN 0309-5606)
    Description: News items and feature articles on technological developments in the industry, reviews of process and operational equipment, and analysis of industrial trends and the effects of legislation on the industry.

622.33   US   ISSN 0192-3862
TN805
FEDERAL COAL MANAGEMENT REPORT. 1977. a. U.S. Department of the Interior, Bureau of Land Management, Washington, DC 20240. TEL 202-208-5717. (Avail. from: Superintendent of Documents, U.S. Government Printing Office, Box 371954, Pittsburgh, PA 15250-7954. TEL 202-783-3238. FAX 202-512-2233) circ. 1,000. **Document type:** government publication.
    Description: Discusses the status of Federal Coal Program for preceding fiscal year.

622.8   US
FEDERAL MINE SAFETY AND HEALTH REVIEW COMMISSION DECISIONS. 1978. m. $91 (foreign $113.75) (effective 1995). U.S. Federal Mine Safety and Health Review Commission, 1730 K St. N.W., 6th Fl., Washington, DC 20006. TEL 202-653-5633. FAX 202-653-5030. (Subscr. to: Superintendent of Documents, U.S. Government Printing Office, Box 371954, Pittsburgh, PA 15250-7954. TEL 202-512-1800. FAX 202-512-2250) circ. 300. (back issues avail.) **Indexed:** MEDOC. **Document type:** government publication.

690   GW   ISSN 0174-6979
FELSBAU; Fachzeitschrift fuer Ingenieurgeologie, Geomechanik, Projektierung und Bauausfuehrung. 1983. 6/yr. DM.98. (Oesterreichische Gesellschaft fuer Geomechanik, AU) Verlag Glueckauf GmbH, Postfach 185620, 45206 Essen, Germany. TEL 02054-92412023. FAX 02054-924129. **Indexed:** Geol.Abstr. **Document type:** trade publication.

549   FJ   ISSN 0252-2462
J961
FIJI. MINERAL RESOURCES DEPARTMENT. ANNUAL REPORT. (Text in English) 1953. a. price varies. Mineral Resources Department, P.M. Bag, Suva, Fiji. Ed. Peter Rodda. circ. 500. **Document type:** government publication.
    Former titles: Fiji. Mineral Resources Division. Annual Report; (until 1978): Fiji. Department of Lands and Mineral Resources. Annual Report (ISSN 0252-2470); (until 1972): Fiji. Geological Survey. Annual Report (ISSN 0252-2489)
    Description: Summary of the year's activities, statistics of mining and exploration.

549   FJ   ISSN 0379-296X
FIJI. MINERAL RESOURCES DEPARTMENT. ECONOMIC INVESTIGATION. (Text in English) 1962. irreg. price varies. Mineral Resources Department, P.M. Bag, Suva, Fiji. Ed. Peter Rodda. circ. 300. **Indexed:** GeoRef. **Document type:** monographic series.
    Supersedes (in 1972): Fiji. Geological Survey. Economic Investigation (ISSN 0428-3279)
    Description: Results of mineral explorations.

622   UK   ISSN 0141-3244
TN13
FINANCIAL TIMES INTERNATIONAL YEAR BOOKS: MINING. 1887. a. £150. Longman Group UK Ltd., Westgate House, 6th Fl., The High, Harlow, Essex CM20 1YR, England. TEL 0279-442601. FAX 0279-444501. (Dist. in U.S. and Canada by: St. James Press, 425 N. Michigan Ave., Chicago, IL 60611) adv.: B&W page £730, color page £1155; 202 x 154. **Document type:** trade publication.
—CCC.
    Formerly: Mining Year Book.

622   RU   ISSN 0015-3273
TN4   CODEN: FTRIAR
FIZIKO-TEKHNICHESKIE PROBLEMY RAZRABOTKI POLEZNYKH ISKOPAEMYKH. English translation: Journal of Mining Science (US ISSN 1062-7391) 1965. bi-m. $143 (effective 1996). Rossiiskaya Akademiya Nauk, Sibirskoe Otdelenie, Morskoi pr. 2, 630090 Novosibirsk, Russia. FAX 3832-35-60-02. Ed. M.V. Kurlenya. index. circ. 450. (tabloid format) **Indexed:** Chem.Abstr., Geotech.Abstr., INIS Atomind., Met.Abstr., World Alum.Abstr. **Document type:** academic/scholarly publication.
—BLDSC (0389.990000); CASDDS. **CCC.**

549 560   HU
FRAGMENTA MINERALOGICA ET PALEONTOLOGICA. (Text in English, German) 1970. a. $25 (effective 1995). Magyar Termeszettudomanyi Muzeum - Hungarian Natural History Museum, Baross u. 13, 1088 Budapest, Hungary. TEL 36-1-1130035. FAX 36-1-1138820. Ed. A. Voros. charts; illus.; circ. 200 (paid). (back issues avail.) **Document type:** academic/scholarly publication.
    Description: Contains papers written by museum staff members or based on material deposited there.

FRANCE. ADMINISTRATION DES DIRECTIONS REGIONALES DE L'INDUSTRIE, DE LA RECHERCHE ET DE L'ENVIRONNEMENT. ANNUAIRE. see *ENERGY*

FRANCE. BUREAU DE RECHERCHES GEOLOGIQUES ET MINIERES. MANUELS ET METHODES. see *EARTH SCIENCES — Geology*

622   GW
FUER UNSERE MITARBEITER. 1974. s-a. free. Gewerkschaft Walter, P.O. Box 101313, Stauderstr. 213, 45327 Essen-Katernberg, Germany. Ed. Degenhard Merkle. bk.rev. circ. 3,000. (back issues avail.)
    Description: News and information on the mining company, featuring new techniques in shaft building, new projects, and more.

622   GW   ISSN 0178-501X
FUEHRUNGSKRAFT. Cover title: V D F Fuehrungskraft. 6/yr. DM.60. (Verband der Fuehrungskraefte in Bergbau und Energiewirtschaft) B E W Verwaltungsgesellschaft mbH, Alfredstr. 77-79, 45130 Essen, Germany. TEL 0201-772011. circ. 8,500. **Document type:** trade publication.

FUNDACION BARILOCHE. INSTITUTO DE ECONOMIA DE LA ENERGIA. PUBLICACIONES. see *ENERGY*

GAS SUPPLY AND DEMAND STUDY. see *PETROLEUM AND GAS*

338.7   ZR
GECAMINES ANNUAL REPORT/GECAMINES RAPPORT ANNUEL. (Editions in English and French) a. Generale des Carrieres et des Mines, Division des Relations Publiques, B.P. 8714, Kinshasa, Zaire. charts; stat.

622   ZR
GENERALE DES CARRIERES ET DES MINES. MONOGRAPHIE. irreg. (approx. 4/yr.). Generale des Carrieres et des Mines, Division des Relations Publiques, B.P. 450, Lubumbashi, Zaire. **Document type:** government publication.
    Formerly: Generale des Carrieres et Mines du Zaire. Monographie.

GEOLOGICA CARPATHICA; international geological journal. see *EARTH SCIENCES — Geology*

GEOLOGICA CARPATHICA - CLAYS; international clay journal. see *EARTH SCIENCES — Geology*

GEOLOGICAL, MINING AND METALLURGICAL SOCIETY OF INDIA. BULLETIN. see *EARTH SCIENCES — Geology*

GEOLOGIE EN MIJNBOUW/GEOLOGY AND MINING; an international journal. see *EARTH SCIENCES — Geology*

GEOLOGISCHES JAHRBUCH. REIHE D: MINERALOGIE. PETROGRAPHIE, GEOCHEMIE, LAGERSTAETTENKUNDE. see *EARTH SCIENCES — Geology*

GEOLOGISCHES LANDESAMT BADEN-WUERTTEMBERG. ABHANDLUNGEN. see *EARTH SCIENCES*

GEOLOGISCHES LANDESAMT BADEN-WUERTTEMBERG. JAHRESHEFTE. see *EARTH SCIENCES*

553   RU   ISSN 0016-7770
                            CODEN: GRMAA9
GEOLOGIYA RUDNYKH MESTOROZHDENII. English edition: Geology of Ore Deposits (ISSN 1075-7015) (Text in Russian; summaries in English) 1959. bi-m. $144 (effective 1996). (Rossiiskaya Akademiya Nauk) Interperiodica, Ul. Profsoyuznaya 90, Moscow Moscow, Russia. TEL 7-095-3360066. FAX 7-095-3360666. Ed. V.J. Smirnov. adv.; bk.rev.; bibl.; charts; illus.; index. circ. 2,750. (tabloid format) **Indexed:** Chem.Abstr., Eng.Ind., Geo.Abstr., INIS Atomind., Ref.Zh. **Document type:** academic/scholarly publication.
—CASDDS. **CCC.**

553   RU   ISSN 1075-7015
QE390   CODEN: GODEER
GEOLOGY OF ORE DEPOSITS. Russian translation: Geologiya Rudnykh Mestoroshdenii (ISSN 0016-7770) 1993. 6/yr. $635 in U.S. & Canada (elsewhere $693) (effective 1995). (Russian Academy of Sciences) Interperiodica, Ul. Profsoyuznaya 90, Moscow 117864, Russia. TEL 7-095-3360066. FAX 7-095-3660666. (Subscr. to: Interperiodica, Box 1831, Birmingham, AL 35201-1831. TEL 205-995-1567. FAX 205-995-1588) **Document type:** academic/scholarly publication.
—BLDSC (0411.797000).

622 551   MX   ISSN 0185-1314
TN4   CODEN: GEOMDZ
GEOMIMET. 1973. bi-m. $25 to non-members. Asociacion de Ingenieros de Minas, Metalurgistas y Geologos de Mexico, A.C., Departamento de Circulacion, Paseo de la Reforma 51, Piso 18-801, Col. Revolucion, Delegacion Cuauhtemoc, 06030 Mexico, D.F., Mexico. Ed. Raul Morales Garcia. adv.; bk.rev.; charts; illus.; stat. circ. 10,000. (reprint service avail. from UMI, ISI) **Indexed:** Chem.Abstr., INIS Atomind.
—BLDSC (4147.592000); CASDDS.
    Description: Covers the energy resources sector of Mexico.

GEOMINAS. see *EARTH SCIENCES*

GEOPHYSICAL DIRECTORY. see *EARTH SCIENCES — Geophysics*

338.2   US
GEORGIA GEOLOGIC SURVEY. CIRCULAR 2. MINING DIRECTORY OF GEORGIA. (Subseries of its Circular series) 18th ed., 1981. irreg., latest 1990 ed. free. Department of Natural Resources, Georgia Geologic Survey, 19 Martin Luther King Jr. Dr., S.W., Rm. 400, Atlanta, GA 30334. TEL 404-656-3214. Ed. P. Allgood.
    Description: Listing by commodity and cross-referenced by county of all materials mined in Georgia with mine locations.

622   US
GEORGIA GEOLOGIC SURVEY. CIRCULAR 3. THE MINERAL INDUSTRY OF GEORGIA. (Subseries of its Circular series) 1977. irreg., latest 1989 ed. free. Department of Natural Resources, Georgia Geologic Survey, 19 Martin Luther King Jr. Dr., S.W., Rm. 400, Atlanta, GA 30334. TEL 404-656-3214.
    Description: Information on commodities mined.

338.2   US   ISSN 0433-5473
TN24.G4
GEORGIA GEOLOGICAL SURVEY. INFORMATION CIRCULAR. 1933. irreg., no.90, 1992. price varies. Department of Natural Resources, Georgia Geologic Survey, 19 Martin Luther King Jr. Dr., S.W., Rm. 400, Atlanta, GA 30334. TEL 404-656-3214. Ed. P. Allgood.
    Description: Hydrologic or geologic reports discussing regional hydrology or mineral resources.

MINES AND MINING INDUSTRY 4757

622   UK   ISSN 0960-3182
TN1.A1   CODEN: GGENE3
GEOTECHNICAL AND GEOLOGICAL ENGINEERING.
1983-1990; resumed 1991. q. £160 to institutions in E.C. nations (N. America $280; elsewhere £175) (effective 1995). Chapman & Hall, Journals Department (Subsidiary of: International Thomson Publishing Services), 2-6 Boundary Row, London SE1 8HN, England. TEL 0171-865-0066. FAX 0171-522-9623. TELEX 290164 CHAPMA G. E-mail: journal@chall.mhs.compuserve.com. (Dist. by: International Thomson Publishing Services Ltd., Cheriton House, North Way, Andover, Hants. SP10 5EB, England. TEL 01264-342713. FAX 01264-342807; N. American subcr. to: Chapman & Hall, Journals Promotion Department, One Penn Plaza, 41st Fl., New York, NY 10019. TEL 212-564-1060. FAX 212-564-1505) Eds. D.G. Toll, J.M. Kemeny. adv.; index. (reprint service avail. from UMI) **Indexed:** Geo.Abstr., Geol.Abstr. **Document type:** academic/scholarly publication.
—BLDSC (4158.921500); Faxon; SWETS; UMI; UnCover. **CCC.**
    Formerly: International Journal of Mining and Geological Engineering (ISSN 0269-0136)
    Description: Publishes papers relating to the planning, construction and operation of mines, both surface and underground.
    Refereed Serial

622 658   FR   ISSN 0295-4397
TN2
GERER ET COMPRENDRE/TO MANAGE AND TO UNDERSTAND. (Text in French; summaries in English, German, Russian, Spanish) q. 382 F. (foreign 450 F.) (effective 1995). (Annales des Mines) Editions E S K A, 22 rue Monge, 75005 Paris, France. TEL 43-06-80-42. FAX 44-24-06-94. Ed. Francois Baratin; Pub. Serge Kebabtchieff. adv. **Document type:** trade publication.
—Ei; Faxon; SWETS. **CCC.**
    Formerly: Annales des Mines. Gerer et Comprendre; Supersedes in part: Annales des Mines (ISSN 0003-4282)
    Description: Discusses the mangement, administration, and organization of companies. Publishes studies and testimony of instructors and executives.

622   GW   ISSN 0340-7896
TN3   CODEN: GLUEAJ
GLUECKAUF; Fachzeitschrift fuer Rohstoff, Bergbau und Energie. (Text in German; editions in Chinese, Russian also avail.) 1865. 10/yr. DM.358 (foreign DM.482). Verlag Glueckauf GmbH, Postfach 185620, 45206 Essen, Germany. TEL 02054-92412023. FAX 02054-924129. Ed. Bernd Litke. adv.; B&W page DM.3330; trim 210 x 297. bk.rev.; bibl.; illus.; pat.; stat. circ. 6,500. **Indexed:** C.I.S. Abstr., Chem.Abstr., Dok.Arbeitsmed., ELLIS, Eng.Ind., Excerp.Med., Fuel & Energy Abstr., INIS Atomind. **Document type:** trade publication.
—CASDDS; Ei; Faxon; SWETS. **CCC.**
    Description: Covers technical, economic and safety aspects of underground and open-pit mining, including transportation and processing related topics.

622   GW   ISSN 0017-1387
TN3   CODEN: GKFRAA
GLUECKAUF-FORSCHUNGSHEFTE; Zeitschrift zur Verbreitung von Forschungsergebnisse im Bergbau. 1940. 4/yr. DM.490 (foreign DM.595). Verlag Glueckauf GmbH, Postfach 185620, 45206 Essen, Germany. TEL 02054-92412023. FAX 02054-924129. bk.rev.; bibl.; charts; illus.; pat.; stat.; index. circ. 1,000. (tabloid format) **Indexed:** C.I.S. Abstr., Eng.Ind., Excerp.Med., Fuel & Energy Abstr., INIS Atomind. **Document type:** academic/scholarly publication.
—BLDSC (4196.007000); CASDDS; Ei; Faxon; SWETS. **CCC.**

622   GW   ISSN 0176-4101
GLUECKAUF MINING REPORTER. (Text in English) 1959. irreg. free. Verlag Glueckauf GmbH, Postfach 185620, 45206 Essen, Germany. TEL 02054-92412023. FAX 02054-924129. **Document type:** bulletin.
    Former titles (until 1983): Mining Reporter (ISSN 0343-0073); Bergbau-Reporter (ISSN 0172-1585); (until 1971): Progress in Mining (ISSN 0079-6476)

622 338.2741   US   ISSN 1353-0178
GOLD (YEAR). 1990. a. $95. Gold Institute, Administrative Office - Institut de l'Or, Bureau Administratif, 1112 16th St., N.W., Ste. 240, Washington, DC 20036-4823. TEL 202-835-0185. FAX 202-835-0155. (Co-sponsor: Gold Field Mineral Services Ltd.) charts.
    Description: Presents current picture of each aspect of the gold supply and demand equation in global terms.

622   AT   ISSN 0816-455X
GOLD GAZETTE. 1985. fortn. Aus.$155 (effective 1995). Resource Information Unit Ltd., 79 Hay St., Subiaco, W.A. 6008, Australia. TEL 61-9-382-3955. FAX 61-9-388-1025. Ed. Andrea Maxey. adv.: B&W page Aus.$1010, color page Aus.$1885; trim 262 x 187; adv. contact: Anna Barrett. charts; illus.; stat.; tr.lit.; index. circ. 3,500.
    Description: Contains hard news stories related to the Australian gold industry, stock market news, latest in equipment and technology and some international coverage.

622 610   US
GOLD INSTITUTE. INTERNATIONAL CONFERENCE ON GOLD & SILVER IN MEDICINE. PROCEEDINGS. irreg., latest 1994. $75 (foreign $85). Gold Institute, Administrative Office - Institut de l'Or, Bureau Administratif, 1112 16th St., N.W., Ste. 240, Washington, DC 20036-4823. TEL 202-835-0185. FAX 202-835-0155. (Co-sponsor: Silver Institute) **Document type:** proceedings.
    Description: Reports on new clinical research on gold in England, Canada, the Netherlands and the United States.

338.2 669   US   ISSN 1058-6164
HG289
GOLD NEWS/NOUVELLES DE L'OR. 1976. bi-m. $25 (foreign $30). Gold Institute, Administrative Office - Institut de l'Or, Bureau Administratif, 1112 16th St., N.W., Ste. 240, Washington, DC 20036-4823. TEL 202-835-0185. FAX 202-835-0155. Ed. John H. Lutley. circ. 2,000. (back issues avail.)

622   US   ISSN 0745-6344
GOLD PROSPECTOR. 1968. bi-m. $2.50 per no. Gold Prospectors Association of America, Inc., Box 3040, Fallbrook, CA 92088-3040. TEL 619-728-6620. FAX 619-728-4815. Ed. Perry Massie. circ. 75,000. **Document type:** trade publication.
—UnCover.

622   RU   ISSN 0017-2278
TN4   CODEN: GOZHA6
GORNYI ZHURNAL. 1825. m. $165 (effective 1996). (Gosudarstvennyi Komitet po Chernoi i Tsvetnoi Metallurgii) Izdatel'stvo Nedra, Pl. Belorusskogo Vokzala, 3, 125047 Moscow, Russia. TEL 250-52-55. Ed. A.V. Baronenkov. adv.; bk.rev.; charts; illus.; index. circ. 11,500. **Indexed:** C.I.S. Abstr., Chem.Abstr., Eng.Ind., Fuel & Energy Abstr., INIS Atomind.
—CASDDS. **CCC.**

622   US
GOWER FEDERAL SERVICE - MINING. 1962. irreg. (approx 14/yr.). $315 (effective 1992). Rocky Mountain Mineral Law Foundation, Porter Administration Bldg., 7039 E. 18th Ave., Denver, CO 80220. TEL 303-321-8100. FAX 303-321-7657. circ. 125. (looseleaf format; back issues avail.)
● Also available online. Vendor(s): West Services, Inc. (Gower Federal Service).
    Description: Publishes decisions of the Department of the Interior, Interior Board of Land Appeals, and reports natural resource information from the Federal Register pertaining to mining issues.

622   US
GOWER FEDERAL SERVICE - MISCELLANEOUS LAND DECISIONS. 1972. irreg. (approx 8/yr.). $165 (effective 1992). Rocky Mountain Mineral Law Foundation, Porter Administration Bldg., 7039 E. 18th Ave., Denver, CO 80220. TEL 303-321-8100. FAX 303-321-7657. circ. 100. (looseleaf format; back issues avail.)
● Also available online. Vendor(s): West Services, Inc. (Gower Federal Service).
    Description: Publishes decisions of the Department of the Interior, Interior Board of Land Appeals, pertaining to public land use issues.

GOWER FEDERAL SERVICE - ROYALTY VALUATION AND MANAGEMENT. see *PETROLEUM AND GAS*

GREAT BRITAIN. NATURAL ENVIRONMENT RESEARCH COUNCIL. BRITISH GEOLOGICAL SURVEY. OVERSEAS GEOLOGY AND MINERAL RESOURCES. see *EARTH SCIENCES — Geology*

622   SW   ISSN 0432-7632
GRUVARBETAREN. 1904. m. SEK 125. Svenska Gruvindustriarbetarefoerbundet, P.O. Box 83, 772 22 Graengesberg 1, Sweden. FAX 240-20728. TELEX 12742 FOTEX S. adv. circ. 9,000.
    Former titles (until 1957): Gruvindustriarbetaren; (until 1926): Gruvarbetaren.

553   UK   ISSN 0072-8713
GUIDE TO THE COALFIELDS. 1948. a. (issued Jun.). £107.40($171.85) Argus Business Media Ltd., Fuel and Metals Journals (Subsidiary of: Argus Press Group), Queensway House, 2 Queensway, Redhill, Surrey RH1 1QS, England. TEL 01737-768611. FAX 01737-761685. TELEX 948669 TOPJNL G. **Document type:** directory.
—BLDSC (4226.000000).

HARRIS MISSOURI DIRECTORY OF MANUFACTURERS. see *BUSINESS AND ECONOMICS — Trade And Industrial Directories*

HEALTH & SAFETY RESOURCE. see *OCCUPATIONAL HEALTH AND SAFETY*

HERCYNICA. see *EARTH SCIENCES — Geology*

HIROSHIMA UNIVERSITY. JOURNAL OF SCIENCE. SERIES C. EARTH AND PLANETARY SCIENCES. see *EARTH SCIENCES — Geology*

HOKKAIDO UNIVERSITY. FACULTY OF SCIENCE. JOURNAL SERIES 4: GEOLOGY AND MINERALOGY. see *EARTH SCIENCES — Geology*

338   JA
HONPO KOGYO NO SUSEI/MINING YEARBOOK OF JAPAN.* (Text in Japanese; captions in English or Japanese) 1906. a. Ministry of International Trade and Industry, Research and Statistics Division - Tsusho Sangyo Chosakai, 1-3-1 Kasumigaseki, Chiyoda-ku, Tokyo 100, Japan. TEL 03-501-1511. stat.

622   JM   ISSN 0254-8631
I B A REVIEW. 1975. biennial. $50. International Bauxite Association, P.O. Box 551, Kingston 5, Jamaica, W.I. TEL 809-926-4535. FAX 809-929-4020. TELEX 2428 ITNLBA JA. Ed. Shirley Davis. circ. 300. (avail. in microfiche from CIS) **Indexed:** IIS, Met.Abstr., World Alum.Abstr.

622   GW
I D R. (Industrie Diamanten Rundschau) 1967. q. DM.36. L.N. Schaffrath, Graphischer Betrieb, Martin-Luther-Platz 27, 40212 Dusseldorf, Germany. Ed. Walter Weiland. adv.; bk.rev. circ. 3,000. (back issues avail.; reprint service avail.)

622   US   ISSN 1043-108X
TN343
I E E E MINING INDUSTRY TECHNICAL CONFERENCE. CONFERENCE RECORD. 1979. biennial. price varies. (I E E E, Industry Applications Society) Institute of Electrical and Electronics Engineers, Inc., 345 E. 47th St., New York, NY 10017-2394. TEL 212-705-7900. FAX 212-705-7682. (Subscr to: Box 1331, 445 Hoes Lane, Piscataway, NJ 08855-1331)
—BLDSC (5804.050000); UMI.
    Formerly (until 1985): Mining Industry Technical Conference. Conference Record (ISSN 0740-9869)

IDAHO. GEOLOGICAL SURVEY. BULLETIN. see *EARTH SCIENCES — Geology*

IDAHO. GEOLOGICAL SURVEY. INFORMATION CIRCULAR. see *EARTH SCIENCES — Geology*

338.2 553   US
TN24.I3   CODEN: ILMNAS
ILLINOIS MINERALS. 1954. irreg., no.110, 1992. price varies. State Geological Survey, Natural Resources Bldg., 615 E. Peabody Dr., Champaign, IL 61820. TEL 217-333-4747. abstr.; bibl.; charts; illus.; stat. **Indexed:** AESIS, Geo.Abstr., Geol.Abstr., GeoRef.
    Former titles: Illinois Minerals Notes (ISSN 0094-9442); Formed by the merger of: Illinois. State Geological Survey. Industrial Mineral Notes (ISSN 0073-4853); Illinois. State Geological Survey. Mineral Economic Briefs (ISSN 0073-5116)

MINES AND MINING INDUSTRY

622 US
ILLINOIS MINING INSTITUTE. PROCEEDINGS. 1928. a. $15 (free to members, mining schools and technical libraries). Illinois Mining Institute, 615 E. Peabody, Champaign, IL 61820. TEL 217-333-5115. Ed. H.H. Damberger. adv. circ. 1,400. **Document type:** proceedings.

INDIAN JOURNAL OF GEOLOGY. see *EARTH SCIENCES — Geology*

549 II ISSN 0019-5928
TN103 CODEN: INMLA2
INDIAN MINERALOGIST. (Text in English) 1960. s-a. Rs.75($12) Mineralogical Society of India, Manasa Gangothri, Mysore 670 006, India. Ed. A.S. Janardhan. adv.; bk.rev.; abstr.; charts; illus. circ. 500. **Indexed:** Chem.Abstr.
—CASDDS.

549 II ISSN 0019-5936
TN4 CODEN: INMIAR
INDIAN MINERALS. (Text in English) 1947. q. Rs.220($79.20) Government of India, Department of Publications, Civil Lines, New Delhi 110 054, India. TEL 11-2517409. adv.; bk.rev.; charts; illus. circ. 1,800. **Indexed:** C.R.I.Abstr., C.R.I.Curr.Cont., Chem.Abstr., Eng.Ind., Geo.Abstr., Geol.Abstr. **Document type:** government publication.
—CASDDS.

622 II ISSN 0445-7897
CODEN: IMYBAP
INDIAN MINERALS YEAR BOOK. (Text in English) 1959. a. $72. Indian Bureau of Mines, Controller General, Nagpur 440 001, India.

622 II ISSN 0019-5944
INDIAN MINING & ENGINEERING JOURNAL. (Text in English) 1962. m. Rs.120($40) (Mining Engineers' Association of India) I M E Publications, Plot No. 1457, Laxmisagarpatna, Bhubaneswar 751 006, India. TEL 0674-51224. Ed. J.F. De Souza. adv.: B&W page $300; trim 27 x 20. bk.rev.; charts; illus.; mkt.; stat.; tr.lit.; index. circ. 3,500. (also avail. in microform) **Indexed:** AESIS, Fuel & Energy Abstr. **Incorporates:** Mineral Markets.

INDIAN SCHOOL OF MINES. ANNUAL REPORT. see *EDUCATION*

INDRESCO INC. MARION DIVISION. NEWS AND REVIEW. see *MACHINERY*

622 SP ISSN 0210-2307
CODEN: INMIDU
INDUSTRIA MINERA. 1958. m. (10/yr.) 5500 ptas. Consejo Superior de Colegios de Ingenieros de Minas, Rios Rosas 19 Bis, 28003 Madrid, Spain. TEL 1-411-46-11. Ed. Fernando Evia Cangas. adv.; bk.rev.; abstr.; bibl.; charts; pat.; stat.; tr.lit.; index. circ. 3,000. **Indexed:** Chem.Abstr, Ind.SST.
—CCC.

622 669 553 IT ISSN 0391-1586
TN4 CODEN: INMRAK
INDUSTRIA MINERARIA; miniere e cave, metallurgia, geologia applicata, fonti di energia. 1927; N.S. 1950. bi-m. L.80000 (foreign L.90000) (effective 1995). (Associazione Mineraria Italiana) Servizio Italiano Pubblicazioni Internazionali s.r.l., Viale L. Pasteur, 6, 00144 Rome, Italy. TEL 39-6-5918586. FAX 39-6-5924819. Ed.Bd. adv.: B&W page L.650000. bk.rev.; charts; illus.; mkt.; stat.; index. circ. 3,000. **Indexed:** Cadscan, Chem.Abstr., INIS Atomind., Lead Abstr., Zincscan. **Document type:** trade publication.
—BLDSC (4441.500000); CASDDS.
Former titles (until 1956): Industria Mineraria d'Italia e d'Oltremare (ISSN 0367-892X); (until 1936): Industria Mineraria (ISSN 0019-7696)

622 UK ISSN 0957-0160
INDUSTRIAL CLAYS. 1989. irreg. £50.50. Industrial Minerals Information Ltd. (Subsidiary of: Metal Bulletin plc.), Park House, Park Terrace, Worcester Park, Surrey KT4 7HY, England. TEL 0171-827-9977. FAX 0181-337-8943. **Document type:** trade publication.

338.2 660 UK ISSN 0019-8544
TN1 CODEN: IMINBG
INDUSTRIAL MINERALS. 1967. m. $420. Metal Bulletin plc, Park House, Park Terrace, Worcester Park, Surrey KT4 7HY, England. TEL 0171-827-9977. FAX 0181-337-8943. (U.S. subscr. to: Metal Bulletin Inc., 220 Fifth Ave., New York, NY 10001-7781. TEL 212-213-6202. FAX 212-213-1870) Ed. Joyce Griffiths. adv.; bk.rev.; charts; illus.; stat.; index. circ. 3,600. **Indexed:** AESIS, Br.Ceram.Abstr., Br.Geol.Lit., Ceram.Abstr., Chem.Abstr., INIS Atomind., Key to Econ.Sci., Met.Abstr., PROMT, World Alum.Abstr., World Surf.Coat. **Document type:** trade publication.
—BLDSC (4458.150000); CASDDS; Ei; Faxon; SWETS; UnCover. CCC.
Description: Covers non-metallic mineral producers internationally.

338.2 660 US ISSN 0269-1701
INDUSTRIAL MINERALS DIRECTORY - WORLD GUIDE TO PRODUCERS AND PROCESSORS. 1977. irreg. $210. Metal Bulletin Inc., 220 Fifth Ave., New York, NY 10001-7781. TEL 212-213-6202. FAX 212-213-1870. Ed. Joyce Griffiths. adv. **Document type:** directory.
—BLDSC (4458.185000).
Formerly (until 1986): Industrial Minerals Directory (ISSN 0141-5263); Incorporates (1979): Industrial Minerals Merchants, Agents and Processors (ISSN 0143-263X)
Description: Directory of international non-metallic mineral producers; includes a buyers guide.

622 UK ISSN 0957-4433
INDUSTRIAL MINERALS: GEOLOGY AND WORLD DEPOSITS. 1984. irreg., vol.2, 1990. £55. Industrial Minerals Information Ltd. (Subsidiary of: Metal Bulletin plc.), Park House, Park Terrace, Worcester Park, Surrey KT4 7HY, England. TEL 0171-827-9977. FAX 0181-337-8943. **Document type:** trade publication.

622 CN ISSN 0835-5134
INDUSTRIAL SPECIALTIES NEWS. 1987. s-m. $557. Blendon Information Services, 126 Willowdale Ave., Ste. 1, Willowdale, ON M2N 2Y2, Canada. TEL 416-223-5397. FAX 416-223-8532. Ed. Robert V. Orchard. index. (looseleaf format; back issues avail.) **Document type:** newsletter.
●Also available online. Vendor(s): Data-Star, Knight-Ridder, Inc., Dow Jones News Retrieval.
Description: Contains business news for senior executives in the industrial minerals sector.

622 GW ISSN 0341-3489
INDUSTRIE DER STEINE UND ERDEN. 6/yr. DM.124 (foreign DM.146). (Steinbruch Berufsgenossenschaft) Schlueterische Verlagsanstalt GmbH und Co., Hans-Boeckler-Allee 7, 30173 Hannover, Germany. TEL 0511-8550-0. FAX 0511-8550-100. (Subscr. to: Postfach 5440, 30054 Hannover, Germany) circ. 10,095. **Document type:** trade publication.
—CCC.

549 FR ISSN 0999-5714
CODEN: INMTDT
INDUSTRIE MINERALE MINES ET CARRIERES. TECHNIQUES. (Supplement to: Mines et Carrieres (ISSN 0994-2556)) (Text in French; summaries in English, French) 1972. 5/yr. 1633.60 F. per no. Societe de l'Industrie Minerale Mines et Carriers, 41 rue de la Grange aux Belles, 75010 Paris, France. TEL 42-02-07-92. FAX 42-06-69-30. Ed. Eric Massy-Delhotel. adv. contact: Daniel Gilbert. bibl.; charts; illus. **Indexed:** C.I.S. Abstr., Cadscan, Chem.Abstr., INIS Atomind., Lead Abstr., Met.Abstr., World Alum.Abstr., Zincscan. **Document type:** trade publication.
—BLDSC (4470.340500); CASDDS; SWETS. CCC.
Former titles (until 1988): Industrie Minerale, Mines et Carrieres. Techniques (ISSN 0766-1207); (until 1984): Industrie Minerale. Minéralurgie (ISSN 0240-9542); Which was formed by the 1980 merger of: Industrie Minerale. Mine (ISSN 0367-8989); Industrie Minerale. Minéralurgie (ISSN 0367-8962).

622 BL ISSN 0101-5931
HD9554.B8
INFORMATIVO ANUAL DA INDUSTRIA CARBONIFERA. 1979. a. 2 BTN($2) Departamento Nacional do Producao Mineral, Setor Autarquias Norte, Quadra 1, Bloco B, 70040 Brasilia D.F., Brazil. TEL 061-224-2670.

622 IT ISSN 0020-0700
INFORMATORE DEL MARMISTA. 1962. m. L.150000 (foreign L.180000). Giorgio Zusi Editore, Adriano Garbini 15, 37135 Verona, Italy. TEL 39-45-820-0808. FAX 39-45-8200820. Ed. Giorgio Zusi. adv.; bk.rev.; stat. circ. 4,500.
Description: Covers techniques in the manufacturing of marble, precious stones and granite. Includes articles on various equipment and machinery used in this field.

622 CL ISSN 0717-0572
INGENIERO ANDINO. (English edition avail. bi-w.) 1991. w. $350. G & T International, Perez Valenzuela 1098, Oficina 98 - Providencia, Santiago 09, Chile. TEL 56-2-235-8100. FAX 56-2-235-8068. (Subscr. to: P.O. Box 3074, Correo Central, Santiago, Chile) Eds. Ricardo Cortes, Raul Ferro. bk.rev.; index. (back issues avail.) **Document type:** newsletter.
Description: Reports on mining and energy activities in Chile, Peru and Bolivia.

INJURY EXPERIENCE IN SAND AND GRAVEL MINING. see *OCCUPATIONAL HEALTH AND SAFETY — Abstracting, Bibliographies, Statistics*

622 US ISSN 0145-8701
CODEN: PIBABP
INSTITUTE FOR BRIQUETTING AND AGGLOMERATION. PROCEEDINGS. 1947. s-a. $50. Institute for Briquetting and Agglomeration, 179 Riverview Acres Rd., Hudson, WI 54016. TEL 715-549-6342. TELEX 715-549-5678. adv.; index. **Document type:** proceedings.
—BLDSC (2023.670000); CASDDS.

622 SA ISSN 0020-2983
CODEN: JMSVAW
INSTITUTE OF MINE SURVEYORS OF SOUTH AFRICA. JOURNAL/INSTITUUT VAN MYNOPMETERS VAN SUID-AFRIKA. JOERNAAL. 1923. q. R.32 (effective 1993). Institute of Mine Surveyors of South Africa, P.O. Box 27943, Yeoville 2143, South Africa. TEL 27-11-4873511. Ed. A.W. Harris. adv.; charts; illus.; index every vol. covering 8 issues. circ. 600. **Indexed:** Eng.Ind., Ind.S.A.Per.
—UnCover.

622 UK
INSTITUTE OF QUARRYING, NORTHERN IRELAND. YEAR BOOK. a. (Institute of Quarrying, Northern Ireland) Main Stream Publications, 139 Thomas St., Portadown, Co. Armagh BT62 3BE, N. Ireland. TEL 01762-334272. FAX 01762-351046. **Document type:** corporate report.

622 669 II ISSN 0257-442X
TN1 CODEN: JIEDEK
INSTITUTION OF ENGINEERS (INDIA). MINING ENGINEERING DIVISION. JOURNAL. (Text in English) 1920. s-a. Rs.40($5) Institution of Engineers (India), Mining Engineering Division, 8 Gokhale Rd., Calcutta 700 020, India. TEL 033-288334. FAX 033-288345. TELEX 0217885 IEIC IN. Ed. S.P. Misra. adv.; charts; illus.; index. circ. 3,000. **Indexed:** Chem.Abstr., Eng.Ind., Fluidex, INIS Atomind., INSPEC, Met.Abstr. **Document type:** academic/scholarly publication.
—BLDSC (4794.050000); CASDDS; Ei.
Formerly (until 1984): Institution of Engineers (India). Mining and Metallurgy Division. Journal (ISSN 0020-3394)

622 669 UK ISSN 0371-7844
TN1 CODEN: TIMNAQ
INSTITUTION OF MINING AND METALLURGY. TRANSACTIONS. SECTION A: MINING INDUSTRY. 1892. 3/yr. £65 all three sections £162; all three sections, with Minerals Industry International £210 (effective 1996). Institution of Mining and Metallurgy, 44 Portland Pl., London W1N 4BR, England. TEL 0171-580-3802.
FAX 0171-436-5388. Ed. M.J. Jones. adv.; bibl.; charts; illus. circ. 3,000. **Indexed:** AESIS, Br.Geol.Lit., Br.Tech.Ind., Cadscan, Chem.Abstr., Copper Abstr., Energy.Info.Abstr., Eng.Ind., Environ.Abstr., Ergon.Abstr., Geo.Abstr., Geol.Abstr., IDA, Lead Abstr., Met.Abstr., World Alum.Abstr., Zincscan. **Document type:** academic/scholarly publication.
—Faxon; Genuine Article; SWETS; UMI; UnCover. CCC.
Formerly: Institution of Mining and Metallurgy. Bulletin and Transactions. Section A: Mining Industry.

622 669 550 UK ISSN 0371-7453
TN260 CODEN: TIAEA7
INSTITUTION OF MINING AND METALLURGY. TRANSACTIONS. SECTION B: APPLIED EARTH SCIENCE. 1892. 3/yr. £65 (all sections £162) (effective 1996). Institution of Mining and Metallurgy, 44 Portland Pl., London W1N 4BR, England. TEL 0171-580-3802.
FAX 0171-436-5388. Ed. M.J. Jones. adv.; bibl.; charts; illus.; index. circ. 2,160. **Indexed:** AESIS, Br.Geol.Lit., Br.Tech.Ind., Cadscan, Chem.Abstr., Energy Info.Abstr., Eng.Ind., Environ.Abstr., Ergon.Abstr., Geo.Abstr., Geol.Abstr., Lead Abstr., Met.Abstr., Petrol.Abstr., World Alum.Abstr., Zincscan. **Document type:** academic/scholarly publication.
—CASDDS; Genuine Article; SWETS; UMI; UnCover. CCC.
Formerly: Institution of Mining and Metallurgy. Bulletin and Transactions. Section B: Applied Earth Science.

622 669 UK ISSN 0371-9553
TN496 CODEN: TMEMAB
INSTITUTION OF MINING AND METALLURGY. TRANSACTIONS. SECTION C: MINERAL PROCESSING & EXTRACTIVE METALLURGY. 1892. 3/yr. £54($126) all three sections $316; all three sections plus Minerals Industry International $410. Institution of Mining and Metallurgy, 44 Portland Pl., London W1N 4BR, England. TEL 071-580 3802.
FAX 071-436-5388. Ed. M.J. Jones. adv.; bibl.; charts; illus.; index. circ. 2,400. **Indexed:** AESIS, Br.Geol.Lit., Br.Tech.Ind., Cadscan, Chem.Abstr., Chem.Eng.Abstr., Energy Info.Abstr., Eng.Ind., Environ.Abstr., Ergon.Abstr., Lead Abstr., Met.Abstr., T.C.E.A., World Alum.Abstr., Zincscan. **Document type:** trade publication.
—CASDDS; Genuine Article; SWETS; UMI; UnCover. CCC.
Formerly: Institution of Mining and Metallurgy. Bulletin and Transactions. Section C: Mineral Processing and Extractive Metallurgy.

622 US
INTERNATIONAL CALIFORNIA MINING JOURNAL. 1931. m. $21.95 (effective 1995). California Mining Journal, Inc., Box 2260, Aptos, CA 95001. TEL 408-662-2899. FAX 408-662-3014. Ed. Kenneth L. Harn. adv. contact: Diane Craig. bk.rev.; charts; mkt.; stat.; circ. 12,000 (paid). **Indexed:** Cal.Per.Ind. (1978-), GeoRef. **Document type:** trade publication.
—UnCover.
Formerly: California Mining Journal (ISSN 0008-1299)
Description: International mining publication for miners, prospectors, financiers, and others who deal with the entire mining industry. Contains articles on mining processes, mining law, and current events.

622 382 US ISSN 0146-3845
HD9540.1
INTERNATIONAL COAL. a. $150 (non-profit institutions $95). National Coal Association, 1130 17th St., N.W., Washington, DC 20036. TEL 202-463-2640. **Indexed:** SRI.
Formerly: World Coal Trade (ISSN 0084-148X)

622 UK ISSN 0260-4299
INTERNATIONAL COAL REPORT. (Subseries avail.: Coal Statistics Monthly (ISSN 0268-0343)) 1980. fortn. (25/yr.). £630($975) (foreign £650). Financial Times Energy Publishing (Subsidiary of: Pearson Professional Ltd.), Maple House, 149 Tottenham Court Rd., London W1P 9LL, England. TEL 0171-896-2241. FAX 0171-896-2275. Ed. Gerard McCloskey; Pub. David Hurst. bk.rev.; charts; stat. (also avail. in microform from UMI; weekly fax service avail.; back issues avail.) **Indexed:** Fluidex (1973-), Fluidex, PROMT. **Document type:** newsletter.
●Also available online. Vendor(s): Data-Star, Knight-Ridder, Inc., Lexis-Nexis.
—BLDSC (4538.690000); UMI.
Description: Provides news and analysis for the international coal trade, concentrating on price coverage for spot and contract business.

622 338.2 US
INTERNATIONAL COAL REVIEW. m. $100. National Coal Association, 1130 17th St., N.W., Washington, DC 20036. TEL 202-463-2640. **Indexed:** SRI.

INTERNATIONAL DREDGING REVIEW. see ENGINEERING — Hydraulic Engineering

INTERNATIONAL EROSION CONTROL ASSOCIATION. CONFERENCE PROCEEDINGS. see CONSERVATION

INTERNATIONAL EROSION CONTROL ASSOCIATION. PRODUCTS & SERVICES DIRECTORY. see BUSINESS AND ECONOMICS — Trade And Industrial Directories

622 UK ISSN 0952-8628
INTERNATIONAL GOLD MINING NEWSLETTER. 1974. m. £210($375) combined subscr. with International Quarterly. Mining Journal Ltd., 60 Worship St., London EC2A 2HD, England. TEL 0171-216-6060. FAX 0171-216-6050. Ed. Richard Morgan. circ. 650. (reprint service avail. from UMI) **Document type:** newsletter.
—CCC.

INTERNATIONAL JOURNAL OF COAL GEOLOGY. see EARTH SCIENCES — Geology

622 669 NE ISSN 0301-7516
TN500 CODEN: IJMPBL
INTERNATIONAL JOURNAL OF MINERAL PROCESSING. 1974. m. fl.1440($878) (effective 1996). Elsevier Science B.V., P.O. Box 211, 1000 AE Amsterdam, Netherlands. TEL 31-20-4853911.
FAX 31-20-4853598. TELEX 18582 ESPA NL. E-mail: nlinfo-f@elsevier.nl; usinfo-f@elsevier.com; forinfo-kyf04035@niftyserve.or.jp; Site addr.: http://www.elsevier.nl/. (Subscr. in U.S. and Canada to: Elsevier Science Inc., Box 882, Madison Sq. Sta., New York, NY 10159-0882. TEL 212-989-5800. FAX 212-633-3990) Ed.Bd. bk.rev.; bibl.; charts; illus. (also avail. in microform from UMI) **Indexed:** AESIS, Br.Ceram.Abstr., C.R.I.Abstr., Cadscan, Ceram.Abstr., Chem.Abstr., Curr.Cont., Environ.Abstr., Fluidex, Fuel & Energy Abstr., Geo.Abstr., Geol.Abstr., Ind.Sci.Rev., Lead Abstr., Met.Abstr., Sci.Cit.Ind., Soils & Fert., World Alum.Abstr., Zincscan. **Document type:** academic/scholarly publication.
—BLDSC (4542.362000); CASDDS; Ei; Faxon; Genuine Article; SWETS; UMI; UnCover. CCC.
Description: Covers all aspects of the processing of solid-mineral materials such as metallic and non-metallic ores, coals and other solid sources of secondary materials, etc.
Refereed Serial

INTERNATIONAL JOURNAL OF ROCK MECHANICS AND MINING SCIENCES & GEOMECHANICS ABSTRACTS. see MINES AND MINING INDUSTRY — Abstracting, Bibliographies, Statistics

622.31 NE
INTERNATIONAL JOURNAL OF SURFACE MINING, RECLAMATION AND ENVIRONMENT. Cover title: I J S M. (Text in English) 1987. q. fl.155($90) A.A. Balkema, P.O. Box 1675, 3000 BR Rotterdam, Netherlands. TEL 31-10-4145822.
FAX 31-10-4135947. Ed. R.K. Singhal. **Document type:** academic/scholarly publication.
—Ei; SWETS. CCC.
Incorporates: International Journal of Environmental Issues in Minerals and Energy Industry (ISSN 0928-4206); Former titles (until vol.8, 1994): International Journal of Surface Mining and Reclamation (ISSN 0920-8119); International Journal of Surface Mining.
Description: Examines all aspects of surface mining technology and waste disposal systems relating to coals, oilsands, industrial minerals and metalliferous deposits. Includes computer applications and automation processes.

549 GW ISSN 0074-7017
INTERNATIONAL MINERALOGICAL ASSOCIATION. PROCEEDINGS OF MEETINGS. (Proceedings usually published in host country) 1959. irreg. (every 4 yrs.). price varies. International Mineralogical Association, c/o Dr. S.S. Hafner, Institute of Mineralogy, Univ. of Marburg, Meerweinstr., 35043 Marburg, Germany. TELEX 482-372-UMR-D. adv. **Indexed:** Mineral.Abstr. **Document type:** proceedings.

622.331 553.21 FI ISSN 0782-7784
CODEN: IPEJE8
INTERNATIONAL PEAT JOURNAL. (Text in English; summaries in German, Russian) 1986. irreg., latest 1992. FIM 100($20) International Peat Society, Kuokkalantie 4, SF-40420 Jyska, Finland. TEL 358-41-674042. FAX 358-41-677405. Ed.Bd. bk.rev. **Document type:** academic/scholarly publication.
—BLDSC (4544.895500); CASDDS.

622.331 553.21 FI ISSN 0355-1008
CODEN: BIPSDV
INTERNATIONAL PEAT SOCIETY. BULLETIN/INTERNATIONALE MOOR- UND TORF-GESELLSCHAFT. MITTEILUNGEN. (Text in English) 1972. irreg. (approx. a.). $20. International Peat Society, Kuokkalantie 4, SF-40420 Jyska, Finland. TEL 358-41-674042.
FAX 358-41-677405. Ed.Bd. illus. circ. 1,000. **Indexed:** Biol.Abstr., Geo.Abstr. **Document type:** bulletin.

622 II ISSN 0047-1003
INTERNATIONAL PRESS CUTTING SERVICE: MINES & MINERALS (COAL AND ORES). 1967. w. $65. International Press Cutting Service, Box 63, Allahabad 211001, India. Ed. N. Khanna. bk.rev.; index. circ. 1,200. (processed)

622 UK ISSN 0952-3553
INTERNATIONAL QUARTERLY. 1957. q. £210($375) Mining Journal Ltd., 60 Worship St., London EC2A 2HD, England. TEL 0171-216-6060.
FAX 0171-216-6050. Ed. Richard Morgan. circ. 650. (reprint service avail. from UMI) **Document type:** trade publication.
—CCC.
Former titles: International Quarterly Review of South African Gold Shares; Quarterly Review of South African Gold Shares (ISSN 0143-3415)

INTERNATIONAL SOCIETY OF EXPLOSIVES ENGINEERS. ANNUAL MEMBERSHIP DIRECTORY AND DESK REFERENCE. see ENGINEERING — Chemical Engineering

INTERNATIONAL SOCIETY OF EXPLOSIVES ENGINEERS. CONFERENCES ON EXPLOSIVES AND BLASTING TECHNIQUE. PROCEEDINGS. see ENGINEERING — Chemical Engineering

622.33 US
INTERNATIONAL TECHNICAL CONFERENCE ON COAL UTILIZATION & FUEL SYSTEMS. PROCEEDINGS. 1975. a. $395. Coal & Slurry Technology Association, 1156 15th St., N.W., Ste. 525, Washington, DC 20005. TEL 202-296-1133. FAX 212-223-3504. Ed. Barbara A. Sakkestad. **Document type:** proceedings.

IRON & STEELMAKER. see METALLURGY

ITOGI NAUKI I TEKHNIKI: GEOKHIMIYA - MINERALOGIYA - PETROGRAFIYA. see EARTH SCIENCES — Geology

549 RU ISSN 0202-7437
ITOGI NAUKI I TEKHNIKI: OBOGASHCHENIE POLEZNYKH ISKOPAEMYKH. irreg., vol.23, 1989. 3.30 Rub. Vsesoyuznyi Institut Nauchno-Tekhnicheskoi Informatsii (VINITI), Baltiiskaya ul. 14, Moscow A-219, Russia. (Subscr. to: Mezhdunarodnaya Kniga, Dimitrova ul. 39, 113095 Moscow, Russia)
—BLDSC (0126.641000).

622 RU ISSN 0202-7410
ITOGI NAUKI I TEKHNIKI: RAZRABOTKA MESTOROZHDENII TVERDYKH POLEZNYKH ISKOPAEMYKH. (Text in Russian) 1968. irreg., vols.44-46, 1989. price varies. Vsesoyuznyi Institut Nauchno-Tekhnicheskoi Informatsii (VINITI), Baltiiskaya ul. 14, Moscow A-219, Russia. (Subscr. to: Mezhdunarodnaya Kniga, Dimitrova ul. 39, 113095 Moscow, Russia)
—BLDSC (0140.220000).

622 RU ISSN 0202-7380
TN263 CODEN: INRMCW
ITOGI NAUKI I TEKHNIKI: RUDNYE MESTOROZHDENIYA. (Text in Russian) 1967. irreg., vols.18-20, 1988. price varies. Vsesoyuznyi Institut Nauchno-Tekhnicheskoi Informatsii (VINITI), Baltiiskaya ul. 14, Moscow A-219, Russia. (Subscr. to: Mezhdunarodnaya Kniga, Dimitrova ul. 39, 113095 Moscow, Russia)
—BLDSC (0154.095000).

556 338.2 IV
IVORY COAST. DIRECTION DES MINES ET DE LA GEOLOGIE. RAPPORT PROVISOIRE SUR LES ACTIVITIES DU SECTEUR. irreg. Direction des Mines et de la Geologie, c/o Ministry of Mining, BP V50, Abidjan, Ivory Coast. **Indexed:** GeoRef.

IZVESTIYA VYSSHIKH UCHEBNYKH ZAVEDENII. SERIYA GEOLOGIYA I RAZVEDKA. see EARTH SCIENCES — Geology

MINES AND MINING INDUSTRY

622 JM ISSN 0254-5241
J B I JOURNAL. (Text in English, Spanish) 1980. a. $12.50 to individuals; institutions $20. Jamaica Bauxite Institute, Hope Gardens, P.O. Box 355, Kingston 6, Jamaica, W.I. TEL 809-92-72073. FAX 809-92-71159. TELEX 2309 JAMBAUX JA. Ed.Bd. adv.; bk.rev. circ. 300. **Indexed:** Met.Abstr., World Alum.Abstr.
 Supersedes (1976-1979): J B I Digest.
 Description: Contains original socio-economic, legal and technical articles, highlighting development issues as they affect the Third World, with special reference to aluminium but not excluding other mineral industries.

622 JM ISSN 1018-2160
J B I QUARTERLY; the Jamaica bauxite alumina sector. 1991. q. J.$200($20) Jamaica Bauxite Institute, Hope Gardens, P.O. Box 355, Kingston 6, Jamaica, W.I. TEL 809-92-72073. FAX 809-92-71159. TELEX 2309 JAMBAUX JA. adv. contact: Dennis E. Morris.
 Description: Provides relevant data on the Jamaican bauxite and alumina sector.

622 GW ISSN 0943-9056
JAHRBUCH FUER BERGBAU, ERDOEL UND ERDGAS, PETROCHEMIE, ELEKTRIZITAET, UMWELTSCHUTZ. 1893. a. DM.168 (CD-ROM DM.780). Verlag Glueckauf GmbH, Postfach 185620, 45206 Essen, Germany. TEL 02054-92412023. FAX 02054-924129. adv. **Indexed:** GeoRef.
 Document type: trade publication.
 ● Also available on CD-ROM.
 Former titles (until 1991): Jahrbuch fuer Bergbau, Oel und Gas, Elektrizitaet, Chemie (ISSN 0179-3675); (until 1984): Jahrbuch fuer Bergbau, Energie, Mineraloel und Chemie (ISSN 0075-255X); (until 1966): Jahrbuch des Deutschen Bergbaus (ISSN 0446-3781)

338.7 II ISSN 0304-7164
HD9506.I44
JAMMU & KASHMIR MINERALS LIMITED. ANNUAL REPORT. Key Title: Annual Report - Jammu & Kashmir Minerals Limited. (Text in English) a. Jammu & Kashmir Minerals Limited, Srinagar, India. **Document type:** corporate report.

JAPAN METAL BULLETIN. see METALLURGY

JEWELRY MAKING, GEMS AND MINERALS; gems, gem cutting, minerals, silverwork, geology. see HOBBIES

622 AT ISSN 0075-3777
JOBSON'S MINING YEAR BOOK. 1957. a. Aus.$275. Riddell Information Services Pty. Ltd., 19 Havilah St., Chatswood, N.S.W. 2067, Australia. TEL 61-2-9352700. FAX 61-2-9352777. adv. circ. 2,000. **Document type:** directory.
 Description: Provides information on all Australian and New Zealand mining, oil and gas companies.

338.2 US
JOHANNESBURG GOLD & METAL MINING ADVISOR.★
1980. m. $225. Johannesburg Publications USA, Inc., 503 Sharpsburg Cir., Birmingham, AL 35213. Ed. Brendan Ryan.
 Description: Analysis of South African gold and strategic metals mines, using present value analysis and computer generated financial forecasts.

622 DK
JOINT COMMITTEE ON MINERAL RESOURCES IN GREENLAND. ANNUAL REPORT. Eskimo edition: Kalatdlitnunane Augtitagssanik Atortugssiagssiat Pivdlugit. Faellesraadet Naluaerut. (Text in Danish and Greenlandic) 1980. a. free. Energiministeriet, Raastofforvaltningen for Groenland - Ministry of Energy, Slotsholmsgade 1, 1, Slotsholmsgade 4, DK-1216 Copenhagen K, Denmark. TEL 45-33-92-75-00. FAX 45-33-13-30-17. TELEX 15505 ENRGY DK.
 Formerly: Faellesraadet Vedroerende Mineraliske Raastoffer i Groenland. Beretning (ISSN 0107-3117)
 Description: Deals with the questions concerning mineral resources in Greenland which have been discussed by the Committee during the reporting period.

JOURNAL DU MINEUR. see LABOR UNIONS

JOURNAL OF APPLIED GEOPHYSICS. see EARTH SCIENCES — Geophysics

622.33 US ISSN 0732-8087
TP325 CODEN: JCQUDK
JOURNAL OF COAL QUALITY. 1982. q. $39 to individuals (foreign $48); institutions $46 (foreign $55). Center for Coal Science, 313 T C N W, Western Kentucky University, Bowling Green, KY 42101. TEL 502-745-6244. FAX 502-745-6293. Ed. George Vourvopoulos. adv. circ. 4,000.
 Document type: academic/scholarly publication, proceedings.
 —BLDSC (3486.355000); CASDDS; CIS; Ei; Faxon; SWETS; UnCover.

JOURNAL OF EXPLOSIVES ENGINEERING. see ENGINEERING — Chemical Engineering

JOURNAL OF MINERALOGY, PETROLOGY AND ECONOMIC GEOLOGY. see EARTH SCIENCES — Geology

622 338.2 662 II ISSN 0022-2755
TN1 CODEN: JMMFAM
JOURNAL OF MINES, METALS AND FUELS. 1953. m. $55. Books & Journals Private Ltd., 6-2 Madan St., Calcutta 700 072, India. TEL 91-33-271711. FAX 91-33-2482973. Ed. A.K. Ghose. adv.; bk.rev.; charts; illus.; tr.lit. circ. 2,761. **Indexed:** AESIS, C.I.S.Abstr., C.R.I.Abstr., Chem.Abstr., Eng.Ind., Fuel & Energy Abstr., GeoRef.
 —CASDDS; Ei; Faxon; UnCover.
 Description: Covers mineral exploration, coal and metal mining, petroleum and natural gas, mineral beneficiation, coal preparation, mining equipment and research, smelting and refining, fuel technology, education and research.

622 550 II ISSN 0971-1899
JOURNAL OF MINING RESEARCH. (Text in English) q. Rs.1000($120) (Central Mining Research Station) New Age International Pvt. Ltd., Journals Division, 4835-24 Ansari Rd., Daryaganj, New Delhi 110 002, India. TEL 91-11-3267996. FAX 91-11-3267437. TELEX 031-66507-WELIN. circ. 500. **Document type:** academic/scholarly publication.

622 551 US ISSN 1062-7391
TN4 CODEN: JMCIEJ
JOURNAL OF MINING SCIENCE. English translation of: Fiziko-tekhnicheskie Problemy Razrabotki Poleznykh Iskopaemykh (RU ISSN 0015-3273) bi-m. $1295 (foreign $1515) (effective 1996). (Russian Academy of Sciences, Siberian Division, RU) Plenum Publishing Corp., Consultants Bureau, 233 Spring St., New York, NY 10013-1578. TEL 212-620-8468. FAX 212-463-0742. TELEX 23-421139. Ed. M.V. Kurlenya. (also avail. in microfilm from JSC; back issues avail.) **Indexed:** Curr.Cont., Energy Ind., Energy Info.Abstr., Eng.Ind. **Document type:** academic/scholarly publication.
 —BLDSC (0415.210000); Ei; Faxon; Genuine Article; UMI; UnCover. **CCC.**
 Formerly (until 1992): Soviet Mining Science (ISSN 0038-5581)
 Refereed Serial

622 GW ISSN 0022-7951
  CODEN: KASTAL
KALI UND STEINSALZ. 1952. 3/yr. DM.59.50. (Kaliverein Hannover e.V.) Verlag Glueckauf GmbH, Postfach 185620, 45206 Essen, Germany. TEL 02054-92412023. FAX 02054-924129. Ed. Otto Lenz. bk.rev. circ. 700. (back issues avail.) **Document type:** trade publication.
 —CASDDS. **CCC.**

622.33 CC ISSN 1001-3946
KANCHA KEXUE JISHU/SITE INVESTIGATION - SCIENCE AND TECHNOLOGY. (Text in Chinese; abstracts in Chinese, English) 1983. bi-m. $42. Yejin Gongye Bu, Kancha Kexue Jishu Yanjiusuo - Ministry of Metallurgic Industry, Institute of Prospecting Science and Technology, 51 Dongfeng Zhonglu, Baoding, Hebei 071067, People's Republic of China. TEL 0312-336001. FAX 0312-334561. Ed. Chen Tingzhang; Pub. Gao Xianning. adv.: page $500. circ. 3,000. **Document type:** bibliography.
 Description: Covers engineering geology, geotechnical engineering, hydrogeology, engineering surveying, and engineering geophysical prospecting.

662 PL ISSN 1230-0446
TP315 CODEN: KSMGAA
KARBO - ENERGOCHEMIA - EKOLOGIA. Key Title: Karbo. (Text in Polish; summaries in English, French, German, Russian) 1956. m. 480000 Zl. (foreign $71) (effective 1993). (Instytut Chemiczni Przerobki Wegla) Wydawnictwo Czasopism i Ksiazek Technicznych SIGMA - NOT, Ul. Zamkowa 1, 41-803 Zabrze 3, Poland. TEL 48-22-180918. FAX 48-22-192187. TELEX 814550 SIGMA PL. Ed. Henryk Zielinski. adv. contact: Henryk Zielinski. bk.rev.; circ. 400 (paid). **Indexed:** Chem.Abstr., Fuel & Energy Abstr., INIS Atomind.
 —BLDSC (5085.699600); CASDDS.
 Formerly (until 1992): Koks, Smola, Gaz (ISSN 0023-2823)

KEYSTONE COAL INDUSTRY MANUAL. see BUSINESS AND ECONOMICS — Trade And Industrial Directories

622.33 US ISSN 1047-4269
KING'S COAL EXPORT REPORT. 1984. w. $547. King Publishing Co., Box 52210, Knoxville, TN 37950. TEL 615-584-6294. (back issues avail.)
 Formerly: King's Coal Export Week (ISSN 0749-0658)
 Description: Ship-by-ship listing all coal and petcoke exports from U.S. ports.

622.33 531.64 US
KING'S COALSTATS. 1987. m. $695 print ed.; floppy disk $3000. King Publishing Co., Box 52210, Knoxville, TN 37950. TEL 615-584-6294. (also avail. in diskette format)

622 US ISSN 0749-9043
KING'S INTERNATIONAL COAL TRADE. 1984. w. $895. King Publishing Co., Box 52210, Knoxville, TN 37950. TEL 615-584-6294. (back issues avail.)
 Description: Contains marketing report for international coal industry.

622.33 US ISSN 0749-1719
KING'S NORTHERN COAL. 1980. w. $687. King Publishing Co., Box 52210, Knoxville, TN 37950. TEL 615-584-6294. (back issues avail.)
 Description: Marketing report for the coal industry with emphasis on northeastern states.

622.33 US ISSN 0749-1697
KING'S SOUTHERN COAL. 1980. w. $687. King Publishing Co., Box 52210, Knoxville, TN 37950. TEL 615-584-6294. (back issues avail.)
 Description: Market report for the coal mining industry with emphasis on southern states.

622.33 US ISSN 0749-1700
KING'S WESTERN COAL. 1983. w. $687. King Publishing Co., Box 52210, Knoxville, TN 37950. TEL 615-584-6294. (back issues avail.)
 Description: Market report for the coal industry with an emphasis on western states.

KOMPASS; Zeitschrift fuer Sozialversicherung im Bergbau. see INSURANCE

KONINKLIJK NEDERLANDS GEOLOGISCH MIJNBOUWKUNDIG GENOOTSCHAP. VERHANDELINGEN. see EARTH SCIENCES — Geology

622.33 526.3 CC ISSN 1001-358X
KUANGSHAN CELIANG/MINE SURVEYING. (Text in Chinese) q. foreign Y100. Meitan Kexueyuan, Tangshan Fenyuan - Central Coal Mining Reseearch Institute, Tangshan Branch, No. 21, Xinhuanxi Rd., Tangshan, Hebei 063012, People's Republic of China. TEL 2822145. Ed. Cui Jixian. **Document type:** academic/scholarly publication.

622.33 551 CC ISSN 1001-5892
KUANGSHAN DIZHI. (Text in Chinese) q. Zhongguo Dizhi Xuehui, Kuangshan Dizhi Zhuanye Weiyuanhui, Sanlidian, Guilin, Guangxi 541004, People's Republic of China. TEL 444987.

622.33 CC ISSN 1001-5809
KUANGSHAN JISHU/MINING TECHNOLOGY. (Text in Chinese) bi-m. Yejin Bu, Anshan Heise Yejin Kuangshan Sheji Yanjiusuo, Anshan, Liaoning 114002, People's Republic of China. TEL 537630. Ed. Qian Zhanxun.

MINES AND MINING INDUSTRY

622   CC   ISSN 1003-5923
KUANGSHAN YALI YU DINGBAN GUANLI/GROUND PRESSURE AND STRATA CONTROL. Short title: G P S C. (Text in Chinese) 1984. q. Y20 (foreign $20). (Zhongguo Guangye Daxue - China University of Mining & Technology) China National Coal Ministry, Strata Control Centre, Xuzhou, Jiangsu Province 221008, People's Republic of China. TEL 0516-888653. FAX 0516-888682. (Dist. overseas by: China International Book Trading Corp., P.O. Box 399, Beijing, P.R. China) (Co-sponsor: Production Bureau of China National Coal Corporation) Eds. Li Hongchang, Cui Menggen. adv. contact: Cao Shenggen. **Document type:** academic/scholarly publication.
—BLDSC (4219.237000).
  Description: Covers researches on ground pressure theory and strata control, and engineering practices of coal industry.

KYOTO UNIVERSITY. FACULTY OF SCIENCE. MEMOIRS. SERIES OF GEOLOGY AND MINERALOGY. see *EARTH SCIENCES — Geology*

622   LB
LAMCO NEWS.* 1966. q. free. Lamco J.V. Operating Company, Box 69, Monrovia, Liberia. Ed. Louis A. Wah. circ. 5,600.

LANDESMUSEUM JOANNEUM. ABTEILUNG FUER GEOLOGIE UND PALAEONTOLOGIE. MITTEILUNGEN. see *PALEONTOLOGY*

549   GW   ISSN 0176-1285
LAPIS; die aktuelle Monatsschrift fuer Liebhaber und Sammler von Mineralien und Edelsteinen. 1976. m. DM.99.60 (foreign DM.104.40). Christian Weise Verlag GmbH, Orleansstr. 69, 81667 Munich, Germany. TEL 089-4802933. FAX 089-6886160. Ed. Stefan Weiss; Pub. Christian Weise. adv. contact: Viola Moenius. bk.rev.; index. circ. 12,000. (back issues avail.) **Document type:** bulletin.
—BLDSC (5786.145000).
  Description: Covers mineralogy, gemology and mining for collectors and dealers of minerals and gems.

300   UK   ISSN 0959-8219
LATIN AMERICAN MINING LETTER. 1982. s-m. £396($620) (effective 1996). M I I D A Ltd., P.O. Box 2137, London NW10 6TN, England. TEL 0181-961-7407. FAX 0181-961-7487. Ed. Michael Wood. adv. contact: Anna Wolf. bk.rev. circ. 200. **Document type:** newsletter.
  Description: News and analysis of the metal and mineral industry of South and Central America and the Carribean.

622   CL   ISSN 0717-0580
LATINOMINERIA. 1991. 4/yr. $40 (free to qualified personnel). G and T International, Matilde Salamanca 736, Santiago 09, Chile. TEL 562-209-8100. FAX 562-209-8101. Eds. Ricardo Cortes, Roly Solis. adv.: B&W page $2700, color $3400; trim 10 7/8 x 8 1/8. bk.rev.; charts; illus.; index. circ. 10,000. (back issues avail.)

622 351.823   US   ISSN 1051-533X
LEGAL QUARTERLY DIGEST OF MINE SAFETY AND HEALTH DECISIONS.* 1990. q. $325. Legal Publication Services, 2008 N. Emerson St., Arlington, VA 22207-1948. TEL 703-276-9796. FAX 703-243-3562. Ed. Melanie Aclander. index. **Document type:** abstracting/indexing.
  Description: Summarizes legal decisions, mine safety issues and health cases.

622   AU   ISSN 0259-0751
LEOBENER GRUENE HEFTE. NEUE FOLGE. irreg., no.10, 1992. price varies. Montanhistorischer Verein fuer Oesterreich, Postfach 1, A-8704 Leoben, Austria. **Document type:** monographic series.

LETTRE AFRIQUE ENERGIES. see *PETROLEUM AND GAS*

LIBERIA. MINISTRY OF LANDS, MINES AND ENERGY. ANNUAL REPORT. see *ENGINEERING — Civil Engineering*

LIGHT RAILWAY NEWS. see *TRANSPORTATION — Railroads*

LIGHT RAILWAYS. see *TRANSPORTATION — Railroads*

622   GY
LINMINE NEWS. 1971. q. free. Linden Mining Enterprise Ltd., Public Relations Section, P.O. Box 27, Mackenzie, Linden, Guyana. FAX 592-4-2795. TELEX GY-2245. Ed. Jenny George-Parkinson. bk.rev. circ. 3,000. **Document type:** corporate report.
  Former titles (until 1992): Guymine News; Guybau News.
  Description: Promotes the bauxite industry. Contains current and major events and developmental issues.

LITHOLOGY AND MINERAL RESOURCES. see *EARTH SCIENCES — Geology*

LITHOS; an international journal of mineralogy, petrology, and geochemistry. see *EARTH SCIENCES — Geology*

552 622   RU   ISSN 0024-497X
    CODEN: LPIKAQ
LITOLOGIYA I POLEZNYE ISKOPAEMYE. 1963. bi-m. $123. (Rossiiskaya Akademiya Nauk, Otdelenie Nauk o Zemle) Izdatel'stvo Nauka, 90 Profsoyuznaya ul., 117864 Moscow, Russia. (Dist. in U.S. by: Victor Kamkin Inc., 4956 Boiling Brook Pkwy., Rockville, MD 20852. TEL 301-881-5973. FAX 301-881-1637) Ed. N.M. Strakhov. bk.rev.; bibl. (tabloid format) **Indexed:** Chem.Abstr., GeoRef., INIS Atomind.
—CASDDS. **CCC.**

622.184   US
LOCATING GOLD, GEMS, & MINERALS; the prospector's guide. 1947. bi-m. $6. United Prospectors Inc., 166 West H St., Benicia, CA 94510. Ed. Walter J. Price. adv. circ. 200.
  Former titles: Locating Gold (ISSN 0024-5658) & Panning Gold.

LUXEMBOURG. SERVICE CENTRAL DE LA STATISTIQUE ET DES ETUDES ECONOMIQUES. INDICATEURS RAPIDES. SERIE C: EMPLOI ET CHOMAGE - SIDERURGIE - FINANCES- TRANSPORT ET COMMERCE. see *BUSINESS AND ECONOMICS — Abstracting, Bibliographies, Statistics*

622   AT
M I M A G. 1948. 3/yr. free. M.I.M. Holdings Ltd., 410 Ann St., Brisbane, Qld. 4000, Australia. FAX 61-7-839-4009. Ed. J. Weinthal. circ. 12,000. (back issues avail.) **Document type:** consumer publication, corporate report, newsletter.
  Description: Includes a blend of information on current activities and initiatives by the company, information about the metals it produces and their downstream uses, and a variety of historical and feature articles.

622 546   US
    CODEN: AMIRB8
M I R L REPORTS. 1964. irreg. price varies. University of Alaska at Fairbanks, Mineral Industry Research Laboratory, 212B O'Neill Bldg., Box 757240, Fairbanks, AK 99775-7240. TEL 907-474-7135. FAX 907-474-5400. circ. 350. (back issues avail.) **Indexed:** GeoRef. **Document type:** monographic series.
  Description: Covers topics in coal, gold, and mineral exploration, mining, and processing, along with geological engineering and other topics.

M M I J INTERNATIONAL CONFERENCES. PROCEEDINGS. (Mining and Materials Processing Institute of Japan) see *METALLURGY*

338.2   II   ISSN 0377-1482
HD9506.I4
M M T C NEWS. (Text in English) 1973. q. free. Minerals and Metals Trading Corp. of India Ltd., 9 - 10 Bahadur Shah Zafar Marg, New Delhi, India. Ed. Preeti Chaturvedi. illus. circ. 6,000. **Document type:** newsletter.

622   SA
M S O A BULLETIN. (Text in Afrikaans, English) 1919. bi-m. R.50. Mine Surface Officials' Association of South Africa, 41 Biccard St., Braamfontein, Johannesburg, South Africa. FAX 27-11-403-2449. Ed. R.H. Botha. adv. circ. 16,000. **Document type:** bulletin.
  Formerly: M S O A Journal (ISSN 0024-8428)

669   TU   ISSN 0024-9416
    CODEN: MDCKAP
MADENCILIK; maden muhendisleri odasi dergisi. (Text in Turkish; summaries in English, French, German) 1961. q. TL.400000($25) (effective 1993). Turk Muhendis ve Mimar Odalari Birligi, Maden Muhendisleri Odasi - Union of Chambers of Engineers and Architects of Turkey, Chamber of Mining Engineers, Selanik Cad. 19-3, 06650 Ankara, Turkey. TEL 4-1251080. FAX 4-1175290. Ed. Tevfik Guyaguler. adv. contact: Remzi Gedikoglu. bk.rev.; abstr.; bibl.; charts; illus.; stat.; index; circ. 5,000 (controlled). (also avail. in diskette format) **Indexed:** Chem.Abstr.
—CASDDS.
  Description: Addresses technological development, working conditions and safety, mineral processing and more. Evaluates different methods and practices in production.

338.2   MY
MALAYSIAN CHAMBER OF MINES. COUNCIL REPORT. (Text in English) a. Malaysian Chamber of Mines, 8th Fl., West Block, Wisma Selanger Dredging, Jalan Ampang, P.O. Box 12560, 50782 Kuala Lumpur, Malaysia. TEL 03-2616171. FAX 03-2616179.
  Formerly: States of Malaya Chamber of Mines. Council Report (ISSN 0302-6620)

338.2   MY
MALAYSIAN CHAMBER OF MINES. YEARBOOK. 1966. a. M.$10. Malaysian Chamber of Mines, 8th Fl., West Block, Wisma Selanger Dredging, Jalan Ampang, P.O. Box 12560, 50782 Kuala Lumpur, Malaysia. TEL 03-2616171. FAX 03-2616179. stat.
  Formerly: States of Malaya Chamber of Mines. Yearbook.

MANITOBA. ENERGY AND MINES. ANNUAL REPORT SERIES. see *ENERGY*

MANITOBA ENERGY AND MINES. GEOLOGICAL REPORT. see *EARTH SCIENCES — Geology*

622   US
MARION MILITARY INSTITUTE BULLETIN.* 1904. q. Marion Military Institute, 1101 Washington St., Marion, AL 36756-3213. TEL 205-683-9894. Ed. John K. Bibler. circ. 10,000.

622   GW   ISSN 0174-1357
TN273
DAS MARKSCHEIDEWESEN. 1879. 3/yr. DM.120. Verlag Glueckauf GmbH, Postfach 185620, 45206 Essen, Germany. TEL 02054-924112023. FAX 02054-924129. adv.; bk.rev.; bibl.; charts; index. **Document type:** trade publication.
—BLDSC (5381.699700).
  Formerly (until 1979): Mitteilungen aus dem Markscheidewesen (ISSN 0026-685X)

622 690 720   IT   ISSN 0047-603X
MARMI GRANITI PIETRE; rivista specializzata del settore marmifero. 1959? bi-m. L.50000 (foreign L.65000). Globo Editoriale s.r.l., Via S. Calimero, 1, 20122 Milan, Italy. TEL 02-58309823. FAX 02-58309739. adv.; charts; illus. circ. 10,000.
  Description: Covers topics on marble, granite and stones.

622.351   IT
MARMO ET INDUSTRIA. Assomarmi, Via Nomentana 251, 00161 Rome, Italy. TEL 39-6-44404429. FAX 39-6-4403335.

622   IT
MARMOMACCHINE. (Text in Italian; summaries in English) 1972. bi-m. $120. Promorama s.r.l., Via Cenisio 50, 20154 Milan, Italy. TEL 39-2-3450344. FAX 39-2-316836. Ed. Flavio Marabelli. adv. circ. 7,000.

622   IT
MARMOMACCHINE INTERNATIONAL. (Text in English; summaries in French, German, Spanish) 1993. q. $50. Promorama s.r.l., Via Cenisio 50, 20154 Milan, Italy. TEL 39-2-347556. FAX 39-2-316836. Ed. Flavio Marabelli. adv.: B&W page L.4000000, color page L.5000000. circ. 10,000. **Document type:** trade publication.
  Description: Covers the entire production cycle of marble and natural stone. Covers international market trends. Profiles products, companies, and trade fairs.

MINES AND MINING INDUSTRY

622 720   IT   ISSN 0393-876X
MARMOR. 1983. q. L.60000 (foreign L.70000). Giorgio Zusi Editore, Via Adriano Garbini 15, 37135 Verona, Italy. TEL 39-45-8200808. FAX 39-45-8200820. Ed. Giorgio Zusi. adv.; bk.rev. circ. 5,400.

MATERIALS AND COMPONENTS IN FOSSIL ENERGY APPLICATIONS. see *ENERGY*

622   PL   ISSN 0208-7448
TN345
MECHANIZACJA I AUTOMATYZACJA GORNICTWA; czasopismo naukowo-techniczne. (Text in Polish; summaries in English, Russian) 1962. m. 456800 Zl. Przedsiebiorstwo Obslugi Gornictwa - POMAG, A.W. Korfantego 83a, 40-161 Katowice, Poland. TEL 48-32-598-011. FAX 48-32-597-819. TELEX 0312595. (Co-sponsor: Ministerstwo Przemyslu i Handlu) (back issues avail.)
Description: Covers electrical engineering and automation in mines.

MEITAN JINGJI YANJIU/COAL ECONOMICS STUDY. see *BUSINESS AND ECONOMICS*

622.33   CC   ISSN 0253-9993
TN799.9   CODEN: MTHPDA
MEITAN XUEBAO/CHINA COAL SOCIETY. JOURNAL. (Text in Chinese) 1964. bi-m. $10.80 per no. Zhongguo Meitan Xuehui - China Coal Society, Hepingli, Beijing 100013, People's Republic of China. TEL 86-1-4214931. FAX 86-1-4219234. Ed. Zhao Hongyou. circ. 1,000. **Indexed:** Chem.Abstr. **Document type:** academic/scholarly publication.
—CASDDS.
Description: Publishes R & D reports and academic papers in the field of mining sciences, including coalfield geology and prospecting, mine construction, ground pressure and support, mine ventilation and safety, and coal chemistry.

MEMOIRES POUR SERVIR A L'EXPLICATION DES CARTES GEOLOGIQUES ET MINIERES DE LA BELGIQUE. see *EARTH SCIENCES — Geology*

622   US
METAL INDUSTRY INDICATORS. m. free. U.S. Bureau of Mines, Office of Public Information, 810 Seventh St., N.W., MS-1040, Washington, DC 20241-0001. TEL 202-501-9649. FAX 202-219-2493. (Subscr. to: U.S.B.M., Box 19070, Pittsburgh, PA 15236) (also avail. by fax) **Document type:** newsletter, government publication.
●Also available online.

622   US
METAL MINING: LATIN AMERICAN INDUSTRIAL REPORT. (Avail. for each of 20 Latin American countries) 1985. a. $235 per country report. Aquino Productions, Box 15760, Stamford, CT 06901. TEL 203-325-3138. Ed. Andres C. Aquino.

622 699   US
METALS ALERT. (Telex service) d. price varies. McGraw-Hill, Inc., 1221 Ave. of the Americas, New York, NY 10020. TEL 212-521-2000.

669 549   II   ISSN 0026-0959
TN600   CODEN: MEMRAZ
METALS AND MINERALS REVIEW. (Text in English) 1961. m. Rs.150. L. K. Pandeya, Ed. & Pub., 105-C Block F, New Alipore, Calcutta 700053, India. **Indexed:** Chem.Abstr., GeoRef.
—CASDDS.
Description: Highlights mining, metallurgy, geology and fuel technology.

622   CN
METALS ECONOMICS GROUP STRATEGIC REPORT. 1988. bi-m. Can.$975. Metals Economics Group, 1718 Argyle St., Ste. 300, Halifax, NS B3J 3N6, Canada. TEL 902-429-2880. FAX 902-429-6593. Ed. Marilyn Beamish. **Document type:** newsletter.

622 338.2   US   ISSN 0026-0975
HD9506.A1
METALS WEEK. 1930. w. $770 (foreign $825). McGraw-Hill, Inc., Commodity Services Group, 1221 Avenue of the Americas, 42nd Fl., New York, NY 10020. TEL 212-512-2000. Ed. Ken Jacobson. mkt.; stat. (also avail. in microform from UMI) **Indexed:** Cadscan, Lead Abstr., Zincscan.
●Also available online. Vendor(s): Knight-Ridder, Inc. (File no.624/McGRAW-HILL PUBLICATIONS ONLINE), Dow Jones News Retrieval (MW), Lexis-Nexis (METLWK), NewsNet (ML01).
—SWETS.
Formerly: E-MJ Metal and Mineral Markets (Engineering and Mining Journal).

622 669   US
METALS WEEK PRICE NOTIFICATION SERVICE. (Telex service) d., w., and m. price varies. McGraw-Hill, Inc., 1221 Ave. of the Americas, New York, NY 10020. TEL 212-521-2000.

622   UK   ISSN 0369-1632
                  CODEN: MQRYAT
MINE AND QUARRY. 1924. m. £55 in the UK; Europe £75; elsewhere £100. Herald House Ltd., 96 Dominion Rd., Worthing, W. Sussex BN14 8JP, England. TEL 01903-821082. FAX 01903-821081. Ed. Tim Fryer. adv.; bk.rev.; abstr.; charts; illus.; stat. circ. 4,112. (reprint service avail. from UMI) **Indexed:** AESIS, Br.Geol.Lit., Br.Tech.Ind., C.I.S. Abstr., Chem.Abstr., Eng.Ind, Excerp.Med., Fluidex, Fuel & Energy Abstr., GeoRef., W.R.C.Inf. **Document type:** trade publication.
—BLDSC (5775.800000); CASDDS; Ei; Faxon; SWETS; UnCover.
Formerly: Mining and Minerals Engineering (ISSN 0026-5152)
Description: Explores equipment, technical articles, people, industry and company news, and project reports.

622   US   ISSN 1049-1805
MINE & QUARRY TRADER; merchandising everything for the mining and quarry industries. 1976. m. $18. Allied Publications, 7355 N. Woodland, Box 603, Indianapolis, IN 46206-0603. TEL 317-297-5500. FAX 317-299-1356. circ. 22,000. **Document type:** trade publication.

622.8 613.62   US   ISSN 1040-8223
KF3574.M5   CODEN: MRREEE
MINE REGULATION REPORTER. 1983. bi-w. $785 (foreign $815). Pasha Publications Inc., 1616 N. Ft. Myer Dr., Ste. 1000, Arlington, VA 22209-3107. TEL 703-528-1244. FAX 703-528-1253. Ed. Wayne Barber. index. (looseleaf format) **Document type:** newsletter.
—CCC.
Formerly: Surface Mining Reporter (ISSN 0739-4020)
Description: Covers mining regulation agencies, new regulations, administrative law decisions, with analysis of recent decisions and appeals.

549   AT
MINE REHABILITATION HANDBOOK. 1989. irreg. free. Australian Mining Industry Council, P.O. Box 363, Dickson, A.C.T. 2602, Australia. FAX 61-6-279-3699.
Description: Provides practical guidance on how to rehabilitate areas disturbed by mining in a sensible, scientific way. Outlines the broad principles and practices that should be used as the basis for rehabilitation.

622   SA   ISSN 0026-4504
MINE VENTILATION SOCIETY OF SOUTH AFRICA. JOURNAL. (Text in Afrikaans and English) 1948. m. R.440 (effective 1994). Mine Ventilation Society of South Africa, P.O. Box 93480, Yeoville, Johannesburg 2143, South Africa. TEL 27-11-487-1049. FAX 27-11-648-1876. Ed. D. Walters. adv. contact: Mrs. S. Moseley. bk.rev.; index, cum.index every 10 yrs. circ. 1,250. (also avail. in microform from UMI; back issues avail.; reprint service avail. from UMI) **Indexed:** C.I.S. Abstr., Eng.Ind., Fluidex, Fuel & Energy Abstr., Ind.S.A.Per., INIS Atomind.
—BLDSC (4826.500000); Faxon; UMI.

622   AT
THE MINER. 1977. m. $75. Peter Isaacson Publications Pty. Ltd., 45-50 Porter St., Prahran, Vic. 3181, Australia. TEL 03-245-7777. FAX 03-245-7606. adv.; bk.rev. circ. 7,719. (back issues avail.) **Indexed:** AESIS.
Former titles (until 1987): Miner Newspaper (ISSN 0155-4468); Miner Magazine.

669   BL   ISSN 0100-6908
                  CODEN: MINMAJ
MINERACAO METALURGIA. 1936. m. $60. (Mineracao Metalurgia) Editora Scorpio Ltda., Rua do Catete, 202, Grupo 301, CEP 22.220 Rio de Janeiro, RJ, Brazil. FAX 205-0648. Ed. Wilson Costa. adv.; bibl.; charts; illus.; stat. circ. 15,000. **Indexed:** Chem.Abstr., GeoRef., Met.Abstr., World Alum.Abstr. —BLDSC (5776.570000); CASDDS.
Former titles (until 1968): Engenharia, Mineracao, Metalurgia (ISSN 0013-7685); (until 1951): Mineracao Metalurgia (ISSN 0026-4520)

622   AT   ISSN 0313-6086
TN122.S7
MINERAL INDUSTRY QUARTERLY. 1976. q. free. Department of Mines and Energy, P.O. Box 151, Eastwood, S.A. 5063, Australia. FAX 08-272-7597. cum.index: vols.1-48. (back issues avail.) **Indexed:** AESIS, Eng.Ind., GeoRef. **Document type:** government publication.
—BLDSC (5778.150000); UnCover.
Description: Current information and news items on all aspects of the South Australian mineral industry.

622   GY
MINERAL INDUSTRY SURVEY; a quarterly newsletter. q. Geology and Mines Commission, Upper Brickdam, P.O. Box 1028, Georgetown, Guyana. FAX 592-2-53047. TELEX GUY GEOL 3042. charts. **Document type:** newsletter.

MINERAL LAW NEWSLETTER. see *LAW*

553   II   ISSN 0379-5187
MINERAL RESEARCH. * (Text in English) s-a. Rs.6. Directorate of Geology, Mining, and Groundwater Development, Old Secretariat Building, Nagpur, Maharashtra, India. illus. **Indexed:** GeoRef.

549   TU   ISSN 0026-4563
HD9506.A1   CODEN: BMRXAD
MINERAL RESEARCH AND EXPLORATION INSTITUTE OF TURKEY. BULLETIN. * Turkish edition: Maden Tetkik ve Arama Genel Mudurlugu Yayinlarindan (ISSN 1015-3705) (Text in English) 1953. s-a. $30. General Directorate of Mineral and Exploration - Maden Tetkik ve Arama Genel Mudurlugu, Ankara, Turkey. TEL 90-4-287-34-30. FAX 90-4-287-9188. TELEX 42741-42040 MTATR. circ. 1,500. **Indexed:** Biol.Abstr. **Document type:** bulletin.
—CASDDS; UnCover.

MINERAL REVIEW. see *EARTH SCIENCES — Geology*

622   II   ISSN 0026-4571
TN1   CODEN: MIWEA6
MINERAL WEALTH. (Text in English or Gujarati) 1965. s-a. Rs.10.10. Directorate of Geology and Mining, 0-1 New Mental Hospital Bldg., Aswara, Ahmedabad 16, India. Ed. Shri J.V. Bhatt. adv. circ. 500. **Indexed:** Chem.Abstr., GeoRef.

622   CL   ISSN 0026-458X
TN43   CODEN: MINCAN
MINERALES. (Text in Spanish; abstracts in English) 1945. q. $50 (effective 1995). Instituto de Ingenieros de Minas de Chile, Casilla 14668, Correo 21, Santiago, Chile. TEL 6953849. FAX 6972351. Ed. Jorge Menacho. adv.; bk.rev.; illus. circ. 1,000. **Indexed:** Chem.Abstr., Fluidex, GeoRef. **Document type:** academic/scholarly publication.
—BLDSC (5786.000000); CASDDS.
Refereed Serial

549   XO   ISSN 0369-2086
QE381.C8   CODEN: MSLOBI
MINERALIA SLOVACA. (Text in Czech and Slovak; abstracts and summaries in English) 1969. bi-m. $92. (Geological Research Spisska Nova Ves) Alfa, Hurbanovo nam. 3, 815 89 Bratislava, Slovakia. TEL 33-14-41. FAX 42-7-594-43. Ed. Pavol Grecula. **Indexed:** Chem.Abstr. **Document type:** trade publication.
—BLDSC (5786.100000); CASDDS.

MINES AND MINING INDUSTRY 4763

549 GW ISSN 0939-6640
MINERALIEN-WELT; Magazin fuer das Sammeln Schoener Steine. 1990. bi-m. DM.69 (foreign DM.80). Bode Verlag, Postfach 405, 45716 Haltern, Germany. TEL 02364-16107. FAX 02364-169273. Ed. Rainer Bode. circ. 6,700. **Document type:** consumer publication.

MINERALIUM DEPOSITA; international journal of geology, mineralogy, and geochemistry of mineral deposits. see EARTH SCIENCES — Geology

549 PL ISSN 0032-6267
QE381.P6 CODEN: MNLPBK
MINERALOGIA POLONICA. (Text with summaries in Polish and Russian) 1970. q. membership. Polskie Towarzystwo Mineralogiczne, Al. Mickiewicza 30, Krakow, Poland. Ed. Witold Zabinski. charts; illus.; index. **Indexed:** Chem.Abstr., GeoRef., Mineral.Abstr.
—BLDSC (5786.460000); CASDDS.

549 JA ISSN 0544-2540
QE351 CODEN: MJTOAS
MINERALOGICAL JOURNAL. (Text in English) 1953. q. $50. Mineralogical Society of Japan, Nogizaka Bldg., 6-41, Akasaka 9-chome, Minato-ku, Tokyo 107, Japan. (Dist. by: Business Center for Academic Societies Japan, 5-16-9 Honkomagome, Bunkyo-ku, Tokyo 113, Japan. TEL 03-5814-5811. FAX 03-5814-5822) adv.; bk.rev.; abstr. circ. 800. **Indexed:** Chem.Abstr., GeoRef., Mineral.Abstr. **Document type:** academic/scholarly publication.
—BLDSC (5787.000000); CASDDS; Faxon; UnCover.

549 UK ISSN 0026-461X
QE351 CODEN: MNLMBB
MINERALOGICAL MAGAZINE. 1876. q. £135($225) Mineralogical Society, 41 Queen's Gate, London SW7 5HR, England. TEL 0171-584-7516. FAX 0171-823-8021. Ed. A.M. Clark. adv. contact: A.P. Jones. bk.rev.; charts; illus.; index. circ. 2,000. (also avail. in microfiche from BHP) **Indexed:** AESIS, Br.Ceram.Abstr., Br.Geol.Lit., Cadscan, Chem.Abstr., Curr.Cont., Deep Sea Res.& Oceanogr.Abstr., Fuel & Energy Abstr., Geo.Abstr., Geol.Abstr., GeoRef., Ind.Sci.Rev., Lead Abstr., Zincscan. **Document type:** academic/scholarly publication.
—BLDSC (5788.000000); CASDDS; Faxon; Genuine Article; SWETS; UnCover.

549 JA ISSN 0454-1146
CODEN: KOBZAI
MINERALOGICAL SOCIETY OF JAPAN. JOURNAL/KOBUTSUGAKU ZASSHI. (Text in Japanese; summaries in English) 1952. 3/yr. Mineralogical Society of Japan - Nihon Kobutsu Gakkai, 6-41, Akasaka 9-chome, Minato-ku, Tokyo 107, Japan. **Indexed:** Chem.Abstr., INIS Atomind., Jap.Per.Ind.
—CASDDS.

549 KR ISSN 0204-3548
QE351 CODEN: MINZDR
MINERALOGICHESKII ZHURNAL; vsesoyuznyi nauchno-teoreticheskii zhurnal. (Text in Russian; summaries in English, Russian) 1979. bi-m. $266 (effective 1996). (Akademiya Nauk Ukrainy, Otdelenie Geologii, Geofiziki i Geokhimii) Vidavnitstvo Naukova Dumka, Vul. Tereshchenkivska 3, 252601 Kiev, Ukraine. TEL 044-244-4068. FAX 044-224-7060. (Dist. by: Mezhdudarodnaya Kniga, B. Yakimanka 39, 117049 Moscow, Russia) Ed. N.P. Shcherbak. **Indexed:** Chem.Abstr., GeoRef.
—BLDSC (0115.340000); CASDDS.
Formerly: Regional'naya i Geneticheskaya Mineralogiya i Konstitutsiya i Svoystva Mineralov.

549 552 AU ISSN 0930-0708
QE351 CODEN: MIPEE9
MINERALOGY AND PETROLOGY. 1872. 12/yr. (in 3 vols., 4 nos./vol.). DM.936($680) (effective 1996). Springer-Verlag, Sachsenplatz 4-6, Postfach 89, A-1201 Vienna, Austria. TEL 0222-3302415. FAX 0222-3302426. (Subscr. in N. America to: Springer-Verlag New York, Inc., 44 Hartz Way, Secaucus, NJ 07096-2491. TEL 201-348-4033. FAX 201-348-4505) Ed. E.F. Stumpfl. adv.; bk.rev.; charts; illus.; index. (also avail. in microfiche from UMI; back issues avail.) **Indexed:** Chem.Abstr., Curr.Cont., Eng.Ind., GeoRef., Met.Abstr. **Document type:** academic/scholarly publication.
—BLDSC (5790.340000); CASDDS; Ei; Faxon; Genuine Article; SWETS; UMI; UnCover. **CCC.**
Formerly: T M P M - Tschermaks Mineralogische und Petrographische Mitteilungen (ISSN 0041-3763)

622 US ISSN 0747-9182
CODEN: MMPRE8
MINERALS AND METALLURGICAL PROCESSING. 1984. q. $90. Society for Mining, Metallurgy and Exploration, Box 625002, Littleton, CO 80162-5002. TEL 303-973-9550. FAX 303-973-3845. Ed. Roshan B. Bhappu; Pub. Joseph A. Zullo. adv.; circ. 600 (paid). (also avail. in microfilm from UMI) **Indexed:** AESIS, Chem.Abstr., Eng.Ind., Excerp.Med., Soils & Fert. **Document type:** trade publication.
—BLDSC (5790.620000); CASDDS; Ei; Faxon; Genuine Article; SWETS; UMI; UnCover. **CCC.**
Refereed Serial

MINERALS AND ROCKS; monograph series of theoretical and experimental studies. see EARTH SCIENCES — Geology

622 UK ISSN 0892-6875
TN1 CODEN: MENGEB
MINERALS ENGINEERING; an international journal devoted to innovation and developments in mineral processing and extractive metallurgy. 1988. m. £410($652) (effective 1996). Elsevier Science Ltd., Pergamon, P.O. Box 800, Kidlington, Oxford OX5 1DX, England. TEL 44-1865-843000. FAX 44-1865-843010. E-mail: nlinfo-f@elsevier.nl; usinfo-f@elsevier.com; forinfo-kyf04035@niftyserve.or.jp; Site addr.: http://www.elsevier.nl/. (Subscr. in U.S. and Canada to: Elsevier Science, 660 White Plains Rd., Tarrytown, NY 10591-5153. TEL 914-524-9200. FAX 914-333-2444) Ed. B.A. Wills. (also avail. in microfilm from UMI; back issues avail.) **Document type:** academic/scholarly publication.
—BLDSC (5790.678000); CASDDS; Ei; Faxon; Genuine Article; SWETS; UMI. **CCC.**
Description: Reports developments in mineral processing technology and applications.
Refereed Serial

622 AT ISSN 1037-4930
MINERALS GAZETTE. 1988. m. Aus.$105 (effective 1995). Resource Information Unit Ltd., 79 Hay St., Subiaco, W.A. 6008, Australia. TEL 61-9-382-3955. FAX 61-9-388-1024. Ed. Doug Wilkinson. adv.; B&W page Aus.$960, color page Aus.$1650; trim 297 x 210. charts; illus.; stat.; tr.lit.; index. circ. 2,500. (back issues avail.)
Formerly: Metals Gazette (ISSN 1032-3821)
Description: Contains hard news stories related to the Australian mining industry, stock market news, latest in equipment and technology and some international coverage.

622 669 UK ISSN 0955-2847
TN1 CODEN: MINIEB
MINERALS INDUSTRY INTERNATIONAL. bi-m. £60 (effective 1996). Institution of Mining and Metallurgy, 44 Portland Pl., London W1N 4BR, England. TEL 0171-580-3802. FAX 0171-436-5388. Eds. S.N. Dunton, M.J. Jones. adv.; bk.rev. circ. 5,000. **Indexed:** AESIS, Cadscan, Lead Abstr., Zincscan. **Document type:** trade publication.
—Faxon; SWETS. **CCC.**
Formerly: I M M Bulletin (ISSN 0308-9789)

549 AT ISSN 0727-3800
MINERALS INDUSTRY SURVEY. 1978. a. free. Australian Mining Industry Council, P.O. Box 363, Dickson, A.C.T. 2602, Australia. FAX 61-6-279-3699. **Indexed:** AESIS.
Description: Provides a statistical description of the industry for the financial year.

622 918 US
MINERALS: LATIN AMERICAN INDUSTRY REPORT. 1985. a. $235 per country report. Aquino Productions, Box 15760, Stamford, CT 06901. TEL 203-325-3138. Ed. Andres C. Aquino.

549 US
MINERALS RESEARCH LABORATORY NEWSLETTER. 1959. q. free. North Carolina State University, Minerals Research Laboratory, 180 Coxe Ave., Asheville, NC 28801. TEL 704-251-6155. Ed. Louis M. Schlesinger. circ. 300. (looseleaf format) **Document type:** newsletter.
Supersedes: Minerals Research Laboratory Bulletin (ISSN 0026-4652)
Refereed Serial

549 US ISSN 0076-8952
TN23 CODEN: MYEAAG
MINERALS YEARBOOK. (Issued in 3 vols.: Vol.1: Minerals, Metals, and Fuels; Vol.2: Area Reports - Domestic; Vol.3: Area Reports - International) 1932. a. (in 3 vols.). U.S. Bureau of Mines, Office of Public Information, 810 Seventh St., N.W., MS-1040, Washington, DC 20241-0001. TEL 202-501-9649. FAX 202-219-2493. (Orders to: Superintendent of Documents, U.S. Government Printing Office, Box 371954, Pittsburgh, PA 15250-7954. TEL 202-512-1800. FAX 202-512-2250; Or: Bernan, 4611-F Assembly Dr., Lanham, MD 20706. TEL 301-459-7666. FAX 301-459-0056) stat. (also avail. in microfiche from BHP,PMC) **Document type:** government publication.
●Also available online.
—BLDSC (5791.000000); CASDDS.
Description: Reports mineral data on a commodity, state, and foreign-country basis.

MINERAUX ET FOSSILES. see PALEONTOLOGY

622 PE ISSN 0026-4679
TN52
MINERIA. 1952. bi-m. $55. Instituto de Ingenieros de Minas del Peru, Las Camelias 555-2, Lima 27, Peru. TEL 51-14-423190. FAX 51-14-424393. Ed. Jorge Vargas Fernandez. adv.; illus.; mkt. circ. 10,000. **Indexed:** Chem.Abstr. **Document type:** academic/scholarly publication.

622 669 665.5 CL ISSN 0716-1042
HD9506.C5
MINERIA CHILENA. 1980. m. $80. Editec Ltda., Matilde Salamanca 736, Santiago 09, Chile. TEL 56-2-209-8100. FAX 56-2-209-8101. (Subscr. to: P.O. Box 3074, Correo Central, Santiago, Chile) Eds. Ricardo Cortes, Roly Solis. adv.: B&W page $1350, color page $1700; trim 10 7/8 x 8 1/8. bk.rev.; index. circ. 10,000. (back issues avail.) **Document type:** trade publication.

622 MX ISSN 0187-490X
LA MINERIA EN MEXICO. 1981. biennial. Mex.$15($4.92) Instituto Nacional de Estadistica Geografia e Informatica, Secretaria de Programacion y Presupuesto, Prol. Heroe de Nacozari, 2301, Sur, Puerta 11, Acceso, 20270 Aguascalientes, Ags., Mexico. TEL 91-49-18-19-48. FAX 91-491-80739.

622.33 US ISSN 1040-5860
MINERIA PAN-AMERICANA. (Text in Spanish) 1987. q. $30. Mineria Pan-Americana, Inc., 9500 S. Dadeland Blvd., Ste. 550, Miami, FL 33156-2819. TEL 305-670-4818. FAX 305-670-4820. Ed. Juan Escalante. adv.: B&W page $1655, color page $2355; trim 8 1/4 x 10 3/4. circ. 7,239. (back issues avail.) **Document type:** trade publication.
Description: Covers mining equipment and new products, international trade fairs, methods of mining exploration and production, minerals processing and transport.

622 BL
MINERIOS; extracao & processamento. (Text in Portuguese and Spanish) 1978. m. $60. E M E P Editorial Ltda., Rua Diogo Moriera 124, CEP 05423 Sao Paolo, Brazil. TEL 814-5022. FAX 813-0545. TELEX 1180007 EMED BR. (In U.S.: Box 59761, Chicago, IL 60659. TEL 708-674-7188) Ed. Joseph Young. circ. 11,800.
Description: Covers new mineral projects, advances in equipment and process technology, and improvements in prospecting and geology techniques of mineral producers of the third world.

622 MX
MINERO-NOTICIAS. 1963. m. Publi-News Latinoamericana, S.A.C.V., Colima 436, Mexico 7 D.F., Mexico. Ed. Roberto J. Marquez. adv.

622 US ISSN 0890-6157
MINERS NEWS. 1985. bi-m. $25. Graphic One, Inc., 7289 Franklin Rd., Box 5694, Boise, ID 83705. TEL 208-375-3680; 800-624-7212. FAX 208-375-0975. Ed. Shirley White; Pub. Gary White. adv.: B&W page $1695, color page $2245; trim 11 3/8 x 17 5/8; adv. contact: Arnie Weber. circ. 6,739. **Document type:** trade publication.
Description: Provides the industry with in-depth coverage of events, plus feature stories and regular columns.

MINES AND MINING INDUSTRY

622 AT ISSN 1034-8794
TN122.S7 CODEN: MRSAE7
MINES AND ENERGY REVIEW, SOUTH AUSTRALIA. 1903. a. price varies. Department of Mines and Energy, P.O. Box 151, Eastwood, S.A. 5063, Australia. TEL 08-274-7597. FAX 08-272-7597. Ed. J.F. Drexel. charts; illus.; stat.; index, cum.index: vols.1-146. circ. 700. (back issues avail.) **Indexed:** AESIS, Aus.Rd.Ind., C.R.I.Abstr., Can.B.P.I., Eng.Ind., GeoRef. **Document type:** government publication.
Former titles: Mineral Resources Review (ISSN 0026-525X); Mining Review (ISSN 0365-6985); Review of Mining Operations.
Description: A collection of technical articles and reviews on South Australian geology and the mineral industry; contains South Australian mineral production statistics.

622 FR ISSN 0994-2556
TN2 CODEN: INMNCA
MINES ET CARRIERES; revue de l'industrie minerale. (Supplement avail.: Mines et Carrieres: Les Techniques (ISSN 0999-5714)) 1855. m. 684.07 F. (foreign 905 F.). (Societe de l'Industrie Minerale) Editions E S K A, 27 rue Dunois, 75013 Paris, France. TEL 44-06-80-42. FAX 44-24-06-94. (Subscr. to: Societe de l'Industrie Minerale, 41-47 rue de la Grange aux Belles, 75010 Paris, France. TEL 42-02-07-92. FAX 42-06-69-30) Ed.Bd. adv.; bk.rev.; abstr.; bibl.; charts; illus.; tr.lit.; index. circ. 4,300. **Indexed:** C.I.S. Abstr., Chem.Abstr., Copper Abstr., Eng.Ind., Excerp.Med., Fuel & Energy Abstr., Geotech.Abstr., INIS Atomind., Met.Abstr., World Alum.Abstr. **Document type:** trade publication.
—BLDSC (5795.625000); CASDDS; Ei; SWETS. **CCC.**
Former titles (until 1988): Industrie Minerale, Mines et Carrieres (ISSN 0296-2918); (until 1984): Industrie Minerale (ISSN 0302-2129); Which was formed by the 1971 merger of: Revue de l'Industrie Minerale (ISSN 0035-1431); Mines et Chimie (ISSN 0398-9194).
Description: Discusses issues concerning mines and quarries.

622 US ISSN 0096-4859
CODEN: MMCOAW
MINES MAGAZINE. 1910. 7/yr. $30 in US and Canada; elsewhere $35; or membership. Colorado School of Mines Alumni Association, Inc., Box 1410, Golden, CO 80402. TEL 303-273-3291. FAX 303-273-3165. E-mail: minesmag@mines.colorado.edu. Ed. Richard W. Haugh. adv.; bk.rev.; charts; illus.; tr.lit.; circ. 6,000. circ. 6,000 (paid). **Indexed:** Chem.Abstr., Excerp.Med., GeoRef. **Document type:** consumer publication.
—BLDSC (5796.000000); Faxon; UMI; UnCover.
Formerly (until 1932): Colorado School of Mines Magazine (ISSN 0095-8719).

622 613.62 EI ISSN 0588-702X
MINES SAFETY AND HEALTH COMMISSION. REPORT/ORGANE PERMANENT POUR LA SECURITE DANS LES MINES DE HOUILLE. RAPPORT. 1959. a. free. Commission of the European Communities, L-2985 Luxembourg, Luxembourg. adv. contact: Rebecca Zahn. **Document type:** corporate report.
Formerly (until 1966): European Coal and Steel Community. Organe Permanent pour la Securite dans les Mines de Houille. Rapport.

622 II ISSN 0970-7204
MINETECH. (Text in English) 1976. q. free. Central Mine Planning & Design Institute Ltd. (Subsidiary of: Coal India Limited), Publications Wing, Gondwana Place, Kanke Rd., Ranchi 834008, Bihar, India.

622 FR ISSN 0026-5071
MINEURS DE FRANCE. 1949. m. 50 F. Charbonnages de France, 2 rue de Metz, 57802 Freyming-Merlebach, France. FAX 87-81-75-19. Ed. Francis Schaefer. adv.; bk.rev.; film rev.; play rev.; charts; illus.; stat. circ. 30,000. **Document type:** corporate report.

622 FR ISSN 0989-7577
MINEURS DE FRANCE: EDITION CENTRE-MIDI. 1971. 11/yr. free. Houilleres de Bassin du Centre et du Midi, 8 rue Frachon, 42007 St. Etienne Cedex 1, France. TEL 77-42-33-53. FAX 77-41-75-15. TELEX 300 794. adv.; bk.rev. circ. 7,000.
Former titles: Centre Midi Magazine; Mineur d'Auvergne (ISSN 0026-5063).
Description: Explores coal mining and resources.

622 AT ISSN 0812-0293
MINFO; New South Wales mining and exploration quarterly. 1983. q. free. Department of Mineral Resources, P.O. Box 536, St. Leonards, N.S.W. 2065, Australia. TEL 02-901-8262. Ed. H. Basden. circ. 4,000.

338.7 II
MINING AND ALLIED MACHINERY CORPORATION. ANNUAL REPORT. (Text in English) a. Mining and Allied Machinery Corporation, Durgapur, India. illus. **Document type:** corporate report.

622 AT
MINING & CONSTRUCTION METHODS AND EQUIPMENT. 1973. irreg. Finecraft Publishing Co., Box 260, Neutral Bay Junction, N.S.W. 2089, Australia. Ed. Fiona Stewart.

338.2 622 SA ISSN 1017-4249
MINING AND ENGINEERING & ELECTRONICS INDUSTRIES (YEAR). (Text in English) a. (South African Foreign Trade Organisation) SAFTO, Publishing Division, P.O. Box 782706, Sandton 2146, South Africa. TEL 27-11-883-3737. FAX 27-11-883-6569. TELEX 4-24111 SA. adv. contact: Dorine Pretorius. **Document type:** directory.
Formerly: Mining and Engineering (Year).

622 551 CU
MINING AND GEOLOGY.* (Text in Spanish; summaries in English, Russian, Spanish) 1983. 3/yr. $21. Ediciones Cubanas, P.O. Box 605, Havana, Cuba. TEL 36655. adv. circ. 1,000. (back issues avail.)

MINING AND MATERIALS PROCESSING INSTITUTE OF JAPAN. METALLURGICAL REVIEW. see *METALLURGY*

MINING AND PETROLEUM LEGISLATION SERVICE. see *LAW*

622 UK ISSN 0965-7029
MINING & QUARRYING TECHNOLOGY INTERNATIONAL (YEAR). 1987. a. £55. Sterling Publications Ltd. (Subsidiary of: Sterling Publishing Group PLC), 86-88 Edgware Rd., London W2 2YW, England. TEL 071-258-0066. Ed. Anthony Sharkey. **Document type:** trade publication.
Former titles (until 1992): MinTech (Year) (ISSN 0955-548X); (until 1989): Mining Technology International (ISSN 0951-9661)

549 613.1 AT
MINING AND THE ENVIRONMENT. 1976. irreg., latest 4th ed. free. Australian Mining Industry Council, P.O. Box 363, Dickson, A.C.T. 2602, Australia. FAX 61-6-279-3699. **Document type:** trade publication.
Description: Provides an insight into the effect mining has on the environment and useful current information on the nature, extent and specific activities of the mining industry in Australia.

622 UK ISSN 0076-8995
HD9506.U6
MINING ANNUAL REVIEW. 1935. a. £78($140) Mining Journal Ltd., 60 Worship St., London EC2A 2HD, England. TEL 0171-216-6060. FAX 0171-216-6050. Ed. Chris Hinde. adv. circ. 10,049. (also avail. in microfilm; microfiche; reprint service avail. from UMI) **Indexed:** AESIS, Br.Geol.Lit., Cadscan, GeoRef., Lead Abstr., Ref.Zh., Zincscan. **Document type:** trade publication.
●Also available online. Vendor(s): Lexis-Nexis.
—BLDSC (5799.330000).
Description: Covers mining activity worldwide through over 130 specially commissioned individual country articles and technical reviews of the latest developments in technology in mineral exploration, surface mining, underground mining and in mineral and coal processings.

622 US ISSN 1055-9957
HD9506.U6
MINING BUSINESS DIGEST. 1987. m. Lumac Enterprises, Inc., 11 Robin Crest Ln., Littleton, CO 80123.
Formerly (until 1991): Western Minerals Activity Report (ISSN 0896-8527)

622 UK
MINING DIRECTORY: MINING AND MINE EQUIPMENT COMPANIES WORLDWIDE; the standard reference work for the mining industry. 1982. a. £89($159) to individuals; advertisers free. Don Nelson Publications Ltd., P.O. Box 193, Barnet, Herts EN4 8LP, England. TEL 0181-368-5534. FAX 0181-368-7010. TELEX 297761-BTIEQ-G. adv. **Document type:** directory, trade publication.
Formerly: Mining Directory: Mines & Mining Equipment and Service Companies Worldwide (Year) (ISSN 0262-7965)

622 US ISSN 0026-5187
TN1 CODEN: MIENAB
MINING ENGINEERING. 1949. m. $100. Society for Mining, Metallurgy and Exploration, Box 625002, Littleton, CO 80162-5002. TEL 303-973-9550. FAX 303-973-3845. Ed. Tim O'Neill; Pub. Joseph A. Zullo. adv.; bk.rev.; illus.; tr.lit.; index; circ. 17,000 (paid). (also avail. in microform from UMI; reprint service avail. from UMI) **Indexed:** A.S.& T.Ind., Acid Rain Abstr., Acid Rain Ind., AESIS, Appl.Mech.Rev., C.R.I.Abstr., CAD CAM Abstr., Chem.Abstr., Comput.Abstr., Energy Info.Abstr., Eng.Ind., Environ.Abstr., Excerp.Med., Fuel & Energy Abstr., Geo.Abstr., GeoRef., INIS Atomind., Met.Abstr., Ocean.Abstr., Petrol.Abstr., Pollut.Abstr., RICS, Robomat., Sel.Water Res.Abstr., Soils & Fert., World Alum.Abstr. **Document type:** trade publication.
—BLDSC (5803.000000); CASDDS; Ei; Faxon; SWETS; UMI; UnCover. **CCC.**
Description: Directed to engineering professionals in the mining and mineral processing industries.
Refereed Serial

622 628 UK ISSN 0969-4218
MINING ENVIRONMENTAL MANAGEMENT. 1993. q. £45($80) Mining Journal Ltd., 60 Worship St., London EC2A 2HD, England. TEL 0171-216-6060. FAX 0171-216-6050. Ed. Nathalie Rosin. adv. contact: Mike Bellenger. **Document type:** trade publication.
Description: Encourages communication within the industry and between the mining industry and other elements of society.

622 551 669 II ISSN 0371-9588
TN1 CODEN: TMGMAL
MINING, GEOLOGICAL AND METALLURGICAL INSTITUTE OF INDIA. TRANSACTIONS. (Text in English) 1906. s-a. Rs.50 (foreign $10). Mining, Geological & Metallurgical Institute of India, 29 Chowringhee Rd., Calcutta 700016, India. Ed. S.C. Ray. adv.; bibl.; charts; illus. circ. 2,500. **Indexed:** GeoRef.

622 CN ISSN 0316-2281
HD9506.C2
MINING IN CANADA - FACTS & FIGURES. French edition: Mines au Canada - Faits et Chiffres (ISSN 0316-2311) 1964. a. free. Mining Association of Canada, 350 Sparks St., No. 1105, Ottawa, Ont. K1R 7S8, Canada. TEL 613-233-9391. Ed. Robert Keyes. adv. contact: Gisele Jacob. charts; stat. circ. 12,000. **Indexed:** CS Ind. **Document type:** trade publication.

622 RH
MINING IN ZIMBABWE. 1950. a. Z.$40 (foreign Z.$42.10). Thomson Publications Zimbabwe (Pvt) Ltd., Thomson House, P.O. Box 1683, Harare, Zimbabwe. TEL 263-4-736835. FAX 263-4-752390. TELEX 24705 ZW. **Document type:** trade publication.
Former titles: Mining in Zimbabwe Rhodesia; Mining in Rhodesia (ISSN 0076-8987)

622 UK ISSN 0026-5225
TN1 CODEN: MJOLAS
MINING JOURNAL. 1835. w. £255($455) combined subscription with Mining Magazine and Mining Annual Review. Mining Journal Ltd., 60 Worship St., London EC2A 2HD, England. TEL 0171-216-6060. FAX 0171-216-6050. Ed. Roger Ellis. adv. contact: Mike Bellenger. bk.rev.; illus.; index. circ. 4,535. (also avail. in microfiche; reprint service avail. from UMI; back issues avail.) **Indexed:** AESIS, Br.Geol.Lit., Chem.Abstr., Energy Ind., Energy Info.Abstr., Eng.Ind., Excerp.Med., Fuel & Energy Abstr., GeoRef., Key to Econ.Sci., Met.Abstr., PROMT, World Alum.Abstr. **Document type:** trade publication.
—Faxon; UMI. **CCC.**
Description: International coverage of political, financial and technical news affecting the mining industry.

MINING LEGISLATION: WORLD (BY COUNTRY). see *LAW — International Law*

338.4 622   US
MINING MACHINERY AND MINERAL PROCESSING EN ESPANOL. (Text in Spanish) 1987. q. $60 (free to qualified personnel). Foundation Publications, Inc., 5600 S.W. 135th Ave., Ste. 111, Miami, FL 33183-5135. TEL 305-388-4890. FAX 305-388-4991. Ed. Jose A. Climent; Pub. Jerry Estevez. adv.: B&W page $2143, color page $3152; trim 8 x 10 7/8; adv. contact: Pablo Aguila. bibl.; tr.lit. circ. 17,016. **Document type:** trade publication.
    Supersedes in part: Construction and Mining Machinery en Espanol.
    Description: Contains technical news, new products reviews, job stories and machinery applications stories for readers in 22 Spanish-speaking countries.

622   UK   ISSN 0308-6631
TN1   CODEN: MMALAD
MINING MAGAZINE. 1909. m. £47($85) Mining Journal Ltd., 60 Worship St., London EC2A 2HD, England. TEL 0171-216-6060. FAX 0171-216-6050. Ed. Tony Brewis. adv. contact: Mike Bellenger. bk.rev.; abstr.; bibl.; illus.; mkt.; pat.; stat.; index. circ. 12,454. (also avail. in microfiche; reprint service avail. from UMI) **Indexed:** AESIS, Art & Archaeol.Tech.Abstr., Br.Ceram.Abstr., Br.Tech.Ind., Cadscan, Chem.Abstr., Eng.Ind., Excerp.Med., Fluidex, Fuel & Energy Abstr., Geo.Abstr., GeoRef., HRIS, IDA, Key to Econ.Sci., Lead Abstr., Met.Abstr., PROMT, Soils & Fert., World Alum.Abstr., Zincscan. **Document type:** trade publication.
    ●Also available online. Vendor(s): Lexis-Nexis.
    —BLDSC (5805.000000); CASDDS; Ei; Faxon; SWETS; UMI; UnCover. CCC.

622   ZA
MINING MIRROR; Zambia's mining industry newspaper. 1973. 12/yr. Z.$62.40. Zambia Consolidated Copper Mines Ltd., P.O. Box 71605, Ndola, Zambia. TELEX ZA 30104. Ed.Bd. adv.; bk.rev.; charts; illus. circ. 35,000. **Document type:** trade publication.
    Supersedes: Mufulira Mirror (ISSN 0047-8326); Roan Antelope (ISSN 0048-8437)

622   SA   ISSN 1022-5455
MINING MIRROR. 1988. m. (11/yr.) R.99 (Southern Africa R.125; elsewhere R.260) (effective Aug. 1995). Brooke Pattrick (Pty) Ltd., P.O. Box 422, Bedfordview 2008, South Africa. TEL 27-11-6224666. FAX 27-11-6167196. Ed. Hendrik Vorster. adv. contact: John Pattrick. circ. 5,348 (controlled). **Document type:** trade publication.
    Incorporates: Drilling News.
    Description: Covers all aspects of the mining industry.

622   SA
MINING NEWS. (Text in English, occasionally in Afrikaans) m. Chamber of Mines of South Africa, P.O. Box 809, Johannesburg 2000, South Africa. TEL 27-11-4987100. FAX 27-11-8368070. Ed. C. du Toit Thom. adv.; circ. controlled. **Document type:** newspaper.
    Description: For mining industry personnel in South Africa.

MINING NEWSLETTER. see *OCCUPATIONAL HEALTH AND SAFETY*

622   SA
MINING R & D NEWS. 1983. q. free. C S I R, Division of Mining Technology, P.O. Box 91230, Auckland Park 2006, South Africa. Ed. C. Langbridge. circ. 3,500. **Document type:** newsletter.
    Supersedes (in July 1993): Chamber of Mines Research Organization. R and D News.
    Description: Informs the mining industry of current developments, progress made in research, and consultancy services.
    Refereed Serial

622   US   ISSN 0026-5241
MINING RECORD. 1889. w. $39. Howell Publishing Co., Box 37510, Denver, CO 80237. TEL 303-770-6791. FAX 303-770-6796. Ed. Don E. Howell. adv.; mkt. circ. 6,000.
    Formerly: Mining and Natural Resources Record.

622 333   AT   ISSN 0314-4607
MINING REVIEW. 1968. q. free. Australian Mining Industry Council, P.O. Box 363, Dickson, A.C.T. 2602, Australia. FAX 61-6-279-3699. Ed. P.C. Waterman. adv.; bk.rev.; index. circ. 5,500. **Indexed:** AESIS, Aus.Rd.Ind., Gdlns.
    —UnCover. CCC.
    Former titles (until 1976): Australian Mining Industry Council. Newsletter (ISSN 0314-4593); (until 1973): Australian Mining Industry Council. Monthly Newsletter (ISSN 0313-7317)
    Description: Promotes debate on matters of interest to the mining industry.

622   CN   ISSN 0711-3277
MINING REVIEW. 1977. bi-m. membership. (British Columbia and Yukon Chamber of Mines) Naylor Communications Ltd., 124 W. 8th St., North Vancouver, BC V7M 3H2, Canada. TEL 604-985-8711. (Subscr. to: 100 Sutherland Ave., Winnipeg, MB R2W 3C7, Canada) adv. circ. 2,500. **Indexed:** GeoRef. **Document type:** trade publication.
    Formerly: Mining Exploration and Development Review (ISSN 0318-1766)

622   UK
TN1
MINING TECHNOLOGY (DONCASTER). 1960. m. £80 to non-members (rest of Europe £84; elsewhere £95.50) (effective 1996). Institution of Mining Engineers, Danum House, South Parade, Doncaster, S. Yorks. DN1 2DY, England. TEL 01302-320486. FAX 01302-340554. Ed. G.J.M. Woodrow. adv. contact: Sylvia Beckett. bk.rev.; bibl.; illus.; index. circ. 4,500. (back issues avail.) **Indexed:** Br.Geol.Lit., Br.Tech.Ind., C.I.S. Abstr., Chem.Abstr., Eng.Ind., Fuel & Energy Abstr., GeoRef., HRIS, Met.Abstr., W.R.C.Inf. **Document type:** trade publication.
    —Ei; Faxon; UnCover.
    Formerly (until Dec. 1994): Mining Engineer (ISSN 0026-5179); **Incorporates:** Institution of Mining Engineers. Transactions (ISSN 0371-9634)
    Description: Serves engineers in mining and related fields worldwide.

622   UK   ISSN 0026-5276
TN1   CODEN: MNGTB7
MINING TECHNOLOGY (MANCHESTER). 1920. 10/yr. £45 (foreign £65). (Institution of Mining, Electrical & Mining Mechanical Engineers) Marylebone Press Ltd., Lloyds House, 18 Lloyd St., Manchester M2 5WA, England. TEL 061-832-6541. FAX 061-832-8129. TELEX 669362. Ed. Peter Dalby. adv.; bk.rev.; abstr.; charts; illus.; tr.lit.; index. circ. 3,500. **Indexed:** AESIS, Br.Tech.Ind., C.I.S. Abstr., Eng.Ind., Excerp.Med., Fuel & Energy Abstr., INSPEC, Met.Abstr., World Alum.Abstr. **Document type:** trade publication.
    —BLDSC (5807.400000); Ei; Faxon; SWETS; UnCover.
    Formerly: Mining Electrical and Mechanical Engineer.

622   US   ISSN 1047-7551
MINING WORLD NEWS. 1989. m. $44 in U.S.; Canada $49; (foreign $63). Mining International Publishing Co., 100 W. Grove St., Ste. 240, Reno, NV 89509-4027. TEL 702-827-1115. FAX 702-827-1292. Ed. Dorothy Y. Kosich. adv. contact: Kristin Souza. circ. 30,000. **Document type:** trade publication.

622.33   SA
MINTEK. SPECIAL PUBLICATIONS. 1975. irreg., latest no.13, 1989. price varies. Mintek, Private Bag X3015, Randburg 2125, South Africa. TEL 011-793-3511. FAX 011-793-2413. TELEX 4-24867 SA.
    Formerly: Council for Mineral Technology (MINTEK). Special Publication.
    Description: Covers various aspects of metallurgy and mineral technology, including research, production, and conferences.

622.33   SA
MINTEK REPORTS. 1966. irreg. (approx. 20-30/yr.). $400. Mintek, Private Bag X3015, Randburg 2125, South Africa. TEL 011-793-3511. FAX 011-793-2413. bibl.; illus. **Indexed:** Chem.Abstr., INSPEC, Met.Abstr., Mineral.Abstr., Nucl.Sci.Abstr.
    Former titles: M I N T E K Reports; N I M Reports.
    Description: Deals with mineral processing research.

MINES AND MINING INDUSTRY   4765

622.33   SA   ISSN 1010-2582
MINTEK RESEARCH DIGEST. 1974. bi-m. free. Mintek, Private Bag X3015, Randburg 2125, South Africa. TEL 011-793-3511. FAX 011-793-2413.
    Former titles: M I N T E K Research Digest; N I M Research Digest.

549   RU
MIR KAMNYA/WORLD OF STONES. (Text in English; supplementary sheet in Russian) 1993. q. $52 (effective thru 1996). Plus Ltd. Publishing, P.O. Box 162, 103050 Moscow, Russia. TEL 7-95-2033574. FAX 7-95-2926511. (Subscr. in US to: H. Obodda, Box 51, Short Hills, NJ 07078) Ed. Alexander Evseev. adv.; bk.rev. circ. 3,000.
    Description: Popular-science mineralogical journal for mineralogists and collectors.
    Refereed Serial

549   GW   ISSN 0341-6356
    CODEN: MSMDDQ
MONOGRAPH SERIES ON MINERAL DEPOSITS. (Text in English or German) 1962. irreg. $108 (effective 1996). Gebrueder Borntraeger Verlagsbuchhandlung, Johannesstr. 3A, 70176 Stuttgart, Germany. TEL 0711-625001. FAX 0711-625005. Ed. G. Friedrich. **Document type:** academic/scholarly publication, monographic series.
    —BLDSC (5917.555000). CCC.
    Formerly (until 1975): Clausthaler Hefte zur Lagerstaettenkunde und Geochemie der Mineralischen Rohstoffe (ISSN 0578-4697)

MONTANA. BUREAU OF MINES AND GEOLOGY. BULLETIN. see *EARTH SCIENCES — Geology*

MONTANA. BUREAU OF MINES AND GEOLOGY. MEMOIR. see *EARTH SCIENCES — Geology*

622   US   ISSN 0077-1104
MONTANA. BUREAU OF MINES AND GEOLOGY. MONTANA MINING DIRECTORY. (Subseries of Open-File Reports) a. Bureau of Mines and Geology, Montana Tech of the University of Montana, Butte, MT 59701-8997. TEL 406-496-4167. FAX 406-496-4451. **Document type:** government publication, directory.
    Formerly: Montana. Bureau of Mines and Geology. Directory of Mining Enterprises.
    Description: Each listing includes type of ore produced, mining district, property location, owners' and operators' names and addresses, mill capacity, number of employees, and yearly status.

MONTANA. BUREAU OF MINES AND GEOLOGY. SPECIAL PUBLICATIONS. see *EARTH SCIENCES — Geology*

MUENCHNER GEOWISSENSCHAFTLICHE ABHANDLUNGEN. REIHE B: ALLGEMEINE UND ANGEWANDTE GEOLOGIE. see *EARTH SCIENCES — Geology*

622   ZR   ISSN 0541-4873
MWANA SHABA; journal d'entreprise de la Gecamines. 1957. m. Generale des Carrieres et des Mines, Division des Relations Publiques, B.P. 450, Lubumbashi, Zaire.

N R R I NOW. (Natural Resources Research Institute) see *EARTH SCIENCES*

NAMIBIA BRIEF. see *BUSINESS AND ECONOMICS — International Development And Assistance*

622   US   ISSN 0192-7329
NATIONAL INDEPENDENT COAL LEADER; dedicated to safety in the mining industry. 1960. m. $6. National Independent Coal Operators Association, 1514 Front St., Richlands, VA 24641. TEL 703-963-9011. Ed. Louis Hunter. adv.; bk.rev. circ. 13,000. **Document type:** newspaper.
    Description: Explores coal mining and resources.

NATIONAL RESEARCH INSTITUTE FOR POLLUTION AND RESOURCES. ANNUAL REPORT/KOGAI SHIGEN KENKYUJO NENPO. see *ENVIRONMENTAL STUDIES*

NATIONAL RESEARCH INSTITUTE FOR POLLUTION AND RESOURCES. SCIENCE REPORT/KOGAI SHIGEN KENKYUJO HOKOKU. see *ENVIRONMENTAL STUDIES*

MINES AND MINING INDUSTRY

622.33 551.4   US
NATIONAL SYMPOSIUM ON MINING. PROCEEDINGS.
1979. a. $45. (University of Kentucky, Office of Engineering Services - Continuing Education) O E S Publications, Office of Engineering Services, University of Kentucky, Lexington, KY 40506-0046. TEL 606-257-3343. FAX 606-257-3342. Eds. R. William DeVore, Donald H. Graves. circ. 300. (back issues avail.) **Document type:** proceedings.
    Former titles: National Symposium on Mining, Hydrology, Sedimentology and Reclamation. Proceedings (ISSN 1046-3887); (until 1987): Symposium on Surface Mining, Hydrology, Sedimentology and Reclamation. Proceedings (ISSN 0735-0686)

NATIONAL UNION OF COAL MINE WORKERS. JOURNAL.
see *LABOR UNIONS*

549   GW   ISSN 0077-7757
QE351   CODEN: NJMIAK
NEUES JAHRBUCH FUER MINERALOGIE. ABHANDLUNGEN. 1807. 6/yr. (in 2 vols, 3 nos./vol.). $308 per vol. (effective 1996). E. Schweizerbart'sche Verlagsbuchhandlung, Johannesstr. 3A, 70176 Stuttgart, Germany. TEL 0711-625001. FAX 0711-625005. Ed.Bd. adv. (also avail. in microfiche from BHP) **Indexed:** Art & Archaeol.Tech.Abstr., Biol.Abstr., Br.Ceram.Abstr., Br.Geol.Lit., Chem.Abstr. **Document type:** academic/scholarly publication.
    —BLDSC (6079.000000); CASDDS; Genuine Article; SWETS; UnCover. **CCC.**
    Supersedes and continues volume numbering of: Neues Jahrbuch fuer Mineralogie, Geologie und Palaeontologie. Abhandlungen. Abt. B.

549   GW   ISSN 0028-3649
QE351   CODEN: NJMMAW
NEUES JAHRBUCH FUER MINERALOGIE. MONATSHEFTE. (Text in English and German) 1900. 12/yr. $532 (effective 1996). E. Schweizerbart'sche Verlagsbuchhandlung, Johannesstr. 3A, 70176 Stuttgart, Germany. TEL 0711-625001. FAX 0711-625005. Ed.Bd. bk.rev.; bibl.; charts; illus. **Indexed:** Art & Archaeol.Tech.Abstr., Br.Geol.Lit., Chem.Abstr., Curr.Cont., Ind.Sci.Rev., Int.Aerosp.Abstr. **Document type:** academic/scholarly publication.
    —BLDSC (6080.200000); CASDDS; Ei; Faxon; Genuine Article; SWETS; UnCover. **CCC.**

NEVADA. BUREAU OF MINES AND GEOLOGY. BULLETIN. see *EARTH SCIENCES — Geology*

NEVADA. BUREAU OF MINES AND GEOLOGY. EDUCATIONAL SERIES. see *EARTH SCIENCES — Geology*

NEVADA. BUREAU OF MINES AND GEOLOGY. LISTS. see *EARTH SCIENCES — Geology*

NEVADA. BUREAU OF MINES AND GEOLOGY. OPEN-FILE REPORT. see *EARTH SCIENCES — Geology*

NEVADA. BUREAU OF MINES AND GEOLOGY. PAMPHLET. see *EARTH SCIENCES — Geology*

NEVADA. BUREAU OF MINES AND GEOLOGY. REPORT. see *EARTH SCIENCES — Geology*

NEVADA. BUREAU OF MINES AND GEOLOGY. SPECIAL PUBLICATIONS. see *EARTH SCIENCES — Geology*

NEVADA MINERAL INDUSTRY (YEAR). see *EARTH SCIENCES — Geology*

622   NL   ISSN 0758-6485
NEW CALEDONIA. SERVICE DES MINES ET DE L'ENERGY. RAPPORT ANNUEL. 1915. a. 760 F. Service des Mines et de l'Energie, Noumea, New Caledonia. FAX 687-272345. illus. circ. 210. **Document type:** government publication.

622   US   ISSN 0096-4581
TN24.N6   CODEN: NEXBAJ
NEW MEXICO. BUREAU OF MINES AND MINERAL RESOURCES. BULLETIN. 1915. irreg., no.145, 1993. price varies. Bureau of Mines and Mineral Resources, Socorro, NM 87801. TEL 505-835-5410. **Indexed:** GeoRef. **Document type:** government publication.
    —UnCover.

622   US   ISSN 0548-5975
    CODEN: NMMMAJ
NEW MEXICO. BUREAU OF MINES AND MINERAL RESOURCES. MEMOIR. 1956. irreg., no.47, 1988. price varies. Bureau of Mines and Mineral Resources, Socorro, NM 87801. TEL 505-835-5410. **Indexed:** GeoRef. **Document type:** government publication.

622   US   ISSN 0098-7077
TN24.N6   CODEN: NMXMB7
NEW MEXICO. BUREAU OF MINES AND MINERAL RESOURCES. PROGRESS REPORT. Key Title: Progress Report - New Mexico Bureau of Mines & Mineral Resources. (First 7 nos. were designated "Target Exploration" Reports) 1972. irreg., no.10, 1978. price varies. Bureau of Mines and Mineral Resources, Socorro, NM 87801. TEL 505-835-5410. **Indexed:** GeoRef. **Document type:** government publication.

NEW MEXICO DIRECTORY OF MANUFACTURERS. see *BUSINESS AND ECONOMICS — Trade And Industrial Directories*

622   AT   ISSN 1039-1975
NEW SOUTH WALES. DEPARTMENT OF MINERAL RESOURCES. ANNUAL REPORT. 1988. a. price varies. Department of Mineral Resources, P.O. Box 536, St. Leonards, N.S.W. 2065, Australia. index. circ. 475. **Indexed:** AESIS, GeoRef. **Document type:** government publication.
    Formerly (until 1991): New South Wales. Department of Minerals and Energy. Annual Report (ISSN 1033-0852); Formed by the merger of: New South Wales. Department of Mineral Resources. Annual Report (ISSN 0818-6855); New South Wales. Department of Energy. Annual Report (ISSN 1032-2582); Which was formerly: New South Wales. Department of Mines. Annual Report (ISSN 0077-8664); New South Wales. Energy Authority. Annual Report (ISSN 0158-0809); New South Wales. Department of Mineral Resources and Development. Annual Report (ISSN 0727-9256).
    Description: Details the activities of the department for the financial year and includes audited statements.

NEW SOUTH WALES. GEOLOGICAL SURVEY. METALLOGENIC STUDY AND MINERAL DEPOSIT DATA SHEETS. see *EARTH SCIENCES — Geology*

622 559   AT   ISSN 0077-8729
NEW SOUTH WALES. GEOLOGICAL SURVEY. MINERAL INDUSTRY SERIES. 1967. irreg., no.44, 1979. price varies. Department of Mineral Resources, P.O. Box 536, St. Leonards, N.S.W. 2065, Australia. Ed. H. Basden. circ. 400. **Indexed:** AESIS, GeoRef. **Document type:** government publication.

622 559   AT   ISSN 0077-8737
    CODEN: MRWGDA
NEW SOUTH WALES. GEOLOGICAL SURVEY. MINERAL RESOURCES SERIES. Variant title: Geological Survey of N.S.W. Mineral Resources. 1898. irreg., no.46, 1989. price varies. Department of Mineral Resources, P.O. Box 536, St. Leonards, N.S.W. 2065, Australia. Ed. H. Basden. index. circ. 400. **Indexed:** AESIS, GeoRef. **Document type:** government publication.
    —BLDSC (5779.900000); UnCover.
    Description: Comprehensive treatises on the geology, distribution mining history of particular minerals.

622   AT   ISSN 0727-5757
NEW SOUTH WALES MINERAL INDUSTRY REVIEW. 1980. a. Department of Mineral Resources, P.O. Box 536, St. Leonards, N.S.W. 2065, Australia. TEL 02-901-8262. circ. 1,000. **Document type:** government publication.

622 333.79   CN
NEWFOUNDLAND. DEPARTMENT OF MINES AND ENERGY. GEOLOGICAL SURVEY BRANCH. CURRENT RESEARCH. 1980. a. Department of Mines and Energy, Geological Survey Branch, P.O. Box 8700, St. John's, NF A1B 4J6, Canada. TEL 709-729-3159. FAX 709-729-3493. Ed. C.P.G. Pereira. illus.; circ. 500 (paid). **Document type:** government publication.
    Former titles (until 1990): Newfoundland. Department of Mines and Energy. Geological Survey of Newfoundland. Current Reserch (ISSN 0843-4972); (until 1988): Newfoundland. Department of Mines and Energy. Mineral Development Division. Current Research.
    Description: Presents annual results of studies in all aspects of Newfoundland and Labrador earth science.
    Refereed Serial

622 553   CN   ISSN 1189-6108
NEWFOUNDLAND. DEPARTMENT OF MINES AND ENERGY. GEOLOGICAL SURVEY BRANCH. ORE HORIZONS. 1991. biennial. price varies. Department of Mines and Energy, P.O. Box 8700, St. John's, NF A1B 4J6, Canada. TEL 709-729-3159. FAX 709-729-3493. Eds. H.S. Swinden, A. Hogan. illus.; circ. 600 (paid). **Document type:** government publication.
    Description: Collection of descriptive articles dealing with mineral deposits, exploration case histories, and mineral development projects in the province.
    Refereed Serial

622 550   NR   ISSN 0022-2763
NIGERIAN MINING AND GEOSCIENCES SOCIETY. JOURNAL. (Text primarily in English; occasionally in French with English summaries) s-a. $50 per no. Nigerian Mining and Geosciences Society, University of Ibadan, Department of Geology, Ibadan, Nigeria. TEL 234-2-8101100-104. TELEX CAMPUS 31128 NG, IBA LIB 31233 NG. Ed. A. Azubuike Elueze. adv.: page $4000; adv. contact: A. Azubuike Elueze. bk.rev.; abstr.; charts; illus.; stat.; index. circ. 1,000. (reprint service avail.) **Indexed:** Chem.Abstr., Curr.Cont. (1994-), Geo.Abstr., GeoRef. **Document type:** academic/scholarly publication.
    Former titles (until 1963): Nigerian Mining and Geosciences Society. Journal; Nigerian Mining, Geological and Metallurgical Society. Journal.
    Description: Takes a multidisciplinary look at the geosciences, mining, metallurgy, materials science, and environmental studies.
    Refereed Serial

NIIGATA UNIVERSITY. FACULTY OF SCIENCE. SCIENCE REPORTS. SERIES E: GEOLOGY AND MINERALOGY/NIIGATA DAIGAKU RIGAKUBU KENKYU HOKOKU. E-RUI, CHISHITSU KOBUTSUGAKU. see *EARTH SCIENCES — Geology*

NONFERROUS METALS SOCIETY OF CHINA. TRANSACTIONS. see *METALLURGY*

622 551   US   ISSN 0961-1444
TN1
NONRENEWABLE RESOURCES. 1992. 4/yr. $218 (foreign $238) (effective 1995). (International Association for Mathematical Geology) Oxford University Press, Journals, 2001 Evans Rd., Cary, NC 27513. TEL 919-677-0977; 800-852-7323. FAX 919-677-1714. E-mail: jnlorders@oup-usa.org. (Subscr. outside N. America to: Oxford University Press, Journals, Walton St., Oxford OX2 6DP, England. TEL 44-1865-56767. FAX 44-1865-267773) Ed. Richard McCammon. adv.; bk.rev. circ. 200. **Indexed:** Environ.Per.Bibl. (1992-), Geo.Abstr., Geol.Abstr. **Document type:** academic/scholarly publication.
    —BLDSC (6117.340400); Faxon; UMI. **CCC.**
    Description: Covers topics in natural resource economics, management, and exploration.
    Refereed Serial

MINES AND MINING INDUSTRY

622 CN ISSN 0029-3164
HD9506.C2
THE NORTHERN MINER; devoted to the mineral resources industry of Canada. 1915. w. Can.$70. Southam Magazine Group, 1450 Don Mills Rd., Don Mills, ON M3B 2X7, Canada. TEL 416-445-6641. FAX 416-442-2272. Ed. Olav Svela. adv. contact: Brian Warriner. bk.rev.; charts; illus.; mkt.; stat.; tr.lit. circ. 18,000. (tabloid format; also avail. in microfilm from CML) **Indexed:** Can.B.P.I., Can.Per.Ind., PROMT. **Document type:** newspaper.
●Also available online. Vendor(s): Southam Electronic Publishing.
—BLDSC (6151.020000).
Description: Reports on all mines and metals.

622 FR ISSN 1012-9324
O E C D COAL INFORMATION. a. price varies. Organization for Economic Cooperation and Development, 2 rue Andre-Pascal, 75775 Paris Cedex 16, France. (U.S. orders to: O.E.C.D. Publications and Information Center, 2001 L St., N.W., Ste. 700, Washington, DC 20036-4910. TEL 202-785-6323) (also avail. in microfiche from OEC,CIS) **Indexed:** IIS.
—BLDSC (3290.085000).
Formerly (until 1986): Coal Information Report.

622 RU ISSN 0202-3776
TN500 CODEN: OBOGAD
OBOGASHCHENIE RUD. (Text in Russian) 1956. bi-m. $80 (effective 1993). Mekhanobr - Tekhnika Corp., 21 Liniya, 8a, 199026 St. Petersburg, Russia. TEL 812-713-9978. FAX 812-218-1449. TELEX 121419 MEOBR SU. Ed. Pavlova. adv.: page $200; adv. contact: Chistyakova. bk.rev. circ. 1,200. **Indexed:** Chem.Abstr., Ref.Zh.
—CASDDS.

622 665 US ISSN 0271-0315
TN858.A1 CODEN: OSSPDC
OIL SHALE SYMPOSIUM PROCEEDINGS. 1964. a. $25. (Colorado School of Mines) Colorado School of Mines Press, Golden, CO 80401.
TEL 303-273-3607. (reprint service avail. from UMI) **Indexed:** API Catal., API Hlth.& Environ., API Oil., API Pet.Ref., API Pet.Subst., API Transport., Chem.Abstr., GeoRef.
—CASDDS.

622 CN ISSN 0708-2061
ONTARIO GEOLOGICAL SURVEY. AGGREGATE RESOURCES INVENTORY PAPER. 1979. irreg. price varies. Ontario Geological Survey, 933 Ramsey Lake Rd., Sudbury, ON P3E 6B5, Canada.
TEL 416-314-3800. FAX 416-314-3797. (Subscr. to: Mines & Mineral Information Centre, Rm. M2-17, MacDonald Block, 900 Bay St., Toronto, ON M7A 1C3, Canada) (back issues avail.) **Document type:** government publication.

622 CN
ONTARIO GEOLOGICAL SURVEY. EXPLORATION TECHNOLOGY DEVELOPMENT FUND, SUMMARY OF RESEARCH. (Subseries of: Ontario Geological Survey. Miscellaneous Paper (ISSN 0704-2752)) 1983. a. price varies. Ontario Geological Survey, 933 Ramsey Lake Rd., Sudbury, Ont. P3E 6B5, Canada.
TEL 416-314-3800. FAX 415-314-3797. (Subscr. to: Mines & Minerals Information Centre, Rm. M2-17, MacDonald Block, 900 Bay St., Toronto, Ont. M7A 1C3, Canada) (back issues avail.) **Document type:** government publication.
Formerly: Ontario Geological Survey. Exploration Technology Development Fund Grants (ISSN 0826-791X)

ONTARIO GEOLOGICAL SURVEY. GUIDE BOOKS. see EARTH SCIENCES — Geology

549 CN ISSN 0706-4551
ONTARIO GEOLOGICAL SURVEY. MINERAL DEPOSITS CIRCULAR. 1950. irreg. (1-2/yr.). price varies. Ontario Geological Survey, 933 Ramsey Lake Rd., Sudbury, ON P3E 6B5, Canada.
TEL 416-314-3800. FAX 416-314-3797. (Subscr. to: Mines & Minerals Information Centre, Rm. M2-17, MacDonald Block, 900 Bay St., Toronto, ON M7A 1C3, Canada) (back issues avail.) **Indexed:** GeoRef. **Document type:** government publication.
—UnCover.
Formerly: Ontario. Division of Mines. Mineral Resource Circulars.

622 CN ISSN 0704-2752
CODEN: MPOSDQ
ONTARIO GEOLOGICAL SURVEY. MISCELLANEOUS PAPER. 1960. irreg. (3-4/yr.). price varies. Ontario Geological Survey, 933 Ramsey Lake Rd., Sudbury, ON P3E 6B5, Canada. TEL 416-314-3800.
FAX 416-314-3797. (Subscr. to: Mines & Minerals Information Centre, Rm. M2-17, MacDonald Block, 900 Bay St., Toronto, ON M7A 1C3, Canada) (back issues avail.) **Indexed:** GeoRef. **Document type:** government publication.
—BLDSC (5815.214000); CASDDS.
Formerly: Ontario. Division of Mines. Miscellaneous Papers.

622 CN ISSN 0709-4671
TA705.4.C22
ONTARIO GEOLOGICAL SURVEY. NORTHERN ONTARIO ENGINEERING GEOLOGY TERRAIN STUDY. irreg. price varies. Ontario Geological Survey, 933 Ramsey Lake Rd., Sudbury, ON P3E 6B5, Canada.
TEL 416-314-3800. FAX 416-314-3797. (Subscr. to: Mines & Minerals Information Centre, Rm. M2-17, MacDonald Block, 900 Bay St., Toronto, ON M7A 1C3, Canada) (back issues avail.) **Document type:** government publication.

622 557 CN ISSN 0704-2582
QE191 CODEN: OGSRD2
ONTARIO GEOLOGICAL SURVEY. REPORT. 1960. irreg. (3-10/yr.). price varies. Ontario Geological Survey, 933 Ramsey Lake Rd., Sudbury, ON P3E 6B5, Canada. TEL 416-314-3800. FAX 416-314-3797. (Subscr. to: Mines & Minerals Information Centre, Rm. M2-17, MacDonald Block, 900 Bay St., Toronto, ON M7A 1C3, Canada) (back issues avail.) **Indexed:** Chem.Abstr., GeoRef. **Document type:** government publication.
—CASDDS; UnCover.
Former titles: Ontario Geological Survey. Geological Report; Ontario Geological Survey. Geological Report, Geoscience Report (ISSN 0381-1778); Ontario. Division of Mines. Geological Reports; **Incorporates:** Ontario. Division of Mines. Geochemical Reports.

622 551 CN ISSN 0838-3677
TN27.O4
ONTARIO GEOLOGICAL SURVEY. REPORT OF ACTIVITIES, RESIDENT GEOLOGISTS. (Subseries of: Ontario. Geological Survey. Miscellaneous Paper (ISSN 0704-2752)) 1967. a. price varies. Ontario Geological Survey, 933 Ramsey Lake Rd., Sudbury, ON P3E 6B5, Canada. TEL 416-314-3800.
FAX 416-314-3797. (Subscr. to: Mines & Minerals Information Centre, Rm. M2-17, MacDonald Block, 900 Bay St., Toronto, ON M7A 1C3, Canada) circ. 1,000. (also avail. in microfiche; back issues avail.) **Document type:** government publication.
Formerly: Ontario Geological Survey. Annual Report of the Regional and Resident Geologists.

622 ISSN 0704-2590
CODEN: OGSSD5
ONTARIO GEOLOGICAL SURVEY. STUDY. irreg. price varies. Ontario Geological Survey, 933 Ramsey Lake Rd., Sudbury, ON P3E 6B5, Canada.
TEL 416-314-3800. FAX 416-314-3797. (Subscr. to: Mines & Minerals Information Centre, Rm. M2-17, MacDonald Block, 900 Bay St., Toronto, ON M7A 1C3, Canada) (back issues avail.) **Indexed:** Chem.Abstr., GeoRef. **Document type:** government publication.
—CASDDS.
Formerly: Ontario. Division of Mines. Geological Circular, Geoscience Study.

622 CN ISSN 0829-8203
QE191
ONTARIO GEOLOGICAL SURVEY. SUMMARY OF FIELD WORK. (Sub-series of: Ontario Geological Survey. Miscellaneous Paper (ISSN 0704-2752)) 1968. a. price varies. Ontario Geological Survey, 933 Ramsey Lake Rd., Sudbury, ON P3E 6B5, Canada.
TEL 416-314-3800. FAX 416-314-3797. (Subscr. to: Mines & Minerals Information Centre, Rm. M2-17, MacDonald Block, 900 Bay St., Toronto, ON M7A 1C3, Canada) (back issues avail.) **Document type:** government publication.

622 CN
ONTARIO GEOLOGICAL SURVEY. SUPPLEMENT TO M.P.77. (Sub-series of: Ontario Geological Survey. Miscellaneous Paper (ISSN 0704-2752)) 1978. a. price varies. Ontario Geological Survey, 933 Ramsey Lake Rd., Sudbury, ON P3E 6B5, Canada.
TEL 416-314-3800. FAX 416-314-3797. (Subscr. to: Mines & Minerals Information Centre, Rm. M2-17, MacDonald Block, 900 Bay St., Toronto, ON M7A 1C3, Canada) (back issues avail.) **Document type:** government publication.

338.2 CN ISSN 0714-122X
HD9506.C23
ONTARIO MINERAL SCORE. 1980. a. Can.$15. Ministry of Northern Development and Mines, Mineral Sector Analysis Branch, 4th Fl., 159 Cedar St., Sudbury, Ont. P3E 6A5, Canada. TEL 705-670-7235.
FAX 705-670-7246. Eds. D. Romani, J. Webb. circ. 1,700. **Document type:** government publication.
Description: Provides a statistical compilation of volume and value of mineral production, employment, wages and costs in Ontario mining industry as well as summaries of Ontario mineral exploration data.

622 UK ISSN 0964-6027
OPENCAST MINING (YEAR). a. Strata Publishing Ltd., 65 Tweedy Rd., Bromley, Kent BR1 3NH, England. TEL 081-663-3331. FAX 081-464-5637. Ed. Simon Jarvis. **Document type:** corporate report.
—BLDSC (6266.314000).

622 SA ISSN 0030-4050
HC517.S7
OPTIMA. 1951. s-a. free to shareholders. Anglo American & De Beers of South Africa, P.O. Box 61587, Marshalltown 2107, South Africa. Ed. Ingrid Staude. charts; illus.; stat.; index. circ. 40,000. **Indexed:** AESIS, Cadscan, Field Crop Abstr., Geo.Abstr., GeoRef., Herb.Abstr., Ind.S.A.Per., Int.Polit.Sci.Abstr., Key to Econ.Sci., Lead Abstr., Met.Abstr., Mid.East: Abstr.& Ind., World Alum.Abstr., Zincscan.
—Faxon; UnCover.

OREGON. DEPARTMENT OF GEOLOGY AND MINERAL INDUSTRIES. BULLETIN. see EARTH SCIENCES — Geology

622 SP
PANORAMA MINERO. 1981. a. 2500 ptas. Instituto Tecnologico Geominero de Espana, Cristobal Bordiu, 34, 28003 Madrid, Spain. TEL 34-1-3495730. FAX 34-1-3495762.
Description: Covers the national and international industry of mining.

622 US ISSN 0886-0912
PAY DIRT. ROCKY MOUNTAIN EDITION. 1979. m. $25. Copper Queen Publishing Co., Inc., Drawer 48, Bisbee, AZ 85603. TEL 602-432-2244.
FAX 602-432-2247. Ed. Gary Dillard; Pub. William Epler. adv.: B&W page $570; trim 8 1/2 x 11; adv. contact: Caryl Larkins. circ. 3,996. **Document type:** trade publication.
—UnCover.
Incorporates: Pay Dirt. Intermountain Edition (Nevada, Utah and Colorado); Pay Dirt. Big Sky Edition (Idaho, Montana and Wyoming).
Description: Covers mining industry in Colorado, Idaho, Montana, Nevada, Utah and Wyoming.

622 US ISSN 0886-0920
PAY DIRT. SOUTHWESTERN EDITION. 1938. m. $25. Copper Queen Publishing Co., Inc., Drawer 48, Bisbee, AZ 85603. TEL 602-432-2244.
FAX 602-432-2247. Ed. Gary Dillard; Pub. William Epler. adv.: B&W page $570; trim 8 1/2 x 11; adv. contact: Caryl Larkins. bk.rev. circ. 4,651. **Document type:** trade publication.
—UnCover.
Incorporates: Pay Dirt. Arizona Edition; Pay Dirt. New Mexico Edition.
Description: Covers mining industry in Arizona, New Mexico and Southern California.

MINES AND MINING INDUSTRY

622
TN58.D4 — UK — ISSN 0031-3637
PEAK DISTRICT MINES HISTORICAL SOCIETY. BULLETIN. 1959. s-a. £11($20) to individuals; institutions £18($34). Peak District Mining Historical Society, c/o Peak District Mining Museum, Matlock Bath, Derbyshire DE4 3NR, England. TEL 01629-583834. Ed. Trevor D. Ford. adv. contact: Lynn Willies. bk.rev.; charts; illus.; cum.index. circ. 500. **Indexed:** Br.Archaeol.Abstr., Geo.Abstr. **Document type:** academic/scholarly publication.
—BLDSC (2676.680000).

338.2 — US
PENNSYLVANIA. DEPARTMENT OF ENVIRONMENTAL RESOURCES. ANNUAL REPORT ON MINING ACTIVITIES. 1870. a. $16.13 (PA residents $17.10) for 1993 edition. Department of Environmental Resources, Bureau of Deep Mine Safety, Box 8463, Harrisburg, PA 17105-8463. TEL 717-783-7515. FAX 717-772-2774. (Subscr. to: Pennsylvania State Bookstore, State Records Center Bldg., 1825 Stanley Dr., Harrisburg, PA 17125) Ed. Patsie Nichols. stat. circ. 1,000. **Document type:** government publication.
Former titles: Pennsylvania. Office of Mines and Land Protection. Annual Report; (until 1973): Pennsylvania. Anthracite, Bituminous Coal and Oil and Gas Divisions. Annual Report.

PENNSYLVANIA BAR ASSOCIATION. ENVIRONMENTAL, MINERAL & NATURAL RESOURCES LAW SECTION. NEWSLETTER. see ENVIRONMENTAL STUDIES

549 550 — IT — ISSN 0369-8963
QE351 — CODEN: PEMIA7
PERIODICO DI MINERALOGIA. 1930. 3/yr. L.110000. (Universita degli Studi di Roma La Sapienza) Bardi Editore, Salita de'Crescenzi 16, 00186 Rome, Italy. FAX 06-6878576. index. circ. 300. (back issues avail.) **Indexed:** Geol.Abstr.
—CASDDS.
Description: Covers mineralogy, mining industry, crystallography, geochemistry, earth sciences, vulcanology and petrology.

622 — PH — ISSN 0048-3842
TN113
PHILIPPINE MINING & ENGINEERING JOURNAL. 1970. m. Business Masters International, 55 U.E. Tech. Avenue, University Hills, Subdivision Malabon, Rizal, Philippines. adv.; bk.rev.; illus.; stat. circ. 5,000. **Indexed:** AESIS, Ind.Phil.Per.

622 — PH — ISSN 0085-4875
PHILIPPINE MINING AND ENGINEERING JOURNAL. MINING ANNUAL AND DIRECTORY. Included as July issue of Phillipine Mining and Engineering Journal. 1971. a. P.3($15) Business Masters International, 55 U.E. Tech. Avenue, University Hills, Subdivision Malabon, Rizal, Philippines. Ed. Luciano B. Quitlong. adv. circ. 10,000.

PHOSPHORUS AND POTASSIUM; covers all aspects of world phosphate and potash fertilizer industry. see ENGINEERING — Chemical Engineering

549 — GW — ISSN 0342-1791
QE351 — CODEN: PCMIDU
PHYSICS AND CHEMISTRY OF MINERALS. (Text in English) 1977. 8/yr. DM.1498($1088) (effective 1996). (International Mineralogical Association) Springer-Verlag, Heidelberger Platz 3, 14197 Berlin, Germany. TEL 030-8207-0. FAX 030-8214091. E-mail: orders@springer.de. (Subscr. in N. America to: Springer-Verlag New York, Inc., 44 Hartz Way, Secaucus, NJ 07096-2491. TEL 201-348-4033. FAX 201-348-4505) Ed.Bd. abstr.; bibl.; charts; illus.; stat.; index. (also avail. in microform from UMI; back issues avail.; reprint service avail. from ISI) **Indexed:** Br.Ceram.Abstr., Ceram.Abstr., Chem.Abstr., Curr.Cont., Geol.Abstr., GeoRef., INSPEC, Phys.Ber., Soils & Fert. **Document type:** academic/scholarly publication.
—BLDSC (6478.217000); CASDDS; Ei; Faxon; Genuine Article; SWETS; UMI; UnCover. **CCC.**
Description: Supports interdisciplinary work in mineralogy and physics or chemistry, with particular emphasis on applications of modern techniques and new theories.

622 — US — ISSN 0032-0293
TN1 — CODEN: PIQUAN
PIT & QUARRY. 1916. m. $35. Advanstar Communications, Inc., 7500 Old Oak Blvd., Cleveland, OH 44130. TEL 216-826-2839. FAX 216-891-2726. (Subscr. to: 131 W. First St., Duluth, MN 55802. TEL 800-346-0085) Ed. Robert Drake. adv.; bk.rev.; charts; illus.; tr.lit. circ. 21,672. (also avail. in microform from UMI) **Indexed:** A.S.& T.Ind., Bus.Ind., C.I.S. Abstr., C.R.I.Abstr., C.R.I.Curr.Cont., Chem.Abstr., Eng.Ind., Excerp.Med., GeoRef., PROMT, SRI, Tr.& Indus.Ind. **Document type:** trade publication.
—Ei; Faxon; SWETS; UMI; UnCover. **CCC.**
Formerly: Cement - Mill and Quarry (ISSN 0095-9952)
Description: Covers crushed stone, sand and gravel, cement, lime, gypsum, and related products and applications.

622 — US
PIT & QUARRY MINING REFERENCE MANUAL & BUYERS GUIDE; equipment and technical reference manual for nonmetallic industry. 1907. a. $25. Advanstar Communications, Inc., 7500 Old Oak Blvd., Cleveland, OH 44130. TEL 216-826-2839. FAX 216-891-2726. (Subscr. to: 131 W. First St., Duluth, MN 55802. TEL 800-346-0085) Ed. Robert Drake. adv.; index. circ. 21,000. **Document type:** trade publication.
Former titles: Pit and Quarry Handbook and Buyers Guide; Pit and Quarry Handbook and Purchasing Guide (ISSN 0079-2128)

622 — UK — ISSN 0268-7305
PLATINUM (YEAR). 1985. s-a. free. Johnson Matthey PLC, 78 Hatton Garden, London EC1N 8JP, England. TEL 0171-269-8000. FAX 0171-269-8201. Ed. A.J. Cowley. circ. 16,000. **Document type:** trade publication.
—BLDSC (6538.180000).
Description: Survey and analysis of the supply and demand for platinum and platinum group metals (palladium, rhodium, ruthenium, iridium) and developments in their markets.

549 — GW — ISSN 1120-317X
QE351
PLINIUS. (Supplement to: European Journal of Mineralogy (ISSN 0935-1221)) 1989. bi-m. $34 (effective 1996). (Societa Italiana di Mineralogia e Petrologia, IT) E. Schweizerbart'sche Verlagsbuchhandlung, Johannesstr. 3A, 70176 Stuttgart, Germany. TEL 0711-625001. FAX 0711-625005. **Document type:** academic/scholarly publication.

622 — PL — ISSN 0372-9508
TN4 — CODEN: ZNSGAY
POLITECHNIKA SLASKA. ZESZYTY NAUKOWE. GORNICTWO. (Text in Polish; summaries in English, German, Russian) 1959. irreg. price varies. Politechnika Slaska, Katowicka 7, 44-100 Gliwice, Poland. FAX 371655. TELEX 036-304. (Dist. by: Ars Polona, Krakowskie Przedmiescie 7, 00-068 Warsaw, Poland) Ed. Walwry Szuscik. circ. 205. **Indexed:** Chem.Abstr.
—BLDSC (9512.327100); CASDDS.

622 — PL — ISSN 0324-9670
POLITECHNIKA WROCLAWSKA. INSTYTUT GORNICTWA. PRACE NAUKOWE. KONFERENCJE. (Text in Polish; summaries in English and Russian) 1971. irreg., no.14, 1992. price varies. Wydawnictwo Politechniki Wroclawskiej, Wybrzeze Wyspianskiego 27, 50-370 Wroclaw, Poland. FAX 22-36-64. TELEX 712559 PWRPL. (Dist by: Ars Polona-Ruch, Krakowskie, Przedmiescie 7, Warsaw, Poland) **Document type:** proceedings.
—Ei.

622 — PL — ISSN 0324-9689
TN275.A1 — CODEN: PIGKEF
POLITECHNIKA WROCLAWSKA. INSTYTUT GORNICTWA. PRACE NAUKOWE. MONOGRAFIE. (Text in Polish; summaries in English, Russian) 1973. irreg., no.32, 1992. price varies. Wydawnictwo Politechniki Wroclawskiej, Wybrzeze Wyspianskiego 27, 50-370 Wroclaw, Poland. FAX 22-36-64. TELEX 71-22-54 PWRPL. (Dist. by: Ars Polona-Ruch, Krakowskie Przediescie 7, Warsaw, Poland) illus. **Document type:** monographic series.

622 — PL — ISSN 0370-0798
POLITECHNIKA WROCLAWSKA. INSTYTUT GORNICTWA. PRACE NAUKOWE. STUDIA I MATERIALY. (Text in Polish; summaries in English and Russian) 1970. irreg., no.32, 1992. price varies. Wydawnictwo Politechniki Wroclawskiej, Wybrzeze Wyspianskiego 27, 50-370 Wroclaw, Poland. FAX 22-36-64. TELEX 712559 PWRPL. (Dist. by: Ars Polona-Ruch, Krakowskie Przedmiescie 7, Warsaw, Poland) **Document type:** academic/scholarly publication.

622 — PL — ISSN 0079-3280
TN275 .A1
POLSKA AKADEMIA NAUK. ODDZIAL W KRAKOWIE. KOMISJA GORNICZO-GEODEZYJNA. PRACE: GORNICTWO. (Text in Polish; summaries in English, Russian) 1965. irreg., no.29, 1992. price varies. Polska Akademia Nauk, Oddzial w Krakowie, Komisja Gorniczo-Geodezyjna, Ul. Slawkowska 17, 31-016 Krakow, Poland. TEL 48-12-224853. FAX 48-12-222791. Ed. Zbigniew Strzelecki. **Document type:** monographic series.
—BLDSC (6586.570000).

PORTUGAL. SERVICOS GEOLOGICOS. COMUNICACOES. see EARTH SCIENCES — Geology

622 — US — ISSN 0146-7204
HD9536.A1
POWELL GOLD INDUSTRY GUIDE & INTERNATIONAL MINING ANALYST. 1976. q. $120 (foreign $140). Reserve Research Ltd., Box 4135, Portland, ME 04101. TEL 207-774-4971. Ed. Larson M. Powell. charts; stat. (back issues avail.)

622 — CN — ISSN 1181-6414
PROSPECTOR EXPLORATION & INVESTMENT BULLETIN. 1980. 6/yr. Can.$35 for 12 issues. K W Publishing Ltd., 1268 W. Pender St., Vancouver, BC V6E 2S8, Canada. TEL 604-688-2038. FAX 604-688-2038. Ed. A. Leonard. adv. circ. 25,000. (tabloid format)
Formerly: Northwest Prospector Miners and Developers Bulletin (ISSN 0824-6149)

622 — PL — ISSN 0033-216X
TN4 — CODEN: PRGOAI
PRZEGLAD GORNICZY. (Text in Polish; summaries in English, French, German and Russian) 1912. m. 144 Zl.($25.20) (Glowny Instytut Gornictwa) Wydawnictwo "Slask", Al. W. Korfantego 51, 40-161 Katowice, Poland. TEL 583221. TELEX 312326. (Dist. by: Ars Polona - Ruch, Krakowskie Przedmiescie 7, Warsaw, Poland) (Co-sponsor: Stowarzyszenie Inzynierow i Technikow Gornictwa) Ed. Jerzy Malara. adv.; bk.rev.; abstr.; bibl.; charts; illus.; index. circ. 2,800. (also avail. in microfilm; microfiche) **Indexed:** C.I.S. Abstr., Ceram.Abstr., Chem.Abstr., Eng.Ind., Geotech.Abstr.
—BLDSC (6942.300000); CASDDS; Faxon.

PUBLIC LAND & RESOURCES LAW DIGEST. see LAW

622 — AT
QUARRY. 1973. m. Aus.$50. Morgan Trade Publications, 52 St. Kilda Rd., Melbourne, Vic. 3182, Australia. TEL 03-5101242. FAX 03-510-9024. Ed. Kerrie O'Brien. adv.; bk.rev. circ. 6,250.

622.35 — UK — ISSN 0950-9526
TN950.A1
QUARRY MANAGEMENT. 1918. m. £32. (Institute of Quarrying) Quarry Managers' Journal Ltd., 7 Regent St., Nottingham NG1 5BY, England. TEL 0602-411315. FAX 0602-484035. Ed. Bernard Hill. adv.; bk.rev.; charts; illus.; tr.lit.; index. circ. 6,265. (reprint service avail. from UMI) **Indexed:** AESIS, Br.Geol.Lit., Br.Tech.Ind., C.I.S. Abstr., C.R.I.Abstr., Geo.Abstr., GeoRef., HRIS, Intl.Civil Eng.Abstr., RICS, Soft.Abstr.Eng., W.R.C.Inf. **Document type:** trade publication.
—BLDSC (7168.950000); Ei; SWETS.
Formerly (until Jun. 1984): Quarry Management and Products (ISSN 0305-9421); Incorporates: Quarry Managers' Journal (ISSN 0033-5274); Cement, Lime and Gravel (ISSN 0008-8862)
Description: For the quarrying, opencast and related industries, covering technical and management topics.

QUEBEC (PROVINCE). MINISTERE DE L'ENERGIE ET DES RESSOURCES. RAPPORT ANNUEL. see ENERGY

MINES AND MINING INDUSTRY 4769

622 AT ISSN 0033-6149
TN1 CODEN: QGMJAZ
QUEENSLAND GOVERNMENT MINING JOURNAL. 1900. m. Aus.$90. (Queensland Department of Minerals and Energy) Magazine Publishing Company, 4 Wandoo St., Fortitude Valley, Qld. 4005, Australia. TEL 61-7-252-9677. FAX 61-7-252-4667. Ed. Michael Holliday. adv.: B&W page Aus.$1490, color page Aus.$2490; trim 275 x 210; adv. contact: Trevor Kirk. bk.rev.; abstr.; charts; illus.; mkt.; stat.; tr.lit. circ. 2,500. (also avail. in microform from PMC) **Indexed:** AESIS, Aus.Rd.Ind., Chem.Abstr., Fuel & Energy Abstr., Geo.Abstr., GeoRef., Met.Abstr. **Document type:** government publication, trade publication.
—BLDSC (7214.000000); UnCover.
Description: Provides information on developments in the geological, mining and mineral processing industries in Queensland. Also covers world trends.

QUICK RELEASE TO THE MINERAL STATISTICS OF INDIA. see MINES AND MINING INDUSTRY — Abstracting, Bibliographies, Statistics

R I C INSIGHT. (Rare-earth Information Center) see METALLURGY

R I C NEWS. (Rare-earth Information Center) see METALLURGY

622 UK
R J B NEWSCENE. 1961. m. £9 (overseas £16) (effective 1995-1996). R J B Mining, Harworth Park, Blyth Rd., Doncaster, S. Yorks. DN11 8DB, England. Ed. Stuart Oliver. adv.: B&W page £1800; color page £2500. bk.rev.; charts; illus.; circ. 12,000 (paid). (tabloid format) **Indexed:** Fuel & Energy Abstr. **Document type:** newspaper.
Formerly (until Jan. 1995): Coal News (ISSN 0009-997X)

RAW MATERIALS REPORT; journal of mineral policy, business and environment. see BUSINESS AND ECONOMICS — International Development And Assistance

622 RU ISSN 0034-026X
CODEN: RZONAV
RAZVEDKA I OKHRANA NEDR. 1935. m. 27 Rub. (Profsoyuz Rabochikh Geologorazvedochnykh Rabot) Izdatel'stvo Nedra, Pl. Belorusskogo Vokzala, 3, 125047 Moscow, Russia. TEL 250-52-55. (Co-sponsor: Ministerstvo Geologii) Ed. V.I. Kuzmenko. bk.rev.; bibl.; charts; illus. circ. 8,400. **Indexed:** Biol.Abstr., Chem.Abstr., Eng.Ind., GeoRef.
—BLDSC (0140.000000); CASDDS. **CCC.**

622 658 FR
CODEN: ANMSA3
REALITES INDUSTRIELLES. (Text in French; summaries in English, German, Russian, Spanish) 1794. 7/yr. 790 F. (foreign 950 F.) (includes Gerer et Comprendre) (effective 1995). (Annales des Mines) Editions E S K A, 22 rue Monge, 75005 Paris, France. TEL 44-06-80-42. FAX 44-24-06-94. Ed. Francois Baratin; Pub. Serge Kebabtchieff. adv.; bk.rev.; abstr.; illus.; stat.; index, cum.index every 10 yrs. circ. 3,500. (back issues avail.) **Indexed:** C.I.S. Abstr., Chem.Abstr., Curr.Cont., Eng.Ind., Fuel & Energy Abstr., Geo.Abstr., GeoRef., INIS Atomind., Met.Abstr., Risk Abstr., World Alum.Abstr. **Document type:** trade publication, academic/scholarly publication.
—**CCC.**
Formerly: Annales des Mines. Dossiers Documentaires; Supersedes in part: Annales des Mines (ISSN 0003-4282)
Description: Aims to find the common threads in the technological, economic, and social aspects of business and industry and in the management of firms.

RECLAMATION NEWSLETTER. see ENVIRONMENTAL STUDIES

622 AT ISSN 0725-9158
REGISTER OF AUSTRALIAN MINING. 1976. a. Aus.$325 (effective 1995). Resource Information Unit Ltd., 79 Hay St., Subiaco, W.A. 6008, Australia. TEL 61-9-382-3955. FAX 61-9-388-1025. Ed. Doug Wilkinson. adv.: B&W page Aus.$1570, color page Aus.$2700; trim 297 x 210. charts; illus.; stat.; tr.lit.; index. (back issues avail.)
—BLDSC (7337.325000).
Formerly (until 1980): Australian Mines Handbook (ISSN 0314-3554)
Description: Detailed list of mines and prospects covering 34 different commodities across Australia.

622 JA
REPORT OF OVERSEAS MINING INVESTIGATION: INDIA, PAKISTAN, BANGLADESH/KAIGAI KOGYO JIJO CHOSA HOKOKUSHO: INDO, PAKISUTAN, BANGURADESSHU.* (Text in Japanese) irreg. Konzoku Kogyo Jigyodan, Shigen Joho Senta - Metal Mining Agency of Japan, Mineral Resources Information Center, 25-5, Toranomon 1-chome, Minato-ku, Tokyo 105, Japan. charts; illus.

622 JA
REPORT OF OVERSEAS MINING INVESTIGATION: MADAGASCAR, SWAZILAND/KAIGAI KOGYO JIJO CHOSA HOKOKUSHO: MADAGASUKARU, SUWAJIRANDO.* (Text in Japanese) irreg. Kinzoku Kogyo Jigyodan, Shigen Joho Senta - Metal Mining Agency of Japan, Mineral Resources Information Center, 25-5, Toranomon 1-chome, Minato-ku, Tokyo 105, Japan. charts; illus.

338.2 US ISSN 0747-7333
TN24.O3
REPORT ON OHIO MINERAL INDUSTRIES; with directories of reporting coal and industrial mineral operations. 1872. a. $9.94. Ohio Department of Natural Resources, Division of Geological Survey, 4383 Fountain Square Dr., Columbus, OH 43224-1362. TEL 614-265-6576. FAX 614-447-1918. Ed. Sherry Weisgarber. index. circ. 1,700. **Document type:** government publication.
Former titles (until 1981): Ohio. Division of Mines. Report (ISSN 0078-401X); Ohio. Division of Mines. Annual Report with Coal and Industrial Mineral Directories of Reporting Firms.

RESERVES OF COAL, PROVINCE OF ALBERTA. see ENERGY

RESOURCES POLICY. see ENERGY

622 GW ISSN 0724-4495
REVIER UND WERK. 1950. bi-m. Rheinbraun AG, Stuettgenweg 2, 50935 Cologne, Germany. TEL 0221-48022273. FAX 0221-4801356. Ed. Wolfgang Trees. bk.rev. circ. 34,000. **Document type:** trade publication.

338.2 TZ ISSN 0082-1659
REVIEW OF THE MINERAL INDUSTRY IN TANZANIA. Title varies: Tanzania. Mines Division. Review of the Mineral Industry. (Former name of issuing body: Mineral Resources Division) 1965. a. free. Ministry of Water, Energy and Minerals, Mines Division, Box 903, Dodoma, Tanzania. Ed. Anthony Muze. circ. 400. **Document type:** government publication.

622 628.1 CL ISSN 0716-9620
REVISTA DE DERECHO DE MINAS Y AGUAS. 1990. a. $60. Universidad de Atacama, Instituto de Derecho de Minas y Aguas, Moneda 673, 8o piso, Santiago, Chile. TEL 6986682. FAX 6969177.

622 SP ISSN 0210-8356
TN87 CODEN: REMIEX
REVISTA DE MINAS. 1979. a. 2250 ptas. Universidad de Oviedo, Escuela Tecnica Superior de Ingenieros de Minas, Independencia 13, 33004 Oviedo, Spain. (Subscr. to: Servicio de Publicaciones, Un. de Oviedo, Calle Arguelles 19, 33003 Oviedo, Spain. TEL 34-85-104486. FAX 34-85-104488) Ed. Jose Martinez Alvarez. bk.rev.; illus. circ. 500. **Indexed:** Ind.SST.
—CASDDS.

622 CU
REVISTA DE MINERIA Y GEOLOGIA. 3/yr. $24 in N. America; S. America $25; Europe $26. (Ministerio de Mineria y Geologia, Centro de Informacion Cientifico-Tecnico) Ediciones Cubanas, Obispo No. 527, Apdo. 605, Havana, Cuba. bibl.; charts; illus. **Indexed:** GeoRef.
Formerly (until 1984): Mineria en Cuba.

REVISTA MINELOR. see PETROLEUM AND GAS

622 BO ISSN 0252-8460
REVISTA MINERA BAMIN. no.87, Jan.-Mar., 1976. q. Banco Minero de Bolivia, Departamento de Relaciones Publicas, Casilla Correo 1410, La Paz, Bolivia.

622 SP ISSN 0214-0217
ROC MAQUINA. English edition (ISSN 1130-8362) 5/yr. Virgen de Begona 14-16, 48006 Bilbao, Spain. TEL 4-415-28-00. FAX 4-416-78-45. Ed. Gregorio Nieves.
Formerly (until 1987): Marmomacchine (ISSN 0214-0209)

622.33 SP ISSN 0378-3316
ROCAS Y MINERALES; tecnicas y procesos de minas y canteras. 1972. m. 7500 ptas. (Europe 18000 ptas.; elsewhere 20000 ptas.) (effective 1995). Editorial Rocas y Minerales, C. Arturo Baldasano, 15 bajo, 28043 Madrid, Spain. TEL 34-1-4151804. FAX 34-1-4151661. Eds. Laureano Fueyo, Carlos Vivas Escribano. adv.: B&W page $910; trim 255 x 180. bk.rev.; illus.; circ. 6,000 (controlled). (back issues avail.) **Indexed:** Ind.SST. **Document type:** trade publication.
—**CCC.**
Description: Covers developments in mining preparation and extraction techniques, mechanical processing of rocks and minerals, washing techniques and more.

ROCK MECHANICS AND ROCK ENGINEERING. see EARTH SCIENCES — Geology

622 US ISSN 0080-3375
CODEN: RMESDA
ROCK MECHANICS - FELSMECHANIK - MECHANIQUE DES ROCHES. SUPPLEMENT. 1970. irreg. price varies. Springer-Verlag, 175 Fifth Ave., New York, NY 10010. TEL 212-460-1500. FAX 212-473-6272. (Also: Berlin, Heidelberg, Tokyo and Vienna) (also avail. in microform from UMI; reprint service avail. from ISI) **Indexed:** Geo.Abstr., GeoRef., Geotech.Abstr. **Document type:** academic/scholarly publication.
—UMI. **CCC.**
Continues: Felsmechanik und Ingenieurgeologie. Rock Mechanics and Engineering Geology. Supplement.

622 US ISSN 0035-7464
TN950 CODEN: ROPRA5
ROCK PRODUCTS; industry's recognized authority. (International ed. avail.) 1897. m. $36. Intertec Publishing Corp., 29 N. Wacker Dr., Chicago, IL 60606. TEL 312-726-2802. FAX 312-726-4103. Ed. Richard Hunta. adv.; illus.; tr.lit.; pat.; index. circ. 23,068. (also avail. in microform from UMI; reprint service avail. from UMI) **Indexed:** A.S.& T.Ind., AESIS, C.R.I.Abstr., C.R.I.Curr.Cont., Chem.Abstr., Eng.Ind., Excerp.Med., GeoRef., PROMT.
—CASDDS; Ei; Faxon; SWETS; UMI; UnCover. **CCC.**
Description: Covers the production and distribution of sand and gravel, crushed stone, cement, lime, gypsum, slag, lightweight aggregates and other nonmetallic minerals.

549 551 US ISSN 0035-7529
QE351 CODEN: ROCMAR
ROCKS AND MINERALS; mineralogy, geology, lapidary. 1926. bi-m. $38 to individuals; institutions $66. (Helen Dwight Reid Educational Foundation) Heldref Publications, 1319 Eighteenth St., N.W., Washington, DC 20036-1802. TEL 202-296-6267. FAX 202-296-5149. Ed. Marie Huizig. adv. contact: Raymond Rallo. bk.rev.; charts; tr.lit.; index. circ. 4,000. (also avail. in microform; back issues avail.; reprint service avail.) **Indexed:** Chem.Abstr., Geol.Abstr., GeoRef., Mineral.Abstr., Petrol.Abstr. **Document type:** academic/scholarly publication.
●Also available on CD-ROM. Producer(s): University Microfilms International.
—BLDSC (8002.500000); CASDDS; Faxon; UMI; UnCover. **CCC.**
Description: Articles geared towards the amateurs in the field of mineralogy, geology and paleontology. *Refereed Serial*

622 US ISSN 1061-5245
ROCKY MOUNTAIN COAL MINING INSTITUTE. PROCEEDINGS. 1913. a. $25. Rocky Mountain Coal Mining Institute, 3000 Youngfield, Ste. 324, Lakewood, CO 80215. TEL 303-238-9099. FAX 303-238-0509. Ed. Doris Finnie. adv.; circ. 1,000 (controlled). **Document type:** proceedings.

MINES AND MINING INDUSTRY

622 340 665.5
333.33   US   ISSN 0886-747X
KF1819.A2
ROCKY MOUNTAIN MINERAL LAW INSTITUTE. PROCEEDINGS. 1955. a. $130. Rocky Mountain Mineral Law Foundation, 7039 E. 18th Ave., Denver, CO 80220. Ed. Karen Kaiser. circ. 1,050. (also avail. in microfilm from RRI; back issues avail.; reprint service avail. from RRI,WSH) **Indexed:** C.L.I., Leg.Per. **Document type:** proceedings.
—UnCover. CCC.
Description: Covers mining, oil and gas, landmen, environmental, and water law.

549   RM   ISSN 1220-5621
                CODEN: DSSGDY
ROMANIAN JOURNAL OF MINERALOGY. (Text in English, French and Rumanian; summaries in English and French; contents page in French) 1907. 5/yr. price varies. Institutul Geologic al Romaniei, Str. Caransebes Nr. 1, 78344 Bucharest, Rumania. TEL 40-1-6656625. FAX 40-1-3128444. E-mail: girbhr@roearn.ici.ro. bk.rev. **Indexed:** Bull.Signal., Ref.Zh. **Document type:** academic/scholarly publication.
—BLDSC (8019.636250); CASDDS.
Supersedes in part (in 1992): Institutul de Geologie si Geofizica. Dari de Seama ale Sedintelor. 1. Mineralogie, Petrologie (ISSN 1221-4671); Which was formerly: Institutul de Geologie si Geofizica. Dari de Seama ale Sedintelor. 1. Mineralogie, Petrologie, Geochimie (ISSN 0378-0589); (until 1974): Institutul Geologic. Dari de Seama ale Sedintelor. 1. Mineralogie, Petrologie, Geochimie (ISSN 1010-9420); Supersedes in part (in 1970): Comitetul de Stat al Geologiei. Dari de Seama ale Sedintelor (ISSN 0366-9726)

622   UK
ROSKILL'S METALS DATABOOK. 1987. a. £210. Roskill Information Services Ltd., 2 Clapham Rd., London SW9 0JA, England. TEL 0171-582-5155. FAX 0171-793-0008. circ. 75. **Document type:** corporate report.

ROSSING MAGAZINE. see CONSERVATION

622   UK   ISSN 0080-4495
ROYAL SCHOOL OF MINES, LONDON. JOURNAL. 1951. a. £1. Royal School of Mines Union, Prince Consort Road, London SW7 2BP, England. TEL 01-589 5111. Ed. Frank W.A.A. Lucas. adv.; bk.rev. circ. 2,000. **Indexed:** Cadscan, Lead Abstr., Zincscan.

622   YU   ISSN 0035-9637
TN4.B4
RUDARSKI GLASNIK/BULLETIN OF MINES. (Text in Serbo-Croatian; summaries in English, German and Russian) 1962. q. 278 din.($26) Rudarski Institut-Beograd - Mining Institute - Belgrade, Batajnicki Put 2, Belgrade, Yugoslavia. FAX 011-614-632. TELEX 11830 YU RI. Ed. Marunic Djuro. adv.; bk.rev.; abstr.; bibl.; charts; illus.; index. circ. 1,000. **Indexed:** C.I.S. Abstr., Chem.Abstr., Eng.Ind., GeoRef., Ref.Zh.

669   XV   ISSN 0035-9645
TN4   CODEN: RMZBAR
RUDARSKO-METALURSKI ZBORNIK/MINING AND METALLURGY QUARTERLY. (Text and summaries in English, German, Slovenian) 1953. q. $40. Univerza v Ljubljani, Fakulteta za Naravoslovje in Tehnologijo, Askerceva 20, Box 594, 61001 Ljubljana, Slovenia. TEL 386-61-1254121. FAX 386-61-1258114. Ed. Vasilij Gontazev. adv.; bk.rev.; charts; illus.; index. circ. 1,030. (also avail. in microform from UMI) **Indexed:** Chem.Abstr., Eng.Ind., GeoRef., Met.Abstr., World Alum.Abstr.
—BLDSC (8048.000000); CASDDS; UMI.
Description: Publishes articles, scientific discussions and reports on mining, metallurgy and geology.
Refereed Serial

RUDARSTVO - GEOLOGIJA - METALURGIJA. see METALLURGY

RUDY I METALE NIEZELAZNE. see METALLURGY

622   SA
S A MINING WORLD. m. Phase Four (Pty) Ltd., P.O. Box 784279, Sandton 2146, South Africa. TEL 011-444-4566. FAX 011-444-7888. adv.
Formerly: Mining World S A.

613.62 614.85   AT
S I M T A R S. q. Aus.$24. (Queensland Department of Minerals and Energy, Safety in Mines Testing and Research Centre) Magazine Publishing Company, 4 Wandoo St., Fortitude Valley, Qld. 4006, Australia. TEL 61-7-252-9677. FAX 61-7-252-4667. Ed. Michael Holliday. adv.: B&W page Aus.$1485, color page Aus.$2356; trim 275 x 210; adv. contact: Trevor Kirk. circ. 3,500. **Document type:** trade publication.
Description: Covers news and legislation pertaining to safety in mining and confined spaces, occupational health, research, etc.

622   GW
SAARBERG. 1871. bi-m. Saarbergwerke AG, Trierer Str. 1, 66111 Saarbruecken, Germany. TEL 0681-405-3425. FAX 0681-4053274. circ. 21,000. (back issues avail.) **Document type:** trade publication.
Formerly: Bergmannsfreund.
Description: Covers all aspects of mining.

622   GW
SAARBRUECKER BERGMANNSKALENDER. 1873. a. DM.15. Saarbergwerke AG, Trierer Str. 1, 66111 Saarbruecken, Germany. TEL 0681-405-3425. circ. 18,000. (back issues avail.) **Document type:** bulletin.
Description: Information on miners and mining.

SALT AND HIGHWAY DEICING NEWSLETTER. see TRANSPORTATION — Roads And Traffic

622.33   CN   ISSN 0839-8518
TN26
SASKATCHEWAN ENERGY & MINES. ANNUAL REPORT. 1954. a. Saskatchewan Energy & Mines, 1914 Hamilton St., Regina, SK S4P 4V4, Canada. TEL 306-787-2528. FAX 306-787-2527. charts; illus. **Document type:** government publication.
Former titles: Saskatchewan Mineral Resources. Annual Report; Saskatchewan. Department of Mineral Resources. Annual Report (ISSN 0581-8109)

338.2 665.5   CN   ISSN 0707-2570
HD9506.C23
SASKATCHEWAN ENERGY & MINES. MINERAL STATISTICS YEARBOOK. 1964. a. Can.$50. Saskatchewan Energy and Mines, Petroleum Statistics Branch, 1914 Hamilton St., Regina, SK S4P 4V4, Canada. TEL 306-787-2528. FAX 306-787-2527. **Document type:** government publication.
Former titles: Saskatchewan Mineral Resources. Mineral Statistical Yearbook (ISSN 0080-651X); Saskatchewan. Department of Mineral Resources. Statistical Yearbook.
Description: Includes a summary section on mineral production, disposition, value of disposition and provincial revenues from minerals, and a detailed section containing monthly, annual and historical data on each of fuel, industrial and metallic minerals.

622   SZ   ISSN 0370-9213
                CODEN: SCSTBM
SCHWEIZER STRAHLER. 1964. q. 63 SFr. Schweizer Vereinigung der Strahler und Mineraliensammler (S V S M), Postfach 101, CH-3608 Thun, Switzerland. TEL 033-364996. Ed. Paul Hottinger. adv. contact: Beatrix Elsasser. bk.rev. circ. 3,200. **Document type:** academic/scholarly publication.
—CASDDS.
Refereed Serial

549 552   SZ   ISSN 0036-7699
QE351   CODEN: SMPTA8
SCHWEIZERISCHE MINERALOGISCHE UND PETROGRAPHISCHE MITTEILUNGEN/BULLETIN SUISSE DE MINERALOGIE ET PETROGRAPHIE/BOLLETTINO SVIZZERO DI MINERALOGIA E PETROGRAFIA/SWISS BULLETIN OF MINERALOGY AND PETROLOGY; eine europaeische Zeitschrift fuer Mineralogie, Geochemie und Petrographie. (Text in English, French, German, Italian) 1921. 3/yr. 220 SFr. Staeubli Verlag AG, Raeffelstr. 11, Postfach, CH-8045 Zurich, Switzerland. TEL 01-4615858. FAX 01-4612272. adv.; bk.rev.; charts; illus.; index. **Indexed:** Chem.Abstr., GeoRef. **Document type:** bulletin.
—BLDSC (8119.000000); CASDDS; Faxon; UnCover.

338.4   GW
SECONDARY ALUMINIUM; Europe, Japan, USA. (Text in English) 1965. a. DM.25. Organisation of European Aluminum Smelters, Postfach 200840, 40105 Duesseldorf, Germany. TEL 0211-451933. FAX 0211-431009. Ed. Guenter Kirchner. circ. 4,000. **Document type:** trade publication.
Former titles (until 1988): Aluminium Smelters; Organisation of European Aluminum Smelters. Economic Situation of the Aluminum Smelters in Europe (ISSN 0474-4829)

SEGURIDAD. see OCCUPATIONAL HEALTH AND SAFETY

622   JA   ISSN 0286-7184
SEIMITSU CHOSA HOKOKUSHO/METAL MINING AGENCY OF JAPAN. CLOSE EXAMINATION REPORT. (Text in Japanese) 1965. a. Kinzoku Kogyo Jigyodan - Metal Mining Agency of Japan, 24-14, Toranomon 1-chome, Minato-ku, Tokyo 105, Japan. illus. **Document type:** academic/scholarly publication.
Supersedes in part (in 1968): Chishitsu Kozo Chosa Hokokusho (ISSN 0286-7176)

SERIES ON MINING ENGINEERING. see ENGINEERING — Industrial Engineering

622   CC   ISSN 1000-1603
                CODEN: SKKXEJ
SHANXI KUANGYE XUEYUAN XUEBAO/SHANXI MINING INSTITUTE LEARNED JOURNAL. (Text in Chinese; abstracts in English) q. $2 per no. Shanxi Kuangye Xueyuan - Shanxi Mining Institute, 23 Yingze Dajie, Taiyuan, Shanxi 030024, People's Republic of China. TEL 643200. Ed. Sheng Jianhuan. **Document type:** academic/scholarly publication.

SHIGEN CHISHITSU/RESOURCE GEOLOGY. see EARTH SCIENCES — Geology

622   JA   ISSN 0916-1740
TN275.A1   CODEN: SHSOEB
SHIGEN SOZAI/MINING AND MATERIALS PROCESSING INSTITUTE OF JAPAN. (Text in Japanese; summaries in English) 1885. m. 22400 Yen. Mining and Materials Processing Institute of Japan - Shigen, Sozai Gakkai, Nogizaka Bldg., 9-6-41 Akasaka, Minato-ku, Tokyo 107, Japan. TEL 03-3402-0541. FAX 03-3403-1776. Ed.Bd. adv.; bk.rev. circ. 4,000. **Document type:** academic/scholarly publication.
—BLDSC (4827.700000); CASDDS.
Formerly (until 1988): Nihon Kogyokaishi - Mining and Metallurgical Institute of Japan. Journal (ISSN 0369-4194)

SHIGEN TO KANKYO/NATIONAL INSTITUTE FOR RESOURCES AND ENVIRONMENT. JOURNAL. see ENVIRONMENTAL STUDIES

338.2 669   US   ISSN 0730-8132
SILVER INSTITUTE LETTER; information on silver for industry. 1971. bi-m. $20 (foreign $25). Silver Institute, 1112 16th St., N.W., Ste. 240, Washington, DC 20036. TEL 202-835-0185. FAX 3202-835-0155. Ed. John H. Lutley. circ. 4,000. (also avail. in microfiche from CIS; back issues avail.) **Indexed:** SRI.
Description: Covers recent developments on the uses of silver in the areas of art, finance, mining, coins and photography.

622   US   ISSN 0037-6329
TN1
SKILLINGS' MINING REVIEW. 1912. w. $30 (effective Jan. 1995). Skillings' Mining Review, Inc., First Bank Pl., No.728, 130 W. Superior St., Duluth, MN 55802-2083. TEL 218-722-2310. FAX 218-722-0134. Ed. David Skillings; Pub. David Skillings. adv.; bk.rev.; charts; illus.; stat.; index. circ. 4,000. **Indexed:** AESIS, Geo.Abstr., PROMT. **Document type:** newsletter.
—BLDSC (8295.850000); Faxon; UnCover.

549   SP   ISSN 0210-6558
SOCIEDAD ESPANOLA DE MINERALOGIA. BOLETIN. 1978. a. 5000 ptas. Sociedad Espanola de Mineralogia, Alenza 1, 28003 Madrid, Spain.

MINES AND MINING INDUSTRY 4771

M

338.2 FR ISSN 1163-5959
SOCIETE DE L'INDUSTRIE MINERALE GUIDE DES MINES ET CARRIERES. 1855. a. 663.65 F. Societe de l'Industrie Minerale, 41-47, rue de la Grange aux Belles, 75010 Paris, France. TEL 42-02-07-92. FAX 42-06-69-30. adv.; index.
 Former titles: Societe de l'Industrie Minerale Mines et Carrieres. Annuaire (ISSN 1154-8878); Societe de l'Industrie Minerale. Annuaire (ISSN 0081-0797)

338.7 IV ISSN 0250-3697
SOCIETE POUR LE DEVELOPPEMENT MINIER DE LA COTE D'IVOIRE. RAPPORT ANNUEL. 1962. a. free. Societe pour le Developpement Minier de la Cote d'Ivoire, 01.B.P. 2816, Abidjan 01, Ivory Coast. FAX 011-225-440821. TELEX 26162 SODMI. illus. **Indexed:** GeoRef.

SOCIETY OF EXPLOSIVES ENGINEERS. SYMPOSIUM ON EXPLOSIVES AND BLASTING RESEARCH. PROCEEDINGS. see *ENGINEERING — Chemical Engineering*

622 551 SA
SOUTH AFRICA. DEPARTMENT OF MINERAL AND ENERGY AFFAIRS. ANNUAL REPORT. (Text in Afrikaans and English) N.S. 1947. a. price varies. Department of Mineral and Energy Affairs, Private Bag X59, Pretoria 0001, South Africa. TEL 27-12-3179000. FAX 27-12-3223416. (Orders to: Government Printer, Bosman St., Private Bag X85, Pretoria 0001, South Africa. FAX 27-12-3230009) circ. 1,000. **Indexed:** GeoRef. **Document type:** government publication.
 Formerly: South Africa. Department of Mines. Annual Report; Incorporates: South Africa. Geological Survey. Report of the Chief Director of the Geological Survey; South Africa. Minerals Buro. Report of the Chief Director of the Minerals Buro.
 Description: Reflects the department's activities with regard to the optimum utilization and safe exploitation of mineral and energy resources and the rehabilitation of the surface.

SOUTH AFRICAN INSTITUTE OF MINING AND METALLURGY. JOURNAL. see *METALLURGY*

SOUTH AFRICAN INSTITUTE OF MINING AND METALLURGY. MONOGRAPH SERIES. see *METALLURGY*

SOUTH AFRICAN LAPIDARY MAGAZINE. see *EARTH SCIENCES*

622 620 SA ISSN 0257-7623
SOUTH AFRICAN MINING, COAL, GOLD AND BASE MINERALS. 1891. m. R.117.42 (foreign R.143) (effective 1994). Thomson Publications (Subsidiary of: Times Media Ltd.), P.O. Box 56182, Pinegowrie 2123, South Africa. TEL 27-11-789-2144. FAX 27-11-789-3196. Ed. Bill Krige. adv.; illus.; mkt.; stat.; index. circ. 4,978. (also avail. in microfilm from UMI,PMC) **Indexed:** AESIS, Eng.Ind., Excerp.Med. (until 19??), GeoRef., Ind.S.A.Per., INIS Atomind. **Document type:** trade publication.
 —BLDSC (8342.300000); Faxon; SWETS; UnCover.
 Formed by the 1985 merger of: South African Mining and Engineering Journal (ISSN 0038-2477); **Formerly (until 1919):** South African Mining Journal (ISSN 0370-8349); Coal, Gold and Base Minerals of Southern Africa (ISSN 0530-0029); **Formerly (1953-1964):** Coal and Base Minerals of Southern Africa (ISSN 0366-7103); Incorporates: South African Mining Equipment.

SOUTH AUSTRALIA. DEPARTMENT OF MINES AND ENERGY. SPECIAL PUBLICATIONS. see *EARTH SCIENCES*

622 CN ISSN 0840-6723
TN26
SOUTHAM MINING GROUP'S MINING SOURCEBOOK. 1891. a. Can.$77.58 (foreign $89). Southam Magazine Group, 1450 Don Mills Rd., Don Mills, ON M3B 2X7, Canada. TEL 416-445-6641. FAX 416-442-2261. Ed. Richard Fish; Pub. Doug Donnelly. adv. circ. 2,970. **Document type:** directory.
 Former titles (until 1989): Canadian Mining Journal's Reference Manual and Buyers' Guide (ISSN 0315-9140); Canadian Mining Manual (ISSN 0068-9319)

622 665 UK
SOUTH - EAST ASIA MINING, OIL & GAS NEWSLETTER. 1989. s-m. £396($792) (effective Jan. 1996). Francophone Business Publishing, Box 704, 28 Barclay Rd., London SW6 1EH, England. TEL 0171-736-7604. Ed. R. Purdy. adv. contact: J. Gravell. bk.rev.; stat.; tr.lit. (back issues avail.) **Document type:** newsletter.
 Formerly: Southeast Asia Mining Letter (ISSN 0957-1566)
 Description: Examines metals, mining, oil, coal, and gas in Asia and Oceania. Examines development from exploration and investments to trading and end-use for an international audience.

338.2 622 RU ISSN 0132-1269
SOVETSKII SHAKHTER.* 1952. m. 16.80 Rub. (Profsoyuz Rabochikh Ugol'noi Promyshlennosti, Tsentral'nyi Komitet) Profizdat, Ul. Myasnitskaya 13, 101000 Moscow, Russia. TEL 095-924-5740. Ed. F.S. Bocharov. bk.rev.; charts; illus.; stat.; index. circ. 101,720.

SPAIN. INSTITUTO TECNOLOGICO GEOMINERO DE ESPANA. COLECCION MEMORIAS. see *EARTH SCIENCES — Geology*

SPAIN. INSTITUTO TECNOLOGICO GEOMINERO DE ESPANA. COLECCION TEMAS GEOLOGICOS - MINEROS. see *EARTH SCIENCES*

SPAIN. INSTITUTO TECNOLOGICO GEOMINERO DE ESPANA. INFORMES. see *EARTH SCIENCES — Geology*

622 US
SPEAKERS' PAPERS: SPEECHES FROM THE GOLD AND SILVER INSTITUTES' (YEAR) ANNUAL MEETING. a. $90 (foreign $105). Gold Institute, Administrative Office - Institut de l'Or, Bureau Administratif, 1112 16th St., N.W., Ste. 240, Washington, DC 20036-4823. TEL 202-835-0185. FAX 202-835-0155.
 Description: Contains current information direct from industry leaders and experts.

354.489 DK ISSN 0907-5321
KDZ3471
SPECIFICATIONS OF MINERAL AND HYDROCARBON LICENSES IN GREENLAND. 1981. a. free. Ministry of Environment and Energy, Mineral Resources Administration for Greenland, Kompagnistraede 15, DK-1208 Copenhagen K, Denmark. TEL 45-33-92-75-00. FAX 45-33-13-30-17. TELEX 15505 ENRGY DK.
 Formerly (until 1992): Specifications of Mineral Concessions and Licences in Greenland (ISSN 0107-430X)
 Description: Provides information about the principles, content, etc. of the mineral resources system for Greenland; lists existing mineral and hydrocarbon exploration and prospecting licenses in Greenland

STANDING COMMITTEE ON ENERGY, MINES AND RESOURCES. MINUTES OF PROCEEDINGS AND EVIDENCE. see *ENERGY*

338.2 CN ISSN 0707-2767
TN806.C2
STATISTICAL REVIEW OF COAL IN CANADA. 1971. a. Energy, Mines and Resources Canada, Mineral Policy Sector, 460 O'Connor St., Ottawa, ON K1A 0E4, Canada. TEL 613-995-1118. FAX 613-992-5565. stat. **Document type:** government publication.
 Formerly: Coal in Canada, Supply and Demand (ISSN 0700-284X)

622 665.5 US
HD9685.U4
STEAM - ELECTRIC PLANT FACTORS (YEAR). a. $125 to individuals; non-profit organizations $100. National Coal Association, 1130 17th St., N.W., Washington, DC 20036. TEL 202-463-2640. **Indexed:** SRI.
 Former titles: Steam Electric Fuels (ISSN 0090-3884); Steam - Electric Plant Factors (ISSN 0081-5411)

STEELMAKING CONFERENCE: PROCEEDINGS. see *METALLURGY*

622 GW ISSN 0039-1018
TN950
STEINBRUCH UND SANDGRUBE; unabhaengige Fach-Zeitschrift fuer Steinbrueche, Kies- und Sandgruben, Betonsteinwerke. 1904. m. DM.70 (foreign DM.100). Verlagsgesellschaft Gruetter, Postfach 910708, 30427 Hannover, Germany. TEL 0511-4603-300. FAX 0511-4609-320. Ed. K.-H. Mueller. adv. contact: Thomas Janz. bk.rev.; illus.; index. circ. 10,500. **Document type:** trade publication.
 —CCC.

622 US ISSN 8750-9210
STONE REVIEW. 1985. bi-m. $48 (effective 1994). National Stone Association, 1415 Elliot Pl., N.W., Washington, DC 20007-2599. TEL 202-342-1100. FAX 202-342-0702. Ed. Frank E. Atlee; Pub. Robert G. Bartlett. adv. contact: Frank E. Atlee. circ. 4,000. **Document type:** trade publication.
 Formed by the Jan. 1985 merger of (1974-1984): Stone News; (1964-1984): Limestone.
 Description: Provides a communication forum for the crushed stone industry, facilitating the exchange of information on industry technology, trends, developments and concerns.

338.2 622 661.2 UK ISSN 0039-4890
CODEN: SULPAW
SULPHUR; covers all aspects of world sulphur and sulphuric acid industry. 1953. bi-m. £340($495) British Sulphur Publishing (Subsidiary of: C R U Publishing Ltd.), 31 Mount Pleasant, London WC1X OAD, England. TEL 0171-837-5600. FAX 0171-837-0292. TELEX 918918 SULFEX G. Ed. R. Mansor. bk.rev.; charts; illus.; mkt.; stat.; index. circ. 639. (also avail. in microform from UMI; reprint service avail. from UMI) **Indexed:** Chem.Abstr., Soils & Fert. **Document type:** trade publication.
 —BLDSC (8516.800000); CASDDS; SWETS; UMI; UnCover.

622 BL ISSN 0101-2053
HD9506.B7
SUMARIO MINERAL. 1981. a. 3 BTN($3) Departamento Nacional da Producao Mineral, Setor de Autarquias Norte, Quadra 1, Bloco B, 70040 Brasilia D.F., Brazil. TEL 061-224-2670. circ. 2,500.

338.2 665.5 CN ISSN 0833-9600
HD9506.C2
SURVEY OF MINES AND ENERGY RESOURCES. 1980. a. Can.$67.50. Financial Post Co., Ltd., 333 King St., E., Toronto, Ont. M5A 4N2, Canada. TEL 416-350-6477. FAX 416-350-6501. Ed. Steven Pattison. adv. circ. 11,000.
 —BLDSC (8550.601000).
 Formerly: Financial Post Survey of Mines and Energy Resouces (ISSN 0227-1656); Which was formed by the merger of: Financial Post Survey of Mines (ISSN 0071-5085); Financial Post Survey of Energy Resources (ISSN 0705-7091)
 Description: Investment and financial information on publicly owned mining and resource companies in Canada.

SURVEYING AUSTRALIA. see *ENGINEERING — Civil Engineering*

622 SW ISSN 0039-6435
SVENSK BERGS- & BRUKSTIDNING. 1922. 6/yr. SEK 120 (effective 1990). B & J Invest AB, P.O. Box 6040, S-20011 Malmoe, Sweden. FAX 40-79737. Ed. Joergen Dahlkvist. circ. 3,000.

T H - ERS EXPRESS; adventure bulletin. (Treasure Hunt) see *HOBBIES*

T I Z INTERNATIONAL; Powder & Bulk Magazin. (Tonindustrie-Zeitung) see *ENGINEERING — Chemical Engineering*

622 CC ISSN 0494-6162
TANKUANG GONGCHENG. (Text in Chinese) bi-m. Dizhi Kuangchan Bu, Kantan Jishu Yanjiusuo, 26, Baiwanzhuang Lu, Beijing 100037, People's Republic of China. TEL 8311133. Ed. Wang Decong.

622 II
TECHNICAL INFORMATION DIGEST. (Text in English) 1976. q. free. Central Mine Planning & Design Institute Ltd. (Subsidiary of: Coal India Limited), Publications Wing, Gondwana Place, Kanke Rd., Ranchi 834008, Bihar, India.

MINES AND MINING INDUSTRY

622   **HU**   ISSN 0324-4628
TN275.A1   CODEN: PTUADT
TECHNICAL UNIVERSITY FOR HEAVY INDUSTRY. PUBLICATIONS. SERIES A, MINING. (Text in English, German, Russian) irreg., vol.45, no.1-4, 1988. Nehezipari Muszaki Egyetem, Miskolc, Hungary. TEL 46-65111. FAX 46-69554. TELEX 62223-NMEMIS. Ed.Bd. bibl.; index. circ. 350. **Indexed:** C.R.I.Abstr., C.R.I.Curr.Cont.

TECHNIKA POSZUKIWAN GEOLOGICZNYCH, GEOSYNOPTYKA I GEOTERMIA/EXPLORATION TECHNOLOGY, GEOSYNOPTICS AND GEOTHERMAL ENERGY. see *EARTH SCIENCES — Geology*

622   **GW**   ISSN 0040-1501
TECHNISCHE UNIVERSITAET CLAUSTHAL. MITTEILUNGSBLATT. 1960. s-a. DM.7.50. Technische Universitaet Clausthal, Agricolastrasse 2, 38678 Clausthal, Germany. circ. 1,800.
—CCC.
    Formerly: Technische Hochschule der Bergakademie Clausthal. Mitteilungsblatt.

622   **CN**
TECHNOLOGY FOCUS NEWSLETTER. 3/yr. free. Canada Centre for Mineral and Energy Technology, 555 Booth St., Ottawa, Ont. K1A 0G1, Canada. FAX 613-995-3192. TELEX 053-3395. **Document type:** newsletter.

622   **US**   ISSN 0196-0792
TN345
TECHNOLOGY NEWS. 1974. irreg. free. U.S. Bureau of Mines, Office of Public Information, 810 Seventh St., N.W., MS-1040, Washington, DC 20241. TEL 202-501-9649. FAX 202-219-2493. (Subscr. to: U.S.B.M., MS-6201, 810 Seventh St., N.W., Washington, DC 20241-0002) **Document type:** government publication, academic/scholarly publication.
—BLDSC (8758.960000).
    Description: Reports on recent U.S.B.M. research

TED SLANKER'S MARKET UPDATE. see *BUSINESS AND ECONOMICS — Investments*

622   **AA**
TEKNIKA/TECHNIQUE. (Text in Albanian; summaries in French) q. $3.08. Ministere des Resources Minerales et Energetiques - Ministry of Energy and Mineral Resources, Tirana, Albania. **Document type:** trade publication, government publication.

TEXAS ENERGY. see *ENERGY*

TIANRANQI GONGYE/NATURAL GAS INDUSTRY. see *PETROLEUM AND GAS*

TOHOKU DAIGAKU SOZAI KOGAKU KENKYUJO IHO/TOHOKU UNIVERSITY. INSTITUTE FOR ADVANCED MATERIALS PROCESSING. BULLETIN. see *METALLURGY*

549 551   **JA**   ISSN 0371-3903
    CODEN: STUMAR
TOHOKU UNIVERSITY. SCIENCE REPORTS. SERIES 3: MINERALOGY, PETROLOGY AND ECONOMIC GEOLOGY/TOHOKU DAIGAKU RIKA HOKOKU. DAI 3-SHU, GANSEKIGAKU KOBUTSUGAKU KOSHOGAKU. (Text in English) 1921. a. Tohoku Daigaku, Rigakubu - Tohoku University, Faculty of Science, Aoba, Aramaki, Aoba-ku, Sendai-shi, Miyagi-ken 980, Japan. **Indexed:** Chem.Abstr., INIS Atomind.
—CASDDS; UnCover.

622   **FR**
TRAVAILLEUR DU SOUS-SOL. 24/yr. 263 rue de Paris, 93515 Montreuil Cedex, France. TEL 48-51-82-25. circ. 83,000.

622   **FR**   ISSN 0982-0655
TRIBUNE DE LA REGION MINIERE. 1952. w. Syndicat des Mineurs, Confederation Generale du Travail, 32 rue Casimir-Beugnet, 62300 Lens (Pas-de-Calais), France. adv. circ. 78,000.
    Formerly (until 1986): Tribune des Mineurs (ISSN 0982-0663)

622   **US**   CODEN: PSRMA6
TN5
U S SYMPOSIUM ON ROCK MECHANICS. PROCEEDINGS. 1961. irreg. $80. Colorado School of Mines, Golden, CO 80401. TEL 303-273-3000. Eds. Fun-Den Wang, George B. Clark. (reprint service avail. from UMI) **Document type:** proceedings.
    Formerly (until 1975): Symposium on Rock Mechanics. Proceedings (ISSN 0586-3031)

622 662   **RU**   ISSN 0041-5790
    CODEN: UGOLAR
UGOL'. 1925. m. $110 (effective 1996). (Ministerstvo Ugol'noi Promyshlennosti) Izdatel'stvo Nedra, Pl. Belorusskogo Vokzala, 3, 125047 Moscow, Russia. TEL 250-52-55. Ed. G.V. Krasnikovskii. adv.; bk.rev.; bibl.; charts; illus.; stat.; index. circ. 8,945. **Indexed:** C.I.S. Abstr., Chem.Abstr., Eng.Ind., Fuel & Energy Abstr.
—BLDSC (0383.000000); CASDDS. **CCC.**

622 662.6   **KR**   ISSN 0041-5804
    CODEN: UGOUAK
UGOL' UKRAINY. (Text in Russian) 1957. m. $147 (effective 1996). Izdatel'stvo Tekhnika, Pushkinskaya 28, Kiev, Ukraine. adv.; charts; illus.; index. circ. 10,000. **Indexed:** C.I.S.Abstr., Chem.Abstr., Eng.Ind., Fuel & Energy Abstr.
—CASDDS. **CCC.**

622   **XR**   ISSN 1210-7697
TN4   CODEN: UGPREK
UHLI - RUDY - GEOLOGICKY PRUZKUM. (Text in Czech; summaries in English, German, Russian) 1992. m. 240 Kc. Zamestnavatelsky Svaz Dulniho a Naftoveho Prumyslu, Skretova 6, 120 59 Prague 2, Czech Republic. TEL 42-2-24215373. Ed. Evzen Synek. adv.; bk.rev.; charts; illus.; pat. circ. 2,800. **Indexed:** C.I.S. Abstr., Chem.Abstr., Fuel & Energy Abstr.
—BLDSC (9080.501100); CASDDS.
    Formed by the merger of (1957-1994): Geologicky Pruzkum (ISSN 0016-772X); (1992-1994): Uhli - Rudy (ISSN 1210-1699); Which was formed by the merger of (1953-1992): Uhli (ISSN 0041-5812); (1953-1992): Rudy (ISSN 0483-5093)

338.2   **UK**   ISSN 0957-4697
HD9506.G7
UNITED KINGDOM MINERALS YEARBOOK. 1973. a. price varies. Natural Environment Research Council, British Geological Survey, Kingsley Dunham Centre, Keyworth, Nottingham NG12 5GG, England. TEL 0115-936-1000. FAX 0115-936-2000. TELEX 378173 BGSKEY G. (Subscr. to: H.M.S.O., Circulation Officer, Nine Elms Ln., London SW8 5DR, England) stat. **Document type:** government publication.
—BLDSC (9096.455000).
    Supersedes (in 1989): United Kingdom Mineral Statistics (ISSN 0308-5090)

UNITED MINE WORKERS JOURNAL. see *LABOR UNIONS*

550   **UN**   ISSN 0082-8114
TN1.A1   CODEN: UNEMAT
UNITED NATIONS. ECONOMIC AND SOCIAL COMMISSION FOR ASIA AND THE PACIFIC. MINERAL RESOURCES DEVELOPMENT SERIES. 1952. irreg., no.63. price varies. United Nations Economic and Social Commission for Asia and the Pacific (ESCAP), United Nations Bldg., Rajamnern Ave., Bangkok 10200, Thailand. (Dist. by: United Nations Publications, Rm. DC2-0853, New York, NY 10017; or Distribution and Sales Section, Palais des Nations, CH-1211 Geneva 10, Switzerland) (back issues avail.)

622 614
U.S. BUREAU OF MINES. ANNUAL RESEARCH REPORT. a. U.S. Bureau of Mines, Office of Public Information, 810 Seventh St., N.W., MS-1040, Washington, DC 20241-0001. TEL 202-501-9649. FAX 202-219-2493. (Orders to: U.S.B.M., Box 19070, Pittsburgh, PA 15236; Or: Bernan, 4611-F Assembly Dr., Lanham, MD 20706. TEL 301-459-7666. FAX 301-459-0056) illus.; stat. (also avail. by fax) **Document type:** government publication.
●Also available online.
    Description: Reports U.S.B.M. research on mine safety, reclamation, public health, and materials science.

622   **US**   ISSN 0082-9129
TN23   CODEN: XBMBAJ
U.S. BUREAU OF MINES. BULLETIN. 1910. irreg. price varies. U.S. Bureau of Mines, Office of Public Information, 810 Seventh St., N.W., MS-9800, Washington, DC 20241-0001. (also avail. in microfiche from PMC) **Indexed:** AESIS, Petrol.Abstr. **Document type:** bulletin, government publication.
—CASDDS.
    Description: Reports final results of major projects.

622   **US**
U.S. BUREAU OF MINES. INFORMATION CIRCULARS. 1925. irreg. price varies. U.S. Bureau of Mines, Office of Public Information, 810 Seventh St., N.W., MS-1040, Washington, DC 20241-0001. TEL 202-501-9649. FAX 202-219-2493. (Orders to: National Technical Information Service, 5285 Port Royal Rd., Springfield, VA 22161. TEL 703-487-4650. FAX 703-321-8547) (also avail. in microfiche from NTI) **Indexed:** AESIS, Chem.Abstr., GeoRef., Petrol.Abstr., Pollut.Abstr. **Document type:** government publication.
    Description: Reports the results of various economic and special studies.

U.S. BUREAU OF MINES. OFFICE OF TECHNOLOGY TRANSFER. PATENTS. see *PATENTS, TRADEMARKS AND COPYRIGHTS*

622   **US**   ISSN 1066-5552
TN23   CODEN: XBMIA6
U.S. BUREAU OF MINES. REPORT OF INVESTIGATIONS. 1919. irreg. free. U.S. Bureau of Mines, Office of Public Information, 810 Seventh St., N.W., MS-9800, Washington, DC 20241-0001. TEL 202-501-9358. FAX 202-501-9958. (Orders to: National Technical Information Service, 5285 Port Royal Rd., Springfield, VA 22161. TEL 703-487-4650. FAX 703-321-8547) (also avail. in microfiche from PMC) **Indexed:** AESIS, Chem.Abstr., GeoRef., INSPEC, Petrol.Abstr., Soils & Fert. **Document type:** government publication, monographic series.
    Description: Reports on U.S.B.M. research on mining and metals.

322   **US**
U.S. BUREAU OF MINES. SPECIAL PUBLICATIONS. irreg. price varies. U.S. Bureau of Mines, Office of Public Information, 810 Seventh St., N.W., MS-9800, Washington, DC 20241-0001. TEL 202-501-9649. FAX 202-219-2493. (Orders to: Superintendent of Documents, U.S. Government Printing Office, Box 371954, Pittsburgh, PA 15250-7954. TEL 202-512-1800. FAX 202-512-2250) **Document type:** government publication.
    Description: Discusses new mining and mine-control technologies.

U.S. DEPARTMENT OF THE INTERIOR. A L J DECISIONS. see *PUBLIC ADMINISTRATION*

U.S. DEPARTMENT OF THE INTERIOR. INTERIOR BOARD OF LAND APPEALS. see *PUBLIC ADMINISTRATION*

622.33   **US**   ISSN 0736-4504
TN805.A3
U.S. ENERGY INFORMATION ADMINISTRATION. COAL PRODUCTION (YEAR). Variant title: Annual Coal Production Report. 1976. a. $7.50. U.S. Energy Information Administration, National Energy Information Center, EI-231, James Forrestal Bldg., Rm. 1F-048, 1000 Independence Ave., S.W., Washington, DC 20585. TEL 202-586-8800. (Orders to: National Technical Information Service, 5285 Port Royal Rd., Springfield, VA 22161. TEL 703-487-4650. FAX 703-321-8547; Or: Superintendent of Documents, U.S. Government Printing Office, Box 371954, Pittsburgh, PA 15250-1954. TEL 202-512-1800. FAX 202-512-2250; Or: Bernan, 4611-F Assembly Dr., Lanham, MD 20706. TEL 800-274-4447. FAX 301-459-0056) charts; stat. **Document type:** government publication.
    Formerly: Coal Production Annual; Incorporates (in 1983): Coal-Pennsylvania Anthracite.

U.S. ENERGY INFORMATION ADMINISTRATION. QUARTERLY COAL REPORT. see *ENERGY*

U.S. ENERGY INFORMATION ADMINISTRATION. WEEKLY COAL PRODUCTION. see *ENERGY*

MINES AND MINING INDUSTRY 4773

622.8   US
U.S. MINE SAFETY AND HEALTH ADMINISTRATION. INFORMATIONAL REPORT. irreg. U.S. Department of Labor, Mine Safety and Health Administration, 4015 Wilson Blvd., Arlington, VA 22203.
   Formerly: U.S. Mining Enforcement and Safety Administration. Informational Report (ISSN 0097-9376)

549   IT
UNIVERSITA DEGLI STUDI DI FERRARA. ISTITUTO DI MINERALOGIA. ANNALI. NUOVA SERIE. SEZIONE: SCIENZE DELLA TERRA. (Text in Italian; summaries in English, French and Italian) vol.1, no.7, 1973. irreg. Universita degli Studi di Ferrara, Istituto di Mineralogia, C.so Ercole 1o d'Este 32, 44100 Ferrara, Italy. FAX 0532-206468. bibl.; charts.

622 546   US   ISSN 0568-8760
TN24.A4
UNIVERSITY OF ALASKA. MINERAL INDUSTRY RESEARCH LABORATORY. ANNUAL REPORT OF RESEARCH PROGRESS. a. University of Alaska at Fairbanks, Mineral Industry Research Laboratory, 212B O'Neill Bldg., Box 757240, Fairbanks, AK 99775-7240. TEL 907-474-7135. FAX 907-474-5400. **Document type:** catalog.

UNIVERSITY OF TEXAS AT AUSTIN. BUREAU OF ECONOMIC GEOLOGY. MINERAL RESOURCE CIRCULARS. see *EARTH SCIENCES — Geology*

622   RH   ISSN 0254-2951
UNIVERSITY OF ZIMBABWE. INSTITUTE OF MINING RESEARCH. REPORT. Variant title: I M R Open Report. no.104, 1990. irreg., no.126, 1990. University of Zimbabwe, Institute of Mining Research, P.O. Box MP 167, Mount Pleasant, Harare, Zimbabwe. **Document type:** monographic series.
  —BLDSC (7624.260000).
  Description: Discusses specific aspects of the mining and minerals industries in Zimbabwe and neighboring states.

UNIWERSYTET SLASKI W KATOWICACH. PRACE NAUKOWE. PROBLEMY PRAWNE GORNICTWA. see *LAW*

622   GW   ISSN 0343-8198
UNSER BETRIEB. 1968. 3/yr. Deilmann - Haniel GmbH, Haustenbecke 1, 44319 Dortmund, Germany. TEL 0231-28910. FAX 0231-2891362. bk.rev. circ. 13,000. **Document type:** trade publication.

333.8   FR
URANIUM: RESOURCES, PRODUCTION AND DEMAND/URANIUM: RESSOURCES, PRODUCTION ET DEMANDE. (Text in English, French) 1965. biennial. price varies. Organization for Economic Cooperation and Development, Nuclear Energy Agency, 12 bd. des Iles, 92130 Issy-les-Moulineaux, France. TEL 45-24-10-15. FAX 45-24-11-10. (U.S. subscr. to: O.E.C.D. Publications and Information Center, 2001 L St., N.W., Ste. 700, Washington, DC 20036-4095. TEL 202-785-6323) charts; illus. circ. 2,030. (also avail. in microfiche)
  Description: Compares uranium supply data with the nuclear industry's requirements until the year 2030. Reviews exploration, resources and production.

UTAH GEOLOGICAL SURVEY. BULLETIN. see *EARTH SCIENCES — Geology*

UTAH GEOLOGICAL SURVEY. SPECIAL STUDIES. see *EARTH SCIENCES — Geology*

UTAH GEOLOGICAL SURVEY. SURVEY NOTES. see *EARTH SCIENCES — Geology*

V W D - MONTAN. see *BUSINESS AND ECONOMICS — Investments*

622 338.2   VE   ISSN 0798-5851
VENEZUELA. MINISTERIO DE ENERGIA Y MINAS. CARTA SEMANAL. vol.13, 1970. w. free. Ministerio de Energia y Minas, Torre Norte, Centro Simon Bolivar, Caracas, Venezuela. (Subscr. to: Ministerio de Energia y Minas, Biblioteca, Torre Oeste Piso 2, Parque Central, Caracas-Venezuela) stat. **Document type:** government publication.
  Formerly: Venezuela. Ministerio de Minas e Hidrocarburos. Carta Semanal (ISSN 0042-3394)

622 338.2   VE
VENEZUELA. MINISTERIO DE ENERGIA Y MINAS. INFORMATIONS. (Text in French) 1967. bi-m. free. Ministerio de Energia y Minas, Torre Norte, Centro Simon Bolivar, Caracas, Venezuela. (processed) **Document type:** government publication.
  Formerly: Venezuela. Ministerio de Minas e Hidrocarburos. Informations (ISSN 0042-3408)

622 665   VE
VENEZUELA. MINISTERIO DE ENERGIA Y MINAS. MEMORIA Y CUENTA. 1952. a. free. Ministerio de Energia y Minas, Torre piso 16, Relaciones Publicas, Caracas, Venezuela. charts; stat. **Indexed:** GeoRef. **Document type:** government publication.
  Formerly: Venezuela. Ministerio de Minas e Hidrocarburos. Memoria y Cuenta (ISSN 0083-5374)

622 665.5   VE
VENEZUELA. MINISTERIO DE ENERGIA Y MINAS. QUARTERLY BULLETIN. Spanish edition: Actividades Petroleras (ISSN 0001-7582) (Text in English) q. Ministerio de Energia y Minas, Torre Norte, Centro Simon Bolivar, Caracas, Venezuela. (Subscr. to: Ministerio de Energia y Minas, Biblioteca Torre Oeste, Piso 2, Parque Central, Caracas, Venezuela) charts; stat. **Document type:** bulletin, government publication.
  Former titles: Venezuela. Ministerio de Energia y Minas. Monthly Bulletin; Venezuela. Ministerio de Minas e Hidrocarburos. Monthly Bulletin (ISSN 0042-3416)

622   GW   ISSN 0302-4938
HD95531
VEREIN DEUTSCHER KOHLENIMPORTEURE. JAHRESBERICHT. a. Verein Deutscher Kohlenimporteure e.V., Glockengiesserwall 19, 20095 Hamburg, Germany. TEL 040-327484. FAX 040-326772. TELEX 2161360-KBR-D. **Document type:** corporate report.

553 622   US
VIRGINIA. DIVISION OF MINERAL RESOURCES. PUBLICATIONS. 1959. irreg. price varies. Department of Mines, Minerals and Energy, Division of Mineral Resources, Box 3667, Charlottesville, VA 22903. TEL 804-293-5121. FAX 804-293-2239. **Indexed:** GeoRef. **Document type:** government publication.
  Former titles: Virginia. Division of Mineral Resources. Bulletin; Virginia. Division of Mineral Resources. Information Circular (ISSN 0083-632X); Virginia. Division of Mineral Resources. Mineral Resources Report (ISSN 0083-6338); Virginia. Division of Mineral Resources. Report of Investigations (ISSN 0083-6346); Virginia. Division of Mineral Resources. Reports.

VIRGINIA INDUSTRIAL DIRECTORY. see *BUSINESS AND ECONOMICS — Trade And Industrial Directories*

549   US   ISSN 0042-6652
TN24.8.V8   CODEN: VAMIAB
VIRGINIA MINERALS. 1954. q. free to residents. Department of Mines, Minerals and Energy, Division of Mineral Resources, Box 3667, Charlottesville, VA 22903. TEL 804-293-5121. FAX 804-293-2239. Ed. Eugene K. Roden. bk.rev.; charts; illus.; maps; stat.; cum.index in vol.10 and vol.20. **Indexed:** Chem.Abstr., GeoRef. **Document type:** government publication.
  —Faxon.

622   FI   ISSN 0042-9317
VUORITEOLLISUS/BERGSHANTERINGEN.* (Text in English, Finnish, Swedish) 1943. s-a. FIM 30. Vuorimiesyhdistys-Bergsmannaforeningen r.y. - Mining and Metallurgical Society of Finland, Ins. Lars Heikel, SF-00820 Helsinki, Finland. Ed. Martti Sulonen. adv.; charts; illus.; stat.; cum.index: 1943-1969. circ. 2,300. **Indexed:** GeoRef.
  —BLDSC (9259.500000).

WASHINGTON (STATE). DEPARTMENT OF NATURAL RESOURCES. DIVISION OF GEOLOGY AND EARTH RESOURCES. BULLETIN. see *EARTH SCIENCES — Geology*

557.97   US   ISSN 0147-1783
TN24.W2   CODEN: ICDRD3
WASHINGTON (STATE). DEPARTMENT OF NATURAL RESOURCES. DIVISION OF GEOLOGY AND EARTH RESOURCES. INFORMATION CIRCULAR. Key Title: Information Circular - State of Washington, Department of Natural Resources, Division of Geology and Earth Resources. 1939. irreg., no. 89, 1994. price varies. Department of Natural Resources, Division of Geology and Earth Resources, 1111 Washington St., 5E, Box 47000, Olympia, WA 98504-7000. TEL 206-902-1450. FAX 206-902-1785. **Document type:** government publication, monographic series.
  —BLDSC (4489.055000).
  Description: Provides technical geological information on the state of Washington.

338.2   US
WEST VIRGINIA. OFFICE OF MINER'S HEALTH, SAFETY & TRAINING. REPORT & DIGEST DIRECTORY. 1883. a. $10. Office of Miner's Health, Safety & Training, 1615 Washington St. E., Charleston, WV 25311. TEL 304-348-3500. circ. 2,500. **Document type:** government publication, directory.
  Formed by the merger of: West Virginia. Department of Mines. Annual Report; West Virginia. Department of Mines. Directory of Mines (ISSN 0083-8462)

338.2   US   ISSN 0091-5513
HD9547.W39
WEST VIRGINIA COAL FACTS.* 1971. a. $10. West Virginia Coal Association, 1301 Laidley Tower, Charleston, WV 25301. TEL 304-342-4153. Ed. Mark Polen. stat.; illus. circ. 5,000.

622   US   ISSN 0083-842X
TN1
WEST VIRGINIA COAL MINING INSTITUTE. PROCEEDINGS. 1919. irreg. $7.50. West Virginia Coal Mining Institute, 213 White Hall, Morgantown, WV 26506. Ed. Jay Hilary Kelley. **Document type:** proceedings.

622   US
WEST VIRGINIA MINERAL INDUSTRIES DIRECTORY. 1971. biennial. $25 per no. Geological and Economic Survey, Box 879, Morgantown, WV 26507-0879. TEL 304-594-2331. **Document type:** directory, government publication.
  Former titles: West Virginia Mineral Producers and Processors Directory; West Virginia Mineral Producers Directory.
  Description: Lists by commodity and county all mineral producers in West Virginia, with addresses and phone numbers.

622   AT   ISSN 0510-2014
WESTERN AUSTRALIA. GEOLOGICAL SURVEY. MINERAL RESOURCES BULLETIN. 1945-1984; resumed 199? irreg. price varies. Geological Survey of Western Australia, 100 Plain St., E. Perth, W.A. 6004, Australia. TEL 61-9-222-3333. FAX 61-9-222-3633. circ. controlled. (also avail. in microfiche; back issues avail.) **Indexed:** AESIS, GeoRef. **Document type:** monographic series.

622 549   AT   ISSN 0814-9488
WESTERN CONTRACTOR. 1985. m. Aus.$70. Regal Focus Pty. Ltd., Ste. 6, 272 Hay St., Subiaco, Perth, W.A. 6008, Australia. TEL 61-9-388-1440. FAX 61-9-388-3646. Ed. Mark Mentiplay. adv. contact: Tom Green. tr.lit. circ. 4,000. (back issues avail.) **Document type:** trade publication.
  Description: Western Australia's independent industry magazine providing hard news and information on construction, mining, oil and gas, earthmoving, transport, quarrying, technology and services of contracting industry.

622   US   ISSN 0162-9026
TN12
WESTERN MINING DIRECTORY. 1977. a. $49. Howell Publishing Co., Box 37510, Denver, CO 80237. TEL 303-770-6794. FAX 303-770-6790. Ed. Don E. Howell. circ. 10,000. (back issues avail.) **Document type:** directory.

WESTERN MINING NEWS. see *BUSINESS AND ECONOMICS — Investments*

622   AT   ISSN 0312-4584
WHAT MINING MEANS TO AUSTRALIANS. 1978. irreg. free. Australian Mining Industry Council, P.O. Box 363, Dickson, A.C.T. 2602, Australia. FAX 61-6-279-3699.

MINES AND MINING INDUSTRY — ABSTRACTING, BIBLIOGRAPHIES, STATISTICS

622   UK   ISSN 1351-3915
WHO OWNS WHO IN MINING. 1992. a. £180. Roskill Information Services Ltd., 2 Clapham Rd., London SW9 OJA, England. TEL 0171-582-5155. FAX 0171-798-0008. charts; stats.; circ. 100 (paid). (back issues avail.) **Document type:** directory.

622   AT   ISSN 0817-6353
WHO'S PEGGING. 1970. w. Aus.$475. Pex Publications Pty. Ltd., P.O. Box 158, Claremont, W.A. 6010, Australia. TEL 61-9-3833477. FAX 61-9-3851485. Ed. John Lipscombe. (back issues avail.) **Document type:** newsletter.
Description: Australia's prospecting newsletter listing all mineral tenements by applicant, location and number.

622   PL   ISSN 0043-5120
WIADOMOSCI GORNICZE. 1950. m. $39. (Stowarzyszenie Inzynierow i Technikow Gornictwa) Wydawnictwo "Slask", Al. W. Korfantego 51, 40-161 Katowice, Poland. (Dist. by: Ars Polona-Ruch, Krakowskie Przedmiescie 7, Warsaw, Poland) Ed. Marian Gustek. adv.; bk.rev. circ. 2,850. **Indexed:** C.I.S. Abstr.

622   US
WOMEN IN MINING NATIONAL QUARTERLY. 1981. q. $10. Women in Mining National, 1801 Broadway, Ste. 400, Denver, CO 80202. TEL 303-298-1535. Ed. Susan Hanel. circ. 600. **Document type:** trade publication.
Description: Educates members on all aspects of the minerals industry.

WORLD COAL. see ENERGY

338.2   UK   ISSN 0950-2262
WORLD COPPER DATABOOK. 1974. irreg., latest 1992. $191. Metal Bulletin plc, Park House, Park Terrace, Worcester Park, Surrey KT4 7HY, England. TEL 0171-827-9977. FAX 0181-337-8943. (U.S. subscr. to: Metal Bulletin Inc., 220 Fifth Ave., New York, NY 10001-7781. TEL 212-213-6202. FAX 212-213-1870) Ed. Richard Serjeantson. adv. **Document type:** directory.
Supersedes: World Copper Survey (ISSN 0260-3403); Which was formerly: Copper Survey.
Description: Provides data on mines, smelters, refineries, wire rod operations, copper alloys and alloy ingot makers.

622   US
WORLD MINE PRODUCTION OF GOLD. 1979. a. $50. Gold Institute, Administrative Office - Institut de l'Or, Bureau Administratif, 1112 16th St., N.W., Ste. 240, Washington, DC 20036-4823. TEL 202-835-0185. FAX 202-835-0155. Ed. John H. Lutley. (back issues avail.) **Indexed:** SRI.
Description: Production of each of 58 countries known to produce at least 1,000 troy ounces of gold from underground, surface and alluvial sources.

622   PL
WORLD MINING CONGRESS. REPORT. (Published in Host Country) (Text mainly in English and Russian) 1958. triennial since 1976; latest 16th, 1994, Sofia, Bulgaria. World Mining Congress, International Organizing Committee, c/o Ing. M. Najberg, Secretary-General, Ul. Krucza 36, 00-921 Warsaw, Poland. TEL 48-2-628-5980. FAX 48-2-628-8938. circ. 2,250.
Formerly: International Organizing Committee of World Mining Congresses. Report (ISSN 0074-2775)

622   UK   ISSN 0746-729X
TN345
WORLD MINING EQUIPMENT. 1982. 11/yr. $208. Metal Bulletin plc, Park House, Park Terrace, Worcester Park, Surrey KT4 7HY, England. TEL 0171-827-9977. FAX 0181-337-8943. (U.S. subscr. to: Metal Bulletin Inc., 220 Fifth Ave., New York, NY 10001-7781. TEL 212-213-6202. FAX 212-213-1870) Ed. Kyran Casteel. adv.; bk.rev. circ. 18,000. (back issues avail.) **Indexed:** AESIS, Br.Geol.Lit., C.I.S. Abstr., Energy Info.Abstr., Fluidex, Fuel & Energy Abstr., Met.Abstr., Tr.& Indus.Ind. **Document type:** directory.
—BLDSC (9356.684000); Faxon; SWETS; UMI; UnCover. **CCC.**
Formed by the merger of (1977-1982): Mining Equipment International; (1974-1982): World Coal (ISSN 0361-7483); (1948-1982): World Mining (ISSN 0043-8707)
Description: Covers mines and mining equipment, decision makers with purchasing power in such companies.

338.2   US   ISSN 1059-6992
HD9536.A1
WORLD SILVER SURVEY. 1990. a. $45 (foreign $55). Silver Institute, 1112 16th St., N.W., Ste. 240, Washington, DC 20036-4823. TEL 202-835-0185. FAX 202-835-0155.

622   CC   ISSN 1000-8918
CODEN: WYHUEZ
WUTAN YU HUATAN. (Text in Chinese) q. Dizhi Kuangchan Bu, Hangkong Wutan Yaogan Zhongxin, 29, Xueyuan Lu, Haidian-qu, Beijing 100083, People's Republic of China. TEL 2018811. Ed. Yuan Xuecheng.
—BLDSC (4148.800000); CASDDS.

622   CC   ISSN 1000-9930
CODEN: XKUXEM
XIANGTAN KUANGYE XUEYUAN XUEBAO/JOURNAL OF XIANGTAN MINING INSTITUTE. (Text in Chinese; abstracts in English) 1983. q. Y4 per no. Xiangtan Kuangye Xueyuan - Xiangtan Mining Institute, Xiangtan, Hunan 411201, People's Republic of China. TEL 22357. TELEX 64096 XMI CN. (Dist. overseas by: China National Publications Import & Export Corp., P.O. Box 88, Beijing, P.R. China) Ed. LI Chibo. adv. **Document type:** academic/scholarly publication.
—CASDDS; Ei.
Description: Covers mine engineering, drilling, coalfield geology and prospecting, machinery, automation, architecture, management, and the chemical coal industry. Includes information on academic developments and activities.

622.33 526.9   CC   ISSN 1001-3571
XUANMEI JISHU/COAL PREPARATION TECHNOLOGY. (Text in Chinese) bi-m. foreign Y100. Meitan Kexueyuan, Tangshan Fenyuan - Central Coal Mining Research Institute, Tangshan Branch, No. 21, Xinhuanxi Rd., Tangshan, Hebei 063012, People's Republic of China. TEL 2822145. Ed. Liu Feng. **Document type:** academic/scholarly publication.

622 331.8   UK
YORKSHIRE MINER. 1959. m. £4 (foreign £11). National Union of Mineworkers - Yorkshire Area, Miners' Offices, 2 Huddersfield Rd., Barnsley, S. Yorkshire S70 2LS, England. TEL 0226-284006. FAX 0226-285486. Ed. Mark Hebert. adv.; bk.rev. circ. 17,500. (tabloid format) **Document type:** trade publication.
Description: Covers the Yorkshire miners, their union, families and communities. Also includes articles of general interest.

622 669.3   ZA
ZAMBIA CONSOLIDATED COPPER MINES LTD. ANNUAL REPORT AND ACCOUNTS. (Text in English) a. Zambia Consolidated Copper Mines Ltd., P.O. Box 30048, Lusaka, Zambia. TELEX ZA 30104. **Document type:** corporate report.

622   ZA
ZAMBIA INDUSTRIAL AND MINING CORPORATION. ANNUAL REPORT. (Text in English) s-a. Zambia Industrial and Mining Corp. Ltd., Zimco Information and Publicity Unit, P.O. Box 30090, Lusaka, Zambia. **Document type:** directory.

338.2   ZA   ISSN 0076-9010
ZAMBIA MINING YEARBOOK. 1955. a. free. Copper Industry Service Bureau, Kitwe, Zambia. (Dist. by: American Metal Climax, Inc., 1270 Ave. of the Americas, New York, NY 10026) circ. 500.
Formerly: Copperbelt of Zambia Mining Industry Year Book.

ZBORNIK RADOVA MUZEJA RUDARSTVA I METALURGIJE BOR. see ARCHAEOLOGY

ZHONGGUO YOUSE JINSHU XUEBAO. see METALLURGY

622   CC   ISSN 1005-9792
TN4   CODEN: ZGDXFY
ZHONGNAN GONGYE DAXUE XUEBAO. English edition: Central South University of Technology. Journal (ISSN 1005-9784) (Text in Chinese; summaries in English) 1956. bi-m. $7.50. Central South University of Technology, Institute of Mining and Metallurgy - Zhongnan Jishu Daxue Kuangye Xueyuan, Changsha, Hunan, People's Republic of China. FAX 4731-82817. TELEX 98190. (Dist. by: China International Book Trading Corp. (Guoji Shudian), P.O. Box 2820, Beijing 100044, P.R.C.) Ed. Huang Baiyun. adv. circ. 2,500. **Document type:** academic/scholarly publication.
—CASDDS.
Formerly: Zhongnan Kuangye Xueyuan Xuebao (ISSN 0253-4347)

ZIMBABWE. MINISTRY OF LANDS AND NATURAL RESOURCES. REPORT OF THE SECRETARY FOR LANDS AND NATURAL RESOURCES. see CONSERVATION

ZIMBABWE ENGINEER. see ENGINEERING

MINES AND MINING INDUSTRY — Abstracting, Bibliographies, Statistics

622   AT   ISSN 0313-704X
A E S I S QUARTERLY. (Australian Earth Sciences Information System) 1976. q. Aus.$325 to individuals; educational organizations Aus.$275. Australian Mineral Foundation, 63 Conyngham St., Glenside, S.A. 5065, Australia. TEL 61-8-3790444. FAX 61-8-3794634. TELEX AA 87437. index. circ. 500. **Indexed:** AESIS.
●Also available online. Vendor(s): Info-One International Pty Ltd.
Also available on CD-ROM.

338.2   CN   ISSN 0380-4321
ALBERTA COAL INDUSTRY, ANNUAL STATISTICS. 1973. a. Can.$40. Alberta Energy and Utilities Board, 640 Fifth Ave., S.W., Calgary, Alta. T2P 3G4, Canada. TEL 403-297-8311. FAX 403-297-7040. TELEX 03-821717. illus.; stat.
Formerly: Cumulative Annual Statistics, Alberta Coal Industry (ISSN 0837-2608)
Description: Statistical data on coal and the coal industry in Alberta including production, supply and disposition, plant operations and inventories.

622   UN
HD9555.A1   CODEN: ABCEEZ
ANNUAL BULLETIN OF COAL STATISTICS FOR EUROPE AND NORTH AMERICA. (Text in English, French and Russian) 1966. a., vol.25, 1992. price varies. Economic Commission for Europe (ECE), Palais des Nations, CH-1211 Geneva 10, Switzerland. TEL 022-740-0921. FAX 022-917-0036. (Orders in N. America to: United Nations Publications, Rm. DC2-853, New York, NY 10017. TEL 212-963-8302. FAX 212-963-6489; Or: Unipub, 4611-F Assembly Dr., Lanham, MD 20706. TEL 301-459-7666. FAX 301-459-0056) (also avail. in microfiche from CIS) **Indexed:** IIS. **Document type:** government publication, bulletin.
Formerly: Annual Bulletin of Coal Statistics for Europe (ISSN 0066-3808)
Description: Summarizes developments and trends of coal supply, production, and exports and imports for Europe and North America.

622.33 338.2   FR
ASSOCIATION TECHNIQUE DE L'IMPORTATION CHARBONNIERE. MONTHLY STATISTICS. m. Association Technique de l'Importation Charbonniere, 149 rue de Longchamp, 75016 Paris, France.

MINES AND MINING INDUSTRY — ABSTRACTING, BIBLIOGRAPHIES, STATISTICS

622 319.4   AT   ISSN 1033-0542
AUSTRALIA. BUREAU OF STATISTICS. ACTUAL AND EXPECTED PRIVATE MINERAL EXPLORATION, AUSTRALIA. 1974. q. Aus.$10.50 per no. Australian Bureau of Statistics, P.O. Box 10, Belconnen, A.C.T. 2616, Australia. TEL 062-527911. FAX 062-516009. circ. 258. **Document type:** government publication.
   Formerly (until 1989): Private Mineral Exploration, Australia.
   Description: Covers actual and expected expenditure and metres drilled by private organizations exploring for minerals and petroleum.

338.2   AT
HD9506.A7
AUSTRALIA. BUREAU OF STATISTICS. AUSTRALIAN MINING INDUSTRY. 1971. a. Aus.$33. Australian Bureau of Statistics, P.O. Box 10, Belconnen, A.C.T. 2616, Australia. TEL 062-527911. FAX 062-516009. circ. 475. **Document type:** government publication.
   Formed by the merger of (1992-1993): Mining Industry, Australia (ISSN 1321-2028); (1968-1993): Mining Production, Australia (ISSN 1321-1633); Which was formerly: Mineral Production, Australia (ISSN 0311-8975)
   Description: Provides a broad picture of the structure of the mining industry.

622   AT   ISSN 0727-159X
AUSTRALIA. BUREAU OF STATISTICS. CENSUS OF MINING ESTABLISHMENTS: DETAILS OF OPERATIONS BY INDUSTRY CLASS, AUSTRALIA. 1968. a. Aus.$21. Australian Bureau of Statistics, P.O. Box 10, Belconnen, A.C.T. 2616, Australia. **Document type:** government publication.
   Description: Contains number of mining establishments, employment, wages, and value of turnover.

622   AT   ISSN 0312-1585
HD9506.A7
AUSTRALIA. BUREAU OF STATISTICS. FOREIGN OWNERSHIP AND CONTROL OF THE MINING INDUSTRY, AUSTRALIA. 1963. irreg., latest 1987. Australian Bureau of Statistics, P.O. Box 10, Belconnen, A.C.T. 2616, Australia. **Document type:** government publication.
   Description: Provides statistics about employment, wages and salaries, turnover, value added and fixed capital expenditure of mining establishments.

622   AT
AUSTRALIA. BUREAU OF STATISTICS. MINING INDUSTRY, AUSTRALIA, PRELIMINARY. 1972. a. Aus.$11. Australian Bureau of Statistics, P.O. Box 10, Belconnen, A.C.T. 2616, Australia. **Document type:** government publication.
   Formerly: Census of Mining Establishment: Summary of Operations by Industry Class, Australia, Preliminary (ISSN 1031-2137)
   Description: Contains statistics on the number of mining establishments, employment, wages and salaries, turnover, value of stocks and purchases.

622 310   AT
AUSTRALIA. BUREAU OF STATISTICS. MINING TECHNOLOGY STATISTICS, AUSTRALIA. 1991. irreg., latest 1994. Aus.$22. Australian Bureau of Statistics, P.O. Box 10, Belconnen, A.C.T. 2616, Australia. **Document type:** government publication.
   Description: Gives summary information on the spread of micro-electronic based technologies in mining establishments in Australia.

622   AT   ISSN 1030-9039
AUSTRALIA. BUREAU OF STATISTICS. PRICE INDEXES OF MATERIALS USED IN COAL MINING, AUSTRALIA. 1988. m. Aus.$11 per no. Australian Bureau of Statistics, P.O. Box 10, Belconnen, A.C.T. 2616, Australia. **Document type:** government publication.
   Description: Measures price movements of materials used in the mining of coal.

622   AT   ISSN 1034-5388
AUSTRALIAN BUREAU OF AGRICULTURAL AND RESOURCE ECONOMICS. QUARTERLY MINERAL STATISTICS. 1989. q. Aus.$65. Australian Bureau of Agricultural and Resource Economics, G.P.O. Box 1563, Canberra, A.C.T. 2601, Australia. TEL 61-2-272-2211. Ed. Andrew Wright. **Document type:** government publication.
   Formed by the merger of (1986-1989): Australian Mineral Industry. Quarterly Summary Statistics (ISSN 1030-3340); (1987-1989): Base Metal Statistics (ISSN 1030-3499); (1981-1989): Major Energy Statistics (ISSN 0727-260X); Metal, Ore and Concentrate Prices (ISSN 1034-5361); (1987-1989): Mineral Sands Statistics (ISSN 1034-537X); (1948-1989): Australian Mineral Industry Quarterly (ISSN 0155-9419); Which was formerly (until 1977): Australian Mineral Industry Quarterly Review Quarterly Statistics (ISSN 0004-9751).
   Description: Provides up-to-date national statistics on mine production and exports.

622 669   MX   ISSN 0187-5027
HD9506.M6
AVANCE DE INFORMACION ECONOMICA. INDUSTRIA MINEROMETALURGICA. 1986. m. Mex.$77($26) Instituto Nacional de Estadistica, Geografia e Informatica, Secretaria de Programacion y Presupuesto, Prol. Heroe de Nacozari 2301 Sur, Puerta 11, Acceso, 20270 Aguascalientes, Ags., Mexico. TEL 49-18-19-48. FAX 491-807-39. circ. 800.

622 016   HU   ISSN 0231-0651
BANYASZATI SZAKIRODALMI TAJEKOZTATO/MINING ABSTRACTS. 1949. m. 8600 Ft. Orszagos Muszaki Informacios Kozpont es Konyvtar (O.M.I.K.K.) - National Technical Information Centre and Library, Muzeum u. 17, Box 12, 1428 Budapest, Hungary. (Subscr. to: Kultura, Box 149, 1389 Budapest, Hungary) Ed. Denes Panto. index. circ. 260. **Document type:** abstracting/indexing.
   Supersedes (in 1982): Muszaki Lapszemle. Banyaszat - Technical Abstracts. Mining (ISSN 0027-495X)

312 622   GW
BERGBAU IN DER BUNDESREPUBLIK DEUTSCHLAND. 1949. a. DM.68. (Bundesministerium fuer Wirtschaft) Trans Tech Publications, Postfach 1254, 38670 Claustahl-Zellerfeld, Germany. TEL 05323-9697-0. FAX 05323-969796. stat. (tabloid format) **Document type:** government publication.
   Formerly: Statistische Mitteilungen der Bergbehoerden der Bundesrepublik.

550 016   YU   ISSN 0351-7543
BILTEN DOKUMENTACIJE. RUDARSTVO I GEOLOGIJA/BULLETIN OF DOCUMENTATION. MINING AND GEOLOGY. 1950. bi-m. $264. Jugoslovenski Centar za Tehnicku i Naucnu Dokumentaciju - Yugoslav Center for Technical and Scientific Documentation (YCTSD), Sl. Penezica-Krcuna 29-31, Box 724, 11000 Belgrade, Yugoslavia. Ed. Ljiljana Kojic-Bogdanovic.

622   BL
BRAZIL. DEPARTAMENTO NACIONAL DA PRODUCAO MINERAL. SERIE BIBLIOGRAFIA. 1978. irreg., no.12, 1985. price varies. Departamento Nacional da Producao Mineral, Setor Autarquias Norte, Quadra 1, Bloco B, 70040 Brasilia D.F., Brazil. TEL 061-224-2670. **Document type:** government publication, bibliography.

549   CN   ISSN 0825-6896
TN27.B9
BRITISH COLUMBIA. MINISTRY OF ENERGY, MINES AND PETROLEUM RESOURCES. MINERAL RESOURCES DIVISION. SUMMARY OF OPERATIONS. a. Can.$3.15. Ministry of Energy, Mines and Petroleum Resources, Mineral Resources Division, 5th Fl., 1810 Blanshard St., Victoria, BC V8V 1X4, Canada. (Subscr. to: Crown Publications, 521 Fort St., Victoria, BC V8W 1E7, Canada. TEL 604-386-4636) (back issues avail.) **Document type:** government publication.
   Former titles: British Columbia. Ministry of Energy, Mines and Petroleum Resources. Mineral Resources Branch. Summary of Operations (ISSN 0825-6446); British Columbia. Ministry of Energy, Mines and Petroleum Resources. Annual Report (ISSN 0228-0078)

622   US
BUREAU OF MINES PUBLICATIONS AND ARTICLES (YEAR). a. U.S. Bureau of Mines, Office of Public Information, 810 Seventh St., N.W., MS-1040, Washington, DC 20241. TEL 202-501-9649. FAX 202-219-2493. (Subscr. to: Superintendent of Documents, U.S. Government Printing Office, Box 371954, Pittsburgh, PA 15250-7954. TEL 202-512-1800. FAX 202-512-2250) **Document type:** abstracting/indexing, government publication.
   Description: Compiles publications and articles issued by U.S.B.M. staff.

C A SELECTS. COAL SCIENCE AND PROCESS CHEMISTRY. see CHEMISTRY — Abstracting, Bibliographies, Statistics

549   CN   ISSN 0380-7797
CANADA. STATISTICS CANADA. CANADA'S MINERAL PRODUCTION: PRELIMINARY ESTIMATES. (Catalogue 26-202) (Text in English and French) 1924. a. Can.$22($26) (foreign $31). Statistics Canada, Publications Sales and Services, Ottawa, Ont. K1A 0T6, Canada. TEL 613-951-7277. FAX 613-951-1584. (also avail. in microform from MML)
   Description: Early estimates on mineral production by class and province; quantities and values.

622.33   CN   ISSN 0380-6847
HD9554.C29
CANADA. STATISTICS CANADA. COAL AND COKE STATISTICS. (Catalogue 45-002) (Text in English and French) 1921. m. Can.$100($120) (foreign $140). Statistics Canada, Publications Sales and Services, Ottawa, Ont. K1A 0T6, Canada. TEL 613-951-7277. FAX 613-951-1584. (also avail. in microform from MML)
   —CCC.
   Former titles (until 1950): Coal and Coke Statistics for Canada (ISSN 0829-9781); (until 1949): Monthly Report on Coal and Coke Statistics for Canada (ISSN 0829-9773)
   Description: Covers production, imports, exports, stocks and disposition of coal by province and supply and disposition of coke in Canada.

622.33   CN   ISSN 0705-436X
HD9554.C29
CANADA. STATISTICS CANADA. COAL MINES. (Catalogue 26-206) (Text in English and French) 1917. a. Can.$22($26) (foreign $31). Statistics Canada, Publications Sales and Services, Ottawa, Ont. K1A 0T6, Canada. TEL 613-951-7277. FAX 613-951-1584. bibl. (also avail. in microform from MML)
   Description: Data on the number of mines, employment, payroll, cost of fuel and electricity, production, disposition, exports and imports and supply and demand of coal by province.

338.2   CN   ISSN 0575-8645
HD9506.C2
CANADA. STATISTICS CANADA. GENERAL REVIEW OF THE MINERAL INDUSTRIES, MINES, QUARRIES AND OIL WELLS. (Catalogue 26-201) (Text in English and French) 1949. a. Can.$22($26) (foreign $31). Statistics Canada, Publications Sales and Services, Ottawa, Ont. K1A 0T6, Canada. TEL 613-951-7277. FAX 613-951-1584. (also avail. in microform from MML)
   Description: Final statistics of the mining industry, including production and value of minerals by kind and province, historical tables of values and principal statistics.

622 016   II
CENTRAL MINE PLANNING & DESIGN INSTITUTE. CURRENT AWARENESS SERVICE. (Text in English) 1976. bi-m. free. Central Mine Planning & Design Institute Ltd. (Subsidiary of: Coal India Limited), Library, Archives and Documentation Entre, Gondwana Place, Kanke Rd., Ranchi 834008, Bihar, India.

622.33   US   ISSN 0276-1890
HD9540.1   CODEN: CSAIE8
COAL STATISTICS INTERNATIONAL. 1981. m. $548 (foreign $578). McGraw-Hill, Inc., Energy & Business Newsletters, 1221 Ave. of the Americas, 36th Fl., New York, NY 10020. TEL 212-512-6410. Ed. John Higgins. (reprint service avail. from UMI)

MINES AND MINING INDUSTRY — ABSTRACTING, BIBLIOGRAPHIES, STATISTICS

622   US   ISSN 0893-973X
HD9541
COALDAT PRODUCTIVITY REPORT. (Avail. in Controlling Company Format; State - County Format) 1981. q. $545 (foreign $585). Pasha Publications Inc., 1616 N. Ft. Myer Dr., Ste. 1000, Arlington, VA 22209-3107. TEL 703-528-1244. FAX 703-528-1253. **Document type:** newsletter.
  Formerly (until 1986): Productivity Report.
  Description: Gives production statistics for each mine, including past performance and ownership data.

CURRENT BIBLIOGRAPHY ON SCIENCE AND TECHNOLOGY: EARTH SCIENCE, MINING AND METALLURGY/KAGAKU GIJUTSU BUNKEN SOKUHO. KINZOKU KOGAKU, KOZAN KOGAKU, CHIKYU NO KAGAKU-HEN. see *EARTH SCIENCES — Abstracting, Bibliographies, Statistics*

622 669.3   CL   ISSN 0716-8462
ESTADISTICAS DEL COBRE Y OTROS MINERALES ANUARIO. 1981. a. $100 or exchange basis. Comision Chilena del Cobre, Augustinas 1161, 4o Piso, Santiago, Chile. TEL 562-6726219. FAX 562-6723584. circ. 500. **Document type:** directory.
  Supersedes: Produccion y Exportaciones Chilenas de Cobre.
  Description: Contains statistical information on metallic and non-metallic mining. Data on copper and its by-products.

622 338   SP
ESTADISTICAS MINERA DE ESPANA. a. 2000 ptas. Ministerio de Industria, Direccion General de Minas y Combustibles, Paseo de la Castellana 160, Madrid 28046, Spain. FAX 259-84-80.
  Formerly: Estadisticas Minera y Metalurgica de Espana (ISSN 0071-156X)

338.2   GR   ISSN 0072-7415
GREECE. NATIONAL STATISTICAL SERVICE. ANNUAL STATISTICAL SURVEY ON MINES, QUARRIES AND SALTERNS. (Text in English and Greek) 1960. a. $5. National Statistical Service of Greece, Statistical Information and Publications Division - Ethniki Statistiki Yperesia tes Ellados, 14-16 Lykourgou, 101 66 Athens, Greece. TEL 30-1-3244-748. FAX 30-1-3222-205. TELEX 216734 ESYE GR. (back issues avail.) **Document type:** government publication.
  Formerly (until 1961): Greece. National Statistical Service. Results of the Annual Statistical Surveys on Mines, Quarries and Salterns.

553 622 669 016   UK   ISSN 0268-2516
I M M ABSTRACTS AND INDEX; a survey of world literature on the economic geology and mining of all minerals (except coal), mineral processing and non-ferrous extraction metallurgy. 1950. bi-m. £215 to non-members; members $142 (effective 1996). Institution of Mining and Metallurgy, 44 Portland Pl., London W1N 4BR, England. TEL 0171-580-3802. FAX 0171-436-5388. Ed. M. McGarr. abstr. circ. 1,000. (reprint service avail.) **Indexed:** AESIS, Fluidex. **Document type:** abstracting/indexing.
  ●Also available online. Vendor(s): European Space Agency (IMMAGE).
  —BLDSC (4369.630000). **CCC.**
  Formerly: I M M Abstracts (ISSN 0019-0020)

338.2   II   ISSN 0027-0261
INDIAN BUREAU OF MINES. BULLETIN OF MINERAL INFORMATION. (Text in English, Hindi) 1961. q. Rs.140($50.40) Indian Bureau of Mines, New Secretariat Bldg., Civil Lines, Nagpur 400001, India. (processed) **Indexed:** Chem.Abstr.
  Former titles: Indian Bureau of Mines. Bulletin of Mineral Statistics and Information; Indian Bureau of Mines. Monthly Bulletin of Mineral Statistics.

338.2 310   II
INDIAN GRANITE EXPORTERS' PERFORMANCE MONITOR. (Text in English, French, German, Italian) 1986. m. $500. Commercial Information Services, No.1 Beena Building, 6th Road, T.P.S. IV, Bandra, Bombay 400 050, India. TEL 91-22-6426703. Ed. C. Moonjely. circ. 300.
  Description: Statistics relating to quantity, prices and turnover of each participating granite exporter in India.

622 016   UK   ISSN 0148-9062
TA706   CODEN: IRMGBG
INTERNATIONAL JOURNAL OF ROCK MECHANICS AND MINING SCIENCES & GEOMECHANICS ABSTRACTS. 1964. 8/yr. £785($1249) (effective 1996). Elsevier Science Ltd., Pergamon, P.O. Box 800, Kidlington, Oxford OX5 1DX, England. TEL 44-1865-843000. FAX 44-1865-843010. (Subscr. in U.S. and Canada to: Elsevier Science, 660 White Plains Rd., Tarrytown, NY 10591-5153. TEL 914-524-9200. FAX 914-333-2444) Ed. J.A. Hudson. adv. contact: Rosemarie Fazzolari. bk.rev.; abstr.; charts; illus.; index. circ. 1,400. (also avail. in microfilm from UMI; reprint service avail. from UMI) **Indexed:** Appl.Mech.Rev., C.I.S. Abstr., Cadscan, Curr.Cont., Eng.Ind., Excerp.Med., Fuel & Energy Abstr., Geo.Abstr., Geol.Abstr., Geotech.Abstr., HRIS, Ind.Sci.Rev., INIS Atomind., INSPEC, Intl.Civil Eng.Abstr., Lead Abstr., Petrol.Abstr., Sci.Cit.Ind., Soft.Abstr.Eng., W.R.C.Inf., Zincscan. **Document type:** academic/scholarly publication, abstracting/indexing.
  ●Also available online. Vendor(s): Orbit Search Service (GEOM).
  —BLDSC (4542.542000); Ei; Faxon; Genuine Article; SWETS; UMI; UnCover. **CCC.**
  Formerly: International Journal of Rock Mechanics and Mining Sciences (ISSN 0020-7624); Incorporates: Rock Mechanics Abstracts (ISSN 0035-7456)
  Description: Original research, new developments and case studies in rock mechanics and rock engineering, for mining and civil applications, with comprehensive coverage of significant literature.
Refereed Serial

622   IR   ISSN 0075-0514
IRANIAN MINERAL STATISTICS. (Text in English and Persian) 1962. a. free. Ministry of Finance and Economic Affairs, Bureau of Statistics, Tehran, Iran. **Document type:** government publication.

622   US
IRON & MANGANESE ORE DATABOOK. 1986. irreg. $170. Metal Bulletin Inc., 220 Fifth Ave., New York, NY 10001-7781. TEL 212-213-6202. FAX 212-213-1870. Eds. Henry Cooke, John Bailey. **Document type:** trade publication.
  Formerly: Iron Ore Databook (ISSN 0950-2548)
  Description: Worldwide production statistics and analysis of iron and manganese production.

338.2 315   KO
KOREA (REPUBLIC). NATIONAL STATISTICAL OFFICE. REPORT ON MINING AND MANUFACTURING SURVEY. (Text in English and Korean) 1967. a. 25000 Won($48) National Statistical Office, Hanta Bldg., 647-15, Yoksam-dong, Kangnam-gu, Seoul 135-080, S. Korea. TEL 02-222-1971. (Subscr. to: the Korean Statistical Association, Room 302, Chungok Building, 561-30, Sinsa-dong, Gangnam-gu, Seoul 135-120, S. Korea. TEL 02-517-0382. FAX 02-725-4347) circ. 800. **Document type:** government publication.
  Formerly: Korea (Republic). National Bureau of Statistics. Report on Mining and Manufacturing Survey (ISSN 0075-6849)

622 310   MY   ISSN 0126-818X
HD9506.M36
MALAYSIA. DEPARTMENT OF MINES. STATISTICS RELATING TO THE MINING INDUSTRY OF MALAYSIA. (Text in English and Malay) 1951. a. M.$25. Department of Mines - Jabatan Galian Malaysia, Jbu Pejabat, Tingkat 22, Banguna Tabung Maji, Jalan Tun Razak, 50656 Kuala Lumpur, Malaysia. **Document type:** government publication.

549   MY   ISSN 0127-6794
MALAYSIA. DEPARTMENT OF STATISTICS. MONTHLY TIN STATISTICS OF MALAYSIA. (Text in English) m. M.$3 per no. Department of Statistics, Wisma Statistik, Jalan Cenderasari, 50514 Kuala Lumpur, Malaysia. TEL 03-2922133. **Document type:** government publication.

622   US
▼**MINE SAFETY AND HEALTH NEWS.*** 1994. bi-w. (24/yr.). $475 (diskette $525). Legal Publication Services, 2008 N. Emerson St., Arlington, VA 22207-1948. TEL 703-276-9796. FAX 703-243-3562. Ed. Melanie Aclander. index. (also avail. in diskette format) **Document type:** newsletter.
  Description: Covers proposed and final rules, policies of the Mine Safety and Health Administration and court cases of the Federal Mine Safety and Health Review Commission.

622   US   ISSN 0886-0564
MINERAL INDUSTRY SURVEYS. (Comprises multiple subseries: state, international, commodity annual reviews.) a. (plus m. and q. reports). free. U.S. Bureau of Mines, Office of Public Information, 810 Seventh St., N.W., MS-1040, Washington, DC 20241-0001. TEL 202-501-9649. FAX 202-219-2493. (Orders to: U.S.B.M., Box 19070, Pittsburgh, PA 15236) charts. (also avail. in microfiche from CIS; reprint service avail. from CIS; also avail. by fax) **Indexed:** AESIS, Amer.Stat.Ind. (1973-). **Document type:** government publication.
  ●Also available online.
  —BLDSC (5778.200000).
  Incorporates (in 1995): Mineral Commodity Summaries (ISSN 0160-5151)
  Description: Compiles current data on individual mineral commodities and mining activity in each state.

549   UK   ISSN 0026-4601
QE351   CODEN: MAMMAQ
MINERALOGICAL ABSTRACTS; a quarterly journal of abstracts in English, covering the world literature of mineralogy and related subjects. 1959. q. £165($260) Mineralogical Society, 41 Queen's Gate, London SW7 5HR, England. TEL 0171-584-7516. FAX 0171-823-8021. Ed. R.A. Howie. bk.rev.; abstr.; index. circ. 1,800. **Indexed:** AESIS, Anal.Abstr., Br.Ceram.Abstr., Chem.Abstr., GeoRef. **Document type:** abstracting/indexing.
  ●Also available on CD-ROM.
  —BLDSC (5786.700000).

549   JA
MINERALOGICAL SOCIETY OF JAPAN. ANNUAL MEETING ABSTRACTS/NIHON KOBUTSU GAKKAI NENKAI KOEN YOSHISHU. (Text in English, Japanese) a. 3000 Yen. Mineralogical Society of Japan - Nihon Kobutsu Gakkai, 6-41, Akasaka 9-chome, Minato-ku, Tokyo 107, Japan.

622 338.2   US
NATIONAL COAL ASSOCIATION. WEEKLY STATISTICAL SUMMARY. w. $100 (foreign $150). National Coal Association, 1130 17th St., N.W., Washington, DC 20036. TEL 202-463-2640. **Document type:** newsletter.
  Description: Presents statistical data on coal production and consumption, electrical output and steel production. Also includes data on U.S. petroleum production, stocks and imports.

622   US   ISSN 0364-1376
NEW PUBLICATIONS OF THE BUREAU OF MINES. bi-m. free. U.S. Bureau of Mines, Office of Public Information, 810 Seventh St., N.W., MS-1040, Washington, DC 20241-0001. TEL 202-501-9649. FAX 202-219-2493. (Orders to: U.S.B.M., Box 19070, Pittsburgh, PA 15236) abstr.; bibl. **Document type:** catalog, bibliography, government publication.
  Description: Lists new publications available from the U.S. Bureau of Mines

622.33 310   AT   ISSN 1034-2109
NEW SOUTH WALES COAL YEARBOOK (YEAR). 1989. a. Aus.$55 (typically set in Dec.). Joint Coal Board, G.P.O. Box 3842, Sydney, N.S.W. 2001, Australia. TEL 02-235-9752. FAX 02-223-1896. circ. 2,000.
  Description: Contains a comprehensive range of statistics on the N.S.W. coal industry. Includes profiles of producers, individual mines and port facilities and details of coal export brands-specifications with marketing contracts.

338.2   NZ   ISSN 1170-9154
HD9506.N45
NEW ZEALAND ANNUAL MINING REVIEW. 1972. a. NZ.$20. Ministry of Commerce, Energy and Resources Division, Resource Information Unit, P.O. Box 1473, Wellington, New Zealand. TEL 04-472-0030. FAX 04-471-0187. Ed.Bd. circ. 800. **Document type:** government publication.
  Former titles: New Zealand. Ministry of Energy. Annual Returns of Production from Quarries and Mineral Production Statistics (ISSN 0112-2584); New Zealand Mineral Production Statistics; New Zealand. Ministry of Energy. Mines Division. Annual Returns of Production from Quarries and Mineral Production Statistics. (ISSN 0304-0968); New Zealand. Mines Department. Annual Returns of Production from Quarries and Mineral Production Statistics.

MINES AND MINING INDUSTRY — ABSTRACTING, BIBLIOGRAPHIES, STATISTICS 4777

ONTARIO MINERAL SCORE. see *MINES AND MINING INDUSTRY*

338.2 016   FR   ISSN 1146-5182
P A S C A L. F 41: GISEMENTS METALLIQUES ET NON METALLIQUES. (Printed format ceased Jan. 1995) (Text in English, French) 1984. 10/yr. (Bureau de Recherches Geologiques et Minieres) Centre National de la Recherche Scientifique, Institut de l'Information Scientifique et Technique, 2 allee du Parc de Brabois, 54514 Vandoeuvre-Les-Nancy Cedex, France. TEL 83-50-46-00. FAX 83-50-46-50. adv. contact: Veronique Guinvarc'h. (also avail. in microfiche) **Document type:** bibliography.
●Also available online. Vendor(s): European Space Agency (File no.14), Knight-Ridder, Inc. (File no.144), Telesystemes - Questel.
Also available on CD-ROM.
 Former titles: P A S C A L Folio. F 41: Gisements Metalliques et Non-Metalliques. Economie Miniere (ISSN 0761-182X); P A S C A L Folio. Part 41: Gisements Metalliques et Non-Metalliques. Economie Miniere; Which supersedes (in 1984): Bulletin Signaletique: Bibliographie des Sciences de la Terre. Section 221. Gisements Metalliques et Non Metalliques. Economie Miniere; Bulletin Signaletique: Bibliographie des Sciences de la Terre. Section 221. Gisements Metalliques et Non Metalliques (ISSN 0304-1301); Which supersedes: Bulletin Signaletique: Bibliographie des Sciences de la Terre. Section 221. Cahier B. Gitologie, Economie Miniere (ISSN 0300-9270).

553.21 016   IE   ISSN 0031-367X
PEAT ABSTRACTS. 1951. 3/yr. I£20. Bord na Mona, Peat Research Centre, Droichead Nua, Co. Kildare, Ireland. TEL 045-31201. FAX 045-33240. Ed. Tony McKenna. adv.; bk.rev.; circ. 210. (processed) **Indexed:** Hort.Abstr. **Document type:** abstracting/indexing.

---

622 317   CN   ISSN 0709-292X
HD9506.C2
PRODUCTION OF CANADA'S LEADING MINERALS. (Text in English and French) 1979. m. free. Energy, Mines and Resources Canada, Mineral Policy Sector, Publishing Division, 460 O'Connor, Ottawa, Ont. K1A 0E4, Canada. TEL 819-956-4802. FAX 613-992-5565. (Subscr. to: Supply and Services Canada, Canada Communication Group - Publishing, Ottawa, Ont. K1A 0S9, Canada) Ed. H. Martin. stat. circ. 1,400. (looseleaf format; back issues avail.) **Indexed:** CS Ind. **Document type:** government publication.

---

622   EI   ISSN 1015-6275
TP325   **CODEN:** PCRSEI
PROGRESS IN COAL STEEL AND RELATED SOCIAL RESEARCH; a European journal. (Supplement to: Euro Abstracts) (Text in English) 4/yr. 84 ECU (180 ECU with Euro Abstracts). (European Coal and Steel Community) Commission of the European Communities, 200 rue de la Loi, B-1049 Brussels, Belgium. Ed. Clement Andre. adv. contact: Rebecca Zahn. abstr.; bibl.; pat. **Indexed:** Br.Ceram.Abstr. **Document type:** abstracting/indexing, newsletter.
—BLDSC (6867.725000); SWETS.

---

622 338.2   MY   ISSN 0025-1313
QUARTERLY BULLETIN OF STATISTICS RELATING TO THE MINING INDUSTRY OF MALAYSIA. 1947. q. M.$6. Department of Mines - Jabatan Galian Malaysia, Ibu Pejabat, Tingkat 22, Banguna Tabung Haji, Jalan Tun Razak, 50656 Kuala Lumpur, Malaysia. stat. circ. 140. **Document type:** government publication.

---

622   II
QUICK RELEASE TO THE MINERAL STATISTICS OF INDIA. (Text in English) m. Rs.240($86.40) Indian Bureau of Mines, New Secretariat Bldg., Nagpur 400001, India. stat.

---

622 016   RU   ISSN 0130-8904
REFERATIVNYI ZHURNAL. GORNOE DELO. 1964. bi-m. $550 (effective 1996). Vsesoyuznyi Institut Nauchno-Tekhnicheskoi Informatsii (VINITI), Baltiiskaya ul., 14, Moscow A-219, Russia. (Subscr. to: Mezhdunarodnaya Kniga, B. Yakimanka 39, 117049 Moscow, Russia) **Document type:** abstracting/indexing.

---

622 016   RU   ISSN 0373-6415
REFERATIVNYI ZHURNAL. GORNOE I NEFTEPROMYSLOVOE MASHINOSTROENIE. 1964. m. $179 (effective 1996). Vsesoyuznyi Institut Nauchno-Tekhnicheskoi Informatsii (VINITI), Baltiiskaya ul., 14, Moscow A-219, Russia. (Subscr. to: Mezhdunarodnaya Kniga, Dimitrova ul. 39, 113095 Moscow, Russia) **Document type:** abstracting/indexing.
—CCC.
 Formerly: Gornye Mashiny (ISSN 0034-2394)

338.2 316.8   SA   ISSN 1013-7297
SOUTH AFRICA. CENTRAL STATISTICAL SERVICE. CENSUS OF MINING. (Report No. 20-01-01) triennial, latest 1990. R.8.80 (foreign R.10). Central Statistical Service - Sentrale Statistiekdiens, Private Bag X44, Pretoria 0001, South Africa. TEL 27-12-310-8911. FAX 27-12-310-8500. (Orders to: Government Printing Works, Private Bag X85, Pretoria 0001, South Africa) **Document type:** government publication.
 Former titles: South Africa. Central Statistical Service. Mining: Financial Statistics; South Africa. Department of Statistics. Mining: Financial Statistics.

338.2 316.8   SA
SOUTH AFRICA. CENTRAL STATISTICAL SERVICE. STATISTICAL RELEASE. CENSUS OF MINING. (No. P2001) irreg. free. Central Statistical Service - Sentrale Statistiekdiens, Private Bag X44, Pretoria 0001, South Africa. TEL 27-12-310-8911. FAX 27-12-310-8500. **Document type:** government publication.

338.2 316.8   SA
SOUTH AFRICA. CENTRAL STATISTICAL SERVICE. STATISTICAL RELEASE. MINING - FINANCIAL STATISTICS. (No. P2042) q. free. Central Statistical Service - Sentrale Statistiekdiens, Private Bag X44, Pretoria 0001, South Africa. TEL 27-12-310-8911. FAX 27-12-310-8500. **Document type:** government publication.

338.2 316.8   SA
SOUTH AFRICA. CENTRAL STATISTICAL SERVICE. STATISTICAL RELEASE. MINING - PRODUCTION AND SALES. (No. P2041) m. free. Central Statistical Service - Sentrale Statistiekdiens, Private Bag X44, Pretoria 0001, South Africa. TEL 27-12-310-8911. FAX 27-12-310-8500. **Document type:** government publication.

315.61   TU
TURKEY. DEVLET ISTATISTIK ENSTITUSU. MADEN ISTATISTIKLERI/TURKEY. STATE INSTITUTE OF STATISTICS. MINING STATISTICS. (Text in English, Turkish) 1967. a., latest 1990. $25. Devlet Istatistik Enstitusu - State Institute of Statistics, Necatibey Caddesi No. 114, 06100 Ankara, Turkey. TEL 90-312-4185027. FAX 90-312-4170432. circ. 1,030. **Document type:** government publication.
 Formerly: Turkey. Devlet Istatistik Enstitusu. Madencilik Istatistikleri.

---

622   US
U.S. BUREAU OF MINES. ANNUAL REPORTS: COMMODITIES. BORON. a. U.S. Bureau of Mines, Office of Public Information, 810 Seventh St., N.W., MS-9800, Washington, DC 20241-0001. TEL 202-501-9358. FAX 202-501-9958. (Subscr. to: Superintendent of Documents, U.S. Government Printing Office, Box 371954, Pittsburgh, PA 15250. TEL 202-512-1800. FAX 202-512-2250) charts. **Document type:** government publication.

---

622   US
U.S. BUREAU OF MINES. MINERAL INDUSTRY SURVEYS: ALABAMA. (Subseries of: Mineral Industry Surveys (ISSN 0886-0564)) a. free. U.S. Bureau of Mines, Office of Public Information, 810 Seventh St., N.W., MS-1040, Washington, DC 20241-0001. TEL 202-501-9649. FAX 202-219-2493. (Orders to: U.S.B.M., Box 19070, Pittsburgh, PA 15236) charts. (also avail. by fax) **Document type:** government publication.
●Also available online.
 Formerly (until 1995): U.S. Bureau of Mines. Annual Report: Alabama.

---

622   US
U.S. BUREAU OF MINES. MINERAL INDUSTRY SURVEYS: ALASKA. (Subseries of: U.S. Bureau of Mines. Mineral Industry Surveys (ISSN 0886-0564)) a. free. U.S. Bureau of Mines, Office of Public Information, 810 Seventh St., N.W., MS-1040, Washington, DC 20241-0001. TEL 202-501-9649. FAX 202-219-2493. (Orders to: U.S.B.M., Box 19070, Pittsburgh, PA 15236) charts. (also avail. by fax) **Document type:** government publication.
●Also available online.
 Formerly (until 1995): U.S. Bureau of Mines. Annual Report: Alaska.

---

622   US
U.S. BUREAU OF MINES. MINERAL INDUSTRY SURVEYS: ARIZONA. (Subseries of: U.S. Bureau of Mines. Mineral Industry Surveys (ISSN 0886-0564)) a. free. U.S. Bureau of Mines, Office of Public Information, 810 Seventh St., N.W., MS-1040, Washington, DC 20241-0001. TEL 202-501-9649. FAX 202-219-2493. (Orders to: U.S.B.M., Box 19070, Pittsburgh, PA 15236) charts. **Document type:** government publication.
 Formerly (until 1995): U.S. Bureau of Mines. Annual Report: Arizona.

---

622   US
U.S. BUREAU OF MINES. MINERAL INDUSTRY SURVEYS: ARKANSAS. (Subseries of: U.S. Bureau of Mines. Mineral Industry Surveys (ISSN 0886-0564)) a. free. U.S. Bureau of Mines, Office of Public Information, 810 Seventh St., N.W., MS-1040, Washington, DC 20241-0001. TEL 202-501-9649. FAX 202-219-2493. (Orders to: U.S.B.M., Box 19070, Pittsburgh, PA 15236) charts. (also avail. by fax) **Document type:** government publication.
●Also available online.
 Formerly (until 1995): U.S. Bureau of Mines. Annual Report: Arkansas.

---

622   US
U.S. BUREAU OF MINES. MINERAL INDUSTRY SURVEYS: CALIFORNIA. (Subseries of: U.S. Bureau of Mines. Mineral Industry Surveys (ISSN 0886-0564)) a. free. U.S. Bureau of Mines, Office of Public Information, 810 Seventh St., N.W., MS-1040, Washington, DC 20241-0001. TEL 202-501-9649. FAX 202-219-2493. (Orders to: U.S.B.M., Box 19070, Pittsburgh, PA 15236) charts. (also avail. by fax) **Document type:** government publication.
●Also available online.
 Formerly (until 1995): U.S. Bureau of Mines. Annual Report: California.

---

622   US
U.S. BUREAU OF MINES. MINERAL INDUSTRY SURVEYS: COLORADO. (Subseries of: U.S. Bureau of Mines. Mineral Industry Surveys (ISSN 0886-0564)) a. free. U.S. Bureau of Mines, Office of Public Information, 810 Seventh St., N.W., MS-1040, Washington, DC 20241-0001. TEL 202-501-9619. FAX 202-219-2493. (Orders to: U.S.B.M., Box 19070, Pittsburgh, PA 15236) charts. (back issues avail.) **Document type:** government publication.
●Also available online.
 Formerly (until 1995): U.S. Bureau of Mines. Annual Report: Colorado.

---

622   US
U.S. BUREAU OF MINES. MINERAL INDUSTRY SURVEYS - COMMODITIES: ABRASIVE MATERIALS. (Subseries of: Mineral Industry Surveys (ISSN 0886-0564)) a. (also issued in m. and q. editions). free. U.S. Bureau of Mines, Office of Public Information, 810 Seventh St., N.W., MS-1040, Washington, DC 20241-0001. TEL 202-501-9649. FAX 202-219-2493. (Orders to: U.S.B.M., Box 19070, Pittsburgh, PA 15236) charts. (also avail. by fax) **Document type:** government publication.
●Also available online.

MINES AND MINING INDUSTRY — ABSTRACTING, BIBLIOGRAPHIES, STATISTICS

622 US
U.S. BUREAU OF MINES. MINERAL INDUSTRY SURVEYS - COMMODITIES: ALUMINUM, BAUXITE, AND ALUMINA. (Subseries of: Mineral Industry Surveys (ISSN 0886-0564)) a. (also issued in m. and q. editions). free. U.S. Bureau of Mines, Office of Public Information, 810 Seventh St., N.W., MS-1040, Washington, DC 20241-0001. (Orders to: U.S.B.M., Box 19070, Pittsburgh, PA 15236) (also avail. in microfiche from CIS; also avail. by fax; reprint service avail. from CIS) **Indexed:** Amer.Stat.Ind. (1973-). **Document type:** government publication.
●Also available online.
Formed by the merger of: U.S. Bureau of Mines. Annual Reports - Commodities: Aluminum; Formed by the merger of: U.S. Bureau of Mines. Annual Reports - Commodities: Bauxite; Both of which superseded: U.S. Bureau of Mines. Annual Reports - Commodities: Bauxite and Aluminum; And: U.S. Bureau of Mines. Annual Reports - Commodities: Alumina.
Description: Contains statistical information on the production, import, and export of aluminum, bauxite, and alumina.

622 US
U.S. BUREAU OF MINES. MINERAL INDUSTRY SURVEYS - COMMODITIES: ANTIMONY. (Subseries of: U.S. Bureau of Mines. Mineral Industry Surveys (ISSN 0886-0564)) a. (also issued in m. and q. editions). free. U.S. Bureau of Mines, Office of Public Information, 810 Seventh St., N.W., MS-1040, Washington, DC 20241-0001. TEL 202-501-9649. FAX 202-219-2493. (Orders to: U.S.B.M., Box 19070, Pittsburgh, PA 15236) (also avail. in microfiche from CIS; also avail by fax; reprint service avail. from CIS) **Indexed:** Amer.Stat.Ind. (1973-).
●Also available online.
Description: Contains statistical information on the production, import, and export of antimony.

622 US
U.S. BUREAU OF MINES. MINERAL INDUSTRY SURVEYS - COMMODITIES: BARITE. (Subseries of: Mineral Industry Surveys (ISSN 0886-0564) a. (also issued in m. and q. editions). free. U.S. Bureau of Mines, Office of Public Information, 810 Seventh St., N.W., MS-1040, Washington, DC 20241-0001. TEL 202-501-9649. FAX 202-219-2493. (Orders to: U.S.B.M., Box 19070, Pittsburgh, PA 15236) (also avail. by fax) **Document type:** government publication.
●Also available online.
Description: Contain statistical information on the production, import, and export of barite.

622 US
U.S. BUREAU OF MINES. MINERAL INDUSTRY SURVEYS - COMMODITIES: BISMUTH. (Subseries of: Mineral Industry Surveys (ISSN 0886-0564)) a. (also issued in m. and q. editions). free. U.S. Bureau of Mines, Office of Public Information, 810 Seventh St., N.W., MS-1040, Washington, DC 20241-0001. TEL 202-501-6949. FAX 202-219-2493. (Orders to: U.S.B.M., Box 19070, Pittsburgh, PA 15236) (also avail. in microfiche from CIS; also avail. by fax; reprint service avail. from CIS) **Indexed:** Amer.Stat.Ind. (1973-). **Document type:** government publication.
●Also available online.
Description: Contains statistical information on the production, consumption, import and export of bismuth.

622 US
U.S. BUREAU OF MINES. MINERAL INDUSTRY SURVEYS - COMMODITIES: BORON. (Subseries of: Mineral Industry Surveys (ISSN 0886-0564)) a. (also issued in m. and q. editions). free. U.S. Bureau of Mines, Office of Public Information, 810 Seventh St., N.W., MA-1040, Washington, DC 20241-0001. TEL 202-501-9649. FAX 202-219-2493. (Orders to: U.S.B.M., Box 19070, Pittsburgh, PA 15236) stat. (also avail. by fax) **Document type:** government publication.
●Also available online.
Description: Contains statistical information on the production, import and export of boron.

622 US
U.S. BUREAU OF MINES. MINERAL INDUSTRY SURVEYS - COMMODITIES: BROMINE. (Subseries of: Mineral Industry Surveys (ISSN 0886-0564)) a. (also issued in m. and q. editions). free. U.S. Bureau of Mines, Office of Public Information, 810 Seventh St., N.W., MS-1040, Washington, DC 20241. TEL 202-501-9649. FAX 202-219-2493. (Orders to: U.S.B.M., Box 19070, Pittsburgh, PA 15236) charts. (also avail. by fax) **Indexed:** Amer.Stat.Ind. (1973-). **Document type:** government publication.
●Also available online.
Description: Supplies statistical information on the production and import and export of bromine.

622 US
CODEN: MISCDH
U.S. BUREAU OF MINES. MINERAL INDUSTRY SURVEYS - COMMODITIES: CADMIUM. (Subseries of: Mineral Industry Surveys (ISSN 0886-0564)) a. (also issued in m. and q. editions). free. U.S. Bureau of Mines, Office of Public Information, 810 Seventh St., N.W., MS-1040, Washington, DC 20241-0001. TEL 202-501-9649. FAX 202-2109-2493. (Orders to: U.S.B.M., Box 19070, Pittsburgh, PA 15236) (also avail. in microfiche from CIS; also avail. by fax; reprint service avail. from CIS) **Indexed:** Amer.Stat.Ind. (1973-). **Document type:** government publication.
●Also available online.
—CASDDS.
Description: Contains statistical information on the production, distribution, consumption, import, and export of cadmium.

622 US
U.S. BUREAU OF MINES. MINERAL INDUSTRY SURVEYS - COMMODITIES: CEMENT. (Subseries of: Mineral Industry Surveys (ISSN 0886-0564)) a. (also issued in m. and q. editions). free. U.S. Bureau of Mines, Office of Public Information, 810 Seventh St., N.W., MS-1040, Washington, DC 20241-0001. TEL 202-501-9649. FAX 202-219-2493. (Orders to: U.S.B.M., Box 19070, Pittsburgh, PA 15236) (also avail. in microfiche from CIS; also avail. by fax; reprint service avail. from CIS) **Indexed:** Amer.Stat.Ind. (1973-). **Document type:** government publication.
●Also available online.
Description: Provides data and activity highlights on cement.

622 US
U.S. BUREAU OF MINES. MINERAL INDUSTRY SURVEYS - COMMODITIES: CHROMIUM. (Subseries of: Mineral Industry Surveys (ISSN 0886-0564)) a. (also issued in m. and q. editions). free. U.S. Bureau of Mines, Office of Public Information, 810 Seventh St., N.W., MS-1040, Washington, DC 20241-0001. TEL 202-501-9469. FAX 202-219-2493. (Orders to: U.S.B.M., Box 19070, Pittsburgh, PA 15236) (also avail. in microfiche from CIS; also avail. by fax; reprint service avail. from CIS) **Indexed:** Amer.Stat.Ind. (1973-). **Document type:** government publication.
●Also available online.
Description: Provides statistical information on the production, distribution, and consumption of chromium.

622 US
U.S. BUREAU OF MINES. MINERAL INDUSTRY SURVEYS - COMMODITIES: CLAYS. a. (also issued in m. and q. editions). free. U.S. Bureau of Mines, Office of Public Information, 810 Seventh St., N.W., MS-1040, Washington, DC 20241-0001. TEL 202-501-9649. FAX 202-219-2493. (Orders to: U.S.B.M., Box 19070, Pittsburgh, PA 15236) stat. (also avail. by fax) **Document type:** government publication.
●Also available online.
Description: Provides data and activity highlights on clays.

622 US
U.S. BUREAU OF MINES. MINERAL INDUSTRY SURVEYS - COMMODITIES: COBALT. (Subseries of: Mineral Industry Surveys (ISSN 0886-0564)) a. (also issued in m. and q. editions). free. U.S. Bureau of Mines, Office of Public Information, 810 Seventh St., N.W., MS-1040, Washington, DC 20241-0001. TEL 202-501-6349. FAX 202-219-2493. (Orders to: U.S.B.M., Box 19070, Pittsburgh, PA 15236) (also avail. in microfiche from CIS; also avail. by fax; reprint service avail. from CIS) **Indexed:** Amer.Stat.Ind. (1973-). **Document type:** government publication.
●Also available online.
Description: Provides statistical information on the production, consumption, and distribution of cobalt.

622 US
U.S. BUREAU OF MINES. MINERAL INDUSTRY SURVEYS - COMMODITIES: COLUMBIUM (NIOBIUM) AND TANTALUM. (Subseries of: Mineral Industry Surveys (ISSN 0886-0564)) a. (also issued in m. and q. editions). free. U.S. Bureau of Mines, Office of Public Information, 810 Seventh St., N.W., MS-1040, Washington, DC 20241-0001. TEL 202-501-9649. FAX 202-219-2493. (Orders to: U.S.B.M., Box 19070, Pittsburgh, PA 15236) (also avail. by fax) **Indexed:** Amer.Stat.Ind. (1973-).
●Also available online.
Description: Provides data and activity highlights on columbium and tantalum.

622 US
U.S. BUREAU OF MINES. MINERAL INDUSTRY SURVEYS - COMMODITIES: CONSTRUCTION SAND AND GRAVEL. (Subseries of: U.S. Bureau of Mines. Mineral Industry Surveys (ISSN 0886-0564)) a. (also issued in m. and q. editions). free. U.S. Bureau of Mines, Office of Public Information, 810 Seventh St., N.W., MS-1040, Washington, DC 20241. TEL 202-501-9649. FAX 202-219-2493. (Orders to: U.S.B.M., Box 19070, Pittsburgh, PA 15236) (also avail. by fax) **Indexed:** Amer.Stat.Ind. (1973-). **Document type:** government publication.
●Also available online.
Formerly: U.S. Bureau of Mines. Mineral Industry Surveys. Principal Construction Sand and Gravel Producers in the U.S.

622 US
U.S. BUREAU OF MINES. MINERAL INDUSTRY SURVEYS - COMMODITIES: CRUSHED STONE. (Subseries of: Mineral Industry Surveys (ISSN 0886-0564)) a. (also issued in m. and q. editions). free. U.S. Bureau of Mines, Office of Public Information, 810 Seventh St., N.W., MS-1040, Washington, DC 20241-0001. TEL 202-501-9649. FAX 202-219-2493. (Orders to: U.S.B.M., Box 19070, Pittsburgh, PA 15236) (also avail. by fax) **Indexed:** Amer.Stat.Ind. (1973-). **Document type:** government publication.
●Also available online.
Supersedes in part: Mineral Industry Surveys. Stone - Crushed and Dimension; In part: Mineral Industry Surveys. Prinicpal Crushed Stone Producers in the U.S.

622 US
U.S. BUREAU OF MINES. MINERAL INDUSTRY SURVEYS - COMMODITIES: DIMENSION STONE. (Subseries of: U.S. Bureau of Mines. Mineral Industry Surveys (ISSN 0886-0564)) a. (also issued in m. and q. editions). free. U.S. Bureau of Mines, Office of Public Information, 810 Seventh St., N.W., MS-1040, Washington, DC 20241-0001. TEL 202-501-9649. FAX 202-219-2493. (Orders to: U.S.B.M., Box 19070, Pittsburgh, PA 15236) (also avail. by fax)
●Also available online.
Supersedes in part: U.S. Bureau of Mines. Mineral Industry Surveys. Stone - Crushed and Dimension.

622 US
U.S. BUREAU OF MINES. MINERAL INDUSTRY SURVEYS - COMMODITIES: FELDSPAR. (Subseries of: Mineral Industry Surveys (ISSN 0886-0564)) a. (also issued in m. and q. editions). free. U.S. Bureau of Mines, Office of Public Information, 810 Seventh St., N.W., MS-1040, Washington, DC 20241-0001. TEL 202-501-9649. FAX 202-219-2493. (Orders to: U.S.B.M., Box 19070, Pittsburgh, PA 15236) (also avail. in microfiche from CIS; also avail. by fax; reprint service avail. from CIS) **Indexed:** Amer.Stat.Ind. (1973-). **Document type:** government publication.
●Also available online.
Description: Provides statistical information on the production, distribution and consumption of feldspar.

622 US
U.S. BUREAU OF MINES. MINERAL INDUSTRY SURVEYS - COMMODITIES: FLUORSPAR. (Subseries of: Mineral Industry Surveys (ISSN 0886-0564)) a. (also issued in m. and q. editions). free. U.S. Bureau of Mines, Office of Public Information, 810 Seventh St., N.W., MS-1040, Washington, DC 20241-0001. TEL 202-501-9649. FAX 202-219-2493. (Orders to: U.S.B.M., Box 19070, Pittsburgh, PA 15236) (also avail. in microfiche from CIS; also avail. by fax; reprint service avail. from CIS) **Indexed:** Amer.Stat.Ind. (1973-). **Document type:** government publication.
●Also available online.
Description: Provides data and activity highlights on fluorspar.

MINES AND MINING INDUSTRY — ABSTRACTING, BIBLIOGRAPHIES, STATISTICS

622 US
U.S. BUREAU OF MINES. MINERAL INDUSTRY SURVEYS - COMMODITIES: GEMSTONES. (Subseries of: Mineral Industry Surveys (ISSN 0886-0564)) a. (also issued in m. and q. editions). free. U.S. Bureau of Mines, Office of Public Information, 810 Seventh St., N.W., MS-1040, Washington, DC 20241-0001. TEL 202-501-9649. FAX 202-219-2493. (Orders to: U.S.B.M., Box 19070, Pittsburgh, PA 15236) (also avail. by fax) **Indexed:** Amer.Stat.Ind. (1973-). **Document type:** government publication.
●Also available online.
Description: Provides data and activity highlights on gemstones.

622 US
U.S. BUREAU OF MINES. MINERAL INDUSTRY SURVEYS - COMMODITIES: GOLD. (Subseries of: U.S. Bureau of Mines. Mineral Industry Surveys (ISSN 0886-0564)) a. (also issued in m. and q. editions). free. U.S. Bureau of Mines, Office of Public Information, 810 Seventh St., N.W., MS-1040, Washington, DC 20241-0001. TEL 202-501-9649. FAX 202-219-2493. (also avail. in microfiche from CIS; also avail. by fax; reprint service avail. from CIS) **Indexed:** Amer.Stat.Ind. (1973-). **Document type:** government publication.
●Also available online.
Supersedes in part: U.S. Bureau of Mines. Mineral Industry Surveys: Gold and Silver.

622 US
U.S. BUREAU OF MINES. MINERAL INDUSTRY SURVEYS - COMMODITIES: GRAPHITE. (Subseries of: Mineral Industry Surveys (ISSN 0886-0564)) a. (also avail. in m. and q. editions). free. U.S. Bureau of Mines, Office of Public Information, 810 Seventh St., N.W., MS-1040, Washington, DC 20241-0001. TEL 202-501-9649. FAX 202-219-2493. (Orders to: U.S.B.M., Box 19070, Pittsburgh, PA 15236) charts. (also avail. by fax) **Document type:** government publication.
●Also available online.

622 US
U.S. BUREAU OF MINES. MINERAL INDUSTRY SURVEYS - COMMODITIES: GYPSUM. (Subseries of: Mineral Industry Surveys (ISSN 0886-0564)) a. (also avail. in m. and q. editions). free. U.S. Bureau of Mines, Office of Public Information, 810 Seventh St., N.W., MS-1040, Washngton, DC 20241-0001. TEL 202-501-9649. FAX 202-219-2493. (Orders to: U.S.B.M., Box 19070, Pittsburgh, PA 15236) (also avail. in microfiche from CIS; also avail. by fax; reprint service avail. from CIS) **Indexed:** Amer.Stat.Ind. (1975-). **Document type:** government publication.
●Also available online.
Description: Provides data on the production, distribution and consumption of gypsum.

622 US
U.S. BUREAU OF MINES. MINERAL INDUSTRY SURVEYS - COMMODITIES: HELIUM. (Subseries of: Mineral Industry Surveys (ISSN 0886-0564)) a. (also issued in m. and q. editions). free. U.S. Bureau of Mines, Office of Public Information, 810 Seventh St., N.W., MS-1040, Washington, DC 20241-0001. TEL 202-501-9649. FAX 202-219-2493. (Orders to: U.S.B.M., Box 19070, Pittsburgh, PA 15236) charts. (also avail. by fax) **Document type:** government publication.
●Also available online.

622 US
U.S. BUREAU OF MINES. MINERAL INDUSTRY SURVEYS - COMMODITIES: INDUSTRIAL EXPLOSIVES AND BLASTING AGENTS. (Subseries of: Mineral Industry Surveys (ISSN 0886-0564)) a. (also issued in m. and q. editions). free. U.S. Bureau of Mines, Office of Public Information, 810 Seventh St., N.W., MS-1040, Washington, DC 20241-0001. TEL 202-501-9649. FAX 202-219-2493. (Orders to: U.S.B.M., Box 19070, Pittsburgh, PA 15236) (also avail. by fax) **Document type:** government publication.
●Also available online.
Description: Statistical information on the production, distribution and consumption of blasting explosives and blasting agents.

622 US
U.S. BUREAU OF MINES. MINERAL INDUSTRY SURVEYS - COMMODITIES: INDUSTRIAL SAND AND GRAVEL. (Subseries of: U.S. Bureau of Mines. Mineral Industry Surveys (ISSN 0886-0564)) a. (also issued in m. and q. editions). free. U.S. Bureau of Mines, Office of Public Information, 810 Seventh St., N.W., MS-1040, Washington, DC 20241-0001. TEL 202-501-9649. FAX 202-219-2493. (Orders to: U.S.B.M., Box 19070, Pittsburgh, PA 15236) (also avail. by fax) **Document type:** government publication.
●Also available online.
Formerly: U.S. Bureau of Mines. Mineral Industry Surveys. Industrial Sand and Gravel Producers in the U.S.

622 US
U.S. BUREAU OF MINES. MINERAL INDUSTRY SURVEYS - COMMODITIES: IODINE. (Subseries of: Mineral Industry Surveys (ISSN 0886-0564)) a. (also issued in m. and q. editions). free. U.S. Bureau of Mines, Office of Public Information, 810 Seventh St., N.W., MS-1040, Washington, DC 20241. TEL 202-501-9649. FAX 202-219-2493. (also avail. by fax)
●Also available online.
Description: Provides data and activity highlights on iodine.

622 US
U.S. BUREAU OF MINES. MINERAL INDUSTRY SURVEYS - COMMODITIES: IRON AND STEEL. (Subseries of: Mineral Industry Surveys) a. (also issued in m. and q. editions). free. U.S. Bureau of Mines, Office of Public Information, 810 Seventh St., N.W., MS-1040, Washington, DC 20241-0001. TEL 202-501-9649. FAX 202-219-2493. (Orders to: U.S.B.M., Box 19070, Pittsburgh, PA 15236) (also avail. in microfiche from CIS; also avail. by fax; reprint service avail. from CIS) **Indexed:** Amer.Stat.Ind. (1973-). **Document type:** government publication.
●Also available online.
Description: Provides data on the production, distribution, and consumption of iron and steel scrap.

622 US
U.S. BUREAU OF MINES. MINERAL INDUSTRY SURVEYS - COMMODITIES: IRON ORE. (Subseries of: Mineral Industry Surveys (ISSN 0886-0564)) a. (also issued in m. and a. editions). free. U.S. Bureau of Mines, Office of Public Information, 810 Seventh St., N.W., MS-1040, Washington, DC 20241. TEL 202-501-9649. FAX 202-219-2493. (Subscr. to: U.S.B.M., Box 19070, Pittsuurgh, PA 15236) (also avail. in microfiche from CIS; also avail. by fax; reprint service avail. from CIS) **Indexed:** Amer.Stat.Ind. (1973-). **Document type:** government publication.
●Also available online.
Description: Provides data on all aspects of iron ore production.

622 US
U.S. BUREAU OF MINES. MINERAL INDUSTRY SURVEYS - COMMODITIES: KYANITE AND RELATED MINERALS. (Subseries of: Mineral Industry Surveys (ISSN 0886-0564)) a. (also issued in m. and q. editions). free. U.S. Bureau of Mines, Office of Public Information, 810 Seventh St., N.W., MS-1040, Washington, DC 20241-0001. TEL 202-501-9649. FAX 202-219-2493. (Orders to: U.S.B.M., Box 19070, Pittsburgh, PA 15236) (also avail. by fax) **Document type:** government publication.
●Also available online.
Description: Provides preliminary data and activity highlights on kyanite and related minerals.

622 US
U.S. BUREAU OF MINES. MINERAL INDUSTRY SURVEYS - COMMODITIES: LEAD. (Subseries of: U.S. Bureau of Mines. Mineral Industry Surveys (ISSN 0886-0564)) a. (also issued in m. and q. editions). free. U.S. Bureau of Mines, Office of Public Information, 810 Seventh St., N.W., MS-1040, Washington, DC 20241-0001. TEL 202-501-9649. FAX 202-219-2493. (Orders to: U.S.B.M., Box 19070, Pittsburgh, PA 15236) (also avail. in microfiche from CIS; also avail. by fax; reprint service avail. from CIS) **Indexed:** Amer.Stat.Ind. (1973-).
●Also available online.
Formerly: U.S. Bureau of Mines. Mineral Industry Surveys. Lead Industry.
Description: Provides worldwide data on mine production of lead, including pig metal.

622 US
U.S. BUREAU OF MINES. MINERAL INDUSTRY SURVEYS - COMMODITIES: LIME. (Subseries of: Mineral Industry Surveys (ISSN 0886-0564)) a. (also issued in m. and q. editions). free. U.S. Bureau of Mines, Office of Public Information, 810 Seventh St., N.W., MS-1040, Washington, DC 20241-0001. TEL 202-501-9649. FAX 202-219-2493. (Orders to: U.S.B.M., Box 19070, Pittsburgh, PA 15236) (also avail. in microfiche from CIS; also avail. by fax; reprint service avail. from CIS) **Indexed:** Amer.Stat.Ind. (1973-). **Document type:** government publication.
●Also available online.
Description: Provides data on the production, import, export and consumption of lime.

622 US
U.S. BUREAU OF MINES. MINERAL INDUSTRY SURVEYS - COMMODITIES: LITHIUM. (Subseries of: Mineral Industry Surveys (ISSN 0886-0564)) a. (also issued in m. and q. editions). free. U.S. Bureau of Mines, Office of Public Information, 810 Seventh St., N.W., MS-1040, Washington, DC 20241-0001. TEL 202-501-9649. FAX 202-219-2493. (Orders to: U.S.B.M., Box 19070, Pittsburgh, PA 15236) charts. (also avail. by fax) **Indexed:** Amer.Stat.Ind. (1973-). **Document type:** government publication.
●Also available online.
Description: Reviews mining activity in the U.S. for lithium.

622 US
U.S. BUREAU OF MINES. MINERAL INDUSTRY SURVEYS - COMMODITIES: MAGNESIUM AND MAGNESIUM COMPOUNDS. (Subseries of: U.S. Bureau of Mines. Mineral Industry Surveys (ISSN 0886-0564)) a. (also issued in m. and q. editions). free. U.S. Bureau of Mines, Office of Public Information, 810 Seventh St., N.W., MS-1040, Washington, DC 20241-0001. TEL 202-501-9649. FAX 202-219-2493. (Orders to: U.S.B.M., Box 19070, Pittsburgh, PA 15236) (also avail. in microfiche from CIS; also avail. by fax; reprint service avail. from CIS) **Indexed:** Amer.Stat.Ind. (1973-). **Document type:** government publication.
●Also available online.
Formerly: U.S. Bureau of Mines. Mineral Industry Surveys. Magnesium.
Description: Provides data on the production, import, export and consumption of magnesium worldwide, with emphasis on the U.S.

622 US
U.S. BUREAU OF MINES. MINERAL INDUSTRY SURVEYS - COMMODITIES - MANGANESE. (Subseries of: Mineral Industry Surveys (ISSN 0886-0564)) a. (also issued in m. and q. editions). free. U.S. Bureau of Mines, Office of Public Information, 810 Seventh St., N.W., MS-1400, Washington, DC 20241. TEL 202-501-9649. FAX 202-219-2493. (Orders to: U.S.B.M., Box 19070, Pittsburgh, PA 15236) (also avail. in microfiche from CIS; also avail. by fax; reprint service avail. from CIS) **Indexed:** Amer.Stat.Ind. (1973-). **Document type:** government publication.
●Also available online.
Description: Contains data on foreign and U.S. manganese production, distribution and consumption.

622 US
U.S. BUREAU OF MINES. MINERAL INDUSTRY SURVEYS - COMMODITIES: MERCURY. (Subseries of: Mineral Industry Surveys (ISSN 0886-0564)) a. (also issued in m. and q. editions). free. U.S. Bureau of Mines, Office of Public Information, 810 Seventh St., N.W., MS-1040, Washington, DC 20241-0001. TEL 202-501-9649. FAX 202-219-2493. (also avail. in microfiche from CIS; also avail. by fax; reprint service avail. from CIS) **Indexed:** Amer.Stat.Ind. (1973-). **Document type:** government publication.
●Also available online.
Description: Presents data on worldwide mine production, distribution and consumption of mercury.

622 US
U.S. BUREAU OF MINES. MINERAL INDUSTRY SURVEYS - COMMODITIES: MICA. (Subseries of: Mineral Industry Surveys (ISSN 0886-0564)) a. free. U.S. Bureau of Mines, Office of Public Information, 810 Seventh St., N.W., MS-1040, Washington, DC 20241-0001. TEL 202-501-9649. FAX 202-219-2493. (Orders to: U.S.B.M., Box 19070, Pittsburgh, PA 15236) charts. (also avail. by fax) **Indexed:** Amer.Stat.Ind. (1973-). **Document type:** government publication.
●Also available online.

MINES AND MINING INDUSTRY — ABSTRACTING, BIBLIOGRAPHIES, STATISTICS

622 US
U.S. BUREAU OF MINES. MINERAL INDUSTRY SURVEYS - COMMODITIES: MOLYBDENUM. (Subseries of: Mineral Industry Surveys (ISSN 0886-0564)) a. (also issued in m. and q. editions). free. U.S. Bureau of Mines, Office of Public Information, 810 Seventh St., N.W., MS-1040, Washington, DC 20241-0001. TEL 202-512-9649. FAX 202-219-2493. (Orders to: U.S.B.M., Box 19070, Pittsburgh, PA 15236) (also avail. in microfiche from CIS; also avail. by fax; reprint service avail. from CIS) **Indexed:** Amer.Stat.Ind. (1973-). **Document type:** government publication.
●Also available online.
Description: Presents data on U.S. production, distribution and consumption of molybdenum.

622 US
U.S. BUREAU OF MINES. MINERAL INDUSTRY SURVEYS - COMMODITIES: NICKEL. (Subseries of: Mineral Industry Surveys (ISSN 0886-0564)) a. (also issued in m. and q. editions). free. U.S. Bureau of Mines, Office of Public Information, 810 Seventh St., N.W., MS-1040, Washington, DC 20241-0001. TEL 202-501-9649. FAX 202-219-2493. (Orders to: U.S.B.M., Box 19070, Pittsburgh, PA 15236) (also avail. in microfiche from CIS; also avail. by fax; reprint service avail. from CIS) **Indexed:** Amer.Stat.Ind. (1973-). **Document type:** government publication.
●Also available online.
Description: Provides worldwide coverage of the production, distribution and consumption of nickel.

622 US
U.S. BUREAU OF MINES. MINERAL INDUSTRY SURVEYS - COMMODITIES: NITROGEN. (Subseries of: Mineral Industry Surveys (ISSN 0886-0564)) a. free. U.S. Bureau of Mines, Office of Public Information, 810 Seventh St., N.W., MS-1040, Washington, DC 20241-0001. TEL 202-501-9649. FAX 202-219-2493. (Orders to: U.S.B.M., Box 19070, Pittsburgh, PA 15236) charts. (also avail. by fax) **Document type:** government publication.
●Also available online.

622 US
U.S. BUREAU OF MINES. MINERAL INDUSTRY SURVEYS - COMMODITIES: NONRENEWABLE ORGANIC MATERIALS. (Subseries of: Mineral Industry Surveys (ISSN 0886-0564)) a. (also issued in m. and q. editions). charts. U.S. Bureau of Mines, Office of Public Information, 810 Seventh St., N.W., MS-1040, Washington, DC 20241-0001. TEL 202-501-9649. FAX 202-219-2493. (Orders to: U.S.B.M., Box 19070, Pittsburgh, PA 15236) charts. (also avail. by fax) **Indexed:** Amer.Stat.Ind. (1973-). **Document type:** government publication.
●Also available online.

622 US
U.S. BUREAU OF MINES. MINERAL INDUSTRY SURVEYS - COMMODITIES: PEAT. (Subseries of: Mineral Industry Surveys (ISSN 0886-0564)) a. (also issued in m. and q. editions). free. U.S. Bureau of Mines, Office of Public Information, 810 Seventh St., N.W., MS-1040, Washington, DC 20241-0001. TEL 202-501-9649. FAX 202-219-2493. (Orders to: U.S.B.M., Box 19070, Pittsburgh, PA 15236) (also avail. by fax) **Document type:** government publication.
●Also available online.
Description: Provides preliminary data and activity highlights on peat.

622 US
U.S. BUREAU OF MINES. MINERAL INDUSTRY SURVEYS - COMMODITIES: PHOSPHATE ROCK. (Subseries of: Mineral Industry Surveys (ISSN 0886-0564)) a. (also issued in m. and q. editions). free. U.S. Bureau of Mines, Office of Public Information, 810 Seventh St., N.W., MS-1040, Washington, DC 20241-0001. TEL 202-501-9649. FAX 202-219-2493. (Orders to: U.S.B.M., Box 19070, Pittsburgh, PA 15236) charts. (also avail. by fax) **Document type:** government publication.
●Also available online.

622 US ISSN 0191-4421
CODEN: MISPDM
U.S. BUREAU OF MINES. MINERAL INDUSTRY SURVEYS - COMMODITIES: PLATINUM-GROUP METALS. (Subseries of: Mineral Industry Surveys (ISSN 0886-0564)) a. (also issued in m. and q. editions). free. U.S. Bureau of Mines, Office of Public Information, 810 Seventh St., N.W., MS-1400, Washington, DC 20241-0001. TEL 202-501-9649. FAX 202-219-2493. (Orders to: U.S.B.M., Box 19070, Pittsburgh, PA 15236) (also avail. in microfiche from CIS; also avail. by fax; reprint service avail. from CIS) **Indexed:** Amer.Stat.Ind. (1973-). **Document type:** government publication.
●Also available online.
—CASDDS.
Description: Provides data on worldwide production, distribution and consumption of platinum, with emphasis on the U.S.

622 US
U.S. BUREAU OF MINES. MINERAL INDUSTRY SURVEYS - COMMODITIES: POTASH. (Subseries of: Mineral Industry Surveys (ISSN 0886-0564)) a. (also issued in m. and q. editions). free. U.S. Bureau of Mines, Office of Public Information, 810 Seventh St., N.W., MS-1040, Washington, DC 20241-0001. TEL 202-501-9649. FAX 202-219-2493. (Orders to: U.S.B.M., Box 19070, Pittsburgh, PA 15236) charts. (also avail. by fax) **Indexed:** Amer.Stat.Ind. (1973-). **Document type:** government publication.
●Also available online.
Supersedes in part: Mineral Industry Surveys: Potash - Crop Year; In part: Mineral Industry Surveys. Potash - Annual Preliminary.

622 US
U.S. BUREAU OF MINES. MINERAL INDUSTRY SURVEYS - COMMODITIES: RARE EARTHS - THE LANTHANIDES, YTTRIUM, AND SCANDIUM. (Subseries of: Mineral Industry Surveys (ISSN 0886-0564)) a. (also issued in m. and q. editions). free. U.S. Bureau of Mines, Office of Public Information, 810 Seventh St., N.W., MS-1040, Washington, DC 20241-0001. TEL 202-501-9649. FAX 202-219-2493. (Orders to: U.S.B.M., Box 19070, Pittsburgh, PA 15236) charts. (also avail. by fax) **Indexed:** Amer.Stat.Ind. (1973-). **Document type:** government publication.
●Also available online.

622 US
U.S. BUREAU OF MINES. MINERAL INDUSTRY SURVEYS - COMMODITIES: RECYCLING IRON AND STEEL SCRAP. (Subseries of: Mineral Industry Surveys (ISSN 0886-0564)) a. (also issued in m. and q. editions). free. U.S. Bureau of Mines, Office of Public Information, 810 Seventh St., N.W., MS-1040, Washington, DC 20241-0001. TEL 202-501-9649. FAX 202-219-2493. (Orders to: U.S.B.M., Box 19070, Pittsburgh, PA 15236) charts. (also avail. by fax) **Indexed:** Amer.Stat.Ind. (1973-). **Document type:** government publication.
●Also available online.

622 US
U.S. BUREAU OF MINES. MINERAL INDUSTRY SURVEYS - COMMODITIES: SALT. (Subseries of: Mineral Industry Surveys (ISSN 0886-0564)) a. (also issued in m. and q. editions). free. U.S. Bureau of Mines, Office of Public Information, 810 Seventh St., N.W., MS-9800, Washington, DC 20241-0001. TEL 202-501-9649. FAX 202-219-2493. (Orders to: U.S.B.M., Box 19070, Pittsburgh, PA 15236) (also avail. by fax) **Document type:** government publication.
●Also available online.
Description: Contains statistical information on the production, import, export, and consumption of salt.

622 US
U.S. BUREAU OF MINES. MINERAL INDUSTRY SURVEYS - COMMODITIES: SILICON. (Subseries of: Mineral Industry Surveys (ISSN 0886-0564)) a. (also issued in m. and q. editions). free. U.S. Bureau of Mines, Office of Public Information, 810 Seventh St., N.W., MS-1040, Washington, DC 20241-0001. TEL 202-501-9649. (Orders to: U.S.B.M., Box 19070, Pittsburgh, PA 15236) (also avail. in microfiche from CIS; also avail. by fax; reprint service avail. from CIS) **Indexed:** Amer.Stat.Ind. (1976-). **Document type:** government publication.
●Also available online.
Description: Contains data on the production, import, export and consumption of silicon.

622 US
U.S. BUREAU OF MINES. MINERAL INDUSTRY SURVEYS - COMMODITIES: SILVER. (Subseries of: U.S. Bureau of Mines. Mineral Industry Surveys (ISSN 0886-0564)) a. (also issued in m. and q. editions). free. U.S. Bureau of Mines, Office of Public Information, 810 Seventh St., N.W., MS-1040, Washington, DC 20241-0001. TEL 202-501-9649. FAX 202-219-2493. (Orders to: U.S.B.M., Box 19070, Pittsburgh, PA 15250) charts. (also avail. by fax) **Indexed:** Amer.Stat.Ind. (1973-). **Document type:** government publication.
●Also available online.
Supersedes in part: U.S. Bureau of Mines. Mineral Industry Surveys: Gold and Silver.

622 US
U.S. BUREAU OF MINES. MINERAL INDUSTRY SURVEYS - COMMODITIES: SLAG - IRON AND STEEL. (Subseries of: Mineral Industry Surveys (ISSN 0886-0564)) a. (also issued in m. and q. editions). U.S. Bureau of Mines, Office of Public Information, 810 Seventh St., N.W., MS-1040, Washington, DC 20241-0001. TEL 202-501-9649. FAX 202-219-2493. (Orders to: U.S.B.M., Box 19070, Pittsburgh, PA 15236) charts. (also avail. by fax) **Document type:** government publication.
●Also available online.

622 US
U.S. BUREAU OF MINES. MINERAL INDUSTRY SURVEYS - COMMODITIES: SODA ASH. (Subseries of: Mineral Industry Surveys (ISSN 0886-0564)) a. free. U.S. Bureau of Mines, Office of Public Information, 810 Seventh St., S.W., MS-1040, Washington, DC 20241-0001. TEL 202-501-9649. FAX 202-219-2493. (Orders to: U.S.B.M., Box 19070, Pittsburgh, PA 15236) charts. (also avail. by fax) **Indexed:** Amer.Stat.Ind. (1973-). **Document type:** government publication.
●Also available online.
Description: Reviews mining activity in the U.S. for soda ash.

622 US
U.S. BUREAU OF MINES. MINERAL INDUSTRY SURVEYS - COMMODITIES: SODIUM SULFATE. (Subseries of: U.S. Bureau of Mines. Mineral Industry Surveys (ISSN 0886-0564)) a. (also issued in m. and q. editions). free. U.S. Bureau of Mines, Office of Public Information, 810 Seventh St., N.W., MS-1040, Washington, DC 20241-0001. TEL 202-501-9649. FAX 202-219-2493. (Orders to: U.S.B.M., Box 19070, Pittsburgh, PA 15236) (also avail. by fax) **Document type:** government publication.
●Also available online.
Formerly: U.S. Bureau of Mines. Mineral Industry Surveys. Sodium Compounds.
Description: Provides estimates of data and activity highlights on sodium compounds.

622 US
U.S. BUREAU OF MINES. MINERAL INDUSTRY SURVEYS - COMMODITIES: SULFUR. (Subseries of: Mineral Industry Surveys (ISSN 0886-0564)) a. (also issued in m. and q. editions). free. U.S. Bureau of Mines, Office of Public Information, 810 Seventh St., N.W., MS-1400, Washington, DC 20241-0001. TEL 202-501-9649. FAX 202-219-2493. (Orders to: U.S.B.M., Box 19070, Pittsburgh, PA 15236) (also avail. in microfiche from CIS; also avail. by fax; reprint service avail. from CIS) **Indexed:** Amer.Stat.Ind. (1973-). **Document type:** government publication.
●Also available online.
Description: Provides data on the production and consumption of fresh and recovered sulfur.

622 US
U.S. BUREAU OF MINES. MINERAL INDUSTRY SURVEYS - COMMODITIES: TIN. (Subseries of: Mineral Industry Surveys (ISSN 0886-0564)) a. (also issued in m. and q. editions). free. U.S. Bureau of Mines, Office of Public Information, 810 Seventh St., N.W., MS-1040, Washington, DC 20241-0001. TEL 202-501-9649. FAX 202-219-2493. (Orders to: U.S.B.M., Box 19070, Pittsburgh, PA 15236) charts. (also avail. in microfiche from CIS; also avail. by fax; reprint service avail. from CIS) **Indexed:** Amer.Stat.Ind. (1973-). **Document type:** government publication.
●Also available online.
Description: Presents data on tin mining and consumption.

MINES AND MINING INDUSTRY — ABSTRACTING, BIBLIOGRAPHIES, STATISTICS   4781

622   US
U.S. BUREAU OF MINES. MINERAL INDUSTRY SURVEYS - COMMODITIES: TITANIUM. (Subseries of: Mineral Industry Surveys (ISSN 0886-0564)) a. (also issued in m. and q. editions). free. U.S. Bureau of Mines, Office of Public Information, 810 Seventh St., N.W., MS-1040, Washington, DC 20241-0001. TEL 202-501-9649. FAX 202-219-2493. (Orders to: U.S.B.M., Box 19070, Pittsburgh, PA 15236) charts. (also avail. in microfiche from CIS; also avail. by fax; reprint service avail. from CIS) **Indexed:** Amer.Stat.Ind. (1973-). **Document type:** government publication.
●Also available online.
   Description: Provides data on the production and consumption of titanium.

622   US
U.S. BUREAU OF MINES. MINERAL INDUSTRY SURVEYS - COMMODITIES: TUNGSTEN. (Subseries of: Mineral Industry Surveys (ISSN 0886-0564)) a. (also issued in m. and q. editions). free. U.S. Bureau of Mines, Office of Public Information, 810 Seventh St., N.W., MS-1040, Washington, DC 20241-0001. TEL 202-501-9649. FAX 202-219-2493. (Orders to: U.S.B.M., Box 19070, Pittsburgh, PA 15236) charts. (also avail. in microfiche from CIS; also avail. by fax; reprint service avail. from CIS) **Indexed:** Amer.Stat.Ind. (1973-). **Document type:** government publication.
●Also available online.
   Description: Provides data on the production and consumption of tungsten concentrate, ammonium paratungstate, and intermediate products.

622   US
U.S. BUREAU OF MINES. MINERAL INDUSTRY SURVEYS - COMMODITIES: VANADIUM. (Subseries of: Mineral Industry Surveys (ISSN 0886-0564)) a. (also issued in m. and q. editions). free. U.S. Bureau of Mines, Office of Public Information, 810 Seventh St., N.W., MS-1040, Washington, DC 20241-0001. TEL 202-501-9649. FAX 202-219-2493. (Orders to: U.S.B.M., Box 19070, Pittsburgh, PA 15236) charts. (also avail. in microfiche from CIS; also avail. by fax; reprint service avail. from CIS) **Indexed:** Amer.Stat.Ind. (1973-). **Document type:** government publication.
●Also available online.
   Description: Presents data on vanadium mining and consumption.

622   US
U.S. BUREAU OF MINES. MINERAL INDUSTRY SURVEYS - COMMODITIES: ZINC. (Subseries of: U.S. Bureau of Mines. Mineral Industry Surveys (ISSN 0886-0564)) a. (also issued in m. and q. editions). free. U.S. Bureau of Mines, Office of Public Information, 810 Seventh St., N.W., MS-1040, Washington, DC 20241-0001. TEL 202-501-9649. FAX 202-219-2493. (Orders to: U.S.B.M., Box 19070, Pittsburgh, PA 15236) charts. (also avail. in microfiche from CIS; also avail. by fax; reprint service avail. from CIS) **Indexed:** Amer.Stat.Ind. (1974-). **Document type:** government publication.
●Also available online.
   Formerly: U.S. Bureau of Mines. Mineral Industry Surveys: Zinc Industry and Smelter Production.
   Description: Provides data on zinc mining and consumption.

622   US
U.S. BUREAU OF MINES. MINERAL INDUSTRY SURVEYS - COMMODITIES: ZIRCONIUM AND HAFNIUM. (Subseries of: Mineral Industry Surveys (ISSN 0886-0564)) a. (also issued in m. and q. editions). free. U.S. Bureau of Mines, Office of Public Information, 810 Seventh St., N.W., MS-1040, Washington, DC 20241-0001. TEL 202-501-9649. FAX 202-219-2493. (Orders to: U.S.B.M., Box 19070, Pittsburgh, PA 15236) charts. (also avail. by fax) **Indexed:** Amer.Stat.Ind. (1973-). **Document type:** government publication.
●Also available online.

622   US
U.S. BUREAU OF MINES. MINERAL INDUSTRY SURVEYS: CONNECTICUT. (Subseries of: U.S. Bureau of Mines. Mineral Industry Surveys (ISSN 0886-0564)) a. free. U.S. Bureau of Mines, Office of Public Information, 810 Seventh St., N.W., MS-1040, Washington, DC 20241-0001. TEL 202-501-9649. FAX 202-219-2493. (Orders to: U.S.B.M., Box 19070, Pittsburgh, PA 15236) charts. (also avail. by fax) **Document type:** government publication.
●Also available online.
   Formerly (until 1995): U.S. Bureau of Mines. Annual Report: Connecticut.

622   US
U.S. BUREAU OF MINES. MINERAL INDUSTRY SURVEYS: DELAWARE. (Subseries of: U.S. Bureau of Mines. Mineral Industry Surveys (ISSN 0886-0564)) a. free. U.S. Bureau of Mines, Office of Public Information, 810 Seventh St., N.W., MS-1040, Washington, DC 20241-0001. TEL 202-501-9649. FAX 202-219-2493. (Orders to: U.S.B.M., Box 19070, Pittsburgh, PA 15236) charts. (also avail. by fax) **Document type:** government publication.
●Also available online.
   Formerly (Until 1995): U.S. Bureau of Mines. Annual Report: Delaware.

622   US
U.S. BUREAU OF MINES. MINERAL INDUSTRY SURVEYS: FLORIDA. (Subseries of: U.S. Bureau of Mines. Mineral Industry Surveys (ISSN 0886-0564)) a. free. U.S. Bureau of Mines, Office of Public Information, 810 Seventh St., N.W., MS-1040, Washington, DC 20241-0001. TEL 202-501-9649. FAX 202-219-2493. (Orders to: U.S.B.M., Box 19070, Pittsburgh, PA 15236) charts. (also avail. by fax) **Document type:** government publication.
●Also available online.
   Formerly (until 1995): U.S. Bureau of Mines. Annual Report: Florida.

622   US
U.S. BUREAU OF MINES. MINERAL INDUSTRY SURVEYS: GEORGIA. (Subseries of: U.S. Bureau of Mines. Mineral Industry Surveys (ISSN 0886-0564)) a. free. U.S. Bureau of Mines, Office of Public Information, 810 Seventh St., N.W., MS-1040, Washington, DC 20241-0001. TEL 202-501-9649. FAX 202-219-2493. (Orders to: U.S.B.M., Box 19070, Pittsburgh, PA 15236) charts. (also avail. by fax) **Document type:** government publication.
●Also available online.
   Formerly (until 1995): U.S. Bureau of Mines. Annual Report: Georgia.

622   US
U.S. BUREAU OF MINES. MINERAL INDUSTRY SURVEYS: HAWAII. (Subseries of: U.S. Bureau of Mines. Mineral Industry Surveys (ISSN 0886-0564)) a. free. U.S. Bureau of Mines, Office of Public Information, 810 Seventh St., N.W., MS-1040, Washington, DC 20241-0001. TEL 202-501-9649. FAX 202-219-2493. (Orders to: U.S.B.M., Box 19070, Pittsburgh, PA 15236) charts. (back issues avail.) **Document type:** government publication.
●Also available online.
   Formerly (until 1995): U.S. Bureau of Mines. Annual Report: Hawaii.

622   US
U.S. BUREAU OF MINES. MINERAL INDUSTRY SURVEYS: IDAHO. (Subseries of: U.S. Bureau of Mines. Mineral Industry Surveys (ISSN 0886-0564)) a. free. U.S. Bureau of Mines, Office of Public Information, 810 Seventh St., N.W., MS-1040, Washington, DC 20241-0001. TEL 202-501-9649. FAX 202-219-2493. (Orders to: U.S.B.M., Box 19070, Pittsburgh, PA 15236) charts. (also avail. by fax) **Document type:** government publication.
●Also available online.
   Formerly (until 1995): U.S. Bureau of Mines. Annual Report: Idaho.

622   US
U.S. BUREAU OF MINES. MINERAL INDUSTRY SURVEYS: ILLINOIS. (Subseries of: U.S. Bureau of Mines. Mineral Industry Surveys (ISSN 0886-0564)) a. free. U.S. Bureau of Mines, Office of Public Information, 810 Seventh St., N.W., MS-1040, Washington, DC 20241-0001. TEL 202-501-9649. FAX 202-219-2493. (Orders to: U.S.B.M., Box 19070, Pittsburgh, PA 15236) charts. (also avail. by fax) **Document type:** government publication.
●Also available online.
   Formerly (until 1995): U.S. Bureau of Mines. Annual Report: Illinois.

322   US
U.S. BUREAU OF MINES. MINERAL INDUSTRY SURVEYS: INDIANA. (Subseries of: U.S. Bureau of Mines. Mineral Industry Surveys (ISSN 0886-0564)) a. free. U.S. Bureau of Mines, Office of Public Information, 810 Seventh St., N.W., MS-1040, Washington, DC 20241-0001. TEL 202-501-9649. FAX 202-219-2493. (Orders to: U.S.B.M., Box 19070, Pittsburgh, PA 15236) charts. (also avail. by fax) **Document type:** government publication.
●Also available online.
   Formerly (until 1995): U.S. Bureau of Mines. Annual Report: Indiana.

622   US
U.S. BUREAU OF MINES. MINERAL INDUSTRY SURVEYS: IOWA. (Subseries of: U.S. Bureau of Mines. Mineral Industry Surveys (ISSN 0886-0564)) a. free. U.S. Bureau of Mines, Office of Public Information, 810 Seventh St., N.W., MS-1040, Washington, DC 20241-0001. TEL 202-501-9649. FAX 202-219-2493. (Orders to: U.S.B.M., Box 19070, Pittsburgh, PA 15236) charts. (also avail. by fax) **Document type:** government publication.
●Also available online.
   Formerly (until 1995): U.S. Bureau of Mines. Annual Report: Iowa.

622   US
U.S. BUREAU OF MINES. MINERAL INDUSTRY SURVEYS: KANSAS. (Subseries of: U.S. Bureau of Mines. Mineral Industry Surveys (ISSN 0886-0564)) a. free. U.S. Bureau of Mines, Office of Public Information, 810 Seventh St., N.W., MS-1040, Washington, DC 20241-0001. TEL 202-501-9649. FAX 202-219-2493. (Orders to: U.S.B.M., Box 19070, Pittsburgh, PA 15236) charts. (also avail. by fax) **Document type:** government publication.
●Also available online.
   Formerly (until 1995): U.S. Bureau of Mines. Annual Report: Kansas.

622   US
U.S. BUREAU OF MINES. MINERAL INDUSTRY SURVEYS: KENTUCKY. (Subseries of: U.S. Bureau of Mines. Mineral Industry Surveys (ISSN 0886-0564)) a. free. U.S. Bureau of Mines, Office of Public Information, 810 Seventh St., N.W., MS-1040, Washington, DC 20241-0001. TEL 202-501-9649. FAX 202-219-2493. (Orders to: U.S.B.M., Box 19070, Pittsburgh, PA 15236) charts. (also avail. by fax) **Document type:** government publication.
●Also available online.
   Formerly (until 1995): U.S. Bureau of Mines. Annual Report: Kentucky.

622   US
U.S. BUREAU OF MINES. MINERAL INDUSTRY SURVEYS: LOUISIANA. (Subseries of: U.S. Bureau of Mines. Mineral Industry Surveys (ISSN 0886-0564)) a. free. U.S. Bureau of Mines, Office of Public Information, 810 Seventh St., N.W., MS-1040, Washington, DC 20241-0001. TEL 202-501-9649. FAX 202-219-2493. (Orders to: U.S.B.M., Box 19070, Pittsburgh, PA 15236) charts. (also avail. by fax) **Document type:** government publication.
●Also available online.
   Formerly (until 1995): U.S. Bureau of Mines. Annual Report: Louisiana.

622   US
U.S. BUREAU OF MINES. MINERAL INDUSTRY SURVEYS: MAINE. (Subseries of: U.S. Bureau of Mines. Mineral Industry Surveys (ISSN 0886-0564)) a. free. U.S. Bureau of Mines, Office of Public Information, 810 Seventh St., N.W., MS-1040, Washington, DC 20241-0001. TEL 202-501-9649. FAX 202-219-2493. (Orders to: U.S.B.M., Box 19070, Pittsburgh, PA 15236) charts. (also avail. by fax) **Document type:** government publication.
●Also available online.
   Formerly (until 1995): U.S. Bureau of Mines. Annual Report: Maine.

622   US
U.S. BUREAU OF MINES. MINERAL INDUSTRY SURVEYS: MARYLAND. (Subseries of: U.S. Bureau of Mines. Mineral Industry Surveys (ISSN 0886-0564)) a. free. U.S. Bureau of Mines, Office of Public Information, 810 Seventh St., N.W., MS-1040, Washington, DC 20241-0001. TEL 202-501-9649. FAX 202-219-2493. (Orders to: U.S.B.M., Box 19070, Pittsburgh, PA 15236) charts. (also avail. by fax) **Document type:** government publication.
●Also available online.
   Formerly (until 1995): U.S. Bureau of Mines. Annual Report: Maryland.

MINES AND MINING INDUSTRY — ABSTRACTING, BIBLIOGRAPHIES, STATISTICS

622 US
U.S. BUREAU OF MINES. MINERAL INDUSTRY SURVEYS: MASSACHUSETTS. (Subseries of: U.S. Bureau of Mines. Mineral Industry Surveys (ISSN 0886-0564)) a. free. U.S. Bureau of Mines, Office of Public Information, 810 Seventh St., N.W., MS-1040, Washington, DC 20241-0001. TEL 202-501-9649. FAX 202-219-2493. (Orders to: U.S.B.M., Box 19070, Pittsburgh, PA 15236) charts. (also avail. by fax) **Document type:** government publication. ●Also available online.
Formerly (until 1995): U.S. Bureau of Mines. Annual Report: Massachusetts.

622 US
U.S. BUREAU OF MINES. MINERAL INDUSTRY SURVEYS: MICHIGAN. (Subseries of: Mineral Industry Surveys (ISSN 0886-0564)) a. free. U.S. Bureau of Mines, Office of Public Information, 810 Seventh St., N.W., MS-1040, Washington, DC 20241-0001. TEL 202-501-9649. FAX 202-219-2493. (Orders to: U.S.B.M., Box 19070, Pittsburgh, PA 15236) charts. (also avail. by fax) **Document type:** government publication. ●Also available online.
Formerly (until 1995): U.S. Bureau of Mines. Annual Report: Michigan.

322 US
U.S. BUREAU OF MINES. MINERAL INDUSTRY SURVEYS: MINNESOTA. (Subseries of: U.S. Bureau of Mines. Mineral Industry Surveys (ISSN 0886-0564)) a. free. U.S. Bureau of Mines, Office of Public Information, 810 Seventh St., N.W., MS-1040, Washington, DC 20241-0001. TEL 202-501-9649. FAX 202-219-2493. (Orders to: U.S.B.M., Box 19070, Pittsburgh, PA 15236) charts. (also avail. by fax) **Document type:** government publication. ●Also available online.
Formerly (until 1995): U.S. Bureau of Mines. Annual Report: Minnesota.

622 US
U.S. BUREAU OF MINES. MINERAL INDUSTRY SURVEYS: MISSISSIPPI. (Subseries of: U.S. Bureau of Mines. Mineral Industry Surveys (ISSN 0886-0564)) a. free. U.S. Bureau of Mines, Office of Public Information, 810 Seventh St., N.W., MS-1040, Washington, DC 20241-0001. TEL 202-510-9649. FAX 202-219-2493. (Orders to: U.S.B.M., Box 19070, Pittsburgh, PA 15236) charts. (also avail. by fax) **Document type:** government publication. ●Also available online.
Formerly (until 1995): U.S. Bureau of Mines. Annual Report: Mississippi.

622 US
U.S. BUREAU OF MINES. MINERAL INDUSTRY SURVEYS: MISSOURI. (Subseries of: U.S. Bureau of Mines. Mineral Industry Surveys (ISSN 0886-0564)) a. free. U.S. Bureau of Mines, Office of Public Information, 810 Seventh St., N.W., MS-1040, Washington, DC 20241-0001. TEL 202-501-9649. FAX 202-219-2493. (Orders to: U.S.B.M., Box 19070, Pittsburgh, PA 15236) charts. (also avail. by fax) **Document type:** government publication. ●Also available online.
Formerly (until 1995): U.S. Bureau of Mines. Annual Report: Missouri.

622 US
U.S. BUREAU OF MINES. MINERAL INDUSTRY SURVEYS: MONTANA. (Subseries of: U.S. Bureau of Mines. Mineral Industry Surveys (ISSN 0886-0564)) a. free. U.S. Bureau of Mines, Office of Public Information, 810 Seventh St., N.W., MS-1040, Washington, DC 20241-0001. TEL 202-501-9649. FAX 202-219-2493. (Orders to: U.S.B.M., Box 19070, Pittsburgh, PA 15236) charts. (also avail. by fax) **Document type:** government publication. ●Also available online.
Formerly (until 1995): U.S. Bureau of Mines. Annual Report: Montana.

622 US
U.S. BUREAU OF MINES. MINERAL INDUSTRY SURVEYS: NEBRASKA. (Subseries of: U.S. Bureau of Mines. Mineral Industry Surveys (ISSN 0886-0564)) a. free. U.S. Bureau of Mines, Office of Public Information, 810 Seventh St., N.W., MS-1040, Washington, DC 20241-0001. TEL 202-501-9649. FAX 202-219-2493. (Orders to: U.S.B.M., Box 19070, Pittsburgh, PA 15236) charts. (also avail. by fax) **Document type:** government publication. ●Also available online.
Formerly (until 1995): U.S. Bureau of Mines. Annual Report: Nebraska.

622 US
U.S. BUREAU OF MINES. MINERAL INDUSTRY SURVEYS: NEVADA. (Subseries of: U.S. Bureau of Mines. Mineral Industry Surveys (ISSN 0886-0564)) a. free. U.S. Bureau of Mines, Office of Public Information, 810 Seventh St., N.W., MS-1040, Washington, DC 20241-0001. TEL 202-501-9649. FAX 202-219-2493. (Orders to: U.S.B.M., Box 19070, Pittsburgh, PA 15236) charts. (back issues avail.) **Document type:** government publication. ●Also available online.
Formerly (until 1995): U.S. Bureau of Mines. Annual Report: Nevada.

622 US
U.S. BUREAU OF MINES. MINERAL INDUSTRY SURVEYS: NEW HAMPSHIRE. (Subseries of: U.S. Bureau of Mines. Mineral Industry Surveys (ISSN 0886-0564)) a. free. U.S. Bureau of Mines, Office of Public Information, 810 Seventh St., N.W., MS-1040, Washington, DC 20241-0001. TEL 202-501-9649. FAX 202-219-2493. (Orders to: U.S.B.M., Box 19070, Pittsburgh, PA 15236) charts. (also avail. by fax) **Document type:** government publication. ●Also available online.
Formerly (until 1995): U.S. Bureau of Mines. Annual Report: New Hampshire.

622 US
U.S. BUREAU OF MINES. MINERAL INDUSTRY SURVEYS: NEW JERSEY. (Subseries of: U.S. Bureau of Mines. Mineral Industry Surveys (ISSN 0886-0564)) a. free. U.S. Bureau of Mines, Office of Public Information, 810 Seventh St., N.W., MS-1040, Washington, DC 20241-0001. TEL 202-501-9649. FAX 202-219-2493. (Orders to: U.S.B.M., Box 19070, Pittsuburgh, PA 15236) charts. (also avail. by fax) **Document type:** government publication. ●Also available online.
Formerly (until 1995): U.S. Bureau of Mines. Annual Report: New Jersey.

622 US
U.S. BUREAU OF MINES. MINERAL INDUSTRY SURVEYS: NEW MEXICO. (Subseries of: U.S. Bureau of Mines. Mineral Industry Surveys (ISSN 0886-0564)) a. free. U.S. Bureau of Mines, Office of Public Information, 810 Seventh St., N.W., MS-1040, Washington, DC 20241-0001. TEL 202-501-9649. FAX 202-219-2493. (Orders to: U.S.B.M., Box 19070, Pittsburgh, PA 15236) (also avail. by fax) **Document type:** government publication. ●Also available online.
Formerly (until 1995): U.S. Bureau of Mines. Annual Report: New Mexico.

622 US
U.S. BUREAU OF MINES. MINERAL INDUSTRY SURVEYS: NEW YORK. (Subseries of: U.S. Bureau of Mines. Mineral Industry Surveys (ISSN 0886-0564)) a. free. U.S. Bureau of Mines, Office of Public Information, 810 Seventh St., N.W., MS-1040, Washington, DC 20241-0001. TEL 202-501-9649. FAX 202-219-2493. (Orders to: U.S.B.M., Box 19070, Pittsburgh, PA15236) charts. (also avail. by fax) **Document type:** government publication. ●Also available online.
Formerly (until 1995): U.S. Bureau of Mines. Annual Report: New York.

622 US
U.S. BUREAU OF MINES. MINERAL INDUSTRY SURVEYS: NORTH CAROLINA. (Subseries of: U.S. Bureau of Mines. Mineral Industry Surveys (ISSN 0886-0564)) a. free. U.S. Bureau of Mines, Office of Public Information, 810 Seventh St., N.W., MS-1040, Washington, DC 20241-0001. TEL 202-501-9649. FAX 202-219-2493. (Orders to: U.S.B.M., Box 19070, Pittsburgh, PA 15236) charts. (also avail. by fax) **Document type:** government publication. ●Also available online.
Formerly (until 1995): U.S. Bureau of Mines. Annual Report: North Carolina.

622 US
U.S. BUREAU OF MINES. MINERAL INDUSTRY SURVEYS: NORTH DAKOTA. (Subseries of: U.S. Bureau of Mines. Mineral Industry Surveys (ISSN 0886-0564)) a. free. U.S. Bureau of Mines, Office of Public Information, 810 Seventh St., N.W., MS-1040, Washington, DC 20241-0001. TEL 202-501-9649. FAX 202-219-2493. (Orders to: U.S.B.M., Box 19070, Pittsburgh, PA 15236) charts. (also avail. by fax) **Document type:** government publication. ●Also available online.
Formerly (until 1995): U.S. Bureau of Mines. Annual Report: North Dakota.

622 US
U.S. BUREAU OF MINES. MINERAL INDUSTRY SURVEYS: OHIO. (Subseries of: U.S. Bureau of Mines. Mineral Industry Surveys (ISSN 0886-0564)) a. free. U.S. Bureau of Mines, Office of Public Information, 810 Seventh St., N.W., MS-1040, Washington, DC 20241-0001. TEL 202-501-9649. FAX 202-219-2493. (Orders to: U.S.B.M., Box 19070, Pittsburgh, PA 15236) charts. (also avail. by fax) **Document type:** government publication. ●Also available online.
Formerly (until 1995): U.S. Bureau of Mines. Annual Report: Ohio.

622 US
U.S. BUREAU OF MINES. MINERAL INDUSTRY SURVEYS: OKLAHOMA. (Subseries of: U.S. Bureau of Mines. Mineral Industry Surveys (ISSN 0886-0564)) a. free. U.S. Bureau of Mines, Office of Public Information, 810 Seventh St., N.W., MS-1040, Washington, DC 20241-0001. TEL 202-501-9649. FAX 202-219-2493. (Orders to: U.S.B.M., Box 19070, Pittsburgh, PA 15236) charts. (also avail. by fax) **Document type:** government publication. ●Also available online.
Formerly (until 1995): U.S. Bureau of Mines. Annual Report: Oklahoma.

622 US
U.S. BUREAU OF MINES. MINERAL INDUSTRY SURVEYS: OREGON. (Subseries of: U.S. Bureau of Mines. Mineral Industry Surveys (ISSN 0886-0564)) a. free. U.S. Bureau of Mines, Office of Public Information, 810 Seventh St., N.W., MS-1040, Washington, DC 20241-0001. TEL 202-501-9649. FAX 202-219-2493. (Orders to: U.S.B.M., Box 19070, Pittsburgh, PA 15236) charts. (also avail. by fax) **Document type:** government publication. ●Also available online.
Formerly (until 1995): U.S. Bureau of Mines. Annual Report: Oregon.

622 US
U.S. BUREAU OF MINES. MINERAL INDUSTRY SURVEYS: PENNSYLVANIA. (Subseries of: U.S. Bureau of Mines. Mineral Industry Surveys (ISSN 0886-0564)) a. free. U.S. Bureau of Mines, Office of Public Information, 810 Seventh St., N.W., MS-1040, Washington, DC 20241-0001. TEL 202-501-9649. FAX 202-219-2493. (Orders to: U.S.B.M., Box 19070, Pittsburgh, PA 15236) charts. (also avail. by fax) **Document type:** government publication. ●Also available online.
Formerly (until 1995): U.S. Bureau of Mines. Annual Report: Pennsylvania.

622 US
U.S. BUREAU OF MINES. MINERAL INDUSTRY SURVEYS: PUERTO RICO. (Subseries of: U.S. Bureau of Mines. Mineral Industry Surveys (ISSN 0886-0564)) a. free. U.S. Bureau of Mines, Office of Public Information, 810 Seventh St., N.W., MS-1040, Washington, DC 20241-0001. TEL 202-501-9649. FAX 202-219-2493. (Orders to: U.S.B.M., Box 19070, Pittsburgh, PA 15236) charts. (also avail. by fax) **Document type:** government publication. ●Also available online.
Formerly (until 1995): U.S. Bureau of Mines. Annual Report: Puerto Rico.

622 US
U.S. BUREAU OF MINES. MINERAL INDUSTRY SURVEYS: RHODE ISLAND. (Subseries of: U.S. Bureau of Mines. Mineral Industry Surveys (ISSN 0886-0564)) a. free. U.S. Bureau of Mines, Office of Public Information, 810 Seventh St., N.W., MS-1040, Washington, DC 20241-0001. TEL 202-501-9649. FAX 202-219-2493. (Orders to: U.S.B.M., Box 19070, Pittsburgh, PA 15236) charts. (also avail. by fax) **Document type:** government publication. ●Also available online.
Formerly (until 1995): U.S. Bureau of Mines. Annual Report: Rhode Island.

622 US
U.S. BUREAU OF MINES. MINERAL INDUSTRY SURVEYS: SOUTH CAROLINA. (Subseries of: U.S. Bureau of Mines. Mineral Industry Surveys (ISSN 0886-0564)) a. free. U.S. Bureau of Mines, Office of Public Information, 810 Seventh St., N.W., MS-1040, Washington, DC 20041-0001. TEL 202-501-9649. FAX 202-219-2493. (Orders to: U.S.B.M., Box 19070, Pittsburgh, PA 15236) charts. (Also avail. by fax) **Document type:** government publication. ●Also available online.
U.S. Bureau of Mines. Annual Report: South Carolina.

622 US
U.S. BUREAU OF MINES. MINERAL INDUSTRY SURVEYS: SOUTH DAKOTA. (Subseries of: U.S. Bureau of Mines. Mineral Industry Surveys (ISSN 0886-0564)) a. free. U.S. Bureau of Mines, Office of Public Information, 810 Seventh St., N.W., MS-1040, Washington, DC 20041-0001. TEL 202-501-9649. FAX 202-219-2493. (Orders to: U.S.B.M., Box 19070, Pittsburgh, PA 15236) charts. (also avail. by fax) **Document type:** government publication.
●Also available online.
Formerly (until 1995): U.S. Bureau of Mines. Annual Report: South Dakota.

622 US
U.S. BUREAU OF MINES. MINERAL INDUSTRY SURVEYS: TENNESSEE. (Subseries of: U.S. Bureau of Mines. Mineral Industry Surveys (ISSN 0886-0564)) a. free. U.S. Bureau of Mines, Office of Public Information, 810 Seventh St., N.W., MS-1040, Washington, DC 20241-0001. TEL 202-501-9649. FAX 202-219-2493. (Orders to: U.S.B.M., Box 19070, Pittsburgh, PA 15236) charts. (also avail. by fax) **Document type:** government publication.
●Also available online.
Formerly (until 1995): U.S. Bureau of Mines. Annual Report: Tennessee.

322 US
U.S. BUREAU OF MINES. MINERAL INDUSTRY SURVEYS: TEXAS. (Subseries of: U.S. Bureau of Mines. Mineral Industry Surveys (ISSN 0886-0564)) a. free. U.S. Bureau of Mines, Office of Public Information, 810 Seventh St., N.W., MS-1040, Washington, DC 20041-0001. TEL 202-501-9649. FAX 202-219-2493. (Orders to: U.S.B.M., Box 19070, Pittsburgh, PA 15236) charts. (also avail. by fax) **Document type:** government publication.
●Also available online.
Formerly (until 1995): U.S. Bureau of Mines. Annual Report: Texas.

662 US
U.S. BUREAU OF MINES. MINERAL INDUSTRY SURVEYS: UTAH. (Subseries of: U.S. Bureau of Mines. Mineral Industry Surveys (ISSN 0886-0564)) a. free. U.S. Bureau of Mines, Office of Public Information, 810 Seventh St., N.W., MS-1040, Washington, DC 20241-0001. TEL 202-501-9649. FAX 202-219-2493. (Orders to: U.S.B.M., Box 19070, Pittsburgh, PA 15236) charts. (back issues avail.) **Document type:** government publication.
●Also available online.
Formerly (until 1995): U.S. Bureau of Mines. Annual Report: Utah.

622 US
U.S. BUREAU OF MINES. MINERAL INDUSTRY SURVEYS: VERMONT. (Subseries of: U.S. Bureau of Mines. Mineral Industry Surveys (ISSN 0886-0564)) a. free. U.S. Bureau of Mines, Office of Public Information, 810 Seventh St., N.W., MS-1040, Washington, DC 20241-0001. TEL 202-501-9649. FAX 202-219-2493. (Orders to: U.S.B.M., Box 19070, Pittsburgh, PA 15236) charts. (also avail. by fax) **Document type:** government publication.
●Also available online.
Formerly (until 1995): U.S. Bureau of Mines. Annual Report: Vermont.

622 US
U.S. BUREAU OF MINES. MINERAL INDUSTRY SURVEYS: VIRGINIA. (Subseries of: U.S. Bureau of Mines. Mineral Industry Surveys (ISSN 0886-0564)) a. free. U.S. Bureau of Mines, Office of Public Information, 810 Seventh St., N.W., MS-1040, Washington, DC 20241-0001. TEL 202-501-9649. FAX 202-219-2493. (Orders to: U.S.B.M., Box 19070, Pittsburgh, PA 15236) charts. (also avail. by fax) **Document type:** government publication.
●Also available online.
Formerly (until 1995): U.S. Bureau of Mines. Annual Report: Virginia.

622 US
U.S. BUREAU OF MINES. MINERAL INDUSTRY SURVEYS: WASHINGTON. (Subseries of: U.S. Bureau of Mines. Mineral Industry Surveys (ISSN 0886-0564)) a. free. U.S. Bureau of Mines, Office of Public Information, 810 Seventh St., N.W., MS-1040, Washington, DC 20241-0001. TEL 202-501-9649. FAX 202-219-2493. (Orders to: U.S.B.M., Box 19070, Pittsburgh, PA 15236) charts. (back issues avail.) **Document type:** government publication.
●Also available online.
Formerly (until 1995): U.S. Bureau of Mines. Annual Report: Washington.

622 US
U.S. BUREAU OF MINES. MINERAL INDUSTRY SURVEYS: WEST VIRGINIA. (Subseries of: U.S. Bureau of Mines. Mineral Industry Surveys (ISSN 0886-0564)) a. free. U.S. Bureau of Mines, Office of Public Information, 810 Seventh St., N.W., MS-1040, Washington, DC 20241-0001. TEL 202-501-9649. FAX 202-219-2493. (Orders to: U.S.B.M., Box 19070, Pittsburgh, PA 15236) charts. (back issues avail.) **Document type:** government publication.
●Also available online.
Formerly (until 1995): U.S. Bureau of Mines. Annual Report: West Virginia.

622 US
U.S. BUREAU OF MINES. MINERAL INDUSTRY SURVEYS: WISCONSIN. (Subseries of: U.S. Bureau of Mines. Mineral Industry Surveys (ISSN 0886-0564)) a. free. U.S. Bureau of Mines, Office of Public Information, 810 Seventh St., N.W., MS-1040, Washington, DC 20241-0001. TEL 202-501-9649. FAX 202-219-2493. (Orders to: U.S.B.M., Box 19070, Pittsburgh, PA 15236) charts. (back issues avail.) **Document type:** government publication.
●Also available online.
Formerly (until 1995): U.S. Bureau of Mines. Annual Report: Wisconsin.

662 US
U.S. BUREAU OF MINES. MINERAL INDUSTRY SURVEYS: WYOMING. (Subseries of: U.S. Bureau of Mines. Mineral Industry Surveys (ISSN 0886-0564)) a. free. U.S. Bureau of Mines, Office of Public Information, 810 Seventh St., N.W., MS-1040, Washington, DC 20241-0001. TEL 202-501-9649. FAX 202-219-2493. (Orders to: U.S.B.M., Box 19070, Pittsburgh, PA 15236) charts. (also avail. by fax) **Document type:** government publication.
●Also available online.
Formerly (until 1995): U.S. Bureau of Mines. Annual Report: Wyoming.

622 VE
VENEZUELA. MINISTERIO DE ENERGIA Y MINAS. ANUARIO ESTADISTICO MINERO. 1965. a. Bs.1000. Ministerio de Energia y Minas, Direccion de Planificacion y Economia Minera, Torre Oeste, Piso 4, Centro Simon Bolivar, Caracas, Venezuela. **Document type:** government publication.
Former titles (until 1986): Hierro; Venezuela. Ministerio de Minas e Hidrocarburos. Oficina de Economia Minera. Hierro y Otros Datos Estadisticos (ISSN 0083-5382)

VENEZUELA. MINISTERIO DE ENERGIA Y MINAS. APENDICE ESTADISTICO. see *ENERGY* — *Abstracting, Bibliographies, Statistics*

VENEZUELA. MINISTERIO DE ENERGIA Y MINAS. MEMORIA. see *ENERGY* — *Abstracting, Bibliographies, Statistics*

338.2 310 UK ISSN 0951-9475
WORLD MINERAL STATISTICS; world production, exports and imports. 1978. a. price varies. Natural Environment Research Council, British Geological Survey, Kingsley Dunham Centre, Keyworth, Nottingham NG12 5GG, England. TEL 0115-936-1000. FAX 0115-936-2000. TELEX 378173 BGSKEY G. (Subscr. to: Mining Journal Books Ltd., 60 Worship St., London EC2A 2HD, England) circ. 1,000. **Document type:** abstracting/indexing, government publication.
—BLDSC (9356.674690).
Supersedes: Institute of Geological Sciences, London. Statistical Summary of the Mineral Industry (ISSN 0073-9367)

549 016 GW ISSN 0514-7115
CODEN: ZMKMA5
ZENTRALBLATT FUER MINERALOGIE. TEIL I: KRISTALLOGRAPHIE, MINERALOGIE. (Text in English and German) 1807. 7/yr. $201 per no. (effective 1996). E. Schweizerbart'sche Verlagsbuchhandlung, Johannesstr. 3A, 70176 Stuttgart, Germany. TEL 0711-625001. FAX 0711-625005. Ed. B. Baader. adv.; bk.rev.; abstr.; bibl.; index. **Indexed:** Bull.Signal., Chem.Abstr., GeoRef. **Document type:** academic/scholarly publication.
—CCC.

549 551 016 GW ISSN 0514-7123
CODEN: ZMGMAJ
ZENTRALBLATT FUER MINERALOGIE. TEIL II: PETROGRAPHIE, TECHNISCHE MINERALOGIE, GEOCHEMIE UND LAGERSTAETTENKUNDE. (Text in English and German) 1807. 13/yr. $349 per no. (effective 1996). E. Schweizerbart'sche Verlagsbuchhandlung, Johannesstr. 3A, 70176 Stuttgart, Germany. TEL 0711-625001. FAX 0711-625005. Ed.Bd. adv.; bk.rev.; abstr.; bibl.; index. **Indexed:** Bull.Signal., Chem.Abstr., GeoRef. **Document type:** academic/scholarly publication.
—CCC.

ZHONGGUO DIZHI WENZHAI. see *EARTH SCIENCES* — *Abstracting, Bibliographies, Statistics*

MINES AND MINING INDUSTRY — Computer Applications

622 551 US ISSN 1068-4425
COMPUTERS & MINING. 1985. m. $90 (foreign $115). Gibbs Associates, Box 706, Boulder, CO 80306. TEL 303-444-6032. Ed. Betty L. Gibbs. adv.; bk.rev. circ. 200. (looseleaf format; back issues avail.) **Document type:** newsletter.
Description: Computer applications for earth sciences, mining and geology.

622 US
EARTH SCIENCE SOFTWARE DIRECTORY. biennial. $75 (foreign $95). Gibbs Associates, Box 706, Boulder, CO 80306. TEL 303-444-6032. **Document type:** directory.
Formerly: Directory of Mining Programs.
Description: Lists commercial and public-domain computer programs for mining applications.

MINICOMPUTERS

see *Computers–Minicomputers*

MOTION PICTURES

A M I A NEWSLETTER. (Association of Moving Image Archivists) see *LIBRARY AND INFORMATION SCIENCES*

791.4 BE
A S. 1978. bi-m. 700 BEF (foreign 1000 BEF). De Andere Film, Ommeganckstraat 21, 2018 Antwerp, Belgium. TEL 32-3-2341640. FAX 32-3-2262764. Ed. Tom Paulus. adv. contact: Harry Eysakkers. bk.rev. **Indexed:** Film Lit.Ind. (1980-). **Document type:** bulletin.
Formerly (until no.119, 1994): Andere Sinema (ISSN 0773-5855)

778.53 FR ISSN 0986-1351
A S - ACTUALITE DE LA SCENOGRAPHIE. 5/yr. Editions A.S., 58 rue Servan, 75011 Paris, France. TEL 47-00-19-64. FAX 43-55-81-94. Ed. Michel Gladyrewsky. circ. 5,000.

791 XR ISSN 0775-9746
A S I F A NEWS. (Text in English, French, Russian) no.15, 1967. q. $35 to non-members (effective 1992). Association Internationale du Film d'Animation - International Association of Animated Film, P.O.B. 248, 15200 Prague 52, Czech Republic. TEL 42-2-7980923. FAX 42-2-365854. Ed. Stanislav Ulver. adv.: B&W page $735. bk.rev.
Formerly (until 1988): International Animated Film Association. Bulletin (ISSN 0538-4281)
Description: Aimed at professionals working in the field of animation cinema.

791.43 US
A V C COMMUNICATOR. 1959. 6/yr. $60. Association of Visual Communicators, 8130 La Mesa Blvd., Ste. 406, La Mesa, CA 91941-6437. TEL 619-461-1600. FAX 619-461-1606. Ed. Betty I. Lovgaris. adv.; bk.rev.; illus. circ. 65,000. **Document type:** newsletter.
Former titles: A V C Visions; A V C Communicator & Communicator (South Pasadena); I F P A Communicator (ISSN 0099-1090); I F P A Newsletter.
Description: Provides data to producers of corporate, industrial, educational and promotional programs in any individual medium. Focuses on the association's CINDY and VCDY competitions and on their winners.

MOTION PICTURES

A V GUIDE; the learning media newsletter. see
EDUCATION — Teaching Methods And Curriculum

ABEL VALUE NEWS; panem et circenses/bread and circuses. see *THEATER*

778.5 791.43 US
ACADEMY AWARDS FOR DISTINGUISHED ACHIEVEMENTS. a. $3. Academy of Motion Picture Arts and Sciences, 8949 Wilshire Blvd., Beverly Hills, CA 90211-1972. TEL 310-247-3000. FAX 310-859-9351. E-mail: bwoodward@oscars.org. Ed. Byerly Woodward. **Document type:** directory.

791.43 792 384.55 US
ACADEMY PLAYERS DIRECTORY. 3/yr. $65 per no. Academy of Motion Picture Arts and Sciences, 8949 Wilshire Blvd., Beverly Hills, CA 90211. TEL 310-247-3000. FAX 310-859-9351. E-mail: players@oscars.org. Ed. Patricia L. Citrano. **Document type:** directory.

791.43 SP
ACCION. 1992. m. 3500 ptas.($90) Ediciones Jardin S.L., C. Ferraz, 11 1o, 28008 Madrid, Spain. TEL 34-1-5470529. FAX 34-1-5415055. Ed. Mariano Alonso. adv. contact: Hector Alonso. circ. 50,000. (back issues avail.) **Document type:** consumer publication.
  Description: Reports on actors, current films, new videos, and future film plans.

791.43 384.55 CN ISSN 1198-6093
ACROSS THE BOARD; production news. 1987. q. National Film Board of Canada - Office National du Film du Canada, P.O. Box 6100, Sta. Centre-Ville, Montreal, PQ H3C 3H5, Canada. TEL 514-283-0740. FAX 514-496-2573. Eds. Shawn Goldwater, Philip Lewis. circ. 4,500. pp./issue: 4. (back issues avail.) **Document type:** newsletter.
  Formerly (until July 1992): In Production ... Update.
  Description: Covers N.F.B. films and videos in production with particular focus on ethnic and social issues, including women's issues.

791.43 380.1 US
ADAM FILM WORLD GUIDE DIRECTORY OF ADULT FILM. a. $8.95. Knight Publishing Corp., 8060 Melrose Ave., Los Angeles, CA 90046. TEL 213-653-8060. FAX 213-655-9452. Ed. Tim Connelly. adv. contact: Douglas Johnson. **Document type:** directory.
  Former titles: Adam Film World Guide Directory; Adam Film World Guide.
  Description: Lists distributors, producers and other companies involved in adult video.

AFTERIMAGE. see *PHOTOGRAPHY*

AGENCIES: WHAT THE ACTOR NEEDS TO KNOW. see *BUSINESS AND ECONOMICS — Trade And Industrial Directories*

ALLIGATOR. see *MUSIC*

778.53 UK ISSN 0958-9090
AMATEUR CINE ENTHUSIAST. 1990. q. £14. Porthallow Looe, Cornwall PL13 2JB, England. TEL 01503-72616. Ed. J. Shearsmith. adv.; bk.rev.; film rev.; charts; illus. circ. 1,500. **Document type:** consumer publication.

791.43 384.55 UK ISSN 0961-5091
AMATEUR FILM AND VIDEO MAKER. 1932. bi-m. £20. (Institute of Amateur Cinematographers) Film Maker Publications Ltd., 24 C W. St., Epsom, Surrey KT18 7RJ, England. TEL 081-644-0839. FAX 081-644-0839. Ed. Tony Pattison. adv. contact: Tony Pattison. bk.rev. circ. 2,500. **Document type:** consumer publication.
  Formerly: Amateur Film Maker.

791.43 US ISSN 0002-7928
TR845
AMERICAN CINEMATOGRAPHER; international journal of motion picture production techniques. 1919. m. $24. (American Society of Cinematographers) A S C Holding Corporation, Box 2230, Los Angeles, CA 90078. TEL 213-969-4333. FAX 213-876-4973. (Subscr. to: Box 2230, Hollywood, CA 90078) Ed. David Heuring. adv.; bk.rev.; film rev.; charts; illus.; stat.; index, cum.index. circ. 32,000. (also avail. in microform from UMI) **Indexed:** Chem.Abstr., Film Lit.Ind. (1973-), Int.Ind.Film Per., Intl.Ind.TV. **Document type:** trade publication.
—BLDSC (0812.460000); Ei; Faxon; SWETS; UMI; UnCover.

791.4 US ISSN 0195-8267
PN1993
AMERICAN CLASSIC SCREEN. 1977. bi-m. $15. (National Film Society, Inc.) American Classic Screen, Inc., Box 7150, Shawnee Mission, KS 66207. TEL 913-341-1919. Ed. John C. Tibbetts. adv.; bk.rev. circ. 20,000. (back issues avail.) **Indexed:** Film Lit.Ind.

791.4 384.55 US
AMERICAN FILM & VIDEO REVIEW. 1962. a. free. (American Educational Film and Video Center) Eastern College, St. Davids, PA 19087. TEL 215-341-5935. Ed. John A. Baird, Jr. circ. 30,000. **Document type:** catalog.
  Formerly: American Film Review (ISSN 0065-8308)

330.1 US
AMERICAN FILM INSTITUTE MONOGRAPH SERIES. 1983. irreg. price varies. Praeger Publishers (Subsidiary of: Greenwood Publishing Group Inc.), 88 Post Rd. W., Box 5007, Westport, CT 06881-5007. TEL 203-222-3571. FAX 203-222-1502. **Document type:** monographic series.

778.5 US ISSN 0279-0041
PN1993.5.U6
AMERICAN PREMIERE MAGAZINE; business magazine of the film industry. 1979. q. $16 (free to qualified personnel). American Premiere, Ltd., 8421 Wilshire Blvd., Penthouse Ste., Beverly Hills, CA 90211. TEL 213-852-0434. Ed. Susan Royal. adv.; bk.rev.; film rev. circ. 17,500. **Indexed:** Film Lit.Ind. (1982-). **Document type:** trade publication.
  Formerly: Premiere (ISSN 0274-7766)

791.43 II
ANANDALOK. (Text in Bengali) 1975. fortn. newsstand price: Rs.12. Ananda Bazar Patrika Ltd., 6 Prafulla Sarkar St., Calcutta 700 001, India. TEL 33-274880. TELEX 33-303240. Ed. Dulendra Bhownick. adv.: B&W page Rs.22500, color page Rs.45000; trim 16 x 23.5; adv. contact: S.N. Roychoudhury. circ. 59,618.

740 US ISSN 1061-0308
NC1765
ANIMATION JOURNAL. 1993. s-a. $21.55 to California residents (other U.S. $20; Canada and Mexico $25; elsewhere $30); institutions $40 (Canada and Mexico $45; elsewhere $50). (University of Southern California, School of Cinema and TV) A J Press, 2011 Kingsboro Circle, Tustim, CA 92680-6733. TEL 714-544-6255. E-mail: maureenf@aol.com. Ed. Maureen Furniss. bk.rev. circ. 500. (back issues avail.) **Indexed:** Int.Ind.Film Per. **Document type:** academic/scholarly publication.
  Description: Publishes scholarly investigations on all subjects related to animation, with emphasis on research informed by the concerns of contemporary cultural studies scholarship and on papers that address issues pertinent to the study of art in its popular forms.
  Refereed Serial

ANIMATION MAGAZINE. see *ART*

778.53 384.55 UK ISSN 0964-5586
ANIMATOR. 1982. s-a. £8 for 4 nos. (overseas £16). Filmcraft Publications, 13 Ringway Rd., Park St., St. Albans, Herts. AL2 2RE, England. TEL 01727-872607. Ed. David Jefferson. adv. contact: David Jefferson. bk.rev.; circ. 1,500 (paid). **Indexed:** Film Lit.Ind. (1986-). **Document type:** newsletter.
  Description: Examines film animation professionally, as a hobby, from a student's perspective, by computer, and independent animation as well. Covers different approaches, techniques, and players. Includes festival reports and equipemnt news.

778.53 US ISSN 1069-2088
ANIMATRIX; a journal of the UCLA Animation Workshop. 1984. a. $5. University of California at Los Angeles, Department of Film and Television, 405 Hilgard Ave., Los Angeles, CA 90024. TEL 310-825-5829. FAX 310-825-3383. bk.rev. circ. 500. **Indexed:** Film Lit.Ind. (1988-). **Document type:** academic/scholarly publication.

778.5 FR ISSN 0180-3492
ANNEE DU CINEMA. 1977. a. price varies. Editions Calmann-Levy, 3 rue Auber, 75009 Paris, France. illus.

791.43 384.55 FR ISSN 0991-7799
ANNUAIRE DU CINEMA, TELEVISION, VIDEO. 1948. a. 1100 F.($82) S.N. Bellefaye, 38 rue Etienne Marcel, 75002 Paris, France. TEL 42-33-52-52. FAX 42-33-39-00. adv.
  Formerly (until 1985): Annuaire du Cinema et Television (ISSN 0066-2968)

778.5 US ISSN 0163-5123
PN1993
ANNUAL INDEX TO MOTION PICTURE CREDITS. 1976. a. $64. Academy of Motion Picture Arts and Sciences, 8949 Wilshire Blvd., Beverly Hills, CA 90211-1972. TEL 310-247-3000. FAX 310-859-9351. Ed. Byerly Woodward. circ. 999. **Document type:** directory.
  Superseded: A M P A S Credits Bulletin; Formerly (until 1979): Screen Achievement Records Bulletin (ISSN 0147-2313)
  Description: Contains approximately 15,000 individual credits, and credits for feature films opening in LA area. Index by title, craft, individual names and distributors. Based on primary sources from producers-distributors.

791.43 384.55 IT
ANNUARIO DEGLI ATTORI/EUROPEAN PLAYERS' DIRECTORY. (In 2 vols.: Attrici e Giovani Interpreti; Attori) 1970. a. L.200000. Star Edizioni Cinematografiche s.r.l., Viale Parioli 12, 00197 Rome, Italy. TEL 39-6-8070007. FAX 39-6-80665119. Eds. Marco Guidone, Emi Onorati. adv.: color page L.2900000. circ. 3,600. **Document type:** directory.

791.4 LE ISSN 0003-7397
ARAB FILM AND TELEVISION CENTER NEWS. (Editions in Arabic, English and French) 1965. s-m. free to qualified personnel. Ministry of Information, Arab Film & Television Centre, Box 3434, Beirut, Lebanon. film rev.; illus.; stat.; cum.index. circ. 3,000.

700 US ISSN 1062-9459
N367
ART ON SCREEN; the newsletter of film & video on the visual arts. 1992. 2/yr. free to qualified personnel. Program for Art on Film, 2875 Broadway, 2nd Fl., New York, NY 10025-7805. TEL 212-854-9570. FAX 212-854-9577. E-mail: artfilm@columbia.edu. Ed. Susan Delson. circ. 10,000 (controlled). (looseleaf format) **Document type:** newsletter.
  Description: Disseminates information on the presentation of the visual arts in film, video, television and interactive computer programs, including news of the Program's activities and services, new releases on film and video, and events in the international art and media world.

778.53 PO
ARTE 7; revista tecnica de cinema. q. Esc.500 per no. Terramar, Apart. 112, 2726 Mem Martins Codex, Portugal. TEL 9202104. Ed. Manuel Costa e Silva. circ. 2,000.

ARTIBUS ET HISTORIAE; international journal for visual arts. see *ART*

MOTION PICTURES   **4785**

ARTS AND ENTERTAINMENT LAW REVIEW. see *LAW*

778.53   US   ISSN 1059-440X
PN1993.5.A75
ASIAN CINEMA. 1984. s-a. $20 to individuals; institutions $30; students $10. Asian Cinema Studies Society, Film Department, c/o Prof. Cynthia Contreras, Brooklyn College, Brooklyn, NY 11210-2889. Ed. Mira Reym Binford. adv.; bk.rev. circ. 375. Indexed: Film Lit.Ind. (1986-). **Document type:** academic/scholarly publication.

ASSOCIATION OF TALENT AGENTS. NEWSLETTER. see *THEATER*

778.53   US
ATLANTA FILM AND VIDEO NEWS. 1990. q. Real Estate News Corp., 2600 W. Peterson, Ste. 100, Chicago, IL 60659. TEL 312-465-5151. FAX 312-465-7246. Ed. Steven Polydoris. adv.: B&W page $915, color page $1460; trim 8 1/2 x 11. circ. 3,200. **Document type:** trade publication.

778.534   GW
ATLAS FILMSZENE. 1985. q. Atlas Film & AV GmbH & Co. KG, Ludgerstr. 14-18, 47057 Duisburg, Germany. TEL 0203-308270. Ed. Jaimi Stueber. (back issues avail.)
    Description: Reports on new films being produced and screened.

791   IT   ISSN 0394-8080
ATTUALITA CINEMATOGRAFICHE. 1964. a. price varies. (Parrocchia di Santa Maria della Scalla in San Fedele) Edizioni Letture, Piazza San Fedele 4, 20121 Milan, Italy. TEL 011-02-722711. FAX 011-02-72023481. circ. 1,000.

AUDIO VISUAL. see *EDUCATION — Teaching Methods And Curriculum*

AUDIOVISIVI. see *EDUCATION — Teaching Methods And Curriculum*

778.53 384.55   GW   ISSN 0179-2555
AUGEN-BLICK; Marburger Hefte zur Medienwissenschaft. 1986. 3/yr. DM.24 (foreign DM.30) (effective 1996). (Philipps Universitaet Marburg, Institut fuer Neuere Deutsche Literatur) Schueren Presseverlag GmbH, Deutschhausstr. 31, 35037 Marburg, Germany. TEL 06421-63084. FAX 06421-681190. circ. 1,000. **Document type:** academic/scholarly publication.
—CCC.

791.43 384.55   AT   ISSN 1033-7741
AUSTRALIAN CATALOGUE OF NEW FILMS AND VIDEOS. a. Aus.$75 (foreign Aus.$95); Aus.$245 for CD-ROM. Australian Catalogue, P.O. Box 204, Albert Park, Vic. 3206, Australia. TEL 61-3-525-5302. FAX 61-3-537-2325. Ed. Peter Tapp. (also avail. in diskette format) **Document type:** catalog, consumer publication.
● Also available on CD-ROM.
    Formerly: Filmviews Catalogue (ISSN 1031-4377)
    Description: Comprehensive listing of all currently released films and videos available in Australia. Includes all imported and Australian produced titles, listed alphabetically under subject headings.

791.43   AT   ISSN 0313-7031
AUSTRALIAN FILM INSTITUTE NEWSLETTER. 1976. q. Aus.$40 membership. Australian Film Institute, 49 Eastern Rd., S. Melbourne, Vic. 3205, Australia. TEL 61-3-696-1844. FAX 61-3-696-7972. Ed. Ruth Jones. bk.rev.; film rev.; tr.lit. circ. 7,000. (back issues avail.) **Document type:** newsletter.

AUSTRALIAN FILM, TELEVISION AND RADIO SCHOOL ANNUAL REPORT. see *EDUCATION — Higher Education*

AUSTRALIAN FILM, TELEVISION AND RADIO SCHOOL HANDBOOK. see *EDUCATION — Higher Education*

791.4   FR   ISSN 0045-1150
PN1993
AVANT-SCENE CINEMA. 1961. 11/yr. 582 F. (foreign 726 F.) (effective 1996). Editions de l' Avant Scene, 6 rue Git-le-Coeur, 75006 Paris, France. TEL 1-46-34-28-20. FAX 1-43-54-50-14. illus.; index, cum.index: 1961-1977. (back issues avail.) **Indexed:** Arts & Hum.Cit.Ind., Curr.Cont., Film Lit.Ind. (1974-), Int.Ind.Film Per., Intl.Ind.TV, Pt.de Rep. (1979-), RILM.
—BLDSC (1837.118000); Faxon; SWETS; UnCover.

AXE FACTORY REVIEW. see *LITERATURE*

778.53   PO
B C - BOLETIM CINEMATOGRAFICO. 1951. 12/yr. Esc.1.100 (effective 1995). Rua Candido dos Reis 114-3o, 2780 Oeiras, Portugal. TEL 351-1-4420701. FAX 351-1-4429781. TELEX 64563 SENACI P. Ed. Francisco Perestrello. circ. 1,500 (paid).
    Refereed Serial

778 384.55   UK
B F I FILM AND TELEVISION HANDBOOK (YEAR). 1983. a. £14.95. British Film Institute, 21 Stephen St., London W1P 1PL, England. TEL 071-255-1444. FAX 071-508-9456. Eds. David Leafe, Terry Ilott. adv. contact: Robert Winter.
    Former titles (until 1994): Film and Television Handbook (Year) (ISSN 0956-8409); (until 1989): B F I Film and Television Yearbook (ISSN 0267-8764)

BARBARA EDEN'S OFFICIAL FAN CLUB NEWSLETTER. see *CLUBS*

791.43   CC
BEIJYING HUABAO/BEIJING FILM STUDIO PICTORIAL. (Text in Chinese) bi-m. $30.60. Beijing Dianying Zhipian Chang - Beijing Film Studio, Beijing, People's Republic of China. (Dist. in US by: China Books & Periodicals, Inc., 2929 24th St., San Francisco, CA 94110. TEL 415-282-2994) illus.

791.43   IT   ISSN 0006-0577
PN1993
BIANCO E NERO. (Text in Italian; summaries in English and Italian) 1933. q. L.56000($43) (foreign L.80000). (Centro Sperimentale Cinematografia) E R I Edizioni R A I, Via Arsenale 41, 10121 Turin, Italy. TEL 011-8800. FAX 011-534732. bk.rev.; film rev.; illus.; index. **Indexed:** Arts & Hum.Cit.Ind., Curr.Cont., Film Lit.Ind. (1973-1988), Int.Ind.Film Per., Intl.Ind.TV.

778.5   US   ISSN 0744-723X
BIG REEL.* 1973. m. $25. Antique Trader Publications, Box 1050, Dubuque, IA 52004. TEL 919-427-5850; 800-334-7165. FAX 919-427-7372. Ed. Rhonda K. Lemons. adv.; bk.rev.; film rev. circ. 4,500. (tabloid format)
    Description: Forum for film buffs to buy, trade and sell films, photographs, videotapes, publications, posters, and projectors.

778.534 910.03   US
BLACK CAMERA. 1985. s-a. donation. Smith Research Center, 2805 E. 10th St., Ste. 180-181, Indiana University, Department of Afro-American Studies, Bloomington, IN 47408. TEL 812-855-6041. FAX 812-855-5678. Ed. Gloria Gibson-Hudson. bk.rev. circ. 1,000. (back issues avail.) **Document type:** newsletter.
    Description: Provides insightful information about African-Americans in film.

778.53 910.03   US   ISSN 1055-8780
PN1995.9.N4
BLACK FACE. 1989. q. Black Filmmaker Foundation, 375 Greenwich St., New York, NY 10013. TEL 212-941-3944.

778 910.03   US   ISSN 0887-5723
PN1995.9.N4
BLACK FILM REVIEW. 1985. q. $12 to individuals; institutions $24. Sojourner Productions, Inc., 2025 I St. N.W., Ste. 213, Washington, DC 20006. TEL 202-466-2753. Ed. Jacquie Jones. adv.; film rev. circ. 5,000. (back issues avail.) **Indexed:** Film Lit.Ind. (1986-).
—Faxon; UnCover.

791.43   GW
BLICKPUNKT: FILM. (Text in German; summaries in English and German) 1976. 52/yr. DM.420. Casablanca Verlag GmbH, Stahlgruberring 11a, 81829 Munich, Germany. TEL 089-4209030. FAX 089-42090311. Ed. Ulrich Hoecherl. adv.; bk.rev.; charts; stat. circ. 3,500. (back issues avail.) **Document type:** consumer publication.

778.53   AU
BLIMP; Film Magazine. (Text and summaries in English and German) 1985. q. $40 (students $32). Muchargasse 12-III-10, A-8010 Graz, Austria. TEL 0316-679950. FAX 0316-679960. (Dist. in US by: Bernhard DeBoer, Inc., 113 E. Centre St., Nutley, NJ 07110. TEL 201-667-9300) Ed. Bogdan Grbic. adv.: B&W page $1510; adv. contact: Eva Lorenz. circ. 5,000. **Indexed:** Film Lit.Ind. (1988-). **Document type:** consumer publication.
    Description: Analyzes film, video and media art as forms of cultural practices for academic and non-academic audiences.

BOERNEFILM & VIDEO. see *CHILDREN AND YOUTH — For*

BOLERO; mode beaute cinema travel. see *CLOTHING TRADE — Fashions*

BOMB; artists, writers, actors, directors. see *ART*

791.4   US   ISSN 0006-8527
PN1993
BOXOFFICE; the business magazine of the motion picture industry. 1920. m. $30. R L D Communications, 6640 Sunset Blvd., Ste. 100, Hollywood, CA 90028. TEL 213-465-1186. FAX 213-465-5049. (Subscr. to: 819 S. Wabash Ave., Chicago, IL 60605) Ed. Ray Greene. adv.; bk.rev.; film rev.; charts; illus.; stat. circ. 8,000. **Indexed:** Film Lit.Ind. (1973-). **Document type:** trade publication.
● Also available online. Vendor(s): CompuServe, Inc. —UnCover.
    Description: News and articles covering the motion picture exhibition, distribution, production and related industries.

790   GW   ISSN 0406-9595
BRAVO. 1956. w. $120. Heinrich Bauer Verlag (Muenchen), Charles-de-Gaulle-Str. 8, 81737 Munich, Germany. TEL 089-6786-501. FAX 089-6702033. (Dist. in U.S. by: G L P International, Inc., 153 S. Dean St., Englewood, NJ 07631-3513. TEL 201-871-1010. FAX 201-871-0870) Ed. Gerald Buechelmaier. adv.; film rev.; illus. circ. 1,300,000. **Document type:** consumer publication.

778.5   US   ISSN 0147-4049
BRIGHT LIGHTS. 1974-1981; resumed 1993. q. $20 (foreign $28). Box 420987, San Francisco, CA 94142-0987. TEL 513-641-4048. FAX 513-641-2049. E-mail: bright@iglou.com. Ed. Gary Morris; Pub. Gregory Battle. adv.; bk.rev.; film rev.; illus. circ. 2,500. **Indexed:** Int.Ind.Film Per., Int.Ind.Film Per.
    Description: Contains profiles of film stars and directors, documentation from the studio era, studies of film themes, as well as related news.

BULAWAYO THIS MONTH. see *TRAVEL AND TOURISM*

791.43   BU   ISSN 0007-3911
BULGARIAN FILMS. Russian edition (ISSN 0204-8205); French edition (ISSN 0204-8973); English edition (ISSN 0204-8884) 1960. 8/yr. $24. Bulgarian Film Industry, 135-A Rakovski St., Sofia 1000, Bulgaria. TEL 88 32 89. TELEX 22 447 FILMEX BG. Ed. Ivan Stoyanovich. adv.; bk.rev.; film rev. circ. 20,000 (English ed. 1,500; French ed. 1,500; Russian ed. 17,000). **Indexed:** Film Lit.Ind. (1977-), Int.Ind.Film Per., Intl.Ind.TV.
    Description: Reports on films in production, screenplays and previews. Includes reviews and interviews.

THE BULLET (NASHVILLE). see *COMMUNICATIONS — Television And Cable*

BUSINESS EDUCATION FILMS CATALOG. see *BUSINESS AND ECONOMICS*

778.53 330   UK
THE BUSINESS OF FILM. 1982. m. £95($190) Bookpress Ltd., 24 Charlotte St., London W1P 1HJ, England. TEL 071-580-0141. FAX 071-255-1264. Ed. Michael Goodridge. charts; stat.; tr.lit.; circ. 6,000 (paid). (back issues avail.)

MOTION PICTURES

778.53 658.8 UK ISSN 0269-641X
BUSINESS RATIO REPORT: FILM & TELEVISION PRODUCERS, DISTRIBUTORS; an industry sector analysis. 1986. a. I C C Business Ratios Ltd., Freepost, Field House, Hampton, Mddx. TW12 1BR, England. TEL 081-783-0977. FAX 081-783-1940. charts; stat. **Document type:** trade publication.
—BLDSC (3925.682170).

C C U M C LEADER. (Consortium of College and University Media Centers) see EDUCATION — Teaching Methods And Curriculum

791 FR ISSN 0526-6513
C.I.C.A.E. BULLETIN D'INFORMATION. 1965. irreg. $20. Confederation Internationale des Cinemas d'Art et d'Essai - International Art Cinemas Confederation, c/o Jean Lescure, 22 rue d'Artois, 75008 Paris, France. FAX 45-61-13-65. Ed. Jean Lescure. circ. 1,000.

778.53 GW ISSN 0938-233X
C I C I M: REVUE POUR LE CINEMA FRANCAIS. 1981. q. DM.35 (foreign DM.40). Institut Francais de Munich, Centre d'Information Cinematographique, Kaulbachstr. 13, 80539 Munich, Germany. TEL 089-28662824. FAX 089-28662866. Ed. Heiner Gassen. adv.; bk.rev. circ. 2,000. **Indexed:** Film Lit.Ind. (1987-). **Document type:** academic/scholarly publication.
Description: Provides information on all aspects of French cinema.

791.43 II ISSN 0970-7190
C.T.A. JOURNAL. 1943. m. Rs.30($3) Cine Technicians' Association of South India, 150 Usman Rd., T'nagar, Madras 17, India. Ed. B. Janardana Rao. adv.; bk.rev.; illus.; tr.lit. circ. 1,000.
Formerly (until 1973): Cine Technicians' Association of South India. Journal (ISSN 0009-6970)

791.4 US ISSN 0007-9219
P87
C T V D: CINEMA - T V - DIGEST;* a quarterly review of the serious, foreign-language cinema-T V-press. 1962. irreg. $3 for 4 nos. (foreign $4). Hampton Books, 1102 Barnwell St., Columbia, SC 29201-3804. TEL 803-276-6870. Ed. Ben Hamilton. adv.; bk.rev.; film rev.; illus. circ. 550. (back issues avail.)

778.5 FR ISSN 0764-8499
CAHIERS DE LA CINEMATHEQUE. 1970. 4/yr. 220 F. (EC 260 F., elsewhere 280 F.). Institut Jean Vigo, 21 rue Mailly, 66000 Perpignan, France. TEL 68-66-30-33. Ed. Marcel Orns. adv.; bk.rev.; film rev.; illus. **Indexed:** Film Lit.Ind. (1975-), Int.Ind.Film Per. (until 1995), Intl.Ind.TV.

778.5 FR ISSN 0008-011X
PN1993
CAHIERS DU CINEMA. 1951. m. $85. Editions de l'Etoile, 9 Passage de la Boule Blanche, 75012 Paris, France. TEL 1-43-43-92-20. FAX 43-43-95-04. TELEX 215 092 F. Ed. Thierry Jousse. adv.; bk.rev.; film rev.; illus. circ. 80,000. (also avail. in microfiche) **Indexed:** Arts & Hum.Cit.Ind., Curr.Cont., Film Lit.Ind. (1973-), Int.Ind.Film Per., Intl.Ind.TV, Pt.de Rep. (1989-).
—BLDSC (2948.800000); Faxon.

788.53 BE ISSN 0775-9479
CAHIERS DU SCENARIO. 1986. q. Universite Libre de Bruxelles, Institut de Sociologie, 44 Ave. Jeanne, CP124-B, 1050 Brussels, Belgium. **Indexed:** Film Lit.Ind. (1989-).

CALIFORNIA POINTS AND AUTHORITIES. see LAW

778.5 US ISSN 0270-5346
PN1995.9.W6
CAMERA OBSCURA; a journal of feminism and film theory. 1976. 3/yr. $25 to individuals (foreign $35); institutions $45 (foreign $55). Indiana University Press, Journals Division, 601 N. Morton St., Bloomington, IN 47404. TEL 812-855-9449. FAX 812-855-7931. Ed.Bd. adv.; bk.rev.; film rev.; bibl.; charts; illus. circ. 939. (also avail. in microform; back issues avail.; reprint service avail. from ISI) **Indexed:** Alt.Press Ind., Arts & Hum.Cit.Ind., Film Lit.Ind. (1976-), Int.Ind.Film Per., Int.Ind.Film Per., Intl.Ind.TV, Stud.Wom.Abstr. **Document type:** academic/scholarly publication.
—BLDSC (3016.149800); Faxon; Genuine Article; SWETS; UMI; UnCover.
Description: Presents current perspectives on the national and international film scene.

778.53 FR ISSN 0248-8868
CAMERA - STYLO. 1981. irreg. 18 rue des Fosses Saint Jacques, 75005 Paris, France. **Indexed:** Film Lit.Ind. (1984-).

791.43 CN
CAMPUS REEL. 1983. q. Can.$12 (US Can.$18). Entertainment Media Services Inc., 900 A Don Mills Rd., Ste. 1000, Don Mills, ON M3C 1V6, Canada. TEL 416-445-4020. FAX 416-445-2894. Ed. Sandra I. Stewart; Pub. Brian A. Stewart. adv. contact: Randy Stewart, Donnalyn Coyne. circ. 253,000. **Document type:** consumer publication.
Description: Previews upcoming films.

338.4 CN ISSN 1181-6708
PN1993.5.C2
CANADA. STATISTICS CANADA. FILM AND VIDEO/CANADA. STATISTIQUE CANADA. LE FILM ET LA VIDEO; culture statistics - statistiques de la culture. (Catalogue 87-204) (Text in English, French) 1983. a. Can.$22($26) Statistics Canada, Ottawa, ON K1A 0T6, Canada.
Former titles (until 1989): Canada. Statistics Canada. Film and Video in Canada (ISSN 0847-124X); (until 1987): Canada. Statistics Canada. Culture Statistics. Film Industry, Tables (ISSN 0831-733X)
Description: Provides details on all aspects of the Culture Statistics Program's Film and Video Surveys including highlights and methodology.

CANADA COUNCIL ANNUAL REPORT AND SUPPLEMENT/RAPPORT ANNUEL DU CONSEIL DES ARTS DU CANADA ET SON SUPPLEMENT. see ART

791.43 CN ISSN 0705-548X
CANADIAN FILM SERIES. 1976. irreg., no.6, 1981. price varies. Canadian Film Institute, 2 Daly, Ottawa, ON K1N 6E2, Canada. TEL 613-232-6727. FAX 613-232-6315.

778.5 700 AT ISSN 0158-4154
PN1993
CANTRILLS FILMNOTES. 1971. q. $18 to individuals (foreign $20); institutions, libraries $30 (foreign $33). (Australian Film Commission) Arthur & Corinne Cantrill, Eds. & Pubs., Box 1295L, G.P.O., Melbourne, Vic. 3001, Australia. TEL 61-3-380-6416. bk.rev.; film rev.; illus.; cum.index: nos.1-52 (1971-1986). circ. 1,000. (back issues avail.) **Indexed:** Film Lit.Ind. (1976-), Int.Ind.Film Per., Intl.Ind.TV.
—UnCover.
Description: Covers independent, experimental film and video art with a pan-Pacific emphasis.

778.5 792 UK ISSN 0142-6079
CASTINGDEX. 1979. a.? £18. P.O. Box 11, London SW15 6AY, England. TEL 0181-789-0408. FAX 0181-780-1977. (Subscr. to: P.O. Box 100, Broadstairs, Kent CT10 1UJ, England. TEL 01843-860885) Ed. Vaune Craig-Raymond.

791.43 371.912 US ISSN 0093-7215
HV2591
CATALOG OF CAPTIONED FILMS FOR THE DEAF.* a. Associations for Education of the Deaf, Special Materials Project, c/o Assoc. Builder Contra., 4061 Powder Mill Rd., Beltsville, MD 20705-3149. **Document type:** catalog.

778.5 384.55 NE
CATALOGUS FILMS EN VIDEO. irreg. fl.52.50. Nederlands Filminstituut, Postbus 515, Hilversum, Netherlands. illus. **Document type:** catalog.
Formerly: 3 D Film Gids.

778.53 US ISSN 1057-9427
PN1998.A1
CELEBRITY ACCESS: THE DIRECTORY (YEAR); or how and where to write the rich and famous. 1989. a. $25 (foreign $30). Celebrity Access Publications, 20 Sunnyside Ave., Ste. A241, Mill Valley, CA 94941. TEL 415-389-8133. Ed. Thomas Burford. bk.rev. circ. 2,000. **Document type:** directory.
Description: Provides information and a resource base for locating celebrities mainly of film and television, but also other areas of prominence like sports, music, science, military, religion, art, and politics.
Refereed Serial

791.43 780 US
CELEBRITY BIRTHDAY GUIDE. 1992. biennial. $10.95. Axiom Information Resources, Box 8015-T, Ann Arbor, MI 48107. TEL 313-761-4842. Ed. Pat Wilson. **Document type:** directory.
Description: Lists the birthdays of thousands of celebrities - past and present.

791.43 780 US ISSN 1068-4298
CELEBRITY COMMUNICATOR. m. $29.95. Axiom Information Resources, Box 8015-T, Ann Arbor, MI 48107. TEL 313-761-4842. FAX 313-761-3276. Ed. Pat Wilson. **Document type:** newsletter.
Description: For those who write to celebrities. Its purpose is to exchange information and identify ways to improve these communications.

791.43 780 US
CELEBRITY DIRECTORY. 1984. biennial, 4th ed. $39.95. Axiom Information Resources, Box 8015-T, Ann Arbor, MI 48107. TEL 313-761-4842. Ed. Pat Wilson. **Document type:** directory.
Description: Covers the entire spectrum of celebrities.

791.43 FR ISSN 0397-8435
PN1993.5.F7
CENTRE NATIONAL DE LA CINEMATOGRAPHIE. BULLETIN D'INFORMATION. Cover title: Informations C N C. (Supplements avail.) 1947. 6/yr. 180 F.($3) Centre National de la Cinematographie, 12 rue de Lubeck, 75784 Paris Cedex 16, France. TEL 44-34-36-09. Ed. D. Wallon. bk.rev.; charts; illus.; stat.; index. circ. 10,000. **Document type:** bulletin.

CERBERUS; het magazine voor science fiction, fantastiek & griezel. see LITERATURE — Science Fiction, Fantasy, Horror

791.43 II
CHANDRIKA. (Text in Malayalam) 1935. m.? Muslim Printing & Publishing Co. Ltd., Y.M.C.A. Rd., No. 64, Calicut 673 001, India. TEL 55021. Ed. Mankada T. Abdul Azeez. adv. contact: T. Moideen Koya. cols./p.: 8.

791.43 FR ISSN 0339-8978
CHANGER LE CINEMA. 1976. m. 50 F. 15 rue des Ursulines, 75005 Paris, France. Dir. Maria Landau.

791.43 SW ISSN 0045-6349
CHAPLIN. (Devoted to cinema, cinematography and photography.) 1959. bi-m. SEK 245 in Scandinavia; in Europe SEK 300; elsewhere SEK 360. Svenska Filminstitutet - Swedish Film Institute, P.O. Box 27126, S-102 52 Stockholm, Sweden. TEL 46-8-665-1100. FAX 46-8-665-1820. TELEX 13326 FILMINS S. Eds. Jannike Aahlund, Per Axel Nordfeldt. adv.; B&W page SEK 7150, color page SEK 11150; trim 190 x 252. bk.rev.; film rev.; illus.; index; circ. 5,200 (controlled). **Indexed:** Film Lit.Ind. (1973-), Int.Ind.Film Per., Intl.Ind.TV. **Document type:** abstracting/indexing, trade publication.

778 US
CHICAGO FILM & VIDEO NEWS. bi-m. Real Estate News Corp., 2600 W. Peterson Ave., Chicago, IL 60659-4031. TEL 312-465-7246. FAX 312-465-7218. Ed. Donna B. Proske. adv.

MOTION PICTURES 4787

791.43 CC
PN1993.5.C4
CHINA SCREEN/ZHONGGUO YINMU. (Text in Chinese, English) 1980. q. $12. Zhongguo Dianying Shuchu Shuru Gongsi - China Film Import & Export Corp., 25 Xinjiekouwai Dajie, Beijing 100088, People's Republic of China. (Dist. overseas by: China International Book Trading Corp., P.O. Box 399, Beijing, P.R.C.; Dist. in US by: China Books and Periodicals, 2929 24th St., San Francisco, CA 94110) Indexed: Film Lit.Ind. **Document type:** consumer publication.
—UnCover.
 Formerly: China's Screen (ISSN 0577-893X)
 Description: Covers new Chinese films. Contains feature articles on actors, actresses, directors, and films.

791.43 II
CHITRABHOOMI. (Text in Telugu) 1980. w. newsstand price: Rs.3. Kakatiya Publications, 5-8-55A, Nampally Station Rd., Hyderabad 500 001, India. TEL 201181. Ed. D. Bheem Reddy. adv.: B&W page Rs.8000, color page Rs.16000; adv. contact: P. Madhusudhan Reddy. cols./p.: 5.

791.43 II
CHITRABHUMI. (Text in Malayalam) 1982. w. Mathrubhumi Printing & Publishing Co. Ltd., Calicut 1, India. TEL 56655. Ed. M.T. Vasudevan Nair; Pub. M.J. Vijaya Padman. adv.: B&W page Rs.3000, color page Rs.4000. circ. 25,426.

791.43 II
CHITRALOK. (Text in Gujarati) 1952. w. Lok Prakashan Ltd., Gujarat Samachar Bhavan, Khanpur, P.O. Box 254, Ahmedabad 380 001, India. Ed. Shreyans Shah. circ. 18,900.

778.534 IT
CIAK SI GIRA. 1985. m. L.48600. Silvio Berlusconi Editore S.p.A., Corso Europa, 5-7, 20122 Milan, Italy. TEL 39-2-77941. Ed. Gigi Vesigna. adv.: color page L.20800000. circ. 107,472.

791.4 790 II
CINE ADVANCE. (Text in English) 1954. w. Rs.85($50) Swadeshwari Printers and Publishers Pvt. Ltd., 74 Lenin Saranee, Calcutta 700 013, India. TELEX 215882-NEWS-IN. Ed. Ajay Agarwal. adv.: bk.rev.; film rev.; play rev.; illus. circ. 70,000. (looseleaf format)

791.4 BE ISSN 1016-9660
CINE & MEDIA. (Text and summaries in English, French, Spanish) 1980. bi-m. 875 BEF($25) (effective 1994). International Catholic Organization for Cinema and Audiovisual - Organisation Catholique Internationale du Cinema et de l'Audiovisuel, Rue du Saphir 15, 1040 Brussels, Belgium. TEL 32-2-734-42-94. FAX 32-2-734-32-07. TELEX (0402) 6105905 GMA LU. Ed. Robert Molhant. adv.: B&W page 24000 BEF ($800); trim 210 x 290. bk.rev.; film rev.; video rev.; illus. circ. 9,000.
 Supersedes (in 1988): O C I C Info (English Edition) (ISSN 0771-0518); O C I C Info (Edition Francaise) (ISSN 0771-0461); Which was formerly (until 1982): O C I C Informations (ISSN 0772-2761)
 Description: Covers cinematographic and video productions from all over the world, especially those largely ignored by the more industrialized countries.

778.5 II
CINE BLITZ. m. Rs.210 (foreign Rs.306). Blitz Publications Private Ltd., 17-17H, Cawasji Patel St., Fort, Bombay 400 001, India. TEL 2047166. FAX 2047984. TELEX 011-6801-BLTZ-IN. Ed. Ms. R.K. Mehta. adv.: B&W page Rs.20000, color page Rs.40000; trim 245 x 180; adv. contact: Milind Wagh. film rev. circ. 117,536.

778.53 CN ISSN 0820-8921
CINE-BULLES. 1982. q. Can.$13.67 (foreign Can.$15). Association des Cinemas Paralleles du Quebec, 4545 Ave. Pierre de Coubertin, Case Postale 1000 Succ. M, Montreal, PQ H1V 3R2, Canada. TEL 514-252-3021. FAX 514-251-8038. Ed. Michel Euvrard. adv. contact: Martine Mauroy. bk.rev. Indexed: Film Lit.Ind. (1988-), Int.Ind.Film Per. **Document type:** academic/scholarly publication.

778.5 CU ISSN 0009-6946
CINE CUBANO. 1960. q. C.$12($10) in N. America; S. America $12; Europe $17. Instituto Cubano del Arte e Industria Cinematograficos (ICAIC), Dpto. Publicaciones, Calle 23, No.1115, Apdo. 55, Havana, Cuba. (Dist. by: Ediciones Cubanas, Obispo No. 527, Apdo. 605, Havana, Cuba) Ed. Gloria Villazon Hernandez. circ. 20,000. **Indexed:** Film Lit.Ind. (1973-), Int.Ind.Film Per., Intl.Ind.TV.

791.4 BE ISSN 0773-2279
CINE-FICHES DE GRAND ANGLE. 1972. m. 1132 BEF (foreign 1557 BEF) (effective 1996). (Centre de Documentation Cinematographie) A.S.B.L Grand Angle-Opvac, Rue d'Arschot 29, 5660 Mariembourg, Belgium. TEL 32-60-312168. FAX 32-60-312937. Ed. Jacques Noel. adv.: bk.rev.; film rev.; illus.; index. circ. 3,500. **Indexed:** Film Lit.Ind. (1986-).
 Formerly: Grand Angle; Incorporates (in 1983): Cinemaniac (ISSN 0770-1640)

CINE NEWS. see PHOTOGRAPHY

791.43 VE
CINE-OJA. 1967. 4/yr. $15. Sociedad Civil Cine al Dia, Apdo. 50446, Sabana Grande, Caracas, Venezuela. Ed. Alfredo Roffe. adv.: bk.rev.; film rev.; illus.; circ. 2,500 (controlled). (also avail. in microform from UMI) **Indexed:** Film Lit.Ind., Int.Ind.Film Per., Intl.Ind.TV.
 Formerly (until no.25, 1984): Cine al Dia (ISSN 0009-692X)
 Description: Includes essays on the economic and cultural development of the Venezuelan and Latinamerican cinema.

791.4 BE ISSN 0045-6918
CINE-REVUE. 1920. w. Cine-Revue, S.A., Rue de Danemark, 1060 Brussels, Belgium. Ed. M. Leempoel. adv.: bk.rev.; film rev.; illus. circ. 3,000,000. **Indexed:** Film Lit.Ind. (1974-).

778.53 384.55 SP
CINE & TELE INFORME. 1961. 12/yr. 9860 ptas. (Europe $185; America $250; elsewhere $300 (effective 1995). Gran Via 64, 28013 Madrid, Spain. TEL 34-1-5412129. FAX 34-1-5598110. Ed. Antonio Carballo Sanchez. adv. contact: Isabel Alberca. circ. 6,000. **Document type:** trade publication.
 Formerly: Cine Informe.

778.53 CN ISSN 0826-9866
PN1993
CINEACTION!; radical film criticism & theory. 1985. 3/yr. Can.$18 to individuals; institutions Can.$35. 40 Alexander St., Apt. 705, Toronto, ON M4Y 1B5, Canada. TEL 416-964-3534. adv. contact: R. Wood. circ. 2,500. **Indexed:** Film Lit.Ind. (1985-). **Document type:** academic/scholarly publication.
—UnCover. **CCC.**

791.43 US ISSN 0009-7004
PN1993
CINEASTE. 1967. q. $16 to individuals (foreign $26); institutions $33 (foreign $40). Cineaste Publishers, Inc., 200 Park Ave. S., Ste. 1601, New York, NY 10003. TEL 212-982-1241. FAX 212-982-1241. (Subscr. to: Box 2242, New York, NY 10009) Ed. Gary Crowdus. adv.: bk.rev.; film rev.; index; circ. 9,000 (paid). (also avail. in microform from UMI; back issues avail.) **Indexed:** Alt.Press Ind., Arts & Hum.Cit.Ind., Curr.Cont., Film Lit.Ind. (1973-), Int.Ind.Film Per., Intl.Ind.TV, Left Ind. (1986-), M.L.A., Media Rev.Dig., Sociol.Abstr. **Document type:** consumer publication.
 •Also available online. Vendor(s): University Microfilms International.
—BLDSC (3198.635800); Faxon; Genuine Article; UMI; UnCover.
 Description: Features contributions from many of America's most articulate and outspoken writers, critics, and scholars. Focuses on both the art and politics of the cinema.

791.43 UK ISSN 0957-6290
CINEBLITZ INTERNATIONAL; Asian film sensation. 1989. m. £18($42) Cine Asia Publications, 152A Ealing Rd., Wembly, Middx. HA0 4PY, England. TEL 0181-903-8662. FAX 0181-900-1718. Ed. Rita Mehta; Pub. Rajesh Mehra. adv.; film rev. circ. 30,495. (back issues avail.) **Document type:** consumer publication.

778.534 SZ ISSN 1018-2098
CINEBULLETIN; Zeitschrift der schweizerischen Filmbranche. (Text in French, German) 1975. m. 55 SFr. (foreign 70 SFr.). Schweizerisches Filmzentrum, Neugasse 6, Postfach, CH-8031 Zurich, Switzerland. TEL 01-2725330. FAX 01-2725350. Ed. Michael Scuhhauser. adv.: B&W page 900 SFr.; trim 186 x 278. circ. 2,800. **Document type:** bulletin.

792 IT
CINECORRIERE. 1948. m. L.15000. c/o Alberto Crucilla, Ed., Circonvallazione Clodia 80, 00195 Rome, Italy. TEL 6-311-136. adv. circ. 5,000.

791.43 IT ISSN 0009-7020
CINECRONACHE.* N.S. 1967. m. Circolo del Cinema di Rovigo, Via All'ara 8, Rovigo, Italy. Dir. Gianluigi Ceruti. film rev.

791.4 AT ISSN 0813-1600
CINEDOSSIER. 1982. w. (50/yr.). Aus.$425 (foreign Aus.$575). Australian Film Institute, Research and Information Centre, 49 Eastern Rd., Melbourne, Vic. 3205, Australia. TEL 61-3-696-1844. FAX 61-3-696-7972. Ed. James Sabine. bk.rev.; film rev.; index, cum.index: 1982-1991.
 Description: Press clips from over 40 Australian newspapers concerning film news, production plans, and interviews.

778.5 051 US ISSN 0145-6032
PN1995.9.H6
CINEFANTASTIQUE. 1970. 6/yr. $27. 7240 W. Roosevelt Rd., Forest Park, IL 60130. TEL 708-366-5566. Ed. Frederick S. Clarke. adv. contact: Elaine Fiedler. bk.rev.; film rev.; illus.; stat.; index. circ. 40,000. (back issues avail.) **Indexed:** Film Lit.Ind. (1973-), M.M.R.I., Media Rev.Dig. **Document type:** consumer publication.
—UnCover.

791.43 US ISSN 0011-1056
TR858
CINEFEX; the journal of cinematic illusions. 1980. q. $26. Cinefex, Box 20027, Riverside, CA 92516. TEL 909-788-9828. FAX 909-788-1793. Ed. Jody Duncan; Pub. Don Shay. adv. contact: Bill Lindsay. bk.rev.; circ. 25,000 (paid). **Indexed:** Film Lit.Ind. (1980-), Int.Ind.Film Per., Intl.Ind.TV.
—UnCover.
 Description: Covers motion picture special effects: optical, physical, makeup and digital.

791.43 IT ISSN 0009-7039
PN1993
CINEFORUM; rivista di cultura cinematografica. 1961. m. (10/yr.). L.80000 (foreign L.100000) (typically set in Jan.). Federazione Italiana dei Cineforum, Via Pascoli 3, 24121 Bergamo, Italy. TEL 39-35-244703. FAX 39-35-233129. Ed. Sandro Zambetti; Pub. Bruno Fornara. adv.: B&W page L.1000000; adv. contact: Matteo Zambetti. bk.rev.; film rev.; index. circ. 5,000. **Indexed:** Arts & Hum.Cit.Ind., Curr.Cont., Film Lit.Ind. (1973-), Int.Ind.Film Per., Intl.Ind.TV. **Document type:** consumer publication.

791.43 384.55 792 SP ISSN 0069-4134
CINEGUIA; annuario espanol del espectaculo y audiovisuales. 1960. a. 5000 ptas. (Europe 7000 ptas.). F.M. Editores, S.A., Mauricio Legendre, 16, 28046 Madrid, Spain. TEL 1-323-51-15. FAX 1-323-11-51. adv. circ. 4,800.

778.5 BG
CINEMA. (Text in Bengali) 1974. w. Tk.0.50 per issue. 81 Motijheel C/A, Dhaka 1000, Bangladesh. Ed. Sheikh Fazlur Rahman Maruf. circ. 11,000. **Indexed:** Intl.Ind.TV.

778.5 SZ
CINEMA; unabhaengige schweizerische Filmzeitschrift - revue cinematographique independent suisse. 1951. a. 24 SFr. Stroemfeld Verlag AG, Oetlingerstr. 19, Postfach 79, CH-4007 Basel, Switzerland. TEL 061-6924180. FAX 061-6912406. E-mail: stroemfeld@clients.switch.ch. Eds. Janis Osolin, Alfred Messerli. adv.: bk.rev.; illus. circ. 2,600. **Indexed:** Film Lit.Ind. (1976-), Intl.Ind.TV. **Document type:** academic/scholarly publication.

791.43 IT
CINEMA. (Includes a videocassette.) m. L.235000. E R I Edizioni R A I, Via Arsenale 41, 10121 Torino, Italy. TEL 011-8800. FAX 011-534732.

ULRICH'S INTERNATIONAL PERIODICALS DIRECTORY 1996

MOTION PICTURES

791.43   TS
CINEMA. (Text in Arabic) 1988. q. exchange basis. Cultural Foundation, Culture and Arts Department, P.O. Box 2380, Abu Dhabi, United Arab Emirates. TEL 215300. FAX 336059. TELEX 22414 CULCEN EM. circ. 1,000.
Description: Covers international film news and presents an overview of world film-making activity, and discusses the department's film series.

791.43 028.5   GW   ISSN 0720-020X
CINEMA. m. DM.72 (foreign DM.79.20); newsstand price: DM.6.50. Kino Verlag GmbH, Milchstr. 1, 20148 Hamburg, Germany. TEL 040-44198-0. FAX 040-458519. Ed. Klaus Dahm. adv. contact: Andre Hauke. circ. 210,649. **Document type:** consumer publication.

778.5   FR   ISSN 0045-6926
PN1993
CINEMA (YEAR). 1953. s-m. 180 F. (foreign 246 F.). Editions Temps Libres, 101 av. du General Leclerc, 75014 Paris, France. TEL 40-44-49-29. FAX 40-44-53-79. (Subscr. to: B.P. 544, 75667 Paris Cedex 14, France) Ed. Pascal Brack. adv.; bk.rev. circ. 30,000. **Indexed:** Film Lit.Ind. (1973-), Int.Ind.Film Per., Intl.Ind.TV, Pt.de Rep. **Document type:** newsletter.

792   IT   ISSN 0392-9981
CINEMA D'OGGI. 1967. fortn. L.30000. A.N.I.C.A., Viale Regina Margherita 286, 00198 Rome, Italy. TEL 6-88-41-271. Ed. Carmine Cianfarani. adv. circ. 11,000.

791.43   IT
CINEMA DOMANI. 1961. bi-m. Rolando Jotti, Via Cerquetti 67, 00152 Rome, Italy. film rev. (back issues avail.)

778.5   IT   ISSN 0390-1556
CINEMA E CINEMA. 3/yr. L.50000 (foreign L.90000) (effective 1994). Cooperativa Libraria Universitaria Editrice Bologna, Via Marsala 24, 40126 Bologna, Italy. TEL 051-220736. FAX 051-237758. Dir. Lorenzo Pellizzaro. **Indexed:** Film Lit.Ind. (1986-).

791.43   II
CINEMA EXPRESS. (Text in Tamil) 1980. fortn. newsstand price: Rs.5. Indian Express (Madurai) Ltd., Express Estates, Mount Rd., Madras 600 002, India. TEL 8260551. Ed. V. Ramamurthy. adv.: B&W page Rs.3000, color page Rs.4500; trim 230 x 180. circ. 32,575.

791.43   US   ISSN 0009-7101
PN1993
CINEMA JOURNAL. 1961. q. $25 to individuals; institutions $40. (Society for Cinema Studies) University of Texas Press, Box 7819, Austin, TX 78713. TEL 512-471-4531. FAX 512-320-0668. TELEX 776453-UTEXPRES AUS. E-mail: leah@utpress.ppb.utexas.edu. (Co-sponsor: Society of Cinemetologists) Ed. David Oesser. adv.: B&W page $160; adv. contact: Leah Dixon. bk.rev. circ. 1,500. **Indexed:** Amer.Bibl.Slavic & E.Eur.Stud., Arts & Hum.Cit.Ind., Curr.Cont., Film Lit.Ind. (1973-), Int.Ind.Film Per., Intl.Ind.TV, M.L.A., Mid.East: Abstr.& Ind. **Document type:** academic/scholarly publication.
—BLDSC (3198.639000); Faxon; Genuine Article; UMI; UnCover.
Formerly: Society of Cinematologists. Journal.
Description: Examines history of the motion picture industry.
Refereed Serial

778   IT
CINEMA LOMBARDIA; periodico d'informazione a cura della sezione regionale dell'A.N.E.C. 1975. m. (Associazione Nazionale Esercenti Cinema (A.N.E.C.)) A.G.I.S. Lombarda, Piazza Luigi di Savoia 24, 20124 Milan, Italy. TEL 66 90 241. Ed. Viviana Giorgi. adv.; film rev.; abstr.; charts; illus. circ. 800. (looseleaf format)
Description: Provides news of regional association activities and reprints news articles dealing with the film industry.

791.43   IT   ISSN 0009-711X
CINEMA NUOVO; rassegna bimestrale di cultura. 1952. bi-m. L.40000 (foreign L.60000) (effective 1994). Edizioni Dedalo s.r.l., Casella Postale 362, 70100 Bari, Italy. TEL 39-80-5311413. FAX 39-80-5311414. (Edit. addr.: Via Gacinta Pezzana 110, 10097 Rome, Italy. TEL 39-6-8076464. FAX 39-6-8840586) Dir. Guido Aristarco. adv.: B&W page L.2500000. bk.rev.; bibl.; film rev.; illus.; index. circ. 14,000. **Indexed:** Film Lit.Ind. (1973-), Int.Ind.Film Per., Intl.Ind.TV.
—SWETS; UMI.
Description: Reviews the cinema and its future.

791.43   AT   ISSN 0311-3639
PN1993.5.A8
CINEMA PAPERS. 1974. bi-m. Aus.$37.50. M T V Publishing Ltd., 116 Argyle St., Fitzroy, Vic. 3065, Australia. TEL 61-3-94162644. FAX 61-394164088. Ed. Scott Murray. adv.; bk.rev. (back issues avail.) **Indexed:** Film Lit.Ind. (1975-), Int.Ind.Film Per.
—BLDSC (3198.640200); UnCover.
Description: The production guide to who's making what in Australia. Includes features, interviews, news, reviews and a complete list of the latest censorship decisions.

791.43 320   FR   ISSN 0335-6280
CINEMA POLITIQUE; dans la perspective d'une vie passionnante. bi-m. 75 F. Association pour le Developpement et la Promotion par le Cinema, 20 bd. de l'Hopital, 75005 Paris, France. Ed. Dominique Loeillet. illus.

791.43   IT   ISSN 0009-7152
CINEMA SOCIETA. 1966. q. L.10000($12) Giorgio Trentin, Ed. & Pub., Via di Porta Maggiore, 81, 00185 Rome, Italy. TEL 06-7027687. bk.rev.; film rev. circ. 2,500.

791   PK
CINEMA THE WORLD OVER. (Text in English) 1975. m. Rs.40. National Film Development Corporation, c/o K.S. Hosain, 204-205 Hotel Metropole, Karachi, Pakistan.

778.5   FR
CINEMA 9. 1969. m. 25 F. Chemin des Fosses, 77880 Moncourt-Frononville, France. Ed. Pierre Y. Dhuiege. adv.; illus.

778.53   PO
CINEMA 15. 12/yr. Rua Correia Teles 22 2o, 1300 Lisbon, Portugal. TEL 68-78-80. Ed. Vittoriano Rosa.

778.53   FR   ISSN 0243-4504
CINEMACTION. 1978. irreg. (approx 4/yr.), no.75, 1995. 500 F. for 4 nos. Editions Corlet S.A., Z.I. Route de Vire, 14110 Conde sur Noireau, France. TEL 31699127. FAX 31694129. Ed. Guy Hennebelle; Pub. Charles Corlet. (back issues avail.) **Indexed:** Film Lit.Ind. (1990-), Int.Ind.Film Per. **Document type:** monographic series.
Description: In-depth critical coverage of topics relating to the cinema, including profiles of filmmakers, national cinemas, genre films.

778.53   II
CINEMARANJANI; cine-weekly. w. Andhra Patrika, 14-14-21 Mallikarjuna Rao St., Gandhinagar, Vijayawada 520 003, India. TEL 61247. adv.

791.43   IT   ISSN 0009-7160
CINEMASUD; rivista neorealista di avanguardia e del cinema politico. 1958. q. L.40000 (foreign L.50000). Via degli Imbimbo 45, 83100 Avellino, Italy. TEL 0825-21119. Ed. Camillo Marino. adv.; illus.; charts. **Indexed:** Film Lit.Ind. (1990-).
Description: Covers the world of cinema and film techniques.

778.5   UY   ISSN 0797-2059
CINEMATECA REVISTA. 1977. irreg., approx. 10/yr. $8 for 4 nos. Cinemateca Uruguaya, Lorenzo Carnelli 1311, Casilla de Correo 1170, Montevideo, Uruguay. TEL 598-2-482460. FAX 598-2-494572. TELEX 22043 CIMTECA UY. Ed.Bd. adv.; bk.rev. circ. 2,000. (back issues avail.) **Indexed:** Intl.Ind.TV.
Formerly: Cinemateca.

791.43   US   ISSN 0886-6570
CINEMATOGRAPH; a journal of film and media art. 1985. biennial. $12 to individuals; institutions and foreign $25. (Foundation of Art in Cinema) San Francisco Cinematheque, 480 Potrero, San Francisco, CA 94110. TEL 415-558-8129. FAX 415-558-0455. Ed. Albert Kilchesty. adv.; circ. 1,800. (also avail. in microform from UMI) **Indexed:** Film Lit.Ind. (1986-1988). **Document type:** academic/scholarly publication.
—UMI.

CINEMATOGRAPHERS, PRODUCTION DESIGNERS, COSTUME DESIGNERS & FILM EDITORS GUIDE. see BUSINESS AND ECONOMICS — Trade And Industrial Directories

778.5   US   ISSN 0162-0126
PN1993
CINEMONKEY;* a serious film journal. 1976. irreg. $7. Cinemonkey Inc., 1435 N.E. 72nd, Portland, OR 97213. TEL 503-248-0849. Ed. Douglas Holm. adv.; bk.rev.; film rev.
Formerly: Scintillation (ISSN 0147-5789)

791.43 384.55   US
▼**CINESCAPE.** 1994. m. $19.95; newsstand price: $4.95. Sendai Publishing Group, 1920 Highland Ave., Ste. 222, Lombard, IL 60148. TEL 708-916-7222. FAX 708-916-7227. Ed. Edward Gross; Pub. Steve Harris. adv.: B&W page $4150. circ. 250,000 (paid). **Document type:** consumer publication.

791.43   IT   ISSN 0024-1458
CINESCHEDARIO - LETTURE DRAMMATICHE.* vol.19, 1964. m. L.2000. Centro Salesiano Dello Spettacolo, Via M. Ausiliatrice 32, 10121 Turin, Italy. Ed. Marco Bongioanni. film rev.; play rev.; illus.
Formerly: Letture Drammatiche.

791.43   IT
CINESCOPIO. 1980. m. (11/yr.). L.95000. Gruppo Editoriale J C E, Via Ferri 6, 20092 Cinisello Balsamo (MI), Italy. TEL 39-2-660251. FAX 39-2-6127620. TELEX 352376 JCE MIL I. Ed. Ruben Castelfranchi. adv.: B&W page L.2200000, color page L.3600000; trim 210 x 280. circ. 25,000. **Document type:** consumer publication.

791.43   AG
CINESET. 6/yr. Giribone 1325, Piso 5, Apto. 4, Buenos Aires, Argentina. adv.

791.43   FR
CINETHIQUE. 1969. s-a. Editions Cinethique, B.P. 65, 75722 Paris Cedex 15, France. Ed. Gerard Leblanc. adv.; bk.rev.; film rev. circ. 6,000. (also avail. in microfilm; back issues avail.; reprint service avail. from UMI) **Indexed:** Film Lit.Ind., Intl.Ind.TV.

CINEVIDEO 20. see COMMUNICATIONS — Video

700   US   ISSN 0895-805X
CINEVUE. 1986. 4/yr. $10. Asian CineVision, Inc., 32 E. Broadway, New York, NY 10002. TEL 212-925-8685. Ed. Bill J. Gee. adv.; bk.rev. circ. 16,000.

778.5   US
CITADEL FILM SERIES. 1959. 6/yr. Citadel Press (Subsidiary of: Lyle Stuart Inc.), 120 Enterprise Ave., Secaucus, NJ 07094. TEL 212-736-1141. FAX 212-486-2231. Ed. Allan J. Wilson.

778.5   II
CITRABIKSHANA/CHITRA-BIKSHAN. (Text in Bengali) m. Rs.1.25 per no. Cine Central, 2 Chowringhee Rd., Calcutta 700013, India.

791.43   US   ISSN 0275-8423
PN1995.9.C54
CLASSIC IMAGES. 1962. m. $31 (foreign $42). Muscatine Journal (Subsidiary of: Lee Enterprises, Inc.), 301 Third St. E., Box 809, Muscatine, IA 52761. TEL 319-263-2331. FAX 319-262-8042. Ed. Bob King. adv.; bk.rev.; film rev.; bibl.; illus.; cum.index. circ. 3,800. (tabloid format; also avail. in microfilm from UMI; back issues avail.; reprint service avail. from UMI) **Indexed:** Film Lit.Ind. (1973-), Int.Ind.Film Per., Media Rev.Dig. **Document type:** newspaper, consumer publication.
 —UMI.
 Former titles (until 1979): Classic Film - Video Images (ISSN 0164-5560); (until 1978): Classic Film Collector (ISSN 0009-8329); Eight MM Collector.
 Description: Contains articles on classic films, film personalities, film history.

808.23   US   ISSN 1073-7049
PN1995.9.S3
CLIFFHANGER. Issued with: Under Western Skies (ISSN 0279-6244) 1983. irreg. $13 for 4 nos. World of Yesterday, Rte. 3, Box 263H, Waynesville, NC 28786. TEL 704-648-5647. Ed. Linda S. Downey. adv.: page $25; 7 x 9 1/2. bk.rev.; film rev.; music rev.; circ. 950 (paid). (back issues avail.) **Document type:** consumer publication.
 Description: Offers a look back at old-time suspense dramas as seen in movie palaces, on T.V., and heard on the radio.

CLUB MODELE. see *CLOTHING TRADE* — *Fashions*

778   BL
COLECAO CINEMA.* vol. 14, 1982. irreg. Editora Paz e Terra, Rua Sao Jose 90, S.L. lll Centro, 20010-020 Rio de Janeiro, RJ, Brazil.

778   SP
COLECCION DIRECTORES DE CINE. q. 3000 ptas. (effective 1995). Ediciones J C, Monteleon, 35, 28010 Madrid, Spain. TEL 34-1-4469692. Ed. Juan Carlos Gonzalez Reutero. **Document type:** monographic series.

791.43   SP
COLECCION IMAGENES. irreg., latest no.19. price varies. Ediciones J C, Monteleon, 35, 28010 Madrid, Spain. TEL 34-1-4469692. **Document type:** monographic series.

COLLECTING HOLLYWOOD: THE MOVIE POSTER PRICE GUIDE. see *HOBBIES*

791.43   US
COLUMBIA FILM VIEW. 1985. 3/yr. $7.50. Columbia University, School of the Arts, Film Division, 513 Dodge Hall, New York, NY 10027. TEL 212-280-2842. Eds. Jennifer Robinson, David Wezoer. adv.; bk.rev. circ. 1,000. **Indexed:** Film Lit.Ind. (1986-).
 Formerly: Columbia Film Review.

COMPARATIVE LITERARY AND FILM STUDIES: EUROPE, JAPAN, AND THE THIRD WORLD. see *LITERATURE*

CONSORTIUM FOR DRAMA & MEDIA IN HIGHER EDUCATION. NEWSLETTER. see *THEATER*

CONTEMPORARY ART CENTRE OF SOUTH AUSTRALIA. BROADSHEET. see *ART*

791.4   AT   ISSN 1030-4312
PN1993
CONTINUUM. 1987. biennial. Murdoch University, Centre for Research in Culture and Communication, Murdoch, W.A. 6150, Australia. **Indexed:** Int.Ind.Film Per.
 —BLDSC (3425.720550); UnCover.

778.5   US
COUNCIL ON INTERNATIONAL NONTHEATRICAL EVENTS. YEARBOOK; Golden Eagle film awards. 1962. a. $12. Council on International Nontheatrical Events, Inc., 1001 Connecticut Ave., N.W., Ste. 638, Washington, DC 20036. TEL 202-785-1136. FAX 202-785-4114. Ed. Joy Parisi. film rev.; illus.; stat. circ. 2,500. **Document type:** catalog, directory.

CRIMSON HEROES. see *LITERATURE* — *Science Fiction, Fantasy, Horror*

791.43   UK   ISSN 0015-1203
CRITIC. 1950. w. £15.75. Critics' Guild, 9 Compayne Gardens, London N.W.6, England. Ed. Dore Silverman. bk.rev.; film rev.; music rev.; play rev.
 Formerly: Film Critics' Guild. Bulletin.

778.53   SP   ISSN 0214-462X
CUADERNOS CINEMATOGRAFICOS. 1968. irreg., no.7, 1991. 1200 ptas. Universidad de Valladolid, Secretariado de Publicaciones, C. Juan Mambrilla, 14, 47003 Valladolid, Spain. TEL 983-423000. FAX 34-83-290300. TELEX 26357. **Document type:** monographic series, academic/scholarly publication.

808.23   SP
CUADERNOS DEL AULA DEL CINE. 1991. irreg., no.2, 1992. Universidad de Salamanca, Servicio de Publicaciones, C. Arguelles 19, 33003 Oviedo, Spain. TEL 34-85-104486. FAX 34-85-104488. **Document type:** monographic series.

CUE SHEET. see *MUSIC*

791.43
CULT MOVIE; bimestrale di cultura e politica cinematografica. (Text in Italian) 1980. bi-m. L.15000. Circolo Ricreativo ENEL, Via del Sole 10, 50123 Florence, Italy. Ed.Bd. adv.; bk.rev.; film rev. circ. 5,000.

291.43   US   ISSN 0748-8580
PN1993
CURRENT RESEARCH IN FILM. 1985. a. price varies. Ablex Publishing Corporation, 355 Chestnut St., Norwood, NJ 07648. TEL 201-767-8450. FAX 201-767-6717. TELEX 135-393. Ed. Bruce A. Austin. **Indexed:** Film Lit.Ind. (1985-). **Document type:** academic/scholarly publication.
 —BLDSC (3501.957600); Faxon.

DAILY VARIETY; news of the entertainment industry. see *COMMUNICATIONS* — *Television And Cable*

DANCE ON CAMERA NEWS. see *DANCE*

791.43   CC   ISSN 1002-4646
DANGDAI DIANYING/CONTEMPORARY CINEMA. (Text in Chinese) 1984. bi-m. Y12. China Film Art Research Centre, 25-B Xinjiekouwai Dajie, Beijing 100088, People's Republic of China. TEL 2014422. FAX 2014316. (Dist. outside China by: China National Publications Foreign Trading Corp., P.O. Box 782, Beijing, China) Ed. Chen Bo. film rev. circ. 8,000.
 Description: Covers the fields of film theory, film review, film history, film techniques, and film markets.

791.437   DK   ISSN 0418-3304
DANISH FILMS. (Text in English) 1985. a. free. Danish Film Institute, Store Soendervoldstraede, DK-1419 Copenhagen, Denmark. FAX 45-31-576700. TELEX 31465 DFILM DK. Ed. Vicki Synnott. adv.; illus. circ. 5,000.

791.43   CC   ISSN 0492-0929
DAZHONG DIANYING/POPULAR CINEMA. (Text in Chinese) 1950. m. Y18($85.50) Zhongguo Dianying Chubanshe - China Film Press, 22, Beisanhuan Donglu, Beijing 100013, People's Republic of China. (Dist. outside China by: China International Book Trading Corp., P.O. Box 399, Beijing, P.R.C.; Dist. in US by: China Books & Periodicals, Inc., 2929 24th St., San Francisco, CA 94110. TEL 415-282-2994) Eds. Cai Shiyong, Ma Rui.

016.79   DK   ISSN 0907-4821
DENMARK. STATENS FILMCENTRAL. S F C FILM KATALOGET. 1950. biennial. free. Statens Filmcentral - National Film Board of Denmark, 27 Vestergade, 1456 Copenhagen K, Denmark. TEL 45-33-132686. FAX 45-33-130203. Eds. Claus Hasselberg, Ben Ohmsen. circ. 40,000.
 Former titles: Denmark. Statens Filmcentral. S F C Catalogue; Denmark. Statens Filmcentral. S F C Film and Video Catalogue (ISSN 0070-3621)

791.430   DK   ISSN 0905-5266
DENMARK. STATENS FILMCENTRAL. VIDEO (YEAR). 1977. a. free. Statens Filmcentral - National Film Board of Denmark, Vestergade 27, DK-1456 Copenhagen K, Denmark. TEL 45-33-13-26-86. FAX 45-33-13-02-03. Ed. Claus Hasselberg.
 Former titles: Denmark. Statens Filmcentral. Film og Video (ISSN 0905-0973); (until 1989): Denmark. Statens Filmcentral. S F C - 16 MM Film (ISSN 0105-5526)

778.53   US
DETROIT FILM AND VIDEO NEWS. 1990. q. $7.50. Real Estate News Corp., 2600 W. Peterson, Ste. 100, Chicago, IL 60659. TEL 312-465-7246. FAX 312-465-7218. Ed. Donna B. Proske. adv. circ. 3,500.
 Description: Reports on the industry's progress in the Detroit Metro area and throughout Michigan. Covers trends, equipment, innovations, new facilities, services and technology.

778.53 791.4   CC   ISSN 1000-0151
DIANSHI DIANYING WENXUE/T V AND FILM LITERATURE. Short title: D D W. (Text in Chinese) 1981. bi-m. Y22.80($5) (Shanghai Shi Wenxue Yishujie Lianhehui - Shanghai Literature and Art Association) Dianshi Dianying Wenxue Zazhishe, 238 Yan'an Xilu, Shanghai 200040, People's Republic of China. TEL 21-2581568. Ed. Zhu Liang-yi. adv.; film rev.; illus. circ. 20,000.
 Description: Introduces new Chinese and foreign television, movie works, and literature. Contains stories, scripts, and biographical articles.

778.53   CC   ISSN 0257-0173
DIANYING CHUANGZUO/CINEMATIC CREATION. (Text in Chinese) 1977. m. Y7.80($61.20) (Beijing Dianying Zhipianchang - Beijing Movie Studios) Dianying Chuangzuo Zazhishe, Beisanhuan Zhonglu, Beijing 100088, People's Republic of China. (Dist. outside China by: China International Book Trade Corporation (Guoji Shudian), P.O. Box 399, Beijing, P.R.C.; Dist. in US by: China Books & Periodicals, Inc., 2929 24th St., San Francisco, CA 94110) Ed. Wang Taorui. adv.; film rev.
 Description: Covers China's film industry.

791.43   CC   ISSN 0493-2374
DIANYING GUSHI/FILM STORIES. (Text in Chinese) m. $33.20. (Shanghai Dianying Faxing Fangying Gongsi - Shanghai Film Distribution and Projection Company) Dianying Gushi Bianjibu, 322 Anfu Lu, Shanghai 200031, People's Republic of China. TEL 4332839. (Dist. in US by: China Books & Periodicals, Inc., 2929 24th St., San Francisco, CA 94110. TEL 415-282-2994)

791.4   CC
DIANYING HUAKAN/FILM PICTORIAL.* (Text in Chinese) m. $49.40. Shaanxi Sheng Dianying Gongsi, No. 24 Wenyi Nanlu, Xi'an, Shaanxi 710054, People's Republic of China. TEL 719514. (Dist. in US by: China Books & Periodicals, Inc., 2929 24th St., San Francisco, CA 94110. TEL 415-282-2994)

791.43   CC
DIANYING JIESHAO. (Text in Chinese) m. Shanxi Dianying Faxing Fangying Gongsi - Shanxi Film Distribution & Projection Company, 58 Yingze Dajie, Taiyuan, Shanxi 030001, People's Republic of China. TEL 443862. Ed. Hua Zhongzhuang.

791.4   CC
DIANYING SHIJIE/FILM WORLD. (Text in Chinese) m. $40.40. Changchun Dianying Zhipianchang - Changchun Film Studio, 16 Hongqi Jie, Changchun, Jilin 130021, People's Republic of China. TEL 53511. (Dist. in US by: China Books & Periodicals, Inc., 2929 24th St., San Francisco, CA 94110. TEL 415-282-2994) Ed. Zhao Ziming.

791.43   CC   ISSN 0495-5692
DIANYING WENXUE/FILM LITERATURE. (Text in Chinese) 1958-1966; resumed 1978. m. Y19.20 (effective 1991). Changchun Dianying Zhipianchang - Changchun Film Studio, 16 Hongqi Jie, Changchun, Jilin 130021, People's Republic of China. (Dist. outside China by: China Publications Foreign Trade Corp., P.O. Box 782, Beijing, P.R.C.) Ed. Zhu Jing. circ. 190,000.

4790 MOTION PICTURES

778.53   CC
DIANYING XINZUO/NEW FILMS. (Text in Chinese) bi-m. $24.80. Dianying Xinzuo Bianjibu - New Film Editorial Department, 796 Huaihai Zhonglu, Shanghai, People's Republic of China. (Dist. in US by: China Books & Periodicals, Inc., 2929 24th St., San Francisco, CA 94110) Ed.Bd. adv.

791.43   CC   ISSN 0257-0181
DIANYING YISHU/FILM ART. Variant English title: Cinema Art. (Text in Chinese) 1956. m. Y12($44) (Zhongguo Dianyingjia Xiehui - China Film Association) Zhongguo Dianying Chubanshe - China Film Press, 22 Beisanhuan Donglu, Beijing 100013, People's Republic of China. TEL 4219977. (Dist. outside China by: China International Book Trading Corp., P.O. Box 399, Beijing, P.R.C.; Dist. in US by: China Books & Periodicals, Inc., 2929 24th St., San Francisco, CA 94110) Eds. Guo Wei, Wang Renyin. adv.; bk.rev.; film rev. circ. 5,000.
—UnCover.
Formerly (until July 1959): Zhongguo Dianying.
Description: Covers all aspects of filmmaking, including scriptwriting, directing, acting, cinematography, sound recording, and editing. Critiques current Chinese filmmakers and their works, researches film history, and introduces foreign works on film theory.

791.43   CC   ISSN 1003-5834
DIANYING YUEBAO/MOVIE MONTHLY. (Text in Chinese) bi-m. Guangxi Dianying Zhipian Chang - Guangxi Film Studio, 26 You'ai Beilu, Nanning, Guangxi 530001, People's Republic of China. TEL 34261. Ed. Gao Honghao.

791.43   CC   ISSN 1006-4478
DIANYING ZHI YOU/FILM'S FRIENDS. (Text in Chinese) 1979. m. Y21.60 (effective 1995). Fujian Sheng Dianying Faxing Fangying Gongsi - Film Distribution and Projection Company of Fujian Province, 229 Baima Lu, Fuzhou, Fujian 350001, People's Republic of China. TEL 7520114. FAX 7530341. (Dist. overseas by: Jiangsu Publications Import & Export Corp., 56 Gao Yun Ling, Nanjing, Jiangsu, P.R.C.) Eds. Sa Bendun, Zhang Xuan. adv.; bk.rev. circ. 100,000.

791.43   CC   ISSN 1001-5582
DIANYING ZUOPIN/FILM SCRIPTS. (Text in Chinese) bi-m. E'mei Dianying Zhipian Chang - E'mei Film Studio, Chengdu, Sichuan 610072, People's Republic of China. TEL 669571. Ed. Liang Husheng.

778.53   MX   ISSN 0188-1485
PN1993.5.M4
DICINE; revista de difusion e investigacion cinematograficas a.c. 1983. bi-m. Mex.$100 (America $80; elsewhere $80) (effective 1995 & 1996). Dicine A.C., Leonardo da Vinci 161-A, 03700 Mexico D.F., Mexico. TEL 525-598-60-86. Ed. Nelson Carro. adv.; bk.rev. circ. 5,000. (back issues avail.) **Indexed:** Film Lit.Ind. (1988-).

778.53 791.43   US
DIGEST OF THE U F V A. bi-m. membership. University Film Video Association, Western Michigan University, Communication Department, Kalamazoo, MI 49008. TEL 616-381-4023. FAX 616-387-3999. E-mail: lipkin@wmich.edu. (Alt addr.: c/o George Wehbl, School of Cinema, University of Southern California, University Park, MC 2212, Los Angeles, CA 90089) Eds. Steve Lipkin, Denise Hartsough. circ. 850. **Document type:** newsletter.

778.534   US
DIRECTORY OF HISPANIC TALENT. 1979. biennial. Hispanic Organization of Latin Artists, 250 W. 65th St., New York, NY 10023-6403. TEL 212-595-8286. FAX 212-799-6718. circ. 1,400. **Document type:** directory.
Description: Distributed nationally to casting directors and producers.

778.53   SP   ISSN 0212-7245
DIRIGIDO POR...; revista de cine. 1972. m. 5250 ptas. (Europe $72; elsewhere $102). Dirigido por... S.L., Consell de Cent 304, 2o 1o, 08007 Barcelona, Spain. TEL 34-3-4876202. FAX 34-3-4880896. Dir. Enrique Aragones. adv. contact: Jose Maria Latorre. bk.rev.; film rev.; circ. 15,000 (paid). **Indexed:** Int.Ind.Film Per. (until 1995). **Document type:** consumer publication.
Description: Publishes studies of the works of the great directors, alternating classic with modern film. Includes interviews, dossiers, and reports on film festivals.

791.43   GW   ISSN 0931-1416
DISKURS FILM. 1987. irreg., no.6, 1994. DM.49.50. Diskurs Film Verlag Schaudig & Ledig GbR, Tristanstr. 13, 80804 Munich, Germany. TEL 089-365229. Ed. Klaus Kanzog; Pubs. E. Ledig, M. Schaudig. **Document type:** academic/scholarly publication.

DRAGON. see LITERATURE

778.5 792 791.4   US
DRAMA-LOGUE. 1969. w. $55. Drama-Logue, Inc., Box 38771, Los Angeles, CA 90038. TEL 213-464-5079. Ed. Faye Bordy. adv.; bk.rev. circ. 75,000. **Document type:** trade publication.
Formerly: Hollywood Drama-Logue (ISSN 0272-2720)

DUCKBURG TIMES. see HOBBIES

791.43 384.55   IT
DUEL; mensile di cinema, immagini e televisione. m. L.80000 (Europe $100; US & Japan $200). Duel Edizioni s.r.l., Via Pietro Mascagini 3-5, 00199 Rome, Italy. TEL 39-6-8608913. FAX 39-6-8608930. adv.; B&W page L.4200000, color page L.6000000.

778.5   NE
DUTCH FILM. (Text in English) irreg. Ministerie van Welzijn Volksgezondheid en Cultuur, Publieksvoorlichting, Postbus 5406, 2280 HK Rijswijk, Netherlands. TEL 31-70-3405764. Ed. Pieter van Lierop. illus. **Document type:** government publication.

DZAR BICHIG/PUBLICITY HERALD. see COMMUNICATIONS — Television And Cable

791.43   GW   ISSN 0176-2044
E P D FILM. 1984. m. DM.72. Gemeinschaftswerk der Evangelischen Publizistik e.V., Postfach 500550, 60439 Frankfurt a.M., Germany. TEL 069-58098104. FAX 069-58098100. TELEX 176997347. Ed. Hans Hafenbrack, Bettina Thienhaus; Pub. Norbert Janowski. adv. contact: Claus Mertens. bk.rev.; film rev.; index. circ. 7,000. (back issues avail.) **Indexed:** Film Lit.Ind. (1988-), Int.Ind.Film Per. **Document type:** academic/scholarly publication.
Description: Articles on film theory, criticism, history and economy.

791.43   US   ISSN 0891-6780
PN1993
EAST-WEST FILM JOURNAL. Variant title: East West Film Journal. 1986. s-a. $15 to individuals (foreign $17); institutions $25 (foreign $30). East-West Center, Program on Cultural Studies, 1777 East-West Rd., Honolulu, HI 96848. Ed. Wimal Dissanayake. adv.; bk.rev. circ. 310. (back issues avail.; reprint service avail. from UMI) **Indexed:** Arts & Hum.Cit.Ind., Curr.Cont., Film Lit.Ind. (1986-), Int.Ind.Film Per. **Document type:** academic/scholarly publication.
—Faxon; Genuine Article; UnCover.
Description: Provides a forum where Asian cinema can be introduced to other Asian and Western audiences.
Refereed Serial

791   US   ISSN 1075-0851
▼**ECHOES & MIRRORS;** comparative studies of film. 1994. s-a. $10. Mount Wachusett Community College, 444 Green St., Gardner, MA 01440-1000. TEL 508-632-6600. Ed. Edward R. Cronin.
Description: Provides a forum for the comparative study of motion pictures, particularly studies that demonstrate the influence of one film on another, studies that examine films and their remakes and studies that illuminate different directorial approaches to the same material.

791.43   CN   ISSN 0844-1111
ECHOS VEDETTES. (Text in French) 1963. w. Can.$126.89. 801 est, rue Sherbrooke, 2e etage, Montreal, PQ H2L 4X9, Canada. TEL 514-521-7111. FAX 514-521-7115. adv.; bk.rev. circ. 170,000. (tabloid format; also avail. in microform) **Document type:** newspaper.

778.5   FR   ISSN 0769-1920
ECRAN FANTASTIQUE. 1970. m. 250 F. Editions de Tournon, 44-48 rue Brocca, 75008 Paris, France. TEL 46-37-13-90. FAX 43-36-60-87. Ed. Alain Schlockoff. adv.; bk.rev.; film rev.; illus. circ. 50,000.

EDUCATIONAL TECHNOLOGY RESEARCH & DEVELOPMENT. see EDUCATION — Teaching Methods And Curriculum

EGYPTE - SPORTS - CINEMA. see SPORTS AND GAMES

791.43   XV   ISSN 0013-3302
PN1993
EKRAN; revija za film in televizijo. 1962. m. 1500 SLT. Zveza Kulturnih Organizacij Slovenije, Ulica Talcev 6-II, 61104 Ljubljana, Slovenia. TEL 0368-61318353. Eds. Stojan Pelko, Miha Zadnikar. adv.; film rev.; illus. circ. 2,000. **Indexed:** Film Lit.Ind. (1973-), Int.Ind.Film Per. (until 1995), Intl.Ind.TV. **Document type:** bulletin.

ELVIRA. see LITERATURE — Science Fiction, Fantasy, Horror

ELVIS MONTHLY. see MUSIC

791.43   CN
EN PRIMEUR; edition campus. 1991. q. Can.$12 (in US Can.$18). Entertainment Media Services Inc., 900 A Don Mills Rd., Ste. 1000, Don Mills, ON M3C 1V6, Canada. TEL 416-445-0100. FAX 416-445-2894. Ed. Sandra I. Stewart; Pub. Brian A. Stewart. adv. contact: Randy Stewart, Donnalyn Coyne. circ. 50,000. **Document type:** consumer publication.
Description: Provides previews of upcoming films.

EN PRIMEUR JEUNESSE. see CHILDREN AND YOUTH — For

ENCLITIC; the timely taken seriously. see LITERARY AND POLITICAL REVIEWS

ENSEMBLE; the new variety arts review. see THEATER

ENTERTAINMENT AND SPORTS LAWYER. see LAW

ENTERTAINMENT INDUSTRY OUTLOOK. see BUSINESS AND ECONOMICS — Economic Situation And Conditions

ENTERTAINMENT LAW REPORTER; motion pictures, television, radio, music, theater, publishing, sports. see LAW

THE ENTERTAINMENT MAGAZINE ON-LINE. see MUSIC

ENTERTAINMENT PLUS. see MUSIC

791.43   US   ISSN 1063-5343
ENTERTAINMENT RESEARCH REPORT; the unbiased content report for current films. 1991. s-m. $29.95. Entertainment Research Group, Box 810608, Boca Raton, FL 33481. TEL 407-395-1150; 800-322-1296. FAX 407-395-6129. Ed. David Winston. (back issues avail.)
Description: Provides content information about current movies focusing on potentially objectionable material in language, adult situations, violence and relationship.

EL ESPECTACULAR. see COMMUNICATIONS — Television And Cable

ETIN. see LIBRARY AND INFORMATION SCIENCES

791.43   FR   ISSN 0014-1992
PN1994
ETUDES CINEMATOGRAPHIQUES. 1960. irreg. 165 F. for 10 nos. Lettres Modernes, 45 rue Saint-Andre, 14123 Fleury sur Orne, France. TEL 31-84-47-06. FAX 31-84-48-09. Ed. Michel Esteve. bibl.; illus. **Indexed:** Arts & Hum.Cit.Ind., Curr.Cont., Intl.Ind.TV.

791.43 700   GW
EUROPEAN MEDIA ART FESTIVAL. (Text in English, German) 1988. a. DM.35. International Experimental Film Workshop, Postfach 1861, 49008 Osnabrueck, Germany. TEL 0541-21658. FAX 0541-28327. E-mail: emaf@bionic.zer.de. adv.: page $1500. circ. 1,000. (back issues avail.) **Document type:** catalog.
●Also available online.
Also available on CD-ROM.

EYEPIECE. see PHOTOGRAPHY

808.23 UK
F I A F CLASSIFICATION SCHEME FOR LITERATURE ON FILM AND TELEVISION. irreg., 2nd edition, 1992. £35. International Federation of Film Archives (F I A F) - Federation Internationale des Archives du Film, 6 Nottingham St., London W1M 3RB, England. TEL 0171-224-1203. FAX 0171-224-0991.

FACE TO FACE WITH TALENT. see COMMUNICATIONS — Television And Cable

791.43 US ISSN 0736-3745
FACETS FEATURES. 1975. bi-m. $12 (effective 1994). Facets Multimedia, Inc., 1517 W. Fullerton Ave., Chicago, IL 60614. TEL 312-281-9075. FAX 312-929-5437. TELEX 20-6701. Ed. Milos Stehlik; Pub. David Edelberg. adv. contact: Catherine Foley. bk.rev.; film rev.; illus. circ. 50,000. **Document type:** consumer publication.
Formerly (until 1980): Focus Chicago (ISSN 0362-0905)
Description: Covers the world of international films and video, including new foreign, independent and classic releases.

778.53 384.55 MX
FAMA. fortn. Avda. Eugenio Garza Sada Sur 2245, Col. Roma, Apdo. 3128, Monterrey, NL, Mexico. TEL 83-59-2525. circ. 250,000.

778.534 US
FAME AND FORTUNE.* q. Dell Magazines, 1540 Broadway, New York, NY 10036. TEL 212-354-6500. FAX 212-782-8338.

791.43 US ISSN 0278-4203
PN1995.9.H6
FAMOUS MONSTERS.* 1958-19??; resumed 1994. 4/yr. $7.95. Box 9669, N. Hollywood, CA 91609. Ed. Forrest J. Ackerman. adv.; bk.rev.; film rev.; illus. circ. 200,000.
Formerly: Famous Monsters of Filmland (ISSN 0014-7443)

FANDOM DIRECTORY. see HOBBIES

778.53 SP
FANTASTIC MAGAZINE. 1992. m. 4400 ptas. Comunicacion y Publicaciones, S.A., Gran Via de les Corts Catalanes, 133, 2o, 08014 Barcelona, Spain. TEL 34-3-223-03-53. FAX 34-3-421-61-50. Ed. Elisenda Nadal. circ. 60,000. **Document type:** consumer publication.

791.43 371.33 US
FAST FOREWORD.* 1974. m. $35 to individuals; institutions $85. Association of Audio Visual Technicians, Box 101264, Denver, CO 80250. Ed. Elsa Kaiser. adv.; bk.rev. circ. 1,200. (back issues avail.)

791.43 GW ISSN 0015-0142
CODEN: FNKTAH
FERNSEH- UND KINO-TECHNIK; Fachzeitschrift fuer professionelle. 1946. 11/yr. DM.183 (foreign DM.193.20). (Fernseh- und Kinotechnische Gesellschaft) Huethig GmbH, Postfach 102869, 69018 Heidelberg, Germany. TEL 06221-489-0. FAX 06221-489482. TELEX 461727-HUEHD-D. Ed. N. Bolewski. adv.; B&W page DM.3100; trim 210 x 297; adv. contact: Horst Schuerer. bk.rev.; abstr.; bibl.; charts; illus.; pat.; index; circ. 5,226. **Indexed:** Chem.Abstr., Film Lit.Ind. (1973-), INSPEC. **Document type:** trade publication.
—SWETS. CCC.
Description: Trade journal for professional video, film and television technology.

778.5 FR ISSN 0336-9331
FICHES DU CINEMA. 1934. w. 340 F. (foreign 490 F.) Chretien Medias Cinema, 12 rue Mgr. Gibier, 78000 Versailles, France. TEL 39670398. FAX 39515280. Ed. Pierre Deschamps. film rev. circ. 3,000.
Description: Short reviews and ratings of current films.

791.43 US
FILAMENT. 1981. a. free. Wright State University, Department of Theatre Arts, Dayton, OH 45435. Ed. Glenn Lalich. circ. 1,500. (back issues avail.) **Indexed:** Film Lit.Ind.

791.43 PL ISSN 0137-463X
FILM. 1946. w. $208. Pulawska 61, 02-595 Warsaw, Poland. TEL 48-22-455325. FAX 48-22-454651. Ed. Maciej Pawlicki. film rev.; illus.; index. circ. 149,400.

791.43 UK ISSN 0015-1025
FILM. 1952. q. £25 (effective 1996). British Federation of Film Societies, 21 Stephen St., London W1P 1PL, England. TEL 0171-734-9300. FAX 0171-734-9093. Ed. T. Brownlie. adv.; bk.rev.; film rev.; illus.; index. circ. 2,500. (also avail. in microfilm from WMP; back issues avail.) **Indexed:** Film Lit.Ind. (1973-1987), Media Rev.Dig. **Document type:** trade publication.
—UnCover.
Description: Contains practical information on running film societies as well as news of film availability.

791.43 IR ISSN 1019-6382
FILM. (English supplement avail.) (Text in Persian) 1982. m. $52. P.O. Box 11365-5876, Tehran, Iran. TEL 98-21-679373. FAX 98-21-6459971. Ed. Massoud Mehrabi. circ. 50,000. **Document type:** consumer publication.
Description: Covers the cinema of Iran and the world and promotes knowledge of the art of film.

778.53 IT
FILM. (Includes a videocassette.) m. L.235000 (effective 1992). E R I Edizioni R A I, Via Arsenale 41, 10121 Turin, Italy. TEL 011-8800. FAX 011-534732. **Indexed:** Int.Ind.Film Per.

FILM A DIVADLO. see COMMUNICATIONS — Television And Cable

791.43 XR ISSN 0015-1068
FILM A DOBA; ctvrtletnik pro filmovou a televizni kulturu. (Text in Czech; summaries in English, French and Russian) 1954. q. 72 Kc.($61.30) Sdruzeni Pratel Odborneho Filmoveho Tisku, Parizska 9, 110 00 Prague 1, Czech Republic. Ed. Eva Zaoralova. bk.rev.; abstr.; charts; illus.; index. circ. 7,000. **Indexed:** Film Lit.Ind. (1973-), Int.Ind.Film Per., Intl.Ind.TV.

778.5 DK ISSN 0109-2774
FILM AARBOGEN. 1949. a. DKK 59.75. Carlsen Forlag A-S, Krogshoejvej 32, DK-2880 Bagsvaerd, Denmark. TEL 45-44-44-32-33. FAX 45-44-44-36-33. illus.
Formerly: Aarets Bedste Film.

791.43 FR
FILM AFRICAIN. 6/yr. 150 F. Marche International du Film d'Amiens, 36 rue de Noyon, 80000 Amiens, France. TEL 22-91-01-44. FAX 22-92-53-04. TELEX 140754 CHAMCO.

778.5 900 US ISSN 0360-3695
PN1995.2
FILM & HISTORY. 1972 N.S. q. $15 to individuals; institutions $25. Historians Film Committee, New Jersey Institute of Technology, Newark, NJ 07102. TEL 201-596-3291. Ed. Gregory W. Bush. adv.: page $150. bk.rev.; film rev.; illus. circ. 420. (tabloid format) **Indexed:** Amer.Hist.& Life, Film Lit.Ind. (1985-), Hist.Abstr., Int.Ind.Film Per., Intl.Ind.TV. **Document type:** academic/scholarly publication.
—BLDSC (3925.682100); Faxon; UnCover.
Supersedes: Historians Film Committee Newsletter.
Description: Articles and reviews which analyze moving image documents and their use in society.

791.43 SW ISSN 0345-3316
FILM OCH T V. 1973. q. SEK 250. P.O. Box 2068, S-103 12 Stockholm, Sweden. TEL 46-8-402-08-31. FAX 46-8-402-08-27. Ed. Mari Edman. circ. 2,000. **Document type:** consumer publication.

778.534 384.55 US ISSN 1041-1933
FILM & VIDEO; the production magazine. 1984. m. free to qualified personnel. Phillips Business Information, Inc., 1201 Seven Locks Rd., Potomac, MD 20854. TEL 301-340-1520. FAX 301-424-4297. E-mail: pbi@phillips.com. adv.; illus. (back issues avail.) **Document type:** trade publication.
Incorporates (1981-1995): In Motion (ISSN 0889-6208); Formerly: Film and Video Production.
Description: Covers all areas of the production and post-production process within the teleproduction, commercial, music video and motion picture industries.

791.43 658 AT
FILM AUSTRALIA BUSINESS & MANAGEMENT CATALOGUE. 1989. biennial. free. Film Australia Pty. Ltd., Eton Rd., Lindfield, N.S.W. 2070, Australia. TEL 413-8777. FAX 416-5672. TELEX 22734. circ. 30,000. **Document type:** catalog.

572 700 028.5 370 AT
FILM AUSTRALIA EDUCATION CATALOGUE. 1970. biennial. free. Film Australia Pty. Ltd., Eton Rd., Lindfield, N.S.W. 2070, Australia. TEL 413 8777. FAX 416-5672. TELEX 22734. circ. 20,000. (back issues avail.) **Document type:** catalog.
Formerly: Film Australia Catalogue.

791.43 614.42 AT
FILM AUSTRALIA HEALTH & WELFARE CATALOGUE. 1990. biennial. free. Film Australia Pty. Ltd., Eton Rd., Lindfield, N.S.W. 2070, Australia. TEL 413-8777. FAX 416-5672. TELEX 22734. circ. 15,000. **Document type:** catalog.

791.43 US
FILM BILL. 1970. m. (George Fenmore, Inc.) Film Bill, Inc., 250 W. 54 St., New York, NY 10019. TEL 212-977-4140. FAX 212-977-4404. Ed. George Fenmore. adv. contact: Toddy Gelfand. bk.rev.; circ. 500,000. (controlled). **Document type:** consumer publication.

778.534 384.55 CN ISSN 0831-5175
FILM CANADA YEARBOOK. 1986. a. Can.$25. Cine-Communications, P.O. Box 152, Sta. R, Toronto, ON M4G 3Z3, Canada. TEL 416-696-2382. FAX 416-696-6496. Ed. Patricia Thompson. adv.: B&W page Can.$825; trim 7 x 9 1/2; adv. contact: Deborah Tiffin. **Document type:** directory.
Description: Directories of companies and people in the film and television business in Canada. Information on film and video production companies, including post-production, labs, editing, casting and support services; distributors; exhibitors; TV and pay TV; government agencies; unions; guilds and associations.

778.5 US
FILM CLIPS; a publication for film & video professionals. 1979. bi-m. $25. San Jose Convention and Visitors Bureau, Film and Video Commission, 333 W. San Carlos St., Ste. 1000, San Jose, CA 95110-2720. TEL 408-295-9600. FAX 408-295-3937. Ed. Vicki Ellis; Pub. Joe O'Kane. adv.: B&W page $250; 7 1/2 x 10; adv. contact: Vicki Ellis. illus.; circ. 3,975 (controlled). **Document type:** newsletter.
Description: Covers events of interest to film and video professionals; contains a directory of firms, services, and agencies working in the industry.

791.43 US ISSN 0015-119X
PN1993
FILM COMMENT. 1962. bi-m. $24.95 (effective Jan. 1993). Film Society of Lincoln Center, 70 Lincoln Center Plaza, New York, NY 10023-6595. TEL 212-875-5610. FAX 212-875-5636. Ed. Richard T. Jameson; Pub. Joanne Koch. adv. contact: Tony Impavidio. bk.rev.; film rev.; illus.; index. circ. 40,000. (also avail. in microfilm from UMI; back issues avail.; reprint service avail. from UMI,ISI) **Indexed:** Acad.Ind., Arts & Hum.Cit.Ind., Bk.Rev.Ind. (1977-), Chic.Per.Ind., Child.Bk.Rev.Ind. (1977-), Curr.Cont., Film Lit.Ind. (1973-), Hum.Ind., Int.Ind.Film Per., Intl.Ind.TV, Mag.Ind., Media Rev.Dig., PMR, R.G. **Document type:** consumer publication.
●Also available online. Vendor(s): University Microfilms International.
Also available on CD-ROM. Producer(s): University Microfilms International.
—BLDSC (3925.690000); Faxon; Genuine Article; SWETS; UMI; UnCover.
Description: Offers film criticism and history and elegant, personal writing about film as an art, as a medium, and as an element of modern life.

M

MOTION PICTURES

FILM COMPOSERS GUIDE. see BUSINESS AND ECONOMICS — Trade And Industrial Directories

778.5   US   ISSN 0163-5069
PN1993
FILM CRITICISM. 1976. 3/yr. $15 to individuals (foreign $18); institutions $18 (foreign $21). Allegheny College, Meadville, PA 16335. TEL 814-332-4343. Ed. I. Lloyd Michaels. adv.; bk.rev.; film rev. circ. 500. **Indexed:** Amer.Bibl.Slavic & E.Eur.Stud., Arts & Hum.Cit.Ind., Bk.Rev.Ind. (1983-), Child.Bk.Rev.Ind. (1983-), Curr.Cont., Film Lit.Ind. (1978-), Hum.Ind., Int.Ind.Film Per., Intl.Ind.TV, LCR, M.L.A., Media Rev.Dig.
—BLDSC (3925.705000); Faxon; Genuine Article; UnCover.

791.43   US   ISSN 0015-1211
PN1993
FILM CULTURE. 1955. irreg. $20 (foreign $26) for 4 issues. Film Culture Non-Profit, Inc., 32 Second Ave., New York, NY 10003. TEL 212-505-5181. FAX 212-477-2714. Ed. Jonas Mekas. adv.; bk.rev.; cum.index. circ. 3,000. (also avail. in microfilm from UMI; back issues avail.; reprint service avail. from UMI) **Indexed:** Acad.Ind., Art Ind., Arts & Hum.Cit.Ind., Curr.Cont., Film Lit.Ind. (1973-), Int.Ind.Film Per., Intl.Ind.TV, Media Rev.Dig. **Document type:** academic/scholarly publication.
—Faxon; UMI; UnCover.

791.43   NE
▼**FILM CULTURE IN TRANSITION.** (Text in English) 1994. irreg. price varies. Amsterdam University Press, Prinsengracht 747-751, 1017 JX Amsterdam, Netherlands. TEL 31-20-4200050. FAX 31-20-4203214. Ed. Thomas Elsaesser. **Document type:** monographic series.
Description: Publishes studies of film and television culture from a European perspective.

791.43 700   UK   ISSN 0141-3538
FILM DIRECTIONS. 1977. q. £4. Queen's Film Theatre, 25 College Gdns., Belfast BT9 6BS, N. Ireland. FAX 0232-663733. Ed. Michael Open. adv.; bk.rev.; illus. circ. 2,500. **Indexed:** Film Lit.Ind. (1985-), Intl.Ind.TV.

FILM DIRECTORS: A COMPLETE GUIDE. see BUSINESS AND ECONOMICS — Trade And Industrial Directories

791   UK   ISSN 0305-1706
FILM DOPE. 1972. q. £24.20. 74 Julian Rd., Nottingham NG2 4AN, England. Eds. Derek Owen, Bob Baker. adv.; bk.rev. circ. 2,000. (back issues avail.) **Indexed:** Film Lit.Ind. (1974-), Int.Ind.Film Per. **Document type:** bibliography, directory.

791.43   GW   ISSN 0015-1149
FILM-ECHO - FILMWOCHE. 1947. s-w. DM.515. Verlag Horst Axtmann GmbH und Co., Marktplatz 13, 65183 Wiesbaden, Germany. TEL 0611-36098-0. FAX 0611-372878. Ed. Bernd Jetschin. adv.; bk.rev.; film rev.; illus.; stat. circ. 4,000. **Document type:** consumer publication.
Incorporating: Filmblaetter.

791.43   GW   ISSN 0071-4879
FILM-ECHO FILMWOCHE. VERLEIH-KATALOG. 1949. a. DM.125. Verlag Horst Axtmann GmbH und Co., Marktplatz 13, 65183 Wiesbaden, Germany. TEL 0611-36098-0. FAX 0611-372878. Ed. Horst Axtmann. adv.; bk.rev. circ. 1,500. **Document type:** catalog.

791.4   BE   ISSN 0015-1084
FILM & TELEVISIE - VIDEO. (Text in Dutch) 1956. 10/yr. 1200 BEF (foreign 1600 BEF) (effective 1995). Katolieke Filmliga, Haachtsesteenweg 35, 1030 Brussels, Belgium. TEL 32-2-2170096. FAX 32-2-2170233. Ed. Ronnie Pede. adv.: B&W page 15000 BEF, color page 25000 BEF; 297 x 210. bk.rev.; film rev.; index. circ. 10,000. **Indexed:** Film Lit.Ind. (1975-), Int.Ind.Film Per., Intl.Ind.TV.
Formerly: Film en Televisie (ISSN 0015-122X)
Description: Covers film, television and video productions and festivals, with interviews and reviews.

791.43   US
FILM ENCYCLOPEDIA. irreg., 2nd ed., 1994. $25. Harper Collins Publishers, 10 E. 53rd St., New York, NY 10022. TEL 212-207-7500. FAX 212-207-7936. Ed. Ephraim Katz.

791.43 384.55   XO
FILM FAN SAT. 1991. m. 15.90 Sk. per issue. Euroskop, Inc., Pribinova 25, 819 37 Bratislava, Slovakia. TEL 42-7-2104181. FAX 42-7-2104152. Ed. Peter Nagel. adv. contact: J. Sokolova. film rev.; video rev. circ. 35,000. **Document type:** consumer publication.
Formerly (until 1994): Film Fan (ISSN 0862-8130)
Description: Designed mainly for young age groups, covers film and video reviews, includes satellite programs.

791.43   FR   ISSN 0397-8702
FILM FRANCAIS.* 1945. w. 1900 F. S A R L Cinema de France, 103 bd. Saint-Michel, 75005 Paris, France. TEL 43-29-40-90. FAX 43-29-14-05. TELEX 204 012. Ed. Pierre Rival. adv.; bk.rev.; film rev.; illus. circ. 15,250.
Formerly: Film Francais-Cinematographie Francais (ISSN 0015-1262)

778.5 900   UK   ISSN 0892-2160
PN1993   CODEN: FIHIE6
FILM HISTORY; an international journal. 1987. q. £30 to individuals; institutions £70. John Libbey & Company Ltd., 13 Smiths Yard, Summerley St., London SW18 4HR, England. TEL 0181-847-2777. FAX 0181-947-2664. E-mail: libbey@earlsfield.win-uk.net. Ed. Richard Koszarski. **Indexed:** Int.Ind.Film Per. **Document type:** academic/scholarly publication.
—BLDSC (3925.745000); UMI; UnCover. CCC.
Description: Covers all aspects of the historical development of international cinema, and the social, technological, and economic context against which this has occurred.
Refereed Serial

791.43   IR   ISSN 1021-6510
FILM INTERNATIONAL; a cross-cultural review. (Text in English) 1993. q. DM.32 to individuals; institutions DM.60 (includes supplements). P.O. Box 11635-5875, Tehran 11389, Iran. TEL 98-21-677292. FAX 98-21-6459971. Ed. Behzad Rahimian; Pub. Massoud Mehrabi. adv.; bk.rev.; film rev.; illus.
Description: Provides an international perspective on current trends in the film industry, including extended interviews with film producers and directors, reports from international film festivals, discussions of Iranian cinema, and profiles of other national and regional film industries.

791.43   US   ISSN 0199-7300
FILM JOURNAL. 1934. m. $40. Pubsun Corp., 244 W. 49th St., Ste. 200, New York, NY 10019. TEL 212-246-6460. FAX 212-265-6428. adv.; film rev.; illus.; index. circ. 9,200. **Indexed:** Film Lit.Ind. (1974-).
Formerly: Independent Film Journal (ISSN 0019-3712)

791.43   IR   ISSN 1022-2138
FILM-KHANE-YE MELLI-E IRAN. NAME-YE/NATIONAL FILM ARCHIVE OF IRAN. QUARTERLY. Variant English title: Iranian National Film Quarterly. (Text in Farsi; summaries in English) 1989. q. $19. National Film Archive of Iran - Film-khane-ye Melli-e Iran, P.O. Box 5158, Teheran 11365, Iran. TEL 021-311242. TELEX 215642 RECU IR. Eds. Mohammad Hassan Khoshnevis, Gholam Heydari. illus.

778.5   DK   ISSN 0108-772X
FILM MAGASINET. 1982. bi-m. DKK 5 per no. Ulshoejvej 16, 4400 Kalundborg, Denmark. illus.

790 659.152   II
FILM MIRROR. (Text in English) 1962. m. Rs.10. Film Mirror, 26-F Connaught Place, New Delhi 110 001, India. TEL 011-3312329. FAX 011-4621636. Ed. Harbhajan Singh. film rev. circ. 40,000.

778.5 780   US
FILM MUSIC BUYER'S GUIDE. 1977. a. $9.95. R T S, Box 93897, Las Vegas, NV 89193-3897. TEL 702-896-1300.
Description: Soundtrack titles, composer, record numbers, years of release and current market value of recordings.

791.43   NO   ISSN 0015-1351
FILM OG KINO; Norsk filmblad. 1930. 9/yr. NOK 250 in Scandinavia; elsewhere NOK 400. Kommunale Kinematografers Landsforbund, Kongensgaten 23, N-0153 Oslo, Norway. TEL 22-41-1251. FAX 47-22-42-62-95. Ed. Kalle Loechen. adv.; bk.rev.; film rev.; charts; illus.; index. circ. 3,800. **Indexed:** Film Lit.Ind. (1980-), Int.Ind.Film Per. (until 1995), Intl.Ind.TV.
—CCC.
Formerly: Norsk Filmblad.

791.43   US
FILM PREVIEW REPORTS.* 1970. m. Federation of Motion Picture Councils, 142 N. Tucker, Memphis, TN 38104. TEL 901-725-4987. adv.; film rev.; illus.

FILM PRODUCERS, STUDIOS, AGENTS AND CASTING DIRECTORS GUIDE. see BUSINESS AND ECONOMICS — Trade And Industrial Directories

791.43   US   ISSN 0015-1386
PN1993
FILM QUARTERLY. 1945. q. $23 to individuals (foreign $29); institutions $49 (foreign $55) (effective 1996). University of California Press, Journals Division, Berkeley, CA 94720. TEL 510-643-7154. FAX 510-642-9917. Ed. Ann Martin. adv.; bk.rev.; film rev.; illus.; index. circ. 7,600. (also avail. in microform from UMI; back issues avail.; reprint service avail. from UMI) **Indexed:** Acad.Ind., Access (1978-1990), Amer.Bibl.Slavic & E.Eur.Stud., Art Ind., Arts & Hum.Cit.Ind., Bk.Rev.Ind. (1968-), Chic.Per.Ind., Child.Bk.Rev.Ind. (1968-), Curr.Cont., Film Lit.Ind. (1973-), Hum.Ind., Int.Ind.Film Per., Intl.Ind.TV, Mag.Ind., Media Rev.Dig., Mid.East: Abstr.& Ind., R.G. **Document type:** academic/scholarly publication.
—BLDSC (3925.840000); Faxon; Genuine Article; SWETS; UMI; UnCover. CCC.
Formerly: Quarterly of Film, Radio and Television.
Description: Contains articles and interviews focusing on experimental, documentary, and special-interest films.
Refereed Serial

791.43   US   ISSN 0361-722X
PN1993
FILM READER. 1975. a. $8.50 to individuals; libraries $10. Dept. of Radio - TV - Film, Northwestern University, Evanston, IL 60208. TEL 708-491-7315. Ed. James Schwoch. adv.; bk.rev. circ. 1,000. (also avail. in microfilm from UMI; reprint service avail.) **Indexed:** Arts & Hum.Cit.Ind., Curr.Cont., Film Lit.Ind., Intl.Ind.TV, Media Rev.Dig.

791.43   II
FILM REKHA. (Text in Hindi) 1968. m. Rs.72. Surender Kumar Gupta, Rangbhumi Bhawan, 5-A-15, Ansari Rd., Daryaganj, New Delhi 110002, India. TEL 2279149. adv.; B&W page Rs.2000, color page Rs.4000; trim 240 x 180.

791.43   UK   ISSN 0957-1809
PN1993
FILM REVIEW. (Supplement avail.: Film Review Special) m. £27 (U.S. & Canada $65; rest of world £30) (includes Film Review Special). Visual Imagination Ltd., 9 Blades Ct., Deodar Rd., London SW15 2NU, England. TEL 0181-875-1520. FAX 0181-875-1588. (Subscr. to: P.O. Box 371, London SW14 8JL, England; Canada and US subscr. to: Box 156, Manorville, NY 11949) adv. (back issues avail.) **Document type:** consumer publication.
—SWETS; UnCover.

778   US   ISSN 0737-9080
PN1995
FILM REVIEW ANNUAL. 1981. a. $125. Jerome S. Ozer, Ed. & Pub., 340 Tenafly Rd., Englewood, NJ 07631-1747. TEL 201-567-7040. index. circ. 800. (back issues avail.) **Document type:** academic/scholarly publication.
Description: Compiles film reviews from selected newspapers, magazines, and scholarly journals.

791.43   UK   ISSN 0967-8816
PN1993
FILM REVIEW SPECIAL. q. £27 (U.S. & Canada $65; rest of world £30) (includes Film Review). Visual Imagination Ltd., 9 Blades Ct., Deodar Rd., London SW15 2NU, England. TEL 0181-875-1520. FAX 0181-875-1588. (Subscr. to: P.O. Box 371, London SW14 8JL, England; US and Canada subscr. to: Box 156, Manorville, NY 11949) **Document type:** consumer publication.

MOTION PICTURES 4793

790.2 780 HU ISSN 0015-1416
FILM, SZINHAZ, MUZSIKA. w. $54. Lapkiado Vallalat, Lenin korut 9-11, 1073 Budapest 7, Hungary. TEL 222-408. (Subscr. to: Kultura, Box 149, H-1389 Budapest, Hungary) Ed. Zoltan Iszlai. illus. circ. 30,000.

778.53 US
FILM - TAPE WORLD. 1988. m. $30. Media Publications, 461 2nd St., No 104, San Francisco, CA 94107-1416. TEL 415-543-6100. Ed. Steven Goldstein. adv. contact: Johanna Ward. circ. 5,000. (tabloid format; back issues avail.) **Document type:** trade publication.
Description: Trade publication for the film and video commmunity of Northern California.

791.43 US ISSN 0896-6389
FILM THREAT. 1985; N.S. 6/yr. $11.85 (foreign $21.85). Film Threat, Inc., 9171 Wilshire Blvd., Ste. 300, Beverly Hills, CA 90210. TEL 310-858-7155. FAX 310-274-7985. Ed. Christian Gore. adv.: B&W page $1520, color page $2375; adv. contact: Justin McCormack. bk.rev. circ. 125,000. **Indexed:** Film Lit.Ind. (1988-). **Document type:** consumer publication.
Description: Unique pop culture and movie magazine. Features celebrities and coverage from big studio releases to independent films.

FILM THREAT VIDEO GUIDE. see *COMMUNICATIONS — Video*

791.43 384.55
778.534 GW ISSN 0323-3227
FILM UND FERNSEHEN; Zeitschrift fuer Theorie und Praxis des Film- und Fernsehschaffens. 1973. bi-m. DM.36 (foreign DM.51). Filmverband Brandenburg e.V., Am Bassin 4, 14467 Potsdam, Germany. TEL 0331-21608. FAX 0331-21609. (Dist. by: Inter Abo Betreuungs GmbH, Postfach 53, 12435 Berlin, Germany) Ed.Bd. bk.rev.; index. circ. 2,000. (back issues avail.) **Indexed:** Film Lit.Ind. (1975-), Int.Ind.Film Per. **Document type:** academic/scholarly publication.
Description: Covers news, reviews and discussions of new movies playing in the theatre and on television throughout the world.

791.43 GW ISSN 0173-4970
FILM UND FERNSEHEN IN FORSCHUNG UND LEHRE. 1978. a. DM.25. Hochschule fuer Bildende Kunste Braunschweig, Postfach 2538, 38015 Braunschweig, Germany. TEL 0531-3919123. (Co-sponsor: Institut fuer Medienwissenschaft und Film Braunschweig) Ed. Helmut Korte. index. circ. 1,000. **Document type:** academic/scholarly publication.
Description: Research results concerning academic instruction and writing about film and television in German-speaking countries.

791.43 GW
FILM UND KRITIK. 1992. irreg. DM.20 per no. Stroemfeld Verlag, Postfach 180147, 60082 Frankfurt a.M., Germany. TEL 069-955226-0. FAX 069-95522624. Ed.Bd. **Document type:** academic/scholarly publication.

791.43 GW ISSN 0343-5571
FILM UND TV KAMERAMANN. 1950. m. DM.84.20. l. Weber Verlag, Ohrmstr. 15, 80802 Munich, Germany. TEL 089-38308680. FAX 089-38308683. Ed. Evelyn Mueller. adv.: B&W page DM.1530, color page DM.3000; trim 199 x 131; adv. contact: Heike Schacknies. bk.rev.; charts; illus.; index. circ. 9,443. **Indexed:** Film Lit.Ind. (1979-). **Document type:** trade publication.
Formerly: Deutsche Kameramann (ISSN 0012-0340)

778 US
FILM WORLD. 1968. m. $4.95. Knight Publishing Corp., 8060 Melrose Ave., Los Angeles, CA 90046. TEL 213-653-8060. FAX 213-655-9452. Ed. Timothy Connelly. adv.; bk.rev.; film rev.; play rev. circ. 150,000. (back issues avail.)

FILM WORLD DIRECTORY OF ADULT FILM & VIDEO. see *BUSINESS AND ECONOMICS — Trade And Industrial Directories*

778 US ISSN 0743-6335
FILM WORLD GUIDE. Key Title: Adam Film World Guide. Adam Film World Directory of Adult Films. bi-m. $4.95 per no. Knight Publishing Corp., 8060 Melrose Ave., Los Angeles, CA 90046. TEL 213-653-8060. FAX 213-655-9452.

FILM WRITERS GUIDE. see *BUSINESS AND ECONOMICS — Trade And Industrial Directories*

791.43 SW ISSN 0071-4925
FILMAARSBOKEN/FILM YEAR BOOK (YEAR). 1968. a. $25. (Swedish Film Institute) Proprius Foerlag AB, P.O. Box 10251, S-100 55 Stockholm, Sweden. TEL 46-8-660-96-02. FAX 46-8-660-97-49. Ed. Bertil Wredlund. adv.; illus. circ. 1,500. **Document type:** directory.
Description: Reports on the film repertoire in Sweden. Gives full data on producers, directors, scriptwriters, cinematographers, actors and Swedish release dates and a synopsis of each film. Includes TV films.

011.37 DK ISSN 0107-0940
FILMATISEREDE BOEGER. (Supplements avail.) 1974. a. DKK 668 (incl. supplements) (effective 1996). Dansk BiblioteksCenter as, Tempovej 7-11, DK-2750 Ballerup, Denmark. TEL 45-44-97-40-00. FAX 45-44-68-24-42.

778.53 SZ ISSN 0257-7852
FILMBULLETIN. 1958. bi-m. 54 SFr. Postfach 137, Hard 4, CH-8408 Winterthur, Switzerland. TEL 053-2226444. FAX 052-2220051. Ed. Walter Vian. adv.: B&W page 850 SFr.; adv. contact: Leo Rinderer. circ. 3,000. **Indexed:** Film Lit.Ind. (1985-). **Document type:** bulletin.

791.43 IT ISSN 0015-1513
FILMCRITICA; rivista mensile di studi sul cinema. (Includes section: Lo Spettatore Critico) 1950. m. L.65000 (foreign L.90000). Editori del Grifo, Via Montecavallo 16, 53045 Montepulciano (SI), Italy. TEL 0578-717090. FAX 0578-717091. Ed. Edorado Bruno. adv.; bk.rev.; film rev.; illus.; index. (also avail. in microform from UMI; reprint service avail. from UMI) **Indexed:** Film Lit.Ind. (1973-), Int.Ind.Film Per., Intl.Ind.TV.
—UMI.

778.53 IT
FILMCRONACHE; rivista bimestrale di cultura cinematografica. 1987. bi-m. Associazione Nazionale Circoli Cinematografici Italiani, Via Nomentana 251, 00161 Rome, Italy. TEL 06-86-67-29. Ed. Enzo Nata.

791.43 II ISSN 0015-1548
FILMFARE. (Editions in English, Hindi) 1952. fortn. $12 for English ed.; Hindi ed. $10. Bennett, Coleman & Co. Ltd. (Bombay), Times of India Bldg., Dr. Dadabhai Naoroji Rd., Bombay 400 001, India. TEL 22-4150271. TELEX 1173504. (U.S. subscr. to: M-s. Kalpana, 42-75 Main St., Flushing NY 11355) Ed. Rauf Ahmed. adv.; bk.rev.; film rev.; illus. circ. 106,500.

778.53 GW ISSN 0176-1110
FILMFAUST; internationale Filmzeitschrift. 1976. 6/yr. DM.116 (foreign DM.130). Filmfaust Verlag, Liebigstr. 44, 60323 Frankfurt a.M., Germany. TEL 069-727517. Eds. Bion Steinborn, Christine von Eichel-Streiber. adv.; bk.rev. circ. 12,500. **Indexed:** Film Lit.Ind. (1987-), Int.Ind.Film Per. **Document type:** consumer publication.

778.53 US ISSN 0895-0393
FILMFAX;* the magazine of unusual film and television. bi-m. 1320 Dakton St., Evanston, IL 60202-2719. **Indexed:** Film Lit.Ind. (1987-).

778.53 SW ISSN 0345-3057
FILMHAEFTET; kritisk tidskrift foer analys av roerliga bilder. 1973. q. SEK 150 (effective 1995). P.O. Box 10156, S-100 55 Stockholm, Sweden. TEL 46-8-16-12-77. FAX 46-8-661-03-04. E-mail: bolin@jmk.su.se. Ed. Goeran Bolin. adv. contact: Margareta Roennberg. bk.rev. circ. 700. **Indexed:** Film Lit.Ind. (1987-). **Document type:** academic/scholarly publication.

791.43 II
FILMI DUNIYA. (Text in Hindi) 1958. m. Rs.120. 16 Darya Canj, New Delhi 110 002, India. TEL 011-3278087. FAX 011-3279341. Ed. Narendra Kumar; Pub. Narendra Kumar. adv.: B&W page Rs.15000, color page Rs.30000; 360 x 240. circ. 109,064.

791.43 II
FILMI KALIYAN. (Text in English) 1969. m. 4675-B/21, Ansari Rd., Darya Ganj, New Delhi 110 002, India. TEL 3272080. Ed. V.S. Dewan. adv.: B&W page Rs.8000, color page Rs.24000; trim 240 x 180. circ. 108,104.

791.43 NO ISSN 0015-1556
FILMJOURNALEN; pop topp. 1940. m. NOK 60. Kaare Messel Birkelund, Ed. & Pub., Parkveien 5, Oslo 3, Norway. film rev.; play rev. circ. 16,300.
—CCC.

791.43 SW ISSN 0283-5983
FILMJOURNALEN. 1985. q. Svensk Filmindustri, S-117 88 Stockholm, Sweden.

791.43 SW ISSN 1100-7362
FILMKONST. Variant title: Tidskriften Filmkonst. 1989. q. SEK 230 (effective 1995). Goeteborg Film Festival - Filmkonst, P.O. Box 7079, S-402 32 Goeteborg, Sweden. TEL 46-31-410546. FAX 46-31-410063. Ed. Gunnar Bergdahl.

791.43 SW ISSN 0347-5425
FILMKRETS; tidskriften foer film- och videointresserade. Variant title: Tidskriften Filmkrets. 1976. 5/yr. SEK 90 (effective 1991). Foereningen Filmkrets, Karlbergsv. 75, S-113 35 Stockholm, Sweden.

791.43 GW ISSN 0015-1572
PN1995
FILMKRITIK. 1957. m. DM.88. Filmkritiker Kooperative, Kreittmayrstr. 3, 80335 Munich, Germany. adv.; bk.rev.; film rev.; illus.; index. circ. 5,000. **Indexed:** Arts & Hum.Cit.Ind., Curr.Cont., Film Lit.Ind, Intl.Ind.TV.

791.43 HU ISSN 0015-1580
PN1993
FILMKULTURA. (Text in Hungarian; summaries in English) 1965. m. $42. Magyar Film Intezet - Hungarian Film Institute, Varosligeti fasor 38, Budakeszi u. 51-B, 1021 Budapest, Hungary. TEL 36-1-1767-106. Ed. Ivan Forgacs. adv.: B&W page $1000; adv. contact: Vera Suranyi. bk.rev.; film rev.; illus. circ. 5,000. (tabloid format; also avail. in microfilm from UMI; reprint service avail. from UMI) **Indexed:** Film Lit.Ind. (1973-), Int.Ind.Film Per., Intl.Ind.TV.
Description: Deals with classical and contemporary film art abroad and in Hungary.

791.43 AU ISSN 0015-1599
FILMKUNST; Zeitschrift fuer Filmkultur und Filmwissenschaft. 1949. q. S.370. Oesterreichische Gesellschaft fuer Filmwissenschaft, Kommunikations- und Medienforschung, Rauhensteingasse 5, A-1010 Vienna, Austria. TEL 01-5129936. FAX 01-5135330. adv.; bk.rev.; film rev.; illus. circ. 600. **Indexed:** Film Lit.Ind. (1975-), Int.Ind.Film Per. **Document type:** trade publication.
Description: Scientific studies and essays on motion pictures and television.

778.5 UK
FILMLOG; index of feature film production and casting in Britain. 1986. m. £37.50. P.O. Box 11, London SW15 6AY, England. TEL 081-789-0408. FAX 081-780-1977. (Subscr. to: P.O. Box 100, Broadstairs, Kent CT10 1UJ, England. TEL 0843-860885) Ed. Vaune Craig-Raymond. circ. 4,000. **Document type:** abstracting/indexing.
Description: Lists jobs in the motion picture industry.

MOTION PICTURES

778.53   US   ISSN 1063-8954
PN1993
FILMMAKER; the magazine of independent film. q. $14 to individuals; institutions $35. 104 W. 29th St., 12th Fl., New York, NY 10001-5310. TEL 800-345-6624. FAX 212-465-8525. (Subscr. to: 1625 Olympic Blvd., Santa Monica, CA 90404-3822) Eds. Scott Macaulay, Holldy Willis; Pub. Karol Martesko. adv.; bk.rev. **Indexed:** Film Lit.Ind. (1989-). **Document type:** trade publication, consumer publication.
   Formed by the 1992 merger of: Off-Hollywood Report (ISSN 1045-1706) & Montage.
   Description: Presents an insider's look at the business and creative aspects of independent film production.

792   US
FILMMAKER'S REVIEW. 1976. q. $15. Columbia Filmmakers, 313 Ferris Booth Hall, Columbia University, New York, NY 10027. Ed. Jim Berger. adv.; bk.rev.; illus. circ. 5,000.

FILMNET MAGAZINE. see COMMUNICATIONS — Television And Cable

778.53   AT   ISSN 1036-8701
FILMNEWS. 1975. m. Aus.$55. P.O. Box 341, Kings Cross, N.S.W. 2011, Australia. TEL 61-2-356-2631. FAX 61-2-356-2904. Ed. Paul Kalina. adv. contact: Sue Procter. circ. 10,500. **Indexed:** Film Lit.Ind. (1989-).
   Description: Publishes news, reviews and interviews about production, distribution, exhibition and broadcast of independent film and video in Australia.

791.43   XR   ISSN 0015-1645
PN1998
FILMOVY PREHLED; mesicnik pro film a video. 1939. m. 66 Kc. Narodni Filmovy Archiv, Narodni tr. 40, 111 21 Prague 1, Czech Republic. (Subscr. to: PNS ustred ni expedice a dovoz tisku Praha, Kafkova 19, 160 00 Praha 6, Czech Republic) Ed. Tomas Bartosek. circ. 5,000.

791.43   SW   ISSN 0015-1661
FILMRUTAN; tidskrift foer film och filmstudios. 1958. q. SEK 100($9) in Scandinavia; elsewhere SEK 120 (typically set in Jan.). Sveriges Foerenade Filmstudios, P.O. Box 82, S-851 02 Sundwall, Sweden. FAX 0-60-129892. Ed. Roger Tereus. adv.; bk.rev.; film rev.; illus. circ. 1,500. **Indexed:** Arts & Hum.Cit.Ind., Curr.Cont., Film Lit.Ind., Int.Ind.Film Per., Intl.Ind.TV.

778.5   FR
FILMS ET DOCUMENTS;* revue des techniques audio-visuelles. 5/yr. 60 F. Federation Francaise du Cinema Educatif, 71 rue du l'Ouest, 75014 Paris, France. TEL 43-35-27-81. adv. circ. 1,000.

791.43   US   ISSN 0015-1688
PN1993
FILMS IN REVIEW. 1950. bi-m. $18. National Board of Review of Motion Pictures, Inc., Box 589, New York, NY 10021. TEL 212-628-1594. Ed. Robin Little. adv.; bk.rev.; film rev.; illus. circ. 58,600. (also avail. in microform from UMI; reprint service avail. from UMI) **Indexed:** Art Ind., Bk.Rev.Ind. (1981-), Child.Bk.Rev.Ind. (1981-), Film Lit.Ind. (1973-), Int.Ind.Film Per., Intl.Ind.TV, Media Rev.Dig., Mid.East: Abstr.& Ind., Ref.Sour.
   —BLDSC (3926.720000); Faxon; UMI; UnCover.

791.4352   DK   ISSN 0107-1033
PN1997.8
FILMSAESONEN: DANSK FILMFORTEGNELSE. 1980. a. DKK 248 (effective 1996). (Danske Filmmuseum) Dansk BiblioteksCenter as, Tempovej 7-11, DK-2750 Ballerup, Denmark. TEL 45-44-97-40-00. FAX 45-44-68-24-42. Ed. Anne Jespersen. illus. circ. 1,200.

791.43   AU   ISSN 0015-1696
FILMSCHAU.* 1951. w. S.130. Katholische Filmkommission fuer Oesterreich, Singerstr. 7, Vienna 1, Austria. Ed. Richard Emele. adv.; film rev.; illus.; stat. circ. 5,000.

791.43   SZ
FILMSTELLEN V S E T H - V S U. DOKUMENTATION. 4/yr. Filmstellen V S E T H - V S U, Leonhardstr. 15, CH-8092 Zurich, Switzerland. TEL 01-2564294. Ed.Bd. **Document type:** bulletin.

778.5   IT
FILMSTUDIA. 1974. m. free. Via Orti d'Alibert, 1c, 00165 Rome, Italy. film rev.; illus. circ. 7,000.

791.43   SW   ISSN 0348-5706
FILMTIDNINGEN. 1977. bi-m. Interlecta Publishing, P.O. Box 45045, S-10 30 Stockholm, Sweden.
   Formerly (until 1978): Ciceronen.

791.43   DK
FILMVIDENSKABELIG AARBOG. 1973. a. price varies. Koebenhavns Universitet, Institut for Film- & Mediavidenskab, Njalsgade 78, DK-2300 Copenhagen S, Denmark. TEL 45-35-32-81-01. FAX 45-35-32-81-10. illus. circ. 500.
   Supersedes in part (in 1978): Koebenhavns Universitet. Institut for Filmvidenskab. Skrifter.

778.53   GW   ISSN 0940-2322
FILMWAERTS. 1986. q. DM.38 (foreign DM.46). Schueren Presseverlag GmbH, Deutschhausstr. 31, 35037 Marburg, Germany. TEL 06421-63084. FAX 06421-681190. adv.; bk.rev. **Indexed:** Film Lit.Ind. (1989-), Int.Ind.Film Per. **Document type:** consumer publication.

791.43   GW   ISSN 0173-542X
FISCHER FILM ALMANACH (YEAR). 1980. a. Fischer Taschenbuch Verlag GmbH, Geleitstr. 25, 60599 Frankfurt a.M., Germany. Ed.Bd. **Document type:** bulletin.

778.5   808.8   UK
FLICKERS 'N' FRAMES. no.14, 1991. 4/yr. £5.50($14) c/o John Peters, 299 Southway Dr., Southway, Plymouth, Devon PL6 6QN, England. (Subscr. in U.S. to: Anne Marsden, 1052 Calle del Cerro, No. 708, San Clemente, CA 92672. TEL 714-361-3791) bk.rev.; film rev.; video rev.
   Description: Publishes film criticism and original science fiction stories.

791.43   UK
FLICKS; magazine for moviegoers. 1985. m. £15 (Europe £24.50; elsewhere £47.50). Flicks Publications Ltd., Filmer Studios, 75 Filmer Rd., London SW6 7JF, England. TEL 071-384-1818. Ed. Quentin Falk. circ. 443,300. (back issues avail.)

791.43   FR   ISSN 1242-1898
FOCALES; revue d'histoire et de theorie du cinema et de la television. 1992. biennial. 200 F. Presses Universitaires de Nancy, 25 rue Baron Louis, 54001 Nancy Cedex, France. TEL 83-37-37-65. Ed. Odile Bachler. circ. 1,500. **Indexed:** Int.Ind.Film Per.
   Description: Studies film through different methods and approaches which correspond to historical and sociological interests of viewers, students and teachers of film.

FOTO. see PHOTOGRAPHY

FOTO - CINE. see PHOTOGRAPHY

791.43   YU   ISSN 0015-8704
FOTO-KINO REVIJA; jugoslovenski casopis za fotografijui amaterski film. (Text in Serbo-Croatian) 1948. m. 144 din.($5) Foto Savez Jugoslavije, Bulevar Revolucije 44, Belgrade, Yugoslavia. Ed. Milanka Saponja.

FOTOCAMARA CON POPULAR PHOTOGRAPHY. see PHOTOGRAPHY

778.53   SP
FOTOGRAMAS Y VIDEO. 1946. m. 4800 ptas. Comunicacion y Publicaciones, S.A., Gran Via de les Corts Catalanes 133 2o, 08014 Barcelona, Spain. TEL 34-3-223-03-53. FAX 34-3-421-61-50. Ed. Elisenda Nadal. circ. 200,000. **Document type:** consumer publication.
   Former titles: Fotogramas (ISSN 0212-2340); (until 1980): Nuevo Fotogramas (ISSN 0212-2332); (until 1968): Fotogramas (ISSN 0212-2324)

FOTOMUNDO. see PHOTOGRAPHY

FOTON; fotografia, cine y sonida (photography, amateur movie and sound). see PHOTOGRAPHY

780   384.55   363.49   US
FRAMELINE NEWS. 1985. q. $35 (effective Jan. 1994). Frameline, 346 Ninth St., San Francisco, CA 94103. TEL 415-703-8650. FAX 415-861-1404. Ed. Kathleen Wilkinson. circ. 3,000 (paid). (back issues avail.)
   Description: Devoted to lesbian and gay film and video.

791.43   301.412   GW   ISSN 0343-7736
FRAUEN UND FILM. 1974. s-a. DM.30. Stroemfeld Verlag, Postfach 180147, 60082 Frankfurt a.M., Germany. TEL 069-955226-0. FAX 069-95522624. Eds. Heide Schluepmann, Gertrud Koch. adv.; bk.rev. circ. 3,000. **Indexed:** Film Lit.Ind. (1986-), Int.Ind.Film Per., Intl.Ind.TV. **Document type:** academic/scholarly publication.

530   US   ISSN 0748-5247
FREEDONIA GAZETTE;* the magazine devoted to the Marx brothers. 1978. s-a. $11. Paul G. Wesolowski, Ed. & Pub., 335 Fieldstone Dr., New Hope, PA 18938-1012. TEL 215-862-9734. FAX 215-654-0408. (Also: Raymond D. White, 137 Easterly Rd., Leeds LS8 2RY, England) adv.; bk.rev.; play rev.; illus. circ. 400. (back issues avail.; reprint service avail. from ISI,UMI)

778.5   CN   ISSN 0704-9536
FREEZE FRAME. 1977. q. free. Edmonton Film Society, 6243 - 112 A St., Edmonton, Alta. T6H 3K4, Canada.
   Formerly: Film Edmonton.

791.43   028.5   US
FROM PAGE TO SCREEN. 1992. 5/yr. $35. Gale Research Inc., 835 Penobscot Bldg., Detroit, MI 48266. TEL 313-961-2242. FAX 313-961-6083. Eds. George Wilson, Joyce Moss.
   Description: Lists information and evaluations of over 1400 motion picture adaptations of books for children and youth.

791.43   US
FROSTBITE FALLS FAR-FLUNG FLIER!. 1986. q. $10. Box 39, Macedonia, OH 44056-0039. TEL 216-467-1074. Ed. Charles Ulrich; Pub. Gary David. bk.rev. circ. 250. **Document type:** newsletter.
   Description: Dedicated to Jay Ward cartoons, specifically "Rocky & Bullwinkle".

791.43   II
G. (Text in English) 1989. m. newsstand price: Rs.18. 62, Vaju Kotak Marg, Fort, Bombay 400 001, India. TEL 2611526. Ed. Bhawna Somaya; Pub. Madhuri Kotak. adv.: B&W page Rs.25000, color page Rs.50000; 263 x 270. circ. 45,268.

GADNEY'S GUIDES TO INTERNATIONAL CONTESTS, FESTIVALS & GRANTS IN FILM & VIDEO, PHOTOGRAPHY, TV-RADIO BROADCASTING, WRITING & JOURNALISM. see COMMUNICATIONS

GEORGE EASTMAN HOUSE - INTERNATIONAL MUSEUM OF PHOTOGRAPHY AND FILM. ANNUAL REPORT. see PHOTOGRAPHY

GEORGE EASTMAN HOUSE - INTERNATIONAL MUSEUM OF PHOTOGRAPHY AND FILM. NEWSLETTER. see PHOTOGRAPHY

778.5   HK
GOLDEN MOVIE NEWS/CHIA HO TIEN YING. m. HK.$60. (Ssu Hai Chu Pan Shih Yeh Yu Hsien Kung Ssu) Four Seas Publications Ltd., 1st Fl., 122B Argyle St., Kowloon, Hong Kong. illus.

778.53   PO
GRANDE ILUSAO; revista de cinema. irreg., no.15-16, 1994. price varies. Edicoes Afrontamento, Lda., Rua de Costa Cabral, 859, Apdo. 2009, 4201 Porto Codex, Portugal. TEL 351-2-529271. FAX 351-2-591777. (Subscr. to: Cineclube do Norte, Apdo. 4178, 4003 Porto Codex, Portugal) Ed. Regina Guimaraes.

778.53   IT   ISSN 0393-3857
PN1993
GRIFFITHIANA. 1978. s-a. $18 to individuals; institutions $40 (effective 1993-94). Cineteca del Friuli, Via Osoppo 26, 33014 Gemona, Italy. TEL 39-432-970542. FAX 39-432-980458. Ed. Livio Jacob. adv.; bk.rev. circ. 2,500. **Indexed:** Film Lit.Ind. (1990-), Int.Ind.Film Per.

MOTION PICTURES 4795

791.43 US
GRINDHOUSE. irreg. $1 per no. Box 1370, Murray Hill Sta., New York, NY 10156. Ed. J. Adler.

LE GRIOT; hebdomadaire des spectacles, du cinema et de la culture. see *GENERAL INTEREST PERIODICALS — Africa*

778.53 384.55 US
GUIA FAMILIAR. (Text in Spanish) 1979. w. Box 9090, Van Nuys, CA 91409. TEL 818-781-2605. FAX 818-781-2625. adv.: B&W page $2916.50; 7 3/8 x 9 7/8. circ. 229,644 (controlled).
 Description: Covers movies, Hollywood and TV.

791 355 US
GUIDE TO GOVERNMENT-LOAN FILMS. irreg., latest 1975. $9.95. Serina Press, 70 Kennedy St., Alexandria, VA 22305. TEL 703-548-4080.
 Formerly: Guide to Military-Loan Films (ISSN 0072-8586)

791.43 IR ISSN 1022-3134
GUZARISH-I FILM/REPORTAGE DU FILM. 1990. m. Vali Asar St., P.O. Box 15115-38, Teheran, Iran.

791.43 US ISSN 1050-8996
H B O'S GUIDE TO MOVIES ON VIDEOCASSETTE AND CABLE TV. (Home Box Office) 1990. a. Harper Collins Publishers, 10 E. 53rd St., New York, NY 10022. TEL 800-242-7737.

790 US ISSN 1055-7482
HALLIWELL'S FILM GUIDE (YEAR). 1977. a. $21 paperback; hardcover $50 (effective 1996). Harper Collins Publishers, 10 E. 53rd St., New York, NY 10022. TEL 800-242-7737.

HECHOS DE MASCARA. see *LABOR UNIONS*

HISTORICAL JOURNAL OF FILM, RADIO AND TELEVISION. see *HISTORY*

LE HIT PARADE. see *MUSIC*

778.53 US ISSN 1062-5518
PN1998.3.H58
HITCHCOCK ANNUAL. 1992. a. $7 (foreign $9). Hitchcock Annual Corporation, Box 540, Gambier, OH 43022. Ed. Christopher Brookhouse. adv.; bk.rev. circ. 800. **Document type:** academic/scholarly publication.
 —CCC.
 Description: Publishes essays on Hitchcock's life and films.
 Refereed Serial

HOLLYWOOD ACTING COACHES AND TEACHERS DIRECTORY. see *EDUCATION — Teaching Methods And Curriculum*

791.43 US
▼**HOLLYWOOD COLLECTIBLES.** 1994. m. $22; newsstand price: $3.95. H & S Media, Inc., 2900 N. Meade St., Ste. 4, Appleton, WI 54911. TEL 414-830-1701. Pub. Jim Mohr. adv.: B&W page $280. circ. 60,000 (paid). **Document type:** consumer publication.

917 US ISSN 0018-3660
PN1993
HOLLYWOOD REPORTER. 1930. d. $175. Hollywood Reporter, 5055 Wilshire Blvd., Los Angeles, CA 90036-4396. TEL 213-525-2000. FAX 213-525-2372. Ed. Robert J. Dowling. adv. contact: Lynne Segall. bk.rev.; film rev.; play rev. circ. 29,000. (also avail. in microfilm from BHP,KTO) **Document type:** newspaper.
 ●Also available online. Vendor(s): Lexis-Nexis.
 —CCC.

700 US
PN1998.A1
HOLLYWOOD REPORTER BLU-BOOK DIRECTORY. 1978. a. $55. Hollywood Reporter, 5055 Wilshire Blvd., Los Angeles, CA 90036-4396. TEL 213-525-2184. FAX 213-525-2390. Eds. Randall Tierney, Thea de Hart. bk.rev. circ. 5,000. **Document type:** directory.
 Former titles: Hollywood Reporter Studio Blu-Book Directory (ISSN 0278-419X)

778.5 US
HOLLYWOOD STUNTMEN'S HALL OF FAME NEWS. 1978. 6/yr. $35. Hollywood Stuntmen's Hall of Fame, Inc., 111 E. 100 North, Box 277, Moab, UT 84532-0277. TEL 801-259-6100. FAX 801-259-7780. Ed. John Gilbert Hagner. adv. contact: Doricca Brewer. bk.rev. circ. 375. **Document type:** newsletter.
 Formerly (until 1980): Falling for Stars News.

791.43 367 US
HOPPY TALK. 1991. q. $15. Friends of Hopalong Cassidy, 6310 Friendship Dr., New Concord, OH 43762-9708. TEL 614-826-4850. Ed. Laura Bates. adv.; bk.rev.; circ. 400 (paid). (back issues avail.) **Document type:** newsletter.
 Description: News about William Boyd's career in silent films and his role of Hopalong Cassidy. Stresses the collecting of toys endorsed by Boyd.

791.43 CC ISSN 1002-9974
HUANQIU YINMU HUAKAN/WORLD SCREEN. (Text in Chinese) 1985. m. $60. Zhongguo Dianying Chubanshe - China Film Press, 22 Beisanhuan Donglu, Beijing 100013, People's Republic of China. TEL 4219977. Ed. Cui Junyan.

778 380 US
I D A MEMBERSHIP AND SURVIVAL GUIDE. biennial. $30 to non-members. International Documentary Association, 1551 S. Robertson Blvd., Ste. 201, Los Angeles, CA 90035. TEL 310-284-8422. FAX 301-785-9334. E-mail: idf@netcom.com. Eds. Brenda Reiswerg, Kerry Neal. adv. **Document type:** directory.
 Description: Lists members of the IDA, an international listing of film and video makers, broadcasters, documentary funders, distributors, crew and talent.

IMAGE (ROCHESTER, 1952); journal of photography and motion pictures. see *PHOTOGRAPHY*

791.4 UK ISSN 0950-2114
TR845 CODEN: IMATEV
IMAGE TECHNOLOGY; technology of motion picture film, sound, television, audio, visual. 1936. 10/yr. £65 (overseas £80) (effective Jan. 1995). British Kinematograph Sound and Television Society, M6-14 Victoria House, Vernon Pl., London WC1B 4DJ, England. TEL 0171-242-8400. FAX 0171-405-3560. Ed. John Gainsborough. adv. contact: Alan Fuller. bk.rev.; bibl.; charts; illus.; index; circ. 2,500 (paid). (also avail. in microfilm from UMI; reprint service avail. from UMI) **Indexed:** Br.Tech.Ind., Chem.Abstr., Film Lit.Ind. (1991-), INSPEC. **Document type:** trade publication, directory.
 —BLDSC (4368.992950); Ei; SWETS; UMI.
 Former titles: B K S T S Journal (ISSN 0305-6996) & British Kinematography, Sound and Television (ISSN 0007-1358); British Kinematography.

791.43 SP
IMAGENES DE ACTUALIDAD. 1985. m. 4000 ptas. (Europe $71; elsewhere $102). Dirigido por... S.L., Consell de Cent 304, 2o 1o, 08007 Barcelona, Spain. TEL 34-3-4876202. FAX 34-3-4880896. Ed. Enrique Aragones. adv. contact: Jose Maria Latorre. bk.rev.; film rev.; music rev.; video rev.; circ. 45,000 (paid). **Document type:** consumer publication.
 Description: Publishes reports about recent and future films, interviews with American stars of the moment, articles, dossiers, reports on the main film festivals.

778.53 IT
IMMAGINE. q. Associazione Italiana per le Ricerche di Storia del Cinema, Via Yser 8, Rome, Italy. **Indexed:** Film Lit.Ind. (1986-).

791.43 FR
IMPACT. bi-m. Mad Movies, 4 rue Mansart, 75009 Paris, France. TEL 48-74-70-83. Ed. Denis Trehin. circ. 65,000.

791.43 UK ISSN 0964-6957
IMPACT (HUDDERSFIELD); the action movie magazine. 1992. m. £21.50 (foreign £45). M A I Publications, Revenue Chambers, St. Peter's St., Huddersfield HD1 1EL, England. TEL 01484-435011. FAX 01484-422177. (Dist. by: Comag, Tavistock Rd., W. Drayton, Middx. UB7 7QE, England. TEL 01895-444055) Ed. Bey Logan. adv.: B&W page $650, color page $1150; trim 275 x 187; adv. contact: Moira Spencer. bk.rev.; film rev.; video rev. **Document type:** consumer publication.

778.534 US
IN FOCUS (LOS ANGELES). 1984. s-a. $25 membership. Friends of Visual Communications, 263 S. Los Angeles St., Ste. 307, Los Angeles, CA 90012. TEL 213-680-4462. FAX 213-687-4848. Eds. Russell Leong, Joyce Nako; Pub. Linda Mabalot. film rev.; video rev.; illus. circ. 3,000. **Document type:** newsletter.
 Description: For supporters of Asian-American work in visual communications.

IN HER OWN IMAGE; films and videos empowering women for the future - a media network guide. see *WOMEN'S INTERESTS*

791.43 384.55 US ISSN 0731-5198
PN1993
INDEPENDENT FILM AND VIDEO MONTHLY. 1978. m. (10/yr.). $45 to individuals; libraries $75. (Association of Independent Video and Filmmakers) Foundation for Independent Video & Film, 625 Broadway, 9th Fl., New York, NY 10012. TEL 212-473-3400. FAX 212-677-8732. E-mail: aivf@tmn.com. Ed. Patricia Thomson; Pub. Ruby Lerner. adv. contact: Laura D. Davis. circ. 30,000. (back issues avail.) **Indexed:** Alt.Press Ind., Film Lit.Ind. (1983-). **Document type:** trade publication.
 Description: Covers the technical, legislative, marketing, and artistic facets of film and video production (especially independent production), with new technology articles, conference reports, filmmaker profiles and announcements of festivals.

015 II ISSN 0377-7359
PN1998
INDIAN FILMS. (Text in English) 1972. a. Rs.40. Motion Picture Enterprises, Alaka Talkies, Poona 411030, India. Ed. B.V. Dharap. adv.; illus.; index. circ. 1,200.

791 II
INDIAN MOTION PICTURE ALMANAC. (Text in English) a. Rs.40. Shot Publications, 3-B Madan St., Calcutta 700013, India. illus.
 Incorporating: Bengal Motion Picture Diary and General Information.

574 610 GW ISSN 0073-8417
INSTITUT FUER DEN WISSENSCHAFTLICHEN FILM. PUBLIKATIONEN ZU WISSENSCHAFTLICHEN FILMEN. SEKTION BIOLOGIE. (Text in English, French or German; summaries in English, French and German) 1963. irreg. Institut fuer den Wissenschaftlichen Film, Nonnenstieg 72, 37075 Goettingen, Germany. TEL 0551-50240. FAX 0551-5024400. **Document type:** academic/scholarly publication.

778.53 FR
INSTITUTE JEAN VIGO. ARCHIVES. 5/yr. 80 F. (foreign 100 F.). Institut Jean Vigo, 21 rue Mailly, 66000 Perpignan, France. TEL 68-66-30-33. **Indexed:** Film Lit.Ind. (1988-), Int.Ind.Film Per.

INTERNATIONAL ALLIANCE OF THEATRICAL STAGE EMPLOYEES AND MOVING PICTURE MACHINE OPERATORS OF THE UNITED STATES AND CANADA. OFFICIAL BULLETIN. see *LABOR UNIONS*

778.53 UK
INTERNATIONAL DIRECTORY OF FILM AND T V DOCUMENTATION COLLECTIONS. 1988. irreg., 4th edition, 1994. £50. International Federation of Film Archives (F I A F) - Federation Internationale des Archives du Film, 6 Nottingham St., London W1M 3RB, England. TEL 0171-224-1203. FAX 0171-224-0991. Ed. Frances Thorpe. bk.rev. **Document type:** directory.
 Description: Describes more than 100 major collections (in over forty countries) of published and unpublished material relating to television and film.

778.53 US
INTERNATIONAL DIRECTORY OF FILMS AND FILMMAKERS. (In 5 vols.: vol.1: Films, vol.2: Directors, vol.3: Actors and Actresses, vol.4: Writers and Production Artists, vol.5: Title Index) irreg., latest 2nd ed. $495 for 5 vol. set (vols.1-4: $115 each; vol.5: $65). Gale Research Inc., 835 Penobscot Bldg., Detroit, MI 48226. TEL 313-961-2242. FAX 313-961-6083. bibl.; illus. **Document type:** directory.

MOTION PICTURES

791 US ISSN 0074-462X
INTERNATIONAL DIRECTORY OF 16MM FILM COLLECTORS. 1971. irreg. (approx. biennial). $15. (16mm Filmland) Evan H. Foreman, Ed. & Pub., P.O. Drawer F, Mobile, AL 36601. TEL 205-432-8406. circ. 1,000. (tabloid format) **Document type:** directory.

791.43 572 US ISSN 0742-5333
PN1995.9.D6
INTERNATIONAL DOCUMENTARY. 1982. m. $70 membership. International Documentary Foundation, 1551 S. Robertson Blvd., Ste. 201, Los Angeles, CA 90035. TEL 310-284-8422. FAX 310-785-9334. Ed. Diana Rico. adv. contact: Kathryn Turnas. bk.rev. circ. 2,500. (back issues avail.) **Indexed:** Film.Lit.Ind. (1990-). **Document type:** trade publication.
Description: Devoted to non-faction film and video. Provides valuable information for documentary filmmakers and their audience.

791.43 UK ISSN 0074-6053
PN1993.3
INTERNATIONAL FILM GUIDE. 1964. a. £18.95. Variety, 34-35 Newman St., London W1P 3PD, England. TEL 0171-637-3663. FAX 0171-580-5559. (Dist. in U.S. by: Samuel French Trade, 7623 Sunset Blvd., Los Angeles, CA 90046) Ed. Peter Cowie. adv.; bk.rev. **Document type:** trade publication.
Description: Covers film production, festivals, archives and schools in more than 60 countries.

791.43 US ISSN 1043-8122
PN1993.3
INTERNATIONAL MOTION PICTURE ALMANAC; reference tool of the film industry. 1929. a. $91. Quigley Publishing Co., 159 W. 53 St., New York, NY 10019. TEL 212-247-3100. FAX 212-489-0871. Ed. Barry Monush; Pub. Martin Quigley. adv. contact: James Maser. (also avail. in microfilm from BHP) **Indexed:** Child.Auth.& Illus., Perf.Arts Biog.Master Ind. **Document type:** trade publication.

778.5 IT
INTIMITA DELLA FAMIGLIA. 1946. w. L.139000. Industrie Grafiche Cino del Duca S.p.A., Via Borgogna 5, 20122 Milan, Italy. TEL 02-781051. Eds. Giorgio Galluzzo, Sandra Rudoni. adv.; B&W page L.16330000, color page L.29400000. circ. 468,000.
Former titles: Intimita; Intimita della Famiglia (ISSN 1121-130X)

IRIS; a revista que e a sua imagem. see *PHOTOGRAPHY*

791.43 RU ISSN 0130-6405
ISKUSSTVO KINO. (Text in Russian; summary in English) 1931. m. $115 (effective 1996). Soyuz Rabotnikov Kinematografii - Russian Filmmakers' Union, Ul. Usievicha, 9, 125319 Moscow, Russia. FAX 7-095-1510272. (Dist. in North & South America by: Panorama of Russia, Box 44-1658, Somerville, MA 02144) Ed. Daniil Dondurei. bk.rev.; film rev.; illus.; index. circ. 12,000. **Indexed:** Film Lit.Ind. (1973-), Int.Ind.Film Per., Intl.Ind.TV.

ISLAND - EAR. see *MUSIC*

791 IS ISSN 0792-8610
ISRAEL FILM CENTRE INFORMATION BULLETIN. (Text in English) 1969. a. free. Israel Film Centre, P.O. Box 299, Jerusalem, Israel. TEL 972-2-220608. FAX 972-2-236303. Ed. Marilyn Mordechai. **Document type:** government publication, bulletin, catalog.
Supersedes: Israel Film Centre. Information Bulletin (ISSN 0334-2727); **Former titles:** Israel Films (ISSN 0075-1170); (until 1970): Films from Israel (ISSN 0376-5733)
Description: Provides information on local and international filmmaking in Israel. Serves as a catalogue of Israeli feature films.

778.5 IS ISSN 0333-9882
ISRAEL FILM INDUSTRY DIRECTORY. (Text in English) 1976. irreg., latest 1994. Israel Film Centre, P.O. Box 299, Jerusalem, Israel. TEL 972-2-220608. FAX 972-2-236303. adv. **Document type:** directory.
Formerly: Filmmakers and Film Production Services of Israel.

770 GW ISSN 0075-2509
JAHRBUCH DES KAMERAMANNS. 1959. a. DM.29.80. l. Weber Verlag, Ohmstr. 15, 80802 Munich, Germany. TEL 089-38308680. FAX 089-38308683. adv. contact: Heike Schacknies. **Document type:** bulletin.

778.534 GW ISSN 0931-1920
JAHRBUCH FUER VIDEOFILMER. 1985. a. DM.28. Fachverlag Schiele und Schoen GmbH, Markgrafenstr. 11, 10969 Berlin, Germany. TEL 030-253752-0. FAX 030-2517248. Ed. W. Strauss. index. circ. 5,000. **Document type:** consumer publication.
Formerly: Canon Jahrbuch fuer Videofilmer.

JANASUDHA DAILY. see *LITERARY AND POLITICAL REVIEWS*

JANASUDHA MONTHLY. see *LITERARY AND POLITICAL REVIEWS*

JANASUDHA WEEKLY. see *LITERARY AND POLITICAL REVIEWS*

778.534 II
JEE: FILM & T V FORTNIGHTLY. (Text in Gujarati) 1958. fortn. Rs.100($49) Madhuri Kotak, Ed. & Pub., 62 Vaju Kotak Marg, Bombay 400 001, India. TEL 91-22-2611526. FAX 22-2615895. TELEX 011-78298 JEE IN. (Subscr. to: 132 Andheri Industrial Estate, Veera Desai Road, Andheri, Bombay 400 058, India) adv.; B&W page Rs.15000, color page Rs.30000; 177 x 247. circ. 95,000. **Document type:** consumer publication.
Formerly: Jee: Film Fortnightly.

791.43 II
JEMINE CINEMA. (Text in Tamil) 1981. w. newsstand price: Rs.2.50. Palaniappan Ramasamy, Ed. & Pub., 9 Thirumurthy Nagar 1st St., Nungambakkam, Madras 600 034, India. TEL 8278596. adv.; B&W page Rs.3500; 235 x 165. circ. 25,502.

778.53 FR ISSN 0758-4202
JEUNE CINEMA.* 1964. bi-m. Federation Jean Vigo, 21 rue Mailly, 66000 Perpignan, France. **Indexed:** Film Lit.Ind. (1973-), Int.Ind.Film Per.

791.43 384.55 US ISSN 0742-4671
PN1993
JOURNAL OF FILM AND VIDEO. 1947. q. $15 (foreign $24). University Film and Video Association, c/o Georgia State University, Department of Communication, Atlanta, GA 30303. TEL 404-651-3200. FAX 404-651-1409. Ed. Frank P. Tomasulo. adv.; bk.rev.; film rev.; index, cum.index. circ. 1,300. (also avail. in microform from UMI; back issues avail.) **Indexed:** Abstr.Pop.Cult., Arts & Hum.Cit.Ind., C.I.J.E., Curr.Cont., Educ.Tech.Abstr., ERIC, Film Lit.Ind. (1973-), Int.Ind.Film Per., Intl.Ind.TV. **Document type:** academic/scholarly publication.
—Faxon.
Former titles (until 1984): University Film and Video Association. Journal; (until 1981): University Film Association. Journal (ISSN 0041-9311); University Film Producers Association. Journal.
Description: Publishes scholarly articles on film and video.
Refereed Serial

791.43 BE
JOURNAL OF FILM PRESERVATION. (Text in English, French) 1991. s-a. $45 (effective 1995). Federation Internationale des Archives du Film - International Federation of Film Archives, c/o Brigitte van der Elst, Exec.Sec., 190 rue Franz Merjay, B-1180 Brussels, Belgium. TEL 32-2-3430691. FAX 32-2-3437622. Ed. P. Cherchi-Usai. adv.; bk.rev. **Indexed:** Int.Ind.Film Per. **Document type:** bulletin.
Formerly (until Oct. 1993): F I A F Bulletin (ISSN 1017-1126)

791.43 US ISSN 0195-6051
PN1993
JOURNAL OF POPULAR FILM AND TELEVISION. 1972. q. $34 to individuals; institutions $66. (Helen Dwight Reid Educational Foundation) Heldref Publications, 1319 Eighteenth St., N.W., Washington, DC 20036-1802. TEL 202-296-6267. FAX 202-296-5149. Ed. Lisa Culd Neikirk. adv. contact: Raymond Rallo. bk.rev.; bibl.; illus.; index, cum.index. circ. 800. (processed; also avail. in microform; reprint service avail.) **Indexed:** Acad.Ind., Amer.Bibl.Slavic & E.Eur.Stud., Amer.Hist.& Life, Arts & Hum.Cit.Ind., Bk.Rev.Ind. (1980-), Chic.Per.Ind., Child.Bk.Rev.Ind. (1980-), Commun.Abstr., Curr.Cont., Film Lit.Ind. (1973-), Hist.Abstr., Int.Ind.Film Per., Intl.Ind.TV, M.L.A., Ref.Sour. **Document type:** academic/scholarly publication.
●Also available online. Vendor(s): University Microfilms International.
Also available on CD-ROM. Producer(s): University Microfilms International.
—BLDSC (5041.141000); Faxon; Genuine Article; UMI; UnCover. **CCC.**
Formerly: Journal of Popular Film (ISSN 0047-2719)
Refereed Serial

778.5 US ISSN 0146-5546
JUMP CUT; a review of contemporary media. 1974. irreg. (1-2/yr.). $20 (foreign $22) for 4 nos. Jump Cut Associates, Box 865, Berkeley, CA 94701. TEL 510-658-4482. Ed.Bd. adv.; bk.rev.; film rev.; illus. circ. 6,000. (also avail. in microform from UMI; back issues avail.; reprint service avail. from UMI) **Indexed:** Alt.Press Ind., Chic.Per.Ind., Film Lit.Ind. (1974-), Int.Ind.Film Per., Intl.Ind.TV, Left Ind. (1986-), Media Rev.Dig., Sociol.Abstr.
—BLDSC (5075.007000); Faxon; UMI; UnCover.

JUYING YUEBAO/DRAMA & FILM MONTHLY. see *THEATER*

K & C. (Kunst en Cultuur) see *ART*

791.43 UA
KAWAKEB. 1952. w. Dar al- Hilal, 16 Sharia Muhammad Ezz el-Hilal, Cairo, Egypt. TEL 02-27954. TELEX 92703. Ed. Hosn Shah. circ. 86,381.

791.43 384.5 UK
KEMPS FILM, T V AND VIDEO YEARBOOK. 1956. a. £65. Reed Information Services, Division of Reed Telepublishing Ltd. (Subsidiary of: Reed Elsevier group), Windsor Court, E. Grinstead House, E. Grinstead, W. Sussex RH19 1XA, England. TEL 01342-326972. FAX 01342-335977. TELEX 95127-INFSER-G. Ed. Claire Crossfield; Pub. Richard Woolley. adv.; B&W page £1420, color page £2200; trim 265 x 128; adv. contact: Jerry Odlin. circ. 7,000. **Document type:** directory.
Former titles: Kemps International Film and Television Year Book (ISSN 0142-0690); Kemps Film and Television Year Book (International) (ISSN 0075-5427)
Description: Comprehensive international directory for professionals involved in the film industry.

791 JA ISSN 0023-1460
KINDAI EIGA. 1945. m. 13000 Yen. Kindai-Eiga Corp., Owaricho Bldg., 2F, 6-8-3 Ginza, Chuo-ku, Tokyo 104, Japan. TEL 03-5568-2811. FAX 03-5568-2818. Ed. Keiji Oguri; Pub. Shuzo Kosugi. adv.; film rev.; circ. controlled. (processed) **Document type:** consumer publication.

KINDER JUGEND FILM KORRESPONDENZ. see *CHILDREN AND YOUTH — For*

791.43 YU
KINEMATOGRAFIJA U SRBIJI - UPOREDO S F R J. (Subseries of: Biblioteka Dokumentacije) 1969. a. latest 1988, published in 1991. 480 din.($21) Institut za Film, Beograde, Cika Ljubina 15, Belgrade, Yugoslavia. FAX 3811-634253. Ed. P. Golubovic. stat. circ. 500.
Formerly: Kinematografija u Srbiji (ISSN 0350-2651)

778.53 GW ISSN 0936-3777
KINEMATOGRAPH. 1984. irreg. Deutsches Filmmuseum, Schaumainkai 41, 60596 Frankfurt a.M., Germany. FAX 069-21237881. Ed. Walter Schobert. adv. **Indexed:** Film Lit.Ind. (1986-). **Document type:** monographic series.

MOTION PICTURES

778.53 CK ISSN 0121-3776
KINETOSCOPIO. 1990. bi-m. Col.19000($350) Centro Colombo Americano, Apdo. Aereo 8734, Medellin, Colombia. TEL 574-513-4444.
FAX 574-513-2666. Ed. Paul Bardwell. adv. contact: Ana Ramos. bk.rev.; film rev. circ. 3,500. **Document type:** academic/scholarly publication.
Description: Covers international cinema with a special focus on Latin American cinema through in-depth articles and dossiers. Includes information on all films currently being shown in the country, interviews, and coverage of international film festivals.
Refereed Serial

791.43 PL ISSN 0023-1673
PN1993
KINO. 1966. m. $54. Oficyna "Kino" - Zaklad Agencji Dystrybucji Filmowej, Ul. Kredytowa 5-7, 00-056 Warsaw, Poland. TEL 48-22-266785.
FAX 48-22-268380. (Dist. by: Ars Polona-Ruch, Krakowskie Przedmiescie 7, Warsaw, Poland. TEL 48-22-267622) Ed. Tadeusz Sobolewski. bk.rev.; film rev.; illus.; index. circ. 30,000. **Indexed:** Film Lit.Ind. (1973-), Int.Ind.Film Per., Intl.Ind.TV.

791.43 II
KINO. (Text in English) irreg., latest 1990. Rs.25($10) per no. (Cine Club of Calcutta) Harihar Press, 93-2 Sitaram Ghosh St., Calcutta 700 009, India. Ed. Anjan Ghosh.
Description: Discusses classic films and significant contemporary films.

778.53 GW
KINO (BERLIN). german film and international reports. 1979. 4/yr. $3 per no. Helgolaender Ufer 6, 10557 Berlin, Germany. TEL 030-3916167.
FAX 030-3912424. Ed. Ronald Holloway; Pub. Dorothea Holloway. adv.; bk.rev. circ. 2,500.
Indexed: Film Lit.Ind. (1985-). **Document type:** consumer publication.

791.43 GW ISSN 0930-7966
KINO (HAMBURG); das aktuelle Filmprogramm. m. DM.37.80 (foreign DM.45); newsstand price: DM.3.50. Verlagsgruppe Milchstrasse, Milchstr. 1, 20148 Hamburg, Germany. TEL 040-44198-0. FAX 040-458519. Ed. Helmut Fiebig. adv. contact: Andre Hauke. circ. 105,462. **Document type:** consumer publication.

778.53 GW
KINO; FILME DER BUNDESREPUBLIK DEUTSCHLAND. irreg. Export Union des Deutschen films e.V., Tuerkenstr. 93, 80799 Munich, Germany. **Indexed:** Film Lit.Ind. (1982-).

791.43 GW
KINO NEWS. 1986. m. DM.100. T und M Verlagsgesellschaft mbH, Borkumstr. 2, 13189 Berlin, Germany. TEL 030-47805133.
FAX 030-47805131. Ed. Christoph Meier-Siem. adv.; bk.rev.; film rev.; illus. circ. 1,500,000. (tabloid format) **Document type:** consumer publication.

791.43 GW
KINO NEWS OESTERREICH. 1989. m. DM.100. T und M Verlagsgesellschaft mbH, Borkumstr. 2, 13189 Berlin, Germany. TEL 030-47805133.
FAX 030-47805131. Ed. Christoph Meier-Siem. adv.; bk.rev.; film rev.; illus. circ. 241,000. (tabloid format) **Document type:** consumer publication.

791.43 GW
KINOHIT. m. Kinohit Verlags GmbH, Otto-Hahn-Str. 15-17, 85521 Ottobrunn, Germany.
TEL 089-6090034. FAX 089-6090789. Ed. Guenter Dringenberg. adv. contact: Brigitte Dembinski. circ. 151,603. **Document type:** consumer publication.

778.5 BU ISSN 0323-9993
PN1993
KINOIZKUSTVO. 1946. m. 5 lv.($10) Komitet za Izkustvo i Kultura, 7 Levsky St., 1000 Sofia, Bulgaria. (Co-sponsors: Suiuz na Kinodeitsite; Suiuz na Bulgarskite Pisatel) Ed. Emil Petrov. bk.rev.; film rev.; illus.; index. circ. 7,500. **Indexed:** Film Lit.Ind., Int.Ind.Film Per., Intl.Ind.TV.

778.534 GW
KINOMAGAZIN; Kino und Kultur. 1985. m. DM.10. Studio Kino GmbH, Mainzerstr. 8, 66111 Saarbruecken, Germany. TEL 0681-399297.
FAX 0681-374556. adv. circ. 10,000. (back issues avail.)

791.43 RU ISSN 0023-1681
KINOMEKHANIK. 1937. m. 17.40 Rub. Ministerstvo Kul'tury, Moscow, Russia. Ed. Y.A. Fadeyev. **Indexed:** Chem.Abstr., Photo.Abstr.

791.43 AU
KINOSCHRIFTEN. irreg., no.1, 1988. varies. Synema - Gesellschaft fuer Film und Medien, Neubuagasse 36, A-1070 Vienna, Austria. **Document type:** monographic series.

791.43 GW
KINTOP. 1992. a. DM.30. Stroemfeld Verlag, Postfach 180147, 60082 Frankfurt a.M., Germany.
TEL 069-955226-0. FAX 069-95522624. **Indexed:** Int.Ind.Film Per. **Document type:** academic/scholarly publication.

791.43 384.55 DK ISSN 0904-4159
KLIP. 1966. 4/yr. DKK 160 (typically set in Jan.). Dansk Filmlaererforening, Dronning Sofiesvej 2, DK-4000 Roskilde D, Denmark.
TEL 45-42-37-36-34. FAX 45-33-91-52-42. Ed. Frans Rasmussen. adv.; bk.rev. circ. 5,300.
Document type: academic/scholarly publication.
Formerly: Film U V (ISSN 0107-9522)
Description: Publishes articles on television, feature films and documentaries, and educational video programs.

778.5 KO
KOREA FILM CATALOG. a. Motion Picture Promotion Corporation, K.P.O. Box 605, Seoul, S. Korea.
TEL 02-755-9291. FAX 02-774-0531. illus.

791.43 DK ISSN 0023-4222
PN1993
KOSMORAMA. 1954. q. DKK 170 (effective 1994). Danske Filmmuseum, Store Soendervoldstraede 4, DK-1419 Copenhagen K, Denmark.
TEL 45-31-57-65-00. FAX 45-31-57-13-12. Ed. Maren Pust. bk.rev.; illus.; index. circ. 2,000. (also avail. in microform from MIM; microfilm from WMP) **Indexed:** Arts & Hum.Cit.Ind., Curr.Cont., Film Lit.Ind. (1973-), Int.Ind.Film Per., Intl.Ind.TV.
Description: Covers national and international cinema with articles, interviews and reviews.

791.43 GW ISSN 0171-5208
KULLERAUGEN; Arbeitshilfen fuer Film-Interessierte. 1977. s-a. Verlag Brigitte Tast, Laaseweg 4, 31174 Schellerten, Germany. TEL 05123-4330.
FAX 05123-2015. circ. 1,000. (back issues avail.) **Document type:** bulletin.

791.43 GW ISSN 0174-2582
KULLERAUGEN - MATERIALSAMMLUNG. 1978. s-a. Verlag Brigitte Tast, Laaseweg 4, 31174 Schellerten, Germany. TEL 05123-4330.
FAX 05123-2015. circ. 1,000. (back issues avail.) **Document type:** bulletin.

791.43 JA
KUROMA/CHROMA. (Text in Japanese) 1986. m. 22020 Yen. Seibundo Shinkosha Publishing Co. Ltd., 1-13-7 Yayoi-cho, Nakano-ku, Tokyo 164, Japan. Ed. Hiroshi Nishihara. circ. 10,000.

778.53 PL ISSN 0452-9502
KWARTALNIK FILMOWY. 1951-1962; resumed 1965. q. $20. Polska Akademia Nauk, Instytut Sztuki - Polish Academy of Science, Institute of Art, Ul. Dluga 28, 00-950 Warsaw, Poland. TEL 48-22-313271.
FAX 48-22-313149. (Dist. by: AMOS, ul. Zuga 12, 01-806 Warsaw, Poland. TEL 48-22-346521) Ed. Janusz Gazda. bk.rev.; illus.; index. circ. 2,000. **Document type:** academic/scholarly publication.

LADYSLIPPER CATALOG AND RESOURCE GUIDE OF RECORDS, TAPES, COMPACT DISCS AND VIDEOS BY WOMEN. see *WOMEN'S INTERESTS*

791.43 SA ISSN 0023-8481
LARA LAMONT.* 1967. m. R.2. Golden Film Productions (Edms) Bpk, Dunwell-Gebou 112, Jorrissenstraat, Braamfontein, Johannesburg, South Africa.

791.43 US
LEONARD MALTIN'S MOVIE AND VIDEO GUIDE. 1969. a. newsstand price: $7.99. Signet Books, Penguin USA, 375 Hudson St., New York, NY 10014.
TEL 212-366-2594. **Document type:** consumer publication.
Description: Reviews new, old, and classic films available on videotape and laserdisc.

791.43 DK ISSN 0108-5697
LEVENDE BILLEDER. 1975. m. DKK 280 (foreign DKK 380). Forlaget Sankt Peder af 1985 ApS, Meinungsgade 8D, 3.sal, DK-2200 Copenhagen N, Denmark. TEL 31-39-73-90. FAX 35-37-89-76. Ed. Peder Bundgaard. adv.; bk.rev.; film rev.; abstr.; index. circ. 10,000. **Indexed:** Film Lit.Ind. (1980-).
Supersedes: Film (ISSN 0015-1017)

791.43 800 US
LIFESTYLES OF THE BODILY DISMEMBERED. bi-m.? per no. 1702 Burns Ave., St. Paul, MN 55106. Ed. Jason Stephenson.

LIGHTING DIMENSIONS. see *ARCHITECTURE*

791.43 UK ISSN 0959-1915
THE LIST. 1985. fortn. £35. 14 High St., Edinburgh EH1 1TE, Scotland. TEL 0131-558-1191.
FAX 0131-557-8500. Ed. Lila Rawlings; Pub. Robin Hodge. adv.; bk.rev.; film rev.; play rev. circ. 12,000. **Document type:** consumer publication.
Description: Contains comprehensive listings for cinema in Glasgow and Edinburgh. Includes all forms of music, theater, art, and dance for people 18-35 years old.

801 778.5 US ISSN 0090-4260
PN1995.3
LITERATURE - FILM QUARTERLY. 1973. q. $16 to individuals; libraries $32; foreign $36 (effective Jan. 1995). Salisbury State University, Salisbury, MD 21801. TEL 410-543-6446. FAX 410-543-6068. Ed. James M. Welsh. adv. contact: Anne R. Welsh. bk.rev.; film rev.; illus. circ. 800. (also avail. in microfilm from UMI; back issues avail.) **Indexed:** Abstr.Engl.Stud., Arts & Hum.Cit.Ind., Bibl.Engl.Lang.& Lit., Child.Lit.Abstr., Curr.Cont., Film Lit.Ind. (1973-), Hum.Ind., Int.Ind.Film Per., Intl.Ind.TV, LCR, M.L.A., Media Rev.Dig. **Document type:** academic/scholarly publication.
●Also available on CD-ROM.
—BLDSC (5276.721100); Faxon; Genuine Article; SWETS; UMI; UnCover.
Description: Focuses on the problems of adapting and transferring fiction and drama to film. Covers various film genres, theory and criticism. Features interviews with screenwriters, directors and actors. Circulates from coast-to-coast in roughly 30 foreign countries.
Refereed Serial

778.534 US ISSN 1047-9775
LOCATION PRODUCTION GUIDE. 1988. a. $6.95. Box 10067, Blacksburg, VA 24062-0067. Ed. Phil Flora. circ. 14,918.
Description: Lists film and video production professionals and service companies nationwide.

778.5 384.55 US ISSN 1058-3238
LOCATION UPDATE; the magazine of film and video production. 1985. m. $25.95 (foreign $49.95). Location Update, Inc., 2301 Bellevue Ave., Los Angeles, CA 90026-4017. TEL 213-461-8887. FAX 213-469-3711. adv.; circ. 30,000 (controlled). **Document type:** trade publication.
Description: Covers elements that evolve when filming and video taping on local and distant location, as well as studios and soundstages.

778.53 US
LOCATIONS. 1987. s-a. $5 per no. Association of Film Commissioners International, I-25 and College Dr., Cheyenne, WY 82002. TEL 307-777-7777. adv. circ. 17,000.
Description: Lists AFCI members and their services. Covers on-location productions, national and international filming, location highlights, laws and regulations, finance and budgets, news and events.

791 US
LOS ANGELES CINEMATHEQUE. 1973. m. $10 in L.A. county; others $5. Los Angeles Cinematheque, Inc., Box 24548, Los Angeles, CA 90024. Ed. Jared Rutter. adv.; bk.rev. circ. 2,000.

791 IT
LUMIERE. 1984. q. L.10000. Bulzoni Editore, Via dei Liburni, 14, I-00185 Rome, Italy. Ed. Giacomo Gambetti.

M A I N. (Media Arts Information Network) see *COMMUNICATIONS — Television And Cable*

M 3. see *CLUBS*

MOTION PICTURES

791.43 II ISSN 0024-9432
MADHURI. (Text in Hindi) 1960. fortn. Rs.260($20) Bennett, Coleman & Co., Ltd. (Bombay), Times Bldg., Dr. D.N. Rd., Bombay 400001, India. TEL 4150271. (U.S. subscr. to: M/s Kalpana, 42-75 Main St., Flushing, NY 11355) Ed. Vinod Tiwari. adv.; bk.rev.; film rev. circ. 115,000.

778 US ISSN 0739-2141
PN1993.3
MAGILL'S CINEMA ANNUAL. (Update to: Magill's Survey of Cinema) 1982. a. $50. Salem Press, Inc., Magill Books, Box 1097, Englewood Cliffs, NJ 07632. TEL 201-871-3700. FAX 201-871-8668. Ed. F.N. Magill. film rev. **Document type:** consumer publication.
●Also available online. Vendor(s): Knight-Ridder, Inc..
Description: Contains reviews of films released during the previous calendar year, as well as interviews, obituaries, and lists of major awards.

778.53 384.55 US ISSN 1073-8924
PN1995.9.P7
MARKEE. 1986. m. $34. H J K Publications, Inc., 655 Fulton St., Ste. 9, Sanford, FL 32771. TEL 407-324-1733. FAX 407-324-1766. Ed. Janet Karcher. adv.; circ. 18,500 (controlled). **Document type:** trade publication.
Description: For the Southeast and Southwest film and video industries.

MARQUEE. see THEATER

MARTIN & OSA JOHNSON SAFARI MUSEUM WAIT-A-BIT NEWS. see MUSEUMS AND ART GALLERIES

791.43 II
MAYAPURI. (Text in Hindi) 1974. w. newsstand price: Rs.5. A-5, Mayapuri, New Delhi 110 064, India. TEL 11-591439. FAX 91-11-5418596. TELEX 031-76125 MPLP IN. Ed. A.P. Bajaj. adv.; B&W page Rs.8000, color page Rs.16000; 290 x 210. circ. 168,482. **Document type:** newspaper.

MEDIA DIGEST; a bi-monthly media resource for education. see EDUCATION — Teaching Methods And Curriculum

791.43 PL ISSN 0867-2253
MEDIA REPORTER.* 1957. fortn. $23. c/o Ars Polona-Ruch, Krakowskie Przedmiescie 7, Warsaw, Poland. TEL 48-22-200281. Ed. Zygmunt Marcinczak. abstr. circ. 100,000.
Formerly: Ekran (ISSN 0013-3299)

778.5 DK ISSN 0903-8981
MEDIELAERERFORENINGEN FOR GYMNASIET OG H F. MEDDELELSER. 1978. irreg. (3-4/yr.) membership. Medielaererforeningen for Gymnasiet og H F, c/o Lisbet Borker, Norgesgade 31, DK 2300 Copenhagen S, Denmark. bk.rev.; illus. circ. 200.
Formerly: Foreningen af Filmlaerer i Gymnasiet. Meddelelser (ISSN 0900-6664)

MEDIENCONCRET; Magazin fuer die paedagogische Praxis. see COMMUNICATIONS

MEDIENWISSENSCHAFT; Zeitschrift fuer Rezensionen ueber Veroeffentlichungen zu saemtlichen Medien. see COMMUNICATIONS — Television And Cable

MEDIUM (NEW YORK). see ETHNIC INTERESTS

791.43 FR ISSN 1242-0492
PN1993
LE MENSUEL DU CINEMA. 1946. m. 260 F. 17 rue Sorgentino, 06300 Nice, France. adv.; film rev.; illus. (also avail. in microform from UMI; reprint service avail. from UMI) **Indexed:** Arts & Hum.Cit.Ind., Curr.Cont., Film Lit.Ind. (1973-), Int.Ind.Film Per., Intl.Ind.TV, Pt.de Rep.
—Genuine Article; UMI.
Formerly (until 1992): Revue du Cinema (ISSN 0019-2635)

METAPHYSICAL REVIEW. see LITERARY AND POLITICAL REVIEWS

METRO; media and education magazine. see EDUCATION — Teaching Methods And Curriculum

778.53 US ISSN 0886-8719
MIDNIGHT MARQUEE. 1963. irreg. $8. 4000 Glenarm Ave., Baltimore, MD 21206. TEL 410-665-1198. bk.rev. circ. 1,800. **Indexed:** Film Lit.Ind. (1975-).
Description: Dedicated to the serious study of horror, fantasy, and science fiction films.

778.5 RU ISSN 0134-9090
MIFY I REAL'NOST'. irreg. 1.17 Rub. per no. (Goskino, Institut Teorii i Istorii Kino) Izdatel'stvo Iskusstvo, Vorotnikovskii pereulok 11, Moscow, Russia. Ed.Bd. film rev. circ. 25,000.

778.53 US ISSN 1064-5586
MILLENNIUM FILM JOURNAL. 1977. s-a. $14 to individuals; institutions $20. Millennium Film Workshop, Inc., 66 E. Fourth St., New York, NY 10003. TEL 212-673-0090. (Dist. by: Bernhard DeBoer, Inc., 113 E. Centre St., Nutley, NJ 07110) Eds. Tony Pipolo, Grahame Weinbren. adv.; B&W page $160; trim 6 x 9. illus.; index. circ. 2,000. (also avail. in microfilm; back issues avail.) **Indexed:** Film Lit.Ind. (1978-).

778.5 US ISSN 0164-9655
TR845
MILLIMETER;* the magazine of the motion picture and television production industries. 1973. m. $60. Penton Publishing (New York) (Subsidiary of: Pittway Company), 122 E. 42nd St., Rm. 900, New York, NY 10168-0002. TEL 212-477-4700. Ed. Alison Johns. adv.; bk.rev.; film rev. circ. 30,000. **Indexed:** Film Lit.Ind. (1974-), Intl.Ind.TV, Media Rev.Dig. **Document type:** trade publication.
—UMI; UnCover. CCC.
Description: Reports on the motion picture and television production industries for production professionals involved in the commissioning, shooting and postproduction of commercials, programming and movies. Feature articles cover the various aspects of the creative process--from business to technique and technology.

791.43 US ISSN 1070-5104
PN1993
MODERN SCREEN'S COUNTRY MUSIC. 1930. m. $19.95 (foreign $24.95). Sterling - Macfadden Partnership, 35 Wilbur St., Lynbrook, NY 11563. TEL 516-593-1220. FAX 516-593-0065. adv.; film rev.; illus. (also avail. in microform from UMI) **Document type:** consumer publication.
Former titles (until 1993): Modern Screen's Country Music Special (ISSN 1068-0373); (until 1991): Modern Screen (ISSN 0026-8429)

791.43 CI ISSN 0026-8895
MOJ PAS. (Text in Serbo-Croatian) 1954. m. $12.50. Kinoloski Savez Hrvatske, Ilica 61, Zagreb, Croatia. Ed. Vesna Sekalec.

778.53 BE ISSN 0771-4874
LE MONITEUR DU FILM EN BELGIQUE. Dutch edition: Filmvakblad van Belgie (ISSN 0771-7504) (Text in French) 1980. m. Rue de Framboisier 35, 1180 Brussels, Belgium. **Indexed:** Film Lit.Ind. (1987-).
Formerly (until 1981): Press and Film Service (ISSN 0771-4823)

MONKEES, BOYCE & HART PHOTO FAN CLUB; the photo club. see CLUBS

791.43 808.838 US ISSN 1082-930X
MONSTERSCENE. 1992. q. newsstand price: $5.95. Gogo Entertainment Group, 1036 S. Ahrens Ave., Lombard, IL 60148. Pubs. William N. Harrison, Stephen D. Smith. adv. contact: Christine L. Smith. film rev.; video rev. **Document type:** consumer publication.
Description: Covers horror movie history, actors, directors, collectibles and videos.

791.43 US
THE MOTION PICTURE GUIDE ANNUAL. 1986. a. $159.95. Baseline - CineBooks, 835 Broadway, 4th Fl., New York, NY 10003. TEL 212-254-8235. FAX 908-665-6688. TELEX 138 755. (Dist. by: R.R. Bowker, A Reed Reference Publishing Company, 121 Chanlon Rd., Box 31, New Providence, NJ 07974. TEL 800-521-8110) illus.
Description: Detailed entries, reviews, and anecdotes about hundreds of domestic and foreign features released in the US during the previous year.

791.43 US ISSN 0742-8839
MOTION PICTURE INVESTOR; newsletter on analysis of private and public values of movies and movie stock. 1984. m. $595. Paul Kagan Associates, Inc., 126 Clock Tower Place, Carmel, CA 93923. TEL 408-624-1536. FAX 408-624-1536. TELEX 408-625-3225. charts; index. **Document type:** newsletter.
Description: Covers investment in public and private movie production and distribution companies. Tracks the movement and value of motion picture stocks.

MOTION PICTURE, T V & THEATRE DIRECTORY; for services & products. see BUSINESS AND ECONOMICS — Trade And Industrial Directories

791.43 II ISSN 0027-1632
MOTION PICTURES TECHNICAL BULLETIN. (Text in English) vol.12, 1969. q. Processlabs Private Ltd., S.V. Road, Dahisar, Bombay 68, India. Ed. Krishna Gopal. circ. 350. **Document type:** bulletin.

791.43 UK ISSN 0027-268X
PN1993
MOVIE. 1962. irreg. c/o Ian Cameron, Ed. & Pub., P.O. Box 1, Moffat, Dumfriesshire DG10 9SU, Scotland. TEL 0683-20808. FAX 0683-20012. bk.rev.; film rev.; illus. **Indexed:** Arts & Hum.Cit.Ind., Curr.Cont., Film Lit.Ind. (1975-), Int.Ind.Film Per. (until 1995), Intl.Ind.TV, Media Rev.Dig.

791.43 II ISSN 0971-3182
MOVIE. (Text in English) 1981. m. newsstand price: Rs.20. India Book House Pvt. Ltd., Mahalaxmi Chambers, 5th Fl., 22 B. Desai Rd., Bombay 26, India. TEL 022-4940147. Ed. Dinesh Raheja; Pub. Krishan Kakkar. adv.; B&W page Rs.17000, color page Rs.34000; bleed 210 x 275. circ. 71,100.

791.43 US
MOVIE CLUB MAGAZINE. 1981. bi-m. $21 (foreign $31) (effective 1993). Gateway Entertainment, Inc., 12 Moray Court, Baltimore, MD 21236. TEL 410-256-5944. Ed. Don Dohler. adv. contact: Glenn Barnes. bk.rev. circ. 5,000. **Document type:** consumer publication.
Former titles (until 1993): Cinema News; Amazing Cinema.
Description: Devoted to movies and video-laser disc collecting. Includes articles on classic and new movies, video-laser previews and reviews, and behind-the-scenes of filmmaking.

791.43 UK ISSN 0951-421X
MOVIE INTERNATIONAL. 1983. m. £18 (Europe £30; elsewhere £36). 55 The Broadway, Southall, Middlesex UB1 1JY, England. TEL 0181-574-2222. FAX 0181-813-9911. Ed. Dinesh Raheja; Pub. Neermal Suri. adv.; bk.rev. circ. 22,000. (back issues avail.) **Document type:** consumer publication.

791.43 US
MOVIE LIST BOOK. irreg., 2nd ed., 1994. F & W Publications, Inc., Betterway Books, 1507 Dana Ave., Cincinnati, OH 45207. TEL 800-289-0963. FAX 513-531-4082.

791 JA ISSN 0047-8288
MOVIE - T V MARKETING. (Text in English) 1953. m. 30000 Yen (effective 1996). Movie - TV Marketing, Box 30, Central Post Office, Tokyo 100-91, Japan. TEL 03-3587-2855. FAX 03-3587-2820. Ed. Asia M. Ireton. adv. circ. 100,000. **Document type:** trade publication.
Former titles (umtil 1966): Movie Marketing; (until 1962): Far East Film News (ISSN 0425-7111)

791 JA ISSN 0085-3577
MOVIE - T V MARKETING GLOBAL MOTION PICTURE YEAR BOOK. (Text in English) 1955. a. 10000 Yen. Movie - TV Marketing, Box 30, Central Post Office, Tokyo 100-91, Japan. TEL 03-3587-2855. FAX 03-3587-2820. Ed. Asia M. Ireton. adv. circ. 100,000. (also avail. in microform from UMI) **Document type:** trade publication.

791.43 US
MOVIE WEEKLY. 1987. w. $22. E W A Publications, 275 Bay 37th St., Brooklyn, NY 11214. TEL 718-996-5406. FAX 718-373-1352. Ed. Kevin Brown. adv. contact: Adrienne Knoll. bk.rev.; film rev, illus.; circ. 158,000 (paid). (tabloid format) **Document type:** newspaper.
Description: Contains personality interviews, production features, as well as film and video reviews.

MOTION PICTURES 4799

791.43   US   ISSN 1055-0917
PN1993
MOVIELINE. 1989. m. $15. Movieline, Inc., Attn.: B.L. Shepherd, Circ. Dir., 1141 S. Beverly Dr., Los Angeles, CA 90035. TEL 213-282-0711. Eds. Virginia Campbell, Edward Margulies. adv.; bk.rev. circ. 100,000. **Indexed:** Access (1993-). **Document type:** consumer publication.
  Description: Highlights lifestyles of film and movie makers.

778.5   ISSN 0885-5021
MOVIETONE NEWS.* 1971. 10/yr. $7 to individuals; institutions $10. Seattle Folklore Society, Box 30141, Seattle, WA 98103-0141. TEL 206-782-0505. Ed. Richard T. Jameson. adv.; bk.rev.; film rev.; index. circ. 1,000. (back issues avail.) **Indexed:** Film Lit.Ind., Intl.Ind.TV.

791.43   UK   ISSN 0959-6992
MOVING PICTURES INTERNATIONAL. 1990. m. £75. Moving Pictures International Ltd. (Subsidiary of: Reed Elsevier plc.), 151-153 Wardour St., London W1V 3TB, England. TEL 0171-287-0070. FAX 0171-287-9637. Ed. David Jenkinson. adv. contact: JoJo Dye. **Document type:** consumer publication.

MULTI - IMAGES. see ADVERTISING AND PUBLIC RELATIONS

N A P A M A NEWS. (National Association of Performing Arts Managers and Agents) see THEATER

N A R M C HIGHLIGHTS. (National Association of Regional Media Centers) see LIBRARY AND INFORMATION SCIENCES

791.43 647.968 US
N A T O NEWS. 1967. m. $50. National Association of Theatre Owners, 4605 Lankershim Blvd., No. 340, N. Hollywood, CA 91602. TEL 818-506-1778. FAX 818-506-0269. Ed. Jim Kozak. circ. 3,000. **Document type:** trade publication.
  Former titles: N A T O News and Views (ISSN 0279-120X); N A T O Flash Bulletin.

791.43   NE   ISSN 0927-2127
N F M - PROGRAMMA. 1970. m. fl.30 includes membership. Stichting Nederlands Filmmuseum, Vondelpark 3, 1071 AA Amsterdam, Netherlands. TEL 31-20-5891400. FAX 31-20-6833401. film rev.; bibl.; illus. circ. 17,500. **Document type:** bulletin.
  Former titles (until 1991): N F M Programmakrant (ISSN 0922-3207); (until 1988): Filmmuseum Cinematheek Journal; (until 1974): Filmmuseum-Cinematheek (ISSN 0016-2639)
  Description: Includes a program of the films shown daily at the museum, with brief film descriptions and discussion of program themes.

791.43   NE   ISSN 0926-3411
N F M - THEMAREEKS. 1991. irreg. fl.5 per issue. Stichting Nederlands Filmmuseum, Vondelpark 3, 1071 AA Amsterdam, Netherlands. TEL 31-20-5891400. FAX 31-20-6833401. Ed. Rene Wolf. illus. circ. 1,250. **Document type:** monographic series.
  Description: In-depth original articles and translations on specific film themes, directors or genres.

791.43
NAKED! SCREAMING! TERROR!. m.? $1 per no. Box 67, Oberlin, OH 44074-0067. Ed. David Todarello.
  Description: Covers horror movies.

791.43   II
NANA FILM WEEKLY. (Text in Malayalam) w. newsstand price: Rs.4. R. Krishnaswamy Memorial Building, Lekshminada, Kollam 691 023, Kerala, India. TEL 0474-72403. FAX 0474-70710. TELEX 0886-296 RKAY. Ed. B.A. Rajakrishnan. adv.; B&W page Rs.6000, color page Rs.12000; 250 x 180; adv. contact: N. Krishnan. circ. 63,200.

NATIONAL FILM AND SOUND ARCHIVE NEWSLETTER. see SOUND RECORDING AND REPRODUCTION

791.43   IR
NATIONAL FILM ARCHIVE OF IRAN. BULLETIN. (Text in English) 1989. q. free. National Film Archive of Iran - Film-khane-ye Melli-e Iran, P.O. Box 5158, Teheran 11365, Iran. TEL 021-311242. TELEX 215462 RECU IR. Eds. Mohammad Hassan Khosnevis, Fereydoun Khameneipour. illus. **Document type:** bulletin.

791.43   II   ISSN 0042-2444
NAV-CHITRAPAT. (Text in Hindi) 1932. m. Rs.1.50($0.40) per no. Satyendra Shyam, Ed. & Pub., 92 Daryaganj, Delhi, India. TEL 11 272482. adv.; bk.rev.; film rev.; illus. circ. 36,000. (tabloid format)

NEW ORLEANS REVIEW. see LITERATURE

791.43   US   ISSN 0362-3688
PN1995
NEW YORK TIMES FILM REVIEWS. 1913. biennial. Times Books (Subsidiary of: Random House, Inc.), 201 E. 50th St., New York, NY 10022-7703. TEL 212-751-2600. illus.

791.43   NZ   ISSN 0113-8596
NEW ZEALAND FILM. Variant title: N Z Film. 1980. 2/yr. New Zealand Film Commission, P.O. Box 11-546, Wellington, New Zealand. TEL 4-385-9754. FAX 64-4-384-9719. TELEX NZ-30386. Ed. Lindsay Shelton. circ. 4,000. **Document type:** trade publication.
  Description: Presents a summary of production information about New Zealand movies.

791.43   US
NEWS REEL.* 1968. m. Federation of Motion Picture Councils, 142 N. Tucker, Memphis, TN 38104. bk.rev.; film rev.; illus. **Indexed:** World Text.Abstr.

384   US   ISSN 0737-3988
NEWSBANK REVIEW OF THE ARTS: FILM AND TELEVISION. 1972. m. (plus q. and a. cum.). price varies. NewsBank, Inc., 58 Pine St., New Canaan, CT 06840-5426. TEL 203-966-1100. FAX 203-966-6254. (microfiche)
  ●Also available on CD-ROM.

778.53   VN
NGHE THUAT DIEN ANH/CINEMATOGRAPHY. 1984. fortn. 65 Tran Hung Dao, Hanoi, Socialist Republic of Vietnam. TEL 52473. Ed. Dang Nhat Minh.

778.5   IT
NOTE DI TECNICA CINEMATOGRAFICA. 1963. q. free. Associazione Tecnica Italiana per la Cinematografia e la Televisione, Viale Regina Margherita 286, 00198 Rome, Italy. TEL 396-44-231-480. FAX 396-4404128. Ed. Mario Bernardo. adv.; bk.rev. circ. 800. **Document type:** trade publication.

778.53   RM   ISSN 1220-1200
NOUL CINEMA. 1963. m. $35 in Europe; US $40. Noul Cinema Editions, Piata Presei Libere 1, 41917 Bucharest, Rumania. TEL 40-1-2223332. Ed. Adina Darian. adv.; bk.rev. circ. 100,000. **Document type:** consumer publication.
  Formerly (until 1990): Cinema (ISSN 0578-2910)

NUEVA LENTE; publicacion mensual de fotografia y cine. see PHOTOGRAPHY

791.4
NUOVA GUIDA CINEMATOGRAFICA. 1960. w. (in 5 vols.) L.210000($3) Ente dello Spettacolo, Via Palombini 6, 00165 Rome, Italy. circ. 6,000. **Document type:** directory.
  Formerly: Guida allo Spettacolo (ISSN 0017-5188)
  Description: Guide to motion pictures.

791.43   IT
NUOVO CINEMA EUROPEO. (Text in English and Italian) 1975. w. L.30000($70) (effective 1993). Ideaform, Via Castelfidardo 20, 50137 Florence, Italy. TEL 55-611568. FAX 55-611569. Ed. Paolo di Maira. adv. circ. 10,000. **Document type:** trade publication.

OBJEKTIVET. see PHOTOGRAPHY

OCTOBER. see ART

791.43   AU
OESTERREICHISCHE GESELLSCHAFT FUER FILMWISSENSCHAFT, KOMMUNIKATIONS- UND MEDIENFORSCHUNG. MITTEILUNGEN. 1952. bi-m. S.5. Oesterreichische Gesellschaft fuer Filmwissenschaft, Kommunikations- und Medienforschung, Rauhensteingasse 5, A-1010 Vienna, Austria. TEL 01-5129936. FAX 01-5135330. index. circ. 800. **Document type:** newsletter.
  Formerly: Oesterreichische Gesellschaft fuer Filmwissenschaft. Mitteilungen (ISSN 0029-9146)

790.2   AU   ISSN 0029-9057
DER OESTERREICHISCHER FILMAMATEUR. 1966. bi-m. S.100. Klub der Kinoamateure Oesterreichs, Neubaugasse 36, A-1070 Vienna, Austria. Ed. Peter Gruber. adv.; bk.rev.; bibl. circ. 1,500. (looseleaf format) **Document type:** newsletter.
  Description: For the amateur filmmaker.

791.43   US
OLD TIME WESTERN FILM CLUB NEWSLETTER. 1970. bi-m. free. Old Time Western Film Club, Box 142, Siler City, NC 27344. Ed. Milo Holt. circ. 500. **Document type:** newsletter.
  Description: Encourages interest in old time Westerns, and news of the Club's screeings of Westerns.

051   US
ON LINE.* 1989. m. $9.95. Michaelson Entertainment, 515 West End Ave., Ste. 30, New York, NY 10024-4345. TEL 212-737-8100. Ed. Orli Low. circ. 250,000.
  Description: Examines plot lines of recent movie releases.

791   IS
ON LOCATION - ISRAEL. (Text in English) 1970. irreg., latest 1994. free. Israel Film Centre, P.O. Box 299, Jerusalem, Israel. TEL 972-2-220608. FAX 972-2-236303. circ. 2,500.
  Former titles: Filmmaking in Israel (ISSN 0792-8629); (until 1973): Israel Film-Making Plus (ISSN 0075-1162); Film.
  Description: Provides information for foreign filmmakers on locations and filming conditions in Israel

778.534 006.6   US   ISSN 1067-6120
PN1995.9.P7
ON PRODUCTION AND POST-PRODUCTION. 1992. 8/yr. $43 (foreign $72; airmail $89) (effective 1995). On Production Inc., 17337 Ventura Blvd., Ste. 308, Encino, CA 91316. TEL 818-907-6682. Ed. Howard Kunin. circ. 29,000. **Document type:** trade publication.
  Description: For producers, directors, production managers, video facility managers, editors, agents and post-production executives who need to keep current about the production and post-production industry's latest developments. Focuses on news, trends and feature stories covering the production and post-production industries.

ON THE STREET. see MUSIC

791.43   UK
ORIENT EXPRESS. 1991. q. £6. Astounding Comics, 61 Pyle St., Newport, Isle of Wight PO30 1UL, England. Ed. Kevin Lyons. film rev.; video rev.; illus.
  Description: Critical review of cinema from the Far East, including Japanese anime (animation), live action and monster movies, B movies from the Philippines, and Hong Kong horror and comedy productions, with articles on the backgrounds of individual film directors, producers and their productions.

791.43 808.838 US
OTHER DIMENSIONS; the journal of multimedia horror. 1993. irreg., approx. a., no.2, 1994. $5 per no. Necronomicon Press, Box 1304, West Warwick, RI 02893. TEL 404-828-7161. FAX 401-738-1625. Ed. Stefan Dziemianowicz.
  Description: Looks at contemporary manifestations of horror in entertainment and art forms. Includes interviews with filmmakers and producers, discussions of science fiction and horror films, and examinations of the cultural significance of the iconography of horror.

791.43 780   UK
OVERALL THERE IS A SMELL OF FRIED ONIONS. 1991. m. £12($23) P.O. Box 73, West PDO, Nottingham NG7 4DG, England. TEL 0115-953-8333. FAX 0115-953-8333. Ed. Paul Kilbride. adv.: page £350; trim 277 x 190; adv. contact: Paul Kilbride. bk.rev.; charts; film rev.; music rev.; play rev.; circ. 5,000.

PALMER VIDEO MAGAZINE. see COMMUNICATIONS — Video

ULRICH'S INTERNATIONAL PERIODICALS DIRECTORY 1996

4800 MOTION PICTURES

791.43 780.42   US   ISSN 1050-5504
PAST TIMES: THE NOSTALGIA ENTERTAINMENT NEWSLETTER. 1990. q. $11. Past Times Publishing Co., 7308 Fillmore Dr., Buena Park, CA 90620. TEL 714-956-2246. Ed. Randy Skretvedt; Pub. Jordan Young. adv.; bk.rev.; film rev.; music rev. circ. 5,000. **Document type:** newsletter.
 Description: Perpetuates the entertainment of the 1920s through the 1940s, covering movies, music, radio programs, pop culture, actors, musicians and personalities.

PERFORMING ARTS BUYERS GUIDE: FOOTNOTES. see *DANCE*

808.23   UK
PERIPHERAL VISIONS. no.2, 1995. irreg. £3($7) 28 Hillside Ave., Kilmalcolm, Renfrew PA13 4QL, Scotland. Ed. Iain McLachlan.
 Description: Provides 50 detailed reviews of genre films.

791.43 100   US
PERSISTENCE OF VISION. 1984. a. $15 to individuals; institutions $20. City University of New York, Film Faculty, c/o Tony Pipolo, Ed., 53-24 63rd St., Maspeth, NY 11378. TEL 718-779-3936. adv.; bk.rev. circ. 1,000. (back issues avail.) **Indexed:** Film Lit.Ind. (1985-), Int.Ind.Film Per., M.L.A. **Document type:** academic/scholarly publication.

778.534 384.55   CN
PERSISTENCE OF VISION. 1982. q. membership. Film and Video Arts Society of Alberta, 9722 102nd St., Edmonton, AB T5K 0X4, Canada. TEL 403-429-1671. FAX 403-424-0194. adv.; bk.rev. circ. 100. **Document type:** newsletter.
 Formerly: F A V A Newsletter.

791.43   II   ISSN 0031-6164
PESUM PADAM. (Text in Tamil) 1942. m. Rs.60 (foreign Rs.480). Ramanath Publications Private Ltd., 325 Arcot Rd., Kodambakkam, Madras 600 024, India. Ed. K. Natarajan. adv.; film rev. circ. 42,000.

791.43   US   ISSN 1083-2920
THE PHANTOM OF THE MOVIES' VIDEOSCOPE. 1993. q. $19.97 for 6 issues; newsstand price: $4.25. Phan Media, Box 216, Ocean Grove, NJ 07756. FAX 908-988-9180. Ed. Joe Kane. circ. 10,000. **Document type:** consumer publication.
 Description: Reviews recent releases in genre video.

PHOTO-CINE-EXPERT (1979); la revue suisse au service des photographes et cineastes. see *PHOTOGRAPHY*

770 791.43   FR
PHOTOMAGAZINE; magazine des photographes et cineastes amateurs. 1920. m. 210 F. (foreign 330 F.). Editions Denis Jacob, 103 bd. St-Michel, 75005 Paris, France. FAX 43-29-14-05. Ed. D.J. Presse. adv.; film rev.; charts; illus.; mkt.; tr.lit.; index. circ. 100,000.
 Former titles: Photocinema; Nouveau Photocinema (ISSN 0398-9372); Photo-Cinema, Film, Amateur-Son (ISSN 0031-8477)

791.43 747   UK   ISSN 0263-7553
PICTURE HOUSE. 1982. irreg. £12 (overseas £15) includes membership. Cinema Theatre Association, 5 Coopers Close, Burgess Hill, W. Sussex RH15 8AN, England. TEL 01444-246893. (Subscr. addr.: Flat 30, Cambridge Court, Cambridge Rd., Southend-on-Sea, Essex, SS1 1EJ, England) Ed. Allen Eyles. illus. circ. 1,350. (back issues avail.) **Indexed:** Film Lit.Ind. (1989-). **Document type:** academic/scholarly publication.
 —BLDSC (6498.627000).
 Description: Contains articles on U.K. cinema buildings, circuits, architects and more.

791.43   II
PICTURPOST. (Text in English) 1943. m. 325 Arcot Rd., Madras 600 024, India. TEL 44-422064. Ed. K. Natarajan. circ. 11,000.

PITANJA; mjesecnik: drustvo, znanost, kultura. see *LITERATURE*

PLAYBACK; Canada's broadcast and production journal. see *COMMUNICATIONS — Television And Cable*

PLUG; maandelijks informatieblad. see *THEATER*

791.43   FR   ISSN 0079-2535
POINTS. FILMS. 1971. irreg. price varies. Editions du Seuil, 27 rue Jacob, 75261 Paris Cedex 06, France.
 —CCC.

791.43   FR   ISSN 0048-4911
PN1993
POSITIF. m. Societe Nouvelle des Edition Opta, 1 quai de Conti, 75006 Paris, France. Ed.Bd. adv.; bk.rev.; film rev.; illus. **Indexed:** Arts & Hum.Cit.Ind., Curr.Cont., Film Lit.Ind. (1973-), Int.Ind.Film Per., Intl.Ind.TV, Pt.de Rep. (1981-).
 —BLDSC (6558.810000); SWETS.

POST SCRIPT (COMMERCE); essays in film and the humanities. see *HUMANITIES: COMPREHENSIVE WORKS*

791   US
PRE-VUE ENTERTAINMENT MAGAZINE. 1991. bi-m. $10 (Canada $20) free in movie theaters. National Pre-Vue Network, 7825 Fay Ave., La Jolla, CA 92037. TEL 619-456-5577. FAX 619-542-0114. Ed. Penny Langford; Pub. Penny Langford. adv.: B&W page $4000, color page $5000; trim 5 5/16 x 8 5/16. circ. 100,000 (controlled). **Document type:** consumer publication.
 Description: Highlights new music and movies. Targeted to moviegoers.
 Refereed Serial

051   US   ISSN 0894-9263
PN1993
PREMIERE (NEW YORK). 1987. m. $19.98 in U.S.; elsewhere $31.98. Hachette Publications, Inc. (Subsidiary of: Hachette Filipacchi Press), 1633 Broadway, New York, NY 10019. TEL 212-767-6000. FAX 212-767-5631. (Subscr. to: Box 52293, Boulder, CO 80322. TEL 303-504-1464. FAX 303-504-7455) Ed. Susan Lyne; Pub. Mark Furlong. adv. contact: Mark Furlong. bk.rev. circ. 600,000. **Indexed:** Access (1988-), Film Lit.Ind. (1987-), Mag.Ind. **Document type:** consumer publication.
 —BLDSC (6607.641200); Faxon; SWETS; UMI; UnCover.
 Description: Fills the gap between scholarly film magazines and fan magazines. Contains interviews, investigative reports, profiles of new and old releases, and behind-the-scenes looks at film production.

791.43   FR   ISSN 0399-3698
PREMIERE: LE MAGAZINE DU CINEMA. m. $29.39. 23-25, rue de Berri, 75388 Paris Cedex 08, France. (Subscr. to: 90, rue de Flandre, 75974 Paris Cedex 19, France) Ed. Jean Hohman.

791.43 384.55   CN
PREMIERE VIDEO MAGAZINE. 1984. m. Can.$20($25) Videomania Inc., 1314 Britannia Rd. East, Mississauga, Ont. L4W 1C8, Canada. TEL 416-564-1033. FAX 416-564-3398. Ed. Salah Bachir. adv.; film rev.; tr.lit. circ. 9,000. (back issues avail.) **Document type:** trade publication.
 Formerly: Premiere.

778.5   US
PREVIEW THEATER BROCHURE. m. $20. American Film Institute, John F. Kennedy Center for the Performing Arts, Washington, DC 20566. TEL 202-828-4000. film rev.; circ. controlled. (tabloid format)
 Formerly: American Film Institute Theater Brochure.

791.43 800   US   ISSN 0199-9257
P92.U5
PREVUE. Variant title: Mediascene Prevue. 1972. bi-m. $19.95. Box 4489, Reading, PA 19606. TEL 215-370-0666. FAX 215-370-0867. Ed. J. Steranko. adv.; bk.rev.; film rev.; illus. circ. 240,000. (back issues avail.) **Document type:** consumer publication.
 Formerly (until Aug. 1980): Media Scene.

791.43   IT
PRIMISSIMA. 1990. m. Tamtam Comunicazioni s.r.l., Via Bisagno 28, 00199 Rome, Italy. TEL 39-6-86214662. FAX 39-6-86215022. Ed. Giampiero Cinelli. adv.: color page L.10000000. **Document type:** consumer publication.

791.43   II
PRIYA. (Text in Hindi) 1956. m. Rs.1.50($0.40) per no. 92 Daryaganj, Delhi 110 002, India. TEL 11-262472. Ed. Satyendra Smyam. adv.; bk.rev.; film rev.; illus. circ. 28,000. (tabloid format)
 Formerly (until 1960): Lalita (ISSN 0023-740X)

778.5 791 371.3   US   ISSN 1067-439X
PRODUCER. 1990. bi-m. $15. Testa Communications, Inc., 25 Willowdale Ave., Port Washington, NY 11050. TEL 516-767-2500. FAX 516-767-9335. Ed. Ken McGorry. adv.: B&W page $2365, color page $3190; trim 9 x 10 7/8. charts; illus.; stat.; tr.lit. circ. 15,000. (back issues avail.) **Document type:** trade publication.
 Formerly: Producers Quarterly (ISSN 1053-6450)
 Description: For producers, directors, editors, videographers, composers--all creative people.

PRODUCER'S MASTERGUIDE; the international production manual for motion pictures, television, commercials, cable and videotape industries in the United States, Canada, the United Kingdom, Bermuda, the Caribbean Islands, Mexico, South America, Europe, the Far East, Australia and New Zealand. see *BUSINESS AND ECONOMICS — Trade And Industrial Directories*

778.5 792   UK   ISSN 0142-632X
PRODUCTION AND CASTING REPORT. Abbreviated title: P C R. 1968. w. £201.50. P.O. Box 11, London SW15 6AY, England. TEL 0181-789-0408. FAX 0181-780-1977. (Subscr. to: P.O. Box 100, Broadstairs, Kent CT10 1UJ, England. TEL 01843-860885) Ed. Vaune Craig-Raymond. adv. circ. 4,000. **Document type:** trade publication.
 Incorporates: Who's Where Weekly; Which superseded in part: Who's Where Weekly and Who's Who of Casting Directors (ISSN 0142-6311)
 Description: Covers advance production and casting news in the film, television and theater industry.

778   GW   ISSN 0932-0393
PROFESSIONAL PRODUCTION. 1987. m. DM.59. Verlag Gerhard Spiehs, Baeckergasse 10, 82288 Kottgeisering, Germany. TEL 08144-1541. FAX 08144-1496. circ. 4,000.

PROFIFOTO; magazine for professional photography and electronic imaging. see *PHOTOGRAPHY*

791.43   FI   ISSN 0356-4096
PROJEKTIO. 1960. q. FIM 20. Suomen Elokuvakerhojen Liitto SEKL - Federation of Finnish Film Societies, Yrjonkatu 11 A 5, 00120 Helsinki 12, Finland. Ed. Jukka Vilhunen. adv.; bk.rev. circ. 5,000.

791.43   GW   ISSN 0341-5910
PUBLIKATIONEN ZU WISSENSCHAFTLICHEN FILMEN. SEKTION ETHNOLOGIE. (Text in English, French or German; summaries in English, French and German) 1963. irreg. Institut fuer den Wissenschaftlichen Film, Nonnensteig 72, 37075 Goettingen, Germany. TEL 0551-5024-0. FAX 0551-5024400. **Document type:** academic/scholarly publication.
 Formerly: Institut fuer den Wissenschaftlichen Film. Publikationen zu Wissenschaftlichen Filmen. Sektion Voelkerkunde.

791.43 900   GW   ISSN 0341-5937
PN1993
PUBLIKATIONEN ZU WISSENSCHAFTLICHEN FILMEN. SEKTION GESCHICHTE, PUBLIZISTIK. (Text in German; summaries in English, French and German) 1963. irreg. Institut fuer den Wissenschaftlichen Film, Nonnensteig 72, 37075 Goettingen, Germany. TEL 0551-5024-0. FAX 0551-5024400. **Document type:** academic/scholarly publication.
 Formerly: Publikationen zu Wissenschaftlichen Filmen. Sektion Geschichte, Paedagogik (ISSN 0073-8441)

610 791.43   GW   ISSN 0341-5929
PUBLIKATIONEN ZU WISSENSCHAFTLICHEN FILMEN. SEKTION MEDIZIN. (Text in English, French or German; summaries in English, French and German) 1970. irreg. Institut fuer den Wissenschaftlichen Film, Nonnensteig 72, 37075 Goettingen, Germany. TEL 0551-5024-0. FAX 0551-5024400. **Document type:** academic/scholarly publication.

MOTION PICTURES 4801

791.43 GW ISSN 0344-9300
PUBLIKATIONEN ZU WISSENSCHAFTLICHEN FILMEN. SEKTION PSYCHOLOGIE, PAEDAGOGIK. (Text in English, French or German; summaries in English, French and German) 1979. irreg. Institut fuer den Wissenschaftlichen Film, Nonnenstieg 72, 37075 Goettingen, Germany. TEL 0551-5024-0. FAX 0551-5024400. Document type: academic/scholarly publication.

500 791.43 GW ISSN 0073-8433
T65.5.M6
PUBLIKATIONEN ZU WISSENSCHAFTLICHEN FILMEN. SEKTION TECHNISCHE WISSENSCHAFTEN, NATURWISSENSCHAFTEN. (Text in English, French or German; summaries in English, French and German) 1963. irreg. Institut fuer den Wissenschaftlichen Film, Nonnenstieg 72, 37075 Goettingen, Germany. TEL 0551-5024-0. FAX 0551-5024400. Document type: academic/scholarly publication.

791.43 BG
PURBANI. (Text in Bengali) 1951. w. 1 Ramkrishna Mission Rd, Dhaka 1203, Bangladesh. TEL 2-256503. Ed. Khondker Shahadat Hossain. circ. 22,000.

778.5 384.55 US
PYRAMID FILM AND VIDEO CATALOG. 1960. biennial. free. Pyramid Film & Video, Box 1048, Santa Monica, CA 90406-1048. TEL 310-828-7577. FAX 310-453-9083. Ed. Julie Lawson. film rev. circ. 60,000. Document type: catalog.
   Description: Lists a variety of films and videos distributed by Pyramid.

791.43 IT ISSN 0393-8379
PN1993
QUADERNI DI CINEMA; bimestrale di cultura e politica cinematografica. 1981. bi-m. L.45000 (Europe L.55000; America, Asia, Africa L.75000). Via Benedetto Varchi 57, 50132 Florence, Italy. TEL 055-243144. Ed. Gaetano Strazzulla. adv.; bk.rev. circ. 5,000. (back issues avail.) Indexed: Film Lit.Ind. (1985-).

778.5 791.4 US ISSN 1050-9208
PN1994 CODEN: QRFVEF
QUARTERLY REVIEW OF FILM AND VIDEO. Abbreviated title: Q R F V. 1976. 4/yr. (in 1 vol., 4 nos./vol.) 65 ECU to individuals (effective 1996). Harwood Academic Publishers, c/o International Publishers Distributor, 820 Town Center Dr., Langhorne, PA 19047. TEL 215-750-2642. FAX 215-750-6343. (Subscr. to: International Publishers Distributor, P.O. Box 90, Reading, Berkshire RG1 8JL, England. TEL 0734-560-080) Ed. Michael Renov. bk.rev.; index. (also avail. in microform; reprint service avail. from UMI) Indexed: Amer.Bibl.Slavic & E.Eur.Stud., Bk.Rev.Ind. (1980-), Chicago Psychoanal.Lit.Ind., Child.Bk.Rev.Ind. (1980-), Curr.Cont., Film Lit.Ind. (1976-), Hum.Ind., Int.Ind.Film Per., Intl.Ind.TV, M.L.A.
   —BLDSC (7206.700000); Faxon; UnCover. **CCC.**
   Formerly (until 1989): Quarterly Review of Film Studies (ISSN 0146-0013)
   Refereed Serial

778.5 US
QUORUM QUOTES.* 1970. q. membership. International Quorum of Film and Video, c/o Film House, 230 Chamberlain Bend, Nashville, TN 37228. TEL 615-255-4000. FAX 615-256-3380. Ed. Barbara Blair. adv.; bk.rev.; film rev.; illus. circ. 500.

R T S VIDEO GAZETTE. see *COMMUNICATIONS — Video*

791.43 SU
RAABTA. (Text in Urdu) m. Transcontinental Corp., P.O. Box 9935, Jeddah, Saudi Arabia. TEL 651-3857. circ. 58,000.
   Description: Entertainment and movie news.

791.43 II
RANGBHUMI. (Text in Hindi) 1941. m. 5A-15 Ansari Rd., Darya Ganj, Delhi 110 002, India. TEL 11-274667. Ed. S.K. Gupta. circ. 30,000.

791 CN ISSN 0085-543X
PN1995.9.E9
RECUEIL DES FILMS. 1955. a. Can.$16.95. Office des Communications Sociales, 1340 Est, bd. St-Joseph, Montreal, PQ H2J 1M3, Canada. TEL 514-524-8223. FAX 514-524-8522. adv.; film rev. circ. 1,500.

791.43 US ISSN 0034-2238
REEL.* 1968. s-a. membership (avail. upon request to libraries, advertising agencies). Screen Actors Guild, New York Branch, 1515 Broadway, 44th Fl., New York, NY 10036-8901. Ed. Elizabeth Pennell. adv.; charts; illus. circ. 12,000.

778 US ISSN 0890-5231
RELEASE PRINT. 1979. 10/yr. $35 membership. Film Arts Foundation, 346 Ninth St., 2nd Fl., San Francisco, CA 94103. TEL 415-552-8760. FAX 415-552-0882. Ed. Robert Anbian. adv.; bk.rev.; film rev.; video rev. circ. 3,400. (back issues avail.) Document type: newsletter.
   Description: Covers public policy and the media arts, interviews with independent filmmakers, criticism, a local calendar and international information.

788.53 973 US
▼**REMEMBER;** the people and news we can't forget. 1994. bi-m. $14.97; newsstand price: $2.50. P M Publications, 6 Prowitt St., Norwalk, CT 06855. TEL 203-866-6688. Ed. Randall Beach; Pub. William Kanter. adv.; B&W page $2400. circ. 100,000 (paid). Document type: consumer publication.

778.5 791.43 US
REMINDER LIST OF ELIGIBLE RELEASES; annual Academy awards for distinguished achievements. a. $5. Academy of Motion Picture Arts and Sciences, 8949 Wilshire Blvd., Beverly Hills, CA 90211-1972. TEL 310-247-3000. FAX 310-859-9351. Ed. Byerly Woodward.
   Description: List of films with cast that are eligible for Academy awards consideration.

REPERTORY REPORT. see *THEATER*

791.43 RU ISSN 0034-4648
REPERTUAR KHUDOZHESTVENNOI SAMODEYATEL'NOSTI. 1955. s-m. $10.20. Izdatel'stvo Iskusstvo, Sobinovsky per. 3, 103009 Moscow, Russia. TEL 095-203-5872. Ed. L. Gamazova. circ. 55,000.

791.43 BE ISSN 0774-0115
PN1993.5.B4
REVUE BELGE DU CINEMA. (Text in French) 1963. a. 1300 BEF (foreign 1800 BEF). A P E C, 73, av. des Coccinelles, B-1170 Brussels, Belgium. TEL 32-2-672-94-59. Ed. Josette Debacker. bk.rev.; bibl.; illus. circ. 2,000. (back issues avail.) Indexed: Film Lit.Ind. (1974-), Int.Ind.Film Per. Document type: academic/scholarly publication.
   Description: Publishes critical articles examining in detail specific films, filmmakers, national film industries or styles, cinematic genres or movements. Issues are frequently devoted to a single theme or topic.

778.53 CN ISSN 0847-5911
PN1993.5.A1
REVUE CANADIENNE D'ETUDES CINEMATOGRAPHIQUES/CANADIAN JOURNAL OF FILM STUDIES. (Text in English, French) 1990. s-a. $35. Film Studies Association of Canada, c/o School for Studies in Art & Culture, Film Studies, Carleton University, 1125 Colonel by Drive, Ottawa, Ont. K1S 5B6. TEL 613-788-2600. FAX 613-788-3575. Ed. Zuzana M. Pick. adv.: page $250; 5 1/2 x 8. bk.rev. Document type: academic/scholarly publication.

778.5 CN ISSN 0843-6827
PN1993
REVUE DE LA CINEMATHEQUE. (Text in French) 1989. bi-m. $20 (foreign Can.$25). Cinematheque Quebecoise, 335 bd. de Maisonneuve E., Montreal, PQ H2X 1K1, Canada. TEL 514-842-9763. FAX 514-842-1816. Eds. Pierre Veronneau, Pierre Jutras. adv.; illus. circ. 40,000. (back issues avail.) Indexed: Can.B.P.I., Film Lit.Ind. (1989-), Int.Ind.Film Per., Intl.Ind.TV, Media Rev.Dig., Pt.de Rep. (1983-). Supersedes: Copie Zero (ISSN 0709-0471)

791.43 US ISSN 0035-7081
RIVISTA TECNICA DI CINEMATOGRAFIA; elettroacustica, televisione. (Text in English, French, German and Italian) 1950. s-a. free. Edizione Cinemeccanica S.p.A., Viale Campania 23, Milan, Italy. TEL 39-2-718941. FAX 39-2-70100470. Dir. Mariarosa Cecchi. adv. contact: Luigi Branca. charts; illus.; index; circ. 5,000 (controlled). Document type: trade publication.

791.43 JA
ROADSHOW. (Text in Japanese) 1972. m. Shueisha Inc., 5-10, 2-chome, Hitotsubashi, Chiyoda-ku, Tokyo 101-50, Japan. Ed. Mantaro Hanami. circ. 350,000.

791.43 US
ROGER EBERT'S VIDEO COMPANION. a. $16.95. Andrews and McMeel (Subsidiary of: Universal Press Syndicate), 4900 Main St., Kansas City, MO 64112. TEL 816-932-6700. Document type: consumer publication.
   Description: Reviews films available on videotape.

ROLLING STONE. see *MUSIC*

778.53 RM
ROMANIAN FILM. irreg. Romaniafilm, 25 Juliu Fucik St., Bucharest, Rumania. Indexed: Film Lit.Ind. (1978-), Int.Ind.Film Per. (until 1995).

791.43 367 DK ISSN 0902-1523
ROMANSK FILMKLUB. 1980. a. DKK 40 to non-members. Romansk Filmklub, Schleppegrellsgade 8, st. tv., DK-2200 Copenhagen N, Denmark. TEL 45-31-35-80-34. Ed. Hans Joergen Rundsten. adv. contact: Bent Johannsen. Document type: bulletin.
   Former titles (until 1983): R F Medlemsblad (ISSN 0109-0631); (until 1980): Romansk Filmklub. Medlemsblad (ISSN 0106-214X)

791.43 GW
RONDELL PROGRAMM. 1983. bi-m. Freizeitung Rondell, Lewitstr. 2b, 40547 Duesseldorf, Germany. TEL 0211-588915. circ. 7,500.

778 US
RUTGERS FILMS IN PRINT SERIES. 1982. irreg., latest 1993. price varies. Rutgers University Press, 109 Church St., New Brunswick, NJ 08901. TEL 908-932-7762. FAX 908-932-7039. Ed.Bd. film rev. Document type: monographic series.
   Description: In-depth studies of individual films, trends in filmmaking, and the works of individual directors. Discusses films from America and around the world.

778.53 US
PN1993.5.U65
S A G CALLSHEET. 1986. q. Screen Actors Guild, 5757 Wilshire Blvd., Los Angeles, CA 90036-3600. TEL 213-549-6652. FAX 213-549-6698. Indexed: Film Lit.Ind. (1988-). Document type: trade publication.
   Formerly (until 1994): Screen Actor Hollywood (ISSN 0890-5266)

791.43 AT ISSN 0036-1135
S C J.* (Sydney Cinema Journal) q. Aus.$3.50. c/o Ken Quinell & Michael Thornhill, Eds., Box 4430, Sydney, N.S.W., Australia. adv.; film rev.; illus.

791.4 US ISSN 0036-1682
TR845 CODEN: SMPJDF
S M P T E JOURNAL. 1916. m. $90 (effective 1995). Society of Motion Picture and Television Engineers, 595 W. Hartsdale Ave., White Plains, NY 10607-1824. TEL 914-761-1100. FAX 914-761-3115. TELEX 4995348. Ed. Jeffrey B. Friedman; Pub. Jeffrey B. Friedman. adv. contact: Marilyn Waldman. bk.rev.; abstr.; bibl.; illus.; index, cum.index every 5 yrs. circ. 10,500. (also avail. in microform from UMI,PMC; reprint service avail. from UMI) Indexed: A.S.& T.Ind., Appl.Mech.Rev., ASCA, Chem.Abstr., Curr.Cont., Eng.Ind., Excerpt.Med., Film Lit.Ind. (1973-), Graph.Arts Lit.Abstr., INSPEC, Photo.Abstr. Document type: trade publication.
   —BLDSC (8313.080000); CASDDS; Ei; Faxon; Genuine Article; SWETS; UMI; UnCover.
   Refereed Serial

791.43 384.55 US
SAN JOSE FILM & VIDEO PRODUCTION BINDER. 1981. m. $10. San Jose Film & Video Commission, 333 W. San Carlos St., Ste. 1000, San Jose, CA 95110. TEL 408-295-9600; 800-726-5673. FAX 408-295-3937. Ed. Vicki Ellis; Pub. Joe O'Kane. adv. contact: Vicki Ellis. circ. 1,000 (controlled). Document type: directory.
   Former titles (until 1992): San Jose Film and Video Commission Directory; Best Performance Film and Video Directory.
   Description: Covers local crew personnel available for hire, sample of locations available for filming, general services, and permit information.

MOTION PICTURES

SANTA ANA MOUNTAIN SERIES. see *HISTORY — History Of North And South America*

791.43   CE
SARASAVIYA. (Text in Sinhala) 1963. w. Lake House, D.R. Wijewardene Mawatha, P.O. Box 1168, Colombo 10, Sri Lanka. TEL 1-21181. Ed. Granville Silva. circ. 56,000.

741.5   US
SCANNERS. 1987. m. $10 (effective 1992). Southern California Anime Network, Box 261702, San Diego, CA 92126-1702. Ed. Adam Chaney.
    Description: Covers Japanese anime and comic, including English translations of Japanese animation, and news of events.

791.43   US
SCAREAPHANALIA. m. $0.60 per no. Box 489, Murray Hill Sta., New York, NY 10156-0489. Ed. Michael Gingold. film rev.; index.
    Description: Contains interviews with horror movie directors and performers.

778.53   US
SCENE (NEW YORK, 1990); at the movies. 1990. m. $12 (free in movie theaters). Scene, 240 E. 79th St., Ste. 10D, New York, NY 10021. TEL 212-737-8100. adv. contact: Liz Cohen. circ. 1,500,000 (controlled). **Document type:** consumer publication.
    Description: Covers new movies, actors and actresses, producers and directors.

791.43   GW   ISSN 0177-3739
SCHMALFILM; die Zeitschrift fuer Filmamateure. 1948. 6/yr. DM.88.80. Fachverlag Schiele und Schoen GmbH, Markgrafenstr. 11, 10969 Berlin, Germany. TEL 030-253752-0. FAX 030-2517248. Ed. R. Rendez-Voigt. adv.; bk.rev.; film rev.; illus.; stat.; mkt.; pat.; tr.mk.; index. circ. 2,800. **Document type:** bulletin.
    —CCC.
    Former titles (until 1985): Schmalfilm und Videofilmen (ISSN 0176-2230); (until 1979): Schmalfilm (ISSN 0036-620X)

SCIENCE FICTION ENTERTAINMENT. see *LITERATURE — Science Fiction, Fantasy, Horror*

SCIENCE FICTION MEDIA; Informationsdienst fuer science fiction and fantasy. see *LITERATURE — Science Fiction, Fantasy, Horror*

SCREEN. see *EDUCATION — Teaching Methods And Curriculum*

791.43   JA
SCREEN. (Text in Japanese) 1946. m. 14000 Yen. Kindai-Eiga Corp., Owaricho Bldg., 2F, 6-8-3 Ginza, Chuo-ku, Tokyo 104, Japan. TEL 03-5568-2811. FAX 03-5568-2818. Ed. Hisayuki Ui; Pub. Shuzo Kosugi. **Document type:** consumer publication.

SCREEN. see *COMMUNICATIONS — Television And Cable*

791.43   II   ISSN 0036-9551
SCREEN (BOMBAY). (Text in English) 1951. w. newsstand price: Rs.5. Indian Express Newspapers (Bombay) Pvt. Ltd., Express Towers, Nariman Point, Box 867, Bombay 400 021, India. TEL 022-2022627. FAX 022-2022139. TELEX 011-82585 INEX IN. Ed. Udaya Tara Nayar; Pub. V. Ranganathan. adv.; film rev. circ. 109,864. cols./p.: 8.

SCREEN ACTOR. see *LABOR UNIONS*

791.43 332   UK   ISSN 0965-9587
SCREEN FINANCE. s-m. £495($742) (effective 1995). Financial Times Telecoms & Media Publishing (Subsidiary of: Financial Times Group), Maple House, 149 Tottenham Court Rd., London W1P 9LL, England. TEL 0171-896-2234.
FAX 0171-896-2256. Pub. Helen Nicol. (also avail. in microform from UMI) **Document type:** newsletter.
●Also available online. Vendor(s): Lexis-Nexis.
    Description: Provides global reporting on the film industry: finance, production, exhibition and distribution.

791.4   UK   ISSN 0307-4617
PN1993.5.G7
SCREEN INTERNATIONAL. 1912. w. $175. E M A P Media (Subsidiary of: E M A P Business Communications), 33-39 Bowling Green Ln., London EC1R 0DA, England. TEL 0171-837-1212. FAX 0171-833-4519. E-mail: 74431,1401@compuserve.com. (Subscr. to: Readerlink, Audit House, 260 Field End Rd., Eastcote, Ruislip, Mddx. HA4 9LT, England. TEL 0181-868-4499. FAX 0181-429-3117) Ed. Oscar Moore; Pub. Eileen Dignan. adv.; B&W page £2057, color page £2882; trim 383 x 283; adv. contact: Anne-Marie Flyn. bk.rev.; film rev.; illus.; stat. circ. 9,585. **Document type:** trade publication.
    —CCC.
    Former titles: Screen International and Cinema T V Today; (until 1975): Cinema T V Today.
    Description: Aimed at senior personnel in the entertainment industry.

791   UK
SCREEN INTERNATIONAL FILM AND T V YEARBOOK. 1945. a. £60 (outside Europe £65). E M A P Media (Subsidiary of: E M A P Business Communications), 33-39 Bowling Green Ln., London EC1R 0DA, England. TEL 0171-837-1212. FAX 0171-833-4519. E-mail: 74431,1401@compuserve.com. (Subscr. to: Readerlink, Audit House, 260 Field End Rd., Eastcote, Ruislip, Mddx. HA4 9LT, England. TEL 0181-868-4499. FAX 0181-429-3117) Ed. Oscar Moore; Pub. Eileen Dignan. adv.; B&W page £1190, color page £1690; adv. contact: Alan Lowne. illus. circ. 7,000. **Document type:** directory.
    Former titles: International Film and T V Yearbook; British Film and T V Yearbook (ISSN 0068-1997)

791.43   US   ISSN 0080-8288
SCREEN WORLD. 1949. a. $19.95. Crown Publishers, Inc., 201 E. 50th St., New York, NY 10022. TEL 212-254-1600. Ed. John Willis.
    —Faxon.

791.43   II   ISSN 0971-2305
SCREEN WORLD. Variant title: Screen World Annual. (Text in English) 1987. a. Rs.500. Screen World Publication, 22-1738, M.H.B., Borivali, Bombay 400092, India. Ed. Rajendra Ojha. adv. **Document type:** directory.

791.43   UK
SCREENWRITER. 1992. q. £10. L S W - Screenwriter Publications, 187 Manygate Ln., Shepperton, Middx. TW17 9ER, England. TEL 01932-232952. (Subscr. to: L S W, 84 Wardour St., London W1V 3LF, England. TEL 0171-434-0942) Ed. Paul Gallagher. circ. 1,500. **Document type:** trade publication.
    Description: To inform, educate and entertain on screenwriting and the film industry.

778.53   FR   ISSN 0993-2097
SCRIPT. 1988. q. 100 F. (foreign 110 F.). Association pour la Fondation Internationale du Cinema et de l'Audiovisuel, 50 av. Marceau, 75008 Paris, France. TEL 47-23-70-30. FAX 47-20-78-17. Ed. Marie-Claude Cazin-Boujnah. adv.; bk.rev. **Indexed:** Film Lit.Ind. (1990-). **Document type:** bibliography.
    Description: Devoted to the preservation of the memory of film and television.

SCRIPTWRITERS MARKET. see *LITERATURE*

791   IT   ISSN 0037-0932
SEGNALAZIONI CINEMATOGRAFICHE. 1934. s-m. L.35000. Ente dello Spettacolo, Via Palombini 6, 00165 Rome, Italy. film rev. circ. 35,000. **Document type:** newspaper.

778.534   IT   ISSN 0393-3865
PN1993
SEGNOCINEMA; rivista cinematografica bimestrale. 1981. 6/yr. L.35000 (foreign L.60000). Cineforum di Vincenza, Via Giovanni Prati 34, 36100 Vicenza, Italy. TEL 0444-30097. film rev.; bibl.; illus.; index. circ. 5,000. (back issues avail.) **Indexed:** Film Lit.Ind. (1981-), Int.Ind.Film Per.

791.43   DK   ISSN 0106-2484
SEKVENS. 1973. irreg. (approx. 1/yr.). price varies. Koebenhavns Universitet, Institut for Film- & Medievidenskab, 78 Njalsgade, DK-2300 Copenhagen S, Denmark. TEL 45-35-32-81-01. FAX 45-35-32-81-10.
    Former titles (until 1978): Skrifter fra Institut for Filmvidenskab (ISSN 0105-3671); (until 1976): Koebenhavns Universitet. Institut for Filmvidenskab (ISSN 0105-3663)

778.534   FR   ISSN 0996-7109
SEPTIEME ARTIFICE; les arriere-cours de la grande boutique. m. 158 F. Art of Septieme, c/o Nadja de Lesseps, 29, rue Fondary, 75015 Paris, France.

791.43   CN   ISSN 0037-2412
PN1993
SEQUENCES. (Text in French) 1955. 8/yr. Can.$34 to individuals (foreign $52); institutions Can.$42. 1340, boul. St-Joseph est, Montreal, PQ H2J 1M3, Canada. TEL 514-729-6391. FAX 416-477-2821. (Subscr. to: C.P. 444, Outremont, PQ H2V 9Z9, Canada) Ed. Leo Bonneville. adv.; bk.rev.; film rev.; illus.; cum.index. circ. 3,500. (also avail. in microform from BNQ; back issues avail.) **Indexed:** Can.Per.Ind., Film Lit.Ind. (1973-), Int.Ind.Film Per., Intl.Ind.TV, Pt.de Rep. (1979-). **Document type:** consumer publication.
    Description: Provides reviews, interviews with actors and directors.

778.53 384.55   BL   ISSN 0104-1592
SET; cinema & video. (Supplement avail. bi-m.: Video Erotico) 1987. m. $85. Editora Azul, S.A., Av. Nacoes Unidas, 5777, 05479-900 Sao Paulo SP, Brazil. TEL 11-816-7866. FAX 11-813-9115. (Subscr. to: Rua do Curtume 769, 05065-900 Sao Paulo SP, Brazil. TEL 011-823-9100) Ed. Jose Augusto Lemos. adv.; color page $9500; trim 208 x 274. film rev.; video rev.; illus.; stat. circ. 42,000. **Document type:** consumer publication.
    Description: Presents reviews of new film releases. Profiles actors and actresses.

SHANGHAI YISHUJIA/SHANGHAI ARTIST. see *THEATER*

791.4   CC
SHANGYING HUABAO/SHANGHAI FILM STUDIO PICTORIAL. (Text in Chinese) m. $80. (Shanghai Dianying Zhipianchang - Shanghai Film Studio) Shangying Huabao Bianjibu, 595 Caoxibei Lu, Shanghai 200030, People's Republic of China. TEL 86-21-4386433. FAX 86-21-4382300. (Dist. in US by: China Books & Periodicals, Inc., 2929 24th St., San Francisco, CA 94110. TEL 415-282-2994)

791.43   CC
SHIJIE DIANYING/WORLD FILMS. (Text in Chinese) bi-m. Zhongguo Dianyingjia Xiehui - China Film Makers Association, 22 Beisanhuan Donglu, Beijing 100013, People's Republic of China. TEL 4219977.

791.43   UK
SHIVERS. m. £18 (U.S. and Canada $44; rest of world £20). Visual Imagination Ltd., 9 Blades Ct., Deodar Rd., London SW15 2NU, England. TEL 081-875-1520. FAX 081-875-1588. **Document type:** consumer publication.

792   US   ISSN 1074-5297
SHOOT. 1990. w. $69. B P I Communications, Inc. (New York), 1515 Broadway, New York, NY 10036. TEL 212-764-7300. FAX 212-536-5321. Ed. Peter Caranicas. circ. 15,000. **Document type:** trade publication.
    —UMI.
    Formerly: Back Stage Shoot (ISSN 1055-9825)
    Description: For the commercial production and advertising industries. Special feature issues cover industry events such as the Clio Awards, NAB Convention, ITS Convention, and SMPTE.

SHOOT COMMERCIAL PRODUCTION DIRECTORY. see *COMMUNICATIONS — Television And Cable*

791.43   UK   ISSN 0037-4806
PN1993
SIGHT AND SOUND; the international film monthly. 1932. m. £36 in US & Canada. British Film Institute, 21 Stephen St., London W1P 1PL, England. TEL 071-255-1444. FAX 071-436-2327. TELEX 27624-BFILDN-G. (Subscr. to: Tower Publishing Services, Tower House, Sovereign Park, Market Harborough, Leics. LE16 9EF, England. TEL 0858-468888. FAX 0858-432164; U.S. subscr. to: Eastern News Distributors Inc., 1671 E. 16th St., Ste. 176, Brooklyn, NY 11229-2901) Ed. Philip Dodd; Pub. Caroline Moore. adv.: B&W page £880; color page £1350; adv. contact: Mark Pearson. bk.rev.; film rev.; illus.; index. circ. 35,000. (also avail. in microform from MIM; microfilm from WMP) **Indexed:** Acad.Ind., Art Ind., Arts & Hum.Cit.Ind., Bk.Rev.Ind. (1976-), Br.Hum.Ind., Child.Bk.Rev.Ind. (1976-), Curr.Cont., Film Lit.Ind. (1973-), Gdlns., Hum.Ind., Int.Ind.Film Per., Intl.Ind.TV, Media Rev.Dig., Mid.East: Abstr.& Ind. **Document type:** academic/scholarly publication, consumer publication.
—BLDSC (8275.270000); Faxon; Genuine Article; SWETS; UnCover. **CCC.**
Incorporates: Monthly Film Bulletin (ISSN 0027-0407)
Description: Contains authoritative and entertaining articles on contemporary and classic cinema from Hong Kong to Hollywood. Reviews every feature film given major distribution and lists the full credits for each one.

SILVER SCREEN. see *BUSINESS AND ECONOMICS — Investments*

778   BN   ISSN 0587-0054
SINEAST/FILM MAKER; filmski casopis. (Text in Serbo-Croatian) 1967. q. $15. Kino Savez Bosne i Hercegovine, Strosmajerova 1-II, 71000 Sarajevo, Bosnia Hercegovina. TEL 071 217-002. (Co-sponsor: SIZ Kinematografije Bosne i Hercegovine) Ed. Nikola Stojanovic. adv.; bk.rev.; film rev.; cum.index: 1967-1983. circ. 2,000. (back issues avail.)
Description: Discusses film history, film makers, film events.

791.43   IT
SIPARIO. 1946. m. L.70000 (Europe L.125000, elsewhere L.160000). Cama s.a.s., Via S. Marco 34, 20121 Milan, Italy. TEL 39-2-6572654. FAX 39-2-6552014. Ed. Mario Maria Giorgetti. adv.: B&W page L.3179000, color page L.5500000. circ. 23,000. **Indexed:** M.L.A.

079.54   IT
SITARA TELUGU FILM WEEKLY. (Text in Telugu) 1976. w. newsstand price: Rs.3. Eenadu Complex, Somajiguda, Hyderabad 500 482, India. TEL 223422. TELEX 0425-6521. Ed. Ramoji Rao. adv.: B&W page Rs.10000, color page Rs.20000; 420 x 280; adv. contact: I. Venkat. circ. 53,326. cols./p.: 5.

791.43   IT
SIVARANJANI; Telugu film weekly. (Text in Telugu) 1985. w. newsstand price: Rs.4. Padma Arun Publishers Pvt. Ltd., 7-1, Azamabad Industrial Area, Hyderabad 600 020, India. TEL 616261. TELEX 0425-6894 UDYM IN. Ed. A. Bala Reddy. adv.: B&W page Rs.14000, color page Rs.20000; 400 x 260; adv. contact: K.R.P. Reddy. circ. 73,392.

778.5 384.55   NE   ISSN 0166-1787
SKRIEN. 1968. 6/yr. fl.62.50 (foreign fl.92) (effective 1995-1996). (Ministerie van Welzijn, Volksgezondheid en Cultuur, Afdeling Film) Stichting Skrien, Vondelpark 3, 1071 AA Amsterdam, Netherlands. TEL 31-20-6893831. FAX 31-20-6890438. E-mail: skrien@xs4all.nl. Ed. Mieke Bernink. adv.; bk.rev.; film rev. circ. 5,000. **Indexed:** Film Lit.Ind. (1973-), Int.Ind.Film Per., Intl.Ind.TV.
—SWETS.
Description: Publishes articles and essays on film, television, film and TV production in the Netherlands, film history and theory.

791.433 384.55   DK   ISSN 0107-8119
SMALFILM OG VIDEO. 1953. 6/yr. DKK 60. Danmarks Film- og Videoamatoerer, c/o Hans Michael Lind, Kongevej 35 A, lejl. 26, DK-2300 Copenhagen, Denmark. adv.: B&W page DKK 500; adv. contact: Aage Hertzum. illus.
Former titles (until 1981): Smalfilm (ISSN 0107-8100); Smalfilmbladet.

SMASH HITS MAGAZINE. see *MUSIC*

778.534   SP   ISSN 1130-5541
SOCIEDAD DE ESTUDIOS VASCOS. CUADERNOS DE SECCION. CINEMATOGRAFIA. 1986. irreg. Eusko Ikaskuntza, Legazpi, 10-1, 20004 Donostia-San Sebastian, Spain. TEL 425111.

SOUNDTRACK!. see *MUSIC*

SPECIAL EFFECTS & STUNTS GUIDE. see *BUSINESS AND ECONOMICS — Trade And Industrial Directories*

778.53 384.55   US   ISSN 1051-0230
PN1993
SPECTATOR (LOS ANGELES). 1982. 2/yr. $10 to individuals (foreign $15); institutions $20 (foreign $25). University of Southern California, School of Cinema - Television, University Park, Los Angeles, CA 90089-2211. TEL 213-740-3334. FAX 213-740-9471. Ed. Marsha Kinder. bk.rev. **Indexed:** Film Lit.Ind. (1985-). **Document type:** academic/scholarly publication.

791.43   GW   ISSN 0071-4933
SPIELFILMLISTE. 1958. a. DM.11.50. (Institut Jugend, Film, Fernsehen) KoPaed Verlag, Pfaelzer-Wald-Str. 64, 81539 Munich, Germany. TEL 089-68989200. FAX 089-68989111. Ed. Hans Strobel. adv. circ. 3,500. **Document type:** consumer publication.
Formerly: Filmliste.

SPOTLIGHT CHILDRENS. see *THEATER*

778.5   CE
SRI LANKA FILM ANNUAL. (Text in Sinhalese) no. 28, 1975. a. Rs.6.95. National Catholic Film Office, St. Phillip Neri's Church, Katukurunda, Kalutara, Sri Lanka. film rev.

STAGE SCREEN & RADIO. see *LABOR UNIONS*

STAGECAST-IRISH STAGE AND SCREEN DIRECTORY. see *THEATER*

791.43   II   ISSN 0038-9862
STAR & STYLE. 1965. m. newsstand price: Rs.15. Maurya Publications Pvt. Ltd., No.20-21, Centaur Hotel, Juhu Beach, Juhu Tara Rd., Bombay 400 049, India. TEL 6116632. Ed. Vanit Jain. adv.: B&W page Rs.12000, color page Rs.24000; bleed 205 x 270. circ. 87,000.

791.43 780   US   ISSN 1060-9997
CT120
STAR GUIDE (YEAR); where to contact movie, TV stars and other celebrities. 1987. a. $12.95. Axiom Information Resources, Box 8015-T, Ann Arbor, MI 48107. TEL 313-761-4842. Ed. Pat Wilson. circ. 8,000. **Document type:** directory.
Description: Publishes the names and addresses of over 3,000 celebrities in the entertainment field, sports, politics, business, art, and print media.

STAR TREK: THE OFFICIAL FAN CLUB MAGAZINE. see *COMMUNICATIONS — Television And Cable*

STARLOG; magazine of the future. see *COMMUNICATIONS — Television And Cable*

778.534   BE   ISSN 0776-0698
STARS. (Text in French) 1988. q. 755 BEF (foreign 849 BEF) (effective 1996). A.S.B.L. Grand Angle-Opvac, Rue d'Arschot 29, 5660 Mariembourg, Belgium. TEL 32-60-312168. FAX 32-60-312937. Ed. Jacques Noel. adv.; bk.rev.; film rev.; illus. circ. 1,500. **Indexed:** Film Lit.Ind. (1990-).
Description: Covers the lives and careers of stars and other actors in the film industry.

791.43   GW
STARS; Kino, Szene, Musik. 1990. m. DM.100. T und M Verlagsgesellschaft mbH, Borkumstr. 2, 13189 Berlin, Germany. TEL 030-47805133. FAX 030-47805131. Ed. Christoph Meier-Siem. adv.; bk.rev.; film rev.; illus. circ. 500,000. (tabloid format) **Document type:** consumer publication.

STELLE FILANTI. see *BIOGRAPHY*

MOTION PICTURES   4803

778.5   NE
STICHTING FILM EN WETENSCHAP. CATALOGUE 16MM FILMS AND VIDEO PROGRAMMES.* 1978. irreg. Stichting Film en Wetenschap, Zeeburgerkade 8, 1019 HA Amsterdam, Netherlands. TEL 31-20-6659086. FAX 31-20-6652966.
Formerly: Stichting Film en Wetenschap. Catalogue 16mm Films.

STUDII SI CERCETARI DE ISTORIA ARTEI. SERIA TEATRU, MUZICA, CINEMATOGRAFIE/STUDIES AND RESEARCH IN ART HISTORY. SERIES: THEATRE, MUSIC, CINEMATOGRAPHY. see *THEATER*

SUN BELT JOURNAL. see *BUSINESS AND ECONOMICS*

SUSHMITA. see *LITERATURE*

791.43   AT
SYDNEY FILM FESTIVAL PROGRAMME. 1954. a. Aus.$15($20) Sydney Film Festival, P.O. Box 950, Glebe, N.S.W. 2037, Australia. TEL 61-2-6603844. FAX 61-2-6928793. TELEX 75111. Ed. Paul Byrnes. adv. contact: Jennifer Neighbour. film rev. circ. 5,000. (back issues avail.) **Document type:** catalog.

384.55   US
SYNC: THE REGENT JOURNAL OF FILM AND VIDEO. 1985. s-a. $5. Regent University, College of Communication and the Arts, School of Television and Film, Virginia Beach, VA 23464-9800. TEL 804-523-7943. FAX 804-424-7051. film rev.; video rev.; bibl.; illus. circ. 400. **Document type:** academic/scholarly publication.
Formerly (until vol.7): Film Witness.
Description: Displays the research of graduate students in the discipline.

371.3 791.43   NE   ISSN 0039-8330
T F C NIEUWS. (Text in Dutch) 1968. 4/yr. free. (Technisch Film Centrum) T F C Audiovisuele Media, Arnhemsestraatweg 17, 6881 NB Velp, Netherlands. TEL 31-85-693111. FAX 31-85-646818. adv.; film rev.; illus.; circ. 10,000. (controlled). **Document type:** newsletter.
Formerly: Visualeiten.
Description: Provides information about training videos and films, methods and guides available in Belgium and the Netherlands.

T.G.I.F. CASTING NEWS. see *OCCUPATIONS AND CAREERS*

T V COLLECTOR. see *COMMUNICATIONS — Television And Cable*

791.4   US
T V M S TIGER BEAT. 1957. bi-m. $14.95 (foreign $19.95). Sterling - Macfadden Partnership, 35 Wilbur St., Lynbrook, NY 11563. TEL 516-593-1220. FAX 516-593-0065. adv.; bk.rev.; film rev.; rec.rev.; illus.; circ. 150,000 (paid). **Document type:** consumer publication.
Supersedes: T V and Movie Screen (ISSN 0041-4492)
Description: Covers film, television, and pop music stars admired by teenagers.

TAKE ONE; the video entertainment newspaper. see *COMMUNICATIONS — Video*

791.4 384.55   FR   ISSN 0247-6010
TECHNICIEN DU FILM ET DE LA VIDEO; magazine d'information des professionnels du cinema, de la television, et de l'audio-visuel. 1954. m. 350 F. (foreign 450 F.). Editions Dujarric, 33 av. des Champs-Elysees, 75008 Paris, France. TEL 43-59-24-84. FAX 42-25-59-97. (Subscr. to: IF Diffusion, 31 Champs-Elysees, 75008 Paris, France. TEL 42-56-00-19) Ed. Henriette Dujarric. adv.; illus.; tr.lit. **Document type:** trade publication.
Formerly (until 1980): Technicien du Film (ISSN 0040-103X); Incorporates (in 1973): Technique, l'Expoitation Cinematographique (ISSN 1142) ; which was formed by the merger of: Exploitation Cinematographique (ISSN 1142-6063); Technique Cinematographique (ISSN 1142-6055); both of which supersede (in 1969): Technique, l'Exploitation Cinematographique (ISSN 1142-6047); Which was formed by the merger of (1949-1965): Exploitation Cinematographique (ISSN 1142-6039); (1930-1965): Technique Cinematographique (ISSN 1142-6020).

TECHTRENDS; for leaders in education and training. see *EDUCATION — Teaching Methods And Curriculum*

MOTION PICTURES

TEKHNIKA KINO I TELEVIDENIYA/MOTION PICTURE AND TELEVISION TECHNOLOGY. see COMMUNICATIONS — Television And Cable

778.5 CN ISSN 0837-2446
TELEFILM CANADA ANNUAL REPORT. 1968. a. free. Canadian Film Development Corporation, Telefilm Canada, 600 rue de la Gauchetiere, Ouest, 25th Fl., Montreal, PQ H3B 4L2, Canada. TEL 514-283-6363. circ. 3,000. **Document type:** corporate report.
Formerly (until 1984): C F D C Annual Report (ISSN 0382-2273)

TELERAMA. see COMMUNICATIONS — Television And Cable

778.53 US ISSN 1063-9063
TEN THOUSAND WORDS!. 1976. 10/yr. $75. Behavioral Images, Inc., 302 Leland St., Ste. 101, Bloomington, IL 61701-5646. TEL 309-829-3931. FAX 309-829-9677. Ed. Steve Johnson. bk.rev.; index. circ. 3,000. (also avail. in talking book; reprint service avail.) **Document type:** newsletter.
Description: Strategies, research, terminology, bibliographies, case studies about appraisal of all AV media for any purpose.

791.43 384.55 US
THEY WON'T STAY DEAD. 1989. q. $12. Brian Johnson, Ed. & Pub., 11 Werner Rd., Greenville, PA 16125. TEL 412-588-3471. adv. contact: Brian Johnson. bk.rev.; music rev.; circ. 500 (paid). **Document type:** newsletter.
Description: Covers cult films, music, and sensationalistic nonfiction.

THIS IS THE SPINAL TAP ZINE. see MUSIC

790 US
TIAN WAI TIAN/SKY OUTSIDE SKY. (Text in Chinese) m. $35.90. China Books & Periodicals, Inc., 2929 24th St., San Francisco, CA 94110. TEL 415-282-2994. FAX 415-282-0994.

791.43 AG ISSN 0040-7283
TIEMPO DE CINE.* 1960. m. $1.25 per no. Cineclub Nucleo, Lavalle 2016, 8 Piso, Of. 17, Buenos Aires, Argentina. Ed. Hector Vena. adv.; illus.

791.4 II ISSN 0040-7836
PN1993
TIME & TIDE; Indian journal of international films - TV festivals. (Text in English) 1952. fortn. Rs.120 (foreign $45). 1 Ansari Rd., Daryaganj, New Delhi 110 002, India. TEL 91-11-327-2046. FAX 91-11-327-1454. Ed. Devendra Kumar. adv.; bk.rev.; film rev.; illus. circ. 50,000. (tabloid format; also avail. in record) **Document type:** trade publication.
Description: Details festival activities as well as socio-economic and political aspects of the Indian film industry.

TOUCH MAGAZINE. see MUSIC

778.534 GW ISSN 0942-430X
TREFFPUNKT KINO. 1984. m. DM.20. Casablanca Verlag GmbH, Stahlgruberring 11a, 81829 Munich, Germany. TEL 089-4209030. FAX 089-42090311. Eds. Peter von Schall, Ulrich Scheele. adv.; film rev. circ. 350,000. (back issues avail.) **Document type:** consumer publication.
Formerly: Treffpunkt Film.

791.43 CN ISSN 0823-678X
TRIBUTE. 1984. bi-m. Can.$17.50 (in U.S. Can.$24.50, elsewhere Can.$31.50). Tribute Publishing, Inc., 900 A Don Mills Rd., Ste. 1000, Don Mills, ON M3C 1V6, Canada. TEL 416-445-0544. FAX 416-445-2894. Ed. Sandra I. Stewart. adv. contact: Donnalyn Coyne. circ. 600,000 (controlled). (back issues avail.) **Document type:** consumer publication.
Formerly: Tribute Goes to the Movies (ISSN 0826-1210)
Description: Focuses on new movies, actors, and directors in the entertainment business.

ULTIMO (MUENSTER); Muensters Stadtmagazin. see LITERARY AND POLITICAL REVIEWS

808.23 US ISSN 0279-6244
UNDER WESTERN SKIES. Issued with: Cliffhanger (ISSN 1073-7049) 1978. irreg. $14 for 4 nos. World of Yesterday, Rte. 3, Box 263H, Waynesville, NC 28786. TEL 704-648-5647. Ed. Linda S. Downey; Pub. Linda S. Downey. adv.: page $25; 9 1/2 x 7. bk.rev.; film rev.; music rev.; circ. 1,000 (paid). (back issues avail.) **Document type:** consumer publication.
Description: Deals with the Old West we remember from the silver screen, the smaller screen of the T.V., and that magical box, the radio.

770 UK ISSN 0267-8497
PN1995.9.E96
UNDERCUT. 1981. s-a. £8($30) to individuals; institutions £14. (Arts Council of Great Britain) Undercut, c/o 17 West Grove, London SE10 8QT, England. (Subscr. to: Undercut, c/o 47 George Downing Estate) Ed. Nina Danino. adv.; bk.rev. circ. 1,000. (back issues avail.) **Indexed:** Film Lit.Ind. (1985-).
Description: Focuses on British artists working on film and video.

UNION CATALOG OF MOTION PICTURE MUSIC. see MUSIC

791.43 SG ISSN 0253-195X
UNIR CINEMA; revue du cinema africain. (Text in French) no.36, 1973. q. 1000 Fr.CFA. Diocese de Saint-Louis, B.P. 160, Rue Neuville 1, Saint-Louis, Senegal. TEL 61-10-27. FAX 61-24-08. (Subscr. to: P.J. Vast, 8 rue Duret, B.P. 160, Saint-Louis, Senegal) Ed. Pierre Sagna. adv.; bk.rev.; film rev. circ. 1,000. **Document type:** bulletin.
Description: Provides news from the African cinema.

UNIR: ECHO DE SAINT LOUIS. see LITERATURE

UNIVERSITA DEGLI STUDI DI PARMA. ISTITUTO DI STORIA DELL'ARTE. CATALOGHI. see ART

URB. see MUSIC

791.43 MY
UTUSAM FILEM DAN FESHEN. fortn. 46M Jalan Lima, Off Jalan Chan Sow Lin, Kuala Lumpur, Malaysia. TEL 03-487055. Ed. Mustafa Bin Abdul Rahim. circ. 35,000.

V R; mensile di videoregistrazione creativa. (Video Review) see COMMUNICATIONS — Video

VARIETY. see THEATER

791.43 US ISSN 0897-4373
PN1993
VARIETY'S FILM REVIEWS. 1907. biennial, latest vol.23 for years 1993-1994. $187 (effective 1994); 23-vol. set (1907-1994) $1750. R.R. Bowker, A Reed Reference Publishing company, 121 Chanlon Rd., New Providence, NJ 07974. TEL 908-464-6800. FAX 908-665-6688. TELEX 138 755. (Subscr. to: Order Dept., Box 31, New Providence, NJ 07974-9903. TEL 800-521-8110) cum.index. (back issues avail.) **Document type:** directory, academic/scholarly publication.
Description: Contains all full feature film reviews, both foreign and domestic. Lists the principal cast and credits, running time, first show date, studio, country of origin, and English translation of titles in a foreign language. These reviews are published according to review date and are fully indexed in the Film Title Index and the Director Index.

778.53 US ISSN 1066-8810
PN1992.95
VARIETY'S VIDEO DIRECTORY PLUS. 1986. a. $495. R.R. Bowker, A Reed Reference Publishing company, 121 Chanlon Rd., New Providence, NJ 07974. TEL 908-665-2866. FAX 908-665-3528. TELEX 138 755. (avail. for MS-DOS version) **Document type:** bibliography, directory.
●Available only on CD-ROM. Producer(s): Bowker - Reed Reference Electronic Publishing.

791.43 US ISSN 0149-1830
PN1993 CODEN: VLTREI
VELVET LIGHT TRAP; review of cinema. 1971. s-a. $18 to individuals; institutions $35 (foreign $39). University of Texas Press, Box 7819, Austin, TX 78713. TEL 512-471-4531. FAX 512-320-0668. TELEX 776453 UTEXPRES AUS. E-mail: leah@utpress.ppb.utexas.edu. Ed.Bd. adv. contact: Leah Dixon. bk.rev.; illus. circ. 500. (also avail. in microform from UMI; reprint service avail. from UMI) **Indexed:** Film Lit.Ind. (1973-), Int.Ind.Film Per. —BLDSC (9154.302000); Faxon; UnCover.
Description: Features critical essays exploring alternative methodological approaches to the analysis of American film and television. Studies debate about critical theoretical and historical issues.

VERONICA; weekblad voor radio en TV. see COMMUNICATIONS — Television And Cable

778.5 AT ISSN 1036-1839
VICTORIA. STATE FILM CENTRE. VIDEO CATALOGUE. 1954. irreg. price varies. State Film Centre of Victoria, 17 St. Andrews Pl., E. Melbourne, Vic. 3002, Australia. Ed.Bd. circ. 6,000. **Document type:** catalog.
Former titles (until 1988): Victoria. State Film Centre. New Films and Videotapes (ISSN 0810-4476); Victoria. State Film Centre. New Films.

VIDEO AKTIV. see COMMUNICATIONS — Video

VIDEO & FILMS. see COMMUNICATIONS — Video

791.43 GW
VIDEO FILMFUEHRER. 1993. a. DM.19.80. Vereinigte Motor-Verlage GmbH und Co. KG, Leuschnerstr. 1, 70162 Stuttgart, Germany. TEL 0711-1821226. FAX 0711-1821349. Ed. Tim Cole; Pub. Gernot Hempelmann. adv. contact: Peter Michael Heyde. circ. 30,000. **Document type:** directory.

VIDEO MAGAZINE. see COMMUNICATIONS — Video

791.43 US
VIDEO MAGAZINE GUIDE (YEAR). a. newsstand price: $7.99. Ballantine Books, 210 E. 50th St., New York, NY 10022. TEL 212-751-2600. **Document type:** consumer publication.
Description: Rates well-known and obscure feature and made-for-TV films.

VIDEO PLUS FILM; mesicnik pro audiovizualni tvorby a techniku. see COMMUNICATIONS — Video

791.43 US ISSN 0196-8793
VIDEO REVIEW.* 1980-1992 (Apr.); resumed. 8/yr. $15.97 (foreign $35.97). Media Works Group Inc., P.O. Box 2047, Larchmont, NY 10538-8247. TEL 914-576-8800. FAX 914-576-8841. Ed. Kurt Zahner. adv.: B&W page $7880, color page $9775; trim 8 x 10 1/2. bk.rev. circ. 175,000. (also avail. in microform from UMI; reprint service avail. from UMI) **Indexed:** Mag.Ind. **Document type:** trade publication.
●Also available online. Vendor(s): University Microfilms International.
—UMI; UnCover.
Description: Covers the entire home entertainment industry.

VIDEO UIT & THUIS. see COMMUNICATIONS — Video

778.53 US ISSN 0888-3297
VIDEO VISION.* (Text in English, Spanish) 1984. bi-m. $14.95. Video Vision, Inc., 7454 S.W. 48th St., Miami, FL 33155. TEL 305-262-1505. Ed. Lomberto L. Perez. adv.
Description: Contains articles on video equipment and cassettes. Includes information on new video releases in English and Spanish.

778.53 384.55 US
VIDEOHOUND'S GOLDEN MOVIE RETRIEVER. 1992. a. $17.95. Gale Research Inc., 835 Penobscot Bldg., Detroit, MI 48226. TEL 313-961-2242. FAX 313-961-6083.

791.43 UK
VIDEOLOG. fortn. £180. Trade Service Information Ltd., Cherryholt Rd., Stamford, Lincs. PE9 2HT, England. TEL 01780-64331. FAX 01780-482067. circ. 1,570 (paid). **Document type:** directory.

VIEWFINDER. see EDUCATION — Teaching Methods And Curriculum

MOTION PICTURES — ABSTRACTING, BIBLIOGRAPHIES, STATISTICS

791.43   CN   ISSN 0840-4313
VISUAL MEDIA. (Text in English, French) 1972. 5/yr. Can.$45 (US Can.$50, elsewhere Can.$65). Association for the Advancement of Visual Media - Association pour l'Avancement des Medias Visuels, 3-1750 The Queensway, Ste. 1341, Etobicoke, ON M9C 5HS, Canada. TEL 416-761-6056. Ed. Dorothy Smith. adv.: page Can.$139; adv. contact: Dorothy Smith. bk.rev.; film rev.; index. circ. 350. (also avail. in microform from MML) **Indexed:** Can.B.P.I. **Document type:** consumer publication, directory.
    Formerly (until 1988): Newsletter Called Fred (ISSN 0315-6923); **Supersedes:** Ontario Film Association. Bulletin (ISSN 0030-2910)

778.5   FR
VIVRE LE CINEMA. 1977. irreg. Editions Jacques Glenat, 6 rue Lieutenant Chanaron, 38000 Grenoble, France. Ed. Gilbert Hus.

VYTVARNICTVO, FOTOGRAFIA, FILM; mesacnik pre zaujmovu umelecku cinnost. see *ART*

792   US
WE REMEMBER DEAN INTERNATIONAL. 1978. bi-m. $17 (Canada $19; elsewhere $25). (We Remember Dean International) Sylvia Bongiovanni, Ed. & Pub., Box 5025, Fullerton, CA 92635. adv. contact: Sylvia Bongiovanni. bk.rev. circ. 600. **Document type:** newsletter.
    Formerly: We Remember Dean.
    Description: Dedicated to preserving the memory of James Dean.

791.43   US
▼**WESTERN CLIPPINGS.** 1995. bi-m. $25 (outside N. America $30). Boyd Magers, Ed. & Pub., 1901 Page Pl. N.E., Albuquerque, NM 87112. TEL 505-292-0049. **Document type:** consumer publication.
    Description: Covers contemporary and historic westerns made for the silver screen and T.V.

791.43   US
WESTERNS & SERIALS. 1974. s-a. $12 (foreign $16). Norman Kietzer, Ed. & Pub., Rt. 1, Box 103, Vernon Center, MN 56090. TEL 507-549-3677. FAX 507-549-3788. adv.; bk.rev. circ. 2,000. (back issues avail.)
    Former titles: Favorite Westerns; Serial World.
    Description: Club magazine for those interested in old westerns and serials.

WHAT'S ON VIDEO AND CINEMA. see *COMMUNICATIONS — Video*

WHO'S WHO IN CANADIAN FILM AND TELEVISION (YEAR)/QUI EST QUI AU CINEMA ET A LA TELEVISION AU CANADA. see *BIOGRAPHY*

WHO'S WHO ON THE SCREEN. see *BIOGRAPHY*

778.534   US   ISSN 0160-6840
PN1993
WIDE ANGLE; a film quarterly of theory, criticism and practice. 1978. q. $24 to individuals (foreign $32.80); institutions $58 (foreign $66.80). (Athens Center for Film and Video) Johns Hopkins University Press, Journals Publishing Division, 2715 N. Charles St., Baltimore, MD 21218. TEL 410-516-6987. FAX 410-516-6968. Ed. Ruth Bradley. adv. contact: Tara Dorai-Berry. bk.rev.; film rev.; illus.; index. circ. 1,150. (also avail. in microform from UMI; back issues avail.) **Indexed:** Arts & Hum.Cit.Ind., Curr.Cont., Film Lit.Ind. (1976-), Int.Ind.Film Per., Intl.Ind.TV, M.L.A., Media Rev.Dig. **Document type:** academic/scholarly publication.
    —BLDSC (9315.557500); Faxon; Genuine Article; UMI; UnCover. **CCC.**
    Description: Presents current scholarship in film studies and examines topics ranging from international cinema to the history and aesthetics of film.

791.43   UK   ISSN 0269-2600
WORLD CINEMA. 1986. a. £19.95. Flicks Books, 29 Bradford Rd., Trowbridge, Wilts. BA14 9AN, England. TEL 01225-767728. FAX 01225-760418. Pub. Matthew Stevens. bibl.; illus.; stat.; circ. 3,000 (paid). (back issues avail.) **Document type:** academic/scholarly publication.
    —BLDSC (9353.225000).

WORLD OF FANDOM. see *LITERATURE — Science Fiction, Fantasy, Horror*

778.5 384.55   US
WORLDWIDE DIRECTORY OF FILM AND VIDEO FESTIVALS AND EVENTS. 1988. a. $20. Council on International Nontheatrical Events, Inc., 1001 Connecticut Ave., N.W., Ste. 638, Washington, DC 20036. TEL 202-785-1136. FAX 202-785-4114. Ed. Jay Gemski. circ. 3,000. **Document type:** directory.

791.43   UK   ISSN 0043-9452
WRANGLER'S ROOST; a magazine for the B-Western aficionado. 1970. 3/yr. $7.50. Colin Momber Photography, 23 Sabrina Way, Stoke Bishop, Bristol 9, England. adv.; bk.rev.; film rev. circ. 350. (processed) **Document type:** consumer publication.

WRITERS GUILD OF AMERICA, EAST. NEWSLETTER. see *LITERATURE*

XIJU YU DIANYING/THEATRE AND CINEMA. see *THEATER*

YINGJU XINZUO/NEW FILM AND PLAY SCRIPTS. see *LITERATURE*

791.43 792   CC
YINGJU YISHU/ART OF FILM AND DRAMA. (Text in Chinese) bi-m. Guangxi Wenhua Ting - Guangxi Bureau of Cultural Affairs, 13 Minzhu Lu, Nanning, Guangxi 530023, People's Republic of China. TEL 27924. Ed. Cai Liyang.

YINGSHI WENXUE/FILM AND TELEVISION LITERATURE. see *LITERATURE*

791.43   CC
YINMU NEIWAI/AROUND FILM. (Text in Chinese) m. Sichuansheng Dianying Faxing Fangying Gongsi - Sichuan Film Distribution and Projection Company, 21 Qingnian Lu, Chengdu, Sichuan 610016, People's Republic of China. TEL 22921-160.

778.53   NO   ISSN 0800-1464
PN1993
Z; filmtidsskrift. 1983. 4/yr. NOK 180. Norsk Filmklubforbund, Teatergaten 3, N-0180 Oslo, Norway. TEL 47-22-11-42-17. FAX 47-22-20-79-81. Ed. Jon Iversen. adv.; bk.rev.; film rev, illus. circ. 2,500. **Indexed:** Film Lit.Ind. (1986-).
    Description: Focuses on film theory and film history. Covers Norwegian short and feature films, as well as international films, with emphasis on art films.

ZEITSCHRIFT FUER URHEBER- UND MEDIENRECHT. see *LAW*

778.43   GW   ISSN 0724-7656
ZELLULOID. 1978. irreg. (2-4/yr.) DM.18($13) Arbeitsgemeinschaft fuer Medientheorie und -praxis e.V., c/o Filmhaus, Luxemburger Str. 72, D-5000 Cologne 1, Germany. adv.; bk.rev. circ. 1,000. (back issues avail.) **Indexed:** Film Lit.Ind. (1987-).

ZHONGGUO DIANYING NIANJIAN/CHINA FILM YEARBOOK. see *MOTION PICTURES — Abstracting, Bibliographies, Statistics*

ZHONGGUO GUANGBO YINGSHI/CHINESE RADIO, FILM AND TELEVISION. see *COMMUNICATIONS — Radio*

ZHURNAL NAUCHNOI I PRIKLADNOI FOTOGRAFII. see *PHOTOGRAPHY*

778.53   CN   ISSN 0707-9389
24 IMAGES. (Text in French) 1979. bi-m. Can.$23.75 to individuals; institutions Can.$29.50 (foreign Can.$38). 3962 rue Laval, Montreal, PQ H2W 2J2, Canada. TEL 514-286-1688. Ed. Marie-Claude Loiselle; Pub. Claude Racine. adv.; bk.rev. circ. 10,800. (back issues avail.) **Indexed:** Film Lit.Ind. (1985-), Int.Ind.Film Per., Pt.de Rep. (1981-).
    Description: Covers the history and future of Quebec cinema, its celebrated producers and directors along with those less well known. Offers reviews and interviews.

384.55   BL
1000 VIDEOS. 1989. a. Editora Azul, S.A., Av. Nacoes Unidas, 5777, 05479-900 Sao Paulo SP, Brazil. TEL 11-816-7866. FAX 11-813-9115. TELEX 11-83178 EDAZ. Ed. Angelo Rossi. adv.: color page $7000; trim 208 x 274. illus. circ. 30,000. **Document type:** consumer publication, directory.
    Description: Critical guide to movies on video available in Brazil. Arranged by genre.

MOTION PICTURES — Abstracting, Bibliographies, Statistics

BIO-BIBLIOGRAPHIES IN THE PERFORMING ARTS. see *THEATER — Abstracting, Bibliographies, Statistics*

BOERNEBIBLIOTEKSKATALOG. BILLED- OG LYDMEDIER. see *CHILDREN AND YOUTH — Abstracting, Bibliographies, Statistics*

791 016   UK   ISSN 1357-0048
PN1998.A1
THE BRITISH NATIONAL FILM & VIDEO GUIDE. Abbrevated title: B N F V G. 1963. q. (plus a. supplement). £120 (includes a. supplement); supplement only, £90 (effective 1996). British Library, National Bibliographic Service, Boston Spa, Wetherby, W. Yorks. LS23 7BQ, England. TEL 01937-546585. FAX 01937-546586. (Subscr. to: Turpin Distribution Services, Blackhorse Rd., Letchworth, Herts. SG6 1HN, England. TEL 01462-672555. FAX 01462-480947) (Co-sponsor: British Film Institute) bibl.; index. circ. 1,000. (also avail. in microform from WMP) **Document type:** catalog, directory, bibliography.
    —BLDSC (2331.040000). **CCC.**
    Formerly (until 1991): British National Film and Video Catalogue (ISSN 0266-805X); (until 1984): British National Film Catalogue (ISSN 0007-1552)
    Description: Records details of more than 500 films and videos available for nontheatrical hire or purchase within the U.K., including educational and training films, independent productions, documentaries, T.V. programs and feature films.

791.43   FR
C N C STATISTIQUES. a. Centre National de la Cinematographie, 12 rue Lubeck, 75784 Paris Cedex 16, France. TEL 44-34-36-09.

791.43   CN   ISSN 0380-6294
PN1993.5.C2
CANADA. STATISTICS CANADA. MOTION PICTURE THEATRES AND FILM DISTRIBUTORS. (Catalogue 63-207) (Text in English and French) 1930. a. Can.$20($21) (foreign $21). Statistics Canada, Publications Sales and Services, Ottawa, Ont. K1A 0T6, Canada. TEL 613-951-7277. FAX 613-951-1584. (also avail. in microform from MML)
    Description: Covers motion picture theaters, regular and drive-in, film distributors and videotape production, establishments, employment, revenue and expenses, theatre capacity, amusement taxes.

791.43 780   US
CELEBRITY BIRTHDAY DIRECTORY. 1992. biennial. $10.95. Axiom Information Resources, Box 8015-T, Ann Arbor, MI 48107. TEL 313-761-4842. Ed. Pat Wilson. **Document type:** directory.
    Description: Covers the birthdays of today's celebrities as well as birthdays of celebrities past and present.

791.43   GW
CINEGRAPH; Lexikon zum deutschsprachigen Film. 1984. 2/yr. Edition Text und Kritik GmbH, Levelingstr. 6a, 81673 Munich, Germany. TEL 089-432929. FAX 089-433997. Ed. Hans-Michael Bock. (looseleaf format) **Document type:** bulletin.

791.43 384.55   DK   ISSN 0108-8882
DENMARK. STATENS FILMCENTRAL. STATISTIK OVER UDLEJNING AF 16 MM FILM OG VIDEO OG OVERSIGT OVER 16 MM FILM OG VIDEOKASSETTER I DEPONERING. 1976. a. Statens Filmcentral, Vestergade 27, DK-1456 Copenhagen K, Denmark. TEL 45-33-13-26-86. FAX 45-33-13-02-03. Ed. Claus Hasselberg.
    Formerly (until 1983): Denmark. Statens Filmcentral. Statistik Over Udlejning af 16 MM Film (ISSN 0105-5070)

791.43 778.59   AT   ISSN 0811-1235
FILM AND VIDEO ACQUISITIONS; new film and video acquisitions of the National Film and Video Lending Collection. 1983. q. Aus.$45 (effective 1995). National Library of Australia, Publications Section, Cultural and Educational Serices Division, Canberra, A.C.T. 2600, Australia. TEL 61-6-262-1365. FAX 61-6-273-4493. circ. 600. (reprint service avail. from ISI,UMI)

FILM & VIDEO FINDER. see *EDUCATION — Abstracting, Bibliographies, Statistics*

791.43 016   US   ISSN 0093-6758
Z5784.M9
FILM LITERATURE INDEX. 1973. q. $325 (foreign $350) includes bound a. cum.; bound a. cum. only $125 (foreign $135) (effective July 1994). Film and Television Documentation Center, State University of New York at Albany, Richardson 390C, 1400 Washington Ave., Albany, NY 12222. TEL 518-442-5745. FAX 518-442-5232. Eds. Linda Provinzano, Deborah Sternklar. bk.rev.; bibl.; circ. 500 (paid). **Document type:** abstracting/indexing.
—BLDSC (3925.800000).
Description: Indexes international periodical literature on film, television and video, by author and subject.

FILM UND FERNSEHEN IN FORSCHUNG UND LEHRE. see *MOTION PICTURES*

778.5   DK   ISSN 0106-8180
FILMREGISTRET. (Supplements avail.) 1962. a. DKK 794. Dansk BiblioteksCenter as, Tempovej 7-11, DK-2750 Ballerup, Denmark. TEL 45-44-97-40-00. FAX 45-44-68-24-42.

FILMS: THE VISUALIZATION OF ANTHROPOLOGY. see *ANTHROPOLOGY — Abstracting, Bibliographies, Statistics*

791.43   GW   ISSN 0071-4941
FILMSTATISTISCHES TASCHENBUCH. 1957. a. DM.29 (foreign DM.40). Spitzenorganisation der Filmwirtschaft e.V., Kreuzberger Ring 56, 65205 Wiesbaden, Germany. TEL 0611-7789114. FAX 0611-7789139. Ed. Carsten Pfaff. circ. 900. **Document type:** trade publication.

791   US   ISSN 0072-8462
GUIDE TO GOVERNMENT-LOAN FILMS VOLUME 1: THE CIVILIAN AGENCIES. 1969. irreg., 6th ed., 1980. $9.95. Serina Press, 70 Kennedy St., Alexandria, VA 22305. TEL 703-548-4080. Ed. Daniel Sprecher.

016.791 791.43   UK   ISSN 1355-1671
▼**INTERNATIONAL FILMARCHIVE C D - R O M.** 1994. s-a. £295($450) (includes International Index to Film Periodicals; International Index to Television Periodicals (1983-present)). International Federation of Film Archives (F I A F) - Federation Internationale des Archives du Film, 6 Nottingham St., London W1M 3RB, England. TEL 0171-224-1203. FAX 0171-224-0991. **Document type:** abstracting/indexing, bibliography.
●Available only on CD-ROM.
Description: Lists film and television periodicals from all over the world. Contains F.I.A.F. membership lists, a bibliography to members' publications, a directory of holdings of 125 institutions worldwide, a glossary of filmographic terms, a bibliography of national filmographies from 60 countries, and a listing of members' silent film holdings.

016.791 791.43   UK   ISSN 0000-0388
Z5784.M9
INTERNATIONAL INDEX TO FILM PERIODICALS. 1972. a. £90($140) (price for cumulative microfiche service varies). International Federation of Film Archives (F I A F) - Federation Internationale des Archives du Film, 6 Nottingham St., London W1M 3RB, England. TEL 0171-224-1203. FAX 0171-224-0991. Ed. Michael Moulds. bibl. (also avail. in microfiche from IFA; back issues avail.) **Document type:** abstracting/indexing.
●Also available on CD-ROM.
—BLDSC (4541.050000).

778.5 016   US   ISSN 0363-7778
LB1043.Z9
MEDIA REVIEW DIGEST; the only complete guide to reviews of non-book media. 1970. a. $245. Pierian Press, Box 1808, Ann Arbor, MI 48106. TEL 313-434-5530. FAX 313-434-6409. Ed. Mary K. Hashman. cum.index. **Document type:** abstracting/indexing.
Formerly: Multi Media Reviews Index (ISSN 0091-5858)
Description: Reviews and evaluations of all forms of non-book media appearing in 140 periodicals and reviewing services.

778.5   MX
MEXICO. CENTRO DE INFORMACION TECNICA Y DOCUMENTACION. INDICE DE PELICULAS. a. (Centro de Informacion Tecnica y Documentacion) Servicio Nacional de Adiestramiento Rapido de la Mano de Obra en la Industria, Calzada Atzcapotzalco-la Villa 209, Mexico 16, D.F., Mexico.

338 016   US   ISSN 1044-3967
LB1043.Z9
N I C E M INDEX TO A V PRODUCERS AND DISTRIBUTORS. (Audio Visual) 1971. irreg., 9th ed. 1994. $89. (National Information Center for Educational Media) Plexus Publishing, Inc., 143 Old Marlton Pike, Medford, NJ 08055-8750. TEL 609-654-4888. FAX 609-654-4309.
Description: Provides the name, address, phone number and type of media produced or distributed of companies and institutions involved in nonprint media.

NATIONAL UNION CATALOG. AUDIOVISUAL MATERIALS. see *BIBLIOGRAPHIES*

PERFORMING ARTS BIOGRAPHY MASTER INDEX. see *THEATER — Abstracting, Bibliographies, Statistics*

PSYCHOLOGICAL CINEMA REGISTER; films and video in the behavioral sciences. see *PSYCHOLOGY — Abstracting, Bibliographies, Statistics*

PUBLIC AFFAIRS VIDEO ARCHIVES. CATALOG. see *POLITICAL SCIENCE*

778.53   CN   ISSN 0840-7703
QUEBEC (PROVINCE). BUREAU DE LA STATISTIQUE. PROJECTIONS CINEMATOGRAPHIQUES AU QUEBEC.. q. Can.$33. Bureau de la Statistique, 200 chemin Ste-Foy, Quebec, PQ G1R 5T4, Canada. TEL 418-691-5150. FAX 418-643-4129.

REFERATIVNYI ZHURNAL. FOTOKINOTEKHNIKA. see *PHOTOGRAPHY — Abstracting, Bibliographies, Statistics*

016 791.4   CN   ISSN 0315-7326
SIXTEEN MM FILMS AVAILABLE IN THE PUBLIC LIBRARIES OF METROPOLITAN TORONTO. 1969. irreg. Can.$80. Metropolitan Toronto Library Board, 789 Yonge St., Toronto, ON M4W 2G8, Canada. TEL 416-393-7020. FAX 416-393-7229. Eds. Josephine Tsui, Jytte Birnbaum. adv. contact: Mario Bernardi. **Document type:** catalog.

778.53 316.8   SA
SOUTH AFRICA. CENTRAL STATISTICAL SERVICE. CENSUS OF SOCIAL, RECREATIONAL AND PERSONAL SERVICES - MOTION PICTURE AND VIDEO PRODUCTION. (Report No. 94-01-01) irreg., latest 1988. R.4.40 (foreign R.4.80). Central Statistical Service - Sentrale Statistiekdiens, Private Bag X44, Pretoria 0001, South Africa. TEL 27-12-310-8911. FAX 27-12-310-8500. (Orders to: Government Printing Works, Private Bag X85, Pretoria 0001, South Africa) **Document type:** government publication.

791.43 316.8   SA
SOUTH AFRICA. CENTRAL STATISTICAL SERVICE. CENSUS OF SOCIAL, RECREATIONAL AND PERSONAL SERVICES - MOTION PICTURE DISTRIBUTION AND PROJECTION AND VIDEO DISTRIBUTION SERVICES. (Report No. 94-02-01) irreg., latest 1988. R.4.40 (foreign R.4.80). Central Statistical Service - Sentrale Statistiekdiens, Private Bag X44, Pretoria 0001, South Africa. TEL 27-12-310-8911. FAX 27-12-310-8500. (Orders to: Government Printing Work, Private Bag X85, Pretoria 0001, South Africa) **Document type:** government publication.

016 371.42   DK   ISSN 0900-3479
UDDANNELSE OG ERHVERV KATALOG. 1967. a. free. Raadet for Uddannelses og Erhvervsvejledning, Aebeloegade 7, 2100 Copenhagen OE, Denmark. Ed. Bodil Sneslev. circ. 8,000.

778.53   CC
ZHONGGUO DIANYING NIANJIAN/CHINA FILM YEARBOOK. (Text in Chinese) a. Zhongguo Dianyingjia Xiehui - China Film Association, 15 Beihuan Xilu, Beijing 100082, People's Republic of China. TEL 66-2251. Ed. Cheng Jihua. adv.

MUNICIPAL GOVERNMENT

see *Public Administration–Municipal Government*

MUSEUMS AND ART GALLERIES

A M U NEWS. (American Malacological Union, Inc.) see *BIOLOGY — Zoology*

069 500   US   ISSN 0147-7889
QH83
A S C NEWSLETTER (WASHINGTON). 1973. bi-m. $21 to individuals; libraries $35. Association of Systematics Collections, 730 11th St., N.W., 2nd Fl., Washington, DC 20001. TEL 202-347-2850. E-mail: MNHEN024@SIVM.SI.EDU. Ed. Mike Schauff. adv.; bk.rev. circ. 1,200. **Document type:** newsletter.
—BLDSC (1739.065000).
Description: Provides news of collections, curatorial positions, funding sources, ASC workshops, jobs, computer-software trends, profiles of member institutions and affiliate societies, biological survey activities, and legislation and regulations affecting systematists.

707.4 069.9   US
A S I POSTEN. 1969. 11/yr. membership. American Swedish Institute, 2600 Park Ave., Minneapolis, MN 55407. TEL 612-871-4907. Ed. Janice M. McElfish. adv. circ. 7,000. (back issues avail.)
Supersedes (as of 1982): Happenings; Which superseded: American Swedish Institute. Bulletin.

708 370 500 600   US   ISSN 0895-7371
A S T C NEWSLETTER. 1974. bi-m. $30 to non-members (foreign $40); members $15 (foreign $20). Association of Science-Technology Centers, 1025 Vermont Ave. N.W. 5th Fl., Washington, DC 20005. TEL 202-783-7200. FAX 202-783-7207. Ed. Chris Raymond. charts; illus. circ. 3,700. **Document type:** newsletter.
Description: Reports on new interactive exhibitions at member institutions, issues related to informal science education and to science museums and related institutions.

ADLER MUSEUM BULLETIN. see *MEDICAL SCIENCES*

ADOMUS. see *PHOTOGRAPHY*

069.9   US
AFRICAN AMERICAN MUSEUMS ASSOCIATION. ANNUAL MEETING REPORT.* a. African American Museums Association, Box 548, Wilberforce, OH 45384-0548.

708.5   IT
AGARTE. (Text in Italian; summaries in English) 1950. 9/yr. free. Galleria Agarte, Via Babuino 124, 00187 Rome, Italy. Ed. Giuseppe Tedesco. illus.; mkt. circ. 2,000.
Formerly (until 1989): Medusa (ISSN 0025-8571)

AGENDA. see *ART*

510   JA   ISSN 0385-1354
AKITA-KENRITSU HAKUBUTSUKAN KENKYU HOKOKU/AKITA PREFECTURAL MUSEUM. ANNUAL REPORT. (Text in Japanese; summaries in English, Japanese) 1976. a. Akita Prefectural Museum - Akita-kenritsu Hakubutsukan, Ushiroyama, Kanashi Niozaki, Akita-shi, Akita-ken 010-01, Japan.

069 500   JA   ISSN 0065-5554
QH188
AKIYOSHI-DAI KAGAKU HAKUBUTSUKAN HOKOKU. (Text in English or Japanese; summaries in English) 1961. irreg., no. 6, 1969. Akiyoshi-dai Museum of Natural History - Akiyoshi-dai Kagaku Hakubutsukan, Akiyoshi, Shuho-cho, Mine-gun, Yamaguchi-ken 754-05, Japan. (Co-sponsor: Akiyoshi-dai Science Museum) Ed. M. Ota. **Document type:** bulletin.

069   HU   ISSN 0324-542X
ALBA REGIA. (Text in English, German) 1960. a. 2700 Ft. or exchange basis. Musei Stephani Regis, P.O. Box 78, 8002 Szekesfehervar, Hungary. TEL 22-315-583. Ed. J. Fitz. bk.rev. (back issues avail.) **Indexed:** A.I.C.P.
Description: Covers archaeology, ethnography, and local history.

MUSEUMS AND ART GALLERIES

ALBURY & DISTRICT HISTORICAL SOCIETY. BULLETIN. see HISTORY — History Of Australasia And Other Areas

708   US   ISSN 0002-5739
N650
ALLEN MEMORIAL ART MUSEUM. BULLETIN. 1943. 2/yr. $30 (foreign $33) (effective 1993). Oberlin College, Allen Memorial Art Museum, Oberlin, OH 44074. TEL 216-775-8665. FAX 216-775-8799. Ed. Marjorie E. Wieseman. illus.; cum.index: vols.1-30. circ. 2,000. (also avail. in microform from UMI; back issues avail.; reprint service avail. from UMI) **Indexed:** Art Ind., Artbibl.Mod., RILA. **Document type:** bulletin.
—BLDSC (2384.700000); Faxon; UMI; UnCover.
Description: Scholarly articles on exhibitions and objects from the permanent collection.

708.1   US   ISSN 0065-6410
ALLIED ARTISTS OF AMERICA. EXHIBITION CATALOG. 1914. a. $3. Allied Artists of America, 15 Gramercy Park S., New York, NY 10003. TEL 212-582-6411. adv. circ. 3,000.

945   IT   ISSN 0569-1346
ALTAMURA. a. membership. Museo Civico, Biblioteca, Palazzo degli Studi, Altamura, Italy. Ed. Celio Sabini. bibl.; illus.

069   GW   ISSN 0440-1417
AM101
ALTONAER MUSEUM IN HAMBURG. NORDEUTSCHES LANDESMUSEUM. JAHRBUCH. 1963. a. DM.50 (effective 1996). Altonaer Museum in Hamburg, Museumstr. 23, 22765 Hamburg, Germany. TEL 040-3807480. FAX 040-38072122. Ed. Gerhard Kaufmann. circ. 1,500. **Document type:** academic/scholarly publication.

069 500   US
AMERICAN MUSEUM OF NATURAL HISTORY. ANNUAL REPORT. 1870. a. American Museum of Natural History, 79th St. at Central Park W., New York, NY 10024-5192. TEL 212-769-5100. FAX 212-769-5006. E-mail: scipubs@amnh.org. bibl.; charts; illus. circ. 5,000. **Document type:** corporate report.

AMERICAN MUSEUM OF NATURAL HISTORY. BULLETIN. see BIOLOGY — Zoology

069   US
AMERICAN SWEDISH HISTORICAL MUSEUM NEWSLETTER. 1957? 3/yr. $35 includes membership. American Swedish Historical Museum, 1900 Pattison Ave., Philadelphia, PA 19145. TEL 215-389-1776. FAX 215-389-7701. Ed. Ann Barton Brown. bk.rev.; illus. circ. 800. **Document type:** newsletter.
Formerly (until 1987): Museum Expressen.

069.5   GR   ISSN 0302-1033
QH151   CODEN: AMUGAY
ANNALES MUSEI GOULANDRIS; contributiones ad historiam naturalem graeciae et regionis mediterraneae. (Text in English, French, German, Italian and Latin; summaries in English and Greek) 1973. a. $20. Goulandris Natural History Museum, 13 Levidou St., 145 62 Kifissia, Greece. TEL 301-8015870. FAX 301-8080-674. Ed. W.T. Stearn. circ. 1,000. **Indexed:** GeoRef. **Document type:** academic/scholarly publication.
Description: Covers the natural history of Greece and the Mediterranean.

ANNALS OF THE CAPE PROVINCIAL MUSEUMS: HUMAN SCIENCES. see ANTHROPOLOGY

ANNALS OF THE CAPE PROVINCIAL MUSEUMS: NATURAL HISTORY. see SCIENCES: COMPREHENSIVE WORKS

ANNUAL BIBLIOGRAPHY OF MODERN ART. see ART

708   RM
ANUARUL MUZEULUI NATIONAL DE ISTORIE A ROMANIEI. (Text in Rumanian; summaries in English, French) 1974. a. Muzeul National de Istorie a Romaniei, Calea Victoriei Nr.12, Bucharest, Rumania. TEL 614-90-78. Ed.Bd. bk.rev.; illus. **Indexed:** Numis.Lit. **Document type:** academic/scholarly publication.
Formerly (until 1983): Muzeul National (ISSN 1015-0323)

069   GW   ISSN 0402-7817
ARBEITS UND FORSCHUNGSBERICHTE ZUR SAECHSISCHEN BODENDENKMALPFLEGE. 1953. a. price varies. (Landesamt fuer Archaeologie mit Landesmuseum fuer Vorgeschichte Dresden) Konrad Theiss Verlag GmbH und Co., Villastr. 11, 70190 Stuttgart, Germany. TEL 0711-26861-01. FAX 0711-26861-15. Ed. Judith Oexle. **Indexed:** A.I.C.P., Anthropol.Lit., Br.Archaeol.Abstr., NAA. **Document type:** academic/scholarly publication.
—BLDSC (1585.970000).

ARBEITSBLAETTER FUER RESTAURATOREN. see ARCHAEOLOGY

ARCHIVES ET BIBLIOTHEQUES DE BELGIQUE/ARCHIEF- EN BIBLIOTHEEKWEZEN IN BELGIE. see HISTORY — History Of Europe

ARCHIVIST. see HISTORY — History Of North And South America

ARGO. see HISTORY — History Of Europe

069.9 336.2   SW   ISSN 0284-3242
ARGUS (DALAROE); aarsbok foer Tullmuseum och Tullhistoriska Foereningen. 1987. a. SEK 60 membership (effective 1995). Tullmuseum, Tullhuset, S-130 54 Dalaroe, Sweden. Ed. Jan Berggren. **Document type:** academic/scholarly publication.

069 700   US
ARIZONA ARTISTS GUILD NEWS. m. membership. Arizona Artists Guild, 8912 N. 4th St., Phoenix, AZ 85020. Ed. Cathy McCormick. circ. 500.

355.009485   SW   ISSN 0349-1048
ARMEMUSEUM - MEDDELANDE. 1938. a. SEK 150 to non-members; members SEK 100. Armemuseum - Royal Army Museum, P.O. Box 14095, S-104 41 Stockholm, Sweden. TEL 46-8-788-95-60. FAX 46-8-662-68-31. (Co-sponsor: Foereningen Armemusei Vaenner) Ed. Johan Engstroem. circ. 2,000.
Formerly (until vol.11, 1950): Foereningens Armemusei Vaenner Meddelanden (ISSN 0284-1983)
Description: Features articles on military history, uniforms and weapons, particularly that of Sweden.

700   HU   ISSN 0133-6673
ARS DECORATIVA/IPARMUVESZET. (Text in English, German, Hungarian) 1973. a. exchange basis. Iparmuveszeti Muzeum, Hopp Ferenc Keletazsiai Muveszeti Muzeum - Museum of Applied Arts, Ulloi ut 33-37, 1091 Budapest 9, Hungary. TEL 2175-222. FAX 2175-838. Ed. Zsuzsa Lovag. circ. 1,000 (controlled). **Indexed:** Artbibl.Mod., Numis.Lit. **Document type:** bulletin.
—BLDSC (1697.380000).
Supersedes: Iparmuveszeti Muzeum. Evkonyve.

069   US
ART (NEW YORK). 1988. 3/yr. membership only. American Federation of Arts, 41 E. 65th St., New York, NY 10021. TEL 212-988-7700. (And: 2510 Channing Way, Ste. 4, Berkeley, CA 94704-2315) Ed. Nancy Jones. circ. 2,000. (tabloid format; back issues avail.)
Description: Addresses issues within the museum field.

ART AND DESIGN. see ART

708   AT   ISSN 0066-7935
N3948
ART BULLETIN OF VICTORIA. 1959. a. Aus.$10. National Gallery of Victoria, 180 St. Kilda Rd., Melbourne, Vic. 3004, Australia. TEL 61-3-2080222. FAX 61-3-2080245. TELEX AA 151258. Ed. Sonia Dean. circ. 2,500. **Indexed:** Artbibl., Aus.P.A.I.S., RILA. **Document type:** academic/scholarly publication.
—UnCover.
Supersedes (in 1966): National Gallery of Victoria. Annual Bulletin.
Description: Publishes research on the Gallery's collection of Australian and international art by scholars and researchers.

ART CELLAR EXCHANGE; a service for buying and selling art. see ART

ART DEALERS ASSOCIATION OF AMERICA. DIRECTORY. see BUSINESS AND ECONOMICS — Trade And Industrial Directories

L'ART ET LA MER. see ART

708   CN   ISSN 0082-5018
N910.T6
ART GALLERY OF ONTARIO. ANNUAL REPORT. 1967. a. Art Gallery of Ontario, 317 Dundas St. W., Toronto, ON M5T 1G4, Canada. TEL 416-977-0414. FAX 416-979-6646. Ed. Beverly Carret. circ. 2,500. **Document type:** corporate report.

069   CN   ISSN 1191-9868
ART GALLERY OF ONTARIO. JOURNAL. bi-m. Art Gallery of Ontario, 317 Dundas St. W., Toronto, ON M5T 1G4, Canada. TEL 416-979-6660. FAX 416-977-8547. Ed. Aldona Satterhwaite. charts; illus. circ. 26,000. **Document type:** newsletter.
Former titles: A G O News (ISSN 0829-4437); Art Gallery of Ontario. The Gallery (ISSN 0709-8413); Art Gallery of Ontario. Coming Events (ISSN 0044-9024)

708   US   ISSN 0069-3235
N81
ART INSTITUTE OF CHICAGO. MUSEUM STUDIES. 1966-1978; resumed 1984. s-a. $20 to individuals (foreign $30); institutions $32 (foreign $42); members $15 (foreign $25). Art Institute of Chicago, 111 S. Michigan Ave., Chicago, IL 60603. TEL 312-443-3540. FAX 312-443-1334. Eds. Robert V. Sharp, Michael Sittenfeld. illus.; index. circ. 10,500. (back issues avail.) **Indexed:** Art Ind., Artbibl.Mod., Arts & Hum.Cit.Ind., Avery Ind.Archit.Per., Curr.Cont., RILA. **Document type:** academic/scholarly publication.
—BLDSC (5989.740000); Faxon; Genuine Article; UnCover.
Description: Articles pertain to the museum's permanent collection.

ART MARKETING SOURCEBOOK. see BUSINESS AND ECONOMICS — Trade And Industrial Directories

ART MONTHLY. see ART

ART NEWS INTERNATIONAL DIRECTORY OF CORPORATE ART COLLECTIONS. see ART

708   US
ART NOW GALLERY GUIDE: BOSTON - NEW ENGLAND EDITION. 1981. m. (except Aug.). $20. Art Now, Inc., 97 Grayrock Rd., Box 5541, Clinton, NJ 08809. TEL 908-638-5255. FAX 908-638-8737. adv. circ. 9,000. **Document type:** consumer publication.
Former titles: Art Now: Boston and New England Gallery Guide; Art Now: Boston Gallery Guide.
Description: Information about exhibitions at galleries and museums, plus gallery-area maps.

708   US
ART NOW GALLERY GUIDE: CHICAGO - MIDWEST EDITION. 1981. m. (except Aug.). $20. Art Now, Inc., 97 Grayrock Rd., Box 5541, Clinton, NJ 08809. TEL 908-638-5255. FAX 908-638-8737. Ed. Valerie Frasca. adv. circ. 14,000. **Document type:** consumer publication.
Formerly: Art Now: Chicago and Midwest Gallery Guide; Formed by the merger of (1981-1982): Art Now: Midwest Gallery Guide; (1980-1982): Art Now: Chicago Gallery Guide.
Description: Information about exhibitions at galleries and museums, plus gallery-area maps.

708.1   US
ART NOW GALLERY GUIDE: EUROPE EDITION. 1990. bi-m. $15. Art Now International, Inc., 97 Garyrock Rd., Box 5541, Clinton, NJ 08809. TEL 908-638-5255. FAX 908-638-6461. Ed. Bridget Daley. adv. circ. 25,000. **Document type:** consumer publication, directory.
Description: Information about exhibitions at galleries and museums in Europe, plus gallery-area maps.

MUSEUMS AND ART GALLERIES

069.5   US   ISSN 1059-7689
N510
ART NOW GALLERY GUIDE: INTERNATIONAL EDITION.
1982. m. (except Aug.). $35. Art Now, Inc., 97 Grayrock Rd., Box 5541, Clinton, NJ 08809. TEL 908-638-5255. FAX 908-638-8737. Ed. Bernice Shor. adv. circ. 5,000. **Document type:** consumer publication.
   Former titles: Art Now Gallery Guide: National Edition; Art Now: U S A - National Art Museum and Gallery Guide (ISSN 0745-5720)
   Description: Information about exhibitions at galleries and museums across the US and Europe, plus gallery-area maps.

708.1   US
ART NOW GALLERY GUIDE: NEW YORK EDITION. 1969. m. (except Aug.). $30. Art Now, Inc., 97 Grayrock Rd., Box 5541, Clinton, NJ 08809. TEL 908-638-5255. FAX 908-638-8737. Ed. Bernice Shor. adv. circ. 38,000. **Document type:** consumer publication.
   Former titles: Art Now: New York Gallery Guide; Art Now Gallery Guide.
   Description: Information about exhibitions at galleries and museums, plus gallery-area maps.

708   US
ART NOW GALLERY GUIDE: PHILADELPHIA EDITION. 1981. m. (except Aug.). $20. Art Now, Inc., 97 Grayrock Rd., Box 5541, Clinton, NJ 08809. TEL 908-638-5255. FAX 908-638-8737. adv. circ. 8,500. **Document type:** consumer publication.
   Formerly: Art Now: Philadelphia Gallery Guide.
   Description: Information about exhibitions at galleries and museums, plus gallery-area maps.

069.5   US
ART NOW GALLERY GUIDE: SOUTHEAST EDITION. 1983. m. (except Aug.). $20. Art Now, Inc., 97 Grayrock Rd., Box 5541, Clinton, NJ 08809. TEL 908-638-5255. FAX 908-638-8737. Ed. Valerie Frasca. adv. circ. 7,000. **Document type:** consumer publication.
   Formerly: Art Now: Southeast Gallery Guide.
   Description: Information about exhibitions at galleries and museums, plus gallery-area maps.

708   US
ART NOW GALLERY GUIDE: SOUTHWEST EDITION. 1981. m. (except Aug.). $20. Art Now, Inc., 97 Grayrock Rd., Box 5541, Clinton, NJ 08809. TEL 908-638-5255. FAX 908-637-8787. Ed. Susan Houseweart. adv. circ. 6,000. **Document type:** consumer publication.
   Former titles: Art Now: Southwest Gallery Guide; Art Now: Texas, Arizona, New Mexico Gallery Guide.
   Description: Information about exhibitions at galleries and museums, plus gallery-area maps.

708   US
ART NOW GALLERY GUIDE: WEST COAST EDITION. 1983. m. (except Aug.). $20. Art Now, Inc., 97 Grayrock Rd., Box 5541, Clinton, NJ 08809. TEL 908-638-5255. FAX 908-638-8737. Ed. Susan Houseweart. adv. circ. 12,000. **Document type:** consumer publication.
   Former titles: Art Now Gallery Guide: California - Northwest Edition; Art Now: California and Northwest Gallery Guide; Formed by the merger of (1980-1983): Art Now: California Gallery Guide; Art Now: Northwest Gallery Guide.
   Description: Information about exhibitions at galleries and museums, plus gallery-area maps.

ARTIFACTS (COLUMBIA). see *ART*

069.9   US
THE ARTISAN. 1983. 2/yr. $35. Artisans School, Box 539, Rockport, ME 04856. TEL 207-236-6071. FAX 207-236-8367. Ed. Hope Sage. bk.rev. circ. 4,000.
   Formerly: Apprentice (ISSN 1064-1327)

069 700   US
ARTSFOCUS. 1968. bi-m. membership. Colorado Springs Fine Arts Center, 30 W. Dale St., Colorado Springs, CO 80903. TEL 719-634-5581. Ed. Julia Morrill. circ. 4,000. (back issues avail.) **Document type:** newsletter.
   Description: Covers exhibitions, performing arts series, library, art school, and volunteer and staff activities.

ASPECTEN VAN DE VERZAMELING BEELDHOUWKUNST EN KUNSTNIJVERHEID. see *ART*

069   FR
ASSOCIATION GENERALE DES CONSERVATEURS DE MUSEES ET COLLECTIONS PUBLIQUES DE FRANCE. ANNUAIRE. 1960. biennial. 150 F. Editions Person, 34 rue de Penthievre, 75008 Paris, France. adv.

069   UK   ISSN 0142-887X
ASSOCIATION OF INDEPENDENT MUSEUMS BULLETIN. 1977. bi-m. £25. Association of Independent Museums, Park Cottage, West Dean, Chichester, W. Sussex PO18 ORX, England. TEL 01243-63364. D. Zeuner. adv.; bk.rev. circ. 1,500. **Document type:** bulletin.
   Description: Details the activities of independent museums throughout the U.K.

069   CN   ISSN 0849-5858
ASSOCIATION OF MANITOBA MUSEUMS. NEWSLETTER. 4/yr. membership. Association of Manitoba Museums, 422 - 167 Lombard Ave., Winnipeg, MB R3B 0T6, Canada. bk.rev. circ. 350. **Document type:** newsletter.

591 594   NZ   ISSN 0067-0456
                   CODEN: BUKIAN
AUCKLAND INSTITUTE AND MUSEUM. BULLETIN. 1941. irreg., no.15, 1995. price varies. Auckland Institute and Museum, Private Bag 92018, Auckland 1, New Zealand. FAX 64-9-3799-956. circ. 300. (back issues avail.) **Indexed:** A.I.C.P., Biol.Abstr., GeoRef. **Document type:** bulletin, monographic series.

069.7   NZ   ISSN 0067-0464
Q93   CODEN: RAUIA7
AUCKLAND INSTITUTE AND MUSEUM. RECORDS. 1930. a. price varies. Auckland Institute and Museum, Private Bag 92018, Auckland 1, New Zealand. FAX 64-9-3799-956. Eds. Nigel Prickett, Brian Gill. index. circ. 300. (back issues avail.) **Indexed:** Anthropol.Lit., Biol.Abstr., Deep Sea Res.& Oceanogr.Abstr., GeoRef., Ind.N.Z.Per., So.Pac.Per.Ind. **Document type:** academic/scholarly publication.
   —BLDSC (7314.000000); UnCover.
   Refereed Serial

AUSTRALIAN MUSEUM, SYDNEY. RECORDS. see *SCIENCES: COMPREHENSIVE WORKS*

AUSTRALIAN MUSEUM, SYDNEY. RECORDS SUPPLEMENTS. see *SCIENCES: COMPREHENSIVE WORKS*

069 387   AT   ISSN 0813-0523
AUSTRALIAN SEA HERITAGE. 1984. q. Aus.$27.80 (effective 1995 & 1996). Sydney Maritime Museum, P.O. Box 431, Rozelle, N.S.W. 2039, Australia. TEL 61-2-810-2299. FAX 61-2-810-1756. Ed. Graeme Andrews. adv. contact: Sally Gregg. bk.rev.; charts; illus.; stat. circ. 6,000. (back issues avail.)
   —UnCover.
   Description: Reflects the on going work of Australia's museums in preserving maritime history, and provides outlet for articles on Australian maritime history.

069   US   ISSN 0739-7747
AM1
AVISO. 1968. m. $33. American Association of Museums, 1225 Eye St., N.W., Ste. 200, Washington, DC 20005. TEL 202-289-1818. FAX 202-289-6578. Ed. Lauren Lantos. tr.lit. circ. 15,000. **Document type:** newsletter.
   —CCC.
   Supersedes (in 1975): A A M Bulletin (ISSN 0044-7536)
   Description: Current events covering museums; lists over 100 jobs available throughout US museums each month.

708.1   US   ISSN 0045-3242
B A C A CALENDAR OF CULTURAL EVENTS. 1971. a. $20. (Brooklyn Arts and Culture Association, Inc.) Brooklyn Arts Council, 195 Cadman Plaza W., Brooklyn, NY 11201. TEL 718-625-0080. FAX 718-625-3294. Ed. Charles Reichenthal. circ. 15,000. **Document type:** newsletter.

069   UK
B A F M NEWSLETTER. q. membership. British Association of Friends of Museums, c/o Sue Drought, 31 Southwell Park Rd., Camberly, Surrey GU15 3QG, England. TEL 01276-66617. Ed. Rosemary Silvester. adv. contact: Rosemary Silvester. **Document type:** newsletter.

069   UK   ISSN 0965-8297
B M MAGAZINE. 1969. 3/yr. £10 (overseas £14). British Museum Society, Great Russell St., London WC1B 3DG, England. TEL 0171-637-9983. FAX 0171-323-8614. adv. contact: Elizabeth Foy. bk.rev.; circ. 10,000 (controlled). **Indexed:** RILA. **Document type:** academic/scholarly publication, bulletin.
   —BLDSC (2330.596500).
   Formerly (until 1990): British Museum Society. Bulletin.
   Description: Contains news and information about current and forthcoming museum exhibitions, news, and other events.

BAKKEN LIBRARY AND MUSEUM. see *LIBRARY AND INFORMATION SCIENCES*

700 913   BG
BANGLADESH LALIT KALA. (Text in English) 1975. s-a. Tk.100($15) Dhaka Museum, G.P.O. Box 355, Dhaka 2, Bangladesh.

069   DK   ISSN 0109-8489
BANGSBOMUSEET. AARBOG. 1984. a. DKK 60. Bangsbo Museets Forlag, Frederikshavn, Denmark. TEL 98423111. FAX 98430597. Dir. Hans Munk Pedersen. circ. 1,000.

708   CN
BEAVERBROOK ART GALLERY. ANNUAL REPORT. 1987. a. Beaverbrook Art Gallery, P.O. Box 605, Fredericton, NB E3B 5A6, Canada. TEL 506-458-8545. FAX 506-459-7450. circ. 1,500. **Document type:** newsletter.

069   GW   ISSN 0138-4279
BEITRAEGE ZUR UR- UND FRUEHGESCHICHTE DER BEZIRKE ROSTOCK, SCHWERIN UND NEUBRANDENBURG. 1967. irreg. price varies. (Museum fuer Ur- und Fruehgeschichte Schwerin) VEB Deutscher Verlag der Wissenschaften, Postfach 1216, 1080 Berlin, Germany. Ed. Horst Keiling.

708   GW
BELSER KUNST KATALOG; internationales Verzeichnis der Ausstellungskataloge. a. DM.12. Chr. Belser Verlag, Pfizerstr. 5-7, 70184 Stuttgart, Germany. TEL 0711-2191410. FAX 0711-2191413. circ. 60,000. **Document type:** directory.

708   GW
BELSER KUNST QUARTAL; internationale Vorschau auf Kunstausstellungen und Auktionen. 1965. q. DM.40. Chr. Belser Verlag, Pfizerstr. 5-7, 70184 Stuttgart, Germany. TEL 0711-2191410. FAX 0711-2191413. Ed. Reiner Brouwer. adv.; circ. 33,000 (controlled). **Document type:** bulletin.

069   IS
BETH HATEFUTSOTH. s-a. free. Beth Hatefutsoth - Museum of the Jewish Diaspora, P.O. Box 39359, Tel Aviv 61392, Israel. TEL 972-3-6462020.

BIBLIOTHEQUES ET MUSEES. see *HISTORY — History Of Europe*

THE BIOLOGY CURATOR. see *BIOLOGY*

069   GW
BODENDENKMALPFLEGE IN MECKLENBURG-VORPOMMERN. 1964. a. price varies. (Museum fuer Ur- und Fruehgeschichte Schwerin) Deutscher Verlag der Wissenschaften, Postfach 1216, 1080 Berlin, Germany. Ed. Horst Keiling. **Indexed:** Anthropol.Lit., Br.Archaeol.Abstr., NAA.
   Formerly: Bodendenkmalpflege in Mecklenburg (ISSN 0067-9461)

707.4   GW
BOKULT. irreg. (2-4/yr.). Museum Bochum, Kortumstr. 147, 44787 Bochum, Germany.

069   US   ISSN 0084-7992
BOWDOIN COLLEGE. MUSEUM OF ART. OCCASIONAL PAPERS. 1972. irreg., no.3, 1988. price varies. Bowdoin College, Museum of Art, Walker Art Bldg., Brunswick, ME 04011. TEL 207-725-3275. **Indexed:** RILA.
   Formerly: Walker Art Museum. Bulletin.

BRIMLEYANA; the zoological journal of the southeastern United States. see *BIOLOGY — Zoology*

MUSEUMS AND ART GALLERIES 4809

708.1 CN ISSN 0045-3005
BRITISH COLUMBIA MUSEUMS ASSOCIATION. MUSEUM ROUND UP. 1957. 6/yr. Can.$47. British Columbia Museums Association, 514 Government St., Victoria, BC V8V 4X4, Canada. TEL 604-387-3315. Ed. Linda & David Tanaka. adv. circ. 500. **Document type:** newsletter.

BRITISH SCHOOL AT ROME. PAPERS. ARCHAEOLOGY, HISTORY, HISTORY OF ART. see *ARCHAEOLOGY*

069 US ISSN 1042-9034
AM101
THE BROOKLYN MUSEUM REPORT. 1986. q.? Brooklyn Museum, 200 Eastern Pkwy., Brooklyn, New York, NY 11238. TEL 718-638-5000. FAX 718-638-3731. Ed. Elaine Koss. adv. contact: Sallie Williams.

708 BX ISSN 0084-8131
BRUNEI MUSEUM. SPECIAL PUBLICATION/MUZIUM BRUNEI. PENERBITAN KHAS. (Text in English and Malay) 1972. irreg., latest no. 17. price varies. Brunei Museum, Kota Batu, Bandar Seri Begawan, Brunei Darussalam. Ed. P.M. Dato Sharifiddin. circ. 1,000.

708 BX ISSN 0068-2918
BRUNEI MUSEUM JOURNAL. (Text in English) 1969. a. B.$10. Brunei Museum, Kota Batu, Bandar Seri Begawan, Brunei Darussalam. Ed. P.M. Dato Sharifiddin. illus. circ. 3,000. **Indexed:** A.I.C.P., Anthropol.Lit., Bibl.Ling., E.I.

708 BX
BRUNEI MUSEUM JOURNAL. MONOGRAPH. (Text in English) 1970. irreg., no.6, 1986. B.10 (US B.$20) per no. Brunei Museum, Kota Batu, Bander Seri Begawan, Brunei Darussalam.

069 708 US ISSN 0882-651X
BUGEYE TIMES. 1976. q. membership. Calvert Marine Museum, Box 97, Solomons, MD 20688. TEL 410-326-2042. FAX 410-326-6691. Ed. Paul L. Berry. cum.index: 1976-1992. circ. 2,000. (back issues avail.) **Document type:** newsletter.
  Description: Provides information of interest to the Calvert Marine Museum; includes past and coming events; short reports on topics related to local maritime history, paleontology, or marine biology.

702.8 CN ISSN 1180-3223
C C I NEWSLETTER. 1988. s-a. free. Canadian Conservation Institute - Institut Canadien de Conservation, 1030 Innes Rd., Ottawa, ON K1A 0C8, Canada. TEL 613-998-3721. FAX 613-998-4721. **Document type:** newsletter, bulletin.
  Formerly (until 1992): Canadian Conservation Institute. Newsletter (ISSN 1193-4808)

702.8 333.7 CN ISSN 0706-4152
AM145
C C I TECHNICAL BULLETINS/I C C BULLETINS TECHNIQUES. (Text in English and French) 1975. irreg., latest no.16. Can.$6. Canadian Conservation Institute - Institut Canadien de Conservation, 1030 Innes Rd., Ottawa, ON K1A 0C8, Canada. TEL 613-998-3721. FAX 613-998-4721. (Affiliate: National Museums of Canada) bibl.; illus. (back issues avail.) **Document type:** bulletin.
  Description: Disseminates information on current techniques and principles of conservation of use to curators and conservators of Canada's cultural artifacts.

069 708 US
C F A NEWS (MIAMI). 1982. q. membership. Center for Fine Arts, 101 W. Flagler St., Miami, FL 33130. TEL 305-375-3000. FAX 305-375-1725. Ed. Fran Ames. adv. contact: Risa Parsons. circ. 11,000. (tabloid format; back issues avail.) **Document type:** newsletter.
  Description: Features fine art, design, photography, and sculpture at the center of current exhibitions.

C MAGAZINE; the magazine of contempory art. see *ART*

069 BL
CADERNOS MUSEOLOGICOS. 1989. irreg. Instituto Brasileiro do Patrimonio Cultural, Coordenadoria Geral de Acervos Museologicos, Avda. Rio Branco 46, 2o andar, 20090 Rio de Janeiro RJ, Brazil. TEL 55-21-2965115 ext. 254.
  Description: Contains theoretical and technical texts on museum science.

610 US ISSN 0882-6447
CADUCEUS; a humanities journal for medicine and the health sciences. 1985. 3/yr. $45 to individuals; institutions $60 (effective 1995-1996). S I U School of Medicine, Department of the Medical Humanities, The Pearson Museum, Box 19230, Springfield, IL 62794-9230. FAX 217-782-9132. Ed. John S. Haller, Jr. bk.rev.; illus. circ. 200. (back issues avail.) **Indexed:** Amer.Hist.& Life (1993-), Hist.Abstr. (1993-), Ind.Med. **Document type:** academic/scholarly publication.
  —BLDSC (2947.201000).
  Refereed Serial

CAHIER VINCENT. see *ART*

063 BE ISSN 0776-1317
CAHIERS DE MARIEMONT; bulletin du Musee royal de Mariemont. 1970. a. 200 Fr. Musee Royal de Mariemont, B-7140 Morlanwelz-Mariemont, Belgium. TEL 064-21-21-93. FAX 064-26-29-24. (Co-sponsor: Ministere de la Communaute Francaise) Ed. Guy Donnay. circ. 1,500.

069 CN ISSN 0701-0281
THE CAIRN. 1977. 3/yr. Can.$25. Whyte Museum of the Canadian Rockies, 111 Bear St., Box 160, Banff, AB T0L 0C0, Canada. TEL 403-762-2291. FAX 403-762-8919. E-mail: can-wmcr@lmmedia.ca. Ed. Pat Lee. adv.; circ. 2,500 (controlled). **Document type:** newsletter.
  Description: Describes the current art gallery, heritage exhibitions and upcoming events for members and the public.

506 US ISSN 0008-0829
Q1
CALIFORNIA ACADEMY OF SCIENCES. ACADEMY NEWSLETTER. 1940. m. membership. California Academy of Sciences, Golden Gate Park, San Francisco, CA 94118. TEL 415-750-7142. Ed. Sheri Ketchum. circ. 25,000. **Document type:** newsletter.
  Refereed Serial

069 US
CALIFORNIA MUSEUM DIRECTORY; a guide to 1,200 museums, zoos, botanic gardens, and historic buildings open to the public. 1980. irreg., 2nd ed., 1991. $25. California Institute of Public Affairs, Box 189040, Sacramento, CA 95818. TEL 916-442-CIPA. FAX 916-442-2478. (Affiliate: The Claremont Graduate School) Ed. Jennifer T. Caughman. index. circ. 1,000. **Document type:** directory.
  Description: Guide to approximately 1,200 museums and similar institutions in California, including many smaller and specialized museums. Indexed by geographical areas, subject, and name of institution.

CANADIAN ARTISTS SERIES. see *ART*

069 CN ISSN 0820-8336
CANADIAN MUSEUM OF FLIGHT & TRANSPORTATION. MUSEUM NEWSLETTER. 1975. q. membership. Canadian Museum of Flight & Transportation, Unit 200, 5333 216th St. Langley Airport, Langley, BC V3A 4R1, Canada. TEL 604-532-0035. FAX 604-532-0056. Ed. Brad Thomas. adv. contact: George Proulx. bk.rev.; illus.; circ. 2,000 (controlled). **Document type:** newsletter.
  Description: Describes the museum's activities, functions and services. Includes articles on historic aviation.

069 DK
CARLSBERGFONDET AARSSKRIFT. 1974. a. DKK 188 (prices typically set in Oct.). (Carlsbergfondet) Forlaget Rhodos, H.C. Andersens Blvd. 35, DK-1553 Copenhagen K, Denmark. FAX 33156188. TELEX 33 15 61 88.
  Formerly: Frederiksborgmuseet. Aarskrift (ISSN 0105-9858)

069 UK
CARMARTHEN MUSEUM. PUBLICATION. 1975. irreg. price varies. Carmarthen Museum, Abergwili, Carmarthen, Wales. TEL 0267-231691. Ed. C.J. Delaney. illus.

069 US
THE CARNEGIE. ANNUAL REPORT. 1898. a. The Carnegie, 4400 Forbes Ave., Pittsburgh, PA 15213. TEL 412-622-3131. FAX 412-622-1970. Ed. Pamela S. Pochapin. circ. 5,000.
  Formerly: Carnegie Institute. Annual Report.
  Description: Activity reports of each of four museums that comprise The Carnegie: the Museum of Art, the Andy Warhol Museum, the Museum of Natural History, and the Science Center, with lists of capital projects, exhibitions, loans, acquisitions, contributors, education programs, and visiting scholars.

069.9 US
CARNEGIE INTERNATIONAL. triennial. Carnegie Museum of Art, 4400 Forbes Ave., Pittsburgh, PA 15213. TEL 412-622-8833. FAX 412-622-3112. **Document type:** catalog.
  Description: Exhibition catalogue of international contemporary art.

069.094894 DK
CARTHA. 1982. a. DKK 100. Kerteminde Museum, Strandgade, 5300 Kerteminde, Denmark. Ed. Kurt Risskov Soerensen. illus. circ. 750.
  Formerly: Kerteminde Museum. Aarsskrift (ISSN 0109-047X)

069 700 US
CARTOON TIMES. 1986. q. $35 includes membership to individuals; families $50. Cartoon Art Museum, c/o Lara Pepp, Publist, 814 Mission St., San Francisco, CA 94103-3018. TEL 415-CAR-TOON. FAX 415-243-8666. Ed. Jerry Kruse. circ. 800. **Document type:** newsletter.
  Formerly: Cartoon Art Museum Newsletter.
  Description: Informs cartoon art museum members of museum's activities (exhibits, events, classes). Includes articles on cartoonists, and associated art work and graphics.

069 US
CHARLES H. MACNIDER MUSEUM NEWSLETTER. 1966. bi-m. membership. Charles H. MacNider Museum, 303 Second St., S.E., Mason City, IA 50401-3988. TEL 515-421-3666. Ed. Richard E. Leet. circ. 1,600. **Document type:** newsletter.
  Description: Informs museum members, the public and professional colleagues about events, activities, and exhibitions occurring at the museum.

CHICAGO ARCHITECTURE FOUNDATION NEWS. see *ARCHITECTURE*

CHICAGO ARTISTS' NEWS. see *ART*

069 BL ISSN 0103-2909
CIENCIAS EM MUSEUS. (Text mainly in Portuguese; abstracts in English) 1989. a. Cr.$85000($15) to individuals; institutions Cr.$91000($22) (effective 1990). Conselho Nacional de Desenvolvimento Cientifico e Tecnologico, Museu Paraense Emilio Goeldi, Caixa Postal 399, 66017-970 Belem, Para, Brazil. TEL 091-228-2341. FAX 091-299-1412. TELEX 091-1419. Ed.Bd. charts; illus.

708 US ISSN 1064-2242
N550
CINCINNATI ART MUSEUM. ANNUAL REPORT. 1930; N.S. 1950. a. free. Cincinnati Art Museum, Eden Park, Cincinnati, OH 45202. TEL 513-721-5204. FAX 513-721-0129. Ed. Gretchen Mehring. circ. 5,000. (also avail. in microform from UMI; reprint service avail. from UMI) **Indexed:** Art Ind., Artbibl.Mod., RILA.
  —UMI.
  Formerly: Cincinnati Art Museum. Bulletin (ISSN 0069-4061)

CIRCUIT RIDER (FRANKFURT). see *HISTORY — History Of North And South America*

069.5 IT
CIVICI MUSEI VENEZIANI D'ARTE E DI STORIA. BOLLETTINO. q? Civici Muesi Veneziani d'Arte e di Storia, S. Marco 52, 30100 Venice, Italy. TEL 041-5225625. FAX 041-5200935.

MUSEUMS AND ART GALLERIES

069 745.5　　US　　ISSN 1046-2252
COLLECTIONS (COLUMBIA). 1988. 3/yr. membership. Columbia Museum of Art, 1112 Bull St., Columbia, SC 29201. TEL 803-799-2810. FAX 803-343-2150. Ed. Salvatore G. Cilella. adv.; cum.index: 1988-1989. circ. 3,000. **Indexed:** RILA. **Document type:** academic/scholarly publication.
  Description: Presents articles on European and American art.

709.5　　SZ　　ISSN 0010-0781
COLLECTIONS BAUR. BULLETIN. (Text in French) 1965. s-a. 5 SFr. per no. Fondation Alfred et Eugenie Baur-Duret, 8 Rue Munier-Romilly, CH-1206 Geneva, Switzerland. TEL 022-3461729. FAX 022-7891845. Ed. Frank Dunand. circ. 1,000. **Document type:** bulletin.
  Description: Features descriptions and history of objects in the collection of Japanese and Chinese artifacts. Includes museum events and activities.

069　　US
COLUMN. bi-m. $30 includes membership. Arnot Art Museum, 235 Lake St., Elmira, NY 14901. TEL 607-734-3697. FAX 607-734-5687. Ed. Carolyn J. Warner. circ. 1,500. (tabloid format) **Document type:** newsletter.
  Description: Articles on current exhibitions, artists, events of interest to members and general public.

COMMUNITY HISTORY. see HISTORY — History Of Australasia And Other Areas

069.1 920　　US
CONFLUENCE (WENATCHEE). 1984. q. $25 membership. North Central Washington Museum Association, 127 S. Mission St., Wenatchee, WA 98801. TEL 509-664-5989. FAX 509-664-5997. Ed. Mary L. Thomsen. adv.; bk.rev.; circ. 1,000 (paid). (tabloid format; back issues avail.)
  Description: Covers regional history.

508.074　　US
CONSERVE O GRAM. base vol. plus. s-a. supplements. $56 (foreign 70). U.S. National Park Service, Interior Bldg., Rm. 3104, 18th and C Sts., Washington, DC 20240. TEL 202-208-4621. (Subscr. to: Superintendent of Documents, U.S. Government Printing Office, Box 371954, Pittsburgh, PA 15250-7954. TEL 202-512-1800. FAX 202-512-2250) (looseleaf format) **Document type:** government publication.
  Description: Contains technical advice on the care and preservation of museum artifacts and guides N.P.S. staff in carrying out projects identified in collection management planning documents.

069　　US
CONSTITUTION CHRONICLE. 1976. q. membership. U S S Constitution Museum Foundation, Box 1812, Boston, MA 02129. TEL 617-426-1812. FAX 617-242-0496. Ed. Stephanie M. Nichols. circ. 14,000. (tabloid format) **Document type:** newsletter.
  Formerly (until 1981): U S S Constitution Museum. News and Notes.
  Description: Keeps members of the U.S.S. Constitution Museum informed of museum activities and exhibits.

069　　GW
COOLIBRI; Kultur Freizeit Programm im Ruhrgebiet. 1983. m. DM.40. Roland Scherer Verlag und Werbeservice GmbH, Viktoriastr. 75, 44787 Bochum, Germany. TEL 0234-60342. FAX 0234-60345. Ed. Werner Dickob. adv.: B&W page DM.11560, color page DM.20260; trim 190 x 260. circ. 204,000. **Document type:** consumer publication.

708　　IT　　ISSN 0070-0479
CORPUS VASORUM ANTIQUORUM. ITALIA. 1927. irreg., no.67, 1986. price varies. (Museo Nazionale di Villa Giulia) L'Erma di Bretschneider, Via Cassiodoro 19, 00193 Rome, Italy. TEL 06-687-41-27. FAX 06-687-41-29. Ed. Mr. Barbieri.

930　　NE
CORPUS VASORUM ANTIQUORUM (NETHERLANDS). irreg., no.4, 1991. price varies. (Rijksmuseum van Oudheiden, Leiden) E.J. Brill, P.O. Box 9000, 2300 PA Leiden, Netherlands. TEL 31-71-5353500. FAX 31-71-5317532. TELEX 39296 BRILL NL. (In N. America: E.J. Brill, 24 Hudson St., Kinderhook, NY 12106. TEL 800-962-4406. FAX 518-758-1959) **Document type:** monographic series.

CORRAL DUST. see HISTORY

069　　US
COURIER (NEWARK). bi-m. membership. Mid-Atlantic Association of Museums, Box 817, Newark, DE 19715-0817. TEL 302-731-1424.
  Description: Communicates among museum personnel in the District of Columbia, Maryland, Delaware, New Jersey, Pennsylvania, and New York fostering current museum practices.

069 700　　US
COWBOY ARTISTS OF AMERICA NEWSLETTER. 1983. q. $25 membership. Cowboy Artists of America Museum, 1550 Bandera Hwy., Box 1716, Kerrville, TX 78029. TEL 210-896-2553. FAX 210-896-2556. Ed. Diana Comer. circ. 1,200. **Document type:** newsletter.
  Refereed Serial

CRAS; tidsskrift for kunst og kultur. see ART

069 574　　US　　ISSN 0011-3069
QH70　　　　CODEN: CRTRAH
CURATOR. 1958. q. $30 to individuals; institutions $55. American Museum of Natural History, Central Park W. at 79th St., New York, NY 10024-5192. TEL 212-873-1498. FAX 212-769-5233. E-mail: scipubs@amnh.org. (Subscr. to: Dept. HHH, Box 3000, Denville, NJ 07834. TEL 201-627-2427) Ed. Samuel M. Taylor. adv.; bk.rev.; charts; illus.; index, cum.index. circ. 1,500. (also avail. in microform from UMI; reprint service avail. from UMI) **Indexed:** Amer.Hist.& Life (until 1987), Art & Archaeol.Tech.Abstr., Biol.Abstr., Br.Archaeol.Abstr., Deep Sea Res.& Oceanogr.Abstr., GeoRef., Hist.Abstr. (until 1987). **Document type:** trade publication.
  —BLDSC (3493.500000); Faxon; SWETS; UMI; UnCover.

069　　CN　　ISSN 0384-9627
CURRENTLY: ONTARIO MUSEUM NEWS. 1972. bi-m. Can.$20. Ontario Museum Association, George Brown House, 50 Baldwin St., Toronto, ON M5T 1L4. TEL 416-348-8672. FAX 416-348-0438. E-mail: can-oma@immedia.ca. adv.; bk.rev. circ. 2,000. (back issues avail.) **Document type:** newsletter.
  Formerly: Ontario Museum News.
  Description: Issues of interest to workers in Ontario museums.

069　　SW　　ISSN 0070-2528
DAEDALUS. (Text in Swedish; summaries and occasional paper in English) 1931. a. SEK 225. Tekniska Museet - National Museum of Science and Technology, P.O. Box 27842, S-115 93 Stockholm, Sweden. TEL 46-8-6631085. FAX 46-8-6604519. Ed. Jan-Erik Pettersson. adv.; cum.index. circ. 3,000. **Indexed:** Acad.Ind., Amer.Bibl.Slavic & E.Eur.Stud., Arts & Hum.Cit.Ind., CLOSS, Curr.Cont., Educ.Admin.Abstr., G.Soc.Sci.& Rel.Per.Lit., High.Educ.Curr.Aware.Bull., M.L.A., Mag.Ind., P.A.I.S., SSCI.

069.5　　US　　ISSN 1067-8808
N531.D38
DAVID & ALFRED SMART MUSEUM OF ART. BULLETIN. 1988. a. membership. David & Alfred Smart Museum of Art, University of Chicago, 5550 S. Greenwood Ave., Chicago, IL 60637. TEL 312-702-0180. FAX 312-702-3121. Ed. Stephanie D'Alessandro. illus. circ. 1,000. **Document type:** bulletin.
  Formerly (until 1989): David and Alfred Smart Gallery Bulletin (ISSN 1041-6005)
  Description: Contains articles concerning art objects in the Smart collection; reports on exhibitions, accessions, loans, events, and gifts to the Museum, and programs for Museum audiences.

069 708　　CN　　ISSN 0703-6507
DAWSON AND HIND. (Text in English) 1971. irreg., latest vol.15, no.2. Can.$15. Association of Manitoba Museums, 422-167 Lombard Ave., Winnipeg, Man. R3B 0T6, Canada. Ed. Marilyn de von Flindt. bk.rev. circ. 400.

708　　US
DAYTON ART INSTITUTE. ANNUAL REPORT.* 1931. a. $3.50. Dayton Art Institute, 456 Belmonte Park N., Dayton, OH 45405-4700. TEL 513-223-5277. FAX 513-223-3140. Ed. Pat Obert Koepnick. circ. 4,000. **Indexed:** Artbibl.Mod.
  Supersedes in part: Dayton Art Institute. Annual Report and Bulletin; Formerly (until 1984): Dayton Art Institute. Annual Report (ISSN 0070-3028)

DEINSEA. see BIOLOGY — Zoology

708　　US
DELAWARE ART MUSEUM QUARTERLY. 1984. q. membership. Delaware Art Museum, 2301 Kentmere Pkwy., Wilmington, DE 19806. TEL 302-571-9590. FAX 302-571-0220. Ed. Lise Monty. circ. 5,000. **Document type:** newsletter.
  Formerly: Delaware Art Museum Bulletin.

069 900　　DK　　ISSN 0084-9308
AS281.A2
DENMARK. NATIONALMUSEET. NATIONALMUSEETS ARBEJDSMARK. 1928. a. Nationalmuseet, Frederiksholms Kanal 12, 1220 Copenhagen K, Denmark. TEL 45-33-13-44-11. FAX 45-33-47-33-30. **Indexed:** Numis.Lit.
  Formerly (until 1958): Fra Nationalmuseets Arbejdsmark.

DESIGN QUARTERLY. see ARCHITECTURE

509　　GW　　ISSN 0012-1339
AM101
DEUTSCHES MUSEUM. ABHANDLUNGEN UND BERICHTE. 1929. irreg. membership. R. Oldenbourg Verlag GmbH, Rosenheimerstr. 145, 81671 Munich, Germany. TEL 089-45051-0. FAX 089-45051207. (Subscr. to: Postfach 801360, 81613 Munich, Germany) bibl.; charts; illus. circ. 7,000. **Indexed:** Chem.Abstr. **Document type:** monographic series.

069　　US
DOINGS. 1983. 4/yr. free. Georgia Museum of Art, University of Georgia, Athens, GA 30602. TEL 404-542-3255. E-mail: ltyner@uga.cc.uga.edu. Ed. William Eiland. circ. 16,000.
  Formerly: Georgia Museum of Art. News.

DOMSPATZ; Zeitschrift fuer Fulda. see THEATER

700　　GW　　ISSN 0418-0615
DRESDENER KUNSTBLAETTER. 1956. bi-m. DM.4.50. Staatliche Kunstsammlungen Dresden, Albertinum, Georg-Treu-Platz 2, 01067 Dresden, Germany. TEL 0351-4953056. FAX 0351-4956019. Ed. Karin Perssen. bk.rev.; abstr.; illus.; index. circ. 2,000. (back issues avail.) **Indexed:** Artbibl.Mod., Numis.Lit., RILA. **Document type:** newsletter.
  —BLDSC (3623.400000).

707.4　　GW
DUESSELDORFER MUSEEN. 1981. q. free. Landeshauptstadt Duesseldorf, Oberstadtdirektor Presseamt, Postfach 101120, 40002 Duesseldorf, Germany. TEL 0211-8993131. FAX 0211-8994179. circ. 20,000. **Document type:** government publication.
  Description: Covers museum exhibitions in Dusseldorf.

THE EARLY BIRD. see HISTORY — History Of North And South America

069 700　　US　　ISSN 1070-8618
EARTHSONG. 1960. q. $30 membership. Heard Museum, 22 E. Monte Vista Rd., Phoenix, AZ 85004-1480. TEL 602-252-8840. FAX 602-252-9757. Ed. Juliet Martin. circ. 5,000. **Document type:** newsletter.
  Former titles (until 1993): Heard Museum Newsletter (ISSN 1052-6544); (until 1990): Heard Museum (ISSN 1049-8729); (until vol.10, no.1, 1968): Museum Notes (Phoenix).
  Description: Covers art exhibits and educational programs.
  Refereed Serial

069 700 659.1　　CN　　ISSN 1192-6341
EMPA. 1980. q. Can.$25($15) membership. Museum of Promotional Arts, Toronto, Box 400, Adelaide St. Sta., Toronto, ON M5C 2J5, Canada. TEL 416-925-5888. Ed. Frances E.M. Johnston. illus. circ. 200.
  Description: Aims to make people aware of and appreciate the promotional arts: advertising, packaging, book illustration, religious arts, signs.

MUSEUMS AND ART GALLERIES 4811

069 700 CN
EUROPEAN AND AMERICAN PAINTING, SCULPTURE AND DECORATIVE ARTS, VOLUME 1: 1300-1800. French edition: Peinture, Sculpture et Arts Decoratifs Europeens et Americains, Volume 1: 1300-1800. 1987. biennial. $97.50. National Gallery of Canada, Publications Division, c/o Irene Lillico, 380 Sussex Dr., Ottawa, ON K1N 9N4, Canada. TEL 613-990-0537. FAX 613-990-7460. (Dist. by: University of Chicago Press, 5801 Ellis Ave., Chicago, IL 60637-1496 U.S.A.) illus. **Document type:** catalog.
Description: Catalogs the permanent collection at the National Gallery of Canada

069 US
EVERSON MUSEUM OF ART BULLETIN. 1959. q. $35 to non-members. Everson Museum of Art, 401 Harrison St., Syracuse, NY 13202. TEL 315-474-6064. Ed. Linda M. Herbert. adv.; bibl.; illus. circ. 3,500. **Document type:** bulletin.

069 UK
EXETER CITY MUSEUMS & ART GALLERY. q. free. Exeter Museums Service, Royal Albert Memorial Museum, Queen Street, Exeter, Devon EX4 3RX, England. TEL 01932-265858. FAX 01392-421252. Ed. Ruth Randall. circ. 3,000. **Document type:** newsletter.
Former titles: Museums of Exeter; Exeter Museum News; Exeter Museums Bulletin and View; Exeter Museums News Event and Exhibitors.
Description: Contains retrospective news and information about Exeter's four museums, including exhibition reviews and news of recent acquisitions.

069 DK ISSN 0108-3643
F R A M. (Fra Ringkoebing Amts Museer) 1982. a. DKK 98. Museumsraadet i Ringkoebing Amt, Hjerl Hedes Frilandsmuseum, Hjerl Hedevej 14, 7830 Vinderup, Denmark. Ed. Soeren Toftgaard Poulsen. illus. circ. 3,600. **Indexed:** NAA.

FACULTAD DE ODONTOLOGIA DE BUENOS AIRES. MUSEO Y CENTRO DE ESTUDIOS HISTORICOS. REVISTA. see *MEDICAL SCIENCES — Dentistry*

FINGERPRINTS. see *CHILDREN AND YOUTH — For*

FINSKT MUSEUM. see *ARCHAEOLOGY*

FOLK ART. see *ART*

708.1 355 970 US ISSN 1071-7110
FORT CONCHO GUIDON. 1982. q. $5 to non-members. (Fort Concho Museum) Fort Concho Museum Press, 213 E. Ave. D, San Angelo, TX 76903-7099. TEL 915-657-4443. adv. contact: Cora Pugmire. circ. 1,200. (back issues avail.) **Document type:** newsletter.
Formerly: Fort Concho Members Dispatch.

FORT TICONDEROGA MUSEUM. BULLETIN. see *MILITARY*

948 DK ISSN 0107-4849
FRA BORNHOLMS MUSEUM. 1980. a. DKK 150. Bornholms Museum, Sct. Mortensgade 29, 3700 Roenne, Denmark. TEL 45-56-95-07-35. FAX 45-56-95-07-45. Ed. Ann Vibeke Knudsen. illus. circ. 3,000.
Formerly: Nyt fra Bornholms Museum.

069 GW ISSN 0177-011X
FREUNDESKREIS BLAETTER. 1976. s-a. DM.4. Freundeskreis Freilichtmuseum Suedbayern e.V., 82439 Grossweil, Germany. TEL 08851-1850. FAX 08851-18511. Ed. Helmut Keim. circ. 2,000. **Document type:** bulletin.

069 US
FRIENDS FOR LONG ISLAND'S HERITAGE. NEWS AND INFO. irreg. (every 6-8 wks.). membership. Friends for Long Island's Heritage, 1864 Muttontown Rd., Syosset, NY 11791. TEL 516-571-7600. FAX 516-571-7623. Ed. Loretta Schorr. **Document type:** newsletter.
Formerly: Enquirer Newsletter.
Description: Contains local history of Long Island, with special events indicated.

069 US
FRIENDS' QUARTERLY (ENFIELD). 1988. q. $36 membership. Museum at Lower Shaker Village, Rt. 4A, Enfield, NH 03748. TEL 603-632-4346. Ed. Deborah L. Coffin. illus. circ. 600. **Document type:** newsletter.
Description: Covers news and activities of the local museum.

FUJIAN WENBO/FUJIAN RELICS AND MUSEUM. see *ARCHAEOLOGY*

708.6 780 SP ISSN 1130-9849
FUNDACION LA CAIXA. PANORAMA. (Editions in Catalan, Spanish) 1991. m. free. Fundacion la Caixa, Via Laietana, 56, pral., 08003 Barcelona, Spain. TEL 93-404-60-76. Ed. Jesus Val Jarrin. illus. circ. 130,000.
Formerly (until 1991): Fundacio Caixa de Pensiones. Informatiu (ISSN 1130-7870).
Description: Covers art exhibits and musical performances supported by the foundation.

069 930.1 SW ISSN 0282-7301
DL621
FYND. 1968. s-a. SEK 50 (membership). Fornminnesfoereningen i Goeteborg, Goeteborgs Arkeologiska Museum, Norra Hamngatan 14, S-411 14 Goeteborg, Sweden.
Formerly (until 1985): Fyndmeddelanden.

069 IT ISSN 0072-0070
NC27.i8
GABINETTO DISEGNI E STAMPE DEGLI UFFIZI. CATALOGHI.. 1951. irreg., no.77, 1994. price varies. Casa Editrice Leo S. Olschki, Casella Postale 66, 50100 Florence, Italy. TEL 39-55-6530684. FAX 39-55-6530214. circ. 2,000.

069 IT ISSN 1122-0848
GABINETTO DISEGNI E STAMPE DEGLI UFFIZI. INVENTARIO. 1986. irreg., no.3, 1992. price varies. Casa Editrice Leo S. Olschki, Casella Postale 66, 50100 Florence, Italy. TEL 39-55-6530684. FAX 39-55-6530214. **Document type:** monographic series.

708.9 PY ISSN 1017-2823
GALERIA MICHELE MALINGUE. CATALOGO. (Text in English, Spanish) 1988. q. $50. Distribuidor Internacional Publicaciones Paraguayas, P.O. Box 2507, Ayoreos e-4a y 5a, Asuncion, Paraguay. TEL 595-21-495367. FAX 595-21-447460. Ed. Adriana Almada. circ. 1,000.

708 GW ISSN 0072-0089
GALERIE NIERENDORF, BERLIN. KUNSTBLAETTER. 1963. irreg., no.51, 1989. price varies. Galerie Nierendorf, Hardenbergstr. 19, 10623 Berlin, Germany. TEL 030-7856060. FAX 030-3129327. Ed. Florian Karsch. circ. 2,000.

708 AU
GALERIE SANCT LUCAS. GEMAELDE ALTER MEISTER. 1930. a. S.500. Galerie Sanct Lucas, Josefsplatz 5, Palais Pallavicini, A-1010 Vienna, Austria. FAX 0513-320316. illus. **Document type:** catalog.

708.5 IT
GALLERIA DEL CAVALLINO. MOSTRE. 1956. a. $10. Edizioni del Cavallino, Castello 5269-A, 30122 Venice, Italy. FAX 39-41-5210642. Ed. Paolo Cardazzo. illus. circ. 3,000.

708 AT ISSN 0814-7833
GALLERY. 1968. m. Aus.$47. (National Gallery Society of Victoria) Mount Eagle Publications, P.O. Box 84, Heidelberg, Vic. 3084, Australia. TEL 61-3-459-3911. Ed. Hugo Leschen. adv.; index. circ. 13,000. **Document type:** bulletin.
Description: Monthly issue of the Victoria National Gallery Society.

708.1 US
GALLERY ASSOCIATION BULLETIN. 1983. 3/yr. $12. Gallery Association of New York State, Box 345, Hamilton, NY 13346-0345. TEL 315-824-2510. FAX 315-824-1683. circ. 950. **Document type:** bulletin.

069.9 US
GAZETTE (CLAYTON). 1969. q. membership. Antique Boat Museum, 750 Mary St., Clayton, NY 13624. TEL 315-686-4104. FAX 315-686-2775. Ed. Judy Foster. adv.; bk.rev. circ. 1,700. **Document type:** newsletter.

GELDERS ERFGOED. see *HISTORY — History Of Europe*

069 JA ISSN 0435-219X
GENDAI NO ME. (Text in Japanese) 1954. m. National Museum of Modern Art, Tokyo, 3 Kitanomaru Koen, Chiyoda-ku, Tokyo 102, Japan. TEL 03-3214-2561. FAX 03-3213-1340. Ed. Yukio Kondo. **Document type:** newsletter.
Description: Contains articles on exhibitions and events of the three institutions, for the purpose of supplying fundamental information.

GERALD R. FORD FOUNDATION. NEWSLETTER. see *LIBRARY AND INFORMATION SCIENCES*

069 940 AU ISSN 1013-6800
GESELLSCHAFT FUER VERGLEICHENDE KUNSTFORSCHUNG IN WIEN. MITTEILUNGEN. 1930. q. S.250. Gesellschaft fuer Vergleichende Kunstforschung in Wien, Bundesdenkmalamt, Hofburg-Saeulenstiege, A-1010 Vienna, Austria. (Subscr. to: Institut fuer Kunstgeschichte der Universitaet Wien, Universitaetsstr. 7, A-1010 Vienna, Austria) Ed. Eckart Vancsa. adv.; bk.rev. **Indexed:** Artbibl.Mod., RILA. **Document type:** bulletin.

GIFU-KEN HAKUBUTSUKAN CHOSA KENKYU HOKOKU/GIFU PREFECTURAL MUSEUM. BULLETIN. see *SCIENCES: COMPREHENSIVE WORKS*

069 XV ISSN 0350-2929
DR1475.G67
GORISKI LETNIK. 1974. a. 400 din. Goriski Muzej, Raziskovalna Skupnost Slovenije, Adranska 16 A, Ljubljana, Slovenia. **Indexed:** Amer.Hist.& Life (until 1987), Hist.Abstr. (until 1987).

760 RU ISSN 0077-1562
GOSUDARSTVENNYI MUZEI IZOBRAZITEL'NYKH ISKUSSTV IM. PUSHKINA. SOOBSHCHENIYA. (Text in Russian; summaries in English or French) 1960. irreg., no.10, 1992. price varies. Gosudarstvennyi Muzei Izobrazitel'nykh Iskusstv im. Pushkina - Pushikin Museum of Fine Arts, Volkhonka 12, 121019 Moscow, Russia. TEL 203-6974. FAX 203-4674. Ed. I.E. Danilova. **Document type:** academic/scholarly publication.
Description: Publishes articles on art history and archaeology. Includes catalogue of the current exhibitions.

069 CH
GUANXUN ZAZHI/TAIWAN MUSEUM OF ART. NEWSLETTER. (Text in Chinese) s-a. free. Taiwan Shengli Meishuguan, 2, Wuchuan W. Rd., Taichung, Taiwan, Republic of China. TEL 3723552. FAX 3721195. Ed. Kunfu Liu. **Document type:** newsletter.

069 JA ISSN 0911-9892
HAKUBUTSUKAN KENKYU/MUSEUM STUDIES. (Text in Japanese) 1928. m. 8000 Yen. Japanese Association of Museums - Nihon Hakubutsukan Kyokai, Shoyu-Kaikan 3-3-1, Kasumigaseki, Chiyoda-ku, Tokyo 100, Japan. TEL 03-3591-7190. **Indexed:** RILA.
Incorporates (in 1986): Hakubutsukan Nyusu.

016.9173 US ISSN 0093-1047
Z999
HARRIS AUCTION GALLERIES. COLLECTORS' AUCTION. Key Title: Collectors' Auction (Baltimore). 1962. 6/yr. $25 for 8 nos. Harris Auction Galleries, Inc., 873-875 N. Howard St., Baltimore, MD 21201. TEL 301-728-7040. Eds. Barr Harris, Christopher Bready. circ. 1,000.

HARVARD UNIVERSITY ART MUSEUMS REVIEW. see *ART*

948.91 DK ISSN 0108-0393
HELSINGOER KOMMUNES MUSEER. AARBOG. 1981. a. DKK 120. Helsingoer Kommunes Museer, Hestemoellestraede 1, DK-3000 Helsingoer, Denmark. illus. **Indexed:** NAA.
Formerly (until 1977): Helsingoer Bymuseum. Aarbog (ISSN 0106-0317)

HERITAGE AND HISTORY. see *HISTORY — History Of North And South America*

069 US
HISTORIC DEERFIELD QUARTERLY. 1952. q. free. Historic Deerfield, Inc., Box 321, Deerfield, MA 01342. TEL 413-774-5581. FAX 413-773-7415. Ed. Grace Friary. circ. 3,000. (tabloid format) **Document type:** newsletter.

HISTORIC FARM BUILDINGS GROUP. JOURNAL. see *ARCHITECTURE*

MUSEUMS AND ART GALLERIES

708.8 948.9   DK   ISSN 0905-4723
HISTORISK FORENING FOR VISHERRED, BOV MUSEUM.
1978. a. DKK 60. Historisk Forening for Visherred, Bov Museum, Padborgvej 27, DK-6330 Padborg, Denmark. TEL 45-74-67-16-18.
Formerly (until 1989): Fra Bov Museum (ISSN 0106-8229)

HIWA KAGAKU HAKUBUTSUKAN KENKYU HOKOKU/HIWA MUSEUM FOR NATURAL HISTORY. MISCELLANEOUS REPORTS. see *SCIENCES: COMPREHENSIVE WORKS*

069   GW
HOHENLOHER FREILANDMUSEUM MITTEILUNGEN.
1980. a. DM.8. Hohenlohe Freilandmuseum, Postfach 100180, 74501 Schwaebisch Hall, Germany. TEL 0791-84061. **Document type:** bulletin.

069 952   JA   ISSN 0287-9433
HOKKAIDO KAITAKU KINENKAN KENKYU NENPO/HISTORICAL MUSEUM OF HOKKAIDO. ANNUAL REPORT. (Text in Japanese; summaries in English) 1972. a. free. Hokkaido Kaitaku Kinenkan - Historical Museum of Hokkaido, Konoppporo, Atsubetsu-cho, Atsubetsu-ku, Sapporo-shi, Hokkaido 004, Japan. TEL 898-0456. FAX 898-2657. circ. 1,000.

069   JA   ISSN 0918-3159
GN301
HOKKAIDORITSU HOPPO MINZOKU HAKUBUTSUKAN KENKYU KIYO/HOKKAIDO MUSEUM OF NORTHERN PEOPLES. BULLETIN. (Text in Japanese) 1992. a. Hokkaidoritsu Hoppo Minzoku Hakubutsukan, 313-1 Shiomi, Abashiri-shi, Hokkaido 093, Japan.

HORIZONT; veszprem megyei kozmuvelodesi tajekoztato. see *CLUBS*

707.4   US
HUNTINGTON LIBRARY, ART COLLECTIONS, AND BOTANICAL GARDENS. CALENDAR. 1936. bi-m. $40. Huntington Library, Art Collections and Botanical Gardens, 1151 Oxford Rd., San Marino, CA 91108. TEL 818-405-2170. FAX 818-405-0225. Ed. Catherine M. Babcock. illus. circ. 8,000.
Former titles: Huntington Library, Art Gallery and Botanical Gardens. Collections; Huntington Library, Art Gallery and Botanical Gardens. Calendar; Henry E. Huntington Library and Art Gallery. Calendar of Exhibitions (ISSN 0018-0408)

069   US
I A S M H F NEWSLETTER. 1971. bi-m. $20. International Association of Sports Museums and Halls of Fame, 101 W. Sutton Pl., Wilmington, DE 19810-4115. TEL 302-475-7068. FAX 302-475-7038. Ed. Al Cartwright. adv.; bk.rev. circ. 200. **Document type:** newsletter.
Formerly: Association of Sports Museums and Halls of Fame. Newsletter.
Description: Covers association and member news.

069.094   FR   ISSN 0018-8999
I C O M NEWS. French edition: Nouvelles de l'I C O M. Spanish edition: Noticias del I C O M. 1948. q. 260 F. to non-members. International Council of Museums - Conseil International des Musees, c/o Maison de l'Unesco, 1 rue Miollis, 75732 Paris Cedex 15, France. TEL 47-34-05-00. FAX 43-06-78-62. TELEX UNESCO 270 602. Ed. Therese Hogan. adv.: B&W page 6000 F.; trim 171 x 247; adv. contact: Valerie Julien. bk.rev.; abstr.; bibl. circ. 13,000. **Indexed:** Art & Archaeol.Tech.Abstr., Br.Archaeol.Abstr., Chem.Abstr. **Document type:** newsletter.
—BLDSC (4362.060000).
Description: Provides news of I.C.O.M. activities, its international committees, and topics of interest to museum workers. Reports on stolen art, illicit traffic, and conferences and events.

069 500   US   ISSN 0196-7703
E78.I18
IDAHO MUSEUM OF NATURAL HISTORY. OCCASIONAL PAPERS. 1958. irreg. price varies. Idaho Museum of Natural History, Idaho State University, Box 8096, Pocatello, ID 83209. TEL 208-236-2603. Ed. Skip Lohse. circ. 500. **Document type:** monographic series.
Formerly: Idaho State University Museum. Occasional Papers (ISSN 0073-4551)

069   US   ISSN 0737-5093
IDAHO MUSEUM OF NATURAL HISTORY. SPECIAL PUBLICATION. no. 2, 1971. irreg. price varies. Idaho Museum of Natural History, Idaho State University, Box 8096, Pocatello, ID 83209-0009. TEL 208-236-2603. Ed. Barry L. Keller. **Document type:** monographic series.

069 520   JA
IKOMAYAMA UCHU KAGAKUKAN NYUSU. (Text in Japanese) 1969. irreg. Ikomayama Uchu Kagakukan - Mount Ikoma Space Science Museum, 2312-1, Nahata-cho, Ikoma-shi, Nara-ken 630-02, Japan.
Description: News of the museum.

069 500   US   ISSN 0095-2893
ILLINOIS. STATE MUSEUM. INVENTORY OF THE COLLECTIONS. 1969. irreg., no.1, pt.6, 1986. free. Illinois State Museum, Springfield, IL 62706. TEL 217-782-7386. FAX 217-782-1254. **Indexed:** Sport Fish.Abstr., Wild.Rev. **Document type:** monographic series.
Refereed Serial

069.095   II   ISSN 0019-5987
INDIAN MUSEUM BULLETIN. (Text in English) 1966. a. Rs.100($20) Indian Museum, Calcutta, 27 Jawaharlal Nehru Rd., Calcutta 700016, India. TEL 91-33249-5699. FAX 91-33249-5696. Ed. S.S. Biswas. bk.rev.; charts, illus.; index, cum.index: 1966-1969. circ. 500. **Indexed:** Numis.Lit. **Document type:** bulletin.
—BLDSC (4423.250000).

708.7   US
INDIANAPOLIS MUSEUM OF ART. PREVIEWS MAGAZINE. 1911. bi-m. membership. Indianapolis Museum of Art, 1200 W. 38th St., Indianapolis, IN 46208. TEL 317-923-1331. FAX 317-926-8931. Ed. Julie King. illus. circ. 15,000. **Indexed:** RILA. **Document type:** bulletin.
Former titles (until 1987): Indianapolis Museum of Art. Quarterly Magazine (ISSN 0894-8828); Indianapolis Museum of Art. Newsletter; Indianapolis Museum of Art. Bulletin (ISSN 0004-3060); Art Association of Indianapolis. Bulletin.

069   CI   ISSN 0350-2325
INFORMATICA MUSEOLOGICA. (Text in Serbo-Croatian; summaries in English) 1970. q. $24 (effective Oct. 1990). Muzejski Dokumentacioni Centar, Mesnicka 5, 41000 Zagreb, Croatia. FAX 38-41-430-851. Ed. Branka Sulc. bk.rev. circ. 1,000.

INSTITUTE OF DIVING. NEWSLETTER. see *SPORTS AND GAMES*

355.8075   FI   ISSN 0074-168X
INTERNATIONAL ASSOCIATION OF MUSEUMS OF ARMS AND MILITARY HISTORY. CONGRESS REPORTS. 1957. triennial, 9th, 1981, Washington. membership. International Association of Museums of Arms and Military History, c/o Markku Melkko, P.O. Box 266, FIN-00171 Helsinki, Finland. FAX 358-0-1616390. circ. controlled. **Document type:** proceedings.

INTERNATIONAL SWIMMING HALL OF FAME HEADLINES. see *SPORTS AND GAMES*

INTERP CENTRAL CLEARINGHOUSE NEWSLETTER. see *ENVIRONMENTAL STUDIES*

INVENTAIRE GENERAL DES MONUMENTS ET DES RICHESSES ARTISTIQUES DE LA FRANCE. see *ARCHITECTURE*

IRISH ARTS REVIEW YEARBOOK. see *ART*

069   US
IROQUOIS INDIAN MUSEUM. MUSEUM NOTES. 1981. irreg. $20. Iroquois Indian Museum, Box 7, Caverns Rd., Howes Cave, NY 12092. TEL 518-296-8949. FAX 518-296-8955. Ed. John P. Ferguson. circ. 1,100. **Document type:** newsletter.
Formerly: Schoharie Museum of the Iroquois Indian. Museum Notes.
Description: Reviews museum events, programs and activities

069   IS   ISSN 0333-7499
N3750.J5
ISRAEL MUSEUM JOURNAL. (Text in English) 1965. a. $7.50. Israel Museum, P.O. Box 71117, Jerusalem, Israel. FAX 972-2-631833. Ed.Bd. adv.; charts; illus. circ. 3,000. **Indexed:** Artbibl.Mod., Avery Ind.Archit.Per., Numis.Lit., RILA. **Document type:** academic/scholarly publication.
Formerly: Israel Museum News (ISSN 0021-227X)

708.194   US   ISSN 0362-1979
N582.M25
THE J. PAUL GETTY MUSEUM JOURNAL. 1974. a. $70. J. Paul Getty Museum, 17985 Pacific Coast Highway, Malibu, CA 90265. TEL 310-459-7611. FAX 310-454-8156. (Orders to: J. Paul Getty Book Distribution Center, Box 2112, Santa Monica, CA 90407-2112. TEL 800-223-3431) Ed. John Harris. illus.: cum.index: vols.1-20 in vol.20, 1992. circ. 1,000. (back issues avail.) **Indexed:** Art Ind., Avery Ind.Archit.Per., RILA. **Document type:** academic/scholarly publication.
—Faxon.
Description: Compendium of articles pertaining to the museum's permanent collection, with notes on recent acquisitions.
Refereed Serial

655.5   GW   ISSN 0075-2193
Z1000
JAHRBUCH DER AUKTIONSPREISE FUER BUECHER, HANDSCHRIFTEN UND AUTOGRAPHEN; Ergebnisse der Auktionen in Deutschland, den Niederlanden, Oesterreich und der Schweiz. 1950. a. DM.380. Dr. Ernst Hauswedell und Co. Verlag, Rosenbergstr. 113, 70193 Stuttgart, Germany. FAX 0711-6369010. adv. circ. 1,200. (back issues avail.; reprint service avail. from KTO) **Document type:** bibliography.
Formerly: Jahrbuch der Auktionspreise.

069 708   GW   ISSN 0075-2207
N3
JAHRBUCH DER BERLINER MUSEEN. 1959. a. price varies. (Staatliche Museen Preussischer Kulturbesitz Berlin) Gebr. Mann Verlag GmbH, Lindenstr. 76, 10969 Berlin, Germany. TEL 030-2591-3589. FAX 030-2591-3537. (Subscr. to: 10888 Berlin, Germany) (reprint service avail.) **Indexed:** Artbibl.Mod., Arts & Hum.Cit.Ind., Avery Ind.Archit.Per., Curr.Cont., RILA. **Document type:** academic/scholarly publication.

069   GW   ISSN 0938-6998
JAHRBUCH FUER GLOCKENKUNDE. 1989. a. DM.58 membership. Deutsches Glockenmuseum, Talstr. 19, 35751 Greifenstein, Germany. TEL 06449-6460. Eds. Konrad Bund, Joerg Poeltgen. circ. 600. **Document type:** bulletin.

069   JA   ISSN 0040-8948
JAPAN. NATIONAL MUSEUM NEWS. (Text in Japanese) 1947. m. 1,500 Yen. Tokyo National Museum - Tokyo Kokuritsu Hakubutsukan, 13-9 Ueno Park, Taito-ku, Tokyo 110, Japan. TEL 03-3822-1111. FAX 03-3822-9130. bk.rev. circ. 17,000. (tabloid format)

069   GR
JEWISH MUSEUM OF GREECE. NEWSLETTER. (Text in English) 1981. q. membership. Jewish Museum of Greece, 36 Queen Amalias Ave., 105 58 Athens, Greece. TEL 323-1577. (Dist. in U.S. by: American Friends of the Jewish Museum of Greece, Box 2010, New York, NY 10185-0017. TEL 212-661-9843) Ed. N. Stavroulakis. bk.rev. circ. 1,500. **Document type:** newsletter.
Description: Covers the heritage of the Sephardic and Romaniot communities in the Hellenic world. Includes acquisition news.

708.1   US
N742.S5
JOHN & MABLE RINGLING MUSEUM OF ART. 1964. q. membership. John and Mable Ringling Museum of Art Foundation, 5401 Bay Shore Rd., Sarasota, FL 34243-2161. TEL 813-359-5700. FAX 813-359-5745. Ed. Barbara Linick. illus.; circ. 5,000. (controlled). **Document type:** newsletter.
Former titles: Ringling Museums (ISSN 0731-7956); Ringling Museums Newsletter (ISSN 0035-5461)

MUSEUMS AND ART GALLERIES 4813

707.4 US
JOSLYN NEWS; a publication for members. 1974. bi-m. membership. Joslyn Art Museum, 2200 Dodge St., Omaha, NE 68102. TEL 402-342-3300. FAX 402-342-2376. Ed. Jennifer Rubin. illus.; circ. 7,500 (controlled). **Document type:** newsletter.
Former titles: Joslyn Art Museum Members' Calendar; Joslyn Art Museum Calendar of Events.

JOURNAL OF DECORATIVE AND PROPAGANDA ARTS. see *ART*

069 UK ISSN 0260-9126
JOURNAL OF EDUCATION IN MUSEUMS. 1980. a. £7 (foreign £8). Group for Education in Museums, c/o Sue Morse, Fleet Air Arm Museum, Royal Naval Air Station, Yeovilton, Yeovil, Somers. BA22 8HT, England. adv.; bk.rev.; illus. circ. 800. (back issues avail.)
—BLDSC (4973.150500).
Description: Covers all aspects of museum education both in Britain and abroad.

069 II ISSN 0970-9894
AM1
JOURNAL OF INDIAN MUSEUMS.* (Text in English) a. Museums Association of India, c/o National Museum of Natural History, F I C C I, Museum Building, Barakhamba Road, New Delhi 110002, India. **Indexed:** Art & Archaeol.Tech.Abstr.

069 JA ISSN 0288-2051
JOURNAL OF KOKUGAKUIN UNIVERSITY/KOKUGAKUIN ZASSHI. (Text in Japanese) 1894. m. Kokugakuin University, 4-10-28 Higashi, Shibuya-ku, Tokyo 150, Japan. Ed. Futaki Keiichi. **Document type:** academic/scholarly publication.
—UnCover.

069.095 529 CH ISSN 0256-257X
QH1 CODEN: QJTMAW
JOURNAL OF TAIWAN MUSEUM. Key Title: Taiwan Shengli Bowuguan Jikan. (Text in English) 1948. s-a. Taiwan Provincial Museum - Tai-wan Sheng Li Po Wu Kuan, 2 Siangyang Rd., Taipei, Taiwan 100, Republic of China. FAX 3140939. Ed. C.I. Chang. charts; illus. **Indexed:** Biol.Abstr., Field Crop Abstr., Forest.Abstr., Herb.Abstr., Hort.Abstr., Rev.Appl.Entomol. **Document type:** academic/scholarly publication.
—BLDSC (4905.296000); UnCover.
Formerly (until 1983): Taiwan Museum. Quarterly Journal (ISSN 0039-9116)

JOURNAL OF THE AUSTRALIAN WAR MEMORIAL. see *MILITARY*

069.9 UK ISSN 0954-6650
AM221 CODEN: JHCOE2
JOURNAL OF THE HISTORY OF COLLECTIONS. 1989. s-a. £60($110) (effective 1996). Oxford University Press, Oxford Journals, Walton St., Oxford OX2 6DP, England. TEL 01865-267907. FAX 01865-267773. TELEX 837330-OXPRES-G. E-mail: jnlorders@oup.co.uk. (U.S. subscr. to: Oxford University Press Inc., 2001 Evans Rd., Cary, NC 27513. TEL 919-677-0977. FAX 919-677-1714) Eds. Oliver Impey, Arthur MacGregor. adv. contact: Jane Parker. bk.rev. circ. 800. **Document type:** academic/scholarly publication.
—BLDSC (5000.740000); Faxon; SWETS; UMI; UnCover. **CCC.**
Description: Dedicated to the study of collections, ranging from the contents of palaces and accumulations in more modest households, to the most systematic collection of academic institutions.

639.2074 700 US
K W M NEWSLETTER. 1982. q. membership. Kendall Whaling Museum, 27 Everett St., Box 297, Sharon, MA 02067. TEL 617-784-5642. Ed. Robert A. Kotta. circ. 600. **Document type:** newsletter.

069 AU ISSN 0022-7587
KAERNTNER MUSEUMSSCHRIFTEN. 1954. irreg. price varies. Landesmuseum fuer Kaernten, Museumgasse 2, A-9021 Klagenfurt, Austria. TEL 0463-536-30567. FAX 0463-53630540. Ed. Gernot Piccottini. adv. contact: Raimund Schnablegger. circ. 200. **Document type:** monographic series.

KAMISHIHORO-CHO HIGASHI TAISETSU HAKUBUTSUKAN KENKYU HOKOKU/HIGASHI TAISETSU MUSEUM OF NATURAL HISTORY. BULLETIN. see *SCIENCES: COMPREHENSIVE WORKS*

069 JA
KANAGAWA-KEN HAKUBUTSUKAN KYOKAI KAIHO/KANAGAWA-KEN MUSEUM GAZETTE. (Text in Japanese) 1958. irreg. 500 Yen. Kanagawa-ken Hakubutsukan Kyokai - Museums Association of Kanagawa Prefecture, 5-60 Minami-Nakadori, Naka-ku, Yokohama-shi, Kanagawa-ken 231, Japan. TEL 045-201-0926. FAX 045-201-7364. circ. controlled. **Document type:** bulletin.
Description: A bulletin of natural and cultural sciences.

KANAGAWA-KENRITSU HAKUBUTSUKAN KENKYU HOKOKU. SHIZEN KAGAKU/KANAGAWA PREFECTURAL MUSEUM. BULLETIN. NATURAL SCIENCE. see *SCIENCES: COMPREHENSIVE WORKS*

069 KE
KENYA MUSEUM SOCIETY. CHAIRMAN'S REPORT. 1971. a. $40. Kenya Museum Society, c/o Kenya National Museums, P.O. Box 40658, Nairobi, Kenya. Ed. Esmond Martin. adv. circ. 2,000. **Document type:** corporate report.

KITAKAMI-SHIRITSU HAKUBUTSUKAN KENKYU HOKOKU/KITAKAMI CITY MUSEUM. BULLETIN. see *SCIENCES: COMPREHENSIVE WORKS*

KITAKYUSHU SHIRITSU SHIZENSHI HAKUBUTSUKAN KENKYU HOKOKU/KITAKYUSHU MUSEUM OF NATURAL HISTORY. BULLETIN. see *SCIENCES: COMPREHENSIVE WORKS*

708 GW ISSN 0075-6326
KLEINE MUSEUMSHEFTE. 1967. irreg. vol.9, 1981. price varies. Rheinland Verlag GmbH, Abtei Brauweiler, Postfach 2140, 50250 Pulheim, Germany. TEL 02234-8051. FAX 02234-82503. (Dist. by: Dr. Rudolf Habelt GmbH, Am Buchenhang 1, 53115 Bonn, Germany. TEL 0228-232016. FAX 0228-232017) **Document type:** monographic series.

069.094891 DK ISSN 0107-931X
KOEGE MUSEUM. 1976. a. DKK 80. Koege Museum, Noerregade 4, DK-4600 Koege, Denmark. TEL 45-53-65-02-62. Ed. Gunnar Solvang.
Formerly: Koege Museum. Aarbog.

069.094 GW ISSN 0933-257X
AM51.C64
KOELNER MUSEUMS BULLETIN. 1961. q. plus special issues. DM.35. Museumsdienst Koeln, Schaerenstr. 1b, 50676 Cologne, Germany. FAX 0221-2214544. Ed.Bd. adv.; bk.rev.; illus.; cum.index in prep. (1961-1975). circ. 2,500. **Indexed:** Artbibl.Mod., RILA. **Document type:** bulletin.
Former titles: Museen der Stadt Koeln. Bulletin (ISSN 0178-4218); Museen in Koeln. Bulletin (ISSN 0027-3813)
Description: Reports on new acquisitions, exhibitions, and research.

500 069 JA
KOKURITSU KAGAKU HAKUBUTSUKAN NENPO. (Text in Japanese) 1972. a. Monbusho, Kokuritsu Kagaku Hakubutsukan - Ministry of Education, National Science Museum, 7-20 Ueno Koen, Taito-ku, Tokyo 110, Japan.
Description: Annual report of the museum.

KOMATSU-SHIRITSU HAKUBUTSUKAN KENKYU KIYO/KOMATSU CITY MUSEUM. MEMOIRS. see *SCIENCES: COMPREHENSIVE WORKS*

069 500.9 JA
KOTONOURA. (Text in Japanese) 1986. q. Wakayama-kenritsu Shizen Hakubutsukan Tomo no Kai, Wakayama-kenritsu Shizen Hakubutsukan, 370-1 Funao, Kainan-shi, Wakayama-ken 642, Japan.
Description: Publishes news of Wakayama Prefecture's natural science museum.

096 US
KRESGE FOUNDATION. ANNUAL REPORT. a. Kresge Foundation, Box 3151, 3215 W. Big Beaver Rd., Troy, MI 48007-3151. TEL 313-643-9630. FAX 313-643-0588.

069 GW ISSN 0344-5690
T14.7 CODEN: KUTEEN
KULTUR UND TECHNIK. 1977. q. DM.39.80. (Deutsches Museum) C.H. Beck'sche Verlagsbuchhandlung, Wilhelmstr. 9, 80801 Munich, Germany. TEL 089-38189-338. FAX 089-38189398. adv.: B&W page DM.3700, color page DM.6475; trim 260 x 186. bk.rev.; circ. 12,551 (controlled). **Document type:** academic/scholarly publication.
Description: Examines the inter-relationships of culture and technology.

069 708 SW ISSN 0282-5902
KULTURENS VAERLD. 1985. q. SEK 210. Stiftelsen Kulturens Vaerld, P.O. Box 14056, S-200 24 Malmoe, Sweden. TEL 46-87-35-55-80. FAX 46-87-30-28-07. Ed. Bertil Heddelin. adv.; bk.rev.; illus. circ. 31,000. **Indexed:** NAA, Numis.Lit.

KULTURMILJOEVAARD; information. see *ARCHAEOLOGY*

KUNST & MUSEUMJOURNAAL. see *ART*

069 GW ISSN 0937-9541
KUNST IN KOELN. Variant title: K I K: Kunst in Koeln. 1965. m. free. Generaldirektion der Museen Koeln, St.-Apern-Str. 17-21, 50667 Cologne, Germany. TEL 0221-2212334. Ed. Karin Bolenius. circ. 900. **Document type:** newsletter.
Description: Press release by the museums of the city of Cologne.

069 GW ISSN 0023-5474
N3
KUNSTCHRONIK; Monatsschrift fuer Kunstwissenschaft, Museumswesen und Denkmalpflege. 1948. m. DM.106. (Zentralinstitut fuer Kunstgeschichte in Muenchen) Verlag Hans Carl GmbH, Andernacherstr. 33a, 90411 Nuernberg, Germany. TEL 0911-95285-0. FAX 0911-9528548. Ed. P. Diemer. adv.; bk.rev.; bibl.; charts; illus.; index. circ. 2,600. **Indexed:** Avery Ind.Archit.Per., RILA. **Document type:** bulletin.
—Faxon; SWETS. **CCC.**

KUNSTREPORT. see *ART*

KURASHIKI-SHIRITSU SHIZENSHI HAKUBUTSUKAN KENKYU HOKOKU/KURASHIKI MUSEUM OF NATURAL HISTORY. BULLETIN. see *SCIENCES: COMPREHENSIVE WORKS*

069 JA ISSN 0913-1558
KURASHIKI-SHIRITSU SHIZENSHI HAKUBUTSUKANPO. (Text in Japanese) 1986. a. free. Kurashiki-shiritsu Shizenshi Hakubutsukan - Kurashiki Museum of Natural History, 6-1 Chuo 2-chome, Kurashiki, Okayama 710, Japan. TEL 0864-25-6037. FAX 0864-25-6038. circ. 1,000.
Description: Annual report of the museum.

KUSHIRO-SHIRITSU HAKUBUTSUKAN KIYO/KUSHIRO CITY MUSEUM. MEMOIRS. see *SCIENCES: COMPREHENSIVE WORKS*

069 JA ISSN 0288-9102
KYODO TO HAKUBUTSUKAN. (Text in Japanese) 1953. s-a. Tottori-kenritsu Hakubutsukan - Tottori Prefectural Museum, 2-124 Higashi-machi, Tottori-shi, Tottori-ken 680, Japan. FAX 0857-26-8041. circ. 1,000.

069 AU ISSN 0007-280X
LANDESMUSEUM FUER KAERNTEN. BUCHREIHE. 1954. irreg. price varies. Landesmuseum fuer Kaernten, Museumgasse 2, A-9021 Klagenfurt, Austria. TEL 0463-536-30567. FAX 0463-53630540. Ed. Gernot Piccottini. adv. contact: Raimund Schnablegger. circ. 400. **Indexed:** GeoRef. **Document type:** monographic series.

708 940 GW ISSN 0070-7201
LANDESMUSEUM FUER VORGESCHICHTE, DRESDEN. VEROEFFENTLICHUNGEN. 1952. irreg., vol.17, 1985. price varies. VEB Deutscher Verlag der Wissenschaften, Postfach 1216, 1080 Berlin, Germany. Ed. Werner Coblenz.

708 940 GW ISSN 0072-940X
LANDESMUSEUM FUER VORGESCHICHTE, HALLE. VEROEFFENTLICHUNGEN. 1964. irreg. price varies. (Landesmuseum fuer Vorgeschichte, Halle) VEB Deutscher Verlag der Wissenschaften, Postfach 1216, 1080 Berlin, Germany. Ed. H. Behrens.

MUSEUMS AND ART GALLERIES

069 675 US ISSN 0898-0128
LEATHER CONSERVATION NEWS. 1983. s-a. $15. Minnesota Historical Society, Objects Conservation Laboratory, 345 Kellogg Blvd. W., St. Paul, MN 55407. TEL 612-297-5774. FAX 612-296-9961. Ed. Paul S. Storch. bk.rev.; cum.index: 1983-1993. circ. 250. (back issues avail.) **Document type:** academic/scholarly publication.
—BLDSC (5179.386500).
Description: Publishes materials science research on leather and practical studies of treatments of leather cultural objects. Disseminates information about leather conservation, preservation and restoration to workers in the field and other interested parties.

707.4 GW
LEBENDIGES DARMSTADT; Veranstaltungsvorschau. 1950. m. DM.50. Verkehrsverein Darmstadt e.V., Luisenplatz 5, 64283 Darmstadt, Germany. TEL 06151-20228. **Document type:** bulletin.
Description: Provides a calendar of performances and events within the city of Darmstadt.

708.2 UK ISSN 0024-0257
LEEDS ARTS CALENDAR. 1947. s-a. £15. Leeds Arts Collections Fund, Temple Newsam House, Leeds 15, Yorkshire, England. FAX 0532-602285. Ed. Anthony Wells-Cole. adv.; illus. circ. 450. (also avail. in microform from UMI) **Indexed:** Artbibl.Mod., Br.Hum.Ind., RILA. **Document type:** academic/scholarly publication.
—BLDSC (5181.260000); UMI.

LIBRARY COMPANY OF PHILADELPHIA. OCCASIONAL MISCELLANY. see *HISTORY — History Of North And South America*

069 IC ISSN 1021-6626
LISTASAFN SIGURJONS OLAFSSONAR. ARBOK. (Text in Icelandic; summaries in English) 1986. a. ISK 1500. Sigurjon Olafsson Museum, Laugarnestanga 70, IS-105 Reykjavik, Iceland. TEL 354-553-2906. FAX 354-581-4553. Ed. Birgitta Spur. **Document type:** academic/scholarly publication.

069 US
LITHOPHANE COLLECTOR'S CLUB BULLETIN.* 1975. bi-m. $18 includes membership. Blair Museum of Lithophanes and Carved Waxes, Lithophanes Collector's Club, 608 Madison Ave., Ste. 1523, Toledo, OH 43604-1148. TEL 419-243-4115. bk.rev. circ. 175.
Description: For individuals interested in the history and collection of lithophanes and related art objects.

LITHUANIAN MUSEUM REVIEW. see *ETHNIC INTERESTS*

708 US ISSN 0047-4851
LIVING HISTORICAL FARMS BULLETIN. 1970. bi-m. membership. Association for Living Historical Farms and Agricultural Museums, Conner Prairie Fishers, IN 46038. TEL 317-776-6000. FAX 317-776-6014. Ed. Stephen L. Cox. adv.; bk.rev.; bibl. circ. 1,200. **Document type:** bulletin.

LIVINGSTONE MUSEUM. RESEARCH NOTES. see *HISTORY — History Of Africa*

739 SW ISSN 0024-5372
LIVRUSTKAMMAREN. (Text in English or Swedish; summaries in English, French or German) 1937. s-a. SEK 64. Kungliga Livrustkammaren - Royal Armoury, Kungliga Slottet, Slottsbacken 3, S-111 30 Stockholm, Sweden. TEL 46-8-666-44-68. FAX 46-8-666-44-68. Ed. Anne-Marie Dahlberg. bk.rev. **Document type:** academic/scholarly publication.
Refereed Serial

708 US
LOCUS (NEW YORK). 1975. irreg., latest 1989. $49. Filsinger and Company Ltd., 288 W. 12th St., New York, NY 10014. TEL 212-243-7421. Ed. Cheryl Filsinger.
Description: Provides cross-references to over 450 New York City galleries and their historical and contemporary artists and photographers with an index to gallery specialities, geographical sections, and a city museum list.

708 US
LOCUS SELECT. 1975? irreg., latest 1992. $49. Filsinger and Company Ltd., 288 W. 12th St., New York, NY 10014. TEL 212-243-7421.
Description: Provides cross-references to selected galleries nationwide and their artists and photographers.

069 974 US ISSN 0024-5828
F104.M99
LOG OF MYSTIC SEAPORT. 1948. q. membership. Mystic Seaport Museum, Inc., Mystic, CT 06355. TEL 203-572-5347. FAX 203-572-5326. Ed. Andrew W. German. bk.rev.; illus.; index. circ. 21,000. **Indexed:** Amer.Hist.& Life, Hist.Abstr. **Document type:** academic/scholarly publication.
—UMI.
Description: Contains articles of scholarly and general interest on American maritime history and art, as well as information on Mystic Seaport and its collections.

708 AT ISSN 0817-8445
LOOK MAGAZINE. 1985. m. Aus.$56 (effective Aug. 1995). (Art Gallery Society of New South Wales) Mount Eagle Publications, P.O. Box 84, Heidelberg, Vic. 3084, Australia. TEL 61-3-459-3911. FAX 61-3-457-5249. Ed. Wendy Symonds. adv. contact: Brett Lloyd Jones. bk.rev. circ. 16,500. **Document type:** academic/scholarly publication, bulletin.
Description: A monthly sponsored by the Art Gallery Society of New South Wales.

THE LOOKDOWN. see *EARTH SCIENCES — Oceanography*

069.097 US ISSN 0024-6492
LORE. 1951. 4/yr. $10 membership. (Friends of the Milwaukee Public Museum) Milwaukee Public Museum, 800 W. Wells St., Milwaukee, WI 53233. TEL 414-278-2710. FAX 414-223-1396. bk.rev.; film rev.; illus.; index. circ. 10,000. **Indexed:** Anthropol.Lit.

M A C REVISTA. (Museu de Arte Contemporanea) see *ART*

070.5 700 US ISSN 0893-0279
M O M A. 1993. 3/yr. $60 membership. Museum of Modern Art, 11 W. 53 St., New York, NY 10019-5498. TEL 212-708-9400. FAX 212-708-9889. TELEX 623 70 MODART. Eds. Lucy O'Brien, Tavia Fortt. illus. circ. 50,000. **Document type:** academic/scholarly publication.
—UnCover.
Description: Publishes articles related to exhibitions at the Museum of Modern Art.

069 GW
M P Z ANGEBOT. 1988. s-a. free. Museums-Paedagogisches Zentrum, Barer Str. 29, 80799 Munich, Germany. TEL 089-23805192. FAX 089-23805197. (back issues avail.) **Document type:** directory.
Former titles: Angebote fuer Schulen, Kinder- und Jugendgruppen Fortbildungsangebote fuer Paedagogen; M P Z - Kooperationsprojekt; Schuler im Museum.
Description: News about program for children and youth groups in museums in the Greater Munich area.

069 GW
M P Z INFO; Sonderausstellungen Muenchner Museen. 2/yr. free. Museums-Paedagogisches Zentrum, Barer Str. 29, 80799 Munich, Germany. TEL 089-23805192. **Document type:** bulletin.

069.097 US ISSN 1073-0893
M U C. 1988. bi-m. $40. Midwest Museums Conference, P.O. Box 11940, St. Louis, MO 63112-0040. TEL 314-454-3110. FAX 313-454-3162. Ed. Esther Hockett. bk.rev.; bibl.; charts; illus. circ. 800. **Indexed:** GeoRef. **Document type:** newsletter.
Former titles: Midwest Museums Conference. News Brief (ISSN 1071-8184); (until vol.48, no.4, 1988): Midwest Museums Conference Quarterly (ISSN 0026-3443)

069.9 296 US
MAGNES NEWS. 1968. 3/yr. $35 membership. Judah L. Magnes Museum, 2911 Russell St., Berkeley, CA 94705. TEL 510-549-6950. FAX 510-849-3650. Ed. Paula Friedman. bk.rev.; illus. circ. 2,500. **Document type:** newsletter.
Description: Covers activities of the museum. Includes a calendar of exhibitions.
Refereed Serial

069 II
MAHARAJA SAWAI MAN SINGH II MEMORIAL SERIES. 1971. irreg., no.8, 1987. price varies. Maharaja Sawai Man Singh II Museum, City Palace, Jaipur 302 002, India. Ed. Gopal Narayan Bahura. circ. 1,100.

069 II
MANIPUR STATE MUSEUM. BULLETIN. (Text in English) 1972. a. Rs.3. Manipur State Museum, Publications Sub-Committee, Imphal 759001, Manipur, India. **Document type:** bulletin.

069 CN ISSN 0715-0105
MANITOBA MUSEUM OF MAN AND NATURE. ANNUAL REPORT. 1966. a. membership. Manitoba Museum of Man and Nature, 190 Rupert Ave., Winnipeg, MB R3B ON2, Canada. TEL 204-956-2830. FAX 204-942-3679. TELEX 94236-79. circ. 3,000 (controlled).
Formerly (until 1984): Manitoba Museum of Man and Nature. Biennial Report (ISSN 0076-3888)

069 520 CN ISSN 0843-9133
MANITOBA MUSEUM OF MAN AND NATURE. HAPPENINGS. bi-m. membership. Manitoba Museum of Man and Nature, 190 Rupert Ave., Winnipeg, MB R3B ON2, Canada. TEL 204-956-2830. FAX 204-942-3679. Ed. J.V. Moroz. circ. 2,600. (tabloid format)

069 708 US
MARTIN & OSA JOHNSON SAFARI MUSEUM WAIT-A-BIT NEWS. 1980. q. $15. Martin and Osa Johnson Safari Museum, Inc., 111 N. Lincoln Ave., Chanute, KS 66720. TEL 316-431-2730. Eds. Conrad G. Froehlich, Barbara E. Henshall. bk.rev. circ. 500. (looseleaf format; back issues avail.) **Document type:** newsletter.
Formerly: Johnson Safari Wait-a-Bit Newsletter.

MASTERPIECES IN THE NATIONAL GALLERY OF CANADA/CHEFS-D'OEUVRE DE LA GALERIE NATIONALE DU CANADA. see *ART*

069 GW
MATERIALEN ZUR BODENDENKMALPFLEGE IM RHEINLAND. 1992. irreg., no.4, 1995. price varies. (Landschaftsverband Rheinland, Rheinisches Amt fuer Bodendenkmalpflege) Rheinland Verlag GmbH, Abtei Brauweiler, Postfach 2140, 50250 Pulheim, Germany. TEL 02234-8051. FAX 02234-82503. (Dist. by: Dr. Rudolf Habelt GmbH, Am Buchenhang 1, 53115 Bonn, Germany. TEL 0228-232016. FAX 0228-232017) **Document type:** monographic series.

069 PL ISSN 0076-5236
MATERIALY ZACHODNIO-POMORSKIE. (Text in Polish; summaries in English, French and German) 1957. a. price varies. Muzeum Narodowe, Szczecin, Staromlynska 27, 70-561 Szczecin, Poland. TEL 48-91-335066. FAX 48-91-347894. (Dist. by: Ars Polona- Ruch, Krakowskie Przedmiescie 7, Warsaw, Poland) Ed. Wladyslaw Filipowiak. bk.rev. circ. 700. **Indexed:** Numis.Lit. **Document type:** monographic series.
Description: Publishes papers on various fields: archaeology, ethnology, numismatics, history, history of art, sociology, museum management.
Refereed Serial

MAURITIANA (ALTENBURG). see *SCIENCES: COMPREHENSIVE WORKS*

015.73 US ISSN 0195-105X
MEMBERS CALENDAR; the Museum of Modern Art. m.(11/yr.). $60 membership. Museum of Modern Art, 11 W. 53 St., New York, NY 10019-5498. FAX 212-708-9889. TELEX 623 70 MODART. Ed. Tavia Fortt. illus. circ. 50,000.
Description: Publishes schedule of events at the museum with description of exhibitions and film programs.

MUSEUMS AND ART GALLERIES

708.1   US
MEMPHIS BROOKS MUSEUM OF ART. THE BROOKS. 1955. q. $16 membership. Memphis Brooks Museum of Art, Inc., Board of Directors, 1934 Poplar Ave., Overton Park, Memphis, TN 38104. TEL 901-722-3500. FAX 901-722-3522. Ed. E.A. Carmean, Jr. circ. 6,000. **Document type:** newsletter.
   Former titles (until Dec. 1993): Memphis Brooks Museum of Art. Inside Brooks; (until Feb. 1992): Memphis Brooks Museum of Art. Newsletter; Brooks Memorial Art Gallery. Newsletter.

508.074 069   FR   ISSN 0985-116X
MESOGEE. 1882. a. newsstand price: 80 F. (Museum d'Histoire Naturelle de Marseille) Imprimerie Municipale Ceter Marseille, Palais Longchamp, 13004 Marseille, France. TEL 91-62-30-78. FAX 91-50-72-02. adv. contact: Michele Dufrenne. **Document type:** bulletin.
—BLDSC (5682.634200).
   Former titles (until 1986): Musee d'Histoire Naturelle de Marseille. Bulletin (ISSN 0398-2106); (until 1976): Museum d'Histoire Naturelle de Marseille. Bulletin (ISSN 0366-4392); (until 1937): Musee d'Histoire Naturelle de Marseille. Annales (ISSN 0994-8023)

708.1471   US   ISSN 0077-8958
N610
METROPOLITAN MUSEUM JOURNAL. 1968. a. $60. Metropolitan Museum of Art, 1000 Fifth Ave., New York, NY 10028. TEL 212-879-5500. FAX 212-472-8725. (Orders to: University of Chicago Press, Journals Division, Box 37005, Chicago, IL 60637. TEL 312-753-3347. FAX 312-753-0811) Ed. Barbara Born. illus. (back issues avail.) **Indexed:** Artbibl.Mod., Arts & Hum.Cit.Ind., Avery Ind.Archit.Per., Curr.Cont., RILA.
—Faxon.
   Description: Contains first-time investigations and critical reassessments of individual works; monographic surveys relating objects to their cultural contexts; new information drawing on archival research and technical analyses, and other scholarly articles.

708.7   US   ISSN 0026-1521
N610
METROPOLITAN MUSEUM OF ART BULLETIN. 1905; N.S. 1942. q. $25. Metropolitan Museum of Art, 1000 Fifth Ave., New York, NY 10028. Ed. Joan Holt. illus.; index. circ. 112,000. **Indexed:** Amer.Hist.& Life, Art & Archaeol.Tech.Abstr., Art Ind., Artbibl.Mod., Arts & Hum.Cit.Ind., Avery Ind.Archit.Per., Curr.Cont., Hist.Abstr., Mid.East: Abstr.& Ind., Numis.Lit., RILA. **Document type:** bulletin.
—BLDSC (5748.989000); Faxon; UMI; UnCover.
   Description: General information on art in the museum's collections, each issue organized around a category or an artist.

069 977.4   US   ISSN 0076-8235
MICHIGAN STATE UNIVERSITY. MUSEUM PUBLICATIONS. CULTURAL SERIES. 1961. irreg., vol.1, no.3, 1967. price varies. Michigan State University, Museum, East Lansing, MI 48824. TEL 517-355-2370. (And: Exchange Dept., MSU Library, East Lansing, MI 48824) index at end of each completed vol. circ. 1,850. **Document type:** academic/scholarly publication, monographic series.

MIDWEST MUSEUM BULLETIN. see *ART*

508.074   JA   ISSN 0911-2111
MIKUMANO GENERAL MUSEUM. RESEARCH REPORTS. (Text in Japanese) 1985. a. Mikumano Sogo Shiryokan Kenkyu linkai - Mikumano General Museum, Research Committee, Shingushi Kyoiku linkai, 6760-1 Shingu, Shingu-shi, Wakayama-ken 647, Japan.

MILLER NOTES. see *MUSIC*

069.9 700   US
MINT MUSEUM MEMBERNEWS. 1986. bi-m. $30 membership. Mint Museum of Art, 2730 Randolph Rd., Charlotte, NC 28207. TEL 704-337-2000. FAX 704-337-2101. E-mail: MintNews@aol.com. Ed. Phil Busher. circ. 8,250. (looseleaf format) **Document type:** newsletter.
   Formerly (until 1986): Mint Museum Newsletter.
   Description: Coverage of current art exhibitions, art issues affecting the museum, additions and spotlights to the collections, educational programs, films and affiliate organization news.

MISUL CHARYO/NATIONAL MUSEUM JOURNAL OF ARTS. see *ART*

708.1   US
MONTCLAIR ART MUSEUM. BULLETIN - NEWSLETTER. 1929. bi-m. membership. Montclair Art Museum, 3 South Mountain Ave, Montclair, NJ 07042-1747. TEL 201-746-5555. FAX 201-746-9118. Eds. Cathy Fazekas, Anne-Marie Nolin. adv. contact: Anne-Marie Nolin. illus. circ. 5,000. **Document type:** newsletter, bulletin.
   Formed by the merger of: Montclair Art Museum. Bulletin (ISSN 0027-0059); Montclair Art Museum. Newsletter.

069   RM
MONUMENTE ISTORICE SI DE ARTA. (Text in Rumanian; summaries in English, French, Russian) s-a. 100 lei($73) Ministerul Culturii, Piata Presei Libere 1, Sector 1, Bucharest, Rumania. (Subscr. to: Calea Grivitei 66-68, Box 12201, Bucharest, Rumania) illus. **Indexed:** Numis.Lit.
   Former titles: Revista Muzeelor si Monumentelor. Monumente Istorice si de Arta; Revista Muzeelor si Monumentelor. Monumente.

069.5 708.5   IT
MONUMENTI MUSEI E GALLERIE PONTIFICIE MUSEO GREGORIANO ETRUSCO. CATALOGHI. 1985. irreg., no.2, 1989. price varies. L'Erma di Bretschneider, Via Cassiodoro 19, 00193 Rome, Italy. TEL 06-687-41-27. FAX 06-687-41-29.

061   US
MOSAIC (ST. PETERSBURG). q. limited distribution. Museum of Fine Arts, St. Petersburg, 225 Beach Dr. North East, St. Petersburg, FL 33701. TEL 813-896-2667. FAX 813-894-4638. Ed. Don Baldwin. illus. **Indexed:** Abstr.Engl.Stud., Curr.Adv.Ecol.Sci.
   Description: News and announcements of art acquisitions, events, and exhibits by the Museum of Fine Arts, St. Petersburg, Florida.

707   US   ISSN 0027-3627
N11.M83
MUNSON-WILLIAMS-PROCTOR INSTITUTE. BULLETIN. 1941. m. free to members. Munson-Williams-Proctor Institute, 310 Genesee St., Utica, NY 13417-4799. TEL 315-797-0000. FAX 315-797-5608. Ed. Joe Schmidt. illus. circ. 5,000. (tabloid format) **Document type:** bulletin.
   Description: Presents upcoming events and information on programming.

069.097   CN   ISSN 0820-0165
MUSE (OTTAWA). (Text in English and French) 1966. 4/yr. Can.$26.75 (in US Can.$34.25, elsewhere Can.$42.80). Canadian Museums Association, 280 Metcalf St., Ste. 400, Ottawa, ON K2P 1R7, Canada. TEL 613-567-0099. FAX 613-233-5438. Ed. Aline Michaud. adv.; bk.rev.; illus. circ. 2,200. (back issues avail.) **Indexed:** Amer.Hist.& Life, Art & Archaeol.Tech.Abstr., Can.B.P.I., Can.Per.Ind., Hist.Abstr. **Document type:** newsletter.
   Formerly: C M A Gazette - A M C Gazette (ISSN 0317-6045)
   Description: Provides a forum for the expression of ideas, opinions and research in museology.

069.09493   BE   ISSN 0778-1350
MUSEA NOSTRA. Variant title: Reeks Musea Nostra. (Editions in Dutch, French) 1987. irreg., latest vol.31. 595 BEF per vol. paperbound; clothbound 950 BEF per vol. Credit Communal de Belgique, Services Ventes, 44 Bd. Pacheco, 1000 Brussels, Belgium. TEL 32-2-2224112. FAX 32-2-2225752. (Dist. by: Exhibitions International, Leuvensteenweg 18, 3080 Tervuren, Belgium. TEL 32-7-7679414. FAX 32-7-7675115) illus. (back issues avail.) **Document type:** monographic series.
   Description: Presents an overview of the origins and collections of specific museums in Belgium, with a discussion of the most significant works in the collection.

069   FR   ISSN 0181-1525
N6490
MUSEE NATIONAL D'ART MODERNE. CAHIERS. 1979. 4/yr. Editions du Centre Georges Pompidou, Musee National d'Art Moderne, 75191 Paris cedex 04, France. FAX 42-77-29-49. TELEX MNAM 214024. Ed. Y. Michaud. adv.; bk.rev. circ. 3,300. **Indexed:** Artbibl.Mod., Arts & Hum.Cit.Ind., Curr.Cont., RILA. —SWETS.
   Description: Specializes in contemporary art history and aesthetics. Includes information on the current activities of MNAM at the Pompidou Center.

069   PL   ISSN 0027-3791
N3160
MUSEE NATIONAL DE VARSOVIE. BULLETIN. (Text in various languages) 1960. q. $34. Muzeum Narodowe w Warszawie - National Museum in Warsaw, Al. Jerozolimskie 3, 00-495 Warsaw, Poland. TEL 48-2-6211031. FAX 48-2-6228559. (Dist. by: Ars Polona-Ruch, Krakowskie Przedmiescie 7, 00-068 Warsaw, Poland) Ed. Anna Kozak. illus. circ. 500. **Indexed:** Artbibl.Mod., RILA. **Document type:** bulletin.

069   GW   ISSN 0720-7883
MUSEEN IN SCHLESWIG-HOLSTEIN; Mitteilungen aus Oeffentlichen Museen und Sammlungen. 1980. 2/yr. free. Amt Landesmuseumsdirektor, Schloss Gottorf, 24837 Schleswig, Germany. TEL 04621-9365-0. FAX 04621-936555. (Co-sponsor: Ministerium fuer Wissenschaft, Forschung und Kultur) Ed. Dr. Bernd Brandes-Druba. circ. 20,000. (back issues avail.) **Document type:** newspaper.
   Description: Museums and their activities in Schleswig-Holstein.

069 700   CN   ISSN 0706-098X
MUSEES. 1978. irreg. Can.$42.50 (effective 1995). Societe des Musees Quebecois, C.P. 8888, Succ. Centre-Ville, UQAM, Montreal, PQ H3C 3P8, Canada. TEL 514-987-3264. FAX 514-987-3379. E-mail: RNET(CAN-SMQ@IMMEDIA.CA). Ed. Helene Panaioti. adv. circ. 1,500. (back issues avail.) **Indexed:** Pt.de Rep. (1989-).
   Description: Looks at museum-related subjects from around the world.
   Refereed Serial

069.094   SZ   ISSN 0027-3821
AM68.G4   CODEN: MSGVAD
MUSEES DE GENEVE; revue des musees et collections de la ville de Geneve. 1944. m. free. Beaux-Arts et Culture, Hotel Municipal, Geneva, Switzerland. Ed. Andre Cornellini. adv.; bibl.; illus.; cum.index: 1944-1964, 1965-1979. circ. 5,000. **Indexed:** Amer.Hist.& Life, Artbibl.Mod., GeoRef., Hist.Abstr., RILA.
—BLDSC (5986.700000).

069.094   FR   ISSN 0027-383X
AM46.A1
MUSEES ET COLLECTIONS PUBLIQUES DE FRANCE. 1932. s-a. 30 F. (Association Generale des Conservateurs de Musees et Collections Publiques de France) Editions Person, Pavillon Mollien - Palais du Louvre, 75001 Paris, France. TEL 42-60-39-26. Ed. J.H. Person. adv.; bk.rev.; charts; illus.; index.

069.094   FR   ISSN 0521-7032
MUSEES ET MONUMENTS LYONNAIS. BULLETIN. 1952. q. 300 F. (effective 1995). Musee de Beaux Arts, Association des Amis du Musee, Palais St. Pierre, 20 Place des Terreaux, 69001 Lyon, France. TEL 78-28-07-66. FAX 78-28-12-45. Ed. Philippe Durey. illus.; index. circ. 700. **Indexed:** Artbibl.Mod., RILA. **Document type:** bulletin.

MUSEES ROYAUX D'ART ET D'HISTOIRE. BULLETIN/KONINKLIJKE MUSEA VOOR KUNST EN GESCHIEDENIS. BULLETIN. see *HISTORY* — *History Of Europe*

MUSEUMS AND ART GALLERIES

708　　　　　　　　BE　ISSN 0027-3856
N1830
MUSEES ROYAUX DES BEAUX-ARTS DE BELGIQUE. BULLETIN/KONINKLIJKE MUSEA VOOR SCHONE KUNSTEN VAN BELGIE. BULLETIN. (Text in Dutch, French) 1952. irreg., latest 1994 (for years 1989-1991). price varies. Musees Royaux des Beaux-Arts de Belgique - Koninklijke Musea voor Schone Kunsten van Belgie, Museumstr. 9, 1000 Brussels, Belgium. TEL 32-2-5083211. FAX 31-2-5083232. Ed. Andre A. Moerman. illus.; index. circ. 600. Indexed: Art Ind., Artbibl.Mod., RILA. **Document type:** academic/scholarly publication, bulletin.
—SWETS.
  Description: Publishes articles reflecting the life of the museum, including discussions of exhibitions, acquisitions and technical matters.

069.094891　　　DK　ISSN 0108-917X
MUSEET FOR HOLBAEK OG OMEGN. AARSBERETNING. 1921. a. DKK 15. Museumsforeningen for Holbaek og Omegn, Klosterstraede 14-16, 4300 Holbaek, Denmark. TEL 45-53-43-23-53. Ed. J.L. Oestergaard Christensen. adv.; illus. circ. 1,800.
  Formerly: Museet for Holbaek og Omegn.

069　　　　　　　　IT　ISSN 0083-5447
MUSEI CIVICI VENEZIANI. BOLLETTINO. 1956. q. price varies. Musei Civici Veneziani, Venice, Italy. TEL 041-5225625. FAX 041-5200935. Ed.Bd. adv. circ. 1,650. (also avail. in microform; back issues avail.) **Indexed:** Avery Ind.Archit.Per., RILA. **Document type:** bulletin.
  Description: Covers art and history of Venice.

069　　　　　　　　IT　ISSN 0523-9346
AM55.R6
MUSEI COMUNALI DI ROMA. BOLLETTINO. 1954; N.S. 1987. irreg., no.5, 1992. L.45000. (Associazione Amici dei Musei di Roma) L'Erma di Bretschneider, Via Cassiodoro 19, 00193 Rome, Italy. TEL 06-687-41-27. FAX 06-687-41-29. **Document type:** bulletin.

913　　　　　　　　IT　ISSN 0391-9293
MUSEO ARCHEOLOGICO DI TARQUINIA. MATERIALI. 1980. irreg., vol.12, 1986. price varies. Giorgio Bretschneider, Via Crescenzio 43, I-00193 Rome, Italy. (back issues avail.)

708.5　　　　　　　IT
MUSEO BODONIANO. BOLLETTINO. 1972. a. L.70000. Museo Bodoniano, Biblioteca Palatina, Palazzo della Pilotta, 43100 Parma, Italy. TEL 0521-235662. bk.rev. circ. 80,000. **Document type:** bulletin.
  Description: Covers the history of printing art.

069.5 914.5　　　　IT
MUSEO CIVICO ARCHEOLOGICO UGO GRANAFEI DI MESAGNE. TESTI E MONUMENTI. 1977. irreg., no.7, 1990. price varies. L'Erma di Bretschneider, Via Cassiodoro 19, 00193 Rome, Italy. TEL 06-687-41-27. FAX 06-687-41-29.

069　　　　　　　　CK
MUSEO DE ARTE COLONIAL DE BOGOTA. BOLETIN INFORMATIVO. 1975. m. free. Museo Colonial de Bogota, Carrera 6 no. 9-77, Bogota, Colombia. circ. 500.

301.2　　　　　　　DR
MUSEO DEL HOMBRE DOMINICANO. SERIE CATALOGOS Y MEMORIAS. 1976. irreg., no. 41. Museo del Hombre Dominicano, Calle Pedro Henriquez Urena, Plaza de la Cultura, Santo Domingo, Dominican Republic. illus.

301.2　　　　　　　DR
MUSEO DEL HOMBRE DOMINICANO. SERIE MESA REDONDA CONFERENCIAS. 1974. irreg., no.12, 1981. price varies. Museo del Hombre Dominicano, Calle Pedro Henriquez Urena, Plaza de la Cultura, Santo Domingo, Dominican Republic. illus.

069　　　　　　　　SP　ISSN 0210-8143
AM101.M238
MUSEO DEL PRADO. BOLETIN. 1978. a. 2332 ptas. (foreign 2800 ptas.). Museo del Prado, Paseo del Prado, sn, 28014 Madrid, Spain. TEL 34-1-4292092. FAX 34-1-420-0794. TELEX 44949. Ed. Alfonso E. Perez Sanchez.
  Description: Provides information on the activities of the Prado Museum.

708　　　　　　　　IT
MUSEO DELLA CIVILTA ROMANA. STUDI E MATERIALI. 1938. irreg., no.13, 1989. price varies. L'Erma di Bretschneider, Via Cassiodoro, 19, 00193 Rome, Italy. TEL 06-687-41-27. FAX 06-687-41-29.
  Formerly: Museo dell'Impero Romano. Studi e Materiali (ISSN 0080-3936)

069　　　　　　　　PE　ISSN 0304-2367
F3401
MUSEO NACIONAL. REVISTA. 1932. a. $30. (Museo Nacional de la Cultura Peruana) Industrial Grafica S.A., Apdo. 3048, Lima 100, Peru. Ed. Rosalia Avalos de Matos. circ. 1,000. **Indexed:** A.I.C.P., Amer.Hist.& Life, Anthropol.Lit., Hisp.Amer.Per.Ind. (1969-1987), Hist.Abstr.

500.907　　　　　　CL　ISSN 0716-0224
QH119
MUSEO NACIONAL DE HISTORIA NATURAL. PUBLICACION OCASIONAL. 1963. irreg., no.45, 1989. $12. Museo Nacional de Historia Natural, Casilla 787, Santiago, Chile. Ed. Daniel Frassinetti Cabeza.

709.5　　　　　　　IT
MUSEO NAZIONALE D'ARTE ORIENTALE. SCHEDE. no. 6, 1974. irreg. Museo Nazionale d'Arte Orientale, Via Merulana 248, Rome 00185, Italy. bibl.

708.6 296　　　　　SP　ISSN 0214-6975
DS135.S75
MUSEO SEFARDI. NOTICIAS. 1989. s-a. Museo Sefardi, C. Samuel Levi, s-n, 45002 Toledo, Spain.

708.9　　　　　　　AG
MUSEO Y MONUMENTO NACIONAL "JUSTO JOSE DE URQUIZA". SERIE 3. no. 14, 1981. Museo y Monumento Nacional Justo Jose de Urquiza, Palacio San Jose, Entre Rios, Argentina.

069　　　　　　　　CN　ISSN 0380-4623
MUSEOGRAMME. (Text in English and French) 1973. 6/yr. Can.$26.75 (in US Can.$34.25; elsewhere Can.$42.80). Canadian Museums Association, 280 Metcalf St., Ste. 400, Ottawa, ON K2P 1R7, Canada. TEL 613-567-0099. FAX 613-233-5438. adv. **Document type:** newsletter.
  Description: Membership newsletter of the association.

069　　　　　　　　IT
MUSEOLOGIA SCIENTIFICA. vol.9, 1992. q. L.75000 (foreign L.100000). Associazione Nazionale Musei Scientifici Orti Botanici Giardini Zoologici Acquari, c/o Museo Civico di Storia Naturale, Corso Venezia 55, 20121 Milan, Italy. TEL 045-8012860. Ed. Sandro Ruffo.

069.95 500　　　　IT　ISSN 0541-377X
MUSEOSCIENZA. 1962-1976, no.6; N.S. 1991. s-a. L.25000 per no. Museo Nazionale della Scienza e della Tecnica Leonarda da Vinci, Via San Vittore 21, 20123 Milan, Italy. TEL 39-2-48010040. Ed.Bd; Pub. Roberto De Mattei. adv.; bk.rev.; bibl.; charts; illus. circ. 2,000.

069.095　　　　　JA　ISSN 0027-4003
MUSEUM. (Text in Japanese; title and contents page in English) 1951. m. $29.75. Museum Shuppan Co., Ltd., Asahi-jinbocho Plaza, 2-14 Jinbo-cho, Chiyoda-ku, Tokyo 101, Japan. Ed. Shigeru Muramatsu. adv.; bk.rev.; illus.; index. circ. 6,000. Indexed: Art & Archaeol.Tech.Abstr., So.Pac.Per.Ind. —UnCover.

708　　　　　　　　NE　ISSN 0077-2275
MUSEUM BOYMANS-VAN BEUNINGEN. AGENDA - DIARY. (Text in Dutch and English) 1949. a. fl.29.95. Museum Boymans-van Beuningen, Museumpark 18-20, Postbus 2277, 3000 CG Rotterdam, Netherlands. TEL 31-10-4419400. FAX 31-10-4360500. TELEX 25572 MUBOY NL. circ. 30,000.

MUSEUM ETHNOGRAPHERS GROUP. NEWSLETTER. see *ANTHROPOLOGY*

MUSEUM FUER UR- UND FRUEHGESCHICHTE DER BEZIRKE POTSDAM, FRANKFURT - ODER UND COTTBUS. VEROEFFENTLICHUNGEN. see *HISTORY*

069　　　　　　　　US
MUSEUM HIGHLIGHTS. 1982. q. $25. (Maricopa County Historical Society) Desert Caballeros Western Museum, Box 1446, Wickenburg, AZ 85358. TEL 602-684-2272. Ed. Cheryl Taylor. circ. 600. **Document type:** newsletter.
  Description: Covers donating exhibitions, programs, educational activities and collections management of South-Western art and history.

069 708　　　　　UK　ISSN 1350-0775
AM1
MUSEUM INTERNATIONAL. French edition (ISSN 1020-2226) (Text in English) 1948. q. £55($86) (foreign £55) (effective 1996). (Unesco) Basil Blackwell Ltd., 108 Cowley Rd., Oxford OX4 1JF, England. TEL 0865-791100. FAX 0865-791347. TELEX 837022 OXBOOK G. (Subscr. to: P.O. Box 87, Oxford OX2 0DT, England. TEL 0865-791155. FAX 0865-791927) Ed. Y.R. Isar. charts; illus.; index, cum.index: 1948-1973. **Indexed:** Art Ind., Avery Ind.Archit.Per., Chem.Abstr., DAAI, Mid.East: Abstr.& Ind. **Document type:** academic/scholarly publication.
—BLDSC (5987.708000); Genuine Article; SWETS; UMI; UnCover.
  Former titles (until 1993): Museum (English Edition) (ISSN 0027-3996); (until 1971): Museum (Bilingual Edition) (ISSN 1012-4225); Supersedes (1920-1948): Mouseion (ISSN 0369-1349)

069　　　　　　　　UK　ISSN 0964-7775
AM121
MUSEUM MANAGEMENT AND CURATORSHIP. q. £177($282) (effective 1996). Butterworth - Heinemann, Part of the Reed Elsevier group, Linacre House, Jordan Hill, Oxford OX2 8DP, England. TEL 0865-310366. FAX 0865-310898. TELEX 83111 BHPOXF G. (Subscr. to: Elsevier Science Ltd., P.O. Box 800, Kidlington, Oxford OX5 1DX, England. TEL 44-865-843000. FAX 44-865-843010; Subscr. in U.S. and Canada to: Elsevier Science, 660 White Plains Rd., Tarrytown, NY 10591-5153. TEL 914-524-9200. FAX 914-333-2444) Eds. P. & C. Cannon-Brooks. (also avail. in microform from UMI; back issues avail.) **Indexed:** Art & Archaeol.Tech.Abstr., Br.Archaeol.Abstr., Br.Tech.Ind. **Document type:** academic/scholarly publication.
—BLDSC (5987.763000); SWETS; UMI. **CCC.**
  Formerly: International Journal of Museum Management and Curatorship (ISSN 0260-4779)
  Description: Provides an international forum for the exchange of information among museum professionals. Encourages a continuous reassessment of the disciplines governing the establishment, care, presentation and understanding of museum collections.
  Refereed Serial

069　　　　　　　　AT　ISSN 1320-2677
MUSEUM MATTERS. 1975. q. Aus.$25. Museums Australia (N.S.W.) Inc., c/o Museum of Applied Arts & Sciences, P.O. Box K346, Haymarket, N.S.W. 2000, Australia. TEL 61-2-217-0133. FAX 61-2-217-0355. Ed. Verena Mauldon. adv.; bk.rev.; charts; illus.; tr.lit. circ. 500. (back issues avail.) **Document type:** newsletter.
  Formerly (until 1993): Museums Association of Australia. Quarterly News.
  Description: Contains technical information on museological and conservation issues as well as museum news.

069　　　　　　　　AT　ISSN 1038-1694
MUSEUM NATIONAL. 1982. q. Museums Australia (Victoria) Inc., 24 Queens Parade, N. Fitzroy, Vic. 3068, Australia. TEL 61-3-4863399. FAX 61-3-4863788. adv.; bk.rev. circ. 1,500. (back issues avail.)
  Formed by the merger of (1982-1992): Muse News (ISSN 0728-8948); (1986-1992): A M A A News (ISSN 0810-1027)

MUSEUMS AND ART GALLERIES　4817

069.097　　US　　ISSN 0027-4089
AM1　　　　　　　CODEN: MUNSAJ
MUSEUM NEWS. 1924. bi-m. $38. American Association of Museums, 1225 Eye St., N.W., Ste. 200, Washington, DC 20005. TEL 202-289-1818. FAX 202-289-6578. Ed. John Strand. adv.; bk.rev.; illus.; index. circ. 15,000. **Indexed:** Abstr.Anthropol., Art & Archaeol.Tech.Abstr., Artbibl.Mod., Arts & Hum.Cit.Ind., Avery Ind.Archit.Per., Bk.Rev.Ind. (1965-1986), Br.Archaeol.Abstr., Child.Bk.Rev.Ind. (1965-1986), Curr.Cont. **Document type:** trade publication.
—BLDSC (5987.890000); Faxon; Genuine Article; SWETS; UnCover. **CCC.**
　Description: Magazine for museum professionals and others interested in all types of museums.

069　　　　　US　　ISSN 0027-4097
N714.P7
MUSEUM NOTES (PROVIDENCE). (Not published 1992-1995) 1913. a. $7.50 membership. Rhode Island School of Design, Museum of Art, 224 Benefit St., Providence, RI 02903-2723.
TEL 401-454-6500. FAX 401-454-6556. Ed. Judith A. Singsen. circ. 6,400. **Document type:** bulletin.
　Formerly: Rhode Island School of Design. Bulletin.
　Description: Covers museum acquisitions and articles relating to the museum's collections.

069 700 979　　US
MUSEUM NOTES (SPOKANE). 1960? q. $25. Eastern Washington State Historical Society, Cheney Cowles Museum, W. 2316 First Ave., Spokane, WA 99204. TEL 509-456-3931. FAX 509-456-7690. Ed. Glenn Mason. circ. 1,500. (back issues avail.) **Document type:** newsletter.
　Description: To inform members of events, programs, exhibits, acquisitions, future plans.

708　　　　　SW　　ISSN 0081-5691
DS714
MUSEUM OF FAR EASTERN ANTIQUITIES. BULLETIN. 1929. a. SEK 300. Oestasiatiska Museet - Museum of Far Eastern Antiquities, Skeppsholmen, P.O. Box 16381, S-103 27 Stockholm, Sweden.
TEL 08-666-4400. FAX 08-611-2845. Ed. Jan Wirgin. circ. 600. (back issues avail.) **Indexed:** A.I.C.P., M.L.A. **Document type:** bulletin.
—BLDSC (2624.500000).

MUSEUM OF FINE ARTS, BOSTON. JOURNAL. see *ART*

708.1　　　　US　　ISSN 0018-6708
N576.H7
MUSEUM OF FINE ARTS, HOUSTON. BULLETIN. 1971. 2/yr. Museum of Fine Arts, Houston, 1001 Bissonnet, Houston, TX 77005.
TEL 713-639-7512. Pub. Diane Lovejoy. charts; illus. circ. 10,000. **Indexed:** Artbibl.Mod. **Document type:** bulletin.
—BLDSC (2624.600000).

069　　　　　US
MUSEUM OF THE AMERICAN PIANO. NEWSLETTER. 1988. q. membership. Museum of the American Piano, 211 W. 58th St., New York, NY 10019.
TEL 212-246-4646. adv.; charts; illus. circ. 2,000. (looseleaf format) **Document type:** newsletter.

069.9　　　　US　　ISSN 0198-7763
MUSEUM OF THE GREAT PLAINS NEWSLETTER. 1977. a. $15 includes Great Plains journal. Institute of the Great Plains, Box 68, Lawton, OK 73502.
TEL 405-581-3460. Ed. Steve Wilson. circ. 1,000. (looseleaf format; back issues avail.) **Document type:** newsletter.
　Description: Covers activities of Museum of the Great Plains.

MUSEUM OF VICTORIA. MEMOIRS. see *BIOLOGY — Zoology*

MUSEUM OF VICTORIA. OCCASIONAL PAPERS. see *BIOLOGY — Zoology*

MUSEUM RECORD. see *GENEALOGY AND HERALDRY*

069　　　　　UK　　ISSN 0954-0423
MUSEUM REPORTER. 1988. 4/yr. free. National Museums of Scotland, Chambers St., Edinburgh EH1 1JF, Scotland. TEL 0131-225-7534.
FAX 0131-220-4819. Ed. Barbara Buchan. bk.rev. circ. 6,000. **Document type:** newsletter.
　Description: Collections and activities of the National Museums.

MUSEUM STORE. see *BUSINESS AND ECONOMICS — Marketing And Purchasing*

069　　　　　US
MUSEUM TRUSTEESHIP. 1986. 5/yr. membership. Museum Trustee Association, 1200 19th St., N.W., Ste. 300, Washington, DC 20036-2401.
TEL 202-857-1180. FAX 202-223-4579. Ed. Miriam T. Sample. adv. contact: Phyllis J. Doak. circ. 6,000. (back issues avail.) **Document type:** newsletter.
　Description: Publishes articles and newsworthy pieces on the subject of museum governance, the roles and responsibilities of museum trustees, trustee education, and legislative updates.

069　　　　　UK
MUSEUM VISITOR. 1984. a. £15 (to overseas libraries). British Association of Friends of Museums, c/o Sue Drought, 31 Southwell Park Rd., Camberly, Surrey GU15 3QG, England. TEL 01276-66617. Ed. Rosemary Silvester. adv. contact: Rosemary Silvester. bk.rev. circ. 2,500.
　Formerly (until 1992): British Association of Friends of Museums.
　Description: Covers activities of the association, the museums they support and matters relating to volunteers in museums.

069 700　　US　　ISSN 0740-0403
N520
MUSEUM YEAR. 1962. a. $3. Museum of Fine Arts, Boston, 465 Huntington Ave., Boston, MA 02115. TEL 617-267-9300. FAX 617-267-0280. Ed. Cynthia Purvis. circ. 27,000.
　Formerly: Boston Museum of Fine Arts. Museum Year. Annual Report.
　Description: Annual report of the Boston Museum of Fine Arts, focusing on annual projects and exhibits, staff activities, publications, programs, and curatorial acquisitions.

500.907　　CN　　ISSN 1191-0925
MUSEUMNEWS; from the Nova Scotia Museum Complex, 25 branches throughout Nova Scotia. 1985. bi-m. free. Nova Scotia Museum, 1747 Summer St., Halifax, NS B3H 3A6, Canada.
TEL 902-429-4610. Ed. John Henniear Shuh. circ. 10,000.
　Former titles (until 1992): Museum News and Views from the Nova Scotia Museum Complex (ISSN 0828-2773); (until 1985): News and Views from the Nova Scotia Museum Complex (ISSN 0842-7666); Which was formed by the merger of: Latest Word from the Nova Scotia Museum (ISSN 0703-2277); Nova Scotia Museum Program of Events (ISSN 0225-5006)
　Description: Covers events and offers information about provincial museums, historic houses, and restored mills.

708 059　　UK　　ISSN 0141-6723
N1020
MUSEUMS AND GALLERIES IN GREAT BRITAIN AND IRELAND. 1955. a. £7.45. Reed Information Services (Subsidiary of: Reed Elsevier group), Windsor Court, E. Grinstead House, E. Grinstead, W. Sussex RH19 1XA, England. TEL 01342-335832.
FAX 01342-335948. TELEX 95127-INFSER-G. Ed. Deborah Valentine. adv. circ. 12,000.
—BLDSC (5989.900000).
　Formerly: Museums and Galleries (ISSN 0077-2267)
　Description: Leading guide to the local and national collections of the British Isles.

708　　　　　UN　　ISSN 0077-233X
MUSEUMS AND MONUMENTS SERIES. French edition: Musees et Monuments (ISSN 0251-5040) 1952. irreg., vol.20, 1987. price varies. Unesco, 7-9 Place de Fontenoy, 75700 Paris, France.
TEL 45-77-16-10. (Dist. in U.S. by: Unipub, 4611-F Assembly Dr., Lanham, MD 20706-4391) **Indexed:** GeoRef.

069　　　　　AT　　ISSN 0812-7883
MUSEUMS AUSTRALIA. 1983. a. Museums Australia (Victoria) Inc., 24 Queens Parade, N. Fitzroy, Vic. 3068, Australia. TEL 61-3-4863399.
FAX 61-3-4863788. adv. circ. 1,600. (back issues avail.)

069 917.971　　CN
MUSEUMS IN MANITOBA (YEAR)/MUSEES DU MANITOBA (YEAR); preserving Manitoba's heritage. (Text in English, French) free. (Culture, Heritage and Citizenship - Culture, Patrimoine et Citoyennete) Association of Manitoba Museums, Ste. 422, 167 Lombard Ave., Winnipeg, MB R3B 0T6, Canada. TEL 204-947-1782. **Document type:** government publication, bulletin.
　Description: Lists and describes the many museums throughout the province of Manitoba.

069.094　　UK　　ISSN 0027-416X
AM1
MUSEUMS JOURNAL. 1901. m. £40 to individuals; institutions £60. Museums Association, 42 Clerkenwell Close, London EC1R OPA, England. TEL 071-250-1834. FAX 071-250-1929. Ed. Maurice Davies. adv.; bk.rev. circ. 4,600. (also avail. in microform from BHP) **Indexed:** A.I.C.P., Art Ind., Artbibl.Mod., Br.Archaeol.Abstr., Br.Geol.Lit., Br.Hum.Ind., Br.Tech.Ind., DAAI, RILA. **Document type:** bulletin.
—BLDSC (5990.000000); Faxon; SWETS; UnCover.
　Incorporates (1961-1989): Museums Bulletin.
　Description: Covers new developments, opinions, technical data, historical material and reviews of museums and galleries.

069　　　　　GW　　ISSN 0933-0593
MUSEUMS JOURNAL. 1987. q. DM.32 (foreign DM.44). Museumspaedagogischer Dienst Berlin, Chausseestr. 123, 10115 Berlin, Germany. TEL 030-283973. FAX 030-2826183. Ed. Gerhard Riecke. adv.; B&W page DM.2400; adv. contact: Michael Gottschling. bk.rev.; illus.; circ. 7,000 (paid). (back issues avail.) **Document type:** academic/scholarly publication.

069　　　　　II
MUSEUMS NEWSLETTER.* irreg. Museums Association of India, c/o National Museum of Natural History, F I C C I, Museum Building, Barakhamba Road, New Delhi 110002, India.

069 708　　GW
MUSEUMS OF THE WORLD. (Text in English) 1973. irreg., 5th ed., 1995. DM.598 325. K.G. Saur Verlag KG, A part of Reed Reference Publishing, Ortlerstr. 8, 81373 Munich, Germany.
TEL 089-76902-0. FAX 089-76902150. (Subscr. to: Postfach 701620, 81316 Munich, Germany; N. America subscr. to: K.G. Saur, 121 Chanlon Rd., Box 31, New Providence, NJ 07974-9903, USA. TEL 908-665-3576) adv. **Document type:** directory.
　Description: Lists museums in over 180 countries, providing a broad outline of historical, geographical and ethnological information. Subject index describes museum holdings.

069　　　　　UK　　ISSN 0307-7675
MUSEUMS YEARBOOK. (Includes: Directory of Museums and Art Galleries of the British Isles) 1956. a. £65 to non-members; members £32.50. Museums Association, 42 Clerkenwell Close, London EC1R OPA, England. TEL 071-250-1834.
FAX 071-250-1929. Ed. Sheena Barbour. circ. 2,000. **Document type:** directory.
—BLDSC (5990.105000).
　Formerly: Museums Calendar (ISSN 0580-2652)
　Description: Contains addresses, staff, admission fees, attendance and facilities.

069.094895　　DK　　ISSN 0108-8858
MUSEUMSAVISEN. 1980. s-a. membership. Holsted-Broerup-Vejen Egnens Museumsforening, c/o Henry Nielsen, Melvangvej 2, Askov, DK-6600 Vejen, Denmark. TEL 05-363343. illus.

069 948.95　　DK　　ISSN 0902-3690
MUSEUMSFORENINGEN FOR LAESOE. LAESOE MUSEUM. 1983. a. DKK 50. Laesoe Museum, Museumsforeningen for Laesoe, Gl. Oesterby Skole, DK-9940 Laesoe, Denmark. TEL 45-98-49-80-45. FAX 45-98-49-80-45. Ed. Jens Soerensen. circ. 700. **Document type:** monographic series.
　Formerly (until 1984): Museumsforeningen for Laesoe (ISSN 0109-5854)

069　　　　　GW　　ISSN 0027-4178
MUSEUMSKUNDE. 1905. 3/yr. DM.60. Deutscher Museumsbund e.V., Erbprinzenstr. 13, Postfach 6209, 76133 Karlsruhe, Germany.
TEL 0721-175161. FAX 0721-175110. (Subscr. to: Rheinland Verlag, Ehrenfriedstr. 19, 5024 Pulheim 2) Ed. Siegfried Rietschel. adv.; bk.rev.; index. circ. 2,000. **Indexed:** Artbibl.Mod., RILA. **Document type:** bulletin.

MUSEUMS AND ART GALLERIES

069.094 NO ISSN 0027-4186
MUSEUMSNYTT. 1951. s-a. NOK 175. N K K M - Norske Kunst- og Kulturhistoriske Museer - Norwegian Museums of Art and Social History, Ullevaalsv. 11, N-0165 Oslo, Norway. TEL 47-22-20-14-02. FAX 47-22-11-23-37. Ed.Bd. adv.; bk.rev.; bibl.; illus. circ. 1,200. **Indexed:** Art & Archaeol.Tech.Abstr., NAA.

069 GW ISSN 0931-4857
MUSEUMSVERBAND FUER NIEDERSACHSEN UND BREMEN. MITTEILUNGSBLATT. 1966. s-a. DM.40. Museumsverband fuer Niedersachsen und Bremen e.V., c/o Staatliches Naturhistorisches Museum, Pockelsstr. 10a, 38106 Braunschweig, Germany. TEL 0531-3914354. FAX 0531-3914370. Ed. Juergen Hevers. (back issues avail.) **Document type:** bulletin.
Description: For staff members of museums in Lower Saxony and Bremen.

069 930.1 TU
MUZE/MUSEUM. (Text in Turkish, summaries in English) no.4, 1991. a. exchange basis. Ministry of Culture, General Directorate of Monuments and Museums - Kultur Bakanligi, Anitlar ve Muzeler Genel Mudurlugu, 06100 Ulus - Ankara, Turkey. TEL 90-312-3104960. FAX 90-312-3111417. Ed. Aysegul Uguroglu. illus.
Description: Covers the art, history, architecture and archaeology of Turkey, with reports on recent exhibitions, new finds, current excavations and research, noteworthy architectural sites, and discussions of restoration and conservation.

MUZEJ BRODSKOG POSAVLJA. VIJESTI; godisnjak. see HUMANITIES: COMPREHENSIVE WORKS

069 XR ISSN 0027-5255
MUZEJNI A VLASTIVEDNA PRACE. (Text in Czech; contents page also in English, French, German and Russian) 1961. q. 40 Kc. (Narodni Muzeum, Ustredni Muzeologicky Kabinet) Nakladatelstvi a Vydavatelstvi Pierot, spol. s r.o., Stefanikova 29, 150 00 Prague 5, Czech Republic. (Co-sponsor: Spolecnost Pratel Starozitnosti) Ed. Frantiska Hyndrakova. bk.rev. circ. 1,600. **Indexed:** Numis.Lit.

MUZEJSKI VJESNIK/MUSEUM NEWS MAGAZINE. see ARCHAEOLOGY

069 XO ISSN 0027-5263
MUZEUM; metodicky, studijny a informacny bulletin. (Text in Slovak; contents page and summaries in English) 1954. q. exchange basis. Slovenske Narodne Muzeum, Muzeologicke Informacne Centrum, Vajanskeho Nabrezie 2, 814 36 Bratislava, Slovakia. TEL 07-335-463. Ed. Maria Rihakova. bk.rev.; charts; illus. circ. 500. **Document type:** bulletin.
Description: Guidance, information and study material for museum and art gallery workers.

MUZEUM LITERATURY IM. ADAMA MICKIEWICZA. BLOK-NOTES. see LITERATURE

069.5 709 PL ISSN 0208-8193
MUZEUM NARODOWE W KRAKOWIE. KATALOGI ZBIOROW/NATIONAL MUSEUM IN CRACOW. CATALOGUES OF THE COLLECTIONS. (Text in English, Polish) 1973. irreg., latest 1994. price varies. Muzeum Narodowe w Krakowie - National Museum in Cracow, Ul. J. Pilsudskiego 12, 31-109 Krakow, Poland. (Subscr. to: Ars-Polona, Krakowskie Przedmiescie 7, Warsaw, Poland) Ed. Ewa Harenczyk.

069 UK
N E M S ANNUAL REPORT. a. £2. North of England Museums Service, House of Recovery, Bath Lane, Newcastle-upon-Tyne NE4 5SQ, England. TEL 091-222-1661. FAX 091-261-4725. adv.; bk.rev. **Document type:** corporate report.

069 UK ISSN 0267-2618
N E M S NEWS. 1983. q. £6 to non-members. North of England Museums Service, House of Recovery, Bath Lane, Newcastle-upon-Tyne NE4 5SQ, England. TEL 091-222-1661. FAX 091-261-4725. Ed. Martyn Ladds. adv.; bk.rev. circ. 450. **Document type:** newsletter.
Description: Forum for debate and information on issues relating to the professional practice of museums in the north east region of England.

069 500 JA
N K H NAGAOKA-SHIRITSU KAGAKU HAKUBUTSUKANPO. (Text in Japanese) irreg. Nagaoka-shiritsu Kagaku Hakubutsukan - Nagaoka Municipal Science Museum, 2-1 Yanagihara, Nagaoka-shi, Niigata-ken 940, Japan.

069 500 JA ISSN 0916-6319
NAGOYA DAIGAKU FURUKAWA SOGO KENKYU SHIRYOKAN HOKOKU/NAGOYA UNIVERSITY FURUKAWA MUSEUM. BULLETIN. (Text and summaries in English and Japanese) 1985. a. free. Nagoya Daigaku, Sogo Kenkyu Shiryokan - Nagoya University, University Museum, 1 Furo-cho, Chikusa-ku, Nagoya 464-01, Japan. TEL 052-781-5111. FAX 052-783-1394. circ. 1,000. **Document type:** academic/scholarly publication.
—BLDSC (2629.021000).
Formerly (until 1989): Nagoya Daigaku Sogo Kenkyu Shiryoukan Houkoku - Nagoya University Museum. Bulletin. (ISSN 0912-5604)

NAGOYA KAGAKUKAN NYUSU/SCIENCE MUSEUM NEWS. see SCIENCES: COMPREHENSIVE WORKS

600 069 XR
NARODNI TECHNICKE MUZEUM. CATALOGUES OF COLLECTIONS. (Text in English) 1956. irreg. exchange basis. Narodni Technicke Muzeum, Kostelni 42, 170 78 Prague 7, Czech Republic. **Document type:** catalog.

NATIONAL DIRECTORY OF NONPROFIT ORGANIZATIONS. see SOCIAL SERVICES AND WELFARE

708 UK ISSN 0953-024X
NATIONAL GALLERIES OF SCOTLAND. BULLETIN. 1981. 6/yr. free. National Galleries of Scotland, Information Department, Belford Rd., Edinburgh EH4 3DR, Scotland. TEL 0131-556-8921. FAX 0131-332-4939. Ed. Emma Peto. illus. circ. 40,000. **Document type:** bulletin.
Formerly (until 1987): National Galleries of Scotland. News (ISSN 0261-3220)
Description: Photographic and informational brochure on temporary exhibits, permanent displays, new acquisitions, and current activities at the Gallery.

NATIONAL GALLERY, LONDON. TECHNICAL BULLETIN. see ART

069 708 CN ISSN 0826-9726
NATIONAL GALLERY OF CANADA CATALOGUE. CANADIAN ART. French edition: Musee des Beaux-Arts du Canada. Catalogue. Art Canadien (ISSN 0826-9734) (In 2 vols.: currently Vol.1: A-F and Vol.2: G-K published) 1988. irreg. $74.95. National Gallery of Canada, Publications Division, c/o Irene Lillico, 380 Sussex Dr., Ottawa, ON K1N 9N4, Canada. TEL 613-990-0537. FAX 613-990-7460. (Dist. by: University of Chicago Press, 5801 Ellis Ave., Chicago, IL 60637-1496) illus. **Document type:** catalog.
Description: Information on the gallery's holdings.

354.689 RH
NATIONAL GALLERY OF ZIMBABWE. ANNUAL REPORT AND BALANCE SHEET AND INCOME AND EXPENDITURE ACCOUNT. 1953. a. free. National Gallery of Zimbabwe, P.O. Box CY848, Causeway, Harare, Zimbabwe. illus. circ. 400. **Document type:** corporate report.
Former titles: National Gallery of Zimbabwe - Rhodesia. Annual Report and Balance Sheet and Income and Expenditure Account; National Gallery of Rhodesia. Annual Report and Balance Sheet and Income and Expenditure Account.

069 SI
NATIONAL MUSEUM. MEMOIRS SERIES. irreg. price varies. National Museum, Stamford Rd., Singapore 0617, Singapore. TEL 3377355. FAX 3309568.

069 SA
NATIONAL MUSEUM, BLOEMFONTEIN. ANNUAL REPORT. a. free. National Museum, Bloemfontein - Nasionale Museum, Bloemfontein, P.O. Box 266, Bloemfontein, South Africa. TEL 27-51-479609. FAX 27-51-479681. Eds. C. Lynch, J. Haasbroek. circ. 60. **Document type:** corporate report.

069 JA
NATIONAL MUSEUM OF MODERN ART. ANNUAL REPORT. (Text in English and Japanese) 1957. a. National Museum of Modern Art, Tokyo, 3 Kitanomaru Koen, Chiyoda-ku, Tokyo 102, Japan. TEL 03-3214-2561. FAX 03-3213-1340. circ. 1,000. **Document type:** government publication.
Description: Listing of all exhibitions, events, and collected works of the three institutions.

708 PH ISSN 0076-3756
NATIONAL MUSEUM OF THE PHILIPPINES. ANNUAL REPORT. (Text in English) 1967. a. free. National Museum of the Philippines, Padre Burgos Street, Manila, Philippines. TEL 48-14-27. FAX 632-530-0229. Ed. Rosario B. Tantoco. circ. 500 (controlled). (processed) **Document type:** corporate report.
Description: Contains the accomplishments of the National Museum in the fields of science, culture and education during the year under review.

708 TZ ISSN 0082-1675
NATIONAL MUSEUMS OF TANZANIA. ANNUAL REPORT. 1966. a. $0.60. National Museums of Tanzania, P.O. Box 511, Dar es Salaam, Tanzania. TEL 255-51-31365. FAX 255-51-20843. adv.; bk.rev. circ. 5,000. **Indexed:** A.I.C.P. **Document type:** consumer publication.

709.5 CH ISSN 1011-9078
NATIONAL PALACE MUSEUM. MONTHLY OF CHINESE ART. Key Title: Gugong Wenwu Yuekan. (Text in Chinese) 1983. m. $153. National Palace Museum - Kuo Li Ku Kung Po Wu Yuan, Wai Shuang Hsi, Shih Lin, Taipei, Taiwan, Republic of China. FAX 02-882-1440. (US subscr. to: World Journal Bookstore, 141-07 20th Ave., Whitestone, NY 11357. TEL 718-748-8889) Ed. Chang Yueh-yun. bk.rev.; illus.; index. circ. 10,000.
Description: Presents articles, analysis, and photographs of Chinese art and antiques from the museum's collection.

069.095 709.5 CH ISSN 1011-9086
N3750.T32
NATIONAL PALACE MUSEUM. NEWSLETTER. Key Title: Gugong Zhanlan Tongxun. Variant title: National Palace Museum. Newsletter & Gallery Guide. (Text in Chinese and English) 1968. q. free. National Palace Museum, Wai Shuang Hsi, Shih Lin, Taipei, Taiwan, Republic of China. FAX 886-2-8821440. Eds. Veronica de Jong, Chen Hui-Hsia. charts; illus. circ. 25,000. **Document type:** newsletter.
Description: Highlights of the National Palace Museum's newest publications, exhibitions and activities.

069.095 CH ISSN 1011-906X
N3750.T32
NATIONAL PALACE MUSEUM BULLETIN. Key Title: Gugong Tongxun Yingwen Shuangyuekan. (Text in English) 1966. bi-m. $30. National Palace Museum - Kuo Li Ku Kung Po Wu Yuan, Wai Shuang Hsi, Shih Lin, Taipei, Taiwan, Republic of China. FAX 886-28821440. Eds. Ge Wangzhang, Dora C.Y. Ching. bibl.; illus.; index. circ. 1,000. **Indexed:** Art & Archaeol.Tech.Abstr. **Document type:** bulletin.
Description: Articles of scholarly research on artistic and cultural subjects.

709.5 CH ISSN 1011-9094
NATIONAL PALACE MUSEUM RESEARCH QUARTERLY. Key Title: Gugong Xueshu Jikan. (Text in Chinese) 1966. q. $54. National Palace Museum - Kuo Li Ku Kung Po Wu Yuan, Wai-Shuang-Hsi, Shih-Lin, Taipei, Taiwan, Republic of China. FAX 886-2-8821440. Ed. Fung Ming-chu. charts; illus.; index. circ. 1,000.
Formerly (until 1983): National Palace Museum Quarterly (ISSN 0454-675X)
Description: Journal to further an atmosphere of scholarly and professional exchange.

NATIONAL SCIENCE MUSEUM. BULLETIN. SERIES E: PHYSICAL SCIENCES AND ENGINEERING/KOKURITSU KAGAKU HAKUBUTSUKAN KENKYU HOKOKU. E RUI, RIKOGAKU. see ENGINEERING

NATURAL HISTORY MUSEUM. BIENNIAL REPORT FOR SCIENCE. see SCIENCES: COMPREHENSIVE WORKS

NATURAL HISTORY MUSEUM. TRIENNIAL REPORT. see SCIENCES: COMPREHENSIVE WORKS

MUSEUMS AND ART GALLERIES   4819

069 500.9   US   ISSN 0748-6936
QH70.U62
NATURAL HISTORY MUSEUM OF LOS ANGELES REPORT. 1983. biennial. Natural History Museum of Los Angeles, 900 Exposition Blvd., Los Angeles, CA 90007.

500.907   AU   ISSN 0028-095X
NATURHISTORISCHES MUSEUM IN WIEN. MONATSPROGRAMM. 1949. m. S.3. Naturhistorisches Museum in Wien, Burgring 7, Postfach 417, A-1014 Vienna, Austria. FAX 0222-935254. circ. 4,400. (looseleaf format) **Document type:** newsletter.

708.1   US
NELSON-ATKINS MUSEUM OF ART. CALENDAR OF EVENTS. 1934. 10/yr. membership. Nelson-Atkins Museum of Art, 4525 Oak St., Kansas City, MO 64111-1873. TEL 816-561-4000. FAX 816-561-7154. Ed. Gina Kelley. illus. circ. 16,000. **Document type:** newsletter.
   Formerly: Nelson Gallery and Atkins Museum. Gallery Events (ISSN 0047-9322)

069   GW   ISSN 0028-3282
AM49
NEUE MUSEUMSKUNDE; Theorie und Praxis der Museumsarbeit. (Text in German; contents page and summaries in English, French, and Russian) 1958. q. DM.61.20. (Ministerium fuer Kultur, Rat fuer Museumswesen) Deutscher Verlag der Wissenschaften, Johannes-Dieckmann-Str. 10, 1080 Berlin, Germany. Ed. Heinz Schilling. adv.; bk.rev.; abstr.; bibl.; charts; illus.; index. (tabloid format) **Indexed:** Art & Archaeol.Tech.Abstr.

708   US   ISSN 0077-7919
NEVADA. STATE MUSEUM, CARSON CITY. OCCASIONAL PAPERS. 1968. irreg., no.4, 1980. price varies. Nevada State Museum, Department of Anthropology, Publications Office, Capitol Complex, Carson City, NV 89710. TEL 702-687-4810. circ. 1,000. **Document type:** monographic series.

708   US   ISSN 0077-7927
AM101
NEVADA. STATE MUSEUM, CARSON CITY. POPULAR SERIES. 1965. irreg., no.10, 1990. price varies. Nevada State Museum, Publications Office, Capitol Complex, Carson City, NV 89710. TEL 702-687-4810. Ed.Bd. circ. 1,000.

069   US
NEVADA STATE MUSEUM NEWSLETTER. 1972. bi-m. free to members. Nevada State Museum, Publications Office, Capitol Complex, Carson City, NV 89710. TEL 702-687-4810. Ed. Jack Gibson. bk.rev.; circ. 1,000 (controlled). **Document type:** newsletter.

NEW CRYSTAL PALACE MATTERS. see *ARCHITECTURE*

069 974 745.1   US
NEW GLEANINGS. 1976. q. free to qualified personnel. Historic Cherry Hill, 523 1-2 S. Pearl St., Albany, NY 12202. TEL 518-434-4806. Ed. Liselle LaFrance. bk.rev. price. 700. (looseleaf format; back issues avail.) **Document type:** newsletter.
   Description: Covers activities of the museum including fundraising and new research.

069
NEW MUSEUM NEWSLETTER. 1977. q. $35. New Museum of Contemporary Art, Public Relations, 583 Broadway, New York, NY 10012. TEL 212-219-1222. FAX 212-431-5328. Ed. Charlayne Haynes. circ. 15,000. **Document type:** newsletter.
   Formerly: New Museum News.

069   UK
NEW RESEARCH IN MUSEUM STUDIES: AN INTERNATIONAL SERIES. 1990. irreg., no. 4, 1994. £42. Athlone Press Ltd., 1 Park Dr., London NW11 7SG, England. TEL 0181-458-0888. FAX 0181-201-8115. (Dist. in the U.S. by: Athlone Press, 165 First Ave., Atlantic Highlands, NJ 07781. TEL 908-872-1441) Ed. Susan Pearce. bk.rev.; film rev.; abstr.; bibl.; illus.; stat.; index. (back issues avail.) **Document type:** monographic series.

069   US
NEW YORK (CITY). MUSEUM OF THE CITY OF NEW YORK. ANNUAL REPORT. 1923. a. free. Museum of the City of New York, Fifth Ave. and 103rd St., NY 10029. TEL 212-534-1672. FAX 212-423-0758. Ed. Billie Heller. charts; illus. circ. 5,000. **Document type:** corporate report.
   Supersedes (1970?-1982): New York (City). Museum of the City of New York. Bulletin.

069.097   US
NEWARK MUSEUM. EXHIBITIONS & EVENTS. 1944. bi-m. $6 to non-members. Newark Museum Association, 49 Washington St., Box 540, Newark, NJ 07101. TEL 201-596-6550. illus. circ. 12,500. **Indexed:** Amer.Hist.& Life, Hist.Abstr. **Document type:** newsletter.
   Formerly (until 1983): Newark Museum. News Notes (ISSN 0028-9256)

NEWSBANK REVIEW OF THE ARTS: FINE ARTS AND ARCHITECTURE. see *ART*

708.1   US   ISSN 0029-2567
N715.R2
NORTH CAROLINA MUSEUM OF ART. BULLETIN. 1957. irreg. $4. North Carolina Museum of Art, c/o Lisa Eveleigh, 2110 Blue Ridge Rd., Raleigh, NC 27607. TEL 919-833-1935. illus. circ. 1,000. **Indexed:** Artbibl.Mod., RILA. **Document type:** bulletin.

069   US   ISSN 0892-2896
NORTH CAROLINA MUSEUM OF ART. PREVIEW. 1957. s-a. $25 membership. North Carolina Museum of Art, c/o Lisa Eveleigh, 2110 Blue Ridge Rd., Raleigh, NC 27607. TEL 919-833-1935. Eds. Nancy Margolis, Lisa Everleigh. illus. circ. 10,000.
   Former titles (until 1983): North Carolina Museum of Art. Calendar (ISSN 0146-1680); (until 1975): North Carolina Museum of Art. Calendar of Art Events (ISSN 0149-6603); Which incorporates: North Carolina Museum of Art. Report (ISSN 0899-8507)

069   US   ISSN 1070-468X
NORTH CAROLINA NATURALIST. 1993. q. free. Friends of the North Carolina State Museum of Natural Sciences, Box 27647, Raleigh, NC 27611. TEL 919-733-7450. FAX 919-733-1573. bk.rev. circ. 2,000. **Document type:** consumer publication.
   Description: Promotes the museum across the state. Educates and informs the membership of the friends about the museum and the natural history of North Carolina.

NOTIZIARIO VINCIANO. see *ART*

NYE FAMILY NEWSLETTER. see *GENEALOGY AND HERALDRY*

069   CN   ISSN 0704-5824
OCCASIONAL; an occasional journal for Nova Scotia Museums. 1973. s-a. free. Nova Scotia Museum, 1747 Summer St., Halifax, NS B3H 3A6, Canada. TEL 902-429-4610. Ed. Deborah Trask. bk.rev.; index. circ. 600.

708   SZ
OEFFENTLICHE KUNSTSAMMLUNG BASEL. MUSEUM FUER GEGENWARTSKUNST. JAHRESBERICHT. 1904. irreg., latest 1991. price varies. Oeffentliche Kunstsammlung Basel, Museum fuer Gegenwartskunst, St.-Alban-Graben 16, CH-4010 Basel, Switzerland. TEL 061-2710828. FAX 061-2710845. Ed. Johannes Stueckelberger. **Document type:** bulletin.
   Former titles: Oeffentliche Kunstsammlung. Museum fuer Gegenwart. Jahresbericht; Oeffentliche Kunstsammlung. Jahresbericht (ISSN 0067-4311)

708.1   AU   ISSN 0083-615X
N25
OESTERREICHISCHE GALERIE. MITTEILUNGEN. 1957. a. S.120. Oesterreichische Galerie, Prinz Eugen-Str. 27, A-1037 Vienna, Austria. FAX 784337. Ed.Bd. adv.; illus. circ. 1,200. (tabloid format) **Indexed:** Artbibl.Mod.
   —BLDSC (5862.930000).
   Description: Includes art reviews and a report of the gallery's activities.

069   US   ISSN 0090-6700
AM10.A2
OFFICIAL MUSEUM DIRECTORY. 1961. a., 25th edition, 1995. $189.95 to non-members; members $134. (American Association of Museums) R.R. Bowker, A Reed Reference Publishing company, 121 Chanlon Rd., New Providence, NJ 07974. TEL 908-464-6800. FAX 908-665-6688. TELEX 138 755. (Subscr. to: R.R. Bowker, Order Dept., Box 31, New Providence, NJ 07974-9903. TEL 800-521-8110) adv.; index. **Document type:** directory.
   Description: Lists more than 7,000 institutions in 85 categories, including museums, art associations, nature centers, aquariums, botanical gardens, planetariums, zoos, and others. Lists where they are, what they exhibit, and who manages them.

708.4   FR
OFFICIEL DES GALERIES. no.155, 1976. m. 15 rue du Temple, 75004 Paris, France. Ed. J. Wolman. adv.

069 500   JA   ISSN 0385-0285
OKINAWA KENRITSU HAKUBUTSUKAN KIYO/OKINAWA PREFECTURAL MUSEUM. BULLETIN. (Text in Japanese) 1975. a. Okinawa Kenritsu Hakubutsukan - Okinawa Prefectural Museum, 1-1 Shuri Onaka-cho, Naha-shi, Okinawa-ken 903, Japan. TEL 098-884-2243. FAX 098-886-4353. Ed. Katumori Kugai. **Document type:** bulletin.

069   JA   ISSN 0385-0293
OKINAWA KENRITSU HAKUBUTSUKAN NENPO/OKINAWA PREFECTURAL MUSEUM. ANNUAL REPORT. (Text in Japanese) 1975. a. Okinawa Kenritsu Hakubutsukan, 1-1 Shuri Onaka-cho, Naha-shi, Okinawa-ken 903, Japan. TEL 098-884-2243. FAX 098-886-4353.

069   CN   ISSN 1188-9578
ONTARIO MUSEUM ANNUAL/ANNUAIRE DES MUSEES DE L'ONTARIO. (Text in English, French) 1971. a. Can.$10 to individuals; institutions Can.$15. Ontario Museum Association, George Brown House, 50 Baldwin St., Toronto, ON M5T 1L4, Canada. TEL 416-348-8672. FAX 416-348-0438. E-mail: can-oma@immedia.ca. Ed.Bd. adv.; bk.rev.; circ. 1,500 (controlled). (also avail. in microfilm from MML; back issues avail.; reprint service avail. from MML) **Indexed:** Art & Archaeol.Tech.Abstr., Can.Per.Ind. **Document type:** bulletin.
   —CCC.
   Former titles (until 1992): Museum Quarterly (ISSN 0822-5931); Ontario Museum Quarterly (ISSN 0822-5923)
   Description: Concentrates on museum studies including administration, collections management, conservation, education, exhibit design and research. Reviews publications, conferences and exhibitions; presents research and thesis abstracts.
   Refereed Serial

OPENBAAR KUNSTBEZIT IN VLAANDEREN. see *ART*

069   US
ORANGE EMPIRE RAILWAY MUSEUM GAZETTE. 1956. m. membership. Orange Empire Railway Museum, Inc., Box 548, Perris, CA 92571-0548. TEL 909-943-3020. FAX 909-943-2676. Ed. Paul Hammond. circ. 1,400. **Document type:** newsletter.
   Description: Covers the documents, technology, history, and impact of rail transportation industry in the West.

708   NE   ISSN 0922-775X
ORANJE-NASSAU MUSEUM. JAARBOEK. 1975. a. fl.29.50. Vereniging "Oranje-Nassau Museum", Surinamestraat 34, 2585 GK The Hague, Netherlands. TEL 31-70-3631990.

935 069   US
ORIENTAL INSTITUTE MUSEUM PUBLICATIONS. 1951. irreg., latest 1994. price varies. University of Chicago, Oriental Institute, 1155 E. 58th St., Chicago, IL 60637. TEL 312-702-9508. FAX 312-702-9853. illus. (back issues avail.) **Document type:** monographic series.
   Description: Describes materials in the Near Eastern collections of the museums.

MUSEUMS AND ART GALLERIES

069   JA   ISSN 0389-8105
OSAKA-SHIRITSU SHIZENSHI HAKUBUTSUKAN KANPO/OSAKA MUSEUM OF NATURAL HISTORY. ANNUAL REPORT. (Text in Japanese) 1964. a. Osaka-shiritsu Shizenshi Hakubutsukan - Osaka Museum of Natural History, 1-23 Nagai Koen, Higashi-Sumiyoshi-ku, Osaka-shi, Osaka-fu 546, Japan. Ed. Yorio Miyatake. circ. 1,200. **Indexed:** Biol.Abstr., Jap.Per.Ind.

069.094 948.1   NO   ISSN 0030-6703
DL401   CODEN: OTTADD
OTTAR. 1954. 5/yr. NOK 125. Tromsoe Museum, University of Tromsoe, N-9037 Tromsoe, Norway. TEL 47-77-64-50-00. FAX 47-77-68-91-58. Ed. Rob Barrett. adv.; charts; illus.; cum.index: nos.1-190 (1954-1990). circ. 6,000. **Indexed:** Anthropol.Lit., GeoRef., NAA. **Document type:** academic/scholarly publication.

069   PE
PACHACAMAC; revista de investigaciones. 1992. s-a.? Museo de la Nacion, Apdo. Postal 6150, Lima 100, Peru. Ed. Carlos Guerrero Zevallos.

069 978.8   US
PACIFIC CURRENTS. 1985. q. membership. University of Washington, Thomas Burke Memorial Washington State Museum, DB-10, Seattle, WA 98195. TEL 206-543-5592. FAX 206-685-3039. Ed. Ruth Pelz. bk.rev. circ. 1,300. (looseleaf format; back issues avail.) **Document type:** newsletter.
Formerly: Thomas Burke Memorial Washington State Museum Newsletter.
Description: Designed to build interest in the areas of natural history, Northwest and Native arts, as well as culture by the museum.

069   US
LAS PALABRAS (TAOS). 1979. q. membership. Millicent Rogers Museum, Box A, Taos, NM 87571. TEL 505-758-2462. FAX 505-758-5751. Ed. Robert Bonney; Pub. Robert Bonney. circ. 1,500. **Document type:** newsletter.
Description: Covers the collection and interpretation of the art, history, and culture of the Native American, Hispanic, and Anglo peoples of the Southwest, focusing on Taos and northern New Mexico.

069   US   ISSN 1074-0457
PEABODY ESSEX MUSEUM COLLECTIONS. 1859. q. $25 (foreign $30) (effective 1995). Peabody Essex Museum, East India Sq., Salem, MA 01970. TEL 508-745-1876. FAX 508-744-0036. Ed. William T. La Moy. adv.; bk.rev.; index, cum.index through 1969. circ. 1,100. (also avail. in microform from UMI; reprint service avail. from UMI; back issues avail.) **Indexed:** Amer.Hist.& Life, Arts & Hum.Cit.Ind., Biol.Abstr., Curr.Cont., Hist.Abstr. **Document type:** academic/scholarly publication.
—BLDSC (6413.749000); Faxon; Genuine Article; UMI; UnCover.
Formerly (until vol.129, no.4, Oct. 1993): Essex Institute Historical Collections (ISSN 0014-0953)
Description: Highlights and promotes all facets of the Museum's international holdings in arts and culture.

069   US
PEABODY ESSEX MUSEUM MAGAZINE. 1987. q. $25 membership. Peabody Essex Museum, East India Sq., Salem, MA 01970. TEL 508-745-1876. FAX 508-744-6776. Ed. Dorothy Chen-Courtin. illus. circ. 3,200.
Supersedes: Peabody Museum of Salem. Register.
Description: Covers new exhibitions and items of interest to museum members.

069 500   US   ISSN 0079-0354
AM101   CODEN: PSSEAL
PEARCE-SELLARDS SERIES. 1963. irreg., no.48, 1991. Texas Memorial Museum, University of Texas at Austin, 2400 Trinity, Austin, TX 78705. TEL 512-471-1604. **Indexed:** Biol.Abstr.

PENNSYLVANIA HERITAGE. see HISTORY — History Of North And South America

708.1   US   ISSN 0031-7160
PHAROS (ST. PETERSBURG). 1963. biennial. membership. Museum of Fine Arts, St. Petersburg, 225 Beach Dr. N.E., St. Petersburg, FL 33701. TEL 813-896-2667. FAX 813-894-4638. Ed. Diane Lesko. illus. circ. 5,500. **Indexed:** RILA.
Description: Scholarly research and studies on art history, acquisitions, and collections.

708.1   US   ISSN 0031-7314
N685
PHILADELPHIA MUSEUM OF ART. BULLETIN. 1903. q. $20 (foreign $25) (effective 1995). Philadelphia Museum of Art, Box 7646, Philadelphia, PA 19101. TEL 215-235-8700. FAX 215-235-8715. Ed. George Marcus. illus.; circ. 7,000 (paid). **Indexed:** Art & Archaeol.Tech.Abstr., Art.Ind., Artbibl.Mod., Arts & Hum.Cit.Ind., Avery Ind.Archit.Per., Curr.Cont., RILA. **Document type:** academic/scholarly publication, bulletin.
—Faxon; UnCover.

500.907   GW   ISSN 0343-7620
     CODEN: PABKDZ
PHILIPPIA. (Text in German; summaries in English) 1970. s-a. DM.15. Naturkundemuseum der Stadt Kassel, Steinweg 2, 34117 Kassel, Germany. TEL 0561-7874014. FAX 0561-7874040. circ. 800. (back issues avail.) **Document type:** academic/scholarly publication.

069   PH   ISSN 0117-0686
AM79.P6
PHILIPPINES. REPUBLIC. NATIONAL MUSEUM PAPERS. (Text in English) 1990. s-a. $10. National Museum of the Philippines, Padre Burgos St., Manila, Philippines. TEL 48-14-27. FAX 632-530-0229. (Co-sponsor: Concerned Citizens for the National Museum, Inc.) Eds. Jesus T. Peralta, Rosario B. Tantoco. circ. 500 (controlled). **Document type:** academic/scholarly publication.
Description: Contain brief scientific papers on anthropology, archaeology, botany, geology, zoology and conservation.

069   US
PONY EXPRESS MAIL. 1972. m. $10 (effective 1992). Pony Express Historical Association, Inc., Box 1022, 12th and Penn, St. Joseph, MO 64502. TEL 816-232-8206. (Co-sponsors: Patee House Museum; Jesse James Home) Ed. Gary Chilcote. circ. 325 (paid). (looseleaf format) **Document type:** newsletter.
Description: Chronicles news and activities of the Patee House Museum, headquarters of the Pony Express, and the Jesse James Home, and events pertaining to the Pony Express and Jesse James.

069.5   US   ISSN 8755-2035
N719
PORTICUS. 1978. biennial. $8.50. University of Rochester, Memorial Art Gallery, 500 University Ave., Rochester, NY 14607. TEL 716-473-7720. FAX 716-473-6266. Ed. Candace Adelson. circ. 1,500. (back issues avail.) **Indexed:** Art Ind., Artbibl.Mod., RILA. **Document type:** academic/scholarly publication.
Description: Scholarly articles on the museum's collection, exhibitions, and lectures.

069   US
PORTLAND ART MUSEUM NEWSLETTER. 1949. m. membership. Portland Art Museum, 1219 S.W. Park Ave., Portland, OR 97205. TEL 503-226-2811. FAX 503-226-2842. Ed. Diane Kantor. adv.; circ. 20,000 (controlled). **Document type:** newsletter.
Former titles (until 1991): Oregon Art Institute Newsletter; Portland Art Association Newsletter; Portland Art Association Calendar; Portland Art Museum Calendar.

069 025   US
PRESERVATION TIPS. 1993. q. $10. Chicora Foundation, Inc., 861 Arbutus Dr., Box 8664, Columbia, SC 29202-8664. TEL 803-787-6910. FAX 803-787-6910. Ed. Michael Trinkley. circ. 250. **Document type:** newsletter.
Description: Contains information on preserving archives, historic sites, museums and libraries.

708.1   US   ISSN 0032-843X
N1
PRINCETON UNIVERSITY. ART MUSEUM. RECORD. 1942. s-a. $12 (effective 1993). Princeton University, Art Museum, Princeton, NJ 08544-1018. TEL 609-258-4341. FAX 609-258-5949. Ed. Jill Guthrie. bibl.; illus.; cum.index every 10 yrs. circ. 1,500. (also avail. in microform from UMI; reprint service avail. from UMI) **Indexed:** Art Ind., Artbibl.Mod., RILA. **Document type:** academic/scholarly publication, bulletin.
—Faxon; UMI; UnCover. **CCC.**
Description: Gives history and criticism on pieces in the museum's collection.

387 979 069.9   US   ISSN 0891-2661
QUARTERDECK. 1973. q. $15. Columbia River Maritime Museum, Inc., 1792 Marine Dr., Astoria, OR 97103. TEL 503-325-2323. FAX 503-325-2331. Ed. Karen Carpenter. illus. circ. 1,900. (back issues avail.) **Document type:** newsletter.
Formerly (until Fall 1989): Quarterdeck Review.
Description: News, historical vignettes, and announcements pertaining to the activities of the Columbia River Maritime Museum in Oregon.

069 708   AT   ISSN 1039-8090
QUEEN VICTORIA MUSEUM AND ART GALLERY. ANNUAL REPORT. 1902. a. free. Queen Victoria Museum and Art Gallery, c/o Kaye Dimmack, Wellington St., Launceston, Tas. 7250, Australia. TEL 003-316777. FAX 003-345230. Ed. C.B. Tassell. circ. 500.

069 708 500   AT   ISSN 0085-5278
AM101   CODEN: RQVMAY
QUEEN VICTORIA MUSEUM AND ART GALLERY. LAUNCESTON, TASMANIA. RECORDS. 1942. irreg., no.101, 1993. price varies. Queen Victoria Museum and Art Gallery, c/o Kaye Dimmack, Wellington Street, Launceston, Tasmania 7250, Australia. TEL 003-316777. FAX 003-345230. Ed. C.B. Tassell. circ. 250. **Indexed:** AESIS, Biol.Abstr., GeoRef.
—BLDSC (7324.000000).

069   AT
QUEEN VICTORIA MUSEUM AND ART GALLERY. OCCASIONAL PAPERS. 1989. irreg., no.6, 1992. Queen Victoria Museum and Art Gallery, c/o Kaye Dimmack, Wellington St., Launceston, Tas. 7250, Australia. TEL 003-316777. FAX 003-345230. Ed. C.B. Tassel. circ. 100.

069.7   AT   ISSN 0079-8835
QH1   CODEN: MQUMA8
QUEENSLAND MUSEUM, BRISBANE. MEMOIRS. 1912. irreg. price varies. Queensland Museum, P.O. Box 3300, South Brisbane, Qld. 4101, Australia. TEL 61-7-840-7664. FAX 61-7-846-1918. Ed. P.A. Jell. circ. 650. **Indexed:** AESIS, Anthropol.Lit., Aus.Sci.Ind., Biol.Abstr., Geo.Abstr., Geol.Abstr., GeoRef., Rev.Appl.Entomol., Zoo.Rec. **Document type:** academic/scholarly publication.
—BLDSC (5629.800000); UnCover.

069 708   US
R C H A NEWSLETTER. 1971. q. $12.50 to individuals; institutions $20 (includes: R C H A Technical Information Sheet). Regional Council of Historical Agencies, Box 28, Cooperstown, NY 13326-0028. TEL 607-547-4131. Ed. Elizabeth A. Callahan. adv.; bk.rev.; bibl. (tabloid format; back issues avail.) **Document type:** newsletter.

069 708   US
R C H A TECHNICAL INFORMATION SHEET. 1971. irreg. $20 to individuals; institutions $25 (includes: R C H A Newsletter). Regional Council of Historical Agencies, Box 28, Cooperstown, NY 13326-0028. TEL 607-754-4131. Ed. Elizabeth A. Callahan. bibl. (tabloid format; back issues avail.)

R.E. OLDS TRANSPORTATION MUSEUM NEWSLETTER. see TRANSPORTATION

708   CN   ISSN 0035-7154
R.L.C.'S MUSEUM GAZETTE. 1966. irreg. Richard L. Coulton, Ed. & Pub., Bentley, Alta. T0C 0J0, Canada. adv.; bk.rev.; abstr.; charts; tr.lit.; cum.index. circ. 400. (processed)

069   AG
REVISTA DEL MUSEO AMERICANISTA. 1969. a. Museo Americanista de Antropologia, Historia, Numismatica y Ciencias Naturales, Manuel Castro 254, Lomas de Zamora, Buenos Aires, Argentina.

069   RM   ISSN 1220-1723
REVISTA MUZEELOR. (Text in Rumanian; summaries in English, French, Russian) 1964. 10/yr. 360 lei($91) Ministerul Culturii, Piata Presei Libere 1, Sector 1, Bucharest, Rumania. (Subscr. to: Calea Grivitei, 66-68, Box 12201, Bucharest, Ruamnia) Ed. Gavril Sarafoleanu. bk.rev.; bibl.; charts; illus. Indexed: Numis.Lit.
—BLDSC (7867.600000).
Formerly (until 1990): Revista Muzeelor si Monumentelor. Seria Muzee (ISSN 1220-1731); Which was formed by the 1974 merger of: Revista Muzeelor (ISSN 0035-0206) & Revista Monumentelor Istorice (ISSN 0253-1569); Which was previously (1908-1970): Boletinul Comisi Unii Monumentelor Istorice (ISSN 1220-1715)

708.4   FR   ISSN 0035-2608
REVUE DU LOUVRE ET DES MUSEES DE FRANCE. (Text in French; summaries in English, German) 1951. bi-m. 450 F. (foreign 550 F.). Editions de la Reunion des Musees Nationaux, 49 rue Etienne Marcel, 75001 Paris, France. TEL 40-13-48-49. FAX 40-13-48-61. Ed. Jean-Pierre Cuzin. adv.; bk.rev.; illus.; index. circ. 13,000. Indexed: Art & Archaeol.Tech.Abstr., Art Ind., Artbibl.Mod., Arts & Hum.Cit.Ind., Avery Ind.Archit.Per., Curr.Cont., RILA.
—SWETS.

069 948.91   DK   ISSN 0107-928X
ROMU. 1980. a. DKK 70. Roskilde Museums Forlag, Sankt Ols Gade 15, DK-4000 Roskilde, Denmark. TEL 42-36 60 44. FAX 46-32-16-47. Eds. Flemming Rasmussen, Frank Birkebaek. illus. circ. 1,200. Indexed: NAA. Document type: academic/scholarly publication.

ROYAL AUSTRALIAN HISTORICAL SOCIETY. TECHNICAL INFORMATION SERVICE. see *HISTORY — History Of Australasia And Other Areas*

069   CN   ISSN 0840-7681
ROYAL BRITISH COLUMBIA MUSEUM. SPECIAL PUBLICATIONS. irreg. price varies. Royal British Columbia Museum, 675 Bellville St., Victoria, BC V8V 1X4, Canada. TEL 604-387-6357. (Subscr. to: Crown Publications, 546 Yates St., Victoria, BC V8W 1K8, Canada. TEL 604-386-4636) Ed. Gerry Truscott. (back issues avail.) Document type: government publication.

069 500   CN   ISSN 0843-5383
ROYAL BRITISH COLUMBIA MUSEUM MEMOIRS. 1988. irreg. price varies. Royal British Columbia Museum, 675 Bellville St., Victoria, BC V8V 1X4, Canada. TEL 604-387-6357. (Subscr. to: Crown Publications, 546 Yates St., Victoria, BC V8W 1K8, Canada. TEL 604-386-4636) Ed. Gerry Truscott. (back issues avail.) Indexed: Sport Fish.Abstr., Wild.Rev. Document type: government publication.

708 AM101   CN   ISSN 0082-5115
ROYAL ONTARIO MUSEUM. ANNUAL REPORT. 1949. a. free. Royal Ontario Museum, Publications, 100 Queen's Park, Toronto, ON M5S 2C6, Canada. TEL 416-586-5581. FAX 416-586-5827. Document type: corporate report.

500.907 700   CN   ISSN 0316-1269
ROYAL ONTARIO MUSEUM. HISTORY, TECHNOLOGY AND ART MONOGRAPHS. 1973. irreg. price varies. Royal Ontario Museum, Publications, 100 Queen's Park, Toronto, ON M5S 2C6, Canada. TEL 416-586-5581. FAX 416-586-5827. (Subscr. to: University of Toronto Press, Order Fulfilment Division, 5201 Dufferin St., Downsview, ON M3H 5T8, Canada. TEL 416-667-7791) Ed.Bd. bibl. Document type: monographic series.
—BLDSC (4318.575000).

SADO HAKUBUTSUKAN KENKYU HOKOKU/PUBLICATIONS FROM THE SADO MUSEUM. see *SCIENCES: COMPREHENSIVE WORKS*

708.1   US
ST. LOUIS ART MUSEUM. BULLETIN. 1914; N.S. 1965. s-a. $10. St. Louis Art Museum, Publications Department, No. 1 Fine Arts Dr., Forest Park, St. Louis, MO 63110. TEL 314-721-0072. FAX 314-721-6172. Ed. Mary Ann Steiner. illus.; circ. 17,000 (paid). Indexed: Artbibl.Mod., RILA. Document type: bulletin.
Formerly: City Art Museum of Saint Louis. Bulletin (ISSN 0009-7691)

SAITAMA-KENRITSU SHIZENSHI HAKUBUTSUKAN KENKYU HOKOKU/SAITAMA MUSEUM OF NATURAL HISTORY. BULLETIN. see *SCIENCES: COMPREHENSIVE WORKS*

SAITO HO-ON KAI MUSEUM OF NATURAL HISTORY. RESEARCH BULLETIN. see *SCIENCES: COMPREHENSIVE WORKS*

069   II   ISSN 0304-8152
N3750.H9
SALAR JUNG MUSEUM. ANNUAL REPORT. (Text in English or Hindi) a. Salar Jung Museum, Hyderabad 500 002, Andhra Pradesh, India. TEL 523211.

069   II
SALAR JUNG MUSEUM BI-ANNUAL RESEARCH JOURNAL. (Text in English) 1970. s-a. Rs.55 price varies. Salar Jung Museum, Hyderabad 500 002, Andhra Pradesh, India. TEL 523211. Ed. M.L. Nigam. illus.

500.907   US
SANTA BARBARA MUSEUM OF NATURAL HISTORY. MUSEUM BULLETIN. 1925. bi-m. membership. Santa Barbara Museum of Natural History, 2559 Puesta del Sol Rd., Santa Barbara, CA 93105. TEL 805-682-4711. FAX 805-569-3170. Ed. Suzanne Farwell. bk.rev.; charts; illus. circ. 5,000. Document type: newsletter.
Formerly: Museum Talk.
Description: Provides a bimonthly notice of the museum exhibits, field trips, events, and programs, including articles about natural history, American Indian studies, and the environment.

069   GW
SCHLESWIG-HOLSTEINISCHEN LANDESMUSEUM. JAHRBUCH. 1986. biennial. (Schleswig-Holsteinischen Landesmuseum) Wachholtz Verlag GmbH, Rungestr. 4, 24537 Neumuenster, Germany. TEL 04321-906270. FAX 04321-906275. Document type: bulletin.

069 913   US
SCIENCE MUSEUM NEWS. 1976. s-a. free. Association of Science Museum Directors, c/o The Carnegie Museum of Natural History, 4400 Forbes Ave., Pittsburgh, PA 15213. TEL 412-622-3377. FAX 412-622-8837. Ed. Elizabeth R. Mertz. circ. 200 (controlled). Document type: newsletter.
Description: Articles directed to the natural history and science museum directors.

069   UK   ISSN 0266-6898
SCOTTISH MUSEUM NEWS. 1981. 2/yr. £10. Scottish Museums Council, County House, 20-22 Torphichen St., Edinburgh EH3 8JB, Scotland. TEL 031-229-7465. FAX 031-229-2728. Ed. Wilma Alexander. adv.; bk.rev.; circ. 1,500 (controlled). Document type: newsletter.
Formerly: Omnigatherum.
Description: Information on events in Scottish museums. Includes the work of the Council.

069 387   US
SEA HISTORY'S GUIDE TO AMERICAN & CANADIAN MARITIME MUSEUMS. 1990. irreg. $11.95. National Maritime Historical Society, 5 John Walsh Blvd., Charles Point, Peekskill, NY 10566-0068. TEL 914-737-7878. Ed. Joseph M. Stanford. Document type: directory.
Description: Alphabetical listing of Maritime Museums in the U.S. and Canada.

385   US
SEASHORE TROLLEY MUSEUM DISPATCH. 1958. bi-m. membership. New England Electric Railway Historical Society, Inc., Box A, Kennebunkport, ME 04046. TEL 207-967-2712. Ed. Robert E. Kelly. bk.rev. circ. 1,550. Indexed: Amer.Hist.& Life, Hist.Abstr. Document type: newsletter.

SEFUNIM. see *ARCHAEOLOGY*

069 976   US
SHILOH SCRAPBOOK. 1978. q. $10 membership (effective 1995-1996). Shiloh Museum of Ozark History, 118 W. Johnson Ave., Springdale, AR 72764. TEL 501-750-8165. FAX 501-750-8171. Ed. Susan Young. circ. 2,500. (looseleaf format; back issues avail.) Document type: newsletter.
Formerly (until 1995): Shiloh Museum. Newsletter.
Description: Discusses history of Ozark Mountain region and museum programs for people of all ages.

SHIRETOKO HAKUBUTSUKAN KENKYU HOKOKU/SHIRETOKO MUSEUM. BULLETIN. see *SCIENCES: COMPREHENSIVE WORKS*

SHIZEN KYOIKUEN HOKOKU/MINISTRY OF EDUCATION. NATIONAL SCIENCE MUSEUM. INSTITUTE FOR NATURE STUDY. MISCELLANEOUS REPORTS. see *SCIENCES: COMPREHENSIVE WORKS*

069 550.9   JA   ISSN 1340-2285
SHIZENSHI DAYORI. (Text in Japanese) 1985. irreg. Saitama-kenritsu Shizenshi Hakubutsukan - Saitama Museum of Natural History, 1417-1 Nagatoro, Nagatoro-machi, Chichibu-gun, Saitama-ken 369-13, Japan. TEL 81-0494-66-0404. FAX 81-0494-69-1002.
Description: Reports news of the museum.

069 387   AT   ISSN 1033-4688
SIGNALS. 1988. q. membership only. Australian National Maritime Museum, Public Affairs Section, G.P.O. Box 5131, Sydney, N.S.W. 2001, Australia. TEL 61-2-552-7777. FAX 61-2-552-2318. E-mail: anmmfp@ozemail.com.au. Ed. Jeffrey Mellefont. bk.rev. circ. 5,000.
—UnCover.
Description: Publishes Australian maritime heritage articles, members information, museum news.

SLATE. see *ART*

SMITHSONIAN. see *SOCIAL SCIENCES: COMPREHENSIVE WORKS*

SOCIETE HISTORIQUE DE SAINT-BONIFACE. BULLETIN. see *HISTORY — History Of North And South America*

069   BP
SOLOMON ISLANDS MUSEUM ASSOCIATION. JOURNAL. 1975. a. Solomon Islands Government Printing, Box 313, Honiara, Solomon Islands.

574 500.907   US
SONORENSIS. ANNUAL REPORT. 1957. a. membership. Arizona-Sonora Desert Museum, Inc., 2021 N. Kinney Rd., Tucson, AZ 85743. TEL 602-833-1380. FAX 602-883-2500. Document type: corporate report.
Formerly: Arizona-Sonora Desert Museum. Annual Report.

069   SA   ISSN 0370-8314
AM89.A1   CODEN: SAMAAM
SOUTHERN AFRICAN MUSEUMS ASSOCIATION. BULLETIN. (Text in Afrikaans, English) 1936. s-a. $60. Southern African Museums Association - Suider-Afrikaanse Museumvereniging, P.O. Box 29294, Sunnyside, Pretoria 0132, South Africa. Ed. R.C. de Jong. adv.; B&W page R.120. bk.rev.; charts; illus.; index every 2 yrs. circ. 800. Indexed: Zoo.Rec. Document type: bulletin, proceedings.
Formerly: Southern African Museums Association. Publication (ISSN 0036-0791)

069   US   ISSN 0073-4985
SOUTHERN ILLINOIS UNIVERSITY. UNIVERSITY MUSEUM STUDIES. 1968. irreg., no. 11, 1977. price varies. Southern Illinois University at Carbondale, University Museum, Carbondale, IL 62901. TEL 618-453-5388. FAX 618-453-3253. Document type: academic/scholarly publication, monographic series.

623   US   ISSN 0896-7466
SPINDRIFT (PHILADELPHIA). 1963. 3/yr. $35 membership. Philadelphia Maritime Museum, 321 Chestnut St., Philadelphia, PA 19106. TEL 215-925-5439. FAX 215-625-9635. Ed. Keith Mason. circ. 5,000. Document type: newsletter.
Description: Carries articles on museum exhibits and programs and Delaware Valley maritime history.

SPORVEJSMUSEET SKJOLDENAESHOLM. AARSBERETNING. see *TRANSPORTATION — Railroads*

709   GW   ISSN 0075-5133
STAATLICHE KUNSTHALLE KARLSRUHE. BILDHEFTE. 1958. irreg. price varies. Staatliche Kunsthalle Karlsruhe, Hans-Thoma-Str. 2, 76133 Karlsruhe, Germany. TEL 0721-9263355. FAX 0721-9266788. Document type: catalog.

MUSEUMS AND ART GALLERIES

709   GW   ISSN 0067-284X
N6886.B27
STAATLICHE KUNSTSAMMLUNGEN IN BADEN-WUERTTEMBERG. JAHRBUCH. 1964. a. DM.60. Deutscher Kunstverlag GmbH, Nymphenburgerstr. 84, 80603 Munich, Germany. TEL 089-121516-0. FAX 089-12151616. circ. 600. **Indexed:** Artbibl.Mod., RILA. **Document type:** bulletin.

069 792   BE   ISSN 0773-9559
NX555.A57
STAD ANTWERPEN. CULTUREEL JAARBOEK. (Text in Dutch; summaries in English, French, German) 1983. a. 250 BEF. Stad Antwerpen, 6de Directie, Stadhuis, B-2000 Antwerp, Belgium. TEL 32-3-2328428. FAX 32-3-2251282. TELEX 31807 HAVANT. Ed. Luc Gorsele. bk.rev. circ. 1,500. (back issues avail.) **Document type:** government publication.
Description: Presents various cultural and social events in and around Antwerp.

069   GW   ISSN 0078-2777
STADTBIBLIOTHEK NUERNBERG. AUSSTELLUNGSKATALOG. 1955. irreg., vol. 99, 1992. price varies. Stadtbibliothek Nuernberg, Egidienplatz 23, 90317 Nuernberg, Germany. **Document type:** catalog.

708   US
STANFORD UNIVERSITY MUSEUM OF ART JOURNAL. 1971. biennial. $10. Stanford University, Stanford Museum of Art, Stanford, CA 94305. TEL 415-725-0466. FAX 415-725-0464. E-mail: ehf.bsb@forsythe.stanford.edu. Eds. Bernard Barryte. circ. 1,500. **Indexed:** Artbibl.Mod., RILA. **Document type:** academic/scholarly publication.
Formerly: Stanford Museum (ISSN 0085-6665)
Description: Contains facts on selected works of art in the museum and a list of acquisitions for the two-year period with descriptions of all exhibits in both the museum and nearby gallery.

069   US
THE STATESMAN (SPIEGEL GROVE). 1981. q. free. Rutherford B. Hayes Presidential Center, Spiegel Grove, Fremont, OH 43420-2796. TEL 419-332-2081. FAX 419-332-4952. circ. 7,000. (back issues avail.) **Document type:** newsletter.
Description: News about the Hayes Presidential Center, its collections, exhibits, and programs that are available to the public.

069 797.123   US
STATION LOG. 1981. q. $10 membership. Hull Lifesaving Museum, 1117 Nantasket Ave., Box 221, Hull, MA 02045. TEL 617-925-LIFE. Ed. Lory Newmyer. film rev.; illus. circ. 1,250. (back issues avail.)
Description: Keeps members and visitors informed of museum activities and history.

069   NO   ISSN 0333-0656
STAVANGER MUSEUM. AARBOK. (Text in Norwegian; summaries in English) 1890. a. NOK 150. Stavanger Museum, N-4005 Stavanger, Norway. TEL 04-526035. FAX 04-529380. Ed. Randi Skotheim. circ. 1,000.
—BLDSC (1592.500000).
Former titles (until 1947): Stavanger Museum. (ISSN 0333-3884); (until 1901): Stavanger Museums Aarsberetning (ISSN 0333-3892)

069 914.83   NO   ISSN 0333-0664
STAVANGER MUSEUM. SKRIFTER. (Text in Norwegian; summaries in English) 1920. irreg., vol.11, 1985. price varies. Stavanger Museum, N-4005 Stavanger, Norway. illus. **Document type:** monographic series.

STEARNS NEWSLETTER; the Stearns collection of musical instruments at the University of Michigan. see MUSIC

069   US
STRECKER MUSEUM NEWS. 1971. irreg., approx. 4/yr. free. Baylor University, John. K. Strecker Museum, Box 97154, Waco, TX 76798. TEL 817-755-1110. FAX 817-755-1173. Ed. David Lintz. circ. 2,000. (looseleaf format; back issues avail.) **Document type:** newsletter.
Description: Covers the museum and its research, other programs, museum studies, Strecker associates, volunteers, donors, and interested friends.

069   HU   ISSN 0133-3046
STUDIA COMITATENSIA. (Text in Hungarian; summaries in English, German, and Russian) 1972. irreg., vol.27, 1994. price varies or on exchange basis. Pest Megyei Muzeumok Igazgatosaga - Direction of Pest County Museums, Fo ter 6, H-2000 Szentendre, Hungary. TEL 26-310-244. FAX 26-310-790. illus. circ. 800. **Indexed:** A.I.C.P.
Description: Interdisciplinary studies on Pest County. Includes art, history, sociology, culture, anthropology, ethnology, archeology, literature and history.

STUDIA DO DZIEJOW DAWNEGO UZBROJENIA I UBIORU WOJSKOWEGO. see MILITARY

069   II   ISSN 0081-8259
STUDIES IN MUSEOLOGY. (Text in English) 1965. a. Rs.10($2.) Maharaja Sayajirao University of Baroda, Department of Museology, Sayaji Park, Baroda 390002, Gujarat, India. Ed. V.H. Bedekar. bk.rev. circ. 400.

STUDII SI CERCETARI DE ISTORIA ARTEI. SERIA ARTA PLASTICA. see ART

069.094   SW   ISSN 0039-6885
SVENSKA MUSEER. 1932. bi-m. SEK 200 (effective 1996). Svenska Museifoereningen - Swedish Museums Association, P.O. Box 27151, S-102 52 Stockholm, Sweden. TEL 46-8-240589. FAX 46-8-660-6034. Ed. Gunilla Cedrenius. adv. contact: Aase Aasard. bk.rev.; charts; illus.; stat.; cum.index every 10 yrs. circ. 4,000. **Indexed:** NAA. **Document type:** bulletin.

708.1   CN   ISSN 0845-8081
TABLEAU (FREDERICTON). 1970. 3/yr. free. Beaverbrook Art Gallery, P.O. Box 605, Fredericton, NB E3B 5A6, Canada. TEL 506-458-8545. FAX 506-459-7450. Dir. Ian G. Lumsden. circ. 1,400. **Document type:** newsletter.
Formerly (until 1988): Beaverbrook Art Gallery (ISSN 0045-1592)
Description: Features a message from the director, exhibitions held, programs available, recent aquisitions, staff news, list of members, etc.

708   CN
TABLEAU (WINNIPEG); involving people in the visual arts. bi-m. Winnipeg Art Gallery, 300 Memorial Blvd., Winnipeg, MB R3C 1V1, Canada. **Document type:** newsletter.
Description: Discusses exhibits and events at the Winnipeg Art Gallery.

TAIDE. see ART

708.9   MG
TALOHA. (Text in French and Malagasy) 1965. irreg., no.10, 1987. FMG.5400. Universite de Madagascar, Musee d'Art et d'Archeologie, B.P. 564 Isoraka, Antananarivo, Madagascar. **Indexed:** A.I.C.P., Anthropol.Lit.
Description: Articles on the archeology, anthropology, history and art of ancient Madagascar.

069   NE   ISSN 0920-7430
TENTOONSTELLINGSBOEKJE. Variant title: Nederlandse TentoonstellingsAgenda. (Supplement to: Vitrine (ISSN 0922-226X)) 1959. 8/yr. (Openbaar Kunstbezit) S D U Uitgeverij Koninginnegracht, Postbus 30446, 2500 EA The Hague, Netherlands. TEL 31-70-3429700. FAX 31-70-3634903. circ. 38,500.
Formerly (until 1987): Tentoonstellingsagenda (ISSN 0040-3520)
Description: Covers complete listing of exhibitions in Dutch museums, galeries and other cultural institutions, as well as a number of exhibitions in museums and galeries in nearby foreign countries.

069 574   US   ISSN 0040-3733
AM101   CODEN: TRRAB8
TERRA. 1962. q. $12 to non-members. Natural History Museum of Los Angeles County, 900 Exposition Blvd., Los Angeles, CA 90007. TEL 213-744-3330. FAX 213-742-0730. Ed. Robin Simpson. illus.; index. circ. 25,000. **Indexed:** Abstr.Anthropol., Anthropol.Lit., Art & Archaeol.Tech.Abstr., Curr.Adv.Ecol.Sci., Deep Sea Res.& Oceanogr.Abstr., NAA. **Document type:** consumer publication.
—UnCover.
Formerly: Museum Alliance Quarterly (ISSN 0027-402X)
Description: Concerns natural history, anthropology, and history.

060   US   ISSN 0082-3074
QH105.T4   CODEN: TXMBAR
TEXAS MEMORIAL MUSEUM. BULLETIN. 1960. irreg., no.36, 1994. price varies. Texas Memorial Museum, University of Texas at Austin, 2400 Trinity, Austin, TX 78705. TEL 512-471-1604. (reprint service avail. from UMI) **Indexed:** Biol.Abstr., GeoRef.

069   US   ISSN 0738-6788
TEXAS MEMORIAL MUSEUM. CONSERVATION NOTES. 1982. q. $4. University of Texas, Austin, Texas Memorial Museum, Materials Conservation Laboratory, 2400 Trinity, Austin, TX 78705. Ed. Georg Zapper. circ. 1,600. **Indexed:** Anthropol.Lit.

069 500   US   ISSN 0082-3082
                          CODEN: TMMMBI
TEXAS MEMORIAL MUSEUM. MISCELLANEOUS PAPERS. 1968. irreg., no. 8, 1990. price varies. Texas Memorial Museum, University of Texas at Austin, 2400 Trinity, Austin, TX 78705. TEL 512-471-1604. (reprint service avail. from UMI) **Indexed:** Biol.Abstr., GeoRef.

060   US
TEXAS MEMORIAL MUSEUM. MUSEUM NOTES. 1938. irreg., no. 12, 1974. price varies. Texas Memorial Museum, University of Texas at Austin, 2400 Trinity, Austin, TX 78705. TEL 512-471-1604. Ed. Georg Zappler. (reprint service avail. from UMI)

TEXAS MEMORIAL MUSEUM. SPELEOLOGICAL MONOGRAPHS. see EARTH SCIENCES — Geology

TEXAS TECH UNIVERSITY. MUSEUM. SPECIAL PUBLICATIONS. see BIOLOGY

677   US
TEXTILE MUSEUM BULLETIN. 1971. q. membership. Textile Museum, 2320 S St., N.W., Washington, DC 20008. TEL 202-667-0441. Ed. Maury Sullivan. circ. 4,500. **Document type:** newsletter.
Formerly: Textile Museum Newsletter.
Description: Includes exhibition information, calendar of events, development, travel, education, special events, and Museum Shop news.

709 735.22   DK   ISSN 0085-7262
N1925
THORVALDSENS MUSEUM. MEDDELELSER. (Text in Danish; summaries in English) 1917. irreg., latest 1994. price varies. Thorvaldsens Museum, Porthusgade 2, DK-1213 Copenhagen K, Denmark. TEL 45-33-32-15-32. FAX 45-33-32-17-71. Ed.Bd. illus.; index. circ. 1,200.
Description: Contains studies about Danish art during the first half of the 19th century - the Golden Age of Danish Art.

069   SZ
THURGAUISCHE MUSEUM. MITTEILUNGEN. 1946. irreg., latest 1974. 3 Fr. Thurgauische Museumsgesellschaft, CH-8500 Frauenfeld, Switzerland. Ed. H. Guhl-Widmer.

069   AU   ISSN 0379-0231
DB761
TIROLER LANDESMUSEUM FERDINANDEUM, INNSBRUCK. VEROEFFENTLICHUNGEN. 1825. a. Tiroler Landesmuseum Ferdinandeum, Museumstr. 15, A-6020 Innsbruck, Austria. TEL 0512-59489. FAX 0512-5948988. Ed. Josef Ladurner. circ. 450. **Document type:** academic/scholarly publication.

TOCHIGI-KENRITSU HAKUBUTSUKAN KENKYU HOKOKUSHO/TOCHIGI PREFECTURAL MUSEUM. MEMOIRS. see SCIENCES: COMPREHENSIVE WORKS

TOKYO-TO TAKAO SHIZEN KAGAKU HAKUBUTSUKAN KENKYU HOKOKU/TAKAO MUSEUM OF NATURAL HISTORY. SCIENCE REPORT. see SCIENCES: COMPREHENSIVE WORKS

069   US   ISSN 0730-2231
Q11.S8
TORCH (WASHINGTON). 1954. m. free. Smithsonian Institution, Office of Public Affairs, 900 Jefferson Dr., Rm. 2410, Washington, DC 20560. TEL 202-357-2627. Ed. Mary Combs. bk.rev.; illus. circ. 10,400. (tabloid format)
Formerly (until 1980): Smithsonian Torch (ISSN 0037-7341)

TOTTORI-KENRITSU HAKUBUTSUKAN KENKYU HOKOKU/TOTTORI PREFECTURAL MUSEUM. BULLETIN. see SCIENCES: COMPREHENSIVE WORKS

MUSEUMS AND ART GALLERIES

500   JA
TOYAMA TO SHIZEN. (Text in Japanese) q. Toyama-shi Kagaku Bunka Senta - Toyama Science Museum, 1-8-31 Nishi-nakano-machi, Toyama-shi, Toyama-ken 939, Japan. TEL 0764-92-2123. FAX 0764-21-5950. Ed. Michiharu Goto. **Document type:** newsletter.
  Description: Contains news of the center.

TRANSVAAL MUSEUM. BULLETIN. see *BIOLOGY — Zoology*

069 930.1   SA   ISSN 0255-0172
CODEN: TMMOER
TRANSVAAL MUSEUM. MONOGRAPHS. 1983. irreg., no.8, 1993. Transvaal Museum, P.O. Box 413, Pretoria 0001, South Africa. TEL 27-12-322-7632. FAX 27-12-322-7939. Ed. A. Dreyer. bibl.; index. Indexed: Zoo.Rec. **Document type:** monographic series.
—BLDSC (9026.687000).
  Description: Contributions in archaeology, zoology, and systematics in particular.

069 910   US   ISSN 1072-0073
N4390
TRAVELER'S GUIDE TO ART MUSEUM EXHIBITIONS. 1989. a. Museum Guide Publications, Inc., Box 25369, 1619 31st St. N.W., Washington, DC 20007.
  Formerly (until 1992): Traveler's Guide to Museum Exhibitions (ISSN 1041-0724)

707.4   US   ISSN 0733-463X
TRAVELING EXHIBITION INFORMATION SERVICE. NEWSLETTER. (Editions in English and French) 1980. bi-m. $35. Humanities Exchange, Inc., Box 1608, Largo, FL 34649. TEL 813-581-7328. FAX 813-585-6398. Ed. S.R. Howarth. adv. circ. 600. **Document type:** newsletter.
  Description: Provides descriptions of traveling exhibits in arts, humanities and sciences available for loan.

069   US
TRITON MUSEUM OF ART. MEMBERS' BULLETIN. 1968. bi-m. membership. Triton Museum of Art, 1505 Warburton Ave., Santa Clara, CA 95050. TEL 408-247-3754. FAX 408-247-3796. Ed. Jill Bryant. circ. 1,500 (controlled). (back issues avail.) **Document type:** bulletin, newsletter.

069.9   US   ISSN 1041-9632
TROLLEY FARE. 1953. bi-m. $25 membership. Pennsylvania Railway Museum Association, 1 Museum Rd., Washington, PA 15201. TEL 412-228-9256. FAX 412-228-9675. Ed. Harold M. Englund. circ. 600. (back issues avail.) **Document type:** newsletter.
  Description: Covers streetcar preservation and restoration, plus operations of existing street railways and light rail systems, and reports on the planning and progress of new systems worldwide.

069.094   NO   ISSN 0085-7394
TROMSOE MUSEUM. SKRIFTER. (Text in English, Norwegian) 1925. irreg., 1994, vol.25. price varies. N-9037 Tromsoe, Norway. Indexed: Biol.Abstr., NAA. **Document type:** academic/scholarly publication.

069   NZ   ISSN 1173-4337
AM101.W4715
TUHINGA: RECORDS OF THE MUSEUM OF NEW ZEALAND TE PAPA TONGAREWA. 1975. irreg. price varies. Museum of New Zealand, Board of Trustees, Buckle St., P.O. Box 467, Wellington, New Zealand. TEL 64-4-385-9609. FAX 64-4-385-6035. E-mail: Mary.Cresswell@actrix.gen.nz. Ed. M.M. Cresswell. bk.rev.; bibl.; charts; illus. circ. 550. Indexed: Anthropol.Lit., Biol.Abstr., Deep Sea Res.& Oceanogr.Abstr., Sport Fish.Abstr., Wild.Rev., Zoo.Rec.
—BLDSC (5987.876000).
  Supersedes (in June 1995): Museum of New Zealand Records (ISSN 1171-6908); (in 1992): National Museum of New Zealand Records (ISSN 0110-943X); Dominion Museum Records; Dominion Museum Records in Ethnology.
  Refereed Serial

708.1   US
U A B VISUAL ARTS GALLERY. SELECTIONS FROM THE PERMANENT SELECTION. 1981. irreg. free. University of Alabama at Birmingham, Visual Arts Gallery, 101 Honors House, Birmingham, AL 35294. TEL 205-934-4941. FAX 205-975-6639. TELEX 888826 UAB BHM. Ed. John M. Schnorrenberg. circ. 2,200. (back issues avail.)
  Description: Consists of an illustrated catalogue with essays about works in the Gallery.

708.1   US
U A B VISUAL ARTS GALLERY PAPERS. 1977. irreg. (6-10/yr.). free. University of Alabama at Birmingham, Visual Arts Gallery, 101 Honors House, Birmingham, AL 35294. TEL 205-934-4941. FAX 205-975-6639. TELEX 888826 UAB BHM. Eds. John M. Schnorrenberg, Antoinette Spanos Johnson. circ. 475. (back issues avail.) **Document type:** monographic series.
  Description: Contains biographies of artists exhibiting in the Gallery.

708.7   CN   ISSN 0824-5991
UKRAINIAN CULTURAL AND EDUCATIONAL CENTRE. VISTI - NEWS. (Text in English and Ukrainian) 1976. s-a. membership. Ukrainian Cultural and Educational Centre, 184 Alexander Ave. E., Winnipeg, MB R3B 0L6, Canada. TEL 204-942-0218. FAX 204-943-2857. Ed. Rick Horocholyn. circ. 2,000. **Document type:** newsletter.
  Description: Informs members of activities, events, and recent archival, museum, library and art collections.

069 700   US   ISSN 0737-7665
N8837
U.S. NATIONAL ENDOWMENT FOR THE ARTS. APPLICATION GUIDELINES: MUSEUMS. Key Title: Museums - National Endowment for the Arts. a. free. U.S. National Endowment for the Arts, Public Information Office, 1100 Pennsylvania Ave., N.W., Washington, DC 20506. TEL 202-682-5400. **Document type:** government publication.
  Formerly: N E A Grantmaking Programs: Museums.
  Description: Offers grant application guidelines.

069.9   BL
UNIVERSIDADE DE SAO PAULO. MUSEU PAULISTA. COLECAO. SERIE DE MOBILIARIO. irreg. Universidade de Sao Paulo, Museu Paulista, Caixa Posta 42503, Parque da Independencia, 04263 Sao Paulo, Brazil. Ed. Setembrino Petri.
  Supersedes in part (in 1975): Museu Paulista. Colecao (ISSN 0080-6382)

069   US   ISSN 0093-7436
AM101.F3
UNIVERSITY OF ALASKA MUSEUM. ANNUAL REPORT. a. University of Alaska Museum, 907 Yukon Dr., Fairbanks, AK 99775-1200. TEL 907-474-7505. FAX 907-474-5469. circ. controlled.

069 700   US
UNIVERSITY OF CALIFORNIA AT LOS ANGELES. FOWLER MUSEUM OF CULTURAL HISTORY. MONOGRAPH SERIES. irreg., no.28. price varies. University of California at Los Angeles, Fowler Museum of Cultural History, Los Angeles, CA 90024. TEL 213-825-4361. FAX 213-206-7007. (back issues avail.) **Document type:** monographic series.

069 700   US
UNIVERSITY OF CALIFORNIA AT LOS ANGELES. FOWLER MUSEUM OF CULTURAL HISTORY. OCCASIONAL PAPERS. 1969. irreg., no.5, 1985. price varies. University of California at Los Angeles, Fowler Museum of Cultural History, Los Angeles, CA 90024. TEL 213-825-4361. FAX 213-206-7007. (back issues avail.) **Document type:** monographic series.
  Formerly: University of California at Los Angeles. Museum of Cultural History. Occasional Papers (ISSN 0068-628X)

069 700   US
UNIVERSITY OF KENTUCKY ART MUSEUM NEWSLETTER. 1986. s-a. free. University of Kentucky Art Museum, Rose and Euclid Sts., Lexington, KY 40506-0241. TEL 606-257-5716. FAX 606-258-1994. Ed. Harriet Fowler. circ. 3,000. (tabloid format) **Document type:** newsletter.
  Description: Provides information on acquisitions, exhibitions and programs of the museum.

708   US   ISSN 0270-1642
UNIVERSITY OF MICHIGAN. MUSEUMS OF ART AND ARCHAEOLOGY. BULLETIN. 1978. a. $10 per no. Kelsey Museum of Archaeology, University of Michigan Museum of Art, Department of the History of Art, 434 S. State St., Ann Arbor, MI 48109-1390. TEL 313-747-3307. FAX 313-763-8976. Ed. Margaret A. Lourie. circ. 500. (reprint service avail. from UMI) Indexed: Avery Ind.Archit.Per., RILA. **Document type:** bulletin.
  Supersedes (N.S. 1965-1977): University of Michigan. Museum of Art. Bulletin (ISSN 0076-8391)
  Refereed Serial

708   US   ISSN 0077-8583
N512.A5
UNIVERSITY OF NEW MEXICO ART MUSEUM. BULLETIN. 1965. irreg., latest no.14, 1981-83. $7. University of New Mexico, Art Museum, FAC 1017, Albuquerque, NM 87131. TEL 505-277-4001. Ed. Peter Walch. circ. 1,000. Indexed: Artbibl.Mod., RILA. **Document type:** bulletin.
  Description: Provides information and illustrations on recent acquisitions.

708   US
N716.V45
V M F A CALENDAR. 1940. bi-m. $5 to non-members. Virginia Museum of Fine Arts, Publications Dept., 2800 Grove Ave., Richmond, VA 23221-2466. TEL 804-367-0534. Ed. Monica S. Rumsey. illus. circ. 17,500. **Document type:** newsletter.
  Former titles: Virginia Museum of Fine Arts Bulletin (ISSN 0363-3519); Virginia Museum Bulletin (ISSN 0042-6687)
  Description: Newsletter and calendar of art exhibitions and related events held at the Virginia Museum and at affiliated arts organizations throughout Virginia.

069   US
VALENTINE MUSEUM NEWS. 1898. q. $40 membership. The Valentine, 1015 E. Clay St., Richmond, VA 23219. TEL 804-649-0711. FAX 804-643-3510. Ed. Margaret Tinsley. circ. 3,000. (back issues avail.) **Document type:** newsletter.
  Formerly (until 1985): Visitor.

708   CN   ISSN 0083-5161
VANCOUVER ART GALLERY. ANNUAL REPORT. 1932. a. free. Vancouver Art Gallery, 750 Hornby St., Vancouver, BC V6Z 2H7, Canada. TEL 604-682-4668. FAX 604-682-1086. circ. 9,000. **Document type:** corporate report.

069   CN   ISSN 1192-1838
VANCOUVER ART GALLERY. COLLECTIONS. 1992. irreg. donation. Vancouver Art Gallery, 750 Hornby St., Vancouver, BC V6Z 2H7, Canada. TEL 604-682-4668. FAX 604-682-1086. **Document type:** monographic series.
  Description: Highlights artists and works of art in the Gallery Collection.

069   CN   ISSN 0838-3626
VANCOUVER ART GALLERY. MEMBER'S CALENDAR. 5/yr. membership. Vancouver Art Gallery, 750 Hornby St., Vancouver, BC V6Z 2H7, Canada. TEL 604-682-4668. FAX 604-682-1086. **Document type:** bulletin.
  Description: Provides a schedule of events and exhibitions at the Gallery.

069   SW   ISSN 0083-5536
AM101
VARBERGS MUSEUM. AARSBOK. 1950. a. SEK 60 (effective 1990). Stiftelsen Hallands Laensmuseer. Halmstad och Varberg, 432 44 Varberg, Sweden. FAX 0340-14722. Dir. Thomas Thieme. **Document type:** proceedings.

954.9 069   BG
VARENDRA RESEARCH MUSEUM. JOURNAL. (Text in English) 1972. a. Tk.15($3) Varendra Research Museum, University of Rajshahi, Rajshahi, Bangladesh.

VENDSYSSEL NU OG DA. see *HISTORY — History Of Europe*

VENTURA COUNTY HISTORICAL SOCIETY QUARTERLY. see *HISTORY — History Of North And South America*

MUSEUMS AND ART GALLERIES

069   CI   ISSN 0042-6083
VIJESTI MUZEALACA I KONZERVATORA HRVATSKE. (Text in Croatian, summaries in German; index in English, French) 1960. bi-m. $12. Muzejsko Drustvo Hrvatske, Mesnicka 5, 41000 Zagreb, Croatia. (Co-sponsor: Drustvo Konzervatora Hrvatske) Ed. Zdenko Kuzmic. bk.rev.; bibl.; illus.
    Supersedes: Drusto Muzejsko-Konzervatorskih Radnika N.R. Hrvatske. Vijesti.

VISITOR BEHAVIOR. see *PSYCHOLOGY*

708   CN   ISSN 0712-9238
VISTA (REGINA). 1973. 4/yr. free. Norman Mackenzie Art Gallery, 3475 Albert St., Regina, Sask. S4S 6X6, Canada. TEL 306-522-4242. FAX 306-569-8191. Eds. Kathryn Weisshaar, Bonnie Schaffer. adv. contact: Bonnie Schaffer. bk.rev.; illus. circ. 4,500. **Document type:** newsletter.
    Former titles: Mackenzie M A G; N - M A G; N M A G Review (ISSN 0384-1022); Norman Mackenzie Art Gallery. Newsletter (ISSN 0384-1014)
    Description: Information on exhibitions, permanent collection, events, education classes and volunteer news.

VISUAL RESOURCES; an international journal of documentation. see *ART*

069   NE   ISSN 0922-226X
VITRINE; museummagazine. 1988. 8/yr. fl.82.50 includes Tentoonstellingsboekje. S D U Uitgeverij Koninginnegracht, Postbus 30466, 2500 GK The Hague, Netherlands. TEL 31-70-3429700. FAX 31-70-3634903. adv.; illus. circ. 1,900. **Document type:** consumer publication.
—SWETS.

600   NO   ISSN 0048-2277
T183
VOLUND. Represents: Norsk Teknisk Museum. Yearbook. (Text in Norwegian; summaries in English) 1953. a. NOK 80. Norsk Teknisk Museum - Norwegian Museum of Science and Technology, Kjelsaasveien 143, N-0491 Oslo 4, Norway. TEL 47-22-22-25-50. FAX 47-22-22-29-50. Ed. Gunnar Nerheim. adv.; bk.rev.; illus. circ. 2,500.

090   XO
VYROCNE SPRAVY O CINNOSTI SLOVENSKYCH MUZEI. 1966. a. free. Slovenske Narodne Muzeum, Muzeologicke Informacne Centrum, Vajanskeho Nabrezie 2, 814 36 Bratislava, Slovakia. TEL 07-335-471. Ed. Ilja Okali.
    Former titles: Vyrocne Spravy o Cinnosti Slovenskych Muzei a Galerii; Ustredna Sparava Muzei a Galerii. Vyrocne Spravy o Cinnosti Slovenskych Muzei; Slovenske Narodne Muzeum. Muzeologicky Kabinet. Vyrocne Spravy o Cinnosti Slovenskych Muzei.

508.074   JA
WAKAYAMA KENRITSU SHIZEN HAKUBUTSUKAN KANPO/WAKAYAMA PREFECTURAL MUSEUM OF NATURAL HISTORY. ANNUAL REPORT. (Text in Japanese) 1983. a. Wakayama Kenritsu Shizen Hakubutsukan - Wakayama Prefectural Museum of Natural History, 370-1 Funao, Kainan-shi, Wakayama-ken 642, Japan.

WALTERS ART GALLERY BULLETIN. see *ART*

069 708   US   ISSN 1042-3311
NK9712
WARD FOUNDATION NEWS. q. Ward Foundation, Inc., 909 S. Schumaker Dr., Salisbury, MD 21802. TEL 410-742-4988. Ed. Sheri Olsen Kelly. adv. contact: Sheri Olsen Kelly. circ. 8,000. **Document type:** newsletter.

069   CN
WELLAND HISTORICAL MUSEUM NEWSLETTER. 1988. q. Can.$12 membership. Welland Historical Museum, 65 Hooker St., Welland, ON L3C 5G9, Canada. TEL 416-732-2215. Ed. Bill Sanderson. circ. 450. (looseleaf format) **Document type:** newsletter.

069   US
WELLESLEY COLLEGE FRIENDS OF ART NEWSLETTER. 1965. a. membership. Davies Museum and Cultural Center, Wellesley College, Wellesley, MA 02181. TEL 617-283-2081. FAX 617-235-2064. E-mail: IN%NBunn@wellesley.edu. Ed. Nancy Gunn. circ. 5,000. **Document type:** newsletter.
    Description: Provides current information on acquisitions, benefits, exhibitions, publications, educational programs, and editorial viewpoints.

069 913   CC   ISSN 1000-7954
WEN BO/JOURNAL OF MUSEUMS & ARCHAEOLOGY. Variant English title: Relics and Museology. (Text in Chinese) 1984. bi-m. $3. Shaanxi Sheng Wenwu Shiye Guanli-ju - Shaanxi Provincial Administration of Archaeological Data, Beilin Bowuguan, Sanxue Jie, Xi'an, Shaanxi 710001, People's Republic of China. TEL 7240894. (Dist. in US by: China Books & Periodicals, Inc., 2929 24th St., San Francisco, CA 94110. TEL 415-282-2994) Ed. Chen Quanfang. adv. contact: Wuang Chunhui. bk.rev.; circ. 3,000. circ. 4,000 (paid). **Document type:** academic/scholarly publication.
    Description: Covers research achievements and academic discussions on archaeology and museology.

WEST COAST PEDDLER; oldest journal of antiques, art & collectibles in the Pacific states. see *ANTIQUES*

069   AT
WESTERN AUSTRALIAN MUSEUM. ANNUAL REPORT. 1960. a. Western Australian Museum, Perth, W.A., Australia. FAX 328-8686. circ. 1,000. **Indexed:** Apic.Abstr., GeoRef. **Document type:** government publication.
    Formerly: Western Australia Museum, Perth. Report of the Museum Board (ISSN 0083-8721)

069 708   AT   ISSN 0312-3162
QH1   CODEN: REMUDY
WESTERN AUSTRALIAN MUSEUM. RECORDS. 1974. irreg. Aus.$10. Western Australian Museum, Francis St., Perth, W.A. 6000, Australia. Ed.Bd. circ. 263. **Indexed:** Aus.Sci.Ind., Biol.Abstr. So.Pac.Per.Ind.
—BLDSC (7325.306000).
    Formerly: Western Australia. Public Library, Museum and Art Gallery. Record.

069   AT   ISSN 0313-122X
WESTERN AUSTRALIAN MUSEUM. RECORDS. SUPPLEMENT. 1975. irreg. price varies. Western Australian Museum, Francis St., Perth, W.A. 6000, Australia. FAX 09-328-8686. **Indexed:** Aus.Sci.Ind, Biol.Abstr. **Document type:** government publication.
—BLDSC (7325.308000).

069.9   US
WHISPERS NEAR THE INGLENOOK. 1978. q. $15. 1890 House Museum and Center for Victorian Arts, 37 Tompkins St., Cortland, NY 13045. Dir. John H. Nozynski. circ. 1,300.

WHO'S WHO IN AMERICAN ART. see *BIOGRAPHY*

708 069   US
WILDFOWL ART JOURNAL. q. $35. Ward Foundation, Inc., 909 S. Schumaker Dr., Salisbury, MD 21801. TEL 410-742-4988. Ed. Sheri Olsen Kelly. adv. contact: Sheri Olsen Kelly. circ. 8,000. (back issues avail.) **Document type:** academic/scholarly publication.
    Description: Covers wildfowl art, with emphasis on carving.

069   US
WILLIAM HAMMOND MATHERS MUSEUM. OCCASIONAL PAPERS AND MONOGRAPHS. 1974. irreg. Indiana University, William Hammond Mathers Museum, 601 E. Eighth St., Bloomington, IN 47405. TEL 812-855-6873. FAX 812-855-0205. **Document type:** monographic series.
    Formerly: Indiana University Museum. Occasional Papers and Monographs.

708 709   US   ISSN 0084-0416
N9
WINTERTHUR PORTFOLIO: A JOURNAL OF AMERICAN MATERIAL CULTURE. 1964. 3/yr. $33 to individuals; institutions $76. (Henry Francis Du Pont Winterthur Museum) University of Chicago Press, Journals Division, 5720 S. Woodlawn Ave., Chicago, IL 60637. TEL 312-702-7600. TELEX 25-4603. (Subscr. to: Box 37005, Chicago, IL 60637) Ed. Catherine E. Hutchins. adv. contact: Renee Payne. bk.rev.; charts; illus.; index; circ. 1,800 (paid). (back issues avail.; reprint service avail. from UMI,ISI) **Indexed:** Amer.Hist.& Life, Archit.Per.Ind., Art Ind., Artbibl.Mod., Artbibl., Arts & Hum.Cit.Ind., Avery Ind.Archit.Per., Br.Tech.Ind., Curr.Cont., Hist.Abstr., Ind.Bk.Rev.Hum., M.L.A., RILA. **Document type:** academic/scholarly publication.
—BLDSC (9319.800000); Faxon; Genuine Article; UMI; UnCover. **CCC.**
    Incorporates: Winterthur Conference Report (ISSN 0084-0408)
    Description: Contains articles on the arts in America and the historical context in which they developed. Emphasizes analytical studies that integrates artifacts into their cultural framework.
Refereed Serial

069.9   US
WOODROW WILSON BIRTHPLACE NEWSLETTER. 1973. q. membership. Woodrow Wilson Birthplace Foundation, Inc., Box 24, Staunton, VA 24401. TEL 703-885-0897. FAX 703-886-9874. Ed. Susan E. Klaffky. bk.rev. circ. 1,000. (tabloid format; back issues avail.) **Document type:** newsletter.
    Description: Provides coverage of Presidential museum activities, including exhibits, seminars, lectures, collections, and school programs.

708   US   ISSN 0084-3539
N10
YALE UNIVERSITY ART GALLERY BULLETIN. Key Title: Bulletin - Yale University Art Gallery. 1926. a. $7 per no. Yale University Art Gallery, Box 208271, New Haven, CT 06520-8271. TEL 203-432-0660. FAX 203-432-7159. Ed. Leslie Baier. circ. 2,100. (also avail. in microform from UMI; reprint service avail. from UMI) **Indexed:** Artbibl.Mod., Artbibl., Avery Ind.Archit.Per., RILA. **Document type:** bulletin.
—Faxon; UMI; UnCover.
    Formerly: Yale Art Gallery Bulletin (ISSN 0360-3180)
    Description: Articles and notes relating to works in the Gallery's collection. Includes annual director's report and a complete acquisitions list for the previous year.

069 500   JA
YAMA TO HAKUBUTSUKAN/MOUNTAIN AND MUSEUM. (Text in Japanese) 1956. m. 1230 Yen. Omachi-shiritsu Omachi Sangaku Hakubutsukan - Omachi Alpine Museum, 8056-1, Kamisakae-cho, Omachi-shi, Nagano-ken 398, Japan. FAX 0261-22-0211. circ. 1,000.
    Description: Contains reviews and news of the museum.

YAMAGUCHI KENRITSU YAMAGUCHI HAKUBUTSUKAN KENKYU HOKOKU/YAMAGUCHI MUSEUM. BULLETIN. see *SCIENCES: COMPREHENSIVE WORKS*

YOKOSUKA-SHI HAKUBUTSUKAN KENKYU HOKOKU. SHIZEN KAGAKU/YOKOSUKA CITY MUSEUM. SCIENCE REPORT. see *SCIENCES: COMPREHENSIVE WORKS*

YOKOSUKA-SHI HAKUBUTSUKAN SHIRYOSHU/YOKOSUKA CITY MUSEUM. MISCELLANEOUS REPORT. see *SCIENCES: COMPREHENSIVE WORKS*

069 500   JA   ISSN 0385-8472
QH188
YOKOSUKA-SHI HAKUBUTSUKANPO/YOKOSUKA CITY MUSEUM. ANNUAL REPORT. (Text in Japanese) a. Yokosuka-shi Shizen Hakubutsukan - Yokosuka City Museum, 95, Fukadadai, Yokosuka-shi, Kanagawa-ken 238, Japan.

708   ZA   ISSN 0084-4977
ZAMBIA. NATIONAL MUSEUMS BOARD. REPORT. a. K.1. National Museums Board, Livingstone Museum, Box 498, Livingstone, Zambia. **Document type:** government publication.

069 BS
ZEBRA'S VOICE; lentswe la pitse ya naga. (Text in English; summaries in Setswana) q. free to S A D C C countries. National Museum, Monuments and Art Gallery, Independence Ave., P.B. 114, Gaborone, Botswana. TEL 374616. Ed. S.A. Hughes. circ. 5,000. (back issues avail.)

069 CC
ZHONGGUO BOWUGUAN/CHINESE MUSEUMS. (Text in Chinese, English) q. $3 per no. Zhongguo Bowuguan Xuehui - China Museum Society, 29 Wusi Dajie, Beijing 100009, People's Republic of China. TEL 4015577. FAX 5123119. Ed. Su Donghai. circ. 4,000. **Document type:** academic/scholarly publication.

069 CC
ZIJINCHENG/FORBIDDEN CITY. (Text in Chinese) bi-m. Gugong Bowuyuan - Palace Museum, Beijing 100009, People's Republic of China. TEL 5132255.

ZOO - NACHRICHTEN; Allwetterzoo - Nachrichten. see BIOLOGY — Zoology

MUSEUMS AND ART GALLERIES — Abstracting, Bibliographies, Statistics

069.094891 DK ISSN 0105-6433
BYHORNET; nyt fra Ballerup Egnsmuseet i Pederstrup. 1972. a. DKK 20. Ballerup Historical Society - Co-sponsor: Ballerup Egnsmuseum, Egnsmuseet Lindbjerggaard, Pederstrupvej 51-53, Pederstrup, DK-2750 Ballerup, Denmark. TEL 45-44-97-11-13. FAX 45-44-77-27-18. Ed. Jorgen O. Bjerregaard. circ. 500. **Document type:** academic/scholarly publication.

060
CATALOG OF MUSEUM PUBLICATIONS AND MEDIA; a directory and index of publications and audiovisuals available from U.S. and Canadian institutions. 1972. irreg., latest ed. 1979. $275. Gale Research Inc., 835 Penobscot Bldg., Detroit, MI 48226. TEL 313-961-2242. FAX 313-961-6083. TELEX 810-221-7086. Eds. Paul Wasserman, Esther Herman. index. **Document type:** directory.
Former titles: Museum Catalog of Publications and Media; Museum Media.
Description: Compendium of books, periodicals, audio and audiovisual material available from American and Canadian museums.

069.5 011 II
CONCISE DESCRIPTIVE CATALOGUE OF ARABIC MANUSCRIPTS IN THE SALAR JUNG MUSEUM AND LIBRARY. (Text in English) 1957. irreg., lastest vol.6, 1989. Rs.50. Salar Jung Museum, Hyderabad 500 002, Andhra Pradesh, India. TEL 523211. Ed. Mohamed Ashraf.
Formerly: Catalogue of Arabic Manuscripts in Salar Jung Museum.

069.5 011 II
CONCISE DESCRIPTIVE CATALOGUE OF THE PERSIAN MANUSCRIPTS IN THE SALAR JUNG MUSEUM AND LIBRARY. (Text in English) 1965. irreg., latest vol.9, 1988. Rs.72 price varies. Salar Jung Museum, Hyderabad 500 002, Andhra Pradesh, India. Ed. Mohmed Ashraf. illus.
Formerly: Catalogue of Persian Manuscripts in Salar Jung Museum.

HERITAGE RECORD SERIES. see BIBLIOGRAPHIES

069 700 US
LIBRARY CATALOG OF THE METROPOLITAN MUSEUM OF ART. 1980. irreg. $750. G.K. Hall & Co., c/o MacMillan Publishing USA, 866 Third Ave., 18th Fl., New York, NY 10022. TEL 212-702-6789. (Subscr. to: Simon & Schuster, Library Reference Order Processing, 200 Old Tappan Rd., Old Tappan, NJ 07675. TEL 800-223-2336) **Document type:** catalog.
Description: Lists materials cataloged by the Metropolitan Museum of Art Library. Lists bound books, exhibition catalogs, dealer's catalogs, serial publications, magazines, and catalogs of important public and private collections.

069 UK ISSN 0267-8594
MUSEUM ABSTRACTS. 1985. 12/yr. £50 (foreign £100). Scottish Museums Council, 20-22 Torphichen St., Edinburgh EH3 8JB, Scotland. TEL 031-229-7465. FAX 031-229-2728. **Document type:** abstracting/indexing.
—CCC.
Incorporates: Museum Abstracts International (ISSN 0960-0183)
Description: Covers museums and museum management, heritage interpretation, exhibit design and display, tourism, conservation, and the arts.

708 010 AU
OESTERREICHISCHES MUSEUM FUER VOLKSKUNDE. KATALOGE. 1946. irreg., no.61, 1993. price varies. Verlag Ferdinand Berger und Soehne GmbH, Wiener Str. 21-23, A-3580 Horn, Austria. TEL 02982-4161232. FAX 02982-2317235. **Document type:** catalog.

MUSIC

see also Dance; Sound Recording and Reproduction

780.23 US ISSN 0002-0990
A G M A ZINE. 1936. 5/yr. free. American Guild of Musical Artists, 1727 Broadway, New York, NY 10019-5284. Ed. Dianne James. bk.rev.; illus.; circ. 6,000 (controlled). **Document type:** newsletter.
Description: For artists, stage directors, and stage management in the fields of opera, dance and concert.

A H A! HISPANIC ARTS NEWS. (Association of Hispanic Arts) see ART

A I C F NEWSLETTER. (America-Israel Cultural Foundation) see ART

780 US
A L S JOURNAL. 1977. 2/yr. $25 to institutions. American Liszt Society, Inc., 210 Dovenshire Dr., Rochester, NY 14625. Ed. Mark Wait. adv.; bk.rev.; abstr.; bibl. circ. 550. (also avail. in microform from UMI; reprint service avail. from UMI,ISI) **Indexed:** Amer.Bibl.Slavic & E.Eur.Stud., Music Artic.Guide, Music Ind., RILM. **Document type:** academic/scholarly publication.
—UMI; UnCover.
Formerly: American Liszt Society. Journal (ISSN 0147-4413)

789 US ISSN 1043-5379
ML1050
THE A M I C A NEWS BULLETIN. 1963. bi-m. membership. Automatic Musical Instrument Collectors' Association, c/o John Fisher, 73 Navada, Rochester, MI 48309. adv.; bk.rev.; index. circ. 950. (processed) **Document type:** newsletter.
Former titles: Automatic Musical Instrument Collectors' Association. News Bulletin (ISSN 0884-0644); (until 1973): A M I C A Bulletin (ISSN 0884-0652); (until 1972): Automatic Musical Instrument Collectors' Association. News Bulletin (ISSN 0884-0660)
Description: Contains news and articles of interest to owners, collectors, and sellers of antique automatic musical instruments that run on perforated paper rolls.

780 US ISSN 0747-3060
A M O A LOCATION. Key Title: Location (Chicago). bi-m. membership. Amusement and Music Operators Association, 401 N. Michigan Ave., Chicago, IL 60611. TEL 312-245-1021. FAX 312-321-6869. Ed. Fred Newton. circ. 2,000 (controlled). **Document type:** newsletter.

780 US ISSN 0402-012X
A M S NEWSLETTER (PHILADELPHIA). 1971. 2/yr. free with subscr. to journal. American Musicological Society, 201 S. 34th St., Philadelphia, PA 19104-6313. TEL 215-898-8698. **Document type:** newsletter.

789.91 US ISSN 0361-2147
A P M MONOGRAPH SERIES. (Antique Phonograph Monthly) 1973. irreg. $15. A P M Press, 502 E. 17th St., Brooklyn, NY 11226. TEL 718-941-6835. Ed. Allen Koenigsberg. adv.; bk.rev. circ. 2,000. **Document type:** monographic series.
Description: Devoted to the history of the phonograph and popular music.

780 US
A R C E NEWSLETTER SAMVADI. (Text in English) 1982. q. American Institute of Indian Studies, Archives and Research Centre for Ethnomusicology, B-29 Defence Colony, New Delhi 110 024, India. TEL 91-11-4694149. FAX 91-11-698150. E-mail: rkiv@arce.ernet.in. Ed. Shubha Chaudhuri. circ. 200. **Document type:** newsletter.
Description: Aims to stimulate ethnomusicology in India and develop an archive of Indian performing and oral arts.

780 800 070.5 920 US
A S C A P BIOGRAPHICAL DICTIONARY. irreg. 4th ed. 1980. $41.95. American Society of Composers, Authors and Publishers, One Lincoln Plaza, New York, NY 10023. TEL 212-621-6222. FAX 212-721-0955. **Indexed:** Child.Auth.& Illus., Perf.Arts Biog.Master Ind.

780.23 US ISSN 0197-7849
ML27.U5
A S C A P IN ACTION. (Supplement avail.: Play Back (ISSN 1059-6925)) 1967. 4/yr. free. American Society of Composers, Authors and Publishers, One Lincoln Plaza, New York, NY 10023. TEL 212-595-3050. FAX 212-721-0955. Ed. Murdoch McBride. circ. 40,000. (also avail. in microfilm from UMI; reprint service avail. from UMI) **Indexed:** Music Artic.Guide, Music Ind.
—Faxon; UMI; UnCover.
Former titles (until 1979): A S C A P Today (ISSN 0001-2424); A S C A P News (ISSN 1043-3791)

780.23 US ISSN 0145-5265
A S C A P SYMPHONIC CATALOG. irreg. American Society of Composers, Authors and Publishers, One Lincoln Plaza, New York, NY 10023. TEL 212-595-3050. FAX 212-721-0955. **Document type:** catalog.

786.97 US ISSN 0001-2734
A T G BULLETIN.* Variant title: Accordion Teachers' Guild Newsletter. 1946. q. membership. Accordion Teachers' Guild, International, P.O. Box 22342, Kansas City, MO 64113. Ed. Lisa Cleveland. bk.rev. circ. 200. (processed; back issues avail.) **Document type:** bulletin.

ABHANDLUNGEN ZUR KUNST-, MUSIK- UND LITERATURWISSENSCHAFT. see ART

780 IT
ACCADEMIA DEI CONCORDI ROVIGO. COLLANA DI MUSICHE. no.12, 1977. irreg. price varies. Giardini Editori e Stampatori, Via Santa Bibbiana 28, 56100 Pisa, Italy. TEL 050 502531.

780 IT
ACCADEMIA NAZIONALE DI SANTA CECILIA. ANNUARIO. 1972? a. L.50000. (Accademia Nazionale di Santa Cecilia) Libreria Musicale Italiana Editrice, Via di Arsina 196F, Casella Postale 198, 55100 Lucca, Italy. TEL 39-583-394464. FAX 39-583-394469. Ed. Laura Ciancio.

787 US ISSN 1049-9261
ML1015.G9
ACOUSTIC GUITAR. 1990. m. $36 (Canada $51; elsewhere $66) (effective July 1995). String Letter Press, Inc., Box 767, San Anselmo, CA 94979-0767. TEL 415-485-6946. FAX 415-485-0831. E-mail: acguitar@aol.com. Ed. Jeffrey Pepper Rodgers; David A./Kusternab. adv. contact: Susan Malone. bk.rev.; rec.rev. circ. 50,000. **Document type:** consumer publication.
Description: Written by and for musicians to cover a variety of musical styles, including transcriptions from recordings and solo pieces for guitars.

780 920 GW ISSN 0001-6233
ACTA MOZARTIANA. 1954. 3/yr. DM.60 membership. Deutsche Mozart-Gesellschaft e.V., Karlstr. 6, 86150 Augsburg, Germany. TEL 0821-518588. FAX 0821-157228. Ed. Ulrich Konrad. adv. contact: Friedhelm Brosniak. bk.rev.; charts; illus. circ. 2,900. **Indexed:** Arts & Hum.Cit.Ind., Curr.Cont., Music Ind., RILM. **Document type:** bulletin.
Formerly (until 1992): Deutsches Mozartfest.

MUSIC

780.01 GW ISSN 0001-6241
ML5
ACTA MUSICOLOGICA. (Text in English, French, German) 1928. 2/yr. DM.135 membership. (International Musicological Society, SZ) Baerenreiter Verlag, Heinrich-Schuetz-Allee 35, 34131 Kassel, Germany. TEL 0561-3105-0. FAX 0561-3105240. (Subscr. in US to: Educational Music Service, 13 Elkay Dr., Chester, NY 10918. TEL 914-469-5790. FAX 914-469-5817) Ed. Helmut Federhofer. adv.; bibl.; illus.; index, cum.index: vols.1-25 (1928-1953). **Indexed:** Curr.Cont., Music Ind., RILM. **Document type:** academic/scholarly publication.
—Faxon; Genuine Article; SWETS; UnCover. **CCC.**

786.5 GW ISSN 0567-7874
ML5
ACTA ORGANOLOGICA. 1967. a. (Gesellschaft der Orgelfreunde e.V.) Verlag Merseburger Berlin GmbH, Postfach 103880, 34038 Kassel, Germany. illus. **Indexed:** RILM. **Document type:** academic/scholarly publication.

780 GW ISSN 0001-6942
ACTA SAGITTARIANA. (Text in English, French and German) 1963. a. DM.40 to individuals; institutions DM.50; students DM.20. Internationale Heinrich Schuetz-Gesellschaft e.V., Heinrich-Schuetz-Allee 35, 34131 Kassel, Germany. TEL 0561-3105-0. FAX 0561-3105-240. TELEX 992376-BAERRD. Ed. Sieglinde Froehlich. adv.; bk.rev.; illus. circ. 1,500. **Indexed:** Music Ind. **Document type:** newsletter.

781.7 GW ISSN 0001-7965
AD MARGINEM; Randbemerkungen zur musikalischen Volkskunde. 1964. 2/yr. free. Universitaet zu Koeln, Institut fuer Musikalische Volkskunde, Gronewaldstr. 2, 50931 Cologne, Germany. TEL 0221-470-5269. Eds. Wilhelm Schepping, Gisela Probst-Effah. bk.rev.; abstr.; circ. controlled. (looseleaf format; back issues avail.) **Indexed:** RILM. **Document type:** academic/scholarly publication.

ADAM INTERNATIONAL REVIEW. see *LITERATURE*

780 BE ISSN 0001-8171
ADEM; driemaandelijks tijdschrift voor muziekkultuur. 1965. q. 950 BEF. Madrigaal V.Z.W., Herestraat 53, B-3000 Leuven, Belgium. FAX 32-16-22-2477. Ed. P. Schollaert. adv.; bk.rev. circ. 1,800. (reprint service avail. from UMI) **Indexed:** Music Ind., RILM.
—BLDSC (0680.420000); SWETS.

780 681 374 US
ADVANCE BAND MAGAZINE; the international voice of adult bands. 1977. q. membership. Association of Concert Bands, 2533 S. Maple Ave., Ste. 102, Tempe, AZ 85282-3559. TEL 602-894-6687. Dir. Toni Ryon. adv.; bk.rev.; bibl.; illus. circ. 2,000. (back issues avail.) **Document type:** newsletter.
Former titles (until 1991): A B C Newsmagazine; (until 1987): A B C Newsletter.
Description: For band directors and band music enthusiasts and music educators. Focuses on community concert and band advancement in America and abroad.

780 US ISSN 1062-404X
AESTHETICS IN MUSIC SERIES. 1983. irreg., vol.5, 1994. Pendragon Press, 41 Ferry Rd., Stuyvesant, NY 12173-9720. TEL 518-828-3008. FAX 518-828-2368. **Document type:** monographic series.
—BLDSC (0730.421000).

780 SA ISSN 0065-4019
ML5
AFRICAN MUSIC. (Text in English, French) 1948. irreg. (approx. a.), vol.7, no.2, 1993. R.22($22) International Library of African Music, Institute of Social and Economic Research, Rhodes University, Grahamstown 6140, South Africa. TEL 27-461-318557. FAX 27-461-24411. Ed. Andrew Tracey. adv.; bk.rev.; index. circ. 500. (reprint service avail. from SWZ) **Indexed:** A.I.C.P., Anthropol.Lit., Curr.Cont.Africa, Curr.Cont., Ind.S.A.Per., Music Ind., RILM. **Document type:** academic/scholarly publication.
—BLDSC (0732.900000); UnCover.
Supersedes (in 1954): African Music Society. Newsletter.

781.7 KE
AFRICAN MUSICOLOGY. 1983. a. $5. (University of Nairobi, Institute of African Studies) Eleza Services Ltd., P.O. Box 14925, Nairobi, Kenya. Eds. A. Darkwa, W.A. Omondi. **Indexed:** M.L.A.

AGENDA CLAVE; guia practica de la industria musical y del espectaculo. see *BUSINESS AND ECONOMICS — Trade And Industrial Directories*

781.7 IR
AHANG. (Text in Farsi) 1988. q. Rs.960 per no. Center of Music and Revolutionary Songs, Vahdat Hall, Arfa St., Hafiz Ave., Teheran, Iran.
Description: Covers Iranian music.

780 PL ISSN 0239-7080
AKADEMIA MUZYCZNA. PRACE SPECJALNE. 1984. irreg. exchange basis. Akademia Muzyczna, Ul. Zacisze 3, 40-025 Katowice, Poland. TEL 48 32 155-4017. (Dist. by: Ars Polona Ruch, Krakowskie Przedmiescie 7, 00-068 Warsaw, Poland)
Formerly: Panstwowa Wyzsza Szkola Muzyczna. Prace Specjalne.

780 PL
AKADEMIA MUZYCZNA. SKRYPTY. 1984. irreg. exchange basis. Akademia Muzyczna, Ul. Zacisze 3, 40-025 Katowice, Poland. TEL 48 32 155-4017. (Dist. by: Ars Polona Ruch, Krakowskie Przemiescie 7, 00-068 Warsaw, Poland)
Formerly: Panstwowa Wyzsza Szkola Muzyczna. Skrypty.

780 PL
AKADEMIA MUZYCZNA. SPRAWOZDANIA. a. exchange basis. Akademia Muzyczna, Ul. Zacisze 3, 40-025 Katowice, Poland. TEL 48 32 155-4017. (Dist. by: Ars Polona-Ruch, Krakowskie Przedmiescie 7, 00-068 Warsaw, Poland)
Formerly: Panstwowa Wyzsza Szkola Muzyczna. Sprawozdania.

780 PL
AKADEMIA MUZYCZNA. WYDAWNICTWA OKOLICZNOSCIOWE. irreg. exchange basis. Akademia Muzyczna, Ul. Zacisze 3, 40-025 Katowice, Poland. TEL 48 32 155-4017. (Dist. by: Ars Polona Ruch, Krakowskie Przedmiescie 7, 00-068 Warsaw, Poland)
Formerly: Panstwowa Wyzsza Szkola Muzyczna. Wydawnictwa Okolicznosciowe.

780 AJ
AKADEMIYA NAUK AZERBAIJANA. MUZEI ISTORII. TRUDY. (Text in Azerbaijani and Russian) vol.9, 1973. irreg. 1.50 Rub. per no. Izdatel'stvo Elm, Ul. Narimanova, 31, Baku 370073, Azerbaijan. Ed. P. Azizbekova. illus. circ. 500.
Formerly: Akademiya Nauk Azerbaidzhankoi S.S.R. Muzei Istorii. Trudy.

780 NE ISSN 0929-3787
AKKOORD. 1951. 5/yr. fl.27.50. Stichting L O A M, Keizerstraat 3, 3512 EA Utrecht, Netherlands. TEL 31-30-302301. FAX 31-30-300280. adv.; B&W page fl.1400, color page fl.3400. bk.rev.; illus. circ. 16,000. **Document type:** consumer publication.
Formerly (until 1993): Huismuziek (ISSN 0018-7097)
Description: Covers music history, building of musical instruments, music interpretation, music making, musicians, association news, and reports of music events. Includes list of courses and activities, classified adds.

780 301 US
ALARM CLOCK; women in alternative music and female vocalists. 1990. 4/yr. $6 for 3 issues. Box 1551, Royal Oak, MI 48068. TEL 313-542-1797. Ed. Allen Salyer. bk.rev.; rec.rev. circ. 200.

780 CN ISSN 0838-7796
ALL ACCESS PASS. 1987. m. 3 Manorcrest Street, Bramlea, Ont. L6S 2W6, Canada. TEL 416-791-5574. (tabloid format)

ALLEGRO. see *LABOR UNIONS*

783 282 GW
ALLGEMEINER CAECILIEN-VERBAND. SCHRIFTENREIHE. irreg., latest no.15. price varies. Allgemeiner Caecilien-Verband, Andreasstr. 9, 93059 Regensburg, Germany. TEL 0941-84339. **Document type:** monographic series.

780 621.389 778 US
ALLIGATOR. 1983. m. $24. See You Later, Alligator, Box 50842, New Orleans, LA 70150-0842. TEL 504-469-8887. Ed. Barbara Coppersmith; Pub. Roy Lambert. adv. contact: Judy Boyett. bk.rev.; film rev. circ. 25,000. (tabloid format; back issues avail.) **Document type:** newspaper.

ALTA FEDELTA. see *SOUND RECORDING AND REPRODUCTION*

780 GW ISSN 0942-9034
ALTE MUSIK AKTUELL; aktuelle Information fuer alte Musik. 1985. m. (11/yr.). DM.42. Pro Musica Antiqua, Postfach 100830, 93008 Regensburg, Germany. TEL 0941-52687. FAX 0941-53094. Ed. Stephan Schmid. index. circ. 1,500. (back issues avail.) **Document type:** bulletin.

ALTERNATE ROOTS NEWSLETTER. see *THEATER*

780 IT ISSN 1120-4540
AMADEUS. 1989. m. L.15900 per no. De Agostini - Rizzoli Periodici, Via Vigliani 19, 20148 Milan, Italy. TEL 02-4816355. FAX 02-4818968. Ed. Pietro Boroli. adv.; B&W or color page L.15000000. circ. 47,460. **Document type:** consumer publication.

780 US ISSN 0065-6704
AMATEUR CHAMBER MUSIC PLAYERS. DIRECTORY. (Overseas Directory or North American Directory published in alternate years) 1969. a. contribution. Amateur Chamber Music Players, Inc., 1123 Broadway, Ste. 304, New York, NY 10010-2007. TEL 212-645-7424. Ed. Susan M. Lloyd. circ. 4,000. **Document type:** directory.

780 US
AMATEUR CHAMBER MUSIC PLAYERS. NEWSLETTER. 1947. 3/yr. membership. Amateur Chamber Music Players, Inc., 1123 Broadway, Ste. 304, New York, NY 10010-2007. TEL 212-645-7424. Eds. Susan M. Lloyd, Sally R. Bagg. circ. 4,000. **Document type:** newsletter.
Formerly: Amateur Chamber Music Players. Annual Newsletter.

780 RU
AMATEUR MUSIC ACTIVITIES. 8/yr. 17.80 Rub. Izdatel'stvo Muzyka, Ul. Neglinnaya 14, Moscow 103031, Russia. TEL 924-81-63. FAX 921-83-53.

780 CN ISSN 0227-4310
AMATEUR MUSICIAN/MUSICIEN AMATEUR. 1955. 2/yr. $25 to individuals; students $13. Canadian Amateur Musicians (CAMMAC), 1751 Richardson, Ste. 2509, Montreal, Que. H3K 1G6, Canada. TEL 514-932-8755. FAX 514-932-9811. Ed. Ralph Aldrich. adv.; bk.rev. circ. 2,000. **Document type:** newsletter.
Refereed Serial

789.5 US ISSN 0093-1330
ML27.U5
AMERICAN BELL ASSOCIATION. DIRECTORY. Key Title: Directory - American Bell Association. a. (some vols. accompanied by supplemental directory) $22 membership. American Bell Association, Route 1, Box 286, Natrona Heights, PA 15065. TEL 412-295-9623. **Document type:** directory.

780.6 US ISSN 8756-8357
ML410.B81
AMERICAN BRAHMS SOCIETY. NEWSLETTER. 1983. s-a. $25. American Brahms Society, University of Washington, School of Music DN-10, Seattle, WA 98195. TEL 206-543-0400. Ed. Virginia Hancock. bk.rev. circ. 1,500. (back issues avail.) **Indexed:** Music Artic.Guide. **Document type:** newsletter.
Description: Essays on Brahms and his music; reports on new publications and research on Brahms and his circle.

784 US ISSN 0002-788X
AMERICAN CHORAL FOUNDATION. RESEARCH MEMORANDUM SERIES. 1959. s-a. $30 (Canada $32.50; elsewhere $35) includes American Choral Review. American Choral Foundation, Inc., c/o Chorus America (APVE), 2111 Sansom St., Philadelphia, PA 19103. TEL 215-563-2430. FAX 215-563-2431. Ed. Walter Collins. bibl. circ. 6,000. (processed) **Indexed:** Music Artic.Guide. **Document type:** academic/scholarly publication.

784 US ISSN 0002-7898
AMERICAN CHORAL REVIEW. 1958. s-a. membership only. American Choral Foundation, Inc., c/o Chorus America (APVE), 2111 Sansom St., Philadelphia, PA 19103. TEL 215-563-2430. FAX 215-563-2431. Ed. Alfred Mann. adv.; bk.rev.; bibl.; charts; illus. circ. 6,000. (back issues avail.) **Indexed:** Arts & Hum.Cit.Ind., Curr.Cont., Music Artic.Guide, Music Ind., RILM. **Document type:** academic/scholarly publication.
—UnCover.

780 US
AMERICAN COMPOSERS ALLIANCE BULLETIN. 1938. irreg. American Composers Alliance, 170 W. 74th St., New York, NY 10023. TEL 212-362-8900. FAX 212-874-8605. circ. controlled. (back issues avail.; reprint service avail.) **Document type:** bulletin.
Description: Contains articles and a list of works by and about American composers.

780 US ISSN 0888-8701
AMERICAN HANDEL SOCIETY. NEWSLETTER. 1986. 3/yr. $30. American Handel Society, Inc., c/o University of Maryland, Department of Music, College Park, MD 20742. TEL 301-405-5523. bk.rev. circ. 170. **Indexed:** RILM. **Document type:** newsletter.
Description: Conducts research in the life and work of the composer.

787.5 US ISSN 0002-869X
ML1
AMERICAN HARP JOURNAL. 1967. s-a. $25 to individuals; libraries $15. American Harp Society, Inc., c/o Suzanne L. Moulton, Ed., 10889 W. 65th Way, Arvada, CO 80004. TEL 201-836-8909. (Subscr. to: c/o Charles Jensen, Business Mgr., 187 W. Palisade Ave., Englewood, NJ 07631. TEL 201-569-4674) adv.; bibl.; illus. circ. 3,700. (back issues avail.) **Indexed:** Music Artic.Guide, Music Ind. **Document type:** trade publication.
—UnCover.

780 GW ISSN 0065-8855
AMERICAN INSTITUTE OF MUSICOLOGY. MISCELLANEA. 1951. irreg. (American Institute of Musicology, US) Haenssler Verlag, Postfach 1220, 73762 Neuhausen, Germany. TEL 07158-177-114. FAX 07158-177119. Ed. Frank D'Accone. **Document type:** monographic series.

780.6 US ISSN 0749-341X
AMERICAN LISZT SOCIETY. NEWSLETTER. 1984. s-a. $25 individual membership; institutions $30; students $15 (effective 1992-93). American Liszt Society, Inc., 210 Dovenshire Dr., Rochester, NY 14625. (Subscr. to: c/o Nancy Hallsted, ALS Memb. Sec., 9212 Villa Dr., Bethesda, MD 20817) Ed. Mark R. Hansen. circ. 500. **Document type:** newsletter.
Description: Covers regional activities and worldwide society events, member activities and information on the annual festival.

787 US ISSN 1041-7176
ML755
AMERICAN LUTHERIE. 1973. q. $36 (Canada and Mexico $40; elsewhere $46) includes membership. Guild of American Luthiers, 8222 S. Park, Tacoma, WA 98408. TEL 206-472-7853. Ed. Tim Olsen. adv.; bk.rev.; illus. circ. 2,500. **Indexed:** RILM. **Document type:** academic/scholarly publication.
Former titles (until 1985): Guild of American Luthiers. Quarterly; (until vol.4): G.A.L. Newletter.
Description: Information sharing system for string instrument makers and repairers of all interests and skill levels.

780 US ISSN 0734-4392
ML1
AMERICAN MUSIC. 1983. q. $30 to individuals (foreign $37); institutions $45 (foreign $52). (Sonneck Society) University of Illinois Press, 1325 S. Oak St., Champaign, IL 61820. TEL 217-333-0950. FAX 217-244-8082. Ed. Josephine Wright. adv.; bk.rev.; rec.rev.; illus. circ. 1,650. (also avail. in microform from UMI) **Indexed:** Arts & Hum.Cit.Ind., Curr.Cont., Music Artic.Guide, Music Ind., RILM. **Document type:** academic/scholarly publication.
—BLDSC (0845.800000); Faxon; Genuine Article; UMI; UnCover. **CCC.**
Refereed Serial

780.7 US ISSN 0003-0112
ML1
AMERICAN MUSIC TEACHER. 1951. bi-m. $16 to non-members. Music Teachers National Association, Inc., Carew Tower, 441 Vine St., Ste. 505, Cincinnati, OH 45202-2814. TEL 513-421-1420. FAX 513-421-2503. Ed. Michael Oxley. adv.; bk.rev. circ. 27,000. (also avail. in microform from UMI; microfiche from MUE; back issues avail.; reprint service avail. from UMI) **Indexed:** Bk.Rev.Ind. (1980-), Child.Bk.Rev.Ind. (1980-), Educ.Ind., Music Artic.Guide, Music Ind. **Document type:** trade publication.
●Also available online. Vendor(s): University Microfilms International.
—BLDSC (0845.850000); Faxon; UMI; UnCover.
Description: Presents features articles on aesthetics, composition, criticism, interpretation, musicology and performances.

781.9 US ISSN 0362-3300
ML1
AMERICAN MUSICAL INSTRUMENT SOCIETY. JOURNAL. Key Title: Journal of the American Musical Instrument Society. 1975. a. $35 includes membership. American Musical Instrument Society, c/o Albert R. Rice, 6114 Corbin Ave., Tarzana, CA 91356-1011. TEL 818-776-9446. FAX 310-471-1278. Ed. Martha Clinkscale. adv.; bk.rev.; bibl.; charts; illus. circ. 1,000. **Indexed:** Arts & Hum.Cit.Ind., Curr.Cont., Music Artic.Guide, Music Ind., RILM.
—Faxon; Genuine Article; UnCover.

781.9 US ISSN 0160-2365
ML1
AMERICAN MUSICAL INSTRUMENT SOCIETY. NEWSLETTER. 1971. 3/yr. $35 membership (foreing $40) (effective 1996). American Musical Instrument Society, c/o Albert R. Rice, 6114 Corbin Ave., Tarzara, CA 91356-1011. TEL 818-776-9446. FAX 310-471-1278. E-mail: RiceA@cgs.edu. Ed. Harrison Powley. **Indexed:** Curr.Cont., Music Ind. **Document type:** newsletter.

780 US ISSN 0003-0139
ML27.U5
AMERICAN MUSICOLOGICAL SOCIETY. JOURNAL. 1948. 3/yr. $40 (includes AMS Newsletter, AMS Directory, Doctoral Dissertations in Musicology). American Musicological Society, 201 S. 34th St., Philadelphia, PA 19104-6316. TEL 215-898-8698. Ed. Richard Kramer. adv.; bk.rev.; charts; illus.; index. circ. 4,500. **Indexed:** Arts & Hum.Cit.Ind., Curr.Cont., Hum.Ind., Ind.Bk.Rev.Hum., Music Artic.Guide, Music Ind., RILM.
—Faxon; SWETS; UnCover.

780 US
AMERICAN MUSICOLOGICAL SOCIETY. STUDIES AND DOCUMENTS. 1948. irreg., no.6, 1972. price varies. American Musicological Society, 201 S. 34th St., Philadelphia, PA 19104-6316. TEL 215-898-8698.

786.6 US ISSN 0164-3150
ML1
THE AMERICAN ORGANIST. 1967. m. $42 to non-members (foreign $52). American Guild of Organists, 475 Riverside Dr., Ste. 1260, New York, NY 10115. TEL 212-870-2310. FAX 212-870-2163. (Co-sponsor: Royal Canadian College of Organists) Ed. Anthony Baglivi. adv.; bk.rev.; bibl.; charts; illus.; stat.; tr.lit.; index, cum.index. circ. 25,000. (also avail. in microfilm from UMI) **Indexed:** Music Artic.Guide, Music Ind., RILM. **Document type:** newsletter.
—Faxon; UMI; UnCover.
Incorporates (in 1979): A G O Times (ISSN 0362-5907); **Formerly (until 1978):** Music (ISSN 0027-4208)

789.91 US ISSN 0003-0716
ML1
AMERICAN RECORD GUIDE. (Not published 1972-1975) 1935. bi-m. $29 to individuals; institutions $36. Record Guide Productions, 4412 Braddock St., Cincinnati, OH 45204. TEL 513-941-1116. FAX 513-941-1112. E-mail: usr1438a@tso.uc.edu. Ed. Donald R. Vroon. adv.; bk.rev.; rec.rev.; illus.; index; circ. 11,000 (paid). (also avail. in microform; reprint service avail. from UMI) **Indexed:** Access, Bk.Rev.Ind. (1965-1982), Child.Bk.Rev.Ind. (1965-1982), Mag.Ind., Music Artic.Guide, Music Ind., PMR, R.G. **Document type:** consumer publication.
●Also available online. Vendor(s): University Microfilms International.
—Faxon; UMI.
Formerly: American Music Lover.
Description: Publishes feature articles and reviews music in concert and 600 classical recordings per issue.

788.53 US ISSN 0003-0724
AMERICAN RECORDER. 1960. 5/yr. $25 (foreign $30). American Recorder Society, Inc., Box 631, Littleton, CO 80160-0631. TEL 303-347-1120. E-mail: 74363.3365@compuserve.com. Ed. Benjamin Dunham; Pub. Gail Littleton. adv.; bk.rev.; music rev.; rec.rev.; illus.; cum.index every 5 yrs. circ. 4,000. (also avail. in microform from UMI; back issues avail.; reprint service avail. from UMI) **Indexed:** Music Artic.Guide, Music Ind., RILM. **Document type:** bulletin.
—BLDSC (0853.530000); Faxon; UMI; UnCover.

780
AMERICAN RECORDER SOCIETY MEMBERS' LIBRARY. (Supplement to: American Recorder) 1986. irreg. membership. American Recorder Society, Inc., Box 631, Littleton, CO 80160-0631.
TEL 303-347-1120. Ed. Benjamin Dunham. circ. 4,000. (looseleaf format; back issues avail.)
Document type: bulletin.
Description: Sheet music for recorder consort.

780
AMERICAN RECORDER SOCIETY NEWSLETTER. 1980. 5/yr. membership. American Recorder Society, Inc., Box 631, Littleton, CO 80160-0631.
TEL 303-347-1120. Ed. Benjamin Dunham. circ. 4,000. (looseleaf format) **Document type:** newsletter.
Description: Calendar of recorder and early music events worldwide, and news of society's activities.

AMERICAN REVIEW. see *ART*

780 US ISSN 0896-8993
AMERICAN SONGWRITER. 1984. bi-m. $16.95. 121 17th Ave. S., Nashville, TN 37203.
FAX 615-742-1123. Ed. Vernell Hackett; Pub. Jim Sharp. adv. contact: Rick Hogan. bk.rev.; illus.; circ. 5,000 (paid). **Document type:** trade publication.

787 780.7 US ISSN 0003-1313
ML27.U5
AMERICAN STRING TEACHER.* 1950. q. $35 includes membership. American String Teachers Association, 400 S. Land Ave., Ste. 1, Pittsburgh, PA 15208-2902. FAX 214-490-4219. (Subscr. to: ASTA National Office, 4020 McEwen, Ste. 105, Dallas, TX 75244. TEL 214-233-3116) Ed. Jody Atwook. adv.; bk.rev.; music rev. circ. 7,500. **Indexed:** Music Artic.Guide., Music Ind.
—Faxon; UnCover.

780 US ISSN 0193-5372
AMERICAN SUZUKI JOURNAL. 1972. 6/yr. $35 to members. Suzuki Association of the Americas, Box 17310, Boulder, CO 80308-7310.
TEL 303-444-0948. FAX 303-444-0984. adv.; bk.rev. circ. 6,200. **Indexed:** Music Artic.Guide.
—Faxon; UnCover. **CCC.**
Description: Publication of interest to teachers, parents, and educators dedicated to the advancement of the Suzuki method of music education in the western world.

787 US ISSN 0898-5987
AMERICAN VIOLA SOCIETY. JOURNAL. 1973. irreg. (approx. s-a). $30. American Viola Society, Brigham Young University, Provo, UT 84602.
TEL 801-378-4953. FAX 801-378-5973. Ed. David Dalton. adv.: B&W page $100. bk.rev. circ. 1,000. (back issues avail.) **Indexed:** Music Artic.Guide, RILM. **Document type:** academic/scholarly publication.
Supersedes (after no.28, 1985): American Viola Society. Newsletter.

MUSIC

780 FR ISSN 0154-7283
AMIS DE L'OEUVRE ET LA PENSEE DE GEORGES MIGOT. BULLETIN D'INFORMATION. 1976. 2/yr. 120 F. (Amis de l'Oeuvre et la Pensee de Georges Migot) Institut de Musicologie, 22, rue Descartes, 67084 Strasbourg Cedex, France. Ed. Dr. Marc Honegger. circ. 200.

780 GW ISSN 0569-9827
ANALECTA MUSICOLOGICA. (Vols. 1-11 published by Boehlau-Verlag) 1963. irreg., vol.28, 1993. price varies. (Deutsches Historisches Institut in Rom, Musikgeschichtliche Abteilung, IT) Laaber-Verlag, Regensburger Str. 19, 93164 Laaber, Germany. TEL 09498-2307. FAX 09498-2543. illus. **Indexed:** RILM. **Document type:** monographic series.

780.7 IT ISSN 1121-001X
ANALISI; rivista di teoria e pedagogia musicale. 1990. 3/yr. L.40000 membership (effective 1995). G. Ricordi & C. S.p.A., Via Berchet 3, 20121 Milan, Italy. TEL 39-2-88812. FAX 39-2-88812-212. (Co-sponsor: Societa Italiana di Analisi Musicale) Ed. Marco de Natale. bk.rev. **Document type:** academic/scholarly publication.

785 US ISSN 0091-7176
ML1
THE ANCIENT TIMES. 1973. q. $15 (membership). Company of Fifers & Drummers, Inc., Box 525, Ivoryton, CT 06442. Ed. Bill Pace. adv.; bk.rev.; illus. circ. 2,000. **Document type:** newsletter.

781.57 US
AND ALL THAT JAZZ. 1973. 2/yr. New Orleans Jazz Club of California, Box 1225, Kerrville, TX 78029. TEL 210-896-2285. circ. 4,000. **Document type:** catalog.

780 US
ANDY'S FRONT HALL. (Includes: Buyer's Guide & Source Book) 1977. s-a. $2. Front Hall Enterprises, Inc., Wormer Rd., Box 307, Voorheesville, NY 12186. TEL 518-765-4193. FAX 518-765-4344. E-mail: fennig@aol.com. Ed. Kay L. Spence. bk.rev. circ. 8,000. **Document type:** catalog.
Description: Covers books, recordings and instruments of folk and traditional music.

780 SZ
ANNALES PADEREWSKI. 1979. irreg., approx. 1/yr. 10 SFr. Societe Paderewski a Morges, Centre Culturel, CH-1110 Morges, Switzerland. TEL 021-803-0711. bk.rev. circ. 1,000. **Document type:** bulletin.
Description: Publication containing reminiscences about the life of the Polish pianist. Includes society's news.

780 US ISSN 1062-4058
ANNOTATED REFERENCE TOOLS IN MUSIC SERIES. (Text in English, French and German) 1978. irreg., vol.4, 1991. Pendragon Press, 41 Ferry Rd., Stuyvesant, NY 12173-9720. TEL 518-828-3008. FAX 518-828-2368. (back issues avail.) **Document type:** monographic series.

780 US ISSN 1051-287X
ML156.2
ANNOUNCED...; this month in classical recordings. 1988. m. $28 (foreign $44). Bushnell Corporation, 880 W. Williams Rd., Bloomington, IN 47404. TEL 812-339-2258. TELEX 966420. Ed. Vinson Bushnell. adv. circ. 200. **Document type:** catalog.
Description: Provides a current source of information about new recordings of classical music in the United States.

780 793 FR ISSN 1244-2267
ANNUAIRE MUSIQUE ET DANSE. 1988. a. Association Departementale pour le Developpement des Arts, Haute-Garonne, 5 rue Jules-Chalande, 31000 Toulouse, France.
Formerly: Annuaire Musical et Choregraphique de la Haute-Garonne (ISSN 0993-2127)

384.554 FR ISSN 0066-3565
ANNUAIRE O.G.M.. (Partie 1: Radio, Television, HiFi, Electronique, Electroacoustique; Partie 2: Musique) a. 640 F. per vol. (Office General de la Musique) Editions Louis Johanet, 68 rue Boursault, 75017 Paris, France. adv.

780 UK
ANNUAL CHART SUMMARIES. 1983. a. $4. Chart Watch, 8 Worcester House, Bumpstead Rd., Haverhill, Suffolk CB9 8QB, England. circ. 70.

786 US
ANNUAL ORGAN HANDBOOK; regional survey of historical pipe organs. 1956. a. $27 (includes subscr. to: Tracker). Organ Historical Society, Inc., Box 26811, Richmond, VA 23261. TEL 804-353-9226. FAX 804-353-9266. Ed. Alan Laufman. adv.; illus. circ. 3,000. **Document type:** proceedings.
Supersedes: Organ Historical Society. National Convention (Proceedings).

785.4 US ISSN 0731-0641
ML3505.8
ANNUAL REVIEW OF JAZZ STUDIES. 1973. a. $39.50. (Institute of Jazz Studies) Transaction Periodicals Consortium, Rutgers University, New Brunswick, NJ 08903. TEL 201-932-2280. FAX 201-932-3138. Ed. Edward Berger. adv.; bk.rev.; bibl. circ. 1,000. (also avail. in microform from MIM,UMI; reprint service avail. from UMI) **Indexed:** Amer.Hist.& Life, Curr.Cont., Hist.Abstr., Music Ind., RILM. **Document type:** academic/scholarly publication.
—UMI; UnCover. **CCC.**
Formerly (until 1981): Journal of Jazz Studies; Incorporates: Studies in Jazz Discography (ISSN 0093-3686)

780 IT
ANNUARIO MUSICALE ITALIANO. 1981. biennial. L.70000. Comitato Nazionale Italiano Musica (CIDIM), Via Vittoria Colonna 18, 00193 Rome, Italy. TEL 39-6-68802402. FAX 39-6-6874989. Ed. Walter Vergnano. adv. **Document type:** directory.

780 306 US
ANTHEM. irreg. $1 per no. Box 158324, Nashville, TN 37215. Ed. Keith A. Gordon.
Description: Covers music and other areas of popular culture, including comparative reviews of men's magazines.

780 745.1 US ISSN 0361-2147
TS2301
ANTIQUE PHONOGRAPH MONTHLY. 1973. q. $15. A P M Press, 502 E. 17th St., Brooklyn, NY 11226. TEL 718-941-6835. Ed. Allen Koenigsberg. adv.; bk.rev.; charts; illus.; cum.index: 1973-1990. circ. 2,000. (back issues avail.) **Indexed:** RILM.
Description: Covers the history of recorded sound from 1877 to 1930, and restoration of antique phonographs.

ANUARIO FLAMENCO Y GUIA DE FESTIVALES. see *DANCE*

780 SP ISSN 0211-3538
ML32.S7
ANUARIO MUSICAL. 1946. a. 3000 ptas. (foreign 4500 ptas.). Consejo Superior de Investigaciones Cientificas (C.S.I.C.), Institucion "Mila I. Fontanals", Vitruvio, 8, 28006 Madrid, Spain. TEL 93-2429123. FAX 93-2429123. **Indexed:** Music Ind., RILM.
Description: Covers musicology, ethnomusicology and musical investigation.

APPLAUS; Muenchner Kulturmagazin. see *THEATER*

780 330 UK ISSN 0960-6254
APPLAUSE; the international live music business monthly. 1989. m. £40 (Europe £50; U.S. $110; elsewhere £75). Applause Publications Ltd., 132 Liverpool Rd., London N1 1LA, England. TEL 44-71-700-0248. FAX 44-71-700-0301. Ed. Fiona Marley. adv.; stat. circ. 5,700. (back issues avail.) **Document type:** trade publication.
Description: Contains information about the business of planning and promoting national and international live music tours for managers, booking agents, promoters, and venue owners. Includes supplier companies.

051 US
THE AQUARIAN WEEKLY. 1969. w. $99. Arts Weekly, Inc., Box 137, Montclair, NJ 07042. TEL 201-783-4346. FAX 201-783-5057. Ed. Mike Daley. adv.: B&W page $1352; trim 11 x 14 3/4; adv. contact: Diane Hein. bk.rev.; film rev.; illus.; tr.lit. circ. 40,000. (tabloid format; also avail. in microfilm) **Document type:** newspaper.
Former titles (until Oct. 1992): East Coast Rocker; (until 1986): Aquarian (ISSN 0739-1919)
Description: Covers the New York area alternative music world.

780 GW
ARBEITSGEMEINSCHAFT FUER RHEINISCHE MUSIKGESCHICHTE. MITTEILUNGEN. 1955. q. membership. Arbeitsgemeinschaft fuer Rheinische Musikgeschichte e.V., c/o Musikwissenschaftliches Institut der Universitaet zu Koln, Albertus-Magnus-Platz, 50931 Cologne, Germany. TEL 0221-470-2249. FAX 0221-470-5151. TELEX 888-2291-UNIK-G. Ed. K.W. Niemoeller. bk.rev.; cum.index. circ. 400. **Indexed:** RILM.

780 GW ISSN 0003-9292
ML5
ARCHIV FUER MUSIKWISSENSCHAFT. (Supplement avail.) (Text in English and German) 1918. q. DM.140. Franz Steiner Verlag Wiesbaden GmbH, Birkenwaldstr. 44, 70191 Stuttgart, Germany. TEL 0711-2582-0. FAX 0711-2582390. (Subscr. to: Postfach 101061, 70009 Stuttgart, Germany) Ed. H.H. Eggebrecht. adv.; charts; illus.; index. circ. 800. (back issues avail.) **Indexed:** Arts & Hum.Cit.Ind., Curr.Cont., Music Ind., RILM. **Document type:** academic/scholarly publication.
—Faxon; Genuine Article. **CCC.**

780 GW ISSN 0570-6769
ARCHIV FUER MUSIKWISSENSCHAFT. BEIHEFTE. (Text in English and German) irreg., vol.36, 1995. price varies. Franz Steiner Verlag Wiesbaden GmbH, Birkenwaldstr. 44, 70191 Stuttgart, Germany. TEL 0711-2582-0. FAX 0711-2582390. (Subscr. to: Postfach 101061, 70009 Stuttgart, Germany) **Document type:** monographic series.

780.903 IT
ARCHIVUM MUSICUM; collana di testi rari. 1978. irreg. price varies. Studio per Edizioni Scelte, Lungarno Guicciardini 9, 50125 Florence, Italy. Ed.Bd.

ARISTOS. see *ART*

780 US ISSN 0518-6129
ARIZONA MUSIC NEWS. 1956. 3/yr. $15 to non-members. Arizona Music Educators Association, Inc., 5347 E. 19th St., Tucson, AZ 85711. TEL 602-544-0929. Ed. Bill Richardson. adv.: page $265; 7 1/2 x 10; adv. contact: Carol Vogt. tr.lit. circ. 1,000. **Document type:** academic/scholarly publication.
Description: Covers issues in music education at all levels.

ARKANSAS COUNTRY DANCER. see *DANCE*

783 028.5 IT ISSN 0391-5425
ARMONIA DI VOCI. 1946. bi-m. L.38000 (foreign L.46000) (effective 1996). (Centro Catechistico Salesiano) Editrice Elle Di Ci, Corso Francia 214, 10096 Leumann (Turin), Italy. TEL 39-11-9591091. FAX 39-11-9572900. Ed. Antonio Fant. adv. circ. 1,500.

780 US ISSN 0146-5856
ML410.S283
ARNOLD SCHOENBERG INSTITUTE. JOURNAL. (Text in English, German) 1976. s-ar. $18 to individuals (foreign $23); institutions $30 (foreign $35). Arnold Schoenberg Institute, c/o University of Southern California, University Park, MC-1101, Los Angeles, CA 90089-1101. TEL 213-740-4090. Ed. Paul Zukofsky. adv. contact: Cindy Jansen. bk.rev.; bibl. circ. 800. (also avail. in microfilm; back issues avail., reprint service avail. from UMI) **Indexed:** Arts & Hum.Cit.Ind., Curr.Cont., Music Artic.Guide, Music Ind., RILM. **Document type:** academic/scholarly publication.
—Faxon; Genuine Article; UnCover.
Supersedes: Arnold Schoenberg Institute. Bulletin.
Description: Provides the latest research and scholarship about Arnold Schoenberg's life and work, and also offers source material or unpublished material written by the composer.

781.65 US
ARNOLD SHAW RESEARCH CENTER FOR POPULAR MUSIC. NEWSLETTER. m. University of Nevada at Las Vegas, Arnold Shaw Research Center for Popular Music, 4505 S. Maryland Pkwy., Box 455053, Las Vegas, NV 89154-5053. Ed. Bill Willard. **Document type:** newsletter.
Description: Discusses the lives and works of jazz legends.

782　　　　　　　US　　ISSN 1043-3848
ARS LYRICA: JOURNAL OF LYRICA. 1981. irreg., approx 1/yr. $15 to individuals; libraries $25. Lyrica Society for Word-Music Relations, 90 Church St., Guilford, CT 06437. TEL 203-453-1503. FAX 203-432-2522. Ed. Louis E. Auld. bk.rev.; circ. 250 (controlled). **Document type:** academic/scholarly publication.
  Description: Articles and other works dealing with relations of words and music in any aspect.
  Refereed Serial

780　　　　　　　SA　　ISSN 0379-6485
ARS NOVA. (Text in Afrikaans, English) 1969. a. R.9.20 (overseas $3.71) (effective 1996). University of South Africa, Department of Musicology, P.O. Box 392, Pretoria 0001, South Africa. FAX 27-12-429-3221. TELEX 350068. Ed. Bernard van der Linde. adv.; bk.rev. circ. 450. (back issues avail.) **Document type:** academic/scholarly publication.

786.6　　　　　　GW　　ISSN 0004-2919
ARS ORGANI; Zeitschrift fuer das Orgelwesen. 1951. q. DM.7 per no. (Gesellschaft der Orgelfreunde e.V.) Verlag Merseburger Berlin GmbH, Postfach 103880, 34038 Kassel, Germany. adv.; bk.rev.; music rev, illus. **Indexed:** Music Ind., RILM. **Document type:** consumer publication.

700 793　　　　　BL　　ISSN 0102-3357
ART.* (Text occasionally in English) 1981. 2/yr. $20 (foreign $30). (Universade Federal da Bahia, Escola de Musica e Artes Cenicas) Grafica Universitaria, Rua Augusto Viana s-n, Canela, 40000 Salvador BA, Brazil. Ed. Paulo Lima. abstr. circ. 500. **Indexed:** Music Ind.

ART AND CULTURE. see *ART*

ARTES. see *ART*

780　　　　　　　CI　　ISSN 0587-5455
ML5
ARTI MUSICES/MUSICOLOGICAL YEARBOOK. (Text in Croatian; summaries in English, German) 1969. a. $18. Muzicka Akademija u Zagrebu, Muzikoloski Zavod - Zagreb Academy of Music, Institute of Musicology, Berislaviceva 16, 41000 Zagreb, Croatia. Ed.Bd. adv.; bk.rev.; bibl.; illus. **Indexed:** Music Ind., RILM.
  —BLDSC (1734.075500).

700　　　　　　　GW　　ISSN 0004-3885
ARTIST; Fachzeitschrift fuer Musiker. 1883. s-m. DM.90. Zeitschriften Verlag RBDV, Pressehaus Am Martin-Luther-Platz, Postfach 1135, 4000 Duesseldorf 1, Germany. TEL 0211-505-2616. FAX 0211-505-2555. TELEX 8582495. Ed. Helmut Schwanen. adv.; bk.rev.; illus. circ. 3,000. **Indexed:** Artbibl.Mod.
  —CCC.

786.97 789　　　　FR　　ISSN 0004-3907
ARTISTES ET VARIETES;* revue de l'accordeoniste et des instrumentistes de rythme. 1945. 8/yr. 95 F. Enterprise Generale de Fabrication et de Publicite, 2 bis, rue de la Baume, 75008 Paris, France. TEL 48-83-50-07. FAX 48-83-99-48. Ed. Andre Fournet. adv.; bk.rev.; music rev.; play rev.; illus. circ. 25,000.
  Formerly: Revue de l'Accordeoniste et des Instrumentistes de Rythme.

ARTS MANAGEMENT. see *THEATER*

ARTS MANAGEMENT WEEKLY. see *BUSINESS AND ECONOMICS — Management*

ARTSBOARD. see *THEATER*

ARTSFOCUS. see *MUSEUMS AND ART GALLERIES*

ARTSPACE (COLUMBUS). see *ART*

780 950　　　　　US　　ISSN 0044-9202
ML1
ASIAN MUSIC. 1968. s-a. $25 to individuals; institutions £30. Society for Asian Music, Dept. of Asian Studies, Cornell University, 388 Rockefeller Hall, Ithaca, NY 14853. TEL 607-255-5049. FAX 607-254-2877. Ed. Martin F. Hatch. adv.; bk.rev.; rec.rev. circ. 600. **Indexed:** Arts & Hum.Cit.Ind., Curr.Cont., M.L.A., Music Artic.Guide, RILM. **Document type:** academic/scholarly publication.
  —BLDSC (1742.701000); Faxon; Genuine Article; UnCover. **CCC.**

780.6　　　　　　SP
ASOCIACION DE COMPOSITORES SINFONICOS ESPANOLES. BOLETIN. 1978. s-a. Asociacion de Compositores Sinfonicos Espanoles, Francisco de Rojas 5, Madrid 10, Spain. adv. circ. 1,500.

780　　　　　　　IT
ASOLOMUSICA NEWS; periodico di musica, cultura e spettacolo. 1992. q. free. Asolo Musica, Via Robert Browning 141, 31011 Asolo (TV), Italy. TEL 0423-950150. FAX 0423-529890. **Document type:** newspaper.

ATTITUDE PROBLEM; multipurpose nonconformist rag. see *CHILDREN AND YOUTH — For*

789.91 612.381　　US　　ISSN 0004-752X
TK6540
AUDIO. 1947. m. $24. Hachette Filipacchi Magazines, 1633 Broadway, New York, NY 10019. TEL 212-767-6000. (Subscr. to: Box 52548, Boulder, CO 80321-2548. TEL 800-274-8808) Ed. Eugene Pitts III. adv.; bk.rev.; rec.rev.; illus.; index. circ. 115,000. (also avail. in microform from UMI; reprint service avail. from UMI) **Indexed:** A.S.& T.Ind., Acad.Ind., Mag.Ind., Music Ind. **Document type:** consumer publication.
  —BLDSC (1787.800000); Faxon; UMI; UnCover.
  Description: For serious stereo enthusiasts.

AUDIO CARPETORIUM; the newsletter for people who have it. see *SOUND RECORDING AND REPRODUCTION*

AUDIO MEDIA. see *SOUND RECORDING AND REPRODUCTION*

AUDIOPHILE. see *SOUND RECORDING AND REPRODUCTION*

780 792　　　　　US　　ISSN 1074-0740
AUSTIN CHRONICLE. 1981. w. $60 (Europe $135) (effective thru June 1995). Austin Chronicle Corporation, Box 49066, Austin, TX 78765. TEL 512-454-5766. FAX 512-458-6910. E-mail: XEPHYR@BGA.COM. Ed. Louis Black; Pub. Nick Barbaro. adv.; bk.rev. circ. 80,000. **Document type:** newspaper.
  Description: Focuses on local entertainment, culture and politics.

781.7　　　　　　AT
AUSTRALIAN COUNTRY MUSIC CAPITAL NEWS. 1975. m. Aus.$30 (foreign Aus.$100). B.A.L. Marketing, P.O. Box 497, Tamworth, N.S.W. 2340, Australia. FAX 067-650345. adv. contact: Terry Hill. bk.rev. circ. 6,000. **Document type:** consumer publication.
  Formerly: Capital News.

781.7　　　　　　AT
AUSTRALIAN COUNTRY MUSIC NEWSLETTER. no.36, May 1979. 3/yr. $2.50. Don & Noela Gresham, Box 186, Murwillumbah, N.S.W. 2484, Australia. illus. **Document type:** newsletter.

781.7　　　　　　AT　　ISSN 0726-1292
AUSTRALIAN SONGS. SERIES. 1986. irreg. Aus.$7 per no.; catalogue Aus.$2. Sound Austral, 34 Lucerne Cres., Frankston, Vic. 3199, Australia. TEL 61-3-789-2205. Ed. Frank Hinz. (back issues avail.; catalogue of titles avail.)
  Description: Collection of folkloric and community songs of Australia.

780.7 374　　　　AT　　ISSN 0312-9950
AUSTRALIAN STRING TEACHER. 1976. s-a. Aus.$40. Australian String Teachers Association, 5 Oakridge Rd., Aberfoyle Park, S.A. 5159, Australia. TEL 61-8-270-2145. Ed. Catherine Milligan. adv.; bk.rev.; circ. 1,000 (paid). **Document type:** academic/scholarly publication.
  Description: Acts as a forum for players, teachers, students, makers and repairers. Encourages the writing of music for string instruments, promotes performances.
  Refereed Serial

780　　　　　　　AU
AUSTRIA CREATIV. 10/yr. Austria Creativ Verein zur Foerderung Oesterreichischer Kuenstler in Europa, Hietzinger Hauptstr. 130, A-1130 Vienna, Austria. TEL 0222-8779850. FAX 0222-8775979. Ed.Bd. **Document type:** consumer publication.

AUTORES. see *THEATER*

780　　　　　　　FR　　ISSN 0764-2873
AVANT-SCENE OPERA. (Text in language of author and French) 1976. 7/yr. 550 F. (foreign 710 F.)(effective 1994). Editions Premieres Loges, 15 rue Tiquetonne, 75002 Paris, France. TEL 1-42-33-51-51. FAX 1-42-33-80-91. Ed. Michel P. Azdro. **Indexed:** Curr.Cont., RILM.

781.64　　　　　US　　ISSN 1072-5032
AXCESS. 1993. 9/yr. $25. Axcess Ventures, Box 9309, San Diego, CA 92169. **Indexed:** Access (1995-).

780　　　　　　　US
B A MAGAZINE. vol.6, 1977. irreg. Brooklyn Academy of Music, 30 Lafayette Ave., Brooklyn, NY 11217. TEL 718-636-4100. illus.

780　　　　　　　UK　　ISSN 0144-9621
B A S C A NEWS. 1951. q. £20 to non-members. British Academy of Songwriters, Composers & Authors, 34 Hanway St., London W1P 9DE, England. TEL 0171-436-2261. FAX 0171-436-1913. Ed. Amanda Harcourt. adv.; bk.rev.; illus. circ. 3,500. **Document type:** newsletter.
  Incorporates: Songwriter's Guild News.

781.68　　　　　UK　　ISSN 0966-7180
B B C MUSIC MAGAZINE; the complete monthly guide to classical music. (Includes compact disc of recorded music) 1992. m. $6 per no. (British Broadcasting Corporation) B B C Music Magazine, Rm. A1044, Woodlands, 80 Wood Ln., London W12 0TT, England. TEL 0181-576-3283. FAX 0181-576-3292. (U.S. subscr. to: B.B.C. Classical Music Service, Box 30622, Tampa, Fl 33630-0622. TEL 800-257-1100) Ed. Fiona Maddocks; Pub. Heather Aycott. adv. contact: Jonathan Gifford. music rev.; illus. **Document type:** consumer publication.
  Description: Reviews new classical music releases, broadcasts and performances.

780 398　　　　　US　　ISSN 0897-2907
B D A A NEWSLETTER. 1978. q. $20 includes membership. Balalaika and Domra Association of America, 2225 Madison Sq., Philadelphia, PA 19146. TEL 215-985-4678. Ed. Maxwell McCollough. film rev.; illus. circ. 500. (tabloid format; back issues avail.) **Document type:** newsletter.
  Description: Perpetuates the playing of the balalaika and domra, and related instruments.

780.7 370　　　　US　　ISSN 1072-9526
B D GUIDE. (Band Director) 1987. 5/yr. (during school yr.). $15. Village Press, 2779 Aero Park Dr., Traverse City, MI 49684. TEL 616-946-3712. FAX 616-946-3289. (Subscr. to: Box 629 Traverse City, MI 49685) Ed. Kenneth Neidig. adv.; bk.rev. circ. 20,000. (back issues avail.) **Document type:** trade publication.
  Description: In-service education publication for high school, junior high, community and four-year college, and military band directors.

780　　　　　　　SZ
B K G V INFORMATION. q. Birbach 9, CH-3326 Krauchthal, Switzerland. TEL 034-511930. Ed. Alfred Iseli. circ. 1,500.

780　　　　　　　US　　ISSN 1042-6736
ML3469
B M I: MUSIC WORLD. 1962. 4/yr. free to qualified personnel. Broadcast Music Inc., 320 W. 57th St., New York, NY 10019. TEL 212-586-2000. Ed. Robin Ahrold. abstr. circ. 100,000. (processed; also avail. in microfilm from UMI) **Indexed:** Music Artic.Guide, Music Ind.
  —UMI.
  Formerly (until 1987): B M I: The Many Worlds of Music (ISSN 0045-317X)

780.6　　　　　　GW
B M R - CORRESPONDENZ; Informationen - Berichte - Kommentare. 1979. bi-m. free. Bayerischer Musikrat e.V., Linprunstr. 16 Rgb., 80335 Munich, Germany. TEL 089-5234054. FAX 089-529704. **Document type:** newsletter.

781.57　　　　　FI　　ISSN 0784-7726
B N. (Blues News) (Text in Finnish) 1968. bi-m. FIM 150. Finnish Blues Society, PL 257, 00531 Helsinki 53, Finland. TEL (358 0) 760 755. Ed. Pertti Nurmi. adv.; bk.rev.; rec.rev. circ. 1,300.
  Description: Covers all forms of Afro-American music.

MUSIC

B P I STATISTICAL HANDBOOK. (British Phonographic Industry) see *MUSIC — Abstracting, Bibliographies, Statistics*

780 US
B-SIDE. bi-m. $18. Box 1860, Birlington, NJ 08016. TEL 609-387-9424. Ed. Carol Schutzbank; Pub. Sandra A. Garcia. adv.

BABYFISH LOST ITS MOMMA. see *LITERATURE — Poetry*

780 US ISSN 0005-3600
ML410.B1
BACH. 1970. 2/yr. $20 membership (libraries $26). Riemenschneider Bach Institute, Baldwin-Wallace College, 275 Eastland Rd., Berea, OH 44017. TEL 216-826-2207. FAX 216-826-3239. Ed. Elinore L. Barber. charts; illus.; index. circ. 800. (tabloid format) **Indexed:** Arts & Hum.Cit.Ind., Curr.Cont., Music Artic.Guide, Music Ind., RILM. **Document type:** academic/scholarly publication.
—Faxon; Genuine Article; UnCover.
Description: Provides articles concerned with Bach styles, forms, and performance practices, with a historical background.

780 GW ISSN 0084-7682
ML410.B1
BACH-JAHRBUCH. 1904. a. price varies. (Bach-Archiv Leipzig) Evangelische Verlagsanstalt, Burgstr. 1-5, 04109 Leipzig, Germany. Eds. H-J. Schulze, C. Wolff. bk.rev.; bibl.; charts; illus. circ. 3,000. **Indexed:** RILM. **Document type:** academic/scholarly publication.
—BLDSC (1854.630000).
Description: Contains scientific findings, bibliographies and facsimilies.

BACKBOARD. see *LITERATURE — Poetry*

780.42 US ISSN 0746-990X
ML420.S77
BACKSTREETS. 1980. q. $18 (foreign $25). Backstreets Publishing Inc., Box 51225, Ste. Rear B, Seattle, WA 98115. FAX 206-728-8827. Ed. Charles R. Cross. adv.; bk.rev. circ. 20,000. (back issues avail.)
Description: Deals with the music and performances of Bruce Springsteen and other Jersey shore acts.

784 GW
BADISCHE SAENGERZEITUNG; Organ des Badischen Saengerbundes. 1972. m. DM.23.54. Badischer Saengerbund e.V., Gartenstr. 56a, 76133 Karlsruhe, Germany. TEL 0721-849669. FAX 0721-853886. Ed. Bernd J. Schorn. adv.; B&W page DM.1200; trim 263 x 185. circ. 8,000. **Document type:** bulletin.

BALL MAGAZINE. see *LITERARY AND POLITICAL REVIEWS*

780 NO ISSN 0332-5148
BALLADE; tidsskrift for ny musikk. 1977. q. NOK 385 in Nordic countries; elsewhere $75 (effective 1996). (International Society for Contemporary Music (ISCM), Norwegian Section) Scandinavian University Press, P.O. Box 2959 Toeyen, N-0608 Oslo, Norway. TEL 47-22-57-54-00. FAX 47-22-57-53-53. Ed. Morten Eide Pedersen. adv.; bk.rev.; rec.rev. circ. 20,000. **Indexed:** Music Ind.

780.6 US ISSN 0885-7113
BALUNGAN. 1984. 2/yr. $16 to individuals (foreign $21); institutions $30 (foreign $35). American Gamelan Institute, Box 1052, Lebanon, NH 03766-4052. TEL 603-448-8837. Ed. Jody Diamond. adv. contact: David Fuqua. bk.rev. circ. 800. **Document type:** academic/scholarly publication.
—UnCover.
Description: Focuses on all forms of gamelan, Indonesian performing arts, and their international counterparts.
Refereed Serial

780.42 US ISSN 0194-5793
BAM: THE CALIFORNIA MUSIC MAGAZINE; beat attitudes music. 1976. fortn. $25. Bam Publications, Inc., 3470 Buskirk Ave., Pleasant Hill, CA 94523. TEL 510-934-3700. FAX 510-934-3958. Ed. Dennis Erokan. adv. contact: Steven Gellman. bk.rev. circ. 130,000. (tabloid format) **Document type:** consumer publication.
Formerly (until 1977): B A M: Bay Area Music.
Description: Covers developments in popular music from a California perspective.

785 US
BAND FAN; the Detroit Concert Band newsletter. 1972. q. $15. Detroit Concert Band, Inc., 7443 E. Butherus, Ste. 100, Scottsdale, AZ 85260. TEL 602-948-9870. Ed. John Stafford. adv.; bk.rev. circ. 10,000. **Document type:** newsletter.
Description: Contains editorials, concert reviews and classified ads.

785.067 JA ISSN 0005-4933
BAND JOURNAL. (Text in Japanese) 1959. m. 880 Yen. Ongaku No Tomo Sha Corp., Kagurazaka 6-30, Shinjuku-ku, Tokyo 162, Japan. TEL 03-3235-2111. FAX 03-3235-2129. adv.: B&W page 240000 Yen, color page 448000 Yen; trim 275 x 210. bk.rev.; illus. circ. 720,000.
Description: Contains commentaries, lectures, analysis of compositions and reports on items of interest. Also includes scores for parts in the supplement of each issue to make the publication practical.

785 US ISSN 0084-7704
BAND MUSIC GUIDE. 1959. irreg. $28. Instrumentalist Co., 200 Northfield Rd., Northfield, IL 60093-3390. TEL 708-446-5000; 800-323-5559. Pub. James T. Rohner.

780 US ISSN 0887-9036
BANDWORLD; the international band magazine. 1985. 5/yr. $18 (foreign $33) (effective May 1993). W I B C, Inc., 407 Terrace St., Ashland, OR 97520. TEL 503-482-5030. Ed. M. Max McKee. index. circ. 22,000. (tabloid format; also avail. in diskette format; back issues avail.) **Document type:** academic/scholarly publication.
Description: Details tips and information for music students and band directors.

780 US ISSN 0190-1559
ML1
BANJO NEWSLETTER; the 5-string banjo magazine. 1973. m. $22 (foreign $27). Banjo Newsletter, Inc., Box 3418, Annapolis, MD 21403-0418. TEL 800-759-7425. FAX 410-482-7252. Ed. Nonald Nitchie. adv.; bk.rev.; illus.; index. circ. 6,900. **Indexed:** Music Ind. **Document type:** newsletter.
Description: Contains information on the 5-string banjo, a musical instrument used in folk and classical music. Includes tablature for the instrument.

781.7 793 CN ISSN 0840-4267
ML5
BANSURI. 1984. a. Can.$7 to institutions. Raga-Mala Performing Arts of Canada, 216 Varsity Green Bay N.W., Calgary, Alta. T3B 3A8, Canada. TEL 403-288-0048. Ed. Jagannath Wani. bk.rev. circ. 700.

787 US
BASS MAGAZINE HALL OF FAME YEARBOOK (YEAR). a. $24.95 (foreign $100). (International Bassists' - Bass Players Hall of Fame Museum) Earthentics, 33 Essex St., Hackensack, NJ 07601. TEL 201-488-2055. FAX 201-489-5057. circ. 41,188.
Description: Educational tool for teachers and students to enhance and maintain levels of music education and history for the electric and string bass instrument players.

780 US ISSN 1050-785X
BASS PLAYER; for electric and string bass musicians. 8/yr. $29.97 (foreign $39.95). Miller Freeman Inc. (San Mateo) (Subsidiary of: United Newspapers Group), 411 Borel Ave., Ste. 100, San Mateo, CA 94402. TEL 415-358-9500. FAX 415-358-8728. (Subscr. to: Box 57324, Boulder, CO 80322-7324) Ed. Jim Roberts; Pub. Pat Cameron. adv. contact: Ricc Sandoval. circ. 20,000. (also avail. in microfilm from UMI; reprint service avail. from UMI) **Document type:** consumer publication.
—UMI; UnCover. **CCC.**
Supersedes in part (in 1989): G P I Collector's Edition (ISSN 1044-6656)
Description: For professional, semi-pro and amateur bass players in all styles.

BATON. see *PHILATELY*

780 UK
BAX SOCIETY BULLETIN.* 1969. q. Bax Society, Ed. Paul Podro, 103 Cheyneys Ave., Canons Park, Edgware, Middlesex, England. bk.rev.; bibl.

784.5 NO ISSN 0801-5279
BEAT. 1985. 4/yr. NOK 150. Beat Bulldog, c/o Aller Familiejournalen, P.O. Box 250 Oekern, N-0133 Oslo 1, Norway.

780 790.2 US
THE BEAT (HIGHLAND). 1977. m. $20. Lounges Publications, 2613 41st St., Highland, IN 46322. TEL 219-922-9131. FAX 219-922-9131. E-mail: BEATBOSS2AOL.COM. Ed. Tom Lounges. adv.: B&W page $575, spot-color page $650; trim 101/4 x 13. bk.rev.; circ. 35,000 (controlled). **Document type:** newspaper.

780 US ISSN 1063-5319
ML3469
THE BEAT (LOS ANGELES); reggae, African, Caribbean, world music. 1982. bi-m. $15. Bongo Productions, Box 65856, Los Angeles, CA 90065. TEL 213-257-2328. FAX 213-257-2461. Ed. C.C. Smith. adv. contact: Amy Sharafi. bk.rev.; circ. 15,000 (paid). (back issues avail.) **Document type:** consumer publication.
Formerly: Reggae and African Beat.
Description: Popular and traditional music of the Caribbean, Africa and Brazil, and the new world beat movement.

780.42 US ISSN 0274-6905
BEATLEFAN. 1978. bi-m. $15. Goody Press, Box 33515, Decatur, GA 30033. TEL 404-633-5587. FAX 404-321-3109. Ed. William King. adv.: B&W page $140; 7 x 9 3/4; adv. contact: Leslie King. bk.rev. circ. 16,000. **Document type:** newsletter, consumer publication.
Description: News and features for fans and collectors of the Beatles and the group's individual members: John Lennon, Paul McCartney, George Harrison, Ringo Starr.

780.42 UK ISSN 0261-1600
BEATLES BOOK MONTHLY. 1963. m. £27 (elsewhere in Europe £32; U.S. £35) (effective 1995-1996). Beat Publications Ltd., 43-45 St. Mary's Rd., Ealing, London W5 5RQ, England. TEL 0181-579-1082. FAX 0181-5666-2024. Ed. John Dean. adv.; illus. circ. 11,000. **Document type:** consumer publication.

780.42 US
BEATLES: GOOD DAY SUNSHINE. 1980. bi-m. $12 (foreign $22). Liverpool Productions, 397 Edgewood Ave., New Haven, CT 06511-4013. TEL 203-865-8131. FAX 203-565-3535. Ed. Charles F. Rosenay. adv. contact: Mike Streeto. bk.rev.; film rev.; play rev.; illus.; tr.lit. circ. 5,200. (back issues avail.) **Document type:** newsletter.
Former titles: Good Day Sunshine; Incorporates: Dark Horse & Here, There and Everywhere (ISSN 1041-4118)
Description: For Beatles fans, collectors and appreciators of music from the '60s; includes news, reviews, convention reports, and photos.

780.42 NE
BEATLES VISIE. 1980. q. $12. Vereniging Nederlandse Beatles Fanclub, Box 1464, 1000 BL Amsterdam, Netherlands. Ed. Bertus Elzenaar. adv.; bk.rev. circ. 600. (microfiche)
Formerly: Nota Beatles.

780 US
BEATS MAGAZINE. 1987. m. free. The Wiz, 1300 Federal Blvd., Carteret, NJ 07008. TEL 908-602-1900. FAX 908-602-0030. Ed. Lori Senger. adv. circ. 85,000.
Description: Provides news, artist interviews, and concert and product reviews of all genres of music, including video.

785.067 NO ISSN 0802-6343
ML1342
BEDRE KORPS. 1980. bi-m. NOK 265. Vanebo Fagpresse A-S, P.O. Box 130, N-2260 Kirkenaer, Norway. Ed. Odd H. Vanebo. adv. circ. 12,000.
Formerly (until 1990): Janitsjar'n (ISSN 0332-9437)

MUSIC 4831

780.92 US ISSN 1059-5031
ML410.B42
BEETHOVEN FORUM. 1992. a. price varies. University of Nebraska Press, 312 N. 14th St., Box 880484, Lincoln, NE 68588-0484. TEL 402-472-3581. FAX 402-472-6214. **Document type:** academic/scholarly publication.
Description: Serves as an international venue for articles, notes, queries, critical exchanges, and reviews of scholarship of the classical composer.
Refereed Serial

780 GW ISSN 0522-5949
BEETHOVEN-JAHRBUCH. 1954. biennial. price varies. Verein Beethoven-Haus, Postfach 2463, 53014 Bonn, Germany. TEL 0228-658245. FAX 0228-692744. Ed. Sieghard Brandenburg. bk.rev.; bibl. circ. 1,000. **Indexed:** RILM. **Document type:** academic/scholarly publication.

780 US ISSN 0898-6185
BEETHOVEN NEWSLETTER. 1986. 3/yr. $45 membership; students $20; institutions $20 (foreign $30). San Jose State University, Center for Beethoven Studies, One Washington Sq., San Jose, CA 95192-0171. TEL 408-924-4590. FAX 408-924-4365. (Co-sponsor: American Beethoven Society) Ed. William Meredith. bk.rev. circ. 1,000. **Indexed:** Music Artic.Guide, Music Ind., RILM. **Document type:** newsletter.
Description: Devoted to the life and music of the composer.

780 CN
BEETLE. 1970. m. Can.$7.50. Entertainment Publications, Inc., Box 5696, Postal Stn. A, Toronto, Ont., Canada. Ed. Debbie Brioux. adv.; bk.rev.; film rev.; play rev. circ. 150,000.

780 CC ISSN 1002-767X
BEIFANG YINYUE/NORTHERN MUSIC. (Text in Chinese) 1980. bi-m. (Heilongjiang Sheng Wenlian) Beifang Yinyue Zazhishe, 16, Yaojingjie, Nangang-qu, Harbin, Heilongjiang 150006, People's Republic of China. TEL 30847. Ed. Shu Feng.

780 AU ISSN 0067-5067
BEITRAEGE ZUR HARMONIKALEN GRUNDLAGENFORSCHUNG. 1968. irreg., no.12, 1980. price varies. Musikverlag Elisabeth Lafite, Hegelgasse 13-22, A-1010 Vienna, Austria. TEL 526869. **Document type:** monographic series.

780 AU
BEITRAEGE ZUR JAZZFORSCHUNG/STUDIES IN JAZZ RESEARCH. (Text in German) 1969. irreg., vol.8, 1986. price varies. (International Society for Jazz Research) Akademische Druck- und Verlagsanstalt Dr. Paul Struzl, Schoenaugasse 6, A-8010 Graz, Austria. TEL 0316-813460. Eds. Alfons M. Dauer, Franz Kerschbaumer. (back issues avail.) **Indexed:** RILM. **Document type:** academic/scholarly publication.

789 US ISSN 0092-8666
ML1
BELL TOWER. 9/yr. membership. American Bell Association, 7210 Bellbrook Dr., San Antonio, TX 79423. Ed. Ron Weaver. illus. circ. 2,600. **Document type:** catalog.

780 378 US ISSN 1052-3839
MT4.B7
BERKLEE TODAY; a forum for contemporary music and musicians. 1989. 3/yr. free. Berklee College of Music, 1140 Boylston St., Boston, MA 02215. TEL 617-266-1400. FAX 617-247-8788. Ed. Mark Small. adv.: B&W page $1100, color page $1400. circ. 26,000. (back issues avail.) **Document type:** academic/scholarly publication.
Description: Provides a forum for contemporary music and musicians; features college news, musical instruction pieces; contains editorials dealing with current issues in the music industry, and a survey of new publications, recordings, and professional achievements of Berklee alumni.

780 FR ISSN 1140-7417
BEST; le mensuel du rock. 1968. m. 228 F. (foreign 350 F.). Editions Mederic, 45 rue Mederic, 92100 Clichy, France. TEL 47-37-03-99. FAX 42-70-18-27. Ed. Gerard Clairiot.

780.42 JA
BEST HIT. (Text in Japanese) 1983. m. 5880 Yen. Gakken Co., Ltd., 40-5, 4 chome, Kamiikedai, Ohta-ku, Tokyo 145, Japan. Ed. Kin'ichi Iina.

BEST OF VIDEO & MUSIC. see *COMMUNICATIONS — Video*

780 PL ISSN 0860-2786
BIBLIOTEKA CHOPINOWSKA. 1959. irreg. price varies. Polskie Wydawnictwo Muzyczne, Al. Krasinskiego 11a, 31-111 Krakow, Poland. TEL 48-12-227044. FAX 48-12-220174. Ed. Mieczyslaw Tomaszewski. adv. contact: Teresa Wlochynska. **Document type:** academic/scholarly publication.
Description: Survey of the books on Chopin's life and work.

780 PL ISSN 0208-9963
BIBLIOTEKA RES FACTA. 1970. irreg. price varies. Polskie Wydawnictwo Muzyczne, Al. Krasinskiego 11a, 31-111 Krakow, Poland. TEL 48-12-227044. FAX 220174. (Subscr. to: Polskie Wydawnictwo Muzyczne, Foreign Trade Dept., Al. Krasinskiego 11a, 31-111 Krakow, Poland. TEL 48-12-227328) Ed. Michal Bristiger. adv. contact: Teresa Wlochynska. **Indexed:** RILM. **Document type:** academic/scholarly publication.
Description: Contains articles by Polish authors and translations of contemporary articles by foreign writers that contribute new valuable aspects to the scientific knowledge of music.

780 PL ISSN 0067-7779
BIBLIOTEKA SLUCHACZA KONCERTOWEGO. SERIA WPROWADZAJACA. 1954. irreg. price varies. Polskie Wydawnictwo Muzyczne, Al. Krasinskiego 11a, 31-111 Krakow, Poland. TEL 48-12-227044. FAX 48-12-220174. Ed. Mieczyslaw Tomaszewski. adv. contact: Teresa Wlochynska.
Description: Covers popular way famous symphonic and concert works.

780 NE
BIBLIOTHEEK NEDERLANDSE MUZIEK. 1991. a. fl.39.50. Uitgeversmaatschappij Walburg Pers BV, Postbus 4159, 7200 BD Zutphen, Netherlands. TEL 31-5750-10522. FAX 31-5750-41025. (Co-sponsor: Centrum Nederlandse Muziek) **Document type:** monographic series.

781.57 GW ISSN 0171-9505
ML156.4.J3
BIELEFELDER KATALOG - JAZZ. a. DM.29.80. Vereinigte Motor-Verlage GmbH und Co. KG, Leuschnerstr. 1, 70174 Stuttgart, Germany. TEL 0711-18201. FAX 0711-1821669. (Subscr. to: Postfach 106036, 70049 Stuttgart, Germany) Ed. Manfred Scheffner; Pub. Uwe Hagen. adv. contact: Peter Michael Heyde. circ. 5,000. **Document type:** catalog.

789.91 GW ISSN 0721-7153
ML156.2
BIELEFELDER KATALOG - KLASSIK. 1952. s-a. DM.29.80. Vereinigte Motor-Verlage GmbH und Co. KG, Leuschnerstr. 1, 70174 Stuttgart, Germany. TEL 0711-18201. FAX 0711-1821669. (Subscr. to: Postfach 106036, 70049 Stuttgart, Germany) Ed. Christa Hartmann; Pub. Uwe Hagen. adv. contact: Peter Michael Heyde. circ. 12,500. **Document type:** catalog.
Formerly: Bielefelder Katalog (ISSN 0006-2103)

781.64 UK
BIG. fortn. £23 (foreign £28) (effective 1995-1996). E M A P - Metro, Mappin House, 4 Winsley St., London W1N 7AR, England. TEL 0171-436-1515. FAX 0171-312-8191. (Subscr. to: Tower Publishing Services Ltd., Tower House, Sovereign Park, Lathkill St., Market Harborough, Leics. LE16 9EF, England. TEL 01858-468811. FAX 01858-432164) adv. **Document type:** consumer publication.

780 US
BIG APPLE BLUES. 1981. irreg. $10. Eric Lesselbaum, Ed. & Pub., c/o Dr. Boogie, Box 655, Bronxville, NY 10708. adv.; bk.rev.; music rev. circ. 250. **Document type:** newsletter.
Description: Covers blues performances in New York metro area.

BIG BOPPER. see *CHILDREN AND YOUTH — For*

780 US
THE BIG TAKEOVER. 1980. 2/yr. $16 for 4 nos. 249 Eldridge St., No. 14, New York, NY 10002. TEL 212-533-6057. E-mail: JRABIO@aol.com. Ed. Jack Rabid. adv.: color page $200. circ. 8,000. **Document type:** consumer publication.
Description: Covers concerts, recordings of new music, and interviews.

791 US ISSN 0006-2510
PN2000
BILLBOARD (NEW YORK). 1894. w. $209. B P I Communications, Inc. (New York), 1515 Broadway, New York, NY 10036. TEL 212-764-7300; 800-344-7119. FAX 212-536-5358. (Alt. addr.: 9107 Wilshire Blvd., Beverly Hills, CA 90036) circ. 46,675. (also avail. in microform from UMI,KTO; microfilm from BHP,KTO; reprint service avail. from UMI) **Indexed:** Bus.Ind., Music Ind., PMR, Tr.& Indus.Ind.
● Also available online. Vendor(s): Knight-Ridder, Inc. —BLDSC (2060.700000); UMI. **CCC.**
Description: Newsweekly for the music and home entertainment industries.

780.42 US
BILLBOARD HISTORY OF ROCK 'N ROLL. 1992. a. $100. B P I Communications, Inc. (New York), 1515 Broadway, New York, NY 10036. TEL 212-764-7300; 800-344-7119. FAX 212-944-1719. (And: 5055 Wilshire Blvd., Los Angeles, CA 90036) rec.rev.
● Available only on CD-ROM.
Description: Combines CD-Audio and CD-ROM technologies to list top-selling recording artists by year, and also includes a feature article section.

780 US ISSN 0067-8600
BILLBOARD'S INTERNATIONAL BUYER'S GUIDE OF THE MUSIC - RECORD - TAPE INDUSTRY. 1958. a. $83. B P I Communications, Inc. (New York), 1515 Broadway, New York, NY 10036. TEL 212-764-7300; 800-344-7119. FAX 212-944-1719. (And: 5055 Wilshire Blvd., Los Angeles, CA 90036) (also avail. in microfilm from KTO; reprint service avail. from UMI) **Document type:** directory.
Formerly (until 1960): Billboard. International Buyer's Guide of the Music - Record Industry.
Description: Worldwide music and video business to business directory.

780 US ISSN 0732-0124
ML1
BILLBOARD'S INTERNATIONAL TALENT AND TOURING DIRECTORY; the music industry's worldwide reference source: talent, talent management, booking agencies, promoters, venue facilities, venue services and products. 1978. a. $73. B P I Communications, Inc. (New York), 1515 Broadway, New York, NY 10036. TEL 212-764-7300; 800-344-7119. FAX 212-944-1719. (And: 5055 Wilshire Blvd., Los Angeles, CA 90036) circ. 15,000. (also avail. in microfilm from KTO) **Document type:** directory.
Formerly: Billboard's International Talent Directory (ISSN 0190-9649); Incorporates: Billboard's on Tour (ISSN 0361-5383); Campus Attractions (ISSN 0067-8597); Which was formerly (1964-1968): Billboard. Music on Campus.
Description: Source for US and international talent, booking agencies, facilities, services and products.

792 US
BILLBOARD'S YEAR-END AWARDS ISSUE. 1970. a. $9.95. B P I Communications, Inc. (New York), 1515 Broadway, New York, NY 10036. TEL 212-764-7300; 800-344-7119. FAX 212-944-1719. (And: 5055 Wilshire Blvd., Los Angeles, CA 90036) circ. 45,000. (also avail. in microfilm from KTO)
Former titles: Billboard's Year-End Issue Talent in Action; Billboard's Year-End Awards - Talent in Action; Billboard's Talent in Action.

781.7 367 US
BILLIE JO WILLIAMS INTERNATIONAL FAN CLUB. 1982. q. $10 to individuals; senior citizens $7. Box 1408, N. Wilkesboro, NC 28659. Ed. Billie Jo Williams. (back issues avail.)
Description: Provides news of the artist, including his show dates, merchandise price list and photos.

780.42 BL ISSN 0104-1649
BIZZ. (Supplements avail.: Letras Traduzidas, Rock em CD) 1985. m. $40.80. Editora Azul, S.A., Av. Nacoes Unidas, 5777, 05479-900 Sao Paulo SP, Brazil. TEL 11-816-7866. FAX 11-813-9115. (Subscr. to: Rua do Curtume 769, 05065-900 Sao Paulo, Brazil. TEL 011-823-9100) Ed. Carlos C. Arruda. adv.: color page $12700; 208 x 274. music rev.; rec.rev.; illus.; stat. circ. 39,000. **Document type:** consumer publication.
Description: Covers all aspects of the pop-rock music industry. Contains articles, interviews and reviews.

MUSIC

BLACK BEAT. see *CHILDREN AND YOUTH — For*

BLACK DOG MAGAZINE. see *LITERATURE*

780 910.03   US   ISSN 0276-3605
ML3556
BLACK MUSIC RESEARCH JOURNAL. 1980. s-a. $35 (foreign $40). Center for Black Music Research, Columbia College Chicago, 600 S. Michigan Ave., Chicago, IL 60605. TEL 312-663-1600. FAX 312-663-9019. E-mail: cbmr@mail.columb.edu. Ed. Samuel A. Floyd, Jr. index. circ. 808. Indexed: Arts & Hum.Cit.Ind., Music Artic.Guide, Music Ind., RILM. **Document type:** trade publication.
—BLDSC (2105.965600); Faxon; Genuine Article; UnCover.
   Description: Broad range of research in black music.
   Refereed Serial

780.65 910.03   US   ISSN 1043-9455
ML2999
BLACK SACRED MUSIC; a journal of theomusicology. 1987. s-a. $20 to individuals (foreign $20); institutions $40 (foreign $52). Duke University Press, Box 90660, Durham, NC 27708-0660. TEL 919-687-3600. FAX 919-688-4574. Ed. Jon Michael Spencer. Indexed: Music Artic.Guide, RILM.
—Faxon; UMI.
   Formerly (until 1989): Journal of Black Sacred Music (ISSN 0891-9321)
   Refereed Serial

BLAETTER DER FREIEN VOLKSBUEHNE BERLIN. see *THEATER*

780   GW   ISSN 0344-8231
DIE BLASMUSIK. 1950. m. DM.31. (Bund Deutscher Blasmusikverbaende e.V.) Verlag Die Blasmusik, Am Maerzengraben 6, 79112 Freiburg, Germany. TEL 07664-1431. FAX 07664-5123. Ed. K. Schulz. adv.: B&W page DM.990; trim 260 x 185. bk.rev.; bibl.; illus.; stat. circ. 6,300. (back issues avail.) **Document type:** consumer publication.
   Formerly: Allgemeine Volksmusikzeitung.

781.64   US
▼**BLENDER**; the interactive pop culture magazine. 1994. bi-m. $49.95. 25 W. 39th St., Ste. 1103, New York, NY 10018. adv. **Document type:** consumer publication.
●Available only on CD-ROM.
   Description: Provides a fast-paced multimedia look into contemporary music.

780.904   US   ISSN 0889-5635
BLITZ; the rock and roll magazine for thinking people. 1975. q. $15 for 6 issues. Box 48124, Los Angeles, CA 90048-0124. TEL 818-997-3294. Ed. Michael McDowell; Pub. Michael McDowell. adv. contact: Virginia McDowell. bk.rev.; charts; illus.; stat.; circ. 5,000 (paid). (back issues avail.) **Document type:** consumer publication.
   Description: Focus on obscure and underrated artists in rock and roll music, with a record collector's perspective.

781.57   NE   ISSN 0921-2558
ML5
BLOCK; magazine for blues. 1975. q. fl.24 (foreign fl.37.50). Postbus 244, 7600 AE Almelo, Netherlands. TEL 31-546-819976. FAX 31-546-820106. Ed. Rien Wisse. adv.; bk.rev.; circ. 4,000. (back issues avail.) Indexed: Alt.Press Ind. **Document type:** consumer publication.

780   IT
BLU AND BLU; mensile di musica tutta italiana. m. (Athena 2001 Coop. a.r.l.) Edizioni L.E.T.I. s.r.l., Via E.Q. Visconti, 20, 00193 Rome, Italy. TEL 06-3144512. circ. 80,500.

781.7   GW   ISSN 0936-2479
ML3519
BLUEGRASS - BUEHNE; old time and bluegrass magazine. 1981. bi-m. DM.30($20) Eberhardtstr. 14-4, 89073 Ulm, Germany. TEL 0731-21393. Ed. Eberhard Finke. adv.; bk.rev. circ. 600. **Document type:** bulletin.

781.62   CN   ISSN 1180-761X
ML3519
BLUEGRASS CANADA MAGAZINE; uniting bluegrassers. 1989. bi-m. Can.$21($27) Jim Jesson, Ed. & Pub., 1-231 Victoria St., Kamloops, BC V2C 2A1, Canada. TEL 604-579-9282. FAX 604-579-5818. **Document type:** consumer publication.

780   US   ISSN 0006-5129
BLUEGRASS MUSIC NEWS. 1950. 4/yr. $15 in the U.S.; Canada $18; elsewhere $20. Kentucky Music Educators Association, c/o Hazel O. Carver, Ed., 1007 Granville Ln., Russellville, KY 42276. TEL 502-726-6427. FAX 502-726-7879. adv.: B&W page $260; 7 1/2 x 10. bk.rev.; charts; illus. circ. 2,000. **Document type:** academic/scholarly publication.
   Description: Articles on music education.

781.7   US   ISSN 0006-5137
ML1
BLUEGRASS UNLIMITED. 1966. m. $21 (foreign $30) (effective Jan. 1994). Bluegrass Unlimited Inc., Box 111, Broad Run, VA 22014. TEL 703-349-8181; 800-258-4727. FAX 703-341-0011. Ed. Peter V. Kuykendall. adv.; bk.rev.; rec.rev.; illus. circ. 23,717. Indexed: Music Ind., Pop.Mus.Per.Ind., RILM. **Document type:** consumer publication.
—Faxon.
   Description: Covers old-time, traditional country music and bluegrass.

780   US
BLUEMONT MUSE. 1979. bi-m. Bluemont Concert Series, Box 208, Leesburg, VA 22075. TEL 703-777-0574. Ed. Peter H. Dunning. circ. 5,000.

781.57   IT
IL BLUES. 1982. q. L.20000. Editori Blues e Dintorni, Piazza Grandi 12, I-20135 Milan, Italy. (Subscr. to: c/o Mario Grandi, viale Tunisia 15, 20124 Milan, Italy) Ed.Bd. adv.; bk.rev. circ. 2,000. (tabloid format; back issues avail.)

781.57   US   ISSN 1066-4068
BLUES ACCESS. 1990. q. $12 (Canada or Mexico $14; Europe and elsewhere $20) (effective 1995). Cary Wolfson, Ed. & Pub., 1455 Chestnut Pl., Boulder, CO 80304-3153. TEL 303-443-7245. FAX 303-939-9729. E-mail: bluzacces@aol.com. adv.; B&W page $590; adv. contact: Cary Wolfson. bk.rev. **Document type:** consumer publication.
●Also available online.
   Description: Features reviews and articles pertaining to blues music and the people who make it. Contains a complete listing of all new CD releases, in-depth festivals information, plus access to a variety of blues resources.

781.57   UK
BLUES & RHYTHM; the gospel truth. 1984. every 5 weeks. $34; newsstand price: £2.85. 1 Cliffe Ln., Thornton, Bradford, W. Yorks. BD13 3DX, England. TEL 01234-826158. FAX 01234-826180. E-mail: tbone99eworld.com. Ed. Tony Burke. adv. contact: Tony Watson. bk.rev.; rec.rev.; circ. 2,000 (paid). **Document type:** newsletter, academic/scholarly publication.
   Description: Covers all aspects of blues, R&B, and gospel; and includes articles, discographies, and letters.

781   UK   ISSN 0045-2297
BLUES & SOUL MUSIC REVIEW. 1966. fortn. £71. Napfield Ltd., 153 Praed St., London W2 RL, England. TEL 071-402-6869. FAX 071-224-8227. Ed. R. Killbourn. adv.; bk.rev.; illus. circ. 65,000.
   Incorporates: Black Music and Jazz Review (ISSN 0307-2169)

781.57   US
BLUES AT THE FOUNDATION. q. free to members. Blues Foundation, 174 Beale St., Memphis, TN 38103. TEL 901-527-2583. FAX 901-529-4030. circ. 3,000 (controlled).

780   US
THE BLUES AUDIENCE.* m. $12. 104 Old Nelson Rd., Marlborough, NH 03455-4004. TEL 603-827-3952. **Document type:** consumer publication.
   Description: Performance listings for New England blues bands and clubs.

781.57   US
BLUES RESEARCH. 1959. irreg., no.17, 1975. $1 per no. Record Research, 65 Grand Ave., Brooklyn, NY 11205. TEL 718-857-7003. Eds. Anthony Rotante, Paul Sheatsley. charts; illus.

780   US   ISSN 1076-6162
BLUES REVUE. bi-m. $20 (foreign $30). Rt. 2, Box 118, W. Union, WV 26456. TEL 304-782-1971. FAX 304-782-1993. E-mail: BluesRevue@aol.com. Ed. Andrew M. Robble. bk.rev. circ. 44,000. **Document type:** consumer publication.
   Formerly: Blues Revue Quarterly.

781.573   UK   ISSN 0006-5153
ML5
BLUES UNLIMITED. 1963. 4/yr. £7.50($15) B U Publications Ltd., 36 Belmont Park, Lewisham, London S.E. 13, England. Ed.Bd. adv.; bk.rev.; illus. circ. 4,000. Indexed: M.L.A.

780 793   PE
BOLETIN DE MUSICA Y DANZA.* 1978. Instituto Nacional de Cultura, Departamental Ancash, Oficion Numero. 363, Huaras, Peru. Dir. Domingo Sanchez. bk.rev. (processed)

BOMBAY ART SOCIETY'S ART JOURNAL. see *ART*

780   US
BOMP. 1966. 6/yr. $12 for 8 issues. Bomp Magazine, Box 7112, Burbank, CA 91510. Ed. Gregory Shaw. adv.; bk.rev. circ. 40,000.
   Formerly: Who Put the Bomp (ISSN 0039-7873)

789.91   NE   ISSN 0166-1426
BOOGIE WOOGIE AND BLUES COLLECTOR. (Text in Dutch and English) 1968. q. (Blues Record Centre) Dutch Blues and Boogie Organisation, Postbus 12538, 1100 AM Amsterdam, Netherlands. TEL 31-20-6961111. FAX 31-20-6961111. (Subscr. to: Maasdrielhof 175, 1106 NG Amsterdam, Netherlands) Ed. Martin van Olderen. adv.; bk.rev. circ. 9,000. (back issues avail.)

780   US
BOOM!; strictly raggamuffin. 1993. bi-m. newsstand price: $2.50. Boom Publications, Inc., Box 286, Boston, MA 02123. TEL 617-437-8437. Ed. Christina Pazzanese.

785   US   ISSN 8755-5832
BOOMBAH HERALD; a band history newsletter. 1973. s-a. $10. 15 Park Blvd., Lancaster, NY 14086. Ed. Loren D. Geiger. adv.; bk.rev.; illus.; tr.lit.; rec.rev.; cum.index. circ. 100. (tabloid format; back issues avail.) **Document type:** academic/scholarly publication, newspaper.
   Description: Seeks to preserve the heritage of the concert band in the USA and around the world. Articles cover band histories and composer biographies.

781.973   US   ISSN 0006-7598
BOOSEY AND HAWKES NEWSLETTER. 1965. 3/yr. free. Boosey and Hawkes, Inc., 24 E. 21st St., New York, NY 10010-7200. TEL 212-228-3300. FAX 212-473-5730. TELEX 650-284-8790 MCI. Ed. Steven Swartz. bk.rev.; illus.; music rev.; circ. 10,000 (controlled). **Document type:** newsletter.
   Description: Provides articles and information about the work of composers published by Boosey and Hawkes and its affiliates.

BOP. see *CHILDREN AND YOUTH — For*

780   US
BORDER X-INGS. q. $2.50 per no. Box 5173, North Bergen, NJ 07047. Ed. Mary Ann O'Brien.
   Description: Features Irish rock music and Celtic life.

786   US   ISSN 0524-1170
BOSTON ORGAN CLUB NEWSLETTER.* 1965. irreg. $5. Organ Historical Society, Boston Organ Club, Box 863, Claremont, NH 03743. Ed. E.A. Boadway. adv.; bk.rev. circ. 300.

MUSIC 4833

780.15 US
BOSTON SYMPHONY ORCHESTRA PROGRAM. 1882. w. during season. $75. Boston Symphony Orchestra, Program Office, Symphony Hall, Boston, MA 02115. TEL 617-266-1492. FAX 617-638-9367. TELEX TWX-710-321-9283. Ed. Marc Mandel. adv.; bk.rev.; index. circ. 234,000. (also avail. in microform from UMI,BHP; microfilm from KTO; reprint service avail. UMI)
—UMI.
Formerly: Boston Symphony Orchestra Program Book-Notes (ISSN 0006-8020)

780 NE ISSN 1380-4545
DE BOUWBRIEF. 1975. q. fl.57 (effective 1992). Vereniging voor Muziek en Instrumentenbouw, Huismuziek, c/o Stichting L O A M, Keizerstraat 3, 3512 EA Utrecht, Netherlands. TEL 31-30-302301. FAX 31-30-300280. Ed. A. Riesthuis. adv.; bk.rev.; illus. circ. 1,500.
Description: Devoted to the building and designing of musical instruments. Covers materials, tools, and measurements. Includes announcements of events, exhibitions, and courses.

780 920 GW ISSN 0341-941X
ML5
BRAHMS STUDIEN. 1976. biennial. DM.30. Johannes Brahms Gesellschaft, Internationale Vereinigung e.V., Trostbruecke 4, 20457 Hamburg, Germany. Ed. Martin Meyer. adv.; bk.rev.; illus. circ. 500. **Indexed:** RILM. **Document type:** academic/scholarly publication.
Formerly: Brahms-Gesellschaft Hamburg. Jahresgabe.

780.9 US
BRAHMS STUDIES. irreg. price varies. University of Nebraska Press, 312 N. 14th St., Box 880484, Lincoln, NE 68588-0484. TEL 402-472-3581. FAX 402-472-6213. Ed. David Brodbeck. index. **Document type:** academic/scholarly publication.
Description: Seeks to develop and publish new studies on the work, life, and milieu of the composer.
Refereed Serial

BRAILLE MUSIC MAGAZINE. see *HANDICAPPED — Visually Impaired*

780 SZ
BRASS BAND. m. Baselstr. 23C, CH-4537 Wiedlisbach, Switzerland. TEL 065-763727. FAX 065-762644. Ed. Werner Obrecht. adv.; B&W page 877 SFr.; trim 176 x 266. circ. 4,000.

780 US
BRASS BAND NOTES. 1970. bi-m. $7 includes membership. Chatfield Brass Band, Inc., 81 Liberty Ln., Box 578, Chatfield, MN 55923. TEL 507-867-3275. Ed. Rita Kramer. circ. 200.

784.18 UK ISSN 0961-6373
BRASS BAND WORLD; an independent magazine for bands. 1991. m. £24.50 (rest of Europe £35; elsewhere £40) (effective 1995). Caron Publications, Peak Press Bldg., Eccles Rd., Chapel-en-le-Frith, Stockport, Ches. SK12 6HB, England. TEL 01298-812816. FAX 01298-815220. Ed. Robert G. Mulholland. adv.: page £370; trim 210 x 297; adv. contact: Sally Bowker. music rev. circ. 4,000. (back issues avail.) **Document type:** trade publication.
Description: Aimed at brass-band players and enthusiasts; contains profiles of bands and individual players, reviews, and interviews.

780 SZ ISSN 0303-3848
ML5
BRASS BULLETIN; international magazine for brass players. (Text in English, French and German) 1971. 4/yr. 53 SFr.($41) to individuals; students 42 SFr.($32.50). P.O. Box, CH-1630 Bulle, Switzerland. TEL 029-24422. FAX 029-21350. Ed. Jean-Pierre Mathez. adv.; bk.rev.; bibl.; illus. circ. 7,000. (back issues avail.) **Indexed:** Music Ind., RILM. **Document type:** bulletin.
—BLDSC (2273.640000); Faxon; UnCover.

780 US ISSN 0197-8845
BRASS PLAYERS GUIDE (YEAR). 1975. a. $4 (effective 1992). Robert King Music Sales, Inc., 140 Main St., Bldg. 15, N. Easton, MA 02356. FAX 508-238-2571. Ed. Dennis Hugh Avey. adv. circ. 20,000. **Document type:** catalog.

780 US ISSN 0363-454X
BRASS RESEARCH SERIES. irreg. Brass Press, c/o RKMS, 140 Main St., N. Easton, MA 02356. FAX 508-238-2571. Ed. Stephen L. Glover.
Description: Music history and research.

BRAVO. see *MOTION PICTURES*

BRAVURA STUDIES IN MUSIC. see *MUSIC — Abstracting, Bibliographies, Statistics*

BRIO. see *LIBRARY AND INFORMATION SCIENCES*

780 UK
ML21
BRITISH AND INTERNATIONAL MUSIC YEARBOOK. 1972. a. £19.95. Rhinegold Publishing Ltd., 241 Shaftesbury Ave., London WC2H 8EH, England. TEL 0171-333-1760. FAX 0171-333-1769. Ed. Felicity Rich. adv.; stat.; index. **Indexed:** RILA. **Document type:** directory.
—BLDSC (2330.700000).
Former titles: British Music Yearbook (ISSN 0306-5928); Music Yearbook.
Description: Comprehensive directory of British classical music industry.

785 UK ISSN 0007-0319
BRITISH BANDSMAN. 1887. w. £31.50($71) British Bandsman Ltd., London End, Beaconsfield, Bucks., England. Ed. Peter Wilson. adv.; bk.rev.; illus.
Incorporates: Brass Band News & International Bandsman.

781.97 016 UK ISSN 0068-1407
BRITISH CATALOGUE OF MUSIC. 1957. 3/yr. (annual cum. incorporates contents of 2 previous issues). £69($140) (foreign £75). (Publisher £75). British Library, Bibliographic Services) Bowker - Saur Ltd., A part of Reed Reference Publishing, Maypole House, Maypole Rd., E. Grinstead, W. Sussex RH19 1HH, England. TEL 44-01342-330100. FAX 44-1342-330191. E-mail: custserv@bowker-saur.co.uk. bibl.; index. circ. 600. **Document type:** catalog.
●Also available online.
—BLDSC (2292.600000).
Description: Lists music recently published in the U.K. and received by the Copyright Receipt Office of the British Library, music available in the U.K. via a sole agent, and post-1980 acquisitions of the British Library.

780.7 CN ISSN 0705-9019
BRITISH COLUMBIA MUSIC EDUCATOR. 1959. s-a. Can.$53.50 to non-members; members Can.$25; students Can.$12. (B.C. Music Educators' Association) B.C. Teachers' Federation, 100-550 W. 6th Ave., Vanouver, BC V5Z 4P2, Canada. TEL 604-871-1848. FAX 604-871-2291. adv.; bk.rev.; illus.; stat.; index. circ. 1,200. **Indexed:** Can.Educ.Ind. **Document type:** trade publication.
Description: Covers the study and teaching of music.

780 UK
BRITISH FEDERATION OF FESTIVALS. YEARBOOK. 1921. a. £6. British Federation of Festivals, 198 Park Ln., MacClesfield, Ches. SK11 6UD, England. FAX 01625-503229. Ed. Liz Whitehead. adv. contact: Liz Whitehead. circ. 2,500. **Document type:** directory.
Formerly: British Federation of Music Festivals. Yearbook (ISSN 0309-8044)
Description: Contains detailed information about affiliated festivals in the U.K., Hong Kong, and Bermuda. Includes music, dance, speech, and drama festivals for amateurs.

780.1 305.8 UK ISSN 0968-1221
ML3797.6
BRITISH JOURNAL OF ETHNOMUSICOLOGY. a. £12 to individuals; institutions £15 (includes Newsletter). International Council for Traditional Music (U.K. Chapter), c/o Centre of Music Studies, School of Oriental and African Studies, Thornhaugh St., Russell Sq., London WC1H OXG, England. Ed.Bd. adv.; bk.rev.; music rev. (back issues avail.) **Document type:** academic/scholarly publication.
—BLDSC (2307.785000).
Formerly (until 1992): International Council for Traditional Music (U K Chapter). Bulletin.
Description: Publishes scholarly essays on traditional ethnic music.
Refereed Serial

650 UK ISSN 0265-0517
ML5
BRITISH JOURNAL OF MUSIC EDUCATION. 1984. 3/yr. £47($73) (effective 1996). Cambridge University Press, Edinburgh Bldg., Shaftesbury Rd., Cambridge CB2 2RU, England. TEL 01223-312393. FAX 01223-315052. TELEX 851817256. (N. American addr.: Cambridge University Press, 40 W. 20th St., New York, NY 10011. TEL 212-924-3900. FAX 212-691-3239) Eds. John Paynter, Keith Swanwick. adv.; bk.rev. (also avail. in microform from UMI; back issues avail.; reprint service avail. from SWZ) **Indexed:** Cont.Pg.Educ., Mult.Ed.Abstr., RILM, Tech.Educ.Abstr. **Document type:** academic/scholarly publication.
—BLDSC (2311.890000); Faxon; UMI; UnCover. CCC.
Description: Covers classroom music teaching, individual instrumental teaching and group teaching, and music in higher education.

780 UK ISSN 0007-1463
BRITISH MOUTHPIECE; brass & military band journal. 1958. w. £11. Mechanics Institute, Spring St., Shuttleworth, Nr. Ramsbottom, Lancashire, England. Ed. E.C. Buttress. adv.; bk.rev.; abstr.; charts; illus.; rec.rev.; tr.lit. circ. 4,000.

780.6 UK ISSN 0958-5664
ML5
BRITISH MUSIC. 1979. a. £5. British Music Society, 7 Tudor Gardens, Upminster, Essex RM14 3DE, England. TEL 01708-224795. Ed. Beryl Kington. adv.; B&W page £50; adv. contact: Stephen C. Trowell. circ. 600. **Document type:** academic/scholarly publication.
—BLDSC (2330.620000).
Formerly (until vol.10, 1988): British Music Society. Journal (ISSN 0143-7402)
Description: Covers British opera, chamber music, orchestral music; reviews of artists, works, interviews and more.

BRITISH PERFORMING ARTS YEARBOOK. see *THEATER*

780 616.89 UK ISSN 0953-7511
ML3919
BRITISH SOCIETY FOR MUSIC THERAPY. BULLETIN. 1987. 3/yr. (included to members free with subscr. of "Journal"). British Society for Music Therapy, 69 Avondale Ave., E. Barnet, Herts. EN4 8NB, England. Ed. Denize Christophers. **Document type:** bulletin.
—BLDSC (2425.300000).

780 US ISSN 1075-0371
BROWBEAT. 1993. 2/yr. $3 per issue. Rage Rage Rage Publishing, Box 11124, Oakland, CA 94611-1124. TEL 510-652-2441. FAX 510-652-2464. E-mail: rizzi@netcom.com. Site addr.: http://www.meer.net/~browbeat. (Dist. by: Fine Print, 6448 Hwy. 209 E., No. B-104, Austin, TX 78723. TEL 800-874-7082) Ed. Mike Rizzi. bk.rev.; film rev.; music rev.; illus.; circ. 1,500 (paid). (back issues avail.) **Document type:** consumer publication.
Description: Devoted to dissonant music in all genres, with emphasis on Japanese underground music. Includes interviews and discographies.

780.42 US ISSN 0192-9097
BUDDY; the original Texas music magazine. 1973. m. 11258 Goodnight Ln., Ste. 102, Dallas, TX 75229-3395. TEL 214-484-9010. FAX 214-484-8785. Ed. Ron McKeown. adv.; bk.rev. circ. 50,000. **Document type:** newspaper.

BUEHNE. see *THEATER*

780 BU
BULGARSKA MUSIKA; organ na suyuza no Bulgarskite kompozitori i na komiteta za kultura. 10/yr. 7. Komiteta a Kultura, Iv. Vazov 2, Sofia, Bulgaria. Ed. Dimitr Zenginor. **Indexed:** Music Ind.

780.1 US ISSN 0739-5639
ML1
THE BULLETIN OF HISTORICAL RESEARCH IN MUSICAL EDUCATION. 1980. 3/yr. $20. University of Kansas, M E M T Division, 311 Baily Hall, Lawrence, KS 66045-2344. TEL 913-864-4784. Ed. George Heller. bk.rev.; bibl. circ. 227. (back issues avail.) **Indexed:** Music Ind. **Document type:** academic/scholarly publication, bulletin.
—Faxon; UnCover.
Description: Contains research in music education history in the U.S. and elsewhere.
Refereed Serial

M

MUSIC

787 658.8   UK   ISSN 0956-2346
BUSINESS RATIO REPORT: MUSICAL INSTRUMENTS; an industry sector analysis. 1989. a. I C C Business Ratios Ltd., Freepost, Field House, Hampton, Mddx. TW12 1BR, England. TEL 081-783-0977. FAX 081-783-1940. charts; stat. **Document type:** trade publication.

780 026   CN   ISSN 0383-1299
C A M L NEWSLETTER/A C B M NOUVELLES. (Text in English and French) 1972. 3/yr. Can.$65($20) to individuals; institutions Can.$80; student Can.$25. Canadian Association of Music Libraries, c/o Bibliographic Services Dept., Metropolitan Toronto Reference Library, 789 Yonge St., Toronto, ON M4W 2G8, Canada. TEL 416-393-7024. FAX 416-393-7229. E-mail: au441@freenet.toronto.on.ca. Ed. Cheryl Martin. adv.; B&W page Can.$30. bk.rev. circ. 190. (back issues avail.) **Document type:** newsletter.
  Supersedes: Canadian Music Library Association. Newsletter (ISSN 0383-1280)
  Description: Features association news, conference reports, book and music reviews and library articles.

780   CN
C A M M A C SOUTHERN ONTARIO REGION NEWSLETTER. 1970. m. Can.$35. Canadian Amateur Musicians, Southern Ontario Region - Musiciens Amateurs du Canada, 283 Bogert Ave., Toronto, ON M2N 1L4, Canada. TEL 416-250-8527. Ed. Claudia Morawetz. adv. contact: Nora Mular-Richards. circ. 400 (controlled). **Document type:** newsletter.
  Description: Provides news and information about upcoming musical events, activities and workshops of interest to amateur musicians of all ages and abilities in the southern Ontario region.

C A NEWS. (Christians in the Arts Networking, Inc.) see *ART*

780   US   ISSN 1053-7694
ML1
C A S JOURNAL. 1964. s-a. $45 to individuals (foreign $50); institutions $55 (foreign $60). Catgut Acoustical Society, c/o Carleen M. Hutchins, Sec., 112 Essex Ave., Montclair, NJ 07042. TEL 201-744-4029. FAX 201-744-9197. Ed. Edward Wall. bk.rev.; charts; illus.; index. circ. 800. (back issues avail.) **Indexed:** Forest Prod.Abstr.
  —UnCover.
  Former titles: Catgut Acoustical Society. Journal (ISSN 0882-2212); (until 1984): Catgut Acoustical Society Newsletter (ISSN 0576-9280)

780   CN   ISSN 0711-9828
C B C CLASSICAL RECORD REFERENCE BOOK. (Text in English and French) 1980. a. Canadian Broadcasting Corporation, 1400 E. Rene Levesque, Montreal, PQ H3C 3A8, Canada. TEL 514-285-3211.

780 910.03   US   ISSN 1043-1241
C B M R DIGEST. 1988. s-a. free to qualified personnel. Center for Black Music Research, Columbia College Chicago, 600 S. Michigan Ave., Chicago, IL 60605-1996. TEL 312-663-1600. FAX 312-663-9019. E-mail: cbmr@mail.columb.edu. Ed. Suzanne Flandreau. **Document type:** newsletter.

780 910.03   US   ISSN 1042-8836
C B M R MONOGRAPHS. 1989. irreg. $10 (foreign $13). Center for Black Music Research, Columbia College Chicago, 600 S. Michigan Ave., Chicago, IL 60605. TEL 312-663-1600. FAX 312-663-9019. E-mail: cbmr@mail.columb.edu. Ed. Samuel A. Floyd, Jr. circ. 450. **Document type:** monographic series.
  Description: Covers broad range of research in black music.

783   US
C C M UPDATE. (Contemporary Christian Music) 1983. 50/yr. $120. C C M Communications, 107 Kenner Ave., Nashville, TN 37205-2207. TEL 614-386-3011. FAX 615-386-3380. (Subscr. to: Box 55995, Boulder, CO 80322) Ed. John W. Styll. adv. circ. 5,000. **Document type:** consumer publication.
  Formerly (until 1986): MusicLine (ISSN 0746-7656)
  Description: Contains news and information about the contemporary gospel music industry, including airplay and sales reports.

C C T NEWSLETTER. (Choreographers Theatre) see *DANCE*

780   UK   ISSN 0967-4411
C D CLASSICS. 1992. m. £70 for 6 issues. Northern & Shell Publications, Northern & Shell Bldg., P.O. Box 381, Millharbour, London E14 9TW, England. TEL 44-171-987-5090. FAX 44-171-987-2160. Ed. Kate Price-Thomas. adv.: color page £1375; adv. contact: Zoe Almeida. circ. 80,000. **Document type:** consumer publication.

780   US   ISSN 1062-6883
ML156.9
C D GUIDE. (Compact Disc) s-a. $22.97. Connell Communications, Inc. (Subsidiary of: International Data Group), 86 Elm St., Peterborough, NH 03458.

780   US   ISSN 1044-1700
ML156.9
C D REVIEW. (Compact Disc) 1984. m. $22.97 (effective Jul. 1993). Connell Communications, Inc. (Subsidiary of: International Data Group), 86 Elm St., Peterborough, NH 03458. TEL 603-924-7271. FAX 603-924-7013. (Subscr. to: P.O. Box 538, Peterborough, NH 03458) Ed. Lou Warrycia; Pub. Ellen Holmes. adv. contact: Brian Vorillencourt. circ. 95,000. (also avail. in microfilm from UMI) **Document type:** consumer publication.
  —UMI.
  Formerly: Digital Audio and Compact Disc Review (ISSN 0743-619X)
  Description: A multi-category music magazine covering pop, rock, classical, jazz, folk, blues, world, country and new age styles. Offers reviews, reports on new stereo equipment and interviews with recording artists.

780   AU   ISSN 0574-9468
C I A REVUE. 1953. a. Confederation Internationale des Accordeonistes, c/o Walter Mauer, Sec. Gen., Dietrichgasse 51-19, 1030 Vienna, Austria. FAX 1-74830320. circ. 1,000.

780.7   US   ISSN 0007-845X
C I M NOTES. 1973. bi-m. (Sept.-June). free. Cleveland Institute of Music, 11021 E. Boulevard, Cleveland, OH 44106. TEL 216-791-5000. FAX 216-791-3063. E-mail: XX365@po.cwru.edu. Ed. Rory Sanders. illus.; circ. 10,000 (controlled). **Document type:** newsletter.
  Description: Provides information on events at the Cleveland Institute of Music and on faculty, student, and trustee activities. Scholarly articles are also included as well as profiles on alumni and donors.

370   US   ISSN 0007-8638
C M E A NEWS. 1947. q. $10. California Music Educators Association, 3924 Cottonwood Dr., Concord, CA 94519. TEL 510-685-3237. FAX 510-687-5246. Ed. Jerri Burke. adv. circ. 3,100. **Indexed:** Music Artic.Guide.

780.42 384.55   US   ISSN 0890-0795
C M J NEW MUSIC REPORT. (College Media Journal) 1978. w. $295. College Media Inc., 11 Middle Neck Rd., Ste. 400, Great Neck, NY 11021-3308. TEL 516-466-6000. FAX 516-466-7159. Ed. Scott Decker; Pub. Robert Haber. adv.; bk.rev.; film rev. circ. 3,000. (back issues avail.) **Document type:** trade publication.
  Former titles: Progressive Media (ISSN 0731-5708); C M J Progressive Media (ISSN 0195-7430)

780   US   ISSN 0162-6973
ML3505.8
CADENCE (REDWOOD); the review of jazz & blues: creative improvised music. 1976. m. $30 (foreign $35). Cadence Jazz & Blues Magazine Ltd., Cadence Bldg., Redwood, NY 13679-9612. TEL 315-287-2852. FAX 315-287-2860. Ed. Robert Rusch. adv. contact: Fred Dallas. bk.rev.; index. circ. 7,500. **Indexed:** Abstr.Pop.Cult, Microcomp.Ind., Music Ind., Pop.Mus.Per.Ind.
  —Faxon.
  Description: Features interviews, oral histories, news and coverage of record scenes.

780   RU
CADENCIES TO MOZART'S CONCERTS. a. 3.60 Rub. Izdatel'stvo Muzyka, Ul. Neglinnaya 14, Moscow 103031, Russia. TEL 924-81-63. FAX 921-83-53.

780.7   US   ISSN 0007-9405
CADENZA. 1942. 3/yr. $8 to non-members. Montana Music Educators Association, 3833 Audubon Way, Billings, MT 59102. TEL 406-652-1419. Ed. Ed Harris. adv.; illus. circ. 1,000.
  Description: Forum covering the study and teaching of music.

780.7   CN   ISSN 0703-8380
CADENZA. s-a. Can.$35. (Saskatchewan Music Educators' Association) Saskatchewan Teachers' Federation, Box 1108, Saskatoon, SK S7K 3N3, Canada. Ed. Ian Cochrane. bk.rev. circ. 500. **Document type:** newsletter.
  Former titles: S M E A. Journal (ISSN 0317-5073); S M E A. Newsletter (ISSN 0381-9051)

780.92   FR   ISSN 0395-1200
ML410.D28
CAHIERS DEBUSSY. 1974. a. 120 F. Centre de Documentation Claude Debussy, IRCAM, 31, rue Saint-Merri, 75004 Paris, France. TEL 42-77-06-39. Ed. Francois Lesure. adv.; illus. **Indexed:** RILM.

780   US   ISSN 0886-4594
CALENDAR FOR NEW MUSIC. 1979. m. (13/yr.). $13 (foreign $16) (students $9). SoundArt Foundation, Inc., Box 850, Philmont, NY 12565-0850. FAX 518-672-4775. Ed. William Hellermann. adv. circ. 6,500. **Document type:** newsletter.
  Former titles (until 1982): New Music News; Formerly (until 1981): New Music Calendar.

780.7   US
CALIFORNIA STUDIES IN 19TH CENTURY MUSIC. 1980. irreg., no.8, 1990. price varies. University of California Press, 2120 Berkeley Way, Berkeley, CA 94720. TEL 510-642-4247. FAX 510-643-7127. (Orders to: California-Princeton Fulfillment Services, 1445 Lower Ferry Rd., Ewing, NJ 08618. TEL 800-777-4726. FAX 800-999-1958) (back issues avail.) **Document type:** monographic series.
  Description: Discusses theory in music of the 19th century.
  Refereed Serial

782.1   UK   ISSN 0954-5867
ML1699
CAMBRIDGE OPERA JOURNAL. 1989. 3/yr. £49($79) (effective 1996). Cambridge University Press, Edinburgh Bldg., Shaftesbury Rd., Cambridge CB2 2RU, England. TEL 01223-312393. FAX 01223-315052. TELEX 851817256. (N. American addr.: Cambridge University Press, Journals Dept., 40 W. 20th St., New York, NY 10011. TEL 212-924-3900. FAX 212-691-3239) Eds. A. Groos, R. Parker. adv.; bk.rev. (back issues avail.) **Document type:** academic/scholarly publication.
  —BLDSC (3015.966900); Faxon; SWETS; UMI; UnCover. **CCC.**
  Description: Addresses audiences from a variety of disciplines, ranging from musicology to literature, theater, and history.

780   UK
CAMBRIDGE STUDIES IN MUSIC THEORY AND ANALYSIS. 1992. irreg. Cambridge University Press, Edinburgh Bldg., Shaftesbury Rd., Cambridge CB2 2RU, England. TEL 01233-312393. FAX 01233-315052. TELEX 851817256. (N. American addr.: Cambridge University Press, Journals Dept., 40 W. 20th St., New York, NY 10011. TEL 212-924-3900. FAX 212-691-3239) **Document type:** monographic series.

780.01   UK
CAMBRIDGE STUDIES IN PERFORMANCE PRACTICE. no.3, 1994. irreg. Cambridge University Press, Edinburgh Bldg., Shaftesbury Rd., Cambridge CB2 2RU, England. TEL 01223-312393. FAX 01223-315052. TELEX 817256. (N American addr.: Cambridge University Press, 40 W. 20th St., New York, NY 10011. TEL 212-924-3900. FAX 212-691-3239) **Document type:** monographic series.

CANADA'S ATLANTIC FOLKLORE AND FOLKLIFE SERIES. see *FOLKLORE*

MUSIC

785.06 CN ISSN 0833-9503
CANADIAN BAND ASSOCIATION (ONTARIO) INC. NEWSLETTER. 1971. q. membership. Canadian Band Association (Ontario) Inc., 21 Tecumseh St., Brantford, ON N3S 2B3, Canada. TEL 519-753-1858. Ed. Frank McKinnon. adv.; bk.rev. circ. 170. (processed) **Document type:** newsletter.
   Formerly: Canadian Band Directors Association. Newsletter (ISSN 0381-9159)
   Description: Promotes and develops the musical, educational and cultural values of bands in Ontario.

785 CN ISSN 0703-9077
CANADIAN BAND JOURNAL. 1975. q. Can.$20 (foreign Can.$28). Unison, Inc., P.O. Box 5005, Red Deer, AB T4N 5H5, Canada. TEL 403-342-3216. FAX 403-341-5474. Ed. Keith Mann; Pub. Keith Mann. adv.; bk.rev.; music rev.; index. circ. 3,500. (CD reviews) **Document type:** consumer publication.
   Description: A professional journal for instrumental music educators and performers.

780 CN ISSN 0045-4575
CANADIAN COIN BOX. 1946. 10/yr. Can.$28. N C C Publishing, 106 Lakeshore Rd. E., Ste. 209, Mississauga, Ont. L5G 1E38, Canada. TEL 519-376-9680. FAX 416-271-6373. Ed. Sandra Anderson. adv.; B&W page Can.$810; trim 8 1/2 x 11; adv. contact: Pete Wilkinson. circ. 1,861.
   Description: News for the coin-operated entertainment industry.

781.7 CN ISSN 0829-5344
ML3563
CANADIAN FOLK MUSIC BULLETIN. (Text in English, French) 1965. q. Can.$20($20) to individuals; students and seniors Can.$16($16); institutions Can.$20($20); subscribers receive both Journal and Bulletin. Canadian Society for Musical Traditions, P.O. Box 4232, Sta. C, Calgary, AB T2T 5N1, Canada. Eds. George Lyon, John Leeder. bk.rev. circ. 500. **Indexed:** M.L.A. **Document type:** bulletin.
   —UnCover.
   Formerly: Canadian Folk Music Society Newsletter (ISSN 0576-5234)

780 CN ISSN 0068-8746
CANADIAN FOLK MUSIC JOURNAL. (Text in English and French) 1973. a. Can.$20($20) to individuals; students and seniors Can.$16($16); institutions Can.$20($20); subscribers receive both Journal and Bulletin. Canadian Society for Musical Traditions, P.O. Box 4232, Sta. C, Calgary, Alta. T2T 5N1, Canada. Eds. Edith Fowke, Jay Rahn. bk.rev. circ. 500. **Indexed:** M.L.A., Music Ind.

CANADIAN MUSIC DIRECTORY. see *BUSINESS AND ECONOMICS — Trade And Industrial Directories*

780.7 CN ISSN 0008-4549
ML5
CANADIAN MUSIC EDUCATOR. Variant title: Canadian Journal of Research in Music Education. 1959. 3/yr. Can.$25 membership includes newsletter, journal and research journal. Canadian Music Educators Association, National Office, 16 Royaleigh Ave., Etobicoke, ON M9P 2J5, Canada. TEL 416-244-3745. FAX 416-235-1833. Ed. Brian Roberts. adv. contact: Donna Ferron. bk.rev.; charts; illus.; stat.; index. circ. 2,800. (back issues avail.) **Document type:** academic/scholarly publication.
   —UnCover.
   Incorporates: Canadian Music Educators Association. Newsletter (ISSN 0045-5172)

780.7 CN ISSN 1193-9567
ML5
CANADIAN MUSIC TEACHER. 1935. 3/yr. membership. Canadian Federation of Music Teachers' Associations, 616 Andrew St., Thunder Bay, ON P7B 2C9, Canada. Ed. Laura Gresch. adv.; bk.rev. circ. 4,000.
   Former titles (until 1991): Music News (ISSN 1187-676X); (until 1990): Canadian Federation of Music Teachers' Association. Newsletter (ISSN 0381-6494); (until 1975): Canadian Music Teacher (ISSN 0319-6356); (until 1971): Canadian Federation of Music Teachers' Association. News Bulletin (ISSN 0008-3534)

780 CN ISSN 0225-9435
CANADIAN MUSIC TRADE. 1979. bi-m. Can.$10($16) Norris - Whitney Communications Inc., 23 Hannover Dr., No. 7, St. Catharines, ON L2W 1A3, Canada. TEL 905-641-3471. FAX 905-641-1648. Ed. Shauna Kennedy. adv.; circ. 3,000. (controlled). **Document type:** trade publication.

780 CN ISSN 0708-9635
ML3848
CANADIAN MUSICIAN. 1979. bi-m. Can.$16($21) Norris - Whitney Communications Inc., 23 Hannover Dr., No. 7, St. Catharines, ON L2W 1A3, Canada. TEL 905-641-3471. FAX 905-641-1648. Ed. Shauna Kennedy. adv.; circ. 28,000. (back issues avail.) **Indexed:** Can.B.P.I., Can.Per.Ind., CMI, Music Ind. **Document type:** trade publication.
   —UnCover.

782.1 CN ISSN 0844-384X
CANADIAN OPERA COMPANY MAGAZINE. 1978. National Theatre Publications, 30 St. Clair Ave. W. No. 805, Toronto, ON M4V 3A1, Canada. TEL 416-926-7595. FAX 416-926-0407.

782.1 CN ISSN 0820-4896
CANADIAN OPERA COMPANY NEWS. 1982. 3/yr. Can.$50. Canadian Opera Company, 227 Front St. E., Toronto, ON M5A 1E8, Canada. TEL 416-363-6671. FAX 416-363-5584. circ. 14,000.
   Formerly (until 1986): C O C News (ISSN 0822-8922)
   Description: Information on forthcoming productions, as well as other activities and events.

780 CN ISSN 0710-0353
ML5
CANADIAN UNIVERSITY MUSIC REVIEW/REVUE DE MUSIQUE DES UNIVERSITES CANADIENNES. (Text in English and French) 1971. N.S. 1980. a. Can.$35 (foreign Can.$45). University of Toronto Press, Journals Department, 5201 Dufferin St., Downsview, ON M5H 5T8, Canada. TEL 613-667-7781. FAX 416-667-7881. Eds. Carl Morey, Marcelle Guertin. adv.; bk.rev. circ. 400. (also avail. in microfilm from UMI; back issues avail.; reprint service avail. from UMI) **Indexed:** Music Ind., RILM. **Document type:** academic/scholarly publication.
   —UMI; UnCover.
   Formerly: Canadian Association of University Schools of Music. Journal. (ISSN 0315-3541)

780 SP
CANCIONES CIFRADAS - J L A.* m. 330 ptas.($7) Ediciones Anel, San Vicente Ferrer 13, Granada, Spain. adv.; charts; illus. circ. 38,750. (back issues avail)
   Formerly: Acordes Cifrados para Guitarra.

783 IT
CANTUS PLANUS; rivista bimestrale di canti monodici delle liturgie latine. (Text in Latin) 1992. q. L.38000 (DM.61, 210 F., 54 SFr., 3850 ptas.) (effective 1992). Casa Musicale Edizioni Carrara, Via Calepio 4, Casella Postale 158, 24100 Bergamo, Italy. Ed. Angelo Rosso. **Document type:** consumer publication.

781.7 398 UK ISSN 0967-0599
CANU GWERIN/FOLK SONG. 1909. a. £5 (foreign £6). Welsh Folk-Song Society, c/o Mrs. B.L. Roberts, Hafan, Cricieth, Gwynedd, Wales. Eds. Rhidian Griffiths, Rhiannon Ifans. bk.rev. circ. 250. (back issues avail.) **Document type:** bulletin.
   Formerly (until 1978): Welsh Folk-Song Society. Journal.

780 IT ISSN 0394-2988
CAR AUDIO & FM; la prima rivista di musica in auto. 1986. m. L.80000 (foreign L.250000). Editore Progest s.r.l., Via Rovereto, 6, 00198 Rome, Italy. TEL 39-6-8591972. FAX 39-6-8558885. Ed. Gianni Caserta. adv. contact: Giovanni B. Rodinis. **Document type:** academic/scholarly publication.

780 IT ISSN 1120-7116
CAR STEREO E F M. 1989. bi-m. L.48000 (foreign L.190000). Editore Progest s.r.l., Via Rovereto, 6, 00198 Rome, Italy. TEL 39-6-8552084. FAX 39-6-8558885. Ed. Giovanni B. Rodinis. adv.: B&W page L.7250000, color page L.11600000.

789.5 US ISSN 0730-5001
ML1039
CARILLON NEWS. 1969. s-a. $5. Guild of Carillonneurs in North America, c/o Margo Halsted, Ed., University of Michigan, 900 Burton Tower, Ann Arbor, MI 48109-1270. TEL 313-764-2539. bk.rev. circ. 525. **Document type:** newsletter.
   Formerly: Randschriften; a Newsletter for the Guild of Carillonneurs (ISSN 0085-5383)

CARNEGIE MAGAZINE; dedicated to art, science, literature and music. see *ART*

784 IT ISSN 1120-4621
CARTELLINA; rivista bimestrale di didattica e musica corale. 1977. bi-m. L.50000 (foreign L.60000). Edizioni Suvini Zerboni, Via M.F. Quintiliano 40, 20138 Milan, Italy. TEL 0039-2-5084365. FAX 0039-2-5084261. Ed. Giovanni Acciai. adv.; bk.rev.; bibl.; cum.index. circ. 3,000. (back issues avail.)

789.91 US ISSN 0008-7289
ML1
CASH BOX;* the international music-record weekly. 1942. w. $185. Cash Box Publishing Co., Inc., 51 E. 8th St., Ste. 155, New York, NY 10003-6494. TEL 212-586-2640. Ed. Fred Goodman. adv.; illus.; rec.rev.; index. circ. 20,339. **Indexed:** Music Ind.

CASSETTE GAZETTE; audio magazine. see *LITERATURE*

780 FR
CATALOGUE GENERAL CLASSIQUE. a. 352 F. Diapason - Harmonie, 9-13 rue Colonel Pierre Avia, 75754 Paris Cedex 15, France.

781.64 US
CATALOGUE OF CONTEMPORARY MUSIC. irreg. (2-4/yr.) free. (American Composers Alliance) American Composers Edition, 170 W. 74th St., New York, NY 10023. TEL 212-362-8900. FAX 212-874-8605. Ed.Bd. (back issues avail.) **Document type:** catalog.
   Description: Sales and rental performance materials (scores and parts) for 20th century music written by members of ACA.

781.7 UK
CATALOGUE OF CONTEMPORARY WELSH MUSIC. irreg. £3 per no. Guild for the Promotion of Welsh Music, 94 Walter Rd., Swansea SA1 5QA, Wales. Ed. Robert Smith. **Document type:** catalog.

780 GW ISSN 0069-116X
ML113
CATALOGUS MUSICUS. 1963. irreg. price varies. (International Association of Music Libraries) Baerenreiter Verlag, Heinrich-Schuetz-Allee 35, 34131 Kassel, Germany. TEL 0561-3105-0. FAX 0561-3105240. (Subscr. in US to: Educational Music Service, 13 Elkay Dr., Chester, NY 10918. TEL 914-469-5790. FAX 914-469-5817) (Co-sponsor: International Musicological Society) Ed.Bd. **Document type:** academic/scholarly publication.

780 282 US ISSN 1059-9088
CATHOLIC MUSIC EDUCATOR. 1992. 5/yr. $18. National Association of Pastoral Musicians, New Music Educator Division, 225 Sheridan St., N.W., Washington, DC 20011. TEL 202-723-5800. FAX 202-723-2262. Ed. Rev. Virgil Funk. adv.; bk.rev.; illus. circ. 700.
   Description: Reports on news, issues and teaching materials for Catholic music educators.

268 782.5 028.5 US ISSN 1046-378X
ML1
CELEBRATE CHORAL MUSIC. q. $13.25. Southern Baptist Convention, Sunday School Board, 127 Ninth Ave., N., Nashville, TN 37234. TEL 800-458-2772.
   Formerly (until 1990): Opus One (ISSN 0162-430X)
   Description: Provides easy music an accompaniments in a variety of styles for younger youth choirs.

783 IT ISSN 0008-8706
CELEBRIAMO; rivista bimestrale di musica vocale per la liturgia. 1970. bi-m. L.48000 (foreign L.54000). Casa Musicale Edizioni Carrara, Casella Postale 158, Via Calepio 4, 24100 Bergamo, Italy. TEL 035-243618. Dir. Vittorio Carrara. adv.: B&W page L.600000. circ. 5,000.
   Supersedes: Organista; Musica Sacra; Scholare Assemblea; Lodiamo Il Signore; Fiori dell'Organo; Maestri dell'Organo.

CELEBRITY BIRTHDAY GUIDE. see *MOTION PICTURES*

CELEBRITY COMMUNICATOR. see *MOTION PICTURES*

CELEBRITY DIRECTORY. see *MOTION PICTURES*

CENTRE CULTUREL FRANCAIS DE YAOUNDE. PROGRAMME SAISON. see *ART*

780 FR ISSN 0998-6413
CENTRE INTERNATIONAL DE RECHERCHES EN ESTHETIQUE MUSICALE. CAHIERS. musique du XXe siecle. 1986. s-a. 340 F. Centre International de Recherche en Esthetique Musicale, B.P. 4174, 76723 Rouen Cedex, France. TEL 35-71-62-25. FAX 32-10-00-72. Ed. M. Biget. **Document type:** bibliography, monographic series.

780 020 IT
CENTRO INTERNAZIONALE DI RICERCA SUI PERIODICI MUSICALI. BOLLETTINO. 1992. s-a.? Centro Internazionale di Ricerca sui Periodici Musicali, Via del Conservatorio, 31 - bis, 43100 Parma, Italy. TEL 0521-236613. (Dist. by: UMI, 300 N. Zeeb Rd., Ann Arbor, MI 48106-1346) (Co-sponsor: Centro di Studi sull'Ottocento Musicale) Ed. Marcello Conati. **Document type:** bulletin.

783 XV ISSN 0351-496X
CERKVENI GLASBENIK. (Text in Slovenian; summaries in English) 1878. q. 810 SLT($13.50) (Sovenske Rimskokatoliske Skofije) Druzina, Cankarjevo Nabrezje 3-I, 61101 Ljubljana, Slovenia. TEL 061-221-324. Ed. Edo Skulj. circ. 1,500.

780 US ISSN 1071-1791
ML1
CHAMBER MUSIC. 1978. q. $60. Chamber Music America, 545 Eighth Ave., New York, NY 10018. TEL 212-244-2772. FAX 212-244-2776. Ed. Gwendolyn Freed; Pub. Leonard R. Levine. adv.; bk.rev. circ. 12,500. **Indexed:** Music Artic.Guide, Music Ind. **Document type:** consumer publication.
—Faxon.
   Former titles (until 1986): Chamber Music Magazine (ISSN 8755-0725); (until 1983): American Ensemble (ISSN 0197-3144)
   Description: News, features, profiles, events, and lists pertaining to chamber, instrumental ensembles, vocal ensembles, jazz ensembles, concert presenters, and audiences.

780 US
CHAMBER MUSIC DIRECTORY. 1978. a. $60. Chamber Music America, 545 Eighth Ave., New York, NY 10018. TEL 212-244-2772. Pub. Len Levine. adv. circ. 15,000. **Document type:** directory.
   Formerly: Chamber Music America. Membership Directory (ISSN 0277-4054)

781.7 CN
CHANSONS. 1984. bi-m. Can.$15 to individuals; institutions Can.$18; foreign Can.$24. Office des Communications Sociales, 1340 Est, bd. St-Joseph, Montreal, PQ H2J 1M3, Canada. TEL 514-524-8223. FAX 514-524-8522. (back issues avail.)
   Formely: Chansons d'Aujourd'hui (ISSN 0227-5023)
   Description: Covers music from francophone countries.

784 FR ISSN 0980-3785
CHANT CHORAL MAGAZINE. 4/yr. 140 F. (effective Jan. 1994). A Coeur Joie, Les Passerelles, 24 ave J. Masset, 69387 Lyon Cedex 09, France. TEL 78-83-19-61. Ed. Francois Harquel. adv. circ. 13,500. (back issues avail.)

780.7 028.5 FR
CHANTE ET RIS. q. A Coeur Joie, Les Passerelles, 24 ave J. Masset, 69387 Lyon Cedex 09, France. TEL 78-83-19-61. Ed. Monique Gelas. adv. circ. 4,000. (back issues avail.)

784 CN ISSN 1192-1900
CHANTER. 1976. q. Can.$10. Alliance des Chorales du Quebec, 4545 av. Pierre De Coubertin, C.P. 1000 Succursale M, Montreal, PQ H1V 3R2, Canada. TEL 514-252-3020. FAX 514-251-8038. TELEX 05-829647 SECADMIBEC. Ed. Daniel Gauvreau. adv. contact: Chantal Paquette. bk.rev.; rec.rev.; illus.; index. circ. 6,000. (back issues avail.)
   Formerly (until 1992): A l'Ecoute (ISSN 0700-3900)
   Description: Covers choral music and singers.

780 UK ISSN 0262-9577
CHART WATCH. 1981. q. $22.60. ChartWatch, 8 Worcester House, Bumpstead Rd., Haverhill, Suffolk CB9 8QB, England. Eds. Neil Rawlings, John Hancock. adv.; bk.rev.; charts. circ. 300.

380.1 IT
CHI E DOVE. (Special issue of Musica e Dischi) 1971. a. L.25000. Editoriale Musica e Dischi, Via De Amicis 47, 20123 Milan, Italy. TEL 39-2-58105737. FAX 39-2-8323843. Ed. Mario de Luigi. **Document type:** directory.
   Description: Lists addresses of people and companies operating in the Italian music business.

CHI SONO. see *BIOGRAPHY*

CHICAGO MAGAZINE. see *TRAVEL AND TOURISM*

787 US
CHICAGO SYMPHONY ORCHESTRA. q. Orchestral Association, 220 South Michigan Ave., Chicago, IL 60604-2270. TEL 312-435-8122. FAX 312-435-0126. Ed. Denise Wagner. adv.

780 IT ISSN 0069-3391
CHIGIANA; rassegna annuale di studi musicologici. 1964. a. price varies. Accademia Musicale Chigiana, Siena, Via di Citta 89, 53100 Siena, Italy. FAX 39-577-288124. (Dist. by: Casa Editrice Leo S. Olschki, Casella Postale 66, 50100 Florence, Italy. TEL 39-55-6350684) Ed. G. Burchi. bk.rev. circ. 500. **Indexed:** RILM.
   Formerly: Accademia Musicale Chigiana. Quaderni (ISSN 0065-0714)

780 RU
CHILDREN - MUSICIANS. 3/yr. 9.70 Rub. Izdatel'stvo Muzyka, Ul. Neglinnaya 14, Moscow 103031, Russia. TEL 924-81-63. FAX 921-83-53.

782.5 264 028.5 US ISSN 0895-7428
M2193
THE CHILDREN'S CHOIR. q. $13.50. Southern Baptist Convention, Sunday School Board, 127 Ninth Ave., N., Nashville, TN 37234. TEL 800-458-2772.
   Description: Contains choir music and activities directed to children ages 6-11 (grades 1-6).

780 US
CHILDREN'S CHOIR NEWSLETTER. 1953. q. $5. (Americas Boychoir Federation) Shallway Foundation, Shallway Bldg., Connellsville, PA 15425. TEL 412-628-3939. FAX 412-628-0682. (Co-sponsor: International Children's Choir Federation) Ed. John B. Shallenberger. circ. 1,400. (looseleaf format; back issues avail.) **Document type:** newsletter.
   Former titles: Americas Boychoir - International Children's Choir Federation. Newsletter; Children's Choir Newsletter.

781.7 US ISSN 0192-3749
ML336
CHINESE MUSIC. 1978. q. $25 to individuals; institutions $49. Chinese Music Society of North America, One Heritage Plaza, Box 5275, Woodridge, IL 60517-0275. TEL 708-910-1551. FAX 708-910-1561. Ed. Sin-Yan Shen. adv. contact: B.J. Jefferson. bk.rev.; rec.rev.; index; circ. 1,200 (paid). (also avail. in microform from UMI; back issues avail.) **Indexed:** Music Artic.Guide, Music Ind., RILM. **Document type:** academic/scholarly publication.
—UMI; UnCover.
   Formerly: Chinese Music General Newsletter.
   Description: Covers all phases of research and performance activities in Chinese music and its relation with music of the world. Provides a forum for original papers concerned with musicology, composition, acoustics, analysis, orchestration, musicians, global interactions, intercultural studies, and musical instruments.
Refereed Serial

780.01 HK
CHINESE UNIVERSITY OF HONG KONG. CHUNG CHI COLLEGE. MUSIC DEPARTMENT. HOLDINGS OF THE CHINESE MUSIC ARCHIVES. (Text in English and Chinese) 1974. a. Chinese University of Hong Kong, Chung Chi College, Music Department, Shatin, New Territories, Hong Kong. illus.

787 IT ISSN 1121-3531
CHITARRE; rivista di tecnica musicale e chitarristica. 1986. m. L.80000 (Europe L.80000; elsewhere L.120000). Edizioni Lakota, Via Pietro Mascagni 3-5, 00199 Rome, Italy. FAX 6-8608930. Ed. Andrea Carpi. adv.; bk.rev. circ. 20,000.

780 UK ISSN 0968-7262
ML5
CHOIR & ORGAN. 1993. 6/yr. £13.50($27) Orpheus Publications Ltd., 7 St. John's Rd., Harrow, Middlesex HA1 2EE, England. TEL 0181-863-2020. FAX 0181-424-9945. Ed. Basil Ramsey. adv. contact: Matthew Power. **Document type:** consumer publication.
—BLDSC (3181.538610); UnCover.

784 US
CHOIR HERALD. bi-m. Lorenz Publishing Co., 501 E. 3rd St., Box 802, Dayton, OH 45401-0802. TEL 513-228-6118. FAX 513-223-2042. Ed. Hugh S. Livingston, Jr. adv. contact: Larry Pugh. **Document type:** trade publication.

784 CN ISSN 0822-4749
CHOIRS ONTARIO. 1970. 4/yr. membership. Ontario Choral Federation, 100 Richmond St., E., Ste. 200, Toronto, ON M5C 2P9, Canada. TEL 416-363-7488. FAX 416-363-8236. Ed. Bev. Jahnke. adv. **Document type:** newsletter.
   Description: Information and articles of interest to Ontario Choirs and other choral enthusiasts.

784 GW ISSN 0940-600X
CHOR. 1947. q. DM.2. Deutschen Allgemeinen Saengerbundes e.V., Barbarastr. 7, 44357 Dortmund, Germany. TEL 0231-333352.

782.5 AU
CHOR AKTUELL; oesterreichische Saengerzeitung. q. S.240. Oesterreichischer Saengerbund, Opernring 11-5, A-1010 Vienna, Austria. TEL 01-5869494. FAX 01-58694944. adv.; bk.rev. **Indexed:** RILM. **Document type:** newsletter.

784 US ISSN 0009-5028
ML1
CHORAL JOURNAL. 1959. m. (Aug.-May). membership; libraries $15 (effective 1995 & 1996). American Choral Directors Association, Box 6310, Lawton, OK 73506-0310. TEL 405-355-8161. FAX 405-248-1465. Ed. John Silantien. adv. contact: Frank Fulmgr. bk.rev.; rec.rev.; illus.; index, cum.index: vols.1-32; circ. 18,000 (paid). (also avail. in microfilm from UMI; microfiche from UMI; reprint service avail. from UMI) **Indexed:** Music Artic.Guide, Music Ind., RILM. **Document type:** academic/scholarly publication.
—Faxon; UMI; UnCover.
   Description: Publishes articles of both a practical and scholarly nature which explore various aspects of choral conducting.
Refereed Serial

780 US ISSN 0069-3758
CHORD AND DISCORD. 1933. irreg. (every 3-4 yrs.) free. Bruckner Society of America Inc., 2150 Dubuque Rd., Iowa City, IA 52240-9632. TEL 319-351-5758. Ed. Charles Eble. circ. 750. **Document type:** academic/scholarly publication.

784 028.5 US ISSN 0412-2801
ML1
CHORISTERS GUILD LETTERS. 1949. 10/yr. $40. Choristers Guild, 2834 W. Kingsley Rd., Garland, TX 75041. TEL 214-271-1521. FAX 214-840-3113. Ed. Donald F. Jensen. adv. contact: Kathy Guttierrez. bk.rev.; bibl.; charts; illus.; index. circ. 8,500. (back issues avail.) **Indexed:** Music Artic.Guide. **Document type:** newsletter.
   Description: Focuses on music with young people. Includes articles, news releases, reviews, and study plans pertaining to choral compositions, with announcements and news on the members and activities of the guild.

MUSIC   4837

784 658.048   AU
CHORMAGAZIN. 1974. q. S.4. Oesterreichischer Arbeiter-Saengerbund, Arndtstr. 27, A-1120 Vienna, Austria. TEL 0222-830220. FAX 0222-67660127. Ed. Georg Stockreiter. charts; illus.
Formerly: Oesterreichische Arbeitersaenger.

780   GW   ISSN 0172-2255
DER CHORSAENGER. 1951. q. membership. Mitteldeutscher Saengerbund e.V., Ulmenstr. 16, 34117 Kassel, Germany. TEL 0561-15888. FAX 0561-107567. Ed. Helmuth Breiter. adv.; bk.rev. circ. 3,800. **Document type:** newsletter.

784   GW
CHORSZENE. 1980. s-a. free. Staedtischen Musikvereins zu Duesseldorf e.V., Heinrich-Heine-Allee 22, 40213 Duesseldorf, Germany. TEL 0211-329191. circ. 5,000. (back issues avail.)

784   CN   ISSN 0821-1108
CHORUS. 1976. q. Can.$20. Nova Scotia Choral Federation, 1809 Barrington St., Ste. 901, Halifax, NS B3J 3K8, Canada. TEL 902-423-4688. FAX 902-422-0881. E-mail: NSCF@FOX.NSTN.CA. Ed. Susan Marsh. adv.; B&W page Can.$100. circ. 350.
Description: Articles of interest to members and choral music enthusiasts. Information on federation programs and services.

780   US   ISSN 1044-7857
CHORUS!.* 1989. m. $19.95. (Norcross Music Association) D S C Publishing, Box 2318, Duluth, GA 30136. TEL 404-497-1902. Ed. Mark Gresham. adv.; bk.rev. circ. 3,000. (tabloid format; back issues avail.) **Indexed:** Music Artic.Guide. **Document type:** newspaper.
Description: For the choral music enthusiast, whether singer, listener, educator, conductor or composer; contains interviews, articles, reviews, concert calendar.

781.62   FR   ISSN 1241-7076
CHORUS; les cahiers de la chanson. 1992. q. 250 F. (Europe 290 F.; N. America 320 F.). Editions du Verbe, B.P. 28, 28270 Brezolles, France. TEL 16-737-43-66-60. FAX 16-37-43-62-71. Ed. Fred Hidalgo. adv. contact: Fred Hidalgo. bk.rev.; music rev.; index. circ. 15,000. **Document type:** consumer publication.
Description: Studies the news and history of French songs and music.

780.1   US
CHRISTIAN MUSIC DIRECTORIES: PRINTED MUSIC. 1976. a. (plus q. updates). $160. Resource Publications, Inc., 160 E. Virginia St., San Jose, CA 95112. TEL 408-286-8505. FAX 408-287-8748. circ. 1,200 (paid). **Document type:** directory.
Formerly: Music Locator (ISSN 0899-0115)
Description: Lists religious music by title, composer and songbook or collection.

783 621.389 200   US   ISSN 1048-6844
ML156.4.R4
CHRISTIAN MUSIC DIRECTORIES: RECORDED MUSIC. 1974. a. $160 (effective 1995). Resource Publications, Inc., 160 E. Virginia St., No. 290, San Jose, CA 95112. TEL 408-286-8505. FAX 408-287-8748. circ. 1,200 (paid). **Document type:** directory.
Former titles (until 1989): Recording Locator (ISSN 0899-0123); (until 1981): Musicatalog.
Description: Lists religious music available in recorded form by artist, title and album name.

783   UK   ISSN 0307-6334
ML5
CHURCH MUSIC QUARTERLY. 1963. q. membership. Royal School of Church Music, Addington Palace, Croydon CR9 5AD, England. TEL 0181-341-6408. FAX 0181-340-0021. Ed. Trevor Ford. adv. contact: Anne Hastings. bk.rev.; rec.rev.; bibl.; charts; illus.; circ. 14,500 (controlled). (reprint service avail. from UMI) **Document type:** bulletin.
Formerly: Promoting Church Music (ISSN 0033-1112)
Description: Contains articles, interviews, profiles, news and information.

781.7 200   US   ISSN 1071-9903
THE CHURCH MUSIC REPORT. 1984. m. $39.95. T C M R Communications Inc., Box 1179, Grapevine, TX 76099-1179. TEL 817-488-0141. FAX 817-481-4191. Ed. William H. Rayborn. adv.; bk.rev. circ. 6,600. **Document type:** newsletter.

781.7   US   ISSN 0009-6466
ML1
THE CHURCH MUSICIAN. 1950. q. $23.95. Southern Baptist Convention, Sunday School Board, 127 Ninth Ave., N., Nashville, TN 37234. TEL 800-251-5933. circ. 20,000. **Indexed:** Chr.Per.Ind., Music Ind., South.Bap.Per.Ind.
Description: Contains professional articles for church music directors and other church music leaders.

786   US   ISSN 0890-9032
M21
CHURCH PIANIST. 1984. bi-m. $22.95. Lorenz Publishing Co., 501 E. Third St., Box 802, Dayton, OH 45401-0802. TEL 513-228-6118. FAX 513-223-2042. Ed. Hugh S. Livingston, Jr. adv. contact: Larry Pugh. **Document type:** trade publication.

784   US
CI KAN/VERSES. (Text in Chinese) bi-m. $20.50. China Books & Periodicals, Inc., 2929 24th St., San Francisco, CA 94110. TEL 415-282-2994. FAX 415-282-0994.

CIAO 2001. see CHILDREN AND YOUTH — For

780.7   SP
CICLO VIDA Y OBRA. no.6, 1983. Asociacion de Compositores Sinfonicos Espanoles, Teatro Real, Calle Carlos III, Madrid, Spain.

786.6   UK
CINEMA ORGAN. 1953. q. membership. Cinema Organ Society, 3 Dorothy Farm Rd., Rayleigh, Essex SS6 8RE, England. Ed. Tony Bernard Smith. adv.; bk.rev.; illus. circ. 2,050.

780.904   CN   ISSN 1183-1693
CIRCUIT; revue nord-americaine de musique du XXe siecle. 1991. s-a. Can.$32 to individuals; institutions Can.$51. (Nouvel Ensemble Moderne) Presses de l'Universite de Montreal, C.P. 6128, Succ. A, Montreal, PQ H3C 3J7, Canada. FAX 514-343-5727. (Subscr. to: Periodica, C.P. 444, Outremont, PQ H2V 4R6, Canada. TEL 514-274-5468) Ed. Jean-Jacques Nattiez. **Document type:** academic/scholarly publication.

791.3   US   ISSN 0009-7365
ML3533.8
CIRCUS.* 1969. m. $22. Circus Enterprises Corp., 6 W. 18th St., New York, NY 10011. TEL 212-242-4902. FAX 212-242-5734. Ed. Gerald Rothberg. adv. contact: Gary Victor. bk.rev.; film rev.; rec.rev.; illus. circ. 307,092. (also avail. in microform from UMI)
—UMI.
Former titles (until 1979): Circus Weekly (ISSN 0164-9248); (until 1978): Circus (ISSN 1044-2553)
Description: Popular music publication that covers music news and rock-and-roll personalities.

780   UK
CITY OF BIRMINGHAM SYMPHONY ORCHESTRA. BROADSHEET. a. free. City of Birmingham Symphony Orchestra, Paradise Pl., Birmingham B3 3RP, England. FAX 0121-223-2423. circ. 250,000. (broadsheet format)

780   UK
CITY OF BIRMINGHAM SYMPHONY ORCHESTRA. SUMMER SEASON BROCHURE. a. free. City of Birmingham Symphony Orchestra, Paradise Pl., Birmingham B3 3RP, England. FAX 0121-233-2423. circ. 150,000.
Formerly: City of Birmingham Symphony Orchestra. Prom Prospectus.

780   IT
CIVICA SCUOLA DI MUSICA. QUADERNI. 1980. q. free. Civica Scuola di Musica, Via Stilicone 36, 20142 Milan, Italy. TEL 02-313334. FAX 02-3315697. Ed. Massimilano Carraro. circ. 2,500. **Document type:** academic/scholarly publication.
●Also available online.

786   US   ISSN 1054-5824
CLAPPER. 1973. q. $15. North American Guild of Change Ringers, c/o Kathryn Almy, 9855 Milo Rd., Plainwell, MI 49080. adv.; bk.rev.; circ. 350 (paid). **Document type:** newsletter.
Description: Provides information regarding educational materials, activities and issues concerning the practice of change ringing for guild members.

780   US   ISSN 0361-5553
ML1
CLARINET. 1973. q. $30 (foreign $40). International Clarinet Association, College of Music, University of North Texas, Denton, TX 76203. TEL 817-565-4096. FAX 817-565-2002. Ed. James Gillespie. adv.; bk.rev.; charts; illus.; stat. circ. 3,000. (back issues avail.) **Indexed:** Music Artic.Guide, Music Ind. **Document type:** academic/scholarly publication.
—Faxon; UnCover.
Description: Contains articles and a wide range of subjects written by the world's leading performers, teachers and scholars. Topics include performance and pedagogy, care and repair, acoustics and instrument design, repertoire, history, and reviews of new publications and recordings. Also includes reports on clinics, master classes, and activities of the membership.

788   UK   ISSN 0260-390X
CLARINET AND SAXOPHONE. vol.5, 1980. q. membership. Clarinet and Saxophone Society of Great Britain, 26 Monks Orchard, Wilmington, Kent, England. illus.
—BLDSC (3274.376500).
Formerly: C A S S News (ISSN 0308-9053)

780   FR   ISSN 0761-9553
ML929
CLARINETTE MAGAZINE. (Text in French; summaries in English) 1984. q. 180 Fr. Clarinette Magazine, 5 rue des Fleurs, 67550 Vendenheim, France. Ed. Jean-Marie Paul. adv.; bk.rev. circ. 700.
Description: All aspects about the Clarinet; interviews with players, information on composers, special events, competitions, new records and scores.

780   UK   ISSN 0959-7204
CLASSIC C D; the magazine you can listen to. 1990. m. £39($80) (includes m. extracts on CD). Future Publishing, 30 Monmouth St., Bath BA1 2AB, England. TEL 01225-442244. FAX 01225-462986. (Subscr. to: Future Publishing, Somerton, Somerset TA11 6BR, England. TEL 01225-822511) Ed. R. Ainsley. adv.; bk.rev.; music rev.; index. circ. 75,000. (back issues avail.) **Document type:** consumer publication.
Description: Presents new recordings of classical music with news, features, and other articles of general interest.

780   FI   ISSN 1236-0325
CLASSICA. 1990. q. FIM 390. Yhtyneet Kuvalehdet oy, Maistraatinportti 1, FIN-00240 Helsinki, Finland. TEL 358-0-156-6524. FAX 358-0-156-6505. Ed. Liisa Tikkanen. adv.; B&W page FIM 5700, color page SEK 9500. circ. 10,881.
Description: Focuses on classical music and related subjects: concerts, sound recordings, reproduction equipment.

787   UK   ISSN 0950-429X
CLASSICAL GUITAR. 1982. m. £35 (rest of Europe £39.95 ($64.35); the Americas and S. Africa £56.65 ($101.75); elsewhere £60.50 ($111.10); newsstand price: £2.20 ($4.50). Ashley Mark Publishing Co., Olsover House, 43 Sackville Rd., Newcastle-upon-Tyne NE6 5TA, England. TEL 0191-276-0448. FAX 0191-276-1623. Ed. Maurice J. Summerfield. adv.; B&W page £420, color page £695; trim 264 X 180; adv. contact: Simer Turnbull. circ. 8,500. (back issues avail.) **Document type:** consumer publication.
—Faxon; UnCover.
Description: Aimed at a player, a teacher, or a listener. Devoted to the classical guitar, with some flamenco and some lute coverage.

MUSIC

780   UK   ISSN 0961-2696
CLASSICAL MUSIC. 1976. fortn. £71. Rhinegold Publishing Ltd., 241 Shaftesbury Ave., London WC2H 8EH, England. TEL 0171-333-1742. FAX 0171-333-1769. (Subscr. to: P.O. Box 47, Gravesend, Kent DA12 2AN, England) Ed. Keith Clarke. adv.; bk.rev. **Document type:** trade publication.
—BLDSC (3274.556900).
    Former titles: Classical Music and Album Reviews; (until Sept. 1978): Classical Music Weekly (ISSN 0308-9762)

787   CN   ISSN 1185-9717
ML5
CLASSICAL MUSIC MAGAZINE. 5/yr. 121 Lakeshore Rd. E., Ste. 207, Mississuaga, ON L5G 1E5, Canada. TEL 905-271-0339. FAX 905-271-9748. Ed. Rick Macmillian. **Document type:** consumer publication.
—BLDSC (3274.556970).

786.2   UK   ISSN 0969-5818
CLASSICAL PIANO. 1993. bi-m. £12 (foreign £20). Rhinegold Publishing Ltd., 241 Shaftesbury Ave., London WC2H 8EH, England. TEL 0171-333-1724. FAX 0171-333-1769. Ed. Jessica Duchen. **Document type:** consumer publication.
    Description: Magazine for pianists, technicians and lovers of piano music.

780   RU
CLASSICS OF WORLD MUSIC CULTURE. a. 3.10 Rub. Izdatel'stvo Muzyka, Ul. Neglinnaya 14, Moscow 103031, Russia. TEL 924-81-63. FAX 921-83-53.

780   SP
CLAVE PROFESSIONAL. m. Clave Professional, Av. Gaudi 10, 2o 1a, 08025 Barcelona, Spain. TEL 34-3-3475199. FAX 34-3-4561729. Ed. Carlos Bosch; Pub. Jordi Rueda. adv. contact: Elisa Munoz. **Document type:** trade publication.

786   US   ISSN 0009-854X
ML1
CLAVIER; a magazine for pianists and organists. 1962. 10/yr. $18. Instrumentalist Co., 200 Northfield Rd., Northfield, IL 60093-3390. TEL 708-446-5000; 800-323-5559. Pub. James T. Rohner. adv.; bk.rev.; rec.rev.; illus.; index. circ. 18,000. **Indexed:** Amer.Bibl.Slavic & E.Eur.Stud, Arts & Hum.Cit.Ind., Curr.Cont., Educ.Ind., Music Artic.Guide, Music Ind., RILM.
—Faxon; UnCover.

786   US   ISSN 0279-0858
ML3930.A2
CLAVIER'S PIANO EXPLORER. 1981. 10/yr. $6. Instrumentalist Co., 200 Northfield Rd., Northfield, IL 60093-3390. TEL 708-446-5000; 800-323-5559. Ed. Ann Rohner Callis; Pub. James T. Rohner. circ. 73,000.

CLOCKWATCH REVIEW; a journal of the arts. see LITERATURE

781.7   US   ISSN 0896-372X
ML1
CLOSE UP MAGAZINE. Running title: C M A Close Up. 1959. m. membership only. Country Music Association, Inc., One Music Circle S., Nashville, TN 37203-4312. TEL 615-244-2840. FAX 615-726-0314. Ed. Janet E. Williams. bk.rev.; illus. circ. 8,000. **Document type:** trade publication.
    Formerly: Close-Up (ISSN 0009-9449)

781.6   SW   ISSN 1103-3568
CLOSE-UP MAGAZINE. 1991. q. SEK 130. S A Tidnings AB, P.O. Box 1617, S-60046 Norrkoeping, Sweden. TEL 46-11-18-03-30. FAX 46-11-10-00-11. Ed. Robert Becirovic. circ. 15,000 (paid). **Document type:** consumer publication.
    Description: Specializes in speed, death, hardcore and black metal music. Sometimes includes CDs.

781.57   CN   ISSN 0820-926X
ML5
CODA MAGAZINE; the journal of jazz and improvised music. 1958. 6/yr. Can.$25.68 (foreign $24). Coda Publications, P.O. Box 1002, Sta. O, Toronto, ON M4A 2N4, Canada. TEL 416-593-7230. FAX 416-593-7230. Ed. Bill Smith; Pub. John Norris. adv.; bk.rev.; rec.rev.; circ. 3,000 (paid). (also avail. in microfilm from UMI,MML; back issues avail.; reprint service avail. from UMI, MML) **Indexed:** Can.B.P.I., Can.Per.Ind., CMI, Music Ind., New Per.Ind., Pop.Mus.Per.Ind. **Document type:** consumer publication.
—Faxon; UMI; UnCover.
    Formerly: Coda (ISSN 0010-017X)
    Description: Contains articles and interviews covering the entire spectrum of the music.

780 700   SP
COLECCION ETHOS. (In 2 series: Musica, Arte) 1980. irreg., no.17, 1992. price varies. Universidad de Oviedo, Area de Musicologia, Servicio de Publicaciones, C. Arguelles, 19, 33003 Oviedo, Spain. TEL 34-85-210160. FAX 34-85-218352. Dirs. Emilio Casares Rodicio, Angel Medina Alvarez. **Document type:** academic/scholarly publication, monographic series.

780   IT
COLLANA DI MUSICHE VENEZIANE INEDITE O RARE. 1962. irreg., no.8, 1973. price varies. Casa Editrice Leo S. Olschki, Casella Postale 66, 50100 Florence, Italy. TEL 39-55-6530684. FAX 39-55-6530214. **Document type:** monographic series.

780   FR   ISSN 0224-747X
COLLECTION PSYCHOLOGIE ET PEDAGOGIE DE LA MUSIQUE. 1978. irreg. price varies. Editions Scientifiques et Psychologigues, 6 bis, rue Andre-Chenier, 92130 Issy-les-Moulineaux, France. TEL 46-45-38-12. FAX 40-95-73-32. TELEX 370 105 F. (back issues avail.)

780   UK   ISSN 0261-2550
COLLECTORS ITEMS. 1980. 6/yr. £17 (Europe £19.50; America £25; elsewhere £26). J & M Records, P.O. Box 276, Taunton TA3 6YZ, England. TEL 01823-481234. FAX 01823-480167. Ed. John Holley. bk.rev.; bibl. circ. 1,000. (back issues avail.) **Document type:** consumer publication.
    Description: Contains material of interest to jazz and blues collectors.

785   US   ISSN 0742-8480
ML1299
COLLEGE BAND DIRECTORS NATIONAL ASSOCIATION JOURNAL. 1984. irreg. $15 for 2 issues. College Band Directors National Association, c/o A-R Editions Inc., 801 Deming Way, Madison, WI 53717. Ed. James Arrowood. bk.rev. circ. 1,100.
—Faxon; UnCover.

780 378   US
COLLEGE MUSIC SOCIETY. NEWSLETTER. bi-m. $37 membership. College Music Society, 202 W. Spruce St., Missoula, MT 29802-4202. TEL 406-721-9616. FAX 406-721-9419. Ed. K. Marie Stolba. bk.rev. circ. 3,000. (back issues avail.) **Document type:** newsletter.

780   US   ISSN 0069-5696
ML1
COLLEGE MUSIC SYMPOSIUM. 1961. a. $25. College Music Society, 202 W. Spruce St., Missoula, MT 59802. TEL 406-721-9616. FAX 406-721-9419. Ed. Ann Dhu McLucas. adv.: page $175; trim 7 x 9 1/2. bk.rev. circ. 4,500. **Indexed:** Arts & Hum.Cit.Ind., Curr.Cont., Music Artic.Guide, Music Ind., RILM. **Document type:** academic/scholarly publication.
—BLDSC (3311.175000); Faxon; Genuine Article; UMI; UnCover.
    Refereed Serial

780   US   ISSN 0147-0108
M2
COLLEGIUM MUSICUM: YALE UNIVERSITY. 1955. irreg. price varies. (Yale University, Department of Music) A-R Editions, Inc., 801 Deming Way, Madison, WI 53717. TEL 608-836-9000. FAX 608-831-8200. Eds. Leon Plantinga, James Grier. circ. 413. (back issues avail.) **Indexed:** Music Ind., RILM. **Document type:** academic/scholarly publication.

COLOQUIO: ARTES; revista de artes visuais musica e bailado. see ART

780.7 370   US   ISSN 0010-1672
COLORADO MUSIC EDUCATOR.* 1953. q. $1.75 to non-members. Colorado Music Educators Association, 1309 Rollingwood La., Fort Collins, CO 80525-1945. Ed. Kevin J. McCarthy. adv.; bk.rev.; illus. circ. 2,200. **Indexed:** Music Artic.Guide.
—UnCover.
    Description: Presents study and teaching methods.

COMPANY NORTH AMERICA. see LITERARY AND POLITICAL REVIEWS

780   PL
COMPENDIUM MUSICUM. (Text in Polish; summaries in English) 1983. irreg. price varies. Polskie Wydawnictwo Muzyczne, Al. Krasinskiego 11a, 31-111 Krakow, Poland. TEL 48-12-227044. FAX 48-12-220174. adv. contact: Teresa Wlochynska. **Document type:** academic/scholarly publication.
    Description: Series of elementary textbooks covering all fields of music.

780   US
COMPOSER - U S A. 1932. 3/yr. $20. National Association of Composers - U S A, Box 49652, Barrington Sta., Los Angeles, CA 90049. TEL 310-541-8213. Ed. Albert Bennerk. adv.; bk.rev. circ. 600. (tabloid format) **Indexed:** Music Artic.Guide. **Document type:** newsletter.

780 927   US   ISSN 0069-8016
COMPOSERS OF THE AMERICAS/COMPOSITORES DE AMERICA. 1955. a. $7. Organization of American States, 1889 F St., N.W., Washington, DC 20006. TEL 703-941-1617. circ. 2,000.

789.91   NE
COMPOSERS' VOICE; Dutch contemporary music on compact discs. 1975. irreg. Donemus Amsterdam, Paulus Potterstraat 14, 1071 CZ Amsterdam, Netherlands. TEL 31-20-6764436. (Dist. in U.S. and Canada by: Records International, Box 1140, Goleta, CA 93116)
    Formerly: Donemus Audio-Visual Series.

780   GW
CONCENTUS MUSICUS. 1973. irreg., vol.9, 1992. price varies. (Deutsches Historisches Institut in Rom, Musikgeschichtliche Abteilung, IT) Laaber-Verlag, Regensburger Str. 19, 93164 Laaber, Germany. TEL 09498-2307. FAX 09498-2543. illus. **Document type:** monographic series.

CONCERT. see CHILDREN AND YOUTH — For

780   US
CONCERTINA & SQUEEZEBOX; international journal for reed musicians. 1983. q. $20. J.M. Cowan, Ed. & Pub., Box 6706, Ithaca, NY 14851. adv.; bk.rev. circ. 1,200. **Document type:** newsletter, academic/scholarly publication.
    Former titles: Concertina and Free Reed; Concertina.
    Description: Covers concertinas, accordions, bandoliers and other reed instruments.

745   UK
THE CONDUCTOR. 1947. q. £2 to non-members. National Association of Brass Band Conductors, Marrey, 7 Carr View Rd., Hepworth, Huddersfield HD7 7HN, England. TEL 01484-683793. FAX 01484-608512. Ed. Jeffrey Turner. adv. contact: Jeffrey Turner. bk.rev.; music rev.; circ. 300 (paid). (back issues avail.) **Document type:** bulletin.
    Description: Assists members with problems, stimulates interest, and improves the standards of musicianship as well as enhancing prestige.
    Refereed Serial

780   US   ISSN 0734-1032
ML457
CONDUCTORS' GUILD. JOURNAL. 1980. q. $30 (effective 1995). Conductors' Guild, Inc., Box 3361, W. Chester, PA 19381. TEL 215-430-6010. FAX 215-430-6010. E-mail: conguild@aol.com. Ed. Jacques Voois. adv.; bk.rev. circ. 1,500. **Indexed:** Music Artic.Guide, RILM. **Document type:** academic/scholarly publication.
—UnCover.

MUSIC 4839

780 US
CONDUCTORS' GUILD NEWSLETTER. 1978. q. $60. Conductors' Guild, Inc., Box 3361, West Chester, PA 19381. TEL 610-430-6010. FAX 610-430-6010. E-mail: conguild@aol.com. (Alt. addr.: S. High St., Rm.6, West Chester, PA 19382) Ed. Lauren Green. circ. 1,500. **Document type:** newsletter.

781.7 ZR ISSN 0010-5775
CONGO DISQUE;* revue de la musique congolaise moderne. vol.5, 1967. B.P. 6112, Kinshasa 6, Zaire. adv.; illus.

781 US ISSN 1076-2485
CONNECTIONS (ROXBURY). 1986. q. $30 U.S. membership; non U.S. $35; low income U.S. member $18; non-U.S. $23; family membership $45; newsstand price: $5. Music for People, 7 Middletown Rd., Roxbury, NH 03431. TEL 603-352-4941. FAX 603-352-8377. Ed. Bonnie S. Insull. adv. contact: Bonnie Insull. bk.rev. circ. 1,000. (back issues avail.) **Document type:** newsletter.
 Description: Articles on musical improvisation, self-expression, creativity, music and healing.

780.7 SZ ISSN 0010-6550
CONSERVATOIRE DE MUSIQUE DE GENEVE. BULLETIN. 1933. 10/yr. 30 SFr. Conservatoire de Musique de Geneve, Case Postale 5155, CH-1211 Geneva 11, Switzerland. TEL 022-3117633. FAX 022-3121810. Ed.Bd. adv. circ. 3,500. **Document type:** bulletin.

780 UK ISSN 0268-9111
ML467
CONSORT. 1929. a. plus Bulletin 3/yr. £12 (foreign £15). Dolmetsch Foundation Inc., 15 Hamlyn Ave., Hull HU4 6BT, England. Ed. Gwilym Beechey. adv.; bk.rev.; charts; illus.; cum.index: 1929-1987. circ. 900. (also avail. in microfilm; reprint service avail. from UMI) **Indexed:** Br.Hum.Ind., Music Ind., RILM. —UnCover.

CONTACTS & FACILITIES IN THE AUSTRALIAN ENTERTAINMENT INDUSTRY. see *THEATER*

780 IT
CONTATTO DISCOGRAFICO. m. A W F Productions International, Largo Olgiata 15, is. 75, 6-6, 00123 Rome, Italy. TEL 39-6-30880255. FAX 39-6-30888687. Ed. Gianluca Zanna; Pub. Alessandro Cerreoni. adv. **Document type:** trade publication.

782 US
CONTEMPORARY A CAPPELLA NEWSLETTER. 1990. bi-m. $15 to individuals; institutions $20 (effective 1995-96). Contemporary A Cappella Society of America, 1850 Union, Ste. 1441, San Francisco, CA 94123. TEL 415-563-5224. FAX 415-921-2834. Ed. Deke Sharon. adv.; bk.rev.; music rev.; rec.rev. circ. 4,000. (back issues avail.)
 Description: Contains news, articles, reviews and interviews for a cappella groups and fans.

780 US ISSN 1049-3379
CONTEMPORARY CHRISTIAN MUSIC. Short title: C C M. 1978. m. $19.95. C C M Communications, 107 Kenner Ave., Nashville, TN 37205-2207. TEL 614-386-3011. FAX 614-386-3380. Ed. John W. Styll. adv.; bk.rev.; rec.rev. circ. 80,000. (back issues avail.) **Document type:** consumer publication.
 Former titles (until 1986): Contemporary Christian (ISSN 0746-0066); (until 1983): Contemporary Christian Music (ISSN 0164-6664)
 Description: Seeks to promote spiritual growth by using contemporary Christian mucis as a "window" into issues of life and faith.

780 IE
CONTEMPORARY MUSIC CENTRE. LIBRARY CATALOGUE (YEAR). a. Contemporary Music Centre, 95 Lower Baggot St., Dublin 2, Ireland. TEL 01-6612105. FAX 01-6762639. E-mail: info@cmc.ie. Ed. Eve O'Kelly. **Document type:** catalog.

780 US ISSN 0749-4467
ML197
CONTEMPORARY MUSIC REVIEW. 1984. 2/yr. 69 ECU (effective 1996). Harwood Academic Publishers, c/o International Publishers Distributor, 820 Town Center Dr., Langhorne, PA 19047. TEL 215-750-2642. FAX 215-750-6343. (Subsc. to: International Publishers Distributor, PO Box 90, Reading, Berkshire, RG1 8JL, England. TEL 44-173-456-8316) Ed Nigel Osborne. (also avail. in microform; back issues avail.)
 —BLDSC (3425.192200). **CCC.**
 Description: Covers composition today - its techniques, aesthetics, technology and its relationship to other disciplines as well as current thought.
 Refereed Serial

780 US ISSN 0891-5415
CONTEMPORARY MUSIC STUDIES. irreg., latest vol.9. price varies. Harwood Academic Publishers, c/o International Publishers Distributor, 820 Town Center Dr.553, PA 19047. TEL 215-750-2642. FAX 215-750-6343. (UK subscr. to: Box 90, Reading, Berkshire RG1 8JL, England. TEL 0734-560-080) Ed. Nigel Osborne. (also avail. in microform) **Document type:** monographic series.
 —BLDSC (3425.192250).
 Refereed Serial

920 US ISSN 1044-2197
ML385
CONTEMPORARY MUSICIANS. 1989. s-a. $55 (effective Nov. 1992). Gale Research Inc., 835 Penobscot Bldg., Detroit, MI 48226. TEL 313-961-2242; 800-877-4253. FAX 313-961-6083. TELEX 810-221-7086. (also avail. in magnetic tape; diskette format)
 ●Also available online. Vendor(s): Lexis-Nexis.
 Description: Contains approximately 100 biographical entries on artists in the music business.

782.5 264 US ISSN 1046-3801
M2198
CONTEMPORARY PRAISE. 1974. q. $13.25. Southern Baptist Convention, Sunday School Board, 127 Ninth Ave., N., Nashville, TN 37234. TEL 800-458-2772.
 Formerly (until 1990): Gospel Choir (ISSN 0362-0417)
 Description: Provides music and accompaniments for ensembles and youth choirs

780 US
CONTEMPORARY RECORD SOCIETY. SOCIETY NEWS MAGAZINE. 1983. s-a. $40 (foreign $65). Contemporary Record Society, 724 Winchester Rd., Broomall, PA 19008. TEL 215-544-5920. FAX 215-544-5921. Ed. John Perotti. adv.: page $1200; 7 1/3 x 10; adv. contact: Jack Shusterman. bk.rev.; music rev.; rec.rev.; video rev.; index. circ. 90,000. (back issues avail.) **Document type:** trade publication.
 Description: Includes members' progress notes, award and performance possibilities, concert listings, employment opportunities and feature articles of renowned composers and performers.

780 US ISSN 0705-6656
CONTINUO; an early music magazine. 1977. 6/yr. $30 in U.S.; Canada $35; elsewhere $63; newsstand price: $6. Matthew James Redsell, Ed.& Pub., Box 327, Hammondsport, NY 14840. TEL 607-569-2489. adv.: B&W page $150; trim 7 1/4 x 9 3/4. bk.rev. circ. 1,200. **Document type:** newsletter.
 —Faxon.
 Supersedes: Early Music Directory (ISSN 0705-6648); Which was formerly: Toronto Early Music Directory (ISSN 0229-9690)

780 AT ISSN 0310-6802
ML26
CONTINUO. 1970. s-a. Aus.$35. International Association of Music Libraries Archives & Documentation Centres (Australian Branch), Performing Arts Library, University of Adelaide, Adelaide, S.A. 5001, Australia. TEL 08-2285489. FAX 08-232-3689. TELEX UNIVD AA 89141. Ed. Gordon Abbott. adv.; bk.rev. circ. 90. (back issues avail.) **Indexed:** Aus.P.A.I.S.

780 BE ISSN 0779-1569
CONTREPOINTS. (Text in French) 1992. 5/yr. 1000 BEF. Opera Royal de Wallonie, 1, rue des Dominicains, 4000 Liege, Belgium. TEL 32-41-214720. FAX 32-41-210201. Ed. Paul Danblon. circ. 2,000.
 Formerly: Prologue.

780 US ISSN 0190-4922
ML1
CONTRIBUTIONS TO MUSIC EDUCATION. 1972. a. $5 to individuals; institutions $7.50. Hugh A. Glauser School of Music, Kent State University, Kent, OH 44242-0001. TEL 216-672-2397. E-mail: dhamann@kentum.kent.edu. Ed. Don Hamann. bk.rev. circ. 550. **Indexed:** Music Ind. **Document type:** academic/scholarly publication.
 —BLDSC (3461.026000); Faxon; UnCover.
 Description: Covers experimental, descriptive, theoretical, and historical research in music education.

780 US ISSN 0193-9041
CONTRIBUTIONS TO THE STUDY OF MUSIC AND DANCE. 1981. irreg. price varies. Greenwood Press, Inc. (Subsidiary of: Greenwood Publishing Group Inc.), 88 Post Rd. W., Box 5007, Westport, CT 06881-5007. TEL 203-226-3571. FAX 203-222-1502.
 —BLDSC (3461.454100).

780 GW ISSN 0070-0363
CORPUS MENSURABILIS MUSICAE. 1948. irreg. (American Institute of Musicology, US) Haenssler Verlag, Postfach 1220, 73762 Neuhausen, Germany. TEL 07158-177-114. FAX 07158-177119. Ed. Frank D'Accone. **Document type:** monographic series.
 Description: Examines Medieval and Renaissance compositions.

780 GW
CORPUS OF EARLY KEYBOARD MUSIC; transcription of all known sources of keyboard music of the 14th and 15th centuries. 1963. irreg. price varies. (American Institute of Musicology, US) Haenssler Verlag, Postfach 1220, 73762 Neuhausen, Germany. TEL 07158-177-114. FAX 07158-177119. Ed. John Caldwell. **Document type:** monographic series.

780 GW ISSN 0070-0460
ML170
CORPUS SCRIPTORUM DE MUSICA. (Text mainly in Latin) 1950. irreg. (American Institute of Musicology, US) Haenssler Verlag, Postfach 1220, 73762 Neuhausen, Germany. TEL 07158-177-114. FAX 07158-177119. Ed. Gilbert Reaney.

780 310 US
COST OF DOING BUSINESS SURVEY: OPERATING PERFORMANCE COMPARISONS FOR MUSIC PRODUCT DEALERS. a. $35 to members; non-members $50. National Association of Music Merchants Inc., 5140 Avenida Encinas, Carlsbad, CA 92008-4391. TEL 619-438-8001.
 Formerly: Survey of Operating Performance for Music Dealers.
 Description: Reports statistical data supplied by music products retailers on sales volume and product line.

780.7 370 US ISSN 0010-9894
ML1
COUNCIL FOR RESEARCH IN MUSIC EDUCATION. BULLETIN. Key Title: Bulletin of the Council for Research in Music Education. 1963. q. $17 to individuals; institutions $25; students $10 (effective Jan. 1995). University of Illinois at Urbana-Champaign, School of Music, 1114 W. Nevada, Urbana, IL 61801. TEL 217-333-1027. FAX 217-244-4585. E-mail: crme@vmd.cso.uiuc.edu. Eds. Eunice Boardman, John Grashel. bk.rev.; charts; index. circ. 2,000. (also avail. in microform from UMI; back issues avail.; reprint service avail. from UMI) **Indexed:** Arts & Hum.Cit.Ind., Child Devel.Abstr., Cont.Pg.Educ., Curr.Cont., Educ.Ind., Mid.East: Abstr.& Ind., Mult.Ed.Abstr., Music Artic.Guide, Music Ind., Psychol.Abstr., Res.High.Educ.Abstr., RILM. **Document type:** academic/scholarly publication.
 —BLDSC (2462.570000); Faxon; UMI; UnCover.
 Description: Presents articles, doctoral dissertation critiques, and conference papers for the international music profession.
 Refereed Serial

ULRICH'S INTERNATIONAL PERIODICALS DIRECTORY 1996

4840 MUSIC

781.642 CN ISSN 1180-8047
COUNTRY; Canada's country music magazine. 1989. bi-m. Can.$16($20) Jim Baine, Ed. & Pub.; R.R. 1, Holstein, ON N0G 2A0, Canada. TEL 519-334-3246. FAX 519-334-3366. adv. contact: Jim Baine. film rev. **Document type:** consumer publication.
  Description: Covers country music from a Canadian perspective.

781.7 051 US ISSN 1043-4488
COUNTRY AMERICA. 1989. 10/yr. $16.97. Meredith Corporation, 1716 Locust St., Des Moines, IA 50309-3023. TEL 515-284-3000; 800-374-8739. FAX 515-284-3035. Ed. Richard Krumme. circ. 1,000,000.
  Description: Entertainment and lifestyle magazine targeted to people who opt for country music and the country way of life.

781.7 UK ISSN 0011-0094
COUNTRY AND WESTERN ROUNDABOUT.* 1962. q. 15s.($2.) c/o R.F. Benson, Ed., 21 Roseacres, Takeley, Dunmow, Essex, England. adv.; bk.rev.; rec.rev.; illus. circ. 1,000.

780 CN ISSN 1189-0061
COUNTRY CANADA (KELOWNA). 1989. irreg. Canadian Chart Research, 2724 Cordova Way, Kelowna, BC V1Z 2N3, Canada.

781.7 US
COUNTRY CRAZY. 1976. 3/yr. $6. Jammie Ann Club - Rebel International Fan Club, Box 3525, York, PA 17402. FAX 717-792-3060. circ. 3,500.

COUNTRY DANCE AND SONG. see **DANCE**

781.62 US ISSN 1066-0453
ML3523
COUNTRY FEVER. 1992. bi-m. newsstand price: $2.95. Larry Flynt Publications, Inc., 9171 Wilshire Blvd., Ste. 300, Beverly Hills, CA 90210. TEL 310-858-7100. FAX 310-275-3857. adv. **Document type:** consumer publication.

780 US ISSN 0733-8759
ML459 .D6
COUNTRY HERITAGE. 1982. bi-m. $9.50 (Canada $11). Country Heritage Productions, RR 3, Box 76-D, Clarksville, AR 72830-9316. E-mail: Northgrass@aol.com. Ed. Matt Nozzolio. adv.; illus. circ. 300. **Document type:** consumer publication. Incorporates (1976-1982): Resophonic Echoes (ISSN 0273-3242); Which was formerly (1974-1976): Dobro Nut.
  Description: Centers around Dobro and other resonator guitars. Also covers traditional country music in general.

781.7 US ISSN 0090-4007
ML1
COUNTRY MUSIC. 1972. bi-m. $15.98. Silver Eagle Publishers, 329 Riverside Ave., Westport, CT 06880. TEL 203-221-4950. FAX 203-221-4948. Ed. Rochelle Friedman. adv.: B&W page $15600, color page $21840; trim 8 1/8 x 10 7/8. bk.rev.; film rev.; illus. circ. 679,000. **Indexed:** Access (1984-), Mag.Ind., PMR, Pop.Mus.Per.Ind. —UMI; UnCover.

780 CN ISSN 0714-8356
COUNTRY MUSIC NEWS; the voice of country music in Canada. 1980. m. Can.$25($40) 97594 Canada Ltd., P.O. Box 7323, Vanier Terminal, Ottawa, ON K1L 8E4, Canada. TEL 613-745-6006. FAX 613-745-0576. Ed. Larry Delaney; Pub. Larry Delaney. adv. contact: Joanne Delaney. bk.rev. circ. 12,500. (tabloid format; back issues avail.) **Document type:** newspaper.
  Description: Covers the country music scene in Canada; aimed at both fans and the industry.

784 AT
COUNTRY MUSIC NEWSLETTER. 1970. 3/yr. Earl Heywood Fan Club, P.O. Box 186, Murwillumbah, N.S.W. 2484, Australia. Ed. Don Gresham, Noela Gresham. **Document type:** newspaper.

781.7 UK ISSN 0591-2237
ML5
COUNTRY MUSIC PEOPLE. 1970. m. £30. Music Farm Ltd., 225A Lewisham Way, London SE4, England. TEL 0181-692-1106. FAX 0181-469-3091. Ed. Craig Baguley. adv.; bk.rev. circ. 21,000. **Document type:** consumer publication.
  Description: Reports on American country music, including artist features and record reviews.

781.7 UK ISSN 0140-5721
COUNTRY MUSIC ROUND UP. 1976. m. £15.60 (rest of Europe £23.90; N. America £30.40; elsewhere £32.40); newsstand price: £1.30. Country Music Round-up Publishing Co., P.O. Box 111, Waltham, Grimsby DN37 0YN, England. TEL 01472-821707. FAX 01472-821808. Ed. John Emptage; Pub. John Emptage. adv. contact: Doreen Holder. bk.rev.; music rev. circ. 18,500. **Document type:** newspaper.
  Description: Country music magazine for Britain and abroad. Includes artist profiles, record reviews, tour schedules, and regional reports.

780 US ISSN 0273-1428
ML18
COUNTRY MUSIC SOURCEBOOK. Variant title: Billboard's Country Music Sourcebook. a. $43. B P I Communications, Inc. (New York), 1515 Broadway, New York, NY 10036. TEL 212-764-7300; 800-344-7119. FAX 212-944-1719. (And: 5055 Wilshire Blvd., Los Angeles, CA 90036) adv. circ. 47,000. (also avail. in microfilm from KTO)
  Description: Radio stations, performing artists, booking agents, personal managers and recording companies listed.

789.4 SW ISSN 0283-5835
COUNTRY NEWS. 1975. q. SEK 99 in Scandinavia; Europe SEK 135; elsewhere SEK 140. Svenska Countrymusikfoereningen, Richertsgatan 8, S-412 60 Goeteborg, Sweden. TEL 46-31-169139. Ed. Thomas Buskhagen. bk.rev. circ. 1,400. **Document type:** bulletin.
  Description: Devoted to all types of country music, from country-rock to bluegrass. Reviews all albums sold in Sweden.

781.7 US ISSN 0011-0248
COUNTRY SONG ROUNDUP.* 1949. m. $25. Country Song Roundup, Inc., 210 E. State Rt. 4, Ste. 401, Paramus, NJ 07652-5103. TEL 201-487-6124. FAX 201-487-7965. Ed. Celeste Gomes. adv.; bk.rev.; rec.rev.; illus. circ. 200,000. **Document type:** trade publication.
  Description: Covers country music, lyrics, and articles about singers and songwriters.

781.62 US
COUNTRYBEAT. q. newsstand price: $2.95. London Publishing Co., Box 910, Ft. Washington, PA 19034. TEL 215-643-6385. FAX 215-628-3571. adv. **Document type:** consumer publication.

780 200 US ISSN 1045-0815
ML2999
CREATOR;* the bimonthly magazine of balanced music ministries. 1978. bi-m. $32.95 (Canada $44; elsewhere $54). Church Music Associates, Inc., 4631 Cutwater Dr., Hilliard, OH 43026-7813. TEL 614-889-0012. FAX 614-792-3585. Ed. Paul Oakley. adv.; bk.rev.; index. circ. 6,000. (back issues avail.)
  Description: Focuses on music program for all denominations, emphasizing balance of music and worship styles.

780 CN
CRESCENDO. 1958. bi-m. Toronto Musicians' Association, 101 Thorncliffe Park Dr., Toronto, Ont. M4H 1M2, Canada. TEL 416-421-1020. FAX 416-421-7011. Ed. George Zarras. adv.; circ. 5,600. (controlled). **Indexed:** RILM.

780 MX ISSN 0185-1896
CUADERNOS DE MUSICA. 1981. irreg., latest 1985. price varies. Universidad Nacional Autonoma de Mexico, Instituto de Investigacione Esteticas, Circuito Mtro. Mario de la Cueva, Ciudad de la Investigacion en Humanidades - Zona Cultural, 04000 Mexico, D.F., Mexico.

780 791.43 US ISSN 0888-9015
ML2074
CUE SHEET. 1984. q. $35 to individuals; institutions $50. Society for the Preservation of Film Music, Box 93536, Los Angeles, CA 90093-0536. FAX 818-248-5775. Ed. Marsha Berman. adv.; bk.rev.; circ. 800 (paid). (back issues avail.) **Indexed:** Film Lit.Ind. (1988-), Int.Ind.Film Per.
  Description: Provides news and studies on the art of composing for film. Features interviews with film composers.

781.7 IT ISSN 0393-2893
CULTURE MUSICALI; quaderni di etnomusicologia. 1982. s-a. L.30000. (Societa Italiana di Etnomusicologia) Libreria Musicale Italiana Editrice, Via di Arsina 196F, 55100 Lucca, Italy. TEL 39-583-394464. FAX 39-583-394469. Ed. Roberto Leydi. abstr.

780 US
CURIOUS GOODS.* q. $2.25 per no. 1804 E. Stark Rd., Dallas, TX 75253-5603. Ed. Jerry Rutherfod. music rev.
  Description: Covers music production and established music bands.

CURRENT ISSUES IN MUSIC EDUCATION. see **EDUCATION — Teaching Methods And Curriculum**

780.01 US ISSN 0011-3735
ML1
CURRENT MUSICOLOGY. 1965. 2/yr. $16 to individuals; institutions $24; students $13. Columbia University, Department of Music, New York, NY 10027. TEL 212-854-1632. Ed. Karen Painter. adv. contact: Michael von der Linn. bk.rev.; abstr.; bibl.; charts; illus.; stat.; cum.index every 5 yrs.; circ. 1,500 (paid). (also avail. in microfilm from UMI; back issues avail.; reprint service avail. from UMI) **Indexed:** Amer.Bibl.Slavic & E.Eur.Stud., Arts & Hum.Cit.Ind., Curr.Cont., Hum.Ind., Ind.Bk.Rev.Hum., Mid.East: Abstr.& Ind., Music Artic.Guide, Music Ind., RILM, RILM. **Document type:** academic/scholarly publication.
  —Faxon; SWETS; UMI; UnCover.

780 US
CUT. q. $2.50 per no. 11 Julian St., Norwich, CT 06360. Ed. Steve Erickson.
  Description: Contains interviews with musicians and bands, and articles on music trends.

780 US ISSN 8755-7622
THE CUTTING EDGE (ORLANDO); unearthing the best in the underground. 1984. bi-m. $10. 8303 Hilton Way, Orlando, FL 32810. TEL 407-298-6927. Ed. Dan Kennedy. adv.; bk.rev. circ. 350. (back issues avail.) **Document type:** newsletter.
  Description: Covers Christian rock music of all styles.

780 US ISSN 0895-6936
CYMBIOSIS; the marriage of music and magazine. 1986. q. $39.98. Cymbiosis, Inc., 6201 W. Sunset Blvd., Ste. 80, Hollywood, CA 90028-8704. TEL 213-463-3808. FAX 213-463-5426. Ed. Ric Levine. adv.; bk.rev. circ. 15,000. (audio cassette) **Indexed:** RILM.
  ●Also available on CD-ROM.
  Description: Articles feature six new age, jazz and progressive artists included in a one-hour music sampler.

780 XR ISSN 1211-0264
ML5
CZECH MUSIC. (Text in English) 1964. 6/yr. $20 in Europe; overseas $25. Cesky Hudebni Fond, Hudebni Informacni Stredisko - Czech Music Foundation, Music Information Center, Besedni 3, 118 00 Prague 1 - Mala Strana, Czech Republic. TEL 42-2-24510075. FAX 42-2-539720. Ed. Wanda Dobrovska. adv.; bk.rev.; illus.; index. circ. 1,000. **Indexed:** Music Ind. **Document type:** bulletin. —UnCover.
  Formerly (until 1995): Music News from Prague (ISSN 0027-4410).
  Description: Contains calendar of symphony concerts, interviews and new works.

780 FR
D I S C INSTRUMENTS INTERNATIONAL. 1973. 7/yr. 200 F. Editions Mediapresse, 148 rue de Paris, 92100 Boulogne, France. Ed. Alain Douarche. adv.; bk.rev. circ. 35,000.
  Formerly: D I S C International.

MUSIC

780 UK ISSN 0965-4364
D J MAGAZINE. (Disc Jockey) 1986. fortn. (25/yr.) £36.75($105) (overseas £68.25). Nexus Media Ltd., Nexus House, Azalea Dr., Swanley, Kent BR8 8HY, England. TEL 01322-660070. FAX 01322-667633. circ. 20,000. **Document type:** trade publication.
Formerly (until 1991): Jocks (ISSN 0951-5143)

780.42 US ISSN 1045-9693
D J TIMES. m. Testa Communications, Inc., 25 Willowdale Ave., Port Washington, NY 11050-3716. TEL 516-767-2500. FAX 516-767-9335. Ed. Chuck Arnold. circ. 13,000.

780.7060489 DK ISSN 0108-9188
D M P F MEDLEMMER. 1975. a. free. Dansk Musikpaedagogisk Forening, Noerrebrogade 45 A, 3-sal t.v., DK-2200 Copenhagen N, Denmark.
Former titles (until 1982): Dansk Musikpaedagogisk Forening. Medlemsliste (ISSN 0107-3001); Statsproevede Musikpaedagoger.

780 DK ISSN 0106-5629
ML5
D M T. 1925. 8/yr. DKK 225. Dansk Musik Tidsskrift, c/o Musikvidenskabeligt Institut, Koebenhavns Universitet, Klerkegade 2, DK-1308 Copenhagen, Denmark. TEL 45-33-15-07-26. FAX 45-33-91-81-39. Ed. Anders Beyer. adv.: B&W page DKK 1930. bk.rev.; charts; illus.; index. circ. 1,100. (back issues avail.) Indexed: Music Ind., RILM. **Document type:** academic/scholarly publication.
Formerly (until 1966): Dansk Musiktidsskrift (ISSN 0011-6386)

DAILY VARIETY; news of the entertainment industry. see
COMMUNICATIONS — Television And Cable

781.62 SW ISSN 0280-6584
DALARNAS SPELMANSBLAD; tidning foer Dalarnas Spelmansfoerbund. 1981. q. SEK 70 (foreign SEK 100). Dalarnas Spelmansfoerbund - Association of Folk Musicians in Dalarna, Kung Magnigatan, S-791 62 Falun, Sweden. TEL 46-0-232-62-10. Ed. Tomas Fahlander. **Document type:** newsletter.

DANCE AND MUSIC SERIES. see DANCE

780.42 793.3 IT ISSN 1121-290X
DANCE MUSIC MAGAZINE. 1992. m. L.50000 (with CD L.185000). Ermitage s.r.l., Piazza Trento e Trieste 1, 40137 Bologna, Italy. TEL 39-51-341754. FAX 39-51-342220. Ed. Roberto Rossi Gandolfi. adv.: color page L.6850000; adv. contact: Marco Ultrocchi. circ. 80,000. **Document type:** consumer publication.

DANCING U S A. see DANCE

781.7 DK ISSN 0905-3964
DANSK FOLKEMUSIK.* 1980. irreg. membership. (Folkemusikhusringen) Filligutten, Koege, Denmark.
Formerly (until 1989): Folkemusikhusringen (ISSN 0107-7074)

780.9489 DK ISSN 0905-6300
DANSK MUSIK AARBOG (YEAR)/DANISH MUSIC YEARBOOK. 1990. a. DKK 250($40) (typically set in Dec.). Dansk Musik Aarbog ApS, Vendersgade 25, DK-1363 Copenhagen K, Denmark. TEL 33-93-97-00. FAX 33-14-51-75. Ed. Nils Harbo. adv. circ. 10,000.
Description: Contains articles and statistics on the Danish popular music industry. Directories of the Danish record industry, sheet music publishing, composers and performers. Lists of releases, first performances, charts, and manufacturers listed by product.

016.78 DK ISSN 0105-8045
DANSK MUSIKFORTEGNELSE/DANISH NATIONAL BIBLIOGRAPHY: MUSIC. 1933. a. DKK 263.60 (effective 1996). (Kongelige Bibliotek, Musikafdeling) Dansk BiblioteksCenter as, Tempovej 7-11, DK-2750 Ballerup, Denmark.
TEL 45-44-97-40-00. FAX 45-44-68-24-42.
Document type: bibliography.

786 DK ISSN 0107-4857
ML549.8
DANSK ORGELAARBOG/DANISH ORGAN YEARBOOK/DAENISCHES ORGELJAHRBUCH. (Text in Danish; summaries in English and German) 1982. biennial. Kr.93.95. Danske Orgelselskab, Doennerupvej 2, DK-2720 Vanloese, Denmark. Ed. Henrik F. Norfelt. bk.rev.; illus. circ. 1,200.

780 US ISSN 0898-1558
ML410.M674
DARIUS MILHAUD SOCIETY NEWSLETTER. 1985. s-a. $20. Darius Milhaud Society, 15715 Chadbourne Rd., Cleveland, OH 44120. TEL 216-921-4548. Ed. Katharine M. Warne. circ. 2,000. (back issues avail.) **Document type:** newsletter.

780 GW ISSN 0418-3878
ML5
DARMSTAEDTER BEITRAEGE ZUR NEUEN MUSIK. irreg., vol.20, 1994. DM.28.50. Schott Musik International GmbH, Weihergarten 5, 55116 Mainz, Germany. TEL 06131-246-0. FAX 06131-246211. **Document type:** consumer publication.
—BLDSC (3533.750000).

780 UK ISSN 0306-0373
ML410.D35
DELIUS SOCIETY JOURNAL. 1973. q. £15 (N. America $31; elsewhere £18). 82 Farley Hill, Luton, Beds. LU1 5EG, England. Ed. Stephen Lloyd. bk.rev. circ. 420. Indexed: Music Ind. **Document type:** academic/scholarly publication.

DENVER ARTS CENTER PROGRAMS. see THEATER

780 US
DETROIT MONOGRAPHS IN MUSICOLOGY. STUDIES IN MUSIC. 1971. irreg. price varies. Harmonie Park Press, 23630 Pinewood, Warren, MI 48091-4759. TEL 810-755-3080. **Document type:** monographic series.
Formerly: Detroit Monographs in Musicology.
Description: Monographs on musicology.

781.64 GW
DEUTSCH ROCK. 1979. m. free. Postfach 100809, 42008 Wuppertal, Germany. TEL 0202-754886. Ed. Raimund Naumann. bk.rev. **Document type:** consumer publication.

780 GW ISSN 0417-2051
ML5
DEUTSCHE GESELLSCHAFT FUER MUSIK DES ORIENTS. MITTEILUNGEN. (Text in English and German) 1962. irreg. DM.28. (Deutsche Gesellschaft fuer Musik des Orients) Verlag der Musikalienhandlung Karl-Dieter Wagner, Marienstr. 13, 99817 Eisenach, Germany. TEL 03691-624901. illus. (back issues avail.) Indexed: A.I.C.P. **Document type:** monographic series.

782.1 GW
DEUTSCHE OPER BERLIN AKTUELL. 1981. m. Deutsche Oper Berlin, Richard-Wagner-Str. 10, 10585 Berlin, Germany. TEL 030-34381. FAX 030-3438232. adv. circ. 30,000. **Document type:** newsletter.
Formerly: Opernjournal.

780 GW ISSN 0415-7435
DEUTSCHES MUSIKLEBEN (YEAR). English edition: Music in Germany (ISSN 0173-5136) 1954. a. free. Inter Nationes e.V., Kennedyallee 91-103, 53175 Bonn, Germany. TEL 0228-880-0. FAX 0228-880457. TELEX 17228308. Ed. Marianne Goebel. circ. 9,500. **Document type:** directory.
Description: Chronological list of the year's most important music festivals and competitions, and events of musicological interest.

781.7 US ISSN 0092-0789
ML1
DEVIL'S BOX. 1969. q. $7. Tennessee Folklore Society, 305 Stella Dr., Madison, AL 35758. Ed. Stephen F. Davis. rec.rev. Indexed: M.L.A.

780 US ISSN 0197-7784
ML1000
DEVOTEE;* magazine for chamber music players and listeners. q. $12. Devotee Publications Inc., 93 Killarney Ct., Niskayuna, NY 12309-1460. Ed. Paul Elistta. Indexed: Music Artic.Guide, Music Ind.

DIALOGUE IN INSTRUMENTAL MUSIC EDUCATION. see EDUCATION — Teaching Methods And Curriculum

786.6 US ISSN 0012-2378
ML1
DIAPASON; devoted to the organ, the harpsichord, the carillon and church music. 1909. m. $18. Scranton Gillette Communications, Inc., 380 E. Northwest Hwy., Des Plaines, IL 60016-2282. TEL 708-298-6622. FAX 708-390-0408. TELEX 206041 MSG RLY. Ed. Jerome Butera. adv.; bk.rev.; illus. elec. circ. 5,000. (also avail. in microform from UMI; reprint service avail. from UMI) Indexed: Music Artic.Guide, Music Ind., RILM. **Document type:** trade publication.
—BLDSC (3580.210500); Faxon; UMI; UnCover. CCC.
Description: Technical reviews and compositional analysis on the organ, the harpsichord, and church music, with recital announcements, reviews of new releases and instruments, and classified ads.

780 FR
DIAPASON. (Supplement avail.) 1955. 11/yr. 274 F. (with supplement 354 F.). Diapason - Harmonie, 9-13 rue Colonel Pierre Avia, 75754 Paris Cedex 15, France. TEL 1-46-62-20-00. FAX 1-46-62-25-33. adv.; bk.rev. circ. 70,000. (also avail. in microfilm) Indexed: Music Ind., RILA, RILM.

785 CN ISSN 0705-6249
DIRECTORY OF CANADIAN ORCHESTRAS AND YOUTH ORCHESTRAS/ANNUAIRE CANADIEN DES ORCHESTRES ET ORCHESTRES DES JEUNES. (Text in English, French) 1976. a. Can.$17.50. Association of Canadian Orchestras, 56 The Esplanade, Ste. 311, Toronto, ON M5E 1A7, Canada. TEL 416-366-8834. FAX 416-366-1780. (Co-sponsor: Ontario Federation of Symphony Orchestras) **Document type:** directory.
Description: Current list of orchestra personnel.

780 370 US ISSN 0742-2520
ML128.I64
DIRECTORY OF INTERNATIONAL MUSIC EDUCATION DISSERTATIONS IN PROGRESS. (Not published in 1990) 1963. biennial. $10. Council for Research in Music Education, University of Illinois, 1114 W. Nevada, Urbana, IL 61801. TEL 217-333-1027. Ed. Marilyn P. Zimmerman. circ. 1,500. (back issues avail.) **Document type:** academic/scholarly publication, directory.
Formerly: Approved Doctoral Dissertations in Progress in Music Education.

780 US ISSN 0098-664X
ML13
DIRECTORY OF MUSIC FACULTIES IN COLLEGES & UNIVERSITIES U S AND CANADA. 1967. a. $55 (effective Nov. 1994). C M S Publications, Inc., Box 8208, Missoula, MT 59807. TEL 406-728-2002; 800-729-0235. FAX 406-721-9419. E-mail: mu__cms@lewis.umt.edu. Dir. Robby D. Gunstream. circ. 4,000. Indexed: Music Ind., RILM. **Document type:** directory.
Formerly: Directory of Music Faculties in American Colleges and Universities (ISSN 0419-3040)
Description: Includes approximately 31,000 music faculty and 1,850 postsecondary institutions.

780 US
DIRECTORY OF SUMMER CHAMBER MUSIC WORKSHOPS, SCHOOLS & FESTIVALS. biennial. $14. Chamber Music of America, 545 Eighth Ave., New York, NY 10018. TEL 212-244-2772. FAX 212-244-2776. Ed. D. Sasscer. (back issues avail.) **Document type:** directory.

780 US ISSN 1047-4315
ML3551
DIRTY LINEN; the magazine of folk, electric folk, traditional and world music. 1988. bi-m. $20 (foreign $30) (effective 1996); newsstand price: 3.95. Dirty Linen, Ltd., Box 66600, Baltimore, MD 21239-6600. TEL 410-583-7973. FAX 410-337-6735. E-mail: editor@dirtylinen.com. Ed. Paul Hartman. adv. page $725; adv. contact: Linda Cohn. bk.rev. circ. 13,000. (back issues avail.) **Document type:** consumer publication.

780 621.389 US ISSN 0731-843X
ML1
DISC COLLECTOR. 1950. m. $5 (foreign $10). Disc Collector Publications, Box 315, Cheswold, DE 19936. TEL 302-674-3149. Ed. Lou Deneumoustier. adv.; bk.rev. circ. 1,100. (processed) **Document type:** newsletter.
Formerly: Disc Collector's Newsletter (ISSN 0070-6655)

MUSIC

DISCO & DANCING. see *DANCE*

780.42   UK   ISSN 0960-3972
DISCO CLUB AND LEISURE INTERNATIONAL. 1976. m. £25 (foreign £85). Nexus Media Ltd., Warwick House, Azalea Dr., Swanley, Kent BR8 8HY, England. TEL 01322-660070. FAX 01322-667633. Ed. Paul Fowler. adv. contact: Jay Green. circ. 13,720. (back issues avail.) **Document type:** consumer publication.
    Former titles (until 1990): Disco and Club Trade International (ISSN 0959-1397); (until 1984): Disco International and Club News.

789.91   GW   ISSN 0943-0830
DISCO MAGAZIN. 1958. m. DM.75.60. Gildefachverlag GmbH & Co. KG, Postfach 1351, 31043 Alfeld, Germany. TEL 05181-80040. adv.; illus.; rec.rev. circ. 5,000.
    Former titles (until 1992): Sigerts Fachmagazin fuer die Unterhaltungs-Gastronomie (ISSN 0930-7192); (until 1986): Musik-Info (ISSN 0176-5019); Musik-Informationen (ISSN 0027-4712).

781.57   UK   ISSN 0012-3544
DISCOGRAPHICAL FORUM. 1960. irreg. £2($4) 44 Belleville Rd., London SW11 6QT, England. TEL 071-228-3193. Ed. Malcom Walker. adv.; bk.rev.; bibl.; stat. circ. 600. (processed)
    Description: Focuses on jazz music.

780.1   US   ISSN 0095-8115
DISCOGRAPHY SERIES. 1969. irreg., no.20, 1990. price varies. J.F. Weber, Ed. & Pub., 194 Roosevelt Dr., Utica, NY 13502. TEL 315-732-4747. bibl. circ. 300. **Document type:** monographic series.

789.91   IT
DISCOTECA HI FI.* 1959. m. Casa Editrice Discoteca s.r.l., Via Monforte 15, 20122 Milan, Italy. Ed. Ornella Zanuso Mauri. adv.; bk.rev.; illus. circ. 20,000.
    Former titles: Discoteca Alta Fedelta (ISSN 0012-3560); Discoteca.

780 745.1   US   ISSN 0896-8322
DISCOVERIES (PORT TOWNSEND); magazine for collective records & CD's. 1987. m. $21. Antique Trader Publications, Box 1050, Dubuque, IA 52004. TEL 800-364-5593. FAX 800-531-0880. Ed. Jerry Osborne. adv.; bk.rev. circ. 20,000. **Document type:** consumer publication.
    Description: Devoted to the hobby of music collecting: buy, sell, trade records, CDs and related memoribilia.

780.42   GW   ISSN 0724-6978
DISCRET; Fach-Journal der Unterhaltungsgastronomie. 1983. m. DM.84. Brigitte Tecklenborg Verlag, Lindenstr. 4, 48565 Steinfurt, Germany. TEL 02552-3933. Ed. Hubert Tecklenborg. circ. 5,900.

781.57   US
DISC'RIBE;* a journal of discographical information. 1980. irreg. (approx. a.) $5 for 4 issues. Wildmusic Company, 1665 Federal Ave., Los Angeles, CA 90025-2946. Ed. David Wild. adv. circ. 200.

780   SZ
DISSONANZ. 1984. q. 40 SFr. (foreign 50 SFr.) Schweizer Tonkuenstlerverein, Moehrlistr. 68, CH-8006 Zurich, Switzerland. TEL 01-3632025. Ed. Christoph Keller. adv. contact: Christoph Keller. bk.rev. circ. 1,700. **Indexed:** RILM. **Document type:** academic/scholarly publication, newsletter.

780   NE
DIVITIAE MUSICAE ARTIS. SERIES A vol.3, 1975. irreg. price varies. Uitgeverij Frits Knuf B.V., Box 720, 4116 ZJ Buren, Netherlands.

781.57   NE   ISSN 0166-2309
DOCTOR JAZZ MAGAZINE. (Text in Dutch; occasionally in English) 1963. q. fl.25. Vijverweg 3, 5461 AL Veghel, Netherlands. TEL 31-4130-63542. (Subscr. to: Kopslaan 34 2082 EJ Santpoort, Netherlands) Ed. Yvo R. von Holtz. adv.; bk.rev.; circ. 850 (controlled). (back issues avail.) **Document type:** bulletin.
    Description: Contains information and research on traditional and classic jazz, blues and related music.

780   PL   ISSN 0860-3944
DOCUMENTA CHOPINIANA. (Text in English and Polish) 1970. irreg. price varies. Polskie Wydawnictwo Muzyczne, Al. Krasinskiego 11a, 31-111 Krakow, Poland. TEL 48-12-227044. FAX 48-12-220174. Ed. Mieczyslaw Tomaszewski. adv. contact: Teresa Wlochynska. **Document type:** academic/scholarly publication.
    Description: Covers Chopin's life and work.

780   BE
DOCUMENTA MUSICAE NOVAE; critical edition of contemporary music sources. (Text in English, Flemish, French) 1968. irreg., vol.6, 1980. $12. Rijksuniversiteit te Gent, Seminarie voor Musicologie, Blandijnberg 2, B-9000 Ghent, Belgium. Ed. Herman Sabbe. circ. 200. **Indexed:** RILM.

DOMSPATZ; Zeitschrift fuer Fulda. see *THEATER*

782.1   UK   ISSN 0307-1448
ML410.D7
DONIZETTI SOCIETY. JOURNAL. 1974. s-a. $15. Donizetti Society, 56 Harbut Rd., London SW11 2RB, England. illus.

780   UK
DONIZETTI SOCIETY NEWSLETTER. 1973. q. £8($15) Donizetti Society, c/o John R. Carter, 56 Harbut Rd., London SW11 2RB, England. bibl. **Document type:** newsletter.

780.42   GW
DOORS QUARTERLY MAGAZINE. (Text in English) 1983. q. DM.35($25) Am Oelvebach 5, 47809 Krefeld, Germany. TEL 02151-571862. FAX 02151-571862. Ed. Rainer Moddemann. adv.; bk.rev. circ. 2,000. (back issues avail.) **Document type:** newsletter.
    Description: Examines rock music of the 60's.

788.705   US   ISSN 0741-7659
ML929
THE DOUBLE REED. 1978. 4/yr. membership. International Double Reed Society, c/o Lowry Riggins, 626 Lakeshore Dr., Monroe, LA 71203-4032. TEL 318-343-5715. FAX 318-345-1159. Eds. Daniel Stolper, Ron Klimko. adv.; bk.rev.; illus. circ. 3,600. **Indexed:** Music Artic.Guide. **Document type:** newsletter. —Faxon; UnCover.
    Formed by the merger of (1973-1977): To the World's Oboists (ISSN 0091-9683); (1969-1977): To the World's Bassoonists (ISSN 0828-1475)

780.904   US   ISSN 0012-5768
ML1
DOWN BEAT; jazz, blues, and beyond. 1934. m. $29 (foreign $35). Maher Publications, Inc., 180 W. Park Ave., Elmhurst, IL 60126. TEL 708-941-2030; 800-535-7496. FAX 708-941-3210. (Subscr. to: Box 1071, Skokie, IL 60076) Eds. Frank Alkyer, John Ephland. adv.; bk.rev.; rec.rev.; illus. circ. 98,441. (also avail. in microform from UMI; reprint service avail. from UMI) **Indexed:** Acad.Ind., Arts & Hum.Cit.Ind., Bk.Rev.Ind. (1977-), Child.Bk.Rev.Ind. (1977-), Curr.Cont., Mag.Ind., Music Artic.Guide, Music Ind., PMR, R.G., RILM.
●Also available online. Vendor(s): University Microfilms International.
—Faxon; SWETS; UMI; UnCover.
    Description: Articles for musicians and listeners interested in contemporary music.

DRAGON. see *LITERATURE*

DREAD TIMES; news for the Nazarite. see *RELIGIONS AND THEOLOGY*

DREAM GUYS. see *CHILDREN AND YOUTH — For*

789.1   US
DRUM! (SAN JOSE).* 1991. bi-m. free to qualified personnel. 1275 Lincoln Ave., No. 13, San Jose, CA 95125. TEL 408-971-9794. FAX 408-971-0382. Ed. Andy Doerschuk. circ. 30,000 (controlled).
    Description: For California drummers and music enthusiasts.

780   US
DRUM BUSINESS. 1993. bi-m. $24. Modern Drummer Publications, Inc., 870 Pompton Ave., Cedar Grove, NJ 07009. TEL 201-239-4140. FAX 201-239-7139. Ed. Kevin Kearns. adv.; B&W page $1510. **Document type:** trade publication.

785.067   US   ISSN 0012-6748
DRUM CORPS NEWS.* 1961. s-m. (Jun.-Aug.); 4/mo. (Sep.-May). $10.50. Tri-Star Enterprises, Inc., Box 108, Prudential Ctr., Boston, MA 02199. TEL 617-266-0299. Ed. Andy Uzarins. adv.; illus. circ. 15,000. **Indexed:** Music Artic.Guide.

780   ISSN 0164-3223
ML1306
DRUM CORPS WORLD. 1971. 20/yr. $48 (Canada $56; elsewhere $59). Drum Corps Sights & Sounds, Inc., Box 8052, Madison, WI 53708-8052. TEL 608-241-2292. FAX 608-241-4974. Ed. Steven Powers; Pub. Steve Vickers. adv. contact: Jeff Collins. bk.rev.; illus.; stat.; circ. 5,300 (paid). (tabloid format; back issues avail.) **Document type:** newspaper.
    Description: Provides information on the worldwide drum and bugle corps activity; includes schedules, contest reviews and results, news and press releases.

786.9   US   ISSN 1052-3324
ML1030
DRUMS & DRUMMING. bi-m. Miller Freeman Inc. (San Mateo), 411 Borel Ave., Ste. 100, San Mateo, CA 94402. TEL 415-358-9500. FAX 416-358-8728. (Subscr. to: Box 58590, Boulder, CO 90322-8590)
    Supersedes in part (in 1989): G P I Collector's Edition (ISSN 1044-6656)

780   GW   ISSN 0176-8832
DRUMS & PERCUSSION. 1982. 6/yr. DM.32 (foreign DM.40). S Z V KG, Schellingstr. 39-43, 80799 Munich, Germany. TEL 089-23726-0. FAX 089-23726125. Ed. Manfred von Bohr. adv. contact: Olav Bjerke. circ. 7,000. **Document type:** consumer publication.

780   US
DUB CATCHER.* q. $20. 121 Prospect Pl., No. 2, Brooklyn, NY 11217-2917.
    Description: Covers dancehall which is incorporating both hip-hop and reggae while maintaining its own distinct personality; features record and concert reviews.

780   US   ISSN 1072-8686
DUB MISSIVE; Reggae & Soca magazine. 1988. bi-m. $9. Amra Enterprises, Inc., Box 677850, Orlando, FL 32867-7850. TEL 407-381-9907. Ed. Dianne A. Adams; Pub. Lascelles A. Adams. adv.; B&W page $1250; adv. contact: Las Adams. bk.rev.; music rev.; circ. 20,000 (paid). **Document type:** consumer publication.
    Description: Covers local and international Reggae and Soca recording artistis.

DUE SOUTH; the biggest guide to what's on in the South. see *ARTS AND HANDICRAFTS*

787.9   US   ISSN 0098-3527
ML1
DULCIMER PLAYERS NEWS. 1975. q. $18. Madeline MacNeil, Ed. & Pub., Box 2164, Winchester, VA 22604. TEL 703-678-1305. FAX 703-678-1151. adv.; bk.rev.; illus.; index. circ. 4,000. —UnCover.
    Description: For players and builders of hammered and mountain dulcimers.

DUMPSTER TIMES. see *LITERATURE*

785.0671   XO
DYCHOVA HUDBA. irreg. price varies. Zdruzenie Dychovych Hudieb na Slovensku, Bastova 4, 816 29 Bratislava, Slovakia.

780   NE   ISSN 0012-7418
DYNAMITE INTERNATIONAL. (Text in English) 1961. bi-m. $12. International Cliff Richard Movement, P.O. Box 94164, 1090 GD Amsterdam, Netherlands. TEL 31-30-618272. FAX 31-21-5518010. Ed. Anton Husmann. adv.; illus. circ. 10,000.
    Formerly: Dynamite.
    Description: Provides international news of interest to fans of Cliff Richard, a British singer.

780.42   GW
E B - METRONOM; Musik magazin. 1984. bi-m. DM.22($16) E B - Metronom Verlag, Hospeltstr. 66, 50825 Cologne, Germany. TEL 0221-543506. FAX 0221-542620. Ed. Gisela Lobisch. bk.rev. circ. 16,000. (back issues avail.) **Document type:** bulletin.

MUSIC 4843

781.64 384.55   UK
E.P. MAGAZINE. 1991. m. £6. Vigilante Publications, 9 Dukesbridge Ct., Duke St., Reading, Berks RG1 4SA, England. TEL 01734-581878. Ed. Jon Ewing. adv. contact: Emma Coop. bk.rev. (back issues avail.). **Document type:** consumer publication.
  Description: News and information on music, films, television and other activities for young people in eastern England.

EARLY DRAMA, ART, AND MUSIC REVIEW. see *THEATER*

784   US   ISSN 0899-8132
ML549.8
EARLY KEYBOARD JOURNAL. 1982. a. $25 membership (institutions $30; students $12.50) (includes Newsletter) (effective Jul. 1994-Jul. 1996). Southeastern Historical Keyboard Society & Midwestern Historical Keyboard Societies, Box 32022, Charlotte, NC 28232-2022. TEL 910-842-4322. FAX 910-560-6437. E-mail: kjacob@cybernetics.net. Eds. Lilian Pruett, Thomas G. MacCracken. adv. contact: Karen Jacob. bk.rev. circ. 500. **Indexed:** RILM. **Document type:** academic/scholarly publication.
  —UnCover.
  Refereed Serial

786 371.3   US   ISSN 0882-0201
ML549.8
EARLY KEYBOARD STUDIES NEWSLETTER. 1984. q. $40. Westfield Center for Early Keyboard Studies, One Cottage St., Easthampton, MA 01027. TEL 413-527-7664. FAX 413-527-7689. Ed. Gregory Hayes. adv. contact: Lynn Edwards. bk.rev.; illus. circ. 750. (back issues avail.). **Document type:** newsletter.
  Description: Fosters appreciation and understanding of keyboard music from the Renaissance through the Baroque, Classical, and Romantic eras. Emphasis is on historical performance practices and circumstances.
  Refereed Serial

780   UK   ISSN 0306-1078
ML5
EARLY MUSIC. 1973. q. £52($92) (effective 1996). Oxford University Press, Oxford Journals, Walton St., Oxford OX2 6DP, England. TEL 01865-267773. FAX 01865-267773. TELEX 837330-OXPRES-G. E-mail: jnlorders@oup.co.uk. (U.S. subscr. to: Oxford University Press Inc., 2001 Evans Rd., Cary, NC 27513. TEL 919-677-0977. FAX 919-677-1714) Ed. Tess Knighton. adv. contact: Arthur Boyars. bk.rev.; illus.; index, cum.index. circ. 4,200. (also avail. in microform from UMI; reprint service avail. from UMI) **Indexed:** Amer.Hist.& Life, Arts & Hum.Cit.Ind., Curr.Cont., Hist.Abstr., Music Ind., RILM. **Document type:** academic/scholarly publication.
  —BLDSC (3642.993000); Faxon; Genuine Article; SWETS; UMI; UnCover. **CCC.**
  Description: Covers the field of Medieval, Renaissance, Baroque and Classical music history, critical surveys and performance practice.

780   UK   ISSN 0261-1279
ML169.8
EARLY MUSIC HISTORY. 1982. 1/yr. £53($92) (effective 1996). Cambridge University Press, Edinburgh Bldg., Shaftesbury Rd., Cambridge CB2 2RU, England. TEL 01223-312393. FAX 01223-315052. TELEX 851817256. (N. American addr.: Cambridge University Press, Journals Dept., 40 W. 20th St., New York, NY 10011. TEL 212-924-3900. FAX 212-691-3239) Ed. Iain Fenlon. adv.; bk.rev. (also avail. in microform from UMI; back issues avail.) **Indexed:** Amer.Hist.& Life (1992-), Arts & Hum.Cit.Ind., Curr.Cont., Hist.Abstr. (1992-), RILM. **Document type:** academic/scholarly publication.
  —BLDSC (3642.998100); Faxon; Genuine Article; UMI; UnCover. **CCC.**
  Description: Encourages British, American and European work in manuscript studies, analytical work, iconography, textual criticism, and the relationship between music and society before 1700.

788   US
EARLY MUSIC NEWSLETTER. vol.16, 1976. m. (Sep.-June). $20. New York Recorder Guild, c/o Eleanor Brodkin, Ed., 197 New York Ave., Dumont, NJ 07628. adv.; bk.rev. circ. 185. **Document type:** newsletter.

780   UK   ISSN 0144-8072
EARLY MUSIC RECORD SERVICES. MONTHLY REVIEW. 1980. m. £4.25. Early Music Record Services, 53 Ashton St., Saffron Walden, Essex CB10 2AQ, England.

780   UK   ISSN 1352-0059
EARLY MUSIC TODAY. 1993. bi-m. £12 (foreign £20). Rhinegold Publishing Ltd., 241 Shaftesbury Ave., London WC2H 8EH, England. TEL 0171-333-1744. FAX 0171-333-1769. Ed. Lucien Jenkins. **Document type:** consumer publication.
  Description: News magazine for people involved in the promotion, performance, study or sheer enjoyment of early music.

781.57   US
EARSHOT JAZZ; a mirror and focus for the jazz community. vol.8, no.5, 1992. m. Earshot Jazz, 3429 Fremont Pl., Ste. 309, Seattle, WA 98103. TEL 206-547-6763. Ed. Andrew Freund.

780.42   US
EAST END LIGHTS; the Elton John magazine. 1990. q. $26. Voice Communications Corp., Box 760, New Baltimore, MI 48047. TEL 810-949-7900. FAX 810-949-2217. Ed. Tom Stanton. circ. 1,400. **Document type:** consumer publication, newsletter.
  Description: Focuses on the rock star for devoted fans and collectors.

EASTERN RAINBOW. see *LITERATURE*

785.067   US   ISSN 0012-8902
EASTERN REVIEW (BROOKLYN); the voice of drum & bugle corps. 1956. m. $20 (Canada $28). Eastern Review, Inc., Box 495, Brooklyn, NY 11201. Ed. R.P. Bellarosa. adv.; bk.rev.; music rev.; charts; illus.; stat. circ. 4,000. (tabloid format)
  Formerly (until vol.20, no.3): Drum Corps Review (ISSN 0094-3649)

780   US   ISSN 0147-345X
MT4.R5
EASTMAN NOTES. 1966. a. free to qualified personnel. University of Rochester, Eastman School of Music, 26 Gibbs St., Rochester, NY 14604. TEL 716-274-1040. illus. circ. 11,000. **Indexed:** Music Artic.Guide. **Document type:** newsletter.
  Former titles: Notes from Eastman (1979); Eastman Notes (1976); Notes from Eastman (ISSN 0550-0958).
  Description: Alumni newsletter.

780.01   US   ISSN 1071-9989
EASTMAN STUDIES IN MUSIC. irreg. price varies. University of Rochester Press, c/o Robert Easton, Man. Ed., Box 41026, Rochester, NY 14604. TEL 716-275-0419. FAX 716-271-8778. **Indexed:** RILM. **Document type:** monographic series, academic/scholarly publication.
  Former titles (until 1994): Studies in Music (ISSN 1054-0911); Studies in Musicology.

780   US
EASY REEDING. 1985. q. $10 one time fee. Hohner Inc., 10223 Sycamore Dr., Ashland, VA 23005. TEL 804-550-2700. FAX 804-550-9625. (Subscr. to: Hohner Inc., Dept. HNL, Box 9375, Richmond, VA 23227) Ed. Jack C. Kavoukian. adv. contact: Jack C. Kavoukian. circ. 3,000. **Document type:** newsletter.
  Description: For those interested in the harmonica, its music and artists, related events and activities.

780 808   US
ECHO ROOM. 1988. 4/yr. $4. 211 Morris St., Phillipsburg, NJ 08865. TEL 908-213-0994. Eds. Steve Gilbert, Rab Sharpe. adv.

780.7   FR   ISSN 0013-1415
EDUCATION MUSICALE; revue culturelle et pedagogique de tout l'enseignement de la musique. (5 supplements yearly) 1945. 10/yr. 350 F. (foreign 390 F.). 23 rue Benard, 75014 Paris, France. TEL 45-42-34-07. FAX 45-43-26-74. Ed. C. Negiar. adv.; rec.rev.; charts. circ. 7,000. **Indexed:** RILM.
  Description: Presents study and teaching methods.

780   US   ISSN 0363-4558
EDWARD H. TARR SERIES. irreg. Brass Press, c/o RKMS, 140 Main St., N. Easton, MA 02356. FAX 508-238-2571.
  Description: Music for trumpet.

783 200   FR   ISSN 0013-2357
EGLISE QUI CHANTE. 1957. bi-m. 157 F. (foreign 190 F.). (Association Saint-Ambroise) Editions du Cerf, 29 bd. Latour-Maubourg, 75340 Paris Cedex 07, France. TEL 44-18-12-12. FAX 45-56-04-27. (Subscr. to: Service Abonnements, 3 chemin des Prunais, 94350 Villiers-sur-Marne, France) Ed. J. Lebon. adv.; charts; index.

EIGHTEENTH-CENTURY STUDIES. see *HISTORY*

780   GW
EISERNE LERCHE; Hefte fuer eine demokratische Musikkultur. q. DM.8. Verlag Plaene GmbH, Postfach 827, 4600 Dortmund 1, Germany. illus.

789   US   ISSN 0884-4720
ML1380
ELECTRONIC MUSICIAN. 1976. m. $24 (foreign $44). Act III Publishing, 6400 Hollis, Ste. 12, Emeryville, CA 94608. TEL 510-653-3307. FAX 510-635-5142. (Subscr. to: Box 41094, Nashville, TN 37204. TEL 800-888-5139) Ed. Bob O'Donnell. adv.; bk.rev.; rec.rev.; software rev. circ. 50,677. (back issues avail.) **Indexed:** Amer.Hist.& Life, Hist.Abstr., Music Ind.
  —Faxon; UnCover.
  Formerly (until 1985): Polyphony (ISSN 0163-4534).
  Description: High-tech music equipment and applications magazine.

780 621.3   US   ISSN 0160-1148
ELECTRONOTES. 1972. m. $25. Musical Engineering Group, One Pheasant Ln., Ithaca, NY 14850. TEL 607-272-8030. Ed. Bernie Hutchins. bk.rev.; abstr.; bibl.; charts; illus. circ. 1,000. (back issues avail.)
  Formerly: Electronotes Newsletter.

780.92   UK   ISSN 0143-1269
ELGAR SOCIETY. JOURNAL. 1973. 3/yr. £15 (effective 1995). Elgar Society, c/o John Greig, Treasurer, Orchard Barn, Derringstone St., Barham, Canterbury, Kent CT4 6QB, England. TEL 01227-831841. Ed. Geoffrey Hodgkins. adv.; bk.rev. circ. 1,400. **Document type:** academic/scholarly publication.
  Formerly: Elgar Society. Newsletter (ISSN 0309-4405).

051   US   ISSN 1070-2164
ELVIS INTERNATIONAL FORUM. 1993. q. $19.95. Darwin Lamm, Ed. & Pub., Box 3373, Thousand Oaks, CA 91359. TEL 805-379-4012. adv.: B&W page $5000. illus. circ. 80,000. **Document type:** consumer publication.
  Description: Informative and entertaining articles about Elvis Presley.

780   UK   ISSN 0013-6484
ELVIS MONTHLY. 1958. m. £12($33) Heanor Record Centre Ltd., 6 Empire Rd., Leicester LE3 5HE, England. TEL 0116-253-7271. FAX 0106-253-1875. (Subscr. to: Spotlight Magazine Distribution Ltd., 1 Benwell Rd., Holloway, London N7 7AX, England) Pub. Todd Slaughter. adv. contact: Todd Slaughter. bk.rev.; film rev.; illus. circ. 50,000. **Document type:** consumer publication.
  Description: Contains articles on Elvis Presley, his music, and his fans.

ELVIS NOW FAN CLUB. see *CLUBS*

780   US
ELVIS WORLD. 1986. q. $15 (effective Jun. 1993). Burk Enterprises, Box 16792, Memphis, TN 38186-0792. TEL 901-327-1128. FAX 901-323-1528. Ed. Connie Lauridsen Burk. adv.: B&W page $325. bk.rev. circ. 5,300. (back issues avail.) **Document type:** consumer publication.
  Description: Features rare photos and stories (factual) of Elvis Presley.

781.64   UK   ISSN 0957-4948
EMPIRE. 1989. m. £28.20 (foreign £36.45) (effective 1995-1996). E M A P - Metro, Mappin House, 4 Winsley St., London W1N 7AR, England. TEL 0171-436-1515. FAX 0171-312-8191. (Subscr. to: Tower Publishing Services Ltd., Tower House, Sovereign Park, Lathkill St., Market Harborough, Leics. LE16 9EF, England. TEL 01858-468811. FAX 01858-432164) adv. **Document type:** consumer publication.

MUSIC

781.7 UK ISSN 0013-8231
ML5
ENGLISH DANCE AND SONG. 1936. q. £30 (includes Folk Music Journal). English Folk Dance and Song Society, Cecil Sharp House, 2 Regents Park Rd., London NW1 7AY, England. Ed. Dave Arthur. adv.; bk.rev.; rec.rev.; illus. circ. 5,000. (also avail. in microform from UMI; reprint service avail. from UMI) Indexed: A.I.C.P., M.L.A., Music Ind., RILM.
—BLDSC (3773.400000); Faxon; UMI; UnCover.
Incorporates: E F D S S News (ISSN 0012-7647)

ENTERTAINMENT AND SPORTS LAWYER. see LAW

780.42 US
ENTERTAINMENT EYES. 1979. m. $12.60. Alsaman Rec. and Comm. Group, Inc., Box 8263, Haledon, NJ 07508. TEL 201-942-6810. Eds. Maureen Ellis, Samuel Cummings. adv.; bk.rev.; bibl.; charts. circ. 10,000. (back issues avail.)

780 791.43 US
THE ENTERTAINMENT MAGAZINE ON-LINE. 1977. m. free. S W Alternatives, Inc., Box 3355, Tucson, AZ 85722. TEL 602-623-3733. E-mail: rezucker@rtd.com; Site addr.: http://www.rfd.com/emol/ Ed. Robert E. Zucker; Pub. Robert E. Zucker. adv.: page $999; adv. contact: Robert Zucker. bk.rev.; film rev.; music rev.; play rev. circ. 50,000. (back issues avail.) **Document type:** newspaper.
●Available only online.
Former titles: Entertainment Magazine (ISSN 0883-1890); (until 1985): Southwest Alternatives Institute. Magazine (ISSN 0742-9568); Which incorporated (1981-1982): Tucson Teen (ISSN 1044-954X)
Description: Explores music, theatre, video, film, and the arts with articles and interviews, as well as a comprehensive Arizona calendar of events, new music, and video release guide. Includes national and Southwest regional coverage.

780 791.43 US
ENTERTAINMENT PLUS. w. Box 11707, Rock Hill, SC 29731. TEL 803-329-4000.

782 FR ISSN 0013-8975
ENTR'ACTE;* la revue des theatres lyriques. 1955. s-m. 36 F. 29 Bd. Voltaire, 75011 Paris, France. Ed. Stephane Wolff. adv.; illus.

780 NE ISSN 0924-560X
ML5
ENTR'ACTE; muziek journal. vol.3, 1977. 10/yr. fl.79.50 to individuals; students fl.69.50. Impresariaat, Paulus Potterstraat 12, 1071 CZ Amsterdam, Netherlands. TEL 31-20-6620727. FAX 31-20-6751206. Ed. Sytze Smit. adv.; bk.rev.; illus. circ. 15,000. Indexed: Excerp.Med. **Document type:** consumer publication.
Former titles (until Sep. 1989): Muziek en Dans (ISSN 0166-0535); M D.

780 SP
ENTRE MUSICOS. 24/yr. Avda. de America 25, 1o, 28002 Madrid, Spain. TEL 1-589-77-89. FAX 1-256-36-87. Ed. Luis Bomati. circ. 36,000.

780 IT ISSN 1122-9462
L'ERBA MUSICA; rivista di pedagogia speciale e di cultura musicale. 1991. q. L.35000 (effective 1995) L.40000 (effective 1996). Laboratorio di Musicologia Applicata, Via Plana 45, 20155 Milan, Italy. TEL 39-2-33000026. FAX 39-2-33003350. Ed. Francesca Martinez. adv. contact: Pierangelo Sequeri. **Document type:** academic/scholarly publication.

780 US
ERNEST BLOCH SOCIETY. BULLETIN. 1967. a. $3.50. Ernest Bloch Society, c/o Susan Bloch, Ed., 448 Riverside Dr., New York, NY 10027. bk.rev. circ. 2,000. **Document type:** bulletin.
Former titles: Ernest Bloch Society. Newsletter; (until 1983): Ernest Bloch Society. Bulletin (ISSN 0071-1195)
Description: Devoted entirely to correspondence between the composer and his friends and colleagues.

790.92 US ISSN 1053-9948
ML410.K7365
ERNST KRENEK ARCHIVE. NEWSLETTER. 1990. 3/yr. $10. Ernst Krenek Archive, University of California, San Diego, La Jolla, CA 92093-0175. TEL 619-534-2759. FAX 619-534-0189. E-mail: sroman@ucsd.edu. Ed. Garrett H. Bowles. **Document type:** newsletter.

780 US ISSN 0421-3653
ERTONG YINYUE/CHILDREN'S MUSIC. (Text in Chinese) 1957. bi-m. $18. China Books & Periodicals, Inc., 2929 24th St., San Francisco, CA 94110. TEL 415-282-2994. FAX 415-282-0994.

780.42 AG
ESCENARIOS; de musica popular argentina. 1990. m. Editorial Escenarios, Juncal 971, 4o A, Buenos Aires, Argentina. TEL 393-6298.

780 IT
ESERCIZI MUSICA E SPETTACOLO. 1978. a. Universita degli Studi di Perugia, Centro di Studi Musicali in Umbria, Catteedra di Storia della Musica, Piazza Morlacchi 11, 06123 Perugia, Italy. TEL 075-5853734. FAX 075-5853732. Ed. Massimo Bogianckino.
Formerly: Esercizi Arte Musica Spettacolo (ISSN 0393-6791)

EL ESPECTACULAR. see COMMUNICATIONS — Television And Cable

780 306 FR ISSN 0299-3201
ETHNOMUSICOLOGIE. (Subseries of: Bibliotheque de la S E L A F) 1985. irreg., no.5, 1990. price varies. Societe d'Etudes Linguistiques et Anthropologiques de France (SELAF), 52 bd St. Michel, 75006 Paris, France. (Dist. by: Editions Peeters s.p.r.l., Bondgenotenlaan 153, B-3000 Louvain, Belgium. TEL 32-16-235170. FAX 32-16-228500) (back issues avail.) **Document type:** monographic series.

781.7 US ISSN 0014-1836
ML1
ETHNOMUSICOLOGY. 1953. 3/yr. $50 to individuals and institutions; students $25. Society for Ethnomusicology, Morrison Hall 005, Indiana University, Bloomington, IN 47405-2501. TEL 812-855-6672. FAX 812-855-6673. Ed. James Cowdery. bk.rev.; film rev.; rec.rev.; bibl.; charts; illus.; index, cum.index: vols.1-10, 11-20, 21-30. circ. 2,000. (also avail. in microform from UMI; back issues avail.; reprint service avail. from UMI) **Indexed:** A.I.C.P., Abstr.Anthropol., Amer.Bibl.Slavic & E.Eur.Stud., Anthropol.Lit., Arts & Hum.Cit.Ind., Chic.Per.Ind., Curr.Cont.Africa, Curr.Cont., Hum.Ind., Ind.Bk.Rev.Hum., M.L.A., Mid.East: Abstr.& Ind., Music Ind., Ref.Sour., RILM, So.Pac.Per.Ind., SSCI. **Document type:** academic/scholarly publication.
—BLDSC (3815.150000); Faxon; Genuine Article; SWETS; UMI; UnCover. **CCC.**
Description: Explores the music of peoples throughout the world. Articles represent current theoretical attitudes and research in this and related fields.
Refereed Serial

783 FR ISSN 0071-2086
ETUDES GREGORIENNES; revue de musicologie religieuse. (Text in English, French and Italian) 1954. irreg, latest vol.20, 1981. price varies. Editions Abbaye Saint-Pierre de Solesmes, 72300 Sable sur Sarthe, France. Dir. D. Jean Claire. bk.rev. circ. 500. **Indexed:** RILM.

780 KO
EUMAK DONG-A. 1984. m. Dong-A Ilbo, 139 Sejongno, Chongno-gu, Seoul, S. Korea. TEL 02-721-7114. Ed. Kwon O-Kie. circ. 85,000.

786.23 GW ISSN 0014-2387
EURO PIANO; information & service. (Text in English, French, German, Italian) 1960. q. DM.80. (Union Europaeischer Pianomacher-Fachverbaende) Verlag Erwin Bochinsky GmbH, Muenchenerstr. 45, 60329 Frankfurt a.M., Germany. TEL 069-239521. Ed. Rita Orgel. adv. contact: Winfried Kumetat. charts; illus.; stat. circ. 2,000. **Document type:** trade publication.
—**CCC.**
Description: Information and workshop service for piano manufacturers. Features latest technology, computerization, association news and events, readers' comments.

780.65 781.64 FR ISSN 1154-5399
EURO POP; international rock & pop music directory. (Text in English) 1990. a. 320 F. Centre d'Information du Rock et des Varietes, Parc de la Villette, 211 av. Jean-Jaures, 75019 Paris, France. TEL 42-00-12-11. FAX 42-00-64-46. Ed. Stephane Davet. **Document type:** directory.

780 338 NE
▼**EUROFILE ARTISTS, VENUES AND TOURING DIRECTORY**. 1994. a. fl.135($90) B P I Communications, Rijnsburgstraat 11, 1059 AT Amsterdam, Netherlands. TEL 31-20-6691961. FAX 31-20-66919412. Ed. Cesco van Gool. (also avail. in diskette format) **Document type:** directory.
Description: References source for the European talent and touring industry, including information on management company and record label for major musical acts, and contacts for concert venues, concert promoters, hotels, and touring related service companies.

EUROFILE MUSIC INDUSTRY DIRECTORY. see BUSINESS AND ECONOMICS — Trade And Industrial Directories

780 GW ISSN 0939-2106
EUROPEAN MUSIC CATALOG OF SCORES. 9/yr. Harrassowitz Verlag, Taunusstr. 5, 65183 Wiesbaden, Germany. TEL 0611-530-0. FAX 0611-530560. E-mail: 100024.761@compuserve.com. (Subscr. in N. America to: Harrassowitz, Box 10, Columbia, MD 21045-0010. TEL 410-964-3011. FAX 410-964-3013) **Document type:** directory.
Formerly: European Music Catalog.

786 SZ
EUROPIANO. q. Schweizerischer Verband der Klavierbauer und -stimmer, c/o E. Schoeckle, Lindenfeldweg 9, 4106 Therwil, Switzerland. TEL 031-840036.

781.57 DK
EVELYN BOOSTER. 1977. m. free. Fajabefa-Aarhus, Aabogade 36, DK-8200 Aarhus N, Denmark. TEL 86-10-66-33. adv. circ. 800. **Document type:** newsletter, trade publication.
Formerly (until 1980): Fajabefa Nyt (ISSN 0105-5933)

781.7 AT ISSN 1036-109X
EVERYONE'S SONGS. 1977. irreg. Aus.$7 per no.; catalogue Aus.$2. Sound Austral, 34 Lucerne Cres., Frankston, Vic. 3199, Australia. TEL 61-3-789-2205. Ed. Frank Hinz. (back issues avail.; catalogue of titles avail.)
Formerly (until 1990): Everyone's Songs. Series (ISSN 0159-1991)
Description: Collection of folkloric and community songs of Australia.

780.01 US ISSN 0276-6795
ML1
EX TEMPORE. 1981. s-a. $10 to individuals; institutions $14. c/o Deptartment of Music, Texas Christian University, Ft. Worth, TX 76129. adv. circ. 200. (back issues avail.)

782.5 286 US ISSN 1046-3798
ML1
EXALTATION. 1974. q. $13.25. Southern Baptist Convention, Sunday School Board, 127 Ninth Ave., N., Nashville, TN 37234. TEL 800-458-2772.
Formerly (until 1990): Choral Praise (ISSN 0362-0409)
Description: Contains anthem music for youth and adult choirs.

EXETER STUDIES IN AMERICAN & COMMONWEALTH ARTS. see LITERATURE

780 US
EXIT (NEW YORK); alternative music. 1990. bi-m. Exit Magazine, Box 5173, New York, NY 10185. TEL 718-278-4310. Ed. Leslie Kobyluck.

781 US ISSN 0883-0754
EXPERIMENTAL MUSICAL INSTRUMENTS. 1985. q. $24 (Canada & Mexico $27, elsewhere $34). Experimental Musical Instruments, Box 784, Nicasio, CA 94946. TEL 415-662-2182. Ed. Bart Hopkin. adv.; bk.rev.; bibl.; charts; illus.; cum.index; circ. 900 (paid). (back issues avail.) Indexed: Music Artic.Guide, UPDATE. **Document type:** newsletter.
  Description: Devoted to new and unusual acoustic and electro-acoustic musical instruments and sound sculpture.

783 NE
EXPRESSIE. 1975. a. $15. Continental Sound, Postbus 80165, 3009 GB Rotterdam, Netherlands. FAX 010-4559022. Ed. Leen la Riviere. adv.; bk.rev. circ. 1,500.
  Formerly: Gospel Informatie-Handboek.

787 US ISSN 0196-187X
ML1
F I G A. 1960. bi-m. $18 (Canada $24.50; elsewhere $35). Fretted Instrument Guild of America, 2344 S. Oakley Ave., Chicago, IL 60608. TEL 312-376-1143. Ed. Glen Lemmer. adv.; bibl. circ. 2,000. **Document type:** newsletter.
  Former titles: F I G A Review (ISSN 0196-1861); (until 1980): F I G A News (ISSN 0014-5890)

F M GUIDE. see COMMUNICATIONS — Radio

781.57 UK ISSN 0969-5214
FABLE BULLETIN: VIOLIN IMPROVISATION STUDIES. 1993. irreg. £100 to insitutions (for all issues through 1999). Anthony Barnett, Ed. & Pub., 14 Mount St., Lewes, E. Sussex BN7 1HL, England. TEL 01273-479393. music rev. circ. 200. (looseleaf format) **Document type:** academic/scholarly publication.
  Description: Contains original research on various aspects of improvisational jazz, including discography and musical scores.

780.42 UK ISSN 0263-1210
THE FACE. 1980. m. $48. Wagadon Ltd., 3rd Fl. Block A, Exmouth House, Pine St., London EC1R 0JL, England. TEL 071-837-7270. FAX 071-837-3906. (Subscr. to: P.O. Box 500, Leicester LE99 0AA, England) Ed. Sheryl Garratt. adv. contact: Rod Sopp. bk.rev.; illus. circ. 105,000. Indexed: DAAI. **Document type:** consumer publication.
  Description: Primary focus is on music, fashion and youth culture.

780.42 US ISSN 0882-2921
ML3533.8
FACES ROCKS.* 1983. irreg., latest June 1993. $19 (foreign $25). Faces Magazines, Inc., 210 E. State Rt. 4, Ste. 401, Paramus, NJ 07652-5013. TEL 201-843-8964. FAX 201-843-8636. Ed.Bd. adv.; illus. circ. 100,000. **Document type:** consumer publication.
  Description: Features hard rock and heavy metal music.

780 GW ISSN 0930-0171
FACHBLATT MUSIK MAGAZIN. m. DM.78 (foreign DM.84). S Z V KG, Schellingstr. 39-43, 80799 Munich, Germany. TEL 089-23726-0. FAX 089-23726125. Ed. Horst Stachelhaus. adv. contact: Sabine Frischmuth. **Document type:** consumer publication.

789.91 US ISSN 0148-9364
ML156.9
FANFARE; the magazine for serious record collectors. 1977. bi-m. $34. Fanfare, Inc., 273 Woodland St., Tenafly, NJ 07670. (Subscr. to: Box 720, Tenafly, NJ 07670) Ed. Joel Flegler. adv.; bk.rev. circ. 26,000. (back issues avail.) Indexed: Music Artic.Guide, Music Ind., RILM. **Document type:** consumer publication.
  —Faxon; UnCover.

780 UK ISSN 0967-9081
FANFARE. 1968. a. £3($10) Royal Military School of Music, Kneller Hall, Twickenham, Middx. TW2 7DU, England. Ed. Major Gordon Turner. adv.; bk.rev. circ. 4,500.

780 SZ
FANFARE. 6/yr. Obere Neugut 25, CH-3280 Murten, Switzerland. TEL 031-7477416. Ed. E. Scheidegger. circ. 1,300.

780 US
FARANDULA INTERNACIONAL. (Text in Spanish) 1993. m. $18. Ibarra Brothers, 3266 21st St., San Francisco, CA 94110. TEL 415-826-6700. FAX 415-826-6701. Ed. Arturo Ibarra.

781.57 IT
FARE MUSICA. 1980. m. L.60000 (Europe L.90000). Ediscreen s.r.l., Via Calderini, 68, 00196 Rome, Italy. Dir. Enzo Perilli. adv.: B&W page L.3148000, color page L.5035000. circ. 80,000. (back issues avail.)

781.7 US ISSN 8755-9137
ML3551
FAST FOLK MUSICAL MAGAZINE. 1984. 10/yr. $100 (foreign $125) (effective 1992). Fast Folk Musical Magazine, Inc., Box 938, Village Sta., New York, NY 10014. TEL 212-274-1636. FAX 212-927-1831. Ed. Jack Hardy. adv.; bk.rev. circ. 1,500. (includes compact discs)
  Description: Focuses on the contemporary folk singer-songwriter scene. Each CD contains a dozen or more songs, while the print publication contains articles, news and commentaries, interviews, lyrics, and biographies of performers-authors.

FAVES. see CHILDREN AND YOUTH — For

780 621.389 IT ISSN 1121-5313
FEDELTA DEL SUONO. 1991. m. L.70000 (Europe L.130000; elsewhere L.150000). Mozart Editrice s.r.l., Via Rismondo 1o, 05100 Terni, Italy. TEL 0744-428398. FAX 0744-428401. Ed. Gianfranco Maria Binari. adv. contact: German Ruscitto. **Document type:** consumer publication.

781.57 US
FEDERATION JAZZ. 1985. 6/yr. $25 to non-members (effective 1995 & 1996). Federation of Jazz Societies, 2787 Del Monte St., W. Sacramento, CA 95691. TEL 916-372-5277. FAX 916-372-3479. (Ed. Addr.: 14 W. Jordan St., Ste. 1-H, Pensacola, FL 32501. TEL 904-433-8382. FAX 904-438-4091) Ed. F. Norman Vickers. adv.; bk.rev.; illus.; circ. 300 (controlled). **Document type:** newsletter.
  Description: Covers the activities of the federation and its members. Includes items of interest to jazz enthusiasts.

780 AT ISSN 1039-4354
FELLOWSHIP OF AUSTRALIAN COMPOSERS. JOURNAL. irreg. free to members. Fellowship of Australian Composers, P.O. Box 265, Carlingford, N.S.W. 2118, Australia. TEL 61-2-869-0451. Ed. John Colborne-Veel. adv. contact: John Colborne-Veel. **Document type:** newsletter.

780 GW ISSN 0939-4664
FERMATE; rheinisches Musikmagazin. 1982. q. DM.25; newsstand price: DM.6.80. Verlag Christoph Dohr, Kasselberger Weg 120, 50769 Cologne, Germany. TEL 0221-707002. FAX 0221-704395. Ed. Christoph Dohr. adv.: page DM.700. bk.rev. (back issues avail.) **Document type:** newsletter.

780.1 US ISSN 1062-4074
FESTSCHRIFT SERIES. 1977. irreg., vol.15, 1994. Pendragon Press, 41 Ferry St., Stuyvesant, NY 12173-9720. TEL 518-828-3008. FAX 518-828-2368. (back issues avail.) Indexed: RILM. **Document type:** monographic series.

780 792 AU
FESTSPIEL - ILLUSTRIERTE. (Text in English, German) 1981. a. S.88. Verlag fuer Kunst und Kultur, Weinberggasse 24, A-1190 Vienna, Austria. TEL 0222-3181924. FAX 0222-3181925. Pub. Angele Zobl. adv.: color page S.38000; adv. contact: Angele Zobl. circ. 40,000 (paid). **Document type:** consumer publication.

781.7 AG
FICTA-DIFUSORA DE MUSICA ANTIQUA. 1977. s-a. Centro de Musica Antiqua, Mexico 1208, 1097 Buenos Aires, Argentina. Ed. Jorge V. Gonzalez. adv.; bk.rev. circ. 1,500.

FILM MUSIC BUYER'S GUIDE. see MOTION PICTURES

FILM, SZINHAZ, MUZSIKA. see MOTION PICTURES

787 US
FIRST BASS. 1987. q. $14.95 (foreign $24.95). (Bass Players Hall of Fame Museum) First Bass International, 33 Essex St., Hackensack, NJ 07601. TEL 201-489-5057. FAX 201-489-2508. Ed. Joe Campagna. bk.rev.
  Description: Directed to the electric and acoustic bass player of all ages, levels and backgrounds with emphasis on the intelligent creative reader, thinker and music lover. Educational tool for students and guide for consumers.

780 AT ISSN 0311-0559
FLAUTIST. 1971. q. Aus.$35 (students & pensioners Aus.$25). Victorian Flute Guild, Inc., P.O. Box 95, Malvern, Vic. 3144, Australia. TEL 03-822-2241. FAX 03-822-6676. Ed. J. Mainka. adv.; bk.rev.; circ. 400 (paid). **Document type:** newsletter.
  Description: Publishes articles relevent to flute players.

780 US
FLIPSIDE.* q. $2.50 per no. Box 60790, Pasedena, CA 91116.
  Description: Features punk music and interviews with new bands.

FLORIDA FOLKLIFE RESOURCE DIRECTORY. see FOLKLORE

784 US ISSN 0160-5119
ML1
FLORIDA FRIENDS OF BLUEGRASS SOCIETY. NEWSLETTER. bi-m. Florida Friends of Bluegrass Society, 7318 Sequaia Dr., Tampa, FL 33617. illus. **Document type:** newsletter.

780.7 US ISSN 0046-4155
ML1
FLORIDA MUSIC DIRECTOR. 1947. 10/yr. $12. Florida Music Educators Association, c/o Vicki Miazga, Man. Ed., 207 Office Plaza Dr., Tallahassee, FL 32301. TEL 904-878-6844. FAX 904-942-1793. (Co-sponsor: Florida State Music Teachers Association) Ed. Charles Hoffer. adv. contact: Vicki Miazga. bk.rev.; illus. circ. 4,875. Indexed: Music Artic.Guide. **Document type:** trade publication, academic/scholarly publication.
  Formerly: Music Director (ISSN 0027-4313); Incorporates: Florida Music Teacher.
  Refereed Serial

780.01 UK
FLOURISH!. 1966. 2/yr. Trinity College London, 16 Park Crescent, London W1N 4AP, England. TEL 0171-323-2320. FAX 0171-323-5201. Ed. Charles Franklyn. adv.; bk.rev.; rec.rev. circ. 10,000. **Document type:** newsletter.
  Formerly (until 1994): Trinity Magazine.

780 US ISSN 0744-6918
ML929
FLUTE TALK; a magazine for flutists and flute teachers. 1980. 10/yr. $15. Instrumentalist Co., 200 Northfield Rd., Northfield, IL 60093-3390. TEL 708-446-5000; 800-323-5559. Ed. Kathleen Goll-Wilson; Pub. James T. Rohner. adv.; bk.rev.; rec.rev. circ. 12,000. Indexed: Music Artic.Guide. —UnCover.

780 US ISSN 8756-8667
ML27.U5
FLUTIST QUARTERLY. 1974. q. $30. National Flute Association, Inc., c/o Phyllis Pemberton, Box 800597, Santa Clarita, CA 91380-0597. TEL 805-297-5287. Ed. Susan Phelps. adv.; bk.rev. circ. 4,500. (also avail. in microfilm from BHP) Indexed: Music Artic.Guide.
  —Faxon.
  Formerly: National Flute Association. Newsletter.

780 US
FLUXBUCKET. 1990. s-a. $12 (effective May 1993). Box 151481, Altamonte, FL 32715. Ed. Craig Michaels. circ. 700. **Document type:** consumer publication.
  Description: Promotes avant, esoteric and difficult music (mainly of an electronic nature). Each issue includes a cassette tape representing the artists profiled.

FOLIO (NORTH HOLLYWOOD). see COMMUNICATIONS — Radio

FOLK ARTS NOTES. see FOLKLORE

MUSIC

781.7 US ISSN 1076-4119
FOLK ERA TODAY!. 1981. q. $8. Folk Era Productions, Inc., 17 Middle Dunstable Rd., Nashua, NH 03062. TEL 603-888-3457. Ed. Bob Grand. adv.; bk.rev. circ. 15,000. (back issues avail.)
Former titles: Folk Era Newsletter; Kingston Korner Newsletter.
Description: Covers popular acoustic folk music.

780 US ISSN 0094-8934
ML1
FOLK HARP JOURNAL. 1973. q. $16 to institutions; free to members. International Society of Folk Harpers and Craftsmen, Inc., 4718 Maychelle Dr., Anaheim, CA 92807-3040. TEL 714-998-5717. FAX 714-998-5717. Ed. Nadine Bunn. adv.; bk.rev.; bibl.; charts; illus. circ. 1,400. **Indexed:** Music Ind. **Document type:** consumer publication.
Description: Covers folk (nonpedal) harp playing, construction, and history. Aims to provide communication among harpers and builders.

FOLK IN KENT. see *DANCE*

781.7 GW ISSN 0934-6449
ML3544
FOLK-MICHEL. 1977. bi-m. DM.30 (foreign DM.37.20). Losemund Verlag, Postfach 1269, 53582 Bad Honnef, Germany. TEL 02224-76510. (Subscr. to: Ulrike Wellmann, Resedastr. 14, 52134 Herzogenrath, Germany) Ed. Bernhard Hanneken. adv.; bk.rev.; cum.index. circ. 1,600. **Document type:** newsletter.
Formerly (until 1987): Michel - Zeitschrift fuer Volksmusik.
Description: Provides information on international and national folk music, both traditional and contemporary.

781.7 793.31 UK ISSN 0531-9684
FOLK MUSIC JOURNAL. 1965. a. English Folk Dance and Song Society, Cecil Sharp House, 2 Regents Park Rd., London NW1 7AY, England. Ed. Ian Russell. adv.; bk.rev.; cum.index. circ. 5,000. (also avail. in microform from UMI; back issues avail.) **Indexed:** Arts & Hum.Cit.Ind., Br.Hum.Ind., Curr.Cont., M.L.A., Music Ind.
—BLDSC (3974.572000); UnCover.
Supersedes: English Folk Dance and Song Society. Journal.

781.7 793.31 UK ISSN 1350-8083
FOLK NORTH-WEST. 1977. 4/yr. £5. North-West Federation of Folk Clubs, 118 Bolton Rd., Aspull, Wigan WN2 1XF, England. TEL 0942-833292. (Subscr. to: 7 Sunleigh Rd., Hindley, Wigan, Lancashire, England) Ed. Nigel Firth. adv.; bk.rev.; play rev. circ. 1,000. (back issues avail.) **Document type:** consumer publication.
Formerly: North-West Federation of Folk Clubs Newsletter.
Description: News and articles on folk music in Northwest England.

781.7 UK ISSN 0951-1326
FOLK ROOTS. 1979. m. £25.60 (foreign £31). Southern Rag Ltd., P.O. Box 337, London N4 1TW, England. TEL 0181-340-9651. FAX 0181-348-5626. Ed. Ian A. Anderson. adv. contact: Gina Jennings. bk.rev. circ. 13,000. (back issues avail.) **Document type:** consumer publication.
Formerly (until 1985): Southern Rag.

FOLKBLAD PIBROCH. see *FOLKLORE*

781.7 GW
FOLKBRIEF; news & views. (Supplement avail.) (Text in German; summaries in English, French) 1979. m. DM.33.80. Folk-Edition, Burgstr. 9, 48301 Nottuln, Germany. TEL 02502-6151. FAX 02502-1825. bk.rev. (back issues avail.)
Formerly (until 1986): Folkblatt.

781.7 398 US
FOLKSONG IN THE CLASSROOM; a network of teachers of history, literature, music and the humanities - a newsletter. 1980. 3/yr. $10 to individuals (foreign $8); institutions $15. Box 925, Starbridge, MA 01566. TEL 508-347-3434. Ed. John W. Scott. bk.rev.; rec.rev. circ. 1,500. (back issues avail.) **Indexed:** ERIC. **Document type:** newsletter.
Description: Contains sheet music and lyrics, historical analysis, correspondence from readers; instructional guidance and materials for classroom teaching.

780.01 UK
FOMRHI QUARTERLY. 1975. q. £10.50 (rest of Europe £12; elsewhere £13.50). Fellowship of Makers and Researchers of Historical Instruments, Faculty of Music, St. Aldate's, Oxford OX1 1DB, England. FAX 01365-276128. bk.rev.; cum.index.; circ. 700 (controlled). (back issues avail.) **Document type:** academic/scholarly publication.
Description: Promotes the authenticity of the reproduction and preservation of historical musical instruments.

780 SP
FONO 2;* la revista de los jovenes y de la musica. m. 480 ptas.($9) Ediciones Anel, San Vicente Ferrer 13, Granada, Spain. adv.; bk.rev.; film rev.; charts; illus. circ. 30,000. (back issues avail.)
Formerly (1963-1969): Fonorama.

789.91 621.389 GW ISSN 0015-6140
FONOFORUM. 1957. m. DM.84 (foreign DM.96). S Z V KG, Schellingstr. 39-43, 80799 Munich, Germany. TEL 089-23726-0. FAX 089-23726-125. Ed. Soeren Meyer-Eller. adv. contact: Kurt Erzinger. bk.rev.; rec.rev.; illus.; tr.lit.; index. circ. 38,000. **Indexed:** RILM. **Document type:** consumer publication.

780 IT ISSN 1120-8260
FONTI MUSICALI IN ITALIA; studi e ricerche. 1987. a. Comitato Nazionale Italiano Musica, Via Vittoria Colonna 18, 00139 Rome, Italy. TEL 06-6542402. (Co-sponsor: Societa Italiana di Musicologia) Eds. Dinko Fabris, Marcello Ruggieri.

784 RU
FOR A LOVER OF VOCAL MUSIC. a. 2.10 Rub. Izdatel'stvo Muzyka, Ul. Neglinnaya 14, Moscow 103031, Russia. TEL 924-81-63. FAX 921-83-53.

780 384.55 UK
FOR THE RECORD; the music trade monthly. m. £25 (Europe £40; elsewhere £55). 57-63 Brownfields, Welwyn Garden City, Herts. AL7 1AN, England. TEL 0707-333716. FAX 0707-375167. TELEX 297222. Ed. Gaynor Edwards. adv. contact: Tim Jones. circ. 5,000. **Document type:** trade publication.

FORCED EXPOSURE. see *LITERARY AND POLITICAL REVIEWS*

780 RU
FOREIGN COMPOSERS. 2/yr. 2.10 Rub. per issue. Izdatel'stvo Muzyka, Ul. Neglinnaya 14, Moscow 103031, Russia. TEL 924-81-63. FAX 021-83-53.

780.01 AU
FORSCHUNGEN ZUR AELTEREN MUSIKGESCHICHTE. 1976. irreg., no.5, 1984. price varies. (Universitaet Wien, Musikwissenschaftliches Institut) Wilhelm Braumueller, Universitaets-Verlagsbuchhandlung GmbH, Servitengasse 5, A-1092 Vienna, Austria. TEL 01-3191159. FAX 01-3102805. Ed. Walter Pass. circ. 500. **Document type:** monographic series.

780 GW ISSN 0173-5187
ML110
FORUM MUSIKBIBLIOTHEK; Beitraege und Informationen aus der musikbibliothekarischen Praxis. 1980. q. DM.38. Deutsches Bibliotheksinstitut, Abt. 1 - Publikationen, Alt-Moabit 101A, 10559 Berlin, Germany. TEL 030-39077-0. FAX 030-39077100. Ed.Bd. circ. 300. **Indexed:** LISA. **Document type:** bulletin.

782 SW ISSN 0284-477X
FOTNOTEN. 1988. bi-m. Laerarfoerbundet, P.O. Box 12239, S-102 26 Stockholm, Sweden. TEL 46-8-737-65-00. circ. 6,000.

781.7 US ISSN 0887-1892
FOUNDER'S SOUNDER. 1979. s-a. free. (Middle Atlantic Regional Gospel Music Festival) Middle Atlantic Regional Press, 100 Bryant St., N.W., Washington, DC 20001-1631. TEL 202-265-7609. Ed. E. Myron Noble. **Document type:** newsletter.
Description: Covers African American gospel music and current events of MARGMF.

780
FRANZ LISZT STUDIES SERIES. 1991. irreg. Pendragon Press, 41 Ferry Rd., Stuyvesant, NY 12173-9720. TEL 518-828-3008. FAX 518-828-2368. Ed. Michael Saffle. **Document type:** monographic series.
Formerly: American Liszt Society Studies Series (ISSN 1062-4031)

780 US ISSN 1062-4082
FRENCH OPERA IN THE 17TH AND 18TH CENTURIES. 1984. irreg., latest no.10. Pendragon Press, 41 Ferry St., Stuyvesant, NY 12173-9720. TEL 518-828-3008. FAX 518-828-2368. **Document type:** monographic series.

780 US
FRIENDS OF JULIO INTERNATIONAL NEWSLETTER. Abbreviated title: F O J I Newsletter. 1986. q. $18 membership. Friends of Julio International, 28 Farmington Ave., Longmeadow, MA 01106. TEL 413-567-0845. Ed. Isabel Butterfield. circ. 150. (looseleaf format) **Document type:** newsletter.
Description: Reports on Julio's concerts, albums, tour schedules, benefits; includes photos of Julio.

787 IT
FRONIMO; rivista trimestrale di chitarra e liuto. 1972. q. L.30000 (foreign L.40000). Edizioni Suvini Zerboni, Via M.F. Quintiliano, 40, 20138 Milan, Italy. TEL 0039-2-5084365. FAX 0039-2-5084261. Ed. Gianni Marinato. adv.; bk.rev.; bibl.; charts; illus.; index. circ. 7,000. **Indexed:** RILM.

781.7 398 VE
FUNDACION DE ETNOMUSICOLOGIA Y FOLKLORE. ANUARIO. 1975. a. $15. Fundacion de Etnomusicologia y Folklore, Apdo. 81015, Prados del Este, Caracas 1080-A, Venezuela. TEL 612118. FAX 627296. bk.rev.; illus.
Formerly (until 1989): Centro para las Culturas Populares y Tradicionales. Boletin; Supersedes (in 1987): Instituto Interamericano de Etnomusicologia y Folklore. Revista.

FUNDACION LA CAIXA. PANORAMA. see *MUSEUMS AND ART GALLERIES*

780.42 MX
FURIA MUSICAL. 1993. fortn. Mex.$4($1.50) per no. Provenemex, S.A. de C.V., Lucio Blanco 435, Azcapotzalco 02400 Mexico DF, Mexico. TEL 352-32-66. Dir. Jesus Gallegos. rec.rev. **Document type:** consumer publication.
Description: Contains interviews with and stories about musical celebrities.

789.5 US ISSN 0827-5955
ML1
G C N A BULLETIN. 1940. a. $4 to non-members. Guild of Carillonneurs in North America (San Antonio), c/o George Gregory, Ed., 132 Linda Dr., San Antonio, TX 78216. TEL 210-822-0416. (Subscr. to: William DeTurk, Bok Tower Gardens, Box 3810, Lake Wales, FL 33853) adv.; bk.rev. circ. 500. **Document type:** academic/scholarly publication.
Description: Covers the carillon, the players and their music.

780 382 JA
G S R. (Gakki Shoho Review) 1980. bi-m. $36. Gakki Shoho-Sha Co., Ltd., Gakki Kaikan Bldg., 5th Fl., 2-18-21 Sotokanda, Chiyoda-ku, Tokyo 101, Japan. Ed. Toshio Suganuma. adv.

780 US ISSN 1078-2303
GAJOOB. 1988. irreg. (2-3/m.). $15 for 9 issues (includes audio cassette). Box 3201, Salt Lake City, UT 84110. TEL 801-364-5110. E-mail: gajoob@utw.com. Ed. Bryan Baker. adv.; circ. 1,500 (paid). **Document type:** newsletter.
●Also available online.
Description: Provides a comprehensive coverage of do-it-yourself recording, craft and artists.

781.91 JA
GAKKI SHOHO/MUSIC TRADE IN JAPAN. (Text in Japanese) 1950. m. 10000 Yen($50) Gakki Shoho-Sha Co., Ltd., Gakki Kakan, 5th Fl., 2-18-21, Sotokanda, Chiyoda-ku, Tokyo 101, Japan. Ed. Yuichi Sayama. adv.; bk.rev.; mkt.; stat. circ. 5,000.
Formerly: Musical Instruments News (ISSN 0016-3945)

MUSIC 4847

780.01 UK ISSN 0072-0127
ML5
GALPIN SOCIETY JOURNAL; for the study of musical instruments. 1948. a. £18($42) to individuals (rest of Europe £24; elsewhere £28); institutions £30 (U.S. subscr. $50) (effective Apr. 1995). Galpin Society, c/o Pauline Holden, 2 Quinton Rise, Oadby, Leicester LE2 5PN, England. Ed. David Rycroft. adv.; bk.rev.; index. circ. 1,400. (also avail. in microfilm from UMI; reprint service avail. from SWZ,UMI) Indexed: Arts & Hum.Cit.Ind., Br.Hum.Ind., Curr.Cont., Music Ind., RILM. **Document type:** academic/scholarly publication.
—BLDSC (4067.550000); UMI; UnCover.

784.96 NE ISSN 0016-5239
GAUDEAMUS. 1945. 6/yr. fl.7.50($2.) Vereniging Het Maastrichts Mannenkoor - Maastricht Male Choir, Arkebijsruwe 87, 6218 RW Maastricht, Netherlands. adv.; illus.

780.904 NE ISSN 0533-9215
GAUDEAMUS INFORMATION (ENGLISH EDITION). 1966. 6/m. free. Gaudeamus Foundation, Swammerdamstr. 38, 1091 RV Amsterdam, Netherlands. TEL 31-20-6947349. FAX 31-20-6947258. E-mail: gaud@xs4all.nl. Ed. H. Heuvelmans. adv.; bk.rev.; music rev. circ. 11,000. **Document type:** newsletter.
Description: Devoted to contemporary music; contains information on concerts, festivals, competitions, records and scores.

780.65 US
THE GAVIN REPORT. w. 140 Second St., 2nd Fl., San Francisco, CA 94105-3727. TEL 415-495-1990. FAX 415-495-2580. Ed. Ron Fell.

784 GW
DER GEMEINDECHOR. 1879. bi-m. DM.7.50. (Christlicher Saengerbund e.V.) Verlag Singende Gemeinde, Westfalenweg 207, 42111 Wuppertal, Germany. TEL 0202-750633. FAX 0202-755304. Ed. Max Koehler. **Document type:** bulletin.

781.7 RU
GEMS OF RUSSIAN AND SOVIET MUSIC. a. 3.50 Rub. per issue. Izdatel'stvo Muzyka, Ul. Neglinnaya 14, Moscow 103031, Russia. TEL 924-81-63. FAX 921-93-53.

780 US ISSN 1048-3713
MT1
GENERAL MUSIC TODAY. 1987. 3/yr. $13. Music Educators National Conference, 1806 Robert Fulton Dr., Reston, VA 22091. TEL 703-860-4000. FAX 703-860-4826. Ed. Keith P. Thompson. Indexed: RILM.
—Faxon.
Description: Publishes articles on emerging trends, effective lesson ideas, and new material for teaching general music at all levels.

780 US ISSN 0046-5798
ML1
GEORGIA MUSIC NEWS. 1940. q. $16. Georgia Music Educators Association, c/o Mary Leglar, Ed., University of Georgia School of Music, Athens, GA 30602. TEL 706-542-2763. FAX 706-542-2773. adv. contact: Linda Sabella. bk.rev. circ. 2,472. Indexed: Music Artic.Guide. **Document type:** academic/scholarly publication.
Refereed Serial

784 CC ISSN 0454-0816
GEQU/SONGS. (Text in Chinese) 1952. m. $23.50. Renmin Yinyue Chubanshe, Beijing, People's Republic of China. (Dist. in US by: China Books & Periodicals, Inc., 2929 24th St., San Francisco, CA 94110. TEL 415-282-2994)

781.57 GW
GERMAN BLUES CIRCLE INFO. 1976. m. DM.20. Fritz Marschall, Ed. & Pub., Ringelstr. 1, 60385 Frankfurt a.M., Germany. Ed.Bd. adv.; film rev.; illus. circ. 600. (back issues avail.)

780.43 IT
GIORNALE DELLA FILARMONICA. 1992. m. free. Accademia Filarmonica Romana, Via Flaminia 118, 00195 Rome, Italy. TEL 06-32-01-752. FAX 06-32-10-410. Ed. Stefano Catucci. **Document type:** academic/scholarly publication.

780 IT ISSN 1120-6195
IL GIORNALE DELLA MUSICA. 1985. m. L.65000($70) E.D.T. s.r.l., Via Alfieri 19, 10121 Torino, Italy. TEL 011-5621496. FAX 011-545296. Ed. Enzo Peruccio. adv. contact: Gina Allegretti. bk.rev. circ. 20,000.
Description: Contains information about musical events, new recordings and music publications, Italian university musicological activities.

GIORNALE DELLO SPETTACOLO. see DANCE

GIORNO POETRY SYSTEMS L P'S, C D'S, CASSETTES & GIORNO VIDEO PAK SERIES. see LITERATURE — Poetry

780.42 US ISSN 1072-8082
GIRL GROUPS GAZETTE; 60's rock 'n roll. 1987. q. $20 (effective Jan. 1993). (Girl Groups Fan Club) Fan Club Publishing, Box 69A04, Dept. UL, W. Hollywood, CA 90069. TEL 213-650-5112. Ed. Louis Wendruck; Pub. Louis Wendruck. adv.; bk.rev. circ. 10,000. (back issues avail.) **Document type:** newsletter.
Description: Covers news and developments relating to female rock 'n roll groups and singers of the 1960s and 70s.

787.8 SW ISSN 0283-474X
GITARR OCH LUTA. 1968. q. SEK 160. Svenska Gitarr och Luta Saellskapet - Swedish Guitar and Lute Society, c/o Jacobsson, Svartviksslingan 71, S-161 29 Bromma, Sweden. TEL 46-8-25-56-40. FAX 46-33-76-66. Ed. Karin Jonsson. adv.: B&W page SEK 850; adv. contact: Margareta Roerby. bk.rev. circ. 700. **Document type:** newsletter.
Description: Contains articles on guitar and lute music; musicians, instrument makers, composers, sheet music and discs. Essays on music history.

780 GW ISSN 0172-9683
GITARRE & LAUTE; das Magazin fuer alle Gitarristen und Lautenisten. 1979. bi-m. DM.49.50. Gitarre & Laute Verlags GmbH, Friedrich-Schmidt-Str. 46A, Postfach 410408, 50933 Cologne, Germany. TEL 0221-493477. FAX 0221-4973716. Ed. Peter Paeffgen. adv. circ. 6,500. Indexed: RILM.
—CCC.

780 GW ISSN 0934-7674
GITARRE UND BASS. m. DM.78 (foreign DM.102). M M - Musik Media Verlag GmbH, Aindlingerstr. 17-19, 86167 Augsburg, Germany. TEL 0821-7904-0. FAX 0821-7904129. Ed. Dieter Roesberg. circ. 36,215. **Document type:** consumer publication.

780 SZ
GLAREANA. 1951. s-a. 30 SFr. to individuals; institutions 50 SFr. Gesellschaft der Freunde alter Musikinstrumente, Oberwilerstr. 122, CH-4054 Basel, Switzerland. Ed. Veronika Gutmann. adv.; bk.rev.; bibl. Indexed: RILM. **Document type:** bulletin.
Description: Contains news and information concerning old and ancient musical instruments. Features reports of events, exhibitions, museums, history.

780 620.2 US ISSN 1045-5027
GLASS AUDIO. 1988. 6/yr. $28. Audio Amateur Publications, Box 176, Peterborough, NH 03458. TEL 603-924-9464. FAX 603-924-9467. Ed. Edward T. Dell, Jr. adv. contact: Martha Povey. circ. 6,000 (paid). (back issues avail.) Indexed: Ind.How To Do It (1988-). **Document type:** consumer publication.
Description: Covers high quality audio reproduction using vacuum tube technology; hands-on; and project orientation.

782.5 264 US ISSN 0731-0781
GLORY SONGS. q. $12.25. Southern Baptist Convention, Sunday School Board, 127 Ninth Ave., N., Nashville, TN 37234. TEL 800-458-2772.
Description: Provides simplified choir music for smaller-membership churches.

782.1 UK ISSN 0434-1066
GLYNDEBOURNE FESTIVAL PROGRAMME BOOK. 1952. a. £10. (Glyndebourne Festival Opera) Glyndebourne Productions Ltd., Glyndebourne, Lewes, E. Sussex BN8 5UU, England, England. TEL 01273-812321. FAX 01273-812783. TELEX 931211395 GO G. Ed. Helen O'Neill. adv. circ. 3,000. **Document type:** consumer publication.

780 US ISSN 8750-2577
GOLDMINE; the record collector's marketplace. 1974. bi-w. $36.95. Krause Publications, Inc., 700 E. State St., Iola, WI 54990. TEL 715-445-2214. FAX 715-445-4087. TELEX 556461 KRAUSE PUB UD. Ed. Jeff Tamarkin. adv.; bk.rev.; illus.; music rev. circ. 32,985. (also avail. in microform from UMI) **Document type:** consumer publication.
—UMI.
Description: Articles on collecting and selling recordings (LPs, tapes, and CDs) in all music fields. Market information on rare and out-of-print records, as well as new releases. Offers dealer lists and private sources of sales and features discographies, interviews, and record reviews.

GONG. see CHILDREN AND YOUTH — For

780.7 US ISSN 0017-2235
GOPHER MUSIC NOTES. 1930. q. $8. Minnesota Music Educators Association, c/o Robert I. Iverson, Ed., 1104 Pine View Rd., Alexandria, MN 56308. TEL 612-763-6135. adv.; bk.rev.; tr.lit. circ. 4,600. (tabloid format) Indexed: Music Artic.Guide.

783.7 US
GOSPEL MUSIC ASSOCIATION. RESOURCE GUIDE. 1971. a. $34.95 (free to qualified personnel). Gospel Music Association, Inc., 1205 Division St., Nashville, TN 37203-4011. TEL 615-242-0303. FAX 615-254-9755. Ed. Bruce Koblish. adv. contact: Tim Marshall. illus. circ. 15,000. **Document type:** directory.
Former titles: Gospel Music Official Directory; Complete Guide to Gospel Music; Gospel Music (ISSN 0197-2715); Gospel Music Association. Annual Directory; Gospel Music Association. Annual Directory and Yearbook (ISSN 0362-7330); Gospel Music Directory and Yearbook.
Description: Contains over 7000 listings of those involved in the Gospel music industry: artists, managers, booking agents, licensing companies, professional organizations, publishers, radio stations, retailers, record companies, etc.

783 DK ISSN 0106-9586
GOSPEL TIME. 6/yr. DKK 60. Nonnetittvoenget 4, DK-5270 Odense, Denmark.

780 US
GOSPEL TODAY; America's leading gospel news magazine. 1990. bi-m. $20. Horizon Concepts, 2201 Murfreesboro Rd., Bldg. C, Ste. 206, Nashville, TN 37217. TEL 615-360-9444. FAX 615-361-1274. (Subscr. to: Box 292494, Nashville, TN 37229. TEL 800-472-6731) Ed. Phil Petrie; Pub. Teresa Hairston. adv. contact: James L. Nowlin. bk.rev.; illus. circ. 30,000. **Document type:** consumer publication.
Formerly: Score (Nashville).
Description: Covers African American gospel news and events. Includes convention calendars, health and beauty tips and family-oriented subjects.

783 GW ISSN 0017-2499
ML5
GOTTESDIENST UND KIRCHENMUSIK. 1951. bi-m. DM.18. Druckhaus Pastyrik, Kleiner Johannes 8, 91253 Pegnitz, Germany. TEL 09241-73316. FAX 09241-73333. Ed. Ruth Engelhardt. adv.; bk.rev.; abstr.; index. circ. 3,000. Indexed: Music Ind. **Document type:** bulletin.
—BLDSC (4203.300000).

780 US ISSN 0141-5085
ML410.G75
GRAINGER SOCIETY JOURNAL. 1978. s-a. $28 membership. Percy Grainger Society, 7 Cromwell Pl., White Plains, NY 10601. (Subscr. to: Matthew McGarrell, Brown University, Department of Music, Providence, RI 02912) Ed. Matthew McGarrell. adv.; bk.rev. circ. 500. Indexed: Music Ind. **Document type:** bulletin.
Formerly: Grainger Journal.
Description: To promote the life and works of Percy Grainger.

MUSIC

784 UK ISSN 0017-310X
ML5
GRAMOPHONE. 1923. m. £30.80($75) Gramophone Publications Ltd., 177-179 Kenton Rd., Harrow, Mddx. HA3 OHA, England. TEL 0181-907-4476. FAX 0181-907-0073. Ed. James Jolly. adv.; bk.rev.; rec.rev.; illus.; index. circ. 65,941. (back issues avail.) **Indexed:** Music Ind. **Document type:** consumer publication.
—BLDSC (4209.000000); Faxon; SWETS; UMI; UnCover.
Description: Reviews all major classical recordings released in the U.K. and reports audio-equipment news and reviews.

784 UK
ML156.2
THE GRAMOPHONE CLASSICAL CATALOGUE. 1953. s-a. £79. Retail Establishment Data Publishing Ltd., Paulton House, 8 Shepherdess Walk, London N1 7LR, England. TEL 0171-490-0049. FAX 0171-253-1308. adv. circ. 4,500. **Document type:** catalog.
●Also available online.
Also available on CD-ROM.
Former titles: Classical Catalogue (ISSN 0961-5237); Gramophone Classical Catalogue (ISSN 0309-4367); Gramophone Classical Record Catalogue.
Description: Lists all classical CDs, LPs, cassettes, DATs, DCCs, minidiscs, videos, and laserdiscs available in the U.K. since 1985.

784 UK
THE GRAMOPHONE GOOD C D GUIDE. (Compact Disc); reviews of the best CDs you can buy. 1988. a. Gramophone Publications Ltd., 177-179 Kenton Rd., Harrow, Mddx. HA3 OHA, England. TEL 0181-907-4476. FAX 0181-907-0073. Ed. Maire Taylor. **Document type:** consumer publication.
Description: Reviews high-quality classical music recordings available on compact disc.

780.42 SP
GRAN MUSICAL. 1969. m. $110. (Sociedad Espanola de Radiodifusion) Nuevas Ediciones, S.A., Gran Via 32-2, Madrid 28013, Spain. FAX 341-347-0709. TELEX 27638 SER E. Ed. Rafael Revert. adv.; bk.rev.; illus. circ. 60,000.
Formerly (until 1972): Musical.

780 US ISSN 0434-3336
LE GRAND BATON. 1964. irreg. $15 (foreign $15). Sir Thomas Beecham Society, Inc., 33 Williamsburg Ct., Littlestown, PA 17341. TEL 717-359-9638. Ed. Joseph G. Ayers. bk.rev.; charts; illus.; music rev.; circ. 500 (paid). **Indexed:** Music Artic.Guide.
Description: For music lovers and collectors, focusing on life and times of Sir Thomas Beecham.

LE GRAND HUIT. see *THEATER*

GRAY AREAS. see *GENERAL INTEREST PERIODICALS — United States*

781.7 US ISSN 0272-0264
GREENWOOD ENCYCLOPEDIA OF BLACK MUSIC. 1981. irreg. price varies. Greenwood Press, Inc. (Subsidiary of: Greenwood Publishing Group Inc.), 88 Post Rd. W., Box 5007, Westport, CT 06881-5007. TEL 203-226-3571. FAX 203-222-1502.

783 NE ISSN 0017-4122
ML5
GREGORIUSBLAD; tijdschrift tot bevordering van liturgische muziek. 5/yr. fl.22.50. (Landelijke Commissie voor Liturgische Muziek) Nederlandse Sint-Gregoriusvereniging, Stadhouderskade 70, Amsterdam 8, Netherlands. Ed. Piet Visser. bk.rev.; music rev.; charts; illus.; cum.index. **Indexed:** CERDIC.
—SWETS.

780.7 XV ISSN 0017-4343
GRLICA/TURTLEDOVE; revija za glasbeno vzgojo. 1969. bi-m. 200 din.($7) Zveza Drustev Glasbenih Pedagogov Slovenije, Kidriceva 5, Ljubljana, Slovenia. Ed. Jakob Jez. bk.rev. circ. 1,300.
Description: Covers the study and teaching of music.

780.01 GW
GROSSE KOMPONISTEN. 1990. fortn. DM.12.90 per no. c/o Marshall Cavendish, Paulstr. 3, 20095 Hamburg, Germany. TEL 040-322175. FAX 040-338769.

GUILDNOTES. see *ART*

780 UK ISSN 0962-2640
GUITAR. 1991. m. £55. Northern & Shell Publications, Northern & Shell Bldg., P.O. Box 381, Millharbour, London E14 9TW, England. TEL 44-171-987-5090. FAX 44-171-987-2160. Ed. Paul Trynka. adv.: color page £1200; adv. contact: Graham Butterworth. circ. 50,000. **Document type:** consumer publication.

787 US ISSN 0270-9325
ML1
GUITAR AND MANDOLIN. 1978. bi-m. $12. Michael I. Holmes, Ed. & Pub., 15 Arnold Place, New Bedford, MA 02740. TEL 617-993-0156. adv.; bk.rev.; illus. circ. 3,000.
Formerly (until 1980): Mandolin Notebook (ISSN 0148-5482)

787 US ISSN 0738-937X
GUITAR FOR THE PRACTICING MUSICIAN. 1983. m. $27.95. Cherry Lane Magazines, Inc., 10 Midland Ave., Port Chester, NY 10573. TEL 914-937-8601. FAX 914-937-0614. (Subscr. to: Box 53063, Boulder, CO 80322-3062) Ed. Harvey Newquist; Pub. Howard Cleff. adv. contact: Barbara Seerman. circ. 170,000 (paid). **Document type:** consumer publication.
—UnCover.
Description: Contains note-for-note transcriptions to todays best-selling songs. Features interviews, music news, instructional playing tips, artist profiles and informative guitar techniques.

787.61 US ISSN 0017-5463
ML1
GUITAR PLAYER; for professional and amateur guitarists. 1967. m. $29.95 (foreign $44.95). Miller Freeman Inc. (San Mateo) (Subsidiary of: United Newspapers Group), 411 Borel Ave., Ste. 100, San Mateo, CA 94402. TEL 415-358-9500. FAX 415-358-9216. Owner(s): RILM. (Subscr. to: Box 58590, Boulder, CO 80322-8590) Ed. Joe Gore; Pub. Pat Cameron. adv. contact: Ross Garnick. bk.rev.; charts; illus.; cum.index. circ. 135,003. (also avail. in microfilm from UMI; reprint service avail. from UMI) **Indexed:** Mag.Ind., Music Artic.Guide, Music Ind., PMR. **Document type:** consumer publication.
—Faxon; UMI; UnCover. **CCC**.
Description: For professional, semi-pro and amateur guitar players in all styles.

787.61 US ISSN 0017-5471
ML1
GUITAR REVIEW. 1946. q. $24 (foreign $28). Albert Augustine, Ltd., 40 W. 25th St., New York, NY 10010. TEL 212-924-4651. FAX 212-242-2220. Ed. Rose L. Augustine. adv.; bk.rev.; rec.rev.; illus. circ. 4,000. (back issues avail.) **Indexed:** Arts & Hum.Cit.Ind., Curr.Cont., Music Artic.Guide, Music Ind., RILM.
—BLDSC (4230.231000); Faxon; UnCover.

787 780.7 US ISSN 1058-0220
GUITAR SCHOOL. 1989. bi-m. $10.50. Harris Publications, Inc., 1115 Broadway, New York, NY 10010. TEL 212-807-7100. Ed. Brad Tolinski. adv. circ. 100,688.
Description: Contains sheet music with instructional lessons and transcriptions to today's songs and classic songs.

787 US ISSN 1045-6295
ML1015.G9
GUITAR WORLD. 1980. 12/yr. $19.94. Harris Publications, Inc., 1115 Broadway, 8th fl., New York, NY 10010. TEL 212-807-7100. FAX 212-627-4678. Ed. Brad Tolinski. circ. 132,317. **Document type:** consumer publication.
Description: Contains interviews and transcriptions.

797.87 786.2 FR ISSN 0760-7997
GUITARE ET CLAVIERS. m. 350 F. Carredas, 132 rue du Faubourg St. Denis, 75010 Paris, France. TEL 40-35-73-73. FAX 40-35-25-29. Ed. Daniel Savides. adv.: B&W page 13000 F., color page 19000 F.; trim 210 x 280; adv. contact: Jean-Michel Herve. bk.rev.; music rev.; software rev.; video rev.; index. (back issues avail.)
Formed by the merger of: Claviers Magazine (ISSN 0247-9141) & Guitare Magazine (ISSN 0248-1375)

780 UK ISSN 0953-7023
GUITARIST. 1984. m. £22.50 (foreign £25). Music Maker Publications Ltd., Alexander House, Forehill, Ely, Cambs CB7 4AF, England. TEL 0353-665577. FAX 44-353-662489. (U.S. addr.: Music Maker Publications, Inc., 21601 Devonshire St., Ste. 212, Chatsworth, CA 91311. FAX 818-407-0931) Ed. Nev Marten. circ. 30,000.

787.87 FR ISSN 0997-3443
GUITARIST MAGAZINE. 1989. m. 270 F. (foreign 370 F.); newsstand price: 29 F. Master Press International, 10 rue de la Paix, 92100 Boulogne, France. TEL 46-03-15-51. FAX 46-03-89-69. Ed. Dany Giorgetti. adv.: page 19000 F.; adv. contact: Alain Versini. s-a. index. circ. 50,000. **Document type:** consumer publication.

787 US ISSN 0434-9350
GUITARRA MAGAZINE. 1979. bi-m. $15.50. Sherry - Brener, Inc., 3145 W. 63rd St., Chicago, IL 60629. Ed. James Sherry. adv.; bk.rev. circ. 4,500. (back issues avail.) **Indexed:** Music Artic.Guide.
Description: Classic and flamenco guitar and music.

780 DK ISSN 0108-321X
GYMNASIEMUSIK; medlemsorientering. 1982. 10/yr. membership. Gymnasieskolernes Musiklaererforening, c/o Kirsten Dollerup, Vestervangsparken 16, DK-8355 Solbjerg, Denmark.
Formerly: Gymnasieskolernes Musiklaererforening Medlemsorientering (ISSN 0108-4054)

H D K MAGAZIN. (Hochschule der Kuenste Berlin) see *ART*

780 621.389 IT
H.M. HEAVY METAL & HARD ROCK; quindicinale di musica specializzata. fortn. (Athena 2001 Coop a.r.l.) Edizioni L.E.T.I. s.r.l., Via E.Q. Visconti, 20, 00193 Rome, Italy. TEL 06-386353. circ. 120,000.

780.6 UK ISSN 0262-7272
HALLE YEAR BOOK. 1858. a. £3. Halle Concerts Society, Heron House, Albert Sq., Manchester M2 5HD, England. TEL 0161-834-8363. FAX 0161-832-1669. Ed. Philip Slorick. adv. circ. 6,000. **Document type:** bulletin.
Formed by the merger of: Halle; And: Halle Prospectus.
Description: Lists activities of the Halle Orchestra. Includes a preview of the season's concerts, news of the sponsoring society and sponsorship, lists of members and patrons, and articles on music.

780.6 UK
HALLMARK. 1946. s-a. membership. Halle Concerts Society, Heron House, Albert Sq., Manchester M2 5HD, England. TEL 0161-834-8363. FAX 0161-832-1669. TELEX 666140. Ed. Philip Slorick. adv. circ. 6,500. **Document type:** newsletter.
Former titles (until 1992): Halle News; Halle Magazine.
Description: Features current activities of the Halle Concerts Society.

780 GW ISSN 0342-8303
HAMBURGER JAHRBUCH FUER MUSIKWISSENSCHAFT. 1974. a. DM.82. Verlag der Musikalienhandlung Karl-Dieter Wagner, Marienstr. 13, 99817 Eisenach, Germany. TEL 03691-624901. **Indexed:** RILM. **Document type:** academic/scholarly publication.

781.7 286 US ISSN 8756-7407
M147
HANDBELLS; for directors and ringers. 1985. q. $19.25. Southern Baptist Convention, Sunday School Board, 127 Ninth Ave., N., Nashville, TN 37234. TEL 800-458-2772. FAX 615-251-3866. Ed. Sharron Lyon. circ. 15,000.
Description: Contains music for beginning and advanced handbell choirs. Includes articles for leaders and ringers regarding all aspects of usage: inspirational, practical, and technical.

THE HANDBOOK OF U K RECORDING & DUPLICATING (YEAR). see *BUSINESS AND ECONOMICS — Trade And Industrial Directories*

780　　　　　GW　　ISSN 0440-2863
ML410.P32
HANS - PFITZNER - GESELLSCHAFT. MITTEILUNGEN. 1954. s-a. free to members. (Hans-Pfitzner-Gesellschaft e.V.) Verlag Dr. Hans Schneider GmbH, Mozartstr. 6, 82323 Tutzing, Germany. TEL 08158-3050. FAX 08158-7636. Ed. Reinhard Seebohm. bk.rev.; play rev.; bibl.; illus. circ. 250. **Indexed:** Music Ind., RILM. **Document type:** newsletter.

780　　　　　US
HARD 'N' FAST. 1988. m. $15. Qmax Press Services Inc., 1651 Dublin Rd., Dresher, PA 19025-1243. TEL 215-654-9200. FAX 215-654-1895. E-mail: qmax@netcom.com. Ed. Alex Richter. adv.: B&W page $200. circ. 5,000. (back issues avail.) **Document type:** newsletter.
　Description: News, interviews and reviews relating to rock music.

780　　　　　US
HARMONICA. 6/yr. $30. Harmonica Information Press, 203 14th Ave., San Francisco, CA 94118-1007. bk.rev.; rec.rev.; video rev. **Document type:** consumer publication.
　Description: For beginners to advanced; contains interviews; covers history, styles, theory, instruments, diatonic, chromatic, extended techniques.

780　　　　　SZ
HARMONIENACHRICHTEN. 6/yr. Poststr. 8, CH-8332 Russikon, Switzerland. TEL 01-2162855. circ. 1,200.

786.9　　　　　GW　　ISSN 0938-6629
HARMONIKA INTERNATIONAL. 1931. q. DM.34. (Deutscher Harmonikaverband e.V.) Hohner Verlag GmbH, Postfach 1150, 78635 Trossingen, Germany. TEL 07425-20425. FAX 07425-20-521. TELEX 760727-HOHN-D. Ed. Wolfgang Layer. adv.: B&W page DM.2560; trim 185 x 255; adv. contact: Evelyn Rohrbach. bk.rev.; illus. circ. 32,000. **Document type:** consumer publication.
　Formerly (until 1989): Harmonika-Revue.

784.96　　　　　US　　ISSN 0017-7849
HARMONIZER. 1942. 6/yr. $18 to non-members (foreign $27). (Society for the Preservation and Encouragement of Barber Shop Quartet Singing in America, Inc.) SPEBSQSA, Inc., 6315 Third Ave., Kenosha, WI 53143-5199. TEL 414-653-8440. FAX 414-654-4048. Ed. Dan Daily. adv.; music rev.; illus.; index; circ. 36,000 (paid). **Document type:** proceedings.

780　　　　　US　　ISSN 1062-4090
HARMONOLOGIA - STUDIES IN MUSIC THEORY. 1978. irreg., no.9, 1995. Pendragon Press, 41 Ferry St., Stuyvesant, NY 12173-9720. TEL 518-828-3008. FAX 518-828-2368. **Document type:** monographic series.

787　　　　　SZ　　ISSN 1017-1142
HARPA; internationale Musik- und Harfenzeitschrift. (Text in English, French, German) 1991. q. 60 SFr. Internationales Harfen Zentrum, Dorneckstr. 105, CH-4143 Dornach, Switzerland. TEL 061-7018866. FAX 061-7018858. Ed. Rudolf Frick. bk.rev.; abstr.; bibl.; illus.; music rev.; index; circ. 1,500. (back issues avail.) **Document type:** bulletin.

786.221　　　　　UK　　ISSN 0953-0797
HARPSICHORD AND FORTEPIANO. 1973. s-a. £12($6) 20 Chisholm Rd., Richmond, Surrey TW10 6JH, England. TEL 0181-940-9661. E-mail: ruxbury@delphi.com. (Subscr. to: Sout Botton Farm, Mytholmroyd, Hebden Gridge, W. Yorks. HX7 5JS, England. TEL 01422-882751. FAX 01422-886157) Ed. David Bray; Pubs. Jeremy & Ruth Burbridge. adv. contact: Graham Williams. bk.rev.; illus. circ. 800. (back issues avail.) **Indexed:** RILM. **Document type:** academic/scholarly publication.
　—UnCover.
　Supersedes (in 1987): English Harpsichord Magazine and Early Keyboard Instrument Review (ISSN 0306-4395).

780　　　　　US　　ISSN 0073-0629
HARVARD PUBLICATIONS IN MUSIC. 1967. irreg., no.18, 1994. price varies. Harvard University, Department of Music, Music Bldg. G6, Cambridge, MA 02138. TEL 617-495-2791.
FAX 617-496-8081. (Subscr. to: Harvard University Press, 79 Garden St., Cambridge, MA 02138. TEL 617-495-2606) **Document type:** monographic series, academic/scholarly publication.
　Refereed Serial

780　　　　　UK　　ISSN 1350-1267
HAYDN SOCIETY JOURNAL. 1980. a. £7.50($15) Haydn Society, University of Lancaster, Music Department, Bailrigg, Lancaster LA1 4YW, England. TEL 01524-593777. FAX 01524-847298. Ed. Denis McCaldin. adv. contact: S. Birchall. music rev. circ. 200. **Document type:** academic/scholarly publication.
　Formerly (until 1992): Haydn Society Newsletter.
　Description: Disseminates scholarly studies and reviews of research into the work of Franz Joseph Haydn.
　Refereed Serial

780 920　　　　　GW　　ISSN 0440-5323
HAYDN - STUDIEN. (Text in English and German) 1965. a. price varies. (Joseph Haydn-Institut e.V.) G. Henle Verlag, Forstenrieder Allee 122, 81476 Munich, Germany. FAX 089-7598240. (U.S. dist. by: G. Henle USA, Inc., 2446 Centerline Industrial Drive, Maryland Heights, MO 63043-0753) Ed. Dr. Horst Walter. adv.; bk.rev.; illus.; index. circ. 750. **Indexed:** Arts & Hum.Cit.Ind., Curr.Cont., RILM. **Document type:** academic/scholarly publication.
　—SWETS.

780.42 363.49　　　　　US
HEADBANGER. 1989. m. $10. Gay Metal Society, Box 802784, Chicago, IL 60680-2784.
TEL 708-780-0746. Ed. Chris Baker. adv.; bk.rev.; film rev.; music rev.; rec.rev.; bibl.; charts; illus. circ. 500. **Document type:** newsletter.
　Description: Contains music news and reviews, notices and commentary.

780　　　　　GW
HEARTBEAT!. (Text in English) 1984. q. $5 per no. Hans-Juergen Klitsch, Ed. & Pub., Moselstr. 2, 26419 Schortens, Germany. TEL 04461-82283. adv.; bk.rev. **Document type:** consumer publication.

783 200　　　　　US　　ISSN 0889-5252
ML3529
HEARTSONG REVIEW; resource guide for New Age music of the spirit. 1986. s-a. $8. Box 5716, Eugene, OR 97405-0716. Ed. Jennifer Washburn. adv.; bk.rev.; film rev.; index. circ. 10,000. (back issues avail.) **Document type:** consumer publication.
　Description: Reviews of vocal and instrumental music for inspirational and therapeutic purposes; a consumer's resource guide.

780.42　　　　　SP
HEAVYROCK; metal magazine. 1982. m. M C Ediciones, S.A., C. Monestir 23, 08034 Barcelona, Spain. TEL 93-2804344. FAX 2803974. Dir. Mariscal Romero. **Document type:** consumer publication.

DER HEIMATPFLEGER; Zeitschrift fuer Volkstanz, Volksmusik, Brauchtum und Heimatpflege. see *FOLKLORE*

780　　　　　MX　　ISSN 0018-1137
ML5
HETEROFONIA; revista musical semestral. 1968. s-a. Mex.$70 (foreign $30) (effective 1995). Centro Nacional de Investigacion, Documentacion e Informacion Musical, Liverpool 16, Col. Juarez, 06600 Mexico, D.F., Mexico. TEL 52-5-5466140. Ed. Juan Jose Escorza. adv. contact: Lourdes Rebollo. bk.rev.; music rev.; abstr.; illus.; index. circ. 1,000. **Indexed:** Arts & Hum.Cit.Ind., Curr.Cont., Music Ind., RILM. **Document type:** academic/scholarly publication.
　Refereed Serial

780　　　　　UK　　ISSN 0142-6230
HI-FI NEWS AND RECORD REVIEW. 1956. m. £42.60. Link House Magazines Ltd., Link House, Dingwall Ave., Croydon, Surrey CR9 2TA, England.
TEL 0181-686-2599. FAX 0181-760-0973. (Subscr. to: R F S, 120-126 Lavender Ave., Mitcham, Surrey CR4 3HP, England) Ed. Steve Harris. adv.; bk.rev.; rec.rev.; charts; illus.; tr.lit.; index. circ. 27,456. (also avail. in microform from UMI) **Indexed:** Br.Tech.Ind. **Document type:** consumer publication.
　—BLDSC (4307.181000); UMI.
　Incorporates: Audio Record Review (ISSN 0018-1226)
　Description: Explores classical, pop and jazz music. Includes hi-fi equipment reviews and ratings, articles, and news of product developments.

HI-FI STEREO; la rivista di musica e alta fedelta. see *SOUND RECORDING AND REPRODUCTION*

780.42　　　　　US
HI-TECH HOME WEEKLY. w. $180. B B S Press Service Inc., 8125 S.W. 21st St., Topeka, KS 66615-1515. TEL 913-478-3157. FAX 913-478-1189. Ed. Alan Bechtold. circ. 375,000.
　Formerly: Online Digital Music Review.
　Description: Provides news and reviews covering music, video and computer technology for home entertainment, education and utility.

789.91 621.389　　　　　BE
HIFI MUSIQUE. REVUE DES DISQUES ET DE LA HAUTE FIDELITE. 1950. bi-m. 950 Fr. Editions Dereume, Rue Golden Hope,1, 1620 Drogenbos, Belgium. Ed. Serge Martin. adv.; bk.rev.; charts; illus. circ. 5,000.
　Formerly: Revue des Disques et de la Haute Fidelite (ISSN 0035-1970)

HIFI & MUSIK. see *SOUND RECORDING AND REPRODUCTION*

789.91　　　　　GW　　ISSN 0178-6156
HIFI VISION. 1985. m. Spezial Zeitschriftenverlagsgesellschaft mbH, Schellingstr. 39-43, 80799 Munich, Germany.
TEL 089-23726-0. FAX 089-23726200. Ed. Walter Schild. adv. contact: Anja Rezsucha. circ. 50,507. **Document type:** consumer publication.

780　　　　　DK　　ISSN 0108-657X
HIGH FIDELITY. (Edition in Swedish) 1967. m. DKK 385. Audio Media A-S, St. Kongensgade 72, DK-1264 Copenhagen K, Denmark. Ed. Michael Madsen. adv.; illus.; tr.lit.; index. circ. 21,000. (back issues avail.) **Indexed:** Acad.Ind.

HIGH PERFORMANCE REVIEW; definitive magazine for audiophiles & music lovers. see *SOUND RECORDING AND REPRODUCTION*

780.42　　　　　US
HIGH VOLTAGE. bi-m. $2.95 per no. Michael John Publishing, 102 Triangle Rd., Somerville, NJ 08876. TEL 908-906-0500.

780.904　　　　　GW　　ISSN 0172-956X
ML410.H685
HINDEMITH - JAHRBUCH/ANNALES HINDEMITH. 1971. a. DM.22.40. (Paul-Hindemith-Institut) Schott Musik International GmbH, Weihergarten 5, 55116 Mainz, Germany. TEL 06131-246-0. FAX 06131-246211. bk.rev. circ. 1,200. **Indexed:** RILM. **Document type:** bulletin.

780.42　　　　　UK
HIP HOP CONNECTION. 1988. m. £16 (foreign £19). Popular Publications Ltd., Alexander House, 38 Forehill, Ely, Cambs. CB7 4AF, England.
TEL 0353-665577. FAX 0353-662489. Ed. Chris Hunt. adv. (back issues avail.) **Document type:** consumer publication.

HISPANIC AMERICAN ARTS; all you want or must know, about everything, in all the fields of Hispanic American arts. see *ART*

780
HISTORIA DE LA MUSICA POP ESPANOLA.* m. 3800 ptas. Ediciones Anel, San Vicente Ferrer 13, Granada, Spain. adv. circ. 20,000.

MUSIC

780   IT   ISSN 0073-2516
HISTORIAE MUSICAE CULTORES BIBLIOTECA. 1952. irreg., vol.74, 1994. price varies. Casa Editrice Leo S. Olschki, Casella Postale 66, 50100 Florence, Italy. TEL 39-55-6530684. FAX 39-55-6530214. circ. 1,000. **Document type:** monographic series.

780   US   ISSN 1045-4616
ML933
HISTORIC BRASS SOCIETY JOURNAL. 1989. a. $20 to individuals; institutions $25 (includes Newsletter). Historic Brass Society, Inc., 148 W. 23rd St., No. 2A, New York, NY 10011. TEL 212-627-3820. FAX 212-627-3820. E-mail: jjn@research.attt.com. Ed. Stewart Carter. adv.: B&W page $110. bk.rev.; bibl.; charts; illus.; circ. 800 (paid). (back issues avail.) **Indexed:** Music Ind., RILM. **Document type:** academic/scholarly publication, newsletter.
—UnCover.
Description: Scholarly articles on the entire range of historic brass music subjects.
Refereed Serial

780   US   ISSN 1045-4594
ML929.5
HISTORIC BRASS SOCIETY NEWSLETTER. 1989. a. $20 to individuals; institution $25 (includes Journal). Historic Brass Society, Inc., 148 West 23rd St., No. 2A, New York, NY 10011. TEL 212-627-3820. FAX 212-627-3820. E-mail: jjn@research.att.com. Ed. Stewart Carter. bk.rev.; rec.rev.; bibl.; charts; illus.; circ. 800 (paid). (back issues avail.) **Indexed:** Music Ind., RILM. **Document type:** newsletter.
—UnCover.
Description: Practical articles concerning the early brass music field.
Refereed Serial

780   US   ISSN 1043-2523
ML651
HISTORICAL HARPSICHORD SERIES. 1984. irreg., vol.4, 1995. Pendragon Press, 41 Ferry St., Stuyvesant, NY 12173-9720. TEL 518-828-3008. FAX 518-828-2368. **Document type:** monographic series.

780   US   ISSN 0898-8587
ML1
HISTORICAL PERFORMANCE; the journal of early music America. 1988. s-a. $30 (foreign $45). Early Music America, 11421 1/2 Bellflower Rd., Cleveland, OH 44106-3990. TEL 216-229-1685. FAX 216-229-1688. E-mail: bxs6@po.cwru.edu. Ed. Stewart Carter. adv.; bk.rev.; charts; illus. circ. 3,000. (back issues avail.) **Indexed:** Music Artic.Guide. **Document type:** academic/scholarly publication, trade publication.
—Faxon; UnCover.
Description: Covers current news, scholarship, and events in the field of historical performance in North America.

780   UK   ISSN 0967-1579
HIT C D. 1992. m. £70 for 6 issues. Northern & Shell Publications, Northern & Shell Bldg., P.O. Box 381, Millharbour, London E14 9TW, England. TEL 44-171-987-5090. FAX 44-171-987-2160. Ed. Tony Horkins. adv.: color page £3500; adv. contact: Jackie Forbes. circ. 150,000. **Document type:** consumer publication.

781.64 791.43   US   ISSN 1044-5056
LE HIT PARADE. (Text in English, French) 1988. bi-m. $12. P.O. IBox 925, Camp Hill, PA 17011-0925. TEL 717-763-0355; 800-835-7537. FAX 717-763-0844. Ed. John Snoddy. circ. 3,000. (back issues avail.) **Document type:** newsletter.
Description: Dedicated to French language popular arts. Major emphasis on music, but includes film.

780   US   ISSN 0162-0266
HIT PARADER. 1954. m. $29. Hit Parader Publications, Inc., 210 Rt. 4 E., Ste. 401, Paramus, NJ 07652-5116. Ed. Andy Secher. adv.; bk.rev.; charts; illus.; tr.lit. circ. 150,000. **Indexed:** PMR. **Document type:** consumer publication.
Description: For fans of hard rock and heavy metal music.

780   SA   ISSN 1022-3061
HIT SONGS; songwords to classic & current chart hits. 1993. q. newsstand price: R.9.98. J T Publishing, P.O. Box 17134, Doornfontein 2028, South Africa. illus. **Document type:** consumer publication.

780   US   ISSN 0073-2516
HITMAKERS SERIES. irreg. (1-2/yr.). $21.95 per no. Watson - Guptill Publications, 1515 Broadway, New York, NY 10036. (Subscr. to: 1695 Oak St., Lakewood, NJ 08701. TEL 800-451-1741. FAX 908-363-0338)

780.7   GW   ISSN 0936-2940
HOCHSCHULE FUER MUSIK KOELN. JOURNAL. 1982. s-a. free. Hochschule fuer Musik Koeln, Dagobertstr. 38, 50668 Cologne, Germany. TEL 0221-912818111. FAX 0221-131204. Ed. Franz Mueller-Heuser. adv. **Document type:** academic/scholarly publication.
Description: Music and reports on the school and the world of musicology and teaching methods.

HOCHSCHULE FUER MUSIK UND DARSTELLENDE KUNST MOZARTEUM IN SALZBURG. JAHRESBERICHT. see *EDUCATION*

HOLIDAYS AT THE KINDERGARTEN. see *CHILDREN AND YOUTH — For*

780.7   US   ISSN 0046-7928
ML1
HORN CALL. 1971. s-a. $25 membership. International Horn Society, 2227 Gershwin Dr., P.O. Box 1724, Durant, OK 74702. TEL 405-924-5859. FAX 405-924-7313. Ed. Paul Mansur. adv.; bk.rev.; index. circ. 3,000. (also avail. in looseleaf format; back issues avail.) **Indexed:** Music Artic.Guide.
—UnCover.
Description: Covers reviews, horn, new music, recordings, history, biography, and research at all educational levels.

786   US
HORN CALL ANNUAL. a. $25 (membership). International Horn Society, c/o Ellen Powley, Exc. Secretary, 2220 N. 140 E., Provo, UT 84604. TEL 801-377-3026.
Description: Covers detailed and scholarly research studies pertaining to the horn.
Refereed Serial

780   US
HOT HOUSE; jazz nightlife guide. m. $14 (foreign $27). On Target Features - Hot House, 18 Whippoorwill Ln., Rockaway Township, NJ 07866. TEL 201-627-5349. Ed. Gene Kalbacher.

780   US
HOT LINE NEWS. 1980. bi-m. membership. Musicians National Hot Line Association, 277 E. 6100 S., Salt Lake City, UT 84107. Ed. Nancy Zitting. circ. 1,000. **Document type:** newsletter.
Description: Helps musicians find bands and helps bands find musicians and gigs.

780.43   US
HOUSTON SYMPHONY MAGAZINE. 1914. 11/yr. free at concerts. (Houston Symphony Orchestra) Gulf Breese Associates Inc., 5615 Kirby Dr., Ste. 600, Houston, TX 77005. TEL 713-524-3000. FAX 713-524-8213. Ed. Connie Juvan-Savoy; Pub. Marlene Walker. adv. contact: Marlene Walker. circ. 28,000.
Description: Contains program notes for the month's concerts, biographies, interviews, history, social events, corporate sponsor articles, symphony and city news.

780   CC   ISSN 1003-7721
HUANG ZHONG. (Text in Chinese) 1986. q. $20 (effective 1996). Wuhan Yiyue Xueyuan, No. 255, Jiefang Lu, Wuchang, Wuhan, Hubei 430060. People's Republic of China. TEL 027-8872571. Ed. Zhou Zhenxi. bk.rev. **Document type:** academic/scholarly publication.
Refereed Serial

780   XR   ISSN 0323-1283
ML5
HUDEBNI NASTROJE. (Text in Czech; summaries in English, German, Russian) 1964. bi-m. 30 Kc.($22.10) (Ceske Hudebni Nastroje) V A N N, Okruzni 700, 500 03 Hradec Kralove, Czech Republic. TELEX 194-260. (Subscr. to: Artia, Ve Smeckach 30, 111 27 Prague 1, Czech Republic) Ed. Vaclav Korbel. adv.; bk.rev.; bibl.; charts; illus.; index. circ. 3,000. (also avail. in microfilm) **Indexed:** RILM.
Description: Devoted to researching, developing and using musical instruments. Deals with acoustics, musicology and musical pedagogy.

780   XR   ISSN 0018-6996
HUDEBNI ROZHLEDY. 1948. m. 120 Kc. Asociace Hudebnich Umelcu a Vedcu, Kafkova 19, 160 00 Prague 6, Czech Republic. TEL 4222-532931. (Dist. by: PNS, zav.01, Administrace Vyvozu Tisku, Kovpakova 26, 160 00 Prague 6, Czech Republic) (Svaz Autoru a Interpretu) Ed. Jan Smolik. adv.; bk.rev.; bibl.; illus.; index. circ. 4,200. **Indexed:** Music Ind., RILM.

780   XR   ISSN 0018-7003
ML5
HUDEBNI VEDA/MUSICOLOGY. (Text mainly in Czech; summaries in English, German, Russian) 1964. q. DM.141. Ceska Akademie Ved, Ustav pro Hudebni Vedu, Puskinovo nam. 9, 160 00 Prague 6, Czech Republic. (Dist. in Western countries by: Kubon & Sagner, P.O. Box 34 01 08, 8000 Munich 34, Germany) bk.rev.; rec.rev.; bibl.; illus.; index. **Indexed:** Arts & Hum.Cit.Ind., CERDIC, Curr.Cont., Music Ind., RILM.
Description: Deals with various branches of the musical sciences, e.g., the history of music, aesthetics and musical theory as well as the musical sociology and popular music.

HUDEBNI VYCHOVA. see *EDUCATION*

780   XO   ISSN 0862-416X
HUDOBNY ARCHIV. (Text in Slovak; summaries also in German and Russian) 1974. irreg. price varies. Matica Slovenska, Slovenska Narodna Kniznica, Archiv Literatury a Umenia, Ul. L Novomeskeho 32, 036 52 Martin, Slovakia. TEL 42-842-38706. FAX 42-842-32454. Eds. Emanuel Muntag. **Indexed:** RILM. **Document type:** proceedings.

781.57 780.42   XO   ISSN 0323-133X
HUDOBNY ZIVOT. s-m. $60. (Slovkoncert) Vydavatel'stvo Obzor, Spitalska 35, 815 85 Bratislava, Slovakia. **Indexed:** RILM.

780   HU   ISSN 0238-9401
ML248
HUNGARIAN MUSIC QUARTERLY. (Text in English) 1970. q. $16. Editio Musica Budapest, Vorosmarty ter 1, P.O. Box 80, 1366 Budapest 5, Hungary. FAX 138-2732. TELEX 225500. Ed. Antal Boronkay. adv.; bk.rev. circ. 5,000.
—UnCover.
Formerly (until 1989): Hungarian Music News (ISSN 0441-5973)

786   US   ISSN 0191-6785
HURDY GURDY. 1972. 4/yr. $18. Amateur Organists & Keyboard Association International, 6436 Penn Ave., S., Minneapolis, MN 55423. TEL 612-866-0463. Ed. Crane J. Bodine. adv.; illus. circ. 5,000.

783.9   US   ISSN 0018-8271
ML1
HYMN; a journal of congregational song. 1949. q. $45 membership. Hymn Society in the United States and Canada, Headquarters, Texas Christian University, Box 30854, Fort Worth, TX 76129. TEL 817-921-7608. Ed. David Music. adv. contact: David P. Schaap. bk.rev.; index. circ. 3,500. (back issues avail.) **Indexed:** Chr.Per.Ind., Music Artic.Guide, Music Ind., Rel.& Theol.Abstr. (1978-), Rel.Ind.One. **Document type:** academic/scholarly publication.
—BLDSC (4352.607000); Faxon; UMI; UnCover.

780   UK   ISSN 0018-828X
ML5
HYMN SOCIETY OF GREAT BRITAIN AND IRELAND. BULLETIN. 1937. q. £8($18) Hymn Society of Great Britain and Ireland, c/o Rev. Michael Garland, St. Nicholas Rectory, Curdworth, Sutton Coldfield, W. Midlands B76 9ES, England. TEL 01675-470384. Ed. Bernard Massey. bk.rev.; rec.rev.; cum.index every 3 yrs. circ. 228. (also avail. in microfilm from WMP; back issues avail.) **Document type:** bulletin.
Refereed Serial

HYMNOLOGISKE MEDDELELSER; tidsskrift om salmer. see *RELIGIONS AND THEOLOGY — Protestant*

780.42   US   ISSN 1065-6200
HYPE. 1991. m. $25 (foreign $45). 305 E. Pine St., Seattle, WA 98122. TEL 206-233-9814. FAX 206-343-5173. adv.; bk.rev.; rec.rev. circ. 15,000. (tabloid format; back issues avail.) **Document type:** consumer publication.
Description: Features interviews, fiction and alternative music reviews.

781.57 US ISSN 0098-9487
ML156.9
I A J R C JOURNAL. 1967. q. $25 to individuals; libraries $40. International Association of Jazz Record Collectors, 127 Briarcliff La., Bel Air, MD 21014. TEL 410-838-7542. FAX 410-638-0497. (Subscr. addr.: c/o Edward E. Nickel, Box 538, Wingate, NC 28174) Ed. Phil Oldham. adv.: B&W page $100; adv. contact: Phil Oldham. bk.rev. circ. 2,200. (back issues avail.) Indexed: Music Ind. **Document type:** academic/scholarly publication.
—UnCover.
  Description: Covers news, reviews and research articles on the subject of jazz music and musicians and related fields of interest to the collector and interested public.

780 US ISSN 1082-1872
I A W M JOURNAL. 1977. 3/yr. $50. 1210 W. Wynnewood Dr., Wynnewood, PA 19096. TEL 610-642-1852. FAX 610-649-8649. E-mail: sglickma@haverford.edu. Ed. Sylvia Glickman. adv.; bk.rev. circ. 1,000. (back issues avail.) Indexed: Music Artic.Guide. **Document type:** newsletter.
—UnCover.
  Former titles (until 1995): A W C News Forum; (until 1982): A W C News (ISSN 0193-0850)
  Description: Provides articles on women in the field of music.

782.1 GW
I B S AKTUELL. 1981. 5/yr. DM.25. Interessenvereins des Bayerischen Staatsopernpublikums e.V., Gartenstr. 22, 80082 Munich, Germany. TEL 089-3003798. Ed. Helga Schmidt. adv.; bk.rev. circ. 850. **Document type:** bulletin.

781.7 367 US
I F C O CLUB HOUSE. 1993. q. $25 (foreign $35). Tri-Son, Inc., Box 40328, Nashville, TN 37204-0328. TEL 615-371-9596. FAX 615-371-9597. Ed. Loudilla Johnson. circ. 2,000 (paid). **Document type:** consumer publication, directory.
  Description: Profiles country music artists, their fans, and their fan club officers.

781.7 367 US
I F C O JOURNAL. 1965. q. $25. (International Fan Club Organization) Tri-Son, Inc., Box 40328, Nashville, TN 37204-0328. TEL 615-371-9596. FAX 615-371-9597. Ed. Loudilla Johnson. circ. 800. **Document type:** directory, consumer publication.

780 US
I M A BULLETIN.* 1984. q. $40. International M I D I Association, 23634 Emelita St., Woodland Hills, CA 91367-5917. TEL 310-649-6434. FAX 310-215-3880. bk.rev. circ. 2,500. (back issues avail.) **Document type:** bulletin, newsletter.
  Description: Covers all aspects of MIDI: musical instruments and digital interface.

780 BE ISSN 1017-7515
I S O NEWS. (Text in English, French, German) 1969. 5/yr. 1250 BEF (effective 1995 & 1996). (International Society of Organbuilders) I S O Publications, Martelarenplein 6, 3000 Leuven, Belgium. TEL 32-41-541601. FAX 32-41-524197. Ed. Gerard Pels. adv.; bk.rev. circ. 2,200. Indexed: Music Ind. **Document type:** newsletter.
  Formerly: I S O Information (ISSN 0579-5613)

780 US
I T G JOURNAL. 1976. q. $26. International Trumpet Guild, Drawer 2025, Columbia, SC 29202. (Subscr. to: Bryan Goff, School of Music, Florida State University, Tallahasse, FL 32306. TEL 904-385-0639) Ed. Anne F. Hardin. adv.; bk.rev. circ. 6,000. Indexed: Music Artic.Guide, Music Ind. **Document type:** academic/scholarly publication.
—UnCover.
  Formerly: International Trumpet Guild. Journal (ISSN 0363-2849); Incorporates (1976-1988): International Trumpet Guild. Newsletter (ISSN 0363-2857)
  Refereed Serial

IDOL OF MY HEART ELVIS PRESLEY FAN CLUB NEWSLETTER. see *CLUBS*

780 US
ILLINOIS ENTERTAINER. 1974. m. $35. Roberts Publishing, Inc., 124 W. Polk St., Ste. 103, Chicago, IL 60605-2069. TEL 312-922-9333. FAX 312-922-9369. E-mail: ieeditors@aol.com. Ed. Michael Harris; Pub. David Roberts. adv. contact: Scott-Assmann, Pete Vernon. bk.rev.; rec.rev. circ. 80,000. **Document type:** consumer publication, trade publication.
  Description: Covers the music, film and video industries nationally and in the Chicago area.

780.7 US ISSN 0019-2147
ILLINOIS MUSIC EDUCATOR. vol.30, 1970. 5/yr. $10 to non-members. Illinois Music Educators Association, c/o Dr. Don Davis, Ed., 72 Marchelle, Springfield, IL 62702. TEL 217-787-6323. adv.; bk.rev.; illus. circ. 3,000.
  Description: Presents teaching methods and current association activities.

IN THE GROOVE. see *ANTIQUES*

780 US ISSN 0360-4365
ML1
IN THEORY ONLY. 1975. irreg. $15 to individuals (foreign $23); institutions $20 (foreign $28). Michigan Music Theory Society, c/o School of Music, University of Michigan, 700 Burton Memorial Tower, Ann Arbor, MI 48109-1270. TEL 313-936-0425. FAX 313-763-5097. Ed. Kristin Y. DeKoster. adv.; bk.rev.; bibl.; charts; illus.; index. circ. 500. (also avail. in microform from UMI; reprint service avail. from UMI) Indexed: Music Artic.Guide, Music Ind., RILM.
—BLDSC (4372.465000); Faxon; UMI; UnCover.

780 UK ISSN 0951-6220
INCORPORATED SOCIETY OF MUSICIANS YEARBOOK. 1898. a. £22. Incorporated Society of Musicians, 10 Stratford Pl., London W1N 9AE, England. TEL 0171-629-4413. FAX 0171-408-1538. circ. 7,500.
  Formerly: Incorporated Society of Musicians Handbook.
  Description: Reports activities of the society with membership lists in the United Kingdom and elsewhere.

690 UK ISSN 0073-5744
INCORPORATED SOCIETY OF ORGAN BUILDERS. JOURNAL. 1949. irreg. £3.50. Incorporated Society of Organ Builders, Petersfield, Hants GU32 3AT, England. Ed. C.J. Gordon Wells. circ. 400.

780 II ISSN 0251-012X
ML5
INDIAN MUSICOLOGICAL SOCIETY. JOURNAL. 1970. a. $15. Indian Musicological Society, Jambu Bet, Dandia Bazar, Baroda 390 001, India. TEL 555388. Ed. R.C. Mehta. adv.; bk.rev. circ. 1,000. (also avail. in microform from UMI; reprint service avail. from UMI) Indexed: Arts & Hum.Cit.Ind., Curr.Cont., Music Ind., RILM. **Document type:** academic/scholarly publication.
—Genuine Article; UMI; UnCover.
  Formerly: Sangeet Kala Vihar (ISSN 0036-4320)

INDIAN RECORDS; film, classical, popular. see *SOUND RECORDING AND REPRODUCTION*

780 US ISSN 0742-2490
INDIANA DIRECTORY OF MUSIC TEACHERS. 1941. a. $16 (educators $12). Indiana University, School of Music, Music Education Department, Bloomington, IN 47405. TEL 812-855-2051. Ed. Karen Gast. index. circ. 220. **Document type:** directory.
  Description: Lists faculties-teachers of music at Indiana public and parochial schools, colleges and universities, and state schools and hospitals. Addresses and telephone numbers included.

780.7 US ISSN 0273-9933
ML1
INDIANA MUSICATOR. 1945. q. $15 to non-members. Indiana Music Educators Association, Ball State University, School of Music, Muncie, IN 47306. TEL 317-285-5496. FAX 317-285-1139. Ed. JoDee Marshall. adv.; bk.rev.; circ. 2,000 (controlled). Indexed: Music Artic.Guide. **Document type:** academic/scholarly publication.

780.7 US ISSN 0271-8022
MT6
INDIANA THEORY REVIEW. 1977. 2/yr. $12. Indiana University, School of Music, Graduate Theory Association, Bloomington, IN 47405. TEL 812-855-0168. Ed. Vincent Benitez. bk.rev.; abstr.; charts. circ. 175. (back issues avail.) Indexed: Music Ind., RILM. **Document type:** academic/scholarly publication.
—Faxon; UnCover.
  Description: Articles on music theory.

INFORMAZIONI E STUDI VIVALDIANI. see *BIOGRAPHY*

780 US
INK DISEASE. irreg. $2.50 per no. 4563 Marmion Way, Los Angeles, CA 90065. music rev.
  Description: Features rock music, interviews and band photos.

780 AU
INNSBRUCKER BEITRAEGE ZUR MUSIKWISSENSCHAFT. 1977. irreg. price varies. Edition Helbling KG, Kaplanstr. 9, Postfach 416, A-6021 Innsbruck Neu Rum, Austria. Ed. Guenter Moesmer. adv. contact: Guenter Moesmer. charts; illus.; index. **Document type:** monographic series.

INSIDE ARTS. see *THEATER*

781.7 US ISSN 0891-0537
ML3519
INSIDE BLUEGRASS. 1974. m. $18. Minnesota Bluegrass and Old Time Music Association, Box 11419, Saint Paul, MN 55111-0419. TEL 612-688-7757. Ed. Bob Waltz. adv. contact: Alice Sizer. bk.rev. circ. 1,000. (back issues avail.)

780 CN
INSIDE TRACKS. bi-m. 93 Goulding Ave., N. York, Ont. M2M 1L3, Canada. TEL 416-229-9213. Ed. Stephen Hubbard. circ. 5,000 (controlled).

780 IT ISSN 0073-8611
INSTITUTA ET MONUMENTA. SERIE I: MONUMENTA. 1954. irreg., latest 1991. price varies. Fondazione "Claudio Monteverdi", Via Ugolani Dati 4, 26100 Cremona, Italy. TEL 39-372-26580. Ed. Raffaello Monterosso. **Document type:** academic/scholarly publication.

780 IT ISSN 0392-629X
INSTITUTA ET MONUMENTA. SERIE II: INSTITUTA. 1969. irreg., vol.12, 1989. price varies. Fondazione "Claudio Monteverdi", Via Ugolani Dati 4, 26100 Cremona, Italy. TEL 39-372-26580. Ed. Raffaello Monterosso. circ. 500 (controlled). **Document type:** monographic series.

781.5 US
INSTITUTE FOR STUDIES IN AMERICAN MUSIC. MONOGRAPHS. 1973. irreg., no.33, 1991. price varies. Institute for Studies in American Music, Conservatory of Music, Brooklyn College, City University of New York, Brooklyn, NY 11210. TEL 718-951-5655. FAX 718-951-4858. Ed. Carol Oja. **Document type:** monographic series, academic/scholarly publication.

780 US ISSN 0145-8396
ML28.B81
INSTITUTE FOR STUDIES IN AMERICAN MUSIC. NEWSLETTER. Short title: I S A M Newsletter. 1971. s-a. free. Institute for Studies in American Music, Conservatory of Music, Brooklyn College, City University of New York, Brooklyn, NY 11210. TEL 718-951-5655. FAX 718-951-6140. Ed. Carol Oja. adv. contact: Ray Allen. bk.rev.; bibl. circ. 4,200. Indexed: Music Artic.Guide. **Document type:** newsletter.
—BLDSC (6107.390500).

INSTITUTO BRASIL - ESTADOS UNIDOS. BOLETIM. see *EDUCATION*

780.7 US ISSN 0020-4331
INSTRUMENTALIST; a magazine for school and college band and orchestra directors, professional instrumentalists, teacher-training specialists in instrumental music education and instrumental teachers. 1946. m. $22. Instrumentalist Co., 200 Northfield Rd., Northfield, IL 60093-3390. TEL 708-446-5000; 800-323-5559. Ed. Catherine Sell; Pub. James T. Rohner. adv.; bk.rev.; rec.rev.; illus.; index, cum.index. circ. 19,000. Indexed: Educ.Ind., Jun.High.Mag.Abstr., Music Artic.Guide, Music Ind., RILM.
—BLDSC (4528.900000); Faxon; UnCover.

781.91 GW ISSN 0934-3962
ML5
INSTRUMENTBAU-ZEITSCHRIFT - MUSIK INTERNATIONAL. 1880. m. DM.82 (foreign DM.98). (Musik International Instrumentenbau) Verlag Franz Schmitt, Kaiserstr. 99-101, 53721 Siegburg, Germany. TEL 02241-64039. FAX 02241-53891. Ed. Carsten Duerer. adv.; charts; illus.; index. circ. 4,200. Indexed: RILM. Document type: trade publication.
Former titles (until 1988): Musik International (ISSN 0720-0439); (until 1980): Instrumentbau (ISSN 0342-1775); (until 1975): Instrumentbau-Zeitschrift (ISSN 0020-4390)

780 GW ISSN 0936-014X
INSTRUMENTENBAU REPORT; aktuelle Informationen fuer Musikfreunde und Instrumentenbauer. 1984. s-a. DM.16. Laerchenstr. 23, 85604 Zorneding, Germany. TEL 08106-22476. Ed. Wilhelm Erlewein. adv.; bk.rev. circ. 1,200. (back issues avail.) Document type: consumer publication.

780 PL
INSTRUMENTY OD A DO Z. 1966. irreg. price varies. Polskie Wydawnictwo Muzyczne, Al. Krasinskiego 11a, 31-111 Krakow, Poland. TEL 48-12-227044. FAX 48-12-220174. adv. contact: Teresa Wlochynska. Document type: monographic series.
Description: Series about musical instruments: their history, description, sound properties, orchestral use.

780 100 US ISSN 1073-6913
ML1
INTEGRAL. 1987. a. $12 to individuals (foreign $16); institutions $16 (foreign $20). Eastman School of Music, 26 Gibbs St., Rochester, NY 14604. Ed. Nancy Rogers. bk.rev. (back issues avail.) Indexed: Music Artic.Guide, RILM. Document type: academic/scholarly publication.
Description: Articles and reviews on music theory, analysis, criticism and their relationship to composition and performance.
Refereed Serial

780 US
INTENSITY. 1990. 6/yr. $14. 2502 W. Opal St., Pasco, WA 99301-3352. TEL 509-545-6747. Ed. John Book. adv. (back issues avail.)
Description: Covers new music bands from Washington.

780 US
INTENT TO KILL.* irreg. $5 per issue. Brian Baltin, Ed. & Pub., 171 Corona Ave., Long Beach, CA 90803-3318.

780 US ISSN 0195-6655
ML1
INTER-AMERICAN MUSIC REVIEW. 1979. s-a. $22. Theodore Front Musical Literature, Inc., 16122 Cohasset St., Van Nuys, CA 91406. TEL 818-994-1902. FAX 818-994-0419. Ed. Robert Stevenson. bk.rev.; bibl.; illus.; circ. 500 (paid). Indexed: Curr.Cont, Hisp.Amer.Per.Ind. (1979-), Music Ind., RILM. Document type: academic/scholarly publication.
—UnCover.

780 GW
INTERCULTURAL MUSIC STUDIES. 1990. 2/yr. International Institute for Traditional Music, Winkler Str. 20, 14193 Berlin, Germany. TEL 030-8262853. FAX 030-8259991. E-mail: iitm@netmbx.netmbx.de. (Subscr. to: Florian Noetzel Verlag, Postfach 580, 26353 Wilhelmshaven, Germany. TEL 04421-43003. FAX 04421-42985) Ed. M.P. Baumann. Document type: academic/scholarly publication.

781.57 US
INTERMISSION (LONG BEACH). 1968. m. $15 (effective 1993). New Orleans Jazz Club of Southern California, Box 15212, Long Beach, CA 90815. TEL 310-867-7501. Ed. Norman Burnham. adv.; bk.rev. circ. 500. (back issues avail.) Document type: newsletter.
Description: Preservation and education of Dixieland jazz. Information on scheduled jazz shows and places to perform jazz music.

780 US
INTERNATIONAL ALBAN BERG SOCIETY NEWSLETTER. 1968. a. $10 to individuals; libraries $15; students $6. International Alban Berg Society, Ph.D. Program in Music, City University of New York, 33 W. 42 St., New York, NY 10036. TEL 212-642-2389. Ed. Joan Allen Smith. circ. 300. (back issues avail.) Indexed: RILM. Document type: newsletter.

781.7 UK
INTERNATIONAL BAGPIPE DIRECTORY. 1993. a. £7.50. Blackfriars Music, 49 Blackfriars St., Edinburgh EH1 1NB, Scotland. TEL 0131-557-3090. FAX 0131-556-2552. Pub. Willie Haines. adv. contact: Willie Haines. circ. 1,000. Document type: directory.

780 US ISSN 0272-2062
INTERNATIONAL BANJO.* 1980. q. $16. International Banjo, Inc., 3431 Snowbell Ct., Orlando, FL 32810-2970. Ed. Pat Terry, Jr. adv.; bk.rev.; charts; illus.; tr.lit. circ. 2,000.

781.57 US
INTERNATIONAL BLUEGRASS. 1985. bi-m. $20. International Bluegrass Music Association, 207 E. Second St., Owensboro, KY 42303. TEL 502-684-9025. FAX 502-686-7863. Ed. Nancy Cardwell. bk.rev. circ. 1,000. (back issues avail.) Document type: newsletter.
Description: News, articles and how-to features aimed at bluegrass music professionals and fans.

784 US ISSN 0896-0968
INTERNATIONAL CHORAL BULLETIN. (Text in English, French, German, Spanish) 1981. q. $40 to individuals; libraries $15. International Federation for Choral Music, c/o Michael J. Anderson, Deputy Scty-Gen., University of Illinois at Chicago, Dept. of Performing Arts (M/C 255), 1040 West Harrison St., LO18, Chicago, IL 60607-7130. TEL 312-996-8744. FAX 312-996-0954. Ed. Jutta Tagger. adv. circ. 1,800. (back issues avail.) Indexed: Music Artic.Guide. Document type: bulletin.
—UnCover.
Description: Articles dealing with choral music and choral activities throughout the world. Lists festivals, workshops and competitions.

780 IT
INTERNATIONAL CONGRESS OF VERDI STUDIES. PROCEEDINGS. (Text in English, French, German, Italian, Spanish) irreg. price varies. Istituto Nazionale di Studi Verdiani, Strada della Repubblica 56, 43100 Parma, Italy. TEL 0521-286044. FAX 0521-287949. Document type: proceedings.

781.7 US ISSN 0739-1390
ML26
INTERNATIONAL COUNCIL FOR TRADITIONAL MUSIC. BULLETIN. (Text in English, French and German) 1948. s-a. International Council for Traditional Music, c/o Department of Music, Columbia University, New York, NY 10027. TEL 212-678-0332. FAX 212-678-2513. TELEX 220094 COLU UR. Ed. Dieter Christensen. circ. 1,400. (back issues avail.) Indexed: A.I.C.P., RILM. Document type: bulletin.
Formerly (until 1981): International Folk Music Council. Bulletin (ISSN 0020-6768)

780.1 305.8 UK
INTERNATIONAL COUNCIL FOR TRADITIONAL MUSIC (UK CHAPTER). NEWSLETTER. s-a. £12 to individuals; institutions £15 (includes British Journal of Ethnomusicology). International Council for Traditional Music (U.K. Chapter), c/o Centre of Music Studies, School of Oriental and African Studies, Thornhaugh St., Russell Sq., London WC1H 0XG, England. Ed.Bd. adv.; bk.rev.; music rev. (back issues avail.) Document type: newsletter.
Description: Publishes less formal articles on the ethnic study of music.

788.705 US ISSN 0092-0827
ML1
INTERNATIONAL DOUBLE REED SOCIETY JOURNAL. 1973. 4/yr. International Double Reed Society, c/o Lowry Riggins, 626 Lakeshore Dr., Monroe, LA 71203-4032. TEL 318-343-5715. FAX 318-345-1159.
—Faxon; UnCover.

781.7 SW
INTERNATIONAL FOLK MUSIC COUNCIL. INTERNATIONALE ARBEITSTAGUNG DER STUDY GROUP ON FOLK MUSICAL INSTRUMENTS. (Supplement to: Musikhistoriska Museets Skrifter) 6th, 1977. irreg. $57. A W I International AB, P.O. Box 4627, S-116 91 Stockholm, Sweden. TEL 468-6408800. FAX 468-641-1180. Ed. Erich Stockmann. illus.

786 US
INTERNATIONAL HORN SOCIETY. DIRECTORY. a. $25 membership. International Horn Society, c/o Ellen Powley, Exe. Secretary, 2220 N. 1400 E., Provo, UT 84604. TEL 801-377-3026. Document type: directory.

786 US
INTERNATIONAL HORN SOCIETY. NEWSLETTER. q. $25 membership. International Horn Society, c/o Ellen Powley, Exec. Secretary, 2220 N. 1400 E., Provo, UT 84604. TEL 801-377-3026. Document type: newsletter.
Description: Keeps members informed of immediate horn news and activities.

781.57 SZ
▼**INTERNATIONAL JAZZFESTIVAL GUIDE.** (Text in English) 1995. a. 15 SFr. Jazztime-Verlag, CH-5430 Wettingen, Switzerland. TEL 056-272141. FAX 056-272601. Ed. Eduard Keller. Document type: consumer publication.

780 GW ISSN 0723-9769
INTERNATIONAL JOSEPH MARTIN KRAUS-GESELLSCHAFT. MITTEILUNGEN. 1983. irreg. DM.50 membership. Internationale Joseph Martin Kraus-Gesellschaft e.V., Kellereistr. 25-29, 74722 Buchen, Germany. TEL 06281-8898. Ed.Bd. bk.rev. Document type: proceedings.

780.7 UK ISSN 0255-7614
INTERNATIONAL JOURNAL OF MUSIC EDUCATION. (Abstracts in French, German, Spanish) 1967. s-a. $20 (typically set in Jan.). International Society for Music Education, University of Reading - Music Education Centre, Bulmershe Ct., Reading RG6 1HY, England. TEL 01734-318846. FAX 01734-352080. Eds. Jack Dobbs, Anthony Kemp. adv.; bk.rev.; music rev.; illus. circ. 2,500. (also avail. in microform from UMI; microfiche from KTO; back issues avail.; reprint service avail. from UMI) Indexed: Aus.Educ.Ind., Cont.Pg.Educ., Music Ind., RILM. Document type: academic/scholarly publication.
—Faxon; UMI; UnCover.
Formerly (until 1983): Australian Journal of Music Education (ISSN 0004-9484)
Description: Reports on various aspects of music education throughout the world.

780 GW ISSN 0941-9535
ML5
INTERNATIONAL JOURNAL OF MUSICOLOGY. (Text in English, French, German, Italian, Spanish) 1992. a. DM.126. Peter Lang GmbH Europaeischer Verlag der Wissenschaften, Eschborner Landstr. 42-50, 60489 Frankfurt a.M., Germany. TEL 069-7807050. FAX 069-785893. Eds. Elliott Antokoletz, Michael von Albrecht. adv.; B&W page DM.800; trim 115 x 169; adv. contact: Rita Bebenroth. circ. 400. Document type: academic/scholarly publication.
—BLDSC (4542.368700).

781.7 US ISSN 1074-746X
ML12
INTERNATIONAL LATIN MUSIC BUYER'S GUIDE. 1992. a. $60. Billboard Directories, 1515 Biway, New York, NY 10076. TEL 212-536-5025. FAX 212-536-5055. Pub. Ronald E. Willman. adv. Document type: directory.
Description: Lists critical Latin Music contacts in the U.S., Mexico, Central America, South America, Spain and Portugal.

780.6   US   ISSN 0748-5735
INTERNATIONAL LEAGUE OF WOMEN COMPOSERS. NEWSLETTER. 1975. 3/yr. $25 to individuals; students and senior citizens $15; institutions $35. International League of Women Composers, c/o Elizabeth Hayden Pizer, Box 670, S. Shore Rd., Pr. Peninsula, NY 13693. TEL 315-649-5086. Ed. Sally Reid. adv.; bk.rev.; illus. circ. 600. (looseleaf format; back issues avail.) **Indexed:** Music Artic.Guide. **Document type:** newsletter.
   Description: Promotes serious concert music composed by women. Informs readers of activities, opportunities, and events.

331.8 780   US   ISSN 0020-8051
ML1
INTERNATIONAL MUSICIAN. 1901. m. $20 to non-members. American Federation of Musicians of the United States and Canada, 1501 Broadway, New York, NY 10036. TEL 212-869-1330. FAX 212-302-4374. Ed. Stephen R. Sprague. adv.; bk.rev.; illus. circ. 155,000. (tabloid format; also avail. in microform from UMI; reprint service avail. from UMI) **Indexed:** Music Artic.Guide, Music Ind., PMR. **Document type:** newspaper.
   —Faxon; UMI.

780.65   IT
INTERNATIONAL RECORDS NEWS. (Text in English) 1982. m. L.30000($35) Fini Editions, 18 Via Monte Battaglia, 40046 Inola, Italy. Ed. Francesco Fini. bibl.; charts.

780   CI   ISSN 0351-5796
INTERNATIONAL REVIEW OF THE AESTHETICS AND SOCIOLOGY OF MUSIC. (Text in English, French, German; summaries in English and Croatian) 1970. s-a. $28. Muzicka Akademija u Zagrebu, Muzikoloski Zavod, Berlislaviceva 16, 41001 Zagreb, Croatia. Ed. Ivo Supicic. adv.; bk.rev.; bibl. circ. 1,250. (reprint service avail. from SWZ) **Indexed:** Curr.Cont., Music Ind., RILM.
   —BLDSC (4545.980000); Faxon; SWETS; UnCover.
   Formerly: International Review of Music Aesthetics and Sociology (ISSN 0047-1208)

INTERNATIONAL SINATRA SOCIETY NEWSLETTER. see *CLUBS*

780.7   UK
INTERNATIONAL SOCIETY FOR MUSIC EDUCATION. PROCEEDINGS. biennial. $34 (effective 1994-1995). International Society for Music Education, University of Reading - Music Education Centre, Bulmershe Ct., Reading RG6 1HY, England. TEL 01734-318846. FAX 01734-352080. Ed. Heath Lees. circ. 1,700. (back issues avail.) **Document type:** proceedings.
   Formerly (until 1988): International Society for Music Education. Yearbook.

780   US   ISSN 0892-0532
ML920
INTERNATIONAL SOCIETY OF BASSISTS. JOURNAL. 1982. 3/yr. $30 (foreign $35). International Society of Bassists, 4020 McEwen, No. 105, Dallas, TX 75244. TEL 214-233-9107. FAX 214-490-4219. Ed. Madeleine Crouch. adv.; bk.rev.; bibl.; illus. circ. 2,600. **Indexed:** Music Artic.Guide.
   —Faxon; UnCover.
   Formed by the 1982 merger of: International Society of Bassists. Newsletter; Bass World; Which was formerly: Probas.

780   US   ISSN 0145-3513
ML1
INTERNATIONAL TROMBONE ASSOCIATION. JOURNAL. 1971. 3/yr. $20. International Trombone Association, Music Department, North Texas State University, TX 76203. Ed. Vern Kagarice. adv.; bk.rev. circ. 3,500. **Indexed:** Music Ind.
   —Faxon; UnCover.
   Formerly (until 1981): International Trombone Association. Newsletter.

780   US   ISSN 0363-5708
INTERNATIONAL TROMBONE ASSOCIATION SERIES. irreg. Brass Press, c/o RKMS, 140 Main St., N. Easton, MA 02356. FAX 508-238-2571. Ed. Stephen L. Glover.

780   UK   ISSN 0307-2894
INTERNATIONAL WHO'S WHO IN MUSIC AND MUSICIANS' DIRECTORY. 1935. biennial. £87.50. Melrose Press Ltd., 3 Regal Ln., Soham, Ely, Cambridgeshire CB7 5BA, England. TEL 01353-721091. FAX 01353-721839. (Dist. in U.S. by: International Publication Services, Taylor-Francis, Inc., 1900 Frost Rd., Ste.101, Bristol, PA 19007-1598) Ed. Jocelyn Timothy; Pub. Nicholas Law. adv. contact: Jean Pearson. **Indexed:** Child.Auth.& Illus., Perf.Arts Biog.Master Ind. **Document type:** directory.
   —BLDSC (4552.112000).
   Formerly: Who's Who in Music and Musicians' International Directory (ISSN 0083-9647)

780   AU   ISSN 0020-9325
INTERNATIONALE STIFTUNG MOZARTEUM. MITTEILUNGEN. 1952. s-a. S.350. Internationale Stiftung Mozarteum, Schwarzstr. 26, Postfach 34, A-5024 Salzburg, Austria. TEL 0662-88940-10. FAX 0662-882419. Ed. Rudolph Angermueller. adv. contact: Rudolph Angermueller. bk.rev.; illus.; index. circ. 2,000. **Indexed:** Music Ind., RILM. **Document type:** newsletter.
   Description: Features historical and musical information, reviews and analysis of his works, Mozart's contemporaries, foundation news, and news of Mozart societies. Includes announcement of events and exhibitions.

780.6   GW   ISSN 0579-8353
INTERVALLE; A M J Informationen. s-a. Arbeitskreis Musik in der Jugend, Adersheimer Str. 60, 38304 Wolfenbuettel, Germany. TEL 05331-46016. FAX 05331-43723. Ed. Rolf Pasdzierny. adv.; bk.rev. (back issues avail.) **Document type:** bulletin.
   Description: Reports on the activities of the Arbeitskreis.

780.7   US   ISSN 0021-0609
IOWA MUSIC EDUCATOR. 1946. 3/yr. $9. Iowa Music Educators Association, c/o Lance Lehmberg, Ed., Dept. of Music, Morningside College, Sioux City, IA 51106. TEL 712-274-5218. FAX 712-274-5101. E-mail: hllool@chicf.morningside.edu. adv.: B&W page $150; 8 1/2 x 11. bk.rev.; tr.lit. circ. 1,400. **Document type:** academic/scholarly publication.

780   IE   ISSN 0332-298X
ML3654
IRISH FOLK MUSIC STUDIES/EIGSE CHEOL TIRE. 1972. irreg. £3. Folk Music Society of Ireland, 15 Herietta St., Dublin 1, Ireland. Ed. Hugh Shields. adv.; bk.rev.; bibl. circ. 1,000. **Indexed:** RILM.

781.7 793.31   US
IRISH MUSIC AND DANCE ASSOCIATION NEWSLETTER. (Text in English, Gaelic) 1983. m. $12. Irish Music and Dance Association, Box 65187, St. Paul, MN 55165. TEL 612-227-5090. Ed. Sean T. Kelly. adv. circ. 275. (looseleaf format) **Document type:** newsletter.
   Description: Covers items of interest to the Irish community in Minnesota.

IRISH PERFORMING ARTS YEARBOOK. see *THEATER*

780 791.43   US   ISSN 1041-3812
ISLAND - EAR. 1978. bi-w. $40. Island - Ear Inc., Box 309, Island Park, NY 11558. TEL 516-889-6045. FAX 516-889-5513. Ed. Alvin Eng. adv. contact: Arie Nadboy. circ. 30,000. (tabloid format; back issues avail.)
   Description: Covers entertainment on Long Island.

ISLENSK HLJODRITASKRA/BIBLIOGRAPHY OF ICELANDIC SOUND RECORDINGS. see *BIBLIOGRAPHIES*

781.7   IS   ISSN 0334-2026
ISRAEL STUDIES IN MUSICOLOGY. (Text in English) 1978. irreg. $15. Israel Musicology Society, P.O. Box 503, Jerusalem, Israel. (Editorial addr.: c/o Dept. of Musicology Bar-Ilan University, Ramat Gan 55900, Israel. TEL 972-5318405. FAX 972-3-5344622) Ed. Bathia Churgin. bk.rev.; circ. 500 (paid). **Indexed:** RILM. **Document type:** academic/scholarly publication.
   Description: Publishes scholarly articles on musicological topics, including music theory and ethnomusicology.
   Refereed Serial

MUSIC   4853

M

783   IT
ISTITUTO DI MUSICA "VINCENZO AMATO". QUADERNI; teologia,filologia ed estetica nella musica sacra. 1985. irreg. Istituto di Musica "Vincenzo Amato", Via SS. Salvatore, No.1, 90134 Palermo, Italy. TEL 091-323392. Ed. Gino Lo Galbo.
   Description: Contains a collection of didactic and cultural initiatives unfolded in the course of each year of musical activity. Also publishes contributions from institutions that research and perform music.

780   GW   ISSN 0937-1095
JAHRBUCH ALTE MUSIK. 1989. a. (Akademie fuer Alte Musik) Florian Noetzel Verlag, Heinrichshofen Buecher, Valoisstr. 11, 26382 Wilhelmshaven, Germany. (Dist. in N. America by: C.F. Peters Corp., 373 Park Ave. S., New York, NY 10016) Eds. Thomas Albert, Gisela Jaacks. **Document type:** bulletin.

782.1   GW   ISSN 0938-4952
JAHRBUCH DER BAYERISCHEN STAATSOPER. 1959. a. DM.28. (Gesellschaft zur Foerderung der Muenchner Opernfestspiele) F. Bruckmann Muenchen Verlag und Druck GmbH, Nymphenburgerstr. 86, 80636 Munich, Germany. TEL 089-125701. FAX 089-1257269. circ. 5,000. (back issues avail.) **Document type:** bulletin.

JAHRBUCH FUER LITURGIK UND HYMNOLOGIE. see *RELIGIONS AND THEOLOGY*

780 398   GW   ISSN 0075-2703
ML5
JAHRBUCH FUER MUSIKALISCHE VOLKS- UND VOELKERKUNDE. 1968. irreg. price varies. (Freie Universitaet Berlin, Vergleichende Musikwissenschaft) Verlag der Musikalienhandlung Karl-Dieter Wagner, Marienstr. 13, 99817 Eisenach, Germany. TEL 03691-624901. Ed. Josef Kuckertz. **Indexed:** A.I.C.P., Anthropol.Lit., RILM. **Document type:** academic/scholarly publication.

782   GW   ISSN 0724-8156
ML1699
JAHRBUCH FUER OPERNFORSCHUNG. (Text in English, French, and German) 1985. irreg. DM.49. Peter Lang GmbH Europaeischer Verlag der Wissenschaften, Eschborner Landstr. 42-50, 60489 Frankfurt a.M., Germany. TEL 069-7807050. FAX 069-785893. **Indexed:** RILM. **Document type:** academic/scholarly publication.

784.4 398   GW   ISSN 0075-2789
ML3630
JAHRBUCH FUER VOLKSLIEDFORSCHUNG. 1928. a. price varies. (Deutsches Volksliederarchiv) Erich Schmidt Verlag GmbH & Co. (Bielefeld), Viktoriastr. 44A, 33602 Bielefeld, Germany. TEL 0521-583080. (Subscr. to: Postfach 102451, 33524 Bielefeld, Germany) Ed. Rolf Wilhelm Brednich. adv.; bk.rev.; index. (back issues avail.) **Indexed:** Curr.Cont., M.L.A., RILM. **Document type:** academic/scholarly publication.
   —Genuine Article.

780   US
JAM RAG. 1985. 20/yr. $16. Jam Rag Press, Box 20076, Ferndale, MI 48220. TEL 313-542-8090. FAX 315-542-9826. Ed. Tom Ness. adv. contact: Susan Ness. bk.rev. circ. 20,000. **Document type:** newspaper, consumer publication.
   Description: For ages 15-40, covers underground music scene, rock bands, politics, environmental issues, and local news.

780 792   JM
JAMAICA PICTORIAL. bi-m. Jam.$15($14) for 12 issues. J.S.M. Press, 121 King St., Kingston, Jamaica, W.I.

JAUNA GAITA. see *ART*

781.5   SZ
JAZZ. (Text in German) 1968. m. 30 Fr.($10.) Hochuli AG, Box 4132, Mutteuz, Switzerland. Ed. Freddy J. Angstman. adv.; bk.rev.; rec.rev.; bibl.; charts; illus.; stat.; index, cum.index; circ. 10,000. (controlled).
   Formerly: Jazz - Rhythm and Blues (ISSN 0021-5619)

781.65   GW
JAZZ (YEAR). 1993. a. DM.12. Lamuv Verlag GmbH, Nikolaikirchhof 7, 37073 Goettingen, Germany. TEL 0551-44024. FAX 0551-41392. Ed. Alwin Meyer. **Document type:** bulletin.

4854   MUSIC

781.57   US
JAZZ ARCHIVIST. 1986. s-a. $15 membership. Hogan Jazz Archive, Howard-Tilton Memorial Library, Tulane University, New Orleans, LA 70118. TEL 504-865-5688. FAX 504-865-6773. Ed. Dr. John J. Joyce. bk.rev. circ. 1,000. **Document type:** newsletter.
  Description: Presents short, scholarly articles based on research conducted at the Archive, news of exhibits, recent donations and related features.

781.57   GW
JAZZ CLUB KARLSRUHE E.V.; termine, veranstaltungen, news. 1985. bi-m. DM.17.50($10) Piduch Verlag, Am Hang 21, 76437 Rastatt, Germany. TEL 07222-53514. Ed. Georg Kleinert. adv.; bk.rev. circ. 8,000.

781.57   AT   ISSN 0155-9680
JAZZ DOWN UNDER. 1974. bi-m. Aus.$3.60. Box 202, Camden, N.S.W. 2570, Australia. Ed. Peter Hume. adv.; illus.

780.7   US   ISSN 0730-9791
ML1
JAZZ EDUCATORS JOURNAL. 1968. 4/yr. $25 (effective 1995-96). International Association of Jazz Educators, Box 724, Manhattan, KS 66502-0006. TEL 913-776-8744. FAX 913-776-6190. E-mail: IAJE@KSUVM.KSU.EDU. Ed. Antonio Garcia. adv.; bk.rev.; film rev.; bibl.; cum.index. circ. 7,500. (back issues avail.) **Indexed:** Music Ind. **Document type:** academic/scholarly publication.
  —BLDSC (4663.429300); Faxon; UnCover.
  Former titles: National Association of Jazz Educators. Newsletter; N A J E Educator (ISSN 0047-8741)

780.79   DK   ISSN 0900-064X
JAZZ FESTIVALS AND RELATED MAJOR JAZZ EVENTS. DIRECTORY. (Text in English) approx. biennial. DKK 100 in Nordic countries; rest of Europe and Mediterranean countries DKK 115; elsewhere DKK 130. Danish Jazz Center, Borupvej 66 B, DK-4683 Roennede, Denmark. TEL 45-56-71-13-27. FAX 45-56-71-17-49. Ed. Mette Fanoe. **Document type:** directory.

781.57   PL   ISSN 0324-8801
ML3505.8
JAZZ FORUM. (Supplements avail.) 1965. m. $32. For Jazz, Inc., Nowogrodzka 49, 00-695 Warsaw, Poland. TEL 48-22-219451. FAX 48-22-6217758. Ed. Pawel Brodowski. adv.; bk.rev.; rec.rev.; illus. circ. 12,000. (also avail. in microform from UMI; back issues avail.; reprint service avail. from UMI) **Indexed:** Music Ind. **Document type:** trade publication.

781.57   FR   ISSN 0021-5643
ML5
JAZZ HOT; la revue internationale de jazz. 1935. 11/yr. 350 F. (effective 1995). Jazz Hot Publications, 66 rue Villiers-de-l'Isle-Adam, B.P. 405, 75969 Paris Cedex 20, France. TEL 43-66-74-88. FAX 43-66-72-60. Ed. Yves Sportis. adv.; rec.rev.; illus. **Indexed:** Music Ind.

781.57   UK
JAZZ IN THE MIDLANDS. 1984. q. £7.50. (Jazz Central) Jazz Central Ltd., 29/30 Guildhall Buildings, Navigation Street, Birmingham B2 4BT, England. TEL 0 273 571536. Ed. Alan James. adv. circ. 15,000. (back issues avail.)
  Description: Features news of tours, festivals, workshops, performances, record reviews and competitions. Also contains performance guide for local jazz music.

781.57 658.048   US
JAZZ INTERACTIONS. 1965. s-m. $25. Jazz Interactions, Inc., Box 268, Glen Oaks, NY 11004. TEL 718-465-7500. Ed. R. Neufeld. adv. circ. 300. (back issues avail.)
  Description: Comprehensive listing of jazz clubs and artists in NYC and its vicinity. Includes information on free summer jazz park concerts.

781.57   UK   ISSN 0140-2285
ML5
JAZZ JOURNAL INTERNATIONAL. 1948. m. £34 (foreign £43) (effective 1996). Jazz Journal Ltd., 1-5 Clerkenwell Rd., London EC1M 5PA, England. TEL 0171-608-1348. FAX 0171-608-1292. Ed. Eddie Cook. adv.; bk.rev.; rec.rev.; illus.; index. circ. 12,000. (also avail. in microform from UMI; back issues avail.) **Indexed:** Music Ind. **Document type:** consumer publication.
  —Faxon; UMI; UnCover.
  Formerly (until April 1977): Jazz Journal (ISSN 0021-5651); Incorporates: Jazz and Blues.
  Description: Various issues contain: personal interviews with leading Jazz musicians, career appraisals, discographical information, readers' letters, CD reviews, news previews and reports, of interest to jazz enthusiasts as well as musicians.

781.57   FR   ISSN 0021-566X
ML5
JAZZ MAGAZINE. 1954. m. 265 F. (foreign 327 F.) (effective 1995). Publications Filipacchi, 63 Champs-Elysees, 75008 Paris, France. TEL 33-1-40-74-74-55. FAX 33-1-40-74-74-91. (Subscr. to: 99 rue d'Amsterdam, 75008 Paris. TEL 42-80-68-55) Ed. Philippe Carles. adv.; bk.rev.; rec.rev.; illus. circ. 25,000. (also avail. in microform from UMI; reprint service avail. from UMI) **Indexed:** Music Ind. **Document type:** consumer publication.
  —UMI.

781.57   US
JAZZ NEWSLETTER. m. New Orleans Jazz Club of California, Box 1225, Kerrville, TX 78029. TEL 210-896-2285. **Document type:** newsletter.

781.65   US
JAZZ NOTES. 1978. m. $20. Twin Cities Jazz Society, Box 4487, St. Paul, MN 55104-0487. TEL 612-633-0329. E-mail: GJVASQUEZ@AOL.COM. Eds. Genaro & Jessica Vasquez. adv.; rec.rev. **Document type:** newsletter.
  Description: Reviews and previews events of interest to jazz musicians and people who love jazz.

781.57   NE   ISSN 0166-7025
JAZZ NU; maandblad voor jazz en geimproviseerde muziek. 1978. m. fl.72 (foreign fl.125) (effective 1993). Uitgeverij Scala bv, Postbus 28009, 3828 ZG Hoogland, Netherlands. TEL 31-33-806896. FAX 31-33-802281. Ed. Bert Huisjes. adv.; bk.rev.; illus.; index. circ. 6,000. (back issues avail.)
  Description: For jazz muscians and aficionados.

781.57   SZ
JAZZ PASSION. (Text in French) m. Rue a Ornette, CH-1333 Lussy-sur-Morges, Switzerland. TEL 021-701-1071. (Subscr. to: c/o Catherine Montandon, Rue de l'Industrie 35, CH-1030 Bussigny) adv.; bk.rev.; illus.
  Description: Provides festival coverage, interviews and information to jazz fans of Switzerland.

781.65   US
JAZZ PLAYER. 1993. bi-m. $35 (foreign $45) (includes instructional compact disc). Dorn Publications, Inc., Box 206, Medfield, MA 02052. music rev.; video rev. **Document type:** trade publication.
  Description: Helps jazz musicians improve their technique. Also contains articles and columns to enthusiasts of all forms of jazz.

781.57   GW   ISSN 0021-5686
ML5
JAZZ PODIUM. 1952. m. DM.55 (foreign DM.71.50). Jazz Podium Verlags GmbH, Vogelsangstr. 32, 70197 Stuttgart, Germany. TEL 0711-636699. FAX 0711-632893. Ed. Gudrun Endress. adv.; B&W page DM.1210, color page DM.3160; trim 185 x 261. bk.rev. circ. 12,000. **Indexed:** Music Ind. **Document type:** newsletter.

781.57   UK
JAZZ RAG. 1986. bi-m £9.50 (overseas £11.50). Big Bear Music Group, P.O. Box 944, Edgbaston, Birmingham B16 8UT, England. TEL 0121-454-7020. FAX 0121-454-9996. Ed. Jim Simpson; Pub. Jim Simpson. adv. contact: Esther Blaine. bk.rev.; film rev.; rec.rev.; illus. circ. 10,000. (back issues avail.) **Document type:** consumer publication.
  Description: Reviews of jazz releases, CDs, videos, books, and live concerts. Includes interviews and news.

781.57   UK   ISSN 0021-5716
JAZZ TIMES. 1964. m. membership. British Jazz Society, 10 Southfield Gardens, Twickenham, Middlesex, England. Ed. John G. Boddy. adv.; bk.rev.; film rev.; rec.rev.; illus. circ. 10,000.

781.57   US   ISSN 0749-4564
ML3505.8
JAZZ WORLD. 1972. bi-m. $35 includes supplement. World Jazz Society, Box 777, Times Square Sta., New York, NY 10108-0777. TEL 201-939-0836. Ed. Jan A. Byrczek. adv.; bk.rev. circ. 6,000. (back issues avail.) **Indexed:** Music Ind.
  Former titles (until 1984): Jazz World Index (ISSN 0886-1927); (until 1981): Jazz Echo (ISSN 0277-5980); (until 1979): Swinging Newsletter.

781.57   GW
JAZZ ZEITUNG. 1976. m. DM.30. Titurelstr. 9, 81925 Munich, Germany. TEL 089-983360. FAX 089-981886. Ed. Hans Ruland. adv.; bk.rev. circ. 10,000. **Document type:** consumer publication.
  Description: Jazz portraits, record reviews, information about concerts and musicians in and around Munich.

785.4   AG
JAZZBAND. 1972. bi-m. $7. c/o Alberto Miguel Consiglio, 2291 Yerbal, Buenos Aires, Argentina. adv.; bk.rev.; illus. circ. 10,000.

780   AU   ISSN 0075-3572
ML5
JAZZFORSCHUNG/JAZZ RESEARCH. (Text and summaries in English and German) 1969. a. price varies; free to members. (International Society for Jazz Research) Akademische Druck- und Verlagsanstalt Dr. Paul Struzl, Schoenaugasse 6, A-8010 Graz, Austria. TEL 0316-813460. FAX 0316-81346024. (Co-sponsors: Hochschule fuer Musik und Institut fuer Jazz Darstellende Kunst) **Indexed:** Music Ind., RILM. **Document type:** academic/scholarly publication.

781.57   GW   ISSN 0021-5724
ML5
DER JAZZFREUND; Mitteilungsblatt fuer Jazzfreunde in Ost und West. 1956. q. DM.27. Von-Stauffenberg-Str. 24, 58708 Menden, Germany. TEL 02373-63776. Ed. Gerhard Conrad. bk.rev.; rec.rev. (processed) **Document type:** consumer publication.

781.57   US   ISSN 0741-5885
JAZZIZ. 1983. m. $12.95. Jazziz Magazine, Inc., 3620 N.W. 43rd St. Ste. D, Gainesville, FL 32606. TEL 904-375-3705. FAX 904-375-7268. Ed. Michael Fagien. adv.; B&W page $2375, color page $3325; trim 8 3/8 x 11 1/8. bk.rev. circ. 150,000. (reprint service avail.) **Indexed:** Music Artic.Guide, RILM.
  —UMI; UnCover.
  Description: Music lifestyle publication devoted to jazz and music for adults.

781.57 973   US   ISSN 0890-6440
ML3505.8
JAZZLETTER. 1981. 12/yr. $60 (foreign $70). Box 240, Ojai, CA 93024-0240. TEL 805-640-8307. FAX 805-640-0253. E-mail: Jazzlet@IX.netcom.com. Ed. Gene Lees. adv.; bk.rev.; cum.index. circ. 2,000. (back issues avail.) **Document type:** newsletter.
  Description: Biographical portraits of major artists, and articles on the evolution and contemporary state of American jazz.

781.57   AT
JAZZLINE. 1975. q. Aus.$3.00 per no. Victorian Jazz Club, P.O. Box 2421v, Melbourne, Vic. 3001, Australia. Ed. Judi Anderson. adv.; bk.rev. circ. 500.

781.57   US   ISSN 8756-6540
JAZZLINE. 1965. s-m. $25. Jazz Interactions, Inc., Box 268, Glen Oaks, NY 11004. TEL 718-465-7500. Ed. R. Neufeld. circ. 250.
  Description: Provides information on jazz and jazz events in the New York metropolitan area.

781.57   US
JAZZMEN'S REFERENCE BOOK; Jazz World Direct. 1973. a. $95 to non-members. Jazz World Society, Box 777, Times Square Sta., New York, NY 10108-0777. Ed. Jan Byrczek. adv. circ. 8,000.

MUSIC 4855

781.57 US ISSN 0198-6805
JAZZOLOGIST. 1963. irreg. (4-6/yr.) $8. New Orleans Jazz Club of California, Box 1225, Kerrville, TX 78029. TEL 210-896-2285. Ed. Mort Enob. adv.; bk.rev.; rec.rev.; bibl. circ. 5,000. **Document type:** newspaper.

781.57 US ISSN 1055-5722
ML3505.8
JAZZSOUTH. 1989. q. free. Southern Arts Federation, 181 14th St., Ste. 400, Atlanta, GA 30309. TEL 404-874-7244. FAX 404-873-2148. Ed. Tom Campbell. illus.; music rev.; circ. 3,000 (controlled). (back issues avail.) **Document type:** newsletter.
Description: Reports on Southern jazz performances, funding opportunities, educational programs, recordings, publications, and other jazz news in the region.

781.57 US ISSN 0272-572X
ML1
JAZZTIMES; America's jazz magazine. 1972. 10/yr. $21.95 (Canada $35.95; elsewhere $59.95). Jazz Times Inc., 7961 Eastern Ave., Ste. 303, Silver Spring, MD 20910-4898. TEL 301-588-4114. FAX 301-588-5531. Ed. Mike Joyce. adv.; bk.rev.; illus. circ. 65,000. (also avail. in microfiche from UMI; reprint service avail. from UMI) **Indexed:** Music Artic.Guide. **Document type:** consumer publication.
—Faxon; UMI; UnCover.
Supersedes: Radio Free Jazz (ISSN 0145-5125)
Description: Comprehensive consumer jazz publication covering swing and big band to Brazilian, blues and contemporary jazz.

780 FR ISSN 1155-3464
JE CHANTE!; la revue de la chanson francaise. (Supplement avail.: Discographies (ISSN 1155-3472)) 1990. bi-m. 200 F. 36-44 rue de Wattignies, 75012 Paris, France. TEL 43-46-83-07. (Subscr. to: 39 ave du Centre, 78189 Saint-Quentin-en-Yvelines. TEL 30-64-02-68) Ed. Rene Bellaiche.

781.6 SW ISSN 0345-5653
ML5
JEFFERSON; Scandanavian magazine for blues and related music. 1968. q. SEK 120 to individuals; institutions SEK 130; newsstand price: SEK 35.64. Scandinavian Blues Association, P.O. Box 4020, S-102 61 Stockholm, Sweden. FAX 46-8-702-21-18. Ed. Tommy Loefgren. adv.; bk.rev.; bibl. circ. 2,000.
Formerly (until vol.7, 1969): Jefferson Blues Magazine.
Description: Contains related music styles like zydeco, rock 'n roll, gospel, and reggae.

780 US
JERSEY BEAT. 1982. q. $3 per no. 418 Gregory Ave., Weehawken, NJ 07087. TEL 201-864-9054. E-mail: jimjbeat@aol.com. Ed. Jim Testa. adv.; bk.rev. circ. 5,000.
Description: Covers the alternative music world, focusing on the New Jersey area.

781.57 US ISSN 0740-5928
JERSEY JAZZ. 1973. 11/yr. $25. New Jersey Jazz Society, Box 173, Brookside, NJ 07926. TEL 201-543-2039. Ed. Don Robertson. adv.; bk.rev.; illus.; circ. 1,500 (controlled). **Document type:** newsletter.
Description: Covers traditional and mainstream jazz.

780 US ISSN 0886-7437
JET LAG.* m. $12. 3980 Bowen St., A, St. Louis, MO 63116-3145. TEL 314-383-5841.
Description: Presents articles, interviews and reviews of new records and performance artists. Covers rock, progressive and classical music.

780 CC
JIANGSU YINYUE/JIANGSU MUSIC. (Text in Chinese) m. Jiangsu Wenxue Yishu Jie Lianhehui - Jiangsu Literary and Art Circle Association, 126 Ninghai Lu, Nanjing, Jiangsu 210024, People's Republic of China. TEL 306362. Ed. Xie Hua.

780 US
JOHNNY WINTER. q. $5 (foreign $10). Johnny Winter International Fan Club, 2442 N.W. Market, Ste. 208, Seattle, WA 98107. **Document type:** consumer publication, newsletter.

783 IE
JOINT COMMITTEE FOR CHURCH MUSIC IN IRELAND. NEWSLETTER. 1977. q. free. Joint Committee for Church Music in Ireland, R.E. Resource Centre, Mount Argus Rd., Dublin 6, Ireland. Ed. David Bedlow. adv.; bk.rev. circ. 1,000. **Document type:** newsletter.

780 US
JOLSON JOURNAL. 1950. 2/yr. $18. International Al Jolson Society, c/o Dolores Kontowicz, 11520 W. James Ave., Franklin, WI 53132. TEL 414-529-2868. bk.rev.; illus. circ. 1,000. **Document type:** consumer publication.

780 US
JOLSONEWS. q. membership. International Al Jolson Society, c/o Dolores Kontowicz, 11520 W. James Ave., Franklin, WI 53132. TEL 414-529-2868. **Document type:** newsletter.
Formerly: Jolson Journalette.

780 GW ISSN 0446-9577
JOSEPH HAAS GESELLSCHAFT. MITTEILUNGENSBLATT. 1950. a. membership. Joseph Haas Gesellschaft e.V., c/o Wolfgang Haas, Kreuzeckstr. 18, 82049 Pullach, Germany. TEL 089-794345. Ed. Siegfried Gmeinwieser. bk.rev.; bibl.; index. circ. 300.

JOURNAL OF AESTHETICS AND ART CRITICISM. see ART

780 694 US ISSN 1048-2482
ML549.8
JOURNAL OF AMERICAN ORGANBUILDING. 1986. q. $12 (foreign $16). American Institute of Organbuilders, Box 130982, Houston, TX 77219-0982. TEL 713-529-2212. Ed. Howard Maple. adv.; bk.rev.; circ. 600 (paid). (back issues avail.) **Document type:** trade publication.
Description: Includes technical articles and product reviews for pipe organ builders and tuning and maintenance technicians.

786.067 US ISSN 0021-9207
JOURNAL OF BAND RESEARCH. 1964. s-a. $7. (American Bandmasters Association) Troy State University Press, Troy, AL 36082. TEL 205-670-3258. FAX 205-566-6500. (Co-sponsors: College Band Directors National Association; National Band Association; American School Band Directors Association) Ed. Jon R. Persol. bk.rev.; abstr.; bibl.; charts; illus.; stat.; cum.index: vols.1-8; circ. 950 (paid). (also avail. in microform from UMI; reprint service avail. from UMI) **Indexed:** Arts & Hum.Cit.Ind., Curr.Cont., Music Artic.Guide, Music Ind., RILM. **Document type:** academic/scholarly publication.
—Faxon; Genuine Article; UMI; UnCover.

JOURNAL OF BRITISH MUSIC THERAPY. see EDUCATION — Special Education And Rehabilitation

780.01 US ISSN 0092-0517
ML1
JOURNAL OF COUNTRY MUSIC. 1970. 3/yr. $18. Country Music Foundation, Inc., 4 Music Square E., Nashville, TN 37203. TEL 615-256-1639. FAX 615-255-2245. Ed. Paul F. Kingsbury. adv.; bk.rev.; rec.rev.; bibl. circ. 4,000. (back issues avail.) **Indexed:** Arts & Hum.Cit.Ind., Curr.Cont., M.L.A., RILM. **Document type:** consumer publication.
—Faxon; Genuine Article; UnCover.
Formerly: Country Music Foundation News Letter.
Description: Presents biographical reviews of performers and their musical development, question-and-answer interviews with performers and music business people, and overview essays on historical development of specific styles of music.

783.02 US ISSN 0197-0100
ML3195
JOURNAL OF JEWISH MUSIC AND LITURGY. (Text in English and Hebrew) 1976. a. $8. Cantorial Council of America, c/o Yeshiva University, 500 W. 185th St., New York, NY 10033. TEL 212-960-5353. Ed. Macy Nulman. bk.rev. circ. 300.
—BLDSC (5009.550000).
Description: Informs the professional and layman of aspects of Jewish music and liturgy from the Biblical period to present.

780 US ISSN 1057-0837
MT1
JOURNAL OF MUSIC TEACHER EDUCATION. 1991. 2/yr. $13. Music Educators National Conference, 1806 Robert Fulton Dr., Reston, VA 22091-4348. TEL 703-860-4000. FAX 703-860-4826. Ed. Hilary Apfelstadt. bk.rev. **Document type:** academic/scholarly publication.
Description: Serves as a clearinghouse for ideas among professors of music education.

781 US ISSN 0022-2909
ML1
JOURNAL OF MUSIC THEORY. 1957. s-a. $21 to individuals; institutions $27; students $18. Yale University, School of Music, Box 208310, New Haven, CT 06520. TEL 203-432-2985. FAX 203-432-2983. Ed. Thomas Denske. adv.; bk.rev.; bibl.; charts; illus.; index. circ. 1,700. (also avail. in microform from MIM,UMI; reprint service avail. from UMI) **Indexed:** Arts & Hum.Cit.Ind., Curr.Cont., Ind.Bk.Rev.Hum., Music Artic.Guide, Music Ind., RILM, SSCI. **Document type:** academic/scholarly publication.
—Faxon; Genuine Article; SWETS; UMI; UnCover.

780 US ISSN 0891-7639
MT10
JOURNAL OF MUSIC THEORY PEDAGOGY. 1987. a. $30. University of Oklahoma, School of Music, Parrington Oval, Norman, OK 73019. TEL 405-325-2081. Ed. Mary Wennerstrom. adv. contact: Alice M. Lanning. bk.rev. circ. 600. (back issues avail.) **Indexed:** Music Artic.Guide, Music Ind., RILM. **Document type:** academic/scholarly publication.
—Faxon; UnCover.
Description: International publication for music theorists and music theory teachers that combines scholarly research with practical applications of pedagogical issues. Devoted exclusively to matters directly related to the problems and solutions of teaching and learning music theory.
Refereed Serial

615.837 US ISSN 0022-2917
ML1 CODEN: JMUTA2
JOURNAL OF MUSIC THERAPY. 1964. q. $95 (foreign $105) (effective 1996). National Association for Music Therapy, Inc., 8455 Colesville Rd, Ste. 930, Silver Spring, MD 20910-3392. TEL 301-589-3300. FAX 301-589-5175. Ed. Jayne Standley. bk.rev.; charts; illus.; index. circ. 6,000. (also avail. in microform from UMI; reprint service avail. from UMI) **Indexed:** Arts & Hum.Cit.Ind., Curr.Cont., Educ.Ind., Except.Child Educ.Abstr., Hosp.Lit.Ind., Music Artic.Guide, Music Ind., Psychol.Abstr. (1964-), RILM. **Document type:** academic/scholarly publication.
—BLDSC (5021.160000); Faxon; UMI; UnCover.
Description: Reports research in the area of music therapy and the use of music in treatment and rehabilitation settings.
Refereed Serial

780.7 US ISSN 0141-1896
ML5
JOURNAL OF MUSICOLOGICAL RESEARCH. 1974. 4/yr. (in 1 vol., 4 nos./vol.) 97 ECU (effective 1996). Gordon and Breach Science Publishers, c/o International Publishers Distributor, 820 Town Center Dr., Langhorne, PA 19047. TEL 215-750-2642. FAX 215-750-6343. (Subscr. to: International Publishers Distributor, P.O. Box 90, Reading, Berkshire RG1 8JL, England. TEL 44-173-456-8316) Ed. Ralph P. Locke. adv.; bk.rev.; illus. (also avail. in microform) **Indexed:** Arts & Hum.Cit.Ind., Br.Hum.Ind., Curr.Cont., Ind.Bk.Rev.Hum., Music Artic.Guide, Phil.Ind., RILM. **Document type:** academic/scholarly publication.
—BLDSC (5021.163000); Faxon; SWETS; UnCover. CCC.
Formerly: Music and Man (ISSN 0306-2082)
Description: Focuses on study and teaching.
Refereed Serial

MUSIC

780.01 US ISSN 0277-9269
ML1
JOURNAL OF MUSICOLOGY; a quarterly review of music history, criticism, analysis, and performance practice. 1982. q. $70 (foreign $75) (effective 1996). University of California Press, Journals Division, 2120 Berkeley Way, Berkeley, CA 94720. TEL 510-643-7154. FAX 510-642-9917. Ed. Marian C. Green. adv.; bk.rev. circ. 1,400. (also avail. in microform from UMI; back issues avail.) **Indexed:** Arts & Hum.Cit.Ind., Curr.Cont., Hum.Ind., Music Artic.Guide, Music Ind., RILM. **Document type:** academic/scholarly publication.
—BLDSC (5021.163700); Faxon; Genuine Article; SWETS; UMI; UnCover. **CCC.**
Description: Examines music history, criticism, analysis, and performance practice.
Refereed Serial

JOURNAL OF NEW MUSIC RESEARCH. see COMPUTERS — Computer Music

780.7 US ISSN 0022-4294
ML1
JOURNAL OF RESEARCH IN MUSIC EDUCATION. 1953. q. $25. (Society for Research in Music Education) Music Educators National Conference, 1806 Robert Fulton Dr., Reston, VA 22091-4348. TEL 703-860-4000. FAX 703-860-4826. Ed. Harry E. Price. circ. 3,300. (also avail. in microform from UMI; reprint service avail. from UMI,KTO) **Indexed:** Arts & Hum.Cit.Ind., C.I.J.E., Cont.Pg.Educ., Curr.Cont., Educ.Ind., Music Artic.Guide, Music Ind., Psychol.Abstr., RILM, SSCI.
—BLDSC (5052.020000); Faxon; SWETS; UMI.
Description: Covers research on music education, its history and possible future directions.
Refereed Serial

784 US
JOURNAL OF RESEARCH IN SINGING AND APPLIED VOCAL PEDAGOGY. 1977. s-a. $25 (foreign $30) (effective 1995-96). International Association for Research in Singing, Texas Christian University, Department of Music, Box 32887, Ft. Worth, TX 76129-0001. TEL 817-921-7602. FAX 817-92107333. Ed. Vincent Russo. adv. contact: Vincent Russo. bk.rev. circ. 500. **Indexed:** Music Artic.Guide, Music Ind., RILM. **Document type:** academic/scholarly publication.
—UnCover.
Formerly: Journal of Research in Singing (ISSN 0272-6440)
Description: Intends to increase the knowledge of the singing voice and the practical application of that knowledge.

780 US ISSN 0364-2216
ML1
JOURNAL OF THE GRADUATE MUSIC STUDENTS AT THE OHIO STATE UNIVERSITY. 1969. irreg., no.6, 1977. Ohio State University, School of Music, 1899 N. College Rd., Columbus, OH 43210. TEL 614-422-6571.

780 US
JUBILATION. q. membership. Paul Anka Admiration Society, 2136 Lincoln Ave., Apt. J, Alameda, CA 94501. TEL 415-769-9562.
Description: News and information on the life and performing career of singer and songwriter Paul Anka.

780 IT ISSN 0022-5711
JUCUNDA LAUDATIO. 1963. q. L.10000. Padri Benedettini, Isola di Giorgio Maggiore, 30124 Venice, Italy. charts.

780.7 US ISSN 1064-1580
MT4.N3
JUILLIARD JOURNAL; monthly newspaper. 1962. 8/yr. $15 (free to qualified personnel). Juilliard School, Lincoln Center, New York, NY 10023. TEL 212-799-5000. FAX 212-724-0263. Ed. Jane Rulansky. adv. contact: Nancy Szakacs. bk.rev.; illus. circ. 14,500. (also avail. in microform from UMI; reprint service avail. from UMI) **Indexed:** Music Artic.Guide. **Document type:** newspaper.
—UMI.
Formerly (until 1985): Juilliard News Bulletin (ISSN 0022-6173)

780 US ISSN 1062-4104
JUILLIARD PERFORMANCE GUIDES. 1983. irreg., no.4, 1994. Pendragon Press, 41 Ferry St., Stuyvesant, NY 12173-9720. TEL 518-828-3008. FAX 518-828-2368. **Document type:** monographic series.

781.57 UK ISSN 1351-5551
JUKE BLUES. 1985. q. £13.50 (foreign £16). P.O. Box 148, London W9 1DY, England.
FAX 0171-286-2993. (In U.S.: c/o Dick Shurman, 3S 321 Winfield Rd., Warrenville, IL 60555) Ed. Cilla Huggins. adv.; B&W page £200($320), color page £350($575); trim 278 x 190. bk.rev. circ. 5,000. **Document type:** consumer publication.
Description: Contains articles, news and reviews about Black American blues music.

JUKEBOX COLLECTOR. see HOBBIES

780 FR ISSN 0296-6395
JUKEBOX MAGAZINE. 1984. m. 370 F. (foreign 470 F.); newsstand price: 35 F. Jacques Leblanc Editions S.A.R.L., 32 bd. de Vaugirard, 75015 Paris, France. TEL 43-35-52-52. FAX 43-21-97-00. Ed. Jacques Leblanc; Pub. Jacques Leblanc. adv.: page 14200 F.; adv. contact: Annie Vincent. film rev.; music rev.; video rev. circ. 26,500. (back issues avail.) **Document type:** consumer publication.
Description: Covers popular music and record collecting.

780 US ISSN 0022-6629
ML1
JUNIOR KEYNOTES. 1927. 4/yr. $4. National Federation of Music Clubs, 1336 N. Delaware St., Indianapolis, IN 46202. TEL 317-638-4003. FAX 317-638-0503. Ed. Mary Alice Cox. adv.; bk.rev.; illus. circ. 6,000.
Description: Contains organization news.

JUNKANOO. see THEATER

780.7 US ISSN 0022-8702
ML1
KANSAS MUSIC REVIEW. 1938. 4/yr. $3 to non-members. Kansas Music Educators Association, Wichita State University, School of Music, Wichita, KS 67260-0053. TEL 316-689-3103. FAX 316-689-3951. Ed. James Hardy. adv.; bk.rev.; music rev.; illus. circ. 3,000. **Indexed:** Music Artic.Guide, Music Ind. **Document type:** academic/scholarly publication, trade publication.
—UnCover.
Description: Presents study and teaching methods.

780 RU
KAZANSKII GOSUDARSTVENNYI PEDAGOGICHESKII INSTITUT. VOPROSY ISTORII, TEORII MUZYKI I MUZYKAL'NOGO VOSPITANIYA. SBORNIK. 1970. irreg. price varies. Kazanskii Gosudarstvennyi Pedagogicheskii Institut, Ul. Mezjlauk, 1, 420021 Kazan, Russia. Ed.Bd. circ. 600.
Description: Contains the research of theoretical and historical materials about professional training of the school musical teachers.

786 US ISSN 0735-8660
ML552
KERAULOPHON. 1968. q. $5. Organ Historical Society, Greater New York City Chapter, Box 194, Pepperell, MA 01463. TEL 508-433-5784. E-mail: ogasapiaj@woods.uml.edu. (Subscr. to: Box 104, Harrisville, NH 03450) Ed. John Ogasapian. adv.; bk.rev.; bibl. circ. 100. (looseleaf format; back issues avail.) **Indexed:** RILM. **Document type:** newsletter.
Description: Articles, reviews, research queries, notices pertaining to the history of organs and organ building in New York City.

781.64 UK ISSN 0262-6624
KERRANG!. w. £60 (foreign £88) (effective 1995-1996). E M A P - Metro, Mappin House, 4 Winsley St., London W1N 7AR, England. TEL 0171-436-1515. FAX 0171-312-8191. (Subscr. to: Tower Publishing Services Ltd., Tower House, Sovereign Park, Lathkill St., Market Harborough, Leics. LE16 9EF, England. TEL 01858-468811. FAX 01858-432164) circ. 67,649. **Document type:** consumer publication.
Description: Covers heavy metal music for young men.

786 AT ISSN 0310-8260
KEY VIVE. 1973. q. Aus.$3.50. Australian Society for Keyboard Music, 9 Glenroy Ave., Middle Cove, N.S.W. 2068, Australia. Ed.Bd. adv.; bk.rev.; charts; illus. circ. 700.

786 US ISSN 0730-0158
ML1
KEYBOARD; for all keyboard players. 1975. m. $29.95 (foreign $44.95). Miller Freeman Inc. (San Mateo) (Subsidiary of: United Newspapers Group), 411 Borel Ave., Ste. 100, San Mateo, CA 94402. TEL 415-359-9500. FAX 415-358-9527. (Subscr. to: Box 58528, Boulder, CO 80322-8528) Ed. Dominic Milano; Pub. Pat Cameron. adv. contact: Vicki Hartung. bk.rev.; charts; illus.; cum.index. circ. 69,000. (also avail. in microform from UMI; reprint service avail. from UMI) **Indexed:** Music Artic.Guide, Music Ind., RILM.
—BLDSC (5091.840500); Faxon; SWETS; UMI. **CCC.**
Formerly (until 1981): Contemporary Keyboard (ISSN 0361-5820)
Description: For keyboard musicians of all styles and levels of ability. Teaches how to put more music in your technology.

786 US ISSN 0273-9526
KEYBOARD CLASSICS; the magazine you can play. 1981. bi-m. $16.97. Keyboard Classics, Inc., 223 Katonah Ave., Katonah, NY 10536. TEL 914-232-8108. FAX 914-232-1205. (Subscr. to: Box 58529, Boulder, CO 80322. Tel.: 800-759-3036) Ed. Stuart Isacoff. adv.; bk.rev.; illus. circ. 50,000. **Indexed:** Music Artic.Guide, Music Ind.

786 US
KEYBOARD COMPANION; a practical magazine on early-level piano study. 1990. q. $17 in the U.S.; Canada $25; elsewhere $31 (effective 1996). Keyboard Companion, Box 24-C-54, Los Angeles, CA 90024. TEL 310-474-8966. FAX 310-475-0092. E-mail: kcompanion@aol.com. Ed. Richard Chronister. adv. contact: Patrick Meader. illus. circ. 15,000. **Document type:** consumer publication.

780 UK ISSN 0962-2675
KEYBOARD REVIEW. 1985. m. £17.50 (foreign £20). Music Maker Publications Ltd., Alexander House, Forehill, Ely, Cambs CB7 4AF, England. TEL 0353-665577. FAX 0353-662489. (U.S. addr.: Music Maker Publications, Inc., 22024 Lassen St., Ste. 118, Chatsworth, CA 91311. TEL 818-407-07444) Ed. Malcolm Harrison. adv.; bk.rev. circ. 18,000.
Formerly (until 1991): Home Keyboard Review (ISSN 0957-6371)

786.6 US
KEYBOARD TEACHER. 1964. bi-m. (except Jul. and Aug.). membership. Keyboard Teachers Association International, Inc., 361 Pin Oak Ln., Westbury, NY 11590-1941. Ed. Albert DeVito. circ. 2,000. **Document type:** newsletter.
Former titles: Organ Teacher; N A O T Notes (ISSN 0027-5948)

780 GW ISSN 0178-4641
KEYBOARDS. m. DM.78 (foreign DM.102). Musik Media Verlag GmbH, Aindlingerstr. 17-19, 86167 Augsburg, Germany. TEL 0821-79049. FAX 0821-7904129. Ed. Reinhard Schmitz. adv. contact: Peter Waschke. circ. 34,464. **Document type:** consumer publication.

786 621.389 FR ISSN 0981-2008
KEYBOARDS MAGAZINE. 1987. m. 270 F. (foreign 370 F.); newsstand price: 29 F. Master Press International, 10 rue de la Paix, 92100 Boulogne, France. TEL 46-03-15-51. FAX 46-03-89-69. Ed. Dany Giorgetti. adv.: page 21000 F.; adv. contact: Alain Versini. bk.rev.; s-a. index. circ. 50,000. **Document type:** consumer publication.
Description: Covers musical and home studio equipment, artists and professionals in the industry.

780 US ISSN 0199-6657
KICKS. 1979. a. Norton Records, Box 646, Cooper Station, New York, NY 10003. TEL 718-789-4438. FAX 718-398-9215. Eds. Billy Miller, Miriam Linna. adv.; bk.rev.; film rev.; rec.rev. circ. 10,000. **Document type:** consumer publication.
Description: Covers rock & roll and popular culture.

MUSIC   4857

783 GW ISSN 0023-1800
ML5
DER KIRCHENCHOR. 1940. q. DM.15. (Verband Evangelischer Kirchenchoere Deutschlands) Baerenreiter Verlag, Heinrich-Schuetz-Allee 35, 34131 Kassel, Germany. TEL 0561-3105-0. FAX 0561-3105240. (Subscr. in US to: Educational Music Service, 13 Elkay Dr., Chester, NY 10918. TEL 914-469-5790. FAX 914-469-5817) Ed. Otto Brodde. adv.; bk.rev.; index. circ. 6,500. Indexed: Music Ind. Document type: academic/scholarly publication.
—CCC.

783 GW ISSN 0174-2116
KIRCHENMUSIKALISCHE MITTEILUNGEN. 1967. q. Amt fuer Kirchenmusik, St. Meinradweg 6, 72108 Rottenburg, Germany. TEL 07472-169430. circ. 3,500.

780 200 GW ISSN 0939-4761
ML5
KIRCHENMUSIKALISCHE NACHRICHTEN. 1950. q. DM.12. Evangelische Kirche in Hessen und Nassau in Frankfurt, Amt fuer Kirchenmusik, Miquelallee 7, 60487 Frankfurt a.M., Germany. TEL 069-2477190. bk.rev. circ. 1,800. Document type: newsletter.

780 282 GW ISSN 0075-6199
KIRCHENMUSIKALISCHES JAHRBUCH. 1876. a. price varies. Allgemeiner Caecilien-Verband, Andreasstr. 9, 93059 Regensburg, Germany. TEL 0941-84339. Ed. Prof. Guenther Massenkeil. bk.rev. Indexed: Music Ind., RILM. Document type: bulletin.

783 GW ISSN 0023-1819
DER KIRCHENMUSIKER. 1950. bi-m. DM.30. (Verband Evangelischer Kirchenmusiker Deutschlands) Verlag Merseburger Berlin GmbH, Postfach 103880, 34038 Kassel, Germany. Ed. Klaus-Juergen Gundlach. adv.; bk.rev.; rec.rev.; illus.; index. circ. 7,600. Indexed: RILM. Document type: bulletin.
—CCC.

780 NE ISSN 0929-161X
KLANK & SHOW. m. fl.29.50. Koninklijke Nederlandse Federatie van Muziekverenigingen, Swerts de Landasstraat 83, 6814 DC Arnhem, Netherlands. TEL 31-85-451146. FAX 31-85-458698. (Co-sponsor: Algemene Nederlandse Unie van Muziekverenigingen) Ed. A.J. Gossink. adv.; bk.rev.; rec.rev.; illus.
Formed by the 1993 merger of: Muziek en Show (ISSN 0929-1601); Formerly (1980-1987): Muziek (ISSN 0929-1598) & A N U M Klanken (ISSN 0929-158X); Which supersedes: Musica (ISSN 0027-450X)
Description: Publishes news and information relating to music, performance and related matters.

780 NE ISSN 0030-3836
KLANK EN WEERKLANK. 1970. irreg. (7-8/yr.). fl.3. Stichting Vrienden van het Brabants Orkest - Foundation Friends of the Brabant Orchestra, Postbus 230, 5600 AE Eindhoven, Netherlands. TEL 31-40-655699. FAX 31-40-463459. Ed.Bd. adv.; bk.rev.; illus. circ. 4,500.
Supersedes: Opmaat.

789.5 NE ISSN 0023-2181
KLOK EN KLEPEL. 1959. s-a. fl.20. Nederlandse Klokkenspel-Vereniging, Wielengahof 21, 2625 LJ Delft, Netherlands. TEL 31-15-563034. Ed. Loek Boogert. adv.; bk.rev.; illus. circ. 500. Indexed: Music Ind. Document type: bulletin.
Description: Covers carillons, carillon music and the history of bells.

780 SZ
KNABENMUSIK DER STADT ZUERICH. MITTEILUNGSBLATT. 6/yr. Postfach 6817, CH-8023 Zurich, Switzerland. TEL 01-9802903. circ. 1,200.

780 US
KODALY ENVOY. 1975. q. $30 to libraries. Organization of American Kodaly Educators, 1457 S. 23rd St., Fargo, ND 58103-3708. TEL 701-235-0366. FAX 701-241-7051. Ed. Alan Strong. adv.; bk.rev.; illus.; index; circ. 1,600 (paid). Indexed: Music Ind. Document type: trade publication.
Refereed Serial

780.7 CN ISSN 1180-1344
KODALY SOCIETY OF CANADA. ALLA BREVE. (Text in English and French) 1976. 2/yr. Can.$10 to individuals; institutions Can.$15. Kodaly Society of Canada, 19 Grey Owl, Elmira, ON N3B 1S4, Canada. Ed. Jeanette Panagapka; Pub. Phil Baldwin. adv. contact: Heather Morris. bk.rev. circ. 550. (back issues avail.) Document type: academic/scholarly publication.
Former titles: Kodaly Society of Canada. Notes; Kodaly Institute of Canada. Notes (ISSN 0700-3269)

780 GW
KOELN KONTAKTER; ein Handbuch durch die Musikszene Koeln. 1991. biennial. DM.10. E B - Metronom Verlag, Hospeltstr. 66, 50825 Cologne, Germany. TEL 0221-543506. FAX 0221-542620. Ed. Gisela Lobisch. circ. 5,000. Document type: bulletin.

780 GW
KOELNER BEITRAEGE ZUR MUSIKFORSCHUNG. irreg., vol.181, 1993. price varies. Gustav Bosse Verlag, Heinrich-Schuetz-Allee 35, 34131 Kassel, Germany. TEL 0561-31050. Ed. Berthold Kloss. Document type: monographic series.

780 SW ISSN 1400-2450
KOERLIVET. 1928. q. SEK 80 (effective 1994). Sveriges Koerfoerbund, P.O. Box 38014, S-100 64 Stockholm, Sweden. Ed. Inger Laurell. adv.; bk.rev.; bibl.; charts; illus. circ. 15,000.
Formerly (until 1994): Musiklivet - Vaar Saang (ISSN 0027-4836).

780.7 GW
KONGRESSBERICHT BUNDESSCHULMUSIKWOCHE. 1955. biennial. price varies. (Verband Deutscher Schulmusiker) Schott Musik International GmbH, Weihergarten 5, 55116 Mainz, Germany. TEL 06131-246-0. FAX 06131-246211. Ed. Dieter Zimmerschied. circ. 800. (back issues avail.) Document type: monographic series.
Formerly: Vortraege der Bundesschulmusikwoche (ISSN 0172-9624)

780.6 SW ISSN 0023-3560
KONSERTNYTT. 1965. 4/yr. free. Stockholms Konserthusstiftelse - Stockholm Concert Hall Foundation, P.O. Box 7083, S-103 87 Stockholm, Sweden. TEL 46-8-786-02-00. FAX 46-8-791-73-30. Ed. Lotta Bjelkeborn. adv. contact: Paola Costa. circ. 15,000. (also avail. in audio cassette)

780 PL
KONTRAPUNKTY. 1986. irreg. price varies. Polskie Wydawnictwo Muzyczne, Al. Krasinskiego 11a, 31-111 Krakow, Poland. TEL 48-12-227044. FAX 48-12-220174.

780 GW ISSN 0721-5398
KONZERT ALMANACH; Termine, Programme, Sitzplaene und Preise klassischer Konzerte. 1981. a. DM.39.80. Heel-Verlag GmbH, Hauptstr. 354, 53639 Koenigswinter, Germany. FAX 02223-23028. adv. circ. 6,000. Document type: directory.

781.7 SW ISSN 0349-7208
KOUNTRY KORRAL; Scandinavia's country music magazine. 1968. bi-m. SEK 110($8) to members. Lillies Ohlsson, Ed. & Pub., Box 8014, S-720 08 Vaesteraas, Sweden. adv.; bk.rev.; bibl.; charts; illus. circ. 2,500.
Former titles (until vol.3, 1981): Nya Kountry Korral Magazine; (until vol.3, 1980): Kountry Korral Magazine; (until 1980): Kountry Korral (ISSN 0023-429X)

KULTUR NEWS. see *ART*

780 JA ISSN 1341-5050
KUNITACHI ONGAKU DAIGAKU KENKYU KIYO/KUNITACHI COLLEGE OF MUSIC. MEMOIRS. (Text in English, French, German, Italian, Japanese) 1966. a. Kunitachi Ongaku Daigaku - Kunitachi College of Music, 5-1 Kashiwa-cho 5-chome, Tachikawa-shi, Tokyo 190, Japan. Ed. H Okamura. illus. circ. 800. Document type: newsletter.

780.6 US ISSN 0899-6407
KURT WEILL NEWSLETTER. 1983. 2/yr. free. Kurt Weill Foundation for Music, 7 E. 20th St., New York, NY 10003-1106. TEL 212-505-5240. FAX 212-353-9663. Ed. David Farneth. bk.rev. circ. 6,000. Document type: newsletter.
—Faxon; UnCover.
Description: Devoted to the life and works of Kurt Weill and Lotte Lenya. Includes feature articles, news about current productions and publications, bibliographies, and critical reviews of performances, books and recordings.

780.7 JA ISSN 0388-7502
KYOIKU ONGAKU, CHUGAKU KOKO-BAN/EDUCATIONAL MUSIC, JUNIOR HIGH AND HIGH SCHOOL. (Text in Japanese) m. 880 Yen. Ongaku No Tomo Sha Corp., Kagurazaka 6-30, Shinjuku-ku, Tokyo 162, Japan. TEL 03-3235-2111. FAX 03-3235-5731. adv.; B&W page 120000 Yen, color page 300000 Yen; trim 257 x 182. circ. 35,000.
Formerly: Educational Music, Secondary School.
Description: Presents study and teaching methods.

780.7 JA ISSN 0388-7480
KYOIKU ONGAKU, SHOGAKU-BAN/EDUCATIONAL MUSIC, ELEMENTARY SCHOOL. (Text in Japanese) 1946. m. 880 Yen. Ongaku No Tomo Sha Corp., Kagurazaka 6-30, Shinjuku-ku, Tokyo 162, Japan. TEL 03-3235-2111. FAX 03-3235-5731. adv.; B&W page 120000 Yen, color page 300000 Yen; trim 257 x 182. circ. 35,000.
Description: Presents study and teaching methods.

783 SW ISSN 0281-286X
ML5
KYRKOMUSIKERNAS TIDNING. Short title: K M T. 1935-1982; resumed 1984. 17/yr. SEK 225 (typically set in Jan.). Kyrkomusikernas Riksfoerbund (KMR), Sveriges Laerarfoerbund, P.O. Box 12229, S-102 26 Stockholm, Sweden. FAX 46-8-619-0088. Ed. Stellan Sagvik. adv.; bk.rev.; illus. circ. 4,100.
Former titles (until 1984): Svensk Kyrkomusik. Uppl. A - B. och Uppl.B; (until 1970): K M T - K S F; Formed by the 1967 merger of Kyrkosaangsfoerbundet; (until 1967): Kyrkomusikernas Tidning (ISSN 0347-416X)

LADYSLIPPER CATALOG AND RESOURCE GUIDE OF RECORDS, TAPES, COMPACT DISCS AND VIDEOS BY WOMEN. see *WOMEN'S INTERESTS*

780.7 GW ISSN 0047-3979
LANDESVERBAND DER TONKUENSTLER UND MUSIKLEHRER. MITTEILUNGSBLATT. vol.26, 1976. q. membership. Landesverband der Tonkuenstler und Musiklehrer, Hamburg Kulturell, Husumer Str. 31, 20249 Hamburg, Germany. Ed. Walter Gehlert. adv.; bk.rev.; bibl. Document type: bulletin.
Description: Covers the study and teaching of music.

780 UK
LASERLOG. w. £240. Trade Service Information Ltd., Cherryholt Rd., Stamford, Lincs. PE9 2HT, England. TEL 01780-64331. FAX 01780-482067. circ. 1,000 (paid). Document type: directory.

781.7 US ISSN 0163-0350
ML199
LATIN AMERICAN MUSIC REVIEW/REVISTA DE MUSICA LATINO AMERICANA. 1980. s-a. $20 to individuals; institutions $35. University of Texas Press, Box 7819, Austin, TX 78713. TEL 512-471-4531. FAX 512-320-0668. TELEX 776453 UTEXPRES AUS. E-mail: leah@utpress.ppb.utexas.edu. Ed. Gerard H. Behague. adv. contact: Leah Dixon. bk.rev.; index. circ. 450. (also avail. in microform from UMI; reprint service avail. from UMI) Indexed: Arts & Hum.Cit.Ind., Chic.Per.Ind., Curr.Cont., Hisp.Amer.Per.Ind. (1980), M.L.A., Music Ind., RILM, RILM. Document type: academic/scholarly publication.
—Faxon; Genuine Article; SWETS; UMI; UnCover. CCC.
Description: Examines all aspects of the written and oral musical traditions of Latin America.

780 US
LATIN BEAT MAGAZINE; salsa, afro-antillana, latin jazz and more ... 1991. m. (11/yr.). $20 (Canada $35; elsewhere $50). 15900 Crenshaw Blvd., Ste. 1-223, Gardena, CA 90249. TEL 310-516-6767. FAX 310-532-6784. adv.

MUSIC

781.7 JA ISSN 0288-8661
LATINA. (Text in Japanese) 1952. m. 6360 Yen. Musica Iberoamericana Co., 1-13-6 Ebisu, Shibuya-ku, Tokyo, Japan. FAX 03-443-7123. Ed. Kenji Honda. adv.; illus. circ. 30,000.
Formerly: Musica Iberoamericana (ISSN 0027-4534)

781.7 US
LATVJU MUZIKA. (Text in Latvian) 1968. a. $8. Latvian Choir Association in the United States, Inc., 7886 Anita Dr., Philadelphia, PA 19111. (Subscr. to: 3322 St. Antoine Ave., Kalamazoo, MI 49007) Ed. Roberts Zuika. bk.rev. circ. 1,200. (back issues avail.)

787 US ISSN 1056-5329
ML420.L277
LEAD BELLY LETTER; to appreciate and celebrate Lead Belly music. 1990. 4/yr. $15 in U.S.; Canada $17.50; elsewhere $22. Lead Belly Society, Box 6679, Ithaca, NY 14851. TEL 607-273-6615. FAX 607-844-4810. Ed. Sean Killeen. bk.rev. circ. 3,000. **Document type:** academic/scholarly publication, newsletter.
Description: Devoted to furthering appreciation of Lead Belly music. Contains critical articles and little known photographs.
Refereed Serial

780 UK ISSN 0960-6297
ML5
LEADING NOTES; journal of the National Early Music Association. 1984. s-a. £5 (free to members). National Early Music Association, 8 Covent Garden, Cambridge CB1 2HR, England. TEL 01223-315681. Ed. Ann Lewis. adv.; bk.rev. circ. 1,000. **Document type:** academic/scholarly publication.
—BLDSC (5162.875600).
Formerly (until 1991): N E M A Journal (ISSN 0951-6573)

780 US
LEBLANC BELL. 1977. q. free. G. Leblanc Corporation, 7001 30th Ave., Kenosha, WI 53141-1415. TEL 414-658-1644. FAX 414-658-2824. Ed. Leon Pascucci; Pub. Vito Pascucci. bk.rev.; circ. 35,000 (controlled). (back issues avail.)
Description: Contains feature stories, opinion columns, and new product information of interest to music educators and retailers.

780.42 US ISSN 0892-1830
LEFSETZ LETTER; first in music analysis. 1986. bi-w. $110. 2128 Oak St., Ste. B, Santa Monica, CA 90405. TEL 310-450-3798. Ed. Robert Scott Lefsetz. **Document type:** newsletter.

780 GW
▼**LEIPZIGER BEITRAEGE ZUR BACH-FORSCHUNG.** 1995. irreg. (Bach-Archiv Leipzig) Georg Olms Verlag, Hagentorwall 7, 31134 Hildesheim, Germany. TEL 05121-1501-0. FAX 05121-150150. Ed. H.-J. Schulze. **Document type:** monographic series.

LEISURE INDUSTRY REPORT. see *LEISURE AND RECREATION*

780 AT
LEMON. irreg., no.13, 1992. John & Louise Dickinson, Eds. & Pubs., P.O. Box 651, Glebe, N.S.W.

780 910.03 US ISSN 1080-0646
▼**LENOX AVENUE: A JOURNAL OF INTERARTISTIC INQUIRY.** 1995. a. $35 (foreign $40). Center for Black Music Research, Columbia College, 600 S. Michigan Ave., Chicago, IL 60605. TEL 312-663-1600. FAX 312-663-9019. E-mail: cbmr@mail.colum.edu. Ed. Samuel A. Floyd Jr. circ. 300.
Description: Research relating to ways of inquiring into the black expressive arts, both singly and as multimode presentations.
Refereed Serial

780 US ISSN 0961-1215
ML197 CODEN: LMJOEQ
LEONARDO MUSIC JOURNAL. (Includes compact disc of recorded music) 1991. a. $30 (foreign $35). (International Society for the Arts, Sciences and Technology) M I T Press, 55 Hayward St., Cambridge, MA 02142. TEL 617-253-2889. FAX 617-258-6779. E-mail: journals-orders@mit.edu. Ed. Roger L. Malina.
Indexed: Music Artic.Guide.
—BLDSC (5182.620000); Genuine Article; SWETS; UnCover. **CCC.**
Description: Addresses the role of science and technology in contemporary music and multimedia art forms using sound.
Refereed Serial

780.7 RU
LESSONS OF MASTERSHIP. a. 1.70 Rub. Izdatel'stvo Muzyka, Ul. Neglinnaya 14, Moscow 103031, Russia. TEL 924-81-63. FAX 921-83-53.

780.42 US ISSN 1056-4179
ML417.E9
LETTER FROM EVANS. 1989. q. $20. C S C S Publications, 2712 Cady Way, Winter Park, FL 32792-4856. TEL 407-678-7113. FAX 407-678-7049. Ed. Win Hinkle. adv.; bk.rev. circ. 600.

780 FR ISSN 0766-916X
LETTRE DU MUSICIEN. 1984. 15/yr. 260 F. (foreign 310 F.) B.P. 64, 75722 Paris Cedex 15, France. TEL 47-34-06-91. FAX 42-73-18-47. Ed. Michele Worms. adv. circ. 5,000. **Document type:** newsletter.

LIAISON; la revue des arts en Ontario francais. see *ART*

780.6 GW ISSN 0460-0932
DAS LIEBHABERORCHESTE. 1956. 2/yr. DM.10. Bund Deutscher Liebhaberorchester e.V., Gaussstr. 68, 27580 Bremerhaven, Germany. TEL 0471-86157. Ed. Hans Linder. adv.: page DM.600; trim 176 x 122. bk.rev.; bibl.; music rev.; circ. 4,700. (back issues avail.) **Document type:** newsletter.

784 GW ISSN 0024-290X
ML5
LIED UND CHOR; Zeitschrift fuer das gesamte Chorwesen. 1908. m. DM.30.50. (Deutscher Saengerbund e.V.) Verlags- und Vertriebs-GmbH fuer Chorbedarf, Bernhardstr. 166, 50968 Cologne, Germany. TEL 0221-371033. Ed. Wolfgang Steffen. adv.; bk.rev.; illus. circ. 21,000. **Document type:** newsletter.

780 US ISSN 1068-8404
LIGHTNING STRIKES. 1977. 2/yr. $10 (effective 1994-1996). (Lou Christie International Fan Club) Universal Mind Press, c/o Harry Young, Ed., Box 748, Chicago, IL 60690-0748. TEL 312-241-5412. adv.; bk.rev. circ. 650. (back issues avail.)
Description: Covers all aspects of the career and music of Lou Christie.

781.7 ZR
LIKEMBE. bi-m. K.350. Maison d'Editions "Jeunes pour Jeunes", B.P. 9624, Kinshasa 1, Zaire. Ed. Mulongo Mulunda Mukena. illus.

780 US
THE LIL'RHINO GAZETTE. 1986. q. $18. Box 14139, Arlington, TX 76094-1139. TEL 817-794-0772. Ed. K. Kelly R. North. adv.; bk.rev.; music rev. circ. 1,000.
Description: Contains interviews with musicians and reviews of alternative and underground music, videos, books, comics and fanzines.

780 US
LINGNAN YINYUE/LINGNAN MUSIC. (Text in Chinese) bi-m. $14. China Books & Periodicals, Inc., 2929 24th St., San Francisco, CA 94110. TEL 415-282-2994. FAX 415-282-0994.

780 BN ISSN 0024-4244
LIRA. 1974. m. 3 din. per no. Opstinska Konferencija Muzicke Omladine, AVNOJ-a 5, Bihac, Bosnia Hercegovina. Ed. Safet Curtovic.

781.57 DK ISSN 0109-1212
LISTE OVER RYTMISKE SPILLESTEDER I DANMARK. 1982. a. price varies. Danske Jazzcenter, Borupvej 66, 4683 Roennede, Denmark. Ed. Arnvid Meyer. circ. 2,500.
Formerly: Liste over Danske Jazzklubber og Huse.

780.9481 NO ISSN 0804-3086
ML5
LISTEN TO NORWAY. (Text in English) 1993. 3/yr. free. Norwegian Music Information Centre, Tollbugt. 28, N-0157 Oslo, Norway. TEL 47-22-42-90-90. FAX 47-22-42-90-91. Ed. Mona Levin.
Incorporates (1981-1993): Norwegian Music Information Center. Bulletin (ISSN 0801-1087)

780.92 SW ISSN 0263-0249
LISZT SAECULUM. (Text in English, German) 1971. s-a. SEK 300 membership. International Liszt Centre, Synaalsvaegen 5, S-161 49 Bromma, Sweden. TEL 46-8-25-17-16. FAX 46-8-25-17-36. Ed. Lennart Rabes. adv.; bk.rev. circ. 400. **Document type:** academic/scholarly publication.
Formerly (until vol.23, 1978): I.L.C. Quarterly.
Description: Presents original material and research articles, as well as news of the organization and other Liszt associations.
Refereed Serial

780 UK ISSN 0141-0792
LISZT SOCIETY. JOURNAL. (Supplement avail.) 1976. a. £15 (foreign £18) membership. Liszt Society Ltd., 135 Stevenage Road, Fulham, London SW6 6PB, England. TEL 0171-381-9751. FAX 0171-381-2406. Ed. Michael Short. bk.rev.; bibl. circ. 300. **Document type:** academic/scholarly publication.
Formerly: Liszt Society, London. Newsletter (ISSN 0459-5084)
Description: Contains original articles and reviews.

LITERARNO - MUZEJNY LETOPIS. see *LITERATURE*

780 DK
LITTLE RICHARD NEWS. 1986. irreg. (2-3/yr.). DKK 100. Mjoelner Edition, Oeregaardsvaengevej 15, DK-4720 Praestoe, Denmark. FAX 53-79-30-28. Ed. John Garodkin. adv.; bk.rev. circ. 400.

LITURGY 90. see *RELIGIONS AND THEOLOGY — Roman Catholic*

787 IT
LIUTERIA MUSICA CULTURA. 3/yr. L.25000 (foreign L.30000). (Associazione Liuteria Italiana) Cooperativa Editoriale Liutaria, Via Radaelli 4, 26100 Cremona, Italy. TEL 0372-20357. Ed. Gianpaolo Gregori.
Description: Covers the music of the lute.

780.65 647.968 UK
LIVE!. 1989. 10/yr. £25 (foreign £75). Nexus Media Ltd., Warwick House, Azalea Dr., Swanley, Kent BR8 8HY. TEL 01322-660070. FAX 01322-667633. Ed. Mike Lethby. adv.: page £1000; adv. contact: Jay Green. circ. 14,500 (paid). (back issues avial.) **Document type:** trade publication.
Formerly: Live! Pro Light and Sound.
Description: Trade journal for live performance industry.

780 GW
LIVE IN CONCERT. 1984. 11/yr. DM.40. Spezial Zeitschriftenverlagsgesellschaft mbH, Schellingstr. 39-43, 80797 Munich, Germany. TEL 089-23726-0. FAX 089-23726125. circ. 328,475. **Document type:** consumer publication.
Formerly: Concert.

780 SZ
LIVE MUSIC MONITOR.* m. Show How AG, Alte Forchstr. 10, CH-8126 Zumikon, Switzerland. Ed. Benny Furth. circ. 20,000.

781.64 US ISSN 1059-4809
LIVE WIRE. 1991. bi-m. newsstand price: $2.95. J.Q. Adams Productions (New York), 28 W. 25th St., New York, NY 10010. TEL 212-647-0222. FAX 212-647-0236. adv. **Document type:** consumer publication.

782 UK ISSN 0966-9000
LIVERPOOL CLASSICAL PAPERS. 1988. irreg., no.3, 1993. Liverpool Classical Monthly, University of Liverpool, Box 147, Liverpool L69 3BX, England. Ed. H.D. Jocelyn. **Document type:** monographic series.
—BLDSC (5281.130600).

MUSIC 4859

781.573   US   ISSN 0024-5232
ML1
LIVING BLUES; a journal of the African American blues tradition. 1970. bi-m. $18 (Canada $24; overseas $30). University of Mississippi, Center for the Study of Southern Culture, University, MS 38677-9836. TEL 601-232-5742. FAX 601-232-7842. Ed. D. Nelson. adv.; bk.rev.; rec.rev.; video rev.; illus. circ. 17,000. (also avail. in microfilm from UMI; back issues avail.). Indexed: Abstr.Folk.Stud., M.L.A., Music Ind., Pop.Mus.Per.Ind., RILM.
— Faxon; UMI; UnCover.
   Description: Features interviews with blues musicians and spotlights performers on the blues scene.

781.573   US   ISSN 1044-1026
ML12
LIVING BLUES BLUES DIRECTORY. Variant title: Blues Directory. 1989. a. $25. University of Mississippi, Center for the Study of Southern Culture, University, MS 38677-9836. TEL 601-232-5742. FAX 601-232-7842. Document type: directory.
   Description: Includes listings of blues artists and agents, festival dates, radio shows, record labels, night clugs, blues societies, and other resources pertinent to the blues.

780   UK
LONDON COLLEGE OF MUSIC MAGAZINE. 1960. s-a. £7.50. London College of Music, Polytechnic of West London, St. Mary's Rd., Ealing, London W5 5RF, England. TEL 0181-579-5000. FAX 0181-566-1353. adv.; bk.rev.; circ. controlled. (processed)
   Description: For students, staff and LCM Society members.

781.7 367   US
LORETTA LYNN FAN CLUB. 1963. q. $12. (Loretta Lynn International Fan Club) Tri-Son, Inc., Box 40328, Nashville, TN 37204-0328. TEL 615-371-9597. FAX 615-371-9597. Ed. Loudilla Johnson. circ. 2,000 (paid). Document type: bulletin.
   Description: Chronicles Loretta Lynn and her activities, concerts, recordings, and other music endeavors.

780   US
LOS ANGELES SONGWRITERS SHOWCASE MUSEPAPER. Cover title: Songwriters Musepaper. 1986. m. $29 (Canada $32; elsewhere $50). Music & Arts Foundation of America, Los Angeles, Box 93759, Hollywood, CA 90093. TEL 213-467-7823. Ed. John Braheny. adv. circ. 20,000. Document type: trade publication.

780   RM
LUCRARI DE MUZICOLOGIE. (Text in Rumanian; summaries in English, or French, or German) 1965. a. price varies. Academia de Muzica "Gheorge Dima", Str. I.C. Bratianu 25, 3400 Cluj-Napoca, Rumania. Ed. Dan Voiculescu. circ. 300. Indexed: RILM.

781.6   NE   ISSN 0024-7286
LUISTER. 1952. 12/yr. fl.79.50 (effective 1995). Wegener Tijl Tijdschriften Groep B.V., Postbus 9943, 1006 AP Amsterdam, Netherlands. TEL 31-20-5182828. FAX 31-20-5182843. Ed. Paul Korenhof. adv.; bk.rev.; rec.rev. circ. 18,518. Document type: consumer publication.
— SWETS.
   Description: Covers classical music.

780   UK   ISSN 0952-0759
ML5
THE LUTE. 1959. a. £20 (subscr. includes newsletter). Lute Society, 103 London Rd., Oldham, Lancs OL1 4BW, England. TEL 0161-624-4369. Ed. M. Spring. adv.; bk.rev. circ. 400. (back issues avail.). Indexed: RILM. Document type: academic/scholarly publication.
   Formerly (until 1982): Lute Society Journal (ISSN 0460-007X)

780   US   ISSN 0076-1524
ML1
LUTE SOCIETY OF AMERICA. JOURNAL. 1968. a. membership. Lute Society of America, c/o Beedle Hinely, Box 1328, Lexington, VA 24450. TEL 703-463-5812. Ed. Victor Coelho. adv.; bk.rev.; index. circ. 600. Indexed: RILM.
— UnCover.

780   US
LUTE SOCIETY OF AMERICA. QUARTERLY. q. membership. Lute Society of America, c/o Beedle Hinely, Box 1328, Lexington, VA 24450. TEL 703-463-5812. Ed. Phillip Rukavina. Indexed: Music Artic.Guide.
   Formerly: Lute Society of America. Newsletter.

780   SZ
LUZERNER SAENGERBLATT. 8/yr. Stauffacherweg 2a, CH-6006 Luzern, Switzerland. Ed. Edwin Wartenweiler. circ. 1,850. Document type: consumer publication.

786   US
LYRA (LONG ISLAND CITY); the music magazine. 1935. q. free to libraries, colleges and conservatories. Steinway & Sons, Steinway Pl., Long Island City, NY 11105. TEL 718-721-2600. Ed. Leo Spellman. bk.rev.; illus. circ. 45,000. Document type: newsletter.
   Formerly (until 1994): Steinway News.
   Description: Provides tips on caring for Steinway pianos and information on piano competitions. Profiles new Steinway artists.

782.1   US   ISSN 0024-7839
LYRIC OPERA NEWS. 1956. 2/yr. membership. Lyric Opera of Chicago, 20 N. Wacker Dr., Chicago, IL 60606. TEL 312-332-2244. FAX 312-419-8345. Ed. Alfred Glasser. adv. contact: Susan Mathieson. bk.rev.; music rev.; illus. circ. 23,000. Indexed: Music Artic.Guide. Document type: newsletter.

780   IT
LYRICA. 1993. m. L.199000 (foreign L.249000). Ermitage s.r.l., Piazza Trento e Trieste 1, 40137 Bologna, Italy. TEL 39-51-341754. FAX 051-342220. Ed. Alberto Spano. adv.: color page L.4850000; adv. contact: Marco Ultrocchi. circ. 78,000. Document type: consumer publication.

780.42   CN
M E A T. 1989. m. Can.$25($30) M E A T Communications, Inc., P.O. Box 35, Sta. O, Toronto, ON M4A 2M8, Canada. TEL 416-699-8486. FAX 416-690-6697. Ed. Drew Masters. circ. 35,000 (controlled).

780   GW   ISSN 0722-9119
M M BRANCHEN HANDBUCH. 1980. a. DM.59.50. (Musik Markt) Josef Keller Verlag, Postfach 1455, 82317 Starnberg, Germany. TEL 08151-7710. Ed.Bd. index. Document type: bulletin.

780 621.389   UK   ISSN 1350-4312
ML73
M T. 1981. m. Music Technology (Publications) Ltd. (Subsidiary of: Music Maker Publications (Holdings) plc), Alexander House, Forehill, Ely, Cambs CB7 4AF, England. TEL 0353-665577. FAX 0353-662489. (U.S. addr.: Music Maker Publications Inc., 22024 Lassen St., Ste. 118, Chatsworth, CA 91311) Ed. Nigel Lord. adv. contact: Colin McKee. bk.rev. circ. 50,000. Indexed: RILM. Document type: consumer publication.
   Former titles (until 1993): Music Technology (ISSN 0957-6606); (until 1986): Electronics and Music Maker.
   Description: Latest technology in music, covering keyboards, guitars, drums, woodwinds, and other types of musical instruments. Includes articles on sound recording and reproduction, performance reviews, interviews, and profiles of industry leaders.

780   US   ISSN 0740-5812
MADAMINA!. 1980. s-a. $20. Music Associates of America, 224 King St., Englewood, NJ 07631. TEL 201-569-2898. FAX 201-569-7023. Ed. George Sturm. adv. circ. 5,000. (back issues avail.). Document type: bulletin.

780.903   IT
MADRIGALISTI DELL'ITALIA CENTRO-SETTENTRIONALE. 1980. irreg., no.6, 1993. price varies. Casa Editrice Leo S. Olschki, Casella Postale 66, 50100 Florence, Italy. TEL 39-55-6530684. FAX 39-55-6530214. Document type: monographic series.

MAGAZIN FESTSPIELE. see THEATER

780.42   FR   ISSN 0223-8756
MAGAZINE DE LA DISCOTHEQUE ET DES DISC-JOCKEYS. 1980. 6/yr. 150 F. Phil Organisation, 11 rue du Pas-de-Roquille, 17640 Vaux sur Mer, France. TEL 46-39-22-22. FAX 46-39-93-90. Ed. Phil Borgogno. adv.: B&W page 20800 F.; 297 x 210; adv. contact: Phil Borgogno. circ. 6,000.

781.7   HU   ISSN 0025-0384
ML5
MAGYAR ZENE. 1960. q. $18. (Magyar Zenemuveszek Szovetsege) Lapkiado Vallalat, Lenin korut 9-11, 1073 Budapest 7, Hungary. TEL 222-408. (Subscr. to: Kultura, Box 149, H-1389 Budapest, Hungary) bk.rev.; abstr.; bibl. Indexed: Arts & Hum.Cit.Ind., Curr.Cont., RILM.

MAILOUT; arts work with people. see ART

780 792   AT
MAJOR ATTRACTIONS. ANNUAL DIARY. 1978. a. Sydney Opera House Trust, G.P.O. Box 4274, Sydney N.S.W. 2001, Australia. TEL 02-250-7827. FAX 02-252-1161.

780   PL
MALA BIBLIOTEKA OPEROWA. 1955. irreg. price varies. Polskie Wydawnictwo Muzyczne, Al. Krasinskiego 11a, 31-111 Krakow, Poland. TEL 48-12-227044. FAX 48-12-220174. Ed. Mieczyslaw Tomaszewski. adv. contact: Teresa Wlochynska. Document type: monographic series.
   Description: Covers the most popular Polish and foreign operas: music, libretto, work's origin.

780   PL
MALE MONOGRAFIE MUZYCZNE; monografie popularne. 1952. irreg. price varies. Polskie Wydawnictwo Muzyczne, Al. Krasinskiego 11a, 31-111 Krakow, Poland. TEL 48-12-227044. FAX 48-12-220174. Ed. Stanislaw Haraschin. adv. contact: Teresa Wlochynska. Document type: monographic series.
   Description: Presents life and work of great composers.

780   US
THE MANDOCRUCIAN'S DIGEST. s-a. $3.25 per no. Box 3585, Winchester, VA 22601. Ed. Niles Hokkanen.
   Description: Covers mandolin and other stringed instruments.

MANNHEIMER LIEDERTAFEL. MITTEILUNGEN. see CLUBS

780   CN   ISSN 1189-0150
MAPLE MUSIC. 1989. irreg. Canadian Chart Research, 2724 Cordova Way, Kelowna, BC V1Z 2N3, Canada.

MARCAN HANDBOOK OF ARTS ORGANISATIONS. see ART

780.42   US   ISSN 0364-815X
ML1
MARQUEE (NORWALK). m. $6. World Wide Publishing Co., Box 509, Norwalk, CA 90650. TEL 213-864-2741. illus. Indexed: Avery Ind.Archit.Per.

780.7   US   ISSN 0025-4312
MARYLAND MUSIC EDUCATOR. 1954. 4/yr. $8 to non-members. Maryland Music Educators Association, c/o Thomas W. Fugate, Ed., 27 Meadow Ln., Thurmont, MD 21788. TEL 301-271-7269. FAX 301-271-7032. Ed. Thomas W. Fugate. adv.: B&W page $150; trim 7 x 9 5/8. bk.rev.; illus.; circ. 1,400 (controlled). Indexed: Music Artic.Guide.
   Description: Covers all areas of music education: choral, band, orchestra, general music, research, music teachers and supervisors.

780.42   XR
MASARYKOVA UNIVERSITA. FILOZOFICKA FAKULTA. SBORNIK PRACI. H: RADA HUDEBNEVEDNA. 1966. irreg. (approx. a). price varies. Masarykova Universita, Filozoficka Fakulta, A. Novaka 1, 660 88 Brno, Czech Republic. FAX 41-211241. bk.rev. Document type: proceedings.
   Formerly: Universita J.E. Purkyne. Filozoficka Fakulta. Sbornik Praci. H: Rada Hudevnedna (ISSN 0231-522X)
   Description: Series Musicologica provides articles in the various fields of the theory and history of music: Czech, German, Russian, Italian, modern, folk and more.

ULRICH'S INTERNATIONAL PERIODICALS DIRECTORY 1996

MUSIC

780.7 US ISSN 0147-2550
MASSACHUSETTS MUSIC NEWS. 1953. q. $8. Massachusetts Music Educators Association, Inc. (Subsidiary of: Music Educators National Conference), c/o J. Anthony DiGiore, Ed., 93 Greenleaf Ave., P.O. Box 532, West Springfield, MA 01090-0532. TEL 413-739-9065. FAX 413-788-9251. adv.: B&W page $160; trim 8 1/2 x 11. bk.rev.; film rev.; music rev.; illus.; stat. circ. 1,500. **Indexed:** Music Artic.Guide. **Document type:** newsletter.
Formerly: M.M.E.A. Music News (ISSN 0024-8258)
Description: Documents the progress of music education in Massachusetts.

780 UK
MASSENET SOCIETY. NEWSLETTER. no.2, 1975. q. £4. Massenet Society, c/o Stella J. Wright, Flat 2, 79 Linden Gardens, London W2 4EU, England. Ed. Frank Granville Barker. **Document type:** newsletter.

781.62 PL ISSN 0860-3391
MATERIALY DO POLSKIEJ MUZYKI LUDOWEJ. 1957. irreg. price varies. Polskie Wydawnictwo Muzyczne, Al. Krasinskiego 11a, 31-111 Krakow, Poland. TEL 48-12-227044. FAX 48-12-220174.
Description: Series containing collections of songs and tunes from authentic recordings of folk singers, musicians and bands.

786.2 US ISSN 0360-8484
ML423.M42
THE MATTHAY NEWS. 1927. 2/yr. $30. American Matthay Association, 100 Minty Dr., Dayton, OH 45415. Ed. Elizabeth Vandevander. bk.rev.; illus. circ. 250. **Document type:** academic/scholarly publication.

780 US
MAXIMUMROCKNROLL. 12/yr. $36; newsstand price: $2. Box 460760, San Francisco, CA 94146-0760. adv.; bk.rev.; music rev. (back issues avail.) **Document type:** bulletin.

789 US ISSN 1045-795X
ML1
MECHANICAL MUSIC. 1954. 3/yr. $30. Musical Box Society International, 887 E. Orange Ave., St. Paul, MN 55106. TEL 612-774-2590. FAX 612-772-2464. Ed. Angelo Rulli. adv.; bk.rev.; illus. circ. 3,000. **Indexed:** Music Ind. **Document type:** bulletin, directory.
Former titles: Musical Box Society International Technical Journal; Musical Box Society International. Bulletin; Musical Box Society. Bulletin (ISSN 0027-4577)
Description: Technical articles about the restoration of antique musical mechanical instruments.

MEDICAL PROBLEMS OF PERFORMING ARTISTS. see *MEDICAL SCIENCES*

MEDIUM (NEW YORK). see *ETHNIC INTERESTS*

780 GW ISSN 0543-4033
MEISTERWERKE DER MUSIK. 1965. irreg., vol.63. DM.26.80. Wilhelm Fink Verlag, Ohmstr. 5, 80802 Munich, Germany. TEL 089-348017. FAX 089-341378. **Document type:** monographic series.

781.5 XR ISSN 0025-8997
MELODIE. monthly for jazz and pop music. 1963. m. 60 Kc.($52.10) (GoJa, Agentura Gott-Janecek) JA Manager Services, Vrsovicka 101, 100 00 Prague 10, Czech Republic. Ed. Jan Dobias. adv.; bk.rev.; charts; illus.; index. circ. 90,000. (tabloid format)

780 UK ISSN 0025-9012
ML5
MELODY MAKER. 1926. w. $105. I P C Magazines, Specialist Magazine Group (Subsidiary of: Reed Elsevier group), King's Reach Tower, Stamford St., London SE1 9LS, England. TEL 071-261-6229. FAX 0444-440619. TELEX 892084 REEDBP G. (Dist. by: Quadrant Subscription Services, Oakfield House, Perrymount Rd., Haywards Heath, W. Sussex RH16 3DH, England. TEL 0444-440421) Ed. Alan Jones. adv.; bk.rev.; film rev.; play rev.; charts; illus. circ. 68,300. (also avail. in microform from UMI) **Indexed:** Music Ind. **Document type:** consumer publication.
—UMI. **CCC.**

781 SW ISSN 1103-0968
MELOS; en musiktidskrift. (Text in English, Swedish) 1992. q. SEK 240 in the Nordic countries; elsewhere SEK 290. Kantat HB, P.O. Box 27728, S-102 53 Stockholm, Sweden. TEL 46-8-664-16-20.

789.91 UK ISSN 0266-8033
MEMORY LANE. 1968. q. £12($30) (typically set in Feb.). Memory Lane, 226 Station Rd., Leigh-on-Sea, Essex SS9 3BS, England. Ed. Ray Pallett. adv. contact: Ray Pallett. bk.rev. circ. 2,000. **Document type:** consumer publication.
Description: Covers popular music from 1920-1950: jazz, dance bands, big bands.

780 792 US ISSN 1044-1875
MEMPHIS STAR.* m. $10. 1333 Carr Ave., Memphis, TN 36104-4500. TEL 901-452-7827. Ed. David Wayne Brown. adv.; bk.rev.
Description: Looks at music, theater, and the movies, mainly from an entertainment perspective. Includes record industry news.

780 NE ISSN 0025-9462
MENS EN MELODIE. 1946. 10/yr. fl.62 (foreign fl.119) (effective 1993). Uitgeverij Scala bv, Postbus 28009, 3828 ZG Hoogland, Netherlands. TEL 31-33-806896. FAX 31-33-802281. Ed. P. Peters. adv.; bk.rev.; bibl.; illus.; index. circ. 4,500. **Indexed:** Music Ind., RILM.
—BLDSC (5678.461000); SWETS.
Description: Covers classical music for enthusiasts and players.

780 UK ISSN 0967-442X
METAL C D. 1992. m. £70 for 6 issues. Northern & Shell Publications, Northern & Shell Bldg., P.O. Box 381, Millharbour, London E14 9TW, England. TEL 44-171-987-5090. FAX 44-171-987-2160. Ed. Kirk Blows. adv.: color page £1755; adv. contact: Elspeth Thomson. circ. 100,000. **Document type:** consumer publication.

780 US ISSN 1068-2872
METAL EDGE. 1957. m. $24.95 (foreign $29.95). Sterling - Macfadden Partnership, 35 Wilbur St., Lynbrook, NY 11563. TEL 516-593-1220. FAX 516-593-0065. adv.; bk.rev.; film rev.; illus. circ. 299,369. **Document type:** consumer publication.
Formerly: T V Picture Life (ISSN 1059-8006); (until 1984): T V Picture Life (ISSN 0039-856X)
Description: Covers hard rock - heavy metal music and musicians. Includes interviews and information on contests.

780.904 SZ ISSN 0955-1190
METAL HAMMER; the international hard rock & heavy metal magazine. 1984. m. DM.75 (foreign DM.93). Z A G Zeitschriften Verlag, Baarerstr. 22, CH-6301 Zug, Switzerland. TEL 042-222020. FAX 042-215268. (Subscr. in Germany to: Werinherstr. 71, 81541 Munich. TEL 089-9234310. FAX 089-9234312) Ed. Andrea Nieradzik. adv. contact: Heiko Heinemann. bk.rev. circ. 86,703. (back issues avail.) **Document type:** consumer publication.

781.64 US
METAL MANIACS. bi-m. $18 (foreign $23). Sterling - Macfadden Partnership, 35 Wilbur St., Lynbrook, NY 11563. TEL 516-593-1220. FAX 516-593-0065. adv. **Document type:** consumer publication.

780 US ISSN 1056-2826
ML3533.8
METAL REVOLUTION. q. Flip Magazines, Inc., 801 Second Ave., New York, NY 10017. TEL 212-661-7878.

780 GW
METAL STAR. m. DM.65. Klaus Schultz Verlagsgesellschaft mbH, Boeckmannstr. 15, 20099 Hamburg, Germany. TEL 040-241617. FAX 040-249448. Ed. Klaus Schultz. adv. contact: Soraya Wilms. circ. 35,700. **Document type:** consumer publication.

783 UK
METHODIST CHURCH MUSIC SOCIETY NOTES. 1970. s-a. £10. Methodist Church Music Society, c/o Frank Pagden, Ed., Grove Manse, Town St., Horsforth, Leeds LS18 4RJ, England. adv.; bk.rev. circ. 1,000. (also avail. in microform from WMP) **Document type:** newsletter.
Formerly: Methodist Church Music Society Bulletin (ISSN 0047-6919)

780 US
METRONOME MAGAZINE. 1986. m. $20. Brian M. Owens, Ed. and Pub., P.O. Box 921, Billerica, MA 01821. rec.rev. circ. 30,000. (tabloid format; back issues avail.)
Description: Focuses on music and entertainment. Contains interviews with local, national and international musicians.

785 069 US
MILLER NOTES. 1975. 5/yr. $20 membership (foreign $25). Glenn Miller Birthplace Society, Box 61, Clarinda, IA 51632. TEL 712-542-2461. Ed. Wilda Martin. adv. contact: Marvin Negley. bk.rev. circ. 700. (looseleaf format)
Description: Presents news of personnel associated with big band leader Glenn Miller, his records, and the Society's festival.

784.2 780.15 US ISSN 1046-5413
MILWAUKEE SYMPHONY ORCHESTRA. Variant title: Milwaukee Symphony Program. 1980. s-m. free. Encore, Inc., 4532 N. Oakland Ave., Milwaukee, WI 53211. TEL 414-964-5669. Ed. John Stone. adv. contact: Trenny Aiken.
Formerly: Milwaukee Symphony Orchestra. Stagebill.

781.7 CC
MINZU MINJIAN YINYUE/NATIONAL AND FOLK MUSIC. (Text in Chinese) q. Y4.80. (Guangdongsheng Minjian Yinyue Yanjiushi - Guangdong Folk Music Research Office) Minzu Minjian Yinyue Bianjibu, 79 Wende Lu, 7th Floor, Guangzhou, Guangdong 510030, People's Republic of China. TEL 340465. Eds. Lin Yun, Ma Ming.
Description: Introduces folk music popular among nationalities in Guangdong Province.

780 XR ISSN 0544-4136
ML3797
MISCELLANEA MUSICOLOGICA. (Text in Czech; summaries in German) 1956. irreg. (approx. a.). 19.50 Kc. per no. Universita Karlova, Filosoficka Fakulta, Katedra Dejin Hudby, Divadla a Filmu, Nam. J. Palacha 1, 116 38 Prague 1, Czech Republic. Ed. Frantisek Muzik. illus. circ. 770. **Indexed:** A.I.C.P., CERDIC.
—BLDSC (5812.407000).

780.7 US
MISSISSIPPI MUSIC EDUCATOR. 1941. 3/yr. $6. Mississippi Music Educators Association, c/o Larry W. Newell, Ed., 2106 Bob White Dr., Tupelo, MS 38801-6181. TEL 601-842-7909. adv.; bk.rev.; film rev.; illus.; stat.; tr.lit. circ. 550.
Formerly: Mississippi Notes (ISSN 0026-6353)

781.57 US ISSN 0742-4612
MISSISSIPPI RAG; the voice of traditional jazz and ragtime. 1973. m. $20 (foreign $22). Mississippi Rag, Inc., 1401 W. 76th St. 250, Minneapolis, MN 55423-3846. TEL 612-861-2446. FAX 612-861-4621. Ed. Leslie Carole Johnson. adv. contact: Jody Hughes. bk.rev.; rec.rev.; illus. circ. 4,200. (tabloid format; back issues avail.) **Indexed:** Music Ind., Pop.Mus.Per.Ind. **Document type:** newspaper.
Description: Historical articles, current jazz and ragtime news, photos and articles on performers and festivals, listings of gigs and festivals.

780 US ISSN 0085-350X
ML1
MISSOURI JOURNAL OF RESEARCH IN MUSIC EDUCATION. 1962. a. $2 (effective 1996). Missouri Music Educators Association, c/o Martin J. Bergee, 140 Fine Arts. Missouri University, Columbia, MO 65211. TEL 417-887-5252. FAX 314-882-5071. (Subscr. to: Conservatory of Music, 4949 Cherry, University of Missouri-Kansas City, MO 64110. TEL 816-235-2907) Ed. John Hylton. circ. 200. **Indexed:** Music Artic.Guide, Music Ind. **Document type:** academic/scholarly publication.
—UnCover.
Description: Reports of original research related to music teaching and learning.
Refereed Serial

780.7 US ISSN 0026-6701
MISSOURI SCHOOL MUSIC. 1945. 4/yr. $6. Missouri Music Educators Association (Marshfield), Box 690, Marshfield, MO 65706. adv.; illus. circ. 3,000.

MUSIC

780   UK   ISSN 0957-6622
MIXMAG. 1983. m. newsstand price: £1.95. D M C Publishing Ltd., P.O. Box 89, London W2 3GP, England. TEL 0171-602-3977. FAX 0171-602-8707. E-mail: mixmag@intermedia.co.uk. (Subscr. in the U.S. to: Mixmag New York, 666 Broadway, Ste. 3, New York, NY 10012. TEL 212-777-6676. FAX 212-777-7167) Ed. Dom Phillips; Pub. Tony Prince. adv.: B&W page £1000, color page £1400; trim 300 x 230; adv. contact: Peter Fox. film rev. circ. 43,000. **Document type:** consumer publication.
   Description: Contains information about dance music and the club culture scene.

781.71   SW   ISSN 0345-8105
MIXTUREN. 1970. 6/yr. SEK 160. Frikyrkliga Studiefoerbundet, Box 479, S-101 29 Stockholm, Sweden. TEL 46-8-698-44-13. FAX 46-8-698-44-28. Ed. Torgny Erseus.
   Description: Focuses on congregational and Church music; includes sheet music supplements.

780   FR   ISSN 1159-070X
MODAL. s-a. 450 F. Geste Editions, Maison des Ruralies, B.P. 1, 79230 Vouille, France. TEL 49-75-67-71. Ed. Jean-Loic Le Quellec.
   Description: Covers ethnomusicology, French tradition music and dance.

780   US   ISSN 0194-4533
ML1035
MODERN DRUMMER. 1977. m. $29.95 (effective 1994). Modern Drummer Publications, Inc., 870 Pompton Ave., Cedar Grove, NJ 07009. TEL 201-239-4140. FAX 201-239-7139. (Subscr. to: Box 480, Mt. Morris, IL 61054. TEL 800-551-3786) Ed. Ronald L. Spagnardi. adv. contact: Bob Berenson. bk.rev.; illus. circ. 102,000. **Indexed:** Music Ind., RILM. **Document type:** consumer publication.
   —Faxon; UMI; UnCover.
   Incorporates (in 1988): Modern Percussionist (ISSN 8750-7838)
   Description: Articles, news, profiles, advice, and equipment specs for the contemporary percussionist.

781.57   IT
MODERN JAZZ. (Text in English) irreg. Ruggero Stiassi, Ed. & Pub., Via Putti 3, Bologna, Italy. adv.; rec.rev. (processed)

786.6   US
MODERN KEYBOARD. 1988. bi-m. $2.95 per no. Harris Publications, Inc., 1115 Broadway, 8th Fl., New York, NY 10010. TEL 212-807-7100. adv. circ. 65,000.
   Description: Combines rock & roll music with new technology. Features include interviews profiling top keyboard artists and MIDI technology for the beginner. Covers the basics from home studio and computer music to sequencers and synthesizers.

781.46   UK
MOJO. m. £28.20 (foreign £36.45) (effective 1995-1996). E M A P - Metro, Mappin House, 4 Winsley St., London W1N 7AR, England. TEL 0171-436-1515. FAX 0171-312-8191. (Subscr. to: Tower Publishing Services Ltd., Tower House, Sovereign Park, Lathkill St., Market Harborough, Leics. LE16 9EF, England. TEL 01858-468811. FAX 01858-432164) adv. **Document type:** consumer publication.

MOLODEZHNAYA ESTRADA. see *CHILDREN AND YOUTH — For*

780.42   US
MONDO 2000. q. Box 10171, Berkeley, CA 94709. TEL 415-845-9018. Ed. Alison Kennedy.

MONKEES, BOYCE & HART PHOTO FAN CLUB; the photo club. see *CLUBS*

780.01   US   ISSN 1062-4112
MONOGRAPHS IN MUSICOLOGY SERIES. 1983. irreg., vol.10, 1992. Pendragon Press, 41 Ferry St., Stuyvesant, NY 12173-9720. TEL 518-828-3008. FAX 518-828-2368. **Document type:** monographic series.

780   SP   ISSN 0210-4083
ML5
MONSALVAT. 1973. m. 5000 ptas. Ediciones de Nuevo Arte Thor, Plaza Gala Placidia 1-16, 08006 Barcelona, Spain. TEL 93 218 11 97. FAX 932184638. Ed. Jose Manuel Infiesta Monterde. adv.; bk.rev.; illus. circ. 20,000. **Indexed:** RILM.

780   PL
MONUMENTA MUSICAE IN POLONIA. SERIES B: COLLECTANEA MUSICAE ARTIS. 1964. irreg. (Polska Akademia Nauk, Instytut Sztuki) Polskie Wydawnictwo Muzyczne, Al. Krasinskiego 11a, 31-111 Krakow, Poland. TEL 48-12-227044. FAX 48-12-220174. Ed. J. Morawski. adv. contact: Teresa Wlochynska. **Document type:** abstracting/indexing.
   Formerly: Monumenta Musicae in Polonia. Series B: Fontes Artis Musicae; **Supersedes in part:** Monumenta Musicae in Polonia (ISSN 0077-1465)

780   PL   ISSN 0239-8834
MONUMENTA MUSICAE IN POLONIA. SERIES C: TRACTATUS DE MUSICA. (Text in Latin, Polish; summaries in English) 1984. irreg. (Polska Akademia Nauk, Instytut Sztuki) Polskie Wydawnictwo Muzyczne, Al. Krasinskiego 11a, 31-111 Krakow, Poland. TEL 48-12-227044. FAX 48-12-220174. Ed. Henryk Kowalewicz. adv. contact: Teresa Wlochynska. **Document type:** abstracting/indexing.
   Supersedes in part: Monumenta Musicae in Polonia (ISSN 0077-1465)
   Description: Covers both transcriptions of music treatises and their translation into Polish with comprehensive source-based critical commentaries.

780   PL   ISSN 0239-9954
MONUMENTA MUSICAE IN POLONIA. SERIES D: BIBLIOTHECA ANTIQUA. 1975. irreg. (Polska Akademia Nauk, Instytut Sztuki) Polskie Wydawnictwo Muzyczne, Al. Krasinskiego 11a, 31-111 Krakow, Poland. TEL 48-12-227044. FAX 48-12-220174. Ed. Jerzy Morawski. adv. contact: Teresa Wlochynska. **Document type:** monographic series.
   Supersedes in part: Monumenta Musicae in Polonia (ISSN 0077-1465)
   Description: Contains the reprints of the treatises and music editions from the 16th and 17th centuries.

780   US   ISSN 0077-1503
MONUMENTS OF RENAISSANCE MUSIC. 1967. irreg., vol.7, 1986. price varies. University of Chicago Press, 5801 S. Ellis Ave., Chicago, IL 60637. TEL 312-702-7899. Ed. Howard M. Brown. (reprint service avail. from UMI,ISI)
   Refereed Serial

780.7   RU
MONUMENTS OF WORLD MUSICAL SCIENCE. a. 4.60 Rub. Izdatel'stvo Muzyka, Ul. Neglinnaya 14, Moscow 103031, Russia. TEL 924-81-63. FAX 921-83-53.

781.7   US   ISSN 0278-0763
ML1
MORAVIAN MUSIC JOURNAL. (Supplement to: Moravian Music Foundation Newsletter) 1957. q. $10. Moravian Music Foundation, 20 Cascade Ave., Winston-Salem, NC 27127. TEL 919-725-0651. FAX 919-725-4514. Ed. Nola Reed Knouse. adv.; bk.rev.; bibl. circ. 4,000. (back issues avail.) **Indexed:** Music Artic.Guide, Music Ind. **Document type:** academic/scholarly publication.
   —Faxon; UnCover.
   Former titles: Moravian Music Foundation. Bulletin (ISSN 0147-7013); Moravian Music Foundation. News Bulletin (ISSN 0027-1020)

780   US
MOTORBOOTY; the big daddy of the Bozo underground. 1987. s-a. $14. Clownskull Graphics, Box 02007, Detroit, MI 48202. TEL 313-871-8419. FAX 313-871-4840. E-mail: mbootyl@aol.com. Eds. Mark Dancey, Danny Plotnick. adv. circ. 10,000. **Document type:** consumer publication.
   Description: Covers music, comics, subculture and satire.

MOVEMENTS IN THE ARTS. see *ART*

780   GW   ISSN 0077-1805
MOZART - JAHRBUCH. (Text in English, French and German) 1950. a. price varies. (Internationale Stiftung Mozarteum, AU) Baerenreiter Verlag, Heinrich-Schuetz-Allee 35, 34131 Kassel, Germany. TEL 0561-3105-0. FAX 0561-3105240. (Subscr. in US to: Educational Music Service, 13 Elkay Dr., Chester, NY 10918. TEL 914-469-5790. FAX 914-469-5817) Ed.Bd. adv.; index. circ. 1,000. **Indexed:** RILM. **Document type:** academic/scholarly publication.
   —BLDSC (5980.708000); SWETS.

781.7 780.42   IT   ISSN 1121-354X
IL MUCCHIO SELVAGGIO; mensile di musica e cultura rock. 1977. m. L.70000. Editore Lakota, Via Pietro Mascagni, 3-5, 00199 Rome, Italy. TEL 06-8608913. FAX 06-8608930. Ed. Massimo Stefani. adv.: B&W page L.2600000, color page L.4200000. illus.

780   GW
MUENCHNER PHILHARMONIKER. 1985. s-m. DM.26. Muenchner Philharmoniker, Kellerstr. 4, 81667 Munich, Germany. TEL 089-480980. FAX 089-48098525. **Document type:** bulletin.

784.4   AT   ISSN 0157-3381
MULGA WIRE. 1954. 6/yr. Aus.$8. Bush Music Club Inc., P.O. Box 433, Sydney, N.S.W. 2001, Australia. Eds. Colin Fong, Linda Scott. adv.; bk.rev.; illus. circ. 300. **Document type:** newsletter.
   Incorporates (in 1979): Singabout; Journal of Australian Folksong (ISSN 0037-5632)

780.01 572   GW
MUSEUM FUER VOELKERKUNDE, BERLIN. VEROEFFENTLICHUNGEN. NEUE FOLGE. ABTEILUNG: MUSIKETHNOLOGIE. 1961. irreg., vol.8, 1991. price varies. Staatliche Museen zu Berlin - Preussischer Kulturbesitz, Generalverwaltung, Stauffenbergstr. 41, 10785 Berlin, Germany. TEL 030-266-6. FAX 030-2662612. **Document type:** monographic series.

MUSEUM OF THE AMERICAN PIANO. NEWSLETTER. see *MUSEUMS AND ART GALLERIES*

780   US   ISSN 0895-1543
ML128.P63
MUSI - KEY; the reference guide of note. 1987. bi-m. $300. 10260 N. Alder Spring Dr., Tucson, AZ 85737-9477. Eds. Randy Rucker, Linda Rucker. circ. 1,000. **Document type:** catalog.
   ●Also available on CD-ROM.
   Description: Lists popular and standard music currently in print, both sheets and collections.

780   IT   ISSN 0392-5536
MUSIC. 1978. m. L.60000. (Athena 2001 Coop.) Edizioni L.E.T.I. s.r.l., Viale E. Q. Visconti, 20, 00198 Rome, Italy. TEL 06-3222780. FAX 06-3210651. Ed. Francesco Puzzo. adv.: B&W page L.5100000, color page L.9200000. circ. 53,000.
   Description: Covers various topics in music.

780   II
MUSIC ACADEMY. CONFERENCE SOUVENIR. (Text in English, Sanskrit or Tamil) 1940. a. Rs.15. Music Academy, 306 T.T.K. Rd., Royapettah, Madras 600014, India.
   Description: Contains articles on music contributed by international writers, and documented programmes of music and dance recitals.

780   II   ISSN 0970-3101
MUSIC ACADEMY. JOURNAL. (Text in English, Sanskrit, Tamil) 1929. a. Rs.15($3) Music Academy, 306 T.T.K. Rd., Royapettah, Madras 600014, India. **Document type:** academic/scholarly publication.
   —UnCover.
   Description: Devoted to the advancement of the science and art of music.

780 US
MUSIC ACCESS; the interactive music monthly. 1990. m. $12. Music Access, Inc., 90 Fifth Ave., Brooklyn, NY 11217. TEL 718-398-2146. FAX 718-230-5539. Ed. Danny Nelson. adv. contact: Mike Gunderloy. music rev. **Document type:** directory.
●Also available online.
Formerly (until Apr., 1993): Music Access Directory.
Description: Lists all recorded music excerpts accessible by regular telephone. Categories include classical, rock and pop, jazz and blues, country and folk, contemporary, children's, and experimental. Features more than 1200 selections each month.

780 US
MUSIC ADDRESS BOOK; how to reach anyone who's anyone in music. 1989. irreg. Harper Collins Publishers, 10 E 53rd St., New York, NY 10022. TEL 212-207-7741. FAX 212-207-7145. Ed. Nancy Pesla.

780 UK ISSN 0262-5245
MUSIC ANALYSIS. 1982. 3/yr. £108($217) (foreign £135) (effective 1996). Basil Blackwell Ltd., 108 Cowley Rd., Oxford OX4 1JF, England. TEL 0865-791100. FAX 0865-791347. TELEX 837022-OXBOOK-G. Ed. Derrick Puffett. adv.; bk.rev. circ. 800. (reprint service avail. from SWZ,UMI) **Indexed:** Arts & Hum.Cit.Ind., Curr.Cont., RILM.
—BLDSC (5990.185300); Genuine Article; SWETS; UnCover. **CCC**.

780.42 US
MUSIC & AUDIO REVIEWS.* m. $2.95 per no. W G E Publishing, Inc., 70 State Rte. 202 N, Peterborough, NH 03458-1107.

780.65 FR ISSN 1151-3470
MUSIC AND BUSINESS. 1973. 6/yr. 300 F. Master Press International, 10 rue de la Paix, 92100 Boulogne, France. TEL 1-46-03-15-51. FAX 1-46-03-47-88. Ed. Marc Rouve. circ. 5,000. **Document type:** trade publication.
Former titles (until 1990): D I S C (Disques, Instruments, Sonorisations, Clubs) (ISSN 0337-8837); (until 1975): Disque (ISSN 0337-8829)
Description: Offers advice for the growth of the business, presents new materials, studies of the French market and international news.

780 341.758 UK ISSN 0968-0322
MUSIC & COPYRIGHT. 1992. s-m. £580($870) in the U.K. and overseas (effective 1995). Financial Times Telecoms & Media Publishing (Subsidiary of: Financial Times Group), Maple House, 149 Tottenham Court Rd., London W1P 9LL, England. TEL 0171-896-2234. FAX 0171-896-2256. Pub. Helen Nicol. **Document type:** newsletter.
—UMI.
Description: Provides global reporting on the commercial aspects of the music industry.

MUSIC & DANCE NEWS. see *DANCE*

780.7 US
MUSIC AND ENTERTAINMENT INDUSTRY EDUCATORS' NOTES. Short title: M I E A Notes. 1978. q. $6. Music Industry Educators Association, c/o Music Department, New York State University, Oneonta, NY 13820. TEL 703-568-6863. Ed. Janet Nepkie. circ. 500. (looseleaf format) **Document type:** newsletter.
Formerly: Music Industry Educators' Notes.

780.07 UK ISSN 0027-4224
ML5
MUSIC AND LETTERS. 1920. q. £52($98) (effective 1996). Oxford University Press, Oxford Journals, Walton St., Oxford OX2 6DP, England. TEL 01865-267907. FAX 01865-267773. TELEX 837330-OXPRES-G. E-mail: jnlorders@oup.co.uk. (U.S. subscr. to: Oxford University Press Inc., 2001 Evans Rd., Cary, NC 27513. TEL 919-677-0977. FAX 919-677-1714) Eds. Nigel Fortune, Tim Carter. adv. contact: Rosemary Dooley. bk.rev.; music rev.; illus.; index, cum.index: vols.1-40, 1920-1959. circ. 1,600. (also avail. in microform from UMI; reprint service avail. from SWZ) **Indexed:** Abstr.Engl.Stud., Arts & Hum.Cit.Ind., Br.Hum.Ind., Can.Rev.Comp.Lit., Curr.Cont., Hum.Ind., Ind.Bk.Rev.Hum., M.L.A., Music Ind., RILM. **Document type:** academic/scholarly publication.
—BLDSC (5990.190000); Faxon; Genuine Article; SWETS; UMI; UnCover. **CCC**.
Description: Covers all fields of musical enquiry, from earliest times to present day. Includes wide range of reviews: scholarly editions of music of the past; new music.

780 UK ISSN 0085-3607
MUSIC AND LIFE. 1950. irreg. (3-4/yr.). £1.20. Music Group of the Communist Party, c/o George Burn, Ed., 17 Huntingdon Rd., London N.2, England. circ. 300. (processed)

784 UK ISSN 0305-4438
ML5
MUSIC AND LITURGY. 1974. 6/yr. £18 (Europe £19; elsewhere £21). Society of St. Gregory, 33 Brockenhurst Rd., Addiscombe, Croydon CR0 7DR, England. FAX 0181-654-3379. Ed. Ann Moynihan. adv.; bk.rev. circ. 1,000. (also avail. in microform from UMI) **Indexed:** Br.Hum.Ind., Cath.Ind., CERDIC. **Document type:** bulletin.
—UMI.
Formed by the merger of: Church Music (ISSN 0009-644X); Life and Worship (ISSN 0024-5119)

780 384.5 NE
MUSIC & MEDIA; Europe's radio active newsweekly. (Text in English) 1984. w. fl.397($270) (effective 1993). B P I Communications, Rijnsburgstraat 11, 1059 AT Amsterdam, Netherlands. TEL 31-20-6691961. FAX 31-20-6691941. Ed. Machgid Bakker; Pub.. Philip Alexander. adv. circ. 7,500. **Document type:** trade publication.
Description: Covers the European radio and music industries.

780 621.389 658 US ISSN 0894-1238
ML1092
MUSIC AND SOUND RETAILER; the newsmagazine for musical instrument and sound product merchandisers. 1978. m. $18 free to qualified personnel. Testa Communications, Inc., 25 Willowdale Ave., Port Washington, NY 11050. TEL 516-767-2500. FAX 516-767-9335. Ed. Jon Mayer. adv.; charts; illus.; stat.; tr.lit. circ. 10,000. (tabloid format; back issues avail.) **Document type:** trade publication.
Former titles: Music and Sound Electronics Retailer; Sound Arts Merchandising Journal.
Description: For professional musicians and retailers.

MUSIC AND THE TEACHER. see *EDUCATION — Teaching Methods And Curriculum*

780 IE
MUSIC ASSOCIATION OF IRELAND. ANNUAL REPORT. 1975. a. Music Association of Ireland, 5 North Frederick St., Dublin 1, Ireland. TEL 01-746060. stat.

780 028.5 RU
MUSIC AT THE KINDERGARTEN. a. 3 Rub. Izdatel'stvo Muzyka, Ul. Neglinnaya 14, Moscow 103031, Russia. TEL 924-81-63. FAX 921-83-53.

780 US
MUSIC BIZ 411. a. Soundtrack Publishing, 317 Skyline Lake Dr., Box 609, Ringwood, NJ 07456. TEL 201-831-1317. FAX 201-831-8672. **Document type:** directory.
Description: Lists U.S. record distributors, radio stations, print media, booking agents, and clubs.

780 US
MUSIC BIZ 411 INTERNATIONAL. a. Soundtrack Publishing, 317 Skyline Lake Dr., Box 609, Ringwood, NJ 07456. TEL 201-831-1317. FAX 201-831-8672. **Document type:** directory.
Description: Lists record distributors, retailers, radio stations, print media, booking agents, and clubs outside the U.S.

745.1 780 UK ISSN 0027-4275
MUSIC BOX. 1962. q. $17. Musical Box Society of Great Britain, c/o Broadgate Printing Company, Crondel Rd., Exhall, Coventry CV7 9NH, England. Ed. Robert Clarson-Leach. adv.; bk.rev.; bibl.; charts; illus.; index. cum.index every 8 nos. circ. 2,500.
—BLDSC (5990.235000).

780 681 UK ISSN 0269-0292
MUSIC BUSINESS; the monthly magazine for the musical instrument and allied trade. 1986. m. £15 (foreign £30) (includes Music Business Directory). Feedback Publications Ltd., Valley View, Greenbanks, Llandogo, Monmouth, Gwent NP5 4TG, Wales. TEL 01594-530117. FAX 01594-530755. (Subscr. to: Grosvenor House, Police Station Ln., Bushey, Herts. WD2 1BR, England. TEL 0181-950-4984. FAX 0181-950-0302) Ed. Peter Pulham; Pubs. Sandie Smith, Peter Pulham. adv.: B&W page £575; color page £795; adv. contact: Sandie Smith. music rev.; circ. 3,550 (paid). (back issues avail.) **Document type:** trade publication.

780 681 UK
MUSIC BUSINESS DIRECTORY. a. £15 (foreign £30) (includes subscr. to Music Business). Feedback Publications Ltd., Valley View, Greenbanks, Llandogo, Monmouth, Gwent NP5 4TG, Wales. TEL 01594-530117. FAX 01594-530755. (Subscr. to: Grosvenor House, Police Station Ln., Bushey, Herts. WD2 1BR, England. TEL 0181-950-4984. FAX 081-950-0302) Ed. Peter Pulham; Pubs. Sandie Smith, Peter Pulham. adv.: B&W page £575; color page £795; adv. contact: Sandie Smith. circ. 3,550 (paid). **Document type:** directory.
Description: Lists more than 700 distributors, manufacturers, printed-music suppliers, and sales agents. Also contains brand names, product sources, and a general information section.

780 UK
MUSIC BUSINESS INTERNATIONAL. 1991. m. £75. Spotlight Publications Ltd. (Subsidiary of: Morgan-Grampian plc), Ludgate House, 245 Blackfriars Rd., London SE1 9UR, England. TEL 071-620-3636. FAX 071-401-8036. Ed. Steve Hurst. adv. contact: Rudi Blackette. circ. 8,000. **Document type:** trade publication.
Description: Overview of the worldwide music market.

THE MUSIC CATALOG ON C D - R O M. see *BIBLIOGRAPHIES*

MUSIC CATALOGING BULLETIN. see *LIBRARY AND INFORMATION SCIENCES*

780 IT
MUSIC CITY; l'ipermercato dell'informazione musicale. m. L.120000. Edizioni Milano Publishing s.r.l., Via Marconi 28, 20091 Bresso (MI), Italy. TEL 39-2-66502365. FAX 39-2-66502742. Ed. Roberto Casiraghi. adv. contact: Roberto Ronchetti.

781.5 US ISSN 0027-4291
MUSIC CITY NEWS. 1963. m. $23.50 (typically set in Jan.). Music City News Publishing Co., Inc., Box 22975, 50 Music Sq. W., Nashville, TN 37202. TEL 615-329-2200. Ed. Lydia Dixon-Harden. adv.; bk.rev.; illus. circ. 150,000. **Document type:** newsletter.
Description: Focuses on country music and entertainers.

780 US ISSN 0161-2654
ML1
MUSIC CLUBS MAGAZINE. 1922. 4/yr. $6. National Federation of Music Clubs, 1336 N. Delaware St., Indianapolis, IN 46202. TEL 317-638-4003. FAX 317-638-0503. Ed. Isabella Laude. adv.; bk.rev.; film rev.; music rev. circ. 4,000. (also avail. in microform from UMI) **Indexed:** Music Artic.Guide, Music Ind.
—UMI.
Description: Promotes American music and musicians.

MUSIC

780.65 US
MUSIC CONNECTION. 1977. fortn. $40. Music Connection Inc., 6640 Sunset Blvd., Ste. 201, Hollywood, CA 90028. FAX 213-462-3123. Ed. Michael Dolan. adv. contact: Eric Bettelli. bk.rev. circ. 75,000. **Document type:** trade publication.

780 US
MUSIC CRITICS ASSOCIATION. NEWSLETTER. 1963. q. Music Critics Association, 7 Pine Ct., Westfield, NJ 07090. TEL 908-233-8468. FAX 908-233-8468. Ed. A.H. Cohen. circ. 1,000. (back issues avail.) **Document type:** newsletter.

780 CN ISSN 0820-0416
ML21.C3
MUSIC DIRECTORY CANADA. 1983. biennial. Can.$29.95. Norris - Whitney Communications Inc., 23 Hannover Dr., No. 7, St. Catherines, ON L2W 1A3, Canada. TEL 905-641-3471. FAX 905-641-1648. Ed. Jim Norris. circ. 6,000. **Document type:** directory.

780.7 UK
MUSIC EDUCATION YEARBOOK. 1984. a. £13.95. Rhinegold Publishing Ltd., 241 Shaftesbury Ave., London WC2H 8EH, England. TEL 0171-333-1761. FAX 0171-333-1769. Ed. Annabel Carter. **Document type:** academic/scholarly publication.
—BLDSC (2330.640000).
Former titles (until 1994): Music Teachers' Yearbook (ISSN 1353-548X); (until 1993): British Music Education Yearbook (ISSN 0266-2329)
Description: Complete guide to music education at all levels from pre-school to post-graduate.

780.7 US ISSN 0027-4321
ML1
MUSIC EDUCATORS JOURNAL. 1914. 6/yr. $60 (institutional subscriptions only). Music Educators National Conference, 1806 Robert Fulton Dr., Reston, VA 22091. TEL 703-860-4000. FAX 703-860-1531. Ed. Jeanne Spaeth. adv.; bk.rev.; illus.; index. circ. 64,000. (also avail. in microform from UMI; reprint service avail. from UMI) **Indexed:** Arts & Hum.Cit.Ind., Bk.Rev.Ind. (1965-), C.I.J.E., Child.Bk.Rev.Ind. (1965-), Cont.Pg.Educ., Curr.Cont., Educ.Ind., Except.Child.Educ.Abstr., Mult.Ed.Abstr., Music Artic.Guide, Music Ind., PMR, RILM, So.Pac.Per.Ind., Sp.Ed.Needs Abstr. **Document type:** academic/scholarly publication.
—BLDSC (5990.270000); Faxon; UMI; UnCover.
Description: Presents study and teaching methods.

MUSIC FILE. see EDUCATION — Teaching Methods And Curriculum

780 CN
MUSIC FOR ONE MUSIC FOR ALL. 1988. a. Can.$10. Saskatchewan Music Festival Association, 201 - 1819 Cornwall St., Regina, SK S4P 2K4, Canada. Ed. Doris Covey Lazecki. circ. 2,500. **Document type:** academic/scholarly publication.
Description: The written history of the Association.

780 US ISSN 0898-8757
MUSIC FOR THE LOVE OF IT. (Feb. issue includes A C M P Summer Music Workshop Directory) 1988. bi-m. $20. Ted Rust, Ed. & Pub., 67 Parkside Dr., Berkeley, CA 94705. TEL 510-654-9134. FAX 510-654-4656. adv.; bk.rev.; illus.; circ. 500 (paid). (looseleaf format; back issues avail.) **Document type:** newsletter.

780.1 US ISSN 0885-503X
MUSIC FORUM. 1967. irreg., vol.6, pt.1, 1988. price varies. Columbia University Press, 562 W. 113th St., New York, NY 10025. TEL 212-666-1000. Ed. Felix Salzer. illus. **Indexed:** Music Ind., RILM.

780 US ISSN 1071-2801
MUSIC FROM CHINA. NEWS/CHANG FENG YUE XUN. (Text in Chinese and English) 1991. q. $10. Music from China - Chang Feng Zhongyuetuan, 170 Park Row, Ste. 12-D, New York, NY 10038. TEL 212-962-5698. Eds. Chen Yi, Paul Shackman. bk.rev.; music rev.; circ. 1,200. (back issues avail.) **Document type:** newsletter.
Description: Aims to foster interest in Chinese music. Introduces musicians, works, and events.

780 US
MUSIC IN AMERICAN LIFE. irreg. University of Illinois Press, 1325 S. Oak St., Champaign, IL 61820. TEL 217-333-0950. FAX 217-244-8082. (reprint service avail. from UMI) **Document type:** academic/scholarly publication, monographic series. *Refereed Serial*

780 057.85 PL ISSN 0860-911X
MUSIC IN POLAND. (Text in English) 1966. s-a. free. Polish Music Council, Fredry 8, 00-097 Warsaw, Poland. (Co-sponsor: Ministry of Culture and Arts) bk.rev.; bibl. circ. 900.
—BLDSC (5990.381250); UnCover.
Description: Contains articles especially on Polish music and musical life in Poland.

780 AU
MUSIC IN THE MEDIA - I M Z BULLETIN. (Text in English, French, German) 1961. m. (10/yr.). membership. International Music Centre - Internationales Musikzentrum, Lothringerstr. 20, A-1030 Vienna, Austria. TEL 01-7130777. FAX 01-7130777-77. Ed. Monika Gelbmann. bk.rev. circ. 1,500. **Indexed:** RILM. **Document type:** bulletin.
Former titles: Music and Media - I M Z Bulletin; I M Z Bulletin (ISSN 0019-0071); I M Z Information (ISSN 0538-8783)

780 IS
MUSIC IN TIME. 1984. a. free. Jerusalem Rubin Academy of Music and Dance, Campus Givat Ram, Jerusalem 91904, Israel. TEL 972-2-759911. FAX 972-2-527713. Ed. Mrs. Michal Smoira-Cohn. circ. 1,000. **Document type:** academic/scholarly publication.
Description: Covers musical activities in Israel and subjects of interest to the music and dance world. Presents contributions from internationally-known musicians and music educators.

780.65 381 US ISSN 1050-1681
MUSIC INC. 11/yr. $16. Maher Publications, Inc., 180 Park Ave., Elmhurst, IL 60126. TEL 708-941-2030. FAX 708-941-3210. (Subscr. to: 180 W. Park Ave., Elmhurst, IL 60126) Ed. Edward Enright. circ. 8,754.
Former titles (until 1990): Up Beat Monthly (ISSN 0892-113X); Up Beat (ISSN 0164-7121)

780 UK ISSN 0951-5135
ML5
MUSIC JOURNAL. 1929. m. £22. Incorporated Society of Musicians, 10 Stratford Pl., London W1N 9AE, England. TEL 0171-629 4413. FAX 0171-408-1538. Ed. Neil Hoyle. circ. 5,000. (back issues avail.)
Description: Carries general musical news and reports of members' activities.

781.7 264 028.5 US ISSN 0027-4372
ML1
THE MUSIC LEADER. 1970. q. $17.95. Southern Baptist Convention, Sunday School Board, Music Department, MSN 170, 127 Ninth Ave., N., Nashville, TN 37234-0001. TEL 615-251-2513; 800-458-2772. FAX 615-251-3866. Ed. Anne Trudel. circ. 36,000. **Document type:** trade publication.
Formerly: Children's Music Leader.
Description: Provides advice to church music leaders and contains lesson plans for all ages of preschool and children's choirs.

780 US ISSN 0580-289X
MUSIC LIBRARY ASSOCIATION. NEWSLETTER. Key Title: Newsletter - Music Library Association. Variant title: M L A Newsletter. 1969. q. membership. Music Library Association, Box 487, Canton, MA 02021. TEL 617-828-8450. Ed. Michael J. Rogan. **Document type:** newsletter.
Description: Published in order to keep the membership of the association abreast of events, ideas, and trends related to music librarianship.

MUSIC LIBRARY ASSOCIATION. NOTES. see LIBRARY AND INFORMATION SCIENCES

MUSIC LIBRARY ASSOCIATION. TECHNICAL REPORTS; information for music media specialists. see LIBRARY AND INFORMATION SCIENCES

780 JA
MUSIC LIFE. (Text in Japanese) 1952. m. 6000 Yen. Shinko Music Publishing Co. Ltd., 2-1, Ogawa-machi, Kanda, Chiyoda-ku, Tokyo, Japan. Ed. Kaoruko Togo.

782.5 264 028.5 US ISSN 0162-4377
ML1
MUSIC MAKERS (NASHVILLE). q. $10.95. Southern Baptist Convention, Sunday School Board, 127 Ninth Ave., N., Nashville, TN 37234. TEL 800-458-2772. **Indexed:** Perf.Arts Biog.Master Ind.
Description: Presents choir music for children in grades 1-3.

780 658 DK ISSN 0108-5328
MUSIC MANAGEMENT & INTERNATIONAL PROMOTION; the magazine behind the business news. Variant title: M M I P. 1983. bi-m. DKK 21.25 per no. Music Management International, Postbox 77, 2650 Hidovre, Denmark. illus.

780 UK
MUSIC MART. 1987. m. Maze Media Ltd., Castle House, 97 High St., Colchester, Essex CO1 1TH, England. TEL 01206-795640. FAX 01206-795640. Ed. Steve Wright. adv. contact: Sylvia Linscott. **Document type:** consumer publication.
Formerly: Music & Equipment Mart (ISSN 0956-6619)
Description: Product reviews of guitars, basses and keyboards.

780 CN ISSN 0702-9012
MUSIC MCGILL. 1976. s-a. free. McGill University, Faculty of Music, 555 Sherbrooke St. W., Montreal, Que. H3A 1E3, Canada. TEL 514-398-4535. Ed. John Grew. circ. 4,500.

780 US ISSN 0891-1002
ML1
MUSIC NEWS;* the monthly report. 1984. m. $20. Keyboard Press, Ltd., 3829 Legation St., N.W., Washington, DC 20015-2701. TEL 301-474-0050. Eds. Bradford Gowen, Maribeth Gowen. bk.rev. circ. 700.

781.24 US ISSN 0258-963X
MUSIC NOTATION NEWS. 1986. q. $40 for 2 yrs. (Music Notation Modernization Association) Notation Research Press, Box 241, Kirksville, MO 63501. TEL 816-665-8098. FAX 816-665-8098. (Subscr. to: Michael Laschober, Treas., 10 Briar Path, Arnold, MO 63010) Ed. Tom Reed. bk.rev. (back issues avail.) **Document type:** academic/scholarly publication.
Description: Research on new methods of music notation.

780 US ISSN 0027-4437
MUSIC NOW. 1951. q. membership. Southeastern Composers' League, Mississippi University for Women, Box W-70, Colombus, MS 39701. TEL 601-329-7203. FAX 601-329-7348. E-mail: RMONT@SUNMUW1.MUW.EDU. Ed. Richard Montalto. adv.; bk.rev.; circ. 600 (paid). (processed) **Indexed:** Music Artic.Guide. **Document type:** newsletter.

MUSIC O C L C USERS GROUP. NEWSLETTER. see LIBRARY AND INFORMATION SCIENCES

MUSIC OF THE SPHERES; a quarterly magazine of art and music for the New Age. see NEW AGE PUBLICATIONS

780 US ISSN 1066-8217
MUSIC OF THE UNITED STATES OF AMERICA. (Subseries of: Recent Researches in American Music (ISSN 0147-0078)) 1993. q. price varies. A-R Editions, Inc., 801 Deming Way, Madison, WI 53717. TEL 608-836-9000. Ed. Richard Crawford. **Document type:** academic/scholarly publication.

780 US
MUSIC PAPER. 1979. m. $12. Sound Resources, Box 304, Manhasset, NY 11030. TEL 516-883-8898. FAX 516-883-2577. Ed. Karen A. Cavill; Pub. Bill Russo. adv.; music rev. circ. 70,000. **Document type:** consumer publication, trade publication.
Description: Covers contemporary music and high-fidelity equipment for musicians and music lovers.

780.01 US ISSN 0730-7829
ML1
MUSIC PERCEPTION. 1983. q. $104 (foreign $110) (effective 1996). University of California Press, Journals Division, 2120 Berkeley Way, Berkeley, CA 94720. TEL 510-643-7154. FAX 510-642-9917. Ed. Diana Deutsch. adv.; bk.rev.; illus.; index. circ. 900. (also avail. in microform from UMI; back issues avail.) **Indexed:** Arts & Hum.Cit.Ind., Curr.Cont., Music Ind., Psychol.Abstr. (1983-), RILM. **Document type:** academic/scholarly publication.
—BLDSC (5990.381000); Faxon; Genuine Article; SWETS; UMI; UnCover. **CCC.**
 Description: Focuses on scientific and musical approaches to the study of musical phenomena.
 Refereed Serial

MUSIC REFERENCE SERVICES QUARTERLY. see *LIBRARY AND INFORMATION SCIENCES*

780 JA ISSN 0289-2278
MUSIC RESEARCH/ONGAKU KENKYU. 1972. a. free. Music Research Institute, Osaka College of Music - Osaka Ongaku Daigaku Ongaku Kenkyujo, 1-1-4 Meishinguchi, Toyonaka, Osaka 561, Japan. FAX 06-866-8490. Ed. Nobuo Nishioka. adv.; bk.rev.; illus. circ. 1,000. **Indexed:** RILM. **Document type:** academic/scholarly publication.
 Former titles (until 1982): Music Culture; (until 1978): Data of Music in Western Japan; (until 1975): Data of Music in Kansai District.
 Description: Contains papers on music culture, modern music, folk music, acoustics, music physiology, and music education.

780.7 CN ISSN 0700-3838
MUSIC RESEARCH NEWS. 1976. s-a. membership. Canadian Music Research Council, c/o Robert Walker, Simon Fraser University, Faculty of Education, Burnaby, B.C., Canada. TEL 604-291-3192. bk.rev.; bibl. circ. 100.

780 UK ISSN 0027-4445
ML5
MUSIC REVIEW. 1940. q. £50. Black Bear Press Ltd., Kings Hedges Rd., Cambridge CB4 2PQ, England. Ed. A.F. Leighton Thomas. adv.; bk.rev.; music rev.; rec.rev.; index. circ. 1,000. (also avail. in microform from UMI; reprint service avail. from KTO) **Indexed:** Arts & Hum.Cit.Ind., Br.Hum.Ind., Curr.Cont., Hum.Ind., Ind.Bk.Rev.Hum., Music Ind., RILM.
—BLDSC (5990.400000); Faxon; SWETS; UMI; UnCover.

780.7 UK ISSN 0027-4461
ML5
MUSIC TEACHER. 1909. m. £44. Rhinegold Publishing Ltd., 241 Shaftesbury Ave., London WC2H 8EH, England. TEL 0171-333-1747. FAX 0171-333-1769. (Subscr. to: P.O. Box 47, Gravesend, Kent DA12 2AN, England) Ed. Tim Homfray. adv.; bk.rev.; music rev. (also avail. in microform from UMI) **Indexed:** Cont.Pg.Educ., Music Ind. **Document type:** academic/scholarly publication.
—BLDSC (5990.420000); UMI; UnCover.
 Formerly: Music Teacher and Piano Student.
 Description: Presents study and teaching methods.

780.7 RU
MUSIC TEACHERS LIBRARY. 2/yr. 1.50 Rub. per issue. Izdatel'stvo Muzyka, Ul. Neglinnaya 14, Moscow 103031, Russia.

780 US ISSN 0195-6167
MT6
MUSIC THEORY SPECTRUM. 1979. s-a. $45 to individuals (outside N. America $60); institutions $48 (outside N. America $63); students $20 (outside N. America $35). Society for Music Theory, College of Music, Temple University, Philadelphia, PA 19122. TEL 215-204-8316. FAX 215-204-4957. E-mail: cfolio@vm.temple.edu. Ed. Joel Lester. adv.; bk.rev. circ. 1,100. (back issues avail.) **Indexed:** Music Artic.Guide, Music Ind., RILM. **Document type:** academic/scholarly publication.
—BLDSC (5990.425000); Genuine Article; UnCover.

780 US ISSN 0734-7367
ML3920
MUSIC THERAPY. 1981. a. $20 to individuals; institutions and libraries $30. American Association for Music Therapy, Box 80012, Valley Forge, PA 19484-0012. TEL 215-265-4006. FAX 215-265-1011. Ed. David Marcus. bk.rev. circ. 1,000. (back issues avail.) **Indexed:** Psychol.Abstr. (1981-).
—BLDSC (5990.429000).

780 150 US ISSN 0734-6875
ML3920
MUSIC THERAPY PERSPECTIVES. 1983. 2/yr. $85 (foreign $95) (effective 1996). National Association for Music Therapy, Inc., 8455 Colesville Rd., Ste. 930, Silver Spring, MD 20910-3392. TEL 301-589-3300. FAX 301-589-5175. Eds. Mary Scovel, Brian Wilson. adv. (back issues avail.) **Indexed:** Psychol.Abstr. (1987-). **Document type:** academic/scholarly publication.
—BLDSC (5990.435100); UnCover.
 Description: Focuses on the theory, practice and administration of music therapy.
 Refereed Serial

782.5 286 US ISSN 0164-7180
MUSIC TIME. w. $11.75. Southern Baptist Convention, Sunday School Board, 127 Ninth Ave., N., Nashville, TN 37234. TEL 800-458-2772.
 Description: For preschool choir members and their parents.

780 US ISSN 0027-4488
ML1
MUSIC TRADES. 1890. m. $14 (includes Purchaser's Guide to the Music Industries). Music Trades Corporation, c/o Paul A. Majeski, Ed., Box 432, 80 West St., Englewood, NJ 07631. TEL 201-871-1965. adv.; charts; illus. circ. 7,200. (also avail. in microform from UMI; reprint service avail. from UMI) **Indexed:** Music Ind., PROMT. **Document type:** trade publication.
—UMI; UnCover.

780 310 US ISSN 0197-4173
ML3795
MUSIC U S A;* annual statistical review of the musical instrument industry. 1957? a. $15. American Music Conference, 5140 Avenida Encinas, Carlsbad, CA 92008. TEL 619-431-9124. Ed. Paul Bjorneberg. circ. 1,750. **Indexed:** SRI.

780 US ISSN 1065-0229
MUSIC VIDEO MAGAZINE. Cover title: Clip. 1991. m. David Bernstein, Ed. & Pub., Box 17705, Irvine, CA 92713. TEL 714-262-9336. adv. **Document type:** consumer publication.
 Description: Covers developments and releases in the music video industry.

658.8 789.91 UK ISSN 0265-1548
ML3790
MUSIC WEEK. 1959. w. £110 (foreign £136). Spotlight Publications Ltd. (Subsidiary of: Morgan-Grampian plc), Ludgate House, 245 Blackfriars Rd., London SE1 9UR, England. TEL 071-620-3636. FAX 071-401-8036. Ed. Steve Redmond. adv. contact: Jonathan Roberts. bk.rev.; rec.rev.; charts. circ. 13,468. **Document type:** trade publication.
 Incorporates: R M; **Former titles:** Music and Video Week; (until Jul. 1981): Music Week; Record Retailer (ISSN 0034-1606)
 Description: News for the music industry and music retailer.

780 UK ISSN 0267-3290
MUSIC WEEK DIRECTORY. 1976. a. £35. Spotlight Publications Ltd., Ludgate House, 245 Blackfriars Rd., London SE1 9UR, England. TEL 071-620-3636. FAX 071-401-8036. **Document type:** directory.
 Former titles (until 1984): Music and Video Week Directory (ISSN 0264-3383); Music and Video Week Yearbook; Music Week Industry Year Book.
 Description: Directory of UK record and music industry institutions, companies and individuals.

780 GW ISSN 0027-4518
ML5
MUSICA; Zweimonatsschrift fuer alle Gebiete des Musiklebens. 1946. bi-m. DM.56. Baerenreiter Verlag, Heinrich-Schuetz-Allee 35, 34131 Kassel, Germany. TEL 0561-3105-0. FAX 0561-3105240. (Subscr. in US to: Educational Music Service, 13 Elkay Dr., Chester, NY 10918. TEL 914-469-5790. FAX 914-469-5817) Ed.Bd. adv.; bk.rev.; bibl.; illus.; index. circ. 11,000. **Indexed:** Music Ind., RILM. **Document type:** academic/scholarly publication.
—Faxon; Genuine Article; SWETS; UMI. **CCC.**

780 789.91 IT ISSN 0392-5544
MUSICA; informazione musicale e discografica. 1977. bi-m. L.49000 (foreign L.112000) (effective Oct. 1993). Edizioni Diapason Milano, Via Ampere 60, 20131 Milan, Italy. TEL 02-2367615. Dir. Umberto Masini. adv.; bk.rev.; film rev.; index. circ. 35,000. (back issues avail.)

780 CU ISSN 1010-4615
MUSICA. q. Ministerio de Cultura, UNEAC, Casa de las Americas, 3 y G, Vedado, Havana, Cuba.

780.902 BE ISSN 0771-7016
MUSICA ANTIQUA; aktuele informatie over oude muziek. 1984. q. 700 BEF (foreign 800 BEF). Alamire vzw, P.O. Box 45, 3990 Peer, Belgium. TEL 32-11-632-164. FAX 32-11-63-49-11. Ed. Herman Baeten; Pub. Herman Baeten. adv.; B&W page 10000 BEF, color page 34000 BEF; trim 300 x 210. bk.rev.; music rev. circ. 2,000. **Indexed:** RILM. **Document type:** academic/scholarly publication.
 Description: Scholarly and general coverage of early music, including musicology topics, interviews, reports on music fairs, festivals, and conferences.

780 950 US ISSN 0140-6078
ML330
MUSICA ASIATICA. 1978. irreg. (approx. a.), vol.3, 1981. price varies. Oxford University Press, 200 Madison Ave., New York, NY 10016. TEL 212-679-7300. Ed. Laurence Picken. illus. **Indexed:** Anthropol.Lit., RILM.
—BLDSC (5990.535000).

780 UK ISSN 0580-2954
MUSICA BRITANNICA; a national collection of music. 1951. irreg. price varies. (Musica Britannica Trust) Stainer and Bell Ltd., P.O. Box 110, Victoria House, 23 Gruneisen Rd., London N3 1DZ, England. FAX 0181-343-3024. Ed. Paul Doe. circ. 1,100. **Document type:** academic/scholarly publication.

780 700 792 IT
MUSICA, CINEMA, IMMAGINE, TEATRO. irreg., latest no.13. price varies. Angelo Longo Editore, Via Paolo Costa 33, 48100 Ravenna, Italy. TEL 39-544-217026. FAX 39-544-217554. Ed. Gianfranco Casadio. circ. 1,500. **Document type:** monographic series.
 Former titles: Musica, Cinema, Teatro; Musica, Immagine, Teatro.

780 IT
MUSICA D'OGGI; periodico di cultura musica spettacolo. 1975. m. L.20000. Musica d'Oggi, Via Romolo Balzani, 64-6, 00177 Rome, Italy. Ed. Dino Cafaro. adv.; bk.rev. circ. 30,000. (tabloid format)

780.9 GW ISSN 0077-2461
MUSICA DISCIPLINA; yearbook of the history of music, Medieval and Renaissance. (Text in English; occasionally in French, German, Italian) 1946. a. DM.81.50. (American Institute of Musicology, US) Haenssler Verlag, Postfach 1220, 73762 Neuhausen, Germany. TEL 07158-177-114. FAX 07158-177119. Eds. Gilbert Reaney, Frank D'Accone. **Indexed:** Arts & Hum.Cit.Ind., Curr.Cont., Music Ind., RILM. **Document type:** academic/scholarly publication.
—BLDSC (5990.610000); UnCover.

780.904 780.7 IT ISSN 0391-4380
MT3.18
MUSICA DOMANI; trimestrale di cultura e pedagogia musicale. 1971. q. L.30000 (foreign L.35000). G. Ricordi & C. S.p.A., Via Berchet, 2, Milan, Italy. TEL 39-2-88812. FAX 39-2-88812212. TELEX 310177 RICOR I. Ed. Maurizio Della Casa. adv.; bk.rev. circ. 4,500. (back issues avail.) **Document type:** academic/scholarly publication.

780   IT
MUSICA E CULTURA. 1987. 3/yr. L.27000 (foreign L.35000) (effective 1988). Editrice Turris, Via Bertesi, 1, 26100 Cremona, Italy. Ed. Giacomo Fornari.

789.91   IT   ISSN 0027-4526
MUSICA E DISCHI. (Includes supplements) 1945. m. L.100000 (foreign L.150000). Editoriale Musica e Dischi, Via De Amicis 47, 20123 Milan, Italy. TEL 39-2-58105737. FAX 39-2-8323843. Ed. Mario de Luigi. adv. contact: Emanuela Masserani. rec.rev.; illus.; bibl. **Indexed:** Music Ind. **Document type:** trade publication.
    Description: Information on music industry, audio (professional) and home video.

780   IT   ISSN 0394-0187
MUSICA E DOSSIER. 1986. m. L.57000. Giunti Gruppo Editoriale S.p.A., Via Vincenzo Gioberto, 34, 50121 Florence, Italy. TEL 055-66791. FAX 055-268312. Ed. Francesco Cristino.

780   AG
MUSICA HOY; opera danza teatro conciertos. vol.12, 1993. m.? Arg.$5 per no. Musica Hoy Producciones, Donato Alvarez 419, 1406 Buenos Aires, Argentina. TEL 54-1-6324591. Ed. Juan Gelaf.

781.57   IT   ISSN 0027-4542
ML5
MUSICA JAZZ. 1945. m. L.144000 (foreign L.230000). (Messaggerie Musicali) Rusconi Editori S.p.A., Servizio Abbonamenti, Viale Sarca 235, 20126 Milan, Italy. TEL 02-66191. FAX 02-6619-2737. Dir. Pino Candini. adv.; bk.rev.; film rev, music rev, play rev, rec.rev, bibl, illus.; index. circ. 40,000. (back issues avail.) **Indexed:** Music Ind.

781.7   US   ISSN 0147-7536
ML1
MUSICA JUDAICA. (Text in English and Hebrew) 1976. a. $25. American Society for Jewish Music, 155 Fifth Ave., New York, NY 10010. TEL 212-533-2601. FAX 212-533-2601. Ed. Israel J. Katz. adv.; bk.rev. circ. 1,500. **Indexed:** Ind.Jew.Per., Music Ind., RILM.
    —BLDSC (5990.665000).

780   PL   ISSN 0077-247X
ML170
MUSICA MEDII AEVI. (Text in Polish; summaries in English) 1965. irreg. price varies. (Polska Akademia Nauk, Instytut Sztuki) Polskie Wydawnictwo Muzyczne, Al. Krasinskiego 11a, 31-111 Krakow, Poland. TEL 48-12-227044. FAX 48-12-220174. Ed. Jerzy Morawski. adv. contact: Teresa Wlochynska. **Indexed:** RILM. **Document type:** academic/scholarly publication.
    —BLDSC (5990.670000).
    Description: Covers the field of Medieval music.

780   PL
DE MUSICA MUNDI. 1988. irreg. price varies. Polskie Wydawnictwo Muzyczne, Al. Krasinskiego 11a, 31-111 Krakow, Poland. TEL 48-12-227044. FAX 48-12-220174.
    Description: Series containing comprehensive studies and monographs by musicologists from Jagiellonian and Warsaw Universities.

786   JA   ISSN 0289-3630
MUSICA NOVA. (Text in Japanese) m. 860 Yen. Ongaku No Tomo Sha Corp., Kagurazaka 6-30, Shinjuku-ku, Tokyo 162, Japan. TEL 03-3235-2675. FAX 03-3260-6415. adv.: B&W page 174000 Yen, color page 360000 Yen; trim 257 x 182. circ. 65,000.
    Description: Directed at pianists and piano instructors.

780.7   IT
MUSICA - REALTA. 1980. 3/yr. L.70000 (foreign L.90000). Libreria Musicale Italiana Editrice, Via di Arsina 196F, 55100 Lucca, Italy. Ed. Luigi Pestalozza. adv.: B&W page L.750000.

783 282   GW   ISSN 0179-356X
MUSICA SACRA. bi-m. DM.59. Allgemeiner Caecilien-Verband, Andreasstr. 9, 93059 Regensburg, Germany. TEL 0941-84339. (also avail. in microfiche from IDC) **Indexed:** RILM. **Document type:** bulletin.

780   IT
MUSICA VIVA. 1977. m. L.70000. Sigel S.r.l., Via Andrea Doria 50, 20124 Milan, Italy. TEL 02-72002878. FAX 02-8693624. TELEX 321118 NIM I. Ed. Lorenzo Arruga. adv.: B&W page L.4500000, color page L.6000000. bk.rev.; rec.rev.; illus. circ. 20,000. (back issues avail.)

780   SP
MUSICA Y TECNOLOGIA - KEYBOARD. 11/yr. Corcega 89 entlo., 08029 Barcelona, Spain. TEL 3-230-97-90. FAX 3-230-97-90. Ed. Josep-Oriol Tomas. circ. 15,000.

783   IT   ISSN 0027-4569
MUSICAE SACRAE MINISTERIUM. 1964. irreg. $25 to non-members (effective 1994). Consociatio Internationalis Musicae Sacrae, c/o PIMS, Via di Torre Rossa 21, 00165 Rome, Italy. TEL 39-6-6638792. FAX 39-6-6985378. TELEX 504-2024 DIRGENTEL VA. Ed. Rudolf Pohl. bk.rev.; abstr.; index. circ. 400. **Indexed:** RILM. **Document type:** academic/scholarly publication.

790   US   ISSN 0735-7788
ML12
MUSICAL AMERICA INTERNATIONAL DIRECTORY OF THE PERFORMING ARTS. 1960. a. $80 (effective 1995). K-III Directory Corp., 424 W. 33rd St., 11th Fl., New York, NY 10001-3604. TEL 212-714-3100. FAX 212-695-5025. Ed. Sedgwick Clark. adv. circ. 15,000. **Document type:** directory.
    Formerly (until 1968): Musical America Annual Directory Issue (ISSN 0580-308X)

780.9489   DK   ISSN 0027-4585
MUSICAL DENMARK. 1952. s-a. free. Danish Musical Information Center, Graabroedretorv 16, DK-1154 Copenhagen K, Denmark. TEL 45-33-11-20-66. FAX 45-33-32-20-16. Ed. Bendt Viinholt Nielsen. bibl.; illus. circ. 8,000. (back issues avail.) **Indexed:** Music Ind. **Document type:** academic/scholarly publication, bulletin, newsletter.
    —UnCover.

780   US   ISSN 0160-3876
ML1
MUSICAL HERITAGE REVIEW MAGAZINE. 1977. 18/yr. membership only. Musical Heritage Society, 1710 Highway 35, Ocean, NJ 07712. TEL 201-531-7000. adv.; bk.rev.; circ. controlled.

780 001.3   SW   ISSN 0349-988X
MUSICAL INTERPRETATION RESEARCH. Short title: M I R. 1982. irreg. price varies. Mirage, Raadmansgatan 3, 4tr., S-11425 Stockholm, Sweden. TEL 08-108052. Ed. Nils-Goran Sundin. bk.rev. (back issues avail.) **Indexed:** RILM.
    Description: Concerns the artistic aspects of musical performance, particularly the aesthetics of conductors.

MUSICAL MAINSTREAM (LARGE-PRINT EDITION). see HANDICAPPED — Visually Impaired

658.8 781.91   US   ISSN 0027-4615
ML1
MUSICAL MERCHANDISE REVIEW; pianos, musical instruments, organs, accessories. 1879. m. $24. Larkin-Pluznick-Larkin, Inc., 100 Wells Ave., Box 9103, Newton, MA 02159-9103. TEL 617-964-5100. FAX 617-964-2752. Ed. Don Johnson. adv.; bk.rev.; film rev.; rec.rev.; illus.; mkt.; pat.; tr.lit.; tr.mk.; index; circ. 12,000. (controlled). **Document type:** trade publication.

780.7   UK   ISSN 0027-4623
ML5
MUSICAL OPINION; serious music journal. 1877. m. £23 (foreign £35) (subscr. includes section of Organ World. Musical Opinion Ltd., 2 Princes Rd., St. Leonards-on-Sea, East Sussex TN37 6EL, England. TEL 0424-715167. FAX 0424-712214. Ed. Denby Richards. adv. contact: Liz Biddle. bk.rev.; music rev.; rec.rev.; illus. circ. 5,000. (also avail. in microform from UMI,WMP) **Indexed:** Br.Hum.Ind., Music Ind., RILM. **Document type:** consumer publication.
    —BLDSC (5990.770000); Faxon; UMI; UnCover.
    Description: Covers classical music for the music enthusiast and for the professional musician.

780   US   ISSN 0027-4631
ML1
MUSICAL QUARTERLY. 1915. q. £45($64) (effective 1996). Oxford University Press, Journals, 2001 Evans Rd., Cary, NC 27513. TEL 919-677-0977; 800-852-7323. FAX 919-677-1714. E-mail: jnlorders@oup-usa.org. (Subscr. outside N. America to: Oxford University Press, Journals, Walton St., Oxford OX2 6DP, England. TEL 44-1865-56767. FAX 44-1865-267773) Ed. Leon Botstein. adv.; bk.rev.; bibl.; illus.; index, cum.index: 1915-1959, vols.1-45. circ. 2,300. (also avail. in microform from UMI,PMC) **Indexed:** Acad.Ind., Amer.Bibl.Slavic & E.Eur.Stud., Arts & Hum.Cit.Ind., Bk.Rev.Dig., Bk.Rev.Ind. (1965-), Can.Rev.Comp.Lit., Child.Bk.Rev.Ind. (1965-), Curr.Cont., Hum.Ind., Ind.Bk.Rev.Hum., Mag.Ind., Music Artic.Guide, Music Ind., R.G., RILM. **Document type:** academic/scholarly publication.
    —BLDSC (5990.790000); Faxon; Genuine Article; SWETS; UMI; UnCover. **CCC.**
    Description: Contains original articles covering the entire range of musical composition and performance, from early music to the Classical-Romantic tradition to twentieth-century jazz and pop to the latest developments in theory and practice.

MUSICAL SHOW; devoted to the amateur presentation of Broadway musical shows on the stage. see THEATER

780   UK   ISSN 0027-4666
ML5
MUSICAL TIMES; a monthly journal for serious music lovers. 1844. m. £26.40($60) Orpheus Publications Ltd., 7 St. John's Rd., Harrow, Middlesex HA1 2EE, England. TEL 0181-863-2020. FAX 0181-424-9945. Ed. Antony Bye. bk.rev.; music rev.; rec.rev.; index. circ. 6,000. (also avail. in microform from UMI,WMP; reprint service avail. from UMI) **Indexed:** Arts & Hum.Cit.Ind., Br.Hum.Ind., Curr.Cont., Ind.Bk.Rev.Hum., Music Ind., RILM. **Document type:** consumer publication.
    —BLDSC (5990.810000); Faxon; SWETS; UnCover.

780.7 301.412   US   ISSN 0737-0032
ML82
MUSICAL WOMAN. 1983. irreg., latest 1992. price varies. Greenwood Press, Inc. (Subsidiary of: Greenwood Publishing Group Inc.), 88 Post Rd. W., Box 5007, Westport, CT 06881-5007. TEL 203-226-3571. FAX 203-222-1502.
    —Faxon.

780   IT   ISSN 0027-4674
MUSICALBRANDE; arvista Piemonteisa. (Text in Italian and Piedmontese dialect) 1959. q. L.30000. Corso Palermo 11, 10152 Turin, Italy. TEL 39-11-853826. Ed. Alfredo Nicola. adv.: page L.450000. bk.rev.; illus. circ. 1,100.

780.43   IT
MUSICALIA; il fascino della musica. 1992. bi-m. L.8000 per no. Via Alatri, 30, 00171 Rome, Italy. TEL 06-215-51-22. FAX 06-215-51-22. Ed. Enrico Castiglione. **Document type:** consumer publication.

MUSICALS; das Musicalmagazin. see THEATER

780.903   IT   ISSN 1122-0783
MUSICHE DEL RINASCIMENTO ITALIANO. 1990. irreg., no.2, 1990. price varies. Casa Editrice Leo S. Olschki, Casella Postale 66, 50100 Florence, Italy. TEL 39-55-6530684. FAX 39-55-6530214. **Document type:** monographic series.

780.01   IT   ISSN 1122-4282
MUSICHE RINASCIMENTALI SICILIANE. 1970. irreg., no.14, 1994. price varies. Casa Editrice Leo S. Olschki, Casella Postale 66, 50100 Florence, Italy. TEL 39-55-6530684. FAX 39-55-6530214. circ. 1,000. **Document type:** monographic series.

MUSIC

780 US ISSN 0733-5253
ML1
MUSICIAN. 1976. 12/yr. $19.97 (foreign $31.97) (effective 1994). B P I Communications, Inc. (New York), 1515 Broadway, New York, NY 10036. TEL 212-764-7300. (Subscr. to: Box 1923, Marion, OH 43302. TEL 800-347-6969) Ed. Bill Flanagan. adv.; illus. circ. 115,000. (also avail. in microform from UMI; reprint service avail. from UMI) **Indexed:** Music Artic.Guide, Music Ind., New Per.Ind. **Document type:** consumer publication.
—UMI; UnCover. **CCC.**
Incorporates (1986-1990): Gig Magazine (ISSN 1048-8952); Former titles (until 1982): Musician, Player and Listener (ISSN 0161-9543); (until 1977): Music America (ISSN 0145-5419)
Description: Features industry news, record reviews and interviews of today's leading rock and jazz music makers.

780 SZ
MUSICIEN NEUCHATELOIS. 6/yr. Plage 12, CH-2072 St. Blaise, Switzerland. TEL 038-335433. Ed. Donald Bacuzzi. circ. 2,000.

780 CN ISSN 0226-8620
MUSICK. 1979. q. Can.$10($12) Vancouver Society for Early Music, 1254 W. Seventh Ave., Vancouver, BC V6H 1B6, Canada. TEL 604-732-1610. FAX 604-732-1602. Ed.Bd. adv. contact: Jose Verstappen. bk.rev. circ. 4,000. **Document type:** academic/scholarly publication, newsletter.
—Faxon; UnCover.
Description: Covers medieval, Renaissance, baroque and classical music.

780 US
MUSICK OF THE FIFES & DRUMS SERIES. 1976. irreg., latest 1981. price varies. Colonial Williamsburg Foundation, Box 1776, Williamsburg, VA 23187-1776. TEL 804-220-7349. Ed. John C. Moon.

780 NE ISSN 0165-5884
MUSICMAKER; maandblad voor de muziekbeoefenaar. (Text in Dutch) 1977. m. fl.85. Misset (Subsidiary of: Reed Elsevier plc), Postbus 4, 7000 BA Doetinchem, Netherlands. TEL 31-8340-49911. FAX 31-8340-63638. Ed. Jaap van Eik. adv.: B&W page fl.3378, color page fl.5773; trim 215 x 285; adv. contact: Cor van Nek. circ. 20,700. **Document type:** trade publication.
Description: For amateur and professional musicians in the Netherlands and Belgium.

780.1 781.7 SP
MUSICOLOGIA ESPANOLA. 1975. irreg. Ministerio de Educacion y Ciencia, Comisaria Nacional de la Musica, Madrid 3, Spain.

780.01 BE
MUSICOLOGICA NEOLOVANIENSIA STUDIA. 1980. irreg., no.7, 1992. price varies. Association des Diplomes Histoire Art et Archeologie, College Erasme, Place Blaise Pascal 1, B-1348 Louvain-la-Neuve, Belgium. FAX 32-10-472579. **Document type:** monographic series.

780 XO ISSN 0581-0558
ML5
MUSICOLOGICA SLOVACA. 1969. irreg. price varies. (Slovenska Akademia Vied, Umenovedny Ustav) Veda, Publishing House of the Slovak Academy of Sciences, Klemensova 19, 814 30 Bratislava, Slovakia. (Dist. by: Slovart, Nam. Slobody 6, 817 64 Bratislava, Slovakia) **Indexed:** Music Ind., RILM.

780 AT ISSN 0155-0543
MUSICOLOGICAL SOCIETY OF AUSTRALIA. NEWSLETTER. 1977. 3/yr. Aus.$40 membership. Musicological Society of Australia, G.P.O. Box 2404, Canberra, A.C.T. 2601, Australia. Ed. David Pear. circ. 300. (back issues avail.) **Document type:** newsletter.
Description: Carries news of Australian musicology and musicologists as well as international matters of interest to members.

780 GW ISSN 0077-2496
MUSICOLOGICAL STUDIES AND DOCUMENTS. (Text in English; occasionally in French) 1948. irreg. (American Institute of Musicology, US) Haenssler Verlag, Postfach 1220, 73762 Neuhausen, Germany. TEL 07158-177-114. FAX 07158-177119. Ed. Armen Carapetyan. **Document type:** monographic series.
—BLDSC (5990.880000).

780 US ISSN 0275-5866
MUSICOLOGY; a book series. Key Title: Musicology Series. 1979. irreg., latest vol.16. (effective 1996). Gordon & Breach Science Publishers, c/o International Publishers Distributor, 820 Town Center Dr., Langhorne, PA 19047. TEL 215-750-2642. FAX 215-750-6343. (Subscr. to: International Publishers Distributor, P.O. Box 90, Reading, Berkshire RG1 8JL, England. TEL 44-173-456-8316) Ed. F.J. Smith. **Document type:** monographic series.
Refereed Serial

450 AT ISSN 0814-5857
ML5
MUSICOLOGY AUSTRALIA. 1964. a. Aus.$35 or membership Aus.$40. Musicological Society of Australia, G.P.O. Box 2404, Canberra, A.C.T. 2601, Australia. Ed. Michael Noone. adv.; bk.rev. circ. 450. (back issues avail.) **Indexed:** Aus.P.A.I.S., Music Ind., RILM.
—BLDSC (5990.890100); UnCover.
Formerly: Musicology (ISSN 0077-250X)
Description: Features articles on the music of Europe, America, Asia, Indian Ocean, Pacific Ocean, Australian Aborigines and Australian musical composition.

MUSICOPYRIGHT INTELLIGENCE; a newsletter of financial success through copyright ownership. see *PATENTS, TRADEMARKS AND COPYRIGHTS*

780 SP ISSN 0212-7067
MUSICOS. 1980. 6/yr. Nicaragua 137, entlo. 1o, 08029 Barcelona, Spain. TEL 3-239-52-70. Ed. M. Martinez Santin. circ. 10,000.
Formerly (until 1983): Instrumento Musical (ISSN 0211-1705)

780.7 SA ISSN 0256-8837
MUSICUS. (Text in Afrikaans and English) 1973. 2/yr. R.26.20 (overseas $7.80) (effective 1996). University of South Africa, Department of Music, P.O. Box 392, Pretoria 0001, South Africa. FAX 27-12-429-2533. TELEX 350068. Ed. H.H. van der Spuy. adv.; bk.rev. circ. 2,000. (reprint service avail. from UMI) **Document type:** academic/scholarly publication.
Description: Presents articles written on different aspects of music and music examinations and their success.

780 700 CN ISSN 0225-686X
ML5
MUSICWORKS; journal of sound explorations. (Text in English, French) 1978. 3/yr. Can.$39 to individuals; institutions Can.$60. Music Gallery, 179 Richmond St., Toronto, ON M5V 1V3, Canada. TEL 416-977-3546. FAX 416-204-1048. Ed. Gayle Young. adv. contact: Nadine Theriault. bk.rev.; bibl.; charts; illus.; circ. 2,400 (paid). (also avail. in microfilm from MML; includes cassette or CD; back issues avail.) **Indexed:** Can.B.P.I. **Document type:** consumer publication.
Description: Explores, from the artist's perspective, contemporary (including ethnic and indigenous) thought about music and sound.

780.5 FI ISSN 0355-1059
MUSIIKKI. 1971. q. Fmk.70. Suomen Musiikkitieteellinen Seura, Vironkatu 1, 00170 Helsinki 17, Finland. Ed. Erkki Salmenhaara. adv.; bk.rev. circ. 600.

780 GW ISSN 0930-8954
ML21.G3
MUSIK - ALMANACH; Musikleben in der Bundesrepublik Deutschland. 1986. triennial. DM.72. (German Music Council) Gustav Bosse GmbH und Co. KG, Postfach 101420, 34014 Kassel, Germany. Ed. Margot Wallscheid. adv. contact: Hildegard Pfalz. **Document type:** bulletin.

780 792 SZ ISSN 0931-8194
MUSIK & THEATER; die aktuelle Kulturzeitschrift. 1979. m. (10/yr.). 85 SFr. M & T Verlag AG, Geltenwilenstr. 8a, CH-9001 St. Gallen, Switzerland. TEL 071-235555. FAX 071-236745. Ed. Andrea Meuli. adv.; rec.rev.; illus.
Description: News and information from the music and theater world. Includes lists of new records and performances, announcements of events, and classified ads.

780 GW
MUSIK AUS DER STEIERMARK. 1959. irreg. (4-6/yr.). price varies. (Styrian Composers Society) Musikverlag Schulz GmbH, Am Maerzengraben 6, 79112 Freiburg, Germany. FAX 07664-5123. Ed. Wolfgang Suppan. adv. contact: Klaus Schulz. circ. 200. **Document type:** newsletter.
Description: Publication of contemporary music by young composers. Features musical arrangements for all instruments. Each issue includes a single piece of music.

780 GW ISSN 0254-5187
MUSIK-EXPRESS, SOUNDS. 1967. m. Medien Verlagsgesellschaft mbH, Werinherstr. 71, 81541 Munich, Germany. TEL 089-9234-367. FAX 089-6913064. TELEX 523854. Ed. Helmut Werb. adv. contact: Constanze Jandt. circ. 110,367. **Document type:** consumer publication.
Formed by 1983 merger of: Musik-Express (ISSN 0723-4651); Sounds (ISSN 0724-6501)

780 SW ISSN 0077-2518
MUSIK I SVERIGE. (Text in English, German and Swedish) 1969. irreg. price varies. Svenskt Musikhistoriskt Arkiv, Box 16326, S-103 26 Stockholm, Sweden. TEL 46-8-6664560. FAX 46-8-666-4565. (Co-sponsor: Svenska Samfundet foer Musikforskning) **Indexed:** RILM. **Document type:** monographic series.

780 GW
▼**MUSIK IN BADEN-WUERTTEMBERG.** 1994. a. DM.58. (Gesellschaft fuer Musikgeschichte in Baden-Wuerttemberg) Metzler-Verlag, Kernerstr. 43, 70182 Stuttgart, Germany. Ed. Helmut Voelkl. **Document type:** bulletin.

780 GW ISSN 0937-583X
MUSIK IN BAYERN. s-a. Verlag Dr. Hans Schneider GmbH, Mozartstr. 6, 82323 Tutzing, Germany. TEL 08158-3050. FAX 08158-7636. **Indexed:** RILM. **Document type:** academic/scholarly publication.
—Genuine Article.

780.7 GW ISSN 0027-4704
ML5
MUSIK IN DER SCHULE; Zeitschrift fuer Theorie und Praxis des Musikunterrichts. 1949. 6/yr. DM.51. Paedagogischer Zeitschriftenverlag, Postfach 269, 10107 Berlin, Germany. TEL 030-20343431. FAX 030-20343432. Ed. Wolfgang Wunder. adv.; bk.rev.; abstr.; illus.; index. circ. 3,200. **Indexed:** Music Ind., RILM. **Document type:** academic/scholarly publication.
—SWETS.
Description: Presents study and teaching methods.

780 GW ISSN 0931-3311
MUSIK - KONZEPTE; die Reihe ueber Komponisten. 1977. 4/yr. DM.71. Edition Text und Kritik GmbH, Levelingstr. 6a, 81673 Munich, Germany. TEL 089-432929. FAX 089-433997. Eds. Heinz-Klaus Metzger, Rainer Riehn. **Indexed:** RILM. **Document type:** academic/scholarly publication.

780.7 GW ISSN 0027-4747
ML5
MUSIK UND BILDUNG; Zeitschrift fuer Theorie und Praxis der Musikerziehung. 1969. bi-m. DM.65. (Verband Deutscher Schulmusikerzieher) Schott Musik International GmbH, Weihergarten 5, 55116 Mainz, Germany. TEL 06131-246-0. FAX 06131-246211. Ed.Bd. adv.: B&W page DM.1660; trim 260 x 185; adv. contact: Karin Krappen. bk.rev.; music rev.; rec.rev.; bibl.; charts; illus.; index. circ. 9,000. **Indexed:** Music Ind., RILM. **Document type:** consumer publication.
Supersedes: Musik im Unterricht, Ausgaben A and B.

780 301 AU ISSN 0259-076X
MUSIK UND GESELLSCHAFT. 1967. irreg., no.23, 1995. price varies. Hochschule fuer Musik und Darstellende Kunst, Institut fuer Musiksoziologie, Schubertring 14, A-1010 Vienna, Austria. **Document type:** monographic series.

783　　　　　　SZ　　ISSN 0027-4763
MUSIK & GOTTESDIENST. 1947. bi-m. 72 SFr. Gotthelf Verlag, Badenerstr. 69, CH-8026 Zurich, Switzerland. FAX 01-2418242. Eds. Heinz-Roland Schneeberger, Andreas Marti. adv.; bk.rev. circ. 3,700. (also avail. in microform from UMI; reprint service avail. from UMI) **Indexed:** Music Ind., RILM. **Document type:** bulletin.
—UMI.
Incorporates: Der Evangelische Kirchenchor.

783　　　　　　GW　　ISSN 0027-4771
ML5
MUSIK UND KIRCHE. 1930. bi-m. DM.56. Baerenreiter Verlag, Heinrich-Schuetz-Allee 35, 34131 Kassel, Germany. TEL 0561-3105-0. FAX 0561-3105240. (Subscr. in US to: Educational Music Service, 13 Elkay Dr., Chester, NY 10918. TEL 914-469-5790. FAX 914-469-5817) Ed.Bd. adv.; bk.rev.; bibl.; illus. circ. 4,000. **Indexed:** Arts & Hum.Cit.Ind., Curr.Cont., Music Ind., RILM. **Document type:** academic/scholarly publication.
—Faxon; Genuine Article. **CCC**

780.7　　　　GW　　ISSN 0937-9568
MUSIK UND UNTERRICHT. 1976. bi-m. DM.81 (foreign DM.84.60). Erhard Friedrich Verlag GmbH, Im Brande 17, 30926 Seelze, Germany. TEL 0511-40004-0. FAX 0511-4000444. (Subscr. to: Postfach 100150, 30917 Seelze, Germany) index. circ. 2,300. (back issues avail.) **Indexed:** RILM. **Document type:** academic/scholarly publication.
—**CCC.**
Formerly (until 1990): Zeitschrift fuer Musikpaedagogik (ISSN 0341-2830)

780.92　　　　SW　　ISSN 0345-8210
MUSIKANT. 1967. 5/yr. SEK 25 membership. Riksfoerbundet Sveriges Amatoerorkestrar, P.O. Box 3128, S-580 03 Linkoeping, Sweden. TEL 46-13-14-95-90. FAX 46-13-13-71-34.
Formerly: R S A O.

787　　　　　　GW　　ISSN 0172-8989
ML3469
MUSIKBLATT; Zeitschrift fuer Gitarre, Folklore und Lied. 1974. bi-m. DM.42. W. Ulrichs Musikblattverlag, Tannenweg 14, 37085 Goettingen, Germany. TEL 0551-796606. FAX 0551-792681. Ed. Wieland Ulrichs. adv. contact: Thomas Mueller. bk.rev.; bibl.; illus.; index. circ. 3,000. (back issues avail.) **Document type:** consumer publication.

780　　　　　　DK　　ISSN 0108-0040
MUSIKBRANCHENS AARBOG. 1982. a. DKK 29.75. Danplay, Krohsgade 1, 2100 Copenhagen OE, Denmark. Ed. Uffe Egekvist. adv.; bk.rev.; illus. circ. 7,000.

782.1　　　　　SW
MUSIKDRAMATIK. 1978. q. SEK 150. Foereningen MusikDramatik, P.O. Box 4038, S-102 61 Stockholm, Sweden. TEL 46-8-643-95-44. Ed. Torbjoern Eriksson. bk.rev. **Document type:** consumer publication.
Former titles: M D - Musikdramatik (ISSN 0283-5754); (until 1984): Tidskriften Musikdramatik (ISSN 0281-8884); (until 1981): Musikdramatik (ISSN 0349-7259)
Description: Features articles on opera, interviews with artists, performance criticism, and reviews of recordings.

331.881178094　　DK　　ISSN 0905-9962
MUSIKEREN. 1911. m. (11/yr.). DKK 308. Musikeren ApS, Vendersgade 25, 1363 Copenhagen K, Denmark. FAX 33-337517. Ed. Henrik Strube. adv. contact: Kristian Nielsen. circ. 6,000. **Document type:** consumer publication, trade publication.
Formerly (until 1990): Dansk Musiker Tidende (ISSN 0902-9141)

780 331.7　　　SW　　ISSN 0027-478X
ML5
MUSIKERN. 1908. 10/yr. SEK 200. Svenska Musikerfoerbundet - Swedish Musicians Union, P.O. Box 43, S-101 20 Stockholm, Sweden. (Co-sponsors: Kulturarbetarfoerbundet; LO-Foerbundet foer Verksamma inom Kultur- och Noejessektorn) Ed. Ammi Lennander. adv.; bk.rev.; charts; illus.; mkt. circ. 11,000. (also avail. in audio cassette) **Indexed:** Music Ind. **Document type:** trade publication.
Former titles (until 1920): Svenska Musikerfoerbundets Tidning; (until 1910): Musikern.

780　　　　　　AU　　ISSN 0027-4798
MUSIKERZIEHUNG; Zeitschrift der Musikerzieher Oesterreichs. 1947. 5/yr. S.300. Oe B V Paedagogischer Verlag GmbH, Schwarzenbergstr. 5, A-1015 Vienna, Austria. FAX 0222-51405210. adv.; bk.rev.; rec.rev.; bibl.; charts; illus.; index. circ. 1,800. **Indexed:** Arts & Hum.Cit.Ind., Music Ind., RILM. **Document type:** academic/scholarly publication.

780.01　　　　GW　　ISSN 0027-4801
ML5
DIE MUSIKFORSCHUNG. 1947. q. DM.110 or membership. (Gesellschaft fuer Musikforschung) Baerenreiter Verlag, Heinrich-Schuetz-Allee 35, 34131 Kassel, Germany. TEL 0561-3105-0. FAX 0561-3105240. (Subscr. in US to: Educational Music Service, 13 Elkay Dr., Chester, NY 10918. TEL 914-469-5790. FAX 914-469-5817) Eds. C.-H. Mahling, W. Doemling. adv.; bk.rev.; abstr.; bibl.; charts; illus.; index. circ. 2,500. **Indexed:** Curr.Cont., Music Ind., RILM. **Document type:** academic/scholarly publication.
—Faxon; Genuine Article; SWETS. **CCC**

780　　　　　　GW　　ISSN 0935-2562
ML5.I579
MUSIKFORUM - REFERATE UND INFORMATIONEN DES DEUTSCHEN MUSIKRATES. no.9, 1968. 3/yr. free. Deutscher Musikrat, Am Michaelshof 4-a, 53177 Bonn, Germany. FAX 0228-352650. Eds. Richard Jakoby, Andreas Eckhardt.
Formerly (until 1988): International Music Council. German Committee. Referate Informationen (ISSN 0538-8791)

780　　　　　　GW　　ISSN 0027-481X
ML5
MUSIKHANDEL. 1949. 8/yr. DM.40. (Gesamtverband Deutscher Musikfachgeschaefte e.V.) Musikhandel Verlagsgesellschaft mbH, Friedrich-Wilhelm-Str. 31, 53113 Bonn, Germany. FAX 0228-235916. (Co-sponsor: Deutsches Musikverleger-Verband e.V.) adv.; bk.rev.; rec.rev.; charts; illus. circ. 2,450. **Indexed:** Music Ind. **Document type:** trade publication.
—BLDSC (5991.113500).
Description: Trade publication for sheet music, musical instruments and record retailers. Features news, record reviews, new publications, and available positions.

681.8　　　　　GW　　ISSN 0027-4828
ML5
DAS MUSIKINSTRUMENT. 1952. m. DM.112. Verlag Erwin Bochinsky GmbH, Muenchenerstr. 45, 60329 Frankfurt a.M., Germany. TEL 069-239521. Ed.Bd. adv. contact: Winfried Kumetat. bk.rev.; charts; illus.; pat.; index. circ. 5,500. **Indexed:** RILM. **Document type:** trade publication.
—**CCC.**
Description: International trade magazine devoted to the manufacturing, trade, handicraft and research of musical instruments and musical electronics.

780.7　　　　　NO　　ISSN 0802-8176
MUSIKK - FOKUS. 1980. 10/yr. NOK 300 in Norway; other Nordic countries NOK 325; elsewhere NOK 350; newsstand price: NOK 35. N M M - Nordisk Musiker- og Musikkpedagogforening, P.O. Box 210, N-4301 Sandnes, Norway. TEL 47-51-66-54-57. FAX 47-51-62-27-00. Ed. Kare Holdhus. adv.: B&W page NOK 2600, color page NOK 6000; trim 185 x 260. circ. 2,727 (controlled).
Former titles (until 1990): N M P F - Nytt (ISSN 0800-1782); (until 1982): Norsk Musikkpedagogisk Forening Nytt (ISSN 0333-4317)

780　　　　　　NO　　ISSN 0332-6926
MUSIKK OG SKOLE. 1956. 8/yr. NOK 260. Landslaget Musikk i Skolen, Kongensgate 4, N-0153 Oslo, Norway. TEL 47-22-41-93-80. FAX 47-22-41-93-83. Ed. Torild Wagle Christensen. adv.: B&W page NOK 2700, color page NOK 7900; trim 243 x 210. bk.rev. circ. 2,000. **Indexed:** RILM.

780 658.8　　　GW　　ISSN 0047-8474
DER MUSIKMARKT. 1959. s-m. DM.288. Josef Keller Verlag, Postfach 1455, 82317 Starnberg, Germany. TEL 08151-7710. Ed. Uwe Lencher. adv.; bk.rev. circ. 10,300. **Document type:** bulletin.
—**CCC.**

780　　　　　　SW
MUSIKMUSEETS RAPPORTSERIE. 1984. irreg. price varies. Statens Musiksamlingar, Musikmuseet, P.O. Box 16326, S-103 26 Stockholm, Sweden. TEL 46-8-666-45-30. FAX 46-8-663-91-81. Ed. Krister Malm. circ. 200. **Document type:** monographic series.

780　　　　　　SW　　ISSN 0282-8952
MUSIKMUSEETS SKRIFTER. 1964. irreg., no.24, 1992. price varies. Statens Musiksamlingar, Musikmuseet, Box 16326, S-10326 Stockholm, Sweden. TEL 46-8-666-45-30. FAX 46-8-663-91-81. Ed. Krister Malm. circ. 1,000. **Indexed:** RILM. **Document type:** proceedings.
Formerly: Musikhistoriska Museets. Skrifter (ISSN 0081-5675)

780　　　　　　GW
MUSIKPAEDAGOGISCHE BIBLIOTHEK. 1962. irreg., vol.37, 1993. price varies. Florian Noetzel Verlag, Heinrichshofen Buecher, Valoisstr. 11, 26382 Wilhelmshaven, Germany. (Dist. in U.S. by: C.F. Peters Corp., 373 Park Ave. S., New York, N.Y. 10016) Ed. Walter Kolneder. **Document type:** monographic series.

MUSIKPAEDAGOGISCHE FORSCHUNGSBERICHTE. see
EDUCATION — Teaching Methods And Curriculum

780　　　　　　GW　　ISSN 0177-350X
ML3830
MUSIKPSYCHOLOGIE. 1984. irreg. DM.54. (Deutsche Gesellschaft fuer Musikpsychologie) Florian Noetzel Verlag, Heinrichshofen Buecher, Valoisstr. 11, 26382 Wilhelmshaven, Germany. Ed.Bd. circ. 1,000. (back issues avail.) **Indexed:** RILM. **Document type:** monographic series.

780.5　　　　　SW　　ISSN 0027-4844
ML5
MUSIKREVY; allmaen musiktidsskrift. (Editions in English and German at irregular intervals) 1946. bi-m. SEK 350 in the Nordic countries; Europe SEK 370; elsewhere SEK 460. Musikrevy Tidskriftsaktiebolag AB, P.O. Box 144, S-233 23 Svedala, Sweden. TEL 46-40-40-56-65. FAX 46-40-40-56-65. Ed. Bengt Pleijel; Pub. Ben Hedenberg. adv.; bk.rev.; music rev.; rec.rev.; illus.; index. circ. 14,000.

780　　　　　　GW　　ISSN 0178-8884
MUSIKTEXTE; Zeitschrift fuer neue Musik. 1983. 5/yr. DM.40($25) Verlag MusikTexte, Postfach 102461, 50464 Cologne, Germany. TEL 0221-9520215. FAX 0221-9520216. Ed.Bd. adv.: B&W page DM.500; trim 210 x 297. bk.rev. circ. 1,200. **Indexed:** RILM. **Document type:** consumer publication.

780　　　　　　GW　　ISSN 0177-4182
ML5
MUSIKTHEORIE. 1986. 3/yr. DM.85 (foreign DM.98). Laaber-Verlag, Regenburger Str. 19, 93164 Laaber, Germany. TEL 09498-2307. FAX 09498-2543. index. (back issues avail.) **Indexed:** RILM. **Document type:** academic/scholarly publication.
—Faxon.

780　　　　　　SW
MUSIKTIDNINGEN MUSIKOMANEN. 1980. 6/yr. SEK 100($20) Nya Mediaplan AB, P.O. Box 6903, S-10239 Stockholm, Sweden. circ. 100,020. (back issues avail.)

780　　　　　　DK
MUSIKVEJVISER FOR VEJLE AMT. 1981. a. free. Amtsmusikudvalget of Vejle Amt, Undervisnings- og kulturforvaltningen, Damhaven 12, 7100 Vejle, Denmark. TEL 05-835333. Ed. Anette Duedal. circ. 2,500.
Formerly: Musikvejleder for Vejle Amt.
Description: An index of the musical activity in Vejle Amt.

780　　　　　　CN
MUSIMAGAZINE. 6/yr. Publiart, Inc., 1741 Leprohon, Montreal, PQ H4E 1P3, Canada. TEL 514-769-7032. FAX 514-769-5884. Ed. Karmen Riendeau. adv. contact: Napolean Major. circ. 12,000. **Document type:** trade publication.

681.8 655　　　FR　　ISSN 0027-4852
MUSIQUE ET INSTRUMENTS; la revue des editeurs de musique et des facteurs d'instruments. bi-m. 54 F. E G P, 6 rue de Reims, 94230 Cachan, France. TEL 46-63-27-43. adv.; bibl.; illus.; music rev.

MUSIC

780   FR
MUSIQUES ET TECHNIQUES. 11/yr. Foch - Communications, 98 av. de Versailles, B.P. 267, 75016 Paris, France. TEL 42-81-94-58. FAX 42-81-94-58. Ed. Franck Cadet. circ. 12,000.

780   FI   ISSN 0356-7923
MUUSIKKO/MUSICIAN. 1922. m. FIM 160. Suomen Muusikkojen Liitto r.y. - Finnish Musicians' Union, Pieni Roobertinkatu 16, SF-00120 Helsinki, Finland. TEL 358-0-6803-40-70. FAX 358-0-6803-40-87. Ed. Ahti Vanttinen. adv.; bk.rev.; rec.rev. circ. 4,500. **Document type:** trade publication.

780 370   NE   ISSN 0378-0651
MUZIEK EN ONDERWIJS. 1962. bi-m. fl.15. Vereniging Leraren Schoolmuziek, Laweweg 10, 3815 VG Amersfoort, Netherlands. Ed. Nicky Selen. adv.; bk.rev.; bibl.; illus.; index. circ. 1,000.

783   NE   ISSN 0167-2274
MUZIEKBODE. 1932. m. membership. Nederlandse Federatie van Christelijke Muziekbonden, Hulsmaatstraat 88, 7523 WG Enschede, Netherlands. TEL 31-53-330890. FAX 31-53-342162. adv.; bk.rev.; play rev.; abstr.; bibl.; illus.; stat.; tr.lit. circ. 5,000.
Formerly: Christelijke Muziekbode (ISSN 0009-5176)

658.8 781.91   NE   ISSN 0027-5301
MUZIEKHANDEL. 1950. m. free. Nederlandse Muziek Federatie - N M F, Eikbosserweg 181, 1213 RX Hilversum, Netherlands. TEL 31-35-248104. FAX 31-35-214220. Ed. C. Smit. adv.; bk.rev.; bibl.; mkt.; tr.lit.; circ. 500 (controlled). **Document type:** trade publication.
Description: Trade publication for the music industry. Covers sheet music retailing and publishing as well as musical instruments. Includes reports and announcements of meetings and events.

780 070.5   NE
MUZIEKUITGEVERS NOOT. 7/yr. free to qualified personnel. Nederlandse Muziek Federatie - N M F, Eikbosserweg 181, 1213 RX Hilversum, Netherlands. TEL 31-35-248104. FAX 31-35-214220. **Document type:** trade publication.
Description: News for music publishers.

780   XV   ISSN 0580-373X
MUZIKOLOSKI ZBORNIK/MUSICOLOGICAL ANNUAL. (Text in various languages; summaries in English and Slovene) 1965. a. price varies. Univerza v Ljubljani, Filozofska Fakulteta, Oddelek za Muzikologijo, Askerceva 12, 61000 Ljubljana, Slovenia. TEL 061-150-001. FAX 061-159-337. Ed. Andrej Rijavec. illus.; index. circ. 500. **Indexed:** RILM.

781.7   US
MUZIKOS ZINIOS/MUSIC NEWS. (Text in Lithuanian) 1911. s-a. $10 membership. (Siaures Amerikos Lietuviu Muzikos Sajunga - North American Lithuanian Music Organization) Morkunas Press, c/o Antanas Giedraitis, 7310 S. California Ave., Chicago, IL 60629. TEL 312-737-2421. Eds. Kazys Skaisgirys, Stasys Slizys. circ. 300 (paid). **Document type:** newsletter, bulletin.
Description: Contains news of composers, musicians and singers of Lithuanian descent. Provides information on programs and concerts in the U.S. and abroad.

780   HU   ISSN 0027-5336
MUZSIKA. 1958. m. $23. Lapkiado Vallalat, Lenin korut 9-11, 1073 Budapest 7, Hungary. TEL 121-5440. (Subscr. to: Kultura, Box 149, H-1389 Budapest, Hungary) Ed. Maria Feuer. adv.; bk.rev.; illus. circ. 7,500. **Indexed:** Music Ind., RILM.

780   PL
MUZYCZNE CRACOVIANA. 1983. irreg. price varies. Polskie Wydawnictwo Muzyczne, Al. Krasinskiego 11a, 31-111 Krakow, Poland. TEL 48-12-227044. FAX 48-12-220174.
Description: Series presenting Krakow as artistic center of events, facts, and phenomena connected with music.

781   PL   ISSN 0027-5344
ML5
MUZYKA; kwartalnik poswiecony historii i teorii muzyki. (Text in Polish; summaries in English) 1956. q. $16. Polska Akademia Nauk, Instytut Sztuki, Ul.Dluga 28, 00-950 Warsaw, Poland. TEL 48-22-313271. FAX 48-22-313149. (Dist. by: AMOS, ul. Zuga 12, 01-806 Warsaw, Poland. TEL 48-22-346521) Ed. Katarzyna Morawska. bk.rev.; music rev.; rec.rev.; bibl.; illus. (reprint service avail. for UMI) **Indexed:** Music Ind., RILM.
Description: Covers history and theory of music.

780   PL
MUZYKA MOJA MILOSC. 1970. irreg. price varies. Polskie Wydawnictwo Muzyczne, Al. Krasinskiego 11a, 31-111 Krakow, Poland. TEL 48-12-227044. FAX 48-12-220174.
Description: Series containing essays devoted to the most prominent persons of the world of music.

781.71   PL
MUZYKA POLSKA W DOKUMENTACJACH I INTERPRETACJACH. 1980. irreg. price varies. Polskie Wydawnictwo Muzyczne, Al. Krasinskiego 11a, 31-111 Krakow, Poland. TEL 48-12-227044. FAX 48-12-220174. Ed.Bd. adv. contact: Teresa Wlochynska. **Document type:** academic/scholarly publication.
Description: Papers on Polish music, devoted to composers, material and folklore papers.

780   RU   ISSN 0869-4516
ML5
MUZYKAL'NAYA AKADEMIYA. 1933. q. $80 (effective 1996). Izdatel'stvo Kompozitor, Sadovaya Triumfal'naya ul. 14-12, 103006 Moscow, Russia. TEL 095-209-2384. (Dist. by: Mezhdunarodnaya Kniga, B. Yakimanka 39, 117049 Moscow, Russia; Dist. in U.S. by: Victor Kamkin Inc., 4956 Boiling Brook Pkwy., Rockville, MD 20852. TEL 301-881-5973. FAX 301-881-1637) Ed. Yu.S. Korev. bk.rev.; bibl.; illus.; music rev.; index. circ. 3,000. **Indexed:** Curr.Dig.Sov.Press, Music Ind., RILM.
Formerly: Sovetskaya Muzyka (ISSN 0038-5085)

780 398   RU   ISSN 0135-0064
MUZYKAL'NAYA FOL'KLORISTIKA. (Text in Russian; summaries in English and German) 1973. irreg. (approx. every 5 yrs.) 2 Rub. (Soyuz Kompozitorov Rossiiskoi Federatsii, Fol'klornaya Komissiya) Izdatel'stvo Kompozitor, Sadovaya-Triumfalnaya ul. 14-12, 103006 Moscow, Russia. illus. **Indexed:** M.L.A.

780   RU   ISSN 0027-5352
MUZYKAL'NAYA ZHIZN'. 1957. s-m. $86. (Soyuz Kompozitorov Rossiiskoi Federatsii) Izdatel'stvo Kompozitor, Sadovaya-Triumfalnaya ul. 14-12, 103006 Moscow, Russia. TEL 095-209-7524. (Dist. by: Mezhdunarodnaya Kniga, B. Yakimanka 39, 117049 Moscow, Russia; Dist. in U.S. by: Victor Kamkin Inc., 4956 Boiling Brook Pkwy., Rockville, ND 20852. TEL 301-881-5973. FAX 301-881-1637) Ed. I.E. Popov. index.

780.7   US   ISSN 0027-576X
ML27.U5
N A C W P I JOURNAL. 1952. q. $25 to non-members. (National Association of College Wind & Percussion Instructors) Simpson Publishing Co., c/o Dr. R. Weerts, Ed., Division of Fine Arts, Northeast Missouri State University, Kirksville, MO 63501. TEL 816-785-4442. FAX 816-785-7463. adv.; bk.rev.; charts; illus.; circ. 6,000 (controlled). (also avail. in microform from UMI; reprint service avail. from UMI) **Indexed:** Music Artic.Guide, Music Ind., RILM. **Document type:** academic/scholarly publication.
—Faxon; UMI; UnCover.

658.8 780   US
ML3790
N A M M NEWS. 1947. 10/yr. membership. National Association of Music Merchants Inc., 5140 Avenida Encinas, Carlsbad, CA 92008. TEL 619-438-8001. Ed. Jerry Derloshon. tr.lit.; circ. 10,500 (controlled).
Former titles: N A M M Music Retailer News (ISSN 0027-5913); N A M M Members Monthly Bulletin.

789.91   US
N A R M SOUNDING BOARD. s-m. National Association of Recording Merchandisers, 3 Eves Dr., Ste. 307, Marlton, NJ 08053.

784.9   US   ISSN 0884-8106
ML27.U5
N A T S JOURNAL. 1944. 5/yr. $23 (foreign $27) (effective 1993). National Association of Teachers of Singing, Inc., 2800 University Blvd. N., JU Sta., Jacksonville, FL 32211. TEL 904-744-9022. FAX 904-744-9033. E-mail: wmvessels@aol.com. Ed. James McKinney. adv.; bk.rev.; music rev.; rec.rev.; charts; illus.; index. circ. 6,000. (also avail. in microfilm from UMI; reprint service avail. from UMI) **Indexed:** Music Artic.Guide, Music Ind. **Document type:** academic/scholarly publication.
—Faxon; UMI; UnCover.
Formerly (until May 1985): N A T S Bulletin (ISSN 0027-6073)
Description: Presents study and teaching methods. *Refereed Serial*

N D. see *ART*

780   GW   ISSN 0863-3975
N M! MESSITSCH. 10/yr. DM.50 (foreign DM.60). Nord Ost Rock e.V., Wichertstr. 67, 10439 Berlin, Germany. TEL 030-4497879. FAX 030-4974601. Ed. Wolf Kampmann. adv. contact: Petra Rolf. circ. 20,000. **Document type:** consumer publication.

780   NE   ISSN 0926-0692
N N O MAGAZINE. 1990. bi-m. fl.20. Noord - Nederlands Orkest, Emmaplein 2, P.O. Box 818, 9700 AV Groningen, Netherlands. TEL 31-50-126200. FAX 31-50-138164. Eds. A.L.E. Verberne, K.H.A. Holtman. adv.; bk.rev.; illus.; circ. 3,500 (controlled). (also avail. in microfilm)
Formed by the merger of (1962-1990): Paukenslag (Leeuwarden) (ISSN 0926-7654); N F O Magazine (ISSN 0924-6967)

782.1   US   ISSN 0749-9345
N O A NEWSLETTER. 1977. q. $40 to non-members; institutions $50. National Opera Association, 3904 Griffin Rd., Clinton, NY 13323. TEL 315-853-6292. (Subscr. to: National Opera Association, c/o Jeff Wright, N.W.U. School of Music, 711 Elgin Rd., Evanston, IL 60208-1200) Ed. JoElyn Wakefield-Wright. adv. circ. 1,000. (tabloid format) **Document type:** newsletter.
Description: Opera convention information, notices of competitions for members of the association, articles concerning opera, and news of member activities.

780   US   ISSN 0146-9975
ML1
N S O A BULLETIN. 1959. q. membership; libraries $8. National School Orchestra Association, c/o University of Northern Colorado, Greeley, CO 80639. Ed. Donn L. Mills. bk.rev. circ. 1,200-1,400. (back issues avail.) **Indexed:** Music Artic.Guide, Music Ind.

016.78   US   ISSN 0093-0288
ML1
N U QUARTER NOTES. 1972. 4/yr. free. Northwestern University, Music Library, Evanston, IL 60208. TEL 708-491-3434. Ed. Deborah Campana. bk.rev.; bibl. circ. 350. **Document type:** newsletter.
Formerly (until 1981): 1810 Overture.

N Y C - ON STAGE. see *THEATER*

780   AU
NACHRICHTEN ZUR MAHLER FORSCHUNG. (Text in English and German) 1976. s-a. S.210($20) Internationale Gustav Mahler Gesellschaft, Wiedner Guertel 6, A-1040 Vienna, Austria. TEL 0222-5057330. circ. 1,000. (back issues avail.) **Indexed:** RILM. **Document type:** newsletter.

NARODNI BIBLIOGRAFIE CESKE REPUBLIKY. HUDEBNINY. see *BIBLIOGRAPHIES*

780 792   US
NASHVILLE SCENE.* w. 209 Tenth Ave. S., Ste. 222, Nashville, TN 37203-4101. TEL 615-371-9357.
Description: Covers entertainment, arts and leisure.

781.7   NE
NASHVILLE TENNESSEE. 1984. 11/yr. fl.45. Karel van der Kemp, P.O. Box 570, 2800 AN Gouda, Netherlands. TEL 01682-4877. Ed.Bd. adv.; bk.rev. circ. 9,000.
Description: Devoted to country and rock and roll music, featuring articles and interviews with singers, international news, reports and lists of events and new records, photos.

MUSIC

780   XV   ISSN 0027-8270
NASI ZBORI. (Text in Slovenian; summaries in English) vol.18, 1966. w. 300 din.($30) Zveza Kulturnih Organizacij Slovenije, Kidriceva 5, 61000 Ljubljana, Slovenia. Ed. M. Gobec.

780   SP   ISSN 0213-7305
ML315.7.A7
NASSARRE; revista aragonesa de musicologia. 1985. a. 2500 ptas. Institucion Fernando el Catolico, Plaza de Espana 2, 50071 Zaragoza, Spain. TEL 34-76-288878. FAX 34-76-288869. Ed. Pedro Calahorra.

780   US   ISSN 0547-4175
ML27.U5
NATIONAL ASSOCIATION OF SCHOOLS OF MUSIC. DIRECTORY. 1950. a. $16. National Association of Schools of Music, 11250 Roger Bacon Dr., No. 21, Reston, VA 22090. TEL 703-437-0700. **Document type:** directory.
  Description: Lists accredited institutions and degree programs, with addresses, telephone numbers, and music executives of all member institutions.

780   US   ISSN 0164-2847
ML27.U5
NATIONAL ASSOCIATION OF SCHOOLS OF MUSIC. HANDBOOK. 1930. biennial. $14. National Association of Schools of Music, 11250 Roger Bacon Dr., No. 21, Reston, VA 22090. TEL 703-437-0700. circ. 2,200.

780.7   US   ISSN 0190-6615
ML27.U5
NATIONAL ASSOCIATION OF SCHOOLS OF MUSIC. PROCEEDINGS OF THE ANNUAL MEETING. Key Title: Proceedings of the Annual Meeting - National Association of Schools of Music. 1934. a. $20. National Association of Schools of Music, 11250 Roger Bacon Dr., No. 21, Reston, VA 22090. TEL 703-437-0700. **Indexed:** Music Ind. **Document type:** proceedings.
  Supersedes: National Association of Schools of Music. Proceeding of the Annual Meeting (ISSN 0077-3409)

784.18   US
NATIONAL BAND DIRECTORY; a directory of community bands in the U.S. 1987. biennial. Association of Concert Bands, Inc., 2533 S. Maple Ave., Ste. 102, Tempe, AZ 85282. TEL 602-894-6687. Ed. Toni Ryon. **Document type:** directory.

NATIONAL BRAILLE ASSOCIATION. MUSIC CATALOG. see HANDICAPPED — Visually Impaired

786.3   US   ISSN 0077-4642
NATIONAL GUILD OF PIANO TEACHERS. GUILD SYLLABUS. 1943. a. $1.50. National Guild of Piano Teachers, Box 1807, Austin, TX 78767. TEL 512-478-5775. Ed. Richard Allison. circ. 12,000.

NATIONAL JEWISH ARTS NEWSLETTER. see ETHNIC INTERESTS

NATIONAL LIBRARY SERVICE. MUSIC AND MUSICIANS CIRCULAR SERIES. see HANDICAPPED — Visually Impaired

780.65   US
NATIONAL MUSIC PUBLISHERS' ASSOCIATION. NEWS & VIEWS. 1965. q. free to qualified personnel. National Music Publishers' Association, 711 3rd Ave., 8th Fl., New York, NY 10017-4014. TEL 212-370-5330. FAX 212-953-2471. TELEX 237441 HAFOX UR. Ed. Margaret A. O'Keeffe. illus. circ. 6,000. **Document type:** newsletter.
  Formerly (until 1991): National Music Publishers' Association. Bulletin.

NATIONAL RADIO GUIDE; guide to C B C radio and C B C stereo. see COMMUNICATIONS — Radio

787.9   US   ISSN 1064-0754
ML3188
NATIONAL SACRED HARP NEWSLETTER; covering the country like kudzu. 1985. bi-m. $8. Sacred Harp Publishing Co., Inc., Box 551, Temple, GA 30179. (Subscr. to: Box 1828, Carrollton, GA 30117) Eds. Hugh McGraw, Richard DeLong. circ. 1,500. **Document type:** newsletter.

780   US   ISSN 0732-1503
NEBRASKA MUSIC EDUCATOR. 1940. q. $10. Nebraska Music Educators Association, Box 83046, Lincoln, NE 68501-3046. TEL 402-435-6913. FAX 402-474-3250. E-mail: mveak@lps.esu18.k12.ne.us. Ed. Michael H. Veak. adv.; bk.rev.; circ. 1,550 (controlled). **Indexed:** Music Artic.Guide. **Document type:** academic/scholarly publication.
  —UnCover.
  Description: Membership journal including columns by officers, music reviews, feature articles.
  Refereed Serial

780   NE   ISSN 0928-8120
NEDERLANDS JAZZ ARCHIEF BULLETIN. Key Title: Jazz Archief Bulletin. 1991. q. fl.25. Stichting Nederlands Jazz Archief, Oude Schans 73-77, 1011 KN Amsterdam, Netherlands. TEL 31-20-6271708. FAX 31-20-6271708. Ed. Pim Gras. adv.; B&W page fl.300; adv. contact: Egbert De Bloeme. bk.rev.; illus. circ. 700. (back issues avail.) **Document type:** academic/scholarly publication, bulletin.
  Formerly: National Jazz Archief Bulletin.
  Description: Covers the history of jazz and jazz musicians in the Netherlands from 1920 to the present.

780.65   US   ISSN 1055-663X
NETWORK NEWS (NEW YORK).* 1982. 3/yr. $10 to non-members. Composers' Forum, Inc., 73 Spring St., Rm. 506, New York, NY 10012-5802. TEL 212-334-0216. Ed. Betsy McClelland. adv. circ. 2,500. (tabloid format; back issues avail.) **Indexed:** Music Artic.Guide.
  Description: Announcements, opportunities, and items of interest pertaining to members, other composers, and performers worldwide.

780   GW   ISSN 0077-7714
NEUE MUSIKGESCHICHTLICHE FORSCHUNGEN. 1968. irreg. price varies. Breitkopf und Haertel, Postfach 1707, 65007 Wiesbaden, Germany. TEL 0611-45008-0. FAX 0611-4500859. TELEX 4182647-EB-D. Ed. Lothar Hoffmann-Erbrecht. **Document type:** monographic series.

780   GW   ISSN 0028-3290
NEUE MUSIKZEITUNG. 1952. bi-m. DM.48. (Verband Deutscher Musikschulen) Verlag Neue Musikzeitung, Postfach 100245, 93002 Regensburg, Germany. TEL 0941-798560. FAX 0941-7985650. Ed. Theo Geissler. adv.; bk.rev.; play rev.; illus. circ. 30,000. (tabloid format; also avail. in microfilm from BHP,KTO) **Indexed:** Music Ind. **Document type:** bulletin.
  Formerly: Musikalische Jugend.

780   GW   ISSN 0170-8791
NEUE ZEITSCHRIFT FUER MUSIK. 1834. 6/yr. DM.65. Schott Musik International GmbH, Weihergarten 5, 55116 Mainz, Germany. TEL 06131-246-0. FAX 06131-246211. Ed.Bd. adv.; B&W page DM.1670; trim 260 x 185; adv. contact: Karin Krappen. bk.rev.; music rev.; rec.rev.; charts; illus.; index. circ. 8,000. (also avail. in microfilm from BHP) **Indexed:** Curr.Cont., Music Ind., RILM. **Document type:** consumer publication.
  —BLDSC (6077.827500); Faxon; SWETS.
  Former titles: Melos (ISSN 0025-9020); Neue Zeitschrift fuer Musik (ISSN 0028-3509)

780   US   ISSN 0028-4181
ML156.9
NEW AMBEROLA GRAPHIC. 1971. q. $8 for 2 yrs. (foreign $10). New Amberola Phonograph Co., 37 Caledonia St., St. Johnsbury, VT 05819. Ed. Martin Bryan. adv.; bk.rev. circ. 1,000. **Document type:** consumer publication.
  Description: For collectors of records and phonographs from 1895-1935.

NEW CULTURE; a review of contemporary African arts. see ART

781.7   US   ISSN 1076-3503
NEW ENGLAND FOLK ALMANAC. bi-m. $15 (Canada and Mexico $20; elsewhere $30). Folk Arts Network, Inc., Box 336, Cambridge, MA 02141. TEL 617-661-4708. Pub. Stephen Baird. music rev.; rec.rev. **Document type:** newsletter.
  Description: Lists concert, club and coffeehouse performances, includes performer profiles and interviews.

780   GW
NEW FUNK TIMES. m. Funkateers International, Ehrenstr. 19, 50672 Cologne, Germany. TEL 0221-256199. FAX 0221-256319. Ed. Peter Jebsen.

780.42   UK   ISSN 0260-3330
NEW GANDY DANCER; the magazine for instrumental rock music. 1976. 3-4/yr. $24 for 4 nos. (effective 1996). Dama Publishing, 87 Napier Rd., Swalwell, Newcastle-upon-Tyne NE16 3BT, England. TEL 0191-488-8349. Ed. David Peckett. adv.; bk.rev.; charts, rec.rev. circ. 1,000. **Document type:** newsletter.
  Description: Devoted to instrumental rock music. Includes features and artist profiles.

780.7   US   ISSN 0028-5315
ML1
NEW HAMPSHIRE QUARTER NOTES. vol.20, 1977. a. $10. New Hampshire Music Educators Association, Rt. 5, Box 307, Penacook, NH 03303. TEL 603-648-2692. Ed. Elaine Hashem. adv.; bk.rev.; circ. 800 (controlled). **Indexed:** Music Artic.Guide. **Document type:** newsletter.

780.7   US   ISSN 0028-6265
NEW MEXICO MUSICIAN. 1954. 3/yr. $7. New Mexico Music Educators Association, 93 Mimbres Dr., Los Alamos, NM 87544. FAX 505-672-9840. Ed. Donald E. Gerheart. adv.; bk.rev.; charts; illus. circ. 1,600. **Document type:** newsletter.
  Description: Information of interest to association members.

781.64   IE   ISSN 0791-5268
NEW MUSIC NEWS. 1990. 3/yr. Contemporary Music Centre, 95 Lower Baggot St., Dublin 2, Ireland. TEL 01-6612105. FAX 01-6762639. E-mail: info@cmc.ie. Ed. Eve O'Kelly. **Document type:** bulletin.

780   UK   ISSN 0028-6362
NEW MUSICAL EXPRESS. 1952. w. $105. I P C Magazines, Specialist Magazine Group (Subsidiary of: Reed Elsevier group), King's Reach Tower, Stamford St., London SE1 9LS, England. TEL 071-261-6472. FAX 0444-440619. TELEX 892084 REEDBP G. (Dist. by: Quadrant Subscription Services, Oakfield House, Perrymount Rd., Haywards Heath, W. Sussex RH16 3DH, England. TEL 0444-440421) Ed. Neil Spencer. rec.rev. circ. 123,200. (tabloid format; also avail. in microfilm from RPI) **Document type:** consumer publication.
  —CCC.

780   US   ISSN 0276-7031
ML18
NEW ON THE CHARTS. 1976. m. $185 (limited distribution). Music Business Reference, Inc., 70 Laurel Pl., New Rochelle, NY 10801. TEL 914-632-3349. FAX 914-633-7690. Ed. Leonard Kalikow. adv.; circ. 2,500 (controlled). **Document type:** trade publication.

780.7   US
NEW OXFORD HISTORY OF MUSIC. irreg. price varies. Oxford University Press, 200 Madison Ave., New York, NY 10016. TEL 212-679-7300. Ed.Bd.

780   US
NEW YORK MUSIC. 1993. m. $9. Music Marketing Enterprises, 19 W. 44th St., Ste. 1217, New York, NY 10036. TEL 212-221-7065. Ed. Peter Comas. adv.: B&W page $4594. circ. 75,000. **Document type:** consumer publication.

782.1   US   ISSN 1043-2361
ML3795
NEW YORK OPERA NEWSLETTER. 1987. m. $48 (Canada $54; elsewhere $72) (effective 1992). New York Opera Newsletter, Inc., Box 278, Maplewood, NJ 07040. TEL 201-378-9549. FAX 201-278-2372. Ed. Barry Lenson. circ. 2,200. **Document type:** newsletter.
  Description: Provides specific information for classical vocal artists at all levels, with interviews, articles, and coverage of auditions, competitions, training programs.

781.7 398   US   ISSN 1041-4150
NEW YORK PINEWOODS FOLK MUSIC CLUB NEWSLETTER. 1965. m. (except Aug.) $27 includes membership. Folk Music Society of New York, 817 Broadway, 6th Fl., New York, NY 10003-4760. Ed. Eileen Pentel. adv.; bk.rev. circ. 1,200. **Document type:** newsletter.

MUSIC

783   UK   ISSN 0263-2306
NEWS OF HYMNODY. Abbreviated title: N.O.H. 1981. q. £2.50($7) Grove Books, Ltd., Bramcote, Nottingham NG9 3DS, England. TEL 0115-943-0786. FAX 01115-922-0134. circ. 1,000.

780.948   DK   ISSN 0108-2914
NORDIC SOUNDS. 1982. 4/yr. free. (Nordic Council of Ministers) Nordic Sounds, Klerkegade 2, DK1308 Copenhagen K, Denmark. TEL 45-33-15-07-26. FAX 45-33-91-81-39. Ed. Anders Beyer. bk.rev. circ. 5,000. **Indexed:** Music Ind. **Document type:** academic/scholarly publication.
—BLDSC (6117.931000).

780   NO   ISSN 0029-2044
NORSK MUSIKERBLAD. 1914. 10/yr. NOK 270 in Scandinavia; rest of Europe NOK 350; elsewhere NOK 400. Norsk Musikerforbund - Norwegian Musicians' Union, Youngsgt. 11, N-0181 Oslo, Norway. TEL 47-22-03-14-93. FAX 47-22-03-14-90. Ed. Jan Lothe Eriksen. adv.: B&W page NOK 3700; trim 297 x 210; adv. contact: Bente J. Gundersen. bk.rev. circ. 2,700. **Indexed:** Music Ind. **Document type:** trade publication.
—BLDSC (6144.100000).

780   NO   ISSN 0332-5482
NORSK MUSIKKTIDSSKRIFT. 1964. q. NOK 85($8) Norske Musikklaereres Landsforbund, Youngsgt. 11, 0181 Oslo 1, Norway. Ed. Joerg Johnsen. adv.; bk.rev. circ. 1,700. **Indexed:** RILM.

780.7   US   ISSN 0029-2753
NORTH DAKOTA MUSIC EDUCATOR. 1961. q. $10. North Dakota Music Educator's Association, 4450 San Juan Dr., Fargo, ND 58103. TEL 701-281-0386. Ed. Carolyn Italiano. adv.; bk.rev. circ. 834.

780   UK   ISSN 0261-5096
NORTHUMBRIAN PIPERS' SOCIETY MAGAZINE. 1980. a. £1.25 to members; non-members £1.75. Northumbrian Pipers' Society, c/o Morpeth Chantry Bagpipe Museum, Bridge St., Morpeth, Northumberland NE61 1PZ, England. TEL 0670-519466. Ed. David Geddes. adv.; bk.rev.; rec.rev. circ. 550. **Document type:** newsletter.
Description: News items, articles, and reviews relating to Northumbrian bagpipes and Northumbrian music.

NOSTALGIA. see *SOUND RECORDING AND REPRODUCTION*

780.01   US
NOTES (ANN ARBOR); a publication for friends and supporters of the University Musical Society. 1989. q. free. University Musical Society, c/o University of Michigan, Burton Memorial Tower, Ann Arbor, MI 48109-1270. TEL 313-747-1177. FAX 313-747-1171. Ed. Catherine S. Arcure. adv.; bk.rev. circ. 12,000. (back issues avail.)
Description: Concerned with artists, programming, and composers as they relate to upcoming presentations of the University Musical Society.

780.7   US   ISSN 0029-3946
NOTES A TEMPO. 1951. m. (Sep.-May). $5 (typically set in June). West Virginia Music Educators Association, Inc., Hall of Fine Arts, West Liberty State College, West Liberty, WV 26074-0335. TEL 304-336-8263. FAX 304-336-8285. E-mail: WOLFEIII@WLSVAX.WVNET.EDU. (Alt. addr.: c/o Al Frey, 880 Sherwood Rd., Charlestown, WV 25314. TEL 304-342-0357) Ed. Edward C. Wolf. adv. contact: Edward C. Wolf. stat. circ. 1,190. (processed) **Document type:** newsletter.
Description: Covers all aspects of music education within the state of West Virginia.

780   RU   ISSN 0029-4462
NOTNAYA LETOPIS'. 1931. q. $6.60. (Komitet po Pechati Soveta Ministrov) Izdatel'stvo Kniga, 50, Gorky St., 125047 Moscow, Russia. bibl.; index. circ. 930. (also avail. in microfiche from MUE; back issues avail.)

787   GW   ISSN 0254-9565
NOVA GIULIANIAD; Saitenblaetter fuer die Gitarre und Laute. 1983. s-a. DM.14($10) (Internationale Gitarristische Vereinigung Freiburg e.V.) Orlando Syrg Verlag, Lessingstr. 4, 79100 Freiburg, Germany. TEL 0761-77407. Ed. Joerg Sommermeyer. adv.; bk.rev. circ. 9,000. (back issues avail.)

780   IT   ISSN 0391-3724
NUOVA RASSEGNA DI STUDI MUSICALI. 2/yr. L.40000. (Universita degli Studi di Padova, Centro di Studi Musicali Aggregati) Giardini Editori e Stampatori, Via Santa Bibbiana 28, 56100 Pisa, Italy. TEL 050-502531. Ed. Franco Piva.

780   IT   ISSN 0029-6228
ML5
NUOVA RIVISTA MUSICALE ITALIANA; trimestrale di cultura e informazione musicale. 1967. q. L.60000 (foreign L.85000). E R I Edizioni R A I, Via Arsenale 41, 10121 Turin, Italy. TEL 011-8800. FAX 011-534732. Ed. Dir. Leonardo Pinzauti. adv.: B&W page L.1100000. bk.rev.; rec.rev.; bibl. circ. 3,500. **Indexed:** Arts & Hum.Cit.Ind., Curr.Cont., Music Ind., RILM.
—Faxon; SWETS.

780.904   SW   ISSN 0029-6597
ML5
NUTIDA MUSIK/CONTEMPORARY MUSIC. 1957. q. SEK 200. International Society for Contemporary Music, Swedish Section, c/o Nutida Musik, P.O. Box 208, S-135 27 Tyresoe, Sweden. TEL 46-8-712-17-23. FAX 46-8-712-17-23. Ed. Bo Rydberg. bk.rev.; illus.; cum.index. **Indexed:** Music Ind., RILM.

781.57   SW   ISSN 1102-7428
ML5
O J. Variant title: Orkesterjournalen. 1933. m. SEK 340. Stiftelsen Orkester Journalen, P.O. Box 4206, Oestgoetagatan 44, S-102 65 Stockholm, Sweden. TEL 46-8-642-64-64. FAX 46-702-21-18. Ed. Lars Westin. adv.: B&W page SEK 3800, color page SEK 7000; trim 215 x 290; adv. contact: Nilla Domnerus. bk.rev.; rec.rev. circ. 3,000. (back issues avail.) **Indexed:** Music Ind. **Document type:** newspaper.
Formerly (until 1991): Orkester Journalen (ISSN 0030-5642); Incorporates (in 1991): Jazznytt fraan S.J.R. (ISSN 0047-195X); Which was formerly (until Nov. 1967): Jazznyt.
Description: Focuses on jazz music.

780   PL
OBRZEDY I ZWYCZAJE LUDOWE. 1985. irreg. price varies. Polskie Wydawnictwo Muzyczne, Al. Krasinskiego 11, 31-111 Krakow, Poland. TEL 48-12-227044. FAX 48-12-220174. Ed. Aleksandra Bogucka. adv. contact: Teresa Wlochynska. illus. **Document type:** academic/scholarly publication.
Description: Publishes documents; ethnographic descriptions of traditional rites and customs. Includes narration, quotations of ritual text in dialect, songs and couplets with music.

780   NE   ISSN 0926-0684
ODEON. 1990. 3/yr. fl.15. Nederlandse Opera, Waterlooplein 22, 1011 PG Amsterdam, Netherlands. TEL 31-20-5518922. FAX 31-20-5518311. adv.: B&W page fl.2400; adv. contact: Frank Driessen. circ. 25,000. (back issues avail.)
Description: Contains interviews, background information on staged operas performed by De Nederlanse Opera. Includes cast lists and synopses of operas.

780   AU   ISSN 0023-3048
OESTERREICHISCHE AKADEMIE DER WISSENSCHAFTEN. KOMMISSION FUER MUSIKFORSCHUNG. MITTEILUNGEN. 1956. irreg. price varies. Verlag der Oesterreichischen Akademie der Wissenschaften, Dr. Ignaz-Seipel-Platz 2, A-1010 Vienna, Austria. FAX 0222-5139541.

OESTERREICHISCHE AUTORENZEITUNG. see *PATENTS, TRADEMARKS AND COPYRIGHTS*

784.18   AU
OESTERREICHISCHE BLASMUSIK. 10/yr. S.180. (Oesterreichischer Blasmusikverband) Tuba Musikverlag, Steinamangererstr. 187, A-7400 Oberwart, Austria. TEL 03352-33392. FAX 03352-34130. Ed. Kurt Boehler. circ. 10,000. **Indexed:** RILM. **Document type:** bulletin.

780   GW   ISSN 0078-3471
OESTERREICHISCHE GESELLSCHAFT FUER MUSIK. BEITRAEGE. 1967. irreg. price varies. Baerenreiter Verlag, Heinrich-Schuetz-Allee 35, 34131 Kassel, Germany. TEL 0561-3105-0. FAX 0561-3105240. (Subscr. in US to: Educational Music Service, 13 Elkay Dr., Chester, NY 10918. TEL 914-469-5790. FAX 914-469-5817) Eds. R. Klein, K. Roschitz. **Indexed:** RILM. **Document type:** academic/scholarly publication.

780 920   AU   ISSN 0078-3501
OESTERREICHISCHE KOMPONISTEN DES 20. JAHRHUNDERTS. 1964. irreg. price varies. Musikverlag Elisabeth Lafite, Hegelgasse 13-22, A-1010 Vienna, Austria. TEL 5126869. FAX 5124629. (And: Oesterreichischer Bundesverlag, Schwarzenbergstr. 5, 1015 Vienna 1, Austria) **Document type:** monographic series.

780   AU   ISSN 0029-9316
ML5
OESTERREICHISCHE MUSIKZEITSCHRIFT. 1946. m. S.450. Musikverlag Elisabeth Lafite, Hegelgasse 13-22, A-1010 Vienna, Austria. TEL 5126869. FAX 5124629. Ed. Marion Diederichs-Lafite. adv.; bk.rev.; music rev.; rec.rev.; illus.; index. **Indexed:** Music Ind., RILM. **Document type:** bulletin.
—Faxon.
Incorporates (in 1979): Komponist.

780.01   AU
OESTERREICHISCHER MUSIKRAT - MITTEILUNGEN. 1965. 3/yr. Oesterreichischer Musikrat, Hanuschgasse 3, A-1010 Vienna, Austria. TEL 01-5123143. FAX 01-5122050. (Co-sponsors: Ministry for Education; Ministry for Science, Research and Arts) Ed. Wilfried Scheib. bk.rev. circ. 1,800. (back issues avail.) **Indexed:** RILM. **Document type:** bulletin.

784   AU   ISSN 0473-8624
OESTERREICHISCHES VOLKSLIEDWERK. JAHRBUCH. 1952. a. S.330. Oesterreichisches Volksliedwerk, Gallitzinstr. 1, A-1160 Vienna, Austria. TEL 0222-9144626. FAX 0222-914462613. Ed. Walter Deutsch. bk.rev.; index. circ. 600. **Indexed:** RILM. **Document type:** academic/scholarly publication.
Formerly: Volkslied, Volkstanz, Volksmusik.

780.42   US
OFFENSE NEWSLETTER.* 1982. 12/yr. $7.20. Tet Offensive Productions, Box 12614, Columbus, OH 43212. Ed. Timothy K. Anstaett. bk.rev.; rec.rev. circ. 500. (back issues avail.)
Supersedes (1980-1982): Offense.

786.6   US
THE OFFICIAL ELECTRONIC KEYBOARD BLUEBOOK; used electronic keyboard valuation guide. 1967. a. $50. Hal Leonard Publishing Corporation, 7777 W. Bluemound Rd., Box 13819, Milwaukee, WI 53213. TEL 414-774-3630. FAX 414-774-3259. illus.; stat.; index, cum.index. circ. 2,500.
Formerly (until 1985): Official Organ Blue Book (ISSN 0048-1513)

781.7   US   ISSN 1044-3649
OKLAHOMA BLUEGRASS GAZETTE. 1975. m. $8 membership. Oklahoma Bluegrass Club Inc., 8700 Hillview, Midwest City, OK 73150. TEL 405-737-9944. Ed. Charlie Blackwell. adv.; bk.rev.; illus.; tr.lit. rec. 600. (tabloid format) **Document type:** newspaper.
Description: Keeps members informed of events and bands.

780   US   ISSN 1040-3582
OLD-TIME HERALD; a magazine dedicated to old-time music. 1987. q. $20 to individuals; institutions or overseas $25. Old-Time Music Group, Inc., 1812 House Ave., Durham, NC 27707. TEL 919-416-9433. E-mail: agerrard@nando.net. Ed. Alice Gerrard. adv.; illus. circ. 4,000. **Indexed:** RILM.

780.01   GW
OLDIE - MARKT. 1977. m. DM.156. New Media Verlag, Postfach 1144, 21411 Winsen-Luhe, Germany. TEL 04171-64243. FAX 04171-64355. Ed. Martin Reichold; Pub. Frank Goldmann. adv. contact: Juergen Vanheiden. bk.rev. circ. 15,000. **Document type:** consumer publication.

MUSIC 4871

780 US ISSN 1057-9893
ML1
ON THE AIR MAGAZINE. 1990. m. $29 (effective 1995). Classical Guide, Inc., Box 19600, Denver, CO 80219. TEL 303-986-2022. FAX 303-988-1871. Ed. Ash Morland; Pub. Karen Mohr. adv. contact: Chris Mohr. music rev.; circ. 10 (paid). (back issues avail.) **Indexed:** Music Artic.Guide. **Document type:** consumer publication.
   Description: Contains program listings for classical music stations in nine major markets as well as articles about composers, performing artists, and compact disc reviews.

780.42 US ISSN 0196-1446
ON THE ROCK. 1979. m. $15. Pumpernickel Press, Box 24-8741, Miami, FL 33124. Ed. Chris Freeman. adv.; bk.rev. circ. 2,150.

780 778.534 AT
ON THE STREET. 1980. w. Aus.$52. 2 Bellevue St., Surry Hills, N.S.W. 2010, Australia. FAX 61-2-211-1122. Ed. Dino Scatena; Pub. Nick Walsh. adv. contact: Matt Christie. bk.rev.; film rev.; play rev.; charts; illus. circ. 31,750. (back issues avail.)

780.42 US
ONE SHOT; the magazine of one hit wonders. 1986. s-a. $9 for 3 nos. One Shot Enterprises, Contract Sta. 6, Box 145, 1525 Sherman St., Denver, CO 80203. TEL 303-744-6360. Ed. Steven Rosen. adv.; bk.rev. circ. 250. (back issues avail.)
   Description: Study and appreciation of now-obscure one-hit wonders of rock and pop music.

780.01 JA ISSN 0030-2597
ONGAKU GAKU/JAPANESE MUSICOLOGICAL SOCIETY. JOURNAL. (Text in Japanese; summaries in English) 1954. 3/yr. 7000 Yen($60) Nippon Ongaku Gakkai - Musicological Society of Japan, c/o Tokyo National University of Fine Arts and Music, Department of Musicology, Ueno Park, Taito-ku, Tokyo 110, Japan. (Subscr. to: Academia Music Ltd. 3-16-5 Hongo, Bunkyo-ku, Tokyo 113, Japan) adv.; bk.rev.; abstr.; bibl.; charts; illus. circ. 1,600. **Indexed:** RILM. **Document type:** academic/scholarly publication.
   —BLDSC (6260.282000).
   Description: Aims to present original articles in the field of musicology.

780.01 JA ISSN 0030-2600
ONGAKU GEIJUTSU/ART OF MUSIC. (Text in Japanese) 1946. m. 850 Yen. Ongaku No Tomo Sha Corp., Kagurazaka 6-30, Shinjuku-ku, Tokyo 162, Japan. TEL 03-3235-2111. FAX 03-3235-2110. Ed. Yukio Kurosawa. adv.; B&W page 108000 Yen, color page 320400 Yen; trim 227 x 152. bk.rev. circ. 36,000. **Indexed:** RILM. **Document type:** academic/scholarly publication.
   Description: Specialized in the study and critics of music. Includes research on composers, their works, musical history and aesthetics of music.

780 JA ISSN 0289-3606
ONGAKU NO TOMO/FRIENDS OF MUSIC. (Text in Japanese) 1941. m. 950 Yen. Ongaku No Tomo Sha Corp., Kagurazaka 6-30, Shinjuku-ku, Tokyo 162, Japan. TEL 03-3235-2111. FAX 03-3235-2129. adv.; B&W page 324000 Yen, color page 624000; trim 277 x 210. illus. circ. 150,000.
   Description: Contains commentary and explanations of outstanding works and performances, stories of great composers and musicians, movements of music circles in the world as well as in Japan.

ONGAKU ONKYO KENKYUKAI SHIRYO/ACOUSTICAL SOCIETY OF JAPAN. TRANSACTIONS OF COMMITTEE MEETING ON MUSIC ACOUSTICS. see *PHYSICS — Sound*

780 NE ISSN 0921-1616
OOR. 1971. bi-w. fl.132.50 (foreign fl.260.50) (effective 1995). B.V. Uitgeversmaatschappij .Bonaventura (Subsidiary of: Elsevier N.V.), Postbus 2158, 1000 CD Amsterdam, Netherlands. TEL 31-20-6914111. FAX 31-20-5674398. adv. **Document type:** consumer publication.
   Formerly (until 1984): Muziekkrant Oor (ISSN 0301-6501)

780 US ISSN 0276-8747
ML1
OP; independent music. 1978. bi-m. $8. Lost Music Network, Box 2391, Olympia, WA 98507. Ed. John Foster. adv.; bk.rev.; illus. circ. 10,000. (also avail. in microform from UMI)

780 GW ISSN 0030-3518
ML5
OPER UND KONZERT. 1963. 4/yr. DM.48. Verlag A. Hanuschik, Ungererstr. 19, 80802 Munich, Germany. TEL 089-391442. FAX 089-391482. Ed. Helmut Mauro; Pub. Annie Hanuschik. adv. contact: Winfried Hanuschik. bk.rev.; music rev.; play rev.; rec.rev.; charts; illus. circ. 4,150. **Indexed:** Music Ind. **Document type:** consumer publication.
   —BLDSC (6266.350000).

782.1 UK ISSN 0030-3526
ML5
OPERA. 1950. m. £39. Opera Magazine, 1A Mountgrove Rd., London N5 2LU, England. TEL 0171-359-1037. FAX 0171-354-2700. (Subscr. to: DSB, 2A Sopwith Cres., Shotgate, Wickford, Essex SS11 8YU, England) Ed. Rodney Milnes. adv.; bk.rev.; music rev.; rec.rev.; illus.; index. circ. 11,500. (also avail. in microform from UMI; reprint service avail. from UMI) **Indexed:** Br.Hum.Ind.; Hum.Ind., Music Ind., RILM. **Document type:** consumer publication.
   —BLDSC (6266.400000); Faxon; SWETS; UMI; UnCover.

782.1 IT ISSN 1121-4112
L'OPERA (MILAN). 1987. m. L.90000 (foreign L.110000) (effective 1993). Edizioni di Sabino Lenoci, Via Carlo Botta, 4, 20135 Milan, Italy. TEL 39-2-55193793. FAX 39-2-5460154. adv.; B&W page L.4800000, color page L.6000000. circ. 24,000.

780 792 US
OPERA AMERICA. REPERTOIRE SURVEY. a. $20 to non-members; members $12. Opera America, 1156 15th St., N.W., Ste. 810, Washington, DC 20005-1704. TEL 202-293-4466. FAX 202-393-0735. Ed. Martha Perry. **Indexed:** Music Artic.Guide.
   Description: Catalogs productions presented by Opera America companies over the preceeding season, with analysis of trends in operatic repertoire.

780 792 370 US ISSN 1062-7243
ML27.U5
OPERA AMERICA NEWSLINE. 1972. m. (10/yr.). membership. Opera America, 1156 15th St., N.W., Ste. 810, Washington, DC 20005-1704. TEL 202-293-4466. FAX 202-393-0735. Ed. Martha Perry. adv.; bk.rev.; abstr.; stat. circ. 2,100. (back issues avail.)
   Formerly (until 1991): Intercompany Announcements.
   Description: Reports on opera company activities and information currently affecting the field. Covers legislation, research, and management techniques, conferences, new publications, job listings and auditions.

782.1 US ISSN 0899-3645
ML1699
OPERA ANNUAL U S (YEAR). 1988. a. $48. Jerome S. Ozer, Ed. & Pub., 340 Tenafly Rd., Englewood, NJ 07631-1747. TEL 201-567-7040.
   Description: Examines opera sources throughout the U.S.

782.1 AT ISSN 1320-9299
OPERA AUSTRALASIA. 1978. m. Aus.$40 (effective 1996). Pellinor Pty. Ltd., Level 2, 44 Bridge St., Sydney, N.S.W. 2000, Australia. TEL 61-2-247-2264. FAX 61-2-247-2269. Ed. David Gyger. adv.; B&W page Aus.$1610. bk.rev.; index, cum.index: 1978-1981, 1982-1985, 1986-1989. circ. 1,858. (tabloid format; back issues avail.) **Document type:** newspaper.
   Formerly (until 1994): Opera Australia (ISSN 0155-4980)
   Description: Covers the opera and music theatre in Australasia, with some reference to the international scene.

782.1 AT ISSN 1321-3768
OPERA AUSTRALASIA LIBRETTO SERIES. 1982. irreg. Aus.$8.80 per libretto. Pellinor Pty. Ltd., Level 2, 44 Bridge St., Sydney, N.S.W. 2000, Australia. TEL 61-2-247-2264. FAX 61-2-247-2269. Ed. David E. Gyger. circ. 1,000. (back issues avail.)
   Formerly (until 1994): Official Opera Australia Libretto Series (ISSN 0810-8021)

782.1 CN ISSN 0030-3577
ML5
OPERA - CANADA. 1960. 4/yr. Can.$20 (foreign Can.$28). Opera Canada Publications, Ste. 434, 366 Adelaide St. E., Toronto, ON M5A 3X9, Canada. TEL 416-363-0395. FAX 416-363-0396. Ed. Jocelyn Laurence. adv.; bk.rev.; rec.rev.; illus. circ. 5,500. (also avail. in microform from UMI; back issues avail.; reprint service avail. from UMI) **Indexed:** Can.Per.Ind., CMI, Music Ind., RILM. **Document type:** consumer publication.
   —UMI; UnCover.

782.1 US ISSN 0891-3757
OPERA FANATIC; * the magazine for lovers of expressive singing. 1986. q. $20 (foreign $25). (Bel Canto Society, Inc.) Max Way Data Corp., 100 Newfield Ave., Edison, NJ 08837-3817. Ed. Stefan Zucker. **Indexed:** RILM.

792 UK
▼**OPERA HOUSE (LONDON)**; the magazine of the Royal Ballet, the Royal Opera and the Birmingham Royal Ballet. 1994. 3/yr. membership; newsstand price: £2.50. (Friends of Covent Garden Ltd.) Premiere Magazines, c/o Siri Fischer Hansen, Covent Garden, London WC2E 9DD, England. TEL 0171-212-9412. FAX 0171-836-0231. (Co-sponsor: Royal Opera House Trust) Henrietta Bredin. adv. contact: Sofie Mason. illus. circ. 30,000. **Document type:** consumer publication.
   Description: Reviews opera and ballet performances. Contains articles on opera singers and composers, as well as ballet dancers.

782.1 US ISSN 0030-3585
ML1
OPERA JOURNAL. 1968. q. $45 to individuals; libraries $30; organizations $60. National Opera Association, Inc., Department of Music, University of Nevada - Las Vegas, 4505 Maryland Pkwy., Las Vegas, NV 89154-5025. TEL 702-895-1665. FAX 702-895-4194. E-mail: kimball@cfpa.nevada.edu. Ed. Carol Kimball. adv.; bk.rev.; music rev.; illus.; index, cum.index. circ. 700. (also avail. in microform from UMI; reprint service avail. from UMI) **Indexed:** Music Artic.Guide, Music Ind. **Document type:** academic/scholarly publication.
   —BLDSC (6267.100000); UMI; UnCover.
   Description: Articles on opera, and reviews. *Refereed Serial*

786 US ISSN 0897-6554
ML1699
OPERA MONTHLY. 1988. m. $25. That New Magazine, Inc., 28 W. 25th St., 4th Fl., New York, NY 10010. TEL 212-627-2120. FAX 212-727-9321. (And: Box 816, Madison Sq. Sta., New York, NY 10159) Ed. Thomas E. Steele. adv.; bk.rev. circ. 5,000. (back issues avail.)
   —UnCover.
   Description: Includes reviews and interviews for the opera lover.

782.1 US ISSN 0030-3607
ML1
OPERA NEWS. 1936. m. (May-Nov.); fortn. (Dec.-Apr.). $30. Metropolitan Opera Guild, Inc., 70 Lincoln Center Plaza, New York, NY 10023. TEL 212-769-7080. FAX 212-769-7007. Ed. Patrick J. Smith. adv. contact: Elaine B. Kones. bk.rev.; music rev.; rec.rev.; bibl.; illus.; index; circ. 125,000 (paid). (also avail. in microform from UMI; reprint service avail. from UMI) **Indexed:** Amer.Bibl.Slavic & E.Eur.Stud., Arts & Hum.Cit.Ind., Biog.Ind., Bk.Rev.Ind. (1965-), Child.Bk.Rev.Ind. (1965-), Curr.Cont., Hum.Ind., Mag.Ind., Music Artic.Guide, Music Ind., PMR, R.G., RILM. **Document type:** consumer publication.
   ●Also available online. Vendor(s): University Microfilms International.
   —BLDSC (6267.500000); Faxon; UMI; UnCover.
   Description: Contains interviews with prominent singers and conductors, historical background articles, performance reviews worldwide, plus cast lists, photographs, and plot summaries for weekly Metropolitan Opera radio broadcasts.

MUSIC

782.1 UK ISSN 0958-501X
OPERA NOW. 1989. m. £75. Rhinegold Publishing Ltd., 241 Shaftesbury Ave., London WC2H 8EH, England. TEL 0171-333-1742. FAX 0171-333-1769. Ed. Graeme Kay. adv.; bk.rev.; music rev.; rec.rev. circ. 20,070. **Document type:** consumer publication.
Description: International perspective on the world of opera.

780 US ISSN 0736-0053
ML1699
OPERA QUARTERLY. 1983. q. $36 to individuals (foreign $48); institutions $80 (foreign $92) (effective 1996). Duke University Press, Box 90660, Durham, NC 27708-0660. TEL 919-687-3600. FAX 919-688-4571. Ed. William Ashbrook. adv.; bk.rev.; rec.rev.; illus. circ. 5,000. (back issues avail.) **Indexed:** Arts & Hum.Cit.Ind., Curr.Cont., Music Artic.Guide, Music Ind., RILM.
—BLDSC (6267.512000); Faxon; Genuine Article; UMI; UnCover.
Refereed Serial

782.1 DK ISSN 0900-6354
OPERABLADET ASCOLTA. 1982. 8/yr. DKK 150. Operaens Venner, Anemonevej 4, DK-3500 Vaerloese, Denmark. TEL 45-44-98-71-66. Ed. J. Krisand. adv.; bk.rev.; illus. circ. 3,800.
Formerly (until 1983): Ascolta (ISSN 0108-2124)

782.1 GW ISSN 0935-6398
OPERNGLAS. 1980. m. DM.93.50($100) Opernglas Verlagsgesellschaft mbH, Lappenbergsallee 45, 20257 Hamburg, Germany. TEL 040-8503395. FAX 040-858112. Ed. Michael Lehnert. adv. contact: Christine Muth. bk.rev.; rec.rev. circ. 17,500. **Document type:** consumer publication.
Description: Features opera reviews, interviews, information, artist information and calendar.

782.1 GW ISSN 0030-3690
ML5
OPERNWELT; die internationale Opernzeitschrift. 1959. m. DM.187.90. Erhard Friedrich Verlag GmbH, Im Brande 17, 30926 Seelze, Germany. TEL 0511-400040. FAX 0511-4000444. Eds. Manuel Brug, Thomas Voigt. adv.; illus.; circ. 10,000 (controlled). **Indexed:** Music Ind. **Document type:** consumer publication.
—SWETS. **CCC.**

780 NE ISSN 1382-1822
OPSCENE. 1987. bi-m. fl.35($25) Uitgeverij Papieren Tijger, Postbus 2599, 4800 CN Breda, Netherlands. TEL 31-76-228375. FAX 31-76-228375. Ed. K. Poolman. adv.; music rev.; circ. 1,600 (paid). **Document type:** consumer publication.
Description: Interviews, articles and reviews of avant garde and independent music.

780.01 US ISSN 0882-178X
ML1
OPTION MAGAZINE. 1985. bi-m. $15.95. Supersonic Media, 1522 B Cloverfield Blvd., Santa Monica, CA 90404. TEL 310-449-0120. FAX 310-449-1153. E-mail: OPTIONMAG@AOL.com. Ed. Mark Kemp; Pub. Scott Becker. adv. contact: Scott Becker. bk.rev.; illus. circ. 27,000. (back issues avail.) **Document type:** consumer publication.
—UnCover.
Description: Covers nonmainstream music.

780.7 CN ISSN 0846-3085
OPUS. 1953. q. free. Saskatchewan Registered Music Teachers' Association, Box 120, Meacham, SK S0K 2V0, Canada. TEL 306-376-2054. Ed. Lore Ruschiensky. adv. contact: Lore Ruschiensky. circ. 350. **Document type:** newspaper.
Description: Reports from various branches of the provincial association on activities and competitions.

780 XR ISSN 0862-8505
OPUS MUSICUM. 1969. 10/yr. 90 Kc.($30) Opus Musicum Foundation, Radnicka 10, 60200 Brno, Czech Republic. TEL 42-5-42213567. FAX 42-5-41211597. (Foreign subscr. to: Kubon and Sagner. P.O. Box 340108, 8000 Munich, P.O. Box 34108, Germany) Ed. Eva Drlikova. adv.; bk.rev.; illus. circ. 1,500. **Indexed:** Music Ind., RILM. **Document type:** bulletin.

780.01 IS ISSN 0303-3937
ORBIS MUSICAE; Assaph studies in the arts. (Text in English, French, German) 1971. irreg., no.11, 1994. $15. Tel Aviv University, Department of Musicology, Ramat Aviv 69978, Israel. TEL 972-3-6408332. FAX 972-3-6407358. Ed. David Halperin. bk.rev. circ. 500. (back issues avail.) **Indexed:** Music Ind. **Document type:** academic/scholarly publication, monographic series.
—BLDSC (6277.867000).
Description: Articles in musicology and ethnomusicology by international scholars.

ORBIT MAGAZINE. see LEISURE AND RECREATION

785 GW ISSN 0030-4468
ML5
DAS ORCHESTER; Zeitschrift fuer deutsche Orchesterkultur und Rundfunk-Chorwesen. 1953. 11/yr. DM.102. (Deutsche Orchestervereinigung) Schott Musik International GmbH, Weihergarten 5, 55116 Mainz, Germany. TEL 06131-246-0. FAX 06131-246211. Eds. R. Duennwald, G. Engelmann. adv.: B&W page DM.2755; trim 260 x 185; adv. contact: Karin Krappen. bk.rev.; bibl.; charts; illus.; index. circ. 20,000. **Indexed:** Music Ind., RILM. **Document type:** consumer publication.
—BLDSC (6277.925000); Faxon; SWETS; UnCover.

780.6 CN ISSN 0380-1799
ORCHESTRA CANADA/ORCHESTRES CANADA. (Text in English, French) 1974. bi-m. Can.$22. Association of Canadian Orchestras, 56 The Esplanade, Ste. 311, Toronto, ON M5E 1A7, Canada. TEL 416-366-8834. (Co-sponsor: Ontario Federation of Symphony Orchestras) Ed. Ulla Colgrass. adv. circ. 3,000.
Description: Contains reviews of government legislation, cultural issues, news, people, and orchestras.

780.7 US ISSN 0030-4743
OREGON MUSIC EDUCATOR.* vol.25, 1973. 3/yr. $2 to non-members. 337 W. Riverside Dr., Roseburg, OR 97470. TEL 503-673-6353. Ed. Robert E. Robins. adv.; bk.rev.; illus.; music rev. circ. 2,000. **Indexed:** Music Artic.Guide.
Description: Presents study and teaching methods.

780 US ISSN 0095-2613
ML1
ORFF ECHO. 1968. 4/yr. $35 to individuals; libraries $40. American Orff-Schulwerk Association, 332 Gerard Ave., Elkins Park, PA 19117. TEL 215-635-2622. FAX 215-625-2415. (Subscr. to: c/o Cindi Wobig, Box 391089, Cleveland, OH 44139-1089. TEL 216-543-5366) Ed. Tossi Aaron. adv.; bk.rev. circ. 5,100. **Indexed:** Music Artic.Guide. **Document type:** newsletter.
—UnCover.

780 AT
ORFF-SCHULWERK ASSOCIATION OF QUEENSLAND. BULLETIN.* 1968. m. Aus.$3. Orff-Schulwerk Association of Queensland, c/o Australian National Council of Orff-Schulwerk Association, 32 Cuthbert St., Heathmont, Vic. 3135, Australia.

786.6 UK ISSN 0030-4883
ORGAN; review for its makers, its players and its lovers. 1921. q. £15 (foreign £20). Musical Opinion Ltd., 2 Princes Rd., St. Leonards-on-Sea, E. Sussex TN37 6EL, England. TEL 0424-715167. FAX 0424-712214. Ed. Brian Hick. adv. contact: Liz Biddle. rec.rev.; charts; illus. circ. 2,000. (also avail. in microform from WMP) **Indexed:** Arts & Hum.Cit.Ind., Br.Hum.Ind., Curr.Cont., Music Ind., RILM. **Document type:** academic/scholarly publication.
—BLDSC (6285.300000); Faxon; UnCover.

786 UK ISSN 0306-0357
ORGAN CLUB JOURNAL. 1964. bi-m. $14. Organ Club, c/o Philip Weston, Gen. Sec., 36 Fortismere Ave., London N10 3BL, England. (Subscr. to: James Trelaor, 29 Columbine Close, Huntingdon, Chester CH3 6BQ, England) bk.rev. circ. controlled.

786 US ISSN 0193-6670
M6
ORGAN PORTFOLIO. bi-m. $22.95. Lorenz Publishing Co., 501 E. Third St., Box 802, Dayton, OH 45401-0802. TEL 513-228-6118. FAX 513-223-2042. Ed. Dorothy Wells. adv. contact: Larry Pugh. **Document type:** trade publication.
Description: Includes arrangements for the trained organist.

780 NE ISSN 0078-6098
ORGAN YEARBOOK; a journal for the players and historians of keyboard instruments. (Text in English, French and German) 1970. a. fl.49. Uitgeverij Frits Knuf B. V., Box 720, 4116 ZJ Buren, Netherlands. FAX 31-349-2617. Ed. Peter Williams. adv.; bk.rev. circ. 3,000. (back issues avail.) **Indexed:** Music Ind., RILM.

786 US
ORGANIST. bi-m. $22.95. Lorenz Publishing Co., 501 E. Third St., Box 802, Dayton, OH 45401-0802. TEL 513-228-6118. FAX 513-223-2042. Ed. Gregg Sewell. **Document type:** trade publication.
Description: Arrangements for the organist with little or no training.

786.5 IT
ORGANISTICA. 1992. 3/yr. L.48000 (foreign L.54000). Casa Musicale Edizioni Carrara, Via Calepio 4, 24100 Bergamo, Italy. TEL 035-243-618. Ed. Wilhelm Krumbach. adv.: B&W page L.600000; adv. contact: Vittorio Carrara. **Document type:** consumer publication.

786 UK
ORGANISTS' BENEVOLENT LEAGUE. ANNUAL REPORT. 1909. a. free. Organists' Benevolent League, c/o R.C. Lyne, Ed., 10 Stratford Place, London W1N 9AE, England. circ. 2,500.

786.6 UK ISSN 0048-2161
ORGANISTS' REVIEW. 1913. q. £14 (elsewhere £16.50). (Incorporated Association of Organists) Marcus Knight, 6 Homefield Close, Chelmsford, Essex CM1 2HE, England. TEL 01245-259120. Ed. Paul Hale. adv.; bk.rev.; rec.rev. circ. 5,000. (also avail. in microform from UMI; reprint service avail. from UMI) **Indexed:** Music Ind. **Document type:** bulletin.
—BLDSC (6289.920000); UMI.
Description: Contents include articles on pipe organs, organ music, organ builders, association news, record and tape reviews.

786 786 IT ISSN 0474-6376
ORGANO; rivista di cultura organaria e organistica. 1960. s-a. L.80000. Patron Editore, Via Badini 12, 40050 Quarto Inferiore (Bologna), Italy. Eds. Oscar Mischiati, Luigi Tagliavini. bk.rev.; index. (back issues avail.) **Indexed:** RILM.
—BLDSC (6291.059000).

780 NE ISSN 1382-1377
ORGELDIENST. 1973. bi-m. fl.45. Vereniging van Gereformeerde Kerkorganisten, Heemskerkstraat 7, 9801 KL Zuidhorn, Netherlands. TEL 31-5940-6374. Ed. J. Smelik. bk.rev.
Description: Covers topics relating to church organ music.

786.5 SW
ORGELFORUM. 1979. q. SEK 140 membership. Svenska Orgelsaellskapet, Turingevaegen 77, S-125 43 Aelvsjoe, Sweden. TEL 46-8-647-68-22. Ed. Jan Rostroem. adv. **Document type:** newspaper.

786.6 FR ISSN 0030-5170
ML5
ORGUE; histoire-technique-esthetique-musique. (Supplement avail: Cahiers et Memoires de l'Orgue). 1929. q. 330 F. Association des Amis de l'Orgue, 70 rue de Rivoli, 75004 Paris, France. TEL 42-78-60-23. Ed. Brigitte De Leersnyder. adv.; bk.rev.; bibl.; charts; illus. **Indexed:** Music Ind., RILM.

780 GW ISSN 0932-6111
ORPHEUS. 1972. 13/yr. DM.147 (foreign DM.177). Neue Gesellschaft fuer Musikinformation mbH, Livlaendischestr. 27, 10715 Berlin, Germany. TEL 030-8533287. FAX 030-8542207. Ed. Geerd Heinsen. adv.; bk.rev.; index. circ. 20,000. (back issues avail.; reprint service avail. from KTO) **Document type:** bulletin.

780 FR ISSN 1251-3369
▼**OSTINATO**. 1994. s-a. 300 F. (foreign 350 F.) (effective 1996). Editions Jean Michel Place, 12 rue Pierre et Marie Curie, 75005 Paris, France. TEL 46-33-05-11. FAX 46-34-52-65.

780 UK
OUTLET. 1978. 2/yr. £2.50. Outlet Magazines, 33 Aintree Crescent, Barkingside, Ilford, Essex IG6 2HD, England. TEL 0181-551-3346. Ed. Trev Faull. circ. 6,800. (back issues avail.) **Document type**: consumer publication.
 Description: Small indie label reviews of recordings, listings, reissues and artist discographies.

OVERALL THERE IS A SMELL OF FRIED ONIONS. see *MOTION PICTURES*

780 CN
OVERTURE. 9/yr. free. Winnipeg Symphony Orchestra, 101-555 Main St., Winnipeg, MB R3B 1C3, Canada. TEL 204-949-3950. FAX 204-956-4271. Ed. Geoffrey Hayes. adv. contact: Carol Cassels. circ. 14,000 (controlled). (back issues avail.)
 Description: Provides information on the activities, repertoire, artists and composers featured in the orchestra's annual season.

780 US ISSN 0885-3347
MT125
OVERTURE (BALTIMORE). 1977. 5/yr. free. Baltimore Symphony Orchestra, Inc., 1212 Cathedral St., Baltimore, MD 21201-5545. TEL 410-783-8100. FAX 410-783-8077. TELEX 87770 BAL. Ed. Jan Bedell. adv. circ. 40,000.
 Description: Covers news, upcoming events and interviews with guest artists and members of the Baltimore Symphony Orchestra.

780 331.8 US ISSN 0030-7556
ML1
OVERTURE (LOS ANGELES). 1919. m. membership. Musicians' Union, Local 47 of A.F.M., 817 N. Vine St., Los Angeles, CA 90038. TEL 213-462-2161. Ed. Serena Kay Williams. adv.; charts; illus. circ. 10,000. **Document type**: trade publication.

OVERTURES; the magazine devoted to the musical on stage and record. see *THEATER*

780 US
OXFORD MONOGRAPHS ON MUSIC. irreg. price varies. Oxford University Press, 200 Madison Ave., New York, NY 10016. TEL 212-679-7300.

780 US ISSN 0078-7264
OXFORD STUDIES OF COMPOSERS. irreg., no.19, 1982. price varies. Oxford University Press, 200 Madison Ave., New York, NY 10016. TEL 212-679-7300. Ed. Colin Mason.

780.7 US ISSN 0030-8102
P M E A NEWS. 1952. 4/yr. $8. Pennsylvania Music Educators Association, Inc., c/o R. Merrell, 823 Old Westtown Rd., West Chester, PA 19382. TEL 610-436-9281. adv.; bk.rev.; charts; illus.; index. circ. 5,000. **Indexed**: Music Artic.Guide. **Document type**: trade publication.
 —Faxon; UnCover.
 Description: Professional journal for Pennsylvania music educators.

780 US ISSN 0030-8153
P.M.O. NOTES. 1943. q. free. Purdue University Musical Organizations, Edward C. Elliott Hall of Music, W. Lafayette, IN 47907-1093. TEL 317-494-3941. Ed. Kitty Campbell. illus. circ. 8,500. (processed) **Document type**: newsletter.
 Description: Features articles and pictures on recent events, including musical shows, concerts, tours and student organization activities.

780 UK ISSN 0964-9875
P R S MEMBERS HANDBOOK. 1991. irreg. membership. Performing Right Society Ltd., c/o Terri Anderson, 29-33 Berners St., London W1P 4AA, England. TEL 0171-580-5544. circ. 27,000. **Document type**: bulletin.

780 UK
P R S NEWS. 1976. 2/yr. membership. Performing Right Society Ltd., c/o Terri Anderson, 29-33 Berners St., London W1P 4AA, England. TEL 0171-580-5544. circ. 27,000. **Indexed**: Music Ind. **Document type**: newsletter.
 Former titles: Performing Right News (ISSN 0309-0019); Performing Right (ISSN 0031-5257)
 Description: For organizations related to the music industry, and their members.

PALACE PEEPER. see *THEATER*

780 PL
PAMIETNIKI MUZYCZNE. 1983. irreg. price varies. Polskie Wydawnictwo Muzyczne, Al. Krasinskiego 11a, 31-111 Krakow, Poland. TEL 48-12-227044. FAX 48-12-220174. adv. contact: Tersa Wlochynska. illus.
 Description: Contains memoirs of great artists.

781.62 AU
PANNONISCHE FORSCHUNGSSTELLE OBERSCHUETZEN. ARBEITSBERICHTE - MITTEILUNGEN. 1990. a. Pannonische Forschungsstelle Oberschuetzen, Postfach 12, A-7432 Oberschuetzen, Austria. TEL 03353-669340. Eds. Thomas Hochradner, Bernhard Hoble. bk.rev.; circ. 500. **Document type**: proceedings.

780 CN ISSN 1195-7719
PARADES & PAGEANTRY. 1972. m. Can.$25 to non-members. Ontario Drum Corps Association, P.O. Box 40056, RPO Waterloo Sq., Waterloo, ON N2J 4V1, Canada. TEL 519-742-5811. FAX 519-742-5501. Ed. Betty Schmidt. adv. circ. 325. (back issues avail.) **Document type**: newsletter.
 Formerly: Information Drum Corps; Incorporates (1991-1993): Pageantry Ontario (ISSN 1199-1135)

780 FR ISSN 0247-0357
PAROLES ET MUSIQUE; le mensuel de toutes les musiques. 1980. m. 275 F. Editions de l'Araucaria, 1 rue du Pont-De-Lodi, 75006 Paris, France. Ed. Fred Hidalgo.

780 IT
PASQUINO MUSICALE. 1991. m. (10/yr.). L.40000 (L.125000 with CD). Saturnia Diffusione, Villa II Parnaso, Via Carizia 25, 04018 Sezze Romano (LT), Italy. TEL 39-773-803287. FAX 39-773-803744. Ed. Luciano Della Mea.

PAST TIMES: THE NOSTALGIA ENTERTAINMENT NEWSLETTER. see *MOTION PICTURES*

783 US ISSN 0363-6569
ML1
PASTORAL MUSIC. 1976. bi-m. $27 to libraries. National Association of Pastoral Musicians, 225 Sheridan St., N.W., Washington, DC 20011. TEL 202-723-5800. Ed. Rev. Virgil Funk. adv.; bk.rev.; illus. circ. 9,000. (also avail. in microfilm from UMI; back issues avail.; reprint service avail. from UMI) **Indexed**: Cath.Ind.; CERDIC, Music Artic.Guide, Music Ind. **Document type**: newsletter.
 —Faxon; UMI; UnCover.
 Supersedes: Musart (ISSN 0027-3724)

783 US ISSN 0145-6636
ML2999
PASTORAL MUSIC NOTEBOOK. 1977. bi-m. membership. National Association of Pastoral Musicians, 225 Sheridan St., N.W., Washington, DC 20011. TEL 202-723-5800. Ed. Gordon E. Truitt. circ. 8,500.

789.9 US ISSN 0360-2109
ML156.9
PAUL'S RECORD MAGAZINE. 1975. irreg., nos.17-18, 1978. $10 (foreign $20). Paul E. Bezanker, Ed. & Pub., Box 843, Enfield, CT 06083-0843. adv.; bk.rev.; rec.; rev.; illus.; stat.; index, cum.index. circ. 1,500. **Indexed**: Pop.Mus.Per.Ind.

PEABODY NEWS. see *COLLEGE AND ALUMNI*

787 US
PEDAL STEEL NEWSLETTER. 1973. 10/yr. $20 (foreign $30). Pedal Steel Guitar Association, Inc., Box 20248, Floral Park, NY 11002-0248. Ed. Doug Mack. adv. circ. 1,200. (back issues avail.) **Document type**: newsletter.
 Description: Concerns the pedal steel guitar, how it is played, and those who play it.

781.7 286 US ISSN 0272-9199
ML2999
PEDALPOINT. q. $29.50. Southern Baptist Convention, Sunday School Board, 127 Ninth Ave., N., Nashville, TN 37234. TEL 800-458-2772.
 Description: Provides church organists and pianists with easy and medium-difficulty music.

780 UK ISSN 0967-4667
THE PENGUIN GUIDE TO COMPACT DISCS AND CASSETTES YEARBOOK. 1991. a. Penguin Books Ltd., 27 Wrights Ln., London W8 5TZ, England. Ed. Ivan March. **Document type**: catalog.

780 US ISSN 1046-0292
PENN SOUNDS. 1989. 3/yr. $10. Composer Services Inc., 345 S. 19th St., Philadelphia, PA 19103. TEL 215-985-0963. Eds. Harry D. & Elizabeth R. Hewitt. adv.: B&W page $50. bk.rev.; illus.; index, cum.index: 1989-1993. circ. 250. (looseleaf format; back issues avail.) **Indexed**: Music Artic.Guide. **Document type**: newspaper.
 Description: Serves the needs and interests of Pennsylvania composers. Features biographies of senior Pennsylvania composers, articles on esthetics, as well as technical articles related to composition; and lists Pennsylvania composer activities.
 Refereed Serial

780.6 US
PEOPLE'S SONGLETTER. 4/yr. membership. Newsong Network, 61 Wurts St., Kingston, NY 12401. TEL 914-338-8587.

780 US
PERCUSSION NEWS. bi-m. $40 (students $20); includes Percussive Notes. Percussive Arts Society, Inc., Box 25, Lawton, OK 73502-0025. TEL 405-353-1455. FAX 405-353-1456. Ed. Shawn Brown. **Document type**: newsletter.

789 US ISSN 0553-6502
ML1
PERCUSSIVE NOTES. 1961. 6/yr. $40 (students $20); includes Percussion News. Percussive Arts Society, Inc., Box 25, Lawton, OK 73502-0025. TEL 405-353-1455. FAX 405-353-1456. Ed. James Lambert. adv.; bk.rev.; illus.; index, cum.index. circ. 5,700. (also avail. in microform from UMI; reprint service avail. from UMI) **Indexed**: Music Artic.Guide., Music Ind., RILM. **Document type**: academic/scholarly publication.
 —BLDSC (6423.560000); Faxon; UMI; UnCover.
 Formerly: Percussionist (ISSN 0553-6499); Incorporates: Percussionist and Percussive Notes (ISSN 0031-5168)

790 US ISSN 0882-9314
PERFORMANCE; the international talent weekly. 1970. w. (51/yr.). $189 (first class $259) includes directories. Performance Magazine, 1101 University Dr., Ste. 108, Ft. Worth, TX 76107. TEL 817-338-9444. adv.; bk.rev. circ. 2,400. **Document type**: trade publication.
 Formerly: Performance Newspaper (ISSN 0746-9772)

780 US ISSN 1044-1638
ML1
PERFORMANCE PRACTICE REVIEW. 1988. s-a. $19 to individuals; institutions $38; students $9 (effective 1995). 1422 Knoll Park La., Fallbrook, CA 92028. TEL 619-723-0565. FAX 619-723-0422. Ed. Roland Jackson. adv.; bk.rev.; bibl. circ. 600. **Indexed**: Music Artic.Guide. **Document type**: academic/scholarly publication.
 —Faxon; UnCover.
 Description: Addresses the concerns of historically authentic performance.

PERFORMING ARTS; the theatre & music magazine. see *THEATER*

PERFORMING ARTS AND ENTERTAINMENT IN CANADA. see *THEATER*

780 UK ISSN 0309-0884
ML27.G7
PERFORMING RIGHT YEAR BOOK. 1977. a. membership. Performing Right Society Ltd., c/o Terri Anderson, 29-33 Berners St., London W1P 4AA, England. TEL 0171-580-5544. **Document type**: corporate report.
 Description: Reviews the previous year's activities, including the society's annual report and accounts.

782 US ISSN 1068-9664
ML3469
PERFORMING SONGWRITER. 1993. bi-m. $25.95. Desktop Communications, Box 158159, Nashville, TN 37215. TEL 615-297-6972. FAX 615-383-4812. E-mail: PERFSONG@aol.com. Ed. Lydia L. Hutchinson. adv. contact: Cliff Goldmacher. circ. 9,000.
    Description: A resource magazine for songwriters of any musical genre with indepth interviews, regular columns and festival information.

780 US ISSN 0898-8722
ML410.P29
PERGOLESI STUDIES/STUDI PERGOLESIANI. 1986. irreg., vol.2, 1989. Pendragon Press, 41 Ferry St., Stuyvesant, NY 12173-9720. TEL 518-828-3008. FAX 518-828-2368. **Document type:** monographic series.

781.7 RU
PERSONALITIES. EVENTS. TIMES; albums. 1982. a. 15 Rub. Izdatel'stvo Muzyka, Ul. Neglinnaya 14, Moscow 103031, Russia.

780.904 US ISSN 0031-6016
ML1
PERSPECTIVES OF NEW MUSIC. 1962. s-a. $37 to individuals; institutions $75. Perspectives of New Music, Inc., School of Music DN-10, University of Washington, Seattle, WA 98195. TEL 206-543-0196. FAX 206-543-9285. E-mail: pnm@u.washington.edu. Ed. Benjamin Boretz. adv.; bk.rev.; rec.rev.; charts; illus.; index, cum.index; circ. 1,500 (paid). (also avail. in microform from UMI; back issues avail.; reprint service avail. from UMI) **Indexed:** Amer.Bibl.Slavic & E.Eur.Stud, Arts & Hum.Cit.Ind., Curr.Cont., Ind.Bk.Rev.Hum., Music Artic.Guide, Music Ind., RILM. **Document type:** academic/scholarly publication.
●Also available online. Vendor(s): Information Access Co.
Also available on CD-ROM.
—BLDSC (6428.145900); Faxon; UMI; UnCover.
    Description: Publishes interviews, analyses, technical reports, position papers by composers, sociological and philosophical articles relating to contemporary music.
    Refereed Serial

780 UK ISSN 0266-366X
PETER WARLOCK SOCIETY NEWSLETTER. 1965. 6/m. £8 membership. Peter Warlock Society, 100 Boileau Rd., London W5 3AJ, England. Ed. David Cox. bk.rev. circ. 150. (processed) **Document type:** newsletter.

784 GW ISSN 0031-6687
PFAELZER SAENGER. 1949. m. DM.9. (Pfaelzischer Saengerbund) Pfaelzer Saenger, Hauptstr. 80, 67714 Waldfischbach-Burgalben, Germany. Ed. H.J. Hoffmann. adv. circ. 5,000.

781.7 US
PHILADELPHIA FOLKSONG SOCIETY NEWSLETTER. m. (excl. July-Sept.). membership. Philadelphia Folksong Society, 7113 Emlen St., Philadelphia, PA 19119. TEL 215-247-1300. Ed. Rosemarie Urbano. circ. 1,575.
    Formerly: Tune Up (ISSN 0161-3081)
    Description: Covers community news, membership information, and concert and event listings.

780.6 GW
PHILHARMONISCHE BLAETTER (BERLIN). 1960. 6/yr. DM.25. Berliner Philharmonisches Orchester, Matthaeikirchstr. 1, 10785 Berlin, Germany. TEL 030-254880. FAX 030-2614887. Ed. Helge Gruenewald. adv. contact: Helge Gruenewald. illus. circ. 24,000. (back issues avail.) **Document type:** bulletin.

780 GW
PHILHARMONISCHE BLAETTER (MUNICH). 1985. m. DM.20. Muenchner Philharmoniker, Kellerstr. 4, 81667 Munich, Germany. TEL 089-480980. FAX 089-48098525. adv.
    Description: News about the Munich Philharmonic Orchestra.

780 BE
PHILIPPE DE MONTE OPERA. SERIES A, MOTETS. 1975. irreg., vol.7, 1986. Leuven University Press, Krakenstraat 3, B-3000 Leuven, Belgium. TEL 32-16-324175. FAX 32-16-323782. **Document type:** academic/scholarly publication.

780 BE
PHILIPPE DE MONTE OPERA. SERIES B, MASSES. 1976. irreg., vol.2, 1979. Leuven University Press, Krakenstraat 3, B-3000 Leuven, Belgium. TEL 32-16-324175. FAX 32-16-323782. **Document type:** academic/scholarly publication.

780 BE
PHILIPPE DE MONTE OPERA. SERIES D, MADRIGALS. 1977. irreg., vol.4, 1988. Leuven University Press, Krakenstraat 3, B-3000 Leuven, Belgium. TEL 32-16-324175. FAX 32-16-323782. **Document type:** academic/scholarly publication.

780.65 GW
PHONO PRESS. 1973. s-a. free. Bundesverband der Phonographischen Wirtschaft e.V., Grelckstr. 36, 22529 Hamburg, Germany. TEL 040-580258. FAX 040-582842. circ. 2,000. **Document type:** bulletin.

PHONOLOG REPORTER; all-in-one-reporter. see MUSIC — Abstracting, Bibliographies, Statistics

780.42 IT
PHOTOROCK & RECORDS.* 12/yr. L.20000. Gruppo Editoriale Suono s.r.l., Via Capo Peloro, 30, 00141 Rome, Italy. TEL 893608.

786 FR ISSN 0999-5404
PIANO. 1987. a. 70 F. (foreign 70 F.). B.P. 64, 75722 Paris Cedex 15, France. TEL 47-34-06-91. FAX 42-73-18-47. Ed. Michele Worms. adv.; bk.rev. **Document type:** consumer publication.

786.3 US ISSN 1067-3881
ML1
PIANO & KEYBOARD. 1952. bi-m. $36 (Canada $43.50; elsewhere $51). String Letter Press, Inc., Box 767, San Anselmo, CA 94979-0706. TEL 415-485-6946. FAX 415-485-0831. E-mail: pianokeyb@aol.com. Ed. Tim Pfaff; Pub. David A. Listerman. adv. contact: Rachel Blatt. bk.rev.; music rev.; rec.rev.; illus.; cum.index every 3 yrs. circ. 15,000. (also avail. in microform from UMI; reprint service avail. from UMI,ISI) **Indexed:** Arts & Hum.Cit.Ind., Curr.Cont., Music Artic.Guide., Music Ind., RILM. **Document type:** consumer publication.
—Faxon; Genuine Article; UMI; UnCover.
    Former titles (until 1993): Piano Quarterly (ISSN 0031-9554); (until 1958): Piano Quarterly Newsletter (ISSN 0735-7125).
    Description: Contains interviews with leading pianists, composers and conductors, lessons, reviews of new music, and articles of historical interest to both professional and amateur performers who play the piano.

780 NE ISSN 0920-0983
PIANO BULLETIN. 1982. 3/yr. fl.45($30) (European Piano Teachers Association) E.P.T.A. Netherlands, P.O. Box 613, 2270 AP Voorburg, Netherlands. TEL 31-70-3873848. (Editorial addr.: Havenstraat 12, 2613 VK Delft, Netherlands. TEL 31-15-126695. FAX 31-15-126695) Ed. Christo Lelie. adv. circ. 1,200.
    Description: Information for professional pianists and piano teachers about repertoire, technique, history of music, interpretation, and new recordings.

786.3 US ISSN 0031-9546
PIANO GUILD NOTES. 1945. bi-m. $15. National Guild of Piano Teachers, Box 1807, Austin, TX 78767. TEL 512-478-5775. Ed. Pat McCabe-Leche. adv.; bk.rev.; illus.; circ. 12,000. (also avail. in microfilm from UMI; reprint service avail. from UMI)
—UMI; UnCover.

786 GW ISSN 0173-8607
ML650
PIANO-JAHRBUCH; das deutschsprachige Klavierperiodikum. 1977. irreg. DM.58($14) Piano-Verlag Recklinghausen, Koernerplatz 8, 45661 Recklinghausen, Germany. Ed. Rainer M. Klaas. adv.; bk.rev.; bibl.; illus.; index. circ. 1,300. (back issues avail.)

786 UK ISSN 0267-7253
ML5
PIANO JOURNAL. 1980. 3/yr. £6($12) European Piano Teachers' Association (E.P.T.A.), 28 Emperor's Gate, London SW7 4HS, England. TEL 071-373-7307. Ed. Carola Grindea. adv.; bk.rev.; music rev.; tr.lit. circ. 3,250. (back issues avail.)
—BLDSC (6498.264000).
    Description: Includes articles on pianists and piano teaching, reviews, and association news.

786.23 US ISSN 0031-9562
ML1
PIANO TECHNICIANS JOURNAL.* 1958. m. $85. Piano Technicians Guild, Inc., 3930 Washington St., Kansas City, MO 64111-2925. Ed. Larry Goldsmith. adv.; bk.rev.; charts; illus.; index. circ. 3,900. **Indexed:** Music Ind.
—UnCover.

786 IT
PIANO TIME. 1983. m. L.160000 (Europe L.240000). Ediscreen s.r.l., Via Calderini, 68, 00196 Rome, Italy. TEL 06-3220195. Dir. Enzo Perilli. adv.: B&W page L.2370000, color page L.3830000.

PIANO-TUNERS QUARTERLY. see HANDICAPPED — Visually Impaired

787 US
PITCH (NEW YORK); for the international microtonalist. 1986. q. $62 (Canada $66; elsewhere $70). American Festival of Microtonal Music, Inc., 318 E. 70th St., Ste. 5FW, New York, NY 10021. TEL 212-517-3550. FAX 212-517-5495. Ed. Johnny Reinhard. bk.rev. circ. 1,000. (audio cassette) **Indexed:** RILM. **Document type:** bibliography.

780 331.8 US ISSN 0032-034X
PITTSBURGH MUSICIAN. 1949. m. membership only. Pittsburgh Musicians Union, Local No.60-471, A.F.M., 709 Forbes Ave., Pittsburgh, PA 15219. TEL 412-281-1822. Ed. Vincent Ventresca. adv.; charts; illus.; circ. 1,200 (controlled). **Document type:** newspaper.
    Description: News and items of interest to local union musicians.

785.06 US ISSN 0032-0358
PITTSBURGH SYMPHONY ORCHESTRA PROGRAM. 1926. w. (Sept.-May). $45. Pittsburgh Symphony Society, Heinz Hall, 600 Penn Ave., Pittsburgh, PA 15222. TEL 412-392-4800. FAX 412-392-4909. Ed. Laurette Mumper. adv.; index. circ. 8,550. **Indexed:** Music Ind.

PLACE DES ARTS. MAGAZINE. see THEATER

016.7809 DK ISSN 0109-534X
PLADEANMELDELSER, RYTMISK MUSIK. 1984. fortn. DKK 1653.60 (effective 1996). Dansk BiblioteksCenter as, Tempovej 7-11, 2750 Ballerup, Denmark. TEL 45-44-97-40-00. FAX 45-44-68-24-42.

783 UK ISSN 0961-1371
ML169.8
PLAINSONG & MEDIEVAL MUSIC. 1978. s-a. £40($64) (effective 1996). (Plainsong & Mediaeval Music Society) Cambridge University Press, Edinburgh Bldg., Shaftesbury Rd., Cambridge CB2 2RU, England. TEL 01223-312393. FAX 01223-315052. TELEX 851817256. (N. American addr.: Cambridge University Press, Journals Dept., 40 W. 20th St., New York, NY 10011. TEL 212-924-3900. FAX 212-691-3239) Eds. John Caldwell, Christopher Page. adv.; bk.rev. (back issues avail.) **Indexed:** RILM. **Document type:** academic/scholarly publication.
—UMI; UnCover. CCC.
    Formerly (until 1992): Plainsong and Mediaeval Music Society. Journal (ISSN 0143-4918)
    Description: Covers the entire field of plainchant and medieval music, including monophonic, polyphonic, and liturgical music from the East and West.

DAS PLATEAU. see ART

780.3 US ISSN 1059-6925
ML27.U5
PLAY BACK. Variant title: A S C A P in Action Play Back. (Supplement to: A S C A P in Action (ISSN 0197-7849)) 1990. irreg. American Society of Composers, Authors and Publishers, One Lincoln Plaza, New York, NY 10023. TEL 212-595-3050. FAX 212-721-0955.

PLAY METER. see SPORTS AND GAMES

780 II
PLAYBACK & FAST FORWARD. (Text in English) 1986. m. newsstand price: Rs.20. P.B. No. 16164, B.G. Kher Marg, Bombay 400 006, India. Ed. Anil Chopra. adv.: B&W page Rs.5200, color page Rs.9000; bleed 270 x 205; adv. contact: Nandu Pankar.

MUSIC   4875

786 UK ISSN 0140-7589
PLAYER PIANO GROUP BULLETIN. 1959. q. £10. Player Piano Group, 93 Evelyn Ave., Ruislip, Middlesex HA4 8AH, England. TEL 01895-634288. Ed. Julian Dyer. adv.; bk.rev. circ. 275. (back issues avail.) Document type: bulletin.
  Description: Provides information and opportunities for people interested in player and reproducing pianos.

781.7 PL ISSN 0032-2946
ML5
POLISH MUSIC/POLNISCHE MUSIK. (Text in English and German) 1966. q. $14. Agencja Autorska - Authors' Agency, Hipoteczna 2, P.O. Box 133, 00-950 Warsaw, Poland. TEL 22-27-83-96. FAX 22-27-58-82. TELEX ZAIKS PL 812470. Ed. Jan Grzybowski. adv.; bk.rev. circ. 1,200. Indexed: Music Ind., RILM.
  ●Available only online.
  —UnCover.

781.7 US ISSN 0741-9945
POLISH MUSIC HISTORY SERIES. 1982. irreg., no.5, 1993. price varies. Friends of Polish Music, University of Southern California, School of Music, Los Angeles, CA 90089-0851. TEL 213-877-1906. FAX 818-509-8435. Ed. Wanda Wilk. circ. 1,000. Document type: academic/scholarly publication, bibliography.

780.65 US ISSN 1067-6945
ML13
POLLSTAR. 1981. 50/yr. $295. Promoters On-Line Listings, 4333 N. West Ave., Fresno, CA 93705. TEL 209-224-2631. FAX 209-224-2674. Ed. Gary Bongiovanni. adv. contact: Brad Snavely. circ. 15,000. Document type: trade publication.
  Description: Covers the international concert business. Includes artist itineraries, box office results, news, ratings charts, contacts.

781.7 PL ISSN 0079-3612
POLSKA PIESN I MUZYKA LUDOWA. ZRODLA I MATERIALY. (Text in English and Polish) 1974. irreg. price varies. (Polska Akademia Nauk, Instytut Sztuki) Polskie Wydawnictwo Muzyczne, Al. Krasinskiego 11a, 31-111 Krakow, Poland. TEL 48-12-227044. FAX 48-12-220174. Ed. Ludwik Bielawski. adv. contact: Teresa Wlochynska. Document type: academic/scholarly publication.
  Description: Folklore materials collected from 1945-1962: transcription from tape recordings, critical commentaries.

783 IT
POLYPHONIA; musica sacra corale - sacred choral music - geistliche Vokal-musik. (Text in English, German, Italian) 1991. q. L.30000 (DM.51, 172 F., 43 SFr., 3445 ptas.) (effective 1991). Casa Musicale Edizioni Carrara, Via Calepio 4, Casella Postale 158, 24100 Bergamo, Italy. Ed. Vittorio Carrara.

781.63 SW ISSN 1103-8578
POP. 1992. bi-m. SEK 195; newsstand price: 39. Fanzine Media AB (Subsidiary of: Bonniers AB), Tulegatan 44, S-113 53 Stockholm, Sweden. TEL 46-8-24-99-20. FAX 46-8-24-99-20. E-mail: pop@pi.se. Ed. Pietro Maglio. adv. contact: Terry Ericsson. circ. 13,000 (controlled). pp./issue: 132.

POPCORN. see *CHILDREN AND YOUTH — For*

POPFOTO. see *CHILDREN AND YOUTH — For*

780.904 IT
POPSTER.* 1976. m. L.15000($31) Gruppo Editoriale Suono s.r.l., Via Capo Peloro, 30, 00141 Rome, Italy. TEL 893608. adv.; illus. circ. 11,500.

780.42 XO ISSN 0554-6877
POPULAR. 1951. m. $33. (Ustav Umeleckej Kritiky a Divadelnej Dokumentacie, Bratislava) Obzor, Spitalska 35, 815 85 Bratislava, Slovakia.
  Former titles (until 1969): Maly Repertoar (ISSN 1210-1664); (until 1964): Nasa Praca (ISSN 0465-9279)

781.62 US
POPULAR FOLK MUSIC TODAY. 1989. q. $10. Aztec Corporation, 705 S. Washington St., Naperville, IL 60540-6654. TEL 708-305-0770. FAX 708-305-0782. Ed. Kerry Loudon. adv. contact: Kerry Loudon. circ. 1,500 (paid). (back issues avail.)
  Description: Covers popular folk music for compact disc buyers.

780.42 UK ISSN 0261-1430
ML3469
POPULAR MUSIC. 1982. 3/yr. £59($99) (effective 1996). Cambridge University Press, Edinburgh Bldg., Shaftesbury Rd., Cambridge CB2 2RU, England. TEL 01223-312393. FAX 01223-315052. TELEX 851817256. (N. American addr.: Cambridge University Press, Journals Dept., 40 W. 20th St., New York, NY 10011. TEL 212-924-3900. FAX 212-691-3239) Ed.Bd. adv.; bk.rev. (also avail. in microform from UMI; back issues avail.; reprint service avail. from SWZ) Indexed: Music Ind., RILM. Document type: academic/scholarly publication.
  —BLDSC (6550.760800); Faxon; SWETS; UMI; UnCover. CCC.
  Description: Provides multidisciplinary coverage of all aspects of popular music: musicology, literary studies, sociology, and economic and social history.

780.42 US
POPULAR MUSIC. vol.11, 1986. a. $58. Gale Research Inc., 835 Penobscot Bldg., Detroit, MI 48266. TEL 313-961-2242. FAX 313-961-6083. Ed. Bruce Pollock.
  Description: Presents information on nearly 500 songs of the year.

780.301 US ISSN 0300-7766
ML1
POPULAR MUSIC & SOCIETY. 1972. q. $25. (Bowling Green State University) Popular Press, Bowling Green State University, Bowling Green, OH 43403. TEL 419-372-7866. Ed. Gary Burns. adv.; bk.rev.; stat.; index. circ. 1,000. (processed; also avail. in microform from KTO,MIM,UMI; reprint service avail. from UMI) Indexed: Arts & Hum.Cit.Ind., Bk.Rev.Ind. (1980-), Child.Bk.Rev.Ind. (1980-), Commun.Abstr., Curr.Cont., Ind.Bk.Rev.Hum., Music Ind., RILM, Sage Fam.Stud.Abstr.
  —BLDSC (6550.761000); Faxon; UMI; UnCover.
  Description: Contains articles on all aspects of popular, mainly rock, music and society, authors, and performers.

780 PL
PRACE ARCHIVUM SLASKIEJ KULTURY MUZYCZNEJ. 1972. irreg., no.8, 1980. exchange basis. Akademia Muzyczna, Biblioteka Glowna, Ul. Zacisze 3, 40-025 Katowice, Poland. TEL 32-155-4017. (Dist. by: Ars Polona-Ruch, Krakowskie Przedmiescie 7, 00-68 Warsaw, Poland).

780 CN ISSN 0822-7500
PRAIRIE SOUNDS. 1980. s-a. free. Canadian Music Centre, Prairie Region, 911 Library Tower, 2500 University Dr., N.W., Calgary, AB T2N 1N4, Canada. TEL 403-220-7403. FAX 403-289-4877. Ed. John C. Reid. adv. circ. 2,000. (back issues avail.) Document type: newsletter.
  Description: Focuses on music composed by Canadian composers.

PRELUDE. see *DANCE*

781.64 UK ISSN 0269-7769
PREMIERE; the only magazine to have music instead of words. m. £30 (foreign £38.25) (effective 1995-1996). E M A P - Metro, Mappin House, 4 Winsley St., London W1N 7AR, England. TEL 0171-436-1515. FAX 0171-312-8191. (Subscr. to: Tower Publishing Services Ltd., Tower House, Sovereign Park, Lathkill St., Market Harborough, Leics. LE16 9EF, England. TEL 01858-468811. FAX 01858-432164) Document type: consumer publication.

PRESENTERS HANDBOOK/GUIDE DU DIFFUSEUR. see *ART*

780 SZ
PRESTO. (Text in French, German) 1915. m. (11/yr.). 40 SFr. (foreign 45 SFr.). Schweizerischer Musikerverband, Hotelgasse 1, CH-3000 Bern, Switzerland. TEL 031-3317448. FAX 031-3317329. Ed. Bernard Schenkel. adv.: page 1050 SFr.; trim 185 x 258. bk.rev. circ. 2,500. Document type: bulletin.
  Formerly: Schweizer Musikerblatt - Bulletin Musical Suisse.

PREVUE. see *MOTION PICTURES*

780 700 500 IT
PRIMI PIANI; mensile d'arte, costume, cultura, scienza, spettacolo e turismo. 1964. m. L.15000 (effective 1992). Via Bolzano 32, 00198 Rome, Italy. TEL 841-16-86. Ed. Fernando Luciani. adv.; illus.; stat.; tr.lit.
  Formerly: Pentagramma (ISSN 0031-4889)

782.1 US
PRINCETON SERIES IN OPERA. irreg. price varies. Princeton University Press, 41 William St., Princeton, NJ 08540. TEL 609-258-4900. FAX 609-258-6305. E-mail: jhardy@pupress.princeton.edu. Document type: monographic series.

PRODUCTIV'S HANDBUCH FUER MUSIKER. see *SOUND RECORDING AND REPRODUCTION*

PRODUCTIV'S SOLO. see *SOUND RECORDING AND REPRODUCTION*

780 320 US
PROFANE EXISTENCE. 1989. q. $9. Anarchist Youth Federation, Box 8722, Minneapolis, MN 55408. Ed. Claire Troll. circ. 2,000.
  Formerly: M.A.S.
  Description: Features political coverage of music.

780 CN ISSN 1186-1797
PROFESSIONAL SOUND. 1990. q. Can.$14 (foreign Can.$17). Norris - Whitney Communications Inc., 23 Hannover Dr., No. 7, St. Catharines, ON L2W 1A3, Canada. TEL 905-641-3471. FAX 905-641-1648. Ed. Shauna Kennedy. adv. circ. 10,500. Document type: trade publication.

780 792 US
PROFILE (WASHINGTON). a. $25 to non-members; members $15. Opera America, 1156 14th St., N.W., Ste. 810, Washington, DC 20005-1704. TEL 202-293-4466. FAX 202-393-0735. Ed. Martha Perry. Indexed: SRI.
  Description: provides an overview of Opera America and the professional opera field, with analysis of the most recent professional opera survey, and descriptions of individual Opera America companies.

780.42 US ISSN 0738-8861
PROGRESSIVE PLATTER MUSIC REVIEW.* 1976. m. $15. (New England D J Association) Progressive Platter, 72-74 E. Dedham St., No. 5, Boston, MA 02118-2417. TEL 617-247-1144. (Subscr. to: Kenmore Station, Box 638, Boston, MA 02215) Ed. Cosmo Wyatt. adv.; bk.rev. circ. 10,000.

786 GW
PROLIX; Wochenzeitung im Dreyeckland. (Text in English, French, German) 1975. w. Prolix Verlag GmbH, Goethestr. 23, 79100 Freiburg, Germany. Ed. Daniel Jaeger. circ. 5,000. (back issues avail.)

PROTOKOLLE; Wiener Halbjahresschrift fuer Literatur, Bildende Kunst und Musik. see *LITERATURE*

780 CN ISSN 1199-0643
PROVINCIAL NEWSLETTER. 3/yr. free. British Columbia Registered Music Teachers' Association, 197 Vancouver Ave., Penticton, BC V2A 1A1, Canada. TEL 604-492-8944. Ed. Ernst Schneider. adv.; bk.rev.; circ. 779 C. (looseleaf format; back issues avail.) Document type: newsletter.
  Description: Presents articles on the teaching of music and reports of the branches of the Association.

781.15 UK ISSN 0305-7356
ML5
PSYCHOLOGY OF MUSIC. 1973. s-a. £25($49) (student £10($25)). Society for Research in Psychology of Music and Music Education, Department of Psychology, The University, Leicester LE1 7RH, England. TEL 0116-2522155. FAX 0116-2522067. E-mail: djh@leicester.ac.uk. Ed. David Hargreaves. adv.; bk.rev.; cum.index every 5 vols. circ. 700. Indexed: Psychol.Abstr. (1976-), RILM. Document type: academic/scholarly publication.
  —BLDSC (6946.536000); Faxon; SWETS; UnCover.
  Refereed Serial

MUSIC

780.01 US ISSN 0275-3987
ML3830
PSYCHOMUSICOLOGY; a journal of research in music cognition. 1981. s-a. $21 (foreign $25). Illinois State University, Office of Research in Arts Technology, Normal, IL 61761. TEL 309-438-3575. FAX 309-438-8318. Ed. David Brian Williams. adv.; bk.rev.; bibl.; charts; stat. circ. 300. (back issues avail.) Indexed: Educ.Ind., Music Ind., Psychol.Abstr. (1981-), RILM. **Document type:** academic/scholarly publication.
—BLDSC (6946.540070); Faxon; UnCover.
Description: Serves as a journal of research in music cognition, providing a forum for reports of experimental research, reviews of research and theoretical papers that are based on experimental research.

780 792 JM
PULSE. q. Pulse Ltd., P.O. Box 200, Kingston 5, Jamaica, W.I. Ed. Kingsley Cooper.

780 US ISSN 1062-7626
PULSE!. 1983. 11/yr. $19.95 (Canada $39.95; elsewhere $150). M T S, Incorporated, Tower Records - Pulse!, 2500 Delmonte St., Bldg. C, W. Sacramento, CA 95691. TEL 916-373-2450. FAX 916-373-2480. E-mail: pulsemag@netcom.com. (Subscr. to: Box 919001, W. Sacramento, CA 95691) Ed. Michael Farrace. adv. contact: Bill Bartsche. film rev.; rec.rev.; video rev.; illus.; circ. 22,500 (paid); 300,000 (controlled). **Document type:** consumer publication.
Description: Covers new music and video releases from around the world, with news of bands, musicians, and interviews.

780 US ISSN 1047-4528
PUNCTURE; a magazine of music and the arts. 1982. q. $11. Puncture Magazine, Box 14806, Portland, OR 97214. TEL 503-236-8270. FAX 503-236-0405. E-mail: puncture@teleport.com. Ed. Katherine Spielmann. adv. contact: Steve Connell. bk.rev. circ. 10,000. (back issues avail.) **Document type:** consumer publication.
Description: Presents articles and reviews covering new developments in contemporary music (especially rock & roll) and the arts.

780 US
PURCHASER'S GUIDE TO THE MUSIC INDUSTRIES. 1897. a. free with subscription to Music Trades. Music Trades Corporation, c/o Paul A. Majeski, Box 432, 80 West St., Englewood, NJ 07631. TEL 201-871-1965. Ed. Brian T. Majeski. adv. contact: Anthony C. D'Angeco. circ. 8,000. (reprint service avail. from UMI) **Document type:** trade publication.

781.64 UK ISSN 0955-4955
ML3533.8
Q; the modern guide to music and more. 1986. m. £27.60 (foreign £40) (effective 1995-4996). E M A P - Metro, Mappin House, 4 Winsley St., London W1N 7AR, England. TEL 0171-436-1515. FAX 0171-323-0680. (Subscr. to: Tower Publishing Services Ltd., Tower House, Sovereign Park, Market Harborough, Leics. LE16 9EF, England. TEL 01858-468811. FAX 01858-432164) Ed. Danny Kelly. adv. contact: Mark Williamson. music rev.; illus. (back issues avail.) **Document type:** consumer publication.
Description: Covers the music scene in the U.K. and throughout the world, with extensive reviews of recent releases and reissues, profiles of bands, and interviews with musicians and rock 'n' roll personalities.

780.6 CC
QING YINYUE/LIGHT MUSIC. (Text in Chinese) bi-m. Jilin Sheng Yinyuejia Xiehui - Jilin Musicians' Association, Fu 111, Stalin St., Bldg. No. 14, Changchun, Jilin 130021, People's Republic of China. TEL 884953. Ed. Wang Guanqun.

QU YI/VARIETY SHOW. see THEATER

780 IT
QUADERNI PUCCINIANI. 1982. irreg., no.4, 1992. price varies. Istituto di Studi Pucciniani, Via Circo 18, 20123 Milan, Italy. TEL 2-8057378. FAX 2-4982194. bk.rev. circ. 1,000. **Document type:** academic/scholarly publication.
Description: Contains musical criticism regarding the life and works of Giacomo Puccini.

780 IT
QUADERNI ROSSINIANI. 1954. irreg., no.19, 1976. price varies. (Fondazione Rossini) Casa Editrice Leo S. Olschki, Casella Postale 66, 50100 Florence, Italy. TEL 39-55-6530684. FAX 39-55-6530214. **Document type:** monographic series.

QUAKE. see CHILDREN AND YOUTH — For

780.904 BL
QUALIS; music collection. bi-m. Qualis Editora, Rua Bartira 12, 05009 Perdizes, Sao Paulo SP, Brazil. TEL 011-65-4973.

780 370 US ISSN 1046-9133
MT1
THE QUARTERLY JOURNAL OF MUSIC TEACHING AND LEARNING. 1990. q. $45 (foreign $53). University of Northern Colorado, School of Music, 123 Frazier Hall, Greeley, CO 80639. TEL 303-351-2254. FAX 303-351-1923. Ed. Elza Daugherty. bk.rev.; charts; circ. 450 (paid). **Document type:** academic/scholarly publication.
—UnCover.
Formerly: Center for Research in Music Learning and Teaching Quarterly.
Description: Presents ideas and issues of concern to all involved with music teaching and learning.
Refereed Serial

780 UK
QUARTERNOTE. 1979. q. free to members. Bournemouth Orchestras, Arts Centre, Poole, Dorset BH15 1UF, England. TEL 0202-670611. FAX 0202-687235. Eds. Ted Street, Rachel Bostock. bk.rev.; illus. circ. 2,500. **Document type:** newsletter.
Formerly (until 1988): W O S News.

780 331.8 US
QUARTERNOTE. 1976. q. $5. American Musicians Union, Inc., 8 Tobin Ct., Dumont, NJ 07628. TEL 201-384-5378. Ed. Ben Intorre. adv.; bk.rev.; illus.; circ. 350 (controlled).
Description: Provides information of interest to members of the union.

780 GW ISSN 0079-905X
QUELLENKATALOGE ZUR MUSIKGESCHICHTE. 1966. irreg., vol.25, 1993. Florian Noetzel Verlag, Heinrichshofen Buecher, Valoisstr. 11, 26382 Wilhelmshaven, Germany. (Dist. in U.S. by C. F. Peters Corp., 373 Park Ave. S., New York, N.Y. 10016) Ed. Richard Schaal. **Document type:** monographic series.

784 US ISSN 0885-9442
QUODLIBET. 1967. 3/yr. membership. Intercollegiate Musical Council, Department of Music, Wabash College, Crawfordsville, IN 47933. TEL 317-364-4398. (Subscr. to: Fr. Richard H. Trame, S.J., Exec. Sec., Department of Music, Loyola Marymount University, Los Angeles, CA 90045) Ed. Stanley A. Malinowski. bk.rev. circ. 75. (looseleaf format; back issues avail.)

780 US
R.A.D!; review and discussion of rock & roll. 1992. m. $18 (effective Jan. 1994). Conspiracy M.E.D.I.A., 826 Old Charlotte Pike E., Franklin, TN 37064. TEL 615-791-1624. (And: Box 158324, Nashville, TN 37215) Ed. Keith A. Gordon. adv. contact: Tracey dooling. circ. 3,000. (also avail. in diskette format; back issues avail.) **Document type:** newsletter.
●Also available online.
Description: Contains critical reviews and discussion of popular music, including culture, music journalism, small press publishing and interviews with artists and writers.

780.7 UK
ML5
R C M ANNUAL REVIEW. 1904. a. £10 to non-members. Royal College of Music, Prince Consort Rd., London SW7 2BS, England. TEL 0171-589-3643. FAX 0171-589-7740. Ed. Susan Sturroc. adv.; bk.rev.; music rev.; illus. circ. 5,000. Indexed: Br.Hum.Ind., Music Ind. **Document type:** academic/scholarly publication.
Formerly: R C M Magazine (ISSN 0033-684X)
Description: Journal of general musical interest for undergraduate and post graduate students and professional musicians and musicologists.

780 US ISSN 0889-6607
R I D I M - R C M I INVENTORY OF MUSIC ICONOGRAPHY. 1987. irreg. price varies. (Repertoire Internationale d'Iconographie Musicale. Research Center for Music Iconography) City University of New York, Research Center for Music Iconography, Graduate School and University Center, 33 W. 42nd St., New York, NY 10036. TEL 212-642-2336. FAX 212-642-1873. Ed. Zdravko Blazekovic. circ. 250. Indexed: RILM.
Description: Catalogues of the music iconography in individual museums in the U.S.A.

780 US ISSN 0360-8727
ML26
R I D I M - R C M I NEWSLETTER. 1975. s-a. $10 to individuals; institutions $25. (Repertoire Internationale d'Iconographie Musicale. Research Center for Music Iconography) City University of New York, Research Center for Music Iconography, Graduate School and University Center, 33 W. 42nd St., New York, NY 10036. TEL 212-642-2336. FAX 212-642-1873. Ed. Zdravko Blazekovic. bk.rev. circ. 500. Indexed: RILM. **Document type:** academic/scholarly publication, newsletter.
—Faxon.
Description: Includes scholarly articles on music iconography, reports, inventories, and exhibition reviews.

784.5 NO ISSN 0800-0549
R-O-C-K. (Text in Norwegian and Swedish) 1978. 5/yr. NOK 100($11) Rock and Roll Society of Scandinavia, P.O. Box 59 Furuset, N-1001 Oslo, Norway. TEL 47-22-21-41-30. Ed. Tor Arne Petzold. adv.; bk.rev.; illus. circ. 2,000.
—CCC.
Supersedes (1972-1977): Rock and Roll International Magazine; Whole Lotta Rockin.

780.42 780.7 CN
R P M: REVIEW OF POPULAR MUSIC.* 1981. s-a. Can.$35 to members; institutions Can.$45. International Association for the Study of Popular Music, Mc Gill University, Grad Program in Communication, 3465 Peel Street, Montreal P.Q. H3A IW7, Canada. TEL 613-788-2600. (Subscr. to: Venise Berry, Journalism and Mass Communications, Com. Center No. 207, University of Iowa, Iowa City, IA 52242, USA) Ed. Will Straw. bk.rev. circ. 400.

789.91 CN ISSN 0033-7064
R P M WEEKLY. (Records - Promotion - Music); music, television, radio, film, records, theatre. 1964. w. $126. R P M Music Publications Ltd., 6 Brentcliffe Rd., Toronto, Ont. M4G 3Y2, Canada. TEL 416-425-0257. Ed. Walt Grealis. adv.; bk.rev.; film rev.; play rev.; abstr.; bibl.; charts; illus.; index; circ. 5,000 (controlled). (tabloid format)

789.91 US
R T S MUSIC GAZETTE. 1973. m. $18 to individuals; institutions $10. R T S, Box 93897, Las Vegas, NV 89193-3897. TEL 702-896-1300. Ed. I. Nii. adv.; bk.rev.; illus.; tr.lit.
Description: Information about film music and soundtrack recordings, soundtracks for sale.

RADIO & RECORDS. see COMMUNICATIONS — Radio

780 US
RADIO FREE ROCK.* vol.2, 1978. m. free. Cyco Publishing, 8008 Morningside Dr., Indianapolis, IN 46240-2529. Ed. David F. Myers. adv.; illus. circ. 10,000. (tabloid format)
Incorporates: Gulcher.

785.4 US ISSN 0090-4570
ML1
RAG TIMES. 1967. bi-m. $17 in U.S. and Canada; elsewhere $24. Maple Leaf Club, 15522 Ricky Ct., Grass Valley, CA 95949. Ed. Richard Zimmerman. adv.; bk.rev.; illus. circ. 550. (back issues avail.) **Document type:** newsletter.
Description: News, articles, announcements, and reviews pertaining to rag-time music and musicians across the nation.

781.572 CN ISSN 0033-8672
ML5
RAGTIMER. 1962. bi-m. Can.$8. Ragtime Society, Box 520, Station A, Weston, Ont. M9N 3N3, Canada. bk.rev.; rec.rev. circ. 500. Indexed: Music Ind.

RAMPIKE MAGAZINE. see ART

MUSIC 4877

780.42
RAP EXPRESS.* q. $3.50 per no. Circus Enterprises Corp., 6 W. 18th St., New York, NY 10011. TEL 212-242-4902. FAX 212-242-5734.

780.42 US ISSN 1056-4705
RAP MASTERS.* 1988. m. $24. Word Up! Publications, Inc., 210 E. State Rte. 4, Ste. 401, Paramus, NJ 07652-5103. TEL 201-487-6124. FAX 201-487-9360. Ed. Kate Ferguson. adv. circ. 75,000. **Document type**: consumer publication.
Description: Covers rap music and artists for teenagers.

781.57 US ISSN 1063-1283
ML3531
RAPPAGES. 1991. 9/yr. $19.95 (foreign $29.95). Larry Flynt Publications, Inc., 9171 Wilshire Blvd., Ste. 300, Beverly Hills, CA 90210. TEL 310-858-7100. FAX 310-274-7985. Ed. Sheena Lester. adv. **Document type**: consumer publication.
Description: Covers rap music releases and performers.

RAPPORT; the West Coast review of books, arts & entertainment. see PUBLISHING AND BOOK TRADE

782.1 IT ISSN 0033-9784
RASSEGNA MELODRAMMATICA; corriere de musica. 1890. s-m. L.40000. Via Alfredo Oriani 4, 20122 Milan, Italy. Ed. Vittore Deliliers. adv.; abstr.; illus. circ. 3,500. **Document type**: newspaper.

782.1 IT ISSN 0033-9806
RASSEGNA MUSICALE CURCI; periodico di cultura e attualita musicali. 1948. 3/yr. free. Edizioni Curci s.r.l., Galleria del Corso 4, 20122 Milan, Italy. Ed. Giuseppe Gramitto Ricci. adv.; bk.rev.; music rev.; rec.rev.; illus. circ. 7,000. **Indexed**: Music Ind., RILM.
Description: Covers classical and contemporary music; lists new publications and musical competitions.

RASSEGNA SOVIETICA; rivista bimestrale di cultura. see ART

780 US
RAVINIA FESTIVAL.* 1936. 12/yr. Midwest Publishing Co., 260 E. Chestnut St., Ste. 4306, Chicago, IL 60611-2421. TEL 312-539-8540. Ed. Charlis McMillan. circ. 140,000.
Description: Program book for the viewers of the concert programs in Ravinia Park Pavilion of Chicago's North Shore, during the Ravinia Festival Season each summer.

781.64 UK
RAW. fortn. £49.95 (foreign £51.50) (effective 1995-1996). E M A P - Metro, Mappin House, 4 Winsley St., London W1N 7AR, England. TEL 0171-436-1515. FAX 01858-432164. (Subscr. to: Tower Publishing Services Ltd., Tower House, Sovereign Park, Lathkill St., Market Harborough, Leics. LE16 9EF, England. TEL 01858-468811. FAX 01858-462164) adv. **Document type**: consumer publication.

780 US ISSN 1073-7944
RAY GUN; the bible of music and style. 1992. 10/yr. $25. Ray Gun Publishing, 807 Navy St., Santa Monica, CA 90405. TEL 310-452-6222. Ed. Randy Bookasta. adv.; illus. **Document type**: consumer publication.

780 US ISSN 1050-2831
REAL LIFE IN A BIG CITY. m. $10. 6520 Selma Ave., No. 332, Los Angeles, CA 90028. Ed. Debi Dip.
Description: Features comprehensive interviews with music bands.

781.66 CN ISSN 1185-1937
REAR GARDE.* Variant title: RearGarde. 1986. m. $15. 1455 de Maisonneuve ouest, Montreal, Que. H3G 1M8, Canada. TEL 514-483-5372. Ed. Paul Gott. (tabloid format)

REBA MCENTIRE INTERNATIONAL FAN CLUB NEWSLETTER. see CLUBS

780 US ISSN 0147-0078
RECENT RESEARCHES IN AMERICAN MUSIC. 1977. q. price varies. A-R Editions, Inc., 801 Deming Way, Madison, WI 53717. TEL 608-836-9000. FAX 608-831-8200. Ed. John M. Graziano. (back issues avail.) **Document type**: academic/scholarly publication.

780 US ISSN 0484-0828
M2
RECENT RESEARCHES IN THE MUSIC OF THE BAROQUE ERA. 1964. q. price varies. A-R Editions, Inc., 801 Deming Way, Madison, WI 53717. TEL 608-836-9000. FAX 608-831-8200. Ed. Christopher Wolff. (back issues avail.) **Document type**: academic/scholarly publication.

780 US ISSN 0147-0086
M2
RECENT RESEARCHES IN THE MUSIC OF THE CLASSICAL ERA. 1975. q. price varies. A-R Editions, Inc., 801 Deming Way, Madison, WI 53717. TEL 608-836-9000. FAX 608-831-8200. Ed. Eugene K. Wolf. (back issues avail.) **Document type**: academic/scholarly publication.
Formerly: Recent Researches in the Music of the Classical and Early Romantic Era.

780 US ISSN 0362-3572
M2
RECENT RESEARCHES IN THE MUSIC OF THE MIDDLE AGES AND EARLY RENAISSANCE. 1975. q. price varies. A-R Editions, Inc., 801 Deming Way, Madison, WI 53717. TEL 608-836-9000. FAX 608-831-8200. Ed. Charles M. Atkinson. (back issues avail.) **Document type**: academic/scholarly publication.

780.904 US ISSN 0193-5364
M2
RECENT RESEARCHES IN THE MUSIC OF THE NINETEENTH AND EARLY TWENTIETH CENTURIES. 1979. q. price varies. A-R Editions, Inc., 801 Deming Way, Madison, WI 53717. TEL 608-836-9000. FAX 608-831-8200. Ed. Rufus Hallmark. (back issues avail.) **Document type**: academic/scholarly publication.

780 US ISSN 0486-123X
M2
RECENT RESEARCHES IN THE MUSIC OF THE RENAISSANCE. 1964. q. price varies. A-R Editions, Inc., 801 Deming Way, Madison, WI 53717. TEL 608-836-9000. FAX 608-831-8200. Ed. James Haar. (back issues avail.) **Document type**: academic/scholarly publication.
—Faxon.

780 US ISSN 1066-8209
RECENT RESEARCHES IN THE ORAL TRADITIONS OF MUSIC. 1993. biennial. price varies. A-R Editions, Inc., 801 Deming Way, Madison, WI 53717. TEL 608-836-9000. Ed. Philip V. Bohlman. **Document type**: academic/scholarly publication.

780 IT ISSN 1120-5741
ML5
RECERCARE; rivista per lo studio e la pratica della musica antica - journal for the study and practice of early music. (Text in English, French, German, Italian, Spanish) 1971. s-a. L.35000. (Fondazione Italiana per la Musica Antica) Liberia Musicale Italiana Editrice, P.O. Box 198, 55100 Lucca, Italy. TEL 39-583-394464. FAX 39-538-394469. Ed. Marco Di Pasquale. adv. contact: Thomas Arkell. bk.rev.; abstr. circ. 5,000. **Indexed**: RILM. **Document type**: academic/scholarly publication.
Formerly (until 1988, no.17-18): Flauto Dolce.

780 CN ISSN 0712-8290
THE RECORD.* 1981. w. Can.$225($325) 4211 Young Street Ste 410, Toronto, Ont. M2P 2A9, Canada. TEL 416-533-9417. FAX 416-221-3366. Ed. David Farrell. adv. circ. 1,600.
Description: Includes trade news, sales and airplay statistics, reviews and new releases.

780.42 US ISSN 0745-2594
RECORD (NEW YORK, 1967). m. $12. Straight Arrow Publishers Company, L.P., 1290 Ave. of Americas, New York, NY 10104. TEL 212-484-1616. Ed. David McGee. adv.; illus. circ. 75,000. (also avail. in microfiche from UMI) **Indexed**: C.I.S. Abstr., Music Ind.
—UMI.

789.91 US ISSN 0034-1568
RECORD COLLECTOR (BROOMFIELD); a magazine for collectors of recorded vocal art. 1946. q. $38. c/o Larry Lustig, Ed., 111 Longshots Close, Broomfield, Chelmsford CM1 5DU, England. TEL 01245-441661. FAX 01245-443642. adv.; bk.rev.; rec.rev.; charts; illus.; index. circ. 850. **Indexed**: Music Ind.

789.9 UK ISSN 0261-250X
RECORD COLLECTOR (LONDON). 1979. m. $110. Parker Publishing, 43-45 St. Mary's Rd., Ealing, London W5 5RQ, England. TEL 0181-579-1082. FAX 081-566-2024. Ed. Peter Doggett. bk.rev.; illus. (back issues avail.) **Document type**: consumer publication.

780 US ISSN 8755-6154
ML1
RECORD COLLECTOR'S MONTHLY. 1982. irreg. (4-5/yr.). $15 for 10 issues (foreign $23 for 6 issues). Record Collector's Monthly, Inc., Box 75, Mendham, NJ 07945. TEL 201-543-9520. FAX 201-543-6033. Ed. Don Mennie. adv. contact: Carole Mennie. bk.rev.; rec.rev.; circ. 3,000 (paid). (tabloid format; back issues avail.) **Document type**: newspaper.
Description: Covers collectible recordings from the 1950's and 1960's of vocal groups, blues, R & B, and rock & roll, with emphasis on 45's and LP's.

780 621.389 US ISSN 0557-9147
RECORD EXCHANGER. 1969. q. $11.95. Vintage Records, Box 6144, Orange, CA 92667. TEL 714-639-3383. Ed. Art Turco. adv.; bk.rev.; charts; illus.; index. circ. 22,000.

789.91 JA ISSN 0289-3614
RECORD GEIJUTSU/ART OF RECORDS, DISCOGRAPHY REVIEW. (Text in Japanese) 1952. m. 1000 Yen. Ongaku No Tomo Sha Corp., Kagurazaka 6-30, Shinjuku-ku, Tokyo 162, Japan. TEL 03-3235-2111. FAX 03-3235-2129. adv.: B&W page 312000 Yen, color page 624000 Yen; trim 257 x 182. circ. 150,000.
Description: Carries critical commentaries by authorities in the field that serve as guidelines for new record selections as well as enhances the knowledge of music.

780 UK
RECORD MART. 1968. m. £7.50. 16 London Hill, Rayleigh, Essex, England. Ed. Frank K. Bailey. adv.; tr.lit. circ. 900.

789.91 US ISSN 0034-1592
ML1
RECORD RESEARCH; the magazine of record statistics and information. 1955. bi-m. $10 for 10 issues. 65 Grand Ave., Brooklyn, NY 11205. TEL 718-857-7003. Ed. Len Kunstadt. bk.rev.; illus.; mkt.; stat. (processed) **Indexed**: Music Ind.

RECORD RETAILING DIRECTORY. see BUSINESS AND ECONOMICS — Trade And Industrial Directories

780 US
RECORD ROUNDUP. 1970. bi-m. $5. Rounder Records, One Camp St., Cambridge, MA 02140. TEL 617-661-6308. FAX 617-868-8769. E-mail: rupinfo@rounder.com. Ed. Mark Cadigan. music rev. **Document type**: catalog.

780 GW
RECORD-SERIE. 1962. s-m. DM.52.80. VEB Lied der Zeit Musikverlag, Rosa-Luxemburg-Str. 41, 10178 Berlin, Germany.
Formerly: Standard-Serie (ISSN 0038-9617)

789.91 UK ISSN 0961-3544
ML5
THE RECORDER MAGAZINE. 1963. q. £12. Peacock Press, Scout Bottom Farms, Mytholmroyd, Hebden Bridge, W. Yorks HX7 5JS, England. TEL 01422-882751. FAX 01422-886157. Ed. Andrew Mayes; Pubs. Jeremy Burbidge, Ruth Burbidge. adv.: page £250; trim 264 x 180; adv. contact: Graham Williams. bk.rev.; music rev.; illus. circ. 3,000. **Indexed**: Music Ind., RILM. **Document type**: academic/scholarly publication.
—Faxon, UnCover.
Former titles: Recorder and Music Magazine (ISSN 0306-4409); Recorder and Music (ISSN 0034-1665); **Incorporates**: Recorder News.

MUSIC

786   US   ISSN 0736-9549
REED ORGAN SOCIETY BULLETIN. Short title: R O S Bulletin. 1982. q. $17.50. (Reed Organ Society, Inc.) Reed Organ Society Publications, 6907 Rix St., S.E., Ada, MI 49301. TEL 616-676-1188. (Subscr. to: Reed Organ Society, Inc., Musical Museum, Deansboro, NY 13328. TEL 315-841-8774) Ed. Edward A. Peterson; Pub. Gordon DeYoung. adv.; bk.rev.; bibl. circ. 700. (back issues avail.) **Document type:** bulletin.
    Formerly: Reed Organ Society Newsletter.
    Description: For musicians, historians, collectors and restorers of all types of free-reed instruments, including melodeons, "pump" organs, harmoniums and more.

780   GW   ISSN 0342-4936
REGER-STUDIEN. 1978. irreg. price varies. (Max-Reger-Institut, Bonn) Breitkopf und Haertel, Postfach 1707, 65007 Wiesbaden, Germany. TEL 0611-45008-0. FAX 0611-4500859. TELEX 4182647-EB-D. Ed.Bd. **Indexed:** RILM. **Document type:** monographic series.

780   US   ISSN 1065-3023
REGGAE REPORT. 1983. 10/yr. $22. R R International Magazine Inc., 21300 N.E. 24 Ct., Miami, FL 33180. TEL 305-933-1178; 800-829-4360. FAX 305-933-1077. E-mail: 74467,3070. Ed. Sara Gurgen. adv.; B&W page $1490; color page $2285. bk.rev.; music rev. **Document type:** newsletter.
    Description: Covers all aspects of reggae music and culture.

780   HU   ISSN 0080-0562
REGI MAGYAR DALLAMOK TARA/CORPUS MUSICAE POPULARIS HUNGARICAE. (Text in Hungarian; occasional summaries in German) 1958. irreg. price varies. (Magyar Tudomanyos Akademia, Nepzenekutato Csoport) Akademiai Kiado, Publishing House of the Hungarian Academy of Sciences, P.O. Box 245, H-1519 Budapest, Hungary. TEL 181-2134. FAX 166-6466. TELEX 22-6228 AKNYO H.

780   UK   ISSN 0953-5330
REGISTER OF MUSICIANS IN EDUCATION. 1986. a. £7.50. Incorporated Society of Musicians, 10 Stratford Pl., London W1N 9AE, England. TEL 0171-629-4413. FAX 0171-408-1538. circ. 3,000. **Document type:** directory.
    Description: Lists members working in all fields of music education.

780   UK
REGISTER OF PERFORMERS & COMPOSERS. 1976. a. £11. Incorporated Society of Musicians, 10 Stratford Pl., London W1N 9AE, England. TEL 0171-629-4413. FAX 0171-408-1538. circ. 4,000. **Document type:** directory.
    Formerly: Professional Register of Artists.
    Description: Lists members working professionally as performers, conductors, and composers.

780   UK   ISSN 0951-6239
ML21.G7
REGISTER OF PROFESSIONAL PRIVATE MUSIC TEACHERS. 1987. a. £12. Incorporated Society of Musicians, 10 Stratford Pl., London W1N 9AE, England. TEL 0171-629-4413. FAX 0171-408-1538. circ. 6,000. **Document type:** directory.
    Formerly: Professional Register of Private Teachers of Music.
    Description: Lists professional teachers of music to private pupils.

780.42   US   ISSN 0146-3489
RELIX; music for the mind. Variant title: Dead Relix. 1974. bi-m. $27 (foreign $32). Relix Magazine, Inc, Box 94, Brooklyn, NY 11229. TEL 718-258-0009. Ed. Toni A. Brown. adv. contact: Toni Brown. bk.rev.; film rev.; charts; illus.; stat. circ. 70,000. (back issues avail.) **Indexed:** Music Ind. **Document type:** consumer publication.
    Description: Specializes in music from San Francisco, with a focus on the Grateful Dead. Also covers current blues, folk, reggae and rock music.

780   US   ISSN 0889-8790
ML3469
REMEMBER THAT SONG; newsletter for sheet music collectors. 1981. m. $19. 5623 N. 64th Ave., Glendale, AZ 85301. TEL 602-931-2835. Ed. Lois A. Cordrey. bk.rev.; illus.; circ. 425 (paid). **Document type:** newsletter.
    Description: Covers the historical aspects and implications of collecting American popular music, and the evolution of song, from pre-Civil War to the present day.

780   GW   ISSN 0196-7037
ML169.8
RENAISSANCE MANUSCRIPT STUDIES. 1973. irreg., latest vol.6. (American Institute of Musicology, US) Haenssler Verlag, Postfach 1220, 73762 Neuhausen, Germany. TEL 07158-177-114. FAX 07158-177119. Ed. Charles Hamm. **Document type:** monographic series.

780   US   ISSN 0034-4451
RENFRO VALLEY BUGLE. 1943. m. $9. Renfro Valley Entertainment Center, Inc., 101 Main St., Renfro Valley, KY 40473. TEL 606-256-2638. FAX 606-256-2679. Ed. Anne Brosnan; Pub. Dean L. Henricksen. adv.; illus. circ. 4,000. (tabloid format) **Document type:** newspaper.
    Description: Covers news of the local and national country music scene, with listings of upcoming events, and articles on past and present country music entertainers.

780   CC   ISSN 0447-6573
ML5
RENMIN YINYUE/PEOPLE'S MUSIC. (Text in Chinese; table of contents in English) 1950. bi-m. Y1.50 (foreign $24.30). Zhongguo Yinxie Zazhishe, No. 10, Nongzhanguan Nanli, Beijing 100026, People's Republic of China. (Dist. outside China by: China International Book Trading Corp., P.O. Box 2399, Beijing, P.R.C.; Dist. in US by: China Books & Periodicals, Inc., 2929 24th St., San Francisco, CA 94110. TEL 415-282-2994)
—UnCover.

REPLAY; a professional publication for the coin-operated amusement industry. see *BUSINESS AND ECONOMICS — Production Of Goods And Services*

780.42   US   ISSN 1045-0084
ML476.8
REQUEST. 1989. m. $20. (Musicland - Sam Goody) Request Media Inc., 7630 Excelsior Blvd., Minneapolis, MN 55426. TEL 612-932-7740. FAX 612-932-7797. Ed. Keith Moerer; Pub. Marcia Appel. adv. contact: Brian Maginnis. circ. 575,000. **Document type:** consumer publication.
    Description: Covers pop, rock, R & B, country, rap, jazz, and home video.

780.01   US   ISSN 1049-099X
ML3830
RESEARCH SYMPOSIUM ON THE PSYCHOLOGY AND ACOUSTICS OF MUSIC. PROCEEDINGS. 1977. irreg. price varies. University of Kansas, M E M T Division, 311 Bailey Hall, Lawrence, KS 66045-2344. TEL 913-864-4784. FAX 913-864-3566. Ed. George L. Duerksen. circ. 300. **Document type:** academic/scholarly publication, proceedings.

781   US   ISSN 0749-2472
ML3544
RESOUND. 1982. q. $20. Indiana University, Archives of Traditional Music, Morrison Hall 117, Bloomington, IN 47405-2501. TEL 812-855-4679. FAX 812-855-6673. Ed. Ruth Stone. index. circ. 500. **Indexed:** Anthropol.Lit. **Document type:** bulletin.
    Description: Reports on the Archives' collections of traditional music from all regions of the world.

780   UK
RESOURCES OF MUSIC SERIES. 1969. irreg., no.21, 1985. price varies. Cambridge University Press, Edinburgh Bldg., Shaftesbury Rd., Cambridge CB2 2RU, England. TEL 01223-312393. FAX 01223-315052. ISBN 851817256. (N. American addr.: Cambridge University Press, Journals Dept., 40 W. 20th St., New York, NY 10011. TEL 212-924-3900. FAX 212-691-3239) Ed. John Paynter. **Document type:** monographic series.
    Formerly: Resources of Music (ISSN 0080-1828)

781.7   BL   ISSN 0103-7595
ML5
REVISTA BRASILEIRA DE MUSICA. 1934-1947; resumed 1981. irreg., latest 1986. Universidade Federal de Rio de Janeiro, Escola de Musica, Rua de Passeio 98-Lapa, 20021 Rio de Janeiro, Brazil. adv. circ. 1,000. **Indexed:** Music Ind.
    Description: Covers folk music of Brazil.

780.01   CK
REVISTA COLOMBIANA DE INVESTIGACION MUSICAL. 1985. 2/yr. exchange basis. Universidad Nacional de Colombia, Instituto de Investigaciones Esteticas, Seccion de Musicologia, Bogota, Colombia. Eds. Ellie Duque, Egberto Bermudez. bk.rev. circ. 1,000.

780.01   SP   ISSN 0210-1459
REVISTA DE MUSICOLOGIA. s-a. 700 ptas. Sociedad Espanola de Musicologia, Ordonez, 1, Madrid-29, Spain. Ed. Dionisio Preciado. bibl. **Indexed:** RILM.

780   BL   ISSN 0103-5525
ML5
REVISTA MUSICA. 1990. s-a. exchange basis. Universidade de Sao Paulo, Departamento de Musica, Av. Prof. Lucio Martins Rodrigues 443, 05508 Butanta SP, Brazil. TEL 813-3222. FAX 815-4272. TELEX 80629 UVSI BR.
—BLDSC (7867.248000).

780.7   CL   ISSN 0716-2790
ML5
REVISTA MUSICAL CHILENA. 1945. s-a. $45. Universidade de Chile, Facultad de Artes, Compania 1264, Casilla 2100, Santiago, Chile. TEL 56-2-6781337. FAX 56-2-6711435. Ed. Luis Merino Montero; Pub. Nancy Sattler. adv. contact: Fernando Garcia. bk.rev.; bibl.; charts; illus.; index, cum.index. circ. 450. (also avail. in microfiche) **Indexed:** Hisp.Amer.Per.Ind. (1975-), Music Ind., RILM. **Document type:** academic/scholarly publication.
—Faxon.
    Description: Review of Chilean and Latin American art and indigenous and folk music from the colonial epoch to present.
    Refereed Serial

780.5   VE   ISSN 0254-7376
REVISTA MUSICAL DE VENEZUELA. 1980. 3/yr. Instituto Latinoamericano de Investigaciones y Estudios Musicales Vicente Emilio Sojo, Apdo. Postal 70537, Caracas 1071, Venezuela. **Indexed:** Hisp.Amer.Per.Ind. (1980-).

780.01   BE   ISSN 0771-6788
REVUE BELGE DE MUSICOLOGIE/BELGISCH TIJDSCHRIFT VOOR MUZIEKWETENSCHAP. (Text in Dutch, English, French, and German) 1945. a. 700 BEF($14) Societe Belge de Musicologie, 30 rue de la Regence, 1000 Brussels, Belgium. Eds. H. Vanhulst, R. Wangermee. adv.; bk.rev.; illus. circ. 600. **Indexed:** Music Ind., RILM. **Document type:** academic/scholarly publication.
—SWETS.

780.01   FR   ISSN 0035-1601
REVUE DE MUSICOLOGIE. 1917. s-a. 230 F. Societe Francaise de Musicologie, 2 rue de Louvois, 75002 Paris, France. TEL 47-03-88-50. Eds. Christian Meyer, Joel-Marie Fauquet. adv.; bk.rev.; illus.; cum.index. circ. 1,250. (also avail. in microform from UMI; reprint service avail. from UMI,KTO) **Indexed:** Arts & Hum.Cit.Ind., Curr.Cont., Ind.Bk.Rev.Hum., Music Ind., RILM, RILM.
—Faxon; SWETS; UMI.

REVUE DES ARCHEOLOGUES ET HISTORIENS D'ART DE LOUVAIN. see *ART*

780.1   FR   ISSN 0035-3736
REVUE MUSICALE; revue d'esthetique musicale. 1920. 10/yr. 1200 F. 7 place Saint Sulpice, 75006 Paris, France. TEL 43-26-28-36. Ed. Francis Pinguet. circ. 1,500. (also avail. in microfilm from BHP; reprint service avail. from SWZ) **Indexed:** Arts & Hum.Cit.Ind., Curr.Cont., Music Ind., RILM.
    Formerly: Polyphonie (ISSN 0032-4019)

780   SZ   ISSN 0035-3744
REVUE MUSICALE DE SUISSE ROMANDE. 1948. q. 38 SFr. (Europe 50 SFr.; elsewhere 60 SFr.). Case Postale 3074, CH-1401 Yverdon-les-Bains, Switzerland. TEL 024-212606. FAX 024-217310. Ed. Jacques-Michel Pittier. adv. contact: Rina Tordjman. bk.rev.; music rev.; rec.rev.; charts; illus. circ. 3,000. **Indexed:** Music Ind., RILM. **Document type:** bulletin.

780   UK   ISSN 0957-6592
RHYTHM; for the contemporary drummer, percussionist and programmer. (U.K. Edition) 1987. m. £20 (foreign £25). Music Maker Publications Ltd., Alexander House, Forehill, Ely, Cambs CB7 4AF, England. TEL 0353-665577. FAX 0353-662489. (U.S. addr.: Music Maker Publications Inc., 21601 Devonshire St., Ste. 212, Chatsworth, CA 91311) circ. 20,000. **Document type:** trade publication.
    Description: Includes new electronic drum technology, interviews with rhythm professionals and drumming news.

780.42   US
RHYTHM & NEWS.* vol.5, 1989. m. Tune-In Publications, Inc., 9800 Richmond Ave., Ste. 300, Houston, TX 77042.

781.6   US   ISSN 1074-8660
RHYTHM MUSIC MAGAZINE; global culture. 1992. m. $20 (outside N. America $45); newsstand price: $3; Can.$3.95; £2.25. World Marketing Corp., 972 Massachusetts Ave., Ste. 2-7, Cambridge, MA 02139. TEL 617-497-0256. FAX 617-497-0692. E-mail: rhythm@id.wing.net. (Subscr. to: Box 391894, Cambridge, MA 02139. TEL 617-497-6984) Ed. Larry Blumenfeld; Pubs. Kyle F. Russell, Thomas D. Ganci. adv.: B&W page $4100; adv. contact: Thomas D. Ganci. bk.rev.; film rev.; music rev.; illus.; circ. 78,000 (paid). (back issues avail.) **Document type:** consumer publication.
    Description: Covers the spectrum of world music and culture. Provides a forum for musicians, indigenous peoples, and urban minds to express ideas, thoughts, and insights into global music and culture.

780.65   UK
RHYTHM RAG. no.4, 1977. 4/yr. £1.50 for 5 nos. Cunningham, 190 Camrose Ave., Edgware, Middlesex, England. adv.

780   GW   ISSN 0720-9827
RICHARD STRAUSS BLAETTER; neue Folge. (Text in English, German) 1979. s-a. (Internationale Richard Strauss Gesellschaft, AU) Verlag Dr. Hans Schneider GmbH, Mozartstr. 6, 82323 Tutzing, Germany. TEL 08158-3050. FAX 08158-7636. **Document type:** newsletter.

780   GW
RICHARD WAGNER BLAETTER. (Text in French, German) s-a. (Aktionskreis fuer das Werk Richard Wagners e.V.) Verlag Dr. Hans Schneider GmbH, Mozartstr. 6, 82323 Tutzing, Germany. TEL 08158-3050. FAX 08158-7636. **Document type:** newsletter.

789.5   UK   ISSN 0035-5453
RINGING WORLD. 1911. w. £36. (Central Council of Church Bell Ringers) Ringing World Ltd., Penmark House, Woodbridge Meadows, Guildford, Surrey GU1 1BL, England. TEL 01483-69535. Ed. D.G. Thorne. adv.; bk.rev. circ. 4,500. **Document type:** newsletter.

780.42   US   ISSN 0889-5791
ML3533.8
RIP. m. $24.95. Larry Flynt Publications, Inc., 9171 Wilshire Blvd., Ste. 300, Beverly Hills, CA 90210. TEL 310-858-7100. FAX 310-274-7985. Ed. Lonn Friend. **Document type:** consumer publication.
    Description: Covers heavy metal music for young adults.

780.42   US   ISSN 1059-5899
RIP PHOTO SPECIALS. 1988. q. $2.95 per no. Larry Flynt Publications, Inc., 9171 Wilshire Blvd., Ste. 300, Beverly Hills, CA 90210. TEL 213-858-7100. FAX 213-274-7985. **Document type:** consumer publication.

780.42   US
RIP PRESENTS. q. $2.95 per no. Larry Flynt Publications, Inc., 9171 Wilshire Blvd., Ste. 300, Beverly Hills, CA 90210. TEL 310-858-7100. FAX 310-274-7985. **Document type:** consumer publication.

780.6   IT
RISVEGLIO MUSICALE. (Supplement avail.: Quaderno Organizzativo) 1982. bi-m. L.30000. Anbima, Via Marianna Dionigi 43, 00193 Rome, Italy. Ed. Orazio Giuri. adv.; bk.rev. circ. 15,000.
    Formerly: Risveglio Bandistico.

783   IT   ISSN 0394-6282
ML2999
RIVISTA INTERNAZIONALE DI MUSICA SACRA/INTERNATIONAL CHURCH MUSIC REVIEW/INTERNATIONALE ZEITSCHRIFT FUER KIRCHENMUSIK/REVUE INTERNATIONALE DE MUSIQUE SACREE/REVISTA INTERNACIONAL DE MUSICA SAGRADA. (Text in English, French, German, Italian, Spanish) 1980. s-a. L.70000($42) Libreria Musicale Italiana Editrice, Via di Arsina 196F, Casella Postale 198, 55100 Lucca, Italy. TEL 39-583-394464. FAX 39-583-394469. Ed. Natale Ghiglione. adv.; bk.rev. circ. 700. **Indexed:** RILM.
    Description: Collects contributions from the world's leading authorities on the study and practice of liturgical music throughout the world and thoughout time.

780.01   IT   ISSN 0035-6867
ML5
RIVISTA ITALIANA DI MUSICOLOGIA. 1966. s-a. L.74000 (foreign L.95000) (effective 1995) US $65.50 (effective 1996). (Societa Italiana di Musicologia) Casa Editrice Leo S. Olschki, Casella Postale 66, 50100 Florence, Italy. TEL 39-55-6530684. FAX 39-55-6530214. Ed. M. Conati. adv.; bk.rev. circ. 1,000. **Indexed:** Arts & Hum.Cit.Ind., Curr.Cont., Music Ind., RILM. **Document type:** academic/scholarly publication.
—Faxon; Genuine Article; SWETS.

780.01   IT   ISSN 0394-4395
RIVISTA ITALIANA DI MUSICOLOGIA. QUADERNI. 1966. irreg., no.32, 1994. price varies. Casa Editrice Leo S. Olschki, Casella Postale 66, 50100 Florence, Italy. TEL 39-55-6530684. FAX 39-55-6530214. **Document type:** academic/scholarly publication.

ROAR. see LITERARY AND POLITICAL REVIEWS

780 305.4   US
ROCK AGAINST SEXISM. 1988. q. $3 per issue. Box 390643, Cambridge, MA 02139. TEL 617-437-9593.
    Description: Fights sexism and heterosexism by promoting women rockers and alternatives to mainstream "rock music".

781   FR   ISSN 0048-8445
ROCK & FOLK; pop music, rhythm & blues, jazz chanson. 1966. m. 265 F. (foreign 331 F.). Editions Lariviere, 15-17 quai de l'Oise, 75166 Paris Cedex 19, France. TEL 1-40-34-22-07. FAX 1-40-35-84-41. TELEX 211 678 F. Dir. Christian de la Tullaye. adv.; bk.rev.; film rev.; charts; illus. circ. 115,000. **Indexed:** Pt.de Rep. (1991-).

780.42   GW   ISSN 0930-6994
ROCK & POP L P - PREISKATALOG. 1983. a. DM.48.50. Vereinigte Motor-Verlage GmbH und Co. KG, Leuschnerstr. 1, 70174 Stuttgart, Germany. TEL 0711-18201. FAX 0711-1821756. Ed. Michael Goldmann; Pub. Uwe Hagen. adv. contact: Peter Michael Heyde. bk.rev.; bibl.; charts; illus. circ. 6,000. **Document type:** catalog.

780.42   UK
ROCK & POP STARS. 1979. m. £0.75 per no. Moore Harness Ltd., Gaddline House, Whyteleafe, Surrey, England. Ed. Leonard Holdsworth. adv. circ. 70,000.

784.5   US   ISSN 1068-7653
ML3533.8
ROCK & RAP CONFIDENTIAL. 1983. m. $24. Box 341305, Los Angeles, CA 90034. bk.rev. circ. 6,000. (back issues avail.) **Document type:** consumer publication.
    Former titles (until 1992): Rock and Roll Confidential (ISSN 0891-9372); Dave Marsh's Rock and Roll Confidential (ISSN 0740-2058)
    Description: Exposes rock and roll as an industry whose chief aim is profit.

780.42   US
ROCK & ROLL DISC. 1987. bi-m. $24. Tag Enterprises, Box 17601, Memphis, TN 38187-0601. TEL 901-386-4954. Ed. Tom Graves. adv.; bk.rev. circ. 5,233. (tabloid format; avail. in CD)
    Description: Features renowned music critics on compact discs.

780   UK   ISSN 0965-190X
ROCK C D. 1992. m. £70 for 6 issues. Northern & Shell Publications, Northern & Shell Bldg., P.O. Box 381, Millharbour, London E14 9TW, England. TEL 44-171-987-5090. FAX 44-171-987-2160. Ed. Paul Trynka. adv.: color page £1950; adv. contact: Elspeth Thomson. circ. 60,000. **Document type:** consumer publication.

780.42   US
ROCK FEVER. 5/yr. $2.95. Comics World, 475 Park Ave. S., New York, NY 10016. TEL 212-689-2830.

780   UK   ISSN 0964-3257
ROCK 'N' REEL. 1988. q. £5 (Europe £7; rest of world £10). 8 Dent Pl., Cleator Moor, Cumbria CA25 5EE, England. TEL 0946-812496. Ed. Sean McGhee. adv. circ. 21,000. **Document type:** consumer publication.
    Description: Covers the world roots music scene.

780   US
ROCK 'N' ROLL EXPERIENCE. 1992. m. $27. R J S Entertainment, Box 87, White Marsh, MD 21162. TEL 410-335-0092. FAX 410-335-0098. Ed. Bob Suehs. adv.: B&W page $250; adv. contact: John Gonzalez. bk.rev.; film rev.; music rev. circ. 20,000. (back issues avail.) **Document type:** consumer publication.
    Description: Covers local and national rock 'n' roll artists.

780   JA
ROCK SHOW. (Text in Japanese) 1976. bi-m. 3480 Yen. Shinko Music Publishing Co. Ltd., 2-1, Ogawa-machi, Kanda, Chiyoda-ku, Tokyo, Japan. Ed. Mariko Miyazaki.

780.42   US   ISSN 0890-460X
ML3533.8
ROCKBILL.* 1982. m. $15. Rave Communications, Inc., c/o E.M.C.I. Corp., 24 Richmond Hill Ave., Ste. 8, Stamford, CT 06901-3600. TEL 212-925-7560. Ed. Mike Hammer. adv. circ. 250,000.
    Description: Covers pop-rock music and industry.

781.7   JM
ROCKERS. 1982. bi-m. Rockers Productions, P.O. Box 46, Hagley Park P.O., Jamaica, W.I. Ed. Lynval Gibbons.

780.42   US
ROCKET. 1979. m. $25. Murder, Inc. Publishers, 2028 Fifth Ave., Seattle, WA 98121. TEL 206-728-7625. Ed. Charles Cross. adv. circ. 70,000.
    Description: Covers music, entertainment, popular culture, film and lifestyles in the Pacific Northwest.

780 745.1   US   ISSN 1052-8768
ML156.4.P6
ROCKIN' RECORDS; buyers - sellers reference book and price guide. 1986. a. $39.95. Jellyroll Publishing, Box 29, Boyne Falls, MI 49713. TEL 616-582-6852. FAX 616-582-9713. Ed. Jerry Osborne. adv. circ. 10,000. **Document type:** trade publication, catalog.
    Description: Covers music and the hobby of record collecting, with price information for all size records.

780.904   US   ISSN 0738-7717
ROCKIN' 50S; dedicated to the true rock 'n' roll era. 1976. bi-m. $25. (Buddy Holly Memorial Society) William F. Griggs, Ed.& Pub., Box 6123, Lubbock, TX 79493-6123. TEL 806-799-4299. (Subscr. to: Box 6123, Lubbock, TX 79493) adv.; bk.rev.; film rev.; play rev.; stat. circ. 5,450. (back issues avail.)
    Formerly (until June 1986): Reminiscing.
    Description: For 1950s record collectors. Covers the music, artists and fads of the 1950's rock and roll era.

ROCKSTAR; numero uno. see CHILDREN AND YOUTH — For

780   IT
ROCKYSSIMO. 1987. m. L.3000 per no. Edizioni Coop Athena 2001 a.r.l., Via E. Q. Visconti, 20, 00193 Rome, Italy. TEL 06-3207101. Ed. Salvatore Puzzo. adv.: B&W page L.3970000, color page L.7130000. illus. circ. 122,200.

MUSIC

786   PL   ISSN 0208-5992
ML410.C54
ROCZNIK CHOPINOWSKI. 1956. a. price varies. Towarzystwo im. F. Chopina - Frederick Chopin Society, Ul. Okolnik 1, 00-368 Warsaw, Poland. TEL 48-22-275471. FAX 48-22-279599. adv. contact: Janusz Zabza. bk.rev. Indexed: RILM. Document type: academic/scholarly publication.
Description: Covers Fryderyk Chopin life and work. Publishes articles and research of the most prominent Polish and foreign chopinologists. Also contains Chopin's bibliography and Chopin's chronicle.

RODMAN HALL BULLETIN. see *ART*

780.42   US
ROGUES GALLERY. m. Box 1464, Reseda, CA 91337. TEL 818-781-4104. Ed. Nannette Freeman. circ. 10,000.

780   GW   ISSN 0944-0291
ML929
ROHRBLATT; Magazin fuer Oboe, Klarinette, Fagott und Saxaphon. 1986. q. DM.48 (students DM.42). Verlag Karl Hofmann, Postfach 1360, 73603 Schorndorf, Germany. TEL 07181-402-0. FAX 07181-402111. Ed. Hans-Juergen Mueller. adv.; bk.rev.; index. Indexed: RILM. Document type: consumer publication.
Former titles: Oboe - Klarinette - Fagott (ISSN 0179-8170); Klarinette.
Description: For those interested in the clarinet.

ROLLING BLUNDER REVIEW. see *NEW AGE PUBLICATIONS*

781.5   US   ISSN 0035-791X
AP2
ROLLING STONE. 1967. bi-w. $25.95 (Canada $41; elsewhere $65). Straight Arrow Publishers Company, L.P., 1290 Ave. of Americas, New York, NY 10104. TEL 212-484-1616. FAX 212-759-2966. E-mail: rolling-stone@echonyc.com. (Subscr. to: Box 55329, Boulder, CO 80322-5329. TEL 800-283-1549) Ed. Jann Wenner; Pub. Jann Wenner. adv.; bk.rev.; illus.; rec.rev. circ. 1,175,000. (tabloid format; also avail. in microform from UMI; Braille; back issues avail.) Indexed: Acad.Ind., Bk.Rev.Ind. (1976-), Chic.Per.Ind., Child.Bk.Rev.Ind. (1976-), Curr.Lit.Fam.Plan., Film Lit.Ind. (1973-), Jun.High.Mag.Abstr., Mag.Ind., Media Rev.Dig., Music Ind., PMR, Pop.Per.Ind., TOM. Document type: consumer publication.
●Also available on CD-ROM. Producer(s): University Microfilms International.
—Faxon; SWETS; UMI; UnCover.
Description: Covers all aspects of the pop/rock music industry. Articles, interviews, reviews. Includes features on politics, movies and fashion.

780 791.43   AT   ISSN 1320-0615
ROLLING STONE.* 1972. 13/yr. Aus.$35($50) Rolling Ston, 78 Renwick St., Redfern, N.S.W. 2016, Australia. TEL 61-2-3101433. FAX 61-2-3101315. Ed. Toby Creswell. circ. 35,000. Document type: consumer publication.

780 621.389   US
ROOTS & RHYTHM NEWSLETTER. 1978. irreg. (approx. 6/yr.). $6 (foreign $10). Roots & Rhythm, Inc., 6921 Stockton Ave., El Cerrito, CA 94530. TEL 510-525-1494. FAX 510-525-2904. Ed. Franklyn Scott. adv.; bk.rev.; rec.rev, video rev. circ. 13,000. Document type: newsletter.
Formerly: Down Home Music Newsletter.
Description: Features reviews of blues, country and jazz music.

780   IE
ROYAL IRISH ACADEMY OF MUSIC. PROSPECTUS. 1973. a. free. Royal Irish Academy of Music, 36-38 Westland Row, Dublin, 2, Ireland. circ. 1,000.

780.01   UK   ISSN 0269-0403
ML28.L8
ROYAL MUSICAL ASSOCIATION. JOURNAL. 1874. 2/yr. £45($82) (effective 1995). (Royal Musical Association) Oxford University Press, Oxford Journals, Walton St., Oxford OX2 6DP, England. TEL 01865-267907. FAX 01865-267773. TELEX 837330-OXPRES-G. E-mail: jnlorders@oup.co.uk. (U.S. subscr. to: Oxford University Press Inc., 2001 Evans Rd., Cary, NC 27513. TEL 919-677-0977. FAX 919-677-1714) Ed. Andrew Watney. adv. contact: Rosemary Dooley. bk.rev.; cum.index: vols.1-99. circ. 1,350. (also avail. in microform from BHP; reprint service avail. from KTO) Indexed: Arts & Hum.Cit.Ind., Br.Hum.Ind., Curr.Cont., Music Ind., RILM. Document type: academic/scholarly publication.
—BLDSC (4862.125000); Faxon; Genuine Article; SWETS; UMI; UnCover. **CCC.**
Superseded (in 1987): Royal Musical Association, London. Proceedings (ISSN 0080-4452)
Description: Addresses new research into all branches of musical scholarship - historical musicology and ethnomusicology, theory and analysis, textural criticism, archival research, organology and performing practice.

780   UK   ISSN 0080-4460
ML5
ROYAL MUSICAL ASSOCIATION. R.M.A. RESEARCH CHRONICLE. 1961. a. £22.50 to non-members. Royal Musical Association, c/o John Wagstaff, Faculty of Music, St. Aldate's, Oxford OX1 1DB, England. TEL 01865-276146. FAX 08165-276128. E-mail: libmus@vax.ox.ac.uk. Ed. Jonathan Wainwright. bk.rev. circ. 600. Indexed: Br.Hum.Ind., Music Ind., RILM. Document type: academic/scholarly publication.
—BLDSC (7993.953000); UnCover.
Description: Comprises articles on the history of music, reviews and musicological documentation. *Refereed Serial*

780   PL
ROZPRAWY I SZKICE FILOZOFICZNO-ESTETYCZNE O MUZYCE. 1972. irreg. price varies. Polskie Wydawnictwo Muzyczne, Al. Krasinskiego 11a, 31-111 Krakow, Poland. TEL 48-12-227044. FAX 48-12-220174. adv. contact: Teresa Wlochynska. Document type: academic/scholarly publication.
Description: Covers dissertations and essays about music by Polish authors.

780   PL   ISSN 0035-9610
ML5
RUCH MUZYCZNY; a musical review. 1957. fortn. $49. Ul. Senatorska 13-15, 00-075 Warsaw, Poland. TEL 48-22-261662. (Dist. by: Ars Polona-Ruch, Krakowskie Przedmiescie 7, Warsaw, Poland. TEL 48-22-267622) Ed. Ludwik Erhardt. bk.rev.; illus.; music rev.; rec.rev.; index. circ. 5,000. Indexed: Music Ind., RILM.
—BLDSC (8047.340000).

780   IT   ISSN 1121-3523
RUMORE. 1992. m. L.70000. Apache s.r.l., Via Pietro Mascagni 3-5, 00199 Rome, Italy. TEL 06-860-8913. FAX 06-8608930. Ed. Massimo Stefani. adv.; B&W page L.2600000, color page L.4200000. circ. 40,000. Document type: consumer publication.

780   RU
RUSSIAN CLASSICAL MUSICAL CRITICS. a. 2.20 Rub. Izdatel'stvo Muzyka, Ul. Neglinnaya 14, Moscow 103031, Russia.

786   RU
RUSSIAN PIANO MUSIC. a. 9.70 Rub. Izdatel'stvo Muzyka, Ul. Neglinnaya 14, Moscow 103031, Russia. TEL 924-81-63. FAX 921-83-53.

780   RU
RUSSIAN SYMPHONIC MUSIC. 2/yr. 20 Rub. per issue. Izdatel'stvo Muzyka, Ul. Neglinnaya 14, Moscow 103031, Russia. TEL 924-81-63. FAX 921-83-53.

780 792   DK   ISSN 0107-6280
RYTME; nyt om folkemusik, rock, jazz og teater i Nordjylland. 1981. m. DKK 25. Skraaen, Strandvejen 19, DK-9000 Aalborg, Denmark. TEL 8-122189. Ed. Jorgen Nissen. adv.; bk.rev.; illus. circ. 15,000.

786   US   ISSN 0744-0200
M2062
S A B CHOIR. (Soprano, Alto, Bass) 1981. bi-m. (exc. May, June, Jul., Aug.) $120 (minimum 10 copies). Lorenz Publishing Co., 501 E. Third St., Box 802, Dayton, OH 45401-0802. TEL 513-228-6118. FAX 513-223-2042. Ed. Hugh S. Livingston, Jr. adv. contact: Larry Pugh. Document type: trade publication.
Description: Concerns three-part music.

781.6   SW   ISSN 1101-5152
S A - SOUND AFFECTS. 1988. 6/yr. SEK 195. S A Tidnings AB, P.O. Box 1617, S-600 46 Norrkoeping, Sweden. TEL 46-11-10-00-53. FAX 46-11-10-00-92. music rev, rec.rev. circ. 30,000.
Description: Contains articles and information on pop, rock, alternative, punk.

780   US
S C I JOURNAL OF MUSIC SCORES. Variant title: Journal of Music Scores. 1973. irreg. (2-3/yr.), latest no. 19. price varies. (Society of Composers Inc.) European American Music Corporation, Box 850, Valley Forge, PA 19482-0850. TEL 610-648-0506. FAX 610-889-0242. Ed. Bruce Taub. circ. 175. Indexed: Music Ind.
Formerly: A S U C Journal of Music Scores.
Description: Anthology of music scores written by members of SCI.

780   US
S C MUSICIAN. 1948. 3/yr. $5. (South Carolina Music Educators Association) Wentworth Publishing Co., 6136 North Rd., Orangeburg, SC 29115. TEL 803-534-1006. Ed. Mrs. Johnnie U. Price. adv.: B&W page $125; trim 8 1/2 x 11; adv. contact: Mrs. Johnnie U. Price. circ. 1,774. Document type: academic/scholarly publication.

781.7   US   ISSN 0739-9103
S E M NEWSLETTER. 1966. q. membership. Society for Ethnomusicology, Morrison Hall 005, Indiana University, Bloomington, IN 47405-2501. TEL 812-855-6672. FAX 812-855-6673. Eds. Rene Lysloff, Deborah Wong. circ. 2,000. (processed; also avail. in microform from UMI; back issues avail.; reprint service avail. from UMI) Indexed: A.I.C.P., Music Artic.Guide, Music Ind., RILM. Document type: newsletter.
—BLDSC (8237.350000); UMI.
Former titles: Ethnomusicology Newsletter; Society for Ethnomusicology Newsletter; S E M Newsletter (ISSN 0036-1291)
Description: Covers society news, announces forthcoming conferences and events and profiles noteworthy persons.

S V ZEITUNG. (Sondenhaeuser Verband) see *COLLEGE AND ALUMNI*

783   US   ISSN 0036-2255
SACRED MUSIC. 1874. q. $10. Church Music Association of America, 548 Lafond Ave., St. Paul, MN 55103. Ed. Rev. Richard J. Schuler. adv.; bk.rev.; charts; index. circ. 1,100. (also avail. in microform from UMI; reprint service avail. from UMI,ISI) Indexed: Arts & Hum.Cit.Ind., Cath.Ind., Curr.Cont., Music Artic.Guide, Music Ind. Document type: academic/scholarly publication.
—BLDSC (8062.740000); Faxon; Genuine Article; UMI; UnCover.
Incorporates: Caecilia; Catholic Choirmaster.

781.7   US
SACRED MUSIC NEWS & REVIEW. 1992. m. $39.95. T C M R Communications Inc., Box 1179, Grapevine, TX 76099-1179. TEL 817-488-0141. FAX 817-488-4191. Ed. Timothy Sharp. Document type: newsletter.
Description: Discusses issues in music ministry, news and information pertaining to choral music, notices of publications and recorded music, employment listings.

786   US   ISSN 0036-2263
SACRED ORGAN JOURNAL. 1966. bi-m. $22.95. Lorenz Publishing Co., 501 E. Third St., Box 802, Dayton, OH 45401-0802. TEL 513-228-6118. FAX 513-223-2042. Ed. James Mansfield. adv. contact: Larry Pugh. Document type: trade publication.
Description: Arrangements for liturgical church services.

SADLER'S WELLS THEATRE PROGRAMME. see *THEATER*

781.7   GW   ISSN 0036-2328
ML5
SAENGER- UND MUSIKANTENZEITUNG; Zweimonatschrift fuer Volksmusik. 1958. bi-m. DM.44. B L V Verlagsgesellschaft mbH, Lothstr. 29, 80797 Munich, Germany. TEL 089-12705-0. FAX 089-12705354. Ed. Maria Hildebrandt. adv. contact: Henning Stemmler. bk.rev.; illus. Indexed: RILM. Document type: bulletin.
—CCC.

784   US   ISSN 0036-2336
SAENGER-ZEITUNG.* (Text in English and German) vol.41, 1965. q. membership. Federation of Worker's Singing Societies of the U.S.A., 1729 Springfield Ave., Maplewood, NJ 07040. Ed. Walter Hoops. adv.; music rev. circ. 600.

780   SZ
SAENGERWARTE. 8/yr. Wydaeckerring 69, Postfach 217, CH-8047 Zurich, Switzerland. TEL 01-4919346. Ed. Emil Scheiwiller. circ. 1,100.

780   IT
▼**SAGGIATORE MUSICALE.** 1994. s-a. L.70000 (foreign L.90000) (effective 1995) US $64 (effective 1996). (Universita degli Studi di Bologna, Dipartimento di Musica e Spettacolo) Casa Editrice Leo S. Olschki, Casella Postale 66, 50100 Florence, Italy. TEL 39-55-6530684. FAX 39-55-6530214. Ed. Giuseppina La Face Bianconi. bk.rev. Document type: academic/scholarly publication.

781.62   US
▼**ST. LOUIS FOLK FIRE DANCE AND MUSIC.** 1994. bi-m. $3 or donation. 2920 Shenandoah, St. Louis, MO 63104-1740. TEL 314-771-7619. Ed. Lynn DeVries; Pub. Andrew S. Limani. adv. contact: Andrew S. Limanni. Document type: newsletter.
Description: Source of folk dance and music information.

780   GW
SAITENSPIEL. 1961. 6/yr. DM.65($40) Deutscher Zithermusik-Bund e.V., Ysenburgstr. 9, 80634 Munich, Germany. TEL 089-131437. FAX 089-131437. Ed. Michael Brandlmeier. adv.; bk.rev. circ. 2,000. Document type: bulletin.
Description: All about the zither: composition, instruction, recordings.

780   DK   ISSN 0109-8438
SAMFUNDET TIL UDGIVELSE AF DANSK MUSIK. BULLETIN. 1981. irreg. free. Samfundet til Udgivelse af Dansk Musik - Society for Publication of Danish Music, Graabroedrestraede 18, 1. sal, DK-1156 Copenhagen K, Denmark. TEL 45-33-13-54-45. FAX 45-33-93-30-44.

780.01   GW   ISSN 0085-588X
SAMMLUNG MUSIKWISSENSCHAFTLICHER ABHANDLUNGEN/COLLECTION D'ETUDES MUSICOLOGIQUES. (Text in English, French, and German) 1932. irreg., no.88, 1994. price varies. Verlag Valentin Koerner GmbH, Postfach 304, 76482 Baden-Baden, Germany. TEL 07221-22423. FAX 07221-38697. Document type: monographic series.
Description: Monographs on musicological studies.

SAN DIEGO SOUND POST. see *LABOR UNIONS*

781.57   US
SAN JOSE SYMPHONY MASTERWORKS - SUPER POPS AND FAVORITE CLASSICS PROGRAMS.* 8/yr. Latimer Publications, 617 Veterans Blvd., Ste.213, Redwood City, CA 94063-1404. TEL 415-324-1570. FAX 415-324-4420. Ed. Marlyn Holmes; Pub. Douglas H. Latimer. circ. 14,000.
Description: Contains program guide and notes for the San Jose Symphony Orchestra performances.

780 792   II   ISSN 0036-4339
SANGEET NATAK; journal of Indian music, dance, theatre. (Text in English) 1965. q. Rs.30 to individuals; institutions Rs.50 (foreign $15). Sangeet Natak Akademi - National Academy of Music, Dance and Drama, Rabindra Bhavan, Feroz Sehah Rd., New Delhi 110001, India. TELEX 031-65466-SNA-IN. Ed. Abhijit Chatterjee. bk.rev.; illus. circ. 500. Indexed: RILM.
—UnCover.

SANGER-HILSEN/SINGERS GREETINGS. see *ETHNIC INTERESTS*

780   CN
SASKATCHEWAN MUSIC FESTIVAL ASSOCIATION OFFICIAL SYLLABUS. 1909. tirennial. Can.$5. Saskatchewan Music Festival Association, 201 - 1819 Cornwall St., Regina, SK S4P 2K4, Canada. Ed. Doris Covey Lazecki. adv. circ. 2,500.

780   US
SASSAFRAS. 1986. s-a. membership. People's Music Network for Songs of Freedom and Struggle, c/o Sarah Underhill, RR1 Box 193, Kerhonkson, NY 12446. Document type: newsletter.
Description: News and events for singers, songwriters, musicians and others interested in the links between musical expression and progressive social and political change.

780   YU
SAVEZ ORGANIZACIJA KOMPOZITORA JUGOSLAVIJE. BILTEN. English edition: Union of Yugoslav Composers' Organizations. Bulletin. (Text in Serbo-Croatian) 1972. q. free. Savez Organizacija Kompozitora Jugoslavije - Union of Yugoslav Composers' Organizations, Misarska 12-14, 1000 Belgrade, Yugoslavia. TEL 38-11-334771. FAX 38-11-336-168. Ed. Ivan Kovac. circ. free. Indexed: Music Ind.
Description: Publishes news on union's activities: copyright protection, international cooperation, major music events in the country, news on first performances, awards.

781.65   US   ISSN 0276-4768
SAXOPHONE JOURNAL. 1980. bi-m. $25 (foreign $35); with CD $35 (foreign $45) (effective 1995). Box 206, Medfield, MA 02052. (back issues avail.; compact disc avail.) Indexed: Music Artic.Guide, RILM. Document type: trade publication.
—Faxon; UnCover.
Formerly: Saxophone Sheet.
Description: Provides news to improve playing with regular columns on jazz improvisation, techniques, doubling, career management, new publications, writing and teaching ideas, and reviews.

780   FR   ISSN 1161-8124
SCALA MAGAZINE. 4/yr. P L U S, 16 rue Rodier, B.P. 512, 75009 Paris, France. TEL 42-85-11-78. FAX 42-81-94-58. Ed. Alexandre Zenou. circ. 7,500. Indexed: Geo.Abstr.

SCENARIA. see *THEATER*

780 792   US
SCENERY, COSTUMES, AND MUSICAL MATERIALS DIRECTORY. biennial. $25 to non-members; members $15. Opera America, 1156 15th St., N.W., Ste. 810, Washington, DC 20005. TEL 202-293-4466. FAX 202-393-0735. Ed. Martha Perry. Document type: directory.
Description: Listing of materials available for rent or purchase from Opera America companies.

SCENES MAGAZINE; mensuel suisse d'information culturelle. see *ART*

780   GW
SCHALLPLATTEN A B C. AUSGABE A: SINGLE SCHALLPLATTEN. m. DM.5.50 per no. (Gesamtverband Deutscher Musikfachgeschaefte e.V.) Helmut Sander Verlag, Hohenfriedbergweg 1, 32425 Minden, Germany. TEL 0571-41595. Document type: catalog.

780   GW
SCHALLPLATTEN A B C. AUSGABE B: LANGSPIELPLATTEN UND MUSICASSETTEN. m. DM.6 per no. (Gesamtverband Deutscher Musikfachgeschaefte e.V.) Helmut Sander Verlag, Hohenfriedbergweg 1, 32425 Minden, Germany. TEL 0571-41595. Document type: catalog.

780 028.5   US   ISSN 1048-2180
SCHERZO;* a magazine for music students. 1989. q. $10. Jimm Omodt Music Studio, Box 203, Joseph, OR 97846-0203. TEL 503-287-7009. Ed. Jimm A. Omodt. bk.rev. circ. 500. (back issues avail.)
Description: Articles and activities for beginning to intermediate music students.

780   SP   ISSN 0213-4802
SCHERZO. 1985. m. (10/yr.). 6000 ptas. (Europe 8000 ptas.; America 10000 ptas.). Scherzo Editorial, S.A., Marques de Mondejar, 11 2o D, 28028 Madrid, Spain. TEL 34-3-567622. Dir. Antonio Moral. adv.; bk.rev.; rec.rev.; circ. 15,000 (controlled).
Description: Presents the world of so-called "serious music" (classical, jazz) in Spain. Covers national and foreign events.

780   FR
SCHERZO - GUIDE MUSICAL. 1970. 10/yr. 70 F. Vie Musicale, 27 rue Dareau, 75014 Paris, France. adv.; bk.rev. circ. 12,000.
Formed by the 1975 merger of: Scherzo & Guide Musical.

780.65   US   ISSN 1060-4111
ML427
SCHIRMER - NEWS. 1987. irreg. (1-4/yr.). free. G. Schirmer Inc., 257 Park Ave. S., 20th Fl., New York, NY 10010. TEL 212-254-2100. FAX 212-254-2-13. TELEX 428351. (Co-publisher: Associated Music Publishers Inc.) Ed. E. Matthew. Document type: newsletter.
Description: Contains articles, calendars, and announcements of interest to performers, conductors, and the classical music business.

780   GW   ISSN 0036-6137
SCHLAGER FUER DICH. 1954. q. Lied der Zeit Musikverlag, Rosa-Luxemburg-Str.41, 10178 Berlin, Germany.

780   US   ISSN 0036-6668
ML1
SCHOOL MUSIC NEWS. 1936. 8/yr. (Sep.-May). $16 to non-members. New York State School Music Association, 151 Sweetwater Hills Dr., Hendersonville, NC 28739-8003. TEL 704-891-5145. FAX 704-891-1151. Ed. Robert Campbell. adv.; music rev.; illus.; index. circ. 50,000. (also avail. in microform from UMI; reprint service avail. from UMI) Indexed: Music Artic.Guide.
—UMI; UnCover.

791   GW
SCHOTT AKTUELL. 1961. m. free. Schott Musik International GmbH, Weihergarten 5, 55116 Mainz, Germany. TEL 06131-246885. FAX 06131-246250. Ed.Bd. circ. 2,800. (tabloid format) Document type: consumer publication.

SCHUBERT DURCH DIE BRILLE. see *BIOGRAPHY*

780   GW   ISSN 0174-2345
SCHUETZ-JAHRBUCH. 1979. a. membership. (Internationale Heinrich Schuetz-Gesellschaft e.V.) Baerenreiter Verlag, Heinrich-Schuetz-Allee 35, 34131 Kassel, Germany. TEL 0561-3105-0. FAX 0561-3105240. (Subscr. in US to: Educational Music Service, 13 Elkay Dr., Chester, NY 10918. TEL 914-469-5790. FAX 914-469-5817) Indexed: Music Ind., RILM. Document type: academic/scholarly publication.
Superseded (1966-1973): Sagittarius (ISSN 0080-5408)

780   GW   ISSN 0340-3661
SCHWAEBISCHE SAENGERZEITUNG. 1952. m. DM.33. (Schwaebischer Saengerbund 1879 e.V.) W. Kohlhammer GmbH, Hessbruehlstr. 69, 70565 Stuttgart, Germany. TEL 0711-8363-1. FAX 0711-7863263. Document type: newsletter.

SCHWANN OPUS. see *MUSIC — Abstracting, Bibliographies, Statistics*

780   SZ
SCHWEIZER BEITRAGE ZUR MUSIKWISSENSCHAFT. (Text in German; summaries vary) 1972. irreg. price varies. Paul Haupt AG, Falkenstrasse 14, CH-3001 Bern, Switzerland. TEL 031-3012345. FAX 031-3014669. Ed. Ernst Lichtenhahn. Indexed: RILM. Document type: monographic series.

780   SZ   ISSN 0036-7419
SCHWEIZER MUSIKER-REVUE.* vol.41, 1965. m. 8 SFr. Postfach 19, CH-3114 Wichtrach, Switzerland. Ed. Beat Braendli. adv.; music rev. circ. 4,000.

MUSIC

780 SZ
SCHWEIZER MUSIKPAEDAGOGISCHE BLAETTER. 1912. q. 40 SFr. Schweizerischer Musikpaedagogischer Verband, Hauptstr. 188, CH-2552 Orpund, Switzerland. TEL 032-551557. Ed. Bernhard Billeter. adv. contact: Marlise Zbinden. bk.rev. circ. 5,200. Indexed: RILM. Document type: academic/scholarly publication.

780 SZ
SCHWEIZER VOLKSMUSIK. 6/yr. Riedstr., Postfach 34, CH-3082 Schlosswil, Switzerland. TEL 031-7111639. Ed. Werner Reber. circ. 10,000.

785 SZ
SCHWEIZERISCHE BLASMUSIKZEITUNG. (Text in French, German, Italian) 11/yr. 31 SFr. (foreign 36 SFr.). (National Society of Music from Switzerland) Zollikofer AG, Fuerstenlandstr. 122, CH-9001 St. Gallen, Switzerland. TEL 071-297777. FAX 071-297384. circ. 22,000. (back issues avail.) Document type: consumer publication.

784 SZ
SCHWEIZERISCHE CHORZEITUNG/REVUE SUISSE DES CHORALES. (Text in French, German, Italian) 1978. m. 28 SFr. (foreign 32 SFr.). Union Suisse des Chorales - Schweizerische Chorvereinigung, Scheuchzerstr. 14, CH-8006 Zurich, Switzerland. TEL 01-3612855. FAX 01-3612855. Ed. Theres-Ursula Beiner. adv. circ. 6,500. Document type: bulletin.

780 SZ ISSN 0080-7354
SCHWEIZERISCHE MUSIKFORSCHENDE GESELLSCHAFT. PUBLIKATIONEN. SERIE 2. 1952. irreg., no.34, 1991. price varies. Paul Haupt AG, Falkenplatz 14, CH-3001 Bern, Switzerland. TEL 031-3012345. FAX 031-3014669. Document type: monographic series.
—CCC.

780 SZ
SCHWEIZERISCHE SAENGERZEITUNG. 1911. 9/yr. 7 SFr. Schweizerischer Arbeiter-Saengerverband, Kirchbergerstr. 3, CH-3008 Bern, Switzerland. TEL 031-3724540. (Subscr. to: Markus Grunder, Falkenfluhweg 9, CH-3138 Uetendorf, Switzerland) Ed. Peter Anliker. adv.; bk.rev. circ. 3,000. Document type: newsletter.

780 200 US ISSN 1073-5925
SCREAMS OF ABEL. bi-m. $8. Box 2861, Springfield, VA 22152-2861. Ed. Phil Powell. adv. Document type: newsletter.
Former titles (until Sep. 1992): Cephas - Teeth; (until 1992): Cephas; Incorporates (in 1992): Teeth.
Description: Focuses on Christian heavy metal music; includes concert reviews.

SEATTLE FOLKLORE SOCIETY NEWSLETTER. see FOLKLORE

781.57 US ISSN 0037-0576
ML1
SECOND LINE. 1950. q. $25 membership. New Orleans Jazz Club, 828 Royal St., Ste. 265, New Orleans, LA 70116. TEL 504-455-6847. Ed. Carolyn Stafford. adv.; bk.rev.; bibl.; charts; illus.; stat.; index, cum.index. circ. 1,000. Indexed: Music Ind., RILM.

SECOND SHIFT. see WOMEN'S INTERESTS

051 US
SECOND SKIN. irreg., latest no.6. $2 per issue. Alyssa Isenstein, Ed. & Pub., One Mead Way, Bronxville, NY 10708. rec.rev.

781.64 UK ISSN 0959-8367
SELECT. 1990. m. £22.20 (foreign £27) (effective 1995-1996). E M A P - Metro, Mappin House, 4 Winsley St., London W1N 7AR, England. TEL 0171-436-1515. FAX 0171-312-8191. (Subscr. to: Tower Publishing Services Ltd., Tower House, Sovereign Park, Lathkill St., Market Harborough, Leics. LE16 9EF, England. TEL 01858-468811. FAX 01858-432164) adv. Document type: consumer publication.

781.7 US ISSN 0361-6622
ML3799
SELECTED REPORTS IN ETHNOMUSICOLOGY. 1966. irreg, vol.10, 1994. price varies. University of California at Los Angeles, Department of Ethnomusicology and Systematic Musicology, Box 951657, Los Angeles, CA 90095-1657. TEL 213-825-5947. FAX 213-206-4738. Ed.Bd. illus. circ. 800. (back issues avail.) Indexed: A.I.C.P., Anthropol.Lit., M.L.A., Music Ind., RILM. Document type: monographic series, academic/scholarly publication.
—BLDSC (8235.030000); UnCover.
Refereed Serial

780.01 IT
SEMINARIO DI STUDI E RICERCHE SUL LINGUAGGIO MUSICALE. ATTI. 1971. a. Istituto Musicale F. Canneti, Villa Cordellina-Lombardi, Montecchio Maggiore, Vincenza, Italy. illus.

780 286 US ISSN 1046-4158
ML1
SENIOR MUSICIAN. 1970. q. $8.95. Southern Baptist Convention, Sunday School Board, 127 Ninth Ave., N., Nashville, TN 37234. TEL 800-458-2772.
Description: Contains easy music and provides leader guides for senior adult choir members and their leaders in worship, ministry, and recreation.

SENSIBLE SOUND. see SOUND RECORDING AND REPRODUCTION

SEVENTEENTH CENTURY FRENCH STUDIES. see LITERATURE

780.6 920 US ISSN 1054-6022
ML194
SEVENTEENTH - CENTURY MUSIC. 1984. 2/yr. $10 to non-members. Society for Seventeenth - Century Music, c/o Steven Saunders, Dept. of Music, Colby College, Waterville, ME 04901. FAX 207-872-3237. adv.; bk.rev. circ. 120. Document type: newsletter.
Former titles: Schutz Society Reports; Archer.
Description: Deals with all aspects of the study and performance of music in the Seventeenth century.

783 US
SHALSHELET: THE CHAIN. vol.11, 1976. irreg. membership. Hebrew Union College - Jewish Institute of Religion (New York), One W. Fourth St., New York, NY 10012. TEL 212-674-5300. Ed. B. Ostfeld Horowitz. circ. 200.

780.42 US ISSN 0273-6462
ML1
SHEET MUSIC MAGAZINE. STANDARD PIANO - GUITAR EDITION. 1977. bi-m. $16.97. Sheet Music Magazine, Inc., 223 Katonah Ave., Katonah, NY 10536. TEL 914-232-8108. FAX 914-232-1205. (Subscr. to: Box 58629, Boulder, CO 80322) Ed. Edward Shanaphy; Pub. Edward Shanaphy. adv. contact: Josephine Sblendorio, Man. Ed. bk.rev. circ. 200,000. Document type: consumer publication.
—UnCover.
Description: Contains articles and features of interest to musicians, amateur and professional, together with instructional material and sheet music for several songs.

781.57 UK ISSN 0583-1296
SHOUT. 1967. m. £2.25($6) c/o Clive Richardson, Ed., 46 Slades Drive, Chislehurst, Kent BR7 6JX, England. adv.; film rev.; index. circ. 2,000. (processed)
Formerly: Soul Music.

780.65 GW
SHOW; independent music media service. 1968. 48/yr. DM.513.69($360) Show Organisation Dieter Liffers GmbH, Stumpf 15, 53797 Lohmar, Germany. TEL 02205-6869. FAX 02205-6879. Ed. Dieter Liffers. adv. contact: B&W page DM.1600, color page DM.1800; trim 210 x 296; adv. contact: Ursula Maylahn. bk.rev. circ. 1,600. (looseleaf format; back issues avail.) Document type: newsletter.

789.91 792 US ISSN 8755-9560
ML1699
SHOW MUSIC; the musical theatre magazine. 1981. q. $19. Goodspeed Opera House, P.O. Box 466, East Haddam, CT 06423-0466. TEL 203-873-8664. FAX 203-873-2329. Ed. Max O. Preeo; Pub. John Pike. adv.; bk.rev.; circ. 6,200 (paid). (back issues avail.) Document type: consumer publication.
Description: Reviews new, original cast recordings and related-interest records, videos, and compact disc releases; contains articles on musical theatre personalities and creators.

780 790 UK ISSN 0264-4150
SHOWCALL. 1973. a. £20 for 2 vols. Stage Newspaper Ltd., Stage House, 47 Bermondsey St., London SE1 3XT, England. TEL 0171-403-1818. FAX 0171-403-1418. Ed. Brian Attwood; Pub. Catherine Comerford. adv. contact: Colin Finlay. illus.; index. Document type: directory.

780 UK
SHOWCASE INTERNATIONAL MUSIC BOOK.* 1965. a. £30. Showcase Publications Ltd., 12 Felix Ave., London N8 9TL, England. TEL 0181-348-2332. FAX 0181-340-3750. adv. Document type: directory.
Former titles: Kemps International Music Book (ISSN 0963-8490); Kemps International Music and Recording Industry Yearbook; Kemps International Music and Recording Yearbook; Kemps Music and Record Industry Year Book International (ISSN 0305-7100); Kemps Music and Record Industry Year Book (ISSN 0075-5451)

780 US ISSN 0889-7581
ML1
SIGMA ALPHA IOTA QUARTERLY: PAN PIPES. Key Title: Pan Pipes. vol.63, 1970. 4/yr. $15. Sigma Alpha Iota, International Music Fraternity, c/o Margaret Maxwell, Ed., 8466 N. Lockwood Ridge Rd., Ste. 312, Sarasota, FL 34243. TEL 813-794-0623. (Subscr. to: Executive Office of Sigma Alpha Iota, 4119 Rollins Ave., Des Moines, IA 50312) adv.; bk.rev.; music rev.; rec.rev.; illus. circ. 20,000. Indexed: Music Artic.Guide, Music Ind.
—UnCover.
Formerly (until 1980): Pan Pipes of Sigma Alpha Iota (ISSN 0031-0611)

780 282 FR ISSN 1151-4051
SIGNES MUSIQUES; la revue du chant liturgique. 1990? bi-m. 248 F. (outside E.C. 268 F.). Bayard Presse, 3 rue Bayard, 75393 Paris Cedex 08, France. TEL 44-35-60-60. FAX 44-35-60-91. TELEX 648 094 F. (Subscr. to: B.P. 12, 99505 Paris Entreprises. TEL 46-30-38-00. FAX 46-30-31-67)
Description: Suggests songs to use in conjunction with the liturgy.

780 US
SIN;* art, music, subculture. 1992. m. $30. 624 Broadway, San Diego, CA 92101-5402. TEL 619-239-9746. Ed. Rex Edhlund.

SINATRA INTERNATIONAL. see BIOGRAPHY

784 US ISSN 0037-5624
ML1
SING OUT!; the folksong magazine. 1950. q. $18 to individuals (foreign $21); institutions $25 (foreign $28). Sing Out Corporation, Box 5253, Bethlehem, PA 18015-0253. TEL 610-865-5366. FAX 610-865-5129. Ed. Mark D. Moss. adv. contact: Lynn Koehler. bk.rev.; music rev.; illus.; cum.index; circ. 10,000 (paid). (also avail. in microform from UMI; back issues avail.; reprint service avail. from UMI) Indexed: Access (1976-1987), Alt.Press Ind., Curr.Cont., Mag.Ind., Music Artic.Guide, Music Ind., New Per.Ind. Document type: academic/scholarly publication.
—Faxon; UMI; UnCover.
Description: Selection of songs and articles reflecting a diversity of folk music styles: blues, blue-grass, country, gospel contemporary folk, Celtic, traditional, women's, topical, children's, and seasonal.

SING TO THE LORD. see RELIGIONS AND THEOLOGY — Protestant

780 SZ
SINGEN UND MUSIZIEREN IM GOTTESDIENST. bi-m. 39.50 SFr. (foreign 41.50 SFr.). (Schweizerischer Katholischer Kirchenmusikverband) Ostschweiz Druck und Verlag AG, Oberer Graben 8, CH-9001 St. Gallen, Switzerland. TEL 071-208585. FAX 071-236577. Ed. Herbert Ulrich. adv: B&W page 383 SFr.; trim 140 x 205. circ. 1,800. **Document type:** consumer publication.
 Formerly: Katholische Kirchenmusik.

783 AU ISSN 0037-5721
ML5
SINGENDE KIRCHE; Zeitschrift fuer katholische Kirchenmusik. 1953. q. S.70. Oesterreichische Bischofskonferenz, Oesterreichische Kirchenmusikkommission, Stock-im-Eisen Platz 3-IV, A-1010 Vienna, Austria. TEL 0222-51552-641. FAX 0222-51552-640. Ed. Karl Dorneger. adv.; bk.rev.; abstr.; bibl.; illus. circ. 3,500. **Indexed:** Music Ind., RILM. **Document type:** bulletin.

782.81 UK ISSN 0969-9686
THE SINGER. 1993. bi-m. £12 (foreign £20). Rhinegold Publishing Ltd., 241 Shaftesbury Ave., London WC2H 8EH, England. TEL 0171-333-1720. FAX 0171-333-1769. Ed. Ashutosh Khandekar. adv.: page £900; adv. contact: Geraldine McElearney. music rev.; circ. 8,000. **Document type:** consumer publication.
 —BLDSC (8285.561000).

780 792 US
SINGER'S GUIDE TO THE PROFESSIONAL OPERA COMPANIES. biennial. $25 for non-members; members $15. Opera America, 1156 15th St., N.W., Ste. 810, Washington, DC 20005. TEL 202-293-4466. FAX 202-393-0735. Ed. Martha Perry.
 Formerly: Opera America. Survey of Professional Training-Apprentice Programs.
 Description: Provides information on training, apprenticeship, and artist-in-residence programs at opera companies in North America and elsewhere, with company casting policies and application procedures.

784 US ISSN 1060-3956
SINGING NEWS; the printed voice of gospel music. 1969. m. $19. Singing News, Inc., Box 2810, Boone, NC 28607-2810. TEL 704-264-3700. FAX 704-264-4621. Ed. Jerry Kirksey; Pub. Maurice Templeton. adv. contact: Pam Slaney. bk.rev.; bibl.; illus. circ. 160,000. **Document type:** trade publication.

781.7 XO
SLOVAK MUSIC. (Text in English) 1969. s-a. free. Hudobny Fond, Hudobne Informacne Stredisko - Music Found, Music Information Center, Medena 29, 811 02 Bratislava, Slovakia. TEL 07-333-569. FAX 07-331-380. Ed. Olga Smetanova. bk.rev. circ. 4,000. **Indexed:** Music Ind., RILM. **Document type:** bulletin.
 Description: Contains information on new compositions, composers, musical history and musical education.

SLOVENSKA NARODNA BIBLIOGRAFIA SERIA H: HUDOBNINY. see *MUSIC — Abstracting, Bibliographies, Statistics*

784.7691 786.97 XO
SLOVENSKE LUDOVE PIESNE PRE AKORDEON. irreg., vol.3, 1974. price varies. Opus, Bratislava, Slovakia.

780.7 CN
SLUR; a smooth connection between notes. 1983. q. free. Saskatchewan Band Association, 1840 McIntyre St., Regina, Sask. S4P 2P9, Canada. TEL 306-522-2263. FAX 306-565-2177. Ed. Carol J. McNabb. adv. circ. 300.
 Description: Contains articles and events pertaining to instrumental music programs in Saskatchewan.

781.65 UK ISSN 0260-3004
SMASH HITS. 1978. fortn. £24 (foreign £27) (effective 1995-1996). E M A P - Metro, Mappin House, 4 Winsley St., London W1N 7AR, England. TEL 0171-436-1515. FAX 0171-312-8191. (Subscr. to: Tower Publishing Services Ltd., Tower House, Lathkill St., Market Harborough, Leics. LE16 9EF, England. TEL 01858-468811. FAX 01858-432164) adv. circ. 602,156. **Document type:** consumer publication.

781.57 791.43 AT ISSN 0815-1121
SMASH HITS MAGAZINE. 1984. fortn. Aus.$58.95. Mason Stewart Publishing Pty. Ltd., P.O. Box 746, Darlinghurst, N.S.W. 2010, Australia. FAX 02-360-5367. Ed. James Manning. adv.; bk.rev. circ. 63,000. **Document type:** consumer publication.
 Description: Entertainment magazine covering music, movies and TV.

789.42 AT ISSN 0815-4740
SMASH HITS YEARBOOK. a. Aus.$58.95. Mason Stewart Publishing Pty. Ltd., P.O. Box 746, Darlinghust, N.S.W., Australia. TEL 02-331-5006. FAX 02-360-5367.

780 SP ISSN 0213-0815
ML315.7.B37
SOCIEDAD DE ESTUDIOS VASCOS. CUADERNOS DE SECCION. MUSICA. 1983. irreg. Eusko Ikaskuntza, Legazpi, 10-1, 20004 Donostia-San Sebastian, Spain. TEL 425111.

780 US
SOCIETY FOR ETHNOMUSICOLOGY. SPECIAL SERIES. no. 3, 1971. irreg., no.6, 1992. price varies. Society for Ethnomusicology, Morrison Hall 005, Indiana University, Bloomington, IN 47405-2501. TEL 812-855-6672. FAX 812-855-6673. bibl. (back issues avail.) **Document type:** monographic series.
 Description: Explores the ethnic study of music throughout the world.

780 US
SOCIETY OF COMPOSERS NEWSLETTER. (Former name of issuing body: American Society of University Composers) 1968. 6/yr. membership. Society of Composers, Inc., Box 296, New York, NY 10011-9998. Ed. Ting Ho. bk.rev.; bibl. circ. 900. **Document type:** newsletter.
 Former titles: American Society of University Composers Newsletter; American Society of University Composers News Bulletin; American Society of University Composers Newsletter.

SOCIOLOGY OF MUSIC SERIES. see *SOCIOLOGY*

781.62 SW ISSN 0346-2595
SOERMLANDSLAATEN. 1968. 3-4/yr. SEK 80 (effective 1994). Soedermanlands Spelmansfoerbund, c/o Nils Haeggbom, Bildvaegen 6, S-137 57 Vaesterhaninge, Sweden. TEL 468-500-312-88. Ed. Nils Haeggbom. adv.; bk.rev.

780 SZ
SOLOTHURNISCHES SAENGERBLATT. 6/yr. Roemerstr. 5B, CH-4512 Bellach, Switzerland. TEL 065-383651. Ed. T.U. Beiner-Rolli. circ. 1,200.

SON!. see *ART*

780.904 SP
SONDA;* problema y panorama de la musica contemporanea. 1973. q. Sonda, Juventudes Musicales, San Bernardo 44, Madrid 8, Spain. Ed. Ricardo Parado.

783 US ISSN 0273-2920
SONG OF ZION; newsletter for LDS musicians. 1980. 4/yr. free. Jackman Music Corp., Box 1900, Orem, UT 84059-5900. TEL 801-225-0859. FAX 801-225-0851. Eds. David R. Naylor, Jerry R. Jackman. adv. contact: Virginia King. bk.rev.; bibl.; illus.; tr.lit.; circ. 17,000 (controlled).

781.7 AT ISSN 0726-1306
SONGS OF NEW SOUTH WALES. SERIES. 1988. irreg. Aus.$7 per no.; catalogue Aus.$2. Sound Austral, 34 Lucerne Cres., Frankston, Vic. 3199, Australia. TEL 61-3-789-2205. Ed. Frank Hintz. (back issues avail.; catalogue of titles avail.)
 Description: Collection of folkloric and community songs of New South Wales.

781.7 AT ISSN 1035-6355
SONGS OF NEW ZEALAND. 1990. irreg. Aus.$7 per no.; catalogue Aus.$2. Sound Austral, 34 Lucerne Cres., Frankston, Vic. 3199, Australia. TEL 61-3-789-2205. Ed. Frank Hinz. (back issues avail.; catalogue of titles avail.)
 Description: Collection of folkloric and community songs of New Zealand.

781.7 AT ISSN 0726-1365
SONGS OF NORTHERN TERRITORY. SERIES. 1988. irreg. Aus.$7 per no.; catalogue Aus.$2. Sound Austral, 34 Lucerne Cres., Frankston, Vic. 3199, Australia. TEL 61-3-789-2205. Ed. Frank Hinz. (back issues avail. catalogue of titles avail.)

781.7 AT ISSN 0726-1330
SONGS OF QUEENSLAND. SERIES. 1986. irreg. Aus.$7 per no.; catalogue Aus.$2. Sound Austral, 34 Lucerne Cres., Frankston, Vic. 3199, Australia. TEL 61-3-789-2205. Ed. Frank Hinz. (back issues avail.; catalogue of titles avail.)
 Description: Collection of folkloric and community songs of Queensland.

781.7 AT ISSN 0726-1322
SONGS OF SOUTH AUSTRALIA. SERIES. 1988. irreg. Aus.$7 per no.; catalogue Aus.$2. Sound Austral, 34 Lucerne Cres., Frankston, Vic. 3199, Australia. TEL 61-3-789-2205. Ed. Frank Hinz. (back issues avail.; catalogue of titles avail.)
 Description: Collection of folkloric and community songs of South Australia.

781.7 AT ISSN 0726-1357
SONGS OF TASMANIA. SERIES. 1986. irreg. Aus.$7 per no.; catalogue Aus.$2. Sound Austral, 34 Lucerne Cres., Franskton, Vic. 3199, Australia. TEL 61-3-789-2205. Ed. Frank Hinz. (back issues avail.; catalogue of titles avail.)
 Description: Collection of folkloric and community songs of Tasmania.

781.7 AT ISSN 0726-1314
SONGS OF VICTORIA. SERIES. 1977. irreg. Aus.$7 per no.; catalogue Aus.$2. Sound Austral, 34 Lucerne Cres., Frankston, Vic. 3199, Australia. TEL 61-3-789-2205. Ed. Frank Hinz. (back issues avail.; catalogue of titles avail.)
 Description: Collection of folkloric and community songs of Victoria.

781.7 AT ISSN 0726-1349
SONGS OF WESTERN AUSTRALIA. SERIES. 1988. irreg. Aus.$7 per no.; catalogue Aus.$2. Sound Austral, 34 Lucerne Cres., Frankston, Vic. 3199, Australia. TEL 61-3-789-2205. Ed. Frank Hinz. (back issues avail.; catalogue of titles avail.)
 Description: Collection of folkloric and community songs of Western Australia.

780 US
SONGTALK; the songwriter's newspaper. 1986. q. $30 for 2 yrs. National Academy of Songwriters, 6381 Hollywood Blvd., Ste. 780, Hollywood, CA 90028. TEL 213-463-7178. FAX 213-463-2146. Ed. Paul Zollo. adv. circ. 25,000. **Document type:** newspaper.
 Description: In-depth coverage of songwriting and songwriters, with interviews and feature articles.

784.61 US
SONGWRITERS & LYRICIST CLUB NEWSLETTER. 1984. a. $35 membership. Songwriter and Lyricist Club, Box 23304, Brooklyn, NY 11202-0066. TEL 718-855-5057. Ed. Robert Makinson. adv.; bk.rev. (looseleaf format)
 Formerly (until 1995): Lyric and Melody Newsletter.

780.65 US ISSN 0161-5971
MT67
SONGWRITER'S MARKET. 1979. a. $22.99. F & W Publications, Inc., 1507 Dana Ave., Cincinnati, OH 45207. TEL 513-531-2222. Ed. Cindy Laufenberg. (reprint service avail. from UMI)
 Description: Lists 2500 listings of music publishers, record companies, producers, AD/AV firms, managers, booking agents.

780 UK ISSN 1355-7726
SONIC ARTS NETWORK JOURNAL. 1989. irreg. £15. Sonic Arts Network, Francis House, Francis St., London SW1P 1DE, England. TEL 0171-828-9796. FAX 0171-233-5159. E-mail: sonicart.demon.co.uk. Ed. Pete Stollery. adv. contact: John Cooper. bk.rev. circ. 350. **Document type:** consumer publication.

780 MX
SONIDO;* revista musical. 1976. m. Mex.$200($25) Corporacion Editorial S.A., Lucio Blanco 435, Col. San Juan Tlihuaca, 02400 Mexico D.F., Mexico. circ. 100,000.

MUSIC

780   US
SONNECK SOCIETY BULLETIN; for American music. 1975. 3/yr. membership. (Sonneck Society for American Music) Ouachita Baptist University, Box 3659, Arkadelphia, AR 71998. TEL 419-221-1641. FAX 419-221-0450. Ed. George Keck. adv.; bk.rev.; bibl. circ. 1,000. (also avail. in microform from UMI; reprint service avail. from UMI) **Indexed:** Music Artic.Guide, Music Ind. **Document type:** academic/scholarly publication.
—UMI; UnCover.
 Formerly (until vol.13, 1987): Sonneck Society Newsletter (ISSN 0196-7967)
 Description: Contains brief articles of current interest, essays, and performance news.

780 621.389   IT
SONORA; itinerari oltre il suono. (Includes compact disc of recorded music) (Text in English, Italian) q. L.60000 (foreign L.80000). Materiali Sonori, Pza. della Liberta 13, 52027 S. Giovanni Valdarno, Italy. Ed. Stefano Saletti.

780   US   ISSN 0739-229X
ML1
SONUS. 1980. s-a. $20 to individuals; institutions $25; students $15. 24 Avon Hill, Cambridge, MA 02140. TEL 617-868-0215. Ed. Pozzi Escot. adv. contact: Martin Schreiner. circ. 350. **Indexed:** Music Artic.Guide, RILM. **Document type:** academic/scholarly publication.
—BLDSC (8327.964000); UnCover.

781.57   FR   ISSN 0398-9089
ML5
SOUL BAG; le magazine du Blues et de la Soul. 1970. bi-m. 70 F.($13) Edit 71, 22 rue d'Annam, 75020 Paris, France. (Subscr. to: C.L.A.R.B., 35 rue Trezel, 92300 Levallois-Perret, France) adv. circ. 1,000. (back issues avail.)

780   UK   ISSN 0966-5471
SOUL C D. 1992. m. £70 for 6 issues. Northern & Shell Publications, Northern & Shell Bldg., P.O. Box 381, Millharbour, London E14 9TW, England. TEL 44-171-987-5090. FAX 44-171-987-2160. Ed. Stuart Kirkham. adv.: color page £1700; adv. contact: Paul Cowley. circ. 100,000. **Document type:** consumer publication.

789.91 621.38   GR   ISSN 1105-1302
SOUND & HI FI/IHOS. (Text in Greek) 1973. m. Dr.14000($100) Technical Press S.A., 31 Praxitelous St., 167 77 Athens, Greece. TEL 30-1-9961-861. FAX 30-1-9961-864. Ed. Sophie Cavvatha; Pub. Costas Cavvathas. adv. contact: Yiannis Vrontos. circ. 30,000. (back issues avail.) **Document type:** consumer publication.
● Also available online.
 Description: Discusses music and high-quality high-fidelity equipment.

SOUND & IMAGE. see *SOUND RECORDING AND REPRODUCTION*

780.7   GW   ISSN 0936-0689
SOUND CHECK. 1984. m. DM.69 (foreign DM.79). Presse Project Verlag, Postfach, 85232 Bergkirchen, Germany. TEL 08131-56550. FAX 08131-3288. Ed. Michael van Almsick. circ. 58,000. **Document type:** consumer publication.

780   US   ISSN 8756-6176
ML3469
SOUND CHOICE. 1985. s-a. $20. Audio Evolution Network, Box 1125, Oceano, CA 93445-1125. Ed. David Ciaffardini. adv.; bk.rev. circ. 20,000. (back issues avail.) **Document type:** consumer publication, trade publication.
 Description: Features reviews and news relating to alternative and independent audio, video, multi-media and print.

780   MY
SOUND OF MALAYSIAN'S MUSICIAN/TA MA KO YU CHIH SHENG. (Text in Chinese) 1971. s-a. M.$0.30 per no. 18 Dato Koyah Rd., Penang, Malaysia. illus.

780 621.389   UK   ISSN 0951-6816
SOUND ON SOUND. 1985. m. £35 (Europe £50; world £65). Sound on Sound Ltd., Media House, Burrel Rd., St. Ives, Cambridgeshire PE17 4LE, England. TEL 01480-461244. FAX 01480-492422. Ed. Paul White; Pub. Ian Gilby. adv. contact: Robert Cottee. bk.rev.; index. circ. 31,200. (back issues avail.) **Document type:** consumer publication.
 Description: Provides reviews and information on musicians and record producers, modern music-making instruments and recording gear.

381.7   US   ISSN 0749-0755
ML1
SOUND POST; dedicated to Scandinavian folk music and dance. 1984. q. $15. Hardanger Fiddle Association of America, 2745 Winnetka Ave. N., Ste. 211, Minneapolis, MN 55427. TEL 616-373-6877. E-mail: BM.EIP@RLG.STANFORD.EDU. (Subscr. to: Lucy Ghastin, 7130 Century Ave., Middleton, WI 53562) Ed. Stephen Tabor. adv.; bk.rev.; index; cum.index: 1984-1988. circ. 360. (back issues avail.) **Document type:** newsletter.
 Description: Presents Scandinavian folk music and dance with emphasis on the Norwegian Hardanger fiddle.

780.904   US
SOUND VIEWS; subterranean music and politics. m. free. Greenfeld Communications and Design, 96 Henry St., Ste. 5W, Brooklyn Heights, NY 11201. TEL 718-797-5350. Ed. Lee Greenfeld. adv.: B&W page $235; trim 7 7/16 x 9 7/8. rec.rev.; illus. (back issues avail.)

787   US
SOUNDBOARD. 1974. q. $30 (effective 1994). Guitar Foundation of America, c/o Gunnar Eisel, Gen. Mgr., Box 1240, Claremont, CA 91711. Ed. Peter Danner. adv.; bk.rev.; bibl.; illus. circ. 3,000. (also avail. in microfiche; back issues avail.) **Indexed:** Music Artic.Guide, Music Ind.
—UnCover.
 Formerly: Guitar Foundation of America Soundboard (ISSN 0145-6237)
 Description: Articles feature a wide variety of technical and musical columns, new music, and reviews.

780   AT   ISSN 0811-3149
IN PROCESS
SOUNDS AUSTRALIAN JOURNAL. 1983. q. Aus.$45 to individuals; institutions Aus.$60. Australian Music Centre Ltd., P.O. Box N690, Grosvenor Pl., N.S.W 2000, Australia. TEL 61-2-241-2873. E-mail: amc@slim.slnsw.gov.au. Ed. Cathy Brown-Watt. adv.; bk.rev.; rec.rev. circ. 1,200. **Document type:** academic/scholarly publication.
 Description: Covers issues in contemporary composition and current activities in contemporary Australian music.

780   AT   ISSN 1030-4916
ML360.5
SOUNDS AUSTRALIAN UPDATE. 1977. m. free with subscription to Sounds Australian Journal. Australian Music Centre Ltd., P.O. Box N690, Grosvenor Pl., N.S.W. 2000, Australia. TEL 61-2-241-2873. FAX 61-2-241-2873. E-mail: amc@slim.slnsw.gov.au. Ed. Cathy Brown-Watt. adv.; bk.rev. circ. 1,200. **Document type:** bulletin.
 Formerly (until 1987): A M C News.
 Description: Covers current events in Australian music: concerts, performances, competitions, festivals, etc.

781.64   US
SOUNDS OF DEATH MAGAZINE. 1991. s-a. $15. Independent Media International, Inc., 1069 Pinegate Dr., Kirkwood, MO 63122. TEL 314-966-0976. FAX 314-822-2721. E-mail: sodmag@aol.com. Ed. David Horn. adv.: page $900; trim 8 1/4 x 10 3/4; adv. contact: David Horn. film rev.; music rev.; illus. circ. 10,000. (back issues avail.) **Document type:** consumer publication.
 Description: Covers the death metal subgenre of heavy metal rock.

786 778.5   BE   ISSN 0771-6303
SOUNDTRACK!. Key Title: Soundtrack! Incorporating CinemaScore. 1975. q. 600 BEF($20) Belgian Film Music Society v.z.w., Astridlaan 171, B-2800 Mechelen, Belgium. TEL 15-41-41-07. (Subscr. in U.S. to: Roger Feigelson, 145 N. El Camino Real, No. 210, San Mateo, CA 94401) Ed. Luc Van de Ven. adv.: B&W page 7000 BEF; adv. contact: Daniel Mangodt. bk.rev.; rec.rev.; film rev. circ. 2,400. **Indexed:** Film Lit.Ind. (1983-), Int.Ind.Film Per. **Document type:** consumer publication.
—BLDSC (8330.555000); UnCover.
 Incorporates: CinemaScore (ISSN 0277-9803); Former titles: Soundtrack! The Collector's Quarterly; (until vol.6, 1980): Soundtrack Collector's Newsletter.

780 621.389   US   ISSN 1042-0649
SOUNDTRACK. 1988. bi-m. $75. (Independent Music Association) Soundtrack Publishing, 317 Skyline Lake Dr., Box 609, Ringwood, NJ 07456. TEL 201-831-1317. FAX 201-831-8672. Ed. Don Kulak; Pub. Don Kulak. adv. contact: Mark Wilkins. bk.rev. circ. 10,000. (back issues avail.) **Indexed:** Int.Ind.Film Per. **Document type:** trade publication.
 Description: Provides promotion, marketing and distribution information for independent record labels and retailers. Covers cooperative marketing programs, and cooperative advertising programs with record retailers.

780   US
THE SOURCE (MORRIS). q. Box 586, Morris, IL 61054.

780   US
THE SOURCE (NEW YORK, 1988); the magazine of hip-hop music, culture & politics. 1988. m. $19.95 (Canada $40.95; elsewhere $69.95); newsstand price: $2.95. 594 Broadway, Ste. 510, New York, NY 10012-3233. TEL 212-274-0464; 800-827-0172. FAX 212-274-8334. Ed. Bakari KicWana; Pub. David Mays. adv.: B&W page $6300, color page $8120; trim 8 1/2 x 10 7/8. illus.; circ. 113,548 (paid). **Document type:** consumer publication.

780 975   US
SOURCES OF MUSIC AND THEIR INTERPRETATION, DUKE STUDIES IN MUSIC. 1987. irreg. price varies. Duke University Press, Box 90660, Durham, NC 27708-0660. TEL 919-687-3600. FAX 919-688-4574. Ed. Peter Williams. **Document type:** academic/scholarly publication.

780 616.89   SA   ISSN 1012-2850
SOUTH AFRICAN JOURNAL OF MUSIC THERAPY/SUID-AFRIKAANSE TYDSKRIF VIR MUSIEKTERAPIE. (Text in English) 1982. 3/yr. R.40 (effective 1996). Music Therapy Society of Southern Africa, P.O. Box 361, Florida Hills 1716, South Africa. TEL 27-11-672-2111. (Co-sponsor: Southern African Music Rights Organization) Ed. Jeanne Bull. bk.rev.; film rev.; bibl.; charts; illus.; cum.index. circ. 250. (back issues avail.) **Indexed:** RILM.
 Description: Music for therapeutic purposes.

780.01   SA   ISSN 0258-509X
ML5
SOUTH AFRICAN JOURNAL OF MUSICOLOGY/SUID-AFRIKAANSE TYDSKRIF VIR MUSIEKWETENSKAP. (Text in Afrikaans, English) 1981. a. R.40($20) Musicological Society of Southern Africa, P.O. Box 29958, Sunnyside, Pretoria 0132, South Africa. Ed. R.W. Walton. bk.rev.; cum.index. circ. 300. (back issues avail.) **Indexed:** RILM.

780.7   SA   ISSN 0038-2493
ML5
SOUTH AFRICAN MUSIC TEACHER/SUID-AFRIKAANSE MUSIEKONDERWYSER. (Text in Afrikaans, English) 1931. s-a. free. South African Society of Music Teachers, 20 Erica Pl., Bergvliet 7945, South Africa. TEL 27-21-72-4682. Ed. Michael Whiteman. adv.; bk.rev.; music rev.; circ. 2,000 (controlled). **Indexed:** Ind.S.A.Per., Music Ind., RILM. **Document type:** trade publication.
 Description: Presents information and articles of interest and use to music teachers in South Africa.

SOUTH DAKOTA MUSICIAN. see *EDUCATION*

MUSIC 4885

784 US
SOUTHEASTERN HISTORICAL KEYBOARD SOCIETY. NEWSLETTER. Issued with: Early Keyboard Journal (ISSN 0899-8132) irreg. (approx. 2/yr.) $25 membership (institutions $30; students $12.50) (includes Early Keyboard Journal) (effective Jul. 1994-Jul. 1996). Southeastern Historical Keyboard Society & Midwestern Historical Keyboard Society, Box 32022, Charlotte, NC 28232-2022. TEL 910-842-4322. FAX 910-560-6437. E-mail: kjacob@cybernetics.net. Ed. Karen Jacob. circ. 500. **Document type:** academic/scholarly publication.

780.7 US ISSN 1047-9635
ML1
SOUTHEASTERN JOURNAL OF MUSIC EDUCATION. 1989. a. Georgia Center for Continuing Education, Ste. 295, University of Georgia, Athens, GA 30602.

780.7 US ISSN 0162-380X
SOUTHWESTERN MUSICIAN COMBINED WITH THE TEXAS MUSIC EDUCATOR. 1935. m. (Aug.-May). $15. Texas Music Educators Association, Box 49469, Austin, TX 78765. TEL 512-452-0710. FAX 512-451-9213. Ed. Robert Floyd. adv.; bk.rev.; illus.; index. circ. 8,900. (processed; also avail. in microfiche; reprint service avail. from UMI)
—UMI; UnCover.
  Formerly: Southwestern Musician (ISSN 0038-4895); **Incorporates:** Texas Music Educator.

780 SP
SPAIN. DIRECCION GENERAL DE BELLAS ARTES. SEMANA DE MUSICA EN LA NAVIDAD. irreg. Direccion General de Bellas Artes, Murcia, Spain. illus.

780 IT ISSN 0038-7401
SPETTATORE MUSICALE.* 1966. bi-m. L.3000. Via Nizza 45, 00198 Rome, Italy. Ed.Bd. circ. 1,100.

781.64 808
SPILLED GUTS. bi-m. $10. 12 White Oak Way, Trenton, NJ 08618. Ed. Chris Wagner. adv. contact: Chris Wagner. bk.rev.; music rev. **Document type:** newsletter.
  Description: Covers modern and alternative rock and punk music. Publishes poetry and art reviews.

789.9 US ISSN 0886-3032
ML3533.8
SPIN. 1985. m. $18. Camouflage Associates, 6 W. 18th St., New York, NY 10011. TEL 212-633-8200; 800-829-9093. FAX 212-633-2668. Ed. Bob Guccione, Jr. adv. contact: David Rheins. bk.rev. circ. 400,000. (also avail. in microform from UMI) **Indexed:** Access (1986-). **Document type:** consumer publication.
—UMI; UnCover.
  Description: Aimed at music fans between the ages of 18 and 34. Covers the artists, sounds, styles, attitudes and social issues important to trendsetting young adults.

780 PL
SPOTKANIA (KRAKOW). 1985. irreg. price varies. Polskie Wydawnictwo Muzyczne, Al. Krasinskiego 11, 31-111 Krakow, Poland. TEL 48-12-227044. FAX 48-12-220174. adv. contact: Teresa Wlochynska.
  Description: Literary text connected with music, engravings and musical text.

780 YU ISSN 0490-6659
SRPSKA AKADEMIJA NAUKA I UMETNOSTI. ODELJENJE LIKOVNE I MUZICKE UMETNOSTI. MUZICKA IZDANJA. 1953. irreg. exchange basis. Srpska Akademija Nauka i Umetnosti, Odeljenje Likovne i Muzicke Umetnosti, Knez Mihailova 35, 11001 Belgrade, Serbia, Yugoslavia. FAX 38-11-182-825. TELEX 72593 SANU YU. (Dist. by: Prosveta Export Import Terazije 16, 11001 Belgrade, Serbia, Yugoslavia) circ. 300.

SRPSKA AKADEMIJA NAUKA I UMETNOSTI. ODELJENJE LIKOVNE I MUZICKE UMETNOSTI. POSEBNA IZDANJA. see ART

780 US
STACKHOUSE - ROOSTER BLUES NEWSLETTER. 1989. a. free. Stackhouse - Rooster Blues Records, 232 Sunflower Ave., Clarkside, MS 38614. TEL 601-627-2209. FAX 601-627-9861. Ed. Jim O'Neal; Pub. Jim O'Neal. circ. 10,000. **Document type:** newsletter.
  Description: Gives news, descriptions and commentary about the blues in the Mississippi Delta.

780 US ISSN 1042-9409
ML3469
STAGE & STUDIO. 1980. m. $18. Testa Communications, Inc., 25 Willowdale Ave., Port Washington, NY 11050. TEL 516-767-2500. FAX 516-767-9335. Ed. Robert Seidenberg. adv. circ. 78,000.
  Formerly (until 1989): Music and Sound Output (ISSN 0273-8902)

783 US ISSN 0196-2337
ML1
STANZA. vol.2, 1978. s-a. membership. Hymn Society in the United States and Canada, Headquarters, Texas Christian University, Box 30854, Fort Worth, TX 76129. TEL 817-921-7608. illus. **Document type:** newsletter.

STAR GUIDE (YEAR); where to contact movie, TV stars and other celebrities. see MOTION PICTURES

780 RU
STARS OF MUSIC WORLD. a. 5 Rub. Izdatel'stvo Muzyka, Ul. Neglinnaya 13, Moscow 103031, Russia. TEL 924-81-63. FAX 921-83-53.

780 RU
STARS OF WORLD VARIETY. a. 3.50 Rub. Izdatel'stvo Muzyka, Ul. Neglinnaya 14, Moscow 103031, Russia. TEL 924-81-63. FAX 921-83-53.

780 069 US ISSN 1046-4387
STEARNS NEWSLETTER; the Stearns collection of musical instruments at the University of Michigan. 1986. 3/yr. $30. University of Michigan, School of Music, Ann Arbor, MI 48109. TEL 313-763-4389. FAX 313-763-5097. Ed. James Borders. circ. 400. (back issues avail.) **Document type:** newspaper.
  Description: Contains articles about the Stearns lectures and research on its holdings of over 2,000 instruments worldwide.

780 CN ISSN 1199-8091
ML26
STEFAN WOLPE SOCIETY NEWSLETTER. 1991. q. Stefan Wolpe Society Inc., 035 McLaughlin, York University, North York, ON M3J 1P3, Canada. Ed.Bd. bibl. **Document type:** newsletter.
  Description: Provides a forum for musicians, scholars and the general public interested in the music of Stefan Wolpe. Acts as a medium for news and views, short articles and reviews and as a means of publicizing new publications and coming events.

STEREO. see SOUND RECORDING AND REPRODUCTION

STEREO REVIEW. see SOUND RECORDING AND REPRODUCTION

789.91 US ISSN 0585-2544
TK7881.8
STEREOPHILE; for the high-fidelity stereo perfectionist. 1962. 12/yr. $35 in the U.S. and Canada (foreign $75) (effective 1995). Box 5529, Santa Fe, NM 87502. TEL 505-982-2366. FAX 505-989-8791. E-mail: John Atkinson 74472,255@CompuServe.com. (Subscr. to: Stereophile, Box 469027, Escondido, CA 92046-9901. TEL 619-745-2809) Ed. John Atkinson Jr.; Pub. Larry Archibald. adv.; bk.rev.; index; circ. 60,000. (paid) **Document type:** consumer publication.

780 GR ISSN 1105-1345
STEREOPHONY AND MUSIC. 1975. a. Technical Press, S.A., 31 Praxitelous St., 167 77 Athens, Greece. TEL 30-1-9961-861. FAX 30-1-9961-864. Ed. Sophie Cavvatha; Pub. Costas Cavvathas. circ. 15,000. **Document type:** consumer publication.
  Description: Guide for purchasing of hi-fi equipment.

780 GW ISSN 0172-388X
STEREOPLAY; das internationale HiFi-Magazin. 1979. m. DM.90; newsstand price: DM.8.50. Vereinigte Motor-Verlage GmbH und Co. KG, Leuschnerstr. 1, 70174 Stuttgart, Germany. TEL 0711-18201. FAX 0711-1821669. (Subscr. to: Postfach 106036, 70049 Stuttgart, Germany) Ed. Karl Breh; Pub. Uwe Hagen. adv.: B&W page DM.8200, color page DM.15170; trim 185 x 248; adv. contact: Peter Michael Heyde. charts; illus. circ. 61,726. **Indexed:** Music Ind. **Document type:** consumer publication.
—UMI.
  Incorporates: HiFi Stereophonie (ISSN 0018-1382); Which was formerly: HiFi Stereopraxis.

STERN'S PERFORMING ARTS DIRECTORY; catalogue of classical music and dance artists and attractions, programs, resources and services. see DANCE

780 US
STILL NO SYMPTOMS.* q.? $2.50 per no. 75 Middle Rd., Guilford, CT 06437-1766. Eds. Liz Colker, Dave Cunningham.
  Description: Covers the controversial pop music bands.

780 SW ISSN 0283-3190
STIM NYTT. 1984. s-a. free. Swedish Performing Rights Society, P.O. Box 27327, S-102 54 Stockholm, Sweden. Ed. Margita Jardfelt. charts; illus. circ. 24,000.
  Formerly: Ord och Ton.

780 UK
STIRRINGS FOLK AND ACOUSTIC MUSIC. 1974. q. £5($15) 28 Montgomery Ave., Sheffield, S. Yorkshire S7 1NZ, England. TEL 0114-2589182. E-mail: ah98@cityscupe.co.uk. Ed. Trevor Sommers. adv.: B&W page £40. circ. 700. **Document type:** bulletin.
  Description: Covers regional folk song and dance.

STOHOLOSNYK/STOGOLOSNIK; aktualna svitova kultura. see ART

787.01 UK ISSN 0039-2049
ML5
STRAD; a monthly journal for professionals and amateurs of all stringed instruments played with the bow. 1890. m. £35($75) Orpheus Publications Ltd., 7 St. John's Rd., Harrow, Middlesex HA1 2EE, England. TEL 0181-863-2020. FAX 0181-863-2444. Ed. Brian Yule. adv. contact: Nicola Wildin. bk.rev.; music rev.; rec.rev.; illus. circ. 11,000. (also avail. in microform from UMI,WMP; reprint service avail. from UMI) **Indexed:** Arts & Hum.Cit.Ind., Br.Hum.Ind., Curr.Cont., Music Ind. **Document type:** consumer publication.
—BLDSC (8467.600000); Faxon; UnCover.

STREET ARTISTS' NEWSLETTER. see ART

780 CN ISSN 0841-2650
STREETSOUND; North America's international D.J. authority. 1988. m. Can.$2.98. 174 Spadina Ave., Ste. 506, Toronto, Ont. M5T 2C2, Canada. TEL 416-369-0070. FAX 416-369-1702. Ed. Michael Mannix. adv.; bk.rev. circ. 16,000.

787 US ISSN 0888-3106
ML749.5
STRINGS; the magazine for players and makers of bowed instruments. 1986. bi-m. $42 (Canada $50.75; elsewhere $59.50) (effective July 1995). String Letter Press, Inc., Box 767, San Anselmo, CA 94979-0767. TEL 415-485-6946. FAX 415-485-0831. E-mail: strings1@aol.com. Ed. Mary Van Clay; Pub. David A. Listerman. adv. contact: Jeff Jensen. bk.rev. circ. 15,000. **Indexed:** Music Artic.Guide, Music Ind. **Document type:** consumer publication.
—UMI; UnCover.
  Description: Directed to the practicing and performing musician who wants to play with greater knowledge and craft.

MUSIC

781.6 973.34   DK   ISSN 0906-1061
STRINGS AND SQUARES; bladet for traditionel amerikansk musik og dans i Danmark. 1984. bi-m. DKK 40 (typically set in Oct.). Strings and Squares, c/o Margot Gunzenhause, Hasselvej 18, DK-2830 Virum, Denmark. TEL 45-83-99-83. (Subscr. to: Bent Hjortshoej, Gedevasevej 17, DK-3520 Farum, Denmark) (Co-sponsors: Oldtime, Bluegrass & Country i Danmark; Midtjysk Old Time Music Association; Dansk-Amerikansk Folkemusik Forening; Square Dance Partners) Ed. Palle Aabom. adv.; bk.rev.; illus, rec.rev. circ. 1,000. **Document type:** newsletter.
  Former titles: Lydhullet (ISSN 0109-2480) & Broken Strings (ISSN 0107-4172)
  Description: Covers square and contra dancing, bluegrass, and old-time music events in Denmark.

781.91   IT   ISSN 0039-260X
STRUMENTI & MUSICA. 1947. m. L.3000. Berben Editore, Via Redipuglia 65, 60100 Ancona, Italy. Ed. Bio Boccosi. adv.

780   IT   ISSN 0392-890X
STRUMENTI MUSICALI. 1979. m. (11/yr.) L.53900 (foreign L.107800). Gruppo Editoriale Jackson S.p.A., Via M. Gorki 69, 2092 Cinisello B. (MI), Italy. TEL 39-2-660341. FAX 39-2-66034238. Ed. Pierantonio Palerma. adv.; B&W page L.23000000, color page L.3100000; trim 210 x 280. circ. 11,938.
  Description: Offers special reports, audiotests, reviews and monographs about acoustic and electronic instruments. Also includes interviews with famous musicians.

780   IT   ISSN 0394-4417
STUDI DI MUSICA VENETA. 1968. irreg., no.21, 1994. price varies. (Fondazione Giorgio Cini) Casa Editrice Leo S. Olschki, Casella Postale 66, 50100 Florence, Italy. TEL 39-55-6530684. FAX 39-55-6530214. **Document type:** monographic series.

780   IT
STUDI DI MUSICA VENETA. QUADERNI VIVALDIANI. 1980. irreg., no.7, 1992. price varies. (Fondazione Giorgio Cini) Casa Editrice Leo S. Olschki, Casella Postale 66, 50100 Florence, Italy. TEL 39-55-6530684. FAX 39-55-6530214. **Document type:** monographic series.

780.903   IT   ISSN 1122-0686
STUDI E TESTI PER LA STORIA DELLA MUSICA. 1979. irreg., no.10, 1994. price varies. Casa Editrice Leo S. Olschki, Casella Postale 66, 50100 Florence, Italy. TEL 39-55-6530684. FAX 39-55-6530214. **Document type:** monographic series.

780   IT   ISSN 0391-7789
STUDI MUSICALI. 1972. s-a. L.74000 (foreign L.95000) (effective 1995) US $65.50 (effective 1996). (Accademia Nazionale di Santa Cecilia di Roma) Casa Editrice Leo S. Olschki, Casella Postale 66, 50100 Florence, Italy. TEL 39-55-6530684. FAX 39-55-6530214. Ed. Nino Pirrotta. bk.rev. circ. 1,000. **Indexed:** Arts & Hum.Cit.Ind., RILM. **Document type:** academic/scholarly publication.
  —Genuine Article.

STUDI PIEMONTESI. see *LITERATURE*

782.1   IT   ISSN 0393-2532
STUDI VERDIANI. (Text in English, German, Italian) 1982. a. L.30000($15) Istituto Nazionale di Studi Verdiani, Strada della Repubblica 56, 43100 Parma, Italy.

780   PL
STUDIA I MATERIALY DO DZIEJOW MUZYKI POLSKIEJ. 1955. irreg. price varies. Polskie Wydawnictwo Muzyczne, Al. Krasinskiego 11a, 31-111 Krakow, Poland. TEL 48-12-227044. FAX 48-12-220174. Ed. Tadeusz Strumillo. adv. contact: Teresa Wlochynska. **Document type:** academic/scholarly publication, monographic series.
  Description: Covers Polish composers' lives and work.

780.01   HU   ISSN 0039-3266
STUDIA MUSICOLOGICA ACADEMIAE SCIENTIARUM HUNGARICAE. (Text in English, French, German, Italian, Russian) 1961. 2/yr. $84 (effective 1992). (Magyar Tudomanyos Akademia) Akademiai Kiado, Publishing House of the Hungarian Academy of Sciences, P.O. Box 245, H-1519 Budapest, Hungary. TEL 181-2134. FAX 166-6466. TELEX 22-6228 ANKYO H. Ed. Jozsef Ujfalussy. adv.; bk.rev.; bibl.; charts; index. **Indexed:** Music Ind., RILM. **Document type:** academic/scholarly publication.
  —UnCover. CCC.
  Description: Publishes papers on Hungarian musicology, including topics of music history. Includes reports on congresses, musical notes and records.

780.9481   NO   ISSN 0332-5024
ML3797.1
STUDIA MUSICOLOGICA NORVEGICA. (Text in English, German, Norwegian; summaries in English) 1968. a. NOK 250 in Nordic countries; elsewhere $47 (effective 1996). Scandinavian University Press, P.O. Box 2959-Toeyen, NO-0608 Oslo, Norway. (U.S. addr.: Scandinavian University Press, 200 Meecham Ave., Elmont, NY 11003. TEL 516-352-7300) Ed. Arvid O. Vollsnes. circ. 300. **Indexed:** Music Ind., RILM.
  —CCC.
  Description: Music studies, both general and Norwegian, including the history of music, ethnomusicology, analysis and theory.
  Refereed Serial

780   SW   ISSN 0081-6744
STUDIA MUSICOLOGICA UPSALIENSIA. NOVA SERIES. (1952-58, vols. 1-8; 1965 designated as Nova Series and issued in Acta Universitatis Upsaliensis) irreg. price varies. (Uppsala Universitet) A W I International AB, P.O. Box 4627, S-116 91 Stockholm, Sweden. TEL 468-640-8800. FAX 468-641-1180. Ed. Ingmar Bengtsson.

780   GW   ISSN 0177-7904
STUDIEN UND MATERIALEN ZUR MUSIKWISSENSCHAFT. 1984. irreg., vol.10, 1994. price varies. Georg Olms Verlag, Hagentorwall 7, 31134 Hildesheim, Germany. TEL 05121-1501-0. FAX 05121-150150. (US subscr. to: 111 W. 57th St., New York, NY 10019. TEL 212-757-5237) **Document type:** monographic series.

780   GW   ISSN 0177-7904
STUDIEN ZUR MUSIK. 1982. irreg., vol.14. DM.98. Wilhelm Fink Verlag, Ohmstr. 5, 80802 Munich, Germany. TEL 089-348017. FAX 089-341378. **Document type:** monographic series.

780   GW   ISSN 0081-7341
STUDIEN ZUR MUSIKGESCHICHTE DES NEUNZEHNTEN JAHRHUNDERTS. irreg. price varies. Gustav Bosse Verlag, Heinrich-Schuetz-Allee 35, 34131 Kassel, Germany. TEL 0561-31050. Ed. Berthold Kloss. **Document type:** monographic series.

780.01   GW   ISSN 0930-9578
STUDIEN ZUR MUSIKWISSENSCHAFT; Beihefte der Denkmaeler der Tonkunst in Oesterreich. biennial. Verlag Dr. Hans Schneider GmbH, Mozartstr. 6, 82323 Tutzing, Germany. TEL 08158-3050. FAX 08158-7636. Ed. Othmar Wessely. **Indexed:** RILM. **Document type:** academic/scholarly publication.

780   HU   ISSN 0237-9996
STUDIES IN CENTRAL AND EASTERN EUROPEAN MUSIC. (Text in English) 1967. irreg., vol.5, 1991. price varies. (Magyar Tudomanyos Akademia) Akademiai Kiado, Publishing House of the Hungarian Academy of Sciences, P.O. Box 245, H-1519 Budapest, Hungary. TEL 181-2134. FAX 166-6466. TELEX 22-6228 ANKYO H. Ed. Zoltan Falvy.
  Formerly (until 1980): Musicologica Hungarica (ISSN 0077-2488)

780   CN   ISSN 0703-3052
ML5
STUDIES IN MUSIC. 1976. a. University of Western Ontario, Department of Music History, London, ON, Canada. Ed. Robert Toft. circ. 300. **Indexed:** Music Ind. **Document type:** academic/scholarly publication.

780.9   US   ISSN 0898-0144
STUDIES IN THE HISTORY AND INTERPRETATION OF MUSIC. 1980. irreg., latest no.46. $49.95 per no. Edwin Mellen Press, 415 Ridge St., Box 450, Lewiston, NY 14092. TEL 716-754-2788. FAX 716-754-4056. **Document type:** monographic series.
  —BLDSC (8490.650600).

781.7   JA   ISSN 0039-3851
ML5
STUDIES ON ORIENTAL MUSIC/TOYO ONGAKU KENKYU. (Text in Japanese; summaries in English) 1937. price varies. Japan Publications Trading Co. Ltd., Box 5030, Tokyo International, Tokyo 100-31, Japan. (Or: 1255 Howard St., San Francisco, CA 94103) Ed. Masao Tanabe. adv.; bk.rev.; illus. circ. 4,000. **Indexed:** RILM.

STUDII SI CERCETARI DE ISTORIA ARTEI. SERIA TEATRU, MUZICA, CINEMATOGRAFIE/STUDIES AND RESEARCH IN ART HISTORY. SERIES: THEATRE, MUSIC, CINEMATOGRAPHY. see *THEATER*

THE STUDIO. see *EDUCATION — Teaching Methods And Curriculum*

780   US
SUBURBAN VOICE. 1982. q. $3.50 per issue. Al Quint, Ed. & Pub., Box 2746, Lynn, MA 01903. TEL 617-596-1570. adv. contact: Al Quint. bk.rev.; music rev.; rec.rev. circ. 4,000. **Document type:** consumer publication.
  Description: Provides coverage of punk rock and other energetic musical forms. Includes interviews and editorial commentary.

SUOSIKKI. see *CHILDREN AND YOUTH — For*

780   US
SUPERDOPE. 1991. irreg., no.7, 1994. $3 per issue. 520 Frederick St., Box 33, San Francisco, CA 94117. adv.; bk.rev. circ. 1,600.

781.64   US   ISSN 1054-0180
SUPERSTAR SPECIAL. bi-m. newsstand price: $2.95. Sterling - MacFadden Partnership, 233 Park Ave. S., New York, NY 10003. TEL 212-780-3500. FAX 212-780-3555. adv. **Document type:** consumer publication.

780   II
SURCHHANDA. (Text in Bengali) 1955. m. Rs.30. Nilratan Banerji, Ed. & Pub., Nirala, 2B, Jadar Ghosh Bye Lane, Calcutta 700 061, India. adv.; bk.rev.; illus. circ. 1,200.

367 781.7   US
SUZI DEVERAUX INTERNATIONAL FAN CLUB. 1975. q. $5. 201 Waters Ave., Watertown, TN 37184. TEL 615-237-3020. Ed. Cheryl Ellison. circ. 2,000. (back issues avail.)
  Description: For country music fans interested in Suzi Deveraux's career.

780.01   SW   ISSN 0081-9816
ML5
SVENSK TIDSKRIFT FOER MUSIKFORSKNING/SWEDISH JOURNAL OF MUSICOLOGY/SCHWEDISCHE ZEITSCHRIFT FUER MUSIKFORSCHUNG. Abbreviated title: S T M. (Text in Swedish; occasionally in English and German; summaries in English) 1919. a. SEK 200. (Avdelingen foer Musikvetenskap) Svenska Samfundet foer Musikforskning, Musikhoegskolan i Goeteborg, Avdelingen foer Musikvetenskap, P.O. Box 5439, S-402 29 Goeteborg, Sweden. TEL 031-773-40-86. FAX 031-773-40-89. Eds. Hans Bernskioeld, Ola Stockfelt. adv.; bk.rev.; index, cum.index: 1919-68 (vols. 1-50). circ. 900. **Indexed:** Arts & Hum.Cit.Ind., Curr.Cont., Music Ind., RILM. **Document type:** academic/scholarly publication.
  Description: Consists of articles covering various fields of musicology. Reports are given of unpublished theses in musicology, of research projects and congresses. Also a review section on literature and scholarly editions of music.

780   SW   ISSN 0081-9824
SVENSK VISARKIV. HANDLINGAR. 1967. irreg. SEK 120. A W I International AB, P.O. Box 4627, S-116 91 Stockholm, Sweden. TEL 468-40-8800. FAX 468-461-1180.

780 SW ISSN 0081-9832
SVENSK VISARKIV. MEDDELANDEN. (Text in English and Swedish) irreg. SEK 5. A W I International AB, P.O. Box 4627, S-116 91 Stockholm, Sweden. TEL 468-640-8800. FAX 468-641-1180.

780 SW ISSN 0081-9840
SVENSK VISARKIV. SKRIFTER. 1958. irreg. price varies. A W I International AB, P.O. Box 4627, S-116 91 Stockholm, Sweden. TEL 468-640-8800. FAX 468-641-1180.

780 016 SW ISSN 0586-0709
SVENSKT MUSIKHISTORISKT ARKIV. BULLETIN. (Text in Swedish; glossary in English) 1966. irreg. (approx. 1/yr.) SEK 45. Svenskt Musikhistoriskt Arkiv, Box 16326, S-103 26 Stockholm, Sweden. TEL 8-6664560. circ. 300. Indexed: RILM.
Description: Acquisitions and holdings of the Svenskt Musikhistoriskt Arkiv.

780 CI ISSN 1330-2531
SVETA CECILIJA; casopis za duhovnu glazbu. 1877. q. (Institut za Crkvenu Glazbu u Zagrebu) Hrvatsko Knjizevno Drustvo Cirila i Metoda, Trg Kralja Tomislava 21, 41000 Zagreb, Croatia. TEL 041-431-950. Ed. A. Milanovic. adv.; bk.rev.; illus. circ. 1,200. Indexed: RILM.

781.57 JA ISSN 0039-744X
SWING JOURNAL. (Text in Japanese) 1947. m. 18000 Yen. Swing Journal Co. Ltd., 3-6-24, Shibakoen, Minato-ku, Tokyo 105, Japan. FAX 03-3432-7758. Ed. Kiyoshi Koyama. adv.; bk.rev.; rec.rev.; illus. circ. 250,000.

782.1 792 AT ISSN 0811-0050
SYDNEY OPERA HOUSE. DIARY. 1973. bi-m. $12 (foreign Aus.$20). Sydney Opera House Trust, G.P.O. Box 4274, Sydney, N.S.W. 2001, Australia. TEL 02-250-7414. FAX 02-252-1161. Ed. Charlotte Faunce. circ. 50,000. (back issues avail.) **Document type:** bulletin.
Formerly (until 1983): Sydney Opera House. Monthly Dairy (ISSN 0311-9246)
Description: Calendar of events containing performance details and information on all Sydney Opera House events and facilities.

786 AT ISSN 0817-2285
SYDNEY ORGAN JOURNAL. 1970. bi-m. Aus.$27 membership. Organ Society of Sydney, Box 2348, G.P.O., Sydney, N.S.W. 2001, Australia. Ed. G. Bock. adv.; bk.rev. circ. 700.

780 IT ISSN 1120-9909
SYMPHONIA. Spanish edition (ISSN 1120-9917) 1990. m. L.159000 (foreign L.208000). Ermitage s.r.l., Piazza Trento Trieste 1, 40137 Bologna, Italy. TEL 051-341754. FAX 051-342220. Ed. Alberto Spano. adv.; color page L.4750000; adv. contact: Marco Ultrocchi. circ. 30,000.

785.066 US ISSN 1046-3232
ML1
SYMPHONY. 1948. bi-m. $35 includes membership. American Symphony Orchestra League, 1156 15th St., N.W., Ste. 800, Washington, DC 20005-1704. TEL 202-628-0099. FAX 202-783-7228. Ed. Sandra Hyslop. adv.; bk.rev.; bibl.; charts; illus.; stat.; tr.lit.; index. circ. 17,000. (also avail. in microform from UMI; back issues avail; reprint service avail. from UMI) Indexed: Music Artic.Guide, Music Ind. **Document type:** trade publication.
—UMI; UnCover.
Former titles (until 1989): Symphony Magazine (ISSN 0271-2687); (until Apr. 1980): Symphony News (ISSN 0090-5380); American Symphony Orchestra League. Newsletter (ISSN 0003-1372)
Description: Provides news of the orchestra field, the music world, and the League itself.

780 US ISSN 0275-9381
ML27.U5
SYMPHONY GOLD BOOK. a. $28 to members; non-members $42. American Symphony Orchestra League, 1156 15th St., N.W., Ste. 800, Washington, DC 20005-1702. TEL 202-628-0099. FAX 202-783-7228. circ. 650. **Document type:** corporate report.
Description: A compendium of successful volunteer projects in the areas of ticket sales, fundraising, and educational programs.

780 PL
SYNTEZY. 1972. irreg. price varies. Polskie Wydawnictwo Muzyczne, Al. Krasinskiego 11a, 31-111 Krakow, Poland. TEL 48-12-227044. FAX 48-12-220174. adv. contact: Teresa Wlochynska. **Document type:** monographic series.
Description: Covers history of music, composers.

780 PL ISSN 0239-9148
SZKICE O KULTURZE MUZYCZNEJ XIX WIEKU. STUDIA I MATERIALY. (Text in Polish; summaries in English) irreg., vol.4, 1981. price varies. Polska Akademia Nauk, Instytut Sztuki, Ul. Dluga 28, 00-950 Warsaw, Poland. TEL 48-22-313271. FAX 48-22-313149. Ed. Z. Chechlinska. charts; illus.

T R U K P A C T INFO. (Transvaalse Raad vir die Uitvoerende Kunste) see THEATER

780.6 US ISSN 0363-4787
ML1
T.U.B.A. JOURNAL. 1973. 4/yr. $25 for libraries. Tubists Universal Brotherhood Association, 444 North County St., Waukegan, IL 60085. Ed. Tom Gillette. adv.; bk.rev.; bibl.; charts; illus.; tr.lit.; index. circ. 1,800. (back issues avail.)
—UnCover.
Formerly: T.U.B.A. Newsletter (ISSN 0363-4779)

780 GW ISSN 0082-1969
TASCHENBUECHER ZUR MUSIKWISSENSCHAFT. 1969. irreg., vol.120, 1993. price varies. Florian Noetzel Verlag, Heinrichshofen Buecher, Valoisstr. 11, 26382 Wilhelmshaven, Germany. (Dist. in U.S. by: C. F. Peters Corp., 373 Park Ave. S., New York, N.Y. 10016) Ed. Richard Schaal. **Document type:** monographic series.

780 US ISSN 1069-7446
TEACHING MUSIC. 1993. 6/yr. $60. Music Educators National Conference, 1806 Robert Fulton Dr., Reston, VA 22091. TEL 703-860-4000. FAX 703-860-1531. Ed. Elizabeth Hoffman. (also avail. in microform from UMI)
—UMI; UnCover.
Description: Presents Association news and brief, practical features for the classroom.

TEATRO E STORIA. see THEATER

780 US
TECHNOLOGY WORKS. bi-m. $2 per no. Box 477, Placentia, CA 92670-0477. Ed. Paul Moore.
Description: Covers the movement of new rock music.

TEEN BEAT. see CHILDREN AND YOUTH — For

TEEN BEAT ALLSTARS. see CHILDREN AND YOUTH — For

TEEN STAR ZINE; a newsletter for 10-18 year olds who love the performing arts. see CHILDREN AND YOUTH — For

781.57 SZ
TELEJAZZ (YEAR); schweizer Jazz Handbuch. (Text in German) 1986. a. 20 SFr. Jazztime-Verlag, CH-5430 Wettingen, Switzerland. TEL 056-272141. FAX 056-272601. Ed. Eduard Keller. **Document type:** consumer publication.

TELLUS; the audio magazine series of experimental and innovative sound. see LITERARY AND POLITICAL REVIEWS

780 UK ISSN 0040-2982
ML5
TEMPO (LONDON, 1939); a quarterly review of modern music. 1939. q. £13 (foreign £14.50) (effectie 1996). Boosey & Hawkes Music Publishers Ltd., 295 Regent St., London W1R 8JH, England. (U.S. addr.: Boosey & Hawkes, Inc., Oceanside, NY 11572) Ed. C. MacDonald. adv.; bk.rev.; rec.rev.; charts; illus. Indexed: Br.Hum.Ind., Ind.Bk.Rev.Hum., Music Ind., RILM.
—BLDSC (8790.042000); Faxon; SWETS; UnCover.

780.1 US ISSN 0040-3334
TENNESSEE MUSICIAN. 1948. q. $6 to non-members. Tennessee Music Educators Association, c/o Carl H. Kauffman, Ed., 500 Holly Hill Ct., Nashville, TN 37221. adv.; bk.rev. circ. 2,130.

372.87 US
TEXAS MUSIC EDUCATION PRIMER. 1993. a. Office of the Governor, Texas Music Office, Box 13246, Austin, TX 78711. TEL 512-463-4114. FAX 512-463-4114. **Document type:** government publication.

THEATER HEUTE. see THEATER

THEATER IN GRAZ. see THEATER

786.6 US ISSN 0040-5531
THEATRE ORGAN. vol.17, 1975. bi-m. $25 membership. American Theatre Organ Society, Box 130463, Houston, TX 77219-0463. FAX 503-777-8081. Ed. Grace McGinnis; Pub. Alden Stockebrand. adv.; bk.rev.; illus.; rec.rev.; index. circ. 6,200.
—UnCover.

786.6 UK ISSN 0040-5558
THEATRE ORGAN REVIEW.* 1947. q. 10s.($3.50) Theatre Organ Review, 127 Stratford St., Leeds LS11 6JG, Yorkshire, England. (U.S. subscr. addr.: Bobby Clark, 939 Green St., Orangeburg, SC 29115) Ed. Frank Hare. adv.; illus.; rec.rev. (tabloid format)

780 US ISSN 1062-4139
THEMATIC CATALOGUES SERIES. (Text in English, French and German) 1972. irreg., no.21, 1995. Pendragon Press, 41 Ferry St., Stuyvesant, NY 12173-9720. TEL 518-828-3008. FAX 518-828-2368. **Document type:** monographic series.

780 US ISSN 0741-6156
THEORY AND PRACTICE. 1975. a. $22 to individuals; institutions $30. Music Theory Society of New York State, Inc., College - Conservatory of Music, University of Cincinnati, Cincinnati, OH 45219. Ed. Severine Neff. bk.rev.; bibl. circ. 250. (back issues avail.) Indexed: RILM. **Document type:** academic/scholarly publication.
—BLDSC (8814.628300); UnCover.

THERE AND BACK: TOUR ORGANIZERS HANDBOOK/ALLER RETOUR: GUIDE DU DIRECTEUR DE TOURNEES. see ART

780 US ISSN 1083-0057
THIS IS THE SPINAL TAP ZINE. a. $4.95. Chip Rowe, Ed. & Pub., Box 11967, Chicago, IL 60611-0967. circ. 800 (paid).
Description: Provides an A-to-Z guide to one of England's loudest bands.

780 GW ISSN 0176-6511
TIBIA; Magazin fuer Freunde alter und neuer Blaesermusik. 1976. 4/yr. DM.33 (foreign DM.37). Moeck Verlag & Musikinstrumentenwerk, Postfach 3131, 29231 Celle, Germany. TEL 05141-8853-0. FAX 05141-885342. Ed.Bd. adv.; bk.rev. circ. 4,000. (back issues avail.) Indexed: RILM. **Document type:** consumer publication.

780.42 SW ISSN 0280-6177
TIDSKRIFT FOER TIDIG MUSIK. 1979. q. SEK 220. Foereningen foer Tidig Musik, Schoenfeldtsgraend 1, S-111 27 Stockholm, Sweden. TEL 46-8-791-46-82. FAX 46-8-791-46-82. Ed. Anna Frisk. circ. 1,500. **Document type:** newsletter, trade publication.

780.9031 NE ISSN 0920-0649
TIJDSCHRIFT VOOR OUDE MUZIEK. 1986. q. fl.40 (foreign fl.65) (effective 1995). Organisatie Oude Muziek, Postbus 734, 3500 AS Utrecht, Netherlands. TEL 31-30-362236. FAX 31-30-322798. Ed. Jolande van der Klis. adv. contact: Jolande van der Klis. bk.rev.; music rev. circ. 5,000. (back issues avail.) Indexed: RILM. **Document type:** academic/scholarly publication, consumer publication.
Description: Covers topics in early music, including historical articles, interviews with performers, and listings of concerts and performances.

780 UK
TOCCATA. 1978. 2/yr. £15 (Europe £20). Leopold Stokowski Society, 12 Market St., Deal, Kent CT1 6HS, England. Ed. C.Ducrotoy. adv.; film rev.; play rev.; rec.rev.; abstr.; bibl.; charts; illus.; tr.lit.; index. circ. 2,500. (back issues avail.) **Document type:** consumer publication.

4888 MUSIC

TON - VIDEO REPORT. see *SOUND RECORDING AND REPRODUCTION*

780   SW   ISSN 0346-329X
TONFALLET. 1968. bi-m. SEK 150. Svenska Rikskonserter - The Swedish Concert Institute, P.O. Box 1225, 111 82 Stockholm, Sweden. FAX 10-99-92. Ed. Cecilia Aare. adv.; bk.rev.; bibl.; illus. circ. 4,000.
  Formerly (until 1969): Informationsbulletin - Rikskonserter.

780.42   CC   ISSN 1003-7322
TONGSU GEQU/POPULAR SONGS. (Text in Chinese) 1987. m. Hebei Sheng Yishu Yanjiusuo - Hebei Art Research Institute, 41, Beima Lu, Shijiazhuang, Hebei 050071, People's Republic of China. TEL 743726. Ed. Li Jiang.

780 920   UK   ISSN 0260-7425
ML410.S587
TONIC. 1980. irreg. £12 (foreign £15). Robert Simpson Society, 24 Regent Close, Fleet, Hampshire GU13 9NS, England. TEL 061-3399099. FAX 061-3082687. Ed. Brian Duke. adv.; bk.rev. circ. 200. (back issues avail.) **Document type:** bulletin.
  Description: Discusses the music of Robert Simpson.

780   UK
TOP. 1987. 10/yr. £15. Tower Records, 62-64 Kensington High St., London W8 4PE, England. TEL 071-938-5388. FAX 071-937-5024. Ed. Hugh Fielder. adv.: color page £1795; adv. contact: Jon Newey. bk.rev.; circ. 60,533 (paid). (back issues avail.) **Document type:** consumer publication.

780.42   CN   ISSN 1194-2878
TOP FORTY FOCUS. 1992. bi-m. Can.$6. Suggitt Publishing Ltd., 17317-107 Ave., Edmonton, AB T5S 1E5, Canada. TEL 403-486-5802. FAX 403-481-9267. Ed. Dave Suggitt; Pub. Thomas Suggitt. adv.; B&W page Can.$1995, color page Can.$2535; trim 8 1/8 x 10 3/4; adv. contact: Rob Suggitt. circ. 40,000.

780.42   KO
TOP 10. (Text in English, Korean) 1990. m. 20 Won($30) Sangji Music Publishing Co., Ltd., 83-4 Guro 2-Dong, Guro-Ku, Seoul, Korea. TEL 82-2-867-4544. FAX 82-2-868-5179. TELEX K24393. Ed. Saehoon Oh. adv. (also avail. in talking book; back issues avail.)
  Description: Includes the top 10 Korean and foreign hit songs in piano and guitar arrangements.

785   CN   ISSN 0849-0910
TORONTO SYMPHONY.* 7/yr. free. National Theatre Publications, 30 St. Clair Ave. W. No. 805, Toronto, ON M4V 3A1, Canada. TEL 416-926-7595. FAX 416-926-0407. circ. 30,000.
  Former titles (until 1988): Toronto Symphony Magazine (ISSN 0829-8068); (until 1986): Toronto Symphony Programme Magazine (ISSN 0822-9090); (until 1983): Toronto Symphony News (ISSN 0822-4870); (until 1982): Toronto Symphony News (ISSN 0225-4689); (until 1965): T S O News (ISSN 0225-4697)

780 791.43   UK   ISSN 0969-8019
TOUCH MAGAZINE. 1990. m. £14.50 (foreign £30). Sunray Promotions Ltd., Studio 606, 8 Nursery Rd., London SW9 8BP, England. TEL 0171-738-7308. FAX 0171-738-6313. (Dist. by: Time Out Distribution, Universal House, 251 Tottenham Court Rd., London W1P 0A5, England. TEL 0171-813-6060) Ed. Jaimie D'Cruz. adv.: color page £1255; adv. contact: Joe Pidgeon. bk.rev.; film rev.; charts; circ. 22,000 (paid). **Document type:** consumer publication.
  Description: Upfront guide to the music and lifestyles of youth culture in the U.K. and worldwide.

786.63   US   ISSN 0041-0330
ML1
TRACKER; journal of American pipe organ progress, history, preservation, organbuilding, and performance. 1956. q. $27. Organ Historical Society, Inc., Box 26811, Richmond, VA 23261. TEL 804-253-9226. FAX 804-353-9266. Ed. John K. Ogaspian. adv.; bk.rev.; charts; illus.; stat.; index. circ. 3,800. (also avail. in microfilm from UMI) **Indexed:** Music Artic.Guide. **Document type:** academic/scholarly publication.
  —Faxon; UMI; UnCover.

781.7   US   ISSN 1071-1864
TRADITION (WALNUT). 1976. bi-m. $15. (National Traditional Country Music Association, Inc.) Prairie Press Ltd., Box 438, Walnut, IA 51577. TEL 712-784-3001. FAX 712-784-2010. Ed. Sheila Everhart. adv.; bk.rev.; film rev.; charts; illus.; cum.index: 1976-1989. circ. 2,500. (back issues avail.) **Document type:** consumer publication, newsletter.
  Description: Publication for acoustic music lovers, supporters, performers, fans, preservationists and promoters of all forms of traditional acoustic music: folk, bluegrass, traditional country, western swing, ragtime, hillbilly, etc.

780   UK   ISSN 0306-7440
ML5
TRADITIONAL MUSIC. 1975. 3/yr. £1.20($3) Alan Ward, Ed. & Pub, 90 St. Julian's Farm Rd., London SE27 ORS, England. adv.; bk.rev.; illus. **Indexed:** M.L.A., Music Ind.

780   US   ISSN 1059-5953
ML3544.5
THE TRADITIONAL MUSICLINE. 1987. m. $17.50 (Canada $20). Stephanie P. Ledgin, Ed. & Pub., Box 10598, New Brunswick, NJ 08906. TEL 908-699-0665. adv.: B&W page $165. circ. 2,500. **Document type:** newsletter, consumer publication, trade publication.
  Description: A comprehensive calendar magazine for traditional folk, bluegrass, blues, Cajun and Celtic music concerts, dances and festivals in a six-state area covering Rhode Island, eastern Pennsylvania, Delaware, New York City and Midstate New York, New Jersey and Connecticut; subscriptions include a semi-annual radio program guide and an annual resource guide of venues and organizations.

780   US   ISSN 1041-7494
ML935
TRAVERSO; baroque flute newsletter. 1989. q. $12 (foreign $15). Folkers & Powell, c/o Ardal Powell, Ed., 49 Rte. 23, Hudson, NY 12534. TEL 518-828-9779. bk.rev. **Document type:** newsletter.
  Description: Covers news, information and ideas for all interested in the baroque flute and its music.

780.42   US
TRAX MUSIC GUIDE. 1985. bi-m. $13. Trax Entertainment, 111 N. La Cienega Blvd., Beverly Hills, CA 90211-2206. TEL 310-659-7852. FAX 310-659-7856. E-mail: trax.usa@aol.com. Pub. Jeff Fishman. adv. circ. 1,000. **Document type:** newsletter.
  ●Also available online.
  Description: Contains articles of interest to DJs and others in the music industry, along with new music charts and related news bits.

780.42 028.5   IT
TREND DISCOTEC. 1989. m. L.50000. Edizioni Juvenis, Viale Lunigiana 7, 20125 Milan, Italy. TEL 39-2-66711016. FAX 39-2-6692445. Ed. Enrico Cammarota. adv.: color page L.8500000. circ. 95,000. **Document type:** consumer publication.

781.7   IE   ISSN 0790-004X
ML5
TREOIR; Irish folk music, song, dance, customs and heritage. 1968. q. I£5($20) Comhaltas Ceoltoiri Eireann, 32, Belgrave Sq., Monkstown, Co. Dublin, Ireland. Ed. Labhras O'Murchu. adv.; bk.rev.; illus.; index. circ. 13,000. **Document type:** consumer publication.

780   US
TRI - M NEWS. 1952. s-a. membership. (Music Educators National Conference) Tri - M Music Honor Society, 1806 Robert Fulton Dr., Reston, VA 22901-4348. TEL 800-336-3768. FAX 703-860-1531. Ed. Sandra V. Fridy. circ. 12,000. (tabloid format) **Document type:** newsletter.
  Description: Features articles for and about student members of the association. Distributed to over 12,000 members of more than 2,500 chapters with a listing of awards, chapter activities, and accomplishments of outstanding students.

781.7   US
TRI-SON NEWS; biggest little news sheet in country music. 1963. m. $15. Tri-Son, Inc., Box 40328, Nashville, TN 37204-0328. TEL 615-371-9596. FAX 615-371-9597. Ed. Loudilla Johnson. illus.; tr.lit. circ. 1,200. (looseleaf format) **Document type:** consumer publication, newsletter.
  Description: Covers entertainment with a strong emphasis on country music.

785   US   ISSN 0735-4711
ML19
TRI-STATE BLUEGRASS ASSOCIATION BAND AND FESTIVAL GUIDE. 1981. a. $10. Tri-State Bluegrass Association, R.R. 1, Kahoka, MO 63445. TEL 314-853-4344. Ed. Erma Spray. circ. 5,000. (back issues avail.) **Document type:** directory.
  Description: Contains information on bluegrass music bands and related materials.

780.7   US   ISSN 0041-2511
ML1
TRIAD (DAYTON). 1928. bi-m. $15. Ohio Music Education Association, Dept. of Music, Wright State Univ., 3640 Col. Glenn Hwy, Dayton, OH 45435-9950. TEL 513-873-2346. FAX 513-873-3786. Ed. Sharon H. Nelson. adv. contact: David Meeker. illus. circ. 4,900. **Indexed:** Music Ind. **Document type:** academic/scholarly publication.
  Description: Articles and columns address issues and concerns relevant to music education.

780   US   ISSN 0041-2600
ML1
TRIANGLE OF MU PHI EPSILON. 1906? q. $10. Mu Phi Epsilon International Professional Music Fraternity, c/o Mimi A. Altman, International Executive Office, 763 Deerfield Rd., Ste. 4, Deerfield, IL 60015-4304. TEL 708-940-1222. FAX 708-945-0231. Ed. Gerri Flynn. bk.rev.; illus. circ. 10,000. **Indexed:** Music Ind. **Document type:** trade publication.
  —UnCover.

780   AG   ISSN 0041-2767
TRIBUNA MUSICAL. 1965. s-a. Arg.$20000. Pablo Luis Bardin Ed. & Pub., Av. Libertador 3576, Buenos Aires, Argentina. adv.; illus. circ. 1,500. (tabloid format)

780   SZ   ISSN 1013-6835
ML5
TRIBUNE DE L'ORGUE. 1948. q. 33 SFr. (foreign 45 SFr.). Maison du Prieur, CH-1323 Romainmotier, Switzerland. TEL 024-531446. FAX 024-531150. Ed. Guy Bovet. adv.; bk.rev. circ. 2,000. **Indexed:** Music Ind. **Document type:** academic/scholarly publication.
  Description: Devoted to the organ and its music.

780   UK
TRITSCH - TRATSCH. 1966. s-a. £5 per no. Johann Strauss Society of Great Britain, 12 Bishams Ct., Church Hill, Caterham, Surrey CR3 6SE, England. Ed. Michael O'Sullivan. **Document type:** bulletin.

780   US   ISSN 1061-8856
ML1
TRUMPET AND BRASS PROGRAMS (YEAR). 1989. a. membership. International Trumpet Guild, Drawer 2025, Columbia, SC 29223. TEL 803-788-3379. FAX 803-736-9455. (Subscr. to: Attn. Brian Goff, School of Music, Florida State University, Tallahassee, FL 32306) Ed. Kevin Eisensmith. circ. 6,000. (back issues avail.) **Document type:** bulletin.

780.42   GW
TRUST; Hardcore Magazin. 1986. bi-m. DM.25. Trust Verlag, Salzmannstr. 53, 86163 Augsburg, Germany. TEL 0821-665088. FAX 0821-666964. Ed. Dolf Hermannstaedter. circ. 2,200. **Document type:** consumer publication.

TUITION, ENTERTAINMENT, NEWS, VIEWS. see *ART*

780   GW
DER TURNERMUSIKER. 6/yr. Deutscher Turnerbund e.V., c/o Westharzer Musikhaus Wilhelm Watermann, Postfach 370, 37577 Bad Gandersheim, Germany. TEL 05382-5021. FAX 05382-5613. **Document type:** newsletter.

MUSIC   4889

780.43 US ISSN 1052-3170
ML156.9
TUROK'S CHOICE; the insider's review of new classical recordings. 1990. m. (11/yr.). $13.95. P. Turok, Ed. & Pub., Box 202, Old Chelsea Sta., New York, NY 10113-0202. TEL 212-691-9229. (Alt. addr.: 105 W. 13th St., New York, NY 10021) circ. 1,000. (looseleaf format; back issues avail.) **Document type:** newsletter.
Description: Examines new classical recordings (on cassette or CD-ROM) with information about the artist, format, and commentary.

TURTLE QUARTERLY MAGAZINE. see *ETHNIC INTERESTS*

780.7 UK
TUTOR & TEXTBOOK - ELEMENTARY PIPING & DRUMMING. 1963. irreg. £9. Royal Scottish Pipe Band Association, 45 Washington St., Glasgow G3 8AZ, Scotland. adv. **Document type:** academic/scholarly publication.

787 US
▼**TUTTI.** 1994. 3/yr. 2980 McFarlane Rd., Coconut Grove, FL 33133. Ed. Bob Cannon. adv.; illus.

780 IT ISSN 1121-6514
TUTTI FRUTTI. 1982. m. L.30000($50) (effective 1994). Abrond House Coop.r.l., Via Ovidio 10, 00193 Rome, Italy. TEL 39-6-6833665. FAX 39-6-6832688. Ed. Massimo Bassoli. adv.: color page L.22000000. bk.rev. circ. 112,000. (back issues avail.)

780 IT
TUTTO MUSICA E SPETTACOLO. 1977. m. L.24000; newsstand price: L.3000. Silvio Berlusconi Editore S.p.A., Corso Europa 5-7, 20122 Milan, Italy. TEL 39-2-77941. Ed. Gigi Vesigna. adv.: color page L.22800000. circ. 181,628. (back issues avail.)

780 IT ISSN 1120-8859
TUTTO STRUMENTI. 1985. s-a. L.15000 per no. Ediscreen s.r.l., Via Calderini, 68, 00196 Rome, Italy. TEL 06-3233204. Dir. Enzo Perilli. adv.: B&W page L.3148200, color page L.5035000.

780.42 028.5 IT
TUTTODISCOTECA. 1990. m. L.45000. Edizioni Juvenis, Viale Lunigiana 7, 20125 Milan, Italy. TEL 39-2-66711016. FAX 39-2-6692445. Ed. Enrico Cammarota. adv.: B&W page L.5000000, color page L.7000000. circ. 62,000. **Document type:** consumer publication.

784 288 US
U U M N NOTES. 1983. 3/yr. $10. Unitarian Universalist Musician's Network, c/o D.L. Jackson, 1234 Oak Knoll Dr., Cincinnati, OH 34224. TEL 513-729-4183. Ed. Betty Wylder. adv.; bk.rev. circ. 1,000. (back issues avail.)

780 GW ISSN 0174-6065
UEBEN & MUSIZIEREN; Zeitschrift fuer Musikschule, Studium und Berufspraxis. 1983. 6/yr. DM.45. Schott Musik International GmbH, Weihergarten 5, 55116 Mainz, Germany. TEL 06131-246-0. FAX 06131-246211. Ed.Bd. adv.: B&W page DM.1460; trim 260 x 185; adv. contact: Renate Elsaesser. bk.rev.; bibl.; charts; illus.; index. circ. 6,000. **Indexed:** RILM. **Document type:** trade publication.

780 US
ULTIMATE EARLY CHILDHOOD MUSIC RESOURCE. 1984. a. $19.95 (foreign $29.50). Miss Jackie Music Co., 10001 El Monte, Overland Park, KS 66207. TEL 913-381-3672. Ed. Emily A. Smith. adv.; bk.rev.; index. circ. 1,000. (back issues avail.)
Supersedes (in 1990): Early Childhood Music Quarterly; Which was formerly: Early Childhood Music (ISSN 0747-5446)
Description: Features, news, exercises, programs, and original music, as a guide for teaching pre- and early-schoolers.

ULTIMO (MUENSTER); Muensters Stadtmagazin. see *LITERARY AND POLITICAL REVIEWS*

780.42 IT
ULTIMO BUSCADERO; mensile d'informazione rock. 1980. m. (11/yr.). L.60000 (US L.120000($71)) (effective 1995). Ultimo Buscadero S.r.l., Casella Postale 239, 21013 Gallarate (VA), Italy. TEL 39-331-771027. adv. contact: Paolo Caru. bk.rev. circ. 25,000. (back issues avail.) **Document type:** newspaper.
Refereed Serial

UNGA ATALANTE. see *THEATER*

780.42 US
UNION CATALOG OF MOTION PICTURE MUSIC. 1991. irreg. $50. International Film Music Society, 112 Harvard Ave., Ste. 223, Claremont, CA 91711. Eds. William H. Rosar, Leslie N. Andersen. **Document type:** academic/scholarly publication, catalog.
Description: Facilitates the location of existing musical materials in libraries and repositories throughout the country for films from Hollywood's Golden Age of Film Music, as well as from films being produced today.

780 BU
UNION OF BULGARIAN COMPOSERS. NEWS BULLETIN. (Editions in English and Russian) 1970. q. free. Soyuz na Bulgarski Kompozitori - Union of Bulgarian Composers, 2, Ivan Vazov St., 1000 Sofia, Bulgaria. Ed. Evgueni Pavlov. circ. 600.
Formerly: Music News Bulletin (ISSN 0566-9197)
Description: Features composer awards, Bulgarian music abroad and discographies.

780 US
U.S. NATIONAL ENDOWMENT FOR THE ARTS. APPLICATION GUIDELINES: MUSIC FELLOWSHIPS - COMPOSERS, JAZZ, SOLO RECITALISTS. (In 3 categories: Ensembles; Fellowships; Professional Training) a. free. U.S. National Endowment for the Arts, Public Information Office, 1100 Pennsylvania Ave., N.W., Washington, DC 20506. TEL 202-682-5400. **Document type:** government publication.
Formerly: N E A Grantmaking Programs: Music.
Description: Grant application guidelines.

U.S. NATIONAL ENDOWMENT FOR THE ARTS. APPLICATION GUIDELINES: OPERA - MUSICAL THEATER. see *THEATER*

780.01 UY
UNIVERSIDAD DE LA REPUBLICA. FACULTAD DE HUMANIDADES Y CIENCIAS. REVISTA. SERIE MUSICOLOGIA. irreg. exchange basis. Universidad de la Republica, Facultad de Humanidades y Ciencias, Seccion Revista, Tristan Narvaja 1674, Montevideo, Uruguay. Dir. Beatriz Martinez Osorio.
Supersedes in part: Universidad de la Republica. Facultad de Humanidades y Ciencias. Revista.

UNIVERSIDAD NACIONAL DE COLOMBIA. CENTRO DE ESTUDIOS FOLKLORICOS. MONOGRAFIAS. see *FOLKLORE*

780 AT ISSN 0726-3929
UNIVERSITY OF WESTERN AUSTRALIA. SCHOOL OF MUSIC. MUSIC MONOGRAPH. Key Title: Music Monograph. 1971. irreg. University of Western Australia, School of Music, Nedlands, W.A. 6907, Australia. TEL 61-9-380-2791. FAX 61-9-380-1076. Ed. Frank Callaway. **Document type:** academic/scholarly publication, monographic series.

UNIVERZITA KOMENSKEHO. FILOZOFICKA FAKULTA. ZBORNIK: MUSAICA. see *ART*

785.06 US
UPBEAT. LEXINGTON PHILHARMONIC SOCIETY NEWSLETTER. 1965. 5/yr. free. Lexington Philharmonic Society, 161 N. Mill St., Lexington, KY 40507-1125. adv.; bk.rev. circ. 6,000. (processed) **Document type:** newsletter.
Formerly: Lexington Philharmonic Society Newsletter (ISSN 0024-161X)
Description: Contains organization news.

780.7 371.3 US
UPDATE: APPLICATIONS OF RESEARCH IN MUSIC EDUCATION. 1982. 2/yr. $13. Music Educators National Conference, 1806 Robert Fulton Dr., Reston, VA 22091-4348. FAX 703-860-4826. Ed. Charles A. Elliott. adv.; bk.rev. circ. 1,350. **Indexed:** Music Artic.Guide.
Description: Contains articles to help music educators use research results in their teaching.

781.64 791.43 US
URB. 1990. 10/yr. $15; newsstand price: $2.50. 1680 N. Vine St., Ste. 1012, Los Angeles, CA 90028. TEL 213-993-0291. FAX 213-466-1207. (Dist. adddr.: 1200 Eagle Rock Blvd., Los Angeles, CA 90065. TEL 213-344-1200. FAX 213-256-9999) Ed. Raymond Leon Roker. adv.: B&W $1850, color page $2650; trim 10 x 12. film rev.; music rev.; illus. circ. 40,000. (back issues avail.) **Document type:** consumer publication.
Description: Covers the urban entertainment scene: music, clubs and modern primitive culture for readers 16-30. Includes interviews.

780 US ISSN 0506-306X
V D G S A NEWS. 1964. q. $20 in the U.S. and Canada; elsewhere $30. Viola da Gamba Society of America, Inc., c/o John A. Whisler, Exec.Sec., 1308 Jackson, Charleston, IL 61920-2242. Ed. Lisa Terry. adv.; bk.rev. circ. 850. **Indexed:** Music Ind. **Document type:** academic/scholarly publication, newsletter.

780 IT ISSN 0042-3734
ML410.V4
VERDI. (Text in English, Italian) 1960. irreg. price varies. Istituto Nazionale di Studi Verdiani, Strada della Repubblica 56, 43100 Parma, Italy. illus.; index, cum.index every 3 nos. **Indexed:** RILM.
Description: Discusses origin, musical aspects, libretto, staging, performances and singers of a single opera.

780 920 US ISSN 0160-2667
ML410.V4
VERDI NEWSLETTER. (Text in English and Italian) 1976. a. $15. (American Institute for Verdi Studies) New York University, Department of Music, 24 Waverly Pl., New York, NY 10003. TEL 212-998-2587. FAX 212-995-4147. Ed. Martin Chusid. adv.; bk.rev.; bibl.; charts; illus.; circ. 500 (paid). (back issues avail.) **Indexed:** RILM. **Document type:** academic/scholarly publication, newsletter.
Description: Research into the music, life and times of Giuseppe Verdi.

780.9 NE ISSN 0042-3874
VERENIGING VOOR NEDERLANDSE MUZIEKGESCHIEDENIS. TIJDSCHRIFT. (Text in Dutch, English; summaries in English) 1882. 2/yr. fl.88($50) (effective 1994). Swets & Zeitlinger bv, Hereweg 347, 2161 CA Lisse, Netherlands. TEL 31-2521-35111. FAX 31-2521-15888. TELEX 41325. (Dist. in N. America by: Swets & Zeitlinger, 440 Creamery Way, Ste. A, Exton, PA 19341. TEL 800-447-9387. FAX 610-524-5366) Ed. Arend Jan Gierveld. bk.rev.; cum.index: vols. 1-30. circ. 800. (also avail. in microfiche; back issues avail.; reprint service avail. from SWZ) **Indexed:** Arts & Hum.Cit.Ind., Curr.Cont., Music Ind., RILM. **Document type:** academic/scholarly publication.
—Faxon; Genuine Article; SWETS; UnCover.
Description: Covers the musical historiography of the Low Countries, including research on the life and work of major and minor composers.

780 GW ISSN 0543-1735
VEROEFFENTLICHUNGEN DES MAX-REGER-INSTITUTES. 1966. irreg. price varies. (Max-Reger-Institut) Ferd. Duemmlers Verlag, Kaiserstr. 31-37, 53113 Bonn, Germany. (Subscr. to: Postfach 1480, 53004 Bonn, Germany)

780 GW
VEROEFFENTLICHUNGEN ZUR MUSIKFORSCHUNG. 1973. irreg., vol.11, 1992. price varies. Florian Noetzel Verlag, Heinrichshofen Buecher, Valoisstr. 11, 26382 Wilhelmshaven, Germany. (Dist. in US by: C.F. Peters Corp., 373 Park Ave. S., New York, NY 10016) Ed. Richard Schaal. **Document type:** monographic series.

VERONICA; weekblad voor radio en TV. see *COMMUNICATIONS — Television And Cable*

781.64 US ISSN 1070-4701
ML3469
VIBE. 1993. 10/yr. $18 (Canada $30; elsewhere $50) (effective 1994). Time Inc. Ventures, 205 Lexington Ave., New York, NY 10016. TEL 212-522-7092. (Subscr. to: Box 59580, Boulder, CO 80323-7538. TEL 800-477-3974) Ed. Jonathan Van Meter. adv. contact: Susan Cappa. film rev.; music rev.; illus. **Indexed:** Access (1995-). **Document type:** consumer publication.
Description: Covers rap, hip-hop and related music, fashions and life-styles.

VICE VERSA MAGAZINE. see LITERATURE

780 US
VICTORY MUSIC REVIEW. 1976. m. $20. Victory Music, Box 7515, Bonney Lake, WA 98390. TEL 206-863-6617. Ed. Alicia Healey. adv. contact: Chris Lunn. bk.rev.; rec.rev. circ. 5,500. **Document type:** trade publication.
Description: Covers folk, jazz, new acoustic, songwriter, children's, women's, old time dance, blues, and other acoustic music through reviews.

VIDEO & MUSIC BUSINESS. see BUSINESS AND ECONOMICS — Marketing And Purchasing

VIDEO FILM MUSIC. see COMMUNICATIONS — Video

780 FR ISSN 0083-6109
VIE MUSICALE EN FRANCE SOUS LES ROIS BOURBONS. SERIE 1: ETUDES. (Text in English, French; summaries in French) 1954. irreg. price varies. Editions A. et J. Picard, 82 rue Bonaparte, 75006 Paris, France. FAX 43-26-42-64. **Document type:** academic/scholarly publication, monographic series.

780 FR ISSN 0080-0139
ML270
VIE MUSICALE EN FRANCE SOUS LES ROIS BOURBONS. SERIE 2: RECHERCHES SUR LA MUSIQUE FRANCAISE CLASSIQUE. (Text in English, French; summaries in French) 1960. a. price varies. Editions A. et J. Picard, 82 rue Bonaparte, 75006 Paris, France. FAX 43-26-42-64. Ed. Nobert Dufourcq. **Indexed:** RILM. **Document type:** academic/scholarly publication, monographic series.

780 US
VIERUNDZWANZIGSTELJAHRSSCHRIFT DER INTERNATIONALEN MAULTROMMELVIRTUOSENGENOSSENSCHAFT. (Text in English, French, German, Italian) 1982. irreg. $12 for 2 nos. V I M, 601 N. White St., Mt. Pleasant, IA 52641. TEL 319-385-2659. Ed. Frederick Crane. adv. contact: Frederick Crane. bk.rev.; bibl.; rec.rev.; circ. 75 (paid). **Indexed:** RILM. **Document type:** academic/scholarly publication.
Description: Publishes articles, reviews, checklists, discographies, bibliographies relating to the Jew's harp.

787 US ISSN 1056-8581
ML155
VINTAGE GUITAR. 1990. q. Orion Research Corp., 14555 N. Scottsdale Rd., Ste. 330, Scottsdale, AZ 85254-3457.

781.57 UK ISSN 0042-6369
VINTAGE JAZZ MART. 1953. q. £16 (N. America $26). c/o M. Berresford, R. Shor, P.O. Box 78, Nottingham NG6 8RY, England. TEL 01602-274465. (Subscr. in U.S. to: Box 8184, Radnor, PA 19087) adv.; bk.rev. circ. 1,800. **Document type:** consumer publication.
Description: Jazz record trading and research magazine.

VINTAGE RECORD MART. see SOUND RECORDING AND REPRODUCTION

787 US
VIOLA D'AMORE SOCIETY OF AMERICA. NEWSLETTER. (Text in English; summaries in German) 1977. s-a. $18 membership (effective 1995). Viola d'Amore Society of America, 39-23 47th St., Sunnyside, NY 11104. TEL 718-729-3138. Eds. Myron Rosenblum, Daniel Thomason. adv.; bk.rev.; bibl.; tr.lit. circ. 200. (processed; back issues avail.) **Document type:** newsletter.
Description: Furthers the research, history and performance of the Viola d'Amore.

780 US ISSN 0507-0252
ML1
VIOLA DA GAMBA SOCIETY OF AMERICA. JOURNAL. 1964. a. $20 in the U.S. and Canada; elsewhere $30. Viola da Gamba Society of America, Inc., c/o John A. Whisler, 1308 Jackson, Charleston, IL 61820-2242. Ed. Caroline Cunningham. adv.; bk.rev.; bibl.; illus. circ. 850. (back issues avail.) **Indexed:** Music Ind., RILM. **Document type:** academic/scholarly publication.
—UnCover.

787 US ISSN 0148-6845
ML1
VIOLIN SOCIETY OF AMERICA. JOURNAL. Key Title: Journal of the Violin Society of America. 1973. q. $45. (Violin Society of America) Queens College Press, 65-30 Kissena Blvd., Flushing, NY 11367. TEL 718-520-7773. (Subscr. to: Norman Pickering, 23 Culver Hill, Southampton, NY 11968) Ed. Albert Mell. adv.; bk.rev.; illus. circ. 1,400. (back issues avail.) **Indexed:** Arts & Hum.Cit.Ind., Curr.Cont., Music Artic.Guide, Music Ind., RILM. **Document type:** academic/scholarly publication.
—BLDSC (4912.520000); Faxon; UnCover.
Formerly: Violin Society of America. Bulletin.

VLAANDEREN; tijdschrift voor kunst en letteren. see ART

784 US ISSN 1074-0805
VOICE OF CHORUS AMERICA. 1978. q. $30 membership. Chorus America (APVE), 1811 Chestnut St., Ste. 401, Philadelphia, PA 19103. TEL 215-563-2430. FAX 215-563-2431. Ed. Fred Leise. adv.; bk.rev. circ. 7,000. **Indexed:** Music Artic.Guide. **Document type:** newsletter.

780 US ISSN 0147-4367
ML1
VOICE OF WASHINGTON MUSIC EDUCATORS. 1956. q. $3. Washington Music Educator's Association, c/o Jo Caldwell, Ed., Box 1117, Edmonds, WA 98020-1117. TEL 509-925-3609. FAX 509-925-7150. adv.; illus. circ. 1,500. **Indexed:** Music Artic.Guide.
—UnCover.
Supersedes: Washington Music Educator (ISSN 0043-065X)

784 US
VOLUNTEER CHOIR. bi-m. $120 (for ten copies). Lorenz Publishing Co., 501 E. Third St., Box 802, Dayton, OH 45401-0802. TEL 513-228-6118. FAX 513-223-2042. Ed. Eugene McCluskey. adv. contact: Larry Pugh. **Document type:** trade publication.

780.42 920 US
VOODOO CHILD. 1985. q. $12. Jimi Hendrix Information Management Institute, 4219 Winding Way, Indianapolis, IN 46220-5513. TEL 317-257-JIMI. FAX 317-255-1663. Ed. Ken Voss. adv.; bk.rev.; film rev. circ. 2,200. (back issues avail.) **Document type:** newsletter.
Description: Accumulates and disseminates information regarding the legend and legacy of rock guitarist Jimi Hendrix.

780 AT
VOX. 1960. m. Aus.$12($18) Theater Organ Society of Australia, Victorian Division, 19 Beatty St., Ivanhoe, Vic. 3079, Australia. Ed. Eric Wicks. adv.; bk.rev. circ. 850. (back issues avail)

VYTVARNA VYCHOVA; casopis pro vytvarnou a obecne estetickouvychovu skoli a mimosklni. see EDUCATION

790.2 US ISSN 0092-4113
ML28.W2
W P A S MUSELETTER. 1970. bi-m. $25 membership. Washington Performing Arts Society, 2000 L St., N.W., No. 810, Washington, DC 20036-4907. TEL 202-833-9800. FAX 202-331-7678. Ed. Cristina King. adv. contact: Linda C. Soma. circ. 9,000. **Document type:** newsletter.
Description: Contains membership events, development updates, WPAS news, and a calendar of programs and performances.

782.1 920 UK ISSN 0963-3332
WAGNER. 1980. 3/yr. £15 to individuals; institutions £12. Wagner Society, c/o Michael Bousfield, Meadowview Barn, Bonwycks Pl., Ifieldwood, W. Sussex RH11 0LE, England. (Society addr.: 4 Lucastes Rd., Haywards Heath, W. Sussex RH16 1JL, England. TEL 01444-450829) Ed. Stewart Spencer. adv.; bk.rev. circ. 1,100. **Document type:** academic/scholarly publication.
Description: Contains items of a scholarly nature about the life and works of the composer Richard Wagner.

782.1 920 UK ISSN 0261-3468
ML410.W1
WAGNER NEWS. 1980. 6/yr. £15 to individuals; institutions £12. Wagner Society, c/o Michael Bousfield, Meadowview Barn, Bonwycks Pl., Ifieldwood, W. Sussex RH11 0LE, England. (Society addr.: 4 Lucastes Rd., Haywards Heath, W. Sussex RH16 1JL, England. TEL 01444-450829) Ed. J.J. Pritchard. adv.; bk.rev.; rec.rev. circ. 1,100. **Document type:** newsletter.
Description: Includes news of forthcoming events, reviews and articles of general interest about the works of Richard Wagner.

780 808.81 US
WALT WHITMAN MUSIC LIBRARY. BULLETIN. 1993. m. free. Walt Whitman Music Library, 345 Arguello Blvd., Ste. 307, San Francisco, CA 94118. Ed. Frederick Berndt. **Document type:** bulletin.

780.904 NE
WAPKRANT. m. free. Westlandse Associatie van Popmuzikanten, Langestraat 38, 2691 BH 's-Gravenzande, Netherlands. adv.; bk.rev. circ. 1,500.

780 792 US ISSN 0196-3236
ML1699
WASHINGTON OPERA MAGAZINE. 1974. 3/yr. free to members of the Washington Opera. Washington Opera Guild, Kennedy Center, Washington, DC 20566. TEL 202-416-7850. FAX 202-416-7857. Ed. Eleanor Forrer. adv.; circ. 60,000 (paid); 60,000 (controlled).
Description: Information about opera productions at the Kennedy Center by the Washington Opera. Includes interviews with guest artists, synopsis of the operas, and a calendar of events.

DIE WEBEREIZEITUNG. see GENERAL INTEREST PERIODICALS — Germany

781.7 UK ISSN 0043-244X
WELSH MUSIC/CERDDORIAETH CYMRU. (Text mainly in English) 1959. 3/yr. £2 per no. Guild for the Promotion of Welsh Music, 94 Walter Rd., Swansea SA1 5QA, Wales. Ed. A.J. Heward Rees. adv.; bk.rev.; music rev.; rec.rev.; charts; illus. circ. 450. **Indexed:** RILM.

WEST COAST LINE; a journal of contemporary writing and criticism. see LITERATURE

781.642 GW ISSN 0944-0658
WESTERN MAIL; Fachzeitung fuer Country & Western Kultur. 1987. m. DM.40 (foreign DM.50). Ber Verlag, Treptower Str. 24-25, 12059 Berlin, Germany. TEL 030-6872432. FAX 030-6860083. Ed. Iris Paech; Pub. Kai Ulatowski. adv. contact: Wolfgang Retzlaff. bk.rev. circ. 12,000. **Document type:** newsletter.

784 US
WESTERN PENNSYLVANIA BLUEGRASS COMMITTEE. NEWSLETTER. 1969. m. $10. Western Pennsylvania Bluegrass Committee, Box 5295, Pittsburgh, PA 15206-5295. Ed. George P. Corey; Pub. George P. Corey. adv.; bk.rev. circ. 2,000. **Document type:** newsletter.

WESTWIND (LOS ANGELES); U C L A's journal of the arts. see ART

787 CN
WHAT WAVE. 1984. irreg., approx. a. Can.$7 (outside N. America Can.$8). 17 Erie Ave., London, ON N6J 1H9, Canada. TEL 519-672-0971. FAX 519-672-0971. Ed. Dave O'Halloran. adv.; circ. 1,000 (paid). **Document type:** newsletter.
Description: Covers 50s rockabilly, 60s and 70s punk, 80s garage music.

780.5 CN ISSN 0838-4312
WHAT'S IN A N A M E?. 1987. 2/yr. New Art Music Editions, 799 Beach Ave., Winnipeg, MB R2L 1E1, Canada. **Document type:** newsletter.

780 US ISSN 0043-4752
WHEEL OF DELTA OMICRON. 1915. 4/yr. $5. Delta Omicron International Music Fraternity, c/o M. Diane Blain, 57 Orchard Dr., Worthington, OH 43085. Ed. Carolyn Goodman. illus. circ. 5,500. **Document type:** academic/scholarly publication.
Description: Contains organization news.

MUSIC

781.64 US
THE WHO: THE RELAY. 1982. s-a. $3 per no. Box 1670, New York, NY 10013-1670. Ed. Diane Hatz. (back issues avail.) **Document type:** consumer publication.
Description: Contains items of interest to fans of the rock band The Who.

780 PL
WIEDZA O MUZYCE. 1983. irreg. price varies. Polskie Wydawnictwo Muzyczne, Al. Krasinskiego 11a, 31-111 Krakow. TEL 48-12-227044. FAX 48-12-220174. adv. contact: Teresa Wlochynska. **Document type:** academic/scholarly publication.
Description: Series of text-books for students; it covers various fields of music.

780.43 943 US
WILHELM FURTWAENGLER SOCIETY OF AMERICA. NEWSLETTER. 1989. q. $25 (foreign $30). Wilhelm Furtwaengler Society of America, c/o Hans Raillard, 6400 Lone Pine Rd., Sebastopol, CA 95472-5623. TEL 415-851-3808. FAX 415-851-3151. Ed.Bd; Pub. Dade Thieriot. bk.rev.; music rev. circ. 400. (back issues avail.) **Document type:** newsletter.
Description: Devoted to the furthering of knowledge about Wilhelm Furtwaengler, the late German conductor and composer, and his unique and interpretative art.

780 US ISSN 1051-0788
WILLEM MENGELBERG SOCIETY. NEWSLETTER. 1970. q. $7 (foreign $9). Willem Mengelberg Society, 1408A Marshall St., Manitowoc, WI 54220-5140. Ed. Ronald Klett. bk.rev.; rec.rev. **Document type:** newsletter.
Description: Covers all aspects of the life, recordings and concerts of the orchestral and choral conductor.

780.7 US ISSN 0043-6658
ML1
WISCONSIN SCHOOL MUSICIAN. 1926. q. $12. Wisconsin School Music Association, Inc., 4797 Hayes Rd. No. 3, Madison, WI 53704-3288. TEL 608-249-4566. FAX 608-249-4973. Ed. Michael George. adv.; bk.rev.; illus. circ. 4,300. **Indexed:** Music Artic.Guide.
—UnCover.

780 305.4 US ISSN 1068-2724
WOMEN OF NOTE QUARTERLY; The magazine of historical and contemporary women composers. 1993. q. $20 to individuals (foreign $29); institutions $25 (foreign $34) (effective 1995). Vivace Press, N.W. 310 Wawawai Rd., Pullman, WA 99163-2959. TEL 509-334-4660. FAX 509-334-3551. Ed. Barbara Harbach; Pub. Jonathan Yordy. adv.; bk.rev.; music rev. circ. 5,000. (back issues avail.) **Document type:** academic/scholarly publication.
Description: Profiles female composers and songwriters and discusses their work.
Refereed Serial

780 US
WOMEN'S MUSIC PLUS; directory of resources in women's music & culture. 1977. a. $20 to insitutions. Empty Closet Enterprises, Inc., 5210 N. Wayne, Chicago, IL 60640. TEL 312-769-9009. FAX 312-728-7002. Ed. Toni Armstrong Jr. circ. 2,000.
Description: Contact information (more than 5,500 names, addresses, phone numbers, descriptions) for women's music and culture industry (performers, writers, publishers, festivals, film, video, and concert producers, theatre, bookstores, and periodicals).

WOMEN'S NETWORK; national newsletter for women. see WOMEN'S INTERESTS

780.42 US ISSN 0891-9585
WOODSTOCK SERIES; popular music of today. 1976. irreg., no.2, 1995. price varies. Borgo Press, Box 2845, San Bernardino, CA 92406. TEL 909-884-5813. FAX 909-888-4942. **Document type:** monographic series.
Description: Monographs on popular musicians and music groups of the twentieth century, with discographies and bibliographies.

780.42 028.5 US ISSN 1056-4691
WORD UP! (RIVER EDGE). 1987. 12/yr. $24. Word Up! Publications, Inc., 63 Grand Ave., Ste. 230, River Edge, NJ 07601. TEL 201-487-6124. FAX 201-487-9360. Ed. Kate Ferguson. adv.; bk.rev. circ. 110,000. **Document type:** consumer publication.

781.6 CN ISSN 1195-8316
▼**WORDS & MUSIC.** French edition: Paroles & Musique (ISSN 1195-8324) 1994. q. $20. Society of Composers, Authors and Music Publishers of Canada - Societe Canadienne des Auteurs, Compositeurs et Editeurs de Musique, 41 Valleybrook Dr., Don Mills, ON M3B 2S6, Canada. TEL 416-445-8700. FAX 416-445-7108. Ed. Rick MacMillan.

781.7 JA
WORKS BY JAPANESE COMPOSERS (YEAR). biennial. Japan Federation of Composers, No. 305, 5th Sky Bldg., 3-3-8 Sendagaya, Shibuya-ku, Tokyo 151, Japan. TEL 03-5474-1853. FAX 03-5474-1854.

780 SZ
WORKSHOP. 1988. 10/yr. 61 SFr. Postfach 181, CH-3360 Herzogenbuchsee, Switzerland. TEL 063-661291. FAX 063-661392. Ed. Christian Hunziker. adv. contact: Fernando Palencias. bk.rev. circ. 11,300. **Document type:** trade publication.

784 US
WORLD CHORAL CENSUS. (Text in English, French, German) 1984. a. $15. International Federation for Choral Music, c/o Michael J. Anderson, Deputy Scty-Gen., University of Illinois at Chicago, Dept. of Performing Arts (M/C 255), 1040 West Harrison St., Chicago, IL 60607-7130. TEL 312-996-8744. FAX 312-996-0954. Ed. Claude Tagger. circ. 2,000. **Document type:** bulletin.
Description: Attempts to list all choral organizations in the world.

780 GW ISSN 1019-7117
WORLD NEW MUSIC MAGAZINE. (Text in English) 1991. a. DM.12. (International Society of Contemporary Music) Verlag MusikTexte, Postfach 102461, 50464 Cologne, Germany. TEL 0221-9520215. FAX 0221-9520216. Ed.Bd. adv.: B&W page DM.300. circ. 1,200. **Document type:** consumer publication.

WORLD OF FANDOM. see LITERATURE — Science Fiction, Fantasy, Horror

780 GW ISSN 0043-8774
ML5
THE WORLD OF MUSIC. (Text in English) 1958. 3/yr. $30 to individuals; institutions $36. International Institute for Traditional Music, Winkler Str. 20, 14193 Berlin, Germany. TEL 030-8262853. FAX 030-8259991. E-mail: iitm@netmbx.netmbx.de. (Subscr. to: Florian Noetzel Verlag, Postfach 580, 26353 Wilhelmshaven, Germany. TEL 04421-43003. FAX 04421-42985) Ed. M.P. Baumann. adv.; bk.rev.; music rev.; rec.rev.; illus. circ. 1,500. (reprint service avail. from SWZ) **Indexed:** Arts & Hum.Cit.Ind., Curr.Cont., Music Ind., RILM. **Document type:** academic/scholarly publication.
—BLDSC (9356.730000); Faxon; Genuine Article; SWETS; UnCover. **CCC.**

781.7 264 US ISSN 1046-381X
▼**WORSHIP: RESOURCES FOR THE CHURCH MUSICIAN.** 1995. q. $27.95. Southern Baptist Convention, Sunday School Board, 127 Ninth Ave., N., Nashville, TN 37234. TEL 800-458-2772. **Document type:** bulletin.
Description: Provides church music leaders with worship-planning guides and resources.

780 PL
WSPOLCZESNA PUBLICYSTYKA POLSKA. 1971. irreg. price varies. Polskie Wydawnictwo Muzyczne, Al. Krasinskiego 11a, 31-111 Krakow, Poland. TEL 48-12-227044. FAX 48-12-220174. adv. contact: Teresa Wlochynska.
Description: Contemporary Polish music publicists' writings about music.

780 GW ISSN 0177-6487
ML5
WUERTTEMBERGISCHE BLAETTER FUER KIRCHENMUSIK. 1927. bi-m. DM.20. Evangelische Kirchenmusik in Wuerttemberg, Gerokstr. 19, 70184 Stuttgart, Germany. TEL 0711-243629. FAX 0711-2360642. Ed. Helmut Voelkl. bk.rev. circ. 3,700. (back issues avail.) **Indexed:** RILM. **Document type:** newsletter.

780 PL ISSN 0512-4255
WYCHOWANIE MUZYCZNE W SZKOLE. 1956. 5/yr. $15. (Ministerstwo Edukacji Narodowej) Wydawnictwo Szkolne i Pedagogiczne, Pl. Dabrowskiego 8, 00-950 Warsaw, Poland. TEL 48-22-265451. FAX 48-22-268971. (Dist.by: Ars Polona, Krakowskie Przedmiescie 7, Warsaw, Poland) Ed. Ewa Hoffman-Lipska. circ. 4,000. **Indexed:** RILM.
Description: For music teachers who take care of vocal and instrumental groups in schools and other educational institutions. Publishes articles dealing with music and related fields of knowledge, such as psychology, sociology, music pedagogy, aesthetics, including both Polish and foreign traditions and ideas of music education.

780 800 US ISSN 1051-4155
X MAGAZINE; humor and/or music. 1990. q. $10 (Canada $15; elsewhere $20). Jeff Hansen, Ed. & Pub., Box 1077, Royal Oak, MI 48068-1077. E-mail: xmag@mail.msen.com. Site addr.: http://www.msen.com/nxmag.
●Also available online.

Y S B. (Young Sisters & Brothers) see CHILDREN AND YOUTH — For

780 051 US
YAKUZA. 1992. q. Box 26039, Wilmington, DE 19899-6039. Ed. Dave McGurgan; Pub. Dave McGurgan. adv. contact: Allison Herdan. **Document type:** newsletter.

780 US ISSN 0740-1558
ML1
YEARBOOK FOR TRADITIONAL MUSIC. (Text in English, French, German) 1949. a. $35. International Council for Traditional Music, c/o Department of Music, Columbia University, New York, NY 10027. TEL 212-678-0332. FAX 212-678-2513. TELEX 220094 COLU UR. E-mail: ictm@woof.music.columbia.edu. Ed. Dieter Christensen. bk.rev.; rec.rev.; video rev. circ. 1,300. (reprint service avail. from SWZ) **Indexed:** A.I.C.P., M.L.A., Music Ind., RILM. **Document type:** bulletin.
—Genuine Article; UnCover.
Former titles (until 1980): International Folk Music Council. Yearbook; International Folk Music Council Journal (ISSN 0074-6096)

780 CC
YINXIANG SHIJIE/AUDIO-VISUAL WORLD. (Text in Chinese) m. Shanghai Changpian Zonggongsi - Shanghai Record Corporation, 739 Hengshan Road, Shanghai 200030, People's Republic of China. TEL 4373230. Ed. Liu Senmin.

780 CC
YINYUE AIHAOZHE/MUSIC LOVER. (Text in Chinese) bi-m. $20.30. Shanghai Yiyue Chubanshe - Shanghai Music Publishing Company, 74 Shaoxing Lu, Shanghai 200020, People's Republic of China. TEL 021-4372608. FAX 021-4332452. TELEX 33384. (Dist. in US by: China Books & Periodicals, Inc. 2929 24th St., San Francisco, CA 94110. TEL 415-282-2994) Ed. Chen Xueya. circ. 50,000. **Document type:** consumer publication.
Description: Presents popular music knowledge with illustrations.

780 US ISSN 0513-2436
YINYUE CHUANGZUO/MUSICAL CREATION. (Text in Chinese) q. $27.90. China Books & Periodicals, Inc., 2929 24th St., San Francisco, CA 94110. TEL 415-282-2994. FAX 415-282-0994.

780 CC ISSN 0512-7920
YINYUE SHENGHUO/MUSIC LIFE. (Text in Chinese) m. $35.90. (Zhongguo Yinyuejia Xiehui, Liaoning Fenhui - Chinese Musicians Association, Liaoning Chapter) Yinyue Shenghuo Bianjibu, 74 Bajing Jie, Heping-qu, Shenyang, Liaoning 110003, People's Republic of China. TEL 24778. (Dist. in US by: China Books & Periodicals, Inc., 2929 24th St., San Francisco, CA 94110. TEL 415-282-2994) Ed. Ding Ming.

780	CC
YINYUE SHIJIE/MUSIC WORLD. (Text in Chinese) m. (China Musicians Association, Sichuan Branch) Yiyue Shijie Bianjibu, 85 Hongxing Zhonglu Erduan (Sec. 2), Chengdu, Sichuan 610012, People's Republic of China. TEL 29323.

780.7   CC   ISSN 1004-2172
YINYUE TANSUO/EXPLORATIONS IN MUSIC; the academic periodical of Sichuan Conservatory. Variant title: Sichuan Yinyue Xueyuan Xuebao. (Text in Chinese; table of contents in English) q. Sichuan Yinyue Xueyuan - Sichuan Conservatory of Music, 2, Xinsheng Lu, Xinnan Menwai, Chengdu, Sichuan 610012, People's Republic of China. TEL 552181. Ed. Song Daneng. **Document type:** academic/scholarly publication.

780   CC   ISSN 1003-4218
YINYUE TIANDI/MUSIC WORLD. (Text in Chinese) m. $24.20. Zhongguo Yinyuejia Xiehui, Shaanxi Fenhui - China Musicians Association, Shaanxi Chapter, Wenyi Lu, Tuanjiefang, Building No. 7, Xi'an, Shaanxi 710054, People's Republic of China. TEL 712616. (Dist. in US by: China Books & Periodicals, Inc., 2929 24th St., San Francisco, CA 94110. TEL 415-282-2994) Ed. Wang Yan.

780.7   CC   ISSN 0512-7939
ML5
YINYUE YANJIU/MUSIC RESEARCH. Variant English title: Music Study. (Text in Chinese; table of contents in English) q. $19.50. Renmin Yinyue Chubanshe, Beijing, People's Republic of China. (Dist. outside China by: China International Book Trading Corp., P.O. Box 2820, Beijing, P.R.C.; Dist. in US by: China Books & Periodicals, Inc., 2929 24th St., San Francisco, CA 94110. TEL 415-282-2994) Eds. Zhao Feng, Li Yedao.

780   CC   ISSN 1000-4270
ML5
YINYUE YISHU/ART OF MUSIC. (Text in Chinese; table of contents in English) 1979. q. $16.50. Shanghai Conservatory of Music - Shanghai Yinyue Xueyuan, 20 Fenyang Lu, Shanghai, People's Republic of China. FAX 86-21-4330866. (Dist. outside China by: China International Book Trading Corp., P.O. Box 2820, Beijing, P.R.C.; Dist. in US by: China Books & Periodicals, Inc., 2929 24th St., San Francisco, CA 94110. TEL 415-282-2994) Ed. Jiang Mingdun. adv. contact: Dai Xiaolian. index. **Document type:** academic/scholarly publication.
Description: Covers Chinese and western music, musicology, composition, organology and history.

780.42   US
YO! MAGAZINE. m. $2.95 per no. Ashley Communications, Inc., Box 88427, Los Angeles, CA 90009. TEL 818-885-6800. (And: 19431 Business Center Dr., Northridge, CA 91324) Ed. Dedi Fee. adv. contact: Robert Masset. **Document type:** consumer publication.

780   US
YOU COULD DO WORSE. 1988. 3/yr. $7.50. Box 74647, Cedar Rapids, IA 52407. TEL 319-351-2126. E-mail: ycdworse@aol.com. Ed. Rob Galago; Pub. Rob Galago. circ. 2,000. (back issues avail.) **Document type:** consumer publication.
Formerly (until 1994): File 13.
Description: Provides reviews, interviews, music and features on alternative and/or independent music of all types.

780   JA
YOUNG AUDIO NOW. (Text in Japanese) 1974. a. 680 price varies. Gakken Co. Ltd., 40-5, 4-chome, Kamiikedai, Ohta-ku, Tokyo 145, Japan. Ed. Akira Ohuchi.

780   JA
YOUNG GUITAR. (Text in Japanese) 1969. m. 6000 Yen. Shinko Music Publishing Co. Ltd., 2-1 Ogawa-machi, Kanda, Chiyoda-ku, Tokyo, Japan. Ed. Takashi Yamamoto.

780   UK
YOUNG MUSICIAN. 1981. bi-m. £2.50. Young Musicians Enterprises, St. Albans Lane, Golders Green, London EC4Y 1PN, England. adv.

782.5 264   US   ISSN 0044-0841
ML1
YOUNG MUSICIANS. q. $13.50. Southern Baptist Convention, Sunday School Board, 127 Ninth Ave., N., Nashville, TN 37234. TEL 800-458-2772.
Formerly: Junior Musician.
Description: Provides children in grades 4-6 with choir music and activities.

780   CC   ISSN 1001-5736
YUEFU XIN SHENG. Variant title: Shenyang Yinyue Xueyuan Xuebao. (Text in Chinese) 1983. q. Y6. Shenyang Yinyue Xueyuan - Shenyang Conservatory of Music, No. 1, Sanhao Jie Sec. 2, Heping Qu, Shenyang, Liaoning 110003, People's Republic of China. FAX 0086-24-394193. music rev. circ. 5,000. (back issues avail.) **Document type:** academic/scholarly publication.
Description: Covers music theory, music education, theory of composition technique, music history, music science and technology, research on performance art and ethnomusicology.

780   IS   ISSN 0084-439X
ML3776
YUVAL. (Text in English, French and Hebrew; summaries in English and Hebrew) 1968. irreg., latest vol.6. price varies. (Jewish Music Research Centre) Magnes Press, The Hebrew University, Jerusalem, P.O. Box 7695, Jerusalem 91076, Israel. TEL 972-2-660341. FAX 972-2-633370. Ed. Israel Adler. (back issues avail.) **Indexed:** Ind.Heb.Per., RILM. **Document type:** monographic series.

780 296   IS   ISSN 0334-3758
YUVAL MONOGRAPH SERIES. (Text in English, French, German, Hebrew) 1974. irreg., vol.10, 1995. price varies. (Jewish Music Research Centre) Magnes Press, Hebrew University, Jerusalem, P.O. Box 7695, Jerusalem 91076, Israel. TEL 972-2-660341. FAX 972-2-633370. **Document type:** monographic series.

780   PL   ISSN 0084-442X
Z DZIEJOW MUZYKI POLSKIEJ. 1960. irreg. Bydgoskie Towarzystwo Naukowe, Jezuicka 4, Bydgoszcz, Poland. (Dist. by Ars Polona-Ruch, Krakowskie Przedmiescie 7, Warsaw, Poland)

782.42 028.5   PL
ZASPIEWAJ MI, MAMO. 1985. irreg. price varies. Polskie Wydawnictwo Muzyczne, Al. Krasinskiego 11a, 31-111 Krakow, Poland. TEL 48-12-227044. FAX 48-12-220174.
Description: Series containing well-known nursery rhymes for small children.

ZEITSCHRIFT FUER OSTKIRCHLICHE KUNST HERMENEIA; Beitraege zu Kultur und Kunst, Ikonen und Theologie des Christlichen Ostens. see *ART*

781.7   US
ZHONGGUO YINYUE/CHINESE MUSIC. (Text in Chinese) q. $22.25. China Books & Periodicals, Inc., 2929 24th St., San Francisco, CA 94110. TEL 415-282-2994. FAX 415-282-0994.

780.01   CC
ZHONGGUO YINYUEXUE/MUSICOLOGY IN CHINA. (Text in Chinese; table of contents and summaries in English) 1985. q. (Zhongguo Yishu Yanjiuyuan, Yinyue Yanjiusuo) Wenhua Yishu Chubanshe, 17, Qianhai Xijie, Xicheng Qu, Beijing 100009, People's Republic of China. Ed. Guo Naian. bk.rev. **Document type:** academic/scholarly publication.

780.904   CC   ISSN 1001-9871
ZHONGYANG YINYUE XUEYUAN XUEBAO/CENTRAL CONSERVATORY OF MUSIC. JOURNAL. (Text in Chinese; table of contents in English) no.36, 1989. q. Y6($20.40) Central Conservatory of Music - Zhongyang Yinyue Xueyuan, 43 Baojia Jie, Xi Cheng Qu (West City District), Beijing, People's Republic of China. (Dist. by: China International Book Trading Corporation (Guoji Shudian), P.O. Box 339, Beijing 100044, P.R.C.; Dist. in US by: China Books & Periodicals, Inc., 2929 24th St., San Francisco, CA 94110; 91217) Ed. Yu Run-yang. bk.rev. **Document type:** academic/scholarly publication.
—UnCover.
Description: Publishes research papers on music history, theory of ethnomusicology, composition and conducting, and vocal and instrumental performance; articles on music teaching; selected foreign papers on music; and reviews of performances. Also includes recent vocal and instrumental composition scores.

780   PL
ZRODLA PAMIETNIKARSKO-LITERACKIE DO DZIEJOW MUZYKI POLSKIEJ. 1956. irreg. price varies. Polskie Wydawnictwo Muzyczne, Al. Krasinskiego 11a, 31-111 Krakow, Poland. TEL 48-12-227044. FAX 48-12-220174. Ed. Tadeusz Strumillo. adv. contact: Teresa Wlochynska.
Description: Letters, memoirs, diaries and opinions about Polish musical culture.

ZUGABE. see *THEATER*

780   GW   ISSN 0176-0971
ML5
ZUPFMUSIK MAGAZIN. q. DM.36. (Bund Deutscher Zupfmusiker e.V.) Oertel & Spoerer, Burgstr. 1-7, 72764 Reutlingen, Germany. TEL 07121-302563. FAX 07121-302512. Ed. Ruediger Grambow. adv. contact: Ermo Lehari. illus. **Document type:** consumer publication.
Incorporates: Gitarre.

780   YU   ISSN 0044-555X
ML5
ZVUK; Jugoslovenska muzicka revija. (Text in Serbo-Croatian; summaries in English) 1955. q. DM.10 per no. Savez Organizacija Kompozitora Jugoslavije (SOKOJ), Misarska 12-14, 11000 Belgrade, Yugoslavia. TEL 38-11-334771. FAX 38-11-336-168. Ed. Erika Krpan. adv.; bk.rev.; rec.rev. circ. 1,500. **Indexed:** Music Ind., RILM.
Description: Provides reviews on the most significant music events, musicologial studies, interviews.

780   US
ML3809
1 - 1 JOURNAL. 1985. irreg. $15 to individuals; libraries $25. Just Intonation Network, 535 Stevenson St., San Francisco, CA 94103. TEL 415-864-8123. FAX 415-864-8726. Ed. David B. Doty. adv. contact: Henry S. Rosenthal. bk.rev. circ. 500. **Indexed:** RILM.
Formerly: 1 - 1 Quarterly (ISSN 8756-7717)
Description: Devoted solely to music theory and practice, and instrument construction and modification relating specifically to just intonation.

781.57   AT   ISSN 0313-0797
2 M B S - F M STEREO F M RADIO PROGRAM GUIDE. 1975. m. Aus.$55 (effective 1995 & 1996). Music Broadcasting Society of N.S.W. Co-op Ltd., 76 Chandos St., St. Leonards, N.S.W. 2065, Australia. TEL 61-2-439-4777. FAX 61-2-439-4064. Ed. Celeste Pena. adv.; bk.rev. circ. 8,000. (back issues avail.)
Description: Features mostly classical, specialist jazz, blues, and contemporary-experimental music.

MUSIC — ABSTRACTING, BIBLIOGRAPHIES, STATISTICS

780   US   ISSN 0148-2076
ML1
19TH CENTURY MUSIC. 1977. 3/yr. $33 to individuals (foreign $38); institutions $69 (foreign $74) (effective 1996). University of California Press, Journals Division, 2120 Berkeley Way, Berkeley, CA 94720. TEL 510-643-7154. FAX 510-642-9917. Ed. James Hepokoski. adv.; bk.rev.; index, cum.index. circ. 1,500. (also avail. in microform from UMI; microfiche; back issues avail.; reprint service avail. from UMI) **Indexed:** Curr.Cont., Hum.Ind., Ind.Bk.Rev.Hum., Music Artic.Guide, Music Ind., RILM. **Document type:** academic/scholarly publication.
—BLDSC (9725.475000); Faxon; Genuine Article; SWETS; UMI; UnCover. **CCC.**
    Description: Explores music history and criticism, analysis, and theory, as well as reviews and commentary by guest columnists.
    Refereed Serial

781.6 745.1   US
▼**78 QUARTERLY.** 1994. q. $38. Box 283, Key West, FL 33041. TEL 305-294-2653. Ed. Pete WHelan. adv.: page $500; adv. contact: Pete Whelan. bk.rev. circ. 3,500. (back issues avail.)
    Description: Appeals to collectors of blues and jazz 78-RPM phonograph records from the 1920s and 1930s.

MUSIC — Abstracting, Bibliographies, Statistics

780.42   UK   ISSN 0142-7636
B P I STATISTICAL HANDBOOK. 1992. a. £20. British Phonographic Industry, 25 Savile Row, London W1X 1AA, England. TEL 0171-287-4422. FAX 0171-287-2252. Ed. Peter Scaping. stat.; circ. 1,000 (paid); 1,000 (controlled). (back issues avail.) **Document type:** trade publication.
    Description: Summarizes market size and share and the demographics of purchasing and retailing in the music industry.

780   US   ISSN 1072-5202
ML 156.2
BEST RATED C DS - CLASSICAL. 1992. a. $19.95 (effective 1992). Peri Press, Hemlock Ridge, Box 348, Voorheesville, NY 12186-0348. TEL 518-765-3163; 800-677-4492. FAX 518-765-3158. Ed. Janet Grimes. music rev.
    Description: Selected reviews of award winning classical music available on CD.

780   US   ISSN 1072-5210
ML156.9
BEST RATED C DS - JAZZ, POPULAR ETC.. 1992. a. $19.95 (effective 1992). Peri Press, Hemlock Ridge, Box 348, Voorheesville, NY 12186-0348. TEL 518-765-3163; 800-677-4492. FAX 518-765-3158. Ed. Janet Grimes. music rev.
    Description: Selected reviews of award-winning music available on CDs.

780   PL
BIBLIOGRAFIA MUZYCZNA POLSKICH CZASOPISM NIEMUZYCZNYCH. 1962. irreg. price varies. Polskie Wydawnictwo Muzyczne, Al. Krasinskiego 11a, 31-111 Krakow, Poland. TEL 48-12-227044. FAX 48-12-220174. Ed. Kornel Michalowski. adv. contact: Teresa Wlochynska. **Document type:** bibliography.
    Description: Lists literature about music in 19th and 20th century Poland.

780   PL
BIBLIOGRAFIA POLSKICH CZASOPISM MUZYCZNYCH. 1955. irreg. price varies. Polskie Wydawnictwo Muzyczne, Al. Krasinskiego 11a, 31-111 Krakow, Poland. TEL 48-12-227044. FAX 48-12-220174. Ed. Kornel Michalowski. adv. contact: Teresa Wlochynska. **Document type:** bibliography.
    Description: Reveals valuable and hitherto not fully exploited material based on sources, contained in Polish musical journals.

016 780   NE   ISSN 0084-7844
ML113
BIBLIOGRAPHIA MUSICOLOGICA; a bibliography of musical literature. (Text in various languages) 1970. irreg., vol.3, 1976. fl.500($300) Joachimsthal Publishers, Box 2218, 1180 EE Amstelveen, Netherlands. Ed. A.M. Joachimsthal. (back issues avail.) **Document type:** bibliography.

016.78   US   ISSN 0360-2753
ML136.N5
BIBLIOGRAPHIC GUIDE TO MUSIC. (Text in various languages) a. $250 cloth. G.K. Hall & Co., c/o MacMillan Publishing USA, 866 Third Ave., 18th fl., New York, NY 10022. TEL 212-702-6789. (Subscr. to: Simon & Schuster, Library Reference Order Processing, 200 Old Tappan Rd., Old Tappan, NJ 07675. TEL 800-223-2336) **Document type:** bibliography, abstracting/indexing.
—BLDSC (1964.895000).
    Formerly: Music Book Guide (ISSN 0360-1943)
    Description: Covers musical subjects in book and non-book form.

780   FR   ISSN 1142-3285
Z2165
BIBLIOGRAPHIE NATIONALE FRANCAISE. MUSIQUE. 3/yr. 555 F. (foreign 630 F.) (effective 1995). Bibliotheque Nationale de France, 58 rue de Richelieu, 75002 Paris, France. TEL 47-03-86-10. FAX 47-03-85-86. Ed. P.-A. Berend. **Document type:** bibliography.
—BLDSC (1989.235200).
    Former titles (until 1990): Bibliographie de la France. Supplement 3. Musique (ISSN 0150-5971); (until 1977): Bibliographie de la France. 1ere Partie, Bibliographie Officielle. Supplement 3. Musique (ISSN 1149-6916); (until 1975): Bibliographie de la France. Supplement C. Ouevres Musicales (ISSN 1147-6974); Supersedes in part (in 1946): Bibliographie de la France (ISSN 0006-1344)

780 016   US
BIBLIOGRAPHIES IN AMERICAN MUSIC. 1974. irreg. price varies. College Music Society, 202 W. Spruce St., Missoula, MT 59802. TEL 406-721-9616. FAX 406-721-9419. Ed. James Heintze. adv. contact: Diane Benjamin. **Document type:** bibliography.
    Description: Bibliographies in the field of American music.

780   US   ISSN 0742-6968
BIO-BIBLIOGRAPHIES IN MUSIC. 1985. irreg. price varies. Greenwood Press, Inc. (Subsidiary of: Greenwood Publishing Group Inc.), 88 Post Rd. W., Box 5007, Westport, CT 06881-5007. TEL 203-226-3571. FAX 203-222-1502. **Document type:** bibliography.
—BLDSC (2066.804400).

016   DK   ISSN 0106-729X
BOERNEBIBLIOTHEKSKATALOG. GRAMMOFONPLADER, KASSETTEBAAND. (Not avail. in printed format) 1979. a. (plus supplements). DKK 1339. Dansk BiblioteksCenter a-s, Tempovej 7-11, DK-2750 Ballerup, Denmark. TEL 45-44-97-40-00. FAX 45-44-68-24-42.
●Also available online.
Also available on CD-ROM.
    Formerly: Boernepladier Boernekassetter.

780   UK
BRAVURA STUDIES IN MUSIC. 1979. a. price varies. Bravura Publications, 2 Clovelly Park, Clovelly Drive, Hindhead, Surrey GU26 6RS, England. Ed. Alan Poulton. bibl. circ. 250. (back issues avail.)

015 789.91   BU   ISSN 0323-9365
BULGARSKI GRAMOFONNI PLOCHI. 1974. a. $31. Narodna Biblioteka Sv.sv. Kiril i Metodii, 11, V. Levski Blvd., 1504 Sofia, Bulgaria. TEL 359-2-882811. FAX 359-2-881600. Ed. V. Magneva. bibl. circ. 300.

780 011   US   ISSN 1045-0114
ML156.9
C D REVIEW DIGEST - CLASSICAL; the international indexing service - a guide with excerpts to English language reviews of all music recorded on compact and video laser discs. 1983. q. with a. cumulation. $79. Peri Press, Hemlock Ridge, Box 348, Voorheesville, NY 12186-0348. TEL 518-765-3163; 800-677-4492. FAX 518-765-3158. Ed. Janet Grimes. adv. (back issues avail.) **Document type:** abstracting/indexing.
    Supersedes in part (in 1988): C D Review Digest (ISSN 0890-0213)

780 011   US   ISSN 1045-0122
ML156.4.J3
C D REVIEW DIGEST - JAZZ, POPULAR, ETC.; the international indexing service - a guide with excerpts to English language reviews of all music recorded on compact and video laser discs. 1983. q. with a. cumulation. $79. Peri Press, Hemlock Ridge, Box 348, Voorheesville, NY 12186-0348. TEL 518-765-3163; 800-677-4492. FAX 518-765-3158. Ed. Janet Grimes. adv. (back issues avail.) **Indexed:** RILM. **Document type:** abstracting/indexing.
    Supersedes in part (in 1988): C D Review Digest (ISSN 0890-0213)

780   CN
CADENCE ALL-YEARS INDEX. 1988. a. Can.$28($29) Lord Music Reference Inc., 1540 Taylor Way, West Vancouver, BC V7S 1N4, Canada. (Dist. by: North Country-Cadence, Cadence Bldg., Redwood, NY 13679, USA. TEL 315-287-2852. FAX 315-287-2860) Ed. Tom Lord.

CELEBRITY BIRTHDAY DIRECTORY. see *MOTION PICTURES — Abstracting, Bibliographies, Statistics*

780   DK   ISSN 0107-9816
DANSK LYDFORTEGNELSE. (Not avail. in printed format) 1982. q. DKK 818. Dansk BiblioteksCenter a-s, Tempovej 7-11, DK-2750 Ballerup, Denmark. TEL 45-44-97-40-00. FAX 45-44-68-24-42.
●Also available online.
Also available on CD-ROM.

784   DK   ISSN 0108-2272
DANSK SANGINDEKS; register til sange for boern og voksne. 1982. a. DKK 1350.50 (effective 1996). Dansk BiblioteksCenter a-s, Tempovej 7-11, DK-2750 Ballerup, Denmark. TEL 45-44-97-40-00. FAX 45-44-68-24-42.

780 016   US   ISSN 0070-3885
DETROIT STUDIES IN MUSIC BIBLIOGRAPHY. 1961. irreg., no.73, 1994. price varies. Harmonie Park Press, 23630 Pinewood, Warren, MI 48091-4759. TEL 810-755-3080. **Document type:** bibliography.

780 015   GW
DEUTSCHE NATIONALBIBLIOGRAPHIE. REIHE M. MUSIKALIEN UND MUSIKSCHRIFTEN. 1976. m. DM.309. (Deutsche Bibliothek, Deutsches Musikarchiv) Buchhaendler-Vereinigung GmbH, Postfach 100442, 60004 Frankfurt a.M., Germany. TEL 069-1306-0. FAX 069-1306201. TELEX 413573-BUCHV-D. **Document type:** bibliography.
—BLDSC (3573.164200).
    Former titles: Deutsche Nationalbibliographie: Verzeichnis der Musikalien und Musikschriften (ISSN 0939-0596); Deutsche Bibliographie: Musikalien-Verzeichnis (ISSN 0170-124X)
    Description: Bibliography that lists music scores from German-speaking countries available at the Music Archive.

780 016   US   ISSN 0015-6191
ML5
FONTES ARTIS MUSICAE. (Text in English, French, German) 1953. 4/yr. $33 to individuals; institutions $48. International Association of Music Libraries, Archives and Documentation Centres (U.S.), c/o Susan T. Sommer, Editor in Chief, New York Public Library for the Performing Arts, New York, NY 10023-7498. TEL 212-870-1620. FAX 212-870-1704. (Subscr. to: Robert Follet, Music Library, University of Arizona, Tucson, AZ 85721; Subscr. outside U.S. to: Pamela Thompson, IAML Treasurer, Royal College of Music, Prince Consort Rd., London SW7 2BS, England) Ed.Bd. adv.; bk.rev.; bibl.; index. circ. 2,200. **Indexed:** Arts & Hum.Cit.Ind., Curr.Cont., Lib.Lit., LISA, Music.Ind., RILM. **Document type:** academic/scholarly publication.
—BLDSC (3976.850000); Faxon; UnCover.

780 016   GW   ISSN 0075-2959
Z6811
JAHRESVERZEICHNIS DER MUSIKALIEN UND MUSIKSCHRIFTEN. (In 2 Vols: Teil 1 Alphabetischer Teil; Teil 2 Systematischer Teil und Registerteil) a. DM.160 for both vols. Friedrich Hofmeister Musikverlag GmbH, Karlstr. 10, 04103 Leipzig, Germany.
    Formerly: Jahresverzeichnis der Musikalien und Musikschriften.

MUSIC — ABSTRACTING, BIBLIOGRAPHIES, STATISTICS

780 016 JA
JAPAN FEDERATION OF COMPOSERS. CATALOGUE OF PUBLICATIONS. (Text in Japanese, English) 1970. a. free. Japan Federation of Composers, No. 307, 5th Sky Bldg., 3-3-8 Sendagaya, Shibuya-ku, Tokyo 151, Japan. TEL 03-5474-1853. FAX 03-5474-1854. Ed.Bd. circ. 1,000. **Document type:** catalog.

780 PL
KATALOG POLSKICH DRUKOW MUZYCZNYCH 1800-1963. (Text in English, Polish) 1968. irreg. price varies. Polskie Wydawnictwo Muzyczne, Al. Krasinskiego 11a, 31-111 Krakow, Poland. TEL 48-12-227044. FAX 48-12-220174. adv. contact: Teresa Wlochynska. **Document type:** monographic series.
  Description: Bibliography of music publications printed in Poland and Polish historical documents published abroad.

789.91 US
LASERLOG REPORTER; CD reporter. 1985. fortn. $228. Phonolog Publishing (Subsidiary of: Trade Service Corporation), 10996 Torreyana Rd., Box 85007, San Diego, CA 92138. TEL 619-457-5920. Ed. Bonnie J. Dudley. (looseleaf format)
  Description: Provides a list of CD albums by title and artist.

780 240 US ISSN 1070-6690
THE LIGHTHOUSE (STATE COLLEGE); shining light on today's Christian music. 1992. m. $10. Polarized Publications, 256 E. College Ave., Ste. 302, State College, PA 16801. TEL 814-238-6730. FAX 814-238-6739. E-mail: LIGHTHOUSE@SABINE.PSU.EDU. Eds. Beth Blair, J. Warner Soditus. adv. contact: Vorda Whetsel. circ. 2,000. **Document type:** consumer publication.
  Description: Covers various styles of contemporary Christian music.

780 016 HU ISSN 0133-5782
ML120.H9
MAGYAR NEMZETI BIBLIOGRAFIA. ZENEMUVEK BIBLIOGRAFIAJA. 1977. q. 600 Ft. Orszagos Szechenyi Konyvtar, Budavari Palota F epulet, 1827 Budapest, Hungary. TEL 36-1-175-0096. FAX 36-1-202-0804. TELEX 224226 BIBLN H. (Subscr. to: Kultura Kulkereskedelmi Vallalat, Pf. 149, 1389 Budapest, Hungary) Ed. Eva Kelemen. circ. 200. **Document type:** bibliography.
  Supersedes in part (in 1977): Magyar Nemzeti Bibliografia (ISSN 0373-1766); Also supersedes (1970-1977): Magyar Zenemuvek Bibliografiaja (ISSN 0200-0679)
  Description: Bibliography of musical compositions and recordings published in Hungary and officially deposited in the National Szechenyi Library.

780 PL
MATERIALY DO BIBLIOGRAFII MUZYKI POLSKIEJ. 1954. irreg. price varies. Polskie Wydawnictwo Muzyczne, Al. Krasinskiego 11a, 31-111 Krakow, Poland. TEL 48-12-227044. FAX 48-12-220174. Ed. Tadeusz Strumillo. adv. contact: Teresa Wlochynska. **Document type:** bibliography.
  Description: Covers publications concerning music published and copied in Polish and Polish authors' works published in foreign languages.

MEDIA REVIEW DIGEST; the only complete guide to reviews of non-book media. see MOTION PICTURES — Abstracting, Bibliographies, Statistics

780 US
MELLEN OPERA REFERENCE INDEX. irreg., latest no.25. Edwin Mellen Press, 415 Ridge St., Box 450, Lewiston, NY 14092. TEL 716-754-2766. FAX 716-754-4056. **Document type:** bibliography.

780 793 US
MUSIC AND DANCE PERIODICALS; an international directory and guide book. 1989. irreg. $65. Peri Press, Hemlock Ridge, Box 348, Voorheesville, NY 12186-0348. TEL 518-765-3163; 800-677-4492. FAX 518-765-3158. Ed. Doris Robinson. **Document type:** directory.

MUSIC & MUSICIANS: BRAILLE SCORES CATALOG - CHORAL (LARGE-PRINT EDITION). see HANDICAPPED — Abstracting, Bibliographies, Statistics

MUSIC & MUSICIANS: BRAILLE SCORES CATALOG - INSTRUMENTAL (LARGE-PRINT EDITION). see HANDICAPPED — Abstracting, Bibliographies, Statistics

MUSIC & MUSICIANS: BRAILLE SCORES CATALOG - ORGAN (LARGE-PRINT EDITION). see HANDICAPPED — Abstracting, Bibliographies, Statistics

MUSIC & MUSICIANS: BRAILLE SCORES CATALOG - PIANO (LARGE-PRINT EDITION). see HANDICAPPED — Abstracting, Bibliographies, Statistics

MUSIC & MUSICIANS: BRAILLE SCORES CATALOG - VOCAL. PART I: CLASSICAL (LARGE-PRINT EDITION). see HANDICAPPED — Abstracting, Bibliographies, Statistics

MUSIC & MUSICIANS: BRAILLE SCORES CATALOG - VOCAL. PART II: POPULAR (LARGE-PRINT EDITION). see HANDICAPPED — Abstracting, Bibliographies, Statistics

MUSIC & MUSICIANS: INSTRUCTIONAL CASSETTE RECORDINGS CATALOG (LARGE-PRINT EDITION). see HANDICAPPED — Abstracting, Bibliographies, Statistics

MUSIC & MUSICIANS: INSTRUCTIONAL DISC RECORDINGS CATALOG (LARGE-PRINT EDITION). see HANDICAPPED — Abstracting, Bibliographies, Statistics

MUSIC & MUSICIANS: LARGE-PRINT SCORES AND BOOKS CATALOG (LARGE-PRINT EDITION). see HANDICAPPED — Abstracting, Bibliographies, Statistics

780 016 US ISSN 0027-4240
ML1
MUSIC ARTICLE GUIDE; annotated guide to selected feature articles in American music periodicals with special emphasis on the special needs of school and college music educators. 1965. q. $58. Information Services, Inc., Box 27066, Philadelphia, PA 19118. TEL 215-848-3540. Ed. Morris Henken. index. (also avail. in microfilm from UMI; reprint service avail. from UMI) **Document type:** abstracting/indexing.
—UMI.

780 US ISSN 0146-7883
MUSIC-IN-PRINT SERIES. 1974. irreg. price varies. Musicdata, Inc., Box 48010, Philadelphia, PA 19144-8010. TEL 215-842-0555. FAX 215-842-0597. Ed. Mark Daugherty. adv. contact: Noah Simon. bibl. circ. 2,000. **Document type:** catalog.
  Description: Goal is to locate and catalog all printed music published throughout the world, and to keep the information current by publishing supplements and revised editions.

780 016 US ISSN 0027-4348
ML118
MUSIC INDEX; a subject-author guide to over 300 current international periodicals. CD-ROM edition (ISSN 1066-1514) (Supplement avail. Music Index Subject Heading List) (Entries are in language of country of origin) 1949. m. $1235 (includes Subject Heading List). Harmonie Park Press, 23630 Pinewood, Warren, MI 48091-4759. TEL 810-755-3080. Ed. Nadia Stratelak. bk.rev.; bibl.; cum.index. circ. 900. **Document type:** abstracting/indexing.
●Also available on CD-ROM.
  Description: Bibliography-guide to current music periodicals worldwide.

780 029.5 US ISSN 0094-6478
MUSIC LIBRARY ASSOCIATION. INDEX AND BIBLIOGRAPHY SERIES. 1964. irreg. price varies. Music Library Association, Box 487, Canton, MA 02021. TEL 617-828-8450. Ed. Deborah Campana. circ. 250. **Document type:** abstracting/indexing.
—BLDSC (5879.713700).
  Formerly: Music Library Association. Index Series (ISSN 0077-2445)
  Description: Analytical indexes to music serials and music materials.

780 US ISSN 0736-7740
MUSIC REFERENCE COLLECTION. 1983. irreg. Greenwood Press, Inc. (Subsidiary of: Greenwood Publishing Group Inc.), 88 Post Rd. W., Box 5007, Westport, CT 06881-5007. TEL 203-226-3571. FAX 203-222-1502.
—BLDSC (5990.401500).

016.78 DK
MUSIKALER I DANSKE BIBLIOTEKER/MUSIC IN DANISH LIBRARIES; accessionskatalog/union catalogue. (Text in Danish; summaries in Danish and English) 1971. a. (plus q. updates). DKK 5950. Dansk BiblioteksCenter, Tempovej 7-11, DK-2750 Ballerup, Denmark. TEL 45-44-97-40-00. FAX 45-44-68-24-42.
●Available only online.
  Former titles (until 1993): Musikaler I Danske Biblioteker (Mikroform) (ISSN 0109-0364); (until 1983): Musikalier I Danske Biblioteker (ISSN 0085-3623)

780 016 JA
ONGAKU BUNKEN YOSHI MOKUROKU. 1973. a. 3000 Yen (effective since 1993). R I L M National Committee of Japan, Musashino Music College, 1-13 Hazawa, Nerima-ku, Tokyo 176, Japan. (Affiliate: International Repertory of Music Literature) Ed. Toshiko Sekine. adv. contact: Kazuo Fukushima. bk.rev. circ. 1,000. **Document type:** bibliography.
  Formerly: Nihon Ongaku Bunken Yoshi Mokuroku.
  Description: Annotated bibliography of music literature in Japan.

016.78 UK ISSN 0958-5702
P O P S I. (Popular Song Index) a. £23 (foreign £28); diskette £105 (foreign £110) (effective 1996). British Library, Document Supply Centre, Boston Spa, Wetherby, W. Yorks. LS23 7BQ, England. TEL 01937-546080. FAX 01937-546286. TELEX 557381. (Subscr. to: Turpin Distribution Services Ltd., Blackhorse Rd., Letchworth, Herts. SG6 1HN, England. TEL 01462-672555. FAX 01462-480947) (microfiche; also avail. in diskette format) **Document type:** abstracting/indexing.
—BLDSC (6550.074950).

789.91 US
PHONOLOG REPORTER; all-in-one-reporter. 1948. w. $486. Trade Service Corporation, 10996 Torreyana Rd., Box 85007, San Diego, CA 92186-9982. TEL 619-457-5920. FAX 619-457-1320. Ed. Bonnie J. Dudley. (looseleaf format; also avail. in diskette format)
●Also available on CD-ROM.
  Description: Lists pre-recorded music in all formats. Indexed by album artist, and song title.

780 016 US ISSN 0033-6955
ML1
R I L M ABSTRACTS OF MUSIC LITERATURE. (Repertoire International de Litterature Musicale) CD-ROM version: M U S E, Music Search (ISSN 1054-2639) 1967. s-a. $90 to individuals; institutions $480 (effective 1996). R I L M Abstracts, City University of New York, 33 W. 42nd St., New York, NY 10036. TEL 212-642-2709. FAX 212-642-2642. E-mail: bdm@cunyvms1.gc.cuny.edu. (Co-sponsors: International Association of Music Libraries, Archives, and Documentation Centers; International Council for Traditional Music; International Musicological Society) Ed. Adam P.J. O'Connor. bk.rev.; cum.index every 5 yrs.; circ. 1,500 (controlled). (back issues avail.) **Indexed:** RILM. **Document type:** abstracting/indexing, bibliography, academic/scholarly publication.
●Also available online. Vendor(s): OCLC.
Also available on CD-ROM. Producer(s): NISC (MUSE, Music Search).
—BLDSC (7971.466000).
  Description: Provides broad, international coverage and concise abstracts from the scholarly literature of music, as well as from other related fields.

780 011 US ISSN 0896-6079
REPERTOIRE INTERNATIONAL DE LA PRESSE MUSICALE. 1987. a. $125 per vol. U M I Company, 300 N. Zeeb Rd., Ann Arbor, MI 48106. TEL 313-761-4700; 800-521-0600. FAX 313-761-1203. Ed. H. Robert Cohen. **Document type:** abstracting/indexing.
  Description: Indexes 19th-Century music periodicals in Europe and North America.

780 016　　　　US
ML156.2
SCHWANN ARTIST. 1975. s-a. $15. Schwann Publications, 440 Cerrillos Rd., Ste. B, Santa Fe, NM 87501. TEL 505-988-2126. (Orders to: Schwann Publications, 49 Sheridan Ave., Albany, NY 01210. TEL 800-877-2693) Eds. Kristina Melcher, Geary Kaczorowski; Pub. Bruce Shortz. adv. contact: Mark Fisher. circ. 15,000 (paid). **Document type:** catalog.
Former titles (until 1995): Artist Issue (ISSN 1063-3456); (until 1990): Schwann Artist Issue (Santa Fe) (ISSN 0893-7486); (until 1986): Schwann Artist Issue (Boston) (ISSN 0582-1487)
Description: Lists more than 45,000 classical music compact discs, LPs, cassette tapes, and CD-videos by name of artist, conductor, and orchestra.

789.913　　US　　ISSN 1066-2138
ML156.2
SCHWANN OPUS. 1949. q. $29.95. Schwann Publications (Subsidiary of: Stereophile), 440 Cerrillos Rd., Ste. C, Santa Fe, NM 87501. TEL 505-988-2126. (Subscr. to: Schwann Publications, 49 Sheridan Ave., Albany, NY 12210. TEL 800-877-2693) Eds. Kristina Melcher, Geary Kaczorowski; Pub. Bruce Shortz. adv. contact: Mark Fisher. circ. 21,000 (paid). **Document type:** catalog.
Former titles (until 1991): Opus (ISSN 1047-2355); (until 1990): Schwann-1 Record and Tape Guide (ISSN 0160-1571); Schwann-1, Records and Tapes (ISSN 0098-356X); Schwann Record and Tape Guide (ISSN 0036-715X)
Description: Lists more than 45,000 classical music compact discs, records, and cassettes by composer.

016　　　　US　　ISSN 1065-9161
ML156.2
SCHWANN SPECTRUM. 1949. q. $24.95. Schwann Publications (Subsidiary of: Stereophile), 440 Cerrillos Rd., Ste. B, Santa Fe, NM 87501. TEL 505-988-2126. (Subscr. to: Schwann Publications, 49 Sheridan Ave., Albany, NY 12210. TEL 800-877-2693) Eds. Kristina Melcher, Geary Kaczorowski; Pub. Bruce Shortz. adv. contact: Mark Fisher. circ. 18,000 (paid). **Document type:** catalog.
Former titles (until 1991): Spectrum (Santa Fe) (ISSN 1047-2371); (until 1990): Schwann-2 Record and Tape Guide (ISSN 0271-5783); Schwann-2, Records and Tapes (ISSN 0099-0167)
Description: Lists more than 65,000 compact discs, cassette tapes, LPs, DCCs, minidics, and laserdiscs of all types of popular music.

780　　　　XO
SLOVENSKA NARODNA BIBLIOGRAFIA SERIA H: HUDOBNINY. (Text in German, Slovak; summaries in English, French, German, Slovak) 1981. a. Matica Slovenska, Slovenska Narodna Kniznica, Ul. L. Novomeskeho 32, 036 52 Martin, Slovakia. TEL 0842-313-71. FAX 0842-324-54. TELEX 075 331. Ed. Anna Kucianova. (back issues avail.) **Document type:** bibliography.

780 011　　US　　ISSN 1055-5536
ML136.U5
U.S. LIBRARY OF CONGRESS. MUSIC CATALOG ON MICROFICHE. (Text in various languages) 1973. a. $115 to N. American libraries (foreign libraries $130). (U.S. Library of Congress, Cataloging Distribution Service, Customer Service Section) Advanced Library Systems, Inc., 100 Brickstone Sq., Box 246, Andover, MA 01810-0005. TEL 508-470-0610. FAX 508-475-1072. (Subscr. also to: Superintendent of Documents, U.S. Government Printing Office, Box 317954, Pittsburgh, PA 15250-7954. TEL 202-512-1800. FAX 202-512-2250) (microfiche) **Document type:** bibliography, catalog, government publication.
●Also available on CD-ROM. Producer(s): NISC (Muse).
—BLDSC (5990.243000).
Former titles (until 1989): Music, Books on Music and Sound Recordings (ISSN 0092-2838); U.S. Library of Congress Catalog - Music and Phonorecords (ISSN 0041-7793)

MUSIC — Computer Applications

see also Computers–Computer Music

780　　　　US
A T M I INTERNATIONAL NEWSLETTER. 1977. q. $30 (foreign $40) includes Technology Directory. Association for Technology in Music Instruction, c/o Gary S. Karpinski, Pres., Dept. of Music, University of Massachusetts, Amherst, MA 01003. TEL 413-545-4229. Ed. Barbara Murphy. bk.rev. circ. 325. (tabloid format) **Indexed:** ERIC. **Document type:** newsletter.
Former titles: Association for Technology in Music Instruction Newsletter; National Consortium for Computer-Based Music Instruction. Newsletter.

780　　　　US
A T M I TECHNOLOGY DIRECTORY. a. $30 (foreign $40) includes Newsletter. Association for Technology in Music Instruction, c/o Gary S. Karpinski, Pres., Dept. of Music, University of Massachusetts, Amherst, MA 01003. TEL 413-545-4229. bk.rev. **Document type:** directory.
Description: Includes listings and information about hardware, software, video discs, and other materials related to technology-based music instruction.

780　　　　US
AFTERTOUCH; new music discoveries. 1991. q. $10 (Canada $15; elsewhere $25). Creative Musicians Coalition, 1024 W. Wilcox Ave., Peoria, IL 61604. TEL 309-685-4843. FAX 309-685-4878. Ed. Ron Wallace. adv. contact: Ron Wallace. circ. 7,000. (back issues avail.) **Document type:** catalog, consumer publication, trade publication.
Description: Features write-ups about new music and video art and the artists. Includes articles, feature columns, resource material, a directory, reviews and interviews, and a unique dialogue between artists and listeners.

780 620.2　　US　　ISSN 0148-9267
ML1　　　　　CODEN: CMUJDY
COMPUTER MUSIC JOURNAL. 1977. q. $42 to individuals (foreign $58); institutions $105 (foreign $121); students $30 (foreign $46). M I T Press, 55 Hayward St., Cambridge, MA 02142. TEL 617-253-2889. FAX 617-258-6779. TELEX 921473. E-mail: journals-orders@mit.edu. (Editorial addr.: Box 9496, Berkeley, CA 94709-0496) Ed. Stephen Pope. adv.; bk.rev.; illus. circ. 4,000. (also avail. in microfilm from UMI; back issues avail.; reprint service avail. from UMI) **Indexed:** Arts & Hum.Cit.Ind., Compumath, Comput.Cont., Comput.Rev., Curr.Cont., Eng.Ind., Ind.Sci.Rev., Inform.Sci.Abstr., INSPEC, LAMP, Music Artic.Guide, Music Ind., RILM, Sci.Cit.Ind.
●Also available online.
—BLDSC (3394.113000); Ei; Faxon; Genuine Article; SWETS; UMI; UnCover. **CCC.**
Description: Resource for musicians, composers, scientists, engineers and computer enthusiasts interested in contemporary and electronic music and computer-generated sound.
Refereed Serial

780　　　　US　　ISSN 1046-1744
ML73
COMPUTERS IN MUSIC RESEARCH. 1989. a. $16. Wisconsin Center for Music Technology, School of Music, University of Wisconsin, Madison, WI 53706. TEL 608-263-1900. Ed. John W. Schaffer. bk.rev. circ. 230. (back issues avail.) **Indexed:** Music Ind., RILM. **Document type:** academic/scholarly publication.
—BLDSC (3394.925330); UnCover.
Description: Covers the application of computers and technology to the study of music.
Refereed Serial

780　　　　US　　ISSN 1057-9478
ML73
COMPUTING AND MUSICOLOGY; an international directory of applications. 1985. a. Center for Computer Assisted Research in the Humanities, 525 Middlefield Rd., Ste. 120, Menlo Park, CA 94025. TEL 415-322-3307. FAX 415-329-8365. Eds. Walter B. Hewlett, Eleanor Selfridge-Field. **Document type:** academic/scholarly publication, directory.
—BLDSC (3395.083000).
Description: Covers applications involving both textual and musical information.

781.64　　　UK　　ISSN 0967-0378
FUTURE MUSIC. 1992. m. £37.95 (overseas £80) (includes free compact disc). Future Publishing, 30 Monmouth St., Bath, Avon BA1 2BW, England. TEL 01225-442244. FAX 01225-462986. (Subscr. to: Future Publishing, Freepost, Somerton, Somers. TA11 7BR, England. TEL 01225-822511) Ed. Andy Jones. circ. 23,112. **Document type:** consumer publication.
Description: Contains news, reviews of music equipment, and profiles of musicians. Covers all aspects of computer music.

780　　　　US　　ISSN 1075-1041
ML73.M53
M I D I.* (Musical Instrument Digital Interface) 1992. bi-m. $19.95 (effective 1993). G W Publishing, 592A Washington St., Wellesley, MA 02181-6417. TEL 617-965-6900. Ed. George O'Conor. circ. 15,000.

780　　　　GR
MOUSIKI. m. Dr.5000($40) Epsilon, 176 3rd Septemvriou, 112 51 Athens, Greece. TEL 30-1-8640845. FAX 30-1-8643533. Ed. Nick Grammatikas. music rev. (back issues avail.)

786.7　　　　US
ROLAND USERS GROUP MAGAZINE; the magazine for the electronic musician. vol.11, no.2. s-a. Roland Corporation U S, 7200 Dominion Cir., Los Angeles, CA 90040. TEL 213-685-5141. Ed. Ernie Rideout; Pub. Nancy Kewin. adv.; illus. **Document type:** trade publication.
Description: News, product reviews, information and technical tips for musicians using Roland equipment.

SMALL COMPUTERS IN THE ARTS NEWS. see *ART — Computer Applications*

SYMPOSIUM ON SMALL COMPUTERS IN THE ARTS. PROCEEDINGS. see *ART — Computer Applications*

MYSTERY AND DETECTIVE

see Literature–Mystery and Detective

NEEDLEWORK

746　　　　US
ALL TIME FAVORITE CROCHET. 1985. a. Harris Publications, Inc., 1115 Broadway, 8th fl., New York, NY 10010. TEL 212-807-7100. Ed. Barbara Jacksier. bk.rev. (back issues avail.)
Description: Covers needlework patterns.

746　　　　US　　ISSN 8756-6591
TT835
AMERICAN QUILTER. 1985. q. $18 (foreign $28) includes membership (effective 1995). American Quilter's Society, Box 3290, Paducah, KY 42002-3290. TEL 502-898-7903. FAX 502-898-8890. Ed. Victoria Faoro. adv. contact: Rick Loyd. bk.rev. circ. 70,000. **Document type:** consumer publication.
—Faxon.
Description: Serves today's quilters with articles on quilt designing techniques, study, exhibition, issues, events.

746.4　　　US　　ISSN 0745-6360
ANNIE'S CROCHET NEWSLETTER. 1982. bi-m. $17.95. Annie's Attic, Inc., 1 Annie Ln., Box 212B, Big Sandy, TX 75755. TEL 903-636-4303. Ed. Annie Potter. circ. 114,812 (paid). **Document type:** consumer publication.
Description: For those interested in crochet; includes patterns with instruction and hints.

746　　　　US　　ISSN 1051-3337
ANNIE'S QUICK & EASY PATTERN CLUB. 1980. bi-m. $17.95. Annie's Attic, Inc., 1 Annie Ln., Box 212B, Big Sandy, TX 75755. TEL 903-636-4303. Ed. Annie Potter. circ. 61,057 (paid). **Document type:** consumer publication.
Formerly: Annie's Pattern Club Newsletter (ISSN 0199-7106)
Description: For those interested in all types of needlecrafts; includes patterns with instructions and hints.

NEEDLEWORK

746   UK   ISSN 0268-5175
AUDREY BABINGTON'S WORKBOX. 1984. 4/yr. $9. Workbox Enterprises, Upcott Hall, Bishop's Hull, Taunton, Somerset TA4 1AQ, England. TEL 0823-326561. Ed. Audrey Babington. adv.; bk.rev. circ. 40,000. **Document type:** consumer publication.
Description: For needlecraft enthusiasts: news about embroidery, dollmaking, patchwork and quilting.

THE AUSTRALIAN WOMEN'S WEEKLY HANDMADE; craft, decorating, fashion. see *ARTS AND HANDICRAFTS*

746   US
BETTER HOMES AND GARDENS QUILTING. a. Meredith Corporation, Special Interest Publications, 1716 Locust St., Des Moines, IA 50336. TEL 515-284-3000. Pub. Steve Levinson. adv.: B&W page $12250, color page $16250; adv. contact: Pat Tomlinson. circ. 400,000.

746   NE   ISSN 0165-4721
BIJVOORBEELD. 1968. q. fl.48.50. Spanjaardsgat b.v., Pieterskerkhof 22, 2300 AB Leiden, Netherlands. Ed. Marjan Unger. adv. circ. 7,000.

746   US
BLANKET STATEMENTS. q. American Quilt Study Group, 660 Mission St., Ste. 400, San Francisco, CA 94105-4007. TEL 415-495-0163. FAX 415-495-3516. Ed. Christine Bowman. illus.; circ. 900 (paid). **Document type:** newsletter.
Description: Publishes quilt research articles, circulates news of AQSG and AQSQ members.

746   IT   ISSN 1120-4362
BRAVA CASA. 1974. m. L.57600. Rizzoli Editore-Corriere della Sera, Via A. Rizzoli 2, 20132 Milan, Italy. TEL 02-2588. Ed. Carla Giagnoni. adv.: B&W page L.28200000; 200 x 255; adv. contact: Flavio Biondi. circ. 260,593.
Formerly (until 1985): Brava (ISSN 0392-3193)

746   GW
BURDA BABYMASCHEN. s-a. Verlag Aenne Burda, Am Kestendamm 2, 77652 Offenburg, Germany. TEL 0781-8402. Ed. Iris Hanle-Schmidt. circ. 180,000.

746   GW
BURDA FILETHAEKELN. a. Verlag Aenne Burda, Am Kestendamm 2, 77652 Offenburg, Germany. TEL 0781-8402. Ed. Maria Blumrich. circ. 225,000.

746   GW
BURDA KINDERMASCHEN. q. Verlag Aenne Burda, Am Kestendamm 2, 77652 Offenburg, Germany. TEL 0781-8402. Ed. Iris Hanle-Schmidt. circ. 150,000.

746   GW
BURDA KREUZSTICH. a. Verlag Aenne Burda, Am Kestendamm 2, 77652 Offenburg, Germany. TEL 0781-8402. Ed. Maria Blumrich. circ. 120,000.

746   GW
BURDA MASCHENMUSTER. q. Verlag Aenne Burda, Am Kestendamm 2, 77652 Offenburg, Germany. TEL 0781-8402. Ed. Iris Hanle-Schmidt. circ. 180,000.

BURDA MODEN (ARABIC EDITION). see *BEAUTY CULTURE*

746   UK
BUTTERICK CRAFTS & NEEDLEWORK. 1991. q. £7.80 (foreign £11.50); newsstand price: £1.95. Butterick Company Ltd., New Ln., Havant, Hants. PO9 2ND, England. TEL 01705-486221. FAX 01705-192769. Ed. Gail Goldie. adv.: B&W page £819; color page £1212; adv. contact: Vivien Ryan. bk.rev.; illus.; tr.lit.; circ. 50,000 (paid). **Document type:** consumer publication.
Description: Provides a selection of traditional and trend-setting needlework and crafts, offering color photographs of completed projects, along with step-by-step instructions.

746   CN
CANADA QUILTS MAGAZINE. 1975. 5/yr. Can.$18.50($22) (Canada Quilts) Deborrah Sherman, Ed. & Pub., P.O. Box 39, Sta. A, Hamilton, Ont. L8N 3A2, Canada. TEL 416-523-5828. FAX 416-523-7222. adv.; bk.rev. circ. 3,500. (back issues avail.)
Formerly: Canada Quilts (ISSN 0381-7369)
Description: Contains patterns, instructions, quilting news from across Canada, color photos, product reviews, an antique column and events listed by region.

746   US
CAST ON. 1984. 5/yr. $23 (Canada & Mexico $30; elsewhere $38). Knitting Guild of America, 502 S. Gay St., Ste. 410, Knoxville, TN 37902. TEL 615-524-2401. FAX 615-521-6034. Ed. Carol S. Wigginton. adv. contact: Michelle Renee McDaniel. bk.rev.; bibl.; charts; illus.; tr.lit. circ. 10,000. (back issues avail.) **Indexed:** Ind.How To Do It (1990-).
Description: Provides education and communication for hand and machine knitters wishing to advance the quality of workmanship and creativity in their knitting endeavors.

746   JA
CHARM. (Text in Japanese) 1975. bi-m. 2320 Yen. Shufu-to-Seikatsusha Ltd., 5-7, 3-chome, Kyobashi, Chuo-ku, Tokyo 104, Japan. Ed. Tsuguo Nakamura.

746 745.5   US
CHRISTMAS: YEAR ROUND NEEDLEWORK & CRAFT IDEAS. bi-m. $2.95 per no. Oxmoor Publishing, 2100 Lakeshore Dr., Birmingham, AL 35209. TEL 205-877-6000.

746   US   ISSN 8755-2655
THE CLOTH DOLL; the finest quality cloth doll magazine. 1982. q. $15.95. Judy Beswick, Pub., Box 2167, Lake Oswego, OR 97035. TEL 503-244-3539. Ed. Leta Bergman. adv.; bk.rev. circ. 4,800. **Indexed:** Ind.How To Do It (1984-).
Description: Contains how-to articles, supply sources, features on doll makers, and patterns.

746   US   ISSN 1054-3155
COUNTRY STITCH. bi-m. $2.95 per no. Oxmoor Publishing, 2100 Lakeshore Dr., Birmingham, AL 35209. TEL 205-877-6000.

746   US   ISSN 0887-9818
TT159
CRAFT & NEEDLEWORK AGE ANNUAL TRADE DIRECTORY. a. $40. Hobby Publications, Inc., 225 Gordons Corner Plaza, Box 420, Manalapan, NJ 07726. TEL 908-446-4900. FAX 908-446-5488. Ed. Karen Ancona. circ. 25,000. **Document type:** directory.
Former titles: Annual Basic Industry Trade Directory; Craft, Model and Hobby Industry Annual Trade Directory; Craft and Needlework Age - World of Miniatures Annual Trade Directory.

746   US   ISSN 1060-0493
CREATIVE MACHINE. 1990. q. $16 (effective 1994). Open Chain Publishing, Inc., Box 2634, Menlo Park, CA 94026. TEL 415-366-4440. FAX 415-366-4455. Ed. Robbie Fanning. adv.; bk.rev.; illus.; circ. 5,000 (paid). **Document type:** newsletter.
Description: Projects and advice for sewing machine lovers.

746   US   ISSN 0887-3690
CREATIVE QUILTING. 1986. $24. Grass Roots Publishing Co., Inc., 950 Third Ave., 16th Fl., New York, NY 10022. TEL 212-888-1855. adv.; bk.rev. circ. 225,000. **Document type:** consumer publication.
Description: Features step-by-step instructions and diagrams for various levels of quilters. Each issue contains patterns for different types of quilts. Includes a buyer's guide and articles on well-known quilters.

746   US
CROCHET. 1981. q. $2.50 per no. Harris Publications, Inc., 1115 Broadway, 8th fl., New York, NY 10010. TEL 212-807-7100. Ed. Georgiana Heyda. adv.; illus.
Description: Contains illustrations and detailed instructions for a variety of crochet projects, some submitted by readers.

746   FR   ISSN 0395-6997
CROCHET D'ART. 1974. m. 210 F. Editions de Saxe, 20 rue Croix-Barret, 69358 Lyon Cedex 07, France. TEL 78-72-92-54. FAX 78-72-64-18. Ed. J. Deschavanne. circ. 66,000.
Formerly: Tout le Tricot - Le Crochet et le Tricot d'Art (ISSN 0183-3898)

746   US   ISSN 1074-1798
CROCHET DIGEST. 1981. q. $9.95. House of White Birches Publishing, 306 E. Parr Rd., Berne, IN 46711. TEL 219-589-8741. FAX 219-589-8093. Ed. Laura Scott. circ. 62,000 (paid). (back issues avail.) **Document type:** consumer publication.
Formerly (until 1993): Women's Circle Crochet (ISSN 0279-1978)
Description: Contains patterns for afghans, doilies, toys, clothing, holiday decorations, bazaar items.

746   US   ISSN 8750-8877
CROCHET FANTASY. 1983. 8/yr. $31.60. All American Crafts, Inc., 243 Newton-Sparta Rd., Newton, NJ 07860-2748. TEL 201-383-8080. Eds. Karen Manthey, Janice Edsall. adv. contact: Barbara Smith. bk.rev.; illus. circ. 198,000. **Document type:** consumer publication.
Description: Publication for crochet enthusiasts featuring photographs, instructions, and diagrams for traditional and contemporary garments, accessories, and home decor.

746   US   ISSN 1046-719X
CROCHET HOME. 1987. bi-m. $14.95. Needlecraft Shop, Inc., 206 West St., Big Sandy, TX 75755. TEL 903-636-4011. FAX 903-636-4088. (Subscr. to: 23 Old Pecan Rd., Big Sandy, TX 75755) Ed. Jennifer Simcik. circ. 68,000. (back issues avail.) **Document type:** consumer publication.
Formerly (until 1989): Crochet Fun.
Description: Crochet patterns and instructions for home decorating, toys, and clothing for the beginner and experienced stitcher alike.

746   US
CROCHET PATTERNS. bi-m. P J S Publications, Inc., New Plaza, Box 1790, Peoria, IL 61656. TEL 309-682-6626. Ed. Anne Reed. circ. 200,000. **Document type:** consumer publication.

746   US   ISSN 0164-7962
CROCHET WORLD. 1978. bi-m. $12.97. House of White Birches Publishing, 306 E. Parr Rd., Berne, IN 46711. TEL 219-589-8741. Ed. Susan Hankins. illus. circ. 70,000. **Document type:** consumer publication.
Description: Contains 15 to 25 patterns for afghans and doilies, plus contests and question and answers.

746   US   ISSN 1057-7076
CROCHET WORLD SPECIALS. 1978. q. $9.95. House of White Birches Publishing, 306 E. Parr Rd., Berne, IN 46711. TEL 219-589-8741. Ed. Susan Hankins. circ. 35,000.
Former titles: Crochet Today Fashions (ISSN 1041-0759); Crochet World Omnibook.
Description: Contains 15 to 25 needlework patterns, plus contests and question and answers.

746 745.5   US
CROSS QUICK - CROSS STITCH. m. $3.50 per no. Meredith Corporation, 1716 Locust St., Des Moines, IA 50366. TEL 515-284-2484. FAX 515-284-2700. (Subscr. to: 70 W. 36th St., 15th Fl., New York, NY 10018)

746   US   ISSN 0886-6600
CROSS STITCH & COUNTRY CRAFTS. bi-m. $19.90. Meredith Corporation, 1716 Locust St., Des Moines, IA 50336. TEL 515-284-3000. FAX 515-284-3863. (Alt. addr.: 4118 Lakeside Dr., Richmond, CA 94806. TEL 510-262-7700) Ed. Carol Field Dahlstrom. circ. 2,000,000.

746   US
CROSS STITCH CHRISTMAS. 1990. a. $3.50. Meredith Corporation, 1716 Locust St., Des Moines, IA 50336. TEL 515-284-3000. (Alt. addr.: 4118 Lakeside Dr., Richmond, CA 94806. TEL 510-262-7700) Ed. Joan Cravens. adv.: B&W page $10550, color page $14325; trim 8 x 10 1/2. circ. 600,000. **Document type:** consumer publication.

745.5 UK ISSN 0965-8602
CROSS-STITCH COLLECTION. 1992. bi-m. Future Publishing Ltd., 30 Monmouth St., Bath, Avon BA1 2BW, England. TEL 01225-442244. FAX 01225-462986. (Subscr. to: Future Publishing Ltd., Somerton, Somerset TA11 6BR, England. TEL 01225-822511) Ed. Rebecca Bradshaw. adv. contact: Elizabeth Snow. bk.rev.; circ. 70,873 (paid). (back issues avail.) **Document type:** consumer publication.
Description: Contains a selection of charted designs for experienced cross-stitchers.

746 US
CROSS STITCH COUNTRY. 1993. a. $3.50. Meredith Corporation, 1716 Locust St., Des Moines, IA 50336. TEL 515-284-3000. (Alt. addr.: 4118 Lakeside Dr., Richmond, CA 94806. TEL 510-262-7700) Ed. Joan Cravens. adv.: B&W page $8660, color page $11495; trim 8 x 10 1/2. circ. 500,000. **Document type:** consumer publication.

746 US ISSN 1056-7542
CROSS STITCH! MAGAZINE. 1990. bi-m. $14.95. Needlecraft Shop, Inc., 206 West St., Big Sandy, TX 75755. TEL 903-636-4011. FAX 903-636-4088. (Subscr. to: 23 Old Pecan Rd., Big Sandy, TX 75755) Ed. Jennifer Simcik. circ. 59,000. (back issues avail.) **Document type:** consumer publication.
Description: Presents cross stitch patterns and instructions for home decorating and clothing.

746 US ISSN 1054-3430
CROSS-STITCH PLUS. 1984. bi-m. $12.97. House of White Birches Publishing, 306 E. Parr Rd., Berne, IN 46711. TEL 219-589-8741. Ed. Lana Schurb. adv. circ. 66,000. (back issues avail.) **Document type:** consumer publication.
Former titles: Women's Circle Counted Cross-Stitch; Women's Circle Counted Cross-Stitch and Candlewicking.
Description: Contains 20 or more patterns, interviews with designers and reference material.

746 US ISSN 1055-2871
CROSS-STITCHER. 1983. 6/yr. $14.97. Clapper Communications Companies, 2400 E. Devon Ave., Ste. 375, Des Plaines, IL 60018-4618. TEL 708-635-5800. FAX 708-635-6311. Ed. B.J. McDonald. circ. 64,700. (back issues avail.) **Document type:** consumer publication.

745.5 UK ISSN 0966-811X
CROSS-STITCHER. 1992. m. £28 (foreign £53.80). Future Publishing, 30 Monmouth St., Bath, Avon BA1 2BW, England. TEL 0225-442244. FAX 0225-462986. (Subscr. to: Future Publishing, Somerton, Somerset TA11 6BR, England. TEL 0225-822511) Ed. Mary Lojkine. adv. contact: Elizabeth Snow. circ. 77,021 (paid). (back issues avail.) **Document type:** consumer publication.
Description: Contains cross-stitch projects and articles, as well as news and product reviews.

746 US
ELIZABETH ZIMMERMANN'S WOOL GATHERING. 1959. s-a. $15 for 3 yrs. (foreign $22). Schoolhouse Press, 6899 Cary Bluff, Pittsville, WI 54466. TEL 715-884-2799. FAX 715-884-2829. Ed. Meg Swansen. bk.rev.; video rev.; circ. 9,000 (paid). (back issues avail.) **Document type:** newsletter.
Formerly: Wool Gathering.
Description: Aimed at handknitters; includes complete instructions for an original Meg Swansen or Elizabeth Zimmermann design.

746 SP
ESPECIAL LABORES. 1954. a. H Y M S.A., Aribau 28, 08011 Barcelona, Spain. TEL 3237063. FAX 4541322. Ed. Eulalia Ubach Nuet. adv. circ. 60,000.

746 IT
FANTASTICA MAGLIA.* 1982. m. Curcio Periodici S.p.A., Via IV Novembre 149, 00187 Rome, Italy. Ed. Rosanna Falconi. adv. circ. 245,000.

746 US ISSN 8750-8869
FASHION KNITTING. 1981. bi-m. $29.70. All American Crafts, Inc., 243 Newton-Sparta Rd., Newton, NJ 07860-2748. TEL 201-383-8080. FAX 201-383-8133. Ed. Sally V. Klein. adv. contact: Barbara Smith. illus. circ. 102,000. **Document type:** consumer publication.
Description: Publication for knitting enthusiasts featuring contemporary knitted garment designs, photographs, instructions, diagrams and more.

FASHION POETRY PATTERNS & RECITALS NEWS. see *WOMEN'S INTERESTS*

FIBRE NORTH. see *TEXTILE INDUSTRIES AND FABRICS*

746 US ISSN 0270-2959
TT740
FLYING NEEDLE. 1971. q. $35. Council of American Embroiderers, 588 St. Charles Ave., N.E., Atlanta, GA 30308. TEL 404-873-3550. (Subscr. to: c/o Cheryl Christian, 7912 Eikhorn Mtn. Trail, Tustin, TX 78729) Ed. Jeane Hutchins. adv. contact: Linda Scarman. bk.rev. circ. 3,500. (back issues avail.)
—UnCover.
Description: Covers all areas of fiber using a threaded needle. Includes artists' profiles, information on exhibitions, and how-to articles.

746 US ISSN 1040-3965
FOR THE LOVE OF CROSS STITCH. 1988. 6/yr. $12.95. Leisure Arts, Box 56099, Little Rock, AR 72215-6099. Ed. Anne Van Wagner Young.

746 DK ISSN 0905-4596
HAANDARBEJDE TRIN FOR TRIN. 1974. m. DKK 38.50. Bonniers Specialmagasiner A-S, Strandboulevarden 130, 2100 Copenhagen OE, Denmark. TEL 45-39-29-55-00. FAX 45-39-29-01-99. Ed. Merete Rude. circ. 125,000.
Formerly (until 1990): Alt om Haandarbejde (ISSN 0900-3649)
Description: Features articles on knitting, sewing and crocheting for women, men and children.

746 DK ISSN 0107-1769
HAANDARBEJDETS FREMME/DANISH HANDCRAFT GUILD. 1934. q. DKK 300($55) Selskabet til Haandarbejdets Fremme, Sekretariatet, Fredericiagade 21, DK-1310 Copenhagen, Denmark. TEL 45-33-12-07-15. FAX 45-33-15-07-16. Ed. Ove Storm. adv.; bk.rev. circ. 6,000.

746 GW ISSN 0017-7156
HANDARBEIT. 1964. q. DM.9.60. Zeitschriftenverlag fuer die Frau, Friedrich-Ebert-Str. 76-78, 04109 Leipzig, Germany.

746 US
HANDWORKER. 1953. bi-m. $9. Suennen Publications, Rt. 1, Box 239, Wausaukee, WI 54177. TEL 715-732-6327. Ed. Lucille Suennen. adv.; bk.rev. circ. 2,000. (back issues avail.)

746 CN ISSN 0827-2476
HEDDLE. bi-m. $7.50. Muskoka Publications Group, 27 Dominion St., Box 1906, Bracebridge, Ont. P0B 1C0, Canada. TEL 705-645-5710. FAX 705-645-3928. adv.; bk.rev.
Description: Magazine for spinners and weavers containing personality profiles, features and instructional articles.

HOBBY MERCHANDISER ANNUAL TRADE DIRECTORY. see *HOBBIES*

746 US ISSN 0893-1879
HOOKED ON CROCHET!. 1987. bi-m. $14.95. Needlecraft Shop, Inc., 206 West St., Big Sandy, TX 75755. TEL 903-636-4011. FAX 903-636-4088. (Subscr. to: 23 Old Pecan Rd., Big Sandy, TX 75755) Ed. Jennifer Simcik. circ. 80,000. (back issues avail.) **Document type:** consumer publication.

746 US
HOUSEWIVES' HANDY HINTS, SMALL BUSINESSWOMAN'S NEWSLETTER.* 1980. bi-m. $8. 67 Aberdeen Cir., Leesburg, FL 34788-7615. Ed. Jackie Barlow. circ. 150.

746 US
INSIDE A H S C A. 1978. bi-m. membership. American Home Sewing & Craft Association, 1375 Broadway, New York, NY 10018. TEL 212-302-2150. FAX 212-391-8009. Ed. Joan Katz. circ. 1,600.
Description: News of consumer motivation, education, membership and government relations programs. Includes fashion and home decorating trends and industry news.

746 US ISSN 0740-6746
INTERNATIONAL OLD LACERS, INC. BULLETIN. 1981. q. $15 membership (foreign $22). International Old Lacers, Inc., Box 265, Camden, ME 04843. TEL 207-236-0755. Ed. Susan Penner. adv.: B&W page $150; trim 8 1/2 x 11; adv. contact: Susan Penner. bk.rev.; video rev. circ. 2,000. **Document type:** bulletin.
Description: Provides current news of lace activities, improvement of skills and inspiration for new ventures. Includes features about the history and study of old lace or the preservation and expansion of the crafts of lace, regular tatting column, illustrations of members' work, patterns and ideas.

746 US ISSN 0883-0797
TT778.C76
JUST CROSS STITCH. 1983. bi-m. newsstand price: $3.95. P J S Publications, Inc., News Plaza, Box 1790, Peoria, IL 61656. TEL 309-682-6626. FAX 309-682-7394. **Document type:** consumer publication.

746 US
KEEPSAKE CALENDAR;* (year) cross-stitch collection. 1988. a. $9.97. Craftways Corporation, 1716 Locust St., Des Moines, IA 50309-3038. TEL 510-262-7700. FAX 510-223-6431. (Subscr. to: Dept. KC92, 111 Tenth St., Box 11447, Des Moines, IA 50336-1447) Ed. Joan Cravens. charts. circ. 150,000. (back issues avail.)
Description: Cross-stitch patterns, articles and instructions themed to each month for the needlework hobbyist.

746 II ISSN 0023-107X
KHATOON MASHRIQ. (Text in Urdu) 1937. m. Rs.60. 423, Matia Mahal, Ama Masjid, Delhi-6, India. Ed. Taufiq Farooqi. adv.; bk.rev.; illus. circ. 100,000.

746 DK ISSN 0900-8799
KNIPLEBREVET. 1985. q. DKK 150 membership. Foreningen Knipling i Danmark - Danish Lace Association, P.O. Box 94, DK-6270 Toender, Denmark. Dir. B. Poulsen. adv.: B&W page DKK 1000. bk.rev.; illus.; index. circ. 3,000.
Description: Devoted to lacemaking and lacemakers. Includes patterns.

746.43 US ISSN 0747-9026
KNITTERS. 1984. q. $16 (foreign $20). Golden Fleece Publications, Box 1525, Sioux Falls, SD 57101. TEL 605-338-2450. FAX 605-338-2994. Ed. Elaine Rowley; Pub. Alexis Xenakis. adv. contact: Karen Bright. bk.rev.; charts; illus.; tr.lit. (back issues avail.) **Document type:** consumer publication.
Description: Features techniques and instructions for innovative fashion knitting projects, plus interviews with designers and craftspeople.

681.7 UK ISSN 0268-7135
KNITTING AND SEWING MACHINE TIMES.* 1939. 5/yr. £9.50. Knitting and Sewing Machine Times Ltd., 15c Osborn St., London E1 6TJ, England. Ed. Shirley Barnett. adv. circ. 2,000. **Indexed:** World Text.Abstr.
Formerly (until 1985): Sewing Machine Times (ISSN 0049-030X)
Description: Deals with home sewing and knitting products; extends to allied fields of haberdashery, crafts, and sewing patterns.

746.43 US ISSN 1072-7167
KNITTING DIGEST. bi-m. $14.95. House of White Birches Publishing, 306 E. Parr Rd., Berne, IN 46711. TEL 219-589-8741. FAX 219-589-8093. Ed. Laura Scott. circ. 40,000 (paid). **Document type:** consumer publication.
Formerly: Knitting World (ISSN 0194-8083)
Description: Features 12 to 15 patterns including afghans, clothing, holiday items, dolls and toys all knitted with familiar stitches and a variety of readily available yarns.

KNITTING TECHNOLOGY. see *TEXTILE INDUSTRIES AND FABRICS*

746 US ISSN 1067-0629
KURENAI: JAPANESE EMBROIDERY JOURNAL. 1988. 4/yr. $18. Embroidery Research Press Inc., No. 200 G-4, 10800 Alpharetta Hwy., Roswell, GA 30076. TEL 404-390-0617. FAX 404-512-7837. Ed. Dolly Norton Fehd. bk.rev. circ. 400. **Document type:** academic/scholarly publication.
Description: Devoted to traditional Japanese embroidery. Articles on symbolism, color usage and design elements.

NEEDLEWORK

746   SP   ISSN 0047-3863
LABORES DEL HOGAR. 1926. m. $102.12. H Y M S.A., Aribau 28, 08011 Barcelona, Spain. TEL 3237063. FAX 454-13-22. Ed. Eulalia Ubach Nuet. adv.; bk.rev.; charts; illus. circ. 156,765.

746   UK   ISSN 0308-3039
LACE. 1976. q. £16 Europe £20; rest of world £24. Lace Guild, The Hollies, 53 Audnam, Stourbridge, West Midlands DY8 4AE, England. TEL 01384-390739. FAX 01384-444415. Ed. S. Arnold. adv.: B&W page £280. bk.rev. circ. 9,000. **Document type:** newsletter.

746   US   ISSN 0731-9916
LADY'S CIRCLE PATCHWORK QUILTS.* bi-m. Lopez Publications, Inc., 105 E. 35th St., New York, NY 10016-3877. TEL 212-689-3933. FAX 212-725-2239.
   Description: Features present-day quilts and interviews with quilters around the U.S., and provides instructions for selected designs. Includes antique quilts.

746   US
MCCALL'S CROCHET. bi-m. newsstand price: $2.95. P J S Publications, Inc., News Plaza, Box 1790, Peoria, IL 61656. TEL 309-682-6626. FAX 309-682-7394. **Document type:** consumer publication.

746   US   ISSN 1069-2894
MCCALL'S NEEDLEWORK. 1935. bi-m. $15.98 (effective 1994). (McCall Pattern Co.) Symbol of Excellence Publishers (Subsidiary of: P J S Publications, Inc.), 405 Riverhills Business Park, Birmingham, AL 35242. TEL 205-995-8860. FAX 205-995-8428. (Subscr. to: Box 3218, Harlan, IA 51537. TEL 800-289-3553) Ed. Ashley Cobb. adv.: B&W page $5535, color page $7325; adv. contact: Kip Dubois. bk.rev.; charts; illus. circ. 275,000. (back issues avail.) **Indexed:** Ind.How To Do It (1978-), MELSA. **Document type:** consumer publication.
—UMI.
   Formerly (until June 1993): McCall's Needlework and Crafts (ISSN 0024-8924)
   Description: Contains instructions for a variety of craft projects, including knitting and crocheting, embroidery, sewing and other home-based crafts, to produce fashion items as well as decorative objects.

746   UK   ISSN 0269-9761
MACHINE KNITTING MONTHLY. 1986. m. £21.60 (U.S. £34). Machine Knitting Ltd., 17 Grove Park, Waltham Rd., Maidenhead, Berkshire SL6 3LW, England. TEL 01628-829815. FAX 01628-829816. Ed. Sheila Berriff; Pub. Anne Smith. adv. contact: Brenda Hughes. bk.rev. circ. 47,000. (back issues avail.) **Document type:** consumer publication.
   Description: The latest patterns, features and news for all machine knitters.

746.43 687   UK   ISSN 0266-8505
MACHINE KNITTING NEWS. 1984. m. £22.80 in UK; elsewhere £47. Litharne Ltd., P.O. Box 9, Stratford-upon-Avon, Warwickshire CV37 8RS, England. TEL 0789-720133. FAX 0789-720888. Ed. Lynne Davies. adv. contact: Maggie Michaels. circ. 50,000. **Document type:** bulletin.

746   FR   ISSN 0246-5957
MAGIC CROCHET. no.25, 1983. bi-m. $16.25. Editions de Saxe, 20 rue Croix Barret, 69364 Lyon Cedex 7, France. (U.S. addr.: Robin Hill Park, Rt. 22, Patterson, NY 12563)

MANEQUIM. see *CLOTHING TRADE — Fashions*

MEYERS MODEBLATT. see *CLOTHING TRADE — Fashions*

746   US   ISSN 1065-0245
MINIATURE QUILTS. 6/yr. $15.95. Chitra Publications, 2 Public Ave., Montrose, PA 18801. TEL 717-278-1984. FAX 717-278-2223. **Indexed:** Ind.How To Do It (1991-). **Document type:** consumer publication.
   Description: Covers miniature quilting.

646.4   MX
MODA MOLDES. 1992. bi-m. Editorial Television S.A. de C.V., Lucio Blanco 435, Axcapotzalco 02400 Mexico D.F., Mexico. TEL 352-32-66. Dir. Aida Contreras de Pagano. adv. **Document type:** consumer publication.
   Description: Covers women's fashion. Includes patterns and instructions.

646   BL
MODA MOLDES. (Supplement avail. a.: Moda Moldes Superfacil) m. Editora Globo S.A., Rua do Curtume 665, 05065-001 Sao Paulo SP, Brazil. TEL 55-11-8746000. FAX 55-11-861-2042. adv.; illus.; circ. 138,607 (paid). **Document type:** consumer publication.
   Description: Each issue includes 70 patterns of the latest fashions.

646   BL
MODA MOLDES ESPECIAL INFANTIL. bi-m. Editora Globo S.A., Rua do Curtume 665, 05065-001 Sao Paulo SP, Brazil. TEL 55-11-8746000. FAX 55-11-8612042. adv.; illus.; circ. 37,783 (paid). **Document type:** consumer publication.
   Description: Presents patterns with instructions for practical, inexpensive and current fashions for children up to 14 years.

746 687   UK   ISSN 0957-6673
MODERN MACHINE KNITTING. m. £19.20 (foreign £31). Modern Knitting Ltd., 17 Grove Park, Waltham Rd., Maidenhead, Berkshire SL6 3LW, England. TEL 01628-829815. FAX 01628-829816. Ed. Anne Smith; Pub. Anne Smith. adv. contact: Brenda Hughes. bk.rev. (back issues avail.) **Document type:** consumer publication.
   Description: Presents the latest patterns, features and news, plus letters, hints and tips by UK's leading experts in the field.

MODUS. see *HOME ECONOMICS*

646 028.5   BL
MOLDE FACIL. bi-m. Editora Globo S.A., Rua do Curtume 665, 05065-001 Sao Paulo SP, Brazil. TEL 55-11-8746000. FAX 55-11-8612042. adv.; circ. 18,100 (paid). **Document type:** consumer publication.
   Description: Offers instructions on practical, easy-to-make everyday wear for teenagers and children.

746   US   ISSN 0273-0197
NK9100
NEEDLE AND BOBBIN CLUB BULLETIN. 1916. a. $20 to non-members. Needle and Bobbin Club, c/o Mrs. P. Guth, 955 Fifth Ave., New York, NY 10021. TEL 212-288-5525. Ed. Anne Dahlgren Hecht. adv.; bk.rev.; charts; illus. circ. 375. **Indexed:** Artbibl.Mod.

746.44   US   ISSN 0047-925X
NEEDLE ARTS. 1970. q. $24 (effective Jan. 1991). Embroiderers Guild of America, 335 W. Broadway, Ste. 100, Louisville, KY 40202. TEL 502-589-6956. FAX 502-584-7900. Ed. Jody Jeroy. adv. contact: Carolyn Deutsch. bk.rev.; charts; illus.; tr.lit. circ. 21,000. **Indexed:** Art & Archaeol.Tech.Abstr., Text.Tech.Dig.

746   US
NEEDLEPOINT BULLETIN. 1973. m. $12. Needlepoint, Inc., Box 13165, N. Palm Beach, FL 33408. Ed. Sharlene Weldon. bk.rev.

746   US
NEEDLEWORK RETAILER. 1992. bi-m. free to qualified personnel. Yarn Tree Design, Inc., 117 Alexander Ave., Ames, IA 50010. TEL 515-232-3121; 800-247-3952. FAX 515-232-0789. Ed. Heidi A. Bomgarden; Pub. Larry R. Johnson. adv.: B&W page $1100, color page $1540; trim 8 1/8 x 10 7/8. bk.rev. circ. 16,500. (back issues avail.) **Document type:** trade publication.

746   SA   ISSN 1021-8521
NEEDLEWORK'S CROSS STITCH; beautiful cross stitch designs for you to enjoy. (Text in English) 1993. m. newsstand price: R.9.90. Litharne S.A., P.O. Box 27212, Sunnyside 0132, South Africa. adv.; illus. **Document type:** consumer publication.

746   FI   ISSN 1236-1860
NOVITA; kasityot. q. FIM 130. Yhtyneet Kuvalehdet Oy - United Magazines Ltd., Maistraatinportti 1, SF-00240 Helsinki, Finland. TEL 358-0-156-6524. FAX 358-0-156-6505. Ed. Eeva Sinbasaani. adv.: B&W page FIM 10200, color page FIM 15000; trim 217 x 280; adv. contact: Kauko Kanerva. circ. 42,658. **Document type:** consumer publication.
   Description: Devoted to handicrafts; contains patterns.

746   US   ISSN 1050-9518
OLD TIME CROCHET. 1979. q. $9.95. House of White Birches Publishing, 306 E. Parr Rd., Berne, IN 46711. TEL 219-589-8741. Eds. Anne Jefferson, Marion Kelly. circ. 112,000. **Document type:** consumer publication.
   Formerly (until 1989): Old Time Crochet Patterns and Designs (ISSN 0195-2013)
   Description: Contains reprints of popular patterns and signs from fifty years ago.

746   UK   ISSN 0268-5620
PATCHWORK & QUILTING. 1985. bi-m. £13 (Europe £18; rest of world £19). Traplet Publications Ltd., Traplet House, Severn Dr., Upton-upon-Severn, Worcestershire WR8 0JL, England. TEL 01684-594505. FAX 01684-594586. (Dist. by: Seymour, Windsor House, 1270 London Rd., London SW16 4DH, England. TEL 0181-679-1899. FAX 0181-679-8907; Subscr. in US to: Box 167, Florham Park, NJ 07932; Dist. in US by: Carsten Publications Inc., Box 700, Newton, NJ 07860. TEL 201-383-3355. FAX 201-383-4064) Eds. Elaine Hammond, Dianne Huck. adv. contact: Jane Stephenson. index. (back issues avail.) **Document type:** consumer publication.

746   US
PATCHWORK PATTER. 1973. q. National Quilting Association, Inc., Box 393, Ellicott City, MD 21043. TEL 301-461-5733. adv.; bk.rev.
   Description: Furthers the understanding of quilts, quilting, and the history of this particular craft.

746   UK   ISSN 0957-381X
PATTERNS GALORE. 1989. bi-m. £13.50($14) Litharne Publishing Ltd., P.O. Box 9, Stratford-upon-Avon, Warks. CV37 8RS, England. FAX 01789-720888. Ed. Janet Kirwood. circ. 28,000. **Document type:** consumer publication.
   Description: Provides styles and ideas for the home dress-maker.

746   US
PEACEFUL PIECES. 1983. q. $6. Boise Peace Quilt Project, Box 6469, Boise, ID 83707. TEL 208-378-0293. FAX 208-323-0848. Ed. Lyn McCollum. bk.rev.
   Description: Connects those who make or support fabric arts for peace, justice, and the environment.

746   FR
PEINTURE SUR SOIE AVEC DESSINS. q. 310 F. Editions de Saxe, 20 rue Croix-Barret, 69358 Lyon Cedex 07, France. TEL 78-72-92-54. FAX 78-72-64-18.

746   FR
PEINTURE SUR SOIE SANS DESSINS. q. 156 F. Editions de Saxe, 20 rue Croix-Barret, 69358 Lyon Cedex 07, France. TEL 78-72-92-54. FAX 78-72-64-18.

746   JA
PICHI. (Text in Japanese) 1977. bi-m. 2340 Yen. Gakken Co. Ltd., 40-5, 4-chome, Kamiikedai, Ohta-ku, Tokyo 145, Japan. Ed. Junko Horibe.

746   US   ISSN 1067-2249
TT740
PIECEWORK; all this by hand. 1993. bi-m. $24 (foreign $26). Interweave Press, Inc., 201 E. Fourth St., Loveland, CO 80537. TEL 303-669-7672; 800-645-3675. FAX 303-667-8317. Ed. Veronica Patterson; Pub. Linda Ligon. adv. contact: Barbara Liebler. bk.rev.; charts; illus.; circ. 22,000 (paid). (back issues avail.) **Document type:** consumer publication.
—UnCover.
   Description: Feature stories, rooted in history on quilting, knitting, crochet, embroidery, cross-stitch, needlepoint, lace making, beadwork, dyeing and fine hand sewing.
   Refereed Serial

NEEDLEWORK 4899

746 US
PINGOUIN KNITTING. * irreg. (8-12/yr.) $51 for 12 nos. Pingouin, c/o Laninter Corp., 19 Spear Rd., Ramsey, NJ 07446-1223. circ. 7,200.
 Description: Features illustrated instructions for fashion items using Pingouin-brand yarns.

746 US
PLASTIC CANVAS CRAFTS. 6/yr. $12.97. House of White Birches Publishing, 306 E. Parr Rd., Berne, IN 46711. TEL 219-589-8741. FAX 219-589-8093. circ. 64,000 (paid). Document type: consumer publication.
 Formerly: Plastic Canvas and More.

745.5 US ISSN 1045-1854
PLASTIC CANVAS! MAGAZINE. 1989. bi-m. $14.95. Needlcraft Shop, Inc., 206 West St., Big Sandy, TX 75755. TEL 903-636-4011. FAX 903-636-4088. (Subscr. to: 23 Old Pecan Rd., Big Sandy, TX 75755) Ed. Janet Tipton. circ. 225,000. (back issues avail.) Document type: consumer publication.
 Description: Plastic canvas needlework patterns and instructions for home decorating, toys, and wearables.

746 745.5 US ISSN 1072-6373
PLASTIC CANVAS WORLD. bi-m. $12.97. House of White Birches Publishing, 306 E. Parr Rd., Berne, IN 46711. TEL 219-589-8741. FAX 219-589-8093. Ed. Marjorie Pearl. circ. 63,167. circ. 75,000 (paid). Document type: consumer publication.

746 BL
PONTO DE CRUZ. s-a. Editora Globo S.A., Rua do Curtume 665, 05065-001 Sao Paulo SP, Brazil. TEL 55-11-8746000. FAX 55-11-8612042. circ. 45,000 (paid). Document type: consumer publication.
 Description: Presents craft projects to make by cross-stitch.

746 US ISSN 1048-3659
TT740
QUICK & EASY CRAFTS. 1968. bi-m. $12.97. House of White Birches Publishing, 306 E. Parr Rd., Berne, IN 46711. TEL 219-589-8741. Ed. Beth Schwartz Wheeler. circ. 260,000. Document type: consumer publication.
 Formerly (until 1990): Women's Circle Country Needlecraft (ISSN 0892-8223)
 Description: Contains 20 to 30 patterns, offers designs in various crafts.

746 US ISSN 0885-0631
QUICK AND EASY CROCHET. bi-m. Grass Roots Publishing Co., Inc., 950 Third Ave., 16th Fl., New York, NY 10022-2705. TEL 212-888-1855. FAX 212-838-8420. circ. 300,000. Document type: consumer publication.

745.5 US ISSN 1048-5341
QUICK & EASY PLASTIC CANVAS. 1989. bi-m. $14.95. Needlecraft Shop, Inc., 206 West St., Big Sandy, TX 75755. TEL 903-636-4011. FAX 903-636-4088. (Subscr. to: 26 Old Pecan Rd., Big Sandy, TX 75755) Ed. Janet Tipton. circ. 49,000. (back issues avail.) Document type: consumer publication.
 Description: Plastic canvas needlework patterns and instructions for home decorating, toys and wearables.

746 US ISSN 1045-5965
TT835
QUICK & EASY QUILTING. 1979. bi-m. $14.95. House of White Birches Publishing, 306 E. Parr Rd., Berne, IN 46711. TEL 219-589-8741. Ed. Sandra Hatch. bk.rev. circ. 79,000. Document type: consumer publication.
 Formerly: Quilt World Omnibook.
 Description: Contains patterns and a directory of quilt shows.

746 US ISSN 1059-0684
QUILT. q. Harris Publications, Inc., 1115 Broadway, 8th Fl., New York, NY 10010. TEL 212-807-7100. FAX 212-627-4678. Ed. Jean Eitel. circ. 94,500.

746 US ISSN 1057-7971
QUILT CRAFT. * 1991. bi-m. $11.97. Lopez Publications, Inc., 105 E. 35th St., New York, NY 10016-3877. TEL 212-689-3933. FAX 212-725-2239. Ed. Terri Nyman. circ. 175,000.
 Description: Focuses on quilts for intermediate and beginning quilters. Most designs are originals.

646 US ISSN 0149-8045
TT835
QUILT WORLD. 1976. bi-m. $12.97. House of White Birches Publishing, 306 E. Parr Rd., Berne, IN 46711. TEL 219-589-8741. Ed. Sandra Hatch. adv.; illus.; tr.lit. circ. 55,000. Document type: consumer publication.
 Description: Contains 15 to 20 patterns, plus features and a directory of quilt shows.

746 677 UK ISSN 0954-4933
THE QUILTER. 1979. q. £20 (Europe £24; rest of world £30). The Quilters Guild, OP66, Dean Clough, Halifax, W. Yorks HX3 5AX, England. TEL 01422-347669. FAX 01422-345017. Ed. Vivien Finch. adv. contact: Suzy Barton. bk.rev.; illus. circ. 6,000. Indexed: DAAI. Document type: newsletter.
 Formerly: Quilters Guild. Newsletter (ISSN 0261-7420)

746 677 US ISSN 0274-712X
TT835
QUILTER'S NEWSLETTER MAGAZINE; the magazine for quilt lovers. 1969. m. $18.95. Leman Publications, Inc. (Subsidiary of: Rodale Press, Inc.), 6700 W. 44th Ave., Wheatridge, CO 80033. TEL 303-420-4272. FAX 303-420-7358. (Subscr. to: Box 394, Wheatridge, CO 80034-0394) Ed. Bonnie Leman. adv.; bk.rev.; charts; illus.; cum.index: 1969-1988. circ. 175,000. (back issues avail.) Indexed: Ind.How To Do It (1990-).

746 US ISSN 1040-4457
TT835
QUILTING TODAY. bi-m. $15.95. Chitra Publications, 2 Public Ave., Montrose, PA 18801. TEL 717-278-1984. FAX 717-278-2223. Indexed: Ind.How To Do It (1990-). Document type: consumer publication.
 Description: International quilting magazine.

746 677 US ISSN 1047-1634
QUILTMAKER; the pattern magazine for today's quiltmakers. 1982. 4/yr. $14.95. Leman Publications, Inc. (Subsidiary of: Rodale Press, Inc.), 6700 W. 44th Ave., Wheatridge, CO 80033. TEL 303-420-4272. FAX 303-420-7358. (Subscr. to: Box 394, Wheatridge, CO 80034-0394) Ed. Bonnie Leman. adv.; illus.; cum.index: 1982-1986. circ. 70,000. (back issues avail.) Indexed: Ind.How To Do It (1990-).

RAKAM; mensile di moda e lavori femminili. see **WOMEN'S INTERESTS**

746 687 US ISSN 1076-058X
ROUND BOBBIN. 1965. m. $35 in U.S.; Canada $45; elsewhere $95. International Sewing Machine Association, Inc., P.O. Box 2188, Zanesville, OH 43702-2188. TEL 614-452-4541. FAX 614-452-2552. Ed. Duane R. Meyers. adv.; bk.rev. circ. 5,400. (tabloid format) Document type: trade publication.
 Description: Provides business, marketing, and other information of relevance to independent sewing machine dealers. Includes association and industry developments.

S A G A NEWS. (Smocking Arts Guild of America) see **ARTS AND HANDICRAFTS**

746 GW
SANDRA; tolle Strickmode. (Editions in Dutch, English, French, German, Italian, Russian, Spanish) 1984. m. DM.34.80 (Europe DM.62.40; elsewhere DM.86.40). Gruner und Jahr AG & Co., Am Baumwall 11, 20459 Hamburg, Germany. TEL 040-3703-0. FAX 040-37035617. Ed. Johannes Haller. illus. circ. 166,000. (back issues avail.) Document type: consumer publication.

746 NE
▼**SANDRA;** breimode. 1995. m. fl.39.50 (750 BEF). Vipmedia Publishing en Services, Willemstraat 23, 4811 AJ Breda, Netherlands. TEL 31-76-224265. FAX 31-76-144531. (Subscr. in Belgium to: Vipmedia, Bredabaan 852, 2170 Merksem, Belgium. TEL 32-3-6454294) illus. Document type: consumer publication.

746 646.4 US ISSN 1063-9160
SEW BEAUTIFUL. 1987. 6/yr. $25.95 (effective Sep. 1994); newsstand price: $5. Martha Pullen Co., Inc., 518 Madison St., Huntsville, AL 35801. TEL 205-533-9586. FAX 205-533-9630. Ed. Amelia Johanson. adv.; B&W page $750, color page $825; adv. contact: Kathy McMakin. circ. 60,000 (paid). Document type: consumer publication.
 Description: How-to articles and patterns. Features include heirloom sewing, smocking, embroidery, applique and cross stitch designs, with emphasis on sewing for children.

746 US ISSN 0888-577X
SEW IT SEAMS. 1986. q. $22. Sharon Lewis, Ed. & Pub., c/o Sew It Seams, 333 11th Pl., Kirkland, WA 98033.

SEW NEWS; the newspaper for people who sew. see **CLOTHING TRADE — Fashions**

746 SA
▼**SEW TODAY.** 1994. bi-m. R.49.50. Litharne S.A., P.O. Box 27212, Sunnyside, Pretoria 0132, South Africa. adv.; illus. Document type: consumer publication.
 Incorporates (1992-1993): Patterns Galore (ISSN 1019-7478)

746 US
▼**SEWING DECOR.** 1994. bi-m. $17.98; newsstand price: $3.95. P J S Publications, Inc., News Plaza, Box 1790, Peoria, IL 61656-1790. TEL 309-682-6626. FAX 309-682-7394. Ed. Susan Voigt-Reising; Pub. Jerry Constantino. adv.: B&W page $1950, color page $3000. circ. 100,000 (paid). Document type: consumer publication.

746 UK
▼**SEWING WORLD.** 1995. bi-m. £13 (Europe £18; rest of world £19). Traplet Publications Ltd., Traplet House, Severn Dr., Upton-upon-Severn, Worcestershire WR8 0JL, England. TEL 01684-594505. FAX 01684-594586. (Dist. by: Seymour, Windsor House, 1270 London Rd., London SW16 4DH, England. TEL 0181-679-1899. FAX 0181-679-8907; Subscr. in US to: Box 167, Florham Park, NJ 07932. TEL 201-765-0881; Dist. in US by: Carsten Publications Inc., Box 700, Newton, NJ 07860. TEL 201-383-3355. FAX 201-383-4064) Ed. Myra Coles. adv. contact: Jane Stephenson. Document type: consumer publication.

640 745.5 US ISSN 0080-9446
TS1490
SHUTTLE CRAFT GUILD. MONOGRAPHS. 1960. irreg., latest no.37. price varies. Shuttle Craft Books, Inc., Box 550, Coupeville, WA 98239. TEL 206-678-4648. Ed. Jim Anderst. Document type: monographic series.
 Description: Provides monographs on weaving.

476 US ISSN 1061-3234
SIMPLY CROSS STITCH. 1990. bi-m. $14.95. Needlecraft Shop, Inc., 206 West Street, Big Sandy, TX 75755. TEL 903-636-4011. FAX 903-636-4088. (Subscr. to: 26 Old Pecan Rd., Big Sandy, TX 75755) Ed. Jennifer Simcik. circ. 32,500. (back issues avail.) Document type: consumer publication.
 Description: Presents cross stitch patterns and instructions for home decorating, toys and clothing.

SLOEJDFORUM. see **ARTS AND HANDICRAFTS**

STITCHES. see **CLOTHING TRADE**

746 GW ISSN 0179-0579
STRICK UND SCHICK. m. DM.33.60. Bastei Verlag Gustav H. Luebbe GmbH und Co., Scheidtbachstr. 23-31, 51469 Bergisch Gladbach, Germany. TEL 02202-121-0. FAX 02202-121251. Ed. Karin Nagel. adv. contact: Franz Mueller. circ. 50,584. Document type: consumer publication.

746 US ISSN 0194-4193
STUMPWORK SOCIETY CHRONICLE. 1979. q. $15. Stumpwork Society, 1315 Anderson Ave., No. 23, Ft. Lee, NJ 07024. TEL 201-224-3622. FAX 201-224-3075. Ed. Sylvia C. Fishman. bk.rev. (back issues avail.)

NEW AGE PUBLICATIONS

746   FI   ISSN 1236-3855
SUURI KASITYOLEHTI. 1974. m. FIM 310. Helsinki Media Magazines, P.O. Box 107, Hoylaametie 1A, 00381 Helsinki, Finland. TEL 358-0-1221. FAX 358-0-120-5599. Ed. Tina Toetterman. adv.: B&W page $16850, color page $23300; 194 x 248. circ. 124,130 (paid).
   Formerly (until 1993): Suuri Kasityokerho (ISSN 0355-2098)

646.4 746.4   SW   ISSN 0283-2224
SY & STICKA; vi modemoenster. 1940. s-a. Kooperativa Foerbundet, P.O. Box 5216, S-105 45 Stockholm, Sweden. TEL 46-8-670-65-60. circ. 24,200.
   Former titles (until 1983): Vi Modemoenster; (until 1971): Vaar Moenstertidning.

TAITO. see *ARTS AND HANDICRAFTS*

746   GW
TEXTIL STUNDE; Lehrblaetter fuer Textiles Gestalten und Werken. 1977. s-a. DM.20. A L S Verlag GmbH, Voltastr. 3, 63128 Dietzenbach, Germany. TEL 06074-82160. FAX 06074-27322. Ed. Ingrid Kreide. cum.index: 1977-1994. circ. 22,000. (looseleaf format; back issues avail.) **Document type:** academic/scholarly publication.

746   GW
TEXTILSTUNDE II. 1992. s-a. DM.25. A L S Verlag GmbH, Voltastr. 3, 63128 Dietzenbach, Germany. TEL 06074-82160. FAX 06074-27322. Ed. Ingrid Kreide. cum.index: 1992-1994. circ. 3,000. (looseleaf format; back issues avail.) **Document type:** academic/scholarly publication.

746   US   ISSN 0882-7370
TT697
THREADS. 1985. bi-m. $28. Taunton Press, Inc., 63 S. Main St., Box 5506, Newtown, CT 06470-5506. TEL 203-426-8171. FAX 203-426-3434. Ed. Christine/Timmons. adv. contact: Maureen Larkin. bk.rev.; illus.; index. circ. 150,000. **Indexed:** Access (1994-), DAAI, Ind.How To Do It (1985-). **Document type:** consumer publication.
   —Faxon; UnCover.
   Description: Devoted to the design, materials and techniques of fashion sewing and other needle arts.

746   UK   ISSN 0968-2511
TO & FRO. 1978. bi-m. £10.50 (foreign £15). 17 Grove Park, Waltham Rd., White Waltham, Maidenhead, Berkshire SL6 3LW, England. TEL 01628-829815. FAX 01628-829816. (Dist. by: Seymour, 1270 London Rd., London SW16 4DH, England. TEL 0181-679-1899) Ed. Anne Smith. adv. contact: Brenda Hughes. (back issues avail.) **Document type:** consumer publication.
   Description: Covers all aspects of machine knitting.

746   US   ISSN 1050-0073
TRADITIONAL QUILTER; the leading teaching magazine for creative quilters. 1989. bi-m. $23.70 (effective Sep. 1990). M S C Publishing, Inc., 243 Newton Sparta Rd., Newton, NJ 07860-2748. TEL 201-383-8080. FAX 201-383-8133. (Subscr. to: Box 507, Mt. Morris, IL 61054) Ed. Phyllis Barbieri. adv.; bk.rev. (back issues avail.) **Document type:** consumer publication.
   Description: Teaches quilting, advanced techniques and design. Offers news on quilters and exhibits.

746   US   ISSN 1050-4435
TRADITIONAL QUILTWORKS. bi-m. $15.95. Chitra Publications, 2 Public Ave., Montrose, PA 18801. TEL 717-278-1984. FAX 717-278-2223. **Indexed:** Ind.How To Do It (1990-). **Document type:** consumer publication.
   Description: Covers quilting patterns.

746   US   ISSN 1059-2466
TT753
TREASURES IN NEEDLEWORK.* 1992. q. Craftways, 1716 Locus St., Des Moines, IA 50309-3038. (Subscr. to: Box 54531, Boulder, CO 80322-4531) Ed. Joan Cravens. adv.: B&W page $4500, color page $6000; trim 8 1/4 x 10 3/4. circ. 200,000.

746 646.2   FR   ISSN 0241-0702
TRICOT PRESTIGE. 1979. 4/yr. 105 F. Societe Generale de Publications Illustrees, 10 rue St. Marc, 75002 Paris, France. illus.

746   FR   ISSN 0397-9075
TRICOT - SELECTION. 1967. 10/yr. 215 F. Editions de Saxe, 20 rue Croix-Barret, 69364 Lyons Cedex 7, France. TEL 78-72-92-54. FAX 78-72-64-18. adv. circ. 90,000.

746 646.2   FR
TRICOTS CHICS; layette, adults. 1948. 4/yr. (foreign 105 F.). Societe Generale de Publications Illustrees, 10 rue St. Marc, 75002 Paris, France.

746.434   IT
TUTTO UNCINETTO. m. Edicami Iniziative Editoriali s.r.l., Via Dell'Aprica 18, 20158 Milan, Italy. TEL 39-2-69004773. FAX 39-2-69004776. Ed. Pietro Paolo Cavalletti. adv.: color page L.18000000. circ. 240,000.

746.434   IT
UNCINETTO SELEZIONE.* 1979. m. L.12000. Curcio Periodici S.p.A., Via IV Novembre 149, 00187 Rome, Italy. Ed. Rosanna Falconi. adv. circ. 165,000.

746 305.4   US   ISSN 0277-0628
TT835
UNCOVERINGS; research papers. 1980. a. $18. American Quilt Study Group, 660 Mission St., Ste. 400, San Francisco, CA 94105-4007. TEL 415-495-0163. FAX 415-495-3516. Ed. Virginia Gunn. illus.; index. circ. 900. **Document type:** academic/scholarly publication.
   —UnCover.
   Description: Covers the history of quilts, quiltmaking and textiles. Includes research into women's history and arts.

746   SW   ISSN 0281-3343
VAEVMAGASINET; Scandinavian weaving magazine. (Text in Dutch, English, German, Japanese, Swedish) 1982. q. SEK 180. Foerlags AB Vaevhaesten, P.O. Box 100, S-280 64 Glimaakra, Sweden. TEL 46-44-427-30. FAX 46-44-433-30.

746   GW   ISSN 0940-9297
VERENA; Mode - Maschen - Ideen. 1986. m. Verlag Aenne Burda, Am Kestendamm 2, 77652 Offenburg, Germany. TEL 0781-8402. FAX 0781-843508. Ed. Marianne Muesch; Pub. Aenne Burda. adv. contact: Bodo Schlimpen. circ. 291,853. **Document type:** consumer publication.

746   US   ISSN 0890-9237
TT820
VOGUE KNITTING. 1982. 3/yr. $11.95. Butterick Co., Inc., 161 Ave. of the Americas, New York, NY 10013. TEL 212-620-2500. (Subscr. to: 2900 Beale Ave., Altoona, PA 16603. TEL 800-766-3619) **Document type:** consumer publication.

746   US   ISSN 1042-7643
TT848
WEAVERS. 1981; N.S. 1988. q. $18 (foreign $22). Golden Fleece Publications, Box 1525, Sioux Falls, SD 57101. TEL 605-338-2450. FAX 605-338-2994. Ed. Madelyn Vander Noogt; Pub. Alexis Xenakis. adv. contact: Karen Bright. bk.rev.; charts; illus.; tr.lit.; index. circ. 4,300. (back issues avail.) **Document type:** consumer publication.
   Formerly (until vol.5, no.2): Prairie Wool Companion (ISSN 0743-8907)

793   US
WOMAN'S DAY CHRISTMAS CRAFTS. 1973. a. $2.25. Hachette Magazines, Inc., Woman's Day Special Publications, 1633 Broadway, 45th Fl., New York, NY 10019. TEL 201-767-6000. Ed. Carolyn Galla. adv.; bk.rev.; charts; illus.; tr.lit. (back issues avail.)
   Former titles: Woman's Day Holiday Craft and Granny Square; Granny Square and Craft Ideas; Woman's Day Granny Squares.

746.4   US
TT825
WOMAN'S DAY CHRISTMAS TRADITIONS. 1981. a. $2.95 per no. Hachette Magazines, Inc., Woman's Day Special Publications, 1633 Broadway, 42nd Fl., New York, NY 10019. TEL 212-767-6000. Ed. Lisa Goldstein. adv.; bk.rev.; charts; illus.; tr.lit. circ. 400,000. (back issues avail.)
   Former titles: Woman's Day 101 Sweater and Craft Ideas (ISSN 1056-6503); Woman's Day 101 Needlework and Sweater Ideas; Woman's Day 101 Sweaters You Can Knit and Crochet.
   Description: For the home knitter, contains instructions for sweaters and other knit and crochet items, plus other types of needle crafts

746   US   ISSN 0745-0575
WOMEN'S HOUSEHOLD CROCHET. q. $9.95. House of White Birches Publishing, 306 E. Parr Rd., Berne, IN 46711. TEL 219-589-8741. Ed. Susan Hankins. circ. 42,000. **Document type:** consumer publication.
   Formerly: Crochet for Women Only.

746   US   ISSN 0162-9123
TT697
WORKBASKET; the world's largest needlework and crafts magazine. 1935. bi-m. $12.95. K C Publishing Inc., 700 W. 47th St., Ste. 310, Kansas City, MO 64112. TEL 816-531-5730. FAX 816-531-3873. Ed. Kay M. Olson. adv.: B&W page $9900, color page $12900; trim 5 1/8 x 7 3/8. bk.rev.; illus. circ. 790,228. (also avail. in microfilm from UMI; reprint service avail. from UMI) **Indexed:** Ind.How To Do It (1978-), Mag.Ind., MELSA, PMR. **Document type:** consumer publication.
   ●Also available online. Vendor(s): Knight-Ridder, Inc. —UMI.
   Description: Provides easy-to-follow instructions and guidance on needlework (knitting, tatting, crocheting, stitching, and sewing), crafts, recipes and gardening.

746.44   UK
WORLD OF EMBROIDERY. 1932. q. £12.40($30) (overseas £16.50). (Embroiderers' Guild) E G Enterprises Ltd., P.O. Box 42B, E. Molesey, Surrey KT8 9BB, England. TEL 0181-843-1229. FAX 0181-977-9882. Ed. Valerie Campbell-Harding. adv.; bk.rev.; illus.; index. circ. 14,500. **Indexed:** Artbibl.Mod.; DAAI. **Document type:** consumer publication.
   —UnCover.
   Formerly: Embroidery (ISSN 0013-6611)
   Description: Features current embroidery, both amateur and professional techniques, historical, and ethnographic subjects and design.

746   FR
1000 MAILLES CROCHET D'ART. m. 210 F. Editions de Saxe, 20 rue Croix-Barret, 69358 Lyon Cedex 07, France. TEL 78-72-92-54. FAX 78-72-64-18.

NEW AGE PUBLICATIONS

see also *Astrology; Parapsychology and Occultism*

100   US
A U R A NEWSLETTER.* vol.3, no.2, 1981. 12/yr. $10. Association for Unity, Research and Awareness, c/o Robert Mahlman, 840 Sage Cir.lory Ln., Lincoln, NE 68520-1152.

ACE OF RODS; Wiccan - pagan contacts magazine. see *ARTS AND HANDICRAFTS*

AHKADEN; The Ahkaden. see *PARAPSYCHOLOGY AND OCCULTISM*

133.9   GW   ISSN 0934-4535
ALLGEMEINE ZEITSCHRIFT FUER PARANORMOLOGIE. 1976. q. DM.40 (foreign DM.45). Deutsche Gesellschaft fuer Parapsychologie, Thraenstr. 13, 89077 Ulm, Germany. TEL 0731-33057. Ed. Hildegund Zehmke. bk.rev. circ. 200. **Document type:** academic/scholarly publication.
   Formerly (until 1988): Allgemeine Zeitschrift fuer Parapsychologie (ISSN 0174-0288)

AMMONITE. see *LITERATURE — Poetry*

ANCIENT SKIES. see *AERONAUTICS AND SPACE FLIGHT*

NEW AGE PUBLICATIONS 4901

110 296 US ISSN 1077-0003
▼**ANGEL TIMES.** 1995. bi-m. $26. Angelic Realms Unlimited, 4360 Chamblee-Dunwoody Rd., Ste. 400, Atlanta, GA 30341. TEL 404-986-9787. FAX 404-986-8895. Ed. Linda Whitmon Vephula. circ. 100,000. **Document type:** consumer publication.
Description: Contains articles, art and reviews about God's messengers of love for people of all religions and cultures.

ANGELWATCH. see *RELIGIONS AND THEOLOGY*

110 MX
ANO CERO. 1990. m. 4500 ptas. Editorial Samra, S.A. de C.V., Lucio Blanco 435, Azcapotzalco, 02400 Mexico DF, Mexico. TEL 525-3523266. Ed. Enrique de Vicente.

ANUBIS; Zeitschrift fuer praktische Magie und Psychonautik. see *PARAPSYCHOLOGY AND OCCULTISM*

110 US
AQUARIAN ALTERNATIVES. 1970. irreg. $25. Aquarian Research Foundation, 5620 Morton St., Philadelphia, PA 19144. TEL 215-849-3237. Ed. Art Rosenblum. bk.rev. circ. 500. (looseleaf format; back issues avail.)
Description: Discusses peace issues, and alternatives for the future.

ARCANA; inner dimensions of spirituality. see *RELIGIONS AND THEOLOGY — Other Denominations And Sects*

051 US
ARIZONA NETWORKING NEWS. 1981. bi-m. $15 (foreign $30). Tri-Pyramids, Inc., Box 5477, Scottsdale, AZ 85261-5477. TEL 602-951-1275. FAX 602-951-1295. Ed. Joanne Henning Tedesco. adv.; bk.rev. circ. 60,000. (tabloid format; back issues avail.) **Document type:** newspaper.
Description: Focuses on holistic health.

294.54 CN ISSN 0315-8179
ASCENT (KOOTENAY BAY). 1970. 4/yr. Can.$12.50($10) Yasodhara Ashram Society, Box 9, Kootenay Bay, BC V0B 1X0, Canada. TEL 604-227-9224. FAX 604-227-9494. Ed. Swami Gopalananda. adv. contact: Don Gamble. bk.rev.; bibl.; charts; illus. circ. 1,600. **Document type:** academic/scholarly publication.
Description: Offers an integration of modern Western psychological tools with the practice of Yoga.

ASTROFLASH. see *ASTROLOGY*

AT THE CROSSROADS; feminism, spirituality and New Paradigm science exploring earthly and unearthly reality. see *WOMEN'S STUDIES*

THE AZRAEL PROJECT NEWSLETTER. see *PSYCHOLOGY*

110 UK ISSN 1355-1876
BAELDER; the pan-European fraternity of knowledge. (Text in English) 1990. bi-m (in 12 nos.). £20($38) (European Cultural Centre for Appreciation and Advancement of Regions, Traditions and Heritage) Coxland Press, c/o 60 Elmhurst Rd., Reading, Berks. RG1 5HY, England. TEL 01734-875509. Ed. Marco Lockhorst; Pubs. Stephen B. Cox, Scott Reap. adv. contact: Stephen B. Cox. bk.rev./ circ. controlled. (back issues avail.) **Document type:** newsletter, directory.
Description: Contains articles on the occult, mythology, folklore, ethnography and pagan history. Includes membership directory and reports of coming events.

133 110 US
THE BEACON (MIAMI). 1974. m. $5. Roundtable of the Light Centers, Inc., 1801 S.W. 82nd Pl., Miami, FL 33155. TEL 305-261-0722. Ed. Larry Cuttler. adv.; bk.rev. circ. 450. (tabloid format)

BEYOND P E. see *PHYSICAL FITNESS AND HYGIENE*

BIOFEEDBACK & SELF REGULATION. see *PSYCHOLOGY*

133.91 US ISSN 0895-7657
BODY, MIND & SPIRIT MAGAZINE. Key Title: Body Mind Spirit. 1982. bi-m. $20. Island Publishing Company, Inc., Box 701, Providence, RI 02901. TEL 401-351-4320. FAX 401-272-5767. Ed. Carole Kramer. adv.; bk.rev. circ. 160,000. (back issues avail.)
Formerly (until 1987): Psychic Guide (ISSN 0745-8746)
Description: Provides news and information on all aspects of New Age, from spirit channeling to nutritional supplements.

391.65 US
BODY PLAY AND MODERN PRIMITIVES QUARTERLY. 1992. q. $45 in N. America; elsewhere $55. Insight Books, Box 2575, Menlo Park, CA 94026-2575. TEL 415-324-0543. Ed. Fakir Musafar. adv.; bk.rev.; illus.
Description: Covers the deliberate, ritualized modification of the human body.

181.45 US
BODYWORK SERIES. irreg., latest no.2. Himalayan International Institute (HII), RR1, Box 407, Honesdale, PA 18431. TEL 717-253-4929. FAX 717-253-9078.
Description: Features unique exercises that benefit the health of the nervous system.

133 US ISSN 0006-8233
BOTH SIDES NOW; an alternative journal of aquarian - new age transformations. 1969. irreg., latest no.32. $9 for 10 issues. Free People, 10547 State Hwy. 110 N., Tyler, TX 75704-9537. TEL 903-592-4263. Ed. Elihu Edelson. adv.: page $50; 8 1/2 x 11. bk.rev. circ. 200. (also avail. in microform from UMI) **Document type:** newsletter.
Description: Covers spiritual and political alternatives with emphasis on New Age and Green directions.

181.45 US
BREATH SERIES; a progression of pranayama practices. irreg., latest no.2. Himalayan International Institute (HII), RR1, Box 52, Honesdale, PA 18431. TEL 717-253-4929. FAX 717-253-9078.
Description: Helps readers learn the importance of proper breathing.

133 PY ISSN 1017-2777
BUHARDILLA. 1990. m. Distribuidor Internacional Publicaciones Paraguayas, B.O. Box 2507 y 5a, Ayoreos e-4a y 5a, Asuncion, Paraguay. TEL 595-21-495367. FAX 595-21-447460. adv. circ. 1,000.

110 GW
C S A MAGAZIN; fuer ein gesundes und erfuelltes Leben. 1977. bi-m. DM.40. C S A Europa e.V., Rhoenstr. 1, 61381 Friedrichsdorf, Germany. TEL 06007-661. FAX 06007-7802. bk.rev.; circ. 5,000. (back issues avail.) **Document type:** consumer publication.

133 VE
CABALA; la magia de saber insolito. 1977. m. Bs.70($3) (effective June 1992). Editorial Elite (Subsidiary of: Publicaciones Capriles), Torre de la Prensa, piso 2, Plaza del Panteon, Caracas, Venezuela. TEL 81-49-31-832399. FAX 83-88-35. TELEX 21173 ULTIN VC. Ed. J.P. Leroy. adv.: B&W page Bs.13000, color page Bs.19370; trim 205 x 275. circ. 80,000.

133 US
CATALIST;* rediscovering your personal magic. $5. bi-m. Box 810, Boulder Creek, CA 95006-0810. TEL 408-338-7587. FAX 408-338-3582. Ed. Adam J. Fleischer.
Description: Contains articles on holistic health and spiritual living. Includes a catalog of alternative health-oriented products.

133 US
CATALYST (MARIETTA); a publication resource of New Age newsletters, book reviews, personals, holistic health, UFO's and psychic connections. 1985. a. $9.95 (foreign $14.95). Catalyst, Box 670022, Marietta, GA 30066. bk.rev. **Document type:** directory.
Formerly: Psychic Connections.

658 US
CATALYST DIRECTORY NEWSLETTER. 1985. a. $9.95. Catalyst, Box 670022, Marietta, GA 30066. adv.; bk.rev. circ. 2,000. **Document type:** directory.
Formerly: Catalyst Perspective.
Description: Lists metaphysical, New Age UFO, psychtronics newsletters; "personals" resources, back to earth, holistic health.

133 US
CELEBRATE LIFE! (INDIAN ROCK BEACH). 1988. q. $8. Unimedia Corporation, Box 247, 18395 Gulf Blvd., Ste. 201, Indian Rocks Beach, FL 34635. TEL 813-595-4141. Ed. Marty Johnson. adv. circ. 10,000.
Description: Focuses on positive awareness and self-discovery. Features include unique vacations, health-related travel and leisure, culture, the arts, retreats, workshops and New Thought.

CHRISTIAN NEW AGE QUARTERLY; a bridge supporting dialogue. see *RELIGIONS AND THEOLOGY*

110 133.5 US ISSN 0009-6520
CHURCH OF LIGHT QUARTERLY. 1925. q. $20 (effective 1996). Church of Light Inc., 2341 Coral St., Los Angeles, CA 90031-2916. TEL 213-226-0453. FAX 213-226-0454. Ed. Paul Brewer. adv. contact: Dorothy Wissler. charts; illus. circ. 1,000. **Document type:** academic/scholarly publication, newsletter.
Description: Provides astrological analysis of topical personalities and events, current cycle charts and weather data. Covers mental and spiritual alchemy, sacred tarot, and the hermetic tradition of the Brotherhood of Light.

110 US
COMMON GROUND (SAN ANSELMO); resources for personal transformation. 1973. 4/yr. $10. 305 San Anselmo Ave., Ste. 313, San Anselmo, CA 94960. TEL 415-459-4900. FAX 415-459-4974. TELEX 428701. E-mail: spectrav@ix.netcom.com. Ed. Baha'uddin Andy Alpine. adv.: B&W page $1050. bk.rev.; illus. circ. 90,000. (tabloid format) **Document type:** directory.
Description: Directory of resources for personal growth, with interviews and feature articles on topics relating to personal development.

133 CN ISSN 0849-1224
COMMON GROUND MAGAZINE. 1975. 4/yr. Can.$16.05 (foreign Can.$21). 356 Dupont St., Toronto, ON M5R 1V9, Canada. TEL 416-964-0528. Ed. Julia Woodford. adv. contact: Kathy Pringle. bk.rev.; circ. 50,000 (controlled). (back issues avail.) **Document type:** consumer publication.
Former titles (until 1989): Ontario's Common Ground Magazine (ISSN 0845-471X); *(until 1988):* Canada's Common Ground Magazine (ISSN 0845-4701); *(until 1988):* Common Ground Magazine (ISSN 0840-3953); *(until 1987):* Ontario's Common Ground (ISSN 0820-5779); *(until 1986):* Common Ground (ISSN 0829-6375); *(until 1985):* Toronto's Common Ground (ISSN 0829-6367).
Description: Guide to natural foods and lifestyles.

COMMUNITIES; journal of cooperation. see *BUSINESS AND ECONOMICS — Cooperatives*

100 GW ISSN 0932-5565
CONNECTION; Meditation, Vision, Lebenskunst. 1985. m. DM.68 (foreign DM.78.50). Connection Medien GmbH, Hauptstr. 5, 84494 Niedertaufkirchen, Germany. TEL 08639-6009-0. FAX 08639-1219. Ed. Susann Pasztor; Pub. Wolf Schneider. adv. contact: Heike Bus. bk.rev. circ. 14,000. (back issues avail.) **Document type:** bulletin.

110 GW ISSN 0178-5737
CONTRASTE; Monatszeitung fuer Selbstverwaltung. 1984. m. DM.80. Contraste e.V., Postfach 104520, 69035 Heidelberg, Germany. TEL 06221-162467. FAX 06221-164489. (also avail. in diskette format) **Document type:** newspaper.

133 110 US ISSN 1043-0180
COSMIC CURRENT NEWS. 1983. irreg. $8 (foreign $12) for 4 nos. Cosmic Current News, Box 903203, Palmdale, CA 93590-3203. TEL 805-265-8710. Ed. Albert Rainey. bk.rev. circ. 2,000. (back issues avail.)
Description: Provides information on the new age music.

NEW AGE PUBLICATIONS

133 US ISSN 1058-4196
COSMIC VOICE; cosmic revelations for the New Age. 1955. m. $16. Aetherius Society, 6202 Afton Pl., Hollywood, CA 90028-8298. TEL 213-465-9652. Ed. George King. adv.; illus. circ. 700.
Supersedes: Aetherius Society Newsletter; Cosmic Voice.

110 US
CREATIONS; a showcase of Long Island's creative spirit. 1987. 6/yr. Creations Magazine, Box 407, Seacliff, NY 11579. TEL 516-674-3051. FAX 516-671-7547. Ed. Rosemarie Ceraso. adv. contact: Swami Titi. bk.rev.

DA'AT; Jewish philosophy and Kabbalah. see *PHILOSOPHY*

133 US
DAUGHTERS OF NYX; a magazine of goddess stories, mythology and fairy tales. 4/yr. $14. Box 1187, White Salmon, WA 98672.

DIRECTORY OF INTENTIONAL COMMUNITIES. see *BUSINESS AND ECONOMICS — Trade And Industrial Directories*

DIRECTORY TO CANADIAN PAGAN RESOURCES. see *RELIGIONS AND THEOLOGY*

DOUBLE HEARTLINE. see *RELIGIONS AND THEOLOGY*

333.7 AT
DOWN TO EARTH NORTH EAST AUSTRALIA NEWSLETTER. Short title: D T E - N E A Newsletter. 1977. m. Aus.$25 (foreign Aus.$35). P.O. Box 341, Spring Hill, Qld. 4004, Australia. Ed. Dik Freestun. adv.; bk.rev. circ. 750. (back issues avail.)
Description: Presents information on a wide variety of events and techniques for raising awareness of real needs both personal and global. Special interest in total health and nature.

135.3 154.63 US ISSN 1054-6707
BF1074
DREAM NETWORK; a quarterly journal exploring dreams and myth. 1982. q. $22 (Canada $28; elsewhere $36). 1337 Powerhouse Ln., Ste. 22, Moab, UT 84532. TEL 801-259-5936. FAX 801-259-5936. E-mail: ossanatt@delphi.con. Ed. H. Roberta Ossana. bk.rev.; cum.index: 1982-1991. (back issues avail.)
Document type: consumer publication.
Formerly (until 1989): Dream Network Bulletin.
Description: Provides a forum for exchange of ideas among individuals interested in understanding the symbologic language of dreams, with a focus on dream sharing and exploring relationships between dream and mythology.
Refereed Serial

THE EARTH CHANGES REPORT; the survival guide for the nineties. see *EARTH SCIENCES*

299 631 AT ISSN 0310-222X
EARTH GARDEN. 1972. q. Aus.$19. RMB 427, Trentham, Vic. 3458, Australia. FAX 054-241743. Eds. A.T. Gray, G. Simmons. adv.; bk.rev. circ. 25,000. (also avail. in microfiche) Indexed: Gdns, Pinpointer.

EIDOLON. see *PARAPSYCHOLOGY AND OCCULTISM*

614.7 US
ELYSIUM: JOURNAL OF THE SENSES. Abbreviated title: J O T S. 1961. 4/yr. $6. (Elysium Institute, Inc.) Elysium Growth Press, 814 Robinson Rd., Topanga, CA 90290. TEL 310-455-1000. FAX 310-455-2007. TELEX 6975129. Ed. Art Kunkin; Pub. Ed Lange. adv.; bk.rev. circ. 15,000. (back issues avail.) **Document type:** consumer publication.
Former titles: Journal of the Senses (ISSN 0741-8787); Elysium.

100 US ISSN 0890-538X
EMERGING. 1969. s-a. $25. (Teleos Institute) L P Publications, Box 12009-418, Scottsdale, AZ 85267-2004. TEL 602-948-1800. FAX 602-948-1870. Ed. Mariamne Paulus. illus. circ. 350.
Supersedes (in 1987): Seeker Magazine (ISSN 0886-1285); (in 1982): Seeker Newsletter (ISSN 0145-8361); (in 1972): New Focus (ISSN 0047-9683)
Description: Essays and commentary on spiritual consciousness and evolution, stressing the importance of universal and unconditional love, the study of wisdom teachings, and living life with purpose.

133 100 US
EMSHOCK LETTER. 1977. irreg. (7-12/yr.). $25. Vongrutnorv Og Press, Inc., Box 411, Randall Flat Rd., Troy, ID 83871-0411. TEL 208-835-4902. Ed. Steven E. Erickson. bk.rev. circ. 1,000. (back issues avail.)
Description: Provides an "experiment in consciousness," with no limit on variables.

ENCHANTING NEWS. see *PARAPSYCHOLOGY AND OCCULTISM*

EROTIC EARTHBODY; sacred sexuality, eros and the life force - networking our way toward evolution. see *WOMEN'S INTERESTS*

130 GW ISSN 0003-2921
ESOTERA; neues Denken und Handeln. 1949. m. DM.78 (foreign DM.84). Verlag Hermann Bauer KG, Kronenstr. 2, 79100 Freiburg, Germany. TEL 0761-7082-0. FAX 0761-701811. Ed. Gert Geisler. adv.: B&W page DM.5460, color page DM.7750; trim 221 x 276; adv. contact: Ursula Heist. bk.rev.; bibl.; charts; illus. circ. 60,000. **Document type:** bulletin.
—CCC.
Formerly: Andere Welt.

133 IT
L'ETA DELL'ACQUARIO; the magazine of the new plane of consciousness. 1971. bi-m. L.45000($30) Via Torchio 16, 28075 Grignasco (NO), Italy. TEL 0163-418978. FAX 0163-411095. Ed. Isabella Bresci. adv. contact: Marco Orsi. bk.rev. circ. 1,500. (back issues avail.) **Document type:** consumer publication.

EVERLASTING CIRCLE. see *ARTS AND HANDICRAFTS*

181.45
EXPANDING LIGHT PROGRAM GUIDE. 1981. 2/yr. free. Ananda Church of Self-Realization, 14618 Tyler Foote Rd., Nevada City, CA 95959. TEL 916-292-3496. Ed. Richard McCord. adv. circ. 20,000. **Document type:** catalog.
Former titles: Ananda Program Guide; Ananda.
Description: Describes retreat programs in spiritual growth offered at Ananda Village.

100 US
FAITHIST JOURNAL. 1968. bi-m. $15 (foreign $20) (effective July 1995). Kosmon Publishing, Inc., P.O. Box 4670, Hualapai, AZ 86412-4670. TEL 602-757-4569. Eds. Charles W. Benfield, Kasandra Kares. adv. contact: Kasandra Kares. bk.rev.; abstr.; charts; illus. circ. 275. (back issues avail.) **Document type:** consumer publication.
Description: New Age magazine discussing a variety of subjects such as UFO's, spiritualism, life after death, vegetarianism, astral travel, crystal power and I-Ching.

110 US
FARM NET NEWS. 1983. q. $20. Book Publishing Company, 156 Drakes Ln., Summertown, TN 38483. TEL 615-964-3571. (Subscr. to: 5211 Meadow Creek Dr., Austin, TX 78745. TEL 512-462-3991) Ed. Joy Newcom. circ. 600. **Document type:** newsletter.

133 US
THE FEDERATION FLASH; exploring the frontiers of miraculous probability. 1990. q. $12; newsstand price: $3. Starbuilders, Box 220964, Hollywood, FL 33022-0964. TEL 305-927-7900. FAX 305-927-7659. E-mail: jal__kae@gate.net. Ed. Aldin. illus. circ. 3,000. (back issues avail.) **Document type:** newsletter.
Description: Covers various New Age topics, including ascension, psychological aspects of spirituality, and awakening.

299 UK
FINDHORN FOUNDATION. GUEST PROGRAMME. s-a. free. Findhorn Foundation, The Park, Findhorn, Forres. IV36 0TZ, Scotland. TEL 01309-30311. FAX 01309-30933. E-mail: stewards@eindhorn.org. **Document type:** catalog.
Description: Discusses courses, workshops, and programs and reflects on the Findhorn spiritual philosophy.

133 US ISSN 1046-6029
FIREHEART;* a journal of magic and spiritual transformation. 1988. s-a. $8.50. EarthSpirit Community, Box 365, Medford, MA 02155-0003. TEL 617-395-1023. (And: Box 365, Medford, MA 02155) Ed. Myrriah Lavin. adv.; bk.rev. circ. 3,000. (back issues avail.)
Description: Devoted to magic and nature spirituality and to exploring various traditions such as Wicca, Paganism, Shamanism and New Age spirituality.

FLOATING. see *ALTERNATIVE MEDICINE*

FORESIGHT (BIRMINGHAM). see *PARAPSYCHOLOGY AND OCCULTISM*

129 291.2 US ISSN 1063-3421
FOREVER ALIVE. 1989. q. $24 (effective Sep. 1993). People Forever International, Box 12305, Scottsdale, AZ 85267-2305. TEL 602-922-0300. FAX 602-922-0800. Ed. Herb Bowie. adv.; bk.rev.; circ. 3,000 (paid). (back issues avail.) **Document type:** consumer publication.
Formerly: Eternal Flame.
Description: Covers health, wellness and physical immortality.

FREE SPIRIT (BROOKLYN); a directory and journal of new realities. see *PHILOSOPHY*

133 US ISSN 0738-9264
FUTURIFIC. 1976. m. $70 to individuals (foreign $100); institutions $140 (foreign $170). (Foundation for Optimism) Futurific, Inc., 305 Madison Ave., Concourse 10B, New York, NY 10165. TEL 212-297-0502; 800-696-2836. Ed. Balint Szent-Miklosy; Pub. Balint Szent-Miklosy. adv.; bk.rev.; film rev.; play rev.; software rev. circ. 10,000. **Document type:** academic/scholarly publication.
Description: Newsmagazine of the future, focusing on solutions, not problems. Reviews current events and forecasts their most likely outcomes.

158 US ISSN 1076-7029
GENTLE SURVIVALIST. 1991. 11/yr. $20. Laura Martin-Buehler Co., Box 4004, St. George, UT 84770. Ed. Laura Martin-Buhler. bk.rev. circ. 300. (looseleaf format; back issues avail.) **Document type:** newsletter.
Description: Devoted to physical, mental, emotional, spiritual self-survival technology; simplifying life and alleviating environmental illness. Includes Native teachings and preparedness wisdom.
Refereed Serial

299 150.19 US ISSN 0894-6159
BL624
GNOSIS; a journal of the Western inner traditions. 1985. q. $20 to individuals; libraries $25. Lumen Foundation, Box 14217, San Francisco, CA 94114-0217. TEL 415-255-0400. FAX 415-255-6329. Ed. Richard Smoley; Pub. Jay Kinney. adv. contact: Rashid Patch. bk.rev.; illus. circ. 16,000. **Document type:** consumer publication.
—UnCover.
Description: Features non-sectarian articles and reviews on the mystical and esoteric spiritual paths of the Western world, from the perspectives of comparative religion, history and Jungian psychology.

133 US ISSN 1068-2457
GOLDEN ISIS. 1980. q. $10. Golden Isis Press, Box 21753, St. Petersburg, FL 33742. Ed. Gerina Dunwich. adv.; bk.rev. circ. 3,600. **Document type:** trade publication.
Description: Contains pagan art, Wiccan news, reviews, white magick and goddess-inspired poetry.

615.53 613.2 US
GOOD LIFE TIMES;* choices in health, education and the arts. 1978. m. $20. Association for Wholistic Living, 6970 Central Ave., Lemon Grove, CA 91945-2110. Ed. Dr. Mark Solomon. adv.; bk.rev. circ. 50,000.
Formerly: Wholistic Living News.

NEW AGE PUBLICATIONS

291   US   ISSN 1066-7385
GREEN EGG; a journal of the awakening Earth. 1968-1977; resumed 1988. 4/yr. $18 (Americas $25) (effective 1995). (Church of All Worlds) Green Egg, Box 1542, Ukiah, CA 95482-1542. TEL 707-485-0772. FAX 707-485-8287. E-mail: gemagazine@aol.com. Ed. Maerian Morris; Pub. Oberon Zell. adv.: B&W page $400, color page $800; 7 1/2 x 10; adv. contact: Richard Johnson. bk.rev.; film rev.; bibl.; illus. circ. 10,000. (also avail. in microform from UMI; talking book; back issues avail.) Indexed: Access. Document type: trade publication.
  Description: Contains articles, reviews, letters, poetry, humor, fiction, and information relevant to and promoting Earth-centered spirituality.

DAS GROSSE LEBEN; Makrobiotik-Magazin. see *NUTRITION AND DIETETICS*

613.7 135   CN   ISSN 0827-7982
GUIDE RESSOURCES; nouvelles tendances, nouvelles valeurs. 1985. m. (10/yr.) Can.$31.45. S W A A Communications Inc., 4388 St-Denis St., Ste. 305, Montreal, PQ H2J 2L1, Canada. TEL 514-847-0060. FAX 514-847-0062. Ed. Christian Lamontagne. adv. contact: Louise Gaudreault. bk.rev. circ. 17,184. Indexed: Pt.de Rep. (1989-). Document type: consumer publication.
  Description: Devoted to New Age topics: nutrition, environmental issues, psychology, health and spirituality.

HAKOMI FORUM. see *PSYCHOLOGY*

HEARTSONG REVIEW; resource guide for New Age music of the spirit. see *MUSIC*

HECATE'S LOOM; Canada's national pagan magazine. see *RELIGIONS AND THEOLOGY — Other Denominations And Sects*

HOLISTIC EDUCATION REVIEW. see *EDUCATION*

110   US
HOLISTIC HEALTH DIRECTORY.* a. $5.95. New Age Journal Rising Star Associates, Ltd., 42 Pleasant St., Watertown, MA 02172-2312. TEL 617-787-2005. Document type: directory.
  Description: Lists holistic health care practitioners throughout the U.S., including physicians, physical and occupational therapists, chiropractors, acupuncturists, and natural healers.

100   CN   ISSN 1197-3331
I CREATE; meeting the intensity of the 90's. 1972. q. Can.$18. Integrity International, P.O. Box 9, 100 Mile House, BC V0K 2E0, Canada. TEL 416-395-3166. Ed. Chris Foster. bk.rev. circ. 1,750.
  Former titles (until Jan. 1993): Integrity (ISSN 0848-1660); (until 1989): Integrity International (ISSN 0712-7685); (until 1981): Integrity (ISSN 0700-4826).
  Description: A quarterly publication in practical spirituality.

289.9 100   US   ISSN 1062-1792
INNER JOURNEYS. 1987. q. $5. (Institute for the Development of the Harmonious Human Being, Inc.) Gateways Books and Tapes, Box 370, Nevada City, CA 95959. TEL 916-272-0180. FAX 916-432-1810. E-mail: dougt@dnai.com. Ed. Iven Lourie. adv. contact: Janna Hart. bk.rev. circ. 2,500. (back issues avail.) Document type: trade publication.
  Description: Promotional material and news for bookstores and retailers of metaphysical books.

181.45   US   ISSN 0149-6026
BL624
INNER PATHS. 1977. 12/yr. $15. Inner Paths Publications, Inc., 26 Reichert Circle, Westport, CT 06880. Ed. Louis Rogers. adv.; bk.rev. circ. 33,500. Document type: bulletin.

158   US
INNER SELF; rediscovering wisdom, peace and joy. 1985. m. $28.50. Innerself Publications, 915 S. 21st Ave., No. 2A, Hollywood, FL 33054. TEL 305-923-0730. FAX 305-921-1221. Ed. Marie Russell; Pubs. Marie T. Russell, Iree Russell. adv.: B&W page $570; 7 1/4 x 9 1/4; adv. contact: Alfred Steck. bk.rev.; film rev.; music rev. circ. 10,000.
  Formerly (until 1985): Mighty Natural Magazine.
  Description: Provides an opportunity for increased well-being on all levels - body, mind and spirit.

100   NR   ISSN 0794-7968
INSIGHT MAGAZINE; a magazine for spiritual development. (Text in English) 1987. m. $2 per no. OAL Research Publications Ltd., Cleanjohn House, 90 Ladipo House, P.O. Box 9802, Lagos, Nigeria. TEL 01-523-420. TELEX 27358. Ed. O.A. Lawal. adv. circ. 25,000. (back issues avail.)

INTERSPACE - LINK CONFIDENTIAL NEWSLETTER; the link. see *AERONAUTICS AND SPACE FLIGHT*

155   US
INTUITION; a magazine for the higher potential of the mind. 1993. q. $15 (Canada & Mexico $20; elsewhere $25). Colleen Mauro, Ed. & Pub., Box 460773, San Francisco, CA 94146-0773. TEL 415-949-4240. adv.; bk.rev.; illus. Document type: consumer publication.
  Description: Publishes articles discussing intuition and creativity, including profiles, interviews and news of issues relating to the development and application of intuition in all fields of endeavor.

INTUITIVE EXPLORATIONS. see *PARAPSYCHOLOGY AND OCCULTISM*

JOURNAL FOR THE STUDY OF CONSCIOUSNESS. see *PHILOSOPHY*

JOURNAL OF REGRESSION THERAPY. see *PSYCHOLOGY*

KURSKONTAKTE; der Anzeiger fuer ganzheitliche Bildung und Kultur. see *ALTERNATIVE MEDICINE*

KWAN UM ZEN SCHOOL NEWSLETTER. see *RELIGIONS AND THEOLOGY — Buddhist*

110 001.3 378   US   ISSN 0730-9066
LIFTOFF; a world commonwealth of education, science and culture. 1947. bi-m. $35 membership. World University Roundtable, Box 2470, Benson, AZ 85602-2470. TEL 602-586-2985. Ed. Howard John Zitko. bk.rev. circ. 1,000. (back issues avail.) Indexed: Refug.Abstr. Document type: newsletter.
  Formerly: World University. International Newsletter.
  Description: Discusses matters of spiritual significance from a New Age perspective, as they apply to topics in education, science, and culture.

200 100   US   ISSN 1040-7448
BP605.T78
LIGHT OF CONSCIOUSNESS. 1977. 3/yr. $11. Truth Consciousness at Desert Ashram., 3403 W. Sweetwater Dr., Tuscon, AZ 85745. TEL 520-743-0384. Ed. Sita Stuhlmiller. adv.: B&W page $270. bk.rev. circ. 5,000. (back issues avail.)
  Formerly (until vol.11, no.1, 1988): Truth Consciousness Journal (ISSN 0191-5207)

339.4 158   US
LIVING FREE; a personal journal of self liberation. 1979. bi-m. $12. Living Free, Box 29, Hiler Branch, Buffalo, NY 14223. Ed. Jim Stumm. adv.; bk.rev. circ. 200. (also avail. in microfiche; back issues avail.) Document type: newsletter.
  Description: Survivalists, homesteaders and anarchists discuss self-reliant living.

133 299   US
LLEWELLYN'S NEW WORLDS OF MIND & SPIRIT; new age resources for human potential and magical living. 1980. bi-m. $10 in U.S. and Canada; $20 elsewhere. Llewellyn Worldwide, 84 S. Wabasha St., Box 64383, St. Paul, MN 55164-0383. TEL 612-291-1970. FAX 612-291-1908. Ed. Krista Tempe. adv.: B&W page $975, color page $1170; trim 8 1/4 x 10 3/4; adv. contact: Terry Klingberg. bk.rev. circ. 60,000. (back issues avail) Document type: consumer publication, catalog.
  Former titles: Llewellyn New Worlds; Llewellyn New Times (ISSN 0893-1534)

101   US
LOVE; the journal of the human spirit. 1978. irreg. free. Box 9, Prospect Hill, NC 27314-0009. Eds. Bob Love, Pat Warren. circ. 100.

179.3   US   ISSN 0147-1201
M A I N. (Mark-Age Inform-Nations) 1960. q. $20 (foreign $25). Mark-Age, Inc., Box 290368, Ft. Lauderdale, FL 33329. TEL 305-587-5555. Ed. Pauline Sharpe. bk.rev.; film rev.; play rev.; bibl. circ. 1,000. (back issues avail.) Document type: consumer publication.
  Description: Contains news, educational articles and guidelines for linking of light workers and groups as preparation for the Second Coming and New Age of Aquarius.

700   US   ISSN 1040-4287
MAGICAL BLEND; a transformative journey. 1980. q. $17 (foreign $16). Magical Blend Publishers, 234 W. Third St., Ste. C, Chico, CA 95928. TEL 916-893-9037. FAX 916-894-9076. E-mail: magical@aspen.com. Ed. Jerry Shider. adv. contact: Meg Powers. bk.rev.; film rev.; charts; illus.; tr.lit. circ. 60,000. (back issues avail.) Document type: trade publication.
  •Also available online.
  Description: Contains articles on metaphysics, healing, ancient mysticism, human potentials, transformational psychology, holistic health, interspecies communication as well as philosophy, cyberspace, art and poetry.

MAGICKAL PAGAN NEWS. see *PARAPSYCHOLOGY AND OCCULTISM*

MAGICKAL UNICORN MESSENGER. see *PARAPSYCHOLOGY AND OCCULTISM*

MANTEIA; a magazine for the mantic arts. see *PARAPSYCHOLOGY AND OCCULTISM*

100   US
MASTER OF LIFE. 1976. q. free. Valley of the Sun Publishing Co., Box 38, Malibu, CA 90265. TEL 818-706-0961. FAX 818-706-3606. Ed. Richard Sutphen; Pub. Richard Sutphen. adv.; bk.rev. circ. 250,000. Document type: consumer publication, catalog.
  Formerly: Self - Help Update.
  Description: Promotes mental, physical and philosophical self-sufficiency through awareness and reprogramming techniques.

MEDITATOR'S NEWSLETTER. see *RELIGIONS AND THEOLOGY*

156   GW   ISSN 0177-3852
MERIDIAN;* Zeitschrift fuer Kosmobiologie, Astrologie und angewandte Psychologie. 1979. 6/yr. DM.52. Ebertin-Verlag, Kronenstr. 2, Postfach 167, 7800 Freiberg, Germany.
  Incorporates: Kosmobiologie (ISSN 0023-4214) & Kosmischer Beobachter (ISSN 0177-3844)

110   US
▼**MERLANA'S MAGICHAL MESSAGE**. 1995. 3/yr. $20. Box 1107, Dept. UIPD, Blythe, CA 92226-1107. TEL 619-922-0686. Ed. Marjorie E. Navarro. bk.rev. circ. 1,000. Document type: consumer publication.

133   US
MESSENGER (POMPANO BEACH); a magazine for the golden age. 1980. m. $12. Lily O'Donnell, Ed. & Pub., 1936 S.W. 63rd Terrace, Pompano Beach, FL 33068. TEL 305-972-8951. FAX 305-942-2205. adv.: B&W page $125. circ. 500 (paid).
  Description: Articles on psychic phenomena, new age and spiritual concerns.

METAPSICHICA; rivista italiana di parapsicologia. see *PARAPSYCHOLOGY AND OCCULTISM*

METASCIENCE ANNUAL; a New Age journal of parapsychology. see *PARAPSYCHOLOGY AND OCCULTISM*

NEW AGE PUBLICATIONS

031   US
MILLENNIUM WHOLE EARTH CATALOG; access to tools & ideas for the twenty-first century. 1968. irreg., latest 1994. $30 softcover; hardcover $50. Point Foundation, 27 Gate Five Rd., Sausalito, CA 94965. TEL 415-332-1716. (Co-publisher: HarperSanFrancisco, 1160 Battery St., San Francisco, CA 94111. TEL 415-477-4400. FAX 415-477-4444) Ed. Howard Rheingold. bk.rev. circ. 150,000. **Document type:** catalog.
 Former titles (until 1994): Essential Whole Earth Catalog; Which supersedes in part (in 1974): Whole Earth Catalog (ISSN 0043-5031)
 Description: Provides access to information and resources for self-education in a variety of fields.

133   US
MIND TOOLS. 1984. bi-m. $15. (Crystal Research Foundation) Kryolux, Inc., 27 Hickory St., Box 467, Ellenville, NY 12428-1307. TEL 914-647-3111. Ed. Steven Krulick. adv.
 Formerly: Green Light News.

MINI EXAMINER. see ASTROLOGY

MINSTREL. see PARAPSYCHOLOGY AND OCCULTISM

MIRACLES MAGAZINE. see RELIGIONS AND THEOLOGY

MONTHLY PLANET. see POLITICAL SCIENCE — International Relations

700 780   US   ISSN 0892-2721
MUSIC OF THE SPHERES; a quarterly magazine of art and music for the New Age. 1988. q. $14. Music of the Spheres Publishing, Box 1751, Taos, NM 87571. TEL 505-758-0405. Ed. John Patrick Lamkin. adv.; bk.rev.; film rev.; play rev.; illus. circ. 10,000.
 Description: Focuses on promoting and networking the art and music of the New Age, and to promote world peace.

301   AG   ISSN 0326-0666
MUTANTIA; cuadernos eco-espirituales. 1980. q. $30. Ediciones Mutantia, Casilla 260, Sucursal 12, 1412 Buenos Aires, Argentina. TEL 541-343-4377. FAX 541-331-1033. Dir. Miguel Grinberg. adv.; bk.rev.; illus. circ. 12,000. (also avail. in microfilm; back issues avail.) **Document type:** trade publication.
 Description: Covers documents exploring the building of the 21st century's society, transformational education, focusing on human potentials and alternative ways of living.

MYSTIC MAGIC. see RELIGIONS AND THEOLOGY — Other Denominations And Sects

NATURAL HEALING & NUTRITION ANNUAL. see ALTERNATIVE MEDICINE

NATURAL HEALTH; the guide to well-being. see ALTERNATIVE MEDICINE

NATURE AND HEALTH. see ALTERNATIVE MEDICINE

110   US   ISSN 1041-4878
NETWORK OF LIGHT. bi-m. $10. Box 687, Washington Sta., Buffalo, NY 14205. (tabloid format) **Document type:** consumer publication.
 Description: A bio-regional resource for conscious awareness in whole health, ecology, social responsibility and personal transformation.

133 158   US   ISSN 1070-762X
THE NETWORKER (ASHEVILLE); a common link of the voices for planetary awakening. 1992. m. $16. Delphi Communications, 20 Battery Park Ave., Ste. 612, Asheville, NC 28801. TEL 704-254-6852. FAX 704-258-8332. Ed. Robin Dunn. adv. contact: Al Bouchard. illus. circ. 5,000. (tabloid format) **Document type:** newspaper.
 Description: Covers topics relating to planetary awakening, holistic healing practices, spirituality and related educational issues, healthy life-styles and sustainable technologies.

NEW AGE ASTROLOGY GUIDE (YEAR). see ASTROLOGY

133   US
NEW AGE DIGEST. 1983. irreg. donation or exchange basis. New Age Press, Box 1373, Keala Kekua, HI 96750. TEL 808-328-8013. Ed. Jim Butler. circ. 400.

110 030   US   ISSN 1047-2746
BP605.N48
NEW AGE ENCYCLOPEDIA. biennial. Gale Research Inc., 835 Penobscot Bldg., Detroit, MI 48226. TEL 313-961-2242. FAX 313-961-6083. TELEX 810-221-7086.

110
NEW AGE EXCHANGE;* a magazine of contemporary metaphysical thought. 1986. 6/yr. $18. Zoan Publishing Co., Inc., 705 Bay Blossom Dr., Wilmington, NC 28405. Ed. S. Jasinski. adv.; bk.rev. circ. 1,000. (back issues avail.)

051   US   ISSN 0746-3618
BP605.N48
NEW AGE JOURNAL. 1974. bi-m. (plus a. special issue) $24. New Age Publishing, Inc., 42 Pleasant St., Watertown, MA 02172. TEL 617-926-0200. FAX 617-926-5021. E-mail: editor@newage.com. (Subscr. to: Box 53275, Boulder, CO 80321-327553. TEL 800-234-4556) Ed. Peggy Taylor; Pub. David Thorne. adv.; bk.rev.; illus.; circ. 180,000. (paid). (also avail. in microfiche from UMI) Indexed: Alt.Press Ind., Bk.Rev.Ind. (1981-), Child.Bk.Rev.Ind. (1981-), New Per.Ind. **Document type:** consumer publication.
 —Faxon; UMI; UnCover.
 Former titles (until 1983): New Age Magazine (ISSN 0164-3967); New Age Journal.
 Description: Serves as a discerning chronicle of America's spiritual reawakening, examining such topics as holistic medicine, natural foods, self-help psychology, contemporary mysticism, and green politics.

110 613.7   US
NEW AGE JOURNAL SOURCEBOOK. a. $3.95. New Age Publishing, Inc., 42 Pleasant St., Watertown, MA 02172. TEL 617-926-0200. adv. **Document type:** consumer publication.

070.5   US   ISSN 1042-6566
NEW AGE RETAILER; books, music, merchandise. 1987. bi-m. $25 (foreign $50). Continuity Publishing, Inc., 1300 N. State St., Ste. 105, Bellingham, WA 98225-4730. TEL 360-676-0789; 800-463-9343. FAX 360-676-0789. E-mail: newagere@pacificrim.net. Ed. Dwight Lucky. adv.; bk.rev.; circ. 5,800. (controlled). **Document type:** trade publication.
 Formerly (until 1989): Monthly Report to Booksellers.
 Description: Trade journal focusing on quality material for retailers of new age books, music, videos and sidelines. Includes articles and reviews.

299   US
NEW AGE TEACHINGS. 1967. bi-m. contribution. New Age Teaching Center of Learning, 37 Maple St., Brookfield, MA 01506. TEL 508-867-3754. Ed. Anita Afton. bk.rev. circ. 3,000. **Document type:** newsletter.

100   US   ISSN 1040-2047
NEW DAY HERALD. 1975. bi-m. $25 (effective Mar. 1991). (Church of the Movement of Spiritual Inner Awareness) Mandeville Press, Box 3935, Los Angeles, CA 90051. FAX 213-737-5680. Ed. Stede Barber. adv. circ. 5,000. (tabloid format; back issues avail.) **Document type:** newspaper.
 Formerly (until 1988): Movement Newspaper.

301   US
NEW ENVIRONMENT BULLETIN. 1974. m. $8 in N. America; elsewhere $12.50. New Environment Association, 270 Fenway Dr., Syracuse, NY 13224. TEL 315-446-8009. Ed. Harry Schwarzlander. bk.rev. circ. 150. **Document type:** newsletter.
 Description: Articles, reviews and announcements dealing with a wide range of ecological and social topics; includes reports on activities of the New Environment Association.

100   US   ISSN 0886-4616
NEW FRONTIER; magazine of transformation. 1981. m. $18 (foreign $38) (effective 1994). New Frontier Education Society, 15 Mace Ave., Asheville, NC 28806-2724. TEL 704-251-0109. FAX 704-251-0727. E-mail: 73072.2140@compuserve.com; Site addr.: http://www.consciousnet.com. Ed. Swami Nostradamus Virato. adv.: B&W page $1180. bk.rev.; film rev.; music rev. circ. 60,000. (back issues avail.) **Document type:** consumer publication. ●Also available online.
 Description: Presents informative articles by, and interviews with, internationally respected leaders in the New Age field. Covers holistic health, metaphysics, yoga, natural foods, astrology and latest world news.

613
NEW LIFE; for those who want to make a change. bi-m. $18. Serenity Health Organization, Inc., 218 W. 72nd St., New York, NY 10023. TEL 212-787-1600. Ed. Mark Becker. circ. 60,000.
 Formerly: Serenity's New Life (ISSN 1051-2195)
 Description: Reference and resource guide for holistic health, environment and New Age. Examines consciousness and the human potential, and provides information on products and services.

100   US   ISSN 1044-2782
NEW TIMES (SEATTLE); enriching and changing lives since 1985. 1985. m. $15. Silver Owl Publications, Box 51186, Seattle, WA 98115-1186. TEL 206-524-9071. FAX 206-524-0052. (Alt. addr.: 8618 Roosevelt Way, Seattle, WA 98115) Ed. Rhonda Dicksion; Pub. Krysta Gibson. adv. contact: Krysta Gibson. bk.rev.; illus. circ. 20,000. cols./p.: 6; pp./issue: 24. (broadsheet format; back issues avail.) **Document type:** newspaper.
 Incorporates (in 1991): Inner Woman; Which was formerly: Spiritual Women's Times.
 Description: Examines human potential, peace and numerous spiritual alternatives.

NEXUS (BOULDER); Colorado's holistic journal. see ALTERNATIVE MEDICINE

NIGHTSCAPES; journal of magic, paganism and the occult. see PARAPSYCHOLOGY AND OCCULTISM

133   DK   ISSN 0108-3503
NYT ASPEKT; magazine for alternative living and thinking. 1983. bi-m. DKK 260. Nyt Aspekt, Nannasgade 18, 2200 Copenhagen N, Denmark. TEL 35-82-30-03. FAX 35-82-73-02. Ed. Iben Gaarde-Nissen. adv. contact: Birgit Olsen. bk.rev. circ. 10,000.
 Formed by the merger of: Psykisk Forum (ISSN 0108-7800); U F O Aspekt (ISSN 0107-0258)
 Description: Covers spiritual science, personal growth, health, parapsychology and alternative thinking and living.

133   US
O P E R A NEWSLETTER.* (Former name of issuing body: Organization of Psychic Research Associates) 1975. 6/yr. $15 (effective 1994). Organization of Psychic Educational & Research Associates, Box 720366, Norman, OK 73070-4271. TEL 405-557-8048. Ed. May Harshbarger. adv.; bk.rev.; circ. 240 (paid). **Document type:** newsletter.
 Formerly: O P R A Newsletter.
 Description: News and information regarding psychic phenomena, research and educational activities of interest to members.

ODYSSEY; an adventure in more conscious living. see PHILOSOPHY

289.9   US
OMEGA NEW AGE DIRECTORY. 1972. m. $15. New Age Community Church, 6418 S. 39th Ave., Phoenix, AZ 85041. TEL 602-237-3213. Eds. Joy Rodgers, John Rodgers. adv.; bk.rev.; music rev.; video rev. circ. 25,000. (tabloid format; back issues avail.) **Document type:** newspaper, directory.
 Description: Contains national and local news of interest to the metaphysical community. Includes complete activity and group listings, coverage of holistic health issues and related items.

NEW AGE PUBLICATIONS

100 US
ON COURSE; weekly inspiration for the inner journey. 1983. s-m. $3 per no. Interfaith Fellowship, 459C Carol Dr., Monroe, NY 10950. TEL 914-783-0383. FAX 914-774-7747. Ed. Jon Mundy. adv.; bk.rev.; bibl.; illus. circ. 3,000. (back issues avail.)
  Formerly: Mustard Seed.
  Description: A course in miracles orientation helps bring people of different faiths together. Includes daily meditations, quotations, jokes, parables, prayers, poems, and seasonal perspectives.

299 UK ISSN 0144-8595
ONE EARTH. 1980. q. £7.50($12) (Findhorn Foundation) One Earth Ltd., The Park, Findhorn, Forres N36 0TZ, Scotland. TEL 01309-30311. FAX 01309-30933. Eds. Andrew Murray, Jill Wolcott. adv.; bk.rev. circ. 3,500. (back issues avail.)
  Formerly: One Earth Image (ISSN 0143-8247); Formed by the merger of (1975-1980): Open Letter (ISSN 0308-2423); (1975-1980): On Earth (ISSN 0308-1516).

133 615.89 NE ISSN 0165-5027
ONKRUID; goed voor aarde, lichaam en geest. 1978. bi-m. fl.36.50. Stichting Onkruid, West 32, 1633 JC Avenhorn, Netherlands. TEL 31-2295-42800. FAX 31-2295-42315. (In Belgium: Postbus 10, 8580 Avelgem, Belgium) Ed. Paul Breekveldt; Pub. Paul Breekveldt. adv.; bk.rev.; illus.; circ. 30,000 (paid). (back issues avail.) **Document type:** consumer publication.
  ●Also available online.
  Description: Covers alternative health, environmental and spiritual concerns.

ORGANICA; a magazine of arts & activism. see LITERATURE

OUTLOOK. see RELIGIONS AND THEOLOGY — Other Denominations And Sects

PAGANS FOR PEACE. see RELIGIONS AND THEOLOGY

299 US
PAN-LIME; the newsletter of the Pan Community. m. $15 (Canada and Mexico $16; elsewhere $18). Pen & Pan Publishing, 800 W. Drayton, Ferndale, MI 48220. TEL 810-543-0565. **Document type:** newsletter.
  Description: Informs readers of news and events concerning the Pan community throughout the U.S. and around the world.

THE PANIC RELIEF NEWS. see PSYCHOLOGY

158 US ISSN 1048-3578
PERSONAL DISCOVERY REPORT. 1990. m. $49. Personal Advantage, Box 10882, Portland, OR 97210-0882. TEL 503-228-4972. Ed. Maggie Connolly-Jensen. bk.rev. circ. 1,000. (back issues avail.) **Document type:** newsletter.
  Description: Promotes positive ideas and approaches for better living and personal growth.

100 US
PERSPECTIVE ON CONSCIOUSNESS & PSI RESEARCH. 1979. 12/yr. membership. A.R.E. Press, Box 595, Virginia Beach, VA 23451. TEL 804-428-3588. Ed. Henry Reed. circ. 70,000.

110 US
PHENOMENEWS; exploring human potential, holistic health and living. 1978. m. $14. PhenomeNEWS Inc., 18444 W. 10 Mile Rd., No. 105, Southfield, MI 48075-2626. TEL 810-569-3888. FAX 810-569-4512. Ed. Cindy Saul. adv.: B&W page $540; 9 3/4 x 12 7/8; adv. contact: Gerri MaGee. bk.rev. circ. 40,000. **Document type:** newspaper.

PILGRIMAGE; reflections on the human journey. see MEDICAL SCIENCES — Psychiatry And Neurology

110 US ISSN 1070-0498
POSITIVE TIMES. 1990. q. $14. Partners in Positive Publishing, Inc., Box 244, West Stockbridge, MA 01266-0244. TEL 413-698-3344. Ed. Jacquelyn Wescott; Pub. Jerry D. Posner. adv.; bk.rev.; circ. 2,500 (paid).
  Description: Dedicated to personal growth, self-improvement, mental and emotional healing.

100 BE ISSN 0777-9909
PRESSE-INTER. 1981. q. 1000 BEF (effective 1992). Centre d'Inter-Action Culturelle, 4 rue de la Procession, B-1331 Rosieres, Belgium. TEL 32-2-653-53-24. FAX 32-2-654-1908. Ed. Pierre Houart. adv.; bk.rev.
  Formerly (until 1988): Alternatives (ISSN 0770-4437)
  Description: Examines peace and non-violence in culture and spirituality.

PRIMARY POINT. see RELIGIONS AND THEOLOGY — Buddhist

PSYCHIC READER. see PARAPSYCHOLOGY AND OCCULTISM

PSYCHICAL STUDIES. see PARAPSYCHOLOGY AND OCCULTISM

200 US ISSN 1040-533X
BP500
THE QUEST (WHEATON). 1988. q. $13.97 membership (foreign 16.97) (includes The American Theosophist). Theosophical Society in America, 1926 N. Main St., Box 270, Wheaton, IL 60189-0270. TEL 708-668-1571. FAX 708-665-8791. Ed. William Metzger. adv.: B&W page $500; 8 1/4 x 10 3/4. bk.rev. circ. 25,000.
  Description: Covers philosophy, religion, science, and the arts from a Theosophical perspective.

299 US ISSN 1066-9914
QUINTILE. 1991. 4/yr. free. Alana Lotharius, Ed. & Pub., Box 89, Hales Corners, WI 53130. TEL 414-423-8620. FAX 414-423-8610. bk.rev.

THE RADIANCE TECHNIQUE NEWSLETTER. see ALTERNATIVE MEDICINE

100 US
RAINBOW RAY FOCUS. 6/yr. $12. Magnificent Consummation Inc., Box 1188, Sedona, AZ 86336. Ed. Angel Violet.
  Formerly: Ruby Focus.

100 133 US ISSN 0886-036X
REALITY CHANGE; a global Seth journal. 1980. q. $29.95 (Canada and Mexico $ 36.95; elsewhere $49.95) (effective 1995). Seth Network International, Box 1620, Eugene, OR 97440-1620. TEL 503-686-0803. FAX 503-683-1084. E-mail: sethnet@emerald.com. Ed. Fairlight Lucia; Pubs. Lynda Dahl, Stan Ulkowski. adv.: B&W page $285; 8 1/2 x 11. bk.rev. circ. 1,500. (back issues avail.) **Document type:** consumer publication.
  Description: Explores the concepts and ideas outlined in the 22-volume system of philosophy written by Jane Roberts.

REFLECTIONS QUARTERLY RESOURCE DIRECTORY. see BUSINESS AND ECONOMICS — Trade And Industrial Directories

133 US
RELEVANT TIMES. bi-m. T A O Communications, Box 126, Mountain Lakes, NJ 07046. TEL 201-331-0082. FAX 201-331-0082. Ed. Nancy Dreyfus; Pub. Megan L. McWilliams. adv.; bk.rev.; illus. **Document type:** consumer publication.
  Description: Discusses ethical and healthful living from a New Age perspective.

100 US
REVELATIONS OF AWARENESS; the cosmic newsletter. 1972. 17/yr. $42 membership (effective 1995 & 1996). Cosmic Awareness Communications, Box 115, Olympia, WA 98507. Ed. Avaton. bk.rev. circ. 3,100. (back issues avail.) **Document type:** newsletter.
  Description: Explains UFOs, the alien presence, other mysteries, plus spiritual philosophy, and life-after-death.

301 US
BF309
REVISION: A JOURNAL OF CONSCIOUSNESS AND TRANSFORMATION. 1978. q. $32 to individuals; institutions $53. (Helen Dwight Reid Education Foundation) Heldref Publications, 1319 Eighteenth St., N.W., Washington, DC 20036-1802. TEL 202-296-6267. FAX 202-296-5149. Ed. Adele Mujal. adv. contact: Raymond Rallo. bk.rev.; abstr.; bibl.; charts; stat.; tr.lit. circ. 1,000. (also avail. in microform from UMI; back issues avail.) **Indexed:** Alt.Press Ind., Psychol.Abstr. **Document type:** academic/scholarly publication.
  —BLDSC (7800.565000); UMI; UnCover. **CCC**.
  Formerly: Revision (ISSN 0275-6935)
  Refereed Serial

299 780 US
ROLLING BLUNDER REVIEW. Variant title: Arlo Guthrie's Rolling Blunder Review. no.7, 1988. 4/yr. $5 (effective 1993). (Guthrie Center) Rising Son Records, Box 657, Housatonic, MA 01236-0657. TEL 413-528-5905. Ed. Arlo Guthrie. illus. circ. 5,000. **Document type:** newsletter, catalog.
  Description: Includes the philosophical meanderings of the folksinger, strange adventures of Reuben Clamzo, Recipes from Alice (of Restaurant fame), and the "Get-Stuff" mail order catalogue.

135 US
RON WARMOTH LETTER. 1980. m. $35. Ron Warmoth Letter, Box 4037, Los Angeles, CA 90078. TEL 213-389-3483. Ed. Ron Warmoth. (looseleaf format) **Document type:** newsletter.

SACRED SERPENT. see RELIGIONS AND THEOLOGY — Other Denominations And Sects

SELF & SOCIETY; European journal of humanistic psychology. see PSYCHOLOGY

SELF-REALIZATION. see RELIGIONS AND THEOLOGY

100 UK ISSN 0262-9356
SHARE IT; international journal for celebrating & sharing who we really are. 1979. 2/yr. £3.50 (Europe £3.90; rest of world £4.30) per no. Head Exchange Press, 17 Mackeson Rd., London NW3 2LU, England. TEL 0171-267-0188. E-mail: headexchange@gn.apc.org. Ed. Richard Lang. bk.rev.; illus. circ. 300. (back issues avail.) **Document type:** newsletter.
  Formerly: Nacton Newsletter.
  Description: Provides a forum to explore and discuss the experience and meaning of "seeing who we really are", a contemporary method of self-enquiry by the philosopher Douglas Harding.

THE SKEPTIC. see PARAPSYCHOLOGY AND OCCULTISM

SKEPTIC. see PARAPSYCHOLOGY AND OCCULTISM

SOMATICS; magazine-journal of the mind body arts and sciences. see PHYSICAL FITNESS AND HYGIENE

133 US
SOMNIAL TIMES. 1988. 6/yr. $9 (foreign $12). American Mensa, Dreamers Special Interest Group, c/o Gloria Reiser, Box 561, Quincy, IL 62306-0561. TEL 217-222-9082. Ed. Judith Eir Landaiche. adv.; bk.rev.; circ. 10 (paid). **Document type:** newsletter.
  Description: Shares dreamland adventures and explores the dream state. Shares dreams, reveries, dream programming.

300 US
SPECTRUM MONTHLY UPDATE; celebrating the diversity of all races, religions and cultures. 1965. m. $10. Unity-and-Diversity World Council, 5521 Grosvenor Blvd., Ste. 22, Los Angeles, CA 90066-6915. TEL 310-577-1968. FAX 310-578-1028. Ed. Rev. Leland P. Stewart. adv.; bk.rev. circ. 1,500. (tabloid format) **Indexed:** Abstr.Engl.Stud. **Document type:** newsletter.
  Description: Celebrates the diversity of all races, religions, and cultures.

NEW AGE PUBLICATIONS

110   US   ISSN 1049-9075
SPECTRUM - THE WHOLISTIC NEWS MAGAZINE. 1988. bi-m. $18 (foreign $26). Spectrum Universal, 61 Dutile Rd., Belmont, NH 03220. TEL 603-528-4710. Ed. Roger G. Windsor; Pub. Roger G. Windsor. adv.; circ. 5,000 (paid). (back issues avail.) **Document type:** consumer publication.
    Description: Discusses in digest form nutrition, the environment, medicine, natural healing, and psychology from a wholistic perspective.

133   US
SPIRITUAL EMERGENCE NETWORK NEWSLETTER. 1982. 3/yr. membership. Spiritual Emergence Network, 603 Mission St., Santa Cruz, CA 95060-3653. TEL 408-426-0902. E-mail: emergenc@well.com. Ed. Selene Vega. bk.rev.; bibl.; tr.lit. circ. 3,000. (tabloid format; back issues avail.) **Document type:** newsletter.

131   UK   ISSN 0038-7622
THE SPIRITUAL HEALER; journal of spiritual healing and philosophy. 1953. bi-m. free. Harry Edwards Spiritual Healing Sanctuary Trust, Burrows Lea, Shere, Guildford, Surrey GU5 9QG, England. TEL 01483-202054. Ed. Ramus Branch. adv.; illus.; index; circ. 7,250 (controlled). **Document type:** consumer publication.

133.5   US
STAR BEACON. 1987. m. $15 (Canada $16; elsewhere $24). (U F O Contact Center International, Delta County) Earth Star Publications, Box 117, Paonia, CA 81428. TEL 303-527-3257. Ed. Ann Ulrich. adv.; bk.rev. circ. 500. (looseleaf format; back issues avail.; reprint service avail.) **Document type:** newsletter.
    Description: For UFO percipients offering a wide variety of metaphysical information and promoting spiritual awareness.

STAR TECH; the real cosmic connection. see ASTRONOMY

100   UK
STARFIRE. q. £6. B C M Starfire, London WC1N 3XX, England. illus.

135   US   ISSN 1045-4942
SUBCONSCIOUSLY SPEAKING; you can change your life through the power of your mind. 1985. bi-m. $12 (Canada $15; elsewhere $18). Harriman Publishing Co. (Subsidiary of: Infinity Institute International, Inc.), 4110 Edgeland, Dept. 800, Royal Oak, MI 48073-2251. TEL 810-549-5594. FAX 810-549-5421. Ed. Anne H. Spencer. adv.; bk.rev. circ. 3,500. **Document type:** newsletter.
    Description: To elevate the consciousness of all who read through current information regarding hypnosis, imagery, and healing of body, mind and spirit.

SUBTLE ENERGIES; an interdisciplinary journal of energetic and informational interactions. see ALTERNATIVE MEDICINE

100   US
SUPPORTIVE LIFESTYLES NEWS. 1972. 12/yr. $25. Fellowship of the Inner Light, 620 14 St., Virginia Beach, VA 23451. TEL 703-896-3673. FAX 804-428-6648. Ed. Myrrh Haslam. adv.; bk.rev. (tabloid format)

100   152   US
TAROT NETWORK NEWS. 1981. s-a. $10. Taroco, Box 104, Sausalito, CA 94966. TEL 415-332-9254. Ed. Gary W. Ross; Pub. Jack Hurley. adv. contact: Geri Kepler. bk.rev. circ. 350. (back issues avail.) **Document type:** newsletter.
    Description: Provides a guide to the content and application of the Tarot.

TAROT NEWS; a journal for Tarot enthusiasts. see PARAPSYCHOLOGY AND OCCULTISM

110   US
TEMPLE DOORS;* doctrine of mysteries. 1980. q. $25. Star of Isis Mystery School, Church of the Johannine Wellspring, Box 200202, Austin, TX 78720-0202. TEL 512-737-1733. Ed. Chrystine Star Eagle Hayes. bk.rev. circ. 60. (back issues avail.) **Formerly:** Source.
    Description: Mystery schooling of deeply symbolic, metaphysical studies that include source translations on planetary transformation, inner world Shamanism, angelic transmissions, and spirit heritage.

133   US
TERRITORIAL HERALD. 1981. q. $3 (foreign $5). Ministry of the Interior, RP 200-0203, Box 7075, Laguna Niguel, CA 92607. TEL 714-240-8472. Ed. Marc Ely-Chairin. circ. 200. (back issues avail.)

THEOSOPHICAL HISTORY; a quarterly journal of research. see HISTORY

110   US   ISSN 1073-7421
THRESHOLDS QUARTERLY. 1975. q. $35 membership. School of Metaphysics, National Headquarters, HCR 1, Box 15, Windyville, MO 65783. TEL 417-345-8411. Ed. Barbara Condron. adv.: B&W page $1250; trim 7 1/2 x 10; adv. contact: Laurel Fuller Clark. bk.rev.; illus. circ. 5,000. **Indexed:** Avery Ind.Archit.Per. **Document type:** academic/scholarly publication.
    Formerly: Thresholds Journal.
    Description: Reports on personal development and strategies for spiritual and material success, with interviews and features on business, health, the arts, historical subjects, and more.

TO YOUR HEALTH!; the magazine of healing and hope. see PHYSICAL FITNESS AND HYGIENE

133   US
TOTAL ECLIPSE. 6/yr. $12 (Canada $14, elsewhere $17). Box 1055, Suisun, CA 94585. Ed. J. Taylor Black. **Document type:** consumer publication.

157   200   615.89   US
TRANSFORMATION TIMES; new age journal. 1982. 10/yr. $8. (Christ Light Community Church) Life Resources Unlimited, Box 425, Beavercreek, OR 97004. TEL 503-632-7141. Ed. Connie L. Faubel. adv.; bk.rev. circ. 8,000. (tabloid format) **Document type:** newspaper.

TRANSFORMERS NOTEBOOK. see DRUG ABUSE AND ALCOHOLISM

U F O ENCOUNTER. see AERONAUTICS AND SPACE FLIGHT

100   US   ISSN 1069-9465
UNARIUS LIGHT JOURNAL. 1974. q. $25 (foreign $39). (Unarius Academy of Science Publications) Unarius Publishing, 145 S. Magnolia Ave., El Cajon, CA 92020-4522. TEL 619-444-7062. FAX 619-444-9736. E-mail: Unarius@cts.com. (Dist. addr.: 5425 Tulane Dr., S.W., Atlanta, GA 30336-2323. TEL 404-691-6996) Ed. Barbara Rogers; Pub. Charles L. Spiegel. adv. contact: Frank Garlock. bk.rev.; illus.; cum. index (1974-1995). circ. 5,000. (also avail. in audio cassette; back issues avail.) **Document type:** academic/scholarly publication.
    Formerly (until 1993): Unarius Light Magazine.
    Description: Discusses the psychology of consciousness, past-life history, and the extraterrestrial phenomenon.

133   US
THE UNEXPLAINED; mysteries of life explained. 1960. q. $8. (M U - Metaphysical Union) Krastman Productions, Box 16790, Encino, CA 91416. TEL 818-705-8865. Ed. Hank Krastman. adv.; bk.rev.; circ. 5,000 (paid). (also avail. in video cassette; back issues avail.) **Document type:** consumer publication.

100   US
UNIVERSAL PROUTIST. 1985. m. membership. Proutist Universal, Inc., Box 56466, Washington, DC 20040. TEL 202-829-2278. FAX 202-829-0462. Ed. D. Dhruva. bk.rev.; illus. circ. 4,000. (back issues avail.) **Indexed:** Environ.Abstr.
    Formerly: New Waves (Washington) (ISSN 1040-8185)
    Description: Informs members of developments in the PROUT (Progressive Utilization Theory) movement, social projects, and activities of other progressive organizations.

133   US
THE UNIVERSALIAN; dedicated to expanding conscious awareness. 1985. q. contributions. Universalia, Inc., Box 6243, Denver, CO 80206. Ed. Jan Martin. circ. 1,200. **Document type:** newsletter.
    Description: Expounds the group's religious philosophy of increasing New Age awareness.

200   133   US   ISSN 0748-3406
VENTURE INWARD. 1984. bi-m. membership. Association for Research and Enlightenment, Inc., Box 595, Virginia Beach, VA 23451. TEL 804-428-3588. FAX 804-422-4631. Ed. A. Robert Smith. bk.rev.; index. circ. 35,000. **Document type:** bulletin.
    Supersedes: A.R.E. Journal.
    Description: Publishes articles that relate to the parapsychology, holistic medicine, metaphysical and spiritual concepts contained in the readings of the late psychic Edgar Cayce.

158   US
VIEWS FROM OFF CENTER. 1991. bi-m. Ethical Humanist Society, 38 Old Country Rd., Garden City, NY 11530. TEL 516-739-0042. Eds. Scott Allison, GraceAnn V. Inyard. **Document type:** newsletter.

VISIONS (AGOURA HILLS). see ALTERNATIVE MEDICINE

VITALITY MAGAZINE; Toronto's monthly wellness journal. see ALTERNATIVE MEDICINE

133.9   GW
WEGE MAGAZIN; zur Einheit von Natur und Mensch. 1982. q. DM.18 (foreign DM.27). Verlag Aviva W. Dahlberg, Rennbahnstr. 22, 60528 Frankfurt a.M., Germany. TEL 089-782123. FAX 089-784601. Ed. Wolfgang Dahlberg. adv. circ. 10,000. **Document type:** consumer publication.
    Formerly: Wege... (ISSN 0177-4891)

WELCOME TO PLANET EARTH; journal of new astrology in the contemporary world. see ASTROLOGY

327   AU
WELT SPIRALE UND AGNI YOGA; Zeitschrift fuer Fortschritt und Welterneuerung. 1961. m. S.500. Welt-Spirale - Ethische Gesellschaft fuer Fortschritt und Welterneuerung, Wienerstr. 12, A-4020 Linz, Austria. Ed. Willy Augustat. circ. 1,500.
    Formerly: Welt Agni (ISSN 0043-2555)
    Description: Comments on politics, economics, technical problems, religion, and philosophy on the basis of the theosophical teaching.

051   US   ISSN 0749-5056
AP2
WHOLE EARTH REVIEW. 1974. q. $20. Point Foundation, 27 Gate Five Rd., Sausalito, CA 94965. TEL 415-332-1716. FAX 415-332-3110. Ed. Ruth Kissane. bk.rev.; film rev.; charts; illus.; index. circ. 40,000. (also avail. in microform from UMI; back issues avail.) **Indexed:** Acad.Ind., Access (1978-), Alt.Press Ind., Bk.Rev.Ind. (1989-), CAD CAM Abstr., Child.Bk.Rev.Ind. (1989-), Consum.Ind., Energy Rev., Fut.Surv., Hum.Ind., Microcomp.Ind., New Per.Ind. **Document type:** consumer publication.
    ●Also available online. Vendor(s): Knight-Ridder, Inc., Lexis-Nexis, Ovid Technologies, University Microfilms International.
    —BLDSC (9311.953670); Faxon; UMI; UnCover. CCC.
    Formed by the 1984 merger of: Whole Earth Software Review; CoEvolution Quarterly (ISSN 0095-134X); Which supersedes in part (1968-1974): Whole Earth Catalog (ISSN 0043-5031)

613.2   614.7   US   ISSN 0279-5590
                            CODEN: CMMOD9
WHOLE LIFE TIMES.* 1979. 8/yr. $11.95. Whole Life Company, Inc., 12 Jacob Amsden Rd., Westborough, MA 01581-1766. Ed. Kimberly French. adv.; bk.rev. circ. 140,000. (tabloid format) **Indexed:** Alt.Press Ind., Hlth.Ind.
    —UMI.

WICCAN CANDLE. see PARAPSYCHOLOGY AND OCCULTISM

WICCAN REDE. see RELIGIONS AND THEOLOGY — Other Denominations And Sects

133.5   US
WINGED CHARIOT; a tarot newsletter. 1981. irreg. $15. MoonStar Enterprises, Box 1718, Milwaukee, WI 53201-1718. TEL 414-444-0505. Ed. Tracey A. Hoover. adv.; bk.rev. circ. 100. (looseleaf format; back issues avail.) **Document type:** newsletter.

WINGED MERCURY MISSIVE. see SOCIOLOGY

WINGSPAN: JOURNAL OF THE MALE SPIRIT. see MEN'S STUDIES

133 US ISSN 0740-6754
THE WORD (DALLAS). 1986. q. $15. Word Foundation, Inc., Box 180340, Dallas, TX 75218. TEL 214-348-5006. Ed. Neil F. Avery; Pub. Arnold F. Menze. (tabloid format; back issues avail.)
  Description: Sheds light on problems of human living for individuals seeking to make progress through self-improvement.

181.45 US ISSN 1055-7911
B132.Y6
YOGA INTERNATIONAL. 1981. bi-m. $15 (Canada $20; elsewhere $25). Himalayan International Institute (HII), RR 1, Box 407, Honesdale, PA 18431. TEL 717-253-4929; 800-821-YOGA. FAX 717-253-6360. TELEX 510 600 1805. Ed. Deborah Willoughby. adv.: B&W page $600, color page $740; trim 8 1/4 x 10 7/8; adv. contact: Sewa Hecht. bk.rev.; illus.; circ. 8,000 (paid); 3,000 (controlled). (back issues avail.) **Document type:** consumer publication.
  Supersedes (in July 1991): Dawn (Honesdale) (ISSN 0277-4461)
  Description: Covers the practice of yoga, focusing on bodywork and breathing techniques.

613 US ISSN 0191-0965
YOGA JOURNAL; for health and conscious living. 1975. bi-m. $19.97. California Yoga Teachers Association, 2054 University Ave., Ste. 601, Berkeley, CA 94704-1082. TEL 510-841-9200. FAX 510-644-3101. (Subscr. to: Box 469018, Escondido, CA 92046-9018) Ed Rick Fields. adv.; bk.rev. circ. 85,000. (also avail. in microform from UMI; back issues avail.) **Indexed:** New Per.Ind.
 —UMI.
  Description: Covers yoga, holistic health, psychology, New Age consciousness, meditation and Eastern and Western spirituality.

133.323 GW
ZEITSCHRIFT FUER RADIAESTHESIE UND HARMONIEFINDUNG. 1949. q. DM.32 (foreign DM.40). (Zentrum fuer Radiaesthesie) Herold Verlag Dr. Franz Wetzel und Co. KG, Kirchbachweg 16, 81479 Munich, Germany. Ed. Claus Wetzel. adv.; bk.rev.; bibl.; charts; illus.; index, cum.index: 1950-1961. circ. 2,000. **Document type:** academic/scholarly publication.
  Formerly: Zeitschrift fuer Radiaesthesie (ISSN 0044-3425)

NUCLEAR ENERGY

see Energy-Nuclear Energy

NUCLEAR PHYSICS

see Physics-Nuclear Physics

NUMISMATICS

737 US
A N S NEWSLETTER. 1979. q. American Numismatic Society, Broadway at 155th St., New York, NY 10032. TEL 212-234-3130. FAX 212-234-3381. Ed. Elam Martin. circ. 1,400.

737 XR ISSN 0862-1195
ACTA MUSEI MORAVIAE. SUPPLEMENTUM: FOLIA NUMISMATICA. (Supplement to: Moravske Zemske Muzeum. Casopis. Vedy Spolecenske (ISSN 0323-0570)) (Text in Czech; summaries in English, French, German, Russian) 1986. a. $17.50. Moravske Zemske Muzeum, Zelny trh 6, 65937 Brno, Czech Republic. TEL 42-5-22241. FAX 42-5-25279. Ed. Tatana Kucerovska. illus.; index. circ. 700. **Document type:** academic/scholarly publication.
  Incorporates: Moravskie Numismaticke Zpravy (ISSN 0077-152X)

737.4 US
CJ1
AMERICAN JOURNAL OF NUMISMATICS. SERIES 2. 1866. a. $30. American Numismatic Society, Broadway at 155th St., New York, NY 10032. TEL 212-345-3130. FAX 212-234-3381. circ. 2,400. (back issues avail.)
  Former titles: American Journal of Numismatics (ISSN 1053-8356); (1945-1989): Museum Notes (New York) (ISSN 0145-1413)
  Description: Academic analysis of numismatic objects contributing to the understanding and interpretation of history, political science, archaeology, and art history.

737 US ISSN 0569-6720
CJ15
AMERICAN NUMISMATIC SOCIETY. ANNUAL REPORT. a. free. American Numismatic Society, Broadway at 155th St., New York, NY 10032. TEL 212-234-3130. FAX 212-234-3381. Ed. M.H. Martin. illus.
 —BLDSC (1105.200000).

737.4 US ISSN 0271-4019
ANCIENT COINS IN NORTH AMERICAN COLLECTIONS. 1969. irreg. price varies. American Numismatic Society, Broadway at 155th St., New York, NY 10032. TEL 212-234-3130. FAX 212-234-3381. Eds. M.H. Martin, L.A. Elam. (reprint service avail. from UMI)
  Formerly: Greek Coins in North American Collections (ISSN 0072-744X)
  Description: Covers public and private collections not generally available for inspection.

737 954 II
ANDHRA PRADESH, INDIA. DEPARTMENT OF ARCHAEOLOGY AND MUSEUMS. MUSEUM SERIES. (Text in English) 1961. irreg., no.18, 1975-76. price varies. Department of Archaeology and Museums, Hyderabad 500001, Andhra Pradesh, India. (Or: Publications Bureau, Directorate of Government Printing, Chanchalguda, Hyderabad, Andhra Pradesh, India)
  Former titles: Andhra Pradesh, India. Department of Archaeology and Museums. Museum Objects and Numismatics Series; Andhra Pradesh, India. Department of Archaeology. Museum Series (ISSN 0066-166X)

737 IT ISSN 1121-7464
ANNOTAZIONI NUMISMATICHE. (Includes 2 supplements each year.) 1991. q. L.60000 (effective 1994). Edizioni Ennerre s.r.l., Via San Rocco, 8, 20135 Milan, Italy. FAX 39-2-58309185. Ed. Giorgio Veronelli. bk.rev. **Document type:** academic/scholarly publication.
  Description: Contains news, reviews, discussions and bibliographic notes.

737 US ISSN 0884-0180
CJ3481
ARMENIAN NUMISMATIC JOURNAL. Key Title: Hay Dramagitakan Handes. 1975. q. $12.50 (effective 1995 & 1996). Armenian Numismatic Society, 8511 Beverly Park Place, Pico Rivera, CA 90660-1920. TEL 310-695-0380. Ed. Y.T. Nercessian. bk.rev.; charts; illus.; cum.index: vols.1-15. (back issues avail.) **Indexed:** Numis.Lit.

737 FR ISSN 0004-5543
ASSOCIATION INTERNATIONALE DES NUMISMATES PROFESSIONELS. BULLETIN-CIRCULAR. (Text in English, French) no.49, 1969. membership. International Association of Professional Numismatists, c/o Michel Kampmann, 49 rue de Richelieu, 75001 Paris, France. Ed. J.P. Divo.

737 CN ISSN 0044-9903
ATLANTIC PROVINCES NUMISMATIC ASSOCIATION. NEWSLETTER.* m. Atlantic Provinces Numismatic Association, 25 Honeydale Cresc., Halifax, N.S., Canada. Ed. N.C. Boltz.

737.4 AT ISSN 0004-8887
AUSTRALIAN COIN REVIEW. 1964. m. Aus.$32. Jolyon Sykes, Ed. & Pub., P.O. Box 5, Thirroul, N.S.W. 2515, Australia. TEL 61-42-681434. FAX 61-42-681435. adv.; bk.rev. circ. 7,222. (back issues avail.) **Indexed:** Numis.Lit., Pinpointer. **Document type:** consumer publication.
 —UnCover.
  Description: Devoted to the numismatic world of coins, medallions, medals, tokens, banknotes and share scrips.

AUSTRALIAN NUGGET JOURNAL. see MINES AND MINING INDUSTRY

737 AT ISSN 0004-9875
AUSTRALIAN NUMISMATIC JOURNAL; devoted to the study of coins, tokens, paper money and medals, particularly the issues of Australia. 1949. irreg. membership. South Australian Numismatic Society, G.P.O. Box 80 B, Adelaide, S.A., Australia. Ed. D.J. Rampling. bk.rev.; index, cum.index. circ. 200. **Indexed:** Numis.Lit.

737 US ISSN 0164-0828
BANK NOTE REPORTER; your news and marketplace for all paper money. 1973. m. $29.95. Krause Publications, Inc., 700 E. State St., Iola, WI 54990. TEL 715-445-2214. FAX 715-445-4087. TELEX 55 6461 KRAUSE PUB UD. Ed. David C. Harper. adv. circ. 5,835. (tabloid format; also avail. in microform from UMI) **Indexed:** Numis.Lit.
  Description: News source and marketplace for collectors of U.S. and world paper money, notes, checks and related fiscal paper. Provides current prices for bank notes of the U.S. and world. Includes active buy-sell marketplace for paper money collectors.

737 PL ISSN 0006-4017
BIULETYN NUMIZMATYCZNY/NUMISMATIC BULLETIN. 1965. q. $30. Polskie Towarzystwo Numizmatyczne, Ul. Jezuicka 6, P.O. Box 2, 00-958 Warsaw, 40, Poland. TEL 48-22-313928. Ed. Janusz Kurpiewski; Pub. Janusz Kurpiewski. adv. contact: Lech Kokocinski. bk.rev.; abstr.; bibl.; illus.; cum.index. circ. 1,600. **Indexed:** Numis.Lit. **Document type:** bulletin.

737 UK ISSN 0143-8956
BRITISH NUMISMATIC JOURNAL. (Includes the Society's Annual Proceedings) 1905. a. £24 membership. British Numismatic Society, 35 Coniston Ct., Kendal St., London W2 2AN, England. Eds. M. Delme-Radcliffe, N.J. Mayhew. adv.; bk.rev.; bibl.; charts; illus.; index, cum.index every 10 vols. circ. 650. **Indexed:** Amer.Hist.& Life (until 1991), Br.Archaeol.Abstr., Br.Hum.Ind., Hist.Abstr. (until 1991), Numis.Lit.
 —BLDSC (2331.300000).

737 370 US ISSN 0010-1443
C N L. 1960. q. $15 (effective 1995). Colonial Newsletter Foundation, Inc., Box 4411, Huntsville, AL 35815. TEL 205-881-8678. E-mail: 75021.172@compuserve.com. Ed. James C. Spilman. bk.rev.; charts; illus.; stat.; circ. 350 (paid). (back issues avail.) **Indexed:** Numis.Lit. **Document type:** newsletter.
  Description: Educational medium for communications between individuals interested in early American numismatics.

737 FR ISSN 0008-0373
CAHIERS NUMISMATIQUES. 1964. q. 120 F. (foreign 130 F.). Societe d'Études Numismatiques et Archeologiques, 3 rue des Arts, 92100 Boulogne Billancourt, France. adv.; bk.rev.; bibl.; charts; illus.; stat. circ. 380. **Indexed:** Numis.Lit.

737 US ISSN 0008-0616
CALCOIN NEWS. 1946. q. membership. California State Numismatic Association, 7879 Greenback Ln., Ste. 250, Citrus Heights, CA 95610. Ed. Regan G. Shea; Pub. Jeffrey Sherlin. bk.rev.; charts; illus. circ. 1,000. **Indexed:** Numis.Lit. **Document type:** newsletter.

737 CN ISSN 0702-3162
CANADIAN COIN NEWS. 1963. fortn. Can.$24.49 (US $25.95, elsewhere Can.$38.95). 103 Lakeshore Rd., Ste. 202, St. Catharines, ON L2N 2T6, Canada. TEL 416-493-4400. Ed. Bret Evans; Pub. Paul Fiocca. adv. contact: Lorna McGill. bk.rev.; illus.; stat. circ. 18,500. **Indexed:** Can.B.P.I., CMI, Numis.Lit.
  Formerly: Coin, Stamp, Antique News (ISSN 0010-0439)
  Description: Offers news, auction results, show listings, and price trends for the most popular Canadian coins.

NUMISMATICS

737   CN   ISSN 0008-4573
CANADIAN NUMISMATIC JOURNAL. 1956. 10/yr. Can.$30 (foreign $30) (effective 1996). Canadian Numismatic Association, P.O. Box 226, Barrie, ON L4M 4T2, Canada. TEL 705-737-0845. FAX 705-737-0293. adv. contact: Paul Fiocca. bk.rev.; bibl.; illus.; stat.; index; circ. 1,900 (paid). (also avail. in microform; back issues avail.) **Indexed:** Can.B.P.I., CMI, Numis.Lit.
   Description: Aims to encourage and promote the science of numismatics by acquirement and study of coins, paper money, medals, tokens and all other numismatic items, with special emphasis on material pertaining to Canada.

737   CN   ISSN 0045-5202
CANADIAN NUMISMATIC RESEARCH SOCIETY. TRANSACTIONS. (Text mainly in English, occasionally in French) 1965. a. Can.$16. Canadian Numismatic Research Society, Box 22022, Elmwood Sq. P.O., St. Thomas, ON N5R 6A1, Canada. Ed. Harry N. James. bk.rev. circ. 50. **Indexed:** Numis.Lit. **Document type:** academic/scholarly publication.

737   CN   ISSN 0703-895X
CANADIAN TOKEN. 1972. bi-m. membership. Canadian Association of Token Collectors, 10 Wesanford Place, Hamilton, Ont. L8P 1N6, Canada. Ed. K.A. Palmer. bk.rev. circ. 300. **Indexed:** Numis.Lit.

737.4 700   US   ISSN 1048-0986
CJ201
THE CELATOR; numismatic art of antiquity. 1987. m. $27 (Canada $30; elsewhere $48) (effective 1995). Celator, Inc., Box 123, Lodi, WI 53555. TEL 608-592-4684. FAX 608-592-4684. Ed. Steven A. Sayles; Pub. Wayne G. Sayles. adv.; bk.rev.; bibl.; charts; illus.; tr.lit.; circ. 2,000 (paid). **Indexed:** Numis.Lit. **Document type:** consumer publication.
   Incorporates: Roman Coins and Culture.
   Description: Articles and features about ancient coins and artifacts, connoisseurship and market news.

737   BE   ISSN 0009-0344
CERCLE D'ETUDES NUMISMATIQUES. BULLETIN. 1964. q. 1250 BEF. Cercle d'Etudes Numismatiques, 4 Bd. de l'Empereur, B-1000 Brussels, Belgium. adv.; bk.rev.; charts; illus.; cum.index. (back issues avail.) **Indexed:** Numis.Lit. **Document type:** bulletin.

737   BE
CERCLE D'ETUDES NUMISMATIQUES. DOSSIERS. 1986. irreg., latest vol.2. price varies. Cercle d'Etudes Numismatiques, 4 Bd. de l'Empereur, B-1000 Brussels, Belgium. (back issues avail.) **Document type:** monographic series.

737   BE   ISSN 0069-2247
CERCLE D'ETUDES NUMISMATIQUES. TRAVAUX. 1964. irreg., latest vol.12, 1993. price varies. Cercle d'Etudes Numismatiques, 4 Bd. de l'Empereur, B-1000 Brussels, Belgium. (back issues avail.) **Document type:** monographic series.

737.4   US
CERTIFIED COIN DEALER NEWSLETTER. 1986. w. $117. Coin Dealer Newsletter, Box 7939, Torrance, CA 90504. TEL 310-515-7369. FAX 310-515-7534. Ed. Dennis R. Baker; Pub. Ron Downing. adv. contact: Shane Downing. **Document type:** newsletter.

737   US   ISSN 1066-3061
CHECK COLLECTOR; devoted to the study of security paper. 1974. q. $10 membership. American Society of Check Collectors, c/o Coleman A. Leifer, Sec., Box 577, Garrett Park, MD 20896. TEL 301-493-5755. Ed. Robert D. Hohertz. adv. contact: Robert D. Hohertz. bk.rev.; charts; illus.; circ. 350 (paid). **Document type:** academic/scholarly publication.
   Formerly: Check List.

737.4   CN   ISSN 0045-7019
CITY OF OTTAWA COIN CLUB. MONTHLY BULLETIN. 1968. m. membership. City of Ottawa Coin Club, P.O. Box 55127, 240 Sparks St., Ottawa, ON K1P 1A1, Canada. (Co-sponsor: Canadian Numismatic Association) adv.; bk.rev. circ. 125.

737   US   ISSN 1064-1181
CJ1
CLASSICAL NUMISMATIC REVIEW. 1936. 4/yr. $35. Classical Numismatic Group Inc., Box 479, Lancaster, PA 17608-0479. TEL 717-390-9194. FAX 717-390-9978. (U.K. subscr. to: Seaby Coins, 14 Old Bond St., London W1X 3DB. TEL 071-495-1888) Ed. Kerry K. Wetterstrom. bk.rev.; illus.; tr.bibl.; index. **Indexed:** Br.Archaeol.Abstr., Numis.Lit.
   Formerly: Seaby's Coin and Medal Bulletin (ISSN 0037-0053)

737.4   US   ISSN 1062-8169
COIN DEALER NEWSLETTER. 1963. w. $98. Coin Dealer Newsletter, Box 7939, Torrance, CA 90504. TEL 310-515-7369. FAX 310-515-7534. Ed. Dennis R. Baker; Pub. Ron Downing. adv. contact: Shane Downing. (back issues avail.) **Document type:** newsletter.

737   UK   ISSN 0140-1149
COIN HOARDS. irreg. Royal Numismatic Society, British Museum, London WC1B 3DG, England. (Dist. by: Spink & Son Ltd., 5-7 King St., St. James, London SW1, England) Ed. M.J. Price. **Indexed:** Br.Archaeol.Abstr., Numis.Lit. **Document type:** bulletin. —BLDSC (3292.932000).

737.4   UK
COIN MONTHLY (1980). 1966. m. £44.60. Numismatic Publishing Co., Sovereign House, Brentwood, Essex CM14 4SE, England. adv.; bk.rev.; charts; illus.; mkt.; stat. circ. 10,534. **Indexed:** Numis.Lit.
   Former titles: Coin (ISSN 0143-5485); Coin Monthly (ISSN 0010-0390)

737   UK   ISSN 0958-1391
CJ1
COIN NEWS. 1979. m. £24 (foreign £33). Token Publishing Ltd., 105 High St., Honiton, Devon EX14 8PE, England. TEL 01404-45414. FAX 01404-45313. (Dist. by: Seymour Press Ltd., Windsor House, 1270 London Rd., Norbury, London SW16 4DH, England) Ed. John W. Mussell. adv. contact: Carol Hartman. bk.rev.; index. circ. 12,000. **Document type:** bulletin.
   Formerly: Coin and Medal News (ISSN 0955-4386); **Incorporates:** Medals International.
   Description: Monthly information for collectors of coins and banknotes.

737 332.6   US
COIN PREVIEWER; numismatic investment newsletter. 1974. m. $19.95. 500 N.W. 101st Ave., Coral Springs, FL 33071. TEL 305-755-7930. (Subscr. to: Box 8655, Coral Springs, FL 33075) Ed. Robert J. Leuchten. adv.; bk.rev. circ. 200. (back issues avail.)

737.4   US   ISSN 0010-0412
COIN PRICES. 1967. bi-m. $16.95. Krause Publications, Inc., 700 E. State St., Iola, WI 54990. TEL 715-445-2214. FAX 715-445-4087. TELEX 556461 KRAUSE PUB UD. Ed. Bob Wilhite. adv. circ. 91,580. (also avail. in microform from MIM,PMC,UMI)
   Description: Current market information for U.S. coin investors and collectors, featuring market analysis and auction results.

737.4   US   ISSN 0045-7280
COIN WHOLESALER.* 1970. m. $10. World-Wide Coin Investments Ltd., 3763 Roswell Rd. N.E., Atlanta, GA 30342-4414. TEL 404-262-1810. Ed. Michael G. Nugent. adv.; bk.rev.; illus.; stat. circ. 30,000. (tabloid format)

737.4   US   ISSN 0010-0447
CJ1
COIN WORLD. 1960. w. $28. Amos Press Inc., Box 4315, Sidney, OH 45365. TEL 513-498-0800. FAX 513-498-0812. Ed. Beth Deisher. adv.; bk.rev.; illus.; stat. circ. 70,000. (also avail. in microform from UMI; reprint service avail. from UMI) **Indexed:** Numis.Lit. **Document type:** newspaper, consumer publication.
—UMI.
   Formerly: Numismatic Scrapbook (ISSN 0029-6058)

737 332.6   US
COIN WORLD ANNUAL PRICE GUIDE. 1989. a. $4.99. Signet Books, Penguin USA, 375 Hudson St., New York, NY 10014. TEL 212-366-2594. Ed. Donna Cullen-Dolce.

737.4   UK   ISSN 0307-6571
CJ2471
COIN YEARBOOK. 1968. a. £10.95. Numismatic Publishing Co., Sovereign House, Brentwood, Essex CM14 4SE, England. illus. circ. 20,000.

737.4   US   ISSN 0010-0455
COINAGE. 1964. m. $23. Miller Magazines, Inc., 4880 Market St., Ventura, CA 93003-2888. TEL 805-644-3824. Ed. James L. Miller. (also avail. in microform from UMI) **Indexed:** Numis.Lit.
—UMI.
   Description: History and human stories about coins and coin collecting and investing, plus coverage of medals, ancient coins and currency. Most articles deal with U.S. coins and medals.

737.4   US   ISSN 8756-6265
COINAGE OF THE AMERICAS CONFERENCE. PROCEEDINGS. a. price varies. American Numismatic Society, Broadway at 155th St., New York, NY 10032. TEL 212-234-3130. FAX 212-234-3381. Ed. L.A. Elam. **Document type:** proceedings.

737 332.6   US
COINFIDENTIAL REPORT. 1963. bi-m. $19.95 (effective Mar. 15, 1995). Bale Publications, Box 2727, New Orleans, LA 70176. TEL 504-895-5750. Ed. Don Bale, Jr. adv.; bk.rev.; film rev.; charts; illus.; stat.; tr.lit.; circ. 300 (paid). (processed; back issues avail.) **Document type:** newsletter.
   Description: Highlights in-depth analyses of coins that should be lucrative long and/or short-term investments, and stock recommendations on the major US markets. Includes inside look at the coin and stock markets, and current news briefs and trends in both fields.

737.4   US   ISSN 0010-0471
COINS. 1955. m. $22.95. Krause Publications, Inc., 700 E. State St., Iola, WI 54990. TEL 715-445-2214. FAX 715-445-4087. TELEX 55 6461 KRAUSE PUB UD. Ed. Allan Herbert. adv.; bk.rev.; illus. circ. 54,527. (also avail. in microform from PMC,UMI) **Indexed:** Numis.Lit.
—UMI; UnCover.
   Description: Provides in-depth features on U.S. coins accompanied by full-color photographs, helpful collector columns, and U.S. and world coin hobby news.

737.4   UK   ISSN 0069-4983
COINS MARKET VALUES. a. Link House Magazines Ltd., Link House, Dingwall Ave, Croydon, Surrey CR9 2TA, England. TEL 0181-686-2599. FAX 0181-760-0973. Ed. Richard West. **Indexed:** Numis.Lit. **Document type:** consumer publication.
   Formerly: Coins Annual.
   Description: Examines ancient and modern British coins.

737.4   CN   ISSN 0827-0716
COINS OF CANADA. 1971. a. Can.$8.95. Unitrade Press, 91 Tycos Dr., Toronto, ON M6P 3S2, Canada. TEL 416-787-5658. FAX 416-787-7104. Eds. J.A. Haxby, R.C. Willey. illus.

COLLECTORS' SHOWCASE. see *ANTIQUES*

737   IT
CRONACA NUMISMATICA; mensile di monete, cartamoneta, medaglie e titoli antichi. 1993. m. L.53000 (Europe L.100000; elsewhere L.150000) (effective 1995). Eder s.r.l., Via Orazio 22, 80122 Naples, Italy. TEL 39-81-7611315. FAX 39-81-7611316. Ed. Carlo Alberto De Rosa. adv.: B&W page L.1050000, color page L.2100000; trim 185 x 259; adv. contact: Alf De Rosa. circ. 16,744.

737.4   US
CURRENCY DEALER NEWSLETTER; a monthly report on the current market. 1979. m. $44. Coin Dealer Newsletter, Box 7939, Torrance, CA 90504. TEL 310-515-7369. FAX 310-515-7534. Ed. Dennis R. Baker; Pub. Ron Downing. adv. contact: Shane Downing. (back issues avail.) **Document type:** newsletter.
   Description: Wholesale price guide to old US paper money.

NUMISMATICS

737.4   DK
DANMARKS MOENTER FRA CHR. IV TIL MARGRETHE II, SAMT ISLAND, GROENLAND, FAEROERNE, DANSK VESTINDIEN. 1968. a. DKK 125. Frovin Sieg, Ulbjerg Gl. Skole, DK-8832 Skals, Denmark. TEL 86-697102. (Dist. by: Danske Boghandleres Kommissionsanstalt, Siljangade 6, DK-2300 Copenhagen S, Denmark) illus.
Formerly: Sieg's Moentkatalog. Danmark (Year) (ISSN 0586-4496)

737.4   332.6   US
DAVID HALL'S INSIDE VIEW. 1979. bi-m. $97. David Hall's Rare Coins and Collectibles, 1936 E. Deere Ave., Ste. 102, Santa Ana, CA 92705-5723. TEL 714-261-0509. FAX 714-252-0541. Ed. David Hall. Document type: newsletter.

DEUTSCHE BRIEFMARKEN - REVUE; SD - Sammlerdienst. see PHILATELY

737   GW   ISSN 0933-8527
DEUTSCHES MUENZEN MAGAZIN. 1987. bi-m. DM.34.50. E M S Verlag GmbH, Bientzlestr. 3, 70599 Stuttgart, Germany. TEL 0711-454098. FAX 0711-4570666. Ed. Wolfgang Erzinger. circ. 200,000. Document type: consumer publication.

737.4   380.1   US
DIRECTORY OF COIN COLLECTORS. irreg. $99. 53 Beverly Blvd., San Jose, CA 95116. TEL 408-272-8265. Ed. Debbie Stewart. Document type: directory.

737.4   US   ISSN 0270-8949   CJ1826
EDMUNDS UNITED STATES COIN PRICES. 1980. 2/yr. $10. Edmund Publications Corp., 300 N. Sepulveda Blvd., Ste. 2050, El Segundo, CA 90245-4469. TEL 310-640-7840. Ed. Robert Belloch. circ. 18,000.
Description: Gives comprehensive price breakdowns on all coins circulated, as well as commemorative grading information. Includes photographs.

737   US
ENGRAVINGS. vol.3, no.1, 1993. q. American Bank Note Commemoratives, Inc., 7 High St., Ste. 412, Huntington, NY 11743. TEL 800-533-2262.

737   US
ERROR TRENDS COIN MAGAZINE. 1968. m. $15. Box 158, Oceanside, NY 11572. TEL 516-764-8063. Ed. Arnold Margolis. adv.; bk.rev.; illus. circ. 2,000. (back issues avail.) Document type: consumer publication.
Description: Devoted entirely to coin collectors who specialize in numismatic error coins.

737   US
ERRORSCOPE.* 1963. m. membership. Combined Organizations of Numismatic Error Collectors of America, c/o J.T. Stanton, Pres., Box 15487, Savannah, GA 31416. TEL 912-232-8655. Ed. Stella Teiglang. adv.; bk.rev. circ. 550.
Formerly: Errorgram.

737   NE   ISSN 0014-3030
EUROPEAN NUMISMATICS.* (Text in Dutch, English) 1968. bi-m. fl.7.50.($2.10) Uitgeverij Numismatica Nederland N.V., Darwinplantsoen 26, Amsterdam 6, Netherlands. Ed. S.A.M. Le Loux. adv.; bk.rev.; bibl.; illus.; stat.; tr.lit. Indexed: Numis.Lit.

EUROPHIL NEWS. see PHILATELY

737   US   ISSN 0014-7745
FARE BOX. 1947. m. $16 (effective 1995 & 1996). American Vecturist Association, Box 1204, Boston, MA 02104. TEL 617-277-8111. Ed. John M. Coffee, Jr. adv. contact: Robert M. Butler. bk.rev.; charts; stat. circ. 825. Indexed: Numis.Lit. Document type: newsletter.
Description: For collectors of transportation fare tokens and those interested in urban transportation history.

737.4   US   ISSN 1041-6951   CJ1826
FELL'S U S COINS QUARTERLY INVESTMENT GUIDE. 1991. q. Blockbuster Periodicals, Inc., 2131 Hollywood Blvd., Hollywood, CA 33020. TEL 305-925-5242. Ed. Barbara Newman. circ. 75,000.
Description: For collectors and investors. Highlights numismatic news and expands upon basic beginner information for the advanced collector.

737 700   US   ISSN 0092-5039   CJ5813
FRANKLIN MINT ALMANAC. 1970. 3/yr. free. (Franklin Mint Collectors Society) Franklin Mint, Franklin Center, PA 19091. TEL 610-459-6000. FAX 610-459-6880. Ed. Jack Wilkie. adv.; bk.rev.; illus.; stat.; index, cum.index: 1970-1984; circ. 2,100 (controlled).

FRIMERKER OG MYNTER. see PHILATELY

737   SP   ISSN 0210-2137
GACETA NUMISMATICA. 1966. q. membership. Asociacion Numismatica Espanola, Gran Via de les Corts Catalanes, 627, 08010 Barcelona, Spain. FAX 34-3-3189062. Ed. Josep Pellicer i Bru. adv.; bk.rev.; cum.index in vol.101. circ. 2,000. Indexed: Numis.Lit., Numis.Lit. Document type: academic/scholarly publication.

737   SZ   ISSN 0016-5565
GAZETTE NUMISMATIQUE SUISSE/SCHWEIZER MUENZBLAETTER. (Text in English, French, German) 1949. q. 100 SFr. Societe Suisse de Numismatique - Schweizerische Numismatische Gesellschaft, Niederdorfstr. 43, CH-8001 Zuerich, Switzerland. adv.; illus.; cum.index every 5 yrs. circ. 1,000. Indexed: Numis.Lit. Document type: newsletter.
—BLDSC (8112.370000).

737   GW   ISSN 0931-0681
DER GELDSCHEINSAMMLER; Zeitschrift fuer Papiergeld. 1986. 9/yr. DM.63 (foreign DM.81). H. Gietl Verlag & Publikationsservice GmbH, Postfach 166, 93122 Regenstauf, Germany. TEL 09402-5856. FAX 09402-6635. Ed. Alexander Persijn; Pubs. Heinrich Gietl, Josef Roidl. adv. contact: Kurt Fischer. bk.rev.; index. circ. 3,000. (back issues avail.) Document type: newsletter.

737   GW
GOLD UND SILBER ZUM SAMMELN. a. Dresdner Bank AG, Juergen-Ponto-Platz 2, 60329 Frankfurt a.M., Germany. TEL 069-263-7726. FAX 069-263-7892. TELEX 4189741. circ. 50,000. Document type: consumer publication.

737.4   US   ISSN 0072-8829   CJ1826
GUIDEBOOK OF UNITED STATES COINS. 1946. a. $10.95. Western Publishing Co., Inc., Attn.: Whitman Coin Dept., 1220 Mound Ave., Racine, WI 53404. TEL 414-633-2431. Ed. R.S. Yeoman. illus.; index.
Description: Retail guide of all U.S. coins from 1616 to the present.

737.4   US   ISSN 0072-9949
HANDBOOK OF UNITED STATES COINS. 1941. a. $6.50. Western Publishing Co., Inc., Attn.: Whitman Coin Dept., 1220 Mound Ave., Racine, WI 53404. TEL 414-633-2431. Ed. R.S. Yeoman. illus.; index.
Description: Contains up-to-date wholesale values for all U.S. coins from 1616 to the present.

737   SZ   ISSN 0073-0963
HAUTES ETUDES NUMISMATIQUES. 1966. irreg., no.2, 1967. (Ecole Pratique des Hautes Etudes, Centre de Recherches d'Histoire et de Philologie, FR) Librairie Droz S.A., 11, rue Massot, CH-1211 Geneva 12, Switzerland. TEL 022-3466666. FAX 022-3472391. circ. 500. Document type: monographic series.
—CCC.
Description: Examines ancient coins.

737   GR
HELLENIC NUMISMATIC SOCIETY. BIBLIOTECA. (Text in Greek with English translations) 1993. irreg., no.3. price varies. Hellenic Numismatic Society - Elleniki Nomismatiki Etaireia, Didotou 45, 106 80 Athens, Greece. TEL 30-1-3615-585. FAX 30-1-3934-296. Ed. A.P. Tzamalis. Document type: monographic series.
Description: Covers various topics in Greek numismatics and related issues.

737.4   SZ   ISSN 1013-350X
HELVETISCHE MUENZEN-ZEITUNG.* 1966. 12/yr. H M Z Verlag, Rennweg 6, CH-8034 Zurich, Switzerland. Indexed: Numis.Lit.

737   US
I B N S JOURNAL. 1961. q. $17.50 membership. International Bank Note Society, c/o Milan Alusic, Sec.-Gen., Box 1642, Racine, WI 53401. TEL 414-554-6255. Ed. Steve Feller. adv.; bk.rev.; bibl.; illus.; circ. 2,200 (paid). Indexed: Numis.Lit. Document type: bulletin.
Supersedes: International Bank Note Society Magazine (ISSN 0020-6121)

737.4   BE   ISSN 0777-3781
INTERNATIONAL FAR-EASTERN NUMISMATICS NEWS. 1989. bi-m. Ivan Florine, P.O. Box 75, B-163 Linkebeek, Belgium. Indexed: Numis.Lit.

INTERPHILA; international directory of philately and numismatics. see PHILATELY

INVESTMENT COIN REVIEW. see BUSINESS AND ECONOMICS — Investments

737   IS   ISSN 0021-2288
ISRAEL NUMISMATIC JOURNAL. (Text in English) 1963. irreg. (approx. a.). $35. Israel Numismatic Society, P.O. Box 750, Jerusalem, Israel. FAX 972-2-249779. TELEX 26598. Ed.Bd. bk.rev.; bibl.; charts; illus.; stat. circ. 300. Indexed: New Test.Abstr., Numis.Lit. Document type: academic/scholarly publication.
—BLDSC (4583.866000).

737   IT   ISSN 0578-9923
ISTITUTO ITALIANO DI NUMISMATICA. ANNALI. 1954. a. L.80000 (typically set in May). Istituto Italiano di Numismatica, Palazzo Barberini, Via Quattro Fontane 13, 00195 Rome, Italy. TEL 06-4743603. adv.; bk.rev. circ. 500. (back issues avail.) Indexed: Numis.Lit.

737.4   NE   ISSN 0920-380X
JAARBOEK VOOR MUNT- EN PENNINGKUNDE. (Text in Dutch, occasionally in English, French, German; summaries in English) 1914. a. fl.90 per vol. Koninklijk Nederlands Genootschap voor Munt- en Penningkunde - Royal Dutch Society of Numismatics, c/o The Netherlands Bank, Postbus 98, 1000 AB Amsterdam, Netherlands. Ed.Bd. cum.index. circ. 500. Document type: academic/scholarly publication.

737   GW   ISSN 0075-2711   CJ31
JAHRBUCH FUER NUMISMATIK UND GELDGESCHICHTE. (Text mainly in German; occasionally in English and French) 1949. irreg. price varies. (Bayerische Numismatische Gesellschaft) Verlag Michael Lassleben, Lange Gasse 19, 93183 Kallmuenz, Germany. Ed. J. Kellner. Indexed: Br.Archaeol.Abstr., Numis.Lit. Document type: monographic series.

737   US   ISSN 0308-8677
L A N S A. (Text in English, Spanish) 1973. 3/yr. $8. Latin American Paper Money Society - Sociedad Latinoamericana de Papel Moneda, 3304 Milford Mill Rd., Baltimore, MD 21244. Ed. Arthur C. Matz. adv.; bk.rev.; illus.; index. circ. 400. (back issues avail.) Document type: bulletin, directory.
Description: Covers articles on paper money and related items of Latin America and Iberia for the collector.

LANDESMUSEUM FUER KAERNTEN. BUCHREIHE. see MUSEUMS AND ART GALLERIES

737 900   AU   ISSN 0255-2809
LITTERAE NUMISMATICAE VINDOBONENSES. 1979. irreg. price varies. Verlag der Oesterreichischen Akademie der Wissenschaften, Dr. Ignaz-Seipel-Platz 2, A-1010 Vienna, Austria. FAX 0228-5139541.

737   PL   ISSN 0024-5771
LODZKI NUMIZMATYK.* 1961. q. membership. Polskie Towarzystwo Archeologiczne i Numizmatyczne, Oddzial w Lodzi, Plac Wolnosci 14, Lodz, Poland. Ed. Anatol Gupieniec. bk.rev.; abstr.; bibl.; charts; illus.; stat.; index, cum.index. Indexed: Numis.Lit.

M R I BANKERS' GUIDE TO FOREIGN CURRENCY. (Monetary Research Institute) see BUSINESS AND ECONOMICS — Banking And Finance

NUMISMATICS

737   IQ   ISSN 0002-4058
AL-MASKUKAT.* 1969. a. ID.5000($12) Ministry of Culture and Information, State Organization of Antiquities and Heritage, Jamal Abdul Nasr St., Baghdad, Iraq. TEL 4158355. **Indexed:** Numis.Lit.

737 709   UK   ISSN 0263-7707
CJ5501
THE MEDAL. 1982. 2/yr. £25 (outside Europe £25). British Art Medal Trust, c/o Philip Attwood, Ed., Department of Coins and Medals, British Museum, London WC1B 3DG, England. TEL 0171-323-8260. FAX 0171-323-8171. Eds. Philip Attwood, Mark Jones. adv.; bk.rev.; index every 10 issues. circ. 1,100. **Indexed:** Artbibl.Mod., Numis.Lit., RILA. **Document type:** academic/scholarly publication.
—BLDSC (5424.628800); Faxon.
Description: Contains articles on both the history of the medal and on contemporary medals, reviews of exhibitions, and news about new medallic work. *Refereed Serial*

737 355   SA
MILITARY MEDAL SOCIETY OF SOUTH AFRICA. JOURNAL. (Text in English) 1974. 2/yr. R.30($17) Military Medal Society of South Africa, 1 Jacqueline Ave., Northcliff, Johannesburg 2195, South Africa. TEL 27-11-888-5797. Ed. C.H. Loots. bk.rev.; cum.index. circ. 200. (back issues avail.) **Document type:** newsletter.

737.4   US   ISSN 0149-4279
CJ113
MODERN GOLD COINAGE (YEAR). 1976. a. $50. Gold Institute, Administrative Office - Institut de l'Or, Bureau Administratif, 1112 16th St., N.W., Ste. 240, Washington, DC 20036-4823. TEL 202-835-0185. FAX 202-835-0155. Ed. John H. Lutley. circ. 600. (back issues avail.)
Description: Data on all gold coins issued in the world in each year.

737.4   US   ISSN 0149-7707
CJ1546
MODERN SILVER COINAGE (YEAR). 1973-1993; resumed 1995. a. $40. Silver Institute, 1112 16th St., N.W., Ste. 240, Washington, DC 20036-4823. TEL 202-835-0185. FAX 202-835-0155. Ed. John H. Lutley. stat. (also avail. in microfiche from CIS; back issues avail.) **Indexed:** SRI.
Description: Contains data on all silver coins issued worldwide, with names and addresses of mints from which they can be acquired.

737.4   DK
MOENTER FRA NORDEN SAMT DE BALTISKE LANDE. 1969. a. DKK 165. Frovin Sieg, Ulbjerg Gl. Skole, DK-8832 Skals, Denmark. TEL 86-697102. (Dist. by: Danske Boghandleres Kommissionsanstalt, Siljansgade 6, DK-2300, Copenhagen S. Denmark) **Document type:** catalog.
Formerly: Sieg's Moentkatalog - Norden (Year) (ISSN 0900-9310)

737   DK   ISSN 0900-1409
MOENTSAMLEREN. 1984. s-a. DKK 30 (effective 1996). Moentsamlaren, Noerregade 48, 7400 Herning, Denmark. TEL 97-22-08-45. Ed. Preben Eriksen. adv.; bk.rev.; illus. circ. 4,000.

737   VB   ISSN 0958-1545
MONETA INTERNATIONAL; coins and treasures monthly. 1988. m. $20. c/o Vernon W. Pickering, P.O. Box 704, Road Town - Tortola, British Virgin Islands. TEL 809-49-43510. FAX 809-494-4540. Ed. Giorgio Migliavacca. adv.; bk.rev.; index. circ. 6,000. (tabloid format; back issues avail.)
Description: Covers coin collecting and numismatic research from ancient to modern coins.

737   US
▼**MONEYCARD COLLECTOR.** 1994. m. $14.95; newsstand price: $4.95. Amos Press Inc., Box 783, Sidney, OH 45365. TEL 513-498-0879. FAX 513-498-0808. Ed. Randy Moser; Pub. Murray Church. adv.; B&W page $2750. circ. 50,000. **Document type:** bulletin.

737   SZ   ISSN 0254-461X
MUENZEN-REVUE. 1969. 12/yr. 72 SFr. Verlag Muenzen-Revue, Blotzheimerstr. 40, CH-4055 Basel, Switzerland. FAX 061-445542. adv.; bk.rev.; bibl. circ. 20,000. **Document type:** trade publication.
Description: Features news, history, values, new coins, trade as well as reports of events and auctions for coin hobbyists.

737   SZ   ISSN 0027-3007
MUENZEN UND MEDAILLEN/MONNAIES ET MEDAILLES. 1942. m. free. Muenzen und Medaillen AG, Malzgasse 25, CH-4002 Basel, Switzerland. illus. circ. 12,500.

737   GW   ISSN 0179-3683
MUENZEN- UND MEDAILLENSAMMLER BERICHTE. (Text in English, French and German) 1961. bi-m. DM.48. Kricheldorf Verlag, Guenterstalstr. 16, 79100 Freiburg, Germany. TEL 0761-73913. FAX 0761-709670. bk.rev. circ. 1,000. (back issues avail.) **Document type:** bulletin.

737   GW
MUENZEN UND PAPIERGELD. bi-m. DM.36 (foreign DM.54); newsstand price: DM.6.50. H. Gietl Verlag & Publikationsservice GmbH, Postfach 166, 93122 Regenstauf, Germany. TEL 09402-5856. FAX 09402-6635. Ed. Thomas Gradl; Pubs. Heinrich Gietl, Josef Roidl. adv.; B&W page DM.1480, color page DM.2380; adv. contact: Kurt Fischer. **Document type:** newsletter.

737   RM   ISSN 0256-0844
MUZEUL NATIONAL DE ISTORIE A ROMANIEI. CERCETARI NUMISMATICE. Key Title: Cercetari Numismatice. (Text in Rumanian; summaries in English, French) 1978. irreg. Muzeul National de Istorie a Romaniei, Calea Victoriei, 12, Bucharest, Rumania. TEL 40-1-6149078. **Indexed:** Numis.Lit. **Document type:** academic/scholarly publication.
Formerly: Muzeur de Istorie al Republicii Socialiste Romania. Cercetari Numismatice.

737.4   PL   ISSN 0208-5062
MUZEUM ARCHEOLOGICZNE I ETNOGRAFICZNE, LODZ. PRACE I MATERIALY. SERIA NUMIZMATYCZNA I KONSERWATORSKA. (Text in Polish; summaries in English) 1981. a. price varies. Muzeum Archeologiczne i Etnograficzne w Lodzi, Pl. Wolnosci 14, 91-415 Lodz, Poland. TEL 48-42-328480. FAX 48-42-329740. Eds. Ryszard Grygiel, Jerzy Pininski. circ. 600.

737   US   ISSN 0027-6006
N A S C QUARTERLY. 1959. q. $10 (effective 1992). Numismatic Association of Southern California, Box 2123, Sepulveda, CA 91393. Ed. Jeff Oxman. adv.; bk.rev.; charts; illus.; stat. circ. 700.
Description: Contains articles, coin club and association news.

737   US
NEW JERSEY NUMISMATIC JOURNAL. 1975. q. membership. Garden State Numismatic Association, Inc., Box 787, Pearl River, NY 10965. TEL 201-827-2482. (Subscr. to: Judith Kessler, Correspondence Sec., Box 331, Millville, NJ 08332; Or: Box 3462, Toms River, NJ 08756-3462) Ed. James K. Brandt. adv.; bk.rev.; bibl.; illus. circ. 1,000.

737   GR   ISSN 1105-8579
NOMISMATIKA KHRONIKA. (Translations or summaries in English) 1972. a. $25. Hellenic Numismatic Society - Elleniki Nomismatiki Etaireia, Didotou 45, 106 80 Athens, Greece. TEL 30-1-3615-585. FAX 30-1-3634-296. Ed. A.P. Tzamalis. adv.; bk.rev. circ. 1,000. **Indexed:** Numis.Lit. **Document type:** academic/scholarly publication.
Description: Covers Greek and related numismatics of all periods.

NORDISK FILATELI. see *PHILATELY*

NORDISK JULEMAERKE KATALOG; Nordic Christmas seal catalogue. see *PHILATELY*

737   DK   ISSN 0025-8539
NORDISK NUMISMATISK UNION MEDLEMSBLAD. 1936. 8/yr. DKK 100 (effective 1995). Nordisk Numismatisk Union - Nordic Numismatic Union, c/o Royal Collection of Coins and Medals, National Museum, DK-1220 Copenhagen K, Denmark. FAX 45-33-15-55-21. Ed. Joergen Steen Jensen. adv.; bk.rev.; illus. circ. 2,500. **Indexed:** NAA, Numis.Lit.

737   SZ
NUMIS-POST; Monatszeitschrift fuer den Muenzensammier. 1968. 11/yr. 35 SFr. Numis-Post, Postfach, CH-7310 Bad Ragaz, Switzerland. TEL 081-3022429. FAX 081-3025984. Ed. Ruth Niedermann. **Document type:** newsletter.

737   SP   ISSN 0029-6015
CJ9
NUMISMA. (Text in English, French, Spanish) 1951. bi-m. exchange basis. Sociedad Ibero-Americana de Estudios Numismaticos, c/o Fabrica Nacional de Moneda y Timbre, Museo, Jorge Juan, 106, 28071 Madrid, Spain. Ed. Antonio Beltran Martinez. bk.rev.; bibl.; charts; illus.; stat. **Indexed:** Amer.Hist.& Life, Hist.Abstr., Numis.Lit.

737   FI   ISSN 0355-5615
NUMISMAATIKKO. 1965. 6/yr. FIM 165. Suomen Numismaatikkoliitto, P.O. Box 895, FIN-00101 Helsinki, Finland. TEL 358-31-631-480. FAX 358-31-631-480. Ed. Petri Virolainen. adv.; bk.rev.; cum.index. circ. 1965-1974. circ. 2,500. **Indexed:** Numis.Lit.

737 900   UK   ISSN 0078-2696
NUMISMATIC CHRONICLE AND JOURNAL. 1839. a. membership. Royal Numismatic Society, British Museum, London, WC1B 3DG, England. (Dist. by: Spink & Son Ltd., 5-7 King St., St. James, London SW1, England) Eds. I. Carradice, M. Blackburn. adv.; bk.rev. circ. 1,400. **Indexed:** Br.Hum.Ind., NAA. **Document type:** bulletin.
—BLDSC (6184.719000).

737   UK   ISSN 0029-6023
NUMISMATIC CIRCULAR. 1892. 10/yr. £12 (foreign £30). Spink & Son Ltd., 5 King St., St. James's, London SW1, England. TEL 0171-930-7888. FAX 0171-839-4853. Ed. Douglas Saville. bk.rev.; bibl.; tr.lit.; index. circ. 3,000. **Indexed:** Numis.Lit. **Document type:** catalog.

737   US   ISSN 0029-6031
Z6866
NUMISMATIC LITERATURE. 1947. s-a. $10. American Numismatic Society, Broadway at 155th St., New York, NY 10032. TEL 212-234-3130. FAX 212-234-3381. Ed. L.A. Elam. adv.; abstr.; bibl.; index. (reprint service avail. from UMI) **Indexed:** Amer.Bibl.Slavic & E.Eur.Stud., Br.Archaeol.Abstr., Numis.Lit.

737   US   ISSN 0029-604X
CJ1
NUMISMATIC NEWS. 1952. w. $27.95. Krause Publications, Inc., 700 E. State St., Iola, WI 54990. TEL 715-445-2214. FAX 715-445-4087. TELEX 55 6461 KRAUSE PUB UD. Ed. Bob Wilhite. adv.; bk.rev.; bibl.; charts; illus.; mkt.; stat.; tr.lit. circ. 37,000. (tabloid format; also avail. in microform from UMI,PMC) **Indexed:** Numis.Lit.
Description: Guide to coin collecting hobby, serving collectors of U.S. coins with news and advertising marketplace where coin collectors can buy and sell through the mail.

737   US   ISSN 0078-2718
NUMISMATIC NOTES AND MONOGRAPHS. 1920. irreg. no.165, 1991. price varies. American Numismatic Society, Broadway at 155th St., New York, NY 10032. TEL 212-234-3130. FAX 212-234-3381. Eds. M.H. Martin, L.A. Elam. (reprint service avail. from UMI) **Indexed:** Numis.Lit.

737   II   ISSN 0029-6066
NUMISMATIC SOCIETY OF INDIA. JOURNAL. (Text in English) 1910. s-a. Rs.200($30) Numismatic Society of India, Banaras Hindu University, Varanasi 221005, India. TEL 311074. Ed.Bd. bk.rev.; bibl.; charts; illus.; stat. (back issues avail.) **Indexed:** Numis.Lit.
—UnCover.

737   US   ISSN 0517-404X
NUMISMATIC STUDIES. 1938. irreg. price varies. American Numismatic Society, Broadway at 155th St., New York, NY 10032. TEL 212-234-3130. FAX 212-234-3381. Eds. M.H. Martin, L.A. Elam. circ. 800. (back issues avail.; reprint service avail. from UMI) **Indexed:** Numis.Lit.
—BLDSC (6184.743000).
Description: Scholarly monographs analyzing numismatic materials and their relationship to the understanding and interpretation of history, archaeology, political science, and art history.

737   IT
NUMISMATICA; mensile di scienza, storia, arte, economia delle monete. 1970. m. L.60000($85) Gino Manfredini, Ed. & Pub., Via Ferramola 1-A, 25121 Brescia, Italy. TEL 030-3756211. adv.; bk.rev.; illus. **Indexed:** Numis.Lit. **Document type:** newsletter.

NUMISMATICS

737 SZ
NUMISMATICA E ANTICHITA CLASSICHE. (Supplements avail.) (Text in English, French, German, Italian) 1972. a. 170 SFr. Amici dei Quaderni Ticinesi di Numismatica e Antichita Classiche, Secretariat, C.P. 3157, CH-6901 Lugano, Switzerland. TEL 091-711695. index. circ. 500. (back issues avail.) Indexed: Numis.Lit. Document type: academic/scholarly publication.

737 BE
NUMISMATICA LOVANIENSIA. 1977. irreg., no.14, 1994. price varies. Association des Diplomes Histoire Art et Archeologie, College Erasme, Place Blaise Pascal 1, B-1348 Louvain-la-Neuve, Belgium. TEL 32-10-47-4880. FAX 32-10-472579. (Co-sponsor: Universite Catholique de Louvain, Seminaire de Numismatique Marcel Hoc) Ed. T. Hackens. circ. 2,000. Document type: monographic series.

737 XR ISSN 0078-2726
NUMISMATICA MORAVICA. (Text in Czech; summaries also in English or in French, German, Russian) 1965. irreg., no.6, 1986. price varies. Moravske Zemske Muzeum, Numismaticke Oddeleni, Zelny trh 6, 659 37 Brno, Czech Republic. TEL 42-5-22241. FAX 42-5-25279. Ed. J. Sejbal. illus.; index. circ. 1,200. Indexed: Numis.Lit. Document type: proceedings.
Description: Monographs and materials from the conferences dealing with the questions of the history of the Moravian coinage.

737 XR ISSN 0029-6074
NUMISMATICKE LISTY. (Text in Czech; summaries in English, French, German, Russian) 1945. bi-m. 32.20 Kc.($24) (Narodni Muzeum) Vydavatelstvi Pierot, spol. s r.o., Stefanikova 29, 150 00 Prague 5, Czech Republic. (Dist. by: Artia, Ve Smeckach 30, 111 27 Prague 1, Czech Republic) Ed. Jarmila Haskova. bk.rev.; abstr.; bibl.; illus.; index. circ. 7,500. Indexed: Numis.Lit.

737.4 943.7 XR ISSN 0546-9414
CJ9
NUMISMATICKY SBORNIK. (Text mainly in Czech and Slovak; occasionaly in German and other languages) 1953. irreg., vol.18, 1989. Ceska Akademie Ved, Historicky Ustav, Vysehradska 49, 128 26 Prague 2, Czech Republic. (Subscr. to: Artia, Ve Smeckach 30, 111 27 Prague 1, Czech Republic) Ed. Jiri Sejbal. illus. circ. 1,000. Indexed: Numis.Lit.
—BLDSC (6184.747000).

737 AU
NUMISMATIK SPEZIAL. 1993. 10/yr. S.400. Zeitungsverlag Kuhn und Co. GmbH, Kutschkergasse 42, A-1180 Vienna, Austria. TEL 01-47686. FAX 01-4768621. Ed. Gerd-Volker Weege. adv.: B&W page S.10500, color page S.13500; trim 269 x 197; adv. contact: Werner Deutsch. Document type: consumer publication.

737 FR ISSN 0335-1971
NUMISMATIQUE & CHANGE. 1972. m. 210 F. (foreign 260 F.) S E P S, 12 rue Poincare, 55800 Revigny, France. Ed. R.L. Martin. adv.; bk.rev.; charts; stat. circ. 15,000. Indexed: Numis.Lit.
Formerly: Change (ISSN 0009-1367)

737 GW ISSN 0323-8962
NUMISMATISCHE BEITRAEGE. q. DM.40. (Gesellschaft fuer Heimatgeschichte, Zentraler Fachausschuss fuer Numismatik) V E B Deutsche Verlag der Wissenschaften, Johannes-Dieckmann-Str. 10, 1080 Berlin, Germany. (Orders to: Buchexport, Leninstr. 16, 7010 Leipzig, Germany) Ed. J. Gottschalk.

737 GW ISSN 0937-6488
NUMISMATISCHES NACHRICHTENBLATT. 1952. m. DM.30. Deutsche Numismatische Gesellschaft, Lehrastr. 17, 67346 Speyer, Germany. TEL 06232-35752. Ed. Helfried Ehrend. adv.: B&W page DM.460; trim 140 x 200. bk.rev.; abstr.; bibl.; illus.; index. circ. 4,500. (back issues avail.) Indexed: Numis.Lit. Document type: newsletter.

737 SW ISSN 0078-2734
NUMISMATISKA MEDDELANDEN/NUMISMATIC COMMUNICATIONS. (Text in Swedish; summaries in English, French and occasionally German) 1874. irreg. price varies. Svenska Numismatiska Foereningen, Banergatan 17 nb, S-115 22 Stockholm, Sweden. TEL 08-667-55-98. Ed.Bd. index. circ. 1,000. Indexed: NAA, Numis.Lit.

737 US ISSN 0029-6090
THE NUMISMATIST. 1888. m. $31 to non-members. American Numismatic Association, 818 N. Cascade Ave., Colorado Springs, CO 80903-3279. TEL 719-632-2646. FAX 719-634-4085. Ed. Barbara Gregory. adv.; bk.rev.; charts; illus.; stat.; index, cum.index: vols.1-51, 52-71; circ. 28,000 (controlled). (also avail. in microfiche) Indexed: Amer.Bibl.Slavic & E.Eur.Stud., Numis.Lit. Document type: academic/scholarly publication, consumer publication.
—UnCover.
Incorporates (1987-1994): First Strike (ISSN 0896-4432); Incorporates (1951-1981): A N A Club Bulletin (ISSN 0001-1991)
Description: For collectors of coins, medals, tokens and paper money.

737 BU
NUMIZMATIKA. 1969. q. $1. Suiuz na Bulgarski Filatelisti, Sofia, Bulgaria. (Dist. by: Hemus, 6, Rouski Blvd., 1000 Sofia, Bulgaria) circ. 2,000. Indexed: Numis.Lit.

737 PO ISSN 0871-2743
NUMMUS. (Text in English and Portuguese; summaries in English and French) 1952. a. $25. Sociedade Portuguesa de Numismatica, Rua de Costa Cabral, 664, 4200 Porto, Portugal. TEL 596029. Ed.Bd. bk.rev.; bibl.; charts; illus.; cum.index: 1968-1972. circ. 2,000. Indexed: Numis.Lit. Document type: academic/scholarly publication.
Formerly: Numus - Numismatica, Medalhistica, Arqueologia (ISSN 0085-364X)

737 AU
OESTERREICHISCHE AKADEMIE DER WISSENSCHAFTEN. NUMISMATISCHE KOMMISSION. VEROEFFENTLICHUNGEN. (Subseries of: Oesterreichische Akademie der Wissenschaften. Philosophisch-Historische Klasse. Denkschriften) 1973. irreg. Verlag der Oesterreichischen Akademie der Wissenschaften, Dr. Ignaz-Seipel-Platz 2, A-1010 Vienna, Austria. FAX 0222-5139541. illus.

737 AU ISSN 0029-9359
OESTERREICHISCHE NUMISMATISCHE GESELLSCHAFT. MITTEILUNGEN. 1883. 6/yr. S.300. Oesterreichische Numismatische Gesellschaft, Burgring 5, A-1010 Vienna, Austria. Ed. Karl Schulz. adv. contact: Karl Schulz. bk.rev.; abstr., illus.; cum.index. circ. 700. Document type: bulletin.

737 CN ISSN 0048-1815
ONTARIO NUMISMATIST. 1961. m. Ontario Numismatic Association, Box 40033, Waterloo Sq. P.O., 75 King St., S., Waterloo, ON N2J 4V1. Ed. Bruce H. Raszmann.

PHILA-REPORT; die Sammlerfreundliche Briefmarkenzeitung. see PHILATELY

THE PHILATELIC EXPORTER; world's greatest stamp trade journal. see PHILATELY

737 US
PROOF COLLECTORS CORNER. 1964. bi-m. $15 membership (Junior $10). World Proof Numismatic Association, Box 4094, Pittsburgh, PA 15201. TEL 412-782-4477. FAX 412-782-0227. Ed. Gail P. Gray; Pub. Edward J. Moschetti. bk.rev. Document type: trade publication.
Description: Provides current coverage of numismatic issues, with information on the history and background of coins.

793 US ISSN 0095-263X
CJ1
RARE COIN REVIEW. 1969. bi-m. $19. Bowers and Merena Galleries, Inc., Box 1224, Wolfeboro, NH 03894. TEL 603-596-5095. FAX 603-569-5319. Ed. Q. David Bowers. adv. contact: Chris Karstedt. bk.rev.; bibl.; illus.; circ. controlled. Document type: catalog.
Refereed Serial

737 BE ISSN 0774-5885
REVUE BELGE DE NUMISMATIQUE ET DE SIGILLOGRAPHIE. 1842. a. 2000 BEF. Societe Royale de Numismatique de Belgique, c/o Rozenstraat 22, 3500 Hasselt, Belgium. adv.; bk.rev.; cum.index. circ. 500. Indexed: Numis.Lit. Document type: academic/scholarly publication, bibliography.
Former titles (until 1908): Revue Belge de Numismatique (ISSN 0774-5877); (until 1875): Revue de la Numismatique Belge (ISSN 0774-5869)

737 FR ISSN 0484-8942
REVUE NUMISMATIQUE. 1836. a. 343 F. (Societe Francaise de Numismatique) Societe d'Edition les Belles Lettres, 95 Boulevard Raspail, 75006 Paris, France. TEL 1-45485826. FAX 1-45485860. bk.rev. Indexed: Numis.Lit. Document type: academic/scholarly publication.
—BLDSC (7938.600000).

737 SZ ISSN 0035-4163
REVUE SUISSE DE NUMISMATIQUE/SCHWEIZERISCHE NUMISMATISCHE RUNDSCHAU. (Text in English, French and German) 1890. a. 100 SFr. Societe Suisse de Numismatique - Schweizerische Numismatische Gesellschaft, Niederdorfstr. 43, CH-8001 Zurich, Switzerland. adv.; illus. circ. 1,000. Indexed: Numis.Lit. Document type: bulletin.
—BLDSC (7953.385400).

737 UK ISSN 0080-4487
CODEN: SPRSD5
ROYAL NUMISMATIC SOCIETY. SPECIAL PUBLICATIONS. irreg. Royal Numismatic Society, British Museum, London WC1B 3DG, England. Document type: bulletin.
—BLDSC (8380.400000); CASDDS.

737 US ISSN 0036-4053
SAN DIEGO NUMISMATIC SOCIETY. BULLETIN. 1947. m. membership. San Diego Numismatic Society Inc., 611 Oakwood Way, El Cajon, CA 92021. (Subscr. to: Box 6909, San Diego, CA 92112) Ed. Dorothy Baber. charts; illus. circ. 150. Document type: bulletin.

737.4 UK
SEABY'S STANDARD CATALOGUE OF BRITISH COINS. 1929. a. £12.95. B.T. Batsford Ltd., 4 Fitzhardinge St., London W1H OAH, England. TEL 071-486-8484. FAX 071-487-4296. illus. Document type: catalog.

737 296 US
SHEKEL. 1968. 6/yr. membership. American Israel Numismatic Association, Box 940277, Far Rockaway, NY 11694-0277. TEL 718-634-9266. FAX 3718-318-1455. Ed. Edward Schuman. bk.rev. circ. 3,000. Indexed: Numis.Lit.

737 US ISSN 0037-5616
SINFORMATION. (Text in English; occasionally in French, German, Spanish) vol.9, 1970. q. $10. Society for International Numismatics, Box 943, Santa Monica, CA 90406. TEL 213-396-4662. Ed. Keith Laumer. adv.; bk.rev.; index. circ. 500. (also avail. in microfilm from UMI)

737 XO ISSN 0081-0088
SLOVENSKA NUMIZMATIKA. (Text in Slovak; summaries in German) 1970. approx. biennial. (Slovenska Akademia Vied) Veda, Publishing House of the Slovak Academy of Sciences, Klemensova 19, 814 30 Bratislava, Slovakia. (Dist. by: Slovart, Nam. Slobody 6, 817 64 Bratislava, Slovakia) Ed. Eva Kolnikova. Indexed: Numis.Lit.

737 FR ISSN 0037-9344
SOCIETE FRANCAISE DE NUMISMATIQUE. BULLETIN. 1946. 10/yr. 200 F. Societe Francaise de Numismatique, 58 rue de Richelieu, 75084 Paris Cedex 2, France. bk.rev.; charts; illus.; cum.index every 5 yrs. circ. 950. Indexed: Numis.Lit. Document type: bulletin.

737 IT
SOLDI NUMISMATICA. 1966. m. L.1500 per no. Audiovisivi e Periodici s.r.l., Via Taranto 21, 00182 Rome, Italy. Ed. Mariella Storoni. adv. circ. 65,000.

737 AT
SOUTH AUSTRALIAN NUMISMATIC SOCIETY. NEWSLETTER. q. membership. South Australian Numismatic Society, G.P.O. Box 80 B, Adelaide, S.A., Australia. Document type: newsletter.

NUMISMATICS — ABSTRACTING, BIBLIOGRAPHIES, STATISTICS

STAMP & COIN MART INTERNATIONAL. see *PHILATELY*

737   RM   ISSN 0081-8887
STUDII SI CERCETARI DE NUMISMATICA. 1957. irreg., vol.8, 1984. (Academia Romana) Editura Academiei Romane, Calea Victoriei 125, 79717 Bucharest, Rumania. (Subscr. to: Artexim, Export-Import Presa, Str. Piata Presei Libere nr.1, P.O. Box 33-16, 70055 Bucharest, Rumania) **Indexed:** Numis.Lit.

737.4 769.56   US
SUPERIOR COLLECTOR. (Former name of issuing body: Superior Stamp & Coin Co., Inc.) 1970. bi-m. $10. Superior Auction Galleries of Beverly Hills, 9478 W. Olympic Blvd., Beverly Hills, CA 90212-4299. TEL 800-421-0754. FAX 213-203-0496. Ed. Christopher Bush. adv.; bk.rev.; illus. circ. 12,000. **Document type:** consumer publication.
Supersedes (in 1994): MoneyTalks.
Description: Covers all aspects of coin collecting and offers timely tips. Also lists prices of rare U.S. coins and ancient coins.

737.4   SW   ISSN 0283-071X
SVENSK NUMISMATISK TIDSKRIFT. 1972. 8/yr. SEK 165. Svenska Numismatiska Foereningen, Banergatan 17 nb., S-115 22 Stockholm, Sweden. TEL 46-8-667-55-98. bk.rev.; illus. **Indexed:** NAA, Numis.Lit.
Formerly (until 1986): Myntkontakt.

737   US   ISSN 0271-3993
SYLLOGE NUMMORUM GRAECORUM. Short title: S N G A N S. 1972. irreg., vol.7, 1989. price varies. American Numismatic Society, Broadway at 155th St., New York, NY 10032. TEL 212-234-3130. FAX 212-234-3381. Eds. M.H. Martin, L.A. Elam. (reprint service avail. from UMI)

737   US   ISSN 0039-8233
T A M S JOURNAL. 1961. bi-m. $20. Token and Medal Society, Box 366, Bryantown, MD 20617. TEL 301-274-3441. Ed. David E. Schenkman. adv.; bk.rev.; charts; illus.; index, cum.index; circ. 1,700 (paid). **Indexed:** Numis.Lit.
Formerly: Token and Medal Society. Journal.

737   AT   ISSN 0817-4075
TASMANIAN NUMISMATIST.* 1985. a. Aus.$4.50. Tasmanian Numismatic Society, Inc., 1 Fern Crt., Claremont, Tas. 7011, Australia. TEL 2-278825. bk.rev. circ. 120.

737   US
TIPSICO BULLETIN. 1972. bi-m. $6. Tipsico Coin Co., Box 1128, 2141 Broadway, N. Bend, OR 97459. TEL 503-756-7111. Ed. J. Richard Wagner. adv.; bk.rev.; illus.; circ. 1,000 (controlled).
Formerly: Collector's Choice Bulletin.

TRIBUNA DEL COLLEZIONISTA; mensile culturale di attualita e cronaca filatelica e numismatica. see *PHILATELY*

TRIDENT - VISNYK. see *PHILATELY*

TRIERER ZEITSCHRIFT FUER GESCHICHTE UND KUNST DES TRIERER LANDES UND SEINER NACHBARGEBIETE. see *ARCHAEOLOGY*

737   US
U S COIN COLLECTOR. 1990. bi-m. $18. National Coin Collectors Association, Box 1150, Murphysboro, IL 62966. Ed. William Atkinson.

UKRAINIAN PHILATELIST. see *PHILATELY*

737.4   US
UNITED STATES MINT. WORLD COINAGE REPORT. biennial? United States Mint, 1500 Pennsylvania Ave., N.W., Washington, DC 20220. (Subscr. to: Superintendent of Documents, U.S. Government Printing Office, Box 371954, Pittsburgh, PA 15250-7954. TEL 202-512-1800. FAX 202-512-2250) illus. **Document type:** government publication.
Description: Contains photographs, sketches, and descriptions of coins from all over the world.

069.9 737   BL
UNIVERSIDADE DE SAO PAULO. MUSEU PAULISTA. COLECAO. SERIE DE NUMISMATICA. 1975. irreg. Universidade de Sao Paulo, Museu Paulista, Caixa Postal 42503, Parque da Independencia, 04263 Sao Paulo SP, Brazil. Ed. Antonio Rocha Penteado.
Supersedes in part (in 1975): Museu Paulista. Colecao (ISSN 0080-6382)

737   PL   ISSN 0043-5155
WIADOMOSCI NUMIZMATYCZNE/NUMISMATIC NEWS. 1957. q. $30. Polska Akademia Nauk, Instytut Historii Kultury Materialnej, Al. Solidarnosci 105, 00-190 Warsaw, Poland. (Subscr. to: Ossolineum Pulishing House, Foreign Trade Department, Rynek 9, 50-106 Wroclaw, Poland) Eds. Marta Meclewska, Stanislaw Suchodolski. charts; illus.; index. circ. 740. **Indexed:** Numis.Lit.
Formerly: Wiadomosci Numizmatyczno-Archeologiczne.

737.4   US   ISSN 0145-9090
WORLD COIN NEWS. 1973. bi-m. $25.95. Krause Publications, Inc., 700 E. State St., Iola, WI 54990. TEL 715-445-2214. Ed. Dave Harper. adv.; bk.rev.; bibl.; charts; illus. circ. 9,000. (also avail. in microfilm from PMC) **Indexed:** Numis.Lit.
Description: News and classified-display advertisements for international coin investors and collectors, featuring question-answer and reader-opinion forums.

737.4 769.56   IT
WORLD COLLECTIONS NEWS; mensile di informazioni numismatiche e filateliche. 1982? m. (11/yr.). $30. World Wide Collections S.r.l., Corso Buenos Aires, 20-4, 16129 Genoa, Italy. TEL 39-10-581463. FAX 39-10-561855. Ed. Beppe Barnao. adv.: B&W page L.1000000, color page L.1500000. circ. 4,000. **Document type:** newspaper.

737.4   CC
ZHONGGUO QIANBI/CHINA NUMISMATICS. (Text in Chinese) 1983. q. Y20($46.50) (Zhongguo Qianbi Xuehui) Zhongguo Jinrong Chubanshe, Xijiaomin Xiang 17, Beijing 100031, People's Republic of China. TEL 653858. (Dist. in US by: China Books & Periodicals, Inc., 2929 24th St., San Francisco, CA 94110. TEL 415-282-2994)
Description: Publishes research on numismatics or the history of coins, news of excavations, and interesting anecdotes about coins. Introduces historic coins, presents the experiences of coin collectors, and reports on related events in China and the world.

NUMISMATICS — Abstracting, Bibliographies, Statistics

011 737.4   US
NUMISMATIC BOOKS IN PRINT. 1975. a. $3. Sanford J. Durst Numismatic Publications, Ltd., 11 Clinton Ave., Rockville Centre, NY 11570. TEL 516-766-4444. FAX 516-766-4520. Ed. Sanford J. Durst. circ. 10,000. **Document type:** bibliography.

769.56 737   US
STAMPS, COINS, POSTCARDS & RELATED MATERIALS; a directory of periodicals. 1991. irreg. $29. Peri Press, Hemlock Ridge, Box 348, Voorheesville, NY 12186-0348. TEL 518-765-3163; 800-677-4492. FAX 518-765-3158. Ed. Doris Robinson. **Document type:** bibliography.
Description: Includes data in annotated listings of about 700 current periodicals.

NURSES AND NURSING

see *Medical Sciences–Nurses and Nursing*

NUTRITION AND DIETETICS

616.39   GW   ISSN 0720-7522
A I D VERBRAUCHERDIENST; Zeitschrift fuer Fach-, Lehr- und Beratungskraefte im Bereich Ernaehrung. 1956. m. DM.20. Auswertungs- und Informationsdienst fuer Ernaehrung, Landwirtschaft und Forsten e.V., Konstantinstr. 124, 53179 Bonn, Germany. TEL 0228-84990. FAX 0228-8499177. TELEX 886323-AIDNB-D. bk.rev. circ. 14,500. **Document type:** academic/scholarly publication, government publication.
—BLDSC (9155.778000); SWETS.
Refereed Serial

ADVANCES IN EATING DISORDERS. see *MEDICAL SCIENCES — Psychiatry And Neurology*

613.2 641.1   US   ISSN 1043-4526
TX537   CODEN: AFNREL
ADVANCES IN FOOD AND NUTRITION RESEARCH. 1948. irreg., vol.36, 1992. Academic Press, Inc., 525 B St., Ste. 1900, San Diego, CA 92101-4495. TEL 619-231-0926. FAX 619-699-6715. (Subscr. to: Order Dept., 6277 Sea Harbor Dr., 4th Fl., Orlando, FL 32887. TEL 800-321-5068) Eds. E.M. Mrak, George F. Stewart. index. (reprint service avail. from ISI) **Indexed:** Abstr.Hyg., Biol.Abstr., Biol.& Agr.Ind., Chem.Abstr., Dairy Sci.Abstr., Excerp.Med., Food Sci.& Tech.Abstr., Ind.Med., INIS Atomind., Nutr.Abstr., Trop.Dis.Bull.
—BLDSC (0706.850000); CASDDS; Faxon; SWETS; UnCover. **CCC.**
Formerly (until 1990): Advances in Food Research (ISSN 0065-2628)

613.2   US   ISSN 0149-9483
QP141.A1   CODEN: ANURD9
ADVANCES IN NUTRITIONAL RESEARCH. 1977. irreg., vol.8, 1995. Plenum Publishing Corp., 233 Spring St., New York, NY 10013-1578. TEL 212-620-8000. FAX 212-463-0742. TELEX 23-421139. Ed. Harold H. Draper. (back issues avail.) **Indexed:** Chem.Abstr., Ind.Med., Ind.Sci.Rev., Sci.Cit.Ind. **Document type:** monographic series.
—CASDDS; Faxon.
Description: Provides authoritative accounts of the current state of knowledge regarding major topics of research in the nutritional sciences.
Refereed Serial

613.26   US
AHIMSA. 1960. 4/yr. $18. American Vegan Society, 501 Old Harding Highway, Box H, Malaga, NJ 08328-0908. TEL 609-694-2887. Ed. H. Jay Dinshah. bk.rev.; index, cum.index. **Document type:** newsletter.
Description: Presents total-vegetarian diet, lifestyle, and philosophies.

610 641.1   GW   ISSN 0341-0501
CODEN: AEKPDQ
AKTUELLE ERNAEHRUNGSMEDIZIN; Klinik und Praxis. 1976. bi-m. DM.178.50 (for students and members of the Arbeitsgemeinschaft fuer klinische Diaetetik, Diaetassistentinnen DM.107). Georg Thieme Verlag, Ruedigerstr. 14, 70469 Stuttgart, Germany. TEL 0711-8931-0. FAX 0711-8931298. (Subscr. to: Postfach 104853, 70040 Stuttgart, Germany) Ed.Bd. index. circ. 2,700. (reprint service avail. from UMI) **Indexed:** Chem.Abstr., Curr.Cont., Excerp.Med., Potato Abstr., Sugar Ind.Abstr., Triticale Abstr. **Document type:** academic/scholarly publication.
—BLDSC (0785.735000); CASDDS. **CCC.**

ALIMENTACION, NUTRICION Y SALUD. see *FOOD AND FOOD INDUSTRIES*

641.1   FR
CODEN: ALLVAR
ALIMENTATION ET LA VIE - NOUVELLE PRESENTATION. 1942. q. 65 F. Societe Scientifique d'Hygiene Alimentaire, 16 rue de l'Estrapade, 75005 Paris, France. (Co-sponsor: Association Francaise des Techniciens de l'Alimentation Animale) Ed. Georges le Moan. adv.; bibl.; charts; stat. **Indexed:** Dairy Sci.Abstr., Ind.Vet., Nutr.Abstr., Vet.Bull.
—CASDDS.
Formerly: Alimentation et la Vie (ISSN 0065-6267)

613.2   IT   ISSN 0392-7512
CODEN: ANMTD9
ALIMENTAZIONE NUTRIZIONE METABOLISMO; rivista trimestrale di studi nutrizionali ed endocrino-metabolici. (Text in English, French, Italian; summaries in English, Italian) 1979. q. L.64000($35.70) Societa Editrice Universo, Via Morgagni 1, 00161 Rome, Italy. Ed. Michelangelo Cairella. adv.; bk.rev.; bibl.; charts; illus.; index. circ. 500. (tabloid format; back issues avail.) **Indexed:** Biol.Abstr., Chem.Abstr.
—BLDSC (0787.952000); CASDDS.

612.3 664   SP   ISSN 0212-6400
ALIMENTEC.* 1981. m. 4500 ptas. Ediciones J.S., S.A., Doctor Fleming 32, 61-6a planta, 28036 Madrid, Spain. TEL 1-458-14-68. FAX 1-458-27-92. TELEX SDMAE 46422. Ed. Jose Salgado. circ. 10,000.

ALIMENTOS E NUTRICAO. see *FOOD AND FOOD INDUSTRIES*

ALIVE; Canadian journal of health and nutrition. see *PHYSICAL FITNESS AND HYGIENE*

NUTRITION AND DIETETICS

AMERICAN CHIROPRACTOR. see *MEDICAL SCIENCES — Chiropractic, Homeopathy, Osteopathy*

616.39   US   ISSN 0731-5724
RC620.A1   CODEN: JONUDL
AMERICAN COLLEGE OF NUTRITION. JOURNAL. 1982. 6/yr. $75 to individuals (foreign $115); institutions $150 (foreign $190) (effective 1996). American College of Nutrition, c/o Hospital for Joint Deseases, 301 E. 17th St., New York, NY 10003. TEL 718-283-7906. FAX 718-283-7005. (Subscr. to: Fulco, Box 3000, Denville, NJ 07834. TEL 800-875-2997. FAX 201-627-5872) Ed. Dr. Fima Lifshitz. adv.; bk.rev.; abstr.; index. circ. 1,600. (also avail. in microform; back issues avail.) **Indexed:** Biol.Abstr., Chem.Abstr., Curr.Adv.Biochem., Curr.Adv.Ecol.Sci., Curr.Cont., Excerp.Med., Ind.Med., NRN, Sci.Cit.Ind. **Document type:** academic/scholarly publication.
—BLDSC (4685.780000); CASDDS; Faxon; Genuine Article; SWETS; UMI; UnCover. **CCC.**
Description: Covers nutrition research as it applies to patient care.
Refereed Serial

613.2   US   ISSN 0002-8223
RM214   CODEN: JADAAE
AMERICAN DIETETIC ASSOCIATION. JOURNAL. 1925. m. $100 (Canada $123; elsewhere $170) (effective 1995). American Dietetic Association, 216 W. Jackson Blvd., Ste. 800, Chicago, IL 60606-6995. TEL 312-899-0040. FAX 312-899-1757. Ed. Elaine R. Monsen. adv.: B&W page $3650; trim 8 1/8 x 10 7/8; adv. contact: Vicki Guinta. bk.rev.; abstr.; bibl.; charts; index; circ. 67,200 (paid). (also avail. in microform from PMC,UMI; back issues avail.; reprint service avail. from UMI) **Indexed:** Abstr.Health Care Manage.Stud., Abstr.Hyg., AIM, Art.Hosp.& Tour., Behav.Med.Abstr., Biol.Abstr., Biol.& Agr.Ind., C.I.S. Abstr., Chem.Abstr., Curr.Adv.Biochem., Curr.Adv.Ecol.Sci., Curr.Cont., Dairy Sci.Abstr., Dent.Ind., Diar.Dis.Res, Dok.Arbeitsmed., Environ.Per.Bibl., Excerp.Med., Food Sci.& Tech.Abstr., Gen.Sci.Ind., Helminthol.Abstr., Hlth.Ind., Hosp.Lit.Ind., Ind.Med., INIS Atomind., Int.Nurs.Ind., NRN, Nutr.Abstr., Potato Abstr., Poult.Abstr., Psychol.Abstr., Risk Abstr., Soc.Work Res.& Abstr. **Document type:** academic/scholarly publication.
●Also available online. Vendor(s): University Microfilms International.
—BLDSC (4686.130000); CASDDS; Faxon; Genuine Article; SWETS; UMI; UnCover.
Formerly: American Dietetic Association. Bulletin.
Description: Publishes reports of original research and other papers covering all aspects of dietetics, including nutrition and diet therapy, community nutrition, education, and administration.
Refereed Serial

612.3 613.2   US   ISSN 0002-9165
RC584   CODEN: AJCNAC
AMERICAN JOURNAL OF CLINICAL NUTRITION; a journal reporting the practical application of our world-wide knowledge of nutrition. (Supplement avail.) 1952. m. $115 (foreign $175) (effective 1996). American Society for Clinical Nutrition, Inc., 9650 Rockville Pike, Rm. 2310, Bethesda, MD 20814-3998. TEL 301-530-7026. FAX 301-530-7001. Ed. Dr. Norman Kretchmer. adv.; bk.rev.; bibl.; charts; illus.; index. circ. 7,900. (also avail. in microfilm from PMC,UMI; back issues avail.) **Indexed:** A.S.& T.Ind., Abstr.Hyg., Abstr.Inter.Med., AIM, Anim.Breed.Abstr., Behav.Med.Abstr., Bibl.Dev.Med.& Child.Neur., Biol.Abstr., Biol.& Agr.Ind., Chem.Abstr., CINAHL, Curr.Adv.Biochem., Curr.Cont., Dairy Sci.Abstr., Diar.Dis.Res., Dok.Arbeitsmed., Energy Rev., Environ.Per.Bibl., Excerp.Med., Food Sci.& Tech.Abstr., Helminthol.Abstr., Ind.Med., Ind.Sci.Rev., Ind.Vet., INIS Atomind., Kidney, NRN, Nutr.Abstr., Potato Abstr., Psychol.Abstr., Rev.Plant Path., Rice Abstr., Sci.Cit.Ind., So.Pac.Per.Ind., Soyabean Abstr., Sugar Ind.Abstr., Triticale Abstr., Trop.Dis.Bull., Vet.Bull., World Agri.Econ.& Rural Sociol.Abstr. **Document type:** academic/scholarly publication.
●Also available online. Vendor(s): University Microfilms International.
—BLDSC (0823.000000); CASDDS; Faxon; Genuine Article; SWETS; UMI; UnCover. **CCC.**
Description: Publishes original research contributed by scientists throughout the world, perspective in nutrition, editorials, case reports, special articles, meeting reports. Special supplements are devoted to symposia, workshops, and other long reports.
Refereed Serial

AMERICAN JOURNAL OF HEALTH PROMOTION. see *PUBLIC HEALTH AND SAFETY*

ANALES DE BROMATOLOGIA. see *FOOD AND FOOD INDUSTRIES*

616.39   SZ   ISSN 0250-6807
   CODEN: ANUMDS
ANNALS OF NUTRITION AND METABOLISM; European journal of nutrition, metabolic diseases and dietetics. (Supplement: Bibliotheca Nutritio et Dieta) (Text in English, French, German) 1959. bi-m. 400 SFr.($276) per vol. (Federation of European Nutrition Societies) S. Karger AG, Allschwilerstr. 10, P.O. Box, CH-4009 Basel, Switzerland. TEL 061-3061111. FAX 061-3061234. E-mail: Karger@Karger.ch. Ed. G. Wolfram. adv.; bibl.; charts; illus.; index. circ. 1,250. (also avail. in microform) **Indexed:** Abstr.Hyg., Anim.Breed.Abstr., Biol.Abstr., Biotech.Abstr., Cadscan, Chem.Abstr., Curr.Adv.Ecol.Sci., Curr.Cont., Dairy Sci.Abstr., Dent.Ind., Excerp.Med., Food Sci.& Tech.Abstr., Ind.Med., Ind.Sci.Rev., Lead Abstr., NRN, Nutr.Abstr., Poult.Abstr., Sci.Cit.Ind., Soyabean Abstr., Zincscan. **Document type:** academic/scholarly publication.
—BLDSC (1043.250000); CASDDS; Faxon; Genuine Article; SWETS; UnCover. **CCC.**
Incorporating (1947-1980): Annales de la Nutrition et de l'Alimentation (ISSN 0003-4037); Former titles (until 1980): Nutrition and Metabolism (ISSN 0029-6678); (until 1970): Nutritio et Dieta.
Description: Reports of basic research, primarily on the biochemical and physiological aspects of nutrition.
Refereed Serial

613.2 664 613.7   US   ISSN 1055-6990
TX341
ANNUAL EDITIONS: NUTRITION. 1988. a. $12.95. Dushkin Publishing Group, Sluice Dock, Guilford, CT 06437-9989. TEL 203-453-4351. FAX 203-453-6000. Ed. Charlotte Cook-Fuller; Pub. Ian Nielsen. illus. **Document type:** academic/scholarly publication.
Refereed Serial

613.2   US   ISSN 0199-9885
QP141.A1   CODEN: ARNTD8
ANNUAL REVIEW OF NUTRITION. 1981. a. $48 (foreign $53) (effective Jan. 1995). Annual Reviews Inc., 4139 El Camino Way, Box 10139, Palo Alto, CA 94303-0139. TEL 415-493-4400; 800-523-8635. FAX 415-855-9815. E-mail: annrevu@class.org. Ed. Donald B. McCormick. bibl.; index, cum.index. (also avail. in microform from UMI; back issues avail.; reprint service avail.) **Indexed:** Abstr.Hyg., Biol.Abstr., Chem.Abstr., Curr.Adv.Ecol.Sci., Dent.Ind., Diar.Dis.Res., Ind.Med., Ind.Sci.Rev., Pig News & Info., Potato Abstr., Sci.Cit.Ind., Sugar Ind.Abstr. **Document type:** academic/scholarly publication.
—BLDSC (1524.300000); ADONIS; CASDDS; Faxon; Genuine Article; SWETS; UMI; UnCover. **CCC.**
Description: Original critical reviews of the significant primary literature and current developments in nutrition.

613.2   UK   ISSN 0195-6663
QP136   CODEN: APPTD4
APPETITE; the journal for research on intake, and dietary practices, their control and consequences. 1980. bi-m. £202 (effective 1996). Academic Press Ltd. (Subsidiary of: Harcourt Brace & Company Ltd.), 24-28 Oval Rd., London NW1 7DX, England. TEL 44-171-267-4466. FAX 44-171-482-2293. TELEX 25775 ACPRESS G. (Subscr. to: Harcourt Brace & Company Ltd., Foots Cray High St., Sidcup, Kent DA14 5HP, England. TEL 44-181-300-3322. FAX 44-181-309-0807) Ed.Bd. adv.; bk.rev.; index. **Indexed:** Chem.Abstr., Curr.Adv.Ecol.Sci., Dent.Ind., Excerp.Med., Ind.Med., Ind.Sci.Rev., NRN, Nutr.Abstr., Potato Abstr., Poult.Abstr., Psychol.Abstr. (1980-), Sci.Cit.Ind., Sugar Ind.Abstr. **Document type:** academic/scholarly publication.
—BLDSC (1570.200000); CASDDS; Faxon; Genuine Article; SWETS; UnCover. **CCC.**
Description: Covers the determinants and consequences of eating and drinking disorders. Includes dietary intake, attitudes, and practices.

612.3   VE   ISSN 0004-0622
TX341   CODEN: ALANBH
ARCHIVOS LATINOAMERICANOS DE NUTRICION. (Text in English, French, Portuguese, Spanish) 1966. q. $50 to non-members; members $30; institutions in the Americas $125; institutions elsewhere $150. Sociedad Latinoamericana de Nutricion - Latin American Nutrition Society, Apdo. Postal 62778, Chacao, Caracas 1060, Venezuela. FAX 58-2-284-8543. Ed. Dr. Virgilio Bosch R. adv.; bk.rev.; abstr.; bibl.; charts; index. circ. 1,000. (reprint service avail. from ISI) **Indexed:** Biol.Abstr., Chem.Abstr., Curr.Adv.Ecol.Sci., Curr.Cont., Dairy Sci.Abstr., Dent.Ind., Excerp.Med., Food Sci.& Tech.Abstr., Helminthol.Abstr., Ind.Med., Maize Abstr., NRN, Nutr.Abstr., Potato Abstr., Triticale Abstr.
—BLDSC (1655.300000); CASDDS; Genuine Article; SWETS; UMI. **CCC.**
Formerly: Archivos Venezolanos de Nutricion.
Description: Presents results of research in the fields of food and nutrition conducted in the Americas.

641 613.2   AT   ISSN 1032-1322
TX341
AUSTRALIAN JOURNAL OF NUTRITION AND DIETETICS. 1944. q. Aus.$50 (foreign Aus.$70) (effective 1995). Dietitians Association of Australia, P.O. Box 11, O'Connor, A.C.T. 2601, Australia. TEL 61-6-247-2555. FAX 61-6-257-2184. Ed. Nancy E. Hitchcock. adv. contact: Keerry Moir. bk.rev.; abstr. circ. 2,400. **Indexed:** Curr.Cont., Dairy Sci.Abstr., Food Sci.& Tech.Abstr., Nutr.Abstr. **Document type:** academic/scholarly publication.
—BLDSC (1810.700000); Faxon; UnCover. **CCC.**
Former titles (until Mar. 1989): Journal of Food and Nutrition (ISSN 0728-4713); Food and Nutrition Notes and Reviews (ISSN 0015-6329)
Description: Scientific journal specialising in nutrition and dietetics.
Refereed Serial

613.26   AT
AUSTRALIAN VEGETARIAN. 1962. bi-m. Aus.$4. Vegetarian Society, South Australia, P.O. Box 46, Rundle Sta., Adelaide, S.A. 5000, Australia. Eds. T. Allen, E.M. Fearnside. adv.; bk.rev. circ. 1,000.
Description: Covers cooking methods and philosophies.

613   CN   ISSN 0849-0430
B C D N A NEWS. m. Can.$45. British Columbia Dietitians' and Nutritionists' Association, 1755 W. Broadway Ave., Ste. 402, Vancouver, BC V6J 4S5, Canada. TEL 604-736-3790. FAX 604-736-5606. adv.; bk.rev. circ. 900. (back issues avail.) **Document type:** newsletter.
Former titles (until 1989): B C D N A Newsletter (ISSN 0845-499X); British Columbia Dietitians' and Nutritionists' Association. Newsletter (ISSN 0830-047X)
Description: Provides members with current information on topics and events of interest.

641.4   UK
B N F ANNUAL CONFERENCE PROCEEDINGS. a. price varies. British Nutrition Foundation, High Holborn House, 52-54 High Holborn, London WC1V 6RQ, England. TEL 0171-404-6504. FAX 0171-404-6747. (back issues avail.) **Document type:** proceedings.
Description: Presents papers on diet, nutrition, and health and safety presented at the B.N.F. Annual Conference.

613.2   UK
B N F BRIEFING PAPERS. 1980. irreg. price varies (usually £3-£5). British Nutrition Foundation, High Holborn House, 52-54 High Holborn, London WC1V 6RQ. TEL 0171-404-6504. FAX 0171-404-6747. (back issues avail.) **Document type:** academic/scholarly publication.
Description: Covers nutrition during pregnancy, salt intake, energy balance, food and behavior, and diet.

613.2   UK
B N F MONOGRAPHS. 1980. irreg. price varies. British Nutrition Foundation, High Holborn House, 52-54 High Holborn, London WC1V 6RQ, England. TEL 0171-404-6504. FAX 0171-404-6747. (back issues avail.) **Indexed:** Nutr.Abstr. **Document type:** monographic series.
Formerly: British Nutrition Foundation Newsletter.
Description: Presents the latest scientific thinking in such nutrition topics as energy, fat, protein, carbohydrates, and vitamins and minerals.

NUTRITION AND DIETETICS

641.4 664   UK   ISSN 0141-9684
CODEN: BNUBD6
B N F NUTRITION BULLETIN. 1968. q. £24 with supplement (overseas £32) (effective 1995). British Nutrition Foundation, High Holborn House, 52-54 High Holborn, London WC1V, England. TEL 0171-404-6504. FAX 0171-404-6747. Ed. Margaret Ashwell. index. circ. 1,300. (back issues avail.) **Indexed:** Abstr.Hyg., Biol.Abstr., Chem.Abstr., Curr.Adv.Ecol.Sci., Dairy Sci.Abstr., Food Sci.& Tech.Abstr., Nutr.Abstr., Packag.Sci.Tech., Trop.Dis.Bull. **Document type:** academic/scholarly publication.
—BLDSC (2116.298000); CASDDS.
 Description: Covers the current state of knowledge in clinical nutrition, food processing, food safety, and food policy.

613.2   UK
B N F TASK FORCE REPORTS. 1983. irreg. (1992). price varies. British Nutrition Foundation, High Holborn House, 52-54 High Holborn, London WC1V 6RQ. TEL 0171-404-5604. FAX 0171-404-6747. (back issues avail.) **Document type:** academic/scholarly publication.
 Description: Reports on nutrition in medical education, food intolerance and food aversion, sugars and syrups, and trans-fatty acids.

612.3 617.1   US
BARIATRICIAN. 1986. q. $40 (foreign $50). American Society of Bariatric Physicians, 5600 S. Quebec, Ste. 109A, Englewood, CO 80111-2208. TEL 303-779-4833. Ed. James F. Merker. adv. circ. 1,200. (back issues avail.) **Document type:** academic/scholarly publication.
 Description: Covers medical treatment of obesity and associated conditions.
Refereed Serial

641   US
BASIC AND CLINICAL NUTRITION. 1980. irreg., vol.3, 1981. price varies. Marcel Dekker, Inc., 270 Madison Ave., New York, NY 10016. TEL 212-696-9000. FAX 212-685-4540. TELEX 421419. **Indexed:** Biol.Abstr., Chem.Abstr.
Refereed Serial

641.1   US
BETTER HOMES AND GARDENS EATING RIGHT, LIVING WELL. s-a. Meredith Corporation, Special Interest Publications, 1716 Locust St., Des Moines, IA 50336. TEL 515-284-3000. Pub. Steve Levinson. adv.: B&W page $13450, color page $18350; adv. contact: Pat Tomlinson. circ. 50,000. **Document type:** consumer publication.

613.2   US
BETTER HOMES AND GARDENS LOW-CALORIE RECIPES. 1982. a. $3.50 per no. Meredith Corporation, Special Interest Publications, 1716 Locust St., Des Moines, IA 50309. TEL 515-284-3000. Pub. Steve Levinson. adv.: B&W page $13450, color page $18350; adv. contact: Pat Tomlinson. circ. 500,000.
 Formerly: Diet and Exercise (ISSN 0163-0334)

641.1   US
TX341
BETTER NUTRITION FOR TODAY'S LIVING. m. $24 (foreign $64). Argus Inc., 6151 Powers Ferry Rd., N.W., Atlanta, GA 30339-2941. TEL 404-955-2500. FAX 404-955-0400. Ed. Frank Murray. adv.; illus. (also avail. in microform from UMI; reprint service avail. from UMI) **Indexed:** Hlth.Ind., PMR. **Document type:** trade publication.
●Also available online. Vendor(s): University Microfilms International.
—BLDSC (1947.087000); UMI. **CCC.**
 Formerly (until 1990): Better Nutrition (ISSN 0405-668X); Incorporates (in 1990): Today's Living (ISSN 0743-7285)
 Description: Discusses health foods, vitamin supplements, herbs, cosmetics and bodycare, diet and new products. Includes menus and recipes.

641.1   SZ   ISSN 0067-8198
TX341   CODEN: BNDSA3
BIBLIOTHECA NUTRITIO ET DIETA. (Supplement avail.: Annals of Nutritional Metabolism) (Text in English, French and German) 1960. irreg. (approx. 1/yr.) price varies. S. Karger AG, Allschwilerstr. 10, P.O. Box, CH-4009 Basel, Switzerland. TEL 061-3061111. FAX 061-3061234. E-mail: Karger@Karger.ch. Ed. J.C. Somogyi. (back issues avail.; reprint service avail. from ISI) **Indexed:** Biodet.Abstr., Biol.Abstr., Chem.Abstr., Curr.Cont., Dairy Sci.Abstr., Food Sci.& Tech.Abstr., Ind.Med., Nutr.Abstr. **Document type:** academic/scholarly publication.
—BLDSC (2019.200000); CASDDS; Faxon; SWETS. **CCC.**
Refereed Serial

BIO NACHRICHTEN. see AGRICULTURE — *Crop Production And Soil*

BIOLOGICAL TRACE ELEMENT RESEARCH. see BIOLOGY — *Biological Chemistry*

BLUEBOOK UPDATE. see AGRICULTURE — *Crop Production And Soil*

BOVINE VETERINARIAN. see *VETERINARY SCIENCE*

612.3   AT   ISSN 0729-2759
BREASTFEEDING REVIEW. 1982. s-a. Aus.$30 (foreign Aus.$40). Nursing Mothers' Association of Australia, P.O. Box 231, Nunawading, Vic. 3131, Australia. TEL 61-3-98775011. FAX 61-3-9894-3270. Ed. Jill Finch. adv.; bk.rev. circ. 1,500. (back issues avail.) **Indexed:** CINAHL. **Document type:** academic/scholarly publication.
—UnCover.
 Description: For medical, nursing and allied health professionals, contains current research and developments in all aspects of human lactation.
Refereed Serial

BRITISH FOOD JOURNAL. see *FOOD AND FOOD INDUSTRIES*

612.3   UK   ISSN 0007-1145
TX501   CODEN: BJNUAV
BRITISH JOURNAL OF NUTRITION. (Supplement avail.: Nutrition Research Review (ISSN 0954-4224)) 1947. m. £310($576) (effective 1996). (Nutrition Society) Cambridge University Press, Edinburgh Bldg., Shaftesbury Rd., Cambridge CB2 2RU, England. TEL 01223-312393. FAX 01223-315052. TELEX 851817256. (N. American addr.: Cambridge University Press, Journals Dept., 40 W. 20th St., New York, NY 10011. TEL 212-924-3900. FAX 212-691-3239) Ed. D.A.T. Southgate. adv.; bibl.; charts; index. (also avail. in microform from SWZ,UMI,PMC; back issues avail.) **Indexed:** Abstr.Hyg., Anal.Abstr., Anim.Breed.Abstr., ASCA, Behav.Med.Abstr., Biol.Abstr., Biol.& Agr.Ind., Biotech.Abstr., Chem.Abstr., Curr.Adv.Biochem., Curr.Adv.Ecol.Sci., Curr.Cont., Dairy Sci.Abstr., Dent.Ind., Diar.Dis.Res., Environ.Per.Bibl. (1977-), Excerp.Med., Food Sci.& Tech.Abstr., Helminthol.Abstr., Ind.Med., Ind.Sci.Rev., Ind.Vet., INIS Atomind., Maize Abstr., NRN, Nutr.Abstr., Pig News & Info., Potato Abstr., Poult.Abstr., Protozool.Abstr., Rice Abstr., Sci.Cit.Ind., Small Anim.Abstr., Sorghum & Millets Abstr., Soyabean Abstr., Sugar Ind.Abstr., Triticale Abstr., Trop.Dis.Bull., Vet.Bull. **Document type:** academic/scholarly publication.
—BLDSC (2312.000000); CASDDS; Faxon; Genuine Article; SWETS; UMI; UnCover. **CCC.**
 Description: Devoted to the advancement of the scientific study of nutrition and its application to the maintenance of human and animal health. Includes papers on clinical and human nutrition, as well as general nutrition.

613.2   US   ISSN 0007-7364
BUXOM BELLE COURIER. * 1959. m. $1. Buxom Belles International, Inc., 619 Spencer, Ferndale, MI 48220. Ed. Dee Phillips. charts; illus.; stat. circ. 2,800. (processed)

BWINO: HEALTH CARE NEWS. see *PHYSICAL FITNESS AND HYGIENE*

C M U JOURNAL OF SCIENCE. (Central Mindanao University) see AGRICULTURE

641   FR   ISSN 0007-9960
CODEN: CNDQA8
CAHIERS DE NUTRITION ET DE DIETETIQUE. 1966. bi-m. 434 F. foreign 442 F.) (effective 1996). (Societe de Nutrition et de Dietetique de Langue Francaise) Masson - Periodiques, Villa Laromiguiere, 75005 Paris, France. TEL 1-40-46-62-00. FAX 1-40-46-62-01. Ed. Claude Sautier. adv.; bk.rev.; charts; illus.; circ. 3,500 (controlled). **Indexed:** Biol.Abstr., Chem.Abstr., Curr.Adv.Biochem., Curr.Adv.Ecol.Sci., Curr.Adv.Genetics & Molec.Biol., Curr.Cont., Dairy Sci.Abstr., Excerp.Med. (1994-), Food Sci.& Tech.Abstr., Rural Recreat.Tour.Abstr., World Agri.Econ.& Rural Sociol.Abstr. **Document type:** academic/scholarly publication.
—BLDSC (2950.200000); CASDDS; Faxon; SWETS. **CCC.**
 Description: Establishes a relationship between the medical world and the food industry. Publishes original articles and general reviews.

613.2   JM   ISSN 0376-7655
CAJANUS. 1968. q. free to Caribbean countries; $6 to Third World countries; $12 to US and other developed countries. Caribbean Food and Nutrition Institute, U.W.I. Mona Campus, P.O. Box 140, Kingston 7, Jamaica, W.I. TEL 809-927-1540. FAX 809-927-2657. TELEX 3705. (Co-sponsors: Pan American Health Organization, World Health Organization) Ed. Clare Forrester. bk.rev.; bibl.; charts; index. circ. 2,028. **Indexed:** Dairy Sci.Abstr., Food Sci.& Tech.Abstr., Nutr.Abstr., Rural Ext.Educ.& Tr.Abstr.
 Description: Research articles on nutrition and dietary intake, focusing on the population of the Caribbean.

613.2   US   ISSN 1049-1791
CALORIE CONTROL COMMENTARY. 1979. 2/yr. free in U.S. (foreign $10). Calorie Control Council, 5775 Peachtree-Dunwoody Rd., Ste. 500-G, Atlanta, GA 30342. TEL 404-252-3663. FAX 404-252-0774. Ed. Keith C. Keeney. charts; illus.; stat.; circ. 12,000 (controlled). (back issues avail.) **Document type:** newsletter.
 Description: Newsletter summarizing scientific, regulatory and other developments relating to sweeteners, fat replacers, dieting, weight control and low-calorie - reduced fat foods and beverages.

641   CN   ISSN 0008-3399
CODEN: JCDTAH
CANADIAN DIETETIC ASSOCIATION. JOURNAL/ASSOCIATION CANADIENNE DES DIETETISTES. REVUE. (Text in English, French) 1939. q. Can.$50 (foreign $55). Canadian Dietetic Association - Association Canadienne des Dietetistes, 480 University Ave., Ste. 601, Toronto, ON M5G 1V2, Canada. TEL 416-596-0857. FAX 416-596-0603. Ed. Susan Gatchell. adv. contact: Joan Embury. bk.rev.; abstr.; charts; illus.; index. circ. 5,500. (also avail. in microfilm from UMI) **Indexed:** Biol.Abstr., Chem.Abstr., Curr.Cont., Food Sci.& Tech.Abstr., NRN, Nutr.Abstr. **Document type:** academic/scholarly publication.
—BLDSC (4723.020000); CASDDS; Faxon; Genuine Article; UMI; UnCover.
 Description: Articles and research reports in nutrition, dietetics, food administration and management.
Refereed Serial

613.2   VI
CARIBBEAN DIET DIGEST. Cover title: Dr. Carter's Caribbean Diet Digest. q. $18. Caribbean Diet Institute, PO Box 191, Frederiksted, St. Croix, Virgin Islands.

613.2   US   ISSN 1049-4901
CODEN: CNSEEH
CARNATION NUTRITION EDUCATION SERIES. 1989. irreg., latest vol.3. price varies. Raven Press (Subsidiary of: Wolters Kluwer N.V.), 1185 Ave. of the Americas, New York, NY 10036. TEL 212-930-9500. FAX 212-869-3495. **Document type:** proceedings.
—BLDSC (3053.740000).

CELIAC NEWS. see *MEDICAL SCIENCES — Gastroenterology*

CEYLON JOURNAL OF MEDICAL SCIENCE. see *MEDICAL SCIENCES*

CHICAGO HEALTHCARE. see *PHYSICAL FITNESS AND HYGIENE*

NUTRITION AND DIETETICS

CHILE PEPPER; spicy world cuisine. see *HOME ECONOMICS*

613.2   IT   ISSN 0392-7318
CODEN: CLDID7
CLINICA DIETOLOGICA. 1974. q. L.60000 (foreign L.120000). Societa Editrice Universo, Via G.B. Morgagni 1, 00161 Rome, Italy. Ed. Michelangelo Cairella. **Indexed:** Biol.Abstr., Soyabean Abstr., Sugar Ind.Abstr.
—BLDSC (3286.201000).

613.2   UK   ISSN 0261-5614
CODEN: CLNUDD
CLINICAL NUTRITION. 1982. bi-m. £224($370) (effective 1995). (European Society of Parenteral and Enteral Nutrition) Churchill Livingstone Journals, Robert Stevenson House, 1-3 Baxter's Pl., Leith Walk, Edinburgh EH1 3AF, Scotland. TEL 0131-556-2424. FAX 0131-459-1177. (Subscr. to: Pearson Professional Ltd., P.O. Box 77, Fourth Ave., Harlow, Essex CM19 5AA, England; U.S. subscr. to: Churchill Livingstone, 650 Ave. of the Americas, New York, NY 10011. TEL 212-206-5000) Ed. Marinos Elia. adv. contact: David Dunnachie. bk.rev. circ. 1,125. (also avail. in microform from UMI; back issues avail.) **Indexed:** Chem.Abstr., Curr.Adv.Ecol.Sci., Excerp.Med., NRN. **Document type:** academic/scholarly publication.
—BLDSC (3286.314500); CASDDS; Genuine Article; SWETS; UnCover. **CCC.**

COLLEGE - UNIVERSITY FOODSERVICE WHO'S WHO. see *BUSINESS AND ECONOMICS — Trade And Industrial Directories*

613.2   UK
THE COMPOSITION OF FOOD. (Supplements avail.) irreg., 5th ed., 1993. £35. The Royal Society of Chemistry, Thomas Graham House, Science Park, Milton Rd., Cambridge CB4 4WF, England. TEL 01223-420066. FAX 01223-423623. E-mail: rsc1@rsc.org. (Dist. by: Turpin Distribution Services Ltd., Blackhorse Rd., Letchworth, Herts. SG6 1HN, England. TEL 01462-672555. FAX 01462-480947; Subscr. in N. America to: CRC Press Inc., 2000 Corporate Blvd., N.W., Boca Raton, FL 33431. TEL 407-994-0555) Ed.Bd. **Document type:** trade publication.
Description: Contains revised and updated data on nearly 1,200 foods.

613.2   US
CONNELLY REPORT. m. $48. Met-Rx U S A, Inc., 2112 Business Center Dr., Irvine, CA 92715. Ed. Dr. Scott Connelly. circ. 56,000. **Document type:** newsletter.
Description: Covers health, nutrition, life extension and related topics.

COOKING LIGHT; the magazine of food and fitness. see *HOME ECONOMICS*

616.39   US   ISSN 0191-2453
CODEN: CTNDDU
CURRENT TOPICS IN NUTRITION AND DISEASE. 1977. irreg., vol.22, 1990. price varies. John Wiley & Sons, Inc., Journals, 605 Third Ave., New York, NY 10158. TEL 212-475-7700. bibl.; illus.; index. **Indexed:** Biol.Abstr., Chem.Abstr.
—CASDDS. **CCC.**
Refereed Serial

641.1   US   ISSN 0011-5568
CODEN: DACDAK
DAIRY COUNCIL DIGEST; an interpretive review of recent nutrition research. 1929. bi-m. $12 (foreign $16). National Dairy Council, O'Hare International Center, 10255 W. Higgins Rd., Ste. 900, IL 60018-5616. TEL 708-803-2000. FAX 708-803-2077. index. circ. 25,000. (also avail. in microform from UMI; back issues avail.) **Indexed:** CHNI, Hlth.Ind., Nutr.Abstr. **Document type:** academic/scholarly publication.
—CASDDS; UMI.
Description: Covers recent research information for nutrition professionals. Each issue examines a single topic.

641.5   US   ISSN 1073-8436
DELICIOUS!; guide to natural living. 1985. m. $24 (foreign $44). New Hope Communications, Inc., 1301 Spruce St., Boulder, CO 80302-4832. TEL 303-939-8440. FAX 303-939-9559. Ed. Sue Frederick; Pub. Rick Prill. **Document type:** consumer publication.
Description: Publishes articles on natural foods, herbs vitamins and life-styles.

DIABETES, NUTRITION & METABOLISM, CLINICAL AND EXPERIMENTAL. see *MEDICAL SCIENCES — Endocrinology*

DIET & HEALTH MAGAZINE. see *PHYSICAL FITNESS AND HYGIENE*

612.3   CN   ISSN 0834-3160
DIETETIQUE EN ACTION. (Text in English, French) 1986. 3/yr. $45. Ordre Professionel des Dietetistes du Quebec, 1425 bd. Rene-Levesque O., Bur. 703, Montreal, PQ H3G 1T7, Canada. TEL 514-393-3733. FAX 514-393-3582. Ed. Michel Lefevre. adv.: B&W page Can.$535, color page Can.$1170; trim 8 1/2 x 11. bk.rev. circ. 2,500. **Indexed:** Pt.de Rep. (1989-). **Document type:** bulletin.

641.1   SW   ISSN 0348-0674
DIETISTEN; kostekonomi, kostterapi. 1949. m. (11/yr.). SEK 390 (effective 1991). Svensk Dietistfoerening, P.O. Box 12069, S-102 22 Stockholm, Sweden. Ed. Anne-Marie Tidholm. adv. circ. 2,396.
Former titles (until vol.3, 1977): Svenska Ekonomifoerestaandares Tidskrift (ISSN 0346-2293); (until vol.3, 1968): Svenska Ekonomifoerestaandarinnors Tidskrift; (until vol.7, 1950): Meddelande fraan Svenska Ekonomifoerestaandarinnors Foerening.

DROPPJOURNALEN; tidskrift om nutrition och vaetsketerapi. see *PHARMACY AND PHARMACOLOGY*

613.2   SZ   ISSN 1021-1225
CODEN: DNREEN
DYNAMIC NUTRITION RESEARCH. (Text in English) 1991. irreg., vol.3, 1992. $157 price varies. S. Karger AG, Allschwilerstr. 10, P.O. Box, CH-4009 Basel, Switzerland. TEL 061-3061111. FAX 061-3061234. E-mail: Karger@Karger.ch. Ed. M. Paubert-Braquet. **Document type:** academic/scholarly publication, monographic series.
—BLDSC (3637.137000); CASDDS.
Description: Reflects the increasingly close relationship that is developing between the agrofood sector and health care industries, placing emphasis on the influence of foodstuffs on human biology and pathophysiology.
Refereed Serial

616   US   ISSN 1048-6984
EATING DISORDERS REVIEW; current clinical information for the professional treating eating disorders. 1990. bi-m. $79 (foreign $96) (effective 1996). Quest Publishing Co., Inc., A Division of Raven Press Ltd. (Subsidiary of: Wolters Kluwer N.V.), 1351 Titan Way, Brea, CA 92621. TEL 714-738-6400. FAX 714-525-6258. (Subscr. to: Raven Press, 1185 Ave. of the Americas, New York, NY 10036. TEL 212-930-9500. FAX 212-869-3495) Ed. Dr. Joel Yager; Pub. Mary Waltham. (back issues avail.) **Document type:** newsletter.
—**CCC.**

EATING WELL; the magazine of food & health. see *FOOD AND FOOD INDUSTRIES*

ECOLE NATIONALE SUPERIEURE DE BIOLOGIE APPLIQUEE A LA NUTRITION ET A L'ALIMENTATION. CAHIERS. see *FOOD AND FOOD INDUSTRIES*

613.2   US   ISSN 0367-0244
TX341   CODEN: ECFNBN
ECOLOGY OF FOOD AND NUTRITION; an international journal. 1971. 12/yr. (in 3 vols., 4 nos./vol.). 83 ECU per vol. (effective 1996). Gordon and Breach Science Publishers, c/o International Publishers Distributor, 820 Town Center Dr., Langhorne, PA 19047. TEL 215-750-2642. FAX 215-750-6343. (Subscr. to: International Publishers Distributor, P.O. Box 90, Reading, Berkshire RG1 8JL, England. TEL 44-173-456-8316) Ed.Bd. adv.; bk.rev.; bibl.; charts; illus.; stat.; index. (also avail. in microform; back issues avail.) **Indexed:** A.I.C.P., Abstr.Anthropol., Abstr.Hyg., Abstr.Rural Dev.Trop., Agroforest.Abstr., Biol.Abstr., Cadscan, Chem.Abstr., Curr.Adv.Ecol.Sci., Curr.Cont., Dairy Sci.Abstr., Energy Ind., Energy Info.Abstr., Environ.Per.Bibl. (1991-), Excerpt.Med., Field Crop Abstr., Food Sci.& Tech.Abstr., Geo.Abstr., Herb.Abstr., IDA, Ind.Sci.Rev., Lead Abstr., Maize Abstr., NRN, Nutr.Abstr., Potato Abstr., Rice Abstr., Rural Devel.Abstr., Sci.Cit.Ind., So.Pac.Per.Ind., Soils & Fert., Trop.Dis.Bull., World Agri.Econ.& Rural Sociol.Abstr., Zincscan. **Document type:** academic/scholarly publication.
—BLDSC (3650.043000); CASDDS; Faxon; SWETS; UnCover. **CCC.**
Description: Emphasizes foods and their utilization in satisfying the nutritional needs of mankind, but also extends to nonfood contributions, to obesity and leanness, malnutrition, vitamin requirements, and mineral needs.
Refereed Serial

614   BE   ISSN 0004-5144
EDUCATION SANITAIRE ET NUTRITIONNELLE D'AFRIQUE CENTRALE. 1927. q. 150 BEF. Centre d'Education Sanitaire et Nurtritionnelle d'Afrique Centrale, 11 rue Brialmont, B-1030 Brussels, Belgium. TEL 32-2-2170497. Ed. M.M. Moeremans d'Emaus. circ. 1,000.
Formerly: Assistance aux Maternites et Dispensaires en Afrique Centrale.

664 613   UA   ISSN 1110-0192
EGYPTIAN JOURNAL OF FOOD SCIENCE/AL-MAJALLAH AL-MISRIYYAH LI-ULUM AL-AGHDHIYA. (Text in English; summaries in Arabic and English) 1973. 3/yr. $82 (effective 1996). (Society of Food Science and Technology, Research Department) National Information and Documentation Centre (NIDOC), Tahrir St., Dokki, Awqaf P.O., Cairo, Egypt. TEL 20-2-701696. Ed. A. Alian. illus. circ. 1,000. (reprint service avail. from IRC) **Indexed:** Apic.Abstr., Biol.Abstr., Chem.Abstr., Curr.Pack.Abstr., Dairy Sci.Abstr., ExtraMED, Food Sci.& Tech.Abstr., Hort.Abstr., Nutr.Abstr., Packag.Sci.Tech. **Document type:** academic/scholarly publication.
●Also available on CD-ROM.

613.2   JA
EIYO KANRI NO KENKYU/STUDY ON NUTRITION CONTROL. (Text in Japanese) a. 1900 Yen. Zenkoku Jichitai Byoin Kyogikai - Japan Municipal Hospital Association, Godo Kaikan, 3-27, Kioicho, Chiyoda-ku, Tokyo 102, Japan.

613.2   JA   ISSN 0013-6492
EIYO NIPPON/NUTRITION OF JAPAN. (Text in Japanese) 1958. m. 850 Yen per no. Nihon Eiyoshikai - Japan Dietetic Association, 1-39, Kanda Jinbocho, Chiyoda-ku, Tokyo 101, Japan.

613.2   JA   ISSN 0915-759X
EIYOU HYOKA TO CHIRYO/JAPANESE JOURNAL OF NUTRITIONAL ASSESSEMENT. (Text in Japanese) 1987. 4/yr. 1600 Yen per no. Medikaru Rebyusha - Medical Review Co., Ltd., 7-3, Hiranomachi 1-chome, Chuo-ku, Osaka 541, Japan.

641.1   US   ISSN 0893-4452
ENVIRONMENTAL NUTRITION; the newsletter of diet, nutrition and health. 1977. m. $30 to libraries (foreign $49). Environmental Nutrition, Inc., 52 Riverside Dr. Bldg. 15A, New York, NY 10024-6599. TEL 212-362-2066. (Subscr. to: Box 420451, Palm Coast, FL 32142-0451) Ed. Denise Webb. bk.rev.; index. circ. 100,000. (looseleaf format; back issues avail.) **Indexed:** CHNI, Hlth.Ind. **Document type:** newsletter.
●Also available online. Vendor(s): Information Access Co.
—BLDSC (3791.527600).
Formerly: Environmental Nutrition Newsletter (ISSN 0195-4024)

NUTRITION AND DIETETICS

ENVIRONMENTAL OPPORTUNITIES. see *ENVIRONMENTAL STUDIES*

641.1   IT
ERBORISTERIA DOMANI. 1978. m. (11/yr.) L.86000. Demetrio Benelli, Ed. & Pub., Piazza Wagner 1, 20145 Milan, Italy. TEL 39-2-4816742. FAX 39-2-4817843. adv.: B&W page L.1400000, color page L.2400000. circ. 20,000. **Indexed:** Apic.Abstr. **Document type:** consumer publication.

641.1   GW   ISSN 0014-021X
CODEN: ERUMAT
ERNAEHRUNGS UMSCHAU; Forschung und Praxis. (Includes supplements: Ernaehrungslehre- und Praxis; D G E Info) 1954. m. DM.128.40 (student DM.100.80). (Deutsche Gesellschaft fuer Ernaehrung) Umschau Zeitschriftenverlag Breidenstein GmbH, Stuttgarter Str. 18-24, 60329 Frankfurt a.M., Germany. TEL 069-2600-0. FAX 069-2600-619. (Co-sponsors: Verband Deutscher Diaetassistenten; Guetegemeinschaft Diaetverpflegung) Ed. Sabine Fankhaenel. adv.: B&W page DM.4700, color page DM.7685; trim 176 x 257. bk.rev.; charts; illus.; stat.; index. circ. 11,344. (back issues avail.) **Indexed:** Biol.Abstr., Chem.Abstr., Curr.Adv.Ecol.Sci., Curr.Cont., Dairy Sci.Abstr., Excerp.Med., Food Sci.& Tech.Abstr., INIS Atomind., Nutr.Abstr., Sugar Ind.Abstr. **Document type:** consumer publication.
—CASDDS. **CCC.**

ERNAEHRUNGSDIENST; Handels- und Boersenzeitung fuer die Agrarmaerkte. see *AGRICULTURE — Feed, Flour And Grain*

641.1   US   ISSN 0071-1179
CODEN: ERNFA7
ERNAEHRUNGSFORSCHUNG/NUTRITION RESEARCH; aktuelle Informationen aus Wissenschaft und Praxis. 1956. q. 61 ECU (effective 1996). (Akademie der Wissenschaften, Zentralinstitut fuer Ernaehrung) Harwood Academic Publishers, c/o International Publishers Distributor, 820 Town Center Dr., Langhorne, PA 19047. (Subscr. to: International Publishers Distributor, P.O. Box 90, Reading, Berkshire RG1 8JL, England. TEL 4-173-456-8316) Ed. H.-A. Ketz. charts; illus.; index. **Indexed:** Biol.Abstr., Chem.Abstr., Dairy Sci.Abstr., Excerp.Med., Food Sci.& Tech.Abstr., Maize Abstr., Pig News & Info.
—CASDDS; SWETS. **CCC.**

612.3   GW   ISSN 0721-5118
ERNAEHRUNGSRUNDBRIEF. 1970. q. DM.28. Arbeitskreis fuer Ernaehrungsforschung e.V., Zwerweg 19, 75378 Bad Liebenzell, Germany. TEL 07052-3061. Ed. Petra Kuehne. adv.; bk.rev.; index. circ. 4,000. (back issues avail.) **Document type:** bulletin.

641.1   UK   ISSN 0954-3007
CODEN: EJCNEQ
EUROPEAN JOURNAL OF CLINICAL NUTRITION. 1976. m. £195 to E.C.; elsewhere £205($310). Stockton Press (Subsidiary of: Macmillan Press Ltd.), Houndmills, Basingstoke, Hampshire RG2 2XS, England. TEL 01256-817245. FAX 01256-28339. Pub. Marija Vukovojac. adv. contact: Michael Rowley. circ. 1,000. **Indexed:** Curr.Cont., Dairy Sci.Abstr., Diar.Dis.Res., Excerp.Med., Gen.Sci.Ind., NRN, Nutr.Abstr., Potato Abstr., Rice Abstr., Trop.Dis.Bull. **Document type:** academic/scholarly publication.
—BLDSC (3829.728000); CASDDS; Faxon; Genuine Article; SWETS; UMI; UnCover. **CCC.**
Formerly (until 1987): Human Nutrition. Clinical Nutrition (ISSN 0263-8290); Which superseded in part (in 1981): Journal of Human Nutrition (ISSN 0308-4329); Which was formerly (until 1976): Nutrition (ISSN 0029-6600)

EXERCISE PHYSIOLOGY: CURRENT SELECTED RESEARCH. see *PHYSICAL FITNESS AND HYGIENE*

EXTENDED CARE PRODUCT NEWS. see *PHYSICAL FITNESS AND HYGIENE*

613.2   UN   ISSN 1014-3181
F A O FOOD AND NUTRITION SERIES. Spanish edition: Coleccion F A O, Alimentacion y Nutricion (ISSN 1014-3173); French edition: Collection F A O, Alimentation et Nutrition (ISSN 0253-2549) (Text in English, French and Spanish) 1948. irreg., no.24. 1991. price varies. Food and Agriculture Organization of the United Nations, c/o UNIPUB, 4611-F Assembly Dr., Lanham, MD 20706-4391. TEL 301-459-7666. FAX 301-459-0056. **Indexed:** Ind.Med., Nutr.Abstr., World Agri.Econ.& Rural Sociol.Abstr. **Document type:** monographic series.
—BLDSC (3865.643300).
Formerly: F A O Nutritional Study (ISSN 0071-7088)

613.2   US   ISSN 0895-0040
FELIX LETTER; a commentary on nutrition. 1981. 6/yr. $12 (effective Jan. 1995). Clara Felix, Ed. & Pub., Box 7094, Berkeley, CA 94707. TEL 510-526-6268. bk.rev.; circ. 1,000 (controlled). (back issues avail.) **Document type:** newsletter.
Description: Critical review and commentary on nutrition research. Promotes nutrition as an alternative to or adjunctive to medical approaches to illness.

613.2   GW   ISSN 0720-8731
CODEN: FPEREX
FETT IN DER PARENTERALEN ERNAEHRUNG. 1981. irreg., vol.4, 1993. DM.50. W. Zuckschwerdt Verlag GmbH, Industriestr. 17, 82110 Germering, Germany. TEL 089-894349-0. FAX 089-89434950. Ed. J. Eckart. **Document type:** academic/scholarly publication.
—CASDDS.

572 900   ISSN 0740-9710
TX341   CODEN: FOFWEC
FOOD AND FOODWAYS; explorations in the history and culture of human nutrition. 4/yr. (in 1 vol., 4 nos./vol.). 99 ECU (effective 1996). Harwood Academic Publishers, c/o International Publishers Distributor, 820 Town Center Dr., Langhorne, PA 19047. TEL 215-750-2642. FAX 215-750-6343. (Subscr. to : International Publishers Distributor, PO Box 90, Reading, Berkshire, RG1 8JL, England. TEL 44-173-456-8316) Ed. Steven L. Kaplan. adv. (also avail. in microform) **Indexed:** Amer.Hist.& Life (1993-), Hist.Abstr. (1993-).
—BLDSC (3977.038450); Faxon; UnCover. **CCC.**
Refereed Serial

641.1   UN   ISSN 0379-5721
TX341   CODEN: FNBPDV
FOOD AND NUTRITION BULLETIN. (Text in English) 1978. q. $40 (developing countries $25). United Nations University Press, 53-70, Jingumae 5-chome, Shibuya-ku, Tokyo 150, Japan. TEL 03-3499-2811. FAX 03-3499-2828. TELEX J25442 UNATUNIV. Ed. Dr. Nevin S. Scrimshaw. bk.rev.; cum.index: vols.1-3. circ. 3,800. (also avail. in microfiche from CIS; back issues avail.) **Indexed:** Agroforest.Abstr., Chem.Abstr., Diar.Dis.Res., Food Sci.& Tech.Abstr., IDA, IIS, Rice Abstr., Rural Devel.Abstr., Sorghum & Millets Abstr., World Agri.Econ.& Rural Sociol.Abstr.
—BLDSC (3977.043200); Faxon; SWETS; UnCover.
Supersedes: Protein-Calorie Advisory Group of the United Nations System. P A G Bulletin.

FOOD AND NUTRITION IN HISTORY AND ANTHROPOLOGY. see *ANTHROPOLOGY*

641   US   ISSN 0015-6310
FOOD & NUTRITION NEWS. 1930. 5/yr. free. National Live Stock and Meat Board, 444 N. Michigan Ave., Chicago, IL 60611. TEL 312-467-5520. FAX 312-467-9729. Ed. E. Urenos. bk.rev.; index. circ. 55,000. (reprint service avail. from UMI) **Indexed:** CHNI, Hlth.Ind., Ind.Free Per. **Document type:** newsletter.
—BLDSC (3977.045000).

641.1   GW   ISSN 0721-6912
FOOD COMPOSITION AND NUTRITION TABLES/ZUSAMMENSETZUNG DER LEBENSMITTEL, NAEHRWERT TABELLEN. (Text in English, French and German) irreg. (2-3/yr.) Wissenschaftliche Verlagsgesellschaft mbH, Postfach 101061, 70009 Stuttgart, Germany. TEL 0711-2582-0. FAX 0711-2582-290. **Document type:** trade publication.
—BLDSC (3977.289000).

FOOD HYGIENIC SOCIETY OF JAPAN. JOURNAL/SHOKUHIN EISEIGAKU ZASSHI. see *PUBLIC HEALTH AND SAFETY*

664   UN   ISSN 1014-806X
RA601
FOOD NUTRITION AND AGRICULTURE/ALIMENTATION NUTRITION ET AGRICULTURE/ALIMENTACION NUTRICION Y AGRICULTURA. (Text in English, French and Spanish) 1974. 3/yr. free. Food and Agriculture Organization of the United Nations, Sales & Distribution Section, Via delle Terme di Caracalla, 00100 Rome, Italy. TEL 57971. FAX 6799563. TELEX 610181 FAO. E-mail: publications-sales@fao.org. Ed. Kim Atkinson. bk.rev.; charts; stat.; illus.; cum.index. circ. 10,000. **Indexed:** Abstr.Hyg., Biol.& Agr.Ind., Curr.Adv.Ecol.Sci., Dairy Sci.Abstr., Diar.Dis.Res., Field Crop Abstr., Herb.Abstr., Ind.Med., Mag.Ind., Nutr.Abstr., Rural Devel.Abstr., Rural Recreat.Tour.Abstr., Trop.Dis.Bull., World Agri.Econ.& Rural Sociol.Abstr.
—BLDSC (3981.304500); UnCover. **CCC.**
Formed by the 1991 merger of: Food and Nutrition (ISSN 0304-8942) & Alimentation et Nutrition (ISSN 0251-1452) & Alimentacion y Nutricion (ISSN 0251-1428); **Supersedes:** Nutrition Newsletter (ISSN 0428-9447)
Description: FAO world review of food policy and nutrition. Each issue covers a specific theme, in addition to regular reports of committees and updates on food laws.

FOOD, NUTRITION & HEALTH NEWSLETTER. see *FOOD AND FOOD INDUSTRIES*

613.2 664   US   ISSN 1046-705X
TX543   CODEN: FSTUE2
FOOD STRUCTURE. 1982. q. $100 (foreign $120). Scanning Microscopy International, Inc., Box 66507, AMF O'Hare, Chicago, IL 60666-0507. TEL 312-529-6677. FAX 312-980-6698. Ed. Om Johari. bk.rev.; illus.; cum.index. circ. 300. (back issues avail.) **Indexed:** ASCA, Biol.Abstr., Chem.Abstr., Curr.Adv.Ecol.Sci., Curr.Cont., Dairy Sci.Abstr., Food Sci.& Tech.Abstr., Ind.Sci.Rev., Sci.Cit.Ind., SSCI. **Document type:** academic/scholarly publication.
—BLDSC (3983.600000); CASDDS; Faxon; Genuine Article; SWETS; UnCover. **CCC.**
Formerly (until vol.8, no.2, 1989): Food Microstructure (ISSN 0730-5419)
Description: Covers the structure of foods and feeds with special emphasis on the relation between processing, molecular properties, microstructure and macroscopic behavior.
Refereed Serial

613.2   JA   ISSN 0385-5880
FUKUYAMA AKENOHOSHI GAKUIN EIYO SENMON GAKKO KENKYU KIYO/FUKUYAMA AKENOHOSHI GAKUIN SCHOOL OF DIETETICS. BULLETIN. (Text in Japanese) 1973. irreg. Fukuyama Akenohoshi Gakuin Eiyo Senmon Gakko, 4-1, Nishifukazumachi 3-chome, Fukuyama-shi, Hiroshima-ken 720, Japan.

612.3 616.3   US   ISSN 0890-507X
G I G NEWSLETTER. 1974. q. $25 (Canada & Mexico $30; elsewhere $35). Gluten Intolerance Group of North America, Box 23053, Seattle, WA 98102-0353. TEL 206-325-6980. FAX 206-850-2394. Ed. Elaine I. Hartsook. bk.rev.; index. circ. 1,500. (looseleaf format; back issues avail.) **Document type:** academic/scholarly publication, newsletter.
Description: Contains research reports, food product and drug information, seminar-meeting announcements, activities of national and local interest, and recipes.

641.1 635   US
GARLIC TIMES; the newsletter of lovers of the stinking rose. 1976. a. $21 for 2 yrs. (Lovers of the Stinking Rose) Harris Publishing, 1563 Solan Ave., Ste. 201, Berkeley, CA 94707-2116. Ed. L. John Harris. adv.; bk.rev. circ. 5,000. (back issues avail.) **Document type:** newsletter.

GASTRONOMIE; Fachzeitschrift fuer Restaurant, Kueche und Hotel. see *HOTELS AND RESTAURANTS*

GATHERED VIEW. see *MEDICAL SCIENCES*

613.2 IT ISSN 1122-2239
GIORNALE ITALIANO DI NUTRIZIONE CLINICA E PREVENTIVA. (Text in English, Italian) 1991. 3/yr. L.90000($150) (effective 1995). Casa Editrice Idelson, Via A. De Gasperi 55, 80133 Naples, Italy. TEL 39-81-5524733. FAX 39-81-5518295. Eds. Flaminio Fidanza, Mario Mancini.
Formerly: Rivista Italiana di Nutrizione Clinica e Preventiva.
Description: Presents original data and discusses theoretical and practical aspects of clinical and preventive nutrition.

641.1 IO ISSN 0436-0265
GIZI INDONESIA. (Text in English, Indonesian) q. Rps.1200. (Indonesian Nutrition Association) Akedemi Gizi, Jl. Hang Jebat III/F3, P.O. Box 8 KBB, Kebayoran Baru, Jakarta, Indonesia. Ed. Ig. Tarnotjo. adv.; bk.rev.; illus.

GOOD LIFE TIMES; choices in health, education and the arts. see NEW AGE PUBLICATIONS

613.2 US
GOOD-NEWS-LETTER (WASHINGTON, 1990). 1990. bi-m. free. American Institute for Cancer Research (AICR), 1759 R St., N.W., Washington, DC 20009. TEL 202-328-7744. FAX 202-328-7226. circ. 14,000.
Description: For children ages 7-10. Contains games and puzzles that teach children about good nutrition in an entertaining manner.

GOURMED; magazine for doctors. see MEDICAL SCIENCES

GREAT BODY. see PHYSICAL FITNESS AND HYGIENE

919.204 UK
GREENSCENE; the only magazine for young vegetarians. 1988. 3/yr. £4. Vegetarian Society, Parkdale, Dunham Rd., Altrincham, Chesire WA14 4QG, England. TEL 061-928-0793. FAX 061-926-9182. Ed. Juliet Gellatley. adv.; bk.rev. circ. 10,000. (back issues avail.)

613.2 GW ISSN 0932-2981
DAS GROSSE LEBEN; Makrobiotik-Magazin. 1986. q. DM.60 membership. Ost-West-Bund Verlag, Auf der Juchhoeh 21, 66333 Voelklingen, Germany. TEL 06802-202. FAX 06802-1248. Ed. Richard Theobald. adv.; bk.rev. circ. 10,000. (back issues avail.) **Document type:** consumer publication.

613.2 PK ISSN 0259-3734
HAMDARD NAUNEHAL. 1952. m. R.180($20) Hamdard Foundation, Nizamabad 3, Karachi 74600, Pakistan. TEL 92-21-6616001. FAX 92-21-6641766. TELEX 24529 HAMD PK. Ed. Masood Ahmed Barakaatee. **Document type:** academic/scholarly publication.

HEALTH AND FITNESS (LONDON). see PHYSICAL FITNESS AND HYGIENE

664 613 SA
HEALTH COUNTER NEWS. 1976. m. R.3.20. P.O. Box 961, Noordwyk 1686, South Africa. adv.

613.2 641.1 US ISSN 1055-8241
HEALTH DIET & NUTRITION.* (Supplement avail.) 1991. q. $29.99. Publishing & Business Consultants, 101 W. 64th St., Unit 3, Inglewood, CA 90302-1255. TEL 213-732-3477. FAX 213-732-9123. (Subscr. to: Box 75392, Los Angeles, CA 90075) Ed. Andeson Napoleon Atia. adv. circ. 120,000.
Document type: consumer publication.
Description: Covers basic nutrition information, dietary habits, and personal health care.

613.2 US
HEALTH EXPRESS (LAS VEGAS).* 12/yr. $12. International Academy of Nutritional Consultants, 2375 Tropicana, Ste. 270, Las Vegas, NV 90109. TEL 702-454-1665. adv.

664 US ISSN 0149-9602
HD9001 CODEN: HFBUED
HEALTH FOODS BUSINESS; the business publication of the natural foods industry. 1954. m. $33. P T N Publishing Corp., 445 Broad Hollow Rd., Melville, NY 11747. TEL 516-845-2700. FAX 516-845-7109. Ed. Gina Geslewitz. adv.; bk.rev. circ. 12,300.
—BLDSC (4275.015950).
Description: Reaches health and natural foods retailers with news, information, purchasing guide and surveys.

613.2 616.39 II ISSN 0970-8685
HEALTH FOR THE MILLIONS. 1975. bi-m. Rs.120 (foreign $30). Health for the Millions Trust, Tong Swasthya Bhawan, 40 Institutional Area, New Delhi 110 016, India. TEL 011-668071. FAX 011-6885377. E-mail: vhai@unv.ernet.in. Ed. Anurita Roy Choudhury; Pub. Alok Mukhopadkyay. adv.: B&W page Rs.4000; adv. contact: S. Kannapiran. bk.rev.; bibl.; illus. circ. 3,000. **Indexed:** Curr.Adv.Ecol.Sci. **Document type:** academic/scholarly publication.
Description: Aims to influence decision making and disseminates practical information on health policies and programs affecting the public.

613 362.1 US
RA773
HEALTH NEWS NATURALLY. 1975. q. $9.95. Keats Publishing, Inc., 27 Pine St., Box 876, New Canaan, CT 06840. TEL 203-966-8721. FAX 203-972-3991. Ed. Cheryl Hirsch. adv.; bk.rev.; illus. circ. 150,000. **Indexed:** Hlth.Inc.
—UMI.
Former titles (until 1995): Health News and Review (ISSN 1056-1900); (until 1993): Your Good Health Review and Digest (ISSN 0745-7278); (until 1983): Health Quarterly, Plus Two (ISSN 0199-6673); Health Quarterly (ISSN 0362-6644)

613 UK ISSN 0144-4948
HEALTH NOW. 1977. 6/yr. Health Now Publishing Co. Ltd., 79281 High St., Godalming, Surrey GU7 1AW, England. TEL 0483 426064. FAX 0483-426005. Ed. Alice Peet. adv.; bk.rev. circ. 400,000.

613 US ISSN 0883-8216
HEALTH SCIENCE; living in harmony with nature. 1978. bi-m. $25 (foreign $45). American Natural Hygiene Society, Inc., Box 30630, Tampa, FL 33630. TEL 813-855-6607. Ed. James Michael Lennon. adv.; bk.rev.; charts; illus.; cum.index: 1978-1983. circ. 6,000. (back issues avail.)
Former titles (until vol.8, no.2): Vegetarian Health Science (ISSN 8750-1643); Health Science (ISSN 0161-5874)

613.2 613.7 CN ISSN 0845-8251
HEALTH WATCH. 1989. 4/yr. Can.$12.95. Telemedia Procom Inc., 25 Sheppard Ave., W., North York, ON M2H 6S7, Canada. TEL 416-733-7600. FAX 416-218-3633. Ed. Constance Dragones; Pub. Ashley Harvey. adv. contact: Merrilyn Patterson. circ. 500,000. **Document type:** consumer publication.

HEALTHCARE NEW ORLEANS. see PHYSICAL FITNESS AND HYGIENE

641.1 US ISSN 0897-9251
HEALTHWAYS. 1987. 3/yr. $25 (foreign $30). International Macrobiotic Shiatsu Society, 1122 M St., Eureka, CA 95501-2442. TEL 707-445-2290. FAX 707-445-2391. Ed. Patrick McCarty. bk.rev. circ. 600. **Document type:** newsletter.

HEALTHY EATING. see FOOD AND FOOD INDUSTRIES

613.26 AT ISSN 0158-1015
HEALTHY LIFE NEWS. bi-m. Aus.$12. Marketing Factory Pty. Ltd., 501-13 Spring St., Chatswood, N.S.W., Australia. TEL 02-411-2944. Ed. K. Richards. adv. circ. 200,000.
Description: Covers preventive medicine and health issues.

HEALTHY TIMES. see PHYSICAL FITNESS AND HYGIENE

612.3 613.2 US ISSN 1075-0169
HEALTHY WEIGHT JOURNAL; research, news and commentary across the weight spectrum. 1986. bi-m. $59 (foreign $68) (effective 1996). Healthy Living Institute, 402 S. 14th St., Hettinger, ND 58639. TEL 701-567-2646. FAX 701-567-2602. Ed. Frances M. Berg; Pub. Frances M. Berg. adv.; bk.rev.; abstr.; index. circ. 1,600. (also avail. in microform from UMI; back issues avail.; reprint service avail. from UMI) **Indexed:** CINAHL, Consum.Ind., ERIC, Nurs.Abstr., Soc.Work Res.& Abstr. **Document type:** academic/scholarly publication.
● Also available online. Vendor(s): University Microfilms International.
—UMI. CCC.
Former titles (until 1994): Obesity and Health (ISSN 1044-1522); (until 1989): International Obesity Newsletter (ISSN 0893-2204); Obesity Newsletter (ISSN 0891-4028)
Description: Reports research and information on weight including causes, prevalence, treatment, prevention, health risks of obesity and eating disorders, impact on individuals, social and political issues and the weight loss industry.

HERE'S HEALTH; a monthly guide to health, nutrition, natural food and natural therapy. see PHYSICAL FITNESS AND HYGIENE

613 JA
HIMAN CHIRYO KENKYUKAI KOENSHU/JAPANESE SOCIETY FOR OBESITY THERAPY. PROCEEDINGS. (Text in Japanese) a. Himan Chiryo Kenkyukai, Chiba Daigaku Igakubu Dai 2 Geka, 8-1, Inohana 1-chome, Chuo-ku, Chiba 260, Japan.

613.2 JA ISSN 0289-5137
CODEN: HBSKE6
HIROSHIMA BUNKYO SHOKUMOTSU EIYO KENKYUKAISHI/HIROSHIMA BUNKYO WOMEN'S COLLEGE. SOCIETY FOR FOOD NUTRITION. JOURNAL. (Text in Japanese) 1983. a. Hiroshima Bunkyo Shokumotsu, Eiyo Kenkyukai, Hiroshima Bunkyo Joshi Daigaku Tanki Daigakubu, 2-1, Kabe Higashi 1-chome, Asakita-ku, Hiroshima-shi, Hiroshima-ken 731-02, Japan.

HOME ECONOMICS ASSOCIATION OF VICTORIA. NEWSLETTER. see HOME ECONOMICS

613.2 642.58 US ISSN 0046-7979
HOSPITAL FOOD SERVICE. 1967. bi-m. members only. (American Society for Hospital Food Service Administrators) American Hospital Association, One North Franklin, Chicago, IL 60606. TEL 312-422-3873. FAX 312-422-4579. Ed. Shirley Arniestead. circ. 1,700 (controlled). (looseleaf format) **Document type:** newsletter.

613.2 US ISSN 1062-7723
HOW ON EARTH!; youth supporting compassionate, ecologically sound living. 1992. q. $19 (Canada $21; elsewhere $25). Vegetarian Education Network, Box 339, Oxford, PA 19363-0339. TEL 717-529-8638. FAX 717-529-3000. E-mail: HowOnEarth@aol.com. Ed. Sally Clinton. adv.; bk.rev. (looseleaf format; back issues avail.) **Document type:** consumer publication.
Description: Publishes articles on environmental, animal, and vegetarian issues for teenagers, and provides a forum and activities concerning them. Includes nutritional advice, tips on products to boycott, resources, and telephone numbers, and recipes by and for vegetarian teenagers.

HUMAN ECOLOGY. ANNUAL REPORT. see SOCIAL SCIENCES: COMPREHENSIVE WORKS

613.2 US ISSN 0886-6848
QP141.A1 CODEN: HNUTEP
HUMAN NUTRITION. 1979. irreg., vol.8, 1993. price varies. Plenum Publishing Corp., 233 Spring St., New York, NY 10013-1578. TEL 212-620-8468. FAX 212-463-0742. TELEX 23421139. Eds. Roslyn B. Alfin-Slater, David Kritchev. (back issues avail.) **Document type:** monographic series.
Refereed Serial

HUNGER NOTES. see SOCIOLOGY

4918 NUTRITION AND DIETETICS

613.2 US
I A P N H NEWSLETTER. 1985. q. $12 to non-members. International Association of Professional Natural Hygienists, 204 Stambaugh Bldg., Youngstown, OH 44503. TEL 216-746-5000. FAX 216-746-1836. Ed. Mark A. Huberman. bk.rev. circ. 55. (looseleaf format; back issues avail.) **Document type**: newsletter.
   Description: For primary care doctors.

I B F A N NEWS. (International Baby Food Action Network) see CHILDREN AND YOUTH — About

616.39 US ISSN 0936-4072
I L S I HUMAN NUTRITION REVIEWS. 1986. irreg. price varies. Springer-Verlag, 175 Fifth Ave., New York, NY 10010. TEL 212-460-1500. FAX 212-473-6272. (Also: Berlin, Heidelberg, Tokyo, Vienna) (reprint service avail. from ISI) **Document type**: academic/scholarly publication.

613.2 GW
I L S I MONOGRAPH. irreg., latest 1993. price varies. (International Life Sciences Institute) Springer-Verlag, Heidelberger Platz 3, 14197 Berlin, Germany. TEL 030-8207-1. FAX 030-8214091. (Subscr. in N. America to: Box 2485, Secaucus, NJ 01096-2491. TEL 800-777-4643. FAX 201-777-4505) **Document type**: monographic series.

641.1 II ISSN 0022-3174
TX341 CODEN: IJNDAN
INDIAN JOURNAL OF NUTRITION AND DIETETICS. (Text in English) 1964. m. Rs.150($40) Avinashilingam Institute for Home Science and Higher Education for Women, c/o Rajammal P. Devadas, Ed., Coimbatore 641 043, India. TEL 40241. TELEX 855 459 ADU IN. adv.; bk.rev.; bibl.; charts; stat.; index. circ. 620. **Indexed**: Abstr.Hyg., Biol.Abstr., Chem.Abstr., Curr.Cont., Dairy Sci.Abstr., Diar.Dis.Res., ExtraMED, Field Crop Abstr., Food Sci.& Tech.Abstr., Helminthol.Abstr., INIS Atomind., Maize Abstr., Nutr.Abstr., Plant Breed.Abstr., Poult.Abstr., Seed Abstr., Sorghum & Millets Abstr., Soyabean Abstr., Triticale Abstr., Trop.Dis.Bull., Trop.Oil Seeds Abstr. **Document type**: academic/scholarly publication.
●Also available on CD-ROM.
   —BLDSC (4417.450000); CASDDS; UnCover.
   Formerly (until vol.7, 1970): Journal of Nutrition and Dietetics.
   Description: Research papers and review articles in the fields of nutrition and dietetics.
   Refereed Serial

613.26 II ISSN 0019-6460
INDIAN VEGETARIAN CONGRESS QUARTERLY. 1968. q. $6. Indian Vegetarian Congress, The Grove, No. 1, Eldams Road, Madras 600 018, India. TEL 450-364. Ed. Surendra M. Mehta. adv.; bk.rev.; charts; illus. circ. 1,500.

INFANT NUTRITION. see MEDICAL SCIENCES — Pediatrics

INFUSIONSTHERAPIE UND TRANSFUSIONSMEDIZIN. see MEDICAL SCIENCES — Hematology

613.2 152 US
INSTITUTE FOR POSITIVE WEIGHT MANAGEMENT NEWSLETTER. 1989. q. 10. Institute for Positive Weight Management, Box 1271, Boca Raton, FL 33429-1271. TEL 407-750-7004. Ed. Dr. Lynn Brown. index. circ. 75. (looseleaf format; back issues avail.) **Document type**: consumer publication.
   Description: Provides information for laypersons and professionals regarding weight management.

641 UN ISSN 0533-4179
INSTITUTO DE NUTRICION DE CENTRO AMERICA Y PANAMA (INCAP). INFORME ANUAL. (Editions in English and Spanish) 1950. a. exchange basis. Institute of Nutrition of Central America and Panama (INCAP) - Instituto de Nutricion de Centro America y Panama, Carretera Roosevelt Zona 11, Apdo. Postal 1188, 01901 Guatemala City, Guatemala. TEL 723762. FAX 715658. TELEX 5696 INCAP GU. E-mail: delgado@uclvmz. Ed. Carlos Cipriani. circ. 1,100. **Indexed**: Biol.Abstr., Nutr.Abstr.

INSTITUTO DE TECNOLOGIA DE ALIMENTOS. COLETANEA. see FOOD AND FOOD INDUSTRIES

INSTITUTO DE TECNOLOGIA DE ALIMENTOS. INSTRUCOES PRATICAS. see FOOD AND FOOD INDUSTRIES

INSTITUTO DE TECNOLOGIA DE ALIMENTOS. INSTRUCOES TECNICAS. see FOOD AND FOOD INDUSTRIES

612 NG ISSN 0534-4700
INTER-AFRICAN CONFERENCE ON FOOD AND NUTRITION. PROGRAMA E INFORMACOES. * (Text in English, French and Portuguese) irreg. (Commission for Technical Co-Operation in Africa South of the Sahara) Maison de l'Afrique, B.P. 878, Niamey, Niger.

641 NG ISSN 0538-2785
INTER-AFRICAN CONFERENCE ON FOOD AND NUTRITION. REPORT. * 1949. irreg. (Commission for Technical Co-Operation in Africa, South of the Sahara) Maison de l'Afrique, B.P. 878, Niamey, Niger.

641.1 AT ISSN 0813-9008
CODEN: ICNRDJ
INTERNATIONAL CLINICAL NUTRITION REVIEW. 1981. q. Aus.$54 (New Zealand Aus.$64; elsewhere $69). Integrated Therapies Pty. Ltd., P.O. Box 370, Manly, N.S.W. 2095, Australia. TEL 61-2-99770771. FAX 61-2-99770267. Ed. Robert A. Buist. bk.rev. circ. 2,000. **Indexed**: Chem.Abstr., Curr.Adv.Ecol.Sci., Dairy Sci.Abstr., NRN, Nutr.Abstr. **Document type**: academic/scholarly publication.
   —BLDSC (4538.673500); CASDDS.
   Incorporates: Orthomolecular Review (ISSN 0725-7090)
   Description: Reports recent nutritional research from journals worldwide with original articles emphasizing potential clinical applications.

INTERNATIONAL JOURNAL FOR VITAMIN AND NUTRITION RESEARCH. see PHARMACY AND PHARMACOLOGY

614.7 612.3 370 US ISSN 1044-811X
BF1 CODEN: IJMREU
INTERNATIONAL JOURNAL OF BIOSOCIAL AND MEDICAL RESEARCH; bridging the gap between the natural and social sciences to better understand human behavior. 1979. 2/yr. $25 to individuals; institutions and foreign $50. (Foundation for Biosocial Research) Life Sciences Press, Box 1174, Tacoma, WA 98401-1174. TEL 206-922-0442. FAX 206-922-0479. Ed. Alexander G. Schauss. adv.; bk.rev. circ. 3,500. (back issues avail.) **Indexed**: Excerp.Med., Lang.& Lang.Behav.Abstr., Neurosci.Abstr., Nutr.Abstr., Psychol.Abstr., Sociol.Abstr.
   —BLDSC (4542.155090); UnCover. **CCC**.
   Formerly (until 1989): International Journal for Biosocial Research (ISSN 0731-9169)
   Description: Publishes studies on behavior as it relates to nutrition, neurotoxicology and environmental health.
   Refereed Serial

616.37 US ISSN 0276-3478
RC552.A72 CODEN: INDIDJ
INTERNATIONAL JOURNAL OF EATING DISORDERS. 1981. 8/yr. $592 (foreign $716) (effective 1996). John Wiley & Sons, Inc., Journals, 605 Third Ave., New York, NY 10158. TEL 212-850-6645. FAX 212-850-6021. TELEX 12-7063. (Subscr. outside the Americas to: John Wiley & Sons Ltd., Baffins Ln., Chichester, W. Sussex PO19 1UD, England. TEL 44-1243-779777. FAX 44-1243-776128) Ed. Dr. Michael Strober. adv.; bk.rev.; bibl.; stat. circ. 1,050. (also avail. in microform from UMI; back issues avail.) **Indexed**: Adol.Ment.Hlth.Abstr., Biol.Abstr., Curr.Adv.Ecol.Sci., Excerp.Med., Ind.Med. (1993-), NRN, Psychol.Abstr. (1981-), Risk Abstr., Soc.Sci.Ind., Sp.Ed.Needs Abstr., Stud.Wom.Abstr. **Document type**: academic/scholarly publication.
   —BLDSC (4542.195500); Faxon; Genuine Article; SWETS; UMI; UnCover. **CCC**.
   Description: Publishes basic research, clinical and theoretical articles of scholarly substance on a variety of aspects of anorexia nervosa, bulimia, obesity and other atypical patterns of eating behavior and body weight regulation.
   Refereed Serial

581 UK ISSN 0963-7486
CODEN: IJFNEH
INTERNATIONAL JOURNAL OF FOOD SCIENCES AND NUTRITION. 1973. 6/yr. £84 to individuals; institutions £196 (effective 1996). Carfax Publishing Co., P.O. Box 25, Abingdon, Oxon. OX14 3UE, England. TEL 01235-55535. FAX 01235-553559. (Subscr. in N. America to: 875-81 Massachusetts Ave., Cambridge, MA 02139) Ed. C.J.K Henry. circ. 1,000 (controlled). **Indexed**: Abstr.Hyg., Chem.Abstr., Curr.Pack.Abstr., Diar.Dis.Res., Food Sci.& Tech.Abstr., Hort.Abstr., Nutr.Abstr., Rev.Med.& Vet.Mycol., Trop.Dis.Bull. **Document type**: academic/scholarly publication.
   —BLDSC (4542.254000); CASDDS; Faxon; SWETS; UMI; UnCover. **CCC**.
   Former titles: Food Sciences and Nutrition (ISSN 0954-3465); Human Nutrition. Food Sciences and Nutrition (ISSN 0952-8954); Journal of Plant Foods (ISSN 0142-968X); Plant Foods for Man (ISSN 0306-2686)
   Description: Analyzes the common elements of food science and nutrition. Examines biotechnological, nutritional, and physiological issues.

INTERNATIONAL JOURNAL OF HYGIENE AND NUTRITION IN FOOD SERVICE AND CATERING. see FOOD AND FOOD INDUSTRIES

613 UK ISSN 0307-0565
RC628 CODEN: IJOBDP
INTERNATIONAL JOURNAL OF OBESITY. 1977. m. £110 to individuals; institutions £235. (International Association for the Study of Obesity) Macmillan Press Ltd., Houndmills, Basingstoke, Hants RG21 2XS, England. TEL 01256-817245. FAX 01256-28339. Eds. Michael Stock, Jean-Paul Despres; Pub. Marija Vukovojac. adv. contact: Michael Rowley. bk.rev.; cum.index. circ. 1,500. **Indexed**: Abstr.Hyg., Chem.Abstr., Curr.Adv.Ecol.Sci., Curr.Cont., Dent.Ind., Excerp.Med., Ind.Med., Ind.Sci.Rev., NRN, Nutr.Abstr., Risk Abstr., Sci.Cit.Ind., Soyabean Abstr., Trop.Dis.Bull. **Document type**: academic/scholarly publication.
   —BLDSC (4542.410000); CASDDS; Faxon; Genuine Article; SWETS; UMI; UnCover. **CCC**.
   Description: Reports about animal and human studies in the areas of basic, clinical and applied biochemistry, physiology, and genetics together with the molecular, biochemical, psychological and epidemiological aspects of obesity and related disorders.

613.2 617.1 US ISSN 1050-1606
RC1235 CODEN: ISNUE5
INTERNATIONAL JOURNAL OF SPORT NUTRITION. Short title: I J S N. 1991. q. $40 to individuals (foreign $44); institutions $90 (foreign $94); students $24 (foreign $28). Human Kinetics Publishers, Inc., Box 5076, Champaign, IL 61825-5076. TEL 217-351-5076. FAX 217-351-2674. Ed. Priscilla M. Clarkson. adv. contact: Pamela Anderson. abstr.; bibl.; charts; stat.; index. circ. 760. (back issues avail.) **Indexed**: Excerp.Med. (1995-), Ind.Med. (1993-), Phys.Ed.Ind., Sportsearch. **Document type**: academic/scholarly publication.
   —BLDSC (4542.680800); Genuine Article; UnCover. **CCC**.
   Description: Advances understanding of nutritional aspects of human physical and athletic performance.
   Refereed Serial

INTERNATIONAL SEMINARS IN PAEDIATRIC GASTROENTEROLOGY AND NUTRITION. see MEDICAL SCIENCES — Gastroenterology

IRON METABOLISM. see BIOLOGY — Biological Chemistry

613.2 JA ISSN 0913-8471
IRYOSHOKU/MEDICAL FOODS. (Text in Japanese) 1974. a. Nihon Iryoshoku Kyokai - Japan Medical Foods Association, 6-4, Uchikanda 2-chome, Chiyoda-ku, Tokyo 101, Japan.

613.2 613.2 UK
ISSUES IN NUTRITION AND TOXICOLOGY SERIES. no.2, 1994. irreg. price varies. Chapman & Hall, 2-6 Boundary Row, London SE1 8HN, England. TEL 0171-865-1505. FAX 0171-865-0066. (U.S. addr.: Chapman & Hall, One Penn Plaza, 41st Fl., New York, NY 10119. TEL 212-564-1060. FAX 212-564-1505) **Document type**: monographic series.

613.2   JA   ISSN 0388-127X
J J P E N: JAPANESE JOURNAL OF PARENTERAL AND ENTERAL NUTRITION/YUEKI EIYO JANARU. (Text in Japanese) 1979. m. 23000 Yen. Medikaru Koa - Medical Core Co., Ltd., 8-1, Hatchobori 3-chome, Chuo-ku, Tokyo 104, Japan. TEL 03-3553-7741. FAX 03-3553-7745. Ed. Eiichi Tanaka; Pub. Sansetsu Hayashi. adv. contact: Yoichi Inoue. circ. 3,000. **Document type:** academic/scholarly publication.

613.2   JA   ISSN 0485-1412
                               CODEN: RNEYAW
JAPANESE JOURNAL OF CLINICAL NUTRITION/RINSHO EIYO. (Text in Japanese) 1952. m. 930 Yen per no. Ishiyaku Publishers, Inc., 7-10 Honkomagome 1-chome, Bunkyo-ku, Tokyo 113, Japan. Ed. Hiroshi Miura. adv.; bk.rev.; charts; illus. circ. 16,500. **Indexed:** Chem.Abstr.
—CASDDS.

641   JA   ISSN 0021-5147
                               CODEN: EYGZAD
JAPANESE JOURNAL OF NUTRITION/EIYOGAKU ZASSHI. (Text in Japanese) 1941. bi-m. 4326 Yen (effective 1995). (National Nutrition Society - Kokumin Eiyo Shinkokai) Daiichi Shuppan K.K., 1-39 Kanda Jimbo-cho, Chiyoda-ku, Tokyo 101, Japan. TEL 03-3291-4576. FAX 03-3291-4579. (Subscr. to: Japan Publications Trading Co. Ltd., P.O. Box 5030, Tokyo International, Tokyo 100-31, Japan) Ed. Shuhei Kobayashi. adv.; bk.rev. **Indexed:** Biol.Abstr., Chem.Abstr., Dairy Sci.Abstr., Field Crop Abstr., Food Sci.& Tech.Abstr., INIS Atomind., Maize Abstr., Nutr.Abstr., Rice Abstr., Seed Abstr. **Document type:** academic/scholarly publication.
—CASDDS; UnCover.

641   JA   ISSN 0287-3516
                               CODEN: NESGDC
JAPANESE SOCIETY OF NUTRITION AND FOOD SCIENCE. JOURNAL/NIPPON EIYO SHOKURYO GAKKAISHI. (Text in Japanese; summaries in English) 1947. 6/yr. 18000 Yen to non-members; students 4200 Yen; members 6300 Yen. Japanese Society of Nutrition and Food Science - Nippon Eiyo Shokuryo Gakkai, c/o Business Center for Academic Societies Japan, 5-16-9 Honkomagome, Bunkyo-ku, Tokyo 113, Japan. TEL 03-5814-5801. FAX 03-5814-5820. Ed. Yousuke Seyama. adv. bk.rev. circ. 4,300. **Indexed:** Biol.Abstr., Chem.Abstr., Food Sci.& Tech.Abstr., So.Pac.Per.Ind., Sugar Ind.Abstr. **Document type:** academic/scholarly publication.
—BLDSC (4809.474000); CASDDS; Ei; UnCover.
    Formerly: Food and Nutrition - Eiyo to Shokuryo (ISSN 0021-5376)

613.26   UK   ISSN 0021-681X
JEWISH VEGETARIAN. 1965. q. £10($15) International Jewish Vegetarian Society, 855, Finchley Rd., London NW11 8LX, England. Ed. Shirley Labelda. adv.; bk.rev. circ. 8,000. (tabloid format) **Document type:** consumer publication.

613   US
TX392
JEWISH VEGETARIANS. 1983. q. $12 (outside U.S. $15). Jewish Vegetarians of North America, 6938 Reliance Rd., Federalsburg, MD 21632. TEL 410-754-5550. Ed.Eva R. Mossman. bk.rev.; circ. 600. circ. 900 (paid); 520 (controlled). **Document type:** newsletter.
    Formerly: Jewish Vegetarians of New York (ISSN 0883-1904)
    Description: Discusses Judaism and vegetarianism. Topics include health, ecology, world hunger, animal rights and Jewish holidays.

JIANKANG BAO/HEALTH NEWS. see *PHYSICAL FITNESS AND HYGIENE*

613.2   JA   ISSN 0286-0511
                               CODEN: JEDKD7
JOSHI EIYO DAIGAKU KIYO/KAGAWA NUTRITION COLLEGE. JOURNAL. (Text in English, Japanese) 1970. a. Joshi Eiyo Daigaku, 24-3, Komagome 3-chome, Toshima-ku, Tokyo 170, Japan. **Indexed:** Chem.Abstr., Jap.Per.Ind.
—BLDSC (4810.180000); CASDDS.

641.1   US   ISSN 0021-8960
                               CODEN: JNAPAX
JOURNAL OF APPLIED NUTRITION. 1947. q. $75 to individuals (foreign $100); students $30 (foreign $40). International Academy of Nutrition and Preventive Medicine, Box 18433, Asheville, NC 28814-0433. TEL 704-258-3243. Ed. James Heffley. adv.: B&W page $250; adv. contact: Elizabeth Pavka. bk.rev.; abstr.; charts; illus.; cum.index: 1947-1990. circ. 1,500. (also avail. in microform from UMI; back issues avail.; reprint service avail. from UMI) **Indexed:** Biol.Abstr., Biol.& Agr.Ind., Chem.Abstr., Environ.Per.Bibl. (1974-), Excerp.Med., Nutr.Abstr. **Document type:** academic/scholarly publication.
—BLDSC (4943.500000); CASDDS; EMDOCS; Faxon; SWETS; UMI; UnCover. **CCC.**
    Incorporates: International Academy of Preventive Medicine. Journal (ISSN 0094-324X)
    Description: Scientific reports and reviews that stress practical human applications of macro and micro nutrients in treatment and prevention of diseases.
    Refereed Serial

641.1 640   SA   ISSN 0378-5254
                               CODEN: TDHUDO
JOURNAL OF DIETETICS AND HOME ECONOMICS/TYDSKRIF VIR DIEET- EN HUISHOUDKUNDE. (Text in Afrikaans, English) 1973. 2/yr. R.45. Home Economics Association of Southern Africa, P.O. Box 35269, Menlo Park, Pretoria 0102, South Africa. TEL 27-12-4202854. FAX 27-12-436867. Ed. E. Boshoff. adv.; bk.rev. **Indexed:** INIS Atomind., Nutr.Abstr. **Document type:** academic/scholarly publication.
—CASDDS.

612.3   US
JOURNAL OF HEALTH SCIENCE.* 1981. q. $10. Health News Network, Inc., 6323 Saw Flower St., Portland, OR 97221-1071. Ed. Cameron Stauth. adv.; illus.

JOURNAL OF HUMAN LACTATION. see *MEDICAL SCIENCES — Obstetrics And Gynecology*

613.2   UK   ISSN 0952-3871
                               CODEN: JHNDEO
JOURNAL OF HUMAN NUTRITION AND DIETETICS. 1988. bi-m. £140 (outside Europe £154($248)) (effective 1996). (British Dietetic Association) Blackwell Science Ltd., Osney Mead, Oxford OX2 0EL, England. TEL 01865-206206. FAX 01865-206219. TELEX 83355 MEDBOK G. Ed. Jane Thomas. adv.; bk.rev.; abstr.; bibl.; illus.; index. circ. 3,750. (also avail. in microform from UMI; back issues avail.) **Indexed:** Diab.Cont. **Document type:** academic/scholarly publication.
—BLDSC (5003.419300); CASDDS; Faxon; Genuine Article; SWETS; UMI; UnCover. **CCC.**
    Formerly (until 1987): Human Nutrition. Applied Nutrition (ISSN 0263-8495); Which supersedes in part (in 1981): Journal of Human Nutrition (ISSN 0308-4329); Which was formerly (until 1976): Nutrition (ISSN 0029-6600)
    Refereed Serial

JOURNAL OF MUSCLE FOODS. see *FOOD AND FOOD INDUSTRIES*

NUTRITION AND DIETETICS   4919

641 613   US   ISSN 0022-3166
RM214   CODEN: JONUAI
JOURNAL OF NUTRITION. 1928. m. $90 to non-members; members $45; institutions $185; students $25. American Institute of Nutrition, 9650 Rockville Pike, Bethesda, MD 20814. TEL 301-530-7027. FAX 301-571-1892. Ed. Dr. Willard Visek. adv.; bk.rev.; abstr.; bibl.; charts; illus.; index. circ. 4,430. (also avail. in microform from UMI,PMC; back issues avail.; reprint service avail. from UMI) **Indexed:** Abstr.Anthropol., Abstr.Hyg., Anim.Breed.Abstr., Behav.Med.Abstr., Biol.Abstr., Biol.& Agr.Ind., Biol.Dig., Biotech.Abstr., Cadscan, Chem.Abstr., Curr.Adv.Cancer Res., Curr.Adv.Ecol.Sci., Curr.Cont., Curr.Ref.Fish Res., Dairy Sci.Abstr., Dent.Ind., Diar.Dis.Res., Environ.Per.Bibl., Excerp.Med., Food Sci.& Tech.Abstr., Gen.Sci.Ind., Helminthol.Abstr., Ind.Med., Ind.Sci.Rev., Ind.Vet., Ind.Vet., INIS Atomind., Lead Abstr., Maize Abstr., Nutr.Abstr., Pig News & Info., Plant Breed.Abstr., Poult.Abstr., Rev.Appl.Entomol., Rev.Med.& Vet.Mycol., Rice Abstr., Sorghum & Millets Abstr., Soyabean Abstr., Sport Fish.Abstr., Sugar Ind.Abstr., Triticale Abstr., Trop.Dis.Bull., Trop.Oil Seeds Abstr., Vet.Bull., Wild.Rev., Zincscan, Zoo.Rec. **Document type:** academic/scholarly publication.
—BLDSC (5024.000000); CASDDS; EMDOCS; Faxon; Genuine Article; SWETS; UMI; UnCover. **CCC.**
    Description: Reports of original research in all aspects of nutrition.
    Refereed Serial

641.1   CN   ISSN 0022-3182
QP141.A1
JOURNAL OF NUTRITION EDUCATION. 1969. bi-m. $90 to individuals (outside US & Canada $125); institutions $135 (outside US & Canada $160) (effective 1996). (Society for Nutrition Education) Decker Periodicals, P.O. Box 620, LCD 1, Hamilton, ON L8N 3K7, Canada. TEL 905-522-7017; 800-568-7281. FAX 905-522-7839. (U.S. addr.: Box 785, Lewiston, NY 14092-0785) Ed. Audrey N. Maretzki. adv.; bk.rev.; index. circ. 4,800. (also avail. in microform from UMI; reprint service avail. from UMI,ISI) **Indexed:** Behav.Med.Abstr., C.I.J.E., CINAHL, Cont.Pg.Educ., Curr.Cont., Educ.Ind., Environ.Per.Bibl., Gen.Sci.Ind., Ind.Sci.Rev., Mult.Ed.Abstr., Nutr.Abstr., Sp.Ed.Needs Abstr., Stud.Wom.Abstr., Tech.Educ.Abstr. **Document type:** academic/scholarly publication.
—BLDSC (5024.700000); Faxon; Genuine Article; SWETS; UMI; UnCover. **CCC.**
    Description: Designed to stimulate interest and research in applied nutritional sciences and to disseminate information to educators and others concerned about positive nutritional practices and policies.

JOURNAL OF NUTRITION FOR THE ELDERLY. see *GERONTOLOGY AND GERIATRICS*

641.1   US   ISSN 1055-1379
TX341
▼**JOURNAL OF NUTRITION IN RECIPE & MENU DEVELOPMENT;** innovations in new nutritional product development, dietary substitutes, medically-related issues in food service. 1994. q. $75 (foreign $105) (effective 1996). Haworth Press, Inc., 10 Alice St., Binghamton, NY 13904-1580. TEL 607-722-5857; 800-342-9678. FAX 607-722-1424. TELEX 4932599. Ed. Mahmood A. Khan. adv.; bk.rev. (also avail. in microfiche from UMI; reprint service avail. from HAW) **Indexed:** Food Sci.& Tech.Abstr. **Document type:** academic/scholarly publication.
—Haworth.
    Description: Publishes research and practice papers relating directly to new recipe and menu concepts which are aimed at health promotion.
    Refereed Serial

NUTRITION AND DIETETICS

616.39 UK ISSN 1359-0847
RM214
JOURNAL OF NUTRITIONAL & ENVIRONMENTAL MEDICINE. 1990. q. £58 to individuals; institutions £214 (effective 1996). Carfax Publishing Co., P.O. Box 25, Abingdon, Oxon. OX14 3UE, England. TEL 01235-555335. FAX 01235-553559. (Subscr. in N. America to: Carfax Publishing Co., 875-81 Massachusetts Ave., Cambridge, MA 02139) Eds. Stephen Davies, Damien Downing. **Indexed:** Excerp.Med. (1993-). **Document type:** academic/scholarly publication.
—BLDSC (5024.740000); Faxon; UMI; UnCover. **CCC.**
  Formerly: Journal of Nutritional Medicine (ISSN 0955-6664)
  Description: Aimed at physicians, surgeons, dietitians, nutritionists, clinical biochemists, clinical psychologists, as well as students in these fields. Covers the field of nutrition and its relationship to clinical medicine.
  Refereed Serial

641 US ISSN 0955-2863
QP141.A1 CODEN: JNBIEL
JOURNAL OF NUTRITIONAL BIOCHEMISTRY. 1970. m. $465 to institutions (effective 1996). Butterworth - Heinemann, Part of the Reed Elsevier group, 313 Washington St., Newton, MA 02158. TEL 617-928-2500; 800-366-2665. FAX 617-928-2610. TELEX 880052. (Subscr. to: Elsevier Science Inc., Box 882, Madison Sq. Sta., New York, NY 10159-0882. TEL 212-989-5800. FAX 212-633-3990) Ed. Dr. Steven H. Zeisel. adv.; charts; illus.; index. (also avail. in microfilm from UMI; reprint service avail.; back issues avail.) **Indexed:** Anim.Breed.Abstr., Biol.Abstr., Cadscan, Chem.Abstr., Curr.Adv.Biochem., Curr.Adv.Ecol.Sci., Curr.Cont., Dairy Sci.Abstr., Diar.Dis.Res., Environ.Per.Bibl., Excerp.Med., Food Sci.& Tech.Abstr., Helminthol.Abstr., Herb.Abstr., Ind.Sci.Rev., Ind.Vet., Maize Abstr., Nutr.Abstr., Pig News & Info., Poult.Abstr., Protozool.Abstr., Rev.Med.& Vet.Mycol., Rice Abstr., Risk Abstr., Sorghum & Millets Abstr., Soyabean Abstr., Sport Fish.Abstr., Sugar Ind.Abstr., Triticale Abstr., Trop.Oil Seeds Abstr., Vet.Bull., Weed Abstr., Wild.Rev., Zincscan, Zoo.Rec. **Document type:** academic/scholarly publication.
—BLDSC (5024.730000); CASDDS; Faxon; Genuine Article; SWETS; UMI; UnCover. **CCC.**
  Supersedes (in 1990): Nutrition Reports International (ISSN 0029-6635)
  Description: Forum for advances and issues in nutrition, nutritional biochemistry and food sciences.

JOURNAL OF NUTRITIONAL IMMUNOLOGY. see *MEDICAL SCIENCES — Allergology And Immunology*

615.328 JA ISSN 0301-4800
CODEN: JNSVA5
JOURNAL OF NUTRITIONAL SCIENCE AND VITAMINOLOGY. 1954. bi-m. $145 (effective 1996). (Japanese Society of Nutrition and Food Science) Center for Academic Publications Japan, 2-4-16 Yoyoi, Bunkyo-ku, Tokyo 113, Japan. TEL 03-5817-5821. FAX 03-3817-5830. E-mail: capj@twics.com. (Dist. by: Business Center for Academic Societies Japan, 5-16-9 Honkomagome, Bunkyo-ku, Tokyo 113, Japan. TEL 03-5814-5811) (Co-sponsor: Vitamin Society of Japan) bk.rev.; bibl.; charts; illus.; index. circ. 1,500. **Indexed:** Biol.Abstr., Biotech.Abstr., Chem.Abstr., Curr.Adv.Ecol.Sci., Curr.Cont., Dairy Sci.Abstr., Excerp.Med., Food Sci.& Tech.Abstr., Ind.Med., Ind.Sci.Rev., Ind.Vet., INIS Atomind., Nutr.Abstr., Rice Abstr., Soyabean Abstr., Sugar Ind.Abstr., Vet.Bull. **Document type:** academic/scholarly publication.
—BLDSC (5024.750000); CASDDS; Faxon; Genuine Article; SWETS; UMI; UnCover.
  Formerly (until 1972): Journal of Vitaminology (ISSN 0022-5398)

613.2 US ISSN 1061-2130
QP141.A1 CODEN: JOTNEV
JOURNAL OF OPTIMAL NUTRITION. 1992. q. $75 (foreign $90). Institute for the Study of Optimal Nutrition, 2546 Regis Dr., Davis, CA 95616-1557. TEL 916-756-3311. FAX 916-758-7444. Ed. Brian Leibovitz. bk.rev. **Indexed:** Excerp.Med. (1994-). **Document type:** academic/scholarly publication.
—BLDSC (5026.368000); CASDDS.
  Description: Focuses on elucidating the optimal levels of macronutrients and micronutrients for the prevention and treatment of disease as well as for the maintenance of optimal health.
  Refereed Serial

612.3 US ISSN 0148-6071
RM224 CODEN: JPENDU
JOURNAL OF PARENTERAL AND ENTERAL NUTRITION.
Key Title: J P E N: Journal of Parenteral and Enteral Nutrition. 1979. bi-m. $115 to individuals; institutions $100. American Society for Parenteral and Enteral Nutrition, 8630 Fenton St., Ste. 412, Silver Spring, MD 20910-3805. TEL 301-587-6315. FAX 301-587-3323. Ed. Dr. John L. Rombeau. adv.; B&W page $1300. bk.rev. circ. 10,113. (also avail. in microform from WWS; reprint service avail. from ISI) **Indexed:** CINAHL, I.P.A., Ind.Med., INIS Atomind., Rev.Med.& Vet.Mycol., Soyabean Abstr. **Document type:** academic/scholarly publication.
●Also available online.
—BLDSC (5029.100000); CASDDS; Faxon; Genuine Article; SWETS; UMI; UnCover. **CCC.**
  Description: Research on nutritional deficiency and its treatment, including administration, risks and complications.
  Refereed Serial

JOURNAL OF PEDIATRIC & PERINATAL NUTRITION. see *MEDICAL SCIENCES — Pediatrics*

JOURNAL OF PEDIATRIC GASTROENTEROLOGY AND NUTRITION. see *MEDICAL SCIENCES — Gastroenterology*

616.39 616.6 US ISSN 1051-2276
JOURNAL OF RENAL NUTRITION. 1991. q. $100 (foreign $120) (effective 1996). (National Kidney Foundation, Council on Renal Nutrition) W.B. Saunders Co. (Subsidiary of: Harcourt Brace & Company), Curtis Center, 3rd Fl., Independence Sq. W., Philadelphia, PA 19106-3399. TEL 215-238-7800. FAX 215-238-6445. (Subscr. to: Periodicals Fulfillment, W.B. Saunders Co., 6277 Sea Harbor Dr., 4th Fl., Orlando, FL 32891-4800. TEL 800-654-2452. FAX 800-874-6418) Ed. Dr. Judith A. Beto; Pub. Joan W. Blumberg. adv.: B&W page $570, color page $1445; 7 x 10. bk.rev. circ. 2,017. (back issues avail.) **Document type:** academic/scholarly publication.
—BLDSC (5049.460000); UMI. **CCC.**
  Description: Disseminates renal nutrition-related research and professional education related to the field.
  Refereed Serial

JOURNAL OF SENSORY STUDIES. see *MEDICAL SCIENCES — Psychiatry And Neurology*

JOURNAL OF TEXTURE STUDIES; an international journal of rheology, psychorheology, physical and sensory testing of foods and pharmaceuticals. see *FOOD AND FOOD INDUSTRIES*

KIND ERNAEHRUNG UMWELT. see *MEDICAL SCIENCES — Pediatrics*

613.2 GW ISSN 0174-2469
CODEN: KLEREQ
KLINISCHE ERNAEHRUNG. 1980. irreg., vol.35, 1991. DM.49.80. W. Zuckschwerdt Verlag GmbH, Industriestr. 17, 82110 Germering, Germany. TEL 089-894349-0. FAX 089-89434950. Ed.Bd. **Document type:** academic/scholarly publication.
—BLDSC (5099.366000); CASDDS.

613.2 JA ISSN 0911-565X
KOBE GAKUIN DAIGAKU EIYOGAKUBU RONBUNSHU/KOBE GAKUIN UNIVERSITY. FACULTY OF NUTRITION. JOURNAL. (Text in English, German, Japanese; summaries in English) 1969. a. Kobe Gakuin Daigaku, Eiyogakubu, 518, Ikawadanicho Arise, Nishi-ku, Kobe-shi, Hyogo-ken 673, Japan.

613.2 JA
KOKUMIN EIYO NO GENJO/REPORT OF NATIONAL NUTRITIVE CONDITIONS. (Text in Japanese) 1947. a. 2500 Yen. (Koseisho, Hoken Iryokyoku - Ministry of Health and Welfare, Health Service Bureau) Daiichi Shuppan K.K., 1-39, Kanda Jimbo-cho, Chiyoda-ku, Tokyo 101, Japan. **Document type:** government publication.

574.13 JA ISSN 0368-5209
TX341
KOKURITSU KENKO EIYO KENKYUJO HOKOKU/NATIONAL INSTITUTE OF HEALTH AND NUTRITION. ANNUAL REPORT. (Text in Japanese) 1949. a. exchange basis. Kosei-sho, Kokuritsu Kenko Eiyo Kenkyujo - National Institute of Health and Nutrition, 1-23-1 Toyama-cho, Shinjuku-ku, Tokyo 162, Japan. TEL 03-3203-5721. FAX 03-3203-3278. Ed. S. Kobayashi. **Indexed:** Biol.Abstr. **Document type:** government publication.
—BLDSC (1364.711000).
  Formerly: Kokuritsu Eiyo Kenkyujo Hokoku - National Institute of Nutrition. Annual Report.

613.2 JA ISSN 0913-5537
CODEN: KDKAEH
KOSHIEN DAIGAKU KIYO. A, EIYOGAKUBU HEN/KOSHIEN UNIVERSITY. FACULTY OF NUTRITION. BULLETIN. (Text in Japanese; summaries in English, Japanese) 1970. a. Koshien Daigaku, 10-1 Momijigaoka, Takarazuka-shi, Hyogo-ken 665, Japan. TEL 0797-87-5111. Ed. Hiroyuki Masutani. circ. 500.

KRAUT UND RUEBEN; das Magazin fuer biologischen Gaertnern und naturgemaesses Leben. see *GARDENING AND HORTICULTURE*

L S T NYT. see *FOOD AND FOOD INDUSTRIES*

LET'S LIVE. see *PHYSICAL FITNESS AND HYGIENE*

613.26 NE ISSN 0166-0802
LEVEN EN LATEN LEVEN. bi-m. fl.35. Nederlandse Vegetariersbond, Larenseweg 26, 1221 CM Hilversum, Netherlands. TEL 31-35-834796. FAX 31-35-836152. Dir. Hans van Boven. adv. circ. 5,000. **Document type:** consumer publication.
  Formerly (until 1971): Vegetische Bode.
  Description: Covers topics relating to vegetarianism, nutrition, animal welfare and related matters.

613.2 US
LIFELINELETTER. 1977. bi-m. $35 (free to qualified personnel). Oley Foundation for Home Parenteral & Enteral Nutrition, 214 Hun Memorial, A-23, Albany Medical Center, Albany, NY 12208-3478. TEL 518-262-5079. FAX 518-262-5528. Ed. Roslyn Scheib Dahl. bk.rev. circ. 4,000. **Document type:** newsletter.
  Description: Provides support, education and information on research in the field of home parenteral or enteral nutrition.

613.26 CN ISSN 0834-3543
LIFELINES (TORONTO); the voice of Toronto's vegetarian community. 1954. bi-m. Can.$25. Toronto Vegetarian Association, 736 Bathurst St., Toronto, ON M5S 2R4, Canada. TEL 416-533-3897. E-mail: tva@interlog.com. Site addr.: http://www.interlog.com/ntva/home.html. Ed. Stephen Leckie. adv.; bk.rev. circ. 2,500. **Document type:** newsletter.
  Formerly: Toronto Vegetarian Association. Newsletter (ISSN 0049-4232)
  Description: Information about vegetarianism.

613.2 641.1 US
LIGHT 'N DELIGHTFULLY;* the newsletter for real losers. 1992. m. $30. 10300 Golden Meadow Dr., Apt. 201, Austin, TX 78758-4906. TEL 310-821-5902. Ed. Mary Robbins Jones. circ. 1,000.
  Former title: Light Delight.
  Description: Publishes recipes, new product information, diet and nutrition news and discussions, reviews diet products.

613.2 US
LOW FAT FOR LIFE. m. $15. Coffee Pot Press, Box 3906, Greenville, SC 29608. TEL 803-294-9807. FAX 803-246-7340. Ed. Elizabeth A. Mason. bk.rev.; index; circ. 70 (paid). (tabloid format; also avail. in diskette format; back issues avail.) **Document type:** newsletter.
  Description: Contains recipes for low fat foods, nutritional information, and low fat brand name products.

MAA BRA; specialtidningen foer kropp & sjael. see *PHYSICAL FITNESS AND HYGIENE*

NUTRITION AND DIETETICS

641.1 US
MACROBIOTICS TODAY. 1960. 6/yr. $15 (with membership $20). George Ohsawa Macrobiotic Foundation, 1999 Myers, Oroville, CA 95966. TEL 916-533-7702. FAX 916-533-7908. Ed. Bob Ligon; Pub. Carl Ferre. adv. contact: Bob Ligon. bk.rev. circ. 5,500. **Document type:** consumer publication.
    Formerly (until 1984): G O M F News.
    Description: Contains articles, interviews and news events concerning macrobiotics and alternative health care.

613 FR ISSN 0398-7604
CODEN: MENUDI
MEDECINE ET NUTRITION. 1965. 6/yr. 330 F. (foreign 380 F.) (effective 1993). (Societe d'Hygiene de Langue Francaise) Editions la Simarre, Z.I. No. 2 - rue Joseph-Cugnot, 37300 Joue-les-Tours, France. TEL 47-53-53-66. FAX 47-67-45-05. adv.; bibl.; charts; illus. circ. 10,000. **Indexed:** Biol.Abstr., C.I.S. Abstr., Chem.Abstr., Dairy Sci.Abstr., Excerp.Med., Food Sci.& Tech.Abstr., Nutr.Abstr., Soyabean Abstr.
—BLDSC (5487.732500); CASDDS; SWETS. **CCC.**
    Formerly: Annales d'Hygiene de Langue Francaise (ISSN 0003-4363)
    Description: Publishes original studies on the fundamental and applied aspects of food and nutrition.

613.2 610 II ISSN 0971-4219
MEDICAL AND NUTRITIONAL RESEARCH COMMUNICATIONS. (Text in English) 1993. 3/yr. Rs.60 to individuals (foreign $20); institutions Rs.75 (foreign $75). Kunneth Institute of Medical Sciences, Medical Research Centre, Madichal 629 163, Tamil Nadu, India. TEL 04651-6432. FAX 04651-7400. Ed. S. Krishnamurthy. **Document type:** academic/scholarly publication.
    Description: Publishes papers on all aspects of medicine and nutrition, yoga, meditation, and health care, including various Indian systems of medicine and homeopathy.

MEMPHIS HEALTH CARE NEWS. see *PHYSICAL FITNESS AND HYGIENE*

MILITAER-KUECHENCHEF. see *MILITARY*

616.39 612.015 SZ ISSN 0026-6841
RA421 CODEN: MGLHAE
MITTEILUNGEN AUS DER GEBIETE DER LEBENSMITTELUNTERSUCHUNG UND HYGIENE/TRAVAUX DE CHIMIE ALIMENTAIRE ET D'HYGIENE. (Text mainly in French and German; occasionally in English and Italian) 1910. 6/yr. 66 SFr. Bundesamt fuer Gesundheitswesen, Postfach, CH-3000 Bern 14, Switzerland. (Co-sponsors: Schweizerische Gesellschaft fuer Lebensmittel- und Umweltchemie; Schweizerische Gesellschaft fuer Lebensmittelhygiene) adv.; bk.rev.; bibl.; illus.; index. circ. 1,700. **Indexed:** Anal.Abstr., Biol.Abstr., Biotech.Abstr., Chem.Abstr., Excerp.Med., Food Sci.& Tech.Abstr., Ind.Med., Nutr.Abstr., Packag.Sci.Tech., Potato Abstr., Sugar Ind.Abstr., Vet.Bull. **Document type:** trade publication.
—BLDSC (5878.000000); CASDDS; SWETS.

613.2 US
MODERN NUTRITION NEWS. q. $7. Connaught Press Inc., 212 Hillside Ave., Hillside, NJ 07205. TEL 201-926-0816. Ed. E. Gerald Kay. **Document type:** newspaper.
    Description: Provides a variety of health-related information, viewpoints and new discoveries.

613.2 US
N A A F A NEWSLETTER. 1969. 6/yr. $35 membership. National Association to Advance Fat Acceptance, Inc., P.O. Box 188620, Sacramento, CA 95818. TEL 916-558-6880. FAX 916-558-6881. E-mail: PMCGIOC@prodigy.com. Ed. Sally E. Smith. adv.; bk.rev. circ. 4,000. (back issues avail.) **Document type:** newsletter.
    Description: Provides information regarding obesity research, size discrimination, and advances in the size acceptance movement

613.2 616.1 IT ISSN 0939-4753
CODEN: NMCDEE
N M C D. (Nutrition, Metabolism and Cardiovascular Diseases) (Text in English) 1991. q. DM.298. c/o Prof. Mancini, Inst. Internal Medicine & Metabolic Diseases, Second Medical School, University of Naples, Via S. Pansini, 80131 Naples, Italy. E-mail: orders@springer.de. **Document type:** academic/scholarly publication.
—CASDDS; Genuine Article; UMI. **CCC.**

613.2 US
N N F A TODAY. 1986. m. membership. National Nutritional Foods Association, 150 E. Paularino, Ste. 285, Costa Mesa, CA 92626. TEL 714-966-6632. adv.; bk.rev.; circ. controlled. **Document type:** trade publication.
    Formerly (until Mar. 1993): N N F A Monitor; Which supersedes (1981?-1984): Food for Thought (Oceanside).

613.2 US
N O H A NEWS. 1976. q. $8. Nutrition for Optimal Health Association, Box 380, Winnetka, IL 60093. TEL 708-786-5326. Ed. Marjorie Fisher. bk.rev. circ. 700. (back issues avail.) **Document type:** newsletter.
    Description: Reports on nutritional information and research findings culled from a wide range of scientific sources; includes a column written by members of the professional advisory board.

612.3 641 GW ISSN 0027-769X
TX341 CODEN: NAHRAR
DIE NAHRUNG/FOOD. (Text in English, German) 1957. 6/yr. DM.510($383) (effective 1996). (German Institute for Human Nutrition) V C H Verlagsgesellschaft mbH, Postfach 101161, 69451 Weinheim, Germany. TEL 06201-606-147. FAX 06201-606117. adv. contact: R. Roth. bk.rev.; charts; illus.; index. circ. 450. **Indexed:** Anal.Abstr., Apic.Abstr., Biol.Abstr., Cadscan, Chem.Abstr., Curr.Adv.Ecol.Sci., Curr.Cont., Curr.Pack.Abstr., Dairy Sci.Abstr., Excerp.Med., Field Crop Abstr., Food Sci.& Tech.Abstr., Herb.Abstr., Ind.Med., Ind.Vet., Lead Abstr., Mass Spectr.Bull., Nutr.Abstr., Rev.Plant Path., Soils & Fert., Vet.Bull., Zincscan. **Document type:** academic/scholarly publication.
—BLDSC (6015.300000); CASDDS; Faxon; Genuine Article; SWETS. **CCC.**

NATIONAL FLUORIDATION NEWS; covering reports on research into the toxicity of fluoride, news on accidents, election outcomes and general information on the issue. see *ENVIRONMENTAL STUDIES*

641.1 II ISSN 0377-3744
NATIONAL INSTITUTE OF NUTRITION. ANNUAL REPORT. (Text in English) 1946. a. free. National Institute of Nutrition, Indian Council of Medical Research, Jamai-Osmania, Hyderabad 500 007, India. circ. 1,000. **Document type:** academic/scholarly publication.
    Formerly: Nutrition Research Laboratories. Annual Report.

613.2 GW ISSN 0721-8982
NATUERLICH UND GESUND; Das Magazin fuer Ganzheitliche Lebensfuehrung. 1979. bi-m. Verlag Helmut Preussler, Dagmarstr. 8, 90482 Nuernberg, Germany. Ed. Eberhard Coelle. circ. 35,000. **Document type:** consumer publication.

613.2 GW ISSN 0932-3503
NATUR UND HEILEN; die Monatszeitschrift fuer gesundes Leben. 1924. m. DM.69 (foreign DM.79.20). Verlag Natur und Heilen, Nikolaistr. 5, 80802 Munich, Germany. TEL 089-38015910. FAX 089-38015916. Ed. Anne Devillard; Pub. Hansjoerg Volkhardt. adv. contact: Eva Ziervogel. bk.rev. (back issues avail.) **Document type:** consumer publication.
—BLDSC (6033.868000).

613.2 631 US ISSN 0470-3715
NATURAL FOOD & FARMING. 1953. bi-m. $20. Natural Food Associates, Box 210, Atlanta, TX 75551. Ed. Bill Francis. adv.; bk.rev.; circ. 5,000. **Document type:** consumer publication.

641.1 UK
NATURAL FOOD TRADER. 1960. m. £36 (foreign £48). I B T M Ltd., Queensway House, 2 Queensway, Redhill, Surrey RH1 1QS, England. TEL 0737-768611. FAX 0737-760425. Ed. Paul Rouse. adv.; bk.rev.; illus.; circ. 4,500 (controlled). **Document type:** trade publication.
—CCC.
    Formerly: Health Food Trader (ISSN 0046-7049)
    Description: For health food store professionals.

NATURAL FOODS MERCHANDISER; new ideas, trends, products for the natural and organic foods industry. see *BUSINESS AND ECONOMICS — Marketing And Purchasing*

612.3 AT ISSN 0816-2751
NATURAL HEALTH. 1961. bi-m. Aus.$32 (foreign Aus.$44). Natural Health Society of Australia Ltd., Ste. 28, 541 High St., Penrith, N.S.W. 2750, Australia. TEL 047-215068. Ed. Roger French. adv.; bk.rev. circ. 6,000. (back issues avail.)
    Description: To promote health and well-being through a more natural way of living, recognizing that prevention is far better than cure.

616.39 US
NATURAL HYGIENE SOCIETY OF NEW JERSEY. NEWSLETTER. 1981. 8/yr. $15. Natural Hygiene of New Jersey, Inc., Box 142, Pompton Plains, NJ 07444. TEL 201-839-5919. Ed. John R. Chorba. abstr. circ. 350. (looseleaf format; back issues avail.) **Document type:** newsletter.
    Formerly: American Natural Hygiene Society. New Jersey Chapter. Newsletter.
    Description: Covers various issues in health and hygiene, includes exercise, diet and behavior.

NAUTILUS (INDEPENDENCE). see *PHYSICAL FITNESS AND HYGIENE*

613.2 616.39 SZ
NESTLE FOUNDATION. ANNUAL REPORT. 1969. a. free. Nestle Foundation, 4 Place de la Gare, CH-1003 Lausanne, Switzerland. FAX 021-3203392. Ed. B. Schuerch. circ. 1,500. **Document type:** corporate report.

613.2 US ISSN 0742-2806
CODEN: NNWSDT
NESTLE NUTRITION SERIES. Key Title: Nestle Nutrition Workshop. 1982. irreg., latest vol.32. price varies. Raven Press (Subsidiary of: Wolters Kluwer N.V.), 1185 Ave. of the Americas, New York, NY 10036. TEL 212-930-9500. FAX 212-869-3495. (reprint service avail. from UMI) **Document type:** proceedings.
—BLDSC (6076.609000); CASDDS.
    Refereed Serial

641.1 US
NEW YORK STATE. ASSEMBLY SUBCOMMITTEE ON FOOD, FARM AND NUTRITION POLICY. REPORT.* a. Subcommittee on Food, Farm and Nutrition Policy, Empire State Plaza, 13th Fl., A-4, Albany, NY 12248-0001.

612.3 617.1 US
NEWS FROM A S B P. 1986. bi-m. American Society of Bariatric Physicians, 5600 S. Quebec, Ste. 109A, Englewood, CO 80111-2208. TEL 303-779-4833. **Document type:** newsletter.

613.2 NR ISSN 0189-0913
CODEN: NJNSEP
NIGERIAN JOURNAL OF NUTRITIONAL SCIENCES. 1980. s-a. £N10. (Nutritional Society of Nigeria) Ibadan University Press, Department of Human Nutrition, University of Ibadan, Ibadan, Nigeria. Ed. Dr. Tola Atinmo. circ. 2,000. **Indexed:** ExtraMED. **Document type:** academic/scholarly publication.
●Also available on CD-ROM.
—CASDDS.

612.3 JA ISSN 0912-9405
NIHON JOMYAKU KEICHO EIYO KENKYUKAISHI/JAPANESE SOCIETY OF PARENTERAL AND ENTERAL NUTRITION. JOURNAL. (Text in English, Japanese) 1986. a. Nihon Jomyaku Keicho Eiyo Kenkyukai, Tokyo Jikeikai Ika Daigaku Dai 2 Geka, 25-8, Nishishinbashi 3-chome, Minato-ku, Tokyo 105, Japan.
—BLDSC (4809.475000).

NUTRITION AND DIETETICS

612.3 JA ISSN 0286-8202
CODEN: NREZEN
NIHON RINSHO EIYO GAKKAI ZASSHI/JAPANESE SOCIETY OF CLINICAL NUTRITION. JOURNAL. (Text in Japanese; summaries in English) 1982. 3/yr. 5000 Yen. Nihon Rinsho Eiyo Gakkai, c/o Nihon Gakkai Jimu Senta, 16-9 Honkomagome 5-chome, Bunkyo-ku, Tokyo 113, Japan.
TEL 81-3-5814-5801. Ed. Yoshiya Hata. adv. contact: Nobuhiko Takeda. **Document type:** academic/scholarly publication.
Refereed Serial

641 JA ISSN 0029-0572
NINGEN IGAKU/HUMAN MEDICINE. (Text in Japanese) 1938. m. 2000 Yen($7) Ningen Igakusha, 5-16-23 Senrioka, Settsu-shi 564, Japan. Ed. Takaaki Oura. adv.; bk.rev.; illus.; tr.lit. circ. 20,000.

NISARG ANE AROGYA. see PHYSICAL FITNESS AND HYGIENE

613.2 NE ISSN 0167-4587
CODEN: NUSYD8
NUTRICIA SYMPOSIA. (Text in English) 1964. irreg. price varies. Kluwer Academic Publishers, Postbus 17, 3300 AA Dordrecht, Netherlands.
TEL 31-78-392392. FAX 31-78-392254. TELEX 29245 KAPG NL. (Dist. by: Kluwer Academic Publishers Group, P.O. Box 322, 3300 AH Dordrecht, Netherlands. TEL 31-78-392392. FAX 31-78-546474; N. America dist. addr.: Box 358, Accord Sta., Hingham, MA 02018-0358. TEL 617-871-6600. FAX 617-871-6528) **Document type:** proceedings.
—CASDDS.
Refereed Serial

612.3 SP ISSN 0211-6057
CODEN: NUTCDF
NUTRICION CLINICA; dietetica hospitalaria. 1981. 6/yr. 5000 ptas.($100) (Europe $60). (Sociedad Espanola de Nutricion (S.E.N.)) Alpe Editores, S.A., Pedro Rico, 27, 28029 Madrid, Spain.
TEL 34-1-7338811. FAX 34-1-3159652. Pub. A. Alvarez. adv.: color page 160000 ptas.; 210 x 280; adv. contact: C. Alvarez. charts; circ. 5,000 (controlled). **Indexed:** Chem.Abstr., Excerp.Med., Ind.Med.Esp., Triticale Abstr.
—BLDSC (6187.650000); CASDDS. **CCC.**

641.1 II ISSN 0550-404X
NUTRITION. 1966. q. Rs.8. National Institute of Nutrition, Indian Council of Medical Research, Jamai-Osmania, Hyderabad 500 007, India. Ed. M. Mohanram. circ. 4,000. **Document type:** academic/scholarly publication.
Description: Popular magazine concerning food and nutrition.

613.2 US ISSN 0899-9007
QP141.A1 CODEN: NUTRER
NUTRITION; an international journal of applied and basic nutritional science. 1985. bi-m. $79 (effective 1994). Nutrition, Inc., c/o Dept. of Surgery, 750 E. Adams St., Syracuse, NY 13210.
TEL 315-464-6280. FAX 315-464-6238. (Subscr. to: Box 920, Syracuse, NY 13210-0920) Ed. Dr. Michael Meguid. adv. circ. 20,112. **Indexed:** Ind.Med. (1992-).
—BLDSC (6187.930000); CASDDS; Faxon; Genuine Article; SWETS.
Formerly (until 1987): Nutrition International (ISSN 0888-1294)
Description: Publishes news of current research and practice in the field of applied and basic nutrition.
Refereed Serial

641.1 US ISSN 0885-7792
CODEN: NAHLED
NUTRITION ACTION HEALTHLETTER. 1974. 10/yr. $24. Center for Science in the Public Interest, 1875 Connecticut Ave., N.W., Ste. 300, Washington, DC 20009-5728. TEL 202-332-9110.
FAX 202-265-4954. Ed. Stephen B. Schmidt. bk.rev.; abstr.; bibl. circ. 840,000. (also avail. in microform from UMI; back issues avail.; reprint service avail.) **Indexed:** Alt.Press.Ind., CHNI, Hlth.Ind.
●Also available online. Vendor(s): University Microfilms International.
—BLDSC (6188.025100); UMI.
Formerly: Nutrition Action (ISSN 0199-5510); Incorporating (1976-1980): Intake (New Hyde Park) (ISSN 0732-6920)
Description: News, commentary, features, letters, and advocacy on nutrition and food policy, in order to promote good health.

NUTRITION AND CANCER; an international journal. see MEDICAL SCIENCES — Oncology

613.2 US ISSN 8750-8370
NUTRITION & DIETARY CONSULTANT; America's only journal for the practicing professional. 1979. m. $15.96. American Association of Nutritional Consultants, 1641 E. Sunset Rd., B 117, Las Vegas, NV 89119. TEL 702-361-1132.
FAX 702-739-7225. Ed. Myra E. Zelikovics. adv. circ. 43,000. (back issues avail.) **Document type:** trade publication.
Former titles: Your Nutritional Consultant (ISSN 8750-3395); (until 1984): Nutritional Consultant and Health Express (ISSN 0746-9799); (until 1981): Nutritional Consultant; Incorporates: Herald of Holistic Health Newsletter.
Description: For the nutritional consultant and dietitian in private practice; covers health maintenance, vitamin, mineral herbal therapies, food evaluation and diet management.

641 664 UK ISSN 0034-6659
CODEN: NFSCD7
NUTRITION AND FOOD SCIENCE. 1966. bi-m. £279($459) (effective 1996). M C B University Press Ltd., 60-62 Toller Ln., Bradford, W. Yorks BD8 9BY, England. TEL 01274-499821.
FAX 01274-574143. TELEX 51317-MCBNI-G. Ed. Dilys Wells. adv.; bk.rev.; abstr.; charts; stat.; index. circ. 3,500. (reprint service avail. from SWZ)
Indexed: Art.Hosp.& Tour., Br.Tech.Ind., Chem.Abstr., Curr.Adv.Ecol.Sci., Dairy Sci.Abstr., Food Sci.& Tech.Abstr., Nutr.Abstr., Rural Recreat.Tour.Abstr., Sugar Ind.Abstr., World Agri.Econ.& Rural Sociol.Abstr. **Document type:** academic/scholarly publication.
—BLDSC (6188.070000); CASDDS; Faxon; SWETS.
Formerly: Review of Nutrition and Food Science.

613 UK ISSN 0260-1060
CODEN: NUHEDT
NUTRITION AND HEALTH. 1982. 4/yr. £95($189) (McCarrison Society) A B Academic Publishers, P.O. Box 42, Bicester, Oxon. OX6 7NW, England.
TEL 0869-320949. Ed. Edward Kirby. adv.; bk.rev. (also avail. in microform) **Indexed:** ASSIA, Curr.Adv.Ecol.Sci., Dairy Sci.Abstr., Environ.Per.Bibl. (1985-), Excerp.Med., Ind.Med. **Document type:** academic/scholarly publication.
—BLDSC (6188.073000); CASDDS; Faxon; SWETS UnCover. **CCC.**
Description: Covers preventive medical and nutrition education.

618 US ISSN 0149-2667
CODEN: NUBRD4
NUTRITION AND THE BRAIN. 1975. irreg., latest vol.8. price varies. Raven Press (Subsidiary of: Wolters Kluwer N.V.), 1185 Ave. of the Americas, New York, NY 10036. TEL 212-930-9500.
FAX 212-869-3495. Eds. Richard J. and Judith J. Wurtman. (reprint service avail. from UMI) **Indexed:** Biol.Abstr., Curr.Cont., Sci.Cit.Ind. **Document type:** monographic series.
—BLDSC (6188.040000); CASDDS.
Refereed Serial

613 641 US ISSN 0732-0167
NUTRITION & THE M.D.; a continuing education service for physicians and nutritionists. 1974. m. $48 (foreign $73) (effective 1995). Quest Publishing Co., Inc., A Division of Raven Press Ltd. (Subsidiary of: Wolters Kluwer N.V.), 1351 Titan Way, Brea, CA 92621. TEL 714-738-6400. FAX 714-525-6258.
(Subscr. to: Raven Press, 1185 Ave. of the Americas, New York, NY 10036. TEL 212-930-9500. FAX 212-869-3495) Ed. Dr. Russell Merritt; Pub. Mary Waltham. circ. 4,108. (back issues avail.) **Document type:** newsletter.
—CCC.
Description: Each issue covers a single topic from several aspects.

641.4 CN ISSN 0318-4501
NUTRITION FORUM/FORUM DE NUTRITION. 1966. s-a. membership. Canadian Society for Nutritional Sciences, Department of Foods and Nutrition, University of Manitoba, Winnipeg, MB R3T 2N2, Canada. TEL 613-993-4484. (Dist. by: Department de Nutrition, Universite de Montreal, PQ H30 3J7, Canada) Ed. Vivian Bruce. bk.rev.; circ. controlled.
Formerly (until 1973): Newsletter - Nutrition (ISSN 0318-4498)

613.2 US ISSN 0748-8165
NUTRITION FORUM. 1984. bi-m. $35 to individuals; institutions $50 (effective 1995). Prometheus Books Incorporated, 59 John Glenn Dr., Amherst, NY 14228. TEL 716-691-0133. FAX 716-564-2711. (Editorial addr.: Box 740045, Rego Park, NY 11374. TEL 718-651-8057) Ed. Jack Raso. adv.; bk.rev. circ. 2,000. (looseleaf format) **Indexed:** Hlth.Ind. **Document type:** newsletter.
—BLDSC (6188.285000); UMI.
Description: Publishes investigative journalism concerning health-related nutritional methods and products. Reports news about alternative healthcare, quackery, food science and related subjects.

612 US ISSN 0892-1474
NUTRITION FUNDING REPORT; a monthly guide to locating resources. 1986. m. $45. Nutrition Legislation Services, Box 75035, Washington, DC 20013. TEL 202-488-8879. FAX 202-554-3116. Ed. Lenora Moragne; Pub. Lenora Moragne. **Document type:** newsletter.
Description: Itemizes available resources for nutrition and health-related activities: grants, contracts, scholarships, fellowships, publications, all from charities, corporations, foundations, government and other sources.

613 US ISSN 0164-7202
NUTRITION HEALTH REVIEW. 1976. q. $18 for 2 yrs. Vegetus Publications, 27 Tunbridge Rd., Haverford, PA 19041. TEL 610-896-1853.
FAX 610-896-1857. Ed. Andrew Rifkin; Pub. Frank Ray Rifkin. bk.rev.; illus.; circ. 298,800. (tabloid format; also avail. in microfilm; microform from UMI) **Indexed:** Hlth.Ind. **Document type:** consumer publication, newspaper.
●Also available online. Vendor(s): Information Access Co.
Also available on CD-ROM.
—UMI.

613.2 US ISSN 0884-5336
CODEN: NCPREH
NUTRITION IN CLINICAL PRACTICE. Short title: N C P. 1986. bi-m. $40 to individuals; institutions $70. American Society for Parenteral and Enteral Nutrition, 8630 Fenton St., Ste. 412, Silver Spring, MD 20910. TEL 301-587-6315.
FAX 301-587-3323. Ed. Philip J. Schneider. adv.: B&W page $1040. circ. 8,152. (also avail. in microform from WWS) **Indexed:** CINAHL. **Document type:** academic/scholarly publication.
—BLDSC (6188.130000); Faxon; SWETS; UMI; UnCover. **CCC.**
Description: Multidisciplinary clinical journal providing information on nutritional and metabolic therapy for personnel associated with oral and IV nutrition therapy. Publishes articles, clinical observations, case reports, techniques and procedures.

612.3 US
NUTRITION JOURNAL.* bi-m. Dimon Creative Communications, 3515 W. Pacific Ave., Burbank, CA 91505-1556. TEL 818-845-3748.
FAX 818-954-8916. Ed. Michael Meguid. circ. 12,000.

612 340   US
NUTRITION LEGISLATION NEWS; a twice-monthly report of United States legislative, executive, and regulatory activities. 1985. s-m. $150. Nutrition Legislation Services, Box 75035, Washington, DC 20013. TEL 202-488-8879. FAX 202-554-3116. Ed. Lenora Moragne; Pub. Lenora Moragne. **Document type:** newsletter.
  Former titles: Nutrition Legislation and Regulatory News; Nutrition Legislation News (ISSN 8756-6060)
  Description: Offers regulatory and legislative information covering all aspects of nutrition: research, education, international, food assistance, manpower training, surveillance and monitoring, and food quality and safety.

613   US   ISSN 8756-5919
NUTRITION NEWS (RIVERSIDE). 1976. m. $18 (Canada & Mexico $22; elsewhere $29). Nutrition News, 4108 Watkins Dr., Riverside, CA 92507-4752. TEL 909-784-7500. FAX 909-784-7555. Ed. Siri Khalsa. circ. 90,000 (paid). (tabloid format; back issues avail.) **Document type:** newsletter.
  Description: Reviews health and nutrition related topics, primarily on dietary, herbal and vitamin supplements, for a general audience.

641.1   US   ISSN 0369-6464
TX501
NUTRITION NEWS (ROSEMONT). 1937. 3/yr. $6 (foreign $9). National Dairy Council, O'Hare International Center, 10255 W. Higgins Rd., Ste. 900, Rosemont, IL 60018-5616. TEL 708-803-2000. FAX 708-803-2077. circ. 25,000. (back issues avail.) **Indexed:** CHNI, Nutr.Abstr. **Document type:** newsletter.
  —UMI.
  Description: Provides updates on recent developments in nutrition research, and the latest nutrition education resources. Contains teaching ideas of interest to elementary and secondary teachers and nurses.

NUTRITION NEWS IN ZAMBIA. see *FOOD AND FOOD INDUSTRIES*

613.2   US
NUTRITION NOTES. 1965. q. $30. American Institute of Nutrition, 9650 Rockville Pike, Bethesda, MD 20814. TEL 301-530-7050. FAX 301-571-1892. Ed. Carolyn Berdanier. circ. 2,750. (back issues avail.) **Document type:** newsletter.
  Description: Information on awards, publications, reports, meetings; updates readers (nutrition scientists) on legislation.

612.3   US   ISSN 0740-8684
NUTRITION REPORT. 1983. m. $54. Health Media Communications, 3309 Fourth Ave., San Diego, CA 92109. TEL 619-688-0377. FAX 619-688-9370. Ed.Bd. abstr.; bibl. circ. 4,000. **Document type:** newsletter.
  Description: Provides concise summaries of recently published scientific research on vitamins and minerals.

613.2   UK   ISSN 0271-5317
QP141.A1   CODEN: NTRSDC
NUTRITION RESEARCH. 1981. m. $742 to institutions (effective 1996). Elsevier Science Ltd, Pergamon, P.O. Box 800, Kidlington, Oxford OX5 1DX, England. TEL 44-1865-843000. FAX 44-1865-843010. E-mail: nlinfo-f@elsevier.nl; usinfo-f@elsevier.com; forinfo-kyf04035@niftyserve.or.jp; Site addr.: http://www.elsevier.nl/. (Subscr. in U.S. and Canada to: Elsevier Science, 660 White Plains Rd., Tarrytown, NY 10591-5153. TEL 914-524-9200. FAX 914-333-2444) Ed. Ranjit K. Chandra. index. (also avail. in microfilm from UMI) **Indexed:** Abstr.Hyg., Biol.Abstr., Chem.Abstr., Curr.Adv.Ecol.Sci., Curr.Cont., Dairy Sci.Abstr., Diar.Dis.Res., Energy Ind., Energy Info.Abstr., Excerp.Med., Food Sci.& Tech.Abstr., Ind.Med., Ind.Sci.Rev., Maize Abstr., Nutr.Abstr., Pig News & Info., Poult.Abstr., Rice Abstr., Soyabean Abstr., Triticale Abstr., Trop.Oil Seeds Abstr. **Document type:** academic/scholarly publication.
  —BLDSC (6188.950000); CASDDS; Faxon; Genuine Article; SWETS; UMI; UnCover. **CCC.**
  Incorporates (1975-1993): Progress in Food and Nutrition Science (ISSN 0306-0632); Which was formerly: International Encyclopedia of Food and Nutrition (ISSN 0074-4700)
  Description: Reports on basic and applied research on all aspects of food and nutrition, including relevant topics from the social sciences.
  Refereed Serial

613.2   US   ISSN 0736-0037
NUTRITION RESEARCH NEWSLETTER; a monthly update for food, nutrition, and health professionals. 1983. 10/yr. $96 in the U.S., Canada and Mexico; elsewhere $106. Lyda Associates, Box 700, Palisades, NY 10964. TEL 914-359-8282. FAX 914-359-1229. Ed. Lillian Langseth. index. circ. 5,000. (reprint service avail. from ISI) **Indexed:** Hlth.Ind. **Document type:** newsletter.
  ●Also available online. Vendor(s): Ovid Technologies, Knight-Ridder, Inc.
  —BLDSC (6188.970000); UMI.
  Description: Geared to food, nutrition and health professionals, with articles on diet in health and disease.

612.3   UK   ISSN 0954-4224
QP141.A1   CODEN: NREREX
NUTRITION RESEARCH REVIEWS. (Supplement to: British Journal of Nutrition. (ISSN 0007-4224)) 1988. 1/yr. £50($90) (effective 1996). (Nutrition Society) Cambridge University Press, Edinburgh Building, Shaftesbury Rd., Cambridge CB2 2RU, England. TEL 01223-312393. FAX 01223-315052. TELEX 851817256. (N. American addr.: Cambridge University Press, Journals Dept., 40 W. 20th St., New York, NY 10011. TEL 212-924-3900. FAX 212-691-3239) Ed. M.I. Gurr. (also avail. in microform from UMI; back issues avail.) **Indexed:** Environ.Per.Bibl. (1990-), Sugar Ind.Abstr. **Document type:** academic/scholarly publication.
  —BLDSC (6188.975000); CASDDS; Faxon; SWETS; UMI; UnCover. **CCC.**
  Description: Reviews research on a variety of nutritional problems.

NUTRITION REVIEW. see *MEDICAL SCIENCES*

641   US   ISSN 0029-6643
TX341   CODEN: NUREA8
NUTRITION REVIEWS. 1942. 12/yr. $55 to individuals (foreign $60); institutions $90 (foreign $95). (International Life Sciences Institute - Nutrition Foundation) Allen Press, Inc., Box 1897, Lawrence, KS 66044. TEL 913-843-1234. FAX 913-843-1274. Ed. Robert E. Olson. adv.; bk.rev.; abstr.; bibl.; index. circ. 10,000. (also avail. in microfilm from UMI; reprint service avail. from UMI) **Indexed:** Abstr.Hyg., Acad.Ind., Biol.Abstr., Biol.& Agr.Ind., Cadscan, Chem.Abstr., Curr.Adv.Biochem., Curr.Adv.Ecol.Sci., Curr.Cont., Dairy Sci.Abstr., Dent.Ind., Diar.Dis.Res., Environ.Per.Bibl., Excerp.Med., Food Sci.& Tech.Abstr., Gen.Sci.Ind., Helminthol.Abstr., Hlth.Ind., Ind.Med., Ind.Sci.Rev., Ind.Vet., Lead Abstr., Nutr.Abstr., Protozool.Abstr., Rev.Med.& Vet.Mycol., Rev.Plant Path., Risk Abstr., Trop.Dis.Bull., Vet.Bull. **Document type:** academic/scholarly publication.
  ●Also available online. Vendor(s): University Microfilms International.
  —BLDSC (6189.000000); CASDDS; EMDOCS; Faxon; Genuine Article; SWETS; UMI; UnCover.
  Description: Reports on research in clinical and experimental nutrition.

613.2 641.1   NE   ISSN 0924-4557
CODEN: NUTSDT
NUTRITION SCIENCES. (Text in English) 1982. irreg. price varies. Kluwer Academic Publishers, Postbus 17, 3300 AA Dordrecht, Netherlands. TEL 31-78-392392. FAX 31-78-392254. TELEX 29245 KAPG NL. (Dist. by: Kluwer Academic Publishers Group, P.O. Box 322, 3300 AH Dordrecht, Netherlands. TEL 31-78-392392. FAX 31-78-546474; N. America dist. addr.: Box 358, Accord Sta., Hingham, MA 02018-0358. TEL 617-871-6600. FAX 617-871-6528) **Document type:** monographic series.

641   UK   ISSN 0029-6651
TX501   CODEN: PNUSA4
NUTRITION SOCIETY. PROCEEDINGS. 1941. 3/yr. £144($264) (effective 1996). Cambridge University Press, Edinburgh Bldg., Shaftesbury Rd., Cambridge CB2 2RU, England. TEL 01223-312393. FAX 01223-315052. TELEX 851817256. (N. American addr.: Cambridge University Press, Journals Dept., 40 W. 20th St., New York, NY 10011. TEL 212-924-3900. FAX 212-691-3239) Ed.Bd. adv.; abstr.; bibl.; charts; index. (also avail. in microform from SWZ,UMI,PMC; back issues avail.) **Indexed:** Abstr.Hyg., Anim.Breed.Abstr., Biol.Abstr., Biol.& Agr.Ind., Biotech.Abstr., Cadscan, Chem.Abstr., Curr.Adv.Ecol.Sci., Curr.Cont., Dairy Sci.Abstr., Diar.Dis.Res., Energy Ind., Energy Info.Abstr., Field Crop Abstr., Food Sci.& Tech.Abstr., Helminthol.Abstr., Herb.Abstr., Ind.Med., Ind.Vet., Lead Abstr., Nutr.Abstr., Risk Abstr., Rural Recreat.Tour.Abstr., Triticale Abstr., Trop.Dis.Bull., Vet.Bull., World Agri.Econ.& Rural Sociol.Abstr., Zincscan. **Document type:** proceedings.
  —BLDSC (6780.000000); CASDDS; Faxon; Genuine Article; SWETS; UMI; UnCover. **CCC.**
  Description: Publishes papers presented by invitation at symposia of the society, and abstracts of original communications presented at other meetings.

613.2 612.3   AT   ISSN 0314-1004
CODEN: PNSADB
NUTRITION SOCIETY OF AUSTRALIA. PROCEEDINGS. 1976. a. Aus.$40 in Australia & New Zealand; elsewhere Aus.$45. Nutrition Society of Australia, c/o David Petterson, Publication Officer, 98 Stanley St., Nedlands, W.A. 6009, Australia. TEL 09-368-3365. FAX 09-474-1881. Ed. J.R. Mercer. index. circ. 1,000. (back issues avail.) **Indexed:** Biol.Abstr., Chem.Abstr., Curr.Cont., Sugar Ind.Abstr. **Document type:** proceedings.
  —BLDSC (6779.400000); CASDDS.

641.4 630   II
NUTRITION SOCIETY OF INDIA. PROCEEDINGS. 1967. a. Rs.50($15) Nutrition Society of India, c/o National Institute of Nutrition, PO-Jamai Osmania, Hyderabad 500007, India. Ed.Bd. circ. 1,500. (back issues avail.) **Indexed:** Agroforest.Abstr., Rice Abstr., Soyabean Abstr., Trop.Oil Seeds Abstr.

641   US   ISSN 0029-666X
RA784
NUTRITION TODAY. 1966. bi-m. $40 to individuals; institutions $77 (effective 1995). Williams and Wilkins, 428 E. Preston St., Baltimore, MD 21202. TEL 410-528-4000; 800-638-6423. FAX 410-528-4312. TELEX 87669. Ed. Helen A. Guthrie. adv.; bk.rev.; index. circ. 5,300. (also avail. in microfilm from WWS; reprint service avail.) **Indexed:** A.S.& T.Ind., Bibl.Agri., Biol.Abstr., CHNI, Curr.Cont., Environ.Per.Bibl. (1991-), Gen.Sci.Ind., Hlth.Ind., Nutr.Abstr. **Document type:** academic/scholarly publication.
  —BLDSC (6190.100000); Faxon; SWETS; UnCover. **CCC.**
  Description: Presents articles on developments in nutrition for dieticians, nutritionists, and physicians.

641.1   US   ISSN 0736-0096
NUTRITION WEEK. 1970. w. (48/yr.). $85 to individuals; insitutions $125 (renewal $230); students $40. Community Nutrition Institute, 2001 S St., N.W., Washington, DC 20009. TEL 202-776-0595. FAX 202-776-0599. E-mail: cnii@igc.apc.org. Ed. Dominic Madigan; Pub. Rodney E. Leonard. bk.rev.; bibl.; index. circ. 2,000. **Document type:** newsletter.
  Former titles: C N I Weekly Report (ISSN 0191-0833); C N I Report.
  Description: Offers and independent up-to-date examination of events in food and nutrition policy, be they specific reports on congressional action, or in-depth analyses about the trends shaping nutrition policymaking.

NUTRITION AND DIETETICS

641   JM   ISSN 0255-8203
TX360.C35
NYAM NEWS. 1975. m. free. Caribbean Food and Nutrition Institute, U.W.I. Mona Campus, P.O. Box 140, Kingston 7, Jamaica, W.I. TEL 809-927-1540. FAX 809-927-2657. TELEX 3705. (Co-sponsors: Pan American Health Organization, World Health Organization) Eds. Sadie Campbell, Clare A. Forrester. circ. 700. **Indexed:** Nutr.Abstr.
    Description: Feature service directed mainly at students, teachers and the mass media in the English-speaking Caribbean, giving sample information on topical and pertinent food and nutrition issues.

613.2   JA   ISSN 0910-7258
NYU DAIETTO SERAPI/NEW DIET THERAPY. (Text in Japanese) 1985. q. 1400 Yen per no. Nihon Rinsho Eiyo Kyokai - Japanese Clinical Nutrition Association, Toho Daigaku Igakubu Fuzoku Omori Byoin Eiyobu, 11-1, Omori Nishi 6-chome, Ota-ku, Tokyo 143, Japan.

641.1 633   US
ON YOUR MARK. 1976. q. free. Sugar Association, Inc., 1101 15th St., N.W., No. 600, Washington, DC 20005. TEL 202-785-1122. FAX 202-785-5019. Ed. Michelle Sutton. circ. 10,000. **Document type:** newsletter.
    Formerly: Sugar and Health.
    Description: Covers nutrition, fitness and the role of sugar in nutrition and health.

613.2 051   US
ONE PEACEFUL WORLD. 1989. 4/yr. $30 to individuals; families $50. One Peaceful World, Inc., Box 10, Becket, MA 01223. TEL 413-623-2322. FAX 413-623-8827. Ed. Alex Jack. adv.; bk.rev. circ. 5,000.
    Formerly: Return to Paradise.

ONTARIO WRESTLER MAGAZINE. see SPORTS AND GAMES

641.1   US   ISSN 0195-0924
ORGANIC CONSUMER REPORT. w. $5. Eden Ranch, Box 370, Topanga, CA 90290. TEL 213-455-2065. Ed. Judith Eagan. bk.rev.; circ. controlled.

613.2   GW   ISSN 0178-7624
ORTHOMOLEKULAR; Fachzeitschrift fuer Ernaehrung, Gesundheit und Umwelt. (Text in Dutch, German) 1985. bi-m. DM.139 (foreign DM.159). Ortho-Communications, Lindemannstr. 47, 40237 Dusseldorf, Germany. TEL 0211-684422. FAX 0211-684946. Ed. Diana Evans von Metternich. adv.; bk.rev. circ. 3,250.

664 641   US   ISSN 0748-8394
OUTPOST EXCHANGE; Milwaukee's food and wellness magazine. 1971. m. $11. (Outpost Natural Foods) Outpost Exchange, 102 E. Capitol Dr., Milwaukee, WI 53212. TEL 414-964-7789. FAX 414-961-1961. Ed. Art Blair. adv.; bk.rev. circ. 24,000. **Document type:** consumer publication.

OVER THE GARDEN FENCE; natural living in North Texas. see GARDENING AND HORTICULTURE

641.1   US
P C C SOUND CONSUMER. 1974. 11/yr. $12 to non-members. Puget Consumers Co-op, 4201 Roosevelt Way, N.E., Seattle, WA 98105-6008. TEL 206-547-1222. FAX 206-545-7131. Ed. Kim Runciman. adv.; bk.rev. circ. 43,000. **Document type:** newspaper.
    Formerly: Puget Consumers Co-op Newsletter.

PERSONAL FITNESS. see PHYSICAL FITNESS AND HYGIENE

641   PH   ISSN 0031-7640
TX501   CODEN: PJNUAF
PHILIPPINE JOURNAL OF NUTRITION. 1949. q. $12. Philippine Association of Nutrition, c/o Nutrition Foundation of the Philippines, 107 E. Rodriguez, Sr. Blvd., Quezon City, Philippines. Ed. Velona A. Corpus. adv.; bk.rev.; abstr.; charts; illus.; index. circ. 2,000. (also avail. in microform from UMI; reprint service avail. from UMI) **Indexed:** Biol.Abstr., Chem.Abstr., Dairy Sci.Abstr., ExtraMED, Food Sci.& Tech.Abstr., Nutr.Abstr., Philip.Abstr., Rural Recreat.Tour.Abstr., World Agri.Econ.& Rural Sociol.Abstr.
    ●Also available on CD-ROM.
    —CASDDS.
    Formerly: Nutrition News.

641.1   PH
PHILIPPINES. FOOD AND NUTRITION RESEARCH INSTITUTE. ANNUAL REPORT. (Text in English) 1950. a. Food and Nutrition Research Institute, Science Complex, Bicutan, Tagig, Metro Manila 1604, Philippines. TEL 837-29-34. FAX 837-29-34. (Alt. addr.: DOST Compound, Gen. Santos Ave., Bicutan, Taguig, Metro Manila, Philippines. TEL 823-8934. FAX 823-8934) Ed. Alma M. Jose. circ. controlled.
    Formerly: Philippines. Food and Nutrition Research Center. Annual Report (ISSN 0071-7142)
    Description: A detailed compilation of the institute's various projects and activities. Includes completed research, research in progress, public services, staff papers and publications, staff development, cooperative activities, foreign visitors, financial resources, and technical staff.

PHYSICIANS' GENRX; the official drug reference of FDA prescribing information and therapeutic equivalents. see MEDICAL SCIENCES

613.2   NE   ISSN 0921-9668
TX341   CODEN: PFHNE8
PLANT FOODS FOR HUMAN NUTRITION. (Text in English) 1952. 8/yr. fl.906 to institutions; $581 to institutions in U.S. (effective 1996). Kluwer Academic Publishers, Postbus 17, 3300 AA Dordrecht, Netherlands. TEL 31-78-392392. FAX 31-78-392254. TELEX 29245 KAPG NL. E-mail: SERVICES@WKAP.NL. (Dist. by: Kluwer Academic Publishers Group, Box 322, 3300 AH Dordrecht, Netherlands. TEL 31-78-392392. FAX 31-78-546474; N. America dist. addr.: Box 358, Accord Sta., Hingham, MA 02018-0358. TEL 617-871-6600. FAX 617-871-6528) Ed. Constance V. Kies. adv.; bk.rev.; bibl.; charts; illus. (also avail. in microform from UMI; reprint service avail. from SWZ) **Indexed:** ASCA, Biol.Abstr., Chem.Abstr., Curr.Adv.Biochem., Curr.Adv.Ecol.Sci., Curr.Cont., Excerp.Med., Field Crop Abstr., Food Sci.& Tech.Abstr., Herb.Abstr., Hort.Abstr., I.P.A., Ind.Med., Int.Abstr.Biol.Sci., Maize Abstr., Nutr.Abstr., Plant Breed.Abstr., Potato Abstr., Poult.Abstr., Rice Abstr., Seed Abstr., Soils & Fert., Soyabean Abstr., Triticale Abstr., Trop.Oil Seeds Abstr., VITIS. **Document type:** academic/scholarly publication.
    —BLDSC (6517.500000); CASDDS; Genuine Article; SWETS; UMI. **CCC.**
    Former titles (until 1987): Qualitas Plantarum (ISSN 0377-3205); (until 1973): Qualitas Plantarum et Materiae Vegetabiles (ISSN 0033-5134)
    Description: Publishes reports of original research concerned with the improvement and evaluation of the nutritional quality of plant foods for humans, as they are influenced by biotechnology, plant breeding, cooking and processing, plant and soil ecology, and plant production practices.
    Refereed Serial

POSITIVELY PASTA. see FOOD AND FOOD INDUSTRIES

664 331.88   XR   ISSN 0032-566X
POTRAVINAR. 1946. m. 9.60 Kc.($13.20) N O S Pracovniku Potravinarskeho Prumyslu, Nam. W. Churchilla 2, 113 59 Prague 3, Czech Republic. (Dist. by: Artia, Ve Smeckach 30, 111 27 Prague 1, Czech Republic) Ed. Vladimir Marek.

POTRAVINARSKE AKTUALITY. VYZIVA A LEGISLATIVA. see FOOD AND FOOD INDUSTRIES

PROFESSIONEALLEVATORE. see AGRICULTURE — Poultry And Livestock

REPORT ON INSTITUTIONAL FOODSERVICE. see FOOD AND FOOD INDUSTRIES

641.1   CL   ISSN 0716-1549
REVISTA CHILENA DE NUTRICION. 1980. 3/yr. Sociedad Chilena de Nutricion, Bromatologia y Toxicologia, Universidad de Chile, Fac. de Medicina, Depto. Nutricion, Independencia 1027, Santiago, Chile. Ed. Hector Araya.
    —BLDSC (7848.910000).
    Supersedes (1961-1968): Nutricion, Bromatologia y Toxicologia (ISSN 0550-4023)

616.39 664   CU   ISSN 0864-2133
REVISTA CUBANA DE ALIMENTACION Y NUTRICION. (Text in Spanish; summaries in English, Spanish) 1987. s-a. $28 in S. America; N. America $30; elsewhere $34. Ministerio de Salud Publica, Centro Nacional de Informacion de Ciencias Medicas, Calle E No. 452, e-19 y 21, Plaza de la Revolucion, Apdo. 6520, Havana, Cuba. TEL 809-32-5338. (Dist. by: Ediciones Cubanas, Obispo No. 527, Apdo. 605, Havana, Cuba) (Co-sponsors: Instituto Nacional de Alimentacion y Nutricion; Sociedad Cubana de Alimentacion y Nutricion) Ed. Ana Dolores del Campo. circ. 1,000.
    Description: Covers nutrition and food hygiene.

REVISTA DE INVESTIGACION CLINICA. see MEDICAL SCIENCES

616.1 616.39   AG   ISSN 0034-8600
REVISTA DE NUTRICION Y ATEROSCLEROSIS. 1958. bi-m. free. c/o Mario Campagnoli, Juan B. Alberdi 3255, Buenos Aires, Argentina. adv.; illus. circ. 15,000.

REVUE DE L'INDUSTRIE ALIMENTAIRE. see FOOD AND FOOD INDUSTRIES

641.1   IT   ISSN 0393-5582
RIVISTA ITALIANA DI NUTRIZIONE PARENTERALE ED ENTERALE. (Text in Italian; summaries in English) 1983? 3/yr. L.90000($90) (effective 1994). Wichtig Editore s.r.l., Via Friuli, 72-74, 20135 Milan, Italy. TEL 02-5452306. FAX 02-5451843.
    —BLDSC (7987.442500).

RUNNING & FITNEWS. see PHYSICAL FITNESS AND HYGIENE

613   US
RX WEIGHT CONTROL;* the multidisciplinary newsletter designed to reduce health risk. 1984. bi-m. $18. Nutritional Management, c/o Herbert Kahn, 114 State St., 4th Fl., Boston, MA 02109-2402. Ed.Bd. illus.

613.2   IT
SALVALINEA/WEIGHT WATCHERS. 1978. m. L.40000 (foreign L.64000). Salvalinea s.r.l., Foro Buonaparte 51, 20121 Milan, Italy. TEL 39-2-86454190. FAX 39-2-86454209. Ed. Fiammetta Fadda. adv.: B&W page L.5870000, color page L.10565000. circ. 75,000.

SANTE. see PHYSICAL FITNESS AND HYGIENE

612.3   SW   ISSN 1102-6480
                     CODEN: SJNUEI
SCANDINAVIAN JOURNAL OF NUTRITION/NAERINGSFORSKNING. (Supplement avail.) (Text in English and Nordic languages; summaries in English) 1957. q. SEK 240 (effective 1993). Swedish Nutrition Foundation, Ideon, S-223 70 Lund, Sweden. TEL 46-(0)-46-18-22-80. FAX 46-0-46-18-22-81. Ed. Bo Hallgren. bk.rev.; circ. 2,500 (controlled). (back issues avail.) **Indexed:** Excerp.Med. (1993-).
    ●Also available online.
    —BLDSC (6015.349000).
    Formerly (until vol.36, 1992): Naeringsforskning (ISSN 0027-7878)
    Description: Directed to present state of the art in the various fields within nutrition. Provides readers with information through original and review articles and reports.

SCHOOL FOOD SERVICE AND NUTRITION. see FOOD AND FOOD INDUSTRIES

SCHOOL FOOD SERVICE RESEARCH REVIEW. see FOOD AND FOOD INDUSTRIES

SCHOOL FOODSERVICE WHO'S WHO. see BUSINESS AND ECONOMICS — Trade And Industrial Directories

613.2   GW   ISSN 0931-1068
SCHROT UND KORN. m. Verlag Gesund Essen GmbH, Am Eichwald 24, 64850 Schaafheim, Germany. TEL 06073-80057. FAX 06073-9548. Ed. Renee Herrnkind-Galuschka. adv. contact: Sabine Kauffmann. circ. 145,583. **Document type:** bulletin.

641.1   IT
SCUOLA DELLA SALUTE.* m. L.36000. Curcio Periodici S.p.A., Via IV Novembre 149, 00187 Rome, Italy. Ed. Rosanna Falconi. adv.

NUTRITION AND DIETETICS

613.2   JA   ISSN 0286-6366
CODEN: KSTDD5
SEITOKU EIYO TANKI DAIGAKU KIYO/SEITOKU JUNIOR COLLEGE OF NUTRITION. MEMOIRS. (Text in English, Japanese) 1965. a. Seitoku Eiyo Tanki Daigaku, 4-6, Nishishinkoiwa 1-chome, Katsushika-ku, Tokyo 124, Japan. **Indexed:** Chem.Abstr., Jap.Per.Ind.
—BLDSC (5634.815000); CASDDS.

613.2   JA
SHIGAKEN KOSHU EIYO KATSUDO NO GAIYO/ANNUAL REPORT OF PUBLIC NUTRITION IN SHIGA PREFECTURE. (Text in Japanese) a. Shigaken Kenko Fukushibu - Shiga Prefectural Government, Health and Welfare Division, 1-1, Kyomachi 4-chome, Otsu-shi, Shiga-ken 520, Japan. **Document type:** government publication.

641.1 664   CC
SHIPIN KE-JI/FOOD SCIENCE. (Text in Chinese) m. $0.40 per no. Guoji Shudian, Qikan Bu - China International Book Trading Corp., P.O. Box 399, Beijing 100044, People's Republic of China.

641   JA
SHOKU NI KANSURU JOSEI KENKYU CHOSA HOKOKUSHO/RESEARCH REPORT ON FOOD SCIENCE BY SUBSIDIARY PAYMENTS. (Text in Japanese; summaries in English, Japanese) 1990. s-a. Sukairaku Fudo Saiensu Kenkyujo - Skylark Food Science Institute, 3-CB-5, Nakase 1-chome, Mihama-ku, Chiba-shi, Chiba-ken 261, Japan.

613.2   UK   ISSN 0144-8129
SLIMMING. 1969. 10/yr. £16 (foreign £24) (effective 1995-1996). E M A P - Elan, 20 Orange St., London WC2H 7ED, England. TEL 0171-957-8383. FAX 0171-930-5728. (Subscr. to: Tower Publishing Services Ltd., Tower House, Sovereign Park, Lathkill St., Market Harborough, Leics. LE16 9EF, England. TEL 01858-468811. FAX 01858-432164) adv.; bk.rev. circ. 211,000.
   Formerly (until Mar. 1979): Slimming and Nutrition (ISSN 0049-075X)

616.39 610   UK   ISSN 0264-5807
SOCIETY FOR ENVIRONMENTAL THERAPY. NEWSLETTER. 1981. q. £10 to libraries; students £6; scientists £14. Society for Environmental Therapy, c/o Mrs. Hilary Davidson, 521 Foxhall Rd., Ipswich, Suffolk IP3 8LW, England. Ed. Vicky Rippere. adv.; bk.rev. circ. 350. **Document type:** newsletter.
—BLDSC (6108.344340).

SOUTH PACIFIC FOODS LEAFLET. see *FOOD AND FOOD INDUSTRIES*

613.2   JA   ISSN 0919-9535
CODEN: DTKKEE
SOY PROTEIN RESEARCH COMMITTEE. REPORT. (Text in Japanese; summaries in English) 1980. a. Soy Protein Research Committee, c/o Fuji Oil Co., Ltd., Sumiyoshi-cho 1, Isumisano 598, Japan. TEL 0724-63-1120. FAX 0724-0491. **Indexed:** Chem.Abstr.
—BLDSC (7610.180000); CASDDS.
   Formerly (until 1993): Nutritional Science of Soy Protein (ISSN 0288-6219)

SOYA BLUEBOOK. see *AGRICULTURE — Crop Production And Soil*

614.53   US   ISSN 1048-8413
SPECIALTY COOKING; cookbook magazine. 1989. q. $3.95 per no. Blockbuster Periodicals, Inc., 2131 Hollywood Blvd., Hollywood, FL 33020. TEL 305-925-5242. Ed. Barbara Newman. circ. 65,000.
   Incorporates: Cookbook Series; Good Cooking Series.
   Description: Covers diabetic and low-cholesterol cooking.

613.26   US   ISSN 0744-9860
SPROUTLETTER. 1980. q. $12. Sprouting Publications, Box 62, Ashland, OR 97520. TEL 503-488-2326. FAX 503-488-2326. Ed. Michael Linden. adv.; bk.rev.; charts; illus.; tr.lit.; cum.index. circ. 3,000. (back issues avail.) **Document type:** newsletter.
   Description: Explores nutrition, holistic health, vegetarianism, sprouting, live foods, blue-green algae, acidophilus, enzymes, indoor food gardening; includes recipes and product listings.

SUNFLOWER (MANHATTAN). see *CLUBS*

T O P S NEWS. (Take Off Pounds Sensibly, Inc.) see *PHYSICAL FITNESS AND HYGIENE*

TETSU TAISHA KENKYUKAI PUROGURAMU SHOROKUSHU/CONFERENCE ON CURRENT TOPICS FOR IRON METABOLISM. PROGRAM AND ABSTRACTS. see *BIOLOGY — Biological Chemistry*

613.2   JA   ISSN 0289-8829
TOKAI RINSHO EIYO KENKYUKAISHI/TOKAI SOCIETY OF CLINICAL NUTRITION. JOURNAL. (Text in Japanese) a. $1980. Tokai Rinsho Eiyo Kenkyukai, Nagoya Daigaku Igakubu Dai 2 Geka Kyoshitsu, 65, Tsurumaicho, Showa-ku, Nagoya-shi, Aichi-ken 466, Japanese.

613.2   JA
TOKYO TOMIN NO EIYO JOKYO/REPORT ON NUTRITIVE CONDITIONS IN TOKYO. (Text in Japanese) a. Tokyo Eiseikyoku, Kenko Suishinbu - Tokyo Metropolitan Government, Bureau of Public Health, Public Health Promotion Division, 8-1, Nishishinjuku 2-chome, Shinjuku-ku, Tokyo 163-01, Japan.

613.2   US   ISSN 0883-5691
TOPICS IN CLINICAL NUTRITION. 1986. q. $69 (foreign $83). Aspen Publishers, Inc., 200 Orchard Ridge Dr., Gaithersburg, MD 20878. TEL 301-417-7500. FAX 301-417-7550.
—BLDSC (8867.432800); Faxon; UMI; UnCover. CCC.

641.1   US
TOPS NEWS. m. membership. Tops Club, Inc., 4575 S. Fifth St., Milwaukee, WI 53207-5858. TEL 414-482-0360. Ed. Kathy Davis. circ. 309,512.

613.2 614.58   US   ISSN 0274-6743
TOTAL HEALTH. 1979. bi-m. $16. Total Health Communications, Inc., 165 N. 100 St. E., Ste. 2, Saint George, UT 84770-2505. TEL 801-673-1789. FAX 801-634-9336. Ed. Robert L. Smith; Pub. Robert L. Smith. adv. contact: Katherine Hurd. bk.rev. circ. 95,000. (also avail. in microform from UMI) **Indexed:** Hlth.Ind. **Document type:** consumer publication.
● Also available online. Vendor(s): University Microfilms International.
—UMI.
   Formerly: Trio.
   Description: Presents preventive health care life-style articles covering nutrition, diet, fitness, travel, psychological-spiritual health encompassing mind, body, and spirit.

TRENDS IN FOOD SCIENCE AND TECHNOLOGY. see *FOOD AND FOOD INDUSTRIES*

TRENDS IN FOOD SCIENCE AND TECHNOLOGY (REFERENCE EDITION). see *FOOD AND FOOD INDUSTRIES*

513.2   US   ISSN 0747-4105
CODEN: TUDLET
TUFTS UNIVERSITY DIET AND NUTRITION LETTER. 1983. m. $20. 53 Park Pl., 8th Fl., New York, NY 10007. TEL 212-608-6515. FAX 212-608-5317. (Subscr. to: Box 57857, Boulder, CO 80322) Ed. Stanley N. Gershoff. bk.rev. circ. 280,000. (also avail. in microform; microform from UMI) **Indexed:** Hlth.Ind. **Document type:** newsletter.
● Also available online. Vendor(s): University Microfilms International.
—UMI.

613.2   US
U S D A DIETARY GUIDELINES. irreg. free. U.S. Department of Agriculture, Food and Nutrition Service, 3101 Park Center Dr., Alexandria, VA 22302. TEL 703-756-3062. **Document type:** consumer publication, government publication.

UNIVERSITY OF TEXAS LIFETIME HEALTH LETTER. see *PHYSICAL FITNESS AND HYGIENE*

613.2   SA
V I C MEDICAL UPDATE. 3/yr. free to qualified personnel. Vitamin Information Centre, P.O. Box 182, Isando 1600, South Africa. TEL 27-11-9741887. FAX 27-11-3924034. (Co-sponsor: Roche Products (Pty) Ltd.) **Document type:** academic/scholarly publication, bulletin.
   Description: Provides an accurate, scientific, timely review of current vitamin related issues and research.
   Refereed Serial

613.2   US
V S D C NEWS. 1927. bi-m. $15. Vegetarian Society of the District of Columbia, Box 4921, Washington, DC 20008. TEL 301-589-0722. Ed. Polly Nelson. circ. 1,000. (looseleaf format; back issues avail.) **Document type:** newsletter.
   Description: Promotes vegetarianism in the Washington, DC, metropolitan area. Provides a forum for readers to share views and information; announces society-sponsored events.

613.2   SW   ISSN 0042-2657
TX341   CODEN: VAFOAS
VAAR FODEA. (Text in Swedish; summaries in English) 1949. 8/yr. SEK 260. Statens Livsmedelsverk - National Food Administration, P.O. Box 622, S-751 26 Uppsala, Sweden. FAX 46-18-105848. TELEX 76121 SLVUPS. Ed. Lena Boija. bk.rev.; charts; illus. circ. 5,500. **Indexed:** Chem.Abstr., Dairy Sci.Abstr., Food Sci.& Tech.Abstr., Nutr.Abstr., Sugar Ind.Abstr. **Document type:** government publication.
—BLDSC (9146.020000); CASDDS.
   Description: Covers activities in food control projects, new regulations and current research.

613.26 179.3   UK   ISSN 0307-4811
VEGAN. 1946. q. £7 (overseas £9.80). Vegan Society, 7 Battle Rd., St. Leonards-on-Sea, E. Sussex TN37 7AA, England. TEL 01424-427393. FAX 01424-717064. Ed. Richard Farhall. adv. contact: Keith Bird. bk.rev. circ. 5,000. (back issues avail.) **Document type:** newsletter.
   Description: Supplies information on animal rights, vegan nutrition, health and ecology.

VEGETARIAN ASTROLOGER. see *ASTROLOGY*

613.26   US   ISSN 0049-5905
VEGETARIAN COURIER.* 1960. m. $2. Vegetarian Society of New York, Inc., c/o Murray Mickenberg, 87-12 Clio St., Holliswood, NY 11423. (Or: 1133 Broadway, Rm. 416, New York, NY 10010) bk.rev. circ. 500.

613.26   US   ISSN 1065-6340
TX837
VEGETARIAN GOURMET; easy and healthy cooking! 1992. 5/yr. $15.95 (effective June 1994). Chariot Publishing Inc., 2 Public Ave., Montrose, PA 18801. TEL 717-278-1984. FAX 717-278-2223. (Subscr. to: Box 7641, Riverton, NJ 08077-9141) Ed. Jessica Dubey; Pub. Christiane Meunier. adv.; bk.rev. circ. 90,000. (back issues avail.) **Document type:** consumer publication.
   Description: Contains features and recipes for vegetarians. Includes vegetarian gourmet visits, entertainment, and international fare.

919.204   UK
VEGETARIAN HANDBOOK. 1956. biennial. £3.95. Vegetarian Society, c/o Publications Mgr., Parkdale, Dunham Rd., Altrincham, Ches. WA14 4QG, England. TEL 0161-928-0793. Ed. Jane Bowler. adv. circ. 20,000.
   Former titles: International Vegetarian Health Food Handbook; Vegetarian Handbook (ISSN 0083-5315); Food Reformers' Yearbook.
   Description: Provides a comprehensive list of where to eat, stay, and products available.

613.26   US   ISSN 0885-7636
VEGETARIAN JOURNAL. 1982. bi-m. $20 (effective 1995-1996). Vegetarian Resource Group, Box 1463, Baltimore, MD 21203. TEL 410-366-8343. E-mail: brad@clark.net, or 73052.2610.CompuServe.com. Eds. Charles Stahler, Debra Wasserman. bk.rev.; film rev.; illus. circ. 25,000. (reprint service avail. from UMI) **Document type:** consumer publication.
   Formerly (until 198?): Baltimore Vegetarians (ISSN 0883-1165)
   Description: Covers various aspects of vegetarianism, including health, recipes, ethics, ecology, world hunger, and animal rights.

NUTRITION AND DIETETICS

613.26 US ISSN 0164-8497
TX392
VEGETARIAN TIMES. 1974. 12/yr. $23.95. Cowles Magazines, Inc. (Subsidiary of: Cowles Media Company), 6405 Flank Dr., Box 8200, Harrisburg, PA 17105-8200. TEL 717-657-9555. FAX 717-657-9526. Ed. Luey Moll. adv.; bk.rev.; illus.; tr.lit. circ. 230,000. (also avail. in microform from UMI; reprint service avail. from UMI) **Indexed:** CHNI, Hlth.Ind., New Per.Ind. **Document type:** consumer publication.
—Faxon; UMI; UnCover.
Incorporates: Vegetarian World.
Description: Contains vegetarian recipes, dietary information, advice on buying whole foods and preparing foods for maximum nutritional value, and articles on nutritional approaches to disease, information for travelers and profiles of prominent vegetarians.

613.26 US ISSN 0271-1591
VEGETARIAN VOICE. 1974. q. $20 to individuals; free to libraries. North American Vegetarian Society, Box 72, Dolgeville, NY 13329. TEL 518-568-7636. Ed. Jennie O. Collura. bk.rev.; illus. circ. 7,000. **Indexed:** Alt.Press Ind. (1992-). **Document type:** consumer publication.
Description: Information on nutrition, cooking, health, animal and environmental protection for people interested in vegetarianism, with organization news and reports on annual conferences.

613.26 GW ISSN 0178-9104
DER VEGETARIER; Zeitschrift fuer ethische Lebensgestaltung und Lebensreform. 1949. bi-m. DM.30. Vegetarier Bund Deutschlands e.V., Blumenstr. 3, 30159 Hannover, Germany. TEL 0511-3632050. Ed. Hildegund Scholvien. adv.; bk.rev. circ. 4,000. (back issues avail.) **Document type:** bulletin.

613.262 DK ISSN 0109-8861
VEGETARISK TIDSSKRIFT. irreg. (1-2/yr.), vol.77, 1983. DKK 30. Dansk Vegetar-og Raakostforening, Ny Vestergaardsvej 6, 3500 Vaerloese, Denmark. illus.
Formerly: V F (ISSN 0109-8845)

VIBRANT LIFE; a Christian guide to total health. see *PHYSICAL FITNESS AND HYGIENE*

VIE ET SANTE. see *PHYSICAL FITNESS AND HYGIENE*

613 IT ISSN 1120-4591
VITALITY. 1989. m. L.52800 (foreign L.80000). Rusconi Editori S.p.A., Viale Sarca 235, 20126 Milan, Italy. TEL 02-66191. FAX 02-6619-2480. Ed. M. Picollo. adv.: color page L.24000000. circ. 122,962. (back issues avail.)

613.2 613.7 CN ISSN 0826-2756
VITASANA.* (Text in English, Italian) 1984. m. (10/yr.). $25. VitaSana Magazine Inc., 1100 Caledonia Rd., Ste. 200, Toronto, Ont. M6A 2W5, Canada. TEL 416-785-4975. FAX 416-785-4329. Ed. Elena Caprile. adv.: B&W page Can.$1495, color page Can.$1990; trim 8 1/2 x 11. circ. 21,618.

641.1 IT
VIVERE - GUARIRE. 1952. q. L.7000. Editrice Guarire di Fausto Pistarino, San Felice, Centro Commerciale, Torre 7, 20090 Segrate (Milan), Italy. adv. circ. 50,000.

641 613 FR ISSN 0042-7608
VIVRE EN HARMONIE. 1952. m. 130 F. (effective 1991). Centre Fraternel Vivre en Harmonie, B.P. 492, 95005 Cergy Pontoise Cedex, France. FAX 1-34-64-46-45. Ed. Raymond Dextreit. bk.rev.; bibl.; charts; illus.

VLEES IN VOEDING. see *FOOD AND FOOD INDUSTRIES*

641 NE ISSN 0042-7926
TX341 CODEN: VOEDAK
VOEDING; Netherlands journal of nutrition. (Text in Dutch; occasionally in English) 1939. 10/yr. fl.120 (effective 1993). (Stichting Voeding Nederland) Keesing Noordervliet B.V., P.O. Box 325, 3990 GC Houten, Netherlands. TEL 31-3403-58585. FAX 31-3403-58500. Ed. Dr. W.Th.J.M. Hekkens. adv.: B&W page fl.1300; color page fl.3450; adv. contact: S.O. Nieuwenhuis. bk.rev.; charts; illus.; index. circ. 3,000. **Indexed:** Biol.Abstr., Chem.Abstr., Dairy Sci.Abstr., Food Sci.& Tech.Abstr., Ind.Med., Nutr.Abstr., Rural Recreat.Tour.Abstr., Sugar Ind.Abstr., World Agri.Econ.& Rural Sociol.Abstr.
—BLDSC (9251.000000); CASDDS; SWETS.

613.2 NE ISSN 0922-8012
VOEDINGSMAGAZINE. 1988. bi-m. free. Stichting Zuivel, Voeding en Gezondheid, Zonnebaan 12D, 3606 CA Maarssen, Netherlands. TEL 31-30-412241. FAX 31-30-411840. Ed. G.J. Hiddink. (back issues avail.) **Document type:** trade publication.
Description: Information on nutrition and health matters for general practitioners, registered dieticians, medical specialists in food-related disciplines, and educators in nutrition and health.

612 641 RU ISSN 0042-8833
CODEN: VPITAR
VOPROSY PITANIYA/PROBLEMS OF NUTRITION. 1932. bi-m. $60 (effective 1996). (Nutrition Institute) A-O Nutritec, Ustisnsky pr. 2-14, 109240 Moscow, Russia. (Dist. by: Mezhdunarodnaya Kniga, B. Yakimanka 39, 117049 Moscow, Russia) (Co-sponsor: Ministerstvo Zdravookhraneniya) Ed. V.A. Tutelyan. adv. contact: G.Yu. Sazhinov. index. **Indexed:** Abstr.Hyg., Biol.Abstr., Chem.Abstr., Dairy Sci.Abstr., Dent.Ind., Dok.Arbeitsmed., Food Sci.& Tech.Abstr., Ind.Med., Int.Aerosp.Abstr., Maize Abstr., Nutr.Abstr., Seed Abstr., Triticale Abstr., Trop.Dis.Bull.
—BLDSC (0043.930000); CASDDS. **CCC.**
Description: Publishes original and survey articles, reflecting joint work done by physiologists, biochemists, hygienists, pathophysiologists, clinicians and technologists dealing with problems of nutrition.

641.1 XR
VYZIVA A POTRAVINY. (Supplements avail.: Vyziva v Rodine (ISSN 0322-7502); Vyziva a Spotreba Pozivatin v Cislech (ISSN 0322-7553)) 1946. m. 8 Kc.($1) (effective Jan. 1991). Spolecnost pro Vyzivu, Sobeslavska 40, 130 00 Prague 3, Czech Republic. TEL 29-01-91. (Dist. by: Artia, Ve Smeckach 30, 111 27 Prague 1, Czech Republic) Ed. Milan Starnovsky. circ. 5,500 (controlled). **Indexed:** Biol.Abstr., Chem.Abstr., Dairy Sci.Abstr., Food Sci.& Tech.Abstr., Rural Recreat.Tour.Abstr., World Agri.Econ. & Rural Sociol.Abstr.
Former titles (until 1994): Vyziva; (until 1991): Vyziva Lidu (ISSN 0042-9414)

613.2 641 XO ISSN 0042-9406
VYZIVA A ZDRAVIE/NUTRITION AND HEALTH; journal for rational nutrition. (Text in Slovak; summaries also in English and Russian) 1956. m. $16. Slovenska Spolecnost pre Racionalnu Vyzivu - Slovak Society for Rational Nourishment, Krizna 52 - III, 821 08 Bratislava, Slovakia. (Subscr. to: Slovart, Gottwaldovo nam. 48, 805 32 Bratislava, Slovakia) Ed. Vojtech Spanko. adv.; bk.rev.; charts; illus. circ. 9,000. **Indexed:** Chem.Abstr.

WARSAW AGRICULTURAL UNIVERSITY. S G G W. ANNALS. FOOD TECHNOLOGY AND NUTRITION. see *FOOD AND FOOD INDUSTRIES*

613.2 US ISSN 0043-2180
RM222.2
WEIGHT WATCHERS MAGAZINE. 1968. m. $15.97. Weight Watchers-Twenty-First Corporation, 360 Lexington Ave., New York, NY 10017. TEL 212-370-0644. FAX 212-687-4398. Ed. Lee Haiken. adv.; bk.rev. circ. 1,000,000. (also avail. in microform from UMI; microfiche from KTO) **Indexed:** CHNI, Mag.Ind. **Document type:** consumer publication.
—UMI; UnCover.
Description: For women who want to change their lives for the better. Provides "how-to" tips on smart eating, beauty, fashion, fitness and nutrition.

WELL BEING MAGAZINE; personal and planetary healing. see *PHYSICAL FITNESS AND HYGIENE*

WELLNESS LETTER; the newsletter of nutrition, fitness, and stress management. see *PHYSICAL FITNESS AND HYGIENE*

641.1 US
WELLNESS NOTES.* 1981. 4/yr. $4. (Circle of Life) Lifecircle Publications, 570 Hollibaugh Ave., No. 1, Akron, OH 44310-3927. Ed. Jonathon Miller. bk.rev. circ. 2,000.
Formerly (until 1982): Fruit.

WHOLE LIFE TIMES. see *NEW AGE PUBLICATIONS*

613.2 US
WOMAN'S DAY 101 WAYS TO LOSE WEIGHT AND STAY HEALTHY. 1973. a. Hachette Magazines, Inc., Woman's Day Special Publications, 1633 Broadway, 45th Fl., New York, NY 10019. TEL 212-767-6000. Ed. Andrea Levine. adv.; illus.

612.3 UN ISSN 1010-9099
HV696.F6
WORLD FOOD PROGRAMME JOURNAL. French edition: Programme Alimentaire Mondial. Journal (ISSN 1010-9110); Spanish edition: Programe Mundial de Alimentos (ISSN 1010-9102) 1963. 6/yr. free. Food and Agriculture Organization of the United Nations, Sales & Distribution Section, Via delle Terme di Caracalla, 00100 Rome, Italy. TEL 52251. FAX 52253152. E-mail: publications-sales@fao.org. **Indexed:** Environ.Abstr., IIS, Nutr.Abstr., Rural Recreat.Tour.Abstr., World Agri.Econ.& Rural Sociol.Abstr.
—BLDSC (9355.548000); UnCover.
Formerly (until 1987): World Food Programme News (ISSN 0049-8084)

641.1 SZ ISSN 0084-2230
QP141.A1 CODEN: WRNDAT
WORLD REVIEW OF NUTRITION AND DIETETICS. (Text in English) 1964. irreg. price varies. S. Karger AG, Allschwilerstr. 10, P.O. Box, CH-4009 Basel, Switzerland. TEL 061-3061111. FAX 061-3061234. E-mail: Karger@Karger.ch. Ed. A.P. Simopoulos. (reprint service avail. from ISI) **Indexed:** Abstr.Hyg., Biol.Abstr., Chem.Abstr., Curr.Cont., Dairy Sci.Abstr., Dent.Ind., Food Sci.& Tech.Abstr., Ind.Med., Nutr.Abstr., Rice Abstr., Triticale Abstr., Trop.Dis.Bull. **Document type:** academic/scholarly publication.
—BLDSC (9359.180000); CASDDS; Faxon; SWETS; UnCover. **CCC.**
Refereed Serial

Y M C A WEEKLY NEWS (VANCOUVER, BC). (Vancouver Downtown Young Men's Christian Association) see *PHYSICAL FITNESS AND HYGIENE*

YAOWU SHIPIN FENXI/JOURNAL OF FOOD AND DRUG ANALYSIS. see *FOOD AND FOOD INDUSTRIES*

613.2 CC ISSN 0512-7955
QP141 CODEN: YYHPA4
YINGYANG XUEBAO/JOURNAL OF NUTRITION. (Text in Chinese) 1956-1958; resumed 1982. q. $40 (effective 1996). Zhongguo Yingyang Xuehui - Chinese Nutrition Society, 1 Dali Dao, Heping Qu, Tianjin 300050, People's Republic of China. TEL 86-22-3322197. FAX 86-22-3314818. Ed. Gu Jingfan. **Document type:** academic/scholarly publication.
—CASDDS.

614.8 US
YOUR HEALTH. 1979. bi-m. $30 membership. International Academy of Nutrition and Preventive Medicine, Box 18433, Asheville, NC 28814-0433. TEL 704-258-3243. Ed. Elizabeth Pavka. adv. contact: Elizabeth Pavka. bk.rev. circ. 1,000. (tabloid format; back issues avail.) **Document type:** newsletter.
Description: Written for lay people to inform readers of developments in nutrition and preventive medicine.

ZAMBIA. NATIONAL FOOD AND NUTRITION COMMISSION. ANNUAL REPORT. see *FOOD AND FOOD INDUSTRIES*

641 GW ISSN 0044-264X
QP141.A1 CODEN: ZERNAL
ZEITSCHRIFT FUER ERNAEHRUNGSWISSENSCHAFT/JOURNAL OF NUTRITIONAL SCIENCES/JOURNAL DES SCIENCES DE LA NUTRITION. (Text and summaries in English, French and German) 1960. q. DM.328($238) (effective 1996). Dr. Dietrich Steinkopff Verlag, Saalbaustr. 12, 64283 Darmstadt, Germany. TEL 06151-1745-0. FAX 06151-174510. (Subscr. to: Postfach 111442, 64229 Darmstadt, Germany) Ed.Bd. adv.; bk.rev.; charts; illus.; index. circ. 1,500. (also avail. in microform from UMI) **Indexed:** Biol.Abstr., Chem.Abstr., Curr.Adv.Biochem., Curr.Adv.Cell & Devel.Biol., Curr.Adv.Ecol.Sci., Curr.Cont., Dairy Sci.Abstr., Excerp.Med., Food Sci.& Tech.Abstr., Ind.Med., Nutr.Abstr., Poult.Abstr., Soyabean Abstr. **Document type:** academic/scholarly publication.
—BLDSC (9458.860000); CASDDS; EMDOCS; Faxon; Genuine Article; SWETS; UMI; UnCover. CCC.

613.2 JA
ZEN EISHIKYO GEPPO/JAPANESE ASSOCIATION OF DIETITIAN TRAINING INSTITUTE. MONTHLY BULLETIN. (Text in Japanese) m. Zenkoku Eiyoshi Yosei Shisetsu Kyokai, 16-6, Kitaotsuka, Toshima-ku, Tokyo 170, Japan.

613.1 CH ISSN 1011-6958
CODEN: ZMYZEG
ZHONGHUA MINGUO YINGYANG XUEHUI ZAZHI/CHINESE NUTRITION SOCIETY. JOURNAL. 1976. irreg. Chinese Nutrition Society, National Taiwan Ocean University, 2 Pei-Ning Rd., Keelung, Taiwan, Republic of China. **Indexed:** Excerp.Med. (1994-). **Document type:** academic/scholarly publication.
—CASDDS.

614 PL ISSN 0209-164X
CODEN: ZCMEDQ
ZYWIENIE CZLOWIEKA I METABOLIZM/POLISH JOURNAL OF HUMAN NUTRITION AND METABOLISM. 1974. 2/yr. $52. Instytut Zywnosci i Zywienia - National Food and Nutrition Institute, Ul. Powsinska 61-63, 02-903 Warsaw, Poland. TEL 48-22-422171. FAX 48-22-421103. TELEX 816854. (Dist. by: Ars Polona-Ruch, Krakowskie Przedmiescie 7, Warsaw, Poland) Ed. Swiatoslaw Ziemlanski. circ. 690. **Indexed:** Chem.Abstr., Nutr.Abstr.
—BLDSC (9538.941000); CASDDS.
Formerly: (until 1983): Zywienie Czlowieka (ISSN 0303-7851)

NUTRITION AND DIETETICS —
Abstracting, Bibliographies, Statistics

641.1 016 GW
BIBLIOGRAPHIE NUTRIS, SERIES: ERNAEHRUNGSWISSENSCHAFT. 1971. m. DM.450. Zentralinstitut fuer Ernaehrung, Arthur-Scheunert-Allee 114-116, 14558 Bergholz-Rehbruecke, Germany. Ed. Peter Klingenberg. index. **Document type:** bibliography.
—CCC.
Formerly: Bibliographie "Nahrung und Ernaehrung der Menschen": Ernaehrung (ISSN 0138-208X)

641.1 016 GW
BIBLIOGRAPHIE NUTRIS, SERIES: LEBENSMITTELWISSENSCHAFT. 1971. m. DM.550. Zentralinstitut fuer Ernaehrung, Arthur-Scheunert-Allee 114-116, 1505 Bergholz-Rehbruecke, Germany. Ed. Peter Klingenberg. index. **Document type:** bibliography.
—CCC.
Formerly: Bibliographie "Nahrung und Ernaehrung der Menschen": Lebensmittelwissenschaft (ISSN 0138-2136)

612.3 016 UK
CAB INTERNATIONAL. BUREAU OF NUTRITION. ANNOTATED BIBLIOGRAPHIES. irreg. no. 2, 1967. price varies. CAB International, Bureau of Nutrition, Wallingford, Oxon. OX10 8DE, England. TEL 44-491-832111. FAX 44-491-833508. TELEX 847964 COMAGG G. (U.S. subscr. to: CAB International, North American Office, 845 N. Park Ave., Tucson, AZ 85719. TEL 800-528-4841) bk.rev. **Indexed:** Nutr.Abstr. **Document type:** bibliography.
●Also available online. Vendor(s): Ovid Technologies, CISTI, DIMDI, Knight-Ridder, Inc., European Space Agency.
Formerly: Commonwealth Bureau of Nutrition. Annotated Bibliographies (ISSN 0069-6935)

COMPLEMENTARY MEDICINE INDEX. see *MEDICAL SCIENCES — Abstracting, Bibliographies, Statistics*

613.2 US ISSN 0883-1963
CONSUMER HEALTH AND NUTRITION INDEX. 1985. q. with a. cumulation. $145 (foreign $160). Oryx Press, 4041 N. Central Ave., No. 700, Phoenix, AZ 85012-3397. TEL 602-265-2651. FAX 602-265-6250. Ed. Susan Slesinger; Pub. Phyllis Steckler. bibl. (back issues avail.) **Document type:** abstracting/indexing.
●Also available on CD-ROM. Producer(s): NISC (Consumer Reference Disc).
Description: Comprehensive index to articles on health topics in general and specialized publications, for researchers and medical librarians.

613.2 HO
ENCUESTA NACIONAL DE NUTRICION. (In 8 regional editions) a. Ministerio de Salud Publica, 4a Avda, 3a Calle, Tegucigalpa, D.C., Honduras. **Document type:** government publication.

NUTRICION EN SALUD PUBLICA. see *PUBLIC HEALTH AND SAFETY — Abstracting, Bibliographies, Statistics*

641 016 UK ISSN 0309-1295
QP141.A1
NUTRITION ABSTRACTS AND REVIEWS. SERIES A: HUMAN AND EXPERIMENTAL. Incorporating separate section: Reviews in Clinical Nutrition. 1977. m. £535($960); newsstand price: (effective 1996). CAB International, Wallingford, Oxon. OX10 8DE, England. TEL 01491-832111. FAX 01491-833508. TELEX 847964 COMAGG G. E-mail: cabi@cabi.org. (U.S. subscr. to: CAB International, North American Office, 845 N. Park Ave., Tucson, AZ 85719. TEL 800-528-4841) Ed.Bd. adv.; bk.rev.; index, cum.index: vols.1-10 (in 2 vols.). circ. 1,750. (also avail. in diskette format; back issues avail.) **Indexed:** Abstr.Hyg., Anim.Breed.Abstr., Biol.Abstr., Chem.Abstr., Dairy Sci.Abstr., Forest.Abstr., Ind.Med., JAMA, Trop.Dis.Bull. **Document type:** abstracting/indexing.
●Also available online. Vendor(s): CISTI, DIMDI, European Space Agency (File nos.16 & 124/CAB), Knight-Ridder, Inc., Ovid Technologies (NUTR).
Supersedes in part: Nutrition Abstracts and Reviews (ISSN 0029-6619)
Description: Aimed at research workers, consultants, public health specialists, advisors, and general practitioners.

NUTRITION DE SANTE PUBLIQUE. see *PUBLIC HEALTH AND SAFETY — Abstracting, Bibliographies, Statistics*

613.2 US
PERSPECTIVES IN NUTRITION. 1993. q. $49.50 to individuals; institutions $74.95; residents, students $32.95 (effective 1996). Mosby - Year Book, Inc. (Chicago) (Subsidiary of: Times Mirror Company), 200 N. LaSalle St., Chicago, IL 60601-1080. FAX 312-726-6075. TELEX 206155. Ed. Ronni Chernoff.
Description: Features abstracts of full-length journal articles on issues pertinent to the field of nutrition.

PUBLIC HEALTH NUTRITION. see *PUBLIC HEALTH AND SAFETY — Abstracting, Bibliographies, Statistics*

SCIENCE & TECHNOLOGY ABSTRACTS. see *FOOD AND FOOD INDUSTRIES — Abstracting, Bibliographies, Statistics*

OBSTETRICS AND GYNECOLOGY

see *Medical Sciences–Obstetrics and Gynecology*

OCCUPATIONAL HEALTH AND SAFETY

613.62 US ISSN 1059-1753
A O T A SELF STUDY SERIES. 1990. m. American Occupational Therapy Association, Inc., Box 31220, Bethesda, MD 20824-1220. TEL 301-652-2682. FAX 301-652-7711.

A P E L L NEWSLETTER. (Awareness and Preparedness for Emergencies at Local Level) see *CIVIL DEFENSE*

A S VORORT; Zeitschrift fuer Unfallverhuetung und Grubensicherheitswesen. (Arbeit und Sicherheit) see *MINES AND MINING INDUSTRY*

363.11 CN ISSN 0044-5878
ACCIDENT PREVENTION. 1952. bi-m. Can.$18 (US Can.$24, elsewhere Can.$33). Industrial Accident Prevention Association, 250 Yonge St., 28th Fl., Toronto, ON M5B 2N4, Canada. TEL 416-506-8888. FAX 416-506-8880. bk.rev.; abstr.; illus.; charts. circ. 35,000. **Indexed:** C.I.S. Abstr. **Document type:** trade publication.
—BLDSC (0573.200000).

613.62 658 US ISSN 8756-629X
ADMINISTRATION & MANAGEMENT SPECIAL INTEREST SECTION NEWSLETTER. (Consists of 11 sections: Administration and Management; Developmental Disabilities; Education; Home & Community Health; Gerontology; Mental Health; Physical Disabilities; School Systems; Sensory Integration; Technology; Work Programs) 1985. q. $15. American Occupational Therapy Association, Inc., Box 31220, Bethesda, MD 20824-1220. TEL 301-652-2682. FAX 301-652-7711. **Document type:** newsletter.

ADVANCE FOR OCCUPATIONAL THERAPISTS. see *MEDICAL SCIENCES*

AEROSPACE NEWSLETTER. see *AERONAUTICS AND SPACE FLIGHT*

613.62 614.85 SW ISSN 0280-3097
AKTUELL ARBETSMILJOEFORSKNING. 1981. s-a. free. Arbetsmiljoeinstitutet - Nationan Institute of Occupational Health, S-171 84 Solna, Sweden. TEL 46-8-730-91-00. FAX 46-8-730-98-88. E-mail: klever@nioh.se. Ed. Elisabeth Lagerloef. **Document type:** catalog.
Description: Contains summaries of scientific reports published by the Institute as well as summaries of presentations by researchers from the Institute at international conferences.

614.85 IT ISSN 0393-7054
AMBIENTE E SICUREZZA SUL LAVORO. 9/yr. Edizioni di Protezione Civile s.r.l., Via dell'Acqua Traversa 187-189, 00135 Rome, Italy. TEL 39-6-3313000. FAX 39-6-3313212. TELEX 626462 EPCINF I. Ed. Michele Lepore; Pub. Pier Roberto Pais. adv. contact: Roberto Barberini. circ. 9,000. **Document type:** trade publication.

613.62 US ISSN 0002-8894
RC963 CODEN: AIHAAP
AMERICAN INDUSTRIAL HYGIENE ASSOCIATION JOURNAL.* 1940. m. $120 (Canada and Mexico $145; elsewhere $185) (effective 1996). American Industrial Hygiene Association, 2700 Prosperity Ave., Ste. 250, Fairfax, VA 22031-4307. TEL 703-849-8888. Ed. Samuel Elkin. adv.; bk.rev.; bibl.; charts; illus.; index. circ. 11,300. (also avail. in microfiche; microfilm; reprint service avail. from UMI) **Indexed:** A.S.& T.Ind., Abstr.Hyg., Anal.Abstr., API Catal., API Hlth.& Environ., API Oil., API Pet.Ref., API Pet.Subst., API Transport., B.C.I.R.A., Bibl.Ind., Biodet.Abstr., Biol.Abstr., Br.Ceram.Abstr., C.I.S. Abstr., Cadscan., Chem.Abstr., Curr.Adv.Ecol.Sci., Curr.Cont., Energy Ind., Energy Info.Abstr., Environ.Abstr., Excerp.Med., Fuel & Energy Abstr., Ind.Hyg.Dig., Ind.Med., Ind.Sci.Rev., Ind.Vet., INIS Atomind., Intl.Polym.Sci.& Tech., Lab.Haz.Bull., Lead Abstr., Maize Abstr., Med.& Surg.Dermat., Noise Pollut.Publ.Abstr., Ocean.Abstr., Pollut.Abstr., Poult.Abstr., Protozool.Abstr., RAPRA, Rev.Med.& Vet.Mycol., Risk Abstr., Sci.Cit.Ind., Trop.Dis.Bull., Vet.Bull., Zincscan. **Document type:** trade publication.
●Also available online. Vendor(s): University Microfilms International.
—BLDSC (0819.995000); CASDDS; Faxon; Genuine Article; SWETS; UMI; UnCover. CCC.
Former titles (until 1957): American Industrial Hygiene Association Quarterly (ISSN 0096-820X); (until 1946): Industrial Hygiene.
Description: Offers a broad spectrum of articles together with literature, new products, meeting accouncements, committee activities and other AIHA news.
Refereed Serial

OCCUPATIONAL HEALTH AND SAFETY

613.62 US ISSN 0271-3586
CODEN: AJIMD8
AMERICAN JOURNAL OF INDUSTRIAL MEDICINE. 1980. m. $1571 (foreign $1757) (effective 1996). John Wiley & Sons, Inc., Journals, 605 Third Ave., New York, NY 10158. TEL 212-850-6645. FAX 212-850-6021. TELEX 12-7063. E-mail: SUBINFO@JWILEY.COM. (Subscr. outside the Americas to: John Wiley & Sons Ltd., Baffins Ln., Chichester, W. Sussex PO19 1UD, England. TEL 44-1243-779777. FAX 44-1243-446128) Ed. P.J. Landrigan. adv.; bibl.; charts; illus.; index. (also avail. in microform from UMI; back issues avail.) **Indexed:** Abstr.Hyg., Biol.Abstr., Br.Ceram.Abstr., Cadscan, Chem.Abstr., Curr.Adv.Ecol.Sci., Curr.Cont., Dent.Ind., Excerp.Med., Ind.Med., INIS Atomind., Lab.Haz.Bull., Lead Abstr., Med.& Surg.Dermat., Rev.Med.& Vet.Mycol., Zincscan. **Document type:** academic/scholarly publication.
●Also available online.
—BLDSC (0826.750000); CASDDS; Faxon; Genuine Article; SWETS; UnCover. **CCC.**
Description: Presents both clinical and laboratory findings, as well as general academic and scientific contributions in the fundamental or applied study of occupational disease.
Refereed Serial

615.851 US ISSN 0272-9490
RM735.A1 CODEN: AJOTAM
AMERICAN JOURNAL OF OCCUPATIONAL THERAPY. 1947. 10/yr. $120 (foreign $130) (effective 1996). American Occupational Therapy Association, Inc., Box 31220, Bethesda, MD 20824-1220. TEL 301-652-2682. FAX 301-652-7711. Ed. Elaine Viseltear. adv.; bk.rev.; abstr.; bibl.; charts; illus.; index. circ. 53,000. (also avail. in microform from UMI) **Indexed:** Abstr.Soc.Geront., ASSIA, Bibl.Dev.Med.& Child Neur., Biol.Abstr., C.I.J.E., CINAHL, CLOA, Curr.Cont., Dent.Ind., Dok.Arbeitsmed., Except.Child.Educ.Abstr., Excerp.Med., Hosp.Lit.Ind., IMFL, Ind.Med., Psychol.Abstr. (1950-), Rehabil.Lit., SSCI. **Document type:** academic/scholarly publication.
—BLDSC (0828.750000); Faxon; Genuine Article; SWETS; UMI; UnCover. **CCC.**
Former titles (until 1978): A J O T: The American Journal of Occupational Therapy (ISSN 0161-326X); (until 1977): American Journal of Occupational Therapy (ISSN 0002-9386)
Refereed Serial

613.62 US ISSN 0145-8922
AMERICAN OCCUPATIONAL THERAPY ASSOCIATION. ANNUAL REPORT. 1972. a. American Occupational Therapy Association, Inc., Box 31220, Bethesda, MD 20824-1220. TEL 301-652-2682. FAX 301-652-7711. **Document type:** corporate report.

614.85 338 US ISSN 1047-9090
AMERICAN WINDOW CLEANER; voice of the professional window cleaner. 1986. bi-m. $35 to individuals (Canada $40); institutions and foreign $60 (effective 1995 & 1996). (International Window Cleaning Association) Richard Fabry, Ed. & Pub., 27 Oak Creek Rd., El Sobrante, CA 94803. TEL 510-222-7080. FAX 510-223-7080. E-mail: amerwincln@aol.com. adv.; bk.rev. circ. 9,000. (back issues avail.) **Document type:** trade publication.
Formerly: American Window Cleaner Newsletter.
Description: Provides an industry-wide communication link on new products, techniques, association news, interviews, business advice, and upcoming events.

AMERISURE SAFETY NEWS. see *PUBLIC HEALTH AND SAFETY*

ANGEWANDTE ARBEITSWISSENSCHAFT. see *BUSINESS AND ECONOMICS — Labor And Industrial Relations*

363.11 948.9 DK ISSN 0905-1902
ANMELDTE ARBEJDSULYKKER. YEARBOOK. 1979. a. Danish National Working Environment Service, Analysis and Documentation Office, P.O. Box 858, DK-2100, Copenhagen, Denmark. TEL 45-31-18-20-62. FAX 45-31-18-00-88. Ed. Kirsten Joergensen. circ. 1,000.
Formerly (until 1989): Arbejdsulykker - Aarsstatistik (ISSN 0106-9683)

613.62 UK ISSN 0003-4878
RC963 CODEN: AOHYA3
ANNALS OF OCCUPATIONAL HYGIENE. 1958. bi-m. £340($541) (effective 1996). (British Occupational Hygiene Society, UK) Elsevier Science Ltd., Pergamon, P.O. Box 800, Kidlington, Oxford OX5 1DX, England. TEL 44-1865-843000. FAX 44-1865-843010.
E-mail: nlinfo-f@elsevier.nl; usinfo-f@elsevier.com; forinfo-kyf04035@niftyserve.or.jp; Site addr.: http://www.elsevier.nl/. (Subscr. in U.S. and Canada to: Elsevier Science, 660 WHite Plains Rd., Tarrytown, NY 10591-5153. TEL 914-524-9200. FAX 914-333-2444) Ed. John McK. Ellison. adv.; bk.rev.; charts; illus.; index. circ. 1,800. (also avail. in microfilm from UMI; back issues avail.) **Indexed:** Abstr.Hyg., Biol.Abstr., Biol.Dig., Br.Ceram.Abstr., C.I.S. Abstr., Chem.Abstr., Curr.Adv.Ecol.Sci., Curr.Cont., Ergon.Abstr., Excerp.Med., Helminthol.Abstr., Ind.Hyg.Dig., Ind.Med., Ind.Sci.Rev., Intl.Polym.Sci.& Tech., Lab.Haz.Bull., Med.& Surg.Dermat., Noise Pollut.Publ.Abstr., RAPRA, Rev.Med.& Vet.Mycol., Risk Abstr., Sci.Cit.Ind., Trop.Dis.Bull. **Document type:** academic/scholarly publication.
—BLDSC (1043.300000); CASDDS; Ei; Faxon; Genuine Article; SWETS; UMI; UnCover. **CCC.**
Description: Provides current coverage of news, issues and research in the field.
Refereed Serial

614.85 JA
ANZEN NO SHIHYO/BAROMETER OF OCCUPATIONAL SAFETY. (Text in Japanese) a. 470 Yen (effective 1990). Japan Industrial Safety and Health Association, International Cooperation Department, 5-35-1 Shiba, Minato-ku, Tokyo 108, Japan. TEL 81-3-3452-6841. FAX 81-3-3454-4596.
Description: Educational and promotional booklet for Japan's annual Safety Week.

AOMORIKEN SAGYO RYOHO KENKYU/BULLETIN OF AOMORI OCCUPATIONAL THERAPY. see *MEDICAL SCIENCES — Physical Medicine And Rehabilitation*

613.62 US ISSN 1047-322X
RC963.A1 CODEN: AOEHE9
APPLIED OCCUPATIONAL & ENVIRONMENTAL HYGIENE. 1986. m. $204 to institutions in U.S.; $298 to institutions outside the Americas (effective 1996). (American Conference of Governmental Industrial Hygienists, Inc.) Elsevier Science Inc., 655 Ave. of the Americas, New York, NY 10010. TEL 212-633-3950. FAX 212-633-3990. (Subscr. to: Box 882, Madison Sq. Sta., New York, NY 10159-0882) Ed. J.M. Dement. adv.; bk.rev.; abstr.; charts; illus. circ. 6,500. (back issues avail.) **Indexed:** Chem.Abstr., Curr.Cont., Environ.Abstr., Environ.Per.Bibl., Excerp.Med., Ind.Hyg.Dig. **Document type:** academic/scholarly publication.
—BLDSC (1576.239000); CASDDS; Faxon; SWETS; UnCover. **CCC.**
Formerly (until vol.5, no.1, 1990): Applied Industrial Hygiene (ISSN 0882-8032)
Description: Articles of interest to the occupational and environmental safety and health professional.

614.8 NO ISSN 0332-7124
HD7200
ARBEIDERVERN; working environment journal. 1973. 5/yr. NOK 80. Direktoratet for Arbeidstilsynet - Directorate of Labour Inspection, Fr. Nansens vei 14, P.O. Box 8103 Dep., N-0032 Oslo, Norway. TEL 47-22-957000. FAX 47-11-466214. adv.; illus. circ. 33,000. **Indexed:** C.I.S. Abstr.
—BLDSC (1584.023000). **CCC.**

363.1 NO ISSN 0800-2088
ARBEIDSMILJOE. 1951. 8/yr. NOK 250. Arbeidsmiljoesenteret, P.O. Box 28 Taasen, N-0801 Oslo, Norway. TEL 22236000. FAX 222237055. Ed. Oystein Braaathen. adv. contact: Tom Svendsen. bk.rev. circ. 10,489. **Document type:** bulletin.
—CCC.
Former titles (until 1982): Vern og Velferd Arbejdsmiljoe (ISSN 0332-9127); (until 1980): Vern og Velferd (ISSN 0049-5964)

363.11 NE ISSN 0920-119X
ARBEIDSOMSTANDIGHEDEN. (Supplement avail.: Arbeidsomstandigheden Concreet (ISSN 0929-1105)) 1927. 11/yr. fl.229.50. (Nederlands Instituut voor Arbeidsomstandigheden) Uitgeverij Kluwer B.V., Postbus 23, 7400 GA Deventer, Netherlands. (Editorial addr.: NIA, Postbus 75665, 1070 AR Amsterdam, Netherlands. TEL 31-20-5498611) adv.; bk.rev.; bibl.; illus.; stat. circ. 5,900. **Indexed:** C.I.S. Abstr., Chem.Abstr., Excerp.Med. **Document type:** trade publication.
Formerly: De Veiligheid - Safety (ISSN 0042-3149)

363.11 NE ISSN 0929-1105
ARBEIDSOMSTANDIGHEDEN CONCREET. (Supplement to: Arbeidsomstandigheden (ISSN 0920-119X)) 1992. 11/yr. (Nederlands Instituut voor Arbeidsomstandigheden) Uitgeverij Kluwer B.V., Postbus 23, 7400 GA Deventer, Netherlands. TEL 31-5700-47111. FAX 31-5700-34740. adv. circ. 6,600. **Document type:** trade publication.
Formerly (until 1993): Arbeidsomstandigheden-actueel (ISSN 0927-4480)

614.85 BE ISSN 0770-7649
ARBEIDSVEILIGHEID. (Text in Flemish) 1982. s-m. 5380 BEF. C E D Samsom (Subsidiary of: Wolters Samsom Belgie n.v.), Kouterveld 14, B-1831 Diegem, Belgium. TEL 32-2-7231111. index.
Description: Focuses on latest developments in workers' safety.

613.62 GW ISSN 0946-7599
ARBEIT UND GESUNDHEIT; Zeitschrift fuer Arbeitssicherheit und Gesundheitsschutz. 1949. m. DM.20. Hauptverband der Gewerblichen Berufsgenossenschaften e.V., 53754 Sankt Augustin, Germany. TEL 02241-23101333. Ed. Rudolf Dertinger. **Document type:** bulletin.

ARBEITSMEDIZIN, SOZIALMEDIZIN, UMWELTMEDIZIN; Zeitschrift fuer Praxis, Klinik, Forschung, Begutachtung. see *PUBLIC HEALTH AND SAFETY*

ARBEITSMEDIZIN, SOZIALMEDIZIN, UMWELTMEDIZIN. SUPPLEMENT. see *PUBLIC HEALTH AND SAFETY*

613 DK
ARBEJDSBETINGEDE LIDELSER. YEARBOOK. (Illness at Work) 1983. a. DKK 250. Danish National Working Environment Service., Analysis and Documentation Office, P.O. Box 858, DK-2100 Copenhagen OE, Denmark. TEL 45-31-18-00-88. FAX 45-31-18-20-62. Ed. Kirsten Joergensen. circ. 1,000.

363.11 SW ISSN 0346-7805
ARBETARSKYDD. 1972. 15/yr. SEK 280. Arbetarskyddsstyrelsen, Arbetarskyddsstyrelsen, S-171 84 Solna, Sweden. TEL 46-8-730-99-00. FAX 46-8-730-90-68. Ed. Hans Olof Wiklund. adv.: B&W page SEK 25000, color page SEK 30000; trim 252 x 370; adv. contact: Sylvia Aldenryd. circ. 23,500. cols./p.: 5; pp./issue: 20. (tabloid format) **Document type:** newspaper.
Former titles (until 1975): Aktuell Information (ISSN 0345-0244); (until 1974): Aktuellt fraan Arbetarskyddsverket (ISSN 0345-0252)

614.85 SW ISSN 0282-910X
ARBETARSKYDDSREGLER BYGGARBETE. 1982-1984; resumed 1985. a. SEK 495 (effective 1991). Svensk Byggtjaenst, S-171 88 Solna, Sweden.

614.85 SW ISSN 0348-2138
ARBETARSKYDDSSTYRELSENS FOERFATTNINGSSAMLING. 1978. irreg. SEK 600 (effective 1995). Arbetarskyddsstyrelsen, S-171 84 Solna, Sweden. (Dist. by: S T K - Distribution, Sorterarg. 2, S-162 26 Vaellingby, Sweden) circ. 13,000. **Document type:** government publication.
Formed by the merger of: Arbetarskyddsstyrelsens Meddelanden; Arbetarskyddsstyrelsens Anvisningar.

363.11 NE ISSN 0169-9237
ARBO BULLETIN. 1986. bi-m. (Nederlands Instituut voor Arbeidsomstandigheden) Uitgeverij Kluwer B.V., Postbus 23, 7400 GA Deventer, Netherlands. TEL 31-5700-47111. FAX 31-5700-37533. adv. **Document type:** bulletin.
—SWETS.

OCCUPATIONAL HEALTH AND SAFETY

363.11   NE
ARBO JAARBOEK. 1959. a. (Nederlands Instituut voor Arbeidsomstandigheden) Uitgeverij Kluwer B.V., Postbus 23, 7400 GA Deventer, Netherlands. TEL 31-5700-47111. FAX 31-5700-34740. (Editorial addr.: NIA, Postbus 75665, 1070 AR Amsterdam, Netherlands. TEL 31-20-5498425) adv.; bk.rev. circ. 4,000. **Document type:** trade publication.
    Formerly: Veiligheidsjaarboek (ISSN 0083-534X)
    Description: Yearbook for those professionally occupied with the working environment.

363.11 690   NE   ISSN 1382-7197
ARBOUW JOURNAAL. 1991. 4/yr. fl.50. (Stichting Arbouw) Uitgeverij Kluwer B.V., Postbus 23, 7400 GA Deventer, Netherlands. TEL 31-5700-47111. FAX 31-5700-34740. (Editorial addr.: Postbus 8114, 1005 AC Amsterdam, Netherlands. TEL 31-20-5805580) adv. **Document type:** trade publication.
    Description: Covers issues relating to the improvement of working conditions in the construction industry.

ARCHIVES BELGES DE MEDECINE SOCIALE, HYGIENE, MEDECINE DU TRAVAIL ET MEDECINE. see *PUBLIC HEALTH AND SAFETY*

362.1 613.6   FR   ISSN 0003-9691
    CODEN: AMPMAR
ARCHIVES DES MALADIES PROFESSIONNELLES ET DE MEDECINE DU TRAVAIL ET DE SECURITE SOCIALE. (Text in French; summaries in English) 1938. 8/yr. 930 F. (foreign 1226 F.) (effective 1996). (Societe de Medecine et d'Hygiene du Travail de France) Masson - Periodiques, Villa Laromiguiere, 75005 Paris, France. TEL 1-40-46-62-00. FAX 1-40-46-62-01. Ed. Patrick Hadengue. adv.; bk.rev.; illus.; index. circ. 3,500. (also avail. in microform from UMI; reprint service avail. from ISI) **Indexed:** Abstr.Hyg., Biol.Abstr., C.I.S. Abstr., Chem.Abstr., Curr.Adv.Ecol.Sci., Ergon.Abstr., Excerp.Med., Helminthol.Abstr., Ind.Med., INIS Atomind., Nutr.Abstr., Rev.Plant Path., Trop.Dis.Bull. **Document type:** academic/scholarly publication.
—CASDDS; Faxon; SWETS; UMI. **CCC.**
    Description: Supplies technical, scientific and practical information to practitioners devoted to occupational medicine or professional pathology.

613.62   IT
ARCHIVIO DI SCIENZE DEL LAVORO. vol.9 no.1, 1993. q. L.66000 (foreign L.99000). Istituto Poligrafico e Zecca dello Stato, Via Nomentana 2, 00161 Rome, Italy. TEL 39-6-8559648. (Edit. addr.: Istituto di Medicina del Lavoro dell'Universita Cattolica, Largo A. Gemelli, 8, 00168 Rome, Italy. TEL 39-6-30154359) Ed. Carmelo Bellocco.

ARHIV ZA HIGIJENU RADA I TOKSIKOLOGIJU/ARCHIVES OF INDUSTRIAL HYGIENE AND TOXICOLOGY. see *ENVIRONMENTAL STUDIES — Toxicology And Environmental Safety*

613.62   US   ISSN 0197-7903
N1
ART HAZARDS NEWS. 1978. 5/yr. $24 (Canada $26.50; foreign $29) (effective 1995 & 1996). Center for Safety in the Arts, 5 Beekman St., New York, NY 10038. TEL 212-227-6220. FAX 212-233-3846. Ed. Michael McCann; Pub. Angela Babin. bk.rev.; index. circ. 2,500. (back issues avail.) **Document type:** newsletter.
    Description: News on research and education pertaining to hazards in the arts (including visual and performing arts, and museums and educational facilities), covering such topics as precautions, legislation and regulations, lawsuits, and calendars of events.

ASBESTOS CASE LAW QUARTERLY. see *LAW*

ASIAN ENVIRONMENT; journal of environmental science and technology for balanced development. see *ENVIRONMENTAL STUDIES*

613.62   FR   ISSN 0066-927X
ASSOCIATION FRANCAISE DES TECHNICIENS ET INGENIEURS DE SECURITE ET DES MEDECINS DU TRAVAIL. ANNUAIRE. 1965. a. 360 F. Association Francaise des Techniciens et Ingenieurs de Securite et des Medecins du Travail (AFTIM), 1 place Uranie, 94340 Joinville le Pont, France. TEL 33-1-48-85-70-59. FAX 33-1-48-85-02-99. adv.

613 340   AT
AUSTRALIAN INDUSTRIAL SAFETY, HEALTH & WELFARE. (In 3 vols.) 1979. 10/yr. C C H Australia Ltd., P.O. Box 230, North Ryde, N.S.W. 2113, Australia. TEL 61-2-8571555. FAX 61-2-8571601. (looseleaf format)
    Description: Covers all Australian jurisdictions. Contains case extracts, codes of practice, an index of existing standards, and articles covering new developments.

620.86   US
AUTOMOTIVE, TOOLING, METALWORKING, AND ASSOCIATED INDUSTRIES NEWSLETTER. bi-m. $19 to non-members; members $15. National Safety Council, Periodicals Department, 1121 Spring Lake Dr., Itasca, IL 60143. TEL 708-775-2281. Ed. Kathy Henderson; Pub. Kevin H. Axe. **Document type:** newsletter.
    Former titles: Safety Newsletter: Automotive, Tooling, Metalworking and Associated Industries; Safety Newsletter: Automotive and Machine Shop Section.
    Description: Information and recommendations on various safety issues within the field.

614.85   US
B C S P NEWSLETTER. 1975. 3/yr. membership only. Board of Certified Safety Professionals, 208 Burwash, Savoy, IL 61874. TEL 217-359-9263. Ed. Michael K. Orn. (back issues avail.) **Document type:** newsletter.
    Description: Professional certification in safety, demographics of safety engineers, and regulatory activities.

B G W MITTEILUNGEN. (Berufsgenossenschaft fuer Gesundheitsdienst und Wohlfahrtspflege) see *INSURANCE*

613.62   US   ISSN 1065-3104
KFC584.A15
B N A CALIFORNIA SAFETY & HEALTH REPORT.* 1992. bi-w. $395. M. Lee Smith Publishers & Printers, 162 Fourth Ave., Box 198867, Nashville, TN 37219-8867. TEL 615-242-7395. FAX 615-256-6601. Ed. Glenn Totten. index. (back issues avail.)
    Description: Notification service providing comprehensive coverage of state and local job safety and health developments and related workplace developments.

614.7   FR
BATIMENT - ENTRETIEN. 1968. bi-m. 72 F. 91 rue du Faubourg Saint Denis, 75010 Paris, France. TEL 42-46-55-24. FAX 48-00-05-03. Ed. Bernard Abenesdra. adv. circ. 10,500.

613.62   GW   ISSN 0341-096X
BAU; Mitteilungsblatt. 1949. q. Bau-Berufsgenossenschaft Wuppertal, Eulenbergstr. 15-21, 51065 Cologne, Germany. TEL 0221-6703175. **Document type:** newsletter.

614.85   GW   ISSN 0931-2862
BAU-BERUFSGENOSSENSCHAFT HANNOVER. MITTEILUNGSBLATT. 1976. q. free. Bau-Berufsgenossenschaft Hannover, Hildesheimer Str. 309, 30519 Hannover, Germany. TEL 0511-987-0. FAX 0511-9872440. Ed. Rolf Schaper. adv. contact: Bernard Foerster. bk.rev. circ. 62,000. (back issues avail.) **Document type:** newsletter.

614.85   US   ISSN 0090-7480
T55.A1
BEST'S SAFETY DIRECTORY; safety-industrial hygiene-security. 1946. a. $45. A.M. Best Co., Ambest Rd., Oldwick, NJ 08858. TEL 908-439-2200. FAX 908-439-3296. Ed. Christine Koehler. adv. **Document type:** directory.
—**CCC.**

613.62   RU   ISSN 0409-2961
    CODEN: BZTPAM
BEZOPASNOST' TRUDA V PROMYSHLENNOSTI/LABOUR SAFETY IN INDUSTRY. 1932. m. $90 (effective 1996). Izdatel'stvo Nedra, Pl. Belorusskogo Vokzala, 3, 125047 Moscow, Russia.
—CASDDS.

614.85   XO   ISSN 0322-8347
BEZPECNA PRACA. (Text in Czech or Slovak; summaries in English, German, Russian) 1970. bi-m. $39. Vyskumny a vzdelavaci Ustav Bezpecnosti Prace - Research Institute of Work Security, Stefanikova 47, 814 54 Bratislava, Slovakia. (Dist. by: Slovart, Gottwaldovo nam. 48, 805 32 Bratislava, Slovakia) **Indexed:** C.I.S. Abstr.

613.62   PL   ISSN 0137-7043
BEZPIECZENSTWO PRACY. 1971. m. 13.50 Zl. Centralny Instytut Ochrony Pracy - Central Institute for Labor Protection, Ul. Czerniakowska 16, 00-701 Warsaw, Poland. TEL 48-2-623-3695. FAX 48-2-623-4610. E-mail: JOSE@CIOP.WAW.PL. adv.; bk.rev. circ. 6,500.
    Description: Covers occupational safety and ergonomics.

614.85   GW   ISSN 0935-9451
BILAG BRIEF. 1982. 2/yr. DM.15. Berliner Infoladen fuer Arbeit und Gesundheit e.V., Gneisenaustr. 2a, 10961 Berlin, Germany. TEL 030-6932090. Ed. Eberhard Goebel, Beate Guthke. adv.; bk.rev.; bibl.; illus. circ. 1,200. (back issues avail.) **Document type:** newsletter.

614.85   IS
BITECHUT. (Text in Hebrew) bi-m. Safety and Hygiene Institute, 22 Mazeh St., Tel Aviv, Israel. TEL 03-297311.

613.7   US   ISSN 0275-9101
BODY BULLETIN NEWSLETTER. 1981. m. Rodale Press, Inc., 33 E. Minor St., Emmaus, PA 18098. TEL 610-967-5171. TELEX 847338. **Document type:** newsletter.
—UMI. **CCC.**
    Description: Introduces employees to safe and sensible ways to deal with common health problems.

BRITISH COLUMBIA. MINISTRY OF SKILLS, TRAINING AND LABOUR. NEGOTIATED WORKING CONDITIONS. see *BUSINESS AND ECONOMICS — Labor And Industrial Relations*

613.62 620   US
C S P DIRECTORY. 1975. biennial. $30. Board of Certified Safety Professionals, 208 Barwash Ave., Savoy, IL 61874. TEL 217-359-9263. Ed. Michael K. Orn. adv. circ. 9,500. **Document type:** directory.

613.63 614.85   US   ISSN 1062-6743
C T D NEWS. 1991. m. $147. Center for Workplace Health, 410 Lancaster Ave., Ste. 15, Haverford, PA 19041. TEL 610-896-2770; 800-554-4283. FAX 610-896-2762. Ed. Michael Gauf; Pub. James Kinsella. adv. contact: Bradley Aronson. index. circ. 4,365. (also avail. in diskette format; back issues avail.) **Document type:** newsletter.
    Description: Deals with occupational health and computer injury issues.

613.62   BE   ISSN 0376-7639
    CODEN: CMTVAS
CAHIERS DE MEDECINE DU TRAVAIL/CAHIERS VOOR ARBEIDSGENEESKUNDE. (Text in Dutch, French) 1963. q. 2300 BEF (foreign 2800 BEF). Association Professionnelle Belge des Medecins du Travail - Belgische Beroepsvereniging voor Arbeidsgeneesheren, Ave. de Venus 14, 1410 Waterloo, Belgium. TEL 32-2-3547775. FAX 32-2-3510451. (Subscr. to: c/o Dr. P. Carlier, Rueli aux Pierres de Tailles 16, 1000 Brussels, Belgium) Eds. Dr. P. Genet, Dr. P. Dewilde. abstr.; bibl.; cum.index every 5 yrs.; circ. 600 (paid). **Document type:** bulletin.
—BLDSC (2949.745000); CASDDS.
    Description: Publishes articles on topics of interest to occupational physicians, hygienists, ergonomists, and safety managers.
Refereed Serial

4930 OCCUPATIONAL HEALTH AND SAFETY

613.62   US   ISSN 1054-1209
CAL - O S H A REPORTER. (Occupational Safety and Health Association) 1973. w. $227. Commanon Corp., Box 815, Daville, CA 94526-0815. TEL 415-233-1880. FAX 415-233-1249. Ed. Anne Bell; Pub. John P. McCann. bk.rev.; index. circ. 1,848. (looseleaf format; back issues avail.)
Document type: newsletter.
Former titles: California - O S H A Reporter; Cal - O S H A Reporter.
Description: Written for occupational safety and health practitioners primarily in California. Covers job safety and health, workers' compensation, toxics, risk management and other related issues. Provides detailed coverage of laws, regulations and court cases.

CALIFORNIA. DEPARTMENT OF INDUSTRIAL RELATIONS. BIENNIAL REPORT. see BUSINESS AND ECONOMICS — Labor And Industrial Relations

344   613.62   CN
CANADIAN EMPLOYMENT SAFETY AND HEALTH GUIDE. m. Can.$685. C C H Canadian Ltd., 6 Garamond Ct., North York, ON M3C 1Z5, Canada. TEL 416-441-2992; 800-268-4522. FAX 416-444-9011. **Document type:** trade publication.
Description: Reports on federal and provincial legislation on employment safety and health plus relevant case law.

615.8   CN   ISSN 0008-4174
CANADIAN JOURNAL OF OCCUPATIONAL THERAPY/REVUE CANADIENNE D'ERGOTHERAPIE. Abbreviated title: C J O T. (Text mainly in English, occasionally in French) 1933. 5/yr. Can.$37($52) Canadian Association of Occupational Therapists, 110 Eglinton Ave. West, 3rd Fl., Toronto, ON M4R 1A3, Canada. TEL 416-487-5404. FAX 416-487-0480. Ed. Geraldine Moore. adv.: B&W page Can.$525; 7 1/4 x 9 1/2; adv. contact: Jacqualine Corbett. bk.rev.; bibl.; illus.; index; circ. 434 (paid); 6,172. (reprint service avail. from UMI) Indexed: CINAHL, Excerp.Med. (1994-), Ind.Med., Rehabil.Lit.
—BLDSC (3033.600000); Faxon; SWETS; UMI; UnCover.
Description: Promotes the advancement and growth of theory and practice in occupational therapy and fosters excellence in research and education.

CANADIAN MINING JOURNAL. see MINES AND MINING INDUSTRY

614.8   CN   ISSN 0709-5252
CANADIAN OCCUPATIONAL HEALTH & SAFETY NEWS. 1978. w. (50/yr.). Can.$374.03 (foreign Can.$419). Southam Information and Technology Group, 1450 Don Mills Rd., Don Mills, ON M3B 2X7, Canada. TEL 416-445-6641. FAX 416-442-2200. Ed. Mary Mancini. q. index. **Document type:** newsletter.
Formerly: Canadian Industrial Health and Safety News (ISSN 0701-8983)
Description: Contains the latest legislative and regulatory changes, new techniques and technology, calendars of upcoming conferences and workshops and WHMIS updates.

614   340   CN   ISSN 0704-3724
CANADIAN OCCUPATIONAL SAFETY & HEALTH LAW. 1978. 12/yr. Can.$959 (foreign Can.$1047). Southam Information and Technology Group, 1450 Don Mills Rd., Don Mills, ON M3B 2X7, Canada. TEL 416-445-6641. FAX 416-442-2200. Ed. Mary Mancini. bk.rev.; cum.index. (looseleaf format)

620.86   US
CEMENT, QUARRY AND MINERAL AGGREGATES NEWSLETTER. bi-m. $19 to non-members; members $15. National Safety Council, Peridocals Department, 1121 Spring Lake Dr., Itasca, IL 60143. TEL 708-775-2281. Ed. Kathy Henderson; Pub. Kevin H. Axe. **Document type:** newsletter.
Formerly: Safety Newsletter: Cement, Quarry and Mineral Aggregates Section.
Description: Information and recommendations on various safety issues within the field.

613.62   540   UK   ISSN 0265-5721 CODEN: CHINEK
CHEMICAL HAZARDS IN INDUSTRY. 1984. m. £337($638) in E.C. nations; elsewhere £345 (effective 1996). The Royal Society of Chemistry, Thomas Graham House, Science Park, Milton Rd., Cambridge CB4 4WF, England. TEL 01223-420066. FAX 01223-423429. E-mail: rsc1@rsc.org. (Subscr. to.: Turpin Distribution Services Ltd., Blackhorse Rd., Letchworth, Herts. SG6 1HN, England. TEL 01462-672555. FAX 01462-480947) Ed. Michael Hannant. cum.index. Indexed: Chem.Abstr., World Surf.Coat. **Document type:** abstracting/indexing, bulletin.
●Also available online. Vendor(s): Data-Star (CSNB), Knight-Ridder, Inc. (File no.317), STN International (CSNB).
Also available on CD-ROM. Producer(s): Knight-Ridder, Inc.
—BLDSC (3146.588000). **CCC**.
Description: Provides current awareness of such topics as health and safety, chemical and biological hazards, plant safety, legislation, protective equipment and storage relating to the chemical and allied industries.

330.280   US
CHEMICAL NEWSLETTER. bi-m. $19 to non-members; members $15. National Safety Council, Periodicals Department, 1121 Spring Lake Dr., Itasca, IL 60143. TEL 708-775-2281. Ed. Kathy Henderson; Pub. Kevin H. Axe. **Document type:** newsletter.
Formerly: Safety Newsletter: Chemical Section.

CHEMICAL SAFETY SHEETS. see CHEMISTRY

613.62   US   ISSN 0073-7488
CHEMICAL-TOXICOLOGICAL SERIES. BULLETINS. 1947. irreg., no.8, 1969. price varies. Industrial Health Foundation, Inc., 34 Penn Circle W., Pittsburgh, PA 15206. TEL 412-363-6600. **Document type:** bulletin.
Formerly: Industrial Hygiene Foundation. Chemical-Toxicological Series. Bulletin (ISSN 0537-5215)

613.62   614.85   NE
CHEMIEKAARTEN; gegevens voor veilig werken met chemicalien. (Text in Dutch) 1977. a. fl.189.50. (Nederlandse Instituut voor Arbeidsomstandigheden - Dutch Institute for the Working Environment) Samsom H.D. Tjeenk Willink B.V. (Subsidiary of: Wolters Kluwer N.V.), Postbus 316, 2400 AH Alphen aan den Rijn, Netherlands. TEL 31-1720-66822. FAX 31-1720-66639. (Co-sponsors: Nederlandse Vereniging voor Veiligheidskunde; Vereniging van de Nederlandse Chemische Industrie) circ. 10,000.
Description: Standard work on the effects of chemicals on the human being and prevention possibilities.

CHILD LABOR MONITOR. see CHILDREN AND YOUTH — About

614.85   US   ISSN 8755-2566 CODEN: CIHNEM
CHILTON'S INDUSTRIAL SAFETY & HYGIENE NEWS; news of safety, health and hygiene, environmental, fire, security and emergency protection equipment. 1967. m. $50. Chilton Co., One Chilton Way, Radnor, PA 19089. TEL 215-964-4028. Ed. Dave Johnson. adv.; charts; illus.; tr.lit. circ. 62,000. (tabloid format; also avail. in microform from UMI; reprint service avail. from UMI) Indexed: Curr.Pack.Abstr., Ind.Hyg.Dig.
—UMI. **CCC**.
Former titles (until 1982): Industrial Safety and Hygiene News; (until 1981): Industrial Safety Product News (ISSN 0192-8325); (until 1978): Safety Products News (ISSN 0278-8217)

613.62   338   UN
CLEANER PRODUCTION. (Supplement to: Industry and Environment (ISSN 0378-9993) and Lettre du C F E (ISSN 0999-6249)) s-a. United Nations Environment Programme, Industry and Environment Programme Activity Centre, 39-43 quai Andre Citroen, 73739 Paris Cedex 15, France. TEL 44-37-14-50. FAX 44-37-14-74. TELEX 204 997 F. Ed. G. Clark. illus. **Document type:** newsletter.
Description: Provides information on cleaner technologies and products, actions by governments and organizations to promote cleaner production and the UNEP IEPAC Cleaner Production activities and network.

331.204   US
COAL MINING NEWSLETTER. bi-m. $19 to non-members; members $15. National Safety Council, Periodicals Department, 1121 Spring Lake. Dr., Itasca, IL 60143. TEL 708-775-2281. Ed. Kathy Henderson; Pub. Kevin H. Axe. **Document type:** newsletter.
Formerly: Safety Newsletter: Coal Mining Section.
Description: Information and recommendations on various safety issues within the coal mining industry.

COATINGS, REGULATIONS AND THE ENVIRONMENT. see PAINTS AND PROTECTIVE COATINGS

613.62   US
COMMUNITY AND WORKER RIGHT-TO-KNOW NEWS. fortn. $379. Thompson Publishing Company, 1725 K St., N.W., Ste. 200, Washington, DC 20006. TEL 202-872-4000. Ed. Nancy Nickell. index. **Document type:** newsletter.
Description: Publishes articles on right-to-know and emergency planning, particularly regarding explosions, fires, and spills, aimed at environmental managers seeking information on compliance.

658.3   344.73
613.62   US   ISSN 1077-5889
▼**COMPLIANCE MAGAZINE;** workplace safety, health & environment. 1994. 10/yr. $55 (free to qualified personnel). I H S Publishing Group, Inc., 17730 W. Peterson Rd., Libertyville, IL 60048-0159. TEL 708-362-8711. FAX 708-362-3484. Ed. Brian J. Taylor. adv. contact: Lauren Guthrie. circ. 60,000 (controlled). (tabloid format; back issues avail.) **Document type:** trade publication.
—Ei.
Description: Aims to inform and educate industry professionals responsible for workplace safety, health and environment about existing regulations, significant new laws and recent compliance product developments that affect their operations.

614   MX   ISSN 0185-2353
CONDICIONES DE TRABAJO. 1976. 3/yr. free. Secretaria del Trabajo y Prevision Social, Direccion General de Seguridad e Higiene en el Trabajo, Calzada Azcapotzalco la Villa No. 209, Junto Metro Ferreria, 02020 Mexico, D.F., Mexico. TEL 525-3943344. FAX 525-3942644. Dir. Dr. Juan Antonio Legaspi Velasco. bibl.; charts; illus.; stat. circ. 4,000. **Document type:** government publication.
Description: Covers health insurance, hygiene, and work conditions in the work force.

658.3   US
CONSTRUCTION NEWSLETTER. bi-m. $19 to non-members; members $15. National Safety Council, Periodicals Department, 1121 Spring Lake Dr., Itasca, IL 60143. TEL 708-775-2281. Ed. Kathy Henderson; Pub. Kevin H. Axe. **Document type:** newsletter.
Formerly: Safety Newsletter: Construction Section.
Description: Information and recommendations on various safety issues in construction.

614.85   CN   ISSN 0848-9394
CORPUS OCCUPATIONAL HEALTH AND SAFETY MANAGEMENT HANDBOOK. 1985. biennial. Can.$47.50. Southam Information and Technology Group, 1450 Don Mills Rd., Don Mills, ON M3B 2X7, Canada. TEL 416-445-6641. FAX 416-442-2200. Ed. Mary Mancini. charts; illus. circ. 1,600.
Description: Provides facts, advice and contacts.

614.85   UK
CRONER'S DANGEROUS SUBSTANCES. 1983. bi-m. £158.80 (effective 1993). Croner Publications Ltd. (Subsidiary of: Wolters Kluwer N.V.), Croner House, London Rd., Kingston, Surrey KT2 6SR, England. TEL 081-547-3333. FAX 081-547-2637. Ed. C. Hand. (looseleaf format)
Description: Covers European requirements for dangerous substance classification, packaging and labelling, with emphasis on the United Kingdom.

614.85   340   UK
CRONER'S HEALTH AND SAFETY AT WORK. 1979. bi-m. £103.20 (effective 1993). Croner Publications Ltd. (Subsidiary of: Wolters Kluwer N.V.), Croner House, London Rd., Kingston, Surrey KT2 6SR, England. TEL 081-547-3333. FAX 081-547-2637. Ed. L. Clery. (looseleaf format)
Description: Provides information on health and safety legislation, legal requirements, and related topics.

OCCUPATIONAL HEALTH AND SAFETY

614.85 UK
CRONER'S HEALTH AND SAFETY IN PRACTICE. irreg. Croner Publications Ltd. (Subsidiary of: Wolters Kluwer N.V.), Croner House, London Rd., Kingston-on-Thames, Surrey KT2 6SR, England. TEL 081-547-3333. FAX 081-547-2637. **Document type:** monographic series.

613.62 UK
CRONER'S SUBSTANCES HAZARDOUS TO HEALTH. 1986. base vol. (plus q. updates). £119.40 (effective 1993). Croner Publications Ltd. (Subsidiary of: Wolters Kluwer N.V.), Croner House, London Rd., Kingston, Surrey KT2 6SR, England. TEL 081-547-3333. FAX 081-547-2637. Ed. Dr. Brian Kellard. (looseleaf format) **Document type:** trade publication.
Description: Provides a practical guide to the assessment, measurement, and control of specific hazardous substances.

613.62 US ISSN 0270-3777
T55.3.H3 CODEN: DPIRDU
DANGEROUS PROPERTIES OF INDUSTRIAL MATERIALS REPORT. 1980. bi-m. $210 (Canada $250). Van Nostrand Reinhold, 115 Fifth Ave., New York, NY 10003. TEL 212-254-3232. FAX 212-673-1239. Ed. N. Irving Sax. adv.; bk.rev.; bibl.; charts; illus.; stat.; cum.index; circ. 2,000. (back issues avail.) **Indexed:** Abstr.Bull.Inst.Pap.Chem., C.I.S. Abstr., CAD CAM Abstr., Chem.Abstr., Corros.Abstr., Dent.Ind., Environ.Abstr., Lab.Haz.Bull.
—BLDSC (3518.820000); CASDDS; Faxon; UMI; UnCover. **CCC.**

DELO IN VARNOST; revija za varstvo pri delu. see BUSINESS AND ECONOMICS — Labor And Industrial Relations

DEVELOPMENTAL DISABILITIES SPECIAL INTEREST SECTION NEWSLETTER. see PSYCHOLOGY

DIAGNOSTIC ENGINEERING. see ENGINEERING — Mechanical Engineering

DICTIONNAIRE PERMANENT: SECURITE ET CONDITIONS DE TRAVAIL. see BUSINESS AND ECONOMICS — Labor And Industrial Relations

614.85 FR ISSN 0339-6517
DOCUMENTS POUR LE MEDECIN DU TRAVAIL. 1973. q. 380 F. Institut National de Recherche et de Securite pour la Prevention des Accidents du Travail et des Maladies Professionnelles, Ministere du Travail, Direction des Relations du Travail, 30 rue Olivier-Noyer, 75680 Paris Cedex 14, France. TEL 40-44-30-00. FAX 40-44-30-99. Ed. A. Leprince. bk.rev.; index, cum.index. circ. 10,000. **Indexed:** C.I.S. Abstr. **Document type:** corporate report, newspaper, government publication.
—BLDSC (3609.113080).
Description: Scientific and medical publication for occupational medical practitioners.

614.85 GW ISSN 0340-5567
DOKUMENTATION ARBEITSSCHUTZ UNFALLVERHUETUNG ARBEITSMEDIZIN. (Text in English and German) 1970. 5/yr. DM.30. Berufgenossenschaft der Chemischen Industrie, Bereich Praevention IuD, Postfach 101480, 69004 Heidelberg, Germany. TEL 06221-523431. FAX 06221-523420. bk.rev. circ. 1,900. **Document type:** academic/scholarly publication, bibliography.

613.62 628 US ISSN 1062-5526
E M F HEALTH & SAFETY DIGEST. (Electric and Magnetic Field) 1983. 10/yr. $400. E M F Information Project, 2701 University Ave., S.E., Ste. 203, Minneapolis, MN 55414-3236. TEL 612-623-4600. FAX 612-623-3645. E-mail: emfproj@rsba.com. (Subscr. to: Box 141049, University Sta., Minneapolis, MN 55414-6049) Ed. Janet Lathrop. bk.rev.; bibl.; charts. circ. 500. (looseleaf format; back issues avail.) **Indexed:** Amer.Hist.& Life, Hist.Abstr., Sociol.Abstr.
Former titles: Transmission - Distribution Health and Safety Report (ISSN 0737-5743) & T and D Health and Safety Report (ISSN 0736-5047)
Description: Covers the controversial issues of health effects from electric and magnetic fields.

EDUCATION SPECIAL INTEREST SECTION NEWSLETTER. see EDUCATION

EMPLOYER'S HEALTH & SAFETY MANUAL - ONTARIO. see BUSINESS AND ECONOMICS — Labor And Industrial Relations

363.1 613.62 AT ISSN 0728-635X
EMPLOYERS' REVIEW. 1928. 23/yr. membership only. Employers' Federation of New South Wales, 313 Sussex St., Sydney, N.S.W. 2001, Australia. FAX 61-2-261-1968. Ed. Jill Allen. adv.; bk.rev. circ. 3,300. **Document type:** newsletter.

613.6 363.11 US ISSN 0890-1988
KF3574.G68A497
EMPLOYMENT HEALTH LAW & BENEFITS. 1986. m. $148. Employment Research Institute, Inc., 5009 W. Windsor, Chicago, IL 60630-3926. TEL 312-545-0585. FAX 312-545-0586. Ed. Bernard Farber. index. circ. 200. (looseleaf format; back issues avail.) **Document type:** newsletter.
Description: Reviews all published court decisions in state and federal courts, significant cases of general interest, and summaries of current technical literature relating to employment health law.

331 313.62 US ISSN 0093-1535
EMPLOYMENT SAFETY AND HEALTH GUIDE. 3/yr. (plus w. reports). $800. Commerce Clearing House, Inc., 4025 W. Peterson Ave., Chicago, IL 60646. TEL 312-583-8500.

613.62 US
ENVIRONMENTAL HEALTH AND SAFETY NEWS. 1951. m. free. University of Washington, Department of Environmental Health, School of Public Health and Community Medicine, SC-34 Health Sciences Bldg., Seattle, WA 98195. TEL 206-543-4252. FAX 206-543-8123. Ed. Harvey Checkoway. circ. 3,000. (processed) **Document type:** newsletter.
Formerly: Occupational Health Newsletter (ISSN 0029-7925)

ENVIRONMENTAL HEALTH BRIEFING. see PUBLIC HEALTH AND SAFETY

ERGA. see OCCUPATIONAL HEALTH AND SAFETY — Abstracting, Bibliographies, Statistics

613.62 338.4 US ISSN 0743-6149
HD7269.B92
EVALUATING YOUR FIRM'S INJURY & ILLNESS RECORD. CONSTRUCTION INDUSTRIES. a. U.S. Department of Labor, Bureau of Labor Statistics, 441 G St., N.W., Washington, DC 20212. TEL 202-655-4000. (Subscr. to: Superintendent of Documents, U.S. Government Printing Office, Box 371954, Pittsburgh, PA 15250-7954. TEL 202-512-1800. FAX 202-512-2250; Or: Bureau of Labor Statistics Publications Sales Center, Box 2145, Chicago, IL 60690) **Document type:** government publication.

613.62 338.4 US ISSN 0742-339X
HD8051
EVALUATING YOUR FIRM'S INJURY & ILLNESS RECORD. SERVICE INDUSTRIES. a. U.S. Department of Labor, Bureau of Labor Statistics, 441 G St., N.W., Washington, DC 20212. TEL 202-655-4000. (Subscr. to: Superintendent of Documents, U.S. Government Printing Office, Box 371954, Pittsburgh, PA 15250-7954. TEL 202-512-1800. FAX 202-512-2250; Or: Bureau of Labor Statistics Publications Sales Center, Box 2145, Chicago, IL 60690) **Document type:** government publication.

613.62 388 US ISSN 0742-3403
HD8051
EVALUATING YOUR FIRM'S INJURY & ILLNESS RECORD. TRANSPORTATION & PUBLIC UTILITIES INDUSTRIES. a. U.S. Department of Labor, Bureau of Labor Statistics, 441 G St., N.W., Washington, DC 20212. TEL 202-655-4000. (Subscr. to: Superintendent of Documents, U.S. Government Printing Office, Box 371954, Pittsburgh, PA 15250-7954. TEL 202-512-1800. FAX 202-512-2250; Or: Bureau of Labor Statistics Publications Sales Center, Box 2145, Chicago, IL 60690) **Document type:** government publication.

613.62 381 US ISSN 0742-3411
EVALUATING YOUR FIRM'S INJURY & ILLNESS RECORD. WHOLESALE & RETAIL TRADE INDUSTRIES. a. U.S. Department of Labor, Bureau of Labor Statistics, 441 G St., N.W., Washington, DC 20212. TEL 202-655-4000. (Subscr. to: Superintendent of Documents, U.S. Government Printing Office, Box 371954, Pittsburgh, PA 15250-7954. TEL 202-512-1800. FAX 202-512-2250; Or: Bureau of Labor Statistics Publications Sales Center, Box 2145, Chicago, IL 60690) **Document type:** government publication.

EVERYONE'S BACKYARD. see ENVIRONMENTAL STUDIES — Waste Management

613.62 US ISSN 0738-6583
EXECUTIVE HOUSEKEEPING TODAY. 1980. m. $22 (foreign $28). National Executive Housekeepers Association, 1001 Eastwind Dr., Ste. 301, Westerville, OH 43081. TEL 614-895-7166; 800-EHT-3203. FAX 614-895-1248. Ed. Beth Kramer. adv.: B&W page $885, color page $1490. bk.rev.; index; circ. 7,600 (paid). **Indexed:** Hospit.Ind. **Document type:** trade publication.
—Faxon; UnCover.
Description: Geared to management professionals responsible for institutional housekeeping.
Refereed Serial

620.86 US
FERTILIZER AND AGRICULTURAL CHEMICAL NEWSLETTER. bi-m. $19 to non-members; members $15. National Safety Council, Periodicals Department, 1121 Spring Lake Dr., Itasca, IL 60143. TEL 708-775-2281. Ed. Kathy Henderson; Pub. Kevin H. Axe. **Document type:** newsletter.
Former titles: Safety Newsletter: Fertilizer and Agricultural Chemical Section; Safety Newsletter: Fertilizer Section.
Description: Information and recommendations on various safety issues in the field of fertilizer and agricultural chemicals.

613 US ISSN 1057-994X
FOCUS ON FEDERAL EMPLOYEE HEALTH AND ASSISTANCE. bi-m. $6. U.S. Office of Personnel Management, Employee Health Services Branch, 1900 E. St., N.W., No.7412, Washington, DC 20415. TEL 202-606-1638. FAX 202-606-2613. (Subscr. to: Superintendent of Documents, U.S. Government Printing Office, Washington, DC 20402. TEL 202-783-3238) Ed. Tracey Long. circ. 2,900 (paid). **Document type:** government publication, newsletter.
Description: Provides news and developments in federal employee health and fitness counseling and other health issues affecting federal government employees.

363 US
FOOD & BEVERAGE NEWSLETTER. bi-m. $19 to non-members; members $15. National Safety Council, Periodicals Department, 1121 Spring Lake Dr., Itasca, IL 60143. TEL 708-775-2281. Ed. Kathy Henderson; Pub. Kevin H. Axe. **Document type:** newsletter.
Formerly: Safety Newsletter: Food and Beverage Section.
Description: Information and recommendations on various safety issues in the food and beverage industry.

614.85 664 UK ISSN 0964-9158
FOOD SAFETY BRIEFING. 1991. m. £99 for hardcopy edition; electronic editions £150. Barbour Index, New Lodge Drift Rd., Windsor, Berks. SL4 4RQ, England. TEL 01344-884121. FAX 01344-884112. Ed. D. Denton. bk.rev. (also avail. in diskette format) **Document type:** bulletin, abstracting/indexing.
●Also available online.
Description: Provides summaries of newly published U.K. and E.C. legislation, reports, and other authoritative and official publications on food safety and hygiene and related issues.

634.9 US
FOREST INDUSTRIES NEWSLETTER. bi-m. $19 to non-members; members $15. National Safety Council, Periodicals Department, 1121 Spring Lake Dr., Itasca, IL 60143. TEL 708-775-2281. Ed. Kathy Henderson; Pub. Kevin H. Axe. **Document type:** newsletter.
Formerly: Safety Newsletter: Forest Industries Section.
Description: Information and recommendations on various safety issues in forest industries.

OCCUPATIONAL HEALTH AND SAFETY

363.11 613.6   FR   ISSN 0007-9952
CODEN: CNDIBJ
FRANCE. INSTITUT NATIONAL DE RECHERCHE ET DE SECURITE POUR LA PREVENTION DES ACCIDENTS DU TRAVAIL ET DES MALADIES PROFESSIONNELLES. CAHIERS DE NOTES DOCUMENTAIRES; securite et hygiene du travail. 1956. q. 550 F. Institut National de Recherche et de Securite pour la Prevention des Accidents du Travail et des Maladies Professionnelles, 30 rue Olivier Noyer, 75680 Paris Cedex 14, France. TEL 40-44-30-00. FAX 40-44-30-99. TELEX 203594F INRSPAR F. abstr.; charts; illus.; index, cum.index. circ. 10,000. **Indexed:** C.I.S. Abstr., Chem.Abstr., INIS Atomind., Ref.Zh. **Document type:** academic/scholarly publication.
—BLDSC (2950.000000); CASDDS; SWETS.
Description: Scientific and technical publication in the field of occupational safety and health.

614.85   GW
G I T SPEZIAL ARBEITSSCHUTZ - ARBEITSSICHERHEIT. 1992. 2/yr. DM.35 (students DM.17.50). G I T Verlag GmbH, Roesslerstr. 90, 64293 Darmstadt, Germany. TEL 06151-8090-0. FAX 06151-809045. Ed.Bd. adv.: B&W page DM.8375, color page DM.11255; trim 185 x 260; adv. contact: Frank Urban. circ. 30,000. **Document type:** trade publication.

613.62   GW
GEGENGIFT; Hamburger Hefte fuer Arbeit und Gesundheit. 1986. 2/yr. DM.50 for 5 nos. Gruppe Arbeit und Gesundheit, Informationsstelle Arbeit und Gesundheit, Schanzenstr. 75, 20357 Hamburg, Germany. TEL 040-4392858. FAX 040-4392818. Ed. Henning Wriedt. adv.; bk.rev. circ. 1,500. (back issues avail.) **Document type:** newsletter.
Description: Covers all areas of occupational health; aimed at safety activists and employees.

GENERAL SAFETY DIGEST/DIGEST DE SECURITE GENERALE. see MILITARY

614.85   GW
GERMANY. BUNDESANSTALT FUER ARBEITSSCHUTZ. AMTLICHE MITTEILUNGEN. 1984. q. Bundesanstalt fuer Arbeitsschutz - Federal Institute for Occupational Safety and Health, Friedrich-Henkel-Weg 1-25, 44149 Dortmund, Germany. TEL 0231-9071-306. Ed. Wolfgang Dicke. circ. 90,000. **Document type:** government publication.

GERONTOLOGY SPECIAL INTEREST SECTION NEWSLETTER. see GERONTOLOGY AND GERIATRICS

363.11   NE   ISSN 1381-4508
▼**GEZOND IN BEDRIJF.** 1995. 6/yr. fl.35. (Nederlands Instituut voor Arbeidsomstandigheden) Uitgeverij Kluwer B.V., Postbus 23, 7400 GA Deventer, Netherlands. TEL 31-5700-47060. FAX 31-5700-38040. adv. circ. 10,000. **Document type:** trade publication.

616.98   IT   ISSN 0391-9889
CODEN: GIMLDG
GIORNALE ITALIANO DI MEDICINA DEL LAVORO. (Text in English and Italian; summaries in English) 1979. bi-m. L.80000($100) Giardini Editori e Stampatori, Via Santa Bibbiana 28, 56100 Pisa, Italy. TEL 050-502531. Ed. Francesco Candura. adv.; bk.rev.; index, cum.index. circ. 1,500. (back issues avail.) **Indexed:** Biol.Abstr., Chem.Abstr., Dent.Ind., Excerp.Med., Ind.Hyg.Dig., Ind.Med.
—BLDSC (4178.230000); CASDDS.
Description: Features research papers on various topics of occupational health.

GREAT BRITAIN. DEPARTMENT OF EDUCATION AND SCIENCE. SAFETY IN EDUCATION. see PUBLIC HEALTH AND SAFETY

613.62   JA
GUIDEBOOK ON INDUSTRIAL SAFETY. (Text in Japanese) a. 470 Yen. Japan Industrial Safety and Health Association, International Cooperation Department, 5-35-1 Shiba, Minato-ku, Tokyo 108, Japan. TEL 81-3-3452-6841. FAX 81-3-3454-4596.
Description: Educational and promotional booklet for Japan's annual National Safety Week.

613.62   IS
HABITECHUT. (Text in Arabic) q. Safety and Hygiene Institute, 7 Solomon St., Tel Aviv 66 023, Israel. TEL 03-374933.

614.85   US
HAZARD CONTROL MANAGER. s-a. Board of Certified Hazard Control Management, 8009 Carita Court, Bethesda, MD 20817. TEL 301-984-8969. Ed. Habold M. Gordon. **Document type:** newsletter.
Description: Covers the management of safety programs.

HAZARDOUS MATERIALS NEWSLETTER. see PUBLIC HEALTH AND SAFETY

613.62   UK   ISSN 0964-962X
HAZARDOUS SUBSTANCES. 10/yr. £132 (foreign £154). Monitor Press, Rectory Rd., Great Waldingfield, Sudbury, Suffolk CO10 0TL, England. TEL 01787-378607. FAX 01787-880201. (back issues avail.) **Indexed:** Euro.LJI, Intl.Polym.Sci.& Tech., LJI, RAPRA. **Document type:** newsletter.
—BLDSC (4274.451150).
Description: Covers the storage, transportation, processing, disposal, and laboratory research use of hazardous substances.

614.85   UK   ISSN 0267-7296
HAZARDS MAGAZINE. 1976. q. £9 to individuals (outside Europe £12); institutions £20 (outside Europe £25) (effective 1995). Hazards Publications Ltd., P.O. Box 199, Sheffield S1 1FQ, England. TEL 0114-276-5695. FAX 0114-276-7257. Ed. Rory Gingell. bk.rev.; abstr.; charts; illus.; stat.; index. circ. 500. (back issues avail.) **Indexed:** Br.Tech.Ind. **Document type:** bulletin.
—BLDSC (4274.451570).
Formerly (until 1984): Hazards Bulletin (ISSN 0140-0525)
Description: Aims to help workers organize health and safety concerns through their unions.

613   IE   ISSN 0791-1610
HEALTH & SAFETY. 4/yr. Jude Publications, 2-6 Tara St., Dublin 2, Ireland. TEL 713500. FAX 713074. Ed. Kate Tammemagi. circ. 4,500.

614   UK   ISSN 0141-8246
HEALTH & SAFETY AT WORK. 1978. m. £51 (foreign £84). Tolley Publishing Co. Ltd., Tolley House, 2 Addiscombe Rd., Croydon, Surrey CR9 5AX, England. TEL 0181-686-9141. FAX 0181-686-3155. Ed. Isobel Allen. adv.: B&W page £980; adv. contact: Philip Woodgate. bk.rev. circ. 11,500. (also avail. in microform from UMI; reprint service avail. from UMI) **Indexed:** Account.& Data Proc.Abstr., BMT, Br.Rail.Bd., Br.Tech.Ind., Build.Manage.Abstr., C.I.S. Abstr., Cadscan, Ergon.Abstr., Excerp.Med., Intl.Polym.Sci.& Tech., Lab.Haz.Bull., Lead Abstr., Met.Abstr., Mgmt.& Market.Abstr., RAPRA, World Alum.Abstr., World Surf.Coat., World Text.Abstr., Zincscan. **Document type:** trade publication.
—BLDSC (4274.869800); SWETS. **CCC.**
Description: For safety management.

614   UK
HEALTH AND SAFETY IN INDUSTRY AND COMMERCE; news bulletin. 1977. m. £82.50 (foreign £90.50). Springfield Information Services, P.O. Box 31, Peterborough, Cambs. PE1 1SD, England. TEL 01733-267272. Ed. John Franks. bk.rev.; abstr.; tr.lit. (back issues avail.) **Indexed:** Int.Packag.Abstr., Lab.Haz.Bull., Mgmt.& Market.Abstr. **Document type:** newsletter.

658.4 613.62
614.85   UK   ISSN 1353-5161
▼**THE HEALTH & SAFETY MANAGER'S YEARBOOK.** 1994. a. £35. (Royal Society for the Prevention of Accidents) A P Information Services, Roman House, 296 Golders Green Rd., London NW11 9PZ, England. TEL 0181-455-4550. FAX 0181-455-6381. **Document type:** trade publication.
Description: Provides a complete source of information on this expanding market, covering both the service providers and all key health, safety, and environmental contacts at major U.K. companies.

340 613.62   UK   ISSN 0140-8534
KD3168.A13   CODEN: HSMOE5
HEALTH & SAFETY MONITOR. m. £119 (foreign £141). Monitor Press, Rectory Rd., Great Waldingfield, Sudbury, Suffolk CO10 0TL, England. TEL 0787-378607. FAX 0787-880201. (back issues avail.) **Indexed:** Cadscan, Euro.LJI, Lead Abstr., LJI, Mgmt.& Market.Abstr., Zincscan. **Document type:** newsletter.
—BLDSC (4274.865500).
Description: For senior executives and safety officers, company secretaries and legal representatives as well as union officials.

614   UK   ISSN 0954-5972
HEALTH AND SAFETY OFFICER'S HANDBOOK. 1983. a. £25. Millbank Publications Ltd., 25 Catherine St., London WC2B 5JW, England. TEL 071-379-3036. FAX 071-240-6840. adv.; charts; illus. circ. 2,000. **Document type:** bulletin.

614.85 622.8   CN   ISSN 1198-1229
HEALTH & SAFETY RESOURCE. French edition (ISSN 1198-1237) 1994. bi-m. free. Ontario Natural Resources Safety Association, Box 2050, 690 McKeown Ave., North Bay, ON P1B 9P1, Canada. TEL 705-474-SAFE. FAX 705-472-5800. Ed. Douglas Bennett. bk.rev.; circ. 5,000. circ. 10,000 (controlled). (back issues avail.) **Document type:** trade publication.
Supersedes (in 1994, vol.24, no.4): Safety News.
Description: For the mining, forestry, and pulp and paper industries of Ontario.

HEALTH & SAFETY SPECIFIERS; health, safety and environmental safety. see PUBLIC HEALTH AND SAFETY

614.8   US
HEALTH CARE NEWSLETTER. bi-m. $19 to non-members; members $15. National Safety Council, Periodicals Department, 1121 Spring Lake Dr., Itasca, IL 60143. TEL 708-775-2281. Ed. Kathy Henderson; Pub. Kevin H. Axe. **Document type:** newsletter.
Former titles: Safety Newsletter: Health Care Section; Safety Newsletter: Hospital-Health Care Section.
Description: Information and recommendations on safety issues in the health care field.

613.62   CN
HEALTH IN WORK PLACE. 12/yr. $160. Carswell, One Corporate Plaza, 2075 Kennedy Rd., Scarborough, ON M1T 3V4, Canada. TEL 416-609-8000. FAX 416-298-5094. Ed. Laurie Blake. **Document type:** newsletter.
Description: Covers complex, work-related health problems in straightforward language. Studies precedent-setting court cases in Canada, the US and the world.

HEALTHCARE HAZARDOUS MATERIALS MANAGEMENT. see MEDICAL SCIENCES

HEALTHY HOME & WORKPLACE; timely help for quality living in the 90's. see PUBLIC HEALTH AND SAFETY

HOPE HEALTH LETTER. see PHYSICAL FITNESS AND HYGIENE

613.62   JA   ISSN 0911-3363
HOPPO SANGYO EISEI/JOURNAL OF NORTHERN OCCUPATIONAL HEALTH. (Text in English or Japanese; summaries in English) 1938. biennial. free. Association of Northern Occupational Health - Hoppo Sangyo Eisei Kyoukai, c/o Department of Hygiene and Preventive Medicine, Hokkaido University School of Medicine, Kita-15 nishi-7, Kita-ku, Sapporo 060, Japan. TEL 011-706-5066. FAX 011-717-1140. Ed. Naoki Sugawara. (back issues avail.) **Document type:** academic/scholarly publication.
Formerly: Hoppo Sangyo Eisei Kyoukai Kaishi.

HOSPITAL EMPLOYEE HEALTH. see HOSPITALS

HOSPITAL SAFETY INFORMATION SERVICE. see HOSPITALS

363.11 US
HOW TO WRITE A COMPANY SAFETY MANUAL. base vol. plus a. update. $144 for base vol. Standard Publishing Corp., 155 Federal St., Boston, MA 02110. TEL 617-457-0900; 800-682-5759. FAX 617-457-0608. Ed. Neville C. Tompkins. (looseleaf format) **Document type:** trade publication.
   Description: Advises managers on how to compile occupational safety documents and manuals.

331 US
HUMAN RESOURCES MANAGEMENT - O S H A COMPLIANCE. (Part of: Human Resources Management) base vol. (plus m. reports). $370. Commerce Clearing House, Inc., 4025 W. Peterson Ave., Chicago, IL 60646. TEL 312-583-8500. FAX 708-940-4600.
   Formerly: C C H - O S H A Compliance Guide.
   Description: Provides practical guidance on compliance issues arising under federal OSHA and state OSH Acts. Offers the guidelines and examples needed to eastablish an effective company safety program.

I A Q PRODUCT & SERVICE GUIDE; the directory of products and services for control of indoor air quality. see BUSINESS AND ECONOMICS — Trade And Industrial Directories

614.8 628 331.8 SZ ISSN 0376-9410
I Z A (Illustrierte Zeitschrift fuer Arbeitssicherheit) (Text and summaries in German) 1953. s-m. 25 Fr. Ott Verlag und Druck AG, Laenggasse 57, Postfach 22, CH-3607 Thun, Switzerland. TEL 033 22 16 22. FAX 033-22-20-06. Ed. Alfred Lauchli-Wyss. circ. 3,500.

614 US
IN TOUCH (WASHINGTON).* bi-m. free. International Hand Protection Association, 9812 Falls Rd., Ste. 114-334, Potomac, MD 20854-3976. TEL 202-296-9200. FAX 202-296-0023. Ed. Kathee E. Baker. circ. 280. **Document type:** newsletter.
   Formerly: Hands On Newsletter.

INDIAN JOURNAL OF INDUSTRIAL MEDICINE. see MEDICAL SCIENCES

615.8 II ISSN 0445-7706
INDIAN JOURNAL OF OCCUPATIONAL THERAPY. 1956. 4/yr. $20. All India Occupational Therapists' Association, 136 Sunlight Colony-II, Didharth Enclave, New Delhi 110 014, India. TEL 6832232. Ed. M.S. Warhade. adv.; bk.rev. circ. 750. **Indexed:** Indian Psychol.Abstr. **Document type:** academic/scholarly publication.

613 614 331 IO ISSN 0126-0987
INDONESIAN JOURNAL OF INDUSTRIAL HYGIENE, OCCUPATIONAL HEALTH-SAFETY AND SOCIAL SECURITY/MAJALAH HIGENE PERUSAHAAN, KESEHATAN-KESELAMATAN KERJA, DAN JAMINAN SOSIAL. (Text in English and Indonesian) 1969. q. National Institute of Industrial Hygiene and Occupational Health - Lembaga Nasional Higene Perusahaan dan Kesehatan Kerja, Jl. Jend. A. Yani 69-70, Jakarta, Indonesia. Ed.Bd. charts; stat. (also avail. in microfilm from UMI; reprint service avail. from UMI)

614.85 CN ISSN 0712-774X
INDUSTRIAL ACCIDENT PREVENTION ASSOCIATION. ANNUAL REVIEW. 1918. a. Industrial Accident Prevention Association, 250 Yonge St., 28th Fl., Toronto, ON M5B 2N4, Canada. TEL 416-506-8888. circ. 7,500. **Document type:** corporate report.
   Formerly: Industrial Accident Prevention Association. Annual Report (ISSN 0073-7305)

613.62 658 US
HD49
INDUSTRIAL & ENVIRONMENTAL CRISIS QUARTERLY; international journal of industrial and organizational crises. (Text in English) 1987. q. $50 to individuals; institutions $195 (effective Sep. 1995). Bucknell University, Department of Management, Lewisburg, PA 17837. TEL 717-524-1821. FAX 717-524-1338. E-mail: SHRIVAST@BUCKNELL.EDU. (Co-sponsor: Industrial Crisis Institute Inc., New York) Ed. Paul Shrivastava. bk.rev. circ. 250. (back issues avail.) **Indexed:** Sociol.Abstr. **Document type:** academic/scholarly publication.
   —BLDSC (4445.215000); UMI.
   Formerly: Industrial Crisis Quarterly (ISSN 0921-8106)
   Description: Reports on industrial crises that are caused by technological, economic, social or political factors and that lead to large-scale damage to people and their natural and social environments.
   Refereed Serial

613.62 JA ISSN 0019-8366
RC963 CODEN: INHEAO
INDUSTRIAL HEALTH. (Text in English) 1963. q. membership. National Institute of Industrial Health - Rodo-sho Sangyo Igaku Sogo Kenkyujo, 21-1 Nagao 6-chome, Tama-ku, Kawasaki-shi, Kanagawa-ken 214, Japan. TEL 81-044-865-6111. FAX 81-044-865-6116. Ed. Sohei Yamamoto. charts; illus.; index. circ. 1,100. (reprint service avail.) **Indexed:** Abstr.Hyg., Art & Archaeol.Tech.Abstr., Biol.Abstr., C.I.S. Abstr., Chem.Abstr., Curr.Cont., Dent.Ind., Excerp.Med., Ind.Hyg.Dig., Ind.Med., INIS Atomind., Med.& Surg.Dermat., Trop.Dis.Bull. **Document type:** academic/scholarly publication.
   •Also available online. Vendor(s): Knight-Ridder, Inc., JICST.
   —BLDSC (4454.700000); CASDDS; EMDOCS; Faxon; Genuine Article; UnCover.
   Description: Contains research articles in the area of industrial health.

613.62 340 US ISSN 0890-3018
INDUSTRIAL HEALTH & HAZARDS UPDATE. 1984. m. $269 (Canada $309; elsewhere $339). Merton Allen Associates, InfoTeam Inc., Box 15640, Plantation, FL 33318-5640. TEL 305-473-9560. FAX 305-473-0544. Eds. Merton Allen, David R. Allen. (back issues avail.; reprint service avail.) **Document type:** newsletter.
   •Also available online. Vendor(s): Data-Star, Knight-Ridder, Inc., Human Resources Information Network, NewsNet (LA04).
   —CCC.
   Description: Covers occupational health, safety, hazards, and related subjects. Designed for busy executives in the health, medical, environmental, legal, management, and technological fields of industry, government, commerce, and academia.

613.2 US ISSN 0073-7496
INDUSTRIAL HEALTH FOUNDATION. ENGINEERING SERIES. BULLETINS. 1936. irreg., no.8, 1971. price varies. Industrial Health Foundation, Inc., 34 Penn Circle W., Pittsburgh, PA 15206. TEL 412-363-6600. **Document type:** bulletin.

331.8 613.62 US ISSN 0073-750X
INDUSTRIAL HEALTH FOUNDATION. LEGAL SERIES BULLETINS. 1936. irreg., no.9, 1972. price varies. Industrial Health Foundation, Inc., 34 Penn Circle W., Pittsburgh, PA 15206. TEL 412-363-6600. **Document type:** bulletin.
   Formerly: Industrial Hygiene Foundation of America. Legal Series Bulletin.

331 614 US
INDUSTRIAL HEALTH FOUNDATION. MANAGEMENT SERIES. 1971. irreg., no.2, 1978. price varies. Industrial Health Foundation, Inc., 34 Penn Circle W., Pittsburgh, PA 15206. TEL 412-363-6600. (back issues avail.) **Document type:** monographic series.

613.62 US ISSN 0073-7518
HD7260
INDUSTRIAL HEALTH FOUNDATION. MEDICAL SERIES. BULLETINS. 1937. irreg., no.21, 1982. price varies. Industrial Health Foundation, Inc., 34 Penn Circle W., Pittsburgh, PA 15206. TEL 412-363-6600. **Document type:** monographic series.

613.62 US ISSN 0073-7526
INDUSTRIAL HEALTH FOUNDATION. NURSING SERIES. BULLETINS. 1965. irreg., no.3, 1971. price varies. Industrial Health Foundation, Inc., 34 Penn Circle W., Pittsburgh, PA 15206. TEL 412-363-6600.

331 US ISSN 0147-5401
INDUSTRIAL HYGIENE NEWS. 1978. 7/yr. $25 ($30 outside N. America) (free to qualified personnel). Rimbach Publishing, Inc., 8650 Babcock Blvd., Pittsburgh, PA 15237. TEL 412-364-5366. Ed. David C. Lavender; Pub. Norberta Rimbach. adv.; bk.rev.; tr.lit. circ. 61,725. (tabloid format) **Document type:** trade publication.
   —SWETS.
   Description: Information on occupational health and high technology safety.

614.85 UK ISSN 0267-1476
INDUSTRIAL MAINTENANCE; for factory managers and maintenance professionals. 1957. 10/yr. £30. Nexus Media Ltd., Nexus House, Azalea Dr., Swanley, Kent BR8 8HY, England. TEL 01322-660070. FAX 01322-667633. circ. 23,363. (back issues avail.)

614.85 II ISSN 0301-4746
T55.A1
INDUSTRIAL SAFETY CHRONICLE. (Text in English) 1969. q. Re.40($8) National Safety Council, Central Labour Institute Bldg., Sion, Bombay 400022, India. Ed. A.A. Krishnan. adv.; bk.rev.; illus. circ. 1,500. **Indexed:** C.I.S. Abstr.

363.11 UK ISSN 0262-3226
INDUSTRIAL SAFETY DATA FILE. 1982. m. £90($257) 130. Wilmington Publishing, Wilmington house, Church Hill, Dartford, Kent UA2 7EF, England. TEL 0322-277788. FAX 0322-276476. (Subscr. to: Ferari House, 258 Field End Rd., Ruislip, Middx. HA4 9UX, England. TEL 081-868-4499) Ed. Dina Chase. illus.; s-a. index. circ. 2,500. (looseleaf format) **Indexed:** Br.Tech.Ind., C.I.S. Abstr.
   Supersedes: Industrial Safety (ISSN 0019-8757)

628.5 NE ISSN 0921-9110
INDUSTRIAL SAFETY SERIES. 1987. irreg., vol.3, 1994. price varies. Elsevier Science B.V., Books Division, P.O. Box 211, 1000 AE Amsterdam, Netherlands. TEL 31-20-4853911. FAX 31-20-4853705. TELEX 18582 ESPA NL. E-mail: nlinfo-f@elsevier.nl; usinfo-f@elsevier.com; forinfo-kyf04035@niftyserve.or.jp; Site addr.: http://www.elsevier.nl/. (Subscr. in U.S. and Canada to: Elsevier Science Inc., Box 882, Madison Sq. Sta., New York, NY 10159. TEL 212-989-5800. FAX 212-633-3680) (back issues avail.) **Document type:** monographic series.
   —BLDSC (4462.440000).
   Refereed Serial

INDUSTRIAL VENTILATION; A MANUAL OF RECOMMENDED PRACTICE. see HEATING, PLUMBING AND REFRIGERATION

613.62 UK
INSTITUTE OF OCCUPATIONAL HEALTH. PROCEEDINGS. irreg. University of Birmingham, Institute of Occupational Health, P.O. Box 363, Edgbaston, Birmingham B15 2TT, England. TEL 0121-414-6030. FAX 0121-471-5208. E-mail: institute-of-occupational-health@bham.ac.uk. **Document type:** proceedings.

620.86 US
INTERNATIONAL AIR TRANSPORT NEWSLETTER. 1952. bi-m. $19 to non-members; members $15. National Safety Council, Periodicals Department, 1121 Spring Lake Dr., Itasca, IL 60143. TEL 708-775-2281. Ed. Kathy Henderson; Pub. Kevin H. Axe. **Document type:** newsletter.
   Former titles: Air Transport Newsletter; Safety Newsletter: Air Transport Section (ISSN 0470-2832)
   Description: Information and recommendations on various safety issues in the field of international air transport.

OCCUPATIONAL HEALTH AND SAFETY

613.62 — GW — ISSN 0340-0131
RC963.A1 — CODEN: IAEHDW
INTERNATIONAL ARCHIVES OF OCCUPATIONAL AND ENVIRONMENTAL HEALTH. (Text in English) 1930. 6/yr. DM.1376($1000) (effective 1996). Springer-Verlag, Heidelberger Platz 3, 14197 Berlin, Germany. TEL 030-8207-0. FAX 030-8214091. E-mail: orders@springer.de. (Subscr. in N. America to: Springer-Verlag New York, Inc., 44 Hartz Way, Secaucus, NJ 07096-2491. TEL 201-348-4033. FAX 201-348-4505) Ed. G. Lehnert. adv.; bibl.; charts; illus.; index. (also avail. in microform from UMI; back issues avail.; reprint service avail. from ISI) **Indexed:** Abstr.Hyg., ASCA, Biol.Abstr., C.I.S. Abstr., Cadscan, Chem.Abstr., CINAHL, Curr.Adv.Cancer Res., Curr.Adv.Ecol.Sci., Curr.Cont., Dent.Ind., Excerp.Med., Ind.Med., Ind.Sci.Rev., Lab.Haz.Bull., Lead Abstr., Med.& Surg.Dermat., NRN, Nutr.Abstr., Risk Abstr., Sci.Cit.Ind., Sel.Water Res.Abstr., Trop.Dis.Bull., Zincscan. **Document type:** academic/scholarly publication.
—BLDSC (4536.128000); CASDDS; Faxon; Genuine Article; SWETS; UMI; UnCover. **CCC.**
Former titles (until 1975): International Archives of Occupational Health (ISSN 0020-5923); (until 1970): Internationales Archiv fuer Gewerbepathologie und Gewerbehygiene; (until 1962): Archiv fuer Gewerbepathologie und Gewerbehygiene.
Description: Covers occupational, environmental, and social medicine, and their subdisciplines.

INTERNATIONAL COMMISSION ON RADIOLOGICAL PROTECTION. ANNALS. see *MEDICAL SCIENCES — Radiology And Nuclear Medicine*

613.62 — AT — ISSN 0074-3828
INTERNATIONAL CONGRESS OF OCCUPATIONAL THERAPY. PROCEEDINGS. 1974. irreg., 7th, 1978, Jerusalem. World Federation of Occupational Therapists, 20 Syree Court, Marmion, W.A. 6020, Australia. circ. 1,500. **Document type:** proceedings.

613.85 — PL — ISSN 1232-1087
INTERNATIONAL JOURNAL OF OCCUPATIONAL MEDICINE AND ENVIRONMENTAL HEALTH. (Text in English; summaries in English, Polish) 1988. q. $160 to individuals; institutions $200 (effective 1994). Nofer Institute of Occupational Medicine, P.O. Box 199, Ul. Sw. Teresy 8, 90-950 Lodz, Poland. TEL 48-42-314745. FAX 48-42-348331. (Co-sponsor: Polish Association of Occupational Medicine) Ed.Bd. adv.; bk.rev.; index. circ. 1,000. (back issues avail.) **Indexed:** Excerp.Med., Ind.Med. **Document type:** academic/scholarly publication.
—BLDSC (4542.412000).
Former titles (until 1994): Polish Journal of Occupational Medicine and Environmental Health (ISSN 0867-8383); (until 1991): Polish Journal of Occupational Medicine (ISSN 0860-6536).
Description: Publishes papers concerning industrial hygiene, preventive medicine, diagnosis and treatment of occupational diseases, physiology and psychology of work, toxicological research, environmental toxicology, environmental epidemiology and epidemiological studies devoted to occupational problems.
Refereed Serial

363.11 620.8
613.62
▼**INTERNATIONAL JOURNAL OF OCCUPATIONAL SAFETY AND ERGONOMICS.** 1995. q. $59.50 to individuals; institutions $155. (Centralny Instytut Ochrony Prace, PL - Central Institute for Labor Protection) Ablex Publishing Corporation, 355 Chestnut St., Norwood, NJ 07648. TEL 201-767-8450. FAX 201-767-6716. TELEX 135-393. adv.; bk.rev. circ. 200.
Description: Covers occupational safety and ergonomics for research workers.

INTERNATIONAL SOCIETY FOR RESPIRATORY PROTECTION. JOURNAL. see *MEDICAL SCIENCES — Respiratory Diseases*

IRISH SECURITY NEWS. see *CRIMINOLOGY AND LAW ENFORCEMENT — Security*

614.85 — JA
JAPAN INDUSTRIAL SAFETY AND HEALTH ASSOCIATION. ANNUAL REPORT. a. Japan Industrial Safety & Health Association, International Cooperation Department, 5-35-1 Shiba, Minato-ku, Tokyo 108, Japan. TEL 03-3452-6841. FAX 03-3453-8034.

613.62 — JA
JAPAN INDUSTRIAL SAFETY AND HEALTH ASSOCIATION. INTERNATIONAL COOPERATION DEPARTMENT. GUIDEBOOK ON OCCUPATIONAL HEALTH. (Text in Japanese) a. 470 Yen. Japan Industrial Safety and Health Association, International Cooperation Department, 5-35-1 Shiba, Minato-ku, Tokyo 108, Japan. TEL 03-3452-6841. FAX 03-3453-8034.
Description: Educational and promotional booklet for Japan's annual occupational Health Week.

613.62 — JA
JAPAN INDUSTRIAL SAFETY AND HEALTH ASSOCIATION. INTERNATIONAL COOPERATION DEPARTMENT. OCCUPATIONAL HEALTH. (Text in Japanese) m. 8400 Yen. Japan Industrial Safety and Health Association, International Cooperation Department, 5-35-1 Shiba, Minato-ku, Tokyo 108, Japan. TEL 03-3452-6841. FAX 03-3453-8034.
Description: Magazine for occupational health managers, specialists and practitioners.

614.85 — JA
JAPAN INDUSTRIAL SAFETY AND HEALTH ASSOCIATION. INTERNATIONAL COOPERATION DEPARTMENT. SAFETY. (Text in Japanese) m. 7920 Yen. Japan Industrial Safety and Health Association, International Cooperation Department, 5-35-1 Shiba, Minato-ku, Tokyo 108, Japan. TEL 03-3452-6841. FAX 03-3453-8034.
Description: Magazine for occupational safety managers, specialists and practitioners.

614.85 — JA
JAPAN INDUSTRIAL SAFETY AND HEALTH ASSOCIATION. INTERNATIONAL COOPERATION DEPARTMENT. YEARBOOK OF INDUSTRIAL SAFETY AND HEALTH. (Text in Japanese) a. 5000 Yen. Japan Industrial Safety and Health Association, International Cooperation Department, 5-35-1 Shiba, Minato-ku, Tokyo 108, Japan. TEL 03-3452-6841. FAX 03-3453-8034.
Formerly: Japan Industrial Safety and Health Association. Research and Survey Division. Yearbook of Industrial Safety.
Description: Covers activities and relevant information in the field of industrial safety and health in Japan.

JITSUMU TENBO/SAFETY NEWS ON BOILER AND CRANE ENGINEERING. see *MACHINERY*

658.3 — US — ISSN 0149-7510
JOB SAFETY & HEALTH (WASHINGTON). (Subseries of: B N A Policy and Practice Series; Environment, Safety, and Health Series) 1977. bi-w. $680 (effective July 1995). The Bureau of National Affairs, Inc., 1231 25th St., N.W., Washington, DC 20037. TEL 202-452-4200. FAX 202-822-8092. TELEX 285656 BNAI WSH. (Subscr. to: 9435 Key West Ave., Rockville, MD 20850. TEL 800-372-1033) Ed. Stanley S. Pond. index. (looseleaf format; back issues avail.)
●Also available online. Vendor(s): Human Resources Information Network (CDD, HDD).
—**CCC.**
Description: Review of workplace safety and health regulations, policies, policies and trends.

614.85 — US — ISSN 1057-5820
IN PROCESS
JOB SAFETY AND HEALTH QUARTERLY. 1989. q. $8.50 (foreign $10.65) (effective 1995). U.S. Occupational Safety and Health Administration, Department of Labor, Frances Perkins Bldg., Rm. S2315, 200 Constitution Ave., N.W., Washington, DC 20210. TEL 202-523-8148. (Subscr. to: Superintendent of Documents, U.S. Government Printing Office, Box 371954, Pittsburgh, PA 15250-7954. TEL 202-512-1800. FAX 202-512-2250) (back issues avail.) **Document type:** government publication.
—UnCover.
Description: Features articles on job safety and health topics and contains current information on O.S.H.A. activities.

613.62 — US — ISSN 1059-924X
RC965.A5
JOURNAL OF AGROMEDICINE. 1993. q. $95 (foreign $133) (effective 1996). Haworth Press, Inc., 10 Alice St., Binghamton, NY 13904. TEL 607-722-5857; 800-342-9678. FAX 607-722-1424. Ed. Stanley H. Schuman. adv.: page $300. bk.rev. (also avail. in microfiche from UMI) **Indexed:** Abstr.Anthropol., Biostat., Environ.Per.Bibl., Geo.Abstr., Helminthol.Abstr., IDA, Ref.Zh.
—BLDSC (4926.240000); Haworth.
Description: Focuses on the health effects of agricultural operations on workers and their families, consumers, and the environment.
Refereed Serial

613.62 — UK — ISSN 0954-576X
JOURNAL OF HEALTH AND SAFETY. 1981. 3/yr. £10 (overseas $12.50). British Health and Safety Society, c/o Health & Safety Unit, Aston University, Aston Triangle, Birmingham B4 7ET, England. TEL 0121-359-3621. FAX 0121-333-5809. E-mail: bhss@aston.ac.uk. Ed. Roger C. Clarke. adv.; bk.rev. circ. 400. (back issues avail.) **Document type:** academic/scholarly publication.
—BLDSC (4996.725000).
Formed by the 1988 merger of: British Health and Safety Society. Newsletter (ISSN 0268-0580) & British Health and Safety Society. Reviews Bulletin (ISSN 0268-0572)
Description: Contains articles, conference papers, and more relating to all aspects of occupational health and safety.

JOURNAL OF OCCUPATIONAL AND ENVIRONMENTAL MEDICINE. see *MEDICAL SCIENCES*

613.6 — JA — ISSN 1341-0725
CODEN: SAIGBL
JOURNAL OF OCCUPATIONAL HEALTH/SANGYO EISEIGAKU ZASSHI. (Text in English or Japanese; summaries in English) 1959. 6/yr. 10000 Yen. Japan Society for Occupational Health - Nihon Sangyo Eisei Gakkai, Public Health Bldg., 1-29-8 Shinjuku, Shinjuku-ku, Tokyo 160, Japan. FAX 03-3817-5830. Ed. Akio Sato. adv.; bk.rev.; illus.; index. circ. 5,300. (processed) **Indexed:** Abstr.Hyg., C.I.S.Abstr., Chem.Abstr., Curr.Cont., Excerp.Med., Ind.Hyg.Dig., Ind.Med., Trop.Dis.Bull. **Document type:** academic/scholarly publication.
—BLDSC (4655.500000); CASDDS; EMDOCS.
Formerly: Japanese Journal of Industrial Health - Sangyo Igaku (ISSN 0047-1879)

613 — AT — ISSN 0815-6409
JOURNAL OF OCCUPATIONAL HEALTH AND SAFETY: AUSTRALIA AND NEW ZEALAND. 1985. bi-m. C C H Australia Ltd., P.O. Box 230, North Ryde, N.S.W. 2113, Australia. TEL 61-2-8571555. FAX 61-2-8571601. Eds. Anne Wyatt, Gabrielle Grammeno. adv.; bk.rev.; film rev.; illus.; index, cum.index. (back issues avail.) **Document type:** academic/scholarly publication.
—BLDSC (5026.092000); SWETS; UnCover. **CCC.**
Description: Provides information for occupational health and safety professionals and managers.

615.9 — US — ISSN 1054-044X
RC963.A1 — CODEN: JOMTEE
JOURNAL OF OCCUPATIONAL MEDICINE AND TOXICOLOGY; an international journal. 1992. q. $140 (effective 1994). (International Society of Occupational Medicine and Toxicology) Princeton Scientific Publishing Co., Inc., Box 2155, Princeton, NJ 08543. TEL 609-683-4750. FAX 609-683-0838. Ed. Nachman Brautbar. adv.; bk.rev.; index. circ. 250. (back issues avail.) **Indexed:** Excerp.Med. (1994-). **Document type:** academic/scholarly publication.
—CASDDS. **CCC.**
Description: Publishes basic and applied research in occupational medicine and toxicology, including case reports and risk assessment associated with hazardous wastes and ground water contamination.
Refereed Serial

OCCUPATIONAL HEALTH AND SAFETY

615.8 US ISSN 1053-0487
RC964 CODEN: JOCTEW
JOURNAL OF OCCUPATIONAL REHABILITATION. 1991. q. $225 (foreign $265) (effective 1996). Plenum Publishing Corp., 233 Spring St., New York, NY 10013-1578. TEL 212-620-8000. FAX 212-463-0742. TELEX 23-421139. Ed. Michael Feuerstein. adv. (back issues avail.) **Indexed:** Psychol.Abstr. (1991-). **Document type:** academic/scholarly publication.
—BLDSC (5026.125000). **CCC.**
Description: Multidisciplinary forum for the publication of original research, theoretical papers, review articles, and case studies related to the mechanism and management of work-related disabilities.
Refereed Serial

363.7 UK ISSN 0022-4375
HV675.A1 CODEN: JSFRAV
JOURNAL OF SAFETY RESEARCH. 1982. q. £243($387) (effective 1996). (National Safety Council) Elsevier Science Ltd., Pergamon, P.O. Box 800, Kidlington, Oxford OX5 1DX, England. TEL 44-1865-843000. FAX 44-1865-843010. E-mail: nlinfo-f@elsevier.nl; usinfo-f@elsevier.com; forinfo-kyf04035@niftyserve.or.jp; Site addr.: http://www.elsevier.nl/. (Subscr. in U.S. and Canada to: Elsevier Science, 660 White Plains Rd., Tarrytown, NY 10591-5153. TEL 914-524-9200. FAX 914-333-2444) Ed. Thomas Planek. adv.; bk.rev. (also avail. in microfilm from UMI) **Indexed:** ASCA, Biol.Abstr., C.I.S. Abstr., Curr.Cont., Psychol.Abstr. (1969-), Psyscan, Risk Abstr. **Document type:** academic/scholarly publication.
—BLDSC (5052.130000); Ei; Faxon; Genuine Article; SWETS; UMI; UnCover. **CCC.**
Refereed Serial

614.85 IE ISSN 1052-2263
HD7255.A2
JOURNAL OF VOCATIONAL REHABILITATION. 1991. bi-m. I£116($183) (effective 1996). Elsevier Science Ireland Ltd., P.O. Box 85, Limerick, Ireland. TEL 353-61-472144. FAX 353-61-472144. (Subscr. in U.S. and Canada to: Elsevier Science, Box 882, Madison Sq. Sta., New York, NY 10159-0882. TEL 212-989-5800. FAX 212-633-3990) Ed. Paul Wehman. (also avail. in microform from UMI; back issues avail.) **Document type:** academic/scholarly publication.
—BLDSC (5072.512400); UMI. **CCC.**
Description: Topics range from supported employment to psychiatric impairment, vocational training, and physical disability.
Refereed Serial

613.62 US
KEEPING FIT. 1989. m. $15. Bureau of Business Practice, 24 Rope Ferry Rd., Waterford, CT 06386. TEL 203-442-4365. FAX 203-434-3078. TELEX 966420. Ed. J.A. Grabel.
Formerly: Health Plus.

614.85 JA
KENSETSU KOJI SAIGAI BOSHI TEIANSHU/PROPOSALS FOR INDUSTRIAL SAFETY OF CONSTRUCTION. (Text in Japanese) 1982. s-a. Nihon Doboku Kogyo Kyokai, Kanto Shibu - Japan Civil Engineering Contractors' Association, Kanto Branch, 5-1, Hatchobori 2-chome, Chuo-ku, Tokyo 104, Japan.

KOKUTETSU CHUO HOKEN KANRIJOHO; health control. see *PUBLIC HEALTH AND SAFETY*

614 US
LABOR OCCUPATIONAL HEALTH PROGRAM MONITOR. 1974. s-a. $10. University of California at Berkeley, School of Public Health, Labor Occupational Health Program, 2515 Channing Way, Berkeley, CA 94720. TEL 510-642-5507. FAX 510-643-5698. Ed. Eugene S. Darling. bk.rev.; film rev.; charts; illus. circ. 2,500. (back issues avail.) **Document type:** newsletter.

614.85 661 UK ISSN 0261-2917
CODEN: LHBUD2
LABORATORY HAZARDS BULLETIN. 1981. m. £168($322) in E.C. nations; elsewhere £174 (effective 1996). The Royal Society of Chemistry, Thomas Graham House, Science Park, Milton Rd., Cambridge CB4 4WF, England. TEL 01223-420066. FAX 01223-423429. E-mail: rsc1@rsc.org. (Subscr. to: Turpin Distribution Services Ltd., Blackhore Rd., Letchworth, Herts. SG6 1HN, England. TEL 01462-672555. FAX 01462-480947) Ed. Mike Hannant. adv.; index. cum.index. **Document type:** bulletin.
● Also available online. Vendor(s): Data-Star (CSNB), Knight-Ridder, Inc. (File no.317), STN International (CSNB).
Also available on CD-ROM. Producer(s): Knight-Ridder, Inc.
—BLDSC (5139.870000); SWETS. **CCC.**
Description: Reports on safety measures, potential hazards and new legislation affecting the well-being of employees working in laboratories.

614.85 AT
LABORATORY SAFETY MANUAL. 1992. s-a. C C H Australia Ltd., P.O. Box 230, North Ryde, N.S.W. 2113, Australia. TEL 61-2-8571515. FAX 61-2-8571601. (looseleaf format) **Document type:** trade publication.
Description: Covers health and safety considerations and procedures for laboratories.

LEGAL QUARTERLY DIGEST OF MINE SAFETY AND HEALTH DECISIONS. see *MINES AND MINING INDUSTRY*

614.82 FR
LETTRE D'INFORMATION SUR LA RECHERCHE HYGIENE ET SECURITE. English Edition: Safety Research News (ISSN 0765-913X) 1982. irreg. free. Institut National de Recherche et de Securite pour la Prevention des Accidents du Travail et des Maladies Professionnelles, 30 rue Olivier Noyer, 75680 Paris Cedex 14, France. TEL 40-44-30-00. FAX 40-44-30-99. TELEX 203-594 INSPAR. (Co-sponsors: International Social Security Association; International Section for Research on Prevention of Occupational Risks) Ed. B. Moncelon. bk.rev.
Formerly: I N R S Lettre d'Information sur la Recherche.

614.85 UK
LOSS PREVENTION COUNCIL. REPORT S H E. irreg., no.9, 1993. £20. Loss Prevention Council, 140 Aldersgate St., London EC1A 4HY, England. TEL 071-606-3757. FAX 071-600-1487. **Document type:** monographic series.

614.8 SP ISSN 0212-1050
MAPFRE SEGURIDAD. (Text in Spanish; summaries in English) 1981. q. free. (Fundacion Mapfre) Editorial Mapfre, Ctra. Majadahonda a Pozuelo km. 3500, 28220 Majadahonda (Madrid), Spain. TEL 626-55-17. FAX 626-21-42. adv. contact: Javier Del Busto. cum.index: 1981-1991; circ. 19,510 (controlled). (back issues avail.) **Document type:** trade publication.
Description: Covers accident and fire prevention, industrial hygiene, occupational medicine, and safety at work.

620.86 US ISSN 0160-8509
CODEN: MNNLDV
MARINE NEWSLETTER. bi-m. $19 to non-members; members $15. National Safety Council, Periodicals Department, 1121 Spring Lake Dr., Itasca, IL 60143. TEL 708-775-2281. Ed. Kathy Henderson; Pub. Kevin H. Axe. **Document type:** newsletter.
Formerly: Safety Newsletter: Marine Section.
Description: Information and recommendations on various safety issues in the marine industry.

613.62 FR ISSN 0025-6757
MEDECINE ET TRAVAIL. 1961. q. 1200 F. Syndicat National Professionnel des Medecins du Travail, 12 impasse Mas, 31000 Toulouse, France. TEL 61-99-20-77. FAX 61-62-75-66. Eds. Drs. F. Blanc, M.C. Remesy. adv.; bk.rev. circ. 1,250. **Indexed:** C.I.S. Abstr., Excerp.Med.
—BLDSC (5487.733200).
Description: Publishes articles on occupational medicine, industrial health, hygienics, and safety at work.

613.62 SP
MEDICINA DE LA EMPRESA; publicacion dedicada a la seguridad y medicina del trabajo. 1963. q. 500 ptas.($8) Sociedad Catalana de Seguridad y Medicina del Trabajo, Tapineria, 10 pral., 08002 Barcelona, Spain. Ed. Dr. B. Gardoqui. adv.; bk.rev.; illus.; circ. controlled. **Indexed:** C.I.S. Abstr.

613.62 IT ISSN 0025-7818
RC963 CODEN: MELAAD
MEDICINA DEL LAVORO. (Text in Italian; summaries in English and Italian) 1901. bi-m. L.90000. Istituti Clinici di Perfezionamento, Via Daverio 6, 20122 Milan, Italy. Ed. Enrico C. Vigliani. adv.; bk.rev.; illus.; stat.; index. circ. 1,200. **Indexed:** Abstr.Hyg., Biol.Abstr., C.I.S. Abstr., Chem.Abstr., Ergon.Abstr., Excerp.Med., Ind.Hyg.Dig., Ind.Med., INIS Atomind., Nutr.Abstr., Trop.Dis.Bull.
—BLDSC (5533.600000); CASDDS; EMDOCS; SWETS.

613.6 RU
CODEN: GTPZAB
MEDITSINA TRUDA I PROMYSHLENNAYA EKOLOGIYA. 1957. m. Institut Meditsiny Truda, Prospekt Budennogo, 31, 105275 Moscow, Russia. Ed. N.F. Izmerov. index. **Indexed:** Abstr.Hyg., Bioeng.Abstr., Biol.Abstr., C.I.S. Abstr., Chem.Abstr., Dent.Ind., Excerp.Med., Ind.Hyg.Dig., Ind.Med., INIS Atomind., Int.Aerosp.Abstr., Rev.Med.& Vet.Mycol., Trop.Dis.Bull., World Bibl.Soc.Sec.
—CASDDS; SWETS. **CCC.**
Formerly (until 1993): Gigiena Truda i Professional'nye Zabolevaniya (ISSN 0016-9919)
Description: Covers hygiene in industry and agriculture, physiology of labor, industrial toxicology, clinical picture of occupational diseases.

MEDYCYNA PRACY. see *MEDICAL SCIENCES*

MENTAL HEALTH SPECIAL INTEREST SECTION NEWSLETTER. see *PSYCHOLOGY*

614.85 GW ISSN 0936-1197
MERKBLAETTER GEFAEHRLICHE ARBEITSSTOFFE. 1974. irreg. DM.650. Ecomed Verlagsgesellschaft AG & Co. KG, Rudolf-Diesel-Str. 3, 86899 Landsberg, Germany. TEL 08191-125-0. FAX 08191-125492. Eds. R. Kuehn, K. Birett. circ. 10,500. (looseleaf format) **Document type:** bulletin.

620.86 US
METALS NEWSLETTER. bi-m. $19 to non-members; members $15. National Safety Council, Periodicals Department, 1121 Spring Lake Dr., Itasca, IL 60143. TEL 708-775-2281. Ed. Kathy Henderson; Pub. Kevin H. Axe. **Document type:** newsletter.
Formerly: Safety Newsletter: Metals Section.
Description: Information and recommendations on safety issues in the field of metals.

613.62 US ISSN 0026-251X
MICHIGAN'S OCCUPATIONAL HEALTH. 1955-1991; resumed 1995. s-a. free. Department of Public Health, Division of Occupational Health, Box 30195, Lansing, MI 48909. TEL 517-335-8250. FAX 517-335-8761. charts; illus. circ. 4,500. **Document type:** government publication.
Description: Articles pertaining to industrial hygiene, toxicology, engineering controls and interpretations of federal and state occupational health standards.

622 613.62 SA
MINE MEDICAL OFFICERS' ASSOCIATION OF SOUTH AFRICA. JOURNAL. (Text in English) 1921. irreg. membership. Chamber of Mines of South Africa, P.O. Box 809, Johannesburg 2000, South Africa. TEL 27-11-4987534. FAX 27-11-8343804. charts; illus.; cum.index. circ. 500. (back issues avail.) **Indexed:** Abstr.Hyg., Excerp.Med., Ind.Med., Ind.S.A.Per., Trop.Dis.Bull. **Document type:** academic/scholarly publication.
Formerly: Mine Medical Officers' Association of South Africa. Proceedings (ISSN 0026-4490)

MINE REGULATION REPORTER. see *MINES AND MINING INDUSTRY*

MINES SAFETY AND HEALTH COMMISSION. REPORT/ORGANE PERMANENT POUR LA SECURITE DANS LES MINES DE HOUILLE. RAPPORT. see *MINES AND MINING INDUSTRY*

OCCUPATIONAL HEALTH AND SAFETY

620.86 US
MINING NEWSLETTER. bi-m. $19 to non-members; members $15. National Safety Council, Periodicals Department, 1121 Spring Lake Dr., Itasca, IL 60143. TEL 708-775-2281. Ed. Kathy Henderson; Pub. Kevin H. Axe. **Document type:** newsletter.
Formerly: Safety Newsletter: Mining Section.
Description: Information and recommendations on safety issues in mining.

613.6 363.11 HU ISSN 0027-3619
T55.A1 CODEN: MMUZDM
MUNKAVEDELEM/LABOR SAFETY. (Text in Hungarian; summaries in English, German, Russian) 1955. q. $20. (Szakszervezetek Orszagos Tanacsa, Munkavedelmi Tudomanyos Kutatointezet) Nepszava Lapkiado Vallalat, Rakoczi ut 54, 1964 Budapest 7, Hungary. TEL 222-408. (Subscr. to: Kultura, Box 149, H-1389 Budapest, Hungary) (Co-sponsor: Orszagos Munkaegeszsegugyi Intezet) Ed. Gyula Nagy. adv.; bk.rev. circ. 5,000. **Indexed:** Abstr.Hyg., Chem.Abstr., Trop.Dis.Bull.
—CASDDS.

614.85 US
N I O S H T I C DATABASE. q. price varies. (National Institute for Occupational Safety and Health Technical Information Center, Priorities and Research Analysis Branch) U.S. National Technical Information Service, 5285 Port Royal Rd., Springfield, VA 22161. TEL 703-487-4630. bibl. **Document type:** government publication, directory.
●Also available online. Vendor(s): Knight-Ridder, Inc., Orbit Search Service.
Also available on CD-ROM.
Description: Bibliographic database which cites over 125,000 cases involving hazards and resultant injuries and illnesses in the workplace.

363.11 NE ISSN 0928-4923
N V V K INFO. 1987. 5/yr. (Nederlandse Vereniging voor Veiligheidskunde) Uitgeverij Kluwer B.V., Postbus 23, 7400 GA Deventer, Netherlands. TEL 31-5700-47111. FAX 31-5700-34740. adv.; circ. 1,500 (controlled). **Document type:** trade publication.
Formerly (until 1992): N V V K Nieuws (ISSN 0929-1245)

615.8 JA ISSN 0917-3617
NAGANOKEN SAGYO RYOHOSHIKAI GAKUJUTSUSHI/NAGANO ASSOCIATION OF OCCUPATIONAL THERAPISTS. JOURNAL. (Text in Japanese) 1982. a. Naganoken Sagyo Ryohoshikai, Kakeyu Byoin, 1308, Nishiuchi, Marukomachi, Chiisaagata-gun, Nagano-ken 381-03, Japan. Ed. Yoko Sato. adv. contact: Shigeru Aketa. **Document type:** academic/scholarly publication.

615.82 CN
NATIONAL (TORONTO). bi-m. membership. Canadian Association of Occupational Therapists - Association Canadienne des Ergotherapeutes, 110 Eglinton Ave., W., 3rd Fl., Toronto, ON M4R 1A3, Canada. TEL 416-487-5404. FAX 416-487-0480. circ. 5,652. **Document type:** newsletter.
Description: Reports on current professional events, issues, viewpoints and Association business.

614.85 616.2 SA ISSN 0374-9800
NATIONAL CENTRE FOR OCCUPATIONAL HEALTH. ANNUAL REPORT. 1957. irreg. free. Department of Health, National Centre for Occupational Health, P.O. Box 4788, Johannesburg 2000, South Africa. FAX 27-11-720-6608. Ed. Dr. A.C. Cantrell. circ. 400 (controlled). **Document type:** government publication.
Formerly: National Institute for Occupational Diseases. Annual Report.

614.85 JA
NATIONAL INSTITUTE OF INDUSTRIAL SAFETY. ANNUAL REPORT. (Text in Japanese) 1968. a. free. National Institute of Industrial Safety, Umezono 1-4-6, Kiyose, Tokyo 204, Tokyo 108, Japan. circ. 2,000. (back issues avail.) **Document type:** corporate report.
Formerly (until 1992): Research Institute of Industrial Safety. Annual Report.

613.6 368.5 AU ISSN 1016-0515
NEUE B S; Sicherheitsmagazin. 1965. 10/yr. S.210. (Allgemeine Unfallversicherungsanstalt) Elbemuehl Druck- und Verlagsgesellschaft mbH, Altmannsdorferstr. 154-156, A-1230 Vienna, Austria. TEL 0222-66122. Ed. Ilse Zembaty. adv. contact: Margot Weidner. bk.rev.; abstr.; illus.; stat.; index. circ. 272,850. **Indexed:** C.I.S. Abstr. **Document type:** consumer publication.
—BLDSC (6077.321200).
Formerly (until 1988): Betriebssicherheit - B S (ISSN 0005-3287)

NEW HAMPSHIRE MUNICIPAL PRACTICE SERIES. VOL. 3: PUBLIC HEALTH, SAFETY AND HIGHWAYS. see
PUBLIC ADMINISTRATION — Municipal Government

614.7 US ISSN 1048-2911
RA566.3 CODEN: NESLES
NEW SOLUTIONS; a journal of environmental and occupational health policy. 1990. 4/yr. $40 to individuals and non-profit organizations; institutions and overseas $60. Oil, Chemical & Atomic Workers Union, Box 281200, Lakewood, CO 80228-8200. TEL 303-987-2229. FAX 303-987-1967. E-mail: ocaw@labornet.org. Ed. Charles Levenstein. **Indexed:** Alt.Press Ind., Environ.Abstr., Environ.Per.Bibl. (1991-), P.A.I.S.
—BLDSC (6088.645000); CIS; UnCover.

614.8 374.013 NO
NORWAY. DIREKTORATET FOR ARBEIDSTILSYNET. FORSKRIFTER/REGULATIONS. irreg. price varies. Direktoratet for Arbeidstilsynet - Directorate of Labour Inspection, Fr. Nansens vei 14, P.O. Box 8103 Dep., N-0032-Oslo, Norway. TEL 47-22-95-70-00. FAX 47-22-42-64-58. (Subscr. to: Tiden Norsk Forlag, P.O. Box 8813, Youngstorget, N-0028 Oslo, Norway) charts; illus.
Formerly: Norway. Statens Arbeidstilsyn Direktoratet. Verneregler.

613.62 US ISSN 0888-1626
NOTICIAS DE SEGURIDAD. (Text in Spanish) 1938. m. $32. Inter-American Safety Council, 33 Park Pl., Englewood, NJ 07631. TEL 201-871-0004. FAX 201-871-2074. TELEX 135407. Ed.Bd. adv. circ. 10,000. **Document type:** trade publication.

613.62 363.11 CN ISSN 0827-4576
O H & S CANADA. (Occupational Health & Safety) 1985. bi-m. Can.$88.81 (US Can.$114, elsewhere Can.$124). Southam Information and Technology Group, 1450 Don Mills Rd., Don Mills, ON M3B 2X7, Canada. TEL 416-445-6641. FAX 416-442-2200. Ed. Margaret Nearing. adv.; bk.rev.; charts; illus.; stat.; tr.lit.; index. circ. 7,000. (back issues avail.) **Indexed:** Can.B.P.I., Can.Per.Ind.
—BLDSC (6228.859000); Faxon; UMI.
Description: Provides information on accident prevention, occupational hygiene, laws and standards, workman's compensation.

O O H N A JOURNAL. (Ontario Occupational Health Nurses Association) see MEDICAL SCIENCES — Nurses And Nursing

614.85 US
O S H A NEWS FOR CONSTRUCTION. fortn. $397. (Occupational Safety and Health Administration) Merritt Company, 1661 Ninth St., Box 955, Santa Monica, CA 90406. TEL 310-450-7234. FAX 310-450-7234. Ed. John Hartnett. **Document type:** government publication, newsletter.
Description: Information on what the Federal Occupational Safety and Health Administration plans to do in regard to "1926" Construction regulations.

614.85 US
O S H A NEWS FOR GENERAL INDUSTRY. bi-w. $397. Merritt Company, 1661 Ninth St., Box 955, Santa Monica, CA 90406. TEL 310-450-7234. FAX 310-396-4563. Ed. John Hartnett. **Document type:** newsletter.
Formerly: O S H A News.
Description: Publishes information on what the Federal Occupational Safety and Health Administration plans to do in regard to "1910" General Industry regulations.

O S H A TRAINING BULLETIN FOR SUPERVISORS. (Occupational Safety and Health Administration) see ENVIRONMENTAL STUDIES

613.62 US
O S H A UP TO DATE NEWSLETTER. (U.S. Occupational Safety & Health Administration) m. $34 to non-members; members $28. National Safety Council, Periodicals Department, 1121 Spring Lake Dr., Itasca, IL 60143. TEL 708-775-2281. Ed. Kathleen Henderson; Pub. Kevin H. Axe. circ. 30,000. **Document type:** newsletter.

613.62 614.85 US ISSN 1057-1485
O S H A WEEK. (Occupational Safety and Health Administration) w. $248. Stevens Publishing Corporation, 3630 J.H. Kultgen Frwy., Waco, TX 76706. TEL 817-776-9000. FAX 817-776-9018. Ed. Jerome Ashton; Pub. L. Alan Stevens. **Document type:** newsletter.
—CCC.
Description: Discusses government policy on occupational health and safety.

614.85 UK ISSN 1352-0334
O S H BRIEFING. (Occupational Safety and Health) 1993. m. £99 for hardcopy edition; electronic editions £150. Babour Index, New Lodge Drift Rd., Windsor, Berks. SL4 4RQ, England. TEL 01344-884121. FAX 01344-884112. Ed. D. Denton. bk.rev. (also avail. in diskette format) **Document type:** bulletin, abstracting/indexing.
●Also available online.
Description: Provides concise summaries of newly published U.K. and E.C. legislation, reports, and other documents of an official and authoritative nature. Covers health, safety, fire safety, and related topics.

613.62 BE ISSN 0771-2634
OBJECTIF PREVENTION. 1964. m. 880 BEF. Association Nationale pour la Prevention des Accidents du Travail (ANPAT), 88 Rue Gachard, Bte. 4, B-1050 Brussels, Belgium. TEL 32-2-648-03-37. FAX 32-2-648-68-67. circ. 27,000. (tabloid format)

613.62 616.98 UK ISSN 1351-0711
RC963 CODEN: OEMEEM
OCCUPATIONAL AND ENVIRONMENTAL MEDICINE. 1944. m. £139($240) B M J Publishing Group, B.M.A. House, Tavistock Sq., London WC1H 9JR, England. TEL 0171-383-6270.
FAX 0171-383-6402. (N. American subscr. to: Box 408, Franklin, MA 02038. TEL 800-2-FON-BMJ. FAX 800-2-FAX-BMJ) Ed. Anne Cockroft. adv. contact: Sheila Rowe. bk.rev.; abstr.; charts; illus.; index, cum.index: 1944-1960. (also avail. in microform from UMI; reprint service avail. from UMI) **Indexed:** Abstr.Hyg., API Abstr., API Catal., API Hlth.& Environ., API Oil., API Pet.Ref., API Pet.Subst., API Transport., B.C.I.R.A., Biol.Abstr., Br.Ceram.Abstr., C.I.S. Abstr., CAD CAM Abstr., Cadscan, Chem.Abstr., Cott.& Trop.Fibr.Abstr., Curr.Adv.Ecol.Sci., Curr.Cont., Dent.Ind., Energy Rev., Environ.Abstr., Environ.Per.Bibl. (1981-), Ergon.Abstr., Excerp.Med., Helminthol.Abstr., Ind.Hyg.Dig., Ind.Med., Ind.Sci.Rev., Ind.Vet., Lab.Haz.Bull., Lead Abstr., Med.& Surg.Dermat., Nutr.Abstr., Plant Breed.Abstr., Poult.Abstr., Risk Abstr., Sci.Cit.Ind., Trop.Dis.Bull., Vet.Bull., World Surf.Coat., World Text.Abstr., Zincscan. **Document type:** academic/scholarly publication.
—BLDSC (6227.833000); ADONIS; CASDDS; Faxon; Genuine Article; SWETS; UMI; UnCover. **CCC.**
Formerly (until 1993): British Journal of Industrial Medicine (ISSN 0007-1072)
Description: Focuses on current interest in the whole field of occupational medicine.
Refereed Serial

OCCUPATIONAL ERGONOMICS AND SAFETY. see
BUSINESS AND ECONOMICS — Labor And Industrial Relations

OCCUPATIONAL HEALTH AND SAFETY

614.85 US ISSN 0029-7909
CODEN: OCHAAZ
OCCUPATIONAL HAZARDS; magazine of health & environment. 1938. m. $45 (free to qualified personnel). Penton Publishing (Subsidiary of: Pittway Company), 1100 Superior Ave., Cleveland, OH 44114-2543. TEL 216-696-7000. FAX 216-696-8765. (Subscr. to: Box 95759, Cleveland, OH 44101) Ed. Stephen G. Minter. adv.; bk.rev.; charts; illus.; stat.; tr.lit.; index; circ. 60,000 (controlled). (also avail. in microform from UMI; reprint service avail. from UMI) **Indexed:** ABI Inform, B.P.I., BPIA, Bus.Ind., C.I.S. Abstr., Chem.Abstr., Hlth.Ind., Ind.Hyg.Dig., Lab.Haz.Bull., Pers.Manage.Abstr., PROMT, Tr.& Indus.Ind., Work Rel.Abstr.
●Also available online. Vendor(s): University Microfilms International.
—BLDSC (6228.000000); Faxon; Genuine Article; SWETS; UMI. **CCC.**
Description: News on industrial safety, occupational health, environmental control, insurance, first aid, medical care, and hazardous material control.

613.62 US ISSN 0362-4064
RC963 CODEN: OHSADQ
OCCUPATIONAL HEALTH & SAFETY. (Contains special issue: Asbestos Control Buyer's Guide) m. $49. Stevens Publishing Corporation, 3630 J.H. Kultgen Frwy., Waco, TX 76706. TEL 817-776-9000. FAX 817-776-9018. Ed. Mark Hartley; Pub. Russell Lindsay. adv.; bk.rev.; charts. circ. 85,000. (also avail. in microform from UMI; reprint service avail. from UMI) **Indexed:** Abstr.Hyg., B.P.I., Biol.Abstr., C.I.S. Abstr., Chem.Abstr., CINAHL, Dent.Ind., Ergon.Abstr., Hosp.Lit.Ind., Ind.Hyg.Dig., Ind.Med., INSPEC, Lab.Haz.Bull., Noise Pollut.Publ.Abstr., Pers.Lit., Tr.& Dev.Alert, Trop.Dis.Bull. **Document type:** trade publication.
●Also available online. Vendor(s): University Microfilms International.
—BLDSC (6228.858000); Faxon; SWETS; UMI; UnCover. **CCC.**
Former titles (until vol.45, 1976): International Journal of Occupational Health and Safety (ISSN 0093-2205); Industrial Medicine and Surgery (ISSN 0019-8536)
Refereed Serial

OCCUPATIONAL HEALTH AND SAFETY LAW. see *LAW*

614 US ISSN 0196-058X
OCCUPATIONAL HEALTH & SAFETY LETTER; ...towards productivity and peace of mind. 1971. bi-w. $273 (effective Sep. 1992). Business Publishers, Inc., 951 Pershing Dr., Silver Spring, MD 20910-4464. TEL 301-587-6300. FAX 301-585-9075. Ed. Bryan Morris. (looseleaf format) **Document type:** newsletter.
●Also available online. Vendor(s): NewsNet.
—**CCC.**
Former titles: Workplace Health Safety and Liability Report; Workplace Health and Job Safety Report; Workplace Health; Job Safety and Health Report; Job Safety and Health (Silver Spring) (ISSN 0148-4079)
Description: News for workplace managers on maintaining staff safety; includes Americans with Disabilities Act regulations.

613.62 614.85 US ISSN 0896-3835
CODEN: OHSDE2
OCCUPATIONAL HEALTH & SAFETY NEWS. bi-w. $239. Stevens Publishing Corporation, 3630 J.H. Kultgen Frwy., Waco, TX 76706. TEL 817-776-9000. FAX 817-776-9018. Ed. Jay Fletcher; Pub. L. Alan Stevens. adv. **Document type:** newsletter.
Description: Discusses federal policy regarding occupational health and safety.

613.62 UK ISSN 0969-708X
OCCUPATIONAL HEALTH BULLETIN. 1986. s-a. University of Birmingham, Institute of Occupational Health, P.O. Box 363, Edgbaston, Birmingham B15 2TT, England. TEL 0121-414-6030. FAX 0121-471-5208. E-mail: institute-of-occupational-health@bham.ac.uk. (back issues avail.) **Document type:** bulletin.
Formerly: University of Birmingham. Institute of Occupational Health. Bulletin (ISSN 0958-6040)

613 AT ISSN 1032-0989
OCCUPATIONAL HEALTH MAGAZINE. 1987. m. Aus.$345 includes Newsletter (effective May 1995). Newsletter Information Services, P.O. Box 693, Manly, N.S.W. 2095, Australia. TEL 02-977-7500. FAX 02-977-3310.
Former titles: Occupational Health and Safety Products and Services (ISSN 1032-0970); (until 1988): Products and Services (ISSN 1032-0962)
Description: Provides information service on occupational health and safety. Alerts employers and unions to key developments in workplace safety and health from Australia and throughout the world.

613.62 US
OCCUPATIONAL HEALTH MANAGEMENT. 1991. m. $219. American Health Consultants, Inc., Six Piedmont Center, Ste. 400, Atlanta, GA 30305. TEL 404-262-7436; 800-688-2421. FAX 800-284-3291. Ed. Greg Freeman. circ. 1,220. **Document type:** newsletter.

613 AT
OCCUPATIONAL HEALTH NEWSLETTER. fortn. Aus.$345 includes Occupational Health Magazine (effective May 1995). Newsletter Information Services, P.O. Box 2095, Manly, N.S.W. 2095, Australia. TEL 02-977-7500. FAX 02-977-3310. **Document type:** newsletter.
Description: Provides information on occupational health and safety. Alerts employers and unions to key developments in workplace safety and health from Australia and throughout the world.

658.3 US
OCCUPATIONAL HEALTH NURSING NEWSLETTER. bi-m. $19 to non-members; members $15. National Safety Council, Periodicals Department, 1121 Spring Lake Dr., Itasca, IL 60143. TEL 708-775-2281. Ed. Kathy Henderson; Pub. Kevin H. Axe. **Document type:** newsletter.
Formerly: Safety Newsletter: Occupational Health Nursing Section (ISSN 0466-499X)
Description: Information and recommendations on safety issues in the field of occupational health nursing.

613.62 UK ISSN 0951-4600
OCCUPATIONAL HEALTH REVIEW. 1987. bi-m. £95 (foreign £105). Eclipse Group Ltd., 18-20 Highbury Pl., London N5 1QP, England. TEL 0171-354-5858. FAX 0171-359-4000. Ed. John Ballard. circ. 1,400. (back issues avail.) **Indexed:** Intl.Polym.Sci.& Tech., RAPRA. **Document type:** trade publication.
—BLDSC (6228.990000).
Description: For specialists and nonspecialists in the area of occupational medicine and employee welfare.

363.11 US ISSN 1061-0251
CODEN: OCHYE9
OCCUPATIONAL HYGIENE; risk management of occupational hazards. 1993. 4/yr. 90 ECU (effective 1996). Gordon & Breach Science Publishers, c/o International Publishers Distributor, 820 Town Center Dr., Langhorne, PA 19047. TEL 215-750-2642. FAX 215-750-6343. (Subscr. to: International Publishers Distributor, P.O. Box 90, Reading, Berkshire RG1 8JL, England. TEL 44-173-456-8316) (also avail. in microform)
—CASDDS. **CCC.**
Description: Presents recent developments in the science of anticipation, recognition, evaluation and control of occupational hazards.

613.62 UK ISSN 0141-7568
CODEN: OHMOD4
OCCUPATIONAL HYGIENE MONOGRAPHS. 1978. irreg. price varies. Science and Technology Letters, P.O. Box 81, Northwood, Middlesex HA6 3DN, England. TEL 09274-23586. FAX 09274-25066. Ed. Dr. Donald Hughes. circ. 5,000. (back issues avail.) **Document type:** monographic series.

613.62 616.98 UK ISSN 0962-7480
CODEN: OCMEE8
OCCUPATIONAL MEDICINE. 1951. bi-m. £140($223) (effective 1996). (Society of Occupational Medicine) Butterworth - Heinemann, Part of the Reed Elsevier group, Linacre House, Jordan Hill, Oxford OX2 8DP, England. TEL 0865-310366. FAX 0865-310898. TELEX 83111 BHPOXF G. (Subscr. to: Elsevier Science Ltd., P.O. Box 800, Kidlington, Oxford OX5 1DX, England. TEL 44-865-843000. FAX 44-865-843010; Subscr. to: Elsevier Science, 660 White Plains Rd., Tarrytown, NY 10591-5153. TEL 914-524-9200. FAX 914-333-2444) Ed. D. D'Auria. adv.; bk.rev.; illus.; index. (also avail. in microform from UMI; back issues avail.) **Indexed:** Abstr.Hyg., Biol.Abstr., C.I.S. Abstr., Chem.Abstr., Curr.Adv.Ecol.Sci., Curr.Cont., Excerp.Med., Ind.Med., INIS Atomind., Lab.Haz.Bull., Rev.Med.& Vet.Mycol., Trop.Dis.Bull. **Document type:** academic/scholarly publication.
—CASDDS; Faxon; Genuine Article; SWETS; UMI; UnCover. **CCC.**
Former titles (until 1991): Society of Occupational Medicine. Journal (ISSN 0301-0023); Society of Occupational Medicine Transactions (ISSN 0037-9972)
Description: Covers original and review articles on all aspects of occupational health.
Refereed Serial

613.62 US ISSN 1047-4498
RC963.A1
OCCUPATIONAL MEDICINE (NORWALK). 1990. triennial. Appleton & Lange (Subsidiary of: Simon & Schuster Company), 25 Van Zant St., Box 5630, Norwalk, CT 06855. TEL 203-838-4400.

613.62 US ISSN 0885-114X
RC963.A1 CODEN: SAOME4
OCCUPATIONAL MEDICINE (PHILADELPHIA); state of the art reviews. q. $86 (foreign $96). Hanley & Belfus, Inc., 210 S. 13th St., Philadelphia, PA 19107. TEL 215-546-7293. FAX 215-790-9330. circ. 1,600. (back issues avail.) **Indexed:** Ind.Hyg.Dig.
—BLDSC (6229.620000); CASDDS; Faxon; Genuine Article; SWETS. **CCC.**
Refereed Serial

363 628.5 SA
OCCUPATIONAL SAFETY & ENVIRONMENTAL NEWS. 1993. m. Complete Publishing (Pty.) Ltd., P.O. Box 87745, Houghton 2041, South Africa. TEL 27-11-7892112. FAX 27-11-789-5347. adv.; illus. (tabloid format) **Document type:** trade publication.

363.11 613.6 UK ISSN 0143-5353
T55.A1
OCCUPATIONAL SAFETY AND HEALTH.* 1946. m. £6.75. Royal Society for the Prevention of Accidents, Cannon House, the Priory Queensway, Birmingham B4 6BS, England. Ed. Juliet Russell. adv.; bk.rev.; abstr.; charts; illus.; tr.lit.; index. circ. 12,900. **Indexed:** Abstr.Hyg., Account.& Data Proc.Abstr., Agri.Eng.Abstr., Anbar, B.C.I.R.A., BMT, Br.Ceram.Abstr., Br.Rail.Bd., Br.Tech.Ind., C.I.S. Abstr., Cadscan, Lab.Haz.Bull., Lead Abstr., Mgmt.& Market.Abstr., RAPRA, Repindex, Trop.Dis.Bull., World Text.Abstr., Zincscan.
—BLDSC (6231.100000); Faxon; SWETS.
Formerly: British Journal of Occupational Safety.

344 US ISSN 0092-3435
KF3568.3.A2
OCCUPATIONAL SAFETY AND HEALTH DECISIONS. 1973. irreg. $39.50. Commerce Clearing House, Inc., 4025 W. Peterson Ave., Chicago, IL 60646. TEL 312-583-8500.

OCCUPATIONAL HEALTH AND SAFETY

331 US ISSN 0095-3237
KF3570.A1
OCCUPATIONAL SAFETY & HEALTH REPORTER; a weekly review of workplace health and safety. 1971. w. $1082 (effective July 1995). The Bureau of National Affairs, Inc., 1231 25th St., N.W., Washington, DC 20037. TEL 202-452-4200. FAX 202-822-8092. TELEX 285656 BNAI WSH. (Subscr. to: 9435 Key West Ave., Rockville, MD 20850. TEL 800-372-1033) Ed. Stanley S. Pond. charts; stat.; index. (looseleaf format; back issues avail.) **Indexed:** Ind.Hyg.Dig.
●Also available online. Vendor(s): Human Resources Information Network (CDD, HDD), Knight-Ridder, Inc. (Laborlaw, File no.244).
—BLDSC (6231.205000). **CCC.**
Description: Notification and reference service which provides information on federal and state regulation of occupational safety and health, standards, legislation, enforcement activities, research, and legal decisions.

613.62 UN ISSN 0078-3129
CODEN: OSHSDY
OCCUPATIONAL SAFETY AND HEALTH SERIES. (Editions in English, French and Spanish) 1963. irreg., no.70, 1993. price varies. (International Labour Office) I L O Publications, CH-1211 Geneva 22, Switzerland. TEL 022-799-6111. FAX 022-799-6358. TELEX 415647-ILO-CH. (Dist. in U.S. by: I L O Publications Center, 49 Sheridan Ave., Albany, NY 12210. TEL 518-436-9686. FAX 518-436-7433) (also avail. in microform from ILO) **Document type:** monographic series.
—**CCC.**

613.62 UK ISSN 0966-7903
▼**OCCUPATIONAL THERAPY INTERNATIONAL.** 1994. q. £40($150) to individuals; institutions £80 (effective 1996). Whurr Publishers Ltd., 19b Compton Terrace, London N1 2UN, England. TEL 0171-359-5979. FAX 0171-226-5290. (Subscr. to: Turpin Distribution Services Ltd., Blackhorse Rd., Letchworth, Herts. SG6 1HN, England. TEL 01462-672555. FAX 01462-480947; Subscr. in N. America to: Whurr Publishers Ltd., Box 1897, Lawrence, KS 66044-8897. TEL 913-843-1221. FAX 913-843-1274) adv.: page £150; adv. contact: Sarah Vicary. **Document type:** academic/scholarly publication.
—BLDSC (6231.254800).
Description: Covers clinical research, current practices, technology, professional issues, education, trends in health care, industrial health and other areas of interest to occupational therapists throughout the world.
Refereed Serial

613.62 US ISSN 0893-1712
OCCUPATIONAL THERAPY WEEK. 1939. m. $80 to individuals; institutions $175; foreign $200. American Occupational Therapy Association, Inc., Box 31220, Bethesda, MD 20824-1220. TEL 301-652-2682. FAX 301-652-7711. Ed. Bruce E. Tapper. adv.; charts; illus. circ. 42,000. (tabloid format) **Indexed:** Rehabil.Lit.
—UnCover.
Former titles (until 1985): Occupational Therapy Newspaper; Occupational Therapy; American Occupational Therapy Association. Newsletter.

340 613.62 UK ISSN 1352-2205
OFFICE HEALTH AND SAFETY MONITOR. 1993. m. £119 (foreign £141). Monitor Press, Rectory Rd., Great Waldingfield, Sudbury, Suffolk CO10 0TL, England. TEL 0787-378607. FAX 0787-880201. **Document type:** newsletter.

363.11 UK
OFFICE HEALTH & SAFETY PRACTICE. bi-m. £75 (foreign £84). Tolley Publishing Co. Ltd., Tolley House, 2 Addiscombe Rd., Croydon, Surrey CR9 5AX, England. TEL 0181-686-9141. FAX 0181-686-3155. **Document type:** trade publication.

614.8 US ISSN 0198-7208
HD7260
OHIO MONITOR. 1928. m. free to qualified personnel. Industrial Commission, Division of Safety and Hygiene, 246 N. High St., Columbus, OH 43215. TEL 614-466-3385. Ed. Robert L. McCullough. bk.rev.; abstr.; charts; illus.; stat. circ. 75,000.
—BLDSC (1567.795000).
Formerly: Monitor (ISSN 0026-9751)

ONTARIO HEALTH AND SAFETY LAW; a comprehensive guide to the statute, case-law, policy and procedures. see LAW

658.3 US
PETROLEUM NEWSLETTER. bi-m. $19 to non-members; members $15. National Safety Council, Periodicals Department, 1121 Spring Lake Dr., Itasca, IL 60143. TEL 708-775-2281. Ed. Kathy Henderson; Pub. Kevin H. Axe. **Indexed:** AESIS. **Document type:** newsletter.
Formerly: Safety Newsletter: Petroleum Section.
Description: Information and recommendations on safety issues in the petroleum industry.

PHYSICAL DISABILITIES SPECIAL INTEREST SECTION NEWSLETTER. see HANDICAPPED

658.3 US
POWER PRESS AND FORGING NEWSLETTER. bi-m. $19 to non-members; members $15. National Safety Council, Periodicals Department, 1121 Spring Lake Dr., Itasca, IL 60143. TEL 708-775-2281. Ed. Kathy Henderson; Pub. Kevin H. Axe. **Document type:** newsletter.
Formerly: Safety Newsletter: Power Press and Forging Section.
Description: Information and recommendations on safety issues in the field.

PRACOVNI LEKARSTVI. see MEDICAL SCIENCES

363.11 613.6 FR ISSN 0982-443X
PREVENIR LES RISQUES DU METIER. 1959. q. 24 F. Institut National de Recherche et de Securite pour la Prevention des Accidents du Travail et des Maladies Professionnelles, 30 rue Olivier Noyer, 75680 Paris Cedex 14, France. TEL 40-44-30-00. FAX 40-44-30-99. TELEX 203594F INRSPAR F. Ed. Didier Gout. circ. 240,000. **Indexed:** C.I.S. Abstr. **Document type:** newspaper.
Formerly (until 1984): Risques du Metier (ISSN 0048-8321)

613.6 HT
PREVOYANCE. 1981. s-a. free. Office d'Assurance Accidents du Travail, Maladie et Maternite, B.P. 1324, Port-au-Prince, Haiti. Ed. Gerson Alexis. charts; illus.; stat. circ. 2,000.
Formerly (until 1980): Prevention (ISSN 0048-5241)

658.3 US
PRINTING AND PUBLISHING NEWSLETTER. bi-m. $19 to non-members; members $15. National Safety Council, Periodicals Department, 1121 Spring Lake Dr., Itasca, IL 60143. TEL 708-775-2281. Ed. Kathy Henderson; Pub. Kevin H. Axe. **Document type:** newsletter.
Formerly: Safety Newsletter: Printing and Publishing Section.
Description: Information and recommendations on safety issues in printing and publishing.

620.8 US ISSN 0099-0027
T55.A1 CODEN: PRSAD5
PROFESSIONAL SAFETY. 1956. m. $60. American Society of Safety Engineers, 1800 E. Oakton St., Des Plaines, IL 60018-2187. TEL 708-692-4121. FAX 708-296-3769. Ed. Neal Lorenzi. adv.; bk.rev.; charts; illus.; tr.lit.; index. circ. 30,000. (also avail. in microform from UMI; reprint service avail. from UMI) **Indexed:** A.S.& T.Ind., ABI Inform, C.I.S.Abstr., Eng.Ind., Environ.Per.Bibl., ISMEC, Met.Abstr., Mgmt.& Market.Abstr. **Document type:** trade publication.
●Also available online. Vendor(s): University Microfilms International.
—BLDSC (6864.215000); Ei; Faxon; SWETS; UMI; UnCover. **CCC.**
Formerly (until 1974): American Society of Safety Engineers. Journal (ISSN 0003-1208)
Description: For safety professionals. Features information on developments in the research and technology of accident prevention.

658.382 US
PUBLIC EMPLOYEE NEWSLETTER. bi-m. $19 to non-members; members $15. National Safety Council, Periodicals Department, 1121 Spring Lake Dr., Itasca, IL 60143. TEL 708-775-2281. Ed. Kathy Henderson; Pub. Kevin H. Axe. **Document type:** newsletter.
Formerly: Safety Newsletter: Public Employee Section (ISSN 0470-2840)
Description: Information and recommendations on safety issues for public employees.

PUBLIC SERVICE ASSOCIATION JOURNAL. see PUBLIC ADMINISTRATION

350.162 US
PUBLIC UTILITIES NEWSLETTER. bi-m. $19 to non-members; members $15. National Safety Council, Periodicals Department, 1121 Spring Lake Dr., Itasca, IL 60143. TEL 708-775-2281. Ed. Kathy Henderson; Pub Kevin H. Axe. **Document type:** newsletter.
Formerly: Safety Newsletter: Public Utilities Section (ISSN 0466-5007)
Description: Information and recommendations on safety issues in public utilities.

613.62 614.85
615.9 US ISSN 0361-2546
RA1215
R T E C S. (Registry of Toxic Effects of Chemical Substances) 1971. q. U.S. National Institute for Occupational Safety and Health, 4676 Columbia Pkwy., Cincinnati, OH 45226. TEL 800-356-4674. abstr.; bibl.; index. circ. 10,000. (also avail. in magnetic tape; not avail. in printed format) **Indexed:** MEDOC.
●Also available online. Vendor(s): Canadian Centre for Occupational Health & Safety, Chemical Information Systems, Data-Star, Knight-Ridder, Inc. (File no.336), National Library of Medicine, STN International.
Also available on CD-ROM. Producer(s): SilverPlatter Information, Inc.
Description: Provides information on known toxic and biological effects of chemical substances for use by employers, employees, physicians, industrial hygienists, toxicologists, researchers, and others concerned with the safe handling of chemicals. The absence of a substance from the registry does not indicate that it is not toxic. Includes CODEN files.

614.8 539.2 US ISSN 0740-0640
R895.A1 CODEN: RPMAEI
RADIATION PROTECTION MANAGEMENT; the journal of applied health physics. (Supplement avail.: R P M Directory) 1983. bi-m. $45 to individuals; institutions $395 (effective 1994). R S A Publications, 19 Pendleton Dr., Box 19, Hebron, CT 06248. TEL 203-228-0824. FAX 203-228-4402. Ed. Sharyn Mathews. adv. contact: Sharyn Mathews. bk.rev.; index. circ. 1,200. (back issues avail.) **Indexed:** Chem.Abstr. **Document type:** trade publication.
—BLDSC (7227.994000); CASDDS; Ei.
Description: Presents practical, work-related information on applied radiation protection programs at nuclear power plants, fuel facilities, laboratories and waste disposal facilities. Covers the entire spectrum of industrial health physics topics, as well as respiratory protection, technical management, and relevant computer applications.

620.86 US
RAILROAD NEWSLETTER. bi-m. $19 to non-members; members $15. National Safety Council, Periodicals Department, 1121 Spring Lake Dr., Itasca, IL 60143. TEL 708-775-2281. Ed. Kathy Henderson; Pub. Kevin H. Axe. **Document type:** newsletter.
Formerly: Safety Newsletter: Railroad Section.
Description: Information and recommendations on safety issues for the railroad industry.

362.104 NO ISSN 0805-5238
RAMAZZINI/NORWEGIAN JOURNAL OF OCCUPATIONAL MEDICINE. 1969. 6/yr. NOK 250. Norsk Arbeidsmedisinsk Forening, Fjellvn. 5, N-1324 Lysaker, Norway. TEL 47-67-12-46-00. FAX 47-67-59-10-90. Ed. Dr. Oeivind Larsen. adv.; bk.rev. circ. 1,783. **Document type:** academic/scholarly publication.
Former titles (until 1994): Norsk Tidsskrift for Arbeidsmedisin (ISSN 0803-2394); (until 1991): Norsk Bedriftshelsetjeneste (ISSN 0333-0249); (until 1980): Norsk Fretagshaelsovaerd (ISSN 0332-8910); (until 1978): N I R - Nytt (ISSN 0358-4909)
Description: Covers industrial and occupational medicine, as well as general preventive medicine.

REPETITIVE STRESS INJURY LITIGATION REPORTER. see LAW

OCCUPATIONAL HEALTH AND SAFETY

620.86 US
RESEARCH AND DEVELOPMENT NEWSLETTER. bi-m. $19 to non-members; members $15. National Safety Council, Periodicals Department, 1121 Spring Lake Dr., Itasca, IL 60143. TEL 708-775-2281. Ed. Kathy Henderson; Pub. Kevin H. Axe. **Document type:** newsletter.
 Formerly: Safety Newsletter: Research and Development.
 Description: Information and recommendations on safety issues pertaining to research and development.

613.62 539.7 US
RESPIRATORY PROTECTION NEWSLETTER. 1985. bi-m. $119 in N. America; elsewhere $129. Radiation Safety Associates, Inc., Box 107, Hebron, CT 06248. TEL 203-228-0487. FAX 203-228-4402. Ed. Paul R. Steinmeyer. bk.rev.; index. circ. 150. (looseleaf format; back issues avail.)
 Formerly (until Nov. 1988): Radiological Respiratory Protection Newsletter (ISSN 0882-0953)

614.85 BL
REVISTA DE TERAPIA OCUPACIONAL. (Text in Portuguese; abstracts and index in English, Portuguese) 1990. s-a. exchange basis. Universidade de Sao Paulo, Curso de Terapia Ocupacional, Rua Cipotanea 51, Cidade Universitaria Armando Salles de Oliveira, 05508-900 Sao Paulo SP, Brazil. TEL 011-818-4061. Ed.Bd. bk.rev.; bibl. **Document type:** academic/scholarly publication.

613.62 FR ISSN 0300-0559
REVUE DE MEDECINE DU TRAVAIL. (Summaries in English, French) 1972. bi-m. 500 F.($100) (effective 1995). Groupement National des Medecins du Batiment et des Travaux Publics, 7 rue la Perouse, 75116 Paris, France. TEL 40-69-53-77. FAX 45-53-58-77. Eds. M. Blaizot, M. Amphoux. adv.; bk.rev.; index. circ. 2,000. (back issues avail.) **Document type:** bulletin.
 —BLDSC (7931.800000).
 Description: Covers all subjects concerning occupational health, medicine, and ergonomics industrial toxicologies.

613.62 368 363 IT ISSN 0035-5836
HD7816.I8 CODEN: RIMPAA
RIVISTA DEGLI INFORTUNI E DELLE MALATTIE PROFESSIONALI. 1914. bi-m. L.42000. Istituto Nazionale per l'Assicurazione contro gli Infortuni sul Lavoro, Via 4 Novembre 144, 00187 Rome, Italy. adv.; bk.rev.; abstr.; bibl.; charts; illus.; stat.; index, cum.index. circ. 8,000. **Indexed:** C.I.S. Abstr., Chem.Abstr., World Bibl.Soc.Sec.
 —CASDDS.

613.62 IT ISSN 0391-2825
 CODEN: RMLIDF
RIVISTA DI MEDICINA DEL LAVORO ED IGIENE INDUSTRIALE. 1976. q. L.50000($72) (effective 1995). Casa Editrice Idelson, Via A. DeGasperi, 55, 80133 Naples, Italy. TEL 39-81-5524733. FAX 39-81-5518295. Ed. Luciano Rossi.
 —CASDDS.

610 JA ISSN 0022-443X
 CODEN: ROKAAV
RODO KAGAKU (KAWASAKI, 1924)/JOURNAL OF SCIENCE OF LABOUR. (Text in English, Japanese) 1924. m. 8800 Yen. Institute for Science of Labour - Rodo Kagaku Kenkyujo, 2-8-14 Sugao, Miyamae-ku, Kawasaki 216, Japan. TEL 81-44-977-2121. FAX 81-44-977-7504. Ed. Kazutaka Kogi. adv.; bk.rev.; abstr.; bibl.; index. circ. 2,500. (also avail. in microfilm) **Indexed:** Abstr.Hyg., C.I.S.Abstr., Chem.Abstr., Ergon.Abstr., Ind.Hyg.Dig., Nutr.Abstr., Psychol.Abstr., Trop.Dis.Bull. **Document type:** academic/scholarly publication.
 —BLDSC (5056.230000); UnCover.

610 JA ISSN 0035-7774
 CODEN: ROKAAV
RODO NO KAGAKU (KAWASAKI, 1946)/DIGEST OF SCIENCE OF LABOUR. (Text in Japanese) 1946. m. 11000 Yen. Institute for Science of Labour - Rodo Kagaku Kenkyujo, 2-8-14 Sugao, Miyamae-ku, Kawasaki 216, Japan. TEL 81-44-977-2121. FAX 81-44-97-7504. Ed. Kazutaka Kogi. adv.; bk.rev. circ. 3,000. **Indexed:** Chem.Abstr. **Document type:** academic/scholarly publication.
 —CASDDS.

660.280 US
RUBBER AND PLASTICS NEWSLETTER. bi-m. $19 to non-members; members $15. National Safety Council, Periodicals Department, 1121 Spring Lake Dr., Itasca, IL 60143. TEL 708-775-2281. Ed. Kathy Henderson; Pub. Kevin H. Axe. **Document type:** newsletter.
 Formerly: Safety Newsletter: Rubber and Plastics Section.
 Description: Information and recommendation on safety issues pertaining to rubber and plastics.

S I M T A R S. (Safety in Mines Testing and Research Centre) see MINES AND MINING INDUSTRY

613.62 UK ISSN 0144-4301
S P A I D NEWS. 1980? irreg. £5. Society for the Prevention of Asbestosis and Industrial Diseases, 38 Drapers Rd., Enfield, Middx. EN2 8LU, England. TEL 0707-8730250. Ed. Nancy Tait. circ. 2,000.

331 US
SAFE WORKER. m. $19 to non-members; members $15. National Safety Council, 1121 Spring Lake Dr., Itasca, IL 60143. TEL 708-775-2281. Ed. Kathleen Henderson; Pub. Kevin H. Axe. circ. 190,000.
 Description: On-the-job safety information for non-supervisory personnel.

363 US ISSN 0891-1797
HD7260
SAFETY AND HEALTH; the international safety, health and environmental magazine. 1919. m. $56 to non-members (outside N. America $96); members $45 (outside N. America $85) (effective 1994). National Safety Council, Periodicals Department, 1121 Spring Lake Dr., Itasca, IL 60143. TEL 708-775-2284. FAX 708-775-2285. Ed. Carrie Fearn; Pub. Kevin H. Axe. adv.; bk.rev.; abstr.; bibl.; charts; illus.; stat.; tr.lit.; index, cum.index. circ. 40,000. (also avail. in microform from UMI; reprint service avail. from UMI) **Indexed:** B.P.I., Bus.Ind., C.I.S. Abstr., Chem.Abstr., Hlth.Ind., Ind.Hyg.Dig., Tr.& Dev.Alert, Tr.& Indus.Ind. **Document type:** trade publication.
 —BLDSC (8065.709600); Faxon; Genuine Article; SWETS; UMI; UnCover.
 Former titles (until 1986): National Safety and Health News (ISSN 8756-5366); (until May 1985): National Safety News (ISSN 0028-0100)
 Description: For occupational safety, health and environmental professionals. Provides extensive coverage of international safety, health and environmental issues, including occupational heaalth, traffic safety, environmental health and industrial hygiene.

SAFETY AND HEALTH BULLETIN. see ENVIRONMENTAL STUDIES — Pollution

363.11 613.6 JA
SAFETY & HEALTH IN JAPAN. (Text in English) irreg., no.11, 1994. Japan Industrial Safety and Health Association, International Cooperation Department, 5-35-1, Shiba, Minato-ku, Tokyo 108, Japan. TEL 81-3-3452-6841. FAX 81-3-3454-4596. Dir. Yasuko Matsumoto. **Document type:** newsletter.

SAFETY & INDUSTRY LAW SERVICE N S W. see LAW

614.8
SAFETY COMPLIANCE LETTER; with OSHA highlights. s-m. $95. Bureau of Business Practice, 24 Rope Ferry Rd., Waterford, CT 06386. TEL 203-442-4365. FAX 203-434-3078. TELEX 966420. Ed. Mickele Rubin.
 Formerly: O S H A Compliance Letter (ISSN 0092-5799)

621.95 363.11 SA
SAFETY, HEALTH & PROTECTIVE EQUIPMENT BUYER'S GUIDE. 1993. a. Delinds Publications, P.O. Box 72366, Parkview 2122, South Africa. illus. **Document type:** directory.

363.11 354.7 SA ISSN 0377-8592
T55.A1 .
SAFETY MANAGEMENT/VEILIGHEIDSBESTUUR. (Text in Afrikaans, English) 1958. m. R.45($45) (effective 1996). National Occupational Safety Association (NOSA) - Nasionale Beroepsveiligheidsvereniging, P.O. Box 26434, Arcadia 0007, South Africa. TEL 27-12-217736. FAX 27-12-3242393. TELEX 3-22262 SA. (Co-sponsor: Association of Societies for Occupational Safety and Health) Ed. Tanya Accone. adv. contact: Steve Naude. bk.rev.; film rev.; illus.; stat.; tr.lit. circ. 16,500. **Indexed:** C.I.S. Abstr., Lab.Haz.Bull. **Document type:** trade publication.
 Formerly: Safety in Industry (ISSN 0036-2484); Incorporates: Safety Digest (ISSN 0036-2468)
 Description: Explores the various echelons of management and the workforce in industrial, commercial, financial and governmental undertakings. Emphasis on all aspects of occupational health and safety.

613.62 658 US
SAFETY MANAGEMENT. 1975. m. $85. Bureau of Business Practice, 24 Rope Ferry Rd., Waterford, CT 06386. TEL 203-442-4365. FAX 203-434-3078. TELEX 966420. Ed. Heather Vaughn. **Indexed:** Br.Tech.Ind.

SAFETY NEWS (DENVER). see WATER RESOURCES

363.11 US ISSN 1078-0114
▼**SAFETY NOW.** 1994. m. $70. Bureau of Business Practice, 24 Rope Ferry Rd., Waterford, CT 06386. TEL 203-442-4365. FAX 203-434-3078. Ed. Shelley Wolf. **Document type:** newsletter.

614.85 US
SAFETY PAYS ON THE JOB. 1979. m. $39. Bureau of Business Practice, 24 Rope Ferry Rd., Waterford, CT 06386. TEL 203-442-4365. FAX 203-434-3078. TELEX 966420. Ed. Heather Vaughn.
 Formerly: On the Safety Side.

614.85 US
SAFETY RESOURCES; safety and environmental news for employers. 1990. bi-m. $24 to non-members; members $12. (Florida Employers Safety Association) Gulf Atlantic Communications Corporation, Inc., Box 8068, Lakeland, FL 33802. TEL 813-683-9377. FAX 813-687-0921. Ed. Ernie Neff. adv.; B&W page $1500. circ. 100,000 (controlled). **Document type:** trade publication.
 Description: Addresses safety, health and environmental issues.

331 613 NE ISSN 0925-7535
HD7262 CODEN: SSCIEO
SAFETY SCIENCE. (Text in English, French and German) 1976. 9/yr. fl.906($552) (effective 1996). Elsevier Science B.V., P.O. Box 211, 1000 AE Amsterdam, Netherlands. TEL 31-20-4853911. FAX 31-20-4853598. TELEX 18582 ESPA NL. E-mail: nlinfo-f@elsevier.nl; usinfo-f@elsevier.com; forinfo-kyf04035@niftyserve.or.jp; Site addr.: http://www.elsevier.nl/. (Subscr. in U.S. and Canada to: Elsevier Science Inc., Box 882, Madison Sq. Sta., New York, NY 10159. TEL 212-989-5800. FAX 212-633-3990) Eds. H.S. Eisner, A.R. Hale. adv.; bk.rev.; charts; illus.; index. (also avail. in microform from UMI) **Indexed:** Abstr.Hyg., Agri.Eng.Abstr., Biol.Abstr., C.I.S. Abstr., Curr.Cont., Eng.Ind., Excerp.Med., HRIS, INIS Atomind., Risk Abstr., Trop.Dis.Bull. **Document type:** academic/scholarly publication.
 —BLDSC (8069.124900); Ei; Faxon; Genuine Article; SWETS. **CCC.**
 Formerly (until vol.15, 1992): Journal of Occupational Accidents (ISSN 0376-6349)
 Description: For safety engineers and inspectors, industrial engineers, research scientists, industrial psychologists and ergonomists. Presents research papers on aspects of work-related risks of various occupations.
 Refereed Serial

614 US
SAFETY SIGNALS. 1974. bi-m. membership. Industrial Safety Equipment Association, 1901 N. Moore St., Ste. 808, Arlington, VA 22209. TEL 703-525-1695. FAX 703-528-2148. Ed. Bruce R. Clash. adv.; bk.rev.; circ. 450 (controlled).

OCCUPATIONAL HEALTH AND SAFETY

614.85   AT   ISSN 1321-9553
SAFETY W A. 1972. q. Aus.$10. Industrial Foundation for Accident Prevention, Box 339, Willetton, W.A. 6155, Australia. FAX 61-9-332-3511. Ed. G. Arcus. adv.; bk.rev. circ. 1,700. **Document type:** bulletin.
    Former titles: I F A P Bulletin; I F A P News (ISSN 0311-0311)

620.8   JA   ISSN 0911-8063
SANGYO ANZEN KENKYUJO GIJUTSU SHISHIN/NATIONAL INSTITUTE OF INDUSTRIAL SAFETY. TECHNICAL RECOMMENDATION. (Text in Japanese) 1972. irreg. National Institute of Industrial Safety - Sangyo Anzen Kenkyujo, Umezono 1-4-6, Kiyose, Tokyo 204, Japan. circ. 450. (back issues avail.)
—BLDSC (8710.750000).

613.62 614.7   JA   ISSN 0911-6923
SANGYO ANZEN KENKYUJO KENKYU HOKOKU/NATIONAL INSTITUTE OF INDUSTRIAL SAFETY. RESEARCH REPORT. (Text in Japanese; summaries in English) 1968. a. National Institute of Industrial Safety - Sangyo Anzen Kenkyujo, Umezono 1-4-6, Kiyose, Tokyo 204, Japan. circ. 450. (back issues avail.) **Document type:** academic/scholarly publication.
—BLDSC (7762.851000).
    Formerly: Sangyo Anzen Kenkyujo Hokoku (ISSN 0911-6915)

613.6   FI   ISSN 0355-3140
RC963.A1   CODEN: SWEHDO
SCANDINAVIAN JOURNAL OF WORK, ENVIRONMENT & HEALTH. (Includes supplement) (Text in English) 1975. bi-m. 800($170) (Scandinavian Counries $150; elsewhere $170) (effective 1996). Finnish Institute of Occupational Health, Topeliuksenkatu 41 a A, FIN-00250 Helsinki, Finland. TEL 358-0-4747694. FAX 358-0-8783326. (Co-sponsors: National Institutes of Occupational Health for Sweden, Norway and Denmark) Ed. Sven Hernberg. bk.rev.; illus.; index. circ. 1,600. **Indexed:** Abstr.Hyg., ASCA, ASSIA, Biol.Abstr., C.I.S. Abstr., Chem.Abstr., Curr.Adv.Cancer Res., Curr.Cont., Dent.Ind., Ergon.Abstr., Excerp.Med., Geo.Abstr., Ind.Hyg.Dig., Ind.Med., Psychol.Abstr. (1984-), Sci.Cit.Ind., Sel.Water Res.Abstr., Trop.Dis.Bull., World Surf.Coat.
—BLDSC (8087.568000); CASDDS; Faxon; Genuine Article; SWETS; UMI; UnCover. **CCC.**
    Formed by the merger of: Nordisk Hygienisk Tidskrift (ISSN 0029-1374) & Work - Environment - Health (ISSN 0300-3221)

614   FR   ISSN 0755-2386
SECURITE ET MEDECINE DU TRAVAIL. 1969. q. 100 F. Association Francaise des Techniciens et Ingenieurs de Securite et des Medecins du Travail (AFTIM), 1 place Uranie, 94340 Joinville le Pont, France. Ed. Jacky Bellaguet. adv.; bibl.; charts; illus. **Indexed:** C.I.S. Abstr.
—BLDSC (8217.030000).

614.85 622   SP   ISSN 0378-9551
SEGURIDAD. 1960. q. 800 ptas. Comision de Seguridad en la Industria Siderometalurgica, Apdo. 195, Jose Cueto 40 - 1 Izda., 33400 Aviles (Asturias), Spain. TEL 85-56-29-59. FAX 85-56-28-02. Ed. J.L. Poyal Costa. **Document type:** trade publication.

613.62 371.9   US   ISSN 0279-4128
SENSORY INTEGRATION SPECIAL INTEREST SECTION NEWSLETTER. (Consists of 11 sections: Administration and Management; Developmental Disabilities; Education; Gerontology; Home & Community Health; Mental Health; Physical Disabilities; School System; Sensory Integration; Technology; Work Programs) vol.12, no.4, 1989. q. $15. American Occupational Therapy Association, Inc., Box 31220, Bethesda, MD 20824-1220. TEL 301-652-2682. FAX 301-652-7711. **Document type:** newsletter.
    Formerly: American Occupational Therapy Association. Sensory Integration Specialty Section. Newsletter (ISSN 0194-6358)

620.8   NE
SERIES IN PHYSICAL ERGONOMICS. (Text in English) 1993. irreg., vol.2, 1994. Delft University Press, Stevinweg 1, 2628 CN Delft, Netherlands. TEL 31-15-2783254. FAX 31-15-2781661. Ed. J.M. Dirken. (back issues avail.) **Document type:** monographic series.

613.62   US   ISSN 0732-7722
KF3568.15
SHEPARD'S FEDERAL OCCUPATIONAL SAFETY AND HEALTH CITATIONS. 1981. base vol. (plus q. supplements). $376. Shepard's - McGraw-Hill, Inc., Box 35300, Colorado Springs, CO 80935-3530. TEL 800-525-2474.
    Description: Analysis of federal occupational safety and health cases and statutes.

614.85 613.62   CC
SHIJIE LAODONG ANQUAN WEISHENG DONGTAI/WORLD INDUSTRIAL SAFETY AND HYGIENE DEVELOPMENT. (Text in Chinese) m. Zhongguo Laodong Anquan Weisheng Qingbao Zhongxin - China Industrial Safety and Hygiene Information Center, A-1 Xibahe, Chaoyang-qu, Beijing 100028, People's Republic of China. TEL 4219190. Ed. Wang Zhixin.

613.6 368.5   AU   ISSN 0037-4512
SICHERE ARBEIT; Zeitschrift fuer Arbeitsschutz. 1947. bi-m. S.554 (foreign S.489). (Allgemeine Unfallversicherungsanstalt) Bohmann Druck und Verlag GmbH & Co. KG, Leberstr. 122, A-1110 Vienna, Austria. TEL 0222-74095. Ed. Regina Ender. adv. contact: Erich Peischl. bk.rev.; charts; illus.; stat.; index. circ. 13,000. **Indexed:** C.I.S. Abstr. **Document type:** consumer publication.
—SWETS.

011   US   ISSN 1043-1721
RA399.A1
SOCIETY FOR HEALTH SYSTEMS. JOURNAL. Key Title: Journal of the Society for Health Systems. q. Institute of Industrial Engineers, 25 Technology Park-Atlanta, Norcross, GA 30092. TEL 404-449-0460. circ. 1,000. **Indexed:** Ind.Med. (1989-), Int.Nurs.Ind.
—BLDSC (4888.250000). **CCC.**
    Formerly (until 1989): I E News: Health Services.

613.62   GW
SUEDDEUTSCHE METALL-BERUFSGENOSSENSCHAFT. MITTEILUNGEN. 1947. q. membership. Sueddeutsche Metall-Berufsgenossenschaft, Wilhelm-Theodor-Roemheld-Str. 15, 55130 Mainz, Germany. TEL 06131-802-1. FAX 06131-802-232. **Document type:** bulletin.
    Formerly (until 1993): Sueddeutsche Eisen- und Stahl-Berufsgenossenschaft. Mitteilungen (ISSN 0178-0182)

613.62 613.62   US   ISSN 1066-7660
SYNERGIST. 1989. m. $40. American Industrial Hygiene Association, 2700 Prosperity Ave., Ste. 250, Fairfax, VA 22031. TEL 703-849-8888. FAX 703-207-3561. Ed. Joni M. Lucas. adv. contact: Ronna Bogart. charts; stat.; tr.lit. circ. 11,000. (back issues avail.)
    Description: Provides information on issues affecting the profession and the association.

613.6   GW
     CODEN: TUSZA6
T UE - TECHNISCHE UEBERWACHUNG. SICHERHEIT ZUVERLAESSIGKEIT UND UMWELTSCHUTZ IN WIRTSCHAFT UND VERKEHR. 1960. m. DM.319($131.50) (Verband der Technischen Ueberwachungsvereine e.V.) V D I Verlag GmbH, Heinrichstr. 24, 40239 Duesseldorf, Germany. TEL 0211-6188-0. FAX 0211-6188-112. TELEX 8587743. (Subscr. to: Postfach 101054, 40001 Duesseldorf, Germany) Ed. E. Zimmermann. adv.; bk.rev.; charts; illus, pat.; tr.mk.; index. circ. 6,000. **Indexed:** Chem.Abstr. **Document type:** trade publication.
—BLDSC (8753.500000); CASDDS; Ei; SWETS. **CCC.**
    Former titles: T U Sicherheit und Zuverlaessigkeit in Betrieb und Verkehr (ISSN 0376-1185); T U Technische Ueberwachung (ISSN 0040-1498)

331   IS   ISSN 0792-1322
TAASIOT. (Text in Hebrew) 1986. fortn. IS.50($25) Merav Publishing Industries Ltd., 12 Yad Harutzim, Tel Aviv 67778, Israel. TEL 972-3-6382943. FAX 972-3-6382939. Ed. Sara Skulsky. adv. circ. 12,000. **Document type:** newspaper.

TALLYBOARD. see FORESTS AND FORESTRY

TECHNOLOGY SPECIAL INTEREST SECTION NEWSLETTER. see TECHNOLOGY: COMPREHENSIVE WORKS

658.382   US
TEXTILE NEWSLETTER. bi-m. $19 to non-members; members $15. National Safety Council, Periodicals Department, 1121 Spring Lake Dr., Itasca, IL 60143. TEL 708-775-2281. Ed. Kathy Henderson; Pub. Kevin H. Axe. **Document type:** newsletter.
    Formerly: Safety Newsletter: Textile Section.
    Description: Information and recommendations on safety issues pertaining to the textile industry.

620.1   NE   ISSN 0921-4348
TIJDSCHRIFT VOOR ERGONOMIE. 6/yr. fl.77. Nederlandse Vereniging voor Ergonomie, W.G. Plein 564, 1054 SI Amsterdam, Netherlands. TEL 31-20-6180930. FAX 31-20-6120396. circ. 1,250. **Document type:** trade publication.
—SWETS.

363.11 613.6   UK
TOLLEY'S HEALTH AND SAFETY AT WORK HANDBOOK. a. £46.95. (Royal Society for the Prevention of Accidents) Tolley Publishing Co. Ltd., Tolley House, 2 Addiscombe Rd., Croydon, Surrey CR9 5AF, England. TEL 0181-686-9141. FAX 0181-686-3155. Ed. Malcolm Dewis. **Document type:** trade publication.

613.62   US
TOPHEALTH; the health promotion and wellness letter. (Editions in English, Spanish) 1987. m. price varies. Health Source Corporation, 443 Western Ave., Box 35280, Brighton, MA 02135. TEL 617-244-6965. Ed. Dr. Arnon I. Dreyfuss. **Document type:** newsletter.
    Description: Promotes the good health of members and employees of organizations and corporations.

613.62   US
TOPHEALTH EN ESPANOL; the health promotion and wellness letter. (Text in Spanish) 1990. m. price varies. Health Source Corporation, 443 Western Ave., Box 35280, Brighton, MA 02135. TEL 617-244-6965. Ed. Dr. Arnon Dreyfuss. **Document type:** newsletter.
    Description: Promotes the good health of members and employees of organizations and corporations.

614.85   NE
TOPICS IN SAFETY, RISK, RELIABILITY AND QUALITY. (Text in English) 1991. irreg. price varies. Kluwer Academic Publishers, Postbus 17, 3300 AA Dordrecht, Netherlands. TEL 31-78-392392. FAX 31-78-392254. TELEX 29245 KAPG NL. (Dist. by: Kluwer Academic Publishers Group, P.O. Box 322, 3300 AH Dordrecht, Netherlands. TEL 31-78-392392. FAX 31-78-546474; N. America dist. addr.: Box 358, Accord Sta., Hingham, MA 02018-0358. TEL 617-871-6600. FAX 617-871-6528) Ed. A.Z. Keller. **Document type:** monographic series.
    Formerly (until vol.4, 1995): Topics in Safety, Reliability and Quality (ISSN 0927-1015)
    Description: Publishes studies covering the spectrum of disciplines required to deal with safety, quality and reliability of products, processes and services.
    Refereed Serial

TOXICOLOGY AND INDUSTRIAL HEALTH; an international journal. see ENVIRONMENTAL STUDIES — Toxicology And Environmental Safety

658.382   US
TRADES AND SERVICES NEWSLETTER. bi-m. $19 to non-members; members $15. National Safety Council, Periodicals Department, 1121 Spring Lake Dr., Itasca, IL 60143. TEL 708-775-2281. Ed. Kathy Henderson; Pub. Kevin H. Axe. **Document type:** newsletter.
    Formerly: Safety Newsletter: Trades and Services Section.
    Description: Information and recommendations on safety issues pertaining to trade and services.

TRANSPORTATION SAFETY SPECIAL REPORTS. see PUBLIC HEALTH AND SAFETY

613.62   CN   ISSN 0829-0369
TRAVAIL ET SANTE; revue francophone pour la sante du travail et de l'environnement. 1985. 4/yr. $20. Groupe de Communication Sansectra Inc., P.O. Box 1089, Napierville, PQ J0J 1L0, Canada. TEL 514-245-7285. Ed. Robert Richards. adv. circ. 1,904. **Indexed:** Agri.Eng.Abstr., Pt.de Rep. (1989-).
—BLDSC (9026.990000).

614.331 FR ISSN 0373-1944
HD7262
TRAVAIL ET SECURITE. 1949. m. 350 F. Institut National de Recherche et de Securite pour la Prevention des Accidents du Travail et des Maladies Professionnelles, 30 rue Olivier-Noyer, 75680 Paris Cedex 14, France. TEL 40-44-30-00. FAX 40-44-30-99. TELEX 203594F INRSPAR F. Ed. Didier Gout. bk.rev.; film rev.; bibl.; illus.; cum.index. circ. 65,000. **Indexed:** C.I.S. Abstr., World Surf.Coat. **Document type:** newspaper.
—BLDSC (9027.000000).

613.62 FI ISSN 0041-4816
TYO - TERVEYS - TURVALLISUUS/WORK - HEALTH - SAFETY. 1971. 15/yr. FIM 360. Finnish Institute of Occupational Health, Topeliuksenkatu 41 a A, 00250 Helsinki, Finland. TEL 358-0-47471. FAX 358-0-4747478. Ed. Matti Tapiainen. adv.; bk.rev.; illus. circ. 72,974. **Indexed:** C.I.S. Abstr., Ergon.Abstr.

363.11 UK
U K OFFSHORE HEALTH & SAFETY MANAGEMENT. bi-m. £75 (foreign £78). Tolley Publishing Co. Ltd., Tolley House, 2 Addiscombe Rd., Croydon, Surrey CR9 5AX, England. TEL 0181-686-9141. FAX 0181-686-3155. **Document type:** trade publication.

DER UNFALLCHIRURG. see *MEDICAL SCIENCES — Orthopedics And Traumatology*

363.11 UK
UNITED KINGDOM OFFSHORE HEALTH & SAFETY MANAGEMENT GUIDE. 1980. q. £225. Charles Knight Publishing, Tolley House, 2 Addiscombe Rd., Croydon, Surrey CR9 5AF, England. TEL 0181-686-9141. FAX 0181-686-3155. E-mail: sean_cotter@tolley.ccmail.compuserve.com. Ed. Sean Cotter; Pub. Carol Doyle-Linden. circ. 500 (paid). (looseleaf format) **Document type:** trade publication.
Former titles (until 1995): Whitehead's United Kingdom Offshore Legislation Guide; (until 1994): United Kingdom Offshore Legislation Guide (ISSN 0260-6135)

363.11 UK
▼**UNITED KINGDOM OFFSHORE HEALTH & SAFETY MANAGEMENT NEWSLETTER.** 1994. bi-m. £75. Charles Knight Publishing, Tolley House, 2 Addiscombe Rd., Croydon, Surrey CR9 5AF, England. TEL 0181-686-9141. FAX 0181-686-3155. E-mail: sean_cotter@tolley.ccmail.compuserve.com. Ed. Sean Cotter; Pub. Carol Doyle-Linden. **Document type:** newsletter.

363.1 US
RC965.R25
U.S. NUCLEAR REGULATORY COMMISSION. OCCUPATIONAL RADIATION AT COMMERCIAL NUCLEAR POWER REACTORS AND OTHER FACILITIES. ANNUAL REPORT. Key Title: Occupational Radiation Exposure, Annual Report. 1970. a. U.S. Nuclear Regulatory Commission, Office of Nuclear Regulatory Research, Washington, DC 20555. TEL 301-492-7000. circ. 2,000. **Indexed:** Geo.Abstr.
Former titles: U.S. Nuclear Regulatory Commission. Occupational Radiation Exposure. Annual Report (ISSN 0198-8360) & U.S. Nuclear Regulatory Commission. Annual Occupational Radiation Exposure Report.

344 US ISSN 0094-7776
KF3568.3.A2
U.S. OCCUPATIONAL SAFETY AND HEALTH REVIEW COMMISSION. ADMINISTRATIVE LAW JUDGE AND COMMISSION DECISIONS.* Key Title: O S A H R C Reports. 1975. m. $43. U.S. Occupational Safety and Health Review Commission, 1825 K St. N.W., Washington, DC 20006. TEL 202-634-7943. (Orders to: Superintendent of Documents, U.S. Government Printing Office, Box 371954, Pittsburgh, PA 15250-7954. TEL 202-512-1800. FAX 202-512-2250) Ed. Linda A. Smith. circ. 700. (microfiche) **Document type:** government publication.

613.62 JA ISSN 0387-821X
CODEN: JOUOD4
UNIVERSITY OF OCCUPATIONAL AND ENVIRONMENTAL HEALTH. JOURNAL. Key Title: Journal of U O E H. (Text in English, Japanese; summaries in English) 1979. q. $48. University of Occupational and Environmental Health, Japan, Iseigaoka 1-1, Yahatanishi-ku, Kita-Kyushu 807, Japan. FAX 093-692-4876. Ed. Toshiji Koboyashi. bk.rev.; circ. 900 (controlled). (back issues avail.) **Indexed:** Abstr.Hyg., Biol.Abstr., C.I.S.Abstr., Excerp.Med., Trop.Dis.Bull. **Document type:** academic/scholarly publication.
—BLDSC (4912.250000); CASDDS.
Description: Focuses on occupational and environmental health sciences, but includes articles in other fields of medicine and humanities.

613.62 GW
VERWALTUNGSBERICHT (YEAR). a. Berufsgenossenschaft fuer Gesundheitsdienst und Wohlfahrtspflege, Pappelallee 35-37, 22089 Hamburg, Germany. TEL 040-20207-0. FAX 040-20207-525. **Document type:** bulletin.

363.11 NE ISSN 0926-4205
VOORKOMEN. 1951. bi-m. Nederlands Instituut voor Arbeidsomstandigheden - Dutch Institute for the Working Environment, Postbus 75665, 1070 AR Amsterdam, Netherlands. TEL 31-20-5498425. FAX 31-20-6462310. pat. circ. 160,000.
Formed by the merger of (1970-1990): Techniek en Veiligheid (ISSN 0924-4441) & Doen en Laten (ISSN 0926-4191); Which was formerly (until 1983): Veilig Werken (ISSN 0042-3130)
Description: For workers and scholars; seeks to increase interest and motivation concerning the working environment.

614.85 CN
W H M I S COMPLIANCE MANUAL. (Workplace Hazardous Materials Information Systems) 1989. 3/yr. Can.$139. Carswell, One Corporate Plaza, 2075 Kennedy Rd., Scarborough, ON M1T 3V4, Canada. TEL 416-609-8000. FAX 416-298-5094. Ed. R. Ferguson.
Description: For companies developing and maintaining a program to comply with WHMIS requirements throughout Canada.

614.85 UK
W R A P. 1979. m. £13.50. Royal Society for the Prevention of Accidents, Cannon House, the Priory Queensway, Birmingham B4 6BS, England. TEL 021-200-2461. FAX 021-200-1254. Ed. Stephanie Lennon. circ. 7,669. (tabloid format) **Document type:** academic/scholarly publication.
Formerly: Safety Representative (ISSN 0143-0874); Which incorporated: Look out.

363.11 IE ISSN 1051-9815
RM735.A1
WORK; a journal of prevention, assessment & rehabilitation. 1990. bi-m. I£118($186) (effective 1996). Elsevier Science Ireland Ltd., P.O. Box 85, Limerick, Ireland. TEL 353-61-471944. FAX 353-61-472144. (Subscr. in U.S. and Canada to: Elsevier Science, Box 882, Madison Sq. Sta., New York, NY 10159-0882. TEL 212-989-5800. FAX 212-633-3990) Ed. Karen Jacobs. (also avail. in microform from UMI; back issues avail.) **Document type:** academic/scholarly publication.
—BLDSC (9348.040100); UMI; UnCover. **CCC.**
Description: Each issue is devoted to one topic within the scope of work practice, such as injury prevention, work assessment, and the older worker. *Refereed Serial*

WORK AND STRESS. see *PSYCHOLOGY*

WORK PROGRAMS SPECIAL INTEREST SECTION NEWSLETTER. see *OCCUPATIONS AND CAREERS*

WORKERS' COMPENSATION - BUSINESS MANAGEMENT GUIDE. see *INSURANCE*

613.62 UK ISSN 1351-4792
WORKERS HEALTH INTERNATIONAL NEWSLETTER. Spanish edition: W H I N en Espanol (ISSN 1130-8575) q. £10 (effective 1995). Hazards Publications Ltd., P.O. Box 199, Sheffield S1 1FQ, England. TEL 0114-276-5695. FAX 0114-276-7257. **Document type:** newsletter.

WORKLIFE REPORT. see *BUSINESS AND ECONOMICS — Labor And Industrial Relations*

613.62 614.85 US
▼**WORKPLACE ERGONOMICS.** 1995. bi-m. $30. Stevens Publishing Corporation, 3630 J.H. Kultgen Frwy., Waco, TX 76706. TEL 817-776-9000. FAX 817-776-9018. Ed. Mark Hartley; Pub. Russell Lindsay. adv. **Document type:** trade publication.

613.62 AT
WORKPLACE HEALTH AND SAFETY MANUAL. 1988. q. C H Australia Ltd., P.O. Box 230, North Ryde, N.S.W. 2113, Australia. TEL 61-2-8571555. FAX 61-2-8571601. (looseleaf format)
Description: A topic based approach to sound health and safety practice and administration within the workplace.

614.8 SZ ISSN 0084-165X
WORLD CONGRESS ON THE PREVENTION OF OCCUPATIONAL ACCIDENTS AND DISEASES. PROCEEDINGS. (Proceedings published by national organizing committee) 1955. triennial, 13th, 1993, New Delhi. International Social Security Association, Case Postale 1, CH-1211 Geneva 22, Switzerland. FAX 022-7986385. **Document type:** proceedings.

WUERTTEMBERGISCHE BAU-BERUFSGENOSSENSCHAFT. MITTEILUNGEN. see *BUILDING AND CONSTRUCTION*

331 YU ISSN 0044-1880
ZASTITA RADA. 1959. m. 40 din.($2.67) Jelene Cetkovic 3, Box 723, Belgrade, Yugoslavia. Ed. Katarina Todorovic.

613.62 GW ISSN 0944-2502
CODEN: ZAAEE
ZENTRALBLATT FUER ARBEITSMEDIZIN, ARBEITSSCHUTZ UND ERGONOMIE. 1951. m. DM.198. Dr. Curt Haefner Verlag, Bachstr. 14-16, 69121 Heidelberg, Germany. TEL 06221-49064. (Subscr. to: Postfach 106060, 69050 Heidelberg, Germany) Ed.Bd. adv.; bk.rev.; abstr.; bibl.; charts; illus.; pat.; index. circ. 2,500. **Indexed:** Abstr.Hyg., Biol.Abstr., C.I.S. Abstr., Chem.Abstr., Chem.Infd., Ergon.Abstr., Excerp.Med., Ind.Med., Trop.Dis.Bull. **Document type:** bulletin.
—BLDSC (9500.799500); CASDDS; Faxon; SWETS. **CCC.**
Former titles (until 1992): Zentralblatt fuer Arbeitsmedizin, Arbeitsschutz, Prophylaxe und Ergonomie (ISSN 0173-3338); (until 1980): Zentralblatt fuer Arbeitsmedizin, Arbeitsschutz und Prophylaxe (ISSN 0340-7047); Which was formed by the 1976 merger of: Zentralblatt fuer Arbeitsmedizin und Arbeitsschutz (ISSN 0044-4049); Prophylaxe (Heidelberg) (ISSN 0033-1368)

613.62 CC ISSN 1001-9391
CODEN: ZLWZEX
ZHONGHUA LAODONG WEISHENG ZHIYEBING ZAZHI/CHINESE JOURNAL OF INDUSTRIAL HYGIENE AND OCCUPATIONAL DISEASES. (Text in Chinese) 1983. m. Y81. Tianjin Institute of Industrial Hygiene and Occupational Diseases, 211 Ma Chang Rd., Hexi District, Tianjin 300204, People's Republic of China. TEL 86-22-3280264. Ed. Gang Baoqi. circ. 4,000 (paid); 400 (controlled). **Document type:** academic/scholarly publication.
—BLDSC (3180.354000); CASDDS.
Description: Contains epidemiological investigation on inudstrial hygiene and occupational medicine, and studies on prevention, diagnosis and treatment of occupational diseases.

OCCUPATIONAL HEALTH AND SAFETY — Abstracting, Bibliographies, Statistics

613.62 US
AMERICAN INDUSTRIAL HYGIENE ASSOCIATION. CONFERENCE ABSTRACTS.* a. $20. American Industrial Hygiene Association, 2700 Prosperity Ave., Ste. 250, Fairfax, VA 22031-4307. TEL 703-849-8888.
Description: Abstracts of papers presented at the annual meeting of the American Industrial Hygiene Conference.

OCCUPATIONAL HEALTH AND SAFETY — ABSTRACTING, BIBLIOGRAPHIES, STATISTICS

614.8 016 GW ISSN 0932-2876
ARBEITSMEDIZIN. (Text in English or German) 1975. 4/yr. DM.52. Landesinstitut fuer den Oeffentlichen Gesundheitsdienst des Landes Nordrhein-Westfalen, Westerfeldstr. 35-37, 33611 Bielefeld, Germany. TEL 0521-8007-0. FAX 0521-8007200. (Subscr. to: Postfach 201012, 33548 Bielefeld, Germany) Ed. Eva-Maria Dreitzer; Pub. U. Laaser. bk.rev. circ. 600. **Indexed:** Ergon.Abstr., Ind.Hyg.Dig. **Document type:** abstracting/indexing.
 Former titles: Beruf und Gesundheit - Occupational Health; (until 1985): Dokumentation Arbeitsmedizin - Documentation Occupational Health (ISSN 0340-3238)

614.85 011 DK ISSN 0905-9539
ARBEJDSMILJOET - NETOP NU. 1978. 10/yr. DKK 1200. Arbejdstilsynet, Bibliotek og Dokumentation, Landskronagade 33-35, 2100 Copenhagen Oe, Denmark. TEL 45-31-18-00-88. FAX 45-31-18-35-60. TELEX 45-16-149 AMI DK. Ed. Tove Bruum. circ. 1,000. **Document type:** abstracting/indexing.
 Former titles: (until 1991): Dok (ISSN 0903-6083); (until 1988): S D A - Nyt (ISSN 0108-5417)
 Description: Presents occupational safety and health abstracts.

613.62 US ISSN 0190-9398
CODEN: CSCSDD
C A SELECTS. CHEMICAL HAZARDS, HEALTH & SAFETY. s-w. $220 to non-members; members $65 (effective 1996). Chemical Abstracts Service (Subsidiary of: American Chemical Society), 2540 Olentangy River Rd., Box 3012, Columbus, OH 43210-0012. TEL 614-447-3600. FAX 614-447-3713. TELEX 6842086. **Document type:** abstracting/indexing.
 Description: Covers safety in chemical laboratories and in the chemical and nuclear industries; health and safety of personnel working in these areas or working with hazardous substances.

613.62 011 US ISSN 1047-8124
CODEN: CSOHE7
C A SELECTS. OCCUPATIONAL EXPOSURE & HAZARDS. 1988. s-w. $220 to non-members; members $65 (effective 1996). Chemical Abstracts Service (Subsidiary of: American Chemical Society), 2540 Olentangy River Rd., Box 3012, Columbus, OH 43210-0012. TEL 614-447-3600. FAX 614-337-3713. TELEX 6842986. **Document type:** abstracting/indexing.
 Formerly (until 1989): BIOSIS CAS Selects: Occupational Exposure.
 Description: Covers occupational exposure and related hazards. Includes epidemiological studies on workplace exposure of humans to chemicals, biological agents, radiation, and noise.

331.11 US ISSN 0164-1530
HD7262.5.U62
CALIFORNIA WORK INJURIES AND ILLNESSES. 1945. a. free. Department of Industrial Relations, Division of Labor Statistics and Research, Box 420603, San Francisco, CA 94142-0603. TEL 415-703-5971.
 Supersedes in part (in 1975): California Work Injuries.

614 016 SP ISSN 0213-943X
Z6675.I5
ERGA. 1973. m. 4240 ptas. (CD-Rom ed. 40000 ptas.). Instituto Nacional de Seguridad e Higiene en el Trabajo, Ministerio de Trabajo y Seguridad Social, Calle Dulcet 2-10, 08034 Barcelona, Spain. FAX 343-280-36-42. Ed. Antonio Bonastre. adv. contact: Emilio Castejon. bk.rev.; index, cum.index: 1975-1988. circ. 2,000. **Document type:** bibliography.
 ●Also available on CD-ROM.
 Former titles: (until 1988): Instituto Nacional de Seguridad e Higiene en el Trabajo. Boletin Bibliografico (ISSN 0212-2359); (until 1981): Spain. Servicio Social de Higiene y Seguridad del Trabajo. Boletin Bibliografico (ISSN 0210-069X)

EXPLORATION AND PRODUCTION HEALTH, SAFETY AND ENVIRONMENT. see *PETROLEUM AND GAS — Abstracting, Bibliographies, Statistics*

HEALTH AND SAFETY SCIENCE ABSTRACTS. see *PUBLIC HEALTH AND SAFETY — Abstracting, Bibliographies, Statistics*

613.62 FR ISSN 0335-0274
I N R S BULLETIN DE DOCUMENTATION. 7/yr. 270 F. Institut National de Recherche et de Securite pour la Prevention des Accidents du Travail et des Maladies Professionnelles, 30 rue Olivier Noyer, 75680 Paris Cedex 14, France. TEL 40-44-30-00. FAX 40-44-30-99. TELEX 203594F INRSPAR F. index, cum.index. circ. 2,500. **Document type:** bibliography.
 Description: Contains bibliographic information about occupational safety and health.

613.62 016 US ISSN 0019-8382
CODEN: IHYDA
INDUSTRIAL HYGIENE DIGEST. 1937. m. $150. Industrial Health Foundation, Inc., 34 Penn Circle W., Pittsburgh, PA 15206. TEL 412-363-6600. bk.rev.; index, cum.index every 10 yrs. circ. 1,000. **Indexed:** C.I.S. Abstr., JAMA. **Document type:** abstracting/indexing.
 —BLDSC (4456.480000).

363.11 622 US ISSN 0270-2053
TN295
INJURY EXPERIENCE IN SAND AND GRAVEL MINING. a. U.S. Department of Labor, Mine Safety and Health Administration, 4015 Wilson Blvd., Arlington, VA 22203. TEL 703-235-1452. (Subscr. to: Superintendent of Documents, U.S. Government Printing Office, Box 371954, Pittsburgh, PA 15250-7954. TEL 202-783-3238. FAX 202-512-2250) **Document type:** government publication.
 Former titles: (until 1978): Injury Experience in the Sand and Gravel Industry (ISSN 0191-6645); (until 1978): Injury Experience and Worktime Data for the Sand and Gravel Industry (ISSN 0364-3131)

331.8 016 613 UN ISSN 0074-2147
INTERNATIONAL CATALOGUE OF OCCUPATIONAL SAFETY AND HEALTH FILMS. (Subseries of Occupational Safety and Health Series) (Text in English, French and Spanish) 1969. irreg. (International Labour Office) I L O Publications, CH-1211 Geneva 22, Switzerland. TEL 022-799-6111. FAX 022-798-6358. TELEX 415647-ILO-CH. (Dist. in U.S. by: I L O Publications, 49 Sheridan Ave., Albany, NY 12210. TEL 518-436-9686. FAX 518-436-7433) **Document type:** catalog.

613.62 331 US
IOWA. DIVISION OF LABOR. OCCUPATIONAL INJURIES AND ILLNESSES SURVEY. 1973. a. free. Division of Labor, Bureau of Labor Statistics Section, 1000 E. Grand Ave., Des Moines, IA 50319. TEL 515-281-3606. stat. circ. 300. (processed) **Document type:** government publication.
 Formerly: Iowa. Bureau of Labor. Occupational Injuries and Illnesses Survey (ISSN 0092-6299)

K W O C LIST OF PETROLEUM ABSTRACTS' EXPLORATION & PRODUCTION THESAURUS AND NEW EXPLORATION & PRODUCTION TERMS. see *PETROLEUM AND GAS — Abstracting, Bibliographies, Statistics*

613.62 SP
LANEKO LESIOEN ESTATISTIKAK (YEAR)/ESTADISTICAS DE LA LESIONES PROFESIONALES. a. (Lan eta Gizarte Segurantza Saila - Departamento de Trabajo y Seguridad Social) Eusko Jaurlaritzaren Argitalpen-Zerbitzu Nagusia - Servicio Central de Publicaciones del Gobierno Vasco, Calle Duque de Wellington 2, 01011 Vitoria-Gasteiz, Spain. circ. 2,000.

MEXICO. CENTRO DE INFORMACION TECNICA Y DOCUMENTACION. INDICE DE ARTICULOS SOBRE SEGURIDAD E HIGIENE INDUSTRIAL. see *INSURANCE — Abstracting, Bibliographies, Statistics*

331.11 US ISSN 0196-2132
RC964
OCCUPATIONAL DISEASE IN CALIFORNIA. (Formerly published by California Department of Health) 1979. a. free. Department of Industrial Relations, Division of Labor Statistics and Research, Box 420603, San Francisco, CA 94141-0603. TEL 415-703-5971.

614.85 US
OCCUPATIONAL HEALTH. (Subseries of: Nuclear Regulatory Commission Guides) irreg. price varies. (Nuclear Regulatory Commission) U.S. National Technical Information Service, 5825 Port Royal Rd., Springfield, VA 22161. TEL 703-487-4630.

613.62 310 US ISSN 1063-3820
HD7262.5.U62
OCCUPATIONAL INJURY & ILLNESS INFORMATION. a. free. Department of Labor, Research & Analysis Section, Box 25501, Juneau, AK 99802-5501. TEL 907-465-5083. FAX 907-465-2101. **Document type:** government publication.
 Description: Statistical report on work-related injuries and illnesses in Alaska's work force.

614.8 016 UN ISSN 1010-7053
T55.A1 CODEN: SHWOEV
SAFETY AND HEALTH AT WORK. French edition: Securite et Sante au Travail (ISSN 1010-7061) (Editions in English, French) 1974. 6/yr. $240. International Labour Office, International Occupational Safety and Health Information Centre, CH-1211 Geneva 22, Switzerland. TEL 22-799-67-40. FAX 41-22-798-6253. TELEX 415-647-ILO-CH. Ed.Bd. adv.; bk.rev.; abstr.; index, cum.index. circ. 20,000. (tabloid format) **Indexed:** Ergon.Abstr., Lab.Haz.Bull.
 ●Also available online. Vendor(s): European Space Agency (File no.40/CISDOC), IST-INFORMATHEQUE, Inc., Orbit Search Service, Telesystemes - Questel. Also available on CD-ROM. Producer(s): SilverPlatter Information, Inc.
 —BLDSC (8065.717000); CASDDS.
 Former titles: C I S Abstracts (ISSN 0302-7651); Occupational Safety and Health Abstracts (ISSN 0029-7984)

614.8 016 UN ISSN 1010-7061
SECURITE ET SANTE AU TRAVAIL. English edition: Safety and Health at Work (ISSN 1010-7053) (Editions in English and French) 1974. 6/yr. $240. International Labour Office, International Occupational Safety and Health Information Centre - Bureau International du Travail, Centre International d'Infromations de Securite et de Sante au Travail, CH-1211 Geneva 22, Switzerland. TEL 22-799-6740. FAX 41-22-798-6253. TELEX 415-647-ILO-CH. Ed.Bd. adv.; bk.rev. **Indexed:** C.I.S. Abstr., Ergon.Abstr., Lab.Haz.Bull.
 ●Also available online. Vendor(s): European Space Agency, IST-INFORMATHEQUE, Inc., Orbit Search Service, Telesystemes - Questel.
 Also available on CD-ROM. Producer(s): SilverPlatter Information, Inc.
 Former titles: Bulletin C I S (ISSN 0250-4235); Bulletin Bibliographique de la Prevention (ISSN 0045-3498)

610 613.62 UK ISSN 0262-9836
SELECTED ABSTRACTS ON OCCUPATIONAL DISEASES. 1982. q. £8. Departments of Health and Social Security, Skipton House, Elephant and Castle, London SE1 6LW, England. (Subscr. to: D H S S Publications, No. 2 Site, Manchester Rd., Heywood, Lancs. OL10 2PZ, England) Ed. John Goodier. **Document type:** abstracting/indexing, government publication.

613.62 016 RU ISSN 0202-8905
SIGNAL'NAYA INFORMATSIYA. TEKHNIKA BEZOPASNOSTI. SANITARNAYA TEKHNIKA. 1971. s-m. 17.60 Rub. Vsesoyuznyi Institut Nauchno-Tekhnicheskoi Informatsii (VINITI), Baltiiskaya ul. 14, Moscow A-219, Russia. (Dist. by: Mezhdunarodnaya Kniga, Dimitrova ul. 39, 113095 Moscow, Russia) **Document type:** abstracting/indexing.

614.852 310 US ISSN 0195-9344
WESTERN WOOD PRODUCTS ASSOCIATION. QUARTERLY INJURY & ILLNESS INCIDENCE REPORT. q. $18 (effective Jan. 1995). Western Wood Products Association, Yeon Bldg., 1 522 S.W. Fifth Ave., Portland, OR 97236. TEL 503-761-0134. FAX 503-224-3934. (back issues avail.) **Document type:** trade publication.
 Description: Supplies a year-to-date injury-control index and annual summary of injuries sustained by lumberjacks in Western timber forests.

OCCUPATIONS AND CAREERS

see also Business and Economics–Labor and Industrial Relations

371.42 374.4 US
A A C E BONUS BRIEFS; careers, education, and work pulling together. 1991. a. $15 to non-members. American Association for Career Education, 2900 Amby Pl., Hermosa Beach, CA 90254-2216. TEL 310-376-7318. FAX 310-374-1360. Ed. Pat Nellor Wickwire. circ. 500 (controlled). (back issues avail.) **Document type:** consumer publication.

371.42 374 US ISSN 1074-9551
A A C E CAREERS UPDATE; careers, education and work pulling together. 1982. q. $15 to non-members. American Association for Career Education, 2900 Amby Pl., Hermosa Beach, CA 90254-2216. TEL 310-376-7378. FAX 310-374-1360. Ed. Pat Nellor Wickwire. circ. 500. (back issues avail.) **Document type:** newsletter.
Description: Covers education, work, and careers today.

371.42 394.4 US
A A C E DISTINGUISHED MEMBER SERIES; careers, education, and work pulling together. 1992. a. $15 to non-members. American Association for Career Education, 2900 Amby Pl., Hermosa Beach, CA 90254-2216. TEL 310-376-7378. FAX 310-374-1360. Ed. Pat Nellor Wickwire. circ. 500 (controlled). (back issues avail.) **Document type:** academic/scholarly publication.

A C J S EMPLOYMENT BULLETIN. (Academy of Criminal Justice Sciences) see *BUSINESS AND ECONOMICS — Personnel Management*

371.42 150 UK
A E P APPOINTMENTS BROADSHEET. 1978. w. free. Association of Educational Psychologists, 3 Sunderland Rd., Durham DH1 2LH, England. TEL 0191-3849512. FAX 0191-3865287. Ed. F. Challis. adv. contact: Lynn Flowers. circ. 1,900. (broadsheet format; back issues avail.) **Document type:** newspaper.
Description: Contains advertisements for vacant positions in educational psychology.

A G H E EXCHANGE. (Association for Gerontology in Higher Education) see *GERONTOLOGY AND GERIATRICS*

331.1 US ISSN 0194-3642
A S A EMPLOYMENT BULLETIN. m. $25 (foreign $35). American Sociological Association, 1722 N St., N.W., Washington, DC 20036. TEL 202-833-3410. FAX 202-785-0146. Ed. Nancy Sylvester. **Document type:** bulletin.
Description: Contains current position vacancy listings in academic, applied, and fellowship settings.

A S C E SALARY SURVEY. (American Society of Civil Engineers) see *ENGINEERING — Civil Engineering*

A S P P NEWSLETTER. (American Society of Plant Physiologists) see *BIOLOGY — Botany*

A S - SEKRETARKA. see *BUSINESS AND ECONOMICS — Office Equipment And Services*

371.42 808.02 US
A W P JOB LIST. 8/yr. Associated Writing Programs (Fairfax), Tallwood House, Mail Stop IE3, George Mason University, Fairfax, VA 22030. TEL 703-993-4301. FAX 703-993-4302. circ. 5,000.
Description: Lists jobs for teaching creative writing in universities.

371.42 658.3 IS ISSN 0792-0490
ADAM VEAVODA/MAN AND WORK; journal in labor studies. (Text in English and Hebrew) 1987. s-a. $12. Association of Vocational and Career Counseling in Israel, P.O. Box 9006, Haifa 31090, Israel. TEL 972-4-527785. Ed. Edgar Krau. adv.; bk.rev. circ. 400. Indexed: Psychol.Abstr. (1988-). **Document type:** academic/scholarly publication.

371.42 US
ADVANCE (LIBERTY). 1985. a. Target Marketing, Inc., 5 Victory Ln., Ste. 101, Liberty, MO 64068. TEL 816-781-7557. FAX 816-792-3892. adv.; circ. 250,000 (controlled).
Description: Directed to university career planning and job placement advisors.

371.42 659.1 US ISSN 0882-8253
HF5801
ADVERTISING CAREER DIRECTORY. (Subseries of: Career Advisor Series) 1986. irreg., 5th ed., 1992. $29.92 (softcover $17.95) (effective 1992). Gale Research Inc., 835 Penobscot Bldg., Detroit, MI 48226. TEL 313-961-2242. FAX 313-961-6083. **Document type:** directory.

331 US ISSN 0146-2113
AFFIRMATIVE ACTION REGISTER; the E E O recruitment publication. 1974. m. $15 to individuals; free to qualified personnel. (Affirmative Action, Inc.) Joyce R. Green, Ed. & Pub., 8356 Olive Blvd., St. Louis, MO 63132. TEL 314-991-1335. FAX 314-997-1788. adv.; circ. 60,000 (controlled). **Indexed:** Rehabil.Lit.
Description: All-personnel recruitment publication for female, minority, handicapped, native American and veteran candidate sources and pools.

AGENDA. see *ART*

331.1 US ISSN 1056-5051
AIR JOBS DIGEST. 1986. a. $96. World Air Data, Box 70127, Washington, DC 20088. TEL 301-984-0002. (tabloid format) **Document type:** newspaper.
Description: Lists current open positions in the entire aviation industry, including corporate, commercial and government aviation.

370.15 US
ALABAMA COUNSELING ASSOCIATION. JOURNAL. 1974. s-a. $5 for non-members. Alabama Counseling Association, c/o Dr. Ervin L. Word, Rt. 1CC 50, Sta.36, Livingston University, Livingston, AL 35470. TEL 205-652-9661. FAX 205-652-4065. Ed. Widdell Williamson. adv.; bk.rev.; charts. circ. 2,000. (back issues avail.)
Former titles: Alabama Association for Counseling and Development Journal; Alabama Personnel and Guidance Journal.

371.42 US ISSN 1063-3766
ALASKA CAREER GUIDE; finding the right fit (year). a. Department of Labor, Research & Analysis Section, Box 25501, Juneau, AK 99802-5501. TEL 907-465-4585. FAX 907-465-2101. **Document type:** government publication.
Description: Provides current information to assist students and those making career choices or conducting job searches.

371.42 US ISSN 1063-3715
HD5725.A4
ALASKA INDUSTRY OCCUPATION OUTLOOK TO (YEAR). a. free. Department of Labor, Research & Analysis Section, Box 25501, Juneau, AK 99802-5501. TEL 907-465-4585. FAX 907-465-2101. charts. **Document type:** government publication.
Description: Occupational profiles for 27 major industries and industry groups. Includes occupational estimates for 1990, projections into 1995 and a narrative of the current industry status and outlook.

ALLIED HEALTH GRADUATE. see *MEDICAL SCIENCES*

ALMANAC OF AMERICAN EMPLOYERS. see *BUSINESS AND ECONOMICS — Labor And Industrial Relations*

AMERICAN COLLEGE OF SPORTS MEDICINE. CAREER SERVICES BULLETIN. see *MEDICAL SCIENCES — Sports Medicine*

AMERICAN WINDOW CLEANER; voice of the professional window cleaner. see *OCCUPATIONAL HEALTH AND SAFETY*

THE AMERICAN WORKER. see *BUSINESS AND ECONOMICS — Labor And Industrial Relations*

371.42 917.306 US ISSN 1067-330X
HD2346.U52
ANUARIO HISPANO. (Text in English, Spanish) 1985. a. $17.50 (effective 1995). T I Y M Publishing Company, Inc., 1489 Chain Bridge Rd., Ste. 200, McLean, VA 22101. TEL 703-734-1632. FAX 703-356-0787. Ed. Angela Zavala; Pub. Juan E. Zavala. adv.; circ. 25,000. circ. 50,000 (paid). **Document type:** catalog, directory.
● Also available on CD-ROM.
Description: Covers career opportunities for Hispanics. Includes statistical information, self-marketing strategies and listings of employment services, Hispanic organizations, publications, and T.V. and radio stations.

331.1 II
APPOINTMENTS MARKET WEEKLY.* 1971. w. Rs.1.60. C-7 Chaupatian Colony, Lucknow 5, India. Ed. K.G. Srivastava. adv.; tr.lit.

331.1 US
ARKANSAS. EMPLOYMENT SECURITY DEPARTMENT. ANNUAL REPORT. 1946? a. free. Department of Labor, Employment Security Department, Box 2981, Little Rock, AR 72203. TEL 501-682-3119. charts; stat.; circ. controlled.
Formerly: Arkansas. Department of Labor. Employment Security Division. Annual Report.

ARTSEARCH; the national employment service bulletin for the performing arts. see *THEATER*

331.1 US ISSN 0888-4870
ATHLETICS EMPLOYMENT WEEKLY. 1986. 48/yr. $80. R D S T Enterprises, RR Box 140, Carthage, IL 62321. TEL 217-357-3615. FAX 217-357-3615. circ. 1,600 (paid). (tabloid format) **Document type:** newsletter.
Description: Lists job openings for athletic directors, coaches, assistant coaches and graduate assistants. Covers all sports and all sizes of colleges throughout the United States.

DER AUSBILDER. see *EDUCATION — Adult Education*

373.246 FR ISSN 0005-1969
HF5382
AVENIRS. 1947. 10/yr. 300 F. (foreign 375 F.). Office National d'Information sur les Enseignements et les Professions (ONISEP), 46, 52 rue Albert, 75013 Paris, France. TEL 40-77-60-00. FAX 45-86-60-85. TELEX 202 962 F ONISEP N. bk.rev.; bibl.; charts; illus.; stat.; index. Indexed: Int.Lab.Doc.

AVIATION EMPLOYMENT MONTHLY. see *AERONAUTICS AND SPACE FLIGHT*

371.42 GW
B F Z - INFO. 1986. q. Berufsfoerderungszentrum Essen e.V., Altenessenerstr. 80-84, 45326 Essen, Germany. TEL 0201-3204-272. FAX 0201-3204-276. Ed. Norbert Meyer. circ. 12,000. **Document type:** bulletin.

331.4 UK
B P W NEWS INTERNATIONAL. (Business and Professional Women) (Text in English, French, Spanish) m. £30. International Federation of Business and Professional Women, Studio 16, Cloisters House, Cloisters Business Centre, 8 Battersea Park Rd., London SW8 4BG, England. TEL 0171-738-8323. FAX 0171-622-0528. **Document type:** newsletter.

371.42 663.1 UK
BARTENDER INTERNATIONAL.* 1982. bi-m. £13 to members & qualified personnel. (U K Bartenders' Guild) Adpress Ltd., 91-93 Gordon Rd., Harborne, Brimingham B17 9HA, England. adv. circ. 1,700.

371.42 DK ISSN 0901-313X
BARTENDEREN. 1950. 6/yr. free. Dansk Bartender Laug, Chr. Richartsvej 6, 1951 Frederiksberg C, Denmark. TEL 31-355882. Ed. Per Valet. adv. circ. 1,000.

OCCUPATIONS AND CAREERS

331.1 — GW — ISSN 0173-6574
HD5777
BEITRAEGE ZUR ARBEITSMARKT- UND BERUFSFORSCHUNG. (Text in German) 1970. irreg. (approx. 10/yr.). price varies. Institut fuer Arbeitsmarkt- und Berufsforschung (IAB), Regensburger Str. 104, 90327 Nuernberg, Germany. TEL 0911-1793017. FAX 0911-1793258. TELEX 622348-BA-D. circ. 1,800. (back issues avail.) **Document type:** academic/scholarly publication.

371.42 — GW — ISSN 0931-8895
BERUFLICHE REHABILITATION. 1987. q. DM.44 (foreign DM.59). (Bundesarbeitsgemeinschaft der Berufsbildungswerke) Lambertus-Verlag GmbH, Woelfinstr. 4, 79104 Freiburg, Germany. TEL 0761-36825-25. FAX 0761-37064. Ed. Philibert Magin. adv.; bk.rev. circ. 1,600. **Document type:** bulletin.

371.42 — SZ
BERUFSBILDER. (Text in French, German) s-a. Muehlirain, CH-8153 Rumlang, Switzerland. TEL 01-8173055. FAX 01-8170406. Ed. A. Amacher.

371.42 — GW — ISSN 0341-4515
BERUFSBILDUNG IN WISSENSCHAFT UND PRAXIS. 1972. bi-m. DM.64.50. (Bundesinstitut fuer Berufsbildung) W. Bertelsmann Verlag, Postfach 100633, 33506 Bielefeld, Germany. TEL 0521-91101-0. FAX 0521-9110179. Ed. Henning Bau. **Document type:** government publication.
—CCC.

371.42 — GW
BERUFSPLANUNG FUER DEN MANAGEMENT NACHWUCHS. 1974. a. DM.19.80. Staufenbiel Institut fuer Berufs- und Ausbildungsplanung Koeln GmbH, Konrad-Adenauer-Ufer 33, 50668 Cologne, Germany. TEL 0221-124038. FAX 0221-124030. Ed. Joerg Staufenbiel. circ. 25,000. **Document type:** directory.

371.42 620 — GW
BERUFSPLANUNG FUER INGENIEURE. 1981. a. DM.19.80. Staufenbiel Institut fuer Berufs- und Ausbildungsplanung Koeln GmbH, Konrad-Adenauer-Ufer 33, 50668 Cologne, Germany. TEL 0221-124038. FAX 0221-124030. Ed. Joerg Staufenbiel. circ. 15,000. **Document type:** directory.

371.42 — SZ
BERUFSWAHL UND AUSBILDUNG. s-a. Buchholzstr. 47, Postfach, CH-8053 Zurich, Switzerland. TEL 01-555075. circ. 5,000.

BIOLOGY FOR THE FUTURE (YEAR); higher education courses in biology and related sciences. see EDUCATION — Guides To Schools And Colleges

371.42 — US — ISSN 0006-4122
BLACK CAREERS. 1965. bi-m. $20. Project Magazine Inc., Box 8214, Philadelphia, PA 19101. TEL 215-387-1600. Ed. Emory W. Washington. adv.; bk.rev.; charts; illus. circ. 275,000.
Formerly (until vol.5, no.4, July 1969): Project - Guidelines to Equal Opportunity (ISSN 0033-0892)
Description: Provides job search information and guidance on career preparation, development and advancement to working professionals nationwide in industry, government, business and technology.

BLACK EMPLOYMENT AND EDUCATION. see ETHNIC INTERESTS

371.42 070.5 — US — ISSN 0882-8261
Z477
BOOK PUBLISHING CAREER DIRECTORY. (Subseries of: Career Advisor Series) 1986. irreg., 5th ed., 1992. $29.95 (softcover $17.95) (effective 1992). Gale Research Inc., 835 Penobscot Bldg., Detroit, MI 48226. TEL 313-961-2242. FAX 313-961-6083. Ed. Bradley J. Morgan. **Document type:** directory.

BREAKOUT SERIES. see EDUCATION

371.4 — UK — ISSN 0306-9885
LB1027.5 — CODEN: BJGCDD
BRITISH JOURNAL OF GUIDANCE AND COUNSELLING. 1973. 3/yr. £48 to individuals; institutions £96 (effective 1996). (Careers Research and Advisory Centre) Carfax Publishing Co., P.O. Box 25, Abingdon, Oxon. OX14 3UE, England. TEL 01235-555335. FAX 01235-553559. (Subscr. in N. America to: 875-81 Massachusetts Ave., Cambridge, MA 02139) Ed. Tony Watts. adv.; bk.rev.; abstr.; index. circ. 750. (also avail. in microfiche; back issues avail.) Indexed: ASSIA, FAMLI, High.Educ.Curr.Aware.Bull., Mult.Ed.Abstr., Psychol.Abstr. (1973-), Res.High.Educ.Abstr., Sociol.Educ.Abstr., SOMA, Stud.Wom.Abstr., Tech.Educ.Abstr. **Document type:** academic/scholarly publication.
—BLDSC (2308.700000); SWETS; UMI. **CCC.**
Refereed Serial

371.42 — GW
BUEROBERUFE. 1990. m. DM.66. Friedrich Kiehl Verlag GmbH, Pfaustr. 13, 67063 Ludwigshafen, Germany. TEL 0621-63502-0. FAX 0621-6350222. Ed. Lothar Kurz. circ. 5,000 (paid). (back issues avail.) **Document type:** academic/scholarly publication.

371.42 330 — US — ISSN 1064-8127
HG181
BUSINESS AND FINANCE CAREER DIRECTORY. (Subseries of: Career Advisor Series) 1989. irreg., 2nd ed., 1992. $29.95 (softcover $17.95) (effective 1993). Gale Research Inc., 835 Penobscot Bldg., Detroit, MI 48226. TEL 313-961-2242. FAX 313-961-6083. **Document type:** directory.

331.4 — CN — ISSN 0045-3587
BUSINESS AND PROFESSIONAL WOMAN. (Text in English, French) 1930. 4/yr. Can.$3. (Canadian Federation of Business and Professional Women's Clubs) Val Publications Ltd., 95 Leeward Glenway, Unit 121, Don Mills, ON M3C 2Z6, Canada. TEL 416-424-1393. FAX 416-467-8262. (Subscr. to: 56 Sparks St., Ste. 308, Ottawa, ON K1P 5A9, Canada) Ed. Valerie Dunn. adv.; bk.rev. circ. 5,000. **Document type:** newsletter.
Description: Issues, news, self-help and management skills for businesswomen.

371.42 330 — US
BUSINESS EDGE. 1992. 2/yr. American Passage Media Corp., 215 W. Harrison, Seattle, WA 98119. TEL 206-282-8111. FAX 206-282-1280. adv.: B&W page $12120; trim 8 1/4 x 10 7/8. circ. 250,000.

371.42 658.8 — UK — ISSN 0261-8052
BUSINESS RATIO REPORT: EMPLOYMENT AGENCIES; an industry sector analysis. 1980. a. I C C Business Ratios Ltd., Freepost, Field House, Hampton, Mddx. TW12 1BR, England. TEL 081-783-0977. FAX 081-783-1940. charts; stat. **Document type:** trade publication.

C C E T S W LEAFLET. (Central Council for Education and Training in Social Work) see SOCIAL SERVICES AND WELFARE

371.42 — UK — ISSN 0268-5450
C I O L A DIRECTORY. (Careers Information Officers in Local Authorities); the esssential guide to careers information resources. 1984. a. £18.95. (Careers Research and Advisory Centre) Hobsons Publishing plc., Bateman St., Cambridge CB2 1LZ, England. TEL 01223-354551. FAX 01223-323154. TELEX 81546 HOBCAM G. (Orders to: Biblios Publishers' Distribution Services Ltd., Star Rd., Partridge Green, W. Sussex RH13 8LD, England. TEL 01403-710851. FAX 01403-711143) **Document type:** directory.
Description: Provides information on books, computer programs, journals, and audiovisual resources available to career counselors and librarians.

371.42 — UK
C R A C ANNUAL REPORT. a. £3.50. (Careers Research and Advisory Centre) Hobsons Publishing plc., Bateman St., Cambridge CB2 1LZ, England. TEL 01223-354551. FAX 01223-323154. TELEX 81546 HOBCAM G. (Orders to: Biblios Publishers' Distribution Services Ltd., Star Rd., Partridge Green, W. Sussex RH13 8LD, England. TEL 01403-710851. FAX 01403-711143) **Document type:** corporate report.
Description: Reports on the work and achievements of C.R.A.C. over the previous year, including industry-education link activities and teacher development programs.

371.42 — UK
C R A C CONFERENCE REPORTS. irreg., latest 1994. £9.95 per vol. (Careers Reseach and Advisory Centre) Hobsons Publishing plc., Bateman St., Cambridge CB2 1LZ, England. TEL 01223-354551. FAX 01223-323154. TELEX 81546 HOBCAM G. (Orders to: Biblios Publishers' Distribution Services Ltd., Star Rd., Partridge Green, W. Sussex RH13 8LD, England. TEL 01403-710851. FAX 01403-711143) (back issues avail.) **Document type:** proceedings.
Description: Disseminates key issues brought forth at C.R.A.C. events and suggests an agenda for action.

371.42 — UK
C R A C OCCASIONAL PAPERS. 1989. irreg., latest 1994. £3 per vol. (Careers Research and Advisory Centre) Hobsons Publishing plc., Bateman St., Cambridge CB2 1LZ, England. TEL 01223-354551. FAX 01223-323154. TELEX 81546 HOBCAM G. (Orders to: Biblios Publishers' Directory Services Ltd., Star Rd., Partridge Green, W. Sussex RH13 8LD, England. TEL 01403-710851. FAX 01403-711143) (back issues avail.) **Document type:** monographic series.
Description: Explores various topics in career development.

THE C R A C STUDENTS' GUIDE TO GRADUATE STUDEIS IN THE U K. see EDUCATION — Higher Education

CALIFORNIA PARKS AND RECREATION JOBMARKET. see LEISURE AND RECREATION

371.42 — US
CALIFORNIA PERSONNEL & GUIDANCE ASSOCIATION. MONOGRAPHS. 1960. irreg., no.11, 1977. price varies. California Association for Counseling and Development, 2555 E. Chapman Ave., Ste. 201, Fullerton, CA 92631-3617. TEL 714-871-6460. FAX 714-871-5132. **Document type:** monographic series.

371.42 — II
CAREER & COMPETITION TIMES. (Text in English) 1981. m. Rs.190. Bennett, Coleman & Co. Ltd. (New Delhi), c/o Times of India, 10 Daryaganj, New Delhi 110002, India. TEL 11-3276567. FAX 11-3323346. TELEX 3161337. (U.S. subscr. addr.: Ms. Kalpana, 42-75 Main St., Flushing, NY 11355) Ed. Bidyut Sarkar. circ. 57,000.

371.42 — US — ISSN 0738-7075
HF5381.A1
CAREER CENTER BULLETIN. 1979. q. $29. Columbia University, Center for Research in Career Development, 316 Uris Hall, New York, NY 10027. TEL 212-854-2830. FAX 212-316-1473. bk.rev. circ. 3,500. Indexed: Pers.Lit.
Formerly (until vol.3, no.4): Career Development Bulletin.
Description: Disseminates information on new practices, trends, research in the field of career development and human resources.

371.42 790.1 — US
CAREER CONNECTIONS. 1990. s-m. $249. Stratford American Sports Corp., 2400 E. Arizona Biltmore Circle, Bldg. 2, Ste. 1270, Phoenix, AZ 85016. TEL 602-954-8106. FAX 602-955-3441. Ed. Jay Abraham. adv. contact: Clay Lyons. circ. 1,600 (paid). (back issues avail.) **Document type:** newsletter.
Description: Contains job listings in sports media, sports telemarketing, sales, health and fitness, facility management, sporting goods, event management, college athletics, sports law, professional sports, and leisure and recreation.

OCCUPATIONS AND CAREERS

371.9 US ISSN 0885-7288
LC3981
CAREER DEVELOPMENT FOR EXCEPTIONAL INDIVIDUALS. 2/yr. $20 (foreign $24). Council for Exceptional Children, 1920 Association Dr., Reston, VA 22091. TEL 703-620-3660. FAX 703-264-9494. Eds. Gary Greene, Len Albright. circ. 2,000. (also avail. in microform from UMI) Indexed: C.I.J.E. Document type: newsletter. —UMI; UnCover.
Description: Contains articles on the latest research activities, model programs, and issues in career development and transition planning for exceptional individuals.

371.42 US ISSN 0889-4019
HF5381.A1
CAREER DEVELOPMENT QUARTERLY. 1952. q. $40 to individuals; institutions $55 (effective 1996). (National Career Development Association) American Counseling Association, 5999 Stevenson Ave., Alexandria, VA 22304-3300. TEL 703-823-9800. FAX 703-823-0252. (Subscr. to: Box 2513, Birmingham, AL 35201-2513. TEL 205-995-1567. FAX 205-995-1588) Ed. Mark L. Savickas. adv.; bibl.; charts; index. circ. 8,000. (also avail. in microform from UMI; reprint service avail. from UMI) Indexed: BPIA, C.I.J.E., Coll.Stud.Pers.Abstr., Cont.Pg.Educ., Curr.Cont., Educ.Ind., High.Educ.Curr.Aware.Bull., Int.Lab.Doc., Mult.Ed.Abstr., Psychol.Abstr. (1954-), Psycscan, Soc.Work Res.& Abstr., SSCI, Stud.Wom.Abstr., Tr.& Dev.Alert, Yrbk.Assoc.Educ.& Rehab.Blind.
●Also available online. Vendor(s): University Microfilms International.
—BLDSC (3051.706000); Faxon; Genuine Article; SWETS; UMI; UnCover. CCC.
Formerly: Vocational Guidance Quarterly (ISSN 0042-7764)
Description: Concerned with research, theory, and practice in career development, career counseling, occupational resources, labor market dynamics, and career education.

371.42 US ISSN 1056-5558
CAREER DIRECTIONS. (Editions avail. for Great Lake states.) 1989. q. Directions Publishing, Inc., 21 N. Henry St., Edgerton, WI 53534. TEL 608-884-3367. adv. circ. 112,000.
Description: Directed to college juniors, seniors, and graduate students.

CAREER EDUCATION. see EDUCATION — Adult Education

371.42 US
CAREER FOCUS. 1988. bi-m. $28.95. Communications Publishing Group, Inc., 250 Mark Twain Tower, 106 W. 11th St., Ste. 250, Kansas City, MO 64105-1806. TEL 816-221-4404. FAX 816-221-1112. Ed. Georgia Lee Clark. adv.; bk.rev. circ. 250,000.
Description: Informs and motivates Black and Hispanic young adults, ages 21-45, on preparing, developing and advancing their careers.

371.42 US ISSN 0891-0596
HF5382.5.U5
THE CAREER GUIDE. 1984. a. $450 to commercial institutions; libraries $395. Dun and Bradstreet Information Services (Subsidiary of: Dun & Bradstreet, Inc.), 3 Sylvan Way, Parsippany, NJ 07054-3896. TEL 201-605-6000.
Formerly (until 1985): Dun's Employment Opportunities Directory (ISSN 0740-7289)
Description: Describes career opportunities and hiring practices of 5,000 companies actively seeking resumes.

371.42 340 US
CAREER OPPORTUNITIES BULLETIN. 9/yr. $90 to non-members. Women's Bar Association of D.C., 2009LH St., N.W., Ste. 510, Washington, DC 20036. TEL 202-785-1540. FAX 202-293-3388. Ed. Lora Pollari-Welbes. circ. 1,700. Document type: newsletter.

371.42 US
CAREER OPPORTUNITIES FOR MINORITY COLLEGE GRADUATES. 1991. a. free. Paoli Publishing, Inc., 1708 E. Lancaster Ave., Ste. 287, Paoli, PA 19301. TEL 215-640-9889.
Description: Guide for minorities seeking employment from major US employers. Lists employment opportunities in accounting, advertising, banking and finance, communications, computer sciences, consulting, continuing education, employment agencies, engineering, health care, nursing, and teaching.

371.42 US ISSN 0739-5043
CAREER OPPORTUNITIES NEWS. 1983. 6/yr. $30. Garrett Park Press, Box 190F, Garrett Park, MD 20896. TEL 301-946-2553. Ed. Robert Calvert, Jr. bk.rev.; charts; illus.

CAREER PLANNING & ADULT DEVELOPMENT JOURNAL. see EDUCATION — Adult Education

CAREER PLANNING AND ADULT DEVELOPMENT NETWORK NEWSLETTER; a newsletter for career counselors, educators, and human resource specialists. see EDUCATION — Adult Education

371.42 US
CAREER SUCCESS. 1987. s-a. $0.75. Target Marketing, Inc., 5 Victory Ln., Ste. 101, Liberty, MO 64068. TEL 816-781-7557. FAX 816-792-3892. adv. circ. 400,000.
Description: Reflects the benefits of vocational education. Covers career opportunities, job outlook, success stories and financial aid.

CAREER VISION. see COLLEGE AND ALUMNI

374 US ISSN 0744-1002
HF5381.A1
CAREER WORLD. 1972. m. (Sep.-May). $27.95 (effective 1995-1996). Weekly Reader Corporation, 245 Long Hill Rd., Box 2791, Middletown, CT 06457-9291. TEL 800-446-3355. FAX 609-786-3360. (Subscr. to: 3000 Cindel Dr., Delran, NJ 08075) Ed. Sandra Maccarone; Pub. Richard J. Le Brasseur. bk.rev.; circ. 92,372 (paid). (also avail. in microform from UMI) Indexed: Ind.Child.Mag.
—UMI; UnCover.
Formed by the 1981 merger of: Career World 1 (ISSN 0198-7615); Career World 2 (ISSN 0198-7623); Which was formerly (until 1977): Career World (ISSN 0361-8994); Incorporates: Real World.
Description: Contains informational articles, essays, and photographs on job markets, job search techniques, and prospective business trends pertaining to vocational planning for high school students.

371.42 AT
CAREERS. 1955. a. free. Careers Publishing Pty Ltd., 8 Elliott St., Ascot Vale, Vic. 3032, Australia.

371.42 UK ISSN 0143-9618
CAREERS ADVISER.* 1973. bi-m. £6. Dominion Press Ltd., Signal House, Lyon Rd., Harrow, Middx. HA1 2QE, England. adv. circ. 15,000.

371.42 US ISSN 1065-9935
CAREERS & COLLEGES. 1981. 2/yr. $5 to individuals; institutions $15. E.M. Guild, Inc., 989 Ave. of the Americas; 6th Fl, New York, NY 10018. TEL 212-563-4688. FAX 212-967-2531. Ed. June Rogoznica. adv.; bk.rev.; illus. circ. 500,000. (back issues avail.; reprint service avail.)
Formerly: Careers.
Description: Covers college and career preparation for teens, including higher education, career awareness, financial aid, getting a job, and personal development.

371.42 378.0025 US ISSN 1059-5686
CAREERS & MAJORS. 1989. s-a. $20. Oxendine Publishing, Inc., Box 14081, Gainesville, FL 32604-2081. TEL 904-373-6907. FAX 904-373-8120. Ed. W.H. Oxendine, Jr. circ. 18,000 (controlled).
●Also available online.
Description: Focuses on career opportunities in relation to the college major of choice.

371.42 US
CAREERS AND THE COLLEGE GRAD. 1987. a. $12.95. Careers Group, 260 Center St., Holbrook, MA 02343. TEL 617-767-8100. FAX 617-767-0994. adv. circ. 22,000. Document type: consumer publication.
Description: Lists employers, profiles, career bios, industry reports, feature articles and career opportunities for recruitment purposes.

CAREERS & THE DISABLED. see HANDICAPPED

371.42 620 US
CAREERS AND THE ENGINEER. 1989. 2/yr. $12.95 per no. Careers Group, 260 Center St., Holbrook, MA 02343. TEL 617-767-8100. FAX 617-767-0994. adv. circ. 21,014. Document type: consumer publication.
Description: Lists employers, profiles, career bios, feature articles, industry reports and career opportunities.

371.42 330 US
CAREERS AND THE M B A. (Masters of Business Administration) 1969. 2/yr. $12.95. Careers Group, 260 Center St., Holbrook, MA 02343. TEL 617-767-8100. FAX 617-767-0994. adv. circ. 17,000. Document type: consumer publication.
Description: Lists employers, profiles, career bios, feature articles, industry reports and career trends for recruitment purposes.

331.1 II
CAREERS DIGEST. (Text in English) 1963. m. 21 Shankar Market, Delhi 110 001, India. TEL 11-44726. Ed. O.P. Varma. circ. 35,000.

371.42 UK
CAREERS ENCYCLOPEDIA. 1952. a. £40. Cassell plc., Villiers House, 41-47 Strand, London WC2N 5JE, England. (Subscr. to: Fleets Ln., Poole, Dorset BH15 3AJ, England; Dist. in U.S. by: Cassel, PCS Data Processing Inc., 360 W. 31st St., New York, NY 10001) Ed. Audrey Segal. adv. Document type: directory.
Description: Provides career information to graduates, parents, teachers and career advisers. Covers courses and qualifications in further and higher education and how it relates to particular career areas.

371.42 378 362.4 UK
▼**CAREERS FOR DISABLED GRADUATES.** Variant title: Casebook for Disabled Graduates. (Part of the Equal Opportunities Casebook series) 1994. a. £8.50 (complete set £99.95). (Careers Research and Advisory Centre) Hobsons Publishing plc., Bateman St., Cambridge CB2 1LZ, England. TEL 01223-354551. FAX 01223-323154. TELEX 81546 HOBCAM G. (Orders to: Biblios Publishers' Distribution Services Ltd., Star Rd., Partridge Green, W. Sussex RH13 8LD, England. TEL 01403-710851. FAX 01403-711143)
Description: Recent graduates discuss their careers.

371.42 UK
CAREERS FOR ETHNIC MINORITY GRADUATES. Variant title: Casebook for Ethnic Minority Graduates. a. £8.50 (complete set £99.95). (Careers Research and Advisory Centre) Hobsons Publishing plc., Bateman St., Cambridge CB2 1LZ, England. TEL 01223-354551. FAX 01223-323154. TELEX 81546 HOBCAM G. (Orders to: Biblios Publishers' Distribution Services Ltd., Star Rd., Partridge Green, W. Sussex RH13 8LD, England. TEL 01403-710851. FAX 01403-711143)
Formerly: Racial Equality Casebook.
Description: Recent graduates belonging to ethnic minority groups discuss their careers.

371.42 374 UK
CAREERS FOR MATURE STUDENTS. Variant title: Casebook for Mature Students. (Part of the Equal Opportunities Casebook Series) a. £8.50 (complete set £99.95). (Careers Research and Advisory Centre) Hobsons Publishing plc., Bateman St., Cambridge CB2 1LZ, England. TEL 01223-354551. FAX 01223-323154. TELEX 81546 HOBCAM G. (Orders to: Biblios Publishers' Distribution Services Ltd., Star Rd., Partridge Green, W. Sussex RH13 8LD, England. TEL 01403-710851. FAX 01403-711143)
Description: Recent senior citizen graduates discuss their new careers.

OCCUPATIONS AND CAREERS

371.42 305.4 UK
CAREERS FOR WOMEN GRADUATES. Variant title: Casebook for Women Graduates. (Part of the Equal Opportunities Casebook Series) a. £8.50 (complete set £99.95). (Careers Research and Advisory Centre) Hobsons Publishing plc., Bateman St., Cambridge CB2 1LZ, England. TEL 01223-354551. FAX 01223-323154. TELEX 81546 HOBCAM G. (Orders to: Biblios Publishers' Distribution Services Ltd., Star Rd., Partridge Green, W. Sussex RH13 8LD, England. TEL 01403-710851. FAX 01403-711143)
  Formerly: Hobsons Working Women Casebook.
  Description: Recent female graduates discuss their careers and prospects.

371.42 UK ISSN 0969-6431
CAREERS GUIDANCE TODAY. (Former name of issuing body: Institute of Careers Officers) 1980. q. £4 (typically set in Jul.). Institute of Careers Guidance, 27a Lower High St., Stourbridge, W. Midlands DY8 1TA, England. FAX 01384-440830. adv.; bk.rev. circ. 4,000. Indexed: High.Educ.Curr.Aware.Bull. **Document type:** trade publication.
  Former titles (until 1993): Careers Officer (ISSN 0958-7489) & Careers Journal; Which superseded (in July 1989): Careers Quarterly.

371.42 323.4 378 UK
▼**CAREERS GUIDE FOR SCHOOLS.** (Part of the Equal Opportunities Casebook Series) 1995. a. £15 (complete set £99.95). (Careers Research and Advisory Centre) Hobsons Publishing plc., Bateman St., Cambridge CB2 1LZ, England. TEL 01223-354551. FAX 01223-323154. TELEX 81546 HOBCAM G. (Orders to: Biblios Publishers' Distribution Services Ltd., Star Rd., Partridge Green, W. Sussex RH13 8LD, England. TEL 01403-710851. FAX 01403-711143) **Document type:** directory.
  Description: Advises teachers on careers and equal opportunities for students who belong to an ethnic minority group and addresses issues of discrimination these people may face.

371.42 AT
CAREERS IN HOSPITALS AND HEALTH SERVICES IN VICTORIA. 1969. biennial. Aus.$3.50. Health Department, Victoria, Mayfield Centre, 11-27 Mayfield Ave., Malvern, Vic. 3144, Australia. Ed. Leigh Brown. circ. 2,500.

CAREERS UNLIMITED. see MILITARY

371.42 AT
CAREERS UPDATE. 1971. w. Aus.$45 to individuals and schools; companies Aus.$110. Monash University, Course and Career Centre, Clayton, Vic. 3168, Australia. TEL 03-565-3150. FAX 03-565-3168. Ed. L.H. Parrott. circ. 1,000.
  Formerly: Careers Weekly (ISSN 0310-7418)
  Description: Contains job advertisements and career-related news.

371.42 378 UK
CAREERSCOPE. 1981. 3/yr. £10. (Independent Schools Careers Organisation) Isco Publications, 12A Princess Way, Camberley, Surrey GU15 3SP, England. (Dist. by: Biblios Publishers' Distribution Services Ltd., Star Rd., Partridge Green, W. Sussex RH13 8LD, England. TEL 01403-710851. FAX 01403-711143) Ed. Anna Alston. circ. 49,000. **Document type:** academic/scholarly publication, bulletin.
  Formerly: I S C O Careers Bulletin.
  Description: Deals with careers of all kinds and developments in higher education.

371.42 US ISSN 1074-3642
CARETAKER GAZETTE; number 1 source for caretaker jobs! 1983. bi-m. $24 (effective 1995). Dunn, Inc., HC 76 Box 4022, Garden Valley, ID 83622-9729. TEL 208-462-3993. FAX 208-462-3993. Ed. Thea K. Dunn; Pub. Gary Dunn. adv.; bk.rev.; illus. circ. 2,000. (looseleaf format; back issues avail.) **Document type:** newsletter.
  Description: Provides information on caretaker positions available in U.S. and abroad, includes caretaker classified ads, reader correspondence and profiles successful caretakers. Provides free ads for landowners seeking to hire caretakers.

CHAMBER JOBWATCH. see BUSINESS AND ECONOMICS — Chamber Of Commerce Publications

CHEMISTRY FOR THE FUTURE (YEAR); first degree courses in chemistry and related sciences. see EDUCATION — Guides To Schools And Colleges

CHICAGO SCHOOLS AND CAREERS. see EDUCATION — Guides To Schools And Colleges

371.42 US ISSN 0746-7761
CHIEF - CIVIL SERVICE LEADER. 1897. w. $20. New York Civil Service Employees Publishing Co., Inc., 150 Nassau St., New York, NY 10038. TEL 212-962-2690. Ed. Frank J. Prial. adv. circ. 51,112. **Document type:** newspaper.
  Formerly: Chief (ISSN 0009-3807)
  Description: Concentrates on the civil services field, reaching police officers, firefighters, school teachers, sanitation and postal employees.

CIVIL ENGINEERING FOR THE FUTURE; first degree courses in civil engineering and related subjects. see EDUCATION — Guides To Schools And Colleges

371.42 US ISSN 1042-7848
UB357
CIVILIAN CAREER GUIDE. 1987. a. $14.95 (effective 1993). Grant's Guides, Inc., Box 613, Lake Placid, NY 12946. TEL 800-922-1923. FAX 518-523-2974. Ed. James Grant. adv. circ. 10,000. (back issues avail.) **Document type:** directory.
  Description: For former military personnel entering the civilian job market. Offers economic analyses of the industries most likely to hire former military personnel.

371.42 US
COLLEGE OUTLOOK. bi-a. free. Townsend Outlook Publishing, 20 E. Gregory, Kansas City, MO 64114. TEL 816-361-0616. FAX 816-361-0616. Ed. Kaila King. adv. contact: Karen M. Scott. bk.rev.; circ. controlled. **Document type:** consumer publication.
  Description: Encourages high school juniors (spring edition) and high school seniors (fall edition) to attend college; describes college life, financial aid, and scholarships.

371.42 US ISSN 0147-8826
LB2350.5
COLLEGE PLANNING - SEARCH BOOK. 1975. a. $10. American College Testing, 2201 N. Dodge, Box 168, Iowa City, IA 52243. TEL 319-337-1429.

COLORADO JOB FINDER. see PUBLIC ADMINISTRATION — Municipal Government

331.1 US ISSN 0195-1157
HF5382.5.U5
COMMUNITY JOBS; the national employment newspaper for the non-profit sector. (Former name of issuing body: Community Careers Resource Center) 1977. m. $69 to institutions. ACCESS: Networking in the Public Interest, 30 Irving Pl., 9th Fl., New York, NY 10003. TEL 212-475-1001. FAX 212-475-1199. Ed. Ingrid Johnson. adv.; bk.rev. circ. 11,000. Indexed: Alt.Press Ind. **Document type:** newspaper.
  Description: Nationwide listing of job opportunities in the non-profit sector.

COMPUTER CONTRACTOR. see COMPUTERS — Computer Industry, Vocational Guidance

331.1 US ISSN 0161-3405
CONSTRUCTION EMPLOYMENT GUIDE IN THE NATIONAL AND INTERNATIONAL FIELD. irreg., 7th ed., 1990. $16.50. World Trade Academy Press, Inc., 50 E. 42nd St., Ste. 509, New York, NY 10017-5480. TEL 212-697-4999. FAX 212-949-4001. **Document type:** directory.

CONSULTING OPPORTUNITIES JOURNAL. see BUSINESS AND ECONOMICS — Management

331.1 330 US
CONSULTING RATES AND BUSINESS PRACTICES. ANNUAL SURVEY. 1979. biennial. $25. Professional and Technical Consultants Association, Box 4143, Mountain View, CA 94040. TEL 415-903-8305. FAX 415-967-0995. Ed. Martin van Derpool. circ. 2,000. **Document type:** trade publication.

658 US ISSN 1071-2917
CONTEMPORARY TIMES. 1982. q. $120 to non-members; members $60; non-profit $80. National Association of Temporary and Staffing Services, Inc., 119 S. St. Asaph St., Alexandria, VA 22314. TEL 703-549-6287. FAX 703-549-4808. Ed. Louise Gates Seghers. adv.; bk.rev.; charts; illus.; stat.; index, cum.index. circ. 6,000. (back issues avail.) **Document type:** trade publication.
  Formerly: N A T S News.
  Description: Presents management support articles for the temporary help and staffing industry, and current information on Association and industry activities.

CONTRACT EMPLOYMENT WEEKLY. see BUSINESS AND ECONOMICS — Trade And Industrial Directories

CO-OP - EXPERIENCE - CO-OP MAGAZINE. see EDUCATION — Higher Education

331.1 US ISSN 0892-5232
HF5382.5.U5
CORPORATE JOBS OUTLOOK!. (Supplement avail.: Almanac of American Employers) 1986. bi-m. $169.99. Corporate Jobs Outlook!, P.O. Box 670466, Dallas, TX 75367-0466. TEL 512-755-8810. FAX 512-755-2410. Ed. Jack W. Plunkett. cum.index: 1986-1992. circ. 1,000. (looseleaf format; back issues avail.) **Document type:** newsletter.
  ●Also available online. Vendor(s): Human Resources Information Network.
  Description: Objective reports on growing, hiring employers. Includes ratings for salaries, benefits, and advancement opportunities. Covers training, corporate growth, financial stability, marketing, products and services, and mid-term outlook for America's top employers.

CORPUS CHRISTI MARINER NEWS. see TRANSPORTATION — Ships And Shipping

COUNSELING TODAY. see PSYCHOLOGY

371.2 US ISSN 1041-7877
COUNTY CARE. vol.11, 1975. 7/yr. membership. Medical Arts, Inc., c/o Lloyd R. Chase, Ed., Box 323, Houlton, ME 04730-0323. TEL 207-532-4771. FAX 207-532-0830. adv.; bk.rev.; film rev.; play rev.; bibl.; charts; illus.; stat.; tr.lit. circ. 800. (processed; also avail. in microfiche) **Document type:** newsletter.
  Former titles: Administrative News and Notes; Maine School Administrative District No. 70 News and Notes; Maine School Administrative District No. 29 News and Notes.

371.42 US ISSN 1055-8292
CURRENT EMPLOYMENT.* (Supplement avail.) 1991. q. $29.99. Publishing & Business Consultants, 101 W. 64th St., Unit 3, Inglewood, CA 90302-1255. TEL 213-732-3477. FAX 213-732-9123. (Subscr. to: Box 75932, Los Angeles, CA 90075) Ed. Andeson Napoleon Atia. adv. circ. 120,000. **Document type:** consumer publication.
  Description: Provides updated information on government jobs, with employment trends and forecasts.

DEGREE COURSE GUIDES (YEAR). see EDUCATION — Guides To Schools And Colleges

DIMENSIONS (RIMROCK). see PARAPSYCHOLOGY AND OCCULTISM

371.42 US
DIRECTAIM. 1985. 4/yr. $9.60. Communications Publishing Group, Inc., 250 Mark Twain Tower, 106 W. 11th St., Ste. 250, Kansas City, MO 64105-1806. TEL 816-221-4404. FAX 816-221-1112. Ed. Georgia Lee Clarke. adv. circ. 500,000.
  Formerly: Aim (Kansas City).
  Description: Assists vocational-technical graduates ages 21-35 in their search for career opportunities.

920 CK ISSN 0302-6876
HD8038.C6
DIRECTORIO NACIONAL DE PROFESIONALES. irreg. E C O C Ltda., Calle 17 no. 5-43, Apdo. Aereo 30969, Bogota, Colombia. illus. **Document type:** directory.

DIRECTORY OF INDEPENDENT FURTHER EDUCATION. see EDUCATION — Guides To Schools And Colleges

OCCUPATIONS AND CAREERS

DIRECTORY OF INTERNSHIPS, RESIDENCIES AND REGISTRARSHIPS AVAILABLE IN VICTORIAN HOSPITALS. see HOSPITALS

371.42   US   ISSN 1063-3774
HD3630.U7
DIRECTORY OF LICENSED OCCUPATIONS IN ALASKA (YEAR). a. free. Department of Labor, Research & Analysis Section, Box 25501, Juneau, AK 99802-5501. TEL 907-465-4518. FAX 907-465-2101. **Document type:** government publication.
   Description: Lists Alaska occupations which require licenses issued by various state and federal agencies; the Municipality of Anchorage and by the City and Borough of Juneau.

DIRECTORY OF MODEL - TALENT AGENCIES AND SCHOOLS USA AND INTERNATIONAL. see BUSINESS AND ECONOMICS — Trade And Industrial Directories

DIRECTORY OF OVERSEAS SUMMER JOBS. see BUSINESS AND ECONOMICS — Trade And Industrial Directories

DIRECTORY OF SUMMER JOBS ABROAD. see BUSINESS AND ECONOMICS — Trade And Industrial Directories

DIRECTORY OF SUMMER JOBS IN BRITAIN. see BUSINESS AND ECONOMICS — Trade And Industrial Directories

371.42   US   ISSN 1072-4656
DOWN THE ROAD. 1993. q. $19.95 (effective Jan. 1995). Mike Byrnes & Associates, 2025 N. Third St., Ste. 155, Phoenix, AZ 85004. TEL 602-252-4868. FAX 602-252-8120. Ed. Deborah Fox; Pub. Mike Byrnes. adv. contact: Mike Byrnes. bk.rev. circ. 2,600. (back issues avail.) **Document type:** newsletter, catalog.
   Description: Directed to truck drivers and diesel mechanics training professionals. Contains a calendar, job bank, resource review, school profile, product catalog and feature articles.

DRAMATISTS SOURCEBOOK. see THEATER

E M A JOURNAL. (Employment Management Association) see BUSINESS AND ECONOMICS — Personnel Management

361.73 371.42   US
E S S EMPLOYMENT OPPORTUNITIES. (Executive Search Service) 1963. m. $25 to non-members. National Society of Fund Raising Executives, 1101 King St., Ste. 700, Alexandria, VA 22314. TEL 703-684-0410. FAX 703-684-0540. Ed. Julie Humphrey. adv.; circ. 16,000 (controlled).
   Former titles: Executive Search Service News; E S S Employment Newsletter.
   Description: Information on career opportunities in fund-raising.

371.42 613.1   US   ISSN 1060-5053
EARTHWORK. 1991. m. (11/yr.). $29.95. Student Conservation Association, Box 550, Charlestown, NH 03603. TEL 603-543-1700. FAX 603-543-1828. Ed. Lisa K. Younger; Pub. Scott Izzo. adv.: B&W page $683, color page $1050; trim 8 1/4 x 10 3/4. circ. 6,000. **Document type:** trade publication, bulletin.
   Description: Provides environmental and natural resource management job listings and career information.

ECONOMICS AND BUSINESS FOR THE FUTURE (YEAR); first degree courses in economics and business. see EDUCATION — Guides To Schools And Colleges

371.42   EI
EDUCATION AND TRAINING; vocational training in Europe. French edition: Education, Formation (ISSN 1017-5962) (Editions in Dutch, English, French, German, Italian) 1992. q. free. Task Force: Human Resources, Education, Training and Youth, Rue Archimede 17, Bte. 17, B-1040 Brussels, Belgium. (Dist. in US by: European Community Information Service, 2100 M St., N.W., Ste. 707, Washington, DC 20037) circ. 24,500. **Indexed:** Adol.Ment.Hlth.Abstr., Build.Manage.Abstr., Cont.Pg.Educ., Educ.Tech.Abstr., Rural Recreat.Tour.Abstr., Stud.Wom.Abstr., World Agri.Econ.& Rural Sociol.Abstr.
—BLDSC (3096.985000). **CCC.**
   Formed by the merger of: C E D E F O P News (ISSN 0252-855X) & E U R Y D I C E Info.
   Description: Covers the EEC's member countries. Features employment, job market, job opportunities, education, current problems, government influence, reports of events, etc.

371.42   GW
EDUCATIONAL AND VOCATIONAL GUIDANCE - BULLETIN A I O S P, I A E V G, I V S B B. (Text in English, French and German) 1959. s-a. $15 per no. Association Internationale d'Orientation Scolaire et Professionnelle - International Association for Educational and Vocational Guidance - Internationale Vereinigung fuer Schul- und Berufsberatung, c/o Landesarbeitsamt Berlin-Brandenburg, Friedrichstr. 34, 10969 Berlin, Germany. TEL 030-2532-2600. Ed. Bernhard Jenschke. adv.; bk.rev.; bibl.; charts; illus. circ. 1,600. **Document type:** bulletin.
   Former titles: Bulletin A I O S P-I A E V G-I V S B B (ISSN 0251-2513) & A I O S P Bulletin (ISSN 0044-9504)
   Description: Discusses new methods of counseling, guidance systems in various countries, and information for the everyday work of counselors.

EMERGING PATTERNS OF WORK AND COMMUNICATIONS IN AN INFORMATION AGE. see COMMUNICATIONS

331.1   SZ
L'EMPLOI/STELLE/POSTO. (Text in German, French and Italian) 1974. w. 50 SFr. (foreign 65 SFr.) (Office Federal du Personnel, Service de Placement) Staempfli und Cie AG, Hallerstr. 7-9, CH-3001 Bern, Switzerland. TEL 031-3006666. FAX 031-3006688. illus.; tr.lit. circ. 8,500. (tabloid format) **Document type:** government publication.

EMPLOYMENT IN ALBERTA; a guide to conditions of work and employee benefits. see LAW

EMPLOYMENT IN BRITISH COLUMBIA; a guide to conditions of work and employee benefits. see LAW

EMPLOYMENT IN ONTARIO; a guide to conditions of work and employee benefits. see LAW

EMPLOYMENT LEADER. see BUSINESS AND ECONOMICS — Personnel Management

371.42   US
EMPLOYMENT MARKETPLACE. 1982. q. $15. P T M, Inc., 12015 Robyn Park Dr., St. Louis, MO 63131. TEL 314-569-3095. Pub. A.P. Mueller. adv. contact: Pat Turner. (back issues avail.) **Document type:** trade publication.

331.1   II
EMPLOYMENT NEWS. (Editions in English, Hindi, Urdu) 1976. w. Rs.200. Ministry of Information & Broadcasting, Publications Division, Patiala House, Tilak Marg, New Delhi 110001, India. TEL 11-603856. (Subscr. to: Assistant Business Manager, Employment News, East Block IV, R.K. Puram, New Delhi 110001, India) Ed. D.K. Bharadwaj. circ. 426,000. **Document type:** government publication.
   Description: Strives to upgrade the awareness of the job seeking fraternity about suitable openings in public and private sector and provides a useful component of guidance materail designed to assist them in coping with the prescribed tests.

331.1   US
EMPLOYMENT OPPORTUNITIES (ENGLEWOOD). m. $70 (includes Guildnotes). National Guild of Community Schools of the Arts, Box 8018, Englewood, NJ 07631. TEL 201-871-3337.
   ●Also available online. Vendor(s): NewsNet.
   Description: Announcements of administrative openings in the field of community arts education.

331.1   US
EMPLOYMENT OPPORTUNITIES (WASHINGTON). q. $75. National Association of Business Economists, 1233 20th St., N.W., Ste. 505, Washington, DC 20036-2304. TEL 202-463-6223. FAX 202-463-6239. (back issues avail.)
   Description: A listing of job openings in business and economics, including description of job, qualifications, salary information, and contact person.

331.1   US
EMPLOYMENT PRACTICE GUIDE. 1965. s-m. $870. Commerce Clearing House, Inc., 4025 W. Peterson Ave., Chicago, IL 60646. TEL 312-583-8500. Ed.Bd.

331.1 368   US
EMPLOYMENT SERVICE AND UNEMPLOYMENT INSURANCE OPERATIONS; a monthly summary. m. Employment Security Commission, Labor Market Information Division, 532 Kendal Bldg., 700 Wade Ave., Box 25903, Raleigh, NC 27611. TEL 919-733-2936.

ENTREPRENEURIAL WOMAN. see BUSINESS AND ECONOMICS — Small Business

ENTREPRISE ET CARRIERES. see BUSINESS AND ECONOMICS

363.70023   US
ENVIRONMENTAL CAREER DIRECTORY. (Subseries of: Career Advisor Series) 1993. irreg. Gale Research Inc., 835 Penobscot Bldg., Detroit, MI 48226. TEL 313-961-4424. FAX 313-961-6083. Eds. Bradley J. Morgan, Joseph M. Palmisano. **Document type:** directory.

ENVIRONMENTAL CAREERS ORGANIZATION. CONNECTIONS. see ENVIRONMENTAL STUDIES

EQUAL OPPORTUNITY. see ETHNIC INTERESTS

ERASMUS - THE U K GUIDE. see EDUCATION — Guides To Schools And Colleges

371.42   UK   ISSN 0951-1806
ESCAPE: THE CAREER CHANGE MAGAZINE. 1986. bi-m. £17.50. Weavers Press Publishing Ltd., 113 Abbotts Ann Down, Andover, Hants. SP11 7BX, England. Ed. John T. Wilson. circ. 2,500. **Document type:** newsletter.
   Formerly: Escape Committee.
   Description: Contains articles and features on career change and self-employment.

371.42   GW
EURO-CHALLENGE; international career guide for students and graduates. 1993. a. DM.29.80. Staufenbiel Institut fuer Berufs- und Ausbildungsplanung Koeln GmbH, Konrad-Adenauer-Ufer 33, 50668 Cologne, Germany. TEL 0221-124038. FAX 0221-124030. Ed. Joerg Staufenbiel. circ. 20,000. **Document type:** directory.

371.42   GW
EUROPAEISCHE STUDIENGAENGE UND MBA PROGRAMME IN EUROPA. 1984. biennial. DM.29.80. Staufenbiel Institut fuer Berufs- und Ausbildungsplanung Koeln GmbH, Konrad-Adenauer-Ufer 33, 50668 Cologne, Germany. TEL 0221-124038. FAX 0221-124030. Ed. Joerg Staufenbiel. circ. 5,000. **Document type:** directory.

EXECUTIVE GRAPEVINE, VOLUME 1: DIRECTORY OF EXECUTIVE RECRUITMENT CONSULTANTS - UK EDITION (YEAR); recruitment library. see BUSINESS AND ECONOMICS — Management

EXECUTIVE GRAPEVINE, VOLUME 2: INTERNATIONAL DIRECTORY OF EXECUTIVE RECRUITMENT CONSULTANTS; Grapevine recruitment library. see BUSINESS AND ECONOMICS — Management

EXECUTIVE GRAPEVINE, VOLUME 3: EUROPEAN DIRECTORY OF CAREER MANAGEMENT, OUTPLACEMENT AND ASSESSMENT; Grapevine recruitment library. see BUSINESS AND ECONOMICS — Management

EXECUTIVE GRAPEVINE, VOLUME 4: DIRECTORY OF INTERIM MANAGEMENT AND NON EXECUTIVE DIRECTORS; Grapevine recruitment library. see BUSINESS AND ECONOMICS — Management

OCCUPATIONS AND CAREERS

EXECUTIVE GRAPEVINE, VOLUME 5: DIRECTORY OF ASSESSMENT & DEVELOPMENT CONSULTANTS. see BUSINESS AND ECONOMICS — Management

EXECUTIVE GRAPEVINE, VOLUME 6: LIST OF HUMAN RESOURCE PROFESSIONALS; recruitment library. see BUSINESS AND ECONOMICS — Management

371.42 US
EXPRESSMALE.* 1992. m. $21. S A Publishing Inc., 2108 Fort St., Louisville, KY 40217-1606. TEL 502-589-2719. Ed. Cameron Mason Steele. adv.: B&W page $6100. circ. 60,000.
 Description: Targets 21- to 35-year-old males who are starting their careers.

331.1 US ISSN 0279-2230
FEDERAL CAREER OPPORTUNITIES. 1974. fortn. $175 (online $45/hr.). Federal Research Service, Inc., 243 Church St., N.W., Box 1059, Vienna, VA 22183-1059. TEL 703-281-0200. FAX 703-281-7639. Ed. Katherine A. Dausch; Pub. Judelle A. McArdle. **Document type:** newsletter. •Also available online.
 Description: Updated listings of federal government job vacancies. Includes articles on how to get a federal job.

371.42 US ISSN 0739-1684
FEDERAL JOBS DIGEST. 1980. bi-w. $125 (effective 1996). Breakthrough Publications, Inc., 310 N. Highland Ave., Issining, NY 10562. TEL 914-762-5111. FAX 914-762-4818. (Subscr. to: 325 Pennsylvania Ave. S.E., Washington, DC 20003. TEL 800-824-5000) Ed. Peter E. Ognibene. (tabloid format; back issues avail.) **Document type:** newspaper.
 Description: Specializes in the Federal job market. Each issue contains over 10,000 current openings with the Federal government in the United States and overseas, including all occupations and career levels.

FORDYCE LETTER; commentary and information provided exclusively for those involved in the personnel, search, employment, recruiting and outplacement professions. see LAW — Corporate Law

371.42 IT ISSN 0015-7767
FORMAZIONE E LAVORO. 1963. bi-m. L.7000($15) Ente Nazionale A C L I Istruzione Professionale, Via Giuseppe Marcora 18-20, 00153 Rome, Italy. adv.; bibl.; charts; illus.; stat. circ. 3,000.
—BLDSC (4008.350000).

FREELANCERS OF NORTH AMERICA. see PUBLISHING AND BOOK TRADE

G C C A NEWSLETTER. (Graduate Careers Council of Australia Ltd.) see EDUCATION — Higher Education

331.1 334 US
G E O: GRASSROOTS ECONOMIC ORGANIZING NEWSLETTER. 1984. bi-m. $15 to individuals; institutions $30. GEO, Box 5065, New Haven, CT 06525. TEL 203-389-6194. FAX 203-486-0387. Ed. Len Krimerman. adv.; bk.rev.; film rev.; play rev.; illus. circ. 1,200. (back issues avail.) **Document type:** newsletter.
 Formerly (until 1990): Changing Work (ISSN 0883-1416)
 Description: News articles, interviews, departments, and informational documents in pursuit of democratizing the workplace and effecting worker-community ownership.

371.42 378 UK ISSN 0309-894X
G E T: GRADUATE EMPLOYMENT AND TRAINING (YEAR); 60,000 graduate jobs and courses. a. £13.99. (Careers Research and Advisory Centre) Hobsons Publishing plc., Bateman St., Cambridge CB2 1LZ, England. TEL 01223-354551. FAX 01223-323154. TELEX 81546 HOBCAM G. (Subscr. to: Biblios Publishers' Distribution Services Ltd., Star Rd., Partridge Green, W. Sussex RH13 8LD, England. TEL 01403-710851. FAX 01403-711143) **Document type:** directory.
—BLDSC (4206.826200).
 Formerly (until 1976): Careers Beyond a Degree.
 Description: Guides graduates through the various avenues to the career of their choice. Indexed by degree subject, occupation, and employer type. Details the latest developments in several private- and public-sector industries.

371.42 020 US ISSN 1062-9238
HF5382.75.U6
GETTING THE LOWDOWN ON EMPLOYERS AND A LEG UP ON THE JOB MARKET. 1992. irreg. Washington Researchers Publishing (Subsidiary of: Washington Researchers, Inc.), Box 19005, 20th St. Sta., Washington, DC 20036-9005. TEL 202-333-3499. FAX 202-625-0656. **Document type:** trade publication.

371.42 UK ISSN 0017-2804
GRADUATE CAREERS.* 1961. q. £1.($2.50) Dominion Press Ltd., Dominion House, Signal House, Lyon Rd., Harrow, Middx HA1 2QE, England. Ed. Alex Taylor. adv.; bk.rev.; illus.
 Description: Career opportunities for university graduates.

371.42 378 UK ISSN 0963-1542
GRADUATE CAREERS SERVICES DIRECTORY. a. £15. C S U (Publications) Ltd. (Subsidiary of: Higher Education Careers Services Unit), Armstrong House, Oxford Rd., Manchester M1 7ED, England. TEL 0161-236-9816. FAX 0161-236-8541. **Document type:** directory.
 Description: Lists all U.K. higher education career services personnel.

371.42 AT ISSN 0314-0679
GRADUATE OUTLOOK. 1977. a. New Hobsons Press Pty. Ltd., 553 Elizabeth St., Surry Hills, N.S.W. 2010, Australia. Eds. C. Etteridge, M. Lord. adv.: page Aus.$740; adv. contact: Colin Ritchie. circ. 5,000. **Document type:** directory.

GRADUATING ENGINEER. see ENGINEERING

GRADUATING NURSE. see MEDICAL SCIENCES — Nurses And Nursing

GUIDE TO CAMPUS RECRUITING. see EDUCATION — Guides To Schools And Colleges

371.42 UK
▼**THE GUIDE TO TRAINING IN SECRETARIAL AND OFFICE SKILLS.** 1995. a. £9.99. (Careers Research and Advisory Centre) Hobsons Publishing plc., Bateman St., Cambridge CB2 1LZ, England. TEL 01223-354551. FAX 01223-323154. TELEX 81546 HOBCAM G. (Orders to: Biblios Publishers' Distribution Services Ltd., Star Rd., Partridge Green, W. Sussex RH13 8LD, England. TEL 01403-710851. FAX 01403-711143)
 Description: Advises on secretarial career opportunities and covers PA qualifications, computer skills, office management, and language courses. Profiles universities.

H R D I ADVISORY. (Human Resources Development Institute) see BUSINESS AND ECONOMICS — Labor And Industrial Relations

371.42 IS
HADASSAH CAREER COUNSELING INSTITUTE. ANNUAL REPORT FOR THE YEAR. (Editions in English, Hebrew) 1948. a. free. Hadassah Career Counseling Institute, P.O. Box 1406, Jerusalem, Israel. TEL 972-2-244344. (Co-sponsor: Hadassah Women Zionist Organization of America) Ed. Y. Garty. circ. 1,200. **Document type:** corporate report.
 Former titles: Hadassah Career Guidance Institute. Annual Report for the Year; Hadassah Vocational Guidance Institute. Annual Report for the Year; Hadassah Vocational Guidance Institute. Report (ISSN 0072-9248)

371.42 384.3 UK ISSN 0964-1742
THE HANDBOOK OF INFORMATION TECHNOLOGY (YEAR); the guide to jobs and training in information technology. Abbreviated title: H I T (Year). 1987. a. £11.99. (Careers Research and Advisory Centre) Hobsons Publishing plc., Bateman St., Cambridge CB2 1LZ, England. TEL 01223-354551. FAX 01223-323154. TELEX 81546 HOBCAM G. (Orders to: Biblios Publishers' Distribution Services Ltd., Star Rd., Partridge Green, W. Sussex RH13 8LD, England. TEL 01403-710851. FAX 01403-711143)
—BLDSC (4250.538300).
 Description: Provides career and professional training guidance for persons considering a career in computing. Lists key employers, job opportunities, and qualifications.

658 US ISSN 0741-3092
HD69.C6
HARVARD BUSINESS SCHOOL CAREER GUIDE. MANAGEMENT CONSULTING. biennial. Harvard Business School, Press and Publishing, Operations Dept., Boston, MA 02163. TEL 617-495-6117. FAX 617-495-6985. Ed. Sue C. Marsh.

658.8 US ISSN 0899-7101
HF5415.35
HARVARD BUSINESS SCHOOL CAREER GUIDE. MARKETING. 1988. biennial. Harvard Business School, Press and Publishing, Operations Dept., Boston, MA 02163. TEL 617-495-6117. FAX 617-495-6985. Ed. Sue C. Marsh.

HEALTH CAREER POST. see HOSPITALS

371.42 610 US ISSN 1062-5976
R697.A4
HEALTHCARE CAREER DIRECTORY. (Subseries of: Career Advisor Series) 1993. irreg. $29.95 (softcover $17.95). Gale Research Inc., 835 Penobscot Bldg., Detroit, MI 48226. TEL 313-961-2242. FAX 313-961-6083. Ed. Bradley J. Morgan. **Document type:** directory.
 Description: Contains essays on nursing and medical specialties performed by doctors. Includes listings for professional associations and career resources.

HEALTHCARE EMPLOYMENT JOURNAL; serving healthcare professionals. see MEDICAL SCIENCES

371.42 610 US ISSN 1047-7276
HEALTHCARE TRENDS AND TRANSITION. 6/yr. Nex, Inc., Box 48, Eden, MD 21822. TEL 800-541-9129. FAX 301-749-8769. Ed. Karen Flynn.
—BLDSC (4275.247961).

HELPING OUT IN THE OUTDOORS; a directory of volunteer jobs and internships in parks and forests nationwide. see BUSINESS AND ECONOMICS — Trade And Industrial Directories

371.42 US ISSN 1064-1769
HF5382.75.U6
THE HIDDEN JOB MARKET. 1992. a. $16.95. Peterson's Guides, Inc., 202 Carnegie Center, Box 2123, Princeton, NJ 08543. TEL 609-243-9111. **Document type:** directory.
 Description: Guide to fast-growing technology companies that are still hiring despite the 1990's recession.

331.1 629.1 US ISSN 0749-2960
HIGH TECHNOLOGY CAREERS. 1984. bi-m. $29. High Technology Careers, 4701 Patrick Henry Dr., Ste. 1901, Santa Clara, CA 95054. TEL 408-970-8800. Ed. Cathy Mickelson. adv. contact: Paul Burrows. bk.rev.; tr.lit. circ. 130,000. (tabloid format; reprint service avail.)
 Description: Offers a multitude of job opportunities in the Northern California area, as well as articles on the latest technology topics.

371.42 374 AT
HINTS FOR JOB HUNTERS. 1980. a. Monash University, Course & Career Centre, Wellington Rd., Clayton, Vic. 3168, Australia. TEL 03-565-3150. FAX 03-565-3168. Ed. Linel Parrott.
 Description: Provides tips on planning a job seeking strategy, resume writing and interviews.

HISPANIC ENGINEER. see ENGINEERING

331.1 917.306 US ISSN 0892-1369
HD8081
HISPANIC TIMES MAGAZINE; the nation's only career and business magazine for Hispanics, American Indians and native Americans. (Text in English, Spanish) 1978. 5/yr. $30. Hispanic Times Enterprises, Box 579, Winchester, CA 92596. TEL 909-926-2119. Ed. Gloria J. Davis. adv.; bk.rev. circ. 35,000. (back issues avail.) **Indexed:** Chic.Per.Ind. **Document type:** consumer publication.
—CCC.

OCCUPATIONS AND CAREERS

371.42 378 UK
▼**HOBSONS CITY CASEBOOK.** 1995. a. £8.50 (complete set £99.95). (Careers Research and Advisory Centre) Hobsons Publishing plc., Bateman St., Cambridge CB2 1LZ, England. TEL 01223-323154. FAX 01223-323154. TELEX 81546 HOBCAM G. (Orders to: Biblios Publishers' Distribution Services Ltd., Star Rd., Partridge Green, W. Sussex RH13 8LD, England. TEL 01403-710851. FAX 01403-711143)
   Description: Offers case studies of recent graduates in urban careers.

371.42 371.42 UK ISSN 0266-4097
HOBSONS ENGINEERING CASEBOOK. 1979. a. £8.50 (complete set £99.95). (Careers Research and Advisory Centre) Hobsons Publishing plc., Bateman St., Cambridge, England. TEL 01223-354551. FAX 01223-323154. TELEX 81546 HOBCAM G. (Orders to: Biblios Publishers' Distribution Services Ltd., Star Rd., Partridge Green, W. Sussex RH13 8LD, England. TEL 01403-710851. FAX 01403-711143)
   —BLDSC (4319.840000).
   Description: Recent graduates discuss their engineering careers.

371.42 320 UK ISSN 0266-402X
HOBSONS FINANCE CASEBOOK. 1981. a. £8.99 (includes Actuarial Casebook) (complete set £99.95). (Careers Research and Advisory Centre) Hobsons Publishing plc., Bateman St., Cambridge CB2 1LZ, England. TEL 01223-354551. FAX 01223-323154. TELEX 81546 HOBCAM G. (Orders to: Biblios Publishers' Distribution Services Ltd., Star Rd., Partridge Green, W. Sussex RH13 8LD, England. TEL 01403-710851. FAX 01403-711143)
   Description: Recent graduates discuss their finance careers.

371.42 384.3 UK ISSN 1351-8097
HOBSONS I T CASEBOOK. (Information Technology) a. £8.50 (complete set £99.95). (Careers Research and Advisory Centre) Hobsons Publishing plc., Bateman St., Cambridge CB2 1LZ, England. TEL 01223-354551. FAX 01223-323154. TELEX 81546 HOBCAM G. (Orders to: Biblios Publishers' Distribution Services Ltd., Star Rd., Partridge Green, W. Sussex RH13 8LD, England. TEL 01403-710851. FAX 01403-711143)
   Description: Recent graduates discuss their careers in the industry.

371.42 340 UK
HOBSONS LAW CASEBOOK. a. £8.50 (complete set £99.95). (Careers Research and Advisory Centre) Hobsons Publishing plc., Bateman St., Cambridge CB2 1LZ, England. TEL 01223-354551. FAX 01223-323154. TELEX 81546 HOBCAM G. (Orders to: Biblios Publishers' Distribution Services Ltd., Star Rd., Partridge Green, W. Sussex RH13 8LD, England. TEL 01403-710851. FAX 01403-711143)
   Description: Recent graduates discuss their careers in law.

HOBSONS MANAGEMENT CASEBOOK. see BUSINESS AND ECONOMICS — Management

371.42 658 UK
HOBSON'S MARKETING, RETAILING AND SALES CASEBOOK. a. £8.99 (complete set £99.95). (Careers Research and Advisory Centre) Hobson's Publishing plc., Bateman St., Cambridge CB2 1LZ, England. TEL 01223-354551. FAX 01223-323154. TELEX 81546 HOBCAM G. (Orders to: Biblios Publishers' Distribution Services Ltd., Star Rd., Partridge Green, W. Sussex RH13 8LD, England. TEL 01403-710851. FAX 01403-711143)
   Description: Recent graduates discuss their careers in marketing, retailing, and sales.

350 371.42 UK
▼**HOBSONS PUBLIC SECTOR CASEBOOK.** 1995. a. £8.50 (complete set £99.95). (Careers Research and Advisory Centre) Hobsons Publishing plc., Bateman St., Cambridge CB2 1LZ, England. TEL 01223-354551. FAX 01223-323154. TELEX 81546 HOBCAM G. (Orders to: Biblios Publishers' Distribution Services Ltd., Star Rd., Partridge Green, W. Sussex RH13 8LD, England. TEL 01403-710851. FAX 01403-711143)
   Description: Recent graduates discuss their careers in government.

371.42 500 UK
HOBSONS SCIENCE CASEBOOK. a. £8.99 (includes Physics Casebook) (complete set £99.95). (Careers Research and Advisory Centre) Hobsons Publishing plc., Bateman St., Cambridge CB2 1LZ, England. TEL 01223-354551. FAX 01223-323154. TELEX 81546 HOBCAM G. (Orders to: Biblios Publishers' Distribution Services Ltd., Star Rd., Partridge Green, W. Sussex RH13 8LD, England. TEL 01403-710851. FAX 01403-711143)
   Description: Recent graduates discuss their careers in the natural sciences.

371.42 628 UK
HOBSON'S SCIENCE FOR AND TECHNOLOGY IN THE ENVIRONMENT FOR SCHOOLS CASEBOOK. a. £8.50 (complete set £99.95). (Careers Research and Advisory Centre) Hobsons Publishing plc., Bateman St., Cambridge CB2 1LZ, England. TEL 01223-354551. FAX 01223-323154. TELEX 81546 HOBCAM G. (Orders to: Biblios Publishers' Distribution Services Ltd., Star Rd., Partridge Green, W. Sussex RH13 8LD, England. TEL 01403-710851. FAX 01403-711143)
   Formerly (until 1995): Hobson's Science for Schools Casebook.

371.42 378 UK
HOBSONS SIXTH FORM CASEBOOK. a. £8.50 (complete set £99.95). (Careers Research and Advisory Centre) Hobsons Publishing plc., Bateman St., Cambridge CB2 1LZ, England. TEL 01223-354551. FAX 01223-323154. TELEX 81546 HOBCAM G. (Orders to: Biblios Publishers' Distribution Services Ltd., Star Rd., Partridge Green, W. Sussex RH13 8LD, England. TEL 01403-710851. FAX 01403-711143)
   Description: Contains case studies of school dropouts who have gone into higher education or work. Gives students insight into where their chosen courses can lead at 18 and beyond.

I E E E CAREERS CONFERENCE. CONFERENCE RECORD. see ENGINEERING — Electrical Engineering

371.42 760 686 US ISSN 8756-6664
IMAGE WORLD; careers in graphic communications. 1986. s-a. $10 to industry; students and teachers free. Rochester Institute of Technology, Technical and Education Center of the Graphic Arts, c/o Rochester Institute of Technology, 66 Lomb Memorial Dr., Rochester, NY 14623. TEL 716-475-2549. FAX 716-475-7052. Ed. Sandy Richolson. circ. 150,000. (back issues avail.) **Document type:** trade publication.
   Description: Information on career opportunities in graphic communications for high school and college students.

371.42 US ISSN 1066-5633
INDEPENDENT SCHOLAR; a newsletter for independent scholars and their organizations. 1987. q. $14 (foreign $13). National Coalition of Independent Scholars, Box 5743, Berkeley, CA 94705. TEL 510-549-1922. Ed. Harold Orlans. adv.; bk.rev. circ. 350. (back issues avail.) **Document type:** newsletter.

INDIAN JOURNAL OF TRAINING & DEVELOPMENT. see BUSINESS AND ECONOMICS — Personnel Management

371.42 GW
▼**INDIVIDUELL BEWERBEN.** 1994. biennial. DM.29.80. Staufenbiel Institut fuer Berufs- und Ausbildungsplanung Koeln GmbH, Konrad-Adenauer-Ufer 33, 50668 Cologne, Germany. TEL 0221-124038. FAX 0221-124030. Ed. Joerg Staufenbiel. circ. 20,000. **Document type:** directory.

INFORMATIONEN ZUM ARBEITSLOSENRECHT UND SOZIALHILFERECHT. see SOCIAL SERVICES AND WELFARE

371.42 GW
INFORMATIONEN ZUR BERUFLICHEN BILDUNG. 1970. m. DM.42.40. Deutscher Instituts Verlag GmbH, Postfach 510670, 50942 Cologne, Germany. TEL 0221-3708341. FAX 0221-3708191. TELEX 8882768-IWKD. Ed. Winfried Schlaffke. **Document type:** trade publication.

371.42 620 GW
DAS INGENIEURSTUDIUM. 1979. triennial. DM.29.80. Staufenbiel Institut fuer Berufs- und Ausbildungsplanung Koeln GmbH, Konrad-Adenauer-Ufer 33, 50668 Cologne, Germany. TEL 0221-124038. FAX 0221-124030. Ed. Joerg Staufenbiel. circ. 7,500. **Document type:** directory.

331.1 FR
INNOVATION AND EMPLOYMENT. 4/yr. 170 F. (25 ECU). Organization for Economic Cooperation and Development, 2 rue Andre Pascal, 75775 Paris Cedex 16, France. (U.S. subscr. to: O.E.C.D. Publications and Information Center, 2001 L St., N.W., Ste. 700, Washington, DC 20036-4095. TEL 202-785-6323) (Co-sponsor: Commission of the European Communities) (also avail. in microfiche)

371.42 790.1 US
THE INSIDER (PHOENIX). s-m. $149 for 6 mos. Stratford American Sports Corp., Box 10129, Phoenix, AZ 85064. TEL 602-954-8106. FAX 602-955-3441. Ed. Clay Lyons; Pub. Jay Abraham. **Document type:** trade publication, newsletter.
   Formerly: Sports Careers Newsletter.

371.42 CE
INSTITUTE OF BANKERS OF SRI LANKA. JOURNAL. 1981. s-a. Rs.50 (foreign Rs.100). Institute of Bankers of Sri Lanka, No. 5, Milepost Avenue, Colombo 3, Sri Lanka. TEL 573625. Ed. H.B. Illankone. adv. circ. 5,000.
   Formerly (until 1981): Bankers' Training Institute (Sri Lanka). Bulletin.

371.42 IE ISSN 0332-3641
INSTITUTE OF GUIDANCE COUNSELLORS. JOURNAL. vol.4, 1981. 2/yr. £7. Institute of Guidance Counsellors, c/o H. O'Brien, Curriculum Development Unit, Trinity College, Dublin, Ireland. Ed. Finian Buckley. adv.; bk.rev.; cum.index: vols.1-14. circ. 750.
   Formerly: Career Guidance and Counselling.
   Description: The chief aim of the journal is to disseminate both practical and theoretical ideas among guidance counselors and others involved in education, careers and counselling.

371.42 368 332 US
INSURANCE AND FINANCIAL SERVICES CAREERS. 1960. a. Wallace Witmer Company, 1509 Madison Ave., Memphis, TN 38104. TEL 901-276-5424. adv. circ. 50,650.
   Description: Contains career guidance for college students interested in the insurance and financial services industry.

INTERNATIONAL ASSOCIATION FOR EDUCATIONAL AND VOCATIONAL INFORMATION. STUDIES AND REPORTS. see EDUCATION

371.42 US
INTERNATIONAL ASSOCIATION OF INDEPENDENT SCHOLARS. NEWS & NOTES. q. $30. International Association of Independent Scholars, Box 1453, Reseda, CA 91337. **Document type:** newsletter.

INTERNATIONAL EDUCATOR (WEST BRIDGEWATER). see EDUCATION — International Education Programs

371.42 331.1 US ISSN 0748-8890
INTERNATIONAL EMPLOYMENT HOTLINE. 1980. m. $39. Cantrell Corporation, Box 3030, Oakton, VA 22124. TEL 703-620-1972. Ed. Will Cantrell. adv. circ. 5,000. (looseleaf format) **Document type:** newsletter.
   Description: Reports on developments in the international job market, covering a wide range of overseas job openings for US citizens.

331.1 US ISSN 0890-2305
INTERNATIONAL EMPLOYMENT OPPORTUNITIES DIGEST. 1970. q. $15. International Publications (Subsidiary of: Mid-America Marketing, Inc.), Box 5730, Pompano Beach, FL 33074-5730. Ed. M.W. Vail. (back issues avail.)
   Description: Lists a wide variety of specific overseas employment opportunities with contact name and address.

OCCUPATIONS AND CAREERS

658.3
HF5549.5.C35
UK   ISSN 0955-6214
INTERNATIONAL JOURNAL OF CAREER MANAGEMENT. 7/yr. £939($1559) (effective 1996). M C B University Press Ltd., 60-62 Toller Ln., Bradford, W. Yorks BD8 9BY, England. TEL 01274-499821. FAX 01274-547143. TELEX 51317-MCBUNI-G. (N. American subscr. to: M C B University Press Limited, Box 1943, Birmingham, AL 35202) Ed. Rod Davies. (reprint service avail. from SWZ) **Indexed:** Pers.Manage.Abstr., Tech.Educ.Abstr., Tr.& Dev.Alert. **Document type:** academic/scholarly publication. —BLDSC (4542.161200); UMI. **Description:** Covers theory and practice of all aspects of career management.

INTERNATIONAL JOURNAL OF VOCATIONAL EDUCATION AND TRAINING. see EDUCATION — International Education Programs

658.3
L901
US   ISSN 0272-5460
INTERNSHIPS; 50,000 on-the-job training opportunities for students and adults. 1981. a. $29.95. Peterson's Guides, Inc., 202 Carnegie Center, Box 2123, Princeton, NJ 08543-2123. TEL 609-243-9111. FAX 609-243-9150. Ed. Brian Rushing. **Document type:** directory. **Description:** Current information on 38,000 training opportunities in fields ranging from business to science to theater.

371.42 362.7   US
J A C S VOLUNTEER. 1968. q. free. Joint Action in Community Service, Inc., 5225 Wisconsin Ave. N.W., Ste. 404, Washington, DC 20015. TEL 202-537-0996. FAX 202-363-0239. Ed. Shirley A. Gravely-Currie. circ. 6,000. **Document type:** newsletter. **Description:** Directed to volunteers across the U.S. providing help for ex-Job Corps (disadvantaged youth 16-24 yrs.) students.

J C A H P O OUTLOOK. (Joint Commission on Allied Health Personnel in Ophthalmology) see MEDICAL SCIENCES — Ophthalmology And Optometry

JAPANESE NURSING ASSOCIATION RESEARCH REPORT. see MEDICAL SCIENCES — Nurses And Nursing

JOB BANK. see ENVIRONMENTAL STUDIES — Pollution

371.42   UK   ISSN 0309-9059
JOB BOOK (YEAR). a. £25.99. (Careers Research and Advisory Centre) Hobsons Publishing plc., Bateman St., Cambridge CB2 1LZ, England. TEL 01223-354551. FAX 01223-323154. TELEX 81546 HOBCAM G. (Orders to: Biblios Publishers' Distribution Services Ltd., Star Rd., Partridge Green, W. Sussex RH13 8LD, England. TEL 01403-710851. FAX 01403-711143) **Description:** Provides secondary school students with a comprehensive guide to career, training and education opportunities.

331.7   US
HF5382.5.U5
JOB CHOICES (YEAR); a guide to employment opportunities for college graduates. (Former name of issuing body: College Placement Council, Inc.) 1957. a. $39.95. National Association of Colleges and Employers, 62 Highland Ave., Bethlehem, PA 18017. TEL 610-868-1421. FAX 610-868-0208. Ed. Mimi Collins. adv.; illus. circ. 1,122,000. **Former titles:** C P C Annual (ISSN 0749-7474); College Placement Annual (ISSN 0069-5734) **Description:** Contains information on career planning, the job search, work-related education, graduate schools; administration, business and other nontechnical career options; engineering, sciences, computer field and other technical career options; medical, nursing, and allied health career options.

JOB EXPRESS. see COMPUTERS

331.1   US
JOB EXPRESS REGISTRY. 1984. m. $33 to non-members; members $18 for 3 mos. American Dance Guild, 31 W. 21st St., 3rd Fl., New York, NY 10010. TEL 212-627-3790. **Document type:** directory. **Description:** Lists positions for teachers in colleges, universities, public schools, administrations.

658.3   US
THE JOB FINDER; a checklist of openings for administrative and government research employment in the West. 1954. m. $35. Western Government Research Association, 10900 Los Alamitos Blvd., No. 201, Los Alamitos, CA 90720. TEL 310-785-6694. FAX 310-785-6697. Ed. Mel D. Powell. adv. circ. 2,000. (back issues avail.) **Document type:** newsletter. **Formerly:** Governmental Research News: The Job Finder.

371.42   II
JOB GUIDELINES. (Text in Tamil) 1993. m. newsstand price: Rs.10. 352 Triplicane High Rd., Madras 600 005, India. Ed. G. Asokan. circ. 18,490.

371.42   ISSN 1053-1874
HF5382.75.U6
JOB HUNTER'S SOURCEBOOK; where to find employment leads and other job search resources. 1991. biennial. $55 (effective Dec. 1992). Gale Research Inc., 835 Penboscot Bldg., Detroit, MI 48266. TEL 313-916-2242; 800-877-4253. FAX 313-916-6083. Ed. Michelle LeCompte. (also avail. in diskette format; magnetic tape) **Description:** Identifies and describes job-search handbooks, how-to guides, and directories and often-overlooked information sources.

331 330   US   ISSN 0196-1551
JOB OPENINGS FOR ECONOMISTS. 1974. bi-m. $25 to non-members and institutions; members $15. American Economic Association, 2014 Broadway, Ste. 305, Nashville, TN 37203. TEL 615-322-2595. tr.lit. **Description:** Lists job vacancies.

371 378   FR   ISSN 0751-4794
JOB PRATIQUE MAGAZINE. 6/yr. 23 rue des Appenins, 75017 Paris, France. TEL 42-28-59-00. FAX 42-88-24-58. Ed. Alaine Gonse. circ. 85,000.

331.1   US   ISSN 1070-8952
JOB SEEKER. 1988. fortn. $60 to individuals; institutions $84. Rt. 2, Box 16, Warrens, WI 54666. FAX 608-378-4290. Ed. Becky Potter. **Document type:** newsletter.

331.1   US   ISSN 1061-3285
HF5382.75.U6
JOB SEEKER'S GUIDE TO PRIVATE AND PUBLIC COMPANIES. (In 4 vols.: Vol.1: The West, Vol.2: The Midwest, Vol.3: The Northeast, Vol.4: The South - Mid-Atlantic - Great Plains) 1992. a. $99 per vol.; complete set $365 (effective Dec. 1993). Gale Research Inc., 835 Penobscot Bldg., Detroit, MI 48266. TEL 313-961-2242; 800-877-4253. FAX 313-961-6083. (also avail. in diskette format; magnetic tape) **Description:** Provides detailed employment profiles of more than 15,000 companies of high interest to job seekers.

331.1   US
JOB SERVICE OPENINGS AND STARTING WAGES REPORTS. m. free. Department of Employment and Training Services, Labor Market Information, 10 Senate Ave., Rm. 101, Indianapolis, IN 46204. TEL 317-232-8536. FAX 317-232-6950. **Description:** Lists occupations in local offices by occupational category.

331.1   US   ISSN 0826-788X
JOBMART. 1980. 22/yr. $75 to non-members; members $30. American Planning Association, 1313 E. 60th St., Chicago, IL 60637. TEL 312-955-9100. FAX 312-955-8312. (And: 1776 Massachusetts Ave., N.W., Washington, DC 20036. TEL 202-872-0611) Ed. Grace Williams. adv.; circ. 5,500 (controlled). (tabloid format; reprint service avail. from UMI) **Description:** Lists employment opportunities available in the field of planning and related areas.

JOBS CLEARINGHOUSE. see EDUCATION — Teaching Methods And Curriculum

331.1 100   US
JOBS FOR PHILOSOPHERS. 1973. 5/yr. $30 to institutions. American Philosophical Association, University of Delaware, Newark, DE 19716. TEL 302-831-1112. FAX 302-831-8690. E-mail: beller @brahms.udel.edu. circ. 9,000.

371.42   US
JOBS FROM RECYCLABLES POSSIBILITY NEWSLETTER. 1991. a. $4.50. Update Publicare Co., c/o Prosperity & Profits Unlimited, Box 416, Denver, CO 80201-0416. TEL 303-575-5676. Ed. A. Doyle. circ. 2,000. (looseleaf format) **Document type:** newsletter.

331.1   US   ISSN 1053-654X
JOBS IN RECESSIONARY TIMES POSSIBILITY NEWSLETTER. 1990. a. $7. Continnuus, c/o Prosperity & Profits Unlimited, Box 416, Denver, CO 80201-0416. TEL 303-575-5676. Ed. A.C. Doyle. circ. 1,500. (looseleaf format) **Document type:** newsletter.

371.42   UK   ISSN 0962-9742
JOBSEARCH UK. 1991. w. £22.50 for 18 mos. Trinity Newspapers Southern Ltd., 50-56 Portman Rd., Reading, Berkshire RG3 1BA, England. TEL 0734-503030. FAX 0734-391619. (Subscr. to: Customer Interface, Bradley Pavillions, Peartree Rd., Bradley Stoke North, Bristol, Avon BS12 0BQ, England. TEL 0454-620090) Pub. Peter Thorp. adv. contact: Martin Gardner. (tabloid format; back issues avail.) **Document type:** newspaper. **Description:** Lists jobs and vacancies nationwide.

JOURNAL OF CAREER ASSESSMENT. see PSYCHOLOGY

371.42   US   ISSN 0894-8453
LC1037.5
JOURNAL OF CAREER DEVELOPMENT. 1972. q. $195 (foreign $230) (effective 1996). Human Sciences Press, Inc. (Subsidiary of: Plenum Publishing Corp.), 233 Spring St., New York, NY 10013-1578. TEL 212-620-8000. FAX 212-463-0742. TELEX 23-421139. Ed. Norman C. Gysbers. adv.; bk.rev.; bibl.; charts; illus.; stat.; index. (also avail. in microform from UMI; reprint service avail. from UMI) **Indexed:** Bus.Educ.Ind., C.I.J.E., Coll.Stud.Pers.Abstr., Cont.Pg.Educ., Psychol.Abstr. (1978-), Soc.Work Res.& Abstr., Tech.Educ.Abstr., Tr.& Dev.Alert. **Document type:** academic/scholarly publication. —BLDSC (4954.876000); Faxon; Genuine Article; UMI; UnCover. **CCC. Formerly (until 1984):** Journal of Career Education (ISSN 0164-2502) **Description:** Covers career education, adult career development, career development of special needs population, and career and leisure, focusing on impact of theory and research on practice. *Refereed Serial*

371.42 378   US   ISSN 0884-5352
LB2343.5
JOURNAL OF CAREER PLANNING & EMPLOYMENT; the international magazine of placement and recruitment. 1940. 4/yr. $72 to non-members, includes Spotlight newsletter. National Association of Colleges and Employers, 62 Highland Ave., Bethlehem, PA 18017. TEL 610-868-1421. FAX 610-868-0208. Ed. Mimi Collins. adv.; bk.rev.; charts; illus.; index. circ. 4,200. (also avail. in microform from UMI; reprint service avail. from UMI) **Indexed:** Account.Ind. (1974-), C.I.J.E., Educ.Ind., High.Educ.Curr.Aware.Bull., P.A.I.S., Pers.Lit., Pers.Manage.Abstr., Work Rel.Abstr. ●Also available online. Vendor(s): University Microfilms International. —BLDSC (4954.878500); Faxon; UMI; UnCover. **Formerly:** Journal of College Placement (ISSN 0021-9770)

JOURNAL OF COUNSELING & DEVELOPMENT. see PSYCHOLOGY

JOURNAL OF EMPLOYMENT COUNSELING. see PSYCHOLOGY

371.42 331   II
KARMAKSHETRA. (Text in Bengali) 1980. w. Swarnakshar Prakasani Pvt. Ltd., 29-1A, Old Ballygunge, 2nd Ln., Calcutta 700 019, India. TEL 247-0008. Ed. Asoke Chakraborty; Pub. Amarendra Chakravorty. adv. circ. 59,906. **Description:** Contains news of employment and self-employment opportunities.

658.3 US ISSN 0891-2572
KENNEDY'S CAREER STRATEGIST; a monthly guide to career planning success and job satisfaction. 1986. m. $59. Career Strategies, 1150 Wilmette Ave., Wilmette, IL 60091. TEL 708-251-1661. FAX 708-251-5191. Ed. P. O'Keefe. index. circ. 2,000. (back issues avail.) Document type: newsletter.
 Description: Covers mid-level management on careers, office politics, job hunting for mid-career people in all fields.

KEY - A GUIDE TO COLLEGE AND CAREERS. see EDUCATION — Guides To Schools And Colleges

371.42 UK ISSN 0268-9294
KEY NOTE REPORT: EMPLOYMENT AGENCIES. Variant title: Employment Agencies. irreg. £185. Key Note Publications Ltd., Field House, 72 Oldfield Rd., Hampton, Middlesex TW12 2HQ, England. TEL 0181-783-0755. FAX 0181-783-1720. Document type: trade publication.
●Also available online.
Also available on CD-ROM.
—BLDSC (3737.069300).

371.42 US
▼**KEYS TO SUCCESS.** 1994. s-a. free. Prentice Hall (Subsidiary of: Paramount Publishing), 113 Sylvan Ave., Englewood Cliffs, NJ 07632. Eds. Carol Carter, Sandy Kirshner. adv.; illus. Document type: consumer publication.
 Description: Discusses career challenges and opportunities. Geared toward college students.

L M I REVIEW; a quarterly review of Washington State labor market information. (Labor Market Information) see BUSINESS AND ECONOMICS — Labor And Industrial Relations

331.1 SW ISSN 0024-0230
LEDIGA PLATSER. 1961. 40/yr. SEK 220 (effective 1991). PO Box 1335, 701 13 Oerebro, Sweden. Ed. John H. Larsson. adv.; bk.rev. circ. 12,500.
 Former titles (until vol.17, 1962): Lediga Platser foer Ingenjoerer och Administratoerer; (until vol.16, 1961): Lediga Platser foer Tekniker och Ingenjoerer.

371.42 FR ISSN 1146-1918
LETTRE TOURISTIQUE. 1968. s-m. 240 F. A P I Publication, 400 rue St. Honore, 75001 Paris, France. Eds. C. Lea Kadouch, R.R. Leroux. adv.; bk.rev. circ. 3,200.
 Formerly (until 1986): Agent de Voyages (ISSN 1146-190X)

371.42 GW ISSN 0172-1658
LITERATURINFORMATIONEN ZUR BERUFLICHEN BILDUNG. 1974. 6/yr. DM.100. (Bundesinstitut fuer Berufsbildung, Generalsekretaer) W. Bertelsmann Verlag, Postfach 100633, 33506 Bielefeld, Germany. TEL 0521-91101-0.
FAX 0521-9110179. Ed. Christina Kleinschmitt. bk.rev. (back issues avail.) Document type: bibliography.
●Also available online.

371.42 US ISSN 1052-7664
HF5549.5.E45
LOOKING FOR EMPLOYMENT IN FOREIGN COUNTRIES. 1970. irreg., 10th ed., 1995. $16.50. World Trade Academy Press, Inc., 50 E. 42nd St., Ste. 509, New York, NY 10017. TEL 212-697-4999. FAX 212-949-4001. Document type: trade publication.
 Description: Shows how to find job openings abroad with global corporations and nonprofit and voluntary organizations engaged in overseas relief and development. Profiles 37 nations.

371.42 US
LOS ANGELES JOB BANK (YEAR); the job hunter's guide to Southern California. 1982. a. Adams Publishing (Halbrook), 260 Center St., Holbrook, MA 02343. Ed. Carter Smith. Document type: directory.
 Description: Comprehensive and up-to-date career directory for jobs in Southern California.

371.42 GW
M B A STUDIUM UND BUSINESS SCHOOLS IN DEN U S A. (Masters in Business Administration) 1981. biennial. DM.29.80. Staufenbiel Institut fuer Berufs- und Ausbildungsplanung Koeln GmbH, Konrad-Adenauer-Ufer 33, 50668 Cologne, Germany. TEL 0221-124038. FAX 0221-124030. Ed. Joerg Staufenbiel. circ. 4,000. Document type: directory.

331.1 410 US
M L A JOB INFORMATION LISTS. (In 2 editions: English edition; foreign language edition) 1971. q. $35. Modern Language Association of America, 10 Astor Pl., New York, NY 10003. TEL 212-614-6321. FAX 212-477-9863. Ed. Roy Chustek. circ. 6,000. (reprint service avail. from UMI)
 Description: Lists available college teaching positions in English, comparative literature, linguistics and foreign languages.

MAGAZINE AFFAIRES PLUS. see BUSINESS AND ECONOMICS — Investments

380.1 070.5 US ISSN 0889-8502
PN4797
MAGAZINES CAREER DIRECTORY. (Subseries of: Career Advisor Series) 1986. a. $29.95 (softcover $17.96) (effective Mar. 1993). Gale Research Inc., 835 Penobscot Bldg., Detroit, MI 48226. TEL 313-961-2242. FAX 313-961-6083. Ed. Bradley J. Morgan. Document type: directory.
 Formerly (until 1986): Magazine Publishing Career Directory (ISSN 0882-827X)
 Description: Contains essays discussing some of the industry's varied career paths. Includes listings for related companies, career resources and associations.

371.42 658 US ISSN 0889-8510
HF5415.35
MARKETING AND SALES CAREER DIRECTORY. (Subseries of: Career Advisor Series) 1987. irreg., 4th ed., 1992. $29.95 (softcover $17.95) (effective 1992). Gale Research Inc., 835 Penobscot Bldg., Detroit, MI 48226. TEL 313-961-2242. FAX 313-961-6083. Document type: directory.

MASSAGE AND BODYWORK QUARTERLY. see PHYSICAL FITNESS AND HYGIENE

MATHEMATICS FOR THE FUTURE (YEAR); first degree courses in mathematics and related subjects. see EDUCATION — Guides To Schools And Colleges

371 NP
MATRIMONIAL ADVERTISEMENTS INTERNATIONAL. 1984. q. $100. Siveast Consultants, Inc., USA, c/o P.O. Box 8510, Kathmandu, Nepal. (UK subscr to: Dr. Ramasastry, c/o Overseas Customer Service, Midland Bank Blc., Poultry and Princes St., London EC2, England) Ed. C.V. Ramasastry. circ. 50 (controlled). (looseleaf format) Document type: newsletter.
 Former titles: 100 Livelihood Occupations; Matrimonial, Overseas Jobs and Real Estate International Newsletter (ISSN 0742-8944)

MECHANICAL ENGINEERING FOR THE FUTURE; first degree courses in mechanical engineering and related subjects. see EDUCATION — Guides To Schools And Colleges

MEDICAL CAREERS IN AUSTRALIA. see MEDICAL SCIENCES

MICRO O L M. (Occupations in the Labor Market) see BUSINESS AND ECONOMICS — Labor And Industrial Relations

054.1 FR ISSN 0026-3591
MIGRATIONS; revue des possibilites d'emploi-outre-mer, etranger. 1963. m. 5 F. per issue. Editions Lafayette, 3 rue de Montyon, 75429 Paris 9, France. Dir. Yves Andre. adv. circ. 45,000. Indexed: CERDIC.
 Formerly: France Vie.

371.42 330 US ISSN 1040-1547
MINORITY M B A. 1988. a. $8.95. Peterson's - C O G Publishing, 16030 Ventura Blvd., Ste. 560, Encino, CA 91436. TEL 818-789-5293. FAX 818-789-5488. adv.; bk.rev.; circ. 13,381 (controlled).
 Description: Provides career and job placement information for African-American, Hispanic, Asian-American and women graduate students enrolled in business programs nationwide.

371.42 610.73 US
MINORITY NURSE PROFESSIONAL. 1993. a. Peterson's - C O G Publishing, 16030 Ventura Blvd., Ste. 550, Encino, CA 91436. TEL 818-789-5293. FAX 818-789-5488. Ed. Al Austin. adv.: B&W page $4150, color page $5100; trim 8 x 10 3/4. circ. 25,000.

371.42 659.152 US ISSN 1061-4737
MODEL CALL. 1991. q. $14. Richard Poirier Model and Talent Agency, 3575 Cahuenga Blvd. W., No. 254, Los Angeles, CA 90068-1341. TEL 213-969-9990. FAX 213-850-3382. adv. circ. 20,000. Document type: trade publication.
 Description: Covers the business activities of professional models and talents who work in advertising print media.

MUFACE. see PUBLIC ADMINISTRATION — Municipal Government

371.42 SA ISSN 0027-5425
MY CAREER/MY LOOPBAAN; biennial publication on vocational information/tweejaarlikse publikasie oor beroepsinligting. 1950. biennial. free. Department of Labour - Departement van Arbeid, Private Bag X117, Pretoria 0001, South Africa. TEL 27-12-3106358. FAX 27-12-3222839. Ed. T. Zwiegers. abstr.; bibl.; charts; index, cum.index; circ. 45,000 (controlled). Indexed: Ind.S.A.Per. Document type: government publication.
 Description: Intended for juvenile workseekers in need of careers counselling and placement.

371.42 US
LB2343.5
N A C E NATIONAL DIRECTORY; who's who in career planning, placement, and recruitment. (Former name of issuing body: College Placement Council, Inc.) 1985. a. $47.95 to non-members; members $32.95. National Association of Colleges and Employers, 62 Highland Ave., Bethlehem, PA 18017. TEL 610-868-1421. FAX 610-868-0208. Ed. Marian R. Szakacs. circ. 4,200. Document type: directory.
 Formerly: C P C National Directory (ISSN 8755-8378)
 Description: Contains information on 2,200 colleges, 2,100 employers and 9,400 personnel people in the field. Includes names, addresses, phone numbers, interview schedules, and minority enrollments.

N A I E C NEWSLETTER. (National Association for Industry - Education Cooperation) see BUSINESS AND ECONOMICS — Management

371.42 UK
N I C E C PROJECT REPORTS. 1992. irreg., latest Jan. 1995. £9.95 per vol. (Careers Research and Advisory Centre) Hobsons Publishing plc., Bateman St., Cambridge CB2 1LZ, England. TEL 01223-354551. FAX 01223-323154. TELEX 81546 HOBCAM G. (Orders to: Biblios Publishers' Distribution Services Ltd., Star Rd., Partridge Green, W. Sussex RH13 8LD, England. TEL 01403-710851. FAX 01403-711143) (back issues avail.) Document type: monographic series.
 Description: Covers various issues in career development in secondary schools.

N S B E BRIDGE. (National Society of Black Engineers) see ENGINEERING

371.42 US
N S E E QUARTERLY. 1973. q. $70 (includes membership). National Society for Experiential Education, 3509 Haworth Dr., Ste. 207, Raleigh, NC 27609-7229. TEL 919-787-3263. Ed. Anne Kaplan. adv.; bk.rev. circ. 2,000. (back issues avail.)
 Formerly: Experiential Education.
 Description: Covers college and K-12 programs for experiential education, internships, community-service learning, field education, cooperative education, community-based learning, and action research.

331.1 US ISSN 0744-7140
NATIONAL AD SEARCH. 1968. 50/yr. $235. National Ad Search, Inc., Box 2083, Milwaukee, WI 53201. TEL 414-351-1398; 800-992-2832. Ed. Doris M. Morey. adv. (tabloid format) Document type: newspaper.
 Former titles: Ad Search. The Weekly National Want Ad Digest; Ad Search. The National Want Ad Newspaper.
 Description: Lists over 2,000 want ads, categorized into 55 areas of expertise, compiled from 75 major newspapers throughout the U.S.

OCCUPATIONS AND CAREERS

371   US
NATIONAL ASSOCIATION OF COLLEGES AND EMPLOYERS. SALARY SURVEY; a study of beginning salary offers. (Former name of issuing body: College Placement Council, Inc.) 1960. 4/yr. $220 to non-members. National Association of Colleges and Employers, 62 Highland Ave., Bethlehem, PA 18017. TEL 610-868-1421. FAX 610-868-0208. Ed. Dawn L. Oberman. circ. 4,000. (also avail. in microfiche from CIS) **Indexed**: SRI.
   Formerly: C P C Salary Survey (ISSN 0196-1004)

371.42   US   ISSN 1055-9523
NATIONAL BUSINESS EMPLOYMENT WEEKLY. 1980. w. $199 (effective 1995 & 1996). Dow Jones Newspaper Fund, Inc., Box 300, Princeton, NJ 08543-0300. TEL 609-520-4305; 800-JOB-HUNT. Ed. Tony Lee; Pub. Allen Simeone. adv.; circ. 35,000 (paid). (tabloid format; back issues avail.) **Document type**: consumer publication.
   ●Also available online. Vendor(s): Dow Jones News Retrieval.
   —CCC.
   Description: Aimed at Wall Street Journal readers. Provides career guidance and job-hunting advice.

NATIONAL DIRECTORY OF INTERNSHIPS. see EDUCATION — Higher Education

331.1   US   ISSN 1051-4872
HF5382.5.U5
NATIONAL JOB BANK. 1983. a. $250. Adams Publishing (Holbrook), 260 Center St., Holbrook, MA 02343. TEL 617-767-8100. FAX 617-767-0994. **Document type**: consumer publication.

NATIONAL PARALEGAL EMPLOYMENT & SALARY SURVEY. see LAW

331.1   US   ISSN 0896-3002
HD4904.25
NATIONAL REPORT ON WORK & FAMILY. 1987. s-m. $504. Business Publishers, Inc., 951 Pershing Dr., Silver Spring, MD 20910-4464. TEL 301-587-6300. FAX 301-585-9075. Ed. Richard Hagan. (back issues avail.)
   ●Also available online. Vendor(s): Human Resources Information Network.
   —CCC.
   Description: Covers work and family issues, such as parental leave, elder care, care for sick children, and flexible work time.

NEW SETTLER'S GUIDE FOR WASHINGTON, D.C. AND COMMUNITIES IN NEARBY MARYLAND AND VIRGINIA. see TRAVEL AND TOURISM

371.42   UK   ISSN 0307-8477
NEWSCHECK; with careers service bulletin. 1975. m. free. Careers and Occupational Information Centre, Virginia House, Foulsham, Dereham, Norfolk NR20 5RX, England. Ed. Janet Widmer. adv.; bk.rev. circ. 20,000. **Indexed**: Build.Manage.Abstr., High.Educ.Curr.Aware.Bull.
   —BLDSC (6106.245700).

371.42 070.5   US   ISSN 0889-8499
PN4797
NEWSPAPERS CAREER DIRECTORY. (Subseries of: Career Advisor Series) 1987. irreg., 4th ed., 1993. $29.95 (softcover $17.95) (effective 1993). Gale Research Inc., 835 Penobscot Bldg., Detroit, MI 48226. TEL 313-961-2242. FAX 313-961-6083. Ed. Bradley J. Morgan. **Document type**: directory.
   Description: For people interested in finding positions on the staffs of daily, weekly, business and special interest newspapers.

371   US
NEWSPAPERS, DIVERSITY AND YOU. 1985. a. free. Dow Jones Newspaper Fund, Inc., Box 300, Princeton, NJ 08543-0300. TEL 609-452-2820. FAX 609-520-5804.
   Formerly: Journalism Career Guide for Minorities.
   Description: Offers information on financial aid and programs specifically geared to minorities for the study of print journalism as well as information on journalism careers.

371.42   JA
NIKKEI ADOLE. (Text in Japanese) m. Nikkei Home Publishing, Inc. (Subsidiary of: Nihon Keizai Shimbun, Inc.), 2-2-7 Kanda Tsukasa-cho, Chiyoda-ku, Tokyo 101, Japan. TEL 03-3258-7818. **Document type**: consumer publication.
   Description: Provides information for students preparing to enter business and society. Includes employment and other information directed at young people.

371.42   JA
NIKKEI HANDBOOK FOR JOB SEARCH. a.? Nikkei Custom Publishing Services, Inc. (Subsidiary of: Nihon Keizai Shimbun, Inc.), 2-8-4 Kanda Tsukasa-cho, Chiyoda-ku, Tokyo 101, Japan. TEL 03-5256-6924.
   Description: Contains information on the Japanese economy, industry, employment environment, and the changing job scene for third-year university students who are starting to think about a career.

371.42   JA
NIKKEI PLACEMENT GUIDE. a.? Nihon Keizai Shimbun, Inc., 1-9-5 Ote-machi, Chiyoda-ku, Tokyo 100-66, Japan. TEL 03-3270-0251. FAX 03-5255-2661. TELEX J22308 NIKKEI.
   Description: Provides detailed information for college seniors on job opportunities by corporation.

NIKKEI VOCATIONAL SCHOOL GUIDE. see EDUCATION — Guides To Schools And Colleges

371.2   UK
NORTH WEST JOB CAR AND BARGAIN MART. 1987. w. Guardian Media Group, 164 Deansgate, Manchester M60 2RD, England. TEL 061-832-7200. FAX 061-839-1488. Ed. Mike Hill. adv. contact: J.A. Pacey. circ. 20,000 (paid). (back issues avail.) **Document type**: newspaper.
   Description: Contains articles on job finding, career opportunities in various areas, training, and on-the-job problems.

371.4 340   US   ISSN 1059-6445
KF299.G6
NOW HIRING; government jobs for lawyers. 1952. a. $14.95 to non-members; members $9.95. American Bar Association, Law Student Division, 750 N. Lake Shore Dr., Chicago, IL 60611. TEL 312-988-5000. **Document type**: trade publication.
   Former titles: Washington Want Ads & Federal Government Legal Career Opportunities (ISSN 0065-7476)

371.42   FR
O N I S E P COMMUNIQUE. 20/yr. 105 F. (foreign 132 F.). Office National d'Information sur les Enseignements et les Professions (ONISEP), 46-52 rue Albert, 75013 Paris, France. TEL 40-77-60-00. FAX 45-86-60-85. TELEX 202 962 F ONISEP N.

371.42 331.2 330.9   US   ISSN 0082-9072
OCCUPATIONAL OUTLOOK HANDBOOK. 1946. biennial. $23 (hardcover edition $26) (effective 1995). U.S. Bureau of Labor Statistics, 441 G St., N.W., Washington, DC 20212. TEL 202-219-6611. (Dist. by: Bernan, 4611 Assembly Dr., Lanham, MD 20706. TEL 800-274-4447. FAX 301-459-0056; Subscr. to: Superintendent of Documents, U.S. Government Printing Office, Box 371954, Pittsburgh, PA 15250-7954. TEL 202-512-1800. FAX 202-512-2250; Or: Bureau of Labor Statistics Publications Sales Center, Box 2145, Chicago, IL 60690) Ed. Michael Pilot. **Document type**: government publication.

371.42 331.3 330.9   US   ISSN 0199-4786
HF5382.5.U5   CODEN: OOQUAK
OCCUPATIONAL OUTLOOK QUARTERLY. 1957. q. (Sep.-June). $9.50 (foreign $11.90). U.S. Bureau of Labor Statistics, 441 G St., N.W., Washington, DC 20212. TEL 202-655-4000. (Dist. by: Bernan, 4611-F Assembly Dr., Lanham, MD 20706. TEL 800-274-4447. FAX 301-459-0056; Also avail. from: Superintendent of Documents, U.S. Government Printing Office, Box 371954, Pittsburgh, PA 15250-7954. TEL 202-512-1800. FAX 202-512-2250; Or: Bureau of Labor Statistics Publications Sales Center, Box 2145, Chicago, IL 60690) Ed. Melvin C. Fountain. bibl.; charts; illus.; index. circ. 15,000. (also avail. in microfiche from CIS,UMI; back issues avail.; reprint service avail. from CIS) **Indexed**: ABI Inform, Abstr.Soc.Geront., Amer.Stat.Ind. (1973-), B.P.I., Bus.Ind., C.I.J.E., Ind.U.S.Gov.Per., Mag.Ind., P.A.I.S., Pers.Lit., Tr.& Indus.Ind., Work Rel.Abstr. **Document type**: bulletin, government publication.
   ●Also available online. Vendor(s): University Microfilms International.
   Also available on CD-ROM.
   —BLDSC (6229.700000); Faxon; UMI; UnCover.
   Description: Helps job seekers and career counselors evaluate the prospects of occupations by examining trends and developments.

OCCUPATIONAL PROGRAMS IN CALIFORNIA PUBLIC COMMUNITY COLLEGES. see EDUCATION — Guides To Schools And Colleges

331.1   US   ISSN 8755-0466
OFFICIAL GUIDE TO AIRLINE CAREERS. 1977. irreg., latest 1985. $9.95. International Publishing Company of America, 665 La Villa Dr., Miami Springs, FL 33166. TEL 305-887-1700. FAX 305-885-1923. Ed. Alex Morton. adv. circ. 25,000.

371.42 387.7   US   ISSN 8755-044X
OFFICIAL GUIDE TO FLIGHT ATTENDANTS CAREERS. 1968. biennial. $9.95. International Publishing Company of America, 665 La Villa Dr., Miami Springs, FL 33166. TEL 305-887-1700. FAX 305-885-1923. Ed. Alexander C. Morton. circ. 25,000.
   Former titles: Airline Guide to Stewardess and Stewards Career (ISSN 0065-4914); Annual Guide to Stewardess Career.

331.1   US   ISSN 8755-0431
OFFICIAL GUIDE TO FOOD SERVICE AND HOSPITALITY MANAGEMENT CAREERS. 1982. irreg., latest 2nd ed. $9.95. International Publishing Company of America, 665 La Villa Dr., Miami Springs, FL 33166. TEL 305-887-1700. FAX 305-885-1923. Ed. Alexander C. Morton. circ. 25,000.

331.1 387.7   US   ISSN 8755-0458
G154
OFFICIAL GUIDE TO TRAVEL AGENT & TRAVEL CAREERS. 1980. irreg., latest 1986. $9.95. International Publishing Company of America, 665 La Villa Dr., Miami Springs, FL 33166. TEL 305-887-1700. Ed. Alexander C. Morton. illus. circ. 25,000.

331.1   AT
ON STARTING WORK. irreg. Monash University, Course & Career Centre, Wellington Rd., Clayton, Vic. 3168, Australia. TEL 03-565-3150. FAX 03-565-3168. Ed. Lionel Parrott.
   Description: Manual for students making the transition from tertiary studies to the workforce.

OPERATION ENTERPRISE NEWS. see BUSINESS AND ECONOMICS — Management

OPPORTUNITIES IN THE GAP YEAR. see EDUCATION — Higher Education

371.42 658.3   US   ISSN 0734-1776
ORGANIZE YOUR LUCK!. 1976. 10/yr. $75. Behavioral Images, Inc., 302 Leland St., Ste. 101, Bloomington, IL 61701-5646. TEL 309-829-3931. FAX 309-829-9677. Ed. Stephen C. Johnson. adv.; bk.rev. circ. 3,000. (also avail. in talking book) **Document type**: newsletter.
   —CCC.
   Description: Assists people in finding, getting and keeping their jobs through self-marketing methods.

OCCUPATIONS AND CAREERS

371.42   CN   ISSN 0833-0530
L'ORIENTATION. (Text in English, French) 1964. 3/yr. Can.$20 to individuals; institutions Can.$40. Ordre Professionnel des Conseillers et Conseillères d'Orientation du Quebec, 1100 av. Beaumont, No. 520, Mont-Royal, PQ H3P 3H5, Canada. TEL 514-737-4717. Ed. Louise Landry. adv.; bk.rev.; charts; cum.index. circ. 2,500. **Indexed:** C.I.J.E., Pt.de Rep. (1983-).
    Formerly (until 1987): Orientation Professionnelle - Vocational Guidance (ISSN 0030-5413)

371.42   UK
OXBRIDGE CAREERS HANDBOOK. 1979. a. £5. Oxford University Students Union, New Barnet House, Little Clarendon St., Oxford OX1 2HU, England. TEL 01865-270777. FAX 01865-270778. Ed. David Howard-Jones; Pub. Neil Bradford. adv. contact: Ian Tester. circ. 20,000. **Document type:** directory.

331.1 610.69   US   ISSN 1071-5983
P A CAREER. (Physician Assistants) 1989. m. American Academy of Physician Assistants, 950 N. Washington St., Alexandria, VA 22314. TEL 703-836-2272. FAX 703-684-1924. Ed. Connie Szostak. adv. contact: Connie Szostak. charts; tr.lit.; circ. 19,000. (controlled). (back issues avail.) **Document type:** trade publication.
    Formerly (until 1993): P A J F Employment Magazine (ISSN 1050-2246)
    Description: Covers employment outlooks and information for physician assistants. Includes help wanted ads for physician assistants.

371.42 658   US
P B L BUSINESS LEADER. 1991. 3/yr. $9. Future Business Leaders of America, Phi Beta Lambda, 1908 Association Dr., Reston, VA 22091. TEL 703-860-3334. Ed. Angela Angerosa. adv. circ. 19,735.

333.78 371.42   US
PARK AND RECREATION OPPORTUNITIES JOB BULLETIN. s-m. $60 to institutions (members $35). National Recreation and Park Association, 2775 S. Quincy St., No. 300, Arlington, VA 22206. TEL 703-820-4940. FAX 703-671-6772.
    Description: Provides specific position vacancy listings received by NRPA.

331.1   US   ISSN 0161-2425
HF5549.A2
PERSONNEL CONSULTANT. 1968. bi-m. $60. National Association of Personnel Consultants, 3133 Mt. Vernon Ave., Alexandria, VA 22305. TEL 703-684-0180. FAX 703-684-0071. adv.; bk.rev.; circ. 2,500. (controlled). (tabloid format)
    Formerly: Placement Age.

331.1 320   US
PERSONNEL SERVICE NEWSLETTER. m. $30 membership (foreign $55). American Political Science Association, 1527 New Hampshire Ave., N.W., Washington, DC 20036. TEL 202-483-2512. FAX 202-483-2657. Ed. Joyce Williams. **Document type:** newsletter.
    Description: Lists job positions for political scientists.

331.1   US   ISSN 1070-6615
HF5382.5.U5
PETERSON'S JOB OPPORTUNITIES IN BUSINESS. 1984. a. $19.95. Peterson's Guides, Inc., 202 Carnegie Center, Box 2123, Princeton, NJ 08543-2123. TEL 609-243-9111. FAX 609-243-9150.
    Former titles: Peterson's Job Opportunities for Business and Liberal Arts Graduates (Year) (ISSN 1048-3411); Peterson's Business and Management Jobs (Year) (ISSN 0894-9433); Peterson's Guide to Business and Management Jobs (Year) (ISSN 0749-5021)
    Description: Presents information from hundreds of organizations that recruit employees in the areas of business and management.

331.1 620   US   ISSN 1071-068X
TA157
PETERSON'S JOB OPPORTUNITIES IN ENGINEERING AND TECHNOLOGY (YEAR). 1980. a. $19.95. Peterson's Guides, Inc., 202 Carnegie Center, Box 2123, Princeton, NJ 08543-2123. TEL 609-243-9111; 800-338-3282. FAX 609-243-9150. **Document type:** directory.
—BLDSC (6430.193300). **CCC.**
    Former titles (until 1994): Peterson's Job Opportunities for Engineering, Science and Computer Graduates (Year) (ISSN 1048-342X); Peterson's Engineering, Science, and Computer Jobs (Year) (ISSN 0894-9425); Peterson's Guide to Engineering, Science and Computer Jobs (Year) (ISSN 0730-0980); Peterson's Annual Guide to Careers and Employment for Engineers, Computer Scientists, and Physical Scientists (ISSN 0190-4213)
    Description: Contains data from about 1,000 manufacturing, research, consulting and government organizations hiring technical graduates.

331.1 610   US   ISSN 1071-0671
PETERSON'S JOB OPPORTUNITIES IN HEALTH CARE. a. $19.95. Peterson's Guides, Inc., 202 Carnegie Center, Box 2123, Princeton, NJ 08543-2123. TEL 609-243-9111. FAX 609-243-9150. **Document type:** directory.

371.42 378   UK
PHOENIX (MANCHESTER). 1977. q. £10. (Association of Graduate Careers Advisory Services) C S U (Publications) Ltd. (Subsidiary of: Higher Education Central Services Unit), Armstrong House, Oxford Rd., Manchester M1 7ED, England. TEL 0161-236-9816. FAX 0161-236-8541. adv.: B&W page £700. circ. 1,200 (controlled).
    Description: Analyzes trends, issues, and events within graduate recruitment and higher-education careers advisory work in the U.K.

POLICE CAREER DIGEST. see CRIMINOLOGY AND LAW ENFORCEMENT

351 371.42   US   ISSN 1070-3322
HD3630.U7
PROFESSIONAL AND OCCUPATIONAL LICENSING DIRECTORY. 1993. biennial. Gale Research Inc., 835 Penobscot Bldg., Detroit, MI 48226. TEL 313-961-2242; 800-877-4253. FAX 313-961-6083. TELEX 810-221-7086.

371.42   US   ISSN 1045-9863
HF5382.5.U5
PROFESSIONAL CAREERS SOURCEBOOK. 1989. biennial. $85 (effective Nov. 1993). Gale Research Inc., 835 Penobscot Bldg., Detroit, MI 48266. TEL 313-961-2242; 800-877-4253. FAX 313-961-6083. Eds. Kathleen M. Savage, Joseph M. Palmisano. (also avail. in diskette format; magnetic tape)
    Description: Provides profiles on 118 professions.

371.42   US   ISSN 0190-1796
HD6278.U5   CODEN: PWMIDY
PROFESSIONAL WOMEN AND MINORITIES; a total human resources data compendium. 1975. a., 10th ed., 1992. $125. (Commission on Professionals in Science & Technology) C P S T Publications, 1500 Massachusetts Ave., N.W., Ste. 813, Washington, DC 20005. TEL 202-223-6995. FAX 202-223-6444. Eds. B. Vetter, E. Babco. bibl.; charts; index. circ. 1,000. (reprint service avail. from UMI) **Indexed:** SRI. —CASDDS. **CCC.**
    Description: Comprehensive reference book of data on human resources presented in approximately 400 tables and charts, with breakouts by sex and or minority status.

371.42   UK
PROSPECTS DIRECTORY. 1976. a. £25 (effective 1995). C S U (Publications) Ltd. (Subsidiary of: Higher Education Central Services Unit), Armstrong House, Oxford Rd., Manchester M1 7ED, England. TEL 0161-236-9816. FAX 0161-236-8541. adv.; index. circ. 84,000. **Document type:** directory.
• Also available on CD-ROM.
    Formerly: R O G E T (Register of Graduate Employment and Training) (ISSN 0962-4082)
    Description: Contains recruitment plans and training policies of organizations that employ graduates. Helps individuals find employers meeting their personal criteria.

371.42   UK
PROSPECTS FOR THE FINALIST. 1976. 5/yr. £12.50 (effective 1995). C S U (Publications) Ltd. (Subsidiary of: Higher Education Central Services Unit), Armstrong House, Oxford Rd., Manchester M1 7ED, England. TEL 0161-236-9816. FAX 0161-236-8541. adv.: B&W page £1100. circ. 70,000.
    Former titles (until June 1995): Prospects Plus; Future Vacancies for the Finalist: Jobs for Those Graduating in (Year).
    Description: Aimed at students in their final year of study; lists vacancies for which applications can be made in advance of exams.

371.42   UK
PROSPECTS FOR THE FINALIST. 1976. 5/yr. £10 to students (effective 1994-1995). C S U (Publications) Ltd. (Subsidiary of: Higher Education Careers Services Unit), Armstrong House, Oxford Rd., Manchester M1 7ED, England. TEL 0161-236-9816. FAX 0161-236-9227. adv. circ. 68,000. **Document type:** directory.
    Formerly: Future Vacancies for the Finalist.
    Description: Contains entries from organizations wishing to employ final-year students upon their graduation. Alerts individuals of the up-to-date recruitment plans of employers.

371.42 340   UK
PROSPECTS LEGAL. 1988. a. £13 (effective 1995). C S U (Publications) Ltd. (Subsidiary of: Central Services Unit), Armstrong House, Oxford Rd., Manchester M1 7ED, England. TEL 0161-236-9816. FAX 0161-236-8541. adv. circ. 12,000.
    Formerly (until 1995): R O G E T Legal.
    Description: Contains recruitment plans and training policies of organizations employing trainee solicitors. Helps individuals find employers meeting their personal criteria.

PROSPECTS POSTGRAD. see EDUCATION — Higher Education

371.42   UK
PROSPECTS SCOTLAND. 1989. a. £11 (effective 1995). C S U (Publications) Ltd. (Subsidiary of: Higher Education Careers Services Unit), Armstrong House, Oxford Rd., Manchester M1 7ED, England. TEL 0161-236-9816. FAX 0161-236-9227. adv.; index. circ. 13,000.
    Formerly: R O G E T Scotland.
    Description: Covers recruitment plans and training policies of organizations that employ graduates in Scotland. Helps individuals find employers meeting their personal criteria.

331.1   UK
PROSPECTS TODAY. 1972. fortn. (25/yr.). £58.50 to institutions; students £8.50 (for 6 issues) (effective 1994-1995). C S U (Publications) Ltd. (Subsidiary of: Higher Education Careers Services Unit), Armstrong House, Oxford Rd., Manchester M1 7ED, England. TEL 0161-236-9816. FAX 0161-379-9337. adv.: B&W page £1800. circ. 50,000. **Document type:** trade publication.
    Formerly: Current Vacancies for Graduates.
    Description: Lists immediate vacancies for graduates, featuring jobs, career opportunities, and vocational training.

371.42 658   US   ISSN 0742-9770
    CODEN: PRREED
PRYOR REPORT. 1984. m. $89. Imagine, Inc., Box 1766, Clemson, SC 29678. TEL 800-237-7967. FAX 803-654-7275. Ed. Paul G. Friedman. adv. contact: Rives Cheney. bk.rev. circ. 27,000. **Document type:** newsletter.
—CASDDS.

371.42 659.1   US   ISSN 0882-8288
HM263
PUBLIC RELATIONS CAREER DIRECTORY. (Subseries of: Career Advisor Series) 1986. biennial. $29.95 (softcover $17.95) (effective Mar. 1993). Gale Research Inc., 835 Penobscot Bldg., Detroit, MI 48226. TEL 313-961-2242. FAX 313-961-6083. Ed. Bradley J. Morgan. **Document type:** directory.
    Description: Contains advice on opportunities in corporate communications, international public relations, community affairs, media relations, and with financial and sports organizations.

OCCUPATIONS AND CAREERS

371.42 384.5   US   ISSN 1062-0737
PN1990.55
RADIO AND TELEVISION CAREER DIRECTORY. (Subseries of: Career Advisor Series) 1991. irreg., 2nd ed., 1993. $29.95 (softcover $17.95) (effective 1993). Gale Research Inc., 835 Penobscot Bldg., Detroit, MI 48226. TEL 313-961-2242. FAX 313-961-6083. Ed. Bradley J. Morgan. **Document type:** directory.
Description: Contains essays to help users find on-air and behind-the-scenes opportunities.

REAL TALK. see CHILDREN AND YOUTH — For

331.1   AT
REASONS FOR CHOOSING. irreg. Monash University, Course & Career Centre, Wellington Rd., Clayton, Vic. 3168, Australia. TEL 03-565-3150. FAX 03-565-3168. Ed. Lionel Parrott.
Description: Guide for students preparing to choose an employer and suitable employment.

371.42   US   ISSN 1068-199X
RECAREERING NEWSLETTER. 1992. m. $59. Publications Plus, Inc., 655 Rockland Rd., Ste. 7, Lake Bluff, IL 60044-1700. TEL 708-735-1981. FAX 708-735-0046. Ed. Sharon B. Schuster. bk.rev. **Document type:** newsletter.
Description: Covers career transitions, with particular reference to corporate downsizing and other workplace dislocations.

371.42 613   US
RECRUITMENT DIRECTIONS. 1985. 6/yr. $200. National Association for Healthcare Recruitment, Box 5769, Akron, OH 44372. FAX 216-867-1630. Ed. Karen Hart. adv.; bk.rev. circ. 1,600.

REHABILITATION COUNSELING BULLETIN. see HANDICAPPED

REPORT ON CORPORATE EDUCATIONAL SUPPORT. see EDUCATION — School Organization And Administration

331.1   US
RESUMES FOR EMPLOYMENT IN THE U S AND OVERSEAS. irreg., 3rd ed., 1988. $16.50. World Trade Academy Press, Inc., 50 E. 42nd St., Ste. 509, New York, NY 10017-5480. TEL 212-697-4999. FAX 212-949-4001.
Description: Contains general resumes and cover letter formats, with examples for jobs ranging from administrative assistant to video producer; sources of mailing lists to fit individual skills; requirements for work permits in foreign countries; tips for the interview and after.

REVIEW OF THE ECONOMY AND EMPLOYMENT. see BUSINESS AND ECONOMICS — Economic Situation And Conditions

331.1   FR   ISSN 1167-3656
RHONE METIERS. 1965. bi-m. 66 F. Chambre de Metiers du Rhone, 58 av. Marechal Foch, 69453 Lyon Cedex 06, France. TEL 72-43-43-00. FAX 72-43-43-01. Eds. M. Laroche, Nathalie Beroujon. adv.; bk.rev. circ. 25,000. **Document type:** bulletin.
Formerly: Carrefour des Metiers (ISSN 1167-3664)

331.1   US
ROCKY MOUNTAIN EMPLOYMENT NEWSLETTER. (In 4 editions: Colorado-Wyoming, Idaho-Montana, Arizona-New Mexico, Washington-Oregon) 1975. 18/yr. $105 for 4 edns. Intermountain Publishing and Referral Inc., 311-UB 14th St., Glenwood Springs, CO 81601-3949. TEL 303-945-8991. FAX 303-945-8991. Ed. H. Harrison. circ. 1,000. **Document type:** newsletter.
Description: Designed to assist in relocation to the Rocky Mountain area.

371.4   CN
S C W E A NEWSLETTER. 1981. 3/yr. Can.$20. (Saskatchewan Career - Work Education Association) Saskatchewan Teachers' Federation, Box 1108, Saskatoon, SK S7K 3N3, Canada. Ed. Anna Marie Donovan. **Document type:** newsletter.

331.1 500   US   ISSN 0146-5015
Q149.U5
SALARIES OF SCIENTISTS, ENGINEERS AND TECHNICIANS; a summary of salary surveys. 1965. biennial, 15th ed., 1991. $100. (Commission on Professionals in Science & Technology) C P S T Publications, 1500 Massachusetts Avenue, N.W., Ste. 831, Washington, DC 20005. TEL 202-223-6995. FAX 202-223-6444. Ed. Eleanor L. Babco. charts; illus.; stat. circ. 1,000. (also avail. in microfiche from CIS; reprint service avail. from UMI) **Indexed:** SRI.
—CCC.
Description: Provides information from more than 50 salary surveys on starting and advance salaries in industry, government and educational institutions, with breakouts by field, highest degree, years since first degree, age group, category of employment, work activity, type of employer, geographic area, academic rank, civil service grade and grade distribution, and level of responsibility.

371 658.3   US
SALARY INCREASE SURVEY REPORT. a. Hewitt Associates, 100 Half Day Rd., Lincolnshire, IL 60069-9971. TEL 708-295-5000.

371.42   SZ
SCHWEIZERISCHE ZEITSCHRIFT FUER KAUFMAENNISCHES BILDUNGSWESEN. (Text in French, German, Italian) 1906. 6/yr. 30 SFr. Guisanstr. 9, CH-9010 St. Gallen, Switzerland. TEL 071-302630. FAX 071-302619. Ed. Rolf Dubs. adv.; bk.rev. circ. 1,000. **Document type:** bulletin.

620   US   ISSN 0036-8768
TA157
SCIENTIFIC, ENGINEERING, TECHNICAL MANPOWER COMMENTS. 1963. 9/yr. $90. (Commission on Professionals in Science & Technology) C P S T Publications, 1500 Massachusetts Ave. N.W., Ste. 831, Washington, DC 20005. TEL 202-223-6995. Ed. Betty M. Vetter. bk.rev.; abstr.; bibl.; charts; stat.; index. circ. 1,500. (also avail. in microfilm from UMI; reprint service avail. from UMI) **Indexed:** Pers.Lit.
—UMI. CCC.
Description: Digest of current developments affecting recruitment, training and utilization of scientists, engineers, and technologists.

SILENT NEWS JOB BULLETIN; career opportunities working with deaf and hard-of-hearing people. see HANDICAPPED — Hearing Impaired

THE SIXTHFORMER'S GUIDE TO VISITING UNIVERSITIES AND COLLEGES (YEAR). see EDUCATION — Higher Education

371.42   AT   ISSN 1035-1116
SMART START. 1967. a. New Hobson's Press Pty. Ltd., 553 Elizabeth St., Surry Hills, N.S.W. 2010, Australia. Ed. C. Etteridge. adv.: page Aus.$1975; adv. contact: Colin Ritchie. circ. 15,000. **Document type:** consumer publication.
Former titles (until 1990): Jobs, Careers and Further Studies; Australian School Leavers Yearbook; (until 1981): Opportunities for School Leavers in Australia.

331.1 360   US
SOCIAL SERVICE JOBS. 1975. fortn. $118. Employment Listings for the Social Services, 10 Angelica Dr., Framingham, MA 01701. TEL 508-626-8644. FAX 508-626-8389. Ed. M.B. Sack. circ. 5,000. **Document type:** newsletter.
Description: National listings of current job openings for social workers, psychologists and counselors.

SPONSORSHIP FOR STUDENTS (YEAR); for all students seeking sponsorship for degree - H N D courses. see ADVERTISING AND PUBLIC RELATIONS

331.1   US   ISSN 0162-1068
SPOTLIGHT (BETHLEHEM); bi-weekly newsletter covering career planning, placement, and recruitment. 1977. fortn. $72 to non-members (includes Journal of Career Planning & Employment). National Association of Colleges and Employers, 62 Highland Ave., Bethlehem, PA 18017. TEL 610-868-1421. FAX 610-868-0208. Ed. Mimi Collins.
—BLDSC (8419.861215); UnCover.

STREET ARTISTS' NEWSLETTER. see ART

371.42   UK
STUDENT HELPBOOKS SERIES. irreg. price varies. (Careers Research and Advisory Council) Hobsons Publishing plc., Bateman St., Cambridge CB2 1LZ, England. TEL 01223-354551. FAX 01223-323154. TELEX 81546 HOBCAM G. (Orders to: Biblios Publishers' Distribution Service Ltd., Star Rd., Partridge Green, W. Sussex RH13 8LD, England. TEL 01403-710851. FAX 01403-711143)
Description: Advises students on career options and study skills.

371.42   GW
STUDIEREN NACH DEM STUDIUM. 1989. triennial. DM.25. Staufenbiel Institut fuer Berufs- und Ausbildungsplanung Koeln GmbH, Konrad-Adenauer-Ufer 33, 50668 Cologne, Germany. TEL 0221-124038. FAX 0221-124030. Ed. Joerg Staufenbiel. circ. 6,000. **Document type:** directory.

650 150   US   ISSN 0745-2489
CODEN: SUCSEY
SUCCESS (NEW YORK); the magazine for today's entrepreneurial mind. 1954. m. (10/yr.). $19.97 (foreign $29.97) (effective 1993). Lang Communications, 230 Park Ave., 7th Fl., New York, NY 10169-0014. TEL 212-551-9500. FAX 212-922-2919. (Subscr. to: Box 3038, Harlan, IA 51537-3038. TEL 800-234-7324) Ed. Scott DeGarmo. adv.; bk.rev.; charts; illus. circ. 475,000. (back issues avail.)
—BLDSC (8503.719500); CASDDS; Faxon; UMI; UnCover. CCC.
Formerly: Success Unlimited (ISSN 0039-4424)

331.1   US   ISSN 1064-6701
HF5382.5.U5
SUMMER JOBS (YEAR). 1951. a. $16.95. Peterson's Guides, Inc., 202 Carnegie Center, Box 2123, Princeton, NJ 08543-2123. TEL 800-338-3282. FAX 609-243-9150. Ed. Pat Beusterien. adv.; bk.rev. **Document type:** directory.
—BLDSC (8533.427000).
Formerly (until 1993): Summer Employment Directory of the United States (ISSN 0081-9352)
Description: Publishes names and addresses of employers and summer part-time jobs available to students and teachers. Includes 75,000 summer job openings at resorts, camps, parks, hotels, businesses, conference and training centers, ranches, restaurants and government.

331.1   US
SUMMER JOBS FOR (YEAR); Opportunities in the Federal Government. a. U.S. Office of Personnel Management, 1900 E. St., N.W., Washington, DC 20415. TEL 202-606-0597.

331.1   US   ISSN 0732-2631
SUPPLY AND DEMAND FOR SCIENTISTS AND ENGINEERS. 1977. irreg. $25. (Commission on Professionals in Science & Technology) C P S T Publications, 1500 Massachusetts Ave., N.W., Ste. 831, Washington, DC 20005. TEL 202-223-6995. FAX 202-223-6444. Ed. Betty M. Vetter. charts.
—CCC.

SUPPORTED EMPLOYMENT INFOLINES. see SOCIAL SERVICES AND WELFARE

SURVEY OF FINAL YEAR ACCOUNTING STUDENTS. see BUSINESS AND ECONOMICS — Accounting

790   US
T.G.I.F. CASTING NEWS. 1973. bi-w. $10. T.G.I.F. Enterprise, Box 1683, Hollywood, CA 90028. Ed. R.H. Smith, Jr. adv.; bk.rev.; film rev.; play rev. circ. 20,000.

TEACHER SUPPLY - DEMAND. see EDUCATION — School Organization And Administration

TEACHERS' GUIDE TO OVERSEAS TEACHING; a complete and comprehensive guide of English-language schools and colleges overseas. see EDUCATION — International Education Programs

TEACHING OPPORTUNITIES OVERSEAS - BULLETIN. see EDUCATION

OCCUPATIONS AND CAREERS 4955

371.42 600 US
TECHNOLOGY EDGE. 1992. 2/yr. American Passage Media Corp., 251 W. Harrison, Seattle, WA 95119. TEL 206-282-8111. FAX 206-282-1280. adv.: B&W page $12120; trim 8 1/4 x 10 7/8. circ. 230,000.

371.42 US ISSN 0279-9685
TOMORROW'S BUSINESS LEADER. 1969. q. membership. Future Business Leaders of America - Phi Beta Lambda, 2800 Shirlington Rd., Ste. 706, Arlington, VA 22206. Ed. Angela M. Angerosa. adv.; bk.rev. circ. 220,000.

TORONTO REGION'S TOP EMPLOYERS GUIDE. see *BUSINESS AND ECONOMICS*

TRAINING TODAY. see *EDUCATION*

371.42 910.09 US ISSN 1048-1079
G155.A1
TRAVEL AND HOSPITALITY CAREER DIRECTORY. (Subseries of: Career Advisor Series) 1989. irreg., 2nd ed., 1992. $29.95 (softcover $17.95) (effective 1992). Gale Research Inc., 835 Penobscot Bldg., Detroit, MI 48226. TEL 313-961-2242. FAX 313-961-6083. Ed. Bradley J. Morgan. **Document type:** directory.

371.42 US
TRENDS (LIBERTY); you and your future. 1985. a. Target Marketing, Inc., 5 Victory Ln., Ste. 101, Liberty, MO 64068. TEL 816-781-7557. FAX 816-792-3892. Ed. Lyle Kraft. adv. circ. 400,000.
 Description: Focuses on the opportunities available in vocational schools, two- and four-year colleges, and the military.

371.42 GW
UNI MAGAZIN PERSPEKTIVEN FUER BERUF UND ARBEITSMARKT. 1977. 7/yr. DM.45.50. (Bundesanstalt fuer Arbeit) Transmedia Projekt und Verlags GmbH, Kolpingstr. 18, 68165 Mannheim, Germany. TEL 0621-440000. FAX 0621-4400044. (Subscr. to: DSB Zeitschriften - Abonnements - Verwaltungsgesellschaft mbH, Postfach 1163, 74148 Neckarsulm, Germany) Ed. Manfred Hammes. circ. 210,000. (back issues avail.) **Document type:** bulletin.
 Formerly (until 1991): Uni Berufswahl-Magazin.

UNIQUE OPPORTUNITIES. see *MEDICAL SCIENCES*

371.42 AT ISSN 0312-1771
UNIVERSITY OF NEW SOUTH WALES. FACULTY HANDBOOKS: PROFESSIONAL STUDIES. a. Aus.$5. University of New South Wales, Sydney, N.S.W. 2052, Australia. TEL 61-2-385-2840. FAX 61-2-662-2163.

371.42 331 II
UTTAR PRADESH ROZGAR DIGEST; an employment oriented & consultative Hindi fortnightly. (Text in Hindi) 1978. fortn. Disha Publications Pvt. Ltd., P.B. No. 205, Bazar Gunj, Moradabad 244 001, India. TEL 28925. Ed. Vishwapati Sharma; Pub. Vikas Sharma. adv. contact: Umesh Chandra Vaish. circ. 36,439.

VACATURE; nieuws- en advertentieblad voor het onderwijs. see *EDUCATION*

371.42 US ISSN 1060-5630
Z7164.V6
VOCATIONAL CAREERS SOURCEBOOK. 1992. biennial. $75. Gale Research Inc., 835 Penobscot Bldg., Detroit, MI 48266. TEL 313-961-2242; 800-877-4253. FAX 313-961-6083. Eds. Kathleen M. Savage, Karin Hill. (also avail. in diskette format; magnetic tape)
 Description: Provides profiles describing 135 careers.

371.42 373.246 EI ISSN 0378-5068
LC1041
VOCATIONAL TRAINING. (Editions in Danish, Dutch, English, French, German, Greek, Italian, Portuguese, Spanish) 1977. 2/yr. 10 ECU. (European Center for the Development of Vocational Training) C E D E F O P, Bundesallee 22, 10717 Berlin, Germany. TEL 030-884120. FAX 030-88412222. TELEX 184163-EUCEN-D. circ. 10,000. **Indexed:** Tech.Educ.Abstr.
 —BLDSC (9250.480000); UnCover.
 Formerly: Vocational Training Information Bulletin.
 Description: Specialized source of reference for all those involved in vocational training (decision making, program planning, and administration).

371.42 EI
VOCATIONAL TRAINING INFORMATION BULLETIN. (Text in English) 3/yr. $15. Office for Official Publications of the European Communities, L-2985 Luxembourg, Luxembourg. (Dist. in the U.S. by: Unipub, 4611-F Assembly Dr., Lanham, MD 20706-4391. TEL 800-274-4888. FAX 301-459-0056)

371.426 US
VOCATIONAL TRAINING NEWS; the independent weekly report on employment, training & vocational education. 1970. w. $298 (foreign $363). Capitol Publications Inc., 1101 King St., Ste. 444, Alexandria, VA 22314. TEL 703-683-4100. FAX 703-739-6501. Ed. Jennifer Citta; Pub. Cindy Carter. charts; stat.; s-a. index. (looseleaf format) **Document type:** newsletter.
 —CCC.
 Formed by the 1984 merger of: Manpower and Vocational Education Weekly (ISSN 0047-5785); (1975-1984): Education and Work (ISSN 0194-231X)
 Description: Provides current reports on the federal Job Training Partnership Act and the Carl D. Perkins Vocational Education Act. Includes coverage of adult literacy, dropout prevention, and state education and training initiatives.

WASHINGTON (STATE). EMPLOYMENT SECURITY DEPARTMENT. AFFIRMATIVE ACTION INFORMATION. see *BUSINESS AND ECONOMICS — Labor And Industrial Relations*

331.1 310 US
WASHINGTON (STATE). EMPLOYMENT SECURITY DEPARTMENT. ANNUAL DEMOGRAPHIC INFORMATION. 1976. a. (in 13 vols.). $3 per vol. Employment Security Department, Labor Market and Economic Analysis Branch, LMEA Mailstop 6000, Box 9046, Olympia, WA 98507-9046. TEL 360-438-4800. FAX 360-438-4824. Ed. Jack Schillinger. circ. 400. **Indexed:** SRI. **Document type:** government publication.
 Description: Provides a demographic profile of the state of Washington and its counties, as divided into 13 regions.

WASHINGTON (STATE). EMPLOYMENT SECURITY DEPARTMENT. AREA WAGE SURVEYS. see *BUSINESS AND ECONOMICS — Labor And Industrial Relations*

331.11 US
WASHINGTON (STATE). EMPLOYMENT SECURITY DEPARTMENT. OCCUPATIONAL PROJECTIONS. (Avail. on MicroOLM diskette) a. Employment Security Department, Labor Market and Economic Analysis Branch, Box 9046, Olympia, WA 98507-9046. **Document type:** government publication.
 Description: Lists annual job openings and five-year projections on the basis of Occupational Employment Statistics surveys.

371.42 US ISSN 0740-8501
WASHINGTON COUNSELETTER. 1963. m. (Oct.-May). $32.95. Chronicle Guidance Publications, Inc., Box 1190, Moravia, NY 13118. TEL 315-497-0330. FAX 315-497-3359. bk.rev.; film rev. circ. 5,250. (looseleaf format) **Document type:** newsletter.

658.3 US ISSN 1041-3294
JK2687
THE WESTERN GOVERNMENTAL RESEARCHER. 1983. a. $35. Western Governmental Research Association, 10900 Los Alamitos Blvd. No. 201, Los Alamitos, CA 90720. TEL 310-785-6694. FAX 310-785-6697. Ed. Mel D. Powell. circ. 1,100 (paid). (back issues avail.) **Document type:** academic/scholarly publication.
 —UnCover.
 Formerly (until 1986): Western Governmental Research Journal (ISSN 1041-5165)

371.42 UK
WHAT DO GRADUATES DO? (YEAR). a. £5.95. (Association of Graduate Careers Advisory Services) Hobsons Publishing plc., Bateman St., Cambridge CB2 1LZ, England. TEL 01223-324551. FAX 01223-323154. TELEX 81546 HOBCAM G. (Orders to: Biblios Publishers' Distribution Services Ltd., Star Rd., Partridge Green, W. Sussex RH13 8LD, England. TEL 01403-710851. FAX 01403-711143) Ed. Jenny Jones. stat.
 Description: Lists first-degree graduates as to the type of work in which they are employed.

WHICH DEGREE. ARTS, HUMANITIES, LANGUAGES. see *HUMANITIES: COMPREHENSIVE WORKS*

WHICH DEGREE. ENGINEERING, TECHNOLOGY, GEOGRAPHY. see *ENGINEERING*

WHICH DEGREE. SOCIAL SCIENCES, BUSINESS, EDUCATION. see *SOCIAL SCIENCES: COMPREHENSIVE WORKS*

WHICH DEGREE. WHICH UNIVERSITY: UNIVERSITIES - COLLEGES. see *EDUCATION — Higher Education*

WHICH DEGREE IN BRITAIN (YEAR). see *EDUCATION — Guides To Schools And Colleges*

WINDS OF CHANGE; American Indian education & opportunity. see *ETHNIC INTERESTS*

371.42 GW ISSN 0341-339X
WIRTSCHAFT UND BERUFS - ERZIEHUNG; Zeitschrift fuer Berufsbildung. 1949. m. DM.169.20. W. Bertelsmann Verlag, Postfach 100633, 33506 Bielefeld, Germany. TEL 0521-9110126. FAX 0521-9110179. Ed. A. Kieslinger. **Document type:** academic/scholarly publication.
 —BLDSC (9325.413000). CCC.

371.42 GW
DIE WIRTSCHAFTSWISSENSCHAFTLICHEN FAKULTAETEN. 1977. biennial. DM.29.80. Staufenbiel Institut fuer Berufs- und Ausbildungsplanung Koeln GmbH, Konrad-Adenauer-Ufer 33, 50668 Cologne, Germany. TEL 0221-124038. FAX 0221-124030. Ed. Joerg Staufenbiel. circ. 13,000. **Document type:** directory.

WOMEN IN PUBLIC SERVICE BULLETIN. see *WOMEN'S INTERESTS*

371.42 US ISSN 0273-0022
HD4802
WORK (BOCA RATON). (Subseries of: S I R S Social Issues (ISSN 0740-3127)) 1972. a. price varies; a. supplement $17. Social Issues Resources Series, Box 2348, Boca Raton, FL 33427-2348. TEL 407-994-0079; 800-232-7477. FAX 407-994-4704. (looseleaf format; also avail. in microfiche; back issues avail.)
 Description: Reprints articles that explore the history and meaning of work.

640 338 US
WORK-AT-HOME SOURCEBOOK; how to find "at-home" work that's right for you. 1987. a. $16.95. Live Oak Publications, Box 2193, Boulder, CO 80306. TEL 303-447-1087. Ed. Lynie Arden. illus.; index. **Document type:** directory.
 Description: Provides names, addresses and complete information on over 1,000 companies that have work-at-home programs.

331.1 613.62 US ISSN 1043-1462
WORK PROGRAMS SPECIAL INTEREST SECTION NEWSLETTER. (Consists of 11 sections: Administration and Management; Developmental Disabilities; Education; Gerontology; Home & Community Health; Mental Health; Physical Disabilities; School System; Sensory Integration; Technology; Work Programs) 1987. q. $15. American Occupational Therapy Association, Inc., Box 31220, Bethesda, MD 20824-1220. TEL 301-652-2682. FAX 301-652-7711. **Document type:** newsletter.

WORK TIMES. see *BUSINESS AND ECONOMICS — Economic Situation And Conditions*

4956 OCCUPATIONS AND CAREERS — ABSTRACTING, BIBLIOGRAPHIES, STATISTICS

371.42 910.09 US ISSN 0895-3678
WORKAMPER NEWS; America's guide to working while camping. 1987. bi-m. $23. Workamper News, 201 Hiram Rd., Heber Springs, AR 72543. TEL 501-362-2637. FAX 501-362-2637. Ed. Greg Robus; Pub. Debbie Robus. adv.; bk.rev. circ. 20,000. **Document type:** newsletter.
Description: Provides information on seasonal and year-round employment opportunities in parks and resort areas.

371.42 362.6 US ISSN 0883-2714
WORKING AGE NEWSLETTER. 1984. bi-m. $35 (effective 1996). American Association Retired Persons, Worker Equity Initiative, 601 E St., N.W., Washington, DC 20049. TEL 202-662-4842. Ed. Ronald Allen. circ. 66,000. **Document type:** newsletter.
Description: Covers the latest employment facts and demographic trends affecting employees age 50 and over. Especially pertinent to employers with older employees and to benefits, pension, and personnel directors, specialists in aging, and policy makers.

371.42 910.09 UK
WORKING HOLIDAYS (YEAR). 1952. a. £8.99 (effective 1995). British Council, 10 Spring Gardens, London SW1A 2BN, England. circ. 12,000.
Description: Complete international guide to seasonal job opportunities.

658.3 US
WORKING OPTIONS. 1981. m. $45. Association of Part-Time Professionals, Crescent Plaza, Ste. 216, 7700 Leesburg Pike, Falls Church, VA 22043. TEL 703-734-7975. circ. 1,500. (back issues avail.) **Document type:** newsletter.
Former titles: Part-Time Professional & Association of Part-Time Professionals. National Newsletter (ISSN 0739-2931)
Description: Trends in part-time employment, employer policies, employee profiles and job search information.

354.689 ZA ISSN 0514-5457
ZAMBIA. EDUCATIONAL AND OCCUPATIONAL ASSESSMENT SERVICE. ANNUAL REPORT. a. K.200. Zambia Government Printing Department, P.O. Box 30136, Lusaka, Zambia. stat. **Document type:** government publication.
Description: Annual report on the selection process of talent for Zambia's secondary schools.

ZENTRALER BEWERBERANZEIGER MARKT UND CHANCE. see SOCIAL SERVICES AND WELFARE

OCCUPATIONS AND CAREERS — Abstracting, Bibliographies, Statistics

AMERICAN SALARIES AND WAGES SURVEY. see BUSINESS AND ECONOMICS — Abstracting, Bibliographies, Statistics

ARKANSAS. EMPLOYMENT SECURITY DEPARTMENT. STATISTICAL REVIEW. see BUSINESS AND ECONOMICS — Abstracting, Bibliographies, Statistics

371.42 AT ISSN 1034-0033
AUSTRALIA. BUREAU OF STATISTICS. JOB VACANCIES AND OVERTIME, AUSTRALIA. 1989. q. Aus.$13 per no. Australian Bureau of Statistics, P.O. Box 10, Belconnen, A.C.T. 2616, Australia. **Document type:** government publication.
Formed by the merger of (1981-1989): Overtime, Australia (ISSN 1031-1106); (1977-1989): Job Vacancies, Australia (ISSN 1031-0371)
Description: Estimates the number of job vacancies, job vacancy rates, average hours of overtime worked and percentages of employees working overtime.

371.42 331.1 US ISSN 0276-0355
Z7164.V6
CHRONICLE CAREER INDEX. a. $15.68. Chronicle Guidance Publications, Inc., Box 1190, Moravia, NY 13118. TEL 315-497-0330. FAX 315-497-3359. circ. 6,150.
Former titles: Chronicle Career Index Annual (ISSN 0190-4663); Career Index (ISSN 0576-7296)

331.1 317.2 MX
CLASIFICACION MEXICANA DE OCUPACIONES. 1990. irreg. Instituto Nacional de Estadistica, Geografia e Informatica, Secretaria de Programacion y Presupuesto, Av. Prol. Heroe de Nacozari 2301 S., Puerta 11, Acceso, 20270 Aguascalientes, Ags., Mexico. TEL 91-49-18-19-48. FAX 91-491-80739.

331.1 CN
CLERICAL SALARY SURVEY & EMPLOYMENT PRACTICES (YEAR). a. Can.$350 to non-members; members Can.$300. Board of Trade of Metropolitan Toronto, P.O. Box 60, 1 First Canadian Place, Toronto, ON M5X 1C1, Canada. TEL 416-366-6811.

331.1 CN
DATA PROCESSION SALARY SURVEY & EMPLOYMENT PRACTICES (YEAR). a. Can.$350 to non-members; members Can.$300. Board of Trade of Metropolitan Toronto, P.O. Box 60, 1 First Canadian Place, Toronto, ON M5X 1C1, Canada. TEL 416-366-6811.

EMPLOYMENT AND PAYROLLS IN WASHINGTON STATE BY COUNTY AND INDUSTRY; industries covered by the Employment Security Act and federal employment covered by Title 5, U.S.C. 85. see BUSINESS AND ECONOMICS — Abstracting, Bibliographies, Statistics

331.1 HK
EMPLOYMENT AND VACANCIES STATISTICS IN: WHOLESALE, RETAIL AND IMPORT - EXPORT TRADES, RESTAURANTS AND HOTELS. (Text in English) a. price varies. (Census and Statistics Department) Government Publication Centre, G.P.O. Building, Ground Floor, Connaught Place, Hong Kong, Hong Kong. (Subscr. to: Director of Information Services, Information Services Dept., 1 Battery Path, G-F, Central, Hong Kong) Ed.Bd.

331 HK
EMPLOYMENT AND VACANCY STATISTICS IN: TRANSPORT, STORAGE AND COMMUNICATION FINANCING, INSURANCE, REAL ESTATE AND BUSINESS SERVICES, COMMUNITY, SOCIAL AND PERSONAL SERVICES. (Text in English) a. price varies. (Census and Statistics Department) Government Publication Centre, G.P.O. Building, Ground Floor, Connaught Place, Hong Kong, Hong Kong. (Subscr. to: Director of Information Services, Information Services Dept., 1 Battery Path, G-F, Central, Hong Kong) Ed.Bd.

331.1 690 HK
EMPLOYMENT, WAGES AND MATERIAL PRICES IN THE CONSTRUCTION INDUSTRY. (Text in English) q. HK.$12. (Census and Statistics Department) Government Publication Centre, G.P.O. Bldg., Ground Fl., Connaught Place, Hong Kong, Hong Kong. (Subscr. to: Director of Information Services, Information Services Dept., 1 Battery Path, G-F, Central, Hong Kong) Ed.Bd.

331.1 CN
EXECUTIVE COMPENSATION SURVEY (YEAR). a. Can.$450 to non-members; members Can.$370. Board of Trade of Metropolitan Toronto, P.O. Box 60, 1 First Canadian Place, Toronto, ON M5X 1C1, Canada. TEL 416-366-6811.

331.1 312 JA ISSN 0911-8527
JAPAN. MINISTRY OF HEALTH AND WELFARE. STATISTICS AND INFORMATION DEPARTMENT. REPORT ON SURVEY OF OCCUPATIONAL STATISTICS ON VITAL EVENTS. Key Title: Shokugyo, Sangyobetsu Jinko Dotai Tokei. (Text in English, Japanese) 1951. quinquennial. 5665 Yen. Ministry of Health and Welfare, Statistics and Information Department - Koseisho Daijin Kanbo Tokei Johobu, 7-3 Ichigaya-Honmura-cho, Shinjuku-ku, Tokyo 162, Japan. TEL 03-3260-3181. FAX 03-3269-8824. (Subscr. to: Health & Welfare Statistics Association, 5-13-14 Ropponji, Minato-ku, Tokyo, Japan. TEL 03-3586-3361. FAX 03-3584-4710) **Document type:** government publication.

LABOR FORCE AND EMPLOYMENT IN WASHINGTON STATE. see BUSINESS AND ECONOMICS — Abstracting, Bibliographies, Statistics

331.1 CN
MIDDLE MANAGEMENT & PROFESSIONAL COMPENSATION SURVEY (YEAR). a. Can.$450 to non-members; members Can.$370. Board of Trade of Metropolitan Toronto, P.O. Box 60, 1 First Canadian Place, Toronto, ON M5X 1C1, Canada. TEL 416-366-6811.

MONASH UNIVERSITY. COURSE & CAREER CENTRE. SURVEY OF GRADUATE STARTING SALARIES AS OF 30 APRIL (YEAR). see BUSINESS AND ECONOMICS — Abstracting, Bibliographies, Statistics

NETHERLANDS. CENTRAAL BUREAU VOOR DE STATISTIEK. STATISTIEK VAN HET BEROEPSONDERWIJS: TECHNISCH EN NAUTISCH ONDERWIJS. see EDUCATION — Abstracting, Bibliographies, Statistics

NETHERLANDS. CENTRAAL BUREAU VOOR DE STATISTIEK. STATISTIEK VAN HET HOGER BEROEPSONDERWIJS: AGRARISCH ONDERWIJS. see EDUCATION — Abstracting, Bibliographies, Statistics

371.42 310 UK
STATISTICAL INFORMATION PACKAGE. 1979. q. £195 (effective 1994-1995). C S U (Publications) Ltd. (Subsidiary of: Higher Education Careers Services Unit), Armstrong House, Oxford Rd., Manchester M1 7ED, England. TEL 0161-236-8541. FAX 0161-236-9227. circ. 13,000.
Description: Reviews trends in the U.K. graduate-employment market. Reviews salaries, covers first destination by institution, and forecasts the number of graduates over the following three years.

371.42 UK
STATISTICAL QUARTERLY; Higher Education Unit Services unit salary and vacancy survey. 1979. q. £75 (effective 1994-1995). C S U (Publications) Ltd. (Subsidiary of: Higher Education Careers Services Unit), Armstrong House, Oxford Rd., Manchester M1 7ED, England. TEL 0161-237-5409. FAX 0161-236-9227. Ed. Colin Lawton. circ. 750. **Document type:** trade publication.

331.11 362.5 US
WASHINGTON (STATE). EMPLOYMENT SECURITY DEPARTMENT. MONTHLY JOB SERVICE STATISTICS. m. free. Employment Security Department, Labor Market and Economic Analysis Branch, Box 9046, Olympia, WA 98507-9046. charts. **Document type:** government publication.
Description: Supplies Washington State Job Service data on claims, benefits, and payments for state and county. Includes job application, opening, placement, and referral information.

331.11 US
WASHINGTON (STATE). EMPLOYMENT SECURITY DEPARTMENT. OCCUPATIONAL PROFILES. (Each vol. surveys one-third of the states industries and is published on a 3-year cycle.) a. $45 for complete set (prices for individual counties vary). Employment Security Department, Labor Market and Economic Analysis Branch, Box 9046, Olympia, WA 98507-9046. TEL 360-438-4801. **Document type:** government publication.
Description: Provides wage and salary employment information by occupation for selected manufacturing and nonmanufacturing industries in the state of Washington by county.

WASHINGTON (STATE). EMPLOYMENT SECURITY DEPARTMENT. WEEKLY INSURED UNEMPLOYMENT REPORT. see INSURANCE — Abstracting, Bibliographies, Statistics

WASHINGTON LABOR MARKET. see BUSINESS AND ECONOMICS — Abstracting, Bibliographies, Statistics

OCEANOGRAPHY

see Earth Sciences–Oceanography

OFFICE EQUIPMENT AND SERVICES

see Business and Economics–Office Equipment and Services

ONCOLOGY

see Medical Sciences–Oncology

OPHTHALMOLOGY AND OPTOMETRY

see Medical Sciences–Ophthalmology and Optometry

OPTICS

see Physics–Optics

ORGANIC CHEMISTRY

see Chemistry–Organic Chemistry

ORIENTAL STUDIES

see also History–History of Asia; Linguistics

950   II   ISSN 0304-6214
DS401
A I I S QUARTERLY NEWSLETTER. (Text in English) 1974. q. American Institute of Indian Studies, D-176 Defence Colony, New Delhi 110024, India. Ed. P.R. Mehendiratta. adv.; bk.rev.; bibl.; illus. circ. 1,500.

950   II
A S H PUBLICATION SERIES. (Text in English) irreg., vol.2, 1992. (Association of Studies on Himalayas) Shree Almora Book Depot, Mall Rd., Almora, U.P. 263 601, India. **Document type:** monograph series.
   Description: Explores the civilization of the Himalaya Mountains region.

A S S E S S. see HISTORY — History Of Asia

956   GW   ISSN 0173-1904
ABHANDLUNGEN DES DEUTSCHEN PALAESTINAVEREINS. 1969. irreg., vol.19, 1994. price varies. Harrassowitz Verlag, Taunusstr. 14, 65183 Wiesbaden, Germany. TEL 0611-530-0. FAX 0611-530570. TELEX 4186135. (Subscr. to: Postfach 2929, 65019 Wiesbaden, Germany) Eds. Siegfried Mittmann, Manfred Weippert. **Document type:** monograph series.

950   GW   ISSN 0567-4980
ABHANDLUNGEN FUER DIE KUNDE DES MORGENLANDES. (Text in English, French, and German) irreg., vol.51, no.2, 1995. price varies. (Deutsche Morgenlaendische Gesellschaft) Franz Steiner Verlag Wiesbaden GmbH, Birkenwaldstr. 44, 70191 Stuttgart, Germany. TEL 0711-2582-0. FAX 0711-2582390. (Subscr. to: Postfach 101061, 70009 Stuttgart, Germany) Ed. Tilman Nagel. (also avail. in microfiche from BHP; reprint service avail. from KTO) **Document type:** monograph series.

950   LE   ISSN 0002-3973
AS595.A6
AL-ABHATH. (Text in Arabic and English) 1948. a. $15. American University of Beirut, P.O. Box 1786, Beirut, Lebanon. FAX 002124781995. TELEX 20801 LE. Ed. Ramzi Baalbaki. bk.rev.; bibl. circ. 1,000. **Indexed:** Amer.Hist.& Life, Bibl.Ling., Hist.Abstr., Numis.Lit. **Document type:** academic/scholarly publication.

950   BE   ISSN 0065-0382
PJ3001
ABR-NAHRAIN. (Supplement avail.) (Text in English, French, German) 1959. a. 1200 BEF (effective 1994). (University of Melbourne, Department of Classical and Near Eastern Studies, AT) Editions Peeters s.p.r.l., Bondgenotlenlaan 153, 3000 Leuven, Belgium. TEL 32-16-235170. FAX 32-16-228500. Ed. G. Bunnens. **Indexed:** Bibl.Ling. **Document type:** academic/scholarly publication.
—BLDSC (0549.749300).

950   BE   ISSN 0065-0390
ABR-NAHRAIN. SUPPLEMENTS. 1964. irreg., vol.3, 1992. price varies. (University of Melbourne, Department of Middle Eastern Studies, AT) Editions Peeters s.p.r.l., Bondgenotlenlaan 153, 3000 Leuven, Belgium. TEL 32-16-235170. FAX 32-16-228500. (back issues avail.) **Indexed:** M.L.A. **Document type:** monograph series.

ABSTRACTA IRANICA. see HISTORY — Abstracting, Bibliographies, Statistics

950   HU   ISSN 0001-6446
DS1
ACADEMIA SCIENTIARUM HUNGARICA. ACTA ORIENTALIA. (Text mainly in English, occasionally in French, German, Russian) 1950. 4/yr. $84 (effective 1992). (Magyar Tudomanyos Akademia) Akademiai Kiado, Publishing House of the Hungarian Academy of Sciences, P.O. Box 245, H-1519 Budapest, Hungary. TEL 181-2134. FAX 166-6466. TELEX 22-6228 AKNYO H. Ed. Alice Sarkozy. adv.; bk.rev.; illus.; index. **Indexed:** M.L.A., Old Test.Abstr. —CCC.
   Description: Provides an international forum for original papers in the field of oriental studies, including Turkish, Mongolian, Manchurian, Chinese, Tibetan, Indian, Iranian, and Semitic philology, literature and history.

ACADEMIA SINICA. INSTITUTE OF ETHNOLOGY. BULLETIN. see ANTHROPOLOGY

950   JA   ISSN 0567-7254
DS12
ACTA ASIATICA. (Text in English) 1961. s-a. 8000 Yen. Toho Gakkai - Institute of Eastern Culture, 4-1, Nishi-Kanda 2-chome, Chiyoda-ku, Tokyo 101, Japan. TEL 03-3262-7221. FAX 03-3262-7227. Ed. Jikido Takasaki. bibl. circ. 1,000. **Indexed:** Anthropol.Lit., M.L.A. **Document type:** academic/scholarly publication.
—Faxon; UnCover.
   Description: Introduces recent academic contributions by leading Japanese scholars in the field of Asian and Japanese studies.

950   DK   ISSN 0001-6438
PJ1
ACTA ORIENTALIA. (Text in English, French or German) 1922. a. DKK 420 (effective 1996). (Oriental Societies of Denmark, Finland, Norway and Sweden) Munksgaard International Publishers Ltd., 35 Noerre Soegade, P.O Box 2148, DK-1016 Copenhagen K, Denmark. TEL 33-127030. FAX 33-129387. Ed. Per Kvaerne. bk.rev.; illus. circ. 500. (reprint service avail. from ISI,KTO) **Indexed:** Bibl.Ling., Curr.Cont., M.L.A., Mid.East: Abstr.& Ind.
—UnCover. CCC.
   Refereed Serial

950   GW   ISSN 0720-9061
AEGYPTEN UND ALTES TESTAMENT; Studien in Geschichte, Kultur und Religion Aegypten und des Alten Testaments. 1979. irreg., vol.27, 1994. price varies. Harrassowitz Verlag, Taunusstr. 14, 65183 Wiesbaden, Germany. TEL 0611-530-0. FAX 0611-530570. TELEX 4186135. (Subscr. to: Postfach 2929, 65019 Wiesbaden, Germany) Ed. Manfred Goerg. **Document type:** monograph series.

956   GW   ISSN 0568-0476
AEGYPTOLOGISCHE ABHANDLUNGEN. 1960. irreg., vol.55, 1994. price varies. Harrassowitz Verlag, Taunusstr. 14, 65183 Wiesbaden, Germany. TEL 0611-530-0. FAX 0611-530570. TELEX 4186135. (Subscr. to: Postfach 2929, 65019 Wiesbaden, Germany) Ed. Ursula Roessler-Koehler. **Document type:** monograph series.

950   GW   ISSN 0931-282X
AETAS MANJURICA. 1987. irreg., vol. 4, 1994. price varies. Harrassowitz Verlag, Taunusstr. 14, 65183 Wiesbaden, Germany. TEL 0611-530-0. FAX 0611-530570. (Subscr. to: Postfach 2929, 65019 Wiesbaden, Germany) Ed.Bd. **Document type:** monographic series.

950   GW   ISSN 0170-3196
AETHIOPISTISCHE FORSCHUNGEN. (Text in English and German) irreg., vol.42, 1995. price varies. Harrassowitz Verlag, Taunusstr. 14, 65183 Wiesbaden, Germany. TEL 0611-530-0. FAX 0611-530570. (Subscr. to: Postfach 2929, 65019 Wiesbaden, Germany) Ed. Ernst Hammerschmidt. **Document type:** monographic series.

AFRO-ASIA. see HISTORY

950   GW   ISSN 0568-4447
AKADEMIE DER WISSENSCHAFTEN UND DER LITERATUR, MAINZ. ORIENTALISCHE KOMMISSION. VEROEFFENTLICHUNGEN. (Text in French and German) irreg., vol.40, 1994. price varies. Harrassowitz Verlag, Taunusstr. 14, 65183 Wiesbaden, Germany. TEL 0611-530-0. FAX 0611-530570. **Document type:** monographic series.

956   GW   ISSN 0342-0329
AKTUELLER INFORMATIONSDIENST MODERNER ORIENT/ORIGINAL NEWS AND COMMENTS FROM MIDDLE EASTERN NEWSPAPERS. (Text in English, French, German) 1975. m. DM.120. Deutsches Orient-Institut, Mittelweg 150, 20148 Hamburg, Germany. TEL 040-441481. FAX 040-441484. Ed.Bd. adv. circ. 160. **Document type:** abstracting/indexing.

950   II   ISSN 0970-0994
ALIGARH JOURNAL OF ORIENTAL STUDIES. (Text in English; summaries in Arabic, Persian, Sanskrit) 1984. s-a. Rs.100($20) Viveka Publications, 3-39 Samad Rd., Aligarh 202 001, U.P., India. TEL 0571-24681. Ed. Umesh Chandra Sharma. adv.: page Rs.700. bk.rev. circ. 500. (back issues avail.) **Indexed:** Bibl.Ling. **Document type:** academic/scholarly publication.
   Description: Publishes original contributions on all areas represented in the All-India Oriental Conference.

950   NE   ISSN 0065-6593
ALTBABYLONISCHE BRIEFE IM UMSCHRIFT UND UEBERSETZUNG. 1964. irreg., vol.13, 1993. price varies. E.J. Brill, P.O. Box 9000, 2300 PA Leiden, Netherlands. TEL 31-71-5353500. FAX 31-71-5317532. TELEX 39296 BRILL NL. (In N. America: E.J. Brill, 24 Hudson St., Kinderhook, NY 12106. TEL 800-962-4406. FAX 518-758-1959) Ed. F.R. Kraus. (back issues avail.) **Document type:** monographic series.
   Description: Publishes ancient Babylonian letters from museums and collections throughout the world, with translations and scholarly commentary.
   Refereed Serial

DAS ALTERTUM. see CLASSICAL STUDIES

ALTORIENTALISCHE FORSCHUNGEN. see HISTORY — History Of The Near East

495.1 951   US
AMERICAN JOURNAL OF CHINESE STUDIES. 1984. s-a. $20. American Association for Chinese Studies, 300 Bricker Hall, Ohio State Univerity, Columbus, OH 43210. Ed. Wen Lang Li. adv.; bk.rev. circ. 500. **Document type:** academic/scholarly publication.
   Former titles: Journal of Chinese Studies; American Association for Chinese Studies. Bulletin; American Association for Chinese Studies Newsletter; American Association of Teachers of Chinese Language and Culture. Newsletter.

950   US   ISSN 0065-9541
AMERICAN ORIENTAL SERIES. 1925. irreg. price varies. American Oriental Society, Harlan Hatcher Graduate Library, University of Michigan, Ann Arbor, MI 48109-1205. TEL 313-747-4760. (Subscr. to: Eisenbrauns, Box 275, Winona Lake, IN 46590. TEL 219-269-2011) bk.rev. (reprint service avail. from KTO)

ORIENTAL STUDIES

950 US ISSN 0003-0279
PJ2
AMERICAN ORIENTAL SOCIETY. JOURNAL. (Text in English, French and German) 1842. q. $65. American Oriental Society, Harlan Hatcher Graduate Library, University of Michigan, Ann Arbor, MI 48109-1205. TEL 313-747-4760. Ed. Edwin Gerow. adv.; bk.rev.; charts; illus.; index. circ. 2,300. (also avail. in microform from UMI,PMC; microfiche from IDC; back issues avail.; reprint service avail. from UMI) **Indexed:** Amer.Bibl.Slavic & E.Eur.Stud., Arts & Hum.Cit.Ind., Bibl.Ling., Curr.Cont., Hum.Ind., Ind.Bk.Rev.Hum., New Test.Abstr., Numis.Lit., Old Test.Abstr., Rel.& Theol.Abstr. (1973-), Rel.Ind.One. **Document type:** academic/scholarly publication.
●Also available online. Vendor(s): University Microfilms International.
—BLDSC (4689.390000); Faxon; Genuine Article; SWETS; UMI; UnCover.

950 US ISSN 0003-097X
DS101
AMERICAN SCHOOLS OF ORIENTAL RESEARCH. BULLETIN. Abbreviated title: B A S O R. 1919. q. $42 to individuals (foreign $53); institutions $57 (foreign $68). (American Schools of Oriental Research) Scholars Press, Box 15399, Atlanta, GA 30333-0399. TEL 404-727-2320. FAX 404-727-2348. Eds. Albert Leonard, Jr., James M. Weinstein. bk.rev.; charts; illus.; index. circ. 2,100. (also avail. in microform from UMI; reprint service avail. from SWZ,UMI) **Indexed:** A.I.C.P., Anthropol.Lit., Bibl.Ling., New Test.Abstr., Numis.Lit., Old Test.Abstr., Rel.& Theol.Abstr. (1968-), Rel.Ind.One, Rel.Per. **Document type:** academic/scholarly publication.
—BLDSC (2392.700000); Faxon; Genuine Article; SWETS; UMI; UnCover.
Description: Presents technical reports of original research and ASOR-sponsored excavations, and reviews of current scholarship in the field.

951 930.1 US ISSN 0361-6029
DS101
AMERICAN SCHOOLS OF ORIENTAL RESEARCH. NEWSLETTER. Variant title: A S O R Newsletter. 1938. q. $20 to individuals (foreign $25); institutions $25 (foreign $30). (American Schools of Oriental Research (ASOR)) Scholars Press, Box 15399, Atlanta, GA 30333-0399. TEL 404-727-2320. FAX 404-727-2348. Ed. Victor Matthews. bibl. circ. 1,500. (also avail. in microform from UMI; reprint service avail. from UMI) **Indexed:** A.I.C.P., Anthropol.Lit., Rel.Ind.One. **Document type:** newsletter.
—BLDSC (0856.457000); UMI.
Formerly (until 1966): Archeological Newsletter.
Description: Intended as a means of communicating news to members of the American Schools of Oriental Research (ASOR) and others interested in ASOR's activities in the Middle East.

950 VC
ANALECTA ORIENTALIA. 1931. irreg., no.54, 1994. price varies. (Pontificio Istituto Biblico, Facolta degli Studi per l'Oriente Antico - Pontifical Biblical Institute, Faculty of Ancient Near Eastern Studies) Biblical Institute Press, Piazza della Pilotta 35, 00187 Rome, Italy. TEL 39-6-678-15-67. FAX 39-6-678-05-88.
Description: Devoted to the languages, literatures and history of ancient Near Eastern non-biblical cultures.

ANATOLIAN STUDIES. see *ARCHAEOLOGY*

939.4 US
ANCIENT NEAR EAST: HISTORY AND PHILOLOGY. 1993. irreg. price varies. Nova Science Publishers, Inc., 6080 Jericho Tpke., Ste. 207, Commack, NY 11725-2808. TEL 516-499-3103. **Document type:** monographic series.
Previously announced as: Journal of Ancient Near East: History and Philology.

950 US ISSN 0897-6074
DS41
ANCIENT NEAR EASTERN SOCIETY. JOURNAL. Abbreviated title: J A N E S. 1968. a. $15 to individuals; institutions $25. Ancient Near Eastern Society, Jewish Theological Seminary, 3080 Broadway, New York, NY 10027-4649. TEL 212-678-8847. FAX 212-678-8947. Eds. Edward L. Greenstein, David Marcus. adv.; illus. circ. 400. (also avail. in microfilm; back issues avail.) **Indexed:** Anthropol.Lit., Bibl.Ling., Mid.East: Abstr.& Ind., Old Test.Abstr., Rel.& Theol.Abstr. (1973-), Rel.Ind.One. **Document type:** academic/scholarly publication.
—BLDSC (4697.740000); UMI.
Formerly (until 1982): Columbia University. Ancient Near Eastern Society. Journal (ISSN 0010-2016)
Description: Presents articles on all aspects of the ancient Near East.

954 913 NP
ANCIENT NEPAL. (Text in English and Nepali) 1967. bi-m. Rs.10. Department of Archaeology, Kathmandu, Nepal. TEL 215358. Ed. Khadga Man Shrestha. circ. 500. **Indexed:** Avery Ind.Archit.Per. **Document type:** academic/scholarly publication.

950 FR ISSN 0980-5842
ANNALES DU LEVANT. 1985. a. (Centre Interdisciplinaire de Recherche sur les Relations Internationales au Moyen-Orient) Presses Universitaires de Rennes, 2 rue du Doyen D. Leroy, 35044 Rennes Cedex, France. TEL 99-54-66-35. FAX 99-33-07-95. (Co-sponsor: Equipe de Recherche sur le Systeme Industriel) **Indexed:** Int.Polit.Sci.Abstr.
Description: Studies the economic and political relationships between industrialized and developing countries in the Middle East

956 297 UA ISSN 0570-1716
ANNALES ISLAMOLOGIQUES. (Supplement avail.: Bulletin Critique des Annales Islamologiques (ISSN 0259-7373)) (Text in Arabic, English, French) 1954. a., vol.27, 1994. £E180 (overseas 300 F.). Institut Francais d'Archeologie Orientale du Caire, P.O. Box 11562 Kasr-el-Aini, 37 Sharia Sheikh Aly Youssef, Mounira, Cairo, Egypt. TEL 20-2-3548245. FAX 20-2-3544635. (Dist. by: Boustany's Arab Publishing House, 29 Faggalah St., 11271 Cairo, Egypt. TEL 20-2-4177915. FAX 20-2-3404905; In France: Imprimerie Nationale - D A C F, 27 rue de la Convention, 75732 Paris Cedex 15, France. TEL 33-1-40583292. FAX 33-1-40583057) circ. 800. (back issues avail.) **Indexed:** Bibl.Ling. **Document type:** academic/scholarly publication.
Description: Research of history, archaeology and linguistics from the beginning of Islam to the 19th century.

297 UA ISSN 0254-282X
ANNALES ISLAMOLOGIQUES. SUPPLEMENT. Key Title: Supplement aux Annales Islamologiques. Variant title: Cahiers des Annales Islamologiques. (Text mainly in French, occasionally in English) 1981. irreg., approx a., vol.14, 1992. price varies. Institut Francais d'Archeologie Orientale du Caire, P.O. Box 11562 Kasr-el-Aini, 37 Sharia Sheikh Aly Youssef, Mounira, Cairo, Egypt. TEL 20-2-3548245. FAX 20-2-3544635. (Dist. by: Boustany's Arab Publishing House, 29 Faggalah St., 11271 Cairo, Egypt. TEL 20-2-4177915. FAX 20-2-3404905; In France: Imprimerie Nationale - D A C F, 27 rue de la Convention, 75732 Paris Cedex 15, France. TEL 33-1-40583292. FAX 33-1-40583057) (back issues avail.) **Document type:** monographic series.
Description: Scholarly studies of historical topics, texts and inscriptions relating to Islamic Egypt and neighboring regions.

950 II
ANNALS OF ORIENTAL RESEARCH. (Text in English or various Indian languages) a. University of Madras, c/o Director, Publications Division, Madras 600005, India. TEL 91-44-568778. FAX 91-44-566693. **Indexed:** Bibl.Ling.

068.549 954 BG
ANNUAL GENERAL MEETING OF THE ASIATIC SOCIETY OF BANGLADESH: REPORT OF THE GENERAL SECRETARY. (Text in English) a. Asiatic Society of Bangladesh, 5 Old Secretariat Rd., Ramna, Dhaka, Bangladesh. TEL 2-866582. **Document type:** academic/scholarly publication.

ARAB STRUGGLE. see *HISTORY* — History Of The Near East

953 NE ISSN 0570-5398
PJ6001
ARABICA; revue d'etudes arabes. (Text in Arabic, English, French, German) 1954. 3/yr. fl.140($90) to individuals; institutions fl.215($139) (effective 1996). (Centre National de la Recherche Scientifique, FR) E.J. Brill, P.O. Box 9000, 2300 PA Leiden, Netherlands. TEL 31-71-5353500. FAX 31-71-5317532. TELEX 39296 BRILL NL. E-mail: ejborders@ejbrill.com. (In N. America: E.J. Brill, 24 Hudson St., Kinderhook, NY 12106. TEL 800-962-4406. FAX 518-758-1959) Ed. M. Arkoun. bk.rev.; bibl.; index. (also avail. in microform from SWZ; reprint service avail. from SWZ) **Indexed:** Amer.Hist.& Life, Bibl.Ling., Hist.Abstr., M.L.A., Numis.Lit., Per.Islam. (1991-). **Document type:** academic/scholarly publication.
—Faxon; SWETS; UnCover. CCC.
Description: Studies, documents and notes on the language, literature, history and civilization of the Arab world, with emphasis on multidisciplinary studies of ancient and contemporary problems concerning Arab societies.
Refereed Serial

950 FR ISSN 0044-8613
ARCHIPEL. (Text in English, French, Indonesian) 1971. s-a. 210 F. Association Archipel, Ehess Bureau 732, 54 bd. Raspail, 75270 Paris Cedex 06, France. FAX 45-44-93-11. Ed.Bd. adv.; bk.rev.; bibl.; charts; illus. circ. 1,000. **Indexed:** Amer.Hist.& Life, Bibl.Ling., Bull.Signal., E.I., Hist.Abstr., Int.Polit.Sci.Abstr.
—UnCover.

950 960 NE ISSN 0044-8699
DS1
ARCHIV ORIENTALNI/ORIENTAL ARCHIVES; quarterly journal of African, Asian and Latin-American studies. (Text in English, French, German, Russian) 1929. q. fl.309 (effective 1996). (Czech Academy of Sciences, Oriental Institute, XR) John Benjamins Publishing Co., Amsteldijk 44, P.O. Box 75577, 1070 AN Amsterdam, Netherlands. TEL 31-20-6738156. FAX 31-20-6792956. (In N. America: Box 27519, Philadelphia, PA 19118-0519. TEL 215-836-1200. FAX 215-836-1204) Eds. Blahoslav Hruska, Lubic Obuchova. bk.rev.; bibl.; charts; illus. circ. 1,200. (also avail. in microfiche from IDC; back issues avail.; reprint service avail. from SCH) **Indexed:** A.I.C.P., Amer.Hist.& Life, Bibl.Ling., E.I., Hist.Abstr., M.L.A., Mid.East: Abstr.& Ind., Old Test.Abstr., Per.Islam. (1991-). **Document type:** academic/scholarly publication.
—BLDSC (1621.570000); SWETS; UnCover.
Description: Original papers, review articles and book reviews pertaining to the history, economy, culture and society of African, Asian and Latin American countries.

956 GW ISSN 0724-8822
DS327
ARCHIVUM EURASIAE MEDII AEVI. (Text in English, French) 1975. a. price varies. Harrassowitz Verlag, Taunusstr. 14, 65183 Wiesbaden, Germany. TEL 0611-530-0. FAX 0611-530570. TELEX 4186135. (Subscr. to: Postfach 2929, 65019 Wiesbaden, Germany) Ed.Bd. bk.rev. **Indexed:** Numis.Lit. **Document type:** academic/scholarly publication.

950 US ISSN 1048-1508
ARIZONA STATE UNIVERSITY. CENTER FOR ASIAN STUDIES. MONOGRAPH SERIES. 1967. s-a. $10 per vol. Arizona State University, Center for Asian Studies, Box 871702, Tempe, AZ 85287-1702. TEL 602-965-7184. FAX 602-965-8317. Ed. Stephen R. MacKinnon. circ. 500. **Document type:** monographic series.
Formerly (until 1987): Arizona State University. Center for Asian Studies. Occasional Papers (ISSN 0570-9644)

950 709   US   ISSN 0571-1371
ARS ORIENTALIS; the arts of Asia, Southeast Asia and Islam. 1954. a. $40. Department of History of Art, Tappan Hall, University of Michigan, Ann Arbor, MI 48109-1357. FAX 313-763-8976. Ed. Margaret Lourie. bk.rev. circ. 500. **Indexed:** Avery Ind.Archit.Per. **Document type:** academic/scholarly publication.
—UnCover.
  Supersedes: Ars Islamica.
  Refereed Serial

950   IT
ARTE ORIENTALE IN ITALIA. (Subseries of: Rome (City). Museo Nazionale d'Arte Orientale. Pubblicazione) 1971. irreg. price varies. Museo Nazionale d'Arte Orientale, Via Merulana 248, Rome 00185, Italy. Ed. Giovanni Poncini. illus. circ. 1,000.

ARTIBUS ASIAE; quarterly of Asian art and archaeology for scholars and connoisseurs. see *ART*

ARTIBUS ASIAE SUPPLEMENTA. see *ART*

ARTS ASIATIQUES. see *ART*

ARYANA. see *HISTORY — History Of Asia*

950   US   ISSN 0890-4464
N7280.A1
ASIA INSTITUTE. BULLETIN. Key Title: Bulletin of the Asia Institute. (Text in English, French, German, Spanish) 1987. a. $65 (effective vol.6). Bulletin of the Asia Institute, 3287 Bradway Blvd., Bloomfield Hills, MI 48301. TEL 810-647-7917. FAX 910-647-9223. E-mail: Carol.Bromberg@um.cc.umich.edu. Ed. Carol Altman Bromberg. bk.rev.; circ. 270 (paid). (back issues avail.) **Document type:** academic/scholarly publication.
  Description: For universities, museums, historians, and collectors. Promotes current studies in the art, archaeology, history, and culture of early to mid-Islamic Iran and Central Asia and interconnections with the Far East.
  Refereed Serial

950   US   ISSN 0004-4482
DS501
ASIA MAJOR; a journal of Far Eastern Studies. 1923; N.S. 1952-1975; resumed. irreg., vol.4, no.2, 1991. Princeton University, East Asian Studies, 211 Jones Hall, Princeton, NJ 08544. TEL 609-258-4279. Ed. Denis Twitchett. adv.; bk.rev.; bibl.; illus.; maps. circ. 500. (reprint service avail. from SCH) **Indexed:** Amer.Hist.& Life, Hist.Abstr. **Document type:** academic/scholarly publication.
—Faxon; SWETS; UnCover.

950   UK   ISSN 0306-8374
DS1
ASIAN AFFAIRS. 1903. 3/yr. £30($60) Royal Society for Asian Affairs, 2 Belgrave Sq., London SW1X 8PJ, England. TEL 071-235-5122. FAX 071-259-6771. Ed. Victor Funnell. adv.; bk.rev.; charts; illus.; index. circ. 2,300. (back issues avail.) **Indexed:** Amer.Hist.& Life, Asian-Pac.Econ.Lit., Br.Hum.Ind., Hist.Abstr., Int.Polit.Sci.Abstr., Mid.East: Abstr.& Ind., P.A.I.S., Soc.Sci.Ind. **Document type:** academic/scholarly publication.
—BLDSC (1742.270000); Faxon; SWETS; UnCover.
  Formerly: Royal Central Asian Society. Journal (ISSN 0035-8789)

950 960 490 890   XO   ISSN 0571-2742
DS1   CODEN: AAFSEH
ASIAN AND AFRICAN STUDIES. (Text in English) 1965. a. price varies. Slovak Academy of Sciences, Institute of Oriental and African Studies, Klemensova 19, 813 64 Bratislava, Slovakia. (Dist. in Western countries by: Curzon Press Ltd., 42 Gray's Inn Rd., London WC1, England) Ed. Jozef Genzor. bk.rev.; index. **Indexed:** Bibl.Ling., Curr.Cont.Africa, E.I.

700   US   ISSN 1352-2744
N7262
ASIAN ART AND CULTURE. 1988. 3/yr. £60($90) (effective 1996). (Smithsonian Institution, Arthur M. Sackler Gallery) Oxford University Press, Journals, 2001 Evans Rd., Cary, NC 27513. TEL 919-677-0977; 800-852-7323. FAX 919-677-1714. E-mail: jnlorders@oup-usa.org. (Subscr. outside N. America to: Oxford University Press, Journals, Walton St., Oxford OX2 6DP, England. TEL 44-1865-56767. FAX 44-1865-267773) Ed. Karen Sagstetter. circ. 1,450. **Document type:** academic/scholarly publication.
—Faxon; Genuine Article; UMI; UnCover. CCC.
  Formerly (until 1994): Asian Art (ISSN 0894-234X)
  Description: Provides broad yet detailed examinations of the painting, sculpture, ceramics, textiles, photography, architecture, landscape design, and folk traditions of the region, from antiquity to the present.
  Refereed Serial

ASIAN CHURCH TODAY. see *RELIGIONS AND THEOLOGY*

950   UN
ASIAN CULTURAL CENTRE FOR UNESCO. ORGANIZATION AND ACTIVITIES. (Text in English) biennial. Asian Cultural Centre for Unesco, 6 Fukuro-machi, Shinjuku-ku, Tokyo 162, Japan. TEL 3-269-4435. illus.

ASIAN CULTURAL STUDIES. see *HISTORY — History Of Asia*

950   UN
ASIAN PACIFIC CULTURE; cross-cultural magazine. Short title: A P C. (Text in English) 1972. irreg. $4.20 per issue. Asian Cultural Centre for Unesco, 6, Fukuro-machi, Shinjuku-ku, Tokyo 162, Japan. TEL 03-269-4435. Ed. Taichi Sasaoka. illus. circ. 2,000.
  Formerly: Asian Culture (ISSN 0385-6402)

950   CH
ASIAN PACIFIC CULTURE QUARTERLY. (Text in English) 1973. q. Asian-Pacific Cultural Center, Asian-Pacific Parliamentarians' Union, 6-F, 66 Aikuo East Rd., Taipei, Taiwan, Republic of China. TEL 02-322-2139. FAX 02-322-2138. Ed. Tai-chu Chen. adv.; bk.rev.; index. circ. 3,000.
—UnCover.
  Formerly: Asian Culture Quarterly (ISSN 0378-8911)
  Description: General articles on Asian-Pacific culture and creative writings.

ASIAN PHILOSOPHY. see *PHILOSOPHY*

950   HK   ISSN 0304-8675
DS1
ASIAN PROFILE. (Text in English) 1973. bi-m. $50 to individuals; institutions $80. Asian Research Service, G.P.O. Box 2232, Hong Kong. TEL 5707227. FAX 5128050. TELEX 63899-HX. Ed. Nelson Leung. adv.; bk.rev. (back issues avail.) **Indexed:** Abstr.Rural Dev.Trop., Amer.Hist.& Life, Asian-Pac.Econ.Lit., Geo.Abstr., Hist.Abstr., Int.Polit.Sci.Abstr., Mid.East: Abstr.& Ind., Rural Devel.Abstr., Rural Ext.Educ.& Tr.Abstr., Rural Recreat.Tour.Abstr., Soils & Fert., World Agri.Econ.& Rural Sociol.Abstr. **Document type:** academic/scholarly publication.
—BLDSC (1742.731000); SWETS; UMI; UnCover.

950   JA   ISSN 0917-1479
ASIAN RESEARCH TRENDS; a humanities and social science review. (Text in English) 1962. a. 2200 Yen. Centre for East Asian Cultural Studies for Unesco, Toyo Bunko (Oriental Library), 2-28-21 Honkomagome, Bunkyo-ku, Tokyo 113, Japan. TEL 03-3942-0124. FAX 03-3942-0120. Ed. Yoneo Ishii. circ. 1,000. **Indexed:** Rural Devel.Abstr., World Agri.Econ.& Rural Sociol.Abstr. **Document type:** academic/scholarly publication, bibliography.
—BLDSC (1742.744700); UnCover.
  Supersedes (in 1991): East Asian Cultural Studies (ISSN 0012-8414)
  Description: Presents recent trends in the research on Asia and North Africa done by regional specialists in the various disciplines concerning these areas.

950   PH   ISSN 0004-4679
DS1
ASIAN STUDIES. 1963. a. $12.50 (effective since 1989). University of the Philippines, Asian Center, Diliman, Quezon City 1101, Philippines. FAX 992863. TELEX 2231 UPDIL PU. charts; illus.; stat. circ. 500. **Indexed:** Asian-Pac.Econ.Lit., Bibl.Ling., E.I., Ind.Phil.Per, M.L.A., RILM.
—BLDSC (1742.747000); UnCover.

950   AT   ISSN 0156-0182
ASIAN STUDIES ASSOCIATION OF AUSTRALIA. CONFERENCE PAPERS. 1978. biennial. price varies. University of New South Wales Library, P.O. Box 1, Kensington, N.S.W. 2033, Australia. FAX 02-663-4017. (microfiche) **Document type:** proceedings.

950   US   ISSN 0362-4811
DS1
ASIAN STUDIES NEWSLETTER. 1955. 5/yr. $25 to institutions. Association for Asian Studies, Inc., 1 Lane Hall, University of Michigan, Ann Arbor, MI 48109. TEL 313-665-2490. FAX 313-665-3801. adv. circ. 8,500. (back issues avail.; reprint service avail. from UMI) **Indexed:** A.I.C.P., E.I. **Document type:** newsletter.
  Formerly (until 1971): Association for Asian Studies. Newsletter (ISSN 0004-5403)
  Description: Contains association news, and information on grants, publications, study programs, meetings, exhibits, and employment opportunities.

ASIAN STUDIES REVIEW. see *HISTORY — History Of Asia*

ASIAN SURVEY. see *POLITICAL SCIENCE*

ASIAN THEATRE JOURNAL. see *THEATER*

950   US   ISSN 0893-6870
ASIAN THOUGHT AND CULTURE. irreg. Peter Lang Publishing, Inc., 62 W. 45th St., 4th Fl., New York, NY 10036. TEL 212-302-6740. FAX 212-302-7574. Ed. Charles Wei-hsun Fu. **Document type:** academic/scholarly publication, monographic series.

950   II   ISSN 0571-3161
ASIATIC SOCIETY, CALCUTTA. JOURNAL. (Text in English) vol.18, 1976. a. $9. Asiatic Society, Calcutta, 1 Park St., Calcutta 700 016, India. TEL 91-033-290779. FAX 91-033-290355. TELEX 021 5238 ASIA IN. bk.rev.; bibl.; charts; illus. (also avail. in microfilm from UMI; microfiche from BHP; reprint service avail. from UMI) **Indexed:** A.I.C.P., Numis.Lit.

950   II
ASIATIC SOCIETY, CALCUTTA. MONOGRAPH SERIES. irreg. $10 per vol. Asiatic Society, Calcutta, One Park St., Calcutta 700 016, India. TEL 91-033-290779. FAX 91-033-290355. TELEX 021 5238 ASIA IN. **Document type:** monographic series.

950   II
ASIATIC SOCIETY, CALCUTTA. SEMINAR SERIES. irreg. Asiatic Society, Calcutta, One Park St., Calcutta 700 016, India. TEL 91-033-290779. FAX 91-033-290355. TELEX 021 5238 ASIA IN.

ASIATIC SOCIETY OF BANGLADESH. JOURNAL: HUMANITIES. see *HUMANITIES: COMPREHENSIVE WORKS*

ASIATIC SOCIETY OF BANGLADESH. JOURNAL: SCIENCE. see *SCIENCES: COMPREHENSIVE WORKS*

950   II   ISSN 0004-4709
ASIATIC SOCIETY OF BOMBAY. JOURNAL. 1925. a. price varies. Asiatic Society of Bombay, Town Hall, Bombay 400 023, India. (Subscr. to: Arthur Probsthain, 41 Great Russell St., London, W.C. 1, England) Ed. V.M. Kulkarni. bk.rev.; illus. circ. 1,000. **Indexed:** A.I.C.P., Amer.Hist.& Life, Bibl.Ling., Hist.Abstr. **Document type:** academic/scholarly publication.
—BLDSC (4701.800000).

ORIENTAL STUDIES

950 952   JA   ISSN 0287-6051
ASIATIC SOCIETY OF JAPAN. TRANSACTIONS. (Text in English) 1872. a. 4000 Yen to members; non-members 6000 Yen. Asiatic Society of Japan, C.P.O. Box 592, Tokyo, Japan. TEL 03-3586-1548. FAX 03-3587-0030. Ed. Roger Finch. adv. circ. 500. (also avail. in microfilm from BHP; back issues avail.; reprint service avail. from KTO) **Document type:** academic/scholarly publication.

956   GW   ISSN 0571-320X
ASIATISCHE FORSCHUNGEN. 1959. irreg., vol.129, 1995. price varies. Harrassowitz Verlag, Taunusstr. 14, 65183 Wiesbaden, Germany. TEL 0611-530-0. FAX 0611-530570. TELEX 4186135. (Subscr. to: Postfach 2929, 65019 Wiesbaden, Germany) Ed.Bd. **Document type:** monographic series.

950   SZ   ISSN 0004-4717
DS1
ASIATISCHE STUDIEN/ETUDES ASIATIQUES. (Text in English, French, German) 1947. 4/yr. 85 SFr. (Schweizerische Gesellschaft fuer Asienkunde) Verlag Peter Lang AG, Jupiterstr. 15, CH-3000 Bern 15, Switzerland. TEL 031-9411122. FAX 031-9411131. TELEX 912651-PELA-CH. Ed.Bd. bk.rev.; bibl.; illus.; index. circ. 800. **Indexed:** Bibl.Ling., M.L.A. **Document type:** academic/scholarly publication.
—SWETS; UnCover.

950   FR   ISSN 0992-5473
ASIE EXTREME. 1988. a. 55 F. (Centre de Recherches Asie Orientale) Presses Universitaires de Rennes, 2 rue du Doyen D. Leroy, 35044 Rennes Cedex, France. TEL 99-54-66-35. FAX 99-33-07-95.
Description: Promotes a better understanding of Oriental Asia, past and present.

950   GW   ISSN 0721-5231
DS1
ASIEN; deutsche Zeitschrift fuer Politik, Wirtschaft und Kultur. (Text in English, German; summaries in English) 1981. q. DM.60. Deutsche Gesellschaft fuer Asienkunde e.V., Rothenbaumchaussee 32, 20148 Hamburg, Germany. TEL 040-445891. FAX 040-4107945. Ed. Guenter Schucher. adv.: B&W page DM.500; trim 180 x 120. bk.rev. circ. 1,000. **Indexed:** Asian-Pac.Econ.Lit., Forest.Abstr., Rural Devel.Abstr. **Document type:** academic/scholarly publication.
—UnCover. **CCC.**

950   SP   ISSN 0571-3692
DS1
ASOCIACION ESPANOLA DE ORIENTALISTAS. BOLETIN. (Text in language of authors) 1965. a. 6000 ptas. Asociacion Espanola de Orientalistas, Universidad Autonoma, Edificio Rectorado, 28049 Madrid, Spain. TEL 397-41-12. Ed. F. Valderrama. bk.rev.; charts; illus. circ. 500. (back issues avail.) **Indexed:** Amer.Hist.& Life, Bibl.Ling., Hist.Abstr. **Document type:** bulletin.

950   US   ISSN 0883-8909
DS1
ASSOCIATION FOR ASIAN STUDIES. SOUTHEAST CONFERENCE. ANNALS. 1979. a. $10 to non-members; members $5. Association for Asian Studies, Southeast Region, c/o South Asia Collection, Duke University Library, Durham, NC 27708-0175. TEL 919-660-5841. FAX 919-684-2855. Ed. Lawrence Kessler. adv. circ. 200. **Document type:** proceedings.
—BLDSC (1044.250000).

ASSYRIOLOGICAL STUDIES. see LINGUISTICS

955   IR   ISSN 1017-4109
AYANDEH; Persian journal of Iranian studies. (Text in Persian) 1926. m. $50. Iraj Afshar, Ed. & Pub., P.O. Box 19575-583 Niyavaran, Tehran, Iran. TEL 98-21-283254. adv.; bk.rev.; bibl.; illus.; index. circ. 4,000. **Indexed:** M.L.A. **Document type:** academic/scholarly publication.
Former titles (until 1979): Rahnama-yi Kitab (ISSN 0033-8699); (until 1958): Ayandah (ISSN 0259-9252)

BANGALORE THEOLOGICAL FORUM. see RELIGIONS AND THEOLOGY

950 490   AU   ISSN 0259-0654
BEIHEFTE ZUR WIENER ZEITSCHRIFT FUER DIE KUNDE DES MORGENLANDES. irreg., no.15, 1989. price varies. Universitaet Wien, Institut fuer Orientalistik, Universitaetsstr. 7-V, A-1010 Vienna, Austria. Ed. Arne A. Ambros. **Document type:** monographic series.

BEIRUT REVIEW. see POLITICAL SCIENCE — International Relations

952   AU   ISSN 0522-6759
BEITRAEGE ZUR JAPANOLOGIE. (Text in English and German, summaries in English and Japanese) 1955. irreg., vol.32, 1994. price varies. Universitaet Wien, Institut fuer Japanologie, Universitaetsstr. 7, A-1010 Vienna, Austria. FAX 0222-4020533. Eds. Alexander Slawik, Sepp Linhart. bk.rev. circ. 300. **Indexed:** A.I.C.P. **Document type:** academic/scholarly publication.

950   GW   ISSN 0138-4228
BERLINER TURFANTEXTE. (Text in English and German) 1971. irreg., vol.16, 1993. Akademie Verlag GmbH, Muehlenstr. 33-34, 13187 Berlin, Germany. TEL 030-47889348. FAX 030-47889357. **Document type:** monographic series.

954   II   ISSN 0378-1143
PK101
BHANDARKAR ORIENTAL RESEARCH INSTITUTE. ANNALS. (Text in English) 1919. a. price varies. Bhandarkar Oriental Research Institute, Deccan Gymkhana, Pune 411 004, India. TEL 336932. Eds. R.N. Dandekar, S.D. Laddu. bk.rev. circ. 1,250. **Indexed:** A.I.C.P., Bibl.Ling., M.L.A., Numis.Lit. **Document type:** bulletin.

954   II   ISSN 0378-1984
DS401
BHARATYA VIDYA. (Text in English and Sanskrit) 1939. m. Rps.60. Bharatiya Vidya Bhavan, Kulapnati K.M. Munshi Marg, Bombay 400 007, India. Eds. J.H. Dave, S.A. Upadhyaya. (back issues avail.) **Indexed:** M.L.A.

BIBLICA ET ORIENTALIA. see RELIGIONS AND THEOLOGY — Roman Catholic

BIBLICAL ARCHAEOLOGIST. see ARCHAEOLOGY

BIBLIOTECA DEGLI STUDI CLASSICI E ORIENTALI. see CLASSICAL STUDIES

BIBLIOTHECA ISLAMICA. see RELIGIONS AND THEOLOGY — Islamic

BIBLIOTHECA ORIENTALIS. see HISTORY — Abstracting, Bibliographies, Statistics

950 490   HU   ISSN 0067-8104
BIBLIOTHECA ORIENTALIS HUNGARICA. (Text in English, French and German) 1955. irreg., vol.38, 1992. price varies. (Magyar Tudomanyos Akademia) Akademiai Kiado, Publishing House of the Hungarian Academy of Sciences, P.O. Box 245, H-1519 Budapest, Hungary. TEL 181-2134. FAX 166-6466. TELEX 22-6228 AKNYO H. **Indexed:** New Test.Abstr., Old Test.Abstr.

955   BE
BIBLIOTHEQUE IRANIENNE. (Text in English, French) 1975. irreg., vol.38, 1995. Editions Peeters s.p.r.l., Bondgenotenlaan 153, 3000 Leuven, Belgium. TEL 32-16-235170. FAX 32-16-228500. (back issues avail.) **Document type:** monographic series.

500   GW   ISSN 0170-0006
BOCHUMER JAHRBUCH ZUR OSTASIENFORSCHUNG. 1978. a. DM.89.80. Universitaetsverlag Dr. N. Brockmeyer, Querenburger Hoehe 281, 44801 Bochum, Germany. TEL 0234-706978. circ. 80. **Indexed:** Bibl.Ling.

952   GW   ISSN 0173-7902
BONNER JAPANFORSCHUNGEN. 1979. irreg. Bonner Verein zur Foerderung der Japanforschung, Regina-Pacis-Weg 7, 53113 Bonn, Germany. TEL 0228-737223. FAX 0228-737020. circ. 500. (back issues avail.) **Document type:** academic/scholarly publication, monographic series.

BOSTON THIRD WORLD LAW JOURNAL. see LAW — International Law

954   NE   ISSN 0925-2916
BRILL'S INDOLOGICAL LIBRARY. (Text in English) 1991. irreg.,vol.9, 1995. price varies. E.J. Brill, P.O. Box 9000, 2300 PA Leiden, Netherlands. TEL 31-71-5353500. FAX 31-71-5317532. TELEX 39296 BRILL NL. (In N. America: E.J. Brill, 24 Hudson St., Kinderhook, NY 12106. TEL 800-962-4406. FAX 518-758-1959) Ed. Johannes Bronkhorst. (back issues avail.) **Document type:** monographic series.
Description: Scholarly monographs on topics in Indian religion, language, history and philosophy.
Refereed Serial

952   NE   ISSN 0925-6512
BRILL'S JAPANESE STUDIES LIBRARY. 1989. irreg., no.4, 1993. price varies. E.J. Brill, P.O. Box 9000, 2300 PA Leiden, Netherlands. TEL 31-71-5353500. FAX 31-71-5317532. TELEX 39296 BRILL NL. (In N. America: E.J. Brill, 24 Hudson St., Kinderhook, NY 12106. TEL 800-962-4406. FAX 518-758-1959) (back issues avail.) **Document type:** monographic series.
Description: Scholarly studies of Japanese literary history and traditions, and related topics in linguistics.
Refereed Serial

026.954   UK   ISSN 1350-4711
Z792.B85932
BRITISH LIBRARY. ORIENTAL AND INDIA OFFICE COLLECTIONS. REVIEW. irreg., latest 1993 (for years 1989-1991). £4. British Library Board, 96 Euston Rd., London NW1 2DB, England. (Orders to: British Library, Oriental and India Office Collections, 197 Blackfriars Rd., London SE1 8NG, England. TEL 44-171-412-7000. FAX 44-171-412-7858) **Document type:** corporate report.
—BLDSC (7798.560000).
Formerly (until 1993): British Library. India Office Library and Records and Oriental Collections. Annual Report (ISSN 0954-2019); (until 1988): British Library. Department of Oriental Manuscripts and Printed Books. Annual Report.

950   HU   ISSN 0139-4614
BUDAPEST ORIENTAL REPRINTS, SERIES A. 1977. irreg. price varies or exchange basis. (Korosi Csoma Tarsasag) Magyar Tudomanyos Akademia Konyvtara, Arany Janos u.1, P.O. Box 7, 1361 Budapest, Hungary. Eds. E. Schutz, Eva Apor. **Document type:** monographic series.

BUDDHIST TRADITION SERIES. see RELIGIONS AND THEOLOGY — Buddhist

BULLETIN CRITIQUE DES ANNALES ISLAMOLOGIQUES. see RELIGIONS AND THEOLOGY — Islamic

950   FR   ISSN 0007-4349
BULLETIN DE L'OEUVRE D'ORIENT. 1856. bi-m. 10 F.($1) Association de l'Oeuvre d'Orient, 20 rue du Regard, 75006 Paris, France. Ed. J. Andre Boissonnet. circ. 210,000.

BULLETIN OF CONCERNED ASIAN SCHOLARS. see POLITICAL SCIENCE — International Relations

952   GW   ISSN 0932-268X
BUNKEN; Studien und Materialen zur japanischen Literatur. 1987. irreg., vol.4, 1994. Harrassowitz Verlag, Taunusstr. 14, 65183 Wiesbaden, Germany. TEL 0611-530-0. FAX 0611-530-570. TELEX 4186135. (Subscr. to: Postfach 2929, 65019 Wiesbaden, Germany) Ed. Ekkehard May. **Document type:** monographic series.

949.5   GW   ISSN 0007-7704
BYZANTINISCHE ZEITSCHRIFT. (Text in several languages) 1892. s-a. DM.198. B.G. Teubner GmbH, Postfach 801069, 70510 Stuttgart, Germany. TEL 0711-78901-0. FAX 0711-78901-10. Ed. Peter Schreiner. adv.; bk.rev.; bibl.; illus.; index, cum.index: vols.1-12. circ. 1,000. (reprint service avail. from SCH) **Indexed:** Bibl.Ling., Curr.Cont., M.L.A., Numis.Lit., RILA. **Document type:** academic/scholarly publication.
—Faxon; Genuine Article; SWETS. **CCC.**

ORIENTAL STUDIES 4961

949.5 487   NE   ISSN 0007-7712
CB231
BYZANTINOSLAVICA; revue internationale des etudes byzantines. (Text in English, French, German, Italian, Russian) 1929. 2/yr. fl.260 (effective 1996). (Czech Academy of Sciences, Institute of Greek, Roman and Latin Studies, XR) John Benjamins Publishing Co., Amsteldijk 44, P.O. Box 75577, 1070 AN Amsterdam, Netherlands. TEL 31-20-6738156. FAX 31-20-6792956. (In N. America: Box 27519, Philadelphia, PA 19118-0519. TEL 215-836-1200. FAX 215-836-1204) Ed. Vladimir Vavrinek. bk.rev.; bibl.; illus.; maps; index. circ. 1,100. (back issues avail.) **Indexed:** Bibl.Ling., CERDIC, Curr.Cont., M.L.A., Numis.Lit. **Document type:** academic/scholarly publication.
—Faxon; UnCover.
   Description: International journal devoted to Byzantine studies.
   Refereed Serial

900   BE   ISSN 0378-2506
PA5000
BYZANTION; revue internationale des etudes byzantines. (Text in English, French, German, Greek, Italian) 1924. s-a. 2000 BEF($50) (ASBL Byzantion) Universa, Hoenderstr. 24, B-9200 Wetteren, Belgium. Ed. Prof. P. Yannopoulos. bk.rev.; bibl (reprint service avail. from KTO) **Indexed:** Bibl.Ling., M.L.A., Numis.Lit., RILA. **Document type:** academic/scholarly publication.
—Faxon; UnCover.

950   LE
C E M A M REPORTS. 1974. a. price varies. (Universite Saint-Joseph, Center pour l'Etude du Monde Arabe Modern) Dar el-Machreq S.A.R.L., 2 rue Huvelin, P.O. Box 946, Beirut, Lebanon. TEL 961-1-326469. (Subscr. to: Librairie Orientale, P.O. Box 946, Beirut, Lebanon)

950 011   UK   ISSN 1357-7522
C M E I S OCCASIONAL PAPERS. 1972. irreg., latest no.47. price varies. University of Durham, Centre for Middle Eastern and Islamic Studies, South End House, South Rd., Durham City DH1 3TG, England. TEL 0191-374-2822. FAX 0191-374-2830. Ed. Margaret Greenhalgh. bibl. **Document type:** monographic series.
   Formerly (until 1995): University of Durham. Centre for Middle Eastern and Islamic Studies. Occasional Papers Series (ISSN 0307-0654)

C W A S NEWSLETTER. (Committee on Women in Asian Studies) see WOMEN'S STUDIES

950 495   FR   ISSN 0399-1652
DS501
CAHIERS DE L'ASIE DU SUD-EST. 1977. irreg., latest no.31. price varies. Institut National des Langues et Civilisations Orientales, 2 rue de Lille, 75343 Paris Cedex 07, France. TEL 49-26-42-74. **Description:** Presents articles, translations, summaries and bibliographies on the languages, literatures and civilizations of South-East Asia.

950   FR   ISSN 0767-6468
DS36
CAHIERS DE L'ORIENT. q. 300 F. (Centre de Reflexion sur le Proche-Orient) Societe Francaise d'Edition, d'Impression et de Realisation, 80 rue Saint Dominique, 75007 Paris, France. Ed. Antoine Sfeir. adv.; bk.rev. circ. 1,986. **Document type:** academic/scholarly publication.

CAHIERS DE LA D A F I. see ARCHAEOLOGY

CAHIERS DE LINGUISTIQUE ASIE ORIENTALE. see LINGUISTICS

CAHIERS DU MONDE RUSSE ET SOVIETIQUE. see HISTORY — History Of Europe

950   AU   ISSN 1215-7279
CAHIERS FRANCOPHONES D'EUROPE CENTRE ORIENTALE. (Text in French) 1991. a. S.195 (effective 1996). (Association des Etudes Francophones d'Europe Centre Orientale) Wilhelm Braumueller, Universitaets-Verlagsbuchhandlung GmbH, Servitengasse 5, A-1092 Vienna, Austria. TEL 01-3191159. FAX 01-3102805. **Document type:** academic/scholarly publication.

950   AT
▼CAMBRIDGE ASIA - PACIFIC STUDIES.* 1994. irreg. Department of Foreign Affairs and Trade, Overseas Information Branch, P.O. Box 12, Canberra, A.C.T. 2601, Australia. Ed. John Ravenhill. **Document type:** academic/scholarly publication.
   Description: Covers regionalisation of production, environmental issues, ethnicity and gender, science and technology, the evolving security balance, religion and politics in the Asia-Pacific region.

CELESTINESCA; boletin informativo internacional. see LITERATURE

958   PK
CENTRAL ASIA. (Text in English) 1978. 3/yr. Rs.90($25) University of Peshawar, Area Study Center (Central Asia), Peshawar, Pakistan. Ed. Mohammad Anwar Khan. circ. 200. **Indexed:** Per.Islam. (1991-). **Document type:** academic/scholarly publication.

950 490 890   GW   ISSN 0008-9192
DS785
CENTRAL ASIATIC JOURNAL; international periodical for the languages, literatures, history and archaeology of Central Asia. (Text in English, French, German) 1955. s-a. DM.168. Harrassowitz Verlag, Taunusstr. 14, 65183 Wiesbaden, Germany. TEL 0611-530-0. FAX 0611-530570. TELEX 4186135. (Subscr. to: Postfach 2929, 65019 Wiesbaden, Germany) Ed. Giovanni Stary. adv.; bk.rev.; bibl.; charts; illus.; index. circ. 550. (back issues avail.) **Indexed:** Arts & Hum.Cit.Ind., Bibl.Ling., Curr.Cont., Mid.East: Abstr.& Ind., Numis.Lit. **Document type:** academic/scholarly publication.
—BLDSC (3105.970000); Genuine Article; SWETS; UMI. CCC.

959 490   CN   ISSN 0839-4555
CENTRE D'ETUDES DE L'ASIE DE L'EST. CAHIERS; recherche sur l'Asie de l'Est. (Text in English, French) 1980. irreg., latest no.8. Can.$8 per no. Universite de Montreal, Faculte des Arts et des Sciences, Centre d'Etudes de l'Asie de l'Est, C.P. 6128, Succ. A, Montreal, PQ H3C 3J7, Canada. TEL 514-343-5970. FAX 514-343-7716. Ed. Claude Comtois. bk.rev. circ. 500. (back issues avail.) **Document type:** academic/scholarly publication.
   Description: Presents a multidisciplinary forum that covers all aspects of the Far East. Publishes original manuscripts, notes, essays, documents, bibliographical studies in the field of humanities by specialists of East and Southeast Asia.
   Refereed Serial

CENTRE FOR SOUTH-EAST ASIAN STUDIES. OCCASIONAL PAPERS. see HISTORY — History Of Asia

CENTRE FOR THE STUDY OF THE CIVILIZATIONS OF CENTRAL ASIA. PUBLICATIONS. see HISTORY — History Of Asia

950   JA   ISSN 0009-1537
GT2910
CHANOYU QUARTERLY; tea and the arts of Japan. (Text in English) 1970. q. 4400 Yen($25) Urasenke Foundation, Ogawa Teranouchi Agaru, Kamikyo-ku, Kyoto 602, Japan. TEL 075-411-1178. (Subscr. to: Urasenke Chanoyu Center, 153 E. 69th St., New York, NY 10021, USA. TEL 212-988-6161. FAX 212-517-7594) Ed. Gretchen Mittwer. bk.rev.; bibl.; illus, charts. circ. 2,000. (processed; also avail. in microform from UMI; reprint service avail. from ISI) **Indexed:** Artbibl.Mod., Arts & Hum.Cit.Ind., Curr.Cont. **Document type:** academic/scholarly publication.
—Faxon.
   Description: Covers art, cultural history, literature and philosophy of Japan, in relation to the "tea ceremony".

950   II
CHAUKHAMBHA ORIENTAL RESEARCH STUDIES. 1976. irreg., no.35, 1989. price varies. Chaukhambha Orientalia, Gokul Bhawan, K 37-109 Gopal Mandir Lane, Varanasi 221001, India. **Document type:** monographic series.

951   NE   ISSN 0920-203X
DS701
CHINA INFORMATION; a quarterly journal on contemporary China studies. 1967. q. fl.58.30 to individuals (foreign fl.74.20); institutions fl.79.50 (foreign fl.90); students fl.37.10 (foreign fl.53) (effective 1993). Rijksuniversiteit te Leiden, Sinologisch Instituut, Documentation and Research Centre for Contemporary China, Postbus 9515, 2300 RA Leiden, Netherlands. TEL 31-71-272516. FAX 31-71-272615. E-mail: docchin@rullet.leidenuniv.nl. Ed. W.L. Chong. adv.; bk.rev. circ. 375. **Indexed:** Int.Polit.Sci.Abstr., Key to Econ.Sci. **Document type:** academic/scholarly publication.
—BLDSC (3180.170700); UnCover.
   Formerly (until 1986): China Informatie (ISSN 0577-8832)
   Description: Monitors and provides analyses of recent developments in China and in other Chinese societies throughout the world. Covers issues in politics, economics, law, ecology, culture and society, as well as literature and the arts.
   Refereed Serial

950 700 370   US
CHINA INSTITUTE IN AMERICA. BULLETIN. q. membership only. China Institute in America, Inc., 125 E. 65th St., New York, NY 10021. TEL 212-744-8181. Ed. Helen Geraghty. bk.rev. circ. 1,700.

950 320 300   AT
DS701
THE CHINA JOURNAL. 1979. 2/yr. Aus.$25($25) to individuals; institutions Aus.$30($30); students Aus.$20($20). Australian National University, Research School of Pacific and Asian Studies, Contemporary China Centre, Canberra, A.C.T. 0200, Australia. TEL 06-249-4150. FAX 06-257-3642. Ed. Anita Chan. adv.; bk.rev. circ. 900. **Indexed:** Amer.Hist.& Life, Asian-Pac.Econ.Lit., Aus.P.A.I.S., Geo.Abstr., Hist.Abstr., IDA, Int.Polit.Sci.Abstr., Int.Polit.Sci.Abstr., Polit.Sci.Abstr., Rural Recreat.Tour.Abstr., Sage Urb.Stud.Abstr., World Agri.Econ.& Rural Sociol.Abstr. **Document type:** academic/scholarly publication.
—BLDSC (1806.090000); Genuine Article; UMI; UnCover.
   Formerly: Australian Journal of Chinese Affairs (ISSN 0156-7365)
   Description: Publishes articles that analyze and study different aspects of China's development since 1949.

951   UK   ISSN 0009-4439
CHINA QUARTERLY. 1959. q. £42($80) (effective 1996). (University of London, School of Oriental and African Studies) Oxford University Press, Oxford Journals, Walton St., Oxford OX2 6DP, England. TEL 01865-267907. FAX 01865-267773. E-mail: jnlorders@oup.co.uk. (U.S. subscr. to: Oxford University Press Inc., 2001 Evans Rd., Cary, NC 27513. TEL 919-677-0977. FAX 919-677-1714) Ed. David Shambaugh. adv. contact: Jane Parker. bk.rev.; bibl.; charts; maps; index. circ. 3,100. (also avail. in microfilm from UMI) **Indexed:** A.B.C.Pol.Sci., Acad.Ind., Amer.Hist.& Life, Asian-Pac.Econ.Lit., ASSIA, Curr.Cont., E.I., Hist.Abstr., Int.Lab.Doc., Int.Polit.Sci.Abstr., Key to Econ.Sci., M.L.A., Mid.East: Abstr.& Ind., P.A.I.S., Polit.Sci.Abstr., Ref.Sour., Rural Recreat.Tour.Abstr., Soc.Sci.Ind., SSCI, World Agri.Econ.& Rural Sociol.Abstr. **Document type:** academic/scholarly publication.
●Also available online. Vendor(s): University Microfilms International.
—BLDSC (3180.230000); UnCover. CCC.
   Description: Covers all aspects of modern China studies.

CHINESE AMERICA; history and perspectives. see ETHNIC INTERESTS

951   CH   ISSN 0009-4544
DS701
CHINESE CULTURE. (Text in English) 1957. q. NT.$600($45) China Academy, Institute for Advanced Chinese Studies, P.O. Box 12, Yang Ming Shan, Taiwan, Republic of China. TEL 02-8611861. FAX 02-8617164. Ed. Chang Chi-Yun. adv.; bk.rev.; index. circ. 2,000. (also avail. in microform from UMI; microfiche from IDC) **Indexed:** Amer.Hist.& Life (until 1992), Hist.Abstr. (until 1992). **Document type:** academic/scholarly publication.
—Faxon; UMI; UnCover.

ORIENTAL STUDIES

951   HK   ISSN 0963-5726
CHINESE CULTURE QUARTERLY/CHIU CHOU HSUEH K'AN. (Text in Chinese; table of contents in English) q. HK.$80 (Taiwan NT.$450; elsewhere $15) to individuals; institutions HK.$120 (Taiwan NT.$600; elsewhere $25). Hong Kong Institute for Promotion of Chinese Culture, Rm. 1001-5, Shun Tak Centre, 200 Connaught Rd., Central, Hong Kong. TEL 5-594904. (Subscr. to: Far East Book Company, G.P.O. Box 4892, Hong Kong; Editorial addr.: Kwan-Fong Institute of East Asian Studies, Pace University, New York, NY 10038, USA. TEL 212-488-1832) Ed. Pei-kai Cheng. bk.rev.

950   US   ISSN 1043-643X
D1
CHINESE HISTORIAN. 1987. s-a. $12 to individuals; institutions $20. Chinese Historians in the United States, Inc., Department of History, 1 College Circle, SUNY - Geneseo, Geneseo, NY 14454. Ed. Chen Jian. bk.rev. circ. 200.
    Formerly: Historian (Athens).
    Description: Provides a forum for the exchange of ideas and views among Chinese historians in the United States and other countries.

CHINESE LITERATURE; fiction, poetry, art. see *LITERATURE*

CHINESE SCIENCE. see *SCIENCES: COMPREHENSIVE WORKS*

CHINESE STUDIES IN HISTORY; a journal of translations. see *HISTORY*

951   HK
CHINESE UNIVERSITY OF HONG KONG. INSTITUTE OF CHINESE STUDIES. JOURNAL. 1968. a. HK.$50($8.70) Chinese University of Hong Kong, Institute of Chinese Studies, Shatin, New Territories, Hong Kong. Ed.Bd. adv.; bk.rev.; bibl.; charts; illus. circ. 500. **Indexed:** Amer.Hist.& Life, Hist.Abstr.

CHING FENG; a journal on Christianity and Chinese relition and culture. see *RELIGIONS AND THEOLOGY*

951 895.1   US   ISSN 0193-7774
PL2253
CHINOPERL PAPERS. (Text in Chinese and English) 1969. irreg., no.18, 1995. $22.50 to individuals (foreign $25); institutions $27.50 (foreign £30) (effective 1995). Conference on Chinese Oral and Performing Literature, c/o Bell Yung, Music Department, University of Pittsburgh, Pittsburgh, PA 15260. TEL 412-648-7367. FAX 412-648-2199. Eds. Samuel H.N. Cheung, Lindy Li Mark. bk.rev.; bibl. circ. 200. (back issues avail.) **Indexed:** RILM. **Document type:** academic/scholarly publication.
—UnCover.
    Formerly: Chinoperl News.
    Description: Deals primarily with oral Chinese literature (popular storytelling, opera, ceremonial chanting and folksongs) and various genres of Chinese verse and prose.

962   BE   ISSN 0009-6067
CHRONIQUE D'EGYPTE. (Text in English, French, German, Italian) 1925. s-a. 2500 BEF. Fondation Egyptologique Reine Elisabeth, Parc du Cinquantenaire 10, 1040 Brussels, Belgium. TEL 32-2-74-17-364. Eds. J. Bingen, H. de Meulenaere. bk.rev.; bibl.; illus.; cum.index: vols.1-10, 11-35, 36-50. circ. 1,000. (back issues avail.) **Indexed:** Bibl.Ling., M.L.A. **Document type:** academic/scholarly publication.

CINERAIDER. see *LITERARY AND POLITICAL REVIEWS*

952   FR   ISSN 1164-5857
CIPANGO. a. price varies. Institut National des Langues et Civilisations Orientales, 2 rue de Lille, 75343 Paris Cedex 07, France. TEL 49-26-42-74. FAX 49-26-42-99. Ed.Bd.
    Description: Interdisciplinary study of Japan, past and present.

950   GW   ISSN 0340-6393
CODICES ARABICI ANTIQUI. 1972. irreg., vol.4, 1986. price varies. Harrassowitz Verlag, Taunusstr. 14, 65183 Wiesbaden, Germany. TEL 0611-530-0. FAX 0611-530-570. TELEX 4186135. (Subscr. to: Postfach 2929, 65019 Wiesbaden, Germany) Ed. R.G. Khoury. **Document type:** monographic series.

950   AG
COLECCION ORIENTE-OCCIDENTE. 1976. irreg. price varies. Universidad del Salvador, Instituto Latinoamericano de Investigaciones Comparadas Oriente-Occidente, Callao 853, 1023 Buenos Aires, Argentina. Ed. I. Quiles. circ. 2,000.

954   UK   ISSN 0141-0156
COLLECTED PAPERS ON SOUTH ASIA. 1978. irreg. price varies. University of London, School of Oriental and African Studies, Thornhaugh St., Russell Sq., London WC1H 0XG, England. TEL 0171-637-2388. FAX 0171-436-3844. Ed. Diana Matias; Pub. Martin Daly. adv. contact: Martin Daly. **Document type:** monographic series.
—BLDSC (3306.490000).

956.1   BE
COLLECTION TURCICA. (Text in English, French) 1981. irreg., vol.7, 1994. price varies. Editions Peeters s.p.r.l., Bondgenotenlaan 153, 3000 Leuven, Belgium. TEL 32-16-235170. FAX 32-16-228500. (back issues avail.) **Document type:** monographic series.
    Description: Publishes contributions on topics relating to the history and culture of the Ottoman Empire, Turkey and other Turkic-speaking areas.

COLLECTIONS BAUR. BULLETIN. see *MUSEUMS AND ART GALLERIES*

951   FR   ISSN 0337-792X
COLLEGE DE FRANCE. INSTITUT DES HAUTES ETUDES CHINOISES. MEMOIRS.* 1975. irreg. Diffusion de Boccard, 11 Rue du Medicis, 75006 Paris, France. illus. (reprint service avail. from KTO)

950   FR   ISSN 0248-5095
COLLOQUES LANGUES'O. irreg. price varies. Institut National des Langues et Civilisations Orientales, 2 rue de Lille, 75343 Paris Cedex 07, France. TEL 49-26-42-74.

950   US
COLUMBIA UNIVERSITY. EAST ASIAN INSTITUTE. STUDIES. Variant title: East Asian Institute Series. 1962. irreg., latest 1993. price varies. Columbia University Press, 562 W. 113th St., New York, NY 10025. TEL 212-666-1000. **Document type:** monographic series.

COMMONWEALTH NOVEL IN ENGLISH. see *LITERATURE*

COMMUNICATIONS OF C O L I P S. (Chinese and Oriental Languages Information Processing Society) see *LINGUISTICS — Computer Applications*

COMPUTER AIDED RESEARCH IN NEAR EASTERN STUDIES. see *HISTORY — Computer Applications*

951   UK   ISSN 0085-2856
CONTEMPORARY CHINA INSTITUTE PUBLICATIONS. 1970. irreg., latest 1986. price varies. (Contemporary China Institute, School of Oriental and African Studies, University of London) Cambridge University Press, Edinburgh Bldg., Shaftesbury Rd., Cambridge CB2 2RU, England. TEL 01223-312393. FAX 01223-315052. TELEX 851817256. (N. American addr.: Cambridge University Press, Journals Dept., 40 W. 20th St., New York, NY 10011. TEL 212-924-3900. FAX 212-691-3239) Ed.Bd. **Document type:** academic/scholarly publication.

950   US   ISSN 1053-1866
CONTRIBUTIONS IN ASIAN STUDIES. 1991. irreg. price varies. Greenwood Press, Inc. (Subsidiary of Greenwood Publishing Group Inc.), 88 Post Rd. W., Box 5007, Westport, CT 06881-5007. TEL 203-226-3571. FAX 203-222-1502. **Document type:** monographic series.

CONTRIBUTIONS TO NEPALESE STUDIES. see *HISTORY — History Of Asia*

950   DK   ISSN 1395-4199
COPENHAGEN JOURNAL OF ASIAN STUDIES. (Text in English) 1987. s-a. DKK 170($29) (University of Copenhagen, Center for East and Southeast Asian Studies) Museum Tusculanum Press, Koebenhavns Universitet, Njalsgade 92, DK-2300, Copenhagen S, Denmark. TEL 45-35-32-91-09. FAX 45-35-32-91-13. (Dist. in U.S. and Canada by: Paul & Co., c/o P C S Data Processing, Inc., 360 W. 31st St., New York, NY 10001. TEL 212-564-3730. FAX 212-971-7200) Ed. Kjeld Erik Broedsgaard. **Indexed:** Asian-Pac.Econ.Lit., Int.Polit.Sci.Abstr. **Document type:** academic/scholarly publication.
—BLDSC (3466.106000).
    Formerly (until 1995): Copenhagen Papers in East and Southeast Asian Studies (ISSN 0903-2703)
    Description: Although not entirely limited to papers by Scandinavian scholars, the periodical is meant to demonstrate the breadth and depth of modern East Asian studies in that part of the world.

950   US   ISSN 0734-449X
Z688.A75
CORMOSEA BULLETIN. vol.7, 1974. s-a. $10. Association for Asian Studies, Inc., Committee for Research Materials on Southeast Asia, University of Michigan, One Lane Hall, Ann Arbor, MI 48109. TEL 313-665-2490. FAX 608-265-2754. Ed. Carol Mitchell. bk.rev.; bibl. circ. 200. **Indexed:** E.I. **Document type:** bulletin.
—UnCover.
    Formerly: Cormosea Newsletter.
    Description: Bibliographies and reviews of research materials in Southeast Asian Studies.

950   US   ISSN 1050-2955
CORNELL EAST ASIA SERIES. 1973. irreg., no.76, 1995. price varies. Cornell University, East Asia Program, 140 Uris Hall, Ithaca, NY 14853-7601. TEL 607-255-6222. FAX 607-255-1388. E-mail: kks3@cornell.edu. Ed. David McCann. circ. 2,000. **Document type:** academic/scholarly publication.
—BLDSC (3470.940900).
    Formerly: Cornell East Asia Papers (ISSN 8756-5293)
    Description: Publishes manuscripts on a wide variety of scholarly topics pertaining to East Asia (China, Japan, Korea).

959 011   US
CORNELL MODERN INDONESIA PROJECT PUBLICATIONS. 1958. irreg., no.74, 1995. price varies. Cornell University, Cornell Modern Indonesia Project, 640 Stewart Ave., Ithaca, NY 14850. TEL 607-255-4359. FAX 607-277-1904. TELEX WUI 6713054. Ed. Audrey R. Kahin. **Document type:** monographic series.
—BLDSC (7127.250000).
    Former titles (until no.72, 1993): Cornell University. Modern Indonesia Project Publications. Monographs, Translations, Bibliographies, Interim Reports (ISSN 0589-7300) & Cornell University. Modern Indonesia Project Publications. Monographs, Translations, Bibliographies; Cornell University. Modern Indonesia Project. Monographs.
    Refereed Serial

950   US
CORNELL UNIVERSITY. SOUTHEAST ASIA PROGRAM. TRANSLATION SERIES. 1990. irreg., no.4, 1995. price varies. Cornell University, Southeast Asia Program, 640 Stewart Ave., Ithaca, NY 14850. TEL 607-255-8038. FAX 607-277-1904. TELEX WUI-6713054. (Subscr. to: S E A P Publications, Cornell University, E. Hill Plaza, Ithaca, NY 14850) **Document type:** monographic series.

CORPUS SCRIPTORUM CHRISTIANORUM ORIENTALIUM: AETHIOPICA. see *RELIGIONS AND THEOLOGY — Other Denominations And Sects*

CORPUS SCRIPTORUM CHRISTIANORUM ORIENTALIUM: ARABICA. see *RELIGIONS AND THEOLOGY — Other Denominations And Sects*

CORPUS SCRIPTORUM CHRISTIANORUM ORIENTALIUM: ARMENIACA. see *RELIGIONS AND THEOLOGY — Other Denominations And Sects*

CORPUS SCRIPTORUM CHRISTIANORUM ORIENTALIUM: COPTICA. see *RELIGIONS AND THEOLOGY — Other Denominations And Sects*

CORPUS SCRIPTORUM CHRISTIANORUM ORIENTALIUM: IBERICA. see *RELIGIONS AND THEOLOGY — Other Denominations And Sects*

ORIENTAL STUDIES

CORPUS SCRIPTORUM CHRISTIANORUM ORIENTALIUM: SUBSIDIA. see *RELIGIONS AND THEOLOGY — Other Denominations And Sects*

CORPUS SCRIPTORUM CHRISTIANORUM ORIENTALIUM: SYRIACA. see *RELIGIONS AND THEOLOGY — Other Denominations And Sects*

956   TU   ISSN 0011-281X
CULTURA TURCICA. (Text in English, French, German) 1964. irreg. $10. Turk Kulturunu Arastirma Enstitusu - Turkish Cultural Research Institute, 17 Sok. 38, Bahceivler, Ankara, Turkey. Dir. Sukru Elcin. bk.rev.; dance rev.; film rev.; abstr.; charts; illus.; index. circ. 1,000. (also avail. in microfiche from IDC) **Document type:** academic/scholarly publication.

956 297   NE   ISSN 0169-8257
DE GOEJE STICHTING. UITGAVEN/DE GOEJE FUND. PUBLICATIONS.* 1956. irreg., vol.26, 1988. price varies. De Goeje Stichting - De Goeje Fund, c/o Prof. R. Roolvink, Prins Bernhardtlaan 70, 2252 GZ Voorschoten, Netherlands. FAX 071-317532. (Dist. by: Nederlands Instituut voor het Nabije Oosten, Witte Singel 24, P.O. Box 9515, 2300 RA Leiden, Netherlands) **Document type:** monographic series.

950   GW   ISSN 0341-0137
PJ5
DEUTSCHE MORGENLAENDISCHE GESELLSCHAFT. ZEITSCHRIFT. (Supplement avail.) (Text in English, German) 1847. s-a. DM.168. Franz Steiner Verlag Wiesbaden GmbH, Birkenwaldstr. 44, 70191 Stuttgart, Germany. TEL 0711-2582-0. FAX 0711-2582390. (Subscr. to: Postfach 101061, 70009 Stuttgart, Germany) Ed. Tilman Nagel. adv.; bk.rev.; bibl.; index. circ. 1,200. (also avail. in microfiche from IDC,BHP; back issues avail.; reprint service avail. from KTO) **Indexed:** Bibl.Ling., Numis.Lit. **Document type:** academic/scholarly publication.
—Genuine Article; SWETS. CCC.

950   GW   ISSN 0341-0803
DS57
DEUTSCHE MORGENLAENDISCHE GESELLSCHAFT. ZEITSCHRIFT. SUPPLEMENTA. irreg., vol.10, 1994. price varies. Franz Steiner Verlag Wiesbaden GmbH, Birkenwaldstr. 44, 70191 Stuttgart, Germany. TEL 0711-2582-0. FAX 0711-2582390. (Subscr. to: Postfach 101061, 70009 Stuttgart, Germany) (also avail. in microfiche from BHP) **Document type:** monographic series.

956   GW   ISSN 0012-1169
DEUTSCHER PALAESTINA-VEREIN. ZEITSCHRIFT. (Text in English, French and German) 1878. 2/yr. DM.92. (Deutscher Verein zur Erforschung Palaestinas) Harrassowitz Verlag, Taunusstr. 14, 65183 Wiesbaden, Germany. TEL 0611-530-0. FAX 0611-530570. TELEX 4186135. (Subscr. to: Postfach 2929, 65019 Wiesbaden, Germany) Eds. Manfred Weippert, Siegfried Mittmann. adv.; bk.rev.; illus. circ. 600. (also avail. in microfiche from IDC; back issues avail.; reprint service avail. from KTO) **Indexed:** Bibl.Ling., Mid.East: Abstr.& Ind. **Document type:** academic/scholarly publication.
—Genuine Article. CCC.

954   II
DHANIRAM BHALLA GRANTHAMALA. (Text in Hindi and Sanskrit) irreg., vol.19, 1972. price varies. Vishveshvaranand Vedic Research Institute, P.O. Sadhu Ashram, Hoshiarpur 146021, Punjab, India. Ed. Vishva Bandhu.

956   US   ISSN 1060-4367
DS41
DIGEST OF MIDDLE EAST STUDIES. Abbreviated title: D O M E S. 1992. q. $40 to individuals; institutions $50; students $30. University of Wisconsin at Milwaukee, Milwaukee School of Library and Information Science, Box 413, Milwaukee, WI 53201. TEL 414-229-4707. FAX 414-229-4848. TELEX 4909991372 ALAUI G. E-mail: aman@csd.uwm.edu. Ed. Mohammed Aman. bk.rev. **Indexed:** Bk.Rev.Dig. **Document type:** academic/scholarly publication.
Description: Contains articles and reviews on all topics concerning Islam, Arab countries, Israel, Turkey and Iran. Includes the texts of important Middle East agreements and transcriptions of notable speeches by experts.
Refereed Serial

950 895 495   XR   ISSN 0419-4268
DISSERTATIONES ORIENTALES. (Text in Chinese and English) 1964. irreg. price varies. Ceska Akademie Ved, Orientalni Ustav, Pod Vodarenskou Vezi 4, 182 08 Prague 8, Czech Republic. Ed. Jaroslav Cesar.

950   FR   ISSN 0768-4053
DOCUMENTS D'HISTOIRE MAGHREBINE. 1972. irreg. Librairie Orientaliste Paul Geuthner, 12 rue Vavin, 75006 Paris, France. TEL 33-1-46-34-71-30. FAX 33-1-43-29-75-64. Ed. Chantal de la Veronne.

890   KO
DONG-A MUNHUA/EAST ASIA CULTURE. (Text in Korean.) 1963. irreg., latest no.29. 1500 Won. Seoul National University, Institute of Asian Studies, College of Humanities, San 56-1, Sinlim-dong, Kwanak-ku, Seoul 151-742, S. Korea. FAX 02-871-7244. bk.rev. circ. 500.

950   MP
DORNO, ORNO/EAST & WEST. (Text in Mongolian; summaries in English) 1978. q. Academy of Sciences, Institute of Oriental and International Studies, P.O. Box 48-17, Ulan Bator, Mongolia. Ed. Ts. Batbayar. **Document type:** academic/scholarly publication.
Formerly (until 1991, no.3): Dornodahiny Sudlal - Oriental Studies.
Description: Covers social, political events, history, culture and foreign relations.

EAST. see *GENERAL INTEREST PERIODICALS — Japan*

950   IT   ISSN 0012-8376
AP37
EAST AND WEST. (Text in English) 1951. q. $100. (Istituto Italiano per il Medio ed Estremo Oriente) Herder Editrice e Libreria s.r.l., Piazza Montecitorio 120, 00186 Rome, Italy. TEL 67-94-628. FAX 678-47-51. TELEX 621427 NATEL. adv.; bk.rev.; bibl.; charts; illus.; index. circ. 1,500. **Indexed:** Amer.Hist.& Life, Anthropol.Lit., Bibl.Ling., Hist.Abstr., Numis.Lit. **Document type:** academic/scholarly publication.
—BLDSC (3645.400000); Faxon; UnCover.

950   US
EAST ASIAN HISTORICAL MONOGRAPHS. irreg. Oxford University Press, 200 Madison Ave., New York, NY 10016. TEL 212-679-7300. Ed. Wang Gungwu. **Document type:** monographic series.

EAST ASIAN HISTORY. see *HISTORY — History Of Asia*

950   US
EAST ASIAN RESEARCH AIDS AND TRANSLATIONS. (Text in English or Asian languages) 1984. irreg., vol.5, 1994. price varies. Western Washington University, Center for East Asian Studies, Bellingham, WA 98225-9056. TEL 206-650-3448. Ed. Edward H. Kaplan. **Document type:** monographic series.

950   FR   ISSN 0336-1519
DS531
ECOLE FRANCAISE D'EXTREME-ORIENT. BULLETIN. 1901. irreg., latest vol.80-81, 1993. 280 F. Editions d' Amerique et d'Orient, 11 rue St. Sulpice, 75006 Paris, France. TEL 43-26-86-35. FAX 33-1-43-54-59-54. (also avail. in microfiche from IDC) **Indexed:** A.I.C.P., Amer.Hist.& Life (until 1992), Anthropol.Lit., Bibl.Ling., E.I., Hist.Abstr. (until 1992). **Document type:** academic/scholarly publication, bulletin.
—BLDSC (2496.900000).

950   MX   ISSN 0185-0164
DS1
ESTUDIOS DE ASIA Y AFRICA. 1966. 3/yr. $32 to individuals (foreign $42); institutions $50 (foreign $60) (effective 1995). Colegio de Mexico, A.C., Departamento de Publicaciones, Camino al Ajusco 20, Codigo Postal 01000, Mexico, D.F., Mexico. TEL 525-6455955. FAX 525-6450464. TELEX 1777585 COLME. Ed.Bd. adv.; bk.rev.; cum.index. circ. 1,500. (back issues avail.; reprint service avail. from UMI) **Indexed:** Amer.Hist.& Life, Hist.Abstr., M.L.A.
—SWETS.
Supersedes (in 1974): Estudios Orientales (ISSN 0185-0156)

950   GW
ETHNO-ISLAMICA. 1991. irreg., vol.6, 1994. Ergon-Verlag, Grombuehlstr. 7, 97080 Wuerzburg, Germany. TEL 0931-280084. FAX 0931-282872. Ed. P. Heine. **Document type:** monographic series.

959   BE   ISSN 0531-1926
ETUDES ORIENTALES. 1963. irreg., no.11, 1983. price varies. Librairie-Editions Thanh-Long, 34 rue Dekens, B-1040 Brussels, Belgium. (back issues avail.) **Document type:** monographic series.

ETUDES URBAINES. see *HOUSING AND URBAN PLANNING*

915.66   NE   ISSN 0922-7768
EVLIYA CELEBI'S BOOK OF TRAVELS. (Text in English, Turkish) 1988. irreg., vol.2, 1990. price varies. E.J. Brill, P.O. Box 9000, 2300 PA Leiden, Netherlands. TEL 31-71-5353500. FAX 31-71-5317532. (In N. America: E.J. Brill, 24 Hudson St., Kinderhook, NY 12106. TEL 800-962-4406. FAX 518-758-1959) illus.; maps. (back issues avail.) **Document type:** monographic series.
Description: Publishes scholarly editions of portions of the Seyahatname, with English translation and commentary.

955 297   IR   ISSN 0014-7788
DS251
FARHANG-E IRAN ZAMIN. (Text mainly in Farsi: occasionally in English, French) 1952. q. $40. Iraj Afshar, Ed. & Pub., P.O. Box 19575-583 Niyavaran, Teheran, Iran. TEL 021-283254. bk.rev. circ. 2,000. (also avail. in microfiche) **Indexed:** M.L.A. **Document type:** academic/scholarly publication.

950   AT   ISSN 0085-0586
FLINDERS ASIAN STUDIES LECTURE. 1970. a. price varies. Flinders University of South Australia, School of Social Sciences, Director of Asian Studies, G.P.O. Box 2100, Adelaide, S.A. 5001, Australia. TEL 08-201-2404. FAX 08-201-2566. **Document type:** monographic series.

950   AT
FLINDERS ASIAN STUDIES MONOGRAPH. 1981. irreg. price varies. Flinders University of South Australia, School of Social Sciences, Director of Asian Studies, G.P.O. Box 2100, Adelaide, S.A. 5001, Australia. TEL 08-201-2404. FAX 08-201-2566. **Document type:** monographic series, academic/scholarly publication.

950   PL   ISSN 0015-5675
FOLIA ORIENTALIA. (Text in English, French and German) 1959. a. price varies. Polska Akademia Nauk, Oddzial w Krakowie, Komisja Orientalistyczna - Polish Academy of Sciences, Cracow Section, Commission of Orientalistics, Ul. Slawkowska 17, 31-016 Krakow, Poland. TEL 48-12-224853. FAX 48-12-222791. Ed. Stanislaw Stachowski. bk.rev.; abstr.; bibl. circ. 590. **Indexed:** Bibl.Ling., M.L.A., Numis.Lit., Rel.Islam. (1991-). **Document type:** academic/scholarly publication.
Description: Monographs and research reports from Oriental studies in Poland.

FREE PALESTINE. see *POLITICAL SCIENCE — Civil Rights*

950   GW   ISSN 0170-3307
FREIBURGER ALTORIENTALISCHE STUDIEN. irreg., vol.19, 1995. price varies. Franz Steiner Verlag Wiesbaden GmbH, Birkenwaldstr. 44, 70191 Stuttgart, Germany. TEL 0711-2582-0. FAX 0711-2582390. (Subscr. to: Postfach 101061, 70009 Stuttgart, Germany) Ed. Burkhart Kienast. **Document type:** monographic series.

956   GW   ISSN 0340-6261
FREIBURGER BEITRAEGE ZUR INDOLOGIE. 1968. irreg., vol.27, 1994. price varies. Harrassowitz Verlag, Taunusstr. 14, 65183 Wiesbaden, Germany. TEL 0611-530-0. FAX 0611-530570. TELEX 4186135. (Subscr. to: Postfach 2929, 65019 Wiesbaden, Germany) Ed. Ulrich Schneider. **Document type:** monographic series.

950   GW   ISSN 0724-4703
FREIBURGER FERNOESTLICHE FORSCHUNGEN. 1983. irreg., vol.2, 1992. price varies. Harrassowitz Verlag, Taunusstr. 14, 65183 Wiesbaden, Germany. TEL 0611-530-0. FAX 0611-530570. TELEX 4186135. (Subscr. to: Postfach 2929, 65019 Wiesbaden, Germany) Ed. Peter Greiner. **Document type:** monographic series.

4964 ORIENTAL STUDIES

956 297 GW ISSN 0170-3285
FREIBURGER ISLAMSTUDIEN. irreg., vol.16, 1995. price varies. Franz Steiner Verlag Wiesbaden GmbH, Birkenwaldstr. 44, 70191 Stuttgart, Germany. TEL 0711-2582-0. FAX 0711-2582390. (Subscr. to: Postfach 101061, 70009 Stuttgart, Germany) Ed. Hans Robert Roemer. **Document type:** monographic series.

951 GW ISSN 0429-6656
FREIES ASIEN. 1959. s-m. Deutsch-Chinesische Gesellschaft e.V., Villichgasse 17, 53177 Bonn, Germany. TEL 0228-356535. FAX 0228-357520. Ed. Ingrid Fuchs. bk.rev. circ. 3,500. (looseleaf format; back issues avail.) **Document type:** newsletter.

FU JEN STUDIES; literature & linguistics. see *LITERATURE*

950 II
GANGANATHA JHA KENDRIYA SANSKRIT VIDYAPEETHA. JOURNAL. (Text in English, Hindi, Sanskrit) 1943. q. Rs.60($15) Ganganatha Jha Kendriya Sanskrit Vidyapeetha, Chandrashakhar Azad Park, Allahabad 211002, Uttar Pradesh, India. TEL 0532-600957. Eds. Gaya C. Tripathi, Maya Malaviya. bk.rev.; illus.; index. circ. 1,000. **Document type:** academic/scholarly publication.
  Formerly: Ganganatha Jha Research Institute. Journal (ISSN 0016-4461)
  Description: Devoted to oriental studies in general, and India studies in particular.

890 297 BN ISSN 0350-1418
DB240.5
GAZI HUSREVBEGOVA BIBLIOTEKA. ANALI. (Text in Serbo-Croatian; summaries in English) 1972. a. Gazi Husrevbegova Biblioteka, Obala Pariske Komune 4, 71000 Sarajevo, Bosnia Hercegovina. (Co-sponsor: Starjesinstvo Islamske Zajednice) Ed. Abdurahman Hukic. circ. 1,500. **Indexed:** Amer.Hist.& Life (until 1987), Hist.Abstr. (until 1987).

950 GW ISSN 0016-9080
GESELLSCHAFT FUER NATUR- UND VOELKERKUNDE OSTASIENS. NACHRICHTEN; Zeitschrift fuer Kultur und Geschichte Ostasiens. (Text in English and German) 1926. s-a. DM.70 (members DM.60). Universitaet Hamburg, Seminar fuer Sprache und Kultur Japans, Von Melle Park 6-7, 20146 Hamburg, Germany. TEL 040-41234884. Ed. Herbert Worm. bk.rev.; bibl.; charts; illus. circ. 750. **Indexed:** Amer.Hist.& Life, Hist.Abstr. **Document type:** academic/scholarly publication.
  —CCC.

GHANTA. see *EDUCATION — International Education Programs*

950 GW ISSN 0170-3455
GLASENAPP-STIFTUNG. irreg., vol.38, 1995. price varies. (Glasenapp-Stiftung) Franz Steiner Verlag Wiesbaden GmbH, Birkenwaldstr. 44, 70191 Stuttgart, Germany. TEL 0711-2582-0. FAX 0711-2582390. (Subscr. to: Postfach 101061, 70009 Stuttgart, Germany) **Document type:** monographic series.

959 US
GLOBAL STUDIES: INDIAN AND SOUTH ASIA. 1993. irreg. $13.95. Dushkin Publishing Group, Sluice Dock, Guilford, CT 06437-9989. TEL 203-453-4351. FAX 203-453-6000. Ed. James Norton; Pub. Ian Nielsen. illus. **Document type:** academic/scholarly publication.

954 300 II ISSN 0970-1427
GLORY OF INDIA; quarterly on Indology. (Text in English and Hindi) 1977. q. Rs.40($22) Motilal Banarsidass (Delhi), 40, U.A., Bungalow Rd., Jawahar Nagar, Delhi 110007, India. TEL 11-2911985. FAX 011-2930689. Ed. N.P. Jain. adv.; bk.rev.; abstr.; bibl.

935 950 GW ISSN 0340-6326
GOETTINGER ORIENTFORSCHUNGEN. REIHE I: SYRIACA. irreg., vol.35, 1994. price varies. Harrassowitz Verlag, Taunusstr. 14, 65183 Wiesbaden, Germany. TEL 0611-530-0. FAX 0611-530570. TELEX 4186135. (Subscr. to: Postfach 2929, 65019 Wiesbaden, Germany) **Document type:** monographic series.

950 GW ISSN 0173-2358
GOETTINGER ORIENTFORSCHUNGEN. REIHE II: STUDIEN ZUR SPAETANTIKEN UND FRUEHCHRISTLICHEN KUNST. 1980. irreg., vol.4, III-IV, 1993. price varies. Harrassowitz Verlag, Taunusstr. 14, 65183 Wiesbaden, Germany. TEL 0611-530-0. FAX 0611-530570. TELEX 4186135. (Subscr. to: Postfach 2929, 65019 Wiesbaden, Germany) **Document type:** monographic series.

932 GW ISSN 0340-6342
GOETTINGER ORIENTFORSCHUNGEN. REIHE IV: AEGYPTEN. 1973. irreg., vol.30, 1994. price varies. Harrassowitz Verlag, Taunusstr. 14, 65183 Wiesbaden, Germany. TEL 0611-530-0. FAX 0611-530570. TELEX 4186135. (Subscr. to: Postfach 2929, 65019 Wiesbaden, Germany) Eds. Friedrich Junge, Wolfhart Westendorf. **Document type:** monographic series.

954 NE
▼**GONDA INDOLOGICAL STUDIES.** (Text in English) 1994. irreg., vol.4, 1995. prices varies. Forsten, Postbus 6148, 9702 HC Groningen, Netherlands. TEL 31-50-259104. FAX 31-50-275618. (Dist. in N. America by: John Benjamins Publishing Co., Box 27519, Philadelphia, PA 19118-0519. TEL 215-836-1200. FAX 215-836-1204) (back issues avail.) **Document type:** academic/scholarly publication.

950 NE ISSN 0924-8846
GRONINGEN ORIENTAL STUDIES. (Text in English) 1986. irreg., vol.11, 1995. price varies. Forsten, Postbus 6148, 9702 HC Groningen, Netherlands. TEL 31-50-259104. FAX 31-50-275618. (Dist. in N. America by: John Benjamins Publishing Co., Box 27519, Philadelphia, PA 19118-0519. TEL 215-836-1200. FAX 215-836-1204) illus. (back issues avail.) **Document type:** monographic series, proceedings.
  —BLDSC (4217.975000).
  Description: Publishes studies of Indian religion, art, medicine, science and literature.

951 915.134 CC
GUIZHOU MINZU YANJIU/STUDY OF GUIZHOU NATIONALITIES. (Text in Chinese) q. $20.40. Guizhou Sheng Minzu Yanjiusuo - Guizhou Nationality Research Institute, No. 16, Bianjing Xiang, Bajiaoyan, Guiyang, Guizhou 550001, People's Republic of China. TEL 625623. (Dist. in US by: China Books & Periodicals, Inc., 2929 24th St., San Francisco, CA 94110. TEL 415-282-2994) Ed. Wu Yongqing.

950 CH
HANDBOOK OF ASIAN PACIFIC COUNTRIES AND REGIONS. (Text in English) irreg., 2nd ed., 1992. Asian-Pacific Cultural Center, Asian-Pacific Parliamentarians' Union, 6F, 66 Aikuo East Rd., Taipei, Taiwan 100, Republic of China. TEL 02-322-2139. FAX 02-322-2138. Eds. Chen Tai-Chu, Francis Fine.

930.1 950 NE
HANDBUCH DER ORIENTALISTIK. (Consists of 6 sections: Der Nahe und der Mittlere Osten; Indien; Indonesien, Malaysia und die Philippinen; China; Japan; Handbook of Uralistic Studies) 1952. irreg., latest 1995. price varies. E.J. Brill, P.O. Box 9000, 2300 PA Leiden, Netherlands. TEL 31-71-5353500. FAX 31-71-5317532. TELEX 39296 BRILL NL. (In N. America: E.J. Brill, 24 Hudson St., Kinderhook, NY 12106. TEL 800-962-4406. FAX 518-758-1959) Ed. B. Spuler. illus. (back issues avail.) **Document type:** monographic series, bibliography.
  Description: Scholarly monographs, bibliographies, research tools and reference works on all aspects of Oriental studies, encompassing social, political and cultural history, religions, the sciences, archaeology and linguistics.
  Refereed Serial

950 NE ISSN 0169-9423
HANDBUCH DER ORIENTALISTIK. 1. ABTEILUNG. DER NAHE UND DER MITTLERE OSTEN. 1952. irreg., vol.21, 1995. price varies. E.J. Brill, P.O. Box 9000, 2300 PA Leiden, Netherlands. TEL 31-71-5353500. FAX 31-71-5317532. TELEX 39296 BRILL NL. (In N. America: E.J. Brill, 24 Hudson St., Kinderhook, NY 12106. TEL 800-962-4406. FAX 518-758-1959) Ed. B. Spuler. (back issues avail.) **Document type:** monographic series, bibliography.
  Description: Scholarly monographs, bibliographic works and research tools pertaining to the political, economic, and social history of the Near and Middle East, encompassing studies of religions, the sciences, archaeology (including Egyptology) and linguistics.
  Refereed Serial

954 NE ISSN 0169-9377
HANDBUCH DER ORIENTALISTIK. 2. ABTEILUNG. INDIEN. 1966. irreg., vol.9, 1995. price varies. E.J. Brill, P.O. Box 9000, 2300 PA Leiden, Netherlands. TEL 31-71-5353500. FAX 31-71-5317532. TELEX 39296 BRILL NL. (In N. America: E.J. Brill, 24 Hudson St., Kinderhook, NY 12106. TEL 800-962-4406. FAX 518-758-1959) Ed. B. Spuler. **Document type:** monographic series.
  Description: Scholarly monographs, bibliographies and research tools pertaining to the political, economic, social, linguistic and religious history of the Indian sub-continent.
  Refereed Serial

959 NE ISSN 0169-9571
HANDBUCH DER ORIENTALISTIK. 3. ABTEILUNG. INDONESIEN, MALAYSIA UND DIE PHILIPPINEN. 1972. irreg., latest 1995. price varies. E.J. Brill, P.O. Box 9000, 2300 PA Leiden, Netherlands. TEL 31-71-5353500. FAX 31-71-5317532. TELEX 39296 BRILL NL. (In N. America: E.J. Brill, 24 Hudson St., Kinderhook, NY 12106. TEL 800-962-4406. FAX 518-758-1959) Ed. B. Spuler. **Document type:** monographic series.
  Description: Scholarly monographs on topics in the history, religions, culture and linguistics of Indonesia, the Philippines and Malaysia, including the Cape-Malays in South Africa.
  Refereed Serial

951 NE ISSN 0169-9520
HANDBUCH DER ORIENTALISTIK. 4. ABTEILUNG. CHINA. 1976. irreg., vol.9, 1995. price varies. E.J. Brill, P.O. Box 9000, 2300 PA Leiden, Netherlands. TEL 31-71-5353500. FAX 31-71-5317532. TELEX 39296 BRILL NL. (In N. America: E.J. Brill, 24 Hudson St., Kinderhook, NY 12106. TEL 800-962-4406. FAX 518-758-1959) Ed. B. Spuler. **Document type:** monographic series.
  Refereed Serial

952 NE ISSN 0921-5239
HANDBUCH DER ORIENTALISTIK. 5. ABTEILUNG. JAPAN. 1988. irreg., latest 1994. price varies. E.J. Brill, P.O. Box 9000, 2300 PA Leiden, Netherlands. TEL 31-71-5353500. FAX 31-71-5317532. TELEX 39296 BRILL NL. (In N. America: E.J. Brill, 24 Hudson St., Kinderhook, NY 12106. TEL 800-962-4406. FAX 518-758-1959) Ed. B. Spuler. **Document type:** monographic series.
  Description: Scholarly studies on topics in the religious, literary, social, economic, legal and political history of Japan.
  Refereed Serial

494 NE
HANDBUCH DER ORIENTALISTIK. 8. ABTEILUNG. ZENTRALASIEN. 1988. irreg., vol.2, 1995. price varies. E.J. Brill, P.O. Box 9000, 2300 PA Leiden, Netherlands. TEL 31-71-5353500. FAX 31-71-5317532. TELEX 39296 BRILL NL. (In N. America: E.J. Brill, 24 Hudson St., Kinderhook, NY 12106. TEL 800-962-4406. FAX 518-758-1959) Ed. B. Spuler. (back issues avail.) **Document type:** monographic series.
  Description: Discusses the history and culture of the Central Asian regions, including linguistics of the Uralic languages.
  Refereed Serial

HANDES AMSORYA; Zeitschrift fuer Armenische Philologie. see *LINGUISTICS*

HARVARD ARMENIAN TEXTS AND STUDIES. see *HISTORY — History Of The Near East*

950   US   ISSN 0073-0548
DS501
HARVARD JOURNAL OF ASIATIC STUDIES. 1936. s-a. $30 to individuals; institutions $45 (effective 1992). Harvard-Yenching Institute, 2 Divinity Ave., Cambridge, MA 02138. TEL 617-495-2758. FAX 617-495-7798. Ed. Howard S. Hibbett. bk.rev.; cum.index: 1936-80; index every 5 yrs. circ. 1,200. (also avail. in microform from UMI,MIM; reprint service avail. from UMI,SCH) **Indexed:** Amer.Hist.& Life, Anthropol.Lit., Arts & Hum.Cit.Ind., Bibl.Ling., Bk.Rev.Ind., Curr.Cont., Hist.Abstr., Hum.Ind., Ind.Bk.Rev.Hum., M.L.A., Mid.East: Abstr.& Ind., Soc.Sci.Ind. **Document type:** academic/scholarly publication.
—Faxon; Genuine Article; SWETS; UMI; UnCover.
Description: Covers the languages, literatures, cultures, and histories of the countries in Eastern and Central Asia.

410   SZ   ISSN 0073-0971
HAUTES ETUDES ORIENTALES. 1968. irreg., no.30, 1995. (Ecole Pratique des Hautes Etudes, Centre de Recherches d'Histoire et de Philologie, FR) Librairie Droz S.A., 11, rue Massot, CH-1211 Geneva 12, Switzerland. TEL 022-3466666. FAX 022-3472391. circ. 600. **Document type:** monographic series.
—CCC.
Description: Discusses studies of military, literature and poetry from the Far East.

951   US   ISSN 1055-9884
DS721
HEAVEN EARTH; the Chinese art of living. 1991. 3/yr. $14 (Canada $20; elsewhere $24). China Advocates, Box 22459, San Francisco, CA 94122. TEL 415-665-4505. Ed. Howard Dewar.

HENRY MARTYN INSTITUTE OF ISLAMIC STUDIES. BULLETIN. see *RELIGIONS AND THEOLOGY — Islamic*

961   MR   ISSN 0018-1005
DT301
HESPERIS - TAMUDA. (Text in English, French, Spanish) N.S. 1960. 2/yr. $30 per no. Universite Mohammed V, Faculte des Lettres et des Sciences Humaines, Association des Sciences de l'Homme, Avenue Moulay Cherif, B.P. 1040, Rabat, Morocco. TEL 212-7-771889. FAX 212-7-772068. bk.rev.; bibl.; charts; illus. **Indexed:** A.I.C.P., Amer.Hist.& Life, Hist.Abstr., Numis.Lit. **Document type:** academic/scholarly publication.
Description: Covers the history of North Africa and the Middle East.

935   BE   ISSN 0776-2666
HETHITICA. (Subseries of: Bibliotheque des Cahiers de l'Institut Linguistique de Louvain) 1972. irreg., vol.11, 1992. price varies. (Universite Catholique de Louvain, Institut Linguistique de Louvain) Editions Peeters s.p.r.l., Bondgenotenlaan 153, 3000 Leuven, Belgium. TEL 32-16-235170. FAX 32-16-228500. Ed. R. Lebrun. (back issues avail.) **Document type:** academic/scholarly publication.

958   NP
HIMALAYAN CULTURE. (Text in English or Nepali) 1978. q. Re.38($6) Hari Bangsha Kirant, 20-136 Kamal Pokhari, Kathmandu 711000, Nepal.

890   TI   ISSN 0018-862X
AS653
I B L A. (Text mainly in French; occasionally in Arabic and English) 1937. s-a. 30 din.($39) Institut des Belles Lettres Arabes, 12 rue Jamaa el Haoua, 1008 Tunis, Tunisia. TEL 01-560133. FAX 01-572683. Ed. Jean Fontaine. adv.; bk.rev.; bibl.; index. circ. 850. (also avail. in microfiche) **Indexed:** A.I.C.P., Bibl.Ling., Bull.Signal., Lang.& Lang.Behav.Abstr., M.L.A. **Document type:** academic/scholarly publication.
Description: Covers questions in the field of arts and human sciences concerning the Arab-Muslim world, with special reference to Tunisia.

954 800   II
IMAGE. (Text in English) vol.2, 1977. s-a. Rs.10($3) Image Publication, Sahadevkhunta, Balasore 756001, Orissa, India. Ed. Indu Bhusan Kar. adv.; bk.rev.

INDIAN HORIZONS. see *HISTORY — History Of Asia*

954   II   ISSN 0019-686X
DS401
INDICA. (Text in English) 1964. s-a. Rs.55($10) Heras Institute of Indian History and Culture, St. Xavier's College, Bombay 400 001, India. TEL 22-262-0662. Ed. Aubrey Mascarenhas, S.J. adv.; bk.rev.; illus.; index, cum.index. circ. 400. (back issues avail.) **Indexed:** Amer.Hist.& Life, Hist.Abstr. **Document type:** academic/scholarly publication.
Description: Articles on history, literature, archeology, art and religion.

INDICES VERBORUM LINGUAE MONGOLIAE MONUMENTIS TRADITORUM. see *LINGUISTICS*

INDO-ASIA; fuer Politik, Kultur und Wirtschaft Indiens und Suedost Asiens. see *POLITICAL SCIENCE*

INDO-IRAN JOURNAL. see *POLITICAL SCIENCE*

891 955   NE   ISSN 0019-7246
PK1   **CODEN: IIRJAU**
INDO-IRANIAN JOURNAL. 1957. q. fl.428 to institutions; $274 to institutions in U.S. (effective 1996). Kluwer Academic Publishers, Postbus 17, 3300 AA Dordrecht, Netherlands. TEL 31-78-392392. FAX 31-78-392254. TELEX 29245 KAPG NL. E-mail: SERVICES@WKAP.NL. (Dist. by: Kluwer Academic Publishers Group, P.O. Box 322, 3300 AH Dordrecht, Netherlands. TEL 31-78-392392. FAX 31-78-546474; N. America dist. addr.: Box 358, Accord Sta., Hingham, MA 02018-0358. TEL 617-871-6600. FAX 617-871-6528) Eds. J.W. De Jong, M. Witzel. adv.; bk.rev.; index. (also avail. in microform from UMI; reprint service avail. from SWZ) **Indexed:** Arts & Hum.Cit.Ind., ASCA, Bibl.Ling., Curr.Cont., IBR, IBZ, Ind.Bk.Rev.Hum., Lang.& Lang.Behav.Abstr., M.L.A., Mid.East: Abstr.& Ind., Phil.Ind., Rel.Ind.One, Sociol.Abstr. **Document type:** academic/scholarly publication.
—Faxon; Genuine Article; SWETS; UMI; UnCover. CCC.
Description: Publishes original scholarship on ancient and medieval Indian and Iranian languages, literatures and linguistics, as well as related philosophical and textual issues.
Refereed Serial

954   FR
INDOLOGICA TAURINENSIA. (Text in various languages) 1973. irreg. Association Internationale pour les Etudes Sanskrites - International Association of Sanskrit Studies, c/o C. Caillat, Treas., 52 rue du Cardinal Lemoine, 75231 Paris Cedex 05, France. TEL 33-1-44-27-10-98. (back issues avail.) **Indexed:** Bibl.Ling. **Document type:** academic/scholarly publication, monographic series.
Refereed Serial

991   US   ISSN 0019-7289
DS611
INDONESIA (ITHACA). 1966. s-a. $20 (foreign $25). Cornell University, Southeast Asia Program, 640 Stewart Ave., Ithaca, NY 14850. TEL 607-255-8038. FAX 607-277-1904. TELEX WUI-6713054. Ed. Audrey Kahin. bk.rev.; bibl.; charts; illus.; stat.; index every 3 yrs. circ. 900. (also avail. in microform from UMI; reprint service avail. from UMI; back issues avail.) **Indexed:** Asian-Pac.Econ.Lit., E.I., Int.Polit.Sci.Abstr. **Document type:** academic/scholarly publication.
—BLDSC (4437.630000); SWETS; UMI; UnCover.
Description: Interdisciplinary journal devoted to Indonesia's culture, history and socio-political problems.

INKSTONE; a magazine of haiku. see *LITERATURE — Poetry*

951 291   BE
INSTITUT BELGE DES HAUTES ETUDES CHINOISES. PUBLICATIONS. (Text mainly in French, occasionally in English) 1932. irreg., vol.26, 1995. price varies. Editions Peeters s.p.r.l., Bondgenotenlaan 153, 3000 Leuven, Belgium. TEL 32-16-235170. FAX 32-16-228500. (back issues avail.) **Document type:** monographic series.
Supersedes: Melanges Chinois et Bouddhiques (ISSN 0775-4612)
Description: Publishes studies on the history, cultures and religions of China and surrounding areas, including Nepal, Tibet and Mongolia.

ORIENTAL STUDIES   4965

935 955   BE   ISSN 0553-2841
INSTITUT DES ETUDES IRANIENNES. TRAVAUX. Key Title: Travaux de l'Institut d'Etudes Iraniennes de l'Universite de la Sorbonne Nouvelle. (Text in French) 1966. irreg., vol.14, 1991. price varies. Editions Peeters s.p.r.l., Bondgenotenlaan 153, 3000 Leuven, Belgium. TEL 32-16-235170. FAX 32-16-228500. (back issues avail.) **Document type:** monographic series.
Description: Publishes studies on the history, language and culture of Iran from ancient times to the present.

INSTITUT DOMINICAIN D'ETUDES ORIENTALES DU CAIRE. MELANGES. see *HISTORY — History Of The Near East*

INSTITUT FRANCAIS D'ARCHEOLOGIE ORIENTALE DU CAIRE. BIBLIOTHEQUE D'ETUDE. see *ARCHAEOLOGY*

INSTITUT FRANCAIS D'ARCHEOLOGIE ORIENTALE DU CAIRE. BIBLIOTHEQUE GENERALE. see *ARCHAEOLOGY*

INSTITUT FRANCAIS D'ARCHEOLOGIE ORIENTALE DU CAIRE. BULLETIN. see *ARCHAEOLOGY*

950   II   ISSN 0073-8352
INSTITUT FRANCAIS DE PONDICHERY. DEPARTEMENT D'INDOLOGIE. PUBLICATIONS. (Text in English, French) 1956. irreg.(approx. 4/yr.). price varies. Institut Francais de Pondichery, P.O. Box 33, Pondichery 605 001, India. TEL 91-413-34170. FAX 91-413-29534. TELEX 469224 FRAN IN. (Dist. outside India: Librairie Adrien Maisonneuve, 11 rue Saint Sulpice, 75006 Paris, France) Ed. F. Grimalal. bk.rev.; index. circ. 500. **Indexed:** Bull.Signal.
Formerly: Institut Francais d'Indologie. Publications.

956   GW   ISSN 0073-8387
INSTITUT FUER ASIENKUNDE. SCHRIFTEN. (Text in German; summaries in English) 1957. irreg., no.47, 1986. price varies. Harrassowitz Verlag, Taunusstr. 14, 65183 Wiesbaden, Germany. TEL 0611-530-0. FAX 0611-530570. TELEX 4186135. (Subscr. to: Postfach 2929, 65019 Wiesbaden, Germany) **Document type:** monographic series.

INSTITUTE OF ASIAN STUDIES. JOURNAL. see *SOCIOLOGY*

950 020   HK   ISSN 0161-7397
Z688.A75
INTERNATIONAL ASSOCIATION OF ORIENTALIST LIBRARIANS. BULLETIN. 1971. s-a. $10 to individuals; institutions $12. International Association of Orientalist Librarians, c/o University of Hong Kong Libraries, Pikfulam Rd., Hong Kong, Hong Kong. bk.rev. circ. 200. **Document type:** bulletin.
Formerly: International Association of Orientalist Librarians. Newsletter (ISSN 0146-6992)

950 001.3 300   JA
PJ21
INTERNATIONAL CONFERENCE OF EASTERN STUDIES. TRANSACTIONS. (Text in English) 1957. a. 2300 Yen. Toho Gakkai - Institute of Eastern Culture, 4-1, Nishi-Kanda 2-chome, Chiyoda-ku, Tokyo 101, Japan. TEL 03-3262-7221. FAX 03-3262-7227. Ed.Bd. (back issues avail.) **Indexed:** M.L.A. **Document type:** proceedings.
Formerly (until Feb. 1994): International Conference of Orientalists in Japan. Transactions (ISSN 0538-6012)
Description: Publishes full texts and abstracts of the papers presented at the Conference.

950   HK
INTERNATIONAL DIRECTORY OF CENTERS FOR ASIAN STUDIES. 1975. biennial. $48. Asian Research Service, G.P.O. Box 2232, Hong Kong. TEL 5707227. FAX 5128050. Ed. Nelson Leung. circ. 1,000. **Document type:** directory.

ORIENTAL STUDIES

956 UK ISSN 0020-7438
DS41
INTERNATIONAL JOURNAL OF MIDDLE EAST STUDIES. 1970. q. £90($136) (effective 1996). (Middle East Studies Association of North America - M E S A, US) Cambridge University Press, Edinburgh Bldg., Shaftesbury Rd., Cambridge CB2 2RU, England. TEL 01223-312393. FAX 01223-315052. TELEX 851817256. (N. American addr.: Cambridge University Press, Journals Dept., 40 W. 20th St., New York, NY 10011. TEL 212-924-3900. FAX 212-691-3239) (Co-sponsor: British Society for Middle East Studies) Ed. R.S. Humphreys. adv.; bk.rev. (also avail. in microform from UMI; back issues avail.; reprint service avail. from SWZ,UMI) Indexed: A.B.C.Pol.Sci., Amer.Hist.& Life, Bibl.Ling., Commun.Abstr., Curr.Cont., Geo.Abstr., Hist.Abstr., IDA, Int.Polit.Sci.Abstr., M.L.A., Mid.East: Abstr.& Ind., Polit.Sci.Abstr., Rural Recreat.Tour.Abstr., Soc.Sci.Ind., SSCI, World Agri.Econ.& Rural Sociol.Abstr. **Document type:** academic/scholarly publication.
—BLDSC (4542.358000); Faxon; Genuine Article; SWETS; UMI; UnCover. **CCC**.
Description: Features research on the Middle East from the seventh century to the present day: history, politics, economics, anthropology, sociology, literature and folklore, comparative religion and law.

950 HK
INTERNATIONAL SYMPOSIA ON ASIAN STUDIES. PROCEEDINGS. 1979. a. $125. Asian Research Service, G.P.O. Box 2232, Hong Kong. TEL 5707227. FAX 5128050. Ed. Nelson Leung. **Document type:** proceedings.

IRAN AND CENTRAL ASIA. see HISTORY — History Of The Near East

955 US ISSN 0021-0862
CODEN: IRSTEK
IRANIAN STUDIES. 1968. s-a. $35 to individuals; institutions $40 (foreign $45). Society for Iranian Studies, Middle East Center, DR-05, University of Washington, Seattle, WA 98195. TEL 206-543-4227. FAX 206-685-0668. Ed. Abbas Amanat. adv.; bk.rev.; bibl.; charts; illus. circ. 500. Indexed: Anthropol.Lit., Bibl.Ling., Ind.Islam., M.L.A., Mid.East: Abstr.& Ind. **Document type:** academic/scholarly publication.
—Faxon; SWETS.

950 GW ISSN 0944-1271
IRANICA. 1993. irreg. price varies. Harrassowitz Verlag, Taunusstr. 14, 65183 Wiesbaden, Germany. TEL 0611-530-0. FAX 0611-53070. TELEX 4186135. **Document type:** monographic series.

IRANICA ANTIQUA. see ARCHAEOLOGY

IRANICA ANTIQUA SUPPLEMENTA. see ARCHAEOLOGY

955 GW ISSN 0578-7076
IRANISTISCHE MITTEILUNGEN. (Text in English and German) 1967. irreg. (2-4/yr.). Antigone-Verlag, Postfach 1147, 35105 Allendorf-Eder, Germany. TEL 06452-1800. Ed. Helmhart Kanus-Crede. bk.rev. circ. 50. (back issues avail.) **Document type:** academic/scholarly publication.
Description: Iranian studies.

IRAQ. see ARCHAEOLOGY

AL-ISLAAM. see RELIGIONS AND THEOLOGY — Islamic

297 GW ISSN 0021-1818
DS36
DER ISLAM; Zeitschrift fuer Geschichte und Kultur des Islamischen Orients. (Text in English, German) 1910. s-a. DM.179. Walter de Gruyter and Co., Genthiner Str. 13, 10785 Berlin, Germany. TEL 030-26005-0. FAX 030-26005251. TELEX 184027. (U.S. addr.: Walter de Gruyter, Inc., 200 Saw Mill River Rd., Hawthorne, NY 10532) Eds. Albrecht Noth, Bertold Spuler. adv.; bk.rev.; bibl.; illus. circ. 500. Indexed: Amer.Hist.& Life (until 1992), Bibl.Ling., Curr.Cont., E.I., Hist.Abstr. (until 1992), M.L.A., Numis.Lit., Rel.Ind.One. **Document type:** academic/scholarly publication.
—BLDSC (4583.013000); Faxon; Genuine Article; SWETS. **CCC**.

297 892.7 II ISSN 0021-1834
DS36
ISLAMIC CULTURE. (Text in English) 1927. q. $8. Islamic Culture Board, Opposite Osmania University Post Office, Hyderabad 7, India. Ed. Syed Sirajuddin. adv.; bk.rev.; bibl.; illus.; index. circ. 700. (also avail. in microform from UMI; microfiche from IDC; reprint service avail. from KTO) Indexed: Amer.Hist.& Life, Hist.Abstr., Ind.Bk.Rev.Hum., Mid.East: Abstr.& Ind.
—Faxon; SWETS; UnCover.

ISLAMIC EDUCATION. see EDUCATION

ISLAMIC HISTORY AND CIVILIZATION. see RELIGIONS AND THEOLOGY — Islamic

297 892.7 UK ISSN 0021-1842
D198
ISLAMIC QUARTERLY; a review of Islamic Culture. 1954. q. £20 (outside Europe £25) (effective 1995). Islamic Cultural Centre, 146 Park Rd., London NW8 7RG, England. TEL 0171-724-3363-7. FAX 0171-724-0493. Ed. Ali Mughram al-Ghamdi. bk.rev. circ. 1,500. (back issues avail.) Indexed: Amer.Hist.& Life, Hist.Abstr. **Document type:** academic/scholarly publication.
—BLDSC (4583.030000); SWETS; UMI; UnCover.

ISRAEL EXPLORATION JOURNAL. see ARCHAEOLOGY

950 NE ISSN 0334-4401
PJ3001
ISRAEL ORIENTAL STUDIES. (Text in Arabic, English, French, German) 1971. irreg., vol.14, 1994. price varies. (Tel Aviv University, Faculty of Humanities, IS) E.J. Brill, P.O. Box 9000, 2300 PA Leiden, Netherlands. TEL 31-71-5353500. FAX 31-71-5317532. TELEX 39296 BRILL NL. (In N. America: E.J. Brill, 24 Hudson St., Kinderhook, NY 12106. TEL 800-962-4406. FAX 518-758-1959) Ed.Bd. bk.rev. circ. 1,000. (back issues avail.) Indexed: Bibl.Ling. **Document type:** monographic series.
Description: Publishes original studies on topics relating to the ancient Near East, Judaism, Christianity and Islam, and Indian civilizations.
Refereed Serial

ISSUES & STUDIES. see POLITICAL SCIENCE — International Relations

ISTANBULER MITTEILUNGEN. see ARCHAEOLOGY

950 IT
ISTITUTO UNIVERSITARIO ORIENTALE DI NAPOLI. ANNALI. (Text in English, French, Italian) 1940; N.S. 1944. q. (plus 4 supplements). L.125000($100) Herder Editrice e Libreria s.r.l., Piazza Montecitorio 120, 00186 Rome, Italy. TEL 67-94-628. FAX 678-47-51. TELEX 621427 NATEL. Ed. Luigi Cagni. bk.rev.; bibl. (back issues avail.) Indexed: Bibl.Ling. **Document type:** academic/scholarly publication.
Supersedes: Istituto Orientale di Napoli. Annali (ISSN 0392-6869)

ISTITUTO UNIVERSITARIO ORIENTALE DI NAPOLI. SEMINARIO DI STUDI DEL MONDO CLASSICO. ANNALI. SEZIONE LINGUISTICA. see CLASSICAL STUDIES

952 GW ISSN 0937-2008
IZUMI; Quellen, Studien und Materialen zur Kultur Japans. 1989. irreg., vol.1, 1989. Harrassowitz Verlag, Taunusstr. 14, 65183 Wiesbaden, Germany. TEL 0611-530-0. FAX 0611-530-570. TELEX 4186135. (Subscr. to: Postfach 2929, 65019 Wiesbaden, Germany) Ed. Klaus Kracht. **Document type:** monographic series.

952 059.956 JA ISSN 0385-2318
DS821
JAPAN FOUNDATION NEWSLETTER. (Text in English) 1973. bi-m. free. Japan Foundation, Ark-Mori Bldg., 1-12-32, Akasaka, Minato-ku, Tokyo 107, Japan. TEL 03-5562-3532. FAX 03-5562-3501. bk.rev. circ. 8,000. (back issues avail.) **Document type:** newsletter.
Description: Features cultural highlights, research reports, conference reports and foundation activities. Intended for those interested in Japanese culture and international cultural exchange.

JAPAN LETTER. see BUSINESS AND ECONOMICS — Economic Situation And Conditions

JAPANESE JOURNAL OF RELIGIOUS STUDIES. see RELIGIONS AND THEOLOGY — Other Denominations And Sects

JAPANESE SWORD SOCIETY OF THE U S BULLETIN. see ANTIQUES

952 GW ISSN 0934-9995
JAPANISCHE FACHTEXTE. 1980. irreg., vol.3, 1988. Harrassowitz Verlag, Taunusstr. 14, 65183 Wiesbaden, Germany. TEL 0611-530-0. FAX 0611-530-570. TELEX 4186135. (Subscr. to: Postfach 2929, 65019 Wiesbaden, Germany) Ed. Bruno Lewin. **Document type:** monographic series.

952 US ISSN 1071-4227
JAPANOPHILE. 1974. q. $14 (foreign $20) (effective 1994); newsstand price: $3.95. Japanophile, Box 223, Okemos, MI 48864. TEL 517-669-2109. Ed. Earl R. Snodgrass. adv. contact: Vada L. Davis. bk.rev. circ. 800. (back issues avail.) **Document type:** consumer publication.
Description: Aims to promote understanding between Japanese and Americans. Contains articles, fiction, art and poetry with a special interest in Japanese culture.

JAPANWIRTSCHAFT. see BUSINESS AND ECONOMICS — Economic Situation And Conditions

952 NE
JAPONICA NEERLANDICA. (Text in English) 1985. irreg., vol. 5, 1992. J.C. Gieben, Nieuwe Herengracht 35, 1011 RM Amsterdam, Netherlands. TEL 31-20-6275170. FAX 31-20-6275170. (Dist. in N. America by: John Benjamins Publishing Co., Box 27519, Philadelphia, PA 19118-0519. TEL 215-836-1204. FAX 215-836-1200) **Document type:** monographic series.
Description: Publishes scholarly studies on topics relating to Japanese history and culture.

950 US
JAVANESE LITERATURE IN SURAKARTU MANUSCRIPTS. 1993. irreg. price varies. Cornell University, Southeast Asia Program, 640 Stewart Ave., Ithaca, NY 14850. TEL 607-255-4359. FAX 607-277-1904. (Subscr. to: S E A P Publications, Cornell University, E. Hill Plaza, Ithaca, NY 14850) **Document type:** bibliography.

950 FR ISSN 0021-762X
PJ4
JOURNAL ASIATIQUE. (Text in English, French) 1822. 4/yr. 3000 BEF (effective 1994). (Societe Asiatique, FR) Editions Peeters s.p.r.l., Bondgenotenlaan 153, 3000 Leuven, Belgium. TEL 32-16-235170. FAX 32-16-228500. adv.; bk.rev.; illus.; index. (also avail. in microfiche from IDC; back issues avail.; reprint service avail. from SCH) Indexed: Bibl.Ling., E.I., M.L.A. **Document type:** academic/scholarly publication.
—SWETS.
Refereed Serial

JOURNAL OF AMERICAN - EAST ASIAN RELATIONS. see HISTORY — History Of Asia

JOURNAL OF ARABIC LITERATURE. see LITERATURE

JOURNAL OF ASIAN AND AFRICAN STUDIES. see SOCIOLOGY

950 US ISSN 0162-6795
DS1
JOURNAL OF ASIAN CULTURE. 1977. a. $10. University of California at Los Angeles, Department of East Asian Languages and Cultures, Graduate Students in Asian Studies, 290 Royce Hall, Los Angeles, CA 90024. TEL 213-206-8235. Ed. Adam Schorr. adv.; bk.rev.; charts; illus. circ. 500. Indexed: Amer.Hist.& Life, Hist.Abstr., Sociol.Abstr., Sociol.Abstr. **Document type:** academic/scholarly publication.
Description: Annual publication of graduate students whose research involves various aspects of Asian studies.

ORIENTAL STUDIES

950   US   ISSN 0021-9118
DS501
JOURNAL OF ASIAN STUDIES. 1941. q. $60. Association for Asian Studies, Inc., 1 Lane Hall, University of Michigan, Ann Arbor, MI 48109. TEL 313-665-2490. Ed. Anand A. Yang. adv.; bk.rev.; bibl.; charts; illus.; stat.; index. circ. 10,000. (also avail. in microform from UMI; back issues avail.; reprint service avail. from UMI) **Indexed:** A.B.C.Pol.Sci., Acad.Ind., Amer.Bibl.Slavic & E.Eur.Stud., Amer.Hist.& Life, Anthropol.Lit., Asian-Pac.Econ.Lit., Bibl.Ling., Bk.Rev.Ind., Child.Bk.Rev.Ind. (1965-), Curr.Cont., E.I., Hist.Abstr., Hum.Ind., Ind.Bk.Rev.Hum., Int.Polit.Sci.Abstr., J.of Ferroc., M.L.A., Polit.Sci.Abstr., Ref.Sour., Rural Devel.Abstr., SSCI, Stud.Wom.Abstr. **Document type:** academic/scholarly publication.
●Also available online. Vendor(s): University Microfilms International.
—BLDSC (4947.250000); Faxon; SWETS; UMI; UnCover.
Description: Contains articles about the humanities and social sciences in reference to Asia.

950   KO   ISSN 0021-9126
DS1
JOURNAL OF ASIATIC STUDIES. (Text in Korean; occasionally in English) 1958. s-a. $25. (Korea University, Asiatic Research Center) Korea University Press, 1 Anam-dong, Sungbuk-ku, Seoul 136-70, S. Korea. TEL 02-9261926. FAX 02-9249132. TELEX KOREA-KU-K34138. Ed. Yi Hyun Hwee. **Indexed:** Amer.Hist.& Life, Hist.Abstr., Mid.East: Abstr.& Ind. —UnCover.

JOURNAL OF CHINESE LAW. see LAW

JOURNAL OF CHINESE PHILOSOPHY. see PHILOSOPHY

JOURNAL OF CHINESE RELIGIONS. see RELIGIONS AND THEOLOGY — Other Denominations And Sects

JOURNAL OF CUNEIFORM STUDIES. see ARCHAEOLOGY

950   PH   ISSN 0022-0450
JOURNAL OF EAST ASIATIC STUDIES. 1951. s-a. $12. University of Manila, 546 Dr. M.V. de los Santos St., Manila D-403, Philippines. Ed. Charles O. Houston, Jr. adv.; charts; illus.; index. circ. 500. **Indexed:** A.I.C.P., Amer.Hist.& Life, Hist.Abstr.

JOURNAL OF EGYPTIAN ARCHAEOLOGY. see ARCHAEOLOGY

JOURNAL OF FUKIEN HISTORY. see HISTORY — History Of Asia

JOURNAL OF INDIAN PHILOSOPHY. see PHILOSOPHY

952   US   ISSN 0095-6848
DS801
JOURNAL OF JAPANESE STUDIES. 1974. s-a. $30 (foreign $34) (effective Jul. 1995). Society for Japanese Studies, University of Washington, Box 353650, Seattle, WA 98195-3650. TEL 206-543-9302. FAX 206-685-0668. E-mail: jjs@u.washington.edu. Ed. Susan B. Hanley. adv.; bk.rev. circ. 1,900. (back issues avail.) **Indexed:** Amer.Hist.& Life, Arts & Hum.Cit.Ind., Curr.Cont., Hist.Abstr., M.L.A., Soc.Sci.Ind. (1994-). **Document type:** academic/scholarly publication.
—BLDSC (5009.300000); Faxon; SWETS; UnCover.
Description: Takes a multidisciplinary approach to the study of Japan.
Refereed Serial

950   II   ISSN 0022-3301
PK101
JOURNAL OF ORIENTAL RESEARCH. (Text in English and Sanskrit) 1927. irreg. (approx. a.). 25. Kuppuswami Sastri Research Institute, 84 Royapettah High Rd., Madras 600 004, Mylapore, India. TEL 847320. Ed. S.S. Janaki. bk.rev.; illus.; index. circ. 500. (also avail. in microfiche from IDC)
—BLDSC (5027.325000).
Description: Contributions to Sanskrit and Indological research.

950   HK   ISSN 0022-331X
DS501
JOURNAL OF ORIENTAL STUDIES. (Text in Chinese and English) 1954. s-a. HK.$225 to individuals; institutions HK.$300. University of Hong Kong, Centre of Asian Studies, Pokfulam Rd., Hong Kong. FAX 852-2559-5884. Ed. C. Y. Sin. adv.; bk.rev.; index. circ. 300. (also avail. in microform from UMI; back issues avail.; reprint service avail. from UMI) **Indexed:** Amer.Hist.& Life, Hist.Abstr., Ind.Bk.Rev.Hum. **Document type:** academic/scholarly publication.
—BLDSC (5027.400000); UMI; UnCover.
Description: Covers research from China, Japan and Southeast Asia concerning traditional and contemporary issues in various social sciences.

951   JA
JOURNAL OF SINOLOGICAL STUDIES/SHINAGAKU KENKYU. (Text in Japanese; summaries in English) 1948. s-a. Sinological Society of Hiroshima - Hiroshima Shinagakkai, c/o Hiroshima University, Faculty of Literature, 1-1-89 Higashi-Senda-machi, Hiroshima, Japan.

JOURNAL OF SOUTHEAST ASIAN STUDIES. see HISTORY — History Of Asia

951   US   ISSN 1059-3152
DS751
JOURNAL OF SUNG-YUAN STUDIES. (Text in Chinese and English) 1970. a. $15 to individuals; institutions $25; retired scholars and graduate students $10. c/o James M. Hargett, Ed., Department of East Asian Studies, HU 210, State University of New York, Albany, Albany, NY 12222. TEL 518-422-4233. FAX 518-442-4188. E-mail: HARGETT@CNSVAX.ALBANY.EDU. adv.; bk.rev.; bibl.; illus. circ. 400. **Document type:** academic/scholarly publication.
—UnCover.
Former titles (until no.22, 1989): Bulletin of Sung-Yuan Studies (ISSN 0049-254X); (until vol.14, 1978): Sung Studies Newsletter.

950   CH   ISSN 1022-6230
JOURNAL OF SUNOLOGY. (Text in Chinese) 1985. q. $50. National Sun Yat-sen University, Sun Yat-sen Institute, Kaohsiung, Taiwan 800, Republic of China. TEL 07-5329387003. Ed. Wen-Chun Chen. bk.rev. circ. 1,000. **Document type:** academic/scholarly publication.

JOURNAL OF THE ECONOMIC AND SOCIAL HISTORY OF THE ORIENT/JOURNAL D'HISTOIRE ECONOMIQUE ET SOCIALE DE L'ORIENT. see HISTORY — History Of The Near East

950   UK   ISSN 1356-1863
AS122
JOURNAL OF THE ROYAL ASIATIC SOCIETY. 1827; N.S. 1865; 3rd series 1991. 3/yr. £52($89) (effective 1996). (Royal Asiatic Society of Great Britain and Ireland) Cambridge University Press, Edinburgh Bldg., Shaftesbury Rd., Cambridge CB2 2RU, England. TEL 01223-312393.
FAX 01223-315052. TELEX 8151817256. (N. American addr.: Cambridge University Press, Journals Dept., 40 W. 20th St., New York, NY 10011. TEL 212-924-3900. FAX 212-691-3239) Ed. D.O. Morgan. adv.; bk.rev.; illus.; index. (also avail. in microfiche from IDC,BHP; back issues avail.; reprint service avail. from SCH) **Indexed:** A.I.C.P., Amer.Hist.& Life, Arts & Hum.Cit.Ind., Bibl.Ling., Br.Hum.Ind, Curr.Cont., Hist.Abstr., Mid.East: Abstr.& Ind., Numis.Lit. **Document type:** academic/scholarly publication.
—BLDSC (4853.810000); Faxon; Genuine Article; SWETS; UMI; UnCover. CCC.
Former titles (until 1991): Royal Asiatic Society of Great Britain and Ireland. Journal (ISSN 0035-869X); **Formerly (until 1835):** Royal Asiatic Society of Great Britain and Ireland. Transactions (ISSN 0950-4737); **Incorporates:** Society of Biblical Archaeology. Proceedings.
Description: Covers Asian languages, literatures, history, archaeology, arts, philosophies and religions.
Refereed Serial

950   US   ISSN 1072-5040
DS1
JOURNAL OF THE THIRD WORLD SPECTRUM. 1989. s-a. $28 to individuals (foreign $37); institutions $53 (foreign $63) (effective 1995). Box 44843, Washington, DC 20026-4843. TEL 202-806-7649. Ed. Feraidoon Shams. bk.rev. circ. 300. **Indexed:** Amer.Hist.& Life, Hist.Abstr., Int.Polit.Sci.Abstr., P.A.I.S. **Document type:** academic/scholarly publication.
—BLDSC (5069.099570); UnCover.
Formerly (until Spring 1994): Journal of Asian and African Affairs (ISSN 1044-2979)
Description: Intended to promote critical studies, research and analyses on wide-ranging complex problems confronting the Third World societies. Features concrete research and measured arguments by various contributing scholars and practitioners on economic, political and social facets of life in the Third World settings of Africa, Asia and Latin America.
Refereed Serial

JOURNAL OF TURKOLOGY. see LINGUISTICS

950   UK
K.R. NORMAN COLLECTED PAPERS. irreg., vol.5, 1995. £18.95. Pali Text Society, 73 Lime Walk, Oxford OX3 7AD, England. Ed. R.F. Gombrich. **Document type:** monographic series.

KADMONIOT; quarterly for the antiquities of Eretz-Israel and Biblical lands. see ARCHAEOLOGY

KARATE AND ORIENTAL ARTS. see SPORTS AND GAMES

954   II   ISSN 0022-9210
KASHMIR AFFAIRS. (Text in English) 1959. bi-m. Rs.7.50. Karan Nagar, Jammu, India. Ed. Balraj Puri. adv.; bk.rev.; charts; cum.index.

958   GW
KATALOG DER TIBETISCHEN UND MONGOLISCHEN SACHKULTUR IN EUROPAEISCHEN MUSEEN UND PRIVATSAMMLUNGEN. 1989. irreg. DM.178. Harrassowitz Verlag, Taunusstr. 14, 65183 Wiesbaden, Germany. TEL 0611-530-0. FAX 0611-530570. Eds. Hans Roth, Veronika Ronge. circ. 250 (paid). (back issues avail.) **Document type:** academic/scholarly publication, catalog.

KEILSCHRIFTTEXTE AUS BOGHAZKOI. see ARCHAEOLOGY

KEIRAKU SHINRYO. see ALTERNATIVE MEDICINE

950   HU   ISSN 0133-6193
KELETI TANULMANYOK/ORIENTAL STUDIES. (Text in English, French, German, Hungarian, Russian and Oriental languages) 1976. irreg. price varies or exchange basis. Magyar Tudomanyos Akademia Konyvtara, Arany Janos u.1, P.O. Box 7, 1361 Budapest 5, Hungary. Ed. Eva Apor. **Document type:** monographic series.
Description: Oriental studies and papers on the documents and the history of the Oriental collection of the Academy Library of Hungary.

KENKYUJOHO. see RELIGIONS AND THEOLOGY

950   NE   ISSN 0169-8907
KERN INSTITUTE, LEIDEN. MEMOIRS. irreg., vol.5, 1992. price varies. E.J. Brill, P.O. Box 9000, 2300 PA Leiden, Netherlands. TEL 31-71-5353500. FAX 31-71-5317532. TELEX 39296 BRILL NL. (In N. America: E.J. /Brill, 24 Hudson St., Kinderhook, NY 12106. TEL 800-962-4406. FAX 518-758-1959) **Document type:** monographic series.
Refereed Serial

950   GW   ISSN 0937-2105
KHOJ; a series of modern South Asian studies. 1988. irreg., vol.5, 1994. Harrassowitz Verlag, Taunusstr. 14, 65183 Wiesbaden, Germany. TEL 0611-530-0. FAX 0611-530-570. TELEX 4186135. (Subscr. to: Postfach 2929, 65019 Wiesbaden, Germany) Eds. Richard Barz, Monika Thiel-Horstmann. **Document type:** monographic series.

ORIENTAL STUDIES

950   PH   ISSN 0115-6012
KINAADMAN/WISDOM; a journal of the Southern Philippines. 1979. s-a. P.200. Xavier University, Cagayan de Oro 9000, Philippines.
FAX 63-8822-72-6355. (Dist. by: Bookmark Inc., Box 1171, Manila, Philippines; Dist. in U.S. by: Cellar Book Shop, 18090 Wyoming Ave., Detroit, MI 48221) Ed. Miguel A. Bernad. bk.rev.; bibl. circ. 800. Indexed: Ind.Phil.Per. **Document type:** academic/scholarly publication.
Description: Covers the Southern Philippines and Mindanao topics.

959.8   GW   ISSN 0948-3314
KITA; das Magazin der Deutsch-Indonesische Gesellschaft. (Text in German, Indonesian) 1991. 3/yr. DM.30($25) (Deutsch-Indonesische Gesellschaft e.V.) Omimee Intercultural Publishers, Postfach 501706, 50977 Cologne, Germany. FAX 0221-4303862. (Dist. by: Helga Blazy, Hermann-Pflaume-Str. 39, 50933 Cologne, Germany. FAX 0221-5101631) adv.; bk.rev. (back issues avail.) **Document type:** monographic series.
Formerly (until 1995): D I G Magazin (ISSN 0944-9876)

956   GW   ISSN 0343-1088
KLEINE AEGYPTISCHE TEXTE. 1969. irreg., vol.11, 1994. price varies. Harrassowitz Verlag, Taunusstr. 14, 65183 Wiesbaden, Germany. TEL 0611-530-0. FAX 0611-530570. TELEX 4186135. (Subscr. to: Postfach 2929, 65019 Wiesbaden, Germany) Ed. Wolfgang Helck. **Document type:** monographic series.

KOKUSAI KORYU. see ETHNIC INTERESTS

KONGZI YANJIU/STUDIES ON CONFUCIUS. see PHILOSOPHY

951.9   GW   ISSN 0944-8373
KOREA FORUM. (Text in German, Korean) 1991. 4/yr. DM.30. Korea-Verband im Asienhaus, Bullmannaue 11, 45327 Essen, Germany. TEL 0201-8303812. adv.; bk.rev.; circ. 600. **Document type:** newsletter.

951.9   KO
KOREA FOUNDATION NEWSLETTER. (Text in English) 1992. q. free to qualified personnel. Korea Foundation, Daewoo Foundation Bldg., 526, 5-ga, Namdaemunno, C.P.O. Box 2147, Chung-gu, Seoul, S. Korea. TEL 735-8766. FAX 757-2049. Ed. Hyuck-In Lew. **Document type:** newsletter.

951.9   KO   ISSN 0023-3919
KOREA OBSERVER. 1968. q. $40. Institute of Korean Studies, C.P.O. Box 3410, Seoul 100-634, S. Korea. TEL 02-569-5574. FAX 02-564-1190. Ed. Myong Whai Kim. adv.; bk.rev.; abstr.; charts; stat. circ. 3,500. (processed) Indexed: Asian-Pac.Econ.Lit., Int.Polit.Sci.Abstr. **Document type:** academic/scholarly publication.
—BLDSC (5113.467000); Faxon; UnCover.
Description: Covers the fields of the humanities and social sciences, and promotes cultural exhcanges with other nations.

KOREA UPDATE. see POLITICAL SCIENCE — Civil Rights

950   US   ISSN 0145-840X
DS901   CODEN: KOSTEL
KOREAN STUDIES. 1977. a. $14 per vol. (foreign $15). (University of Hawaii, Center for Korean Studies) University of Hawaii Press, Journals Department, 2840 Kolowalu St., Honolulu, HI 96822. TEL 808-956-8833. FAX 808-988-6052. E-mail: shultz@uhunix.uhcc.hawaii.edu. Ed. Edward J. Shultz. adv.; bk.rev. circ. 150. (back issues avail.; reprint service avail. from UMI,ISI) Indexed: Amer.Hist.& Life, Hist.Abstr., IDA. **Document type:** academic/scholarly publication.
—UMI; UnCover.
Description: Features interdisciplinary and multicultural articles on Korea and the Korean community abroad.
    Refereed Serial

951.9   CN   ISSN 1195-8448
KOREAN STUDIES IN CANADA. q.? University of Toronto, Centre for Korean Studies, 130 St. George St., Toronto, ON M5S 1A5, Canada. TEL 416-978-7568. FAX 416-978-5711. Ed. Eung-Jin Baek.

951.9 700   KO   ISSN 1016-0744
DS901
KOREANA; a quarterly on Korean culture. (Editions in English, Japanese, Spanish) 1987. q. $29. Korea Foundation, 526, 5-ga, Namdaemunno, Chung-gu, C.P.O. Box 2147, Seoul, S. Korea. TEL 02-753-6464. FAX 02-757-2049. S. Chang. adv.; stat. Indexed: M.L.A.

952   JA   ISSN 0913-5200
KYOTO JOURNAL; an international quarterly on culture and Japan. (Text in English) 1987. q. 3500 Yen (N. America $30). Heian Bunka Center, 35 Minamigosho-machi, Okazaki, Sakyo-ku, Kyoto 606, Japan. TEL 075-771-6111. FAX 075-751-1196. E-mail: KYO794JOURNL@TWICS.COM. Ed. John Einarsen; Pub. Shokei Harada. adv.; bk.rev. **Document type:** academic/scholarly publication.

950 895
LALBHAI DALPATBHAI INSTITUTE OF INDOLOGY. PUBLICATIONS. (Text in various languages) q. Rs.250 (effective 1993). Lalbhai Dalpatbhai Institute of Indology, Near Gujarat University, P.O. Navarangpura, Ahmedabad 380009, India. TEL 442463. circ. 500. **Document type:** monographic series.

LEBANON REPORT. see POLITICAL SCIENCE — International Relations

LEVANT MORGENLAND. see RELIGIONS AND THEOLOGY

495   GW
LEXICOGRAPHIA ORIENTALIS. irreg., vol.3, 1994. DM.148. Helmut Buske Verlag GmbH, Richardstr. 47, 22081 Hamburg, Germany. TEL 040-299958-0. FAX 040-2993614. Ed. Marko Snoj. **Document type:** monographic series.

LIBRARY RESEARCH IN ASIA, AFRICA & AUSTRALIA. see LIBRARY AND INFORMATION SCIENCES

LONDON ORIENTAL AND AFRICAN LANGUAGE LIBRARY. see LINGUISTICS

954   UK   ISSN 0142-601X
LONDON STUDIES ON SOUTH ASIA. 1980. irreg. price varies. University of London, School of Oriental and African Studies, Thornhaugh St., Russell Sq., London WC1H 0XG, England. TEL 0171-637-2388. FAX 0171-436-3844. Ed. Diana Matias; Pub. Martin Daly. adv. contact: Martin Daly. bibl.; index. **Document type:** academic/scholarly publication.
—BLDSC (5294.153000). CCC.

297 954   II
M A A S JOURNAL OF ISLAMIC SCIENCE. (Text in English) 1985. s-a. Rs.90($20) to individuals; institutions Rs.225 ($60). Muslim Association for the Advancement of Science, 44, Ahmad Nagar, Dodhpur, Aligarh 202 001, India. TEL 0571-401209. Ed. M. Zaki Kirmani. adv.; bk.rev.; bibl.; cum.index every 5 yrs. circ. 1,000. **Document type:** academic/scholarly publication.
—BLDSC (5319.748000).
Formerly: M A A S Journal of Islamic Sciences (ISSN 0970-1672)
Description: Aims to develop a new synthesis of science on the basis of the principles of Islam.

297 954   II
M A A S NEWSLETTER. (Text in English) bi-m. Muslim Association for the Advancement of Science, 44, Ahmad Nagar, Dodhpur, Aligarh 202 001, India. TEL 0571-401209. **Document type:** newsletter.

297   PK   ISSN 0002-4015
AL-MA'ARIF. (Text in Urdu) 1968. m. Rs.120. Institute of Islamic Culture, 2 Club Rd., Lahore 3, Pakistan. TEL 92-42-6363127. Ed. Rashid Ahmad Jullundhry. bk.rev. circ. 500. **Document type:** academic/scholarly publication.
Formerly: Thaqafat.
Description: Covers issues in Islamic philosophy, Islamic culture and Islamic history.

950   LE
AL-MACHREQ; cultural magazine. 2/yr. $30 in Europe (US & Canada $35). Dar el-Machreq S.A.R.L., 2 rue Hevelin, P.O. Box 946, Beirut, Lebanon. TEL 961-1-326469. (Subscr. to: Dar el-Machreq, P.O. Box 166778, Beirut, Lebanon)

952 001.3 300   BE   ISSN 0495-7725
MAISON FRANCO-JAPONAISE. BULLETIN. (Text in French; summaries in English, French) 1927; N.S. 1951. irreg. (every 2-3 yrs.). price varies. (Maison Franco-Japonaise, JA) Editions Peeters s.p.r.l., Bondgenotenlaan 153, 3000 Leuven, Belgium. TEL 32-16-235170. FAX 32-16-228500. Ed.Bd. bibl. circ. 7,000. (reprint service avail. from KTO) Indexed: MLA. **Document type:** academic/scholarly publication, bulletin.
—CCC.

MAJALLAH-I TAHQIQAT-I TARIKHI/JOURNAL OF HISTORICAL RESEARCH. see HISTORY — History Of The Near East

MANUSCRIPTS OF THE MIDDLE EAST; journal devoted to the study of handwritten materials of the Middle East. see HISTORY — History Of The Near East

572 915.16   CC   ISSN 1000-7873
MANYU YANJIU/MANCHU LANGUAGE STUDIES. (Text in Chinese) 1985. s-a. $20.40. Heilongjiang Manyu Yanjiusuo - Heilongjiang Institute for Manchu Studies, 26 Qingbin Lu, Harbin. TEL 63931. (Dist. in US by: China Books & Periodicals, Inc., 2929 24th St., San Francisco, CA 94110. TEL 415-282-2994) Ed. Liu Jingxian. circ. 1,500. **Document type:** academic/scholarly publication.
Description: Studies on Manchu culture and language.

MANZU WENXUE/MANCHU LITERATURE. see LITERATURE

950   IT
MATERIALI PER IL VOCABOLARIO NEOSUMERICO. COLLANA. 1974. a. L.30000. (Unione Accademica Nazionale) Bonsignori Editore s.r.l., Viale dei Quattro Venti, 47, 00152 Rome, Italy. TEL 06-5881496. FAX 06-5882839. (back issues avail.) **Document type:** monographic series.

MATERIALIEN ZUM INTERNATIONALEN KULTURAUSTAUSCH/STUDIES IN INTERNATIONAL CULTURAL RELATIONS. see POLITICAL SCIENCE — International Relations

MATERIALS AND STUDIES FOR KASSITE HISTORY. see HISTORY — History Of The Near East

MATRIX (URBANA). see LITERATURE — Poetry

956 950   GW   ISSN 0543-1719
MAX FREIHERR VON OPPENHEIM-STIFTUNG. SCHRIFTEN. 1955. irreg., vol.14, 1988. price varies. Gebr. Mann Verlag GmbH, Lindenstr. 76, 10969 Berlin, Germany. TEL 030-2591-3589. FAX 030-2591-3537. (Subscr. to: 10888 Berlin, Germany) (reprint service avail.) **Document type:** monographic series.

MERIDIANS; redefining health. see ALTERNATIVE MEDICINE

950   GW   ISSN 0138-3663
MEROITICA. (Text in English, French, German) 1973. irreg., vol.14, 1994. (Humboldt-Universitaet zu Berlin, Bereich Aegyptologie und Sudan Archaeologie) Akademie Verlag GmbH, Muehlenstr. 33-34, 13187 Berlin, Germany. TEL 030-47889348. FAX 030-47889357. Indexed: Anthropol.Lit. **Document type:** monographic series.
Description: Monographs and source material on ancient Sudanese history and archaeology.

951.9   US   ISSN 1050-3935
MID ATLANTIC BULLETIN OF KOREAN STUDIES. 1984. 2/yr. $5 (free to qualified personnel). Georgetown University, School of Foreign Service, Asian Studies Program, Washington, DC 20057. TEL 202-687-8987. FAX 202-687-1431. E-mail: phb@gunet.georgetown.edu. Ed. Bonnie B.C. Oh. adv. **Document type:** bulletin.

MIDDLE EAST STUDIES ASSOCIATION BULLETIN. see SOCIAL SCIENCES: COMPREHENSIVE WORKS

950   GW   ISSN 0177-1647
MIDDLE EASTERN CULTURE CENTER, JAPAN. BULLETIN. 1984. irreg., vol.7, 1994. price varies. Harrassowitz Verlag, Taunusstr. 14, 65183 Wiesbaden, Germany. TEL 0611-530-0. FAX 0611-530570. TELEX 4186135. (Subscr. to: Postfach 2929, 65019 Wiesbaden, Germany) Ed. H.I.H. Prince Takahito Mikasa. **Document type:** monographic series.

950   US   ISSN 0147-037X
DS753
MING STUDIES. 1975. s-a. $15 to individuals; institutions $20. Hobart & William Smith Colleges, Department of History, Geneva, NY 14456-3397. TEL 315-781-3349. FAX 315-781-3348. Ed. William S. Atwell. adv.; bk.rev.; bibl. circ. 250. (back issues avail.) **Indexed:** Amer.Hist.& Life (until 1994), Hist.Abstr. (until 1994).
—UnCover.
Formerly: Ming Studies Newsletter.

MINZU HUABAO/NATIONALITY PICTORIAL. see *ETHNIC INTERESTS*

951 300   CC   ISSN 0256-1891
MINZU YANJIU/STUDY IN NATIONALITIES. (Text and summaries in Chinese; table of contents in English) 1979. bi-m. Y6.60($26.10) Zhongguo Shehui Kexueyuan, Minzu Yanjiusuo - Chinese Academy of Social Sciences, Institute of Nationalities, 27 Baishiqiao Lu, Beijing 100081, People's Republic of China. TEL 8022288. (Dist. outside China by: China International Book Trading Corporation, P.O. Box 399, Beijing, P.R.C.; Dist. in US by: China Books & Periodicals, Inc., 2929 24th St., San Francisco, CA 94110. TEL 415-282-2994) Ed. Du Rongkun. bk.rev.; circ. 5,000 (controlled). **Indexed:** Bibl.Ling.
Description: Contains historical, social, and economic studies of minority nationalities.

MIRAS-E FARHANGI. see *ARCHAEOLOGY*

950   SP   ISSN 0544-408X
PJ3001
MISCELANEA DE ESTUDIOS ARABES Y HEBRAICOS. 1952. 2/yr. price varies. Universidad de Granada, Servicio de Publicaciones, Antiguo Colegio Maximo, Campus de Cartuja, 18071 Granada, Spain. TEL 34-58-243930. FAX 34-58-242827. Eds. Emilio De Santiago, Ma. Jose Cano. **Indexed:** Amer.Hist.& Life, Bibl.Ling., Hist.Abstr. **Document type:** academic/scholarly publication.
—CCC.

MITHILA INSTITUTE OF POST GRADUATE STUDIES AND RESEARCH IN SANSKRIT LEARNING. BULLETIN. see *LINGUISTICS*

950   IS   ISSN 0017-7083
DS41
HAMIZRAH HEHADASH/NEW EAST. (Text in Hebrew; summaries in English) 1949. a. $30. Israel Oriental Society, Hebrew University, Jerusalem 91905, Israel. Ed. Jacob m. Landau. bk.rev.; bibl.; charts; stat.; index; circ. 2,500 (controlled). **Indexed:** Ind.Heb.Per., Old Test.Abstr. **Document type:** academic/scholarly publication.
Refereed Serial

950   UK   ISSN 0026-749X
DS1
MODERN ASIAN STUDIES. 1967. q. £106($180) (effective 1996). (European Association for South East Asian Studies) Cambridge University Press, Edinburgh Bldg., Shaftesbury Rd., Cambridge CB2 2RU, England. TEL 01223-312393. FAX 01223-315052. TELEX 851817256. (N. American addr.: Cambridge University Press, Journals Dept., 40 W. 20th St., New York, NY 10011. TEL 212-924-3900. FAX 212-691-3239) (Co-sponsor: Australian South East Asian Association) Ed. Gordon Johnson. adv.; bk.rev. (also avail. in microform from UMI; back issues avail.; reprint service avail. from SWZ) **Indexed:** A.B.C.Pol.Sci., Amer.Hist.& Life, Asian-Pac.Econ.Lit., Curr.Cont, E.I., Geo.Abstr., Hist.Abstr., IDA, Int.Polit.Sci.Abstr., Mid.East: Abstr.& Ind., Polit.Sci.Abstr., Rice Abstr., Rural Devel.Abstr., Rural Recreat.Tour.Abstr., Soc.Sci.Ind., SSCI, World Agri.Econ.& Rural Sociol.Abstr. **Document type:** academic/scholarly publication.
—BLDSC (5883.650000); Faxon; Genuine Article; SWETS; UMI; UnCover. **CCC.**
Description: Covers Asia from Pakistan to Japan; studies the impact of modernization during the 19th and 20th centuries on the ancient cultures of these nations.

MODERN CHINA; an international quarterly of history and social science. see *HISTORY — History Of Asia*

MODERN CHINESE LITERATURE. see *LITERATURE*

MODERN MIDDLE EAST SERIES. see *HISTORY — History Of Asia*

951   IT   ISSN 0390-2811
DS701
MONDO CINESE; rivista trimestrale. 1973. q. L.48000 (effective Mar. 1995). Istituto Italo Cinese per gli Scambi Economici e Culturali, Via Carducci, 18, 20123 Milan, Italy. TEL 39-2-8057384. FAX 72000236. Ed.Bd. adv. contact: Alcide Luini. bk.rev.; bibl.; charts; stat. circ. 1,200. (back issues avail.) **Indexed:** Amer.Hist.& Life, Hist.Abstr. **Document type:** academic/scholarly publication.
Description: Covers the development of relations between the Chinese and Italian cultures.

951.7005   US   ISSN 0190-3667
DS793.M7
MONGOLIAN STUDIES. 1962. a. $20. Mongolia Society, Inc., 322 Goodbody Hall, Indiana University, Bloomington, IN 47405-2401. TEL 812-855-4078. FAX 812-855-7500. Ed. John R. Krueger. adv.; bk.rev.; abstr.; bibl.; charts; stat. circ. 475. **Indexed:** Amer.Bibl.Slavic & E.Eur.Stud, Amer.Hist.& Life, Bibl.Ling., Hist.Abstr., M.L.A. **Document type:** academic/scholarly publication.
—UnCover.
Supersedes (in 1974): Mongolian Society Bulletin (ISSN 0026-9654); Which superseded: Mongolia Society Newsletter.
Description: Scholarly research articles and multidisciplinary approaches to Mongolia, past and present.

954   GW   ISSN 0170-8864
MONOGRAPHIEN ZUR INDISCHEN ARCHAEOLOGIE, KUNST UND PHILOLOGIE. irreg., vol.8, 1993. price varies. (Stiftung Ernst Waldschmidt) Dietrich Reimer Verlag, Unter den Eichen 57, 12203 Berlin, Germany. TEL 030-8314081. FAX 030-8316323. Ed. Marianne Yaldiz. **Document type:** monographic series.

MONUMENTA LINGUAE MONGOLICAE COLLECTA. see *LINGUISTICS*

952 390   JA   ISSN 0027-0741
DS821.A1
MONUMENTA NIPPONICA; studies in Japanese culture. (Text in English) 1938. q. 4200 Yen($36) Sophia University, 7-1 Kioi-cho, Chiyoda-ku, Tokyo 102, Japan. Ed. Michael Cooper. bk.rev.; illus.; index, cum.index: vols.1-40. circ. 1,150. (also avail. in microform from UMI) **Indexed:** Amer.Hist.& Life, Arts & Hum.Cit.Ind., Curr.Cont., Hist.Abstr., Ind.Bk.Rev.Hum., M.L.A., SSCI.
—BLDSC (5966.230000); Faxon; UMI; UnCover.

950   GW   ISSN 0254-9948
MONUMENTA SERICA; journal of Oriental studies. (Text in English, French, German) 1934. a., vol.43, 1995. Institut Monumenta Serica, Arnold-Janssen-Str. 20, 53754 Sankt Augustin, Germany. TEL 02241-237431. FAX 02241-205841. Ed. Roman Malek. bk.rev. circ. 400. **Indexed:** Amer.Hist.& Life, Hist.Abstr. **Document type:** academic/scholarly publication.
—SWETS; UnCover. **CCC.**
Description: Scholarly journal dealing with traditional China in the fields of history, language, literature, philosophy and religion.

950   GW   ISSN 0179-261X
MONUMENTA SERICA MONOGRAPH SERIES. (Text in English, French and German) 1937. a. Institut Monumenta Serica, Arnold-Janssen-Str. 20, 53754 Sankt Augustin, Germany. TEL 02241-237431. FAX 02241-205841. TELEX 889559-STEYL-D. Ed. Roman Malek. circ. 500. (back issues avail.) **Document type:** monographic series.
Description: Covers various topics in Chinese history, language, literature, philosophy and religion.

950   RU   ISSN 0320-8095
MOSKOVSKII UNIVERSITET. VESTNIK. SERIYA 14: VOSTOKOVEDENIE. q. $50 (effective 1996). Moskovskii Universitet, Ul. Gertsena 5-7, 103009 Moscow, Russia. bk.rev.; bibl.; index. **Indexed:** Int.Aerosp.Abstr. **Document type:** academic/scholarly publication.

956   GW   ISSN 0077-1880
MUENCHENER INDOLOGISCHE STUDIEN. 1955. irreg., vol.6, 1969. price varies. Harrassowitz Verlag, Taunusstr. 14, 65183 Wiesbaden, Germany. TEL 0611-530-0. FAX 0611-530570. TELEX 4186135. (Subscr. to: Postfach 2929, 65019 Wiesbaden, Germany) Ed. H. Hoffmann. **Document type:** monographic series.

950   GW   ISSN 0170-3668
MUENCHENER OSTASIATISCHE STUDIEN. (Text in English and German) irreg, vol.70, 1995. price varies. Franz Steiner Verlag Wiesbaden GmbH, Birkenwaldstr. 44, 70191 Stuttgart, Germany. TEL 0711-2582-0. FAX 0711-2582390. (Subscr. to: Postfach 101061, 70009 Stuttgart, Germany) Ed.Bd. **Document type:** monographic series.

950   GW   ISSN 0170-3676
MUENCHENER OSTASIATISCHE STUDIEN. SONDERREIHE. (Text in English and German) irreg., vol.4, 1992. price varies. Franz Steiner Verlag Wiesbaden GmbH, Birkenwaldstr. 44, 70191 Stuttgart, Germany. TEL 0711-2582-0. FAX 0711-2582390. (Subscr. to: Postfach 101061, 70009 Stuttgart, Germany) Ed.Bd. **Document type:** monographic series.

MUSEO NAZIONALE D'ARTE ORIENTALE. SCHEDE. see *MUSEUMS AND ART GALLERIES*

954   BE   ISSN 0771-6494
LE MUSEON; revue d'etudes orientales. (Supplement avail.: Bibliotheque du Museon; Publications de l'Institut Orientaliste de Louvain) (Text in English, French) 1881. 4/yr. 3000 BEF (effective 1994). Editions Peeters s.p.r.l., Bondgenotenlaan 153, 3000 Leuven, Belgium. TEL 32-16-235170. FAX 32-16-228500. Ed. B. Coulie. bk.rev.; bibl.; cum.index 1882-1931, 1932-1973. (back issues avail.) **Indexed:** Bibl.Ling., New Test.Abstr., Numis.Lit. **Document type:** academic/scholarly publication.
—SWETS; UnCover.
Description: Studies all aspects of the Christian Near East.

MUSEUM OF FAR EASTERN ANTIQUITIES. BULLETIN. see *MUSEUMS AND ART GALLERIES*

MUSICA ASIATICA. see *MUSIC*

954   II   ISSN 0580-4396
PK401
MYSORE ORIENTALIST. (Text in English and Sanskrit) 1967. a. $5. University of Mysore, Oriental Research Institute, Mysore 5, Karnataka, India. TEL 23136. Ed. B.A. Dodamani. bk.rev. circ. 300. **Document type:** academic/scholarly publication.
Description: Contains studies on Indic peoples.

950   DK   ISSN 0904-4337
DS32.8
N I A S - NYTT/NORDIC NEWSLETTER OF ASIAN STUDIES. (Text in English) 1983. 4/yr. free. (Nordic Institute of Asian Studies) Nordic Institute of Asian Studies, Njalsgade 84, DK-2300 Copenhagen S, Denmark. TEL 45-31-54-88-44. FAX 45-32-96-25-30. Ed. Bd. circ. 2,500. **Document type:** newsletter.
Former titles: C I N A - Nytt (ISSN 0109-4203) & Asien-Studier i Skandinavien (ISSN 0105-7340)
Description: Contains articles and short scholarly reports, conference and symposia reports, information on new and current journals and series of books and forthcoming conferences.

960   DK   ISSN 0904-597X
DS32.9.S34
N I A S REPORT. 1968. irreg. (8/yr.). price varies. Nordic Institute of Asian Studies, Njalsgade 84, DK-2300 Copenhagen S, Denmark. TEL 45-31-54-88-44. FAX 45-32-96-25-30. Ed. Jens Chr. Soerensen. bk.rev. circ. 300. **Indexed:** So.Pac.Per.Ind. **Document type:** academic/scholarly publication.
—BLDSC (6109.726000).
Formerly (until 1989): Scandinavian Institute of Asian Studies. Annual Newsletter (ISSN 0106-3871)

950   GW   ISSN 0935-1051
NAHOST JAHRBUCH. 1988. a. DM.33. (Deutsches Orient Institut) Verlag Leske und Budrich GmbH, Postfach 300551, 51334 Leverkusen, Germany. TEL 02171-2079. FAX 02171-41209. Eds. Thomas Koszinowski, Hanspeter Mattes. bk.rev. **Document type:** academic/scholarly publication.

954   CC   ISSN 1004-1508
NANYA YANJIU JIKAN/SOUTH ASIAN STUDIES QUARTERLY. (Text in Chinese) 1979. a. Y6($2.50) Sichuan University, South Asian Research Institute, Sichuan Daxue Nei, Jiuyanqiao, Chengdu, Sichuan 610064, People's Republic of China. TEL 583875. Eds. Iei Qihuai, Li Dechang. circ. 1,000.
—BLDSC (8348.650800).

ORIENTAL STUDIES

950   CC   ISSN 1003-9856
NANYANG WENTI YANJIU/SOUTHEAST ASIAN STUDIES. (Text in Chinese) q. $20. Xiamen Daxue, Nanyang Yanjiusuo - Xiamen University, Institute of Southeast Asian Studies, c/o Xiamen Daxue Tushuguan, Xiamen, Fujian 361005, People's Republic of China. TEL 592-2086414. Ed. Liao Shaolian. **Document type:** academic/scholarly publication.

950   CC
NANYANG ZILIAO YICONG/SOUTH ASIAN AFFAIRS: A QUARTERLY JOURNAL OF TRANSLATION. (Text in Chinese) q. Xiamen Daxue, Nanyang Yanjiusuo - Xiamen University, Institute of Southeast Asian Studies, c/o Xiamen Daxue Tushuguan, Xiamen, Fujian 361005, People's Republic of China. TEL 592-2086414. Ed. Liao Shaolian. **Document type:** academic/scholarly publication.

NANZAN INSTITUTE FOR RELIGION AND CULTURE. BULLETIN. see *RELIGIONS AND THEOLOGY*

NATIONAL PALACE MUSEUM. NEWSLETTER. see *MUSEUMS AND ART GALLERIES*

950   GW   ISSN 0932-2728
NEAR AND MIDDLE EAST MONOGRAPHS. 1987. irreg., vol.3, 1990. Harrassowitz Verlag, Taunusstr. 14, 65183 Wiesbaden, Germany. TEL 0611-530-0. FAX 0611-530-570. TELEX 4186135. (Subscr. to: Postfach 2929, 65019 Wiesbaden, Germany) Ed.Bd. **Document type:** monographic series.

959 320   NP   ISSN 0251-2653
NEPAL - ANTIQUARY; journal of social-historical research and digest. 1974. bi-m. $30 per no. Office of Nepal-Antiquary, 20-401 Naxal, Kathmandu, Nepal. Ed. Jagadish C. Regmi. circ. 75. (back issues avail.)

958   GW   ISSN 0178-8612
NEPAL INFORMATION. 1967. 2/yr. DM.60($35) Deutsch-Nepalische Gesellschaft e.V., Duesseldorferstr. 58, 51145 Cologne, Germany. TEL 02203-26660. FAX 02203-24001. Ed. Wolf Donner. adv.; circ. 500 (paid). **Document type:** academic/scholarly publication.
  Description: Information on all fields relevant to the socio-economic development of Nepal.

950   GW   ISSN 0720-6615
NEPAL RESEARCH CENTRE. JOURNAL. (Text in English) 1977. a. DM.58. Franz Steiner Verlag Wiesbaden GmbH, Birkenwaldstr. 44, 70191 Stuttgart, Germany. TEL 0711-2582-0. FAX 0711-2582390. (Subscr. to: Postfach 101061, 70009 Stuttgart, Germany) Ed. Albrecht Wezler. **Document type:** academic/scholarly publication.

NEW ASIA REVIEW. see *PUBLISHING AND BOOK TRADE*

956   US   ISSN 0081-8291
NEW YORK UNIVERSITY. STUDIES IN NEAR EASTERN CIVILIZATION. 1968. irreg., latest no.12. New York University Press, 70 Washington Square S., New York, NY 10012. TEL 212-998-2575; 800-996-3833. FAX 212-995-3833. TELEX 235128 NYU UR. Ed. Peter Chelkowski. **Document type:** monographic series.

959   NZ
NEW ZEALAND JOURNAL OF EAST ASIAN STUDIES. 1993. s-a. NZ.$45 to individuals; institutions NZ.$55. University of Waikato, Department of East Asian Studies, Private Bag 3105, Hamilton, New Zealand.

950   CH   ISSN 0253-2875
NEWSLETTER FOR RESEARCH IN CHINESE STUDIES. 1982. q. $40. Center for Chinese Studies, c/o National Central Library, 20 Chung Shan S. Rd., Taipei, Taiwan 10040, Republic of China. TEL 02-314-7321. FAX 02-371-2126. Ed. Pei-ling Tsai. adv.; bk.rev. circ. 2,400.

952   JA   ISSN 0915-0889
DS820.8
NICHIBUNKEN. (Text in English) 1988. a. International Research Center for Japanese Studies (Nichibunken) - Kokusai Nihon Bunka Kenkyu Senta, 3-2 Oeyama-cho, Goryo, Nishikyo-ku, Kyoto 610-11, Japan. TEL 075-335-2222. FAX 075-335-2091.

952   JA   ISSN 0915-0986
DS820.8
NICHIBUNKEN JAPAN REVIEW. (Text in English) 1990. irreg. International Research Center for Japanese Studies (Nichibunken) - Kokusai Nihon Bunka Kenkyu Senta, 3-2 Oeyama-cho, Goryo, Nishikyo-ku, Kyoto 610-11, Japan. TEL 075-335-2222. FAX 075-335-2091.
—BLDSC (6109.899000); UnCover.

952   JA   ISSN 0914-6482
NICHIBUNKEN NEWSLETTER/NIHON BUNKA. (Text in English, Japanese) 1988. m.? International Research Center for Japanese Studies (Nichibunken) - Kokusai Nihon Bunka Kenkyu Senta, 3-2 Oeyama-cho, Goryo, Nishikyo-ku, Kyoto 610-11, Japan. TEL 075-335-2222. FAX 075-335-2091. Ed. Ito Shuntaro. **Document type:** newsletter.

950   XR   ISSN 0029-5302
DS1
NOVY ORIENT/NEW ORIENT. (Text in Czech) 1946. 10/yr. DM.100. Ceska Akademie Ved, Orientalni Ustav, Pod Vrstevnici 5, 140 00 Prague 4, Czech Republic. Ed. Svetozar Pantucek. bk.rev.; charts, illus, maps; index. circ. 2,050. **Indexed:** Amer.Hist.& Life (until 1989), Hist.Abstr. (until 1989).
  Description: Deals with the cultures and civilizations of Asia and Africa; regularly includes studies on developing countries and information about current problems of the Third World.

950 320   UK   ISSN 0960-7935
Z792.B85932
O I O C NEWSLETTER. 1974. s-a. free. (British Library, Oriental and India Office Collections) British Library Board, 96 Euston Rd., London NW1 2DB, England. (Subscr. to: British Library, Oriental and India Office Collections, 197 Blackfriars Rd., London SE1 8NG, England. TEL 44-171-412-7000. FAX 44-171-412-7858) Ed. David Plumb. adv.; bk.rev.; bibl. circ. 880. **Document type:** newsletter.
—BLDSC (6252.638000).
  Former titles: India Office Library and Records Oriental Collections Newsletter (ISSN 0265-1386); India Office Library and Records Newsletter (ISSN 0307-6008)
  Description: News of activities of the library and articles pertaining to its acquisitions, collections, recent publications.

ORBIS MUSICAE; Assaph studies in the arts. see *MUSIC*

950   NE   ISSN 0078-6527
DS1
ORIENS. (Text in English, French, German) 1948. irreg. (approx. biennial), vol.34, 1994. fl.190($108.75) (effective 1993). (Internationale Gesellschaft fuer Orientforschung - Milleterarasi Sark Tetkikleri Cemiyeti - International Society for Oriental Research) E.J. Brill, P.O. Box 9000, 2300 PA Leiden, Netherlands. TEL 31-71-5353500. FAX 31-71-5317532. TELEX 39296 BRILL NL. (In N. America: E.J. Brill, 24 Hudson St., Kinderhook, NY 12106. TEL 800-962-4406. FAX 518-758-1959) Ed. R. Sellheim. bk.rev.; illus.; maps; cum.index: vols.1-10 (1948-1957). (back issues avail.) **Indexed:** Amer.Hist.& Life (until 1990), Bibl.Ling., Hist.Abstr. (until 1990). **Document type:** academic/scholarly publication, monographic series.
—CCC.
  Description: Studies in the culture of Asia and North Africa from antiquity to the present focusing on language, literature, religion and art.
Refereed Serial

950 490 890   GW   ISSN 0030-5197
DS501
ORIENS EXTREMUS; Zeitschrift fuer Sprache, Kunst und Kultur der Laender des fernen Ostens. (Text mainly in German; occasionally in English and French) 1954. 2/yr. DM.138. Harrassowitz Verlag, Taunusstr. 14, 65183 Wiesbaden, Germany. TEL 0611-530-0. FAX 0611-530570. TELEX 4186135. (Subscr. to: Postfach 2929, 65019 Wiesbaden, Germany) Ed.Bd. charts; illus.; index. circ. 350. (back issues avail.) **Indexed:** Amer.Hist.& Life, Bibl.Ling., E.I., Hist.Abstr., M.L.A. **Document type:** academic/scholarly publication.
—SWETS; UnCover. **CCC.**

950   GW   ISSN 0030-5227
DS41
ORIENT; Deutsche Zeitschrift fuer Politik und Wirtschaft des Orients - German journal for politics and economics of the Middle East. 1960. q. DM.138 (students DM.87) (foreign DM.145). (Deutsches Orient-Institut) Verlag Leske und Budrich GmbH, Postfach 300551, 51334 Leverkusen, Germany. TEL 02171-2079. FAX 02171-41209. adv.; bk.rev.; bibl.; charts; illus.; maps. **Indexed:** Bibl.Ling., Curr.Cont.M.E., ELLIS, Geo.Abstr., IDA, Int.Polit.Sci.Abstr., Key to Econ.Sci., P.A.I.S.For.Lang.Ind., Polit.Sci.Abstr. **Document type:** academic/scholarly publication.
—BLDSC (6291.138000). **CCC.**
  Description: Deals with the politics, economy and society of the modern Near and Middle East.

950   FR   ISSN 1161-0344
ORIENT EXPRESS; notes et nouvelles d'archeologie orientale. 1991. 3/yr. 75 F. Orient - Express, c/o Institut d'Art et d'Archeologie, 3 rue Michelet, 75006 Paris, France. FAX 44-07-01-79. **Document type:** newsletter.
  Description: European bulletin specializing in oriental archaeology.

709.5   UK   ISSN 0030-5278
N8
ORIENTAL ART; devoted to the study of all forms of Oriental art. N.S. 1955. q. £24($48) Oriental Art Magazine Ltd., 12 Ennerdale Rd., Richmond, Surrey TW9 3PG, England. Ed. Ann Butler. adv.; bk.rev.; bibl.; illus.; index. (reprint service avail. from KTO) **Indexed:** Art & Archaeol.Tech.Abstr., Art Ind., Artbibl.Mod., Artbibl., Arts & Hum.Cit.Ind., Avery Ind.Archit.Per., Curr.Cont., Ind.Bk.Rev.Hum.
—BLDSC (6291.163000); Faxon; SWETS; UnCover.

ORIENTAL INSTITUTE COMMUNICATIONS. see *ARCHAEOLOGY*

ORIENTAL INSTITUTE MUSEUM PUBLICATIONS. see *MUSEUMS AND ART GALLERIES*

950   AT   ISSN 0030-5340
DS41
ORIENTAL SOCIETY OF AUSTRALIA. JOURNAL. 1961. a. Aus.$15. Oriental Society of Australia, University of Sydney, School of Asian Studies, Sydney, N.S.W. 2006, Australia. FAX 61-2-692-2319. Ed. A.D. Stefanowska. adv.; charts. circ. 500. **Indexed:** Aus.P.A.I.S, E.I.
—BLDSC (4837.600000); UnCover.

939.4   VC   ISSN 0030-5367
PJ6
ORIENTALIA. (Text in English, French, German, Italian) 1920. q. L.110000($100) (effective 1995). (Pontificio Istituto Biblico - Pontifical Biblical Institute) Biblical Institute Press, Piazza Pilotta 35, 00187 Rome, Italy. TEL 39-6-678-15-67. FAX 39-6-678-05-88. Ed. Rev. R.W. Mayer SJ. bk.rev.; bibl.; charts; illus.; index. circ. 650. (also avail. in microfiche from IDC; back issues avail.) **Indexed:** Bibl.Ling., New Test.Abstr., Old Test.Abstr., Rel.Ind.One. **Document type:** academic/scholarly publication.
—Faxon; SWETS; UnCover.
  Description: Consists of ancient Near Eastern studies.

950 200   VC
ORIENTALIA CHRISTIANA ANALECTA. (Text in English, French, German, Italian) 1923. irreg., approx. 3/yr. price varies. (Pontificio Istituto Orientale) Edizioni Orientalia Cristiana, Piazza S. Maria Maggiore 7, 00185 Rome, Italy. TEL 06-446-5589. FAX 06-446-5576. Ed. Robert Taft. circ. 1,000. **Document type:** academic/scholarly publication, monographic series.
  Continues (since 1935): Orientalia Christiana.

950   SW   ISSN 0078-656X
ORIENTALIA GOTHOBURGENSIA. (Subseries of: Acta Universitatis Gothoburgensis) 1969. irreg., no.10, 1995. price varies; also exchange basis. Acta Universitatis Gothoburgensis, P.O. Box 5096, S-402 22 Goeteborg, Sweden. Ed. Jan Retsoe. **Document type:** monographic series.

950   BE   ISSN 0777-978X
ORIENTALIA LOVANIENSIA ANALECTA. (Text in English, French, German) 1974. 3/yr. price varies. Katholieke Universiteit te Leuven, Departement Oosterse en Slavische Studies, Blijde Inkomststraat 21, 3000 Leuven, Belgium. TEL 32-16-325080. FAX 32-16-325025. (Dist. by: Editions Peeters s.p.r.l., Bondgenotenlaan 153, 3000 Leuven, Belgium. TEL 32-16-235170. FAX 32-16-228500) (back issues avail.) **Document type:** monographic series.
   Description: Publishes studies on the history, cultures, languages, religions and cultures of the ancient and modern Near East, North Africa and South Asian regions.

950   BE   ISSN 0085-4522
ORIENTALIA LOVANIENSIA PERIODICA. (Supplement avail.: Orientalia Lovaniensia Analecta (ISSN 0777-978X)) (Text in English, French, German; summaries in English) 1970. a. 1600 BEF. Katholieke Universiteit te Leuven, Departement Oosterse en Slavische Studies, Blijde Inkomststraat 21, 3000 Leuven, Belgium. TEL 32-16-325080. FAX 32-16-325025. (Dist. by: Editions Peeters s.p.r.l., Bondgenotenlaan 153, 3000 Leuven, Belgium. TEL 32-16-235170. FAX 32-16-228500) Ed. G. Pollet. bk.rev.; abstr.; charts; illus.; cum.index. circ. 500. (back issues avail.) **Indexed:** Bibl.Ling., M.L.A., Numis.Lit., Old Test.Abstr. **Document type:** academic/scholarly publication.
   —BLDSC (6291.187400).

950   NE   ISSN 0169-9504
ORIENTALIA RHENO-TRAIECTINA. 1949. irreg., vol.37, 1991. price varies. E.J. Brill, P.O. Box 9000, 2300 PA Leiden, Netherlands. TEL 31-71-5353500. FAX 31-71-5317532. TELEX 39296 BRILL NL. (In N. America: E.J. Brill, 24 Hudson St., Kinderhook, NY 12106. TEL 800-962-4406. FAX 518-758-1959) Ed. J. Gonda. (back issues avail.) **Document type:** monographic series.
   Refereed Serial

950   SW   ISSN 0078-6578
DS1
ORIENTALIA SUECANA. 1952. a. price varies. (Uppsala Universitet) A W I International AB, P.O. Box 4627, S-116 91 Stockholm, Sweden. TEL 468-640-8800. FAX 648-641-1180. Ed. Tryggve Kronholm. circ. 600. **Indexed:** Bibl.Ling., M.L.A., Numis.Lit.
   —BLDSC (6291.191000).

950   SW   ISSN 0345-8997
ORIENTALISKA STUDIER. 1969. q. SEK 100 to individuals; institutions SEK 120. Foereningen foer Orientaliska Studier, University of Stockholm, S-106 91 Stockholm, Sweden. TEL 46-8-16-17-75. Eds. Mirja Juntunen, Joakim Enwall. bk.rev. **Document type:** academic/scholarly publication.

890   GW   ISSN 0030-5383
PJ5
ORIENTALISTISCHE LITERATURZEITUNG; Zeitschrift fuer die Wissenschaft vom ganzen Orient und seinen Beziehungen zu den angrenzenden Kulturkreisen. (Text in English, French, German) 1898. bi-m. DM.198 to individuals; institutions DM.424 (effective 1996). Akademie Verlag GmbH, Muehlenstr. 33-34, 13187 Berlin, Germany. TEL 030-47889348. FAX 030-47889357. Ed. H. Klengel. adv.; bk.rev.; bibl. (also avail. in microfiche from IDC) **Indexed:** New Test.Abstr., Old Test.Abstr. **Document type:** academic/scholarly publication.
   —SWETS; UnCover. CCC.

ORIENTATIONS. see *ART*

953   NE   ISSN 0928-0189
DS35.62
ORIENTATIONS. 1993. irreg. price varies. Editions Rodopi B.V., Keizersgracht 302-304, 1016 EX Amsterdam, Netherlands. TEL 31-20-6227507. FAX 31-20-6380948. E-mail: F.van.der.Zee@Rodopi.nl. (In N. America: 233 Peachtree St., N.E., Ste. 404, Atlanta, GA 30303-1504. TEL 800-225-3998. FAX 404-522-7116) Ed. E. de Moor. **Document type:** academic/scholarly publication, monographic series.
   Description: Studies contacts between Europe and the Arab world.

950   IT   ISSN 0030-5472
D461
ORIENTE MODERNO; rivista mensile d'informazione e di studi per la conoscenza dell'Oriente. 1921. m. L.75000($80) (Istituto per l'Oriente) Herder Editrice e Libreria s.r.l., Piazza Montecitorio, 120, 00186 Rome, Italy. TEL 67-94-628. FAX 678-47-51. (Alt. addr.: Via A. Carconcini 190, 00197 Rome, Italy) Ed. Giovanni Oman. bk.rev.; index, cum.index: 1921-1973. circ. 800. (reprint service avail. from SCH) **Indexed:** Amer.Hist.& Life, Documentatieblad, Hist.Abstr., Int.Polit.Sci.Abstr. **Document type:** academic/scholarly publication.
   —SWETS.

950 410   II   ISSN 0474-9030
OUR HERITAGE. (Text in English, Bengali or Sanskrit) vol.19, 1972. s-a. Sanskrit College, Department of Postgraduate Training and Research, 1 Bankim Chatterjee St., Calcutta 12, India. Ed. B. Bhattacharya. bibl.
   Description: Covers literary subjects.

951   CH
PACIFIC CULTURAL FOUNDATION. ANNUAL REPORT. (Text in English, Chinese) a. Pacific Cultural Foundation, Ste. 807, Palace Office Bldg., 346 Nanking East Rd., Sec. 3, Taipei, Taiwan, Republic of China. TEL 02-752-7424. FAX 02-752-7429. Ed. Brian P. Lew; Pub. Yu-sheng Chang.

959   CU
PAGINAS. a. $8 in S. America; N. America $10; elsewhere $12. (Centro de Estudio Asia y Oceania) Ediciones Cubanas, Obispo No. 527, Apdo. 605, Havana, Cuba.

950   GW   ISSN 0232-3257
PAPYRI AUS DEN STAATLICHEN MUSEEN ZU BERLIN. 1978. irreg. (Stiftung Preussischer Kulturbesitz) Akademie Verlag GmbH, Muehlenstr. 33-34, 13187 Berlin, Germany. TEL 030-47889348. FAX 030-47889357. **Document type:** monographic series.

894 494 947.87   US   ISSN 0031-5508
PERMANENT INTERNATIONAL ALTAISTIC CONFERENCE (PIAC). NEWSLETTER. 1966. irreg. (2-3/yr.) free. Indiana University, Permanent International Altaistic Conference, Goodbody Hall 216, Bloomington, IN 47405. TEL 812-855-0959. FAX 812-855-7500. Ed. Prof. Denis Sinor. adv.; bibl. circ. 750. (processed) **Document type:** newsletter.

THE PHILIPPINES: NEWS AND VIEWS. see *POLITICAL SCIENCE — International Relations*

PHOENIX. see *ARCHAEOLOGY*

950 572   PP   ISSN 0253-2913
POINT SERIES. 1982-1988; resumed 1989. s-a. $14. Melanesian Institute for Pastoral & Socio-Economic Service, P.O. Box 571, Goroka EHP, Papua New Guinea. FAX 675-721-070. Ed. Paul Roche. bk.rev. circ. 1,000. (back issues avail.) **Indexed:** Rel.Ind.One.
   —BLDSC (6541.858000).

POINTS EAST (MENLO PARK). see *ETHNIC INTERESTS*

950   PL   ISSN 0079-4783
POLSKA AKADEMIA NAUK. KOMITET NAUK ORIENTALISTYCZNYCH. PRACE ORIENTALISTYCZNE. (Text and summaries in English, French, German, Polish, and Russian) 1954. irreg., vol.38, 1994. price varies. Wydawnictwo Naukowe P W N, Ul. Miodowa 10, 00-251 Warsaw, Poland. TEL 48-22-312738. FAX 48-22-267163. TELEX 813763 PWN PL. circ. 1,200.

950   PL   ISSN 0079-3426
POLSKA AKADEMIA NAUK. ODDZIAL W KRAKOWIE. KOMISJA ORIENTALISTYCZNA. PRACE. (Text in English, French, German, Polish) 1962. irreg., no.21, 1990. price varies. Polska Akademia Nauk, Oddzial w Krakowie, Komisja Orientalistyczna, Ul. Slawkowska 17, 31-016 Krakow, Poland. TEL 48-12-224853. FAX 48-12-222791. Ed. Stanislaw Stachowski. circ. 700. **Document type:** monographic series.
   —BLDSC (6588.147300).
   Description: Presents Arabic sources concerning the history of Central and Eastern Europe. Also important literary and linguistic works on Oriental subjects.

PORTA LINGUARUM ORIENTALIUM. see *LINGUISTICS*

950   US   ISSN 1067-9847
DS501
POSITIONS; east Asia cultures critique. 1993. 3/yr. $24 to individuals (foreign $33); institute $54 (foreign $63) (effective 1996). Duke University Press, Box 90660, Durham, NC 27708-0660. TEL 919-687-3600. FAX 919-688-4574. Ed. Tani E. Barlow. circ. 650. **Indexed:** Amer.Hist.& Life (1995-), Hist.Abstr. (1995-). **Document type:** academic/scholarly publication.
   —UnCover.
   Description: Offers a forum of debate for all concerned with the social, intellectual, and political events unfolding in East Asia and within the Asian diaspora.

954   II
PRACHYA PRATIBHA. (Text in English, Hindi, Sanskrit) 1973. s-a. Rs.150($30) (effective 1996). Birla Institute of Art and Music, Prachya Niketan, Birla Museum, P.O. Vallabh Bhavan, Bhopal 462004, India. TEL 0755-551388. Ed. Susmita Pande; Pub. Aparna Bajpai. bk.rev. circ. 500. (also avail. in microfilm) **Document type:** academic/scholarly publication.
   Description: A research journal which carries contributions from scholars and savants on indology. Regular features include indian history and culture, archaeology, epigraphy, museology and numismatics.
   Refereed Serial

950 490   US
PRINCETON LIBRARY OF ASIAN TRANSLATIONS. irreg. price varies. Princeton University Press, 41 William St., Princeton, NJ 08540. TEL 609-258-4900. FAX 609-258-6305. E-mail: jhardy@pupress.princeton.edu. **Document type:** monographic series.

PRINCETON PAPERS IN NEAR EAST STUDIES. see *HISTORY — History Of The Near East*

PRINCETON STUDIES ON THE NEAR EAST. see *HISTORY — History Of The Near East*

956   NE   ISSN 0169-9601
PROBLEME DER AEGYPTOLOGIE. 1953. irreg, vol.9, 1994. price varies. E.J. Brill, P.O. Box 9000, 2300 PA Leiden, Netherlands. TEL 31-71-5353500. FAX 31-71-5317532. TELEX 39296 BRILL NL. (In N. America: E.J. Brill, 24 Hudson St., Kinderhook, NY 12106. TEL 800-962-4406. FAX 518-758-1959) Ed. W. Helck. (back issues avail.) **Document type:** monographic series.
   Description: Interpretations of religious, historical and cultural topics in Egyptology.
   Refereed Serial

954   II
PUNJAB UNIVERSITY INDOLOGICAL SERIES. no.24, 1979. irreg. price varies. Vishveshvaranand Vedic Research Institute, P.O. Sadhu Ashram, Hoshiarpur 146021, Punjab, India. Ed. S. Bhaskaran Nair.

950   GW   ISSN 0931-9158
PURANA RESEARCH PUBLICATIONS, TUEBINGEN. 1987. irreg., vol.3, 1992. price varies. Harrassowitz Verlag, Taunusstr. 14, 65183 Wiesbaden, Germany. TEL 0611-530-0. FAX 0611-530570. (Subscr. to: Postfach 2929, 65019 Wiesbaden, Germany) Ed. Heinrich von Stietencron. **Document type:** monographic series.

951.47 300   CC   ISSN 1000-5447
QINGHAI MINZU XUEYUAN XUEBAO/QINGHAI INSTITUTE OF NATIONALITIES. JOURNAL. (Text in Chinese) 1975. q. Y8. Qinghai Minzu Xueyuan - Qinghai Institute of Nationalities, 25 Bayi Lu, Xining, Qinghai 810007, People's Republic of China. TEL 0971-76888. Ed. Li Yankai. bk.rev. circ. 1,500. **Document type:** academic/scholarly publication.
   Description: Focuses on local and ethnic history, minority languages and literatures (including folk literature), economics, education, government policy, religion, law, and arts pertaining to nationalities in Qinghai Province.

ORIENTAL STUDIES

953   IT   ISSN 1121-2306
QUADERNI DI STUDI ARABI. (Text in English, French, Italian) 1983. a. L.80000. (Universita degli Studi di Venezia, Dipartimento di Scienze Storico-Archeologiche e Orientalistiche) Herder Editrice e Libreria s.r.l., Piazza Montecitorio, 117-120, 00186 Rome, Italy. TEL 6794628. FAX 678-47-51. Ed. F. Picchetti Lucchetta. **Document type:** academic/scholarly publication.
—BLDSC (7167.001000).

RECHERCHES D'ARCHEOLOGIE, DE PHILOLOGIE ET D'HISTOIRE. see *ARCHAEOLOGY*

RECORDS OF CIVILIZATION, SOURCES AND STUDIES. see *HISTORY*

RELIGIONS IN THE GRAECO-ROMAN WORLD. see *RELIGIONS AND THEOLOGY*

950   HK   ISSN 0377-3515
PL2658.E1
RENDITIONS; a Chinese-English translation magazine. 1973. s-a. $20 (effective 1994). Chinese University of Hong Kong, Research Centre for Translation, Shatin, New Territories, Hong Kong. TEL 852-26097407. FAX 852-26035149. TELEX 50301-CUHK-HX. E-mail: renditions@cuhk.hk. Eds. Eva Hung, D.E. Pollard. adv.; bk.rev.; bibl.; index. circ. 1,500. (back issues avail.) **Indexed:** Arts & Hum.Cit.Ind., Curr.Cont., M.L.A. **Document type:** academic/scholarly publication.
—UnCover.
Description: Offers translations of traditional and modern Chinese literature. Special issues include poetry, fiction, and prose, as well as regional studies.
Refereed Serial

892.7 297   UA
REPERTOIRE CHRONOLOGIQUE D'EPIGRAPHIE ARABE. (Text in French) 1931. irreg., vol.18, 1991. price varies. Institut Francais d'Archeologie Orientale du Caire, P.O. Box 11562 Kasr-el-Aini, 37 Sharia Sheikh Aly Youssef, Mounira, Cairo, Egypt. TEL 20-2-3548245. FAX 20-2-3544635. (Dist. by: Boustany's Arab Publishing House, 29 Faggalah St., 11271 Cairo, Egypt. TEL 20-2-4177915. FAX 20-2-3404905) (back issues avail.) **Document type:** monographic series.

956   BE   ISSN 1142-2831
DS41
RES ORIENTALES. (Text in French) 1989. a., vol.6, 1994. price varies. (Groupe d'Etudes pour la Civilisation du Moyen-Orient) Editions Peeters s.p.r.l., Bondgenotenlaan 153, 3000 Leuven, Belgium. TEL 32-16-235170. FAX 32-16-228500. Ed. R. Gyeselen. (back issues avail.) **Document type:** monographic series.

950   UK
RESEARCH PAPERS IN EAST ASIAN STUDIES. 1993. a. University of Sheffield, School of East Asian Studies, Sheffield S10 2UJ, England. TEL 01742-729479. FAX 01742-824384. Ed.Bd. **Document type:** academic/scholarly publication.
—BLDSC (7755.034700).

REVISTA AFRICA Y MEDIO ORIENTE. see *GENERAL INTEREST PERIODICALS — Africa*

956   FR   ISSN 0373-6032
PJ3103
REVUE D'ASSYRIOLOGIE ET D'ARCHEOLOGIE ORIENTALE. 1904. a. 410 F. (foreign 470 F.) (effective 1996). Presses Universitaires de France, Departement des Revues, 14 av. du Bois-de-l'Epine, B.P.90, 91003 Evry Cedex, France. TEL 1-60-77-82-05. FAX 1-60-79-20-45. TELEX PUF 600 474 F. (also avail. in microfiche from IDC; reprint service avail. from KTO) **Indexed:** Bibl.Ling., Mid.East: Abstr.& Ind., Old Test.Abstr. **Document type:** academic/scholarly publication.
—Faxon; SWETS. **CCC.**

REVUE D'EGYPTOLOGIE. see *ARCHAEOLOGY*

951.9   UN   ISSN 0251-2416
REVUE DE COREE. (Text in French) 1969. s-a. 10000 Won($24) Korean National Commission for Unesco, B.P. 64 Poste Centrale, Seoul, S. Korea. TEL 822-539-0625. FAX 822-555-6917. TELEX MOCNDM-K-23231-2. Ed. Hu Kwon. adv.; bk.rev.; index, cum.index. circ. 1,800.
Description: Aspects of Korean language, culture, history, education, science and society.

REVUE DE QUMRAN. see *RELIGIONS AND THEOLOGY*

REVUE DES ETUDES ARMENIENNES NOUVELLE SERIE. see *HISTORY — History Of The Near East*

297   FR   ISSN 0336-156X
BP1
REVUE DES ETUDES ISLAMIQUES. 1927. 2/yr. Librairie Orientaliste Paul Geuthner, 12 rue Vavin, 75006 Paris, France. TEL 33-1-46-34-71-30. FAX 33-1-43-29-75-64. TELEX 250 303 PUBLIC PARIS. Ed. D. Sourdel. abstr.; charts. (also avail. in microfiche from IDC; back issues avail.; reprint service avail. from KTO) **Indexed:** E.I., M.L.A. **Document type:** academic/scholarly publication.
—BLDSC (7900.165000); SWETS.
Supersedes (1906-1926): Revue du Monde Musulman.
Description: Cultural, sociological and historical studies of Islamic world.

950   CC   ISSN 1004-2458
RIBEN WENTI YANJIU/JOURNAL OF JAPANESE STUDIES. (Text in Chinese) q. Hebei Daxue - Hebei University, No. 1 Hezuolu Rd., Baoding, Hebei 071002, People's Republic of China. TEL 0312-5022929. FAX 0312-5022648. Ed. Sun Zhizhong. circ. 1,000. **Document type:** academic/scholarly publication.

950   IT   ISSN 0392-4866
PJ6
RIVISTA DEGLI STUDI ORIENTALI. (Text in English, French, German, Italian, Spanish) 1907. q. L.80000($80) (effective 1993). (Universita degli Studi di Roma, Dipartimento di Studi Orientali) Bardi Editore, Salita de'Crescenzi, 16, 00186 Rome, Italy. FAX 06-6878576. Ed. Paolo Daffina. adv.; bk.rev.; bibl. circ. 300. (also avail. in microfiche from IDC) **Indexed:** Bibl.Ling., Int.Z.Bibelwiss., M.L.A. **Document type:** academic/scholarly publication.
Description: Covers all fields of Oriental studies, from the ancient Near East to modern Japan.

950   PL   ISSN 0080-3545
ROCZNIK ORIENTALISTYCZNY. (Text in English, French, German, Polish and Russian) 1914. irreg., vol.49, 1994. price varies. (Polska Akademia Nauk, Komitet Nauk Orientalistycznych) Wydawnictwo Naukowe P W N, Ul. Miodowa 10, 00-251 Warsaw, Poland. Ed. E. Tryjarski. circ. 470. **Indexed:** Amer.Hist.& Life, Bibl.Ling., Hist.Abstr., M.L.A.
—BLDSC (8005.550000).

950   HK   ISSN 0085-5774
DS1
ROYAL ASIATIC SOCIETY. HONG KONG BRANCH. JOURNAL. (Text in English) 1961. a. $24 (typically set in Apr.) (effective 1994). Royal Asiatic Society, Hong Kong Branch, P.O. Box 3864, Hong Kong. TEL 658-6529. FAX 658-5400. Ed. Patrick Hase. bk.rev.; cum.index: vols. 1-10, 11-20. circ. 1,000. (back issues avail.; reprint service avail. from SCH) **Indexed:** A.I.C.P., Amer.Hist.& Life, Hist.Abstr. **Document type:** academic/scholarly publication.
—BLDSC (4758.550000).
Description: Specializes in Hong Kong and South China studies, especially local history, social anthropology, and natural history.

RTAM. see *LINGUISTICS*

954   CN   ISSN 1188-9950
RUNGH; a South Asian quarterly of culture, comment and criticism. 1992. q. Can.$20 to individuals; institutions Can.$27. Rungh Cultural Society, Box 66019, Sta. F, Vancouver, BC V5N 1L4, Canada. TEL 604-254-9320. FAX 604-662-7466. Ed. Zool Suleman. bk.rev. **Document type:** consumer publication.
Description: Provides a platform for South Asian writers, artists, musicians, dancers, video-film makers, photographers, architects, designers, crafts people, cultural administrators and decision makers to discuss and articulate what it means to be South Asian within a western context.

950   FR   ISSN 1144-5726
SAHAND; a Persian journal of political & cultural studies. 1984. q. B.P. 1006-16, 75761 Paris Cedex 16, France. Ed. R. Sharifi.

950   II
SAMBODHI. (Text in English, Gujarati, Hindi, Prakrit and Sanskrit) 1972. q. Rs.25($6.50) Lalbhai Dalpatbhai Institute of Indology, Near Gujarat University, P.O. Navarangpura, Ahmedabad 380009, India. Ed.Bd. bk.rev. circ. 150.

950   GW   ISSN 0940-0265
SANTAG; Arbeiten und Untersuchungen zur Keilschriftkunde. 1990. irreg., vol.2, 1990. Harrassowitz Verlag, Taunusstr. 14, 65183 Wiesbaden, Germany. TEL 0611-530-0. FAX 0611-530-570. TELEX 4186135. (Subscr. to: Postfach 2929, 65019 Wiesbaden, Germany) Eds. Karl Hecker, Walter Sommerfeld. **Document type:** monographic series.

950   SZ   ISSN 0171-7391
SCHWEIZER ASIATISCHE STUDIEN. STUDIENHEFTE. 1978. irreg., vol.13, 1992. 49 SFr. Verlag Peter Lang AG, Jupiterstr. 15, CH-3000 Bern 15, Switzerland. TEL 031-9411122. FAX 031-9411131. TELEX 912651-PELA-CH. **Document type:** academic/scholarly publication.

SCRIPTA MEDITERRANEA. see *HISTORY — History Of The Near East*

SEMITIC STUDY SERIES; new series. see *LINGUISTICS*

951.9   KO   ISSN 1225-0201
SEOUL JOURNAL OF KOREAN STUDIES. (Text in English) 1988. a. 8000 Won (foreign $12). Seoul National University, Institute of Korean Studies, Seoul 151-742, S. Korea. TEL 02-888-5833. FAX 02-871-7244. Ed. Young-woo Han. **Document type:** academic/scholarly publication.
—UnCover.

950   II
SHREYE; international research quarterly. (Text in English, Hindi) 1971. q. free to members. Bharatiya Sahityakar Sangh, 51-1 New Market, Guru Gavind Singh Marg, New Delhi 110 005, India. TEL 11-5725707. Ed. Dr. Mohan Lal Srivastava. adv.; bk.rev. circ. 1,000. **Document type:** academic/scholarly publication.

SINICA LEIDENSIA. see *HISTORY — History Of Asia*

SINO-JUDAICA OCCASIONAL PAPERS. see *ETHNIC INTERESTS*

951   GW   ISSN 0170-3706
SINOLOGICA COLONIENSIA; Ostasiatische Beitraege der Universitaet zu Koeln. irreg., vol.18, 1994. price varies. (Universitaet zu Koeln) Franz Steiner Verlag Wiesbaden GmbH, Birkenwaldstr. 44, 70191 Stuttgart, Germany. TEL 0711-2582-0. FAX 0711-2582390. (Subscr. to: Postfach 101061, 70009 Stuttgart, Germany) Ed. Martin Gimm. **Document type:** monographic series.

950   CH
SINOLOGICAL STUDIES.* (Text in Chinese) vol.15, 1973. bi-m. Wen-Tsai-Lee, 162 Ho-Ping E. Rd., Sec. 1, Taipei, Taiwan, Republic of China. Ed. Hsueh-Chuen Sha. bibl.

SOCIETE FRANCAISE D'EGYPTOLOGIE. BULLETIN. see *ARCHAEOLOGY*

950   UK   ISSN 0262-7280
DS331
SOUTH ASIA RESEARCH. 1980. s-a. £28($48) (effective 1996). (University of London, School of Oriental and African Studies) Oxford University Press, Oxford Journals, Walton St., Oxford OX2 6DP, England. TEL 01865-267907. FAX 01865-267773. E-mail: jnlorders@oup.co.uk. (U.S. subscr. to: Oxford University Press Inc., 2001 Evans Rd., Cary, NC 27513. TEL 919-677-0977. FAX 919-677-1714) Eds. Michael Hutt, Michael Andersen. actv. contact: Jane Parker. bk.rev. circ. 500. (also avail. in microfiche; back issues avail.) **Indexed:** Amer.Hist.& Life, Geo.Abstr., Hist.Abstr., IDA. **Document type:** academic/scholarly publication.
—BLDSC (8348.584000); UnCover. **CCC.**
Description: Interdisciplinary journal concerned with history, ecology, anthropology, languages and literatures, legal systems and religions of South Asia.

ORIENTAL STUDIES

950 II ISSN 0970-3764
SOUTH ASIAN SOCIAL SCIENTIST. (Text in English) 1985. s-a. $15 individuals; institutions $23. South Asian Social Scientists Association, Department of Anthropology, University of Madras, Tamil Nadu, Madras 600 005, India. TEL 568778. TELEX 41-6376-UNOM-IN. Ed. N. Subba Reddy. adv.; bk.rev. circ. 325.
  Description: Offers a forum for discussions between researchers and scholars on the theoretical and empirical on various aspects of the social sceinces.
  Refereed Serial

950 954 II ISSN 0038-285X
DS335
SOUTH ASIAN STUDIES. (Text in English) 1965. s-a. Rs.60($72) University of Rajasthan, South Asian Studies Centre, Research Centre Building, Jaipur 302 004, India. Ed. Dr. Ramakaut. bk.rev.; bibl. Indexed: IDA, Int.Polit.Sci.Abstr.

954 GW ISSN 0584-3170
SOUTH ASIAN STUDIES. (Text in English) irreg., vol.27, 1993. price varies. (Universitaet Heidelberg, Suedasien Institut, New Delhi, Il) Franz Steiner Verlag Wiesbaden GmbH, Birkenwaldstr. 44, 70191 Stuttgart, Germany. TEL 0711-2582-0. FAX 0711-2582390. (Subscr. to: Postfach 101061, 70009 Stuttgart, Germany) Indexed: IDA. Document type: monographic series.

SOUTH EAST ASIA LIBRARY GROUP NEWSLETTER. see *LIBRARY AND INFORMATION SCIENCES*

959 US
SOUTHEAST ASIA PAPERS. (Text in English) 1973. irreg. (1-2/yr.) price varies. University of Hawaii at Manoa, School of Hawaiian, Asian and Pacific Studies, Center for Southeast Asian Studies, c/o Program Coordinator, 1890 East-West Rd., Moore Hall 416, Honolulu, HI 96822. TEL 808-956-2688. FAX 808-956-2682. bibl. circ. 150. (back issues avail.) Indexed: HR Rep., Seed Abstr. Document type: monographic series.
  Formerly: Southeast Asian Studies Working Paper Series.
  Description: Publishes research on Southeast Asia and the Pacific islands, as well as translations of contemporary Southeast Asian Literature.

959 US
SOUTHEAST ASIA PROGRAM SERIES; monographs, translations, bibliographies. 1986. irreg., no.17, 1995. price varies. Cornell University, Southeast Asia Program, 640 Stewart Ave., Ithaca, NY 14850. TEL 607-255-8038. FAX 607-277-1904. TELEX WUI-6713054. (Subscr. to: S E A P Publications, Cornell University, E. Hill Plaza, Ithaca, NY 14850) Document type: monographic series.

950 IT
STUDI ORIENTALI. 1943. irreg., no.12, 1992. price varies. (Universita degli Studi di Roma, Dipartimento di Studi Orientali) Bardi Editore, Salita de Crescenzi 16, 00186 Rome, Italy. FAX 06-6878576. Indexed: Bibl.Ling. Document type: monographic series.

340.09 NE ISSN 0169-8168
STUDIA ET DOCUMENTA AD IURA ORIENTIS ANTIQUI PERTINENTIA. (Text in various languages) 1936. irreg., vol.11, 1984. price varies. (Stichting voor het Niet-Westers Recht) E.J. Brill, P.O. Box 9000, 2300 PA Leiden, Netherlands. TEL 31-71-5353500. FAX 31-71-5317532. TELEX 39296 BRILL NL. (In N. America: E.J. Brill, 24 Hudson St., Kinderhook, NY 12106. TEL 800-962-4406. FAX 518-758-1959) Document type: monographic series.
  Description: Scholarly studies of law and related issues in the ancient Near East.
  Refereed Serial

955 BE ISSN 0772-7852
STUDIA IRANICA. (Supplements avail.: Abstracta Iranica; Studia Iranica. Cahiers) (Text in French) 1972. 2/yr. 2000 BEF (effective 1995). (Association pour l'Avancement des Etudes Iraniennes) Editions Peeters s.p.r.l., Bondgenotenlaan 153, 3000 Leuven, Belgium. TEL 32-16-235170. FAX 32-16-228500. bibl.; illus.; stat. (back issues avail.) Indexed: Bibl.Ling., M.L.A., Numis.Lit. Document type: academic/scholarly publication.
  —SWETS.

955 BE
STUDIA IRANICA. CAHIERS. (Text in English, French) 1982. irreg., vol.13, 1993. price varies. (Association pour l'Avancement des Etudes Iraniennes) Editions Peeters s.p.r.l., Bondgenotenlaan 153, 3000 Leuven, Belgium. TEL 32-16-235170. FAX 32-16-228500. bibl.; illus. (back issues avail.) Document type: monographic series, proceedings.

STUDIA ISLAMICA. see *RELIGIONS AND THEOLOGY — Islamic*

950 FI ISSN 0039-3282
PJ9
STUDIA ORIENTALIA. (Text in English, French and German) 1925. irreg. FIM 200. Finnish Oriental Society, c/o University of Helsinki, Department of Asian and African Studies, P.O. Box 13 (Meritullinkatu 1), SF-00014, Finland. FAX 358-0-191-2094. Ed. Harry Halen. bk.rev.; charts; illus.; cum.index. circ. 700. Indexed: Bibl.Ling.

950 NE ISSN 0281-4528
STUDIA ORIENTALIA LUNDENSIA. (Text in English) 1983. irreg., vol.4, 1990. price varies. Lund University Press, P.O. Box 141, S-221 oo Lund, Sweden. TEL 46-46-31-20-00. FAX 46-46-30-53-38. E-mail: order@studli.se. Ed. Goesta Vitestam. Document type: academic/scholarly publication.
  Refereed Serial

STUDIA PHOENICIA. see *HISTORY — History Of The Near East*

950 VC
STUDIA POHL. (Text in language of author) 1967. irreg., no.15, 1990. price varies. (Pontificio Istituto Biblico) Biblical Institute Press, Piazza della Pilotta 35, 00187 Rome, Italy. TEL 39-6-678-15-67. FAX 39-6-678-05-88.
  Description: Studies concerning the ancient Near East.

950 VC
STUDIA POHL: SERIES MAIOR. (Text mainly in English, occasionally in French or German) 1969. irreg., no.16, 1993. price varies. (Pontificio Istituto Biblico - Pontifical Biblical Institute) Biblical Institute Press, Piazza della Pilotta 35, 00187 Rome, Italy. TEL 39-6-678-15-67. FAX 39-6-678-05-88. charts; illus.
  Description: Contains studies concerning the ancient Near East. Includes photographs, plans, maps and such in a format larger than that of the main series.

STUDIEN ZUR OSTASIATISCHEN SCHRIFTKUNST. see *ART*

STUDIES IN ANCIENT ORIENTAL CIVILIZATION. see *HISTORY — History Of The Near East*

306 950 NE ISSN 1380-782X
STUDIES IN ASIAN ART AND ARCHAEOLOGY. 1969. irreg., vol.16, 1994. E.J. Brill, P.O. Box 9000, 2300 PA Leiden, Netherlands. TEL 31-71-5353500. FAX 31-71-5317532. TELEX 39296 BRILL NL. (In N. America: E.J. Brill, 24 Hudson St., Kinderhook, NY 12106. TEL 800-962-4406. FAX 518-758-1959) Ed. Jan Fonten. (back issues avail.) Document type: monographic series.
  —BLDSC (8489.546000).
  Formerly (until vol.16, 1994): Studies in South Asian Culture (ISSN 0169-9865)
  Description: Scholarly studies of subjects relating to the arts, religions and cultures of Asian societies in prehistoric, ancient and modern periods, with emphasis on art, sculpture and architecture.
  Refereed Serial

STUDIES IN CENTRAL AND EAST ASIAN RELIGIONS. see *RELIGIONS AND THEOLOGY — Buddhist*

950 390 US ISSN 0081-8321
STUDIES IN ORIENTAL CULTURE. 1966. irreg., no.21, 1988. Columbia University Press, 562 W. 113th St., New York, NY 10025. TEL 212-666-1000. Document type: monographic series.

950 US
STUDIES ON EAST ASIA. (Text in English or Asian languages) 1971. irreg., vol.19, 1994. price varies. Western Washington University, Center for East Asian Studies, Bellingham, WA 98225-9056. TEL 206-650-3041. Ed. Edward H. Kaplan. Document type: monographic series.
  Formerly (until vol.13): Western Washington State College. Program in East Asian Studies. Occasional Papers.

959 US
STUDIES ON SOUTHEAST ASIA. 1985. irreg. price varies. Cornell University, Southeast Asia Program, 640 Stewart Ave., Ithaca, NY 14850. TEL 607-255-8038. FAX 607-277-1904. TELEX WUI-6713054. (Subscr. to: S E A P Publications, Cornell University, E. Hill Plaza, Ithaca, NY 14850) Document type: monographic series.

SUI YUAN WEN HSIEN. see *ETHNIC INTERESTS*

950 613.7 US ISSN 0730-1049
GV504
T'AI CHI; the leading international magazine of T'ai Chi Ch'uan. 1977. bi-m. $20 (foreign $30) (effective 1995-1996). Wayfarer Publications, Box 26156-0156, Los Angeles, CA 90026. TEL 213-665-7773. FAX 213-665-1627. Ed. Marvin Smalheiser; Pub. Marvin Smalheiser. adv.; bk.rev.; circ. 30,000 (paid). (back issues avail.) Document type: consumer publication.
  Description: Takes a comparative look at the various styles of T'ai Chi Ch'uan practice, Qigong, and the Chinese philosophy and health principles.

950 US ISSN 1074-5599
▼**TAIWAN STUDIES.** 1995. q. $220 to institutions (foreign $260) (effective Jul. 1995). M.E. Sharpe, Inc., 80 Business Park Dr., Armonk, NY 10504. TEL 914-273-1800; 800-541-6563. FAX 914-273-2106. Document type: academic/scholarly publication.

950 US ISSN 1048-2342
TAIWAN STUDIES NEWSLETTER. 1982. s-a. $10. Taiwan Studies Group, Asian Studies Center, Michigan State University, E. Lansing, MI 48824. TEL 517-353-1680. FAX 517-336-2659. (Co-sponsors: China and Inner Asia Council; Association for Asian Studies) Ed. Jack Williams.

TAMKANG REVIEW; a journal mainly devoted to comparative studies between Chinese and foreign literatures. see *LITERATURE*

950 US ISSN 0737-5034
T'ANG STUDIES. 1982. a. $10 to individuals; institutions $15; students $7.50. T'ang Studies Society, c/o Prof. Michael R. Drompp, Rhodes College, Department of History, 2000 N. Pkwy., Memphis, TN 38112. TEL 901-726-3655. FAX 901-726-3727. E-mail: drompp@rhodes.edu. Ed. Paul W. Kroll. circ. 250. (reprint service avail. from SCH) Document type: academic/scholarly publication.
  —UnCover.
  Description: Surveys scholarly articles relating to China's T'ang Dynasty (618-907).
  Refereed Serial

TARIH. see *HISTORY — History Of The Near East*

TEL AVIV JOURNAL OF ARCHAEOLOGY. see *ARCHAEOLOGY*

TEL AVIV UNIVERSITY. INSTITUTE OF ARCHAEOLOGY. MONOGRAPH SERIES. see *ARCHAEOLOGY*

TEL AVIV UNIVERSITY. INSTITUTE OF ARCHAEOLOGY. OCCASIONAL PUBLICATIONS. see *ARCHAEOLOGY*

951.5 II ISSN 0970-5368
THE TIBET JOURNAL. (Text in English) 1975. q. $30. Library of Tibetan Works and Archives, Dharamshala 176 215, India. TELEX TF 22467. Ed. Pema Khangsar. adv.; bk.rev.; bibl.; charts. circ. 1,000. (back issues avail.) Document type: academic/scholarly publication.
  —BLDSC (8820.637000).
  Description: Provides international information on the study of Tibet.

ORIENTAL STUDIES

950 US ISSN 0735-1364
DS785.A1
TIBET SOCIETY JOURNAL. (Text in English, French, German and Tibetan) 1981. a. $20 (foreign $24). Tibet Society, Inc., Box 1968, Bloomington, IN 47402. TEL 812-335-8222. Ed. Elliot Sperling. bk.rev. circ. 450.
Description: Devoted to all areas of research on Tibet and regions influenced by Tibetan culture.

958 GW ISSN 0935-7505
TIBETAN AND INDO-TIBETAN STUDIES. irreg., vol.5, 1993. price varies. (University of Hamburg, Institute for the Culture and History of India and Tibet) Franz Steiner Verlag Wiesbaden GmbH, Birkenwaldstr. 44, 70191 Stuttgart, Germany. TEL 0711-2582-0. FAX 0711-2582390. (Subscr. to: Postfach 101061, 70009 Stuttgart, Germany) Document type: monographic series.

950 297 JA ISSN 0304-2448
TOHO GAKUHO/DONGFANG XUEBAO. (Text in Japanese; occasionally in Chinese) 1931. a. Kyoto University, Institute for Research in Humanities - Kyoto Daigaku Jinbun Kagaku Kenkyusho, Ushinomiya-cho, Yoshida, Sakyo-ku, Kyoto 606, Japan. illus.
Document type: academic/scholarly publication.
—BLDSC (5027.410000); UnCover.
Description: Covers humanities in East Asia.

900 JA ISSN 0495-7199
TOHOGAKU/EASTERN STUDIES. (Text in Japanese; abstracts in English) 1951. s-a. 3800 Yen. Toho Gakkai - Institute of Eastern Culture, 4-1, Nishi-Kanda 2-chome, Chiyoda-ku, Tokyo 101, Japan. TEL 03-3262-7221. FAX 03-3262-7227. Ed.Bd. bk.rev. (back issues avail.) **Indexed:** M.L.A. —UnCover.
Description: Publishes articles on oriental studies, covering such fields as history, religion, literature, linguistics, art and archaeology.

950 NE ISSN 0082-5433
DS501
T'OUNG PAO; revue internationale de sinologie. (Supplement avail.: T'oung Pao. Monographies (ISSN 0169-832X)) (Text mainly in English, occasionally in French, German) 1890. 2/yr. fl.172($111) (effective 1996). E.J. Brill, P.O. Box 9000, 2300 PA Leiden, Netherlands. TEL 31-71-5353500. FAX 31-71-5317532. TELEX 39296 BRILL NL. E-mail: ejborders@ejbrill.com. (In N. America: E.J. Brill, 24 Hudson St., Kinderhook, NY 12106. TEL 800-962-4406. FAX 518-758-1959) Eds. Jacques Gernet, E. Zuercher. abstr.; index, cum.index: vols.38-55, 1948-1969. (also avail. in microfilm from BHP; reprint service avail. from KTO) **Indexed:** Amer.Hist.& Life, Arts & Hum.Cit.Ind., Bibl.Ling., Hist.Abstr., M.L.A. **Document type:** academic/scholarly publication.
—Faxon; SWETS; UnCover. CCC.
Description: Publishes articles on topics in art, history, linguistics, literature, history of science, and other fields furthering knowledge of traditional Chinese civilization.
Refereed Serial

951 NE ISSN 0169-832X
T'OUNG PAO. MONOGRAPHIES. (Supplement to: T'oung Pao (ISSN 0082-5433)) (Text in English, French, German) 1954? irreg., vol. 16, 1989. price varies. E.J. Brill, P.O. Box 9000, 2300 PA Leiden, Netherlands. TEL 31-71-5353500. FAX 31-71-5317532. TELEX 39296 BRILL NL. (In N. America: E.J. Brill, 24 Hudson St., Kinderhook, NY 12106. TEL 800-962-4406. FAX 518-758-1959) (back issues avail.) **Document type:** monographic series.
Description: Scholarly translations of Chinese historical texts, and critical studies on specific issues in the arts, literature, social, cultural, religious and political history of ancient and modern China.
Refereed Serial

950 GW ISSN 0938-0051
TRAVAUX DU GROUPE DE RECHERCHES ET D'ETUDES SEMITIQUES ANCIENNES. 1982. irreg., vol.4, 1995. Harrassowitz Verlag, Taunusstr. 14, 65183 Wiesbaden, Germany. TEL 0611-530-0. FAX 0611-530-570. TELEX 4186135. (Subscr. to: Postfach 2929, 65019 Wiesbaden, Germany) Document type: monographic series.

950 GW ISSN 0344-5542
TUNGUSICA. 1978. irreg., vol.4, 1992. price varies. Harrassowitz Verlag, Taunusstr. 14, 65183 Wiesbaden, Germany. TEL 0611-530-0. FAX 0611-530570. TELEX 4186135. (Subscr. to: Postfach 2929, 65019 Wiesbaden, Germany) Ed. Michael Weiers. **Document type:** monographic series.

956.1 494 BE ISSN 0082-6847
DR401
TURCICA; REVUE D'ETUDES TURQUES. (Supplements avail.: Cahiers Turcica; Collection Turcica) (Text in English, French, German) 1969. a., vol.27, 1995. 2000 BEF (effective 1995). (Universite des Sciences Humaines de Strasbourg, Association pour le Developpement des Etudes Turques, FR) Editions Peeters s.p.r.l., Bondgenotenlaan 153, 3000 Leuven, Belgium. TEL 32-16-235170. FAX 32-16-228500. (Co-sponsors: Institut Francais d'Etudes Anatoliennes a Istanbul, TU; Universite de Paris, Institut des Etudes Turques, FR) Ed. I. Melikoff. adv.; bk.rev.; index. **Indexed:** Amer.Hist.& Life, Bibl.Ling., Hist.Abstr. **Document type:** academic/scholarly publication.
—BLDSC (9071.840000).

950 GW ISSN 0177-4743
TURCOLOGICA. 1985. irreg., vol.21, 1995. price varies. Harrassowitz Verlag, Taunusstr. 14, 65019 Wiesbaden, Germany. TEL 0611-530-0. FAX 0611-530570. TELEX 4186135. (Subscr. to: Postfach 2929, 65019 Wiesbaden, Germany) Ed. Lars Johanson. **Document type:** monographic series.

956 TU ISSN 0041-4239
TURK KULTURU. 1962. m. $25. Turk Kulturunu Arastirma Enstitusu - Turkish Cultural Research Institute, 17 Sok. 38, Bahceivler, Ankara, Turkey. Dir. Sukru Elcim. bk.rev.; film rev.; play rev.; abstr.; bibl.; charts; illus.; stat.; index. circ. 5,000. (also avail. in microfiche from IDC) **Document type:** academic/scholarly publication.

956.1 TU ISSN 0564-5093
TURK KULTURU ARASTIRMALARI. 1964. a. $10. Turk Kulturunu Arastirma Enstitusu - Turkish Cultural Research Institute, 17 Sok. 38, Bahceivler, Ankara, Turkey. Dir. Sukru Elcin. bk.rev.; film rev.; play rev.; abstr.; bibl.; charts; illus.; stat.; index. circ. 1,000. **Document type:** academic/scholarly publication.

TURK TARIH KURUMU. BELGELER. see HISTORY — *History Of The Near East*

TURK TARIH KURUMU. BELLETEN. see HISTORY — *History Of The Near East*

UNIVERSITE CATHOLIQUE DE LOUVAIN. INSTITUT ORIENTALISTE. PUBLICATIONS. see HISTORY — *History Of Asia*

955 200 LE
UNIVERSITE SAINT-JOSEPH. FACULTE DES LETTRES ET DES SCIENCES HUMAINES. RECHERCHES. SERIE B: ORIENT CHRETIEN. (Previously published by its Institut des Lettres Orientales in 4 series) 1956; N.S. 1971. irreg. price varies. Dar el-Machreq S.A.R.L., 2 rue Huvelin, P.O. Box 946, Beirut, Lebanon. TEL 961-1-326469. (Subscr. to: Librairie Orientale, P.O. Box 946, Beirut, Lebanon) **Document type:** monographic series.

UNIVERSITY OF CHICAGO ORIENTAL INSTITUTE. PUBLICATIONS. see HISTORY — *History Of The Near East*

950 HK ISSN 0378-2689
UNIVERSITY OF HONG KONG. CENTRE OF ASIAN STUDIES. OCCASIONAL PAPERS AND MONOGRAPHS. Key Title: Occasional Papers and Monographs - Centre of Asian Studies. (Text in Chinese or English) 1970. irreg., no.112, 1994. price varies. University of Hong Kong, Centre of Asian Studies, Pokfulam Rd., Hong Kong. FAX 852-2559-5884. TELEX 71919-CEREB-HX. Ed. Edward K.Y. Chen. (processed) **Document type:** monographic series.
—BLDSC (3106.467000).

951 UK ISSN 0308-6119
UNIVERSITY OF LONDON. CONTEMPORARY CHINA INSTITUTE. RESEARCH NOTES AND STUDIES. 1976. irreg., no.10, 1994. £8. University of London, School of Oriental and African Studies, Thornhaugh St., Russell Sq., London WC1H 0XG, England. TEL 0171-637-2388. FAX 0171-436-3844. (Co-sponsor: Contemporary China Institute) **Document type:** academic/scholarly publication.
—BLDSC (7749.760000).

UNIVERSITY OF LONDON. SCHOOL OF ORIENTAL AND AFRICAN STUDIES. BULLETIN. see HUMANITIES: *COMPREHENSIVE WORKS*

915.4 II ISSN 0304-8233
DS339.9.I4
UNIVERSITY OF RAJASTHAN. SOUTH ASIAN STUDIES CENTRE. ANNUAL REPORT. (Text in English) 1966. irreg., latest 1973. University of Rajasthan, South Asian Studies Centre, Gandhi Nagar, Jaipur 302004, India.

UNIVERZITA KOMENSKEHO. FILOZOFICKA FAKULTA. ZBORNIK: GRAECOLATINA ET ORIENTALIA. see *CLASSICAL STUDIES*

VARENDRA RESEARCH MUSEUM. JOURNAL. see *MUSEUMS AND ART GALLERIES*

890 967 MF
VASANT. (Text in Hindi) 1978. q. Rs.80($6) Mahatma Gandhi Institute, Library, Moka, Mauritius. TEL 464-8022. FAX 230-464-8265. Ed. Abhimanyu Unnuth. bk.rev. circ. 500. (back issues avail.)
Description: Provides a representation of Hindi literature being written in Mauritius consolidating a geographical indentity while keeping in touch with trends of world Hindi literature.

950 GW ISSN 0506-7936
VERZEICHNIS DER ORIENTALISCHEN HANDSCHRIFTEN IN DEUTSCHLAND. Short title: V O H D. (Text in English and German) irreg., vol.33, 1995. price varies. (Deutsche Morgenlaendische Gesellschaft) Franz Steiner Verlag Wiesbaden GmbH, Birkenwaldstr. 44, 70191 Stuttgart, Germany. TEL 0711-2582-0. FAX 0711-2582390. (Subscr. to: Postfach 101061, 70009 Stuttgart, Germany) Ed. Hartmut-Ortwin Feistel. **Document type:** monographic series.

950 GW ISSN 0506-7944
VERZEICHNIS DER ORIENTALISCHEN HANDSCHRIFTEN IN DEUTSCHLAND. SUPPLEMENTBAENDE. Abbreviated title: V O H D Supplementbaende. (Text in English and German) irreg., vol.35, 1994. price varies. (Deutsche Morgenlaendische Gesellschaft) Franz Steiner Verlag Wiesbaden GmbH, Birkenwaldstr. 44, 70191 Stuttgart, Germany. TEL 0711-2582-0. FAX 0711-2582390. (Subscr. to: Postfach 101061, 70009 Stuttgart, Germany) Ed. Hartmut-Ortwin Feistel. **Document type:** monographic series.

VESTNIK DREVNEI ISTORII/JOURNAL OF ANCIENT HISTORY. see HISTORY

VIETNAMESE STUDIES. see HISTORY — *History Of Asia*

954 II
VISHVA VICHARAMALA. (Text in Hindi and Sanskrit) irreg. price varies. Vishveshvaranand Vedic Research Institute, P.O. Sadhu Ashram, Hoshiarpur 146021, Punjab, India. Ed. S. Bhaskaran Nair.

954 II
VISHVESHVARANAND VEDIC RESEARCH INSTITUTE. RESEARCH AND GENERAL PUBLICATIONS. (Text in English, Hindi, and Sanskrit) 1921. irreg. price varies. Vishveshvaranand Vedic Research Institute, P.O. Sadhu Ashram, Hoshiarpur 146021, Punjab, India.

954 US
THE VOICE OF BANGLADESH. m. $15. Penta Communications, Inc., 1170 Broadway, Ste. 200, New York, NY 10001. TEL 212-779-8105. FAX 212-683-3925. Ed. S.G. Hasan.
Description: News magazine about Bangladesh.

VOICES FROM ASIA. see LITERATURE — *Poetry*

VOORAZIATISCH-EGYPTISCH GENOOTSCHAP "EX ORIENTE LUX". JAARBERICHT; annuaire de la Societe Orientale Neerlandaise "Ex Oriente Lux". see HISTORY — History Of Asia

VOORAZIATISCH-EGYPTISCH GENOOTSCHAP "EX ORIENTE LUX". MEDEDELINGEN EN VERHANDELINGEN. see HISTORY — History Of Asia

950 960   RU   ISSN 0869-1908
DS1
VOSTOK; Afro-aziatskie obshchestva - istoria i sovremennost' (Text in Russian; summaries in English, content pages in English and French) 1955. bi-m. $108 (effective 1996). (Rossiiskaya Akademiya Nauk, Institut Vostokovedeniya) Izdatel'stvo Nauka, 90 Profsoyuznaya ul., 117864 Moscow, Russia. (Dist. by: Mezhdunarodnaya Kniga, ul. Dimitrova D.39, 113095 Moscow, Russia; Dist. in U.S. by: Victor Kamkin Inc., 4956 Boiling Brook Pkwy, Rockville, MD 20852. TEL 301-881-5973) (Co-sponsor: Rossiiskaya Akademiya Nauk, Institut Afriki) Ed. A.A. Kutzenkov. bk.rev.; bibl.; charts; illus.; index. circ. 3,700. **Indexed:** Amer.Hist.& Life, Bibl.Ling., Bull.Signal., Hist.Abstr., Int.Lab.Doc., Int.Polit.Sci.Abstr., Numis.Lit., Polit.Sci.Abstr., World Agri.Econ.& Rural Sociol.Abstr.
—BLDSC (0045.787000).
    Former titles (until 1991): Narody Azii i Afriki (ISSN 0130-6995); (1959-1961): Problemy Vostokovedeniya.

962   UA   ISSN 0257-4098
VOYAGEURS OCCIDENTAUX EN EGYPTE. Key Title: Collection des Voyageurs Occidentaux en Egypte. (Text in French) 1970. irreg., vol.26, 1990. price varies. Institut Francais d'Archeologie Orientale du Caire, P.O. Box 11562 Kasr-el-Aini, 37 Sharia Sheikh Aly Youssef, Mounira, Cairo, Egypt. TEL 20-2-3548245. FAX 20-2-3544635. (Dist. by: Boustany's Arab Publishing House, 29 Faggalah St., 11271 Cairo, Egypt. TEL 20-2-4177915. FAX 20-2-3404905) (back issues avail.) **Document type:** monographic series.
    Description: Publishes early travel accounts and studies of early European travellers in Egypt, up to and including the Napoleonic invasion.

WAQA'I DAWLAT AL-IMARAT/EMIRATES EVENTS. see HISTORY — History Of The Near East

WASHINGTON - JAPAN JOURNAL. see POLITICAL SCIENCE — International Relations

AL-WATHA'IQ AL-FILASTINIYYAH/PALESTINIAN DOCUMENTS. see HISTORY — History Of The Near East

WATHA'IQ DAWLAT AL-IMARAT/EMIRATES DOCUMENTS. see HISTORY — History Of The Near East

AL-WATHIQA. see HISTORY — History Of The Near East

956 297   NE   ISSN 0043-2539
DS36
DIE WELT DES ISLAMS; internationale Zeitschrift fuer die Geschichte des Islams in der Neuzeit - international journal for the history of modern Islam. (Text in English, French, German) 1913-1943; NS. 1951. 3/yr. fl.175($113) (effective 1996). E.J. Brill, P.O. Box 9000, 2300 PA Leiden, Netherlands. TEL 31-71-5353500. FAX 31-71-5317532. TELEX 39296 BRILL NL. E-mail: ejborders@ejbrill.com. (In N. America: E.J. Brill, 24 Hudson St., Kinderhook, NY 12106. TEL 800-962-4406. FAX 518-758-1959) Eds. Stefan Wild, Werner Ende. bk.rev.; index. (also avail. in microform from SWZ; reprint service avail. from SWZ) **Indexed:** Amer.Hist.& Life, Bibl.Ling., Hist.Abstr. **Document type:** academic/scholarly publication.
—BLDSC (9294.710000); Faxon; SWETS. **CCC**.
    Description: Focuses on the history and culture of the peoples of Islam from the end of the 18th century up to the present, with special attention given to literature.
    Refereed Serial

WENSHI ZHISHI/KNOWLEDGE OF LITERATURE AND HISTORY. see SOCIAL SCIENCES: COMPREHENSIVE WORKS

956   AU   ISSN 0084-0076
Z2831
WIENER ZEITSCHRIFT FUER DIE KUNDE DES MORGENLANDES. (Text in English, French, German and Italian) 1887. a. S.690. Universitaet Wien, Institut fuer Orientalistik, Universitaets Str. 7-V, A-1010 Vienna, Austria. TEL 01-401032599. FAX 01-4020533. Ed.Bd. adv.; bk.rev. circ. 400. (reprint service avail. from SCH) **Indexed:** Bibl.Ling., M.L.A. **Document type:** academic/scholarly publication.

WISCONSIN CHINA SERIES. see HISTORY — History Of Asia

951 915.12   CC   ISSN 1001-5558
DS730
XIBEI MINZU YANJIU/NORTHWEST MINORITIES STUDIES. (Text in Chinese) 1986. s-a. $27.20. Xibei Minzu Yanjiusuo - Northwest Minorities Institute, No. 1, Xibei Xincun, Lanzhou, Gansu 730030, People's Republic of China. TEL 86-931-8464011. FAX 86-931-8487162. (Dist. in US by: China Books & Periodicals, Inc., 2929 24th St., San Francisco, CA 94110. TEL 415-282-2994) Ed. Hao Sumin. circ. 3,000. **Document type:** academic/scholarly publication.

XIZANG WENXUE/TIBETAN LITERATURE. see LITERATURE

951 915.12   CC   ISSN 1000-0003
XIZANG YANJIU/TIBETAN STUDIES. (Editions in Chinese, English, Tibetan) 1981. q (English ed. s-a). $24 for Chinese ed.; Tibetan ed. $21. Xizang Zizhiqu Shehui Kexueyuan - Tibetan Autonomous Region Academy of Social Sciences, Lhasa, Xizang (Tibet) 850000, People's Republic of China. TEL 22638. (Dist. in US by: China Books & Periodicals, Inc., 2929 24th St., San Francisco, CA 94110. TEL 415-282-2994) Ed. Shilai Daoji.
    Description: Covers Tibetan politics, economics, history, religion, literature, art, language, medicine, law and archaeology.

951   CC   ISSN 1003-7942
XUEYU WENHUA/TIBETAN CULTURE. (Editions in Chinese and Tibetan) 1989. q. Y10. Xueyu Wenhua Zazhishe, 2 Dolsingar Road, Lhasa, Xizang (Tibet) 850000, People's Republic of China. TEL 22024. FAX 26689. (Dist. overseas by: Guoji Shudian - China International Book Trade Corp., P.O. Box 399, Beijing, P.R.C.) Ed. Gyamco. adv. contact: Zhong Zhang. circ. 7,000.
    Description: Features Tibetan customs, arts, religion, ancient relics and tourism.

950   US   ISSN 0513-4501
YALE SOUTHEAST ASIA STUDIES. MONOGRAPH SERIES. 1961. irreg., no.38, 1992. Yale University, Council on Southeast Asia Studies, Box 208206, 34 Hillhouse Ave., New Haven, CT 06520. TEL 203-432-3431. FAX 203-432-9381. Ed. M.K. Mansfield. adv. (reprint service avail. from UMI) **Document type:** monographic series.
—BLDSC (9371.210000).

951   CC   ISSN 1003-7527
YANG GUAN. (Text in Chinese) 1979. bi-m. Y6. (Jiuquan Diqu Wenlian) Yang Guan Zazhishe, Xi Dajie, Jiuquan, Guansu 735000, People's Republic of China. TEL 0937-613440. (Dist. overseas by: Jiangsu Publications Import & Export Corp., 56 Gao Yun Ling, Nanjing, Jiangsu, P.R.C.) Ed. Zhao Shuming. adv.; bk.rev. circ. 4,000.
    Description: Includes literary works, profiles of historical figures, legends, and ancient relics and art works along the Silk Road in Western China.

YAQEEN INTERNATIONAL. see RELIGIONS AND THEOLOGY — Islamic

950   GW   ISSN 0932-3201
YARMOUK UNIVERSITY. INSTITUTE OF ARCHAEOLOGY AND ANTHROPOLOGY. SERIES. 1987. irreg., vol.2, 1989. Harrassowitz Verlag, Taunusstr. 14, 65183 Wiesbaden, Germany. TEL 0611-530-0. FAX 0611-530-570. TELEX 4186135. (Subscr. to: Postfach 2929, 65019 Wiesbaden, Germany) Ed. M.M. Ibrahim. **Document type:** monographic series.
—BLDSC (9371.582460).

294.3   JA   ISSN 0386-4251
YOUNG EAST; a quarterly on Buddhism and Japanese culture. (Text in English) 1925-1966; N.S. 1975. q. 2000 Yen($10) (Young East Association) Tohokai, Inc., 6-2-17 Nishitenma, Kita-ku, Osaka 530, Japan. Ed. Nara Yasuaki. circ. 20,000.

951.35 301   CC   ISSN 1001-8913
YUNNAN MINZU XUEYUAN XUEBAO/YUNNAN INSTITUTE OF NATIONALITIES. JOURNAL. (Text in Chinese) 1983. q. Y12 (effective 1996). Yunnan Minzu Xueyuan - Yunnan Institute of Nationalities, Lianhua Chi, Kunming, Yunnan 650031, People's Republic of China. TEL 86-871-5154458. (Dist. overseas by: China International Book Trading Corp., P.O. Box 399, Beijing, P.R.C.) Ed. Huikun Huang. adv.; bk.rev. circ. 2,500. **Document type:** academic/scholarly publication.
—UnCover.
    Description: Contains research papers and reports on political science, philosophy, economics, literature, history, and linguistics relating to ethnic groups in Yunnan Province.
    Refereed Serial

932 490   GW   ISSN 0044-216X
PJ1004
ZEITSCHRIFT FUER AEGYPTISCHE SPRACHE UND ALTERTUMSKUNDE. (Text in English, French, German) 1863. 2/yr. DM.217 (students DM.105) (effective 1996). Akademie Verlag GmbH, Muehlenstr. 33-34, 13187 Berlin, Germany. TEL 030-47889348. FAX 030-47889357. Eds. E. Blumenthal, E. Hornung. bk.rev.; bibl.; illus.; index. (also avail. in microfiche from IDC) **Indexed:** Bibl.Ling. **Document type:** academic/scholarly publication.
—Genuine Article.

956   GW   ISSN 0179-4639
ZEITSCHRIFT FUER GESCHICHTE DER ARABISCH-ISLAMISCHEN WISSENSCHAFTEN. (Text in Arabic, English, French and German) 1984. a. price varies. Institut fuer Geschichte der Arabisch-Islamischen Wissenschaften, Beethovenstrasse 32, 60325 Frankfurt, Germany. TEL 069-756009-0. Ed. Fuat Sezgin. bk.rev. **Indexed:** Bibl.Ling.

956.1   GW   ISSN 0934-0696
HC491
ZEITSCHRIFT FUER TUERKEISTUDIEN. 2/yr. DM.82.50 (students DM.54.40) (foreign DM.85). Verlag Leske und Budrich GmbH, Postfach 300551, 51334 Leverkusen, Germany. TEL 02171-2079. FAX 02171-41209. Ed.Bd. **Document type:** academic/scholarly publication.

951   CC   ISSN 1001-0882
ZHONGGUO SHAOSHU MINZU. (Subseries of: Fuyin Baokan Ziliao) (Text in Chinese) m. Y29.40. Zhongguo Renmin Daxue, Shubao Ziliao Zhongxin - China People's University, Book & Newspaper Information Center, P.O. Box 1122, Beijing 100007, People's Republic of China. TEL 86-10-4015080.
    Description: Reprints papers and articles on China's minority groups.

ZHONGGUO SHEHUI JINGJISHI YANJIU/JOURNAL OF CHINESE SOCIAL AND ECONOMIC HISTORY. see HISTORY — History Of Asia

951 915.12   US
ZHONGGUO ZANGXUE/STUDY - TIBETAN NATIONALITIES. (Editions in Chinese and Tibetan) q. $23.75. China Books & Periodicals, Inc., 2929 24th St., San Francisco, CA 94110. TEL 415-282-2994. FAX 415-292-0994.

ORIENTAL STUDIES — Abstracting, Bibliographies, Statistics

ANNUAL EGYPTOLOGICAL BIBLIOGRAPHY/BIBLIOGRAPHIE EGYPTOLOGIQUE ANNUELLE/JAEHRLICHE AEGYPTOLOGISCHE BIBLIOGRAPHIE. see HISTORY — Abstracting, Bibliographies, Statistics

950 015   II   ISSN 0006-1212
BIBLIOGRAPHIA ASIATICA. 1968. m. Rs.1800($250) K.K. Roy (Private) Ltd., 55 Gariahat Rd., P.O. Box 10210, Calcutta 700 019, India. Ed. K.K. Roy. abstr.; bibl.; index. circ. 1,600. (tabloid format; also avail. in microform) **Document type:** bibliography.

ORNITHOLOGY

950 US ISSN 1046-8765
Z3001
BIBLIOGRAPHIC GUIDE TO EAST ASIAN STUDIES. 1990. a. $200. G.K. Hall & Co., c/o MacMillan Publishing USA, 866 Third Ave., 18th fl., New York, NY 10022. TEL 212-702-6789. (Subscr. to: Simon & Schuster, Library Reference Order Processing, 200 Old Tappan Rd., Old Tappan, NJ 07675. TEL 800-223-2336) **Document type:** bibliography, abstracting/indexing.
 Description: Covers China, Hong Kong, Taiwan, North and South Korea, and Japan, with approximately 3500 listings from LCMARC tapes and the Oriental Division of the New York Public Library. Includes publications about East Asia, materials published in any of the relevant countries, and publications in Chinese, Korean, and Japanese (transliterated into Roman letters).

956 US ISSN 1058-644X
Z3013
BIBLIOGRAPHIC GUIDE TO MIDDLE EASTERN STUDIES. 1991. a. $205. G.K. Hall & Co., c/o MacMillan Publishing USA, 866 Third Ave., 18th fl., New York, NY 10022. TEL 212-702-6789. (Subscr. to: Simon & Schuster, Library Reference Order Processing, 200 Old Tappan Rd., Old Tappan, NJ 07675. TEL 800-223-2336) **Document type:** bibliography, abstracting/indexing.
 Description: Lists all the materials catalogued during the past year by the Library of Congress, the Middle East section of the New York Public Library's Oriental Division, and modern Hebrew language books in the NYPL's Jewish Division.

950 JA ISSN 0524-0654
Z3001
BOOKS AND ARTICLES ON ORIENTAL SUBJECTS PUBLISHED IN JAPAN. (Text in English, Japanese) 1954. a. 4700 Yen. Toho Gakkai - Institute of Eastern Culture, 4-1, Nishi-Kanda 2-chome, Chiyoda-ku, Tokyo 101, Japan. TEL 03-3262-7221. FAX 03-3262-7227. Ed. Jikido Takasaki. (back issues avail.) **Document type:** bibliography, catalog.
 Description: Comprehensive catalogue of books and articles on oriental subjects published in the preceding year.

BULLETIN D'ARABE CHRETIEN. BIBLIOGRAPHIE DES AUTEURS ARABES CHRETIENS. see *HISTORY — Abstracting, Bibliographies, Statistics*

950 016 US ISSN 0008-9044
Z7043
CENTER FOR CHINESE RESEARCH MATERIALS. NEWSLETTER. 1968. s-a. free. Center for Chinese Research Materials, Box 3090, Oakton, VA 22124. TEL 703-281-7731. FAX 703-281-1835. Ed. Pingfeng Chi. bibl.; charts. circ. 1,400. **Document type:** newsletter.

950 016 US
CORNELL UNIVERSITY. LIBRARY. JOHN M. ECHOLS COLLECTION ON SOUTHEAST ASIA. ACCESSIONS LIST. 1959. m. $20 (foreign $25). Cornell University, Kroch Library, Echols Collection, Ithaca, NY 14853. TEL 607-255-7229. FAX 607-277-1904. TELEX WUI-6713054. Ed. John Badgeley. bibl. circ. 150. (back issues avail.) **Document type:** bibliography.
 Formerly (until 1978): Cornell University. Library. Wason Collection. Southeast Asia Accessions List (ISSN 0589-7351)

011 950 US ISSN 0098-4485
Z3001
DOCTORAL DISSERTATIONS ON ASIA; an annotated bibliographical journal of current international research. 1975. a. $20. Association for Asian Studies, Inc., 1 Lane Hall, University of Michigan, Ann Arbor, MI 48109. TEL 313-665-2490. FAX 313-665-2490. Ed. Frank J. Shulman. bibl. circ. 2,500. (back issues avail.) **Document type:** bibliography.
 —SWETS.

950 016 II
INDEX ASIA SERIES IN HUMANITIES. 1965. irreg. price varies. Centre for Asian Dokumentation, K-15, CIT Bldg., Christopher Rd., Calcutta 700 014, India. Ed. S. Chaudhuri. bk.rev.; index. **Document type:** monographic series, abstracting/indexing, bibliography.
 Description: Cumulative index to writings in journals on all aspects of South Asian and Buddhist studies as well as bibliographies on specific topics.

954 015 II ISSN 0019-3844
INDEX INDIA. (Text in English) 1967. q. Rs.1000($100) Rajasthan University Library, Gandhi Nagar, Jaipur 302004, India. TEL 91-141-511866. Ed. Pawan K. Gupta. bibl. circ. 400. **Document type:** abstracting/indexing.
 Description: A documentation list of Indian Newspapers, Index to Indian Periodicals, Index to Foreign Periodicals, Index to Compsite Publications, Index to Biographical Profiles, Index to Book Reviews, and Index to Theses and Dissertations.

950 015 II ISSN 0019-3852
Z3001
INDEX INDO-ASIATICUS. (Text in Bengali, English, Hindi, Sanskrit and other European languages) 1968. q. Rs.850. Centre for Asian Dokumentation, K-15, CIT Bldg., Christopher Rd., Calcutta 700 014, India. (Subscr. to: Central News Agency, P.O. Box 374, New Delhi 110 001, India; Dist. overseas by: Verlag Otto Harrassowitz, Taunusstr. 14, P.O. Box 2929, 6200 Wiesbaden 1, Germany) Ed. SIbadas Chaudhuri. adv.; bk.rev.; bibl.; cum.index. circ. 400. **Document type:** abstracting/indexing.
 Description: Indexes international periodicals of all languages, whose topics relate to the culture of India and ancient Asia.

650
INDEX INTERNATIONALIS INDICUS. 1970. triennial. Rs.1000. Centre for Asian Dokumentation, K-15, CIT Bldg., Christopher Rd., Calcutta 700 014, India. (Dist. by: Verlag Otto Harrassowitz, Taunusstr. 14, P.O. Box 2929, 6200 Wiesbaden 1, Germany) Ed. S. Chaudhuri. adv. circ. 500. **Document type:** abstracting/indexing.
 Description: Lists cumulative articles on indological and buddhistic sutdies published in Indian and foreign periodicals.

959 016 SI ISSN 0046-984X
INSTITUTE OF SOUTHEAST ASIAN STUDIES. LIBRARY. ACCESSIONS LIST. 1968. irreg. vol.8, no.14. free. Institute of Southeast Asian Studies, Heng Mui Keng Terrace, Pasir Panjang, Singapore 0511, Singapore. TEL 7780955. FAX 7781735. TELEX RS 37068 ISEAS. E-mail: pubsunit@merlion.iseas.ac.sg. bibl. (processed) **Document type:** bibliography.

294 016 II ISSN 0970-1435
M L B D NEWSLETTER; monthly of indological bibliography. (Text in English and Hindi) 1979. m. Rs.15($10) Motilal Banarsidass (Delhi), 41 U.A. Bungalow Rd., Jawahar Nagar, Delhi 110 007, India. TEL 011-2911985. FAX 011-2930689. (Dist. in U.K. by: M S Motilal Books Ltd., 73 Lime Walk, Headington, Oxford OX3 7AD; Dist. in U.S. by: South Asia Books, Box 502, Columbia, MO 65205. TEL 314-449-1359) Ed. N.P. Jain. adv.; bk.rev.; abstr.; bibl.; illus. **Document type:** newsletter.
 Description: Focuses on Vedic and Buddhist works of literature and research.

011 SU
MARKAZ AL-MALIK FAISAL LIL-BUHUTH WAL-DIRASAT AL-ISLAMIYYAH. FIHRIS AL-MAKHTUTAT/KING FAISAL CENTER FOR RESEARCH AND ISLAMIC STUDIES. MANUSCRIPT CATALOGUE. 1985. irreg. King Faisal Center for Research and Islamic Studies, P.O. Box 51049, Riyadh 11543, Saudi Arabia. TEL 4652255. FAX 4659993. TELEX 205470. **Document type:** bibliography.

951 011 NP
NEPAL - ANTIQUARY. BIBLIOGRAPHICAL SERIES. 1976. irreg. Rs.250($30) Office of Nepal-Antiquary, 20-401 Naxal, Kathmandu, Nepal. **Document type:** bibliography.

950 GW ISSN 0720-2695
NEUERWERBUNG SUEDASIEN. 1977. 7/yr. DM.33. Universitaetsbibliothek Tuebingen, Orientabteilung, Postfach 2620, 72016 Tuebingen, Germany. TEL 07071-292587. FAX 07071-293123. index. circ. 120. **Document type:** bibliography.
 Description: Collects new literature focusing on language and culture of Southern Asia received in the University of Tuebingen library.

950 GW ISSN 0720-2741
NEUERWERBUNGEN VORDERER ORIENT. 1977. m. DM.33. Universitaetsbibliothek Tuebingen, Orientabteilung, Postfach 2620, 72016 Tuebingen, Germany. TEL 07071-292587. FAX 07071-293123. index. circ. 240. **Document type:** bibliography.
 Description: Contains new literature about ancient history, language, and modern regional studies of the Near and Middle East as well as North Africa.

950 016 HK ISSN 0441-1900
Z3107.H7
UNIVERSITY OF HONG KONG. CENTRE OF ASIAN STUDIES. BIBLIOGRAPHIES AND RESEARCH GUIDES. (Text in Chinese or English) 1970. irreg., no.24, 1987. price varies. University of Hong Kong, Centre of Asian Studies, Pokfulam Rd., Hong Kong. FAX 852-2559-5884. TELEX 71919-CEREB-HX. Ed. Edward K.Y. Chen. (processed) **Document type:** bibliography.

950 RU
VOSTOKOVEDENIE I AFRIKANISTIKA: ZARUBEZHNAYA LITERATURA; referativnyi zhurnal. 1972. q. $62. Rossiiskaya Akademiya Nauk, Institut Nauchnoi Informatsii po Obshchestvennym Naukam, Ul. Krasikova 28-21, 117418 Moscow V-418, Russia. Ed. S.N. Kuznetsova. **Document type:** abstracting/indexing.
 Formerly: Obshchestvennye Nauki za Rubezhom. Vostokovedenie i Afrikanistika (ISSN 0132-7348)

950 GW ISSN 0721-5762
ZEITSCHRIFTENVERZEICHNIS ORIENT. 1991. a. DM.29. Universitaetsbibliothek Tuebingen, Orientabteilung, Postfach 2620, 72016 Tuebingen, Germany. TEL 07071-292587. FAX 07071-293123. **Document type:** directory.

ORNITHOLOGY

see Biology–Ornithology

ORTHOPEDICS AND TRAUMATOLOGY

see Medical Sciences–Orthopedics and Traumatology

OTORHINOLARYNGOLOGY

see Medical Sciences–Otorhinolaryngology

OUTDOOR LIFE

see Sports and Games–Outdoor Life

PACKAGING

660.29 658.7 670 GW ISSN 0941-0295
TP244.A3 CODEN: AERRBV
AEROSOL & SPRAY REPORT. (Text in English, French and German) 1961. 11/yr. DM.396 (foreign DM.417.60) (effective 1996). Huethig GmbH, Postfach 102869, 69018 Heidelberg, Germany. TEL 06221-489226. FAX 06221-489482. TELEX 461727-HUEHDD. Ed. Bernd Braune. adv.: B&W page DM.3680; trim 210 x 275; adv. contact: Karl Dietzow. charts; illus. circ. 3,568. **Indexed:** Chem.Abstr., Curr.Pack.Abstr., Eng.Ind., Excerp.Med., Int.Packag.Abstr., Met.Abstr., Packag.Sci.Tech., World Alum.Abstr. **Document type:** trade publication.
 —BLDSC (0729.835600); CASDDS; Ei; SWETS. CCC.
 Formerly (until 1991): Aerosol Report (ISSN 0001-9313)
 Description: Trade journal for manufacturers of containers, filling and sealing machines, final packaging machines, propellants, valves, pump sprays, seals, protective caps, paints and indoor protective lacquers, and other accessories.

ALCAN INFORMIERT. see *METALLURGY*

PACKAGING

ANNUAL BOOK OF A S T M STANDARDS. VOLUME 15.09. PAPER; PACKAGING; FLEXIBLE BARRIER MATERIALS; BUSINESS COPY PRODUCTS. see ENGINEERING — Engineering Mechanics And Materials

658.7884 US
ANNUAL CAN SHIPMENTS REPORT. 1972. a. $79.50. Can Manufacturers Institute, 1625 Massachusetts Ave., N.W., Washington, DC 20036. TEL 202-232-4677. circ. 500.
  Formerly: Can Manufacturers Institute. Annual Metal Can Shipments Report (ISSN 0068-7014)
  Description: Covers domestic can shipments by market, product, technology and material used.

ANUARIO DEL EMPAQUE. see BUSINESS AND ECONOMICS — Trade And Industrial Directories

ANYAGMOZGATAS-CSOMAGOLAS. see TRANSPORTATION — Ships And Shipping

ASIA PACIFIC FOOD INDUSTRY BUSINESS REPORT. see FOOD AND FOOD INDUSTRIES

AUSTRALIAN LITHOGRAPHER, PRINTER, AND PACKAGER. see PRINTING

658.7 AT ISSN 0004-9921
CODEN: AUPAEH
AUSTRALIAN PACKAGING. 1952. m. Aus.$55. Reed Business Publishing Pty. Ltd. (Subsidiary of: Reed International PLC), 1-5 Railway St., Chatswood, N.S.W. 2067, Australia. TEL 02-372-5222. FAX 02-419-7533. Ed. A. Crane. adv.; bk.rev.; charts; illus.; pat.; tr.lit.; tr.mk. circ. 5,029. **Indexed:** Abstr.Bull.Inst.Pap.Chem., Curr.Pack.Abstr., Int.Packag.Abstr., Packag.Sci.Tech.
  —BLDSC (1817.400000).

658.7 AU ISSN 0005-0563
AUSTROPACK; Zeitschrift fuer alle Gebiete des Verpackungswesens fuer Transport und Verkehr. 1964. m. S.620 (foreign DM.138). Verlag Dr. A. Schendl GmbH, Karlsgasse 15, Postfach 29, A-1041 Vienna, Austria. TEL 0222-5055593. FAX 0222-5055596. Ed. Martin Oegg. adv.: B&W page S.10600; trim 175 x 260; adv. contact: Helmut Mayr. bk.rev.; abstr.; charts; illus.; stat. circ. 1,500. (tabloid format) **Indexed:** Int.Packag.Abstr. **Document type:** trade publication.

658.788 FR
B I C - CODE. (Text in English) 1970. a. 130 SFr. per no. Bureau International des Containers - International Container Bureau, 167 rue de Courcelles, 75017 Paris, France. TEL 47-66-03-90. FAX 47-66-08-91. Ed. P. Fournier. charts.

658.788 JA
BEST OF PACKAGING IN JAPAN. 1990. a. 16000 Yen. Nippo Co. Ltd., 1-19 Misaki-cho 3-chome, Chiyoda-ku, Tokyo 101, Japan. TEL 03-3262-3461. FAX 03-3263-2560.
  Description: Information on packaged goods: food, drugs, cosmetics, confectioneries and daily necessities.

676.3 US
BOARD CONVERTING NEWS. 1984. w. $120. N V Business Publishers Corp., 43 Main St., Avon by Sea, NJ 07717. TEL 908-502-0500. FAX 908-502-9606. Ed. Jim Curley. circ. 4,695. (back issues avail.) **Document type:** newsletter.
  Description: Covers product and current news, transacted board prices for the U.S. and Canada.

676.3 US
BOARD CONVERTING NEWS INTERNATIONAL. fortn. $110. N V Business Publishers Corp., 43 Main St., Avon by Sea, NJ 07717. TEL 908-502-0500. FAX 908-502-9606. (U.K. addr.: Walton House, 90 London Rd., Hooks, Hampshire RG27 9LF, England) Ed. Michael Brunton. circ. 3,092. (back issues avail.) **Document type:** newsletter.
  Description: Covers product news and general news for the European market.

676.3 UK ISSN 1358-0701
BOARD MARKET DIGEST. 1986. m. £175 (overseas £195). Paper Publications Ltd., Church House, Church Ln., Kings Langley, Herts WD4 8JP, England. TEL 01923-261555. FAX 01923-261118. Ed. Lawrence Turk; Pub. Peter Ingram. bk.rev.; circ. 300 (paid). **Document type:** trade publication.
  Description: Provides up-to-date information on prices, market trends, company information and future prospects for the professional buyer of packaging papers and boards.

676.3 658.7 US ISSN 0006-8489
BOXBOARD CONTAINERS. 1892. m. $28. Intertec Publishing Corp., 29 N. Wacker Dr., Chicago, IL 60606. TEL 312-726-2802. FAX 312-726-2574. Ed. Greg. Kishbaugh. adv.: B&W page $3555, color $4920; 8 1/8 x 10 7/8. charts; illus.; tr.lit. circ. 14,250. (also avail. in microform from UMI; reprint service avail. from UMI) **Indexed:** Curr.Pack.Abstr., Graph.Arts Lit.Abstr., Key to Econ.Sci., Packag.Sci.Tech., PROMT.
  —BLDSC (2265.100000).
  Description: Covers corrugated and solid fibre shipping container, folding carton, setup paper box, transparent, fiber can, drum and tube and paperboard mills.

BRITAIN'S TOP 300 PACKAGING MANUFACTURERS. see BUSINESS AND ECONOMICS — Trade And Industrial Directories

BUSINESS RATIO REPORT: FOOD PROCESSING & PACKAGING MACHINERY INDUSTRY; an industry sector analysis. see FOOD AND FOOD INDUSTRIES

676.3 658.8 UK ISSN 0261-9334
BUSINESS RATIO REPORT: PAPER & BOARD PACKAGING; an industry sector analysis. 1976. a. I C C Business Ratios Ltd., Freepost, Field House, Hampton, Mddx. TW12 1BR, England. TEL 081-783-0977. FAX 081-783-1940. charts; stat. **Document type:** trade publication.
  —BLDSC (6358.911000).

658.788 668.4 658.8 UK ISSN 0261-9385
BUSINESS RATIO REPORT: PLASTICS PACKAGING; an industry sector analysis. 1978. a. I C C Business Ratios Ltd., Freepost, Field House, Hampton, Mddx. TW12 1BR, England. TEL 081-783-0977. FAX 081-783-1940. charts; stat. **Document type:** trade publication.

BUSINESS RATIO REPORT: PRINT AND PACKAGING MACHINERY; an industry sector analysis. see PRINTING

C O P E BACKGROUNDERS. (Council on Packaging in the Environment) see ENVIRONMENTAL STUDIES — Toxicology And Environmental Safety

658.788 US
CAN SHIPMENTS REPORT. (Annual edition avail.) 1975. m. $265. Can Manufacturers Institute, 1625 Massachussets Ave., N.W., Washington, DC 20036. TEL 202-232-4677. circ. 750. (back issues avail.)
  Description: Lists domestic (US and US controlled territories) shipment by market, product, material used and technology.

688.8 US
▼**CAN TECHNOLOGY INTERNATIONAL.** 1994. bi-m. $70. Trend Publishing Inc., 625 N. Michigan Ave., Ste. 2500, Chicago, IL 60611-3109. TEL 312-654-2300. FAX 312-654-2323. Ed. Fred Church; Pub. Scott Walker. adv.: B&W page $2625. circ. 5,500. **Document type:** trade publication.

658.7 670 CN ISSN 0008-4654
CODEN: CPAKAN
CANADIAN PACKAGING. 1948. 11/yr. Can.$45. Maclean-Hunter Ltd., Business Publication Division, Maclean-Hunter Bldg., 777 Bay St., Toronto, ON M5W 1A7, Canada. TEL 416-596-6016. Ed. Doug Faulkner. adv.: B&W page $3830, color page $5280; 8 1/8 x 10 7/8. illus. circ. 12,000. (also avail. in microform from UMI) **Indexed:** Abstr.Bull.Inst.Pap.Chem., Art & Archaeol.Tech.Abstr., Can.B.P.I., Chem.Abstr., Curr.Pack.Abstr., Int.Packag.Abstr., Key to Econ.Sci., Packag.Sci.Tech.
  —BLDSC (3043.350000); Faxon. **CCC.**

688.8 UK ISSN 1352-9293
THE CANMAKER. 1987. m. $220. Sayers Publishing Group, 14 Royce Rd., Manor Royal, Crawley, W. Sussex RH10 2NX, England. TEL 0293-619961. FAX 0293-619988. Ed. John Nutting. adv.; bk.rev. circ. 10,000. **Document type:** trade publication.
  Formerly: Canmaker and Canner (ISSN 0953-8690)

676.2 SP
CARTIFLEX; revista informativa del cartonaje y envase flexible. 1988. 6/yr. 4500 ptas. in Europe; America 6000 ptas. Alabrent Ediciones, C. Valencia 501 entlo. 1a, 08013 Barcelona, Spain. TEL 34-3-2653211. FAX 34-3-2651320. Ed. Ramon Arnella Paris. circ. 4,000. **Document type:** trade publication.

658.7 676.3 FR ISSN 0247-8390
CARTONNAGES & EMBALLAGES MODERNES. 1940. m. 550 F. Editions Technorama, 31 place St. Ferdinand, 75017 Paris, France. TEL 1-45-74-67-43. FAX 45-72-63-21. Ed. R. Baschet. adv.; charts; illus. circ. 7,300. **Indexed:** Graph.Arts Lit.Abstr., Key to Econ.Sci.
  Formed by the merger of: Emballage Moderne (ISSN 0013-6565); Cartonnages.
  Description: Deals with paper and board packaging.

658.7 SP
CATALOGO ESPANOL DEL ENVASE, EMBALAJE Y ARTES GRAFICAS APLICADAS. vol.5, 1972. s-a. 22500 ptas. per no. Instituto Espanol del Envase y Embalaje, Breton de los Herreros, 57, bajo H, 28003 Madrid, Spain. TEL 442-34-81. FAX 5383718. TELEX 27307 E. Ed. Luis Sicre. circ. 15,000. (reprint service avail.)
  Formerly: Catalogo Nacional del Envase, Embalaje y Artes Graficas Aplicadas (ISSN 0008-7610)

676 IT
CATALOGO GUIDA DELL'IMBALLAGGIO (YEAR). (Text in English, Italian) 1987. a. L.25000. Gruppo Editoriale Faenza Editrice S.p.A., Via Pier. de Crescenzi, 44, 48018 Faenza, Italy. TEL 39-546-663488. FAX 39-546-660440. Ed. Franco Rossi. adv.: B&W page L.1700000. circ. 5,000.

688.8 NE ISSN 0166-7416
COMPRES; vaktijdschrift voor grafisch managament. 1976. 25/yr. fl.189. Uitgeverij Compres b.v., Postbus 55, 2300 AB Leiden, Netherlands. TEL 31-71-161515. FAX 31-71-121550. Ed. J. Vlak; Pub. H. Verwoert. adv. contact: Robert de Winter. circ. 9,728 (paid). **Document type:** trade publication.

688.8 658.8 UK
CONSUMER PACKAGING: THE INTERNATIONAL MARKET. (Subseries of: Market Direction reports) a. £1595($3190) (effective 1996). Euromonitor, 60-61 Britton St., London EC1M 5NA, England. TEL 0171-251-8024. FAX 0171-608-3149. (Addr. in N. America: Euromonitor International, 122 S. Michigan Ave., Ste. 1200, Chicago, IL 60603. TEL 312-922-1115. FAX 312-922-1157) (looseleaf format) **Document type:** trade publication.
  Description: Analyzes the consumer packaging market for France, Germany, Italy, Spain, the U.K., the U.S., and Japan.

676.3 US ISSN 1067-4586
TS195.A1
CONVERSION Y EMPAQUE. (Text in Spanish) 1992. bi-m. $25. C C International Publishing, Inc., 1680 S.W. Bayshore Blvd., Port St. Lucie, FL 34984. TEL 407-879-6666. FAX 407-879-7388. adv.: B&W page $2815, color page $3690; trim 8 1/4 x 10 7/8. circ. 15,000. **Document type:** trade publication.
  Description: For paper, film and foil converters and package manufacturing and printing professionals throughout Latin America.

CONVERTING TODAY. see PAPER AND PULP

688.8 676 UK ISSN 0266-0350
CONVERTING WORLD. 1983. m. £60. Maclean Hunter Ltd., Maclean Hunter House, Chalk Ln., Cockfosters Rd., Barnet, Herts EN4 0BU, England. TEL 081-975-9759. FAX 081-975-9764. TELEX 299072-MACHUN-G. Ed. Gail Lea. adv. contact: Julian Maddocks. circ. 5,711 (controlled). (tabloid format; back issues avail.) **Document type:** trade publication.

4978 PACKAGING

677.7　　　　　　　FR
CORDERIE FRANCAISE. 1950. m. 120 Fr. Chambre Syndicale Generale de la Corderie, 146 av. des Fusilles, 49400 Saumur, France. TEL 41-67-36-40. FAX 41-67-35-81. TELEX 723 261. Ed. Jean-Jacques Mesnard. adv. circ. 700.

676.3　　　　　　　UK
CORRUGATED AND CARTON BULLETIN. 1972. 10/yr. £185($315) (outside Europe $330). Data Transcripts Ltd., P.O. Box 14, Dorking, Surrey RH5 4YN, England. TEL 01306-884473. Ed. Lynda Crane. bk.rev.; stat. (back issues avail.) **Document type:** newsletter.
　Description: Examines corrugated and folding carton conversion, raw materials, supply and demand, company and product news, equipment and processing, technical trends, and end use.

676.3　　　　　　US　ISSN 1058-0883
TS198.3. P3
CORRUGATED CONTAINERS CONFERENCE (YEAR). (Title varies slightly: Corrugated Conference Proceedings) (1981 held jointly with Testing Conference Proceedings) a. price varies. Technical Association of the Pulp and Paper Industry, Inc., Technology Park-Atlanta, Box 105113, Atlanta, GA 30348. TEL 404-446-1400. FAX 404-446-6947. **Document type:** proceedings.
　Formerly: Technical Association of the Pulp and Paper Industry. Corrugated Containers Conference. Proceedings (Year).
　Refereed Serial

DIRECTORY OF U S AND CANADIAN SCRAP PLASTICS PROCESSORS AND BUYERS. see *BUSINESS AND ECONOMICS — Trade And Industrial Directories*

676.3　　　　　　NE　ISSN 0924-9303
E C M A FOLDING CARTON BULLETIN. (European Carton Makers Association) French edition (ISSN 0924-9311); German edition (ISSN 0924-932X) (Text in English) q. fl.200. European Association of Folding Carton Makers, ECMA Secretariat, Laan Copes van Cattenburch 79, 2585 EW The Hague, Netherlands. TEL 31-70-3603837. FAX 31-70-3636348.
　—BLDSC (3648.101000).
　Formerly (until 1990): E C M A Bulletin.

E E C - TIN IN TINPLATE. (European Economic Community) see *METALLURGY*

688.8　　　　　　NE　ISSN 0921-383X
E F M. (Euro Flexo Magazine) Key Title: EFM. Euro Flexo Magazine. (Text in English, French, German, Italian) 1985. 10/yr. fl.130. Uitgeverij Compres b.v., Postbus 55, 2300 AB Leiden, Netherlands. TEL 31-71-161515. FAX 31-71-121550. Ed. Durk Schilstra; Pub. H. Verwoert. adv. contact: Robert de Winter. illus.; tr.lit.; index; circ. 8,300 (paid). (back issues avail.) **Document type:** trade publication.
　—BLDSC (3664.131700).
　Description: For the packaging and printing industries.

688.8　　　　　　UK　ISSN 1357-0285
E U PACKAGING REPORT. (European Community) m. £260 in Europe; elsewhere £275 (effective 1994). Agra Europe (London) Ltd., 25 Frant Rd., Tunbridge Wells, Kent TN2 5JT, England. TEL 01892-533813. FAX 01892-544895. TELEX 95114 AGRATW G. **Document type:** newsletter.
　Formerly (until 1995): E C Packaging Report (ISSN 0967-7852)
　Description: Covers packaging and packaging waste legislation both nationally and in the E.U.

676.3　　　　　　PO
EMBALAGEM. 6/yr. Praca das Industrias, Lisbon, Portugal.

658.7　670　　　　FR　ISSN 0013-6557
EMBALLAGE DIGEST. (Text in English, French, German and Italian) 1958. m. 180 f. Societe Europeenne de Presse et d'Edition, 142 rue d'Aguesseau, 92100 Boulogne, France. TEL 46-03-15-54. FAX 46-03-97-67. Ed. Emmanuel C. Pottier. adv.; illus. circ. 11,000. **Indexed:** Int.Packag.Abstr., Met.Abstr., Packag.Sci.Tech., World Alum.Abstr.
　—BLDSC (3732.970000).

658.7　　　　　　FR　ISSN 0013-6573
TS158
EMBALLAGES. 1932. 10/yr. 400 F. (foreign 542 F.)(effective Jan. 1994). Groupe Information et Professions, 1 cite Bergere, 75009 Paris, France. TEL 44-69-55-50. FAX 48-01-07-68. TELEX 285 485. Eds. Philippe-Edouerd Grardel, Claude Reny. adv.; bk.rev.; bibl.; illus.; pat.; stat. circ. 10,000. **Indexed:** Abstr.Bull.Inst.Pap.Chem., Curr.Pack.Abstr., Dairy Sci.Abstr., Food Sci.& Tech.Abstr., Int.Packag.Abstr., Key to Econ.Sci., PROMT, World Alum.Abstr.
　—CCC.

658.7　　　　　　NO　ISSN 0013-6581
EMBALLERING. 1939. m. (10/yr.). NOK 360. Selvig Publishing A-S, Postboks 9070 Groenland, 0133 Oslo, Norway. TEL 22-364440. FAX 22-360550. Ed. Terje Lunde. adv.; illus. circ. 4,350. **Indexed:** Abstr.Bull.Inst.Pap.Chem., Int.Packag.Abstr. **Document type:** trade publication.
　—CCC.
　Formerly: Norske Esker.

663　　　　　　　AG　ISSN 0325-0415
ENVASAMIENTO. 1969. m. $150. Editorial Tecnica Siglo XXI, S.A., Talcahuano 374-1p. B, 1013 Buenos Aires, Argentina. Ed. G. Oliveti. adv.; bk.rev.; bibl.; stat. circ. 6,000.
　Description: Raw materials, machines, design and confections, analysis of markets, regulations, adhesion and events.

676.3　　　　　　SP　ISSN 0211-2965
ENVASPRES; equipos y materiales para el envase, embalaje, acondicionamiento, y su presentacion. 1980. 11/yr. 4500 ptas. Pedeca Sociedad Cooperativa, Ltda., Maria Auxiliadora 5, 28040 Madrid, Spain. TEL 1-450-88-37. FAX 1-564-01-37. Ed. J.F. Munoz Requena. circ. 7,000.

676　　　　　　　SP　ISSN 0212-5226
EQUIPACK; revista trimestral de los equipos y medios de produccion y envasado. 1983. q. 6000 ptas. (effective 1995) 8000 ptas. (effective 1996). Grupo Arte y Cemento, S.A., C. Zancoeta 9, 5 y 7, 48013 Bilbao, Spain. TEL 34-4-4410766. FAX 34-4-4419590. Ed. Ignacio Echevarria; Pub. Eduardo Gonzalez del Castillo. adv.: B&W page 70000 ptas., color page 110000 ptas.; 180 x 270; adv. contact: Gerardo Lopez. circ. 4,000. **Document type:** trade publication.

EREKUTORONIKUSU JISSO GIJUTSU/ELECTRONIC PACKAGING TECHNOLOGY. see *ELECTRONICS*

688.8　　　　　　GW
EUROPAEISCHER WIRTSCHAFTSDIENST. VERPACKUNGS-DIENST. fortn. DM.540. E U W I D - Europaeischer Wirtschaftsdienst GmbH, Bleichstr. 20-22, 76593 Gernsbach, Germany. TEL 07224-9397-0. FAX 07224-939750. circ. 2,450. **Document type:** trade publication.

EUROPEAN CONVERTING INDUSTRY DIRECTORY. see *PAPER AND PULP*

670　　　　　　　US　ISSN 1052-2131
　　　　　　　　　　CODEN: EPANEO
EUROPEAN PACKAGING NEWSLETTER AND WORLD REPORT. 1961. m. $240 (foreign $255) (effective 1996). (International Packaging Club, FR) E P N Inc., 669 S. Washington St., Alexandria, VA 22314-4109. TEL 703-519-3907. FAX 703-519-7732. Ed. Pierre J. Louis; Pub. Jack Cameron. **Document type:** newsletter.
　—BLDSC (3829.768230). **CCC.**
　Description: Serves the packaging industry as a clearinghouse for information on techniques, new machinery, and processes from Europe and Asia.

658.7　　　　　　UK
FILM EXTRUSION MATERIALS AND MARKETS BULLETIN. 1988. 10/yr. £185($315) (outside Europe $330). Data Transcripts Ltd., P.O. Box 14, Dorking, Surrey RH5 4YN, England. TEL 01306-884473. Ed. Lynda Crane. (back issues avail.) **Document type:** newsletter.

688.8　350　　　　US
FLEXIBLE PACKAGING ASSOCIATION. LEGISLATIVE UPDATE. irreg. free to qualified personnel. Flexible Packaging Association, 1090 Vermont Ave., N.W., Ste. 500, Washington, DC 20005. TEL 202-842-3880. FAX 202-842-3841. **Document type:** trade publication.
　Description: Describes legislative activity affecting the flexible-packaging industry.

688.8　350　　　　US
FLEXIBLE PACKAGING ASSOCIATION. REGULATORY REVIEW. m. free to qualified personnel. Flexible Packaging Association, 1090 Vermont Ave., N.W., Ste. 500, Washington, DC 20005. TEL 202-842-3880. FAX 202-842-3481. **Document type:** trade publication.
　Description: Covers regulatory activity affecting the flexible-packaging industry.

688.8　　　　　　US
FLEXIBLE PACKAGING ASSOCIATION. UPDATE NEWSLETTER; issues and activities affecting the flexible packaging industry. m. free to qualified personnel. Flexible Packaging Association, 1090 Vermont Ave., N.W., Ste. 500, Washington, DC 20005. TEL 202-842-3880. FAX 202-842-3841. Ed. Catherine Hyde. circ. 1,000. **Document type:** trade publication.
　Description: Covers government policy, public relations, marketing, technology and regulatory affairs, and legal issues affecting flexible packaging products.

658.788　　　　　FR　ISSN 0765-3204
FLEXO-EUROPE. 1983. 6/yr. 400 Fr. Editions Technorama, 31 Place Saint Ferdinand, 75017 Paris, France. TEL 45-74-67-43. FAX 45-72-63-21. Ed. R. Baschet. adv.; bk.rev. circ. 3,300.
　—CCC.
　Description: Deals with flexible packaging, coating and laminating.

658.7　　　　　　UK
FLEXPACK MATERIALS & MARKETS BULLETIN. 1973. 10/yr. £185($315) (outside Europe $330). Data Transcripts Ltd., P.O. Box 14, Dorking, Surrey RH5 4YN, England. TEL 01306-884473. Ed. Lynda Crane. **Document type:** newsletter.
　Description: Examines all flexible packaging such as paper, film and foil, laminates, coatings for all uses, food, pharmaceuticals, cosmetics, industrial markets data, company information and product development.

676.3　　　　　　UK　ISSN 0306-168X
TS1200.A1
FOLDING CARTON INDUSTRY. 1974. bi-m. Brunton Business Publications Ltd., Thruxton Down House, Thruxton Down, Andover, Hampshire SP11 8PR, England. TEL 0264-889533. FAX 0264-889524. Ed. Michael D. Brunton. adv. **Indexed:** Abstr.Bull.Inst.Pap.Chem., Int.Packag.Abstr., Packag.Sci.Tech.
　—BLDSC (3964.570000).
　Description: Covers all technical aspects of folding carton production.

658.7　664.09　　　US
TP368
FOOD & DRUG PACKAGING. 1959. m. $50 (Canada $80, elsewhere $110). Independent Publishing Co., Inc., 210 S. Fifth St., Ste. 202, St. Charles, IL 60174. TEL 708-377-0100. FAX 708-377-1678. Ed. Lisa McTigue Pierce; Pub. Edwin O. Landon. adv.; charts; illus.; tr.lit.; index. circ. 77,365. (tabloid format; also avail. in microform) **Indexed:** Int.Packag.Abstr., PROMT. **Document type:** trade publication.
　—BLDSC (3977.033000).
　Former titles (until 1995): New Food and Drug Packaging (ISSN 1075-3028); (until 1993): Food and Drug Packaging (ISSN 0015-6272)
　Description: Industry journal covering new products, marketing trends and regulatory developments in packaging for the food, drug, pharmaceutical and cosmetic industries.

658.788 668.4 UK ISSN 0951-4554
FOOD, COSMETICS AND DRUGS PACKAGING; an international newsletter. 1978. m. £338($538) (effective 1996). Elsevier Science Ltd., P.O. Box 800, Kidlington, Oxford OX5 1DX, England. TEL 44-1865-843000. FAX 44-1865-843010. E-mail: nlinfo@elsevier.nl; usinfo-f@elsevier.com; forinfo-kyf04035@niftyserve.or.jp; Site addr.: http://www.elsevier.nl/. (Subscr. in U.S. and Canada to: Elsevier Science, 660 White Plains Rd., Tarrytown, NY 10591-5153. TEL 914-524-9200. FAX 914-333-2444) Ed. P. Barnes, R. Coles. bk.rev.; illus.; pat.; stat. (back issues avail.) **Indexed:** Curr.Pack.Abstr., Intl.Polym.Sci.& Tech., RAPRA. **Document type:** newsletter.
●Also available online. Vendor(s): Knight-Ridder, Inc. —BLDSC (3977.292000); SWETS. **CCC**.
Former titles: F C D Packaging; (until Apr. 1983): Plastics in Retail Packaging Bulletin (ISSN 0140-878X)
Description: Presents practical information in concise, readable form, helping management to make well-informed decisions on the developments, application, planning and forecasting of the role of FCD packaging within their own organizations.

FOOD LABELING NEWS. see *FOOD AND FOOD INDUSTRIES*

688.8 664 UK ISSN 1355-0497
FOOD PACKAGING BULLETIN. m. £269 (effective 1996). Research Information Ltd., 222 Maylands Ave., Hemel Hempstead, Herts HP2 7TD, England. TEL 01442-213222. FAX 01442-259395. (back issues avail.) **Document type:** bulletin.

FOOD PACKER INTERNATIONAL DIRECTORY (YEAR). see *BUSINESS AND ECONOMICS — Trade And Industrial Directories*

FOOD REVIEW. see *FOOD AND FOOD INDUSTRIES*

FOOD SAFETY & SECURITY. see *FOOD AND FOOD INDUSTRIES*

FOUR P NEWS; India's leading journal on pulp, paper, printing and packaging. see *PAPER AND PULP*

658.7884 663.19 US
GLASS PACKAGING INSTITUTE. ANNUAL REPORT. 1957. a. free. Glass Packaging Institute, 1801 K St., N.W., Ste. 1105-L, Washington, DC 20006. FAX 202-785-5377. circ. 24,000. **Indexed:** Br.Ceram.Abstr.
Formerly: Glass Containers (ISSN 0072-4637)

658.7 US ISSN 1049-3158
TS2301.C8 CODEN: GPMAEX
GOOD PACKAGING MAGAZINE. 1940. m. $30 (foreign $80) includes annual Western Packaging Directory. Pacific Trade Journals, 1315 E. Julian St., San Jose, CA 95116-1094. TEL 408-286-1661. FAX 408-275-8071. Pub. Jerry Erich. adv.: B&W page $1460, color page $2845; adv. contact: Ken Dean. illus.; tr.lit. circ. 9,600. **Indexed:** Curr.Pack.Abstr., Int.Packag.Abstr. **Document type:** trade publication.
—UnCover.
Formerly: Good Packaging (ISSN 0017-2170)
Description: Focuses on innovative products, equipment and packaging methods in a variety of industries, including cosmetics, film, food processing, machinery, materials handling, pharmaceuticals and plastics.

670 MX
GUIA DEL ENVASE Y EMBALAJE/CONTAINER AND PACKAGING GUIDE. (Text in English, Spanish) 1975. a. $80. Informatica Cosmos, S.A. de C.V., Calz. del Hueso 334-A11, Col. Ex-Hacienda Coapa, 14300 Mexico D.F, Mexico. TEL 525-677-48-68. FAX 525-679-35-75. (Dist. in US by: Schnell Publishing Co., Inc. TEL 212-248-4177. FAX 212-248-4903) Ed. Raul Macazaga. adv.: B&W page $1000; trim 211 x 274; adv. contact: Mary Christen. circ. 5,000. **Document type:** directory.
Formerly: Envase y Embalaje.
Description: Lists overs 1400 suppliers in Mexico. Lists 800 products, containers, materials, accessories, tools and services.

658.788 UK
HANDLING AND PACKAGING PRODUCT INFORMATION CARDS. Variant title: H A P P I Cards. 1982. 4/yr. Trinity Publishing Ltd., Times House, Station Approach, Ruislip, Middx. HA4 8NB, England. TEL 01895-677677. FAX 01895-676027. adv.; circ. 20,000 (controlled). **Document type:** trade publication.

658.788 660 US
TP201
HAZMAT PACKAGER AND SHIPPER; the journal of hazardous materials regulation and distribution. 1990. bi-m. $195. Packaging Research International Inc., Box 3144, W. Chester, PA 19381-3144. TEL 610-436-8292. FAX 610-436-9422. Ed. Vincent Vitollo. adv.; circ. 935 (paid). **Document type:** trade publication.
—BLDSC (3148.740000).
Formerly (until June 1995): Chemical Packaging Review (ISSN 1054-5131)
Description: Covers packaging and distribution issues related to the transport of hazardous materials. Covers U.S. DOT and international regulations and EPA guidelines.

688.8 621.9 JA
HOSO KIKAI SHINBUN/PACKAGING MACHINERY NEWS. (Text in Japanese) 1969. m. 2000 Yen. Nihon Hoso Kikai Kogyokai - Japan Packaging Machinery Manufactures Association, 5-5, Asakusabashi 5-chome, Taito-ku, Tokyo 111, Japan.

HOUSEHOLD & PERSONAL PRODUCTS INDUSTRY; the magazine for the detergent, soap, cosmetic and toiletry, wax, polish and aerosol industries. see *BUSINESS AND ECONOMICS — Marketing And Purchasing*

670 SP ISSN 0300-4171
I D E. (Informacion de Envase y Embalaje) 1959. m. 8000 ptas. (foreign 11000 ptas.). Instituto Espanol del Envase y Embalaje, Breton de los Herreros, 57, bajo H, 28003 Madrid, Spain. TEL 442-34-81. FAX 5383718. TELEX 27307 CLAVE E. Ed. Luis Sicre Canut. adv.; bibl.; index. circ. 8,000. **Indexed:** Ind.SST, Int.Packag.Abstr.
Incorporates (in 1990): Instituto Espanol del Envase y Embalaje. B I U. Boletin Informativo Urgente.
Description: Covers the industry and users of packaging.

658.788 380.1 US
I S T A ANNUAL SAFE TRANSIT CONFERENCE. PROCEEDINGS. 1987. a. $85 to non-members; members $40. International Safe Transit Association, Box 10744, Chicago, IL 60610-0744. TEL 312-645-0083. FAX 312-645-1078. **Document type:** proceedings.
Formerly: N T S A Annual Safe Stransit Conference. Proceedings.
Description: Technical papers presented at the Conference.

658.7 670 IT ISSN 0019-2708
IMBALLAGGIO. 1950. m. L.100000 (foreign L.190000). Gruppo Editoriale Jackson S.p.A., Via Gorki 69, 20092 Cinisello (MI), Italy. TEL 39-2-66034205. FAX 39-2-66034238. Ed. Franco Barbieri. adv.: B&W page L.3260000, color page L.4170000; trim 208 x 271. circ. 7,981. (back issues avail.) **Indexed:** Chem.Abstr., Dairy Sci.Abstr., Food Sci.& Tech.Abstr., Int.Packag.Abstr., Packag.Sci.Tech.
—BLDSC (4369.050000).

658.788 IT ISSN 1120-8767
IMBALLAGGIO E MOVIMENTAZIONE.* 1988. 9/yr. E T M s.r.l., Via Principe Eugenio 3, 20155 Milan, Italy. TEL 2-480-10-095. FAX 2-480-10-011. TELEX 321655 PTNEED I. Ed. Fabrizio Carmagnini. circ. 15,000.

658.788 IT
IMBALLAGGIO NEWS. 1960. m. L.100000 (included with Imballaggio). Gruppo Editoriale Jackson S.p.A., Via Gorki 69, 20092 Cinisello B. (MI), Italy. TEL 39-2-66034205. FAX 39-2-66034238. Ed. Franco Barbieri. adv.: B&W page L.4290000, color page L.5180000; trim 215 x 282. circ. 15,500. (back issues avail.)
Formerly: Giornale dell'Imballaggio.

663.19 IT ISSN 0392-792X
IMBOTTIGLIAMENTO. bi-m. L.35000 (foreign L.90000) (effective 1995). Tecniche Nuove s.p.a., Via C. Menotti 14, 20129 Milan, Italy. TEL 02-75701. FAX 02-7610351. adv.: B&W page L.1650000, color page L.2520000; trim 185 x 266. circ. 6,059.
—BLDSC (4369.057000).
Description: Various technologies for the production of alcoholic and non-alcoholic beverages.

658.823 DK ISSN 0106-9403
IN-PAK; packaging and handling: from process to shelf. 1980. 11/yr. DKK 350. Teknisk Forlag A-S, IN-PAK, Skelbaekgade 4, DK-1780 Copenhagen V, Denmark. TEL 45-53-48-28-00. FAX 45-53-48-22-05. Ed. Gitte Soendergaard. circ. 7,000. **Document type:** trade publication.

INDUSTRIA GRAFICA Y ARTES GRAFICAS. see *PRINTING*

INTERNATIONAL BOTTLER AND PACKER. see *BEVERAGES*

INTERNATIONAL JOURNAL OF RADIOACTIVE MATERIALS TRANSPORT. see *TRANSPORTATION*

676 US ISSN 0020-8191
TS1135
INTERNATIONAL PAPER BOARD INDUSTRY. 1956. m. $55. N V Business Publishers Corp., 43 Main St., Avon by Sea, NJ 07717. TEL 908-502-0500. FAX 908-502-9606. Eds. Michael Brunton, Ted Vilardi. adv.: B&W page $2000, color page $2750; 8 1/2 x 11. bk.rev.; charts; illus.; tr.lit. circ. 9,494. **Indexed:** Abstr.Bull.Inst.Pap.Chem., Int.Packag.Abstr., Key to Econ.Sci., Paper & Bd.Abstr. **Document type:** trade publication.
—BLDSC (4544.860000).

ISRAEL INSTITUTE OF PACKAGING. PACKAGING DIRECTORY. see *BUSINESS AND ECONOMICS — Trade And Industrial Directories*

JESSE MEYERS' BEVERAGE DIGEST. see *BEVERAGES*

660.29 658.7 670 UK ISSN 0021-8502
QC882 CODEN: JALSB7
JOURNAL OF AEROSOL SCIENCE. (Also contains selected translations from: Journal of Aerosol Research, Japan) 1970. 8/yr. £719($1144) (effective 1996). (Gesellschaft fuer Aerosolforschung - Association for Aerosol Research) Elsevier Science Ltd., Pergamon, P.O. Box 800, Kidlington, Oxford OX5 1DX, England. TEL 44-1865-843000. FAX 44-1865-843010. E-mail: nlinfo@elsevier.nl; usinfo-f@elsevier.com; forinfo-kyf04035@niftyserve.or.jp; Site addr.: http://www.elsevier.nl/. (Subscr. in U.S. and Canada to: Elsevier Science, 660 White Plains Rd., Tarrytown, NY, 10591-5153. TEL 914-524-9200. FAX 914-333-2444) Eds. G. Kasper, J.H. Vincent. adv.; bk.rev. circ. 1,000. (also avail. in microfilm from UMI; reprint service avail. from UMI) **Indexed:** Appl.Mech.Rev., Biotech.Abstr., C.I.S. Abstr., Cadscan, Chem.Abstr., Chem.Eng.Abstr., Curr.Cont., Eng.Ind., Environ.Abstr., Environ.Ind., Excerp.Med., Ind.Sci.Rev., INIS Atomind., INSPEC, Lead Abstr., Sci.Cit.Ind., T.C.E.A., Zincscan. **Document type:** academic/scholarly publication.
—BLDSC (4919.060000); CASDDS; Ei; Faxon; Genuine Article; SWETS; UMI; UnCover. **CCC**.
Description: Publishes original papers in basic and applied aerosol research.
Refereed Serial

688.8 NE ISSN 0922-4254
KARTOFLEX MAGAZINE. 1947. bi-m. fl.55($32.50) (Vereniging van Nederlandse Fabrikanten van Kartonnages en Flexibele Verpakkingen, Kartoflex) Uitgeverij Compres b.v., Postbus 55, 2300 AB Leiden, Netherlands. TEL 31-71-161515. FAX 31-71-121550. Ed. Frits de Winter; Pub. H. Verwoert. adv.: B&W page fl.1795; adv. contact: Robert de Winter. bk.rev.; illus.; index. (back issues avail.) **Document type:** trade publication.
Former titles (until 1988): Kartoflexmarkt (ISSN 0921-1772); (until 1987): Kartonnagemarkt (ISSN 0921-1578); (until 1981): Cartonnagebedrijf (ISSN 0008-705X)
Description: For the packaging and printing industries.

PACKAGING

688.8 UK
KEY NOTE MARKET REVIEW: U K PACKAGING INDUSTRY. Variant title: U K Packaging Industry. irreg. £375. Key Note Publications Ltd., Field House, 72 Oldfield Rd., Hampton, Middlesex TW12 2HQ, England. TEL 0181-783-0755. FAX 0181-783-1720. **Document type:** trade publication.
●Also available online.
Also available on CD-ROM.

688.8 UK ISSN 0268-4462
KEY NOTE REPORT: PACKAGING (GLASS). Variant title: Packaging (Glass). irreg. £185. Key Note Publications Ltd., Field House, 72 Oldfield Rd., Hampton, Middlesex TW12 2HQ, England. TEL 0181-783-0755. FAX 0181-783-1720. **Document type:** trade publication.
●Also available online.
Also available on CD-ROM.
—BLDSC (6332.726000).

688.8 UK ISSN 0950-074X
KEY NOTE REPORT: PACKAGING (METALS & AEROSOLS). Variant title: Packaging (Metals & Aerosols). irreg. £185. Key Note Publications Ltd., Field House, 72 Oldfield Rd., Hampton, Middlesex TW12 2HQ, England. TEL 0181-783-0755. FAX 0181-783-1720. **Document type:** trade publication.
●Also available online.
Also available on CD-ROM.

688.8 UK
KEY NOTE REPORT: PACKAGING (PAPER & BOARD). Variant title: Packaging (Paper & Board). irreg. £185. Key Note Publications Ltd., Field House, 72 Oldfield Rd., Hampton, Middlesex TW12 2HQ, England. TEL 0181-783-0755. FAX 0181-783-1720. **Document type:** trade publication.
●Also available online.
Also available on CD-ROM.

688.8 UK
KEY NOTE REPORT: PACKAGING (PLASTICS). Variant title: Packaging (Plastics). irreg. £185. Key Note Publications Ltd., Field House, 72 Oldfield Rd., Hampton, Middlesex TW12 2HQ, England. TEL 0181-783-0755. FAX 0181-783-1720. **Document type:** trade publication.
●Also available online.
Also available on CD-ROM.

688.8 GW ISSN 0171-2713
KOMMENTAR FERTIGPACKUNGSRECHT. 1974. irreg. DM.198. B. Behr's Verlag GmbH, Averhoffstr. 10, 22085 Hamburg, Germany. TEL 040-2270080. FAX 040-2201091. **Document type:** trade publication.

688.8 AU
KOMPACK; Magazin fuer Verpackung, Umwelt und Gemeinde. 1990. bi-m. S.300 (foreign S.420). Media Emap Verlag GmbH, Loquaiplatz 12-7, A-1061 Vienna, Austria. TEL 01-599600. FAX 01-5996021. (Dist. by: Schwoelberger, Joh.-Galler-Str. 10, A-2120 Wolkersdorf, Austria. TEL 02245-3809) Ed. Otto Komarek. adv.: B&W page S.33000, color page S.55000; trim 235 x 330; adv. contact: Harald Eckert. circ. 12,000. **Document type:** trade publication.
Formerly (until 1993): Compack.

676 CN
L M NEWS.* 1971. s-a. (Mardon Packaging International) Lawson Mardon Group Ltd., Corporate Office, 6733 Mississauga Rd., Ste. 700, Mississauga, Ont. L5N 6P6, Canada. TEL 416-821-9711. FAX 416-821-1454. TELEX 06-218572. circ. 7,000.
Former titles: M P I News; Mardon Packaging Review.
Description: Employee publication.

676.2 658.7 UK ISSN 0143-2192
HD9999.L17
LABELS AND LABELLING INTERNATIONAL. Running title: Labels and Labelling. 1979. bi-m. $72. Labels and Labelling Publishers, The White House, 60 High St., Potters Bar, Herts EN6 5AB, England. TEL 0707-56828. FAX 0707-45322. TELEX 892623-LABELX-G. Ed. M.C. Fairley. adv.: B&W page £1180; trim 8 1/4 x 11 5/8. bk.rev. circ. 6,500. **Indexed:** Int.Packag.Abstr., Packag.Sci.Tech., Print.Abstr.
—BLDSC (5137.892000); Ei; SWETS.

688.8 664 GW ISSN 0946-7726
LEBENSMITTEL- UND VERPACKUNGS-TECHNIK. 1956. q. DM.114 (effective 1995). Meisenbach GmbH, Hainstr. 18, 96047 Bamberg, Germany. TEL 0951-861135. FAX 0951-861158. **Document type:** trade publication.

668.802 DK ISSN 0902-4905
LEVERANDOERHAANDBOGEN; emballage og pakkemaskiner. 1979. biennial. DKK 250 (typically set in Jan.). Packaging & Transportation Research Institute, Gregersensvej, P.O. Box 141, DK-2630 Taastrup, Denmark. TEL 45-43-50-44-65. FAX 45-43-50-72-83. Ed. Lisbeth Seemann. adv. contact: Jens-Chr. Soerensen. circ. 10,000. **Document type:** directory.
Formerly: Emballageinstituttets Leverandoerhaandbog (ISSN 0107-3737)
Description: Lists Danish suppliers of packaging materials, machinery and equipment.

LINK (SAN ANTONIO). see FOOD AND FOOD INDUSTRIES

676.3 US
M A R I BOARD CONVERTING NEWS. (Magazine of the Americas Revista Interamericana); the package converting magazine of Latin America. (Text in English, Spanish) 1989. bi-m. $45. N V Business Publishers Corp., 43 Main St., Avon-by-Sea, NJ 07717. TEL 908-502-0500. FAX 908-502-9606. adv.: B&W page $1600, color page $2000; trim 8 x 10 1/2. bk.rev. circ. 2,176. **Document type:** trade publication.
Formerly: Mari.

676 US
M A R I - BOARD CONVERTING NEWS ESPANOL. 1989. bi-m. $45. N V Business Publishers Corp., 43 Main St., Avon by Sea, NJ 07717. TEL 908-502-0500. FAX 908-502-9606. Ed. Ted Vilardi. adv. circ. 2,234. **Document type:** trade publication.
Formerly: Board Converting News Espanol.

676 US
M T J RECYCLING MARKETS. 1963. w. $110. N.V. Business Publishers Corp., 2970 Marion Executive Center, Northbrook, IL 60062. TEL 708-498-5850. FAX 708-498-1187. Ed. Amy Snell. bk.rev.; abstr.; charts; illus.; pat.; stat.; tr.lit. circ. 4,065. **Document type:** trade publication, newsletter.
Formerly: Mill Trade Journal (ISSN 0047-7427)
Description: Reports on pricing and recycling issues in the paper industry, with coverage of plastics and metal rcycling.

688.8 628.5 UK ISSN 0969-4145
MACHINERY UPDATE. bi-m. £16 (Europe £24; rest of world £36). (Processing and Packaging Machinery Association) P P M A Publications Ltd., 404 Brighton Rd., S. Croydon, Surrey CR2 6AN, England. TEL 0181-681-8226. FAX 0181-681-1641. Ed. Michael Maddox. **Document type:** trade publication.

MANIPULACION DE MATERIALES EN LA INDUSTRIA. see BUILDING AND CONSTRUCTION

MATERIAL HANDLING ENGINEERING; technical magazine for material handling, packaging and shipping specialists. see MACHINERY

MATERIAL HANDLING ENGINEERING HANDBOOK AND DIRECTORY. see MACHINERY

MICROELECTRONIC PACKAGING. see ELECTRONICS

663.19 US ISSN 0026-2978
MID-CONTINENT BOTTLER. 1947. bi-m. $9. Fan Publications, Inc., 8575 W. 110th St., Ste. 218, Overland Park, KS 66210-2620. TEL 913-469-8611. FAX 913-469-8626. Ed. Floyd E. Sageser. adv.; bk.rev. circ. 3,585. **Document type:** trade publication.
Description: Coverage of the soft drink industry in a 23-state area bounded on the east by Ohio and the west by Colorado-Wyoming.

670 NE ISSN 0165-294X
MISSETS PAKBLAD. 1970. m. fl.182.50. Misset (Subsidiary of: Reed Elsevier plc), Postbus 4, 7000 BA Doetinchem, Netherlands. TEL 31-8340-49911. FAX 31-8340-43839. TELEX 45481. Ed. P.P. Roessel. adv.: B&W page fl.2973; trim 210 x 297; adv. contact: Cor van Nek. bk.rev.; charts; illus. circ. 6,060. **Indexed:** Excerp.Med., Key to Econ.Sci., Packag.Sci.Tech. **Document type:** trade publication.
—SWETS.
Formerly: Industrieel Verpakken.
Description: Information on packaging for managers of selfpacking industries, product and marketing managers, designers and product engineers.

658.788 II ISSN 0970-602X
MODERN PACKAGING TRENDS. (Text in English) 1984. q. Rs.80($30) Eastern Trade Press Co., 43 Sunder Mahal, Churchgate, Bombay 400 020, India. adv.; bk.rev. circ. 5,000.

688.8 620.85 UK ISSN 0960-7595
MONITOR (LONDON); packaging's environmental news watch. m. £150 (effective 1995). Angel Publishing Ltd., Kingsland House, 361 City Rd., London EC1V 1LR, England. TEL 0171-417-7400. FAX 0171-417-7500. **Document type:** newsletter.

658.788 CN ISSN 1193-9621
N A P P NEWS. q. free. Environment Canada, National Task Force on Packaging, Solid Waste Management Division, Place Vincent Massey, 12th Fl., 351 St. Joseph Blvd., Ottawa, ON K1H 0H3, Canada. TEL 819-997-3060. FAX 819-953-6881. **Document type:** newsletter.

658.788 GW ISSN 0341-0390
TS195.A1
N V. (Neue Verpackung); Magazin fuer zeitgemaesses Verpacken. 1948. m. DM.325.50 (foreign DM.338.50). Huethig GmbH, Postfach 102869, 69018 Heidelberg, Germany. TEL 06221-489298. FAX 06221-489481. TELEX 461727-HUEHD-D. Ed. Collin Weber. adv.: B&W page DM.4420; trim 210 x 297; adv. contact: Brigitte Sebastian. circ. 13,531. **Document type:** trade publication.
—BLDSC (6077.820000); Ei; SWETS. **CCC.**
Description: Package engineering in both food and non-food areas.

NATIONAL PACKING NEWS. see FOOD AND FOOD INDUSTRIES

NEW ZEALAND PACKAGING YEARBOOK. see BUSINESS AND ECONOMICS — Trade And Industrial Directories

658.788 PH
NEWSPACK. 12/yr. Packaging Institute of the Philippines, Comfoods Bldg., no.216, Sen Gil J, Puyat Ave., Makati MM, Philippines. TEL 885422. Ed. Lorenzo Ligot.

NIEUWSBLAD TRANSPORT. see TRANSPORTATION

658.788 NR ISSN 0794-7054
NIGERIAN PACKAGING NEWS. 1987. q. $100. Nigerian Printer Publications, P.O. Box 632, Yaba, Nigeria. TEL 082-221782. Ed. Austin Odiadi. circ. 3,000.
Description: Technological articles and current technology and applications.

658.7 SW ISSN 0039-6494
NORD-EMBALLAGE; foerpackning, lager, transport, materialhantering. Variant title: Emballage. 1934. 10/yr. SEK 475 (effective 1994); newsstand price: SEK 57. Foerlags AB Thorsten Fahlskog, P.O. Box 25, S-162 11 Vaellingby, Sweden. TEL 46-8-870280. FAX 46-8-874815. Ed. Kerstin Fahlskog. adv.: B&W page SEK 13550, color page SEK 18320; trim 178 x 263. bk.rev.; bibl.; charts; illus.; mkt.; pat.; stat.; tr.lit.; tr.mk.; index; circ. 3,800 (controlled). cols./p.: 3. **Indexed:** Int.Packag.Abstr. **Document type:** trade publication.
Incorporates (in 1990): Konsumentfoerpackningar; Former titles (until 1970): Svensk Emballagetidskrift; (until 1962): Svensk Emballage-och Foerpackningstidskrift.
Description: Directed towards the five Nordic countries. Covers developments in consumer packaging, aerosols, printing and design techniques as well as transport handling. The editorial features also cover important business events within the industry and other organisations in Sweden and internationally.

PACKAGING

658.7   AU
O V Z - MITTEILUNGEN. 1956. bi-m. membership. Wirtschaftskammer W I F I Oesterreich, Oesterreichisches Verpackungszentrum, Gumpendorferstr. 6, A-1060 Vienna, Austria. TEL 0222-5869233. FAX 0222-58886267. bk.rev.; illus.; stat. circ. 6,400. **Indexed:** Int.Packag.Abstr., Packag.Sci.Tech. **Document type:** trade publication.
    Formerly (until Oct. 1976): Besser Verpacken (ISSN 0005-9595)

676   US   ISSN 0030-0284
OFFICIAL BOARD MARKETS; "the yellow sheet". 1925. w. $130. Advanstar Communications, Inc., 7500 Old Oak Blvd., Cleveland, OH 44130. TEL 216-836-2839. FAX 216-891-2726. (Subscr. to: 131 W. First St., Duluth, MN 55082. TEL 800-346-0085) Ed. Mark Arzoumanian. adv.; charts; mkt.; stat. circ. 5,068. (also avail. in microform) **Indexed:** Abstr.Bull.Inst.Pap.Chem. **Document type:** trade publication.
  —CCC.
    Description: Covers corrugated container, folding carton and paper recycling industries.

658.7   US   ISSN 0030-0292
OFFICIAL CONTAINER DIRECTORY. 1913. s-a. $60. Advanstar Communications, Inc., 7500 Old Oak Blvd., Cleveland, OH 44130. TEL 216-891-2730. FAX 216-891-9675. (Subscr. to: 131 W. First St., Duluth, MN 55082. TEL 800-346-0085) Ed. Jacqueline Schultz. adv. circ. 3,000. **Document type:** directory, trade publication.
  —CCC.

658.7   PL   ISSN 0030-3348
OPAKOWANIE. (Text in Polish; summaries in English) 1955. m. $20.50. Wydawnictwo Czasopism i Ksiazek Technicznych SIGMA - NOT, Ul. Ratuszowa 11, P.O. Box 1004, 00-950 Warsaw, Poland. TEL 48-22-180918. FAX 48-22-192187. TELEX 814550 SIGMA PL. (Dist. by: SIGMA NOT Ltd., Ul. Bartycka 20, 00-716 Warsaw, Poland) adv.; bk.rev.; abstr.; bibl.; charts; illus.; stat.; index. circ. 700. **Indexed:** Food Sci.& Tech.Abstr., Packag.Sci.Tech.
  —BLDSC (6265.800000).

658.7   UK
P A C. (Pallett and Case Industry) q. Nelton House, 46A High St., Gravesend, Kent DA11 0AY, England. TEL 0474-536535. FAX 0474-536552. Ed. N.H. Smith.

P A T E F A NEWS BULLETIN. (Printing & Allied Trades Employers Federation of Australia) see PRINTING

658.788   US
P H L BULLETIN. (Packaging, Handling, Logistics) 1956. m. $50. National Institute of Packaging, Handling and Logistic Engineers, 6902 Lyle St., Lanham, MD 20706-3454. TEL 301-459-9105. FAX 301-459-4925. Ed. James A. Russell. adv.; bk.rev.; bibl. circ. 850.

688.8 628.5   UK
P P M A MACHINERY DIRECTORY. 1989. a. £45. (Processing and Packaging Machinery Association) P P M A Publications Ltd., 404 Brighton Rd., S. Croydon, Surrey CR2 6AN, England. TEL 0181-681-8226. FAX 0181-681-1641. **Document type:** directory.

688.8   IT
▼**PACK.** 1994. 9/yr. Tecniche Nuove S.p.A., Via Ciro Menotti 14, 20129 Milan, Italy. TEL 39-2-75701. FAX 39-2-7610351. Ed. G. Nardella. adv.; B&W page L.2350000. **Document type:** trade publication.

688.8   SZ
PACK AKTUELL. 1985. 26/yr. Insider Fachverlag, Gotthardstr. 20, Postfach 4418, CH-6304 Zug, Switzerland. Ed. Guido Durisch. circ. 5,300.

688.8 629.8   BE   ISSN 1370-2491
PACK NEWS & MECHNICAL HANDLING NEWS. (Text in Dutch, French) 1983. 8/yr. 2438 BEF. Kluwer Business Press (Subsidiary of: Wolters Kluwer N.V.), Kouterveldstraat 2, 1831 Diegem, Belgium. TEL 32-2-7231111. FAX 32-2-7231512. Ed. Bernard Lefevre; Pub. Bernard Lefevre. circ. 9,500 (controlled). **Document type:** trade publication.
    Formerly (until 1986): Pack News (ISSN 0774-2061)

688.8   BE
PACK NEWSLETTER. (Text in Dutch, French) bi-w. Kluwer Business Press (Subsidiary of: Wolters Kluwer N.V.), Kouterveldstraat 2, 1831 Diegem, Belgium. TEL 32-2-7231111. FAX 32-2-7231512. Ed. Stephane Maillard. **Document type:** newsletter.

676   FR
PACK TECHNOLOGIE. 6/yr. 78 route de la Reine, 92100 Boulogne, France. TEL 46-04-78-26. FAX 46-04-78-26. Ed. Emmanuel Pottier. circ. 7,000.

658.7 670   UK   ISSN 0030-9060
PACKAGING. 1930. bi-m. £62 (foreign £65). Turret Group Plc., Turret House, 171 High St., Rickmansworth, Herts WD3 1SN, England. TEL 01923-777000. FAX 01923-771297. Ed. Norman Shepherd. adv.; illus. **Indexed:** Br.Tech.Ind., Bus.Ind., Curr.Pack.Abstr., Food Sci.& Tech.Abstr., Int.Packag.Abstr., Intl.Polym.Sci.& Tech., Key to Econ.Sci., PROMT, RAPRA. **Document type:** trade publication.
  —BLDSC (6332.200000); Ei; UMI.

676.3 658.788   SA   ISSN 1011-8519
PACKAGING (YEAR). a. free to qualified personnel. (South African Foreign Trade Organisation) SAFTO, Publishing Division, P.O. Box 782706, Sandton 2146, South Africa. TEL 27-11-883-3737. FAX 27-11-883-6569. TELEX 4-24111 SA. adv. contact: Dorine Pretorius. **Document type:** directory.
    Description: Provides information on packaging products and services available for export from South Africa.

658.788   US
PACKAGING AND CONVERTING TECHNOLOGY SERIES. 1987. irreg., vol.6, 1992. price varies. Marcel Dekker, Inc., 270 Madison Ave., New York, NY 10016. TEL 212-696-9000. FAX 212-685-4540. TELEX 421419. **Document type:** monographic series.
    Formerly: Packaging Technology Series.

658.7 670   US   ISSN 0030-9117
HF5770.A1
PACKAGING DIGEST. 1963. 13/yr. $75. Cahners Publishing Company (Des Plaines), Division of Reed Elsevier Inc., 1350 E. Touhy Ave., Box 5080, Des Plaines, IL 60017-5080. TEL 708-635-8800. FAX 708-299-8622. Ed. Robert W. Heitzman; Pub. Frank Sibley. adv.; B&W page $9420, color page $11800; trim 11 x 15 3/4; adv. contact: Maria LeMane. illus.; tr.lit. circ. 109,000. (tabloid format; also avail. in microform from UMI; reprint service avail. from UMI) **Indexed:** Curr.Pack.Abstr., Graph.Arts Lit.Abstr., Int.Packag.Abstr., Tr.& Indus.Ind. **Document type:** consumer publication, trade publication.
  —BLDSC (6332.651000); Ei; Faxon; SWETS; UMI. CCC.
    Description: Articles for makers and prime users of packaging.

658.7   US
▼**PACKAGING DIGEST EDICION LATINOAMERICANA.** 1994. m.? Cahners Publishing Company (Des Plaines), Division of Reed Elsevier Inc., 1350 E. Touhy Ave., Box 5080, Des Plaines, IL 60017-5080. TEL 708-390-2363. FAX 708-635-6856. Ed. Robert Heitzman; Pub. Frank Sibley. adv.; B&W page $3910; 11 x 14.75. circ. 30,584 (controlled).

676 621.9   US
PACKAGING DIGEST MACHINERY - MATERIALS GUIDE. 1979. a. Cahners Publishing Company (Des Plaines), Division of Reed Elsevier Inc., 1350 E. Touhy Ave., Box 5080, Des Plaines, IL 60611. TEL 708-635-8800. FAX 708-299-8622. Ed. Robert Heitzman. adv.; B&W page $8030, color page $10410; 8 1/8 x 10 7/8. circ. 109,000 (controlled).

658.7   US
▼**PACKAGING DIGEST MARKETPLACE EDITION.** 1995. 4/yr. Cahners Publishing Comany (Des Plaines), Division of Reed Elsevier Inc., 1350 E. Touhy Ave., Box 5080, Des Plaines, IL 60017-5080. TEL 708-390-2363. FAX 708-635-6856. Ed. Robert Heitzman. adv.; B&W page $9240; 11 x 14.75. circ. 150,000 (controlled).

688.8   UK
PACKAGING FOCUS. 10/yr. £185($315) (outside Europe $330). Data Transcripts Ltd., P.O. Box 14, Dorking, Surrey RH5 4YN, England. TEL 01306-884473. Ed. Robert A. Higham. (back issues avail.) **Document type:** newsletter.

688.8   BE
PACKAGING GUIDE. (Text in Dutch, French) a. Kluwer Business Press (Subsidiary of: Wolters Kluwer N.V.), Kouterveldstraat 2, 1831 Diegem, Belgium. TEL 32-2-7231111. FAX 32-2-7231512. Ed. Stephane Maillard. **Document type:** directory.

658.7   II   ISSN 0030-9125
                          CODEN: PINDDS
PACKAGING INDIA. (Text in English) 1968. bi-m. Rs.360($120) Indian Institute of Packaging, E-2 MIDC Area, Post Box 9432, Chakala, Andheri East, Bombay 400 093, India. TEL 91-22-8324670. FAX 91-22-8375302. TELEX 011-79042. Ed. P.V. Narayanan. adv.; bk.rev. circ. 2,500.
  —BLDSC (6332.750000).
    Formed by the 1988 merge of: Packaging Digest; Packaging Update; Packaging India.
    Description: Covers technical and economic aspects of the packaging industry as well as new product information.

658.788   UK   ISSN 0269-9834
PACKAGING INDUSTRY DIRECTORY. (Features four buyers' guides: Packaging and Handling Equipment, Containers and Closures, Packaging Materials, Packaging Consultants and Contract Services) a. £79 (foreign £104). Miller Freeman information Services (Subsidiary of: United News & Media), Riverbank House, Angel Ln., Tonbridge, Kent TN9 1SE, England. TEL 01732-362666. FAX 01732-767301. TELEX 957829. Ed. Gwen Young. adv. contact: Elaine Soni. circ. 5,000. **Document type:** directory.
  —BLDSC (6332.780000).
    Formerly: Packaging Review Directory.
    Description: Lists more than 6,000 companies manufacturing, supplying, or distributing materials, products, and services to the packaging and related industries.

658.7   JA   ISSN 0288-3864
TS195.A1   CODEN: PAJAEC
PACKAGING JAPAN. 1980. bi-m. $90 in Asia; US & Europe $158. Nippo Co. Ltd., 3-1-5 Misaki-cho, Chiyoda-ku, Tokyo 101, Japan. FAX 03-3263-2560. TELEX 2322348 PJNIPOJ. (Dist. by: Intercontinental Marketing Corp., I.P.O. Box 5056, Tokyo 100-30, Japan. TEL 81-3-3661-7458. FAX 81-3-3667-9646) Ed. Katsushi Kawamura. adv.; bk.rev.; charts; illus. circ. 10,000. **Document type:** trade publication.
  —BLDSC (6332.810000); Ei.
    Formerly: New Packaging (ISSN 0004-6469)

658.7884   US   ISSN 0078-7698
PACKAGING MACHINERY MANUFACTURERS INSTITUTE. OFFICIAL PACKAGING MACHINERY DIRECTORY. Cover title: Packaging Machinery Directory. 1954. biennial. $29 (effective 1996). Packaging Machinery Manufacturers Institute, 4350 Fairfax Dr., Ste. 600, Arlington, VA 22203-1619. TEL 202-243-8555. FAX 202-243-8556. Ed. Jerry Welcome. index. circ. 50,000. **Document type:** directory.

658.788   US
PACKAGING MARKETPLACE; the practical guide to packaging sources. 1978. irreg. $140. Gale Research Inc., 835 Penobscot Bldg., Detroit, MI 48226. TEL 313-961-2242. FAX 313-961-6083. TELEX 810-221-7086. Ed. Joseph F. Hanlon. **Document type:** directory.
    Description: Directory of packaging manufacturers and jobbers.

658.7   AT   ISSN 0048-2676
PACKAGING NEWS. 1959. m. Aus.$42 (foreign Aus.$115) (effective Feb. 1995). Yaffa Publishing Group, 17-21 Bellevue St., Surry Hills, N.S.W. 2010, Australia. TEL 61-281-2333. FAX 61-2-281-2750. Ed. Sandra Radice. adv.; B&W page Aus.$2100, color page Aus.$3005; trim 297 x 210. circ. 5,517. **Indexed:** Int.Packag.Abstr., Key to Econ.Sci. **Document type:** trade publication.
  —BLDSC (6332.870000).
    Description: For Australian packaging industry management.

PACKAGING

658.7 UK ISSN 0030-9133
CODEN: PKGNAY
PACKAGING NEWS. 1954. m. £60. Maclean Hunter Ltd., Maclean Hunter House, Chalk Lane, Cockfosters Rd., Barnet, Herts EN4 0BU, England. TEL 081-242-3000. FAX 081-242-3185. TELEX 299072-MACHUN-G. Ed. G. Lea. adv.; bk.rev.; charts; illus.; tr.lit. circ. 17,458. Indexed: Abstr.Bull.Inst.Pap.Chem., Curr.Pack.Abstr., Int.Packag.Abstr., Packag.Sci.Tech. **Document type:** trade publication.
—BLDSC (6332.840000).

658.7 UK
PACKAGING NEWS PRODUCT INFORMATION CARDS. 1967. 5/yr. free. Maclean Hunter Ltd., Maclean Hunter House, Chalk Lane, Cockfosters Rd., Barnet, Herts EN4 0BU, England. TEL 081-243-3000. FAX 081-242-3185. TELEX 299072-MACHUN-G. adv. circ. 16,876. **Document type:** bulletin.

677.7 GW ISSN 0933-4165
PACKAGING PRODUCTION INTERNATIONAL. (Text in English and German) 1988. bi-m. DM.96. Verlag fuer Fachliteratur GmbH, Im Weiher 10, 69121 Heidelberg, Germany. TEL 06221-489280. FAX 06221-489279. TELEX 461727-HUEHD-D. Eds. Peter Haberstolz, Collin Weber. adv. circ. 15,000. (back issues avail.)

658.788 SA ISSN 1014-8280
PACKAGING REVIEW SOUTH AFRICA. 1975. m. R.156 (foreign R.237) (effective 1994). (Institute of Packaging, South Africa) National Publishing (Pty) Ltd., P.O. Box 2735, Johannesburg 2000, South Africa. TEL 27-11-835-2221. FAX 27-11-835-1943. (Co-sponsor: Packaging Council) Ed. Gill Loubser. adv.: B&W page R.3080; trim 297 x 210; adv. contact: Susi Moore. illus. circ. 2,990. Indexed: Dairy Sci.Abstr., Ind.S.A.Per., Int.Packag.Abstr., Packag.Sci.Tech. **Document type:** trade publication.
Description: Covers new equipment, processes and materials, market trends and legislative developments affecting raw materials suppliers, converters and users of packaging products.

658.7 UK ISSN 0952-4495
PACKAGING SCOTLAND. q. £15.15 (foreign £17.15). Peebles Publishing Group Ltd., Berius House, Clifton St., Glasgow G3 7LA, Scotland. TEL 0141-331-1022. FAX 0141-331-1395. Ed. G. Lironi. circ. 4,500. **Document type:** trade publication.

670 US ISSN 8755-6189
CODEN: PASTEC
PACKAGING STRATEGIES. 1983. 23/yr. $397 (outside N. America $457) (effective 1996). Packaging Strategies, Inc., 122 S. Church St., West Chester, PA 19382-3223. TEL 610-436-4220. FAX 610-436-6277. Ed. Ben Miyares; Pub. William H. LeMaire. (looseleaf format; back issues avail.) **Document type:** newsletter.
Description: Focuses on emerging trends, technologies and business issues pertaining to the packaging industries. Reports on materials, containers and equipment.

658.7 US
PACKAGING SUPPLIER SOURCE GUIDE. a. $35. Cahners Publishing Company (Des Plaines), Division of Reed Elsevier Inc., 1350 E. Touhy Ave., Box 5080, Des Plaines, IL 60017-5080. TEL 708-635-8800. FAX 708-635-6856. (Subscr. to: 44 Cook St., Denver, CO 80206. TEL 800-662-7776) **Document type:** directory, consumer publication.
Former titles (until 1992): Packaging Casebook Directory; (until 1991): Packaging Buyers Guide.

658.7 US ISSN 1067-411X
CODEN: PTNEN
PACKAGING TECHNOLOGY AND ENGINEERING; the professional journal of packaging. 1987. 10/yr. $69. (Institute of Packaging Professionals) North American Publishing Co., 401 N. Broad St., Philadelphia, PA 19108. TEL 215-238-5300. FAX 215-238-5457. circ. 28,000. (also avail. in microform from UMI; back issues avail.) **Document type:** trade publication.
—BLDSC (6333.016000); UMI. **CCC.**
Formerly (until 1993): Journal of Packaging Technology (ISSN 0892-029X)
Description: Covers all aspects of the packaging industry.

676 335 UK ISSN 0894-3214
TS195.A1 CODEN: PTSCEQ
PACKAGING, TECHNOLOGY AND SCIENCE. 1988. bi-m. $545 (foreign $545) (effective 1996). John Wiley & Sons Ltd., Journals, Baffins Ln., Chichester, W. Sussex PO19 1UD, England. TEL 01243-779777. FAX 01243-776128. TELEX 86290 WIBOOK G. (Subscr. in the Americas to: John Wiley & Sons, Inc., 605 Third Ave., New York, NY 10158. TEL 212-850-6645. FAX 212-850-6021) Ed. F.A. Paine. circ. 189. (also avail. in microform from UMI; back issues avail.; reprint service avail. from SWZ) Indexed: Environ.Per.Bibl., Intl.Polym.Sci.& Tech., RAPRA. **Document type:** academic/scholarly publication.
—BLDSC (6333.018500); CASDDS; Ei; SWETS; UMI. **CCC.**
Description: Provides an international forum for the rapid publication of articles about developments in this field.

658.7 670 UK ISSN 0268-0920
PACKAGING TODAY. 1979. m. £46($174) (outside Europe £58) (effective 1995). Angel Publishing Ltd., Kingsland House, 361 City Rd., London EC1V 1LR, England. TEL 0171-417-7400. FAX 0171-417-7500. Indexed: DAAI, Int.Packag.Abstr. **Document type:** trade publication.
—BLDSC (6333.019400); SWETS. **CCC.**

614.7 AT
PACKAGING TODAY. 1979. q. Aus.$25. Packaging Council of Australia, 15-17 Park St., South Melbourne, Vic. 3250, Australia. FAX 03-690-3514. circ. 4,000. Indexed: Int.Packag.Abstr. **Document type:** bulletin.
Supersedes: Packaging Council of Australia. Legislation and Metrication Newsletter.

658.7 670 UK
PACKAGING TODAY DIRECTORY - REVIEW. 1988. a. £65 (effective 1995). (Institute of Packaging) Angel Publishing Ltd., Kingsland House, 361 City Rd., London EC1V 1LR, England. TEL 0171-417-7400. FAX 0171-417-7500. Ed. Rodney Abbott; Pub. Dennis Cooper. adv. contact: Mike Mikunda. circ. 4,500. **Document type:** directory, trade publication.
Formerly (until 1993): Packaging Directory - Yearbook (ISSN 0956-3350)

658.7 670 UK ISSN 0267-6117
CODEN: PAWEEL
PACKAGING WEEK. 1897. w. £76 (foreign £113). Miller Freeman Publishers Ltd. (Subsidiary of: Morgan Grampian plc.), Benn House, Sovereign Way, Tonbridge, Kent TN9 1RW, England. TEL 01732-364422. FAX 01732-353328. TELEX 95132 BENTON G. Ed. Mary Murphy; Pub. David Barrett. adv. contact: Jessica Mathews. bk.rev.; illus.; stat. circ. 14,004. (also avail. in microform from UMI; reprint service avail. from UMI) Indexed: Curr.Pack.Abstr., Dairy Sci.Abstr., Food Sci.& Tech.Abstr., Int.Packag.Abstr., Intl.Polym.Sci.& Tech., Key to Econ.Sci., PROMT, RAPRA. **Document type:** trade publication.
—BLDSC (6333.019800); SWETS; UMI. **CCC.**
Incorporates (1983-1985): Volume Packaging (ISSN 0264-4045); **Former titles (until 1985):** Packaging Review (ISSN 0048-2684); (until 1945): Boxmakers' Journal and Packaging Review.

688.8 UK ISSN 0964-8879
PACKAGING WORLD INTERNATIONAL. 1991. q. Manor Publishing Ltd., Unit 7, Edison Rd., Highfield Industrial Estate, Hampden Park, Eastbourne, E. Sussex BN23 6PT, England. TEL 01323-507474. FAX 01323-509306. Ed. Mike Hall; Pub. Gary Stolton. adv. contact: Helen Roberts. (back issues avail.) **Document type:** trade publication.
Incorporates (in 1993): Packaging World (ISSN 0964-0487)

688.8 US ISSN 1066-5897
HF5770.A1
PACKER - SHIPPER. 1990. 8/yr. $15 (Canada and Mexico $30; elsewhere $45). Columbia Publishing and Design, 2809-A Fruitvale Blvd., Box 1467, Yakima, WA 98907-1467. TEL 509-248-2452; 800-900-2452. FAX 509-248-4056. Ed. Ken Hodge. circ. 8,508. (back issues avail.) **Document type:** trade publication.

658.788 SW ISSN 0348-260X
PACKMARKNADEN SCANDINAVIA. Short title: Packmarknaden. 1978. 10/yr. SEK 495. Indufa Foerlag AB, P.O. Box 601, 251 06 Helsingborg, Sweden. TEL 46-42-19-99-19. FAX 46-42-19-99-00. Ed. Peter Schulz. adv.: B&W page SEK 14900; trim 211 x 302; adv. contact: Karin Heidne. circ. 5,000. **Document type:** trade publication.
Description: Focuses on the packaging industry as well as the needs and uses of packaging in various industries.

658.7 UK
PACKPLAS INTERNATIONAL. (Text in Arabic) q. £30. International Printing Communications Ltd., P.O. Box 923, Crownhill Industry, Milton Keynes MK8 0AY, England. TEL 0908-561444. FAX 0908-569564. TELEX 826373-PRINT-G. Ed. R. Ghozzi. adv.: B&W page £1365, color page £1595; trim 272 x 186. bk.rev.; circ. 14,000 (controlled). **Document type:** trade publication.
Description: Provides tecnology guides, in-depth features and analysis for the packaging, plastics, converting and allied industries in the Arab world.

660 670 GW ISSN 0343-7183
PACKUNG UND TRANSPORT; Fachmagazin fuer Verpackung, Materialfluss und Logistik. 1968. m. DM.120. Verlagsgruppe Handelsblatt GmbH, Kasernenstr. 67, 40213 Duesseldorf, Germany. TEL 0211-8870. FAX 0211-133522. (Subscr. to: Postfach 102717, 40018 Duesseldorf, Germany) Ed. H. Springborn. circ. 7,400. (reprint service avail. from UMI) Indexed: Key to Econ.Sci. **Document type:** trade publication.
—BLDSC (6333.087000); SWETS.
Former titles: Packung und Transport in der Chemischen Industrie; Packung und Transport im Chemiebetrieb (ISSN 0030-9184)

658.7 FI ISSN 0031-0131
PAKKAUS. (Text in Finnish; summaries in English) 1964. m. Fmk.200. Suomen Pakkausyhdistys - Finnish Packaging Association, Ritarikatu 3, 00170 Helsinki 17, Finland. Ed. Jorma Hamalainen. adv.; bk.rev.; charts; illus.; mkt. circ. 2,900. Indexed: Int.Packag.Abstr., Packag.Sci.Tech.

676 US ISSN 0031-1138
CODEN: PFFCAT
PAPER, FILM AND FOIL CONVERTER. 1927. m. $62.50. Intertec Publishing Corp., 29 N. Wacker Dr., Chicago, IL 60606. TEL 312-726-2802. FAX 312-726-2574. Ed. Robert A. Zuck. adv.: B&W page $3973, color page $5377; trim 8 1/8 x 10 7/8. bk.rev.; charts; illus.; stat.; tr.lit.; index; circ. 39,737 (controlled). (also avail. in microfilm from UMI; reprint service avail. from UMI) Indexed: Abstr.Bull.Inst.Pap.Chem., Art & Archaeol.Tech.Abstr., Chem.Abstr., Curr.Pack.Abstr., Graph.Arts Lit.Abstr., Int.Packag.Abstr., Intl.Polym.Sci.& Tech., Key to Econ.Sci., Packag.Sci.Tech., Paper & Bd.Abstr., PROMT, RAPRA. **Document type:** academic/scholarly publication.
—BLDSC (6362.000000); Ei; Faxon; Genuine Article; SWETS; UMI. **CCC.**
Former titles (until 1953): American Paper Converter (ISSN 0096-090X); (until 1944): Converter (ISSN 0097-4080)

676 658.7 US ISSN 0031-1227
HF5770
PAPERBOARD PACKAGING. 1916. m. $30. Advanstar Communications, Inc., 7500 Old Oak Blvd., Cleveland, OH 44130. TEL 216-826-2839. FAX 216-891-2726. (Subscr. to: 131 W. First St., Duluth, MN 55802. TEL 800-346-0085) Ed. Jackie Schultz. adv.; charts; illus.; mkt.; stat.; index. circ. 14,029. (also avail. in microform from UMI; back issues avail.) Indexed: Abstr.Bull.Inst.Pap.Chem., B.P.I., Bus.Ind., Chem.Abstr., Curr.Pack.Abstr., Graph.Arts Lit.Abstr., Int.Packag.Abstr., Packag.Sci.Tech., Paper & Bd.Abstr., PROMT, SRI, Tr.& Indus.Ind. **Document type:** trade publication.
●Also available online. Vendor(s): Knight-Ridder, Inc.
—BLDSC (6366.300000); Genuine Article; UMI. **CCC.**
Description: Features and news coverage of the corrugated container, folding carton and converted board products market.

PACKAGING

676.2   US   ISSN 0741-4129
HD9999.C74
PAPERBOARD PACKAGING'S INTERNATIONAL CONTAINER DIRECTORY. Variant title: International Container Directory. a. $95. Advanstar Communications, Inc., 7500 Old Oak Blvd., Cleveland, OH 44130. TEL 216-891-2730. FAX 216-891-2675. (Subscr. to: 131 W. First St., Duluth, MN 55802. TEL 800-346-0085) Ed. Jacqueline Schultz. adv. circ. 1,540. **Document type:** directory, trade publication.
    Description: Listing of box plants throughout the world outside of North America; and suppliers of box plants.

PAPERPRINTPACK INDIA. see *PAPER AND PULP*

688.8   NE   ISSN 0922-4084
PERS; tweewekelijk technisch tijdschrift voor grafische vakmensen. 1988. bi-w. fl.147. Uitgeverij Compres b.v., Postbus 55, 2300 AB Leiden, Netherlands. TEL 31-71-161515. FAX 31-71-121550. Ed. O. Visser; Pub. H. Verwoert. adv. contact: Robert de Winter. circ. 20,249. **Document type:** trade publication.

688.8 615   US
PHARMACEUTICAL & MEDICAL PACKAGING NEWS. 1993. m. $60. O & B Communications, 15 Paoli Plaza, Ste. 6, Paoli, PA 19301. TEL 610-647-8585. FAX 610-647-8565. Ed. Jim Wagner; Pub. Stephen Osborne. adv.: B&W page $2995; adv. contact: Michael Bradley. circ. 20,000. **Document type:** trade publication.

658.7   UK
PLASTICS PACKAGING MONITOR. 10/yr. £185($315) (outside Europe $330). Data Transcripts Ltd., P.O. Box 14, Dorking, Surrey RH5 4YN, England. TEL 01306-884473. Ed. Lynda Crane. bk.rev. **Document type:** newsletter.

PLASTICS RECYCLING UPDATE. see *ENVIRONMENTAL STUDIES — Waste Management*

658.788 380.5   US   ISSN 1043-2841
PRESHIPMENT TESTING. 1977. m. membership. International Safe Transit Association, Box 10744, Chicago, IL 60610-0744. TEL 312-645-0083. FAX 312-645-1078. Ed. Ellis Murphy. adv.; bk.rev.; circ. 3,200 (controlled). **Document type:** newsletter.
    Description: Discusses packaging and transportation issues such as preshipment testing of packaged products, transport damage, quality control and customer service.

PREVISIONS GLISSANTES DETAILLEES EN PERSPECTIVES SECTORIELLES (VOL.26): EMBALLAGES. see *BUSINESS AND ECONOMICS — Economic Situation And Conditions*

688.8   NE   ISSN 0925-3874
PRINT BUYER; vaktijdschrift voor drukwerkinkoop en marketing. (Text in Dutch) 1990. m. fl.147. Uitgeverij Compres b.v., Postbus 55, 2300 AB Leiden, Netherlands. TEL 31-71-161515. FAX 31-71-121550. Ed. G. Molenaar; Pub. H. Verwoert. adv. contact: Robert de Winter. circ. 6,050. **Document type:** trade publication.

688.8   NE
PRINT BUYER GUIDE. (Text in Dutch) a. Uitgeverij Compres b.v., Postbus 55, 2300 AB Leiden, Netherlands. TEL 31-71-161515. FAX 31-71-121550. Ed. G. Molenaar; Pub. H. Verwoert. adv.; circ. 6,500 (controlled). **Document type:** trade publication, directory.

664.09   GW   ISSN 0171-8312
PRINTING & PACKAGING; with Arabian food and packaging. (Text in Arabic and English) 1977. q. DM.46. Verlag Peter Wranesch, Postfach 810645, 70523 Stuttgart, Germany. TEL 0711-713781. FAX 0711-799473. Ed. Peter Wranesch. circ. 5,300. **Document type:** trade publication.

PRODUCE MARKETING ASSOCIATION MEMBERSHIP DIRECTORY & BUYER'S GUIDE. see *FOOD AND FOOD INDUSTRIES*

664.09   US
PRODUCE PACKAGING HANDLING DIGEST. 1980. a. Vance Publishing Corporation (Lenexa), 10901 W. 84th Terr., Lenexa, KS 66214-1631. TEL 913-438-8700. FAX 913-438-0695. adv. circ. 16,000. (back issues avail.) **Document type:** trade publication.
    Formerly: Produce Packaging and Materials Handling Digest.

658.788   GW   ISSN 0724-5661
PRODUKTIONSMENGE UND PRODUKTIONSWERT DER VERPACKUNGSINDUSTRIE IN DER BUNDESREPUBLIK. 1954. a. DM.98. R G Verpackung im R K W, Postfach 5867, 65733 Eschborn, Germany. TEL 06196-495200. FAX 06196-495303. stat.; index. circ. 400. (back issues avail.) **Document type:** trade publication.

R C O UPDATE. (Recycling Council of Ontario) see *ENVIRONMENTAL STUDIES — Waste Management*

658.788   IT   ISSN 1120-6136
RASSEGNA DELL'IMBALLAGGIO E CONFEZIONAMENTO. 1979. fortn. L.24000 (foreign L.200000). Editrice Arti Poligrafiche Europee, Via Casella 16, 20156 Milan, Italy. TEL 02-330221. FAX 02-39214341. Ed. Antonio Ghiorzo. adv.: B&W page L.4200000, color page L.5200000; trim 266 x 392. charts; illus.; circ. 10,000 (controlled).
—BLDSC (7294.227510).

RESEARCH & DEVELOPMENT ASSOCIATES FOR MILITARY FOOD AND PACKAGING SYSTEMS. ACTIVITIES REPORT. see *MILITARY*

RESOURCE RECYCLING'S BOTTLE - CAN RECYCLING UPDATE; markets, legislation, research, data, technology, economics. see *ENVIRONMENTAL STUDIES — Waste Management*

670   SZ
SCHWEIZER VERPACKUNGSKATALOG. (Text in French and German) 1942. a. 35 SFr. Verlag Binkert AG, CH-4335 Laufenburg, Switzerland. TEL 064-697272. FAX 064-697333. Ed. Walter Meier-Schmid. adv. contact: Ludwig Binkert. circ. 4,200. **Document type:** catalog.

676.3   CC
SHANGHAI BAOZHUANG/SHANGHAI PACKAGING. (Text in Chinese) q. Zhongguo Chukou Shangpin Baozhuang Yanjiusuo, Shanghai Fensuo - Chinese Institute of Export Commodities Packaging, Shanghai Branch, 97 Yuanmingyuan Lu, Shanghai 200002, People's Republic of China. TEL 3212999.

688.8   JA
SHUKAN HOSO NYUSU/PACKAGING NEWS. (Text in Japanese) 1964. w. 20000 Yen. Hoso Nyususha - Package News Co., Ltd., 134-11, Noshio 1-chome, Kiyose-shi, Tokyo 204, Japan. **Document type:** trade publication.

676.3   UK
SPECIAL PAPER AND BOARD MATERIALS AND MARKETS BULLETIN. q. $300. Data Transcripts Ltd., P.O. Box 14, Dorking, Surrey RH5 4YN, England. TEL 01306-884473. Ed. Lynda Crane. bk.rev. **Document type:** newsletter.

660.29 658.7   US   ISSN 1055-2340
TS198.P7   CODEN: STEMEJ
SPRAY TECHNOLOGY & MARKETING; the magazine of spray pressure packaging. 1956. m. $30. Industry Publications, Inc. (Fairfield), 389 Passaic Ave., Fairfield, NJ 07006. TEL 201-227-5151. FAX 201-227-9219. Ed. M. SanGiovanni. adv.: B&W page $1770, color page $2895; 8 1/4 x 10 7/8. charts; illus.; pat.; tr.mk. (also avail. in microform from UMI; reprint service avail. from UMI) **Indexed:** B.P.I., Biotech.Abstr., Chem.Abstr., Curr.Pack.Abstr., I.P.A., Int.Packag.Abstr., Key to Econ.Sci., PROMT. **Document type:** trade publication.
●Also available online.
—BLDSC (8422.610000); Faxon; SWETS; UMI; UnCover.
    Formerly (until Apr.1991): Aerosol Age (ISSN 0001-9291)

688.8   SZ
TARA. m. 89 SFr. (foreign 115 SFr.). Tara Verlag AG, Postfach 1012, CH-8640 Rapperswil, Switzerland. TEL 055-272874. FAX 055-274524. Ed. Claude Buerki. adv.: B&W page 2097 SFr.; trim 180 x 264; adv. contact: Margrit Ostwaldl. circ. 4,130. **Document type:** trade publication.

670   FR
TECH-EMBAL; annuaire des fournisseurs de l'emballage. 1966. a. 300 F. Editions Technorama, 31 Place Saint Ferdinand, 75017 Paris, France. TEL 1-45-74-67-43. FAX 45-72-63-21. Ed. R. Baschet. circ. 2,000.

676   US   ISSN 0892-7146
    CODEN: TEPAEC
TECHPAK. 1955. bi-w. $460 (foreign $510). McGraw-Hill, Inc., Chemical & Plastics Information Services, 1221 Ave. of the Americas, 43rd Fl., New York, NY 10020. TEL 212-512-6779. FAX 212-512-2989. Ed. Peter Savage. (back issues avail.) **Document type:** newspaper.
—CCC.
    Formerly: Packaging Letter (ISSN 0277-9722)

670 658.788   IT   ISSN 0391-2124
TECNICHE DELL'IMBALLAGGIO. 1970. m. L.96000 (foreign L.140000) (effective 1993). Franco Angeli Editore, Viale Monza 106, 20127 Milan, Italy. TEL 02-28-27-651. adv.; bk.rev.; abstr.; charts; illus.; stat.; tr.lit.; index. circ. 6,000.

TIN INTERNATIONAL. see *METALLURGY*

TRANSPORT, FOERDER- UND LAGERTECHNIK; Schweizerische Fachzeitschrift fuer rationellen Gueterumschlag, Logistik, Transport, Lagerhaltung und Foerdertechnik. see *TRANSPORTATION*

658.7   SZ   ISSN 0042-4277
DIE VERPACKUNG; schweizerische Fachzeitschrift fuer Verpackung, Technologie, Verpackungspsychologie, Package Design, Marketing. 1945. 10/yr. 82 SFr. (foreign 115 SFr.). S H Z Fachverlag AG, Alte Landstr. 43, CH-8700 Kuesnacht, Switzerland. TEL 01-9108022. FAX 01-9105155. Ed. R. Walser. adv.; bk.rev.; charts; illus.; stat. circ. 4,650. **Indexed:** Int.Packag.Abstr., Key to Econ.Sci., Nutr.Abstr. **Document type:** trade publication.

658.7   GW   ISSN 0042-4293
VERPACKUNGS BERATER. 1956. m. DM.199 (foreign DM.218.40). P. Keppler Verlag GmbH und Co. KG, Industriestr. 2, 63150 Heusenstamm, Germany. TEL 06104-6060. FAX 06104-606145. TELEX 410131. Ed. Susanna Stock. adv.; charts; illus. circ. 14,089. **Indexed:** Int.Packag.Abstr., Key to Econ.Sci., Packag.Sci.Tech. **Document type:** trade publication.
—BLDSC (9194.720000); SWETS. **CCC.**

658.7 670   GW   ISSN 0042-4307
    CODEN: VPKRAV
VERPACKUNGS-RUNDSCHAU. (Text in German; contents page in English and German) 1950. m. DM.286.20 (foreign DM.347.40). P. Keppler Verlag GmbH und Co. KG, Industriestr. 2, 63150 Heusenstamm, Germany. TEL 06104-6060. FAX 06104-606145. Ed. F. Heydorn. adv.; bk.rev.; charts; illus.; pat.; index, cum.index. circ. 14,000. **Indexed:** Abstr.Bull.Inst.Pap.Chem., Chem.Abstr., Curr.Cont.; Curr.Pack.Abstr., Dairy Sci.Abstr., Eng.Ind., Excerp.Med., Food Sci.& Tech.Abstr., Int.Packag.Abstr., Key to Econ.Sci., Met.Abstr. **Document type:** trade publication.
—BLDSC (9194.740000); SWETS. **CCC.**

658.7   NE   ISSN 0042-4315
VERPAKKEN. 1948. 10/yr. fl.185 (foreign fl.298.70) (effective 1995). Wegener Tijl Tijdschriften Groep B.V., P.B. 9943, 1006 AP Amsterdam, Netherlands. TEL 31-20-5182828. FAX 31-20-5182843. Ed. A.Th.H van der Kort. circ. 6,652. **Indexed:** Excerp.Med., Packag.Sci.Tech. **Document type:** trade publication.

676.3 604.6   UK   ISSN 0956-4683
WASTE PAPER NEWS. m. £45. Brunton Business Publications Ltd., Thruxton Down House, Thruxton Down, Andover, Hants. SP11 8PR, England. TEL 0264-889533. FAX 0264-889622. Ed. Michael Brunton. bk.rev. circ. 6,000. **Document type:** newsletter.
    Description: Covers methods and technology developments for processing and recycling waste paper.

PACKAGING — ABSTRACTING, BIBLIOGRAPHIES, STATISTICS

677.7   US   ISSN 0740-1809
WIRE ROPE NEWS AND SLING TECHNOLOGY. 1979. bi-m. $20 (Canada $25; elsewhere $30). Box 871, Clark, NJ 07066. TEL 908-486-3221. FAX 908-396-4215. Ed. Conrad Miller; Pub. Edward J. Bluvias. adv. circ. 3,200. **Document type:** trade publication.
—UnCover.
 Description: Aimed at persons who manufacture, distribute, or use wire rope, chain, cordage, and related products and services.

332.6   IR
YEAR BOOK OF INTERNATIONAL EXHIBITIONS. 1993. a. IRI.10000($50) Iran Exports Publication Co. Ltd., P.O. Box 15815-3373, Tehran 15956, Iran. TEL 98-21-8801999. FAX 98-21-890547. **Document type:** directory.
 Description: Provides facts and figures about Iran's economy, export-import regulations, local and foreign investment, joint ventures, customs, insurance and banking rules, and information about the Tehran International Fair.

658.788   US
ZHONGGUO BAOZHUANG/CHINA PACKAGING. (Text in Chinese) q. $44.40. China Books & Periodicals, Inc., 2929 24th St., San Francisco, CA 94110. TEL 415-282-2994. FAX 415-282-0994.

PACKAGING — Abstracting, Bibliographies, Statistics

ANYAGMOZGATASI ES CSOMAGOLASI SZAKIRODALMI TAJEKOZTATO/ABSTRACT JOURNAL FOR MATERIALS HANDLING AND PACKAGING. see TRANSPORTATION — *Abstracting, Bibliographies, Statistics*

658.788 016   RU   ISSN 0131-0526
EKSPRESS-INFORMATSIYA. TARA I UPAKOVKA. KONTEINERY. 1962. 48/yr. $179 (effective 1996). Vsesoyuznyi Institut Nauchno-Tekhnicheskoi Informatsii (VINITI), Baltiiskaya ul., 14, Moscow A-219, Russia. (Subscr. to: Mezhdunarodnaya Kniga, Dimitrova ul. 39, 113095 Moscow, Russia)
 Formerly: Ekspress-Informatsiya. Tara i Upakovka (ISSN 0013-3825)

658.788 016   UK   ISSN 0260-7409
INTERNATIONAL PACKAGING ABSTRACTS. 1944. m. $1150.20. Pira International, Randalls Rd., Leatherhead, Surrey KT22 7RU, England. TEL 0372-376161. FAX 0372-360104. Ed. Fiona Speight. bk.rev.; abstr.; index. circ. 955. (reprint service avail.) **Indexed:** Abstr.Bull.Inst.Pap.Chem., Curr.Pack.Abstr., World Surf.Coat., World Text.Abstr. **Document type:** abstracting/indexing.
●Also available online. Vendor(s): Data-Star, Knight-Ridder, Inc., FIZ Technik, Orbit Search Service (PIRA), STN International.
Also available on CD-ROM. Producer(s): Knight-Ridder, Inc.
—BLDSC (4544.857200). **CCC.**
 Formerly: Packaging Abstracts (ISSN 0030-9087)

658.788 011   GW   ISSN 0722-3218
PACKAGING SCIENCE AND TECHNOLOGY ABSTRACTS/REFERATEDIENST VERPACKUNG. (Text in English and German) 1982. 6/yr. DM.600. (Fraunhofer Institut fuer Lebensmitteltechnologie und Verpackung) International Food Information Service GmbH, Melibocusstr. 52, 60528 Frankfurt a.M., Germany. TEL 069-6690070. FAX 069-66900710. (Subscr. in North America: IFIS North American Desk, c/o National Food Lab., Inc., 6363 Clark Ave., Dublin, CA 94568; in the UK: IFIS Publishing, Lane End House, Shinfield, Reading RG2 9BB, England) Ed. Julia Elze. pat.; index. **Document type:** abstracting/indexing.
●Also available online. Vendor(s): DIMDI, Data-Star, Knight-Ridder, Inc. (File no.252), FIZ Technik, Orbit Search Service, STN International.
 Description: Contains abstracts from journals, books, conference proceedings in packaging technology and engineering.

PAINTS AND PROTECTIVE COATINGS

667.6   UK   ISSN 0966-8268
ADHESIVES & SEALANTS YEARBOOK AND DIRECTORY. a. (issued in Jan.). £73.15($117.05) Argus Business Media Ltd., Fuel and Metals Journals (Subsidiary of: Argus Press Group), Queensway House, 2 Queensway, Redhill, Surrey RH1 1QS, England. TEL 01737-768611. FAX 01737-761685. TELEX 948669 TOPJNL G. **Document type:** directory, trade publication.
 Description: Provides chemical and technical information on adhesives and sealants and raw materials, as well as comprehensive listings of suppliers and manufacturers.

ADVANCES IN ORGANIC COATINGS SCIENCE AND TECHNOLOGY. see CHEMISTRY — *Organic Chemistry*

667.6   US   ISSN 0098-5430
TP934   CODEN: APCJDB
AMERICAN PAINT & COATINGS JOURNAL. 1916. w. $25 (effective 1996). American Paint Journal Co., 2911 Washington Ave., St. Louis, MO 63103. TEL 314-530-0301. Ed. Chuck Reitter. adv.; mkt.; tr.lit.; tr.mk.; index. circ. 5,936. **Indexed:** Anal.Abstr., Bus.Ind., Chem.Abstr, Key to Econ.Sci., PROMT, Tr.& Indus.Ind., World Surf.Coat.
—BLDSC (0847.829000); CASDDS; SWETS; UMI. **CCC.**
 Formerly: American Paint Journal (ISSN 0003-0317)

698   US   ISSN 0003-0325
AMERICAN PAINTING CONTRACTOR. 1924. m. $24. American Paint Journal Co., 2911 Washington Ave., St. Louis, MO 63103. TEL 314-530-0301. Ed. Paul Stoecklein. adv.; illus.; tr.lit.; index. circ. 24,754. **Indexed:** Corros.Abstr. **Document type:** trade publication.
—CCC.
 Formerly (1924-1963): American Painter and Decorator (ISSN 0096-0918)
 Description: Aimed at industrial, commercial and residential painters.

ANNUAL BOOK OF A S T M STANDARDS. VOLUME 06.01. PAINT - TESTS FOR FORMULATED PRODUCTS AND APPLIED COATINGS. see ENGINEERING — *Engineering Mechanics And Materials*

ANNUAL BOOK OF A S T M STANDARDS. VOLUME 06.02. PAINT - PIGMENTS, RESINS AND POLYMERS. see ENGINEERING — *Engineering Mechanics And Materials*

ANNUAL BOOK OF A S T M STANDARDS. VOLUME 06.03. PAINT - FATTY OILS AND ACIDS, SOLVENTS, MISCELLANEOUS; AROMATIC HYDROCARBONS. see ENGINEERING — *Engineering Mechanics And Materials*

698   SZ
APPLICA; Zeitschrift fuer das Maler- und Gipsergewerbe. 1893. 19/yr. 115 SFr. (foreign 150 SFr.). Schweizerischer Maler und Gipsermeister Verband, Grindelstr. 2, CH-8304 Wallisellen, Switzerland. TEL 01-8305959. FAX 01-8301176. Ed. Juergen Hildebrandt. adv. contact: Beat Steinmann. **Indexed:** C.I.S. Abstr., World Surf.Coat. **Document type:** trade publication.

698   AT   ISSN 0816-3596
AUSTRALIAN PAINT AND PANEL. 1982. bi-m. Aus.$30 (foreign Aus.$85) (effective Feb. 1995). Yaffa Publishing Group, 17-21 Bellevue St., Surry Hills, N.S.W. 2010, Australia. TEL 61-2-281-2333. FAX 61-2-281-2750. Ed. Anne McAllister. adv.: B&W page Aus.$2000, color page Aus.$2880; trim 273 x 210. circ. 4,859. **Document type:** trade publication.
 Description: Keeps body repair shops in touch with latest trends, developments, techniques and new products.

698   IT
BOTTEGA DEL COLORE. 1966. m. L.55000($45) (foerign L.80000) (effective 1993). (Federcolor Association of Paint Stores) Gest. Ed. di Daniele Paolucci, Via Menotti, 33, 20129 Milan, Italy. TEL 02-29512541. FAX 02-29404950. adv.; index. circ. 14,000. (back issues avail.)

698   UK
BRITISH DECORATORS ASSOCIATION. MEMBERS REFERENCE HANDBOOK. 1932. a. British Decorators Association, 32 Coton Rd., Nuneaton, Warks. CV11 5TW, England. TEL 01203-353776. FAX 01203-324513. Ed. S.M. Broughton. adv. contact: Heather Saint. abstr.; charts. circ. 2,500. **Document type:** trade publication.

679.6   GW   ISSN 0178-4412
BROSSAPRESS-NACHRICHTENBLATT FUER DIE BUERSTEN- UND PINSELINDUSTRIE. (Text in English, French, German, Italian) 1925. bi-m. DM.286. Verlag Dr. Grueb Nachf., Oelbergweg 8, 79283 Bollschweil, Germany. TEL 07633-7025. FAX 07633-82129. TELEX 772730-BROS-D. Ed. Rainer Grueb. adv. contact: Petra Lehser. bk.rev.; charts; illus.; pat.; stat.; tr.lit. circ. 4,500. (tabloid format) **Document type:** trade publication.
 Formerly: Nachrichtenblatt fuer die Buersten- und Pinselindustrie (ISSN 0027-7487)

BRUSHWARE. see BUILDING AND CONSTRUCTION — *Hardware*

667.6 686.2   UK   ISSN 0261-930X
BUSINESS RATIO REPORT: PAINT & PRINTING INK MANUFACTURERS; an industry sector analysis. 1973. a. I C C Business Ratios Ltd., Freepost, Field House, Hampton, Mddx. TW12 1BR, England. TEL 081-783-0977. FAX 081-783-1940. charts; stat. **Document type:** trade publication.
—BLDSC (6334.650000).

667.6 330.9   UK
C O M E T. 1993. m. £250. Paint Research Association, 8 Waldegrave Rd., Teddington, Middlesex TW11 8LD, England. TEL 081-977-4427. FAX 081-943-4705. **Document type:** bulletin.
 Description: Contains information on coatings, adhesives, inks and their raw materials worldwide.

667.6   SP
CATALOGO DE CHAPA Y PINTURA. 9/yr. 8000 ptas. (foreign 11000 ptas.). Tecnipublicaciones, S.A., C. Albacete 5, 28027 Madrid, Spain. TEL 34-1-3261440. FAX 34-1-3262539.
 Formerly: Chapa y Pintura.

667.6   FR   ISSN 0396-1214
CATALOGUE NATIONAL DU TRAITEMENT DES SURFACES DE L'ANTICORROSION ET DES TRAITEMENTS THERMIQUES. 1963. a. 234 F. C E P P Publications, 25 Rue Dagorno, 75012 Paris, France. TEL 43-47-30-20. FAX 43-46-58-18. Ed. Martine Clavel. adv. circ. 10,000. **Document type:** trade publication.
 Description: Covers the entire French market of surface coatings.

698   CN   ISSN 0225-6363
COATINGS. 1979. bi-m. Can.$30($50) (foreign $60) (effective 1996). Kay Publishing Company Ltd., 406 N. Service Rd., E., Ste. 1, Oakville, ON L6H 5R2, Canada. TEL 905-844-9773. FAX 905-844-5672. Ed. G. Barry Kay; Pub. G. Barry Kay. adv.; bk.rev. circ. 7,600. (back issues avail.) **Document type:** trade publication.
—BLDSC (3292.580000); Ei; Faxon. **CCC.**

667.6 614.85   UK   ISSN 0967-2508
COATINGS, REGULATIONS AND THE ENVIRONMENT. 1981. m. £160. Paint Research Association, 8 Waldegreave Rd., Teddington, Middlesex TW11 8LD, England. TEL 081-977-4427. FAX 081-943-4705. Ed. Christine Ce. abstr.; index. **Indexed:** Curr.Cont. **Document type:** abstracting/indexing.
—BLDSC (3292.608400). **CCC.**
 Former titles (until 1992): Survey on Hazards, Pollution and Legislation in the Coating Field (ISSN 0953-8801); (until 1986): Hazards, Pollution and Legislation in the Coatings Field (ISSN 0262-7116)

COLOR RESEARCH AND APPLICATION. see ENGINEERING — *Chemical Engineering*

667.6   II   ISSN 0588-5094
TP934   CODEN: COSJAZ
COLOUR SOCIETY. JOURNAL. (Text in English) 1962. bi-m. Rs.5 per no. Colour Society, c/o S. P. Potnis, Department of Chemical Technology, Matunga, Bombay 400019, India. Ed. V. Gowrishankar. adv.; bk.rev.; abstr.; index. circ. 400. **Indexed:** Art & Archaeol.Tech.Abstr., Chem.Abstr., World Surf.Coat.
—CASDDS.

660   NE   ISSN 0430-2222
CODEN: FAPVAP
CONGRESS F A T I P E C. Variant title: Federation d'Associations de Techniciens des Industries des Peintures, Vernis, Emaux et Encres d'Imprimerie de l'Europe Continentale. Congress Proceedings. 1951. biennial. (Federation d'Associations de Techniciens des Industries des Peintures, Vernis, Emaux et Encres d'Imprimerie de l'Europe Continentale) Bond voor Materialenkennis, P.O. Box 390, 3330 AJ Zwyndrecht, Netherlands.
—BLDSC (3897.400000); CASDDS. **CCC.**

667.6   SA   ISSN 0377-8711
TA418.74   CODEN: CCSADT
CORROSION AND COATINGS. (Text in English) 1973. m. R.140. (South African Corrosion Institute) George Warman Publications (Pty.) Ltd., P.O. Box 3847, Cape Town 8000, South Africa. TEL 27-21-24-5320. FAX 27-21-26-1332. Ed. Tony Walker. adv. circ. 2,500. **Indexed:** Chem.Abstr., Corros.Abstr., Ind.S.A.Per., INIS Atomind., Met.Abstr., W.R.C.Inf., World Alum.Abstr. **Document type:** trade publication.
—BLDSC (3473.350000); CASDDS; Ei.
Description: Covers the corrosion prevention and surface coatings industry in South Africa.

667.6   SA
CORROSION AND COATINGS BUYER'S GUIDE. 1984. a. R.110. George Warman Publications (Pty.) Ltd., P.O. Box 3487, Cape Town 8000, South Africa. TEL 27-21-24-5320. FAX 27-21-26-1332. **Document type:** trade publication.
Description: Lists suppliers, representatives, manufacturers, corrosion related products and services.

667.6   US   ISSN 1075-3567
CURELETTER. (Buyers' Guide and Supplement avail.) 1984. m. $225 (foreign $247). Captan Associates, Inc., Box 504, Brick, NJ 08723-0504. TEL 908-840-1244. FAX 908-840-1211. Ed. C. Bluestein. adv. bk.rev.; bibl. (back issues avail.) **Document type:** newsletter.

698.1   DK   ISSN 0905-6440
DANSKE MALERMESTRE. 1907. every 3 wks. DKK 285 (typically set in Jan.). Danske Malermestre, Snaregade 12, DK-1205 Copenhagen K, Denmark. TEL 45-33-93-36-00. FAX 45-33-93-42-10. Ed. Adam Pade. adv. contact: Peter Graah. bk.rev.; circ. 3,200. (controlled). **Document type:** trade publication.
Formed by the 1990 merger of: Malertidende (ISSN 0900-4564) & Malermesteren (ISSN 0025-1364)
Description: Provides technical, political and legal information.

667.6   GW   ISSN 0012-009X
TP934   CODEN: DFZTBF
DEFAZET.* (Supplement: Blaetter fuer den Nachwuchs) 1947. m. DM.54. Lack und Chemie Verlag Elvira Moeller GmbH, Postfach 1168, 7024 Filderstadt 1, Germany. Ed. Elvira Moeller. adv.; bk.rev.; abstr.; illus.; pat.; tr.lit.; index. circ. 4,500. **Indexed:** Chem.Abstr., Excerp.Med., PROMT.
—CASDDS.
Formerly: Deutsche Farben-Zeitschrift.

667.6   GW
DAS DEUTSCHE LACKIERERBLATT. 1992. bi-m. DM.72 (foreign DM.84). (Bundesfachgruppe Fahrzeuglackierer) Deutsche Verlags-Anstalt GmbH, Postfach 101012, 70049 Stuttgart, Germany. TEL 0711-2631-0. FAX 0711-2623685. Ed. Michael Rehm. adv.: B&W page DM.3860, color page DM.6410; trim 269 x 185. circ. 5,500. **Document type:** trade publication.

698   GW   ISSN 0012-0448
TT300
DAS DEUTSCHE MALERBLATT. (Supplements avail.) 1928. m. DM.153 (students DM.111). (Hauptverband des Deutschen Maler- und Lackiererhandwerks) Deutsche Verlags-Anstalt GmbH, Postfach 106012, 70049 Stuttgart, Germany. TEL 0711-2631-0. FAX 0711-2631-292. Ed. Armin Scharf. adv.; bk.rev.; charts; illus.; tr.lit.; index. circ. 19,713. **Indexed:** Art & Archaeol.Tech.Abstr., Biodet.Abstr., World Surf.Coat. **Document type:** trade publication.
—BLDSC (3572.700000). **CCC.**
Incorporates (in 1982): Malerzeitung Drei Schilde (ISSN 0025-1372)

698   GW   ISSN 0343-3722
DEUTSCHES TASCHENBUCH FUER MALER UND LACKIERER (YEAR). 1952. a. DM.22. Callwey Verlag, Postfach 800409, 81604 Munich, Germany. TEL 089-436005-0. FAX 089-43600513. Eds. Konrad Gatz, Klaus Halmburger. circ. 10,000. **Document type:** bulletin.

(YEAR) DIRECTORY OF CUSTOM FINISHERS, VENDORS AND CONSULTANTS. see ENGINEERING — Engineering Mechanics And Materials

698 667   FR   ISSN 0012-5709
CODEN: DOLIA8
DOUBLE LIAISON; chimie des peintures. (Text and summaries in English and French) 1954. m. 521 F. (Etude et Realisations de la Couleur) E R E C, 68 rue Jean Jaures, 92800 Puteaux, France. Ed. Annik Chauvel. adv.; abstr.; bibl.; charts; illus.; stat.; index. circ. 4,700. (back issues avail.) **Indexed:** Anal.Abstr., Art & Archaeol.Tech.Abstr., Chem.Abstr., PROMT, World Alum.Abstr., World Surf.Coat.
Description: Information on paints, varnishes, printing inks and adhesives.

667.6   US
THE DROP CLOTH. 10/yr. membership. Texas Council of Painting and Decorating Contractors of America, 1601 Rio Grande, Ste. 440, Austin, TX 78701. TEL 512-479-0425. FAX 512-495-9031. Ed. Lisa Fry. circ. 200. **Document type:** newsletter.
Description: Discusses paints and protective coatings, as well as building and construction.

698   NE   ISSN 0920-2099
EISMA'S VAKPERS; algemeen vakblad voor het schildersbedrijf. 1899. fortn. fl.210. Eisma B.V. Publishers, Celsiusweg 37, Box 340, 8901 BC Leeuwarden, Netherlands. TEL 058-152545. FAX 058-154000. adv.; bk.rev.; illus.; index. circ. 7,000. **Document type:** trade publication.
—SWETS.
Formerly (until 1986): Eisma's Schildersblad (ISSN 0013-287X)

667.6   UK   ISSN 0955-2804
EMULSION POLYMERISATION AND POLYMER EMULSIONS. m. £275. Paint Research Association, 8 Waldegrave Rd., Teddington, Middlesex TW11 8LD, England. TEL 081-977-4427. FAX 081-943-4705. **Document type:** bulletin.

667.6   UK   ISSN 0938-5207
EQUIPMENT, CORROSION, AND CORROSION PROTECTION. m. £118($214) The Royal Society of Chemistry, Thomas Graham House, Science Park, Milton Rd., Cambridge CB4 4WF, England. TEL 01223-420066. FAX 01223-423623. E-mail: rsc1@rsc.org. (Dist. by: Turpin Distribution Services Ltd., Blackhorse Rd., Letchworth, Herts. SG6 1HN, England. TEL 01462-672555. FAX 01462-480947) **Document type:** abstracting/indexing.
Description: Summarizes articles on construction, maintenance and corrosion within the chemical-processing industries.

667.6   GW   ISSN 0930-3847
CODEN: ECJOEF
EUROPEAN COATINGS JOURNAL. (Text in English and French) 1986. m. (10/yr). DM.219. Vincentz Verlag, Schiffgraben 41-43, 30175 Hannover, Germany. TEL 0511-9909816. FAX 0511-9909814. (Subscr. to: Postfach 6247, 30062 Hannover, Germany) Ed. Juergen Nowak. adv.; bk.rev.; bibl.; charts; illus. circ. 8,150. (tabloid format; reprint service avail. from UMI) **Indexed:** Biodet.Abstr., Chem.Abstr., Curr.Cont., Eng.Ind., Met.Abstr., Phys.Ber., Sci.Cit.Ind., World Surf.Coat. **Document type:** trade publication.
—BLDSC (3829.609000); CASDDS; Ei; SWETS. **CCC.**

667.6   UK   ISSN 0964-8666
EUROPEAN COIL COATING ASSOCIATION DIRECTORY. 1990. a. (European Coil Coating Association) Argus Business Media Ltd., International Trade Publications (Subsidiary of: Argus Press Group), Queensway House, 2 Queensway, Redhill, Surrey RH1 1QS, England. TEL 01737-78611. FAX 01737-760510. TELEX 948669 TOPJNL G. **Document type:** directory.

667.6   UK   ISSN 0266-7800
EUROPEAN PAINT AND RESIN NEWS. 1957. m. £150($395) (rest of Europe £195). Information Research Ltd., 262 Regent St., London W1R 5DA, England. FAX 0171-287-9322. Ed. Cvetka Fuller. pat.; tr.lit. circ. 500. (processed; reprint service avail. from UMI) **Indexed:** World Surf.Coat. **Document type:** newsletter.
—BLDSC (3829.768400). **CCC.**
Formerly: Continental Paint and Resin News (ISSN 0010-7735); Incorporates: Phosphating News.
Description: Industry developments, marketing news and statistics, technology developments, symposia and exhibition news of the European paint and resin industry.

667.6   UK   ISSN 0963-8474
TP934   CODEN: EPPJEJ
EUROPEAN POLYMERS PAINT COLOUR JOURNAL. 1879. m. £116.35($235.60) (foreign £235.60). Argus Business Media Ltd., Fuel and Metals Journals (Subsidiary of: Argus Press Group), Queensway House, 2 Queensway, Redhill, Surrey RH1 1QS, England. TEL 01737-768611. FAX 01737-761685. TELEX 948669 TOPJNL G. Ed. Tom Mulligan. adv.; bk.rev.; abstr.; charts; mkt.; pat.; s-a. index. circ. 2,002. **Indexed:** Anal.Abstr., Art & Archaeol.Tech.Abstr., BMT, Chem.Abstr., Chem.Eng.Abstr., Excerp.Med., Intl.Polym.Sci.& Tech., Key to Econ.Sci., PROMT, RAPRA, T.C.E.A., W.R.C.Inf., World Surf.Coat. **Document type:** trade publication.
—BLDSC (6547.743000); CASDDS; Ei; Faxon; SWETS.
Former titles (until 1991): Polymers Paint Colour Journal (ISSN 0370-1158); (until 1970): Paint, Oil and Colour Journal (ISSN 0030-9516); Oil & Colour Trades Journal (ISSN 0369-7088)
Description: Contains information of value to those in the paint, printing inks, and allied industries.

667.6   SW   ISSN 0427-9107
FAERG OCH FERNISSA; tidskrift foer industriell produktmaalning. (English supplement avail.: Industrial Coatings) 1937. q. free. Becker Industrifaerg AB, Box 2041, 195 02 Maersta, Sweden. TEL 8-590-790-00. FAX 8-591-16949. Ed. Birgitta Karlsson. adv.; charts; illus.; tr.lit.; cum.index every 5 yrs. circ. 10,000. **Indexed:** World Surf.Coat. **Document type:** trade publication.

667.6 667.7   DK   ISSN 0106-7559
TP934   CODEN: FLSCDT
FAERG OCH LACK SCANDINAVIA. (Text in Scandinavian languages) 1955. 6/yr. DKK 380 to non-members. Skandinaviska Lackteknikers Foerbund - Federation of Scandinavian Paint and Varnish Technologists, Strandboulevarden 38, DK-2100 Copenhagen, Denmark. TEL 45-42-84-33-98. FAX 45-42-84-72-77. Ed. Mike Symes. adv.: B&W page DKK 8600, color page DKK 14900; adv. contact: Peter Graaf. bk.rev.; charts; illus.; index. circ. 2,200. **Indexed:** Chem.Abstr. **Document type:** trade publication.
—BLDSC (3869.520000); CASDDS.
Formerly (until 1980): Skandinavisk Tidskrift foer Faerg och Lack (ISSN 0037-6094)

DIE FARBE; Zeitschrift fuer alle Zweige der Farbenlehre und ihre Anwendung. see PHYSICS — Optics

667.6   GW   ISSN 0014-7699
CODEN: FALAAA
FARBE UND LACK. 1894. m. DM.140 (foreign DM.174). (Gesellschaft Deutscher Chemiker) Vincentz Verlag, Schiffgraben 43, 30175 Hannover, Germany. TEL 0511-9909812. FAX 0511-9909814. (Subscr. to: Postfach 6247, 30062 Hannover, Germany) (Co-sponsor: Schweizerische Vereinigung der Lack- und Farbenchemiker (SVLFC)) Ed.Bd. adv.; bk.rev.; abstr.; bibl.; charts; illus.; pat. circ. 5,643. (tabloid format; also avail. in microform from UMI; reprint service avail. from UMI) **Indexed:** Anal.Abstr., Art & Archaeol.Tech.Abstr., Biodet.Abstr., C.I.S. Abstr., Cadscan, Chem.Abstr., Curr.Cont., Excerp.Med., INIS Atomind., Int.Packag.Abstr., Intl.Polym.Sci.& Tech., Key to Econ.Sci., Lead Abstr., Packag.Sci.Tech., RAPRA, Sci.Cit.Ind., World Surf.Coat., Zincscan. **Document type:** trade publication.
—BLDSC (3869.000000); CASDDS; Ei; Faxon; SWETS; UMI. **CCC.**

PAINTS AND PROTECTIVE COATINGS

667.6 AU ISSN 0014-7737
FARBENKREIS, OESTERREICHISCHE MALERZEITUNG. m. S.200. (Landesinnung Wien der Maler, Anstreicher und Lackierer) Eugen Ketterl, Anastasius-Grun-Gasse 43, A-1180 Vienna, Austria. Ed. Erwin Berger. circ. 4,000. **Document type:** trade publication.

698.1 DK ISSN 0908-9926
▼**DE FARVER/COLORS**; magasinet for levende byggeri. 1994. q. DKK 160 (effective 1995). Danske Malermestre - Federation of Danish Master Painters, Snaregade 12, DK-1205 Copenhagen K, Denmark. TEL 47-33-93-36-00. FAX 45-33-93-42-10. Ed. Adam Pade. adv. contact: Peter Graah. circ. 15,500.
Description: Features outstanding work by painters and architects with respect to colors and surface coating.

667.6 667.7 FR ISSN 0071-416X
FEDERATION D'ASSOCIATIONS DE TECHNICIENS DES INDUSTRIES DES PEINTURES, VERNIS, EMAUX ET ENCRES D'IMPRIMERIE DE L'EUROPE CONTINENTALE. ANNUAIRE OFFICIEL. OFFICIAL YEARBOOK. AMTLICHES JAHRBUCH. (Text in English, French, German) 1955. biennial. Federation d'Associations de Techniciens des Industries des Peintures, Vernis, Emaux et Encres d'Imprimerie de l'Europe Continentale, Maison de la Chimie, 28 rue Saint Dominique, 75007 Paris, France. adv. circ. 3,000. **Document type:** trade publication.

667.6 II
FINISH. (Text in English) 1993. q. Rs.100($50) Colour Publications Pvt. Ltd., 126-A Dhuruwadi, Off Dr. Nariman Rd., Bombay 400 025, India. TEL 430-9318. TELEX 71242 CEPE IN. circ. 3,205.

698 UK ISSN 0264-2506
TS670.A1 CODEN: FINIE2
FINISHING. 1948. m. £70 (foreign £90). Turret Group Plc., Turret House, 171 High St., Rickmansworth, Herts WD3 1SN, England. TEL 01923-777000. FAX 01923-771297. Ed. Glenn Tomkins. adv.; bk.rev. (also avail. in microfilm from UMI; reprint service avail. from UMI) **Indexed:** Br.Tech.Ind., Cadscan, Chem.Abstr., Eng.Ind., Excerp.Med., INSPEC, Int.Packag.Abstr., ISMEC, Lead Abstr., Met.Abstr., PROMT, World Alum.Abstr., World Surf.Coat., Zincscan. **Document type:** trade publication.
—BLDSC (3928.204000); CASDDS; Ei; SWETS; UMI.
Formerly: Finishing Industries (ISSN 0309-3018); Which incorporated: Industrial Finishing and Surface Coatings (ISSN 0039-6001); Electroplating and Metal Finishing (ISSN 0013-5305); Industrial Finishing (ISSN 0019-8315); Surface Coatings.

667.6 531 011 US
FINISHING LINE, quarterly on finishing and coating technology. 1983. q. $60. Society of Manufacturing Engineers, Association for Finishing Process, One SME Dr., Box 930, Dearborn, MI 48121-0930. TEL 313-271-1500. FAX 313-271-2861. TELEX 2977422 SME UR (VIA RCA). Ed. Sherry Caruso. bk.rev. circ. 3,000. **Document type:** trade publication.

698 IT
FINITURE E COLORE; verniciatura, decorazione e restauro leggero. 1993. 9/yr. L.40000 (foreign L.60000) (effective 1995). BE-MA Editrice s.r.l., Via Teocrito 50, 20128 Milan, Italy. TEL 39-2-2552451. FAX 39-2-57000692. Ed. Dario Marabelli. adv. color page L.5800000; 264 x 394. circ. 25,000.

667.6 660 UK ISSN 0969-6210
▼**FOCUS ON PIGMENTS.** 1994. m. £165($305) (effective 1996). The Royal Society of Chemistry, Thomas Graham House, Science Park, Milton Rd., Cambridge CB4 4WF, England. TEL 01223-420066. FAX 01223-423429. E-mail: rsc1@rsc.org. (Subscr. to: Turpin Distribution Services Ltd., Blackhorse Rd., Letchworth, Herts. SG6 1HN, England. TEL 01462-672555. FAX 01462-480947) Ed. Reg Adams. **Document type:** newsletter.
Description: Monitors developments in the pigment manufacturing and processing industry.

667.6 FR ISSN 0071-9048
FRANCE - PEINTURE. 1953. biennial. 240 F. C E P P Publications, 25 Rue Dagorno, 75012 Paris, France. TEL 43-47-30-20. FAX 43-46-58-18. Ed. Martine Clavel. adv. circ. 9,100.
Description: Directory of paint varnish and allied industries.

698 FR ISSN 1254-4000
GUIDE PRATIQUE DE L'ENTREPRENEUR - PEINTURE. 6/yr. Editions S E R I P, 40 rue Guy Moquet, 94501 Champigny Cedex, France. TEL 48-81-91-91. FAX 48-81-81-77. Ed. Karine Quedreux. circ. 15,000.

667.6 338 UK
GUIDE TO EUROPEAN PRODUCERS OF POLYURETHANE PAINTS & COATINGS. 1993. irreg. £150. I A L Consultants, 314-316 Harbour Yard, Chelsea Harbour, London SW10 0XD, England. TEL 071-376-3676. FAX 071-376-8281. **Document type:** trade publication.

667.6 338 UK
GUIDE TO THE PRODUCERS OF POLYURETHANE ADHESIVES AND SEALANTS IN EUROPE. 1993. irreg. £150. I A L Consultants, 314-316 Harbour Yard, Chelsea Harbour, London SW10 0XD, England. TEL 071-376-3676. FAX 071-376-8281. **Document type:** trade publication.

667.6 676.284 UK
HOME DECOR. 1955. m. £55. Wallcovering, Fabric and Decor Retailers Association, Box 44, Walsall WS3 1TD, England. TEL 01922-31134. FAX 01922-723703. Ed. Christina Gregory. adv. contact: Malcolm Cheshire. bk.rev. circ. 8,500. **Indexed:** World Surf.Coat. **Document type:** trade publication.
Former titles: W P W Decor; Wallpaper, Paint and Wallcovering (ISSN 0043-0153)

667.6 US
INDUSTRIAL FINISHING BUYER'S GUIDE. 1984. a. Hitchcock Publishing (Subsidiary of: Capital Cities - A B C, Inc.), 191 S. Gary Ave., Carol Stream, IL 60188. TEL 708-665-1000. FAX 708-462-2225. TELEX 72-0404. adv. circ. 36,000. **Document type:** consumer publication.

698 US ISSN 1073-4651
TT325.A1 CODEN: IPPOEA
INDUSTRIAL PAINT & POWDER; coatings manufacturing & application. (Supplement avail.: Annual Buyer's Guide) 1924. m. $60 (foreign $75). Hitchcock Publishing (Subsidiary of: Capital Cities - A B C, Inc.), 191 S. Gary Ave., Carol Stream, IL 60188. TEL 708-665-1000. FAX 708-462-2225. (Subscr. to: Box 2155, Radnor, PA 19089) Ed. Donald E. Hegland; Pub. Charles Spahr. adv.; bk.rev.; abstr.; charts; illus.; index. circ. 38,000. (also avail. in microform from UMI; reprint service avail. from UMI) **Indexed:** A.S.& T.Ind., Bus.Ind., CAD CAM Abstr., Ceram.Abstr., Chem.Abstr., Energy Info.Abstr., Eng.Ind., Excerp.Med., Ind.Sci.Rev., Met.Abstr., Robomat. (until 1992), Tr.& Indus.Ind., World Alum.Abstr.
●Also available online. Vendor(s): Knight-Ridder, Inc.
—CASDDS; Ei; Faxon; Genuine Article; SWETS; UMI; UnCover. **CCC.**
Formerly (until 1993): Industrial Finishing (ISSN 0019-8323)
Description: For those involved in formulating, finishing, paint and powder.

667.6 GW ISSN 0019-9109
CODEN: ILBEAE
INDUSTRIE LACKIERBETRIEB. 1933. m. DM.138 (foreign DM.162). (European Coil Coating Association - ECCA) Vincentz Verlag, Schiffgraben 41-43, 30175 Hannover, Germany. TEL 0511-9909832. FAX 0511-9909899. (Subscr. to: Postfach 6247, 30062 Hannover, Germany) Ed. Olaf Lueckert. adv.; bk.rev.; abstr.; bibl.; charts; illus.; pat. circ. 2,463. (tabloid format) **Indexed:** C.I.S. Abstr., Chem.Abstr., Excerp.Med., Packag.Sci.Tech., World Surf.Coat. **Document type:** trade publication.
—BLDSC (4469.000000); CASDDS; SWETS. **CCC.**

667.6 II
INTERNATIONAL PRESS CUTTING SERVICE: PAINT - COLOUR - VARNISH - INKS. 1967. w. $65. International Press Cutting Service, Box 63, Allahabad 211001, India. Ed. N. Khanna. bk.rev.; index. circ. 1,200. (processed)

667.6 UK
INTERNATIONAL RADCURE YEARBOOK & DIRECTORY. a. Argus Business Media Ltd., Fuel and Metals Journals (Subsidiary of: Argus Press Group), Queensway House, 2 Queensway, Redhill, Surrey RH1 1QS, England. TEL 01737-768611. FAX 01737-760510. TELEX 948669 TOPJNL G. **Document type:** trade publication, directory.

698 GW
INTERSTANDOX; information for the world of the car repair painter. (Editions in various languages) 1978. s-a. free. Herberts GmbH, Christbusch 25, 42286 Wuppertal, Germany. TEL 0202-529-0. FAX 0202-529-2809. (back issues avail.) **Document type:** trade publication.

698 GW
INTERSTANDOX EXTRA. 1978. 4/yr. free. Herberts GmbH, Christbusch 25, 42285 Wuppertal, Germany. TEL 0202-529-0. FAX 0202-529-2809. circ. 22,000. (back issues avail.) **Document type:** trade publication.
Description: Information for body shops and car repair painters.

667.6 US ISSN 0361-8773
TP934 CODEN: JCTEDL
J C T: JOURNAL OF COATINGS TECHNOLOGY. 1922. m. $30. Federation of Societies for Coatings Technology, 492 Norristown Rd., Blue Bell, PA 19422-2350. TEL 215-940-0777. FAX 215-940-0292. Ed. Patricia D. Viola; Pub. Robert F. Ziegler. adv.; bk.rev.; charts; illus.; index. circ. 10,000. (also avail. in microform from UMI,PMC; reprint service avail. from UMI) **Indexed:** A.S.& T.Ind., Anal.Abstr., Art & Archaeol.Tech.Abstr., BMT, Chem.Abstr., Corros.Abstr., Curr.Cont., Energy Ind., Energy Info.Abstr., Excerp.Med., Graph.Arts Lit.Abstr., Ind.Sci.Rev., Int.Packag.Abstr., Intl.Polym.Sci.& Tech., Key to Econ.Sci., Met.Abstr., PROMT, RAPRA, Sci.Cit.Ind., World Alum.Abstr., World Surf.Coat. **Document type:** academic/scholarly publication.
—BLDSC (4958.796000); CASDDS; Ei; Faxon; Genuine Article; SWETS; UMI; UnCover. **CCC.**
Former titles: J.P.T. Journal of Paint Technology (ISSN 0022-3352); Federation of Societies for Paint Technology. Official Digest.

JOURNAL OF COATED FABRICS. see *TEXTILE INDUSTRIES AND FABRICS*

667.6 US ISSN 8755-1985
TP934
JOURNAL OF PROTECTIVE COATINGS AND LININGS. 1984. m. $55 (Canada and Mexico $75; overseas $85) (effective 1995). (Steel Structures Painting Council) Technology Publishing Co., 2100 Wharton St., Ste. 31, Pittsburgh, PA 15203. TEL 412-431-8300. FAX 412-431-5428. Ed. Karen Kapsanis; Pub. Harold Hower. adv. B&W page $1585; color page $2585; 8 1/8 x 10 7/8; adv. contact: Bret Thomas. bk.rev.; circ. 15,000 (controlled). (also avail. in microform from UMI; reprint service avail. from UMI) **Indexed:** Corros.Abstr., Excerp.Med., World Surf.Coat. **Document type:** trade publication.
●Also available on CD-ROM.
—BLDSC (5042.940000); Ei; Faxon; SWETS; UMI.
Description: Provides technical and regulatory information about the use of heavy-duty corrosion protective coating for maintaining steel and concrete industrial structures.

667.6 UK ISSN 0954-5212
KEY NOTE REPORT: PAINTS & VARNISHES. Variant title: Paints & Varnishes. irreg. £185. Key Note Publications Ltd., Field House, 72 Oldfield Rd., Hampton, Middlesex TW12 2HQ, England. TEL 0181-783-0755. FAX 0181-783-1720. **Document type:** trade publication.
●Also available online.
Also available on CD-ROM.
—BLDSC (6340.371000).

KOLORISZTIKAI ERTESITO/COLORISTICAL REVIEW. see *ENGINEERING — Chemical Engineering*

667.6 540 HU ISSN 0133-2546
CODEN: KOFIDO
KORROZIOS FIGYELO/CORROSION OBSERVER. (Text in Hungarian; summaries in English) 1961. bi-m. $20 (effective 1995 & 1996). V E K O R Ltd. - Corrosion Protection Organization for Chemical Industry, Egry J. u. 25-A, 8200 Veszprem, Hungary. TEL 36-88-328514. Ed. Mrs. I. Bozso; Pub. M. Horvatth. adv.; bk.rev.; abstr.; bibl.; illus.; index. circ. 600. **Indexed:** Corros.Abstr., INIS Atomind., Met.Abstr. **Document type:** bulletin.
—CASDDS.
Description: Deals with corrosion and corrosion prevention.
Refereed Serial

PAINTS AND PROTECTIVE COATINGS

677.6   RU   ISSN 0130-9013
LAKOKRASOCHNYE MATERIALY I IKH PRIMENENIE. (Text in Russian; abstracts in English, Russian) 1960. m. $102 (effective 1996). (AO "Lakokraska") Journal LKM Ltd., Scherbakovskaya, 3, VNIIK, 105318 Moscow, Russia. TEL 369-97-13. FAX 284-84-02. (Subscr. to: Mezhdunarodnaya Kniga, ul. Dimitrova 39, 117019 Moscow, Russia. TEL 238-46-00) Ed. Boris B. Kudyavtsev. adv.: color page $500; adv. contact: Irina B. Ustimenko. bk.rev.; bibl.; index. circ. 5,000. **Indexed:** Art & Archaeol.Tech.Abstr., Chem.Abstr., INIS Atomind., World Surf.Coat. **Document type:** academic/scholarly publication.
—BLDSC (0095.300000).
   Description: Provides information on paints and coatings in the former USSR (CIS). Covers scientific and production achievements in the paint industry and finishing technology.
Refereed Serial

698   SW   ISSN 0280-8226
MAALARMAESTAREN;* organ foer Sveriges maalarmaestarfoerening. 1960. bi-m. SEK 50 (effective 1990). Sveriges Maalarmaestares Samorganisation, Aengststigen 8, S-172 40 Sundbyberg, Sweden. **Document type:** trade publication.

698   SW   ISSN 0345-7710
MAALARNAS FACKTIDNING. 1887. 9/yr. SEK 150; newsstand price: SEK 16. Svenska Maalarefoerbundet, P.O. Box 1113, S-111 18 Stockholm, Sweden. TEL 46-8-23-25-80. FAX 46-8-791-00-09. Ed. Bengt Skoeld. adv.: B&W page SEK 12600, color page SEK 18900; trim 191 x 268; adv. contact: Margareta Ehrenborg. circ. 25,000. cols./p.: 4. **Document type:** trade publication.

667.6   GW   ISSN 0943-3872
MALER PRAXIS; Informationen fuer das Malerhandwerk. 1973. 4/yr. free. Wegra Verlag GmbH, Frankfurterstr. 10, 71732 Tamm, Germany. circ. 35,000. **Document type:** trade publication.

698   GW   ISSN 0464-7777
DER MALER UND LACKIERERMEISTER. 1950. m. DM.35. Verlag W. Sachon, Schloss Mindelburg, 87714 Mindelheim, Germany. TEL 08261-999-0. FAX 08261-999-132. Ed. Peter Hartmann. adv. contact: Belinda Staimer. charts; illus.; tr.lit. circ. 21,344. **Document type:** trade publication.

698   NO   ISSN 0333-3531
MALEREN. 1908. m. (10/yr.). NOK 280. Malermestrenes Landsforbund, P.O. Box 5479 Maj., N-0305 Oslo, Norway. TEL 47-22-96-11-60. FAX 47-22-96-11-61. Ed. Knut Randem. adv.; bk.rev. circ. 2,000. **Indexed:** C.I.S. Abstr.
   Description: Articles about the construction industry and painting as a trade.

698 747   FR   ISSN 0755-1533
MANUEL GENERAL DE LA PEINTURE ET DE LA DECORATION. 1961. 10/yr. 62 rue la Boetie, 75008 Paris, France. TEL 45-61-04-61. FAX 45-63-95-43. Ed. Josette Lapierre. circ. 7,500.

698   GW   ISSN 0025-2697
NK1700
DIE MAPPE; Deutsche Maler- und Lackierer-Zeitschrift. 1881. m. DM.166.20 (students DM.135.60). Callwey Verlag, Postfach 800409, 81604 Munich, Germany. TEL 089-436005-0. FAX 089-43600513. Ed. Klaus Halmburger. adv.; bk.rev.; bibl.; illus.; stat.; index. circ. 26,500. **Indexed:** Art & Archaeol.Tech.Abstr., World Surf.Coat. **Document type:** trade publication.
—BLDSC (5369.350000). **CCC.**
   Incorporates (in 1991): Farbe und Raum (ISSN 0014-7702)

667.6   US   ISSN 0098-7786
TP934   CODEN: MPCODM
MODERN PAINT AND COATINGS. 1910. m. $52 (foreign $112). Argus Inc., 6151 Powers Ferry Rd., N.W., Atlanta, GA 30339-2941. TEL 404-955-2500. FAX 404-955-0400. Ed. Larry Anderson. adv.: B&W page $2555, color page $3815; 8 1/8 x 10 7/8. bk.rev.; charts; illus.; pat.; tr.lit. circ. 18,712. (also avail. in microform from UMI; reprint service avail. from UMI) **Indexed:** A.S.& T.Ind., Art & Archaeol.Tech.Abstr., Chem.Abstr., Excerp.Med., Ind.Sci.Rev., Int.Packag.Abstr., Key to Econ.Sci., Lead Abstr., PROMT, World Surf.Coat., Zincscan. **Document type:** trade publication.
● Also available online. Vendor(s): University Microfilms International.
—BLDSC (5890.765000); CASDDS; Ei; SWETS; UMI. **CCC.**
   Formerly: Paint and Varnish Production (ISSN 0030-9478)
   Description: Covers current technical developments in the manufacture and use of paints and coatings, including processes, raw materials, equipment and products.

MODERN PAINT & COATINGS PAINT RED BOOK; directory of the paint and coatings industry. see *BUSINESS AND ECONOMICS — Trade And Industrial Directories*

NAVAL STORES REVIEW. see *PAPER AND PULP*

698   SZ
     CODEN: OBSUA7
OBERFLAECHEN WERKSTOFFE; internationale Fachzeitschrift fuer das gesamte Gebiet der Oberflaechentechnik und des Korrosionsschutzes von Metallen und anderen Werkstoffen. (Text in French, German) 1959. 11/yr. 85 SFr. (foreign 119 SFr.). (Schweizerische Galvanotechnische Gesellschaft) S H Z Fachverlag AG, Alte Landstr. 43, CH-8700 Kuesnacht, Switzerland. TEL 01-9108022. FAX 01-9105155. (Co-sponsor: Verband Galvano Betriebe der Schweiz) Ed. Helmut Tannenberger. adv.; bk.rev.; illus.; index. circ. 6,000. **Indexed:** Art & Archaeol.Tech.Abstr., Chem.Abstr., Excerp.Med., Met.Abstr., World Alum.Abstr., World Surf.Coat.
—CASDDS.
   Formerly (until 1992): Oberflaeche (ISSN 0048-1270)

667.6   US   ISSN 0884-3848
PAINT & COATINGS INDUSTRY. (Includes annual Raw Material & Equipment Directory & Buyers Guide) 1918. 11/yr. $44 (Canada $59.08; elsewhere $80). Business News Publishing Company, 755 W. Big Beaver Rd., Ste. 1000, Troy, MI 48084. TEL 313-362-3700. FAX 313-362-0317. (Subscr. to: Box 2600, Troy, MI 48007) Ed. Karen Wojcik Berner. adv. contact: Andrea Kropp. bk.rev.; illus.; pat.; stat.; tr.lit.; index. circ. 18,102. **Indexed:** Chem.Abstr. **Document type:** trade publication.
—BLDSC (6334.249900); Ei. **CCC.**
   Former titles (until 1985): Industry Section of Western Paint and Decorating; Decorative Products World; Paint and Decorating; Western Paint and Decorating; Western Paint Review (ISSN 0043-4027)
   Description: Serves manufacturers, suppliers, distributors in the paint and coatings field with industry news, technology and product coverage.

667.6 686   UK
PAINT AND INK INTERNATIONAL. q. £82.35($169.30) (foreign £105.80). Argus Business Media Ltd., Fuel and Metals Journals (Subsidiary of: Argus Press Group), Queensway House, 2 Queensway, Redhill, Surrey RH1 1QS, England. TEL 01737-768611. FAX 01737-761685. TELEX 948669 TOPJNL G. Ed. Sarah Thomas. **Indexed:** Intl.Polym.Sci.& Tech., RAPRA. **Document type:** trade publication.
   Description: Covers worldwide developments in the paint and printing ink industries, from raw materials to manufacturing processes, equipment, and applications.

667.6   UK   ISSN 0261-5746
TP934   CODEN: PTRNDJ
PAINT AND RESIN. 1931. 6/yr. £62 (foreign £82). Turret Group Plc., Turret House, 171 High St., Rickmansworth, Herts WD3 1SN, England. TEL 01923-777000. FAX 01923-771297. Ed. Norman Shepherd. adv.; bk.rev.; abstr.; bibl.; charts; illus.; stat.; index. **Indexed:** Art & Archaeol.Tech.Abstr., Br.Tech.Ind., C.I.S. Abstr., Cadscan, Chem.Abstr., Excerp.Med., Lead Abstr., World Surf.Coat., Zincscan. **Document type:** trade publication.
—BLDSC (6334.700000); CASDDS; Ei; SWETS.
   Former titles: Paint Manufacture and Resin News; Paint Manufacture (ISSN 0030-9508)

667.6 658   US   ISSN 1067-1110
PAINT DEALER. 1992. 11/yr. $25. 10097 Manchester Rd., Ste. 208, St. Louis, MO 63122-1828. TEL 314-984-0800; 800-984-0801. FAX 314-984-0866. E-mail: primecoat@aol.com; 75051.137@compuserve.com. Ed. Mike Matthews. adv.: B&W page $3600; trim 8 x 10 3/4; adv. contact: Chris Mugler. bk.rev. circ. 23,000. **Document type:** trade publication.
   Description: Covers product innovations, merchandising ideas, store management and industry news.

667.6   II   ISSN 0030-9540
TP934   CODEN: PIDABZ
PAINTINDIA. (Text in English) 1951. m. Rs.350($100) Colour Publications Pvt. Ltd., 126-A Dhurunadi, Off. Dr. Nariman Rd., Bombay 400 025, India. TEL 430-9318. TELEX 71242 CEPE IN. Ed. R.V. Raghavan. adv.; bk.rev.; abstr.; illus.; stat. circ. 5,096. (also avail. in microform from UMI; reprint service avail. from UMI) **Indexed:** Art & Archaeol.Tech.Abstr., Chem.Abstr., W.R.C.Inf., World Surf.Coat.
—BLDSC (6340.003000); CASDDS; UMI.

698   US
PAINTING AND DECORATING CRAFTSMAN MANUAL AND TEXTBOOK. irreg., 5th ed., 1975. $25 to non-members; members $15. Painting and Decorating Contractors of America, 3913 Old Lee Hwy., Ste. 33B, Fairfax, VA 22030. TEL 703-359-0826. FAX 703-359-2576. charts; illus.

698   US   ISSN 0735-9713
TT300
PAINTING AND WALLCOVERING CONTRACTOR. 1938. bi-m. $19.95. Finan Publishing Company, Inc., 8730 Big Bend Blvd., St. Louis, MO 63119. TEL 314-961-6644. FAX 314-961-4809. Ed. Jeffery Beckner; Pub. Thomas J. Finan IV. adv. contact: Kathie Gardner. stat.; circ. 31,000 (controlled). (also avail. in microform from UMI) **Indexed:** Corros.Abstr. **Document type:** trade publication.
—UMI.
   Former titles: P D C A Magazine; Professional Decorating and Coating Action (ISSN 0099-0310); P D C A 74 (ISSN 0038-8416); Spotlights.

667.6   UK   ISSN 0369-9420
TP934   CODEN: PGRTBC
PIGMENT AND RESIN TECHNOLOGY. 1936. 6/yr. £149($229) (effective 1996). M C B University Press Ltd., 60-62 Toller Ln., Bradford, W. Yorks BD8 9BY, England. TEL 01274-777700. FAX 01274-785200. adv.; bk.rev.; abstr.; charts; illus.; tr.lit.; index. circ. 1,419. (also avail. in microfilm from PMC) **Indexed:** Anal.Abstr., Br.Tech.Ind., Cadscan, Chem.Abstr., Excerp.Med., Graph.Arts Lit.Abstr., Intl.Polym.Sci.& Tech., Lead Abstr., PROMT, RAPRA, World Surf.Coat., Zincscan. **Document type:** trade publication.
—BLDSC (6500.145000); CASDDS; Ei; Faxon; SWETS.
   Formerly: Paint Technology (ISSN 0030-9524)

667.5   SP   ISSN 0031-9945
PINTORES. 1961. bi-m. 1200 ptas. Asociacion de Maestros Pintores de Barcelona, Diputacion 297, Pral., 08009 Barcelona, Spain. TEL 3-301-24-00. Ed. A. Palat Ullastres. adv.; illus.; stat. circ. 6,000.

PAINTS AND PROTECTIVE COATINGS

667.6   SP   ISSN 0031-9953
TT300   CODEN: PACIDY
PINTURAS Y ACABADOS INDUSTRIALES. 1958. 8/yr. 8800 ptas.($150) (effective 1993). Ediciones CEDEL, C. Mallorca 257, 08080 Barcelona, Spain. TEL 343-215-6039. FAX 343-215-6088. adv.; bk.rev.; bibl.; charts; illus.; tr.lit.; index. circ. 4,000. **Indexed:** Chem.Abstr., Ind.SST, World Surf.Coat. **Document type:** trade publication.
—BLDSC (6501.510000); CASDDS; Ei.

698   IT   CODEN: PIVEAY
PITTURE E VERNICI EUROPE. 1925. fortn. L.150000. G.B.P. Communications, Via Natale Battaglia 19, 20127 Milan, Italy. TEL 39-2-2828878. FAX 39-2-2610150. Ed. Gian Battista Pecere. adv.: color page L.2460000; trim 175 x 255. bk.rev.; abstr. circ. 5,000. **Indexed:** Art & Archaeol.Tech.Abstr., Biodet.Abstr., Chem.Abstr., Corros.Abstr., Intl.Polym.Sci.& Tech., RAPRA, World Surf.Coat.
—BLDSC (6506.000000); CASDDS.
Former titles: Pitture e Vernici (ISSN 0048-4245); (until 1945): Vernici (ISSN 0372-5634)

667.6   UK   ISSN 0078-7817
POLYMERS PAINT AND COLOUR YEAR BOOK. 1961. a. (issued in Oct.) £106.30($170.10) Argus Business Media Ltd., Fuel and Metals Journals (Subsidiary of: Argus Press Group), Queensway House, 2 Queensway, Redhill, Surrey RH1 1QS, England. TEL 01737-768611. FAX 01737-761685. TELEX 948669 TOPJNL G. Ed. Sarah Thomas. adv. **Document type:** directory.
—BLDSC (6547.744000).
Formerly: Paint, Oil Colour Year Book; Formerly (until 1973): Paint, Oil, Colour Year Book.
Description: Lists manufacturers of paint, printing ink, and raw materials used in the printing process.

667.6   UK   ISSN 0140-8445
POWDER COATINGS BULLETIN. 1978. m. £165($305) (effective 1996). The Royal Society of Chemistry, Thomas Graham House, Science Park, Milton Rd., Cambridge CB4 4WF, England. TEL 01223-420066. FAX 01223-423429. E-mail: rsc1@rsc.org. (Subscr. to: Turpin Distribution Services Ltd., Blackhorse Rd., Letchworth, Herts. SG6 1HN, England. TEL 01462-672555. FAX 01462-480947) Ed. Sid Harris. bk.rev.; charts; pat.; stat. (back issues avail.) **Document type:** bulletin.
—BLDSC (6571.750000).
Description: Covers all aspects of the powder coatings industry, including growth of the market, new product development, and company news.

698   US   ISSN 0032-9940
TS200   CODEN: PRFCAB
PRODUCTS FINISHING. 1936. m. $36 (foreign $60). Gardner Publications, Inc., 6600 Clough Pike, Cincinnati, OH 45244-4090. TEL 513-231-8020. FAX 513-231-2818. Ed. G. Thomas Robison. adv. contact: Donald Kline. bibl.; illus.; tr.lit. circ. 50,000. (also avail. in microform from UMI,PMC; reprint service avail.) **Indexed:** Cadscan, Chem.Abstr., Eng.Ind., Lead Abstr., Met.Abstr., World Alum.Abstr., World Surf.Coat., Zincscan. **Document type:** trade publication.
—BLDSC (6854.000000); CASDDS; Ei; Faxon; Genuine Article; SWETS; UMI. **CCC.**

698   US   ISSN 0478-4251
PRODUCTS FINISHING DIRECTORY. a. $10. Gardner Publications, Inc., 6600 Clough Pike, Cincinnati, OH 45244-4090. TEL 513-231-8020. FAX 513-231-2818. Ed. G. Thomas Robison. adv. contact: Donald Kline. circ. 30,000. **Document type:** directory, trade publication.

698 683   IT   ISSN 1120-9887
PROFESSIONAL.* 1987. 8/yr. L.80000. (Editoriale Tecnica Macchine) E T M, S.r.l, Via Principe Eugenio 3, 20155 Milan, Italy. TEL 39-2-48010095. FAX 39-2-48010011. adv.; B&W page L.1500000. circ. 12,000.
Description: Review for hardware and paint stores, wood-shop and do-it-yourself supermarkets.

698   US
PROFESSIONAL SPRAYING. q. free. Graco Inc., Box 1441, Minneapolis, MN 55440. TEL 612-623-6000. Ed. Mick Lee.

547 698   SZ   ISSN 0300-9440
CODEN: POGCAT
PROGRESS IN ORGANIC COATINGS; an international review journal. (Text in English, French and German) 1972. m. 1380 SFr.($1131) (effective 1996). Elsevier Science S.A., P.O. Box 564, CH-1001 Lausanne 1, Switzerland. TEL 41-21-3207381. FAX 41-21-3235444. TELEX 450620-ELSA-CH. (Subscr. in U.S. and Canada to: Elsevier Science Inc., Box 882, Madison Sq. Sta., New York, NY 10159. TEL 212-989-5800. FAX 212-633-3990) Ed. W. Funke. adv.; bk.rev.; charts; illus.; index. (tabloid format; also avail. in microform from UMI) **Indexed:** Chem.Abstr., Corros.Abstr., Curr.Cont., Eng.Ind., Intl.Polym.Sci.& Tech., Met.Abstr., Phys.Ber., RAPRA, Sci.Cit.Ind., World Alum.Abstr., World Surf.Coat. **Document type:** academic/scholarly publication.
—BLDSC (6872.200000); CASDDS; Ei; Faxon; Genuine Article; SWETS. **CCC.**
Description: Analyzes and publicizes the progress and current state of knowledge in the field of organic coatings and related materials.
Refereed Serial

698   FR   ISSN 0337-4149
QUI FABRIQUE ET FOURNIT QUOI. 1973. a. 200 F. C E P P Publications, 25, rue Dagorno, 75012 Paris, France. TEL 43-47-30-20. FAX 43-46-58-18.
Description: Directory for surface treatments in industry, paints and coatings.

667.6   GW   ISSN 0945-8409
RADCURELETTER. (Text in English) bi-m. DM.150($100) (European Association for the Advancement of Radiation Curing) Vincentz Verlag, Schiffgraben 43, 30175 Hannover, Germany. TEL 0511-9909832. FAX 0511-9909899. Ed. Dr. Lothar Vincentz. adv. contact: Frauke Haentsch. circ. 1,500. **Document type:** trade publication.
—BLDSC (7226.920200).

667.6   US   ISSN 0734-7200
HD9696.R35
REACTIVE CURE SYSTEMS: UV · IR · EB; (Year) buyers' guide. (Supplement annual.) 1980. a. $97 (disk $68); foreign $112 (disk $83). Captan Associates, Inc., Box 504, Brick, NJ 08723-0504. TEL 908-840-1244. FAX 908-840-1211. adv.; bk.rev. (also avail. in diskette format; back issues avail.) **Document type:** directory.
—BLDSC (7300.281800).
Description: Serves the purchasers of commercial radiation curable products and services and the manufacturing equipment used in radiation curing processing.

667   FI   ISSN 0780-086X
RUTER/COATING. Finnish edition: Ruutu (ISSN 0780-0851) (Text in Swedish) 1980. a. Tikkurila Oy, Kuninkaalantie 1, P.O. Box 53, FIN-01301 Vantaa, Finland. TEL 358-0-85-771. FAX 358-0-8577-6900. Ed. Tapio Kaar.

667   FI   ISSN 0780-0851
RUUTU. Swedish edition: Ruter (ISSN 0780-086X) 1980. a. Tikkurila Oy, Kuninkaalantie 1, P.O. Box 53, FIN-01301 Vantaa, Finland. TEL 358-0-85-771. FAX 358-0-8577-6900. Ed. Tapio Kaar.

698   US
S S P C BULLETIN. 1955. q. membership. Steel Structures Painting Council, 4516 Henry St., Ste. 301, Pittsburgh, PA 15213-3728. TEL 412-687-1113. FAX 412-687-1153. Ed. Janet Rex. circ. 6,500. **Document type:** bulletin, newsletter.
Formerly (until 1988): Steel Structures Painting Bulletin.
Description: Serves members by informing them of council initiatives in research, standards, and education.

698   US
S S P C LEAD PAINT BULLETIN. 1992. q. membership. Steel Structures Painting Council, 4516 Henry St., Ste. 301, Pittsburgh, PA 15213-3728. TEL 412-687-1113. FAX 412-687-1153. Ed. Janet Rex. circ. 13,500. **Document type:** bulletin.
Description: Reports on regulations, technology, practices, and other issues concerning industrial lead paint abatement.

SCAFFOLD INDUSTRY ASSOCIATION. NEWSLETTER. see *BUILDING AND CONSTRUCTION*

667.6   UK   ISSN 1350-4789
▼**SEALING TECHNOLOGY.** 1994. m. £272($433) (effective 1996). Elsevier Science Ltd., P.O. Box 800, Kidlington, Oxford OX5 1DX, England. TEL 44-1865-843000. FAX 44-1865-843010. E-mail: nlinfo-f@elsevier.nl; usinfo-f@elsevier.com; forinfo-kyf04035@niftyserve.or.jp; Site addr.: http://www.elsevier.nl/. (Subscr. in U.S. and Canada to: Elsevier Science, 660 White Plains Rd., Tarrytown, NY 10591-5153. TEL 914-524-9200. FAX 914-333-2444) Ed. P. Ray. (also avail. in microform from UMI; back issues avail.) **Document type:** newsletter.
—**CCC.**
Description: Covers new developments in seals, including innovative design, new materials, applications in all industries, environmental and standards issues.

382   II   ISSN 0304-8179
HD9769.L33
SHELLAC EXPORT PROMOTION COUNCIL. ANNUAL REPORT. (Text in English) a. Shellac Export Promotion Council, 14-1-B Ezra St., Calcutta 1, India. stat.

667.6   JA
SHIKIZAI KENKYU HAPPYOKAI KOEN YOSHISHU/PROCEEDINGS ON COLOUR MATERIAL RESEARCH. (Text in English, Japanese) 1970. a. Shikizai Kyokai - Japan Society of Colour Material, 9-12, Iwamotocho 2-chome, Chiyoda-ku, Tokyo 101, Japan. **Document type:** proceedings.

667.6   JA   ISSN 0010-180X
CODEN: SKYOAO
SHIKIZAI KYOKAISHI/JAPAN SOCIETY OF COLOUR MATERIAL. JOURNAL. Variant title: Colour Material. (Text in Japanese; summaries in English) 1927. m. 8500 Yen. Shikizai Kyokai, 9-12, Iwamotocho 2-chome, Chiyoda-ku, Tokyo 101, Japan. Ed. K. Veki. adv.; illus.; pat.; tr.lit.; index. **Indexed:** Chem.Abstr., INIS Atomind., JTA.
—BLDSC (4807.050000); CASDDS.

667.6   IT
▼**SUPERFICI OGGI.** 1994. 9/yr. L.120000 (foreign L.180000). Gruppo Editoriale Rossini, Via Cola di Rienzo 26, 20144 Milan, Italy. TEL 39-2-425201. FAX 39-2-425498. Ed. Aldo Fiacco. adv.: B&W page L.1900000, color page L.2800000. **Document type:** trade publication.

SURFACE COATING & RAW MATERIAL DIRECTORY. see *BUSINESS AND ECONOMICS — Trade And Industrial Directories*

667.6   UK
SURFACE COATING & RAW MATERIAL SPECIFIER. 1992. m. Industrial Trade Journals Ltd., Stakes House, Quebec Sq., Westerham, Kent TN16 1TD, England. TEL 0959-564212. FAX 0959-562325.

667.6   UK   ISSN 0954-3139
SURFACE COATINGS. 1987. irreg., vol.2, 1988. price varies. Elsevier Science Ltd., Books Division, P.O. Box 800, Kidlington, Oxford OX5 1DX, England. TEL 44-1865-843000. FAX 44-1865-843010. E-mail: nlinfo-f@elsevier.nl; usinfo-f@elsevier.com; forinfo-kyf04035@niftyserve.or.jp; Site addr.: http://www.elsevier.nl/. (Subscr. in U.S. and Canada to: Elsevier Science, 660 White Plains Rd., Tarrytown, NY 10591-5153. TEL 914-524-9200) Ed.Bd. (back issues avail.) **Document type:** monographic series.
—BLDSC (8547.785000).
Refereed Serial

667.6	AT	ISSN 0815-709X
		CODEN: SCAUE6

SURFACE COATINGS AUSTRALIA. 1964. 11/yr. Aus.$60 (foreign Aus.$80). Surface Coatings Association Australia Inc., 443 High St., Prahran, Vic. 3181, Australia. TEL 510-6238. FAX 529-6069. (Co-sponsor: Surface Coatings Associaiton New Zealand Inc. (NZ)) adv.: B&W page Aus.$580; color page Aus.$1140; trim 270 x 180; adv. contact: G. Goullet. bk.rev.; circ. 1,350 (controlled). **Indexed:** Aus.Sci.Ind., Chem.Abstr., Corros.Abstr., World Surf.Coat. **Document type:** trade publication.
—BLDSC (8547.793000); CASDDS; SWETS.
Formerly (until 1984): Australian O.C.C.A. Proceedings and News (ISSN 0045-0774)
Description: Covers association activities, news and technical papers of interest and relevance to the surface coatings industries of Australia and New Zealand.

667.9	UK	
TP934		CODEN: JOCCAB

SURFACE COATINGS INTERNATIONAL. 1918. m. £110($200) Oil & Colour Chemists' Association, Priory House, 967 Harrow Rd., Wembley, Mddx. HAO 2SF, England. FAX 0181-908-1219. TELEX 922670 OCCA G. Ed. P.T. Thuitral. adv.; bk.rev.; illus.; index. circ. 3,420. **Indexed:** Art & Archaeol.Tech.Abstr., BMT, Br.Tech.Ind., Cadscan, Chem.Abstr., Excerp.Med., Graph.Arts Lit.Abstr., Intl.Polym.Sci.& Tech., Lead Abstr., Met.Abstr., Print.Abstr., RAPRA, RICS, World Alum.Abstr., World Surf.Coat, Zincscan. **Document type:** trade publication.
—CASDDS; Ei; SWETS.
Formerly (until 1991): Oil and Colour Chemists' Association. Journal (ISSN 0030-1337).

667.6	UK	ISSN 0967-6767

SURFACE TECHNOLOGY INTERNATIONAL. 1992. q. Argus Business Media Ltd., Fuel and Metals Journals (Subsidiary of: Argus Press Group), Queensway House, 2 Queensway, Redhill, Surrey RH1 1QS, England. TEL 01737-768611. FAX 01737-760510. TELEX 948669 TOPJNL G. **Document type:** trade publication.

698	FR	ISSN 0585-9840
TS653.A1		CODEN: SUFPA2

SURFACES (PARIS); finition et protection. 8/yr. 420 F. (foreign 585 F.) (effective May 1995). Editions Ampere, Groupe C.E.P.P., 25, rue Dagorno, 75012 Paris, France. TEL 43-47-30-20. FAX 43-47-30-80. circ. 7,000. **Indexed:** Chem.Abstr., Met.Abstr., World Alum.Abstr., World Surf.Coat.
—BLDSC (8548.070000); CASDDS; Ei; SWETS. CCC.
Incorporates (in 1984): Email Metal.
Description: Surface treatments, coatings and painting in general industry.

667.6	SW	ISSN 0039-6516

SVENSK FAERGHANDEL; tapet - parfym. 1909. 8/yr. SEK 450. Sveriges Faerghandlares Riksfoerbund, Kungsgatan 19, S-105 61 Stockholm, Sweden. TEL 46-8-791-53-90. FAX 46-8-10-3126. Ed. Birgitta Nygren. adv.: B&W page SEK 5700, color page SEK 10900; trim 213 x 302; adv. contact: Roland Nordlander. bk.rev.; illus.; stat. circ. 1,200.
Formerly (until 1967): Svensk Faergteknisk Tidskrift.
Description: Publishes news and analyses of people, products and events in the paint, wallpaper and perfume trade market in Sweden.

667.6	GW	ISSN 0340-8167

TASCHENBUCH FUER LACKIERBETRIEBE (YEAR). 1943. a. DM.34.90. Vincentz Verlag, Schiffgraben 43, 30175 Hannover, Germany. TEL 0511-9909857. FAX 0511-9909899. (Subscr. to: Postfach 6247, 30062 Hannover, Germany) Ed. Dieter Ondratschek. circ. 7,000. **Document type:** trade publication.

667	FI	ISSN 1237-4113

▼**TIKKURILA COATINGS JOURNAL.** (Text in English) 1994. a. Tikkurila Oy, Kuninkaalantie 1, P.O. Box 53, FIN-01301 Vantaa, Finland. TEL 358-0-85-771. FAX 358-08577-6900. TELEX 121505. Ed. Tapio Kaar. circ. 15,000. (back issues avail.) **Document type:** trade publication.

TIKKURILAN VIESTI. see BUILDING AND CONSTRUCTION

TOLE WORLD; decorative painting projects & ideas. see ART

669 698	IT	

TRATTAMENTI E FINITURE;* rivista tecnica dei trattamenti, processi, finiture delle superfici. 1961. m. (8/yr.) L.70000 (foreign L.95000). E T M S.r.l., Via Principe Eugenio 3, 20155 Milan, Italy. TEL 02-48010095. FAX 02-48010011. adv.; bk.rev.; charts; illus.; tr.lit.; index. circ. 15,000. (back issues avail.) **Indexed:** Met.Abstr.
Formerly: Trattamenti e Finitura - Superfici (ISSN 0041-1833)
Description: Technical review concerning treatment processing, protection and finishing of metals as well as processes for treating the metal surface, finishing, protection and paintings.

667.6	NE	ISSN 0042-3904
		CODEN: VERFAL

VERFKRONIEK. 1928. 11/yr. fl.95. Vereniging van Verf- en Drukinktfabrikanten - Association of Paint and Ink Manufacturers in the Netherlands, c/o Mrs. J. van der Kley, Haagse Schouwweg 8F, Postbus 248, 2300 AE Leiden, Netherlands. TEL 31-71-318900. FAX 31-71-318159. adv.; bk.rev.; charts; illus.; stat. circ. 1,000. **Indexed:** Art & Archaeol.Tech.Abstr., C.I.S. Abstr., Chem.Abstr., Key to Econ.Sci., World Surf.Coat. **Document type:** trade publication.
—BLDSC (9156.000000); CASDDS; SWETS.

VERNICIATURA DEL LEGNO. see BUILDING AND CONSTRUCTION — Carpentry And Woodwork

VERNICIATURA E FINITURA DEI PLASTICI. see PLASTICS

698	IT	
		CODEN: RCLRA3

VERNICIATURA INDUSTRIALE. 1968. m. L.90000 (foreign L.160000). Rivista del Colore s.r.l., Via degli Imbriani 10, 20158 Milan, Italy. Ed. Dr. Danilo O. Malavolti. adv.; bk.rev.; abstr.; tr.lit.; index. circ. 3,000. **Indexed:** Chem.Abstr., World Surf.Coat.
—CASDDS.
Formerly: Revista del Colore (ISSN 0048-8348)

667.6		ISSN 0140-8798

WATERBORNE & HIGH SOLIDS COATINGS BULLETIN. 1978. m. £150. Paint Research Association, 8 Waldegrave Rd., Teddington, Middlesex TW11 8LD, England. TEL 081-977-4427. FAX 081-943-4705. bk.rev.; charts; pat.; stat. (back issues avail.) **Document type:** bulletin.

667.6	GW	

WELT DER FARBEN; das Branchen-Magazin. 1981. m. DM.135. R L - Press Renate Wittsack, Ostlandstr. 1, 50858 Cologne, Germany. TEL 02234-73488. FAX 02234-73598. Ed. Renate Wittsack. adv.: B&W page DM.2100, color page DM.2650; trim 250 x 175; adv. contact: Sabine Esener. circ. 1,250. **Document type:** trade publication.
Formerly (until 1993): Phaenomen Farbe.

PAINTS AND PROTECTIVE COATINGS — Abstracting, Bibliographies, Statistics

667.6	US	ISSN 0275-7036
		CODEN: CCIPDO

C A SELECTS. COATINGS, INKS, & RELATED PRODUCTS. s-w. $220 to non-members; members $65 (effective 1996). Chemical Abstracts Service (Subsidiary of: American Chemical Society), 2540 Olentangy River Rd., Box 3012, Columbus, OH 43210-0012. TEL 614-447-3600. FAX 614-447-3713. TELEX 6842086. **Document type:** abstracting/indexing.
Description: Covers the chemistry, chemical and physical properties, and analysis of decorative and protective coatings.

667.6	US	ISSN 0749-7296
		CODEN: CASCEM

C A SELECTS. CORROSION-INHIBITING COATINGS. s-w. $220 to non-members; members $65 (effective 1996). Chemical Abstracts Service (Subsidiary of: American Chemical Society), 2540 Olentangy River Rd., Box 3012, Columbus, OH 43210-0012. TEL 614-447-3600. FAX 614-447-3713. TELEX 6842086. **Document type:** abstracting/indexing.
Description: Covers the formulation and application of coatings intended to prevent corrosion of metallic surfaces.

667.6	US	ISSN 0734-8762
		CODEN: CAPADY

C A SELECTS. PAINT ADDITIVES. s-w. $220 to non-members; members $65 (effective 1996). Chemical Abstracts Service (Subsidiary of: American Chemical Society), 2540 Olentangy River Rd., Box 3012, Columbus, OH 43210-0012. TEL 614-447-3600. FAX 614-447-3713. TELEX 6842086. **Document type:** abstracting/indexing.
Description: Covers materials added to paints (pigmented coatings) other than the basic polymeric binder, solvents, pigments.

667	US	ISSN 0749-7369
		CODEN: CSWCEW

C A SELECTS. WATER-BASED COATINGS. s-w. $220 to non-members; members $65 (effective 1996). Chemical Abstracts Service (Subsidiary of: American Chemical Society), 2540 Olentangy River Rd., Box 3012, Columbus, OH 43210-0012. TEL 614-447-3600. FAX 614-447-3713. TELEX 6842086. **Document type:** abstracting/indexing.
Description: Covers formulation, application, and performance of water-borne coatings, water-soluble coatings, latex coatings, aqueous coatings.

C P I DIGEST; key to world literature serving the coatings, plastics, fibers, adhesives, and related industries. (Chemical Process Industries) see PLASTICS — Abstracting, Bibliographies, Statistics

MARO POLYMER NOTES. see PLASTICS — Abstracting, Bibliographies, Statistics

667.6 016	UK	ISSN 0144-4425

PAINT TITLES. 1984. w. £440. Paint Research Association, 8 Waldegreave Rd., Teddington, Middx TW11 8LD, England. TEL 081-977-4427. FAX 081-943-4705. Ed. S.C. Haworth. bibl. circ. 300. **Indexed:** Curr.Cont. **Document type:** abstracting/indexing.
—UMI. **CCC.**
Refereed Serial

REFERATIVNYI ZHURNAL. KORROZIYA I ZASHCHITA OT KORROZII. see METALLURGY — Abstracting, Bibliographies, Statistics

667.6 016	RU	ISSN 0202-8697

SIGNAL'NAYA INFORMATSIYA. LAKI - KRASKI - ORGANICHESKIE POKRYTIYA. 1970. s-m. 15.20 Rub. Vsesoyuznyi Institut Nauchno-Tekhnicheskoi Informatsii (VINITI), Baltiiskaya ul. 14, Moscow A-219, Russia. (Subscr. to: Mezhdunarodnaya Kniga, Dimitrova ul. 39, 113095 Moscow, Russia) **Document type:** abstracting/indexing.

667.6 011	US	

TECHNICAL RESOURCES ON COATING PROCESSES. a. free. Society of Manufacturing Engineers, Association for Finishing Processes, One SME Dr., Box 930, Dearborn, MI 48121. TEL 313-271-1500. FAX 313-240-8255. TELEX 297742 SME UR (VIA RCA). **Document type:** bibliography.

667.6 016	UK	ISSN 0043-9088
Z7914.P15		

WORLD SURFACE COATING ABSTRACTS. 1960. 13/yr. £940. Paint Research Association, 8 Waldegreave Rd., Teddington, Middx TW11 8LD, England. TEL 081-977-4427. FAX 081-943-4705. Ed. N. Morgan. (also avail. in magnetic tape) **Indexed:** Abstr.Bull.Inst.Pap.Chem., Anal.Abstr., BMT, Curr.Cont., Int.Packag.Abstr. **Document type:** abstracting/indexing.
●Also available online. Vendor(s): Orbit Search Service (WSCA).
—BLDSC (9360.043000); UMI. **CCC.**
Description: Contains abstracts on all aspects of paints, from raw materials to formulations, and their uses.
Refereed Serial

PALEONTOLOGY

A M U NEWS. (American Malacological Union, Inc.) see BIOLOGY — Zoology

ACTA PALAEOBOTANICA. see BIOLOGY — Botany

PALEONTOLOGY

560   PL   ISSN 0567-7920
QE755.P7   CODEN: APGPAC
ACTA PALAEONTOLOGICA POLONICA. (Text in English; summaries in Polish) 1956. q. $40. Polska Akademia Nauk, Instytut Paleobiologii, Al. Zwirki i Wigury 93, 02-089 Warsaw. FAX 48-22-221652. E-mail: paleo asp.biogeo.uw.edu.pl. Ed. Jerzy Dzik. bk.rev.; bibl.; illus. circ. 710. **Indexed:** Biol.Abstr., Deep Sea Res.& Oceanogr.Abstr., GeoRef., Petrol.Abstr., Vet.Bull. **Document type:** academic/scholarly publication.
—BLDSC (0642.500000); UnCover.

ADVANCES IN ARCHAEOLOGICAL AND MUSEUM SCIENCE. see *ARCHAEOLOGY*

560   AT   ISSN 0311-5518
QE758.A1   CODEN: ALCHDB
ALCHERINGA. 1975. s-a. Aus.$65 to individuals; institutions Aus.$95. Geological Society of Australia, Association of Australasian Palaeontologists, 301 George St., Sydney, N.S.W. 2000, Australia. FAX 61-2-290-2198. Ed. J.W. Pickett. bk.rev. circ. 600. **Indexed:** Curr.Cont., Geo.Abstr., Geol.Abstr., GeoRef., Petrol.Abstr. **Document type:** newsletter.
—BLDSC (0786.752000); Genuine Article; PADDS; UnCover. CCC.

ALTENBURGER NATURWISSENSCHAFTLICHE FORSCHUNGEN. see *BIOLOGY*

560   AG   ISSN 0002-7014
QE752.A7   CODEN: AMGHB2
AMEGHINIANA. (Text in English and Spanish; summaries in English) 1957. 4/yr. $55 to individuals (foreign $60); institutions $60 (foreign $70) (effective 1995). Asociacion Paleontologica Argentina, Maipu 645, 1r piso, 1006 Buenos Aires, Argentina. TEL 54-1-3222820. FAX 54-1-3267463. Ed. Beatriz Aguirre-Urreta. adv.: page $1500. bk.rev.; bibl.; index; circ. 800 (paid). (reprint service avail.) **Indexed:** AESIS, Biol.Abstr., Geo.Abstr., Geol.Abstr., GeoRef. **Document type:** academic/scholarly publication.
—CCC.
Description: Publishes papers on all aspects of palaeontology and related areas, such as biostratigraphy and palaeobiology.

551   US   ISSN 0160-8843
       CODEN: ASPLCY
AMERICAN ASSOCIATION OF STRATIGRAPHIC PALYNOLOGISTS. CONTRIBUTIONS SERIES. irreg., no.30, 1995. American Association of Stratigraphic Palynologists Foundation, c/o Vaughn M. Bryant, Jr., Palynology Laboratory, Anthropology Bldg., Texas A & M University, College Station, TX 77843-4352. TEL 409-845-5242. FAX 409-845-4070. **Indexed:** Biol.Abstr., GeoRef.
—BLDSC (3461.370000); SWETS.
Refereed Serial

AMERICAN ASSOCIATION OF STRATIGRAPHIC PALYNOLOGISTS. NEWSLETTER. see *EARTH SCIENCES — Geology*

560   US   ISSN 0192-737X
AMERICAN ASSOCIATION OF STRATIGRAPHIC PALYNOLOGISTS FOUNDATION. FIELD TRIP GUIDE. 1971. a. American Association of Stratigraphic Palynologists Foundation, c/o Vaughn M. Bryant, Jr., Palynology Laboratory, Anthropology Bldg., Texas A & M University, College Station, TX 77843-4352. TEL 409-845-5242. FAX 409-845-4070.

560   US   ISSN 1066-8772
QE701
AMERICAN PALEONTOLOGIST; a newsletter of paleontology. 1992. q. $20 membership. Paleontological Research Institution, 1259 Trumansburg Rd., Ithaca, NY 14850. Ed. Warren D. Allmon. bk.rev. **Document type:** newsletter.
—BLDSC (0849.300000).
Description: Publishes news, essays, features and announcements of interest to paleontologists at all levels and every specialty.

ANCIENT BIOMOLECULES. see *BIOLOGY — Biological Chemistry*

560   FR   ISSN 0753-3969
ANNALES DE PALEONTOLOGIE (VERT - INVERT). (Text in French; summaries in English) 1906. q. 1702 F. (foreign 1937 F.) (effective 1996). Masson - Periodiques, Villa Laromiguiere, 75005 Paris, France. TEL 1-40-46-62-00. FAX 1-40-46-62-01. Ed. Ph. Taquet. illus. circ. 430. (also avail. in microform from UMI; reprint service avail. from ISI) **Indexed:** Biol.Abstr., Br.Geol.Lit. (1972-), Deep Sea Res.& Oceanogr.Abstr., Geol.Abstr., GeoRef. **Document type:** academic/scholarly publication.
—Faxon; UMI; UnCover. CCC.
Formed by the merger of: Annales de Paleontologie: Vertebres (ISSN 0570-1627); Annales de Paleontologie: Invertebres (ISSN 0570-1619); Which superseded in part: Annales de Paleontologie (ISSN 0003-4142)
Description: Contains original articles on paleobotany, paleozoology, and human paleontology.

560 572   XR   ISSN 0003-5572
GN4   CODEN: ATHRAH
ANTHROPOS; studie z oboru anthropologie, paleoethnologie, paleontologie a kvarterni geologie. (Text in Czech and German) 1958. irreg., no.25, 1989. price varies. Moravske Zemske Muzeum, Zelny trh 6, 659 37 Brno, Czech Republic. TEL 42-5-22241. FAX 42-5-25279. Ed. Jan Jelinek. **Indexed:** CERDIC, Curr.Cont.Africa, E.I., Rel.Ind.One. **Document type:** monographic series.
—UnCover.

560   RM
▼**APLICATIILE IN ARHEOLOGIE.** (Text in Rumanian; summaries in English, French) 1994. a. Muzeul National de Istorie a Romaniei, Calea Victoriei, 12, Bucharest, Rumania. TEL 614-90-78. **Document type:** academic/scholarly publication.

ARCHAEOZOOLOGIA; revue international d'archeozoologie. see *ARCHAEOLOGY*

ARGENTINA. MUSEO PROVINCIAL DE CIENCIAS NATURALES. COMUNICACIONES. NUEVA SERIE. see *BIOLOGY*

ARKEOMETRI SONUCLARI TOPLANTISI. see *ARCHAEOLOGY*

500   AT   ISSN 0810-8889
ASSOCIATION OF AUSTRALASIAN PALAEONTOLOGISTS. MEMOIRS. 1983. irreg. price varies. Association of Australasian Palaeontologists, c/o Dr. P.A. Jell, Ed., Queensland Museum, P.O. Box 3300, S. Brisbane, Qld. 4101, Australia. TEL 61-7-840-7664. FAX 61-7-846-1918. (back issues avail.) **Document type:** academic/scholarly publication, monographic series.
—BLDSC (5577.283000).

560 551   GW   ISSN 0077-2070
QE701   CODEN: BSPGBT
BAYERISCHE STAATSSAMMLUNG FUER PALAEONTOLOGIE UND HISTORISCHE GEOLOGIE. MITTEILUNGEN. (Text and summaries in English and German) 1961. a. DM.68. Bayerische Staatssammlung fuer Palaeontologie und Historische Geologie, Richard-Wagner-Str. 10, 80333 Munich, Germany. TEL 089-5203361. FAX 089-5203276. (Dist. by: Gerhard Trenkle, Joerg-Toemlinger-Str. 2, 82152 Planegg, Germany) Ed. Dietrich Herm. **Indexed:** Biol.Abstr. **Document type:** proceedings.

560   AU   ISSN 1017-5563
QE755.A8   CODEN: BPOEDX
BEITRAEGE ZUR PALAEONTOLOGIE. (Text and summaries in English, German) 1976. a. S.600. Institut fuer Palaeontologie, Universitaetsstr. 7, A-1010 Vienna, Austria. TEL 01-401032494. FAX 01-4020533. E-mail: gwi@pal.univie.ac.at. Ed. Gerhard Withalm. circ. 200. (back issues avail.) **Indexed:** Biol.Abstr. **Document type:** academic/scholarly publication.
Formerly (until 1993): Beitraege zur Palaeontologie von Oesterreich.

560   UK   ISSN 0969-1111
BIBLIOGRAPHY OF EUROPEAN PALAEOBOTANY & PALYNOLOGY. 1976. biennial. £5. National Museum of Wales, Department of Botany, Cathays Park, Cardiff CF1 3NP, Wales. TEL 01222-397951. FAX 01222-239829. Ed.Bd. bibl. circ. 125. **Indexed:** Biol.Abstr. **Document type:** bibliography.
Formerly (until 1990): Report on British Palaeobotany and Palynology (ISSN 0266-4755)
Description: Reports on work in progress, publications.

566   US   ISSN 0272-8869
Z6033.V45
BIBLIOGRAPHY OF FOSSIL VERTEBRATES. 1902. a. $135. Society of Vertebrate Paleontology, W. 436 Nebraska Hall, University of Nebraska, Lincoln, NE 68588-0542. TEL 402-472-4604. FAX 402-472-8949. **Indexed:** GeoRef. **Document type:** bibliography.

BOREAS; an international journal of quaternary research. see *EARTH SCIENCES — Geology*

BRIMLEYANA; the zoological journal of the southeastern United States. see *BIOLOGY — Zoology*

BUDOWA GEOLOGICZNA POLSKI. see *EARTH SCIENCES — Geology*

BULLETIN SCIENTIFIQUE DE BOURGOGNE. see *SCIENCES: COMPREHENSIVE WORKS*

560   US   ISSN 0007-5779
       CODEN: BAPLAJ
BULLETINS OF AMERICAN PALEONTOLOGY. 1895. 2/yr. $125 (foreign $130). Paleontological Research Institution, 1259 Trumansburg Rd., Ithaca, NY 14850-1398. TEL 607-273-6623. Ed. Warren D. Allmon. (reprint service avail. from KTO) **Indexed:** Biol.Abstr., Geol.Abstr., GeoRef. **Document type:** academic/scholarly publication, monographic series.
—BLDSC (2827.750000); Faxon; PADDS; UnCover.
Refereed Serial

560   FR   ISSN 0068-5054
QE719
CAHIERS DE MICROPALEONTOLOGIE. 1965. q. (Ecole Pratique des Hautes Etudes, Laboratoire de Micropaleontologie) C N R S Editions, 20-22 rue St. Amand, 75015 Paris, France. TEL 45-33-16-00. FAX 45-33-92-13. TELEX 200 356 F. adv.; bk.rev.; index. circ. 1,500. **Indexed:** Br.Geol.Lit., Geo.Abstr., GeoRef. **Document type:** academic/scholarly publication.
—BLDSC (2949.810000). CCC.

560 572   FR   ISSN 0293-1176
CAHIERS DE PALEOANTHROPOLOGIE. a. price varies. (Centre National de la Recherche Scientifique) C N R S Editions, 20-22 rue St. Amand, 75015 Paris, France. TEL 45-33-16-00. FAX 45-33-92-13. TELEX 200 356 F. adv.; bk.rev.; index; circ. 1,250 (controlled). **Document type:** academic/scholarly publication.

560   FR   ISSN 0766-0502
CAHIERS DE PALEONTOLOGIE. a. price varies. (Centre National de Recherche Scientifique) C N R S Editions, 20-22 rue St. Amand, 75015 Paris, France. TEL 45-33-16-00. FAX 45-33-92-13. TELEX 200 356 F. adv.; bk.rev.; index; circ. 1,500 (controlled). **Document type:** academic/scholarly publication.

560   FR   ISSN 0298-248X
CAHIERS DE PALEONTOLOGIE EST-AFRICAINE. a. price varies. (Centre National de la Recherche Scientifique) C N R S Editions, 20-22 rue St. Amand, 75015 Paris, France. TEL 45-33-16-00. FAX 45-33-92-13. TELEX 200 356 F. adv.; bk.rev.; index; circ. 1,500 (controlled). **Document type:** academic/scholarly publication.

CARNEGIE MUSEUM OF NATURAL HISTORY. ANNALS. see *SCIENCES: COMPREHENSIVE WORKS*

CARNEGIE MUSEUM OF NATURAL HISTORY. BULLETIN. see *SCIENCES: COMPREHENSIVE WORKS*

CENTRAL TEXAS ARCHEOLOGIST. see *ARCHAEOLOGY*

CEPHALOPOD NEWSLETTER. see *BIOLOGY — Zoology*

CHRONOLOGY & CATASTROPHISM REVIEW. see *EARTH SCIENCES — Geology*

COLLANA DI STUDI PALEONTOLOGICI. see *ANTHROPOLOGY*

560   SP   ISSN 0210-7236
       CODEN: CLPAB7
COLOQUIOS DE PALEONTOLOGIA. 1964. a. 1500 ptas. Universidad Complutense de Madrid, Facultad de Geologia, Departamento de Paleontologia, Ciudad Universitaria, 28040 Madrid, Spain.

COLORADO SCHOOL OF MINES. PROFESSIONAL CONTRIBUTIONS. see *MINES AND MINING INDUSTRY*

PALEONTOLOGY

CONTRIBUTIONS IN BIOLOGY AND GEOLOGY. see *BIOLOGY*

560 551 NE ISSN 0165-280X
CONTRIBUTIONS TO TERTIARY AND QUATERNARY GEOLOGY. vol.15, 1976. a., vol.31, 1994. fl.90. Backhuys Publishers - Universal Book Services, P.O. Box 321, 2300 AH Leiden, Netherlands. TEL 31-71-170208. FAX 31-71-171856. (back issues avail.) **Indexed:** Zoo.Rec. **Document type:** monographic series.
—UnCover.
Description: Focuses on paleontology and stratigraphy in Northwestern Europe.

CURRENT RESEARCH IN THE PLEISTOCENE. see *ARCHAEOLOGY*

563 US ISSN 0070-2242
CODEN: SPCFAO
CUSHMAN FOUNDATION FOR FORAMINIFERAL RESEARCH. SPECIAL PUBLICATION. 1952. irreg., latest no.24. price varies. Cushman Foundation for Foraminiferal Research, Invertebrate Paleontology, Museum of Comparative Zoology, Harvard University, MA 02138. Ed. Stephen J. Culver. circ. 600. **Indexed:** Biol.Abstr., Deep Sea Res.& Oceanogr.Abstr., GeoRef. **Document type:** academic/scholarly publication.
—UnCover.

560 591 US ISSN 0886-3806
CYPRIS; international ostracoda newsletter. 1983. a. membership. International Research Group on Ostracoda, c/o Elisabeth M. Brouwers, Ed., U.S. Geological Survey, Federal Center, MS 919, Denver, CO 80225. TEL 303-236-5667. FAX 303-236-5690. bibl. circ. 400. **Document type:** newsletter.
Description: To improve international contacts between ostracode workers.

560 551.7 NE ISSN 0920-5446
CODEN: DPSTEJ
DEVELOPMENTS IN PALAEONTOLOGY AND STRATIGRAPHY. 1975. irreg., vol.13, 1990. Elsevier Science B.V., Books Division, P.O. Box 211, 1000 AE Amsterdam, Netherlands. TEL 31-20-4853911. FAX 31-20-4853705. TELEX 18582 ESPA NL. E-mail: nlinfo-f@elsevier.nl; usinfo-f@elsevier.com; forinfo-kyf04035@niftyserve.or.jp; Site addr.: http://www.elsevier.nl/. (Subscr. in U.S. and Canada to: Elsevier Science Inc., Box 882, Madison Sq. Sta., New York, NY 10159. TEL 212-989-5800) (back issues avail.) **Document type:** monographic series.
—CASDDS.
Refereed Serial

DINO TIMES. see *CHILDREN AND YOUTH — For*

560 US
DINOSAUR REPORT. 1992. q. $25 membership. Dinosaur Society, 200 Carleton Ave., East Islip, NY 11730. TEL 516-277-7855. Ed. Joseph Ramirez. **Document type:** bulletin.
Description: Bulletin of current findings, scientific policy, and other dinosaur-related news of interest to both general and scholarly audiences.

DISTRICT MEMOIR. see *EARTH SCIENCES — Geology*

560 551 JA ISSN 0912-0823
DOJIN/ASSOCIATION OF JAPANESE CAVERS. JOURNAL. (Text in Japanese) 1978. irreg. Nihon Dokutsu Kyokai - Association of Japanese Cavers, Akiyoshidai Kagaku Hakubutsukan, Akiyoshi, Shuhocho, Mine-gun, Yamaguchi-ken 754-05, Japan.

DORTMUNDER BEITRAEGE ZUR LANDESKUNDE. see *BIOLOGY*

EHIME DAIGAKU KIYO. SHIZEN KAGAKU: D SHIRIZU, CHIGAKU/EHIME UNIVERSITY. MEMOIRS. NATURAL SCIENCE: SERIES D, EARTH SCIENCES. see *EARTH SCIENCES — Geology*

560 GW ISSN 0424-7116
QE696 CODEN: EZGWAB
EISZEITALTER UND GEGENWART. 1951. a. $69 (effective 1996). (Deutsche Quartaervereinigung) E. Schweizerbart'sche Verlagsbuchhandlung, Johannesstr. 3a, 70176 Stuttgart, Germany. TEL 0711-625001. FAX 0711-625005. Ed. J. Klostermann. **Indexed:** Anthropol.Lit., Geo.Abstr., Geol.Abstr. **Document type:** academic/scholarly publication.
—CCC.

ERDGESCHICHTE MITTELEUROPAEISCHER REGIONEN. see *EARTH SCIENCES — Geology*

560 GW ISSN 0932-4739
QH274 CODEN: EJPREZ
EUROPEAN JOURNAL OF PROTISTOLOGY. (Text in English, French) 1965. q. DM.568 (foreign DM.574). (Centre National de la Recherche Scientifique, FR) Gustav Fischer Verlag, Wollgrasweg 49, 70599 Stuttgart, Germany. TEL 0711-458030. FAX 0711-4580334. TELEX 7111488-FIBUCH. (Subscr. to: Postfach 720143, 70577 Stuttgart, Germany; U.S. subscr. to: V C H Publishers, Inc., 303 N.W. 12th Ave., Deerfield Beach, FL 33442-1788) Ed.Bd. abstr.; bibl.; charts; illus. circ. 450. **Indexed:** Abstr.Hyg., Biol.Abstr., Chem.Abstr., Curr.Adv.Ecol.Sci., Curr.Cont., Deep Sea Res.& Oceanogr.Abstr., Helminthol.Abstr., Ind.Vet., Protozool.Abstr., Sel.Water Res.Abstr., Soils & Fert., Trop.Dis.Bull., Vet.Bull. **Document type:** academic/scholarly publication.
—BLDSC (3829.737600); CASDDS; Faxon; Genuine Article; SWETS; UnCover. **CCC.**
Formerly: Protistologica (ISSN 0033-1821)

F A C E N A. (Facultad de Ciencias Exactas y Naturales y Agrimensura) see *BIOGRAPHY*

FACIES. see *EARTH SCIENCES*

560 UK
FIELD GUIDE TO FOSSILS. 1983. irreg., no.6, 1994. Palaeontological Association, c/o Lesley Cherns, Dept. of Earth Sciences, University of Wales, P.O. Box 914, Cardiff CF1 3YE, Wales. TEL 01222-874338. (back issues avail.) **Document type:** bulletin.
Refereed Serial

560 PL ISSN 0015-573X
QE696 CODEN: FOQUAN
FOLIA QUATERNARIA. (Text in English, German) 1960. irreg., no.61-62, 1992. price varies. Polska Akademia Nauk, Oddzial w Krakowie, Ul. Slawkowska 17, 31-016 Krakow, Poland. TEL 48-12-224853. FAX 48-12-222791. Ed. Kazimierz Kowalski. **Indexed:** Biol.Abstr., Geo.Abstr., GeoRef., NAA. **Document type:** monographic series.
—BLDSC (3973.700000).
Description: Paleogeography of the Quaternary, mainly of Poland. Papers concern geomorphology, stratigraphy, paleobotany and paleozoology, archaeology of Quaternary sediments.

560 GW ISSN 0175-5021
FOSSILIEN; Zeitschrift fuer Sammler und Hobbypalaeontologen. 1984. bi-m. DM.88.80 (foreign DM.93). Goldschneck Verlag, Postfach 1265, 71399 Korb, Germany. TEL 07151-660119. FAX 07151-660778. Ed. Werner Karl Weidert. adv.; bk.rev. circ. 3,000. (back issues avail.) **Document type:** consumer publication.
Description: For collectors and amateur fossil hunters.

560 JA ISSN 0022-9202
QE701 CODEN: KASKAS
FOSSILS/KASEKI. (Text in Japanese) 1960. s-a. 2300 Yen. Paleontological Society of Japan - Nihon Koseibutsu Gakkai, c/o Business Center for Academic Societies, 16-9 Honkomagome 5-chome, Bunkyo-ku, Tokyo 113, Japan. Ed.Bd. adv.; bk.rev. circ. 400. **Indexed:** Biol.Abstr., GeoRef., Jap.Per.Ind.

560 NO ISSN 0300-9491
QE711.2 CODEN: FOSTDX
FOSSILS AND STRATA; a monograph series in palaeontology and biostratigraphy. (Text in English) 1972. irreg. price varies (effective 1996). Scandinavian University Press, P. O. Box 2959 Toeyen, N-0608 Oslo, Norway. TEL 47-22-57-54-00. FAX 47-22-57-53-53. (U.S. address: Scandinavian University Press, 200 Meacham Ave., Elmont, NY 11003. TEL 516-352-7300) Ed. Stefan Bengtson. (back issues avail.) **Indexed:** Biol.Abstr., Br.Geol.Lit. **Document type:** monographic series.
—BLDSC (4024.380000).

FRAGMENTA MINERALOGICA ET PALEONTOLOGICA. see *MINES AND MINING INDUSTRY*

560.17 FR ISSN 0016-6995
CODEN: GEBSAJ
GEOBIOS; paleontology, stratigraphy, paleoecology. (Text and summaries in English, French) 1968. bi-m. 750 F. in Europe; elsewhere 850 F.) (effective 1996). (Association Eurolypal) Universite de Lyon I, Centre des Sciences de la Terre, 43 bd. du 11 Novembre, 69622 Villeurbanne, France. TEL 72-44-84-87. FAX 72-44-83-82. Ed. P. Racheboeuf. adv.; bk.rev.; index. circ. 850. **Indexed:** Biol.Abstr., Bull.Signal., Curr.Cont., E&P Hlth. (1993-), Ecol.Abstr., Gas Process.& Ppl. (1993-), Geo.Abstr., Geo.Abstr., Helminthol.Abstr., Off.Tech. (1993-), Petrol.Abstr. (1981-), SSCI. **Document type:** bulletin, monographic series.
—BLDSC (4116.902000); Faxon; Genuine Article; PADDS; UnCover.

GEOLOGICA ET PALAEONTOLOGICA. see *EARTH SCIENCES — Geology*

560 XO ISSN 0139-7435
QE755.C95
GEOLOGICKY USTAV DIONYZA STURA. ZAPADNE KARPATY. SERIA PALEONOTOLOGIA. 1974. irreg. Geologicky Ustav Dionyza Stura, Mlynska Dolina 1, 817 04 Bratislava, Slovakia.
—BLDSC (9426.535000).
Supersedes in part (in 1974): Geologicky Ustav Dionyza Stura (ISSN 0036-5262); Which was formerly (until 1964): Geologicky Ustav Dionyza Stura. Geologicke Prace (ISSN 0431-218X); (1941-1952): Statny Geologicky Ustav. Prace (ISSN 0370-1891)

GEOLOGISCHE ABHANDLUNGEN HESSEN. see *EARTH SCIENCES — Geology*

GEOLOGISCHE BUNDESANSTALT. JAHRBUCH. see *EARTH SCIENCES — Geology*

GEOLOGISCHES JAHRBUCH. REIHE A: ALLGEMEINE UND REGIONALE GEOLOGIE B.R. DEUTSCHLAND UND NACHBARGEBIETE, TEKTONIK, STRATIGRAPHIE, PALAEONTOLOGIE. see *EARTH SCIENCES — Geology*

GEOLOGISCHES JAHRBUCH HESSEN. see *EARTH SCIENCES — Geology*

GEOLOGISCHES LANDESAMT BADEN-WUERTTEMBERG. ABHANDLUNGEN. see *EARTH SCIENCES*

GEOLOGISCHES LANDESAMT BADEN-WUERTTEMBERG. JAHRESHEFTE. see *EARTH SCIENCES*

561.05 II ISSN 0376-5156
QE901 CODEN: GPHTAR
GEOPHYTOLOGY; a journal of palaeobotany and allied sciences. (Text in English) 1971. s-a. Rs.800($100) Palaeobotanical Society, 53 University Rd., Lucknow 7, India. TEL 0522-74291. FAX 0522-246169. Ed. Suresh C. Srivastava. bk.rev.; illus. circ. 325. **Indexed:** AESIS, Apic.Abstr., Biol.Abstr., Soils & Fert. **Document type:** academic/scholarly publication.
—Faxon.
Refereed Serial

DER GESCHIEBESAMMLER. see *EARTH SCIENCES — Geology*

GESELLSCHAFT DER GEOLOGIE- UND BERGBAUSTUDENTEN. MITTEILUNGEN. see *EARTH SCIENCES — Geology*

GLACIOLOGY AND QUATERNARY GEOLOGY. see *EARTH SCIENCES — Geology*

GORTANIA; atti del Museo Friulano di Storia Naturale. see *EARTH SCIENCES*

GROENLANDS GEOLOGISKE UNDERSOEGELSE. BULLETIN/GEOLOGICAL SURVEY OF GREENLAND. BULLETIN. see *EARTH SCIENCES — Geology*

GROENLANDS GEOLOGISKE UNDERSOEGELSE. RAPPORT. see *EARTH SCIENCES — Geology*

566 CC ISSN 1000-3118
GUJIZHUI DONGWU XUEBAO/VERTEBRATA PALASIATICA. (Text in Chinese; summaries in English) 1959. q. $91.60. (Zhongguo Kexueyuan, Gujizhui Dongwu yu Gurenlei Yanjiusuo - Academia Sinica, Institute of Vertebrata Palasiatica) Science Press, Marketing and Sales Department, 16 Donghuangchenggen North St., Beijing 100717, People's Republic of China. TEL 4010642. FAX 4019810. adv. circ. 10,000. **Indexed:** Anthropol.Lit. **Document type:** academic/scholarly publication.
—BLDSC (9216.500000).
Description: Publishes research papers and brief notes on vertebrate paleontology, especially on vertebrates found in Asia.
Refereed Serial

560 CC ISSN 1001-4306
GUSHENGWU XUE WENZHAI/PALAEONTOLOGICAL ABSTRACTS. (Text in Chinese) 1986. q. $20. Zhongguo Kexueyuan, Nanjing Dizhi Gushengwu-suo - Chinese Academy of Sciences, Nanjing Institute of Geology and Palaeontology, 39 Beijing Donglu, Nanjing, Jiangsu 210008, People's Republic of China. TEL 86-25-6637537. FAX 86-25-3357026. TELEX 342301 NJIGP CN. Ed. Zhang Wentang. **Document type:** academic/scholarly publication.

560 CC ISSN 0001-6616
QE701 CODEN: KSWHAT
GUSHENGWU XUEBAO/ACTA PALAEONTOLOGICA SINICA. (Text in Chinese; summaries in English) 1950. bi-m. $87.60. (Zhongguo Kexueyuan, Nanjing Dizhi Gushengwu-suo) Science Press, Marketing and Sales Department, 16 Donghuangchenggen North St., Beijing 100717, People's Republic of China. TEL 4010642. FAX 4019810. adv.; bk.rev. circ. 7,000. **Indexed:** Biol.Abstr., Curr.Adv.Ecol.Sci., GeoRef. **Document type:** academic/scholarly publication.
—BLDSC (0643.000000); UnCover.
Description: Contains theses on paleontology, academic discussions, and comments. Introduces new methodology and techniques.
Refereed Serial

574 572 US ISSN 0891-2963
QE701 CODEN: HIBIEW
HISTORICAL BIOLOGY; an international journal of paleobiology. 1988. 8/yr. (2 vols., 4 nos./vol.). 81 ECU per vol. (effective 1996). Harwood Academic Publishers, c/o International Publishers Distributor, 820 Town Center Dr., Langhorne, PA 19047. TEL 215-750-2642. FAX 215-750-6343. (Subscr. to: International Publishers Distributor, PO Box 90, Reading, Berkshire, RG1 8JL, England. TEL 44-173-456-8316) Ed. E. Buffetaut. (also avail. in microform)
—BLDSC (4316.155000); Faxon. **CCC**.
Refereed Serial

560 551 JA ISSN 0912-7798
HOBETSU-CHORITSU HAKUBUTSUKAN KENKYU HOKOKU/HOBETSU MUSEUM. BULLETIN. (Text in English, Japanese; summaries in English) 1984. a. free to institutions. Hobetsu Museum - Hobetsu-choritsu Hakubutsukan, 80-6 Hobetsu, Hobetsu-cho, Yufutsu-gun, Hokkaido 054-02, Japan. TEL 01454-5-3141. Ed. Tsutomu Chitoku. **Document type:** academic/scholarly publication.
Description: Contains mainly paleontological and geological studies of the Hobetsu area of Hokkaido. Includes studies on late Cretaceous-Neogene vertebrate and invertebrate fossils.

560 CC ISSN 1000-3185
HUASHI/FOSSILS. (Text in Chinese) 1973. q. $43. (Zhongguo Kexueyuan, Gujizhui Dongwu yu Gurenlei Yanjiusuo - Academia Sinica, Institute of Vertebrata Palasiatica) Science Press, Marketing and Sales Department, 16 Donghuangchenggen North St., Beijing 100717, People's Republic of China. TEL 4010642. FAX 4019810. adv. circ. 100,000. **Document type:** academic/scholarly publication.
—BLDSC (4024.365000).
Description: For popular reading. Covers the evolution of living things from a paleontological point of view: evolution of plants, invertebrates, vertebrates, and mankind. Also reports on activities, museums, primitive clan customs, and interesting tidbits.

560 JA
IGA BONCHI KASEKISHU/ATLAS OF FOSSILS FROM IGA BASIN. (Text in Japanese) 1981. a. Shigemi Okuyama, Pub., 1096-27 Tateoka, Shijukucho, Ueno-shi, Mie-ken 518, Japan.

INSTITUTE FOR THE STUDY OF EARTH AND MAN NEWSLETTER. see *ARCHAEOLOGY*

560 US ISSN 0096-1191
QL368.F6 CODEN: JFARAH
JOURNAL OF FORAMINIFERAL RESEARCH. 1971. q. $80 to libraries & institutions; members $40 (effective 1995). Cushman Foundation for Foraminiferal Research, Invertebrate Paleontology, Museum of Comparative Zoology, Harvard University, Cambridge, MA 02138. Ed. Scott W. Snyder. adv.; bk.rev.; charts; illus.; index. circ. 800. (back issues avail.) **Indexed:** AESIS, Biol.Abstr., Br.Geol.Lit., Deep Sea Res.& Oceanogr.Abstr., E&P Hlth. (1993-), Ecol.Abstr., Gas Process.& Ppl. (1993-), Geo.Abstr., Geol.Abstr., GeoRef., Ind.Sci.Rev., Off.Tech. (1993-), Petrol.Abstr. (1972-), Sci.Cit.Ind.
—BLDSC (4984.575000); Faxon; SWETS; UnCover.
Supersedes: Cushman Foundation for Foraminiferal Research. Contributions (ISSN 0011-409X)
Refereed Serial

561.1 574 NE ISSN 0921-2728
CODEN: JOUPE8
JOURNAL OF PALEOLIMNOLOGY. (Text in English) bi-m. fl.753 to institutions; $483 to institutions in U.S. (effective 1996). Kluwer Academic Publishers, Postbus 17, 3300 AA Dordrecht, Netherlands. TEL 31-78-392392. FAX 31-78-392254. TELEX 29245 KAPG NL. E-mail: SERVICES@WKAP.NL. (Dist. by: Kluwer Academic Publishers Group, P.O. Box 322, 3300 AH Dordrecht, Netherlands. TEL 31-78-392392. FAX 31-78-546474; N. America dist. addr.: Box 358, Accord Sta., Hingham, MA 02018-0358. TEL 617-871-6600. FAX 617-871-6528) Ed. J.P. Smol. (also avail. in microform from UMI; back issues avail.; reprint service avail. from SWZ) **Indexed:** Biol.Abstr., Chem.Abstr., Ecol.Abstr., Environ.Per.Bibl., Geo.Abstr., Geol.Abstr., Meteor.& Geoastrophys.Abstr., Sel.Water Res.Abstr. **Document type:** academic/scholarly publication.
—BLDSC (5027.995500); Faxon; UMI; UnCover. **CCC**.
Description: Publishes papers concerned with all aspects of the reconstruction and interpretation of lake histories, including paleoenvironmental studies of rivers and wetlands, and research contributions from biological, chemical and geological perspectives.
Refereed Serial

560 US ISSN 0022-3360
QE701 CODEN: JPALAZ
JOURNAL OF PALEONTOLOGY. 1927. bi-m. $99 (effective 1996). Paleontological Society, Business Office, Box 1897, Lawrence, KS 66044-8897. TEL 913-843-1221. Ed.Bd. adv.; bk.rev.; bibl.; charts; illus.; index, cum.index. circ. 3,500. (also avail. in microform from UMI; back issues avail.) **Indexed:** AESIS, Biol.Abstr., Br.Geol.Lit., Curr.Adv.Ecol.Sci., Curr.Cont., Deep Sea Res.& Oceanogr.Abstr., E&P Hlth. (1993-), Gas Process.& Ppl. (1993-), Geo.Abstr., Geol.Abstr., GeoRef., Ind.Sci.Rev., Off.Tech. (1993-), Petrol.Abstr. (1961-), Sci.Cit.Ind., Sport Fish.Abstr., Wild.Rev., Zoo.Rec. **Document type:** academic/scholarly publication.
—BLDSC (5028.000000); Faxon; Genuine Article; PADDS; SWETS; UMI; UnCover. **CCC**.
Description: Publishes contributions in all fields of paleontology, including invertebrate and vertebrate paleontology, micropaleontology, and paleobotany, emphasizing taxonomic, biostratigraphic, paleoecological, paleoclimatological or paleobiogeographic aspects.
Refereed Serial

JOURNAL OF QUATERNARY SCIENCE. see *EARTH SCIENCES — Geology*

560 US ISSN 0272-4634
QE841 CODEN: JVPADK
JOURNAL OF VERTEBRATE PALEONTOLOGY. 1981. q. $125 (effective 1996). Society of Vertebrate Paleontology, W. 436 Nebraska Hall, University of Nebraska, Lincoln, NE 68588-0542. TEL 402-472-4604. FAX 402-472-8949. adv. (back issues avail.) **Indexed:** Geol.Abstr., Sport Fish.Abstr., Wild.Rev., Zoo.Rec. **Document type:** academic/scholarly publication.
—BLDSC (5072.320000); UnCover.
Refereed Serial

560 JA ISSN 0387-1924
KASEKI KENKYUKAI KAISHI/JOURNAL OF FOSSIL RESEARCH. (Text in Japanese; summaries in English, Japanese) 1968. s-a. membership. Kaseki Kenkyukai - Fossil Research Society of Japan, c/o Tsukubu Daigaku Gakko Kyoikubu, Mano Kenkyushitsu, 29-1 Otsuka 3-chome, Bunkyo-ku, Tokyo 112, Japan. **Indexed:** Jap.Per.Ind.

560 JA ISSN 0389-3847
KASEKI NO TOMO/TOKAI FOSSIL SOCIETY. JOURNAL. (Text in Japanese) 1969. irreg. Tokai Kaseki Kenkyukai - Tokai Fossil Society, 9-21, Sawashita-machi, Atsuta-ku, Nagoya-shi, Aichi-ken 456, Japan.

KAZI SONUCLARI TOPLANTISI. see *ARCHAEOLOGY*

KYUSHU UNIVERSITY. DEPARTMENT OF EARTH AND PLANETARY SCIENCES. SCIENCE REPORTS/KYUSHU DAIGAKU RIGAKUBU KENKYU HOKOKU CHIKYU-WAKUSEI-KAGAKU. see *EARTH SCIENCES — Geology*

560 622 551 AU
LANDESMUSEUM JOANNEUM. ABTEILUNG FUER GEOLOGIE UND PALAEONTOLOGIE. MITTEILUNGEN. 1937. irreg. (approx. 1/yr.). price varies. Landesmuseum Joanneum, Abteilung fuer Geologie und Palaeontologie, Raubergasse 10, A-8010 Graz, Austria. illus. **Document type:** bulletin.
Former titles: Landesmuseum Joanneum. Abteilung fuer Geologie, Palaeontologie und Bergbau. Mitteilungen; (until 1972): Joanneum. Museum fuer Bergbau, Geologie und Technik. Mitteilungen.

560.17 NO ISSN 0024-1164
QE701 CODEN: LETHAT
LETHAIA; an international journal of palaeontology and stratigraphy. (Text in English) 1968. q. NOK 920 in Nordic countries; elsewhere $172 (effective 1996). (International Palaeontological Association) Scandinavian University Press, P.O. Box 2959-Toeyen, N-0608 Oslo, Norway. TEL 47-22-57-54-00. FAX 47-22-57-53-53. (U.S. addr.: Scandinavian University Press, 200 Meacham Ave., Elmont, NY 11003. TEL 516-352-7300) Ed. Christina Franzen. illus. circ. 1,300. (also avail. in microform from UMI; back issues avail.; reprint service avail. from ISI) **Indexed:** Abstr.Anthropol., AESIS, Biol.Abstr., Br.Geol.Lit., Curr.Adv.Ecol.Sci., Curr.Cont., Curr.Tit.Ocean., Deep Sea Res.& Oceanogr.Abstr., E&P Hlth. (1993-), Ecol.Abstr., Gas Process.& Ppl. (1993-), Geol.Abstr., GeoRef., Ind.Sci.Rev., Off.Tech. (1993-), Petrol.Abstr. (1970-), Sci.Cit.Ind.
—BLDSC (5184.950000); Faxon; Genuine Article; PADDS; SWETS; UMI; UnCover. **CCC**.
Description: Focuses on geology, especially the fields of palaeontology, stratigraphy and fossils.

MAINZER GEOWISSENSCHAFTLICHE MITTEILUNGEN. see *EARTH SCIENCES — Geology*

MAMMOTH TRUMPET. see *ARCHAEOLOGY*

MAN & ENVIRONMENT. see *ANTHROPOLOGY*

560 NE ISSN 0377-8398
QE719 CODEN: MAMIDH
MARINE MICROPALEONTOLOGY. 1976. 8/yr.
fl.960($585) (effective 1996). Elsevier Science
B.V., P.O. Box 211, 1000 AE Amsterdam,
Netherlands. TEL 31-20-4853911.
FAX 31-20-4853658. TELEX 18582 ESPA NL.
E-mail: nlinfo-f@elsevier.nl; usinfo-f@elsevier.com;
forinfo-kyf04035@niftyserve.or.jp; Site addr.:
http://www.elsevier.nl/. (Subscr. in U.S. and Canada
to: Elsevier Science Inc., Box 882, Madison Sq. Sta.,
New York, NY 10159. TEL 212-989-5800. FAX
212-633-3990) Eds. J. Lipps, H. Thierstein. (also
avail. in microform from UMI; reprint service avail.
from SWZ) Indexed: AESIS, Biol.Abstr., Curr.Cont.,
Deep Sea Res.& Oceanogr.Abstr., E&P Hlth. (1993-
), Ecol.Abstr., Gas Process.& Ppl. (1993-),
Geo.Abstr., Geol.Abstr., GeoRef., Ind.Sci.Rev.,
Mar.Sci.Cont.Tab., Off.Tech. (1993-), Petrol.Abstr.
(1978-), So.Pac.Per.Ind. **Document type:**
academic/scholarly publication.
—BLDSC (5376.400000); Ei; Faxon; Genuine
Article; PADDS; SWETS; UnCover. **CCC.**
Description: Publishes results of research in all
fields of marine micropalaentology of the ocean
basins and continents, including paleoceanography,
evolution, ecology and paleoecology, biology and
paleobiology, biochronology, paleoclimatology,
taphonomy, and the systematic relationships of
higher taxa.
Refereed Serial

560 US ISSN 0198-8565
CODEN: MMPPAW
**MICHIGAN STATE UNIVERSITY. MUSEUM PUBLICATIONS.
PALEONTOLOGICAL SERIES.** 1972. irreg. price varies.
Michigan State University, Museum, East Lansing, MI
48824. TEL 517-335-2370. Ed.Bd. bibl.; charts;
illus. circ. 1,500. **Document type:** academic/scholarly
publication, monographic series.

563 US ISSN 0026-2803
QE701 CODEN: MCPLAI
MICROPALEONTOLOGY. 1954. q. $90 to individuals;
institutions $175. American Museum of Natural
History, Central Park W. at 79th St., New York, NY
10024-5192. TEL 212-769-5545.
FAX 212-769-5009. E-mail: scipubs@amnh.org.
(Subscr. to: 450 Fame Ave., Hanover, PA 17331)
Ed. Dr. John A. Van Couvering. bk.rev.; charts; illus.
circ. 1,000. (also avail. in microform from MIM,UMI;
microfilm; back issues avail.; reprint service avail.
from UMI) Indexed: AESIS, Biol.Abstr., Chem.Abstr.,
Deep Sea Res.& Oceanogr.Abstr., Ecol.Abstr.,
Geo.Abstr., Geol.Abstr., GeoRef., Ocean.Abstr.,
Petrol.Abstr., Pollut.Abstr., Sel.Water Res.Abstr.
Document type: academic/scholarly publication.
—BLDSC (5759.500000); Faxon; Genuine Article;
PADDS; SWETS; UMI; UnCover. **CCC.**
Description: Contains international research on
stratigraphy, systematics, morphology, paleobiology
and paleoecology of all microorganisms with
fossilized hard parts.
Refereed Serial

563 US ISSN 0160-2071
CODEN: MSPUDO
MICROPALEONTOLOGY SPECIAL PAPERS. 1970. irreg.,
no.7, 1993. American Museum of Natural History,
Central Park W. at 79th St., New York, NY
10024-5192. TEL 212-769-5656.
FAX 212-769-5653. E-mail: scipubs@amnh.org. Ed.
John A. Van Couvering. charts; illus.; maps. circ.
625. (reprint service avail. from UMI) Indexed: Deep
Sea Res.& Oceanogr.Abstr., GeoRef. **Document type:**
monographic series.
—BLDSC (5759.550000). **CCC.**
Description: Monographs on micropaleontology,
including biostratigraphy, paleo-ecology, and
systematics in all microfossil groups.

560 622 FR ISSN 0335-6566
MINERAUX ET FOSSILES. 1974. m. 250 F. S E P S, 12
rue Poincare, 558700 Revigny, France. adv.; bk.rev.

MISSISSIPPI GEOLOGY. see *EARTH SCIENCES —
Geology*

560 JA ISSN 0385-0900
QE756.J29 CODEN: MKHKEZ
**MIZUNAMISHI KASEKI HAKUBUTSUKAN KENKYU
HOKOKU/MIZUNAMI FOSSIL MUSEUM. BULLETIN.**
(Text in English, Japanese) 1974. a. Mizunamishi
Kaseki Hakubutsukan - Mizunami Fossil Museum,
Yamanouchi, Akeyocho, Mizunami-shi, Gifu-ken
509-61, Japan. Ed. Hiroaki Karasawa. adv. contact:
Yoshitsugu Okumura. **Document type:** bulletin.

560 JA
**MIZUNAMISHI KASEKI HAKUBUTSUKAN
SENPO/MIZUNAMI FOSSIL MUSEUM. MONOGRAPH.**
(Text in Japanese) 1980. irreg. Mizunamishi Kaseki
Hakubutsukan - Mizunami Fossil Museum,
Yamanouchi, Akeyocho, Mizunami-shi, Gifu-ken
509-61, Japan. Ed. Atsushi Naruse. adv. contact:
Yoshitsugu Okumura. **Document type:** monographic
series.

560 NE ISSN 0168-6151
QE696
MODERN QUATERNARY RESEARCH IN SOUTHEAST ASIA.
1975. a. fl.105($60) A.A. Balkema, P.O. Box 1675,
3000 BR Rotterdam, Netherlands.
TEL 31-10-4145822. FAX 31-10-4135947. (Dist.
in U.S. by: Ashgate Publishins Co., Old Post Rd.,
Brookfield, VT 05036. TEL 800-535-9544. FAX
802-276-3837) Eds. G.-J. Bartstra, W.A. Casparie.
Indexed: Anthropol.Lit., GeoRef. **Document type:**
academic/scholarly publication.
—**CCC.**

560 US ISSN 0736-3907
QE701.M68
MOSASAUR. 1983. irreg. $18. Delaware Valley
Paleontological Society, c/o Stephen J.G. Farrington,
Bus. Mgr., Box 42078, Philadelphia, PA
19101-2078. Ed. William B. Gallagher. circ. 700.
Document type: academic/scholarly publication.
—BLDSC (5967.483650). **CCC.**

560 551 GW ISSN 0177-0950
QE1
**MUENCHNER GEOWISSENSCHAFTLICHE
ABHANDLUNGEN. REIHE A: GEOLOGIE UND
PALAEONTOLOGIE.** (Text in English, French, German)
1984. irreg., vol.28. DM.160. Verlag Dr. Friedrich
Pfeil, Postfach 650086, 81214 Munich, Germany.
TEL 089-742827-0. FAX 089-7242772. Ed.
Friedrich H. Pfeil. circ. 500. **Document type:**
monographic series.
—**CCC.**
Description: Covers geology and paleontology.

560 AG ISSN 0524-9511
QE752.A7
**MUSEO ARGENTINO DE CIENCIAS NATURALES
"BERNARDINO RIVADAVIA." INSTITUTO NACIONAL DE
INVESTIGACION DE LAS CIENCIAS NATURALES.
REVISTA. PALEONTOLOGIA.** 1964. irreg. Museo
Argentino de Ciencias Naturales "Bernardino
Rivadavia", Instituto Nacional de Investigacion de las
Ciencias Naturales, Avda. Angel Gallardo 470,
Casilla de Correo 220-Sucursal 5, Buenos Aires,
Argentina. Indexed: GeoRef.

560 UY
**MUSEO NACIONAL DE HISTORIA NATURAL.
COMUNICACIONES PALEONTOLOGICAS.** (Summaries
in English, Spanish) 1970. irreg. exchange basis.
Museo Nacional de Historia Natural, Casilla de
Correos 399, 11 000 Montevideo, Uruguay. illus.
circ. 1,200.

NATURAL HISTORY CONTRIBUTIONS. see *BIOLOGY*

**NATURHISTORISCHES MUSEUM BASEL.
VEROEFFENTLICHUNGEN.** see *SCIENCES:
COMPREHENSIVE WORKS*

**NATURHISTORISCHES MUSEUM IN WIEN. ANNALEN.
SERIE A, MINERALOGIE UND PETROGRAPHIE,
GEOLOGIE UND PALEONTOLOGIE, ANTHROPOLOGIE
UND PRAEHISTORIE.** see *SCIENCES:
COMPREHENSIVE WORKS*

**NATURWISSENSCHAFTLICHER VEREIN FUER SCHWABEN.
BERICHTE.** see *BIOLOGY*

**NATURWISSENSCHAFTLICHER VEREIN IN HAMBURG.
ABHANDLUNGEN.** see *BIOLOGY — Zoology*

**NATURWISSENSCHAFTLICHER VEREIN IN HAMBURG.
VERHANDLUNGEN.** see *BIOLOGY — Zoology*

**NATUURHISTORISCH GENOOTSCHAP IN LIMBURG.
PUBLICATIES.** see *BIOLOGY*

**NEUES JAHRBUCH FUER GEOLOGIE UND
PALAEONTOLOGIE. ABHANDLUNGEN.** see *EARTH
SCIENCES — Geology*

**NEUES JAHRBUCH FUER GEOLOGIE UND
PALAEONTOLOGIE, MONATSHEFTE.** see *EARTH
SCIENCES — Geology*

560 AT
**NEW SOUTH WALES. GEOLOGICAL SURVEY. MEMOIRS:
PALAEONTOLOGY.** 1888. irreg., no.19, 1982. price
varies. Department of Mineral Resources, P.O. Box
536, St. Leonards, N.S.W. 2065, Australia. TEL 02
901-8262. Ed. H. Basden. circ. 400. Indexed:
GeoRef.
Formerly: New South Wales. Department of Mines.
Memoirs: Palaeontology (ISSN 0077-8699)

560 551 JA ISSN 0913-6746
**NIHON DOKETSUGAKU KENKYUJO
HOKOKU/SPELEOLOGICAL RESEARCH INSTITUTE OF
JAPAN. ANNUAL.** (Text in Japanese) 1969. a. Nihon
Doketsugaku Kenkyujo - Speleological Research
Institute of Japan, c/o Ryusendo Jimusho,
Iwaizumicho, Shimohei-gun, Iwate-ken 027-05,
Japan.

561 JA ISSN 0387-1851
**NIHON KAFUN GAKKAI KAISHI/JAPANESE JOURNAL OF
PALYNOLOGY.** (Text in English, Japanese) 1965. s-a.
Nihon Kafun Gakkai - Palynological Society of Japan,
Toho Daigaku Yakugakubu Shoyakugaku Kyoshitsu,
2-1, Miyama 2-chome, Funabashi-shi, Chiba-ken
274, Japan.

560 JA
QE756.J29 CODEN: TPPJAA
**NIPPONITES/QUARTERLY JOURNAL OF
PALEONTOLOGY.** (Text in English; summaries in
Japanese) 1935. q. $75. (Palaeontological Society
of Japan - Nihon Koseibutsu Gakkai) Business
Center for Academic Societies Japan, 5-16-9
Honkomagome, Bunkyo-ku, Tokyo 113, Japan.
TEL 03-5814-5811. FAX 03-5814-5822. TELEX
2722268 BCHSP J. bibl.; charts; illus.; index. circ.
550. Indexed: Biol.Abstr., GeoRef., Petrol.Abstr.
—PADDS; UnCover.
Formerly: Palaeontological Society of Japan.
Transactions and Proceedings - Nihon Koseibutsu
Gakkai Hokoku Kiji (ISSN 0031-0204)

560 AT ISSN 0159-818X
NOMEN NUDUM. a. Geological Society of Australia,
Association of Australasian Paleontologists, 301
George St., Sydney, N.S.W. 2000, Australia.
FAX 61-2-290-2198. Ed. I.G. Percival. circ. 400.
Indexed: AESIS. **Document type:** newsletter.

**OESTERREICHISCHE GEOLOGISCHE GESELLSCHAFT.
MITTEILUNGEN.** see *EARTH SCIENCES — Geology*

560 PK ISSN 0078-8155
**PAKISTAN. GEOLOGICAL SURVEY. MEMOIRS;
PALEONTOLOGIA PAKISTANICA.** (Text in English)
1956. irreg. price varies. Geological Survey of
Pakistan, c/o Chief Librarian, Box 15, Quetta,
Pakistan. TEL 73055. circ. 1,500. Indexed: GeoRef.

566 GW ISSN 0724-6331
CODEN: PICHEK
PALAEO ICHTHYOLOGICA. (Text in English, French,
German) 1983. irreg., vol.5. DM.140. Verlag Dr.
Friedrich Pfeil, Postfach 650086, 81214 Munich,
Germany. TEL 089-742827-0. FAX 089-7242772.
Ed. Friedrich H. Pfeil. abstr.; bibl.; charts; illus. circ.
500. (back issues avail.) Indexed: Zoo.Rec. **Document
type:** monographic series.
Description: Neontological and paleontological
works on systematics, ecology, and stratigraphy of
fishes.

PALEONTOLOGY

560 550   NE   ISSN 0031-0182
QE500   CODEN: PPPYAB
PALAEOGEOGRAPHY, PALAEOCLIMATOLOGY, PALAEOECOLOGY; an international journal for the geo-sciences. (Supplement avail.: Global and Planetary Change (ISSN 0921-8181)) (Text in English, French and German) 1965. 32/yr. fl.3360($2049) (effective 1996). Elsevier Science B.V., P.O. Box 211, 1000 AE Amsterdam, Netherlands. TEL 31-20-4853911. FAX 31-20-4853598. TELEX 18582 ESPA NL. E-mail: nlinfo-f@elsevier.nl; usinfo-f@elsevier.com; forinfo-kyf04035@niftyserve.or.jp; Site addr.: http://www.elsevier.nl/. (Subscr. in U.S. and Canada to: Elsevier Science Inc., Box 882, Madison Sq. Sta., New York, NY 10159-0882. TEL 212-989-5800. FAX 212-633-3990) Eds. F. Surlyk, E.J. Barron. adv.; bk.rev.; abstr.; bibl.; charts; illus.; index. (also avail. in microform from UMI; reprint service avail. from ISI,SWZ) **Indexed:** AESIS, Biol.Abstr., Br.Archaeol.Abstr., Br.Geol.Lit., Bull.Signal., Chem.Abstr., Curr.Adv.Ecol.Sci., Curr.Cont., Deep Sea Res.& Oceanogr.Abstr., Ecol.Abstr., Environ.Abstr., Geo.Abstr., Geol.Abstr., GeoRef., Meteor.& Geoastrophys.Abstr., Ocean Abstr., Petrol.Abstr., Pollut.Abstr. **Document type:** academic/scholarly publication.
—BLDSC (6343.450000); CASDDS; Ei; Faxon; Genuine Article; PADDS; SWETS; UnCover. **CCC.**
Description: Publishes original studies and comprehensive reviews in the field of palaeo-environmental geology.
Refereed Serial

560   IT
PALAEONTOGRAPHIA ITALICA. 1913. a. L.100000 (foreign L.110000) (effective 1995). Pacini Editore s.r.l., Via A. Gherardesca 1, 56121 Ospedaletto (Pisa), Italy. TEL 39-50-982439. FAX 39-50-983906. Ed. M. Tongiorgi.

551   GW   ISSN 0375-0442
    CODEN: PGABA8
PALAEONTOGRAPHICA. ABT. A: PALAEOZOOLOGIE - STRATIGRAPHIE. (Text in English and German; summaries in English, French, German) 1846. 8/yr. (in 4 vols.). $315 per vol. (effective 1996). E. Schweizerbart'sche Verlagsbuchhandlung, Johannesstr. 3A, 70176 Stuttgart, Germany. TEL 0711-625001. FAX 0711-625005. Ed. W. Haas. illus. **Indexed:** Biol.Abstr., Br.Geol.Lit., GeoRef. **Document type:** academic/scholarly publication.
—BLDSC (6343.603000); Faxon; UnCover. **CCC.**

560   GW   ISSN 0375-0299
    CODEN: PABPAD
PALAEONTOGRAPHICA. ABT. B: PALAEOPHYTOLOGIE. (Text in English, French and German) 1846. 8/yr. (in 4 vols.). $315 per vol. (effective 1996). E. Schweizerbart'sche Verlagsbuchhandlung, Johannesstr. 3A, 70176 Stuttgart, Germany. TEL 0711-625001. FAX 0711-625005. Eds. K. Goth, D. Mai. bibl.; charts; illus.; index. **Indexed:** AESIS, Biol.Abstr., Br.Geol.Lit., Curr.Adv.Ecol.Sci., GeoRef. **Document type:** academic/scholarly publication.
—BLDSC (6343.605000). **CCC.**

560   GW   ISSN 0085-4611
    CODEN: PLTGAH
PALAEONTOGRAPHICA. SUPPLEMENTBAENDE. irreg. price varies. E. Schweizerbart'sche Verlagsbuchhandlung, Johannesstr. 3A, 70176 Stuttgart, Germany. TEL 0711-625001. FAX 0711-625005. **Indexed:** GeoRef. **Document type:** monographic series.
—**CCC.**

560   US   ISSN 0078-8546
QE701   CODEN: PALAAI
PALAEONTOGRAPHICA AMERICANA. 1916. irreg., no.58, 1994. price varies. Paleontological Research Institution, 1259 Trumansburg Rd., Ithaca, NY 14850. TEL 607-273-6623. Ed. Warren D. Allmon. bibl.; charts; illus.; stat. circ. 250. (back issues avail.) **Indexed:** Biol.Abstr., GeoRef. **Document type:** academic/scholarly publication, monographic series.
—BLDSC (6343.610000); UnCover.
Refereed Serial

PALAEONTOGRAPHICAL SOCIETY. MONOGRAPHS (LONDON). see EARTH SCIENCES — Geology

560   SA   ISSN 0078-8554
QE757.A1   CODEN: PBPRAS
PALAEONTOLOGIA AFRICANA. (Text in English) 1953. irreg., vol.30, 1993. price varies. University of the Witwatersrand, Johannesburg, Bernard Price Institute for Palaeontological Research, Wits 2050, South Africa. TEL 27-11-7162870. FAX 27-11-3391620. E-mail: 106GAR@cosmos.wits.ac.za. Ed. B.S. Rubidge. bk.rev.; cum.index: vols.1-20 (1953-1977); circ. 600 (controlled). (back issues avail.) **Indexed:** Biol.Abstr., Bull.Signal., Geo.Abstr., GeoRef., Ind.S.A.Per. **Document type:** academic/scholarly publication, monographic series.
—BLDSC (6343.680000); UnCover.
Description: Publishes original research relating to any aspect of palaentology.

560   CC
PALAEONTOLOGIA CATHAYANA/HUAXIA GUSHENGWU. (Text in English) 1983. irreg., no.4, 1989. price varies. Science Press, Marketing and Sales Department, 16 Donghuangchenggen North St., Beijing 100717, People's Republic of China. TEL 4010642. FAX 4012180. TELEX 210247-SPBJ-CN. (US office: Science Press New York, Ltd., 63-117 Alderton St., Rego Park, NY 11374. TEL 718-459-4638) Ed. Lu Yan-hao. illus.
Description: Publishes papers on all aspects of paleontology, stratigraphy, and paleobiogeography. Includes review articles, short papers of description or discussion of important flora and fauna, news of current research, and occasional translations.
Refereed Serial

560   JA   ISSN 0549-3927
QE701   CODEN: PSJSAI
PALEONTOLOGICAL SOCIETY OF JAPAN. SPECIAL PAPERS. (Text in English) 1951. irreg. Nihon Koseibutsu Gakkai - Palaeontological Society of Japan, Nihon Gakkai Jimu Senta, 16-9 Honkomagome 5-chome, Bunkyo-ku, Tokyo 113, Japan.
—BLDSC (8368.650000).

560   GW   ISSN 0031-0220
    CODEN: PAZEAW
PALAEONTOLOGISCHE ZEITSCHRIFT. (Text in English and German; summaries in English and French) 1914. s-a. $119 (effective 1996). (Palaeontologische Gesellschaft e.V.) E. Schweizerbart'sche Verlagsbuchhandlung, Johannesstr. 3A, 70176 Stuttgart, Germany. TEL 0711-625001. FAX 0711-625005. Ed.Bd adv.; bibl.; charts; illus. (back issues avail.) **Indexed:** Biol.Abstr., Br.Geol.Lit., Curr.Adv.Ecol.Sci., Deep Sea Res.& Oceanogr.Abstr., GeoRef. **Document type:** academic/scholarly publication.
—BLDSC (6345.250000); Faxon; UnCover. **CCC.**

560   UK   ISSN 0031-0239
    CODEN: PONTAD
PALAEONTOLOGY. (Supplement avail.: Special Papers in Palaeontology) 1957. q. £184($365) (foreign £227) (effective 1996). (Palaeontological Association) Basil Blackwell Ltd., 108 Cowley Rd., Oxford OX4 1JF, England. TEL 44-1865-791100. FAX 44-1865-791347. circ. 2,000. **Indexed:** AESIS, Curr.Adv.Ecol.Sci., Deep Sea Res.& Oceanogr.Abstr., Geol.Abstr. **Document type:** academic/scholarly publication.
—BLDSC (6345.200000); Faxon; Genuine Article; PADDS; SWETS; UnCover.

560   FR   ISSN 0031-0247
QE841   CODEN: PLVTAW
PALAEOVERTEBRATA. (Text and summaries in English, French, German, Spanish) 1967. q. 450 F. (foreign 500 F.($95)). U S T L, Laboratoire de Paleontologie, Place E. Bataillon, F-34095 Montpellier Cedex 5, France. TEL 67-14-38-90. FAX 67-04-20-32. Dir. Henri Cappetta. bk.rev.; bibl.; charts; illus.; stat.; tr.lit. circ. 200. (tabloid format) **Indexed:** Bull.Signal., GeoRef.
—BLDSC (6345.210000).

560   US   ISSN 0883-1351
    CODEN: PALAEM
PALAIOS. 1986. bi-m. $147 (effective 1996). S E P M, 1731 E. 71st. St., Tulsa, OK 74136-5108. TEL 918-493-3361. FAX 918-493-2093. Ed. David J. Bottjer. bk.rev. circ. 1,300. (back issues avail.) **Indexed:** AESIS, Curr.Adv.Ecol.Sci., Deep Sea Res.& Oceanogr.Abstr., Ecol.Abstr., Geo.Abstr., Geol.Abstr. **Document type:** academic/scholarly publication.
—BLDSC (6345.214500); CASDDS; Ei; Faxon; Genuine Article; PADDS; SWETS; UMI; UnCover. **CCC.**
Description: Contains comprehensive articles, short papers, invited editorials, and essays devoted to the applications of paleontology in solving geologic problems.
Refereed Serial

560   US   ISSN 0094-8373
QE701   CODEN: PALBBM
PALEOBIOLOGY. 1975. q. $65 (effective 1996). Paleontological Society, Business Office, Box 1897, Lawrence, KS 66044-8897. TEL 913-843-1221. Eds. R. Cowen, P. Signor. adv.; bk.rev.; abstr.; bibl.; charts; illus.; pat.; stat.; index. circ. 2,400. (also avail. in microform from UMI; back issues avail.; reprint service avail. from UMI) **Indexed:** Biol.Abstr., Br.Archaeol.Abstr., Curr.Adv.Ecol.Sci., Curr.Cont., Deep Sea Res.& Oceanogr.Abstr., Ecol.Abstr., Geol.Abstr., GeoRef., Petrol.Abstr., Sci.Cit.Ind., So.Pac.Per.Ind., Sport Fish.Abstr., Wild.Rev., Zoo.Rec. **Document type:** academic/scholarly publication.
—BLDSC (6345.280000); Faxon; Genuine Article; PADDS; SWETS; UMI; UnCover. **CCC.**
Refereed Serial

560 551   US   ISSN 0031-0298
QE701   CODEN: PLBIA
PALEOBIOS. 1967. irreg. $8. University of California at Berkeley, Museum of Paleontology, Berkeley, CA 94720. TEL 510-642-1821. FAX 510-642-1822. Ed. C.J. Bell. bibl.; charts; illus. circ. 800. (back issues avail.) **Indexed:** Biol.Abstr., Deep Sea Res.& Oceanogr.Abstr., GeoRef. **Document type:** academic/scholarly publication.
—UnCover.
Refereed Serial

560 551.6   US
THE PALEOCLIMATE DATA RECORD. 1990. irreg., latest vol.3, no.2, 1992. free. U.S. National Geophysical Data Center, National Oceanic and Atmospheric Administration, 325 Broadway, E-GC, Boulder, CO 80303-3328. TEL 303-498-6826. FAX 303-497-6513. TELEX 592811 NOAA MASC BDR. E-mail: info@ngdc.noaa.gov. (Co-sponsor: World Data Center - A for Paleoclimatology) **Document type:** government publication, newsletter.
Description: Presents news of paleoclimatology projects supported by the National Geophysical Data Center. Lists new research available.

560 551.6   US
PALEOCLIMATE PUBLICATIONS SERIES. 1991. irreg. exchange basis. U.S. National Geophysical Data Center, National Oceanic and Atmospheric Administration, 325 Broadway, E-GC, Boulder, CO 80303-3328. TEL 303-497-6826. FAX 303-497-6513. TELEX 592811 NOAA MASC BDR. E-mail: info@ngdc.noaa.gov. (Co-sponsor: World Data Center - A for Paleoclimatology) stat. **Document type:** government publication.
Description: Publishes research results in fields relevant to paleoclimatology.

560   NE   ISSN 0168-6208
QE993   CODEN: PLEABR
PALEOECOLOGY OF AFRICA; and the surrounding islands. 1966. a., vol.23, 1992. fl.140($80) A.A. Balkema, P.O. Box 1675, 3000 BR Rotterdam, Netherlands. TEL 31-10-4145822. FAX 31-10-4135947. (Dist. in U.S. by: Ashgate Publishing Co., Old Post Rd., Brookfield, VT 05036. TEL 800-535-9544. FAX 802-276-3837) Ed. K. Heine. **Indexed:** Anthropol.Lit., GeoRef., Zoo.Rec. **Document type:** academic/scholarly publication.
—BLDSC (6343.428000). **CCC.**
Former titles: Paleoecology of Africa and the Surrounding Islands; Palaeoecology of Africa and the Surrounding Islands and Antarctica (ISSN 0078-8538)

PALEONTOLOGY 4995

560   IT   ISSN 1121-3361
PALEONTOLOGIA LOMBARDA. 1993. irreg. price varies. Societa Italiana di Scienze Naturali, Corso Venezia 55, 20121 Milan, Italy. TEL 39-2-62085405. (Co-sponsor: Museo Civico di Storia Naturale) Ed. Giovanni Pinna. circ. 1,000. (back issues avail.) **Document type:** monographic series.

560   US   ISSN 0031-0301
QE701   CODEN: PJOUA
PALEONTOLOGICAL JOURNAL. English translation of: Paleontologicheskii Zhurnal (UR ISSN 0031-031X) 1967. bi-m. $894 (Canada and Mexico $954; elsewhere $976.50) (effective 1995). (Russian Academy of Sciences, RU) Scripta Technica, Inc. (Subsidiary of: John Wiley & Sons, Inc.), 7961 Eastern Ave., Silver Spring, MD 20910. TEL 301-588-0484. FAX 301-588-5278. (Dist. by: John Wiley & Sons, Inc., Periodicals Division, 650 Third Ave., New York, NY 10158. TEL 212-850-6645. FAX 212-850-6021; Subscr. outside the Americas to: John Wiley & Sons Ltd., Baffins Ln., Chichester, W. Sussex PO19 1UD, England. TEL 44-1243-779777. FAX 44-1243-446128) (Co-sponsor: American Geological Institute) Ed. Matthew Nitecki. adv. circ. 425. (also avail. in microform from UMI; reprint service avail. from KTO) **Indexed:** Geol.Abstr., GeoRef. **Document type:** academic/scholarly publication.
—BLDSC (0416.675000); Faxon; UMI; UnCover. **CCC.**
    Description: Deals with the anatomy, morphology and taxonomy of extinct animals and plants.
    Refereed Serial

560   US   ISSN 0078-8597
    CODEN: PSMECR
PALEONTOLOGICAL SOCIETY. MEMOIR. 1968. irreg. $16.50 per no. Paleontological Society, Box 1897, Lawrence, KS 66047. TEL 913-843-1221. Ed. Richard D. Hoare. circ. 3,200. **Indexed:** Biol.Abstr., Deep Sea Res.& Oceanogr.Abstr., GeoRef. **Document type:** monographic series.

560   RU   ISSN 0031-031X
QE701   CODEN: PAZHA7
PALEONTOLOGICHESKII ZHURNAL. English translation: Paleontological Journal (US ISSN 0031-0301) 1959. q. 27 Rub. (Rossiiskaya Akademiya Nauk, Institut Paleontologii) Izdatel'stvo Nauka, 90 Profsoyuznaya ul., 117864 Moscow, Russia. (Dist. by: Mezhdunarodnaya Kniga, ul. Dimitrova D.39, 113095 Moscow, Russia) Ed. L.P. Tatarinov. index. circ. 1,200. (tabloid format) **Indexed:** ASCA, Biol.Abstr., Deep Sea Res.& Oceanogr.Abstr., GeoRef. **Document type:** academic/scholarly publication.
—BLDSC (0128.940000); Genuine Article. **CCC.**
    Incorporates: Akademiya Nauk S.S.S.R. Institut Paleontologii. Trudy.

560   BU   ISSN 0204-7217
QE755.B8   CODEN: PSLIDZ
PALEONTOLOGIIA, STRATIGRAFIIA I LITOLOGIIA. (Text in various languages; summaries in Bulgarian, English, French, German) 1975. irreg. price varies. (Bulgarska Akademiia na Naukite, Geologicheski Institut) Publishing House of the Bulgarian Academy of Sciences, Acad. G. Bonchev St., Bldg. 6, 1113 Sofia, Bulgaria. Ed. C. Spasov. illus. circ. 470. (reprint service avail. from IRC) **Indexed:** Biol.Abstr., BSL Geo., GeoRef.
—BLDSC (0129.070000).
    Supersedes in part: Bulgarska Akademiia na Naukite. Geologicheski Institut. Izvestiia.

560   FR   ISSN 0153-9345
GN855.M628   CODEN: PALEDX
PALEORIENT. 1973. biennial. price varies. (Universite de Paris, Laboratoire de Paleontologie Humaine et de Paleontologie des Vertebres) C N R S Editions, 20-22 rue St. Amand, 75015 Paris, France. TEL 45-33-16-00. FAX 45-33-92-13. TELEX 200 356 F. Ed. S. Renimel. adv.; bk.rev.; bibl.; index; circ. 1,500. (controlled) **Indexed:** A.I.C.P., Anthropol.Lit., GeoRef., Mid.East: Abstr.& Ind.
—BLDSC (6345.330000); UnCover.

561 560   US   ISSN 0191-6122
QE993   CODEN: PALYDP
PALYNOLOGY. 1977. a. $30 to individuals; institutions $40. American Association of Stratigraphic Palynologists Foundation, c/o Vaughn M. Bryant, Jr., Palynology Laboratory, Anthropology Bldg., Texas A & M University, College Station, TX 77843-4352. TEL 409-845-5242. FAX 409-845-4070. Ed. David G. Goodman. circ. 950. **Indexed:** Biol.Abstr., Br.Geol.Lit., Geo.Abstr., GeoRef., Ocean.Abstr., Petrol.Abstr., Pollut.Abstr.
—BLDSC (6345.580000); PADDS; UnCover.
    Supersedes (in 1977): Geoscience and Man (ISSN 0072-1395); **Incorporates (1970-1976):** American Association of Stratigraphic Palynologists. Proceedings of the Annual Meeting (ISSN 0270-1316)
    Refereed Serial

PANSTWOWY INSTYTUT GEOLOGICZNY. PRACE. see *EARTH SCIENCES — Geology*

560   GW   ISSN 0724-9012
PISCIUM CATALOGUS. irreg. DM.240. Verlag Dr. Friedrich Pfeil, Postfach 650086, 81214 Munich, Germany. TEL 089-742827-0. FAX 089-7242772. Ed. Werner Schwarzhans. **Document type:** monographic series.

PRIRODNJACKI MUZEJ U BEOGRADU. GLASNIK. SERIJA A: MINEROLOGIJA, GEOLOGIJA, PALEONTOLOGIJA. see *EARTH SCIENCES — Geology*

PROFIL. see *EARTH SCIENCES*

560   IT
GN700
QUATERNARIA NOVA. (Text and summaries in English, French, German, Italian and Spanish) N.S. 1991. a. L.70000 (effective 1992). Istituto Italiano di Paleontologia Umana, Piazza Mincio 2, 00198 Rome, Italy. (Dist. by: Libreria gia Nardecchia s.r.l., Via di Tor di Nona 39, 00186 Rome, Italy. FAX 396-68300010) adv.; bk.rev.; bibl.; charts; illus.; cum.index. circ. 800. **Indexed:** Anthropol.Lit., Br.Archaeol.Abstr., Br.Geol.Lit., Deep Sea Res.& Oceanogr.Abstr., Geo.Abstr., GeoRef.
    Supersedes: Quaternaria (ISSN 0085-5235)
    Description: Contains articles on quaternary prehistory, paleontology and geology.

QUATERNARY PERSPECTIVE. see *EARTH SCIENCES — Geology*

QUATERNARY RESEARCH; an interdisciplinary journal. see *EARTH SCIENCES — Geology*

QUATERNARY RESEARCH/DAIYONKI KENKYU. see *EARTH SCIENCES — Geology*

QUATERNARY SCIENCE REVIEWS; international multidisciplinary review and research journal. see *EARTH SCIENCES — Geology*

RENLEIXUE XUEBAO/ACTA ANTHROPOLOGICA SINICA. see *ANTHROPOLOGY*

561   NE   ISSN 0034-6667
QE993   CODEN: RPPYAX
REVIEW OF PALAEOBOTANY AND PALYNOLOGY; an international journal. (Text in English, French and German) 1967. 20/yr. fl.2390($1457) (effective 1996). Elsevier Science B.V., P.O. Box 211, 1000 AE Amsterdam, Netherlands. TEL 31-20-4853911. FAX 31-20-4853598. TELEX 18582 ESPA NL. E-mail: nlinfo-f@elsevier.nl; usinfo-f@elsevier.com; forinfo-kyf04035@niftyserve.or.jp; Site addr.: http://www.elsevier.nl/. (Subscr. in U.S. and Canada to: Elsevier Science Inc., Box 882, Madison Sq. Sta., New York, NY 10159-0882. TEL 212-989-5800. FAX 212-633-3990) Ed. W. Punt. adv.; bk.rev.; abstr.; bibl.; charts; illus.; index. (also avail. in microform from UMI; reprint service avail. from SWZ) **Indexed:** Abstr.Anthropol., AESIS, Biol.Abstr., Br.Geol.Lit., Bull.Signal., Curr.Adv.Ecol.Sci., Curr.Cont., Deep Sea Res.& Oceanogr.Abstr., Ecol.Abstr., Geo.Abstr., Geol.Abstr., GeoRef., Plant Breed.Abstr., Soils & Fert. **Document type:** academic/scholarly publication.
—BLDSC (7793.830000); Faxon; Genuine Article; PADDS; SWETS; UnCover. **CCC.**
    Description: Aims to stimulate wide interdisciplinary cooperation and understanding among workers in the fields of palaeobotany and palynology.
    Refereed Serial

560   SP   ISSN 0556-655X
QE719   CODEN: RTEMB5
REVISTA ESPANOLA DE MICROPALEONTOLOGIA. 1969. 3/yr. 9800 ptas. to individuals (foreign 12100 ptas.) (effective 1996). Instituto Tecnologico Geominero de Espana, C. Rios Rosas, 23, 28003 Madrid, Spain. TEL 34-1-3495730. FAX 34-1-3495762. adv.; bk.rev. circ. 700. **Indexed:** Biol.Abstr., Deep Sea Res.& Oceanogr.Abstr., GeoRef., Ind.SST.
—BLDSC (7854.110000); SWETS; UnCover. **CCC.**

560   SP   ISSN 0213-6937
    CODEN: RESAE5
REVISTA ESPANOLA DE PALEONTOLOGIA. 1986. s-a. 8000 ptas. (effective 1995) 9000 ptas. (effective 1996). Sociedad Espanola de Paleontologia, c/o Depto. de Geologia, Univ. de Oviedo, 33005 Oviedo, Spain. TEL 34-8-5103135. FAX 34-8-5103103. E-mail: mmchacon@asturias.geol.uniovi.es. Ed. Maria Luisa Martinez Chacon. bk.rev. **Document type:** academic/scholarly publication.
—BLDSC (7854.170000).

563   FR   ISSN 0035-1598
    CODEN: RMCPAM
REVUE DE MICROPALEONTOLOGIE. 1958. q. 240 F. to individuals (foreign 290 F.); institutions 440 F. (foreign 500 F.) (effective 1995). Maison de la Geologie, B.P. 11705, 75224 Paris Cedex 05, France. Ed. Gerard Bignot. adv. contact: M. Neumann. bk.rev.; bibl.; charts; illus. circ. 550. **Indexed:** Br.Geol.Lit., Bull.Signal., Curr.Adv.Ecol.Sci., Deep Sea Res.& Oceanogr.Abstr., Geo.Abstr., Geol.Abstr., GeoRef., Petrol.Abstr., Zoo.Rec. **Document type:** academic/scholarly publication.
—BLDSC (7933.500000); Faxon; PADDS; SWETS; UnCover.
    Description: Original scientific contributions, review papers and short communications, congress and symposium reports dealing with any micropaleontological theme.
    Refereed Serial

REVUE DE PALEOBIOLOGIE. see *EARTH SCIENCES — Geology*

560   NE
RIJKSUNIVERSITEIT TE UTRECHT. DEPARTMENT OF STRATIGRAPHY AND PALEONTOLOGY. SPECIAL PUBLICATIONS. (Text in English) 1974. irreg., no.5, 1989. price varies. Rijksuniversiteit te Utrecht, Department of Stratigraphy and Paleontology, Working Group of Mammal Paleontology - State University of Utrecht, c/o C.W. Drooger, Ed., Budapestlaan 4, P.O. Box 80.021, 3508 TA Utrecht, Netherlands. (Subscr. to: Sales Office, c/o W. Wessels, Budapestlaan 4, 3584 CD Utrecht, Netherlands) (back issues avail.) **Document type:** monographic series.

560.17   IT   ISSN 0035-6883
QE701   CODEN: RPLSAT
RIVISTA ITALIANA DI PALEONTOLOGIA E STRATIGRAFIA. (Text and summaries in English, French) 1895. 3/yr. L.60000 to individuals; institutions and foreign L.130000 (effective 1995). Universita degli Studi di Milano, Dipartimento di Scienze della Terra, Via Mangiagalli 34, 20133 Milan, Italy. TEL 39-2-23698232. FAX 39-2-70638261. Ed. Maurizio Gaetani. bk.rev.; abstr.; bibl.; charts; illus.; index, cum.index. circ. 450. **Indexed:** Biol.Abstr., Deep Sea Res.& Oceanogr.Abstr., Geo.Abstr., Geol.Abstr., GeoRef. **Document type:** academic/scholarly publication.
—BLDSC (7987.480000); PADDS; UnCover.
    Refereed Serial

560   RM   ISSN 1220-5656
QE755.R6
ROMANIAN JOURNAL OF PALEONTOLOGY. 1949. a. Institutul Geologic al Romaniei, Str. Caransebes Nr. 1, 78344 Bucharest, Rumania. TEL 40-1-6656625. FAX 40-1-3128444. E-mail: girbhr@roearn.ici.ro. **Document type:** academic/scholarly publication.
—BLDSC (8019.638800).
    Former titles (until 1991): Institutul de Geologie si Geofizica. Dari de Seama ale Sedintelor. 3. Paleontologie (ISSN 0254-7295); (until 1974): Institutul Geologie. Dari de Seama ale Sedintelor. 3. Paleontologie (ISSN 1010-9439); Supersedes in part (in 1967): Comitetul de Stat al Geologiei. Dari de Seama ale Sedintelor (ISSN 0366-9726)

S.I.S. CHRONOLOGY & CATASTROPHISM WORKSHOP. (Society for Interdisciplinary Studies) see *EARTH SCIENCES — Geology*

PALEONTOLOGY — ABSTRACTING, BIBLIOGRAPHIES, STATISTICS

560   XR   ISSN 0036-5297
QE755.C95   CODEN: SGPABC
SBORNIK GEOLOGICKYCH VED: PALEONTOLOGIE/JOURNAL OF GEOLOGICAL SCIENCES: PALEONTOLOGY. (Text in English, French or German; summaries also in Russian) 1949. irreg. price varies. Cesky Geologicky Ustav, Klarov 3, 118 21 Prague 1, Czech Republic. (Dist. by: Artia, Narodni 25, 111 27 Prague 1, Czech Republic) Ed. Ivo Chlupac. charts; illus. circ. 600. (back issues avail.) **Indexed:** Bull.Signal., Geol.Abstr., GeoRef., Ref.Zh. **Document type:** academic/scholarly publication.
—BLDSC (4992.600000).

560   SZ   ISSN 0080-7389
CODEN: SPAAAX
SCHWEIZERISCHE PALAEONTOLOGISCHE ABHANDLUNGEN/MEMOIRES SUISSE DE PALEONTOLOGIE. (Text in English, French, German, Italian) 1874. irreg. price varies. Kommission der Schweizerischen Palaeontologischen Abhandlungen, c/o Doris Groenhagen, Naturhistorisches Museum, CH-4001 Basel, Switzerland. FAX 061-2665546. Ed. B. Engesser. index. **Indexed:** Biol.Abstr., GeoRef. **Document type:** academic/scholarly publication.
—BLDSC (8119.200000); UMI. **CCC.**

560   GW   ISSN 0037-2110
QE701   CODEN: SLETAE
SENCKENBERGIANA LETHAEA. (Text and summaries in English, French and German) 1919. 6/yr. DM.98. Senckenbergische Naturforschende Gesellschaft, Abt. Schriftentausch, Senckenberganlage 25, 60325 Frankfurt a.M., Germany. TEL 069-7542-1. FAX 069-746238. TELEX 413129. Ed. W. Struve. bibl.; charts; illus.; maps; index, cum.index. circ. 850. **Indexed:** Biol.Abstr., Br.Geol.Lit., Chem.Abstr., Curr.Adv.Ecol.Sci., Deep Sea Res.& Oceanogr.Abstr., Geol.Abstr., GeoRef. **Document type:** academic/scholarly publication.
—BLDSC (8241.000000); UMI; UnCover. **CCC.**

560   SA
SIDNEY HAUGHTON MEMORIAL LECTURES. 1984. biennial. price varies. South African Museum, P.O. Box 61, Cape Town 8000, South Africa. TEL 27-21-243330. FAX 27-21-246716. Ed. Elizabeth Louw. illus.; circ. 450 (controlled). (back issues avail.) **Document type:** academic/scholarly publication, monographic series.
Description: Publishes lectures delivered by invited speakers. Honors Sidney Haughton and his contribution to palaeontology and geology of southern Africa.

560   US   ISSN 0081-0266
QE701   CODEN: SPBYA8
SMITHSONIAN CONTRIBUTIONS TO PALEOBIOLOGY. 1969. irreg., no.79, 1994. free. Smithsonian Institution Press, 470 L'Enfant Plaza, Ste. 7100, Washington, DC 20560. TEL 202-287-3738. FAX 202-287-3637. Ed. Don Fisher. circ. 2,500. (reprint service avail. from UMI) **Indexed:** AESIS, Biol.Abstr., Deep Sea Res.& Oceanogr.Abstr., Geol.Abstr., GeoRef. **Document type:** monographic series.
—BLDSC (8311.610000).

560   IT   ISSN 0375-7633
QE755.I8   CODEN: BSPIAY
SOCIETA PALEONTOLOGICA ITALIANA. BOLLETTINO. (Text in English, French and Italian) 1960. q. L.60000 in Europe; elsewhere L.80000 to individuals; institutions L.100000 (effective 1996). (Consiglio Nazionale delle Ricerche (CNR) - Italian Council for Scientific Research) Mucchi Editori s.r.l., Via Emila Est, 1527, 41100 Modena, Italy. FAX 39-53-218212. (Subscr. to: Dr. Stefano Conti, Treasurer S.P.I., c/o Dipartimento di Scienze della Terra, Piazzale S. Eufemia 19, 41100 Modena, Italy) Ed. E. Serpagli. cum.index: 1960-1983. circ. 700. **Indexed:** Deep Sea Res.& Oceanogr.Abstr., Geol.Abstr. **Document type:** bulletin.
—BLDSC (2231.700000).

SOCIETE BELGE DE GEOLOGIE. BULLETIN/BELGISCHE VERENIGING VOOR GEOLOGIE. BULLETIN. see *EARTH SCIENCES — Geology*

SOCIETE PREHISTORIQUE FRANCAISE. BULLETIN. see *ARCHAEOLOGY*

560   US   ISSN 0096-9117
QE701   CODEN: SVPNAJ
SOCIETY OF VERTEBRATE PALEONTOLOGY. NEWS BULLETIN. 1941. 3/yr. $25. Society of Vertebrate Paleontology, W. 436 Nebraska Hall, University of Nebraska, Lincoln, NE 68588-0542. TEL 402-472-4604. FAX 4025-472-8949. circ. 1,300. **Indexed:** Biol.Abstr., GeoRef. **Document type:** bulletin, newsletter.

SOUTH AFRICAN MUSEUM. ANNALS/SUID-AFRIKAANSE MUSEUM. ANNALE. see *BIOLOGY*

SPELEOLOGICAL SOCIETY OF JAPAN. JOURNAL. see *EARTH SCIENCES*

560   IT   ISSN 0587-1239
STUDI E RICERCHE SUI GIACIMENTI TERZIARI DI BOLCA. (Text and summaries in English, French, Italian) 1969. irreg., vol.6, 1990. L.35000 per no. Museo Civico di Storia Naturale di Verona, Lungadige Porta Vittoria 9, 37129 Verona, Italy. TEL 39-45-8001987. circ. 600. (back issues avail.)

STUDI PER L'ECOLOGIA DEL QUATERNARIO. see *ANTHROPOLOGY*

TERTIARY RESEARCH. see *EARTH SCIENCES — Geology*

TOHOKU DAIGAKU RIGAKUBU CHISHITSUGAKU KOSEIBUTSUGAKU KYOSHITSU KENKYU HOBUN HOKOKU/TOHOKU UNIVERSITY. FACULTY OF SCIENCE. INSTITUTE OF GEOLOGY AND PALEONTOLOGY. CONTRIBUTIONS. see *EARTH SCIENCES — Geology*

TOHOKU UNIVERSITY. SCIENCE REPORTS. SERIES 2: GEOLOGY/TOHOKU DAIGAKU RIKA HOKOKU. DAI 2-SHU, CHISHITSUGAKU. see *EARTH SCIENCES — Geology*

565   NO   ISSN 0085-7386
TRILOBITE NEWS. (Text in English) 1971. a. free. Universitet i Oslo, Paleontologiska Museum, Sarsgate 1, Oslo 5, Norway. Ed. D.L. Bruton. bk.rev.; abstr.; bibl.; index. circ. 250. **Indexed:** Biol.Abstr., GeoRef.

TULANE STUDIES IN GEOLOGY AND PALEONTOLOGY. see *EARTH SCIENCES — Geology*

560   IT
UNIVERSITA DEGLI STUDI DI FERRARA. ISTITUTO DI GEOLOGIA. ANNALI. SEZIONE 15. PALEONTOLOGIA UMANA E PALETNOLOGIA. (Text and summaries in English, French, Italian) 1959. irreg. exchange basis. Universita degli Studi di Ferrara, Istituto di Geologia, C.So Ercole 1 d'Este 32, Ferrara, Italy. circ. 450.
Formerly: Universita degli Studi di Ferrara. Istituto di Geologia, Paleontologia e Paleontologia Umana. Annali. Sezione 15. Paleontologia Umana e Paleontologia (ISSN 0071-4542)

UNIVERSITA DEGLI STUDI DI FERRARA. ISTITUTO DI GEOLOGIA. PUBBLICAZIONI. see *EARTH SCIENCES — Geology*

UNIVERSITAET HAMBURG. GEOLOGISCH-PALAEONTOLOGISCHES INSTITUT. MITTEILUNGEN. see *EARTH SCIENCES — Geology*

560   US   ISSN 1046-8390
QE701   CODEN: UKPCE3
UNIVERSITY OF KANSAS. PALEONTOLOGICAL CONTRIBUTIONS. NEW SERIES. 1947. irreg. price varies. University of Kansas, Paleontological Institute, 121 Lindley Hall, Lawrence, KS 66045. TEL 913-864-3338. FAX 913-864-5276. (Subscr. to: University of Kansas Libraries, Exchange & Gifts Dept., Lawrence, KS 66045) Ed. Roger L. Kaesler. abstr.; bibl. circ. 700. (back issues avail.) **Indexed:** AESIS, Biol.Abstr., Geo.Abstr. **Document type:** academic/scholarly publication.
—BLDSC (6345.323150).
Formed by the 1992 merger of: University of Kansas. Paleontological Contributions. Articles (ISSN 0075-5044) & University of Kansas. Paleontological Contributions. Papers. (ISSN 0075-5052) & University of Kansas. Paleontological Contributions. Monographs (ISSN 0278-9744)
Refereed Serial

560   US   ISSN 0041-9834
UNIVERSITY OF MICHIGAN. MUSEUM OF PALEONTOLOGY. CONTRIBUTIONS. 1924. irreg., vol.28, no.16, 1993. price varies. University of Michigan, Museum of Paleontology, 1529 Ruthven Museums Bldg., 1109 Geddes Rd., Ann Arbor, MI 48109-1079. TEL 313-764-0489. circ. 500. **Indexed:** Biol.Abstr. **Document type:** monographic series.
Refereed Serial

560   US   ISSN 0148-3838
QE701   CODEN: PPUMD3
UNIVERSITY OF MICHIGAN. MUSEUM OF PALEONTOLOGY. PAPERS ON PALEONTOLOGY. 1972. irreg., no.30, 1992. price varies. University of Michigan, Museum of Paleontology, 1529 Ruthven Museums Bldg., 1109 Geddes Rd., Ann Arbor, MI 48109-1079. TEL 313-764-0489. **Indexed:** GeoRef. **Document type:** monographic series.
Refereed Serial

UNIVERSITY OF WYOMING. CONTRIBUTIONS TO GEOLOGY. see *EARTH SCIENCES — Geology*

550   XR
USTREDNI USTAV GEOLOGICKY. ROZPRAVY. (Text in English or German; summaries in Czech and English) 1926. irreg. price varies. Cesky Geologicky Ustav, Klarov 3, 118 21 Prague 1, Czech Republic. (Dist by: Artia, Narodni 25, 111 27 Prague 1, Czech Republic) charts; illus. circ. 650. (back issues avail.) **Indexed:** Bull.Signal., GeoRef., Ref.Zh. **Document type:** academic/scholarly publication.

560   NE   ISSN 0083-4963
QE719   CODEN: UTMBAA
UTRECHT MICROPALEONTOLOGICAL BULLETINS. (Text in English) 1969. irreg., no.42, 1995. price varies. Rijksuniversiteit te Utrecht, Department of Stratigraphy and Paleontology - State University of Utrecht, Budapestlaan 4, P.O. Box 80.021, 3508 TA Utrecht, Netherlands. (Subscr. to: Sales Office, c/o W. Wessels, Budapestlaan 4, 3584 CD Utrecht, Netherlands) Ed. C.W. Drooger. (back issues avail.) **Indexed:** GeoRef. **Document type:** monographic series.
—BLDSC (9135.518000).

560   JA   ISSN 0387-5784
YAMAGUCHI KEIBINGU KURABU KAIHO/YAMAGUCHI CAVING CLUB. REPORT. (Text in Japanese) a. Yamaguchi Keibingu Kurabu - Yamaguchi Caving Club, Akiyoshidai Kagaku Hakubutsukan, Akiyoshi, Shuhocho, Mine-gun, Yamaguchi-ken 754-05, Japan.

560 551   GW   ISSN 0373-9627
QE701   CODEN: ZTLAAN
ZITTELIANA; Abhandlungen der Bayerischen Staatssammlung fuer Palaeontologie und historische Geologie. 1969. irreg., no.20. DM.150. Bayerische Staatssammlung fuer Palaeontologie und Historische Geologie, Richard-Wagner-Str. 10, 80333 Munich, Germany. TEL 089-5203361. FAX 089-5203276. (Dist. by: Gerhard Trenkle, Joerg-Toemlinger-Str. 2, 82152 Planegg, Germany) Ed. Dietrich Herm. **Indexed:** Biol.Abstr., GeoRef. **Document type:** proceedings.
—BLDSC (9514.667000). **CCC.**

PALEONTOLOGY — Abstracting, Bibliographies, Statistics

AMERICAN ASSOCIATION OF STRATIGRAPHIC PALYNOLOGISTS. ABSTRACTS OF PAPERS PRESENTED AT THE ANNUAL MEETINGS. see *EARTH SCIENCES — Abstracting, Bibliographies, Statistics*

560 016   US   ISSN 0300-7227
BIBLIOGRAPHY AND INDEX OF MICROPALEONTOLOGY. (Text in original language with English translation) 1971. m. $75 to individuals, institutions; corporations $600. American Museum of Natural History, Central Park W. at 79th St., New York, NY 10024-5192. TEL 212-769-5656. FAX 212-769-5653. E-mail: scipubs@amnh.org. Eds. Susan Carroll, Sharon Tahirkeli. abstr.; bibl.; index. circ. 150. (looseleaf format; reprint service avail. from UMI) **Document type:** bibliography.
—**CCC.**
Description: Survey of world literature in all fields of micropaleontology, with annual subject and author index.

560   JA
NIHON KOSEIBUTSU GAKKAI NENKAI KOEN YOKOSHU/PALAEONTOLOGICAL SOCIETY OF JAPAN. ABSTRACTS OF THE ANNUAL MEETING. (Text in English, Japanese) a. Nihon Koseibutsu Gakkai - Palaeontological Society of Japan, Nihon Gakkai Jimu Senta, 16-9, Honkomagome 5-chome, Bunkyo-ku, Tokyo 113, Japan.

560 016   FR   ISSN 1146-5247
P A S C A L F 47: PALEONTOLOGIE. (Printed format ceased Jan. 1995) (Text in English, French) 1984. 10/yr. (Bureau de Recherches Geologiques et Minieres) Centre National de la Recherche Scientifique, Institut de l'Information Scientifique et Technique, 2 allee du Parc de Brabois, 54514 Vandoeuvre-Les-Nancy Cedex, France. TEL 83-50-46-00. FAX 83-50-46-50. adv. contact: Veronique Guinvarc'h. abstr. (also avail. in microfiche) **Document type:** bibliography.
●Also available online. Vendor(s): European Space Agency (File no.14), Knight-Ridder, Inc. (File no.144), Telesystemes - Questel.
Also available on CD-ROM.
Former titles: P A S C A L Folio. F 47: Paleontologie (ISSN 0761-1889); P A S C A L Folio. Part 47: Paleontologie; Which superseded (in 1984): Bulletin Signaletique: Bibliographie des Sciences de la Terre. Section 227: Paleontologie (ISSN 0300-9335).

560 016   GW   ISSN 0044-4189
                     CODEN: ZGPGA4
ZENTRALBLATT FUER GEOLOGIE UND PALAEONTOLOGIE. TEIL II: PALAEONTOLOGIE. 1807. 7/yr. @ $67 per no. (effective 1996). E. Schweizerbart'sche Verlagsbuchhandlung, Johannesstr. 3A, 70176 Stuttgart, Germany. TEL 0711-625001. FAX 0711-625005. Eds. Adolf Seilacher, E. Seilacher. adv.; bk.rev.; abstr.; bibl.; index. **Indexed:** Chem.Abstr., Deep Sea Res.& Oceanogr.Abstr. **Document type:** academic/scholarly publication.
—CCC.

PAPER AND PULP

see also Packaging

676   GW   ISSN 0002-5917
A P R. (Allgemeine Papier-Rundschau) (Text in German; summaries in English) 1876. w. DM.270 (foreign DM.315). P. Keppler Verlag GmbH und Co. KG, Industriestr. 2, 63150 Heusenstamm, Germany. TEL 06104-6060. FAX 06104-606145. Ed. Gerhard Brucker; Pub. Eckhart Thomas. adv.: B&W page DM.3350, color page DM.5690. bk.rev.; abstr.; bibl.; charts; illus.; pat.; stat.; index. circ. 6,281. **Indexed:** Abstr.Bull.Inst.Pap.Chem., Int.Packag.Abstr., Packag.Sci.Tech., Paper & Bd.Abstr., PROMT. **Document type:** trade publication.
—BLDSC (0791.900000). **CCC.**

676   MX
A T C P REVISTA. (Text in Spanish; summaries in English) 1960. bi-m. Mex.$64.50($50) (effective 1995). (Asociacion Mexicana de Tecnicos de las Industrias de la Celulosa y del Papel, A.C.) G S A Publicidad, Av. Insurgentes No. 3493, Poseidon No. 504, 14020 Mexico, D.F., Mexico. TEL 525-665-0368. FAX 525-665-0368. TELEX 1773608 CNCPME. Ed. Octavio Tirado. adv.: B&W page $960, color page $1400, adv. contact: Octavio Tirado. bk.rev.; bibl.; charts; illus.; stat.; tr.lit. circ. 1,700. (also avail. in microform; back issues avail.) **Document type:** trade publication.
Description: Information on the technology, manufacture and business administration of the pulp and paper trade industry worldwide.

676   FR   ISSN 0997-7554
                   CODEN: ATIPBH
A T I P. 1947. 6/yr. 1075 F. (foreign 1905 F.). Association Technique de l'Industrie Papetiere, 154 bd. Haussmann, 75008 Paris, France. FAX 33-1-45-63-53-09. Ed. E. Devos. adv.; bk.rev.; charts; illus.; circ. 2,050 (controlled). **Indexed:** C.I.S.Abstr., Chem.Abstr., Forest Prod.Abstr.
—BLDSC (7874.723000); CASDDS.
Former titles (until 1989): Revue A T I P (ISSN 0750-7666); (until 1982): A T I P (ISSN 0004-5896); (until 1966): Association Technique de l'Industrie Papetiere. Bulletin (ISSN 0403-7383)
Description: Disseminates information on innovations and new technologies, research and applications developed in France, in Europe and throughout the world in relation to the pulp, paper, and allied industries.
Refereed Serial

ADHESIVE TRENDS. see *RUBBER*

676   US
ALBANY INTERNATIONAL FELT DIVISION. NEWS. q. Albany International Felt Division, 1373 Broadway, Albany, NY 12204-2697. TEL 518-447-6581. Ed. Maryhelen McDermott. circ. 1,200.

676   US   ISSN 0897-2524
                   CODEN: APADFJ
ALKALINE PAPER ADVOCATE. 1988. 4/yr. $35 to individuals; institutions $45. Abbey Publications, Inc., 7105 Geneva Dr., Austin, TX 78723-1510. TEL 512-929-3992. FAX 512-929-3995. Ed. Ellen McCrady. bk.rev.; index. circ. 500. (tabloid format; back issues avail.) **Document type:** newsletter.
—Ei.
Description: For those interested (papermakers, librarians and paper industry suppliers) in paper permanence and trends in conversion to alkaline papermaking, world wide. Includes current news and events.

676.2   CC
ALMANAC OF CHINA'S PAPER INDUSTRY. (Text in Chinese; summaries in English) 1986. triennial. $100 (effective 1996). China Technical Association of Paper Industry, 6 East Chang'an St., Beijing 100740, People's Republic of China. TEL 86-1-512-1122. (Subscr. to: Zhongguo Zaozhi Xuehui - China Technical Association of the Paper Industry, 12 Guanghua Rd., Beijing 100020, P.R. China. TEL 86-1-500-2880. FAX 86-1-500-4461) Ed. Yu Yiji. adv.; bk.rev./; circ. 6,500 (paid). **Document type:** directory.

676   US
AMERICAN FOREST & PAPER ASSOCIATION. CAPACITY SURVEY. 1958. a. $375 (foreign $395). American Forest & Paper Association, 1111 19th St., N.W., Washington, DC 20036. TEL 202-463-2700. FAX 202-463-2785. circ. 2,500. (also avail. in microfiche from CIS) **Document type:** SRI.
Formerly: American Paper Institute. Capacity Survey.

676   CN
AMERICAN PAPERMAKER. 1938. m. $30 (foreign $45) (free to qualified personnel). Maclean Hunter Ltd., 777 Bay St., Toronto, ON M5W 1A7, Canada. TEL 416-596-5897. FAX 416-593-3170. Ed. Jerry Korneel. adv. circ. 30,500. **Document type:** trade publication.
●Also available online. Vendor(s): Lexis-Nexis.

ANNUAL BOOK OF A S T M STANDARDS. VOLUME 15.09. PAPER; PACKAGING; FLEXIBLE BARRIER MATERIALS; BUSINESS COPY PRODUCTS. see *ENGINEERING — Engineering Mechanics And Materials*

676   AT   ISSN 0003-6757
TS1080   CODEN: APPIA2
APPITA. 1947. bi-m. Aus.$55 to non-members (effective 1992). Technical Association of the Australian and New Zealand Pulp and Paper Industry, Inc., Ste. 47, Level 1, Carlton Clocktower, 255 Drummond St., Carlton, Vic. 3053, Australia. FAX 61-3-348-1206. Ed. Peter J. Brown. adv.: B&W page Aus.$990; trim 297 x 210. bk.rev.; charts; illus.; index. circ. 1,900. (also avail. in microform from UMI) **Indexed:** Abstr.Bull.Inst.Pap.Chem., Anal.Abstr., Biol.Abstr., Chem.Abstr., Chem.Eng.Abstr., Curr.Cont., Energy Ind., Energy Info.Abstr., Forest.Abstr., Forest Prod.Abstr., Ind.Sci.Rev., P.I.R.A., Paper & Bd.Abstr., Sci.Cit.Ind., T.C.E.A.

AUSTRALIAN LITHOGRAPHER, PRINTER, AND PACKAGER. see *PRINTING*

634.9 676   US
B C NEWS. 1986. 5/yr. qualified personnel only. Boise Cascade Corporation, 1111 W. Jefferson St., Box 50, Boise, ID 83728-0001. TEL 208-384-6105. FAX 208-384-7224. Ed. Sue Rourke. circ. 24,265. **Document type:** newsletter.
Former titles (until 1992): Boise Cascade Insight; Boise Cascade Quarterly.
Description: News and information for employees and retirees of Boise Cascade Corporation.

BERITA SELULOSA. see *FORESTS AND FORESTRY*

676   GW
BIRKNER (YEAR) - EUROPEAN AND INTERNATIONAL PAPERWORLD. (Text in English, French, German, Italian, Portuguese, Spanish) 1905. a. DM.290($210) Birkner & Co., Winsbergring 38, 22525 Hamburg, Germany. TEL 040-85308502. FAX 040-85308381. circ. 4,500. **Document type:** directory, trade publication.
●Also available on CD-ROM.
Formed by the 1994 merger of: Europa Birkner & Birkner PaperWorld.

BOARD CONVERTING NEWS. see *PACKAGING*

BOARD CONVERTING NEWS INTERNATIONAL. see *PACKAGING*

676   CU   ISSN 0138-8940
BOLETIN TECNICO PULPA Y PAPEL. 1984. s-a. exchange basis. Union del Papel, Departamento Tecnico, Calle Perla y Primera, Los Pinos, Havana 11800, Cuba. TEL 448651. TELEX 512121. Ed. Francisco Cabrera. bk.rev. circ. 2,000. **Document type:** trade publication.
Description: Offers updated information on pulp, paper and converting issues from both domestic and international industries.

BRITAIN'S TOP 500 PAPER AND BOARD. see *BUSINESS AND ECONOMICS — Trade And Industrial Directories*

676.2   UK   ISSN 0068-2330
BRITISH PAPER AND BOARD INDUSTRY FEDERATION. TECHNICAL ASSOCIATION. TECHNICAL PAPERS. 1960. a. £100. Paper Industry Technical Association, 4 Frecheville Ct., Bury, Lancashire BL9 0UF, England. TEL 0161-764-5858. FAX 0161-764-5353. Ed. M. Marley; Pub. J. Clewley. adv. contact: Frank Colling. index. **Document type:** trade publication.

676   RU   ISSN 0007-5817
                   CODEN: BUMPAK
BUMAZHNAYA PROMYSHLENNOST'. 1922. m. 26.40 Rub. Ministerstvo Tsellyulozno-bumazhnoi Promyshlennosti, Ul. 25 Oktyabrya, Moscow K-12, Russia. Ed. V.N. Shul'gin. bk.rev.; charts; illus.; index. **Indexed:** Abstr.Bull.Inst.Pap.Chem., Chem.Abstr., Forest Prod.Abstr.
—CASDDS.

676 658.8   UK   ISSN 0261-9326
BUSINESS RATIO REPORT: PAPER & BOARD MANUFACTURERS; an industry sector analysis. 1973. a. I C C Business Ratios Ltd., Freepost, Field House, Hampton, Mddx. TW12 1BR, England. TEL 081-783-0977. FAX 081-783-1940. charts; stat. **Document type:** trade publication.
—BLDSC (6358.905000).

BUSINESS RATIO REPORT: PAPER & BOARD PACKAGING; an industry sector analysis. see *PACKAGING*

676 658.8   UK   ISSN 0261-9318
BUSINESS RATIO REPORT: PAPER MERCHANTS; an industry sector analysis. 1973. a. I C C Business Ratios Ltd., Freepost, Field House, Hampton, Mddx. TW12 1BR, England. TEL 081-783-0977. FAX 081-783-1940. charts; stat. **Document type:** trade publication.
—BLDSC (6364.190000).

PAPER AND PULP

676 384 CN
C E P JOURNAL. (Text in English, French) 1977. q. free. Communications, Energy and Paperworkers Union of Canada - Syndicat Canadien des Communications, de l'Energie et du Papier, 350 Albert St., Ste. 1900, Ottawa, ON K1R 1A4, Canada. TEL 613-230-5200. FAX 613-230-5801. Ed. Catherine Hallessey. circ. 145,000. **Document type:** trade publication, newspaper.
  Formerly: C P U Journal (ISSN 0711-1053); Formed by the 1981 merger of: Intercom (English Edition) (ISSN 0229-9402); Intercom (French Edition) (ISSN 0229-9410); Which superseded in part (in 1980): C P U Journal (ISSN 0705-0763)

676 CN ISSN 0705-6710
CANADIAN PAPER ANALYST. 1978. 9/yr. $205. J.D.R. Publications, P.O. Box 300, Westmount Station, Westmount, Que. H3Z 2V5, Canada. TEL 514-933-8749. FAX 514-849-8367. Ed. Jim Rowland. (back issues avail.)

676 CN ISSN 1191-887X
TS1080 CODEN: CPAPE8
CANADIAN PAPERMAKER. 1948. 12/yr. Can.$45. Maclean Hunter Ltd., Business Publication Division, Maclean Hunter Bldg., 777 Bay St., Toronto, ON M5W 1A7, Canada. TEL 416-596-5518. Ed. Wayne Karl. adv.; bk.rev.; abstr.; charts; illus.; mkt.; pat.; stat.; tr.lit.; index. circ. 7,606. (also avail. in microform from UMI; reprint service avail. from UMI) **Indexed:** Abstr.Bull.Inst.Pap.Chem., Can.B.P.I., Chem.Abstr., P.A.I.S, PROMT.
●Also available online. Vendor(s): Lexis-Nexis.
—BLDSC (6367.800000); Faxon. **CCC.**
  Incorporates: Journal des Pates et Papiers (ISSN 0830-887X); Which was formerly (until 1985): Foret etPapier (ISSN 0319-762X) & Pulp and Paper Journal (ISSN 0713-5807); Supersedes in part (in 1982): Canadian Pulp and Paper Industry (ISSN 0008-4867)

676 CN ISSN 0709-602X
HD9839.N43
CANADIAN PULP AND PAPER ASSOCIATION. MONTHLY NEWSPRINT STATISTICS/ASSOCIATION CANADIENNE DES PATES ET PAPIERS. STATISTIQUES MENSUELLES SUR LE PAPIER JOURNAL. (Text in English, French) m. Canadian Pulp and Paper Association - Association Canadienne des Pates et Papiers, Sun Life Bldg., 19th Fl., 1155 Metcalfe St., Montreal, PQ H3B 4T6, Canada. TEL 514-866-6621. FAX 514-866-3035. charts; stat. (looseleaf format)
  Description: Reviews pulp and paper production, stocks, exports, and consumption.

676.1 CN
CANADIAN PULP AND PAPER ASSOCIATION. TECHNICAL SECTION. PROCEEDINGS. 1915. a. Can.$115 to non-members; members Can.$100. Canadian Pulp and Paper Association, Sun Life Bldg., 19th Fl., 1155 Metcalfe St., Montreal, PQ H3B 4T6, Canada. TEL 514-866-6621. FAX 514-866-3035. index. circ. 100. **Indexed:** Abstr.Bull.Inst.Pap.Chem. **Document type:** proceedings.

CELLULOSA E CARTA. see *FORESTS AND FORESTRY — Lumber And Wood*

676 RM ISSN 0008-879X
TS1080 CODEN: CLOZA8
CELULOZA SI HIRTIE. (Text in Rumanian; summaries in English, French, German, Russian) 1951. q. $100. Technical Association for Romanian Pulp and Paper Industry, Calea Grivitei, 21 sect. 1, Bucharest, Rumania. TEL 50-64-30. FAX 50-60-45. TELEX 10944 ICHIM. adv.; bk.rev.; abstr.; bibl.; illus.; pat.; index. circ. 1,000. **Indexed:** Chem. Abstr.
  Supersedes in part: Revista Padurilor-Industria Lemnului-Celuloza si Hirtie (ISSN 0035-029X)

676 FR
CENTRE TECHNIQUE DU PAPIER. FEUILLETS BIBLIOGRAPHIQUES. 1969. m. 985. Centre Technique du Papier, B.P. 7110, 38020 Grenoble Cedex, France. bibl. circ. 200.
  Formerly: Association Technique de l'Industrie Papetiere. Feuillets Bibliographiques. (ISSN 0004-5888)

COMPUTER PAPER (ALBERTA EDITION); Canada's computer information source. see *COMPUTERS*

COMPUTER PAPER (MANITOBA EDITION); Canada's computer information source. see *COMPUTERS*

COMPUTER PAPER (ONTARIO EDITION). see *COMPUTERS*

676 UK ISSN 0010-8189
CONVERTER. 1964. m. £50($88) (foreign £55) (effective 1995). Faversham House Group Ltd., Faversham House, 232a Addington Rd., South Croydon, Surrey CR2 8LE. TEL 44-181-651-7100. FAX 44-181-651-7117. adv.; bk.rev.; charts; illus.; stat.; tr.lit.; index. circ. 4,257. (also avail. in microform from UMI; reprint service avail. from UMI) **Indexed:** Abstr.Bull.Inst.Pap.Chem., Art & Archaeol.Tech.Abstr., Curr.Pack.Abstr., Int.Packag.Abstr., Intl.Polym.Sci.& Tech., Paper & Bd.Abstr., Print.Abstr., RAPRA. **Document type:** trade publication.
—BLDSC (3463.600000); UMI.
  Description: Covers the paper, paperboard, foil, and film converters market.

380 UK ISSN 0309-2143
CONVERTER DIRECTORY; suppliers and services to the U.K. converting industry. a. Faversham House Group Ltd., Faversham House, 232a Addington Rd., South Croydon, Surrey CR2 8LE, England. TEL 44-181-651-7100. FAX 44-181-651-7117. (reprint service avail. from UMI) **Document type:** directory.

676 US ISSN 0746-7141
CONVERTING MAGAZINE. 1979. m. $60 (foreign $65) (free to qualified personnel). Cahners Publishing Company (Des Plaines), Division of Reed Elsevier Inc., 1350 E. Touhy Ave., Box 5080, Des Plaines, IL 60017-5080. TEL 708-635-8800. FAX 708-299-8622. (Subscr. to: 44 Cook St., Denver, CO 80206-5800) Ed. Yolanda Simonsis; Pub. Steve Bowers. adv.: B&W page $3770, color page $4995; trim 7 7/8 x 10 3/4; adv. contact: Diane Pentoney. tr.lit. circ. 40,363. **Document type:** trade publication.
—BLDSC (3463.612000). **CCC.**
  Former titles: Converting Product News (ISSN 0279-4187); Paper and Converting Product News.
  Description: For industries which convert paper, paperboard, plastic, film and foil via printing, coating, laminating, extruding, slitting, forming, sealing and related processes.

676.3 UK ISSN 0264-715X
CONVERTING TODAY. 1987. m. £42($146) (outside Europe £53). Angel Publishing Ltd., Kingsland House, 361 City Rd., London EC1V 1LR, England. TEL 0171-417-7400. FAX 0171-417-7500. Ed. Pauline Covell; Pub. Dennis Cooper. adv. contact: Jeremy Beard. circ. 6,000. **Document type:** trade publication.
—BLDSC (3463.614500); Ei.

CONVERTING WORLD. see *PACKAGING*

CORRUGATED CONTAINERS CONFERENCE (YEAR). see *PACKAGING*

676 GW ISSN 0012-1096
TS1080
DEUTSCHER DRUCKER. (Text in German; index in English and Russian) 1952. m. DM.84 (foreign DM.104.40). Deutscher Drucker Verlag GmbH, Postfach 4124, 73744 Ostfildern, Germany. TEL 0711-444005. FAX 0711-442099. Ed. Theodor Anton. adv.: B&W page DM.4980, color page DM.9235; trim 185 x 263; adv. contact: Michael Schwab. bk.rev.; abstr.; illus.; pat.; tr.lit.; tr.mk.; index. circ. 13,882. **Indexed:** Abstr.Bull.Inst.Pap.Chem., Bibl.Cart., C.I.S. Abstr., Chem.Abstr. **Document type:** trade publication.
  Formerly: Papier und Druck (ISSN 0031-1375)
  Description: Trade publication for the printing and paper manufacturing industries, featuring book production and design, graphic arts, book binding, production development, screen printing, industry news, and reports of events and exhibitions.

676 IT
DICARTA; spazio aperto al mondo della cartoleria. 1980. m. L.16000. Raddicchi Editore S.R.L., Via S. G.B. De la Salle 4, 20132 Milan, Italy. TEL 39-2-26300330. FAX 39-2-2566849. Ed. Lino Radicchi. adv.: B&W page L.2050000, color page L.3050000; trim 290 x 210. circ. 8,908.

676 658.8 UK
DISPOSABLE PAPER PRODUCTS: THE INTERNATIONAL MARKET. (Subseries of: Market Direction reports) a. £1595($3190) (effective 1996). Euromonitor, 60-61 Britton St., London EC1M 5NA, England. TEL 0171-251-8024. FAX 0171-608-3149. (Addr. in N. America: Euromonitor International, 122 S. Michigan Ave., Ste. 1200, Chicago, IL 60603. TEL 312-922-1115. FAX 312-922-1157) (looseleaf format) **Document type:** trade publication.
●Also available online. Vendor(s): Data-Star, Knight-Ridder, Inc.
  Description: Analyzes the market for disposable paper products in France, Germany, Italy, Spain, the U.K., the U.S., and Japan.

DRUCK UND PAPIER. see *PRINTING*

676 US
E S P NEWS. (Environmentally Sound Paper) bi-m. $59. Conservatree Paper Company, 10 Lombard St., Ste.250, San Francisco, CA 94111. TEL 415-433-1000. FAX 415-391-7890. Ed. David Assmann. circ. 25,000. **Document type:** newsletter, trade publication.
  Description: Discusses environmentally sound paper issues, including recycled paper and chlorine-free paper issues.

676 UK
EQUIPMENT, MACHINERY AND MATERIALS. 1991. bi-m. £55 (rest of Europe £75; elsewhere £105). Whitmar Publications Ltd., 30 London Rd., Southborough, Tunbridge Wells, Kent TN4 0RE, England. TEL 01892-542099. FAX 01892-546693. Ed. Martin Swayne. circ. 7,000. **Document type:** trade publication.
  Formerly: Equipment and Machinery (ISSN 0964-0460)

676 GW
EUROPAEISCHER WIRTSCHAFTSDIENST. HOLZ- UND ZELLSTOFF-DIENST. w. DM.635. E U W I D - Europaeischer Wirtschaftsdienst GmbH, Bleichstr. 20-22, 76593 Gernsbach, Germany. TEL 07224-9397-0. FAX 07224-939750. Eds. Casimir Katz, Heike Schweder. circ. 2,110. **Document type:** trade publication.

676 GW
EUROPAEISCHER WIRTSCHAFTSDIENST. INFORMATIONSBRIEF HOLZ - ZELLSTOFF - PAPIER. m. DM.450. E U W I D - Europaeischer Wirtschaftsdienst GmbH, Bleichstr. 20-22, 76593 Gernsbach, Germany. TEL 07224-9397-0. FAX 07224-939750. TELEX 78915-DBV-D. **Document type:** trade publication.

676 GW ISSN 0171-1458
EUROPAEISCHER WIRTSCHAFTSDIENST. PAPIER- UND ZELLSTOFF-DIENST. 1926. w. DM.745. E U W I D - Europaeischer Wirtschaftsdienst GmbH, Bleichstr. 20-22, 76593 Gernsbach, Germany. TEL 07224-9397-0. FAX 07224-939750. TELEX 78915-DBV-D. Ed. Ellen Streckel. circ. 3,360. **Document type:** trade publication.

676 GW
EUROPAEISCHER WIRTSCHAFTSDIENST. PULP AND PAPER SERVICE. (Text in English) 1926. w. DM.955. E U W I D - Europaeischer Wirtschaftsdienst GmbH, Bleichstr. 20-22, 76593 Gernsbach, Germany. TEL 07224-9397-0. FAX 07224-939750. TELEX 78915-DBV-D. Ed. Bernd Hecht. circ. 1,050. **Document type:** trade publication.

676 658.7 UK ISSN 0961-7507
EUROPEAN CONVERTING INDUSTRY DIRECTORY. 1990. a. £27. Kingland House, 361 City Rd., London EC1V 1LR, England. TEL 071-417-7400. FAX 071-417-7500. **Document type:** directory.
  Formerly (until 1991): Converting Today Directory (ISSN 0959-261X)

PAPER AND PULP

676 540   UK   ISSN 1351-4199
▼**FOCUS ON PAPER CHEMICALS.** 1994. m. £165($305) The Royal Society of Chemistry, Thomas Graham House, Science Park, Milton Rd., Cambridge DB4 4WF, England. TEL 01223-420066. FAX 01223-423429. E-mail: rscl@rsc.org. (Subscr. to: Turpin Distribution Services Ltd., Blackhorse Rd., Letchworth, Herts., SG6 1HN, England. TEL 01462-672555. FAX 01462-480947) Ed. Reg Adams. **Document type:** newsletter.
   Description: Covers trends in supply and demand, market prices, and technical developments in chemicals used in the manufacture of paper.

676 686.2 688.8   II   ISSN 0970-3705
FOUR P NEWS; India's leading journal on pulp, paper, printing and packaging. (Text in English) 1988. bi-m. Rs.85($20) 22, Congress Exhibition Rd., Calcutta 700 017, India. TEL 91-33-247-8718. Ed. Sankar Chakraborty. adv.; bk.rev. circ. 5,500.
—BLDSC (4028.053000).

G P MAGAZIN. (Gewerkschaftpost) see
ENGINEERING — Chemical Engineering

GEWERKSCHAFTLICHE UMSCHAU. see
ENGINEERING — Chemical Engineering

676   US   ISSN 0364-1260
GOVERNMENT PAPER SPECIFICATION STANDARDS. irreg. base vols. plus irreg. supplements. $21 (foreign £26.25). U.S. Government Printing Office, c/o Superintendent of Documents, Washington, DC 20402. (Subscr. to: Superintendent of Documents, U.S. Government Printing Office, Box 371954, Pittsburgh, PA 15250. TEL 202-512-1800. FAX 202-512-2250) (looseleaf format) **Document type:** government publication.
   Description: Prescribes standards for paper stock for printing. Contains detailed standard specifications, standards to be used in testing, and color standards.

676.2   CC   ISSN 1001-3911
GUOWAI ZAOZHI/WORLD PULP AND PAPER. (Text in Chinese) 1982. bi-m. $24. Zhongguo Zaozhi Xuehui - China Technical Association of the Paper Industry, 12 Guanghua Lu, Chaoyang-qu, Beijing 100020, People's Republic of China. TEL 86-1-500-2880. FAX 86-1-500-4461. (Co-sponsor: Paper Industry Research Institute of China) Ed. Li Jiawan. adv. contact: Chai Shuping. circ. 3,000.
   Description: Covers news and technological achievements in global pulp and paper industry.

676.2 745.5   US   ISSN 0887-1418
HAND PAPERMAKING. (Includes quarterly newsletter) 1986. s-a. $35 (N. America $40, elsewhere $45). Box 77027, Washington, DC 20013. TEL 301-587-3635. E-mail: HPDURGIN@AOL.COM. Ed. Michael Durgin. adv.; B&W page $275; 9 x 12; adv. contact: Bobbie Lippman. bk.rev.; circ. 1,750 (paid). (back issues avail.) **Indexed:** Ind.How To Do It (1989-). **Document type:** consumer publication.
—BLDSC (4241.594000); Faxon.
   Description: Devoted to advancing traditional and contemporary ideas in the art of Eastern and Western papermaking. Provides information for readers at all levels of expertise and from all perspectives of interest.

676   NE
HANDBOOK OF PAPER SCIENCE; the science and technology of papermaking, paper properties and paper usage. 1980. irreg., vol.2, 1982. price varies. Elsevier Science B.V., Books Division, P.O. Box 211, 1000 AE Amsterdam, Netherlands. TEL 31-20-4853911. FAX 31-20-4853705. TELEX 18582 ESPA NL. E-mail: nlinfo-f@elsevier.nl; usinfo-f@elsevier.com; forinfo-kyf04035@niftyserve.or.jp; Site addr.: http://www.elsevier.nl/. (Subscr. in U.S. and Canada to: Elsevier Science Inc., Box 882, Madison Sq. Sta., New York, NY 10159. TEL 212-989-5800) **Document type:** monographic series.
   Refereed Serial

676   JA
HONSHU PAPER COMPANY (YEAR). ANNUAL REPORT. a. Honshu Paper Co., Ltd., 26-20, Higashi 1-chome, Shibuya-ku, Tokyo 150, Japan. TEL 03-5467-1012. FAX 03-546-1014. **Document type:** corporate report.
   Description: Reports the company's past year business and financial performances. Contains balance sheets, statements of income and retained earnings, and corporate data.

676   UK   ISSN 1010-4054
TS1090
I P H YEARBOOK/ I P H - JAHRBUCH/ANNUAIRE I P H. (Text in English, French, German) 1980. a. 50 SFr. to non-members. International Association of Paper Historians - Internationalen Arbeitsgemeinschaft der Papierhistoriker, c/o Ludwig Ritterpusch, IPH Secretary, Wehrdaertstr. 135, 35041 Marburg, Germany. TEL 06421-81758. **Document type:** newsletter.

676 700   SP   ISSN 0211-2876
IMPREMPRES; tecnicas equipos para las artes graficas e industrias de la transformacion del papel y carton. 12/yr. 4500 ptas. Pedeca Sociedad Cooperativa, Ltda., Maria Auxiliadora 5, 28040 Madrid, Spain. TEL 1-450-88-37. FAX 1-450-94-29. Ed. J.F. Munoz Requena. circ. 7,000.

INDIAN PRINT & PAPER; a journal for printers, papermakers and the allied industries, see PRINTING

676   II   ISSN 0019-6231
TS1171   CODEN: IPPAAW
INDIAN PULP AND PAPER; India's leading journal on paper, printing and packaging. (Text in English) 1946. bi-m. Rs.30($9) R.N. Chatterjee, Ed. & Pub., 15 India Exchange Pl., 3rd Floor, Calcutta 700001, India. adv.; bk.rev.; charts; illus.; index. circ. 3,500. **Indexed:** Abstr.Bull.Inst.Pap.Chem., Chem.Abstr., Cott.& Trop.Fibr.Abstr., Field Crop Abstr., Forest.Abstr., Forest Prod.Abstr.
—CASDDS; UMI.

676   II
INDIAN PULP & PAPER INDUSTRY DESKBOOK. (Text in English) 1978. biennial. $55. Technical Press Publications, 5-1 Convent Street, Colaba, Bombay 400 039, India. TEL 022-2021446. FAX 022-2871499. TELEX 011-83479 CHEM IN. Ed. J.P. Sousa. adv.; bk.rev.; abstr.; charts; illus. circ. 6,400. (also avail. in microform from UMI.)

676   IT   ISSN 0019-7548
                 CODEN: ICAMA4
INDUSTRIA DELLA CARTA. (Text in Italian; summaries in English and Italian) 1962. m. (10/yr.). L.100000 (foreign L.130000). Editrice Arti Poligrafiche Europee, Via Casella 16, 20156 Milan, Italy. TEL 39-2-330221. FAX 39-2-39214341. TELEX 326544 ANTO I. Dir. Osvaldo Gigliotti. adv.: B&W page L.2130000, color page L.2550000; trim 172 x 265. bk.rev.; illus.; stat.; index. circ. 4,000. **Indexed:** Abstr.Bull.Inst.Pap.Chem., Chem.Abstr., PROMT.
—BLDSC (4438.466000); CASDDS; Ei.

INFORMACION TECNICO ECONOMICA. see BUSINESS AND ECONOMICS

676   US   ISSN 0361-4719
                CODEN: IPPICO
INSTRUMENTATION IN THE PULP AND PAPER INDUSTRY. 1960. irreg. price varies. Instrument Society of America, 67 Alexander Dr., Box 12277, Research Triangle Park, NC 27709. TEL 919-549-8411. FAX 919-549-8288. TELEX 802540 ISA DURM. (reprint service avail. from ISI,UMI) **Indexed:** INSPEC. **Document type:** proceedings.
—BLDSC (4529.042000); Ei. CCC.
   Refereed Serial

INTERNATIONAL PAPER BOARD INDUSTRY. see PACKAGING

676   II   ISSN 0047-1038
INTERNATIONAL PRESS CUTTING SERVICE: PAPER - PULP - BOARD - STRAW. 1967. w. $65. International Press Cutting Service, Box 63, Allahabad 211001, India. Ed. N. Khanna. bk.rev.; index. circ. 1,200. (processed)

676 670   US   ISSN 0097-2509
HD9820.3
INTERNATIONAL PULP & PAPER DIRECTORY. 1974. biennial. $237 (Business Travel Editions - Europe $167; Asia-Australasia $167). Miller Freeman, Inc. (Subsidiary of: United Newspapers), 600 Harrison St., San Francisco, CA 94107. TEL 415-905-2200. FAX 415-905-2232. TELEX 278273. Ed. Vincent M. Ridley. **Document type:** directory.
—BLDSC (4545.440000). CCC.

676   GW
              CODEN: DPAWA2
INTERNATIONALE PAPIERWIRTSCHAFT. Short title: I P W. (Text in English and German) 1958. q. DM.147.66 (foreign DM.162). D P W Verlagsgesellschaft mbH, Borsigstr. 1-3, 63150 Heusenstamm, Germany. TEL 06104-6060. FAX 06104-606317. Ed. Martin Swayne. adv.: B&W page DM.4500; trim 185 x 264. bk.rev. circ. 7,500. **Indexed:** Abstr.Bull.Inst.Pap.Chem., Chem.Abstr. **Document type:** trade publication.
—BLDSC (3573.210000); CASDDS. CCC.
   Formerly: Deutsche Papierwirtschaft (ISSN 0070-4296)
   Description: Magazine for economy and technology of manufacturing, finishing and converting of pulp, paper and substitution products of the printing world.

676   SP   ISSN 0368-0789
              CODEN: IVTPA3
INVESTIGACION Y TECNICA DEL PAPEL. (Text in Spanish; summaries in English, French, German and Spanish) 1964. q. 8400 ptas.($105) (Asociacion de Investigacion Tecnica de la Industria Papelera Espanola) Instituto Papelero Espanol, Carr. de la Coruna, Km. 7, 28040 Madrid, Spain. TEL 34-1-3070976. FAX 34-1-3572828. Ed. J.L. Asenjo Martinez. adv.; bk.rev.; bibl.; stat.; index. circ. 1,000. (back issues avail.) **Indexed:** Abstr.Bull.Inst.Pap.Chem., Chem.Abstr., Forest.Abstr., Forest Prod.Abstr., Ind.SST.
—CASDDS. CCC.

676   JA   ISSN 0022-815X
              CODEN: KAGIAU
JAPAN T A P P I JOURNAL/KAMI PA GIKYOSHI. (Text in Japanese; summaries in English) 1947. m. 18000 Yen. Japan Technical Association of the Pulp and Paper Industry, Kami Pulp Kaikan Bldg., 9-11 Ginza 3-chome, Chuo-ku, Tokyo 104, Japan. TEL 81-3-3248-4841. FAX 81-3-3248-4843. Ed. Hironori Fujiwara. adv.; bk.rev.; abstr.; bibl.; charts; illus.; pat.; stat. circ. 5,500. **Indexed:** Abstr.Bull.Inst.Pap.Chem., Chem.Abstr., INIS Atomind., Paper & Bd.Abstr.
—BLDSC (4650.260000); CASDDS.

676.2   CC   ISSN 1004-8405
              CODEN: XKYJFZ
JOURNAL OF CELLULOSE SCIENCE AND TECHNOLOGY. (Text in Chinese; abstracts in English) 1993. q. $20. Guangzhou Research Institute of Chemistry, P.O. Box 1122, Wushan, Guangzhou, Guangdong Province 510650, People's Republic of China. TEL 86-20-705360. FAX 86-20-7705319. Ed. Luo Fukai. circ. 1,000 (controlled). **Document type:** academic/scholarly publication.
—CASDDS.
   Description: Covers R&D activities and achievements in the fields of cellulose chemistry and lignocellulosic chemistry.

676   CN   ISSN 0826-6220
TS1080   CODEN: JPUSDN
JOURNAL OF PULP & PAPER SCIENCE. (Text in English and French) 1975. bi-m. Can.$214($210) (Canada $187.25; elsewhere $235) (effective 1996). Canadian Pulp & Paper Association, Technical Section, Sun Life Bldg., 19th Fl., 1155 Metcalfe St., Montreal, PQ H3B 4T6, Canada. TEL 514-866-6621. FAX 514-866-3035. Ed. D.H. Paterson. charts; illus.; index. circ. 7,500. **Indexed:** Abstr.Bull.Inst.Pap.Chem., Eng.Ind., INSPEC, Paper & Bd.Abstr.
—BLDSC (5043.660000); CASDDS; Ei; Faxon; Genuine Article; SWETS; UnCover. CCC.
   Formerly: Canadian Pulp and Paper Association. Technical Section. Transactions (ISSN 0317-882X)

676   JA   ISSN 0022-8168
KAMI PARUPU TOKEI GEPPO/PAPER & PULP STATISTICAL MONTHLY.* (Text in Japanese) 1953. m. 7680 Yen. Ministry of International Trade and Industry, Research and Statistics Division - Tsusho Sangyo-sho Daijin Kanbo Chosa Tokei-bu, 1-3-1 Kasumigaseki, Chiyoda-ku, Tokyo 100, Japan. TEL 03-3501-1511. charts; stat. circ. 700.

338.4   JA   ISSN 0453-1515
KAMI PARUPU TOKEI NENPO/YEARBOOK OF PULP AND PAPER STATISTICS. (Editions in English and Japanese) 1947. a. 1500 Yen. Japan Paper Association, Kami-Parupu Kaikan Bldg., 9-11 Ginza 3-chome, Chuo-ku, Tokyo 104, Japan. TEL 03-3248-4802. FAX 81-3-3248-4826.

5000 PAPER AND PULP

676 UK ISSN 0269-9028
KEY NOTE REPORT: DISPOSABLE PAPER PRODUCTS. Variant title: Disposable Paper Products. irreg. £185. Key Note Publications Ltd., Field House, 72 Oldfield Rd., Hampton, Middlesex TW12 2HQ, England. TEL 0181-783-0755. FAX 0181-783-1720. **Document type:** trade publication.
● Also available online.
Also available on CD-ROM.
—BLDSC (3598.723500).

KOEHLER RUNDSCHAU. see *ADVERTISING AND PUBLIC RELATIONS*

676.2025489 DK ISSN 0106-1208
KOMPASS SELECT EXPORT. PAPER INDUSTRY, GRAPHIC ARTS. Cover title: Euro Kompass Denmark. Paper and Graphic Arts. (Text in Danish, English, French, German and Spanish) 1980. a. DKK 300 (listed companies DKK 100). Forlaget Kompass Danmark, Oeverroedevej 5, DK-2840 Holte, Denmark. TEL 45-45-41-21-00. FAX 45-45-41-06-65. illus. **Document type:** directory.
● Also available on CD-ROM.
Formerly: Kompass Select Denmark. Paper and Printing.

380 676 US ISSN 1046-5359
TS1088
LOCKWOOD - POST'S DIRECTORY OF THE PULP, PAPER AND ALLIED TRADES. 1873. a. $187 (traveler's edition $177). Miller Freeman, Inc. (Subsidiary of: United Newspapers), 600 Harrison St., San Francisco, CA 94107. TEL 415-905-2200. FAX 212-905-2232. TELEX 278273. (Alt. addr.: 370 Lexington Ave., Ste. 1700, New York, NY 10017) Eds. Vincent M. Ridley, Harry Dyer. adv.; index. circ. 4,600. (reprint service avail. from UMI) **Document type:** directory.
—CCC.
Formerly: Lockwood's Directory of the Paper and Allied Trades (ISSN 0076-0277)
Description: Listing service for the pulp and paper industry, providing indexes of executive offices, industry mills, mill officials, converters, and general paper merchants.

M A R I BOARD CONVERTING NEWS; the package converting magazine of Latin America. (Magazine of the Americas Revista Interamericana) see *PACKAGING*

M A R I - BOARD CONVERTING NEWS ESPANOL. see *PACKAGING*

M T J RECYCLING MARKETS. see *PACKAGING*

676 CK ISSN 0121-6554
MARI - PAPEL. (Text in English, Spanish) 1993. bi-m. Latin Press Inc., Apdo. Postal 67252, Medellin, Colombia. TEL 57-4-284-5232. adv.; B&W page $1550, color page $2000. circ. 2,053 (controlled). **Document type:** trade publication.

676 NE ISSN 0077-1414
MONUMENTA CHARTAE PAPYRACEAE HISTORIAM ILLUSTRANTIA/COLLECTION OF WORKS AND DOCUMENTS ILLUSTRATING THE HISTORY OF PAPER. (Text mainly in English; occasionally in other languages) 1950. irreg. vol.15, 1993. price varies. Paper Publications Society, Universiteits-Bibliotheek, Singel 425, 1012 W P Amsterdam, Netherlands. Ed. J.S.G. Simmons. circ. 500. **Document type:** monographic series.

676 US ISSN 0739-2214
N P T A MANAGEMENT NEWS. 1959. m. $20. National Paper Trade Association, Inc., 111 Great Neck Rd., Ste. 418, Great Neck, NY 11021. TEL 516-829-3070. FAX 516-829-3074. Ed. Edward C. Pasternack. adv.; B&W page $2930; 8 1/4 x 10 7/8. bk.rev.; charts; stat. circ. 21,000. (also avail. in microfiche from CIS) **Indexed:** SRI. **Document type:** trade publication.
Formerly: Current (Great Neck).

667.6 645 US ISSN 0164-4580
TP977
NAVAL STORES REVIEW. 1890. bi-m. $80 (foreign $110). Kriedt Enterprises, Ltd., 129 S. Cortez St., New Orleans, LA 70119-6118. TEL 504-482-3914. Ed. Don E. Neighbors. adv.: B&W page $380, color page $780; trim 8 1/2 x 11. bk.rev.; charts; illus.; mkt. circ. 600. **Indexed:** Chem.Abstr., P.A.I.S., SRI. **Document type:** trade publication.
—BLDSC (6065.480000); CASDDS.
Formerly: Naval Stores Review and Terpene Chemicals (ISSN 0028-1468)
Description: Includes statistical information for international naval stores imports and exports.

NONWOVENS INDUSTRY; the international magazine for the nonwoven fabrics and disposable soft goods industry. see *TEXTILE INDUSTRIES AND FABRICS*

676 SZ
LE NOVEAU SYNDICAT.* 1980. m. Syndicat Industrie et Batiment, 28 avenue de Sevelin, CH-1000 Lausanne 20, Switzerland. Ed. Alfio Guardo. circ. 3,000.
Formerly (until 1993): Germinal.

OFFICIAL BOARD MARKETS; "the yellow sheet". see *PACKAGING*

OFFICIAL CONTAINER DIRECTORY. see *PACKAGING*

P A T E F A NEWS BULLETIN. (Printing & Allied Trades Employers Federation of Australia) see *PRINTING*

676 651.3 AU ISSN 0030-784X
P B S AKTUELL. (Papierwaren, Buerobedarf, Schreibwaren) 1948. s-m. S.300. Johann L. Bondi und Sohn, Industriestr. 2, A-2380 Perchtoldsdorf, Austria. TEL 01-864921. FAX 01-86492144. Ed. Franz Bondi. circ. 3,500. **Document type:** trade publication.

676 AU
P B S - SPIEL MAGAZIN. 11/yr. Verlag Heymann und Jahn, Holochergasse 45, A-1150 Vienna, Austria. TEL 0222-9827191. FAX 0222-982347117. Ed. Helmut Herz. **Document type:** trade publication.
Former titles: P B S Magazin; Papierhandelsfachblatt.

676 US ISSN 1046-4352
TS1080 CODEN: PMAGDY
P I M A MAGAZINE. Key Title: Pima. 1919. m. $50. Paper Industry Management Association, 1699 Wall St., Ste. 212, Mt. Prospect, IL 60056-5782. TEL 708-956-0250. FAX 708-956-0520. Ed. Alan Rooks. adv.; B&W page $2585, color page $3770; trim 8 1/8 x 10 7/8. bk.rev.; abstr.; charts; illus.; stat.; index; circ. 16,611 (controlled). (also avail. in microform from UMI) **Indexed:** A.S.& T.Ind., Abstr.Bull.Inst.Pap.Chem., Eng.Ind, Paper & Bd.Abstr., PROMT. **Document type:** trade publication.
—BLDSC (6501.300000); Ei; Faxon; SWETS; UMI; UnCover. **CCC.**
Former titles: P I M A (ISSN 0161-1364); (until 1978): Paper Industry (ISSN 0197-3991); (until 1977): American Paper Industry (ISSN 0003-0333)
Description: Articles on operations and management, training and staff development written in non-technical language, including interviews with industry executives. Columns focus on management issues or key mill technical processes. Departments focus on news and trends, new products, application stories and personnel changes.

676 686.2 UK ISSN 0262-8600
P I R A ANNUAL REVIEW OF RESEARCH & SERVICES. 1977. a. membership. Paper, Printing & Packaging Industries Research Association, Randalls Rd., Leatherhead, Surrey KT22 7RU, England. illus. **Indexed:** Curr.Pack.Abstr.

676 BE
P P I THIS WEEK. (Paper & Pulp Industry) (Text in English) 1986. w. (48/yr.). 26000 BEF (effective 1995). Miller Freeman Inc., 123 A Chaussee de Charleroi, Bte. 5, 1060 Brussels, Belgium. TEL 32-2-5386040. Ed. Rita Pappens. circ. 1,400 (paid). (tabloid format; back issues avail.) **Document type:** newsletter.

676 BL ISSN 0031-1057
TS1080 CODEN: PAPLA3
PAPEL. (Text in Portuguese; summaries in English) 1939. m. $250. Associacao Tecnica Brasileira de Celulose e Papel, Rua Ximbo, 165, Aclimacao, 04108-040 Sao Paulo, SP, Brazil. TEL 55-11-574-0166. FAX 55-11-571-6485. Ed. Eduardo Correa. adv. contact: Claudio de Campos. illus.; stat.; tr.lit. circ. 3,500. **Indexed:** Chem.Abstr., Corros.Abstr. **Document type:** trade publication.
—BLDSC (6358.400000); CASDDS.

676 US ISSN 0031-1081
TS1080
PAPER AGE.* 1884. m. $20 (foreign $75) (typically set in Sep.). Global Publications, 77 Waldron Ave., Glen Rock, NJ 07452-2830. TEL 201-666-2262. FAX 201-666-9046. Ed. Mark McCready. adv.; bk.rev.; charts; illus.; circ. 31,400 (controlled). **Indexed:** Abstr.Bull.Inst.Pap.Chem., Graph.Arts Lit.Abstr., Int.Packag.Abstr., Paper & Bd.Abstr. **Document type:** trade publication.
—BLDSC (6358.850000).
Description: For global manufacturers and converters of paper, pulp and paperboard products. Provides information about corporate strategies, and plant operations. Profiles the world's pulp and paper companies and suppliers to the industry.

676 338.4 SW ISSN 0281-725X
PAPER & PULP MAKERS' DIRECTORY; Brusewitz nordisk papperskalender. (Text in English) 1991. biennial. SEK 650. Arbor Publishing AB, P.O. Box 26212, S-100 41 Stockholm, Sweden. TEL 46-8-611-60-30. FAX 46-8-679-90-50. Ed. Carina Bertilson. adv.; index. circ. 1,000. **Document type:** consumer publication, trade publication, directory.
Description: Covers paper and pulp production sites in Sweden, Norway, Denmark and Finland. Gives information about capacity and key personnel.

676 SI ISSN 0218-4540
HD9836.A1
PAPER ASIA; for the Asia-Pacific pulp, paper & converting industries. (Text in English) 1985. 9/yr. $140. Toucan Publications Pte. Ltd., 322-C King George's Ave., Singapore 0820, Singapore. TEL 65-2997121. FAX 65-2997545. (Dist. in N. America by: MagnaMedia, 1800 No.4 Rd., Richmond, B.C. V6X 2L2, Canada. TEL 604-273-2710) Ed. Andrew Loh. adv.: B&W page $2200, color page $3500; trim 210 x 297. circ. 5,408. **Document type:** trade publication.
Description: Covers major happenings, new developments, and issues of interest to the paper industry.

676.3 US
PAPER BUYERS' ENCYCLOPEDIA. 1968. a. $90 ($210 for 3 yrs.) (effective 1995 & 1996). Grade Finders, Inc., 662 Exton Commons, Box 944, Exton, PA 19341. TEL 215-524-7070. Ed. Mark Subers. adv. **Document type:** directory, trade publication.
Description: Provides information on paper, sources, distribution channels and grades.

676 UK ISSN 0955-7806
PAPER EUROPE. 1989. m. £63 (rest of Europe £87; elsewhere £122). Whitmar Publications Ltd., 30 London Rd., Southborough, Tunbridge Wells, Kent TN4 0RE, England. TEL 01892-542099. FAX 01892-546693. Ed. Martin White. adv. contact: Rob Mulligan. circ. 14,300. (back issues avail.) **Document type:** trade publication.
—BLDSC (6361.400000).

676 UK ISSN 0950-4478
PAPER EUROPEAN DATA BOOK. 1985. a. £190 (overseas £215). Miller Freeman Information Services (Subsidiary of: United News & Media), Riverbank House, Angel Ln., Tonbridge, Kent TN9 1SE, England. TEL 01732-362666. FAX 01732-767301. TELEX 957829. Ed. Gwen Young. adv. contact: Elaine Soni. charts; stat.; tr.lit. circ. 600. **Document type:** directory.
—BLDSC (6396.832300).
Description: Directed at decision-makers involved with the European paper industry. Provides a statistical analysis of the economies, raw material resources, and a detailed analysis of the pulp and paper industries of Western Europe.

PAPER, FILM AND FOIL CONVERTER. see *PACKAGING*

PAPER AND PULP

676   UK   ISSN 0950-3420
PAPER FOCUS. 1986. m. £72 (foreign £115). Paper Publications Ltd., Church House, Church Ln., Kings Langley, Herts. WD4 8JP, England. TEL 01923-261555. FAX 01923-261118. Ed. Lawrence Turk; Pub. Peter Ingram. adv.: B&W page £1600, color page £2295; trim 268 x 177; adv. contact: Graham Martin. bk.rev. circ. 12,000. **Document type:** trade publication.
—BLDSC (6362.800000).
Description: Features products, techniques, information and ideas for buyers, specifiers and users of paper and board.

676   US   ISSN 1048-8251
PAPER INDUSTRY MAGAZINE. 1984. bi-m. $12. 804 S. Perry, Ste. 101, Montgomery, AL 36103. TEL 334-265-4337. FAX 334-265-4310. (Subscr. to: Box 2268, Montgomery, AL 36102-2268) adv.: B&W page $2710, color page $3800; 11 x 14 1/2. circ. 10,725. (reprint service avail.)
—CCC.
Formerly: Paper Industry Equipment (ISSN 0889-731X)

676   UK
PAPER INDUSTRY TECHNICAL ASSOCIATION. FUNDAMENTAL RESEARCH INTERNATIONAL SYMPOSIA. 1958. 10/yr. £100. Paper Industry Technical Association, 4 Frecheville Ct., Bury, Lancs. BL9 0UF, England. TEL 0161-764-5858. FAX 0161-764-5353. Ed. M. Marley; Pub. J. Clewley. adv. contact: Frank Colling. **Indexed:** Abstr.Bull.Inst.Pap.Chem. **Document type:** proceedings.
Formerly: British Paper and Board Industry Federation. Technical Association. Fundamental Research International Symposia (ISSN 0068-2322)

676   UK
PAPER MARKET DIGEST. 1982. m. £175 (foreign £195). Paper Publications Ltd., Church House, Church Ln., Kings Langley, Herts WD4 8JP, England. TEL 01923-261555. FAX 01923-261118. **Document type:** trade publication.
Description: Provides information on prices, market trends, company information and future prospects for the professional buyer of graphic papers and boards.

676   US
PAPER MERCHANT PERFORMANCE. 1935. a. $300. National Paper Trade Association, Inc., 111 Great Neck Rd., Ste. 603, Great Neck, NY 11021. TEL 516-829-3070. Ed. George Cain. charts; stat. circ. 2,500. **Indexed:** SRI.

338.4   US
PAPER MERCHANT SALES REPORT. 1940. m. membership only. National Paper Trade Association, Inc., 111 Great Neck Rd., Ste. 603, Great Neck, NY 11021. TEL 516-829-3070. Ed. George Cain. circ. 5,000. (also avail. in microfiche from CIS) **Indexed:** SRI.

676   US   ISSN 1072-1223
TS1120.5
PAPER RECYCLER. 1990. m. $327. Miller Freeman, Inc. (Subsidiary of: United Newspapers), 600 Harrison St., San Francisco, CA 94107. TEL 415-905-2200. FAX 415-905-5232. Ed. Debra Adams Garcia. **Document type:** trade publication.

676   SA   ISSN 0254-3494
PAPER SOUTHERN AFRICA; devoted exclusively to the pulp, paper & board industries in Southern Africa. (Text in English) 1980. bi-m. R.96. (Technical Association of the Pulp and Paper Industry of Southern Africa) George Warman Publications (Pty.) Ltd., P.O. Box 3847, Cape Town 8000, South Africa. TEL 27-21-245320. FAX 27-21-261332. Ed. Tony Walker. adv. circ. 1,400. **Indexed:** Abstr.Bull.Inst.Pap.Chem., Ind.S.A.Per., Paper & Bd.Abstr. **Document type:** trade publication.
Description: Technical journal on pulp, paper and board production and processing.

676.142 604.6   US   ISSN 1064-1432
THE PAPER STOCK REPORT. 1990. bi-w. $99 (Canada & Mexico $125; elsewhere $235). McEntee Media Corp., 13727 Holland Rd., Cleveland, OH 44142-3920. TEL 216-362-7979. FAX 216-362-6553. Ed. Ken McEntee. adv.: page $820; trim 8 1/2 X 11; adv. contact: Richard Downing. stat. circ. 2,000. **Document type:** newsletter.
Description: Features news and trends impacting markets for recovered scrap paper.

676   UK   ISSN 0958-6024
TS1080.B73   CODEN: PATEE6
PAPER TECHNOLOGY. m. £95 to non-members in U.K. and Ireland; rest of world £105. Paper Industry Technical Association, 4 Frecheville Ct., Bury, Lancs. BL9 0UF, England. TEL 0161-764-5858. FAX 0161-764-5353. Ed. M. Marley; Pub. J. Clewley. adv.: B&W page £1000, color page £1500; trim 273 x 184; adv. contact: Frank Colling. bk.rev.; abstr.; bibl.; charts; illus.; index, cum.index. circ. 2,700. **Indexed:** Abstr.Bull.Inst.Pap.Chem., Br.Tech.Ind., C.I.S. Abstr., Chem.Abstr., Eng.Ind., Excerp.Med., Graph.Arts Lit.Abstr., Paper & Bd.Abstr., Sh.& Vib.Dig. **Document type:** trade publication.
—BLDSC (6364.750000); CASDDS; Ei; SWETS.
Former titles (until 1989): Paper Technology and Industry (ISSN 0306-252X); (until 1975): Paper Technology (ISSN 0031-1189); Which was formed by the 1960 merger of: British Paper and Board Makers' Association. Technical Section. Proceedings (ISSN 0366-2942); Which was previously (1921-1950): Paper Makers' Association of Great Britain and Ireland. Technical Section. Proceedings (ISSN 0370-0518); And: British Paper and Board Makers' Association. Technical Section. Technical Bulletin (ISSN 0371-5442); Which was previously (until 1950): Paper Makers' Association of Great Britain and Ireland. Technical Section. Technical Bulletin.
Description: Aims to keep readers aware of new technology through technical articles, abstracts, news and latest developments of the pulp, papermaking, non-woven and converting industries.

PAPER TREE LETTER; independent analysis of forest products economics. see FORESTS AND FORESTRY — Lumber And Wood

676   FI   ISSN 0031-1243
HD9765.F4   CODEN: PAPUAU
PAPERI JA PUU/PAPER AND TIMBER. (Text and title in English, Finnish) 1919. 10/yr. FIM 450 (incl. supplements) (effective 1996). (Suomen Metsateollisuuden Keskusliitto) Finnish Paper and Timber Journal Publishing Co., P.O. Box 154, FIN-00131 Helsinki, Finland. TEL 358-0-132-6688. FAX 358-0-630-365. (Co-sponsors: Finnish Woodworking Engineers' Association; Finnish Paper Engineers' Association) Ed. Marja Korpivaara. adv. contact: Irmeli Hannula. bibl.; charts; illus.; stat.; index. circ. 4,000. **Indexed:** Abstr.Bull.Inst.Pap.Chem., C.I.S. Abstr., Chem.Abstr., Curr.Cont., Forest.Abstr., Forest Prod.Abstr., Graph.Arts Lit.Abstr., Paper & Bd.Abstr., PROMT, Risk Abstr. **Document type:** trade publication.
—BLDSC (6366.500000); CASDDS; Ei; Genuine Article; SWETS; UMI.

676   II   ISSN 0048-2862
PAPERPRINTPACK INDIA. (Text in English) 1963. m. Rs.60 (foreign Rs.150). (Shantarani Sons & Co.) Smt. S. Tikku, Pub., 7-104 Nariman Passage, Prabhadevi P.O., Bombay 400 025, India. TEL 4220906. Ed. Somnath Tikku. adv.: B&W page Rs.800, color page Rs.1200. charts; illus. circ. 6,000. **Indexed:** Packag.Sci.Tech. **Document type:** trade publication.
Description: Devoted to developments in the paper, printing, packaging, and other affiliated industries in India. Includes calendar of relevant events.

PAPERWORKER. see LABOR UNIONS

676 338.4   US
PAPERWORLD.* 1991. m. free to qualified personnel. American Papermaker, 57 Executive Park South, N.E., No. 300, Atlanta, GA 30329-2213. TEL 404-841-3333. FAX 404-841-3332. circ. 40,000 (controlled).

676   SZ   ISSN 0031-1316
PAPETERIST/PAPETIER/CARTOLAIO. (Text in French and German) 1919. m. 40 SFr. (Verband Schweizerischer Papeteristen) Buri Druck AG, Eigerstr. 71, CH-3001 Bern, Switzerland. TEL 031-462323. FAX 031-455463. adv.; illus.; mkt.

676.2   CN   ISSN 0048-2889
PAPETIER. (Text in French) 1964. q. free. Association des Industries Forestieres du Quebec, Ltee., 1200 Ave. Germain-des-Pres, Ste-Foy, PQ G1V 3M7, Canada. TEL 418-651-9352. FAX 418-651-4622. Ed. Andre Duchesne. circ. 20,000. **Indexed:** Pt.de Rep. (1979-). **Document type:** trade publication.
—BLDSC (6401.480000).

676   CN   ISSN 0847-2645
PAPETIERES DU QUEBEC. 1990. 4/yr. Can.$23.54($35) (foreign Can.$55). Guy Fortin, 3300 Cote Vertu, Ste. 410, St. Laurent, Que. H4R 2B7, Canada. TEL 514-339-1399. FAX 514-339-1396. Ed. Yves Lavertu. adv. circ. 5,600.
●Also available online.
Description: Addresses the scientific and technical information needs of the pulp and paper industry.

676   GW   ISSN 0031-1340
TS1080   CODEN: PAERAY
DAS PAPIER; Zeitschrift fuer die Erzeugung von Holzstoff, Zellstoff, Papier und Pappe, Chemische Technologie der Cellulose. (Text in German; summaries in English) 1947. m. DM.245.50 (effective 1996). (Verein Zellcheming) Eduard Roether KG, Berliner Allee 56, 64295 Darmstadt, Germany. TEL 06151-3001-16. FAX 06151-314026. Ed. R. Weidenmueller. adv.; bk.rev.; bibl.; charts; illus.; mkt.; pat.; stat.; tr.lit.; index. circ. 4,000. (also avail. in microform from UMI; reprint service avail. from UMI) **Indexed:** Abstr.Bull.Inst.Pap.Chem., Chem.Abstr., Curr.Cont., Excerp.Med., Forest.Abstr., Forest Prod.Abstr., Packag.Sci.Tech., Paper & Bd.Abstr., PROMT, World Text.Abstr. **Document type:** trade publication.
—BLDSC (6402.000000); CASDDS; Ei; Genuine Article; SWETS; UMI. **CCC.**

676   AU   ISSN 1011-0186
TS1080
PAPIER AUS OESTERREICH. (Text in English and German) 1964. 10/yr. S.1180. (Vereinigung Oesterreichischer Papierindustrieller - Association of Austrian Paper Manufacturers) Austropapier Zeitschriftenverlags GmbH, Gumpendorfer Str. 6, A-1061 Vienna, Austria. TEL 01-58886-0. FAX 01-58886-222. Ed. Viktor Bauer. adv. contact: Monika Antal. bk.rev.; illus.; stat.; index. circ. 17,000. **Indexed:** Abstr.Bull.Inst.Pap.Chem. **Document type:** trade publication.
—BLDSC (6403.080000).
Formerly: Oesterreichische Papier (ISSN 0473-8322)

676   FR   ISSN 0031-1367
   CODEN: PCCLAK
PAPIER, CARTON ET CELLULOSE. (Pierre-Jean/Marcel) 1952. m. 890 F. (rest of Euorpe 1000 F.; elsewhere 1190 F.) (effective 1995). E L T A, 18 rue Saint-Fiacre, 75002 Paris, France. TEL 1-42-36-95-59. FAX 1-42-33-83-24. Ed. Martine Defefosse; Pub. Michel Burton. bk.rev.; abstr.; bibl.; charts; illus.; stat. circ. 4,825. **Indexed:** Abstr.Bull.Inst.Pap.Chem., Chem.Abstr., Excerp.Med., Paper & Bd.Abstr. **Document type:** trade publication, newspaper.
—CASDDS. **CCC.**
Description: Includes producers in Europe, suppliers, converters, merchants and agents.

676   FR
PAPIER, CARTON ET CELLULOSE. ANNUAIRE. a. 795 F. E L T A, 18 rue Saint Fiacre, 75002 Paris, France. TEL 1-42-36-95-59. FAX 1-42-33-83-24. **Document type:** trade publication.
Description: Identifies participants, partners and companies in all involved sectors of activity.

338.4   FR   ISSN 1163-6068
PAPIER, CARTON ET CELLULOSE. ANNUAIRE FINANCIER. a. 1957 Fr. E L T A, 18 rue Saint Fiacre, 75002 Paris, France. TEL 1-42-36-95-59. FAX 1-42-33-83-24. **Document type:** trade publication, directory.
Description: Provides financial profiles of more than 400 companies in the paper industry.

PAPER AND PULP

676 FR
PAPIER, CARTON ET CELLULOSE. CATALOGUE DES MATERIELS ET EQUIPEMENTS. a. 290 Fr. E L T A, 18 rue Saint Fiacre, 75002 Paris, France. TEL 1-42-36-95-59. FAX 1-42-33-83-24. **Document type**: catalog, trade publication.
  Description: Covers market offerings of equipment and manufacturers.

676 658.7 FR
PAPIER, CARTON ET CELLULOSE. GUIDE DU PAPIER. a. 400 Fr. E L T A, 18 rue Saint Fiacre, 75002 Paris, France. TEL 1-42-36-95-59. FAX 1-42-33-83-24. **Document type**: trade publication.
  Description: Offers a complete list of products in the industry for purchasers.

676 AU ISSN 0259-7454
PAPIER UND DRUCK. 1895. 24/yr. S.590. Verlagsbuchhandlung Brueder Hollinek und Co. GmbH, Feldgasse 13, A-1238 Vienna, Austria. TEL 0222-885646. FAX 0222-8893647-24. Ed. K. Patschka. adv.; bibl.; charts; illus.; stat. circ. 4,800. **Document type**: trade publication.
  Incorporated (1949-1986): Papier- und Buchgewerbe-rundschau (ISSN 0031-1359); Formerly (until 1986): Oesterreichische Papier-Zeitung (ISSN 0029-9391)

676 GW ISSN 0048-2897
PAPIER UND KUNSTSTOFF VERARBEITER; die fachzeitschrift fuer druck, veredelung und weiterverarbeitung von papier, vollpappe, wellpape, zellglas, kunststoff und folien aller art. 1965. m. DM.186 (foreign DM.204.50). Deutscher Fachverlag GmbH, Mainzer Landstr. 251, 60326 Frankfurt a.M., Germany. TEL 069-759501. FAX 069-75952999. (Subscr. to: Postfach 100606, 60006 Frankfurt a.M., Germany) Ed. W. Werm. circ. 5,756. **Indexed**: Abstr.Bull.Inst.Pap.Chem., Int.Packag.Abstr., Packag.Sci.Tech., Paper & Bd.Abstr. **Document type**: trade publication.
  —CCC.
  Formerly: Papier Verarbeiter.

676 GW ISSN 0940-340X
PAPIER UND KUNSTSTOFF VERARBEITER INTERNATIONAL. 3/yr. DM.50. Deutscher Fachverlag GmbH, Mainzer Landstr. 251, 60326 Frankfurt a.M., Germany. TEL 069-7595-01. FAX 069-7595-2999. adv.: B&W page DM.4220; trim 210 x 297. circ. 10,750. **Document type**: trade publication.
  —BLDSC (6403.106000).
  Description: Covers printing, up-grading and converting of paper, board, solid board, corrugated board, cellophane, plastic film and foil.

676 GW ISSN 0031-1405
DER PAPIERMACHER. 1951. 13/yr. (Vereinigung der Arbeitgeberverbaende der Deutschen Papierindustrie e.V.) Dr. Curt Haefner Verlag, Bachstr. 14-16, 69121 Heidelberg, Germany. TEL 06221-49064. (Subscr. to: Postfach 106060, 69050 Heidelberg, Germany) circ. 70,000. **Indexed**: Abstr.Bull.Inst.Pap.Chem., Paper & Bd.Abstr. **Document type**: trade publication.
  —CCC.

676 XR ISSN 0031-1421
TS1080 CODEN: PCELAU
PAPIR A CELULOZA. (Text in Czech or Slovak; summaries in English, German, Russian) 1945. m. $54.70. Svaz Prumyslu Papiru a Celulozy, Vinohradska 190, 130 61 Prague 3, Czech Republic. (Dist. by: Artia, Ve Smeckach 30, 111 27 Prague 1, Czech Republic) Ed. Josef Korda. adv.; bk.rev.; charts; illus.; pat. circ. 1,700. **Indexed**: Abstr.Bull.Inst.Pap.Chem., C.I.S. Abstr., Chem.Abstr., Forest Prod.Abstr., Paper & Bd.Abstr.
  —BLDSC (6403.200000); CASDDS.

676 NO ISSN 0332-8929
PAPIRHANDLEREN. 1929. m. NOK 420. Norske Papirhandleres landsforbund, Oevre Vollgt. 15, 0158 Oslo 1, Norway. FAX 02-333269. Ed. Dag Helland. adv. circ. 1,300. **Document type**: trade publication.

676 HU ISSN 0031-1448
CODEN: PAPIBT
PAPIRIPAR. (Text in Hungarian; summaries in English and German) 1957. bi-m. $60 (effective 1995 & 1996). Papír- es Nyomdaipari Mueszaki Egyesuelet, Fo utca 68, Pf. 433, 1371 Budapest 2, Hungary. (Subscr. to: Kultura, Box 149, H-1389 Budapest, Hungary) Ed. George Vamos. adv. contact: Anne Wertheim. bk.rev.; abstr.; bibl.; charts; illus.; index. circ. 1,200. **Indexed**: Abstr.Bull.Inst.Pap.Chem., Chem.Abstr., Forest Prod.Abstr., Graph.Arts Lit.Abstr. **Document type**: academic/scholarly publication, trade publication.
  —BLDSC (6403.290000); CASDDS.

PAPIRIPARI ES NYOMDAIPARI SZAKIRODALMI TAJEKOZTATO/PAPER INDUSTRY & PRINTING ABSTRACTS. see *PAPER AND PULP — Abstracting, Bibliographies, Statistics*

676 UK ISSN 0954-8521
TS1088
PHILLIPS' INTERNATIONAL PAPER DIRECTORY. 1904. a. £115 (foreign £135). Miller Freeman Information Services (Subsidiary of: United News & Media), Riverbank House, Angel Ln., Tonbridge, Kent TN9 1SE, England. TEL 01732-362666. FAX 01732-367301. TELEX 957829. Ed. Gwen Young. adv. contact: Elaine Soni. index. circ. 3,100. **Document type**: directory.
  —BLDSC (6461.293500).
  Formerly: Phillips' Paper Trade Directory - Europe-Mills of the World (ISSN 0079-158X); Incorporates: Papermakers' and Merchants' Directory of All Nations (ISSN 0078-9038)
  Description: Contains information on the world's pulp, paper, and paperboard mills. Includes detailed information about converters, merchants, and suppliers worldwide.

PREVISIONS GLISSANTES DETAILLEES EN PERSPECTIVES SECTORIELLES (VOL.25): INDUSTRIE DES PATES, PAPIERS ET CARTONS. see *BUSINESS AND ECONOMICS — Economic Situation And Conditions*

676 604.6 US ISSN 1061-1452
TS1120.5 CODEN: PPREFY
PROGRESS IN PAPER RECYCLING. 1991. q. $85 (foreign $95) (effective 1996). Doshi & Associates Inc., Box 2771, Appleton, WI 54913-2771. TEL 414-832-9101. FAX 414-832-0870. E-mail: MAHEN@AOL.COM. Ed. Marianne L. Fiscus. adv.: B&W page $2300, color page $3595; adv. contact: Judith K. Schiel. bk.rev.; abstr. circ. 700. **Document type**: academic/scholarly publication.
  —BLDSC (6872.350000); CASDDS. **CCC**.
  Description: Publishes articles on science, technology and economics of paper recycling.

676 US ISSN 0033-4081
TS1080 CODEN: PUPAA8
PULP AND PAPER. 1927. m. (s-m. Nov.). $100 (free to qualified personnel). Miller Freeman, Inc. (Subsidiary of: United Newspapers), 600 Harrison St., San Francisco, CA 94107. TEL 415-905-2200. FAX 415-905-2232. TELEX 278273. Ed. Ken L. Patrick. adv.: B&W page $3660, color page $5390; trim 8 1/8 x 10 7/8. bk.rev.; charts; illus.; mkt.; stat.; tr.lit.; index; circ. 40,900 (controlled). (also avail. in microform from UMI; microfiche from CIS; reprint service avail. from UMI) **Indexed**: Abstr.Bull.Inst.Pap.Chem., B.P.I., Bus.Ind., Chem.Abstr., Curr.Pack.Abstr., Excerp.Med., Forest.Abstr., Forest Prod.Abstr., Key to Econ.Sci., Ocean.Abstr., Paper & Bd.Abstr., Pollut.Abstr., PROMT, SRI, Tr.& Indus.Ind., W.R.C.Inf.
  ●Also available online. Vendor(s): Lexis-Nexis, University Microfilms International.
  —BLDSC (7157.000000); CASDDS; Ei; SWETS; UMI; UnCover. **CCC**.

676 US
PULP & PAPER BUYERS GUIDE. a. $55. Miller Freeman, Inc. (Subsidiary of: United Newspapers), 600 Harrison St., San Francisco, CA 94107. TEL 415-905-2200. FAX 415-905-2232. TELEX 278273. Ed. Ken L. Patrick. circ. 37,500. (also avail. in microform; reprint service avail. from UMI) **Document type**: trade publication, consumer publication.

676.12 674 CN ISSN 0316-4004
TS1080 CODEN: PPCAAA
PULP & PAPER CANADA. 1903. m. Can.$55($62) (foreign $136). (Canadian Pulp and Paper Association) Southam Magazine Group (St. Laurent), 3300 Cote Vertu, Ste. 410, St. Laurent, PQ H4R 2B7, Canada. TEL 514-339-1399. FAX 514-339-1396. Ed. Graeme Rodden; Pub. Mark Verbury. adv.: B&W page $3310 color page $4705; 8 1/8 x 10 7/8; adv. contact: Ursel Krieger. bk.rev.; charts; illus.; mkt.; stat.; tr.lit.; index. circ. 10,300. (also avail. in microfiche from UMI) **Indexed**: Abstr.Bull.Inst.Pap.Chem., Acid Rain Abstr., Agri.Eng.Abstr., Bibl.Agri., CAD CAM Abstr., Can.B.P.I., Chem.Abstr., Curr.Cont., Energy Info.Abstr., Environ.Abstr., Excerp.Med., Forest.Abstr., Forest Prod.Abstr., Graph.Arts Lit.Abstr., INSPEC, Paper & Bd.Abstr., Sel.Water Res.Abstr., W.R.C.Inf. **Document type**: trade publication.
  ●Also available online. Vendor(s): Southam Electronic Publishing.
  —BLDSC (7157.050000); CASDDS; Ei; Faxon; Genuine Article; SWETS; UnCover. **CCC**.
  Formerly: Pulp and Paper Magazine of Canada (ISSN 0033-4103); Incorporating: Woodlands Review.
  Description: Addresses the scientific and technical information needs of the pulp and paper industry.

676 CN ISSN 0708-501X
TS1088
PULP & PAPER CANADA DIRECTORY. 1937. a. Can.$85($110) (Subsidiary of: Southam Inc.), 3300 Cote Vertu, Ste. 410, St. Laurent, Que. H4R 2B7, Canada. TEL 514-339-1399. FAX 514-339-1396. Ed. Graeme Rodden; Pub. Mark Yerbury. adv. contact: Ursel Krieger. index. circ. 1,700. **Indexed**: Abstr.Bull.Inst.Pap.Chem. **Document type**: trade publication.
  Former titles: Pulp and Paper Canada Business Directory (ISSN 0317-3550); Canada's Pulp and Paper Business Directory (ISSN 0079-7936)

676 CN ISSN 0709-2563
TS1088
PULP & PAPER CANADA'S ANNUAL & DIRECTORY. 1930. a. Can.$90.95 (foreign $110). Southam Magazine Group (St. Laurent), 3300 Cote Vertu, Ste. 410, St. Laurent, PQ H4R 2B7, Canada. TEL 514-339-1399. FAX 514-339-1396. Ed. Graeme Rodder. adv.; index. circ. 1,500. **Document type**: directory.
  ●Also available online.
  —BLDSC (7157.080000).
  Former titles: Pulp and Paper Canada's Reference Manual and Buyers' Guide; Pulp and Paper Magazine of Canada's Reference Manual and Buyers' Guide (ISSN 0079-7952)
  Description: Gives corporate and technical information (equipment lists and flow charts) of Canada's pulp and paper companies and their mills. Lists suppliers and products plus copmlete address information. Also lists allied and related organizations.

676 US ISSN 0898-6886
PULP & PAPER FORECASTER. 1988. bi-m. $985. Miller Freeman, Inc. (Subsidiary of: United Newspapers), 600 Harrison St., San Francisco, CA 94107. TEL 415-905-2200. FAX 415-905-2232. TELEX 278273. Ed. Will Mies.

338.47 FR
PULP AND PAPER INDUSTRY IN O E C D MEMBER COUNTRIES/INDUSTRIE DES PATES ET PAPIERS DANS LES PAYS MEMBRES DE L'O C D E. (Text in English, French) 1954. a. price varies. Organization for Economic Cooperation and Development, 2 rue Andre-Pascal, 75775 Paris Cedex 16, France. (U.S. Orders to: O.E.C.D. Publications and Information Center, 2001 L St., N.W., Ste. 700, Washington, DC 20036-4910. TEL 202-785-6323) (also avail. in microfiche from OEC,CIS) **Indexed**: IIS.
  Formerly: Pulp and Paper Industry in O E C D Member Countries and Finland - Industrie des Pates et Papiers dans les Pays Membres de l'O C D E et la Finlande (ISSN 0474-5485)

PAPER AND PULP

676   US   ISSN 0190-2172
TS1109   CODEN: CRCFDZ
PULP AND PAPER INDUSTRY TECHNICAL CONFERENCE. CONFERENCE RECORD. Variant title: Annual Pulp and Paper Industry Technical Conference. Conference Record. a. (I E E E, Industry Applications Society) Institute of Electrical and Electronics Engineers, Inc., 345 E. 47th St., New York, NY 10017-2394. TEL 212-705-7900. FAX 212-705-7682. (Subscr. to: Box 1331, 445 Hoes Ln., Piscataway, NJ 08855-1331) Indexed: INSPEC.
—BLDSC (4362.859800); Ei; UMI. **CCC.**
    Formerly: Pulp and Paper Industry Technical Conference. Record (ISSN 0079-7944)
    Description: Development and application of electrical systems related to the manufacture and fabrication of products.

676   US   ISSN 0033-409X
PULP & PAPER INTERNATIONAL. (Annual editions in Chinese, Russian) 1958. m. $115 free to qualified personnel. Miller Freeman, Inc. (Subsidiary of: United Newspapers), 600 Harrison St., San Francisco, CA 94107. TEL 415-905-2200. FAX 415-905-2232. TELEX 278273. (Alt.addr.: 123A Chaussee de Charleroi, Box 5, B-1060 Brussels, Belgium) Ed. John Pearson. adv.: B&W page $3270, color $4840; 8 1/4 x 11 5/8. bk.rev.; charts; illus.; stat.; index. circ. 12,000. Indexed: Abstr.Bull.Inst.Pap.Chem., B.P.I., Bus.Ind., Chem.Abstr., Curr.Pack.Abstr., Eng.Ind., Excerp.Med., Forest.Abstr., Forest Prod.Abstr., Key to Econ.Sci., Ocean.Abstr., Paper & Bd.Abstr., Pollut.Abstr.
●Also available online. Vendor(s): Lexis-Nexis.
—BLDSC (7157.700000); Ei; Faxon; SWETS; UMI. **CCC.**
    Description: Technical and operational reports for improved operations.

676   US
PULP & PAPER INTERNATIONAL FACT & PRICE BOOK. 1980. a. $275. Miller Freeman Inc., 600 Harrison St., San Francisco, CA 94107. TEL 415-905-2200. Ed. Heide Matussek. circ. 500.
    Formerly: Pulp and Paper International Factbook.

676   US   ISSN 0273-3781
HD9821
PULP & PAPER NORTH AMERICAN INDUSTRY FACTBOOK. 1980. biennial. $327. Miller Freeman, Inc. (Subsidiary of: United Newspapers), 600 Harrison St., San Francisco, CA 94107. TEL 415-905-2200. FAX 415-905-2232. TELEX 278273. Ed. Willard E. Mies. circ. 600. (also avail. in microfiche from CIS; reprint service avail. from UMI) Indexed: SRI.
—**CCC.**

676.2   US   ISSN 0748-1608
PULP & PAPER PROJECT REPORT. 1982. m. $379. Miller Freeman, Inc. (Subsidiary of: United Newspapers), 600 Harrison St., San Francisco, CA 94107. TEL 415-905-2200. FAX 415-905-2232. TELEX 278273. Ed. Carl P. Espe. (reprint service avail. from UMI)
—**CCC.**

676   CN   ISSN 0079-7960
TS1080
PULP AND PAPER RESEARCH INSTITUTE OF CANADA. ANNUAL REPORT. 1968. a. free. Pulp and Paper Research Institute of Canada, 570 blvd. St. Jean, Pointe Claire, PQ H9R 3J9, Canada. TEL 514-630-4100. FAX 514-630-4134. TELEX 05-821541. Ed. J.M. MacLeod. circ. 5,000.

676   US   ISSN 0738-0917
PULP & PAPER WEEK. 1979. w. $637. Miller Freeman, Inc. (Subsidiary of: United Newspapers), 600 Harrison St., San Francisco, CA 94107. TEL 415-905-2200. FAX 415-905-2232. TELEX 278273. Ed. Willard E. Mies. stat.; index. (looseleaf format; back issues avail.; reprint service avail. from UMI) Indexed: Abstr.Bull.Inst.Pap.Chem.
—**CCC.**

RECYCLED PAPER NEWS; independent coverage of recycled paper issues. see *ENVIRONMENTAL STUDIES — Waste Management*

REPRODUCTION BULLETIN. see *PRINTING*

REVISTA FORESTAL BARACOA. see *FORESTS AND FORESTRY — Lumber And Wood*

676   SW   ISSN 0348-2650
S T F I MEDDELANDE. SERIES A. 1969. irreg. exchange basis. S T F I - Swedish Pulp and Paper Research Institute, P.O. Box 5604, S-114 86 Stockholm, Sweden. FAX 46-8-411-55-18. TELEX 10880. illus.; cum.index: 1969-1983. circ. 500. Indexed: Abstr.Bull.Inst.Pap.Chem., Forest.Abstr., Forest Prod.Abstr.
—BLDSC (8464.749500).
    Formerly: Svenska Traeforskningsinstitutet. Meddelande. Series A (ISSN 0085-6983)

676.3   BE   ISSN 0774-9856
SCRIPT, LE PAPETIER. Flemish edition: Script, De Papierhandel (ISSN 0774-9848) (Text in French) 1932. bi-m. 1500 BEF. Uitgevery E.G.P. Editions, F. Lenoirstr. 23, B-1090 Brussels, Belgium. FAX 32-2-4259312. Ed. Andre van Oekel. adv. contact: Emile Ryckaert. bk.rev. circ. 4,500.
    Supersedes (in 1986): Papetier (ISSN 0774-9910)

SEKUNDAER-ROHSTOFFE; Fachzeitschrift fuer Rohstoffhandel, Wiederverwertung und Recycling-Technik. see *MACHINERY*

SIA. see *FORESTS AND FORESTRY — Lumber And Wood*

676   AT   ISSN 0310-4389
SOMETHING ON PAPER.* 1973. q. free. Associated Pulp and Paper Mills Ltd., 476 St. Kilda Rd., Melbourne, Vic. 3004, Australia. FAX 03-811-9629. Ed. N. Heydon. circ. 5,000.

676   US   ISSN 0081-2129
SOURCES OF SUPPLY - BUYERS GUIDE. 1924. a. $90. Advertisers and Publishers Service, Inc., Drawer 795, Park Ridge, IL 60068. TEL 708-823-3145. FAX 708-696-3445. Ed. Linda Hapner. adv.; circ. 1,000 (paid). **Document type:** directory.
    Formerly: Source of Supply Directory.

676.2   US   ISSN 0270-5222
TS1080   CODEN: SOPPDD
SOUTHERN PULP & PAPER.* (Annual Review Number) 1938. m. $18. Ernest H. Abernethy Publishing (Subsidiary of: A-S-M Communications, Inc.), 6 Pidemont Ctr. N.E., Ste. 300, Atlanta, GA 30305-1515. Ed. John C. Cook. adv.; bk.rev.; charts; illus.; tr.lit.; index. circ. 10,000. (back issues avail.) Indexed: Abstr.Bull.Inst.Pap.Chem., Chem.Abstr., Paper & Bd.Abstr.
—BLDSC (0850.050000); UMI.
    Formerly: Southern Pulp and Paper Manufacturer (ISSN 0038-4488)

676   SW   ISSN 0283-6831
TS1080   CODEN: SVPAAE
SVENSK PAPPERSTIDNING - NORDISK CELLULOSA. (Text in Swedish) 1898. 12/yr. SEK 845 within the Nordic countries; elewhere SEK 995. (Svenska Pappers- och Cellulosaingenioersfoereningen, SPCI) Arbor Publishing AB, P.O. Box 26212 5, S-100 41 Stockholm, Sweden. TEL 46-8-679-90-11. FAX 46-8-679-90-50. (Co-sponsors: Skogsindustriema, SKR; Svenska Kemistsamfundet) Ed. Anders Fosstroem. adv.; bk.rev.; abstr.; bibl.; charts; illus.; pat.; stat.; index; circ. 7,687 (controlled). Indexed: Abstr.Bull.Inst.Pap.Chem., ASCA, Biol.Abstr., Chem.Abstr., Curr.Cont., Curr.Pack.Abstr., Forest.Abstr., Forest Prod.Abstr., Paper & Bd.Abstr., PROMT, World Text.Abstr. **Document type:** trade publication.
—CASDDS.
    Formerly: Svensk Papperstidning (ISSN 0039-6680)
    Description: Trade journal for the pulp and paper industry.

676   US   ISSN 0734-1415
TS1080   CODEN: TAJODT
T A P P I JOURNAL. 1949. m. membership. Technical Association of the Pulp and Paper Industry, Inc., Technology Park-Atlanta, Box 105113, Atlanta, GA 30348. TEL 404-446-1400. FAX 404-446-6947. adv.; bk.rev.; charts; illus.; mkt.; pat.; tr.lit.; index. circ. 38,000. (also avail. in microform from MIM,PMC) Indexed: A.S.& T.Ind., Abstr.Bull.Inst.Pap.Chem., Acid Rain Abstr., Acid Rain Ind., Anal.Abstr., Art & Archaeol.Tech.Abstr., ASCA, Biol.Abstr., CAD CAM Abstr., Chem.Abstr., Chem.Eng.Abstr., Curr.Biotech.Abstr., Curr.Cont., Curr.Pack.Abstr., Energy Info.Abstr., Eng.Ind., Environ.Abstr., Excerp.Med., Fluidex, Forest.Abstr., Graph.Arts Lit.Abstr., Int.Packag.Abstr., Mass Spectr.Bull., Packag.Sci.Tech., Paper & Bd.Abstr., Risk Abstr., Robomat., Sh.& Vib.Dig., Soils & Fert., Sugar Ind.Abstr., T.C.E.A., Text.Tech.Dig., W.R.C.Inf., World Surf.Coat., World Text.Abstr. **Document type:** academic/scholarly publication.
—BLDSC (8603.948000); CASDDS; Ei; Faxon; Genuine Article; SWETS; UnCover. **CCC.**
    Formerly: T A P P I (ISSN 0039-8241)
    Refereed Serial

676   US   ISSN 1046-4166
TS1176.6.M4   CODEN: PTAIDL
T A P P I PROCEEDINGS (YEAR). 1985. biennial. price varies. Technical Association of the Pulp and Paper Industry, Inc., Technology Park-Atlanta, Box 105113, Atlanta, GA 30348. TEL 404-446-1400. FAX 404-446-6947. **Document type:** proceedings.
—BLDSC (3928.220000); CASDDS. **CCC.**
    Formerly (until 1988): Technical Association of the Pulp and Paper Industry. Annual Meeting Proceedings (ISSN 0272-7269)
    Refereed Serial

676   US   ISSN 1045-618X
TS1109
T A P P I TEST METHODS. 1926. biennial. membership. Technical Association of the Pulp and Paper Industry, Inc., Technology Park-Atlanta, Box 105113, Atlanta, GA 30348. TEL 404-446-1400. FAX 404-446-6947. index. **Document type:** academic/scholarly publication.
—BLDSC (8604.256500). **CCC.**
    Former titles: T A P P I Standards and Provisional Methods; T A P P I Standards and Suggested Methods.
    Refereed Serial

676   US   ISSN 1047-305X
TS1118.F5   CODEN: TCCPDB
TECHNICAL ASSOCIATION OF THE PULP AND PAPER INDUSTRY. COATING CONFERENCE. 1969. a. price varies. Technical Association of the Pulp and Paper Industry, Inc., Technology Park-Atlanta, Box 105113, Atlanta, GA 30348. TEL 404-446-1400. FAX 404-446-6947. **Document type:** proceedings.
—BLDSC (3292.550000); CASDDS. **CCC.**
    Former titles (until 1980): Technical Association of the Pulp and Paper Industry. Coating Conference Proceedings (ISSN 1047-2185); (until 1979): T A P P I Coating Conference (ISSN 0364-2771); (until 1976): Coating Conference (ISSN 1047-2177)
    Refereed Serial

676   US   ISSN 0091-7737
TS1088
TECHNICAL ASSOCIATION OF THE PULP AND PAPER INDUSTRY. DIRECTORY. Key Title: Directory - Technical Association of the Pulp and Paper Industry. Running title: T A P P I Directory. 1919. a. Technical Association of the Pulp and Paper Industry, Inc., Technology Park-Atlanta, Box 105113, Atlanta, GA 30348. TEL 404-446-1400. FAX 404-446-6947. adv. circ. 31,000. **Document type:** directory.
    Formerly (until 1973): Technical Association of the Pulp and Paper Industry. Yearbook (ISSN 0092-3737)

676   US   ISSN 0271-9959
TS1080   CODEN: ECOPD8
TECHNICAL ASSOCIATION OF THE PULP AND PAPER INDUSTRY. ENGINEERING CONFERENCE PROCEEDINGS (YEAR). (In 3 books) a. Technical Association of the Pulp and Paper Industry, Inc., Technology Park-Atlanta, Box 105113, Atlanta, GA 30348. TEL 404-446-1400. FAX 404-446-6947. **Document type:** proceedings.
—BLDSC (8603.700000); CASDDS. **CCC.**
    Refereed Serial

PAPER AND PULP

676 US ISSN 1050-4265
TS1118.F5 CODEN: PACFEQ
TECHNICAL ASSOCIATION OF THE PULP AND PAPER INDUSTRY. FINISHING AND CONVERTING CONFERENCE. PROCEEDINGS (YEAR). a. Technical Association of the Pulp and Paper Industry, Inc., Technology Park-Atlanta, Box 105113, Atlanta, GA 30348. TEL 404-446-1400. FAX 404-446-6947. adv. **Document type:** proceedings.
—BLDSC (6368.300000); CASDDS. **CCC.**
 Formerly: Technical Association of the Pulp and Paper Industry. Paper Finishing and Converting Conference. Proceedings (Year) (ISSN 0738-0313)
 Refereed Serial

676 US
TECHNICAL ASSOCIATION OF THE PULP AND PAPER INDUSTRY. INTERNATIONAL PROCESS & PRODUCT QUALITY CONFERENCE PROCEEDINGS (YEAR). (Each year held jointly with a different TAPPI section) a. price varies. Technical Association of the Pulp and Paper Industry, Inc., Technology Park-Atlanta, Box 105113, Atlanta, GA 30348. TEL 404-446-1400. FAX 404-446-6947. circ. 500. **Indexed:** Chem.Abstr., Eng.Ind. **Document type:** proceedings.
 Former titles: Technical Association of the Pulp and Paper Industry. International Process and Materials Quality Evaluation Proceedings (Year); Technical Association of the Pulp and Paper Industry. Testing Conference Proceedings.
 Refereed Serial

676 US ISSN 0197-4513
 CODEN: NPFRDN
TECHNICAL ASSOCIATION OF THE PULP AND PAPER INDUSTRY. NONWOOD PLANT FIBER PULPING PROGRESS REPORT. 1975. irreg. price varies. Technical Association of the Pulp and Paper Industry, Inc., Technology Park-Atlanta, Box 105113, Atlanta, GA 30348. TEL 404-446-1400. FAX 404-446-6947.
—CASDDS.
 Refereed Serial

676 US ISSN 1049-6289
TS1828
TECHNICAL ASSOCIATION OF THE PULP AND PAPER INDUSTRY. NONWOVENS CONFERENCE. PROCEEDINGS (YEAR). a. price varies. Technical Association of the Pulp and Paper Industry, Inc., Box 105113, Atlanta, GA 30348. TEL 404-446-1400. FAX 404-446-6947. **Document type:** proceedings.
—BLDSC (6117.342700).
 Refereed Serial

676 US ISSN 0197-5153
TS1080 CODEN: TPCPDY
TECHNICAL ASSOCIATION OF THE PULP AND PAPER INDUSTRY. PAPERMAKERS CONFERENCE PROCEEDINGS (YEAR). a. price varies. Technical Association of the Pulp and Paper Industry, Inc., Technology Park-Atlanta, Box 105113, Atlanta, GA 30348. TEL 404-446-1400. FAX 404-446-6947. **Document type:** proceedings.
—CASDDS. **CCC.**
 Refereed Serial

676 US ISSN 1047-3033
TS198.3.P5
TECHNICAL ASSOCIATION OF THE PULP AND PAPER INDUSTRY. POLYMERS, LAMINATIONS & COATINGS CONFERENCE. PROCEEDINGS (YEAR). a. price varies. Technical Association of the Pulp and Paper Industry, Inc., Box 105113, Atlanta, GA 30348. TEL 404-446-1400. FAX 404-446-6947. **Document type:** proceedings.
 Refereed Serial

676 US
TECHNICAL ASSOCIATION OF THE PULP AND PAPER INDUSTRY. PROCESS CONTROL CONFERENCE. PROCEEDINGS (YEAR). a. price varies. Technical Association of the Pulp and Paper Industry, Inc., Box 105113, Atlanta, GA 30348. TEL 404-446-1400. FAX 404-446-6947. **Document type:** proceedings.
 Refereed Serial

676 US ISSN 0275-0899
TS1171 CODEN: PUCPDP
TECHNICAL ASSOCIATION OF THE PULP AND PAPER INDUSTRY. PULPING CONFERENCE PROCEEDINGS (YEAR). a. Technical Association of the Pulp and Paper Industry, Inc., Technology Park-Atlanta, Box 105113, Atlanta, GA 30348. TEL 404-446-1400. FAX 404-446-6947. **Document type:** proceedings.
—BLDSC (8604.110000); CASDDS. **CCC.**
 Refereed Serial

676.2 IT
TECNORAMA INDUSTRIE CARTARIE. 2/yr. Pubblicita Edizioni Associati s.r.l., Via Simone d'Orsenigo 22, 20135 Milan, Italy. TEL 2-551-18-42. FAX 2-551-85-263. Ed. Ugo Carutti.

TRANSPORT AND HANDLING IN THE PULP AND PAPER INDUSTRY; proceedings. 1975. irreg. (Pulp & Paper International Symposium) Miller Freeman, Inc. (Subsidiary of: United Newspapers), 600 Harrison St., San Francisco, CA 94107. TEL 415-905-2200. FAX 415-905-2232. TELEX 278273. illus.; index. (reprint service avail. from UMI) **Document type:** proceedings.

676 UK
THE U K DIRECTORY OF PAPERS AND BOARDS. s-a. £65. Paper Publications Ltd., Church House, Church Ln., Kings Langley, Herts WD4 8JP, England. TEL 01923-261555. FAX 01923-261118. adv.: B&W page £1365, color page £1950; adv. contact: Graham Martin. **Document type:** directory.
 Description: Provides information needed to select the best papers and boards to match a buyer's requirements.

676 GW ISSN 0042-3939
VERHUETET UNFAELLE. 1935. 13/yr. (Papiermacher Berufsgenossenschaft) Dr. Curt Haefner Verlag, Bachstr. 14-16, 69121 Heidelberg, Germany. TEL 06221-49064. (Subscr. to: Postfach 106060, 69050 Heidelberg, Germany) Ed. H. Gross. illus. circ. 75,000. **Indexed:** Abstr.Bull.Inst.Pap.Chem. **Document type:** bulletin.

VORWAERTS. see *LABOR UNIONS*

676 US ISSN 0083-7024
TS1088
WALDEN'S A B C GUIDE AND PAPER PRODUCTION YEARBOOK. 1885. a. $112.50. Walden-Mott Corporation, 225 N. Franklin Tpke., Ramsey, NJ 07446-1600. TEL 201-818-8630. FAX 201-818-8720. Ed. Theresa J. Dougherty; Pub. Alfred S./Walden. adv. contact: Nancy E. Wilbur. index. **Document type:** directory.

676 US
WALDEN'S FIBER & BOARD REPORT. bi-m. $210. Walden-Mott Corporation, 225 N. Franklin Tpke., Ramsey, NJ 07446-1600. TEL 201-818-8630. FAX 201-818-8720. Ed. Gregg B. Fales; Pub. Alfred S. Walden. (back issues avail.) **Document type:** newsletter.
 Description: Publishes timely news of producers and converters; trend information for sales and marketing; market analyses; inventory and price data, including wastepaper pricing, production and shipment figures, imports and exports, and executive appointments and managers on the move.

676 US
WALDEN'S PAPER REPORT. 1971. s-m. $185. Walden-Mott Corp., 225 N. Franklin Tpke., Ramsey, NJ 07446-1600. TEL 201-818-8630. FAX 201-818-8720. Ed. Sylvia Peremes; Pub. Alfred S. Walden. adv.; bk.rev. **Document type:** newsletter.
 Formerly: Walden-Mott Paper Report.

WEYERHAEUSER TODAY. see *FORESTS AND FORESTRY — Lumber And Wood*

676 338.5 SW ISSN 1101-2226
WHO SELLS WHAT? (Text in English) 1993. irreg. (every 3-4 yrs.). SEK 525. Arbor Publishing AB, P.O. Box 26212, S-100 41 Stockholm, Sweden. TEL 46-8-611-60-30. FAX 46-8-679-90-50. Ed. Carina Bertilson. adv.; index. circ. 1,000. **Document type:** consumer publication, trade publication, directory.
 Description: Gives information about enterprises that sell products used in the pulp and paper industry. Also includes a product index with reference to the supplying companies. Concentration is mainly on Europe and the Nordic countries but also includes entries from the U.S.

676 UK ISSN 0307-6040
WHO'S WHO IN CORRUGATED. 1974. a. £50. (International Paper Board Industry) Brunton Business Publications Ltd., Thruxton Down House, Thruxton Down, Andover, Hampshire SP11 8PR, England. Ed. Michael D. Brunton. **Document type:** directory.
 Description: Provides information for the corrugated board industry.

676 US
WHO'S WHO IN PAPER DISTRIBUTION. 1903. a. $75. National Paper Trade Association, Inc., 111 Great Neck Rd., Ste. 418, Great Neck, NY 11021. TEL 516-829-3070. adv.; charts; stat. circ. 2,500. **Document type:** directory.
 Former titles: Who's Who in Paper Distribution and Factbook; Who's Who in Paper Distribution.

676 GW ISSN 0043-7131
TS1080 CODEN: WBPFAZ
WOCHENBLATT FUER PAPIERFABRIKATION; Fachzeitschrift fuer die Papier-, Pappen- und Zellstoff-industrie. 1871. 22/yr. DM.173.60 (foreign DM.198.10). Deutscher Fachverlag GmbH, Mainzer Landstr. 251, 60326 Frankfurt a.M., Germany. TEL 069-7595-01. FAX 069-7595-2999. (Subscr. to: Postfach 100606, 60006 Frankfurt a.M., Germany) (Co-sponsors: Akademischer Papieringenieur-Verein an der TH Darmstadt; Vereinigter Papierfachverband Munchen e.V.; Papiermacher-Berufsgenossenschaft Mainz; Vereinigung Gernsbacher Papiermacher e.V.; Papiertechnische Stiftung Muenchen) Ed. Dr. Manhart Schlegel. adv.; bk.rev.; abstr.; charts; illus.; pat.; stat.; tr.lit.; index. circ. 3,395. (reprint service avail. from ISI) **Indexed:** Abstr.Bull.Inst.Pap.Chem., Chem.Abstr., Curr.Cont., Excerp.Med., Paper & Bd.Abstr., PROMT, Sel.Water Res.Abstr. **Document type:** trade publication.
—BLDSC (9342.000000); CASDDS; Ei; SWETS. **CCC.**

WOODWORKING INTERNATIONAL. see *FORESTS AND FORESTRY — Lumber And Wood*

676.2 UK ISSN 1353-2677
TS1080 CODEN: WOPAED
WORLD PAPER. (Text in English; summaries in French and German) 1879. 10/yr. £82 (foreign £105). Miller Freeman Publishers Ltd. (Subsidiary of: Morgan-Grampian plc.), Benn House, Sovereign Way, Tonbridge, Kent TN9 1RW, England. TEL 01732-364422. FAX 01732-361534. TELEX 95132 BENTON G. Pub. Patrick Wade. adv. contact: Alison Woolley. bk.rev.; abstr.; bibl.; charts; illus.; pat.; stat.; tr.mk. circ. 11,499. (also avail. in microform from UMI; reprint service avail. from UMI) **Indexed:** Abstr.Bull.Inst.Pap.Chem., Br.Tech.Ind., Chem.Abstr., Excerp.Med., Graph.Arts Lit.Abstr., Paper & Bd.Abstr., PROMT. **Document type:** trade publication.
—CASDDS; SWETS; UMI. **CCC.**
 Formerly (until 1993): Paper (ISSN 0306-8234); Incorporating: World's Paper Trade Review (ISSN 0043-9320); Paper-Maker (ISSN 0031-1154)
 Description: International pulp and paper industry's journal.

676.2 CC
ZAOZHI HUAXUE PIN/PAPER CHEMICALS. (Text in Chinese) 1988. q. $24. China Papermaking Chemicals Industry Association, 7 Shihuiba, Changbanxiang, Hangzhou, Zhejiang Province 310014, People's Republic of China. TEL 86-571-8082860. Ed. Wang Fulin. circ. 3,000.
 Description: Covers R&D and technological achievements in the field of paper chemicals both in China and abroad.

676 CC ISSN 1001-6309
ZHI HE ZAOZHI/PAPER AND PAPERMAKING. (Text in Chinese) 1982. bi-m. $30 (effective 1995). Zhongguo Zaozhi Xuehui - China Technical Association of the Paper Industry, 12 Guanghua Lu, Chaoyang-qu, Beijing 100020, People's Republic of China. TEL 86-1-500-2880. FAX 86-1-500-4461. Ed. Liu Renqing. adv. contact: Chen Wanping. circ. 11,000.

676.2 CC ISSN 0254-508X
TS1080 CODEN: ZHZADC
ZHONGGUO ZAOZHI/CHINA PULP AND PAPER. (Text in Chinese; abstracts in English) 1982. bi-m. $30. Zhongguo Zaozhi Xuehui - China Technical Association of the Paper Industry, 12 Guanghua Lu, Chaoyang-qu, Beijing 100020, People's Republic of China. TEL 86-1-500-2880. FAX 86-1-500-4461. Ed. Zhu Yince. adv. contact: Li Ping. circ. 9,500. **Document type:** trade publication.
—CASDDS.

676.2　　　　　　　CC
ZHONGGUO ZAOZHI XUEBAO/TRANSACTIONS OF CHINA PULP AND PAPER. (Text in Chinese; abstracts in English) 1986. a. $10. Zhongguo Zaozhi Xuehui - China Technical Association of the Paper Industry, 12 Guanghua Rd., Beijing 100086, People's Republic of China. TEL 86-1-500-2880. FAX 86-1-500-4461. Ed. Hua Ningxi. circ. 900. **Document type:** academic/scholarly publication.
Description: Covers R&D achievements in China.

PAPER AND PULP — Abstracting, Bibliographies, Statistics

676　　　　US　　ISSN 0734-8711
　　　　　　　　　CODEN: CSPAEP
C A SELECTS. PAPER ADDITIVES. s-w. $220 to non-members; members $65 (effective 1996). Chemical Abstracts Service (Subsidiary of: American Chemical Society), 2540 Olentangy River Rd., Box 3012, Columbus, OH 43210-0012. TEL 614-447-3600. FAX 614-447-3713. TELEX 6842086. **Document type:** abstracting/indexing.
Description: Covers noncellulosic materials added during papermaking; chemicals used for treating freshly formed sheets.

676.3 634.9　　CN　　ISSN 0835-0094
HD9834.C2
CANADA. STATISTICS CANADA. PAPER AND ALLIED PRODUCTS INDUSTRIES. (Catalogue 36-250) (Text in English and French) 1917. a. Can.$35($42) (foreign $49). Statistics Canada, Publications Sales and Services, Ottawa, ON K1A 0T6, Canada. TEL 613-951-7277. FAX 613-951-1584. (also avail. in microform from MML) **Document type:** government publication.
Supersedes: Paper and Allied Products Industries (ISSN 0384-4633)
Description: Annual census of manufactures.

338.4　　　　　CN　　ISSN 0316-4241
HD9839.N4
CANADIAN PULP AND PAPER ASSOCIATION. ANNUAL NEWSPRINT SUPPLEMENT. a. free. Canadian Pulp and Paper Association - Association Canadienne des Pates et Papiers, Sun Life Building, 19th Fl., 1155 Metcalfe St., Montreal, PQ H3B 4T6, Canada. TEL 514-866-6621. FAX 514-866-3035. stat.

676.1　　　　　　　CN
CANADIAN PULP AND PAPER ASSOCIATION. TECHNICAL SECTION. INDICES/ASSOCIATION CANADIENNE DES PATES ET PAPIERS. SECTION TECHNIQUE. LISTES. (Text in English, French) a. Canadian Pulp and Paper Association, Technical Section, 1155 Metcalfe St., Ste. 1900, Montreal, PQ H3B 4T6, Canada. TEL 514-866-6621. FAX 514-866-3035.
Description: Indexes technical papers, authors and branch and committee papers added to the Technical Section Data Base.

676　　　　　　　BE
CONFEDERATION OF EUROPEAN PAPER INDUSTRIES. ANNUAL STATISTICS. 1992. a. 15000 BEF. Confederation of European Paper Industries, 306 av. Louise, B-1050 Brussels, Belgium. TEL 32-2-6274911. FAX 32-2-6468137.
Description: Provides statistics relating to the previous year's paper production and consumption.

676　　　　　　　FR
FRANCE. SERVICE D'ETUDE DES STRATEGIES ET DES STATISTIQUES INDUSTRIELLES. RESULTATS TRIMESTRIELS DES ENQUETES DE BRANCHE. FABRICATION D'ARTICLES DE PAPETERIE. q. 180 F. (foreign 210 F.)(effective 1991). Service d'Etude des Strategies et des Statistiques Industrielles (SESSI), 85 bd. du Montparnasse, 75270 Paris Cedex 06, France. TEL 45-56-42-34. FAX 45-56-40-71. stat.
Description: Provides detailed industry-wide performance statistics for comparative evaluations.

676 016　　　US　　ISSN 1047-2088
Z7914.P2　　　　　CODEN: ABPCAM
INSTITUTE OF PAPER SCIENCE AND TECHNOLOGY. ABSTRACT BULLETIN. (Former name of issuing body: Institute of Paper Chemistry) 1930. m. $2050 per vol. in N. America; elsewhere $2400. Institute of Paper Science and Technology, 500 10th St., N.W., Atlanta, GA 30318. TEL 404-853-9500. Ed. Rosana Bechtel. bk.rev.; index, cum.index. circ. 600. (also avail. in microform from PMC; back issues avail.; reprint service avail.) **Indexed:** Anal.Abstr., Biol.Abstr., Forest.Abstr., Forest Prod.Abstr., Graph.Arts Lit.Abstr., Int.Packag.Abstr., Paper & Bd.Abstr., World Surf.Coat. **Document type:** abstracting/indexing.
●Also available online. Vendor(s): Knight-Ridder, Inc. (File nos.240 & 840/PAPERCHEM).
—CASDDS. **CCC.**
Formerly (until July 1989): Institute of Paper Chemistry. Abstract Bulletin (ISSN 0020-3033)
Description: Abstracts scientific, technical and patent literature about the manufacture of pulp and paper and related areas, including forestry, economics, wood and wood chemistry, nonwovens.

676　　　　　　　JA　　ISSN 0044-0663
MONTHLY STATISTICS OF PAPER DISTRIBUTION/KAMI RYUTSU TOKEI GEPPO.* m. 12000 Yen. Ministry of International Trade and Industry, 1-3-1 Kasumigaseki, Chiyoda-ku, Tokyo 100, Japan. TEL 03-501-1511. Ed.Bd. charts; stat. circ. 600.

676　　　　　　　NE　　ISSN 0168-4361
HD9835.N4
NETHERLANDS. CENTRAAL BUREAU VOOR DE STATISTIEK. PRODUKTIESTATISTIEKEN: PAPIER- EN KARTONINDUSTRIE. a. Centraal Bureau voor de Statistiek, Prinses Beatrixlaan 428, Voorburg, Netherlands. (Orders to: SDU - Publishers, Christoffel Plantijnstraat, The Hague, Netherlands) **Document type:** government publication.
Formed by the merger of: Netherlands. Centraal Bureau voor de Statistiek. Produktiestatistiek van de Papierindustries; Netherlands. Centraal Bureau voor de Statistiek. Produktiestatistiek Strokartonindustrie.

676 016　　　UK　　ISSN 0307-0778
PAPER AND BOARD ABSTRACTS. 1965. m. $907. Pira International, Randalls Rd., Leatherhead, Surrey KT22 7RU, England. TEL 01372-376161. FAX 01372-360104. Ed. Diana Deavin; Pub. Marie Rushton. bk.rev.; index. (reprint service avail.) **Indexed:** Curr.Cont., World Text.Abstr. **Document type:** abstracting/indexing.
●Also available online. Vendor(s): Data-Star, Knight-Ridder, Inc., Orbit Search Service (PIRA), STN International.
Also available on CD-ROM. Producer(s): Knight-Ridder, Inc.
—BLDSC (6358.900000).
Formerly (until 1976): Kenley Abstracts.

676.3 338.4　　US
PAPER DISTRIBUTION DATA SOURCE; market research for the paper and plastics industries. 1990. a. $240. National Paper Trade Association, Inc., 111 Great Neck Rd., Ste. 418, Great Neck, NY 11021. TEL 516-829-3070. Ed. George Cain. stat.
Description: Provides current information on changes in the US paper industry compiled from government, NPTA and other sources, including information on gross sales volume, state by state evaluations, specific product types, and market projections.

676　　　　　　　US　　ISSN 0003-0341
HD9824
PAPER, PAPERBOARD, & WOOD PULP; monthly statistical summary. (Includes Fact Sheet) 1921. m. $435 (foreign $465). American Forest & Paper Institute, 1111 19th St. N.W., Washington, DC 20036. TEL 202-463-2700. FAX 202-463-2785. Ed. Stan Lancey. charts; mkt. circ. 800. (also avail. in microfiche from CIS) **Indexed:** Abstr.Bull.Inst.Pap.Chem., SRI. **Document type:** newsletter, trade publication.
Description: Reports data such as production, inventories, imports and exports for various grades of pulp, paper and paperboard.

676　　　　　　　US
PAPER PRODUCTION RATIO WEEKLY REPORT. w. $195 (foreign $215). American Forest & Paper Association, 1111 19th St. N.W., Washington, DC 20036. TEL 202-463-2700. FAX 202-463-2785.

674 676 016　　HU　　ISSN 0231-0740
PAPIRIPARI ES NYOMDAIPARI SZAKIRODALMI TAJEKOZTATO/PAPER INDUSTRY & PRINTING ABSTRACTS. 1949. m. 7000 Ft. Orszagos Muszaki Informacios Kozpont es Konyvtar (O.M.I.K.K.) - National Technical Information Centre and Library, Muzeum u. 17, Box 12, 1428 Budapest, Hungary. (Subscr. to: Kultura, Box 149, 1389 Budapest, Hungary) Ed. Peter Kalmar. abstr.; index. circ. 230.
Supersedes (in 1983): Muszaki Lapszemle. Faipar, Papir-es Nyomdaipar - Technical Abstracts. Wood and Paper Industry, Printing (ISSN 0027-4992)

676 016　　　PL　　ISSN 0033-2291
TS1080　　　　　　CODEN: PRZPAE
PRZEGLAD PAPIERNICZY/POLISH PAPER REVIEW. 1945. m. $81.50. Wydawnictwo Czasopism i Ksiazek Technicznych SIGMA - NOT, Ul. Ratuszowa 11, P.O. Box 1004, 00-950 Warsaw, Poland. TEL 48-22-180918. FAX 48-22-192187. TELEX 814550 SIGMA PL. (Dist. by: SIGMA NOT Ltd., Ul. Bartycka 20, 00-716 Warsaw, Poland) Ed. Karol Palenik. adv.; bk.rev.; abstr.; charts; illus.; stat.; index. circ. 1,400. **Indexed:** Abstr.Bull.Inst.Pap.Chem., Biol.Abstr., Chem.Abstr., Packag.Sci.Tech.
—BLDSC (6944.000000); CASDDS.

676　　　　　　　US　　ISSN 0731-8863
HD9839.P33
STATISTICS OF PAPER, PAPERBOARD AND WOOD PULP. 1947. a. $365 (foreign $380). Forest & Paper Association, 1111 19th St. N.W., Washington, DC 20036. TEL 202-463-2700. FAX 202-463-2785. Ed. Stan Lancey. (also avail. in microfiche from CIS) **Indexed:** SRI. **Document type:** trade publication.
Former titles: Statistics of Paper and Paperboard (ISSN 0097-4730); Paperboard Industry Statistics.

676 310　　　FR　　ISSN 0997-0991
STATISTIQUES DE L'INDUSTRIE FRANCAISE DES PATES. PAPIERS ET CARTONS. a. 40 F. Confederation Franciase de l'Industrie des Papiers Cartons & Celluloses, 154 bd Haussmann, 75008 Paris, France. TEL 1-45-62-87-07. FAX 1-45-62-82-47. illus.
Continues: Quelques Donnees Statistiques sur l'Industrie Francaise des Pates, Papiers, Cartons (ISSN 0481-0112)

016.6762　　　CC　　ISSN 1002-6762
ZAOZHI WENZHAI/ABSTRACTS OF PAPER MANUFACTURING. (Text in Chinese) bi-m. $36 (effective 1995 & 1996). Paper Industry Research Institute of China, 12 Guanghua Rd., Beijing 100020, People's Republic of China. TEL 86-1-506-0022. FAX 86-1-500-5677. Ed. Shan Naili. adv. contact: Li Weling. circ. 2,000. **Document type:** abstracting/indexing.
Description: A bibliographic, abstract and index publication covering global pulp and paper activities.

PARAPSYCHOLOGY AND OCCULTISM

see also New Age Publications

133　　　　　　　US
A A - E V P NEWS. 1982. q. $20 membership. American Association - Electronic Voice Phenomena, 816 Midship Ct., Annapolis, MD 21401-7387. TEL 410-573-0873. Ed. Sarah Wilson Estep. illus. circ. 300. (back issues avail.) **Document type:** newsletter.
Description: Evidence of death survival as presented through electronic instruments such as: tape recorders, televisions, and computers.

133　　　　　　　FR　　ISSN 0752-2452
BL624
A R I E S. (Text in English, French, German; summaries in French) 1985. 2/yr. 150 F.($20); newsstand price: 75 F. (Association pour la Recherche et l'Information sur l'Esoterisme) Table d'Emeraude, 21 rue de la Huchette, 75005 Paris, France. TEL 43-54-90-96. FAX 40-51-02-67. Ed.Bd. bk.rev. circ. 200. (back issues avail.) **Document type:** academic/scholarly publication, bibliography.
Description: Methodological articles devoted to the approach of the history of Western esotericism and occultism.

PARAPSYCHOLOGY AND OCCULTISM

133.91 — US — ISSN 0044-7919
A S P R NEWSLETTER. 1968. q. $20 to non-members. American Society for Psychical Research, Inc., 5 W. 73rd St., New York, NY 10023. TEL 212-799-5050. FAX 212-496-2497. illus. circ. 2,000. **Document type:** newsletter.

133
BF1001 — US — ISSN 1066-5455
ABRASAX. 1988. q. $20. Abrasax Publications, Box 1219, Corpus Christi, TX 78403-1219. TEL 512-854-7094. (Dist. by: Abyss Books, Box 1022, Easthampton, MA 01027) Ed. James M. Martin. adv.; bk.rev. circ. 200.
Description: Devoted to the study of all aspects of the occult, emphasizing a non-judgemental attitude towards the so-called Left Hand Path (black magic, Satanism).

133 200 — US
ACADEMY OF RELIGION AND PSYCHICAL RESEARCH. PROCEEDINGS. 1980. a. $10 (effective 1995 & 1996). Academy of Religion and Psychical Research, Box 614, Bloomfield, CT 06002-0614. TEL 203-242-4593. Ed. Claire G. Walker. adv. contact: Bayce Batey. circ. 300. (back issues avail.) **Document type:** proceedings.
Description: Interfaces religion and psychical research.

133 — US
AHKADEN; The Ahkaden. 1987. q. $6. Stellar Mind Communications, Ltd., Box 5431, Clinton, NJ 08822. TEL 908-788-6735. FAX 908-788-9545. Pub. Michael E. Morgan. adv. circ. 500. **Document type:** newsletter.
Former titles (until 1995): Yokar Speaks; (until vol.1, no.4): Akhaden.
Description: Covers spiritual cosmology and spiritual wisdom regarding the human condition, along with ongoing initiations, initiate activities, events, tours, health issues, and experimental investigations on scientific data from parapsychological sources. Reports on Earth changes.

ALLGEMEINE ZEITSCHRIFT FUER PARANORMOLOGIE. see NEW AGE PUBLICATIONS

133.91 — US — ISSN 0003-1070
AMERICAN SOCIETY FOR PSYCHICAL RESEARCH. JOURNAL. 1907. q. $40 to individuals; institutions $65; students and senior citizens $20. American Society for Psychical Research, Inc., 5 W. 73rd St., New York, NY 10023. TEL 212-799-5050. FAX 212-496-2497. Ed. Rhea A. White. bk.rev.; abstr.; charts; stat.; index. circ. 2,000. (also avail. in microform from UMI; back issues avail.; reprint service avail. from UMI) **Indexed:** Mid.East: Abstr.& Ind., Psychol.Abstr. (1933-), Soc.Sci.Ind., SSCI. —BLDSC (4693.050000); Genuine Article; UMI; UnCover.
Description: Discusses clairvoyance, extrasensory perception, precognition, psychokinesis, psychic healing.

133.323 — FR — ISSN 0003-1798
AMIS DE LA RADIESTHESIE. 1930. q. 60 F. Association des Amis de la Radiesthesie, 70 rue du General de Gaulle, B.P. 3, 95620 Parmain, France. Ed. H. de France. adv.; bibl.; charts. circ. 500.

ANTHROPOLOGY OF CONSCIOUSNESS. see ANTHROPOLOGY

133.4 — AU
ANUBIS; Zeitschrift fuer praktische Magie und Psychonautik. 1985. 4/yr. S.280($30) Postfach 45, A-1203 Vienna, Austria. adv.; bk.rev. circ. 800.

133 — UK — ISSN 0141-0121
AQUARIAN ARROW. 1977. irreg. £5($10) for 4 nos. Neopantheist Society, BCM-OPAL, London WC1N 3XX, England. TEL 081-348-4178. Ed. Zachary Cox. adv.; bk.rev. circ. 300. (back issues avail.) **Document type:** consumer publication.
Description: Libertarian magazine with a Thelemic/Nietzschean orientation. Focuses on speculative ethics and irony. Contains articles, essays, creative writing, and reader correspondence on the relationship between pantheistic, spiritual philosophies and cultural, psychological and civic development.

133 150 — AT — ISSN 1035-9621
AUSTRALIAN PARAPSYCHOLOGICAL REVIEW. 1983. 2/yr. Aus.$18. Australian Institute of Parapsychological Research Inc., P.O. Box 176, Annandale, N.S.W. 2038, Australia. TEL 61-2-5163291. E-mail: M.Hough@cchs.su.eud.au. Ed. Harvey Irwin. bk.rev.; charts; illus. circ. 400. (back issues avail.) **Document type:** academic/scholarly publication, newsletter.
Former titles: Australian Institute of Parapsychological Research Bulletin & Australian Institute of Psychic Research Bulletin (ISSN 0813-2194)
Description: Promotes scientific study of parapsychological and related phenomena. Emphasis on Australian studies.

133 — FR
AUTRE MONDE. 1978. m. 120 F. G. Gourdon, Ed. & Pub., 10 rue de Crussol, 75011 Paris, France. TEL 48-05-41-10. FAX 48-05-81-54. adv.; illus. circ. 60,000.

133 — US
THE BAHLASTI PAPERS. 1986. m. $27 (effective 1994). Ordo Templi Orientis, Kali Lodge, Box 3096, New Orleans, LA 70177-3096. TEL 504-949-2037. Ed. Soror Chen. bk.rev.; circ. 200 (paid). **Document type:** newsletter.
Description: Forum for creative thought in the areas of the occult, Western ceremonial magick, voodoo, comparative religion and philosophy.

THE BEACON (MIAMI). see NEW AGE PUBLICATIONS

BEACON (NEW YORK). see PHILOSOPHY

133 — US
BEYOND REALITY; the latest discoveries in ESP, UFO's & psychic phenomena. 1972. bi-m. $18. Beyond Reality Magazine, Inc., Box 428, Nanuet, NY 10954. Ed. Harry Belil. adv.; bk.rev.; illus. circ. 40,000. (also avail. in microform; reprint service avail. from UMI)

THE BLACK FLAME. see RELIGIONS AND THEOLOGY — Other Denominations And Sects

BODY, MIND & SPIRIT MAGAZINE. see NEW AGE PUBLICATIONS

133.323 — UK — ISSN 0007-179X
BRITISH SOCIETY OF DOWSERS. JOURNAL. 1933. q. membership only. British Society of Dowsers, Sycamore Barn, Hastingleigh, Ashford, Kent TN25 5HW, England. TEL 01233-750253. Ed. R. Howard. bk.rev.; abstr.; index; circ. 1,250 (controlled). (also avail. in microfilm from UMI; reprint service avail. from UMI) **Document type:** consumer publication. —BLDSC (4719.200000); UMI.

133 — MX
CASOS EXTRAORDINARIOS!; el universo de lo oculto. 1993. fortn. Mex.$3($2) per no. Publicaciones Llergo, Av. Ceylan 517, Col. Industrial Vallejo, 02300 Mexico DF, Mexico. TELEX 17620550. Dir. Gilberto Juarez. **Document type:** consumer publication.
Description: Contains stories of the occult, phenomena, ghosts, crimes, and mysteries.

CATALYST (MARIETTA); a publication resource of New Age newsletters, book reviews, personals, holistic health, UFO's and psychic connections. see NEW AGE PUBLICATIONS

133 808.838 — US
CEMETARY PLOT. 1993. q. $28. Tellstar Productions, Box 1264, Huntington, WV 25714. Ed. Shannon Bridget Murphy. adv.: page $50. film rev.; illus.; index. circ. 1,000. (also avail. in microform; audio cassette; diskette format; back issues avail.) **Document type:** bulletin.

133 — US
CENTRIC.* 1974. 7/yr. $8. Esoteric Philosophy Center, Inc., 8383 Commerce Park Dr., No. 604, Houston, TX 77036-7425. TEL 713-952-9909. Ed. Brett Chandler. adv.; bk.rev.; illus. circ. 15,000.

CHAMP CHANNELS. see BIOLOGY — Zoology

CHURCH OF LIGHT QUARTERLY. see NEW AGE PUBLICATIONS

133.4 110 — US
CINCINNATI JOURNAL OF MAGIC. 1976. a. $6. Black Moon Publishing, Box 19469, Cincinnati, OH 45219-0469. TEL 504-891-6567. Eds. Joe Bounds, Louis Martinie. bk.rev. circ. 1,000.
Description: Collection of night side magicks.

133 — AG — ISSN 0010-6291
CONOCIMIENTO DE LA NUEVA ERA. 1938. m. Arg.$2. Viamonte 1716, 1055 Buenos Aires, Argentina. Ed. Adolfo Bruziks. bk.rev. circ. 8,000.

COSMIC CURRENT NEWS. see NEW AGE PUBLICATIONS

COSMIC VOICE; cosmic revelations for the New Age. see NEW AGE PUBLICATIONS

133 — UK — ISSN 0954-6006
DARK LILY. q. $4 per no. B C M, P.O. Box 3406, London WC1N 3XX, England. Ed. Magdalene Graham.

DAUGHTERS OF NYX; a magazine of goddess stories, mythmaking and fairy tales. see NEW AGE PUBLICATIONS

130 — IT — ISSN 0391-2965
DIMENSIONE PSI; rivista internazionale di parapsicologia. (Text and summaries in English, French, German, Italian, Spanish) 1946. s-a. $6 membership or exchange basis. Associazione Italiana Studi del Paranormale, Via Puggia 47, 16131 Genoa, Italy. Ed.Bd. adv.; bk.rev.; abstr.; bibl.; charts; illus.; index. circ. 3,000.

133 370.15 150
371.42 — US
DIMENSIONS (RIMROCK). 1980. bi-m. $18. Delphi Publications, Box 211, Rimrock, AZ 86335. TEL 602-634-2390. Ed. Jay Harris. adv.; bk.rev. circ. 2,500.

DIRECTORY TO CANADIAN PAGAN RESOURCES. see RELIGIONS AND THEOLOGY

133.4 — US
DRUID HENGE. 1979. 12/yr. $150 to individuals; pagans $15. Craeftgemot Witancoveyne, Inc., Box 499, Deerfield Beach, FL 33441. TEL 305-698-6924. Ed. Janice Scot-Reeder. adv.; bk.rev.

133 — US
▼**E H E NEWS.** 1994. s-a. $15 to individuals; institutions $18 (foreign $20). Exceptional Human Experience Network, Inc., 2 Plane Tree Ln., Dix Hills, NY 11746. TEL 516-271-1243. FAX 516-427-4413. Ed. Rhea A. White. **Document type:** newsletter.
Description: Publishes brief case reports, interviews, reports of persons and organizations interested in exceptional human experience.

THE EARTH CHANGES REPORT; the survival guide for the nineties. see EARTH SCIENCES

ECLECTIC THEOSOPHIST; following the Blavatsky and Point Loma traditions. see PHILOSOPHY

133 — US
EIDOLON.* 1991. 4/yr. $13.88. 456 S. Seventh St., Ann Arbor, MI 48103-4759. TEL 313-662-7691. Ed. Gabriel LaCroix. adv.; bk.rev.
Description: Features a unique blend of reader submitted articles and artwork.

133 — US
ENCHANTING NEWS. 4/yr. $4.50 per no. Fanscifiaroan Church of Wicca, Box 145, Marion, CT 06444.
Description: Includes practical ritual, formulas for incense.

133 — US — ISSN 0731-7840
ENCYCLOPEDIA OF OCCULTISM AND PARAPSYCHOLOGY. 1978. irreg., 3rd ed., 1990. $295. Gale Research Inc., 835 Penobscot Bldg., Detroit, MI 48226. TEL 313-961-2242. FAX 313-961-6083. TELEX 810-221-7086. Ed. Leslie Shepard. **Indexed:** Child.Auth.& Illus.

ESOTERA; neues Denken und Handeln. see NEW AGE PUBLICATIONS

PARAPSYCHOLOGY AND OCCULTISM

133 AU
ESOTERIK HEUTE. 1992. bi-m. S.250. Gesellschaft zur Pflege, Verbreitung und Erforschung Esoterischer Grenzwissenschaften, Wartholzstr. 12, A-2651 Reichenau, Austria. TEL 02666-2967. FAX 02666-29674. adv.: page $1900. circ. 13,500. (back issues avail.) **Document type:** academic/scholarly publication.

133 GW ISSN 0170-4249
ESOTERIK UND WISSENSCHAFT. 1966. 3/yr. DM.18($10) OARCA - Freie Akademie zur Koordinierung von Esoterik und Wissenschaft e.V., Donnersbergerstr. 11, 80634 Munich, Germany. TEL 089-162445. adv. circ. 1,100. **Document type:** bulletin.

133 US ISSN 0277-3600
ESSENTIA. 4/yr. $8. Paracelsus College, 3555 S. 700 East, Salt Lake City, UT 84106. TEL 801-486-6730. Ed. Mary Adams. adv.; illus.

ESSERE. see *PHILOSOPHY*

130 UK ISSN 0168-7263
EUROPEAN JOURNAL OF PARAPSYCHOLOGY. (Text in English) 1974. a. £12. (Parapsychologcial Association) Koestler Chair of Parapsychology, Dept. of Psychology, Univ. of Edinburgh, 7 George Sq., Edinburgh EH8 9JZ, Scotland. TEL 0131-650-3348. FAX 0131-650-3461. Ed. Robert Morris. bk.rev. circ. 250. **Indexed:** Psychol.Abstr. (1983-). **Document type:** academic/scholarly publication. —BLDSC (3829.733400).
 Description: Publishes articles relating to all aspects of parapsychology and psychical research (covering extrasensory perception and psychokinesis) including historical, theoretical and experimental papers.
 Refereed Serial

EXPLORING THE UNKNOWN. see *CHILDREN AND YOUTH — For*

133.05 US ISSN 0014-8776
BF1995
FATE; the world's mysteries explored. 1948. m. $18. Llewellyn Publications, 84 S. Wabasha St., Box 64383, St. Paul, MN 55164. TEL 612-291-1970. FAX 612-291-1908. adv.; bk.rev.; abstr.; illus. circ. 140,000. (also avail. in microform from UMI; back issues avail.; reprint service avail. from UMI) **Indexed:** Access (1975-), Hlth.Ind., Mag.Ind. —UMI.
 Description: Presents true stories, personal vignettes, and biographical profiles pertaining to strange, mystical, and parapsychological experiences.

THE FEDERATION FLASH; exploring the frontiers of miraculous probability. see *NEW AGE PUBLICATIONS*

FIREHEART; a journal of magic and spiritual transformation. see *NEW AGE PUBLICATIONS*

133 UK
FORESIGHT (BIRMINGHAM). 1970. q. £2.50. 44 Brockhurst Rd., Hodge Hill, Birmingham B36 8JB, England. TEL 0121-783-0587. Eds. John W.B. Barklam, Mrs. J. Barklam. adv. contact: John Barklam. bk.rev.; charts; illus. circ. 1,500. **Document type:** consumer publication.
 Description: Examines UFOs, occult and psychic phenomena, and New Age subjects.

FOREVER ALIVE. see *NEW AGE PUBLICATIONS*

001.94 UK ISSN 0308-5899
FORTEAN TIMES; the journal of strange phenomena. 1973. bi-m. £12($30) (other E.C. nations £15 ($30); elsewhere £18 ($36)). John Brown Publishing Ltd., The Boathouse, Crabtree Ln., London SW6 6LU, England. FAX 071-485-5002. E-mail: ft@forteana.win-uk.net. (U.S. subscr. to: Fenner, Reed & Jackson, Box 754, Manhasset, NY 11030. TEL 516-627-3836. FAX 516-627-1972) Eds. Robert J.M. Rickard, Paul Sieveking. adv. contact: Ronnie Hackston. bk.rev.; bibl.; index; circ. 30,000 (paid). (back issues avail.) **Document type:** academic/scholarly publication.
 Description: Provides accounts of paranormal phenomena, experiences, curiosities, mysteries, prodigies, and portents.

133 US ISSN 0886-6791
THE GATE; explore the mysteries. 1985. q. Box 43518, Richmond Hts., OH 44143. Ed. Beth Robbins. adv.; bk.rev.; illus. circ. 200. (back issues avail.) **Document type:** newsletter.

133 US
GHOST TRACKERS NEWSLETTER. 1982. 3/yr. $12 (foreign $20). Ghost Research Society, Box 205, Oaklawn, IL 60454-0205. TEL 708-425-5163. Ed. Dale Kaczmarek. adv.; bk.rev. circ. 200. (looseleaf format; back issues avail.) **Document type:** newsletter.

GREEN EGG; a journal of the awakening Earth. see *NEW AGE PUBLICATIONS*

133 US ISSN 1069-3211
GREEN MAN; a magazine for pagan men. 1993. q. $13. Alan Niven, Ed. & Pub., Box 641, Point Arena, CA 95468. TEL 707-882-2052. FAX 707-882-2793. adv.; bk.rev.; circ. 3,500 (paid).
 Description: Covers rituals, news, eco-paganism, men's wisdom, God and Goddess lore.

133.4 UK ISSN 0966-6427
HARVEST MOON. 1987. 6/yr. £4. 36 Dawes House, Orb Street, London SE17 1RE, England. TEL 071-708-4629. adv.; bk.rev.
 Formerly: Odinn Magazine.

133 US
HECHIZOS. (Text in Spanish) 1987. m. $2.50 per no. Latin American News and Book Inc., 614 Franklin St., Elizabeth, NJ 07206. TEL 908-355-8835. FAX 908-527-9160. Ed. Jesus M. Tenreiro. adv.: B&W page $650; 6 3/4 x 9 1/2. circ. 45,000.
 Description: Covers parapsychology, spiritualism, science fiction and astrology.

133.91 UK
HIDDEN HISTORY. 1965. q. $25. Anomalous Phenomenon Research Association, 5 Frederick Ave., Carlton NG4 1HP, England. TEL 0602-860010. Ed. S.W. Henley. adv.; bk.rev.; illus.; index. circ. 457.
 Former titles (until 1987): Anomalous Phenomenon Review; U F O Research Review (ISSN 0306-9915); N U F O I S Newsletter.
 Description: Contains information about various earth mysteries, folklore, archaeological curiosities, and other super natural phenomena.

133 IC
HUGINN AND MUNINN; interstellar messenger. (Text in English) 1966-1974; resumed 1979. 4/yr. $10. (Felag Nyalssinna) Bioradii Publications, P.O. Box 1159, Reykjavik, Iceland. TEL 354-553-5683. FAX 354-568-9303. Ed. Thorsteinn Gudjonsson. bk.rev. circ. 400. (processed) **Document type:** bulletin, newsletter.
 Former titles: Interstellar Bulletins; Interstellar Communication (ISSN 0020-9740)
 Description: Focuses on philosophy, parapsychology, old Norse religion and lore.

IMAGINATION, COGNITION AND PERSONALITY. see *PSYCHOLOGY*

133 US
INNERGY NEWS.* 4/yr. free. Source of Innergy, Ltd., c/o Flanagan, Box 2285, Sedona, AZ 86336. Ed. Patrick Flanagan. illus. (tabloid format)

130 US
INSIGHTS (MORRISTOWN).* vol. 5, 1976. 10/yr. $10. Jersey Society of Parapsychology, Box 2071, Morristown, NJ 07960. TEL 201-539-1466. Ed. B.J. McKay. bk.rev. circ. 700.

133 US
INTERNATIONAL DIRECTORY OF PSYCHIC SCIENCES. 1986. a. $7. Ghost Research Society, Box 205, Oaklawn, IL 60454-0205. TEL 708-425-5163. Ed. Dale Kaczmarek. circ. 200. (looseleaf format; back issues avail.) **Document type:** directory.
 Description: Lists organizations, groups and individuals associated with the occult in general.

133 110 US
INTUITIVE EXPLORATIONS. 6137. bi-m. $15. Box 561, Quincy, IL 62306-0561. TEL 217-222-9082. E-mail: BRST18A@Prodigy.com. Ed. Gloria Reiser. adv.: B&W page $35. bk.rev. circ. 1,000. (back issues avail.) **Document type:** newsletter.
 Description: Covers all areas of metaphysics, magic, mysticism, manifesting human potential. Acts as a free-flow exchange amongst those individuals who take metaphysics seriously.

IO. see *ANTHROPOLOGY*

133 US
IRIDIS. 1959. 10/yr. $10 (effective 1995). California Society for Psychical Study, Box 844, Berkeley, CA 94701. TEL 510-530-8564. Ed. Grace Furst. bk.rev. **Document type:** newsletter.

JOURNAL OF BORDERLAND RESEARCH. see *SCIENCES: COMPREHENSIVE WORKS*

130 US ISSN 0022-3387
BF1001 CODEN: JPRPAU
JOURNAL OF PARAPSYCHOLOGY; a scientific quarterly dealing with extrasensory perception, the psychokinetic effect and related topics. 1937. q. $30 to individuals; institutions $45 (effective 1995). (Foundation for Research on the Nature of Man) Parapsychology Press, 402 N. Buchanan Blvd., Durham, NC 27701-1728. TEL 919-688-8241. FAX 919-683-4338. E-mail: journal@frnm.org. Ed. John A. Palmer. adv. contact: Emily W. Cook. bk.rev.; abstr.; bibl.; charts; illus.; index; circ. 1,000 (paid). (also avail. in microform from UMI; back issues avail.; reprint service avail. from UMI, ISI) **Indexed:** ASSIA, Biol.Abstr., Curr.Cont., Excerp.Med., Mid.East: Abstr.& Ind., Psychol.Abstr. (1937-), Soc.Sci.Ind., SSCI. **Document type:** academic/scholarly publication. ●Also available online. Vendor(s): University Microfilms International.
 —BLDSC (5028.800000); Faxon; Genuine Article; UMI; UnCover. **CCC.**
 Refereed Serial

133 200 US ISSN 0731-2148
BL65.P3
JOURNAL OF RELIGION & PSYCHICAL RESEARCH; a scholarly quarterly dealing with religion, psychical research, and related topics. 1979. q. $20 (effective thru 1996). Academy of Religion and Psychical Research, Box 614, Bloomfield, CT 06002-0614. TEL 203-242-4593. Ed. Claire G. Walker. adv. contact: Bayce Batey. bk.rev.; index. circ. 300. (back issues avail.) **Indexed:** Rel.Ind.One. **Document type:** academic/scholarly publication.
 —BLDSC (5049.352000).

JOURNAL OF SCIENTIFIC EXPLORATION. see *SCIENCES: COMPREHENSIVE WORKS*

154 UK
THE KABBALIST. 1974. q. £5 (overseas £7). International Order of Kabbalists, 25 Circle Gardens, Merton Park, London SW19 3JX, England. TEL 0181-542-3611. Ed. D.M. Dalton. adv. contact: D.M. Dalton. bk.rev.; bibl.; circ. 3,000 (paid). **Document type:** academic/scholarly publication.

133.91 GR ISSN 0023-4257
KOSMOS TIS PSYCHIS/WORLD OF SOUL. 1947. m. Dr.100($3.50) Psychic Society of Athens, 32 Tsiller St., Athens 905, Greece. Ed. Georgos Sakellaropoulos. bk.rev.; abstr.; bibl.; illus.; tr.mk.; index. circ. 1,000.

133 574.999 IC ISSN 1022-694X
LIFGEISLAR; timarit um lifsamband vid adrar stjoernur. 1975. bi-m. ISK 1000. Felag Nyalssinna, P.O. Box 1159, 121 Reykjavik, Iceland. TEL 354-554-0765. Ed. Ingvar Agnarsson. circ. 580. (back issues avail.)
 Description: Focuses on life after death, life in the universe, contact with extraterrestrials, Icelandic history and the place of Iceland and the Icelandic language among nations.

PARAPSYCHOLOGY AND OCCULTISM

133.91   UK   ISSN 0047-4649
BF1001
LIGHT; a journal of psychic and spiritual studies. 1881. 3/yr. £8.35($17) (rest of Europe £9.50; elsewhere £13.25). College of Psychic Studies, 16 Queensberry Pl., London SW7 2EB, England. TEL 0171-589-3292. FAX 0171-589-2824. Ed. Jean Prince; Pub. Dudley Poplak. bk.rev.; circ. 3,000 (paid). **Document type:** academic/scholarly publication.
   Description: Offers new perspectives on psychic and spirtual studies for those wanting to stay in step with what is happening now.

133.9   US
LIGHT - LINES. 1982. q. donations only. Rock Creek Research & Development Labs, Inc., Box 5195, Louisville, KY 40255-0195. TEL 502-245-6495. Ed. James McCarty. circ. 1,500. (looseleaf format; back issues avail.)

LLEWELLYN'S NEW WORLDS OF MIND & SPIRIT; new age resources for human potential and magical living. see *NEW AGE PUBLICATIONS*

133.4   US
MAGICKAL PAGAN NEWS. (Supplement avail.: Witchcraft Digest (ISSN 0085-8250)) 1970. m. $10 for 8 nos. (Witches Anti-Discrimination Lobby) Hero Press, 153 W. 80th St., Ste. 1B, New York, NY 10024. Ed. Leo Louis Martello. adv.; bk.rev.; film rev.; illus. circ. 2,500. (processed) **Document type:** newsletter.
   Former titles: W I C A Newsletter (ISSN 0049-7754); Witches Newsletter (ISSN 0028-4173); **Supersedes:** New Age Intellectual Newsletter.

133   US
MAGICKAL UNICORN MESSENGER.* 1980. q. $9. Temple of Wicca, Box 261, New Straitsville, OH 43766-0261. Ed. Charles Pugh. adv.; bk.rev.; illus. circ. 200. (tabloid format)
   Description: Informative publication concerning wicca and paganism. Includes articles, news, reviews and forthcoming events.

133   UK
MAGONIA. bi-m. £4 (Europe £5; US $10; rest of world £5.50). John Dee Cottage, 5 James Terrace, Mortlake Churchyard, London SW14 8HB, England. Ed. John Rimmer. **Document type:** bulletin.

133.3 153.4   DK   ISSN 0904-9339
MANTEIA; a magazine for the mantic arts. (Text in English) 1989. irreg. (2-3/yr.). DKK 150($22) Ouroboros, Spilkammeret, c/o K. Frank Jensen, Sankt Hansgade 20, DK-4000 Roskilde, Denmark. TEL 45-42-35-18-08. FAX 45-42-35-20-09. (U.S. subscr.: Sehila Wilding, 17645 Via Sereno, Los Gatos, CA 95030) Ed. K. Frank Jensen. adv.; bk.rev. circ. 200. (N) **Document type:** academic/scholarly publication.
   Description: Devoted to serious study of the mantic arts, including tarot, I-Ching, runes. Historical and symbolic aspects are discussed.

133   GW
MESCALITO - SPRUNG IN DIE UNMOEGLICHKEIT; Magazin fuer Magie und Schamanismus. 1979. q. DM.48. Indianisches Netzwerk BRD, Zornstr. 11A, 67549 Worms, Germany. TEL 06241-56099. Ed. Berthold Roeth. bibl.; illus.; tr.lit. **Document type:** consumer publication.

MESSENGER (POMPANO BEACH); a magazine for the golden age. see *NEW AGE PUBLICATIONS*

133   UK
METAMORPHIC ASSOCIATION PROGRAMME. 1981. 3/yr. £1. Metamorphic Association, 67 Ritherdon Rd., London SW17 8QE, England. TEL 0181-672-5951. Ed. Gaston St. Pierre. illus. circ. 5,000. **Document type:** newsletter.
   Supersedes in part (in 1983): Metamorphic Association Newsletter (ISSN 0262-1533)
   Description: Lists activities and members of the Association.

133   UK
METAMORPHOSIS. 1981. 2/yr. £7. Metamorphic Association, 67 Ritherdon Rd., London SW17 8QE, England. TEL 0181-672-5951. Ed. Gaston St. Pierre. bk.rev.; illus. circ. 1,200. (back issues avail.) **Document type:** newsletter.
   Supersedes in part (in 1983): Metamorphic Association Newsletter (ISSN 0262-1533)
   Description: Articles on the theory and principles behind Metamorphosis and the Metamorphic technique, an approach to self-healing and creative growth.

133.91   IT   ISSN 0026-1076
METAPSICHICA; rivista italiana di parapsicologia. 1946. q. L.45000 or exchange basis. Associazione Italiana Scientifica di Metapsichica, Via S. Vittore 19, 20123 Milan, Italy. TEL 02-4980365. Ed. Pierangelo Garzia. adv.; bk.rev. circ. 1,000. **Document type:** academic/scholarly publication.
   Description: Journal dealing with parapsychological research from world wide conferences. Includes articles contributed by Italian authors interested in this field.

133   US
METASCIENCE ANNUAL; a New Age journal of parapsychology. 1979. a. $25. MetaScience Foundation, Box 32, Kingston, RI 02881. TEL 401-294-2414. Ed. Marc J. Seifer. adv.; bk.rev.; abstr.; bibl.; charts; illus.; stat.; index. circ. 2,500. (back issues avail.) **Document type:** academic/scholarly publication.
   Formerly: MetaScience Quarterly; Which supersedes (1977-1978): Journal of Occult Studies.
   Description: Discusses all fields related to parapsychology.

133   US
MEZLIM; independent journal for the working magus. q. $6 per no. Box 19566, Cincinnati, OH 45219.

133   CN
MINSTREL. 1987. 6/yr. Can.$20. P.O. Box 3068, Winnipeg, MB R3C 4E5, Canada. TEL 204-942-2881. Ed. Stephen Kendall; Pub. Glen Hoban. circ. 100. **Document type:** newsletter.

MOONCIRCLES. see *WOMEN'S INTERESTS*

MUTANTIA; cuadernos eco-espirituales. see *NEW AGE PUBLICATIONS*

133   UK
NEOMETAPHYSICAL DIGEST. 1952. irreg. £2($6) per no. Society of Metaphysicians Ltd., Archers' Court, Stonestile Lane, the Ridge, Hastings, E. Sussex TN35 4PG, England. TEL 01424-751577. FAX 01424-722387. Ed. Eleanor Swift. adv.; bk.rev. circ. 60,000. **Document type:** consumer publication.
   Formerly: Metaphysical Digest.
   Description: Seeks functional solutions to human problems, understanding of consciousness and its manifestations in mysticism, esoterica, psychic phenomena.
   Refereed Serial

133   US
NEW FRONTIERS. 1982. s-a. $15 to non-members. New Frontiers Center, 2313 CTH MM, Rte. 1, Oregon, WI 53575. TEL 608-835-3795. Eds. Mary Jo & Walter Uphoff. bk.rev.; illus. circ. 1,100. (back issues avail) **Document type:** newsletter.
   Description: Includes worldwide reports on psychic phenomena, health issues, life after death, and psi phenomena, including scheduled conferences.

133   US
NEW MOON RISING; journal of magick and wicca. 1989. bi-m. $14 in the U.S.; Canada and Mexico $21; elsewhere $25. Mystic Moon, 8818 Troy St., Spring Valley, CA 91977. TEL 619-466-8064. adv.; bk.rev. circ. 2,000.

133   US
NIGHTSCAPES; journal of magic, paganism and the occult. 6/yr. $13. Box 4559, Dept. 16, Mesa, AZ 85211-4559.

133.4   UK   ISSN 0269-9850
NUIT - ISIS; journal of the nu-equinox. 1986. a. £6.99($17.95) Golden Dawn Publishing, P.O. Box 250, Oxford OX1 1AP, England. TEL 0865-243671. adv.; bk.rev. circ. 1,000.

133   IT
NUOVO MONDO OCCULTO. vol.3, 1971. m. L.15000. (Tayu Center) Istituto Ricerche exo Mediche, Via Dalbono, 30/b, 80055 Portici, Codice Fiscale 94064860631. bk.rev.; bibl.; illus.
   Formerly: Mondo Occulto (ISSN 0047-7869)

O P E R A NEWSLETTER. (Organization of Psychic Educational & Research Associates) see *NEW AGE PUBLICATIONS*

133 200   UK   ISSN 0969-1375
OCCULT OBSERVER. 1991. q. £11.80. Atlantis Bookshop, 2 Tavistock Chambers, Bloomsbury Way, London WC1A 2SE, England.

133 133.5 398 200   US
ORACLE. 1975. 12/yr. $10. Healing Light Center, Box 758, Sierra Madre, CA 91025-0758. TEL 818-306-2170. Ed. Susan Brown. adv.; bk.rev. circ. 1,500. **Document type:** newsletter.
   Formerly: Light Bearer.

PAGANS FOR PEACE. see *RELIGIONS AND THEOLOGY*

133   US   ISSN 0078-9437
PARAPSYCHOLOGICAL MONOGRAPHS. 1958. irreg., latest no.18. price varies. Parapsychology Foundation, 228 E. 71st St., New York, NY 10021. TEL 212-628-1550. **Indexed:** Psychol.Abstr. **Document type:** monographic series.

133   US
PARAPSYCHOLOGY FOUNDATION. PROCEEDINGS OF INTERNATIONAL CONFERENCES. 1953. a. price varies. Parapsychology Foundation, 228 E. 71st St., New York, NY 10021. TEL 212-628-1550. **Document type:** proceedings.

133 615.8   US
PARAPSYCHOLOGY, HYPNOSIS & ALTERNATIVE HEALTH. 1960. m. $100. Enterprises Unlimited, Box 31, F.D.R. Sta., New York, NY 10150. TEL 212-755-9363. Pub. Bell Evans. circ. 1,000. **Document type:** newsletter.

133   US
PARAPSYCHOLOGY-PSYCHIC SCIENCE REPORTS; magazine of psychic phenomena. 1973. m. $18. Gibbs Publishing Company, Box 600927, N. Miami Beach, FL 33160. Ed. James Calvin Gibbs. adv.; bk.rev. circ. 10,000.
   Former titles: Parapsychology-Psychic Science Journal; Parapsychology.

133 289.9   US
PORTAL. q. Hermetic Society of the Golden Dawn, 31849 Pacific Hwy. S., Ste.107, Federal Way, WA 98003.

POWER PLACES OF CALIFORNIA. see *EARTH SCIENCES — Geophysics*

133   UK   ISSN 0032-7182
PREDICTION. 1936. m. £25.20. Link House Magazines Ltd., Link House, Dingwall Ave., Croydon, Surrey CR9 2TA, England. TEL 0181-686-2599. FAX 0181-760-0973. (Subscr. to: R F S, 120-126 Lavender Ave., Mitcham, Surrey CR4 3HP, England) Ed. Jo Logan. adv.; bk.rev.; illus. circ. 21,400. **Document type:** consumer publication.
   Description: Explores astrology, palmistry, tarot, graphology, dream interpretations and methods used to interpret character and events in life. Includes articles, news briefs, questions and answers, and personal advertisements.

133.324   UK   ISSN 0079-4953
PREDICTION ANNUAL. a. Link House Magazines Ltd., Link House, Dingwall Ave., Croydon, Surrey CR9 2TA, England. TEL 0181-686-2599. FAX 0181-760-0973. Ed. Jo Logan. adv.; bk.rev. **Document type:** consumer publication.
   Description: Presents astrological forecasts for each sign of the Zodiac; includes Tarot card projections.

133 001.94   UK   ISSN 0260-8189
PROBE REPORT. 1980. q. £3.40($6.60) Probe, 16 Marigold Walk, Ashton, Bristol BS3 2PD, England. Ed. Ian Mrzyglod. adv.; bk.rev.; illus.; stat. circ. 500. (back issues avail.)

PARAPSYCHOLOGY AND OCCULTISM

133.91   UK
THE PSI RESEARCHER. 1981. 4/yr. membership. Society for Psychical Research, 49 Marloes Rd., Kensington, London W8 6LA, England. TEL 0171-937-8984. Ed. John Beloff. circ. 900. (back issues avail.) **Document type:** newsletter.
   Formerly (until 1991): S P R Newsletter.

133   US
PSYCHIC MESSENGER.* 4/yr. Shafenberg Research Foundation, c/o Alice Shiver, Ed., 3411 Regatta Pl., Oxnard, CA 93030-6416.

133.91   UK   ISSN 0033-2801
PSYCHIC NEWS. 1932. w. £25($45) Psychic Press Ltd., 2 Tavistock Chambers, Bloomsbury Way, London WC1A 2SE, England. TEL 071-405-3340. Ed. Tim Haigh. adv.; bk.rev.; bibl.; charts; illus.; tr.lit. circ. 13,000. **Document type:** newspaper.
   Description: Newspaper covering spiritualism and the paranormal.

133   US
PSYCHIC READER. 1975. m. $13.50. (Church of Divine Man) Deja Vu Publishing, 2210 Harold Way, Berkeley, CA 94704-1425. TEL 510-644-1600. FAX 510-644-1686. E-mail: dejavnpub@aol.com. Ed. Susan Hull Bostwick. adv.; bk.rev. circ. 210,000. (tabloid format; back issues avail.) **Document type:** newspaper.
   Formerly: Psychic Life.
   Description: New age publication that discusses parapsychology, alternative healing, religions and theology.

133.91   US   ISSN 0276-1610
PSYCHIC STUDIES. irreg., vol.4, 1980. price varies. Gordon & Breach Science Publishers, c/o International Publishers Distributor, 820 Town Center Dr., Langhorne, PA 19047. TEL 215-750-2642. FAX 215-750-6343. (Subscr. to: International Publishers Distributor, P.O. Box 90, Reading, Berkshire RG1 8JL, England. TEL 44-173-456-8316) Eds. Stanley Krippner, Irene Hall. **Document type:** monographic series.
   Refereed Serial

133.91   UK   ISSN 0968-6487
PSYCHICAL STUDIES. 1968. 2/yr. £6. Waterbarrow, High Cunsey, Via Ambleside, Cumbna LA22 0LT, England. TEL 015394-46629. Ed. F.I. Hornby. bk.rev. circ. 200. **Document type:** academic/scholarly publication.
   Formerly: Beyond.
   Description: Examines the relation of psychical studies to religion.

500 133   US
PURSUIT - S I T U. vol.2, 1969. q. $12. Society for the Investigation of the Unexplained, Box 265, Little Silver, NJ 07739. TEL 201-842-5229. Ed. Robert C. Warth. bk.rev.; bibl.; charts; illus.; index. circ. 1,500. **Indexed:** Abstr.Folk.Stud.
   —UMI.
   Formerly: Pursuit (ISSN 0033-4685)

133   IT
QUADERNI DI PARAPSICOLOGIA. (Text in Italian; abstracts in English, Italian) 1970. s-a. L.50000($40) includes Bollettino. Centro Studi Parapsicologici, Via L. Valeriani, 39, 40134 Bologna, Italy. TEL 051-6143104. Ed. Piero Cassoli. bk.rev.; abstr. circ. 450. (back issues avail.) **Document type:** academic/scholarly publication.
   Incorporates: Centro Studi Parapsicologici. Bollettino.

133   IT
QUADERNI GNOSIS. (Includes s-a. supplement: Fogli Gnosis) (Text in Italian; summaries in English) 1963. a. L.50000($16) (effective 1996). Istituto Gnosis per la Ricerca sulla Ipotesi della Sopravvivenza, Via Belvedere 87, 80127 Naples, Italy. TEL 39-81-5603497. Ed. Giorgio di Simone. adv.; bk.rev.; bibl.; illus. circ. 500. **Document type:** newsletter.
   Supersedes (in 1981): Informazioni di Parapsicologia (ISSN 0046-9491)
   Description: Presenta articles on the frontier of parapsychology, psychology and all elements favorable to the survival hypothesis.

133 200 800   FR   ISSN 0246-5434
QUESTION DE. 1973. q. 330 F. (Edition Albin Michel) Edition Question de, B.P. 21, 84220 Gordes, France. FAX 90-72-08-38. Dir. Marc de Smedt. adv.; bk.rev.; bibl.; charts; illus. circ. 12,000.
   Former titles: Question de Racines, Pensees, Sciences Eclairees; Question de Spiritualite, Tradition, Litteratures.

130   SZ
RADIAESTHESIE. 1950. q. 40 SFr. (foreign 45 SFr.). Verlag R G S, Postfach 2225, CH-9001 St. Gallen, Switzerland. TEL 071-226621. Ed. Egon Minikus. adv.; bk.rev. circ. 4,000. **Document type:** academic/scholarly publication.
   Formerly: Radiaesthesie - Geopathie - Strahlenbiologie (ISSN 0033-7552)

REALITY CHANGE; a global Seth journal. see *NEW AGE PUBLICATIONS*

RELIGIOUS FREEDOM REPORTER. see *LAW — Constitutional Law*

133.9   FR   ISSN 0151-4016
RENAITRE 2000; revue des investigations psychiques et des recherches theoriques et experimentales sur la survivance humaine. 1977. 4/yr. 250 F. Andre Dumas, Ed. & Pub., 29 Av. des Sablons, 77230 Dammartin-en-Goele, France. bk.rev. circ. 2,000.
   Supersedes (1858-1977): Revue Spirite; **Formerly:** Survie de l'Ame Humaine (ISSN 0049-2655)

133   US   ISSN 0094-7172
RESEARCH IN PARAPSYCHOLOGY; abstracts and papers from the annual convention. 1972. a. price varies. (Parapsychological Association) Scarecrow Press, Inc., 52 Liberty St., Metuchen, NJ 08840. TEL 800-537-7107. Ed. Linda Henkel. **Document type:** abstracting/indexing.
   —BLDSC (7755.048000).
   Formerly (1957-1971): Parapsychological Association. Proceedings.
   Description: Original presentations on empirical, methodological, philosophical, and historical themes.

133.9 299.934   II
REVIEW OF INDIAN SPIRITUALISM. (Text in English) vol.6, 1974. m. Rs.6($3) Sinha Publishing House, 39 S. R. Das Rd., Calcutta 700026, India. Ed. Amiya Kumar Sinha. adv.; bk.rev. circ. 1,000.

133.91   FR   ISSN 0338-2079
REVUE DU MAGNETISME-ETUDE DU PSYCHISME EXPERIMENTAL. 1975. bi-m. 240 F. 1 rue des Moulins de Garance, 59800 Lille, France. Ed. Jean Magnes. bk.rev.; index. circ. 1,000. **Document type:** bulletin.
   Description: Offers an experimental approach to psychic phenomena. Covers magnetism, hypnotism, suggestion, and mediums.

133   FR   ISSN 0484-8934
REVUE METAPSYCHIQUE. 1920. irreg., vol.17, 1983. 40 F. per no. Institut Metapsychique International, 1 Place de Wagram, 75017 Paris, France. TEL 47-63-65-48. bk.rev. circ. 500.

130   NO   ISSN 0803-2718
SKEPSIS. 1991. 2/yr. NOK 150 membership. Foreningen Skepsis, St. Olavsgate 27, N-0166 Oslo, Norway. TEL 47-22-20-35-33. Eds. Erik Tunstad, Terje Emberland. bk.rev. circ. 3,000.
   Description: Devoted to promoting critical examination of paranormal phenomena, pseudo-science and occultism.

133 110   AT   ISSN 0726-9897
THE SKEPTIC. 1981. q. Aus.$35 (effective 1995 & 1996). P.O. Box A2324, Sydney, N.S.W. 200000, Australia. TEL 61-2-417-2071. Ed. Barry Williams. bk.rev. circ. 1,500. (back issues avail.) **Document type:** newsletter.
   Description: Scientific articles on paranormal issues: psychics, astrology, UFOs, alternative medicine, creation "science", new age beliefs.

133 110   US   ISSN 1063-9330
Q174
SKEPTIC. 1992. q. $35 membership. Skeptics Society, 2761 N. Marengo Ave., Altadena, CA 91101. TEL 818-794-3119. FAX 818-794-1301. E-mail: SKEPTICMAG@AOL.com. Ed. Kim Ziel; Pub. Michael Schermer. adv. contact: Frank Miele. bk.rev. circ. 30,000. (back issues avail.) **Indexed:** Access (1995-). **Document type:** academic/scholarly publication, consumer publication.
   Description: Seeks to understand all scientific and pseudoscientific claims objectively.
   Refereed Serial

133   US   ISSN 1060-216X
SKEPTICAL BRIEFS. 1991. q. $18. Committee for the Scientific Investigation of Claims of the Paranormal, Box 703, Buffalo, NY 14226-0703. TEL 716-636-1425. FAX 716-636-1733. Ed. Ken Frazier. circ. 2,600. **Document type:** academic/scholarly publication, consumer publication.

133   US   ISSN 0194-6730
BF1001
SKEPTICAL INQUIRER. 1976. bi-m. $29.50. Committee for the Scientific Investigation of Claims of the Paranormal, Box 703, Buffalo, NY 14226-0703. TEL 716-636-1425. FAX 716-636-1733. Ed. Barry Karr. bk.rev.; charts; illus.; stat.; cum.index. circ. 67,500. (back issues avail.) **Indexed:** Lang.& Lang.Behav.Abstr. **Document type:** academic/scholarly publication, consumer publication.
   —Faxon; Genuine Article; SWETS; UMI; UnCover.
   Formerly (until 1977): Zetetic (ISSN 0148-1096)
   Description: Contains articles, news and comments.

133 200   UK
SKOOB ESOTERICA ANTHOLOGY. 1990. irreg. $11.95 per no. Skoob Books Publishing Ltd., 17 Sicilian Ave., Southampton Row, London WC1A 2QH, England. TEL 0171-405-0030. FAX 0171-404-4398. Ed. Christopher Johnson. adv. contact: Tim Donnelly. bk.rev. **Document type:** monographic series.
   Formerly (until 1992): Skoob Occult Reviews (ISSN 0967-3342)

133.91   UK   ISSN 0037-9751
BF1011
SOCIETY FOR PSYCHICAL RESEARCH. JOURNAL. 1884. 4/yr. £20($36) Society for Psychical Research, 49 Marloes Rd., Kensington, London W8 6LA, England. TEL 0171-937-8984. Ed. John Beloff. adv. contact: Bernard Carr. bk.rev.; charts; index. cum.index published irregularly. **Indexed:** Br.Hum.Ind., Psychol.Abstr. **Document type:** bulletin.
   —Faxon; UnCover. CCC.

133   UK   ISSN 0081-1475
BF1011   CODEN: PPSRA5
SOCIETY FOR PSYCHICAL RESEARCH. PROCEEDINGS. 1882. irreg. membership. Society for Psychical Research, 49 Marloes Rd., Kensington, London W8 6LA, England. TEL 0171-937-8984. Ed. John Beloff. adv. contact: Bernard Carr. **Indexed:** Br.Hum.Ind., Psychol.Abstr. **Document type:** proceedings.

133 299   SW   ISSN 0038-0504
SOEKAREN; tidskrift foer livsfraagor. 1964. 6/yr. SEK 250 0038-0504. Soekarens Foerlag, P.O. Box 10, S-663 21 Skoghall, Sweden. TEL 054-51-89-00. FAX 054-51-89-02. Ed. Sven Magnusson. adv.; bk.rev.; illus. circ. 3,000.

SOMNIAL TIMES. see *NEW AGE PUBLICATIONS*

133.9   US   ISSN 0887-9001
SPIRIT SPEAKS. 1985. bi-m. $24. Spirit Speaks, Inc., Box 85400, Tuscon, AZ 85745. TEL 800-856-9104. FAX 213-826-9197. Ed. Molli Nickell. adv. circ. 35,000.
   Description: Covers channeling in relation to all aspects of every day life.

SPIRITUAL EMERGENCE NETWORK NEWSLETTER. see *NEW AGE PUBLICATIONS*

PARAPSYCHOLOGY AND OCCULTISM — ABSTRACTING, BIBLIOGRAPHIES, STATISTICS

299 US
SPIRITUAL FRONTIERS FELLOWSHIP INTERNATIONAL JOURNAL. bi-m. $40 membership (includes newsletter). Spiritual Frontiers Fellowship International, Box 7868, Philadelphia, PA 19101. TEL 215-222-1991. FAX 215-222-8459. Ed. Frank Tribbe. circ. 2,200. (back issues avail.) **Document type:** newsletter.
Description: Explores consciousness studies.

299 US
SPIRITUAL FRONTIERS FELLOWSHIP INTERNATIONAL NEWSLETTER. m. $40 membership (includes journal). Spiritual Frontiers Fellowship International, Box 7868, Philadelphia, PA 19101. TEL 215-222-1991. FAX 215-222-8459. Ed. Elizabeth W. Fenske. circ. 2,200. (back issues avail.) **Document type:** newsletter.
Description: Explores consciousness studies.

133 US ISSN 0894-8968
STRANGE MAGAZINE. 1987. 3/yr. $13.95. Box 2246, Rockville, MD 20847. TEL 301-460-4789. FAX 301-460-1959. bk.rev. circ. 25,000. (back issues avail.) **Document type:** consumer publication.
Description: Investigates cryptozoology, paranormal phenomena, and other topics worldwide.

SUBCONSCIOUSLY SPEAKING; you can change your life through the power of your mind. see *NEW AGE PUBLICATIONS*

133 MX
SUPERMENTE; nuevo sendero al naturismo. s-m. Editorial Posada, S.A., Oculistas No. 43, Col. El Sifon, 09400 Mexico, D.F., Mexico.

133 UK ISSN 0143-5418
SUT ANUBIS. irreg. £10($20) Occultique, 73 Kettering Rd., Northampton NN1 4AW, England. TEL 01604-27727. Ed. M.J. Lovett. adv.; bk.rev. circ. 500. **Document type:** monographic series.
Description: Original articles on witchcraft, Crowleyanity, ceremonial magic, paganism.

133 US
TAROT NEWS; a journal for Tarot enthusiasts. 1992. bi-m. $15 (overseas $25) (effective 1995); newsstand price: $2.50. Tarot Special Interest Group of American Mensa, Tarot Special-Interest Group, Box 561, Quincy, IL 62306-0561. TEL 217-222-9082. E-mail: brst18a@prodigy.com. Pub. Gloria Reiser. adv.; bk.rev. **Document type:** consumer publication.
●Also available online.
Description: Discusses topics of interest to persons engaged in reading Tarot cards.

TOTAL ECLIPSE. see *NEW AGE PUBLICATIONS*

TRANSFORMATION TIMES; new age journal. see *NEW AGE PUBLICATIONS*

130 FR ISSN 0049-4666
TRIBUNE PSYCHIQUE.* vol. 75, 1972. q. 5 F Societe Francaise d'Etude des Phenomenes Psychiques, 1 rue des Gatines, 75020 Paris, France. Ed. M. Lemoine. bk.rev.; bibl.

TRIDENT. see *RELIGIONS AND THEOLOGY — Other Denominations And Sects*

THE UNEXPLAINED; mysteries of life explained. see *NEW AGE PUBLICATIONS*

299 US
UNICORN (KIRKLAND). 1977. 8/yr. $10. Rowan Tree Church, 9724 132nd Ave., N.E., Kirkland, WA 98033-5222. TEL 206-828-4124. Ed. Rev. Paul Beyerl. bk.rev.; illus.; circ. 150 (paid). **Document type:** newsletter.
Description: Covers modern Neo-Pagan Revival literature.

THE UNIVERSALIAN; dedicated to expanding conscious awareness. see *NEW AGE PUBLICATIONS*

133 US ISSN 1042-7899
UNKNOWN. 1969. m. $22. Luna Ventures, Box 398, Suisun, CA 94585. adv.; bk.rev. (also avail. in microfiche)
Description: Covers anomalies, the mysterious, and the unusual from witchcraft and appearances to Bigfoot and UFOs.

133 US
UNUSUAL. bi-m. $10. T & A Publications, Box 195, Hancock, WI 54943. TEL 715-249-5611. Ed. Wayne Davis. adv.

133 GW ISSN 0174-3538
V T F-POST. 1975. q. DM.60. Verein fuer Tonbandstimmenforschung e.V., Hoehscheider Str. 2, 40591 Duessldorf, Germany. TEL 0211-786439. Ed. Fidelio Koeberle. bk.rev. circ. 2,000. (back issues avail.) **Document type:** newsletter.

VENTURE INWARD. see *NEW AGE PUBLICATIONS*

133 UK
VIEWPOINT AQUARIUS. 1972. bi-m. $13. Box 97, Camberley, Surrey GU15 2LH, England. TEL 01276-21531. Ed. Jean Coulsting. bk.rev. (processed)
Description: Study of occult, yoga, meditation, flying saucers.

VISIONS (AGOURA HILLS). see *ALTERNATIVE MEDICINE*

133.9 MX ISSN 0185-6480
VOZ INFORMATIVA; revista bimestral de filosofia, ciencia y moral. 1952. bi-m. Mex.$120($6) Pino 129, Mexico 4, D.F., Mexico. (And Apdo. Postal M-7057, Mexico 1, D.F., Mexico) Ed. Jose Castol Gonzalez. circ. 1,000.

133.4 US
WHICH WAY? - WITCH WAY?. 12/yr. $150 to individuals; pagans $15. Craeftgemot Witancoveyne, Inc., Box 499, Deerfield Beach, FL 33441. TEL 305-428-9713.

133 CN
WICCAN CANDLE. m. Can.$15. Gently Johnny Productions, 109 Vaughan Rd., Toronto, ON M6P 2L9, Canada. **Document type:** newsletter.

WICCAN REDE. see *RELIGIONS AND THEOLOGY — Other Denominations And Sects*

133.4 UK ISSN 0952-522X
WICCAN WORKSHOP NEWS. 1982. 2/yr. £2. Aurora Aurea, BM Deosil, London WC1N 3XX, England.

THE WISE WOMAN. see *WOMEN'S INTERESTS*

133.4 US ISSN 0085-8250
WITCHCRAFT DIGEST. (Supplement to: Magickal Pagan News) 1970. a. $2. (Witches Anti-Descrimination Lobby) Hero Press, 153 W. 80th St., Ste. 1B, New York, NY 10024. (Co-sponsor: Witches Liberation Movement) Ed. Leo Louis Martello. adv.; bk.rev. circ. 3,000.
Formerly: Witchcraft (ISSN 0014-2840)

133 US
WITCHCRAFT - PAGANISM DIRECTORY. a. $6.50. Ghost Research Society, Box 205, Oaklawn, IL 60454-0205. TEL 708-425-5163. **Document type:** directory.
Description: Lists groups, organizations, and publications dealing specifically with witchcraft and paganism.

133.91 GW ISSN 0028-3479
BF1003
ZEITSCHRIFT FUER PARAPSYCHOLOGIE UND GRENZGEBIETE DER PSYCHOLOGIE. 1957. q. DM.80. Wissenschaftliche Gesellschaft zur Foederung der Parapsychologie e.V., Hildastr. 64, 79102 Freiburg, Germany. TEL 0761-77202. E-mail: lucadou@sun1.ruf.uni-freiburg.de. Ed. Eberhard Bauer. adv.; bk.rev.; illus. circ. 1,000. **Indexed:** Excerp.Med., Psychol.Abstr., SSCI. **Document type:** academic/scholarly publication.
—SWETS.
Supersedes: Neue Wissenschaft.
Refereed Serial

ZEITSCHRIFT FUER RADIAESTHESIE UND HARMONIEFINDUNG. see *NEW AGE PUBLICATIONS*

133 US ISSN 0741-6229
BF1001
ZETETIC SCHOLAR. 1978. irreg. $15 to individuals; institutions $20; foreign $30. Center for Scientific Anomalies Research, Box 1052, Ann Arbor, MI 48106. TEL 517-522-3551. FAX 517-522-3555. (Subscr. to: Department of Sociology, Eastern Michigan University, Ypsilanti, MI 48197) Ed. Marcello Truzzi. bk.rev.; bibl. circ. 600. (back issues avail.) **Indexed:** Lang.& Lang.Behav.Abstr., Sociol.Abstr. **Document type:** academic/scholarly publication.

PARAPSYCHOLOGY AND OCCULTISM — Abstracting, Bibliographies, Statistics

133 US ISSN 1053-4768
BF1001
EXCEPTIONAL HUMAN EXPERIENCE; studies of the psychic - spontaneous - imaginal. 1983. s-a. $30 to individuals; institutions $60 (effective 1996). Exceptional Human Experience Network, Inc., 2 Plane Tree Ln., Dix Hills, NY 11746. TEL 516-271-1243. FAX 516-427-4413. Ed. Rhea A. White. bk.rev.; abstr.; film rev.; index. circ. 350. **Document type:** abstracting/indexing.
●Also available online.
—BLDSC (3835.380000). CCC.
Formerly (until 1990): Parapsychology Abstracts International (ISSN 0740-7629)
Description: Information resource for literature recording parapsychological, imaginal, mystical and peak phenomena, including profiles of investigators, accounts of experiences, methodological and theoretical articles, and abstracts from a broad range of journals covering anomalies, as well as relevant publications in anthropology, philosophy, sociology and other fields.
Refereed Serial

133 US
OCCULT PUBLICATIONS DIRECTORY. a. $6.50. Ghost Research Society, Box 205, Oaklawn, IL 60454-0205. TEL 708-425-5163. **Document type:** directory.
Description: Lists newsletters, directories, and tabloids dealing with the occult in general.

PATENTS, TRADEMARKS AND COPYRIGHTS

A I P L A BULLETIN. (American Intellectual Property Law Association) see *LAW*

602.7 608.7 340 JA ISSN 0385-8863
A.I.P.P.I. JAPANESE GROUP. JOURNAL (INTERNATIONAL EDITION). Key Title: Journal of the Japanese Group of A.I.P.P.I. International Edition. Japanese edition: Shadan Hojin Nihon Kokusai Kogyo Shoyuken Hogo Kyokai Geppo (ISSN 0385-6909) (Text in English) 1976. bi-m. 12900 Yen (effective 1993). International Association for the Protection of Industrial Property, Japanese Group, Toranomon Denki Bldg., 7F, 8-1, Toranomon 2-chome, Minato-ku, Tokyo 105, Japan. TEL 03-3591-5301. FAX 03-3591-1510. TELEX J23684 AIPPIJPN. Eds. Yukio Kubota, Mitsue Dairaku. adv. contact: Mitsuhiko Nagai. cum.index: 1976-1986. circ. 3,000. (back issues avail.) **Document type:** bulletin.
Description: Presents court decisions, current topics, law and practices concerning industrial and intellectual properties in Japan. Also covers international R&D lisencing and technology transfer.

608.7 AT ISSN 1321-7089
ANNUAL RECORD OF DESIGNS OFFICE. PROCEEDINGS. 1907. a. Aus.$55 (effective 1994). Australian Industrial Property Organisation, P.O. Box 200, Woden, A.C.T. 2606, Australia. TEL 06-2832481. FAX 06-2853929. TELEX COMPAT AA 61518. circ. 40. (back issues avail.)
Former titles: Australia. Designs Office. Registered Owners of Designs and Articles in Respect of Which Designs Have Been Registered; Australia. Designs Office. Registered Owners of Designs and Articles in Respect of Which Designs Have Been Registered Under the Designs Act in Australia; Australia. Designs Office. Registered Owners of Designs.
Description: Contains names of applicants for designs, names of subsequent owners entered in the register and name changes.

PATENTS, TRADEMARKS AND COPYRIGHTS

608.7 AT ISSN 1321-7062
ANNUAL RECORD OF PATENT OFFICE PROCEEDINGS. 1904. a. Aus.$60 (effective 1994). Australian Industrial Property Organisation, P.O. Box 200, Woden, A.C.T. 2606, Australia. TEL 06-2832481. FAX 06-2853929. circ. 137. (back issues avail.)
Description: Contains names of applicants for patents; assignments and changes name.

602.7 AT ISSN 1321-7070
ANNUAL RECORD OF TRADE MARKS OFFICE PROCEEDINGS. 1906. a. Aus.$60 (effective 1994). Australian Industrial Property Organisation, P.O. Box 200, Woden, A.C.T 2606, Australia. TEL 06-2832481. FAX 06-2853593. TELEX COMPAT AA 61517. circ. 989.
Description: Contains names of applicants for trade marks, assignments and changes of name, applications accepted.

346.73 608.7 US ISSN 0361-3844
KF3165.A3
ATTORNEYS AND AGENTS REGISTERED TO PRACTICE BEFORE THE U.S. PATENT AND TRADEMARK OFFICE. Variant title: Patent Attorneys and Agents Registered to Practice before the U.S. Patent and Trademark Office. a. $30. U.S. Patent and Trademark Office, General Information Services Division, Crystal Plaza 3, Rm. 2C02, Washington, DC 20231. TEL 703-308-4357. FAX 703-305-7786. (Subscr. to: Superintendent of Documents, U.S. Government Printing Office, Box 371954, Pittsburgh, PA 15250-7954; Or: Bernan, 4611-F Assembly Dr., Lanham, MD 20706. TEL 301-459-7666. FAX 301-459-0056) **Document type:** government publication.
Former titles: Attorneys and Agents Registered to Practice before the U.S. Patent Office (ISSN 0092-5934); Roster of Attorneys and Agents Registered to Practice before the U.S. Patent Office; Directory of Registered Patent Attorneys and Agents (ISSN 0565-9582)
Description: Lists patent attorneys and agents registered to practice before the U.S. Patent and Trademark Office alphabetically and by geographic region.

608.7 AT ISSN 1320-4688
AUSTRALIA. PATENT, TRADE MARKS AND DESIGNS OFFICES. ACTIVITIES REPORT. 1972. a. Aus.$15 (effective 1994). Australian Industrial Property Organisation, P.O. Box 200, Woden, A.C.T. 2606, Australia. FAX 06-2853929. TELEX COMPAT AA61517. illus. circ. 230.
Former titles: Australia. Patent Office. Annual Report of Activities (ISSN 0311-2152); Australia. Patent Office. Report.

340 AT ISSN 0311-2934
KU1104.A13
AUSTRALIAN COPYRIGHT COUNCIL. BULLETIN. 1973. 4/yr. Aus.$52. Australian Copyright Council, Ste. 3, 245 Chalmers St., Redfern, N.S.W. 2016, Australia. TEL 61-2-318-1788. FAX 61-2-698-3536. Ed. Libby Baulch. circ. 600.

341.7582 AT ISSN 1038-1635
AUSTRALIAN INTELLECTUAL PROPERTY JOURNAL. 1990. q. Aus.$215. Law Book Co. Ltd., 44-50 Waterloo Rd., North Ryde, N.S.W. 2113, Australia. TEL 02-936-6444. FAX 02-888-9706. TELEX ASBOOK 27995. Ed. Ann Dufty.
—BLDSC (1801.674300).
Formerly: Intellectual Property Journal (ISSN 1034-3032)
Description: Discusses the developments in intellectual property law in Australia.

608.7 340 AT ISSN 1038-0671
AUSTRALIAN OFFICIAL JOURNAL OF DESIGNS. 1907. fortn. Aus.$220 (effective 1992). Australian Industrial Property Organisation, P.O. Box 200, Woden, A.C.T. 2606, Australia. TEL 06-2832481. FAX 06-2853929. TELEX COMPAT AA 61517. circ. 98. (back issues avail.) **Indexed:** Chem.Abstr., Petrol.Abstr., RAPRA.
Formerly (until 1982): Australian Official Journal of Patents, Trade Marks and Designs (ISSN 0004-9891)
Description: Covers proceedings under the Designs Act, including design applications lodged and registered.

608.7 602.7 AT ISSN 0819-1794
T321.A2 CODEN: AOJPEO
AUSTRALIAN OFFICIAL JOURNAL OF PATENTS. 1904. w. Aus.$370 (effective 1994). Australian Industrial Property Organisation, P.O. Box 200, Woden, A.C.T. 2606, Australia. TEL 06-2832481. FAX 06-2853929. TELEX COMPAT AA 61517. circ. 177. (back issues avail.) **Indexed:** Petrol.Abstr. (1988-).
—CASDDS; PADDS.
Incorporates: Patent Abridgements (ISSN 0729-0470)
Description: Proceedings under the Patents Act, including applications lodged, applications open to public inspection, complete specifications accepted, patents renewed.

608.7 602.7 AT ISSN 0819-1808
AUSTRALIAN OFFICIAL JOURNAL OF TRADE MARKS. 1906. w. Aus.$410 (effective 1994). Australian Industrial Property Organisation, P.O. Box 200, Woden, A.C.T. 2606, Australia. TEL 06-2832481. FAX 06-2853929. TELEX COMPAT AA 61517. circ. 218. (back issues avail.)
Formerly: Australian Official Journal of Patents, Trade Marks and Design. Trade Marks Supplement.
Description: Proceedings under the Trade Marks Act, including applications lodged, accepted, registered, and renewed.

608.7 GW
AUSZUEGE AUS DEN EUROPAEISCHEN PATENTANMELDUNGEN. TEIL 1A. CHEMIE UND HUETTENWESEN. 1968. w DM.1560. Wila Verlag Wilhelm Lampl GmbH, Landsberger Str. 191A, 80687 Munich, Germany. TEL 089-54756-0. FAX 089-54756309. circ. 1,000. **Document type:** abstracting/indexing.
●Also available online.
Supersedes (1968-1994): Auszuege aus den Europaeischen Patentanmeldungen. Teil 1. Grund- und Rohstoffindustrie, Chemie und Huettenwesen, Bauwesen, Bergbau.

608.7 GW
AUSZUEGE AUS DEN EUROPAEISCHEN PATENTANMELDUNGEN. TEIL 1B. GRUND- UND ROHSTOFFINDUSTRIE, BAUWESEN, BERGBAU. w. DM.1560. Wila Verlag Wilhelm Lampl GmbH, Landsberger Str. 191A, 80687 Munich, Germany. TEL 089-54756-0. FAX 089-54756309. **Document type:** abstracting/indexing.
Supersedes (1968-1994): Auszuege aus den Europaeischen Patentanmeldungen. Teil 1. Grund- und Rohstoffindustrie, Chemie und Huettenwesen, Bauwesen, Bergbau.

608.7 GW
AUSZUEGE AUS DEN EUROPAEISCHEN PATENTANMELDUNGEN. TEIL 2A. PHYSIK, OPTIK, AKUSTIK, FEINMECHANIK. w. DM.1560. Wila Verlag Wilhelm Lampl GmbH, Landsberger Str. 191A, 80687 Munich, Germany. TEL 089-54756-0. FAX 089-54756309. circ. 1,500. **Document type:** abstracting/indexing.
●Also available online.
—CCC.
Supersedes in part (1985-1994): Auszuege aus den Europaeischen Patentanmeldungen. Teil 2. Elektrotechnik, Physik, Feinmechanik und Optik, Akustik (ISSN 0177-963X)

608.7 GW
AUSZUEGE AUS DEN EUROPAEISCHEN PATENTANMELDUNGEN. TEIL 2B. ELEKTROTECHNIK. w. DM.1560. Wila Verlag Wilhelm Lampl GmbH, Landsberger Str. 191A, 80687 Munich, Germany. TEL 089-54756-0. FAX 089-54756309. **Document type:** abstracting/indexing.
—CCC.
Supersedes in part (1985-1994): Auszuege aus den Europaeischen Patentanmeldungen. Teil 2. Elektrotechnik, Physik, Feinmechanik und Optik, Akustik (ISSN 0177-963X)

608.7 GW
AUSZUEGE AUS DEN EUROPAEISCHEN PATENTANMELDUNGEN. TEIL 3A. UEBRIGE VERARBEITUNGSINDUSTRIE UND ARBEITSVERFAHREN, FAHRZEUGBAU, ERNAEHRUNG, LANDWIRTSCHAFT. w. DM.1560. Wila Verlag Wilhelm Lampl GmbH, Landsberger Str. 191A, 80687 Munich, Germany. TEL 089-54756-0. FAX 089-54756309. circ. 1,000. **Document type:** abstracting/indexing.
●Also available online.
—CCC.
Supersedes in part (1985-1994): Auszuege aus den Europaeischen Patentanmeldungen. Teil 3. Uebrige Verarbeitungsindustrie und Arbeitsverfahren, Maschinen- und Fahrzeugbau, Ernaehrung, Landwirtschaft (ISSN 0177-9648)

608.7 GW
AUSZUEGE AUS DEN EUROPAEISCHEN PATENTANMELDUNGEN. TEIL 3B. MASCHINENBAU. w. DM.1560. Wila Verlag Wilhelm Lampl GmbH, Landsberger Str. 191A, 80687 Munich, Germany. TEL 089-54756-0. FAX 089-54756-0. **Document type:** abstracting/indexing.
—CCC.
Supersedes in part (1985-1994): Auszuege aus den Europaeischen Patentanmeldungen. Teil 3. Uebrige Verarbeitungsindustrie und Arbeitsverfahren, Maschinen- und Fahrzeugbau, Ernaehrung, Landwirtschaft (ISSN 0177-9648)

810.7 GW ISSN 0720-9339
AUSZUEGE AUS DEN EUROPAEISCHEN PATENTSCHRIFTEN. TEIL 1. GRUND- UND ROHSTOFFINDUSTRIE, CHEMIE UND HUETTEN-WESEN, BAUWESEN UND BERGBAU. 1980. w. DM.1512. Wila Verlag Wilhelm Lampl GmbH, Landsberger Str. 191A, 80687 Munich, Germany. TEL 089-54756-0. FAX 089-54756309. abstr.; pat. circ. 500. **Document type:** abstracting/indexing.
●Also available online.
—CCC.

608.7 GW ISSN 0941-0015
AUSZUEGE AUS DEN EUROPAEISCHEN PATENTSCHRIFTEN. TEIL 2. ELEKTROTECHNIK, PHYSIK, FEINMECHANIK UND OPTIK, AKUSTIK. 1980. w. DM.1512. Wila Verlag Wilhelm Lampl GmbH, Landsberger Str. 191A, 80687 Munich, Germany. TEL 089-54756-0. FAX 089-54756309. circ. 500. **Document type:** abstracting/indexing.

608.7 GW ISSN 0941-0023
AUSZUEGE AUS DEN EUROPAEISCHEN PATENTSCHRIFTEN. TEIL 3. UEBRIGE VERARBEITUNGSINDUSTRIE UND ARBEITSVERFAHREN, MASCHINEN- UND FAHRZEUGBAU, ERNAEHRUNG, LANDWIRTSCHAFT. 1980. w. DM.1512. Wila Verlag Wilhelm Lampl GmbH, Landsberger Str. 191A, 80687 Munich, Germany. TEL 089-54756-0. FAX 089-54756309. circ. 500. **Document type:** abstracting/indexing.

608.7 GW ISSN 0005-0571
AUSZUEGE AUS DEN GEBRAUCHSMUSTERN. 1964. w. DM.1644. Wila Verlag Wilhelm Lampl GmbH, Landsberger Str. 191A, 80687 Munich, Germany. TEL 089-54756-0. FAX 089-54756309. abstr.; illus.; pat. circ. 1,000. **Document type:** abstracting/indexing.
●Also available online.

608.7 GW ISSN 0340-0816
AUSZUEGE AUS DEN OFFENLEGUNGSSCHRIFTEN. TEIL 1. GRUND- UND ROHSTOFFINDUSTRIE, CHEMIE UND HUETTEN-WESEN, BAUWESEN UND BERGBAU. 1968. w. DM.1764. Wila Verlag Wilhelm Lampl GmbH, Landsberger Str. 191A, 80687 Munich, Germany. TEL 089-54756-0. FAX 089-54756309. **Document type:** abstracting/indexing.
●Also available online.

608.7 GW ISSN 0340-0867
AUSZUEGE AUS DEN OFFENLEGUNGSSCHRIFTEN. TEIL 2. ELEKTROTECHNIK, PHYSIK, FEINMECHANIK UND OPTIK, AKUSTIK. 1968. w. DM.1764. Wila Verlag Wilhelm Lampl GmbH, Landsberger Str. 191A, 80687 Munich, Germany. TEL 089-54756-0. FAX 089-54756309. circ. 1,500. **Document type:** abstracting/indexing.
●Also available online.

PATENTS, TRADEMARKS AND COPYRIGHTS

608.7 GW ISSN 0340-0913
AUSZUEGE AUS DEN OFFENLEGUNGSSCHRIFTEN. TEIL 3. UEBRIGE VERARBEITUNGSINDUSTRIE UND ARBEITSVERFAHREN, MASCHINEN- UND FAHRZEUGBAU, ERNAEHRUNG, LANDWIRTSCHAFT. 1968. w. DM.1764. Wila Verlag Wilhelm Lampl GmbH, Landsberger Str. 191A, 80687 Munich, Germany. TEL 089-54756-0. FAX 089-54756309. circ. 1,000. **Document type:** abstracting/indexing.
●Also available online.

608.7 GW ISSN 0178-4250
AUSZUEGE AUS DEN PATENTSCHRIFTEN. 1955. w. DM.1896. Wila Verlag Wilhelm Lampl GmbH, Landsberger Str. 191A, 80687 Munich, Germany. TEL 089-54756-0. FAX 089-54756309. circ. 1,500. **Document type:** abstracting/indexing.
●Also available online.
Former titles: Auszuege aus den Auslegeschriften; Auszuege aus den Patentanmeldungen (ISSN 0005-058X)

AWISHKARA. see *SCIENCES: COMPREHENSIVE WORKS*

340 608.7 US ISSN 0148-7965
B N A'S PATENT, TRADEMARK & COPYRIGHT JOURNAL. 1970. 1101. $999 (effective July 1995). Bureau of National Affairs, 1231 25th St., N.W., Washington, DC 20037. TEL 202-452-4200. FAX 202-833-8092. TELEX 285656 BNAI WSH. (Subscr. to: 9435 Key West Ave., Rockville, MD 20850. TEL 800-372-1033) Ed. James D. Crowne. bk.rev.; abstr.; pat.; stat.; index, cum.index. (looseleaf format; back issues avail.)
●Also available online. Vendor(s): Lexis-Nexis, West Services, Inc. (BNA-PTCJ).
—CCC.
Description: Provides an in-depth review of current developments in the intellectual property field. Covers congressional activity, court decisions, relevant conferences, professional associations, international developments, and actions of the Patent and Trademark Office and the Copyright Office.

608.7 FR ISSN 0750-7674
T271 CODEN: BOPBEN
B.O.P.I. BREVETS D'INVENTION - ABREGES ET LISTES. (Bulletin Officiel de la Propriete Industrielle) w. 2500 F. Institut National de la Propriete Industrielle, 26 bis rue de Saint-Petersbourg, 75800 Paris Cedex 08, France. TEL 42-94-52-52. FAX 42-93-59-30. (Dist. by: Imprimerie National, B.P. 514, 59505 Douai Cedex, France) pat.; index. circ. 900. (also avail. in microfiche; back issues avail.)
—CASDDS; PADDS.
Formerly: B.O.P.I. Abreges (ISSN 0151-0592)
Description: Contains facsimiles of trademarks registered in France with the bibliographical data and the list of products designated in the registration.

608.7 FR ISSN 0223-3401
B.O.P.I. MARQUES. (Bulletin Officiel de la Propriete Industrielle) 1884. w. 1150 F. Institut National de la Propriete Industrielle, 26 bis rue de St. Petersbourg, 75800 Paris Cedex 08, France. TEL 42-94-52-52. FAX 42-93-59-30. (Dist. by: Imprimerie National, B.P. 514, 59505 Douai Cedex, France) tr.mk.; index. circ. 500. (back issues avail.)

608.7 FR ISSN 0429-4092
B.O.P.I. STATISTIQUES. (Bulletin Officiel de la Propriete Industrielle) 1958. a. 50 F. per no. Institut National de la Propriete Industrielle, 26 bis rue de St. Petersbourg, 75800 Paris Cedex 08, France. TEL 42-94-52-52. FAX 42-93-59-30. TELEX 290 368 INPI PARIS. (Dist. by: Imprimerie Nationale, B.P. 514, 59505 Douai Cedex, France) index. circ. 1,200. (back issues avail.)
Description: Contains the statistical data concerning patents, industrial designs, trademarks, trade and business register and the trade directory.

602.75 346.73 US
BASIC FACTS ABOUT REGISTERING A TRADEMARK. a. $2.50. U.S. Patent and Trademark Office, General Information Services Division, Crystal Plaza 3, Rm. 2C02, Washington, DC 20231. TEL 703-308-4357. FAX 703-305-7786. (Also avail. from: Superintendent of Documents, U.S. Government Printing Office, Box 371954, Pittsburgh, PA 15250-7954. TEL 202-512-1800. FAX 202-512-2250; Or: Bernan, 4611-F Assembly Dr., Lanham, MD 20706. TEL 301-459-7666. FAX 301-459-0056) **Document type:** government publication.
Description: Provides brief, nontechnical information about registering a trademark.

608.7 NE ISSN 0165-8964
BENELUX-MERKENBLAD/RECUEIL DES MARQUES BENELUX. (Text in Dutch and French) 1971. m. fl.300 (outside Benelux fl.330). Benelux Merkenbureau - Bureau Benelux des Marques, Bordewijklaan 15, 2591 XR The Hague, Netherlands. TEL 31-70-3491111. FAX 31-70-3475708. circ. 300.
Supersedes: Merkenblad Benelux - Marques Benelux Recueil (ISSN 0026-007X)

608.7 NE ISSN 0165-6023
BENELUX TEKENINGEN- OF MODELLENBLAD/RECUEIL DES DESSINS OU MODELES BENELUX. (Text in Dutch, French) 1975. m. fl.175 (outside Benelux fl.192). Benelux Bureau voor Tekeningen of Modellen - Bureau Benelux des Dessins ou Modeles, Bordewijklaan 15, 2591 XR The Hague, Netherlands. TEL 31-70-3491111. FAX 31-70-3475708. circ. 200.

347.7 NE ISSN 0006-2251
BIJBLAD BIJ DE INDUSTRIELE EIGENDOM. 1933. m. fl.105. Bureau voor de Industriele Eigendom - Netherlands Industrial Property Office, Patentlaan 2, 2288 EE Rijswijk (Z.H.), Netherlands. Ed.Bd. bk.rev.; bibl.; charts; stat.; index. circ. 900. **Indexed:** ELLIS. **Document type:** government publication.

BLAKES REPORT ON INTELLECTUAL PROPERTY. see *LAW*

608.7 602.7 GW ISSN 0930-2980
BLATT FUER PATENT, MUSTER- UND ZEICHENWESEN. 1898. m. DM.84.40. (Deutsches Patentamt) Carl Heymanns Verlag KG, Luxemburgerstr. 449, 50939 Cologne, Germany. TEL 0221-94373-0. FAX 0221-94373901. adv.; pat.; stat.; tr.mkt.; index, cum.index. circ. 2,300. (tabloid format) **Document type:** government publication.
—SWETS.

608.7 VE ISSN 0006-6338
BOLETIN DE LA PROPIEDAD INDUSTRIAL. 1931. m. free. Ministerio de Fomento, Officina de Registro de la Propiedad Industrial, Centro Simon Bolivar, Edificio Sur, Caracas, Venezuela. Ed. Ricardo Pages. index. circ. 600.

608.7 SP ISSN 0211-0121
CODEN: BPMBBC
BOLETIN OFICIAL DE LA PROPIEDAD INDUSTRIAL. 1: MARCAS Y OTROS SIGNOS DISTINTIVOS. 1886. fortn. 35400 ptas. for hardcopy; microfiche 10900 ptas. Ministerio de Industria y Energia, Oficina Espanola de Patentes y Marcas, Panama, 1, 28071 Madrid, Spain. TEL 34-1-3495300. charts; illus.; pat.; index. (also avail. in microfiche)
●Also available online. Vendor(s): Oficina Espanola de Patentes y Marcas.
—CASDDS.
Superseded in part (in 1965): Boletin Oficial de la Propiedad Industrial (ISSN 0038-6413)

608.5 SP ISSN 0211-0105
BOLETIN OFICIAL DE LA PROPIEDAD INDUSTRIAL. 2: PATENTES Y MODELOS DE UTILIDAD. 1886. fortn. 27500 ptas. for hardcopy; microfiche 8400 ptas. Ministerio de Industria y Energia, Oficina Espanola de Patentes y Marcas, Panama, 1, 28071 Madrid, Spain. TEL 34-1-3495300. charts; illus.; pat.; index. (also avail. in microfiche)
●Also available online. Vendor(s): Oficina Espanola de Patentes y Marcas.
Supersedes in part: Boletin Oficial de la Propiedad Industrial. 2: Patentes, Modelos y Dibujos (ISSN 0211-0113); Which superseded in part (in 1965): Boletin Oficial de la Propiedad Industrial (ISSN 0038-6413)

608.5 SP ISSN 0211-013X
BOLETIN OFICIAL DE LA PROPIEDAD INDUSTRIAL. 3: MODELOS Y DIBUJOS INDUSTRIALES Y ARTISTICOS. 1886. fortn. 8300 ptas. for hardcopy; microfiche 2500 ptas. Ministerio de Industria y Energia, Oficina Espanola de Patentes y Marcas, Panama, 1, 28071 Madrid, Spain. TEL 34-1-3495300. charts; illus.; pat.; index.
●Also available online. Vendor(s): Oficina Espanola de Patentes y Marcas.
Supersedes in part: Boletin Oficial de la Propiedad Industrial. 2: Patentes, Modelos y Dibujos (ISSN 0211-0113); Which superseded in part (in 1969): Boletin Oficial de la Propiedad Industrial (ISSN 0038-6413)

602.7 608.7 SP
BOLETIN OFICIAL DE LA PROPIEDAD INDUSTRIAL. 4: RESUMENES DE PATENTES. 1980. fortn. 12000 ptas. for hardcopy; microfiche 3700 ptas. Ministerio de Industria y Energia, Oficina Espanola de Patentes y Marcas, Panama, 1, 28071 Madrid, Spain. TEL 34-1-3495300. FAX 34-1-4572586.
●Also available online. Vendor(s): Oficina Espanola de Patentes y Marcas.
Formerly (until 1989): Boletin Oficial de la Propiedad Industrial. Informacion Tecnologica de Patentes (ISSN 0211-187X)

602.7 US ISSN 1047-6407
T223.V4
BRANDS AND THEIR COMPANIES. (Supplement avail.) 1976. a. $369 (in 2 vols.). Gale Research Inc., 835 Penobscot Bldg., Detroit, MI 48226. TEL 313-961-2242. FAX 313-961-6083. TELEX 810-221-7086. Ed. Susan Stitler.
●Also available online. Vendor(s): Knight-Ridder, Inc..
Formerly: Trade Names Dictionary (ISSN 0272-8818)
Description: Identifies more than 255,000 consumer products and their manufacturers. Entries are arranged alphabetically by trade name and include contact information for product inquiries or complaints.

602.7 US
T223.V4
BRANDS AND THEIR COMPANIES SUPPLEMENT. 1976. a. (except during the publication of Brands and Their Companies). $260. Gale Research Inc., 835 Penobscot Bldg., Detroit, MI 48226. TEL 313-961-2242. FAX 313-961-6083. TELEX 810-221-7086. Ed. Susan Stetler.
Formerly: New Trade Names (ISSN 0272-8826)
Description: Adds 18,000 new trade names and their companies to the listings in the main volumes.

BRITISH GLASS MANUFACTURERS CONFEDERATION. DIGEST OF INFORMATION AND PATENT REVIEW. see *CERAMICS, GLASS AND POTTERY*

602.7 RM ISSN 1220-6091
CODEN: BINMD3
BULETIN OFICIAL DE PROPIETATE INDUSTRIALA. SECTIUNEA MARCI/OFFICIAL BULLETIN FOR INDUSTRIAL PROPERTY. TRADEMARKS SECTION. (Text in Rumanian; summaries in English, French) 1961. m. $800 or exchange basis. Oficiul de Stat pentru Inventii si Marci (OSIM) - State Office for Inventions and Trademarks, 5 Ion Ghica St., Sect. 3, 70418 Bucharest, Rumania. FAX 40-1-3123819. TELEX 11370 ROPAT R. adv. contact: Ecaterina Berendea.
—CASDDS.
Supersedes in part (in 1991): Buletinul de Informare pentru Inventii si Marci - Bulletin for Inventions and Trademarks (ISSN 1012-8883); Which was formerly (until 1978): Buletin de Informare pentru Inventii si Marci (ISSN 0254-2269)

PATENTS, TRADEMARKS AND COPYRIGHTS

602.7 608.7   RM   ISSN 1220-6105
CODEN: BPSIEW
BULETIN OFICIAL DE PROPRIETATE INDUSTRIAL. SECTIUNEA INVENTII/OFFICIAL BULLETIN FOR INDUSTRIAL PROPERTY. INVENTIONS SECTION. (Text in Rumanian; summaries in English, French, German) 1961. m. $960 or exchange basis. Oficiul de Stat pentru Inventii si Marci (OSIM) - State Office for Inventions and Trademarks, 5, Ion Ghica St., Sect. 3, 70418 Bucharest, Rumania. FAX 40-1-3123819. TELEX 11370 ROPAT R. (Co-sponsor: Rumanian Institute for Inventions and Trademarks) adv. contact: Sofia Liliana Dima.
—CASDDS.
    Supersedes in part (in 1991): Buletinul de Informare pentru Inventii si Marci - Bulletin for Inventions and Trademarks (ISSN 1012-8883); Which was formerly (until 1978): Buletin de Informare pentru Inventii si Marci (ISSN 0254-2269)

608.7   RM   ISSN 1223-7728
BULETIN OFICIAL DE PROPRIETATE INDUSTRIALA. SECTIUNEA DESENE SI MODELE INDUSTRIALE/OFFICIAL BULLETIN FOR INDUSTRIAL PROPERTY. INDUSTRIAL DESIGN SECTION. (Text in Rumanian; summaries in English, French, German) 1993. m. $800 or exchange basis. Oficiul de Stat pentru Inventii si Marci (OSIM) - State Office for Inventions and Trademarks, 5, Ion Ghica St., Sect. 3, 70418 Bucharest, Rumania. FAX 40-1-3123819. TELEX 11370 ROPAT R. (Co-sponsor: Rumanian Institute for Inventions and Trademarks) adv. contact: Elena Graciov.

602 608   UK   ISSN 0261-023X
BULLETIN OF INVENTIONS AND SUMMARY OF PATENT SPECIFICATIONS. 1981. q. £24($30) Okikiolu Scientific & Industrial Co., 377 Edgware Rd., London W2 1BT, England. Ed. G.O. Okikiolu. illus.; pat.; index, cum.index. (back issues avail.) **Document type:** academic/scholarly publication, bulletin.
—CCC.
    Description: Reports on new discoveries and inventions.

BUTTERWORTHS LEGAL SERVICES DIRECTORY. see *LAW*

608.7   UK   ISSN 0306-0314
C I P A. 1971. m. £40 to non-members. Chartered Institute of Patent Agents, Staple Inn Bldgs., High Holborn, London WC1V 7PZ, England. TEL 0171-405-9450. FAX 0171-430-0471. Ed. G.F. Arthur. bk.rev.

602.7   US
CALLMANN ON UNFAIR COMPETITION, TRADEMARKS AND MONOPOLIES. 9 base vols. (plus 3/yr. updates). $850. Clark - Boardman - Callaghan Company Ltd., 375 Hudson St., New York, NY 10014. TEL 212-929-7500; 800-221-9428. FAX 212-924-0460. Eds. Rudolf Callmann, Louis Altman. (looseleaf format)
    Description: Provides thorough analysis to unfair competition and trademark laws.

602.7 608.7   CN   ISSN 0825-7256
CANADIAN INTELLECTUAL PROPERTY REVIEW. 1984. s-a. Can.$60. Patent and Trademark Institute of Canada, P.O. Box 1298, Sta. "B", Ottawa, ON K1P 5R3, Canada. TEL 613-234-0516. circ. 1,000. Indexed: Ind.Can.L.P.L. **Document type:** trade publication.
    Formerly: Patent and Trademark Institute of Canada. Bulletin.
    Description: Contains technical papers presented at spring and annual meetings of the institute and submissions to the Editor.

CANADIAN PATENT REPORTER. see *LAW*

608.7   US
CATALOG FOR GOVERNMENT INVENTIONS AVAILABLE FOR LICENSING. Issued with: Abstract Newsletter. Government Inventions Available for Licensing. a. $250. U.S. National Technical Information Service, 3285 Port Royal Rd., Springfield, VA 22161. TEL 703-487-4630. FAX 703-321-8547. TELEX 64617. Ed. Ed Lehmann. (back issues avail.)
    Former titles: Catalog for Government Inventions for Licensing; Catalog for Government Patents Available for Licensing.
    Description: Provides inventor and back-up information to those interested in patent licensing opportunities.

346.04 608.7   US
CODE OF FEDERAL REGULATIONS, TITLE 37: PATENTS, TRADEMARKS, AND COPYRIGHTS. a. $20 for paper edition, microfiche edition $2. U.S. Patent and Trademark Office, General Information Services Division, Crystal Plaza 3, Rm. 2C02, Washington, DC 20231. TEL 703-308-4357. FAX 703-305-7786. (Orders to: Superintendent of Documents, U.S. Government Printing Office, Box 371954, Pittsburgh, PA 15250-7954. TEL 202-512-1800. FAX 202-512-2250) (also avail. in microfiche) **Document type:** government publication.
    Description: Compiles Rules of Practice in Patent Cases, Trademark Rules of Practice, and Copyright Rules of Practice.

341.7582
COMPENDIUM OF COPYRIGHT OFFICE PRACTICE. Variant title: Compendium II. base vol. (plus s-a. supplements). $62 (foreign 77.50) (effective 1995). U.S. Library of Congress, Copyright Office, First St., N.E., Washington, DC 20559. (Subscr. to: Superintendent of Documents, U.S. Government Printing Office, Box 371954, Pittsburgh, PA 15250. TEL 202-512-1800. FAX 202-512-2250) (looseleaf format) **Document type:** government publication.
    Description: Discusses the operating problems and practices for the staff of the Copyright Office

COMPRESSOR NEWS AND PATENTS. see *MACHINERY*

COPYRIGHT; tidskrift foer press- och dokumentaerfotografi. see *PHOTOGRAPHY*

COPYRIGHT BULLETIN; quarterly review. see *LAW*

341.7582   US
COPYRIGHT LAW HANDBOOK. a. Clark - Boardman - Callaghan Company Ltd., 375 Hudson St., New York, NY 10014. TEL 212-929-7500; 800-221-9428. FAX 212-924-0460. Ed. Jeffrey K. Riffer.
    Description: Highlights the significant developments of copyright law in the past year, including new cases, legislation, regulations, and many other developments affecting the copyright practice area.

346.066 340
COPYRIGHT LAW IN BUSINESS AND PRACTICE.* 1989. base vol. (plus s-a. supplement). Maxwell Macmillan, Rosenfeld Launer, 90 Fifth Ave., New York, NY 10011-7629. TEL 800-562-0245. FAX 201-816-3569. Ed. John W. Hazard, Jr.

341.758   US   ISSN 0884-4437
KF2987
COPYRIGHT LAW JOURNAL. 1984. 6/yr. $375. Executive Press, Box 3897, San Francisco, CA 94119. TEL 510-685-5111. Ed. Neil Boorstyn. index. (back issues avail.) **Document type:** newsletter.

320   US
COPYRIGHT LAW REPORTS. 2 base vols. (plus m. updates). $535. Commerce Clearing House, Inc., 4025 W. Peterson Ave., Chicago, IL 60646. TEL 312-583-8500.

347.7   US   ISSN 0069-9950
KF3035.A75
COPYRIGHT LAW SYMPOSIUM. Variant title: A S C A P Copyright Law Symposium. 1950. irreg., no.39, 1992. price varies. (American Society of Composers, Authors, and Publishers) Columbia University Press, 562 W. 113th St., New York, NY 10025. TEL 212-666-1000. (back issues avail.; reprint service avail. from WSH) Indexed: C.L.I., L.R.I., Leg.Per. **Document type:** proceedings.
—Faxon.

340   UN
COPYRIGHT LAWS AND TREATIES OF THE WORLD. 3 base vols. (plus irreg. suppl.). $665 includes Supplement. Unesco, 7-9 Place de Fontenoy, 75700 Paris, France. TEL 577-16-10. (Dist. in U.S. by: Bernan, 4611-F Assembly Dr., Lanham, MD 20706-4391; and by: BNA Customer Service Center, 9435 Key West Ave., Rockville, MD 20850-3397. TEL 800-372-1033) (Co-sponsor: World Intellectual Property Organization) (looseleaf format)
    Description: Presents the copyright laws, orders, and regulations of more than 150 countries, from Afghanistan to Zimbabwe.

340   UN   ISSN 0069-9969
COPYRIGHT LAWS AND TREATIES OF THE WORLD. SUPPLEMENT. irreg., 25th, 1989. $245. Unesco, 7-9 Place de Fontenoy, 75700 Paris, France. TEL 45-77-16-10. (Dist. in U.S. by: Unipub, 4611-F Assembly Dr., Lanham, MD 20706-4391; and by: BNA Customer Service Center, 9435 Key West Ave., Rockville, MD 30850-3397. TEL 800-372-1033) (Co-sponsor: World Intellectual Property Organization) (also avail. in looseleaf format)

340   AT   ISSN 0725-0509
K3
COPYRIGHT REPORTER. 1981. 4/yr. Aus.$135. Australian Copyright Council, Ste. 3, Chalmers St., Redfern, N.S.W. 2016, Australia. TEL 61-2-318-1788. FAX 61-2-698-3536. Ed. Libby Baulch.

340   US   ISSN 0886-3520
KF2987   CODEN: JCUSEZ
COPYRIGHT SOCIETY OF THE U.S.A. JOURNAL. 1953. q. $125 to individuals; non-profit libraries $50; law firms $500. Copyright Society of the U.S.A., 1133 Ave. of the Americas, 33rd FL., New York, NY 10036. adv.; bk.rev.; bibl.; index. circ. 1,000. (also avail. in microfilm from RRI; back issues avail.; reprint service avail. from RRI,UMI,WSH) Indexed: C.L.I., Curr.Cont., L.R.I., Leg.Per., SSCI.
—BLDSC (4732.210000); CASDDS; Faxon; Genuine Article; UnCover. CCC.
    Formerly (until vol.28): Copyright Society of the U.S.A. Bulletin (ISSN 0010-8642)

342.6482   UK   ISSN 0950-2505
K1411.2   CODEN: CWOREV
COPYRIGHT WORLD. 1988. 10/yr. £275. Intellectual Property Publishing Ltd. (Subsidiary of: Armstrong Group Ltd.), Third Fl., Brigade House, Parsons Green, London SW6 4TH, England. TEL 0171-736-7111. FAX 0171-371-7806. Ed. J. Wild. adv. Indexed: Euro.LJI, LJI.
—BLDSC (3470.170000).

342.6482   UK   ISSN 1352-1160
COPYRIGHT YEARBOOK. Cover title: Managing Intellectual Property. Copyright Yearbook. (Supplement to: Managing Intellectual Property (ISSN 0960-5002)) 1993. a. Euromoney Publications plc., Nestor House, Playhouse Yard, London EC4V 5EX, England. TEL 0171-779-8606. FAX 0171-779-8500. (Orders to: Plymbridge Distributors Ltd., Estover, Plymouth PL6 7PZ, England. TEL 01752-779-8610. FAX 01752-695668) Ed. Jeremy Phillips; Pub. Dominic Carman. **Document type:** trade publication.
—BLDSC (3470.175000).

608.7   CU   ISSN 0011-2615
CUBA. OFICINA NACIONAL DE INVENCIONES, INFORMACION TECNICA Y MARCAS. BOLETIN OFICIAL. Short title: O N I I T E M Boletin. 1906. q. $30. Oficina Nacional de Invenciones, Informacion Tecnica y Marcas, Picota no. 15 c/o Luz y Acosta, Havana Vieja, Havana 1, C.P. 10100, Cuba. TEL 61-0185. FAX 537-338212. TELEX 511290. E-mail: oniitem@ceniai.cu. Ed. ablo Diaz Martinez. adv. contact: America Santos Tivera. index; circ. 200 (controlled). (also avail. in microfilm) **Document type:** government publication, bulletin.
    Formerly: Cuba. Registro de la Propriedad Industrial. Boletin Oficial.
    Description: Includes scientific inventions, industrial models, trademarks and other forms of industrial ownership, which are granted by the National Office.

346.489   DK   ISSN 0903-8825
DANSK MOENSTERTIDENDE. 1970. fortn. DKK 600. Patentdirektoratet, Helgeshoej Alle 81, DK-2630 Taastrup, Denmark. TEL 45-43-50-80-00. FAX 45-43-50-80-01. TELEX 16046 DPO DK.

608.7489   DK   ISSN 0011-6416
    CODEN: DAPAA8
DANSK PATENTTIDENDE. 1894. w. DKK 1000. Patentdirektoratet, Helgeshoej Alle 81, DK-2630 Taastrup, Denmark. TEL 45-43-50-80-00------- FAX 45-43-50-80-01. TELEX 16046 DPO DK.
—CASDDS.

PATENTS, TRADEMARKS AND COPYRIGHTS

346.489   DK   ISSN 0903-8809
DANSK VAREMAERKETIDENDE. 1879. w. DKK 1000. Patentdirektoratet, Helgeshoej Alle 81, DK-2630 Taastrup, Denmark. TEL 45-43-50-80-00. FAX 45-43-50-80-01. TELEX 16046 DPO DK. **Document type:** government publication.
    Formerly (1913-1988): Registreringstidende for vare- og faellesmaerker (ISSN 0106-522X)

340   US   ISSN 0070-3176
KF2994.A1
DECISIONS OF THE UNITED STATES COURTS INVOLVING COPYRIGHTS. (Subseries of U.S. Copyright Office. Bulletin) 1910. a. price varies. U.S. Library of Congress, Copyright Office, First St., N.E., Washington, DC 20559. (Dist. by: Superintendent of Documents, U.S. Government Printing Office, Box 371954, Pittsburgh, PA 15250-7954. TEL 202-512-1800. FAX 202-512-2250) cum.index. **Document type:** government publication, bulletin.

608.7489   DK
DENMARK. PATENTDIREKTORATET. BERETNING. 1975. a. free. Patentdirektoratet - Danish Patents and Trademark Office, Helgeshoj Alle 81, DK-2630 Taastrup, Denmark. TEL 45-43-50-80-00. FAX 45-43-50-80-01. TELEX 16046-DPO-DK. Ed. P.L. Thoft. circ. 5,000.
    Former titles: Denmark. Patentdirektorat. Aarsberetning; Denmark. Direktoratet for Patent- og Varemaerkevaesenet. Aarsberetning.

DIRITTO DELL'INFORMAZIONE E DELL'INFORMATICA. see *LAW*

340   IT   ISSN 0012-3420
DIRITTO DI AUTORE. (Text in French and Italian) 1930. q. L.50000 (foreign L.75000). Casa Editrice Dott. A. Giuffre, Via Busto Arsizio 40, 20151 Milan, Italy. TEL 02-38000905. FAX 02-38009582. Ed. Mario Fabiani. adv.; bk.rev.; abstr.; bibl.; index. circ. 900. **Indexed:** ELLIS.
    —SWETS.

341   UK   ISSN 0142-0461
K5   CODEN: EIPRES
E I P R: EUROPEAN INTELLECTUAL PROPERTY REVIEW. 1978. m. £295. Sweet & Maxwell, South Quay Plaza, 7th Fl., 183 Marsh Wall, London E14 9FT, England. TEL 071-538-8686. FAX 071-538-8625. Ed. Cheri Evans. adv. contact: Jackie Wood. bk.rev.; index. (back issues avail.) **Indexed:** ELLIS, Euro.LJI, LJI. **Document type:** bulletin.
    —BLDSC (3829.720960); SWETS; UnCover.
    Description: Recent developments and news for intellectual property lawyers, patent agents, trade mark agents, music publishers and academics.

E P M ENTERTAINMENT MARKETING SOURCEBOOK. see *BUSINESS AND ECONOMICS — Marketing And Purchasing*

608.7   AU   ISSN 1021-9390
E P O SCRIPT. (Text in English, French, German) 1992. a. DM.79. European Patent Office, Schottenfeldgasse 29, Postfach 82, A-1072 Vienna, Austria. TEL 01-521264051. FAX 01-521264192. TELEX 136337-INP-A. **Document type:** bulletin.
    Description: Utilization of patent protection in Europe.

346.01   US
ECKSTROM'S LICENSING IN FOREIGN AND DOMESTIC OPERATIONS: JOINT VENTURES. 2 base vols. (plus s-a. updates). $215. Clark - Boardman - Callaghan Company Ltd., 375 Hudson St., New York, NY 10014. TEL 212-929-7500; 800-221-9428. FAX 212-924-0460. Ed. Terrence F. MacLaren. (looseleaf format)
    Description: Provides practical guidance on the techniques and considerations involved in forming international joint ventures.

346.04   US
ECKSTROM'S LICENSING IN FOREIGN AND DOMESTIC OPERATIONS: TREATISE. 3 base vols. (plus s-a. updates). $345. Clark - Boardman - Callaghan Company, Inc., 375 Hudson St., New York, NY 10014. TEL 212-929-7500; 800-221-9428. FAX 212-924-0460. Eds. Lawrence J. Eckstrom, Steven Z. Szczepanski. (looseleaf format)
    Description: Reference source for the international licensing of intellectual property rights.

346.4 004   US   ISSN 1074-6420
KF807.5
ELECTRONIC CONTRACTING LAW; EDI and business transactions. 1991. a. $85. Clark - Boardman - Callaghan Company Ltd., 375 Hudson St., New York, NY 10014. TEL 212-929-7500; 800-221-9428. FAX 212-924-0460. Ed.Bd.
    Description: Applies existing principles of contract, commercial, and evidence law to electronic data interchange, and provides original interpretation and analysis of existing commentary.

ENERGY INFORMATION DIRECTORY. see *ENERGY*

ENTERTAINMENT MARKETING LETTER. see *BUSINESS AND ECONOMICS — Marketing And Purchasing*

608.7   GW   ISSN 0423-250X
ENTSCHEIDUNGEN DES BUNDESPATENTGERICHTS. 1962. irreg. DM.90. (Deutsches Patentamt) Carl Heymanns Verlag KG, Luxemburgerstr. 449, 50926 Cologne, Germany. TEL 0221-94373-0. FAX 0221-94373901. index. **Document type:** government publication.

608.7   AU   ISSN 0170-9291
EUROPAEISCHES PATENTAMT. AMTSBLATT/EUROPEAN PATENT OFFICE. OFFICIAL JOURNAL. (Text in English, French, German) m. DM.140. European Patent Office, Schottenfeldgasse 29, Postfach 82, A-1072 Vienna, Austria. TEL 01-521264051. FAX 01-521264192. TELEX 136337-INP-A. adv. circ. 3,500. **Document type:** bulletin.
    ●Also available on CD-ROM.
    —SWETS. **CCC.**

608.7   AU   ISSN 0170-9305
                     CODEN: EPATE8
EUROPAEISCHES PATENTBLATT. (Text in English, French and German) w. DM.790. European Patent Office, Schottenfeldgasse 29, Postfach 82, A-1072 Vienna, Austria. TEL 01-521264051. FAX 01-521264192.
    —CASDDS; PADDS. **CCC.**

602.7 658.8   UK   ISSN 0967-4586
EUROPEAN DIRECTORY OF CONSUMER BRANDS AND THEIR OWNERS. 1992. irreg., latest 1995. £255($370) (effective 1996). Euromonitor, 60-61 Britton St., London EC1M 5NA, England. TEL 0171-251-8024. FAX 0171-608-3149. (Addr. in N. America: Euromonitor International, 122 S. Michigan Ave., Ste. 1200, Chicago, IL 60603. TEL 312-922-1115. FAX 312-922-1157) **Document type:** directory.
    Description: Compiles more than 12,000 brand names in 14 product categories and lists their owners.

608.7   AU   ISSN 0724-7729
EUROPEAN PATENT OFFICE. ANNUAL REPORT. (Text in English, French and German) 1978. a. free. European Patent Office, Schottenfeldgasse 29, Postfach 82, A-1072 Vienna. TEL 01-521264051. FAX 01-521264192. TELEX 136337-INP-A. adv. circ. 7,000. (back issues avail.) **Document type:** corporate report.
    —CCC.
    Description: Annual review detailing patent growth, international patent cooperation, new patents and judicial developments.

608.7 341   UK   ISSN 0269-0802
EUROPEAN PATENT OFFICE REPORTS. 1986. 8/yr. £230. Sweet & Maxwell, South Quay Plaza, 7th Fl., 183 Marsh Wall, London E14 9FT, England. TEL 071-538-8686. FAX 071-538-8625. Ed. Nick Gingell. adv. contact: Jackie Wood. bk.rev. (back issues avail.) **Document type:** bulletin.
    —CCC.
    Description: Provides the patent practitioner with ready access to EPO decisions. For all those advising on the European route to patent protection.

608.7   UK
EUROPEAN PATENTS HANDBOOK. irreg. £330. (Chartered Institute of Patent Agents) Longman Group Ltd., Law, Tax and Finance Division, 21-27 Lamb's Conduit St., London WC1N 3NJ, England. TEL 071-242-2548. FAX 071-831-8119. (looseleaf format) **Document type:** bulletin.
    Description: Practical guide to intricacies of processing an application and patent in the European Patent Office.

608.7   AU   ISSN 1022-4025
EUROPEAN QUALIFYING EXAMINATION. (Text in English, French, German) 1993. a. DM.20. European Patent Office, Schottenfeldgasse 29, Postfach 82, A-1072 Vienna, Austria. TEL 01-521264051. FAX 01-521264192. TELEX 136337-INP-A. **Document type:** bulletin.

615 346.04   UK   ISSN 1354-3776
                     CODEN: EOTPEG
EXPERT OPINION ON THERAPEUTIC PATENTS; authoritative analysis of patenting trends. 1991. m. £1750($3150) Ashley Publications Ltd., First Fl., The Library, 1 Shepherds Hill, Highgate, London N6 5QJ, England. TEL 0181-347-5030. FAX 0181-347-5040. Ed.Bd; Pub. James Drake. pat. **Indexed:** Excerp.Med. (1992-). **Document type:** academic/scholarly publication.
    —BLDSC (3842.002960); CASDDS. **CCC.**
    Formerly (until Feb. 1994): Current Opinion on Therapeutic Patents (ISSN 0962-2594)
    Description: Reviews and evaluates patents issued over the preceding six months, profiles companies and their patenting practices, selects the most significant patents issued each month.
    Refereed Serial

F O G R A PATENTSCHAU. (Forschungsgesellschaft Druck e.V.) see *PRINTING*

FEDERAL BIO-TECHNOLOGY TRANSFER DIRECTORY. see *BIOLOGY — Biotechnology*

346.04   FI   ISSN 0355-4481
FINLAND. PATENTTI- JA REKISTERIHALLITUS. MALLIOIKEUSLEHTI/MOENSTERRAETTSTIDNING. (Text in Finnish and Swedish) 1971. m. FIM 1100 (effective 1996). Patentti- ja Rekisterihallitus - National Board of Patents and Registration, Albertinkatu 25, FIN-00180 Helsinki, Finland. FAX 358-0-69395204. (Dist. by: VAPK - Kustannus, P.O. Box 516, SF-00101 Helsinki 10, Finland) Ed. Sirkka-Liisa Lahtinen. circ. 275. **Document type:** government publication, catalog.

346.04   FI   ISSN 0031-2916
                     CODEN: PATPB2
FINLAND. PATENTTI- JA REKISTERIHALLITUS. PATENTTILEHTI/PATENTTIDNING. (Text in Finnish and Swedish) 1889. s-m. FIM 1350 (effective 1996). Patentti- ja Rekisterihallitus - National Board of Patents and Registration, Albertinkatu 25, 00180 Helsinki 18, Finland. FAX 358-0-69395204. (Dist. by: VAPK - Kustannus, P.O. Box 516, SF-00101 Helsinki 10, Finland) Ed. Juhan Rainersalo. index. circ. 520. **Document type:** government publication, catalog.
    —CASDDS.

346.04 608.7   FI   ISSN 0039-9922
FINLAND. PATENTTI- JA REKISTERIHALLITUS. TAVARAMERKKILEHTI/VARUMAERKSTIDNING. (Text in Finnish and Swedish) 1889. s-m. FIM 900 (effective 1996). Patentti- ja Rekisterihallitus - National Board of Patents and Registration, Albertinkatu 25, FIN-00180 Helsinki, Finland. FAX 358-0-69395204. (Dist. by: VAPK - Kustannus, P.O. Box 516, SF-00101 Helsinki 10, Finland) Ed. Sirkka-Liisa Lahtinen. charts; tr.mk. circ. 230. **Document type:** government publication, catalog.
    Former titles: Tavaraleimalehti; Tavaraleimarekisteri Rekisterilehti.

346   UK   ISSN 0141-9455
KD1365.A2
FLEET STREET REPORTS. 1963. m. £298. (European Law Centre Ltd.) Sweet & Maxwell, South Quay Plaza, 7th Floor, 183 Marsh Wall, London E14 9FT, England. TEL 071-538-8686. FAX 071-538-9508. Ed. Chris Rycrofe. adv. contact: Jackie Wood. index. (back issues avail.) **Document type:** bulletin.
    —CCC.
    Formerly: Fleet Street Patent Law Reports (ISSN 0430-6457)
    Description: Reference to all major cases on industrial property law.

FORDHAM INTELLECTUAL PROPERTY, MEDIA & ENTERTAINMENT LAW JOURNAL. see *LAW*

PATENTS, TRADEMARKS AND COPYRIGHTS

346.04 US
FORMS AND AGREEMENTS ON INTELLECTUAL PROPERTY AND INTERNATIONAL LICENSING. 3 base vols. (plus s-a. updates). $345. Clark - Boardman - Callaghan Company. Ltd., 375 Hudson St., New York, NY 10014. TEL 212-929-7500; 800-221-9428. FAX 212-924-0460. Ed. L.W. Melville. (looseleaf format)
  Description: Covers international licensing and intellectual property rights around the world.

LA FRANCE DE L'INDUSTRIE ET SES SERVICES. see *BUSINESS AND ECONOMICS — Trade And Industrial Directories*

FRIDAY MEMO. see *COMPUTERS*

608.7 UK ISSN 1351-3109
FUTURE AND INVENTOR. 1928. q. £15. Institute of Patentees and Inventors, Ste. 505A, Triumph House, 189 Regent St., London W1R 7WF, England. TEL 0171-242-7812. Ed. R. Magnus. adv.; bk.rev.; bibl. circ. 1,500. **Document type:** newsletter.
  Formerly (until 1987): *Inventor* (ISSN 0579-8388)

608.7 US ISSN 0083-3029
GENERAL INFORMATION CONCERNING TRADEMARKS. irreg., latest 1994. $2.25. U.S. Patent and Trademark Office, General Information Services Division, Crystal Plaza 3, Rm. 2C02, Washington, DC 20231. TEL 703-308-4357. FAX 703-305-7786. (Subscr. to: Superintendent of Documents, U.S. Governemnt Printing Office, Box 371954, Pittsburgh, PA 15250-7954; Or: Bernan, 4611-F Assembly Dr., Lanham, MD 20706. TEL 301-459-7666. FAX 301-459-0056) **Document type:** government publication.
  Description: Contains an introduction to general U.S. patent information.

608.7 JA
GEPPO HATSUMEI/MONTHLY REPORT OF INVENTION. (Text in Japanese) 1965. m. 1800 Yen. Hatsumei Kyokai - Japan Institute of Invention and Innovation, 9-14, Toranomon 2-chome, Minato-ku, Tokyo 105, Japan. **Document type:** newspaper.

608.7 GW ISSN 0934-7062
GESCHMACKSMUSTERBLATT. 1988. s-m. DM.60 per 3 mos. (Deutsches Patentamt) Wila Verlag Wilhelm Lampl GmbH, Landsberger Str. 191A, 80687 Munich, Germany. TEL 089-54756-0. FAX 089-54756309. circ. 600. **Document type:** bulletin.

608.7 340 GW ISSN 0016-9420
GEWERBLICHER RECHTSSCHUTZ UND URHEBERRECHT. 1896. m. DM.655($492) (effective 1996). (Deutsche Vereinigung fuer Gewerblichen Rechtsschutz und Urheberrecht) V C H Verlagsgesellschaft mbH, Postfach 101161, 69451 Weinheim, Germany. TEL 06201-606-147. FAX 06201-606117. TELEX 465516-VCHWH-D. (US addr.: V C H Publishers Inc., 220 E. 23rd St., New York, NY 10010-4606. TEL 212-683-8333) Eds. R. Jacobs, U. Krieger. adv. contact: R. Roth. bk.rev.; bibl.; pat.; tr.lit.; index. circ. 3,600. (also avail. in microfilm from VCI; reprint service avail. from ISI,SCH) **Indexed:** ELLIS, INIS Atomind. **Document type:** academic/scholarly publication.
  ●Also available on CD-ROM.
  —SWETS. **CCC.**

608.7 340 GW ISSN 0435-8600
GEWERBLICHER RECHTSSCHUTZ UND URHEBERRECHT. INTERNATIONALER TEIL. 1952. m. DM.655($492) (effective 1996). (Deutsche Vereinigung fuer Gewerblichen Rechtsschutz und Urheberrecht) V C H Verlagsgesellschaft mbH, Postfach 101161, 69451 Weinheim, Germany. TEL 06201-606-147. FAX 06201-606117. TELEX 465516-VCHWH-D. (US addr.: V C H Publishers Inc., 220 E. 23rd St., New York, NY 10010-4606. TEL 212-683-8333) Ed.Bd. adv. contact: R. Roth. circ. 2,500. (also avail. in microfilm from VCI) **Indexed:** ELLIS. **Document type:** academic/scholarly publication.
  ●Also available on CD-ROM.
  —SWETS. **CCC.**

608.7 UK ISSN 0072-5706
GREAT BRITAIN. DEPARTMENT OF TRADE. PATENTS, DESIGN AND TRADE MARKS (ANNUAL REPORT). a. H.M.S.O., P.O. Box 276, London SW8 5DT, England. (reprint service avail. from UMI) **Document type:** government publication.

341.7 US
GRIMES & BATTERSBY REPORT. 1988. 4/yr. free. Grimes & Battersby, 3 Hudson Sq., Box 1311, Stamford, CT 06904-1311. TEL 203-358-0848. FAX 203-348-2720. Eds. Charles Grimes, Gregory Battersby. circ. 2,500. **Document type:** newsletter.

005.74 602 608 FR
GUIDE INTERNATIONAL DES BANQUES DE DONNEES SUR LES BREVETS ET LES MARQUES. 1993. irreg. 390 F. Editions F L A Consultants, 27 rue de la Vistule, 75013 Paris, France. TEL 45-82-75-75. FAX 45-82-46-04. Eds. Aurelie Bordelet, Beatrice Riou. adv. contact: Beatrice Riou.
  Description: Lists 120 databases of patents and trademarks.

GUIDE TO AVAILABLE TECHNOLOGIES; an annual guide to business opportunities in technology. see *TECHNOLOGY: COMPREHENSIVE WORKS*

GUIDE TO MEDICAL DEVICE REGISTRATION IN JAPAN. see *MEDICAL SCIENCES*

HANDBUCH DER DATENBANKEN FUER NATURWISSENSCHAFT, TECHNIK, PATENTE. see *COMPUTERS — Data Base Management*

608.7 JA ISSN 0385-7115
HATSUMEI/INVENTION. (Text in Japanese) 1905. m. 700 Yen per no. Hatsumei Kyokai - Japan Institute of Invention and Innovation, 9-14, Toranomon 2-chome, Minato-ku, Tokyo 105, Japan. **Document type:** trade publication.

608.7 JA
HATSUMEI KOAN NO SHOKAI/INVENTION AND CONTRIVANCE INFORMATION. (Text in Japanese) a. Tokkyocho, Somubu - Patent Office, General Administration, 4-3 Kasumigaseki 3-chome, Chiyoda-ku, Tokyo 100, Japan. **Document type:** government publication.

608.7 JA ISSN 0917-3978
HATSUMEI KYOKAI KOKAI GIHO. GEKKAN/JIII JOURNAL OF TECHNICAL DISCLOSURE MONTHLY. (Text in Japanese) m. 2500 Yen. Hatsumei Kyokai - Japan Institute of Invention and Innovation, 9-14, Toranomon 2-chome, Minato-ku, Tokyo 105, Japan. **Document type:** bulletin.

608.7 JA ISSN 0385-2490
HATSUMEI KYOKAI KOKAI GIHO. HANGETSUKAN/JIII JOURNAL OF TECHNICAL DISCLOSURE SEMIMONTHLY. (Text in Japanese) 1976. s-m. 32400 Yen. Hatsumei Kyokai - Japan Institute of Invention and Innovation, 9-14, Toranomon 2-chome, Minato-ku, Tokyo 105, Japan. **Document type:** bulletin.

608.7 JA
HATSUMEI RAIFU/INVENTION LIFE. (Text in Japanese) 1956. m. 500 Yen per no. Hatsumei Gakkai - Inventors Institute of Japan, 10-12, Hyakunincho 1-chome, Shinjuku-ku, Tokyo 169, Japan.

608.7 JA
HATSUMEI TO SEIKATSU/INVENTION & LIFE. (Text in Japanese) 1962. m. 1800 Yen. Nihon Hatsumei Shinko Kyokai - Japan Society for the Advancement of Inventions, 4-22, Sakuragaokacho, Shibuya-ku, Tokyo 150, Japan.

608.7 JA
HATSUMEI TSUSHIN. (Text in Japanese) 1963. m. 5000 Yen. Hatsumei Tsushinsha, 3-5 Kanda Kajicho, Chiyoda-ku, Tokyo 101, Japan. Ed. K. Kitamura; Pub. K. Yamagata. **Document type:** newspaper.

341.758 608.7 JO ISSN 1023-0432
HIMAYAT AL-MILKIYYAH AL-FIKRIYYAH/PROTECTION OF INTELLECTUAL PROPERTY. (Text in Arabic, English) q. $50. Arab Society for the Protection of Industrial Property, Amman Commercial Center, 9th Fl., Abdali, P.O. Box 92110, Amman, Jordan. TEL 962-6-669603. FAX 962-6-603743. Ed. Mohammad Othman. circ. 1,000. **Document type:** academic/scholarly publication.
  Description: Covers issues relating to copyright, patents, trademarks, industrial designs, technology transfer and licensing, unfair competition, with a review of court cases and draft legislation.

608.7 JA
HOKKAIDO HATSUMEI KOAN NENPO/ANNUAL REPORT OF INVENTION IN HOKKAIDO. (Text in Japanese) 1955. a. Asahikawa Sangyo Gijutsu Joho Senta - Asahikawa Information Center for Industry and Technology, Asahikawa Shiritsu Toshokan, Tokiwa Koen, Asahikawa-shi, Hokkaido 070, Japan.

608.7 CN
HUGHES AND WOODLEY ON PATENTS. 3/yr. Can.$195. Butterworths Canada Ltd., Part of the Reed Elsevier group, 75 Clegg Rd., Markham, ON L6G 1A1, Canada. TEL 905-479-2665. FAX 905-479-2826. Eds. Roger T. Hughes, John M. Woodley. (looseleaf format) **Document type:** trade publication.
  Description: Covers Canadian patent legislation, practice, procedure and case law.

340 CN
HUGHES ON COPYRIGHT AND INDUSTRIAL DESIGN. 3/yr. Can.$195. Butterworths Canada Ltd., Part of the Reed Elsevier group, 75 Clegg Rd., Markham, ON L6G 1A1, Canada. TEL 905-479-2665. FAX 905-479-2826. Ed. Roger T. Hughes. (looseleaf format) **Document type:** trade publication.
  Description: Covers Canadian copyright legislation, practice, procedure and case law.

602.7 CN
HUGHES ON TRADEMARKS. 3/yr. Can.$195. Butterworths Canada Ltd., Part of the Reed Elsevier group, 75 Clegg Rd., Markham, ON L6G 1A1, Canada. TEL 905-479-2665. FAX 905-479-2826. Ed. Roger T. Hughes. (looseleaf format) **Document type:** trade publication.
  Description: Covers Canadian trademarks legislation, pracice, procedures, and case law.

608 GW ISSN 0018-9855
K9   CODEN: IICLDM
I I C. (International Review of Industrial Property and Copyright Law) (Text in part selected from German and international editions of the journal *Gewerblicher Rechtsschutz und Urheberrecht*) (Text in English) 1969. bi-m. DM.484($364) (effective 1996). (Max-Planck-Institute for Foreign and International Patent, Copyright and Competitition Law, Munich) V C H Verlagsgesellschaft mbH, Postfach 101161, 69451 Weinheim, Germany. TEL 06201-606-147. FAX 06201-606117. TELEX 465516-VCHWH-D. (US addr.: V C H Publishers Inc., 220 E. 23rd St., New York, NY 10010-4606. TEL 212-683-8333) Eds. F.-K. Beier, G. Schricker. bk.rev.; index. circ. 1,300. (also avail. in microfilm from VCH; reprint service avail. from ISI) **Indexed:** Curr.Cont., ELLIS, Euro.LJI, SSCI. **Document type:** academic/scholarly publication.
  ●Also available on CD-ROM.
  —BLDSC (4363.680000); CASDDS; Genuine Article; SWETS; UnCover. **CCC.**

608.7 HK ISSN 1011-3649
I P ASIA; intellectual property marketing and communications law. 1988. 10/yr. HK.$4390($595) (effective Jan. 1994). Asia Law & Practice Ltd., 2-F, 29 Hollywood Rd., Central, Hong Kong. TEL 852-544-9918. FAX 852-543-7617. Ed. Chris Hunter. s-a. index. (back issues avail)
  Description: Covers intellectual property legal developments and enforcement news in 16 Asian countries.

340 US
KF2972
I P L NEWSLETTER. 1982. q. membership only. American Bar Association, Intellectual Property Law Section, 750 N. Lake Shore Dr., Chicago, IL 60611. TEL 312-988-5595. FAX 312-988-5500. Ed. Thomas I. O'Brien. **Document type:** newsletter.
  Formerly: *P T C Newsletter* (ISSN 0736-8232)
  Description: Recent developments in intellectual property law, Section activities, calendar of events.

346.04 602.7 UK ISSN 1353-4998
I P LITIGATION YEARBOOK. (Intellectual Property) (Supplement to: *Managing Intellectual Property* (ISSN 0960-5002)) 1992. a. Euromoney Publications plc., Nestor House, Playhouse Yard, London EC4V 5EX, England. TEL 0171-779-8935. FAX 0171-779-8541. **Document type:** trade publication.

IMPACT PUMP NEWS AND PATENTS. see *MACHINERY*

IMPACT VALVES NEWS AND PATENTS. see *MACHINERY*

PATENTS, TRADEMARKS AND COPYRIGHTS

340 UN CODEN: INDPB4
INDUSTRIAL PROPERTY AND COPYRIGHT. French edition: Propriete Industrielle et le Droit d'Auteur. 1995. m. 210 SFr. in Europe; rest of world 300 SFr. World Intellectual Property Organization (WIPO) - Organisation Mondiale de la Proprieté Intellectuelle, Publications Sales and Distribution Unit, 34 Chemin des Colombettes, CH-1211 Geneva 20, Switzerland. TEL 022-730-9111. FAX 022-733-5428. TELEX 412912-OMPI-CH. adv.; bk.rev.; charts; index. circ. 700. (also avail. in microfiche; back issues avail.) **Document type:** bulletin.
—CASDDS; UncOver.
Formed by the merger of (1965-1995): Copyright (ISSN 0010-8626); (1962-1995): Industrial Property (ISSN 0019-8625)
Description: Covers the developments, theory and practical applications of international copyright, neighboring rights and industrial property law.

608.7 NE ISSN 0019-9249 CODEN: INEIAL
DE INDUSTRIELE EIGENDOM. 1912. s-m. fl.450. Bureau voor de Industriele Eigendom - Netherlands Industrial Property Office, Patentlaan 2, 2288 EE Rijswijk (Z.H.), Netherlands. index. **Indexed:** Key to Econ.Sci. **Document type:** government publication.
—CASDDS.

602.7 CU
INFORMACION DE PATENTES. fortn. Academia de Ciencias, Instituto de Documentacion e Informacion Cientifico-Tecnica (I D I C T), Capitolio Nacional, Prado y San Jose, Habana 2, Havana, Cuba.

INFORMATION SOURCES (YEAR). see *COMPUTERS*

340 AT
INSTITUTE OF PATENT ATTORNEYS OF AUSTRALIA. ANNUAL PROCEEDINGS. 1919. irreg., every 3-5 yrs. membership. Institute of Patent Attorneys of Australia, Qantas House, 2 Railway Parade, Camberwell, Vic. 3124, Australia. TEL 03-882-8041. FAX 613-882-8087. bk.rev. circ. 250. **Document type:** proceedings.

340 AT
INTELLECTUAL PROPERTY - COPYRIGHT. base vol. (plus q. updates). $425. Butterworths, Division of Reed International Books Australia Pty. Ltd. (Subsidiary of: Reed Elsevier Australia Pty. Ltd.), 271-273 Lane Cove Rd., North Ryde, N.S.W. 2113, Australia. TEL 02-335-4444. FAX 02-335-4655. (looseleaf format)

340 AT
INTELLECTUAL PROPERTY IN AUSTRALIA: PATENTS, DESIGNS & TRADEMARKS. 2 base vols. (plus updates 4/yr.). $475. Butterworths, Division of Reed International Books Australia Pty. Ltd. (Subsidiary of: Reed Elsevier Australia Pty. Ltd.), 271-273 Lane Cove Rd., North Ryde, N.S.W. 2113, Australia. TEL 02-335-4444. FAX 02-335-4678. (looseleaf format)

INTELLECTUAL PROPERTY JOURNAL. see *LAW*

340 US ISSN 0892-2365
K9 CODEN: IPLAEG
INTELLECTUAL PROPERTY LAW (NEW YORK). 1987. 4/yr. (in 1 vol., 4 nos./vol.). 136 ECU (effective 1996). Harwood Academic Publishers, c/o International Publishers Distributor, 820 Town Center Dr., Langhorne, PA 19047. TEL 215-750-2462. FAX 215-750-6343. (Subscr. to: International Publishers Distributor, PO Box 90, Reading, Berkshire, RG1 8JL, England. TEL 44-173-456-8316) Eds. Allam S. Melser, David C. Gryce. (also avail. in microform; reprint service avail. from WSH) **Document type:** academic/scholarly publication.
—BLDSC (4531.823900). **CCC.**
Refereed Serial

341.7 US
INTELLECTUAL PROPERTY LAW (SPRINGFIELD). 1961. 4/yr. $12. Illinois State Bar Association, Section on Patent, Trademark & Copyright Law, Illinois Bar Center, Springfield, IL 62701. TEL 217-525-1760. FAX 217-525-0712. Eds. Daniel L. Kegan, Bradford Lyerla. (back issues avail.) **Document type:** newsletter.
Formerly: Illinois State Bar Association. Patent, Trademark and Copyright Newsletter (ISSN 0073-5043)

341.7 US
INTELLECTUAL PROPERTY LAW NEWS. 1991. irreg. (2-3/yr.). State Bar of Wisconsin, Intellectual Property Law Section, 402 W. Wilson St., Madison, WI 53703. TEL 608-257-3838. FAX 608-257-5502. circ. 350. (looseleaf format; back issues avail.) **Document type:** newsletter.

608.7 US ISSN 0193-4864
KF3114.A1
INTELLECTUAL PROPERTY LAW REVIEW. 1969. a. $85. Clark - Boardman - Callaghan Company Ltd., 375 Hudson St., New York, NY 10014. TEL 212-929-7500. FAX 212-924-0460. Ed. John D. Norris. index. (reprint service avail. from WSH) **Indexed:** C.L.I., L.R.I., Leg.Per.
—BLDSC (4531.824000); Faxon.
Formerly: Patent Law Review (ISSN 0079-0168)
Description: Covers major developments in patents, trademarks, and copyright, as well as relevant topics affecting practice and procedure.

346.04 AT ISSN 0812-2024
INTELLECTUAL PROPERTY REPORTS (NORTH RYDE, 1982). 1982. 3/yr. Aus.$290. Butterworths, Division of Reed International Books Australia Pty. Ltd. (Subsidiary of: Reed Elsevier Australia Pty. Ltd.), 271-273 Lane Cove Rd., North Ryde, N.S.W. 2113, Australia. TEL 02-335-4444. FAX 02-335-4678.

346 US ISSN 1079-2422
▼**INTELLECTUAL PROPERTY STRATEGIST.** 1994. m. $155. New York Law Publishing Co., 345 Park Ave. S., New York, NY 10010. TEL 212-545-6170. FAX 212-696-1848. Eds. Mary A. Donovan, Marya Lenn Yee. (looseleaf format; back issues avail.) **Document type:** newsletter.

341.7582 346.04 UK
INTELLECTUAL PROPERTY WORLD. 10/yr. £295($495) (effective Feb. 1995). Intellectual Property Publishing Ltd. (Subsidiary of: Armstrong Group Ltd), Third Fl., Brigade House, Parsons Green, London SW6 4TH, England. TEL 0171-736-7111. FAX 0171-371-7806. **Document type:** trade publication.

341.7582 NE
INTELLECTUAL PROPERTY WORLD DESK REFERENCE; a guide to practice by country, state and province. 1993. base vol. (plus a. update). fl.200($115) (effective 1994). (Lex Mundi) Kluwer Law International (Subsidiary of: Wolters Kluwer N.V.), Postbus 85889, 2508 CN The Hague, Netherlands. TEL 31-70-3081500. FAX 31-70-3081515. (Dist. by: Libresso Distribution Centre, P.O. Box 23, 7400 GA Deventer, Netherlands. TEL 31-5700-33155. FAX 31-5700-33834; In N. America: Kluwer Law International, 675 Massachusetts Ave., Cambridge, MA 02139. TEL 617-340-0140. FAX 617-354-8595) Ed. Thomas M.S. Hemnes. (looseleaf format)
Description: Country by country description of the legal protection afforded different categories of intellectual property, including copyright, industrial designs and models, patents, as well as relevant information on matters such as royalties, currency controls, and other issues.

341.758 NE ISSN 0169-1074
INTELLECTUELE EIGENDOM & RECLAMERECHT. Short title: I E R. 1985. 6/yr. W.E.J. Tjeenk Willink B.V. (Subsidiary of: Wolters Kluwer N.V.), Postbus 25, 8000 AA Zwolle, Netherlands. TEL 31-38-211444. FAX 31-38-216500. adv. **Indexed:** ELLIS. **Document type:** trade publication.
—SWETS.

602.7 US ISSN 1050-8376
HD69.B7
INTERNATIONAL BRANDS AND THEIR COMPANIES; international consumer products and their manufacturers, importers and distributors with addresses. 1988. biennial. Gale Research Inc., 835 Penobscot Bldg., Detroit, MI 48226-4094. TEL 800-877-GALE. FAX 313-961-6083. Ed. Susan Stetler. (also avail. in magnetic tape; diskette format)
●Also available online. Vendor(s): Knight-Ridder, Inc..
Formerly: International Trade Names Dictionary (ISSN 0899-7586)

341.758 FR ISSN 0074-2899
INTERNATIONAL CONFEDERATION OF SOCIETIES OF AUTHORS AND COMPOSERS. irreg., no.186, 1976. International Confederation of Societies of Authors and Composers, 11 rue Keppler, 75116 Paris, France.

608.7 UN ISSN 0250-7730
TS171.A1
INTERNATIONAL DESIGNS BULLETIN; bulletin des dessins et modeles internationaux. (Text in English and French) 1979. m. 460 SFr. World Intellectual Property Organization (WIPO) - Organisation Mondiale de la Proprieté Intellectuelle, Publications Sales and Distribution Unit, 34 Chemin des Colombettes, CH-1211 Geneva 20, Switzerland. TEL 022-730-9111. FAX 022-733-5428. TELEX 412912-OMPI-CH. adv.; illus. circ. 420. (back issues avail.) **Document type:** bulletin.
Formerly: Dessins et Modeles Internationaux (ISSN 0011-9520).

608.7 US ISSN 0738-9337
K1536
INTERNATIONAL PATENT LITIGATION; a country-by-country analysis. 1983. base vol. (plus a. suppl.). $250. B N A Books (Subsidiary of: The Bureau of National Affairs, Inc.), 1231 25th St., N.W., Washington, DC 20037. TEL 202-833-7470; 800-960-1220. FAX 202-833-7490. E-mail: books@bna.com. (Subscr. to: BNA Books Distribution Center, 300 Raritan Center Parkway, Box 7816, Edison, NJ 08818-7816. TEL 908-225-5555. FAX 908-417-0482) Ed. Michael N. Meller. (looseleaf format)
Description: Covers patent laws and procedures of 23 industrial nations.

608.7 US
INTERNATIONAL PATENT LITIGATION. SUPPLEMENT. 1990. irreg. $95. B N A Books (Subsidiary of: The Bureau of National Affairs, Inc.), 1231 25th St., N.W., Washington, DC 20037. TEL 202-833-7470; 800-960-1220. FAX 202-833-7490. E-mail: books@bna.com. (Subscr. to: BNA Books Distribution Center, 300 Raritan Center Parkway, Box 7816, Edison, NJ 08818-7816. TEL 908-225-1900. FAX 908-417-0482) Ed. Michael N. Meller.

608 II
INTERNATIONAL PRESS CUTTING SERVICE: LIST OF INDUSTRIAL LICENCES ISSUED. 1977. 3-4/m. $65. International Press Cutting Service, Box 63, Allahabad 211001, India. Ed. Nandi Khanna. (looseleaf format)

340 GW ISSN 0539-1512
INTERNATIONALE GESELLSCHAFT FUER URHEBERRECHT. YEARBOOK. (Text in English, French, German, Italian and Spanish) irreg. Nomos Verlagsgesellschaft mbH und Co. KG, Waldseestr. 3-5, 76530 Baden-Baden, Germany. TEL 07221-20140. FAX 07221-210427. (Subscr. to: Postfach 610, 76484 Baden-Baden, Germany) circ. 1,200. **Document type:** corporate report.

608.7 US ISSN 1044-4742
T339
INVENTING AND PATENTING SOURCEBOOK. 1990. irreg., 2nd ed., 1992. $79. Gale Research Inc., 835 Penobscot Bldg., Detroit, MI 48226. TEL 313-961-2242; 800-877-4253. FAX 313-961-6083. TELEX 810-221-7086. Ed. Robert J. Hoffman. (also avail. in diskette format; magnetic tape)
Description: Guide for inventors, innovators, and marketers of new products. Provides information on how to get funding for your ideas, how to patent or trademark a product without an attorney's assistance, and how to select a company to approach for licensing.

INVENTION INTELLIGENCE. see *SCIENCES: COMPREHENSIVE WORKS*

608.7 US ISSN 0883-9859
INVENTORS' DIGEST. 1985. bi-m. $22 (Canada $27; elsewhere $40). (Affiliated Inventors Foundation) J M H Publishing Co., 4850 Galley Rd., Ste. 209, Colorado Springs, CO 80915. TEL 719-573-4540. FAX 719-573-4679. Pub. Joanne Hayes. adv.: B&W page $500; trim 8 1/2 x 11. bk.rev. circ. 10,000. (back issues avail.) **Document type:** trade publication.
Description: Informs inventors who want to know how to develop and protect their ideas.

608.7   US   ISSN 0899-8841
INVENTOR'S GAZETTE.* 1986. m. $24. Inventors Association of America, 7780 Klusman Ave., Rancho Cucamonga, CA 91730-2712. TEL 714-980-6446. Ed. L. Troy Hall. adv. circ. 480,000. (tabloid format; back issues avail.)
 Description: Articles on inventors and their latest inventions.

INZYNIERIA MATERIALOWA. see *ENGINEERING*

608.7 607.7   IS   ISSN 0021-2326
ISRAEL. MINISTRY OF JUSTICE. PATENT OFFICE. PATENTS AND DESIGNS JOURNAL. (Part A: Patents, Trademarks and Copyrights; Part B: Patents and Designs) (Text in English and Hebrew) 1968. m. IS.658. Ministry of Justice, Patent Office, P.O. Box 354, Jerusalem, Israel. (Subscr. to: Distribution Service of Government Publications, 29-B St., Hakirya, Tel-Aviv, Israel) Ed.Bd. abstr. circ. 150. Indexed: Chem.Abstr. **Document type:** government publication.

340   IT
ITALY. OFFICIO DELLA PROPRIETA LETTERARIA, ARTISTICA E SCIENTIFICA. BOLLETTINO.* m. L.3500. Italy. Istituto Poligrafico dello Stato, Piazza Verdi 10, 00198 Rome, Italy.

608.7   RU   ISSN 0130-1802
T201
IZOBRETATEL' I RATSIONALIZATOR.* 1929. m. $84 (effective 1996). (Society of Soviet Inventors and Innovators, Central Council) Profizdat, Ul. Myasnitskaya 13, 101000 Moscow, Russia. TEL 095-924-5740. Ed. Nina Karaseva. adv. circ. 400,000.

608.7   RU   ISSN 1021-0865
T285.A2   CODEN: OTIZDX
IZOBRETENIYA/INVENTIONS; ofitsial'nyi patentnyi byulleten' 1924. 3/m. $990. Vsesoyuznyi Nauchno-Issledovatel'skii Institut Patentnoi Informatsii (VNIIPI) - All-Russia Scientific and Research Institute of Patent Information, Raushskaya nab. 4, 113035 Moscow, Russia.
TEL 7-095-2393010. FAX 7-095-2311121. TELEX 411093 POISK SU. Ed. E.I. Daich. adv.; illus.; pat.; tr.mk.; index. circ. 11,125. (also avail. in microfiche; microfilm) Indexed: Abstr.Bull.Inst.Pap.Chem., Chem.Abstr. **Document type:** bulletin.
—CASDDS. CCC.
 Formerly (until 1992): Otkrytiya, Izobreteniya (ISSN 0208-287X); Supersedes in part (in 1983): Otkrytiya, Izobreteniya, Promyshlennye Obraztsy, Tovarnye Znaki (ISSN 0007-4020); Formerly: Bulleten' Izobretenii, Promyshlennykh Obraztsov i Tovarnykh Znakov.
 Description: Publishes formulas and drawings of scientific inventions and discoveries listed in the Russian Federal Register. Contains information about any changes in their legal status and description.

608.7   JA
JAPANESE PATENT OFFICE. ANNUAL REPORT. (Text in English) a. Tokkyocho - Patent Office, 4-3, Kasumigaseki 3-chome, Chiyoda-ku, Tokyo 100, Japan.

608.7   JA
JAPANESE PATENTS GAZETTE. UNEXAMINED.* 1974. w. $3980. Japan Patent Information Organization, Sato-Dia Bldg., 4-1-7, Toyo, Koto-ku, Tokyo 135, Japan. TEL 03-5690-5555. FAX 03-5690-5566. Indexed: Dairy Sci.Abstr.
 Formerly: Japanese Patents Gazette. Part 1: Chemical (ISSN 0308-3713)

341.7   US   ISSN 1041-3952
KF2972
JOURNAL OF PROPRIETARY RIGHTS. 1988. m. $359. Aspen Law & Business (Subsidiary of: Wolters Kluwer N.V.), 270 Sylvan Ave., Englewood Cliffs, NJ 07632. TEL 800-223-0231. FAX 201-894-8666. Ed.Bd; Pub. Rick Kravitz. (looseleaf format; back issues avail.) **Document type:** newsletter.

341.7582   JA   ISSN 0289-1395
KANSAI BUNKEN SENTA NYUSU/KANSAI LITERATURE CENTER NEWS. (Text in Japanese) 1959. irreg. (2-3/yr.) Kansai Bunken Senta Shinkokai - Promotion Association of Kansai Literature Center, Osaka Furitsu Yuhigaoka Toshokan, Tokkyo Shiryoka, 2-7 Reijincho, Tennoji-ku, Osaka 543. TEL 06-771-2646.

608.7   FI   ISSN 0789-4767
HF5565
KAUPPAREKISTERILEHTI/HANDELSREGISTER TIDNING. (Text in Finnish, Swedish) 1896. w. FIM 590. Board of Patents and Registration, Albertilkatu 25, 00180 Helsinki 18, Finland. FAX 358-0-6953204. (Susbcr. to: Government Printing Centre, Aikakauslehtien Tilaukset, PL 516, 00101 Helsinki, Finland) Ed. Oscar Wilder. index. circ. 200.
 Formerly: Kaupparekisteri (ISSN 0022-9504)

608.7   JA   ISSN 0287-3125
KOGYO SHOYUKENHO KENKYU/STUDIES ON LAWS OF INDUSTRIAL PROPERTY RIGHTS. (Text in Japanese) 1964. q. 600 Yen per no. Hanabusa Kogyo Shoyuken Kenkyujo Shuppanbu - Hanabusa Institute for the Protection of Industrial Property, Ochanomizu Sukuea B Kan, 1-6, Kanda Surugadai, Chiyoda-ku, Tokyo 101, Japan.

L E S NOUVELLES. (Licensing Executives Society International) see *TECHNOLOGY: COMPREHENSIVE WORKS*

340   US
LATMAN'S THE COPYRIGHT LAW. irreg., 6th ed., 1986. $75. B N A Books (Subsidiary of: The Bureau of National Affairs, Inc.), 1231 25th St., N.W., Washington, DC 20037. TEL 202-833-7470; 800-960-1220. FAX 202-833-7490. E-mail: books@bna.com. (Subscr. to: BNA Books Distribution Center, 300 Raritan Center Parkway, Box 7816, Edison, NJ 08818-7816. TEL 908-225-5555. FAX 908-417-0482) Ed. William F. Patry.
 Description: Reviews statutes, regulations, international conventions, and judicial and administrative rulings on copyrightability; publication and notice; registration and deposit; infringement and remedies; interaction of federal and state laws; historical background; and international issues.

340 600   US
LAW OF HIGH TECHNOLOGY INNOVATION. 1992. base vol. (plus irreg. updates). $90. Butterworth Legal Publishers (Salem) (Subsidiary of: Reed Elsevier plc), 8 Industrial Way, Bldg. C, Salem, NH 03079. TEL 800-548-4001. FAX 603-898-9858. Ed. Aryeh S. Friedman. (looseleaf format)
 Description: Covers existing intellectual property laws affecting high technology as well as addresses deficiencies of the present laws to adequately protect leading edge developments in the high technology arena.

608.7 658   US   ISSN 0741-0107
THE LICENSING BOOK. 1983. m. $36. Adventure Publishing, 1501 Broadway, Ste. 500, New York, NY 10036-5503. TEL 212-575-4510. FAX 212-575-4521. (Overseas addr.: Cascade Publishing, Pippingford Park Manor, Nutley, E. Sussex TN22 3HW, England. TEL 44-825-713611. FAX 44-824-713633) Ed. Rich Levitt; Pub. Ernest Lustenring. adv. circ. 25,000. (tabloid format) **Document type:** newsletter.
 Description: Discusses the commercial use of sports team names.

602.7   US   ISSN 1040-4023
KF3145.A15
LICENSING JOURNAL. 1982. m. $235 (foreign $265). Kent Communications, Ltd., Box 1169, Stamford, CT 06904-1169. TEL 203-358-0848. FAX 203-348-2720. Eds. Charles W. Grimes, Gregory J. Battersby. adv. contact: Catherine DeVito. bk.rev.; index. circ. 1,000. **Document type:** trade publication.
 Formerly (until 1988, vol.7, no.5): Merchandising Reporter (ISSN 0890-135X)
 Description: Covers developments in every major market of licensing, practical aspects of licensing, and industry topics from legal forms and contracts to protection, licensing and enforcement of rights.

608 658.8   US   ISSN 8755-6235
HF5429.255
LICENSING LETTER. 1977. m. $275 (foreign $305). E P M Communications, 488 E. 18th St., Brooklyn, NY 11226. TEL 718-469-9330. FAX 718-469-7124. Ed. Karen Raugust. (back issues avail.)
—CCC.
 Incorporates: Licensing Industry Newsletter.
 Description: News on licensed properties, licensing representatives, manufacturer licenses and statistical data and contact lists.

608.7   UK
LICENSING REPORTER EUROPE. 1985. fortn. £125($250) (effective Jan. 1995). A4 Publications Ltd., Hagley Chambers, Hagley Rd., Stourbridge, W. Midlands DY8 1PS, England. TEL 01384-440591. FAX 01384-440582. Ed. Adam Driscoll; Pub. Francesca Ash. adv. contact: Jerry Wooldridge. charts; stat.; circ. 2,000 (paid). (back issues avail.) **Document type:** newsletter.
 Description: Reports the latest news from licensors, agents, and licensees throughout Europe. Contains previews on trade fairs, statistics on top T.V. programs, and informs on important licensed properties to watch out for and covers legal issues.

351.8 346.04   UK   ISSN 0959-8421
LICENSING REVIEW; the journal for licensing specialists. 1990. q. £72. Benedict Books, P.O. Box 900, Hemel Hempstead, Herts. HP3 ORJ, England.
TEL 0442-834900. FAX 01442-834901. bk.rev. **Document type:** trade publication.
—BLDSC (5207.588000).
 Description: Contains practical articles and editorial views of interest to persons specializing in licensing issues.

608.7 658   UK
LICENSING TODAY.* 1983. m. $60. Toy & Hobby World, 106 Gloucester Pl., London W1H 3DB, England. TEL 212-594-4237. adv. circ. 18,106.

608.7   MW   ISSN 0025-1267
MALAWI PATENT JOURNAL AND TRADE MARKS JOURNAL. 1966. m. K.2 per no. Ministry of Finance, Government Printer, Box 37, Zomba, Malawi. pat.; tr.mk.

341.758 658.575   UK   ISSN 0960-5002
K13
MANAGING INTELLECTUAL PROPERTY. (Supplements avail.: Copyright Yearbook; I P Litigation Yearbook, Trade Mark Yearbook, World I P Contacts Handbook (Year)) 1990. 10/yr. $440 (includes all supplements). Euromoney Publications plc., Nestor House, Playhouse Yard, London EC4V 5EX, England. TEL 0171-779-8686. FAX 0171-779-8500. (Subscr. to: Quadrant Subscription Services, Oakfield House, Perymount Rd., Haywards Heath, Sussex RH16 3DH, England) Ed. Jeremy Phillips; Pub. Dominic Carman. Indexed: Euro.LJI, LJI. **Document type:** trade publication.
●Also available online. Vendor(s): University Microfilms International.
—BLDSC (5359.287960); UMI.

608.7   GW
MARKENBLATT. s-m. DM.150 for 3 mos. (Deutsches Patentamt) Wila Verlag Wilhelm Lampl GmbH, Landsberger Str. 191A, 80687 Munich, Germany. TEL 089-54756-0. FAX 089-54756309. adv.; illus.; tr.mk.; index. circ. 2,000. **Document type:** bulletin.
 Formed by the merger of (1950-1994): Warenzeichenblatt. Teil 1: Angemeldete Zeichen (ISSN 0043-0331); (1950-1994): Warenzeichenblatt. Teil 2: Eingetragene Zeichen (ISSN 0043-034X)

608.7   UN   ISSN 0025-3936
MARQUES INTERNATIONALES. 1893. m. 450 SFr. World Intellectual Property Organization (WIPO) - Organisation Mondiale de la Propriete Intellectuelle, Publications Sales and Distribution Unit, 34 Chemin des Colombettes, CH-1211 Geneva 20, Switzerland. TEL 022-730-9111. FAX 022-733-5428. TELEX 412912-OMPI-CH. adv.; charts; tr.mk.; index. circ. 1,600. (also avail. in microfiche; back issues avail.)
 Description: Covers all marks, registered, renewed, modified, transferred, refused or otherwise. Includes countries of origin and destination, with reproduction of the actual trademarks or service marks.

346.04 341.7   US   ISSN 1070-4043
KF3109
MEALEY'S LITIGATION REPORT: PATENTS. 1993. s-m. $450. Mealey Publications, Inc., P.O. Box 446, Wayne, PA 19087-0446. TEL 610-688-6566. FAX 610-688-7552. Ed. Maureen McGuire. **Document type:** newsletter.
 Description: Covers the highly specialized area of patent litigation, from the district courts to the Federal Circuit to the Supreme Court. Topics include infringement, claim interpretation, licensing agreements, affirmative defenses, trials, jurisdiction and discovery.

PATENTS, TRADEMARKS AND COPYRIGHTS

341.758 US ISSN 1065-9390
KF2972
MEALEY'S LITIGATION REPORTS: INTELLECTUAL PROPERTY. 1992. s-m. $750. Mealey Publications, Inc., Box 446, Wayne, PA 19087-0446. TEL 610-688-6566. FAX 610-688-7552. Ed. Maureen McGuire.
—CCC.
 Description: Timely information on international developments in intellectual property litigation, including copyright, patent and trademark issues, software protection, trade secret and unfair competition disputes, EC standardization efforts, recent court decisions, and more.

MEDIAPLUSNEWS; monthly of information, culture, technological actualities. see *TECHNOLOGY: COMPREHENSIVE WORKS*

602.7 608.7 US
MERCHANT AND GOULD COMPUTER LAW NEWSLETTER. 1988. s-a. Merchant, Gould, Smith, Edell, Welter & Schmidt, 3100 Norwest Ctr., Minneapolis, MN 55402. TEL 612-332-5300. FAX 332-9081. Ed. Kari Bartingale. circ. 2,500. **Document type:** newsletter.
 Description: Contains articles on current topics regarding patent, trademark and copyright protection of computers, electronics and softwares.

608.7 340 GW ISSN 0026-6884
MITTEILUNGEN DER DEUTSCHEN PATENTANWAELTE. 1909. m. DM.148. (Patentanwaltskammer) Carl Heymanns Verlag KG, Luxemburgerstr. 449, 50939 Cologne, Germany. TEL 0221-94373-0. FAX 0221-94373901. adv.; bk.rev.; abstr.; pat.; index. circ. 1,300. (tabloid format) **Document type:** government publication.

MODEL BUSINESS CONTRACTS. see *BUSINESS AND ECONOMICS*

MUSIC & COPYRIGHT. see *MUSIC*

602.7 780 US ISSN 1067-876X
MUSICOPYRIGHT INTELLIGENCE; a newsletter of financial success through copyright ownership. 1993. m. $195 (Canada $220; elsewhere $270). E.S. Proteus, 1657 The Fairway, Ste. 123, Jenkintown, PA 19046. TEL 215-885-3154. Ed. Eric Nemeyer. adv.; bk.rev.; charts; illus.; stat.; index. circ. 2,000. (back issues avail.) **Document type:** newsletter.
 ●Also available online. Vendor(s): CompuServe, Inc. (71553,3665).
 Description: Provides investigative research, news and perspectives on music industry finance, and money-making ideas for success in a growing world of market economy.

608 SW ISSN 0027-6723
N I R NORDISKT IMMATERIELLT RAETTSSKYDD/SCANDINAVIAN JOURNAL ON INTELLECTUAL PROPERTY. (Text in Danish, Norwegian and Swedish; summaries in English) 1932. q. SEK 320 (effective 1990). Stockholms Universitet, Institutet foer Immaterialraett och Marknadsraett, S-106 91 Stockholm, Sweden. Ed. Gunnar Sterner. adv.; bk.rev.; index, cum.index: 1932-1955, 1956-1962, 1963-1969. circ. 1,700.
 Formerly (until 1949): Nordiskt Industriellt Raettsskydd.

NONWOVENS PATENT NEWS. see *TEXTILE INDUSTRIES AND FABRICS*

346.048 NO ISSN 0803-6985
NORSK MOENSTERTIDENDE. 1971. 25/yr. NOK 600($30) Patentstyret - The Norwegian Patent Office, Koebenhavngate 10, P.O. Box 8160, Dep., N-0033 Oslo, Norway. TEL 47-22-38-73-00. FAX 47-22-38-73-01. TELEX 19152 NOPAT N. Ed. Fredny Bade. illus.; pat. circ. 270. **Document type:** government publication.
 Formerly (until 1992): Norsk Tidende for det Industrielle Rettsvern. Del 3: Moenstre (ISSN 0029-2184)

346.048 NO ISSN 0803-6969
 CODEN: NOPAEG
NORSK PATENTTIDENDE. 1911. w. NOK 1000($30) Patentstyret - Norwegian Patent Office, Koebenhavngate 10, P.O. Box 8160 Dep., N-0033 Oslo, Norway. TEL 47-22-38-73-00. FAX 47-22-38-73-01. TELEX 19152 NOPAT N. Ed. Jon Sveinungsen. abstr.; pat.; index. circ. 445. **Indexed:** Chem.Abstr. **Document type:** government publication.
 —CASDDS.
 Formerly (until 1992): Norsk Tidende for det Industrielle Rettsvern. Del 1: Patenter (ISSN 0029-2206)

346.048 NO ISSN 0803-6977
 CODEN: NTAVA
NORSK VAREMERKETIDENDE. 1911. w. NOK 800($30) Patentstyret - The Norwegian Patent Office, Koebenhavngate 10, P.O. Box 8160, Dep., N-0033 Oslo, Norway. TEL 47-22-38-73-00. FAX 47-22-38-73-01. TELEX 19152 NOPAT N. Ed. Fredny Bade. illus.; tr.mk.; index. circ. 330. **Document type:** government publication.
 Formerly (until 1992): Norsk Tidende for det Industrielle Rettsvern. Del 2: Varemerker (ISSN 0029-2192)

340 AU ISSN 0029-8883
OESTERREICHISCHE AUTORENZEITUNG. 1896. q. free. Staatlich Genehmigte Gesellschaft der Autoren, Komponisten, Musikverleger, Baumannstr. 10, A-1030 Vienna, Austria. TEL 0222-71714-0. FAX 0222-71714-107. Ed. Ernst Perbin-Vogl. adv.; bk.rev.; illus.; index. circ. 18,000. **Indexed:** Music Ind., RILM. **Document type:** bulletin.

340 AU ISSN 0029-8921
OESTERREICHISCHE BLAETTER FUER GEWERBLICHEN RECHTSSCHUTZ UND URHEBERRECHT. 1952. bi-m. (4/yr. with Rundfunkrecht). S.1980. (Oesterreichische Vereinigung fuer Gewerblichen Rechtsschutz und Urheberecht) Manzsche Verlags- und Universitaetsbuchhandlung GmbH, Kohlmarkt 16, A-1014 Vienna, Austria. TEL 01-531610. FAX 01-53161181. Eds. Guido Kucsko, Helmut Gamerith. adv.; bk.rev.; index. circ. 900. (also avail. in microfilm; microfiche) **Document type:** bulletin.

602.7 AU ISSN 0029-9782
OESTERREICHISCHER MARKENANZEIGER. 1948. m. S.1300. Oesterreichisches Patentamt, Kohlmarkt 8-10, A-1014 Vienna, Austria. FAX 01-53424520. TELEX 136847. tr.mk.; index. circ. 190. **Document type:** government publication.

602.7 AU
OESTERREICHISCHER MUSTERANZEIGER. 1991. m. S.1300. Oesterreichisches Patentamt, Kohlmarkt 8-10, A-1014 Vienna, Austria. FAX 01-53424520. TELEX 136847-OEPA-A. circ. 120. **Document type:** government publication.

608.7 AU
OESTERREICHISCHER PATENTINHABER- UND ERFINDERVERBAND; Ideen, Erfindungen, Neuheiten. 1909. q. S.80. Oesterreichischer Patentinhaber- und Erfinderverband, Arsenal, Objekt 219, A-1030 Vienna 1, Austria. TEL 0222-789371. FAX 0222-789371.

608.7 AU
▼**OESTERREICHISCHES GEBRAUCHSMUSTERBLATT.** 1994. m. S.660. Oesterreichisches Patentamt, Kohlmarkt 8-10, A-1014 Vienna, Austria. FAX 01-53424520. circ. 100. **Document type:** government publication.

608.7 AU ISSN 0029-9944
 CODEN: ORPBAD
OESTERREICHISCHES PATENTBLATT. 1899. m. (in 2 parts). S.3500. Oesterreichisches Patentamt, Kohlmarkt 8-10, A-1014 Vienna, Austria. FAX 01-53424520. TELEX 136847. bibl.; charts; illus.; pat.; index. circ. 330. **Document type:** government publication.
 Description: Decisions and statistics concerning patents, utility models, trademarks and industrial designs.

608.7 602.7 IE ISSN 0030-0349
OFFICIAL JOURNAL OF INDUSTRIAL AND COMMERCIAL PROPERTY. 1928. fortn. I£155. Government Publications Sales Office, Sun Alliance House, Molesworth St., Dublin 2, Ireland. charts; pat.; tr.mk.; index. **Document type:** government publication.

ONLINE PATENTS, TRADEMARKS, AND SERVICEMARKS DATABASES. see *LIBRARY AND INFORMATION SCIENCES — Computer Applications*

602.7 608.7 CN ISSN 0849-3154
P T I C BULLETIN. 1967. 10/yr. membership. Patent and Trademark Institute of Canada, Box 1298, Sta. B, Ottawa, ON K1P 5R3, Canada. TEL 613-234-0516. Ed. W.J. Galloway. circ. controlled. (looseleaf format) **Document type:** newsletter.
 Formerly: P T I C Newsletter (ISSN 0380-6375)

346.04 608.7 US
PATENT ALTERNATIVE DISPUTE RESOLUTION HANDBOOK. a. $85. Clark - Boardman - Callaghan Company Ltd., 375 Hudson St., New York, NY 10014. TEL 212-929-7500; 800-221-9428. FAX 212-924-0460. Ed.Bd.
 Description: Examines the multitude of options available to solve a client's problems outside of court using the many forums available for Alternative Dispute Resolution.

608.7 346.04 UK
PATENT AND DESIGN YEARBOOK. (Supplement to: Managing Intellectual Property (ISSN 0960-5002)) a. Euromoney Publications plc., Nestor House, Playhouse Yard, London EC4V 5EX, England. TEL 0171-779-8709. FAX 0171-779-8932. Ed. Jeremy Phillips. **Document type:** trade publication.
 Description: Discusses patent and design issues in countries throughout the world.

608.7 CN ISSN 0079-015X
PATENT AND TRADEMARK INSTITUTE OF CANADA. ANNUAL PROCEEDINGS. 1928. a. membership. Patent and Trademark Institute of Canada, Box 1298, Sta. B, Ottawa, ON K1P 5R3, Canada. TEL 613-234-0516. circ. controlled. **Document type:** proceedings.

340 US
PATENT AND TRADEMARK OFFICE NOTICES. w. $83 (foreign $103.75). U.S. Patent and Trademark Office, General Information Services Division, Washington, DC 20231. TEL 703-308-4357. FAX 703-305-7786. (Subscr. to: Superintendent of Documents, U.S. Government Printing Office, Box 371954, Pittsburgh, PA 15250-7954. TEL 202-512-1800. FAX 202-512-2250) **Document type:** government publication.
 Description: Publishes the notices in each weekly edition of the Official Gazette.

602.7 US ISSN 0882-9098
K16
PATENT AND TRADEMARK OFFICE SOCIETY. JOURNAL. 1985. m. Patent and Trademark Office Society, Box 2600, Arlington, VA 22202. (also avail. in microfiche from WSH; reprint service avail. from WSH)
 —Faxon; SWETS. CCC.

346.04 608.7 US
PATENT APPLICATIONS HANDBOOK. a. $95. Clark - Boardman - Callaghan Company Ltd., 375 Hudson St., New York, NY 10014. TEL 212-929-7500; 800-221-9428. FAX 212-924-0460. Ed. Stephen A. Becker.
 Description: Provides guidelines for preparing and prosecuting patent applications.

643.3 608.7 US
PATENT DIGEST. 1946? m. $60. Gas Appliance Manufacturers Association, 1901 N. Moore St., Ste. 1100, Arlington, VA 22209. TEL 703-525-9565. FAX 703-525-8159.
 Description: Reports on relevant patents. Excerpted from Offical Gazette of the U.S. Patent Office.

608.7 602.7 SA ISSN 0031-286X
T319.S7 CODEN: PJIFEH
PATENT JOURNAL INCLUDING TRADEMARKS, DESIGNS AND COPYRIGHT. Key Title: Patentjoernaal Insluitende Handelsmerke, Modelle en Outeursreg. (Text in Afrikaans, English) 1948. m. R.12.50. Government Printer, Bosman St., Private Bag X85, Pretoria 0001, South Africa. TELEX 3230009. Ed. J. Barton. charts; illus.; pat.; tr.mk. **Indexed:** Chem.Abstr., RAPRA. **Document type:** government publication.
 —CASDDS.

PATENTS, TRADEMARKS AND COPYRIGHTS

340 US ISSN 0192-8198
KF3114
PATENT LAW HANDBOOK. a. $75. Clark - Boardman - Callaghan Company Ltd., 375 Hudson St., New York, NY 10014. TEL 212-929-7500; 800-221-9428. FAX 212-924-0460. Ed. Patricia N. Brantley.
—BLDSC (6410.543000).
Description: Comprehensive guide to current patent practice.

346.04 608.7 US
PATENT LAW: LEGAL AND ECONOMIC PRINCIPLES. 1992. a. Clark - Boardman - Callaghan Company Ltd., 375 Hudson St., New York, NY 10014. TEL 212-929-7500; 800-221-9428. Ed. John W. Schlicher.
Description: Describes patent law by explaining how the major rules of patent law relate to the purpose of a patent system. Also surveys how a law and economics approach applied to patent law.

608.7 SW ISSN 0347-500X
PATENT- OCH REGISTRERINGSVERKETS FOERFATTNINGSSAMLING; P R V F S. 1977-1987; resumed 1991. irreg. SEK 4 per page (effective 1991). Patentverket, P.O. Box 5055, S-102 42 Stockholm, Sweden.

608.7 CN ISSN 0008-4670
CODEN: PORCCI
PATENT OFFICE RECORD (CANADA)/GAZETTE DU BUREAU DES BREVETS. (Text and title in English and French) 1873. w. Can.$63($75.60) Industry Canada, Patent Office, 50 Victoria St., Hull, PQ K1A 0C9, Canada. TEL 819-997-2525. (Subscr. to: Supply and Services Canada, Order Adjustment Section, Rm. 2202, 45 Sacre Coeur Blvd., Hull, PQ K1A 0S9, Canada) Ed. Al Goncalves. adv.; bk.rev.; pat.; index. circ. 1,000. **Indexed:** Abstr.Bull.Inst.Pap.Chem., Chem.Abstr., E&P Hlth. (1993-), Gas Process.& Ppl. (1993-), Off.Tech. (1993-), Petrol.Abstr. (1961-). **Document type:** government publication.
—CASDDS; PADDS. **CCC.**
Formerly: Canadian Patent Office Record.
Description: Disseminates technological information, encourages the creation and exploitation of inventions, and informs the public of changes in practice and publishing jurisprudence in respect to patents.

608.7 II
PATENT OFFICE TECHNICAL SOCIETY. JOURNAL. (Text in English) vol.10, 1976. irreg. Rs.15. Patent Office Technical Society, 214, Acharya Jagadish Bose Rd., Calcutta 700 017, India. Ed. N.R. Seth. adv.; bk.rev.; pat.; stat. circ. 250. (also avail. in microfilm from WSH) **Indexed:** C.L.I., Leg.Per., SSCI.

608.7 UK ISSN 0950-2513
K1501.2 CODEN: PAWOEH
PATENT WORLD. 1987. 10/yr. £295($450) (effective Feb. 1995). Intellectual Property Publishing Ltd. (Subsidiary of: Armstrong Group Ltd.), Third Fl., Brigade House, Parsons Green, London SW6 4TH, England. TEL 0171-736-7111. FAX 0171-371-7806. Ed. Melissa Compton-Edwards. adv.; bk.rev. circ. 1,750. **Indexed:** Euro.LJI, LJI. **Document type:** trade publication.
—BLDSC (6412.250000); CASDDS; Ei.

608.7 GW ISSN 0031-2894
CODEN: PATBAR
PATENTBLATT. 1877. w. DM.896. (Deutsches Patentamt) Carl Heymanns Verlag KG, Luxemburgerstr. 449, 50939 Cologne, Germany. TEL 0221-94373-0. FAX 0221-94373901. circ. 1,850. **Indexed:** Abstr.Bull.Inst.Pap.Chem., Chem.Abstr. **Document type:** government publication.
—CASDDS.

602.7 608.7 DK ISSN 0904-275X
PATENTDIREKTORATET ORIENTERER. q. free. Patentdirektoratet, Helgeshoej Alle 81, DK-2630 Taastrup, Denmark. TEL 45-43-50-80-00. FAX 45-43-50-80-01. TELEX 16046 DPO DK.

608.7 YU ISSN 0031-2908
PATENTNI GLASNIK; Sluzbeni list Saveznog Zavoda za Patente. (Text in Croatian, Macedonian, Serbian, Slovenina) 1921. bi-m. 1800 din.($106.40) (effective Aug. 1991). Savezni Zavod za Patente, Uzun Mirkova 1, 11000 Belgrade, Yugoslavia. TEL 011-639-412. FAX 011-639-761. TELEX 12761 SZPAT YU. (Dist. by: Jugoslovenska Knjiga, Trg Republike 5-8, 11000 Belgrade, Yugoslavia) adv. contact: Blagota Zarkovic. illus.; pat.; index. circ. 900.

608.7 JA ISSN 0388-7081
PATENTS AND LICENSING. (Text in English) 1971. bi-m. $120 in Asia; N. America, Europe & Middle East $130; elsewhere $140 (effective 1996). I P L Communications Inc., Room 202, Sun Mansion, 1-11, Azabudai 1-chome, Minato-ku, Tokyo 106, Japan. TEL 03-3589-4749. FAX 03-3291-3764. Ed. Osahito Makiyama. adv.: page $6300. **Indexed:** JTA. **Document type:** trade publication.
Formerly: Patents and Engineering.
Description: Offers the latest information and data concerning intellectual property and licensing.

608.7 340 US
PATENTS AND THE FEDERAL CIRCUIT. (Supplement avail.) 1982. irreg., 3rd ed., 1994. $145. B N A Books (Subsidiary of: The Bureau of National Affairs), 1231 25th St., N.W., Washington, DC 20037. TEL 202-833-7470; 800-960-1220. FAX 202-833-7490. E-mail: books@bna.com. (Subscr. to: BNA Books Distribution Center, 300 Raritan Center Parkway, Box 7816, Edison, NJ 08818-7816. TEL 908-225-5555. FAX 908-417-0482) Ed. Robert L. Harmon.

608.7 340 US
PATENTS AND THE FEDERAL CIRCUIT. SUPPLEMENT. 1989. a. $45. B N A Books (Subsidiary of: The Bureau of National Affairs, Inc.), 1231 25th St., N.W., Washington, DC 20037. TEL 202-833-7470; 800-960-1220. FAX 202-833-7490. E-mail: books@bna.com. (Subscr. to: BNA Books Distribution Center, 300 Raritan Center Parkway, Box 7816, Edison, NJ 08818-7816. TEL 908-225-5555. FAX 908-417-0482) Ed. Robert L. Harmon.

608.7 PH
PHILIPPINE INVENTIONS. q. P.200 (foreign $50). Science and Technology Information Institute, Department of Science and Technology, P.O. Box 3596, Manila, Philippines. TEL 822-0764. (Subscr. to: Dept. of Science and Technology, Bicutan, Taguig, P.O. Box 2131, Manila, Philippines)

608.7 PL ISSN 0137-8015
POLAND. URZAD PATENTOWY. BIULETYN/POLAND. PATENT OFFICE. BULLETIN. 1973. bi-w. 390000 Zl.($520) Urzad Patentowy, Al. Niepodleglosci 188, Warsaw, Poland. TEL 48 22 25-05-84. FAX 48-22-250581. (Dist. by: Ars Polona-Ruch, Krakowskie Przedmiescie 7, Warsaw, Poland) illus. circ. 2,400.

608.7 PL ISSN 0043-5201
CODEN: WIUPA3
POLAND. URZAD PATENTOWY. WIADOMOSCI/POLAND. PATENT OFFICE. NEWS. (Text in Polish; summaries in English and Russian) 1924. m. 156000 Zl.($153) Urzad Patentowy, Al. Niepodleglosci 188, Warsaw, Poland. TEL 48 22 25-05-84. (Dist. by: Ars Polona-Ruch, Krakowskie Przedmiescie 7, Warsaw, Poland) adv.
—CASDDS.

608.7 RU ISSN 0208-2888
PROMYSHLENNYE OBRAZTSY. TOVARNYE ZNAKI. 1924. 4/yr. Vsesoyuznyi Nauchno-Issledovatel'skii Institut Patentnoi Informatsii (VNIIPI), Raushskaya nab. 4, 113035 Moscow, Russia. TEL 7-095-2393010. FAX 7-095-2311121. TELEX 411093 POISK SU. (Subscr. to: NPO "Poisk", Raushskaya nab. 4, 113834, Moscow, Russia) Ed. V.A. Lukanin. adv. circ. 6,375. (also avail. in microfiche; microfilm)
Supersedes in part (in 1983): Otkrytiya, Izobreteniya, Promyshlennye Obraztsy, Tovarnye Znaki (ISSN 0007-4020)
Description: Publishes information about industrial designs, trademarks; contains their graphic representation; also includes information about any relevant changes.

381 FR ISSN 0338-6473
PROPRIETE INDUSTRIELLE BULLETIN DOCUMENTAIRE. 24/yr. 660 F. (Europe 770 F., elsewhere 1100 F.). (Institut National de la Propriete Industrielle) Documentation Francaise, 29 Quai Voltaire, 75344 Paris Cedex 07, France. TEL 1-40-15-70-00. FAX 40-15-72-30. (Subscr. to: 124 rue Henri Barbusse, 93308 Aubervilliers Cedex, France. TEL 48-39-56-00. FAX 48-39-56-01) abstr.; pat. circ. 1,200. (also avail. in microfiche from DFR; back issues avail.) **Document type:** government publication.
Description: Contains information and reports of French and foreign case law and literature in the field of industrial property.

340 UN
LA PROPRIETE INDUSTRIELLE ET LE DROIT D'AUTEUR. English edition: Industrial Property and Copyright. 1885. m. 210 SFr. in Europe; rest of world 300 SFr. World Intellectual Property Organization (WIPO) - Organisation Mondiale de la Propriete Intellectuelle, Publications Sales and Distribution Unit, 34 Chemin des Colombettes, CH-1211 Geneva 20, Switzerland. TEL 022-730-9111. FAX 022-733-5428. TELEX 412912-OMPI-CG. adv.; bk.rev.; charts; index. circ. 700. (also avail. in microfiche; back issues avail.)
Formed by the 1995 merger of (1885-1995): Droit d'Auteur (ISSN 0012-6365); (1885-1995): Propriete Industrielle (ISSN 0033-1430)
Description: Covers the developments, theory and practical applications of international copyright, neighboring rights and industrial property law.

608.7 BE ISSN 0034-1851
T267 CODEN: REBIA8
RECUEIL DES BREVETS D'INVENTION. (Text in Dutch or French) 1854. m. 3000 BEF (foreign 4000 BEF). Ministry of Economic Affairs, Office de la Propriete Industrielle - Dienst voor Industriele Eigendom, 154 Bd. E. Jacqmain, 1210 Brussels, Belgium. TEL 32-2-2064111. Ed.Bd. illus.; pat.; index. circ. 1,000. **Indexed:** RAPRA. **Document type:** government publication.
●Also available online. Vendor(s): BELINDIS.
—BLDSC (7328.000000).

608.7 UK
REGISTER OF PATENT AGENTS. 1889. a. £5. Chartered Institute of Patent Agents, Staple Inn Bldgs., High Holborn, London WC1V 7PZ, England. TEL 0171-405-9450. FAX 0171-430-0471. adv. circ. 2,500. **Document type:** trade publication.

354.489 DK ISSN 0107-590X
REGISTER OVER DANSKE PATENTER UDSTEDT. 1970. a. DKK 400. Patentdirektoratet, Helgeshoej Alle 81, DK-2630 Taastrup, Denmark. TEL 45-43-50-80-00. FAX 45-43-50-80-01.

608.7 338 UK ISSN 0374-4353
CODEN: RSDSBB
RESEARCH DISCLOSURE. 1960. m. £99($165) Kenneth Mason Publications Ltd., 12 North St., Emsworth, Hants. PO10 7DQ, England. TEL 44-1243-377977. FAX 44-1243-379136. **Indexed:** Abstr.Bull.Inst.Pap.Chem., Dairy Sci.Abstr., Food Sci.& Tech.Abstr., Int.Packag.Abstr., Paper & Bd.Abstr., Text.Tech.Dig., World Text.Abstr. **Document type:** bulletin.
—BLDSC (7738.873000); CASDDS. **CCC.**

340 608.7 MX ISSN 0035-0044
REVISTA MEXICANA DE LA PROPIEDAD INDUSTRIAL Y ARTISTICA. 1963. s-a. Mex.$250($14) David Rangel Medina, Ed. & Pub., Cerrada de Xitle No. 19, Pedregal San Angel, Mexico 20, D.F., Mexico. bk.rev.; illus.; pat.; tr.mk.; index. circ. 1,000.

340 RM ISSN 1220-3009
REVISTA ROMANA DE PROPRIETATE INDUSTRIALA/ROMANIAN REVIEW FOR INDUSTRIAL PROPERTY. (Text in Rumanian; summaries in English, French, German) 1961. q. $200 or exchange basis. Oficiul de Stat pentru Inventii si Marci (OSIM) - State Office for Inventions and Trademarks, 5, Ion Ghica St., Sect. 3, 70418 Bucharest, Rumania. FAX 40-1-3123819. TELEX 11370 ROPAT R. adv. contact: Valeriu Geambazu.
Supersedes in part (in 1991): Buletinul de Inventii si Inovatii - Bulletin for Inventions and Innovations.

PATENTS, TRADEMARKS AND COPYRIGHTS

608   FR   ISSN 0242-1623
T201
REVUE INTERNATIONALE DE LA PROPRIETE INDUSTRIELLE ET ARTISTIQUE. 1883. q. 480 F. (effective 1995). Union des Fabricants pour la Protection de la Propriete Industrielle et Artistique, 16 rue de la Faisanderie, 75116 Paris, France. TEL 33-1-45-01-51-11. FAX 33-1-47-04-91-22. Ed. Francois Eyssette. bk.rev.; illus.; tr.mk.; index. circ. 1,800. **Document type:** bulletin.
—SWETS.

340 070 850   FR   ISSN 0035-3515
REVUE INTERNATIONALE DU DROIT D'AUTEUR. (Text in English, French and Spanish) 1953. q. 910 F. 225 av. Charles de Gaulle, 92200 Neuilly, France. FAX 47-15-47-83. bk.rev.; abstr.; index. **Indexed:** ELLIS, RILM.
—SWETS.

308.7 346.04 615
660   US
ROYALTY RATE REPORT FOR THE PHARMACEUTICAL & BIOTECHNOLOGY INDUSTRIES. a. $895 (renewals $250). Intellectual Property Research Associates, 1004 Buckingham Way, Yardley, PA 19067. TEL 215-428-1163. FAX 215-428-1163. Ed. Russell L. Parr.
Description: Contains financial information about technology transfers. Presents financial details about pharmaceutical and biotechnology intellectual property strategic alliances primarily focusing on license fees and royalty rates.

608.7   SZ   ISSN 0036-7974
SCHWEIZERISCHES PATENT-, MUSTER- UND MARKENBLATT/FEUILLE SUISSE DES BREVETS, DESSINS ET MARQUES/FOGLIO SVIZZERO DEI BREVETTI, DISEGNI E MARCHI. (Text in French, German and partly in Italian) 1962. s-m. 456 SFr. (foreign 472 SFr.) for all sections (Edition C); 238 SFr.(foreign 250 SFr.) for trademark section (Edition B); 262 SFr.(foreign 274 SFr.) for patent and design section (Edition A). Bundesamt fuer geistiges Eigentum - Intellectual Property Office, Einsteinstr. 2, CH-3003 Bern, Switzerland. TEL 031-3224967. FAX 031-3224895. (Subscr. to: Binkert AG, Druck und Verlag, CH-4335 Laufenberg, Switzerland.) Ed. Carolle von Ins. adv.; charts; illus.; pat.; index. circ. 255. **Document type:** government publication.

608.7   JA   ISSN 0385-6909
SHADAN HOJIN NIHON KOKUSAI KOGYO SHOYUKEN HOGO KYOKAI GEPPO/INTERNATIONAL ASSOCIATION FOR THE PROTECTION OF INDUSTRIAL PROPERTY. JAPANESE GROUP. JOURNAL. International edition: A.I.P.P.I. Japanese Group. Journal (International Edition (ISSN 0385-8863) (Text in Japanese) 1956. m. 500 Yen per no. Nihon Kokusai Kogyo Shoyuken Hogo Kyokai - International Association for the Protection of Industrial Property, Japanese Group, 8-1, Toranomon 2-chome, Minato-ku, Tokyo 105, Japan. **Document type:** academic/scholarly publication.

608.7   JA
SHINKETSU KOHO/TRIAL DECISION JOURNAL. (Text in Japanese) 1938. 15/m. Tokkyocho - Patent Office, 4-3, Kasumigaseki 3-chome, Chiyoda-ku, Tokyo 100, Japan.

608.781   SW   ISSN 0346-2196
CODEN: SPTGBB
SVENSK PATENTTIDNING; tidningen foer kungoerelser om patentansoekningar och patent. (Supplement avail.: Svensk Patenttidnings Kumulerade Namnregister (ISSN 0347-898X)) 1968. w. SEK 500. Patent- och Registreringsverket, Patentverket, P.O. Box 5055, S-102 42 Stockholm, Sweden.
—CASDDS.

608.781   SW   ISSN 0347-898X
SVENSK PATENTTIDNINGS KUMULERADE NAMNREGISTER. (Supplement to: Svensk Patenttidning (ISSN 0346-2196)) 1977. m. SEK 500. Patent- och Registreringsverket, Patentverket, P.O. Box 5055, S-102 42 Stockholm, Sweden.

608.7   SW   ISSN 0348-324X
SVENSK VARUMAERKESTIDNING. KUNGOERELSE A. (Supplement avail.: Varumaerkesstatistik) 1885. w. SEK 800 (effective 1991). Patent- och Registreringsverket - Patent and Registration Office, P.O. Box 5055, S-102 42 Stockholm, Sweden. illus.; stat.; tr.mk. circ. 640.
Former titles (until 1978): Registrering foer Varumaerken. A; (until 1934): Registreringstidning foer Varumaerken; (until 1886): Registreringstidning foer Varumaerken. Serien A.

608.7   SW   ISSN 0348-3258
SVENSK VARUMAERKESTIDNING. REGISTRERADE VARUMAERKEN. B. (Supplement avail.: Varumaerkesstatistik) 1885. w. SEK 800. Patent- och Registreringsverket - Patent and Registration Office, P.O. Box 5055, S-102 42 Stockholm, Sweden. illus. circ. 640.
Former titles (until 1978): Registreringstidning foer Varumaerken. B; (until 1934): Registreringstidning foer Varumaerken; (until 1886): Registreringstidning foer Varumaerken. Serien B.

608.87   SW   ISSN 0348-3266
SVENSK VARUMAERKESTIDNING. REGISTRERINGSTIDNING FOER VARUMAERKEN. C. (Supplement avail.: Varumaerkesstatistik) 1961. w. SEK 600 (effective 1991). Patent- och Registreringsverket - Patent and Registration Office, P.O. Box 5055, S-102 42 Stockholm, Sweden. illus. circ. 480.
Formerly (until 1978): Registreringstidning foer Varumaerken. C (ISSN 0347-3465)

602.7   SW
SVENSKT VARUMAERKESARKIV/SWEDISH TRADEMARK ARCHIVE; computer-indexed microfiche archive including full information about registered trademarks and pending applications. 1976. a. (in 2 vols., plus w. updates). SEK 6400. Patent- och Registreringsverket - Patent and Registration Office, Box 5055, S-102 42 Stockholm, Sweden.

608   SW
SWEDEN. PATENT- OCH REGISTERERINGSVERKET. AARSBERAETTELSE. 1965. a. free. Patent- och Registreringsverket - Patent and Regitration Office, Box 5055, S-102 42 Stockholm, Sweden. pat.; stat. circ. 3,000.

608.7 602.7   HU   ISSN 0039-8071
T265.5
SZABADALMI KOZLONY ES VEDJEGYERTESITO/PATENT AND TRADE MARK REVIEW. (Text in Hungarian; summaries in English, French, German, Russian) 1896. m. $63. (Orszagos Szabadalmi Hivatal) Lapkiado Vallalat, Lenin korut 9-11, 1073 Budapest 7, Hungary. TEL 222-408. (Subscr. to: Kultura, Box 149, H-1389 Budapest, Hungary) Ed. Laszlo Mezey. pat. (avail. on records) **Indexed:** C.R.I.Abstr., C.R.I.Curr.Cont.

T M A TRADEMARK REPORT. see TOBACCO

608.7   SP   ISSN 0040-179X
TECNICA E INVENCION. 1954. m. $10. Princesa 14, 28008 Madrid, Spain. TEL 2414800. Ed. F. Garcia Cabrerizo. adv.; bibl.; illus.; pat.; circ. 3,000 (controlled).

608.7   JA   ISSN 0285-3353
TOKKYO/PATENTS. (Text in Japanese) 1971. m. 160 Yen per no. Hatsumei Kyokai - Japan Institute of Invention and Innovation, 9-14, Toranomon 2-chome, Minato-ku, Tokyo 105, Japan. (Co-sponsor: Tokkyocho Somubu - Patent Office, General Administration Division) **Document type:** government publication.

608.7   JA   ISSN 0385-9142
TOKKYO NYUSU/PATENT NEWS. (Text in Japanese) 1961. d. Tsusho Sangyo Chosakai - Research Institute on International Trade and Industry, 8-9 Ginza 2-chome, Chuo-ku, Tokyo 104, Japan.

608.7   JA   ISSN 0385-5562
TOKKYO RYUTSU JOHO/PATENT CLEARING INFORMATION. (Text in Japanese) 1976. q. 2000 Yen. Hatsumei Kyokai, Tokkyo Ryutsu Senta - Japan Institute of Invention and Innovation, Patent Clearing Center, 9-14, Toranomon 2-chome, Minato-ku, Tokyo 105, Japan.

608.7   JA
TOKKYO SHUTSUGAN SHOBUN KENSAKUHYO/REFERENCE TABLES OF DISPOSED PATENT APPLICATION. (Text in Japanese) 1967. a. 12000 Yen. Nihon Tokkyo Joho Kiko - Japan Patent Information Organization, 1-7, Toyo 4-chome, Koto-ku, Tokyo 135, Japan.

608.7   JA
TOKKYOCHO NENPO/PATENT OFFICE. ANNUAL GAZETTES. (Text in Japanese) 1948. a. 1090 Yen. Tokkyocho, Somubu - Patent Office, General Administration Division, 4-3 Kasumigaseki 3-chome, Chiyoda-ku, Tokyo 100, Japan. **Document type:** government publication.

608.7   JA
TOKUGIKON/JAPANESE PATENT OFFICE SOCIETY. JOURNAL. (Text in Japanese) 1960. bi-m. Tokkyocho Gijutsu Konwakai - Japanese Patent Office Society, Tokkyocho, 4-3 Kasumigaseki 3-chome, Chiyoda-ku, Tokyo 100, Japan.

602.04 346.04   UK
TRADE MARK YEARBOOK. (Supplement to: Managing Intellectual Property (ISSN 0960-5002)) a. Euromoney Publications plc., Nestor House, Playhouse Yard, London EC4V 5EX, England. TEL 0171-779-8686. FAX 0171-779-8500. Ed. Jeremy Phillips; Pub. Dominic Carman. **Document type:** trade publication.
Description: Discusses trade mark issues in many nations worldwide.

608.7 602.7   CN   ISSN 0041-0438
T226.V1
TRADE MARKS JOURNAL/JOURNAL DES MARQUES DE COMMERCE; consumer and corporate affairs. (Catalogue no. RG42-2) (Text in English and French) 1954. w. Can.$72($86.40) Supply and Services Canada, Ottawa, ON K1A 0S9, Canada. TEL 819-997-2560. illus.; tr.mk. circ. 799.

608.7 602.7   UK   ISSN 0041-0446
TRADE MARKS JOURNAL.* 1876. w. £275. Patent Office, Government Bldgs., Cardiff Rd., Newport, Gwent NP9 1RH, Wales. TEL 01633-812034. adv.; illus. circ. 900. **Indexed:** Intl.Polym.Sci.& Tech., RAPRA, RAPRA. **Document type:** government publication.
—CCC.

608.7 340   IS   ISSN 0334-2425
TRADE MARKS JOURNAL. (Text in English and Hebrew) 1968. m. Distribution Service of Government Publications, 29-B St., Hakirya, Tel Aviv, Israel.

608.7   US   ISSN 0082-5786
T223.V4
TRADEMARK REGISTER OF THE UNITED STATES. 1958. a. $335. Trademark Register, National Press Bldg., 1297, Washington, DC 20045. TEL 202-662-1233. FAX 202-347-4408. Ed. Cyril W. Sernak. adv.; cum.index: 1881-1991. **Document type:** directory.
●Also available online.
Description: Lists all trademarks registered with the U.S. patent and trademark office plus owner data and product information.

602.7   US
TRADEMARK REGISTRATION PRACTICE. base vol. (plus s-a. updates). $120. Clark - Boardman - Callaghan Company Ltd., 375 Hudson St., New York, NY 10014. TEL 212-929-7500; 800-221-9428. FAX 212-924-0460. Ed. James E. Hawes. (looseleaf format)
Description: Covers the handling of federal trademark applications by the U.S. Patent and Trademark Office, beginning with receipt of the application and ending with the issuance of the registration.

602.7   US   ISSN 0041-056X
K24
TRADEMARK REPORTER. (Former name of issuing body: United States Trademark Association) 1911. bi-m. membership. International Trademark Association, 1133 Sixth Ave., New York, NY 10036-6710. TEL 212-768-9887. FAX 212-768-7796. Ed. Steven M. Weinberg. bk.rev.; charts; index, cum.index: 1937-1950, 1951-1960; every 5 yrs. thereafter. circ. 3,200. (also avail. in microfilm from UMI; reprint service avail. from WSH) **Indexed:** C.L.I., L.R.I., Leg.Per. **Document type:** trade publication.
—UMI; UnCover.

PATENTS, TRADEMARKS AND COPYRIGHTS

602.75 UK ISSN 0950-2564
TRADEMARK WORLD. 1986. 10/yr. £295($450) (effective Feb. 1995). Intellectual Property Publishing Ltd. (Subsidiary of: Armstrong Group Ltd.), Third Fl., Brigade House, Parsons Green, London SW6 4TH, England. TEL 0171-736-7111. FAX 0171-371-7806. Ed. Barbara Frenes. adv. **Indexed:** Euro.LJI, LJI. **Document type:** trade publication.
—BLDSC (8881.030930).

608.7 GW ISSN 0041-1310
TRANSPATENT. 1949. 18/yr. DM.576. Transpatent GmbH, Gogrevestr. 11, 40223 Duesseldorf, Germany. TEL 0211-312073. FAX 0211-319784. TELEX 8587428-TTKR. Ed. H.-Jochen Krieger. adv.; bk.rev.; pat.

UNFAIR COMPETITION AND THE I T C. see *BUSINESS AND ECONOMICS — International Commerce*

622 608.7 US
U.S. BUREAU OF MINES. OFFICE OF TECHNOLOGY TRANSFER. PATENTS. irreg. free. U.S. Bureau of Mines, Office of Technology Transfer, Washington, DC 20240. TEL 202-501-9323. **Document type:** government publication.

341.7582 US ISSN 0090-2845
U.S. COPYRIGHT OFFICE. ANNUAL REPORT OF THE REGISTER OF COPYRIGHTS. Key Title: Annual Report of the Register of Copyrights. 1910. a. price varies. U.S. Library of Congress, Copyright Office, First St., N.E., Washington, DC 20559. (Dist. by: Superintendent of Documents, U.S. Government Printing Office, Box 371954, Pittsburgh, PA 15250-7954. TEL 202-512-1800. FAX 202-512-2250) **Document type:** government publication.

608.7 US ISSN 0083-3002
U.S. PATENT AND TRADEMARK OFFICE. ANNUAL REPORT OF THE COMMISSIONER OF PATENTS. 1837. a. price varies. U.S. Patent and Trademark Office, Washington, DC 20231. TEL 703-557-3341. (Subscr. to: Supt. of Documents, Washington, DC 20402)

608.7 US ISSN 0083-3010
U.S. PATENT AND TRADEMARK OFFICE. CLASSIFICATION BULLETINS. irreg. price varies. U.S. Patent and Trademark Office, Washington, DC 20231. TEL 703-557-3341. (Subscr. to: Supt. of Documents, Washington, DC 20402)

608.7 US
U.S. PATENT AND TRADEMARK OFFICE. GUIDE FOR THE PREPARATION OF PATENT DRAWINGS. a. $15. U.S. Patent and Trademark Office, General Information Services Division, Crystal Plaza 3, Rm. 2C02, Washington, DC 20231. TEL 703-308-4357. FAX 703-305-7786. (Orders to: Superintendent of Documents, U.S. Government Printing Office, Box 371954, Pittsburgh, PA 15250-7954) illus. **Document type:** government publication.
Description: Collates and interprets the most pertinent rules from the Code of Federal Regulations, Title 37, Section 1, pertaining to patent illustrations.

608.7 US ISSN 0362-0719
T223 CODEN: INPADL
U.S. PATENT AND TRADEMARK OFFICE. INDEX OF PATENTS ISSUED. (Issued in 2 parts: Part 1, List of Patentees (in 2 vols.); Part 2, Index to Subjects of Inventions) 1920. a. price varies. U.S. Patent and Trademark Office, General Information Services Division, Crystal Park, Bldg. 2, 2121 Crystal Dr., Arlington, VA 22202. TEL 703-308-4357. FAX 703-305-7786. (Subscr. to: Superintendent of Documents, U.S. Government Printing Office, Box 371954, Pittsburgh, PA 15250-7954. TEL 202-512-1800. FAX 202-512-2250; Or: Bernan, 4611-F Assembly Dr., Lanham, MD 20706. TEL 301-459-7666. FAX 301-459-0056) (also avail. in microform from PMC) **Document type:** government publication.
—CASDDS.
Formerly: U.S. Patent Office. Index of Patents Issued from the United States Patent Office (ISSN 0083-3037)
Description: Lists every patentee or assignee recorded when the patent document was issued; lists all patents for the year by U.S. Patent Classification class and official subclass.

608.7 US
U.S. PATENT AND TRADEMARK OFFICE. MANUAL OF CLASSIFICATION. base vol., plus s-a. updates. $82 (foreign $102.50) (includes Index to the U.S. Patent Classification System). U.S. Patent and Trademark Office, General Information Services Division, Crystal Plaza 3, Rm. 2C02, Washington, DC 20231. TEL 703-308-4357. FAX 703-305-7786. (Subscr. to: Superintendent of Documents, U.S. Government Printing Office, Box 371954, Pittsburgh, PA 15250-7954. TEL 202-512-1800. FAX 202-512-2250) (looseleaf format) **Document type:** government publication.
Description: Presents and lists descriptive titles of about 420 classes and 118,000 subclasses into which patented subject matter is classified.

608.7 US
U.S. PATENT AND TRADEMARK OFFICE. MANUAL OF PATENT EXAMINING PROCEDURE. base vol., with q. updates. $97 (foreign $121.25). U.S. Patent and Trademark Office, General Information Services Division, Crystal Plaza 3, Rm. 2C02, Washington, DC 20231. TEL 703-308-4357. FAX 703-305-7786. (Subscr. to: Superintendent of Documents, U.S. Government Printing Office, Box 371954, Pittsburgh, PA 15250-7954. TEL 202-512-1800. FAX 202-512-2250) (looseleaf format) **Document type:** government publication.
Description: Demonstrates the practices and procedures for prosecuting patent applications.

608.7 US ISSN 0098-1133
T223 CODEN: OGUPE7
U.S. PATENT AND TRADEMARK OFFICE. OFFICIAL GAZETTE. PATENTS. 1872. w. $549 (foreign $686.25). U.S. Patent and Trademark Office, General Information Services Division, Crystal City Plaza 3, Rm. 2C02, Washington, DC 20231. TEL 703-308-4357. FAX 703-305-7786. (Subscr. to: Superintendent of Documents, U.S. Government Printing Office, Box 371954, Pittsburgh, PA 15250. TEL 202-512-1800. FAX 202-512-2250) annual indexes sold separately. (also avail. in microform from RPI,PMC; back issues avail.) **Indexed:** Abstr.Bull.Inst.Pap.Chem., Chem.Abstr., Intl.Polym.Sci.& Tech., Petrol.Abstr., RAPRA, World Text.Abstr. **Document type:** government publication.
●Also available on CD-ROM.
—BLDSC (6239.396000); CASDDS; PADDS; UMI.
Supersedes in part (in 1975): U.S. Patent Office. Official Gazette (ISSN 0041-8021)
Description: Compiles the patents, Patent Office notices, and designs issued each week.

602.7 US ISSN 0360-5132
T223.V5
U.S. PATENT AND TRADEMARK OFFICE. OFFICIAL GAZETTE. TRADEMARKS. 1872. w. $460 (foreign $575). U.S. Patent and Trademark Office, General Information Services Division, Crystal Plaza 3, Rm. 2C02, Washington, DC 20231. TEL 703-308-4357. FAX 703-305-7786. (Subscr. to: Superintendent of Documents, U.S. Government Printing Office, Box 371954, Pittsburgh, PA 15250-7954. TEL 202-512-1800. FAX 202-512-2250) (back issues avail.) **Indexed:** Intl.Polym.Sci.& Tech., Petrol.Abstr., RAPRA. **Document type:** government publication.
●Also available on CD-ROM.
—UMI.
Supersedes in part (in 1975): U.S. Patent Office. Official Gazette (ISSN 0041-8021)
Description: Compiles trademarks, trademark names, marks published for opposition, and trademark registrations issued each week.

608.7 US
U.S. PATENT AND TRADEMARK OFFICE. TECHNOLOGY ASSESSMENT AND FORECAST: PUBLICATIONS. irreg. price varies. U.S. Patent and Trademark Office, Office of Information Products Development, Crystal Plaza 2, Rm. 9D30, Washington, DC 20231. TEL 703-308-0322. FAX 703-308-0493. (Also avail. from: Superintendent of Documents, U.S. Government Printing Office, Box 371954, Pittsburgh, PA 15250-7954. TEL 202-512-1800. FAX 202-512-2250) **Document type:** monographic series, government publication.
Description: Surveys the U.S. patent activity of specific technologies or corporations.

602.7 US
U.S. PATENT AND TRADEMARK OFFICE. TRADEMARK MANUAL OF EXAMINING PROCEDURE. 2nd ed., 1993. base vol., plus s-a. updates. $19 (foreign $23.75). U.S. Patent and Trademark Office, General Information Services Division, Crystal Plaza 3, Rm. 2C02, Washington, DC 20231. TEL 703-308-4357. FAX 703-308-7786. (Subscr. to: Superintendent of Documents, U.S. Government Printing Office, Box 371954, Pittsburgh, PA 15250-7954. TEL 202-512-1800. FAX 202-512-2250) (looseleaf format) **Document type:** government publication.
Description: Provides trademark applicants and attorneys with a reference work on the practices and procedures for prosecuting applications to register a trademark at the U.S. Patent and Trademark Office.

608.7 US
U.S. PATENT CLASSIFICATION DEFINITIONS. base vol., plus s-a. updates. $167 (foreign $208.75). U.S. Patent and Trademark Office, General Information Services Division, Crystal Plaza 3, Rm. 2C02, Washington, DC 20231. TEL 703-308-4357. FAX 703-305-7786. (Subscr. to: Superintendent of Documents, U.S. Government Printing Office, Box 371954, Pittsburgh, PA 15250-7954. TEL 202-512-1800. FAX 202-512-2250) (microfiche) **Document type:** government publication.
Description: Gives a detailed definition for each class and official subclass in the Manual of Classification.

608.7 US ISSN 0041-803X
UNITED STATES PATENTS QUARTERLY. 1929. w. $1350 (effective July 1995). The Bureau of National Affairs, Inc., 1231 25th St., N.W., Washington, DC 20037. TEL 202-452-4200. FAX 202-822-8092. TELEX 285656 BNAI WSH. (Subscr. to: 9435 Key West Ave., Rockville, MD 20850. TEL 800-372-1033) Ed. Cynthia J. Bolbach. abstr.; pat.; tr.mk.; index, cum.index every 5 yrs. (back issues avail.)
●Also available online. Vendor(s): Knight-Ridder, Inc. (Patlaw, File 243), Orbit Search Service.
—CCC.
Description: Reports on decisions dealing with patents, trademarks, copyrights, unfair competition, trade secrets, and computer chip protection.

608.7 GW
VIERTELJAEHRLICHES NAMENSVERZEICHNIS ZUM PATENTBLATT. 1950. q. DM.168. Carl Heymanns Verlag KG, Luxemburgerstr. 449, 50939 Cologne, Germany. TEL 0221-94373-0. FAX 0221-94373901. circ. 950. **Document type:** directory.

341.7 US
WASHINGTON STATE BAR ASSOCIATION. INTELLECTUAL AND INDUSTRIAL PROPERTY SECTION. NEWSLETTER. 1983. irreg. $12. Washington State Bar Association, Intellectual and Industrial Property Section, 500 Westin Bldg., 2001 Sixth Ave., Seattle, WA 98121. TEL 206-727-8239. FAX 206-727-8320. **Document type:** newsletter.

608.7 US ISSN 1049-8168
T223.D7
WHO'S INVENTING WHAT?; tracking US patenting activities and trends. 1990. q. (includes a. cum.). $195. Gale Research Inc., 835 Penobscot Bldg., Detroit, MI 48226. TEL 800-877-4253. FAX 313-961-6083. TELEX 810-221-7086. Ed. Donna Wood.
Description: Reporting service on the 80,000-100,000 patents granted by the US Patent and Trademark Office each year. Entries are alphabetically listed by name of company or individual to whom the patents were assigned.

608.7 346.04 UK
WORLD I P CONTACTS HANDBOOK (YEAR). (Supplement to: Managing Intellectual Property (ISSN 0960-5002)) a. Euromoney Publications plc., Nestor House, Playhouse Yard, London EC4V 5EX, England. TEL 0171-779-8935. FAX 0171-779-8541. Ed. Jeremy Phillips; Pub. Dominic Carman. **Document type:** directory.
Description: Lists experts in intellectual property issues worldwide.

PATENTS, TRADEMARKS AND COPYRIGHTS — Abstracting, Bibliographies, Statistics

602.7 608.7   UK   ISSN 0952-7613
K1401.A13
WORLD INTELLECTUAL PROPERTY REPORT. 1987. m. £408($695) B N A International, Inc. (Subsidiary of: The Bureau of National Affairs, Inc.), Heron House, 10 Dean Farrar St., London SW1H 0DX, England. TEL 0171-222-8831. FAX 0171-222-5550. (U.S. addr.: 1231 25th St., N.W., Washington, DC 20037. TEL 202-542-4200) Ed. Joel Kolko. pat.; index. (back issues avail.) **Document type:** newsletter.
    Description: Provides information on copyright, trademark, and unfair-competition issues worldwide.

608.7   UK   ISSN 0172-2190
T210   CODEN: WPAID2
WORLD PATENT INFORMATION; international journal for patent documentation, classification & statistics. 1979. q. £230($366) (effective 1996). (Commission of the European Communities) Elsevier Science Ltd., Pergamon, P.O. Box 800, Kidlington, Oxford OX5 1DX, England. TEL 44-1865-843000. FAX 44-1865-843010. E-mail: nlinfo-f@elsevier.nl; usinfo-f@elsevier.com; forinfo-kyf04035@niftyserve.or.jp; Site addr.: http://www.elsevier.nl/. (Subscr. in U.S. and Canada to: Elsevier Science, 660 White Plains Rd., Tarrytown, NY 10591-5153. TEL 914-524-9200. FAX 914-333-2444) (Co-sponsor: World Intellectual Property Organization) Ed. V.S. Dodd. adv.: B&W page $550, color page $1350. circ. 1,200. (also avail. in microfilm from UMI; reprint service avail. from ISI,UMI) **Indexed:** BPIA, INSPEC, LISA, World Surf.Coat.
   —BLDSC (9356.973000); CASDDS; Ei; Faxon; SWETS; UMI; UnCover. **CCC.**
    Description: Provides a worldwide forum for the exchange of information among professionals working in the patents information and documentation field.
    Refereed Serial

608.7   US
WORLD PATENT LAW AND PRACTICE; patent statutes, regulations and treaties. 1974. 3/yr. $610. Matthew Bender & Co., Inc., 11 Penn Plaza, New York, NY 10001. TEL 212-967-7707. FAX 212-244-3188. (Subscr. to: International Dept., 1275 Broadway, Albany, NY 12204) Ed. John P. Sinnott. index. circ. 500. (looseleaf format)
    Description: Compilation of US and foreign patent statutes, regulations and treaties, and European Intellectual Property Decisions.

608.7   US   ISSN 0278-8047
T201
WORLD TECHNOLOGY; patent licensing gazette. 1968. bi-m. $152 (foreign $165). Techni Research Associates, Inc., Box T, Willow Grove, PA 19090-0922. TEL 610-657-1753. FAX 610-576-7924. Pub. Louis R. Schiffman. bk.rev.; pat. (looseleaf format; back issues avail.; reprint service avail.)
   —BLDSC (9360.068500); UMI.
    Formerly (until 1975): Patent Licensing Gazette (ISSN 0031-2878)
    Description: Covers chemical, mechanical, electrical and general discovery.

608.7 778.1   US   ISSN 0361-4190
T212
XEROX DISCLOSURE JOURNAL. 1976. bi-m. Xerox Corporation (Rochester), Xerox Sq. 020, Rochester, NY 14644. TEL 716-423-3255. Ed. Carole Ann Banke. illus.; index; circ. 500 (controlled). **Indexed:** Graph.Arts Lit.Abstr.
   —Faxon.

608.7   US
ZHONGGUO ZHUANLI BAO/PATENT REVIEW OF CHINA. (Text in Chinese) s-w. $67. China Books & Periodicals, Inc., 2929 24th St., San Francisco, CA 94110. TEL 415-282-2994. FAX 415-282-0994. **Document type:** newspaper.

608.7   FR   ISSN 0223-3398
B.O.P.I. DESSINS & MODELES. (Bulletin Officiel de la Propriete Industrielle) 1910. m. 60 F. Institut National de la Propriete Industrielle, 26 bis rue de St. Petersbourg, 75800 Paris Cedex 08, France. TEL 42-94-52-52. FAX 42-93-59-30. (Dist. by: Imprimerie Nationale, B.P. 514, 59505 Douai Cedex, France) index. circ. 400. (back issues avail.)
    Description: Contains the bibliographical data on the published industrial designs, arranged according to the international classification of industrial designs.

608.7   JA
BEIKOKU TOKKYO SHOROKU. DENKI HEN/U.S. PATENT ABSTRACTS. ELECTRICITY. (Text in Japanese) 1962. 2/m. 4900 Yen. Nihon Tokkyo Joho Kiko - Japan Patent Information Organization, 1-7, Toyo 4-chome, Koto-ku, Tokyo 135, Japan. **Document type:** abstracting/indexing.

608.7   JA
BEIKOKU TOKKYO SHOROKU. DENSHI, TSUSHIN HEN/U.S. PATENT ABSTRACTS. ELECTRONICS, COMMUNICATIONS. (Text in Japanese) 1962. 4/yr. 4900 Yen. Nihon Tokkyo Joho Kiko - Japan Patent Information Organization, 1-7, Toyo 4-chome, Koto-ku, Tokyo 135, Japan. **Document type:** abstracting/indexing.

608.7   JA
BEIKOKU TOKKYO SHOROKU. DORYOKU, DORYOKU KIKAI, BUTSURYU, BUNPAI, RYUTAI NO TORIATSUKAI HEN/U.S. PATENT ABSTRACTS. POWER, POWER MACHINE, PHYSICAL DISTRIBUTION, DISTRIBUTION, LIQUID HANDLING. (Text in Japanese) 1962. 3/m. 4900 Yen. Nihon Tokkyo Joho Kiko - Japan Patent Information Organization, 1-7, Toyo 4-chome, Koto-ku, Tokyo 135, Japan. **Document type:** abstracting/indexing.

608.7   JA
BEIKOKU TOKKYO SHOROKU. KAGAKU IPPAN, ORIMONO HEN/U.S. PATENT ABSTRACTS. GENERAL CHEMISTRY, TEXTILE. (Text in Japanese) 1962. 3/m. 4900 Yen. Nihon Tokkyo Joho Kiko - Japan Patent Information Organization, 1-7, Toyo 4-chome, Koto-ku, Tokyo 135, Japan. **Document type:** abstracting/indexing.

608.7   JA
BEIKOKU TOKKYO SHOROKU. KIKAI YOSO, KIKAI KOSAKU, ZATSUKIKAI HEN/U.S. PATENT ABSTRACTS. MACHINE ELEMENTS, MACHINE CONSTRUCTION, MISCELLANEOUS MACHINES. (Text in Japanese) 1962. 2/m. 4900 Yen. Nihon Tokkyo Joho Kiko - Japan Patent Information Organization, 1-7, Toyo 4-chome, Koto-ku, Tokyo 135, Japan. **Document type:** abstracting/indexing.

608.7   JA
BEIKOKU TOKKYO SHOROKU. MUKI KAGAKU, KINZOKU, BUKI DAN'YAKU HEN/U.S. PATENT ABSTRACTS. INORGANIC CHEMISTRY, METALS, ARMAMENT AND AMMUNITION. (Text in Japanese) 1962. 3/m. 4900 Yen. Nihon Tokkyo Joho Kiko - Japan Patent Information Organization, 1-7, Toyo 4-chome, Koto-ku, Tokyo 135, Japan. **Document type:** abstracting/indexing.

608.7   JA
BEIKOKU TOKKYO SHOROKU. OYO YUKI KAGAKU, NOSUISAN, IJUTSU HEN/U.S. PATENT ABSTRACTS. APPLIED ORGANIC CHEMISTRY, AGRICULTURE AND FISHERY, MEDICINE. (Text in Japanese) 1962. 3/m. 4900 Yen. Nihon Tokkyo Joho Kiko - Japan Patent Information Organization, 1-7, Toyo 4-chome, Koto-ku, Tokyo 135, Japan. **Document type:** abstracting/indexing.

608.7   JA
BEIKOKU TOKKYO SHOROKU. SOKUTEI, SEIMITSU KIKI, INSATSU, ONKYO, KYOIKU HEN/U.S. PATENT ABSTRACTS. MEASURING, PRECISION INSTRUMENT, PRINTING, SOUND RECORDING, EDUCATION. (Text in Japanese) 1962. 3/m. 4900 Yen. Nihon Tokkyo Joho Kiko - Japan Patent Information Organization, 1-7, Toyo 4-chome, Koto-ku, Tokyo 135, Japan.

608.7   JA
BEIKOKU TOKKYO SHOROKU. YUKI KAGAKU HEN/U.S. PATENT ABSTRACTS. ORGANIC CHEMISTRY. (Text in Japanese) 1962. 2/m. 4900 Yen. Nihon Tokkyo Joho Kiko - Japan Patent Information Organization, 1-7, Toyo 4-chome, Koto-ku, Tokyo 135, Japan. **Document type:** abstracting/indexing.

608.7   JA
BEIKOKU TOKKYO SHOROKU. YU'YU KIKAI, KENSETSU, DOBOKU HEN/U.S. PATENT ABSTRACTS. TRANSPORTING MACHINE, CONSTRUCTION, CIVIL ENGINEERING. (Text in Japanese) 1962. 3/m. 4900 Yen. Nihon Tokkyo Joho Kiko - Japan Patent Information Organization, 1-7, Toyo 4-chome, Koto-ku, Tokyo 135, Japan. **Document type:** abstracting/indexing.

608.7 016   UK   ISSN 0007-1609
BRITISH PATENTS ABSTRACTS.* 1951. w. $1470 for chemical, mechanical, electrical. Derwent Publications Ltd., 14 Great Queen St., London WC2B 5DF, England. (U.S. subscr. to: Derwent Inc., 1313 Dolley Madison Blvd., Suite 303, McLean, VA 22101) abstr.; illus. **Indexed:** Intl.Polym.Sci.& Tech., RAPRA. **Document type:** abstracting/indexing.

C A SELECTS. CERAMIC MATERIALS (PATENTS). see CERAMICS, GLASS AND POTTERY — Abstracting, Bibliographies, Statistics

540   US   ISSN 0734-8819
                      CODEN: CAPPEC
C A SELECTS. NOVEL POLYMERS FROM PATENTS. s-w. $220 to non-members; members $65 (effective 1996). Chemical Abstracts Service (Subsidiary of: American Chemical Society), 2540 Olentangy River Rd., Box 3012, Columbus, OH 43210-0012. TEL 614-447-3600. FAX 614-447-3713. TELEX 6842086. **Document type:** abstracting/indexing.
    Description: Covers patents mentioning newly reported polymeric materials.

C A SELECTS. PHARMACEUTICAL CHEMISTRY (PATENTS). see PHARMACY AND PHARMACOLOGY — Abstracting, Bibliographies, Statistics

340   US   ISSN 1050-5156
Z642
COPYRIGHT DIRECTORY: ATTORNEYS, PROFESSORS, GOVERNMENT AGENCIES, CONGRESSIONAL COMMITTEES, SEARCHERS, CLEARINGHOUSES, HOTLINES & ASSOCIATIONS, (YEAR). biennial. $79.95. Copyright Information Services, 1025 Vermont Ave., N.W., Ste. 820, Washington, DC 20005. TEL 206-378-5218. Ed.Bd.

016 608.7   KO
FOREIGN PATENTS INFORMATION BULLETIN. (Text in Korean) 1963. s-m. Korea Institute for Economics and Technology, P.O.B. 250, Seoul, S. Korea. pat. circ. 450. (reprint service avail. from UMI)
    Former titles: Current List on Foreign Patents; Current Bibliography on Foreign Patents.

608.7   US   ISSN 0161-9470
T223
INDEX TO THE U.S. PATENT CLASSIFICATION SYSTEM. irreg. (approx. a.). $16 (free with Manual of Classification). U.S. Patent and Trademark Office, General Information Services Division, Crystal Plaza 3, Rm. 2C02, Washington, DC 20231. TEL 703-308-4357. FAX 703-305-7786. (Subscr. to: Superintendent of Documents, U.S. Government Printing Office, Box 371954, Pittsburgh, PA 15250-7954. TEL 202-512-1800. FAX 202-512-2250; Or: Bernan, 4611-F Assembly Dr., Lanham, MD 20706. TEL 301-459-7666. FAX 301-459-0056) (microfiche) **Document type:** abstracting/indexing, government publication.
    Description: Lists about 65,000 common, informal headings of terms referring to classes or subclasses in the Manual of Classification.

608.7   UN   ISSN 1013-8374
T201
INDUSTRIAL PROPERTY, STATISTICS B. PART 1 - PATENTS/PROPRIETE INDUSTRIELLE, STATISTIQUES B. PARTIE 1 - BREVETS. (Text in English and French) a. 60 SFr. World Intellectual Property Organization (WIPO) - Organisation Mondiale de la Propriete Intellectuelle, Publications Sales and Distribution Unit, 34 chemin des Colombettes, CH-1211 Geneva 20, Switzerland. TEL 022-730-9111. FAX 022-733-5428. TELEX 412912-OMPI-CH. charts. circ. 250. (back issues avail.) **Indexed:** IIS.
—BLDSC (4459.835500).
   Supersedes in part (in 1985): Industrial Property, Statistics B (ISSN 0377-0044)
   Description: Covers year in question, with complete statistics on patent applications and patents granted to residents and nonresidents.

602.7 608.7   UN   ISSN 1013-8382
INDUSTRIAL PROPERTY, STATISTICS B. PART 2 - TRADEMARKS AND SERVICE MARKS, UTILITY MODELS, INDUSTRIAL DESIGNS, VARIETIES OF PLANTS, MICROORGANISMS/PROPRIETE INDUSTRIELLE, STATISTIQUES B. PARTIE 2 - MARQUES DE PRODUITS ET DES SERVICES, MODELES D'UTILITE, DESSINS ET MODELES INDUSTRIELS, OBTENTIONS VEGETALES, MICRO-ORGANISMES. (Text in English and French) a. 60 SFr. World Intellectual Property Organization (WIPO) - Organisation Mondiale de la Propriete Intellectuelle, Publications Sales and Distribution Unit, 34 chemin des Colombettes, CH-1211 Geneva 20, Switzerland. TEL 022-730-9111. FAX 022-733-5428. TELEX 412912-OMPI-CH. charts. (back issues avail.)
—BLDSC (4459.835500).
   Supersedes in part (in 1985): Industrial Property, Statistics B (ISSN 0377-0044)
   Description: Covers year in question with complete statistics on trademark and service mark applications and registrations by residents and nonresidents.

346.04 016   AT   ISSN 1032-7355
INTELLECTUAL PROPERTY REPORTS (NORTH RYDE, 1989); consolidated index and tables. 1989. a. Aus.$65. Butterworths, Division of Reed International Books Australia Pty. Ltd. (Subsidiary of: Reed Elsevier Australia Pty. Ltd.), 271-273 Lane Cove Rd., North Ryde, N.S.W. 2113, Australia. TEL 02-335-4444. FAX 02-335-4655.
   Description: Tables and index of cases reported, cases judicially considered, statutes, etc.

608.7   JA
JAPANESE PATENTS ABSTRACTS. EXAMINED.* 1962. w. $2640. Japan Patent Information Organization, Sato-Dia Bldg., 4-1-7, Toyo, Koto-ku, Tokyo 135, Japan. TEL 03-5690-5555. FAX 03-5690-5566.
   Former titles: Japanese Patents Report. Examined; Japanese Patents Report (ISSN 0011-913X); Japanese Patents Abstracts (ISSN 0021-5333)
   Description: Covers chemical abstracts exclusively.

608.7 016   US   ISSN 0091-0384
TL788.35
N A S A PATENT ABSTRACTS BIBLIOGRAPHY: A CONTINUING BIBLIOGRAPHY. SECTION 1. ABSTRACTS. 1969. s-a. $16.25 per no. U.S. National Aeronautics and Space Administration, Center for Aero Space Information, 800 Elkridge Landing Rd., Linthium Heights, MD 21090-2934. index. **Document type:** government publication, abstracting/indexing.

608.7 016   US
N A S A PATENT ABSTRACTS BIBLIOGRAPHY: A CONTINUING BIBLIOGRAPHY. SECTION 2. INDEXES. 1969. s-a. $16.50 per no. U.S. National Aeronautics and Space Administration, Center for AeroSpace Information, N A S A Access Help Desk, 800 Elkridge Landing Rd., Linthium Heights, MD 21090-2934. TEL 301-621-0390. FAX 301-621-0134. E-mail: help@sti.nasa.gov. index. **Document type:** government publication, abstracting/indexing, bibliography.

608.7   UN   ISSN 0250-7757
                                CODEN: PCGAEB
P C T GAZETTE. (Patent Cooperation Treaty) French edition: Gazette du P C T (ISSN 0250-7749) 1978. w. 600 SFr. World Intellectual Property Organization (WIPO) - Organisation Mondiale de la Propriete Intellectuelle, Publications Sales and Distribution Unit, 34 chemin des Colombettes, CH-1211 Geneva 20, Switzerland. TEL 022-730-9111. FAX 022-733-5428. TELEX 412912-OMPI-CH. adv.; cum.index. circ. 1,000. (also avail. in magnetic tape; back issues avail.) **Indexed:** Potato Abstr., Sugar Ind.Abstr. **Document type:** bibliography.
●Also available online.
—CASDDS; PADDS.
   Description: Contains bibliographic data on applicant, inventor, origin and destination of application published, title, abstract and drawing or formula of invention, arranged in order of International Patent Classification indexes by filing and publication numbers, designated countries, applicant's names and IPC classes.

608.7   RU
▼**PATENT ABSTRACTS IN ENGLISH.** 1994. m. price varies. Vsesoyuznyi Nauchno-Issledovatel'skii Institut Patentnoi Informatsii (VNIIPI) - All-Russia Scientific and Research Institute of Patent Information, Raushskaya nab. 4, 113035 Moscow, Russia. TEL 7-095-2393010. FAX 7-095-2311121. TELEX 411093 POISK SU. Ed. E.I. Daich. **Document type:** abstracting/indexing, bulletin.

608.7 602.7   AT   ISSN 0819-4831
PATENT ABSTRACTS SUPPLEMENT TO THE AUSTRALIAN OFFICIAL JOURNAL OF PATENTS. 1981. w. Aus.$950 (effective 1994). Australian Industrial Property Organisation, P.O. Box 200, Woden, A.C.T. 2606, Australia. TEL 06-2832481. FAX 06-2853929. TELEX COMPAT AA 61517. circ. 50. (back issues avail.)
   Formerly (until 1987): Patent Abstracts Supplement to the Australian Official Journal of Patents, Trade Marks and Designs (ISSN 0729-0489)
   Description: Abstracts of unaccepted complete patent specifications as laid open to public inspection; search materials for the public.

608.7   JA   ISSN 0386-877X
PATENTS ABSTRACTS OF JAPAN. (Text in English) 1977. irreg. Patent Office - Tokkyocho, 4-3 Kasumigaseki 3-chome, Chiyoda-ku, Tokyo 100, Japan. **Document type:** abstracting/indexing, government publication.

602.7   US   ISSN 0099-0809
T223.V4
U.S. PATENT AND TRADEMARK OFFICE. INDEX OF TRADEMARKS ISSUED. a. price varies. U.S. Patent and Trademark Office, General Information Services Division, Crystal Plaza 3, Rm. 2C02, Washington, DC 20231. TEL 703-308-4357. FAX 703-305-7786. (Subscr. to: Superintendent of Documents, U.S. Government Printing Office, Box 371954, Pittsburgh, PA 15250-7954. TEL 202-512-1800. FAX 202-512-2250) **Document type:** abstracting/indexing, government publication.
   Formerly: U.S. Patent Office. Index of Trademarks Issued (ISSN 0083-3045)
   Description: Lists trademark registrants, registration numbers, publication dates; classifies products registered and decisions published during the preceding year.

PEDIATRICS

see Medical Sciences–Pediatrics

PERFUMES AND COSMETICS

see Beauty Culture–Perfumes and Cosmetics

PERSONAL COMPUTERS

see Computers–Personal Computers

PERSONNEL MANAGEMENT

see Business and Economics–Personnel Management

PETROLEUM AND GAS

666.5 553.282   US   ISSN 0149-1423
TN860   CODEN: AABUD2
A A P G BULLETIN. Microform edition (ISSN 0364-9849) 1917. m. $140 (foreign $165) (effective 1996). American Association of Petroleum Geologists, Box 979, Tulsa, OK 74101. TEL 918-584-2555. FAX 918-584-0469. Ed. Kevin Biddle. adv.: B&W page $1800, color page $2595; 8 1/2 10 7/8. bk.rev.; bibl.; illus.; maps; stat.; index, cum.index every 5 yrs. circ. 32,000. (also avail. in microform from PMC,UMI) **Indexed:** A.S.& T.Ind., AESIS, ASCA, Bibl.& Ind.Geol., Biol.Abstr., Br.Geol.Lit. (1972-), Chem.Abstr., Curr.Cont., Curr.Tit.Ocean., Deep Sea Res.& Oceanogr.Abstr., E&P Hlth. (1993-), Energy Info.Abstr., Eng.Ind., Gas Abstr., Gas Process.& Ppl. (1993-), Geo.Abstr., Geol.Abstr., Geotech.Abstr., Ind.Sci.Rev., INIS Atomind., Off.Tech. (1993-), Petrol.Abstr. (1975-), Sci.Cit.Ind., 044866144ergy Abstr.
—BLDSC (0537.502000); CASDDS; CIS; Ei; Faxon; Genuine Article; PADDS; SWETS; UMI; UnCover. **CCC.**
   Formerly: American Association of Petroleum Geologists. Bulletin (ISSN 0002-7464)
   Description: Technical journal of petroleum geology; worldwide in scope and contributions.
   Refereed Serial

666.5   US   ISSN 0195-2986
A A P G EXPLORER. 1979. m. $45 (foreign $50). American Association of Petroleum Geologists, Box 979, Tulsa, OK 74101. TEL 918-584-2555. Ed. Vern Stefanic. adv.: B&W page $3170, color page $4020; 11 1/2 x 15. circ. 32,000. **Indexed:** Petrol.Abstr.
—BLDSC (0537.502300); SWETS; UnCover. **CCC.**
   Description: News periodical for the petroleum industry.
   Refereed Serial

666.5   US   ISSN 0271-8510
                                CODEN: ASTGD6
A A P G STUDIES IN GEOLOGY SERIES. 1975. irreg., no.29, 1989. price varies. American Association of Petroleum Geologists, Box 979, Tulsa, OK 74101. TEL 918-584-2555. cum.index: 1971-75, 1976-80, 1981-85. **Indexed:** AESIS, Bibl.& Ind.Geol., Biol.Abstr., Chem.Abstr.
—BLDSC (0537.506000); CASDDS.
   Description: Book series that documents current, state-of-the-art advances in research applicable to the geological community.
   Refereed Serial

665.5   TS
A D N O C NEWS/AKHBAR A D N O C. (Text in Arabic, English) 1978. m. free. Abu Dhabi National Oil Company, Public Relations Department, P.O. Box 898, Abu Dhabi, United Arab Emirates. TEL 666000. FAX 655745. TELEX 22215 EM. Ed. Khalifa al-Hossani. circ. 5,000 (paid); 3,500 (controlled).
   Formerly (until Dec. 1988): Petroleum Community - Mujtama' al-Bitrul.
   Description: Discusses ADNOC activities and all petroleum projects in Abu Dhabi and the U.A.E.

PETROLEUM AND GAS

665.7 US ISSN 8756-5471
TP700 CODEN: GAERE7
A G A GAS ENERGY REVIEW. m. $50 to non-members; members $40. American Gas Association, 1515 Wilson Blvd., Arlington, VA 22209. TEL 703-841-8400. FAX 703-841-8406. (Subscr. to: Dept. 0765, McLean, VA 22109-0765) charts. circ. 850. (looseleaf format; back issues avail.)
●Also available online. Vendor(s): University Microfilms International.
—BLDSC (4077.410000); UMI.

338.47 665.74 US
A G A RATE SERVICE. 1919. s-a. $300 to non-members; members $175. American Gas Association, 1515 Wilson Blvd., Arlington, VA 22209. TEL 703-841-8400. FAX 703-841-8406. (Subscr. to: Dept. 0765, McLean, VA 22109-0765) Ed. Sheila Rana. circ. 500. (looseleaf format)

665.54 US
A G A SYNTHETIC PIPELINE GAS SYMPOSIUM. PROCEEDINGS. vol.7, 1975. irreg., latest Boston, 1991. $50. American Gas Association, 1515 Wilson Blvd., Arlington, VA 22209. TEL 703-841-8400. FAX 703-841-8406. (Subscr. to: Dept. 0765, McLean, VA 22109-0765) (Co-sponsors: U.S. Energy Research; Development Administration; International Gas Union) **Document type:** proceedings.

665.7 US
A G A THE NATURAL RESOURCE NEWSLETTER. q. $56 to non-members (foreign $66); members $28 (foreign $38). American Gas Association, 1515 Wilson Blvd., Arlington, VA 22209. TEL 703-841-8400. FAX 703-841-8406. (Subscr. to: Dept. 0765, McLean, VA 22109-0765)

665.5 US
A G A TRAINING UPDATE. q. $20 to non-members; members $10. American Gas Association, 1515 Wilson Blvd., Arlington, VA 22209. TEL 703-841-8400. FAX 703-841-8406. (Subscr. to: Dept. 0765, McLean, VA 22109-0765)

A M P L A BULLETIN. (Australian Mining and Petroleum Law Association Ltd.) see MINES AND MINING INDUSTRY

A M P L A YEARBOOK. (Australian Mining and Petroleum Law Association Ltd.) see MINES AND MINING INDUSTRY

A M R E P DATABASE BULLETIN. (Australian Mineral Resource Politics Pty. Ltd.) see MINES AND MINING INDUSTRY

A O S C DIRECTORY. (Association of Oilwell Servicing Contractors) see BUSINESS AND ECONOMICS — Trade And Industrial Directories

665.5 UY ISSN 0253-6005
A R P E L BOLETIN TECNICO. (Text in Spanish; summaries in English, French, Spanish and Portuguese) 1972. q. $56. Asistencia Reciproca Petrolera Estatal Latinoamericana, Box 1006, Montevideo, Uruguay. TEL 407454. FAX 237023. abstr.; bibl.; charts; illus.; stat. **Indexed:** API Abstr., API Catal., API Hlth.& Environ., API Oil., API Pet.Ref., API Pet.Subst., API Transport.
—BLDSC (2219.085000); PADDS.
Formerly: Asistencia Reciproca Petrolera Estatal Latinoamericana. Revista Tecnica.

665.5 UY ISSN 0797-7549
A R P E L HOY. 1967. bi-m. free. Asistencia Reciproca Petrolera Estatal Latinoamericana, Box 1006, Montevideo, Uruguay. FAX 598-2-237023. TELEX 22560 ARPEL UY.
Supersedes (in Sep. 1989): A R P E L Boletin Informativo.

665.5 UK ISSN 0263-5054
ABERDEEN PETROLEUM REPORT. 1981. w. £440 (rest of Europe £445; elsewhere £450) (effective 1996) (includes Europetroleum with Aberdeen Petroleum Quarterly). Aberdeen Petroleum Publishing Ltd., 35 Huntly St., Aberdeen AB1 1TJ, Scotland. TEL 01224-644725. FAX 01224-647574. Ed. Ted Strachan. circ. controlled. (back issues avail.) **Document type:** newsletter.
Description: Provides business intelligence on North Sea oil and gas activities.

ACCESS (GLENSIDE); information and education for the mining and petroleum industry. see MINES AND MINING INDUSTRY

ACTA UNIVERSITATIS DE ATTILA JOZSEF NOMINATAE. ACTA MINERALOGICA - PETROGRAPHICA. see MINES AND MINING INDUSTRY

ADVANCED FOSSIL ENERGY TECHNOLOGIES. see ENERGY

665.5 531.64 US ISSN 0896-5188
ADVANCED OIL AND GAS RECOVERY TECHNOLOGIES. m. $145 in U.S., Canada, Mexico; elsewhere $290. (Department of Energy) U.S. National Technical Information Service, 5285 Port Royal Rd., Springfield, VA 22161. TEL 703-487-4630. Ed. Rivers.
Description: Disseminates international information on all aspects of enhanced and unconventional recovery of petroleum and natural gas. Includes oil shales and tar sands, natural gas production from coal mines, gas hydrates and geopressured systems.

665.5 US
ADVANCES IN CORE EVALUATION. irreg., no.3, 1993. Gordon & Breach Science Publishers, 820 Town Center Dr., Langhorne, PA 19047. TEL 215-750-2642. FAX 215-750-6343. (UK subscr. to: P.O. Box 90, Reading, Berkshire RG1 8JL, England. TEL 01734-560-080) **Document type:** monographic series.

665.5 551 US ISSN 0739-8352
TN860 CODEN: APGEEH
ADVANCES IN PETROLEUM GEOCHEMISTRY. 1984. irreg., vol.2, 1987. Academic Press, Inc., 525 B St., Ste. 1900, San Diego, CA 92101-4495. TEL 619-231-6616. FAX 619-699-6715. (Subscr. to: Order Dept., 6277 Sea Harbor Dr., 4th Fl., Orlando, FL 32887. TEL 800-321-5068) Eds. Jim Brooks, Dietrich Welte. (back issues avail.) **Document type:** academic/scholarly publication.
—CASDDS.
Refereed Serial

665.538 549 FR ISSN 0994-0235
AFRICA ENERGY AND MINING. French edition: Lettre Afrique Energies. 1983. 23/yr. 3800 F.($700) Indigo Publications, 10, rue du Sentier, 75002 Paris, France. TEL 44-88-26-10. FAX 44-88-26-15. Ed. Maurice Botbol. **Document type:** newsletter.
Description: Pertinent information for energy and mining professionals on what's happening on the African continent.

552 TS
AKHBAR AL-BUTRUL WAL-SINA'A/PETROLEUM AND INDUSTRY NEWS. (Text in Arabic) 1970. m. Ministry of Petroleum and Mineral Wealth, P.O. Box 59, Abu Dhabi, United Arab Emirates. TEL 651810. FAX 663414. TELEX 22544 MPMR EM. Ed. Manaa Said al-Otaiba. circ. 2,000 (controlled).
Description: Discusses current developments and news in petroleum and industry, with a focus on the U.A.E.

552 BA
AKHBAR B A P C O. (Text in Arabic; summaries in English) 1957. w. free. Bahrain Petroleum Co. Ltd., Public Relations Department, P.O. Box 25149, Awali, Bahrain. TEL 755055. FAX 755999. TELEX 8214 BAPCO BN. Ed. Khalid Fahad Mehmas. bk.rev. circ. 8,000. **Document type:** newspaper.
Formerly (until 1981): Weekly Star - An-Najma al-Usbou'

665.5 US
ALABAMA PROPANE GAS NEWS. 1950. m. Alabama Propane Gas Association, 660 Adams Ave., Ste. 133, Montgomery, AL 36104-4336. TEL 205-264-9630. FAX 205-264-9641. Ed. Sherry Wood. adv.: B&W page $280; 8 1/2 x 11; adv. contact: Ben Pickering. circ. 500. **Document type:** newsletter.

665 US
ALASKA SUMMARY REPORT - INDEX. 1980. a. free. Outer Continental Shelf Information Program, Offshore Information and Publications Office, Minerals Management Service, 381 Elden St., No. 1400, Herndon, VA 22070-4817. TEL 703-787-1080. circ. 4,000.
Formed by the 1985 merger of: Arctic Summary Report; Bering Sea Summary Report; Alaska Index.
Description: Documents with status of federal offshore oil and gas leasing, exploration, development and production activities.

ALBERTA OIL & GAS DIRECTORY. see BUSINESS AND ECONOMICS — Trade And Industrial Directories

665.74 333.8 CN ISSN 0229-8546
TN873.C22
ALBERTA'S RESERVE OF GAS: COMPLETE LISTING. 1979. a. Can.$250. Alberta Energy and Utilities Board, 640 5th Ave. S.W., Calgary, Alberta T2P 3G4, Canada. FAX 403-297-7040. TELEX 03-821717. (microfiche)

665.538 US ISSN 1072-8767
ALCOHOL OUTLOOK. 1984. m. $545 (foreign $595). Information Resources, Inc., 1925 N. Lynn St., Ste. 1000, Arlington, VA 22204-1717. TEL 703-528-2500. FAX 703-528-1483. **Document type:** newsletter.
—CCC.
Description: Covers alcohol fuels as oxygen additives as well as neat fuels.

665.5 LY
AL-FATEH UNIVERSITY. FACULTY OF PETROLEUM. BULLETIN. a. Al-Fateh University, Faculty of Petroleum, P.O. Box 13040, Tripoli, Libya. TEL 36010. TELEX 20629.

AMERICAN ASSOCIATION OF PETROLEUM GEOLOGISTS. MEMOIR. see EARTH SCIENCES — Geology

665.7 US ISSN 1043-0652
TP700 CODEN: AMGLEH
AMERICAN GAS. 1919. 11/yr. $39 (foreign $70). American Gas Association, 1515 Wilson Blvd., Arlington, VA 22209. TEL 703-841-8400. FAX 703-841-8406. (Subscr. to: Dept. 0765, McLean, VA 22109-0765) Ed. Lois Whetzel. bk.rev.; charts; illus.; stat.; index. circ. 6,200. (also avail. in microfilm) **Indexed:** A.S.& T.Ind., Chem.Abstr., Energy Info.Abstr. (until 1994), Eng.Ind., Environ.Abstr., Environ.Per.Bibl. (1992-), Fuel & Energy Abstr., Gas Abstr., INIS Atomind., Petrol.Abstr., PROMT. **Document type:** trade publication.
●Also available online. Vendor(s): University Microfilms International.
—BLDSC (0815.900000); Ei; Faxon; UMI; UnCover.
Former titles (until 1989): A G A Monthly (ISSN 0885-2413); American Gas Association Monthly (ISSN 0002-8584)

665.7 US ISSN 0362-4994
TN880.A1 CODEN: POAGAB
AMERICAN GAS ASSOCIATION. OPERATING SECTION. PROCEEDINGS. Key Title: Operating Section Proceedings. 1965. a. $10. American Gas Association, 1515 Wilson Blvd., Arlington, VA 22209. TEL 703-841-8400. FAX 703-841-8406. (Subscr. to: Dept. 0765, McLean, VA 22109-0765) illus. **Indexed:** API Abstr., Bibl.& Ind.Geol., Chem.Abstr., Gas Abstr. **Document type:** proceedings.
—BLDSC (6267.890000).

665.5 US ISSN 0145-9198
TN872
AMERICAN OIL & GAS REPORTER. 1958. 12/yr. $28. National Publishers Group, Inc., Box 343, Derby, KS 67037-0343. FAX 316-788-7568. Ed. Bill Campbell; Pub. Charlie Cookson. adv.: B&W page $2040 color page $2900; 8 1/4 x 10 7/8. bk.rev.; tr.lit.; circ. 11,228 (paid). **Indexed:** E&P Hlth. (1993-), Gas Process.& Ppl. (1993-), Off.Tech. (1993-), Petrol.Abstr. (1973, 1975-). **Document type:** trade publication.
—BLDSC (0847.320000); PADDS; UnCover.
Formerly: Mid-America Oil and Gas Reporter.
Description: For the U.S. oil and gas exploration, drilling and production industry.

AMERICAN PETROLEUM INSTITUTE. MONTHLY COMPLETION REPORT. see PETROLEUM AND GAS — Abstracting, Bibliographies, Statistics

PETROLEUM AND GAS 5025

665.75 US
AMERICAN PUBLIC GAS ASSOCIATION. NEWSLETTER. 1962. bi-w. American Public Gas Association, 11094-D Lee Hwy., Ste. 102, Fairfax, VA 22030. TEL 703-352-3890. Ed. Carole Curtis. circ. 1,000. **Document type:** newsletter.
  Formerly: American Public Gas Association. Memorandum Bulletins (ISSN 0065-9894)

665.7
ANALYSES OF NATURAL GASES. (Subseries of: Information Circular) 1917. a. free. U.S. Bureau of Mines, Office of Public Information, 810 Seventh St., N.W., MS-1040, Washington, DC 20241-0001. TEL 202-501-9649. FAX 202-219-2493. (Orders to: National Technical Information Service, 5285 Port Royal Rd., Springfield, VA 22161. TEL 703-487-4650. FAX 703-321-8547; Or: Bernan. 4611-F Assembly Dr., Lanham, MD 20706. TEL 301-459-7666. FAX 301-459-0056) charts. **Document type:** government publication.
  Formerly: Analyses of Natural Gases of the United States (ISSN 0066-149X)
  Description: Contains tables of analyses of natural gases. Purpose of analysis is to identify the helium content of these gases.

665.5 US ISSN 1058-9430
HD9561
ANNUAL AND CUMULATIVE FIELD AND OPERATOR PRODUCTION. AREA, FEDERAL OFFSHORE. PRODUCT, CRUDE. a. Petroleum Information Corporation, Box 2612, Denver, CO 80201-2612. TEL 303-740-7100. FAX 303-694-1754.

665.5 US ISSN 1058-9449
HD9581.U49
ANNUAL AND CUMULATIVE FIELD AND OPERATOR PRODUCTION. AREA, FEDERAL OFFSHORE. PRODUCT, GAS. a. Petroleum Information Corporation, Box 2612, Denver, CO 80201-2612. TEL 303-740-7100. FAX 303-694-1754.

665.5 US ISSN 1058-0077
HD9567.L8
ANNUAL AND CUMULATIVE FIELD AND OPERATOR PRODUCTION. AREA, LOUISIANA OFFSHORE. PRODUCT, GAS. a. Petroleum Information Corporation, Box 2612, Denver, CO 80201-2612. TEL 303-740-7100. FAX 303-694-1754.

665.5 US ISSN 1053-0576
HD9567.N6
ANNUAL AND CUMULATIVE FIELD AND OPERATOR PRODUCTION. AREA, NEW MEXICO. PRODUCT, NORTHWEST CRUDE. a. Petroleum Information Corporation, Box 2612, Denver, CO 80201. TEL 303-740-7100. FAX 303-694-1754.

338.2 US ISSN 1053-0355
HD9567.N6
ANNUAL AND CUMULATIVE FIELD AND OPERATOR PRODUCTION. AREA, NEW MEXICO. PRODUCT, SOUTHEAST CRUDE. a. Petroleum Information Corporation, Box 2612, Denver, CO 80201. TEL 303-740-7100. FAX 303-694-1754.

665.5 US ISSN 1058-0069
HD9567.L8
ANNUAL AND CUMULATIVE FIELD AND OPERATOR PRODUCTION. AREA, SOUTH LOUISIANA ONSHORE. PRODUCT, GAS. a. Petroleum Information Corporation, Box 2612, Denver, CO 80201-2612. TEL 303-740-7100. FAX 303-694-1754.

ANNUAL BOOK OF A S T M STANDARDS. VOLUME 05.01. PETROLEUM PRODUCTS AND LUBRICANTS (1). see *ENGINEERING — Engineering Mechanics And Materials*

ANNUAL BOOK OF A S T M STANDARDS. VOLUME 05.02. PETROLEUM PRODUCTS AND LUBRICANTS (2). see *ENGINEERING — Engineering Mechanics And Materials*

ANNUAL BOOK OF A S T M STANDARDS. VOLUME 05.03. PETROLEUM PRODUCTS AND LUBRICANTS (3): CATALYSTS. see *ENGINEERING — Engineering Mechanics And Materials*

ANNUAL BOOK OF A S T M STANDARDS. VOLUME 05.05. GASEOUS FUELS; COAL AND COKE. see *ENGINEERING — Engineering Mechanics And Materials*

665.5 US
ANNUAL REVIEW OF CALIFORNIA - ALASKA OIL AND GAS EXPLORATION. 1944. a. $50. Munger Oil Information Service, Inc., 9800 S. Sepulveda Blvd., Ste. 723, Box 45738, Los Angeles, CA 90045. TEL 310-645-3282. FAX 310-645-9147. Ed. Averill H. Munger; Pub. Averill Munger. circ. 300. **Document type:** trade publication.
  Formerly: Annual Review of California Oil and Gas Exploration.

665.7 IT
ANNUARIO DEL METANO/NATURAL GAS DIRECTORY. 1985. biennial. L.150000. R E S Editrice s.r.l., Casella Postale 12053, Via Rogoredo 119, 20120 Milan, Italy. TEL 39-2-4159120. Ed. Gerardo Rizzoli. adv.: B&W page L.1500000, color page L.2600000; adv. contact: Ugo Sociale. **Document type:** directory.
  Description: Lists laws and decrees, provides a catalogue of operators, and a guide to distributors, suppliers and producers.

APPLIED ENERGY. see *ENERGY*

665 FR ISSN 0031-6369
ARAB OIL & GAS. French edition: Petrole et Gaz Arabes. (Text in English) 1969. fortn. 9200 F.($1360) Arab Petroleum Research Center, 7 av. Ingres, 75781 Paris Cedex 16, France. FAX 45-20-16-85. Ed. Nicolas Sarkis. adv.: B&W page $2920, color page $4390; trim 190 x 245. bk.rev.; bibl.; stat.; index. circ. 1,800. **Indexed:** Fuel & Energy Abstr.
  —BLDSC (6430.670000).
  Description: Provides news, studies, comments, interviews, texts of laws and agreements on all aspects of the development of the oil and gas industry in the Middle East and Africa.

338.2 FR ISSN 0304-8551
HD9578.A55
ARAB OIL & GAS DIRECTORY. (Text in English) 1974. a. 2460 F.($460) Arab Petroleum Research Center, 7 av. Ingres, 75781 Paris Cedex 16, France. FAX 45-20-16-85. Ed. Nicolas Sarkis. adv.: B&W page $2920, color page $4390; trim 180 x 245; adv. contact: Anne-Marie Happey. illus.; stat. circ. 5,250. **Document type:** directory.
  —BLDSC (1583.258000).
  Description: Provides complete coverage of Arab oil and gas exporting countries, new products, investment figures, survey of all oil producing surveys, addresses of oil companies.

338.2 665.538 FR ISSN 0378-7184
ARAB OIL & GAS MAGAZINE (MONTHLY). (Text in Arabic, English) 1966. m. Arab Petroleum Research Center, 7 av. Ingres, 75781 Paris Cedex 16, France. FAX 45-20-16-85. adv.: B&W page $2920, color page $4390; trim 190 x 250; adv. contact: Anne-Marie Happey. circ. 16,200.
  —BLDSC (1583.255000).

665 LY ISSN 0003-7435
ARAB OIL REVIEW. (Text in English and Arabic) 1964. bi-m. £L7. 4 Sharia Omar Ibn Abdulaziz, Tripoli, Libya. Ed. Naim El-Arady. adv.; illus.; mkt.; tr.lit.; index.

665 622 LY ISSN 0003-7443
ARAB PETROLEUM. 1964. m. Arab Federation of Petroleum Mining & Chemical Workers, P.O. Box 1905, Tripoli, Libya.

ARAMCO WORLD. see *ETHNIC INTERESTS*

665.7 CN ISSN 0849-5416
HD9581.C3
AREAS SERVED BY GAS IN CANADA. 1984. biennial. Can.$60 to non-members; members Can.$30. Canadian Gas Association, Economics - Statistics Department - Association Canadienne du Gaz, 243 Consumers Rd., Ste. 1200, North York, ON M2J 5E3, Canada. TEL 416-498-1994. FAX 416-498-7465.
  Description: Lists distrubutors and areas seved by natural gas, population, number of customers or meters in each area.

665.5 IT
ARGOMENTI ESSO. 1974. m. free. Esso Italiana, Stampa Informazione, Viale Castello della Magliana 25, 00148 Rome, Italy. TEL 06 59952318. Ed. Carlo Angelo Guareschi. charts; illus.; stat. circ. 10,000.
  Formerly (until 1988): Esso Italiana. Informazioni Economiche.
  Description: Analysis of relations between the oil industry and environment. Covers safe industrial activity, measures for the protection of the environment and actions toward a more rational order of marketing.

665.538 658.7 UK ISSN 0957-039X
ARGUS FUNDAMENTALS. 1989. m. £625 (N. America $995). Petroleum Argus Ltd., 93 Shepperton Rd., London N1 3DF, England. TEL 0171-359-8792. FAX 0171-226-0695. **Document type:** trade publication.

665.5 US ISSN 0570-9520
ARIZONA GEOLOGICAL SURVEY. OIL, GAS & HELIUM PRODUCTION. 1958. m. $16. Arizona Geological Survey, 416 W. Congress, Ste. 100, Tuscon, AZ 85701. TEL 520-770-3500. FAX 520-770-3505. stat.; index. circ. 40. (processed) **Indexed:** SRI.

557 622 US
ARIZONA GEOLOGICAL SURVEY. OPEN-FILE REPORTS. irreg. Arizona Geological Survey, 416 W. Congress, Ste. 100, Tucson, AZ 85701. TEL 520-770-3500. FAX 520-770-3505.
  Formerly: Arizona Geological Survey. Special Publication.

665.7 US
ARKANSAS PROPANE GAS NEWS. vol.24, 1972. bi-m. $2. Arkansas Propane Gas Association, Inc., 103 E. 7th St., Ste. 1012, Little Rock, AR 72201. TEL 501-374-8396. Ed. J.P. Lybrand, Jr. adv. circ. 561. (processed) **Document type:** trade publication.
  Formerly: Arkansas L P News (ISSN 0044-8893)

665 US ISSN 0273-4931
TN867
ARMSTRONG OIL DIRECTORIES: LOUISIANA, MISSISSIPPI, ARKANSAS, TEXAS GULF COAST AND EAST TEXAS EDITION. (In 4 regional eds.) 1958. a. $50. Armstrong Oil Directories, c/o Alan Armstrong, Ed., Box 9660, Amarillo, TX 79102-9660. TEL 806-374-1818. FAX 806-374-1838. **Document type:** directory.
  Formerly (until 1980): Armstrong Oil Directories - Louisiana, Texas Gulf Coast, East Texas, Arkansas and Mississippi (ISSN 0073-0254)

665 US
ARMSTRONG OIL DIRECTORIES: MINI BRIEFCASE EDITION; nation-wide coverage. (In 4 regional eds.) a. $100. Armstrong Oil Directories, c/o Alan Armstrong, Ed., Box 9660, Amarillo, TX 79102-9660. TEL 800-375-1838. FAX 806-374-1838. **Document type:** directory.

665 US ISSN 0273-5229
TN867
ARMSTRONG OIL DIRECTORIES: ROCKY MOUNTAIN - CENTRAL UNITED STATES EDITION. (In 4 regional eds.) 1961. a. $50. Armstrong Oil Directories, c/o Alan Armstrong, Ed., Box 9660, Amarillo, TX 79102-9660. TEL 806-374-1818. FAX 806-374-1838. **Document type:** directory.
  Former titles (until 1980): Armstrong Oil Directory - Central United States; Hank Seale Oil Directory - Central United States (ISSN 0073-0238)

665 US ISSN 0277-2280
TN867
ARMSTRONG OIL DIRECTORIES: TEXAS INCLUDING SOUTHEAST NEW MEXICO EDITION. (In 4 regional eds.) 1957. a. $50. Armstrong Oil Directories, c/o Alan Armstrong, Ed., Box 9660, Amarillo, TX 79102-9660. TEL 806-374-1818. FAX 806-374-1838. **Document type:** directory.
  Formerly (until 1980): Hank Seale Oil Directory - Texas Including Southeast New Mexico (ISSN 0073-0262)

665.5 US
ASHLAND NEWS. 1961. m. free. Ashland Oil, Inc., Box 391, Ashland, KY 41114. TEL 606-329-3333. Ed. Lesli S. Christian. charts; illus. circ. 32,000. **Indexed:** Energy Info.Abstr.

PETROLEUM AND GAS

665.5 338.7 US ISSN 0748-4089
HD9576.A1
ASIA - PACIFIC - AFRICA - MIDDLE EAST PETROLEUM.
1979. a. $115 (foreign $185) (with European Petroleum Directory $250 (foreign $345)). PennWell Publishing Co., Box 1260, Tulsa, OK 74101. TEL 918-835-3161. FAX 918-831-9555. TELEX 211012. Ed. Pat Jackson; Pub. Carol Schaefer. adv. **Document type:** directory.
—CCC.
Formerly: Asia - Pacific Petroleum Directory (ISSN 0270-1235); Incorporates (as of 1985): Africa - Middle East Petroleum Directory (ISSN 0197-7830); Which superseded in part: Eastern Hemisphere Petroleum Directory (ISSN 0070-8224)
Description: Lists companies involved in drilling, refining, exploration, pipelines, engineering, field services, construction and other petroleum related operations.

665.5 JA
ASIAN OIL AND GAS. (Text in English) 10/yr. $115. Intercontinental Marketing Corp., I.P.O. Box 5056, Tokyo 100-31, Japan. TEL 81-3-3661-7458. FAX 81-3-3667-9646.

338.47 HK
ASIAN OIL AND GAS. (Text in English) 1980. m. $75 in Asia; elsewhere $90. Publications Ltd., 14th Fl., 200 Lockhart Rd., Hong Kong. TEL 511-1301. FAX 507-4620. Ed. Andrew Burns. circ. 6,042. **Document type:** trade publication.
Description: Oil industry trade journal.

ASPHALT EMULSION MANUFACTURERS ASSOCIATION. NEWSLETTER. see TRANSPORTATION — Roads And Traffic

665.5 US
ASPHALT ROOFING MANUFACTURERS ASSOCIATION. NEWSLETTER. 6/yr. Asphalt Roofing Manufacturers Association, 6000 Executive Blvd., Ste. 201, Rockville, MD 20852-3803. TEL 301-231-9050. FAX 301-881-6572. **Document type:** newsletter.

665.5 US
ASSOCIATION OF OILWELL SERVICING CONTRACTORS. FIELD REPORTS. 1963. m. $125 to non-members. Association of Oilwell Servicing Contractors, 6060 N. Central Expy., Ste. 425, Dallas, TX 75206. TEL 214-692-0771. Ed. Katherine Leidy. circ. 1,225. (back issues avail.) **Document type:** newsletter.

665.5 551 US
ATLANTIC SUMMARY REPORT - INDEX. 1980. a. Outer Continental Shelf Information Program, Offshore Information and Publications Office, Minerals Management Service, 381 Elden St., No. 1400, Herndon, VA 22070-4817. TEL 703-787-1080. circ. 4,000.
Formed by the 1985 merger of: Atlantic Index; Mid-Atlantic Summary Report; Atlantic Summary Report; Which was formerly (until 1983): South Atlantic Summary Report.

ATOMO PETROLIO ELETTRICITA. see ENERGY

665.5 550 AT ISSN 0817-9263
AUSTRALIA. BUREAU OF MINERAL RESOURCES, GEOLOGY AND GEOPHYSICS. AUSTRALIAN PETROLEUM ACCUMULATIONS REPORT. 1986. irreg. price varies. (Bureau of Mineral Resources, Geology and Geophysics) Australian Geological Organisation, G.P.O. Box 378, Canberra, A.C.T. 2601, Australia. FAX 062-725161.

696 AT ISSN 0727-3541
THE AUSTRALIAN GAS INDUSTRY DIRECTORY (YEAR). a. Aus.$38 to non-members; members Aus.$28. Australian Gas Association, G.P.O. Box 323, Canberra, A.C.T. 2601, Australia. TEL 61-6-247-3955. FAX 61-6-249-7402. Ed. Kim Baker. **Document type:** directory.
Former titles: Directory of the Australian Gas Industry (ISSN 0706-666X); Australian Gas Association. Directory.
Description: List members of The Australian Gas Association, Commonwealth and state government energy offices, overseas gas organizations, and suppliers to the gas industry.

665.7 AT ISSN 0004-9166
TP700
THE AUSTRALIAN GAS JOURNAL. 1936. bi-m. Aus.$50. Australian Gas Association, G.P.O. Box 323, Canberra, A.C.T. 2601, Australia. TEL 61-6-247-3955. FAX 61-6-249-7402. Ed. Mal. Grieve. adv.; bk.rev. circ. 2,500. **Indexed:** AESIS, Bibl.& Ind.Geol., Chem.Abstr., Fuel & Energy Abstr., GeoRef.
—BLDSC (1800.600000).

553 AT ISSN 0314-3171
AUSTRALIAN INSTITUTE OF PETROLEUM. ANNUAL REPORT. 1977. a. free. Australian Institute of Petroleum, Ltd., 500 Collins St., Melbourne, Vic. 3000, Australia.

AUTOMOTIVE ENGINEER. see TRANSPORTATION — Automobiles

338.47 US ISSN 0146-5236
HD9561
AUTOMOTIVE FUEL ECONOMY PROGRAM. ANNUAL REPORT TO THE CONGRESS. 1977. a. U.S. Department of Transportation, National Highway Traffic Safety Administration, Washington, DC 20590. TEL 202-655-4000. circ. 200.

665.5 US
AVERAGE CALENDAR DAY ALLOWABLE REPORT. m. $24 (includes Drilling Completion and Plugging Summary). Railroad Commission, Oil and Gas Publications, Drawer 12967, Capitol Sta., Austin, TX 78711. TEL 512-463-7255. (charts) **Document type:** government publication.
Description: Shows the number of wells and allowables by district, with special production factors.

665 BA
B A P C O NEWS. (Text in English) w. free. Bahrain Petroleum Co. B.S.C., P.O. Box 25149, Awali, Bahrain. TEL 755047. FAX 755999. TELEX 8214 BAPCO BN. Ed. Samuel Knight. circ. 1,000. **Document type:** newspaper.
Formerly: B A P C O Daily News.

665 FR ISSN 0300-4554
B I P. (Bulletin de l'Industrie Petroliere) 1964. d. 12300 F. (foreign 12650 F.). Societe d' Information et de Documentation, Bureau d'Informations Professionnelles, 142 rue Montmartre, 75002 Paris, France. FAX 40-39-97-52. TELEX 220528F. Ed. Jacques Marie. bk.rev.; stat. circ. 1,000. (processed) **Indexed:** Chem.Abstr., Petrol.Energy B.N.I., Sci.Cit.Ind.
—BLDSC (2862.090000). CCC.
Description: Daily news and comments on oil and gas in the world.

665.5 UK ISSN 0306-106X
B P NEWS. m. free to qualified personnel. British Petroleum Company p.l.c., Britannic House, 1 Finsbury Circus, London EC2M 7BA, England. Ed. Diana Ching. circ. 21,000. (tabloid format) **Document type:** newspaper.
Description: Tabloid newspaper for BP staff in the London area.

665.5 UK
B P SHIPPING REVIEW. 1986. q. free. B P Shipping Ltd., B P House, Breakspear Way, Hemel Hempstead, Herts. HP2 4UL, England. TEL 01442-213049. FAX 01442-213049. Ed. Allan Carter. bk.rev. circ. 4,500. **Indexed:** BMT. **Document type:** trade publication.
Formerly: B P Fleet News.
Description: Publicity magazine for clients and potential clients of BP Shipping.

665.5 US
B T U HANDBOOK.* (British Thermal Unit) a. $71 (foreign $81). B T U Publishing, Inc. (Subsidiary of: Waterman & Barrett Publishing), 65 Mechanic St., Red Bank, NJ 07701-1803.

665.5 US
B T U WEEKLY.* (British Thermal Unit) w. $427 (foreign $550). B T U Publishing, Inc. (Subsidiary of: Waterman & Barrett Publishing), 65 Mechanic St., Red Bank, NJ 07701-1803.
Description: For producers and users of natural gas.

BASIC OIL LAWS & CONCESSION CONTRACTS: ASIA & AUSTRALASIA. see LAW — International Law

BASIC OIL LAWS & CONCESSION CONTRACTS: CENTRAL AMERICA & CARIBBEAN. see LAW — International Law

BASIC OIL LAWS & CONCESSION CONTRACTS: EUROPE. see LAW — International Law

BASIC OIL LAWS & CONCESSION CONTRACTS: MIDDLE EAST. see LAW — International Law

BASIC OIL LAWS & CONCESSION CONTRACTS: NORTH AFRICA. see LAW — International Law

BASIC OIL LAWS & CONCESSION CONTRACTS: RUSSIA & N I S. see LAW — International Law

BASIC OIL LAWS & CONCESSION CONTRACTS: SOUTH AMERICA. see LAW — International Law

BASIC OIL LAWS & CONCESSION CONTRACTS: SOUTH & CENTRAL AFRICA. see LAW — International Law

629.286 FI ISSN 0045-1738
BENSIINIUUTISET; Huoltamoiden erikoislehti. (Text in Finnish, Swedish) 1958. 11/yr. membership. Suomen Bensiinikauppiaitten Liitto S B L ry., Mannerheimintie 40 D 84, FIN-00100 Helsinki, Finland. TEL 358-0-441-675. FAX 358-0-442-465. Ed. Veikko Ahola. adv.: B&&W page FI 6800, color page FIM 11900. circ. 3,100.
Description: Discusses professional questions concerning oil products and automobile maintenance and automobile equipment.

381.456 DK
▼**BENZIN OG BUTIK.** 1995. q. Dansk Auto Media A-S, Hoejvangen 23, DK-3480 Fredensborg, Denmark. TEL 45-42-28-51-00. FAX 45-42-28-20-15. Ed. Egon Mathiasen. adv.: B&W page DKK 7500, color page DKK 11400; trim 220 x 297. circ. 5,000.

381.456 665.77 DK ISSN 0907-2284
BENZIN-TANKEN. 1931. m. (except Jul.). $10. Centralforhandler Foreningen af Benzinforhandlere i Danmark, Roegevej 93, 2. sal, DK-2630 Taastrup, Denmark. Ed. Ole Holm. adv.; charts; illus.; mkt. circ. 3,000.
Formerly (until 1992): Benzin og Olie Bladet (ISSN 0005-8858)

665.5 658.3 SI ISSN 0005-9153
BERITA SHELL. (Text in English and Malay) 1955. m. free to employees. Shell Eastern Petroleum Pty. Ltd., Shell Tower, 50 Raffles Place, 1 Singapore, Singapore. Ed. Chua Swee Kiat. bk.rev. circ. 3,800.

665 UA ISSN 1110-4708
AL-BITRUL. 1962. m. Egyptian General Petroleum Corporation, Sharia Filastin, P.O. Box 2130, New Maadi, Cairo, Egypt. TEL 02-3531340. TELEX 92049.

665 BL ISSN 0102-9304
CODEN: BGPEEA
BOLETIM DE GEOCIENCIAS DA PETROBRAS. (Summaries in English and Portuguese) 1957. 4/yr. free to qualified personnel. Petroleo Brasileiro S.A., Centro de Pesquisas e Desenvolvimento "Leopoldo A. Miguez de Mello", Setor de Informacao Tecnica e Propriedade Industrial, Cidade Universitaria, Quadra 7-Ilha do Fundao, C.P. 809, 21910 Rio de Janeiro, Brazil. TEL 021-598-6114. Eds. Affonso Celso M. de Paula, Fani Knoploch. abstr.; bibl.; charts; illus.; stat.; index. circ. 2,000. **Indexed:** API Abstr., API Catal., API Hlth.& Environ., API Oil., API Pet.Ref., API Pet.Subst., API Transport., Bibl.& Ind.Geol., Chem.Abstr., E&P Hlth. (1993-), Gas Process.& Ppl. (1993-), Geo.Abstr., Geol.Abstr., Off.Tech. (1993-), Petrol.Abstr. (1970-).
—BLDSC (2159.350000); CASDDS; PADDS. CCC.
Formerly (until 1987): Boletim Tecnico da Petrobras (ISSN 0006-6117)
Description: Covers all aspects of the petroleum industry worldwide with emphasis on Brazil.

665.5 SP
BOLETIN ESTADISTICO DEL PETROLEO. Short title: B E P. 1986. m. free. Ministerio de Economia y Hacienda, Delegacion del Gobierno en Campsa, Capitan Haya, 41, 28020 Madrid, Spain. TEL 582 52 06.

PETROLEUM AND GAS

665.5   GW   ISSN 0342-6580
HD9553.1
BRENNSTOFFSPIEGEL. 1947. m. DM.82. Ceto Verlag GmbH, Goethestr. 34, 34119 Kassel, Germany. TEL 0561-774517. FAX 0561-772562. Ed. Hans-Colin Wulff. adv.: B&W page DM.2350, color page DM.4295; trim 178 x 230; adv. contact: Sonja Burchard. bk.rev. circ. 5,085. **Document type:** trade publication.
   Formerly: Brennstoffhandel.

BRITISH COLUMBIA. MINISTRY OF ENERGY, MINES AND PETROLEUM RESOURCES. ANNUAL REPORT. see *MINES AND MINING INDUSTRY*

BRITISH COLUMBIA. MINISTRY OF ENERGY, MINES AND PETROLEUM RESOURCES. BULLETIN. see *EARTH SCIENCES — Geology*

665.5   UK
BRITISH FLEET. 1968. q. Shell Tankers (UK) Ltd., Shell Centre, London SE1 7PQ, England. Ed. Terence Ryan. circ. 3,500.
   Formerly: British Fleet News.

665.7   UK
BRITISH GAS. ANNUAL REPORT AND ACCOUNTS. 1948. a. free. British Gas plc., Rivermill House, 152 Grosvenor Rd., London SW1V 3JL, England. TEL 071-821-1444. FAX 071-976-5686. TELEX 938529. Ed. John Badler. circ. 2,000,000. **Document type:** corporate report.
   Former titles: British Gas. Report and Accounts & British Gas Corporation. Report and Accounts (ISSN 0072-0216); Gas Council (Great Britain) Report and Accounts.

665.5   531.64   UK
BRITISH GAS. MONITOR. 1985. a. free. British Gas Plc., Rivermill House, 152 Grosvenor Rd., London SW1V 3JL, England. TEL 071-821-1444. FAX 071-630-7538. TELEX 938529. Ed. J.S. Carmichael. charts; illus.; pat. circ. 25,000. **Indexed:** Energy Info.Abstr.
   Formerly: British Gas Corporation. Monitor (ISSN 0268-3296)

665.7   UK
BRITISH GAS: WORKING FOR THE FUTURE; annual review and summary financial statement. a. free. British Gas plc., Rivermill House, 152 Grosvenor Rd., London SWW1V 3JL, England. charts; stat. **Document type:** corporate report.
   Formerly (until 1992): British Gas. Annual Review.

662.6   UK
BRITOIL. ANNUAL REPORT. 1983. a. Britoil PLC, 301 St. Vincent St., Glasgow, G2 5DD, Scotland. TEL 041-204 2525. circ. 50,000.
   Description: Britoil Plc and subsidiaries' annual report for the year;, includes chairman's statement, financial statements and more.

665.7   US   ISSN 0197-8098
TP714
BROWN'S DIRECTORY OF NORTH AMERICAN AND INTERNATIONAL GAS COMPANIES. 1887. a. $265. Advanstar Communications, Inc., 7500 Old Oak Blvd., Cleveland, OH 44130. TEL 216-243-8100. FAX 216-891-2675. (Subscr. to: 131 W. First St., Duluth, MN 55802. TEL 800-346-0085) Ed. Judy Aspling. adv. **Document type:** directory, trade publication.
—CCC.
   Formerly (until 1978): Brown's Directory of North American Gas Companies (ISSN 0068-2888)
   Description: Indexes data concerning personnel, plants and facilities, sales, revenue and other aspects of North American and international gas companies.

338.47   658.8   UK   ISSN 0268-4292
BUSINESS RATIO REPORT: OIL & GAS EXPLORATION & PRODUCTION; an industry sector analysis. 1985. a. I C C Business Ratios Ltd., Freepost, Field House, Hampton, Mddx. TW12 1BR, England. TEL 081-783-0977. FAX 081-783-1940. charts; stat. **Document type:** trade publication.

338.47   658.8   UK   ISSN 0950-6535
BUSINESS RATIO REPORT: OIL & GAS REFINING & DISTRIBUTION; an industry sector analysis. 1986. a. I C C Business Ratios Ltd., Freepost, Field House, Hampton, Mddx. TW12 1BR, England. TEL 081-783-0977. FAX 081-783-1940. **Document type:** trade publication.

665.7   US   ISSN 0007-7259
TP761.B8
BUTANE - PROPANE NEWS. 1939. m. $26 (Canada $38; elsewhere $49) (effective 1996). Butane - Propane News, Inc., 338 E. Foothill Blvd., Box 660698, Arcadia, CA 91006-0698. TEL 818-357-2168. FAX 818-303-2854. Ed. Chuck Elliott. adv.: B&W page $3210, color page $4770; 8 1/8 x 10 7/8. charts; illus.; tr.lit.; index. circ. 18,000. (also avail. in microform from UMI; reprint service avail. from UMI) **Indexed:** Chem.Abstr., Fuel & Energy Abstr.
—UMI.

C O N C A W E REVIEW. see *ENVIRONMENTAL STUDIES*

665.5   330.9   US
C R A PETROLEUM ECONOMICS MONTHLY. m. $2000. Charles River Associates, John Hancock Tower, 200 Clarendon St., Boston, MA 02116. TEL 617-425-3000. FAX 617-425-3132. (And: 1001 Pennsylvania Ave., N.W., Ste. 750, Washington, DC 20004) Ed. Kim Peterson. charts.
   Description: Featuring in-depth articles on world petroleum market.

665.5   US   ISSN 0273-3250
TJ563   CODEN: JCTIDX
C T I JOURNAL. 1980. s-a. $20 to libraries. Cooling Tower Institute, Box 73383, Houston, TX 77273. TEL 713-583-4087. FAX 713-537-1721. Ed. Robert Monroe. adv. contact: Virginia Manser. bk.rev.; illus. circ. 6,000. (back issues avail.) **Indexed:** Corros.Abstr. **Document type:** academic/scholarly publication.
—Ei.

665.5
C T I NEWS. q. price varies. Cooling Tower Institute, Box 73383, Houston, TX 77273. TEL 713-583-4087. FAX 713-537-1721. **Document type:** newsletter.
   Description: Contains news of CTI and its activities, items of general interest concerning cooling towers, a question and answer section and current literature references concerning cooling towers.

665.5   US   ISSN 0362-1243
TN872.C2   CODEN: CDOOAL
CALIFORNIA. DIVISION OF OIL, GAS AND GEOTHERMAL RESOURCES. ANNUAL REPORT OF THE STATE OIL AND GAS SUPERVISOR. 1915. a. free. Division of Oil, Gas, and Geothermal Resources, 801 K St., MS 20-20, Sacramento, CA 95814-3530. TEL 916-445-9686. FAX 916-323-0424. Ed. Susan Hodgson. illus. circ. 2,400. **Indexed:** Bibl.& Ind.Geol. **Document type:** government publication.

665.5
CALIFORNIA. ENERGY COMMISSION. QUARTERLY OIL REPORT. 1987. q. Energy Commission, 1516 Ninth St., Sacramento, CA 95814. TEL 916-324-3009. **Document type:** government publication.

CANADA. ENVIRONMENT CANADA. ENVIRONMENTAL PROTECTION SERIES REPORTS. see *ENVIRONMENTAL STUDIES*

CANADA A-Z; oil, gas, mining directory. see *BUSINESS AND ECONOMICS — Trade And Industrial Directories*

CANADIAN ENERGY NEWS. see *ENERGY*

665.5   CN   ISSN 0316-3547
HD9581.C3
CANADIAN GAS FACTS. a. Can.$60 to non-members; members Can.$30. Canadian Gas Association, 243 Consumers Rd., Ste. 1200, North York, ON M2J 5E3, Canada. TEL 416-498-1994. FAX 416-498-7465.

CANADIAN NATIONAL ENERGY FORUM PROCEEDINGS. see *ENERGY*

340   665.5   CN   ISSN 0384-8965
CANADIAN OIL & GAS. irreg. (4-6/yr.). Can.$1070. Butterworths Canada Ltd., Part of the Reed Elsevier group, 75 Clegg Rd., Markham, ON L6G 1A1, Canada. TEL 905-479-2665. FAX 905-479-2826. Eds. Bennett Jones Verchere, Nigel Bankes. (looseleaf format) **Document type:** trade publication.
   Description: Monitors statutes, regulations and case law for eleven jurisdictions.

665   CN   ISSN 0068-9394
TN867
CANADIAN OIL REGISTER. 1951. a. Can.$158.50. Southam Energy Group, Ste. 300, 999 8th St., S.W., Calgary, AB T2R 1N7, Canada. TEL 403-244-6111. FAX 403-245-8666. Ed. Doreen McArthur. adv. circ. 5,500.

338.27   US
CANADIAN PETROLEUM INDUSTRY. a. $85. Midwest Register, Inc., 1120 E. 4th St., Tulsa, OK 74120. TEL 918-582-2000. FAX 918-587-9349. **Document type:** directory.
   Formerly: Oil Directory of Canada (ISSN 0474-0114)
   Description: Supplies company name, address, phone and fax numbers, division offices, office location, U.S. office if any.

CARBUROL. see *TRANSPORTATION — Automobiles*

CARTA MINERA Y PANORAMA PETROLERO. see *MINES AND MINING INDUSTRY*

551   665.5   FR   ISSN 0396-2687
QE1   CODEN: BCREDP
CENTRES DE RECHERCHES EXPLORATION - PRODUCTION ELF AQUITAINE. BULLETIN. (Supplement avail. (ISSN 0181-0901)) (Text and summaries in French, English) 1967. s-a. 210 F. (effective 1996). (Elf Aquitaine Production) Elf Aquitaine Edition, Av. Larribau, 64018 Pau Cedex, France. TEL 33-59-83-50-73. FAX 33-59-83-42-42. Ed. Jean-Francois Raynaud. abstr.; bibl.; charts; illus. circ. 2,000. **Indexed:** AESIS, Bibl.& Ind.Geol., Bull.Signal., Chem.Abstr., E&P Hlth. (1993-), Gas Process.& Ppl. (1993-), Geol.Abstr., INIS Atomind., Off.Tech. (1993-), Petrol.Abstr. (1978-). **Document type:** bulletin.
—BLDSC (2439.270000); CASDDS; Genuine Article; PADDS; SWETS. **CCC.**
   Formerly (until 1977): Societe Nationale des Petroles d'Aquitaine. Centre de Recherches de Pau. Bulletin (ISSN 0008-9672)
   Description: Publishes the results of general interest arising from research undertaken by Elf Aquitaine, particularly at the research centers or by scientists working in collaboration with Elf Aquitaine.

"CHECK THE OIL!" MAGAZINE; the publication devoted exclusively to Petroliana. see *HOBBIES*

CHEMECA - AUSTRALASIAN CONFERENCE ON CHEMICAL ENGINEERING. PROCEEDINGS. see *ENGINEERING — Chemical Engineering*

CHEMICAL AND PETROLEUM ENGINEERING. see *ENGINEERING — Chemical Engineering*

665.5   668.4   UK
CHEMICALS & POLYMERS NEWS. 1981. m. I C I Chemicals & Polymers Ltd., P.O. Box 54, Weton, Middl., Cleveland TS6 8JA, England.
   Formerly (until 1987): Petrochemicals and Plastics News.

662   US   ISSN 0009-3092
TP315   CODEN: CTFCAK
CHEMISTRY AND TECHNOLOGY OF FUELS AND OILS. English translation of: Khimiya i Tekhnologiya Topliv i Masel (RU ISSN 0023-1169) 1965. m. $1495 (foreign $1750) (effective 1996). (Russian Academy of Sciences, RU) Plenum Publishing Corp., Consultants Bureau, 233 Spring St., New York, NY 10013-1578. TEL 212-762-8468. FAX 212-463-0742. TELEX 23-421139. Ed. Yu.A. Egorov. (also avail. in microfilm from JSC; back issues avail.) **Indexed:** Cadscan, Chem.Eng.Abstr., Chem.Titles, Curr.Cont., Eng.Ind., Excerpt.Med., INIS Atomind., ISMEC, Lead Abstr., T.C.E.A., Zincscan. **Document type:** academic/scholarly publication.
—BLDSC (0410.490000); Ei; Faxon; Genuine Article; SWETS; UMI; UnCover. **CCC.**
   Refereed Serial

665.5   US   ISSN 1055-6842
CHILTON'S QUICK LUBRICATION GUIDE.* 1991. biennial. H.M. Gousha, 320 Soquel Way, Sunnyvale, CA 94086-4101.

PETROLEUM AND GAS

665.5   UK   ISSN 1353-534X
CHINA OIL & GAS REPORT. m. £315($535) I B C Publishing, Gilmoora House, 57-61 Mortimer St., London W1N 7TD, England. TEL 0171-637-4383. FAX 0171-636-6414. (Subscr. in U.S. to: IBC (USA), 290 Eliot St., Box 91004, Ashland, MA 01721-9104. TEL 508-881-2800. FAX 508-881-0982) Ed. Malcolm Nixon. **Document type:** bulletin.
    Description: Explains how China's oil and gas industries function and how Beijing's policies affect foreign companies.

662.338   UK
CHINTHE. 1970. q. free. Burmah Castrol Trading Ltd., Burmah Castrol House, Pipers Way, Swindon, Wilts. SN3 1RE, England. TEL 01793-511521. FAX 01793-513506. TELEX 449221. Ed. Angela Nixon. circ. 9,000. (back issues avail.) **Document type:** newsletter.
    Former titles: Burmah Chinthe; Burmah International.

665.7 333.8   IT   ISSN 0393-0971
CH4 ENERGIA METANO. (Text in Italian; abstracts in English) 1984. bi-m. L.100000 (foreign L.200000) (effective 1995). Associazione Tecnica Italiana del Gas, Via Palmieri 25, 10138 Turin, Italy. TEL 39-11-4345965. FAX 39-11-4472990. Ed. Vincenzo Ferro. adv.: page L.1800000; adv. contact: Concetta Siracusa. circ. 8,000. circ. 8,000 (paid).
    Description: For all gas operators interested in discussing the problems related to natural gas and energy.
    Refereed Serial

COAL & SYNFUELS TECHNOLOGY. see ENERGY

COMBUSTIBLES ET CARBURANTS. see ENERGY

COMITE DE CONTROLE DE L'ELECTRICITE ET DU GAZ. RAPPORT ANNUEL. see ENGINEERING — Electrical Engineering

665.5   US
COMPOSITE CATALOG OF OIL FIELD EQUIPMENT & SERVICES. 1929. biennial. Gulf Publishing Co., Box 2608, Houston, TX 77252-2608. TEL 713-529-4301. FAX 713-520-4433. TELEX 287330 GULF UR. Ed. Robert Rust. adv.; tr.lit.; index. circ. 20,000. (reprint service avail.)

665.5 660   US   ISSN 1042-508X
COMPOUNDINGS. 1988. m. $800 to non-members; members $60. Independent Lubricant Manufacturers Association, 651 S. Washington St., Alexandria, VA 22314. TEL 703-684-5574. FAX 703-836-8503. circ. 2,000. (tabloid format) **Document type:** trade publication, newspaper.
    Description: Features industry trendes; marketing and manufacturing innovations; new plant operations, people in the industry, legislative and regulatory developments, meetings, news and employment and business opportunities

665.5   US
CONOCO COMMENTS. 1970. 4/yr. free. Conoco Inc., 600 N. Pkwy., Houston, TX 77079. TEL 713-293-1000. Ed. Cora Robinson. bk.rev.; charts; illus. circ. 42,000. **Indexed:** Energy Ind., Energy Info.Abstr., Ind.Free Per.
    Formerly (until 1987): Conoco.

665.5   US
CONTRACTS FOR FIELD PROJECTS AND SUPPORTING RESEARCH ON ENHANCED OIL RECOVERY. PROGRESS REVIEW. Short title: Enhanced Oil Recovery. Progress Review. q. free. U.S. Department of Energy, Bartlesville Project Office, Box 1398, Bartlesville, OK 74005. TEL 918-337-4401. (Subscr. to: National Technical Infomation Service, 5285 Port Royal Rd., Springfield, VA 22161. TEL 703-587-4650. FAX 703-321-8547) (Co-sponsor: U.S. Department of Energy. Office of Gas and Petroleum Technology) charts; stat.; maps. **Document type:** government publication.
    Description: Reports on the status of D.O.E.-sponsored enhanced oil recovery and gas recovery projects, along with the results of field tests.

665.5   US
COOLING TOWER INSTITUTE. BIBLIOGRAPHY OF TECHNICAL PAPERS. m. price varies. Cooling Tower Institute, Box 73383, Houston, TX 77273. TEL 713-583-4087. FAX 713-537-1721. **Document type:** bibliography.
    Description: Lists available technical papers which were presented at meetings sponsored by the institute.

665.54 690   US
D C A NEWS. 1961. m. membership. Distribution Contractors Association, 101 W. Renner Rd., Ste. 250, Richardson, TX 75082. TEL 214-680-0261. FAX 214-680-0461. Ed. Dennis J. Kennedy. circ. 500. **Document type:** newsletter.

665.5   GW   ISSN 0938-068X
D G M K BERICHTE. irreg. Deutsche Wissenschaftliche Gesellschaft fuer Erdoel, Erdgas und Kohle e.V., Steinstr. 7, 20095 Hamburg, Germany. TEL 040-32324821. FAX 040-326398. **Document type:** academic/scholarly publication, monographic series.
    —BLDSC (8598.433000).

665.5   YU   ISSN 0352-0870
D I T; strucni casopis. (Text in Serbo-Croatian) 1982. q. $10. Drustvo Inzenjera i Tehnicara "Nafta - Gas", Sutjeska 1, 21000 Novi Sad, Yugoslavia. s-a. TEL 021 615-144. FAX 021-27-157. TELEX 14196. Ed. Milan Mladenovic. adv.; bk.rev. circ. 700. (back issues avail.)

333.8   US
D R I - MCGRAW-HILL ENERGY REVIEW: COAL INDUSTRY FOCUS. Key Title: Coal Industry Focus. s-a. D R I - McGraw-Hill, 24 Hartwell Ave., Lexington, MA 02173. TEL 617-863-5100. FAX 617-860-6332. TELEX 200 284.

665.7 333.79   US
D R I - MCGRAW-HILL ENERGY REVIEW: NATURAL GAS REVIEW. s-a. D R I - McGraw-Hill, 24 Hartwell Ave., Lexington, MA 02173. TEL 617-863-5100. FAX 617-860-6332. TELEX 200 284.

665.5   US   ISSN 0276-5934
DAILY MUNGER OILOGRAM. d. $680. Munger Oil Information Service, Inc., 9800 S. Sepulveda Blvd., Ste. 723, Box 45738, Los Angeles, CA 90045. TEL 310-645-3282. FAX 310-645-9147. Ed. Averill H. Munger. stat. **Document type:** newsletter.
    Description: Provides information on exploration wells, abandonments, map revisions, and developments affecting the industry, with a focus on California, Alaska, Arizona, Nevada, Oregon, and Washington.

665.5   CN   ISSN 0709-681X
DAILY OIL BULLETIN. 1937. 5/w. Can.$785. Southam Magazine & Information Group (Calgary), 999 Eighth St. S.W., Ste. 300, Calgary, AB T2R 1N7, Canada. TEL 403-244-6111. FAX 403-245-8666. Ed. Ian McKinnon; Pub. Rick Charland. m. and a. index. (back issues avail.) **Document type:** newsletter.
    ●Also available online. Vendor(s): Southam Electronic Publishing.

622.33   UK   ISSN 0267-7652
DEVELOPMENTS IN PETROLEUM ENGINEERING. 1985. irreg. price varies. Elsevier Science Ltd., Books Division, P.O. Box 800, Kidlington, Oxford OX5 1DX, England. TEL 44-1865-843000. FAX 44-1865-843010. E-mail: nlinfo-f@elsevier.nl; usinfo-f@elsevier.com; forinfo-kyf04035@niftyserve.or.jp; Site addr.: http://www.elsevier.nl/. (Subscr. in U.S. and Canada to: Elsevier Science, 660 White Plains Rd., Tarrytown, NY 10591-5153. TEL 914-524-9200) Ed. R.A. Dawe. **Document type:** monographic series.
    Refereed Serial

665.6   NE   ISSN 0376-7361
                       CODEN: DPSCDZ
DEVELOPMENTS IN PETROLEUM SCIENCE. (Text in English) 1976. irreg., vol.39, 1993. Elsevier Science B.V., Books Division, P.O. Box 211, 1000 AE Amsterdam, Netherlands. TEL 31-20-4853911. FAX 31-20-4853705. TELEX 18582 ESPA NL. E-mail: nlinfo-f@elsevier.nl; usinfo-f@elsevier.com; forinfo-kyf04035@niftyserve.or.jp; Site addr.: http://www.elsevier.nl/. (Subscr. in U.S. and Canada to: Elsevier Science Inc., Box 882, Madison Sq. Sta., New York, NY 10159. TEL 212-989-5800) (back issues avail.) **Indexed:** Chem.Abstr. **Document type:** monographic series.
    —BLDSC (3579.085800); CASDDS; Ei. **CCC**.
    Refereed Serial

662   RU   ISSN 0320-006X
QA930   CODEN: DIZGAU
DINAMIKA IZLUCHAYUSCHEGO GAZA. 1974. irreg. 0.51 Rub. (Akademiya Nauk S.S.S.R., Vychislitel'nyi Tsentr) Izdatel'stvo Nauka, 90 Profsoyuznaya ul., 117864 Moscow, Russia. TEL 234-05-84.

665.5   CN   ISSN 0847-527X
DIRECTORY OF CERTIFIED APPLIANCES AND ACCESSORIES. a. Can.$24 (yearly revision service Can.$70). Canadian Gas Association, 243 Consumers Rd., Ste. 1200, N. York, ON M2J 5E3, Canada. TEL 416-447-6468. FAX 416-447-7067. **Document type:** directory.

DIRECTORY OF ELECTRIC UTILITY INDUSTRY. see ENGINEERING — Electrical Engineering

665.7   US
DIRECTORY OF MUNICIPAL NATURAL GAS SYSTEMS. a. $25. American Public Gas Association, 11094-D Lee Hwy., Ste. 102, Fairfax, VA 22030. TEL 703-352-3890. Ed. Carole Curtis. adv. circ. 750. **Document type:** directory.

665.5   IT
DISTRIBUZIONE CARBURANTI. 12/yr. Edizioni Commercio, Via Farini 5, 00185 Rome, Italy. TEL 39-6-860941. Ed. Vincenzo Alfonsi. adv.: B&W page L.2750000, color page L.4350000; adv. contact: Vanni Polidori. circ. 30,000.

662.338   CN   ISSN 0228-5630
DRILLING ACTIVITY REPORT. 1953. m. Can.$150. Saskatchewan Energy and Mines, 1914 Hamilton St., Regina, SK S4P 4V4, Canada. TEL 306-787-2528. FAX 306-787-2527. **Document type:** government publication.
    Description: Lists by production and disposition areas and classification of wells.

665.5   US
DRILLING & WELL SERVICING CONTRACTORS;* drilling & well servicing contractors, equipment manufacturers & supply companies. a. $50. Midwest Register, Inc., 1120 E. 4th St., Tulsa, OK 74120. TEL 918-582-2000. FAX 918-587-9349. **Document type:** directory.
    Formerly: Directory of Oil Well Drilling Contractors (ISSN 0415-9764)
    Description: Supplies company name, address, phone and fax number and personnel.

665.5   US
DRILLING COMPLETION AND PLUGGING SUMMARY. m. $24 (includes Average Calendar Day Allowable Report). Railroad Commission, Oil and Gas Publications, Drawer 12967, Capitol Sta., Austin, TX 78711. TEL 512-463-7255. **Document type:** government publication.
    Description: Gives the number of drilling permits issued, oil and gas completions, dry holes, and other information but does not include permits by individual company.

PETROLEUM AND GAS

622.338 US ISSN 0046-0702
TN860
DRILLING CONTRACTOR. 1944. bi-m. $30 (foreign $40). Drilling Contractor Publications, Inc., Box 4287, Houston, TX 77210. TEL 713-578-7171. FAX 713-578-0589. Ed. Mike Killalea. adv.: B&W page $3570, color page $4670; 7 3/4 x 10 7/8. charts; illus.; stat.; tr.lit.; circ. 36,000 (controlled). Indexed: E&P Hlth. (1993-), Fuel & Energy Abstr., Gas Process.& Ppl. (1993-), Off.Tech. (1993-), Petrol.Abstr. (1961-). Document type: trade publication.
—BLDSC (3627.005000); PADDS; UnCover. CCC.
Description: Articles feature new technology and promote cooperation among drilling contractors, operators and oilfield suppliers.

665.5 US
DRILLING PERMITS. d. $325. Offshore Data Services, Inc., Box 19909, Houston, TX 77224-1909. TEL 713-781-2713. FAX 713-781-9594. Document type: abstracting/indexing.
Description: Provides current information on new oil drilling permits filed with state and federal agencies for the Gulf of Mexico and Louisiana.

662.338 US
DRILLING - THE WELLSITE MAGAZINE.* 6/yr. Energy Publications, 4545 Post Oak Place Dr., Ste. 210, Houston, TX 77027-3105. TEL 214-691-3911.
Description: Covers wellsite operations in the energy industry.

665.5 620.85 US ISSN 1054-6464
TD195.M5
E & P ENVIRONMENT. (Exploration & Production) 1990. bi-w. $395 (foreign $410). Pasha Publications Inc., 1616 N. Ft. Myer Dr., Ste. 1000, Arlington, VA 22209-3107. TEL 703-528-1244. FAX 703-528-1253. Ed. Jerry Grisham. (back issues avail.) Document type: newsletter.
●Also available online. Vendor(s): Information Access Co., NewsNet.
—CCC.
Incorporates: Petrosafe.
Description: Covers environmental issues affecting the oil and gas industries, including news of federal and state actions, enforcement and regulation, as well as trends in risk management and liability.

622 665 FR ISSN 0012-7701
E L F AQUITAINE; bulletin mensuel d'informations. 1966. m. free. E L F - Aquitaine, Direction des Relations Publiques et de la Communication, Tour ELF, Cedex 45, 92078 Paris la Defense, France. FAX 47-44-68-21. Ed. B. Lefranc. illus.; stat. circ. 18,500. Indexed: GeoRef.
—CCC.
Former titles: E L F; E R A P. Bulletin Mensuel d'Informations.

622 665 FR ISSN 0249-1729
E L F - AQUITAINE NEWS. (Text in English) 1982. m. free. E L F - Aquitaine, Directions des Relations Publiques et de la Communication, Tour ELF, 92078 Paris La Defense Cedex 45, France. FAX 47-44-32-32. Ed. Brice Lefranc. adv.; charts; illus.; stat. circ. 8,000.
—CCC.

E N I ANNUAL REPORT. (Ente Nazionale Idrocarburi) see *ENERGY*

665.5 UA
EGYPTIAN JOURNAL OF PETROLEUM. (Text in English; summaries in Arabic, English) 1993. 2/yr. $37. Egyptian Petroleum Research Institute, Seventh Region, Madinat Nasr, Cairo, Egypt. TEL 20-2-607847. FAX 20-2-607433. Ed. Bahram M. Mahmoud. (reprint service avail. from IRC) Document type: academic/scholarly publication.

665.5 RU
EKONOMIKA TOPLIVNO-ENERGETICHESKOGO KOMPLEKSA ROSSII; nauchno-tekhnicheskii zhurnal. 1989. 6/yr. Vserossiiskii Nauchno-Issledovatel'nyi Institut Organizatsii, Upravleniya i Ekonomiki Neftegazovoi Promyshlennosti (VNIIOENG), Ul. Nametkina, 14, korp.B, 117420 Moscow, Russia. TEL 7-95-3320099. Ed. A.A. Makarov.
—BLDSC (0397.754000).
Formerly (until 1992): Ekonomika i Khozraschet Predpriyatii Toplivno-energeticheskovo Kompleksa (ISSN 0235-7968)

ENAJI TAIWA. see *ENERGY*

665.5 SP
ENCICLOPEDIA NACIONAL DEL PETROLEO PETROLQUIMICA Y GAS. 1970. a. $180. Oilgas S.A., Paseo de la Habana, 48, 28036 Madrid, Spain. TEL 34-1-5635800. FAX 34-1-5635234. Ed. Carlos Martin. circ. 6,000.
Description: Spanish national encyclopedia on the petroleum, petrochemical and gas activities.

ENERGIEWIRTSCHAFTLICHE TAGESFRAGEN; Zeitschrift fuer Energie-Wirtschaft, Recht und Technik, und Umwelt. see *ENERGY*

ENERGIMAGASINET. see *MINES AND MINING INDUSTRY*

665.5 SI
ENERGY ASIA; weekly newsletter on Asia's energy industry. (Text in English) 1979. w. $150. Petroleum News Publishing Pte. Ltd., 43 Middle Road., 04-00, Singapore 0718, Singapore. TEL 3367128. FAX 3367919. Ed. Julie Bundy. circ. 6,000. (back issues avail.)

ENERGY DIGEST. see *ENERGY*

ENERGY IN JAPAN. see *ENERGY*

ENERGY POLICY; international journal of the political, economic, planning and social aspects of energy. see *ENERGY*

ENERGY PROCESSING - CANADA. see *ENERGY*

ENERGY REPORT. see *ENERGY*

ENERGY REPORT; energy policy and technology news bulletin. see *ENERGY*

333.8 665.5 UK
▼**THE ENERGY REPORT. VOLUME 1. MARKETS IN TRANSITION.** 1994. a. price varies. Department of Trade & Industry, Rm. 2-1-10, 1 Palace St., London SW1E 5HE, England. (Orders to: H.M.S.O., P.O. Box 276, London SW1E 5HE, England. TEL 0171-573-0011) Document type: government publication.
Description: Sets out the main developments in the U.K. energy sector, along with security of the energy supply and environmental concerns.

338.8 665.5 UK ISSN 1354-6864
THE ENERGY REPORT. VOLUME 2: OIL AND GAS RESOUCES IN THE UNITED KINGDOM. 1975. a. price varies. Department of Trade & Industry, Rm. 2-1-10, 1 Palace St., London SW1E 5HE, England. (Orders to: H.M.S.O., P.O. Box 276, London SW8 5DT, England. TEL 0171-873-0011) illus. Document type: government publication.
Formerly (until 1994): Great Britain. Department of Energy. Development of the Oil and Gas Resources of the United Kingdom (ISSN 0269-3429)
Description: Covers exploration and production; includes economic, industrial and environmental aspects.

ENERGY SOURCES; journal of extraction, conversion, & the environment. see *ENERGY*

ENERGY TODAY. see *ENERGY*

ENERGY TRENDS. see *ENERGY*

ENERGY WORLD. see *ENERGY*

665.7 IT ISSN 0071-0687
ENTE NAZIONALE IDROCARBURI. REPORT AND STATEMENT OF ACCOUNTS. a. Ente Nazionale Idrocarburi, Piazzale Enrico Mattei 1, 00144 Rome, Italy.

665 338.2 AU
ERDOEL. 1969. 6/yr. free. Shell Austria AG, Rennweg 12, A-1030 Vienna, Austria. TEL 01-79797-206. FAX 01-79797-201. TELEX 133241-SHEL-A. index. circ. 4,800. Document type: bulletin.
Supersedes: Shell Erdoel-Informationen (ISSN 0037-3567)

665.5 GW ISSN 0179-3187
TN860 CODEN: EEKOEY
ERDOEL - ERDGAS - KOHLE; Aufsuchung und Gewinnung, Verarbeitung und Anwendung, Petrochemie, chemische Kohlenveredlung. (Annual Directory number avail.) (Summaries in English and German) 1884. m. DM.411. (German Scientific Society of Petroleum, Gas and Coal Chemistry) Urban-Verlag GmbH, Postfach 701606, 22016 Hamburg, Germany. TEL 040-6567071. FAX 040-6567075. (Co-sponsors: Austrian Society of Petroleum Sciences) Eds. T. Vieth, H.J. Mager. adv.; bk.rev.; abstr.; bibl.; charts; illus.; stat.; index. circ. 4,100. Indexed: Anal.Abstr., API Abstr., API Catal., API Hlth.& Environ., API Oil., API Pet.Ref., API Pet.Subst., API Transport., Bibl.& Ind.Geol., Br.Geol.Lit., C.I.S.Abstr., Chem.Abstr., Chem.Eng.Abstr., Chem.Infd., E&P Hlth. (1993-), Energy Info.Abstr., Eng.Ind., Excerp.Med. (until 199?), Fluidex, Fuel & Energy Abstr., Gas Process.& Ppl. (1993-), INIS Atomind., Key to Econ.Sci., Off.Tech. (1993-), Petrol.Abstr. (1961-), PROMT, Risk Abstr., Sci.Cit.Ind., T.C.E.A. Document type: trade publication.
—BLDSC (3799.720000); CASDDS; Ei; Genuine Article; PADDS; SWETS. CCC.
Incorporates (in 1995): Erdoel und Kohle, Erdgas, Petrochemie vereinigt mit Brennstoff-Chemie (ISSN 0367-0716); Which was formed by the 1970 merger of: Brennstoff-Chemie (ISSN 0006-9620); And: Erdoel und Kohle, Erdgas, Petrochemie (ISSN 0014-0058); Former titles: Erdoel - Erdgas (ISSN 0724-8555); Erdoel-Erdgas Zeitschrift (ISSN 0014-004X)

ERDOEL-INFORMATIONSDIENST. see *ENERGY*

ERNST & YOUNG'S OIL AND GAS TAX REPORTER. see *BUSINESS AND ECONOMICS — Public Finance, Taxation*

665 MY ISSN 0127-0710
ESSO IN MALAYSIA. (Text in English, Malay) 1962. m. free. Esso Malaysia Berhad, P.O. Box 10601, Kuala Lumpur, Malaysia. TEL 03-2428760. FAX 03-2422521. (Co-sponsor: Esso Production Malaysia Inc.) Ed. Chan Soon Ching. illus. circ. 3,900.
Formerly: Esso News (ISSN 0014-102X)

665.5 NO ISSN 0802-9474
HD9560.1 CODEN: EUJOE5
EUROIL; European oil and gas journal. (Text in English) 1973. m. £80($198) Hart Europe Ltd., P.O. Box 480, 4001 Stavanger, Norway. (Subscr. to: Richard Fry and Associates, Ste. 225, Surrey House, 34 Eden St., Kingston upon Thames, Surrey KT1 1ER, England. TEL 081-549-3444) Ed. Mark Scruton. adv.; bk.rev.; charts; illus.; stat.; tr.lit. circ. 17,000. Indexed: Bibl.& Ind.Geol., BMT, Br.Geol.Lit., Br.Tech.Ind., Energy Info.Abstr., Petrol.Abstr.
—BLDSC (3829.268800); SWETS. CCC.
Formerly (until 1990): Noroil (ISSN 0332-544X)

338.2 665 GW ISSN 0014-2824
EUROPE OIL-TELEGRAM. 1963. 2/w. DM.1265. KG Oil-Telegram GmbH und Co., Carl-Petersen-Str. 70-76, 20535 Hamburg, Germany. FAX 040-256392. Ed. Dieter W. Gripp. adv.; bk.rev. circ. 1,000.
—CCC.

EUROPEAN ASSOCIATION OF PETROLEUM GEOSCIENTISTS. SPECIAL PUBLICATION. see *EARTH SCIENCES — Geology*

665.5 NO ISSN 0332-5210
EUROPEAN OFFSHORE PETROLEUM NEWSLETTER. (Text in English) 1976. w. £570($200) Hart Europe Ltd., P.O. Box 480, 4001 Stavanger, Norway. (Subscr. to: Richard Fry and Associates, Ste. 225, Surrey House, 34 Eden St., Kingston upon Thames, Surrey KT1 1ER, England. TEL 081-549-3444) Ed. Dan Rigden.
—CCC.

665.7 FR ISSN 1152-6564
EUROPEAN OIL & GAS MANAGEMENT DIRECTORY. 1931. a. 685 F. Editions Technip, 27 rue Ginoux, 75737 Paris Cedex 15, France. adv. Document type: directory.
—CCC.
Former titles (until 1990): Guide du Petrole, Gaz, Petrochimie (ISSN 0294-1120); Guide du Petrole, Gaz, Chimie (ISSN 0072-8055)

5030 PETROLEUM AND GAS

665.5 US ISSN 0275-3871
HD9575.A12
EUROPEAN PETROLEUM DIRECTORY. 1979. a. $115 (or $210 as a 2 volume set with Asia-Pacific-Africa-Middle East Directory). Pennwell Publishing Co., Box 1260, Tulsa, OK 74101. TEL 918-835-3161. FAX 918-831-9497. TELEX 211012. Ed. Jonelle Moore. adv. **Document type:** directory.
—CCC.
Supersedes in part: Eastern Hemisphere Petroleum Directory (ISSN 0070-8224)
Description: Lists companies involved in drilling, refining, exploration, pipelines, engineering, field services, construction and any other petroleum-related operations.

665.5 GW ISSN 0342-6947
HD9575.A1
EUROPEAN PETROLEUM YEARBOOK/JAHRBUCH DER EUROPAEISCHEN ERDOELINDUSTRIE/ANNUAIRE EUROPEEN DU PETROLE. Variant title: A N E P. (Text in English, French and German) 1963. a. DM.180. Urban Verlag Hamburg-Wien GmbH, Postfach 701606, 22016 Hamburg, Germany. TEL 040-6567071. FAX 040-6567075. Ed. Thomas Vieth. adv. contact: Harald Jordan. circ. 2,000. **Document type:** directory.
—BLDSC (0900.450000). **CCC**.

665.5 UK
EUROPEAN PUMPS & PUMPING. 1981. irreg. £60. C H W Roles & Associates Ltd., P.O. Box 25, Sunbury-on-Thames, Mddx. TW16 5QB, England. TEL 081-783 0088. Ed. Richard R.S. Tomes. adv. **Document type:** trade publication.
Formerly: British Pump Market.
Description: Practical reference book and buyer's guide to manufacturers and suppliers of pumps and auxiliary equipment available throughout Europe.

665.5 UK ISSN 0956-6333
EUROPETROLEUM; with Aberdeen Petroleum Quarterly. 1989. q. £40 worldwide (effective 1996) (free with Aberdeen Petroleum Report). Aberdeen Petroleum Publishing Ltd., 35 Huntly St., Aberdeen AB1 1TJ, Scotland. TEL 01224-644725. FAX 01224-647574. Ed. Ted Strachan. circ. controlled. (back issues avail.) **Document type:** trade publication.
Formerly: Aberdeen Petroleum Quarterly.
Description: News and business intelligence about the petroleum industry.

EXPERIMENTAL PETROLEUM GEOLOGY/SHUYOU SHIYAN DIZHI. see *EARTH SCIENCES — Geology*

665.5 US
EXPLORATION DAILY. d. $53 per mo. Petroleum Information Corporation, Box 2162, Denver, CO 80201-2162. TEL 303-740-7100. FAX 303-694-1754. **Document type:** newsletter.
Description: Covers important worldwide petroleum exploration news, including wildcats, new discoveries, and land plays.

665.538 US
F M A TODAY. 1976. fortn. membership. Fuel Merchants Association of New Jersey, 66 Morris Ave., Springfield, NJ 07081. TEL 201-467-1400. FAX 201-467-4066. Ed. Marjorie R. Krampf. circ. 900.

FACTS & FIGURES; a graphical analysis of world energy. see *ENERGY*

665.5 333.79 US
FEDERAL TAXATION OF OIL AND GAS TRANSACTIONS. 1958. a. $300. Matthew Bender & Co., Inc., 11 Penn Plaza, New York, NY 10001. TEL 212-967-7707. (Subscr. to: 1275 Broadway, New York, NY 12201) Eds. Cecil L. Smith, Robert Poleroi. (looseleaf format)

FILTRATION NEWS. see *ENVIRONMENTAL STUDIES*

665.5 UK ISSN 0141-3228
HG4821
FINANCIAL TIMES INTERNATIONAL YEAR BOOKS: OIL AND GAS. 1910. a. £140. Longman Group UK Ltd., Westgate House, 6th Fl., The High, Harlow, Essex CM20 1YR, England. TEL 0279-442601. FAX 0279-444501. (Dist. in U.S. and Canada by: St. James Press, 425 North Michigan Ave., Chicago, IL 60611) adv.: B&W page £730, color page £1155; 202 x 154. **Document type:** directory.
—BLDSC (3927.005000). **CCC**.
Formerly: Oil and Petroleum Year Book.

668 UK ISSN 0141-3236
HD9560.3
FINANCIAL TIMES INTERNATIONAL YEAR BOOKS: WHO'S WHO IN WORLD OIL AND GAS. a. £115. Longman Group UK Ltd., Westgate House, 6th Fl., The High, Harlow, Essex CM20 1YR, England. TEL 0279-442601. FAX 0279-444501. adv.: B&W page £545, color page £1100; 202 x 154. **Document type:** directory.
—BLDSC (9312.560000). **CCC**.

665.5 AT
FLAME. 1976. q. free. Australian Gas Light Co., 111 Pacific Highway Nth., Sydney, N.S.W. 2000, Australia. Ed. M. Tesoriero. circ. 4,000.

665.5 UK
FLEET LIST. 1981. q. free. Shell Tankers (UK) Ltd., Shell Centre, London SE1 7PQ, England. Ed. Terence Ryan. adv. circ. 3,500.
Formerly (until 1988): British Fleet List.

FLUESSIGGAS. see *ENERGY*

622 FR ISSN 0046-4481
FORAGES. 1958. q. $25. Institut Francais du Petrole, B.P. 311, 4 av. Bois Preau, 92506 Rueil-Malmaison Cedex, France. TEL 47-52-61-48. TELEX IFP 203 050 F. Ed. Paneleay. adv.; bibl.; charts; illus.; stat.; tr.lit.; index, cum.index. circ. 2,500.
—CCC.

662 US ISSN 0095-1587
KF1870.A15
FOSTER NATURAL GAS REPORT. 1956. w. $1065 (effective 1995). Foster Associates, 1015 15th St., N.W., Washington, DC 20005-2605. TEL 202-408-7710. FAX 202-408-7723. Ed. Edgar David Boshart. index; circ. 1,100 (paid). **Document type:** trade publication, newsletter.
●Also available online. Vendor(s): Lexis-Nexis.
—CCC.

665.5 VE
FRENTE NACIONAL PRO-DEFENSA DEL PETROLEO VENEZOLANO. ACTUACIONES. 1970. irreg. $5 per no. Frente Nacional Pro Defensa del Petroleo Venezolano, Apto. 50514, Caracas 105, Venezuela. circ. 3,000.

662.6 UK ISSN 0016-2361
TP315 CODEN: FUELAC
FUEL; science and technology of fuel and energy. 1922. 15/yr. £895($1424) (effective 1996). Butterworth - Heinemann, Part of the Reed Elsevier group, Linacre House, Jordan Hill, Oxford OX2 8DP, England. TEL 01865-310366. FAX 01865-310898. TELEX 83111 BHPOXF G. (Subscr. to: Elsevier Science Ltd., P.O. Box 800, Kidlington, Oxford OX5 1DX, England. TEL 44-1865-843000. FAX 44-1865-843010; Subscr. in U.S. and Canada to: Elsevier Science, 660 White Plains Rd., Tarrytown, NY 10591-5153. TEL 914-524-9200. FAX 914-333-2444) Ed.Bd. adv.; bk.rev.; illus.; index, cum.index: 1922-1981. (also avail. in microfilm from UMI; back issues avail.) **Indexed:** Acid Rain Abstr., Acid Rain Ind., AESIS, API Abstr., API Catal., API Hlth.& Environ., API Oil., API Pet.Ref., API Pet.Subst., API Transport., Appl.Mech.Rev., Br.Ceram.Abstr., Br.Tech.Ind., Cadscan, Chem.Abstr., Curr.Cont., E&P Hlth. (1993-), Energy Abstr., Energy Info.Abstr., Energy Rev., Eng.Ind., Environ.Abstr., Excerp.Med., Gas Process.& Ppl. (1993-), GeoRef., Ind.Sci.Rev., Lead Abstr., Mass Spectr.Bull., Off.Tech. (1993-), Petrol.Abstr. (1961-1964, 1982-), Sci.Cit.Ind., Zincscan. **Document type:** academic/scholarly publication.
—BLDSC (4048.000000); CASDDS; CIS; Ei; Faxon; Genuine Article; PADDS; SWETS; UMI; UnCover. **CCC**.
Description: Studies the nature, conservation, preparation, use, physical and nuclear properties of gaseous, liquid and solid fuels.
Refereed Serial

388.324 665.538 UK
FUEL OIL NEWS AND ROAD TANKER TRANSPORT. 1977. m. £46.20. Fuel Oil News Ltd., Regent House, Bexton Ln., Knutsford, Ches. WA16 9AB, England. TEL 01565-653283. FAX 01565-755607. Ed. James Smith. adv. contact: Margaret Boydell. **Document type:** trade publication.
Description: Contains news, opinion, and information for the oil fuel distribution trade.

662.6 NE ISSN 0378-3820
TP315 CODEN: FPTEDY
FUEL PROCESSING TECHNOLOGY; an international journal devoted to all aspects of processing coal, oil shale, tar sands and peat. (Text in English) 1978. 15/yr. fl.2075($1265) (effective 1996). Elsevier Science B.V., P.O. Box 211, 1000 AE Amsterdam, Netherlands. TEL 31-20-4853911. FAX 31-20-4853598. TELEX 18582 ESPA NL. E-mail: nlinfo-f@elsevier.nl; usinfo-f@elsevier.com; forinfo-kyf04035@niftyserve.or.jp; Site addr.: http://www.elsevier.nl/. (Subscr. in U.S. and Canada to: Elsevier Science Inc., Box 882, Madison Sq. Sta., New York, NY 10159. TEL 212-989-5800. FAX 212-633-3990) Ed.Bd. (also avail. in microform from UMI) **Indexed:** AESIS, Chem.Abstr., Curr.Cont., Energy Ind., Energy Info.Abstr., Energy Rev., Eng.Ind., Environ.Abstr., Environ.Per.Bibl. (1982-), Excerp.Med., Fuel & Energy Abstr., Gas Abstr., Ind.Sci.Rev., Petrol.Abstr., Sci.Cit.Ind. **Document type:** academic/scholarly publication.
—BLDSC (4052.760000); CASDDS; Ei; Faxon; Genuine Article; SWETS; UnCover. **CCC**.
Description: Deals with the scientific and technological aspects of processing fuels to other fuels, chemicals and by-products.
Refereed Serial

665.538 US ISSN 1062-3744
TP692.5 CODEN: FUREEQ
FUEL REFORMULATION. 1991. bi-m. $149. Hart Publishing, 4545 Post Oak Pl., Houston, TX 77027. TEL 713-993-9320. FAX 713-840-8585. Ed. Rene Gonzalez. adv. circ. 5,000. (also avail. in microform from UMI) **Document type:** trade publication.
—BLDSC (4052.775000); CASDDS; SWETS; UMI. **CCC**.
Description: Analyzes the business, technical and regulatory circumstances associated with the manufacture, supply and use of transportation fuels, reformulated to improve air quality worldwide.

665.7 662 US ISSN 1060-9725
CODEN: FOHCEU
FUELOIL & OIL HEAT WITH AIR CONDITIONING. 1922. m. $20. Industry Publications, Inc. (Fairfield), 389 Passaic Ave., Fairfield, NJ 07006. TEL 201-227-5151. FAX 201-227-9219. Ed. Paul Geiger. adv.; illus.; stat. circ. 13,300. (also avail. in microform from UMI; back issues avail.; reprint service avail.) **Indexed:** B.P.I, Bus.Ind., Chem.Abstr., Fuel & Energy Abstr., Tr.& Indus.Ind. **Document type:** trade publication.
—Faxon; UMI; UnCover.
Former titles (until 1991): Fueloil and Oil Heat (ISSN 1061-141X); (until 1990): Fueloil and Oil Heat Magazine (ISSN 0888-0735); (until 1985): Fueloil and Oil Heat and Solar Systems (ISSN 0148-9801); (until vol.36, no.8, Aug. 1977): Fueloil and Oil Heat (ISSN 0016-2418)

665.5 FR ISSN 0985-200X
G P L ACTUALITE. (Gaz de Petrole Liquefie) (Supplement to: Petrole Informations) 1987. q. Societe d' Information et de Documentation, Bureau d'Informations Professionnelles, 142 rue Montmartre, 75002 Paris, France. TEL 40-26-83-21. FAX 40-39-97-52. TELEX 220 528 BIP.
—BLDSC (6430.701000).

665.5 620 US
G P S A ENGINEERING DATA BOOK. (In 2 vols.) irreg., latest revised 10th ed. $65 to non-members; members $35. Gas Processors Suppliers Association, Box 35584, Tulsa, OK 74153. TEL 918-493-3872. FAX 918-493-3875. Ed. Ronald G. Brunner. **Document type:** trade publication.
Description: Compiles basic design information, current technical data, and approved procedures for use by gas processing personnel to determine operating and design parameters for hydrocarbon processing and related facilities.

665.7 US
G R I D. (Gas Research Institute Digest) 1976. q. free. Gas Research Institute, Member Relations and Communications, 8600 W. Bryn Mawr Ave., Chicago, IL 60631. TEL 312-399-8100. FAX 312-399-8170. TELEX 253812. Ed. Elizabeth Cicchetti. index; circ. 11,000 (controlled). (back issues avail.) **Indexed:** Energy Info.Abstr., Environ.Abstr., Gas Abstr. **Document type:** trade publication.
Description: Natural gas research of a technical nature explained in simplified terms.

665.7 628 SZ
 CODEN: GWASA4
G W A. (Gas - Wasser - Abwasser) (Text in English, French and German) 1921. m. 202 SFr. Schweizerischer Verein des Gas- und Wasserfaches - Societe Suisse de l'Industrie du Gaz et des Eaux, Gruetlistr. 44, CH-8027 Zurich, Switzerland. TEL 01-2883333. FAX 01-2021633. Ed. C. Nagel. adv.; bk.rev.; bibl.; charts; illus.; stat.; index. circ. 1,600. (back issues avail.) **Indexed:** C.I.S. Abstr., Chem.Abstr., Geo.Abstr. **Document type:** trade publication.
—BLDSC (4085.900000); CASDDS; SWETS.
 Former titles: G W A - Gas Wasser Abwasser (ISSN 0036-8008); Schweizerischer Verein von Gas und Wasserfachmaennern. Monatsbulletin.

665.7 NE ISSN 0016-4828
TP700
GAS. (Text in Dutch; summaries in English) 1880. m. (11/yr.). fl.127.20 (effective 1994). Stichting Tijdschrift Openbare Gasvoorziening, Postbus 220, 7300 AE Apeldoorn, Netherlands. TEL 31-55-494949. FAX 31-55-418963. TELEX 49456. Ed. L.F. Kop. adv.; bk.rev.; charts; illus.; pat.; stat.; index. circ. 2,700. (also avail. in microfilm from UMI; reprint service avail. from UMI) **Indexed:** A.S.& T.Ind., Chem.Abstr., Eng.Ind., Excerp.Med., Gas Abstr., Int.Build.Serv.Abstr., Key to Econ.Sci., Met.Abstr. **Document type:** trade publication.
—SWETS.
 Description: Contains information on the gas industry; distribution, applications and supply.

665.538 GW ISSN 0343-2092
TN880.A1
GAS; internationale Zeitschrift fuer wirtschaftliche und umweltfreudliche Energieanwendung. 1949. 6/yr. DM.128 (effective 1996). (Bundesverband der deutschen Gas-und Wasserwirtschaft e.V.) R. Oldenbourg Verlag GmbH, Rosenheimerstr. 145, 81671 Munich, Germany. TEL 089-45051-0. FAX 089-45051207. (Subscr. to: Postfach 801360, 81613 Munich, Germany) (Co-sponsors: Deutscher Verein des Gas-und Wasserfaches; Fachverband Heiz-und Kochgeraete Industrie; Technische Vereinigung der Firmen im Gas-und Wasserfach) adv.; bk.rev. circ. 5,500. **Indexed:** Key to Econ.Sci. **Document type:** trade publication.
—BLDSC (4073.100000). CCC.
 Description: Trade publication for the natural gas industry covering technology, air pollution control, energy savings, economics and international news.

662 AT ISSN 0072-0208
GAS AND FUEL CORPORATION OF VICTORIA. ANNUAL REPORT. 1851. a. free. Gas and Fuel Corporation of Victoria, 171 Flinders St., Melbourne 3000, Vic., Australia. FAX 03-652-4801. TELEX AA31422. Ed. Ray Poudley. circ. 5,500. **Document type:** corporate report.

665.7 UK
GAS APPLIANCES, for installers and retailers. 1991. bi-m. £25 (foreign £40). (Gas Marketing Ltd.) Carter Spencer Publishing Ltd., Chancery Ct., Lincoln Rd., High Wycombe, Bucks. HP12 3RE, England. TEL 01494-442424. Ed. Nicholas Carter. adv.: page £1550; trim 297 x 210; adv. contact: David Spencer. charts; illus.; pat.; stat.; tr.lit.; circ. 30,000. **Document type:** trade publication.
 Description: Provides information for people associated with or interested in the gas and gas appliance industries.

665.5 US ISSN 1048-938X
HD9581.U5
GAS CONSUMPTION OF THE UNITED STATES. 1973. biennial. $3. American Gas Association, 1515 Wilson Blvd., Arlington, VA 22109-0765. TEL 703-841-8400. FAX 703-841-8406. **Document type:** trade publication.
 Formerly: Future Gas Consumption of the United States (ISSN 0740-1493)

665.7 US ISSN 0885-5935
GAS DAILY. 1974. d. (5/wk.). $1047 (foreign $1135). Pasha Publications Inc., 1616 N. Ft. Myer Dr., Ste. 1000, Arlington, VA 22209-3107. TEL 703-528-1244. Ed. Robert Barton. (back issues avail.) **Document type:** newsletter.
●Also available online. Vendor(s): Data-Star, Knight-Ridder, Inc..
—CCC.
 Formerly (until 1985): Inside Gas Markets.

665.7 US ISSN 1068-1299
HD9581.A1
GAS DAILY'S N G. 1993. bi-m. Pasha Publications Inc., 1616 N. Fort Meyer Dr., Ste. 1000, Arlington, VA 22209-3107. TEL 703-528-1244. FAX 703-528-1253. **Document type:** trade publication.
—CCC.

662 US ISSN 0161-4851
TP700
GAS DIGEST;* the magazine of gas operations. 1975. q. $12 to qualified personnel; others $20. Tri-Plek Productions, 11246 S. Post Oak Rd., Ste. 204, Houston, TX 77035-5741. TEL 713-723-7456. Ed. Ken Kridner. adv.; bk.rev. circ. 3,500. **Indexed:** Fuel & Energy Abstr., Petrol.Abstr.

665.7 UK ISSN 0306-6444
TP700 CODEN: GEMABL
GAS ENGINEERING & MANAGEMENT. 1961. 10/yr. £78 to non-members. Institution of Gas Engineers, 21 Portland Pl., London W1N 3AF, England. Ed. Barrie Atkinson. adv.; bibl.; charts; illus.; stat.; index. circ. 6,000. (also avail. in microform from UMI; reprint service avail. from UMI) **Indexed:** API Abstr., API Catal., API Hlth.& Environ., API Oil., API Pet.Ref., API Pet.Subst., API Transport., Br.Ceram.Abstr., Br.Tech.Ind., C.I.S. Abstr., Eng.Ind., Excerp.Med., Fuel & Energy Abstr., Gas Abstr., Int.Build.Serv.Abstr., Met.Abstr., W.R.C.Inf., World Alum.Abstr.
—BLDSC (4077.550000); Ei; Faxon; Genuine Article; SWETS; UMI; UnCover.
 Formerly: Institution of Gas Engineers. Journal (ISSN 0020-3432)

665.7 628 338.2 GW ISSN 0016-4909
 CODEN: GWGEAQ
GAS - ERDGAS - G W F; das Gas- und Wasserfach. 1858. m. DM.368 to non-members; members DM.258 (effective 1996). (Deutsche Verein der Gas -und Wasserfaches Bundesverband der Deutscher Gas- und Wasserwirtschaft (DVGW)) R. Oldenbourg Verlag GmbH, Rosenheimerstr. 145, 81671 Munich, Germany. TEL 089-45051-0. FAX 089-45051207. (Subscr. to: Postfach 801360, 81613 Munich, Germany) adv.; bk.rev.; abstr.; charts; illus.; mkt.; tr.lit.; tr.mk.; index. **Indexed:** API Abstr., API Catal., API Hlth.& Environ., API Oil., API Pet.Ref., API Pet.Subst., API Transport., C.I.S. Abstr., Chem.Abstr., Eng.Ind., Excerp.Med., Fuel & Energy Abstr. **Document type:** trade publication.
—BLDSC (4085.050000); CASDDS; SWETS. **CCC**.
 Description: Trade publication for the gas industry featuring gas production, distribution, installation and technology. Includes events, patents and positions available.

665 US ISSN 0361-4298
TP722
GAS FACTS; a statistical record of the gas utility industry. 1946. a. $55 to non-members; members $28. American Gas Association, Department of Statistics, 1515 Wilson Blvd., Arlington, VA 22209. TEL 703-841-8559. FAX 703-841-8406. (Subscr. to: Dept. 0765, McLean, VA 22109-0765) circ. 3,000. (also avail. in microfiche from CIS) **Indexed:** SRI.
—BLDSC (4077.650000).

665.7 US
TP350
GAS INDUSTRIES MAGAZINE; the executive, administration, operations management and engineering magazine of gas energy supply, pipeline transmission, utility distribution. (Includes s-a. A G A News) 1956. m. $20 (foreign $90). Gas Industries Inc., Box 558, Park Ridge, IL 60068. TEL 312-693-3682. FAX 708-696-3445. Ed. Ruth W. Stidger. adv.: B&W page $2595, color page $3990; 8 1/8 x 10 7/8; adv. contact: William Dannhausen. bk.rev.; circ. 11,000 (controlled). (also avail. in microform) **Indexed:** Corros.Abstr., Gas Abstr. **Document type:** trade publication.
—BLDSC (4077.840000); CIS; Ei; SWETS; UMI. **CCC**.
 Formerly: Gas Industries E and A News (ISSN 0194-2468); Incorporates: Better Schools (Chicago) (ISSN 0363-373X); Industrial Energy (ISSN 0094-1646); Gas in Industry (ISSN 0016-4933)
 Refereed Serial

665.7 UK ISSN 0954-853X
GAS INDUSTRY DIRECTORY (YEAR). 1896. a. £86. Miller Freeman Information Services (Subsidiary of: United News & Media), Riverbank House, Angel Ln., Tonbridge, Kent TN9 1SE, England. TEL 01732-362666. FAX 01732-767301. TELEX 957829. Ed. Gwen Young. adv. contact: Elaine Soni. stat.; index. circ. 1,500. **Document type:** directory.
—BLDSC (4077.940000). **CCC**.
 Former titles: Gas Directory and Who's Who (ISSN 0307-3084); Gas Directory and Undertakings of the World; Incorporates: Gas Journal Directory (ISSN 0072-0240); Gas Industry Directory (ISSN 0072-0232); Who's Who in the Gas Industry (ISSN 0083-9779)
 Description: Provides a complete guide to the U.K. gas industry that includes a classified buyers guide, trade names, and trade associations.

665.7 IT ISSN 0016-495X
GAS LIQUEFATTI - LE APPARECCHIATURE.* vol.16, 1970. bi-m. L.3000. Editrice Sfera, Via Aurelio Saffi 26, 20123 Milan, Italy.

665.5 US ISSN 1065-867X
 CODEN: GBGUEX
GAS MARKETS WEEK. 1974. w. $477 (foreign $507). Pasha Publications Inc., 1616 N. Ft. Myer Dr., Ste. 1000, Arlington, VA 22209-3107. TEL 703-528-1244. FAX 703-528-1253. Ed. Robert Barton. stat. (back issues avail.) **Document type:** newsletter.
—CCC.
 Former titles: Gas Buyers Guide (ISSN 0897-8778); until 1984): Inside Oil and Gas.
 Description: Covers legal, technological and legislative matters affecting the gas industry.

665.7 UK ISSN 0964-8496
GAS MATTERS. Includes: GasBrief. 1988. m. £520 (outside the E.C. £1020). EconoMatters Ltd., 82 Rivington St., London EC2A 3AY, England. TEL 44-171-613-0087. FAX 44-171-613-0094. TELEX 8954111 REPLAY G. Ed. James R. Ball. **Document type:** newsletter.
 Description: Analyzes natural gas news in Europe.

665.5 US
GAS PRICE INDEX. w. $490 (foreign $525) (effective 1995). Intelligence Press Inc., 22648 Glenn Dr., Sterling, VA 20164-4495. TEL 703-318-8848. FAX 703-318-0597. (Subscr. to: Box 70587, Washington, DC 20024)
 Description: Reports on trading activity and pricing within the domestic spot natural gas market.

665.5 US ISSN 0096-8870
TN880.A1 CODEN: PGPAAC
GAS PROCESSORS ASSOCIATION. ANNUAL CONVENTION. PROCEEDINGS. 1921. a. $25. Gas Processors Association, 6526 E. 60th St., Tulsa, OK 74145. TEL 918-493-3872. FAX 918-493-3875. circ. 5,000. **Indexed:** API Catal., API Hlth.& Environ., API Oil., API Pet.Ref., API Pet.Subst., API Transport., Chem.Abstr., Fuel & Energy Abstr., Gas Abstr. **Document type:** proceedings.
—BLDSC (6840.825000); CASDDS; Ei.

665.5 US
GAS PROCESSORS ASSOCIATION. RESEARCH REPORTS. 1971. irreg., latest RR-142. $25 to non-members; members $10. Gas Processors Association, 6526 E. 60th St., Tulsa, OK 74145. TEL 918-493-3872. FAX 918-493-3875.

PETROLEUM AND GAS

665.5 US
GAS PROCESSORS ASSOCIATION. TECHNICAL PUBLICATIONS. irreg. latest TP-19. Gas Processors Association, 6526 E. 60th St., Tulsa, OK 74145. TEL 918-493-4872. FAX 918-493-3875.

665.5 US ISSN 1057-2279
GAS STORAGE REPORT. 1991. m. $457 (foreign $472). Pasha Publications Inc., 1616 N. Ft. Myer Dr., Ste. 1000, Arlington, VA 22209-3107. TEL 703-528-1244. FAX 703-528-1253. Ed. Mark Hand. Document type: newsletter.
—CCC.
 Description: Monitors natural gas storage inventories, withdrawals and injections, open-access storage programs, federal and state regulatory actions, new business ventures, technological innovations and business trends.

665.5 333.8 AT
GAS SUPPLY AND DEMAND STUDY. 1985. triennial. Aus.$150 for participants report; public report Aus.$25. Australian Gas Association, G.P.O. Box 323, Canberra, A.C.T. 2601, Australia. TEL 61-6-247-3955. FAX 61-6-249-7402. Ed. I. Bruce. charts; illus.; stat. (back issues avail.)
 Description: Guide for industry and government to the study of Australia's long-term supply and demand for natural gas.

665.5 DK ISSN 0106-4355
GAS-TEKNIK. 1911. bi-m. DKK 250 (typically set in Jan.). Dansk Gasteknisk Forening, Naturgassens Hus, Dr. Neergaards Vej 5A, DK-2970 Hoersholm, Denmark. TEL 45-766995. FAX 42-57-16-44. Ed. Erik Hansen. adv.; bk.rev. circ. 1,500. Document type: trade publication.
—BLDSC (4087.950000).

665.5 US
GAS TRANSPORTATION MARKETING SERVICE. 1987. m. $556. (Federal Programs Advisory Service) Thompson Publishing Group, 1725 K St., N.W., Ste.200, Washington, DC 20036. TEL 202-872-4000. FAX 202-296-1091. Ed. Gregory Krehbiel. index. circ. 1,200. (looseleaf format; back issues avail.)
 Description: Provides practical guidance for those doing business in the complex regulatory and legal environment of open-access transportation. Contains current comprehensive information on rates, terms, and conditions of major pipelines that provide service under FERC's open-access program.

665.5 US ISSN 1065-8661
GAS TRANSPORTATION REPORT. 1987. w. $377 (foreign $407). Pasha Publications Inc., 1616 N. Ft. Myer Dr., Ste. 1000, Arlington, VA 22209-3107. TEL 703-528-1244. FAX 703-528-1253. Ed. Tom Castleman. Document type: newsletter.
—CCC.
 Formerly (until 1992): Natural Gas Marketing Report; Supersedes: Natural Gas Marketing Pipeline Guide.
 Description: Covers gas transportation rates, capacity brokering, new construction, system bottlenecks, FERC filings and decisions.

GAS TURBINE WORLD. see ENERGY

333.79 665.7 US
GAS UTILITY INDUSTRY. a. $50. Midwest Register, Inc., 1120 E. 4th St., Tulsa, OK 74120. TEL 918-582-2000. FAX 918-587-9349. Document type: directory.
 Formerly: Directory of Gas Utility Companies Worldwide.
 Description: Supplies company name, address, phone and fax number. Includes personnel with their titles.

665.7 628 697 AU ISSN 0016-5018
CODEN: GAWWA6
GAS, WASSER, WAERME. 1947. m. S.1390. (Oesterreichische Vereinigung fuer das Gas- und Wasserfach) Verlag Lorenz, Ebendorferstr. 10, A-1010 Vienna 1, Austria. TEL 01-426695. FAX 01-438693. (Co-sponsor: Fachverband der Gas- und Waermeversorgungsunternehmungen) adv.: B&W page S.17700, color page S.33000; trim 187 x 277. bk.rev.; bibl.; charts; illus. circ. 1,800. Indexed: Chem.Abstr., Eng.Ind., Excerpt.Med., Fuel & Energy Abstr., Gas Abstr., W.R.C.Inf. Document type: trade publication.
—BLDSC (4086.000000).

665.7 UK ISSN 0960-1635
TP700
GAS WORLD INTERNATIONAL. 1884. m. £52 (foreign £65). Oakfield House, Perrymount Rd., Haywards Heath, W. Sussex RH16 3DH, England. TEL 01732-364422. Ed. Alan Bakalor. adv.; bk.rev.; charts; illus.; mkt.; tr.lit. circ. 3,200. (also avail. in microform from UMI; reprint service avail. from UMI) Indexed: Br.Ceram.Abstr., Br.Tech.Ind., C.I.S. Abstr., Chem.Abstr., Eng.Ind., Fuel & Energy Abstr., Gas Abstr., Key to Econ.Sci., Met.Abstr., Petrol.Abstr., PROMT, W.R.C.Inf.
—BLDSC (4087.000000); Ei; UnCover. CCC.
 Former titles: Gas World (ISSN 0308-7654); Gas World and Gas and Coke.

665.7 US ISSN 0016-4976
GASCOPE. 1964. q. free. Institute of Gas Technology, 1700 S Mount Prospect Rd., Des Plaines, IL 60018-1804. TEL 708-768-0513. FAX 708-768-0516. Ed. Carl Sauer. illus. circ. 15,000. (back issues avail.) Indexed: Energy Info.Abstr. Document type: newsletter.
—CIS.
 Description: Provides information about the R and D and educational activities of the Institute.

665.5 AT
GASCOR NEWS. 1950. q. free. Gas and Fuel Corporation of Victoria, 171 Flinders St., Melbourne, Vic. 3000, Australia. TEL 03-652-5056. FAX 03-652-4801. TELEX AA31422. Ed. Ray Proudley. circ. 6,000. (back issues avail.) Document type: newsletter.

665.7 US
GASLINES. 1947. m. Alabama Gas Corporation, 2101 Sixth Ave. N., Birmingham, AL 35203. TEL 205-326-2750. Ed. Christopher Gagliano. circ. 2,000. Document type: newsletter.
 Formerly: Gas Lines.

665.7 SW ISSN 0039-6834
GASNYTT. 1970. q. SEK 400. Svenska Gasfoereningen, Sct. Eriksgatan 44, P.O. Box 49134, S-100 29 Stockholm, Sweden. TEL 46-8-692-1845. FAX 46-8-654-46-15. Ed. Rolf Johansson. adv.: B&W page SEK 7600, color page SEK 12400; trim 185 x 260. bk.rev.; charts; illus.; maps; index; circ. 2,500 (controlled). Indexed: Fuel & Energy Abstr., Gas Abstr. Document type: trade publication.
 Supersedes: Svenska Gasfoereningens Maanadsblad.

665.538 II ISSN 0971-0191
GASOIL. (Text in English and Hindi) 1968. q. free. Oil & Natural Gas Commission, Western Regional Business Centre, Department of PR & Communication, Makarpura Rd., Baroda 390 009, India. TEL 550324. FAX 0265-65996. TELEX 0175-363-576. Eds. S.K. Panigrahy, T. Premnak. circ. 6,000.
 Description: Contains news and information about the commission for employees. Attempts to reflect the future trends of the organization as well as divergent views on its various activities.

665.7 FR ISSN 0016-5328
TP700 CODEN: GAZJAG
GAZ D'AUJOURD'HUI. 1877. 10/yr. 720 F. (foreign 800 F.). Association Technique de l'Industrie du Gaz en France, 62 rue de Courcelles, 75008 Paris, France. TEL 47-54-34-34. FAX 42-27-49-43. TELEX 642 621 F. Eds. Alain Thibault, Claude Bureau. adv.; bk.rev.; abstr.; illus.; stat.; index. circ. 4,000. Indexed: C.I.S. Abstr., Eng.Ind., Gas Abstr., PROMT.
—CASDDS; UMI. CCC.
 Formerly: Journal des Industries du Gaz.

662 FR ISSN 0072-0321
GAZ DE FRANCE. SECRETARIAT GENERAL. SCHEMA D'ORGANISATION PROFOR.* 1966. a. Gaz de France, 23 rue Philibert, 75804 Paris, France.

665.5 FR
GAZETTE. m. 32 rue Saint-Marc, 75002 Paris, France. TEL 42-60-51-58. FAX 46-28-36-10. TELEX 220 064 F ETRAVEXT. Ed. Albert Willemetz. circ. 10,500.

662.6 RU ISSN 0016-5581
CODEN: GZVPAJ
GAZOVAYA PROMYSHLENNOST/GAZ INDUSTRY. 1956. m. $96 (effective 1996). (Nauchno-Tekhnicheskoe Obshchestvo Neftyanoi i Gazovoi Promyshlennosti) Izdatel'stvo Nedra, Pl. Belorusskogo Vokzala, 3, 125047 Moscow, Russia. TEL 250-52-55. (Co-sponsor: Ministerstvo Gazovoi Promyshlennosti) Ed. S.F. Gudkov. bibl.; charts; illus.; stat. circ. 8,000. Indexed: Chem.Abstr., Fuel & Energy Abstr., Gas Abstr., INIS Atomind.
—BLDSC (0047.020000); CASDDS. CCC.

665.5 JA ISSN 0016-5972
GEKKAN SEKIYU/PETROLEUM MONTHLY. (Text in Japanese) 1955. m. newsstand price: 1300Yen. Sekiyu Kogyo Jihyosha, 22-8, Nishinshinbashi 2-chome, Minato-ku, Tokyo 105, Japan. circ. 25,000. (processed)
—BLDSC (8230.050000).

553.28 RU ISSN 0016-7894
CODEN: GENGA9
GEOLOGIYA NEFTI I GAZA. (Text in Russian; contents page in English) 1957. m. $101 (effective 1996). (Ministerstvo Geologii) Izdatel'stvo Nedra, Pl. Belorusskogo Vokzala, 3, 125047 Moscow, Russia. TEL 250-52-55. (Co-sponsors: Ministerstvo Gazovoi Promyshlennosti S.S.S.R.; Ministerstvo Neftedobyvayushchei Promyshlennosti S.S.S.R.; Ministerstvo Geologii S.S.S.R.) Ed. S.P. Maksimov. adv.; bk.rev.; abstr.; bibl.; charts; illus.; stat.; index. circ. 5,000. (tabloid format) Indexed: Chem.Abstr., E&P Hlth. (1993-), Eng.Ind., Gas Process.& Ppl. (1993-), INIS Atomind., Off.Tech. (1993-), Petrol.Abstr. (1961-).
—BLDSC (0047.620000); CASDDS; PADDS. CCC.

GEOPHYSICAL DIRECTORY. see EARTH SCIENCES — Geophysics

338.2
GLOBAL OIL STOCKS & BALANCES. 1990. 12/yr. $795 (effective Apr. 1994). Petroleum & Energy Intelligence Weekly, Inc., 575 Broadway, 4th Fl., New York, NY 10012-3230. TEL 212-941-5500. FAX 212-941-5508. Ed. Jay Butani; Pub. Edward Morse. adv. contact: Gina Norbury. Document type: trade publication.
 Description: Reports and analyzes international oil inventories and supply-demand trends.

GOLOB'S OIL POLLUTION BULLETIN; the international newsletter on oil pollution prevention, control and cleanup. see ENVIRONMENTAL STUDIES — Waste Management

GOSPODARKA PALIWAMI I ENERGIA/FUEL AND ENERGY MANAGEMENT. see ENERGY

665 US
GOWER FEDERAL SERVICE - OIL AND GAS. 1948. irreg. (approx. 14/yr.). $215 (effective 1992). Rocky Mountain Mineral Law Foundation, Porter Administration Bldg., 7039 E. 18th Ave., Denver, CO 80220. TEL 303-321-8100. FAX 303-321-7657. circ. 175. (looseleaf format; back issues avail.)
●Also available online. Vendor(s): West Services, Inc. (Gower Federal Service).
 Description: Publishes decisions of the Department of the Interior, Interior Board of Land Appeals, and reports natural resources information from the Federal Register pertaining to onshore oil and gas issues.

622 US
GOWER FEDERAL SERVICE - OUTER CONTINENTAL SHELF. 1954. irreg. (approx 8/yr.). $150 (effective 1992). Rocky Mountain Mineral Law Foundation, Porter Administration Bldg., 7039 E. 18th Ave., Denver, CO 80220. TEL 303-321-8100. FAX 303-321-7657. (looseleaf format; back issues avail.)
●Also available online. Vendor(s): West Services, Inc. (Gower Federal Service).
 Description: Publishes decisions of the Department of the Interior, Interior Board of Land Appeals, and reports natural resources information from the Federal register, pertaining to offshore oil and gas operations.

PETROLEUM AND GAS

665.5 US
GOWER FEDERAL SERVICE - ROYALTY VALUATION AND MANAGEMENT. 1989. irreg. (8-12/yr.) $500 (effective 1992). Rocky Mountain Mineral Law Foundation, Porter Administration Bldg., 7039 E. 18th Ave., Denver, CO 80220. TEL 303-321-8100. FAX 303-321-7657. cum.index. circ. 100. (looseleaf format; back issues avail.)
Description: Publishes decisions of the Department of the Interior, Minerals Management Service, appeals relating to the collection of minerals royalty on federal lands.

GREMIO DE ESTACIONES DE SERVICIO. REVISTA PROFESIONAL. see *LABOR UNIONS*

GUIDE TO U S G S GEOLOGIC AND HYDROLOGIC MAPS. see *EARTH SCIENCES*

GULF COAST OIL DIRECTORY. see *BUSINESS AND ECONOMICS — Trade And Industrial Directories*

665.5 662.6 US
GULF COAST PETROPROCESS DIRECTORY. (Includes Buyer's Guide) 1990. a. I.E.I., Publishing Division, 1635 W. Alabama, Houston, TX 77006. TEL 713-529-1616. FAX 713-529-0936. Ed. Janis Johnson; Pub. Shawn Wymes. adv. contact: Rob Garza. circ. 4,000. **Document type:** directory.
Description: Covers the petrochemical and refining industry throughout the Gulf Coast area.

665.538 US ISSN 1058-5850
GULF OF MEXICO DRILLING REPORT. 1984. w. $1450. Offshore Data Services, Inc., Box 19909, Houston, TX 77224-1909. TEL 713-781-2713. FAX 713-781-9594. **Document type:** trade publication.
Description: Provides performance and statistical information on drilling activity in the U.S. Gulf of Mexico.

665.5 US
GULF OF MEXICO FIELD DEVELOPMENT LOCATOR. 1986. m. $300. Offshore Data Services, Inc., Box 19909, Houston, TX 77224-1909. TEL 713-781-2713. FAX 713-781-9594. **Document type:** trade publication.
Description: Covers new oil and gas field development projects from the planning stages through final installation.

665.5 US ISSN 1058-5885
GULF OF MEXICO NEWSLETTER. 1986. w. $115. Offshore Data Services, Inc., Box 19909, Houston, TX 77224-1909. TEL 713-781-2713. FAX 713-781-9594. Ed. Blake Wright. circ. 2,175. **Document type:** newsletter.
Description: Follows opportunities, projects, and people in the petroleum drilling and exploration industry along the U.S. Gulf Coast.

665.5 338.2 US
GULF OF MEXICO RIG LOCATOR. 1986. w. $500. Offshore Data Services, Inc., Box 19909, Houston, TX 77224-1909. TEL 713-781-2713. FAX 713-781-9594. **Document type:** trade publication.
Description: Provides location information on all U.S. offshore rigs operating in the Gulf of Mexico.

665 US
GULF OF MEXICO SUMMARY REPORT - INDEX. 1980. a. free. Outer Continental Shelf Information Program, Offshore Information and Publications Office, Minerals Management Service, 381 Elden St., No. 1400, Herndon, VA 22070-4817. TEL 703-787-1080. circ. 4,000.
Formed by the merger of: Gulf of Mexico Index & Gulf of Mexico Summary Report.
Description: Documents on the federal offshore oil and gas leasing, exploration, development and production.

665.5 US
GULF STATES - PERMIAN BASIN PETROLEUM DIRECTORY. 1990. a. $89. Hart Publications, Inc. (Subsidiary of: Phillips Publishing International, Inc.), 1900 Grant St., Ste. 400, Denver, CO 80203. TEL 303-837-1917. FAX 303-837-8585. Ed. Paula Jepperson. adv. contact: Susan Katz. circ. 1,500. (also avail. in diskette format) **Document type:** directory.

GUOWAI YOUQI KANTAN. see *EARTH SCIENCES — Geology*

665 338.2 US ISSN 1075-5365
TN860
HART'S OIL AND GAS WORLD; * regional coverage of U.S. exploration, drilling and production. 1994. bi-m. $59 (foreign $109). Hart Publications, Inc. (Subsidiary of: Phillips Publishing International, Inc.), 1900 Grant St., Ste. 400, Box 1917, Denver, CO 80201. TEL 303-837-1917. FAX 303-837-8585. adv.; bk.rev.; illus.; tr.lit. circ. 4,467. (back issues avail.) **Indexed:** Bibl.& Ind.Geol., Petrol.Abstr.
Document type: trade publication.
—BLDSC (4265.435000); Faxon; UMI; UnCover.
Formed by the 1994 merger of: Gulf Coast Oil and Gas World (ISSN 1070-4914) & Midcontinent Oil and Gas World (ISSN 1071-4790) & Northeast Oil and Gas World (ISSN 1070-4469) & Pacific Oil and Gas World (ISSN 1071-9628) & Southwest Oil and Gas World (ISSN 1071-4804); Western Oil and Gas World (ISSN 1070-6100); Which was formerly: Western Oil World (ISSN 0884-7592); (until 1985): Western Oil Reporter (ISSN 0043-3985); Gulf Coast Oil and Gas World was formerly: Gulf Coast Oil World (ISSN 0884-7967); (until 1985): Gulf Coast Oil Reporter (ISSN 0744-9070); Midcontinent Oil and Gas World was formerly: Midcontinent Oil World (ISSN 0883-7325); Northeast Oil and Gas World was formerly: Northeast Oil World (ISSN 0884-4771); (until 1995): Northeast Oil Reporter (ISSN 0279-7798); Pacific Oil and Gas World was formerly: Pacific Oil World (ISSN 0008-1329); (until 1971): California Oil World (ISSN 0161-9950); Southwest Oil and Gas World was formerly (until 1993): Southwest Oil World (ISSN 0884-6219); (until 1985): Drill Bit (ISSN 0012-6225).

665.5 US
HEROLD'S COMPARATIVE APPRAISAL REPORTS - SECTOR 1. 1948. m. $1295 (foreign $1350). John S. Herold, Inc., 5 Edgewood Ave., Greenwich, CT 06830. TEL 203-869-2585. charts; illus.; stat.
—CCC.
Formerly: Oil Industry Comparative Appraisals 1 (ISSN 1054-7363)
Description: Provides appraisal reports and updates on the largest U.S. public oil and gas companies.

665.5 US ISSN 0886-8662
HG6047.P47
HEROLD'S COMPARATIVE APPRAISAL REPORTS - SECTOR 2. m. $1295 (foreign $1350). John S. Herold, Inc., 5 Edgewood Ave., Greenwich, CT 06830. TEL 203-869-2585.
—CCC.
Formerly: Oil Industry Comparative Appraisals 2.
Description: Appraises the independent exploration and production companies of the US, and the Master Limited Partnership and Royalty Trust industry sectors.

665.5 US ISSN 1052-3111
HD9560.3
HEROLD'S COMPARATIVE APPRAISAL REPORTS - SECTOR 3. $1295 (foreign $1350). John S. Herold, Inc., 5 Edgewood Ave., Greenwich, CT 06830. TEL 203-869-2585.
—CCC.
Formerly: Oil Industry Comparative Appraisals 3.
Description: Appraises Canadian oils and foreign domiciled, integrated and independent oils.

658.8 US ISSN 0018-4764
HOOSIER INDEPENDENT. 1934. q. membership. Indiana Oil Marketers Association, Inc., 101 W. Washington St., Ste. 1338, Indianapolis, IN 46204-3413. FAX 317-875-6721. Ed. Charlene Hillman. adv.: B&W page $338; adv. contact: Robert Hillman. bk.rev.; charts; illus.; tr.lit.; circ. 1,400 (controlled). **Document type:** trade publication, directory.
Description: Covers subjects of interest to independent oil marketers, fuel oil dealers and operators fo convenience stores throughout Indiana.

HOUSTON BUSINESS JOURNAL. see *BUSINESS AND ECONOMICS — Economic Situation And Conditions*

665.5 670 US ISSN 0739-3555
TN867
HOUSTON OIL DIRECTORY. 1971. a. $55. (International Exhibitions, Inc.) I.E.I., Publishing Division, 1635 W. Alabama, Houston, TX 77006. TEL 713-529-1616. FAX 713-529-0936. Ed. Janis Johnson; Pub. Shawn Wymes. adv. contact: Rob Garza. circ. 4,000. **Document type:** directory.
Description: Geared towards exploration & production of the oil and gas industry throughout the state of Texas.

665.5 338.2 US
HOUSTON PETROLEUM INDUSTRY. a. $40. Midwest Register, Inc., 1120 E. 4th St., Tulsa, OK 74120. TEL 918-582-2000. FAX 918-587-9347. **Document type:** directory.
Formerly: Oil Directory of Houston, Texas (ISSN 0471-3877)
Description: Supplies company name, address, phone and fax numbers and personnel information, producers, drilling and well service, pipelines, refineries, gas processing, petrochemical, engineering, equipment manufacturers and suppliers.

HUADONG SHIFAN DAXUE XUEBAO (ZHEXUE SHEHUI KEXUE BAN)/EAST CHINA NORMAL UNIVERSITY. JOURNAL. (SOCIAL SCIENCE EDITION). see *SOCIAL SCIENCES: COMPREHENSIVE WORKS*

HUAGONG ZHI YOU/FRIEND OF CHEMICAL INDUSTRY. see *CHEMISTRY*

HUAXUE YU NIANHE/CHEMISTRY AND ADHESION. see *ENGINEERING — Chemical Engineering*

HUNTING REVIEW. see *AERONAUTICS AND SPACE FLIGHT*

665.5 US
HUTTLINGER'S NATURAL GAS BULLETIN. w. $360. Huttlinger's Energy News, Box 409, Poolesville, MD 20837. TEL 301-972-8100. Ed. Stan Janet. bibl.; stat. (looseleaf format; back issues avail.) **Document type:** newsletter.

665.5 US
HUTTLINGER'S OIL REPORT. w. $360. Huttlinger's Energy News, Box 409, Poolesville, MD 20837. TEL 301-972-8100. Ed. Stan Janet. bibl.; stat. (looseleaf format; back issues avail.)

665.5 690 US ISSN 0744-379X
HUTTLINGER'S PIPELINE REPORT. w. $360. Huttlinger's Energy News, Box 409, Poolesville, MD 20837. TEL 301-972-8100. Ed. Stan Janet. bibl.; stat. (looseleaf format; back issues avail.)

552 CN ISSN 0703-6655
TN873.C22
HYDROCARBON AND BYPRODUCT RESERVES IN BRITISH COLUMBIA. a. Ministry of Energy, Mines and Petroleum Resources, Energy Resources Division, 7th Fl., 1810 Blanshard St., Victoria, BC V8V 1X4, Canada. (Subscr. to: Crown Publications, 521 Fort St., Victoria, BC V8W 1E7, Canada. TEL 604-386-4636) (back issues avail.) **Document type:** government publication.
Formerly (until 1970): Oil, Natural Gas and Byproducts Reserves in British Columbia (ISSN 0703-6663)
Description: Contains tables of the reserves estimated by the division at the end of the year with an explanation of the definitions used throughout. A copy of the stratigraphic correlation chart and a map showing the location of the fields in the province is also included.

665.5 333.91 SI ISSN 0217-1112
HYDROCARBON ASIA. (Text in English) 1991. 8/yr. $54. Asia Pacific Energy Business Publications Pte. Ltd., 2 Shenton Way, No. 05-01, 05 ICB Bldg., Singapore 0106, Singapore. TEL 65-2223422. FAX 65-2225587. TELEX RS 28366 SAFAN. Ed. Jimmie Aung Khin. adv. contact: Eddie Raj. circ. 5,000.

665.5 333.91 SI
HYDROCARBON ASIAN BUSINESS REPORTS. (Text in English) 22/yr. $520. Asia Pacific Energy Business Publications Pte. Ltd., 2 Shenton Way, 05-01, 05 ICB Bldg., Singapore 0106, Singapore. TEL 65-2223422. FAX 65-2225587. TELEX RS 28366 SAFAN.

PETROLEUM AND GAS

665.5 US ISSN 0887-0284
TP690.A1 CODEN: HYPRAX
HYDROCARBON PROCESSING. 1922. m. $24 (foreign $36). Gulf Publishing Co., Box 2608, Houston, TX 77252-2608. TEL 713-529-4301. FAX 713-520-4433. TELEX 287330 GULF UR. Ed. Les Kane. adv.: B&W page $4485, color page $5880; 7 x 10. bk.rev.; charts; illus.; tr.lit.; index. circ. 34,673. (also avail. in microfilm from UMI,PMC; back issues avail.; reprint service avail.) **Indexed:** A.S.& T.Ind., AESIS, API Abstr., API Catal., API Hlth.& Environ., API Oil., API Pet.Ref., API Pet.Subst., API Transport., Chem.Abstr., Chem.Eng.Abstr., Chem.Infd., Curr.Cont., E&P Hlth. (1993-), Energy.Info.Abstr., Energy Rev., Eng.Ind., Excerp.Med., Fluidex, Foul.Prev.Res.Dig., Fuel & Energy Abstr., Gas Abstr., Gas Process.& Ppl. (1993-), HRIS, Ind.Sci.Rev., INIS Atomind., Intl.Polym.Sci.& Tech., ISMEC, Ocean.Abstr., Off.Tech. (1993-), Petrol.Abstr. (1967-), Pollut.Abstr., PROMT, RAPRA, Risk Abstr., Sci.Cit.Ind., Sel.Water Res.Abstr., Soils & Fert., T.C.E.A. —CCC.
 Supersedes in part (in 1966): Hydrocarbon Processing - Petroleum Refiner (ISSN 0096-2406); Which was formerly (until 1961): Petroleum Refiner (ISSN 0096-6517); And (until 1942): Refiner and Natural Gasoline Manufacturer (ISSN 0096-0462).

665.5 US ISSN 0018-8190
TP690.A1 CODEN: IHPRBS
HYDROCARBON PROCESSING INTERNATIONAL EDITION. 1922. m. Gulf Publishing Co., Box 2608, Houston, TX 77252-2608. TEL 713-529-4301. FAX 713-529-4433. Ed. Les Kane. adv. circ. 21,071.
 —BLDSC (4343.100000); CASDDS; Ei; Faxon; Genuine Article; PADDS; SWETS; UMI; UnCover. **CCC**.
 Supersedes in part (in 1966): Hydrocarbon Processing - Petroleum Refiner (ISSN 0096-2406); Which was formerly (until 1961): Petroleum Refiner (ISSN 0096-6517); And (until 1942): Refiner and Natural Gasoline Manufacturer (ISSN 0096-0462).

665.5 UK ISSN 0952-1399
HYDROCARBON TECHNOLOGY INTERNATIONAL. 1987. q. free. Sterling Publications Ltd. (Subsidiary of: Sterling Publishing Group PLC), 86-88 Edgware Rd., London W2 2YW, England. TEL 0171-915-9623. FAX 0171-258-0624. Ed. Peter Harrison. adv.: B&W page £3085, color page £3393; trim 297 x 210; adv. contact: Paul Mason. circ. 12,500 (controlled). (back issues avail.) **Document type:** trade publication.
 —BLDSC (4343.220000).
 Refereed Serial

665 UK ISSN 0967-537X
HYDROCARBONS BRIEF; Russia & the post-Soviet Republics. Variant title: Oil & Gas Hydrocarbons Brief: Russia & the Post-Soviet Republics. w. £270 (foreign £300). Oil & Gas Russia Ltd., P.O. Box 35, Hastings, E. Sussex TN34 2UX, England. TEL 44-424-442741. FAX 44-424-442913. (Subscr. to: Kingsgate Business Centre, 12-50 Kingsgate Rd., Kingston-upon-Thames, Surrey KT2 5AA, England. TEL 44-81-547-2411; And: VNIIOENG, 14 Nametkin St., 117420 Moscow, Russia. TEL 7-095-332-0037) Ed. Nick Terdre. **Document type:** newsletter.
 Description: Covers legal and economic developments of oil and gas production and exports from the Commonwealth of Independent States.

552 CN
HYDROCARBONS RESERVE TAPE. a. Can.$250. Ministry of Energy, Mines and Petroleum Resources, Energy Resources Division, 7th Fl., 1810 Blanshard St., Victoria, BC V8V 1X4, Canada. (Subscr. to: Crown Publications, 546 Yates St., Victoria, BC V8W 1K8, Canada. TEL 604-386-4636) (magnetic tape) **Document type:** government publication.
 Description: Shows all oil and gas reserves in BC and estimates how much has been used and how much is left.

665.5 FR ISSN 0399-094X
HYDROCARBURE.* q. Institut Francais du Petrole, B.P. 311, 4 av. Bois Preau, 92506 Rueil-Malmaison Cedex, France. TEL 47-32-36-92. TELEX 221 987. adv. circ. 4,000.
 —BLDSC (4343.250000).

665.5 540 330 CI
I N A VJESNIK INDUSTRIJE NAFTE. (Text in Croatian) 1964. I N A - Industrija Nafte, Proleterskih b.78, 41000 Zagreb, Croatia. TEL 516-411. Ed. Branko Franjic. circ. 25,000.

655.5 US ISSN 0199-5685
I U P I W VIEWS. 1945. bi-m. $5. International Union of Petroleum & Industrial Workers, 8131 E. Rosecrano Ave., Paramount, CA 90723. FAX 213-408-1073. Ed. Thomas C. Walsh Sr. adv. circ. 9,000. **Document type:** newsletter.

665.5 US ISSN 0073-5108
TN872.I3 CODEN: ILGPA4
ILLINOIS PETROLEUM. 1926. irreg., no.147, 1995. price varies. State Geological Survey, Natural Resources Bldg., 615 E. Peabody Dr., Champaign, IL 61820. TEL 217-333-4747. abstr.; bibl.; charts; illus.; stat. circ. 1,000. **Indexed:** AESIS, Bibl.& Ind.Geol., Geo.Abstr., Geol.Abstr., Petrol.Abstr. —UnCover.

665.5 CN ISSN 0700-5156
IMPERIAL OIL REVIEW/REVUE DE L'IMPERIALE. (Text in English, French) 1917. q. free. Imperial Oil Ltd., 111 St. Clair Ave., W., Toronto, ON M5W 1K3, Canada. TEL 416-968-4111. Ed. Sarah Lawley. illus.; index. circ. 50,000. **Indexed:** Can.B.P.I., Can.Per.Ind., Pt.de Rep. (1989-).
 Former titles: Imperial Oil Limited. Review (ISSN 0380-903X); Imperial Oil Review (ISSN 0019-2910)

665.5 310 US
IMPORTS & EXPORTS OF CRUDE OIL AND PETROLEUM PRODUCTS. 1977. m. $500 (effective 1995). American Petroleum Institute, Publications Section, 1220 L St., N.W., Washington, DC 20005. TEL 202-682-8378. (Subscr. to: 1970 Chain Bridge Rd., McLean, VA 22109-6000) Ed. Claudette Reid. circ. 350. (also avail. in magnetic tape; back issues avail.) **Indexed:** SRI. **Document type:** trade publication.
 Formerly: Imported Crude Oil and Petroleum Products.
 Description: Contains data on crude oil and petroleum product imports. Includes importer, port of entry, country of origin, recipient, destination, quantity in thousands of barrels, API gravity and sulphur content for crude oil imports. For product imports, includes importer, commodity, port of entry, country of origin, quantity in thousands of barrels, and API gravity (except for residual fuel oil imports which have sulphur content instead of API gravity).

INDEPENDENT ENERGY; the industry's business magazine. see *ENERGY*

665.5 350 US
INDEPENDENT GASOLINE MARKETING. 1973. bi-m. membership. Society of Independent Gasoline Marketers of America, 11911 Freedom Dr., No. 590, Reston, VA 22090-5602. TEL 703-709-7000. FAX 703-709-7007. Ed. Angela M. Angerosa. adv.: B&W page $1785, color page $2410; 8 1/4 x 10 7/8; adv. contact: Mary Alice Kutyn. circ. 5,500 (controlled). **Document type:** trade publication.
 Former titles (until 1987): S I G M A Update; Capitol Digest.
 Description: Covers gasoline legislation and issues.

665.5 US
INDEPENDENT LIQUID TERMINALS ASSOCIATION. DIRECTORY OF BULK LIQUID TERMINAL AND ABOVEGROUND STORAGE TANK EQUIPMENT AND SERVICES: SUPPLIERS OF EQUIPMENT & SERVICES. 1982. a. $25. Independent Liquid Terminals Association, 1133 15th St., N.W., Ste. 650, Washington, DC 20005. TEL 202-659-2301. FAX 202-466-4166. Ed. E. Bruce Calvert. index. circ. 900. **Document type:** directory.
 Formerly: Independent Liquid Terminals Association. Directory of Suppliers of Goods and Services.
 Description: Covers suppliers of equipment and services for terminal and tank farm industry.

665.5 US
INDEPENDENT LIQUID TERMINALS ASSOCIATION. DIRECTORY OF BULK LIQUID TERMINAL AND STORAGE FACILITIES. 1975. a. $95. Independent Liquid Terminals Association, 1133 15th St., N.W., Ste. 650, Washington, DC 20005. TEL 202-659-2301. FAX 202-466-4166. Ed. E. Bruce Calvert. index. circ. 900. **Document type:** directory.
 Formerly: Independent Liquid Terminals Association. Directory of Bulk Liquid Storage Facilities.
 Description: Locates 470 bulk liquid terminals and storage facilities, commodities handled and modes served.

665.5 US
INDEPENDENT LIQUID TERMINALS ASSOCIATION. NEWSLETTER. 1975. m. $120. Independent Liquid Terminals Association, 1133 15th St., N.W., Ste. 650, Washington, DC 20005. TEL 202-659-2301. FAX 202-466-4166. Ed. John Prokop. circ. 1,200. **Document type:** newsletter.
 Description: Covers legislation and regulations affecting terminals, the tank farm industry and related industries.

662.338 II ISSN 0971-2542
INDIAN JOURNAL OF PETROLEUM GEOLOGY. (Text in English) 1992. s-a. Rs.600($80) Indian Petroleum Publishers, 100-9, Naishville Road, Dehra Dun 248 001, India. Ed. S.K. Biswas. bk.rev. **Indexed:** E&P Hlth. (1993-), Gas Process.& Ppl. (1993-), Off.Tech. (1993-), Petrol.Abstr. (1993-). **Document type:** academic/scholarly publication.
 —BLDSC (4418.300000); PADDS.
 Description: Provides a forum for the exchange of scientific and technical information concerning petroleum exploration in Southeast Asian countries in particular and the world in general.

665.5 II
INDIAN PETROCHEMICAL INDUSTRY DESKBOOK. (Text in English) 1984. biennial. $55. Technical Press Publications, 5-1 Convent Street, Colaba, Bombay 400 039, India. TEL 022-2021446. FAX 022-2871499. TELEX 011-83479 CHEM IN. Ed. J.P. Sousa. adv.; bk.rev.; abstr.; charts; illus. circ. 6,400.

338.7 II ISSN 0376-9968
HD9576.I54
INDO-BURMA PETROLEUM COMPANY. ANNUAL REPORT. (Text in English) a. Indo-Burma Petroleum Company, Gillander House, Netaji Subhas Rd., P.O. Box 952, Calcutta 700 001, India. stat.

338.47 UK
INDONESIA FINANCIAL ANALYSIS SERVICE. s-a. £7500 (renewals £4800). Arthur Andersen, Petroleum Services Group, 1 Surrey St., London WC2R 2PS, England. TEL 0171-438-3888. FAX 0171-438-3881. TELEX 8812711. Eds. Mike Coulten, Gary Howorth. (diskette format) **Document type:** trade publication.
 Description: Calculates discounted pre- and post-tax cashflows by field and company for Indonesia.

338.47 UK
INDONESIA UPSTREAM PETROLEUM DATABASE. s-a. (in 6 vols.). £3675. Arthur Andersen, Petroleum Services Group, 1 Surrey St., London WC2R 2PS, England. TEL 0171-438-3888. FAX 0171-438-3881. TELEX 8812711. Ed. James Sales. **Document type:** trade publication.
 Description: Provides comprehensive data on the Indonesian upstream petroleum oil and gas industry activity and companies.

665.5 IT ISSN 0073-7275
INDUSTRIA DEL PETROLIO IN ITALIA. a. Direzione Generale delle Fonti di Energia e Industrie di Base, Via Molise 2, 00187 Rome, Italy. charts; stat.

665.5 MX ISSN 0187-487X
HD9574.M6
INDUSTRIA PETROLERA EN MEXICO. 1979. irreg., latest 1988. Mex.$2500($22) Instituto Nacional de Estadistica, Geografia e Informatica, Secretaria de Programacion y Presupuesto, Prol. Heroe de Nacozari, 2301, Sur, Puerta 11, Acceso, 20270 Aguascalientes, Ags., Mexico. TEL 91-49-18-19-48. FAX 91-491-80739. circ. 1,000.

PETROLEUM AND GAS

665.5   GW   ISSN 0341-3756
                        CODEN: IFRGAO
DIE INDUSTRIEFEUERUNG. Short title: I F. 3/yr. DM.35 per no. Vulkan-Verlag GmbH, Postfach 103962, 45039 Essen, Germany. TEL 0201-82002-0. FAX 0201-82002-40. **Document type:** trade publication.
—BLDSC (4474.753000); CASDDS. **CCC.**
Description: Deals with present-day technical and economic problems encountered in various branches of industry as a result of the increasing use of fuels.

665.7   SP   ISSN 1134-3168
▼**INGENIERIA DEL GAS.** Short title: I D G. 1994. bi-m. Oilgas S.A., Paseo de la Habana 48, 28036 Madrid, Spain. TEL 34-1-5632893. FAX 34-1-5635234. Ed. Julian Cid; Pub. Carlos Martin. adv. contact: Esther Navas. circ. 6,500. **Document type:** trade publication.
Description: Covers installation, equipment and gas engineering for domestic, commercial and industrial use of gas.

665.5   MX   ISSN 0185-3899
                        CODEN: INGPAI
INGENIERIA PETROLERA. 1958. m. Mex.$40 (effective 1994). Asociacion de Ingenieros Petroleros de Mexico A.C., Apdo. Postal 53-013, CP-11490 Mexico, D.F., Mexico. TEL 2-54-04-28. FAX 5-31-15-61. Ed. Javier Guirrion Garcia. adv. circ. 4,000. (also avail. in microfilm)

665.5   US   ISSN 8756-3711
INSIDE F E R C'S GAS MARKET REPORT. 1985. bi-w. $815 (foreign $840). (Federal Energy Regulatory Commission) McGraw-Hill, Inc., Energy & Business Newsletters, 1221 Ave. of the Americas, 36th Fl., New York, NY 10020. TEL 212-512-6410. Ed. Larry Foster. (reprint service avail. from UMI)
Document type: government publication.
●Also available online. Vendor(s): Knight-Ridder, Inc. (File no.624/McGRAW-HILL PUBLICATIONS ONLINE), Dow Jones News Retrieval (GSMR), Lexis-Nexis (GASMKT), NewsNet (EY56).
Also available on CD-ROM. Producer(s): SilverPlatter Information, Inc. (McGraw-Hill Energy Library).

665.5   FR   ISSN 0073-8360
TN860   CODEN: IPTCBP
INSTITUT FRANCAIS DU PETROLE. COLLECTION COLLOQUES ET SEMINAIRES. 1964. irreg., vol.51, 1993. price varies. Editions Technip, 27 rue Ginoux, 75737 Paris Cedex 15, France. TEL 45-78-33-80. FAX 45-75-37-11. TELEX EDITECP 200375F. circ. 1,250. **Indexed:** Bull.Signal., Chem.Abstr., Geophys.Abstr., Petrol.Abstr. **Document type:** proceedings.
—BLDSC (3310.488000); CASDDS. **CCC.**

665.5   FR   ISSN 0073-8379
INSTITUT FRANCAIS DU PETROLE. RAPPORT ANNUEL. (Editions in French, English) 1963. a. free. Institut Francais du Petrole (IFP), 1 et 4 av. de Bois-Preau, B.P. No. 311, 92506 Rueil-Malmaison Cedex, France. TEL 47-52-60-00. FAX 47-52-70-00. TELEX IFPA 634 202 F. circ. 13,000 (8,500 French ed., 4,500 English ed.). **Indexed:** Ocean.Abstr., Petrol.Abstr. **Document type:** corporate report.

665   FR
                        CODEN: RFPTBH
INSTITUT FRANCAIS DU PETROLE. REVUE. (Text in English, French; summaries in English, French, Spanish) 1946. 6/yr. 1500 F. Editions Technip, 27 rue Ginoux, 75737 Paris Cedex 15, France. TEL 45-78-33-80. FAX 45-75-37-11. TELEX EDITECP 200375F. bk.rev.; bibl.; charts; illus.; index, cum.index. 1946-1960, 1961-1965, 1966-1970, 1971-1975, 1976-1980, 1981-1985, 1986-1990. circ. 1,400. **Indexed:** API Abstr., API Catal., API Hlth.& Environ., API Oil, API Pet.Ref., API Pet.Subst., API Transport., Appl.Mech.Rev., Bibl.& Ind.Geol., C.I.S. Abstr., Chem.Abstr., Chem.Eng.Abstr., Curr.Cont., Deep Sea Res.& Oceanogr.Abstr., Eng.Ind., Excerp.Med., Geo.Abstr., Geol.Abstr., IDA, Petrol.Abstr., T.C.E.A. **Document type:** proceedings.
—BLDSC (7878.950000); CASDDS; Ei; Genuine Article; PADDS; SWETS; UnCover. **CCC.**
Formerly: Institut Francais du Petrole. Revue et Annales des Liquides Combustibles (ISSN 0020-2274)

665.5   BE   ISSN 0020-2185
                        CODEN: AIBPD9
INSTITUT ROYAL BELGE DU PETROLE. ANNALES/KONINKLIJK BELGISCH PETROLEUM INSTITUUT. ANNALEN. (Text in Dutch, English, French, German) 1967. q. 650 BEF (foreign 1100 BEF) (effective 1993). Institut Royal Belge du Petrole, 4 rue de la Science, 1040 Brussels, Belgium. Ed. Martial Tonnard. adv.: B&W page 12000 BEF, color page 26000 BEF; 250 x 170. bk.rev. circ. 1,000.
—CASDDS.
Description: Contains information concerning all aspects of the petroleum industry in Belgium.

665.5 551   IS   ISSN 0073-8832
INSTITUTE FOR PETROLEUM RESEARCH AND GEOPHYSICS, HOLON, ISRAEL. REPORT. irreg. Institute for Petroleum Research and Geophysics, Box 2286, Holon 58122, Israel. **Document type:** bulletin, corporate report.

INSTITUTE OF ENERGY. JOURNAL. see *ENERGY*

662   US
INSTITUTE OF GAS TECHNOLOGY. ANNUAL REPORT. a. free. Institute of Gas Technology, 1700 S. Mount Prospect Rd., Des Plaines, IL 60018-1804. TEL 708-768-0512. FAX 708-768-0516. Ed. Colleen Taylor Sen. stat. **Document type:** corporate report.
Formerly: Institute of Gas Technology. Director's Report.

INSTITUTIONAL HOLDINGS OF OIL STOCKS. see *BUSINESS AND ECONOMICS — Investments*

665.5   MX   ISSN 0538-1428
TN873.M6   CODEN: RVMPAX
INSTITUTO MEXICANO DEL PETROLEO. REVISTA. (Text in Spanish; summaries in English) 1969. q. $40. Instituto Mexicano del Petroleo, Eje Central Lazaro Cardenas Norte 152, Col. San Bartolo Atepehuacan Mexico 07730, D.F., Mexico. TEL 398-17-99. Ed. Armando Comaduran Cordova. abstr.; charts; illus.; cum.index. circ. 1,500. (back issues avail.) **Indexed:** API Abstr., API Catal., API Hlth.& Environ., API Oil., API Pet.Ref., API Pet.Subst., API Transport., Bibl.& Ind.Geol., Chem.Abstr., Fuel & Energy Abstr., Petrol.Abstr.
—BLDSC (7819.865000); CASDDS; Ei; PADDS; SWETS.

665.5 622 553.28   PL   ISSN 0209-0724
                        CODEN: PGNGDN
INSTYTUT GORNICTWA NAFTOWEGO I GAZOWNICTWA. PRACE. (Text in Polish; summaries in English and Russian) 1950. irreg. (5-7/yr.). price varies. Instytut Gornictwa Naftowego i Gazownictwa, Ul. Lubicz 25A, 31-503 Krakow, Poland. TELEX 0325276 IGNG PL. charts; illus. circ. 1,000. **Indexed:** Chem.Abstr.
—BLDSC (6581.030000); CASDDS.
Formerly: Instytut Naftowy. Prace (ISSN 0032-6232)

665.7   US
INTERNATIONAL BUTANE - PROPANE NEWSLETTER. 1977. s-m. $235. Butane - Propane News, Inc., 338 E. Foothill Blvd., Box 660698, Arcadia, CA 91006-0698. TEL 818-357-2168. FAX 818-303-2854. Ed. Ann Rey. **Document type:** newsletter.

665.7   US   ISSN 0197-2782
                        CODEN: ICLNBT
INTERNATIONAL CONFERENCE ON LIQUEFIED NATURAL GAS. PAPERS. (Papers in English, some in French; abstracts in English and French) 1968. triennial. $100 for 1995 edition. Institute of Gas Technology, 1700 S. Mount Prospect Rd., Des Plaines, IL 60018-1804. TEL 708-768-0815. (Co-sponsors: International Gas Union; International Institute of Refrigeration) Ed. Bonnie Feingold. **Indexed:** Chem.Abstr., Gas Abstr. **Document type:** proceedings.
—BLDSC (4538.829500); CASDDS.
Formerly: International Conference on Liquefied Natural Gas. Proceedings (ISSN 0538-611X)

662.6   CY   ISSN 1010-1179
INTERNATIONAL CRUDE OIL AND PRODUCT PRICES. 1971. s-a. $560. Middle East Petroleum and Economic Publications, P.O. Box 4940, Nicosia, Cyprus. TEL 445431. FAX 474988. TELEX 2198 MEES CY. Ed. Ian Seymour. charts; stat.
—BLDSC (4539.500350); SWETS.
Description: Reviews and analyzes of oil price trends in world markets.

INTERNATIONAL ENERGY OUTLOOK. see *ENERGY*

338.2 665.5   UK   ISSN 0266-9382
INTERNATIONAL GAS REPORT; covering the gas and gas liquids industry worldwide. 1974. fortn. £545($930) (overseas £620). Financial Times Energy Publishing (Subsidiary of: Pearson Professional Ltd.), Maple House, 149 Tottenham Court Rd., London W1P 9LL, England. TEL 0171-896-2241. FAX 0171-896-2275. Ed. David Tudball; Pub. David Hurst. charts; illus.; stat. (back issues avail.) **Document type:** newsletter.
●Also available online. Vendor(s): Data-Star, Knight-Ridder, Inc., Lexis-Nexis.
—SWETS; UMI.
Description: Provides news and analysis covering the natural gas and gas liquids business worldwide, with emphasis on markets.

665.5   US   ISSN 0736-5721
TP345.A1   CODEN: PGRCDV
INTERNATIONAL GAS RESEARCH CONFERENCE. PROCEEDINGS. 1980. irreg., latest Apr. 1992. $225. (Gas Research Institute) Government Institutes, Inc., 4 Research Pl., Ste. 200, Rockville, MD 20850. TEL 301-921-2300. FAX 301-921-0373. **Indexed:** Chem.Abstr. **Document type:** proceedings.
—BLDSC (4540.502000); CASDDS.

665.7   US   ISSN 0276-4040
INTERNATIONAL GAS TECHNOLOGY HIGHLIGHTS. 1971. fortn. $100. Institute of Gas Technology, 1700 S. Mt. Prospect Rd., Des Plaines, IL 60018. TEL 708-768-0512. FAX 708-768-0516. Ed. Colleen Taylor Sen. circ. 2,500. **Document type:** newsletter.
●Also available online.
—SWETS.
Description: Reviews worldwide economic and technological developments in energy, with a focus on natural gas.

338.39   SZ
INTERNATIONAL GAS UNION. PROCEEDINGS OF WORLD GAS CONFERENCES. (Text in English and French) 1931. triennial; 17th, 1988, Washington. International Gas Union - Union Internationale de l'Industrie du Gaz, Grutlistrasse 44, Case Postale 658, CH-8027 Zurich, Switzerland. Ed. J.P. Lauper. **Document type:** proceedings.
Formerly: International Gas Union. Proceedings of Conferences (ISSN 0074-6126)

INTERNATIONAL JOURNAL OF OFFSHORE AND POLAR ENGINEERING. see *ENGINEERING — Mechanical Engineering*

INTERNATIONAL JOURNAL OF SURFACE MINING, RECLAMATION AND ENVIRONMENT. see *MINES AND MINING INDUSTRY*

INTERNATIONAL OFFSHORE FINANCIAL CENTRES. see *BUSINESS AND ECONOMICS — International Commerce*

665.5   US   ISSN 0535-1634
INTERNATIONAL OIL AND GAS DEVELOPMENT YEARBOOK. 1930. a. price varies. International Oil Scouts Association, Box 272949, Houston, TX 77277-2949. circ. 1,500. (back issues avail.)

665 622   US
INTERNATIONAL OIL NEWS. 1993. w. $517 (effective May 1995). William F. Bland, Co., Box 16666, Chapel Hill, NC 27516-6666. TEL 919-490-0700. FAX 919-490-3002. TELEX 965952-BLAND. Ed. Chris R. Schultz. (back issues avail.) **Indexed:** Bibl.& Ind.Geol.
—CCC.
Formed by the 1993 merger of: International Oil News: Suppliers Edition; International Oil News: Management Edition; **Supersedes (in 1986):** International Oil News (ISSN 0043-8855); Which was formerly (1954-1970): World Petroleum Report.
Description: For top executives managing international oil and gas activities.

553.28   US   ISSN 0277-6812
TN860
INTERNATIONAL OIL SCOUTS ASSOCIATION. OFFICIAL PUBLICATION. 1956. q. $10. International Oil Scouts Association, Box 272949, Houston, TX 77277-2949. adv.; bk.rev.; charts; illus. circ. 1,500.
Formerly: International Oil Scouts Association. Official Newsletter (ISSN 0047-0864)

PETROLEUM AND GAS

INTERNATIONAL OIL SCOUTS ASSOCIATION DIRECTORY. see BUSINESS AND ECONOMICS — Trade And Industrial Directories

628.168 US
INTERNATIONAL OIL SPILL CONTROL DIRECTORY. 1980. a. $95. Cutter Information Corp., 37 Broadway, Arlington, MA 02174-5539. TEL 800-888-8939. FAX 617-648-8707. TELEX 650-100-9891 MCIUW. Ed. Faith Yando. adv. (back issues avail.) **Document type:** directory.
Description: Worldwide listing of more than 3,300 products and services for preventing, controlling, and cleaning up oil spills.

665.5 US ISSN 0148-0375
HD9560.1
INTERNATIONAL PETROLEUM ENCYCLOPEDIA. 1968. a. $95. PennWell Publishing Co., Box 1260, Tulsa, OK 74101. TEL 918-835-3161. FAX 918-831-9497. Ed. John C. McCaslin. adv. (also avail. in microfiche from CIS) **Indexed:** SRI.
—BLDSC (4544.914500). **CCC.**
Description: Provides plans, activities, statistics, technology and analysis in all segments of today's worldwide oil and gas businesses. Features new maps, updated country-by-country reports and brand new features on the most timely petroleum industry developments.

665.5 332 US ISSN 0193-9270
INTERNATIONAL PETROLEUM FINANCE; earnings, finances and management strategies in the petroleum industry. 1978. s-m. $580 in N. America (elsewhere $595) (effective 1993). Petroleum Analysis Ltd., Box 130, F.D.R. Sta., New York, NY 10150-0130. TEL 212-755-7484. FAX 212-750-0189. Ed. Dillard Spriggs. stat.; index. (back issues avail.) **Indexed:** Petrol.Energy B.N.I.
—CCC.
Description: Covers financial and regulatory trends and developments affecting the petroleum industry, including exploration projects, acquisitions and investment evaluations.

338.2 665.5 US
INTERNATIONAL PETROLEUM INDUSTRY. a. $85. Midwest Register, Inc., 1120 E. 4th St., Tulsa, OK 74120. TEL 918-582-2000. FAX 918-587-9349. **Document type:** directory.
Formerly: Oil Directory of Companies Outside the U.S. and Canada (ISSN 0472-7711)
Description: Supplies company name, address, phone and fax numbers, telex number, division offices, office locations and U.S. office if known. Divided by sections.

665.5 US
INTERNATIONAL PETROLEUM INDUSTRY DATA SERVICE: AFRICA. (Includes cumulative world data) base vol. (plus q. supplements). $1650 (renewal $600). (International Petroleum Institute) Barrows Co., Inc., 116 E. 66th St., New York, NY 10021. TEL 212-772-1199. FAX 212-288-7242. TELEX 4971238 BARROWS.
Description: Oil and gas economic data.

665.5 US
INTERNATIONAL PETROLEUM INDUSTRY DATA SERVICE: EUROPE. (Includes cumulative world data) base vol. (plus q. supplements). $1650 (renewal $600). (International Petroleum Institute) Barrows Co., Inc., 116 E. 66th St., New York, NY 10021. TEL 212-772-1199. FAX 212-288-7242. TELEX 4971238 BARROWS. Ed. Marta Guerra.
Description: Oil and gas economic data.

665.5 US
INTERNATIONAL PETROLEUM INDUSTRY DATA SERVICE: FAR EAST. (Includes cumulative world data) base vol. (plus q. supplements). $1650 (renewal $600). (International Petroleum Institute) Barrows Co., Inc., 116 E. 66th St., New York, NY 10021. TEL 212-772-1199. FAX 212-288-7242. TELEX 4971238 BARROWS.
Description: Oil and gas economic data.

665.5 US
INTERNATIONAL PETROLEUM INDUSTRY DATA SERVICE: MIDDLE EAST. (Includes cumulative world data) base vol. (plus q. supplements). $1650 (renewal $600). (International Petroleum Institute) Barrows Co., Inc., 116 E. 66th St., New York, NY 10021. TEL 212-772-1199. FAX 212-288-7242. TELEX 4971238 BARROWS. Ed. Marta Guerra.
Description: Oil and gas economic data.

665.5 US ISSN 0276-0061
INTERNATIONAL PETROLEUM INDUSTRY DATA SERVICE: NORTH AMERICA. (Includes cumulative world data) base vol. (plus q. supplements). $1650 (renewal $600). (International Petroleum Institute) Barrows Co., Inc., 116 E. 66th St., New York, NY 10021. TEL 212-772-1199. FAX 212-288-7242. TELEX 4971238 BARROWS. Ed. Marta Guerra.
Description: Oil and gas economic data.

665.5 US
INTERNATIONAL PETROLEUM INDUSTRY DATA SERVICE: SOUTH & CENTRAL AMERICA. (Includes cumulative world data.) base vol. (plus q. supplements). $1650 (renewal $600). (International Petroleum Institute) Barrows Co., Inc., 116 E. 66th St., New York, NY 10021. TEL 212-772-1199. FAX 212-288-7242. TELEX 4971238 BARROWS. Ed. Marta Guerra.
Description: Oil and gas economic data.

665.5 II ISSN 0047-1046
INTERNATIONAL PRESS CUTTING SERVICE: PETROLEUM - PETROCHEMICALS - FERTILISERS - AGRICULTURAL CHEMISTRY. 1967. w. $75. International Press Cutting Service, P.O. Box 63, Allahabad 211001, India. Ed. N. Khanna. bk.rev.; index. circ. 1,200. (processed)

INTERNATIONAL TAXATION SERIES. see BUSINESS AND ECONOMICS — Public Finance, Taxation

665 US
TN872
INTERSTATE OIL AND GAS COMPACT COMMISSION. COMPACT & COMMITTEE BULLETIN. 1958. a. $10. Interstate Oil and Gas Compact Commission, Box 53127, Oklahoma City, OK 73152-3127. TEL 405-525-3556. charts; illus. **Indexed:** E&P Hlth. (1993-), Gas Process.& Ppl. (1993-), INIS Atomind., Off.Tech. (1993-), Petrol.Abstr. (1965-). **Document type:** trade publication.
—PADDS; UnCover.
Formerly: Interstate Oil Compact Commission. Compact & Committee Bulletin (ISSN 1046-2333); Which was formed by the merger of (1942-1986): Oil and Gas Compact Bulletin; (1958-1986): Interstate Oil Compact Commission. Committee Bulletin (ISSN 0020-9732)

665.5 US ISSN 0884-9854
IOWA OIL SPOUT. 6/yr. Petroleum Marketers of Iowa, 321 Sixth Ave., Des Moines, IA 50309-4102. TEL 515-244-6273. Ed. E.A. Kistenmacher. circ. 1,000.

665.5 US
IOWA PETROLEUM DISTRIBUTOR NEWSLETTER. m. Petroleum Marketers of Iowa, 321 Sixth Ave., Des Moines, IA 50309-1903. TEL 515-244-6273. FAX 515-244-1051. Ed. Ron Marr.

665 IR ISSN 0021-079X
IRAN OIL JOURNAL. French edition: Iran Petrole. Farsi edition: Nameh Sanaat-e-Naft. (Text in English) q. free. Petroleum Ministry, Public Relations & Guidance Department, P.O. Box 1863, Central NIOC Bldg., Taleghani Ave., Teheran, Iran. TEL 021-6151. TELEX 212514. Ed. Yegandokht Mostofian.

665.5 IR
IRAN OIL NEWS. 1984. m. free. Petroleum Ministry, Public Relations & Guidance Department, P.O. Box 1863, Central NIOC Bldg., Taleghani Ave., Tehran, Iran. TEL 6153823.
Formerly: Petroleum Newsletter.
Description: Promotes a better understanding of the Petroleum Ministry of Iran and its policies, as well as providing analysis of the accomplishments within the industry. Addresses energy issues and international petroleum affairs.

665.5 IQ
IRAQ OIL NEWS. (Text in English) no. 55, 1980. Ministry of Oil, Baghdad, Iraq.

665.5 RU ISSN 0202-7429
CODEN: IRNGAK
ITOGI NAUKI I TEKHNIKI: RAZRABOTKA NEFTYANYKH I GAZOVYKH MESTOROZHDENII. 1968. irreg., vol.21, 1989. 6.60 Rub. Vsesoyuznyi Institut Nauchno-Tekhnicheskoi Informatsii (VINITI), Baltiiskaya ul. 14, Moscow A-219, Russia. (Subscr. to: Mezhdunarodnaya Kniga, Dimitrova ul. 39, 113095 Moscow, Russia)
—BLDSC (0140.236000).

665.5 JA ISSN 0289-4343
CODEN: JETIEE
J E T I: JAPAN ENERGY & TECHNOLOGY INTELLIGENCE.* (Text in Japanese) 1957. m. 2-15-5 Fujimi, Chiyoda-ku, Tokyo 101, Japan. illus. **Indexed:** Chem.Abstr., INIS Atomind.
—BLDSC (4648.263000); CASDDS.
Formed by the merger of (1953-1983): Sekiyu Bunka (ISSN 0289-4149); (1957-1983): Sekiyu to Sekiyu Kagaku (ISSN 0371-3830)

665.5 US ISSN 0149-2136
TN860 CODEN: JPTJAM
J P T: JOURNAL OF PETROLEUM TECHNOLOGY. 1949. m. $45 to non-members. Society of Petroleum Engineers, Inc., Box 833836, Richardson, TX 75083-3836. TEL 214-952-9393. FAX 214-952-9435. TELEX 163245 SPEUT. Ed. Georgeann Bilich. adv.: B&W page $3595, color page $4590; 8 1/8 x 10 7/8; adv. contact: Doris Tolman. bk.rev./ abstr.; bibl.; charts; illus.; index, cum.index; circ. 55,237 (paid). (also avail. in microform from UMI; back issues avail.; reprint service avail. from SPE) **Indexed:** A.S.& T.Ind., AESIS, API Abstr., API Catal., API Hlth.& Environ., API Oil., API Pet.Ref., API Pet.Subst., API Transport., Appl.Mech.Rev., Bibl.& Ind.Geol., Cadscan, Chem.Abstr., Curr.Cont., Deep Sea Res.& Oceanogr.Abstr., E&P Hlth. (1993-), Energy Ind., Energy Info.Abstr., Energy Rev., Eng.Ind., Environ.Abstr., Environ.Per.Bibl., Excerp.Med., Fuel & Energy Abstr., Gas Abstr., Gas Process.& Ppl. (1993-), INIS Atomind., Lead Abstr., Met.Abstr., Ocean.Abstr., Off.Tech. (1993-), Petrol.Abstr. (1961-), Pollut.Abstr., Risk Abstr., Sh.& Vib.Dig., W.R.C.Inf., Zincscan. **Document type:** academic/scholarly publication, trade publication.
—BLDSC (5031.000000); CASDDS; Ei; Faxon; PADDS; SWETS; UMI; UnCover. **CCC.**
Formerly: Journal of Petroleum Technology (ISSN 0022-3522)
Refereed Serial

665.5 JA ISSN 0916-2623
JAPAN PETROLEUM AND ENERGY TRENDS. (Supplements avail.) (Text in English) 1966. bi-w. (26/yr.). 180000 Yen. Japan Petroleum and Energy Consultants, Ltd. - Nihon Sekiyu Konsarutanto K.K., P.O. Box 1185, Tokyo Central, Tokyo 100-91, Japan. TEL 04-7573-1931. FAX 04-7573-1934. Ed. K. Kurokawa. mkt.; stat.; index. circ. 1,200. (looseleaf format) **Document type:** newsletter.
Former titles: Japan Petroleum and Energy Weekly & Japan Petroleum Weekly (ISSN 0386-6165)
Description: Covers petroleum and energy related news in Japan.

665.5 JA ISSN 0582-4656
TP690.A1 CODEN: BUJPA5
JAPAN PETROLEUM INSTITUTE. BULLETIN. (Text in English) 1959. s-a. Japan Petroleum Institute - Sekiyu Gakkai, COSMO Hirakawa-cho Bldg., 1-3-14 Hirakawa-cho, Chiyoda-ku, Tokyo 102, Japan. TEL 81-3-3221-7301. FAX 81-3-3221-8175. (Subscr. to: Maruzen Co., Ltd., P.O. Box 5050, Tokyo International, Japan) adv. circ. 5,000. **Indexed:** Chem.Abstr., GeoRef. **Document type:** bulletin.
—CCC.

665.5 JA ISSN 0582-4664
JAPAN PETROLEUM INSTITUTE. JOURNAL/SEKIYU GAKKAISHI. (Text in English or Japanese) 1958. bi-m. 14214 to non-members; members 4200Yen. Japan Petroleum Institute, COSMO Hirakawa-cho Bldg., 1-3-14 Hirakawa-cho, Chiyoda-ku, Tokyo 102, Japan. TEL 03-3221-7301. FAX 81-3-3221-8175. (Subscr. to: Maruzen Co., Ltd., P.O. Box 5050, Tokyo International, Japan) circ. 1,500. **Document type:** academic/scholarly publication.

JET FUEL INTELLIGENCE. see TRANSPORTATION — Air Transport

665.53 CC ISSN 1003-9384
JINGXI SHIYOU HUAGONG/SPECIALTY PETROCHEMICALS. (Text in Chinese) 1984. bi-m. Y30. Zhongguo Shiyou Huagong Zonggongsi - SINOPEC, Specialty Petrochemical S & T Information Center, Shanggulin, Dagang-qu, Tianjin 300271, People's Republic of China. TEL 756622. Ed. Sun Luhou.

PETROLEUM AND GAS

665.5   CN   ISSN 0021-9487
CODEN: JCPMAM
JOURNAL OF CANADIAN PETROLEUM TECHNOLOGY. 1962. 10/yr. Can.$135 (foreign $150). Canadian Institute of Mining, Metallurgy and Petroleum, Petroleum Society, 101 6 Ave., S.W., Ste. 320, Calgary, AB T2P 3P4, Canada. TEL 403-237-5112. FAX 403-262-4792. Ed. Catherine Buchanan; Pub. Yvan Jacques. adv. contact: Wes Scott. bk.rev.; abstr.; bibl.; charts; illus.; tr.lit.; index. circ. 5,700. **Indexed:** AESIS, API Abstr., API Catal., API Hlth.& Environ., API Oil., API Pet.Ref., API Pet.Subst., API Transport., Bibl.& Ind.Geol., CAD CAM Abstr., Chem.Abstr., Curr.Cont., E&P Hlth. (1993-), Energy Info.Abstr., Eng.Ind., Environ.Abstr., Environ.Per.Bibl., Fuel & Energy Abstr., Gas Abstr., Gas Process.& Ppl. (1993-), INIS Atomind., Off.Tech. (1993-), Petrol.Abstr. (1963-), Risk Abstr. **Document type:** trade publication.
—BLDSC (4954.750000); CASDDS; CIS; Ei; Faxon; PADDS; SWETS; UnCover.
    Description: Contains news and technical information of specific interest to the petroleum, oil and gas industries.

665.7 547   CC   ISSN 1003-9853
CODEN: JGCHE8
JOURNAL OF NATURAL GAS CHEMISTRY. (Text in English) 1992. q. Academia Sinica, Chengdu Institute of Organic Chemistry, 9 Section 4, Renminnan Rd., Chengdu, Sichuan 610015, People's Republic of China. TEL 581317. Ed. Guangnian Li. **Document type:** academic/scholarly publication.
—BLDSC (5021.196100); CASDDS.

665.5   UK   ISSN 0141-6421
TN870.5   CODEN: JPEGD9
JOURNAL OF PETROLEUM GEOLOGY. 1978. q. £280. Scientific Press Ltd., P.O. Box 21, Beaconsfield, Bucks. HP9 1NS, England. TEL 01494-675139. FAX 01494-670155. Ed. E.N. Tiratsoo. adv.; bk.rev. **Indexed:** AESIS, Bibl.& Ind.Geol., Br.Geol.Lit., Chem.Abstr., Deep Sea Res.& Oceanogr.Abstr., E&P Hlth. (1993-), Gas Process.& Ppl. (1993-), Geo.Abstr., Geol.Abstr., Off.Tech. (1993-), Petrol.Abstr. (1981-). **Document type:** academic/scholarly publication.
—BLDSC (5030.990000); CASDDS; Ei; Faxon; Genuine Article; PADDS; SWETS; UnCover.

665.54   US   ISSN 1055-5056
HD9561
JOURNAL OF PETROLEUM MARKETING. 1988. 7/yr. B M T Communications, Inc., 7 Penn Plaza, New York, NY 10001-3900. TEL 212-594-4120. FAX 212-714-0514. Ed. John Callanan. circ. 19,600.
    Formerly (until 1990): P - The Journal of Petroleum Marketing (ISSN 1050-1754)

665.5   IQ   ISSN 1012-3369
JOURNAL OF PETROLEUM RESEARCH. 1982. s-a. ID.10($15) to individuals; institutions $50. Scientific Research Council, Petroleum Research Centre, P.O. Box 10039, Jadiriyah, Baghdad, Iraq. TELEX 7768929. Ed. A.H. Mohammed. circ. 500. **Indexed:** Chem.Abstr., Eng.Ind., Petrol.Abstr.

665.5   NE   ISSN 0920-4105
TN860   CODEN: JPSEE6
JOURNAL OF PETROLEUM SCIENCE AND ENGINEERING. (Text in English) 1987. 8/yr. fl.960($585) (effective 1996). Elsevier Science B.V., P.O. Box 211, 1000 AE Amsterdam, Netherlands. TEL 31-20-4853911. FAX 31-20-4853598. TELEX 18582 ESPA NL.
E-mail: nlinfo-f@elsevier.nl; usinfo-f@elsevier.com; forinfo-kyf04035@niftyserve.or.jp; Site addr.: http://www.elsevier.nl/. (Subscr. in U.S. and Canada to: Elsevier Science Inc., Box 882, Madison Sq. Sta., New York, NY 10159-0882. TEL 212-989-5800. FAX 212-633-3990) Ed.Bd. adv.; Ed.Bd. adv.; bk.rev.; charts; illus.; stat. (also avail. in microform from UMI; back issues avail.) **Indexed:** Curr.Cont., E&P Hlth. (1993-), Eng.Ind., Gas Process.& Ppl. (1988-), Geo.Abstr., Geol.Abstr., Off.Tech. (1993-). **Document type:** academic/scholarly publication.
—BLDSC (5030.998000); CASDDS; Ei; Faxon; Genuine Article; PADDS; SWETS. **CCC.**
    Description: Covers the fields of petroleum geology, exploration and engineering.
    Refereed Serial

665.538   UK   ISSN 0265-6582
CODEN: JSLUE6
JOURNAL OF SYNTHETIC LUBRICATION: research, development and application of synthetic lubricants and functional fluids. 1984. q. £150($263) (effective 1996). Leaf Coppin Publishing Co., P.O. Box 111, Deal, Kent CT14 6SX, England. TEL 01304-360241. Ed. Stephen Godfree. adv.; bk.rev. **Indexed:** Chem.Abstr., Eng.Ind. **Document type:** academic/scholarly publication.
—BLDSC (5068.042000); CASDDS; Ei; Faxon; SWETS. **CCC.**
    Refereed Serial

665.538   US   ISSN 0742-4787
TJ1075.A2   CODEN: JOTRE9
JOURNAL OF TRIBOLOGY. 1967. q. $120 to non-members; members $29. American Society of Mechanical Engineers, 22 Law Dr., Fairfield, NJ 07007-2300. TEL 800-843-2763. Ed. W.O. Winer. adv.; bk.rev.; charts; illus.; index. circ. 3,547. (also avail. in microform from UMI; reprint service avail. from UMI) **Indexed:** A.S.& T.Ind., API Abstr., API Catal., API Hlth.& Environ., API Oil., API Pet.Ref., API Pet.Subst., API Transport., Appl.Mech.Rev., Br.Rail.Bd., Chem.Abstr., Curr.Cont., Eng.Ind., Fluidex, Ind.Sci.Rev., INIS Atomind., INSPEC, Int.Aerosp.Abstr., ISMEC, Met.Abstr., Nucl.Sci.Abstr., Sh.& Vib.Dig., World Alum.Abstr.
—BLDSC (8897.070000); CASDDS; Ei; Faxon; Genuine Article; SWETS; UMI; UnCover. **CCC.**
    Formerly (until 1983): Journal of Lubrication Technology (ISSN 0022-2305); Supersedes in part (1880-1958): American Society of Mechanical Engineers. Transactions (ISSN 0097-6822).
    Description: Details lubrication and lubricants.
    Refereed Serial

665.7   JA   ISSN 0914-496X
KANREICHI GIJUTSU KENKYU KAIHATSU SENTA HOKOKU/RESEARCH CENTER FOR GAS INDUSTRY IN COLD DISTRICT. TECHNICAL REPORT. (Text in Japanese) 1980. a. Nihon Gasu Kyokai, Hokkaido Bukai, Kanreichi Gijutsu Kenkyu Kaihatsu Senta - Japan Gas Association, Hokkaido Branch, Research Center for Gas Industry in Cold District, Higashi 5-chome, Kita 3-jo, Chuo-ku, Sapporo-shi, Hokkaido 060, Japan.

665.5   US
KANSAS OIL MARKETER. 1920. 6/yr. membership. Kansas Oil Marketers Association, P.O. Box 8479, Topeka, KS 66608-0479. TEL 913-233-9655. FAX 913-354-4374. Ed. Dannis Enderson. circ. 700.

KARBO - ENERGOCHEMIA - EKOLOGIA. see **MINES AND MINING INDUSTRY**

KELLY'S OIL & GAS DIRECTORY. see **BUSINESS AND ECONOMICS** — Trade And Industrial Directories

KHIMICHESKOE I NEFTYANOE MASHINOSTROENIE/CHEMICAL AND OIL INDUSTRY. see **ENGINEERING** — Chemical Engineering

665.5 547.8   RU   ISSN 0023-1169
CODEN: KTPMAG
KHIMIYA I TEKHNOLOGIYA TOPLIV I MASEL. English translation: Chemistry and Technology of Fuels and Oils (US ISSN 0009-3092) 1956. m. $102 (effective 1996). Izdatel'stvo Khimiya, Novaya pl., 10, Moscow K-12, Russia. Ed. I.S. Polyakov. bibl.; charts; illus.; index. circ. 3,270. **Indexed:** Bibl.& Ind.Geol., Chem.Abstr., INIS Atomind., Pollut.Abstr.
—BLDSC (0394.000000); CASDDS; SWETS. **CCC.**

665.5   KU   ISSN 0304-7237
HD9576.K84
KUWAIT NATIONAL PETROLEUM COMPANY. ANNUAL REPORT. (Text in English) 1963. a. Kuwait National Petroleum Company K.S.C., P.O. Box 70, 13001 Safat, Kuwait. TEL 965-2420121. FAX 965-2433839. Dir. Ahmad Abd al-Muhsin al-Mutair. **Document type:** corporate report.

665.5   KU   ISSN 0023-5792
AL-KUWAITI. (Text in Arabic) 1961. m. free. Kuwait Oil Company (K.S.C.), Supdt. Press and Publications Division, P.O. Box 9758 Ahmadi, 61008 Ahmadi, Kuwait. TEL 965-3989111. FAX 965-3983661. TELEX 44226 KUOCO. Ed. Salem R. Al Roomi. film rev.; play rev.; illus.; tr.lit. circ. 6,300.
    Description: Articles on economics, energy, oil industry and science.

KYUSHU UNIVERSITY. DEPARTMENT OF EARTH AND PLANETARY SCIENCES. SCIENCE REPORTS/KYUSHU DAIGAKU RIGAKUBU KENKYU HOKOKU CHIKYU-WAKUSEI-KAGAKU. see **EARTH SCIENCES** — Geology

665.7   US   ISSN 1053-6949
CODEN: LNOBFK
L N G OBSERVER. (Liquefied Natural Gas) 1990. q. $150 (effective 1996). Institute of Gas Technology, 1700 S. Mount Prospect Rd., Des Plaines, IL 60018-1804. TEL 708-768-0512. FAX 708-768-0516. Ed. Colleen Taylor Sen. charts; stat. circ. 2,000. (back issues avail.) **Indexed:** Gas Abstr. **Document type:** newsletter.
●Also available online.
    Description: Covers technological, political, economic and financial developments in the worldwide liquefied natural gas industry.

658.8   US
L O M A LINE. m. membership. Louisiana Oil Marketers Association, 2354 S. Acadian Thwy. Ste. G., Baton Rouge, LA 70808. TEL 504-344-6968. adv. circ. 600. (processed)
    Formerly: L O M A Bulletin.

665.7   US   ISSN 0024-7103
TP761.P4
L P - GAS. 1940. m. (with annual supplement). $18 (supplement $20). Advanstar Communications, Inc., 7500 Old Oak Blvd., Cleveland, OH 44130. TEL 216-826-2839. FAX 216-891-2726. (Subscr. to: 131 W. First St., Duluth, MN 55802. TEL 800-346-0085) Ed. Zane Chastain. adv.; illus.; stat.; tr.lit. circ. 15,321. (also avail. in microform from UMI) **Indexed:** Gas Abstr. **Document type:** trade publication.
—SWETS; UMI. **CCC.**
    Description: Covers gas production, storage, utilization and marketing.

665.5   UK   ISSN 0309-3077
L P GAS REVIEW. 1977. bi-m. £33 (foreign £45). Bouverie Publishing Company Ltd., 147-151 Temple Chambers, Temple Ave., London EC4Y 0DT, England. TEL 0171-583-3030. FAX 0171-583-6481. Ed. Paul Newbon. circ. 4,585. **Document type:** trade publication.
—BLDSC (5300.125000). **CCC.**
    Description: Covers every aspect of liquefied petroleum gas from bulk containerization to site transfer and consumer containers.

665.5   US   ISSN 0023-7418
HD9560.1
LAMP (NEW YORK). 1918. q. free. Exxon Corporation, 225 E. John W. Carpenter Freeway, Irving, TX 75062-2298. TEL 214-444-1116. FAX 214-444-1139. Ed. James B. Davis. illus.; cum.index every 3 yrs.; circ. 650,000 (controlled). **Indexed:** Chem.Abstr., Environ.Abstr., Ind.Free Per., P.A.I.S., PROMT.
—BLDSC (5145.000000); UnCover.

665.5   US   ISSN 1043-7312
LAND RIG NEWSLETTER. 1978. m. $250 (subscr. includes q. summary) (effective 1993). R J M Communications, Box 6645, Lubbock, TX 79493-6645. TEL 806-741-1531. FAX 806-741-1553. Ed. Richard Mason. **Document type:** newsletter.
    Description: Provides market intelligence for the onshore drilling industry and includes business news on emerging onshore drilling markets, financial reports on acquisitions, rig sales, and company performance.

665.5   US   ISSN 0457-088X
HD9561
LANDMAN. 1955. bi-m. $100. American Association of Professional Landmen, 4100 Fossil Creek Blvd., Fort Worth, TX 76137-2791. TEL 817-847-7700. Ed. Le'ann Pembroke Callihan. adv.: B&W page $520, color page $1720. circ. 10,000 (controlled). **Document type:** trade publication.
—BLDSC (5151.751000); UnCover.
    Description: Covers oil and gas exploration, land management and local association news.

PETROLEUM AND GAS

665.5   US
LAWFUL RESERVOIR MARKET DEMAND FOR PRORATED GAS FIELDS. m. $36. Railroad Commission, Oil and Gas Publications, Drawer 12967, Capitol Sta., Austin, TX 78711. TEL 512-463-7255. **Document type:** government publication.
   Description: Publishes data on monthly reservoir demand, along with adjustments and supplemental changes.

665.538   US
LEGISLATIVE AND REGULATORY SERVICE. 1986. q. $695 (foreign $795). Information Resources, Inc., 1925 N. Lynn St., Ste. 1000, Arlington, VA 22209. TEL 703-528-2500. FAX 703-528-1483. **Document type:** trade publication.
   Description: Provides a detailed compendium of federal and state laws and regulations pertaining to the sale, taxation, blending and marketing of motor fuels.

665.5 621.3   FR   ISSN 0754-5215
LETTRE AFRIQUE ENERGIES. English edition: Africa Energy and Mining. 1983. 23/yr. 3800 F.($700) Indigo Publications, 10, rue du Sentier, 75002 Paris, France. TEL 44-88-26-10. FAX 44-88-26-15. Dir. Maurice Botbol. **Document type:** newsletter.

665.5   AT   ISSN 0817-6191
LIPSCOMBE REPORT. w. (by telex); s-w. by fax; every 2-3 mos. (newsletter). Aus.$2700. Pex Publications Pty. Ltd., P.O. Box 158, Claremont, W.A. 6010, Australia. TEL 61-9-3833477. FAX 61-9-3851485. Ed. Don Lipscombe. index. (back issues avail.)
   Description: Monitors oil and gaz exploration and development in Australia, Papua New Guinea and New Zealand.

665.773   JA   ISSN 0024-709X
LIQUEFIED PETROLEUM GAS/L P GASU. (Text in Japanese) 1959. m. newsstand price: 1500Yen. Sangyo Hodo Publications, Inc., 4-7, Tsukiji 3-chome, Chuo-ku, Tokyo 104, Japan. adv.; charts; illus.

LIQUID GAS CARRIER REGISTER. see *TRANSPORTATION — Ships And Shipping*

LIQUIDS HANDLING. see *ENGINEERING*

LITERATURE ABSTRACTS: CATALYSTS - ZEOLITES. see *CHEMISTRY — Abstracting, Bibliographies, Statistics*

665.5   US   ISSN 0024-581X
                                      CODEN: LGALAS
LOG ANALYST. 1962. bi-m. $95. Society of Professional Well Log Analysts, 8866 Gulf Fwy., Ste. 320, Houston, TX 77017. TEL 713-947-8727. FAX 713-947-7181. adv.; bk.rev. circ. 4,500. **Indexed:** AESIS, Bibl.& Ind.Geol., E&P Hlth. (1993-), Eng.Ind., Gas Process.& Ppl. (1993-), Off.Tech. (1993-), Petrol.Abstr. (1963-), W.R.C.Inf. **Document type:** trade publication.
   —BLDSC (5292.304500); Ei; Faxon; PADDS; SWETS; UnCover.

658.8   US
LOMALINE. 1951. q. Louisiana Oil Marketers Association, 2354 S. Acadian Thwy., Ste. G, Baton Rouge, LA 70808. TEL 504-344-6968. Ed. Robert K. Butcher. adv.; charts; illus.; stat. circ. 1,100.
   Formerly (until 1985): Hose and Nozzle (ISSN 0018-5361)

LOUISIANA OIL AND GAS LAW. see *LAW*

665   US
LUBRICATING OILS DATA BOOK. 1975. biennial. $70. Engine Manufacturers Association, 401 N. Michigan Ave., Chicago, IL 60611-4206. TEL 312-644-6610. FAX 312-321-5111. circ. 3,500 (paid). (looseleaf format) **Document type:** catalog.

620   UK   ISSN 0954-0075
                                      CODEN: LUSCEN
LUBRICATION SCIENCE; physics and chemistry of lubricants in tribological systems. 1988. q. £151($265) (effective 1996). Leaf Coppin Publishing Co., P.O. Box 111, Deal, Kent CT14 6SX, England. TEL 01304-360241. Ed. Stephen Godfree. adv.; bk.rev. **Document type:** academic/scholarly publication.
   —BLDSC (5302.080000); CASDDS; Ei. **CCC**. **Refereed Serial**

665.5   US   ISSN 0195-4563
LUNDBERG LETTER. 1974. s-m. $399. Lundberg Survey, Incorporated, Box 3996, N. Hollywood, CA 91609-0996. TEL 818-768-5111. FAX 818-768-0537. Pub. Trilby Lundberg.

665   HU
MAGYAR OLAJIPARI MUZEUM. EVKONYV. 1974. irreg. 117 Ft. Magyar Olajipari Muzeum, Zalaegerszeg, Hungary. illus. circ. 1,000.

665.5   UK   ISSN 0959-499X
MAJOR CHEMICAL AND PETROCHEMICAL COMPANIES OF EUROPE. 1987. a. £185($315) Graham & Trotman Ltd. (Subsidiary of: Kluwer Academic Publishers Group), Sterling House, 66 Wilson Rd., London SW1V 1DE, England. TEL 44-71-821-1123. FAX 44-71-630-5229. (Dist. by: Kluwer Academic Publishers Group, P.O. Box 322, 3300 AH Dordrecht, Netherlands. TEL 31-78-524400. FAX 31-78-524474; N. America library orders to: Gale Research Inc., Penobscot Bldg., Detroit, MI 48226. TEL 313-961-2242; Other N. America orders to: Box 358, Accord Sta., Higham, MA 02018-0358. TEL 617-871-6600. FAX 617-871-6528) Ed. Ruth Whiteside. **Document type:** trade publication.
   —BLDSC (5353.602000).
   Description: Describes the finances, personnel, structure, products, and locations of the most influential chemical and petrochemical companies in Western Europe.

662.338   US
TN872
MARGINAL OIL: FUEL FOR ECONOMIC GROWTH. 1951. a. $2.50. Interstate Oil and Gas Compact Commission, Box 53127, Oklahoma City, OK 73152-3127. TEL 405-525-3556. **Document type:** trade publication.
   Formerly: National Stripper Well Survey (ISSN 0470-3219)

MARINE AND PETROLEUM GEOLOGY. see *EARTH SCIENCES — Geology*

665   US
THE MARKETER; official voice of petroleum marketers in Oklahoma. 1964. q. $12. Oklahoma Petroleum Marketers Association, 6501 N. Western, Oklahoma City, OK 73118. TEL 405-842-6625. FAX 405-842-9564. Ed. Sheryl McFadden. adv.; circ. 1,300 (controlled).
   Former titles: Oil Marketer; Oklahoma Oil Marketer.

665.5   QA
AL-MASH'AL/TORCH. (Text in Arabic, English) 1986. s-m. free. Qatar General Petroleum Corporation, Public Relations Department, P.O. Box 3212, Doha, Qatar. TEL 974-491449. FAX 974-831995. TELEX 4343 PETCOR DH. circ. 4,000.

MATERIALS AND COMPONENTS IN FOSSIL ENERGY APPLICATIONS. see *ENERGY*

665.5   MX
▼**MEXICO PETROLEUM REPORT.** 1994. m. $175. Publications and Information Management Mexico, Paseo de la Reforma 324, Ste. 1-215, 06500 Mexico DF, Mexico. TEL 525-535-7222. FAX 525-208-9675. Ed. Susan Zimmerman; Pub. James S. Wright. adv. contact: Enitze Elizalde. circ. 1,890 (paid). **Document type:** trade publication, newsletter.

665.5   US
MICHIGAN OIL & GAS NEWS. 1932. w. $100. 206 W. Michigan, Ste. 200, Mt. Pleasant, MI 48858. TEL 517-772-5181. FAX 517-773-2970. Ed. Jack Westbrook. circ. 1,843. **Document type:** trade publication.

665.538 658.7   UK   ISSN 0268-7852
MID-WEEK PETROLEUM ARGUS. w. £655 (N. America $940). Petroleum Argus Ltd., 93 Shepperton Rd., London N1 3DF, England. TEL 0171-359-8792. FAX 0171-226-0695. TELEX 21277. **Document type:** trade publication.

665.5   US
MIDCONTIENT PETROLEUM DIRECTORY. 1984. a. $79. Hart Publications, Inc. (Subsidiary of: Phillips Publishing International, Inc.), 1900 Grant St., Ste. 400, Denver, CO 80205. TEL 303-837-1917. FAX 303-837-8585. Ed. Paula Jepperson. adv. contact: Susan Katz. circ. 2,500. (also avail. in diskette format) **Document type:** directory.
   Description: Directory including companies involved in exploration and production, service and supply with the oil and gas industry. Covers Kansas, Missouri, Oklahoma, Arkansas and parts of Nebraska, Iowa and Texas.

338.2 655.5   US
MIDCONTINENT PETROLEUM INDUSTRY. 1945. a. $50. Midwest Register, Inc., 1120 E. 4th St., Tulsa, OK 74120. TEL 918-582-2000. FAX 918-587-9349. **Document type:** directory.
   Formed by the 1992 merger of: Directory of Producers and Drilling Contractors: Kansas; Directory of Producers and Drilling Contractors: Oklahoma.
   Description: Supplies company name, address, phone and fax numbers, personnel, division offices, offshore operations, whether producer of oil or gas and if drilling contractor with rotary or cable tools for OK, KS, MO, IA, NE.

338.47   CY   ISSN 0544-0424
HD9576.N36
MIDDLE EAST ECONOMIC SURVEY. Abbreviated title: M E E S. 1957. w. $1375 (overseas $1,425). Middle East Petroleum and Economic Publications, P.O. Box 4940, Nicosia, Cyprus. TEL 445431. FAX 474988. TELEX 2198 MEES CY. Ed. Ian Seymour. bk.rev.; charts; stat.; index. **Indexed:** Key to Econ.Sci., Petrol.Energy B.N.I. **Document type:** academic/scholarly publication.
   —BLDSC (5761.373500).
   Description: Reviews oil, finance, banking, and political developments in the Middle East and North Africa.

665.7   US
MIDWEST GAS NEWS. 1978. a. Gas Digest, 11246 S. Post Oak, Ste. 206, Houston, TX 77035-5741. TEL 713-723-7456. circ. 2,000 (controlled).

665.5   GW   ISSN 0544-2524
MINERALOEL - MINERALOELRUNDSCHAU; Zeitschrift fuer die Deutsche Mineraloelwirtschaft. 1953. m. DM.60. Uniti Bundesverband Mittelstaendischer Mineraloelunternehmen e.V., Buchtstr. 10, 22087 Hamburg, Germany. TEL 040-2270030. FAX 040-22700338. Ed. Wolfgang Stichler. adv.; bk.rev.; pat. circ. 1,200. **Document type:** trade publication.
   —BLDSC (5790.360000).
   Former titles: Mineraloelrundschau; (until 1972): Uniti.

MINERIA CHILENA. see *MINES AND MINING INDUSTRY*

662.6   GW   ISSN 0341-1893
                                      CODEN: MTCKAZ
MINEROELTECHNIK. 1956. m. DM.111.20. Beratungsgesellschaft fuer Mineraloel-Anwendungstechnik mbH, Buchtstr. 10, 22087 Hamburg, Germany. TEL 040-22700344. FAX 040-2270-0349. Ed. Wolfgang Heine. adv.; bk.rev.; index. circ. 2,000. (back issues avail.) **Document type:** trade publication.
   —BLDSC (5786.420000); CASDDS.
   Description: Reports on mineral oil usage, research results on oil products, fuels, heating oils, lubricants.

MINING AND PETROLEUM LEGISLATION SERVICE. see *LAW*

MINING RECORD. see *MINES AND MINING INDUSTRY*

353.9   US   ISSN 0095-3024
HD9579.G5
MINNESOTA. DEPARTMENT OF REVENUE. PETROLEUM DIVISION. ANNUAL REPORT. Key Title: Annual Report - Petroleum Division. 1973. a. Department of Revenue, Petroleum Division, MS 3333, St. Paul, MN 55146. TEL 612-296-0889. **Document type:** government publication.

PETROLEUM AND GAS 5039

665.5 US
MISSOURI PIPELINE. 1936. m. membership. Missouri Petroleum Marketers Association, 238 E. High St., Jefferson City, MO 65101. TEL 314-635-7117. FAX 314-635-3575. Ed. Jim Keown. adv.; bk.rev.; tr.lit.; circ. 1,400 (controlled).
  Formerly: Missouri Oil Jobber.

665.5 UK
MODERN LIVING AT THE HOME OF GAS. 1938. s-a. British Gas North Thames, North Thames House, London Rd., Staines, Middx. TW18 4AE, England. Ed. Michael Purdie. circ. 1,800,000.
  Formerly: Modern Living with Gas.

665.7 IT
MONDOMETANO. 1986. 6/yr. L.60000 (foreign L.100000). R E S Editrice s.r.l., Casella Postale 12053, Via Rogoredo 119, 20120 Milan, Italy. TEL 39-2-4159120. Ed. Gerardo Rizzoli. adv.: color page L.2300000; 180 x 265; adv. contact: Ugo Sociale. bk.rev. circ. 8,500. Document type: trade publication.
  Description: Covers gas energy, water, safety, environment, and pollution.

665.5 IO
MONTHLY BULLETIN OF THE PETROLEUM AND NATURAL GAS INDUSTRY OF INDONESIA. 1973. m. Directorate General of Oil and Gas, Programming and Reporting Division - Direktorat Jenderal Minyak dan Gas Bumi, Jalan M.H. Thamrin No. 1, Jakarta 10110, Indonesia. TEL 62-21-351215. FAX 62-21-354987. TELEX 44363. charts; stat. circ. 400.

665.5 US
MONTHLY CRUDE OIL PRODUCTION. m. $75. Railroad Commission, Oil and Gas Publications, Drawer 12967, Capitol Sta., Austin, TX 78711. TEL 512-463-7255. Document type: government publication.
  Former titles: Monthly Production of Crude Oil Allowable, Production and Removal from Leases in the State of Texas; Preliminary Statement of Crude Oil Allowable, Production and Removal from Leases in the State of Texas.
  Description: Contains preliminary information on allowables, production, number of wells flowing and pumping, number of delinquent leases, method of disposition, and other data listed by district and field. Also reviews some of the previous month's final data.

665.5 JA ISSN 0016-5069
MONTHLY GASOLINE STAND/GEKKAN GASORIN SUTANDO. (Text in Japanese) 1959. m. 4800 Yen($13) Gekkan Gasorin Sutandosha, 3-2-3 Shinbashi, Minato-ku, Tokyo 105, Japan. Ed. Yoshihide Yoshitake. adv.; bk.rev.; abstr.; charts; illus.; stat.; tr.lit.; index. circ. 80,000.

665 JA ISSN 0016-5964
MONTHLY JOURNAL OF GASOLINE SERVICE STATIONS/GEKKAN KYUSHO NIHON. (Text in Japanese) 1965. m. 6000 Yen($20) Yugyo Hochi Shinbunsha, 2-15-19 Shinkawa, Chuo-ku, Tokyo 104, Japan. Ed. Yoshio Takeda. adv.; bk.rev.; abstr.; bibl.; charts; illus.; pat.; stat.; tr.lit.; index. circ. 30,000.

665.5 US ISSN 0094-2766
TN881.T4
MONTHLY SUMMARY OF TEXAS NATURAL GAS. 1949. m. $19. Railroad Commission, Oil and Gas Publications, Drawer 12967, Capitol Sta., Austin, TX 78711-2967. TEL 512-463-7255. charts; stat. circ. 500. (looseleaf format) Document type: government publication.
  Description: Lists production of gas-well gas, casinghead gas, and natural gas liquids; indicates number of wells; contains some data on cycling, gasoline and pressure maintenance plant operations, and volumes exported and flared.

665.5 MR
MOROCCO. MINISTERE DE L'ENERGIE ET DES MINES. ACTIVITE DU SECTEUR PETROLIER. (Text in French) 1956. irreg. $10. Direction des Mines et de la Geologie, Direction de l'Energie, Rabat, Morocco. stat.
  Formerly: Morocco. Direction des Mines et de la Geologie. Activite du Secteur Petrolier.

665.5 US
MUNGER MAP BOOK. 1957. a. $100. Munger Oil Information Service, Inc., 9800 S. Sepulveda Blvd., Ste. 723, Box 75738, Los Angeles, CA 90045. TEL 310-645-3282. FAX 310-645-9147. Ed. Averill H. Munger. Document type: trade publication.
  Description: Provides a comprehensive atlas with pages for each oil, gas and geothermal field in California and Alaska; also wildcat areas: information on current drilling wells, producers and dry holes.

665.538 US ISSN 0027-6782
TJ1077.A1 CODEN: NLGIA4
N L G I SPOKESMAN. 1937. m. $24 (Canada $36; elsewhere $56). National Lubricating Grease Institute, 4635 Wyandotte St., Kansas City, MO 64112. TEL 816-931-9480. FAX 816-753-5026. Ed. Duane J. Fike. adv.; bk.rev.; pat.; index. circ. 2,600. (also avail. in microfilm from UMI; reprint service avail. from UMI) Indexed: API Abstr., API Catal., API Hlth.& Environ., API Oil., API Pet.Ref., API Pet.Subst., API Transport., Appl.Mech.Rev., Chem.Abstr., Eng.Ind., Fluidex.
  —BLDSC (6113.800000); CASDDS; Ei; SWETS; UMI. **CCC.**
  Description: Contains original articles on the manufacture of lubricating grease or new developments in application methods, as well as other items related to the industry.

665.7 US ISSN 1040-0354
N P G A REPORTS. 1982. fortn. $25. National Propane Gas Association, 1600 Eisenhower Ln., Ste. 100, Lisle, IL 60532. TEL 708-515-0600. FAX 708-515-8774. Ed. James K. Burnham. illus.; stat.
  Formerly: N P L G A Reports (ISSN 0744-4273)
  Description: Covers industry trends for producers and marketers of liquified petroleum gas.

655.5 US
N P N MARKET FACTS. (National Petroleum News) a. $50. Hunter Publishing Limited Partnership, 25 N.W. Point Blvd., Ste. 800, Elk Grove Village, IL 60007-1030. TEL 708-427-9512. FAX 708-427-2006. stat.
  Formerly: N P N Factbook (ISSN 0099-4294)

338.47 UK
N W EUROPE PETROLEUM DATABASE. 1986. s-a. with a. report. £3500. Arthur Andersen, Petroleum Services Group, 1 Surrey St., London WC2R 2PS, England. TEL 0171-438-3888. FAX 0171-438-3881. TELEX 8812711. Eds. Timothy H. Shingler, Gary Howorth. Document type: trade publication.
  Description: Provides information on licences, drilling activity and reserves for the offshore sectors of Norway, the Netherlands, Denmark, and Germany, as well as onshore Denmark and Ireland.

665.5 NZ ISSN 0113-0501
N Z PETROLEUM EXPLORATION NEWS. q. NZ.$80. Ministry of Commerce, Publicity Unit, Crown Minerals Operations Group, Energy and Resources Division, P.O. Box 1473, Wellington, New Zealand. TEL 64-4-472-0030. FAX 64-4-499-0968. adv. contact: R.H. Reid. circ. 1,000. Document type: government publication.
  —PADDS. **CCC.**
  Description: Magazine on petroleum exploration in New Zealand.

665.5 IQ
NAFT WAL ALAM. 1973. m. Ministry of Oil, Baghdad, Iraq. Ed. Tayeh Abdel Karim. adv.

665 CI ISSN 0027-755X
CODEN: NAFYA7
NAFTA. (Text in English) 1950. m. $120. Jugoslavenski Komitet Svjetskog Kongresa za Naftu - Yugoslav Committee of the World Petroleum Congresses, Savska Cesta 64-IV, 41000 Zagreb, Croatia. TEL 38-41-515252. Ed. Stjepan Djurasek. adv.; bk.rev.; charts; illus.; index, cum.index. circ. 2,100. Indexed: Chem.Abstr., Petrol.Abstr., Ref.Zh.
  —CASDDS; SWETS. **CCC.**

665 PL ISSN 0867-8871
TN860 CODEN: NGAZES
NAFTA - GAZ; miesiacznik poswiecony nauce i technice w przemysle naftowym i gazowniczym. (Text in Polish; summaries in English and Russian) 1945. m. $30. Instytut Gornictwa Naftowego i Gazownictwa, Ul. Lubicz 25A, 31-503 Krakow, Poland. TEL 48-12-210033. (Dist. by: Ars Polona- Ruch, Krakowskie Przedmiescie 7, Warsaw, Poland) (Co-sponsors: Stowarzyszenie Inzynierow i Technikow Przemyslu Naftowego, Instytut Technologii Nafty) Ed. Jozef Raczkowski. adv.; bk.rev.; abstr.; bibl.; charts; illus.; stat.; index. circ. 1,460. Indexed: A.I.Abstr., Chem.Abstr., Energy Info.Abstr., Environ.Abstr., Petrol.Abstr.
  —BLDSC (6013.150000); CASDDS; PADDS.
  Formerly (until 1992): Nafta (ISSN 0027-7541)

NANJING DAXUE XUEBAO (ZHEXUE SHEHUI KEXUE BAN)/NANJING UNIVERSITY. JOURNAL (SOCIAL SCIENCE EDITION). see *SOCIAL SCIENCES: COMPREHENSIVE WORKS*

NANKAI XUEBAO. ZHEXUE SHEHUI KEXUE BAN/NANKAI UNIVERSITY. JOURNAL. PHILOSOPHY AND SOCIAL SCIENCES EDITION. see *SOCIAL SCIENCES: COMPREHENSIVE WORKS*

665.5 TS
NASHRAT A D M A/A D M A BULLETIN. (Text in Arabic) 1984. w. Abu Dhabi Marine Operating Company, P.O. Box 303, Abu Dhabi, United Arab Emirates. TEL 776600. FAX 720028. TELEX 22284 ADMA EM. Ed. Ahmed el-Tayeb Ahmed. circ. 2,400 (controlled).
  Description: News of the company's activities and employees.

NATIONAL DRILLERS BUYERS GUIDE. see *WATER RESOURCES*

665.5 US ISSN 0149-5267
NATIONAL PETROLEUM NEWS. 1909. 13/yr. $60 (Canada $69; elsewhere $75). Hunter Publishing Limited Partnership, 25 N.W. Point Blvd., Ste. 800, Elk Grove Village, IL 60007-1030. TEL 708-427-9512. FAX 708-427-2006. Ed. Donald M. Smith; Pub. Arleigh Hupp. adv.: B&W page $4100, color page $4680; 8 x 10 3/4; adv. contact: Arleigh Hupp. bk.rev.; charts; illus.; mkt.; stat.; tr.lit.; s-a. cum.index. circ. 15,364. (also avail. in microform from UMI,PMC; microfiche from CIS; diskette format; reprint service avail. from UMI) Indexed: B.P.I., Chem.Abstr., Petrol.Energy B.N.I., PROMT, SRI, Tr.& Indus.Ind. Document type: trade publication.
  •Also available online. Vendor(s): Knight-Ridder, Inc..
  —BLDSC (6029.000000); SWETS; UMI; UnCover. **CCC.**
  Description: Covers national and regional news, trends, analysis and statistics for petroleum and convenience store executives.

665.5 US
NATIONAL WILDCAT MONTHLY. m. $42 per mo. Petroleum Information Corporation, Box 2162, Denver, CO 80201-2612. TEL 303-740-7100. FAX 303-694-1754. Document type: newsletter.
  Description: Covers new field discoveries in the U.S., with operating and production details, and a statistical evaluation of activity.

665.7 UK ISSN 0140-3222
TN880.A1
NATURAL GAS; for industry and commerce. 1928. bi-m. £40 (foreign £53). Oakfield House, Perrymount Rd., Haywards Heath, W. Sussex RH16 3DH, England. TEL 0732-364422. Ed. Geoff Clarke. adv.; bk.rev.; illus. circ. 29,270. (also avail. in microform from UMI) Indexed: BMT, Br.Tech.Ind.
  —BLDSC (6037.301000).
  Former titles: Industrial and Commercial Gas; Formed by the 1975 merger of: Natural Gas for Industry (ISSN 0305-2028); Natural Gas for Commerce (ISSN 0306-2414); Incorporates: Gas in Industry and Commerce (ISSN 0016-4925)

5040   PETROLEUM AND GAS

338.47 665.7   US   ISSN 0743-5665
NATURAL GAS. 1949. m. $295 to institutions in the U.S. and Canada (elsewhere $345) (effective 1995). John Wiley & Sons, Inc., Journals, 605 Third Ave., New York, NY 10158. TEL 212-850-6645. FAX 212-850-6021. (Subscr. to: Box 2575, Secaucus, NJ 07096-2575) Ed. Isabelle Cohen. **Indexed:** Energy Info.Abstr., Environ.Abstr. **Document type:** newsletter.
—UMI. **CCC.**
 Former titles: Oil and Gas Analyst (ISSN 0744-5725); (until 1983): Oil and Gas Regulation Analyst (ISSN 0274-9033); Oil and Gas Price Regulation Analyst (ISSN 0199-3410)
 Description: Contains articles on financial and regulatory concerns: contracts pricing, purchasing, merging, acquisitions and financing. Examines federal and state regulation.

NATURAL GAS FUELS. see *TRANSPORTATION*

665.7   US   ISSN 1051-3973
TP714
NATURAL GAS INDUSTRY DIRECTORY. Key Title: Worldwide Natural Gas Industry Directory. 1991. a. $150. PennWell Publishing Co. (Tulsa), Box 21288, Tulsa, OK 74121. TEL 918-831-9421. FAX 918-831-9555. **Document type:** directory.

665.5   US   ISSN 0739-1811
NATURAL GAS INTELLIGENCE; weekly gas market newsletter. 1981. w. $790 (foreign $870) (effective 1995). Intelligence Press Inc., 22648 Glenn Dr., Sterling, VA 20164-4495. TEL 703-318-8848; 800-427-5747. FAX 703-318-0597. (Subscr. to: Box 70587, Washington, DC 20024) Ed. Ellen Beswick. circ. 1,000. (back issues avail.) **Document type:** newsletter.
—**CCC.**
 Description: Provides the latest industry news for buyers and sellers of natural gas.

665.7   US
NATURAL GAS POLICY ACT NOTICES OF DETERMINATION (F E R C FORM 121). (Federal Energy Regulatory Commission) m. $500 for 1600 bpi in US, Canada, Mexico; elsewhere $1000. (Department of Energy, Energy Information Administration) U.S. National Technical Information Service, 5825 Port Royal Rd., Springfield, VA 22161. TEL 703-487-4630. (magnetic tape)
 Description: Contains seller codes instead of names.

665.54 338.47   CN
TP714
NATURAL GAS UTILITY DIRECTORY. 1955. a. Can.$80 to non-members; members Can.$40. Canadian Gas Association, Economics and Statistics Department, 243 Consumers Rd., Ste. 1200, North York, ON M2J 5E3, Canada. TEL 416-498-1994. FAX 416-498-7465. (diskette format) **Document type:** directory.
 Former titles: Directory of Natural Gas Company Operations (ISSN 1193-1345); Directory of Gas Distribution, Transmission and Production Companies (ISSN 0840-9455); Canadian Gas Association Directory; Canadian Gas Utilities Directory (ISSN 0576-5269); Directory of Gas Utilities (ISSN 0315-8349)

NATURAL GAS VEHICLE. see *TRANSPORTATION — Automobiles*

665.5   US   ISSN 8756-3037
NATURAL GAS WEEK. 1985. w. $797. Oil Daily Co., 1401 New York Ave., N.W., Ste. 500, Washington, DC 20005. TEL 202-662-0700. FAX 202-347-8089. Ed. John H. Jennrich. bk.rev.
—**CCC.**

665.7   US   ISSN 1042-1440
KF1870.A15
NATURAL GAS YEARBOOK. 1988. a. $95. John Wiley & Sons, Inc., Journals, 605 Third Ave., New York, NY 10158. TEL 212-850-6645. FAX 212-850-6021. (Subscr. to: Box 2575, Secaucus, NJ 07096-2575) Ed. Isabelle Cohen. (also avail. in microform from UMI) **Document type:** trade publication.
 Description: Reports on the financial and regulatory concerns of the natural gas industry.

665.54   US
NEBRASKA PETROLEUM MARKETER. 1917. m. Nebraska Petroleum Marketers, Inc., 1320 Lincoln Mall, Lincoln, NE 68508. TEL 402-474-6691. FAX 402-474-2510. Ed. Fred R. Stone. adv.: B&W page $374; 8 1/2 x 11. tr.lit. circ. 1,860.
 Formerly: Nebraska Oil Jobber.

665.5   US   ISSN 0202-4578
   CODEN: NGNRF2
NEFT, GAZ I NEFTEKHIMIYA ZA RUBEZHOM/OIL, GAS AND PETROCHEMISTRY ABROAD. (Russian version of three US journals: World Oil (ISSN 0043-8790), Pipe Line (ISSN 0032-0145), Hydrocarbon Processing (ISSN 0018-8190)) 1979. m. $188 (effective 1996). Izdatel'stvo Nedra, Pl. Belorusskogo Vokzala, 3, 125047 Moscow, Russia. TEL 250-52-55.
 Description: Covers scientific-technology and production.

665.5   RU
NEFTEGAZONOSNYE I PERSPEKTIVNYE KOMPLEKSY TSENTRAL'NYKH I VOSTOCHNYKH OBLASTEI RUSSKOI PLATFORMY. (Subseries of: Vsesoyuznyi Nauchno-Issledovatel'skii Geologorazvedochnyi Neftyanoi Institut. Trudy) irreg. 1.65 Rub. per issue. (Vsesoyuznyi Nauchno-Issledovatel'skii Geologorazvedochnyi Neftyanoi Institut) Izdatel'stvo Nedra, Pl. Belorusskogo Vokzala, 3, 125047 Moscow, Russia. TEL 250-52-55. illus.

665.5 547.8   RU   ISSN 0028-2421
TP690.A1   CODEN: NEFTAH
NEFTEKHIMIYA. English translation: Petroleum Chemistry (US ISSN 0965-5441) 1961. bi-m. 33.30 Rub. (Rossiiskaya Akademiya Nauk) Izdatel'stvo Nauka, 90 Profsoyuznaya ul., 117864 Moscow, Russia. Ed. P.L. Sanin. index. (tabloid format) **Indexed:** API Abstr., API Catal., API Hlth.& Environ., API Oil., API Pet.Ref., API Pet.Subst., API Transport., Chem.Abstr., Chem.Infd., Curr.Chem.React., Ind.Chem. **Document type:** academic/scholarly publication.
—BLDSC (0124.280000); CASDDS; SWETS. **CCC.**

NEFTENA I VUGLISTNA GEOLOGIIA/PETROLEUM AND COAL GEOLOGY. see *EARTH SCIENCES — Geology*

665.53   KR   ISSN 0548-1406
TP690.A1   CODEN: NEFNBY
NEFTEPERERABOTKA I NEFTEKHIMIYA; respublikanskii mezhvedomstvennyi sbornik nauchnykh trudov. (Text in Russian) 1965. s-a. (Akademiya Nauk Ukrainy, Institut Fiziko-Organicheskoi Khimii i Uglekhimii, Otdelenie Neftekhimii) Vidavnitstvo Naukova Dumka, Vul. Tereshchenkivska 3, 252601 Kiev, Ukraine. TEL 044-224-4068. FAX 044-224-7060. (Dist. by: Mezhdunarodnaya Kniga, B. Yakimanka 39, 117049 Moscow, Russia) Ed. V.T. Sklyar. **Indexed:** Chem.Abstr.
—BLDSC (0124.230000); CASDDS. **CCC.**

665.5   RU   ISSN 0132-2222
NEFTYANAYA I GAZOVAYA PROMYSHLENNOST'. AVTOMATIZATSIYA, TELEMEKHANIZATSIYA I SVYAZ' V NEFTYANOI PROMYSHLENNOSTI; nauchno-tekhnicheskii zhurnal. 1993. m. Vserossiiskii Nauchno-Issledovatel'nyi Institut Organizatsii, Upravleniya i Ekonomiki Neftegazovoi Promyshlennosti (VNIIOENG), Ul. Nametkina, 14, 117420 Moskva, Russia. Ed. L.G. Arusmakesyan. circ. 300.
—BLDSC (0000.767000).

665.5 330   RU   ISSN 0132-2192
NEFTYANAYA I GAZOVAYA PROMYSHLENNOST'. NAUCHNO-TEKHNICHESKII INFORMATSIONNYI SBORNIK. SERIYA: EKONOMIKA I UPRAVLENIE NEFTEGAZOVOI PROMYSHLENNOSTI. irreg? Vserossiiskii Nauchno-Issledovatel'nyi Institut Organizatsii, Upravleniya i Ekonomiki Neftegazovoi Promyshlennosti (VNIIOENG), Ul. Nametkina 14, 117240 Moscow, Russia. Ed. V.M. Nikiforov.
—BLDSC (0124.344500).
 Formerly (until 1992): Neftyanaya Promyshlennost'. Obzornaya Informatsiya. Seriya: Ekonomika i Upravlenie Neftyanoi Promyshlennosti (ISSN 0234-131X)

665.5   RU
NEFTYANAYA I GAZOVAYA PROMYSHLENNOST'. NAUCHNO-TEKHNICHESKII INFORMATSIONNYI SBORNIK. SERIYA: GEOLOGIYA, GEOFIZIKA I RAZRABOTKA NEFTYANYKH MESTOROZHDENII. irreg? Vserossiiskii Nauchno-Issledovatel'nyi Institut Organizatsii, Upravleniya i Ekonomiki Neftegazovoi Promyshlennosti (VNIIOENG), Ul. Nametkina 14, 117410 Moscow, Russia. Ed. B.E. Leshchenko.
 Formerly (until 1992): Neftyanaya Promyshlennost'. Obzornaya Informatsiya. Seriya: Geologiya, Geofizika i Razrabotka Neftyanykh Mestorozhdenii (ISSN 0234-1344)

665.5   RU
NEFTYANAYA I GAZOVAYA PROMYSHLENNOST'. NAUCHNO-TEKHNICHESKII INFORMATSIONNYI SBORNIK. SERIYA: NEFTEPROMYSLOVOE DELO. irreg? Vserossiiskii Nauchno-Issledovatel'nyi Institut Organizatsii, Upravleniya i Ekonomiki Neftegazovoi Promyshlennosti (VNIIOENG), Ul. Nametkina 14, 117410 Moscow, Russia. Ed. V.F. Lesnichii.
 Formerly (until 1992): Neftyanaya Promyshlennost'. Obzornaya Informatsiya. Seriya: Neftepromyslovoe Delo (ISSN 0205-9681)

665.5   RU   ISSN 0130-3872
NEFTYANAYA I GAZOVAYA PROMYSHLENNOST'. STROITEL'STVO NEFTYANYKH I GAZOVYKH SKVAZHIN NA SUSHE I NA MORE; nauchno-tekhnicheskii khurnal. 1993. m. Vserossiiskii Nauchno-Issledovatel'nyi Institut Organizatsii, Upravleniya i Ekonomiki Neftegazovoi Promyshlennosti (VNIIOENG), Ul. Nametkina, 14, 117420 Moscow, Russia. Ed. Yu.V. Vedetskii.
—BLDSC (0173.970000).

665.5   RU   ISSN 0132-3547
NEFTYANAYA I GAZOVAYA PROMYSHLENNOST'. ZASHCHITA OT KORROSII I OKRUZHAYUSHCHEI SREDY; nauchno-tekhnicheskii zhurnal. 1993. Vserossiiskii Nauchno-Issledovatel'nyi Institut Organizatsii, Upravleniya i Ekonomiki Neftegazovoi Promyshlennosti (VNIIOENG), Ul. Nametkina, 14, 117420 Moscow, Russia. Ed. F.M. Sharifullin.
—BLDSC (0070.918000).

665   RU   ISSN 0028-243X
TN860   CODEN: NFTYA7
NEFTYANIK (MOSCOW, 1956). 1956. m. 16.20 Rub. (Ministerstvo Neftyanoi Promyshlennosti) Izdatel'stvo Nedra, Pl. Belorusskogo Vokzala, 3, 125047 Moscow, Russia. TEL 250-52-55. (Dist. by: Mezhdunarodnaya Kniga, ul. Dimitrova 39, Moscow G-200, Russia) charts; illus.; index. **Indexed:** Chem.Abstr.
—BLDSC (0124.380000); CASDDS. **CCC.**

665 622   RU   ISSN 0028-2448
TN860   CODEN: NEKHA6
NEFTYANOE KHOZYAISTVO. 1920. m. $57. (Ministerstvo Neftyanoi Promyshlennosti) Izdatel'stvo Nedra, Pl. Belorusskogo Vokzala 3, 125047 Moscow, Russia. TEL 250-52-55. Ed. V. Philanovsky. adv.; bk.rev.; bibl.; charts; illus.; index. circ. 8,600. (reprint service avail. from UMI) **Indexed:** Bibl.& Ind.Geol., Chem.Abstr., Curr.Cont., Eng.Ind., Petrol.Abstr., Risk Abstr.
—BLDSC (0124.400000); CASDDS; Genuine Article; PADDS. **CCC.**

665.5 340   US
NEGOTIATORS HANDBOOK: ASIA & AUSTRALASIA. biennial. $245. Barrows Co., Inc., 116 E. 66th St., New York, NY 10021. TEL 212-772-1199. FAX 212-288-7242.
 Description: Summary and analysis by area and country of oil laws, taxes, contracts for exploration and exploitation, and other data essential to negotiations.

665.5 340   US
NEGOTIATORS HANDBOOK: CENTRAL AMERICA & CARIBBEAN. biennial. $245. Barrows Co., Inc., 116 E. 66th St., New York, NY 10021. TEL 212-772-1199. FAX 212-288-7242.
 Description: Summary and analysis by area and country of oil laws, taxes, contracts for exploration and exploitation, and other data essential to negotiations.

PETROLEUM AND GAS

665.5 340   US
NEGOTIATORS HANDBOOK: EUROPE. biennial. $245. Barrows Co., Inc., 116 E. 66th St., New York, NY 10021. TEL 212-772-1199. FAX 212-288-7242.
   Description: Summary and analysis by area and country of oil laws, taxes, contracts for exploration and exploitation, and other data essential to negotiations.

665.5 340   US
NEGOTIATORS HANDBOOK: MIDDLE EAST. biennial. $245. Barrows Co., Inc., 116 E. 66th St., New York, NY 10021. TEL 212-772-1199. FAX 212-288-7242.
   Description: Summary and analysis by area and country of oil laws, taxes, contracts for exploration and exploitation, and other data essential to negotiations.

665.5 340   US
NEGOTIATORS HANDBOOK: NORTH AFRICA. biennial. $245. Barrows Co., Inc., 116 E. 66th St., New York, NY 10021. TEL 212-772-1199. FAX 212-288-7242.
   Description: Summary and analysis by area and country of oil laws, taxes, contracts for exploration and exploitation, and other data essential to negotiations.

665.5 340   US
NEGOTIATORS HANDBOOK: SOUTH AMERICA. biennial. $245. Barrows Co., Inc., 116 E. 66th St., New York, NY 10021. TEL 212-772-1199. FAX 212-288-7242.
   Description: Summary and analysis by area and country of oil laws, taxes, contracts for exploration and exploitation, and other data essential to negotiations.

665.5 340   US
NEGOTIATORS HANDBOOK: SOUTH & CENTRAL AFRICA. biennial. $245. Barrows Co., Inc., 116 E. 66th St., New York, NY 10021. TEL 212-772-1199. FAX 212-288-7242.
   Description: Summary and analysis by area and country of oil laws, taxes, contracts for exploration and exploitation, and other data essential to negotiations.

338.47   UK
THE NETHERLANDS FINANCIAL ANALYSIS SERVICE. s-a. £8000 (renewals £5000). Arthur Andersen, Petroleum Services Group, 1 Surrey St., London WC2R 2PS, England. TEL 0171-438-3888. FAX 0171-438-3881. TELEX 8812711. Eds. Mike Coulten, Gary Howorth. (diskette format; for Windows version Lotus) **Document type:** trade publication.
   Description: Calculates discounted pre- and posttax cashflows by field and company for the Netherlands.

NEW WORLDWIDE TANKER NOMINAL FREIGHT SCALE; code name Worldscale. see *TRANSPORTATION — Ships And Shipping*

338.2   NR
HD9577.N5
NIGERIAN NATIONAL PETROLEUM CORPORATION. MONTHLY PETROLEUM INFORMATION. m. Nigerian National Petroleum Corporation, P.M.B. 12701, Lagos, Nigeria. circ. 2,000.
   Formerly: Nigeria. Federal Department of Petroleum Resources. Monthly Petroleum Information (ISSN 0549-2513)

665.7   JA   ISSN 0029-0211
CODEN: NIPGAM
NIHON GASU KYOKAISHI/JAPAN GAS ASSOCIATION. JOURNAL. (Text in Japanese) 1948. m. 4200 Yen. Nihon Gasu Kyokai - Japan Gas Association, 15-12, Toranomon 1-chome, Minato-ku, Tokyo 105, Japan. Ed. Kazutomo Mukoyama. adv. circ. 5,000. **Indexed:** Fuel & Energy Abstr., Gas Abstr., JTA.
   —BLDSC (4805.000000); CASDDS.

NONRENEWABLE RESOURCES. see *MINES AND MINING INDUSTRY*

655.5   NO   ISSN 0964-4636
NOROIL CONTACTS - OFFSHORE DIRECTORY. 1976. 3/yr. £60. Hart Europe Ltd., P.O. Box 480, 4001 Stavanger, Norway. (Subscr. to: Richard Fry and Associates, Ste. 225, Surrey House, 34 Eden St., Kingston upon Thames, Surrey KT1 1ER, England. TEL 081-549-3444) adv. circ. 5,292.
   Formerly: Noroil Contacts.

665.5 338.2   NO
NOROIL NEWSWIRE. (Text in English) 1978. s-w. £1150($1882) Hart Europe Ltd, P.O. Box 480, 4001 Stavanger, Norway. (Subscr. to: Richard Fry and Associates, Ste. 225, Surrey House, 34 Eden St., Kingston upon Thames, Surrey KT1 1ER, England. TEL 081-549-3444) Ed. Mark Scruton.

665.5 338.2   NO   ISSN 0332-5490
NORSK OLJEREVY/NORWEGIAN OIL REVIEW. 1974. 11/yr. NOK 595 in Nordic countries; elsewhere $130 (effective 1996). Scandinavian University Press, P.O. Box 2959 Toeyen, N-0608 Oslo, Norway. TEL 47-22-57-54-00. FAX 47-22-57-53-53. E-mail: subscription@scup.no. (U.S. addr.: Scandinavian University Press, 200 Meecham Ave., Elmont, NY 11003)
   Incorporates (1974-1980): Weekly Norwegian Oil Report (ISSN 0332-7310)

338.2 665.5   NO   ISSN 0801-9207
NORSK PETROLEUMSFORENING. AARBOK/NORWEGIAN PETROLEUM SOCIETY. YEARBOOK. (Text in Norwegian) 1979. a. Norsk Petroleumsforening, P.O. Box 1897, Vika, N-0124 Oslo 1, Norway.

665.7   US
NORTH CAROLINA PROPANE GAS NEWS. m. North Carolina Propane Gas Association, 5112 Bur Oak Circle, Raleigh, NC 27612-3101. TEL 919-787-8485. Ed. Romaine Holt. circ. 800.
   Formerly: Carolina L P Gas News.

665.5   UK
NORTH SEA EXECUTIVE. m. 44 Beech Crescent, Larbert FK5 3EY, England. TEL 0324-562981. Ed. F. Frazer.

665.5   UK
NORTH SEA FACTS. a. Oilfield Publications Ltd., Homend House, P.O. Box 11, Ledbury, Herefordshire HR8 1BN, England. TEL 01531-634563. FAX 01531-634239. **Document type:** directory.

665.5 332   UK
NORTH SEA LETTER. Abbreviated title: N S L. w. (51/yr.). £595($953) (overseas £640) (effective 1994). Financial Times Energy Publishing (Subsidiary of: Pearson Professional Ltd.), Maple House, 149 Tottenham Court Rd., London W1P 9LL, England. TEL 0171-896-2241. FAX 0171-896-2275. Ed. Meg Leitch; Pub. David Hurst. charts; stat. (also avail. in microform from UMI; back issues avail.) **Document type:** newsletter.
   •Also available online. Vendor(s): Data-Star, Knight-Ridder, Inc., Lexis-Nexis.
   Description: Provides news and commentary on events in the oil and gas industry on Europe's northwestern continental shelf.

NORTH SEA RIG FORECAST. see *ENERGY*

665.5   US
NORTHEAST PETROLEUM DIRECTORY. 1988. a. $69. Hart Publications, Inc. (Subsidiary of: Phillips Publishing International, Inc.), 1900 Grant St., Ste. 400, Denver, CO 80203. TEL 303-837-1917. FAX 303-837-8585. Ed. Paula Jepperson. adv. contact: Susan Katz. circ. 1,000. (also avail. in diskette format) **Document type:** directory.
   Description: Directory of oil and gas companies involved in exploration and production, services and supply. Covers a 21 state area of the northeast US and Ontario.

338.2 665.5   US
NORTHEAST PETROLEUM INDUSTRY. 1945. a. $50. Midwest Register, Inc., 1120 E. 4th St., Tulsa, OK 74120. TEL 918-582-2000. FAX 918-587-9349. **Document type:** directory.
   Formerly: Directory of Producers and Drilling Contractors Northeast: Michigan, Indiana, Illinois, Kentucky.
   Description: Supplies company name, address, phone and fax number, personnel, division offices, offshore operations, producers of oil or gas and if drilling contractor with rotary or cable tools, pipelines, refineries, petrochemical, gas processing, manufacturers and suppliers, petroleum engineers, landmen.

338.2   UK
NORTH WEST EUROPE COMPANY REPORT. s-a. £1000. Arthur Andersen, Petroleum Services Group, 1 Surrey St., London WC2R 2PS, England. TEL 0171-438-3888. FAX 0171-438-3881. TELEX 8812711. Eds. Timothy Shingler, Gary Howorth. **Document type:** trade publication.
   Description: Provides a summary of the exploration and production interests of more than 60 of the most active companies with oil and gas interests in the North Sea region and onshore U.K.

NORWAY FINANCIAL ANALYSIS SERVICE. see *BUSINESS AND ECONOMICS — Banking And Finance*

665.5 550   NE   ISSN 0928-8937
NORWEGIAN PETROLEUM SOCIETY. SPECIAL PUBLICATION. Represents: Norwegian Petroleum Society. Annual Conference Proceedings. (Text in English) 1992. irreg., vol.3, 1993. Elsevier Science B.V., Books Division, P.O. Box 211, 1000 AE Amsterdam, Netherlands. TEL 31-20-4853911. FAX 31-20-4853705. E-mail: nlinfo-f@elsevier.nl; usinfo@elsevier.com; forinfo-kyf04035@niftyserve.or.jp; Site addr.: http://www.elsevier.nl/. (Subscr. in U.S. and Canada to: Elsevier Science Inc., Box 882, Madison Sq. Sta., New York, NY 10159-0882. TEL 212-989-5800. FAX 212-633-3680) **Document type:** proceedings.
   —BLDSC (6152.298700). **CCC.**

NOZZLE. see *TRANSPORTATION — Automobiles*

665.5   UK
NWY NEWS. 1960. bi-m. free. British Gas Wales, Public Relations Dept., Helmont House, Churchill Way, Cardiff CF1 4NB, Wales. TEL 0222-239290. FAX 0222-290738. Ed. Andy Weltch. circ. 6,500 (controlled).

338.47   KU
O A P E C ENERGY RESOURCES MONITOR. (Text in Arabic) 1981. q. free. Organization of Arab Petroleum Exporting Countries, P.O. Box 20501, Safat 13066, Kuwait. TEL 965-4844500. FAX 965-4815747. TELEX 22166 NAFARAB KT. circ. 250.
   Description: Coverage of Arab and world developments in petroleum exploration, drilling, production, field development and in alternative energy technology.

382.42   KU   ISSN 1018-595X
O A P E C MONTHLY BULLETIN. (Editions in Arabic, English) 1975. m. $40 to individuals; institutions $60. Organization of Arab Petroleum Exporting Countries, Information Department, P.O. Box 20501, Safat 13066, Kuwait. TEL 965-4844500. FAX 965-4815747. TELEX 22166 NAFARAB KT. adv.; bk.rev.; stat. circ. 750. **Indexed:** Key to Econ.Sci., Mid.East: Abstr.& Ind., World Bank.Abstr. **Document type:** bulletin.
   —BLDSC (6196.539000).
   Formerly: O A P E C News Bulletin; Incorporating (after 1988): Organization of Arab Petroleum Exporting Countries. Current Awareness; Which was formerly: O A P E C Monthly Bulletin of Current Awareness.
   Description: Covers O.A.P.E.C. library's new accessions plus contents of recent periodicals on energy, petroleum, economics and related subjects.

665.5   US
O & A MARKETING NEWS. 1966. bi-m. $20. KAL Publications, Inc., 1037 N. Lake Ave., Pasadena, CA 91104. TEL 818-398-6848. FAX 818-398-6840. Ed. Kathy Laderman. adv.: B&W page $1900, color page $2800; 11 1/2 x 16 3/4; adv. contact: Lynne Kenworthy. circ. 9,000. **Document type:** trade publication.
   Description: Covers the activities of the petroleum aftermarket in 13 western states, including the distribution, merchandising, installation and servicing of gasoline, oil, alternative fuel and automotive aftermarket products.

665.5   FR
O E C D OIL INFORMATION. a. price varies. Organization for Economic Cooperation and Development, 2 rue Andre-Pascal, 75775 Paris Cedex 16, France. (U.S. orders to: O.E.C.D. Publications and Information Center, 2001 L St., N.W., Ste. 700, Washington, DC 20036-4910. TEL 202-785-6323) (also avail. in microfiche from OEC,CIS) **Indexed:** IIS.
   Formerly: O E C D Annual Oil Market Report.

PETROLEUM AND GAS

665.5   UK
O I E S GULF AND WORLD OIL ISSUES SERIES. 1990. irreg., no.10, 1993. Oxford Institute for Energy Studies, 57 Woodstock Rd., Oxford OX2 6FA, England. TEL 01865-311377. FAX 01865-310527. Ed. Sarah Ahmad Khan. **Document type:** monographic series.

665.7   UK
▼**O I E S PAPERS. NATURAL GAS.** 1994. irreg. Oxford Institute for Energy Studies, 57 Woodstock Rd., Oxford OX2 6FA, England. TEL 01865-311377. FAX 01865-310527. Ed. Michael Stoppard. **Document type:** monographic series.

665.5   UK
O I E S PAPERS. WORLD PETROLEUM MARKET. irreg., no.20, 1995. £14 (overseas £16). Oxford Institute for Energy Studies, 57 Woodstock Rd., Oxford OX2 6FA, England. TEL 01865-311377. FAX 01865-310527. **Document type:** academic/scholarly publication.

665.5   AU   ISSN 0474-6279
HD9560.1
O P E C BULLETIN. (Text in English) 1967. 10/yr. S.600. Organization of the Petroleum Exporting Countries, Information Department, Obere Donaustr. 93, A-1020 Vienna, Austria. TEL 43-1-22112-0. FAX 43-1-2164320. TELEX 134474. Ed. Yusufu Turundu. adv.; bk.rev.; charts; illus.; stat.; index. circ. 6,000. (also avail. in microfiche from CIS) **Indexed:** Energy Info.Abstr., Energy Rev., Environ.Abstr., IIS. **Document type:** bulletin.
—BLDSC (6265.940000); Faxon; UnCover.
Description: Includes oil industry news, organization reports, market reviews, statistics, alternative energy news and surveys, OPEC publications and OPEC Fund for International Development news, new acquisitions in the OPEC library, and a calendar of events.

333.79 665.5   UK   ISSN 0277-0180
HD9560.1   CODEN: OPECDI
O P E C REVIEW; an energy and development forum. (Text in English) 1976. q. £98($147) (effective 1995). (Organization of the Petroleum Exporting Countries, Public Information Department, AU) Elsevier Science Ltd., Pergamon, P.O. Box 800, Kidlington, Oxford OX5 1DX, England. TEL 44-1865-843000. FAX 44-1865-843010. E-mail: nlinfo-f@elsevier.nl; usinfo-f@elsevier.com; forinfo-kyf04035@niftyserve.or.jp; Site addr.: http://www.elsevier.nl/. (Subscr. in U.S. and Canada to: Elsevier Science, 660 White Plains Rd., Tarrytown, NY 10591-5153. TEL 914-524-9200. FAX 914-333-2444) Ed. Keith Marchant. circ. 2,000. (also avail. in microfilm from UMI; microfiche from CIS) **Indexed:** AESIS, Asian-Pac.Econ.Lit., C.R.E.J., Energy Info.Abstr., Environ.Per.Bibl. (1992-), Geo.Abstr., IDA, IIS, Key to Econ.Sci., World Bank.Abstr. **Document type:** academic/scholarly publication.
—BLDSC (6265.943000); Faxon; SWETS; UMI; UnCover. **CCC.**
Description: Publishes selected academic papers on energy, Third World development issues and related economic and policy matters.
Refereed Serial

662   US   ISSN 0029-8042
OCEAN OIL WEEKLY REPORT. 1966. w. $375 (outside N. America $435) (effective 1993). PennWell Publishing Co. (Houston), Box 1941, Houston, TX 77251. TEL 713-621-9720. FAX 713-963-6285. Ed. Michael Crowden; Pub. Jack Schirra. cum.index. circ. 1,000. (looseleaf format)
●Also available online.
—CCC.
Description: Provides news and developments in the world's offshore oil and gas industry.

665.5   SP   ISSN 0210-1882
OCTANAJE. 1975. 11/yr. Reina Victoria 70, 3o, 28003 Madrid, Spain. TEL 1-554-79-41. FAX 1-534-16-00. Ed. Francisco Catena. circ. 6,000.

665.5   CN   ISSN 0835-1740
OCTANE. 1987. 4/yr. Can.$24. Maclean Hunter Ltd. (Calgary), Ste. 2450, 101-6th Ave. S.W., Calgary, AB T2P 3P4, Canada. TEL 403-266-8700; 800-561-1294. FAX 403-266-6634. (Subscr. to: 777 Bay St., Toronto, Ont. M5W 1A7, Canada) Ed. David Coll; Pub. David Coll. adv.: B&W page Can.$2450, color page Can.$3530; trim 8 x 10 3/4; adv. contact: Tony Poblete. circ. 7,557. **Document type:** trade publication.

665.5   US   ISSN 1072-8740
OCTANE WEEK. 1986. w. $995 (foreign $1095). Information Resources, Inc., 1925 N. Lynn St., Ste. 1000, Arlington, VA 22204-1707. TEL 703-528-2500. FAX 703-528-1483. Ed. Kevin Adler. **Document type:** newsletter.
●Also available online. Vendor(s): Data-Star, Knight-Ridder, Inc., Dow Jones News Retrieval.
—CCC.
Description: Covers topics of interest to refiners and gasoline marketers regarding the major transformations occurring in the areas of gasoline composition, grade mix, reformulated fuels, octane generation, refining and blending technologies and aromatics.

338.47   AU
OE M V ANNUAL REPORT (YEAR). (Text in English, German) Annual. a. free. Oe M V Aktiengesellschaft, Otto-Wagner-Platz 5, A-1090 Vienna, Austria. TEL 01-40440-0. FAX 01-40440-91. Ed. Dr. Hermann Michelitsch. **Document type:** corporate report.

621.3   US   ISSN 0078-3706
OFF-SHORE TECHNOLOGY CONFERENCE. RECORD. a. Offshore Technology Conference, Program Department, Box 833836, Richardson, TX 75083-3836. **Document type:** proceedings.

338.2 622   US
TN871.3   CODEN: OFSHAU
OFFSHORE (TULSA). 1954. 12/yr. $55 (foreign $72). PennWell Publishing Co., Box 1260, Tulsa, OK 74101. TEL 918-835-3161. Ed. Leonard Le Blanc. adv.: B&W page $2400, color page $3390; 7 x 10. charts; illus.; tr.lit.; circ. 35,500 (controlled). (also avail. in microform from UMI; reprint service avail. from UMI) **Indexed:** A.S.& T.Ind., BMT, Br.Tech.Ind., Deep Sea Res.& Oceanogr.Abstr., Energy Rev., J.of Ferroc., Key to Econ.Sci., Ocean.Abstr., Petrol.Abstr., Pollut.Abstr., SRI, Tr.& Indus.Ind. **Document type:** trade publication.
●Also available online. Vendor(s): Lexis-Nexis.
—BLDSC (6244.200000); PADDS; SWETS; UMI; UnCover. **CCC.**
Formerly: Offshore Incorporating the Oilman; Which incorporates (1973-1988): Offshore (Tulsa) (ISSN 0030-0608); Which was formerly: Oilman (ISSN 0143-6694)
Description: Serves the worldwide petroleum industry in its marine operations, engineering and technology. Includes information pertaining to seismic services, exploration, drilling, production, process, transportation (pipeline, marine, and air), marine and underwater engineering and communications, naval architecture, design and construction, diving services, marine support facilities, and research in oceanography and meteorology.

665.5   UK   ISSN 0956-6732
OFFSHORE BUSINESS; engineering and project management. 4/yr. £390 (foreign £460). Smith Rea Energy Analysts Limited, Hunstead House, Nickle, Chartham, Canterbury, Kent CT4 7PL, England. TEL 0227-738844. FAX 0227-738866. **Document type:** trade publication.
—BLDSC (6244.215250).

665.7   US   ISSN 1058-9694
TN871.3
OFFSHORE CONTRACTORS AND EQUIPMENT WORLDWIDE DIRECTORY. 1969. a. $125. PennWell Publishing Co., Box 1260, Tulsa, OK 74101. TEL 918-835-3161. Ed. Jonell Moore. adv. (back issues avail.)
Former titles: Offshore Contractors and Equipment Directory (ISSN 0475-1310); Worldwide Offshore Contractors Directory (ISSN 0084-2575)
Description: Lists over 6500 companies and personnel in the drilling, construction, geophysical diving, service and supply manufacturing and transportation industries.

665.5 620   UK   ISSN 0305-876X
TC1501
OFFSHORE ENGINEER. 1975. m. £64 (foreign £68). (Institution of Civil Engineers) Thomas Telford Ltd., Thomas Telford House, 1 Heron Quay, London E14 4JD, England. TEL 0171-987-6999. FAX 0171-537-2443. TELEX 298105-CIVILS-G. Ed. Jenny Gregory. adv.; charts; illus. circ. 16,500. (back issues avail.) **Indexed:** AESIS, Bibl.& Ind.Geol., BMT, Br.Geol.Lit., Br.Tech.Ind., Excerp.Med., Fluidex, Fuel & Energy Abstr., Intl.Polym.Sci.& Tech., Key to Econ.Sci., Ocean.Abstr., Petrol.Abstr., Pollut.Abstr., RAPRA.
—BLDSC (6244.225000); Ei; Faxon; PADDS; SWETS; UnCover. **CCC.**
Incorporating: Northern Offshore (ISSN 0332-5237)
Description: Covers engineering, technical and operational facets of offshore oil and gas exploration and production worldwide.

OFFSHORE ENGINEERING. see ENGINEERING — Civil Engineering

665.5 338.2   US   ISSN 1058-5869
OFFSHORE FIELD DEVELOPMENT INTERNATIONAL. 1979. m. $795 (foreign $870). Offshore Data Services, Inc., Box 19909, Houston, TX 77224-1909. TEL 713-781-2713. FAX 713-781-9594. Ed. Anthony Guegel. circ. 900. (also avail. in magnetic tape; diskette format) **Document type:** trade publication.
●Also available online.
Formerly (until 1991): Ocean Construction Locator (ISSN 0276-3680)
Description: Lists information on all offshore platform, pipeline, and mooring terminal projects worldwide, from the planning stages to final installation.

665.5   US   ISSN 1058-5842
OFFSHORE INTERNATIONAL NEWSLETTER. 1973. w. $525 (foreign $560). Offshore Data Services, Inc., Box 19909, Houston, TX 77224-1909. TEL 713-781-2713. FAX 713-781-9594. Ed. Susanne S. Pagano. circ. 695. **Document type:** newsletter.
Incorporates (1984-1991): Offshore Fleet Economics (ISSN 0266-3112); Former titles (until 1991): Offshore Construction Report (ISSN 0147-152X); Ocean Construction and Engineering Report.
Description: Follows offshore oil developments and related concerns worldwide.

665.5   UK   ISSN 1359-6438
OFFSHORE OIL & GAS DIRECTORY. 1972. a. £79 (rest of Europe £96; elsewhere £104-£109). Miller Freeman Information Services (Subsidiary of: United News & Media), Riverbank House, Angel Ln., Tonbridge, Kent TN9 1SE, England. TEL 01732-362666. FAX 01732-767301. TELEX 957829. Ed. Gwen Young. adv. contact: Elaine Soni. circ. 3,500. **Document type:** directory.
—BLDSC (6150.079550).
Former titles (until 1995): North Sea Oil & Gas Directory. (ISSN 0265-5039); (until 1982): North Sea Oil Directory (ISSN 0307-0344)
Description: Provides information for all sectors of the offshore oil and gas industries.

338.47   US
OFFSHORE PETROLEUM INDUSTRY. q. $1900 (renewal $1150). Barrows Co., Inc., 116 E. 66th St., New York, NY 10021. TEL 212-772-1199. FAX 212-288-7242. TELEX 4971238/BARROWS. Ed. Marta Guerra.
Description: Follows world oil and gas offshore operations in all countries. Emphasis on world investment, geological favorability, production, technology and economics.

655.5   US
OFFSHORE PRODUCTION REPORT. m. $43. Railroad Commission, Oil and Gas Publications, Drawer 12967, Capitol Sta., Austin, TX 78711. TEL 512-463-7255. charts; stat. **Document type:** government publication.
Description: Compiles data on oil and gas production by district and field from offshore state waters.

PETROLEUM AND GAS 5043

665.5 338.2 US
OFFSHORE RIG LOCATOR. 1974. m. $545 (foreign $585). Offshore Data Services, Inc., Box 19909, Houston, TX 77224-1909. TEL 713-781-2713. FAX 713-781-9594. Ed. John Chadderdon. circ. 700. (also avail. in magnetic tape; diskette format) **Document type:** trade publication.
●Also available online.
Formerly (until 1984): Offshore Rig Location Report (ISSN 0733-0928)
Description: Provides location information and operating statistics on the activity of all offshore drilling rigs, with analyses of market conditions.

665.5 US ISSN 0147-1481
OFFSHORE RIG NEWSLETTER. 1974. m. $220 (foreign $235). Offshore Data Services, Inc., Box 19909, Houston, TX 77224-1909. TEL 713-781-2713. FAX 713-781-9594. Ed. Tom Marsh. circ. 850. **Document type:** newsletter.
Description: Reports news and events affecting the international offshore drilling market.

665.5 US
OFFSHORE RIG REPORT. 1984. m. $360. PennWell Publishing Co., Box 1260, Tulsa, OK 74101. TEL 918-835-3161. Ed. Mary J. Lutz. (also avail. in diskette format)
Formerly: Worldwide Offshore Rigfinder.

665 NE ISSN 0921-2477
OFFSHORE VISIE. (Text in Dutch, English) 1984. s-m. free to qualified personnel. Uitgeverij Tridens, Postbus 526, 1970 AM IJmuiden, Netherlands. TEL 31-2550-30577. FAX 31-2550-30577. Ed. Hans Heilig. adv.; circ. 3,500 (controlled). (back issues avail.) **Document type:** trade publication.
—SWETS.
Description: Cover news and developments in the offshore petroleum industry.

665.5 CN ISSN 0848-2780
HD9574.C23
OIL ACTIVITY REVIEW. 1982. a. free. Manitoba Energy and Mines, Petroleum Branch, 360-1395 Ellice Ave., Winnipeg, MB R3G 3P2, Canada. TEL 204-945-6315. FAX 204-945-0586. Ed. L.R. Dubreuil. charts; illus.; stat. circ. 700. **Document type:** government publication.
Description: Review of petroleum industry activity in Manitoba.

333.8 US
OIL: AN INTEGRATED INDUSTRY. 1991. a. $395. Dun & Bradstreet Information Services (Murray Hill) (Subsidiary of: Dun & Bradstreet, Inc.), One Diamond Hill Rd., Murray Hill, NJ 07974. TEL 908-665-5224. FAX 908-771-7599. Ed. George Ross.
Description: Analyzes historical and political events affecting the price, supply and demand, and bottom-line profits of the oil industry.

665.5 KU ISSN 0251-415X
OIL AND ARAB COOPERATION. (Text in Arabic; summaries in English) 1975. q. $20 to individuals; $40 to institutions. Organization of Arab Petroleum Exporting Countries, Information Department, P.O. Box 20501, Safat 13066, Kuwait. TEL 965-4844500. FAX 965-4815747. TELEX 22166 NAFARAB KT. Ed. Abdelaziz Al-Abdulla Al-Turki. bk.rev.; abstr. circ. 750. **Indexed:** Mid.East: Abstr.& Ind.
Description: Articles on petroleum sector and economic and social development in Arab countries.

OIL & CHEMICAL WORKER. see *LABOR UNIONS*

OIL AND ENERGY TRENDS. see *ENERGY*

OIL AND ENERGY TRENDS: ANNUAL STATISTICAL REVIEW. see *ENERGY — Abstracting, Bibliographies, Statistics*

665.5 557 US ISSN 0747-5306
TN872.I3
OIL AND GAS; monthly report on drilling in Illinois. 1936. m. $18. State Geological Survey, Natural Resources Bldg., 615 E. Peabody Dr., Champaign, IL 61820. TEL 217-333-4747. bibl.; stat. circ. 200.
Formerly (until 1979): Oil and Gas Drilling in Illinois (ISSN 0193-3531)

665 UK ISSN 0966-4505
OIL AND GAS; Russia, Central Asia and the Caucasus. 1992. q. £90($180) (subscr. includes special suppl.). (Russian Federation, Ministry of Fuel and Energy) Oil & Gas Russia Ltd., P.O. Box 35, Hastings, E. Sussex TN34 2UX, England. TEL 44-424-442741. FAX 44-424-442913. TELEX 0957823-AFINT-G. (Subscr. to: Kingsgate Business Centre, 12-50 Kingsgate Rd., Kingston-upon-Thames, Surrey KT2 5AA, England. TEL 44-81-547-2411; And: VNIIOENG, 14 Nametkin St., 117420 Moscow, Russia. TEL 7-095-332-0037) Ed. Nick Terdre. adv. contact: Hugo Steinnes. circ. controlled. **Document type:** trade publication.
Description: Provides information about the problems and prospects of the oil and gas industry in the former USSR, including structural and organizational procedures, and technological capabilities and equipment. Provides a platform for ideas, opinions, and facts.

OIL AND GAS ACCOUNTING. see *BUSINESS AND ECONOMICS — Accounting*

665.5 531.64 US
OIL AND GAS DEVELOPMENTS IN PENNSYLVANIA.*
1951. a. price varies. (Bureau of Topographic and Geologic Survey, Department of Environmental Resources) Pennsylvania Geological Survey, Environmental Resources, 400 Waterfront Dr., Pittsburgh, PA 15222-4728. TEL 717-787-2169. (Subscr. to: State Book Store, Box 1365, Harrisburg, PA 17105) (back issues avail.)

338.2 US ISSN 0471-380X
OIL & GAS DIRECTORY. 1970. a. $65 (foreign $80) (effective 1995). Geophysical Directory, Inc., 2200 Welch Ave., Box 130508, Houston, TX 77219. TEL 713-529-8789. FAX 713-529-3646. Ed. Claudia La Calli. adv. contact: Claudia LaCalli. circ. 4,000. (also avail. in diskette format) **Document type:** directory.
Description: Lists oil companies, key personnel as well as service and supply companies in the drilling and producing industry.

OIL AND GAS FIELD DESIGNATIONS. see *EARTH SCIENCES — Geology*

665.5 657 UK ISSN 0962-3752
OIL & GAS FINANCE AND ACCOUNTING. 1986. q. £115($200) Langham Publishing, 21 Pointers Close, Isle of Dogs, London E14 3AP, England. TEL 0171-987-8631. Ed. Tudor David. adv.; bk.rev.; index; circ. 200 (paid). (back issues avail.) **Indexed:** Account.Ind. (1987-). **Document type:** trade publication.
—BLDSC (6249.844500).
Formerly: Journal of Oil and Gas Accountancy (ISSN 0267-4920)
Description: Aimed at practising controllers, accountants and academics in relevant disciplines.

665.5 665.7 AT ISSN 1038-1317
OIL & GAS GAZETTE. 1991. m. Aus.$115. Resource Information Unit Ltd., 78 Hay St., Subiaco, W.A. 6008, Australia. TEL 61-9-382-3955. FAX 61-9-388-1025. Ed. Peter Herkenoff. adv.: B&W page Aus.$960, color page Aus.$1125; trim 297 x 210; adv. contact: Liz Keogh. charts; illus.; stat.; tr.lit.; index. circ. 3,500. (back issues avail.)
Description: Contains hard news stories relating to the Australian oil and gas industry, stock market news, latest in equipment and technology and some international coverage.

665.5 US ISSN 1073-0265
OIL & GAS INTERESTS NEWSLETTER.* 1986. m. $397. Hart Publications, Inc. (Subsidiary of: Phillips Publishing International, Inc.), 1900 Grant St., Ste. 400, Denver, CO 80203. TEL 303-837-1917. FAX 303-837-8585. Ed. Jack Stevenson. circ. 1,250. (also avail. in microform from UMI) **Document type:** newsletter.
—UMI. **CCC.**
Description: Provides business news about the domestic oil & gas industry, especially with regard to exploration and production companies. Includes acquisition, joint venture, bankruptcy and restructuring, financing, and merger information.

665.5 US ISSN 0744-5881
HD9561
OIL AND GAS INVESTOR. 1981. m. $195 (foreign $277). Hart Publications, Inc. (Subsidiary of: Phillips Publishing International, Inc.), 4545 Post Oak Place, Ste. 210, Houston, TX 77027. TEL 713-993-9320. Ed. Leslie Haines; Pub. Verna Ray. adv. contact: Bradley Holmes. charts; illus. circ. 6,500. (back issues avail.) **Indexed:** ABI Inform.
●Also available online. Vendor(s): University Microfilms International.
—BLDSC (6249.958000); UMI; UnCover. **CCC.**
Description: Identifies and interprets events, trends, and needs for companies in the North American oil and gas industry, and for members of the financial community regarding opportunities in the upstream and midstream U.S. and international oil and gas industry.

665.5 US ISSN 0030-1388
TN860 CODEN: OIGJAV
OIL & GAS JOURNAL. 1902. w. $52 to qualified personnel (foreign $82); non-operational personnel $95. PennWell Publishing Co., Box 1260, Tulsa, OK 74101. TEL 918-835-3161. Ed. Gene T. Kinney. adv.: B&W page $4140, color page $5490; 8 x 11 1/8. bk.rev.; charts; illus.; mkt.; stat.; tr.lit.; index. circ. 42,500. (also avail. in microform from UMI;PMC; reprint service avail. from UMI) **Indexed:** A.S.& T.Ind., Acid Rain Abstr., Acid Rain Ind., AESIS, API Abstr., API Catal., API Hlth.& Environ., API Oil., API Pet.Ref., API Pet.Subst., API Transport., Bibl.& Ind.Geol., Br.Geol.Lit., Bus.Ind., C.I.S. Abstr., CAD CAM Abstr., Chem.Abstr., Chem.Eng.Abstr., Chem.Infd., Corros.Abstr., Curr.Cont., Deep Sea Res.& Oceanogr.Abstr., Dok.Arbeitsmed., Energy Info.Abstr., Energy.Info.Abstr., Eng.Ind., Environ.Abstr., Excerp.Med., Fluidex, Fuel & Energy.Abstr., Gas Abstr., Geo.Abstr., Geol.Abstr., HRIS, Key to Econ.Sci., Met.Abstr., Mid.East: Abstr.& Ind., Ocean.Abstr., Petrol.Abstr., Petrol.Energy B.N.I., Pollut.Abstr., PROMT, Risk Abstr., Soils & Fert., SRI, T.C.E.A., Tr.& Indus.Ind., W.R.C.Inf., World Alum.Abstr. **Document type:** trade publication.
●Also available online. Vendor(s): Lexis-Nexis, University Microfilms International.
—BLDSC (6250.000000); CASDDS; Ei; Faxon; Genuine Article; PADDS; SWETS; UMI; UnCover. **CCC.**
Description: Covers all segments of the petroleum industry: exploration, drilling, production, refining, processing and pipeline transportation.

338.2 665 UK ISSN 0263-5070
K3911.2
OIL & GAS: LAW AND TAXATION REVIEW. 1982. m. £395 (effective 1994). Sweet & Maxwell, South Quay Plaza, 183 Marsh Wall, London E14 9FT, England. adv.; bk.rev.; index. circ. 350. (back issues avail.) **Indexed:** Euro.LJI, LJI. **Document type:** academic/scholarly publication.
—BLDSC (6250.023000); SWETS.

665.5 BA ISSN 0217-6602
OIL AND GAS NEWS; the petroleum industry weekly for Asia - Pacific - Middle East. w. $565. Al Hilal Publishing & Marketing Group, P.O. Box 224, Manama, Bahrain. TEL 973-293131. FAX 973-293400. TELEX 8981 HILAL BN. (In Singapore: Al Hilal Publishing (Far East) Pte Ltd, 50 Jalan Sultan, 20-06 Jalan Sultan Centre, Singapore 0719. TEL 2939233. FAX 2970862) Ed. Gurdip Singh. adv.: B&W page $2800, color page $3920; 400 x 275. circ. 4,688. (tabloid format) **Document type:** trade publication.
Description: Covers news of trends, products, events and other information for senior personnel in all sectors of the petroleum industry, including oil companies, exploration, supply, marine and offshore contractors, and government agencies.

665.5 UK
OIL & GAS NEWS. w. Caledonian House, Highfield Rd., Ste.222, Feltham, Middx TW13 4BH, England. TEL 081-844-2468. FAX 081-751-2792. TELEX 9312130519-MAG. Ed. J. Rowles. circ. 5,050.

OIL AND GAS POOL DESCRIPTIONS. see *EARTH SCIENCES — Geology*

PETROLEUM AND GAS

665.5   CN   ISSN 0702-8202
OIL AND GAS PRODUCTION REPORT. m. Can.$125. Ministry of Energy, Mines and Petroleum Resources, Energy Resources Division, 7th Fl., 1810 Blanshard St., Victoria, BC V8V 1X4, Canada. TEL 604-356-2743. (Subscr. to: Crown Publications, 546 Yates St., Victoria, BC V8W 1K8, Canada. TEL 604-386-4636) circ. 125. (back issues avail.) **Document type:** government publication.
   Description: Includes a statistical summary of the drilling activity, well count, production and injection of all fluids on a pool basis, disposition of production gas plant and refinery operations, and nominations and estimated requirements by the refineries.

665.5   US   ISSN 0472-7630
KF1845.A2
OIL AND GAS REPORTER. 1952. m. $540. Southwestern Legal Foundation, Box 830707, Richardson, TX 75083. TEL 214-690-2370. (Subscr. to: 1275 Broadway, Albany, NY 12201) Ed. Carol Holgren. index, cum.index. (looseleaf format)
  —CCC.
   Description: Reporter of oil and gas judicial decisions with editorial comments and case digests.

OIL AND GAS TAX QUARTERLY. see *BUSINESS AND ECONOMICS — Public Finance, Taxation*

665.5 665.74   II   ISSN 0537-0094
TN876.I5   CODEN: BONCDF
OIL AND NATURAL GAS COMMISSION. BULLETIN. (Text in English) 1964. s-a. $50. (Oil & Natural Gas Commission) Indian Petroleum Publishers, 100-9, Naishville Road, Dehra Dun 248 001, India. Ed. D.K. Guha. bk.rev. circ. 1,400. (back issues avail.) **Indexed:** Petrol.Abstr. **Document type:** bulletin.
  —CASDDS; PADDS.

662   US
OIL BUYERS' GUIDE. vol. 5, 1975. w. $695 (foreign $795). Bloomberg Financial Markets, 100 Business Park Dr., Box 888, Princeton, NJ 08542-0888. TEL 609-497-3500. FAX 609-683-7523. Ed. Vincent Sgro. charts; stat.

665.5   US
OIL BUYERS' GUIDE INTERNATIONAL. 1981. w. $775 (foreign $875). Bloomberg Financial Markets, 100 Business Park Dr., Box 888, Princeton, NJ 08542-0888. TEL 609-497-3500. FAX 609-683-7523. Ed. Vincent Sgro. charts; stat.

665   US
OIL CAN. 1926. bi-m. $18 to non-members; members $6. Illinois Petroleum Marketers Association, Box 12020, Springfield, IL 62791-2020. TEL 217-544-4609. FAX 217-789-0222. (Co-sponsor: Illinois Association of Convenience Stores) Ed. William Fleischli. adv.: B&W page $375, color page $775; 8 1/2 x 11; adv. contact: Elizabeth Sharkey. illus.; circ. 1,250 (controlled). (back issues avail.) **Document type:** trade publication.
   Description: Contains news about products and personnel in Illinois' petroleum industry.

OIL CHEMICAL RUBBER WORKERS TRADE UNION OF TURKEY. YEARBOOK. see *LABOR UNIONS*

665.5 338.2   US   ISSN 0030-1434
HD9561
OIL DAILY; daily newspaper of the petroleum industry. 1951. d. $897 (Fax delivery avail.). Oil Daily Co., 1401 New York Ave., N.W., Ste. 500, Washington, DC 20005. TEL 202-662-0700. FAX 202-783-8320. stat. (also avail. in microform from UMI; reprint service avail. from UMI) **Indexed:** Bus.Ind., Petrol.Energy B.N.I., Tr.& Indus.Ind. **Document type:** newsletter.
  ●Also available online. Vendor(s): Knight-Ridder, Inc..
  —BLDSC (6250.750000); UMI. **CCC.**

665.53 338   US   ISSN 1066-3002
HD9579.L83
THE OIL DAILY'S LUBRICANTS WORLD. Short title: Lubricants World. 1991. m. $150 ($175 in Canada & Mexico; elsewhere $220) (free to qualified personnel). Oil Daily Company, 1401 New York Ave. N.W., No. 500, Washington, DC 20005. TEL 800-621-0050. FAX 202-783-5918. Ed. John A. Moore. adv.; bk.rev.; circ. 10,000 (controlled). (reprint service avail.) **Document type:** trade publication.
  —BLDSC (6250.757000). **CCC.**
   Description: Covers the lubricants business for user and suppliers, buyers and sellers of lubricants and related products.

665.5   US   ISSN 0195-0576
OIL EXPRESS; exclusive report giving informed petroleum marketers nationwide. w. $247. United Communications Group, 11300 Rockville Pike, Ste. 1100, Rockville, MD 20852-3030. TEL 301-816-8950. Ed. Carole Donoghue.
  —CCC.
   Description: Provides petroleum marketers with the latest news in the industry, plus new approaches in oil marketing.

622 665   US   ISSN 0030-1353
TN871.5
OIL, GAS & PETROCHEM EQUIPMENT. 1954. m. $99. PennWell Publishing Co., Box 1260, Tulsa, OK 74101. TEL 918-835-3161. (Dist. in Japan by: Intercontinental Marketing Corp., I.P.O. Box 5056, Tokyo 100-30, Japan. TEL 81-3-3661-7458. FAX 81-3-3667-9646) Ed. J.B. Avants. adv.; circ. 36,000 (controlled). (tabloid format) **Indexed:** Petrol.Abstr. **Document type:** trade publication.
  —UMI. **CCC.**
   Formerly: Oil and Gas Equipment.
   Description: Serves the operating phases (except marketing) of the petroleum industry, including: exploration, drilling, drilling and well services contracting, production, natural gas processing, refining, petrochemical manufacturing, process plant contracting, design, engineering, oil and gas pipeline contracting, design, engineering and construction.

665.5   US
OIL, GAS & TECHNOLOGY. (Text in Russian) m. Gulf Publishing Co., Box 2608, Houston, TX 77252-2608. TEL 713-529-4301.
   Formerly: Oil, Gas and Petrochemicals Abroad.
   Description: Covers technical articles for people in the gas and oil business.

665.5   GW   ISSN 0342-5622
TN860
OIL GAS EUROPEAN MAGAZINE. (Text in English) 1975. 4/yr. DM.104.60. Urban-Verlag GmbH, Postfach 701606, 22016 Hamburg, Germany. TEL 040-6567071. FAX 040-6567075. Eds. Thomas Vieth, Hans Joerg Mager. circ. 4,000. **Indexed:** Gas Abstr. **Document type:** trade publication.
  —BLDSC (6252.025000); Ei; Genuine Article; PADDS; SWETS. **CCC.**
   Formerly: European Oil and Gas Magazine.

388.47 330.9   US   ISSN 0741-3343
HD9561
OIL INDUSTRY OUTLOOK FOR THE U S A. 1984. a. $150 (foreign $187.50). PennWell Publishing Co., Box 1260, Tulsa, OK 74101. TEL 918-835-3161. Ed. Robert J. Beck. **Indexed:** SRI.
  —CCC.

OIL MARKET REPORT. see *ENERGY*

665.5   US   ISSN 1047-9538
THE OIL MARKETING BULLETIN. w. $695. United Communications Group, 11300 Rockville Pike, Ste. 1100, Rockville, MD 20852-3030. TEL 301-816-8950. FAX 301-816-8945. Ed. Brian Crotty. **Document type:** bulletin.
   Description: Directed to oil company executives providing information on buying trends, pricing and industry news.

338.2 655.5   US
OIL MARKETING INDUSTRY. 1945. a. $65. Midwest Register, Inc., 1120 E. 4th St., Tulsa, OK 74120. TEL 918-582-2000. FAX 918-587-9349. **Document type:** directory.
   Formerly: Directory of Oil Marketing and Wholesale Distributors (ISSN 0070-5993)
   Description: Supplies company name, address, phone and fax number. Includes information about purchasers, marketers and traders of refined products, crude oil and natural gas.

665.5 338.2   IR   ISSN 0030-1450
OIL NEWS. fortn. free. Petroleum Ministry, Public Relations & Guidance Department, P.O. Box 1863, Central NIOC Bldg., Taleghani Ave., Teheran, Iran. TEL 021-6151. TELEX 212514. **Indexed:** Fuel & Energy Abstr.

665.5   UK
OIL NEWS SERVICE NEWSLETTER. 1972. fortn. £97($185) Oil News Service, Springfield House, Dollar, Clackmannanshire, Scotland. Ed. David Gibson. adv.; bk.rev. circ. 800. (back issues avail.) **Document type:** newsletter.

665.538   UK   ISSN 0957-655X
OIL PACKER INTERNATIONAL. 1988. bi-m. £35($78) Binsted Publications Ltd., Walton House, 90 London Rd., Hook, Hants. RG27 9LF, England. TEL 01256-764180. FAX 01256-766102. Ed. Edward C. Binsted; Pub. Edward C. Binsted. circ. 8,000. **Document type:** trade publication.

338.47   US   ISSN 0279-7801
OIL PRICE INFORMATION SERVICE. w. $545. United Communications Group, 11300 Rockville Pike, Ste. 1100, Rockville, MD 20852-3030. TEL 301-816-8950. Ed. Ben Brockwell.
  ●Also available online. Vendor(s): NewsNet (EY02), United Communications Group (PETROSCAN).
  —CCC.
   Description: Gives actual wholesale and spot gasoline, distillate and propane prices each week, plus trends, new sources, and new markets.

OIL SHALE SYMPOSIUM PROCEEDINGS. see *MINES AND MINING INDUSTRY*

665.5 628.168   US
OIL SPILL CONTINGENCY PLANNER; the compliance guide for vessels, facilities, and pipelines. 1992. irreg. $495. Cutter Information Corp., 37 Broadway, Arlington, MA 02174-5539. TEL 617-648-8700. FAX 617-648-8707. TELEX 650-100-9891 MCIUW. Ed. Amy M. Stolls. (looseleaf format; back issues avail.)
   Description: Assists companies involved with transporting oil to better comply with the new and evolving federal, state, and international regulations.

665.5   US   ISSN 0195-3524
TD427.P4
OIL SPILL INTELLIGENCE REPORT; an international weekly newsletter. 1978. w. $537 (foreign $637). Cutter Information Corp., 37 Broadway, Arlington, MA 02174. TEL 617-648-8700. FAX 617-648-8707. TELEX 650 100 9891 MCIUW. Ed. Faith Yando. adv. (back issues avail.) **Document type:** newsletter.
  ●Also available online. Vendor(s): NewsNet (EV32).
  —CCC.
   Description: News and developments around the world relating to oil spills and related events. Covers advances in technology for preventing, controlling, and cleaning up oil spills. Also covers regulations, legislation, treaties, and litigators.

OIL SPILL LAW INFORMATION SERVICE. see *ENVIRONMENTAL STUDIES — Pollution*

628.168   US
OIL SPILL PLANNING MANUAL. 1992. m. $578. Thompson Publishing Group, 1725 K St., N.W., Ste. 200, Washington, DC 20006. TEL 202-872-4000. FAX 202-728-0809. Ed. Charlene Kerwin. circ. 500 (paid). (looseleaf format) **Document type:** newsletter.
   Description: Details requirements for preparing vessel and facility oil spill response plans, as required under the Oil Pollution Act of 1990. Also includes information on planning requirements issued by federal agencies other than E.P.A. and U.S. Coast Guard.

OIL SPILL U S LAW REPORT; legislation, litigation, regulations & enforcement actions. see *LAW*

PETROLEUM AND GAS

665.5 UK ISSN 0261-3247
OIL SPOT. 1978. m. Britoil PLC, 301 St. Vincent St., Glasgow G2 5DD, Scotland. TEL 041-204 2525. illus. **Document type:** newsletter.
  Description: Company newsletter; includes news of company developments, business activities and employees.

665.5 551 NE ISSN 0923-1730
TN860 CODEN: OIREE7
OILFIELD REVIEW. 1950. q. fl.440($268) (effective 1996). (Schlumberger-Doll Research) Elsevier Science B.V., P.O. Box 211, 1000 AE Amsterdam, Netherlands. TEL 31-20-4853911. FAX 31-20-4853598. TELEX 18582 ESPA NL. E-mail: nlinfo-f@elsevier.nl; usinfo-f@elsevier.com; forinfo-kyf04035@niftyserve.or.jp; Site addr.: http://www.elsevier.nl/. (Subscr. in U.S. and Canada to: Elsevier Science Inc., Box 882, Madison Sq. Sta., New York, NY 10159. TEL 212-989-5800. FAX 212-633-3990) Ed. Henry N. Edmundson. bk.rev.; illus. circ. 4,100. (also avail. in microform from UMI; back issues avail.) Indexed: Geol.Abstr. **Document type:** academic/scholarly publication.
  —BLDSC (6252.274680); CASDDS; Ei; Faxon; PADDS; SWETS. **CCC.**
  Formed by the 1990 merger of: Schlumberger Limited. Technical Review; Drilling and Pumping Journal.
  Description: Source of information on seismic surveying, drilling, MWD, well logging, well testing, reservoir stimulation and completion practices.
  Refereed Serial

665.5 SP ISSN 0030-1493
OILGAS. 1967. m. 10000 ptas.($145) in Europe; elsewhere $170. Oilgas S.A., Paseo de la Habana, 48, 28036 Madrid, Spain. TEL 34-1-5632893. FAX 34-1-5635234. Ed. Carlos Martin Palomo. circ. 6,500. Indexed: Gas Abstr., Ind.SST.
  —**CCC.**
  Description: Discusses the petroleum, petrochemical and gas industries' activities.

665.5 UK
OILNEWS AND GAS INTERNATIONAL. m. R A E - L I N Communications, P.O. Box 6, Haddington, E. Lothian EH41 3NQ, Scotland. TEL 062-0822578. FAX 062-822758. TELEX 94026124-AREL-G. Ed. Richard Brown. **Document type:** trade publication.

665.5 CN ISSN 0164-887X
OILPATCH MAGAZINE; the natural resources magazine. 1976. m. Can.$42.95. c/o Master Publications, 2nd Fl., 17560 - 107th Ave., Edmondton, Alta. T5S 1E9, Canada. TEL 403-486-1295. FAX 403-484-0884. Ed. Leah Hyman. adv. circ. 12,000.

665.5 338.2 CN ISSN 0030-1515
CODEN: OLWKAX
OILWEEK. 1954. 51/yr. Can.$99. Maclean-Hunter Ltd. (Calgary), Ste. 2450, 101-6th Ave. S.W., Calgary, AB T2P 3P4, Canada. TEL 403-266-8700; 800-561-1294. FAX 403-266-6634. Ed. David Coll. adv. contact: Tony Poblete. bk.rev.; charts; illus.; maps; mkt.; stat. circ. 10,088. (also avail. in microform from UMI; reprint service avail. from UMI) Indexed: API Abstr., API Catal., API Hlth.& Environ., API Oil., API Pet.Ref., API Pet.Subst., API Transport., Bibl.& Ind.Geol., Can.B.P.I., Chem.Abstr., Petrol.Abstr., PROMT. **Document type:** newsletter, trade publication.
  —BLDSC (6252.620000); Faxon; UnCover. **CCC.**

338.47 381.42282 DK ISSN 0109-3916
OLIEBERETNING. 1979. a. free. Oliebranchens Faellesrepraesentation - Danish Petroleum Industry Association, Vognmagergade 7, P.O. Box 120, DK-1004 Copenhagen K, Denmark. TEL 45-33 11 30 77. FAX 45-33-32-16-18. Sec.Genl. Joergen Posborg. illus. **Document type:** corporate report.
  Formerly: Oliebranchens Faellesrepraesentation. Beretning.

665.5 CN ISSN 0078-5040
ONTARIO PETROLEUM INSTITUTE. ANNUAL CONFERENCE PROCEEDINGS. 1962. a., latest vol.33, 1994. Can.$40 (effective 1995 & 1996). Ontario Petroleum Institute Inc., 555 Southdale Rd. E., Ste. 104, London, ON N6E 1A2, Canada. TEL 519-680-1620. FAX 519-680-1621. Ed. Douglas W. Gilbert. circ. 200 (paid). **Document type:** proceedings.
  —BLDSC (1082.317000). **CCC.**

665.5 CN
ONTARIO PETROLEUM INSTITUTE. NEWSLETTER. bi-m. Can.$35. Ontario Petroleum Institute, 555 Southdale Rd. E., Ste. 104, London, ON N6E 1A2, Canada. TEL 519-680-1620. FAX 519-680-1621. circ. 450. **Document type:** newsletter.

665.5 CN
ONTARIO PETROLEUM INSTITUTE. TECHNICAL PAPERS. a. Can.$40. Ontario Petroleum Institute, 555 Southdale Rd. E., Ste. 104, London, ON N6E 1A2, Canada. TEL 519-680-1620. FAX 519-680-1621.

665.5 CN
ONTARIO PETROLEUM INSTITUTE VOLUMES. 1962. a. Can.$40. Ontario Petroleum Institute, 555 Southdale Rd. E., Ste. 104, London, ON N6E 1A2, Canada. TEL 519-680-1620. FAX 519-680-1621. Ed. Douglas W. Gilbert. circ. 200. **Document type:** proceedings.

553 US ISSN 0078-5741
TN872.07 CODEN: OGOGAE
OREGON. DEPARTMENT OF GEOLOGY AND MINERAL INDUSTRIES. OIL AND GAS INVESTIGATIONS. 1963. irreg., no.18, 1993. price varies. Department of Geology and Mineral Industries, 800 N.E. Oregon St., No. 28, Ste. 965, Portland, OR 97232-2109. TEL 503-731-4100. FAX 503-731-4066.

341.7 KU
ORGANIZATION OF ARAB PETROLEUM EXPORTING COUNTRIES. SECRETARY GENERAL'S ANNUAL REPORT. 1974. a. free. Organization of Arab Petroleum Exporting Countries, P.O. Box 20501, Safat 13066, Kuwait. TEL 965-4844500. FAX 965-4815747. TELEX 22166 NAFARAB KT. charts; stat. circ. 1,000. **Document type:** corporate report.
  Description: Review of Arab and world economics and energy developments plus description of activities of OPEC and its sponsored ventures.

338.2 665.5 AU ISSN 0257-1617
ORGANIZATION OF THE PETROLEUM EXPORTING COUNTRIES. ANNUAL REPORT. 1967. a. Organization of the Petroleum Exporting Countries, Information Department, Obere Donaustr. 93, A-1020 Vienna, Austria. TEL 01-21112-0. FAX 01-2149827. Ed. Yusufu Turundu. (also avail. in microfiche from CIS) Indexed: IIS. **Document type:** corporate report.
  —BLDSC (6265.920000).
  Formerly: Organization of the Petroleum Exporting Countries. Annual Review and Record (ISSN 0474-6317)
  Description: News about world economic situtation for oil-producing countries, developments in the energy market, activities of the secretariat.

665.5 AT ISSN 0310-4184
P E X: AUSTRALIA'S PETROLEUM EXPLORATION NEWSLETTER. 1972. 11/yr. Aus.$220. Pex Publications Pty. Ltd., P.O. Box 158, Claremont, W.A. 6010, Australia. TEL 61-9-3833477. FAX 61-9-3851485. Ed. Don Lipscombe. Indexed: AESIS. **Document type:** newsletter.
  Description: Publishes news, views, comments and analysis.

665.5 US
P G W NEWSLINE. 1928. m. free. Philadelphia Gas Works, 800 W. Montgomery Ave., Philadelphia, PA 19122. TEL 215-684-6564. Ed. Peter A. Hussie. circ. 4,500 (controlled).
  Formerly: P G W News.
  Description: Magazine for PGW employees.

662.6 338 US
PACIFIC COAST OIL DIRECTORY. 1983. a. Hart Publications, Inc. (Subsidiary of: Phillips Publishing International, Inc.), 1900 Grant St., Ste. 400, Denver, CO 80203. FAX 303-837-8585. **Document type:** directory.

PACIFIC - MOUNTAIN OIL DIRECTORY. see *BUSINESS AND ECONOMICS — Trade And Industrial Directories*

665 US
PACIFIC SUMMARY REPORT - INDEX. 1980. a. free. Outer Continental Shelf Information Program, Offshore Information and Publications Office, Minerals Management Service, 381 Elden St., No. 1400, Herndon, VA 22070-4817. TEL 703-787-1080. circ. 4,000.
  Formed by the merger of: Pacific Index; Pacific Summary Report.
  Description: Documents with status of federal offshore oil and gas leasing, exploration, development and production activities.

665 PK ISSN 1017-0626
PAKISTAN JOURNAL OF HYDROCARBON RESEARCH. (Text in English) vol.4, 1992. s-a. Hydrocarbon Development Institute of Pakistan, 230 Nizamuddin Rd. F 7-4, P.O. Box 1308, Islamabad, Pakistan. FAX 92-51-828773. Ed. Hilal A. Reza. **Document type:** academic/scholarly publication.
  —BLDSC (6341.400000).
  Description: Publishes pure and applied research relating to Pakistan in the fields of oil and gas exploration, production, processing, utilization, economics, policy and planning.

665 PK ISSN 0552-9115
PAKISTAN PETROLEUM LIMITED. ANNUAL REPORT. (Text in English) 1952. a. $6. Pakistan Petroleum Ltd., PIDC House, Dr. Ziauddin Ahmad Rd., Karachi 4, Pakistan. Ed. Ahsan Halim. circ. 5,000.
  Description: Presents a complete picture of the company's finances and operations.

665.5 UK
PERFORMANCE. 1990. q. Phillips Petroleum Co. UK Ltd., 35 Guildford Rd., Woking, Surrey GU22 7QT, England. TEL 01483-752657. FAX 01483-752607. Ed. Lynnda Robson. circ. 5,000. **Document type:** newsletter.

338.2 US
▼**PERMIAN BASIN PETROLEUM INDUSTRY.** 1994. irreg. $85. Midwest Register, Inc., 1120 E. 4th St., Tulsa, OK 74120. TEL 918-582-2000. FAX 918-587-9349.

665.5 531.64 SI
PETRO ASIAN BUSINESS REPORTS. (Text in English) 22/yr. $520. Asia Pacific Energy Business Publications Pte. Ltd., 2 Shenton Way, No. 05-01, 05 ICB Bldg., Singapore 0106, Singapore. TEL 65-2223422. FAX 65-2225587. TELEX RS 28366 SAFAN.

665.5 BL
PETROBRAS. CONSOLIDATED REPORT. (Text in English) a. Petroleo Brasileiro S.A., Servico de Relacoes Publicas, Av. Republica do Chile, 65 S-2056, Rio de Janeiro RJ, Brazil. charts; illus.; stat.

665.5 BL ISSN 0103-5266
PETROBRAS NEWS. (Text in English) q. Petroleo Brasileiro S.A., Public Affairs (SERCOM), Caixa Posta 15521, 20132 Rio de Janeiro, RJ, Brazil. TEL 021-262-7126. FAX 021-220-5052. TELEX 021-23335. Ed. Lanning Elwis. charts; illus.; stat. (looseleaf format) Indexed: Energy Info.Abstr.
  Description: Covers news in the petroleum and drilling field.

PETROCHEMICAL EQUIPMENT. see *ENGINEERING — Chemical Engineering*

380 US
PETROCHEMICAL INDUSTRY; petrochemical plants, engineering, construction, equipment manufactures & supply companies. 1991. a. $65. Midwest Register, Inc., 1120 E. 4th St., Tulsa, OK 74120. TEL 918-582-2000. FAX 918-587-9349. **Document type:** directory.

665.5 US
PETROFAX. (Avail in 4 reports: Canada, Products, LPG, Crude) d. $97. Bloomberg Financial Markets, 100 Business Park Dr., Box 888, Princeton, NJ 08542-0888. TEL 609-497-3500. FAX 609-683-7523.

655.5 AT
PETROFAX. (Fax service only) w. (Thu.). Aus.$1440. Pex Publications Pty. Ltd., P.O. Box 158, Claremont, W.A. 6010, Australia. TEL 61-9-3833477. FAX 61-9-3851485. Ed. Don Lipscombe.
  Description: Exploration scouting service provides information on upcoming events with graphical status summary of every well in the region.

PETROLEUM AND GAS

665.5 US
PETROFLASH. d. $2495. Bloomberg Financial Markets, 100 Business Park Dr., Box 888, Princeton, NJ 08542-0888. TEL 609-497-3500. FAX 609-683-7523.
●Available only online.
Description: Computerized daily oil price reporting service.

665.5 FR
PETROLE ET LE GAZ EN AFRIQUE. irreg., latest 1986. 1190 F. I C Publications, 10 rue Vineuse, 75116 Paris, France. TEL 44-30-81-00. FAX 44-30-81-11.

665.5 FR ISSN 0152-5425
TN860 CODEN: PETEDX
PETROLE ET TECHNIQUES. no.241, Feb.1977. m. 500 F. (foreign 552 F.). Association Francaise des Techniciens et des Professionels du Petrole (A F T P), 92038 Paris la Defense, France. TEL 47-17-67-32. FAX 47-17-67-44. Ed. Jacques Moulin. adv. contact: Jacques Moulin. charts; illus.; circ. 3,100 (paid). Indexed: API Abstr., API Catal., API Hlth.& Environ., API Oil., API Pet.Ref., API Pet.Subst., API Transport., Bibl.& Ind.Geol., Chem.Abstr., Petrol.Abstr. **Document type:** trade publication.
—BLDSC (6430.680000); CASDDS; Ei; PADDS; SWETS.
Formerly: Association Francaise des Techniciens du Petrole. Revue (ISSN 0004-5470)

665.5 FR ISSN 0990-5421
TN864 CODEN: PTIFEJ
PETROLE INFORMATIONS. m. 1040 F. Societe d' Information et de Documentation, Bureau d'Informations Professionnelles, 142 rue Montmartre, 75002 Paris, France. FAX 40-39-97-52. TELEX 220528F. Ed. Elisabeth Liegeois. adv.; illus.; tr.lit. circ. 7,757. Indexed: API Abstr., API Catal., API Hlth.& Environ., API Oil., API Pet.Ref., API Pet.Subst., API Transport., Petrol.Abstr.
—BLDSC (6430.700000); Ei; SWETS. CCC.
Former titles: Petrole Informations International (Edition Bilingue) (ISSN 0755-561X); (until 1982): Petrole Informations (ISSN 0150-6463); (until 1969): Petrole Informations, la Revue Petroliere (ISSN 0150-6471)
Description: Comprehensive analysis of developments in the international oil and gas industries.

665.5 SP ISSN 0213-8360
PETROLEO; actualidad nacional e internacional. 1973. w. 40000 ptas.($420) Oilgas S.A., Paseo de la Habana, 48, 28036 Madrid, Spain. TEL 34-1-5632893. FAX 34-1-5635234. Ed. Carlos Martin. circ. 2,000.
Description: Deals with international activities of the petroleum, petrochemical and gas markets.

665.5 US ISSN 0093-7851
TN860 CODEN: PTRIB2
PETROLEO INTERNACIONAL. (Text in Spanish) 1943. bi-m. free to qualified personnel. Keller International Publishing Corporation, 150 Great Neck Rd., Great Neck, NY 11021. TEL 516-829-9210. FAX 516-829-7265. Ed. Victor Prieto. adv.; bk.rev.; charts; illus.; stat. circ. 8,810. (processed) Indexed: Chem.Abstr., GeoRef., Petrol.Abstr., PROMT. **Document type:** trade publication.
—BLDSC (6430.780000); CASDDS; PADDS. CCC.
Former titles: Petroleo y Petroquimica Internacional; Petroleo Interamericano (ISSN 0031-6407)

665.5 VE
PETROLEUM. 1977. 12/yr. Bs.6000 (Latin America $140; N. America $180; elsewhere $280) (effective 1995). Petroleum Editores, S.A., Apdo. 379, Maracaibo 4001-A, Venezuela. TEL 58-61-529435. TELEX 64336 PEMIN UC. Ed. Jorge Zajia. adv.: B&W page $1600, color page $2000; 180 x 255; adv. contact: Aristides Villalobos. bk.rev. circ. 5,000. **Document type:** trade publication.
Formerly (until 1983): Petroleo y Tecnologia.
Description: For professionals and technicians. Covers Latin American oil industry.

PETROLEUM AND CHEMICAL INDUSTRY CONFERENCE. RECORD OF CONFERENCE PAPERS. see ENGINEERING — Chemical Engineering

662.6 II ISSN 0970-3098
TP690.2.A78
PETROLEUM ASIA JOURNAL. (Text in English) 1978. q. Rs.60($30) Himachal Times Group of Newspapers, 57-B Rajpur Rd., P.O. Box 50, Dehra Dun 248001, India. Ed. Dev Kumar Pandhi. adv. circ. 10,000.

661 UK ISSN 0965-5441
TP690.A1 CODEN: PHEME4
PETROLEUM CHEMISTRY. English translation of: Neftekhimiya (RU ISSN 0028-2421) 1962. bi-m. £1150($1829) (effective 1996). (Rossiiskaya Akademiya Nauk, RU) Elsevier Science Ltd., Pergamon, P.O. Box 800, Kidlington, Oxford OX5 1DX, England. TEL 44-1865-843000. FAX 44-1865-843010. (Subscr. in U.S. and Canada to: Elsevier Science, 660 White Plains Rd., Tarrytown, NY 10591-5153. TEL 914-524-9200. FAX 914-333-2444) Eds. K.M. Minachev, E.J. Banji. adv.; bk.rev.; abstr.; bibl.; charts. circ. 1,025. (also avail. in microfilm from UMI; back issues avail.) Indexed: Curr.Cont. **Document type:** academic/scholarly publication.
—BLDSC (0416.687000); Faxon; Genuine Article; SWETS; UMI. CCC.
Formerly (until 1992): Petroleum Chemistry U.S.S.R. (ISSN 0031-6458)
Description: Publishes research papers on the analysis, physical and chemical properties and behavior of individual petroleum constituents, as well as applications of petroleum cheimstry in the manufacture of industrial products.
Refereed Serial

PETROLEUM CONCESSION HANDBOOK. see LAW — International Law

665.5 UK ISSN 0306-395X
HD9560.1 CODEN: PEECDK
PETROLEUM ECONOMIST; the international energy journal. (Editions in English and Japanese) 1934. m. $425. Petroleum Economist Ltd., P.O. Box 105, 25-31 Ironmonger Row, London EC1V 3PN, England. TEL 44-171-251-3501. FAX 44-171-253-1224. Ed. Ian Bourne. adv.; bk.rev.; charts; mkt.; stat.; index. circ. 4,400. (also avail. in microfilm from UMI; reprint service avail. from UMI) Indexed: AESIS, Asian-Pac.Econ.Lit., Bibl.& Ind.Geol., BMT, Br.Geol.Lit., Bus.Ind., Energy Info.Abstr., Fuel & Energy Abstr., Gas.Abstr., Geo.Abstr., Key to Econ.Sci., P.A.I.S., Petrol.Energy B.N.I., PROMT, Tr.& Indus.Ind. **Document type:** bulletin.
—BLDSC (6431.680000); Faxon; SWETS; UMI; UnCover.
Formerly: Petroleum Press Service (ISSN 0031-6504)
Description: Informational articles, editorial commentary, news items, and statistical data pertaining to the marketing, exploratory, technological, and production aspects of the international oil, gas, and other energy-source industries with company profiles.

622 US ISSN 0164-8322
TN860 CODEN: PENGA6
PETROLEUM ENGINEER INTERNATIONAL; the magazine of drilling and production technology: onshore, offshore, worldwide. 1929. m. $59. Hart Publications, Inc. (Subsidiary of: Phillips Publishing International, Inc.), 4545 Post Oak Place, Ste. 210, Houston, TX 77027. TEL 713-993-9320. FAX 713-840-8585. Ed. Russell Wright; Pub. Russell Wright. adv. contact: Russell Laas. charts; illus. circ. 28,000. (also avail. in microform) Indexed: A.S.& T.Ind., AESIS, Bibl.& Ind.Geol., Eng.Ind., Excerp.Med., Gas Abstr., ISMEC, Petrol.Abstr., SRI, SRI. **Document type:** trade publication.
—BLDSC (6432.000000); Ei; Faxon; PADDS; SWETS; UMI; UnCover. CCC.
Supersedes (in 1970): Hydrocarbon News (ISSN 0018-8182); Petro-Chem Engineer (ISSN 0031-6326)
Description: Provides practical engineering, operating and methods technology to maximize profits in oil and gas drilling and production worldwide.

665 NE ISSN 0955-0712
PETROLEUM ENGINEERING AND DEVELOPMENT STUDIES. (Text in English) 1987. irreg., vol.4, 1993. price varies. Kluwer Academic Publishers, Postbus 17, 3300 AA Dordrecht, Netherlands. TEL 31-78-392392. FAX 31-78-392254. TELEX 29245 KAPG NL. (Dist. by: Kluwer Academic Publishers Group, P.O. Box 322, 3300 AH Dordrecht, Netherlands. TEL 31-78-392392. FAX 31-78-546474; N. America dist. addr.: Box 358, Accord Sta., Hingham, MA 02018-0358. TEL 617-871-6600. FAX 617-871-6528) **Document type:** monographic series.
—BLDSC (6432.500000).
Refereed Serial

665.5 US
PETROLEUM EQUIPMENT DIRECTORY. 1955. a. $50. Petroleum Equipment Institute, Box 2380, Tulsa, OK 74101. TEL 918-494-9696. Ed. Robert N. Renkes. adv. circ. 3,000. **Document type:** directory.

665.5 US ISSN 0740-1817
TN872
PETROLEUM FRONTIERS. q. $200. Petroleum Information Corporation, Box 2612, Denver, CO 80201-2612. TEL 303-740-7100. FAX 303-694-1754. **Document type:** academic/scholarly publication.
—BLDSC (6433.146000); Ei; PADDS; UnCover.
Description: Each issue examines petroleum exploration within a particular geographical region, covering stratigraphic and structural analyses, mineralogy, drilling and discovery history, discussions of leasing history and future outlook, and more.

553 AT ISSN 0048-3591
TN860
PETROLEUM GAZETTE. 1952. q. free. Australian Institute of Petroleum Ltd., 500 Collins St., Melbourne, Vic. 3000, Australia. Ed. R.F. Wilkinson. Indexed: AESIS, Aus.Rd.Ind., Bibl.& Ind.Geol., Gdlns.
—BLDSC (6433.200000); UnCover.

553 US ISSN 0553-8882
PETROLEUM GEOLOGY: A DIGEST OF RUSSIAN LITERATURE ON PETROLEUM GEOLOGY. vol.2, 1959. m. $40. Box 171, McLean, VA 22101. Ed. Grace Carrington. charts; illus. circ. 300. Indexed: AESIS, GeoRef, Petrol.Abstr.
—BLDSC (6433.250000); Faxon; PADDS; SWETS.

665.5 552 CH ISSN 0553-8890
TN876.T28 CODEN: PGTWAU
PETROLEUM GEOLOGY OF TAIWAN/T'AIWAN SHIH-YU TI-CHIH. (Text in English) 1962. a. NT.$1200 (foreign $54). Chinese Petroleum Corporation, 83 Chung Hwa Rd., Sec.1, Taipei, Taiwan 100, Republic of China. TEL 02-361-0221. FAX 02-331-7473. TELEX 11215 CHINOL. Ed. Tai-Hsuan Wu. circ. 1,000. Indexed: Bibl.& Ind.Geol., Deep Sea Res.& Oceanogr.Abstr. **Document type:** bulletin.
—BLDSC (6433.500000); CASDDS; PADDS.
Description: Publishes research papers on the geology of Taiwan.

665.5 551 CN
PETROLEUM GEOLOGY SPECIAL PAPER SERIES. 1990. a. price varies. Ministry of Energy, Mines and Petroleum Resources, Energy Resources Division, 7th Fl., 1810 Blanshard St., Victoria, BC V8V 1X4, Canada. (Subscr. to: Crown Publications, 546 Yates St., Victoria, BC V8W 1K8, Canada. TEL 604-386-4636) **Document type:** government publication.

665.5 US ISSN 0747-2528
HD9561
PETROLEUM INDEPENDENT. (Statistical issue avail.: Oil & Natural Gas Producing Industry in Your State) 1929. 6/yr. $60 to non-members. (Independent Petroleum Association of America) Petroleum Independent Publishers, Inc., 1101 16th St., N.W., Washington, DC 20036. TEL 202-857-4774; 800-433-2851. FAX 202-857-4799. Ed. Bruce A. Wells. adv.; charts; illus.; stat. circ. 6,000. Indexed: Gas Abstr., PROMT, SRI. **Document type:** trade publication.
—BLDSC (6433.570000); UnCover.

PETROLEUM AND GAS

665.5 US
PETROLEUM INFORMATION INTERNATIONAL. Title from masthead: P I International. (In 3 editions: Western Hemisphere; Europe, Africa, Middle Easy; Asia Pacific) m. $400 per edition (all 3 editions $1000). Petroleum Information Corporation, Box 2612, Denver, CO 80201-2612. TEL 303-595-7500; 800-OIL-DATA. FAX 303-595-7506.
— **Supersedes** (in 1994): International Trends in Oil and Gas.
— **Description:** Comprehensive coverage of international petroleum developments.

665.5 US ISSN 0480-2160
HD9560.1
PETROLEUM INTELLIGENCE WEEKLY. 1961. w. $1475 (effective Apr. 1994). Petroleum & Energy Intelligence Weekly, Inc., 575 Broadway, 4th Fl., New York, NY 10012-3230. TEL 212-941-5500. FAX 212-941-5508. TELEX 62371 PETROIN. Ed. Sarah Miller. **Indexed:** Fuel & Energy Abstr., Petrol.Energy B.N.I. **Document type:** trade publication.
—BLDSC (6433.630000). **CCC.**
— **Description:** Provides market insights for oil and natural gas executives and government leaders. Includes information and analysis of major industry developments, issues and trends.

665.5 918 US
PETROLEUM: LATIN AMERICAN INDUSTRIAL REPORT. (Avail. for each of 22 Latin American countries) 1985. a. $435 per country report. Aquino Productions, Box 15760, Stamford, CT 06901. TEL 203-325-3138. Ed. Andres C. Aquino.

PETROLEUM LEGISLATION. see LAW — International Law

658.8 US ISSN 0362-7799
HD9561
PETROLEUM MARKETER. 1933. bi-m. $18. G C I Publishing Co., Inc., 1801 Rockville Pike, Ste. 330, Rockville, MD 20852. TEL 301-984-7333. Ed. Colin A. Cambell. adv.; charts; illus.; stat.; tr.lit.; circ. 17,000 (controlled). (processed) **Indexed:** Chem.Abstr. **Document type:** trade publication.
—SWETS; UMI.
— **Formerly:** Petroleum and TBA Marketer (ISSN 0031-644X)

662 US ISSN 0747-5721
HD9563
PETROLEUM MARKETER'S HANDBOOK. 1977. a. $127 (foreign $139). Bloomberg Financial Markets, 100 Business Park Dr., Box 888, Princeton, NJ 08542-0888. TEL 609-497-3500. FAX 609-683-7523.
— **Description:** Lists brokers and traders in petroleum products.

665.54 US ISSN 0273-6268
PETROLEUM MARKETING MANAGEMENT.* 1980. bi-m. membership. Petroleum Marketers Association, 1901 N. Ft. Myer Dr., Ste. 1200, Arlington, VA 22209. Ed. Connie Szostak. adv. circ. 20,886.

338 US ISSN 0741-9643
CODEN: PMMOEH
PETROLEUM MARKETING MONTHLY. 1983. m. $84 (foreign $105). U.S. Energy Information Administration, National Energy Information Center, EI-231, James Forrestal Bldg., Rm. 1F-048, 1000 Independence Ave., S.W., Washington, DC 20585. TEL 202-586-8800. (Subscr. to: Superintendent of Documents, U.S. Government Printing Office, Box 371954, Pittsburgh, PA 15250-7954. TEL 202-512-1800. FAX 202-512-2250) charts; stat. (also avail. in microfiche from CIS; back issues avail.; reprint service avail. from CIS) **Indexed:** Amer.Stat.Ind. (1983-), Energy Info.Abstr. **Document type:** government publication, bulletin.
— **Description:** Provides current information and statistical data on various petroleum products.

PETROLEUM NEWSLETTER. see OCCUPATIONAL HEALTH AND SAFETY

665.5 338.2 US ISSN 0031-6490
HG6047.P47
PETROLEUM OUTLOOK. 1948. m. $520 (foreign $560). Petroleum Economist Ltd., 25-31 Iron Moner Row, London EC1V 3PN, England. TEL 44-71-251-3501. FAX 44-71-253-1224. Ed.Bd. adv.; illus.; stat. circ. 2,500. **Indexed:** Petrol.Energy B.N.I.
—**CCC.**
— **Description:** Corporate and industry developments of 150 oil and gas service companies.

665.5 UK ISSN 0020-3076
TP690.A1 CODEN: PETRB2
PETROLEUM REVIEW. 1947. m. £85 (overseas £100) (effective 1995). Institute of Petroleum, 61 New Cavendish St., London W1M 8AR, England. TEL 0171-467-7100. FAX 0171-255-1472. Ed. Carol Reader; Pub. Sarah Frost Mellor. adv.; bk.rev.; illus.; stat.; tr.lit.; index. circ. 8,500. (also avail. in microfilm from UMI; reprint service avail. from UMI) **Indexed:** AESIS, API Abstr., API Catal., API Hlth.& Environ., API Oil., API Pet.Ref., API Pet.Subst., API Transport., Bibl.& Ind.Geol., BMT, Br.Geol.Lit., Br.Tech.Ind., Chem.Abstr., Eng.Ind., Excerp.Med., Fluidex, Fuel & Energy Abstr., Geo.Abstr., HRIS, Petrol.Abstr., RAPRA. **Document type:** academic/scholarly publication.
—BLDSC (6435.190000); Ei; PADDS; SWETS; UMI; UnCover.
— **Formerly:** Institute of Petroleum Review.

338.47 UK
PETROLEUM SERVICES. WEEKLY SERVICE (OFFSHORE). 1982. w. £1250 (with Onshore report £1600). Arthur Andersen, Petroleum Services Group, 1 Surrey St., London WC2R 2PS, England. TEL 0171-438-3888. FAX 0171-438-3881. TELEX 8812711. Ed. Timothy H. Shingler. (looseleaf format; back issues avail.) **Document type:** trade publication.
— **Former titles:** Petroleum Services. Weekly Service. Offshore Report; (until 1986): Offshore Drilling Report (Year).
— **Description:** Highlights current drilling activity, rig movements and license changes in the offshore sectors of North Sea region.

338.47 UK
PETROLEUM SERVICES. WEEKLY SERVICE (ONSHORE). 1982. w. £550 (with Offshore report £1600). Arthur Andersen, Petroleum Services Group, 1 Surrey St., London WC2R 2PS, England. TEL 0171-438-3888. FAX 0171-438-3881. TELEX 8812711. Ed. Timothy H. Shingler. (looseleaf format; back issues avail.) **Document type:** trade publication.
— **Former titles:** Petroleum Services. Weekly Service. Onshore Report; (until 1986): Onshore Activity Report (Year).
— **Description:** Highlights current drilling activity, rig movements and license changes for onshore U.K., Ireland and France.

338.47 UK
PETROLEUM SERVICES GROUP. MONTHLY FIELD & PRODUCTION REPORT. m. £800. Arthur Andersen, Petroleum Services Group, 1 Surrey St., London WC2R 2PS, England. TEL 0171-438-3888. FAX 0171-438-3881. TELEX 8812711. Ed. Timothy H. Shingler. (looseleaf format; back issues avail.) **Document type:** trade publication.
— **Description:** Presents summary of monthly production rates from the producing fields of northwest Europe. Provides production figures for all the oil, gas and condensate fields in the North Sea and onshore U.K.

PETROLEUM SOFTWARE DIRECTORY. see COMPUTERS — Software

338.2 665 US
PETROLEUM TAXATION & LEGISLATION REPORT. 1957. bi-m. $1500 (renewal $1250). Barrows Co., Inc., 116 E. 66th St., New York, NY 10021. TEL 212-772-1199. FAX 212-288-7242. TELEX 4971238/BARROWS. Ed. Gordon H. Barrows. bk.rev.; charts; mkt.; tr.lit. circ. 6,000.
— **Formerly:** Petroleum Taxation Report (ISSN 0031-6539)
— **Description:** Reviews changes in world oil and gas laws and tax regulations by country.

665.5 UK
PETROLEUM TIMES ENERGY REPORT. 1899. fortn. £154.60 (avail. as package with Petroleum Times Business Reviews). Nexus Media Ltd., Warwick House, Azalea Dr., Swanley, Kent BR8 8HY, England. TEL 01322-660070. FAX 01322-667633. Ed. Bonnie Downing. **Indexed:** PROMT. **Document type:** trade publication.
—BLDSC (6436.015000); SWETS. **CCC.**
— **Formerly:** Petroleum Times Price Report (ISSN 0261-3883)

665.5 IT ISSN 0031-6563
PETROLIERI D'ITALIA. 1954. m. L.60000. Interpetrol, Via Andrea Doria 3, 20124 Milan, Italy. TEL 2-669-1600. FAX 2-66-97-169. Ed. Enzo Fassitelli. adv.; bk.review. circ. 3,200.

PETROLOGY. see EARTH SCIENCES — Geology

PETROLOGY AND STRUCTURAL GEOLOGY. see EARTH SCIENCES — Geology

665.5 531.64 SI ISSN 0129-1122
HD9576.S652
PETROMIN. (Text in English) 1974. m. $110. Asia Pacific Energy Business Publications Pte. Ltd., 2 Shenton Way, No. 05-01, 05 ICB Bldg., Singapore 0106, Singapore. TEL 65-2223422. FAX 65-2225587. TELEX RS 28366 SAFAN. Ed. Jimmie Aung Khin. adv. contact: Eddie Raj.

665.5 SI
PETROMIN ASIA - PACIFIC PETROLEUM MAP. irreg., latest 6th ed. $190. Asia Pacific Energy Business Publications Pte. Ltd., 2 Shenton Way, No. 05-01, 05 ICB Bldg., Singapore 0106, Singapore. TEL 65-2223422. FAX 65-2225587. TELEX RS 28366 SAFAN.

665 SI
PETROMIN OIL & GAS DIRECTORY. a. $50. Asia Pacific Energy Business Publications Pte. Ltd., 2 Shenton Way, No. 05-01, 05 ICB Bldg., Singapore 0106, Singapore. TEL 65-2223422. FAX 65-2225587. TELEX RS 28366 SAFAN. **Document type:** directory.

665.5 AG ISSN 0031-6598
PETROTECNICA.* 1960. bi-m. Arg.$750.($12.) Victor Sulimovich, Ed. & Pub., Maipu 645, Buenos Aires, Argentina. adv.; charts; illus.; index. circ. 3,500.

338.47 UK
PETROVIEW. m. £21000 (renewals £7000). Arthur Andersen, Petroleum Services Group, 1 Surrey St., London WC2R 2PS, England. TEL 0171-438-3888. FAX 0171-438-3881. TELEX 8812711. Eds. James Sales, Graham Saddler. (diskette format) **Document type:** trade publication.
— **Description:** Provides data on licenses, new and existing wells, fields, platforms, and pipelines. Results of queries can be viewed as a map, table, or graph.

665 US
PHILNEWS. 1937; N.S. 1976. m. free to qualified personnel. Phillips Petroleum Company, Corporate Communications, 16 A1 PB, Bartlesville, OK 74004. TEL 918-661-4974. FAX 918-662-2926. Ed. Bill Wertz. illus. circ. 34,000.

665.54 US
TJ930
PIPE LINE & GAS INDUSTRY; crude oil and products pipelines, gas transmission and gas distribution. (International Edition avail.) 1954. m. $24 (foreign $30) (free to qualified personnel). Gulf Publishing Co., Box 2608, Houston, TX 77252-2608. TEL 713-529-4301. FAX 713-520-4433. TELEX 287330 GULF UR. Ed. Buddy Ives. adv.; bk.rev.; charts; illus.; index. circ. 27,819. (also avail. in microfilm from UMI; reprint service avail.) **Indexed:** A.S.& T.Ind., API Abstr., API Catal., API Hlth.& Environ., API Oil., API Pet.Ref., API Pet.Subst., API Transport., Corros.Abstr., Eng.Ind., Fuel & Energy Abstr., Gas Abstr., Met.Abstr., Petrol.Abstr., World Alum.Abstr.
—Faxon; UMI; UnCover. **CCC.**
— **Formerly:** Pipe Line Industry (ISSN 0032-0145)

PETROLEUM AND GAS

622 US ISSN 0032-0188
TP757 CODEN: PLGJAT
PIPELINE & GAS JOURNAL; energy construction, transportation and distribution. (Includes section: Energy Management Report (ISSN 0013-7537)) 1859. m. $22. Oildom Publishing Co. of Texas, Inc., Box 219368, Houston, TX 77218-9368. TEL 713-558-6930. FAX 712-558-7029. Ed. Gary Congram; Pub. O.L. Klinger III. adv.: B&W page $3450, color page $4650; 8 1/4 x 11 1/4; adv. contact: Sherrie Anderson. charts; illus. (also avail. in microform) **Indexed**: A.S.& T.Ind., AESIS, API Abstr., API Catal., API Hlth.& Environ., API Oil, API Pet.Ref., API Pet.Subst., API Transport., Bus.Ind., Chem.Eng.Abstr., Corros.Abstr., Energy Ind., Energy Info.Abstr., Environ.Abstr., Fluidex, Fuel & Energy Abstr., Gas Abstr., Met.Abstr., Petrol.Abstr., PROMT, SRI, Tr.& Indus.Ind., W.R.C.Inf., World Alum.Abstr. **Document type**: trade publication.
—BLDSC (6502.060000); CIS; Ei; Faxon; Genuine Article; PADDS; SWETS; UMI; UnCover. **CCC**.
  Incorporates (in 1990): Pipeline (Houston) (ISSN 0148-4443); **Formerly**: Pipe Line News (ISSN 0032-0153); Pipeline & Gas Journal was formed by the merger of: Pipeline Engineer (ISSN 0096-8293); American Gas Journal.
  Description: Covers engineering and operating methods on cross-country pipelines that transport crude oil products and natural gas.

665.5 US
PIPELINE & GAS JOURNAL ANNUAL DIRECTORY OF PIPELINES AND EQUIPMENT. 1928. a. $75. Oildom Publishing Co. of Texas, Inc., Box 219368, Houston, TX 77218-9368. TEL 713-558-6930. FAX 713-558-7029. Ed. James Watt; Pub. O.L. Klinger III. adv. contact: Elizabeth Ross. stat. circ. 26,000. **Document type**: directory.
  Former titles: Pipe Line Annual Directory of Pipelines; Pipeline Annual Directory.

665.54 US ISSN 0896-1069
TJ930
PIPELINE & UTILITIES CONSTRUCTION. 1945. 12/yr. $50. Oildom Publishing Co. of Texas, Inc., Box 219368, Houston, TX 77218-9368. TEL 713-558-6930. FAX 713-558-7029. Ed. Robert Carpenter; Pub. O.L. Klinger III. adv. contact: Elizabeth Ross. bk.rev.; tr.lit. circ. 28,000. (back issues avail.) **Indexed**: Fuel & Energy Abstr., Geotech.Abstr., Petrol.Abstr. **Document type**: trade publication.
—PADDS. **CCC**.
  Formerly (until 1985): Pipeline and Underground Utilities Construction (ISSN 0032-0196)
  Description: Covers all aspects of underground systems construction as applied to pipelines and distribution systems: water, gas, cable, sewers, and storm drains. Also covers pipeline rehabilitation.

PIPELINE & UTILITIES CONSTRUCTION. ANNUAL DIRECTORY. see BUSINESS AND ECONOMICS — Trade And Industrial Directories

665.54 US ISSN 0197-1506
TJ930
PIPELINE DIGEST. 1963. s-m. $57 (foreign $87). Hart Publications, Inc. (Subsidiary of: Phillips Publishing International, Inc.), 4545 Post Oak Place, Ste. 210, Houston, TX 77027. TEL 713-993-9320. FAX 713-840-8585. Ed. Edward D. Huber; Pub. Paul S. Caplan. adv. contact: Jeffrey W. Evans. bk.rev. circ. 13,692. **Indexed**: Corros.Abstr., Fluidex. **Document type**: trade publication.
—**CCC**.
  Formerly: Universal News (ISSN 0041-820X)
  Description: Reports up-to-date information on construction, maintenance and operation of pipelines worldwide. Interprets industry trends, tracks proposed pipelines, and details the latest technology, legislation and new products and services.

665.54 US ISSN 1062-5801
PIPELINE INDUSTRY (TULSA). a. $50. Midwest Register, Inc., 1120 E. 4th St., Tulsa, OK 74120. TEL 918-582-2000. FAX 918-587-9349. **Document type**: directory.
  Formerly: Pipe Line & Pipe Line Contractors.
  Description: Supplies company name, address, phone and fax numbers, personnel, division offices, size and length of pipes and type of lines, equipment manufacturers, suppliers, contractors, engineering and construction.

665.54 627 UK ISSN 0032-020X
TS280 CODEN: PPIIAU
PIPES AND PIPELINES INTERNATIONAL; pipes, hoses, tubes, pumps, valves. 1956. bi-m. $150. Scientific Surveys Ltd., P.O. Box 21, Beaconsfield, Bucks. HP9 1NS, England. TEL 01494-675139. FAX 01494-670155. Ed. J.N.H. Tiratsoo. adv.; bk.rev.; charts; illus.; pat.; tr.lit.; index. **Indexed**: AESIS, BMT, Br.Tech.Ind., Chem.Abstr., Chem.Eng.Abstr., Eng.Ind., Excerp.Med., Fluidex, Fuel & Energy Abstr., Gas Abstr., Intl.Polym.Sci.& Tech., Met.Abstr., Petrol.Abstr., RAPRA, World Alum.Abstr. **Document type**: trade publication.
—BLDSC (6502.350000); PADDS; SWETS.
  Incorporates (1958-1990): Pipeline Industries Guild Journal (ISSN 0308-3098)
  Description: Technical information on pipes and pipelines research.

665.5 333.79 US
PLATT'S ASIA - PACIFIC - ARAB GULF MARKETSCAN. (Fax, telex service) d. price varies. McGraw-Hill, Inc., 1221 Ave. of the Americas, New York, NY 10020. TEL 212-521-2000.

665.5 333.79 US
PLATT'S CRUDE OIL MARKET WIRE. (Fax, telex service) d. price varies. McGraw-Hill, Inc., 1221 Ave. of the Americas, New York, NY 10020. TEL 212-521-2000.

665.5 333.79 US
PLATT'S CRUDE TANKERWIRE. (Fax. telex service) d. price varies. McGraw-Hill, Inc., 1221 Ave. of the Americas, New York, NY 10020. TEL 212-521-2000.

665.5 333.79 US
PLATT'S EUROPEAN PETROCHEMICALSCAN. (Fax, telex service) w. price varies. McGraw-Hill, Inc., 1221 Ave. of the Americas, New York, NY 10020. TEL 212-521-2000.

665.5 333.79 US
PLATT'S FAR EASTERN PETROCHEMICAL SCAN. (Fax, telex service) w. price varies. McGraw-Hill, Inc., 1221 Ave. of the Americas, New York, NY 10020. TEL 212-521-2000.

633 US
PLATT'S FEEDSTOCK REPORTS. (Fax, telex service) w. price varies. McGraw-Hill, Inc., 1221 Ave. of the Americas, New York, NY 10020. TEL 212-521-2000.

665.5 US
PLATT'S INTERNATIONAL PETROCHEMICAL REPORT. w. $920. McGraw-Hill, Inc., 1221 Avenue of the Americas, New York, NY 10020.
  ●Also available online. Vendor(s): Knight-Ridder, Inc. (File no.624/McGRAW-HILL PUBLICATIONS ONLINE), Dow Jones News Retrieval, Lexis-Nexis, NewsNet (CH20).
  Description: Aimed at executives who manufacture, market and distribute petroleum products.

333.79 665.5 US
PLATT'S L P GASWIRE. (Fax, telex service) s-w. price varies. McGraw-Hill, Inc., 1221 Ave. of the Americas, New York, NY 10020. Ed. Christine Forster. (back issues avail.)

665.5 US
PLATT'S OIL PRICE HANDBOOK. a. $165. McGraw-Hill, Inc., Commodity Services Group, 1221 Ave. of the Americas, 42nd Fl., New York, NY 10020. TEL 212-512-2000. Ed. Halsey Peckworth.

333.79 665.5 US
PLATT'S OILGRAM BUNKERWIRE. (Fax, telex service) s-w. price varies. McGraw-Hill, Inc., 1221 Ave. of the Americas, New York, NY 10020. Ed. Bob Keller. (back issues avail.)
  Formerly (until 1979): Platt's Marine Fuel Bunkerwire.

333.79 665.5 US
PLATT'S OILGRAM MARKETSCAN. EUROPEAN EDITION. (Fax, telex service) 1976. d. price varies. McGraw-Hill, Inc., 1221 Ave. of the Americas, New York, NY 10020. Ed. Therese Stanton. (back issues avail.)

333.79 665.5 US
PLATT'S OILGRAM MARKETSCAN. U S EDITION. (Fax, telex service) 1976. d. price varies. McGraw-Hill, Inc., 1221 Ave. of the Americas, New York, NY 10020. Ed. Joseph Link. (back issues avail.)

665.5 US ISSN 0163-1284
HD9561
PLATT'S OILGRAM NEWS. 1923. d. $1347 (foreign $1457). McGraw-Hill, Inc., Commodity Services Group, 1221 Ave. of the Americas, 42nd Fl., New York, NY 10020. TEL 212-512-2000. Ed. Onnic Marashian. (also avail. in microform from UMI; back issues avail.) **Indexed**: Bus.Ind., Petrol.Energy B.N.I., Tr.& Indus.Ind.
  ●Also available online. Vendor(s): Knight-Ridder, Inc. (File no.624/McGRAW-HILL PUBLICATIONS ONLINE), Dow Jones News Retrieval (PON), Lexis-Nexis (PONEWS), NewsNet (EY74).
—BLDSC (6539.099000).
  Former titles: Platt's Oilgram News Service; Oilgram News Service.

333.79 665.5 US
PLATT'S OILGRAM NEWS - WIRE. (Fax, telex service) d. price varies. McGraw-Hill, Inc., 1221 Ave. of the Americas, New York, NY 10020. Ed. Carol Roncarioli. **Indexed**: Tr.& Indus.Ind.

665.5 US
PLATT'S OILGRAM PRICE REPORT; an international daily oil-gas price and marketing letter. 1923. d. $1517 (foreign $1767). McGraw-Hill, Inc., 1221 Ave. of the Americas, New York, NY 10020. Ed. Joseph Link. (also avail. in microform from UMI)
  ●Also available online. Vendor(s): Knight-Ridder, Inc. (File no.624/McGRAW-HILL PUBLICATIONS ONLINE), Dow Jones News Retrieval (POP), Lexis-Nexis (PPRICE), NewsNet (EY75).
  Former titles: Platts Oilgram Price Service; Oilgram Price Service.

665.5 333.79 US
PLATT'S OLEFINSCAN. (Telex service) w. price varies. McGraw-Hill, Inc., 1221 Ave. of the Americas, New York, NY 10020. TEL 212-521-2000.

333.79 665.5 US
PLATT'S PETROCHEMICALSCAN. (Telex service) w. price varies. McGraw-Hill, Inc., 1221 Ave. of the Americas, New York, NY 10020. Ed. Jorge Montepque. (back issues avail.)

660 US
PLATT'S POLYMERSCAN. (Telex service) w. price varies. McGraw-Hill, Inc., 1221 Ave. of the Americas, New York, NY 10020. Ed. Ashley Seager. (back issues avail.)

665.5 333.79 US
PLATT'S PRODUCT TANKERWIRE. (Fax, telex service) d. price varies. McGraw-Hill, Inc., 1221 Ave. of the Americas, New York, NY 10020. TEL 212-521-2000.

665.7 XR ISSN 0032-1761
CODEN: PVZTAK
PLYN/GAS; manufacture, distribution and utilization of gas. (Text in Czech; summaries in English) 1950. m. $60. Czech Gas and Oil Association, Sokolska 4, 120 00 Prague 2, Czech Republic. (Dist. by: A.L.L. Production, P.O. Box 732, 111 21 Prague 1, Czech Republic) Ed. Otto Smrcek. adv.; bk.rev.; abstr.; charts; illus.; stat.; index. circ. 3,000. (also avail. in microform) **Indexed**: C.I.S. Abstr., Chem.Abstr., Fuel & Energy Abstr., Gas Abstr., Met.Abstr., World Alum.Abstr.
—CASDDS.
  Supersedes (in 1967): Paliva (ISSN 0369-8262)

553 RU
PRIRODNYI GAZ SIBIRI. 1969. irreg. Vsesoyuznyi Nauchno-Issledovatelskii Institut Prirodnykh Gazov, Tyumenskii Filial, Tyumen, Russia. illus.

665.5 FR ISSN 1148-4446
PROFILS I F P. 1989. 3/yr. free. Institut Francais du Petrole, 1 et 4 ave. de Bois Preau, B.P. 311, 92506 Rueil-Malmaison Cedex, France. TEL 47-52-60-00. FAX 47-52-70-00. TELEX 634 202 F. circ. 2,000.

PETROLEUM AND GAS

665.5   PK   ISSN 0033-0574
PROGRESS. (Text in English) 1956. m. Rs.120. Pakistan Petroleum Ltd., c/o Nusrat Nasarullah, Ed., P I D C House, Dr. Ziauddin Ahmed Rd., P.O. Box 3942, Karachi 75530, Pakistan. TEL 92-21-511338. FAX 92-21-510005. TELEX 2869 PPETK PK. bk.rev.; charts; illus.; stat. circ. 5,000. (tabloid format) Document type: newsletter.
    Description: Provides news about the activities of the company in particular, and the Pakistani oil and gas industry in general. Includes activities and achievements of the company's employees.

665.77   CN   ISSN 0033-1260
PROPANE - CANADA. 1968. 6/yr. Can.$30($35) Northern Star Communications, 1600 - 700 4 Ave. W., Calgary, AB T2P 3J4, Canada. TEL 403-263-6881. FAX 403-263-6886. Ed. Scott Jeffrey. adv.; charts; stat.; tr.lit. circ. 5,106. (processed) Indexed: Fuel & Energy Abstr., Gas Abstr. Document type: trade publication.
    —CCC.

PUBLIC UTILITIES FORTNIGHTLY. see *ENGINEERING — Electrical Engineering*

665.5   SU   ISSN 1319-0547
AL-QAFILAH (DHAHRAN)/CARAVAN (DHAHRAN).* (Text in Arabic) 1959. m. free. Saudi Arabian Oil Co., P.O. Box 5000, Dhahran 31311, Saudi Arabia. Ed. Abdullah Y. Al-Hussaini. circ. 12,500. (tabloid format)
    Formerly: Oil Caravan Weekly (ISSN 0030-1418)

QUALITY OF SERVICE REGULATION. see *ENERGY — Electrical Energy*

QUENTIN CAMERON'S OIL & GAS BULLETIN. see *BUSINESS AND ECONOMICS — Investments*

665.5   US
R G D A NEWS. 1945. m. free. Retail Gasoline and Garage Dealers Association, 3865 W. Henrietta Rd., Rochester, NY 14623-3703. TEL 716-328-3950. Ed. Diane M. Kearns. adv. circ. 1,500.
    Description: For the retail gasoline and repair shop industry in Monroe, Ontario, Wayne and Livingston counties.

622   CI
RAFINERIJSKI LIST. 1974. fortn. free. Rafinerija Nafte, Sisak, Sisak, Croatia. Ed. Bozidar Babic.

RANLIAO HUAXUE XUEBAO/JOURNAL OF FUEL CHEMISTRY AND TECHNOLOGY. see *ENGINEERING — Chemical Engineering*

665.5   UK   ISSN 0033-9822
RASSEGNA PETROLIFERA.* 1934. w. L.120000. C E S P E T R O L, c/o Arthur James Chambers, 33 The Avenue, Beckenham, Kent, England. Ed. Giuseppe Jacono. adv.; charts; illus.; mkt.; stat.; index, cum.index.

665.53   US
REFINING & GAS PROCESSISNG. a. $65. Midwest Register, Inc., 1120 E. 4th St., Tulsa, OK 74120. TEL 918-582-2000. FAX 918-587-9349. Document type: directory.
    Formerly: Refining, Construction, Petrochemical and Natural Gas Processing Plants of the World.
    Description: Supplies company name, address, phone and fax numbers, personnel, capacities and refined product, and equipment manufacturers and suppliers.

665.5   US
REPORTER (HOUSTON). bi-w. $35. Marine Reporter, 307 Ravenhead, Houston, TX 77034. TEL 713-943-8555. Ed. Freda Blizzard. circ. 10,300.

665.5   US   ISSN 0190-8715
TP690.A1
REPORTS ON RESEARCH ASSISTED BY THE PETROLEUM RESEARCH FUND. a. American Chemical Society, 1155 16th St., N.W., Washington, DC 20036. TEL 202-872-4600. FAX 202-872-4615. Document type: academic/scholarly publication.
    Formerly: American Chemical Society. Reports of Research Supported by the Petroleum Research Fund.
    Refereed Serial

662   US
RESOURCES (FORT WORTH). vol.22, 1975. 2/yr. free. Union Pacific Resources Company, Box 7, Ft. Worth, TX 76101-0007. TEL 817-737-1000. Ed. James L. Sailer. charts; illus. circ. 12,000.
    Formerly: Cycler.

665.5   US
RESULTS (HOUSTON). 1935. q. Exxon Company, U.S.A., 800 Bell St., Box 2180, Houston, TX 77252-2180. TEL 713-656-8477. FAX 713-656-9742. Ed. Sue Berniard. circ. 30,000. (back issues avail.)
    Formerly (until 1988): Oilways.
    Description: Articles about various industrial concerns, Exxon products, and general technical interest items.

338.2   US   ISSN 0270-7527
TN860
RESUME; an annual review of oil and gas activity in the United States. a. $100. Petroleum Information Corporation, Box 2612, Denver, CO 80201-2612. TEL 303-740-7100. FAX 303-694-1754. stat.
    Description: Reference for oil and gas statistics, including well drilling highlights, new field discoveries, well completions, and comparative analysis.

665.5   MX   ISSN 0188-4107
REVISTA MEXICANA DEL PETROLEO. (Includes annual special issue) (Text in English and Spanish) 1958. bi-m. $70. Ediciones y Publicaciones Petroleras, S.A. de C.V., Morelos 31 Desp. 303, 06040 Mexico D.F., Mexico. TEL 510-99-50. FAX 521-4630. Ed. Roberto Navarrete Espinosa. adv.: B&W page $1800, color page $2480; trim 8 1/4 x 11. charts; illus.; stat.; tr.lit. circ. 15,000. (back issues avail.) Indexed: Gas Abstr.
    Description: Reports on the oil, gas and petrochemical industries throughout Mexico, Central and South America.

665 622   RM   ISSN 1220-2053
         CODEN: REVMEM
REVISTA MINELOR. (Text in Rumanian; summaries in English, French, German and Russian) 1950. m. 160 lei. Ministerul Minelor Petrolului si Geologiei, Oficiul de Informare Documentara, Calea Victoriei 220, Sector 1, 71104 Bucharest, Rumania. TEL 59-79-25. adv.; bk.rev.; bibl.; charts; illus. circ. 1,500. Indexed: Bibl.& Ind.Geol., C.I.S. Abstr., Chem.Abstr., Corros.Abstr., Petrol.Abstr.
    —CASDDS.
    Formerly (until 1990): Mine, Petrol si Gaze (ISSN 0250-3115); Which was formed by the merger of: Petrol si Gaze (ISSN 1220-2037); Minerul (ISSN 1220-2045)

665 338   IT   ISSN 0035-5852
LA RIVISTA DEI COMBUSTIBILI. 1947. m. L.90000 (foreign L.100000) (effective Jan. 1993). Stazione Sperimentale per i Combustibili, Viale A. de Gasperi 3, 20097 S. Donato Milanese (Milan), Italy. TEL 02-510031. FAX 02-514286. TELEX SSC 321622. Ed. P. Cardillo. adv.: B&W page L.800000. bk.rev.; abstr.; illus.; stat.; index. circ. 1,500. (reprint service avail. from UMI) Indexed: API Catal., API Hlth.& Environ., API Oil., API Pet.Ref., API Pet.Subst., API Transport., C.I.S. Abstr., Chem.Abstr., Chem.Eng.Abstr., T.C.E.A.
    —SWETS.

ROCKY MOUNTAIN MINERAL LAW INSTITUTE. PROCEEDINGS. see *MINES AND MINING INDUSTRY*

380   US
ROCKY MOUNTAIN PETROLEUM INDUSTRY. 1945. a. $50. Midwest Register, Inc., 1120 E 4th St., Tulsa, OK 74120. TEL 918-582-2000. FAX 918-587-9349. Document type: directory.
    Formerly: Directory of Producers and Drilling Contractors: Rocky Mountain Region, Williston Basin, Four Corners New Mexico.
    Description: Supplies information on producing, drilling and well service, pipelines, refineries, gas procesing, petrochemicals, engineering, equipment, manufacturers and suppliers, company names, addresses, phone and fax numbers, and personnel for CO, NM, UT, WY, MT, MN, ID, SD, ND.

665   XO   ISSN 0035-8231
         CODEN: ROUHAY
ROPA A UHLIE. (Text in Czech or Slovak; summaries in English, French, German, Russian) 1959. m. $116. (Vyskumny Ustav pre Ropu a Uhlovodikove Plyny - Research Institute of Crude Oil and Hydrocarbon Gases) Obzor, Spitalska 35, 815 85 Bratislava, Slovakia. (Dist. by: Slovart, Gottwaldovo nam. 48, 805 32 Bratislava, Slovakia) Ed. Xeno Liebl. adv.; bk.rev.; abstr.; charts; pat.; stat.; index. circ. 2,000. Indexed: Chem.Abstr., Gas Abstr., Met.Abstr., Ref.Zh., World Alum.Abstr.
    —BLDSC (8023.400000); CASDDS.

665.5   CN   ISSN 0048-864X
         CODEN: ROUGEZ
ROUGHNECK MAGAZINE. 1952. m. Can.$31. Roughneck Publications Ltd., 700 Fourth Ave.,S.W., Ste. 1600, Calgary, AB T2P 3J4, Canada. TEL 403-263-6881. FAX 403-263-6886. Ed. Scott Jeffrey. adv.: B&W page $1385; trim 5 1/4 x 7 1/4; adv. contact: Jim Graham. bk.rev. circ. 6,000. Document type: trade publication.
    Description: Serves the complete upstream sector of the North American oil and gas industry, including drilling, completions, re-entries, workovers, exploration and production.

665.5   UK
ROUSTABOUT. 1972. m. £50 (foreign £55). Roustabout Publications Ltd., Suite 5, International Base, Greenwell Rd., E. Tullos, Aberdeen AB1 4AX, Scotland. TEL 01224-876582. FAX 01224-879757. Ed. Ann Duguid; Pub. Dennis Davidson. adv.: B&W page £880, color page £1410; trim 225 x 170. circ. 10,000. Document type: trade publication.

665.5 621   UK
S E N CONFERENCE PROCEEDINGS. (Subsea Engineering News) 1989. irreg., no.10, 1994. £65. Knighton Enterprises Ltd., 2 Marlborough St., Faringdon, Oxon. SN7 7JP, England. TEL 01367-242525. FAX 01367-241125. Document type: proceedings.

665.5   US   ISSN 1076-0148
S P E ADVANCED TECHNOLOGY SERIES. 1993. irreg. $30.50 to non-members (foreign $32); members $15.50 (foreign $17). Society of Petroleum Engineers, Box 833836, Richardson, TX 75083-3836. TEL 214-952-9393; 800-456-6863. FAX 214-952-9435. TELEX 163245 SPEUT. Document type: monographic series.

665.5   US   ISSN 1064-6671
TN871.2   CODEN: SDCOE5
S P E DRILLING & COMPLETION. 1986. q. $60 to non-members; members $20. Society of Petroleum Engineers, Inc., Box 833836, Richardson, TX 75083-3836. TEL 214-952-9393. FAX 214-952-9435. TELEX 163245 SPEUT. Ed. Georgeann Bilich. adv.: B&W page $1750, color page $2745; adv. contact: Doris Tolman. index; circ. 4,944 (paid). (back issues avail.) Indexed: A.S.& T.Ind., AESIS, Eng.Ind. Document type: trade publication.
    —BLDSC (8361.840900); Ei; Faxon; PADDS; SWETS; UMI; UnCover. CCC.
    Formerly (until 1993): S P E Drilling Engineering (ISSN 0885-9744)
    Refereed Serial

665.5   US   ISSN 0885-923X
TN871.35   CODEN: SFEVEG
S P E FORMATION EVALUATION. 1986. q. $60 to non-members; members $20. Society of Petroleum Engineers, Inc., Box 833836, Richardson, TX 75083-3836. TEL 214-952-9393. FAX 214-952-9435. TELEX 163245 SPEUT. adv.: B&W page $1750, color page $2745; trim 8 1/8 x 10 7/8; adv. contact: Doris Tolman. index; circ. 4,065 (paid). (back issues avail.) Indexed: A.S.& T.Ind., AESIS, Eng.Ind. Document type: trade publication.
    —BLDSC (8361.842000); CASDDS; Ei; Faxon; Genuine Article; PADDS; SWETS; UMI; UnCover. CCC.
    Refereed Serial

PETROLEUM AND GAS

665.5 US ISSN 1064-668X
TN870 CODEN: SPRFEZ
S P E PRODUCTION & FACILITIES. 1986. q. $60 to non-members; members $20. Society of Petroleum Engineers, Inc., Box 833836, Richardson, TX 75080. TEL 214-952-9393. FAX 214-952-9435. TELEX 163245 SPEUT. Ed. Georgeann Bilich. adv.: B&W page $1750, color page $2745; trim 8 1/4 x 10 7/8; adv. contact: Doris Tolman. index; circ. 5,301 (paid). (back issues avail.) **Indexed:** A.S.& T.Ind., AESIS, Eng.Ind. **Document type:** trade publication.
—BLDSC (8361.862900); CASDDS; Ei; Faxon; PADDS; SWETS; UMI; UnCover. **CCC.**
Formerly (until 1993): S P E Production Engineering (ISSN 0885-9221)
Description: Discusses the technical and professional aspects of oil production methods and facilities.
Refereed Serial

665.5 US ISSN 0885-9248
TN871 CODEN: SREEEF
S P E RESERVOIR ENGINEERING. 1986. q. $60 to non-members; members $20. Society of Petroleum Engineers, Inc., Box 833836, Richardson, TX 75083-3836. TEL 214-952-9393. FAX 214-952-9435. TELEX 163245 SPEUT. adv.: B&W page $1750, color page $2745; trim 8 1/4 x 10 7/8. index; circ. 4,816 (paid). (back issues avail.) **Indexed:** A.S.& T.Ind., AESIS, Eng.Ind. **Document type:** academic/scholarly publication, trade publication.
—BLDSC (8361.866000); CASDDS; Ei; Faxon; Genuine Article; PADDS; SWETS; UMI; UnCover. **CCC.**
Refereed Serial

665.5 UK
S P E REVIEW. 1989. m. membership. (Society of Petroleum Engineers) McQuillan Young Communications, 211 Piccadilly, London W1V 9LD, England. TEL 0171-917-2731. FAX 0171-917-2734. (Dist. by: Mailbird, 11 Roslin Sq., Roslin Rd., London W3 8DH, England. TEL 0181-993-6116) Ed. Tricia Young. adv.: page £795; trim 264 x 184; adv. contact: Tricia Young. circ. 4,000. (back issues avail.) **Document type:** newsletter.

665.5 BX
SALAM. (Text in English, Malay) 1953. m. free to employees. Brunei Shell Petroleum Co Sdn Bhd, Seria 7082, Brunei Darussalam. TEL 037-8624. FAX 037-4190. Ed. Molly McDaniel. circ. 9,000. **Document type:** trade publication.

SASKATCHEWAN ENERGY & MINES. ANNUAL REPORT. see *MINES AND MINING INDUSTRY*

SASKATCHEWAN ENERGY & MINES. MINERAL STATISTICS YEARBOOK. see *MINES AND MINING INDUSTRY*

665.5 CN ISSN 0228-5622
SASKATCHEWAN ENERGY & MINES. MONTHLY OIL AND GAS PRODUCTION REPORT. m. Can.$150. Saskatchewan Energy & Mines, 1914 Hamilton St., Regina, SK S4P 4V4, Canada. TEL 306-787-2528. FAX 306-787-2527. **Document type:** government publication.
Description: Lists by production and disposition areas the monthly production of oil, gas and water for units and pools.

553 665 CN ISSN 0707-2562
TN873.C22
SASKATCHEWAN ENERGY & MINES. RESERVOIR ANNUAL. 1963. a. Can.$70. Saskatchewan Energy & Mines, Petroleum and Natural Gas Branch, 1914 Hamilton St., Regina, SK S4P 4V4, Canada. TEL 306-787-2528. FAX 306-787-2527. **Document type:** government publication.
Former titles: Saskatchewan Energy and Mines. Petroleum and Natural Gas Reservoir Annual (ISSN 0704-5743); Saskatchewan Mineral Resources. Petroleum and Natural Gas Reservoir Annual; Saskatchewan. Department of Mineral Resources. Petroleum and Natural Gas Reservoir Annual.
Description: Contains oil and gas reserves data, development and production data, information concerning enhanced recovery projects and related reservoir information.

665 628.1 CN ISSN 1192-1021
SASKATCHEWAN HORIZONTAL WELL PRODUCTION REPORT. q. Can.$200. Saskatchewan Energy and Mines, 1914 Hamilton St., Regina, SK S4P 4V4, Canada. TEL 306-787-2528. FAX 306-787-2527. (diskette format)
Description: Summarizes horizontal well production by pool, by area and by province. Production information includes monthly and cumulative oil, gas and water production, daily oil rates, gas-oil and water-oil ratios and oilcuts.

665 628.1 CN ISSN 1182-9125
SASKATCHEWAN HORIZONTAL WELL SUMMARY. 1990. m. Can.$150. Saskatchewan Energy and Mines, 1914 Hamilton St., Regina, SK S4P 4V4, Canada. TEL 306-787-2528. FAX 306-787-2527. **Document type:** government publication.
Description: Lists all horizontal wells produced, abandoned, drilled, licensed and approved in Saskatchewan. Each well is listed by name, legal description, operator, approval date, spud date, finished drilling date, productive horizontal length, pool and first producing date.

665.5 NO ISSN 0332-5334
SCANDINAVIAN OIL - GAS MAGAZINE. (Text in English) 1973. bi-m. NOK 700. Scandinavian Oil-Gas Publishing, P.O. Box 6865, St. Olavs Plass, N-0130 Oslo, Norway. TEL 47-22-44-72-70. FAX 47-22-44-72-87. TELEX 72737 SCAND N. Ed.Bd. adv.: B&W page NOK 1400, color page NOK 18000; trim 178 x 252; adv. contact: Rolf Skoog. bk.rev. circ. 12,800. **Indexed:** Petrol.Abstr.
—BLDSC (8087.569700); PADDS. **CCC.**

SEDIMENTARY BASINS OF THE WORLD. see *EARTH SCIENCES*

550 665 NE ISSN 0921-0911
SEDIMENTOLOGY AND PETROLEUM GEOLOGY. (Text in English) 1986. irreg. price varies. Kluwer Academic Publishers, Postbus 17, 3300 AA Dordrecht, Netherlands. TEL 31-78-392392. FAX 31-78-392254. TELEX 29245 KAPG NL. (Dist. by: Kluwer Academic Publishers Group, P.O. Box 322, 3300 AH Dordrecht, Netherlands. TEL 31-78-392392. FAX 31-78-546474; N. America dist. addr.: Box 358, Accord Sta., Hingham, MA 02018-0358. TEL 617-871-6600. FAX 617-871-6528) **Indexed:** INSPEC. **Document type:** monographic series.
Refereed Serial

550 II
SEMINAR ON PETROLIFEROUS BASINS OF INDIA. PROCEEDINGS. a. $450. (KDM Institute of Petroleum Exploration, Oil and Natural Gas Commission) Indian Petroleum Publishers, 100-9 Naishville Rd., Dehra Dun 248001, India. Ed. S.K. Biswas. **Document type:** proceedings.

665.5 US
SEVENTY SIX. 1921. m. free. Unocal Corporation, Box 7600, Los Angeles, CA 90051. TEL 213-977-6814. Ed. Art Bentley. circ. 16,000 (controlled). **Indexed:** Energy Info.Abstr. **Document type:** newsletter.

SHANXI DAXUE XUEBAO (SHEHUI KEXUE BAN)/SHANXI UNIVERSITY. JOURNAL (SOCIAL SCIENCE EDITION). see *SOCIAL SCIENCES: COMPREHENSIVE WORKS*

665.5 NE
SHELL-POST. (Text in Dutch; summaries in English) 1959. fortn. free. Shell Nederland B.V., Carel van Bylandtlaan 30, 2596 HR The Hague, Netherlands. Eds. Hanneke Foppes, Samalina Hoorn. bk.rev.; illus. circ. 8,100. (tabloid format)
Formerly: Koninklijke Shell-Post (ISSN 0023-3390)

665.5 NE
SHELL-VENSTER. 1917. bi-m. free. Shell Nederland B.V., Dept. PAC/1, Hofplein 20, Rotterdam, Netherlands. Ed. P. de Wit. bk.rev.; charts; illus.; stat.; index; circ. 51,000 (controlled).
Formerly: Olie (ISSN 0030-2112)

665.5 UK
SHIELD. 1924. 4/yr. free to qualified personnel. British Petroleum Company plc., Britannic House, 1 Finsbury Circus, London EC2M 7BA, England. FAX 071-496-4528. (U.S. dist.: BP America Inc., 200 Public Sq., Cleveland, Ohio 44114-2373) Ed. Valerie Shepard. charts; illus. circ. 100,000. **Indexed:** Fluidex, Geo.Abstr. **Document type:** corporate report.
Former titles: B P Shield; B P Shield International (ISSN 0045-1274)
Description: Covers business issues relating to activities of the BP group throughout the world.

665.6 500 CC ISSN 1000-5870
CODEN: SDXZE7
SHIYOU DAXUE XUEBAO (ZIRAN KEXUE BAN)/UNIVERSITY OF PETROLEUM, CHINA. JOURNAL (NATURAL SCIENCE EDITION). (Text in Chinese; table of contents in English) 1959. bi-m. Y24 (foreign $20). Shiyou Daxue, Xuebao Bianjibu, Dongying, Shandong 257062, People's Republic of China. (Dist. overseas by: China Educational Publications Import & Export Corp., No.15, Xueyuan Lu, Beijing, P.R. China) Ed. Li Lanzhi. **Document type:** academic/scholarly publication.
—BLDSC (4911.950000); CASDDS; Ei; PADDS.

SHIYOU DILI WULI KANTAN/OIL GEOPHYSICAL PROSPECTING. see *EARTH SCIENCES — Geology*

665.5 CC ISSN 1001-2206
SHIYOU GONGCHENG JIANSHE/PETROLEUM ENGINEERING CONSTRUCTION. (Text in Chinese) 1975. bi-m. $3.90 per no. Zhongguo Shiyou Tianranqi Zong Gongsi, Gongcheng Jishu Yanjiusuo - China National Petroleum Corporation, Engineering Technology Research Institute, No.40, Jin-Tang Gonglu, Tanggu Qu, Tianjin 300451, People's Republic of China. TEL 5343589. FAX 022-5344876. (Dist. outside China by: Guoji Shudian - China International Book Trading Corp., P.O. Box 399, Beijing, P.R.C.) Ed. Meng Qingfu. adv. contact: Yan Yiming. circ. 8,000. **Document type:** academic/scholarly publication.
Description: Covers the engineering constructions and technical improvements of oil and gas fields, oil and gas pepelines, oil refineries, chemical plants, and fertilizer plants.

665.5 CC ISSN 1000-8144
TP692.3 CODEN: SHHUE8
SHIYOU HUAGONG/PETROCHEMICAL TECHNOLOGY. (Text in Chinese) 1970. m. $60. Ministry of Chemical Industry, Beijing Research Institute of Chemical Industry - Huaxue Gongye Bu, Beijing Huagong Yanjiuyuan, P.O. Box 1442, Hepingli, Beijing, People's Republic of China. TEL 4216131. FAX 4228661. (Co-sponsor: Chemical Industry & Engineering Society of China, Institute of Petrochemicals) Ed. Jiang Xuequan. adv. circ. 9,500. **Document type:** academic/scholarly publication.
—BLDSC (6430.395000); CASDDS; Ei.
Description: Publishes scientific research papers, technical reports, and reviews on the petrochemical and organic chemical industries.

665.5 CC ISSN 1000-0747
TN870.5 CODEN: SKYKEG
SHIYOU KANTAN YU KAIFA/PETROLEUM EXPLORATION AND DEVELOPMENT. (Text in Chinese) 1974. bi-m. $1.30 per no. Guoji Shudian, Qikan Bu - China International Book Trading Corp., P.O. Box 399, Beijing 100044, People's Republic of China.
—BLDSC (6433.130000); CASDDS.

SHIYOU KUANGCHANG JIXIE/OIL FIELD EQUIPMENT. see *MACHINERY*

665.5 CC ISSN 1000-1441
SHIYOU WUTAN/GEOPHYSICAL PROSPECTING FOR PETROLEUM. (Text in Chinese) 1979. q. $60. Dizhi Kuangchan-bu, Shiyou Wutan Yanjiusuo, 21 Weigang, Nanjing, Jiangsu 210014, People's Republic of China. TEL 86-25-4432191. FAX 86-25-4432005. (Dist. overseas by: China International Book Trading Corp., P.O. Box 399, Beijing, P.R. China) Ed. Zhu Xuan. adv. contact: Gao Lin. circ. 2,500. **Document type:** academic/scholarly publication.
—BLDSC (4156.100000); PADDS.
Description: Covers the technological developments and their applications in geophysical prospecting for petroleum.

PETROLEUM AND GAS

665.5   CC   ISSN 0253-2697
TN860   CODEN: SYHPD9
SHIYOU XUEBAO/ACTA PETROLEI SINICA. (Text in Chinese) 1980. q. $3.80 per no. Guoji Shudian, Qikan Bu - China International Book Trading Corp., P.O. Box 399, Beijing 100044, People's Republic of China. **Indexed:** Bibl.& Ind.Geol., Chem.Abstr, Fluidex, Petrol.Abstr.
—BLDSC (0644.500000); CASDDS; PADDS.

665.5   FR
SOCIETE NATIONALE E L F AQUITAINE. RAPPORT ANNUEL. a. free. E L F - Aquitaine, Direction des Relations Publiques et de la Communication, Tour ELF, Cedex 45, 92078 Paris La Defense, France. charts; illus.; stat.

665.5 622   US
SOCIETY OF PETROLEUM ENGINEERS. REPRINT SERIES. 1958. irreg. price varies. Society of Petroleum Engineers, Inc., Box 833836, Richardson, TX 75083-3836. TEL 214-952-9393. FAX 214-952-9435. TELEX 163245 SPEUT. Ed. G. Bilich. **Indexed:** Eng.Ind., Ocean.Abstr. **Document type:** academic/scholarly publication.
  Formerly: Society of Petroleum Engineers of American Institute of Mining, Metallurgical and Petroleum Engineers. Petroleum Transactions Reprint Series (ISSN 0081-1688)
  Description: Anthologies of classic and important recent technical reports on broad oil and gas drilling, exploration and production topics.
  Refereed Serial

665.5   US   ISSN 0081-1696
TN1   CODEN: TPTEAF
SOCIETY OF PETROLEUM ENGINEERS. TRANSACTIONS. 1925. a. $90 to non-members. Society of Petroleum Engineers, Inc., Box 833836, Richardson, TX 75083-3836. TEL 214-952-9393. FAX 214-952-9435. TELEX 163245 SPEUT. Ed. Georgeann Bilich. charts; illus.; index; circ. 2,900 (paid). (back issues avail.) **Indexed:** Bibl.& Ind.Geol., Chem.Abstr., Eng.Ind., Gas Abstr., Petrol.Abstr. **Document type:** proceedings, trade publication.
—BLDSC (9008.700000).
  Formerly: Society of Petroleum Engineers of American Institute of Mining, Metallurgical and Petroleum Engineers. Transactions.
  Description: Selects technical reports from five S.P.E. journals.
  Refereed Serial

622.338   US   ISSN 0081-1718
TN871.35   CODEN: SPWLA6
SOCIETY OF PROFESSIONAL WELL LOG ANALYSTS. S P W L A ANNUAL LOGGING SYMPOSIUM TRANSACTIONS. 1960. a. price varies. Society of Professional Well Log Analysts, 8866 Gulf Fwy., Ste. 320, Houston, TX 77017. TEL 713-947-8727. FAX 713-947-7181. adv.; bibl.; charts; illus. circ. 2,500. **Indexed:** GeoRef., Petrol.Abstr. **Document type:** proceedings.

665.773   US   ISSN 0038-1500
SOONER L P G TIMES. 1963. m. free. Oklahoma LP-Gas Association, 4200 N. Lindsay, Oklahoma City, OK 73105. TEL 405-424-1775. Ed. Kurt S. Winden. adv.; bk.rev.; charts; illus.; stat. circ. 1,450. (processed)

665.5   US
SOUTH DAKOTA INDEPENDENT OIL JOBBER. m. 221 S. Central, Box 1058, Pierre, SD 57501. TEL 605-224-8606. Ed. Richard Trippler. circ. 1,000.

665.5   US
SOUTH DAKOTA PETROLEUM MARKETER. m. Box 1058, Pierre, SD 57501-1058. TEL 605-224-8606. Ed. Dawna Leitzke Osborne; Pub. Dawna Leitzke Osborne. circ. 500. **Document type:** newsletter.

665.538   US
SOUTH LOUISIANA DRILLING REPORT. 1984. w. $400. Offshore Data Services, Inc., Box 19909, Houston, TX 77224-1909. TEL 713-781-2713. FAX 713-781-9594. **Document type:** abstracting/indexing.
  Formerly: South Louisiana Land Report.
  Description: Covers drilling activity in Louisiana below the 31st parallel.

SOUTH - EAST ASIA MINING, OIL & GAS NEWSLETTER. see MINES AND MINING INDUSTRY

380   US
SOUTHEAST PETROLEUM INDUSTRY. 1945. a. $50. Midwest Register, Inc., 1120 E. 4th St., Tulsa, OK 74120. TEL 918-582-2000. FAX 918-587-934. **Document type:** directory.
  Formerly: Directory of Producers and Drilling Contractors Southeast: Louisiana, Arkansas, Florida, Georgia.
  Description: Supplies company name, address, personnel, division offices, offshore operations, producer of oil or gas and if drilling contractor with rotary or cable tools, pipelines, refineries, petrochemical, gas processing, equipment manufacturers and suppliers, engineers.

665.5   US
SOUTHEASTERN OIL REVIEW. 1926. w. $30. Oil Review Publishing Co., Box 145, Jackson, MS 39205. TEL 601-353-6213. Ed. J. Ishee. adv. circ. 3,200.
  Description: Covers oil and gas exploration and devlopment, drilling and production activities in the Southeastern States.

665.5   SP
SPAIN. MINISTERIO DE ECONOMIA Y HACIENDA, DELEGACION DEL GOBIERNO EN CAMPSA. EL PETROLEO EN LA C E E. (Comunidad Economica Europea) (Supplement to: Memoria) 1986. a. free. Ministerio de Economia y Hacienda, Delegacion del Gobierno en Campsa, Capitan Haya, 41, 28020 Madrid, Spain. TEL 582-5206. FAX 5561819.

665.5   SP
SPAIN. MINISTERIO DE ECONOMIA Y HACIENDA. DELEGACION DEL GOBIERNO EN CAMPSA. MEMORIA. 1969. a. free. Ministerio de Economia y Hacienda, Delegacion del Gobierno en Campsa, Capitan Haya, 41, 28020 Madrid, Spain. TEL 582.52.06. Ed. J.A. Entrent. illus. circ. 2,000.
  Description: Provides information on the petroleum industry and trade.

SPILL SCIENCE & TECHNOLOGY BULLETIN; oils - chemicals - land - marine. see ENVIRONMENTAL STUDIES — Pollution

665.5   IT
STAFFETA QUOTIDIANA PETROLIFERA; e delle altre fonti di energia. 1933. d. L.180000. Rivista Italiana Petrolio s.r.l., Via Aventina 19, 00153 Rome, Italy. TEL 06-5754818. FAX 06-57554906. TELEX 611674 RIVPE. Ed. Marina Cozzi.

STATIONS - SERVICES ACTUALITES. see TRANSPORTATION — Automobiles

STEAM - ELECTRIC PLANT FACTORS (YEAR). see MINES AND MINING INDUSTRY

STEELMAKING CONFERENCE: PROCEEDINGS. see METALLURGY

665 338.47   RU   ISSN 0039-2448
         CODEN: STTRA3
STROITEL'STVO TRUBOPROVODOV. 1956. bi-m. $75 (effective 1996). Izdatel'stvo Nedra, Pl. Belorusskogo Vokzala, 3, 125047 Moscow, Russia. TEL 250-52-55. bk.rev.; charts; illus.; index. **Indexed:** Chem.Abstr, Gas Abstr., Geotech.Abstr.
—CASDDS. CCC.
  Description: Covers the pipe-line construction industry.

665.5   UK   ISSN 0266-2205
SUBSEA ENGINEERING NEWS; including pipeline and floater update. 1984. s-m. £215 in U.K.; Europe £225; elsewhere £240. Knighton Enterprises Ltd., 2 Marlborough St., Faringdon, Oxon SN7 7JP, England. TEL 01367-242525. FAX 01367-241125. Ed. Steven Sasanow. adv.; bk.rev. circ. 350. (back issues avail.) **Indexed:** Petrol.Abstr. **Document type:** newsletter.
  Former titles: S E N Incorporating Oil and Gas Pipeline News; O G P N.
  Description: Covers market information and technical details on subsea and underwater engineering, pipelines, floating production systems, offshore business news and government policy.

665.5 621   UK   ISSN 0962-6085
SUBSEA PRODUCTION YEARBOOK. 1991. a. £110. Knighton Enterprises Ltd., 2 Marlborough St., Faringdon, Oxon SN7 7JP, England. TEL 01367-242525. FAX 01367-241125. Ed. Steve Sasanow. adv. contact: Steve Sasanow. **Document type:** directory.

338.4 665.5   US
SUPPLY, DISTRIBUTION, MANUFACTURING & SERVICE; supply and service companies & equipment manufacturers. a. $65. Midwest Register, Inc., 1120 E. 4th St., Tulsa, OK 74120. TEL 918-582-2000. FAX 918-587-9349. **Document type:** directory.
  Former titles: Supply and Distribution; Oil Well Supply Industry; Directory of Oil Well Supply Companies (ISSN 0415-9772)
  Description: Supplies company name, address, phone and fax number, and personnel information.

338.2 665   US   ISSN 0039-8403
HD9567.T3
T I P R O REPORTER. 1948. a. $10 to non-members. Texas Independent Producers & Royalty Owners Association, 515 Congress Ave., Ste. 1910, Austin, TX 78701. TEL 512-477-4452. FAX 512-476-8070. E-mail: christy.coventry@tipro.org. Ed. Christy O. Coventry. adv. contact: Christy O. Coventry. circ. 4,000 (paid). (back issues avail.) **Document type:** trade publication.

338.2 665   US
T I P R O TARGET NEWSLETTER. irreg. (approx. every 6 wks.). $5 to non-members. Texas Independent Producers & Royalty Owners Association, 515 Congress Ave., Ste. 1910, Austin, TX 78701. TEL 512-477-4452. FAX 512-476-8070. E-mail: christy.coventry@tipro.org. Ed. Christy O. Coventry. circ. 4,000 (paid). **Document type:** newsletter.
  Description: Reports on industry-related topics, with emphasis on government legislation and rulings.

665.5   UK   ISSN 0958-8787
TANKER CHARTER RECORD. 12/yr. Basil Blackwell Ltd., 108 Cowley Rd., Oxford OX4 1JF, England. TEL 0865-791100. FAX 0865-791347. TELEX 837022-OXBOOK-G.
—UMI. CCC.

665.5 333.79   UK   ISSN 1351-301X
▼**TANKER NEWS.** 1994. m. £350($575) (effective 1994). Basil Blackwell Ltd., 108 Cowley Rd., Oxford OX4 1JF, England. TEL 44-865-791100. FAX 44-865-791347.
—UMI. CCC.

665.5   TS
AL-TAWZI/DISTRIBUTION. (Text in Arabic) 1984. m. free. Abu Dhabi National Oil Company, Distribution Division - Sharikat Bitrul Abu Dhabi al-Wataniyyah lil-Tawzi', P.O. Box 4188, Abu Dhabi, United Arab Emirates. TEL 771300. TELEX 22358 FUDIST EM. Ed. Abdullah Majid al-Mansouri. circ. 1,000.
  Description: News of company activities.

665.7 333.8   JA
TENNEN GASU KANKEI SHIRYO/NATURAL GAS RESOURCES. (Text in Japanese) a. Sekiyu Kodan - Japan National Oil Corp., 2-2, Uchisaiwaicho 2-chome, Chiyoda-ku, Tokyo 100, Japan.

665.538   US
TEXAS. RAILROAD COMMISSION. OIL AND GAS DIVISION. ANNUAL REPORT. a. $16. Railroad Commission, Oil and Gas Publications, Drawer 12967, Capitol Sta., Austin, TX 78711. TEL 512-463-7255. charts; stat. (also avail. in microfiche; back issues avail.) **Document type:** government publication.
  Description: Includes oil and gas production by field, arranged by district and by field name. Lists county, discovery date, depth, and total wells for each field. Provides total production figures for gas and crude oil.

665.5   US
TEXAS. RAILROAD COMMISSION. OIL AND GAS DIVISION. CRUDE OIL AND GAS NOMINATIONS. (Subseries of: Statewide Oil and Gas Stocks and Nominations) m. $28. Railroad Commission, Oil and Gas Publications, Drawer 12967, Capitol Sta., Austin, TX 78711. TEL 512-463-7255. charts; stat. **Document type:** government publication.
  Formerly: Texas. Railroad Commission. Oil and Gas Division. Recapitulation of Crude Oil Nominations and Purchases by Company.
  Description: Gives volumes of crude oil nominated for purchase for the following month and the previous month in district and company totals.

PETROLEUM AND GAS

665.5 US
TEXAS. RAILROAD COMMISSION. OIL AND GAS DIVISION. CRUDE OIL NOMINATIONS AND PURCHASES. m. $32. Railroad Commission, Oil and Gas Publications, Drawer 12967, Capitol Sta., Austin, TX 78711. TEL 512-463-7255. charts; stat. **Document type:** government publication.
Formerly: Texas. Railroad Commission. Oil and Gas Division. Summary of Crude Oil Nominations and Purchases by District.
Description: Gives monthly crude oil nominations and purchases by district and totals for each company.

665.5 US
TEXAS. RAILROAD COMMISSION. OIL AND GAS DIVISION. DRILLING PERMIT INDEX. w. and m. issues. $209 for w. ed.; m. ed. $37. Railroad Commission, Oil and Gas Publications, Drawer 12967, Capitol Sta., Austin, TX 78711. TEL 512-463-7255. (microfiche) **Document type:** government publication.
Description: Lists all permits issued by district and by county, showing operator name and ID number, lease name, well number, API number, and permit date and number.

665.5 US
TEXAS. RAILROAD COMMISSION. OIL AND GAS DIVISION. GAS LEASE INDEX. m. Railroad Commission, Oil and Gas Publications, Drawer 12967, Capitol Sta., Austin, TX 78711. TEL 512-463-7255. (microfiche) **Document type:** government publication.
Description: Lists all leases on the gas proration schedule alphabetically within each district and gives field, operator, and gas well ID number.

665.5 US
TEXAS. RAILROAD COMMISSION. OIL AND GAS DIVISION. GAS PRODUCTION LEDGER. (Avail. by RRC district) m. $241 for all 12 parts (prices for individual parts vary). Railroad Commission, Oil and Gas Publications, Drawer 12967, Capitol Sta., Austin, TX 78711. TEL 512-463-7255. charts. (microfiche) **Document type:** government publication.
Description: Gives production, allowable, and production status by field, operator, and well.

665.538 US
TEXAS. RAILROAD COMMISSION. OIL AND GAS DIVISION. GAS PRORATION SCHEDULE. (Avail. by RRC district) s-a. $202 for all 12 parts; microfiche ed. $143 (prices for individual parts vary). Railroad Commission, Oil and Gas Publications, Drawer 12967, Capitol Sta., Austin, TX 78711. TEL 512-463-7255. **Document type:** government publication.
Description: Compiles monthly allowables by well and field.

665.5 US
TEXAS. RAILROAD COMMISSION. OIL AND GAS DIVISION. GAS PURCHASER. m. $135. Railroad Commission, Oil and Gas Publications, Drawer 12967, Capitol Sta., Austin, TX 78711. TEL 512-463-7255. (microfiche) **Document type:** government publication.
Description: Lists gas purchasers alphabetically; for each operator, lists oil leases or gas wells in numerical sequence within district and field. Shows percentage of authorized take for each lease.

665.5 US
TEXAS. RAILROAD COMMISSION. OIL AND GAS DIVISION. GATHERER STRIPOUT. m. $117. Railroad Commission, Oil and Gas Publications, Drawer 12967, Capitol Sta., Austin, TX 78711. TEL 512-463-7255. charts. (microfiche) **Document type:** government publication.
Description: Gives the proration schedule by gatherer; shows district, field name, operator name, lease or ID number, and monthly allowables.

665.5 US
TEXAS. RAILROAD COMMISSION. OIL AND GAS DIVISION. NOTICES OF HEARINGS AND ORDERS. (Avail. by RRC district) w. $533 for all 12 parts (prices for individual parts vary). Railroad Commission, Oil and Gas Publications, Drawer 12967, Capitol Sta., Austin, TX 78711. TEL 512-463-7255. **Document type:** government publication.
Description: Publishes all orders signed by the Railroad Commission and notices of hearings for all proceedings of the Oil and Gas Division.

665.5 US
TEXAS. RAILROAD COMMISSION. OIL AND GAS DIVISION. OIL AND GAS FIELD NAMES. m. $45. Railroad Commission, Oil and Gas Publications, Drawer 12967, Capitol Sta., Austin, TX 78711. TEL 512-463-7255. (microfiche) **Document type:** government publication.
Description: Publishes all names on the Railroad Commission master field list, both active and inactive, showing district, field number, whether oil or gas, and county.

665.5 US
TEXAS. RAILROAD COMMISSION. OIL AND GAS DIVISION. OIL AND GAS NOTICES AND FORMS. m. $12. Railroad Commission, Oil and Gas Publications, Drawer 12967, Capitol Sta., Austin, TX 78711. TEL 512-463-7255. **Document type:** government publication.
Description: Contains notices of procedure changes, requirements, new and revised forms, information on publications, and bulletins of forthcoming seminars of interest.

665.5 US
TEXAS. RAILROAD COMMISSION. OIL AND GAS DIVISION. OIL LEASE INDEX. m. $83. Railroad Commission, Oil and Gas Publications, Drawer 12967, Capitol Sta., Austin, TX 78711. TEL 512-463-7255. (microfiche) **Document type:** government publication.
Description: Lists all leases on the oil proration schedule alphabetically within each district and gives field, operator, and lease number.

665.5 US
TEXAS. RAILROAD COMMISSION. OIL AND GAS DIVISION. OIL LEASES AND GAS WELLS BY DISTRICT AND OPERATOR. m. $113. Railroad Commission, Oil and Gas Publications, Drawer 12967, Capitol Sta., Austin, TX 78711. TEL 512-463-7255. (microfiche) **Document type:** government publication.
Description: Lists operators within each district and shows their oil leases and gas wells, lease or gas ID number, field name and number, and county name and number.

665.5 US
TEXAS. RAILROAD COMMISSION. OIL AND GAS DIVISION. OIL PRODUCTION LEDGER. (Avail. by RRC district) a. $225 for all 12 parts (prices for individual parts vary). Railroad Commission, Oil and Gas Publications, Drawer 12967, Capitol Sta., Austin, TX 78711. TEL 512-463-7255. charts. (microfiche) **Document type:** government publication.
Description: Gives production status by field, operator, and lease.

665.538 US
TEXAS. RAILROAD COMMISSION. OIL AND GAS DIVISION. OIL PRORATION SCHEDULE. (Avail. by RRC district) s-a. $292 for all 12 parts; microfiche ed. $218 (prices for individual parts vary). Railroad Commission, Oil and Gas Publications, Drawer 12967, Capitol Sta., Austin, TX 78711. TEL 512-463-7255. (also avail. in microfiche) **Document type:** government publication.
Description: Compiles monthly allowables listed by well and field.

665.5 US
TEXAS. RAILROAD COMMISSION. OIL AND GAS DIVISION. OPERATOR STRIPOUT. m. $300. Railroad Commission, Oil and Gas Publications, Drawer 12967, Capitol Sta., Austin, TX 78711. TEL 512-463-7255. charts. (microfiche) **Document type:** government publication.
Description: Gives the proration schedule by operator; shows district, field name, operator name, lease or ID number, and monthly allowables.

665.5 US
TEXAS. RAILROAD COMMISSION. OIL AND GAS DIVISION. P-5 ORGANIZATION DIRECTORY. m. $307. Railroad Commission, Oil and Gas Publications, Drawer 12967, Capitol Sta., Austin, TX 78711. TEL 512-463-7255. (microfiche) **Document type:** government publication, directory.
Description: Lists all companies or individuals who have filed an organization report, including operator number, whether active or inactive, address, phone number, company officers, activity by district, and specialty codes.

665.538 US
TEXAS. RAILROAD COMMISSION. OIL AND GAS DIVISION. PRORATED GAS FIELDS - MONTHLY SCHEDULE. (Avail. by RRC district) m. $241 for all 12 parts (prices for individual parts vary). Railroad Commission, Oil and Gas Publications, Drawer 12967, Capitol Sta., Austin, TX 78711. TEL 512-463-7255. **Document type:** government publication.
Formerly: Texas. Railroad Commission. Oil and Gas Division. Gas Monthly Proration Schedule.
Description: Lists monthly allowables for gas fields produced under special field rules.

665.5 US
TEXAS. RAILROAD COMMISSION. OIL AND GAS DIVISION. PURCHASER STRIPOUT. m. $135. Railroad Commission, Oil and Gas Publications, Drawer 12967, Capitol Sta., Austin, TX 78711. TEL 512-463-7255. charts. (microfiche) **Document type:** government publication.
Description: Gives the proration schedule by purchaser; shows district, field name, purchaser name, purchaser systems, lease or ID number, system deliverability, and allowables.

TEXAS LAW OF OIL AND GAS. see *LAW*

TEXAS NATURAL RESOURCES REPORTER. see *WATER RESOURCES*

662.338 US ISSN 0896-8969
TEXAS OIL MARKETER. 1951. q. $20. Texas Oil Marketers Association, 701 W. 15th St., Austin, TX 78701. TEL 512-476-9547. FAX 512-477-4239. E-mail: lockhart@toma.com. Ed. Cheryl Lockhart. adv.: B&W page $720; trim 8 1/2 x 11. illus.; circ. 1,300 (controlled). **Document type:** trade publication.
Formerly: Texas Oil Jobber (ISSN 0040-4527)
Description: Directed to Texas petroleum marketers, and convenience store owners and operators.

380 US
TEXAS PETROLEUM INDUSTRY. 1945. a. $65. Midwest Register, Inc., 1120 E. 4th St., Tulsa, OK 74120. TEL 918-582-2000. FAX 918-587-9349. **Document type:** directory.
Formerly: Directory of Producers and Drilling Contractors: Texas.
Description: Supplies company name, address, phone and fax numbers, personnel, division offices, offshore operations, whether producer of oil or gas and if drilling contractor with rotary or cable tools, pipelines, refineries, petrochemical, gas processing, equipment manufacturers and suppliers, engineers, landman.

665.773 US ISSN 1081-4051
TEXAS PROPANE. 1944. m. (11/yr.). $36 (effective 1995). Texas Propane Gas Association, Box 140735, Austin, TX 78714-0735. TEL 512-836-8620. FAX 512-834-0758. Ed. Ellen Terry; Pub. John Danks. adv. contact: Ellen Terry. illus.; circ. 1,300 (controlled). **Document type:** trade publication.
Former titles (until 1992): Texas L P - Gas News (ISSN 0040-4454); Texas Butane News.
Description: Covers new laws and regulations (both state and federal) affecting the industry, new technology and products, marketing opportunities, and safety issues.

TEXAS PUBLIC UTILITY NEWS. see *ENERGY*

THUONGMAI/COMMERCIAL REVIEW. see *BUSINESS AND ECONOMICS — International Commerce*

665.7 CC
TIANRANQI DIQIOU KEXUE/NATURAL GAS GEOSCIENCE. (Text in Chinese) 1990. bi-m. Y30 (effective 1994). Zhongguo Kexueyuan, Lanzhou Wenxian Qingbo Zhongxin - Chinese Academy of Sciences, Lanzhou Documentation and Information Centre, 236 Tianshui Rd., Lanzhou, Gansu Province 730000, People's Republic of China. TEL 86-931-8842245. FAX 86-931-8825743. Ed.Bd. bk.rev. **Document type:** academic/scholarly publication.
Description: Reviews and reports the latest developments in gas geoscience research, new theories, and methods of natural gas exploration.

PETROLEUM AND GAS

665.7 CC ISSN 1000-0976
TN880.A1 CODEN: TIGOE3
TIANRANQI GONGYE/NATURAL GAS INDUSTRY. (Text in Chinese; summaries in Chinese, English) 1981. bi-m. $60 (effective 1995). (Sichuan Shiyou Guanli-ju - Sichuan Petroleum Administration) Tianranqi Gongye Zazhishe - Natural Gas Industry Journal Agency, No.3, Sec. 1, Fuqing Lu, Chengdu, Sichuan 610051, People's Republic of China. TEL 028-334911. FAX 028-3358727. (Subscr. to: Guoji Shudian - China International Book Trading Corporation, P.O. Box 399, Beijing 100044, P.R.C. TEL 8413063) Ed. Chen Guohua. adv.; charts; illus.; stat.; index. circ. 6,000. (also avail. in diskette format; back issues avail.)
—BLDSC (6037.315000).
Description: Contains articles on exploration and development, drilling-production technology and equipment, storage, transportation, surface construction, gas processing and utilization, reforms and management in the industry.
Refereed Serial

665.7 660 CC ISSN 1001-9219
CODEN: THTKEF
TIANRANQI HUAGONG/NATURAL GAS CHEMICAL INDUSTRY. (Text in Chinese; summaries in English) 1976. bi-m. $35 (effective 1995 & 1996). (Southwest Research Institute of Chemical Industry) Tianranqi Huagong Bianjibu, P.O. Box 445, Chengdu, Sichuan 610041, People's Republic of China. TEL 028-5184616. FAX 028-5184046. (Dist. overseas by: China National Publishing Industry Trade Corp., Box 782, Beijing, P.R. China) (Co-sponsor: Scientific and Technical Information Center for Natural Gas Chemical Industry) Ed. Feng Xiaoting. adv. contact: Xiao Zhenlu. bk.rev. circ. 3,000. **Document type:** academic/scholarly publication.
—BLDSC (6037.308000); CASDDS.

665.773 US ISSN 1048-0935
TODAY'S REFINERY. 1987. m. $25 in U.S. and Canada; elsewhere $60 (free to qualified personnel). Percy Publishing Company, Inc., 170 King St., Box 287, Chappaqua, NY 10514. TEL 914-238-0205. FAX 914-238-0210. Ed. James D. Wall; Pub. Samuel W. Percy. adv.: B&W page $2890, color page $3790; trim 8 1/8 x 10 7/8. circ. 9,874 (controlled). **Document type:** trade publication.
Description: Contains articles, column, abstracts and reviews of interest to petroleum refiners throughout the world.

051 US
THE TRANSPORTER. 1941. bi-m. free to qualified personnel. Shell Oil Products Co., Transportation, Box 2648, Houston, TX 77252-2648. TEL 213-241-5592. FAX 213-241-4048. Ed. Mark Woodruff. circ. 3,000. **Document type:** newsletter.
Formerly (until 1994): Go Devil.
Description: For the employees and retirees of the company.

620 UK ISSN 1354-4063
▼**TRIBOTEST JOURNAL;** method, technique and apparatus in tribology testing and analysis. 1994. q. £95($155) (effective 1996). Leaf Coppin Publishing Co., P.O. Box 111, Deal, Kent CT14 6SX, England. TEL 01304-360241. FAX 01304-360241. **Document type:** trade publication.
—BLDSC (9050.214500).

354 TR
TRINIDAD AND TOBAGO. MINISTRY OF ENERGY. ANNUAL REPORT. 1964. a. free. Ministry of Energy, P.O. Box 96, Port-of-Spain, Trinidad & Tobago, W.I. illus.; stat. circ. 500. **Document type:** government publication.
Former titles: Trinidad and Tobago. Ministry of Energy and Natural Resources. Annual Report; Trinidad and Tobago. Ministry of Energy and Energy-Based Industries. Annual Report; Trinidad and Tobago. Ministry of Petroleum and Mines. Annual Report.

622 338.2 TR
TRINIDAD AND TOBAGO. MINISTRY OF ENERGY. MONTHLY BULLETIN. 1964. m. free. Ministry of Energy, P.O. Box 96, Port-of-Spain, Trinidad & Tobago, W.I. charts; mkt.; index, cum.index. circ. 570. **Document type:** government publication, bulletin.
Former titles: Trinidad and Tobago. Ministry of Energy and Natural Resources. Monthly Bulletin; Trinidad and Tobago. Ministry of Energy and Energy-Based Industries. Monthly Bulletin; Trinidad and Tobago. Ministry of Petroleum and Mines. Monthly Bulletin (ISSN 0026-5322)

665.5 RU ISSN 0869-8740
TRUBOPROVODNYI TRANSPORT NEFTI/OIL PIPELINE TRANPSORT. m. Vserossiiskii Nauchno-Issledovatel'nyi Institut Oganizatsii, Upravleniya i Ekonomiki Neftegazovoi Promyshlennosti (VNIIOENG), Ul. Nametkina, 14, 117240 Moscow, Russia. TEL 7-95-3320025.
—BLDSC (0182.910000).

TURKIYE PETROL KIMYA, LASTIK ISCILEERI SENDIKASI. MAGAZINE. see *RUBBER*

U K GAS REPORT; covering all aspects of the UK gas industry. see *ENERGY*

338.47 UK
U K UPSTREAM PETROLEUM DATABASE. 1984. s-a. with a. reports. £3650. Arthur Andersen, Petroleum Services Group, 1 Surrey St., London WC2R 2PS, England. TEL 0171-438-3888. FAX 0171-438-3881. TELEX 8812711. Eds. Timothy H. Shingler, Gary Howorth.
Description: Provides information on licences, drilling activity and reserves both on- and offshore U.K.

665.5 US ISSN 0082-8599
HD9563
U S A OIL INDUSTRY DIRECTORY. 1962. a. $125. PennWell Publishing Co., Box 1260, Tulsa, OK 74101. TEL 918-835-3161. Ed. Jonelle Moore. adv. circ. 5,000. **Document type:** directory.
—CCC.
Description: Lists headquarters and provides company profiles of the domestic oil industry.

665.5 US
U S A OILFIELD SERVICE, SUPPLY, AND MANUFACTURERS DIRECTORY. 1983. a. $115. PennWell Publishing Co., Box 1260, Tulsa, OK 74101. TEL 918-835-3161. Ed. Jonelle Moore. adv. circ. 1,500. **Document type:** directory.
Former titles: Oilfield Service, Supply, and Manufacturers Worldwide Directory (ISSN 0736-038X); Oilfield Service, Supply, and Manufacturers Directory.
Description: Provides oilfield services, the wholesale and retail sale of oilfield products as well as information on companies engaged in the design, manufacture and construction of equipment used in the oilfield.

665.5 US ISSN 0731-924X
U S CRUDE OIL, NATURAL GAS, AND NATURAL GAS LIQUIDS RESERVES (YEAR) ANNUAL REPORT. 1977. a. $11. U.S. Energy Information Administration, National Energy Information Center, EI-231, James Forrestal Bldg., Rm. 1F-048, 1000 Independence Ave., S.W., DC 20585. TEL 202-586-8800. (Orders to: National Technical Information Service, 5285 Port Royal Rd., Springfield, VA 22161. TEL 703-487-4650. FAX 703-321-8547; Or: Superintendent of Documents, U.S. Government Printing Office, Box 371954, Pittsburgh, PA 15250-7954. TEL 202-512-1800. FAX 202-512-2250; Or: Bernan, 4611-F Assembly Dr., Lanham, MD 20706. TEL 800-274-4447. FAX 301-459-0056) charts. **Document type:** government publication.
Formerly (until 1979): U S Crude Oil and Natural Gas Reserves (ISSN 0272-3670)
Description: Compiles data on proven reserves of crude oil, natural gas, and natural gas liquids in the U.S. and by state.

665.5 US
HD9563
U S OFFSHORE OIL COMPANY CONTACT LIST. 1988. a. $125. Offshore Data Services, Inc., Box 19909, Houston, TX 77224-1909. TEL 713-781-2713. FAX 713-781-9594. **Document type:** directory.
Former titles: Offshore U S Oil Company Operating Personnel Directory (ISSN 1058-5877); Oil Company Operating Personnel Directory.
Description: Lists operating personnel at 267 oil companies operating in the Gulf of Mexico.

665.5 US ISSN 0502-9767
U S OIL WEEK; inside report on trends in petroleum marketing without the influence of advertising. 1967. w. $267 (foreign $317) includes Fuel Oil Update; C-Store Digest; and U S Oil Week's Price Monitor. Capitol Publications Inc., 1101 King St., Ste. 444, Alexandria, VA 22314. TEL 703-683-4100. FAX 703-739-6517. Ed. Jack Peckham. index. **Document type:** newsletter.
●Also available online. Vendor(s): Knight-Ridder, Inc., NewsNet (EY55).
—CCC.
Incorporates (in 1989): C-Store Week (ISSN 0887-4700)
Description: Competitive coverage of profit opportunities and market trends for petroleum marketers across the country. Focuses on ways to thrive in a changing marketplace. Covers industry news; current and pending government regulations; underground tank, insurance and environmental issues.

UIT EUROPOORTKRINGEN; euregionaal management magazine voor het bedrijfsleven van Amsterdam tot en met Vlanderen. see *TRANSPORTATION — Ships And Shipping*

UNDERGROUND FOCUS; the magazine of below-ground damage prevention. see *BUILDING AND CONSTRUCTION*

665.5 US
UNDERGROUND INJECTION CONTROL WELL INVENTORY. m. $94. Railroad Commission, Oil and Gas Publications, Drawer 12967, Capitol Sta., Austin, TX 78711. TEL 512-463-7255. **Document type:** trade publication.
Description: Lists all wells tacked by the Underground Injection Control Department; shows field name, lease name, well number, lease and ID number, status code, and control numbers.

338.47 UK
THE UNITED KINGDOM FINANCIAL ANALYSIS SERVICE. s-a. £8500 (renewals £5300). Arthur Andersen, Petroleum Services Group, 1 Surrey St., London WC2R 2PS, England. TEL 0171-438-3888. FAX 0171-438-3881. TELEX 8812711. Eds. Mike Coulten, Gary Howorth. (diskette format) **Document type:** trade publication.
Description: Calculates discounted pre- and post-tax cashflows by field and company for the U.K.

UNITED KINGDOM OFFSHORE HEALTH & SAFETY MANAGEMENT GUIDE. see *OCCUPATIONAL HEALTH AND SAFETY*

UNITED KINGDOM OFFSHORE HEALTH & SAFETY MANAGEMENT NEWSLETTER. see *OCCUPATIONAL HEALTH AND SAFETY*

665.538 US
U.S. DEPARTMENT OF ENERGY. STRATEGIC PETROLEUM RESERVE OFFICE. ANNUAL REPORT. a. U.S. Department of Energy, Strategic Petroleum Reserve Office, Washington, DC 20545. TEL 202-252-5000. **Document type:** government publication.

PETROLEUM AND GAS

665.7 US ISSN 0736-9808
HD9581.U49
U.S. ENERGY INFORMATION ADMINISTRATION. NATURAL GAS ANNUAL. a. (in 2 vols.). $35 for both vols. U.S. Energy Information Administration, National Energy Information Center, EI-231, James Forrestal Bldg., Rm. 1F-048, 1000 Independence Ave., S.W., Washington, DC 20585. TEL 202-586-8800. (Orders to: National Technical Information Service, 5285 Port Royal Rd., Springfield, VA 22161. TEL 703-487-4650. FAX 703-321-8547; Or: Superintendent of Documents, U.S. Government Printing Office, Box 371954, Pittsburgh, PA 15250-7954. TEL 202-512-1800. FAX 202-512-2250; Or: Bernan, 4611-F Assembly Dr., Lanham, MD 20706. TEL 800-274-4447. FAX 301-459-0056) charts; stat. **Indexed:** Energy Info.Abstr. **Document type:** government publication.
Supersedes (as of 1979): Natural Gas Production and Consumption (ISSN 0732-6629)
Description: Provides information on the supply and disposition of natural gas and summarizes the year's statistical data.

665.7 US ISSN 0737-1713
TN880.A1 CODEN: NGMODK
U.S. ENERGY INFORMATION ADMINISTRATION. NATURAL GAS MONTHLY. 1977. m. $77 (foreign $96.25). U.S. Energy Information Administration, National Energy Information Center, EI-231, James Forrestal Bldg., Rm. 1F-048, 1000 Independence Ave., S.W., Washington, DC 20585. TEL 202-586-8800. (Subscr. to: Superintendent of Documents, U.S. Government Printing Office, Box 371954, Pittsburgh, PA 15250-7954. TEL 202-512-1800. FAX 202-512-2250) charts; stat. (also avail. in microfiche from CIS; back issues avail.; reprint service avail. from CIS) **Indexed:** Amer.Stat.Ind. (1977-), Chem.Abstr., Energy Info.Abstr., PROMT. **Document type:** government publication.
—CASDDS.
Formed by the 1982 merger of: Underground Natural Gas Storage in the United States (ISSN 0275-9535); Natural Gas Monthly Report (ISSN 0731-9479); Which was formerly (until 1981): Natural and Synthetic Gas (ISSN 1063-066X); (until 1980): Natural Gas (ISSN 0191-4464)
Description: Presents data on natural and supplemental gas production, consumption, supply, storage, import and export, and interstate pipeline activities.

388 US
U.S. ENERGY INFORMATION ADMINISTRATION. PETROLEUM MARKETING ANNUAL. 1977. a. $42. U.S. Energy Information Administration, National Energy Information Center, EI-231, James Forrestal Bldg., Rm. 1F-048, Washington, DC 20585. TEL 202-586-1181. (Orders to: National Technical Information Service, 5285 Port Royal Rd., Springfield, VA 22161; Or: Bernan, 4611-F Assembly Dr., Lanham, MD 20706. TEL 800-274-4447. FAX 301-459-0056) charts; stat. **Document type:** government publication.
Description: Reports U.S. petroleum marketing, production, supply, and consumption data.

665.5 US
U.S. ENERGY INFORMATION ADMINISTRATION. PETROLEUM SUPPLY ANNUAL. (In 2 vols.) 1977. a. (in 2 vols.). $42. U.S. Energy Information Administration, National Energy Information Center, EI-231, National Energy Information Center, EI-231, James Forrestal Bldg., Rm. 1F-048, 1000 Independence Ave., S.W., Washington, DC 20585. TEL 202-586-8800. (Orders to: National Technical Information Service, 5285 Port Royal Rd., Springfield, VA 22161. TEL 703-487-4650. FAX 703-321-8547; Or: Bernan, 4611-F Assembly Dr., Lanham, MD 20706. TEL 800-274-4447. FAX 301-459-0056) charts; stat. **Indexed:** Energy Info.Abstr. **Document type:** government publication.
Former titles: Deliveries of Fuel Oil and Kerosene; Sales of Liquid Petroleum Gases and Ethane; Petroleum Refineries in the United States and U.S. Territories; Petroleum Statement.
Description: Compiles annual supply, disposition, and stock data for crude oil, natural gas liquids, liquefied refinery gases, and finished petroleum products.

665.5 US ISSN 0733-0553
HD9561 CODEN: PSMODO
U.S. ENERGY INFORMATION ADMINISTRATION. PETROLEUM SUPPLY MONTHLY. 1975. m. $83 (foreign $103.75). U.S. Energy Information Administration, National Energy Information Center, EI-231, James Forrestal Bldg., Rm. 1F-048, 1000 Independence Ave., S.W., Washington, DC 20585. TEL 202-586-8800. (Subscr. to: Superintendent of Documents, U.S. Government Printing Office, Box 371954, Pittsburgh, PA 15250-7954. TEL 202-512-1800. FAX 202-512-2250) charts; stat. (also avail. in microfiche from CIS; back issues avail.; reprint service avail. from CIS) **Indexed:** Amer.Stat.Ind. (1977-), Chem.Abstr., Energy Info.Abstr., PROMT. **Document type:** government publication.
—CASDDS.
Formed by the 1982 merger of: Monthly Petroleum Statement. Availability of Heavy Fuel Oils by Sulfur Levels (ISSN 0731-0188); U.S. Energy Information Administration. Monthly Petroleum Statistics Report (ISSN 0364-0205)
Description: Provides current statistics on production, import, export, transportation, and supply and disposition of petroleum. Includes occasional feature articles on energy-related subjects.

665.5 US ISSN 1057-5790
U.S. ENERGY INFORMATION ADMINISTRATION. WEEKLY PETROLEUM STATUS REPORT. w. $65 (foreign $81.25). U.S. Energy Information Administration, National Energy Information Center, EI-231, James Forrestal Bldg., Rm. 1F-048, 1000 Independence Ave., S.W., Washington, DC 20585. TEL 202-586-8800. (Subscr. to: Superintendent of Documents, U.S. Government Printing Office, Box 371954, Pittsburgh, PA 15250-7954. TEL 202-512-1800. FAX 202-512-2250) charts; stat. (also avail. in microfiche from CIS; back issues avail.; reprint service avail. from CIS) **Indexed:** Amer.Stat.Ind. (1979-), Energy Info.Abstr. **Document type:** government publication.
●Also available online. Vendor(s): PetroScan.
Description: Provides up-to-date information on the petroleum supply situation in the context of historical information, selected prices, and forecasts.

URJA. see *ENERGY*

665.5 540 II ISSN 0971-2038
CODEN: UOGIE4
URJA OIL AND GAS INTERNATIONAL. (Text in English) 1992. m. Rs.125($40) Urja, P.O. Box 3008, G-82, Sujan Singh Park, New Delhi 110-003, India. TEL 91-11-611536. FAX 91-11-462-8251. Ed. Dipak Basu Chaudhuri. circ. 3,135 (controlled). **Indexed:** Energy Info.Abstr.
—CASDDS; Ei.
Description: Devoted to petroleum and petrochemicals in South Asia. Also covers the world energy scene and developments in India's near-west.

UTILITY REPORTER - FUELS ENERGY & POWER. see *ENERGY*

665.7 SZ
V T A. q. Brunnmattstr. 18, CH-5610 Wohlen, Switzerland. TEL 057-221563. Ed. Konrad Gfeller. circ. 400.

VENEZUELA. MINISTERIO DE ENERGIA Y MINAS. CARTA SEMANAL. see *MINES AND MINING INDUSTRY*

VENEZUELA. MINISTERIO DE ENERGIA Y MINAS. INFORMATIONS. see *MINES AND MINING INDUSTRY*

VENEZUELA. MINISTERIO DE ENERGIA Y MINAS. MEMORIA Y CUENTA. see *MINES AND MINING INDUSTRY*

VENEZUELA. MINISTERIO DE ENERGIA Y MINAS. QUARTERLY BULLETIN. see *MINES AND MINING INDUSTRY*

665 553.28 622 SZ ISSN 0042-1901
VEREINIGUNG SCHWEIZERISCHER PETROLEUM-GEOLOGEN UND -INGENIEURE. BULLETIN/ASSOCIATION SUISSE DES GEOLOGUES ET INGENIEURS DU PETROLE. BULLETIN. Cover title: V S P Bulletin. (Text in English, French, German) 1934. s-a. 50 SFr. Vereinigung Schweizerischer Petroleum-Geologen und -Ingenieure, c/o V. Gschwind, Shell (Switzerland), Bederstr. 66, Postfach, CH-8021 Zurich, Switzerland. FAX 01-2062209. Ed.Bd. adv.; bk.rev.; bibl.; charts; illus.; cum.index. circ. 650. **Indexed:** Bibl.& Ind.Geol. **Document type:** bulletin.
—BLDSC (2404.050000).

655 658.3 US ISSN 0042-5087
VICKERS VOICE. 1954. q. free. Vickers Petroleum Corporation, c/o Total Petroleum, Box 500, Denver, CO 80230. Eds. Derald Linn, Dick Snider. illus. circ. 2,000.

665.5 UK ISSN 0968-6029
VIETNAM OIL & GAS REPORT. m. £315($535) I B C Publishing, Gilmoora House, 57-61 Mortimer St., London W1N 7TD, England. TEL 0171-637-4383. FAX 0171-636-6414. (Subscr. in the U.S. to: IBC (USA), 290 Eliot St., Box 91004, Ashland, MA 01721-9104. TEL 508-881-2800. FAX 508-881-0982) Ed. Malcolm Nixon. **Document type:** bulletin.
Description: Covers the commercial opportunities in Vietnam's oil and gas industry.

665.5 CI
VJESNIK I N A - NAFTAPLIN. (Text in Croatian) 1974. fortn. I N A - Naftaplin, Subiceva 29, 41000 Zagreb, Croatia. TEL 418-011. Ed. Ivo Decak. circ. 8,000.

665.5 GW
VORAN. 1932. 6/yr. Aral AG, Wittener Str. 45, 44789 Bochum, Germany. FAX 0234-3152364. Ed. Roland Mielke. adv.; index. circ. 5,500.
Formerly: Voran Aktuell.

W S E O DISPATCH. (Washington (State) Energy Office) see *ENERGY*

WAERMETECHNIK; internationales Fachorgan fuer Feuerungs- und Haustechnik. see *HEATING, PLUMBING AND REFRIGERATION*

338.7 CN
HD9574.C24
WASCANA ENERGY. ANNUAL REPORT. 1974. a. free. Wascana Energy Inc., 1777 Victoria Ave., P.O. Box 1550, Regina, SK S4P 3C4, Canada. TEL 306-781-8200. FAX 306-781-8364. Ed.Bd. charts; illus. circ. 55,000. **Document type:** corporate report.
Former titles: Saskoil. Annual Report (ISSN 0713-1100); (until 1985): Saskatchewan Oil and Gas Corporation. Annual Report (ISSN 0381-226X)

665.5 US
WEEKLY OILGRAM. w. $580. Munger Oil Information Service, Inc., 9800 S. Sepulveda Blvd., Ste. 723, Box 45738, Los Angeles, CA 90045. TEL 310-645-3282. FAX 310-645-9147. Ed. Averill H. Munger. **Document type:** newsletter.

665.538 658.7 UK ISSN 0268-7844
WEEKLY PETROLEUM ARGUS. 1969. w. £1044 (Europe £1097; Asia £1139; N. America $1540). Petroleum Argus Ltd., 93 Shepperton Rd., London N1 3DF, England. TEL 0171-359-8792. FAX 0171-226-0695. TELEX 21277. Ed. Adrian Binks. bk.rev.; index; circ. controlled. (looseleaf format; back issues avail.) **Document type:** trade publication.
Formerly (until 1985): Europ-Oil Prices.
Description: An analysis of the oil markets and the news and events that affect them.

665.7 US ISSN 0193-4724
WEEKLY PROPANE NEWSLETTER. 1971. w. $175 (effective Jan. 1991). Butane - Propane News, Inc., 338 E. Foothill Blvd., Box 660698, Arcadia, CA 91066-0698. TEL 818-357-2168. FAX 818-303-2854. Ed. Pete Ottman. **Document type:** newsletter.

PETROLEUM AND GAS

662.338   CN   ISSN 0709-3748
WEEKLY WELL ACTIVITY REPORT. 1980. w. Can.$85. Manitoba Energy and Mines, Petroleum Branch, 360-1395 Ellice Ave., Winnipeg, MB R3G 3P2, Canada. TEL 204-945-6577. FAX 204-945-0586. Ed. J.N. Fox. circ. 50. **Document type:** government publication.
    Description: Information on field activities in Manitoba: wells licensed, drilling information and well status.

665.5   US   ISSN 1058-0646
THE WELL SERVICE MARKET REPORT. 1991. m. $250 (effective 1993). R J M Communications, Box 6645, Lubbock, TX 79493-6645. TEL 806-741-1531. FAX 806-741-1533. Ed. Richard Mason. **Document type:** newsletter.
    Description: Provides market intelligence for the international well service industry, including well servicing and workover contractors. Includes business news on emerging markets, financial reports on acquisitions, company performance and surveys of rates and data.

622.338   US   ISSN 0043-2393
TN860
WELL SERVICING. 1961. bi-m. free to qualified personnel. (Association of Oilwell Servicing Contractors) Workover-Well Servicing Publications, Inc., 6060 N. Central Expy., Ste. 428, Dallas, TX 75206. TEL 214-692-0771. Ed. Polly Fisk; Pub. Polly Fisk. adv.: B&W page $1850, color page $2675; trim 8 1/4 x 10 7/8; adv. contact: Katherine Leidy. bk.rev.; illus.; pat.; stat.; tr.lit.; circ. 10,000 (controlled). (back issues avail.) **Indexed:** Petrol.Abstr. **Document type:** trade publication.
    —BLDSC (9294.190000); UnCover.

338.2   US
WESTERN PETROLEUM INDUSTRY. 1945. a. $50. Midwest Register, Inc., 1120 E. 4th St., Tulsa, OK 74120. TEL 918-582-2000. FAX 918-587-9349. **Document type:** directory.
    Formerly: Directory of Producers and Drilling Contractors: California.
    Description: Supplies company name, address, phone and fax number, personnel, division offices, offshore operations, whether producer of oil or gas and if drilling contractor with rotary or cable tools, pipeline companies, refineries, gas processing, petrochemical and equipment manufacturers and suppliers.

553.2 333.79   AT   ISSN 0159-1878
WHO'S DRILLING. 1979. w. Aus.$730. Pex Publications Pty. Ltd., P.O. Box 58, Claremont, W.A. 6010, Australia. TEL 61-9-3833477. FAX 61-9-3851485. Ed. Don Lipscombe. **Document type:** newsletter.
    Description: National exploration newsletter analysing all current and pending wells, rig and vessel movements, and seismic surveys.

665.7   US   ISSN 1052-8776
HD9581.A1
WORLD GAS INTELLIGENCE. 1990. m. $795 (effective 1995). Petroleum & Energy Intelligence Weekly, Inc., 575 Broadway, 4th Fl., New York, NY 10012-3230. TEL 212-941-5500. FAX 212-941-5508. TELEX 62371 PETROIN. Ed. Ira Joseph. **Document type:** trade publication.
    —SWETS.
    Description: Provides concise news and analysis of developments in the international gas industry.

665.5   US   ISSN 1053-9859
WORLD GEOPHYSICAL NEWS. 1984. s-m. $252 (foreign $342). Petroleum Information Corporation, Box 2162, Denver, CO 80201-2162. TEL 303-340-7100. FAX 303-794-1694. stat. **Document type:** newsletter.
    Description: Includes crew location reports, statistical summaries, and industry news.

WORLD L N G - GAS CONTRACTS. see *LAW — International Law*

WORLD NATIONAL OIL COMPANY STATUTES. see *LAW — International Law*

665 338.2   US   ISSN 0043-8790
TN860   CODEN: WOOIAS
WORLD OIL. 1916. m. $28 (foreign $34) (free to qualified personnel). Gulf Publishing Co., Box 2608, Houston, TX 77252-2608. TEL 713-529-4301. FAX 713-520-4433. TELEX 287330 GULF UR. Ed. Robert Snyder. adv.; bk.rev.; charts; illus.; tr.lit.; index. circ. 37,869. (also avail. in microfilm from UMI; reprint service avail.) **Indexed:** A.S.& T.Ind., AESIS, API Abstr., API Oil., Bibl.& Ind.Geol., Bus.Ind., Chem.Abstr., Curr.Cont., Energy Info.Abstr., Energy Rev., Eng.Ind., Environ.Per.Bibl., Fuel & Energy Abstr., Gas Abstr., Mid.East: Abstr.& Ind., Ocean.Abstr., Petrol.Abstr., Pollut.Abstr., PROMT, Risk Abstr., So.Pac.Per.Ind., Tr.& Indus.Ind.
    —BLDSC (9356.950000); CASDDS; Ei; Faxon; Genuine Article; PADDS; SWETS; UMI; UnCover. **CCC**.
    Formerly: Oil Weekly.

662.338 382   UK   ISSN 0950-1029
WORLD OIL TRADE. 1/yr. £285($500) (foreign $500) (effective 1996). Basil Blackwell Ltd., 108 Cowley Rd., Oxford OX4 1JF, England. TEL 0865-791100. FAX 0865-791347. TELEX 837022-OXBOOK-G.
    —UMI. **CCC.**

665.5 340   US
WORLD PETROLEUM EXPLORATION & EXPLOITATION AGREEMENTS. biennial. $695. Barrows Co., Inc., 116 E. 66th St., New York, NY 10021. TEL 212-772-1199. FAX 212-288-7242.
    Description: Features summaries of oil and gas regulations by country, as well as discussion and valuation of production-sharing contracts versus risk contracts and concessions.

665.5   UK   ISSN 0963-5807
WORLD PETROLEUM TRENDS. a. £300. Petroconsultants (U.K.) Ltd., Europa House, 266 Upper Richmond Rd., London SW15 6TQ, England. TEL 0181-780-2500. FAX 0181-780-2036. TELEX 94018027-PUKL-G. **Document type:** trade publication.

WORLD RIG FORECAST. see *ENERGY*

665.5   US
HD9563
WORLDWIDE OFFSHORE RIG OWNERS & PERSONNEL DIRECTORY. 1989. a. $135. Offshore Data Services, Inc., Box 19909, Houston, TX 77224-1909. TEL 713-781-2713. FAX 713-781-9594. **Document type:** directory.
    Former titles: International Offshore Rig Owners Directory (ISSN 1058-6008); Offshore Rig Owners Directory.
    Description: Provides corporate, personnel, and rig information for US and foreign owned offshore rigs, including US and overseas addresses.

665.5   US   ISSN 0084-2583
TP692.3
WORLDWIDE PETROCHEMICAL DIRECTORY. 1962. a. $140. PennWell Publishing Co. (Tulsa), Box 21288, Tulsa, OK 74121. TEL 918-835-3161. Ed. Jonelle Moore. adv. **Document type:** directory.
    —BLDSC (9364.302000). **CCC.**
    Incorporates in part (in 1987): Refining and Petrochemical Technology Yearbook.

665.5   US   ISSN 0146-3349
TN879.5
WORLDWIDE PIPELINES AND CONTRACTORS DIRECTORY. 1976-1984; resumed 1991. a. $135. Pennwell Publishing Co., Box 1260, Tulsa, OK 74101. TEL 918-835-3161. FAX 918-831-9555. Ed. Pat Jackson. adv. **Document type:** directory.
    —BLDSC (9364.304000). **CCC.**

665.73   US   ISSN 0277-0962
TN867
WORLDWIDE REFINING AND GAS PROCESSING DIRECTORY. 1942. a. $140. PennWell Publishing Co., Box 21288, Tulsa, OK 74121. TEL 918-835-3161. Ed. Jonelle Moore. adv. circ. 2,500. (back issues avail.) **Document type:** directory.
    —**CCC.**
    Supersedes in part (in 1987): Refining and Petrochemical Technology Yearbook.
    Description: Lists over 14,000 personnel in over 3,000 plant sites in the United States, Canada, Europe, Latin America, Asia-Pacific, Africa and the Middle East.

665 550   US   ISSN 0160-2829
QE1   CODEN: WGGCAG
WYOMING GEOLOGICAL ASSOCIATION. GUIDEBOOK. 1946. a. membership. Wyoming Geological Association, Box 545, Casper, WY 82602-0545. TEL 307-137-0027. Ed.Bd. adv. (back issues avail.) **Document type:** proceedings.
    —BLDSC (4225.435000).
    Description: Publishes papers on the geology of Wyoming to disseminate knowledge of it among geologists in industry and academia.

665 550   US
WYOMING GEOLOGICAL ASSOCIATION. OIL & GAS FIELDS SYMPOSIUM. irreg. Wyoming Geological Association, Box 545, Casper, WY 82602-0545. TEL 307-237-0027. Ed.Bd. adv. (looseleaf format; back issues avail.) **Document type:** academic/scholarly publication.
    Description: Provides technical data and structural maps of existing oil and gas fields in Wyoming.

XUEXI YU TANSUO/STUDY & EXPLORATION. see *SOCIAL SCIENCES: COMPREHENSIVE WORKS*

665   US   ISSN 0044-0205
YANKEE OILMAN. 1955. m. $15. New England Fuel Institute, Box 37, Beverly, MA 01915-0001. TEL 508-927-1541. FAX 508-921-5120. Ed. Joel Watts. adv.: B&W page $1030, color page $1750 ; trim 8 1/2 x 11. bk.rev.; stat. circ. 7,120. **Document type:** trade publication.
    Description: Contains news and features about the oil heating and petroleum distribution industries in the northeast United States.

665.5   IS
YEDA. (Text in Hebrew) 1960. bi-m. free. Paz Oil Co., Ltd., Business Information Unit, P.O. Box 434, Haifa 31003, Israel. TEL 972-4-567319. FAX 972-4-567366. circ. 3,500.

662.338   CC   ISSN 1001-697X
YOUTIAN DIMIAN GONGCHENG/OIL - GASFIELD SURFACE ENGINEERING. (Text in Chinese) bi-m. $30 (effective 1996). Daqing Shiyou Guanliju - Daqing Bureau of Petroleum Administration, Ranghu Lu, Daqing, Heilongjiang 163712, People's Republic of China. TEL 0459-5592624. Ed. Wang Daoman.

665.5 665.7   CC   ISSN 1001-9308
ZHONGGUO HAISHANG YOUQI (DIZHI)/CHINA OFFSHORE OIL AND GAS (GEOLOGY). (Text in Chinese; abstracts in Chinese, English) 1987. bi-m. $80. China National Offshore Oil Corporation, China Offshore Oil Exploration and Development Research Center, 22 East St., Gaobeidian, Hebei 074010, People's Republic of China. TEL 03235-212799. FAX 03235-212400. Ed. Yang Jiaming. adv.: page $1000; adv. contact: Wei Ziliang. circ. 3,000. **Document type:** academic/scholarly publication.

665.5   CC   ISSN 1001-7682
ZHONGGUO HAISHANG YOUQI (GONGCHENG). (Text in Chinese) bi-m. Nengyuan-bu, Bohai Gongcheng Sheji Gongsi - Ministry of Energy, Bohai Engineering Design Company, P.O. Box 536, No. 13, Tanggu, Tianjin 300452, People's Republic of China. TEL 975661. Ed. Liu Chufan.

665.5   CC   ISSN 1001-4500
    CODEN: ZHPNE2
ZHONGGUO HAIYANG PINGTAI/CHINA OFFSHORE PLATFORM. (Text in Chinese) 1986. bi-m. $24 (effective 1996). (Zhongguo Guoji Haiyang Shiyou Gongcheng Gongsi - China Offshore Industrial Corporation) China State Shipbuilding Corporation, Shipbuilding Technology Research Institute, P.O. Box 4019, No. 851, Zhongshan Nan 2 Lu, Shanghai 200032, People's Republic of China. TEL 021-4399626. FAX 021-4390908. Ed. Xu Xueguang; Pub. Ying Changchun. adv. contact: Chen Zuyu. circ. 1,500. **Document type:** academic/scholarly publication.
    Description: Covers scientific experiments, researches and designs, project management, economic analysis, equipments and safety issues in the field of offshore engineering.
    Refereed Serial

665.5   CC
ZHONGGUO SHIYOU HUABAO/CHINA OIL PICTORIAL. (Text in Chinese) q. No. 3-15 A, Xinkai Lu, Langfang, Hebei 102800, People's Republic of China. TEL 25111.
    Description: Introduces the Chinese petroleum industry and other energy industries.

PETROLEUM AND GAS — ABSTRACTING, BIBLIOGRAPHIES, STATISTICS

ZHONGNAN MINZU XUEYUAN XUEBAO (SHEHUI KEXUE BAN)/SOUTH-CENTRAL COLLEGE FOR NATIONALITIES. JOURNAL (SOCIAL SCIENCE EDITION). see *SOCIAL SCIENCES: COMPREHENSIVE WORKS*

662.6　　　　　CC　　ISSN 1001-5620
ZUANJING YE YU WANJING YE/DRILLING FLUID & COMPLETION FLUID. (Text in Chinese) 1983. bi-m. $40 (effective 1996). North China Petroleum Administration, Drilling Technology Research Institute, P.O. Box 19, Renqiu, Hebei 062550, People's Republic of China. TEL 86-3426-72548. FAX 86-3426-724527. Ed. Zhang Xiaoyuan. adv. contact: Zhang Wanlong. circ. 3,600. **Indexed:** Petrol.Abstr. **Document type:** academic/scholarly publication.
—PADDS.
Description: Covers drilling fluid, well completion fluid and workover fluid.

666.5　　　　　VE
ZUMAQUE.* 1976. q. Sociedad Venezolana de Ingenieros de Petroleo, c/o Colegio de Engenieros de Venezuela, Apdo. 2006, Caracas, Venezuela.

PETROLEUM AND GAS — Abstracting, Bibliographies, Statistics

665.5　　　　　US
A G A GAS INDUSTRY TRAINING DIRECTORY. a. $70 to non-members; members $35. American Gas Association, 1515 Wilson Blvd., Arlington, VA 22209. TEL 703-841-8400. FAX 703-841-8406. (Subscr. to: Dept. 0765, McLean, VA 22109-0765) **Document type:** directory.

665.5　　　　　US　　ISSN 1049-4103
A G A GAS STATS; monthly gas utility statistical report. m. $16 to non-members (foreign $24); members $8 (foreign $16). American Gas Association, Department of Statistics, 1515 Wilson Blvd., Arlington, VA 22209. TEL 703-841-8559. FAX 703-841-8406. (Subscr.to: Dept. 0765, McLean, VA 22109-0765) **Indexed:** SRI.

622 338.2　　　　CN
ALBERTA DRILLING PROGRESS WEEKLY REPORT. 1950. w. Can.$325. Alberta Energy and Utilities Board, 640 Fifth Ave., S.W., Calgary, Alta. T2P 3G4, Canada. TEL 403-297-8311. FAX 403-297-7040. TELEX 03-821717.
—CCC.
Former titles: Alberta Drilling Progress and Pipeline Receipts. Weekly Report (ISSN 0227-3357); Weekly Production and Drilling Statistics (ISSN 0032-9827)
Description: Summary of drilling activity in the province of Alberta.

665.5 016　　　　US　　ISSN 0002-6441
ALPHABETIC SUBJECT INDEX TO PETROLEUM ABSTRACTS. 1961. a. $170. University of Tulsa, Information Services Division, 600 S. College Ave., Tulsa, OK 74104-3189. TEL 918-631-2297; 800-247-8678. FAX 918-599-9361. TELEX 497543. bibl.; cum.index. circ. 500. (microform) **Document type:** abstracting/indexing.
●Also available online. Vendor(s): Knight-Ridder, Inc. (PEP), Orbit Search Service (TULSA).

025.3 665.5　　　　US
Z695.1.P43
AMERICAN PETROLEUM INSTITUTE. CENTRAL ABSTRACTING & INFORMATION SERVICES. THESAURUS. Key Title: Thesaurus - American Petroleum Institute. 1964. a. $125 to non-members; members $55. American Petroleum Institute, Central Abstracting & Information Services, 275 Seventh Ave., New York, NY 10001-6708. TEL 212-366-4040. FAX 212-366-4298. (also avail. in diskette format) **Document type:** abstracting/indexing.
Formerly: American Petroleum Institute. Central Abstracting and Indexing Service. Thesaurus (ISSN 0193-5151); **Supersedes:** American Petroleum Institute. Information Retrieval System, Subject Authority List.
Description: Guide to the indexing system and controlled vocabulary used to prepare the petroleum refining and petrochemicals industries technology databases.

665.5 338.2　　　　US
AMERICAN PETROLEUM INSTITUTE. DIVISION OF STATISTICS. WEEKLY STATISTICAL BULLETIN. Variant title: American Petroleum Institute. Weekly Statistical Bulletin and Monthly Statistical Report. (Includes Monthly Statistical Report) w. $110 (effective 1995). American Petroleum Institute, Publications Section, 1220 L St., N.W., Washington, DC 20005. TEL 202-682-8378. (Subscr. to: 1970 Chain Bridge Rd., McLean, VA 22109-6000) charts; stat. circ. 2,500. (also avail. in microfiche from CIS) **Indexed:** SRI. **Document type:** trade publication.
●Also available online. Vendor(s): PetroScan.
Formerly: American Petroleum Institute. Division of Statistics and Economics. Weekly Statistical Bulletin (ISSN 0003-0457)
Description: For producers, users, traders, and analysts of petroleum. Reports total US and regional data relating to refinery operations and the production of the five major petroleum products: leaded and unleaded motor gasoline, naphtha and kerosine jet fuel, distilled and residual fuel oil.

AMERICAN PETROLEUM INSTITUTE. HEALTH AND ENVIRONMENTAL SCIENCES DEPARTMENT. REPORTS AND OTHER PUBLICATIONS, INDEX AND ABSTRACTS. see *PUBLIC HEALTH AND SAFETY — Abstracting, Bibliographies, Statistics*

665.5　　　　　US
AMERICAN PETROLEUM INSTITUTE. MONTHLY COMPLETION REPORT. 1970. m. $65 (effective 1995). American Petroleum Institute, Publications Section, 1220 L St., N.W., Washington, DC 20005. TEL 202-682-8518. (Subscr. to: 1970 Chain Bridge Rd., McLean, VA 22109-6000) Ed. Hazim Arafa. circ. 500. **Indexed:** SRI. **Document type:** trade publication.
Former titles: Monthly Drilling Completion Report; Monthly Report on Drilling Activity in the U.S.
Description: Provides data on the cumulative number of completions and related footage drilled, by month, for two prior years.

310　　　　　US
AMERICAN PETROLEUM INSTITUTE. MONTHLY STATISTICAL REPORT. 1977. m. $65 (effective 1995). American Petroleum Institute, Publications Section, 1220 L St., N.W., Washington, DC 20005. TEL 202-682-8378. (Subscr. to: 1970 Chain Bridge Rd., McLean, VA 22109-6000) charts; stat. (looseleaf format; also avail. in microfiche from CIS) **Indexed:** SRI.
Description: Analyzes trends and developments in US petroleum supply and demand.

622.338 338.2　　　　US　　ISSN 1045-4020
TN871.2
AMERICAN PETROLEUM INSTITUTE. QUARTERLY COMPLETION REPORT. q. $175 (effective 1995). American Petroleum Institute, Publications Section, 1220 L St., N.W., Washington, DC 20005. TEL 202-682-8378. (Subscr. to: 1970 Chain Bridge Rd., McLean, VA 22109-6000) stat. **Indexed:** GeoRef, SRI. **Document type:** trade publication.
—CCC.
Former titles: Quarterly Drilling Completions; Quarterly Review of Drilling Statistics (ISSN 0033-5789)
Description: Provides information on reported drilling activity, as well as estimates of the total number of wells drilled and footage for the current and recent quarters.

665.7　　　　　UN　　ISSN 0066-3824
HD9581.E8
ANNUAL BULLETIN OF GAS STATISTICS FOR EUROPE/BULLETIN ANNUEL DE STATISTIQUES DE GAZ POUR L'EUROPE. (Text in English, French and Russian) 1955. a. price varies. Economic Commission for Europe (ECE), Palais des Nations, 1211 Geneva 10, Switzerland. TEL 022-917-2609. FAX 022-917-0036. TELEX 412962. (Orders in N. America to: United Nations Publications, Rm. DC2-853, New York, NY 10017. TEL 212-963-8302. FAX 212-932-3489; Or: Unipub, 4611-F Assembly Dr., Lanham, MD 20706. TEL 301-459-7666. FAX 301-459-0056) (also avail. in microfiche from CIS) **Indexed:** IIS. **Document type:** government publication, bulletin.
Description: Reports trends and other developments in natural gas production, stocks, and consumption for Europe and North America.

665.5 338.2　　　　US　　ISSN 0004-1874
ARKANSAS OIL AND GAS STATISTICAL BULLETIN. 1942. m. free. Oil and Gas Commission, Box 1472, El Dorado, AR 71731-1472. TEL 501-862-4965. FAX 501-862-8823. circ. 350 (controlled). (looseleaf format; also avail. in microfiche from CIS) **Indexed:** SRI. **Document type:** government publication.

662.338　　　　　CN
B C WELL TAPE. m. Can.$1500. Ministry of Energy, Mines and Petroleum Resources, Energy Resources Division, 7th Fl., 1810 Blanshard St., Victoria, BC V8V 1X4, Canada. TEL 604-387-5178. (Subscr. to: Crown Publications, 546 Yates St., Victoria, BC V8W 1K8, Canada. TEL 604-386-4636) (magnetic tape) **Document type:** government publication.
Description: Lists every oil and gas well in BC and all drilling and analysis on these wells, such as cores, distance, and formation taps.

338.2　　　　　UK　　ISSN 0263-9815
HD9560.4
B P STATISTICAL REVIEW OF WORLD ENERGY. a. £8. British Petroleum Company plc., Britannic House, 1 Finsbury Circus, London EC2M 7BA, England. FAX 071-496-4528. (Dist. in U.S. by: B P America Inc., 200 Public Sq., Cleveland, Ohio 44114-2375) circ. 35,000.
Formerly: Statistical Review of the World Oil Industry (ISSN 0081-5039)
Description: Compendium of energy statistics covering the previous 10 years.

665.5　　　　　US　　ISSN 0730-5621
HD9564
BASIC PETROLEUM DATA BOOK. 1974. 3/yr. $225 (effective 1995). American Petroleum Institute, Publications Section, 1220 L St., N.W., Washington, DC 20005. TEL 202-682-8378. (Subscr. to: 1970 Chain Bridge Rd., McLean, VA 22109-6000) Ed. Julie Scott. (also avail. in microfiche from CIS) **Indexed:** PROMT, SRI.
—CCC.
Supersedes: Petroleum Facts and Figures; **Incorporates:** American Petroleum Institute. Division of Statistics and Economics. Annual Statistical Review (ISSN 0569-6852)
Description: Provides domestic and world statistical background information. Includes data on energy, reserves, exploration and drilling, production, finance, prices, demand, refining, imports, exports, offshore transportation, natural gas and the Organization of Petroleum Exporting countries.

665.5　　　　　TS
AL-BUTRUL WAL-SINA'A FI ABU DHABI/PETROLEUM AND INDUSTRY IN ABU DHABI. (Text in Arabic) 1970. a. exchange basis. Ministry of Petroleum and Mineral Wealth, P.O. Box 59, Abu Dhabi, United Arab Emirates. TEL 651810. FAX 663414. TELEX 22544 MPMR EM. circ. 1,000.
Description: Statistical review of petroleum and industrial activity in Abu Dhabi.

665　　　　　US　　ISSN 0749-730X
　　　　　　　　　　CODEN: CADMEB
C A SELECTS. DRILLING MUDS. fortn. $220 to non-members; members $65 (effective 1996). Chemical Abstracts Service (Subsidiary of: American Chemical Society), 2540 Olentangy River Rd., Box 3012, Columbus, OH 43210-0012. TEL 614-447-3600. FAX 614-447-3713. TELEX 6842086. **Document type:** abstracting/indexing.
Description: Covers formulation, properties, and performance of aqueous suspensions used in drilling of oil and gas wells.

665.5　　　　　US　　ISSN 0734-8746
　　　　　　　　　　CODEN: CAEREV
C A SELECTS. ENHANCED PETROLEUM RECOVERY. s-w. $220 to non-members; members $65 (effective 1996). Chemical Abstracts Service (Subsidiary of: American Chemical Society), 2540 Olentangy River Rd., Box 3012, Columbus, OH 43210-0012. TEL 614-447-3600. FAX 614-447-3713. TELEX 6842086. **Document type:** abstracting/indexing.
Description: Covers means for stimulating production of oil wells; secondary and tertiary recovery techniques; in-situ retorting of oil shales and tar sands.

C A SELECTS. FUEL & LUBRICANT ADDITIVES. see *CHEMISTRY — Abstracting, Bibliographies, Statistics*

PETROLEUM AND GAS — ABSTRACTING, BIBLIOGRAPHIES, STATISTICS

665.7   CN   ISSN 0068-7103
HD9574.C2
CANADA. STATISTICS CANADA. CRUDE PETROLEUM AND NATURAL GAS INDUSTRY. (Catalogue 26-213) (Text in English and French) 1926. a. Can.$26($31) (foreign $36). Statistics Canada, Publications Sales and Services, Ottawa, Ont. K1A 0T6, Canada. TEL 613-951-7277. FAX 613-951-1584. (also avail. in microform from MML)
 Description: Presents data on the number of establishments, employment, payroll, production, disposition, exports and imports.

665.5   CN   ISSN 0702-6846
HD9574.C2
CANADA. STATISTICS CANADA. CRUDE PETROLEUM AND NATURAL GAS PRODUCTION. m. Can.$100($120) (foreign $140). Statistics Canada, Publications Division, Ottawa, Ont. K1A 0T6, Canada. TEL 613-951-7277. FAX 613-951-1584.
 Description: Estimates the production and disposition of crude petroleum and natural gas, by province, monthly and cumulative.

665.5   CN   ISSN 0527-5318
HD9581.C3
CANADA. STATISTICS CANADA. GAS UTILITIES, TRANSPORT AND DISTRIBUTION SYSTEMS. (Catalogue 57-205) (Text in English and French) 1959. a. Can.$27($32) (foreign $38). Statistics Canada, Publications Sales and Services, Ottawa, Ont. K1A 0T6, Canada. TEL 613-951-7277. FAX 613-951-1584. stat. (also avail. in microform from MML)
 Description: Covers receipts and disposition of natural gas by month and province, pipeline distance, balance sheet, property account, income account, employees and earnings.

665.54   CN   ISSN 0380-4615
CANADA. STATISTICS CANADA. OIL PIPE LINE TRANSPORT. 1951. m. Can.$100($120) (foreign $140). Statistics Canada, Publications Division, Ottawa, Ont. K1A 0T6, Canada. TEL 613-951-7277. FAX 613-951-1584.
 Description: Receipts and deliveries by source and by movement of crude oil and refined petroleum products by gathering and trunk lines, by provinces; barrel-miles, operating revenues. Includes data analysis.

665.5   CN   ISSN 0835-0175
HD9574.C2
CANADA. STATISTICS CANADA. REFINED PETROLEUM AND COAL PRODUCTS INDUSTRIES. (Catalog 45-250) (Text in English and French) 1980. a. Can.$35($42) Statistics Canada, Communications Division, 3rd Fl., R.H. Coats Bldg., Ottawa, ON K1A 0T6, Canada. (also avail. in microform from MML) **Document type:** government publication.
 Formerly (until 1985): Canada. Statistics Canada. Refined Petroleum and Coal Products (ISSN 0319-9045); Which was formed by the merger of (1960-1981): Canada. Statistics Canada. Petroleum Refineries (ISSN 0068-7162); (1970-1981): Canada. Statistics Canada. Miscellaneous Petroleum and Coal Products Industries (ISSN 0384-4757); Which was formerly (until 1970): Canada. Statistics Canada. Other Petroleum and Coal Products Industries (ISSN 0527-6004); (until 1960): Canada. Statistics Canada. Miscellaneous Products of Petroleum and Coal Industry (ISSN 0384-4765); Petroleum Refineries was formerly (until 1960): Canada. Statistics Canada. Petroleum Products Industry (ISSN 0700-0200); (until 1948): Canada. Statistics Canada. Petroleum Products Industry in Canada (ISSN 0824-9342).

662.338   CN
DAILY LIST OF WELL AUTHORIZATIONS. 3/w. Can.$72. Ministry of Energy, Mines and Petroleum Resources, Energy Resources Division, 7th Fl., 1810 Blanshard St., Victoria, BC V8V 1X4, Canada. (Subscr. to: Crown Publications, 546 Yates St., Victoria, BC V8W 1K8, Canada. TEL 604-386-4636) (back issues avail.) **Document type:** government publication.
 Description: Presents relevant data on wells authorized by the Petroleum Resources Division.

EMENTARIO DA LEGISLACAO DO PETROLEO. see
 LAW — Abstracting, Bibliographies, Statistics

310   SP
ESTADISTICA DE PROSPECCION Y PRODUCCION DE HIDROCARBUROS. a. 1000 ptas. Ministerio de Industria, Paseo de la Castellana, 160, Madrid 28046, Spain. FAX 259-84-80.

662.338 614.85   US   ISSN 1067-1013
614.7
EXPLORATION AND PRODUCTION HEALTH, SAFETY AND ENVIRONMENT. 1993. m. $195. University of Tulsa, Information Services Division, 600 S. College Ave., Tulsa, OK 74104-3189. TEL 918-631-2297; 800-247-8678. FAX 918-599-9361. TELEX 497543. E-mail: question@TUred.pa.utulsa.edu. **Document type:** abstracting/indexing.

662.338 614.85   US   ISSN 0894-9204
Z695.1.P43
EXPLORATION AND PRODUCTION THESAURUS. 1965. biennial. $175. University of Tulsa, Information Services Division, 600 S. College Ave., Tulsa, OK 74104-3189. TEL 918-631-2297. FAX 918-599-9361. (looseleaf format) **Document type:** directory.

662 333.79 016   UK   ISSN 0140-6701
TP315   CODEN: FEABDN
FUEL AND ENERGY ABSTRACTS; a summary of world literature on all scientific, technical, commercial and environmental aspects of fuel and energy. 1960. bi-m. £560($891) (effective 1996). (Institute of Energy) Butterworth - Heinemann, Part of the Reed Elsevier group, Linacre House, Jordan Hill, Oxford OX2 8DP, England. TEL 01865-310366. FAX 01865-310898. TELEX 83111 BHPOXF G. (Subscr. to: Elsevier Science Ltd., P.O. Box 800, Kidlington, Oxford OX5 1DX, England. TEL 44-1865-843000. FAX 44-1865-843010; Subscr. in U.S. and Canada to: Elsevier Science, 660 White Plains Rd., Tarrytown, NY 10591-5153. TEL 914-524-9200. FAX 914-333-2444) Ed.Bd. (also avail. in microform from UMI; back issues avail.) **Indexed:** Anal.Abstr., Br.Ceram.Abstr., Chem.Abstr., Fluidex. **Document type:** abstracting/indexing, academic/scholarly publication.
 —UMI. **CCC.**
 Formerly: Fuel Abstracts and Current Titles (ISSN 0016-2388)
 Description: Each issue contains 1,500 abstracts and titles from the international literature dealing with fuel and other energy topics.
 Refereed Serial

665.7 016   US   ISSN 0016-4844
TP700   CODEN: GAABA3
GAS ABSTRACTS. 1945. m. $210 (foreign $225) (effective 1996). Institute of Gas Technology, 1700 S. Mount Prospect Rd., Des Plaines, IL 60018-1804. TEL 708-768-0500. FAX 708-768-0669. Ed. P. Geith. bk.rev.; index. circ. 750. (also avail. in microform from UMI; reprint service avail. from UMI) **Indexed:** Chem.Abstr., Corros.Abstr., Eng.Ind. **Document type:** abstracting/indexing.
 ●Also available online.
 —BLDSC (4075.000000); UMI.

665.5 310   AT
GAS AND FUEL CORPORATION OF VICTORIA. STATISTICS. 1978. a. free. Gas and Fuel Corporation of Victoria, 171 Flinders St., Melbourne, Vic. 3000, Australia. TEL 03-652-5056. FAX 03-652-4801. Ed. Ray Proudley. circ. 5,000. (back issues avail.)

665.7 333.8   AT   ISSN 0157-731X
GAS INDUSTRY STATISTICS (YEAR). 1979. a. Aus.$25 to non-members; members Aus.$15. Australian Gas Association, G.P.O. Box 323, Canberra, A.C.T. 2601, Australia. TEL 61-6-247-3955. FAX 61-6-249-7402. Ed. O. Dilulio. charts; stat. (back issues avail.)
 Description: Australian gas industry statistics and world energy resources.

665.54   US   ISSN 1067-1021
GAS PROCESSING AND PIPELINING. 1993. m. $175. University of Tulsa, Information Services Division, 600 S. College Ave., Tulsa, OK 74104-3189. TEL 918-631-2297; 800-247-8678. FAX 918-599-9361. TELEX 497543. E-mail: question@TUred.pa.utulsa.edu. **Document type:** abstracting/indexing.

665.5   US   ISSN 0894-9190
G105
GEOGRAPHIC THESAURUS. 1973. biennial. $175. University of Tulsa, Information Services Division, 600 S. College Ave., Tulsa, OK 74104-3189. TEL 918-631-2297. FAX 918-599-9361. (looseleaf format) **Document type:** directory.

665.5   US   ISSN 0742-8464
Z6972   CODEN: GPSIEJ
GUIDE TO PETROLEUM STATISTICAL INFORMATION. 1983. biennial. $150 to non-members; members $75. American Petroleum Institute, Central Abstracting & Information Services, 275 Seventh Ave., New York, NY 10001-6708. TEL 212-366-4040. FAX 212-366-4298. **Document type:** abstracting/indexing.
 —BLDSC (4229.842000).
 Description: Lists the recurring statistical features in four sections that regularly appear in 120 energy-related publications and nearly 300 databases.

338.2   US   ISSN 0073-2656
HISTORICAL STATISTICS OF THE GAS INDUSTRY. 1956. irreg. $25 (non-members $50). American Gas Association, Department of Statistics, 1515 Wilson Blvd., Arlington, VA 22209. TEL 703-841-8559. FAX 703-841-8406. (Subscr. to: Dept. 0765, McLean, VA 22109-0765) circ. 1,000.

665.5   II
INDIAN PETROLEUM AND NATURAL GAS STATISTICS. (Text in English) 1976. a. free. Ministry of Petroleum & Chemicals, Department of Petroleum & Natural Gas, Economics and Statistics Division, Shastri Bhawan, New Delhi 110 001, India. FAX 66235. stat.; circ. controlled. **Document type:** government publication.
 Former titles: Indian Petroleum and Petrochemicals Statistics; Indian Petroleum and Chemicals Statistics.

338.27   IO
INDONESIA OIL STATISTICS/STATISTIK PERMINYAKAN INDONESIA. (Text in English) 1971. q. (with a. cum.). Directorate General Oil and Gas, Programming & Reporting Division - Direktorat Jenderal Minyak Dan Gas Bumi, Jln. M.H. Thamrin No. 1, Jakarta 10110, Indonesia. TEL 62-21-30541. FAX 62-21-354987. TELEX 44363. circ. 400.

665.5   US
INTERNATIONAL OIL SPILL DATABASE; international summary and review. a. Cutter Information Corp., 37 Broadway, Arlington, MA 02174. TEL 617-641-5107. FAX 617-648-8707. TELEX 650 100 9891 MCIUW. Ed. Jeff Welch. charts; stat. (also avail. in diskette format)
 Former titles: Worldwide Oil Spill Incident Database; (until 1992): Oil Spill Statistics.
 Description: Provides statistics on oil spills of 10,000 gallons or more, including type of oil spilled, how much, where, source type (tanker, pipeline, rig), name, owner, flag (if vessel), and environmental damage.

665.5 016   UK   ISSN 1052-9292
TN860   CODEN: IPAAET
INTERNATIONAL PETROLEUM ABSTRACTS. 1973. q. $1195 (foreign $1195) (effective 1996). (Institute of Petroleum) John Wiley & Sons Ltd., Journals, Baffins Ln., Chichester, W. Sussex PO19 1UD, England. TEL 01243-779777. FAX 01243-776128. TELEX 86290 WIBOOK G. (Subscr. in the Americas to: John Wiley & Sons, Inc., 605 Third Ave., New York, NY 10158. TEL 212-850-6645. FAX 212-850-6021) Ed. Gretchen E. Taylor. circ. 122. (also avail. in microform from UMI; back issues avail.) **Indexed:** AESIS, Fuel & Energy Abstr. **Document type:** abstracting/indexing.
 ●Also available online. Vendor(s): Orbit Search Service (IPAB)
 —UMI. **CCC.**
 Incorporates: Offshore Abstracts (ISSN 0309-4944)
 Description: Provides an extensive review of the onshore/offshore oil and gas literature, including oil and gas exploration and development, petroleum refining and products, economics and offshore technology.

INTERNATIONAL PETROLEUM STATISTICS REPORT. see
 STATISTICS

PETROLEUM AND GAS — ABSTRACTING, BIBLIOGRAPHIES, STATISTICS

665.773   US
INVENTORIES OF NATURAL GAS LIQUIDS & LIQUIFIED REFINERY GASES. 1956. m. $250 (effective 1995). American Petroleum Institute, Publications Section, 1220 L St., N.W., Washington, DC 20005. TEL 202-682-8378. (Subscr. to: 1970 Chain Bridge Rd., McLean, VA 22109-6000) Ed.Bd. circ. 150. **Document type:** trade publication.
   Formerly (until Apr., 1985): Liquified Petroleum Gas Report (ISSN 0024-421X)
   Description: Presents data on the inventory levels of ethane, propane, isobutane, normal butane and pentanes plus.

665.5   IT
ITALY. MINISTERO DELL'INDUSTRIA DEL COMMERCIO E DELL'ARTIGIANATO; Direzione generale delle fonti di energia e delle industrie di base, bollettino Petrolifero. vol. 30, 1987. q? Ministero dell'Industria del Commercio dell'Artigianato, Direzione Generale delle Fonti di Energia e delle Industrie di Base, Rome, Italy. stat.
   Description: Provides statistical data resulting from surveys of the petroleum firms in various regions of Italy.

665.5   US
JOINT ASSOCIATION SURVEY ON DRILLING COSTS. 1959. a. $110 (Canada $121; elsewhere $137.50) (effective Dec. 1994). American Petroleum Institute, Publications Section, 1220 L St., N.W., Washington, DC 20005. TEL 202-682-8378. (Subscr. to: 1970 Chain Bridge Rd., McLean, VA 22109-6000) circ. 1,600. **Indexed:** SRI. **Document type:** trade publication.
   Description: Provides annual information pertaining to the cost of drilling oil and gas wells and dry holes by state and by depth interval.

662.338 314.85   US   ISSN 0892-4465
Z695.1.P43
K W O C LIST OF PETROLEUM ABSTRACTS' EXPLORATION & PRODUCTION THESAURUS AND NEW EXPLORATION & PRODUCTION TERMS. 1975. a. University of Tulsa, Information Services Division, 600 S. College Ave., Tulsa, OK 74104-3189. TEL 918-631-2297. FAX 918-599-9361.
   Former titles (until 1987): K W O C List of Petroleum Abstracts' Exploration and Production Thesaurus and Addenda Descriptors from the Supplementary Word List (ISSN 0191-2747); (until 1979): K W O C List of Petroleum Abstracts' Exploration and Production Thesaurus and Seldom Used Descriptors from the Supplementary Word List (ISSN 0162-3265)

338.2   UK   ISSN 1350-9071
HD9560.4
KNOW MORE ABOUT OIL: WORLD STATISTICS. a. £1 (first copy free). Institute of Petroleum, 61 New Cavendish St., London W1M 8AR, England. TEL 0171-467-7100. FAX 0171-255-1472. Ed. Lyn Nevin; Pub. Sarah Frost Mellor. stat. **Document type:** academic/scholarly publication.
   —BLDSC (9360.041650).
   Formerly: Oil World Statistics (ISSN 0306-770X)

665.5   LY   ISSN 0075-9260
LIBYA. CENSUS AND STATISTICS DEPARTMENT. REPORT OF THE ANNUAL SURVEY OF PETROLEUM MINING INDUSTRY. (Text in Arabic and English) 1965. a. free. Secretariat of Planning, Census and Statistics Department, P.O. Box 600, Tripoli, Libya. **Document type:** government publication.

665.5 338.2   LY
LIBYA. CENSUS AND STATISTICS DEPARTMENT. REPORT OF THE ANNUAL SURVEY OF UNITS PROVIDING TECHNICAL SERVICES TO THE PETROLEUM MINING INDUSTRY. (Text in Arabic and English) 1965. a. free. Secretariat of Planning, Census and Statistics Department, P.O. Box 600, Tripoli, Libya. **Document type:** government publication.

665.5   US   ISSN 1074-6862
                         CODEN: LOCHEI
LITERATURE ABSTRACT: OILFIELD CHEMICALS. 1981. w. $50 membership only. American Petroleum Institute, Central Abstracting & Information Services, 275 Seventh Ave., New York, NY 10001-6708. TEL 212-366-4040. FAX 212-366-4298. **Document type:** abstracting/indexing.
   ●Also available online. Vendor(s): Orbit Search Service, STN International.
   Former titles (until 1994): Literature and Patent Abstracts: Oilfield Chemicals (ISSN 1065-0547); (until 1992): A P I Abstracts - Oilfield Chemicals.
   Description: Covers the manufacturing and use of chemicals in the oil and gas fields for drilling, well completion and stimulation, oil production, and enhanced recovery. Covers trade magazine articles and scientific journal papers published worldwide, as well as conference papers and patents.

665.5 016   US
LITERATURE ABSTRACTS. 1954. w. price varies. American Petroleum Institute, Central Abstracting & Information Services, 275 Seventh Ave., New York, NY 10001-6708. TEL 212-366-4040. FAX 212-366-4298. Ed. M. Pronin. **Document type:** abstracting/indexing.
   ●Also available online. Vendor(s): Knight-Ridder, Inc., STN International.
   Former titles: A P I Abstracts - Literature; (until 1978): Abstracts of Refining Literature (ISSN 0003-0422); Until 1961: A.P.I. Technical Abstracts (ISSN 0096-5073); Incorporating in part: Abstracts of Health and Environment Literature (ISSN 1065-0490); Abstracts of Petroleum Refining and Petrochemical Literature (ISSN 1065-0512); Abstracts of Petroleum Substitutes Literature (ISSN 1065-0504); Which was formerly titled: Abstracts of Petroleum Substitutes Literature and Patents (ISSN 0003-0414); and Abstracts of Transportation and Storage Literature (ISSN 1065-0520); Which was formerly: Abstracts of Transportation and Storage Literature and Patents (ISSN 0003-0449).
   Description: Abstracts of journal papers; trade magazine articles, meeting papers; dissertations, technical reports; news articles; and other documents on science and technology related to the work of the petroleum refining and petrochemical industry.

LITERATURE ABSTRACTS: FUEL REFORMULATION. see CHEMISTRY — Abstracting, Bibliographies, Statistics

LITERATURE ABSTRACTS: HEALTH & ENVIRONMENT. see MEDICAL SCIENCES — Abstracting, Bibliographies, Statistics

665.5 011   US   ISSN 1065-0512
                         CODEN: LAPPE9
LITERATURE ABSTRACTS: PETROLEUM REFINING AND PETROCHEMICALS. (Part of: Literature Abstracts) 1954. w. American Petroleum Institute, Central Abstracting & Information Services, 275 Seventh Ave., New York, NY 10001-6708. TEL 212-366-4040. FAX 212-366-4298. **Document type:** abstracting/indexing.
   Formerly (until 1991): A P I Abstracts - Petroleum Refining and Petrochemicals.

665.5   US   ISSN 1065-0504
                         CODEN: LAPSEI
LITERATURE ABSTRACTS: PETROLEUM SUBSTITUTES. (Part of: Literature Abstracts) w. American Petroleum Institute, Central Abstracting & Information Services, 275 Seventh Ave., New York, NY 10001-6708. TEL 212-366-4040. FAX 212-366-4298. **Document type:** abstracting/indexing.
   Formerly (until 1991): A P I Abstracts - Petroleum Substitutes.

LITERATURE ABSTRACTS: TRIBOLOGY. see CHEMISTRY — Abstracting, Bibliographies, Statistics

665.5   CN
MANITOBA PETROLEUM ROYALTY AND TAX INFORMATION. 1982. irreg. free. Manitoba Energy and Mines, Petroleum Branch, 360-1395 Ellice Ave., Winnipeg, MB R3G 3P2, Canada. TEL 204-945-6577. FAX 204-945-0586. Ed. L.R. Dubreuil. circ. 400. **Document type:** government publication.
   Description: Irregularly issued booklet with a general overview of petroleum royalty-tax structure and incentive programs operating in Manitoba, Canada.

016 665   FR   ISSN 0752-5508
MEDIAGAZ. 1927. 11/yr. 850 F. (foreign 950 F.). Association Technique de l'Industrie du Gaz en France, 62 rue de Courcelles, 75008 Paris, France. Ed. Alain Thibault. bk.rev.; abstr.; pat.; stat. circ. 200. **Indexed:** Fuel & Energy Abstr. **Document type:** bulletin.
   Formerly (until 1982): Association Technique de l'Industrie du Gaz en France. Bulletin Bibliographique Mensuel.

665.7   US   ISSN 0085-3429
                        CODEN: MGSDA3
MICHIGAN'S OIL AND GAS FIELDS: ANNUAL STATISTICAL SUMMARY. 1964. a. price varies. Department of Natural Resources, Geological Survey Division, Information Services Center, Box 30028, Lansing, MI 48909. TEL 517-334-6907.

665.5   RU
NEFTYANIK (MOSCOW, 1974). (Abstracts from Petroleum Engineer and Pipeline & Gas Journal) 1974. m. 21 Rub. Izdatel'stvo Nedra, Pl. Belorusskogo Vokzala, 3, 125047 Moscow, Russia. TEL 250-52-55. adv. circ. 3,000.
   Formerly: Inzhener - Naftyanik.

338.4   NO   ISSN 0377-1806
TN867
NORWEGIAN OFFSHORE INDEX. (Text in English) 1974. a. free. (Export Council of Norway) Selvig Publishing A-S, P.O. Box 9070 Groenland, 0133 Oslo, Norway. TEL 22-364440. FAX 22-360550. (Co-sponsor: Federation of Norwegian Industries) circ. controlled. **Document type:** abstracting/indexing.
   —CCC.

016.33847   KU
O A P E C LIBRARY INDEX OF PERIODICAL ARTICLES. (Text in Arabic, English) 1982-1989. q. free. Organization of Arab Petroleum Exporting Countries, P.O. Box 20501, Safat 13066, Kuwait. TEL 965-4844500. FAX 965-4815747. TELEX 22166 NAFARAB KT. **Document type:** abstracting/indexing.
   Formerly: O A P E C Library Index.
   Description: Subject index of periodical articles received by OAPEC's library on energy, petroleum and economic development.

665.5 338.2   FR   ISSN 1016-5010
O E C D OIL AND GAS INFORMATION/O C D E DONNEES SUR LE PETROLE ET SUR LE GAZ. (Text in English, French) 1970. a. price varies. Organization for Economic Cooperation and Development, 2 rue Andre-Pascal, 75775 Paris Cedex 16, France. (U.S. orders to: O.E.C.D. Publications and Information Center, 2001 L St., N.W., Ste. 700, Washington, DC 20036-4910. TEL 202-785-6323) charts; stat. (also avail. in microfiche from OEC,CIS; back issues avail.) **Indexed:** IIS.
   Former titles: O E C D. Annual Oil and Gas Statistics - O C D E. Statistiques Annuelles des Hydrocarbures et du Gaz Naturel; Organization for Economic Cooperation and Development. Oil Statistics - Statistiques Petrolieres; Organization for Economic Cooperation and Development. Provisional Oil Statistics - Statistiques Petrolieres Provisoires (ISSN 0029-7062)

338.2 665.5   FR   ISSN 0474-6007
HD9575.A12
O E C D OIL STATISTICS. SUPPLY AND DISPOSAL. (Text in English, French) 1961. irreg. Organization for Economic Cooperation and Development, 2 rue Andre-Pascal, 75775 Paris Cedex 16, France. (U.S. orders to: O.E.C.D. Publications and Information Center, 2001 L St., N.W., Ste. 700, Washington, D.C. 20036-4910. TEL 202-785-6323) (also avail. in microfiche)

PETROLEUM AND GAS — ABSTRACTING, BIBLIOGRAPHIES, STATISTICS

665.5   FR   ISSN 1013-9362
O E C D QUARTERLY OIL STATISTICS AND ENERGY BALANCES. (Text in English, French) vol.2, 1978. q. $175. Organization for Economic Cooperation and Development, 2 rue Andre-Pascal, 75775 Paris Cedex 16, France. (U.S. Orders to: O.E.C.D. Publications and Information Center, 2001 L St., N.W., Ste. 700, Washington, DC 20036-4910. TEL 202-785-6323) (also avail. in microfiche from OEC,CIS) **Indexed:** IIS.
●Also available online.
—BLDSC (7196.850100).
Former titles: Organization for Economic Cooperation and Development. Quarterly Oil and Gas Statistics; Organization for Economic Cooperation and Development. Quarterly Oil Statistics (ISSN 0378-6536)
Description: Provides detailed data on production of crude oil, natural gas, liquids as well as refinery feedstocks, crude oil and product trades; refinery intake and output; final consumption; stock levels and changes.

662.338   US   ISSN 1067-103X
OFFSHORE TECHNOLOGY. 1993. m. $195. University of Tulsa, Information Services Division, 600 S. College Ave., Tulsa, OK 74104-3189. TEL 918-631-2297; 800-247-8678. FAX 918-599-9361. TELEX 497543. E-mail: question@TUred.pa.utulsa.edu. **Document type:** abstracting/indexing.

338.47   US
HD9561
OIL & NATURAL GAS PRODUCING INDUSTRY IN YOUR STATE. (Statistical issue of: Petroleum Independent (ISSN 0747-2528)) 1939. a. $75. (Independent Petroleum Association of America) Petroleum Independent Publishers, Inc., 1101 16th St., N.W., Washington, DC 20036. TEL 202-857-4774; 800-433-2851. FAX 202-857-4799. Ed.Scott Espenshade. adv.; charts; illus.; stat. circ. 7,000. **Indexed:** SRI. **Document type:** trade publication.
Former titles: Oil and Gas Producing Industry in Your State; (until 1984): Oil Producing Industry in Your State.

665.538   US
OIL - ENERGY STATISTICS BULLETIN; and Canadian oil reports. 1923. bi-w. $185. Oil Statistics Company, Inc., Box 189, Whitman, MA 02382. Ed. John J. McGilvray. adv. contact: Jennifer L. McGilvray. **Document type:** newsletter.

OIL IMPORTS INTO THE UNITED STATES AND PUERTO RICO (E I A 814). see *BUSINESS AND ECONOMICS — Abstracting, Bibliographies, Statistics*

338.2 665.5   AU   ISSN 0475-0608
HD9560.4
ORGANIZATION OF THE PETROLEUM EXPORTING COUNTRIES. ANNUAL STATISTICAL BULLETIN. 1965. a. S.690. Organization of the Petroleum Exporting Countries, Information Department, Obere Donaustr. 93, A-1020 Vienna, Austria. TEL 01-21112. FAX 01-2149827. (also avail. in microfiche from CIS; diskette format) **Indexed:** IIS. **Document type:** bulletin.
—BLDSC (1531.944000).
Description: Contains oil and gas data, summary tables and basic indicators of imports, exports, oil reserves, and refined products. Also covers oil transportation, oil prices and the major oil companies. Includes maps.

665.5 016   US
PATENTS ABSTRACTS. 1960. w. price varies. American Petroleum Institute, Central Abstracting & Information Services, 275 Seventh Ave., New York, NY 10001-6708. TEL 212-366-4040. FAX 212-366-4298. **Document type:** abstracting/indexing.
●Also available online. Vendor(s): Orbit Search Service, STN International.
Formerly: A P I Abstracts - Patents; Supersedes (in 1977): A P I Patent Alert; Which was formerly (until 1971): American Petroleum Institute. Abstracts of Refining Patents (ISSN 0003-0430)
Description: Reports worldwide patents related to the work of the petroleum refining and petrochemical industry with coverage in the chemicals and polymers areas.

665.5   MX   ISSN 0186-3401
PEMEX. BOLETIN BIBLIOGRAFICO. (Text in English) vol.31, 1986. m. free. Petroleos Mexicanos, Unidad de Servicios Sociales y Culturales, Biblioteca Central, Marina Nacional 329, Edif. A, Mezzanine, 11300 Mexico, D.F., Mexico. circ. 3,000. **Document type:** abstracting/indexing.
Formerly: Petroleos Mexicanos. Boletin Bibliografico.
Description: Contains abstracts from scientific and technical journals.

665.5 016   US   ISSN 0031-6423
TN860
PETROLEUM ABSTRACTS. 1961. w. (50/yr.). service basis. University of Tulsa, Information Services Division, 600 S. College Ave., Tulsa, OK 74104-3189. TEL 918-631-2297; 800-247-8678. FAX 918-599-9361. E-mail: question@TUred.pa.utulsa.edu. illus.; stat.; index, cum.index. (also avail. in microform) **Document type:** abstracting/indexing.
●Also available online. Vendor(s): Knight-Ridder, Inc. (PEP), Orbit Search Service (TULSA).
Also available on CD-ROM. Producer(s): Knight-Ridder, Inc..
Description: Abstracts from worldwide petroleum-related literature dealing with exploration and production.

665.5   CN
PETROLEUM AND NATURAL GAS PRODUCTION TAPE. m. Can.$1500. Ministry of Energy, Mines and Petroleum Resources, Energy Resources Division, 7th Fl., 1810 Blanshard St., Victoria, BC V8V 1X4, Canada. (Subscr. to: Crown Publications, 546 Yates St., Victoria, BC V8W 1K8, Canada. TEL 604-386-4636) (magnetic tape) **Document type:** government publication.
Description: Lists all oil and gas wells ever drilled in BC, historical production records for all wells from 1954, amounts produced and number of days productive.

665.5 016   US   ISSN 0098-7743
Z6972
PETROLEUM - ENERGY BUSINESS NEWS INDEX. 1975. m. $850. American Petroleum Institute, Central Abstracting & Information Services, 275 Seventh Ave., New York, NY 10001-6708. TEL 212-366-4040. FAX 212-366-4298. **Document type:** abstracting/indexing.
●Also available online. Vendor(s): Data-Star (PEAB), Knight-Ridder, Inc., Orbit Search Service (ABIZ).
Description: Provides access to political, economic, and social news and economic studies that may affect the petroleum, petrochemical, and energy industries.

666.5 338.2   US   ISSN 1047-630X
HD9560.1
PETROLEUM MARKET INTELLIGENCE. (Supplementary data diskettes avail.) 1987. m. $695 ($1095 with data diskettes) (effective 1995). Petroleum & Energy Intelligence Weekly, Inc., 575 Broadway, 4th Fl., New York, NY 10012-3230. TEL 212-941-5500. FAX 212-941-5508. TELEX 62371 PETROIN. Ed. Tom Wallin. charts; illus.; stat. **Document type:** trade publication.
—SWETS.
Description: Provides analyses of regional pricing, production figures, and key statistics on the oil market.

665.5   CN
PETROLEUM TITLES DATA TAPE. m. Can.$4200. Ministry of Energy, Mines and Petroleum Resources, Energy Resources Division, 7th Fl., 1810 Blanshard St., Victoria, BC V8V 1X4, Canada. (Subscr. to: Crown Publications, 546 Yates St., Victoria, BC V8W 1K8, Canada. TEL 604-386-4636) (magnetic tape) **Document type:** government publication.
Description: Contains information on each active provincial petroleum and natural gas tenure inclusive of term, tenure holder, location, rights conveyed, continuation and renewals.

665.7 338.39   US
PROPANE MARKET FACTS; statistical handbook of the LP-gas industry. 1950. a. $8. National Propane Gas Association, 1600 Eisenhower Ln., Ste. 100, Lisle, IL 60532. Ed. M.A. Spear. index. (diskette format) **Indexed:** SRI.
Former titles: Propane Industry Profile; L P - Gas Market Facts (ISSN 0075-9759)
Description: Presents market research information about the industry on a historical basis.

665.5   US
SALES OF NATURAL GAS LIQUIDS AND LIQUIFIED REFINERY GASES (YEAR). a. $110 (effective 1995). American Petroleum Institute, Publications Section, 1220 L St., N.W., Washington, DC 20005. TEL 202-682-8378. (Subscr. to: 1970 Chain Bridge Rd., McLean, VA 22109-6000) **Indexed:** SRI. **Document type:** trade publication.
Description: Provides information on the annual sales to consumers, and internal company use, of ethane, propane, butane and pentanes plus. Data are categorized by state and by the type of use, that is: residential and commercial, industrial, chemical.

665.7   NE   ISSN 0081-5225
TP733.N4
STATISTIEK VAN DE GASVOORZIENING IN NEDERLAND. 1953. a. Centraal Bureau voor de Statistiek, Prinses Beatrixlaan 428, Voorburg, Netherlands. (Orders to: SDU - Publishers, Christoffel Plantijnstraat, The Hague, Netherlands) circ. 375. **Document type:** government publication.

338.4   FR   ISSN 0767-7588
STATISTIQUES DE L'INDUSTRIE GAZIERE EN FRANCE. a. free. Direction du Gaz, de l'Electricite et du Charbon, 97-99, rue de Grenelle, 75700 Paris Cedex, France. FAX 43-19-49-92. TELEX DIGEC 250 757 F. charts; stat. **Document type:** government publication.
Formerly: France. Direction du Gaz et de l'Electricite. Statistiques Officielles de l'Industrie Gaziere en France (ISSN 0429-3843)
Description: Covers statistics in the French gas industry.

SUMMARY OF RATE SCHEDULES OF NATURAL GAS PIPELINE COMPANIES. see *ENERGY — Abstracting, Bibliographies, Statistics*

665.5 310   US
TEXAS PETRO FACTS. a. $11. Railroad Commission, Oil and Gas Publications, Drawer 12967, Capitol Sta., Austin, TX 78711. TEL 512-463-7255. charts; stat. **Document type:** government publication.
Description: Compiles monthly and annual statistical data on energy, energy prices, and the economy. Data are summarized by month and by year for Texas and the entire U.S.

665.8 338.2   US
TRANSPORTATION ACCIDENT BRIEFS. PIPELINE. (Subseries of: Transportation Accident Briefs) irreg. (approx. 6/yr.). price varies. (U.S. Department of Transportation, National Transportation Safety Board) U.S. National Technical Information Service, 5825 Port Royal Rd., Springfield, VA 22161. TEL 703-487-4630. FAX 703-321-8547. **Document type:** government publication.

665.8 338.2   US
TRANSPORTATION ACCIDENT REPORTS. PIPELINE. (Subseries of: Transportation Accident Reports) irreg. (approx. 6/yr.). price varies. (U.S. Department of Transportation, National Transportation Safety Board) U.S. National Technical Information Service, 5825 Port Royal Rd., Springfield, VA 22161. TEL 703-487-4630. FAX 703-321-8547. **Document type:** government publication.

TURKEY. DEVLET ISTATISTIK ENSTITUSU. GAZ VE SU ISTATISTIKLERI/TURKEY. STATE INSTITUTE OF STATISTICS. GAS AND WATER STATISTICS. see *ENERGY — Abstracting, Bibliographies, Statistics*

665.5   US
U.S. DEPARTMENT OF ENERGY. BARTLESVILLE PROJECT OFFICE. PUBLICATION LIST. s-a. free. U.S. Department of Energy, Bartlesville Project Office, Box 1398, Bartlesville, OK 74005. TEL 918-337-4298. (Orders to: National Technical Information Service, 4285 Port Royal Rd., Springfield, VA 22161. TEL 703-487-4650. FAX 703-321-8547) **Document type:** bibliography, government publication.
Description: Lists D.O.E. and D.O.E.-sponsored publications on oil recovery.

338.2 VE
VENEZUELA. MINISTERIO DE ENERGIA Y MINAS. PETROLEO Y OTROS DATOS ESTADISTICOS. English edition: Venezuelan Petroleum Industry. Statistical Data. a. Bs.3000. Ministerio de Energia y Minas, Direccion de Economia de Hidrocarburos, Torre Oeste, Piso 9, Parque Central, Caracas, Venezuela. (Subscr. to: Ministerio de Energia y Minas, Biblioteca Torre Oeste Piso 9, Parque Central, Caracas-Venezuela) **Document type:** government publication.
Formerly: Venezuela. Ministerio de Minas e Hidrocarburos. Oficina de Economia Petrolera. Petroleo y Otros Datos Estadisticos (ISSN 0083-5390)

665.5 US
WEEKLY OXYGENATE REPORT. w. $575 (effective 1995). American Petroleum Institute, Publications Section, 1220 L St., N.W., Washington, DC 20005. TEL 202-682-8378. (Subscr. to: 1970 Chain Bridge Rd., McLean, VA 22109-6000) **Document type:** trade publication.
Description: Summarizes oxygenate production and inventories at the national level and at the PAD district level as well.

PETROLEUM AND GAS — Computer Applications

665.5 US ISSN 1073-6425
PETRO SYSTEMS WORLD; the computer magazine for the oil & gas professional. 1993. bi-m. $59. Hart Publications, 1900 Grant St., Ste. 400, Denver, CO 80203. TEL 303-832-1917. FAX 303-837-8585. Ed. Robert C. Jarvis. adv. contact: Gary Meyer. bk.rev.; abstr.; charts; stat.; tr.lit. circ. 12,000. (back issues avail.) **Document type:** trade publication.
—UMI. CCC.
Description: Targeted to managers with authority for computer hardware, software and consulting services in the petroleum exploration and production industry.

PETS

see also Animal Welfare

636.8 US ISSN 0744-9631
A C F A BULLETIN. 1955. bi-m. $15 membership. American Cat Fanciers Association, Inc., Box 203, Point Lookout, MO 65726. TEL 417-334-5430. FAX 417-334-5540. Ed. Wini Keuler. adv.; circ. 2,000 (paid). (processed) **Document type:** newsletter.

636.8 AT
A C I YEAR BOOK. 1978. a. Aus.$3.50 per no. Australian Cat Federation, Inc., c/o Ms. J. Ruasack, 32 Tarrant St., Prospect, S.A. 5082, Australia. adv. circ. 1,000. (back issues avail)

636 US
SF421
A K C GAZETTE. 1889. m. $28 (Canada $38; elsewhere $43). American Kennel Club, Inc., 51 Madison Ave., New York, NY 10010. TEL 212-696-8333. FAX 212-696-8299. Ed. Diane Vasey. adv.: B&W page $2675, color page $3850; trim 8 1/4 x 10 3/4. bk.rev.; bibl.; illus. circ. 55,000. (also avail. in microform from UMI; reprint service avail. from UMI) **Indexed:** InterActions Bibl.
—UMI; UnCover.
Formerly: Pure-Bred Dogs, American Kennel Gazette (ISSN 0033-4561)

636 US
A M C CENTERSCOPE. 3/yr. donation. Animal Medical Center, 510 E. 62nd St., New York, NY 10021. TEL 212-838-8100. FAX 212-832-9630. Ed. Erin McGrath. illus. circ. 15,000. **Document type:** newsletter.

636.7 US
A M S C O P E NEWSLETTER.* m. American Miniature Schnauzer Club, c/o Carma Ewer, Ed., 8882 Easthills Dr., Sandy, TX 84093-1813. circ. 500. **Document type:** newsletter.

599 AT
ABYSSINIAN. 1967. s-a. Aus.$16. Abyssinian Cat Club of Australasia, G.P.O. Box 2323, Sydney, N.S.W. 2001, Australia. TEL 61-6-2369133. Ed. Diane Royal. adv.; circ. 350. **Document type:** newsletter.

636.7 US
ADVOCATE (OLD BROOKVILLE). 1967. q. $10. Owner Handler Association of America, c/o Mildred Mesh, Six Michaels Ln., Old Brookville, NY 11545. circ. 2,000.

636.7 US
AFGHAN HOUND CLUB OF AMERICA. BULLETIN. 3/yr. membership only. Afghan Hound Club of America, c/o Norma Cozzoni, Ed., 43 W. 612 Tall Oaks Trail, Elburn, IL 60119. TEL 708-365-2050. **Document type:** bulletin.

636.7 US ISSN 8750-9776
SF429.A4
AFGHAN HOUND REVIEW. 1974. bi-m. $40 (foreign $48). Showdogs Publications, Box 30430, Santa Barbara, CA 93130-0430. TEL 805-966-7270. Ed. Bo Bengtson; Pub. Paul Lepiane. adv.: B&W page $145, color page $1000; adv. contact: Francine Reisman. bk.rev. circ. 1,800. **Document type:** trade publication.
Description: Contains information and photographs of Afghan Hound showdogs.

636.7 US
AIREDALE TERRIER CLUB OF AMERICA. NEWSLETTER. 1900. 5/yr. membership. Airedale Terrier Club of America, c/o Aletta Moore, Epoch Farm, 14181 County Rd.-40, Carver, MN 55315. Ed. Richard Schlicht. circ. 700.

636.7 US
AKITA DOG. 1973. m. $15. Akita Club of America, 2155 Hackamore Pl., Riverside, CA 92506. Ed. Debbie de Fonzo. adv. circ. 600.
Formerly: Akita Magazine.

636.7 US ISSN 0745-1296
AKITA WORLD. 1982. bi-m. $48. Hoflin Publishing Ltd., 4401 Zephyr St., Wheat Ridge, CO 80033-3259. TEL 303-934-5656. FAX 303-422-7000.

636.7 US
ALASKAN GANGLINE. 1979. 8/yr. $16. 400 Denali, Wasilla, AK 99687. FAX 907-326-2081. Ed. Lavon Barve. adv. circ. 500.
Description: Explores the sport of dog sledding.

636.7 US ISSN 0199-1310
ALASKAN MALAMUTE CLUB OF AMERICA. NEWSLETTER. m. membership. Alaskan Malamute Club of America, Inc., c/o Kris Campes, Ed., 14134 Walton Dr., Manassas, VA 22111. TEL 703-791-5567. adv.; bk.rev. circ. 800. **Document type:** newsletter.

636 362.42 US ISSN 1069-0743
ALERT (RENTON). 1990. q. $7.50 (foreign $10). Delta Society, Box 1080, 321 Burnett Ave., S., 3rd Fl., Renton, WA 98055. TEL 206-226-7357. FAX 206-226-7357. Ed. Linda M. Hines. circ. 1,000. **Document type:** newsletter.
Description: Deals with service dogs and issues of interest to their owners, trainers, and persons with disabilities.

636 GW ISSN 0720-2849
ALLES FUER DIE KATZ. 1981. bi-m. DM.8.50($4.30) Gabriele Sparrenberger, Ed. & Pub., Postfach 800627, 6230 Frankfurt a.M. 80, Germany. (looseleaf format; back issues avail.)

636.7 US ISSN 0891-5555
ALPENHORN. 1967. bi-m. $20 to non-members. Bernese Mountain Dog Club of America, 5706 Keating Rd., N.W., Olympia, WA 98502. TEL 360-866-7875. Ed. Elizabeth Pearson. adv.; bk.rev. circ. 1,300. **Document type:** newsletter.
Former titles: B M D C A; Bernese Mountain Dog Club of America. Newsletter.
Description: Contains dog-related articles, club news and information.

636.7 US ISSN 0199-7297
SF429.B78
AMERICAN BRITTANY. 1948? m. $25 membership. American Brittany Club, Inc., Box 616, Marshfield, MO 65706. TEL 417-468-6250. FAX 417-468-5860. Ed. Ronnie C. Smith. adv.; bk.rev. circ. 4,000. **Document type:** bulletin.
Description: Covers field trials, shows, hunting and general information on Brittanys.

636.7 US
AMERICAN BULLMASTIFF ASSOCIATION. BULLETIN. 3/yr. $45 membership. American Bullmastiff Association, Inc., c/o Mary Anne Duchin, Box 137 D, Burger Rd., Melbourne, KY 41059. Ed. Chris Lezotte. adv.; bk.rev. circ. 425. **Document type:** bulletin.

AMERICAN CAGE-BIRD MAGAZINE. see *BIOLOGY — Ornithology*

636.932 US
AMERICAN CHECKERED GIANT RABBIT CLUB. NEWS BULLETIN. bi-m. American Checkered Giant Rabbit Club, Box 481, Grand Prarie, TX 75051. TEL 214-264-1099.

636.7 US
AMERICAN CHESAPEAKE CLUB. BULLETIN. bi-m. c/o Patricia A. Puwal, 4439 Sargent Ave., Castro Valley, CA 94546.

636.7 US ISSN 0279-358X
AMERICAN COCKER MAGAZINE. 1981. bi-m. $36. American Cocker Magazine, Inc., 14531 Jefferson St., Midway City, CA 92655. TEL 714-893-0053. Ed. Michael Allen. adv.; bk.rev. circ. 4,000. **Document type:** bulletin.

598 US
AMERICAN DOVE ASSOCIATION NEWSLETTER. 1955. bi-m. $10 to individuals; juniors $5; senior citizens $7.50; families $12.50. American Dove Association, c/o Rita M. Courtney, Ed., Box 21, Milton, KY 40045. adv.; bk.rev.; illus. circ. 400.
Formerly: American Dove Association. Monthly Bulletin.

636 658.048 US
AMERICAN FANCY RAT AND MOUSE ASSOCIATION YEARBOOK. 1985. a. membership. American Fancy Rat and Mouse Association, 9230 64th St., Riverside, CA 92509. TEL 909-685-2350. Ed. Karen Robbins. adv. contact: Karen Robbins. circ. 300. **Document type:** directory.
Description: List of members, officers, champions, show results, trophy winners and dates, veterinarian referrals, addresses of similar clubs, upcoming show and display dates.

636.7 US ISSN 0888-627X
AMERICAN KENNEL CLUB AWARDS; new titles and results from shows, obedience trials, tracking tests, field trials and hunting tests. 1981. m. $40 (Canada $50; elsewhere $55). American Kennel Club, Inc., 51 Madison Ave., New York, NY 10010. TEL 212-696-8260. FAX 212-696-8299. circ. 13,500. (also avail. in microfilm from UMI)
Formerly: American Kennel Club. Show, Obedience and Field Trial Awards (ISSN 0272-4383)
Description: Provides with new titles, and results from shows, obedience trals, tracking tests, field trals hunting tests and lerding and lure coursing tests and trials.

636.7 US
AMERICAN MANCHESTER TERRIER CLUB. NEWSLETTER. 1961. bi-m. membership. c/o Muriel S. Henkel, 4961 N.E. 193 St., Seattle, WA 98155. adv. circ. 200. **Document type:** newsletter.

636.7 US
AMERICAN SALUKI ASSOCIATION. NEWSLETTER. 1963. q. membership only. c/o Sally Bell, 14118 228th St., S.E., Snohomish, WA 98290. circ. 600. **Document type:** newsletter.

636.7 US
AMERICAN SHETLAND SHEEPDOG ASSOCIATION. BULLETIN BOARD. q. membership. American Shetland Sheepdog Association, c/o Susan Beacham, Corresponding Sec., 2125 E. 16th Ave., ID 83854. TEL 208-773-4256. Ed. Diana Rockwell. circ. 714.
Formerly: American Shetland Sheepdog Association. Bulletin.

636.7 US
AMERICAN SPANIEL CLUB. BULLETIN. 1951. q. membership. American Spaniel Club, 848 Old Stevens Creek Rd., Martinez, GA 30907-9227. FAX 706-860-0881. Ed. Barbara J. Hoops. circ. 1,500. **Document type:** newsletter.

PETS

636.932 US
AMERICAN STANDARD CHINCHILLA RABBIT ASSOCIATION. NEWSLETTER. bi-m. American Standard Chinchilla Rabbit Association, c/o Patricia Gest, 1607 Ninth St. W., Palmetto, FL 34221. TEL 813-729-1184. **Document type:** newsletter.

636 FR ISSN 0246-1854
ANIMAL DISTRIBUTION. 1989. 8/yr. 300 F. Editions J, B.P. 30, 78511 Rambouillet Cedex, France. TEL 34-84-70-60. FAX 34-84-70-55. TELEX 695 589. Ed. Eric Leforestier. adv. contact: Francois-Regis Arnoult. circ. 10,000. **Document type:** newspaper, trade publication.

ANIMAL FINDERS' GUIDE. see AGRICULTURE — Poultry And Livestock

636 US
ANIMAL NEWS. 1981. 3/yr. free. Morris Animal Foundation, 45 Inverness Dr. E., Englewood, CO 80112. TEL 303-790-2345. FAX 303-790-4066. Ed. Janice Rooney. bk.rev. circ. 100,000. (tabloid format)
 Formerly (until 1995): Companion Animal News.
 Description: Contains articles on animal health studies, scientific information and updates on awards and honors given by the Morris Animal Foundation.

ANIMAL PEOPLE. see ANIMAL WELFARE

636 US ISSN 0003-360X
ANIMALDOM. 1930. m. (except Aug.). $2 to non-members. Pennsylvania S.P.C.A., 350 E. Erie Ave., Philadelphia, PA 19134. TEL 215-426-6300. Ed. Charlene W. Peters. bk.rev.; illus.; circ. 42,000 (controlled). **Document type:** newsletter.

636 FR ISSN 0296-6700
ANIMALERIE. 1985. 9/yr. Bureau Europeen de Presse et de Publicite, 59 rue du Faubourg-Poissonniere, 75009 Paris, France. TEL 47-70-94-62. FAX 45-23-36-81. Ed. Michel Chansiaux. circ. 10,000.

636 US
▼**ANIMALTOWN NEWS;** news for animal lovers of all kinds. 1994. m. $6. Killian Graphics, Box 91, Chatham, NJ 07928. Ed. Judy Killian. adv. contact: Ron Christopher. bk.rev.; illus. **Document type:** consumer publication.
 Description: Contains a wide variety of general-interest articles on animals and fish kept as pets, including detailed descriptions of specific breeds. Also publishes articles on pet health and how to deal with the loss of a pet.

636 US ISSN 0899-045X
AQUARIUM FISH MAGAZINE; your guide to successful fishkeeping. 1988. m. $23.97. Fancy Publications, 2401 Beverly Blvd., Los Angeles, CA 90057. TEL 213-385-2222. FAX 714-855-8822. (Subscr. to: Box 6040, Mission Viejo, CA 92690) Ed. Edward Bauman. adv. circ. 75,000. (back issues avail.)
 Description: Covers freshwater and saltwater aquariums and ponds and pond fish. Provides information on the hobby for beginners and experienced hobbyists.

636 IT
ARGOS (MILAN, 1987). 1987. m. L.62000 (foreign L.93000). Motta Periodici s.r.l., Via Branda Castiglioni, 2-A, 20156 Milan, Italy. TEL 02-38-00-29-01. FAX 02-38-00-34-67. Ed. Umberto Costamanga. adv.: B&W page L.9000000, color page L.14000000.

636.7 US
ARISTOCRAT.* 1903. q. $30 to non-members. Borzoi Club of America, c/o Sandy Zeboski, Corres. Sec., Box 2149, Spring, TX 77383-2149. TEL 713-320-0419. Ed. Sanoy Zeboski. adv.; bk.rev. circ. 600. **Document type:** newsletter.
 Formerly: Borzoi Yearbook.
 Description: Covers all aspects of living with and raising purebred Borzoi dogs.

636.7 US
ARK (COLORADO SPRINGS).* 1974. bi-m. $15. American Rottweiler Club, c/o W.M. Gruenerwald & Associates, Box 60669, Colorado Springs, CO 80960-0669. Ed. Dorothea Gruenerwald. circ. 1,200.

636.7 US
ASSOCIATION OF OBEDIENCE CLUBS AND JUDGES. NEWSLETTER. 1950. q. Association of Obedience Clubs and Judges, c/o Patricia Scully, 328 Parkside Dr., Suffern, NY 10901. circ. 500. **Document type:** newsletter.

598 AT
AUSTRALIAN CANARY BREEDER. 1970. m. Aus.$1 per no. Canary Breeders' Association of Australia, 13 Robina Rd., Eaglemont, Vic. 3084, Australia. Ed. S.J. Leaney.

636.7 US
AUSTRALIAN TERRIER CLUB OF AMERICA NEWSLETTER. 1959. q. $6 to non-members. Australian Terrier Club of America, c/o Mrs. Milton Fox, 1411 Dorsett Dock Rd., Pt. Pleasant, NJ 08742. TEL 201-899-0557. Ed. Mae Roo. adv. circ. 250. (processed) **Document type:** newsletter.

AVICULTURAL JOURNAL. see BIOLOGY — Ornithology

636.752 DK ISSN 0905-7080
AVLS- OG AARBOG FOR LANGHAARET HOENSEHUND. Key Title: Avls- og Aarbog for Langhaaret Hoensehund (1987). 1982. a. DKK 40. Klubben for den Langhaarede Hoensehund, c/o Peter Werther, Strandvejen 136, DK-3300 Frederiksvaerk, Denmark. illus.
 Former titles (until 1987): T L Aarbog (ISSN 0109-6060); (until 1984): Avls- og Aarbog for Langhaaret Hoensehund (ISSN 0109-6052)

636 UK
BARBARA WOODHOUSE ANIMAL ANNUAL. a. Grandreams Ltd., Jadwin Hse., 205/211 Kentish Town Rd., London, NW5 2JH, England.

636.7 US
BARKS.* 1977? q. $10. Bull Terrier Club of America, 6239 Genoa Rd., Belvidere, IL 61008. Ed. Mary Jung. circ. 400.

636.7 US ISSN 0094-9744
SF429.B15
BASENJI. 1964. m. $22. Jon and Susan Coe, Eds. & Pubs., 789 Linton Hill Rd., Newtown, PA 18940-1207. TEL 215-860-8254. adv.; bk.rev.; illus.; stat. circ. 1,500. (back issues avail.)
 Description: Oriented to the needs & interests of Basenji fanciers & breeders.

636.7 US
BASENJI CLUB OF AMERICA. OFFICIAL BULLETIN. 1942. bi-m. Basenji Club of America, 2435 Hibiscus Dr., Hayward, CA 94545. circ. 600.

636.7 SW ISSN 0345-1321
BASSETBLADET. 1971. q. SEK 130 membership (effective 1991). Svenska Bassetklubben - SBK, c/o I. Dahl, Larkv. 1, S-690 45 Aasbro, Sweden.

636.7 SW ISSN 0283-4138
BEAGLE (TYRESOE). 1953. q. SEK 100 membership (effective 1990). Svenska Beagleklubben, c/o B.J. Ekelund, Kjulav. 3 A, Taaby, Sweden.

636.7 US ISSN 0736-9743
BETTER BEAGLING. 1977. m. $14. Box 142, Essex, VT 05451. TEL 802-878-3616. Ed. Pearl N. Baker. adv.: B&W page $157; trim 8 1/2 x 11. bk.rev. circ. 6,000.
 Formerly: Large Pack.
 Description: Covers breeding and care of beagle hunting hounds.

636.7 US ISSN 0199-8315
BICHON FRISE REPORTER. 1979. q. $32. Reporter Publications, Box 6369, Los Osos, CA 93412. TEL 805-528-2007. FAX 805-528-8200. Ed. Jean Fergus. adv. contact: Jean Fergus. bk.rev. **Document type:** consumer publication.

179.3 US
BIDE-A-WEE NEWS. 1969. q. contribution. Bide-A-Wee Home Association, 410 E. 38th St., New York, NY 10016. FAX 212-532-4210. Ed. George Wirt. bk.rev. circ. 40,000. (back issues avail.) **Document type:** newsletter.

636 598 US
▼**BIRD BREEDER.** 1994. m. $29.97. Fancy Publications, 2401 Beverly Blvd., Los Angles, CA 90057. TEL 714-855-8822. FAX 714-855-8822. adv.; illus.; index.

636.569 UK ISSN 0955-4238
BIRD KEEPER. 1988. bi-m. £8.75($18) I P C Magazines, Specialist Magazine Group (Subsidiary of: Reed Elsevier group), King's Reach Tower, Stamford St., London SE1 9LS, England. TEL 071-261-6116. FAX 071-261-7851. TELEX 892084 REEDBP G. (Dist. by: Quadrant Subscription Services, Oakfield House, Perrymount Rd., Haywards Heath, W. Sussex RH16 3DH, England. TEL 0444-440421) Ed. Peter Moss. **Document type:** consumer publication.
 Description: All aspects of birdkeeping for the beginner and enthusiast.

636 598.2 US ISSN 0891-771X
BIRD TALK. 1982. m. $25.97; newsstand price: $3.50. Fancy Publications, 2401 Beverly Blvd., Los Angeles, CA 90057. TEL 213-385-2222. FAX 714-855-8822. (Subscr. to: Box 57347, Boulder, CO 80322-7347) Ed. Julie Ann Rach. adv. circ. 146,000. **Indexed:** Sport Fish.Abstr., Wild.Rev. **Document type:** consumer publication.
 —UnCover.
 Formerly: International Bird Talk (ISSN 0742-8359)
 Description: Contains information on understanding and caring for all types of cage and aviary birds. Covers species, medical aspects, bird care and behavior, and special birds. Includes questions and answers.

BIRD WORLD. see BIOLOGY — Ornithology

636 US ISSN 1041-1550
SF460
BIRDS U S A. 1989. a. $5.95. Fancy Publications, 2401 Beverly Blvd., Los Angeles, CA 90057. TEL 213-385-2222. FAX 714-855-8822. Ed. Karyn New. adv. circ. 110,500. **Document type:** consumer publication.
 Description: Contains articles on the basics of bird care for the pet bird owner.

636.7 SW ISSN 1101-1491
BJOERNHUNDEN. 1973. q. SEK 120 membership (effective 1990). Svenska Bjoernhundsklubben, c/o E. Forsgren, Mossg. 3, S-931 40 Skellefteaa, Sweden.

636 SW ISSN 0006-4076
BLAA STJAERNAN; djurvaard inom totalfoersvaret. 1965. 6/yr. SEK 180 to non-members. Svenska Blaa Stjaernan, Linneg. 89, P.O. Box 5435, S-114 34 Stockholm, Sweden. TEL 46-8-788-76-97. FAX 46-8-788-76-97. Eds. Karin Wiebe, Nina von Krusenstierna. adv.; bk.rev.; illus. circ. 9,000. **Document type:** newsletter.

636.932 GW
DAS BLAUE JAHRBUCH; ein praktischer Wegweiser fuer den Kaninchenzuechter. 1955. a. DM.6. (Deutscher Kleintier Zuechter) Oertel & Spoerer, Burgstr. 1-7, 72764 Reutlingen, Germany. TEL 07121-302555. FAX 07121-302512. Ed. Ermo Lehari. adv. contact: Ermo Lehari. circ. 10,000. **Document type:** consumer publication.

636.7 SW ISSN 0284-0863
BLODHUNDSKAMRATEN. 1980. q. membership. Svenska Blodhundskamraterna, c/o Marie Edman, Haellan 3155, S-66800 Ed, Sweden. TEL 0534-21021. adv.: B&W page SEK 600. circ. 100. **Document type:** bulletin, newsletter.

636.7 US
BLOODHOUND BULLETIN. 1958. 3/yr. 7275 Jennings Rd., Whitmore Lake, MI 48189. adv. circ. 400.

636.7 US ISSN 0890-8923
BLOODLINES. 1905. 7/yr. $12 (foreign $23). United Kennel Club, Inc., 100 E. Kilgore Rd., Kalamazoo, MI 49001. TEL 616-343-9020. FAX 616-343-7037. Ed. Kerry Knudsen. adv.; bk.rev. circ. 5,000.
 ●Also available online.
 Formerly: Bloodlines Journal (ISSN 0006-5013)
 Description: Devoted to dog sports and family dogs; covers obedience, breeding, tracking, agility, service dogs, therapy dogs, and herding dogs. Also covers obedience of mongrels.

636.7 US
BORDERLINE.* q. membership. Border Terrier Club of America, c/o Patricia Quinn, Ed., Box 545, Silverhill, AL 36576-0545. circ. 200.

PETS

636.7 SW ISSN 1100-0716
BORDERTERRIERBLADET. 1964. s-a. SEK 80 membership (effective 1990). Borderterriersaellskapet (BTS), c/o I. Bergman, Sund, Toretorpsv. 27, S-812 02 Gaestrike-Hammarby, Sweden.

636 US
BORZOI INTERNATIONAL; for people who love Borzoi. 1988. q. $35 (foreign $40). Borzoi International, Inc., 33594 Overland Lane, Solon, OH 44139. TEL 216-248-0067. FAX 216-946-0664. Ed. Sue Vasick-Croley. adv.; bk.rev. circ. 1,550. (back issues avail.)
Description: Covers all aspects of Borzoi ownership worldwide.

636.7 US ISSN 0746-2875
BORZOI QUARTERLY. 1974. q. $40. Hoflin Publishing Ltd., 4401 Zephyr St., Wheat Ridge, CO 80033-3299. TEL 303-934-5656. FAX 303-422-7000. circ. 1,500.

636.7 US
BOSTON QUARTERLY. q. $40. Hoflin Publishing Ltd., 4401 Zephyr St., Wheat Ridge, CO 80033-3299. TEL 303-934-5656. FAX 303-422-7000.

636.7 SW ISSN 0346-9344
BOSTONTERRIERN; tidskrift foer Svenska Terrierringen. 1958. q. SEK 100 membership (effective 1990). Bostonterriern, c/o S. Andersson, Gamla Soedertaeljev. 155 F, S-141 71 Huddinge, Sweden.

636.7 US ISSN 1067-8875
BOXER REVIEW. 10/yr. $30 (foreign $45). M. Drucker, 8760 Appian Way, Los Angeles, CA 90046. Ed. Kris Dahl.

636.7 SW ISSN 0345-1690
BOXERBLADET. 1965. q. SEK 310 membership (effective 1996). Svenska Boxerklubben, c/o Agneta Rainsson, Marens Gaard, S-761 94 Norrtaelje, Sweden. Ed. Maria Berg. circ. 1,500. **Document type:** bulletin, bibliography.

636.596 SW ISSN 0280-7769
BREVDUVESPORT; Svenska Brevduvefoerbundets tidskrift. 1918. 10/yr. SEK 125 (effective 1991). Brevduvesport, c/o I. Langkjaer, Traedgaardsv. 22, S-237 00 Bjaerred, Sweden.

636.7 SW ISSN 0345-1771
BRUKSHUNDEN. 1940. 8/yr. SEK 175 (effective 1994). Svenska Brukshundklubben-SBK Foerbundet, Snoemakarvaegen 29, S-161 47 Bromma, Sweden. TEL 46-8-25-04-50. FAX 46-8-25-10-06. Ed. Gunnar Lundgren; Pub. Gunnar Lundgren. adv.; B&W page SEK 9800, color page SEK 15400; trim 185 x 265. circ. 49,800. cols./p.: 4; pp./issue: 64.

636.7 US
BRUSSELS GRIFFON QUARTERLY. q. c/o Mr. Terry J. Smith, 221 E. Scott, Box 56, Grand Ledge, MI 48837. circ. 80.

BUDGERIGAR BULLETIN. see *BIOLOGY — Ornithology*

636 UK
BUDGERIGAR WORLD. 1974. m. $60. Budgerigar World Ltd., County Press Buildings, Bala, Gwynedd LL23 7PG, Wales. Ed. T.A. Tuxford; Pub. G. Evans. adv. contact: G. Evans. bk.rev.

636.7 US
BULL SHEET.* 1973. irreg. (4-5/yr.). Obedience Steward Club, c/o Maria Coon, Box 1463, Riverhead, NY 11901-0952. circ. 75.

636.7 US
BULLDOGGER. 3/yr. Bulldog Club of America, c/o Rita L. Phethean, 133 Wild Oak Dr., Birmingham, AL 35210-2605. circ. 1,600.

636.7 636.8 BL ISSN 0103-278X
CAES E GATOS. 1985. bi-m. Cr.$60. Gessulli Editores Ltda., Caixa Postal 198, 18540-000 Porto Feliz SP, Brazil. TEL 55-152-623133. FAX 55-152-623919. Ed. Osvaldo Penha Gessulli.

CAGE & AVIARY BIRDS. see *BIOLOGY — Ornithology*

636 CN ISSN 0045-4052
CALQUARIUM. 1959. m. Can.$24 membership. Calgary Aquarium Society, Box 63180, Calgary, AB T2N 4S5, Canada. Ed. Laura Pylypow. adv.; bk.rev. circ. 175.
Description: Articles and news on aquarium keeping. Subject matter is aimed at the average hobbyist.

636.7 IT ISSN 1121-3000
CANI. 1991. 11/yr. L.57000 (foreign L.86000). Editoriale Olimpia S.p.a., Viale Milton 7, 50129 Florence, Italy. TEL 055-473843. FAX 055-499195. Ed. Attilio Vallecchi. adv.; B&W page L.3290000, color page L.4880000. circ. 39,000. **Document type:** consumer publication.

636.7 US ISSN 0746-1410
CANINE CHRONICLE. 1975. m. $85. 2727 E. Oakland Park Blvd., Ste. 303, Fort Lauderdale, FL 33306. Ed. Elizabeth Lockman. adv. circ. 10,000. **Document type:** trade publication.
Description: Covers dog shows, breeders, judges, professional handlers and other topics of interest to pure-bred dog owners.

636.7 364.4 US
CANINE COURIER. 1979. q. $30. United States Police Canine Association, Inc., Rte. 2, Box 221 J, Angier, NC 27501. TEL 919-639-0490. Ed. Richard Rogers. adv.; bk.rev.; circ. 3,000 (controlled). **Document type:** newspaper.

CANINE LISTENER. see *HANDICAPPED — Hearing Impaired*

636.7 US
CASSETTE. 1970. q. $7. c/o Anne Lively, Ed., 2 Hemlock Cove Rd., R.R. No.3, Falmouth, ME 04105. TEL 207-797-9635. adv.; bk.rev. circ. 500.
Description: Articles, letters, and interviews pertaining to dog-breeding and showing, with show results. Focus is on Collies and Shetland sheepdogs.

636.8 UK ISSN 0008-7599
CAT. 1934. bi-m. £10 (elsewhere £15) (effective 1995). Cats Protection League, 17 Kings Rd., Horsham, W. Sussex RH13 5PN, England. TEL 01403-261947. FAX 01403-218414. Ed. H.E. Boothby. adv.; bk.rev. circ. 50,000. **Document type:** consumer publication.

179.3 AT
CAT CALL. 1968. q. membership. Feline Control Council of W.A., P.O. Box 232, Gosnells, W.A. 6110, Australia. TEL 3-61-841933. Ed. R. Payne. adv. circ. 300. **Document type:** consumer publication.
Description: News of interest to members of the council.

636.8 US ISSN 8750-4898
CAT FANCIERS' ALMANAC. 1984. m. $25 (effective 1995 & 1996). Cat Fanciers' Association, 1805 Atlantic Ave., Box 1005, Manasquan, NJ 08736-1005. TEL 908-528-9797. FAX 908-528-7391. Ed. Allene T. Sergi. adv. contact: Leslie Guriea. bk.rev.; cum.index: 1984-1993. circ. 6,000. (back issues avail.) **Document type:** trade publication.
Description: Cat related articles geared toward the breeder and cat show participant.

636.8 US
CAT FANCIERS' ASSOCIATION. ANNUAL YEARBOOK. 1958. a. $36 (foreign $41). Cat Fanciers' Association, Inc., 1805 Atlantic Ave., Box 1805, Manasquan, NJ 08736-1005. TEL 908-528-9797. FAX 908-528-7391. Ed. Marna Fogarty. adv. contact: Thomas H. Dent. bk.rev.; circ. 7,500 (controlled). **Document type:** trade publication.

636.8 AT
CAT FANCIERS' MAGAZINE. 1971. irreg. free. Cat Fanciers' Club of Tasmania, P.O. Box 114, North Hobart, Tas. 7002, Australia. Ed. Danny Cool.

636.8 US ISSN 0892-6514
SF441
CAT FANCY. 1966. m. $21.97; newsstand price: $2.95. Fancy Publications, 2401 Beverly Blvd., Los Angeles, CA 90057. TEL 213-385-2222. FAX 714-855-8822. (Subscr. addr.: Box 52864, Boulder, CO 80322-2864) Ed. Debbi Phillips-Donaldson. **Indexed:** InterActions Bibl. **Document type:** consumer publication.
—UnCover.
Supersedes: International Cat Fancy (ISSN 0199-0640)
Description: Contains information on how to better understand and care for cats. Covers medical problems, care technique, purebreds, personal and fictional stories. Includes questions and answers.

636.8 658.8 US ISSN 1074-7788
CAT INDUSTRY NEWSLETTER. 1992. m. $295. Good Communications, Inc., Box 31292, Charleston, SC 29417. TEL 803-795-9555; 800-968-1738. FAX 803-795-2930. Ed. Heather Siegel; Pub. Ross Becker. **Document type:** newsletter.
Description: Provides marketing and competitive information to makers of cat food and other products for cats.

636.8 US
CAT LOVER. 1991. q. $12. (Cat Lovers of America) Fancy Publications, 2401 Beverly Blvd., Los Angeles, CA 90057. TEL 213-385-2222. FAX 213-385-8565. adv.: B&W page $1200, color page $1800; trim 8 x 10 7/8; adv. contact: Norman Ridker. circ. 10,200. **Document type:** consumer publication.
Description: Covers care and nutrition, feline products and services, news, history, and trivia.

CAT TALK. see *HOBBIES*

636 US ISSN 0163-1926
CAT WORLD. 1973. bi-m. $16.95 (foreign $18.95). Cat World International, Box 35635, Phoenix, AZ 85069. Ed. Tom Corn. adv.; bk.rev.; index. circ. 2,500. (back issues avail.)

636.8 UK ISSN 0952-2875
CAT WORLD. 1982. m. £27.80. Cat World Ltd., 10 Western Rd., Shoreham-by-Sea, W. Sussex BN43 5WD, England. TEL 01273-462000. FAX 01273-455994. Ed. Joan Moore. adv.; bk.rev. circ. 19,500. (back issues avail.) **Document type:** consumer publication.
Description: All about cats: information guides, veterinary articles, handicraft items, breeders and trade advertisements.

636.8 UK
CAT WORLD ANNUAL. 1982. a. £6.85. Cat World Ltd., 10 Western Rd., Shoreham-by-Sea, W. Sussex BN43 5WD, England. TEL 01273-462000. FAX 01273-455994. Ed. Joan Moore. circ. 11,000. **Document type:** consumer publication.
Description: Contains informative articles, stories and photographs for cat lovers.

636.8 US ISSN 1069-6687
CATNIP; a newsletter for caring cat owners. 1993. m. $30 in the U.S.; Canada $42. Tufts University, School of Veterinary Medicine, 203 Harrison Ave., Boston, MA 02111. TEL 800-829-0926. (Subscr. to: Box 420014, Palm Coast, FL 32142-0014) Ed. Dr. Franklin M. Leow. illus. (back issues avail.)
Description: Gives cat owners practical ideas on how to best care for their felines.

636.8 UK ISSN 0260-3837
CATS. 1981. w. £100. Our Dogs Publishing Co. Ltd., 5 James Leigh St., Manchester M1 6EX, England. TEL 061-236-0577. FAX 061-236-5534. Ed. Brian Doyle. bk.rev.; illus.; circ. 7,000 (controlled). **Document type:** newspaper.

636.8 JA
CATS. m. 680 Yen per no. Pet Life Ltd. (Subsidiary of: Midori Group), Ikebukuro Nishiguichi Sky Bldg., 2-14-4 Ikebukuro, Toshima-ku, Tokyo 171, Japan. TEL 03-3980-6955. circ. 50,000. **Document type:** consumer publication.
Description: Provides general information for cat keepers.

636.8 US ISSN 0008-8544
CATS MAGAZINE. 1945. m. $21.97. Cats Magazine, Inc., Box 290037, Port Orange, FL 32129. TEL 904-788-2770. FAX 904-788-2710. Ed. Tracey K. Copeland. adv. contact: Allan Morton. bk.rev.; illus.; index. circ. 192,000. (also avail. in microfilm from UMI; reprint service avail. from UMI) **Indexed:** A.I.P.P. **Document type:** consumer publication.
—UMI; UnCover.
Description: For cat owners, breeders and exhibitors. Covers a broad range of topics including health and nutrition updates, grooming tips and information about cats in general.

636.7 US
CAVALIER KING CHARLES SPANIEL CLUB, U S A. BULLETIN. 1964. q. $10. Cavalier King Charles Spaniel Club, U S A, Inc., c/o Courtney Carter, Sec., 2 Brynwood Ln., Newtown, PA 18940. Ed. Jesse Cleveland. bk.rev. circ. 750.
Formerly: Cavalier King Charles Spaniel Club of America. Bulletin.

636.7 SZ
LE CHIEN MAGAZINE; revue mensuelle specialisee du chien. m. 50 SFr. (foreign 60 SFr.). Presses Centrale Lausanne SA, Rue de Geneve 7, CH-1003 Lausanne, Switzerland. TEL 021-3205901. FAX 021-3205050. Ed. Liliane Mordasiui. adv.; illus. **Document type:** consumer publication.
Formerly: Chien.

636.7 US ISSN 0279-0203
CHIHUAHUA NEWS.* 1981. 10/yr. $12. Dudgeon Publications, 5100 E. Rosehill Ave., Terre Haute, IN 47805. TEL 812-466-3361. Ed. Mollie Dudgeon. adv.; illus. circ. 500.
Description: Discusses dog care and breeding.

636 US ISSN 0273-2335
LOS CHIHUAHUAS. 1976. bi-m. $20. Myrle Hale, Ed. & Pub., 12860 Thonotosassa Rd., Dover, FL 33527. TEL 813-986-2943. adv. circ. 650. (back issues avail.)

636.7 179.3 AT ISSN 0819-5862
CLUMBER SPANIEL CORRESPONDENCE. 1987. bi-m. Aus.$13 (foreign Aus.$19). Erinrac Enterprises, Foott Rd., Upper Beaconsfield, Vic. 3808, Australia. TEL 61-59-44-3383. FAX 61-59-44-3384. Ed. Jan Irving. adv.; B&W page Aus.$35. bk.rev.; illus.; stat. circ. 80. (back issues avail.) **Document type:** consumer publication, newsletter.

636.7 US
COLLIE CLUB OF AMERICA. BULLETIN. bi-m. membership. Collie Club of America, Rt. 2, Ledge Hill Farm, Easton, ME 04740. Ed. Ronald Dow. circ. 3,500.

636.596 FR ISSN 0398-1576
COLOMBOPHILIE; bulletin nationale. 1976. q. 54 bd. Carnot, 59042 Lille Cedex, France. Ed. Marie L. Lesecq.

636 US
COLONIAL ROTTWEILER CLUB NEWSLETTER. 1954. 6/yr. $25 to non-members. Colonial Rottweiler Club, E. Lake Rd., RD 2, Westfield, NY 14787. TEL 716-326-2370. Ed. Norma Dikeman. adv. circ. 600. (back issues avail.) **Document type:** newsletter.

COMMON SENSE PEST CONTROL QUARTERLY. see BIOLOGY — Entomology

COMPANION ANIMAL PRACTICE. see VETERINARY SCIENCE

636.932 IT
CONGLIO. bi-m. Associazione Nazionale Coniglicultori Italiani, Via A. Torlonia 19, 00161 Rome, Italy. TEL 06-854903.

636.7 US ISSN 1067-0920
COONHOUND BLOODLINES. 1973. m. $15 (foreign $23). United Kennel Club, Inc., 100 E. Kilgore, Kalamazoo, MI 49001. TEL 616-343-9020. FAX 616-343-7037. Ed. Kerry Knudsen. adv.; bk.rev. circ. 25,000.
Description: Contains information about raccoon, bobcat and bear hunting, and coonhound field trials.

636.7 US ISSN 0745-9734
CORGI QUARTERLY. 1983. q. $40. Hoflin Publishing Ltd., 4401 Zephyr St., Wheat Ridge, CO 80033-3299. TEL 303-934-5656. FAX 303-422-7000.

636 CN ISSN 0382-4497
COURRIER S P C A/S P C A COURIER. (Text in English, French) 1974. q. $5. Societe Canadienne de Protection des Animaux - Canadian Society for the Protection of Animals, 5215 Ouest, Rue Jean Talon, Montreal, Que. H4P 1X4, Canada. TEL 514-735-2711. circ. 12,000.

636.753 GW ISSN 0011-5231
DACHSHUND. 1946. m. DM.50. Deutscher Teckelklub e.V., Prinzenstr. 38, 47058 Duisburg, Germany. adv.; bk.rev. circ. 29,000. **Document type:** consumer publication.
Description: Highlights dog care and breeding.

636.7 US ISSN 0893-987X
DALMATIAN QUARTERLY. 1987. q. $40. Hoflin Publishing Ltd., 4401 Zephyr St., Wheat Ridge, CO 80033-3299. TEL 303-934-5656. FAX 303-422-7000.

636 GW
DEUTSCHER JAGDTERRIERCLUB. NACHRICHTENBLATT. 1946. q. DM.12. Deutscher Jagdterrierclub e.V., Wolbecker Str. 7, 48324 Sendenhorst, Germany. TEL 02535-8074. circ. 2,800.

636.932 GW
DEUTSCHER KANINCHENZUECHTER. bi-w. Zentralverband Deutscher Kaninchenzuechter e.V., Landenburger Str. 62, 70192 Stuttgart, Germany.

636.7 US
DEW CLAW.* 1928. bi-m. $9 to non-members. Briard Club of America, c/o Jack McLeroth, 1911 Rio Vista Dr., Fort Wayne, IN 46815-8119. Ed. Diane McLeroth. adv.; bk.rev. circ. 700.

636 NE ISSN 0921-5123
DIBEVO VAKBLAD. 1947. m. (11/yr.). fl.74.53. Landelijke Organisatie DIBEVO - Netherlands Organisation of Pet Retailers and Suppliers and Fishing Tackle Trade Organization, Postbus 94, 3800 AB Amersfoort, Netherlands. TEL 31-33-550433. FAX 31-33-552835. Ed. O.T. Kleijne. adv.; bk.rev.; charts; illus.; stat.; circ. 5,770 (controlled). **Indexed:** Key to Econ.Sci. **Document type:** trade publication.
Formerly (until 1988): Dibevo (ISSN 0012-2416)
Description: For pet shop owners, groomers, pet boarding houses, and garden center owners.

636.7 US ISSN 0194-6323
DOBERMAN WORLD; a bimonthly magazine for Doberman lovers. 1979. bi-m. $40. Hoflin Publishing Ltd., 4401 Zephyr St., Wheat Ridge, CO 80033-3299. TEL 303-934-5656. FAX 303-422-7000. **Document type:** consumer publication.

636.7 US ISSN 0194-9756
DOG (MARSHALL). 1979. fortn. Ringside Publications, 4977 Midway Lane, Marshall, WI 53559.

636 US
DOG BREEDING.* 1988. q. $59. Simone Publications, 34 Bristol Ct., Berkeley Heights, NJ 07922-1306. Ed. Peter Simone. adv.; bk.rev.

636.7 US ISSN 0892-6522 SF421
DOG FANCY. 1970. m. $21.97; newsstand price: $2.95. Fancy Publications, 2401 Beverly Blvd., Los Angeles, CA 90057. TEL 714-855-8822. FAX 714-855-3045. (Subscr. address: Box 53264, Boulder, CO 80322-3264) Ed. Kim Thornton. adv.; bk.rev.; illus. circ. 143,000. (back issues avail.) **Indexed:** InterActions Bibl. **Document type:** consumer publication.
Former titles: International Dog Fancy; Dog Fancy (ISSN 0012-4834)
Description: For the dog lover - including professional breeders, show exhibitors and, especially, general pet owners. Covers information on canine diet, grooming, exotic and domestic breeds, medical news and tips for showing.

636.7 658.8 US ISSN 1074-777X
DOG INDUSTRY NEWSLETTER. 1989. m. $295. Good Communications, Inc., Box 31292, Charleston, SC 29417. TEL 803-795-9555; 800-968-1738. FAX 803-795-2930. Ed. Heather Siegel; Pub. Ross Becker. adv. **Document type:** newsletter.
Description: Provides marketing and competitive information to dog food manufacturers and other pet products makers, their advertising agencies, and industry professionals.

636.7 UK ISSN 0012-4885
DOG WORLD. 1919. w. $122. M.J. Boulding, Ed. & Pub., 9 Tufton St., Ashford, Kent TN23 1QN, England. (also avail. in microform from UMI; reprint service avail. from UMI)

636.7 US ISSN 0012-4893
DOG WORLD. 1916. m. $28. P J S Publications, Inc.g Company, 29 N. Wacker Dr., Chicago, IL 60606. TEL 312-726-2802. FAX 312-726-4103. (Dist. by Kable News, 777 3rd Ave., New York, NY 10017) Ed. Donna Marcel. adv.; B&W page $3430, color page $4530. bk.rev.; illus. circ. 58,075. (also avail. in microform from UMI) **Indexed:** InterActions Bibl. —UMI; UnCover.
Description: Covers purebreds for breeders, exhibitors and trainers.

636.8 UK ISSN 0070-7015
DOG WORLD ANNUAL. 1930. a. $18. M.J. Boulding, Ed. & Pub., 9 Tufton St., Ashford, Kent TN23 1QN, England. index.

636.7 CN ISSN 0317-1485
DOGS IN CANADA. 1889. m. Can.$45. Apex Publishers & Publicity Ltd., 89 Skyway Ave., Ste. 200, Etobicoke, ON M9W 6RW, Canada. TEL 416-675-5511. FAX 416-675-6506. Ed. Allan Reznik; Pub. David Bell. adv.; B&W page $1570, color page $2270; trim 8 1/8 X 10 7/8; adv. contact: Ted Cole. bk.rev.; illus. circ. 23,000. **Indexed:** Can.B.P.I., CMI.
Description: Serves the purebred dog breeder & exhibitor. Carries articles on health, training, behavior, shows & trials, genetics and various other aspects of the show dog.

636.7 CN
DOGS IN CANADA ANNUAL. 1959. a. $6.95 per copy. Apex Publishers & Publicity Ltd., 89 Skyway Ave., Ste. 200, Don Mills, ON M9W 6RW, Canada. TEL 416-675-5511. FAX 416-675-6506. (Dist. by: Gordon & Gotch, 110 Jardin Ave., 11, Concord, ON L4K 2T7, Canada) Ed. Allan Reznik; Pub. David Bell. adv.; B&W page $4585, color page $5385; trim 8 1/8 X 10 7/8; adv. contact: Ted Cole. circ. 90,000. **Document type:** consumer publication.
Description: Complete guide for pet owners and owners-to-be, from selection to training and health. Includes cross-Canada directory of dog breeders, with breed descriptions.

636.7 UK ISSN 0266-7975
DOGS MONTHLY. 1983. m. £21 (foreign £30); newsstand price: £1.75. R T C Associates, Ascot House, High St., Ascot, Berkshire SL5 7JG, England. TEL 01344-28269. Ed. Di Johnson; Pub. David Cavill. circ. 17,000 (paid). **Document type:** consumer publication.

636 UK ISSN 0959-891X
DOGS TODAY. 1990. bi-m. £15 (rest of Europe £18; N. America $40; Australia and New Zealand £25) (effective 1995). Pet Subjects Ltd., 6 Station Parade, Sunningdale, Berks. SL5 0EP, England. TEL 01344-875442. FAX 01344-875443. (Dist. in US by: Center for Applied Animal Behavior, 2140 Shattuck Ave., 2406, Berkeley, CA 94704; Dist. by: S M Magazine Distribution Ltd., 6 Leighton Court Rd., Streatham, London SW16 2PG, England. TEL 0181-677-8111) Ed. Beverley Cuddy; Pub. Beverley Cuddy. adv. contact: Mike Lazarus. circ. 60,000. (back issues avail.) **Document type:** consumer publication.

636.7 US ISSN 0895-5581
DOGS U S A. 1986. a. $5.95. Fancy Publications, 2401 Beverly Blvd., Los Angleses, CA 90057. TEL 213-385-2222. FAX 714-855-8822. Ed. Connie Jankowski. adv. circ. 170,000. **Document type:** consumer publication.

PETS

630 GW ISSN 0341-5759
DU UND DAS TIER. 1971. 6/yr. DM.31.40. (Deutscher Tierschutzbund e.V.) Verlag M. und H. Schaper GmbH, Kalandstr. 4, 31061 Alfeld, Germany. TEL 05181-8009-0. FAX 05181-800933. (Subscr. to: Postfach 1642, 31046 Alfeld, Germany) adv.; bk.rev.; illus.; index. circ. 15,000. **Indexed:** Agri.Eng.Abstr., Ind.Vet., Nutr.Abstr., Vet.Bull. **Document type:** bulletin.
—CCC.

636.0887 DK
DYRENE & OS. DKK 98. Forlaget John Vaboe A-S, Emiliekildevej 35, DK-2930 Klampenborg, Denmark. TEL 45-39-40-80-00. FAX 45-39-40-82-80.

636.8 GW ISSN 0013-0826
DIE EDELKATZE; illustrierte Fachzeitschrift fuer Rassekatzenzucht. 1922. bi-m. DM.54 (foreign DM.60). Erster Deutscher Edelkatzenzuechter Verband e.V., Berliner Str. 13, 35614 Asslar, Germany. TEL 06441-8479. Ed. Waltraut Sattler. adv. contact: Waltraut Sattler. bk.rev.; bibl. circ. 15,000. **Document type:** consumer publication.

636 GW
EIN HERZ FUER TIERE. m. DM.44.40 (foreign DM.60). Gong Verlag GmbH, Innere Cramer-Klett-Str. 6, 90403 Nuernberg, Germany. TEL 0911-5325-0. FAX 0911-5325197. Eds. Claus Schmidt, Uschi Birr; Pub. Ludwig Schaclhauser. adv. contact: Edith Arnold. circ. 224,417. **Document type:** consumer publication.

636 591 FI ISSN 0357-8747
ELAINMAAILMA. 1979. m. FIM 254. Helsinki Media Magazines, P.O. Box 107, SF-00381 Helsinki 38, Finland. TEL 358-0-1221. Ed. Jyrki Leskinen. adv.: B&W page FIM 8650, color page FIM 11900; 194 x 248. circ. 46,238 (paid). **Document type:** consumer publication. **Description:** For school-aged children and adults. Articles vary from pets to wildlife and nature.

636.7 US ISSN 0745-6581
ELKHOUND QUARTERLY. q. $40. Hoflin Publishing Ltd., 4401 Zephyr St., Wheat Ridge, CO 80033-3299. TEL 303-934-5656. FAX 303-422-7000.

636.7 US ISSN 0746-4088
ENGLISH COCKER QUARTERLY. q. $40. Hoflin Publishing Ltd., 4401 Zephyr St., Wheat Ridge, CO 80033-3299. TEL 303-934-5656. FAX 303-422-7000.

636.7 US
ENGLISH SETTER ASSOCIATION OF AMERICA. NEWSLETTER. m. membership. English Setter Association of America, c/o Dawn Ronyak, Sec., 114 Burlington Oval, Chardon, OH 44024-1452. FAX 216-729-8413. circ. 1,000. **Document type:** newsletter.

F A B JOURNAL. (Feline Advisory Bureau) see VETERINARY SCIENCE

FAAGLEHOBBY; medlemsblad foer Sveriges samarbetand burfaagelfoereningar. see BIOLOGY — Ornithology

636 US
FAMILY PET.* 1971. q. $2. c/o M. Linda Sabella, Box 25353, Tampa, FL 33622-5353. adv.; bk.rev. circ. 3,000. (back issues avail.)

636.7 US
FIELD ADVISORY NEWS. 1971. bi-m. $30. American Sighthound Field Association, Inc., c/o Vicky Clarke, Ed., Box 399, Alpaugh, CA 93201-0399. adv.; bk.rev. circ. 650. **Document type:** bulletin.

636.7 US
FRENCH BULLDOG CLUB OF AMERICA. NEWSLETTER.* bi-m. French Bulldog Club of America, c/o Richard M. Hover, 86 Gold Rd., Wappingers Falls, NY 12590-3534. circ. 100.

636 US ISSN 0160-4317
SF456
FRESHWATER AND MARINE AQUARIUM. 1978. m. $22. R-C Modeler Corp., 144 W. Sierra Madre Blvd., Sierra Madre, CA 91024. TEL 818-355-1476. circ. 34,000.

636.7 JA
FRIENDS OF DOG/AIKEN NO TOMO. (Text in Japanese) 1952. m. 23100 Yen. Seibundo Shinkosha Publishing Co. Ltd., 1-13-7 Yayoi-cho, Nakano-ku, Tokyo 164, Japan. Ed. Yorimichi Ishii. circ. 65,000.

636.7 US ISSN 1073-7537
FRONT AND FINISH: THE DOG TRAINER'S NEWS. 1970. m. $26. H and S Publications, Inc., Box 333, Galesburg, IL 61402. Ed. Robert T. Self. adv.; bk.rev.; index. circ. 6,500. (also avail. in microform) **Document type:** newspaper.

FUND FOR ANIMALS QUARTERLY. see CONSERVATION

636.7 US
G S P C A "SHORTHAIR". 1954. m. $25. German Shorthaired Pointer Club of America, 18151 Harrison St., Omaha, NE 68136. TEL 402-895-4843. FAX 402-731-2874. Eds. Art and Jean Armbrust. adv.: B&W page $125, color page $400; 7 1/2 x 10 1/8. bk.rev. circ. 3,140. Formerly (until 1986): G S P C A Newsletter. **Description:** Reports on breed activities in show, field trial, hunt test and obedience. Covers training, dog care, nutrition, new products, industry news, dog rescue, and health and welfare.

636 GW ISSN 0016-5824
GEFLUEGEL-BOERSE. 1879. s-m. DM.144. (Bund Deutscher Rassegefluegelzuechter e.V) Verlag Juergens KG, Industriestr. 13, 82110 Germering, Germany. FAX 089-8402351. Ed. D. Juergens. adv.; bk.rev. circ. 45,000. **Document type:** trade publication.

636.8 GW
GELIEBTE KATZE. m. DM.49.20 (foreign DM.61.80). Gong Verlag GmbH, Innere Cramer-Klett-Str. 6, 90403 Nuernberg, Germany. TEL 0911-5325-0. FAX 0911-5325197. Ed. Uschi Birr; Pub. Bob Borrink. adv. contact: Edith Arnold. circ. 42,995. **Document type:** consumer publication.

636.7 US ISSN 0046-5852
SF429.S6
GERMAN SHEPHERD DOG REVIEW. 1922. m. $47. German Shepherd Dog Club of America, c/o Lois Fryslin, E., 30 Far View Rd., Chalfont, PA 18914. TEL 215-322-8044. adv.: B&W page $125, color page $425; trim 6 1/2 x 9 3/4. bk.rev. circ. 5,700. **Description:** Provides information concerning the breeding, raising, training, and showing of German Shepherd dogs.

636.7 US ISSN 0745-1849
GERMAN SHEPHERD QUARTERLY. 1982. q. $40. Hoflin Publishing Ltd., 4401 Zephyr St., Wheat Ridge, CO 80033-3299. TEL 303-934-5656. FAX 303-422-7000.

636.7 US ISSN 1065-0830
GERMAN SHORTHAIRED POINTER NEWS. 1954. m. $20. Shirley L. Carlson, Ed. & Pub., 86 N. Heck Hill Rd., Box 850, Saint Paris, OH 43072. TEL 513-663-4773. adv.; bk.rev.; stat. circ. 1,500. (back issues avail.) **Description:** Focuses on breeding, puppies, competition; includes articles on training.

636.7 US ISSN 0886-098X
SF429.G63
GOLDEN RETRIEVER WORLD; a quarterly magazine for Golden lovers. 1983. q. $40. Hoflin Publishing Ltd., 4401 Zephyr St., Wheat Ridge, CO 80033-3299. TEL 303-934-5656. FAX 303-422-7000. Formerly (until 1985): Golden Retriever Quarterly (ISSN 0746-2492)

636.7 US ISSN 0899-6024
GOOD DOG!; the consumer magazine for dog owners. 1988. 6/yr. $18 (foreign $30). Box 31292, 511 Harbor View Cir., Charleston, SC 29412-3205. TEL 803-795-9555; 800-968-1738. FAX 803-795-2930. Ed. Judi Sklar; Pub. Ross Becker. adv. contact: Doug Ferguson. bk.rev. circ. 35,000. **Document type:** consumer publication. **Description:** Provides test reports on dog food and products for dogs.

636.7 US
GORDON SETTER NEWS. 1947. m. membership. Gordon Setter Club of America, Inc., 10120 DeWitt, DeWitt, MI 48820. Ed. Dianne Avery. adv.; bk.rev. circ. 1,100. **Document type:** newsletter.

636.7 US
GREAT DANE CLUB OF AMERICA. MONTHLY BULLETIN. m. Great Dane Club of America, c/o Pattie Glanz, Gage Rd., RR 5, Brewster, NY 10509. circ. 2,000.

636.7 US ISSN 0889-7727
GREAT DANE REPORTER. 1976. bi-m. $40 in the U.S.; Canada and Mexico $49; elsewhere $58. Tomar Publications, Box 150, Riverside, CA 92502-0150. TEL 909-784-5437. FAX 909-369-7056. Ed. Sally Silva. adv.; bk.rev. circ. 2,000.

636 796 AT
GREYHOUND ADVISER. 1970. m. Aus.$30. Greyhound Racing Control Board (Victoria), 1 Queens Rd., Melbourne, Vic., Australia. TEL 61-3-98673377. FAX 61-3-98662494. (Co-sponsor: National Coursing Association of Victoria) Ed. T. Ryan. adv.; bk.rev.; circ. 6,000 (controlled). **Document type:** trade publication.

636.7 UK ISSN 0017-4165
GREYHOUND OWNER & BREEDER. 1946. w. £6.50 for 6 mos. Greyhound Owner Ltd., 8 Greenford Ave., London W7 3QP, England. Ed. Jim Shepherd. adv.; stat.; cum.index. circ. 9,800. (tabloid format)

636 976 AT ISSN 1320-9507
GREYHOUND RECORDER. 1935. w. Aus.$225. Greyhound Publications Pty. Ltd., 9 East St., Lidcombe, N.S.W. 2141, Australia. TEL 61-2-646-5855. FAX 61-2-646-5433. circ. 11,000. **Document type:** newspaper.

636.7 US ISSN 0199-8366
SF427.5
GROOM & BOARD. 1980. 9/yr. $25. H.H. Backer Associates, Inc., 20 E. Jackson Blvd., Ste. 200, Chicago, IL 60604. TEL 312-663-4040. FAX 312-663-5676. Ed. Karen Long MacLeod. adv.: B&W page $1525, color page $2290; trim 8 1/4 x 10 7/8; adv. contact: Lou Carso. circ. 16,431. (back issues avail.) **Document type:** trade publication.

636.7 NE ISSN 0928-6268
GROOMERS EUROPE; for professional dog groomers. (Text in Dutch, English, French, German) 1991. 4/yr. fl.35. InterMedium Publishers, P.O. Box 1318, 3800 BH Amersfoort, Netherlands. TEL 31-33-947672. FAX 31-33-945886. Ed. Reinder Sterenborg. adv.; illus. **Document type:** trade publication.

636.7 US
GROOMERS VOICE. 1969. q. membership. National Dog Groomers Association of America, c/o Jeffrey L. Reynolds, Box 101, Clark, PA 16113. TEL 412-962-2711. adv. circ. 2,500.

636.596 GW ISSN 0935-5405
DAS GRUENE JAHRBUCH; Ein praktischer Wegweiser fuer den Gefluegel- und Taubenzuechter. 1953. a. DM.6. (Deutscher Kleintier Zuechter) Oertel & Spoerer, Burgstr. 1-7, 72764 Reutlingen, Germany. TEL 07121-302555. FAX 07121-302512. adv. contact: Ermo Lehari. circ. 7,500. **Document type:** consumer publication.

636.7 362.41 US
GUIDE DOG NEWS. 1950. q. membership. Guide Dogs for the Blind, Inc., Box 151200, San Rafael, CA 94915-1200. FAX 415-499-4023. Ed. Jennifer Conroy. circ. 55,000.

636.7 362.41 US
GUIDE LINES (YORKTOWN HEIGHTS). 1954. q. free. Guiding Eyes for the Blind, 611 Granite Springs Rd., Yorktown Heights, NY 10598-3499.

GUN DOG; upland bird and waterfowl dogs. see SPORTS AND GAMES — Outdoor Life

636 179 GW
HAUSTIER; die Zeitschrift fuer den Tierfreund. 1989. bi-m. DM.44. Symposion Verlag, Wagnerstr. 12, 73728 Esslingen, Germany. TEL 0711-350001. FAX 0711-3508766. (Dist. by: Special Interest, Waldstr. 70, 63128 Dietzenbach, Germany. TEL 06074-8235-0) Ed. Uwe Leitmeier; Pub. Hansjoerg Siegeler. adv.: B&W page DM.3400, color page DM.5900; trim 210 x 280. bk.rev.; film rev.; illus.; tele.rev.; circ. 70,000 (paid). (back issues avail.) **Document type:** consumer publication. Formerly: Grosse Haustier Magazin (ISSN 0939-4486)

PETS

636 US ISSN 0193-1997
HEART OF AMERICA AQUARIUM SOCIETY NEWS. vol.24, 1979. m. (11/yr.). $12 to members. Heart of America Aquarium Society, 2029 W. 84th Terr., Leawood, KS 66206. Ed. Betty Ryne. adv. circ. 300.
Description: Provides current news and information on all species of fish, tropical and native.

HENSTON VETERINARY VADE MECUM (SMALL ANIMALS). see VETERINARY SCIENCE

636.7 NE ISSN 0018-4527
HONDENWERELD. 1946. m. fl.64. Stichting de Hondenwereld, Burg. Wijnenstraat 44, Postbus 8, 5720 AA Asten, Netherlands. TEL 04936-91345. FAX 04936-95005. Ed. B. Bosch. adv.; bk.rev.; abstr.; illus.; index. circ. 13,000.

636.7 US ISSN 0018-6384
HOUNDS AND HUNTING. 1903. m. $14. Hounds and Hunting Publishing Co., Box 372, Bradford, PA 16701. TEL 814-368-6154. FAX 814-368-3522. Ed. Robert F. Slike. adv.: B&W page $405. bk.rev.; illus. circ. 12,000.
Description: Covers the breeding, raising, training and handling of Beagle Hounds.

636.7 GW ISSN 0323-4924
DER HUND. m. DM.38.40. Deutscher Bauernverlag GmbH, Brunnenstr. 128, 13355 Berlin, Germany. TEL 030-464060. FAX 030-46406205. Ed. Susanne Kerl. adv. contact: Hans-Juergen Henze. circ. 57,000. Document type: consumer publication.

636.7 SZ
HUNDE HALTUNG ZUCHT SPORT. 1883. fortn. 100 SFr. (Schweizerischen Kynologischen Gesellschaft) Paul Haupt AG, Falkenplatz 11, CH-3001 Bern, Switzerland. TEL 031-3012345. FAX 031-3015469. Ed. Hans Raeber. adv.; charts; illus. circ. 25,000. Document type: bulletin.
—CCC.
Formerly: Schweizer Hundesport (ISSN 0036-7354)

636.7 DK ISSN 0108-6839
HUNDE-JOURNALEN. 1945. 8/yr. DKK 140. Dyrefondet, Ericaparken 23, DK-2820 Gentofte, Denmark. Eds. Aase Reinhard, Annie Bohe Joergensen. adv.; bk.rev. circ. 5,593.

636.7 DK ISSN 0018-7674
HUNDEN. 10/yr. Dansk Kennel Klub, Parkvej 1, 2680 Solroed Strand, Denmark. adv. circ. 27,000.

636.7 NO ISSN 0332-8813
HUNDESPORT. 1900. m. (10/yr.). Norsk Kennel Klub, Hundesport, Nils Hansens vei 20, N-0667 Oslo, Norway. TEL 47-22--65-60-00. Ed. Aud Jorun Lie. adv.: B&W page NOK 7000, color page NOK 9400; trim 185 x 271; adv. contact: Linda Bekkelund. circ. 50,000.
Formerly (until 1955): Norsk Kennel Klubs Tidsskrift (ISSN 0332-9445)

636.7 GW ISSN 0018-7682
HUNDEWELT. (Text in Czech, German) 1928. m. DM.46. Minerva Verlag GmbH, Eichenstr. 72, 41747 Viersen, Germany. TEL 02162-32735. FAX 02162-30215. Ed. Hans-Joachim Swarovsky; Pubs. Heinz Kerbusch, Brigitte Kerbusch. adv. contact: Jutta Swarovsky. circ. 52,000. Document type: consumer publication.

636.7 SW ISSN 0018-7690
HUNDSPORT. 1887. m. (10/yr.). SEK 240. Svenska Kennel Klubben - Swedish Kennel Club, P.O. Box 141, S-161 26 Bromma, Sweden. FAX 46-8-80-85-95. Ed. Torsten Widholm. adv.; bk.rev. circ. 114,388.
Former titles (until 1955): Hundar och Hundsport; (until 1933): Svenska Kennelklubbens Tidskrift; (until 1893): Tidning foer Idrott; Which supersedes (in 1890): Hunden.

636.7 US ISSN 8750-6629
HUNTING RETRIEVER. 1984. bi-m. $15 membership. United Kennel Club, Inc., 100 E. Kilgore Rd., Kalamazoo, MI 49001. TEL 616-343-9020. FAX 616-343-7037. Ed. Kerry Knudsen. adv.; bk.rev. circ. 3,000. Document type: consumer publication.
Description: Official organ of the Hunting Retriever Club, an organization devoted to retriever performance testing.

636.7 US
I G E NEWS. irreg. free. International Guiding Eyes, 13445 Glenoaks Blvd., Sylmar, CA 91342.
Formerly: International Guiding Eyes. Newsletter.

636.8 US ISSN 0899-9570
I LOVE CATS. 1988. bi-m. $24. Grass Roots Publishing Co., Inc., 950 Third Ave., 16th Fl., New York, NY 10022. TEL 212-888-1855. circ. 200,000.
Document type: consumer publication.
Description: Features information necessary for cat owners to help their cats live healthier and happier lives. Includes proper nutrition, veterinarian advice, dental care and stories about cat lovers and their adventures with cats.

636 US
INTERACTIONS (RENTON). 1983. q. $15 (foreign $22). Delta Society, Box 1080, 321 Burnett Ave., S., 3rd Fl., Renton, WA 98055. TEL 206-226-7357. FAX 206-235-1076. Ed. Linda M. Hines. adv.; bk.rev. circ. 10,000. (tabloid format) Indexed: InterActions Bibl (1990-). Document type: consumer publication.
—CCC.
Formerly (until 1991): People, Animals, Environment (ISSN 8755-5875)
Description: Covers interactions of people, animals, and the nature, animal-assisted therapy, and community people-pet programs.

636.974 US
INTERNATIONAL FERRET REVIEW. 1985. bi-m. $20 membership (foreign $30). Ferret Fanciers Club, 711 Chautauqua Ct., Pittsburgh, PA 15214. TEL 412-322-1161. Ed. Mary Field; Pub. Mary Field. adv.; bk.rev.; video rev. circ. 7,000. (back issues avail.) Document type: newsletter.
Description: News and information on ferrets, including breeding, care, legislation, products and exhibitions.

636 US ISSN 1074-780X
INTERNATIONAL PET INDUSTRY NEWS. 1993. m. $295. Good Communications, Inc., Box 31292, Charleston, SC 29417. TEL 803-795-9555; 800-968-1738. FAX 803-795-2930. Ed. Heather Siegel; Pub. Ross Becker. Document type: newsletter.
Description: For executives in the pet products industry. Covers marketing, new products and promotions for pet food and pet products around the world.

636.7 US
IRISH TERRIER CLUB OF AMERICA. NEWSLETTER. 1970. 6/yr. membership. Irish Terrier Club of America, Box 889, Route 2, Scurry, TX 75158. TEL 617-263-2314. Ed. Beth Childers. bk.rev. circ. 350. Document type: newsletter.

636.7 US
IRISH WATER SPANIEL CLUB OF AMERICA. NEWSLETTER. m. membership only. Irish Water Spaniel Club of America, c/o Susan Tapp, 434 Webster Ave., Washington Township, NJ 07675. Document type: newsletter.

636.7 US ISSN 0164-8675
IRISH WOLFHOUND QUARTERLY. 1978. q. $40. Hoflin Publishing Ltd., 4401 Zephyr St., Wheat Ridge, CO 80033-3299. TEL 303-934-5656. FAX 303-422-7000.

636.752 GW ISSN 0021-3950
DER JAGDSPANIEL. 1907. 4/yr. DM.26. Jagdspaniel-Klub e.V., Trainsjochstr. 6, 81825 Munich, Germany. TEL 089-4316172. Ed. Bruno Richter. adv.; charts; illus.; stat.; tr.lit. Document type: consumer publication.

JAGTHUNDEN. see SPORTS AND GAMES — Outdoor Life

636 AU ISSN 0022-8117
KAMERAD TIER. 1965. irreg. (4-6/yr.). membership. Tierschutzaktion "der Blaue Kreis", Goldschlagerstr. 15, A-1150 Vienna, Austria. TEL 0222-9218573. Ed. Kurt Kolar. adv.; bk.rev.; illus. (looseleaf format)

KANARIENFREUND. see BIOLOGY — Ornithology

636.8 GW ISSN 0176-4853
KATZEN EXTRA. 1979. m. DM.70 (foreign DM.106). Symposion Verlag, Wagnerstr. 12, 73728 Esslingen, Germany. TEL 0711-350001. FAX 0711-3508766. Ed. H.A. Siegler. adv. contact: Hans Juergen Maier. circ. 60,000. (back issues avail.) Document type: consumer publication.

636.7 US
KEEZETTE. 1976. bi-m? $10. c/o Carol Cash, Ed. & Pub., 15646 Creekwood Ln., Strongsville, OH 44136. adv.

636 UK
KENNEL AND CATTERY MANAGEMENT. 1983. m. £14. Albatross Publications, P.O. Box 193, Dorking, Surrey RH5 5YF, England. Ed. Carol Andrews. adv.; bk.rev. circ. 4,500. (back issues avail.) Document type: trade publication.
Description: Covers nutrition, hygiene, veterinary advice, breeding, and management.

636.7 UK ISSN 0305-442X
KENNEL CLUB YEARBOOK. a. £5.50. Kennel Club, 1 Clarges St., Piccadilly, London W1Y 8AB, England. Ed. Charles Colborn. circ. 3,000. Document type: bulletin.

636.7 UK ISSN 0022-9962
KENNEL GAZETTE. 1880. m. £25. Kennel Club, 1 Clarges St., London W1Y 8AB, England. Ed. C. Colborn. adv.; bk.rev.; illus. circ. 9,000. Document type: bulletin.
Description: Dog care and breeding.

636.7 US
KERRY BLUEPRINTS. q. $15 (foreign $18). United States Kerry Blue Terrier Club, 602 W. Fernwood Dr., Toronto, OH 43964. Ed. JoAnn Custer. adv. circ. 400.

636 UK ISSN 0268-9308
KEY NOTE REPORT: PET FOODS. Variant title: Pet Foods. irreg. £185. Key Note Publications Ltd., Field House, 72 Oldfield Rd., Hampton, Middlesex TW12 2HQ, England. TEL 0181-783-0755. FAX 0181-783-1720. Document type: trade publication.
●Also available online.
Also available on CD-ROM.
—BLDSC (6428.818500).

636.7 FI ISSN 0355-7235
KOIRAMME - VAARA HUNDAR. 1896. 10/yr. FIM 130. Suomen Kennelliitto - Finska Kennelklubben, Kamreerintie 8, 02770 Espoo, Finland. FAX 358-0-8054603. Ed. Tapio Eerola. adv. circ. 120,000.

636.7 US
KOMONDOR KOMMENTS. 1971. q. $25 (effective 1995). Komondor Club of America, 26036 S.E. 27th St., Issaquah, WA 98027. TEL 206-391-3776. Ed. Lyn W. Bingham. adv. contact: Wynne Smith. bk.rev. circ. 300. Document type: newsletter.

636.7 US ISSN 8750-3557
LABRADOR QUARTERLY. q. $40. Hoflin Publishing Ltd., 4401 Zephyr St., Wheat Ridge, CO 80033-3299. TEL 303-934-5656. FAX 303-422-7000.

636.73 UK ISSN 0260-5627
LABRADOR RETRIEVER CLUB OF WALES. YEARBOOK. 1980. a. £2. Labrador Retriever Club of Wales, c/o M. Williams, 6 Dan-y-Felin, Llantrisant, Pontyclun, Mid Glam CF7 8EH, Wales. adv.; bk.rev.; illus. circ. 500.

636.7 US
LAKELANDER. bi-m. $10. United States Lakeland Terrier Club, 4259 Bear Hollow Trail, Haymarket, VA 22069. circ. 200.

636.7 DK ISSN 0107-8585
LANGHAARS-NYT. 1979. bi-m. DKK 30. Klubben for den Langhaarede Hoensehund, c/o Georg Tronier, Oestergade 15, DK-6520 Toftlund, Denmark. illus.

PETS

636.7   FI   ISSN 0787-6424
LEMMIKKI. 1990. m. FIM 144. Yhtyneet Kuvalehdet Oy - United Magazines Ltd., Maistraatinportti 1, SF-00240 Helsinki, Finland. TEL 358-0-156-6524. FAX 358-0-156-6505. Ed. Hannele Willberg. adv.: B&W page FIM 3750, color page FIM 7500; trim 190 x 270; adv. contact: Eeva Siukosaari. circ. 20,550. **Document type:** consumer publication.
    Description: Reports on animals and how to care for them, as well as items that animal owners buy for their pets.

636.7   US   ISSN 0273-8333
LHASA APSO REPORTER. 1973. b-m. $36. Denise Olejniczak, Ed. & Pub., 74565 Van Dyke, Romeo, MI 48065. TEL 810-752-5674. adv.; bk.rev. circ. 750.

636.7   US
LHASA BULLETIN. bi-m. $7.50 to non-members. c/o Susan S. Giles, Ed., 2372 Wheatland DR., Manakin-Sabot, VA 23103. circ. 750.

LIVE ANIMAL TRADE & TRANSPORT MAGAZINE. see *TRANSPORTATION*

LIVESTOCK ADVISER; an English monthly dedicated to improve the animal wealth of India. see *AGRICULTURE — Poultry And Livestock*

636   GW   ISSN 0342-9989
MAGAZIN DER TIERFREUNDE. 1955. bi-m. free. Zentralverband Zoologischer Fachbetriebe Deutschlands, Fischerfeldstr. 4, 60311 Frankfurt a.M., Germany. Ed. Ivo Baumann. circ. 104,000.

636.7   US   ISSN 0746-4002
MALAMUTE QUARTERLY. 1982. q. $40. Hoflin Publishing Ltd., 4401 Zephyr St., Wheat Ridge, CO 80033-3299. TEL 303-934-5656. FAX 303-422-7000.

636.7   US   8750-5487
MALTESE MAGAZINE. q. $32. Reporter Publications, Box 6369, Los Osos, CA 93412. TEL 805-528-2007. FAX 805-528-8200. Ed. Jean Fergus. adv. contact: Jean Fergus. illus. **Document type:** consumer publication.
    Formerly: Maltese Tails (ISSN 0274-7022)
    Description: News and information of interest to Maltese owners.

636.7   US
MASTIFF JOURNAL.* 1970. q. $25. (Mastiff Club of America) Moore and Ahlers Publishing, c/o Robert Goldblatt, P.O. Box 204, Talmadge, CA 95481-0204. Ed. Deborah Ahlers. adv.; bk.rev. circ. 600.

636.7   US
MATCH SHOW BULLETIN. 1969. m. $20. Myrna Lieber, Ed.& Pub., Box 214, Massapequa, NY 11758. TEL 516-541-3442. FAX 516-541-3442. adv.: B&W page $350; trim 8 3/8 X 10 7/8. circ. 6,700. (back issues avail.) **Document type:** bulletin.
    Description: Lists locations and details of dog match shows, seminars, and training classes.

179.3   AU
MENSCH UND TIER. 1910. q. membership. Liga gegen Tierquaelerei und Missbrauch der Tierversuche, Blindengasse 38, A-1080 Vienna, Austria. Ed. Albert Schwarz. bk.rev. circ. 16,000. **Document type:** newsletter.

MERIGAL; a voice for the dingo. see *CONSERVATION*

636.8   US
MORRIS REPORT. 1987. q. $7.50. 9-Lives Cat Food - Hogan Communications, 150 E. Olive Ave., Ste. 208, Burbank, CA 91502. FAX 818-848-4995. adv.; bk.rev.

363.7   SP   ISSN 0212-4947
MUNDO DEL PERRO. 1980. 12/yr. San Romualdo 26, 28037 Madrid, Spain. TEL 1-206-98-66.

636.7   US
MUSTARD AND PEPPER. 1973. q. $24. Dandie Dinmont Terrier Club of America, 12109 Piney Glen Ln., Potomac, MD 20854. TEL 301-299-2330. FAX 301-299-3107. Ed. Cathy Nelson. adv. circ. 300.

179.3   US
N A C A NEWS. 1978. bi-m. $20. National Animal Control Association, Box 480851, Kansas City, MO 64148-0851. Ed. John Mays. adv.; bk.rev.; film rev.; charts; stat.; tr.lit. circ. 3,500.

636.7   US   ISSN 1047-9112
NATIONAL BELGIAN NEWSLETTER. 1953. bi-m. $20 to non-members; members $10. Belgian Sheepdog Club of America, c/o Marilyn Russell, RFD2, Box 2480, Bangor, ME 04401. Ed. Billye Gaye Viner. adv.; bk.rev. circ. 550. **Document type:** newsletter.

NATIONAL GREYHOUND NEWS. see *SPORTS AND GAMES*

636   US   ISSN 0028-0267
NATIONAL STOCK DOG. 1954. bi-m. $18. National Stock Dog Registry, Box 402, Butler, IN 46721-0402. TEL 219-868-2670. Ed. J.R. Russell. adv.; abstr.; illus. circ. 5,000.
    Description: For the preservation and advancement of the livestock working breeds of America and the world.

636.8   JA
NEKO NO KURABU/CAT CLUB. (Text in Japanese) 1993. m. 14460 Yen. Seibundo Shinkosha Publishing Co. Ltd., 1-13-7 Yayoi-cho, Nakano-ku, Tokyo 164, Japan. Ed. Etsuko Kogayu. circ. 100,000.

636.7   US   ISSN 0194-7206
NEWF-TIDE.* 1969? q. $25. Newfoundland Club of America, Cheney's Point Rd., Ashville, NY 14710. Eds. Allan Saeger, Peggy Saeger. adv.; bk.rev. circ. 3,200.

636.7   US
NORSK ELGHUND QUARTERLY. 1979. q. $20. Norsk Elghund Quarterly, 31 Peck St., Rehoboth, MA 02769. adv. circ. 400.
    Description: Articles on Norwegian Elkhounds.

636.7 179.3   US   ISSN 1041-1496
NORTHEAST CANINE COMPANION. 1986. m. $20 (effective 1995 & 1996). Companion Publishing Co., Box 357, Sudbury, MA 01776. TEL 508-443-8387. FAX 508-443-0183. Ed. Christine Harris; Pub. Alan I. Alford. adv.: B&W page $150; trim 8 1/2 X 11; adv. contact: Ilene Kort. bk.rev. circ. 12,000. (back issues avail.) **Document type:** consumer publication, newspaper.
    Description: For dog fanciers, especially owners of show dogs.

636.7   US
NORWEGIAN ELKHOUND NEWS. 1975? bi-m. $7. Norwegian Elkhound Association of America, Rt. 9, Box 58B, Jonesboro, AR 72401. Ed. Robin L. Anderson. circ. 600.

636.7   US
NORWICH & NORFOLK NEWS. 1962. s-a. $5. Norwich and Norfolk Terrier Club, c/o Mrs. Susan Elay, Mountain Top Rd., Bernardsville, NJ 07924. bk.rev. circ. 700.

636   IT   ISSN 0029-3784
NOSTRI CANI. 1955. m. L.20000 (foreign L.40000)(effective 1992). Ente Nazionale della Cinofilia Italiana, Viale Premuda 21, 20129 Milan, Italy. TEL 02-76021706. FAX 02-783127. (Affiliate: Federation Cynologique Internationale) adv. circ. 75,700.

636.7   US   ISSN 1079-5537
SF431
OFF-LEAD DOG TRAINING. 1972. m. $20. Arner Publications, Inc., 204 Lewis St., Canastota, NY 13032-1115. TEL 315-339-2033. FAX 315-339-2289. Ed. Lorenz D. Arner. adv. contact: Mark Arner. bk.rev.; illus.; stat.; index; circ. 5,000 (paid). (back issues avail.; reprint service avail. from UMI) **Document type:** consumer publication.
    Formerly: Off-Lead (ISSN 0094-0186)
    Description: Communication among professional and amateur dog trainers, animal behaviourists, pet owners, and veterinarians. Presents techniques, events, equipment, seminars and other educational material.

636.7   US
OLD ENGLISH TIMES. 1972. bi-m. $20. Old English Sheepdog Club of America, Inc., c/o Kathryn Bunnell, Corresponding Sec., 14219 E. 79th St., S., Derby, KS 67037. Ed. Sam Middleton. adv.; bk.rev. circ. 1,000.

636.7   NE
ONZE BOSTONS. 5/yr. fl.30. Boston Terrier Club Nederland, c/o Spitaal 27, 8602 VR Sneek, Netherlands. Ed. G.B.L. Legtenberg. bk.rev. circ. 250.

636   DK   ISSN 0106-6714
OPDRAETTERVEJVISEREN. vol.46, 1980. irreg. free. Dansk Kennel Klub, Parkvej 1, Jersie Strand, 2680 Solroed Strand, Denmark. illus.

636.7   US
ORIENT EXPRESS. bi-m. $20. Southern California Chinese Shar Pei Club, 4430 Arista Dr., San Diego, CA 92103.

636.7   US
OUR AFGHANS. 1968. m. $20 (foreign $26). Weddle Publications, 22235 Parthenia St., West Hills, CA 91304-1348. TEL 818-340-8635. Ed. Ruth Weddle. adv.: B&W page $75; adv. contact: Ruth Weddle. bk.rev.; circ. 1,000 (paid).
    Description: Provides news and advice for Afghan hound owners.

636.7   UK   ISSN 0955-9469
OUR DOGS. 1895. w. £96. Our Dogs Publishing Co. Ltd., 5 James Leigh St., Manchester M1 6EX, England. TEL 061-236-0557. FAX 061-236-5534. Ed. William Moores. adv.; bk.rev.; tr.lit. circ. 22,000. (tabloid format; back issues avail.) **Document type:** newspaper.

636.8 179
PARADE OF ROYALTY (YEAR). 1980. a. $22.95. American Cat Fanciers Association, Inc., Box 203, Point Lookout, MO 65726. TEL 417-334-5430. FAX 427-334-5540. Dir. Wini Keuler. adv. circ. 1,200. (back issues avail.)
    Description: Publishes year-end awards, articles of interest to cat fanciers.

636.7   GW
PARTNER HUND. m. DM.49.20 (foreign DM.61.80). Gong Verlag GmbH, Innere Cramer-Klett-Str. 6, 90403 Nuernberg, Germany. TEL 0911-5325-0. FAX 0911-5325197. Ed. Uschi Birr; Pub. Bob Borrink. adv. contact: Edith Arnold. circ. 47,250. **Document type:** consumer publication.

636.7   US
PEKINGESE CLUB OF AMERICA. BULLETIN. q. Pekingese Club of America, Inc., 3 Carolyn ter., Southboro, MA 01772. Ed. Hetty Orringer. circ. 225.

636.7   US
PEKINGESE NEWS.* 1972. 10/yr. $15. Dudgeon Publications, 5100 E, Rosehill Ave., Terre Haute, IN 47805. TEL 812-466-3361. Ed. Mollie Dudgeon. adv.; illus. circ. 1,000.

636.7   US   ISSN 1069-0425
PEMBROKE WELSH CORGI CLUB OF AMERICA. NEWSLETTER.* 1967. q. $10. Pembroke Welsh Corgi Club of America, c/o Bryce Beasley, P.O. Box 804, Forney, TX 75126-0804. adv.; bk.rev. circ. 850. **Document type:** newsletter.

636.7   US
PEPPER 'N SALT. 1960? 3/yr. $20 to members. Standard Schnauzer Club of America, 1884 W. Lake Storey Rd., Galesburg, IL 61401. Eds. John Pazereskis, Dorothy Pazereskis. adv.; illus.; circ. 600 (controlled). **Document type:** bulletin, consumer publication.
    Description: Contains pictures, lists of breeders, dog show results, articles, and other club publications pertaining to the Standard Schnauzer dog.

636.7   MX   ISSN 0188-1469
LOS PERROS DEL MUNDO; la revista de la canofilia Mexicana. 1985. m. Mex.$72. Publitecnic S.A., Calle 4, no. 188, Box 74-290, C.P. 09070, Mexico 13, D.F., Mexico. TEL 685-28-19. FAX 67-06318. Ed. Fernando Ulacia Esteve. adv.; circ. 10,000 (controlled). (back issues avail.)
    Formerly (until 1989): Xolo (ISSN 0186-3851)

636.8 US
PERSPECTIVES ON CATS. 1981. q. $20. Cornell Feline Health Center, College of Veterinary Medicine, Cornell University, Ithaca, NY 14853. TEL 607-253-3414. FAX 607-253-3419. Ed. June E. Tuttle. cum.index: 1981-1993. **Document type:** newsletter.
   Description: Informs owners and breeders about feline health.

636 US ISSN 0098-5406
SF414.7
PET AGE. 1971. m. $25. H.H. Backer Associates, Inc., 20 E. Jackson Blvd., Ste. 200, Chicago, IL 60604. TEL 312-663-4040. FAX 312-663-5676. Ed. Karen Long MacLeod. adv.: B&W page $1525, color page $2290; trim 8 1/4 x 10 7/8; adv. contact: Lou Carso. charts, illus.; stat.; index. circ. 20,100. (back issues avail.) **Document type:** trade publication.

636 658 US ISSN 0191-4766
PET BUSINESS. 1973. m. $24 (foreign $72). Pet Business of Florida, Inc., 5400 N.W. 84th Ave., Miami, FL 33166-3333. TEL 305-592-9890. Ed. Elizabeth McKay. adv.: B&W page $1835, color page $2825; trim 8 1/8 x 10 7/8; adv. contact: Craig Rexford. bk.rev.; tr.lit. circ. 16,000. **Document type:** trade publication.
   Formerly: Aquarium Industry.

PET BUSINESS WORLD. see *BUSINESS AND ECONOMICS — Small Business*

636 US ISSN 1047-3815
PET CARE REPORT. q. Whittle Communications L.P., 333 Main Ave., Knoxville, TN 37902. TEL 615-595-5300. Ed. Anne Krueger.
   Description: Offers tips to owners of small animals. Features include how-to articles dealing with specific problems, such as pregnancy, disease and immunization, and the needs of special pet breeds.

636 US ISSN 0553-8572
SF411
PET DEALER. 1952. m. $25. P T N Publishing Corp., 445 Broad Hollow Rd., Melville, NY 11747. TEL 516-845-2700. FAX 516-845-7109. Ed. Timothy Fox. adv.: B&W page $1680, color page $2530; trim 8 1/2 x 10 7/8. circ. 20,050. **Document type:** trade publication.
   Description: Reaches pet shop retailers with news, information, purchasing guide and surveys.

636 US ISSN 1046-2112
PET FOCUS; the magazine for people who love pets. 1989. bi-m. $10.50. Focus Publications, Inc., 20 Church St., Montclair, NJ 07042. TEL 201-783-7303. Ed. Martin Fitzpatrick. adv.: B&W page $2160. bibl.; illus. circ. 105,000.
   Description: For the layperson, covers pet health issues.

636 US ISSN 1069-0735
PET PARTNERS NEWSLETTER. 1991. 6/yr. $6 (foreign $9). Delta Society, Box 1080, 321 Burnett Ave., S., 3rd Fl., Renton, WA 98055. TEL 206-226-7357. FAX 206-235-1076. Ed. Maureen Fredrickson. circ. 3,000. **Document type:** newsletter.
   Description: Provides "how-to" information for health care professionals and volunteers involved in programs of animal-assisted activities and therapy.

636 UK ISSN 0262-5849
PET PRODUCT MARKETING; the pet trade journal. 1954. m. £21. Frontline Ltd. (Subsidiary of: E M A P - Haymarket Ltd.), Park House, 117 Park Rd., Peterborough PE1 2TR, England. TEL 0733-555161. FAX 62788. TELEX 329292 FRONT G. Ed. Bob Stonebridge. adv.; bk.rev.; illus.; mkt.; pat. circ. 4,427. (tabloid format)
   —CCC.
   Former titles: Pet Product Marketing and Garden Supplies - The Pet Trade Journal; Pet Trade Journal.

636 US ISSN 1068-5979
PET PRODUCT NEWS & P S M. (Supplement avail.: Pet Product News & P S M Buyer's Guide) 1993. m. $36 (free to qualified personnel). Fancy Publications, 2401 Beverly Blvd., Los Angeles, CA 90057. TEL 213-385-2222. FAX 714-855-8822. (Subscr. to: Box 6050, Irvine, CA 92690. TEL 800-426-2516. FAX 714-855-3045) Ed. Scott McElhaney; Pub. Norman Ridker. adv. contact: Andy Lamedman. circ. controlled. **Document type:** trade publication.
   Formed by the 1993 merger of: Pet Supplies Marketing; (1988-1993): Pet Product News (ISSN 0899-2177)
   Description: For pet store operators. Covers industry news, including trade shows, legal issues, corporate takeovers and personnel changes, with emphasis on new products.

636 338 US
PET SERVICES JOURNAL. 1977. bi-m. $50 (foreign $75). American Boarding Kennels Association, 4575 Galley Rd., Ste. 400A, Colorado Springs, CO 80915. TEL 719-591-1113. FAX 719-579-0006. (American Grooming Shop Association) Ed. Pat Colt. adv. contact: Pat Colt. bk.rev.; circ. 1,700 (controlled). **Document type:** newsletter, trade publication.
   Formerly (until 1992): Borderline Magazine.
   Description: Covers the pet care industry and small business person.

636
PET WORLD. m. 520 Yen per no. Pet Life Ltd. (Subsidiary of: Midori Group), Ikebukuro Nishiguchi Sky Bldg., 2-14-4 Ikebukuro, Toshima-ku, Tokyo 171, Japan. TEL 03-3980-6955. circ. 20,000.
   Description: The only magazine of pet industry in Japan.

636.7 UK ISSN 0959-4450
PETDOGS MAGAZINE. 1989. bi-m. £10.50; newsstand price: £1.75. Shires Mace Ltd., P.O. Box B163, Huddersfield HD4 7YZ, England. TEL 01484-460372. FAX 01484-460373. (Dist. by: Seymour, Windsor House, 1270 London Rd., London SW16 4DH, England. TEL 0181-679-1899. FAX 0181-679-8907) Ed. Paula Shires; Pub. Geoff Mace. adv.: B&W page £510, color page £850; trim 297 x 210; adv. contact: Fiona Smith. bk.rev.; circ. 46,370 (paid). (also avail. in audio cassette; back issues avail.)

PETFOOD INDUSTRY. see *FOOD AND FOOD INDUSTRIES*

636 NE ISSN 0928-6241
PETS EUROPE. (Text in English, French, German) 1980. 7/yr. fl.98. InterMedium Publishers, P.O. Box 1318, 3800 BH Amersfoort, Netherlands. TEL 31-33-947672. FAX 31-33-945886. Ed. Reinder Sterenborg. adv.; bk.rev. circ. 8,800. **Document type:** trade publication.
   Formerly (until 1989): I P T O Bulletin (International Pet Trade Organization).

636 CN ISSN 0831-2621
PETS MAGAZINE. 1983. bi-m. Can.$15($18) Moorshead Publications Ltd., 797 Don Mills Rd., 10th Fl., Toronto, ON M3C 3S5, Canada. TEL 416-445-5600. FAX 41-445-8149. Ed. Ed Zapletal. adv.: B&W page $3740, color page $4400; trim 8 1/8 x 10 3/4; adv. contact: Wilf McIlveen. adv. page. 55,000. Indexed: CMI.
   ●Also available online.
   Former titles (until 1985): Pets (ISSN 0715-8947); (until 1983): Pets Magazine (ISSN 0822-8892)
   Description: For the concerned and caring pet owner.

636 CN ISSN 1195-7298
PETS QUARTERLY MAGAZINE. 1992. q. Can.$13 (US $15, elsewhere $20). P Q M, 151 - 8333 Jones Rd., Richmond, BC V6Y 1L5, Canada. TEL 604-244-7450. FAX 604-244-7450. Ed. Val Wilson; Pub. Robert W. Oates. adv.: B&W page Can.$2150, color page Can.$2680; trim 8 3/8 x 10 7/8; adv. contact: Ian Jamieson. bk.rev.; circ. 38,600 (paid); 31,400 (controlled). **Document type:** consumer publication.
   Description: Features stories and phots about people and their pets. Subjects include training, play, adoption, health and nutrition, grooming, travel.

PETS, SUPPLIES, MARKETING. see *BUSINESS AND ECONOMICS — Marketing And Purchasing*

PETS WELCOME; animal lovers' holiday guide. see *TRAVEL AND TOURISM*

636 US
PETSPECTIVES. 1991. m. American Professional Pet Distributors, Inc., 225 E. 6th St., Ste. 230, St. Paul, MN 55101. TEL 612-293-1049. Ed. Robert Buckler. circ. 1,000 (controlled). **Document type:** newsletter.

636 US
PETTPOURI. q. c/o Andrea Pett, Ed. & Pub., 5907 Cahill Ave., Tarzana, CA 91356-1207. TEL 818-343-1249. circ. 2,500.

636.4 US ISSN 1054-5123
PIG TALE TIMES. 1989. bi-m. $18 (Canada $20, elsewhere $22). (International Gold Star Pot Belly Pig Register) Kiyoko and Company, Box 1478, Pacifica, CA 94044. TEL 415-738-8659. FAX 415-359-8768. Ed. Kiyoko Hancock. adv.; bk.rev.; illus. circ. 2,500. (back issues avail.) **Document type:** newsletter, trade publication.
   Description: Provides news and information for pot belly pig owners and enthusiasts.

636.7 362.41
PILOT DOGS. 1950. q. free. Pilot Light, 625 W. Town St., Columbus, OH 43215.

PIPELINE (ROY). see *CLUBS*

636.7 US
POINTER POINTS. q. $8. American Pointer Club, Inc., 1082 Ocean Blvd., Coronado, CA 92118-2801. Ed. Lucy Goodman. circ. 200.

636.7 US ISSN 0744-8546
POMERANIAN REVIEW.* q. $16. American Pomeranian Club, RR3, Box 429, Washington, IN 47501.

636.7 US ISSN 0477-5449
SF429.P85
POODLE REVIEW. 1955. bi-m. $40 (foreign $45). Hoflin Publishing Ltd., 4401 Zephyr St., Wheat Ridge, CO 80033. TEL 303-934-5656. FAX 303-422-7000. Eds. Del and Sara Dahl. adv.; bk.rev.; illus. circ. 1,700.
   Description: Dedicated to poodle breeders and those interested in showing their poodles in competitions.

636.7 US ISSN 0882-2816
POODLE VARIETY. 1977. 5/yr. $40 (foreign $48). Showdogs Publications, Box 30430, Santa Barbara, CA 93130-0430. TEL 805-966-7270. Ed. Bo Bengtson; Pub. Paul Lepiane. adv.: B&W page $145, color page $1000. bk.rev. circ. 2,000. **Document type:** trade publication.
   Description: Information and photographs of poodle showdogs.

636.7 US
PORTUGUESE WATER DOG CLUB OF AMERICA. NEWSLETTER. bi-m. Portuguese Water Dog Club of America, c/o Diana H. Metcalf, 243 Cheswold Ln., Haverford, PA 19041. **Document type:** newsletter.

636 US
POT-BELLIED PIGS; a journal for breeders & pet owners. 1990. bi-m. $25. Sarnan Publications, Box 853, Ooltewah, TN 37363. Eds. Nancy Cardillo, Sara Oster. adv.; illus.

PRATIQUE MEDICALE ET CHIRURGICALE DE L'ANIMAL DE COMPAGNIE. see *VETERINARY SCIENCE*

636 GW
DER PUDEL SPIEGEL. 1952. q. DM.34.20($20) Verband der Pudelfreunde Deutschland e.V., Dorfstr. 27, Postfach 144, 2055 Wohltorf, Germany. circ. 2,400. **Document type:** consumer publication.

636.7 US
PUG DOG CLUB OF AMERICA. BULLETIN. 1966. q. $10. Pug Dog Club of America, c/o Polly J. Lamarine, 61 Fairfax Ave., Meriden, CT 06450. Ed. Alice Faye Sproul. circ. 410.

636.7 US
PULI NEWS. bi-m. Puli Club of America, c/o Laurel Colton, 655 Amesbury Dr., Dixon, CA 95620.

PETS

636   IT
QUA LA ZAMPA. 1990. bi-m. L.5000 per no. Edizioni Internazionale Cioe s.r.l., Via Sebino 16, 00199 Rome, Italy. TEL 06-3295390. Ed. Fabio Piscopo. adv.: B&W page L.4500000, color page L.8000000. **Document type:** consumer publication.

636   IT
QUATTRO ZAMPE. 1987. m. L.48000. Fabbri Rizzoli Edizioni Periodiche srl, Via Mecenate, 87-6, 20138 Milan, Italy. TEL 02-580841. FAX 02-5062865. Ed. Giovanni Giovannini. adv.: color page L.18000000; adv. contact: Flavio Biondi. circ. 43,537.

RABBIT GAZETTE. see *AGRICULTURE — Poultry And Livestock*

636.596   UK   ISSN 0033-7404
RACING PIGEON PICTORIAL. 1970. m. £19($40) Racing Pigeon Publishing Co. Ltd., Unit 13, 21 Wren St., London WC1X 0HF, England. TEL 0171-833-5959. FAX 0171-833-3151. Ed. Colin Osman. adv.; bk.rev. circ. 9,800. **Document type:** bulletin.

636.7   US   ISSN 0899-1111
RANCH DOG TRAINER. 1986. bi-m. $22. Stonehedge Publishing Co., Inc., 7686 State Rte. 17, W. Plains, MO 65775. TEL 417-257-7376. FAX 417-257-7376. E-mail: RDTKC@TOWHSQR.com. Ed. Kathleen Conner. adv. contact: Pat Pall. bk.rev.; circ. 3,000 (paid). **Document type:** consumer publication.
Description: For the livestock producer who uses the stockdog as a livestock-handling tool.

636   US   ISSN 1048-986X
RARE BREEDS JOURNAL. 1987. bi-m. $25 (effective 1995-1996). Box 66, Crawford, NE 69339. TEL 308-665-1431. FAX 308-665-1931. Ed. Maureen Neidhardt. adv.; bk.rev. circ. 3,000. **Document type:** trade publication.

636   US   ISSN 1078-2311
RAT AND MOUSE TALES. 1984. bi-m. membership. American Fancy Rat and Mouse Association, 9230 64th St., Riverside, CA 92509. TEL 909-685-2350. Ed. Karen Robbins. circ. 300. (back issues avail.) **Document type:** newsletter.
Description: Club newsletter with technical, informative, helpful as well as human interest stories, and articles about rats and mice.

636.932   US   ISSN 1069-2045
RAT REPORT. 1992. m. $18 (Canada $19.50; elsewhere $26). Rat Fan Club, 857 Lindo Ln., Chico, CA 95926. TEL 916-899-0605. E-mail: debbie_ducommun@macgate.csuchico.edu. Ed. Debbie Ducommun. circ. 250 (paid). **Document type:** newsletter.
Description: Covers all aspects of pet rats, including tips on getting started, care and feeding, health concerns, letters from pet owners, and featured tricks or projects.

598.1   US   ISSN 1059-0668
REPTILE AND AMPHIBIAN MAGAZINE. 1989. bi-m. $16. Box 3709-A, Rte. 61, R.D. 3, Pottsville, PA 17901. TEL 717-622-6050. FAX 717-622-5858. Ed. Ed. Erica Ramus; Pub. Norman Frank. adv.: B&W page $476, color page $816; trim 5 1/2 x 8 1/2; adv. contact: Gail Frank. bk.rev.; illus. circ. 14,500. **Document type:** consumer publication.
Description: For amateur herpetologists.

636.7   US   ISSN 0279-9693
RETRIEVER FIELD TRIAL NEWS. 1964. 10/yr. $35. 4213 S. Howell Ave., Milwaukee, WI 53207. TEL 414-481-2760. FAX 414-481-2743. (Co-sponsors: National Retriever Club; National Amateur Retriever Club) Ed. Mary C. Knapp. adv.; trim 10 x 13; adv. contact: Jan Nelson. circ. 3,900 (paid). **Document type:** trade publication.
Description: Provides results of trials, tests and other matters of interest to the owners, breeders and trainers of retrievers.

636.7   US   ISSN 8750-3549
RHODESIAN RIDGEBACK QUARTERLY. 1984? q. $40. Hoflin Publishing Ltd., 4401 Zephyr St., Wheat Ridge, CO 80033-3299. TEL 303-934-5656. FAX 303-422-7000.

636.7   US
RIDGEBACK.* q. Rhodesian Ridgeback Club of the United States, c/o Trish Reynolds, 2589 Rittmer Ln., Seneca Falls, NY 13148. adv.

636.7   US   ISSN 1040-8037
ROTTWEILER QUARTERLY. (Text mainly in English; occasionally in German) 1987. q. $40 (foreign $55) (effective Jun. 1995). G R Q Publications, 3355 Conant Ln., Watsonville, CA 95076. TEL 408-728-8461. FAX 408-728-4708. (Subscr. to: Box 900, Aromas, CA 95004) Ed. Robin Stark; Pub. Tomi Edmiston. adv. contact: Tomi Edmiston. circ. 4,500. **Document type:** consumer publication.
Description: Covers training, showing, breeding, working, health issues, statistics and humor for Rottweiler owners.

636.7   US
SAINT FANCIER. 1888. bi-m. membership. Saint Bernard Club of America, c/o Joanne Alstede, 229 Old Turnpike Rd., Califon, NJ 07830. TEL 908-832-9317. adv. circ. 800.

636.7   US
SALUKI CLUB OF AMERICA. NEWSLETTER. q. Saluki Club of America, 3816 E. Waterloo Rd., Akron, OH 44312. circ. 108. **Document type:** newsletter.

636.7   DK   ISSN 0108-2736
SAMOJEDEN.* 1981. bi-m. free. Samoyed Club of Denmark, Ebletoft, Denmark. Ed. Torben Joergensen. adv.; bk.rev.; illus. circ. 500.

636.7   US   ISSN 0161-0651
SF429.S35
SAMOYED QUARTERLY. 1976. q. $40. Hoflin Publishing Ltd., 4401 Zephyr St., Wheat Ridge, CO 80033-3299. TEL 303-932-5656. FAX 303-422-7000.

636   FR   ISSN 0768-8733
SANS LAISSE. 1978. m. 220 F. (foreign 260 F.). Editions du Suran, BP 49, 15 rue Reclosiere, 39160 Saint-Amour, France. TEL 84-48-82-12. FAX 84-48-80-33. Ed. Alain Dupont. index. circ. 9,000. **Document type:** bulletin.
Formerly (until **1987**): Berger Allemand (ISSN 0183-3197)

636.932   US
SATIN NEWS. bi-m. American Satin Rabbit Breeders Association, 2019 N. 13th St., Kansas City, KS 66104. TEL 913-371-4197.

636.7   US
SCHIPPERKE CLUB OF AMERICA. BULLETIN.* q. $7.50 to members; non-members $10. Schipperke Club of America, Box 950, Olalla, WA 98359-0950. Ed. Joie Chandler. adv. circ. 350.

636.7   US   ISSN 0276-1521
SCHNAUZER SHORTS. 1960. 7/yr. $30 (foreign $42). Dan Kiedrowski Company, P.O. Drawer A, LaHonda, CA 94020. TEL 415-747-0549. FAX 415-747-0549. Ed. Denis Shaw. adv.: B&W page $100. circ. 980. **Document type:** consumer publication.
Description: For miniature Schnauzer enthusiasts and breeders.

636.7   US   ISSN 0886-3997
SETTERS, INCORPORATED. 1975. bi-m. $24. 12 Bay Path Ct., Huntington, NY 11743. Ed. Marilyn Sturz. adv.; bk.rev. circ. 1,000.
Formerly: Setters.

636.7   US   ISSN 0745-2012
SHELTIE INTERNATIONAL. 1982. 6/yr. $43. Reporter Publications, Box 6369, Los Osos, CA 93412. TEL 805-528-2007. FAX 805-528-8200. illus. **Document type:** consumer publication.
Description: News and information of interest to Sheltie owners.

636.7   US   ISSN 0744-6608
SHELTIE PACESETTER. 1977. bi-m. $44. Sheltie Pacesetter, Box 3310, Palos Verdes, CA 90274. TEL 310-791-0102. Ed. Nancy Lee Marshall. adv. contact: Nancy Lee Marshall. bk.rev. circ. 3,600. **Document type:** trade publication.
Description: Contains informative articles and photos on the Sheltie.

636.7   US
SHELTIE PACESETTER TRADE SECRETS BOOK. 1982. quinquennial. $14.50 (foreign $15.50). Sheltie Pacesetter, Box 3310, Palos Verdes, CA 90274. TEL 310-791-0102. Ed. Nancy Lee Marshall.
Description: Gives 770 hints for the novice, professional owner, trainer, or breeder of Shelties covering about 70 topics.

636   US
SHIH TZU BULLETIN.* 1951. q. $00 to non-members. American Shih Tzu Club, Inc., 5024 Barkwood Ln., York, PA 17406. FAX 714-879-3738. Ed. Bruce Lane. adv.; illus. circ. 850. **Document type:** bulletin.

636.7   US   ISSN 1040-5801
SHIH TZU REPORTER. 1975. bi-m. $43. Reporter Publications, Box 6369, Los Osos, CA 93412. TEL 805-528-2007. FAX 805-528-8200. **Document type:** consumer publication.

636.8   US
SIAMESE NEWS QUARTERLY. 1960. q. $15 (Canada $18; elsewhere $20). Siamese Cat Society of America, Inc., Box 1149, Green Valley, AZ 85622. TEL 602-967-4459. (Subscr. to: Z. Kozaczka, 917B S. Acapulco, Tempe, AZ 85281) Ed. Shirley Johnson. adv.; bk.rev.; circ. 600 (paid). **Document type:** newsletter.
Description: Provides owners and breeders of Siamese cats with the latest information on breeding, genetics, general care, and health problems.

636   US   ISSN 0583-1776
SF429.S65
SIBERIAN HUSKY CLUB OF AMERICA NEWSLETTER.* vol. 6, 1972. bi-m. $10. Siberian Husky Club of America, Inc., c/o Ken Gentry, 1408 N.E. Tudor Rd., Lee's Summit, MO 64063. Ed. Debbie Swindlehurst. bk.rev.; charts; illus. circ. 800.

636.7   US   ISSN 0274-7286
SIBERIAN QUARTERLY. 1980. q. $40. Hoflin Publishing Ltd., 4401 Zephyr St., Wheat Ridge, CO 80033-3299. TEL 303-934-5656. FAX 303-422-7000.

636.7   US   ISSN 8750-1953
SIGHTHOUND REVIEW. 1984. bi-m. $40 (foreign $48). Showdogs Publications, Box 30430, Santa Barbara, CA 93130-0430. TEL 805-966-7270. Pub. Bo Bengtson. adv.: B&W page $145, color page $1000. bk.rev. circ. 1,800. **Document type:** trade publication.
Description: Contains information and photographs of the sighthound-greyhound breeds.

636.7   US
SILKY TERRIER CLUB OF AMERICA NEWSLETTER. 1953. m. membership. Silky Terrier Club of America, Inc., Box 1132, Alameda, CA 94501-1132. Ed. Louise Coviello. bk.rev.; illus.; stat. circ. 400. (processed) **Document type:** newsletter.

636   US   ISSN 0037-539X
SIMIAN.* 1958. m. $10. Simian Society of America, Inc., 147 School St., Salem, NH 03079-2681. Ed. Barbara E. O'Brien. adv.; bk.rev.; film rev.; bibl.; illus.; index. circ. 3,000.
Formerly: Monkey Business.

636.7   US   ISSN 1072-8899
SKYE TERRIER CLUB OF AMERICA. BULLETIN. 1938. q. $17 (foreign $30). Skye Terrier Club of America, 7 Fox Hill Ave., Bristol, RI 02809. TEL 401-253-8367. E-mail: MPESARE@aol.com. Ed. Michael J. Pesare. adv.; circ. 275 (paid); 200 (controlled). **Document type:** bulletin.
Description: Devoted exclusively to the Skye terrier. Features include specialty show results, health care, breeding, histories of famous Skye terrier kennels, and exhibitions.

636.7   US   ISSN 1043-5034
SPANIELS IN THE FIELD. 1980. q. $30. On the Line, Ltd., 10714 Escondido Dr., Cincinnati, OH 45249. TEL 513-489-2727. FAX 513-489-4105. Ed. Arthur T. Rodger. adv.; bk.rev.; circ. 2,000 (paid). **Document type:** trade publication.
Former titles: On the Line (Cincinnati); Springers on the Line.
Description: Dedicated to the advancement and promotion of all flushing spaniels.

636.596   GW   ISSN 0490-5687
SPORTAUBE. m. Deutscher Bauernverlag GmbH, Brunnenstr. 128, 13355 Berlin, Germany. TEL 030-464060. FAX 030-46406205. **Document type:** consumer publication.

636.7   US
SPOTTER.* 1971. q. membership only. Dalmatian Club of America, c/o Tim Robbins, Ed., Box 3782, Baytown, TX 77522-3782. adv.; bk.rev. circ. 1,000.

636.7 US
STAFFORDSHIRE BULL TERRIER CLUB OF AMERICA. NEWSLETTER.* 3/yr. Staffordshire Bull Terrier Club of America, 5240 Long Island Dr., N.W., Atlanta, GA 30327. adv. **Document type:** newsletter.

636.7 US
TALLY-HO.* bi-m. membership. Basset Hound Club of America, 2009 Adeline Ct., Wayzata, MN 55391. Ed. Sherry Neiberger. circ. 800.

636.7 US
TASSELS AND TAILS. 3/yr. $10. Bedlington Terrier Club of America, 12 Irma Pl., Oceanport, NJ 07757. circ. 330.

636.7 796 US
TEAM AND TRAIL; the musher's monthly news. 1963. m. $25 (Canada $31; elsewhere $45). Team & Trail Publishers, Box 128, Center Harbor, NH 03226-0128. TEL 603-253-6265. FAX 603-253-9513. Ed. Cynthia J. Molburg; Pub. Cynthia J. Molburg. adv.; bk.rev. circ. 1,200. (back issues avail.) **Document type:** newsletter. **Description:** Provides worldwide sled dog racing news and information on other related events.

636.7 US ISSN 0199-6495
TERRIER TYPE. 1961. 11/yr. $40 (foreign $50). Dan Kiedrowski, Drawer A, LaHonda, CA 94020. TEL 415-747-0549. FAX 415-747-0549. Ed. Denis R. Shaw. adv.; B&W page $100; adv. contact: Bob LaRouech. circ. 1,700. **Document type:** consumer publication. **Description:** For show dog enthusiasts and breeders of terriers.

636.7 179.31 US
THERAPY DOGS INTERNATIONAL. MINI-NEWSLETTER. 1980. q. $20 membership. Therapy Dogs International, 6 Hilltop Rd., Mendham, NJ 07945. TEL 201-543-0888. FAX 201-543-0989. E-mail: tdi@qti.net. circ. 4,000. **Description:** Provides qualified handlers of therapy dogs for visitations to instutuions and facilities to provide comfort and companionship by sharing the dog with the disabled, hadicapped, and terminally ill

TIDSSKRIFT FOR KANINAVL. see *AGRICULTURE — Poultry And Livestock*

636.7 AT ISSN 1037-5090
TOP DOG JOURNAL. 1992. m. Aus.$24 (foreign Aus.$48). Erinrac Enterprises, Foott Rd., Upper Beaconsfield, Vic. 3808, Australia. TEL 61-59-44-3383. FAX 61-59-44-3384. Ed. Jan Irving. adv.; B&W page Aus.$200. bk.rev.; illus.; stat. circ. 5,000. (back issues avail.) **Document type:** consumer publication.

179.3 US ISSN 0082-5441
TOURING WITH TOWSER. 1948. biennial. $3. Quaker Professional Services, Box 9001, Chicago, IL 60604-9001. (Orders to: Quaker Professional Services, 585 Hawthorne Court, Galesburg, IL 61401) Ed. Tom O'Shea. circ. 22,500. **Document type:** directory.

TRAVELLING WITH YOUR PET. see *TRAVEL AND TOURISM*

636.7 GW
UNSERE WINDHUNDE.* 1983. m. DM.50. Deutscher Windhundzucht- und Rennverbands e.V., Bleickenallee 16, 22763 Hamburg, Germany. TEL 05129-7341. Ed. August C. Brendel. circ. 4,000.

636 AT
V C A KENNEL GAZETTE. 1932. m. Aus.$40. Victorian Canine Association Inc., Royal Showgrounds, Epsom Rd., Ascot Vale, Vic. 3032, Australia. TEL 61-3-3762255. FAX 61-3-3761772. Ed. Ian R. Hunter. adv. contact: W. Moore. bk.rev. circ. 16,800. **Formerly:** K C C Kennel Gazette.

636.7 SW ISSN 0042-269X
VAARA HUNDAR. 1923. 6/yr. SEK 130 membership (effective 1995). (Svenska Hundklubben - Swedish Cynological Society) Thomas Staeav, Arkeologgatan 18, S-644 35 Torshaella, Sweden. TEL 46-16-35-59-78. FAX 46-18-52-37-10. (Subscr. to: Svenska Hundklubben, Norbyvaegen 57 D, S-752 39, Uppsala, Sweden; Subscr. to: Svenska Hundklubben, Norbyv. 57D, S752 39 Uppsala, Sweden. TEL 18-52-37-10) Ed. Erik Skye. adv.: B&W page SEK 500. bk.rev. **Description:** Publishes articles on club matters, reports on dog shows and obedience competitions, as well as articles on the caring and training of dogs.

636 AT
VICTORIAN CANINE ASSOCIATION GAZETTE DOGS. 1934. m. free to members. Victorian Canine Association Inc., Royal Showgrounds, Epsom Road, Ascot Vale, Vic. 3032, Australia. TEL 61-3-376-2255. FAX 61-3-376-1772. Ed. I.R. Hunter. adv. contact: W. Moore. bk.rev. circ. 16,800. **Formerly:** Kennel Control Council Gazette Dogs. **Description:** Lists pure-bred dog shows, trial and performance tests.

636.7 AT
VICTORIAN CANINE ASSOCIATION JOURNAL. 1957. m. membership. Victorian Canine Association Inc., Royal Showgrounds, Epsom Rd., Ascot Vale, Vic. 3032, Australia. TEL 61-3-376-2255. FAX 61-3-376-1772. Ed. I. Hunter. adv. contact: W. Moore. bk.rev.; illus.; stat. circ. 16,800. **Formerly:** R A S Kennel Control Journal (ISSN 0033-6777)

636.7 JA
WAN. (Text in Japanese) m. 720 Yen per no. Pet Life Ltd. (Subsidiary of: Midori Group), Ikebukuro Nishiguchi Sky Bldg., 2-14-4 Ikebukuro, Toshima-ku, Tokyo 171, Japan. TEL 03-3980-6955. circ. 60,000. **Document type:** consumer publication. **Description:** Provides general information for dog keepers.

636.7 US ISSN 0162-315X
WEIMARANER MAGAZINE. 1949. m. $22 to non-members. Weimaraner Club of America, P.O. Box 110708, Nashville, TN 37222-0708. TEL 615-832-9115. Ed. Dorothy Derr. adv.; bk.rev.; film rev.; illus. circ. 1,800. **Formerly:** Weimaraner (ISSN 0049-710X) **Description:** Includes event reports, articles of interest to the wide variety of activities open to Weimaraners, and lists of top competitors.

636.7 NE
WELSH SPRINGER. 1976. bi-m. membership. Welsh Springer Spaniel Club, 2e Valthermond 2, 7877 TB Tweede Valthermond, Netherlands. adv.; bk.rev. circ. 700.

636.7 US
WESTIE IMPRINT. 1985. q. $17. West Highland White Terrier Club of America, 604 Arlie St., Richmond, VA 23226. TEL 804-288-7424. Ed. Daphne Gentry. adv.: B&W page $65; adv. contact: Daphne Gentry. bk.rev. circ. 1,000. **Formerly (until 1985):** West Highland White Terrier Club of America. Bulletin. **Description:** Provides fanciers of the West Highland White Terrier Club with information on the breed. Contains educational and entertaining articles on the breed and specific dogs.

636.7 US
WHIPPET NEWS.* m. American Whippet Club, 2300 Hillside Ave., Orange City, FL 32763. circ. 210.

636.7 US
WHIPPET NEWSLETTER. m. $8. 1462 Granger Rd., Medina, OH 44256. **Document type:** newsletter.

WHO'S WHO IN LIVE ANIMAL TRADE & TRANSPORT. see *TRANSPORTATION*

636.7 US ISSN 1059-6267
THE WORKING BORDER COLLIE. 1988. 6/yr. $25 (foreign $35) (effective 1995). Bruce Fogt, Pub., 14933 Kirkwood Rd., Sidney, OH 45365. TEL 513-492-2215. adv.; bk.rev.; illus. circ. 2,000. **Description:** Helps farmers and ranchers to train stock dogs. For beginners through top handlers.

636.932 FR
WORLD RABBIT SCIENCE ASSOCIATION. NEWSLETTER. q. 598 F. World Rabbit Science Association, c/o Association Francaise de Cuniculture, B.P. 50, 63370 Lempes, France. TEL 73-92-01-52. FAX 73-92-86-80. Ed. Daniele Marionnet. **Document type:** newsletter.

636.7 US
YORKIE EXPRESS.* 1951. bi-m. membership. Yorkshire Terrier Club of America, 22600 Main Rd., Cutchogue, NY 11935-1265. Ed. Dorothy DeMaula. circ. 2,000.

636.089 UK ISSN 0268-991X
YOU & YOUR VET. 1985. q. British Veterinary Association, 7 Mansfield St., London W1M OAT, England. TEL 0171-636-6541. FAX 0171-637-0620. Ed. Martin Alder. adv. contact: Gillian Notton. bk.rev. circ. 50,000. **Document type:** consumer publication. **Description:** Discusses pet care and veterinary topics of interest to the general public.

636.8 UK ISSN 1353-260X
▼**YOUR CAT.** 1994. m. £21.60 (foreign £30) (effective 1995-1996). E M A P - Pursuit Publishing, Bretton Ct., Bretton, Peterborough, Cambs. PE3 8DZ, England. TEL 01858-468811. FAX 01733-263294. TELEX 32157. (Subscr. to: Tower Publishing Services Ltd., Tower House, Sovereign Park, Lathkill St., Market Harborough, Leics. LE16 9EF, England. TEL 01858-468844. FAX 01858-432164) adv. **Document type:** consumer publication.

636.7 US
▼**YOUR DOG.** 1994. m. $30. Tufts University, School of Veterinary Medicine, 203 Harrison Ave., Boston, MA 02111. TEL 800-829-5116. (Subscr. to: Box 420014, Palm Coast, FL 32142-0014) **Document type:** newsletter. **Description:** Offers practical advice for dog owners.

636.7 UK
▼**YOUR DOG.** 1995. bi-m. £12 (foreign £15.50) (effective 1995-1996). E M A P - Pursuit Publishing, Bretton Ct., Bretton, Peterborough, Cambs. PE3 8DZ, England. TEL 01733-264666. FAX 01733-263294. TELEX 32157. (Subscr. to: Tower Publishing Services Ltd., Tower House, Sovereign Park, Lathkill St., Market Harborough, Leics. LE16 9EF, England. TEL 01858-468811. FAX 01858-432164) adv. **Document type:** consumer publication.

636 US
▼**YOUR PET.** 1994. q. $8. Your Pet Magazine, Inc., 30 Lincoln Plaza, Ste. 6D, New York, NY 10023. TEL 212-489-1416. Ed. Dominique Davis. adv.: B&W page $25353. **Document type:** consumer publication.

636 SP
ZOOHOGAR - ZOOTECNIC. 4/yr. Paseo Bonanova 14, Torre A, 08022 Barcelona, Spain. TEL 3-211-53-04. FAX 3-417-89-60.

636 GW
ZUCHTBUCH FUER DEUTSCHE SCHAEFERHUNDE. 1901. a. DM.45.90. Verein fuer Deutsche Schaeferhunde, Steinerne Furt 71-71a, 86167 Augsburg, Germany. TEL 0821-74002-0. FAX 0821-709298. Ed.Bd. circ. 2,450. **Document type:** trade publication.

PETS — Abstracting, Bibliographies, Statistics

HANDBOOK OF LIVE ANIMAL TRANSPORT. see *TRANSPORTATION — Abstracting, Bibliographies, Statistics*

PHARMACY AND PHARMACOLOGY

see also Drug Abuse and Alcoholism

615 378 US
A A C P NEWS. 1972. m. $25. American Association of Colleges of Pharmacy, 1426 Prince St., Alexandria, VA 22314-2815. TEL 703-739-2330. Ed. Mary Bassler. adv.; bibl.; illus. circ. 2,500.

PHARMACY AND PHARMACOLOGY

615   SW   ISSN 1103-1255
A A F - TIDNINGEN. 1955. q. SEK 100 membership. Apoteksanstaelldas Foerbund (AAF), P.O. Box 176, S-101 23 Stockholm, Sweden.
Former titles (until 1992): Medlemsblad - A A F; (until 1984): A S F Medlemsblad; (until 1963): Apoteksstaederskefoerbundets Medlemsblad.

615   US
A A P S NEWSLETTER. 1986. m. (except Nov.). membership. American Association of Pharmaceutical Scientists, 1650 King St., 2nd Fl., Alexandria, VA 22314-2747. TEL 703-548-3000. FAX 703-684-7349. Ed. Linda M. Williams. circ. 7,000 (controlled). **Document type:** newsletter.

615   US   ISSN 1063-8792
CODEN: ADINE4
A H F S DRUG INFORMATION. 1959. base vol. (plus 3 supplements/yr.). $115 (Canada $144; elsewhere $175). (American Hospital Formulary Service) American Society of Hospital Pharmacists, c/o Jean Rogers, Dir., Mkt. Svcs., 7272 Wisconsin Ave., Bethesda, MD 20814. TEL 301-657-4383. FAX 301-657-1251. Ed. Gerald K. McEvoy. (reprint service avail. from UMI) **Document type:** academic/scholarly publication.
●Also available online. Vendor(s): Ovid Technologies (DIFT), Knight-Ridder, Inc. (File no.229), Lexis-Nexis. Also available on CD-ROM. Producer(s): University Microfilms International.
—BLDSC (0772.282000). **CCC.**
Formerly (until 1984): American Hospital Formulary Service (ISSN 8756-6028)
Description: Contains detailed monographs on virtually every drug entity available in the US. Includes information on uses, cautions, drug interactions, chemistry, stability, pharmacology, pharmaco-kinetics, toxicity, dosage and administration.

615.19   US
A I H P NOTES. 1955. q. membership. American Institute of the History of Pharmacy, Pharmacy Bldg., 425 N. Charter St., Madison, WI 53706. TEL 608-262-5635. Ed. Rosemary Zurlo-Cuva. circ. 1,000. (back issues avail.) **Document type:** newsletter.
Description: News and information on the history of pharmacy and about activities of the institute.

615   US   ISSN 0065-9304
RM300
A M A DRUG EVALUATIONS. 1971-1983; resumed 199? a. $112.95 (Canada $133.95; elsewhere $153.95). (American Medical Association) United States Pharmacopeia, 12601 Twinbrook Pkwy., Rockville, MD 20852. TEL 800-227-8772. FAX 301-816-8148. charts; illus. **Document type:** trade publication.
—CCC.
Description: Lists drugs according to indications, adverse reactions, interactions, contraindications, and dosage.

A P S BULLETIN. (American Pain Society) see *MEDICAL SCIENCES — Anaesthesiology*

615   US   ISSN 1050-5725
A S C P UPDATE. 1969. m. $24 includes membership. American Society of Consultant Pharmacists, 1321 Duke St., Alexandria, VA 22314-3563. TEL 703-739-1300. FAX 703-739-1321. Ed. Joanne Kaldy. bk.rev. circ. 6,500. (looseleaf format; back issues avail.)
Description: News on issues and legislation relevant to members of the American Society of Consultant Pharmacists.

615.1   US   ISSN 0001-2483
A S H P NEWSLETTER. 1968. m. membership. American Society of Hospital Pharmacists, c/o Jean Rogers, Dir., Mkt. Svcs., 7272 Wisconsin Ave., Bethesda, MD 20814. TEL 301-657-4383. FAX 301-657-1251. illus. circ. 25,000. (reprint service avail. from UMI) **Document type:** academic/scholarly publication.
Description: Contains articles on pharmacy and member news.

615   US   ISSN 0199-6037
ACADEMY REPORTER. q. $25 to non-members; members free. American Pharmaceutical Association, 2215 Constitution Ave., N.W., Washington, DC 20037. TEL 202-628-4410. Ed. Naomi U. Kaminsky. circ. 23,000 (controlled). (back issues avail.) **Document type:** newsletter.
—CCC.
Description: Provides commentary by elected officers of academy on pharmacy practice and management and on pharmaceutical research and science; news on pharmacy related events.

615   FR
ACCESSOIREX; le repertoire des accessoires. 1971. a. (updates 10/yr.). 506 F. (effective 1995). Societe d'Editions Medico-Pharmaceutiques (SEMP), 26 rue le Brun, 75013 Paris, France. TEL 1-43-37-83-50. FAX 43-31-94-11. circ. 2,800. (looseleaf format; also avail. in microfiche)

615.1 370.58   US
ACCREDITED PROFESSIONAL PROGRAMS OF COLLEGES AND SCHOOLS OF PHARMACY. Variant title: American Council on Pharmaceutical Education Annual Directory (Years). 1940. a. free. American Council on Pharmaceutical Education, 311 W. Superior St., Chicago, IL 60610. TEL 312-664-3575. FAX 312-664-4652. Ed. Dr. Daniel A. Nona. circ. 10,000. **Document type:** directory.
Formerly: Accredited Colleges of Pharmacy (ISSN 0065-7980)
Refereed Serial

ACTA BIOLOGICA IUGOSLAVICA. SERIJA C: IUGOSLAVICA PHYSIOLOGICA ET PHARMACOLOGICA ACTA. see *BIOLOGY*

615.1   CI   ISSN 1330-0075
CODEN: ACPHE
ACTA PHARMACEUTICA. (Text in English) 1951. q. $40. Croatian Pharmaceutical Society, Masarykova 2-II, HR-41000 Zagreb, Croatia. TEL 041-427944. FAX 041-431301. Ed. Dr. Franc Kozjek. adv.; bk.rev.; charts; illus.; index, cum.index. circ. 1,000. (reprint service avail. from ISI) Indexed: Anal.Abstr., ASCA, Biol.Abstr., Biotech.Abstr., Bull.Signal., Chem.Abstr., Curr.Adv.Ecol.Sci., Curr.Cont., Excerp.Med., Hort.Abstr., I.P.A., Ind.Sci.Rev., INIS Atomind., Ref.Zh., Sci.Cit.Ind. **Document type:** academic/scholarly publication.
●Also available online.
—CASDDS; Faxon; Genuine Article; UMI.
Formerly (until 1992): Acta Pharmaceutica Jugoslavica (ISSN 0001-6667)
Description: Publishes review articles, original papers and preliminary communications dealing with pharmacy and related fields.

615.1   HU   ISSN 0001-6659
CODEN: APHGAO
ACTA PHARMACEUTICA HUNGARICA. (Text mainly in Hungarian; occasionally in English; abstracts in English) 1925. bi-m. $40. Magyar Gyogyszereszeti Tarsasag - Hungarian Pharmaceutical Association, Gyomroi ut 19-21, P.O.B. 27, 1475 Budapest, Hungary. FAX 36-1-2605604. TELEX 22-5067. (Subscr. to: Kultura, Box 149, H-1389 Budapest, Hungary) Ed. Dr. Sandor Gorog. adv. contact: Zoltan Hanko. bk.rev.; charts; illus. circ. 850. (reprint service avail. from IRC) Indexed: Anal.Abstr., Biol.Abstr., Biotech.Abstr., Chem.Abstr., Dent.Ind., Excerp.Med., Hort.Abstr., I.P.A., Ind.Med. **Document type:** academic/scholarly publication.
●Also available online.
—BLDSC (0645.000000); CASDDS.

615.19   TU   ISSN 1010-0849
CODEN: APTUES
ACTA PHARMACEUTICA TURCICA. (Text in English, French or German; summaries in English, Turkish) 1954. q. $15. ETAM A.S. Matbaa Tesisleri, 26470 Eskisehir, Turkey. TEL 90-222-2360051. (Editorial addr.: Anadlou Universitesi Eczacilik Fakultesi Eczacilik Teknolojisi Bolumu, 26470 Eskisehir, Turkey. TEL 90-222-3350580. FAX 90-222-3350127) Ed. Dr. Erden Guler. adv. circ. 1,125. (back issues avail.) Indexed: Anal.Abstr., Biol.Abstr., Chem.Abstr., Excerp.Med., I.P.A. **Document type:** academic/scholarly publication.
—BLDSC (0646.619000); CASDDS.
Formerly (until 1984): Eczacilik Bulteni (ISSN 0367-0236)
Description: Publishes original research and reviews concerning pharmacy , pharmacology, chemistry, biology and biotechnology.
Refereed Serial

ACTA PHYSIOLOGICA ET PHARMACOLOGICA BULGARICA. see *BIOLOGY — Physiology*

615.1   PL   ISSN 0001-6837
CODEN: APPHAX
ACTA POLONIAE PHARMACEUTICA; drug research. (Text and summaries in English) 1937. bi-m. $180 (effective 1995). Polskie Towarzystwo Farmaceutyczne - Polish Pharmaceutical Society, Ul. Dluga 16, 00-238 Warsaw, Poland. TEL 48-22-310241. FAX 48-22-310243. Ed. Aleksander P. Mazurek. charts; illus.; index. Indexed: ASCA, Biol.Abstr., Biotech.Abstr., Chem.Abstr., Curr.Adv.Ecol.Sci., Curr.Chem.React., Excerp.Med., Helminthol.Abstr., Hort.Abstr., I.P.A., Ind.Chem., Ind.Med., Ind.Sci.Rev., INIS Atomind., Nutr.Abstr., Sci.cit.Ind. **Document type:** academic/scholarly publication.
—BLDSC (0659.000000); CASDDS.
Description: Publishes scientific papers on pharmaceutical analysis, natural drugs, pharmacology, and drug synthesis.
Refereed Serial

ACTA TOXICOLOGICA ET THERAPEUTICA; international journal of toxicology, pharmacology and therapy. see *ENVIRONMENTAL STUDIES — Toxicology And Environmental Safety*

615.1   CN
ACTUALITE PHARMACEUTIQUE. English edition: Pharmacist News. (Text in French) 1929. m. Can.$29. Maclean-Hunter Ltd., Business Publication Division, Maclean-Hunter Bldg., 777 Bay St., Toronto, ON M5W 1A7, Canada. TEL 514-845-5141. (Or: 1001 Maisonneuve Ouest, Montreal, PQ H3A 3E1, Canada) Ed. Louise Saint-Pierre. adv.; illus. circ. 4,109. Indexed: I.P.A.
Formerly: Pharmacien (ISSN 0031-692X)
Description: For French-speaking pharmacists in retail and hospital locations.

615   FR   ISSN 0515-3700
ACTUALITES PHARMACEUTIQUES. 1961. m. 580 F. S.U.T.I.P., 175 rue du Faubourg Poissonniere, 75009 Paris, France. FAX 42-82-98-00. adv. Indexed: Biotech.Abstr., Chem.Abstr., I.P.A., INIS Atomind.
●Also available online.
—BLDSC (0677.324000).
Supersedes: Officine et Techniques Pharmaceutiques.

ACUPOLL REPORTS - HEALTH & BEAUTY AIDS, HOUSEHOLD PRODUCTS. see *BEAUTY CULTURE — Perfumes And Cosmetics*

615.9   US   ISSN 1044-2049
RA1190   CODEN: ATDAEI
ACUTE TOXICITY DATA. (Supplement to: American College of Toxicology. Journal) ceased. irreg., approx. a. (American College of Toxicology) Raven Press, 1185 Ave. of the Americas, New York, NY 10036. TEL 212-930-9500. FAX 212-869-3495. cum.index. Indexed: Energy Info.Abstr. **Document type:** academic/scholarly publication.
—CASDDS.
Description: Compilation of experimental data published with brief experimental procedures. Compounds are indexed by chemical names and CAS numbers.
Refereed Serial

615.19 NE ISSN 0169-409X
CODEN: ADDREP
ADVANCED DRUG DELIVERY REVIEWS. (Text in English) 1987. m. fl.2480($1512) (effective 1996). Elsevier Science B.V., P.O. Box 211, 1000 BM Amsterdam, Netherlands. TEL 31-20-4853911. FAX 31-20-4853798. TELEX 18582 ESPA NL. E-mail: nlinfo-f@elsevier.nl; usinfo-f@elsevier.com; forinfo-kyf04035@niftyserve.or.jp; Site addr.: http://www.elsevier.nl/. (Subscr. in U.S. and Canada to: Elsevier Science Inc., Box 882, Madison Sq. Sta., New York, NY 10159. TEL 212-989-5800. FAX 212-633-3990) Ed.Bd. adv.; bk.rev.; index. (also avail. in microform from UMI; back issues avail.) **Indexed:** Biol.Abstr., Chem.Abstr., Curr.Cont., Excerp.Med. **Document type:** academic/scholarly publication.
—BLDSC (0696.845000); ADONIS; CASDDS; Ei; Faxon; Genuine Article; SWETS. **CCC.**
Description: Publishes critical review articles on current and emerging aspects of research into the design and development of advanced drug delivery systems and their application to experimental and clinical therapeutics.
Refereed Serial

615 616.8 US ISSN 0065-2229
RM315 CODEN: ABPYBL
ADVANCES IN BIOCHEMICAL PSYCHOPHARMACOLOGY. 1969. irreg., latest vol.49. price varies. Raven Press, (Subsidiary of: Wolters Kluwer N.V.), 1185 Ave. of the Americas, New York, NY 10036. TEL 212-930-9500. FAX 212-869-3495. Eds. E. Costa, P. Greengard. (reprint service avail. from UMI) **Indexed:** Biol.Abstr., Chem.Abstr., Curr.Cont., Ind.Med., Ind.Sci.Rev. **Document type:** monographic series.
—BLDSC (0699.930000); CASDDS; Faxon; Genuine Article; SWETS. **CCC.**
Refereed Serial

ADVANCES IN CLINICAL CHEMISTRY. see *BIOLOGY — Biological Chemistry*

615 US
▼**ADVANCES IN CLINICAL PHARMACOLOGY.** 1994. irreg. price varies. Raven Press (Subsidiary of: Wolters Kluwer N.V.), 1185 Ave. of the Americas, New York, NY 10036. TEL 212-930-9500. FAX 212-869-3495. Ed. John R. Vane. **Document type:** monographic series.
Refereed Serial

ADVANCES IN COMBUSTION TOXICOLOGY. see *ENVIRONMENTAL STUDIES — Toxicology And Environmental Safety*

615.1 US ISSN 0065-2490
RS1 CODEN: ADRRAN
ADVANCES IN DRUG RESEARCH. 1964. irreg., vol.24, 1993. Academic Press, Inc., 525 B St., Ste. 1900, San Diego, CA 92101-4495. TEL 619-231-0926. FAX 619-699-6715. (Subscr. to: Order Dept., 6277 Sea Harbor Dr., 4th Fl., Orlando, FL 32887. TEL 800-321-5068) Ed. B. Testa. index. (reprint service avail. from ISI) **Indexed:** Biol.Abstr., Biotech.Abstr., Excerp.Med., Ind.Med., Ind.Vet., Vet.Bull. **Document type:** academic/scholarly publication.
—BLDSC (0704.300000); CASDDS; EMDOCS; Faxon; SWETS; UnCover.
Refereed Serial

615.7 UK ISSN 0272-068X
RC483 CODEN: AHPSDD
ADVANCES IN HUMAN PSYCHOPHARMACOLOGY. 1980. irreg., vol.4, 1987. $88. Jessica Kingsley Publishers, 116 Pentonville Rd., London N1 9JB, England. TEL 071-833-2307. FAX 071-837-2917. (Dist. in U.S. by: Taylor & Francis, 1900 Frost Rd., Ste. 101, Bristol PA 19007-1598. TEL 215-785-5800. FAX 215-785-5515) Eds. Graham D. Burrows, John S. Werry. **Indexed:** Chem.Abstr., Excerp.Med. (1992), Psychol.Abstr. **Document type:** academic/scholarly publication.
—CASDDS.
Refereed Serial

ADVANCES IN NEUROPSYCHIATRY AND PSYCHOPHARMACOLOGY. see *MEDICAL SCIENCES — Psychiatry And Neurology*

615.19 US ISSN 1041-004X
CODEN: AVPSEA
ADVANCES IN PARENTERAL SCIENCES. 1985. irreg., vol.5, 1994. price varies. Marcel Dekker, Inc., 270 Madison Ave., New York, NY 10016. TEL 212-696-9000. FAX 212-685-4540. TELEX 421419. Ed. Joseph R. Robinson.
—BLDSC (0709.582000); CASDDS.

615 US ISSN 0065-3136
RS1 CODEN: APHMA8
ADVANCES IN PHARMACEUTICAL SCIENCES. 1964. irreg., vol.6, 1991. Academic Press, Inc., 525 B St., Ste. 1900, San Diego, CA 92101-4495. TEL 619-231-0926. FAX 619-699-6715. (Subscr. to: Order Dept., 6277 Sea Harbor Dr., 4th Fl., Orlando, FL 32887. TEL 800-321-5068) Eds. H.S. Bean, A.H. Beckett. index. (reprint service avail. from ISI) **Indexed:** Biol.Abstr., Biotech.Abstr., I.P.A., Ind.Med. **Document type:** academic/scholarly publication.
●Also available online.
—BLDSC (0709.740000); CASDDS. **CCC.**
Refereed Serial

615.1 US ISSN 1054-3589
RM30 CODEN: ADPHEL
ADVANCES IN PHARMACOLOGY. 1962. irreg., vol.24, 1993. Academic Press, Inc., 525 B St., Ste. 1900, San Diego, CA 92101-4495. TEL 619-231-0926. FAX 619-699-6715. (Subscr. to: Order Dept., 6277 Sea Harbor Dr., 4th Fl., Orlando, FL 32887. TEL 800-321-5068) Ed. S. Garattini. index. (reprint service avail. from ISI) **Indexed:** Biol.Abstr., Biotech.Abstr., Chem.Abstr., Ind.Med., Ind.Sci.Rev., Ind.Vet., Sci.Cit.Ind., Vet.Bull. **Document type:** academic/scholarly publication.
—BLDSC (0709.760000); CASDDS; UnCover. **CCC.**
Former titles (until 1991): Advances in Pharmacology and Chemotherapy (ISSN 0065-3144); Advances in Pharmacology; Advances in Chemotherapy.
Refereed Serial

615 US ISSN 0732-8141
QP801.P68 CODEN: ATLRD6
ADVANCES IN PROSTAGLANDIN, THROMBOXANE, AND LEUKOTRIENE RESEARCH. 1976. irreg., latest vol.23. price varies. Raven Press (Subsidiary of: Wolters Kluwer N.V.), 1185 Ave. of the Americas, New York, NY 10036. TEL 212-930-9500. FAX 212-869-3495. Eds. Bengt Samuelsson, Rodolfo Paoletti. (reprint service avail. from UMI) **Indexed:** Anim.Breed.Abstr., Biol.Abstr., Chem.Abstr., Curr.Adv.Ecol.Sci., Curr.Cont., Ind.Med., Ind.Sci.Rev., Sci.Cit.Ind. **Document type:** proceedings.
—BLDSC (0710.945000); CASDDS; Faxon; Genuine Article; SWETS. **CCC.**
Formerly (until 1982): Advances in Prostaglandin and Thromboxane Research (ISSN 0361-5952)
Refereed Serial

615 US ISSN 0741-238X
ADVANCES IN THERAPY; the international journal of drug, device and diagnostic research. 1984. bi-m. $60 (effective 1995 & 1996). Health Communications Inc., 20 Highland Ave., Metuchen, NJ 08840. TEL 908-548-9130. FAX 908-548-8555. E-mail: gshap@aol.com. Pub. Joel Shapiro. circ. 5,000. (back issues avail.) **Document type:** academic/scholarly publication.
—BLDSC (0711.622500); Faxon; Genuine Article; SWETS. **CCC.**
Description: Publishes studies in clinical medicine and scientific research, case reports, review articles, and other original contributions in the areas of drug therapy, diagnosis, instrumentation, and related fields, as well as proceedings of symposia and special topics.
Refereed Serial

ADVERSE DRUG REACTION BULLETIN. see *MEDICAL SCIENCES*

615 628 UK ISSN 0964-198X
RM302.5 CODEN: ADRRER
ADVERSE DRUG REACTIONS AND TOXICOLOGICAL REVIEWS. 1982. q. £105($190) (effective 1996). Oxford University Press, Oxford Journals, Walton St., Oxford OX2 6DP, England. TEL 01865-56767. FAX 01865-56646. TELEX 837330-OXPRES-G. E-mail: jnlorders@oup.co.uk. (U.S. subscr. to: Oxford University Press Inc., 2001 Evans Rd., Cary, NC 27513. TEL 919-677-0977. FAX 919-677-1714) Ed. J.P. Griffin. adv. circ. 400. **Indexed:** Biol.Abstr., Chem.Abstr., Curr.Adv.Ecol.Sci., Curr.Cont., Excerp.Med., Ind.Med., Ind.Sci.Rev., NRN, Sci.Cit.Ind., SSCI. **Document type:** academic/scholarly publication.
—BLDSC (0712.233000); CASDDS; Faxon; Genuine Article; SWETS; UMI; UnCover. **CCC.**
Formerly (until 1991): Adverse Drug Reactions and Acute Poisoning Reviews (ISSN 0260-647X)
Description: Covers developments in the field of adverse drug reactions and toxicology.

615 DK ISSN 0900-3142
AFHAENGING. 1984. q. free. Landsforeningen for Human Narkobehandling, Lundtoftparken 32, 2800 Kgs. Lyngby, Denmark. Ed. P.T. Pedersen.

615 NR ISSN 0044-6564
AFRICAN JOURNAL OF PHARMACY AND PHARMACEUTICAL SCIENCES. 1970. q. £60($100) (elsewhere $120). African Journal of Pharmacy and Parmaceutical Sciences, 21 Wharf Rd., P.O. Box 399, Apapa, Lagos, Nigeria. Ed. Bode Ladejobi. adv.; bk.rev.; illus. circ. 40,000. **Indexed:** Excerp.Med., I.P.A. **Document type:** academic/scholarly publication.
Description: Reviews and reports the research and other aspects of those sciences which contribute to the discovery, evaluation and development of medicinal substances.

AGRESSOLOGIE; revue internationale de physiobiologie et de pharmacologie appliquees aux effets de l'agression. see *MEDICAL SCIENCES*

AIDS DIRECTORY. see *MEDICAL SCIENCES — Communicable Diseases*

AIDS REFERENCE MANUAL. see *MEDICAL SCIENCES — Communicable Diseases*

AIDS TRAINERS DIRECTORY. see *MEDICAL SCIENCES — Communicable Diseases*

AIDS TREATMENT UPDATE. see *MEDICAL SCIENCES — Communicable Diseases*

THE ALKALOIDS; chemistry and pharmacology. see *CHEMISTRY — Organic Chemistry*

615.1 US ISSN 0002-5690
ALLEGHENY COUNTY PHARMACIST. 1947. m. membership. Allegheny County Pharmaceutical Association, 111 Two Parkway Center, Pittsburgh, PA 15220. TEL 412-922-2440. Ed. Carole F. Ladik. adv.; illus. circ. 800.

ALTERNATIVE METHODS IN TOXICOLOGY SERIES. see *ENVIRONMENTAL STUDIES — Toxicology And Environmental Safety*

615 US
AMERICAN ASSOCIATION OF COLLEGES OF PHARMACY. (YEAR) PROFILE OF PHARMACY FACULTY. 1980. a. $25. American Association of Colleges of Pharmacy, Office of Academic Affairs, 1426 Prince St., Alexandria, VA 22314-2815. FAX 703-836-8982. E-mail: susanaacp@aol.com. Ed. Susan M. Meyer. circ. 2,500.
Formerly: American Association of Colleges of Pharmacy. Annual Survey of Faculty Salaries.

AMERICAN COLLEGE OF TOXICOLOGY. JOURNAL. see *ENVIRONMENTAL STUDIES — Toxicology And Environmental Safety*

PHARMACY AND PHARMACOLOGY

615.1 US ISSN 0190-5279
RS1 CODEN: AMDREK
AMERICAN DRUGGIST. 1871. m. $44. Hearst Corp., American Druggist, 1790 Broadway, Ste. 6, New York, NY 10019-1412. TEL 212-969-7508. FAX 212-969-7557. Ed. Janice Zoeller. adv.; charts; illus.; mkt.stat.; tr.lit. circ. 91,500. (also avail. in microform from UMI; reprint service avail.) **Indexed:** B.P.I., Bus.Ind., Excerp.Med., Hlth.Ind., I.P.A., PROMT, Tr.& Indus.Ind.
●Also available online.
—BLDSC (0812.900000); UnCover.
Formerly: American Druggist Merchandising (ISSN 0090-6638)

615.1 US ISSN 0364-7471
HD9666.4
AMERICAN DRUGGIST BLUE BOOK. a. $52. Hearst Corp., American Druggist, 1790 Broadway, Ste. 6, New York, NY 10019-1412. TEL 212-969-7549. circ. 93,000.
Formerly: American Druggist Blue Price Book.

AMERICAN HERB ASSOCIATION NEWSLETTER. see GARDENING AND HORTICULTURE

615.1 US ISSN 0270-0611
AMERICAN INSTITUTE OF THE HISTORY OF PHARMACY. PUBLICATIONS. 1972. irreg. American Institute of the History of Pharmacy, 425 N. Charter St., Madison, WI 53706. TEL 608-262-5378. **Document type:** monographic series.

615.1 US ISSN 1079-2082
CODEN: AHSPEK
AMERICAN JOURNAL OF HEALTH - SYSTEM PHARMACY. 1945. s-m. $137 (Canada $162). American Society of Health - System Pharmacists, 7272 Wisconsin Ave., Bethesda, MD 20814. TEL 301-657-4383. FAX 301-657-1258. Ed. C. Richard Talley. adv.; bk.rev.; abstr.; bibl.; charts; illus.; tr.lit.; index. circ. 30,000. (also avail. in microform from UMI; back issues avail.; reprint service avail. from ISI,UMI) **Indexed:** Abstr.Health Care Manage.Stud., Abstr.Hosp.Manage.Stud., Biol.Abstr., Biotech.Abstr., Chem.Abstr., CINAHL, Curr.Adv.Cancer Res., Curr.Adv.Ecol.Sci., Curr.Cont., Dairy Sci.Abstr., Dent.Ind., Excerp.Med., Helminthol.Abstr., Hosp.Lit.Ind., I.P.A., Ind.Med., Ind.Sci.Rev., Kidney, Med.& Surg.Dermat., Med.Care Rev., Nutr.Abstr., Sci.Cit.Ind. **Document type:** academic/scholarly publication.
●Also available online.
—BLDSC (0824.770000); CASDDS; Faxon; Genuine Article; SWETS; UMI; UnCover. **CCC.**
Formerly (until 1995): American Journal of Hospital Pharmacy (ISSN 0002-9289); Incorporates (1982-1993): Clinical Pharmacy (ISSN 0278-2677)
Description: Covers all facets of drug use control in hospitals and other organized health care settings. Provides current information on the clinical use of new drugs - current thinking on drug therapy in selected diseases and clinical trials evaluating drug effects and adverse drug reactions.
Refereed Serial

615.1 370 US ISSN 0002-9459
RS110 CODEN: AJPDAD
AMERICAN JOURNAL OF PHARMACEUTICAL EDUCATION. 1937. 4/yr. $40 to individuals (foreign $65); libraries $100. American Association of Colleges of Pharmacy, 1426 Prince St., Alexandria, VA 22314-2815. TEL 703-739-2330. Ed. George H. Cocolas. bk.rev.; bibl.; charts; illus.; index, cum.index every 10 yrs. circ. 2,300. (also avail. in microform from UMI,PMC; back issues avail.) **Indexed:** Biol.Abstr., C.I.J.E., Chem.Abstr., Cont.Pg.Educ., Curr.Adv.Ecol.Sci., Curr.Cont., Excerp.Med., High.Educ.Curr.Aware.Bull., Hosp.Lit.Ind., I.P.A., Ind.Sci.Rev., Sci.Cit.Ind. **Document type:** academic/scholarly publication.
●Also available online.
—BLDSC (0830.000000); CASDDS; Faxon; Genuine Article; SWETS; UMI; UnCover.
Refereed Serial

615.1 614 US ISSN 0730-7780
CODEN: APSHDH
AMERICAN JOURNAL OF PHARMACY; and the sciences supporting public health. 1825-1980; resumed 1981. q. Philadelphia College of Pharmacy and Science, 600 S. 43rd St., Philadelphia, PA 19104-4495. TEL 215-596-8800. Ed. Daniel A Hussar. adv.; bk.rev.; abstr.; bibl.; charts; illus.; tr.lit.; index. circ. 2,500. (also avail. in microform from UMI,PMC; reprint service avail. from UMI) **Indexed:** Biol.Abstr., Chem.Abstr., Curr.Cont., Excerp.Med., I.P.A., Ind.Med., Nutr.Abstr. **Document type:** academic/scholarly publication.
●Also available online.
—BLDSC (0831.100000); CASDDS; Faxon; SWETS; UMI.
Former titles (until 1980): Pharmacy Management (ISSN 0163-464X); (until 1979): American Journal of Pharmacy and the Sciences Supporting Health (ISSN 0002-9467); American Journal of Pharmacy (ISSN 0093-4712)
Refereed Serial

615.1 US ISSN 0160-3450
RS1 CODEN: AMPHDF
AMERICAN PHARMACY. 1912. m. $50 to non-members. American Pharmaceutical Association, 2215 Constitution Ave., N.W., Washington, DC 20037. TEL 202-628-4410. Ed. Marlene Bloom. adv.; bk.rev.; charts; illus.; index. circ. 48,800. (also avail. in microform from UMI,PMC) **Indexed:** Biol.Abstr., Chem.Abstr., Curr.Adv.Ecol.Sci., Curr.Cont., Excerp.Med., Helminthol.Abstr., I.P.A., Ind.Med., Med.Care Rev., MEDSOC, Nutr.Abstr.
●Also available online.
—BLDSC (0850.576000); CASDDS; Faxon; SWETS; UMI; UnCover. **CCC.**
Formerly: American Pharmaceutical Association. Journal (ISSN 0003-0465)
Refereed Serial

617.96 UK ISSN 0966-7954
CODEN: APRIEG
ANAESTHETIC PHARMACOLOGY REVIEW. 1993. q. £60 to individuals (rest of Europe £60; the U.S. $95; elsewhere £68); institutions £85 (rest of Europe £85; the U.S. $145; elsewhere £94). Castle House Publications Ltd., 28-30 Church Rd., Tunbridge Wells, Kent TN1 1JP, England. TEL 01892-539606. FAX 01892-517005. index. **Indexed:** Excerp.Med. (1994-). **Document type:** academic/scholarly publication.
—BLDSC (0859.930000); CASDDS.

615.1 BL ISSN 0003-2441
RS1 CODEN: AFQUEB
ANAIS DE FARMACIA E QUIMICA DE SAO PAULO. (Text in Portuguese; summaries in English) 1924-1964; resumed 1978. s-a. Sociedade de Farmacia e Quimica de Sao Paulo, Avda. Brigadeiro Luis Antonio 393, 7 andar, CEP 01317, Sao Paulo, Brazil. Ed.Bd. adv.; bk.rev.; cum.index every 10 yrs. (1924-1964). circ. 1,500. **Indexed:** Biol.Abstr., Chem.Abstr., I.P.A., Ind.Med.
●Also available online.
—CASDDS.
Formerly (until 1953): Annaes de Sociedade de Pharmacia e Chimica de Sao Paulo (ISSN 0365-7086)
Description: Presents original research in pharmacology and chemistry.

615 658.8 UK
ANALGESICS: THE INTERNATIONAL MARKET. (Subseries of: Market Direction reports) a. £1595($3190) (effective 1996). Euromonitor, 60-61 Britton St., London EC1M 5NA, England. TEL 0171-251-8024. FAX 0171-608-3149. (Addr. in N. America: Euromonitor International, 122 S. Michigan Ave., Ste. 1200, Chicago, IL 60603. TEL 312-922-1115. FAX 312-922-1157) (looseleaf format) **Document type:** trade publication.
●Also available online. Vendor(s): Data-Star, Knight-Ridder, Inc.
Description: Analyzes the market for nonprescription pain relievers in France, Germany, Italy, Spain, the U.K., the U.S., and Japan.

615.19 US ISSN 0099-5428
RS189 CODEN: APDSB7
ANALYTICAL PROFILES OF DRUG SUBSTANCES. 1972. irreg., vol.21, 1992. Academic Press, Inc., 525 B St., Ste. 1900, San Diego, CA 92101-4495. TEL 619-231-0926. FAX 609-699-6715. (Subscr. to: Order Dept., 6277 Sea Harbor Dr., 4th Fl., Orlando, FL 32887. TEL 800-321-5068) Ed. Klaus Florey. (reprint service avail. from ISI) **Indexed:** Chem.Abstr.
—CASDDS.
Refereed Serial

615.1 FR ISSN 0003-4509
RS1 CODEN: APFRAD
ANNALES PHARMACEUTIQUES FRANCAISES. (Text in French; summaries in English) 1943. bi-m. 1239 F. (foreign 1473 F.) (effective 1996). (Academie de Pharmacie) Masson - Periodiques, Villa Laromiguiere, 75005 Paris, France. TEL 1-40-46-62-00. FAX 1-40-46-62-01. Ed. G. Deysson. adv.; bk.rev.; bibl.; illus.; index. circ. 1,500. (reprint service avail. from ISI) **Indexed:** Anal.Abstr., Apic.Abstr., Biol.Abstr., Biotech.Abstr., C.I.S. Abstr., Chem.Abstr., Curr.Adv.Ecol.Sci., Curr.Chem.React., Curr.Cont., Excerp.Med., Helminthol.Abstr., I.P.A., Ind.Chem., Ind.Med., Ind.Sci.Rev., INIS Atomind., Rev.Med.& Vet.Mycol., Sci.Cit.Ind. **Document type:** academic/scholarly publication.
—BLDSC (0992.000000); CASDDS; Faxon; SWETS; UMI. **CCC.**
Description: Publishes original articles, technical notes of interest to practitioners, and meeting reports of the Academy.

615.1 PL ISSN 0867-0609
ANNALES UNIVERSITATIS MARIAE CURIE-SKLODOWSKA. SECTIO DDD. PHARMACIA. (Text in English or Polish; summaries in English) 1988. a. price varies. Uniwersytet Marii Curie-Sklodowskiej, Wydawnictwo, Pl. M. Curie-Sklodowskiej 5, 20-031 Lublin, Poland. TEL 48-81-375304. FAX 48-81-336699. TELEX 0643223. Ed. Romuald Langwinski. circ. 600. **Document type:** academic/scholarly publication.

615.1 US ISSN 1060-0280
RM300 CODEN: APHRER
THE ANNALS OF PHARMACOTHERAPY. (Text in English; summaries in French and Spanish) 1967. m. (July-Aug. combined) $70 to individuals (foreign $85); institutions $120 (foreign $135); libraries $177 (foreign $192) (effective 1995). Harvey Whitney Books Company, Box 42696, Cincinnati, OH 45242. TEL 513-793-3555. FAX 513-793-3600. Ed. Harvey Whitney. adv.; bk.rev.; abstr.; bibl.; charts; illus.; index. circ. 8,000. (also avail. in microform from UMI; back issues avail.; reprint service avail.) **Indexed:** Abstr.Health Care Manage.Stud., Abstr.Hosp.Manage.Stud., Biol.Abstr., Biotech.Abstr., Chem.Abstr., CINAHL, Curr.Adv.Ecol.Sci., Curr.Cont., Dent.Ind., Excerp.Med., Helminthol.Abstr., Hosp.Lit.Ind., I.P.A., Ind.Med., Ind.Sci.Rev., Kidney, Rev.Med.& Vet.Mycol., Sci.Cit.Ind. **Document type:** academic/scholarly publication.
●Also available online.
—BLDSC (1043.417500); CASDDS; Faxon; SWETS; UMI; UnCover.
Former titles (until 1992): D I C P - The Annals of Pharmacotherapy (ISSN 1042-9611); (until 1988): Drug Intelligence and Clinical Pharmacy (ISSN 0012-6578); (until 1969): Drug Intelligence.
Description: Aimed at health care professionals involved in drug therapy. Provides an interdisciplinary approach to the study of pharmacotherapy.
Refereed Serial

ANNUAIRE FOURNI-LABO PHARMACIE (YEAR); cosmetique et alimentaire. see BUSINESS AND ECONOMICS — Trade And Industrial Directories

615.19 UK ISSN 0260-955X
ANNUAL REGISTER OF PHARMACEUTICAL CHEMISTS. 1869. a. £69. Royal Pharmaceutical Society of Great Britain, 1 Lambeth High St., London SE1 7JN, England. TEL 071-735-9141. FAX 071-735-7629. index. circ. 1,000. **Document type:** directory.
Description: Contains an alphabetical list of names and addresses of all registered pharmacists; corporate bodies operating retail pharmacy businesses with the names of their superintendents; and the business titles and addresses of all registered retail pharmacies in country, county and town order.

PHARMACY AND PHARMACOLOGY

615.1   US   ISSN 0065-7743
RS402   CODEN: ARMCBI
ANNUAL REPORTS IN MEDICINAL CHEMISTRY. 1966. irreg., vol.27, 1992. (American Chemical Society, Division of Medicinal Chemistry) Academic Press, Inc., 525 B St., Ste. 1900, San Diego, CA 92101-4495. TEL 619-231-0926. FAX 619-699-6715. (Subscr. to: Order Dept., 6277 Sea Harbor Dr., 4th Fl., Orlando, FL 32887. TEL 800-321-5068) Ed. Denis M. Bailey. (reprint service avail. from ISI) **Indexed:** Biol.Abstr., Chem.Abstr., Curr.Cont., Dairy Sci.Abstr., Ind.Sci.Rev., Sci.Cit.Ind.
—BLDSC (1513.050000); CASDDS; Faxon; SWETS; UnCover. **CCC.**
Refereed Serial

615.1   US   ISSN 0362-1642
RM16   CODEN: ARPTDI
ANNUAL REVIEW OF PHARMACOLOGY AND TOXICOLOGY. 1961. a. $47 (foreign $52) (effective Jan. 1995). Annual Reviews Inc., 4139 El Camino Way, Box 10139, Palo Alto, CA 94303-0139. TEL 415-493-4400; 800-523-8635. FAX 415-855-9815. TELEX 910-290-0275. E-mail: annrevu@class.org. Ed. Arthur K. Cho. bibl.; index, cum.index. (also avail. in microfilm from UMI; back issues avail.; reprint service avail.) **Indexed:** Biol.Abstr., Biotech.Abstr., Chem.Abstr., Curr.Adv.Ecol.Sci., Excerp.Med., Helminthol.Abstr., Ind.Med., Ind.Sci.Rev., Ind.Vet., M.M.R.I., Psychol.Abstr. (1976-), Sci.Cit.Ind., Vet.Bull. **Document type:** academic/scholarly publication.
—BLDSC (1525.880000); ADONIS; CASDDS; EMDOCS; Faxon; Genuine Article; SWETS; UMI; UnCover. **CCC.**
Formerly (until vol.15, 1975): Annual Review of Pharmacology (ISSN 0066-4251)
Description: Original critical reviews of the significant primary literature and current developments in pharmacology and toxicology.

615.1   SZ   ISSN 0066-4758
RM260   CODEN: ANBCB3
ANTIBIOTICS AND CHEMOTHERAPY. (Text in English) 1954. irreg. (approx. 1/yr.). price varies. S. Karger AG, Allschwilerstr. 10, P.O. Box, CH-4009 Basel, Switzerland. TEL 061-3061111. FAX 061-3061234. E-mail: Karger@Karger.ch. Ed. H. Schoenfeld. (reprint service avail. from ISI) **Indexed:** Biol.Abstr., Chem.Abstr., Curr.Adv.Ecol.Sci., Curr.Cont., Ind.Med. **Document type:** academic/scholarly publication.
—BLDSC (1546.980000); CASDDS; Faxon; Genuine Article. **CCC.**
Refereed Serial

ANTIBODY, IMMUNOCONJUGATES, AND RADIOPHARMACEUTICALS. see *MEDICAL SCIENCES* — Oncology

ANTIMICROBIAL AGENTS AND CHEMOTHERAPY. see *BIOLOGY* — Microbiology

616.9 615   US   ISSN 0897-9811
ANTIVIRAL AGENTS BULLETIN; antiviral drug and vaccine development information. 1988. m. $350 (foreign $410). Biotechnology Information Institute, 1700 Rockville Pike, Ste. 400, Rockville, MD 20852. TEL 301-424-0255. FAX 301-424-0257. Ed. Ronald A. Rader. adv.; bk.rev.; pat.; index. (back issues avail.) **Document type:** bulletin.
●Also available online.
—BLDSC (1552.825000).
Description: Covers news, federal activities, patents, and technology transfer information concerning AIDS and antiviral drug and vaccine development.

615   UK   ISSN 0956-3202
CODEN: ACCHEH
ANTIVIRAL CHEMISTRY & CHEMOTHERAPY. (Supplement avail. (ISSN 1350-2816)) 1990. bi-m. £101 to individuals (outside Europe £111($179)); institutions £225 (outside Europe £250($402)) (effective 1996). Blackwell Science Ltd., Osney Mead, Oxford OX2 OEL, England. TEL 01865-206206. FAX 01865-206219. TELEX 83355 MEDBOK G. Ed. Hugh J. Field. adv.; bk.rev.; illus.; index. (also avail. in microform from UMI; back issues avail.) **Indexed:** Excerp.Med. **Document type:** academic/scholarly publication.
—BLDSC (1552.828000); ADONIS; CASDDS; Ei; Faxon; Genuine Article; SWETS; UMI. **CCC.**
Refereed Serial

615   UK   ISSN 1350-2816
CODEN: ATCSE
ANTIVIRAL CHEMISTRY & CHEMOTHERAPY. SUPPLEMENT. irreg. price varies. Blackwell Science Ltd., Osney Mead, Oxford OX2 OEL, England. TEL 01865-240201. TELEX 83355 MEDBOK G. (back issues avail.) **Indexed:** Excerp.Med. (1994-). **Document type:** academic/scholarly publication, monographic series.
—ADONIS.

615   SW   ISSN 0349-2516
APOTEKET (STOCKHOLM); tidning foer apotekens kunder. 1980. 5/yr. Apoteksbolaget - National Corporation of Swedish Pharmacies, S-105 14 Stockholm, Sweden. TEL 46-8-454-70-00. FAX 46-8-454-73-60. Ed. Tom Wall. circ. 500,000. (also avail. in audio cassette) **Document type:** consumer publication.

380.145615   DK   ISSN 0905-6432
APOTEKSASSISTENTEN. 1946. fortn. (22/yr.). Danske Apoteksteknikeres Forening, Skt. Peders Str. 36, DK-1453 Copenhagen K, Denmark. TEL 45-33-12-06-00. FAX 45-33-14-06-66. Ed. Ellen Borgholm Nissen. adv.; B&W page DKK 3700, color page DKK 9100. circ. 6,269 (controlled).

615.1   US   ISSN 0003-6560
APOTHECARY; the business journal for pharmacy. 1888. 4/yr. $16 (free to qualified personnel). (Massachusetts College of Pharmacy and Allied Health Sciences) Health Care Marketing Services, H C M S Inc., Box AP, Los Altos, CA 94023-0179. TEL 415-941-3955. FAX 415-941-2303. Ed. Jerold K. Karabensh; Pub. Janet L. Goodman. adv. contact: Dale C. Osborne. bk.rev.; charts; illus.; index; circ. 65,000 (controlled). (also avail. in microform from UMI; reprint service avail. from UMI) **Indexed:** I.P.A. **Document type:** trade publication.
●Also available online.
—UMI.
Incorporates: Mid-Atlantic Apothecary (ISSN 0026-2943)
Refereed Serial

615   NE   ISSN 0921-0288
APOTHEEKMANAGEMENT. 1987. bi-m. Mediselect B.V., Postbus 28091, 3828 ZH Hoogland, Netherlands. TEL 31-33-808020. FAX 31-33-805881. Pub. J. Blom. adv. **Document type:** trade publication.

615   AU
DIE APOTHEKE. bi-m. Spitalgasse 31, Postfach 75, A-1094 Vienna, Austria. TEL 01-423588. FAX 01-4085355. Ed. H. Jakesz. circ. 98,500.

135   GW   ISSN 0173-1882
APOTHEKE HEUTE. (Supplement to: Deutsche Apotheke Zeitung) 1950. q. DM.6 (free with subscr. to Deutsche Apotheker Zeitung). Deutscher Apotheker Verlag, Postfach 101061, 70009 Stuttgart, Germany. TEL 0711-2582-0. FAX 0711-2582290. Ed. Peter Ditzel. **Document type:** trade publication.
Former titles: Schaufenster (Stuttgart) (ISSN 0173-2110); Aktuelle Schaufenster (ISSN 0568-7632)
Description: Explores store window-dressing and advertising in pharmacies.

615.19   GW   ISSN 0177-9591
APOTHEKE UND KRANKENHAUS. 1985. q. DM.54.60. (Bundesverband Krankenhausversorgender Apotheker e.V.) Deutscher Apotheker Verlag, Postfach 101061, 70009 Stuttgart, Germany. TEL 0711-25820. FAX 0711-2582290. Ed. Klaus Grimm. circ. 2,000. **Document type:** trade publication.
—CCC.
Description: For hospital pharmacists.

615.19   GW
APOTHEKEN KURIER. 1985. m. Pharma-Kurier Verlag GmbH, Borsigstr. 1-3, 63150 Heusenstamm, Germany. TEL 06104-6060. FAX 06104-606117. TELEX 410131.

615.1   GW   ISSN 0066-5347
APOTHEKER - JAHRBUCH. 1915. a. price varies. (Deutscher Apotheker Verein) Wissenschaftliche Verlagsgesellschaft mbH, Postfach 101061, 70009 Stuttgart, Germany. TEL 0711-2582-0. FAX 0711-2582-290. TELEX 723636-DAZD. Ed.Bd. adv.; index, cum.index. **Document type:** trade publication.
Description: Focuses on new pharmaceutical laws and decrees, jurisdiction, statistical data and important addresses.

615.19   GW   ISSN 0720-1028
APOTHEKER JOURNAL; Magazin aus Wissenschaft und Praxis. 1979. m. DM.72. Otto Hoffmanns Verlag GmbH, Possarstr. 9, 81679 Munich, Germany. TEL 089-4702041. Ed. Helmut Becker. adv.; bk.rev. circ. 20,000. **Document type:** trade publication.

615   GW
APOTHEKERKAMMER NIEDERSACHSEN. MITTEILUNGSBLATT. 1947. m. DM.61.60. Richard Boorberg Verlag GmbH und Co., Kestnerstr. 44, 30159 Hannover, Germany. TEL 0511-810592. circ. 4,800. **Document type:** newsletter.

615.1   BE   ISSN 0003-6579
HET APOTHEKERSBLAD. 1950. m. 2920 BEF (foreign 3360 BEF). Algemene Pharmaceutische Bond, Archimedesstraat 11, Brussels 1040, Belgium. TEL 32-2-2302685. FAX 32-2-2306681. Ed. D. Broeckx. adv.; bk.rev.; index. circ. 4,500. **Indexed:** I.P.A.
Description: For Belgian community pharmacists.

615.9   US
APPROVED BIOEQUIVALENCY CODES. 1992. m. $78.50 (effective 1995). Facts and Comparisons, 111 W. Port Plaza, Ste. 400, St. Louis, MO 63146-3098. TEL 800-223-0554. FAX 314-878-5563. Ed. Bernie R. Olin. (looseleaf format)
Description: Lists FDA approved drug substitution information.

615.7   US   ISSN 1048-5996
RM301.45 .A66
APPROVED DRUG PRODUCTS WITH THERAPEUTIC EQUIVALENCE EVALUATIONS. 1980. base vol., with a. supplements; q. updates on magnetic tape. $64 (foreign $80); magnetic tape edition $240 in N. America (elsewhere $480) (effective 1995). U.S. Food and Drug Administration, Office of Public Affairs, 5600 Fishers Ln., Rockville, MD 20857. TEL 301-443-5315. (Subscr. to: Superintendent of Documents, U.S. Government Printing Office, Box 371954, Pittsburgh, PA 15250-7954. TEL 202-512-1800. FAX 202-512-2250; Or: National Technical Information Service, 5825 Port Royal Rd., Springfield, VA 22161. TEL 703-487-4630. FAX 703-321-8547) (Also avail. on magnetic tape.) **Document type:** government publication.
Formerly (until 1985): Approved Prescription Drug Products with Therapeutic Equivalence Evaluations (ISSN 0733-4036)
Description: Contains information required to identify a particular drug product. Includes N.D.A. and A.N.D.A. number for each entry.

615.1 378   US
APPROVED PROVIDERS OF CONTINUING PHARMACEUTICAL EDUCATION. Added title page title: American Council on Pharmaceutical Education Annual Directory (Year). free. American Council on Pharmaceutical Education, 311 W. Superior St., Ste. 512, Chicago, IL 60610. Dir. A. Nona. **Document type:** directory.

615.1   GR   ISSN 0003-8148
ARCHEIA TES PHARMAKEUTIKES (ATHENS). (Text in English, French and Greek) 1932. irreg. Dr.150($3) Greek Pharmaceutical Society, Emm. Benakis 30, Athens 10678, Greece. Ed. N.H. Choulis. adv.; bk.rev.; bibl.; charts; illus.; index. circ. 1,000. **Indexed:** Biol.Abstr., Chem.Abstr.

PHARMACY AND PHARMACOLOGY

615.1 GW ISSN 0365-6233
CODEN: ARPMAS
ARCHIV DER PHARMAZIE. (Text in English) 1822. m. DM.696($498) (effective 1996). (Deutsche Pharmazeutische Gesellschaft, GW) V C H Verlagsgesellschaft mbH, Postfach 101161, 69451 Weinheim, Germany. TEL 06201-606-147. FAX 06201-606117. TELEX 465516-VCHWH-D. (US addr.: V C H Publishers, Inc., 220 E. 23rd St., New York, NY 10010-4606. TEL 212-683-8333) Ed. Prof. Hartmann. adv. contact: R. Roth. bk.rev.; charts; illus.; index. circ. 800. (also avail. in microfilm from VCI; microfiche from BHP; reprint service avail. from ISI) **Indexed:** Anal.Abstr., Biol.Abstr., Chem.Abstr., Crop Physiol.Abstr., Curr.Adv.Ecol.Sci., Curr.Chem.React., Excerp.Med., Helminthol.Abstr., Hort.Abstr., I.P.A., Ind.Chem., Ind.Med., Ind.Sci.Rev., Mass Spectr.Bull., Protozool.Abstr., Sci.Cit.Ind. **Document type:** academic/scholarly publication.
—BLDSC (1622.800000); CASDDS; Faxon; Genuine Article; SWETS; UnCover. **CCC.**

615.1 BE ISSN 0003-9780
CODEN: AIPTAK
ARCHIVES INTERNATIONALES DE PHARMACODYNAMIE ET DE THERAPIE/INTERNATIONAL ARCHIVES OF PHARMACOLOGY. (Text in English) 1894. bi-m. 8000 BEF($240) (effective 1992). Heymans Institute of Pharmacology, De Pintelaan 185, B-9000 Ghent, Belgium. FAX 32-9-240-49-88. Ed. A.F. de Schaepdryver. bk.rev.; charts. circ. 1,000. (also avail. in microfilm from PMC) **Indexed:** Anim.Breed.Abstr., Biol.Abstr., Biotech.Abstr., Chem.Abstr., Curr.Adv.Ecol.Sci., Curr.Chem.React., Curr.Cont., Dairy Sci.Abstr., Excerp.Med., Helminthol.Abstr., I.P.A., Ind.Chem., Ind.Med., Ind.Sci.Rev., Ind.Vet., Pig News & Info., Sci.Cit.Ind., Vet.Bull. **Document type:** academic/scholarly publication.
—BLDSC (1636.000000); CASDDS; Faxon; Genuine Article; SWETS; UMI; UnCover. **CCC.**

615 KO ISSN 0253-6269
CODEN: APHRDQ
ARCHIVES OF PHARMACAL RESEARCH. (Text in English) 1978. s-a. $30. Pharmaceutical Society of Korea, c/o College of Pharmacy, Seoul National University, Seoul 151-742, S. Korea. TEL 02-584-3257. FAX 02-531-1781. Ed. Young Choong Kim. circ. 1,300. (back issues avail.) **Indexed:** Biol.Abstr., Chem.Abstr., Excerp.Med., Ind.Med. **Document type:** academic/scholarly publication.
—BLDSC (1638.975000); CASDDS.

615.9 GW ISSN 0171-9750
RA1190 CODEN: ATSUDG
ARCHIVES OF TOXICOLOGY. SUPPLEMENT. (Text in English) 1978. irreg. price varies. Springer-Verlag, Heidelberger Platz 3, 14197 Berlin, Germany. TEL 030-8207-0. FAX 030-8214091. E-mail: orders@springer.de. (also avail. in microform from UMI; reprint service avail. from ISI) **Indexed:** Chem.Abstr., Dent.Ind., Ind.Med., NRN, Nutr.Abstr. **Document type:** monographic series.
—BLDSC (1643.510100); CASDDS; SWETS. **CCC.**

615 SW ISSN 0283-8567
ARENA; laekemedel, sjukvaard, samhaelle. 1986. q. Representantfoereningen foer Utlaendska Farmacevtiska Industrier, P.O. Box 5522, S-114 85 Stockholm, Sweden.

615.1 FR ISSN 0004-1203
ARGUS DES PHARMACIENS;* journal professionnel et documentaire. 1927. s-m. 24. F. 26 rue Brey, Paris (17), France.

615.1 YU ISSN 0004-1963
CODEN: ARFMAC
ARHIV ZA FARMACIJU. (Text in Serbo-Croatian; summaries in English, French, German or Russian) 1951. 6/yr. 60 din.($23.70) Farmaceutsko Drustvo Srbije, Vojvode Stepe 450, Box 664, 11000 Belgrade, Yugoslavia. Ed. Dubravka Urosev. adv.; bk.rev.; abstr.; bibl.; charts; illus.; index. **Indexed:** Biol.Abstr., Chem.Abstr., Hort.Abstr., I.P.A.
●Also available online.
—CASDDS.

ARHIV ZA HIGIJENU RADA I TOKSIKOLOGIJU/ARCHIVES OF INDUSTRIAL HYGIENE AND TOXICOLOGY. see ENVIRONMENTAL STUDIES — Toxicology And Environmental Safety

615.9 JA
ARIS. (Text in Japanese) 1991. m. 3000 Yen. Odashima Iyaku Joho Senta - Odashima Pharmaceutical Information Center, 68 Oroshimachi, Hanamaki-shi, Iwate-ken 025-03, Japan.

615.1 US
ARIZONA PHARMACIST.* 1947. m. $15 to non-members. (Arizona Pharmaceutical Association) State Pharmaceutical Editorial Association, 223 W. Jackson Blvd., No. 1000, Chicago, IL 60606-6906. TEL 602-258-8121. Ed. Warren Ellison. adv.; illus. circ. 1,300.
Former titles: New Arizona Pharmacist; Arizona Pharmacist (ISSN 0004-1602)

615.9 610 US
ARIZONA POISON CONTROL SYSTEM NEWSLETTER. 1980. q. free. Arizona Poison Control System, University of Arizona, College of Pharmacy, Tucson, AZ 85721. TEL 602-626-1587. FAX 602-626-4063. Ed. Dr. Theodore G. Tong. circ. 3,000. (tabloid format) **Document type:** newsletter.
Description: Updates and reviews about clinical toxicology and poisonings, for physicians, pharmacists and pharmacologists.

615.1 SP ISSN 0004-2927
CODEN: APHRAN
ARS PHARMACEUTICA. (Text in Spanish; summaries in English) 1960. 4/yr. 3500 ptas. (effective 1995). Universidad de Granada, Facultad de Farmacia, Servicio de Publicaciones, Antiguo Colegio Maximo, Campus de Cartuja, 18071 Granada, Spain. TEL 34-58-243930. FAX 34-58-242827. Ed. Jesus Cabo Torres. adv.; bk.rev.; bibl.; charts; illus.; index. circ. 1,000. **Indexed:** Biol.Abstr., Chem.Abstr., Excerp.Med., I.P.A., Ind.Med.Esp., Ind.SST.
●Also available online.
—BLDSC (1697.700000); CASDDS. **CCC.**

ARTERE. see HOSPITALS

615 GW ISSN 0066-8192
ARZNEI-TELEGRAMM. 1970. m. DM.96 individuals; institutions DM.172. Arzneimittel Information Berlin GmbH (A.T.I.), Petzower Str. 7, 14109 Berlin, Germany. TEL 030-8069080. FAX 030-8054203. Ed. U.M. Moebius. bk.rev. circ. 29,000. **Document type:** academic/scholarly publication.
—SWETS.

615.1 GW ISSN 0004-4172
RM301.25 CODEN: ARZNAD
ARZNEIMITTEL-FORSCHUNG/DRUG RESEARCH. (Text in English and German) 1951. m. DM.490. Editio Cantor, Postfach 1255, 88322 Aulendorf, Germany. TEL 07525-2060. FAX 07525-20680. Eds. H.G. Classen, V. Schramm. adv.; bk.rev.; charts; illus.; tr.lit.; index. circ. 5,200. (reprint service avail. from IRC,ISA) **Indexed:** Anal.Abstr., Apic.Abstr., Biol.Abstr., Biotech.Abstr., Chem.Abstr., Chem.Infd., Curr.Adv.Biochem., Curr.Adv.Genetics, Curr.Adv.Cell & Devel.Biol., Curr.Adv.Ecol.Sci., Curr.Adv.Genetics & Molec.Biol., Curr.Biotech.Abstr., Curr.Cont., Dairy Sci.Abstr., Dent.Ind., Excerp.Med., Helminthol.Abstr., I.P.A., Ind.Chem., Ind.Med., Ind.Sci.Rev., Ind.Vet., INIS Atomind., Mass Spectr.Bull, Nutr.Abstr., Protozool.Abstr., Rev.Plant Path., Sci.Cit.Ind., Vet.Bull. **Document type:** academic/scholarly publication.
●Also available online.
—BLDSC (1738.000000); ADONIS; CASDDS; Faxon; Genuine Article; SWETS; UMI. **CCC.**

615.19 GW ISSN 0935-2767
ARZNEIMITTEL ZEITUNG. 1988. fortn. DM.90. Aerzte Zeitung Verlags GmbH, Am Forsthaus Gravenbruch 5, 63263 Neu-Isenburg, Germany. TEL 06102-5060. FAX 06102-5870. Ed. Dieter Eschenbach; Pub. Gerald Kosans. adv. contact: Ute Krille. bk.rev. circ. 8,000. **Document type:** newspaper.
—SWETS.
Description: Information for employers in the pharmaceutical industry.

615 GW
DER ARZNEIMITTELBRIEF; unabhaengiges Informationsblatt fuer den Arzt. 1967. m. DM.69. Westkreuz Druckerei und Verlag, Toepchiner Weg 198-200, 12309 Berlin, Germany. TEL 030-7452047. FAX 030-7453066. Ed.Bd. **Document type:** academic/scholarly publication.

615.19 GW ISSN 0723-6913
ARZNEIMITTELTHERAPIE. 1983. m. DM.42 (students DM.28.20). Wissenschaftliche Verlagsgesellschaft mbH, Postfach 101161, 70009 Stuttgart, Germany. TEL 0711-2582-0. FAX 0711-2582290. Ed.Bd. adv.; bk.rev. circ. 16,600. **Indexed:** Chem.Abstr. **Document type:** academic/scholarly publication.
—BLDSC (1738.120000); SWETS. **CCC.**

615.19 SI ISSN 0217-9687
CODEN: APJPEV
ASIA PACIFIC JOURNAL OF PHARMACOLOGY. 4/yr. S.$250. Singapore University Press Pte. Ltd., 10 Kent Ridge Crescent, Singapore 0511, Singapore. TEL 7761148. FAX 7740652. **Indexed:** Psychol.Abstr. (1992-). **Document type:** academic/scholarly publication.
—BLDSC (1742.260800); CASDDS; Genuine Article; SWETS.
Description: Covers all aspects of experimental and clinical research on synthetic and natural drugs.

615.19 FR
ASSOCIATION DES PHARMACIENS DE L'INDUSTRIE. BULLETIN. 6/yr. Association des Pharmaciens de l'Industrie, 12 av. Victor Hugo, 75116 Paris, France. TEL 45-00-78-18. circ. 3,000. **Document type:** bulletin.

615.1 CN ISSN 0066-9555
ASSOCIATION OF FACULTIES OF PHARMACY OF CANADA. PROCEEDINGS. 1970. a. membership. Association of Faculties of Pharmacy, Faculty of Pharmaceutical Sciences, University of British Columbia, Vancouver, BC V6T 1Z3, Canada. FAX 604-822-4451. Ed. K.G. Moody. circ. 200. **Document type:** proceedings.
Formerly (until vol.26, 1969): Canadian Conference of Pharmaceutical Faculties. Proceedings.

615.9 JA ISSN 0914-7268
ATARASHII YAKUGAKU O MEZASHITE. (Text in Japanese) 1965. a. 1000 Yen. Shin'yakugaku Kenkyusha Gijutsusha Shudan - Japanese Youthful Group for Pharmaceutical Science and Technology, Komatsu Byoin Yakuzaika, 11-6 Kawakatsucho, Neyagawa-shi, Osaka 572, Japan.

615 AT ISSN 0706-3202
AUSTRALIAN INSTITUTE OF PHARMACY MANAGEMENT NEWSLETTER. 1981. bi-m. free to members. Pharmacy Guild of Australia, P.O. Box 36, Deakin, A.C.T. 2600, Australia. TEL 062 81-0911. FAX 062-824745. Ed Ewan D. Brown. circ. 5,000. **Document type:** newsletter.

615 AT ISSN 0310-6810
CODEN: AUHPAI
AUSTRALIAN JOURNAL OF HOSPITAL PHARMACY. 1966. bi-m. Aus.$80. Society of Hospital Pharmacists of Australia, Ste. 2, 31 Coventry St., South Melbourne, Vic. 3205, Australia. TEL 03-690-6733. FAX 03-696-7634. Ed. John S. Low. adv.: B&W page Aus.$1295, color page Aus.$1190; trim 272 x 206; adv. contact: Barry J. Parsons. bk.rev.; abstr.; illus.; stat. circ. 2,200. **Indexed:** Biol.Abstr., Chem.Abstr., Excerp.Med., I.P.A. **Document type:** academic/scholarly publication.
—BLDSC (1808.700000); CASDDS; SWETS; UnCover. **CCC.**
Description: The AJHP aims to assist the development of the practice of hospital pharmacy in Australia.
Refereed Serial

615.1 AT ISSN 0004-8399
AUSTRALIAN JOURNAL OF PHARMACY. 1886. m. Aus.$100. Australian Pharmaceutical Publishing Co. Ltd., 40 Burwood Rd., Hawthorn , Vic. 3122, Australia. TEL 61-3-810-9800. FAX 61-3-819-1706. Ed. Snezna Kerekovic. adv.; bk.rev.; illus.; mkt.; index. circ. 7,600. (also avail. in microfilm from UMI; back issues avail.) **Indexed:** Aus.Sci.Ind., Biol.Abstr., Biotech.Abstr., Chem.Abstr., Excerp.Med., I.P.A. **Document type:** trade publication.

PHARMACY AND PHARMACOLOGY

615   AT   ISSN 0728-4632
AUSTRALIAN PHARMACIST. 1982. 11/yr. Aus.$70 (foreign Aus.$100) (effective 1996). Pharmaceutical Society of Australia, P.O. Box 21, Curtin, A.C.T. 2605, Australia. TEL 61-6-2811366. FAX 61-6-2852869. Ed. J.A. Wissmann. adv.: B&W page Aus.$1325, color page Aus.$2225. bk.rev. circ. 9,653. **Document type:** trade publication.
—BLDSC (1817.685000); UnCover.
Description: Contains news and information, therapeutic management reviews, promotional and advertising material, continuing education material.
Refereed Serial

AUSTRALIAN PHYSIOLOGICAL AND PHARMACOLOGICAL SOCIETY. PROCEEDINGS. see *BIOLOGY — Physiology*

615   AT   ISSN 0312-8008
AUSTRALIAN PRESCRIBER. 1975. q. free. Commonwealth Department of Human Services and Health, P.O. Box 100, Woden, A.C.T. 2606, Australia. TEL 61-6-289-7038. E-mail: australian-prescriber@hhlgcs.ausgovhhcs.telememo.au. Ed. J.S. Dowden. circ. 60,000 (controlled). **Indexed:** Diar.Dis.Res., Excerp.Med. (1995-). **Document type:** academic/scholarly publication, government publication.
—BLDSC (1818.260000); UnCover.
Formerly: Prescriber's Journal (ISSN 0085-5103)
Refereed Serial

615.7   AT   ISSN 1321-9758
AUSTRALIAN PRESCRIPTION PRODUCTS GUIDE. 1959. a. Aus.$124. Australian Pharmaceutical Publishing Co. Ltd, 40 Burwood Rd., Hawthorn, Vic. 3122, Australia. TEL 61-3-810-9800. FAX 61-3-819-1706. Ed. J. Thomas. circ. 5,000. **Document type:** trade publication.
Formerly: Prescription Products Guide (ISSN 0818-4445); Incorporates: Non-Prescription Products Guide (ISSN 0818-4453); Formerly (until 1986): Prescription Proprietaries Guide (ISSN 0729-2333)

615.19   US
AZOAN. 1923. a. free. Alpha Zeta Omega Pharmaceutical Fraternity, c/o Coleman Levin, 9026 Germantown Ave., Philadelphia, PA 19113-2702. circ. 2,000. (back issues avail.)
Description: Fraternity news, officers' reports, chapter reports, and professional articles.

B B S R C SCIENCE BRIEF. (Biotechnology and Biological Sciences Research Council) see *AGRICULTURE*

615   BF
BAHAMAS PHARMACEUTICAL ASSOCIATION. NEWSLETTER. m. Bahamas Pharmaceutical Association, P.O. Box 3730, Nassau NP, Bahamas. **Document type:** newsletter.

615   JA   ISSN 0914-6113
BAIERU BUKKURETTO SHIRIZU/BAYER BOOKLET SERIES. (Text in Japanese) 1988. 5/yr. Baieru Yakuhin K.K. - Bayer Yakuhin, Ltd., 55-1, Honmachi 2-chome, Higashi-ku, Osaka 541, Japan.

615   BG   ISSN 0301-4606
CODEN: BPJLAQ
BANGLADESH PHARMACEUTICAL JOURNAL. (Text in English) 1972. q. Bangladesh Pharmaceutical Society, University of Dhaka, Ramna, Dhaka 2, Bangladesh. **Indexed:** Chem.Abstr., Excerp.Med., I.P.A.
●Also available online.
—CASDDS.

615 540   GW   ISSN 0005-6960
BAYER BERICHTE/BAYER REPORTS. (Editions in English, French, German, Italian, Japanese, Portuguese and Spanish) 1958. s-a. free to stockholders. Bayer AG, 51368 Leverkusen, Germany. TEL 0214-3081759. Ed. Gerti-Rose Beckmann. abstr.; bibl.; charts; illus.; stat. circ. 520,000. **Indexed:** Intl.Polym.Sci.& Tech., RAPRA, Text.Tech.Dig. **Document type:** bulletin.
—BLDSC (1871.139000).

615 150   UK   ISSN 0955-8810
CODEN: BPHAEL
BEHAVIOURAL PHARMACOLOGY; an international forum in which behaviour and pharmacology receive equal attention. 1990. 8/yr. £275($470) to institutions (effective 1995). Rapid Communications of Oxford Ltd., The Old Malthouse, Paradise St., Oxford OX1 1LD, England. TEL 01865-790447. FAX 01865-244012. E-mail: rapidcom@vax.oxford.ac.uk. Ed. Paul Willner. adv. contact: Julie Gribben. (reprint service avail.) **Indexed:** Excerp.Med. (1993-), Psychol.Abstr. (1989-), Sci.Cit.Ind. **Document type:** academic/scholarly publication.
●Also available on CD-ROM.
—BLDSC (1877.630000); ADONIS; CASDDS; Genuine Article; SWETS. **CCC.**
Description: Covers areas ranging from ethopharmacology to the pharmacology of schedule-controlled operant behavior.

615   JA   ISSN 0913-5308
BELLMEDICO/BERU MEDIKO. (Text in Japanese) 1985. bi-m. 300 Yen per no. (Pharma International, Inc.) Kanebo Yakuhin K.K., 3-12, Motoakasaka 1-chome, Minato-ku, Tokyo 107, Japan.

615.1 338
BEYOND THE COUNTER. m. $89 (effective 1994). Facts and Comparisons, 111 W. Port Plaza, Ste. 400, St. Louis, MO 63146-3098. TEL 800-223-0554. FAX 314-878-5563. **Document type:** newsletter, trade publication.
Description: Centers on the business side of pharmacy. Contains useful tips from colleagues on how to make a pharmacy run better and more profitably.

BIO-REGULADORES/REVIEWS ON BIO-REGULATORS. see *BIOLOGY — Bioengineering*

615.1   UK   ISSN 0006-2952
QP901   CODEN: BCPCA6
BIOCHEMICAL PHARMACOLOGY. 1958. 24/yr. $3500 to institutions (effective 1996). Elsevier Science Ltd., Pergamon, P.O. Box 800, Kidlington, Oxford OX5 1DX, England. TEL 44-1865-843000. FAX 44-1865-843010. E-mail: nlinfo-f@elsevier.nl; usinfo-f@elsevier.com; forinfo-kyf04035@niftyserve.or.jp; Site addr.: http://www.elsevier.nl/. (Subscr. in U.S. and Canada to: Elsevier Science, 660 White Plains Rd., Tarrytown, NY 10591-5153. TEL 914-524-9200. FAX 914-333-2444) Eds. Alan C. Sartorelli, P. Alexander. adv.; bk.rev.; charts; illus.; index. circ. 1,150. (also avail. in microfilm from UMI; back issues avail.; reprint service avail. from UMI) **Indexed:** Abstr.Inter.Med., Anal.Abstr., Apic.Abstr., Biol.Abstr., Biotech.Abstr., C.I.S. Abstr., Chem.Abstr., Curr.Adv.Biochem., Curr.Adv.Cancer Res., Curr.Adv.Cell & Devel.Biol., Curr.Adv.Ecol.Sci., Curr.Adv.Genetics & Molec.Biol., Curr.Cont., Dairy Sci.Abstr., Dent.Ind., Excerp.Med., Helminthol.Abstr., Hort.Abstr., I.P.A., Ind.Medi., Ind.Sci.Rev., Ind.Vet., INIS Atomind., Mass Spectr.Bull., Nutr.Abstr., Protozool.Abstr., Psychol.Abstr., Rev.Plant Path., Sci.Cit.Ind., Vet.Bull., Weed Abstr. **Document type:** academic/scholarly publication.
—BLDSC (2067.700000); ADONIS; CASDDS; Faxon; Genuine Article; SWETS; UMI; UnCover. **CCC.**
Description: Publishes research findings in biochemical pharmacology, with particular emphasis on molecular and structural biology and genetics.
Refereed Serial

615.1 574   JA   ISSN 0918-6158
QP501   CODEN: BPBLEO
BIOLOGICAL & PHARMACEUTICAL BULLETIN. (Text in English) 1978. m. 10300 Yen($125) Pharmaceutical Society of Japan - Nihon Yakugakkai, 2-12-15, Shibuya, Shibuya-ku, Tokyo 150, Japan. (Subscr. in US to: Japan Publications Trading Co., Industrial Way, Box 610, Brisbane, CA 94005. FAX 415-469-8038) Ed. Tetsuo Satoh. adv.; charts; stat.; index. circ. 3,700. **Indexed:** Anal.Abstr., Biol.Abstr., Biotech.Abstr., Chem.Abstr., Curr.Adv.Cell & Devel.Biol., Curr.Adv.Ecol.Sci., Curr.Cont., Dent.Ind., Excerp.Med., Ind.Med., Ind.Sci.Rev., Mass Spectr.Bull., Sugar Ind.Abstr. **Document type:** academic/scholarly publication.
—BLDSC (2074.650000); CASDDS; Faxon; Genuine Article; SWETS; UnCover. **CCC.**
Formerly (until 1993): Journal of Pharmacobio-Dynamics (ISSN 0386-846X)

BIOMEDICAL AND ENVIRONMENTAL SCIENCES. see *MEDICAL SCIENCES*

BIOMEDICINE AND PHARMACOTHERAPY. see *MEDICAL SCIENCES*

BIOPHARM. see *VETERINARY SCIENCE*

615   US   ISSN 1040-8304
CODEN: BPRME5
BIOPHARM; the technology and business of biopharmaceuticals. 1987. 9/yr. $59 (foreign $117). Advanstar Communications, Inc., 859 Willamette St., Eugene, OR 97401. TEL 503-343-5020. FAX 503-344-3514. (Subscr. to: 1 E. First St., Duluth, MN 55082. TEL 800-346-0085) Ed. Anne Montgomery. adv. circ. 18,970. (back issues avail.; reprint service avail.) **Indexed:** Telegen. **Document type:** trade publication.
—BLDSC (2089.353500); CASDDS; Genuine Article; SWETS; UMI. **CCC.**
Formerly: Biopharm Manufacturing (ISSN 1040-8045)
Description: Focuses on the science and industry of biogenitically derived pharmaceutical products. Covers scientific and technical applications and issues, regulatory affairs, and business matters for scientists, engineers, managers, technicians, and corporate management.

615   UK   ISSN 0142-2782
CODEN: BDDID8
BIOPHARMACEUTICS & DRUG DISPOSITION. 1980. 9/yr. $845 (foreign $845) (effective 1996). John Wiley & Sons Ltd., Journals, Baffins Ln., Chichester, W. Sussex PO19 1UD, England. TEL 01243-779777. FAX 01243-776128. TELEX 86290 WIBOOK G. (Subscr. in the Americas to: John Wiley & Sons., Inc., 605 Third Ave., New York, NY 10158. TEL 212-850-6645. FAX 212-850-6021) Ed.Bd. circ. 384. (also avail. in microform from UMI; back issues avail.; reprint service avail. from ISI,SWZ,UMI) **Indexed:** Anal.Abstr., Biotech.Abstr., Chem.Abstr., Curr.Adv.Ecol.Sci., Curr.Cont., Dairy Sci.Abstr., Excerp.Med., I.P.A., Ind.Med., Ind.Sci.Rev., Mass Spectr.Bull., Sci.Cit.Ind. **Document type:** academic/scholarly publication.
—BLDSC (2089.355000); ADONIS; CASDDS; Faxon; Genuine Article; SWETS; UMI. **CCC.**
Description: Presents original reports of studies in biopharmaceutics, drug disposition and pharmacokinetics, especially those which have a direct relation to the therapeutic use of drugs.

BIOSYNTHETIC PRODUCTS FOR CANCER CHEMOTHERAPY. see *MEDICAL SCIENCES — Oncology*

BIOTECHNOLOGY THERAPEUTICS. see *BIOLOGY — Biotechnology*

615.328   JA   ISSN 0911-9477
BITAMIN B KENKYU IIKAI KIJI/VITAMIN B RESEARCH COMMITTEE. REPORT. (Text in Japanese) irreg. Bitamin B Kenkyu Iinkai - Vitamin B Research Committee, Nihon Itaria Kyoto Kaikan, 4 Yoshida Ushinomiyacho, Sakyo-ku, Kyoto 606, Japan.

615.328   JA
BITAMIN B KENKYU IINKAI HOKOKUSHO/VITAMIN B RESEARCH COMMITTEE. SHORT NOTE. (Text in Japanese) a. Bitamin B Kenkyu Iinkai - Vitamin B Research Committee, Nihon Itaria Kyoto Kaikan, 4 Yoshida Ushinomiyacho, Sakyo-ku, Kyoto 606, Japan.

615.328   JA
BITAMIN E KENKYU NO SHINPO/ADVANCES IN VITAMIN E RESEARCH. (Text in English, Japanese) 1990. a. 4000 Yen. (Bitamin E Kenkyukai - Association of Vitamin E Research) Kyoritsu Shuppan Co., Ltd., 6-19 Kohinata 4-chome, Bunkyo-ku, Tokyo 112, Japan.

615.1   US   ISSN 0006-503X
BLUE AND GOLD TRIANGLE OF LAMBDA KAPPA SIGMA. 1926. 8 nos. every 2 years. $10. Lambda Kappa Sigma International Pharmaceutical Fraternity, 2565A US Hwy. 23 S., Alpena, MI 49707-4617. FAX 702-456-4309. Ed. Susan McCone. adv.; bk.rev.; illus. circ. 12,000.

PHARMACY AND PHARMACOLOGY

615 US
BLUE BOOK: THE BUYER'S GUIDE FOR PHARMACEUTICAL PACKAGERS.* 1992. a. $50. Avalon Communications, 24 N. Merion Ave., Bryn Mawr, PA 19010-3013. TEL 215-357-4933. adv. circ. 10,146.
 Description: Reference source for pharmaceutical packaging equipment, materials, containers and services.

615.1 IT ISSN 0006-6648
CODEN: BCFAAI
BOLLETTINO CHIMICO FARMACEUTICO. (Text in French, German, Italian; summaries in English) 1861. m. $310. Societa Editoriale Farmaceutica s.r.l., Via Ausonio, 12, 20123 Milan, Italy. TEL 02-89404545. FAX 02-89401168. Ed. G.C. Lubwer. adv. contact: F. Lubner. bk.rev.; pat.; index. circ. 3,000. Indexed: Biol.Abstr., Biotech.Abstr., Chem.Abstr., Excerp.Med., I.P.A., Ind.Med. Document type: academic/scholarly publication, bulletin.
 —BLDSC (2236.000000); CASDDS; SWETS.
 Description: Covers biopharmaceutics, pharmaceutical technology, pharmacokinetics, and industrial pharmacy.

615.19 IT ISSN 1120-8678
BOLLETTINO DI FARMACOSORVEGLIANZA. 1990. bi-m. free. (Societa Italiana per la Verifica e lo Sviluppo dei Farmaci Post-registrazione) Masson S.p.A., Divisione Periodici, Via Statuto 2-4, 20121 Milan, Italy. TEL 02-6367-1. FAX 02-6367-211. Ed. Ettore Ambrosioni. circ. 70,000. Document type: bulletin.

THE BONE AND MINERAL RESEARCH ANNUAL. see MEDICAL SCIENCES — Orthopedics And Traumatology

THE BOOTS COMPANY NEWS. see BUSINESS AND ECONOMICS — Marketing And Purchasing

615 GW ISSN 0722-7159
BRAUNSCHWEIGER VEROEFFENTLICHUNGEN ZUR GESCHICHTE DER PHARMAZIE UND NATURWISSENSCHAFTEN. 1957. irreg., vol.34, 1994. price varies. Deutscher Apotheker Verlag, Postfach 101061, 70009 Stuttgart, Germany. TEL 0711-2582-0. FAX 0711-2582290. Ed. Wolfgang Schneider. Document type: monographic series.
 Formerly: Technische Universitaet Braunschweig. Pharmaziegeschichtlichen Seminar. Veroeffentlichungen (ISSN 0068-0729)

BRITAIN'S PHARMACEUTICAL INDUSTRY. see BUSINESS AND ECONOMICS — Trade And Industrial Directories

617.96 UK ISSN 0306-5251
CODEN: BCPHBM
BRITISH JOURNAL OF CLINICAL PHARMACOLOGY. 1974. m. £349 (outside Europe £384($599)) (effective 1996). (British Pharmacological Society) Blackwell Science Ltd., Osney Mead, Oxford OX2 0EL, England. TEL 01865-240201. FAX 01865-721205. TELEX 83355 MEDBOK G. Eds. L.E. Ramsay, G.T. Tucker. adv.; bk.rev.; abstr.; bibl.; charts; illus.; index. circ. 3,500. (also avail. in microform from UMI; back issues avail.) Indexed: Abstr.Inter.Med., ASCA, Biol.Abstr, Biotech.Abstr., Chem.Abstr., Curr.Adv.Ecol.Sci., Curr.Cont., Dairy Sci.Abstr., Dent.Ind., Excerp.Med., Helminthol.Abstr., I.P.A., Ind.Med., Ind.Sci.Rev., INIS Atomind., Kidney, Med.& Surg.Dermat., Nutr.Abstr., Protozool.Abstr., Sci.Cit.Ind. Document type: academic/scholarly publication.
 ●Also available online.
 —BLDSC (2307.180000); ADONIS; CASDDS; Faxon; Genuine Article; SWETS; UMI; UnCover. CCC.
 Refereed Serial

BRITISH JOURNAL OF CLINICAL RESEARCH. see MEDICAL SCIENCES

615 UK ISSN 0007-1188
CODEN: BJPCBM
BRITISH JOURNAL OF PHARMACOLOGY. 1946. 24/yr. £620 to E.C.; elsewhere £685($1030). (British Pharmacological Society) Stockton Press (Subsidiary of: Macmillan Press Ltd.), Houndmills, Basingstoke, Hampshire RG21 2XS, England. TEL 01256-817245. FAX 01256-28339. Ed. A.T. Birmingham; Pub. Marija Vukovojac. adv. contact: Michael Rowley. charts; illus.; index, cum.index: 1966-1973; 1974-1977; 1978-1983; 1984-1987. circ. 3,000. (also avail. in microform from UMI) Indexed: Biol.Abstr., Biotech.Abstr., C.I.S. Abstr., Chem.Abstr., Curr.Adv.Cancer Res., Curr.Adv.Cell & Devel.Biol., Curr.Adv.Ecol.Sci., Curr.Chem.React., Curr.Cont., Dairy Sci.Abstr., Dent.Ind., Excerp.Med., Helminthol.Abstr., High.Educ.Curr.Aware.Bull., I.P.A., Ind.Chem., Ind.Med., Ind.Vet., INIS Atomind., Nutr.Abstr., Sci.Cit.Ind., Vet.Bull. Document type: academic/scholarly publication.
 ●Also available online.
 —BLDSC (2314.700000); ADONIS; CASDDS; Faxon; Genuine Article; SWETS; UMI; UnCover. CCC.
 Formerly: British Journal of Pharmacology and Chemotherapy.
 Description: Presents original papers in experimental pharmacology.

615.1 UK ISSN 0260-535X
BRITISH NATIONAL FORMULARY. 1981. 2/yr. £9.95. Royal Pharmaceutical Society of Great Britain, 1 Lambeth High St., London SE1 7JN, England. TEL 071-735-9141. FAX 071-735-7629. (Co-sponsor: British Medical Association) Ed. Anne B. Prasad. index. Document type: consumer publication.
 —BLDSC (2331.060000).
 Description: Gives information for prescribers in the National Health Service and other health care professionals about drugs and medicines available on prescriptions in the UK.

615.19 UK
BRITISH PHARMACOPOEIA: MAIN EDITION. 1864. irreg., 1993. £320 (includes a. supplement) (effective 1994). (British Pharmacopoeia Commission) H.M.S.O., Market Towers, 51 Nine Elms Ln., London SW8 5DR, England. TEL 071-873-0011. FAX 071-873-8463. (Subscr. to: H.M.S.O. Publications Centre, P.O. Box 276, London SW8 5DT, England. TEL 071-973-8200) Document type: government publication.
 ●Also available on CD-ROM.
 Description: Compiles official UK standards for medicines.

BRITISH PHARMACOPOEIA: VETERINARY EDITION. see VETERINARY SCIENCE

615.1 UK ISSN 0068-2519
BRITISH SOCIETY FOR THE HISTORY OF PHARMACY. TRANSACTIONS. 1970. irreg. price varies. British Society for the History of Pharmacy, 36 York Pl., Edinburgh EH1 3HU, Scotland. Ed. Dr. J.G.L. Burnby. Document type: academic/scholarly publication.

615.9 615.19 PL ISSN 0365-9445
RA1258 CODEN: BCTKAG
BROMATOLOGIA I CHEMIA TOKSYKOLOGICZNA. (Text in Polish; summaries in English) q. $100 (effective 1995). Polskie Towarzystwo Farmaceutyczne - Polish Pharmaceutical Society, Ul. Dluga 16, 00-238 Warsaw, Poland. TEL 48-22-310241. Ed. Henryk Mlodecki. Indexed: Apic.Abstr., Biol.Abstr., Chem.Abstr, Dairy Sci.Abstr., Excerp.Med., Food Sci.& Tech.Abstr., Maize Abstr., Nutr.Abstr., Pig News & Info., Soils & Fert., Soyabean Abstr., Triticale Abstr., Weed Abstr. Document type: academic/scholarly publication.
 —BLDSC (2349.500000); CASDDS.
 Description: Deals with bromatology and toxicological chemistry. Contains scientific papers.
 Refereed Serial

615 340 US
BUREAU OF VOLUNTARY COMPLIANCE NEWSLETTERS. (Avail. in 35 state editions each with a national news section.) 1979. q. $100. National Association of Boards of Pharmacy Foundation, 700 Busse Hwy., Park Ridge, IL 60068. TEL 708-698-6227. FAX 708-698-0124. Ed. Janice D. Teplitz. circ. 145,000. Document type: newsletter.

789.56 658.8 UK ISSN 0261-9350
BUSINESS RATIO REPORT: PHARMACEUTICAL MANUFACTURERS; an industry sector analysis. 1973. a. I C C Business Ratios Ltd., Freepost, Field House, Hampton, Mddx. TW12 1BR, England. TEL 081-783-0977. FAX 081-783-1940. charts; stat. Document type: trade publication.
 —BLDSC (6444.032000).

615 658.8 UK ISSN 0261-9482
BUSINESS RATIO REPORT: RETAIL & WHOLESALE CHEMISTS; an industry sector analysis. 1981. a. I C C Business Ratios Ltd., Freepost, Field House, Hampton, Mddx. TW12 1BR, England. TEL 081-783-0977. FAX 081-783-1940. charts; stat. Document type: trade publication.
 —BLDSC (7785.434000).

615.9 JA ISSN 0389-9098
CODEN: BYYADW
BYOIN YAKUGAKU/JAPANESE JOURNAL OF HOSPITAL PHARMACY. (Text in English, Japanese; summaries in English) 1975. bi-m. 1500 Yen per no. Nihon Byoin Yakuzaishikai - Japanese Society of Hospital Pharmacists, 12-15-304, Shibuya 2-chome, Shibuya-ku, Tokyo 150, Japan. Indexed: Chem.Abstr., Excerp.Med.
 —BLDSC (4655.180000); CASDDS.

615.1 616.8 NZ ISSN 1172-7047
CODEN: CNDREF
▼**C N S DRUGS.** (Central Nervous System) 1994. m. $680 (effective 1996). Adis International Limited, Private Bag 65901, Mairangi Bay, Auckland 10, New Zealand. TEL 64-9-479-8100. FAX 64-9-479-8145. E-mail: pcl@topgun.adis.co.nz. (Subscr. addr. in US: Adis International Inc., Attn. Subscriptions Dept., Ste. F-10, 940 Town Center Dr., Langhorne, PA 19047. TEL 215-741-5229. FAX 215-841-5251) Ed. Katharine Palmer. Indexed: Curr.Cont., Excerp.Med. (1995-), Sci.Cit.Ind. Document type: academic/scholarly publication.
 —BLDSC (3287.314345); Genuine Article. CCC.
 Description: Covers clinical aspects of psychiatric and neurological pharmacology.

615.1 US
C P F I NEWSLETTER. 1984. q. free. Christian Pharmacists Fellowship International, Box 1667, Buies Creek, NC 27506. TEL 919-814-2014. Ed. James E. Thompson. bk.rev. circ. 2,000. (back issues avail.) Document type: newsletter.
 Description: Communication link and network of Christian pharmacists around the world.

615.19 US
CALIFORNIA JOURNAL OF HEALTH - SYSTEM PHARMACY. 1989. m. $75. California Society of Health - System Pharmacists, 725 30th St., Ste. 208, Sacramento, CA 95816-3842. TEL 916-447-1033. FAX 916-447-2396. Ed. Priscilla N. Richter. adv. circ. 3,800. (back issues avail.)
 Formerly: California Journal of Hospital Pharmacy (ISSN 1072-7809)
 Description: Reports news, and legislature updates.

615.1 US ISSN 0739-0483
CALIFORNIA PHARMACIST. 1954. m. $30 in N. America; elsewhere $40. California Pharmacists Association, 1112 I St., Ste. 300, Sacramento, CA 95814. TEL 916-444-7811 ext. 302. FAX 916-444-7929. Ed. Robert Marshall. adv. contact: Lisa Clark. bk.rev.; charts; illus.; stat.; index. circ. 6,500. Document type: trade publication.
 —BLDSC (3015.180000).
 Formerly: California Pharmacy (ISSN 0008-1388)

615 CN
▼**CANADIAN JOURNAL OF CLINICAL PHARMACOLOGY/JOURNAL CANADIEN DE PHARMACOLOGIE CLINIQUE.** 1994. 4/yr. Can.$84. (Canadian Society for Clinical Pharmacology) Pulsus Group Inc., 2902 S. Sheridan Way, Oakville, ON L6J 7L6, Canada. TEL 905-829-4770. FAX 905-829-4799. Ed. Dr. Neil H. Shear; Pub. Robert B. Kalina. adv.: B&W page Can.$2165, color page Can.$3815; trim 8 1/8 x 10 7/8. circ. 20,000. Document type: academic/scholarly publication.

CANADIAN JOURNAL OF HERBALISM. see ALTERNATIVE MEDICINE

PHARMACY AND PHARMACOLOGY

615.1 CN ISSN 0008-4123
CODEN: CJHPAV
CANADIAN JOURNAL OF HOSPITAL PHARMACY. (Text in English and French) 1948. bi-m. Can.$48. Canadian Society of Hospital Pharmacists, 1145 Hunt Club Rd., Ste. 350, Ottawa, ON K1V 0Y3, Canada. TEL 613-736-9733. FAX 613-736-5660. Ed. Scott Walker. adv.; bk.rev.; abstr.; charts; illus.; pat.; tr.lit.; index. circ. 3,300. (also avail. in microform from UMI; reprint service avail. from UMI) **Indexed:** Biol.Abstr., Biotech.Abstr., Chem.Abstr., Excerp.Med., Hosp.Lit.Ind., I.P.A. **Document type:** academic/scholarly publication.
●Also available online.
—BLDSC (3031.700000); Faxon; UMI; UnCover. **CCC.**
Formerly: Hospital Pharmacist.
Description: Publishes original research, clinical reviews, case reports, and topical discussions on pharmacy practice that are of use and interest to pharmacists engaged in institutional practice.
Refereed Serial

CANADIAN JOURNAL OF PHYSIOLOGY AND PHARMACOLOGY/JOURNAL CANADIEN DE PHYSIOLOGIE ET PHARMACOLOGIE. see *BIOLOGY — Physiology*

615.1 CN ISSN 0828-6914
CODEN: CPJOAC
CANADIAN PHARMACEUTICAL JOURNAL/REVUE PHARMACEUTIQUE CANADIENNE. Short title: C P J - R P C. 1868. 10/yr. Can.$58.85. Canadian Pharmaceutical Association, 1785 Alta Vista Dr., Ottawa, ON K1G 3Y6, Canada. TEL 613-523-7877. FAX 613-523-0445. Ed. Andrew Reinboldt. adv. contact: Keith Health. bk.rev. circ. 12,673. **Indexed:** Biol.Abstr., Biotech.Abstr., Can.B.P.I., Excerp.Med., I.P.A. **Document type:** trade publication.
●Also available online.
—Faxon; SWETS. **CCC.**
Refereed Serial

615 CN
CANADIAN THERAPEUTICS. 1993. 4/yr. Can.$7.50 per no. (foreign Can.$9.50). S T A Communications Inc., 955 bd. St. Jean, Bur. 306, Pointe Claire, PQ H9R 5K3, Canada. TEL 514-695-7623. FAX 514-695-8554. Ed. Paul Brand. adv.: B&W page Can.$1875; trim 8 1/8 x 10 7/8. circ. 30,080.

CANCER BIOTHERAPY. see *MEDICAL SCIENCES — Oncology*

CANCER CHEMOTHERAPY AND PHARMACOLOGY. see *MEDICAL SCIENCES — Oncology*

CANCER CHEMOTHERAPY AND PHARMACOLOGY. SUPPLEMENT. see *MEDICAL SCIENCES — Oncology*

615.5 US ISSN 0276-4296
RM300
CARDIOLOGIST'S COMPENDIUM OF DRUG THERAPY. Spine title: Compendium of Drug Therapy. 1980. a. $49.95 (effective 1994). Compendium Publications Group Ltd., 1 Harmon Meadow Blvd., Secaucus, NJ 07094. TEL 201-864-2400. FAX 201-864-3626. adv. circ. 105,000.

615 US ISSN 0897-3830
CARDIOVASCULAR DRUG ALERTS. m. $59 (Canada $76; elsewehere $83) (effective 1996). M.J. Powers & Co., 65 Madison Ave., Morristown, NJ 07960. TEL 201-898-7220. FAX 201-898-1201. (back issues avail.) **Document type:** newsletter.

CARDIOVASCULAR DRUG REVIEWS. see *MEDICAL SCIENCES — Cardiovascular Diseases*

CARDIOVASCULAR DRUGS AND THERAPY. see *MEDICAL SCIENCES — Cardiovascular Diseases*

615.7 616.1 UK ISSN 0263-7243
CARDIOVASCULAR PHARMACOLOGY. s-m. (diskette m.) £115 (diskette £115; both £175) (effective 1995). S U B I S, Mansion House, 19 Kingfield Rd., Sheffield S11 9AS, England. TEL 0114-2554433. FAX 0114-2554626. E-mail: admin@sheffac.demon.co.uk. (also avail. in diskette format) **Document type:** abstracting/indexing.
—**CCC.**
Description: Current awareness service for researchers in clinical and life sciences. Covers anti-hypertensives, calcium channel blockers, vasoconstrictors, and vasodilators.

615 US ISSN 0528-1725
CAROLINA JOURNAL OF PHARMACY. 1915. m. $25. North Carolina Pharmaceutical Association, Box 151, Chapel Hill, NC 27514. TEL 919-967-2237. Ed. A.H. Mebane III. adv. circ. 3,000. (back issues avail.) **Indexed:** I.P.A.
—BLDSC (3055.300000).
Description: Covers issues related to pharmacy practice with emphasis on North Carolina pharmacy.

CATEGORY REPORT - HEALTH & BEAUTY AIDS. see *BEAUTY CULTURE — Perfumes And Cosmetics*

338.4 643 636.088 US
CATEGORY REPORT - HOUSEHOLD, PET & MISCELLANEOUS PRODUCTS. m. $1000. Marketing Intelligence Service Ltd., 6473D Route 64, Naples, NY 14512-9726. TEL 716-374-6326. FAX 716-374-5217. Ed.Bd. (back issues avail.) **Document type:** newsletter.
Description: Contains detailed product and packaging description and analysis of new foreign and domestic consumer packaged goods.

615.19 282 US
THE CATHOLIC PHARMACIST. Short title: T.C.P. 1968. q. $20 membership. National Catholic Pharmacists Guild of the United States, 1012 Surrey Hills Dr., St. Louis, MO 63117-1438. TEL 314-645-0085. Ed. John Paul Winkelmann. adv.; bk.rev. circ. 375. (back issues avail.) **Document type:** trade publication.
Description: Acquaints members with the latest developments in their church affecting their profession., as well as feature articles and membership news.

CELL CYCLE. see *BIOLOGY — Cytology And Histology*

CELL DIFFERENTIATION. see *BIOLOGY — Cytology And Histology*

CELLULAR AND MOLECULAR MECHANISMS OF INFLAMMATION; receptors of inflammatory cells: structure-function relationships. see *BIOLOGY*

CELLULAR SIGNALLING. see *BIOLOGY — Cytology And Histology*

615 NE
CENTRE FOR MEDICINES RESEARCH WORKSHOP. Running title: C M R Workshop. (Text in English) irreg., vol.4, 1994. price varies. Kluwer Academic Publishers, Postbus 17, 3300 AA Dordrecht, Netherlands. TEL 31-78-392392. FAX 31-78-392254. TELEX 29245 KAPG NL. (Dist. by: Kluwer Academic Publishers Group, P.O. Box 322, 3300 AH Dordrecht, Netherlands. TEL 31-78-392392. FAX 31-78-546474; N. America dist. addr.: Box 358, Accord Sta., Hingham, MA 02018-0358. TEL 617-871-6600. FAX 617-871-6528) **Document type:** proceedings.
Refereed Serial

615.9 FR ISSN 0995-3671
CENTRE NATIONAL DE DOCUMENTATION SUR LES TOXICOMANIES. BULLETIN DE LIAISON. (Supplement avail.: Cahiers Thematiques) 1983. 2/yr. (plus 2 supplements). 100 F. per no. Centre National de Documentation sur les Toxicomanies, 14 ave. Berthelot, 69007 Lyon, France. TEL 72-72-93-07. FAX 78-58-27-14.
Description: Devoted to the study of drug addiction, with a multidisciplinary approach.

615.19 MG
CENTRE NATIONAL DE RECHERCHES PHARMACEUTIQUES. ARCHIVES. a. FMG.8000($5) Centre National de Recherches Pharmaceutiques, B.P. 694, 101 Antananarivo, Madagascar. TEL 33288. (Affiliate: Centre d'Information et de Documentation Scientifique et Technique) (back issues avail.) **Indexed:** P.L.E.S.A.

615 XR ISSN 1210-7816
RS1 CODEN: CSLFEK
CESKA A SLOVESKA FARMACIE/CZECH AND SLOVAK PHARMACY. (Text in Czech or Slovak; summaries in English, German, Russian) 1952. 10/yr. $62.60. (Ceska Lekarska Spolecnost J.E. Purkyne - Czech Medical Society) Nakladatelske tredisko C L S J.E. Purkyne, Sokolska 31, 120 26 Prague 2, Czech Republic. FAX 42-0-202788. (Dist. by: Artia, Ve Smeckach 30, 111 27 Prague 1, Czech Republic) (Co-sponsors: Ceska Farmaceuticka Spolecnost; Slovenska Farmaceuticka Spolecnost) Ed. P. Komarek. adv.; bk.rev.; index. circ. 2,400. **Indexed:** Anal.Abstr., Biol.Abstr., Biotech.Abstr., C.I.S. Abstr., Chem.Abstr., Curr.Adv.Ecol.Sci., Excerp.Med., I.P.A., Ind.Med., INIS Atomind., Protozool.Abstr.
●Also available online.
—BLDSC (3120.258380); CASDDS. **CCC.**
Formerly (until 1994): Ceskoslovenska Farmacie (ISSN 0009-0530)

615 658 US ISSN 1079-1086
CHAIN PHARMACIST. 1992. q. membership. National Association of Chain Drug Stores, Box 1417-D49, Alexandria, VA 22313-1417. TEL 703-549-3001. FAX 703-836-4869. Ed. Mary Ann Wagner. (looseleaf format) **Document type:** newsletter.

CHEMICAL & PHARMACEUTICAL BULLETIN. see *CHEMISTRY*

CHEMICAL RESEARCH IN TOXICOLOGY. see *ENVIRONMENTAL STUDIES — Toxicology And Environmental Safety*

CHEMISCHE RUNDSCHAU; Wochenzeitung fuer Chemie, Pharmazie, und Lebensmitteltechnik. see *CHEMISTRY*

615.1 UK ISSN 0009-3033
CODEN: CHDRA3
CHEMIST & DRUGGIST; for retailer, wholesaler, manufacturer. 1859. w. £103. (Pharmaceutical Society of Northern Ireland, IE) Miller Freman Publishers Ltd. (Subsidiary of: Morgan-Grampian plc), Benn House, Sovereign Way, Tonbridge, Kent TN9 1RW, England. TEL 01732-364422. FAX 01732-361534. TELEX 95132 BENTON G. Ed. John Skelton. adv. contact: Ian Gerrard. bk.rev.; charts; illus.; mkt.; pat.; tr.mk.; s-a. index. circ. 15,413. (also avail. in microform from UMI) **Indexed:** Br.Tech.Ind., Chem.Abstr., I.P.A., PROMT. **Document type:** trade publication.
●Also available online.
—BLDSC (3167.000000); CASDDS; UMI; UnCover. **CCC.**
Incorporates: Retail Chemist (ISSN 0034-6020)

615.1 UK ISSN 0262-5881
CHEMIST & DRUGGIST DIRECTORY. 1868. a. £92. Miller Freeman Information Services (Subsidiary of: United News & Media), Riverbank House, Angel Ln., Tonbridge, Kent TN9 1SE, England. TEL 01732-362666. FAX 01732-367301. TELEX 954829. Ed. Gwen Young. adv. contact: Elaine Soni. circ. 2,900. **Document type:** directory.
—BLDSC (3167.500000).
Description: Lists the pharmaceutical and affiliated trades. Coverage includes tablet and capsule identification guide. Lists multiple retail outlets, wholesalers, pharmaceutical organizations, and drug contraindications.

615 UK ISSN 0266-3023
CHEMIST & DRUGGIST PRICE LIST. (Supplement to: Chemist & Druggist) 1960. m. free. Miller Freeman Publishers Ltd., Sovereign Way, Tonbridge, Kent TN9 1RW, England. TEL 01732-364422. FAX 01732-361534. TELEX 95132 BENTON G. adv. circ. 15,413.

615.1 II ISSN 0009-3041
CHEMIST & DRUGSTORE NEWS. m. Rs.20. India Publications Co., Denabank House, 2nd Fl., 31 Hamam St., Bombay 1, India. Ed. Eric Martin. bk.rev.; circ. controlled.

540 AT
CHEMIST CATALOGUE. a. Permail Pty. Ltd., P.O. Box 56, Artarmon, N.S.W. 2064, Australia. **Document type:** directory.

615.1 PK ISSN 0009-3149
CHEMISTS REVIEW. (Text in English and Urdu) 1957. m. Rs.250. P.O. Box 376, Karachi, Pakistan. Ed. M.Y. Ansari. adv.; bk.rev.; charts; illus. circ. 5,000.

PHARMACY AND PHARMACOLOGY

615.1 — SZ — ISSN 0009-3157
CODEN: CHTHBK
CHEMOTHERAPY; international journal of experimental and clinical chemotherapy. (Text in English) 1960. bi-m. 330 SFr.($253.80) to individuals; institutions 550 SFr.($423) (effective 1996). S. Karger AG, Allschwilerstr. 10, P.O. Box, CH-4009 Basel, Switzerland. TEL 061-3061111. FAX 061-3061234. E-mail: Karger@Karger.ch. Ed. H. Schoenfeld. adv.; bk.rev.; bibl.; charts; illus. circ. 1,300. (also avail. in microfilm) **Indexed:** Biodet.Abstr., Biol.Abstr., Biotech.Abstr., Chem.Abstr., Curr.Adv.Cancer Res., Curr.Cont., Dairy Sci.Abstr., Diar.Dis.Res., Excerp.Med., Helminthol.Abstr., I.P.A., Ind.Med., Ind.Vet., Protozool.Abstr., Rev.Med.& Vet.Mycol., Rev.Plant Path., Sci.Cit.Ind., Vet.Bull. **Document type:** academic/scholarly publication.
—BLDSC (3172.304000); CASDDS; Faxon; Genuine Article; SWETS; UnCover. **CCC.**
Formerly: Chemotherapia.
Refereed Serial

615.9 — JA
CHIBA DAIGAKU YAKUGAKUBU KENKYU GYOSEKI MOKUROKU/CHIBA UNIVERSITY. FACULTY OF PHARMACEUTICAL SCIENCES. LIST OF RESEARCH ACTIVITIES. (Text in Japanese) 1984. biennial. Chiba Daigaku, Yakugakubu - Chiba University, Faculty of Pharmaceutical Sciences, 1-33, Yayoicho, Inage-ku, Chiba-shi, Chiba-ken 263, Japan. TEL 81-43-290-2981. FAX 81-43-290-2974. circ. 300. **Document type:** academic/scholarly publication.

615.9 617.6 — JA — ISSN 0300-029X
CHIKEN ISHIYAKU JOHO/INVESTIGATIONAL DRUG INFORMATION. MEDICAL AND DENTAL. (Text in Japanese) 1970. a. 25000 Yen. Iji Shuppansha, 2-8 Shinkawa 1-chome, Chuo-ku, Tokyo 104, Japan.

615.9 — JA
CHIKEN'YAKU JOHO/INVESTIGATIONAL DRUG REPORT. (Text in English, Japanese) 1970. m. 175100 Yen. Iyakuhin Sangyo Kenkyujo - Drug Business Research Co., Ltd., 25-2, Koishikawa 1-chome, Bunkyo-ku, Tokyo 112, Japan.

615.9 — US
CHINA DRUG PURCHASE AUDIT. (Editions in Chinese, English) 1985. q. $19750. ChinaMetrik, 1010 Wisconsin Ave. N.W., Ste. 310, Washington, DC 20007-3603. TEL 202-337-7327. FAX 202-337-4498. Ed. A. Wolters. index. (back issues avail.) **Document type:** trade publication.
Description: Contains data on purchases of Western-type drugs by sample of 50 major Chinese hospitals.

CHINA PHARMACEUTICAL AND MEDICAL INSTRUMENTS. see *MEDICAL SCIENCES*

CHINESE MEDICAL SCIENCES JOURNAL. see *MEDICAL SCIENCES*

CHIRALITY; the pharmacological, biological, and chemical consequences of molecular asymmetry. see *BIOLOGY — Microbiology*

615.9 — JA — ISSN 0285-0141
CODEN: CHIYDI
CHUGAI IYAKU/MEDICAL CHUGAI. (Text in Japanese) 1948. m. 100 Yen per no. Chugai Seiyaku K.K. - Chugai Pharmaceutical Co., Ltd., 1-9, Kyobashi 2-chome, Chuo-ku, Tokyo 104, Japan.
—CASDDS.

615.9 — JA — ISSN 0288-7223
CHUGAIKAI NYUZU/CHUGAI PHARMACEUTICAL CO., LTD. NEWS. (Text in Japanese) bi-m. Chugai Seiyaku K.K. - Chugai Pharmaceutical Co., Ltd., 1-9, Kyobashi 2-chome, Chuo-ku, Tokyo 104, Japan.

615.19 — SP — ISSN 1131-5253
CODEN: CIPHEA
CIENCIA PHARMACEUTICA; revista espanola del medicamento y del producto sanitario. 1987. 6/yr. 5000 ptas.($100) (Europe $60). Alpe Editores, S.A., Pedro Rico, 27, 28029 Madrid, Spain. TEL 34-1-7338892. FAX 34-1-3159652. Pres. Dr. Jose Maria Sune Arbussa; Pub. A. Alvarez. adv.: color page 160000 ptas.; trim 210 x 280; adv. contact: C. Alvarez. circ. 6,000 (controlled). **Indexed:** Excerp.Med.
—BLDSC (3196.511500). **CCC.**
Formerly (until 1990): Pharmaklinik (ISSN 1011-4386)

CLINICAL AND EXPERIMENTAL PHARMACOLOGY AND PHYSIOLOGY. see *BIOLOGY — Physiology*

615 — JA — ISSN 0917-5857
CODEN: CLCCEJ
CLINICAL CALCIUM. (Text in Japanese) 1991. m. 2575 Yen per no. Iyaku Janarusha - Medicine & Drug Journal Co., Ltd., 2-8, Hiranocho 3-chome, Chuo-ku, Osaka 541, Japan. **Document type:** academic/scholarly publication.
—CASDDS.

615.9 — US
CLINICAL CONSULT. 1982. m. free to members. American Society of Consultant Pharmacists, 1321 Duke St., Alexandria, VA 22314-3563. TEL 703-739-1300. FAX 703-739-1321. Ed. James W. Cooper. (back issues avail.)
Description: Focuses on geriatric drug therapy and, or clinical illness and offers guidance to readers on drug therapy monitoring criteria.

615 — NZ — ISSN 1173-2563
CODEN: CDINFR
CLINICAL DRUG INVESTIGATION. 1989. m. $175 (effective 1996). Adis International Limited, Private Bag 65901, Mairangi Bay, Auckland 10, New Zealand. TEL 64-9-479-8100. FAX 64-9-479-8145. E-mail: pcl@topgun.adis.co.nz. (Subscr. add. in US: Adis International Inc., Attn. Subscriptions Dept., Ste F-10, 940 Town Center Dr., Langhorne, PA 19047. TEL 215-741-5229. FAX 215-741-5251) Ed. Paul Battershill. **Indexed:** Curr.Cont., Excerp.Med., I.P.A., Ind.Med., Sci.Cit.Ind. **Document type:** academic/scholarly publication.
—CASDDS; Faxon; Genuine Article; SWETS; UnCover. **CCC.**
Formerly: Drug Investigation (ISSN 0114-2402)
Description: Committed to the repid publication and indexing of peer-reviewed original ressearch corvering all phases of drug development.

615 616.97 — NZ — ISSN 1172-7039
▼**CLINICAL IMMUNOTHERAPEUTICS.** 1994. m. $680 (effective 1996). Adis International Limited, Private Bag 65901, Mairangi Bay, Auckland 10, New Zealand. TEL 64-9-479-8100. FAX 215-741-5251. E-mail: pcl@topgun.adis.co.nz. (Subscr. add. in US: Adis International Inc., Attn. Subscriptions Dept., Ste. F-10, 940 Town Center Dr., Langhorne, PA 19047. TEL 215-741-5229) Ed. Alan Beedle. **Indexed:** Curr.Cont., Excerp.Med. (1995-), Sci.Cit.Ind. **Document type:** academic/scholarly publication.
—BLDSC (3286.293820); Genuine Article. **CCC.**
Description: Covers clinical aspects of immunopharmacology, immune disorder treatments, clinical use of immunomodulating agents and cytokines.

574 615 — US — ISSN 1068-1191
CLINICAL INVESTIGATOR NEWS. 1993. m. $548 (foreign $578). C T B International Publishing Inc., Box 218, Maplewood, NJ 07040-0218. TEL 201-379-7749. FAX 201-379-1158. Ed. Christopher Brogna; Pub. Oykwe Brogna. bibl.; pat.; stat.; tr.lit. (back issues avail.) **Document type:** newsletter.
Description: Covers new drug study opportunities, which companies are targeting, what compounds, when they plan to begin trials, and where they stand in their research.

615 — US — ISSN 0362-5664
RM315 CODEN: CLNEDB
CLINICAL NEUROPHARMACOLOGY. 1976. bi-m. $146 to individuals (foreign $198); institutions $245 (foreign $294) (effective 1996). Lippincott - Raven Publishers, 227 E. Washington Sq., Philadelphia, PA 19106. TEL 215-238-4200. Ed. Harold L. Klawans. adv. contact: Phyllis Noyes. charts; illus.; index. circ. 3,500. (back issues avail.; reprint service avail. from UMI) **Indexed:** Biol.Abstr., Chem.Abstr., Curr.Adv.Ecol.Sci., Curr.Cont., Excerp.Med., Ind.Med., Ind.Sci.Rev., Psychol.Abstr. (1990-), Sci.Cit.Ind. **Document type:** academic/scholarly publication.
—BLDSC (3286.310600); CASDDS; Faxon; Genuine Article; SWETS; UMI; UnCover. **CCC.**
Description: Features reviews and original investigations on the pharmacology of central nervous system dysfunction.
Refereed Serial

615.19 — US — ISSN 0886-7879
CLINICAL PHARMACOKINETIC NEWSLETTER. 1984. q. $10. Rhode Island Hospital, Department of Pharmacy, 593 Eddy St., Providence, RI 02902. TEL 401-277-5050. Ed. Louis P. Jeffrey, Sc.D. bk.rev.; bibl.; charts; illus.; cum.index. circ. 1,000. (tabloid format)

615 — NZ — ISSN 0312-5963
CODEN: CPKNDH
CLINICAL PHARMACOKINETICS. 1976. m. $680 (effective 1996). Adis International Limited, Private Bag 65901, Mairangi Bay, Auckland 10, New Zealand. TEL 64-9-479-8100. FAX 64-9-479-8145. E-mail: pcl@topgun.adis.co.nz. (Subscr. addr. in US: Adis International Inc., Attn. Subscriptions Dept., Ste. F-10, 940 Town Center Dr., Langhorne, PA 19047. TEL 215-741-5229. FAX 215-741-5251) Ed. Lee Barradell. **Indexed:** Biol.Abstr., Biotech.Abstr., Chem.Abstr., Curr.Adv.Cancer Res., Curr.Adv.Ecol.Sci., Curr.Cont., Dairy Sci.Abstr., Dent.Ind., Excerp.Med., I.P.A., Ind.Med., Ind.Sci.Rev., Kidney, Rev.Med.& Vet.Mycol., Sci.Cit.Ind. **Document type:** academic/scholarly publication.
—BLDSC (3286.327000); CASDDS; Faxon; Genuine Article; SWETS; UnCover. **CCC.**
Description: Provides clinically relevant pharmacokinetic knowledge to aid in the delivery of rational drug therapy.

615 — US — ISSN 0009-9236
RM1 CODEN: CLPTAT
CLINICAL PHARMACOLOGY & THERAPEUTICS. 1960. m. $131 to individuals (Canada $171.20; elsewhere $160); institutions $243 (Canada $291.04; elsewhere $272); students, residents $59 (Canada $94.16; elsewhere $88) (effective 1996); newsstand price: $12.50. (American Society for Pharmacology and Experimental Therapeutics) Mosby - Year Book, Inc. (Subsidiary of: Times Mirror Company), 11830 Westline Industrial Dr., St. Louis, MO 63146-3318. TEL 314-872-8370; 800-325-4177. FAX 314-432-1380. TELEX 44-2402. (Co-sponsor: American Society of Clinical Pharmacology and Therapeutics) Ed. Dr. Marcus M. Reidenberg. adv.: B&W page $895, color page $1620; trim 8 1/4 x 11. charts; illus.; s-a. index. circ. 4,797. (also avail. in microform from UMI; reprint service avail. from UMI) **Indexed:** Abstr.Inter.Med., AIM, ASCA, Behav.Med.Abstr., Biol.Abstr., Biotech.Abstr., Chem.Abstr., CINAHL, Curr.Adv.Ecol.Sci., Dairy Sci.Abstr., Dent.Ind., Excerp.Med., I.P.A., Ind.Med., Ind.Sci.Rev., INIS Atomind., Kidney, Med.& Surg.Dermat., NRN, Nutr.Abstr., Sci.Cit.Ind., Sugar Ind.Abstr. **Document type:** academic/scholarly publication.
●Also available online. Vendor(s): Ovid Technologies.
—BLDSC (3286.330000); ADONIS; CASDDS; Faxon; Genuine Article; SWETS; UMI; UnCover. **CCC.**
Description: Devoted to the study of the nature, action, disposition, efficacy and total evaluation of drugs as they are used in man.
Refereed Serial

615.19 — US
CLINICAL PHARMACOLOGY SERIES. 1983. irreg., vol.18, 1993. price varies. Marcel Dekker, Inc., 270 Madison Ave., New York, NY 10016. TEL 212-696-9000. FAX 212-685-4540. TELEX 421419. **Document type:** monographic series.

615.1072 — US — ISSN 1060-1333
RS122 CODEN: CRRAES
CLINICAL RESEARCH AND REGULATORY AFFAIRS; a journal devoted to documentation of the clinical research process in the pharmaceutical industry. 1983. 4/yr. $435. Marcel Dekker Journals, 270 Madison Ave., New York, NY 10016. TEL 212-696-9000. FAX 212-685-4540. TELEX 421419. (Subscr. to: Box 5017, Monticello, NY 12701) Ed. S.E. Rosenbaum. adv. contact: Eridania Perez. bk.rev.; illus.; charts; stat.; index. (also avail. in microform from RPI) **Indexed:** Biol.Abstr., Curr.Adv.Ecol.Sci., Excerp.Med. **Document type:** academic/scholarly publication.
—BLDSC (3286.372100); Faxon; Genuine Article; SWETS; UMI; UnCover. **CCC.**
Formerly (until 1992): Clinical Research Practices and Drug Regulatory Affairs (ISSN 0735-7915)
Description: For rapid communication of new and significant data pertaining to the documentation of the industrial clinical research process.
Refereed Serial

CLINICAL TRIALS MONITOR. see *MEDICAL SCIENCES*

PHARMACY AND PHARMACOLOGY

615.1   SP   ISSN 0009-7314
CODEN: CFPBE5
COLEGIO OFICIAL DE FARMACEUTICA. CIRCULAR FARMACEUTICA. (Supplement avail.: Informatiu) 1943. 4/yr. 1000 ptas. to non-members. Colegio Oficial de Farmaceuticos de la Provincia de Barcelona, Pau Claris 94, 08010 Barcelona, Spain. adv.; charts; illus. Indexed: I.P.A.
●Also available online.
—CASDDS.

615.1   SP   ISSN 0214-0470
COLEGIO OFICIAL DE FARMACEUTICOS DE LA PROVINCIA DE BARCELONA. INFORMATIU. (Supplement to: Colegio Oficial de Farmaceuticos. Circular Farmaceutica (ISSN 0009-7314) 1969. m. membership. Colegio Oficial de Farmaceuticos de la Provincia de Barcelona, Pau Claris 94, 08010 Barcelona, Spain. Indexed: Chem.Abstr., GeoRef.
Formerly (until 1986): Butlleti Informatiu de Circular Farmaceutica (ISSN 0212-0674)

615.7   IT   ISSN 0390-8739
COLLEGAMENTO. 1957. m. (10/yr.) L.50000. (Unione Tecnica Italiana Farmacisti) Utet Periodici Scientifici s.r.l., Via P. Giuria 20, 10125 Turin, Italy. TEL 39-2-29003555. FAX 39-2-6599049. Ed. Luigi Casanova. adv.: B&W page L.3340000, color page L.5000000; trim 185 x 246; adv. contact: Corrado Trevisan. circ. 18,500. Indexed: I.P.A.
●Also available online.

615.1   US   ISSN 0010-163X
COLORADO JOURNAL OF PHARMACY. 1958. q. $5. University of Colorado, School of Pharmacy, Box 297, Boulder, CO 80309-0297. TEL 303-492-6278. Ed. James A. Roth. illus. circ. 1,500. Indexed: Biol.Abstr.

COMMENTS ON TOXICOLOGY. see ENVIRONMENTAL STUDIES — Toxicology And Environmental Safety

615.19 658.8   UK   ISSN 0960-376X
COMMUNITY PHARMACY. 1980. m. £58 (foreign £48) (included Beauty Counter). Miller Freeman Publishers Ltd. (Subsidiary of: Morgan-Grampian plc.), Sovereign Way, Tonbridge Wells, Kent TN9 1RW, England. TEL 01732-364422. FAX 01732-361534. Ed. Anne Anstice. adv. contact: Kate Haysom. illus.; circ. 13,813 (controlled). Document type: trade publication.
—BLDSC (3363.647500).
Formerly (until 1986): O T C Medication (ISSN 0260-518X)
Description: For persons involved with pharmacies and pharmaceuticals. Discusses product news, nonprescription medications, and pharmacy in business.

COMPARATIVE BIOCHEMISTRY AND PHYSIOLOGY. PART C: COMPARATIVE PHARMACOLOGY & TOXICOLOGY. see BIOLOGY — Biological Chemistry

615   CN   ISSN 0069-7966
COMPENDIUM OF PHARMACEUTICALS AND SPECIALTIES. French edition: Compendium des Produits et Specialites Pharmaceutiques (ISSN 0317-2813) (Editions in English and French) 1960. a. Can.$108 (French edition Can.$112). Canadian Pharmaceutical Association, 1785 Alta Vista Dr., Ottawa, ON K1G 3Y6, Canada. TEL 613-523-7877. FAX 613-523-0445. Ed. C. Krogh. bk.rev. circ. 95,000. Document type: catalog.
●Also available on CD-ROM.
—BLDSC (3363.971000).

615.329
CONNECTICUT PHARMACIST. 1943. q. $12. Connecticut Pharmacists Association, 35 Cold Spring Rd., Ste. 125, Rocky Hill, CT 06067-3167. TEL 203-563-4619. FAX 203-257-8241. Ed. Daniel C. Leone. adv. circ. 1,949.

615.328   US   ISSN 0888-5109
THE CONSULTANT PHARMACIST. 1986. m. $45 to individuals (foreign $65); institutions $75 (foreign $95). American Society of Consultant Pharmacists, 1321 Duke St., Alexandria, VA 22314-3563. TEL 703-739-1300. FAX 703-739-1321. Ed. L. Michael Posey. adv. circ. 11,000. (back issues avail.) Indexed: Abstr.Soc.Geront.
—BLDSC (3423.763000).
Description: Publishes articles, news and information relevant to pharmacy practice in long-term care facilities, prisons, hospices, adult day care centers, home health care, and other related extended care facilities and settings.

615.9   US   ISSN 0738-0615
CONSUMER PHARMACIST; drug information newsletter. 1982. bi-m. $48. Elba Medical Foundation, 1818 N. Turnbull Dr., Box 1403, Metairie, LA 70004-1403. TEL 504-833-3600. Ed. John F. DiMaggio. adv.; bk.rev. circ. 6,000.

615   SW   ISSN 0280-610X
CONTENTA SEROMO. 1982. bi-m. Svenska AB Serono, Turebergsv. 11a, S-191 47 Sollentuna, Sweden.

CONTROLLED RELEASE SERIES. see CHEMISTRY — Organic Chemistry

CONTROLLED RELEASE SOCIETY. INTERNATIONAL SYMPOSIUM ON CONTROLLED RELEASE OF BIOACTIVE MATERIALS. PROCEEDINGS. see CHEMISTRY — Organic Chemistry

615.1   IT   ISSN 0010-9207
CORRIERE DEL FARMACISTA. 1945. m. L.2500.($4.) Armando Giordano, Ed. & Pub., Piazza d'Aosta 37, 80047 San Giuseppe Vesuviano, Naples, Italy. adv.; abstr. Indexed: Chem.Abstr., Ind.Med.

615 658.8   UK
COUGH AND COLD REMEDIES: THE INTERNATIONAL MARKET. (Subseries of: Market Direction reports) a. £1595($3190) (effective 1996). Euromonitor, 60-61 Britton St., London EC1M 5NA, England. TEL 0171-251-8024. FAX 0171-608-3149. (Addr. in N. America: Euromonitor International, 122 S. Michigan Ave., Ste. 1200, Chicago, IL 60603. TEL 312-922-1115. FAX 312-922-1157) (looseleaf format) Document type: trade publication.
●Also available online. Vendor(s): Data-Star, Knight-Ridder, Inc.
Description: Analyzes the market for nonprescription cough and cold remedies for France, Germany, Italy, Spain, the U.K., the U.S., and Japan.

615.19   US   ISSN 0743-4863
RS201.V43   CODEN: CRTSEO
CRITICAL REVIEWS IN THERAPEUTIC DRUG CARRIER SYSTEMS. 1985. q. $84 to individuals; institutions $295 (effective 1996). Begell House Inc., 79 Madison Ave., Ste. 1201, New York, NY 10016-7892. TEL 212-725-1999. FAX 212-213-8368. E-mail: 74353.2052@compuserve.com. Ed. Stephen D. Bruck. Indexed: Excerp.Med. (1995-). Document type: academic/scholarly publication.
—BLDSC (3487.483700); CASDDS; Faxon; Genuine Article; SWETS. CCC.
Description: Publishes comprehensive, multidisciplinary critical review papers encompassing the basic biological, medical, pharmaceutical, and physical sciences with emphasis on clinical applications.

CRITICAL REVIEWS IN TOXICOLOGY. see ENVIRONMENTAL STUDIES — Toxicology And Environmental Safety

615.1   IT   ISSN 0011-1783
CODEN: CRFMAY
CRONACHE FARMACEUTICHE. (Text in English, French and Italian) 1958. bi-m. L.60000($60) (effective 1993). Societa Italiana di Scienze Farmaceutiche, Via Giorgio Jan. 18, 20129 Milan, Italy. TEL 39-2-29513303. FAX 39-2-29520179. Ed. Piero Sensi. adv.: B&W page L.420000; 210 x 280. bk.rev.; abstr.; bibl.; illus.; index. circ. 1,300. Indexed: Biol.Abstr., Biotech.Abstr., Chem.Abstr., Excerp.Med., I.P.A.
—CASDDS.

CUBA. CENTRO DE INFORMACION Y DOCUMENTACION AGROPECUARIO. BOLETIN DE RESENAS. SERIE: PLANTAS MEDICINALES. see BIOLOGY — Botany

CURRENT CARDIOVASCULAR DRUGS (YEAR). see MEDICAL SCIENCES — Cardiovascular Diseases

615.9   JA   ISSN 0911-2847
CURRENT CONCEPTS IN HOSPITAL PHARMACY/BYOIN YAKKYOKU. (Text in Japanese) 1985. 3/yr. Standard McIntyre - Sutandado Makkintaiya, 3-7 Irifune 2-chome, Chuo-ku, Tokyo 104, Japan.

CURRENT ISSUES IN TOXICOLOGY. see ENVIRONMENTAL STUDIES — Toxicology And Environmental Safety

615   NE   ISSN 1381-6128
▼**CURRENT PHARMACEUTICAL DESIGN.** (Text in English) 1995. 6/yr. fl.278 to individuals (outside Europe $139); institutions fl.693 (outside Europe $365) (effective 1996). Bentham Science Publishers BV, P.O. Box 75676, 1118 ZS Schipol, Netherlands. TEL 31-20-6720924. FAX 31-20-6720924. Ed.Bd. adv. contact: T. Lucas. Document type: academic/scholarly publication.
Description: Publishes timely in-depth reviews in therapeutic areas of drug design, including CNS agents, anti-cancer agents, anti-inflammatory and anti-allergy agents, cardiovascular, hematological, endocrine, metabolic, and anti-infection agents.
Refereed Serial

615.1   AT   ISSN 0311-905X
CURRENT THERAPEUTICS; journal of clinical pharmacology and therapeutics. 1960. m. Aus.$110 (effective 1995). Adis International Pty. Ltd, 9 Rodborough Rd., Frenchs Forest, N.S.W. 2089, Australia. TEL 61-2-9759100. FAX 61-2-9759199. Ed. Frances Westwick. adv.; bk.rev.; abstr.; charts. circ. 22,000. Indexed: Excerp.Med., Rev.Plant Path. Document type: academic/scholarly publication.
—BLDSC (3504.605000); Faxon; Genuine Article; SWETS; UnCover. CCC.
Formerly: New Ethicals (ISSN 0028-5064)

615   UK
CURRENT TOPICS IN DRUG RESEARCH. irreg. Graffham Press Ltd., 6 York Pl., Edinburgh EH1 3EP, Scotland. TEL 0131-556-7887. FAX 0131-556-1129. (back issues avail.) Document type: monographic series, academic/scholarly publication.

CURRENT TOPICS IN ENVIRONMENTAL AND TOXICOLOGICAL CHEMISTRY. see ENVIRONMENTAL STUDIES — Toxicology And Environmental Safety

615.9 616.2   NE   ISSN 0890-1449
RM388   CODEN: CTPTEL
CURRENT TOPICS IN PULMONARY PHARMACOLOGY AND TOXICOLOGY. (Text in English) 1986. irreg., vol.3, 1987. price varies. Elsevier Science B.V., Books Division, P.O. Box 211, 1000 AE Amsterdam, Netherlands. TEL 31-20-4853911. FAX 31-20-4853705. TELEX 18582 ESPA NL. E-mail: nlinfo-f@elsevier.nl; usinfo-f@elsevier.com; forinfo-kjf04035@niftyserve.or.jp; Site addr.: http://www.elsevier.nl/. (Subscr. in U.S. and Canada to: Elsevier Science Inc., Box 882, Madison Sq. Sta., New York, NY 10159. TEL 212-989-5800) Ed. M.A. Hollinger. (back issues avail.) Document type: monographic series.
—CASDDS.
Refereed Serial

CURRENTS IN TOXICOLOGY AND THERAPY. see MEDICAL SCIENCES

615.1   US
D C A T DIGEST. 1960. 9/yr. membership only. Drug, Chemical and Allied Trades Association, Two Roosevelt Ave., 3rd Fl., Syosset, NY 11791. TEL 516-496-3317. FAX 516-496-2231. Ed. Art Cavaler; Pub. Richard J. Lerman. stat. circ. 2,000. Document type: bulletin.
Formerly: D C A T Bulletin (ISSN 0300-7340)

615   JA   ISSN 0913-5006
CODEN: DDSYEI
D D S: DRUG DELIVERY SYSTEM. (Text in Japanese; summaries in English) 1986. bi-m. 1500 Yen per no. Nihon D D S Gakkai - Japan Society of Drug Delivery System, Seimarianna Daigaku Nanbyo Chiryo Kenkyu Senta, 16-1, Sugao 2-chome, Miyamae-ku, Kawasaki-shi, Kanagawa-ken 216.
—BLDSC (3629.104800); CASDDS.

615   JA   ISSN 0917-3099
D I NYUSU/DRUG INFORMATION NEWS. (Text in Japanese) 1989. bi-m. Komaki Shimin Byoin Iyakuhin Johoshitsu - Komaki City Hospital, Drug Information Room, 1-20, Jobushi, Komaki-shi, Aichi-ken 485, Japan.

PHARMACY AND PHARMACOLOGY

615.1   NE   ISSN 0165-6112
D W: DROGISTEN WEEKBLAD; onafhankelijk vakblad voor drogisterij, parfumerie, reformzaak. 1968. w. (Thu.) fl.96. Van der Weij Periodieken B.V., Postbus 285, 1200 AG Hilversum, Netherlands. TEL 31-35-249741. FAX 31-35-210951. adv.: B&W page fl.4350, color page fl.6450; 280 x 394. bk.rev.; film rev.; abstr.; charts; illus.; mkt.; pat.; stat. circ. 6,500. (tabloid format) **Indexed:** Key to Econ.Sci. **Document type:** trade publication.
    Former titles: Drogisten Weekblad; (until 1975): Drogistenblad de Vergulde Gaper (ISSN 0012-6349)

615.9   JA   ISSN 0286-8016
    CODEN: DYDNDM
DAIICHI YAKKA DAIGAKU KENKYU NENPO/DAIICHI COLLEGE OF PHARMACEUTICAL SCIENCES. ANNUAL REPORT. (Text in English, Japanese) 1971. a. Daiichi Yakka Daigaku - Daiichi College of Pharmaceutical Sciences, 22-1 Tamagawacho, Minami-ku, Fukuoka-shi, Fukuoka-ken 815, Japan. **Indexed:** Chem.Abstr., Jap.Per.Ind.
—CASDDS.

615.1   DK   ISSN 0105-7480
DANSKE LAEGEMIDDELSTANDARDER. 1978. a. DKK 188. (Sundhedsstyrelsen, Farmaceutiske Laboratoriet) Nyt Nordisk Forlag Arnold Busck A-S, Koebmagergade 49, DK-1150 Copenhagen K, Denmark. TEL 45-33-11-11-03. FAX 45-33-93-44-90. **Document type:** government publication.

DE TEXTOS. see SOCIOLOGY

615   FR
DELTA SEMP. (In 2 vols.) 1990. q. (vol.2 s-a.). 1020 F. (effective 1995). Societe d'Editions Medico-Pharmaceutiques (SEMP), 26 rue le Brun, 75013 Paris, France. TEL 1-43-37-83-50. FAX 1-43-31-94-11. circ. 800.

DEMENTIA. see MEDICAL SCIENCES — Psychiatry And Neurology

615 354.489   DK   ISSN 0109-9930
DENMARK. SUNDHEDSSTYRELSEN. LAEGEMIDDELAFDELINGEN. AARSBERETNING.* 1981. a. free. (Sundhedsstyrelsen, Laegemiddelafdelingen) Sundhedsstyrelsen, Amaliegade 13, DK-1012 Copenhagen K, Denmark. (Subscr. to: Statens Informationstjeneste, P.O. Box 1103, DK-1009 Copenhagen K, Denmark)

615   JA   ISSN 0916-1147
DENSHO TO IGAKU/TRADITION AND MEDICINE. (Text in Japanese) 1988. s-a. 800 Yen. Tokyo Yakka Daigaku, Doitsugo Kenkyushitsu - Tokyo College of Pharmacy, Department of German Language, 1432-1, Horinouchi, Hachioji-shi, Tokyo 192-03, Japan. TEL 0426-76-5842. FAX 0426-76-5825. Ed. Nobuo Shida. adv. contact: Noriko Miyamoto. bk.rev. **Document type:** academic/scholarly publication.
    Description: Focuses on holistic traditional medicine.

615.1   GW   ISSN 0011-9849
DER DEUTSCHE APOTHEKER; die aktuelle Zeitschrift fuer pharmazeutische Berufe. 1949. m. DM.80. Verlag "Der Deutsche Apotheker", Hans-Thoma-Str. 1, 61440 Oberursel, Germany. TEL 06171-55012. FAX 06171-55142. Ed. Siegfried Beyer-Enke. adv.; bk.rev.; bibl.; charts; illus.; index. circ. 17,000. Indexed: Biol.Abstr., Chem.Abstr., I.P.A. **Document type:** trade publication.
●Also available online.
—CCC.

615.1   GW   ISSN 0011-9857
    CODEN: DAZEA2
DEUTSCHE APOTHEKER ZEITUNG; vereinigt mit Sueddeutsche Apotheker-Zeitung. Unabhaengige pharmazeutische Zeitschrift fuer Wissenschaft und Praxis. 1861. w. DM.175.20 (students DM.109.80). Deutscher Apotheker Verlag, Postfach 101061, 70009 Stuttgart, Germany. TEL 0711-2582-0. FAX 0711-2582290. Ed.Bd. adv.; bk.rev.; charts; illus.; index. circ. 32,500. (also avail. in microfilm from PMC) **Indexed:** Anal.Abstr., Biol.Abstr., Biotech.Abstr., Chem.Abstr., Excerp.Med., I.P.A. **Document type:** trade publication.
●Also available online.
—BLDSC (3563.000000); CASDDS; SWETS. **CCC.**

615.19   GW   ISSN 0174-0164
DEUTSCHE DROGISTEN ZEITUNG. Short title: D D Z. 1945. m. DM.60. E S Fachschriften Verlag GmbH, Paul-Gerhardt-Allee 24, 81245 Munich, Germany. TEL 089-8347077. FAX 089-8341962. circ. 13,000. **Document type:** trade publication.

615.9   GW   ISSN 0934-4640
DEUTSCHE GESELLSCHAFT FUER PHARMAKOLOGIE UND TOXIKOLOGIE. MITTEILUNGEN. 1988. irreg. DM.24 (free to members). (Deutsche Gesellschaft fuer Pharmakologie und Toxikologie) Wissenschaftliche Verlagsgesellschaft mbH, Postfach 101061, 70009 Stuttgart, Germany. TEL 0711-2582-0. FAX 0711-2582290. Ed. W. Braun. **Document type:** academic/scholarly publication.

615   NE   ISSN 0167-6431
    CODEN: DEPHDQ
DEVELOPMENTS IN PHARMACOLOGY. (Text in English) 1980. irreg. price varies. (Commission of the European Communities) Kluwer Academic Publishers, Postbus 17, 3300 AA Dordrecht, Netherlands. TEL 31-78-392392. FAX 31-78-392254. TELEX 29245 KAPG NL. (Dist. by: Kluwer Academic Publishers Group, P.O. Box 322, 3300 AH Dordrecht, Netherlands. TEL 31-78-392392. FAX 31-78-546474; N. America dist. addr.: Box 358, Accord Sta., Hingham, MA 02018-0358. TEL 617-871-6600. FAX 617-871-6528) **Document type:** monographic series.
—CASDDS.
    Refereed Serial

DI CYAN BULLETIN. see MEDICAL SCIENCES — Psychiatry And Neurology

615.19 610   US   ISSN 1054-9609
DIAGNOSTICS INTELLIGENCE. 1990. 12/yr. $414 (foreign $434). C T B International Publishing Inc., Box 218, Maplewood, NJ 07040-0218. TEL 201-379-7749. FAX 201-379-1158. Ed. Christopher Brogna; Pub. Oykwe Brogna. **Document type:** newsletter.
—CCC.
    Description: For executives in the medical in vitro diagnostics business. Covers the latest in research, new markets, new product launches, regulatory affairs, litigation, business opportunities, finance and patents.

615   MX
DICCIONARIO DE ESPECIALIDADES FARMACEUTICAS. 1944. a. $70 (effective Dec. 1991). Ediciones P L M, S.A. de C.V., San Bernardino 17, Col. del Valle, 03100 Mexico, D.F., Mexico. TEL 687-1766. FAX 536-5027. TELEX 1772912 EPLMME. Ed. Dr. Rogelio Silis. adv. circ. 60,000.

615   BL
DICIONARIO DE ESPECIALIDADES FARMACEUTICAS. 1971. a. $70. Editora de Publicacoes Cientificas Ltda., Rua Major Suckow, 30 a 36, 20911 Rio de Janeiro RJ, Brazil. TEL 021-201-3722. FAX 021-261-3749. Ed. Jose Maria de Sousa e Melo. adv. circ. 60,000.

615   US   ISSN 1073-4414
DICKINSON'S F D A REVIEW. (U.S. Food and Drug Administration); human & animal drugs - biologics - medical devices. m. $685 in N. America; elsewhere $745 (effective 1996). Ferdic Inc., Box 367, Las Cruces, NM 88004-0367. TEL 505-527-8634. FAX 505-527-8858. Ed. James G. Dickinson. charts; bibl. (back issues avail.) **Document type:** newsletter.
    Formed by the merger of (1985-1994): Dickinson's F D A (ISSN 0885-159X); (1992-1994): Dickinson's F D A Inspection (ISSN 1063-2433)
    Description: Reviews F.D.A. enforcement of regulations of drugs, biologics, and medical devices.

615   FR   ISSN 0419-1153
DICTIONNAIRE VIDAL. 1914. a. (plus updates 3/yr.). 515 F. (foreign 670 F.). O.V.P. - Editions du Vidal, 11 rue Quentin Bauchart, 75008 Paris, France. TEL 47-23-90-91. FAX 47-20-72-89. TELEX OVP 603 506 F. circ. 185,000.
●Also available on CD-ROM.
    Supersedes: Dictionnaire des Specialites Pharmaceutiques.
    Description: Directory to ethical pharmaceuticals, diagnostic products and OTC products.

615 658.8   UK
DIGESTIVE REMEDIES: THE INTERNATIONAL MARKET. (Subseries of: Market Direction reports) a. £1595($3190) (effective 1996). Euromonitor, 60-61 Britton St., London EC1M 5NA, England. TEL 0171-251-8024. FAX 0171-608-3149. (Addr. in N. America: Euromonitor International, 122 S. Michigan Ave., Ste. 1200, Chicago, IL 60603. TEL 312-922-1115. FAX 312-922-1157) (looseleaf format) **Document type:** trade publication.
●Also available online. Vendor(s): Data-Star, Knight-Ridder, Inc.
    Description: Analyzes the market for nonprescription digestive remedies in France, Germany, Italy, Spain, the U.K., the U.S., and Japan.

DIRECTORY OF ADVERTISING AGENCIES. see ADVERTISING AND PUBLIC RELATIONS

DIRECTORY OF HIGH VOLUME INDEPENDENT DRUG STORES (YEAR). see BUSINESS AND ECONOMICS — Trade And Industrial Directories

615   BL   ISSN 0070-6612
DIRETORIO BRASILEIRO DA INDUSTRIA FARMACEUTICA. 1968. biennial. free. Associacao Brasileira da Industria Farmaceutica, Rua Beira Rio, 57 7o, 04548-050 Sao Paulo SP, Brazil. TEL 011-820-3775. TELEX 011-822-6628. Ed. Jose Eduardo Bandeira de Mello. adv. **Document type:** directory.

615.19   NE   ISSN 0168-7921
    CODEN: DIPHDK
DISCOVERIES IN PHARMACOLOGY. (Text in English) 1983. irreg., vol.3, 1986. price varies. Elsevier Science B.V., Books Division, P.O. Box 211, 1000 AE Amsterdam, Netherlands. TEL 31-20-4853911. FAX 31-20-4853705. TELEX 18582 ESPA NL. E-mail: nlinfo-f@elsevier.nl; usinfo-f@elsevier.com; forinfo-kyf04035@niftyserve.or.jp; Site addr.: http://www.elsevier.nl/. (Subscr. in U.S. and Canada to: Elsevier Science Inc., Box 882, Madison Sq. Sta., New York, NY 10159. TEL 212-989-5800) Eds. M.J. Parnham, J. Bruinvels. (back issues avail.) **Document type:** monographic series.
—CASDDS. **CCC.**
    Refereed Serial

DISPENSING DOCTORS' ASSOCIATION. JOURNAL. see MEDICAL SCIENCES

615   UK
DIURETIC AGENTS. irreg. Marius Press, P.O. Box 15, Carnforth LA6 1HW, England. Eds. S. Johnson, F.N. Johnson. **Document type:** monographic series.

DOJIN NYUSU/DOJIN NEWS. see CHEMISTRY — Analytical Chemistry

DOKUMENTATION ARBEITSSCHUTZ UNFALLVERHUETUNG ARBEITSMEDIZIN. see OCCUPATIONAL HEALTH AND SAFETY

DONJINDO NEWSLETTER. see CHEMISTRY — Analytical Chemistry

615   JA   ISSN 0389-746X
DORAGGU MAGAJIN/DRUG MAGAZINE. (Text in Japanese) 1958. m. 3-15, Nihonbbashi Honcho 2-chome, Chuo-ku, Tokyo 103, Japan.

DR. MED. MABUSE. see MEDICAL SCIENCES

615   SZ
DROGA INFORMATIONS.* m. Gebr. Aeschbacher AG, CH-3076 Worb, Switzerland. Ed. T. Waegli. circ. 1,100.

615.4   GW   ISSN 0945-4500
DROGERIE & PARFUEMERIE. 1930. m. DM.65. P I B - Verlag, Postfach 1427, 82004 Unterhaching, Germany. TEL 089-6127021. FAX 089-6127112. adv. circ. 11,500.
    Formerly (1954-1993): Deutsche Drogerie (ISSN 0722-9518); Which incorporates (in 1991): D D F - Journal (ISSN 0720-633X); Former titles (until 1981): D D F. Drogeriewaren - Fachenmagazin (ISSN 0720-6348); (1965-1977): D D F - Das Drogisten Fachblatt (ISSN 0011-4804)

DROGFRITT LIV; folkets vael. see DRUG ABUSE AND ALCOHOLISM

PHARMACY AND PHARMACOLOGY

615   **SZ**
DROGISTENSTERN. 10./yr. Laengfeldweg 119, CH-2501 Biel, Switzerland. TEL 032-425055. FAX 032-425058. TELEX 34252. circ. 330,000.

615   **SP**
DROGUERIA ACTUALIDAD. 6/yr. Via Agusta 59, 8o 812, 08006 Barcelona, Spain. TEL 3-2378865. FAX 3-415-86-88. Ed. S. Beltran Nunez. circ. 15,000.

615   **SW**   **ISSN 0348-9361**
DROPPJOURNALEN; tidskrift om nutrition och vaetsketerapi. 1979-1981; resumed 1984. q. Kabi Pharmacia, S-112 87 Stockholm, Sweden.

615   **US**   **ISSN 0148-0545**
RA1190   **CODEN: DCTODJ**
DRUG AND CHEMICAL TOXICOLOGY; an international journal for rapid communication. 1978. 4/yr. $450. Marcel Dekker Journals, 270 Madison Ave., New York, NY 10016. TEL 212-696-9000. FAX 212-685-4540. TELEX 421419. (Subscr. to: Box 5017, Monticello, NY 12701) Ed. Gerald Fisher. (also avail. in microform from RPI) **Indexed:** Biol.Abstr., Biotech.Abstr., Chem.Abstr., Curr.Adv.Ecol.Sci., Curr.Cont., Environ.Abstr., Environ.Per.Bibl. (1981-), Excerp.Med., I.P.A., Ind.Med., Ind.Sci.Rev., Ind.Vet., Pig News & Info., Pollut.Abstr., Rev.Med.& Vet.Mycol., Sci.Cit.Ind., Vet.Bull., Weed Abstr. **Document type:** academic/scholarly publication.
●Also available online.
—BLDSC (3627.985000); ADONIS; CASDDS; Faxon; Genuine Article; SWETS; UMI; UnCover. **CCC.**
Refereed Serial

615.9   **US**
DRUG AND CHEMICAL TOXICOLOGY SERIES. 1984. irreg., vol.9, 1993. price varies. Marcel Dekker, Inc., 270 Madison Ave., New York, NY 10016. TEL 212-696-9000. FAX 212-685-4540. TELEX 421419. Eds. F.J. DiCarlo, F.W. Oehme.
Refereed Serial

DRUG AND COSMETIC CATALOG. see **BEAUTY CULTURE — Perfumes And Cosmetics**

DRUG AND COSMETIC INDUSTRY. see **BEAUTY CULTURE — Perfumes And Cosmetics**

615.5   **UK**   **ISSN 0012-6543**
DRUG AND THERAPEUTICS BULLETIN. 1963. m. £41. (Consumers' Association) Which? Ltd., 2 Marylebone Rd., London NW1 4DF, England. TEL 0171-830-6171. FAX 0171-830-6220. (Subscr. to: Consumers' Association, Castlemead, Gascoyne Way, Herts. SG14 1LH, England. TEL 01992-587773) Ed. Dr. J.Collier. cum.index. circ. 99,000. (reprint service avail. from UMI) **Indexed:** Dent.Ind., Excerp.Med., FAMLI, I.P.A., Ind.Med. **Document type:** bulletin.
—BLDSC (3629.100000).
Description: Provides impartial and expert information for doctors and pharmacists on the clinical use of drugs.

615   **JA**   **ISSN 0289-9922**
DRUG APPROVAL AND LICENSING PROCEDURES IN JAPAN. Japanese edition: Iyakuhin Seizo Shishin (ISSN 0911-9329) (Text in English) 1973. a. 56000 Yen. (Society of Japanese Pharmacopoeia) Yakugyo Jiho Co., Ltd., 2-36 Kanda Jimbo-cho, Chiyoda-ku, Tokyo 101, Japan.
Description: Explains Japanese pharmaceutical approval procedures.

615   **SP**
DRUG DATA REPORT. (Text in English) 1979. m. $950 (effective 1996). J.R. Prous, S.A. International Publishers, Apdo. de Correos 540, 08080 Barcelona, Spain. TEL 343-459-2220. FAX 343-458-1535. adv. contact: P. Blancafort. bibl.; charts; index, cum.index: 1985-1994. (back issues avail.)
●Also available online. Vendor(s): Knight-Ridder, Inc. Also available on CD-ROM.
—BLDSC (1085.017500). **CCC.**
Formerly: Annual Drug Data Report (ISSN 0379-4121)
Description: Contains essential drug information in a condensed monograph form. Publishes about 10,000 new compounds each year.

615.19   **US**   **ISSN 1071-7544**
RS199.5   **CODEN: DDELEB**
DRUG DELIVERY; journal of delivery and targeting of therapeutic agents. 1992. q. $144 (foreign $164). Academic Press, Inc., Journal Division, 525 B St., Ste. 1900, San Diego, CA 92101-4495. TEL 619-230-1840. FAX 619-699-6800. (Subscr. to: Box 620000, Orlando, FL 32891-8340. TEL 800-543-9534) Ed. Alfred Stracher. index. (back issues avail.) **Indexed:** Chem.Abstr., Excerp.Med. (1995-). **Document type:** academic/scholarly publication.
—BLDSC (3629.104600); CASDDS; SWETS. **CCC.**
Formerly (until 1993): Drug Targeting and Delivery (ISSN 1058-241X)
Description: Focuses on drug delivery technology at the theoretical as well as practical level. Includes basic research, development, and application principles on the molecular, cellular, and higher levels of targeting sites, as well as physical, chemical and immunokinetic modes of delivery.
Refereed Serial

615.19   **US**   **ISSN 1055-9612**
RS420   **CODEN: DDDIEV**
DRUG DESIGN AND DISCOVERY. 1986. 4/yr. (in 1 vol., 4 nos./vol.). 187 ECU (effective 1996). Harwood Academic Publishers, c/o International Publishers Distributor, 820 Town Center Dr., Langhorne, PA 19047. TEL 215-750-2642. FAX 215-750-6343. (Subscr. to: International Publishers Distributor, PO Box 90, Reading, Berkshire, RG1 8JL, England. TEL 44-173-456-8316. FAX 0734-568211) Eds. G.L. Olson, J. Saunders. (also avail. in microform) **Indexed:** Excerp.Med.
—BLDSC (3629.115420); CASDDS; Faxon; SWETS; UnCover. **CCC.**
Formerly: Drug Design and Delivery (ISSN 0884-2884)
Refereed Serial

615.19   **GW**   **ISSN 0343-4842**
CODEN: DDEVD6
DRUG DEVELOPMENT AND EVOLUTION. 1977. irreg. price varies. Gustav Fischer Verlag, Wollgrasweg 49, 70599 Stuttgart, Germany. TEL 0711-458030. FAX 0711-4580334. TELEX 7111-488-FIBUCH. (Subscr. to: Postfach 720143, 70577 Stuttgart, Germany; U.S. address: VCH Publishers Inc., 303 N.W. 12th Ave., Deerfield Beach, FL 33442-1788) illus. **Indexed:** Chem.Abstr. **Document type:** academic/scholarly publication.
—CASDDS; UMI. **CCC.**

615   **US**   **ISSN 0363-9045**
RS402   **CODEN: DDIPD8**
DRUG DEVELOPMENT AND INDUSTRIAL PHARMACY. 1974. 20/yr. $1295. Marcel Dekker Journals, 270 Madison Ave., New York, NY 10016. TEL 212-696-9000. FAX 212-685-4540. TELEX 421419. (Subscr. to: Box 5017, Monticello, NY 12701) Ed. Christopher T. Rhodes. (also avail. in microform from RPI) **Indexed:** Biol.Abstr., Biotech.Abstr., Chem.Abstr., Curr.Adv.Ecol.Sci., Curr.Cont., Excerp.Med., Helminthol.Abstr., I.P.A., Ind.Sci.Rev., Sci.Cit.Ind. **Document type:** academic/scholarly publication.
●Also available online.
—BLDSC (3629.116000); ADONIS; CASDDS; Faxon; Genuine Article; SWETS; UMI; UnCover. **CCC.**
Formerly: Drug Development Communications (ISSN 0095-5183)
Refereed Serial

615.19   **US**   **ISSN 0272-4391**
CODEN: DDREDK
DRUG DEVELOPMENT RESEARCH. 1981. m. $1884 (foreign $207) (effective 1996). John Wiley & Sons, Inc., Journals, 605 Third Ave., New York, NY 10158. TEL 212-850-6645. FAX 212-850-6021. TELEX 12-7063. E-mail: SUBINFO@JWILEY.COM. (Subscr. outside the Americas to: John Wiley & Sons Ltd., Baffins Ln., Chichester, W. Sussex PO19 1UD, England. TEL 44-1243-779777. FAX 44-1243-776128) Eds. Harbans Lal, Stuart Fielding. adv.; bibl.; charts; illus.; index. (also avail. in microform from UMI; back issues avail.) **Indexed:** Biol.Abstr., Biotech.Abstr., Chem.Abstr., Curr.Adv.Cell & Devel.Biol., Curr.Adv.Ecol.Sci., Curr.Cont., Excerp.Med., Ind.Sci.Rev., Rev.Med.& Vet.Mycol., Sci.Cit.Ind. **Document type:** academic/scholarly publication.
—BLDSC (3629.119000); ADONIS; CASDDS; Faxon; Genuine Article; SWETS; UnCover. **CCC.**
Description: Refelects original research reports and comprehensive reviews about the systematic studies in pharmacology and toxicology, as related to the development of safe and efficacious drugs.
Refereed Serial

615.1 660   **UK**   **ISSN 1359-6446**
▼**DRUG DISCOVERY TODAY.** Announced for publication in 1996. m. £480 to institutions; $764 to institutions (effective 1996). Elsevier Science Ltd., Oxford Fulfilment Centre, P.O. Box 800, Kidlington, Oxford OX5 1DX, England. TEL 44-1865-843000. FAX 44-1865-843010. (Subscr. in U.S. and Canada to: Elsevier Science, 660 White Plains Rd., Tarrytown, NY 10591-5153. TEL 914-524-9200. FAX 914-333-2444) adv. **Document type:** academic/scholarly publication, trade publication.
Refereed Serial

615.5   **SW**   **ISSN 0282-5783**
DRUG EFFECTS IN CLINICAL CHEMISTRY. 1977. triennial. SEK 300 (effective 1992). Apoteksbolaget AB - National Corporation of Swedish Pharmacies, 105 14 Stockholm, Sweden.
—BLDSC (3629.122000).
Former titles (until 1992): Drug Interference and Drug Effects in Clinical Chemistry; (until 1986): Drug Interference and Effects in Clinical Chemistry; (until 1984): Drug Effects in Clinical Chemistry; (until 1978): Laekemedels Paaverkan paa Laboratorieundersoekningar.

615.1   **US**   **ISSN 0277-9714**
RM300
DRUG FACTS AND COMPARISONS. 1947. m. (with a. edition). $200 (a. edition $110). Facts and Comparisons, 111 W. Port Plaza, Ste. 400, St. Louis, MO 63146-3098. TEL 800-223-0554. FAX 314-878-5563. Ed. Bernie R. Olin. index. (looseleaf format)
●Also available online.
—BLDSC (3629.126000).
Formerly: Facts and Comparisons (ISSN 0014-6617)
Description: Reference guide listing over 16,000 drugs, including Rx and OTC, arranged by therapeutic class. Facilitates comparisons of costs, brands, and drugs.

615 614.4   **US**   **ISSN 1061-2335**
DRUG G M P REPORT. (Good Manufacturing Practices) 1992. m. $427. Washington Business Information, Inc., c/o Karen Harrington, 1117 N. 19th St., Arlington, VA 22209. TEL 703-247-3434. FAX 703-247-3421. Ed. Dennis Melamed. (looseleaf format) **Document type:** newsletter.
—**CCC.**
Description: Reports on good manufacturing practices as they relate to the pharmaceutical industry.

615.06   **NE**   **ISSN 0921-2582**
CODEN: DRDIER
DRUG INDUCED DISORDERS. 1985. irreg., vol.5, 1992. price varies. Elsevier Science B.V., Books Division, P.O. Box 211, 1000 AE Amsterdam, Netherlands. TEL 31-20-4853911. FAX 31-20-4853705. TELEX 18582 ESPA NL. E-mail: nlinfo-f@elsevier.nl; usinfo-f@elsevier.com; forinfo-kyf04035@niftyserve.or.jp; Site addr.: http://www.elsevier.nl/. (Subscr. in U.S. and Canada to: Elsevier Science Inc., Box 882, Madison Sq. Sta., New York, NY 10159. TEL 212-989-5800) (back issues avail.) **Document type:** monographic series.
—BLDSC (3629.141000); CASDDS.
Refereed Serial

PHARMACY AND PHARMACOLOGY

615.1 US ISSN 0092-8615
RM1 CODEN: DGIJB9
DRUG INFORMATION JOURNAL. 1966. q. $225 (academic $65) (effective 1993). Drug Information Association, Box 3113, Maple Glen, PA 19002. TEL 215-628-2288. FAX 215-641-1229. Ed. Thomas Teal. adv.; index. circ. 12,500. (also avail. in microfilm from UMI; back issues avail.) **Indexed:** Biol.Abstr., Chem.Abstr., Curr.Adv.Ecol.Sci., Excerp.Med., I.P.A., LISA. **Document type:** academic/scholarly publication.
●Also available online.
—BLDSC (3629.160000); CASDDS; EMDOCS; Faxon; SWETS; UMI; UnCover. **CCC.**
Formerly: Drug Information Bulletin (ISSN 0012-656X)
Refereed Serial

615.7 US
DRUG INTERACTION FACTS. (Includes 3 quarterly updates) q. $95 (a. bound ed. $49.95) (effective 1994). Facts and Comparisons, 111 W. Port Plaza, Ste. 400, St. Louis, MO 63146-3098. TEL 800-223-0554. FAX 314-878-5563. Ed. David S. Tatro. (also avail. in diskette format) **Description:** Reference for drug and food interactions of clinical significance, suspected but unsubstantiated interactions, with concise synopsis of onset, severity and documentation.

615.7 US
DRUG INTERACTIONS AND UPDATES. 1981. base vol. (plus q. updates). $87.50 (foreign $100). Applied Therapeutics, Inc., Box 5077, Vancouver, WA 98668. TEL 360-253-7123. FAX 360-253-8475. Eds. Philip D. Hansten, John R. Horn. adv. contact: Steven B. Naught. (looseleaf format; back issues avail.) **Document type:** academic/scholarly publication, newsletter.
—BLDSC (3629.241000).
Former titles: Drug Interactions (Vancouver); (until vol.8, no.11, 1989): Drug Interactions Newsletter (ISSN 0271-8707); Incorporates (in 1989): Drug Interactions (Philadelphia).
Description: Concise and authoritative guide to drug-drug interactions. Includes a comprehensive index.

615 US ISSN 0090-9556
RM301 CODEN: DMDSAI
DRUG METABOLISM AND DISPOSITION. 1973. m. $85 to individuals; institutions $140 (effective 1995). (American Society for Pharmacology and Experimental Therapeutics, Inc.) Williams & Wilkins, 428 E. Preston St., Baltimore, MD 21202. TEL 410-528-4000; 800-638-6423. FAX 410-528-4132. Ed. Dr. Raymond F. Novak. adv.; bk.rev.; illus.; index. circ. 1,212. (also avail. in microfilm from WWS; back issues avail.) **Indexed:** Biol.Abstr., Biotech.Abstr., Chem.Abstr., Curr.Adv.Ecol.Sci., Curr.Cont., Dairy Sci.Abstr., Excerp.Med., Helminthol.Abstr., Ind.Med., Ind.Sci.Rev., Ind.Vet., INIS Atomind., Mass Spectr.Bull., Nutr.Abstr., Protozool.Abstr., Rev.Med.& Vet.Mycol., Sci.Cit.Ind., Vet.Bull. **Document type:** academic/scholarly publication.
—BLDSC (3629.325000); CASDDS; EMDOCS; Faxon; Genuine Article; SWETS; UnCover. **CCC.**
Description: Covers metabolism of pharmacological agents or drugs and environmental chemicals, reactants and preservatives for pharmacologists, toxicologists and medical chemists.
Refereed Serial

615.19 UK ISSN 0792-5077
RM302 CODEN: DMDIEQ
DRUG METABOLISM AND DRUG INTERACTIONS. (Text in English) 1972. q. $250 (effective 1996). Freund Publishing House Ltd., Ste. 500, Chesham House, 150 Regent St., London W1R 5FA, England. (And: P.O. Box 35010, Tel Aviv, Israel. TEL 972-3-5628540. FAX 972-3-5628538) Ed. N. Kingsley. adv.; bk.rev.; index. (back issues avail.) **Indexed:** Chem.Abstr., Curr.Adv.Ecol.Sci., Excerp.Med., Ind.Med. **Document type:** academic/scholarly publication.
—BLDSC (3629.326000); CASDDS; SWETS.
Former titles (until 1988): Reviews on Drug Metabolism and Drug Interactions (ISSN 0334-2190); (until vol. 3): Reviews on Drug Interactions (ISSN 0048-7546)

615 US ISSN 0199-7912
DRUG METABOLISM NEWSLETTER. q. $4 to non-members; members $3. American Society for Pharmacology and Experimental Therapeutics, Drug Metabolism Division, 9650 Rockville Pike, Bethesda, MD 20814. **Document type:** newsletter.

DRUG METABOLISM REVIEWS. see *MEDICAL SCIENCES*

615.1 II ISSN 0026-8194
DRUG NEWS. 1937. m. Rs.25. India Publications Co., Denabank House, 2nd Fl., 31 Hamam St., Bombay 1, India. Ed. Eric Martin. **Indexed:** PROMT.

615.19 SP ISSN 0214-0934
CODEN: DNPEED
DRUG NEWS & PERSPECTIVES; the international drug newsmagazine. (Text in English) 1988. 10/yr. $650 (effective 1996). J.R. Prous, S.A. International Publishers, Apdo. de Correos 540, 08080 Barcelona, Spain. TEL 343-459-2220. FAX 343-458-1535. adv. contact: P. Blancafort. bk.rev.; illus.; cum.index: 1985-1994. (back issues avail.)
●Also available online. Vendor(s): Knight-Ridder, Inc. Also available on CD-ROM.
—BLDSC (3629.340000); SWETS. **CCC.**
Description: For scientists and managers in pharmaceutical research and development.

615.7 US ISSN 0731-5163
DRUG NEWSLETTER. m. $59.50. Facts and Comparisons, 111 W. Port Plaza, Ste. 400, St. Louis, MO 63146-3098. TEL 800-223-0554. FAX 314-878-5563. **Document type:** newsletter.
Description: Summarizes new findings and recent developments in drug therapy. Information on investigational drugs, OTCs, actions, reactions and interactions and more.

615 616 US ISSN 1074-2913
▼**DRUG RESISTANCE WEEKLY.** 1994. w. $995. Charles W. Henderson, Ed. & Pub., Box 5528, Atlanta, GA 31107-0528. TEL 404-377-8895. FAX 404-378-5411. TELEX 78-2661. (Subscr. to: Box 830409, Birmingham, AL 35283-0409. TEL 800-633-4931. FAX 205-995-1588) (also avail. in microform from UMI) **Document type:** newsletter.
—UMI. **CCC.**
Description: Concentrates on therapeutic drug resistance in disease treatments, including cancer, TB, AIDS, and numerous infections.

615 NZ ISSN 0114-5916
CODEN: DRSAEA
DRUG SAFETY. 1986. bi-m. $660 (effective 1996). Adis International Limited, Private Bag 65901, Mairangi Bay, Auckland 10, New Zealand. TEL 64-9-479-8100. FAX 64-9-479-8145. E-mail: pcl@topgun.adis.co.nz. (Subscr. addr. in US: Adis International Inc., Attn. Subscriptions Dept., Ste. F-10, 940 Town Center Dr., Langhorne, PA 19047. TEL 215-741-5229. FAX 215-741-5251) Ed. Kathy Fraser. **Indexed:** Curr.Cont., Excerp.Med., Ind.Med., Med.& Surg.Dermat., Sci.Cit.Ind. **Document type:** academic/scholarly publication.
—BLDSC (3629.395000); CASDDS; Faxon; Genuine Article; SWETS; UnCover. **CCC.**
Former titles (until 1990): Medical Toxicology and Adverse Drug Experience (ISSN 0113-5244); (until 1987): Medical Toxicology (ISSN 0112-5966)
Description: Provides evaluations of adverse drug experience. Articles are designed to assist in the correct, safe utilisation of today's drugs.

615 UK ISSN 1355-5618
CODEN: DRSTFY
▼**DRUG STABILITY.** 1995. q. £120 (U.S. & Canada $200). Radcliffe Medical Press Ltd., 18 Marcham Rd., Abingdon, Oxon OX14 1AA, England. TEL 01235-528820. FAX 01235-528830. Eds. A. Li Wan, S. Yoshioka. adv.; bk.rev.; circ. 1,000 (paid). **Document type:** academic/scholarly publication.
—CASDDS.
Description: Research, reviews and stability profiles of drug substances and biotechnical products.

DRUG STORE MARKET GUIDE; a detailed distribution analysis of chain and wholesale drug store industry. see *BUSINESS AND ECONOMICS — Trade And Industrial Directories*

615.329 US
DRUG STORE NEWS REFERENCE FOR PHARMACY PRACTICE. 1960. a. $2. Lebhar-Friedman, Inc., 425 Park Ave., New York, NY 10022. TEL 212-756-5000. adv. circ. 56,537.

615.19 574.192 UK ISSN 0952-0317
DRUG TARGETING. s-m. (diskette m.) £115 (diskette £115; both £175) (effective 1995). S U B I S, Mansion House, 19 Kingfield Rd., Sheffield S11 9AS, England. TEL 0114-2554433. FAX 0114-2554626. E-mail: admin@sheffac.demon.co.uk. bk.rev. (also avail. in diskette format; looseleaf format; back issues avail.) **Document type:** abstracting/indexing.
—CCC.
Description: Current awareness service for researchers in clinical and life sciences.

616.86 US ISSN 0001-7094
CODEN: ORTHDZ
DRUG THERAPY. 1971. m. $70 to institutions (foreign $95) (effective 1995). Excerpta Medica, Inc., Core Publishing Division (Subsidiary of: Reed Elsevier Medical group), 105 Raider Blvd., Belle Mead, NJ 08052. TEL 908-874-8550. FAX 908-874-0707. (Subscr. to: Box 3085, Princeton, NJ 08543-3085) adv.; bk.rev. circ. 110,000. (also avail. in microform from UMI; reprint service avail. from UMI) **Indexed:** Curr.Cont., Helminthol.Abstr., I.P.A., Nutr.Abstr.
●Also available online.
—Faxon; Genuine Article; SWETS; UMI; UnCover. **CCC.**

615.1 US ISSN 0012-6616
CODEN: DGTNA7
DRUG TOPICS. 1857. s-m. $58 (foreign $104). Medical Economics Publishing Co., Inc., Five Paragon Dr., Montvale, NJ 07645. TEL 201-358-7200. FAX 201-573-1045. Ed. Val Cardinale. adv.; bk.rev.; charts; illus.; mkt.; pat.; tr.lit. circ. 95,000. (also avail. in microform from RPI,UMI) **Indexed:** ABI Inform., B.P.I., Bus.Ind., Hlth.Ind., I.P.A., PROMT, Tr.& Indus.Ind. **Document type:** trade publication.
●Also available online. Vendor(s): University Microfilms International.
—BLDSC (3629.450000); Faxon; SWETS; UMI; UnCover. **CCC.**
Description: Publishes current trends and developments affecting the pharmacy field. Includes merchandising, government affairs, management, professional and clinical news, and continuing education.

615.7 US ISSN 0884-8998
DRUG UTILIZATION REVIEW. 1985. m. $299. American Health Consultants, Inc., Six Piedmont Center, Ste. 400, Atlanta, GA 30305. TEL 404-262-7436; 800-688-2421. FAX 800-284-3291. Ed. Theresa Waldron. circ. 1,485. (back issues avail.; reprint service avail.) **Document type:** newsletter.

615.7 AT
DRUG WISE. 1977. 6/yr. Aus.$60 (foreign Aus.$75) (effective Feb. 1995). Drug Wise, P.O. Box 4051, Auburn South, Vic. 3122, Australia. FAX 61-3-3801789. Ed. Stuart Baker. bk.rev.; index. circ. 1,000. (back issues avail.) **Document type:** newsletter.
Supersedes (in Jan. 1995): Pharmabulletin.
Description: Technical articles on psychopharmacology and related topics.

615.1 NZ ISSN 0012-6667
RM1 CODEN: DRUGAY
DRUGS; international journal of current therapeutics and applied pharmacology reviews, featuring drug evaluations on drugs, review articles on drugs and drug therapy, and practical therapeutics articles. 1971. m. $970 (effective 1996). Adis International Limited, Private Bag 65901, Mairangi Bay, Auckland 10, New Zealand. TEL 64-479-8100. FAX 64-9-479-8145. E-mail: pcl@topgun.adis.co.nz. (Subscr. addr. in US: Adis International Inc., Attn. Subscription Dept., Ste. F-10, 940 Town Center Dr., Langhorne, PA 19047. TEL 215-741-5229. FAX 215-741-5251) Ed. Stephen Coleman. adv.; abstr.; bibl.; charts; illus. **Indexed:** Biol.Abstr., Biotech.Abstr., Chem.Abstr., Curr.Adv.Cancer Res., Curr.Cont., Dent.Ind., Excerp.Med., Helminthol.Abstr., I.P.A., Ind.Med., Ind.Sci.Rev., Med.& Surg.Dermat., Protozool.Abstr., Sci.Cit.Ind. **Document type:** academic/scholarly publication.
—BLDSC (3629.600000); CASDDS; Faxon; Genuine Article; SWETS; UnCover. **CCC.**
Description: Features comprehensive drug evaluations on new and established drugs, review articles on all aspects of drugs and drug therapy and practical therapeutic articles.

PHARMACY AND PHARMACOLOGY

615.58   NZ   ISSN 1170-229X
RC953.7   CODEN: DRAGE6
DRUGS & AGING. 1991. m. $425 to individuals; institutions $680 (effective 1996). Adis International Limited, Private Bag 65901, Mairangi Bay, Auckland 10, New Zealand. TEL 64-9-479-8100. FAX 64-9-479-8145. E-mail: pcl@topgun.adis.co.nz. (Subscr. addr. in US: Adis International Inc., Attn. Subscription Dept., Ste. F-10, 940 Town Center Dr., Langhorne, PA 19047. TEL 215-741-5229. FAX 215-741-5251) Ed. Claire Berkahn. **Indexed:** Curr.Cont., I.P.A., Ind.Med., Sci.Cit.Ind. **Document type:** academic/scholarly publication.
—BLDSC (3629.612000); Genuine Article; SWETS; UnCover. **CCC.**
   Description: Promotes rational, safe pharmacotherapy in older patients.

DRUGS AND BIOLOGY GUIDANCE MANUAL. see *PUBLIC HEALTH AND SAFETY*

615.9 610.73 614.8   US   ISSN 8756-5935
DRUGS AND DEVICE RECALL BULLETIN. 1985. m. $50. Rx-Data-Pac Service, 8907 Terwilliger's Tr., Cincinnati, OH 45249. TEL 513-489-0943. Ed. Dr. I.H. Goodman. (looseleaf format; back issues avail.) **Document type:** bulletin.
   Description: Current data on FDA recalls.

615.7   US   ISSN 0360-2583
                                  CODEN: DPHSDS
DRUGS AND THE PHARMACEUTICAL SCIENCES. 1975. irreg., vol.66, 1994. price varies. Marcel Dekker, Inc., 270 Madison Ave., New York, NY 10016. TEL 212-696-9000. FAX 212-685-4540. TELEX 421419 MARDEEK. Ed. J. Swarbrick.
—BLDSC (3629.630000); CASDDS. **CCC.**
   Refereed Serial

615   NZ   ISSN 1172-0360
                                  CODEN: DTHPEE
DRUGS & THERAPY PERSPECTIVES. 1993. m. $110 to individuals; institutions $245; students $60 (effective 1996). Adis International Limited, Private Bag 65901, Mairangi Bay, Auckland 10, New Zealand. TEL 64-9-479-8100. FAX 64-9-479-8145. E-mail: pcl@topgun.adis.co.nz. (Subscr. addr. in US: Adis International Inc., Attn. Subscription Dept., Ste. F-10, 940 Town Center Dr., Langhorne, PA 19047. TEL 215-741-5229. FAX 215-741-5251) Ed. Janet Kenyon. **Indexed:** Excerp.Med. (1995-).
—BLDSC (3629.665000); SWETS. **CCC.**
   Description: Provides objective reviews of new drugs, desease treatment algorithms, brief economic evaluations of new drugs.

615   US   ISSN 1051-7723
RS51
DRUGS AVAILABLE ABROAD. 1990. a. $89.95. Gale Research Inc., Box 33477, Detroit, MI 48232-9852. TEL 800-877-4253. FAX 313-961-6083. TELEX TWX 810-221-7086.
   Description: Gives comprehensive and usable guide to pharmaceuticals not yet approved by the U.S. Food and Drug Administration but currently available for sale outside the United States. Offers complete information on the uses, precautions, producers, and U.S. governmental approval status of more than 1000 drugs.

615.9   JA
DRUGS IN JAPAN; ethical drugs. 1978. a. 21000 Yen. Japan Pharmaceutical Information Center - Nihon Iyaku Joho Senta, 3rd Fl., Nagai-Kinenkan, 2-12-15 Shibuya, Shinbuyaku-ku, Tokyo 150, Japan. TEL 03-5466-1811.

615.1   GW   ISSN 0012-6683
RS1   CODEN: DRMGAS
DRUGS MADE IN GERMANY. (Text in English) 1958. 4/yr. DM.40. Editio Cantor, Postfach 1255, 88341 Aulendorf, Germany. TEL 07525-2060. FAX 07525-20680. Ed. Viktor Schramm. adv.; bk.rev.; charts; illus.; pat.; tr.lit. circ. 5,200. (reprint service avail. from IRC,ISI) **Indexed:** Biol.Abstr., Biotech.Abstr., Chem.Abstr., Excerp.Med., I.P.A., Ind.Med.
●Also available online.
—BLDSC (3629.900000); SWETS. **CCC.**

615 619   SP   ISSN 0377-8282
RM1   CODEN: DRFUD4
DRUGS OF THE FUTURE. (Text in English) 1976. m. $950 (effective 1996). J.R. Prous, S.A. International Publishers, Apdo. de Correos 540, 08080 Barcelona, Spain. TEL 343-459-2220. FAX 343-458-1535. adv. contact: P. Blancafort. index, cum.index: 1976-1994. circ. 3,000. (back issues avail.) **Indexed:** Biol.Abstr., Chem.Abstr., Excerp.Med.
●Also available on CD-ROM.
—BLDSC (3629.840000); Faxon; Genuine Article; SWETS. **CCC.**
   Description: Offers comprehensive drug monographs on new compounds, including their synthesis, pharmacological action, pharmacokinetics and metabolism, toxicity, and clinical studies.

615.1   SP   ISSN 0025-7656
                                  CODEN: MDACAP
DRUGS OF TODAY/MEDICAMENTOS DE ACTUALIDAD. (Text in English) 1965. 8/yr. $450 (effective 1996). J.R. Prous, S.A. International Publishers, Apdo. de Correos 540, 08080 Barcelona, Spain. TEL 343-459-2220. FAX 343-458-1535. adv. contact: P. Blancafort. bk.rev.; index, cum.index. circ. 3,000. (also avail. in microform from PMC) **Indexed:** Biol.Abstr., Chem.Abstr., Excerp.Med.
—BLDSC (3630.105000); CASDDS; EMDOCS; SWETS; UnCover. **CCC.**
   Description: Provides physicians and other healthcare professionals with practical, up-to-date monographs on recently approved and launched drugs.

619   SZ   ISSN 0378-6501
                                  CODEN: DECRDP
DRUGS UNDER EXPERIMENTAL AND CLINICAL RESEARCH. Short title: Drugs under Research. 1977. m. 400 SFr. Bioscience Ediprint, Inc., Rue Alexandre-Gavard 16, 1227 Carouge-Geneva, Switzerland. TEL 022-3003383. FAX 022-3002489. TELEX 423355-BIOS-CH. Ed. A. Bertelli. (also avail. in microform from UMI; reprint service avail. from UMI) **Indexed:** Biol.Abstr., Chem.Abstr., Curr.Adv.Ecol.Sci., Curr.Cont., Excerp.Med., Rev.Med.& Vet.Mycol., Sci.Cit.Ind. **Document type:** academic/scholarly publication.
—BLDSC (3629.820000); CASDDS; Faxon; Genuine Article; SWETS; UMI; UnCover. **CCC.**
   Description: Devoted to the study of compounds and molecules which may have possible therapeutic application. Covers animal and clinical pharmacology, medicinal chemistry, toxicology, teratology, mutagenesis, drug metabolism, pharmacokinetics, and clinical trials.

615   SP
EFP-OTC. 12/yr. Garcia-Plata S.A., Marques de Urquijo 10, 28008 Madrid, Spain. TEL 1-559-83-92. FAX 1-248-56-63. circ. 20,000.

615.19   KE   ISSN 0046-094X
RM1
EAST AFRICAN PHARMACEUTICAL JOURNAL. q. P.O. Box 4290, Nairobi, Kenya.

615.1   II   ISSN 0012-8872
                                  CODEN: EAPHA6
EASTERN PHARMACIST. (Text in English) 1958. m. $60. 507 Ashok Bhawan, 93, Nehru Place, New Delhi 110019, India. TEL 6433315. Ed. M.C. Bazaz. adv.; bk.rev.; charts; illus.; mkt.; pat.; tr.lit.; tr.mk.; circ. 5,000 (paid). **Indexed:** Chem.Abstr., Curr.Adv.Ecol.Sci., I.P.A. **Document type:** trade publication, newspaper.
—BLDSC (3646.800000); CASDDS.
   Refereed Serial

615.1   UA   ISSN 0301-5068
-RS1   CODEN: EJPSBZ
EGYPTIAN JOURNAL OF PHARMACEUTICAL SCIENCES. (Text in English; summaries in Arabic, English) 1960. 6/yr. $157 (effective 1996). (Pharmaceutical Society of Egypt, Research Department) National Information and Documentation Centre (NIDOC), Tahrir St., Dokki, Awqaf P.O., Cairo, Egypt. TEL 20-2-701696. Ed. A.A. Abd el-Rahman. charts; illus. circ. 1,750. (reprint service avail. from IRC) **Indexed:** Biol.Abstr., Chem.Abstr., ExtraMED, Food Sci.& Tech.Abstr., Hort.Abstr., I.P.A., Nutr.Abstr. **Document type:** academic/scholarly publication.
●Also available online.
Also available on CD-ROM.
—BLDSC (3664.410000); CASDDS; Faxon.
   Former titles (until 1972): United Arab Republic Journal of Pharmaceutical Sciences (ISSN 0301-5076); Journal of Pharmaceutical Sciences of the United Arab Republic (ISSN 0022-3557)

615.9   RU   ISSN 0869-2092
RS1   CODEN: EKFAE9
EKSPERIMENTAL'NAYA I KLINICHESKAYA FARMAKOLOGIYA/EXPERIMENTAL AND CLINICAL PHARMACOLOGY. (Text in Russian; summaries in English) 1938. bi-m. $114 (effective 1996). (Rossiiskaya Akademiya Meditsinskikh Nauk) Izdatel'stvo Meditsina, Petroverigskii pereulok 6-8, 101000 Moscow, Russia. TEL 095-294-8785. (Dist. by: Mezhdunarodnaya Kniga, B. Yakimanka 39, 117049 Moscow, Russia. TEL 7-095-2384600. FAX 7-095-2384634) (Co-sponsor: Nauchnoe Obshchestvo Farmakologov) Ed. D.A. Kharkevich. adv. contact: V.F. Strizhova. index. (tabloid format) **Indexed:** Biol.Abstr., Biotech.Abstr., Chem.Abstr., Curr.Adv.Ecol.Sci., Curr.Cont., Dent.Ind., Excerp.Med., Helminthol.Abstr., I.P.A., Ind.Med., Ind.Sci.Rev., INIS Atomind., Nutr.Abstr., Psychol.Abstr. (1943-), Sci.Cit.Ind. **Document type:** academic/scholarly publication.
—BLDSC (0397.988500); CASDDS; SWETS; UnCover. **CCC.**
   Formerly (until 1992): Farmakologiya i Toksikologiya (ISSN 0014-8318)
   Description: Publishes articles devoted to the pharmacological study of medicinal preparations and of the effects produced by various poisons on animals and man.

615   US   ISSN 1061-6098
                                 CODEN: EMPHFR
EMERGING PHARMACEUTICALS. 1992. 12/yr. $457 (foreign $477). C T B International Publishing Inc., Box 218, Maplewood, NJ 07040-0218. TEL 201-279-7749. FAX 201-7379-1158. Ed. Christopher Brogna; Pub. Oykwe Brogna. (back issues avail.) **Document type:** newsletter.
—CASDDS. **CCC.**
   Description: Focuses on the earliest stages of drug development - from discovery through preclinical trials and on small molecule drugs.

615.7   AT   ISSN 1034-8719
ENCAPSULATOR. 1977. q. Monash Medical Centre, Pharmacy Department, 246 Clayton Rd., Clayton, Vic. 3168, Australia. TEL 61-3-550-2596. FAX 61-3-550-2595. Ed. Ian Larmour. circ. 1,000. (back issues avail.) **Document type:** bulletin.
   Formerly (until 1989): Pharmacy Bulletin.
   Refereed Serial

EOS; rivista di immunologia ed immunofarmacologia. see *MEDICAL SCIENCES — Allergology And Immunology*

EPILEPSY RESEARCH. see *MEDICAL SCIENCES — Psychiatry And Neurology*

EPILEPSY RESEARCH SUPPLEMENTS. see *MEDICAL SCIENCES — Psychiatry And Neurology*

615.1   GR   ISSN 1011-6575
                                  CODEN: EKFFE
EPITHEORESE KLINIKES FARMAKOLOGIAS KAI FARMAKOKINETIKAS. International edition: Review of Clinical Pharmacology and Pharmacokinetics (ISSN 1011-6583) (Text in Greek; summaries in English) 1983. q. Pharmakon Press, 20 Daskalaki St., 115 26 Athens, Greece. TEL 30-1-7778-101. **Indexed:** Excerp.Med. **Document type:** academic/scholarly publication.
—BLDSC (3794.274000); CASDDS.

PHARMACY AND PHARMACOLOGY

615.321 635.7   IT   ISSN 1121-2896
L'ERBORISTA. 1992. bi-m. L.30000 (foreign L.70000) (effective 1995). Tecniche Nuove s.p.a., Via C. Menotti, 14, 20129 Milan, Italy. TEL 39-2-75701. FAX 39-2-7610351. adv.: B&W page L.1650000, color page L.2550000; trim 184 x 250. circ. 5,458.

615   SP   ISSN 1130-104X
ESCAPARATE FARMACEUTICO. 1990. 4/yr. 5700 ptas.($74) (effective 1992). Publica, S.A., Ecuador, 75, entlo., 08029 Barcelona, Spain. TEL 34-3-3215046. FAX 34-3-3221972.

615   IT
ESPRESSO FARMACEUTICO. 10/yr. Edizioni Effe Emme, Via Caldara 8, 20122 Corbetta (Milan), Italy. TEL 2-977-03-10. FAX 2-977-23-63. Ed. Mario Bernardi. circ. 9,000.

ETHNOBOTANY. see *BIOLOGY — Botany*

615 614.4   US   ISSN 1056-179X
EUROPE DRUG & DEVICE REPORT. 1991. bi-m. $797. Washington Business Information, Inc., c/o Karen Harrington, 1117 N. 19th St., Arlington, VA 22209. TEL 703-247-3434. FAX 703-247-3421. (Co-publisher: Thomas Lesser Publishing) Ed. Sara Lewis. (looseleaf format) **Document type:** newsletter.
—CCC.
Description: Reports on European rules and standards for the pharmaceutical and device and diagnostic products industries.

615   IT   ISSN 1122-2441
EUROPEAN BULLETIN OF DRUG RESEARCH. (Text in English) vol.3 no.1, Jan. 1994. 3/yr. L.120000($120) Europharma 2000 s.r.l., Via Ghibellina 81, 50122 Florence, Italy. TEL 39-55-2478982. FAX 39-55-2478982. Ed.Bd.
—BLDSC (3829.497500).
Description: Publishes original and innovative papers dealing with all aspects of drug research and development, such as medicinal chemistry, design and synthesis of new active substances, pharmacology and pharmacognosy, pharmaceutics and biopharmaceutics, and new drug-delivery systems.

615.1   GW   ISSN 0031-6970
CODEN: EJCPAS
EUROPEAN JOURNAL OF CLINICAL PHARMACOLOGY. (Text in English) 1968. 12/yr. (in 2 vols., 6 nos./vol.). DM.1596($1159) (effective 1996). Springer-Verlag, Heidelberger Platz 3, 14197 Berlin, Germany. TEL 030-8207-0. FAX 030-8214091. E-mail: orders@springer.de. (Subscr. in N. America to: Springer-Verlag New York, Inc., 44 Hartz Way, Secaucus, NJ 07096-2491. TEL 201-348-4033. FAX 201-348-4505) Ed.Bd. adv.; bk.rev.; illus. (also avail. in microform from UMI; reprint service avail. from ISI) **Indexed:** Abstr.Inter.Med., Biol.Abstr., Biotech.Abstr., C.I.S. Abstr., Chem.Abstr., Curr.Adv.Cancer Res., Curr.Adv.Ecol.Sci., Curr.Cont., Dairy Sci.Abstr., Dent.Ind., Excerp.Med., Ind.Med., Ind.Sci.Rev., INIS Atomind., Kidney, Med.& Surg.Dermat., Sci.Cit.Ind. **Document type:** academic/scholarly publication.
—BLDSC (3829.728100); ADONIS; CASDDS; EMDOCS; Faxon; Genuine Article; SWETS; UMI; UnCover. **CCC.**
Description: Publishes original papers, short communications, and letters to the editor on all aspects of clinical pharmacology and drug therapy in man. Focuses on clinical pharmacology and pharmacokinetics.

615.7   SZ   ISSN 0378-7966
CODEN: EJDPD2
EUROPEAN JOURNAL OF DRUG METABOLISM AND PHARMACOKINETICS. (Text in English and French) 1976. q. 295 SFr.($140) (effective 1996). Editions Medecine et Hygiene, Case Postale 456, CH-1211 Geneva 4, Switzerland. TEL 022-3469355. FAX 022-3475610. Ed. A. Benakis. **Indexed:** Biol.Abstr., Biotech.Abstr., Curr.Adv.Ecol.Sci., Dent.Ind., Excerp.Med., I.P.A., Ind.Med., Ind.Sci.Rev., Sci.Cit.Ind. **Document type:** academic/scholarly publication.
●Also available online.
—BLDSC (3829.728300); CASDDS; Genuine Article; UnCover. **CCC.**

615   UK   ISSN 1352-4755
▼**EUROPEAN JOURNAL OF HERBAL MEDICINE.** 1994. 3/yr. £19.50 (EC £21; foreign £27) to individuals; institutions £27(EC £30; foreign £33). National Institute of Medical Herbalists, 56 Longbrook St., Exeter EX4 6AH, England. TEL 01392-426022. FAX 01392-498963. Ed. Michael McIntyre. **Document type:** academic/scholarly publication.
—BLDSC (3829.729870).

615   GW   ISSN 0939-9437
EUROPEAN JOURNAL OF HOSPITAL PHARMACY. 1984. q. DM.48. Medpharm GmbH Scientific Publishers, Postfach 101061, 70009 Stuttgart, Germany. TEL 0711-25820. FAX 0711-2582-290. Ed. Dr. Jochen Kotwas. circ. 8,000. **Document type:** trade publication.

EUROPEAN JOURNAL OF MEDICINAL CHEMISTRY. see *BIOLOGY — Biological Chemistry*

615.1   NE   ISSN 0928-0987
RM301.25   CODEN: EPSCED
EUROPEAN JOURNAL OF PHARMACEUTICAL SCIENCES. (Text and summaries in English) 1993. bi-m. fl.556($339) (effective 1996). (European Federation for Pharmaceutical Sciences) Elsevier Science B.V., P.O. Box 211, 1000 AE Amsterdam, Netherlands. TEL 31-20-4853911. FAX 31-20-4853598. TELEX 18582 ESPA NL. E-mail: nlinfo@elsevier.nl; usinfo-f@elsevier.com; forinfo-kyf04035@niftyserve.or.jp; Site addr.: http://www.elsevier.nl/. (Subscr. in U.S. and Canada to: Elsevier Science Inc., Box 882, Madison Sq. Sta., New York, NY 10159-0882. TEL 212-989-5800. FAX 212-633-3990) Eds. Hans E. Junginger, Gerald J. Mulder. adv.; index. (also avail. in microform from UMI) **Indexed:** Anal.Abstr., ASCA, Biol.Abstr., Biotech.Abstr., Chem.Abstr., Curr.Adv.Ecol.Sci., Curr.Chem.React., Curr.Cont., Dairy Sci.Abstr., Excerp.Med. (1993-), Helminthol.Abstr., I.P.A., Ind.Chem., Ind.Med., Ind.Sci.Rev., INIS Atomind., Sci.Cit.Ind. **Document type:** academic/scholarly publication.
—BLDSC (3829.733850); CASDDS; Ei; Faxon; Genuine Article; SWETS; UMI; UnCover. **CCC.**
Formed by the merger of (1977-1992): Acta Pharmaceutica Fennica (ISSN 0356-3456); Which was formerly (1928-1976): Farmaseuttinen Aikakauslehti (ISSN 0367-259X); (1989-1992): Acta Pharmaceutica Nordica (ISSN 1100-1801); Which was formed by the merger of (1964-1988): Acta Pharmaceutica Suecica (ISSN 0001-6675); (1983-1988) Norwegica Pharmaceutica Acta (ISSN 0800-2606); Which was formerly (1939-1982): Norsk Farmaceutisk Selskap. Meddlelser (ISSN 0029-1927) & Farmaci. Scientific Edition (ISSN 0904-0897); Which was formerly (until 1987): Archiv for Pharmaci og Chemi. Scientific Edition (ISSN 0302-248X); (1926-1972): Dansk Tiddskrift for Farmaci (ISSN 0011-6513).
Description: Publishes original multidisciplinary research, short communications and reviews in the pharmaceutical sciences, from both academia and industry, including topics such as drug bioanalysis, medicinal chemistry and drug delivery, biomedical drug research and drug targeting, pharmacokinetics, pharmacodynamics, drug metabolism and toxicology, as well as pharmaceutical biotechnology.
Refereed Serial

615   GW   ISSN 0939-6411
CODEN: EJPBEL
EUROPEAN JOURNAL OF PHARMACEUTICS AND BIOPHARMACEUTICS. (Text in English, French and German) 1955. bi-m. DM.282. (Arbeitsgemeinschaft fuer Pharmazeutische Verfahrenstechnik e.V.) Wissenschaftliche Verlagsgesellschaft mbH, Postfach 101061, 70009 Stuttgart, Germany. TEL 0711-2582-0. FAX 0711-2582-290. TELEX 723636-DAZ-D. Ed. R. Gurny. circ. 2,000. **Indexed:** Biotech.Abstr., Chem.Abstr., Excerp.Med., I.P.A. **Document type:** academic/scholarly publication.
●Also available online.
—BLDSC (3829.733900); CASDDS; Faxon; Genuine Article; SWETS. **CCC.**
Formerly: Acta Pharmaceutica Technologica (ISSN 0340-3157)

615.1   NE   ISSN 0014-2999
CODEN: EJPHAZ
EUROPEAN JOURNAL OF PHARMACOLOGY; an international journal. 1967. 70/yr. (in 23 vols.). fl.9315($5680) includes Environmental Toxicology and Pharmacology Section, Molecular Pharmacology Section (effective 1995). Elsevier Science B.V., P.O. Box 211, 1000 AE Amsterdam, Netherlands. TEL 31-20-4853911. FAX 31-20-4853598. TELEX 18582 ESPA NL. E-mail: nlinfo-f@elsevier.nl; usinfo-f@elsevier.com; forinfo-kyf04035@niftyserve.or.jp; Site addr.: http://www.elsevier.nl/. (Subscr. in U.S. and Canada to: Elsevier Science Inc., Box 882, Madison Sq. Sta., New York, NY 10159-0882. TEL 212-989-5800. FAX 212-633-3990) Ed. D. de Wied. adv.; charts; illus. (also avail. in microform from UMI; reprint service avail. from ISI) **Indexed:** Apic.Abstr., Biol.Abstr., Biotech.Abstr., Chem.Abstr., Curr.Adv.Ecol.Sci., Curr.Cont., Dairy Sci.Abstr., Dent.Ind., Excerp.Med., Helminthol.Abstr., Ind.Med., Ind.Sci.Rev., Ind.Vet., INIS Atomind., Int.Abstr.Biol.Sci., Psychol.Abstr., Sci.Cit.Ind., Vet.Bull. **Document type:** academic/scholarly publication.
—BLDSC (3829.734000); ADONIS; CASDDS; Faxon; Genuine Article; SWETS; UnCover. **CCC.**
Description: Publishes full length papers as well as short and rapid communications on all aspects of pharmacology.
Refereed Serial

EUROPEAN JOURNAL OF PHARMACOLOGY. ENVIRONMENTAL TOXICOLOGY AND PHARMACOLOGY SECTION. see *ENVIRONMENTAL STUDIES — Toxicology And Environmental Safety*

615   NE   ISSN 0922-4106
CODEN: EJPPET
EUROPEAN JOURNAL OF PHARMACOLOGY. MOLECULAR PHARMACOLOGY SECTION. (Section of: European Journal of Pharmacology (ISSN 0014-2999)) (Text in English) 1989. 12/yr. (in 4 vols.; 3 nos./vol.). fl.1840($968) (effective 1995). Elsevier Science B.V., P.O. Box 211, 1000 AE Amsterdam, Netherlands. TEL 31-20-4853911. FAX 31-20-4853598. TELEX 18582 ESPA NL. E-mail: nlinfo@elsevier.nl; usinfo-f@elsevier.com; forinfo-kyf04035@niftyserve.or.jp; Site addr.: http://www.elsevier.nl/. (Subscr. in U.S. and Canada to: Elsevier Science Inc., Box 882, Madison Sq. Sta., New York, NY 10159-0882. TEL 212-989-5800. FAX 212-633-3990) Ed.Bd. (also avail. in microform from UMI; reprint service avail. from ISI) **Indexed:** Biol.Abstr., Chem.Abstr., Curr.Cont., Excerp.Med., Ind.Med. **Document type:** academic/scholarly publication.
—ADONIS; CASDDS; Faxon; Genuine Article; SWETS; UnCover. **CCC.**
Description: Contains original information on interactions at the molecular level of substances in biological systems.
Refereed Serial

EUROPEAN NEUROPSYCHOPHARMACOLOGY. see *MEDICAL SCIENCES — Psychiatry And Neurology*

EUROPEAN UNION AIDS DIRECTORY. see *MEDICAL SCIENCES — Communicable Diseases*

615.19   US
EVALUATION OF DRUG INTERACTIONS. 1988. a. (updates 6/yr.) $229 (updates $89.95). Professional Drug Systems, Inc., 530 Maryville Centre Dr., Ste. 250, St. Louis, MO 63141. TEL 314-275-8848; 800-366-4737. FAX 314-275-8819. Eds. Frederic Zucchero, Mark Hogan. (looseleaf format) **Document type:** monographic series.
●Also available online.
Description: Comprehensive reference source fo prescription and OTC drug conflicts.

615   FR   ISSN 0755-8309
EVOLUTION PHARMACEUTIQUE. m. 120 F. Union Nationale des Grandes Pharmacies, 57 rue Spontini, 75116 Paris, France. TEL 45-53-60-90. Dir. J. Vigan. adv. circ. 4,500.

EXPERIMENTAL AND CLINICAL PSYCHOPHARMACOLOGY. see *PSYCHOLOGY*

EXPERIMENTAL AND TOXICOLOGIC PATHOLOGY. see *MEDICAL SCIENCES*

PHARMACY AND PHARMACOLOGY

615.1   UK   ISSN 1354-3784
CODEN: CIDREE
EXPERT OPINION IN INVESTIGATIONAL DRUGS; authoritative analysis of R&D trends. 1992. m. £1260($2260) Ashley Publications Ltd., First Fl., The Library, 1 Shepherds Hill, Highgate, London N6 5QJ, England. TEL 0181-347-5030. FAX 0181-181-5040. Ed.Bd; Pub. James Drake. **Indexed:** Excerp.Med. (1994-). **Document type:** academic/scholarly publication.
—BLDSC (3842.002953); CASDDS.
Formerly (until 1994): Current Opinion in Investigational Drugs (ISSN 0967-8298)
Description: Highlights important pharmacological and pharmaceutical developments, covers meetings and conferences, and reviews important worldwide developments.
Refereed Serial

615   SW
F A S S - LAEKEMEDEL I SVERIGE. 1966. a. SEK 382. LINFO - Laekemedelsinformation AB, P.O. Box 17608, S-118 92 Stockholm, Sweden. Dir. Anna-Greta Hedstrand. **Document type:** catalog.
Formerly: F A S S - Farmacevtiska Specialiteter i Sverige (ISSN 0430-1080)

636.089   SW   ISSN 0347-1136
F A S S VET. (Farmacevtiska Specialiteter i Sverige); foeretechning oever laekemedel foer veterinaermedicinsk bruk. Variant title: Farmaceutiska Specialiteter i Sverige Veteriaermedicin. 1973. a. SEK 169 (effective 1993). LINFO - Laekemedelsinformation AB, P.O. Box 17608, S118 92 Stockholm, Sweden. Dir. Anna-Greta Hedstrand. **Document type:** catalog.

F D A COMPLIANCE POLICY GUIDANCE. MANUAL. (U.S. Food and Drug Administration) see *FOOD AND FOOD INDUSTRIES*

F D A CONSUMER. (U.S. Food and Drug Administration) see *CONSUMER EDUCATION AND PROTECTION*

F D A ENFORCEMENT REPORT. (U.S. Food and Drug Administration) see *CRIMINOLOGY AND LAW ENFORCEMENT*

F D A HOTLINE. see *PUBLIC HEALTH AND SAFETY*

F D A INSPECTION OPERATIONS MANUAL. see *FOOD AND FOOD INDUSTRIES*

615.1   US   ISSN 1063-8067
F D A MEDICAL BULLETIN. 1970. irreg. free. U.S. Food and Drug Administration, Office of Public Affairs, 5600 Fisher's Ln., Rockville, MD 20857. TEL 301-443-3220. (Orders to: National Technical Information Service, 5285 Port Royal Rd., Springfield, VA 22161. TEL 703-487-4650. FAX 703-321-8547) Ed. Judith Willis. (back issues avail.) **Indexed:** Curr.Lit.Fam.Plan., Excerp.Med., I.P.A., Ind.Med., ind.U.S.Gov.Per., Med. Care Rev., MEDOC, Telegen. **Document type:** government publication.
●Also available online. Vendor(s): Ovid Technologies (DIOG), Data-Star, Knight-Ridder, Inc.
—BLDSC (3901.292580).
Formerly (until 1990): F D A Drug Bulletin (ISSN 0361-4344)
Description: Reports on new drug approvals, adverse reactions, biological end-products and medical and radiological devices.

F D C CONTROL NEWSLETTER. (Food, Drug, and Cosmetics) see *FOOD AND FOOD INDUSTRIES*

615.1   US   ISSN 0276-4318
RM300
FAMILY PHYSICIAN'S COMPENDIUM OF DRUG THERAPY. Spine title: Compendium of Drug Therapy. 1980. a. $49.95 (effective 1994). Compendium Publications Group Ltd., 1 Harmon Meadow Blvd., Secaucus, NJ 07094. TEL 201-864-2400. FAX 201-764-3626.
Formerly: Osteopathic Physician's Compendium of Drug Therapy (ISSN 0272-7064)
Refereed Serial

615.19 660   AU
FARBE AKTUELL PLUS. m. Verlag Johann L. Bondi und Sohn GmbH, Industriestr. 2, A-2380 Perchtoldsdorf, Austria. TEL 01-864921. FAX 01-86492144. **Document type:** trade publication.
Formerly: Farbe Aktuell.

615   YU
FARMACEUT. bi-m. Farmaceutsko Drustvo Vojvodine, Bulevar Revolucije 32, Novi Sad, Yugoslavia. Ed. Olga Stefanovic.

615.1   XO   ISSN 0014-8172
CODEN: FAOBAS
FARMACEUTICKY OBZOR. (Text in Czech or Slovak; summaries in English, German, Russian) 1931. m. $90. Ministerstvo Zdravotnictva, Institut pre Dalsie Vzdelavanie Pracovnikov, Limbova 12, 833 39 Bratislava, Slovakia. (Dist. by: Slovart, Gottwaldovo nam. 48, 805 32 Bratislava, Slovakia) Ed.Bd. adv.; bk.rev.; abstr.; charts; illus.; stat.; index. circ. 2,500. **Indexed:** Anal.Abstr., Biol.Abstr., Chem.Abstr., Excerp.Med., I.P.A., INIS Atomind.
●Also available online.
—BLDSC (3881.850000); CASDDS.

615   SP   ISSN 0213-7283
FARMACEUTICO. 1984. 15/yr. 7500 ptas. (America 10500 ptas.). Muntaner 374, 4o, 08006 Barcelona, Spain. TEL 34-3-2090255. FAX 34-3-2020643. Ed. Javier March; Pub. Josep Ma. Ferrando. adv. contact: Jose Mayoral. bk.rev. circ. 18,304. **Document type:** academic/scholarly publication.
Description: Addressed to all pharmacists, to the pharmaceutical industry, and to pharmacy services in hospitals.

615   SP   ISSN 0214-4697
FARMACEUTICO HOSPITALES. 1988. 10/yr. 6500 ptas. Ediciones Mayo, S.A., Muntaner 374, 4a, 08006 Barcelona, Spain. TEL 34-3-2090090. FAX 34-3-2020643. Ed. Josep M. Ferrando. circ. 2,000. **Document type:** academic/scholarly publication.

615   SP
FARMACEUTICOS. 12/yr. Apolonio Morales 6, 28036 Madrid, Spain. TEL 1-403-50-14. FAX 1-457-99-18. Ed. J. Velez Garcia Neto. circ. 18,581.

615.1   DK   ISSN 0014-8199
FARMACEUTISK TIDENDE. (Text in Danish; summaries in English) 1890. w. DKK 300. Dansk Farmaceutforening - Danish Pharmacists' Association, Toldbbodgade 36, 1253 Copenhagen K, Denmark. Ed. Knud Soerensen. adv.; bk.rev.; abstr.; bibl.; charts; illus.; stat.; index, cum.index. circ. 3,697. **Indexed:** Chem.Abstr., I.P.A.
●Also available online.

615.1   CI   ISSN 0014-8202
CODEN: FAGLAI
FARMACEUTSKI GLASNIK. (Text in Croatian; summaries in English) 1907. m. $100. Hrvatsko Farmaceutsko Drustvo, Masarykova 2, 41000 Zagreb, Croatia. TEL 41-427944. FAX 41-431301. Ed. Dr. Oleg Cupahin. adv.; bk.rev.; abstr.; bibl.; charts; illus.; stat.; index. circ. 1,600. **Indexed:** Biol.Abstr., Biotech.Abstr., Chem.Abstr., Excerp.Med., I.P.A. **Document type:** academic/scholarly publication.
●Also available online.
—BLDSC (3884.000000); CASDDS.
Formerly (until 1944): Farmaceutski Vjesnik.

615.1   XV   ISSN 0014-8229
CODEN: FMVTAV
FARMACEVTSKI VESTNIK; strokovno glasilo slovenske farmacije. (Text in Serbo-Croatian, Slovenian; summaries English) 1950. q. $50. Slovensko Farmacevtsko Drustvo, P.O. Box 311, Masera Spasica 10, 61001 Ljubljana, Slovenia. TEL 061-221-078. Ed. Ales Krbavcic. adv.; bk.rev.; charts; illus.; tr.lit.; index. circ. 1,900. (reprint service avail. from UMI) **Indexed:** Biol.Abstr., Biotech.Abstr., Chem.Abstr., I.P.A.
●Also available online.
—CASDDS; UMI.

615.1   DK   ISSN 0903-9198
CODEN: APCEAR
FARMACI. 1844. m. DKK 400($27) Danmarks Apotekerforening - Danish Pharmaceutical Association, Bredgade 54, 1260 Copenhagen K, Denmark. TEL 45-33-76-76-00. FAX 45-33-76-76-99. Ed. Jens Povelsen. adv.; bk.rev.; abstr.; charts; illus.; index. circ. 2,500. (back issues avail.) **Indexed:** Biol.Abstr., Chem.Abstr., I.P.A., INIS Atomind. **Document type:** academic/scholarly publication, trade publication.
●Also available online.
—BLDSC (3885.270000); CASDDS.
Formerly: Archiv for Pharmaci og Chemi (ISSN 0003-8938)
Description: Directed primarily to Danish community pharmacists.

615.1   RM   ISSN 0014-8237
CODEN: FRMBAZ
FARMACIA/PHARMACY. (Text in Rumanian; summaries in English, French, German, Russian) 1953. 4/yr. $20. Uniunea Societatilor De Stiinte Medicale Din Republica Socialista Rumania, Str. Progresului No. 8, Bucharest, Rumania. (Subscr. to: ILEXIM, Str. 13 Decembrie Nr. 3, P.O. Box 136-137, Bucharest, Rumania) Ed.Bd. adv.; bk.rev.; adv.; charts. **Indexed:** Abstr.Bulg.Sci.Med.Lit., Biotech.Abstr., Chem.Abstr., Excerp.Med., I.P.A.
●Also available online.
—BLDSC (3886.000000); CASDDS.

615   SP   ISSN 0212-6583
CODEN: FACLE2
FARMACIA CLINICA. 1983. bi-m. Rasgo Editorial S.A., Llansa 16, Dpcho. 2, 08015 Barcelona, Spain. TEL 3-4231619. **Indexed:** Excerp.Med. **Document type:** academic/scholarly publication.
—BLDSC (3886.160000); CASDDS. CCC.

615 658   SP   ISSN 1130-6343
CODEN: FAHOE
FARMACIA HOSPITALARIA. 1977. bi-m. 6500 ptas.($65) (effective 1995). Sociedad Espanola de Farmacia Hospitalaria, C. Echegaray 13, 3o, 28014 Madrid, Spain. TEL 34-1-4202798. (Dist. by: Editorial Garsi, S.A., Juan Bravo 46, 28006 Madrid, Spain. TEL 34-1-4021212) Ed. Ramon Pla Poblador. circ. 2,000. **Indexed:** Excerp.Med.
—BLDSC (3886.200000); CASDDS.

615   IT   ISSN 1121-1350
FARMACIA NATURALE. Key Title: Natom. Farmacia Naturale. 1983. m. (9/yr.) L.70000 (foreign L.190000) (effective 1995). Tecniche Nuove s.p.a., Via C. Menotti, 14, 20129 Milan, Italy. TEL 02-75701. FAX 02-7610351. adv.: B&W page L.2830000, color page L.3820000; trim 184 x 250. circ. 12,866.
Former titles (until 1990): Natom (ISSN 0394-8196); (until 1985): Naturopatia Omeopatia (ISSN 0394-8188)

615.1   IT   ISSN 0014-8245
FARMACIA NUOVA; bollettino dei farmacisti Piemontesi. vol.26, 1970. m. Via Oglianico 4, 10149 Turin, Italy. Ed. Cristoforo Masino. adv. **Indexed:** Biol.Abstr., Chem.Abstr. **Document type:** newspaper.

615   SP
FARMACIA PROFESIONAL.* 11/yr. Haymarket, S.A., Travesera Gracia 17-21 5o 2o, 08022 Barcelona, Spain. TEL 3-237-22-66. FAX 237-66-88. Ed. Enrique Medrano. circ. 8,500.

615   IT
FARMACIA REGIONE. 10/yr. Via E. Filiberto 190, 00185 Rome, Italy. TEL 6-75-73-679. FAX 6-75-95-647. circ. 16,000.

615.19   SW   ISSN 1102-8033
FARMACIFACKET. 1932. m. (11/yr.) SEK 275 (effective 1991). Apoteksstjaenstemannafoerbundet, Vaestmannagatan 66, 113 25 Stockholm, Sweden. FAX 08-342147. Ed. Anita Westin-Jameson. adv. circ. 7,856.
Former titles (until 1991): Apotekstjaenstemannen (ISSN 0281-6040); (until 1983): Apotekstknikern (ISSN 0345-0945); (until 1956): Tekniska Apotekspersonalens Tidskrift; (until vol.4, 1932): Meddelande fraan Sveriges Tekniska Apotekspersonals Foerbundscentralstyrelse.

PHARMACY AND PHARMACOLOGY

615 IT ISSN 0014-8253
FARMACISTA SOCIALE; periodico indipendente dei farmacisti d'Italia. 1965. m. L.10000. (Farmacisti d'Italia) Dr. Franco Ricciardi, Ed. & Pub., Trav. D. Fontana 53-57, Naples, Italy. adv.; bibl.; illus.; stat.; tr.lit. circ. 8,000. (tabloid format)

615.1 PL ISSN 0014-8261
FARMACJA POLSKA. (Text in Polish; contents in English, Russian) 1945. fornt. $150 (effective 1995). Polskie Towarzystwo Farmaceutyczne - Polish Pharmaceutical Society, Dluga 16, 00-238 Warsaw, Poland. TEL 48-22-310241. FAX 48-22-310243. Ed. Jerzy Lazowski. adv.; bk.rev.; charts; illus.; tr.lit.; index. circ. 4,000. (back issues avail.) **Indexed:** Anal.Abstr., Biotech.Abstr., Chem.Abstr., Excerp.Med., I.P.A.
●Also available online.
—BLDSC (3887.000000); CASDDS.
Description: Devoted to scientific and social and professional problems of pharmacy.

615.1 IT ISSN 0014-827X
FARMACO. (Text in English) 1945. m. L.330000 (Europe L.500000; elsewhere L.550000) (effective 1995). Societa Chimica Italiana, Viale Liegi, 48, 00198 Rome, Italy. TEL 39-6-8549691. FAX 39-6-8548734. Ed. Giovanni Rodighiero. adv.; bk.rev.; charts; illus.; tr.lit.; index. circ. 1,500. (also avail. in microfilm from PMC) **Indexed:** Anal.Abstr., Biol.Abstr., Biotech.Abstr., Chem.Abstr., Chem.Infd.; Curr.Adv.Ecol.Sci., Curr.Chem.React., Dairy Sci.Abstr., Excerp.Med., Food Sci.& Tech.Abstr., I.P.A., Ind.Chem., Ind.Med., Mass Spectr.Bull., Nutr.Abstr., Protozool.Abstr., Rev.Med.& Vet.Mycol., Sci.Cit.Ind. **Document type:** academic/scholarly publication.
—BLDSC (3887.500000); Genuine Article; SWETS; UMI.
Description: Publishes original scientific papers and articles on various aspects of medicinal chemistry and pharmaceutical sciences.

615.19 SP ISSN 0214-8935
FARMACOTERAPIA/JOURNAL OF PHARMACOLOGY. 1984. 6/yr. 8000 ptas. (foreign $100). Editores Medicos, S.A., C. Gabriela Mistral 2, 28035 Madrid, Spain. TEL 34-1-3860033. FAX 34-1-3739907. circ. 12,000.
—CCC.

615.1 KR ISSN 0367-3057
RS1 CODEN: FRZKAP
FARMATSEVTYCHNYI ZHURNAL. (Text in Ukrainian; summaries in Russian) 1928-1942; resumed 1958. bi-m. $77 (effective 1996). Vidavnitstvo Naukova Dumka, Ul. Tereshchenkivska 3, Kieg 252 601, Ukraine. (Subscr. to: Mezhdunarodnaya Kniga, Moscow, G-200, Russia) charts; illus.; index. circ. 7,900. **Indexed:** Anal.Abstr., Apic.Abstr., Biol.Abstr., Biotech.Abstr., Chem.Abstr., Excerp.Med., I.P.A., Ind.Med., INIS Atomind.
—BLDSC (0389.100000); CASDDS.

615 BU ISSN 0428-0296
CODEN: FMTYA2
FARMATSIA. (Text in Bulgarian; summaries in English, Russian) 1951. bi-m. 16 lv.($10) (Ministerstvo na Narodnoto Zdrave) Izdatelstvo Meditsina i Fizkultura, 11, Pl. Slaveikov, Sofia, Bulgaria. (Dist. by: Hemus, 6, Rouski Blvd., 1000 Sofia, Bulgaria) (Co-sponsor: Nauchno Druzhestvo po Farmatsija) Ed. E. Minkov. circ. 1,133. **Indexed:** Abstr.Bulg.Sci.Med.Lit., Chem.Abstr., Excerp.Med., I.P.A., Ind.Med.
—BLDSC (0389.190000); CASDDS.

615.1 SW ISSN 0014-8520
FARMIS - REPTILEN. Variant title: Reptilen. (Text occasionally in English) 1959. 8/yr. SEK 100($6.50) Farmaceutiska Studentkaaren, P.O. Box 8036, S-750 08 Uppsala, Sweden. Ed. Richard Gavatin. adv.; bk.rev.; circ. 1,200. (controlled).
Formerly (until vol.3, 1964): Reptilen.

615.1 JA ISSN 0014-8601
CODEN: FARUAW
FARUMASHIA/PHARMACY. (Text in Japanese) 1965. m. $120 to members. Pharmaceutical Society of Japan - Nihon Yakugakkai, 12-15, Shibuya 2-chome, Shibuya-ku, Tokyo 150, Japan. Ed. Shigeo Iwasaki. adv.; bk.rev.; film rev.; abstr.; bibl.; charts; mkt.; stat.; tr.lit.; index; circ. 22,000 (controlled). **Indexed:** Chem.Abstr.
—BLDSC (3896.500000); CASDDS. **CCC.**

615 IT
FEDERFARMA NOTIZIE; organo d'informazione settimanale dei titolari di farmacia. Bound with: Farma 7. 1986. w. L.220000($150) to non-members. Editoriale Giornalidea s.r.l., Via Sebenico, 14, 20124 Milan, Italy. TEL 02-688875. FAX 02-6888780. Ed. Sossio Guarnaccia. adv.; bk.rev. circ. 17,000. (back issues avail.)
Formerly (until 1986): Farmacia Notizie.

789.56 UK
FINANCIAL SURVEY. COMPANY DATA FOR SUCCESS: PHARMACEUTICAL MANUFACTURERS & DISTRIBUTORS. a. I C C Financial Surveys Ltd., Field House, 72 Oldfield Rd., Hampton, Mddx. TW12 2HQ, England. TEL 081-783-0977. FAX 081-783-1940. charts; stat. **Document type:** trade publication.
Formerly (until 1991): Financial Survey Company Directory. Pharmaceutical Manufacturers and Distributors (ISSN 0952-4819)

615 JA
FINE D I WEEKLY. (Text in Japanese) 1988. w. Fukujin Co., Ltd., 23-5, Hatanaka 1-chome, Niza-shi, Saitama-ken 352, Japan.

FITOTERAPIA; rivista di studi ed applicazioni delle piante medicinali. see BIOLOGY — Botany

615.1 US ISSN 0897-4616
FLORIDA PHARMACY TODAY. 1937. m. $25. Florida Pharmacy Association, 610 N. Adams St., Tallahassee, FL 32301. TEL 904-222-2400. Ed. Rod Persnell. adv.; bk.rev.; illus. circ. 3,200.
Former titles: Florida Pharmacy Journal (ISSN 0161-746X); Florida Pharmaceutical Journal (ISSN 0015-4202); Florida Pharmacist.

FOCUS ON PULMONARY PHARMACOLOGY AND TOXICOLOGY. see ENVIRONMENTAL STUDIES — Toxicology And Environmental Safety

615 SZ
FOLIA PHARMACEUTICA. 9/yr. Verlag Diethelm AG, Postfach 203, CH-8808 Pfaeffikon, Switzerland. TEL 01-7849693. FAX 01-7843503. circ. 8,500.

615 JA ISSN 0015-5691
CODEN: NYKZAU
FOLIA PHARMACOLOGICA JAPONICA/NIHON YAKURIGAKU ZASSHI. (Text in Japanese; summaries in English) 1925. m. 12000 Yen (foreign $200). Japanese Pharmacological Society, Editorial Office - Nihon Yakuri Gakkai Henshuubu, Kantohya Bldg., Gokmachi-Ebisugawa, Nakagyo-ku, Kyoto 604, Japan. TEL 075-252-4641. FAX 075-252-4618. Ed. Minoru Watanabe. adv.; illus.; index. circ. 6,500. (also avail. in microform from UMI; reprint service avail. from UMI, ISI) **Indexed:** Biol.Abstr., Biotech.Abstr., Chem.Abstr., Curr.Adv.Ecol.Sci., Curr.Cont., Dairy Sci.Abstr., Dent.Ind., Excerp.Med., Helminthol.Abstr., Ind.Med., Ind.Sci.Rev., Nutr.Abstr. **Document type:** academic/scholarly publication.
●Also available online.
—BLDSC (3973.500000); CASDDS; Genuine Article.
Refereed Serial

615 664 UK ISSN 0265-203X
TX553.A3 CODEN: FACOEB
FOOD ADDITIVES AND CONTAMINANTS; analysis, surveillance, evaluation, control. 1984. 8/yr. £352($580) (effective 1996). Taylor & Francis Ltd., Rankine Rd., Basingstoke, Hants. RG24 8PR, England. TEL 44-1256-840366. FAX 44-1256-479438. TELEX 858540. E-mail: info@tandf.co.uk. (Subscr. in N. America to: Taylor & Francis Inc., 1900 Frost Rd., Ste. 101, Bristol, PA 19007-1598. TEL 44-1256-840366. FAX 44-1256-479438) Eds. Dr. R. Walker, M.E. Knowles. **Indexed:** Anal.Abstr., Biodet.Abstr., Curr.Adv.Cancer Res., Curr.Adv.Ecol.Sci., Dairy Sci.Abstr., Environ.Abstr., Environ.Per.Bibl. (1991-), Excerp.Med., Food Sci.& Tech.Abstr., Ind.Vet., Int.Packag.Abstr., NRN, Packag.Sci.Tech., Pig News & Info., Poult.Abstr., Rev.Med.& Vet.Mycol., Soyabean Abstr., Triticale Abstr., Vet.Bull. **Document type:** trade publication.
—BLDSC (3977.001000); CASDDS; Faxon; Genuine Article; SWETS. **CCC.**
Description: Contains original research and review articles relating to the detection, determination, occurence, persistence, safety evaluation and control of naturally occurring and man-made additives and contaminants in the food chain.
Refereed Serial

FOOD AND DRUG ADMINISTRATION. REGULATORY MANUAL. see LAW

FOOD AND DRUG LETTER. see BUSINESS AND ECONOMICS — Production Of Goods And Services

FOOD & DRUG PACKAGING. see PACKAGING

FOOD AND DRUG REPORT. see LAW

FOOD & DRUGS INDUSTRY BULLETIN. see LAW

615.1 SZ ISSN 0071-786X
CODEN: FAZMAE
FORTSCHRITTE DER ARZNEIMITTELFORSCHUNG/PROGRESS IN DRUG RESEARCH/PROGRES DES RECHERCHES PHARMACEUTIQUES. (Text in English, French and German) 1959. irreg. (1-2/yr.). Birkhaeuser Verlag, P.O. Box 133, CH-4010 Basel, Switzerland. TEL 061-2717400. FAX 061-2717666. Ed. Ernst Jucker. **Indexed:** Biol.Abstr., Biotech.Abstr., Chem.Abstr., Excerp.Med., I.P.A., Ind.Med. **Document type:** academic/scholarly publication.
●Also available online.
—BLDSC (6868.200000); CASDDS; EMDOCS; Faxon; SWETS; UnCover. **CCC.**

615.6 610.5 CC
FUJIAN YIYAO ZAZHI/FUJIAN MEDICAL AND PHARMACOLOGICAL JOURNAL. (Text in Chinese) bi-m. Y12. Fujiansheng Yixue Kexue Yanjiusuo - Fujian Institute of Medical Sciences, 21 Mishu Xiang, Wusi Lu, Fuzhou, Fujian 350001, People's Republic of China. TEL 521704. (Dist. overseas by: Jiangsu Publications Import & Export Corp., 56 Gao Yun Ling, Nanjing, Jiangsu, P.R.C.) (Co-sponsor: Fujian Public Health Bureau - Fujiansheng Weisheng Ting) Ed. Hu Xizhong. **Document type:** academic/scholarly publication.
Description: Presents research results and developments in pharmacology and the medical sciences.

615 JA ISSN 0913-1736
FUKUOKA DAIGAKU YAKUGAKU KIYO/FUKUOKA UNIVERSITY. PHARMACEUTICAL BULLETIN. (Text in English, Japanese; summaries in English) 1963. a. Fukuoka Daigaku, Sogo Kenkyujo - Fukuoka University, Central Research Institute, 19-1, Nanakuma 8-chome, Joan-ku, Fukuoka-shi, Fukuoka-ken 814-01, Japan. **Indexed:** Chem.Abstr.
—BLDSC (6442.780000).

615 JA
FUKUOKA SOCIETY OF HOSPITAL PHARMACY. DRUG INFORMATION NEWS. (Text in Japanese) 1965. q. membership. Fukuokaken Byoin Yakuzaishikai, Kyushu Daigaku Igakubu Fuzoku Byoin Yakuzaibu, 1-1, Maidashi 3-chome, Higashi-ku, Fukuoka-shi, Fukuoka-ken 812, Japan.

615 JA ISSN 0288-724X
FUKUYAMA DAIGAKU YAKUGAKUBU KENKYU NENPO/FUKUYAMA UNIVERSITY. FACULTY OF PHARMACY & PHARMACEUTICAL SCIENCES. ANNUAL REPORT. (Text in English, Japanese; summaries in English) 1982. a. Fukuyaka Daigaku, Yakugakubu, 985, Mikura, Higashimuracho, Fukuyama-shi, Hiroshimaken 729-02, Japan.

FUNDAMENTAL AND APPLIED TOXICOLOGY. see ENVIRONMENTAL STUDIES — Toxicology And Environmental Safety

615.19 FR ISSN 0767-3981
CODEN: FCPHEZ
FUNDAMENTAL AND CLINICAL PHARMACOLOGY. (Text in English) 1970. bi-m. 2235 F. in France; foreign 2615 F.($511) (effective 1996). (Association des Pharmacologistes) Editions Scientifiques Elsevier, 141 rue de Javel, 75747 Paris, France. TEL 33-1-45589063. (Subscr. in U.S. and Canada to: Elsevier Science Inc., Box 882, Madison Sq. Sta., New York, NY 10159. TEL 212-989-5800) Ed.Bd. adv.; bk.rev.; index. (also avail. in microform from UMI) **Indexed:** Curr.Adv.Biochem., Curr.Cont., Excerp.Med., Ind.Med., INIS Atomind., Sci.Cit.Ind. **Document type:** academic/scholarly publication.
—BLDSC (4056.033000); ADONIS; CASDDS; Faxon; Genuine Article; SWETS. **CCC.**
Description: Publishes full-length articles and short communications in the entire field of pharmacology from molecular studies to clinical investigations.
Refereed Serial

PHARMACY AND PHARMACOLOGY

615 340   JA
G M P REGULATIONS OF JAPAN. (Text in English, Japanese) irreg., latest 5th ed. $240. (Ministry of Health and Welfare, Pharmaceutical Affairs Bureau, Inspection and Guidance Division) Yakuji Nippo, Ltd., 1, Kanda Izumicho, Chiyoda-ku, Tokyo 101, Japan. TEL 81-3-3862-2141. FAX 81-3-5821-8757.
Description: Covers G.M.P. provisions on drugs, sterile drug preparations, bulk pharmaceutical chemicals, medical devices, cosmetics and more.

GAIKOKU BUNKEN DAIJESUTO. KAKU IGAKU/FOREIGN LITERATURE DIGEST. NUCLEAR MEDICINE. see *MEDICAL SCIENCES — Radiology And Nuclear Medicine*

615   JA
GAIKOKU IYAKU JOHO/INTERNATIONAL DRUG REPORT. (Text in English, Japanese) 1970. m. 175100 Yen. Iyakuhin Sangyo Kenkyujo - Drug Business Research Co., Ltd., 25-2, Koishikawa 1-chome, Bunkyo-ku, Tokyo 112, Japan.

615   JA   ISSN 0288-349X
GAKUJUTSU ZASSHI/KYOTO COLLEGE OF PHARMACY. SCIENTIFIC JOURNAL. (Text in Japanese) 1968. a. Kyoto Yakka Daigaku, Jichikai Gakujutsubu Shokubutsu Kenkyubu - Kyoto College of Pharmacy, 5 Misasagi Nakauchi-cho, Yamashina-ku, Kyoto-shi, Kyoto-fu 607, Japan. **Document type:** academic/scholarly publication.

GAN YAKURI/JAPANESE JOURNAL OF OCULAR PHARMACOLOGY. see *MEDICAL SCIENCES — Ophthalmology And Optometry*

GASTRIC SECRETION. see *BIOLOGY — Physiology*

GASTROINTESTINAL HORMONES. see *MEDICAL SCIENCES — Gastroenterology*

615   TU   ISSN 1015-9592
CODEN: GUEDE
GAZI UNIVERSITESI ECZACILIK FAKULTESI DERGISI. 1985. s-a. $75. Gazi Universitesi, Eczacilik Fakultesi - Gazi University, Faculty of Pharmacy, 06330 Etiler - Ankara, Turkey. TEL 90-312-2227225. FAX 90-312-2235018. Ed. Dr. Bilge Sener. **Indexed:** Excerp.Med. **Document type:** academic/scholarly publication.
—BLDSC (3659.741500); CASDDS.
Refereed Serial

615   JA   ISSN 0387-9690
GEKKAN OROSHI YAKUGYO/JAPAN PHARMACEUTICAL WHOLESALERS ASSOCIATION. JOURNAL. (Text in Japanese) 1977. m. 600 Yen per no. Nihon Iyakuhin Oroshigyo Rengokai, 7-4, Nihonbashi 2-chome, Chuo-ku, Tokyo 103, Japan.

615.19   GW   ISSN 0942-2951
GELBE LISTE PHARMINDEX. 1971. q. DM.97. I M P Kommunikation (Subsidiary of: Medizinische Media Informations GmbH), Am Forsthaus Gravenbruch 9, 63263 Neu-Isenburg, Germany. TEL 06102-5020. FAX 06102-53779. Ed. Marianne Kaemmer-Reusch. adv.: B&W page DM.14100; trim 225 x 148; adv. contact: Christel Neumann. circ. 43,000. **Document type:** trade publication.
Formerly: Liste Pharmindex (ISSN 0344-015X)

615   NE   ISSN 0304-4629
CODEN: GNMBA
GENEESMIDDELENBULLETIN. (Supplement to: Medisch Contact (ISSN 0024-1234)) 1967. m. free to qualified personnel. (Koninklijke Nederlandse Maatschappij tot Bevordering der Geneeskunst - Royal Dutch Society for the Advancement of Medicine) Stichting Geneesmiddelenbulletin, Lomanlaan 85, 3526 XC Utrecht, Netherlands. TEL 31-30-802660. circ. 28,178. **Indexed:** Excerp.Med. **Document type:** trade publication.
—BLDSC (4096.468000); SWETS.

615.1   UK   ISSN 0306-3623
RM1   CODEN: GEPHDP
GENERAL PHARMACOLOGY. 1970. 8/yr. $1650 to institutions (effective 1996). Elsevier Science Ltd., Pergamon, P.O. Box 800, Kidlington, Oxford OX5 1DX, England. TEL 44-1865-843000. FAX 44-1865-843010. E-mail: nlinfo-f@elsevier.nl; usinfo-f@elsevier.com; forinfo-kyf04035@niftyserve.or.jp; Site addr.: http://www.elsevier.nl/. (Subscr. in U.S. and Canada to: Elsevier Science, 660 White Plains Rd., Tarrytown, NY 10591-5153. TEL 914-524-9200. FAX 914-333-2444) Ed. G.A. Kerkut. adv.; bk.rev.; abstr.; charts; illus.; stat.; mitre. circ. 1,000. (also avail. in microfilm from UMI; back issues avail.; reprint service avail. from UMI) **Indexed:** Biol.Abstr., Biotech.Abstr., Chem.Abstr., Curr.Adv.Biochem., Curr.Adv.Ecol.Sci., Curr.Cont., Dent.Ind., Excerp.Med., Ind.Med., Ind.Sci.Rev., Ind.Vet., Maize Abstr., Poult.Abstr., Sci.Cit.Ind., Triticale Abstr., Vet.Bull. **Document type:** academic/scholarly publication.
—BLDSC (4106.710000); ADONIS; CASDDS; Faxon; Genuine Article; SWETS; UMI; UnCover. **CCC.**
Formerly: Comparative and General Pharmacology (ISSN 0010-4035)
Description: Covers all aspects of pharmacology.
Refereed Serial

615.1 332.6   US   ISSN 1076-884X
GENERIC LINE. 1984. w. $280. Scitec Services, 5324 Sinclair Rd., Columbus, OH 43229. TEL 614-433-0648. FAX 614-433-0432. Ed. Ronald M. Schwartz. **Document type:** newsletter.
Description: Covers the generic-drug industry.

615   US   ISSN 1061-2270
GENESIS REPORT - RX; business implications of technology innovation in pharmaceuticals. 1991. bi-m. $995 (foreign $1050) (effective Jul. 1995). Genesis Group Associates, Inc., 29 Park St., Montclair, NJ 07042. TEL 201-509-7735. FAX 201-509-7745. Ed. Robert E. Hannan. **Document type:** newsletter.
—BLDSC (4111.842000).

615.1   GW   ISSN 0939-334X
GESCHICHTE DER PHARMAZIE. (Supplement to: Deutsche Apotheker Zeitung) 1948. 4/yr. DM.12 (free with subscr. to Deutsche Apotheker Zeitung). (Internationale Gesellschaft fuer Geschichte der Pharmazie) Deutscher Apotheker Verlag, Postfach 101061, 70009 Stuttgart, Germany. TEL 0711-2582-0. FAX 0711-2582290. Ed. W.D. Mueller-Jahncke. bk.rev.; illus.; index. **Document type:** trade publication.
—BLDSC (4162.518000).
Former titles: Beitraege zur Geschichte der Pharmazie (ISSN 0341-0099); Zur Geschichte der Pharmazie (ISSN 0044-5509)

615.19   JA   ISSN 0434-0094
CODEN: GYDKA9
GIFU YAKKA DAIGAKU KIYO/GIFU PHARMACEUTICAL UNIVERSITY. NEWSLETTER. (Text in Japanese) 1951. a. free. Gifu Yakka Daigaku, 101, Yotsubaso, 15-13, Takadanobaba 1-chome, Shinjuku-ku, Tokyo 169, Japan. FAX 0582-37-5797. Ed.Bd. **Indexed:** Chem.Abstr.
—CASDDS.

615   JA   ISSN 0285-1458
GINKAI. (Text in Japanese) 1964. m. 500 Yen per no. Senju Seiyaku K.K. - Senju Pharmaceutical Co., Ltd., 5-8, Hiranomachi 2-chome, Chuo-ku, Osaka 541, Japan.

615   JA   ISSN 0288-6537
GINSHENG REVIEW. (Text in Japanese; summaries in English) 1983. m. Yakuyo Ninjin Kenkyukai - Medical Society for Red Ginseng Research, Nikkan Korai Ninjin K.K., 11-10, Motomachi Dori 3-chome, Chuo-ku, Kobe-shi, Hyogo-ken 650.

615.19   IT   ISSN 0393-8476
GIORNALE DEL FARMACISTA. 1986. fortn. (20/yr.) L.17000 (effective 1994). (Federazione degli Ordini dei Farmacisti Italiani) Masson S.p.A., Divisione Periodici, Via Statuto 4, 20121 Milan, Italy. TEL 02-6367-1. FAX 02-6367-211. Ed. G. Carlo Meani. adv.: B&W page L.6250000, color page L.7400000; trim 266 x 390. circ. 17,000. (tabloid format)

GIORNALE DI NEUROPSICOFARMACOLOGIA. see *MEDICAL SCIENCES — Psychiatry And Neurology*

615   IT   ISSN 1120-3749
GIORNALE ITALIANO DI FARMACIA CLINICA; epidemiologia - informazione - ricerca. 1987. 4/yr. L.264000($160) (effective 1996). (Societa Italiana di Farmacia Ospedaliera - Italian Society of Hospital Pharmacy) Pensiero Scientifico Editore s.r.l., Via Bradano 3-C, 00199 Rome, Italy. TEL 06-86207158. FAX 06-86207160. Ed. Nello Martini. adv.; bk.rev.; bibl. circ. 2,000. **Indexed:** Excerp.Med. **Document type:** academic/scholarly publication.
—BLDSC (4178.215500).

THE GIST. see *FOOD AND FOOD INDUSTRIES*

615   CC   ISSN 1000-8535
R97.7.C5
GUANGZHOU YIYAO/GUANGZHOU MEDICINE AND PHARMACOLOGY. (Text in Chinese) 1970. bi-m. Y2 per no. Guangzhou Weisheng Ju - Guangzhou Health Bureau, No. 484, Renmin Beilu, Guangzhou, Guangdong 510180, People's Republic of China. TEL 8853547. Ed. Yan Shufeng. **Document type:** academic/scholarly publication.

615.1   FR   ISSN 1155-1852
GUIDE NATIONAL DE PRESCRIPTION DES MEDICAMENTS. Abbreviated title: G N P. 1987. a. 370 F. (foreign 390 F.) O.V.P. - Editions du Vidal, 11, rue Quentin Bauchart, 75384 Paris Cedex 08, France. TEL 47-23-90-91. FAX 47-20-72-89. TELEX OVP 643 506 F. (Dist. by: EM-INTER, Allee de la Croix-Bossee, 94234 Cachan Cedex, France. TEL 45-46-15-00) circ. 10,000.
Description: Provides product category information and selection, 8,000 ethical pharmaceuticals classified.

615.329   CC   ISSN 1001-8751
GUOWAI YIYAO (KANGSHENGSU FENCE)/WORLD NOTES ON ANTIBIOTICS. (Text in Chinese) bi-m. $90. Sichuan Kangjunsu Gongye Yanjiusuo - Sichuan Industrial Institute of Antibiotics, 9 Shanbanqiao Lu, Chengdu, Sichuan 610051, People's Republic of China. TEL 444641. TELEX 60111 SIIA CN.

615   CC   ISSN 1001-6856
GUOWAI YIYAO (ZHIWUYAO FENCE)/WORLD NOTES ON HERBAL MEDICINE. (Text in Chinese) bi-m. Guojia Yiyao Guanli-ju, Tianjin Yaowu Yanjiusuo, 308, Anshan Xidao, Tianjin 300193, People's Republic of China. TEL 711320. Ed. Liu Deyan.

615   JA
H O P NYUSU/HOKKAIDO HOSPITAL PHARMACISTS' NEWSLETTER. (Text in Japanese) 1991. s-a. Hokkaido Byoin Yakuzaishikai, Hokkaido Daigaku Fuzoku Byoin Yakuzoku Byoin Yakuzaibu, Nishi 5-chome, Kita 14-jo, Kita-ku, Sapporo-shi, Hokkaido 060, Japan. **Document type:** newsletter.

615   SW   ISSN 1102-3899
HAELSOKURIREN; tidningen om haelsa och egenvaerd. 1991. q. Svenska Defence, P.O. Box 812, S-851 23 Sundsvall, Sweden.

615   SW   ISSN 0346-9751
HAESSLE INFORMATION. 1967. 10/yr. Haessle Laekemedel, S-431 83 Moelndal, Sweden.

615.9   NE
HANDBOOK OF ENDOTOXIN. 1984. irreg., vol.4, 1986. price varies. Elsevier Science B.V., Books Division, P.O. Box 211, 1000 AE Amsterdam, Netherlands. TEL 31-20-4853911. FAX 31-20-4853705. TELEX 18582 ESPA NL. E-mail: nlinfo-f@elsevier.nl; usinfo-f@elsevier.com; forinfo-kyf04035@niftyserve.or.jp; Site addr.: http://www.elsevier.nl/. (Subscr. in U.S. and Canada to: Elsevier Science Inc., Box 882, Madison Sq. Sta., New York, NY 10159. TEL 212-989-5800) Ed. R.A. Proctor. **Document type:** monographic series.
Refereed Serial

615.19   US   ISSN 0171-2004
CODEN: HEPHD2
HANDBOOK OF EXPERIMENTAL PHARMACOLOGY. 1950. irreg. price varies. Springer-Verlag, 175 Fifth Ave., New York, NY 10010. TEL 212-460-1500. FAX 212-473-6272. (Also: Berlin, Heidelberg, Tokyo and Vienna) (reprint service avail. from ISI) **Indexed:** Chem.Abstr. **Document type:** academic/scholarly publication.
—BLDSC (4250.460000); CASDDS; UnCover. **CCC.**

HANDBOOK OF NATURAL TOXINS. see *MEDICAL SCIENCES*

PHARMACY AND PHARMACOLOGY

615.9 US
HANDBOOK ON INJECTABLE DRUGS. (Supplement avail.) irreg., latest 7th ed. $119 to non-members; members $95. American Society of Hospital Pharmacists, c/o Jean Rogers, Dir., Mkt. Svcs., 7272 Wisconsin Ave., Bethesda, MD 20814. TEL 301-657-4383. FAX 301-657-1251. Ed. Lawrence A. Trissel. **Document type:** academic/scholarly publication.
●Also available online. Vendor(s): Ovid Technologies (DIFT), Knight-Ridder, Inc. (File no.229). Also available on CD-ROM.
Description: Comprehensive coverage of injectable drugs used in admixtures including investigational drugs. Monographs are cross-referenced and arranged according to non-proprietary name.

615 636 GW
HANDBUCH MEDIKAMENTE. 1982. biennial. DM.58. Kamlage Verlag GmbH, Iburgerstr. 112, 49082 Osnabrueck, Germany. TEL 0541-52371. FAX 0541-54879. circ. 20,000 (paid). **Document type:** directory.
Description: Directory of pharmaceuticals used by veterinarians and farmers.

615 CC ISSN 1001-8131
HARBIN YIYAO/HARBIN MEDICINE. (Text in Chinese) q. Zhonghua Yixuehui, Harbin Fenhui, 34, Xi 5 Daojie, Daoli-qu, Harbin, Heilongjiang 150010, People's Republic of China. TEL 413165. Ed. Zhao Zhongwu.

615 US
HARPER HOSPITAL, PHARMACY & THERAPEUTICS NEWSLETTER. 1970. bi-m. free. Harper Hospital (Detroit), 3990 John, Detroit, MI 48201. TEL 313-745-2006. FAX 313-745-1793. Ed. Margo Farber. circ. 500. (processed) **Document type:** newsletter.
Former titles: Harper-Grace Hospitals, Pharmacy and Therapeutics Newsletter; Harper-Grace Hospital Drug Therapy Newsletter; Grace Hospital Drug Therapy Newsletter.

615 JA ISSN 0914-9864
HATTATSU YAKURI YAKUBUTSU CHIRYO KENKYUKAI ZASSHI/JAPANESE JOURNAL OF DEVELOPMENTAL AND THERAPEUTIC PHARMACOLOGY. (Text in Japanese; summaries in English) 1988. a. Hattatsu Yakuri Yakubutsu Chiryo Kenkyukai, Asahikawa Ika Daigaku Shonika, 3-11, 5-go, Nishikagura 4-sen, Asahikawa-shi, Hokkaido 078, Japan.

615.1 US ISSN 0073-1420
HAYES DRUGGIST DIRECTORY. 1912. a. $375. Edward N. Hayes, Publisher, 4229 Birch St, Newport Beach, CA 92660. TEL 714-756-9063. FAX 714-756-0921.

615 CC
HEBEI YIYAO/JOURNAL OF HEBEI MEDICINE. (Text in Chinese) 1973. bi-m. Hebei Yixue Kexueyuan - Hebei Academy of Medical Sciences, 62 Qingyuan Jie, Shijiazhuang, Hebei 050021, People's Republic of China. TEL 0311-612687. Ed. Wang Rongjie. **Document type:** academic/scholarly publication.

HERBALGRAM. see *BIOLOGY — Botany*

615.329 II ISSN 0018-1935
RM265 CODEN: HINAAU
HINDUSTAN ANTIBIOTICS BULLETIN. 1958. q. Rs.60 (foreign $15). Hindustan Antibiotics Ltd., Editorial and Advertisement Office, Pimpri, Poona 411 018, India. TELEX 0146-279 IN. Ed. Dr. S.R. Naik. adv.; bk.rev.; bibl.; charts; illus.; index. circ. 400. **Indexed:** Biol.Abstr., Chem.Abstr., Excerp.Med., Ind.Med., Indian Sci.Abstr., Rev.Plant Path. **Document type:** bulletin.
—BLDSC (4315.100000); CASDDS.
Description: Features documentation of research in and on biotechnicology and antibiotics.

615 JA ISSN 0388-2616
CODEN: HBYNDA
HIROSHIMAKEN BYOIN YAKUZAISHIKAI GAKUJUTSU NENPO/HIROSHIMA SOCIETY OF HOSPITAL PHARMACISTS. ANNUAL RESEARCH REPORT. (Text in Japanese) 1975. a. Hiroshimaken Byoin Yakuzaishikai, Hiroshima Daigaku Igakubu Byoin Yakuzaibu, 2-3, Kasumi 1-chome, Minami-ku, Hiroshima-shi, Hiroshima-ken 734, Japan. Ed. Yoshida Minoru. **Document type:** academic/scholarly publication.
—CASDDS.

615 JA ISSN 0389-4061
HIROSHIMAKEN HOSPITAL PHARMACISTS ASSOCIATION. DRUG INFORMATION NEWS. (Text in Japanese) 1973. q. Hiroshimaken Byoin Yakuzaishikai, Hiroshima Daigaku Igakubu Byoin Yakuzaibu, 2-3, Kasumi 1-chome, Minami-ku, Hiroshima 734, Japan. Ed. Masayoshi Okigawa. **Document type:** newsletter.

HIV AND AIDS TREATMENTS DIRECTORY. see *MEDICAL SCIENCES — Communicable Diseases*

615 JA ISSN 0917-5431
HOHSEN JOURNAL. (Text in Japanese) 1990. a. Gifu Yakka Daigaku Dosokai, Tokyo Shibu - Alumni Association of the Gifu Pharmaceutical University, Tokyo Branch, 101, Yotsubaso, 15-13, Takadanobaba 1-chome, Shinjuku-ku, Tokyo 169, Japan.

615 JA ISSN 0917-0936
HOKKAIDO BYOIN YAKUZAISHIKAISHI/HOKKAIDO SOCIETY OF HOSPITAL PHARMACISTS. JOURNAL. (Text in Japanese) 1960. s-a. Hokkaido Byoin Yakuzaishikai, Hokkaido Daigaku Fuzoku Byoin Yakuzaibu, Nishi 5-chome, Kita 14-jo, Kita-ku, Sapporo-shi, Hokkaido 060, Japan.

615 JA ISSN 0917-5245
HOKURIKU DAIGAKU YAKUGAKUBU SOYAKU KENKYU SHISETSU NENPO/HOKURIKU UNIVERSITY. RESEARCH LABORATORY FOR DEVELOPMENT OF MEDICINE. ANNUAL REPORT OF ACTIVITIES. (Text in English, Japanese; summaries in English) 1988. a. Hokuriku Daigaku, Yakugakubu Soyaku Kenkyu Shisetsu, Ho-3, Kanakawamachi, Kanazawa-shi, Ishikawa-ken 920-11, Japan.

HOME HEALTH PRODUCTS. see *MEDICAL SCIENCES*

615 JA ISSN 0441-2559
CODEN: HYDKAK
HOSHI YAKKA DAIGAKU KIYO/HOSHI COLLEGE OF PHARMACY. (Text in English, Japanese; summaries in English) 1951. a. Hoshi Yakka Daigaku, 4-41, Ebara 2-chome, Shinagawa-ku, Tokyo 142, Japan. **Indexed:** Biol.Abstr., Chem.Abstr.

615.1 US ISSN 0098-6909
RA975.5.P5 CODEN: HOFOD9
HOSPITAL FORMULARY. 1966. m. $40. Advanstar Communications, Inc., 7500 Old Oak Blvd., Cleveland, OH 44130. TEL 216-826-2839. FAX 216-891-2726. (Subscr. to: 131 W. First St., Duluth, MN 55802. TEL 800-346-0085) Ed. Karen Sprague. adv.; bk.rev.; abstr.; bibl.; charts; index. circ. 31,488. (also avail. in microform from UMI) **Indexed:** Biol.Abstr., Biotech.Abstr., C.I.N.L., Curr.Cont., Excerp.Med., I.P.A. **Document type:** trade publication.
●Also available online.
—CASDDS; EMDOCS; Faxon; Genuine Article; SWETS; UMI; UnCover. **CCC.**
Formerly (until 1975): Hospital Formulary Management (ISSN 0018-5655)
Description: Focuses on institutional medicine: clinical tests, drug therapy, drug distribution systems, P&T Committee administration and the socio-economic aspects of health care.

615 UK ISSN 1352-7967
▼**THE HOSPITAL PHARMACIST.** 1994. bi-m. £25. The Pharmaceutical Press, 1 Lambeth High St., London SE1 7JN, England. TEL 071-735-9141. FAX 071-735-7629. **Document type:** trade publication.
—BLDSC (4333.206900).

615 US ISSN 1052-3146
CODEN: HPRPEC
HOSPITAL PHARMACIST REPORT. 1987. m. $39 (foreign $55). Medical Economics Publishing Co., Inc., Five Paragon Dr., Montvale, NJ 07645. TEL 201-358-7200. FAX 201-573-1045. Ed. Val Cardinale. adv. circ. 20,000. (also avail. in microform from UMI) **Document type:** trade publication.
—UMI.
Description: Reports on clinical, professional, business, government and legal news and trends affecting hospital pharmacy management.

615.1 US ISSN 0018-5787
CODEN: HOPHAZ
HOSPITAL PHARMACY. 1966. m. $99 to individuals (foreign $140); institutions $135 (foreign $160) (effective 1996); newsstand price: $15. Lippincott - Raven Publishers, 227 E. Washington Sq., Philadelphia, PA 19106. TEL 215-238-4200. Ed. Neil M. Davis. adv.; illus.; index.; circ. 30,425. circ. Pub. Marcia E. Serepy. (also avail. in microform from UMI) **Indexed:** Abstr.Health Care Manage.Stud., Biol.Abstr., Excerp.Med., Hosp.Lit.Ind., I.P.A.
—BLDSC (4333.207200); Faxon; Genuine Article; SWETS; UMI; UnCover. **CCC.**

615.9 618.73 US ISSN 0739-957X
HOSPITAL PHARMACY DIRECTOR'S MONTHLY MANAGEMENT SERIES. 1979. m. $50. Rx-Data-Pac Service, 8907 Terwilliger's Tr., Cincinnati, OH 45249. TEL 513-489-0943. (looseleaf format)
Description: Contains practical management information for pharmacy managers.

615.1 CN
HOSPITAL PHARMACY IN ONTARIO. 1964. 4/yr. membership. Canadian Society of Hospital Pharmacists, Ontario Branch, c/o 1145 Hunt Club Rd., Ste. 350, Ottawa, ON K1V 0Y3, Canada. Ed. Rosemarie Pavlakovic. circ. 1,000. **Document type:** newsletter.

615.19 658 US ISSN 0739-9561
HOSPITAL PHARMACY SERVICE INSTANT UP-DATE. 1978. m. $70. Rx-Data-Pac Service, 8907 Terwilliger's Tr., Cincinnati, OH 45249. TEL 513-489-0943. Ed. Dr. I.H. Goodman. (looseleaf format; back issues avail.)
Description: Contains current data with "its-a-fact" quizzes, to help meet JCAHO requirements for in-service staff. Includes photocopy rights.

HUAXI YIKE DAXUE XUEBAO/WEST CHINA UNIVERSITY OF MEDICAL SCIENCES. JOURNAL. see *MEDICAL SCIENCES*

HUMAN & EXPERIMENTAL TOXICOLOGY; an international journal. see *ENVIRONMENTAL STUDIES — Toxicology And Environmental Safety*

HUMAN PSYCHOPHARMACOLOGY: CLINICAL AND EXPERIMENTAL. see *MEDICAL SCIENCES — Psychiatry And Neurology*

HUMAN REPRODUCTION. see *MEDICAL SCIENCES — Obstetrics And Gynecology*

615 JA ISSN 0916-7587
HYOGOKEN YAKUZAISHIKAISHI/HYOGO PHARMACEUTICAL SOCIETY. JOURNAL. (Text in Japanese) 1951. m. 300 Yen per no. Hyogoken Yakuzaishikai, 45-3, Shimoyamate Dori 6-chome, Chuo-ku, Kobe-shi, Hyogo-ken 650, Japan.

615.1 NE ISSN 1024-0268
I P S F NEWS BULLETIN. (Text in English, French, German and Spanish) 1960. 3/yr. fl.15. International Pharmaceutical Students Federation, Andries Bickerweg 5, 2517 JP The Hague, Netherlands. TEL 31-70-3631925. FAX 31-70-3633914. E-mail: Keithvh@minnie.iaccess.za. Ed. Keith van Heerden. adv.: B&W page $500. charts; illus.; index. circ. 2,000. **Indexed:** I.P.A. **Document type:** bulletin.
Description: Contains articles, news, information and a calendar of worlwide pharmaceutical events of interest to pharmaceutical students.

615 IE ISSN 0332-2130
I P U REVIEW. 1976. 11/yr. I£30. Irish Pharmaceutical Union, 140 Grange Rd., Dublin 14, Ireland. TEL 01-4931801. FAX 01-4931801. Ed. David Butler. adv.: B&W page I£330, color page I£530; trim 210 x 297; adv. contact: Michael Ryan. bk.rev. circ. 1,600. **Document type:** trade publication.
—BLDSC (4567.487500).
Description: Primary objectives are to reflect the authentic views of the pharmaceutical profession, to acquaint pharmacists of Union policy and information, and to ensure that developments in pharmacy are published and commented on as they occur.

I V S. (Index of Veterinary Specialists) see *VETERINARY SCIENCE*

I V S DESK REFERENCE. see *VETERINARY SCIENCE*

PHARMACY AND PHARMACOLOGY

615 JA ISSN 0285-1199
ICHIYAKU SOMOKU TSUSHIN/DAIICHI SEIYAKU CO., LTD. NEWS. (Text in Japanese) bi-m. Daiichi Seiyaku Co., Ltd., 14-10, Nihonbashi 3-chome, Chuo-ku, Tokyo 103, Japan.

615.1 US ISSN 0019-1221
IDAHO PHARMACIST. 1964. s-a. $15. Idaho State Pharmaceutical Association, 1365 N. Orchard, Ste. 316, Boise, ID 83706. TEL 208-376-2273. FAX 208-376-5814. Ed. Jo An Condie. adv.: page $275; trim 7 1/2 x 9 3/4. stat. circ. 500. **Document type:** newsletter.
Description: For registered pharmacists, pharmacies, hospitals, wholesale drug houses, colleges of pharmacy faculty members and students, drug travelers, nursing associations.

615 JA ISSN 0389-3898
CODEN: IGYAEI
IGAKU TO YAKUGAKU/JOURNAL OF MEDICINE AND PHARMACEUTICAL SCIENCE. (Text in Japanese) 1975. m. 2000 Yen per no. Shizen Kagakusha Co., Ltd., 1-4, Iidabashi 2-chome, Chiyoda-ku, Tokyo 102, Japan. **Indexed:** Chem.Abstr.
—BLDSC (5017.383000); CASDDS.

615.1 US ISSN 0195-2099
ILLINOIS PHARMACIST. 1909. bi-m. $36. Illinois Pharmacists Association, 223 W. Jackson Blvd., Ste. 1000, Chicago, IL 60606-6906. TEL 312-939-7300. Ed. Mark Pilkington. adv. contact: James Flanigan. circ. 42,024. (also avail. in microform from UMI; reprint service avail. from UMI) **Document type:** trade publication.
—BLDSC (4365.470000).
Formerly: Illinois Journal of Pharmacy (ISSN 0147-8222); Which was formed by the 1977 merger of: C R D A News; Illinois Pharmacist (ISSN 0019-2163); Which was formerly: Illinois Drug Process (ISSN 0007-9030)

615 616.9 US
IMMUNOFACTS VACCINES & IMMUNOLOGIC DRUGS. 1993. base vol. (plus s-a. updates). $89.95. Facts and Comparisons, 111 W. Port Plaza, Ste. 400, St. Louis, MO 63146-3098. TEL 800-223-0554. FAX 314-878-5563. (looseleaf format)
Description: Provides information on all vaccines, toxoids, immune globulins, immunologic mediators and modulators, hypersensitivity agents and related non-immunologics.

IMMUNOPHARMACOLOGY. see MEDICAL SCIENCES — Allergology And Immunology

615 US ISSN 0892-3973
CODEN: IITOEF
IMMUNOPHARMACOLOGY AND IMMUNOTOXICOLOGY. 1979. 4/yr. $237 to individuals; institutions $475. Marcel Dekker Journals, 270 Madison Ave., New York, NY 10016. TEL 212-696-9000. FAX 212-685-4540. TELEX 421419 MARDEEK. (Subscr. to: Box 5015, Monticello, NY 12701) Ed. Michael A. Chirigos. (also avail. in microform from RPI) **Indexed:** Biol.Abstr., Biol.Dig., Biotech.Abstr., Chem.Abstr., Curr.Adv.Ecol.Sci., Curr.Cont., Excerp.Med., Helminthol.Abstr., Ind.Med., Ind.Sci.Rev., Sci.Cit.Ind., Sugar Ind.Abstr. **Document type:** academic/scholarly publication.
—BLDSC (4369.760200); ADONIS; CASDDS; Faxon; Genuine Article; SWETS; UMI; UnCover. **CCC.**
Former titles: Journal of Pharmacology and Immunotoxicology; Journal of Immunopharmacology (ISSN 0163-0571)
Refereed Serial

IN VITRO TOXICOLOGY; a journal of molecular and cellular toxicology. see ENVIRONMENTAL STUDIES — Toxicology And Environmental Safety

615.9 FR
INCOMPATEX. 1984. a. 440 F. (effective 1994). Societe d'Editions Medico-Pharmaceutiques (SEMP), 26 rue Lebrun, 75013 Paris, France. TEL 1-43-37-83-50. FAX 1-43-31-94-11. circ. 2,200. (looseleaf format)
Description: Contains 3,000 references to drug interactions and contra-indications.

615 UK ISSN 0963-0759
THE INDEPENDENT COMMUNITY PHARMACIST. 1990. m. £45. Plestor House, Farnham Rd., W. Liss, Hants. GU33 6JQ, England. TEL 01730-894059. FAX 01703-895298. Ed. Steve Titmarsh; Pub. Peter Hopkinson. adv. contact: Paul Fenton. bk.rev. circ. 12,000. **Document type:** trade publication.

615 GW
INDEX NOMINUM. (Text in English, French and German) 1956. biennial. DM.398. Medpharm GmbH Scientific Publishers, Postfach 101061, 70009 Stuttgart, Germany. FAX 0711-2582290. **Document type:** monographic series.

615.1 II ISSN 0019-4360
INDIAN & EASTERN PHARMACY.* (Text in English) 1968. m. Rs.40. L. K. Pandeya, Ed. & Pub., Block F, 105C New Alipore, Calcutta 700053, India.

615.1 II ISSN 0019-462X
HD9672.I5 CODEN: INDRBA
INDIAN DRUGS. (Text in English) 1963. 15/yr. Indian Drug Manufacturers Association, 102B Poonan Chambers, Dr. A.B. Rd., Worli, Bombay 400018, India. TEL 91-22-4924178. adv.; bk.rev.; charts; tr.lit. circ. 6,000. **Indexed:** Anal.Abstr., Biol.Abstr., Chem.Abstr., Excerp.Med.
—BLDSC (4396.180000); CASDDS; EMDOCS; SWETS; UnCover.

615.1 II ISSN 0019-4638
CODEN: IDPIA6
INDIAN DRUGS AND PHARMACEUTICALS INDUSTRY. (Text in English) 1966. bi-m. Rs.20. Chary Publications, 14 Sidh Prasad, Ghatkopar Mahul Rd., Tilak Nagar, Bombay 400089, India. Ed. S.T. Chary. adv.; bk.rev.; illus.; stat. circ. 4,000.
—CASDDS.

615.1 II ISSN 0019-526X
RA975.5.P5 CODEN: IJHPBU
INDIAN JOURNAL OF HOSPITAL PHARMACY. (Text in English) 1965. bi-m. Rs.150($20) (free to members). Indian Hospital Pharmacists' Association, R-566 New Rajinder Nagar, New Delhi 110 060, India. TEL 5754344. Ed. B.D. Miglani. adv.: page Rs.1000; 220 x 160. bk.rev.; charts; illus.; stat.; index. circ. 5,000. **Indexed:** Biol.Abstr., Chem.Abstr., Excerp.Med., I.P.A. **Document type:** academic/scholarly publication.
●Also available online.
—CASDDS.
Description: Aims to develop advanced technology for the manufacture of several vital drugs ranging from antiasthmatics and cardiovascular medicines to antibacterials, antiarthritics, antiparasitics and medical aerosols.

615.1 II ISSN 0019-5464
RS119.I5 CODEN: IJPEB3
INDIAN JOURNAL OF PHARMACEUTICAL EDUCATION. 1967. q. Rs.150($20) Association of Pharmaceutical Teachers of India, c/o College of Pharmaceutical Sciences, Manipal 576 119, India. TEL 91-8252-71201. FAX 91-8252-70500. TELEX 833209 VVHC IN. E-mail: pgr@kmc.ernet.in. Ed. P. Gundu Rao. adv.; bk.rev. circ. 1,100. **Indexed:** Biol.Abstr., Chem.Abstr., I.P.A. **Document type:** academic/scholarly publication.
—BLDSC (4418.700000); CASDDS.

615.1 II ISSN 0250-474X
CODEN: IJSIDW
INDIAN JOURNAL OF PHARMACEUTICAL SCIENCES. (Text in English) 1939. bi-m. Rs.500($100) Indian Pharmaceutical Association, Kalina Santacruz East, Bombay 400098, India. Ed. A.K. Kapadia. adv.: page Rs.900; trim 24 x 19. bk.rev. circ. 1,200. (also avail. in microfilm from UMI; reprint service avail. from UMI) **Indexed:** Anal.Abstr., Biol.Abstr., Biotech.Abstr., Chem.Abstr., Excerp.Med., ExtraMED, Hort.Abstr., I.P.A., Mass Spectr.Bull., Nutr.Abstr., Plant Grow.Reg.Abstr., Rev.Med.& Vet.Mycol., Seed Abstr., Soils & Fert., Sugar Ind.Abstr. **Document type:** academic/scholarly publication.
●Also available online.
Also available on CD-ROM.
—BLDSC (4418.750000); CASDDS; Faxon; UMI; UnCover.
Formerly (until 1978): Indian Journal of Pharmacy (ISSN 0019-5472)

615 II ISSN 0253-7613
CODEN: INJPD2
INDIAN JOURNAL OF PHARMACOLOGY. (Text in English) 1969. q. Rs.800($80) Indian Pharmacologial Society, Department of Pharmacology, Jipmer, Pondicherry 605006, India. TEL 413-36380. FAX 413-38132. Ed. C. Adithan. adv.: page $100. bk.rev. circ. 1,450. **Indexed:** Biol.Abstr., Chem.Abstr., Curr.Adv.Ecol.Sci., Excerp.Med., ExtraMED. **Document type:** academic/scholarly publication.
●Also available on CD-ROM.
—CASDDS.
Description: Contains original research articles, and reviews on pharmacology, clinical pharmacology, chemotherapy, ethnopharmacology and molecular biology related to drug action.
Refereed Serial

INDIAN JOURNAL OF PHYSIOLOGY AND PHARMACOLOGY. see BIOLOGY — Physiology

615.19 II
INDIAN PHARMACEUTICAL DIRECTORY. (Text in English) 1988. triennial. $110. Technical Press Publications, 5-1 Convent Street, Colaba, Bombay 400 039, India. TEL 022-2021446. FAX 022-2871499. TELEX 011-83479 CHEM IN. Ed. J.P. Sousa. adv.; bk.rev.; abstr.; charts; illus. circ. 12,000. **Document type:** directory.

615.1 II ISSN 0073-6635
INDIAN PHARMACEUTICAL GUIDE. (Text in English) 1963. a. $80. Pamposh Publications, 506 Ashok Bhawan, 93 Nehru Pl., New Delhi 110019, India. TEL 6432797. Ed. Mohan C. Bazaz. adv. circ. 5,000. **Document type:** directory.
Description: Contains various information on drugs and pharmaceuticals produced in India for local consumption and exports.

615 US
INDIANA PHARMACIST.* m. Indiana Pharmacists Association, 729 N. Pennsylvania St., Indianapolis, IN 46204-1128. adv. circ. 2,600.

615.19 SP ISSN 0213-5574
INDUSTRIA FARMACEUTICA; investigacion y production. 1986. bi-m. 11300 ptas.($173) (effective 1995). Editorial Alcion, S.A., Triana, 53, 28016 Madrid, Spain. TEL 34-1-457-64-00. FAX 34-1-457-39-45. TELEX 49236 QUMI E. Ed. Ramon R. Madrid. adv.; bk.rev.; index. circ. 2,000.

INDUSTRIAL CROPS AND PRODUCTS. see AGRICULTURE — Crop Production And Soil

615 BL ISSN 0104-0219
INFARMA. bi-m. free. Conselho Federal de Farmacia, SBS Quadra 01, Bloco K, 70093-900 Brasilia D.F., Brazil. TEL 061-224-68-49. FAX 061-224-68-25. bk.rev.; illus.; circ. 10,000. (controlled).
Formerly (until 1991): Brazil. Conselho Federal de Farmacia. Relatorio.

615 NE ISSN 0923-9405
CODEN: IDTSEQ
INFLAMMATION AND DRUG THERAPY SERIES. (Text in English) 1987. irreg., vol.5, 1992. price varies. Kluwer Academic Publishers, Postbus 17, 3300 AA Dordrecht, Netherlands. TEL 31-78-392392. FAX 31-78-392254. TELEX 29245 KAPG NL. (Dist. by: Kluwer Academic Publishers Group, P.O. Box 322, 3300 AH Dordrecht, Netherlands. TEL 31-78-392392. FAX 31-78-546474; N. America dist. addr.: Box 358, Accord Sta., Hingham, MA 02018-0358. TEL 617-871-6600. FAX 617-871-6528) **Document type:** monographic series.
—BLDSC (4478.845200); CASDDS.
Refereed Serial

PHARMACY AND PHARMACOLOGY

615   SZ   ISSN 1023-3830
RM1   CODEN: INREFB
INFLAMMATION RESEARCH. (Supplements avail.) (Text in English) 1969. 14/yr. 1280.60 SFr. (foreign 1303.40 SFr.). (European Histamine Research Society) Birkhaeuser Verlag, P.O. Box 133, CH-4010 Basel, Switzerland. TEL 061-2717400. FAX 061-2717666. (Dist. in N. America by: Springer-Verlag, Mercedes Distribution Center, 160 Imlay St., Brooklyn, NY 11231, USA) Co-sponsors: European Workshop on Inflammation; American Inflammation Research Association; British Inflammation Research Association) Ed. M.J. Parnham. index. circ. 900. **Indexed:** Apic.Abstr., Biol.Abstr., Biotech.Abstr., Chem.Abstr., Curr.Adv.Biochem., Curr.Adv.Cancer Res., Curr.Adv.Ecol.Sci., Curr.Cont., Dairy Sci.Abstr., Dent.Ind., Excerp.Med., Helminthol.Abstr., Ind.Med., Ind.Sci.Rev., Nutr.Abstr., Rev.Plant Path., Sci.Cit.Ind. **Document type:** academic/scholarly publication.
—BLDSC (4478.845300); ADONIS; CASDDS; EMDOCS; Faxon; Genuine Article; UMI; UnCover. **CCC.**
Formerly (until 1995): Agents and Actions (ISSN 0065-4299)

616.047   NE   ISSN 0925-4692
CODEN: IAOAES
INFLAMMOPHARMACOLOGY; an international interdisciplinary journal publishing original articles and topical reviews on inflammation and pharmacology. (Text in English) 1991. q. fl.417 to institutions; $267 to institutions in U.S. (effective 1996). Kluwer Academic Publishers, Postbus 17, 3300 AA Dordrecht, Netherlands. TEL 31-78-392392. FAX 31-78-392254. TELEX 29245 KAPG NL. E-mail: SERVICES@WKAP.NL. (Dist. by: Kluwer Academic Publishers Group, P.O. Box 322, 3300 AH Dordrecht, Netherlands. TEL 31-78-392392. FAX 31-78-546474; N. America dist. addr.: Box 358, Accord Sta., Hingham, MA 02018-0358. TEL 617-871-6600. FAX 617-871-6528) Ed. K.D. Rainsford. (also avail. in microform from UMI; back issues avail.) **Indexed:** Chem.Abstr., Excerp.Med. (1992-), Inpharma, Int.Abstr.Biol.Sci., Reac. **Document type:** academic/scholarly publication.
—BLDSC (4478.845700); CASDDS; UMI. **CCC.**
Description: Publishes papers on all aspects of inflammation and its pharmacological control.
Refereed Serial

615   SP   ISSN 0210-9417
INFORMACION TERAPEURICA DE LA SEGURIDAD SOCIAL. 1977. m. free. Centro de Informacion de Medicamentos, Km. 2 Carretera Majadahonda-Pozuelo, 28220 Majadahonda (Madrid), Spain.

615   SW   ISSN 1101-7104
INFORMATION FRAAN LAEKEMEDELSVERKET. 1976. bi-m. Laekemedelsverket, P.O. Box 26, S-751 03 Uppsala, Sweden.
Formerly (until 1990): Information fraan Socialstyrelsens Laekemedelsavdeling (ISSN 0347-5107)

615   IT   ISSN 0073-7984
INFORMATORE FARMACEUTICO. (In 3 vols.: Vol.1. Specialita Medicinali, Vol.2. Parafarmaceutici, Vol.3. Indirizzi) 1940. a. L.385000 (foreign L.425000) includes Notiziario Medico Farmaceutico. Organizzazione Editoriale Medico-Farmaceutica, Via Edolo 42, Box 10434, 20125 Milan, Italy. TEL 2-67-50-51. FAX 2-67-50-52-02. (U.S. dist.: Drug Intelligence & Clinical Pharmacy, Box 42435, Cincinnati OH 45242) Ed. Dr. Lucio Marini. adv.: B&W page L.3550000, color page L.4800000; trim 180 x 260. circ. 4,457.

615   IT   ISSN 1121-1644
INFORMAZIONI SUI FARMACI. 1977. bi-m. L.80000($60) (foreign L.120000 ($90) (effective 1995). Farmacie Comunali Riunite di Reggio Emilia, Servizio Informazione e Documentazione Scientifica, Via Doberdo 9, 42100 Reggio Emilia, Italy. TEL 39-522-543450. FAX 39-522-550146. Ed. Gian Franco Nasi. bk.rev.; charts; stat.; index. circ. 7,000. (tabloid format; back issues avail.) **Document type:** bulletin.
Description: Covers topics in clinical pharmacology for physicians and pharmacists and relevant issues of health policy and health education.
Refereed Serial

INHALATION TOXICOLOGY. see *ENVIRONMENTAL STUDIES — Toxicology And Environmental Safety*

658   UK
INSTITUTE NEWS. 1978. q. £30. Institute of Pharmacy Management International, 17 Wood View, Birkby Park, Huddersfield, W. Yorks. HD2 2DT, England. TEL 01484-535125. Ed. Malcolm Ian Almond. circ. 1,000. (back issues avail.) **Document type:** newsletter.
Formerly: Journal of Management and Communication (ISSN 0958-482X)
Description: Covers management, finance and pharmacy practice.

INTERKANTONALE KONTROLLSTELLE FUER HEILMITTEL. MONATSBERICHT/OFFICE INTERCANTONAL DE CONTROLE DE MEDICAMENTS. BULLETIN MENSUEL/UFFICIO INTERCANTONALE DI CONTROLLO DEI MEDICAMENTI. BOLLETTINO MENSILE. see *MEDICAL SCIENCES*

615   SZ   ISSN 1019-2069
INTERNATIONAL ACADEMY FOR BIOMEDICAL AND DRUG RESEARCH. 1992. irreg. price varies. S. Karger AG, Allschwilerstr. 10, P.O. Box, CH-4009 Basel, Switzerland. TEL 061-3061111. FAX 061-3061234. E-mail: Karger@Karger.ch. Ed.Bd. **Document type:** academic/scholarly publication.
—BLDSC (4535.592200).
Refereed Serial

INTERNATIONAL CLINICAL PSYCHOPHARMACOLOGY. see *PSYCHOLOGY*

615   NE   ISSN 0074-3879
INTERNATIONAL CONGRESS OF PHARMACEUTICAL SCIENCES. PROCEEDINGS. a., 1994, Lisbon. International Pharmaceutical Federation - Federation Internationale Pharmaceutique, c/o Alan W. Davidson, Sec.-Gen., Andries Bickerweg 5, 2517 JP The Hague, Netherlands. TEL 31-70-36312925. FAX 31-70-363914. **Document type:** proceedings.

INTERNATIONAL CONGRESS ON CLINICAL CHEMISTRY. ABSTRACTS. see *BIOLOGY — Biological Chemistry*

INTERNATIONAL CONGRESS ON CLINICAL CHEMISTRY. PAPERS. see *BIOLOGY — Biological Chemistry*

615   US
INTERNATIONAL DIRECTORY OF INVESTIGATORS IN PSYCHOPHARMACOLOGY.* 1973. irreg. U.S. Public Health Service, Alcohol, Drug Abuse and Mental Health Administration, 5600 Fishers Lane, Rockville, MD 20857. TEL 301-496-4000. (Co-sponsor: World Health Organization) Ed. Alice A. Leeds. circ. 6,000.

INTERNATIONAL DRUG THERAPY NEWSLETTER. see *MEDICAL SCIENCES — Psychiatry And Neurology*

INTERNATIONAL FEDERATION OF CLINICAL CHEMISTRY. JOURNAL. see *BIOLOGY — Biological Chemistry*

615.328   US   ISSN 0300-9831
QP771   CODEN: IVEBBN
INTERNATIONAL JOURNAL FOR VITAMIN AND NUTRITION RESEARCH. 1930. q. $151. Hogrefe & Huber Publishers, Box 2487, Kirkland, WA 98083. TEL 206-820-1500. FAX 206-823-8324. Ed. P. Walter. adv.: bk.rev.; abstr. circ. 800. **Indexed:** Biol.Abstr., Chem.Abstr., Curr.Adv.Ecol.Sci., Dairy Sci.Abstr., Excerp.Med., Food Sci.& Tech.Abstr., Ind.Med., Ind.Sci.Rev., Ind.Vet., Maize Abstr., Nutr.Abstr., Pig News & Info., Poult.Abstr., Rev.Med.& Vet.Mycol., Sci.Cit.Ind., Soyabean Abstr., Sport Fish.Abstr., Triticale Abstr., Trop.Dis.Bull., Trop.Oil Seeds Abstr., Vet.Bull., Wild.Rev. **Document type:** academic/scholarly publication.
—BLDSC (4542.698000); CASDDS; Faxon; Genuine Article; SWETS; UnCover. **CCC.**
Formerly: Internationale Zeitschrift fuer Vitamin-Forschung (ISSN 0020-9406)
Description: Provides a scientific international forum for work on the two vast and closely connected research fields of vitaminology and nutrition.

615.1   GW   ISSN 0946-1965
RM1   CODEN: ICTHEK
INTERNATIONAL JOURNAL OF CLINICAL PHARMACOLOGY AND THERAPEUTICS. (Text in English) 1967. m. DM.340($165) Dustri-Verlag Dr. Karl Feistle, Bahnhofstr. 9, 82041 Deisenhofen, Germany. TEL 089-613861-0. FAX 089-613-5412. Ed. G. Hitzenberger. adv.; bibl.; charts; illus. circ. 1,200. **Indexed:** Biol.Abstr., Biotech.Abstr., Chem.Abstr., Curr.Adv.Ecol.Sci., Curr.Cont., Dairy Sci.Abstr., Dent.Ind., Excerp.Med., Helminthol.Abstr., I.P.A., Ind.Med., Ind.Sci.Rev., INIS Atomind., Psychol.Abstr., Sci.Cit.Ind., SSCI. **Document type:** academic/scholarly publication.
—CASDDS; Faxon; Genuine Article; SWETS; UnCover. **CCC.**
Former titles (until 1994): International Journal of Clinical Pharmacology, Therapy and Toxicology (ISSN 0174-4879); (until 1980): International Journal of Clinical Pharmacology and Biopharmacy (ISSN 0340-0026); Internationale Zeitschrift fuer Klinische Pharmakologie, Therapie und Toxikologie (ISSN 0020-9392)

615.19   SZ   ISSN 0251-1649
CODEN: CPHRDE
INTERNATIONAL JOURNAL OF CLINICAL PHARMACOLOGY RESEARCH. Short title: Clinical Pharmacology Research. 1981. bi-m. 330 SFr. Bioscience Ediprint Inc., Rue Alexandre-Gavard 16, CH-1227 Carouge-Geneva, Switzerland. TEL 022-3003383. FAX 022-3002489. TELEX 423355-BIOS-CH. Ed. A. Bertell. (reprint service avail. from UMI) **Indexed:** Excerp.Med., Kidney, Rev.Med.& Vet.Mycol. **Document type:** academic/scholarly publication.
—BLDSC (4542.170800); CASDDS; Faxon; Genuine Article; SWETS; UMI. **CCC.**

INTERNATIONAL JOURNAL OF DRUG POLICY. see *DRUG ABUSE AND ALCOHOLISM*

INTERNATIONAL JOURNAL OF IMMUNOPATHOLOGY AND PHARMACOLOGY. see *MEDICAL SCIENCES — Allergology And Immunology*

615 616.97   UK   ISSN 0192-0561
CODEN: IJIMDS
INTERNATIONAL JOURNAL OF IMMUNOPHARMACOLOGY. 1979. m. £472($751) (effective 1996). Elsevier Science Ltd., Pergamon, P.O. Box 800, Kidlington, Oxford OX5 1DX, England. TEL 44-1865-843000. FAX 44-1865-843010.
E-mail: nlinfo-f@elsevier.nl; usinfo-f@elsevier.com; forinfo-kyf04035@niftyserve.or.jp; Site addr.: http://www.elsevier.nl/. (Subscr. in U.S. and Canada to: Elsevier Science, 660 White Plains Rd., Tarrytown, NY 10591-5153. TEL 914-524-9200. FAX 914-333-2444) Ed.Bd. adv. circ. 1,250. (also avail. in microfilm from UMI; reprint service avail. from UMI) **Indexed:** Biol.Abstr., Biotech.Abstr., Chem.Abstr., Curr.Adv.Ecol.Sci., Curr.Cont., Excerp.Med., Helminthol.Abstr., Ind.Med., Ind.Sci.Rev., Ind.Vet., Protozool.Abstr., Rev.Med.& Vet.Mycol., Sci.Cit.Ind, Vet.Bull. **Document type:** academic/scholarly publication.
—BLDSC (4542.301000); ADONIS; CASDDS; Faxon; Genuine Article; SWETS; UMI; UnCover. **CCC.**
Description: Publishes contributions of clinical relevance which integrate pharmacology and immunology.
Refereed Serial

INTERNATIONAL JOURNAL OF ORIENTAL MEDICINE/GUOJI HANFANG YIYAO ZAZHI. see *ALTERNATIVE MEDICINE*

615   UK   ISSN 0260-6267
CODEN: IPTMDN
INTERNATIONAL JOURNAL OF PHARMACEUTICAL TECHNOLOGY & PRODUCT MANUFACTURE. 1979. 4/yr. £60($126) Childwall University Press Ltd., Box 78, London NW11 0PG, England. TEL 01-455-0011. FAX 01-458-2278. TELEX 8954242-POWDER-G. Ed. Dr. N.A. Armstrong. **Indexed:** Biol.Abstr., Biotech.Abstr., Excerp.Med. —CASDDS.

615 NE ISSN 0378-5173
CODEN: IJPHDE
INTERNATIONAL JOURNAL OF PHARMACEUTICS. (Text in English) 1978. 30/yr. fl.6420($3915) (effective 1996). Elsevier Science B.V., P.O. Box 211, 1000 AE Amsterdam, Netherlands. TEL 31-20-4853911. FAX 31-20-4853598. TELEX 18582 ESPA NL. E-mail: nlinfo-f@elsevier.nl; usinfo-f@elsevier.com; forinfo-kyf04035@niftyserve.or.jp; Site addr.: http://www.elsevier.nl/. (Subscr. in U.S. and Canada to: Elsevier Science Inc., Box 882, Madison Sq. Sta., New York, NY 10159. TEL 212-989-5800. FAX 212-633-3990) Ed. P.F. D'Arcy. adv. (also avail. in microform from UMI; back issues avail.; reprint service avail. from SWZ) **Indexed:** Biodet.Abstr., Biol.Abstr., Biotech.Abstr., Chem.Abstr., Curr.Cont., Dairy Sci.Abstr., Excerp.Med., I.P.A., Ind.Sci.Rev., INIS Atomind., Sci.Cit.Ind., Sugar Ind.Abstr. **Document type:** academic/scholarly publication.
●Also available online.
—BLDSC (4542.454000); ADONIS; CASDDS; Faxon; Genuine Article; SWETS; UnCover. **CCC.**
Description: Publishes research results dealing with all aspects of pharmaceutics including physical, chemical, analytical, biological and engineering studies related to drug delivery.
Refereed Serial

615 NE ISSN 0925-1618
CODEN: IJPYEW
INTERNATIONAL JOURNAL OF PHARMACOGNOSY. (Text in English, French and German) 1954. q. $170 to individuals; institutions $317. Swets & Zeitlinger bv, Heereweg 347, 2161 CA Lisse, Netherlands. TEL 31-2521-35111. FAX 31-2521-15888. TELEX 41325. (Dist. in N. America by: Swets & Zeitlinger, 440 Creamery Way, Ste. A, Exton, PA 19341. TEL 800-447-9387. FAX 610-524-5366) Ed. John M. Pezzuto. adv.; bk.rev.; charts; illus. (also avail. in microform from SWZ; reprint service avail. from SWZ) **Indexed:** Biol.Abstr., Biotech.Abstr., Chem.Abstr., Curr.Adv.Ecol.Sci., Excerp.Med., Forest.Abstr., Forest Prod.Abstr., Hort.Abstr., Ind.Vet., Ornam.Hort., Seed Abstr. **Document type:** academic/scholarly publication.
—BLDSC (4542.454200); CASDDS; SWETS; UnCover. **CCC.**
Former titles: Pharmacognosy; International Journal of Crude Drug Research (ISSN 0167-7314); Quarterly Journal of Crude Drug Research (ISSN 0033-5525)

615 UK ISSN 0961-7671
INTERNATIONAL JOURNAL OF PHARMACY PRACTICE. 1991. q. £64 (foreign £72). Royal Pharmaceutical Society of Great Britain, 1 Lambeth High St., London SE1 7JN, England. TEL 071-735-9141. FAX 071-735-7629. TELEX 9312131542-PS-G. Ed. Douglas Simpson. adv. circ. 1,000. **Document type:** academic/scholarly publication.
—BLDSC (4542.454300).

INTERNATIONAL JOURNAL OF PSYCHOSOMATICS. see *MEDICAL SCIENCES*

INTERNATIONAL MOCHIDA MEMORIAL SYMPOSIUM. see *MEDICAL SCIENCES*

615 UN ISSN 0257-3717
INTERNATIONAL NARCOTICS CONTROL BOARD. REPORT FOR (YEAR). French edition (ISSN 0257-3725); Spanish edition (ISSN 0257-3733) 1968. a. $12. (International Narcotics Control Board - Organe International de Controle des Stupefiants) United Nations Publications, Room DC2-0853, New York, NY 10017. TEL 212-963-8302; 800-253-9646. FAX 212-963-3489. (Or Vienna International Centre, P.O. Box 500, 1400 Vienna, Austria) (also avail. in microfiche from CIS) **Indexed:** IIS.
—BLDSC (7524.185000).
Former titles: United Nations. International Narcotics Control Board. Annual Report; United Nations. Permanent Central Opium Board. Report of the Permanent Central Opium Board on its Work; United Nations. Permanent Central Opium Board. Report to the Economic and Social Council on the Work of the Permanent Central Narcotics (Opium) Board (ISSN 0082-8343)
Description: Focuses on the operation of the international drug control system, with an analysis of the world drug situation.

INTERNATIONAL PRESS CUTTING SERVICE: CHEMICAL PROCESS ENGINEERING. DRUGS - PHARMACEUTICALS. see *ENGINEERING — Chemical Engineering*

615.19 SZ ISSN 1013-9222
INTERNATIONAL SYMPOSIA ON THE PHARMACOLOGY OF THERMOREGULATION. (Text in English) irreg., 8th 1991, Odense. price varies. S. Karger AG, Allschwilerstr. 10, P.O. Box, CH-4009 Basel, Switzerland. TEL 061-3061111. FAX 061-3061234. E-mail: Karger@Karger.ch. (reprint service avail. from ISI) **Indexed:** Biol.Abstr., Curr.Cont., Ind.Med. **Document type:** monographic series.
Refereed Serial

INTERNATIONAL SYMPOSIUM ON QUANTUM BIOLOGY AND QUANTUM PHARMACOLOGY. PROCEEDINGS. see *BIOLOGY*

INTERNATIONAL UPDATE. see *MEDICAL SCIENCES — Communicable Diseases*

615.1 GW ISSN 0074-9729
CODEN: ISHPAO
DER INTERNATIONALEN GESELLSCHAFT FUER GESCHICHTE DER PHARMAZIE. VEROEFFENTLICHUNGEN. NEUE FOLGE. (Text in English and German) 1953; N.S. irreg., vol.58, 1990. Wissenschaftliche Verlagsgesellschaft mbH, Postfach 101061, 70009 Stuttgart, Germany. TEL 0711-2582-0. FAX 0711-2582-290. TELEX 723636-DAZ-D. Ed. Wolfgang-Hagen Hein. **Document type:** monographic series.
—CASDDS.

615.5 US ISSN 0276-4342
RM300
INTERNIST'S COMPENDIUM OF DRUG THERAPY. Spine title: Compendium of Drug Therapy. 1980. a. $49.95. Compendium Publications Group Ltd., 1 Harmon Meadow Blvd., Secaucus, NJ 07094. TEL 201-864-2400. FAX 201-864-3626.

615 US ISSN 0167-6997
RC271.C5 CODEN: INNDDK
INVESTIGATIONAL NEW DRUGS; the journal of anti-cancer agents. 1983. q. fl.498 to institutions; $319 to institutions in U.S. (effective 1996). Kluwer Academic Publishers Boston, Box 358, Accord Sta., Hingham, MA 02018-0358. TEL 617-871-6600. FAX 617-871-6528. TELEX 200190. (Dist. outside N. America by: Kluwer Academic Publishers Group, P.O. Box 322, 3300 AH Dordrecht, Netherlands. TEL 31-78-392392. FAX 31-78-546474) Ed. Dr. Daniel D. Von Hoff. adv.; bk.rev. (also avail. in microform from UMI; back issues avail.; reprint service avail. from SWZ,UMI) **Indexed:** ASCA, Chem.Abstr., Curr.Cont., Excerp.Med., Ind.Med., Ind.Sci.Rev., Int.Abstr.Biol.Sci., Sci.Cit.Ind., Telegen. **Document type:** academic/scholarly publication.
—BLDSC (4559.885000); CASDDS; Faxon; Genuine Article; SWETS; UMI; UnCover. **CCC.**
Refereed Serial

615 US ISSN 0889-7735
IOWA PHARMACIST.* m. Iowa Pharmacist Association, 8515 Douglas No. 16, Des Moines, IA 50322. adv. circ. 2,100.
—BLDSC (4566.550000).

615.1 IE ISSN 0332-0707
IRISH PHARMACY JOURNAL.* 1923. m. £3. 37 Northuberland Rd., Dublin 4, Ireland. TEL 600551. Ed. P. O'Sullivan. adv.; bk.rev.; illus.; tr.lit. circ. 2,000. **Indexed:** I.P.A.
—BLDSC (4574.640000).
Formerly (until 1972): Irish Chemist and Druggist (ISSN 0021-1109)

ISHI SHIKAISHI YAKUZAISHI CHOSA/SURVEY ON PHYSICIANS, DENTISTS AND PHARMACEUTISTS. see *MEDICAL SCIENCES*

615.1 IS ISSN 0017-7865
ISRAEL PHARMACEUTICAL JOURNAL/HA-ROKEACH HA-IVRI/ASSOCIATION PHARMACEUTIQUE D'ISRAEL. JOURNAL. (Text in English, French and Hebrew) 1941. 6/yr. Pharmaceutical Association of Israel, P.O. Box 566, Tel Aviv 65 112, Israel. Eds. E. Menczel, Z. Tomer. adv.; charts; illus. circ. 5,000. **Indexed:** Biol.Abstr., Chem.Abstr., Excerp.Med., I.P.A.
●Also available online.

615 574.192 JA ISSN 0288-2906
IYAKU ANZENSEI KENKYUKAI KAIHO/JAPANESE SOCIETY FOR BIOPHARMACEUTICAL STATISTICS. BULLETIN. (Text in English, Japanese) 1979. q. 1000 Yen per no. (Iyaku Anzensei Kenkyukai) Saientisutosha - Scientist Inc., 3-2, Kanda Surugadai, Chiyoda-ku, Tokyo 101, Japan.

615 574.192 JA
IYAKU ANZENSEI KENKYUKAI TEIREIKAI SHIRYO/PROCEEDINGS OF REGULAR MEETINGS ON BIOPHARMACEUTICAL STATISTICS. (Text in English, Japanese) q. (Iyaku Anzensei Kenkyukai - Japanese Society for Biopharmaceutical Statistics) Saientisutosha - Scientist Inc., 3-2, Kanda Surugadai, Chiyoda-ku, Tokyo 101, Japan. **Document type:** proceedings.

615 JA
IYAKU DAIJESUTO/PHARMACEUTICAL DIGEST. (Text in Japanese) m. 45000 Yen. Iyakuhin Sango Kenkyujo - Drug Business Research Co., Ltd., 25-2, Koishikawa 1-chome, Bunkyo-ku, Tokyo 112, Japan.

615 JA ISSN 0287-4741
IYAKU JANARU/MEDICINE AND DRUG JOURNAL. (Text in Japanese) 1965. m. 2163 Yen per no. Iyaku Janarusha - Medicine & Drug Journal Co., Ltd., 2-8, Hiranocho 3-chome, Chuo-ku, Osaka 541, Japan.
—BLDSC (5534.005700).

615 JA ISSN 0579-2762
IYAKU NO MON/GATEWAY TO MEDICINE. (Text in Japanese) 1961. bi-m. Torii Yakuhin K.K., 4-1, Nihonbashi Honcho 3-chome, Chuo-ku, Tokyo 103, Japan.
—BLDSC (4589.217000).

IYAKU TOKKYO SHOROKU/MEDICINE - PATENTS ABSTRACTS. see *PHARMACY AND PHARMACOLOGY — Abstracting, Bibliographies, Statistics*

615 JA ISSN 0912-2141
IYAKUHIN FUKUSAYO BUNKEN GEPPO/MONTHLY REPORT ON ADVERSE REACTIONS TO DRUGS. (Text in Japanese) 1986. m. (Nihon Iyaku Joho Senta - Japan Pharmaceutical Information Center) Chuwa Insatsu K.K., 2-14, Irifune 2-chome, Chuo-ku, Tokyo 104, Japan.

615 JA ISSN 0286-6153
IYAKUHIN FUKUSAYO JOHO/INFORMATION ON SIDE EFFECTS OF DRUGS. (Text in Japanese) 1977. irreg. 3800 Yen per no. Yakuma Kohosha, 47-8-202, Koenji Minami 3-chome, Suginami-ku, Tokyo 166, Japan.

615 JA ISSN 0911-9329
IYAKUHIN NO FUKUSAYO. ANNUAL REPORT/ADVERSE REACTIONS TO DRUGS. ANNUAL REPORT. (Text in Japanese) 1990. a. 5460 Yen. Chugai Igakusha, 62, Yaraicho, Shinjuku-ku, Tokyo 162, Japan.

615 JA
IYAKUHIN SEIZO SHISHIN. English edition: Drug Approval and Licensing Procedures in Japan (ISSN 0289-9922) (Text in Japanese) 1962. a. (Society of Japanese Pharmacopoeia) Yakugyo Jiho Co., Ltd., 2-36 Kanda Jimbo-cho, Chiyoda-ku, Tokyo 101, Japan.

615.9 JA ISSN 0385-5015
CODEN: ISSKEY
IYAKUHIN SOGO SAYO KENKYU/RESEARCH ON DRUG ACTIONS AND INTERACTIONS. (Text in Japanese) 1975. s-a. 3000 Yen. Iyakuhin Sogo Sayo Kenkyukai - Research Society of Drug Actions and Interactions, Hirosaki Daigaku Igakubu Yakurigaku Kyoshitsu, 5, Zaifucho, Hirosaki-shi, Aomori-ken 036, Japan. bk.rev. circ. 1,200.
—CASDDS.

615.19 JA ISSN 0915-163X
J A P I C WEEKLY BULLETIN. (Text in Japanese) 1973. w. (Japan Pharmaceutical Information Center - Nihon Iyaku Joho Senta, 3rd Fl., Nagai-Kinenkan, 2-12-15 Shibuya, Shibuya-ku, Tokyo 150, Japan. FAX 03-5466-1814. Ed. H. Miyake. bk.rev.; cum.index. circ. 600. **Document type:** bulletin.
Formerly: Japan Pharmaceutical Information Center. Information.

615 JA ISSN 0918-3566
J P M A UPDATE. (Text in English) 1991. s-a. Japan Pharmaceutical Manufacturers Association - Nihon Seiyaku Kogyo Kyokai, 4-1, Nihonbashi Honcho 3-chome, Chuo-ku, Tokyo 103, Japan.

615.9 JA
JAPAN PHARMA INSIGHT; current business news, side effects of drugs, investigational drug reports. 1985. m. $1500. O.T.O. Research Corporation, Takeuchi Bldg., 1-34-12 Takatanobaba, Shinjuku-ku, Tokyo 160, Japan. Ed. Koichi Ogawa. circ. 175.

PHARMACY AND PHARMACOLOGY

615   JA   ISSN 0917-7825
JAPAN PHARMACEUTICAL REFERENCE. (Text in English) 1989. irreg., latest 3rd ed. $180. Japan Medical Products International Trade Association (JAMPITA), Ninjin Bldg., 7-1 Nihonbashi-Honcho 4-chome, Chuo-ku, Tokyo 103, Japan. TEL 81-3-3241-2106. FAX 81-3-3241-2109. Ed. Kuniichiro Ohno. adv.
Document type: academic/scholarly publication.
Description: Introduces pharmaceutical administration and new drugs in Japan.

615   JA   ISSN 0917-8678
JAPANESE ETHICAL PHARMACEUTICAL TARIFF. (Text in English) 1984. biennial. 21000 Yen per no. Pharmadata Publishing, 519-1, Minamicho, Marutamachi Agaru, Higashisanbongi Dori, Kamigyo-ku, Kyoto 602, Japan.

JAPANESE JOURNAL OF ANTIBIOTICS. see *MEDICAL SCIENCES*

616.89   JA   ISSN 1340-7007
CODEN: NKRZE5
JAPANESE JOURNAL OF CHEMOTHERAPY. (Text in English, Japanese) 1953. m. $170 per mo. (effective 1995). Nihon Kagaku Ryoho Gakkai - Japan Society of Chemotherapy, 2-20-8 Kamiosaki, Shinagawa-ku, Tokyo 141, Japan. TEL 81-3-3493-7129. FAX 81-3-5434-0843. Ed. Keisuke Sunakawa. adv.; abstr.; index. circ. 4,000. **Indexed:** Biol.Abstr., Biotech.Abstr., Chem.Abstr., Curr.Adv.Ecol.Sci., Curr.Cont., Excerp.Med., I.P.A., Ind.Med., Ind.Sci.Rev., Protozool.Abstr. **Document type:** academic/scholarly publication.
—BLDSC (3172.305000); CASDDS; UMI.
Formerly (until 1994, vol.42): Nihon Kagaku Ryoho Gakkai Zasshi - Chemotherapy (ISSN 0009-3165)
Refereed Serial

615.1   JA   ISSN 0021-5198
QP901   CODEN: JJPAAZ
JAPANESE JOURNAL OF PHARMACOLOGY. (Supplement avail.) (Text in English) 1951. m. 20000 Yen (foreign $325) (effective Jan. 1995). Japanese Pharmacological Society, Editorial Office - Nihon Yakuri Gakkai Henshuubu, Kantohya Bld., Gokomachi-Ebisugawa, Nakagyo-ku, Kyoto 604, Japan. TEL 075-252-4641. FAX 075-252-4618. Ed. Minoru Watanabe. illus.; index. circ. 2,700. (also avail. in microform from UMI; reprint service avail. from UMI, ISI) **Indexed:** Biol.Abstr., Biotech.Abstr., Chem.Abstr., Curr.Cont., Dent.Ind., Excerp.Med., Helminthol.Abstr., Ind.Med., Ind.Sci.Rev., Ind.Vet., INIS Atomind., JTA, Nutr.Abstr., P.A.I.S., Psychol.Abstr., Rev.Med.& Vet.Mycol., Sci.Cit.Ind. **Document type:** academic/scholarly publication.
●Also available online.
—BLDSC (4657.000000); CASDDS; EMDOCS; Faxon; Genuine Article; SWETS; UMI; UnCover. **CCC.**
Description: Publishes original research on the interactions between chemicals and biological systems.
Refereed Serial

JAPANESE JOURNAL OF TOXICOLOGY/CHUDOKU KENKYU. see *ENVIRONMENTAL STUDIES — Toxicology And Environmental Safety*

JAPANESE JOURNAL OF TOXICOLOGY AND ENVIRONMENTAL HEALTH. see *ENVIRONMENTAL STUDIES — Toxicology And Environmental Safety*

615   JA
JAPANESE PHARMACOPOEIAL FORUM. Variant title: J P Forum. (Text in English, Japanese) 1992. q. $100. Society of Japanese Pharmacopoeia, 2-12-15, Shibuya, Shibuya-ku, Tokyo 150, Japan. TEL 81-3-3400-5634. FAX 81-3-3400-3158. (Subscr. to: Yakuji Nippo, Ltd., Kanda Izumicho, Chiyoda-ku, Tokyo 101, Japan. TEL 81-3-3862-2141. FAX 81-3-3866-8408)

615.19   JA   ISSN 0021-5201
JAPANESE WEEKLY ON PHARMACY AND CHEMISTRY/YAKUGYO SHINBUN.* Alternate title: Weekly Drug News. (Text in Japanese) 1946. w. 3000 Yen. 1-13-12 Kikawa-nishino-cho, Higoshi-yodogawa-ku, Osaka, Japan. Ed. Y. Taguchi. adv.; bk.rev.; abstr.; bibl.; stat. circ. 20,000. **Indexed:** Biol.Abstr., Chem.Abstr., I.P.A.
Formerly: Japanese Journal of Pharmacy and Chemistry.

JILIN ZHONGYIYAO/JILIN TRADITIONAL CHINESE MEDICINE. see *ALTERNATIVE MEDICINE*

615   JA   ISSN 0913-5340
JOSAI DAIGAKU YAKUGAKUBU KENKYU GYOSEKISHU/JOSAI UNIVERSITY. PHARMACEUTICAL BULLETIN. (Text in English, Japanese; summaries in English) 1979. a. Josai Daigaku, Yakugakubu - Josai University, Faculty of Pharmaceutical Science, 1-1, Keyakidai, Sakado-shi, Saitama-ken 350-02, Japan.

615.19   FR   ISSN 0291-1981
CODEN: JPCLDE
JOURNAL DE PHARMACIE CLINIQUE; international journal of clinical pharmacy. (Text in English or French; summaries in English, French) 1982. q. 480 F. to individuals; institutions 800 F.; students 285 F. (effective 1995). John Libbey Eurotext, 127 av de la Republique, 92120 Montrouge, France. TEL 1-46-73-06-60. FAX 1-40-84-09-99. (Subscr. to: A T E I, 23-25 rue Fernand Combette, 93100 Montreuil sous Bois, France. TEL 48-59-58-11. FAX 48-59-57-99) Ed. Pierre A. Sado. circ. 1,300. **Indexed:** Chem.Abstr., Excerp.Med. **Document type:** academic/scholarly publication.
—BLDSC (5032.050000); CASDDS. **CCC.**
Description: Papers on all aspects of pharmaceutical sciences applied to human use.

615   FR   ISSN 0047-2166
CODEN: JPBEAJ
JOURNAL DE PHARMACIE DE BELGIQUE. (Monographic supplements accompany some nos.) 1919; N.S. 1945. bi-m. 819 F. (foreign 863 F.) (effective 1996). (Association Pharmaceutique Belge, BE) Masson - Periodiques, Villa Laromiguiere, 75005 Paris, France. TEL 1-40-46-62-00. FAX 1-40-46-62-01. Eds. M. Delfosse, J. Vervaeren. adv.; illus. (reprint service avail. from ISI) **Indexed:** Biol.Abstr., Biotech.Abstr., Chem.Abstr., Curr.Adv.Biochem., Excerp.Med., Hort.Abstr., I.P.A., Ind.Med., Ind.Sci.Rev., Risk Abstr., Sci.Cit.Ind. **Document type:** academic/scholarly publication.
—BLDSC (5032.000000); CASDDS; EMDOCS; SWETS. **CCC.**
Description: Contains original papers and reviews covering the entire field of pharmaceutical sciences: pharmacology, pharmakokinetics, pharmaceutical chemistry, galenics and phytotherapy.

JOURNAL OF ANALYTICAL TOXICOLOGY. see *ENVIRONMENTAL STUDIES — Toxicology And Environmental Safety*

JOURNAL OF ANTIBIOTICS; an international journal devoted to research on bioactive microbial products. see *MEDICAL SCIENCES*

JOURNAL OF APPLIED TOXICOLOGY. see *ENVIRONMENTAL STUDIES — Toxicology And Environmental Safety*

615   UK   ISSN 0144-1795
CODEN: JAPHDU
JOURNAL OF AUTONOMIC PHARMACOLOGY. 1980. bi-m. £93.50 to individuals in Europe; elsewhere £103($166); institutions in Europe £305; elsewhere £336($540) (effective 1996). Blackwell Science Ltd., Osney Mead, Oxford OX2 0EL, England. TEL 01865-206206. FAX 01865-206219. TELEX 83355 MEDBOK G. Ed. K.J. Broadley. adv.; abstr.; bibl.; illus.; index. circ. 300. (also avail. in microform from UMI; back issues avail.) **Indexed:** Apic.Abstr., Biol.Abstr., Excerp.Med., Ind.Med., Ind.Sci.Rev., Sci.Cit.Ind. **Document type:** academic/scholarly publication.
—BLDSC (4949.900000); ADONIS; CASDDS; Faxon; Genuine Article; SWETS; UMI; UnCover. **CCC.**
Refereed Serial

615.328   UK   ISSN 0792-6855
CODEN: RCBPEJ
JOURNAL OF BASIC AND CLINICAL PHYSIOLOGY AND PHARMACOLOGY. 1980. q. $250 (effective 1996). (Israel Physiological and Pharmacological Society) Freund Publishing House Ltd., Ste. 500, Chesham House, 150 Regent St., London W1R 5FA, England. (Alt. addr.: P.O. Box 35010, Tel Aviv, Israel. TEL 972-3-5628540. FAX 972-3-5628538) Eds. M. Horowitz, Y. Oron. adv.; bk.rev.; illus. (back issues avail.) **Indexed:** Biol.Abstr., Chem.Abstr., Curr.Adv.Ecol.Sci., Excerp.Med., I.P.A., Ind.Med. **Document type:** academic/scholarly publication.
—BLDSC (4951.117000); CASDDS; Faxon.
Former titles (until 1987): Reviews in Clinical and Basic Pharmacology (ISSN 0334-1534); (until 1985): Reviews in Pure and Applied Pharmacological Sciences (ISSN 0197-2839)

615 519.5   US   ISSN 1054-3406
RS57   CODEN: JBSTEL
JOURNAL OF BIOPHARMACEUTICAL STATISTICS. 1991. 3/yr. $40 to individuals; institutions $295. Marcel Dekker Journals, 270 Madison Ave., New York, NY 10016. TEL 212-696-9000. FAX 212-685-4540. TELEX 421419. (Subscr. to: Box 5017, Monticello, NY 12701) Ed. K.E. Peace. **Indexed:** Curr.Ind.Stat., Excerp.Med. (1994-), Ind.Med. (1993-), Stat.Theor.Meth.Abstr. **Document type:** academic/scholarly publication.
—BLDSC (4953.910000); SWETS; UMI. **CCC.**
Description: Applications of statistics in biopharmaceutical research and development and expositions of statistical methodology with applicability to such work.
Refereed Serial

615 616.1   US   ISSN 0160-2446
RM345   CODEN: JCPCDT
JOURNAL OF CARDIOVASCULAR PHARMACOLOGY. 1979. m. $335 to individuals (foreign $422); institutions $640 (foreign $766) (effective 1996); newsstand price: $66. Lippincott - Raven Press, 276 Washington Sq., Philadelphia, PA 19106. TEL 215-238-4200. Ed. Paul M. Vanhoutte. adv. contact: Phyllis Noyes. bk.rev.; index. circ. 2,500. (back issues avail.; reprint service avail. from UMI) **Indexed:** Biotech.Abstr., Chem.Abstr., Curr.Cont., Excerp.Med., Ind.Med., Ind.Sci.Rev., INIS Atomind., Kidney, Sci.Cit.Ind. **Document type:** academic/scholarly publication.
—BLDSC (4954.868000); CASDDS; Faxon; Genuine Article; SWETS; UMI; UnCover. **CCC.**
Description: Publishes extensive reports on major new drugs affecting the heart and blood vessels.
Refereed Serial

JOURNAL OF CHEMOTHERAPY. see *MEDICAL SCIENCES — Oncology*

JOURNAL OF CHILD AND ADOLESCENT PSYCHOPHARMACOLOGY. see *MEDICAL SCIENCES — Psychiatry And Neurology*

JOURNAL OF CLINICAL ONCOLOGY. see *MEDICAL SCIENCES — Oncology*

615.1   US   ISSN 0091-2700
CODEN: JCPCBR
JOURNAL OF CLINICAL PHARMACOLOGY. 1960. m. $205 to individuals (foreign $260); institutions $250 (foreign $305) (effective 1996); newsstand price: $27. (American College of Clinical Pharmacology) Lippincott - Raven Publishers, 227 E. Washington Sq., Philadelphia, PA 19106. TEL 215-238-4200. (Subscr. to: 12107 Insurance Way, Hagerstown, MD 21740) Ed. Dr. Deborah L. Keefe; Pub. Marcia E. Serepy. adv. contact: Kathleen Phelan. bk.rev.; charts; illus.; index. circ. 2,429. (also avail. in microform from UMI; back issues avail.) **Indexed:** Biol.Abstr., Biotech.Abstr., Chem.Abstr., Curr.Cont., Dent.Ind., Excerp.Med. (1993-), I.P.A., Ind.Med., Ind.Sci.Rev., INIS Atomind., Kidney, Med.& Surg.Dermat., Psychol.Abstr., Sci.Cit.Ind. **Document type:** academic/scholarly publication.
●Also available online.
—BLDSC (4958.680000); CASDDS; EMDOCS; Faxon; Genuine Article; SWETS; UMI; UnCover. **CCC.**
Former titles: Journal of Clinical Pharmacology and New Drugs (ISSN 0021-9754); Journal of New Drugs (ISSN 0096-0284)
Description: Geared towards clinical pharmacologists and physicians concerned with and responsible for the appropriate selection, investigation and prescribing of drugs.
Refereed Serial

615 UK ISSN 0269-4727
CODEN: JCPTED
JOURNAL OF CLINICAL PHARMACY AND THERAPEUTICS. 1976. bi-m. £249.50 in Europe; elsewhere £273($440) (effective 1996). Blackwell Science Ltd., Osney Mead, Oxford OX2 0EL, England. TEL 01865-206206. FAX 01865-206219. TELEX 83355 MEDBOK G. Eds. A. Li Wan Po, M.J. Kendall. adv.; bk.rev.; abstr.; bibl.; index. circ. 410. (also avail. in microform from UMI; back issues avail.; reprint service avail. from ISI) **Indexed:** ASCA, Biol.Abstr., Biotech.Abstr., Chem.Abstr., CINAHL, Excerp.Med., I.P.A., Ind.Med., Ind.Sci.Rev., Med.& Surg.Dermat., Rev.Med.& Vet.Mycol., Sci.Cit.Ind. **Document type:** academic/scholarly publication.
—BLDSC (4958.685000); ADONIS; CASDDS; Faxon; Genuine Article; SWETS; UMI; UnCover. **CCC.**
 Former titles: Journal of Clinical and Hospital Pharmacy (ISSN 0143-3180); Journal of Clinical Pharmacy (ISSN 0308-6593)
 Refereed Serial

615.19 US ISSN 0271-0749
CODEN: JCPYDR
JOURNAL OF CLINICAL PSYCHOPHARMACOLOGY. 1981. bi-m. $98 to individuals; institutions $145 (effective 1995). Williams & Wilkins, 428 E. Preston St., Baltimore, MD 21202. TEL 410-528-4000; 800-638-6423. FAX 410-528-4312. Ed. Dr. David J. Greenblatt. adv.; bk.rev. circ. 9,000. (microfilm; back issues avail.) **Indexed:** A.D.& D., Adol.Ment.Hlth.Abstr., Chem.Abstr., Chic.Per.Ind., Curr.Cont., Dent.Ind., Excerp.Med., Ind.Med., Ind.Sci.Rev., Psychol.Abstr. (1988-), Sci.Cit.Ind. **Document type:** academic/scholarly publication.
—BLDSC (4958.691000); CASDDS; Faxon; Genuine Article; SWETS; UnCover. **CCC.**
 Description: Publishes clinical papers for psychiatrists on antipsychotic-, antianxiety-, antidepressant- medications and stimulants.
 Refereed Serial

615.19 US ISSN 1066-7865
CODEN: JCDDE7
JOURNAL OF CLINICAL RESEARCH AND DRUG DEVELOPMENT. 1987. 4/yr. $185 to institutions (foreign $215) (effective 1995). (Associates of Clinical Pharmacology) Elsevier Science Inc., 655 Ave. of the Americas, New York, NY 10010. TEL 212-989-5800. FAX 212-633-3990. TELEX 420643 AEP UI. (Subscr. to: Box 882, Madison Sq. Sta., New York, NY 10159-0882) Ed. Dr. Allen Cato. (also avail. in microform from UMI; back issues avail.) **Indexed:** Biol.Abstr., Excerp.Med. **Document type:** academic/scholarly publication.
—BLDSC (4958.710000); ADONIS; Faxon; SWETS. **CCC.**
 Former titles (until 1993): Journal of Clinical Research and Pharmacoepidemiology (ISSN 1047-0336); (until 1990) Journal of Clinical Research and Drug Development (ISSN 0889-5813)
 Description: Offers practical information on drug development. Provides a forum for the exchange of information and ideas among individuals involved in clinical research.
 Refereed Serial

JOURNAL OF CONTROLLED RELEASE. see *BIOLOGY — Biological Chemistry*

615 UK ISSN 1357-9215
RM300 CODEN: JDDVEY
JOURNAL OF DRUG DEVELOPMENT AND CLINICAL PRACTICE. 1988. q. £105($185) Gardiner - Caldwell Communications Ltd., Old Ribbon Mill, Pitt St., Macclesfield, Ches. SK11 7PT, England. TEL 01625-618507. FAX 01625-614161. Ed. David Caldwell. bk.rev. (back issues avail.) **Indexed:** Excerp.Med. **Document type:** academic/scholarly publication.
—BLDSC (4970.530500); CASDDS; Faxon; Genuine Article.
 Formerly (until 1995): Journal of Drug Development (ISSN 0952-9500)
 Description: Publishes original research papers on subjects relevant to pharmaceutical medicine.
 Refereed Serial

615.1 UA ISSN 0085-2406
JOURNAL OF DRUG RESEARCH OF EGYPT. Cover title: Journal of Drug Research. (Text in English; summaries in Arabic and English.) 1968. a. $12. National Organisation for Drug Control and Research, Drug Research and Control Center, 6, Abou-Hazem St., Pyramids Ave., Box 29, Cairo, Egypt. Ed.Bd. bk.rev.; illus. **Indexed:** Anal.Abstr., Biol.Abstr., Chem.Abstr., Excerp.Med., Food Sci.& Tech.Abstr., I.P.A., Mass Spectr.Bull., Nutr.Abstr. **Document type:** academic/scholarly publication.
●Also available online.
—BLDSC (4970.580000).

615 US ISSN 1061-186X
CODEN: JDTAEH
JOURNAL OF DRUG TARGETING. 1993. q. 148 ECU (effective 1996). Harwood Academic Publishers, c/o International Publishers Distributor, 820 Town Center Dr., Langhorne, PA 19047. TEL 215-750-2642. FAX 215-750-6343. (Subscr. to: International Publishers Distributor, PO Box 90, Reading, Berkshire, RG1 8JL, England. TEL 44-173-456-8316) (also avail. in microform) **Indexed:** Excerp.Med. (1994-), Ind.Med. (1994-). **Document type:** academic/scholarly publication.
—CASDDS; SWETS. **CCC.**
 Description: Publishes papers and reviews on all aspects of drug delivery and targeting, and the design and characterization of carrier systems, with an emphasis on 'in vivo' evaluation.

615.19 IE ISSN 0378-8741
CODEN: JOETD7
JOURNAL OF ETHNOPHARMACOLOGY; an interdisciplinary journal devoted to bioscientific research on indigenous drugs. 1979. m. I£632($999) (effective 1996). Elsevier Science Ireland Ltd., P.O. Box 85, Limerick, Ireland. TEL 353-61-471944. FAX 353-61-472144. (Subscr. in U.S. and Canada to: Elsevier Science Inc., Box 882, Madison Sq. Sta., New York, NY 10159. TEL 212-989-5800. FAX 212-633-3990) Ed.Bd. bk.rev.; abstr. (also avail. in microform from UMI; reprint service avail. from SWZ) **Indexed:** Anthropol.Lit., Biol.Abstr., Chem.Abstr., Cott.& Trop.Fibr.Abstr., Curr.Cont., Excerp.Bot., Excerp.Med., Field Crop Abstr., Forest.Abstr., Forest Prod.Abstr., Hort.Abstr., I.P.A., Ind.Med., Ind.Sci.Rev., Ind.Vet., Protozool.Abstr., Rev.Med.& Vet.Mycol., Sci.Cit.Ind., Seed Abstr., Trop.Oil Seeds Abstr., Weed Abstr. **Document type:** academic/scholarly publication, abstracting/indexing.
—BLDSC (4979.602400); CASDDS; Faxon; Genuine Article; SWETS; UnCover. **CCC.**
 Description: Publishes articles concerned with the observation and experimental investigation of the biological activities of plant and animal substances used in the traditional medicine of past and present cultures. Also provides abstracts of current literature screened from more than 100 journals.
 Refereed Serial

615.1 MM ISSN 1023-3857
▼**JOURNAL OF EUROMED PHARMACY.** (Text in English) 1994. s-a. University of Malta, Department of Pharmacy, Msida, Malta. **Document type:** academic/scholarly publication.

615.7 155.67 US ISSN 8756-4629
CODEN: JGDTEF
JOURNAL OF GERIATRIC DRUG THERAPY. 1987. q. $175 (foreign $245) (effective 1996). Haworth Press, Inc., 10 Alice St., Binghamton, NY 13904. TEL 607-722-5857; 800-342-9678. FAX 607-722-1424. Ed. James Cooper. adv.; bk.rev. circ. 318. (also avail. in microfiche from UMI; reprint service avail. from HAW,ISI) **Indexed:** Abstr.Soc.Geront., Curr.Cont., Excerp.Med., Human Resour.Abstr., IMFL, Psychol.Abstr. (1986-), Ref.Zh., Sage Fam.Stud.Abstr., Soc.Work Res.& Abstr., Sociol.Abstr.
—BLDSC (4995.073000); Faxon; Haworth; UnCover.
 Description: Covers drug therapy and related issues in the geriatric population.
 Refereed Serial

615 US ISSN 0197-1522
RB46.5 CODEN: JOUIDK
JOURNAL OF IMMUNOASSAY. 1980. 4/yr. $395. Marcel Dekker Journals, 270 Madison Ave., New York, NY 10016. TEL 212-696-9000. FAX 212-685-4540. TELEX 421419. (Subscr. to: Box 5017, Monticello, NY 12701) Ed. W.H.C. Walker. (also avail. in microform from RPI) **Indexed:** Abstr.Hyg., Biol.Abstr., Chem.Abstr., Curr.Adv.Ecol.Sci., Excerp.Med., Ind.Med., Ind.Sci.Rev., Ind.Vet., INIS Atomind., Sci.Cit.Ind., Telegen, Vet.Bull. **Document type:** academic/scholarly publication.
—BLDSC (5004.560000); CASDDS; Faxon; Genuine Article; SWETS; UMI; UnCover. **CCC.**
 Formerly: Immunological and Molecular Probes.
 Refereed Serial

615 JA ISSN 0389-1194
JOURNAL OF INTENSIVE CARE MEDICINE. (Text in Japanese; summaries in English, Japanese) 1977. m. 2000 Yen per no. Igaku Tosho Shuppan Ltd., 28-1, Hongo 2-chome, Bunkyo-ku, Tokyo 113, Japan.

615 US ISSN 0194-5106
JOURNAL OF KANSAS PHARMACY. 1964. q. $18. Kansas Pharmacists Association, 1308 SW. 10th Ave., Topeka, KS 66604-1299. TEL 913-232-0439. FAX 913-232-3764. Ed. Jenith Hoover. adv.: B&W page $475, color page $793; trim 8 1/2 x 11; adv. contact: Jenith Hoover. illus.; stat.; tr.lit.; circ. 1,200 (controlled). **Document type:** trade publication.

615.19 US ISSN 0898-2104
RS201.L55 CODEN: JLREE7
JOURNAL OF LIPOSOME RESEARCH. 1988. 5/yr. $395. Marcel Dekker Journals, 270 Madison Ave., New York, NY 10016. TEL 212-696-9000. FAX 212-685-4540. TELEX 421419 MARDEEK. (Subscr. to: Box 5017, Monticello, NY 12701) Ed. Leaf Huang. (also avail. in microform from RPI) **Indexed:** Telegen. **Document type:** academic/scholarly publication.
—BLDSC (5010.505000); CASDDS; Faxon; SWETS; UMI. **CCC.**
 Description: Presents high quality liposome research. Subjects are broad, ranging from biophysical analysis of liposome membranes to clinical applications of liposome-encapsulated drugs.
 Refereed Serial

JOURNAL OF MAINTENANCE IN THE ADDICTIONS; innovations in research, theory, & practice. see *DRUG ABUSE AND ALCOHOLISM*

JOURNAL OF MEDICAL AND PHARMACEUTICAL MARKETING. see *BUSINESS AND ECONOMICS — Marketing And Purchasing*

615.19 610 US ISSN 0022-2623
RS402 CODEN: JMCMAR
JOURNAL OF MEDICINAL CHEMISTRY. 1958. bi-w. $586 to non-members (foreign $668); members $54 (foreign $136). American Chemical Society, 1155 16th St., N.W., Washington, DC 20036. TEL 800-333-9511. FAX 614-447-3671. (Subscr. to: Membership and Subscription Services, Box 3337, Columbus, OH 43210. TEL 614-447-3776) Ed. Dr. Philip S. Portoghese. adv.; bk.rev.; charts; index. circ. 4,272. (also avail. in microfiche; microfilm; back issues avail.; reprint service avail. from UMI) **Indexed:** Biol.Abstr., Biotech.Abstr., Chem.Abstr., Curr.Adv.Biochem., Curr.Adv.Cancer Res., Curr.Adv.Ecol.Sci., Curr.Chem.React., Curr.Cont., Dairy Sci.Abstr., Dent.Ind., Excerp.Med., Helminthol.Abstr., Ind.Chem., Ind.Med., Ind.Sci.Rev., INIS Atomind., Mass Spectr.Bull., Nutr.Abstr., Poult.Abstr., Protozool.Abstr., Rev.Med.& Vet.Mycol., Rev.Plant Path., Sci.Cit.Ind., Vet.Bull. **Document type:** academic/scholarly publication.
●Also available online. Vendor(s): STN International (CJACS).
—BLDSC (5017.200000); CASDDS; EMDOCS; Faxon; Genuine Article; SWETS; UMI; UnCover. **CCC.**
 Formerly: Journal of Medicinal and Pharmaceutical Chemistry (ISSN 0095-9065)
 Description: Focuses on the relationship of chemistry to biological activity. Provides valuable research findings and comprehensive book reviews on medicinal chemistry and related areas.
 Refereed Serial

PHARMACY AND PHARMACOLOGY

616.01 UK ISSN 0265-2048
RS201.C3 CODEN: JOMIEF
JOURNAL OF MICROENCAPSULATION. 1984. bi-m. £236($390) (effective 1996). Taylor & Francis Ltd., Rankine Rd., Basingstoke, Hants. RG25 8PR, England. TEL 44-1256-840366. FAX 44-1256-479438. TELEX 858540. E-mail: info@tandf.co.uk. (Subscr. in N. America to: Taylor & Francis Inc., 1900 Frost Rd., Ste. 101, Bristol, PA 19007-1598. TEL 44-1256-840366. FAX 44-1256-479438) Ed. Dr. T.L. Whateley. **Indexed:** Curr.Adv.Ecol.Sci., Intl.Polym.Sci.& Tech., RAPRA, Sugar Ind.Abstr. **Document type:** academic/scholarly publication.
—BLDSC (5019.530000); CASDDS; Faxon; Genuine Article; SWETS. **CCC.**
Description: Devoted to the preparation, properties and uses of individually encapsulated small particles. Its scope extends beyond microcapsules to all other small-particle dosage forms involving preparative manipulating.
Refereed Serial

615 SA
▼**JOURNAL OF MODERN PHARMACY;** up-to-the-minute practical pharmacy. Variant title: Modern Pharmacy. (Text in English) 1994. m. R.148.68 (free to qualified personnel). National Publishing (Pty) Ltd., P.O. Box 2271, Clareinch 7740, South Africa. TEL 27-21-611140. FAX 27-21-611389. adv.; illus. **Document type:** trade publication.
Description: For pharmacists in community, hospital and health clinic pharmacies.

547.7 US ISSN 0163-3864
QH1 CODEN: JNPRDF
JOURNAL OF NATURAL PRODUCTS. (Text mainly in English; occasionally in French or German.) 1938. m. $290 (Canada & Mexico $299; Europe $308; elsewhere $318) (effective 1996). American Society of Pharmacognosy, c/o David J. Slatkin, Treasurer, Chicago College of Pharmacy, 555 31st St., Downers Grove, IL 60515. TEL 708-971-6417. FAX 708-971-6097. (Co-sponsor: Lloyd Library and Museum) Ed. A. Douglas Kinghorn. bk.rev.; charts; illus.; stat.; index. circ. 1,950. (back issues avail.) **Indexed:** Agroforest.Abstr., Anal.Abstr., Biol.Abstr., Biol.& Agr.Ind., Biotech.Abstr., Chem.Abstr., Chem.Infd., Curr.Adv.Biochem., Curr.Adv.Ecol.Sci., Curr.Biotech.Abstr., Curr.Chem.React., Curr.Cont., Deep Sea Res.& Oceanogr.Abstr., Excerp.Bot., Excerp.Med., Field Crop Abstr., Forest.Abstr., Helminthol.Abstr., Herb.Abstr., Hort.Abstr., I.P.A., Ind.Chem., Ind.Med., Ind.Sci.Rev., Ind.Vet., Mass Spectr.Bull., Ornam.Hort., Plant Breed.Abstr., Plant Grow.Reg.Abstr., Protozool.Abstr., Rev.Med.& Vet.Mycol., Rev.Plant Path., Seed Abstr., So.Pac.Per.Ind., Soyabean Abstr., Vet.Bull., Weed Abstr. **Document type:** trade publication.
●Also available online.
—BLDSC (5021.225000); CASDDS; Faxon; SWETS; UnCover.
Formerly (until vol.42, 1979): Lloydia (ISSN 0024-5461)
Description: Covers natural products research - chemistry, biochemistry and biology of naturally occurring compounds.
Refereed Serial

615.9 US ISSN 1058-8108
CODEN: JNTOER
JOURNAL OF NATURAL TOXINS. 1992. s-a. $100 to individuals; institutions $200 (foreign $230). Alaken, Inc., 305 W. Magnolia St., Ste. 196, Ft. Collins, CO 80521. TEL 303-223-5348. FAX 303-226-8655. (back issues avail.) **Indexed:** Sport Fish.Abstr., Wild.Rev., Zoo.Rec. **Document type:** academic/scholarly publication.
—BLDSC (5021.300200); CASDDS; UnCover.

JOURNAL OF OCULAR PHARMACOLOGY. see *MEDICAL SCIENCES — Ophthalmology And Optometry*

615.19 UK ISSN 0731-7085
CODEN: JPBADA
JOURNAL OF PHARMACEUTICAL AND BIOMEDICAL ANALYSIS. 1983. m. fl.1763($1075) (effective 1996). Elsevier Science Ltd., Pergamon, P.O. Box 800, Kidlington, Oxford OX5 1DX, England. TEL 44-1865-843000. FAX 44-1865-843010. E-mail: nlinfo-f@elsevier.nl; usinfo-f@elsevier.com; forinfo-kyf04035@niftyserve.or.jp; Site addr.: http://www.elsevier.nl/. (Subscr. in U.S. and Canada to: Elsevier Science, 660 White Plains Rd., Tarrytown, NY 10591-5153. TEL 914-524-9200. FAX 914-333-2444) Eds. Anthony Fell, Christopher M. Riley. (also avail. in microfilm from UMI) **Indexed:** Chem.Abstr., Curr.Adv.Ecol.Sci., Excerp.Med., Hort.Abstr., Mass Spectr.Bull., Rev.Med.& Vet.Mycol. **Document type:** academic/scholarly publication.
—BLDSC (5031.600000); ADONIS; CASDDS; Faxon; Genuine Article; SWETS; UMI. **CCC.**
Description: Publishes research reports and reviews on pharmaceutical and biomedical analysis.
Refereed Serial

615 610 NR ISSN 0331-0604
JOURNAL OF PHARMACEUTICAL AND MEDICAL SCIENCES. 1977. bi-m. $115.20. Fred Atoki Publishing Co. Ltd., Plot 25 Kekere-Ekun St., Orile-Iganmu, Box 7313, Lagos, Nigeria. Ed. F.O. Atoki. adv.; illus. circ. 16,000.

615 616.9 US
▼**JOURNAL OF PHARMACEUTICAL CARE IN INFECTIOUS DISEASE MANAGEMENT.** 1994. q. $75 (foreign $105) (effective 1996). Haworth Press, Inc., 10 Alice St., Binghamton, NY 13904. TEL 800-342-9678. FAX 607-722-1424. Ed. Steven L. Barriere. adv.: page $300. bk.rev. (also avail. in microfiche)
—Haworth.
Description: Provides information for pharmacists on the most recent advances in the management of infectious diseases.
Refereed Serial

615 US ISSN 1056-4950
RM319 CODEN: JPPSEX
JOURNAL OF PHARMACEUTICAL CARE IN PAIN & SYMPTOM CONTROL. 1993. q. $85 (foreign $119) (effective 1996). Haworth Press, Inc., 10 Alice St., Binghamton, NY 13904. TEL 607-722-5857; 800-342-9678. FAX 607-722-1424. TELEX 4932599. Ed. Arthur Lipman. adv.; bk.rev. (also avail. in microfiche from UMI; reprint service avail. from HAW) **Indexed:** Excerp.Med. (1994-). **Document type:** academic/scholarly publication.
—BLDSC (5031.860000); Haworth.
Refereed Serial

615.19 658 US ISSN 0883-7597
CODEN: JPMMEY
JOURNAL OF PHARMACEUTICAL MARKETING AND MANAGEMENT. 1986. q. $150 (foreign $210) (effective Mar. 1995). Haworth Press, Inc., 10 Alice St., Binghamton, NY 13904. TEL 607-722-5857; 800-342-9678. FAX 607-722-1424. TELEX 4932599. Ed. Mickey C. Smith. adv.; bk.rev. (also avail. in microfiche from UMI; back issues avail.; reprint service avail. from HAW) **Indexed:** Biostat., Human Resour.Abstr., Ind.Med., P.A.I.S., Sage Fam.Stud.Abstr., Tr.& Indus.Ind.
—BLDSC (5031.880000); Haworth; UnCover.
Description: Devoted to solving problems of management and the marketing of pharmaceutical products and services.
Refereed Serial

615 UK ISSN 0958-0581
CODEN: JPMDE7
JOURNAL OF PHARMACEUTICAL MEDICINE. 1991. q. £143 (outside Europe £157($253)) (effective 1996). (Society of Pharmaceutical Medicine) Blackwell Science Ltd., Osney Mead, Oxford OX2 0EL, England. TEL 01865-206206. FAX 01865-206219. TELEX 83355 MEDBOK G. Eds. B. Dickson, M. Young. adv.; bk.rev.; illus.; index. circ. 550. (also avail. in microform from UMI; back issues avail.) **Document type:** academic/scholarly publication.
—BLDSC (5031.883000); ADONIS; UMI. **CCC.**
Refereed Serial

615.1 JA ISSN 0372-7629
CODEN: YAKUA2
JOURNAL OF PHARMACEUTICAL SCIENCE AND TECHNOLOGY/YAKUZAIGAKU. (Text in English and Japanese; summaries in English) 1940. q. 5356 Yen. (Academy of Pharmaceutical Science and Technology) Business Center for Academic Societies Japan, 5-16-9 Honkamagome, Bunkyo-ku, Tokyo 113, Japan. TEL 03-5814-5811. FAX 03-5814-5822. TELEX 2722268 BCJSP J. circ. 1,200. **Indexed:** Biol.Abstr., Chem.Abstr., I.P.A. **Document type:** academic/scholarly publication.
—BLDSC (5031.890000); CASDDS. **CCC.**
Formerly: Archives of Practical Pharmacy.

615.1 US ISSN 0022-3549
RS1 CODEN: JPMSAE
JOURNAL OF PHARMACEUTICAL SCIENCES. vol.50, 1961. a. $85 to individuals; institutions $310. American Pharmaceutical Association, 2215 Constitution Ave., N.W., Washington, DC 20037. TEL 202-628-4410. FAX 202-783-2351. (Alt. addr.: American Chemical Society, 1155 Sixteenth St., N.W., Washington, DC 20036) Ed. William I. Higuchi. adv.; bk.rev.; bibl.; charts; illus.; index. circ 5,400. (back issues avail.) **Indexed:** Anal.Abstr., Biol.Abstr., Biotech.Abstr., Chem.Abstr., Chem.Infd., Curr.Adv.Cancer Res., Curr.Adv.Ecol.Sci., Curr.Chem.React., Curr.Cont., Dairy Sci.Abstr., Dent.Ind., Excerp.Med., Helminthol.Abstr., Hort.Abstr., I.P.A., Ind.Chem., Ind.Med., Ind.Sci.Rev., INIS Atomind., Mass Spectr.Bull., Nutr.Abstr., Rev.Plant Path., Sugar Ind.Abstr., Vet.Bull. **Document type:** academic/scholarly publication.
●Also available online.
—BLDSC (5031.900000); CASDDS; EMDOCS; Faxon; Genuine Article; SWETS; UMI; UnCover. **CCC.**
Description: Primary research in pharmaceutical science; graduate level and above.
Refereed Serial

615.19 US ISSN 0896-6966
CODEN: JPHAE7
JOURNAL OF PHARMACOEPIDEMIOLOGY; innovations in research and practice. 1989. s-a. $75 (foreign $105) (effective 1996). Haworth Press, Inc., 10 Alice St., Binghamton, NY 13904. TEL 607-722-5857; 800-342-9678. FAX 607-722-1424. TELEX 4932599. Ed. Jack E. Fincham. adv.; bk.rev. (also avail. in microform from HAW; reprint service avail. from HAW) **Indexed:** Biostat., Excerp.Med. (1993-). **Document type:** academic/scholarly publication.
—BLDSC (5032.500000); Haworth.
Description: Facilitates the dissemination and exchange of findings, assessments, and reports of research and practice dealing with the outcomes of drug treatment.
Refereed Serial

615 US ISSN 0090-466X
RM1 CODEN: JPBPBJ
JOURNAL OF PHARMACOKINETICS AND BIOPHARMACEUTICS. 1973. bi-m. $425 (foreign $495) (effective 1996). Plenum Publishing Corp., 233 Spring St., New York, NY 10013-1578. TEL 212-620-8000. FAX 212-463-0742. TELEX 23-421139. Eds. Leslie Z. Benet, Malcolm Rowland. adv.; index. (also avail. in microfilm from JSC; back issues avail.) **Indexed:** Biol.Abstr., Biotech.Abstr., Chem.Abstr., Curr.Adv.Ecol.Sci., Curr.Cont., Excerp.Med., I.P.A., Ind.Med., Ind.Sci.Rev., INIS Atomind. **Document type:** academic/scholarly publication.
—BLDSC (5032.600000); ADONIS; CASDDS; EMDOCS; Faxon; Genuine Article; SWETS; UMI. **CCC.**
Refereed Serial

JOURNAL OF PHARMACOLOGICAL AND TOXICOLOGICAL METHODS. see *ENVIRONMENTAL STUDIES — Toxicology And Environmental Safety*

PHARMACY AND PHARMACOLOGY

615.1   US   ISSN 0022-3565
RS1   CODEN: JPETAB
JOURNAL OF PHARMACOLOGY AND EXPERIMENTAL THERAPEUTICS. 1909. m. (4 vols./yr.). $190 to individuals; institutions $340 (effective 1995). (American Society of Pharmacology and Experimental Therapeutics) Williams & Wilkins, 428 Preston St., Baltimore, MD 21202. TEL 410-528-4000; 800-638-6423. FAX 410-528-4312. Ed. J.A. HArvey. adv.; bibl.; charts; illus.; index. circ. 2,885. (also avail. in microfilm from WWS) **Indexed:** Apic.Abstr., Biol.Abstr., Biotech.Abstr., Chem.Abstr., Curr.Adv.Ecol.Sci., Curr.Cont., Dairy Sci.Abstr., Dent.Ind., Excerp.Med., Helminthol.Abstr., I.P.A., Ind.Med., Ind.Sci.Rev., Ind.Vet., INIS Atomind., Kidney, Med.& Surg.Dermat., Nutr.Abstr., Psychol.Abstr. (1968-), Rev.Med.& Vet.Mycol., Vet.Bull. **Document type:** academic/scholarly publication.
●Also available online.
—BLDSC (5033.000000); CASDDS; EMDOCS; Faxon; Genuine Article; SWETS; UnCover. **CCC.**
   Description: Documents interactions of chemicals with biological systems for pharmacologists, toxicologists and biochemists.
Refereed Serial

615.1   UK   ISSN 0022-3573
     CODEN: JPPMAB
JOURNAL OF PHARMACY AND PHARMACOLOGY. 1949. m. £175 (foreign £195). Royal Pharmaceutical Society of Great Britain, 1 Lambeth High St., London SE1 7JN, England. TEL 071-735-9141. FAX 071-735-7629. Ed. Joseph Chamberlain. adv.; bibl.; charts; illus.; index. circ. 2,500. (also avail. in microfilm from PMC) **Indexed:** Abstr.Hyg., Anal.Abstr., Apic.Abstr., Biol.Abstr., Biotech.Abstr., Chem.Abstr., Curr.Adv.Ecol.Sci., Curr.Chem.React., Curr.Cont., Dairy Sci.Abstr., Dent.Ind., Excerp.Med., Helminthol.Abstr., I.P.A., Ind.Med., Ind.Sci.Rev., Ind.Vet., INIS Atomind., Med.& Surg.Dermat., Nutr.Abstr., Protozool.Abstr., Trop.Dis.Bull., Vet.Bull. **Document type:** academic/scholarly publication.
—BLDSC (5034.000000); CASDDS; EMDOCS; Faxon; Genuine Article; SWETS; UnCover. **CCC.**
   Description: Publishes original research papers and reviews articles about the development and evaluation of medicinal substances.

615   US   ISSN 0897-1900
RS1   CODEN: JPPREU
JOURNAL OF PHARMACY PRACTICE. 1988. bi-m. $121 (foreign $180) (effective 1996). W.B. Saunders Co. (Subsidiary of: Harcourt Brace & Company), The Curtis Center, 3rd Fl., Independence Sq. W., Philadelphia, PA 19106-3399. TEL 215-238-7800. FAX 215-238-6445. (Subscr. to: W.B. Saunders Co., Periodicals Dept., 6277 Sea Harbor Dr., 4th Fl., Orlando, FL 32887-4800. TEL 800-654-2452. FAX 800-874-6418) Ed. Dr. James T. O'Donnell; Pub. Joan W. Blumberg. adv.: B&W page $630, color page $1430; 7 x 10; adv. contact: Steve Gray. circ. 773. **Document type:** academic/scholarly publication.
—BLDSC (5034.020000); UMI. **CCC.**
   Description: Devoted to exploring new practice areas and therapies, giving current information on new drugs, pharmacokinetics, drug administration, and adverse drug reactions.

615 371.3   US   ISSN 1044-0054
     CODEN: JOPTET
JOURNAL OF PHARMACY TEACHING. 1990. q. $75 (foreign $105) (effective 1996). Haworth Press, Inc., 10 Alice St., Binghamton, NY 13904. TEL 607-722-5857; 800-342-9678. FAX 607-722-1424. TELEX 4932599. Ed. Robert A. Buerki. (also avail. in microform from UMI; reprint service avail. from HAW)
—BLDSC (5034.025000); Haworth.
   Description: Focuses on the communication of information with the goal of improved teaching in pharmacy.
Refereed Serial

615.329   US   ISSN 8755-1225
     CODEN: JPTEEB
JOURNAL OF PHARMACY TECHNOLOGY. 1985. bi-m. $40 to individuals; institutions $68; libraries $99. Harvey Whitney Books Company, Box 42696, Cincinnati, OH 45242. TEL 513-793-3555. FAX 513-793-3600. Ed. Harvey Whitney. adv.; bk.rev.; abstr.; bibl.; charts; illus.; index. circ. 3,000. (also avail. in microform from UMI; back issues avail.; reprint service avail.) **Indexed:** Abstr.Health Care Manage.Stud., Chem.Abstr., Curr.Adv.Ecol.Sci., Excerp.Med., I.P.A. **Document type:** academic/scholarly publication.
—BLDSC (5034.030000); CASDDS; Faxon; UMI.
   Description: Aimed at pharmacists and technicians. Covers therapeutic trends, current research and organizational, legal and educational activities. Includes information on new drugs and medical products and equipment.
Refereed Serial

JOURNAL OF PHYSIOLOGY AND PHARMACOLOGY. see
BIOLOGY — Physiology

JOURNAL OF PLANAR CHROMATOGRAPHY - MODERN T L C. see CHEMISTRY — Analytical Chemistry

JOURNAL OF PSYCHOACTIVE DRUGS; a multidisciplinary forum. see DRUG ABUSE AND ALCOHOLISM

615.7 616.8   UK   ISSN 0269-8811
     CODEN: JOPSEQ
JOURNAL OF PSYCHOPHARMACOLOGY. 1987. q. £115($195) (effective 1996). Oxford University Press, Oxford Journals, Walton St., Oxford OX2 6DP, England. TEL 01865-267907. FAX 01865-267773. TELEX 387330-OXPRES-G. E-mail: jnlorders@oup.co.uk. (U.S. subscr. to: Oxford University Press Inc., 2001 Evans Rd., Cary, NC 27513. TEL 919-677-0977. FAX 919-677-1714) Eds. David Nutt, B.E. Leonard. adv.; bk.rev. circ. 850. **Indexed:** Excerp.Med., Psychol.Abstr. (1987-). **Document type:** academic/scholarly publication.
—BLDSC (5043.450000); CASDDS; Genuine Article; SWETS; UMI. **CCC.**
   Formerly: British Association for Psychopharmacology. Journal.
   Description: Presents research and review papers representing a wide range of subjects connected with psychopharmacology, from drug effects on molecular systems to epidemiological studies.

615.19 330.9   US   ISSN 0896-6621
HD9666.1   CODEN: JRPEE5
JOURNAL OF RESEARCH IN PHARMACEUTICAL ECONOMICS. 1989. q. $120 (foreign $168) (effective 1996). Haworth Press, Inc., 10 Alice St., Binghamton, NY 13904. TEL 607-722-5857; 800-342-9678. FAX 067-722-1424. TELEX 4932599. Ed. Mickey Smith. adv.; bk.rev. (also avail. in microfiche from HAW; reprint service avail. from HAW) **Indexed:** Soc.Work Res.& Abstr.
—BLDSC (5052.026000); Haworth.
   Description: Devoted to the analysis of economic questions and concerns related to the use of pharmaceutical products and services.
Refereed Serial

615.9 500 610   II   ISSN 0253-7249
     CODEN: JSRMDB
JOURNAL OF SCIENTIFIC RESEARCH IN PLANTS & MEDICINES. (Text in English) 1981. s-a. Rs.150 to individuals; institutions Rs.300. Yogi Pharmacy Ltd. (Hardwar), Research & Publication Division, P.O. Gurukul Kangri, Hardwar 249404, India. TEL 91-133-426208. FAX 91-1333-426296. Ed. C.S. Trivedi. bk.rev. circ. 5,000. (back issues avail.) **Indexed:** Biol.Abstr., Forest.Abstr., Hort.Abstr., Seed Abstr. **Document type:** trade publication.
—CASDDS.
   Description: Covers the manufacturing of medicines and medicinal products from plants, herbs, and mineral rarely found on the higher altitudes of the Himalayan ranges.

615.19   SW   ISSN 0281-0662
JOURNAL OF SOCIAL AND ADMINISTRATIVE PHARMACY. (Supplement avail.) 1983. 4/yr. SEK 400 in Nordic countries; elsewhere SEK 500; newsstand price: SEK 160. Swedish Pharmaceutical Press, P.O. Box 1136, S-111 81 Stockholm, Sweden. TEL 46-8-723-50-00. FAX 46-8-14-95-80. Ed. Lars-Einar Frykloef.
—BLDSC (5064.714000); SWETS.

JOURNAL OF TOXICOLOGIC PATHOLOGY. see
ENVIRONMENTAL STUDIES — Toxicology And Environmental Safety

JOURNAL OF TOXICOLOGICAL SCIENCES. see
ENVIRONMENTAL STUDIES — Toxicology And Environmental Safety

615.9   US   ISSN 0731-3829
RL803   CODEN: JTOTDO
JOURNAL OF TOXICOLOGY. CUTANEOUS AND OCULAR TOXICOLOGY. 1982. 4/yr. $297.50 to individuals; institutions $595. Marcel Dekker Journals, 270 Madison Ave., New York, NY 10016. TEL 212-696-9000. FAX 212-685-4540. TELEX 421419 MARDEEK. (Subscr. to: Box 5014, Monticello, 12701) Ed. Edward M. Jackson. (also avail. in microform from RPI) **Indexed:** Biol.Abstr., Chem.Abstr., Curr.Adv.Ecol.Sci., Curr.Cont., Energy Rev., Environ.Abstr., Environ.Per.Bibl. (1982-), Excerp.Med., Ind.Sci.Rev., Lab.Haz.Bull., Sci.Cit.Ind. **Document type:** academic/scholarly publication.
—BLDSC (5069.738500); CASDDS; Faxon; Genuine Article; SWETS; UMI; UnCover. **CCC.**
   Description: Explores the phenomena of cutaneous and ocular irritation, sensitization, phototoxicity and photoallergenicity of cosmetics, etc. Contains in vitro and in vivo research as well as the clinical description, diagnosis, and treatment of such effects.
Refereed Serial

615.9   US   ISSN 0731-3837
RA1190   CODEN: JTTRD9
JOURNAL OF TOXICOLOGY. TOXIN REVIEWS. 1982. 3/yr. $287.50 to individuals; institutions $575. Marcel Dekker Journals, 270 Madison Ave., New York, NY 10016. TEL 212-696-9000. FAX 212-685-4540. TELEX 421419 MARDEEK. (Subscr. to: Box 5017, Monticello, NY 12701) Eds. W.T. Shier, A.T. Tu. (also avail. in microform from RPI) **Indexed:** Biol.Abstr., Chem.Abstr., Curr.Adv.Ecol.Sci., Environ.Abstr., Excerp.Med., Ind.Sci.Rev., Ref.Zh., Sci.Cit.Ind., Sport Fish.Abstr., Wild.Rev. **Document type:** academic/scholarly publication.
—BLDSC (5069.741000); CASDDS; Faxon; Genuine Article; SWETS; UMI; UnCover. **CCC.**
   Description: Provides a readily identifiable source of reviews bringing together information on toxins (their characteristics, activities and mechanisms of action) from the full range of clinical and scientific disciplines on which toxins impinge.
Refereed Serial

JOURNAL OF TOXICOLOGY AND ENVIRONMENTAL HEALTH. see ENVIRONMENTAL STUDIES — Toxicology And Environmental Safety

JOURNAL OF TOXICOLOGY: CLINICAL TOXICOLOGY. see
ENVIRONMENTAL STUDIES — Toxicology And Environmental Safety

615   JA
     CODEN: WIGAES
JOURNAL OF TRADITIONAL MEDICINES. (Text in English or Japanese; abstracts in English) 1967. 4/yr. 10000 Yen($95) (Medical and Pharmaceutical Society for Wakan-Yaku) Chuo Insatsu Co., 1-4-5, Shimookui, Toyama 930-01, Japan. TEL 0764-32-6572. (Subscr. to: Toyama Medical & Pharmaceutical University, Research Institute for Wakan-Yaku, Toyama 930-01, Japan. TEL 81-764-34-2281. FAX 81-764-34-5056) Ed. Hiroshi Watanabe. adv. circ. 1,300. (back issues avail.) **Document type:** academic/scholarly publication.
—CASDDS.
   Former titles (until 1994): Medical and Pharmaceutical Society for Wakan-Yaku. Journal (ISSN 0289-730X); (until 1984): Wakan-Yaku Shinpojumu (ISSN 0388-7413)
   Description: Contains chemical, pharmaceutical, pharmacological and clinical studies on Sino-Japanese traditional medicines.
Refereed Serial

PHARMACY AND PHARMACOLOGY

615 636.089 UK ISSN 0140-7783
CODEN: JVPTD9
JOURNAL OF VETERINARY PHARMACOLOGY AND THERAPEUTICS. 1978. bi-m. £282 in Europe; elsewhere £310.50($499) (effective 1996). (Association for Veterinary Clinical Pharmacology & Therapeutics) Blackwell Science Ltd., Osney Mead, Oxford OX2 0EL, England. TEL 01865-206206. FAX 01865-206219. TELEX 83355 MEDBOK G. (Co-sponsors: American College of Veterinary Pharmacology and Therapeutics; European Association for Veterinary Pharmacology and Toxicology) Eds. P. Lees, A. Aronson. adv.; bk.rev.; bibl. circ. 550. (also avail. in microform from UMI; back issues avail.; reprint service avail. from ISI) Indexed: Biotech.Abstr., Chem.Abstr., Curr.Adv.Ecol.Sci., Dairy Sci.Abstr., Excerp.Med. (1992-), Ind.Med., Ind.Sci.Rev., Ind.Vet., Pig News & Info., Poult.Abstr., Protozool.Abstr., Rev.Med.& Vet.Mycol., Small Anim.Abstr., Sport Fish.Abstr., Vet.Bull., Wild.Rev. **Document type:** academic/scholarly publication.
—BLDSC (5072.420000); ADONIS; CASDDS; Faxon; Genuine Article; SWETS; UMI; UnCover. CCC.
Refereed Serial

615 SW ISSN 1102-285X
JOURNALEN (STOCKHOLM); aktuellt fraan Kabi Pharmacia AB. 1988. 10/yr. Kabi Pharmacia AB, S-112 87 Stockholm, Sweden.

615 JA ISSN 0348-5188
KAERNAN; information fraan Pharmacia Therapeutics Nordic AB. 1977. irreg. (4-5/yr.). Pharmacia Therapeutics Nordic AB, P.O. Box 839, S-201 80 Malmoe, Sweden.

KAGAKU RYOHO NO RYOIKI/ANTIBIOTICS AND CHEMOTHERAPY. see *MEDICAL SCIENCES — Obstetrics And Gynecology*

KANAGAWA SEISHIN YAKURI/KANAGAWA JOURNAL OF PSYCHOPHARMACOLOGY. see *PSYCHOLOGY*

615 JA ISSN 0285-4775
CODEN: KKBYDO
KANAGAWAKEN BYOIN YAKUZAISHIKAI KAISHI/KANAGAWA HOSPITAL PHARMACISTS ASSOCIATION. JOURNAL. (Text in Japanese) 1968. 3/yr. Kanagawaken Byoin Yakuzaishikai - Kanagawaken Hospital Pharmacists Association, Kitasato Byoin, 15-1, Kitasato 1-chome, Sagamihara-shi, Kanagawa-ken 228, Japan.
—CASDDS.

615 JA ISSN 0912-0262
KANEYAKU HYAKUMI DANSU. (Text in Japanese) 1978. q. 500 Yen per no. Konebo Yakuhin K.K. - Kanebo Pharmaciscals, Ltd., 3-12, Motoakasaka 1-chome, Minato-ku, Tokyo 107, Japan.

615 JA
KANPOYAKUHO/CHINESE DRUG NEWS. (Text in Japanese) 1983. 3/yr. Kinokuniya Kan'yakkyoku, 2-14, Sotokanda 1-chome, Chiyoda-ku, Tokyo 101, Japan.

KAOHSIUNG JOURNAL OF MEDICAL SCIENCES. see *MEDICAL SCIENCES*

615.9 JA ISSN 0287-2358
KAPUSERU/CAPSULE. (Text in Japanese) 1982. irreg. Nihon Seiyaku Kogyo Kyokai - Japan Pharmaceutical Manufacturers Association, 4-1 Nihonbashi Honcho 3-chome, Chuo-ku, Tokyo 103, Japan.

615 JA ISSN 0289-4750
KATEIYAKU KENKYU/RESEARCH ON HOME MEDICINES. (Text in Japanese) 1982. a. Toyamaken Kateiyaku Kaihatsu Kenkyukai - Toyama Research Society for Home Medicine, 1-7, Shinsogawa, Toyama-shi, Toyama-ken 930, Japan.

615 JA ISSN 0910-6057
KENKYU YAKUBUTSU JOHO. (Text in Japanese) 1965. bi-m. Iyakuhin Sangyo Kenkyujo - Drug Business Research Co., Ltd., 25-2, Koishikawa 1-chome, Bunkyo-ku, Tokyo 112, Japan.

615 US ISSN 0194-567X
THE KENTUCKY PHARMACIST. 1878. m. $30. Kentucky Pharmacists Association, Inc., 1228 U.S. 127 S., Frankfort, KY 40601. TEL 502-227-2303. FAX 502-227-2258. Ed. Robert L. Barnett, Jr. adv.; bk.rev. circ. 1,800.
—BLDSC (5089.654000).

615 UK ISSN
KEY NOTE MARKET REVIEW: U K PHARMACEUTICAL INDUSTRY. Variant title: U K Pharmaceutical Industry. irreg £375. Key Note Publications Ltd., Field House, 72 Oldfield Rd., Hampton, Middlesex TW12 2HQ, England. TEL 0181-783-0755. FAX 0181-783-1720. **Document type:** trade publication.
●Also available online.
Also available on CD-ROM.

615 UK ISSN 0956-8956
KEY NOTE REPORT: O T C PHARMACEUTICALS. Variant title: O T C Pharmaceuticals. irreg. £185. Key Note Publications Ltd., Field House, 72 Oldfield Rd., Hampton, Middlesex TW12 2HQ, England. TEL 0181-783-0755. FAX 0181-783-1720. **Document type:** trade publication.
●Also available online.
Also available on CD-ROM.

615 UK ISSN 1352-7134
KEY NOTE REPORT: PRESCRIBED PHARMACEUTICALS. Variant title: Prescribed Pharmaceuticals. irreg. £185. Key Note Publications Ltd., Field House, 72 Oldfield Rd., Hampton, Middlesex TW12 2HQ, England. TEL 0181-783-0755. FAX 0181-783-1720. **Document type:** trade publication.
●Also available online.
Also available on CD-ROM.
—BLDSC (6609.698000).

615 UK ISSN 1352-6979
KEY NOTE REPORT: RETAIL CHEMISTS & DRUG STORES. Variant title: Retail Chemists & Drug Stores. 1993. irreg. £185. Key Note Publications Ltd., Field House, 72 Oldfield Rd., Hampton, Middlesex TW12 2HQ, England. TEL 0181-783-0755. FAX 0181-783-1720. **Document type:** trade publication.
●Also available online.
Also available on CD-ROM.
—BLDSC (7785.500400).

615.1 RU ISSN 0023-1134
RS402 CODEN: KHFZAN
KHIMIKO-FARMATSEVTICHESKII ZHURNAL. English translation: Pharmaceutical Chemistry Journal (US ISSN 0091-150X) 1967. m. $193 (effective 1996). (Tsentr Khimii i Lekarstvernykh Sredstv) Izdatel'stvo Meditsina, Petroverigskii pereulok 6-8, 101000 Moscow, Russia. TEL 7-095-2948785. (Dist. by: Mezhdunarodnaya Kniga, B. Yakimanka 39, 117049 Moscow, Russia. TEL 7-095-2384600. FAX 7-095-2384634) Ed. R.G. Glushkov. bk.rev.; play rev.; bibl.; charts; illus.; index. Indexed: Anal.Abstr., Biol.Abstr., Biotech.Abstr., Chem.Abstr., Chem.Infd., Cott.& Trop.Fibr.Abstr., Curr.Adv.Ecol.Sci., Curr.Cont., Excerp.Med. (1993-), Helminthol.Abstr., Hort.Abstr., I.P.A., Ind.Chem., Ind.Sci.Rev., Plant Grow.Reg.Abstr., Soils & Fert., Sugar Ind.Abstr.
●Also available online.
—BLDSC (0391.922000); CASDDS; EMDOCS; Genuine Article; SWETS.
Description: Publishes articles on scientific-technical and production activities of chemo-pharmaceutic enterprises.

615.1 JA ISSN 0023-1657
KINKI UNIVERSITY. BULLETIN OF PHARMACY/KINKI DAIGAKU YAKUGAKUBU KIYO. 1959. irreg. Kinki University, Faculty of Pharmaceutical Sciences, 321 Kowakae, Higashiosaka, Osaka, Japan. Ed. Shoji Takemura. circ. 1,000. Indexed: Biol.Abstr., Chem.Abstr., I.P.A.

615 JA ISSN 0914-5079
KITASATO DAIGAKU DAIGAKUIN YAKUGAKU KENKYUKA RINSHO YAKUGAKU TOKURON KIYO/KITASATO UNIVERSITY. CLINICAL PHARMACY BULLETIN. (Text in Japanese) 1982. a. Kitasato Daigaku, Yakugakubu - Kitasato University, Faculty of Pharmacy, 9-1, Shirogane 5-chome, Minato-ku, Tokyo 108, Japan.

615 SW ISSN 0280-6185
KLINIK & TERAPI. 1965. 8/yr. Astra Laekemedel AB, S-151 85 Soedertalje, Sweden.
Former titles (until 1982): Astra-Nytt; (until 1970): Information fraan Astra Laekemedel AB.

615 GW
KLINISCHE PHARMAKOLOGIE. 1990. irreg., vol.9, 1993. W. Zuckschwerdt Verlag GmbH, Industriestr. 17, 82110 Germering, Germany. TEL 089-894349-0. FAX 089-89434950. Eds. H. Kewitz, J. Drews. **Document type:** academic/scholarly publication.

615 JA ISSN 0911-9191
KOBE GAKUIN DAIGAKU YAKUGAKKAISHI/KOBE GAKUIN UNIVERSITY. PHARMACEUTICAL SOCIETY. ANNUAL BULLETIN. (Text in Japanese) 1977. a. Kobe Gakuin Daigaku, Yakugakubu - Kobe Gakuin University, Faculty of Pharmaceutical Science, 518, Arise, Ikawadanicho, Nishi-ku, Kobe-shi, Hyogo-ken 673, Japan.

615 JA ISSN 0911-9183
KOBE GAKUIN DAIGAKU YAKUGAKUBU KIYO/KOBE GAKUIN UNIVERSITY. FACULTY OF PHARMACEUTICAL SCIENCES. MEMOIRS. (Text in English, Japanese) 1978. every 5 yrs. Kobe Gakuin Daigaku, Yakugakubu, 518, Arise, Ikawadanicho, Nishi-ku, Kobe-shi, Hyogo-ken 673, Japan.

615.9 JA ISSN 0912-2133
KOKUNAI IYAKUHIN FUKUSAYO ICHIRAN/LIST OF ADVERSE REACTIONS TO DRUGS. (Text in Japanese) 1975. s-a. 50000 Yen. Japan Pharmaceutical Information Center - Nihon Iyaku Joho Senta, 3rd Fl., Nagai-Kinenkan, 2-12-15 Shibuya, Shibuyaku, Tokyo 150, Japan. FAX 03-5466-1814. Ed. H. Miyake. circ. 1,000.

615 JA ISSN 0915-1656
KOKUNAI IYAKUHIN TENPU BUNSHO JOHO/PACKAGE INSERT INFORMATION OF DOMESTIC MEDICATION. (Text in Japanese) m. 30000 Yen to non-members; members 15000Yen. Nihon Iyaku Joho Senta - Japan Pharmaceutical Information Center, Nagai Kinenkan, 12-15, Shibuya 2-chome, Shibuya-ku, Tokyo 150, Japan.

615 JA ISSN 0388-211X
KOKUSAI IYAKUHIN JOHO/INTERNATIONAL PHARMACEUTICAL INTELLIGENCE. (Text in Japanese) 1972. m. 104200 Yen. Kokusai Shogyo Shuppan K.K. - Kokusai Shogyo Publishing Corp., 14-5, Ginza 6-chome, Chuo-ku, Tokyo 104, Japan.

615 JA
KONNICHI NO CHIRYOYAKU/TODAY'S PHARMACY. (Text in Japanese) 1977. a. 4200 Yen. Nankodo Co., Ltd., 42-6, Hongo 3-chome, Bunkyo-bu, Tokyo 113, Japan.

615.4 KO ISSN 0253-3073
RS160 CODEN: SYHJAM
KOREAN JOURNAL OF PHARMACOGNOSY. Key Title: Sengyakhak-Hoeji (Sehur). (Text in English or Korean; summaries in English) 1970. q. $40. Korean Society of Pharmacognosy, c/o Natural Products Research Institute, 28 Yungun-dong, Chongro-gu, Seoul 110 460, S. Korea. FAX 02-742-9951. Ed. Hye Sook Yum-Choi. adv.; bk.rev. circ. 800. (back issues avail.) Indexed: Chem.Abstr., Excerp.Med. **Document type:** academic/scholarly publication.
—BLDSC (5113.572000); CASDDS.

615 KO ISSN 0377-9459
RM1 CODEN: TYCPAQ
KOREAN JOURNAL OF PHARMACOLOGY/TAEHAN YANGNIHAK CHAPCHI. Key Title: Daihan Yangrihak Jabji. (Text in English; summaries in Korean) 1965. s-a. free. Society of Pharmacology, c/o Dept. of Pharmacology, College of Medicine, 28 Yunkun-dong, Chongro-ku, Seoul 110, S. Korea. FAX 02-745-7996. Ed. Chan-Woong Park. circ. 500. (back issues avail.) Indexed: Biol.Abstr., Chem.Abstr., Excerp.Med. **Document type:** academic/scholarly publication.
—BLDSC (5113.572300); CASDDS.
Refereed Serial

615 KO ISSN 1225-5467
RM301.28
KOREAN SOCIETY FOR CLINICAL PHARMACOLOGY AND THERAPEUTICS. JOURNAL. (Text in Korean) 1993. s-a. $30 (effective 1996). Korean Society for Clinical Pharmacology and Therapeutics, c/o Seoul National University College of Medicine, Department of Neuropsychiatry, 28 Yongon-dong, Chongno-gu, Seoul 110-744, S. Korea. TEL 740-8286. FAX 745-7996. Ed. Jung Sang Lee; Pub. Chung Kyoon Lee. adv. contact: Myoung Mook Lee. **Document type:** academic/scholarly publication.
—BLDSC (4812.343900).
Description: Publishes articles dealing with the effects of drugs, including pharmacodynamics, clinical trials, pharmacoepidemiology, pharmacogenetics and other studies of drugs.
Refereed Serial

615 JA ISSN 0912-5027
KOSEI BUSSHITSU RYOHO/INDICATIONS IN ANTIBIOTIC THERAPY. (Text in Japanese) 1985. s-a. Sutandado Makkintaiya - Standard McIntyre, 3-7, Irifune 2-chome, Chuo-ku, Tokyo 104, Japan.

615 GW ISSN 0173-7597
CODEN: KRANDZ
KRANKENHAUSPHARMAZIE. 1950. m. DM.186. (Arbeitsgemeinschaft Deutscher Krankenhausapotheker) Deutscher Apotheker Verlag, Postfach 101061, 70009 Stuttgart, Germany. TEL 0711-2582-0. FAX 0711-2582290. Ed. Peter Frank. **Indexed:** Biotech.Abstr., Chem.Abstr., I.P.A. **Document type:** trade publication.
—BLDSC (5118.146200); CASDDS; Genuine Article. **CCC.**
Formerly (until 1980): Krankenhaus-Apotheke (ISSN 0075-7071)

615 JA ISSN 0916-4758
KURAYA YAKUHO/KURAYA MEDICAL WEEKLY. (Text in Japanese) 1986. w. Kuraya Yakuhin K.K., Gakujutsubu, 24-7, Hongo 5-chome, Bunkyo-ku, Tokyo 133, Japan.

615 JA ISSN 0911-3371
KURINIKARU FAMASHI/CLINICAL PHARMACY. (Text in Japanese) 1985. q. 1200 Yen per no. Hirokawa Shoten - Hirokawa Publishing Co., 27-14, Hongo 3-chome, Bunkyo-ku, Tokyo 113, Japan.

615 JA
KURINIKARU FAMASHI SHINPOJUMU KOEN YOSHISHU/SYMPOSIUM ON CLINICAL PHARMACY. (Text in Japanese) biennial. Pharmaceutical Society of Japan - Nihon Yakugakkai, 12-15, Shibuya 2-chome, Shibuya-ku, Tokyo 150, Japan. Ed. Keiko Kubonoya.

615 JA ISSN 0285-2713
KURINIKARU NYUSU/DAIICHI PURE CHEMICALS CO., LTD. CLINICAL NEWS. (Text in Japanese) 1980. 3/yr. Daiichi Kagaku Yakuhin K.K. - Daiichi Pure Chemicals Co., Ltd., 13-5, Nihonbashi 3-chome, Chuo-ku, Tokyo 103, Japan.

615 JA
KUSURI HAKUBUTSUKAN DAYORI/NAITO MUSEUM. SEMI-ANNUAL REPORT. (Text in Japanese) 1978. s-a. free. Naito Kinen Kursuri Hakubutsukan - Naito Museum of Pharmaceutical Science and Industry, Kawashima-cho, Hashima-gun, Gifu-ken 501-61, Japan. TEL 058689-2101. FAX 058689-2197. **Document type:** bulletin.

615 JA ISSN 0287-6485
CODEN: KNCHDX
KUSURI NO CHISHIKI/FRONTIERS IN MEDICINE. (Text in Japanese) 1950. m. 1500 Yen. Hoken Dojinsha Inc., 12-2, Fujimi 2-chome, Chiyoda-ku, Tokyo 102, Japan. TEL 03-3664-7750.
—CASDDS.

615 JA ISSN 0452-9731
CODEN: KYDKAJ
KYORITSU YAKKA DAIGAKU KENKYU NENPO/KYORITSU COLLEGE OF PHARMACY. ANNUAL REPORT. (Text in English, Japanese; summaries in English) 1955. a. Kyoritsu Yakka Daigaku, 5-30, Shiba Koen 1-chome, Minato-ku, Tokyo 105, Japan. **Indexed:** Chem.Abstr.
—BLDSC (1320.500000); CASDDS.

615 JA ISSN 0288-111X
KYOTOFU YAKUZAISHIKAI SHIKEN KENKYU SENTA NENPO/KYOTO PREFECTURAL PHARMACEUTICAL ASSOCIATION. ANNUAL REPORT OF THE LABORATORY. (Text in Japanese) 1980. a. Kyotofu Yakuzaishikai, Shiken Kenkyu Senta, Kyotofu Yakuzaishi Kaikan, 563, Umebayashicho, Yamato Oji Higashi Iru 5-chome, Goji Dori, Higashiyama-ku, Kyoto 605, Japan.

615 JA ISSN 0368-7279
CODEN: KYYKBN
KYUSHU YAKUGAKKAI KAIHO/KYUSHU PHARMACEUTICAL SOCIETY. JOURNAL. (Text in Japanese; summaries in English) 1927. a. Kyushu Yamaguchi Yakugakkai, c/o Kyushu Daigaku Igakubu Fuzoku Byoin Yakuzaibu, 1-1, Maidashi 3-chome, Higashi-ku, Fukuoka-shi, Fukuoka-ken 812, Japan. **Indexed:** Chem.Abstr.
—BLDSC (5136.400000); CASDDS.

615 JA ISSN 0911-9205
LABORATORY FRIENDS. (Text in Japanese) 1970. q. Chugai Seiyaku K.K. - Chugai Pharmaceutical Co., Ltd., 1-9, Kyobashi 2-chome, Chuo-ku, Tokyo 104, Japan.

615.1 DK ISSN 0106-1275
LAEGEFORENINGENS MEDICINFORTEGNELSE. 1963. biennial. DKK 340 (effective 1995). Laegeforeningens Forlag, Esplanaden 8A, DK-1263 Copenhagen K, Denmark. TEL 45-31-38-55-00. FAX 45-33-15-28-58.

615.1 DK ISSN 0105-287X
LAEGEMIDDELKATALOGET. (Supplements avail.: Laegemiddelkatalogets Prisliste (DK 0105-4600); Beretning fra Naevnet for Medicinsk Informationsmateriale for Aaret (Year) (DK 0903-9732)) 1976. a. DKK 360.80. Laegemiddelkataloget, Stroedamvej 50 B, DK-1360 Copenhagen K, Denmark. TEL 45-33-11-31-55. FAX 45-33-33-74-20. (Co-sponsors: Danmarks Apotekerforening, Foreningen af Danske Medicinfabrikker, Medicinindustriforeningen) DR. Mogens Brandt Kristensen. **Document type:** catalog.

615.5 SW ISSN 0347-8343
LAEKEMEDELSBOKEN. 1977. a. SEK 250 (effective 1995). Apoteksbolaget, S-105 14 Stockholm, Sweden. Ed. Signe Bogentoft.

615.19 US ISSN 0734-4961
CODEN: LRNSEP
LAWRENCE REVIEW OF NATURAL PRODUCTS. 1980. m. $60. Facts and Comparisons, 111 West Port Plaza, Ste. 400, St. Louis, MO 63146-3098. TEL 800-223-0554. FAX 314-878-5563. (looseleaf format; back issues avail.) **Indexed:** Biol.Abstr., I.P.A. **Document type:** newsletter.
Former titles: Lawrence Review of Natural Products Monograph System; Lawrence Review of Natural Products.
Description: Provides referenced reviews of the history, chemistry, pharmacology and toxicity of natural products of medical, social and economic interest.

LECTINS. see *BIOLOGY — Biological Chemistry*

LEKARSKY OBZOR. see *MEDICAL SCIENCES*

615 FR ISSN 0984-452X
LETTRE DU PHARMACOLOGUE. m. 360 F. Edimark, 207 rue Gallieni, 92100 Boulogne, France. TEL 48-25-11-59. FAX 46-03-94-37. Ed. P. Jaillon.
—BLDSC (5185.215200).

615.1 FR ISSN 1145-4881
LETTRE MENSUEL DE FRANCE PHARMACIE LABORATOIRES. 1945. 11/yr. 450 F. (foreign 690 F.). 41 rue Gambetta, 92100 Boulogne Billancourt, France. TEL 46-04-52-46. FAX 46-05-65-47. Ed. Roger Baert. adv.; bk.rev.; illus. circ. 1,500. **Indexed:** Chem.Abstr., I.P.A.
●Also available online.
Former titles (until 1989): France Pharmacie Laboratoires (ISSN 0998-6804); (until 1988): France Pharmacie (ISSN 0015-9697)

LIAONING ZHONGYI ZAZHI/LIAONING JOURNAL OF TRADITIONAL CHINESE MEDICINE. see *ALTERNATIVE MEDICINE*

615 NE ISSN 1381-3145
▼**LIJFBLAD.** 1995. m. Mediselect B.V., Postbus 28091, 3828 ZH Hoogland, Netherlands. TEL 31-33-808020. FAX 31-33-805881. Ed. M. Meulepas; Pub. J. Blom. adv.; circ. 10,000 (controlled). **Document type:** trade publication.
Description: Covers drug store products and educational matters for salespersons in drug stores and pharmacies.

LIPOSOMES. see *BIOLOGY — Biological Chemistry*

615 UK
THE LOCUM. bi-m. The Old Fire Sta., 69 Albion St., Birmingham B1 3EA, England. TEL 021-233-0233. FAX 021-233-0723. circ. 3,500.

LOOKOUT - NONFOODS. see *BEAUTY CULTURE — Perfumes And Cosmetics*

615 US ISSN 0192-3838
LOUISIANA PHARMACIST.* 1943. bi-m. $20. Louisiana Pharmacists Association, Box 14446, Baton Rouge, LA 70898-4446. Ed. Linda Foreman. adv.; illus. circ. 2,000.

615.1 FR ISSN 0024-7804
CODEN: LYPHAD
LYON PHARMACEUTIQUE. 1930. 8/yr. 815 F. in France; foreign 915 F.($183) (effective 1996). Editions Scientifiques Elsevier, 141 rue de Javel, 75747 Paris, France. TEL 33-1-45589063. (Subscr. in U.S. and Canada to: Elsevier Science Inc., Box 882, Madison Sq. Sta., New York, NY 10159. TEL 212-989-5800) Ed. B. Poggi. adv.; charts; illus. circ. 2,500. (reprint service avail. from ISI, UMI) **Indexed:** Biol.Abstr., Biotech.Abstr., Chem.Abstr., Excerp.Med. (1993-), I.P.A. **Document type:** academic/scholarly publication.
—BLDSC (5312.000000); CASDDS; EMDOCS. **CCC.**
Description: Publishes scientific articles for students, pharmacists and hospital practitioners in the pharmacological and biological fields at the post-graduate level.
Refereed Serial

615.1 FI ISSN 0024-8045
M D S. (Text in Finnish; summaries in English and Swedish) 1901. bi-m. FIM 150. Yliopiston Farmasiakunta r.y. - University Pharmaceutical Association, Biokeskus 1 B, PLJ 6, Viikinkaari 1, 00014 Helsingin Yliopisto, Finland. Ed. Liisa Rantanon. adv.; bk.rev.; charts; illus.; pat.; stat.; tr.lit. circ. 1,000. (looseleaf format)

615 UK ISSN 0957-9095
M I M S. (Monthly Index of Medical Specialties) 1959. m. £64 (effective 1995). Haymarket Medical Ltd., 30 Lancaster Gate, London W2 3LP, England. TEL 0171-413-4095. (Subscr. to: Galleon, P.O. Box 219, Woking, Surrey GU21 1ZW, England. TEL 01483-733800) Ed. Colin Duncan. adv. contact: Jackie Caldwell. circ. 59,950. **Document type:** trade publication.

615 UK ISSN 0140-4415
M I M S AFRICA. 1961. bi-m. £23 (foreign £26) (effective 1996) (free to medical profession and to hospitals in East, West and Central Africa). A.E. Morgan Publications Ltd., Stanley House, 9 West St., Epsom, Surrey KT18 7RL, England. TEL 01372-741411. FAX 01372-744493. Ed. Frances Wilson; Pub. Terence Morgan. adv. contact: Peter Louatt. circ. 8,300. **Document type:** trade publication.
Former titles: African M I M S (ISSN 0002-0079); African Medical Practitioner.
Description: Listing of prescribable drugs for medical practitioners.

615.19 AT ISSN 0725-4709
M I M S ANNUAL. 1977. a. Aus.$150.05. M I M S Australia, 48 Albany St., Crows Nest, N.S.W. 2065, Australia. Ed. Linda H. Badewitz-Dodd. adv.; charts. circ. 24,000.
Description: Full disclosure information on all pharmaceuticals available for prescription in Australia.

615.19 AT ISSN 1035-5723
M I M S BI-MONTHLY. 1963. bi-m. Aus.$143.15. M I M S Australia, 48 Albany St., Crows Nest, N.S.W. 2065, Australia. Ed. Linda H. Badewitz-Dodd. adv. circ. 24,000.
Description: Therapeutically classified prescribing information on all products available for prescription in Australia.

PHARMACY AND PHARMACOLOGY

615 UK
M I M S CARIBBEAN. 1970. bi-m. £21.50 (foreign £23) (effective 1996). A.E. Morgan Publications Ltd., Stanley House, 9 West St., Epsom, Surrey KT18 7RL, England. TEL 01372-741411. FAX 01372-744493. Ed. Frances Wilson; Pub. Terence Morgan. adv. contact: Peter Louatt. circ. 2,600. **Document type:** trade publication.
  Description: Listing of prescribable drugs for medical practitioners.

615 SA ISSN 0076-8847
M I M S DESK REFERENCE. 1965. a. M I M S, Division of Times Media Limited, P.O. Box 2059, Pretoria 0001, South Africa. TEL 27-12-3485010. FAX 27-12-477716. Ed. Jacques Sayman. adv.; index. circ. 8,500.
  Formerly: M I M S Reference Manual.
  Description: Contains details of human medicines, tablet and capsule indentification chart, and a reference section.

M I M S DRUGS AND SPORT. see *MEDICAL SCIENCES — Sports Medicine*

615 UK ISSN 0302-4172
M I M S MIDDLE EAST. 1971. bi-m. £26.30 (foreign £29.40) (effective 1996). A.E. Morgan Publications Ltd., Stanley House, 9 West St., Epsom, Surrey KT18 7RL, England. TEL 01372-741411. FAX 01372-744493. Ed. Frances Wilson; Pub. Terence Morgan. adv. contact: Peter Louatt. circ. 19,000. **Document type:** trade publication.
  Description: Listing of prescribable drugs for qualified medical practitioners.

MAGNESIUM RESEARCH. see *METALLURGY*

615 US ISSN 1075-2358
MANAGED PHARMACEUTICAL REPORT. m. $287. Capitol Publications Inc., 1101 King St., Ste. 444, Alexandria, VA 22314. TEL 703-683-4100. FAX 703-739-6501. Ed. Justin McGuire. **Document type:** newsletter.
  —CCC.
  Description: Briefing service on managed pharmaceuticals that helps subscribers identify new business opportunities and keep costs down.

615 UA ISSN 1110-1318
  CODEN: MJPSEO
MANSOURA JOURNAL OF PHARMACEUTICAL SCIENCES/MAJALLAT AL-MANSURAH LIL-ULUM AL-SAYDALIYYAH. (Text in Arabic, English) 1986. s-a. $80. University of Mansoura, Faculty of Pharmacy, University P.O. 35516, Mansoura, Egypt. **Indexed:** ExtraMED. **Document type:** academic/scholarly publication.
  •Also available on CD-ROM.
  Refereed Serial

615 AG
MANUAL FARMACEUTICO. 1960. m. $240. Alfa Beta S A C I F Y S, Melian 3136, 1430 Buenos Aires, Argentina. Ed. Juan Marrari. adv. circ. 15,000.

615 US ISSN 0085-3100
MARIO NEGRI INSTITUTE FOR PHARMACOLOGICAL RESEARCH. MONOGRAPHS. Key Title: Monographs of the Mario Negri Institute for Pharmacological Research. 1970. irreg., latest 1993. price varies. Raven Press (Subsidiary of: Wolters Kluwer N.V.), 1185 Ave. of the Americas, New York, NY 10036. TEL 212-930-9500. FAX 212-869-3495. Ed. Silvio Garattini. (reprint service avail. from UMI) **Indexed:** Biol.Abstr., Chem.Abstr., Curr.Cont. **Document type:** proceedings.
  Description: Proceedings of international biomedical symposia covering pharmacological problems.
  Refereed Serial

615 UK ISSN 0263-5364
MARTINDALE: THE EXTRA PHARMACOPOEIA. 1883. quinquennial. £125. Royal Pharmaceutical Society of Great Britain, 1 Lambeth High St., London SE1 7JN, England. TEL 071-735-9141. FAX 071-735-7629. (Dist. in U.S. by: Rittenhouse Book Distributors, Philadelphia, PA 19406) Ed. James E. Reynolds. index. **Document type:** catalog.
  •Also available online. Vendor(s): Data-Star, Knight-Ridder, Inc. (File no.141)
  Incorporates: Squires Companion.
  Description: Provides a concise summary of the properties, actions and uses of drugs and medicines for the practising pharmacists and medical practitioners.

615.1 US ISSN 0025-4347
MARYLAND PHARMACIST. 1925. m. $10. Maryland Pharmacists Association, 650 W. Lombard St., Baltimore, MD 21201. TEL 410-727-0746. FAX 410-725-2253. Ed. David G. Miller. adv.; bk.rev.; charts; illus. circ. 1,400. **Indexed:** Alt.Press Ind., Chem.Abstr., I.P.A.

615.1 378 US ISSN 0025-4789
MASSACHUSETTS COLLEGE OF PHARMACY. BULLETIN. 1911. 4/yr. free to qualified personnel. Massachusetts College of Pharmacy and Allied Health Sciences, 179 Longwood Ave., Boston, MA 02115. TEL 617-732-2800. FAX 617-732-2801. Ed. James J. Larkin. illus. circ. 8,000. **Document type:** newsletter.
  Description: Contains organization news.

MATERIA MEDICA POLONA; the Polish journal of medicine and pharmacy. see *MEDICAL SCIENCES*

MED AD NEWS. see *BUSINESS AND ECONOMICS — Marketing And Purchasing*

613 SP ISSN 0214-3178
MEDICAL LETTER. Spanish translation of: Medical Letter on Drugs and Therapeutics (US ISSN 0025-732X) 1979. s-m. $84 (effective 1995). J.R. Prous, S.A. International Publishers, Apdo. de Correos 540, 08080 Barcelona, Spain. TEL 343-458-2220. FAX 343-458-1535. adv. contact: P. Blancafort. index. circ. 2,600. (looseleaf format; back issues avail.)

615 US ISSN 0025-732X
MEDICAL LETTER ON DRUGS AND THERAPEUTICS (ENGLISH EDITION). French, Italian, Japanese and Spanish translations: Medical Letter. 1959. fortn. $37.50 (residents, interns & medical student $18.75). Medical Letter, Inc., 1000 Main St., New Rochelle, NY 10801. TEL 914-235-0500. FAX 914-576-3377. Ed. Dr. Mark Abramowicz. index, cum. index every 5 yrs. circ. 150,000. (also avail. in microform from UMI; back issues avail.; reprint service avail. from UMI) **Indexed:** AIM, CINAHL, Curr.Cont., Dent.Ind., Diar.Dis.Res., Excerp.Med., FAMLI, Helminthol.Abstr., I.P.A., Ind.Med., Ind.Sci.Rev.
  •Also available online. Vendor(s): University Microfilms International.
  —BLDSC (5529.700000); ADONIS; EMDOCS; Genuine Article; UMI.
  Description: Provides unbiased, critical evaluations of drugs for physicians and other members of the health professions.

615 JA ISSN 0910-6316
MEDICAL LETTER ON DRUGS AND THERAPEUTICS (JAPANESE EDITION). (Text in Japanese) 1985. bi-w. 10000 Yen. Iyakuhin Sangyo Kenkyujo - Japanese Society of Medical Imaging Technology, 25-2, Koishikawa 1-chome, Bunkyo-ku, Tokyo 112, Japan.

MEDICAL MALPRACTICE: PHARMACY LAW. see *LAW — Civil Law*

610 658.8 US ISSN 0025-7354
HD9665.1 CODEN: MMKMBX
MEDICAL MARKETING & MEDIA. Short title: M M & M. 1966. 12/yr. $75 to individuals; institutions $100. C P S Communications, Inc., 7200 W. Camino Real, Ste. 215, Boca Raton, FL 33433. TEL 407-368-9301. FAX 407-368-7870. Ed. David Gideon. adv.; bk.rev.; charts; illus.; stat.; index; circ. 12,800 (controlled). (also avail. in microform from UMI; back issues avail.; reprint service avail.) **Indexed:** ABI Inform., BPIA, I.P.A., PROMT. **Document type:** trade publication.
  •Also available online. Vendor(s): Lexis-Nexis, University Microfilms International.
  —BLDSC (5529.950000); Faxon; SWETS; UMI. CCC.
  Formerly: Pharmaceutical Marketing and Media.
  Description: For the pharmaceutical, medical, marketing and advertising industry providing intra-industry communication and an information link with other industries and government.

615.1 JA ISSN 0025-7427
MEDICAL PHARMACY. (Text in Japanese) 1967. bi-m. 300 Yen per no. Daiichi Seiyaku Co., Ltd., 14-10, Nihonbashi 3-chome, Chuo-ku, Tokyo 103, Japan. adv.; index. circ. 6,500. **Indexed:** Chem.Abstr.

615.19 US ISSN 0199-4905
MEDICAL SCIENCES BULLETIN; focus on clinical pharmacology: theory and practice. 1977. m. $30 (first class $33; foreign airmail $43). Pharmaceutical Information Associates, Ltd., 2761 Trenton Rd., Levittown, PA 19056. TEL 215-949-0490. FAX 215-949-2594. E-mail: pialtd@ix.netcom.com; Site addr.: http://pharminfo.com. Ed. Robert Hand; Pub. Lawrence E. Liberti. bk.rev.; charts; illus.; index; circ. 1,000 (paid). (back issues avail.) **Indexed:** CHNI. **Document type:** newsletter.
  Description: Provides an account of new advances in pharmacology and therapeutics; reviews international medical literature, and reports on trends and controversies in clinical pharmacology and health care.

615 658.8 UK
MEDICATED SKINCARE: THE INTERNATIONAL MARKET. (Subseries of: Market Direction report) a. £1595($3190) (effective 1996). Euromonitor, 60-61 Britton St., London EC1M 5NA, England. TEL 0171-251-8024. FAX 0171-608-3149. (Addr. in N. America: Euromonitor International, 122 S. Michigan Ave., Ste. 1200, Chicago, IL 60603. TEL 312-922-1115. FAX 312-922-1157) (looseleaf format) **Document type:** trade publication.
  •Also available online. Vendor(s): Data-Star, Knight-Ridder, Inc.
  Description: Analyzes the market for nonprescription medicated skin care products for France, Germany, Italy, Spain, the U.K., the U.S., and Japan.

615.19 US ISSN 0198-6325
RM300 CODEN: MRREDD
MEDICINAL RESEARCH REVIEWS. 1981. bi-m. $570 (foreign $663) (effective 1996). John Wiley & Sons, Inc., Journals, 605 Third Ave., New York, NY 10158. TEL 212-850-6645. FAX 212-850-6021. TELEX 12-7063. E-mail: SUBINFO@JWILEY.COM. (Subscr. outside the Americas to: John Wiley & Sons Ltd., Baffins Ln., Chichester, W. Sussex PO19 1UD, England. TEL 44-1243-779777. FAX 44-1243-776128) Ed. George de Stevens. adv. circ. 700. (also avail. in microform from UMI; back issues avail.) **Indexed:** Chem.Infd., Curr.Adv.Biochem., Curr.Adv.Ecol.Sci., Curr.Cont.Ind.Med., Ind.Sci.Rev., Sci.Cit.Ind. **Document type:** academic/scholarly publication.
  —BLDSC (5533.992000); ADONIS; CASDDS; Faxon; Genuine Article; SWETS; UMI. CCC.
  Description: Embraces all aspects of research addressing the study of disease and the consequent development of therapeutic agents.
  Refereed Serial

615 DK ISSN 0900-4858
MEDICINTAKST. 1955. irreg. DKK 50. Sundhedsstyrelsen, Amaliegade 13, 1012 Copenhagen K, Denmark. (Dist. by: Staten Information, P.O. Box 1103, 1009 Copenhagen K, Denmark)

615 SA ISSN 1021-6987
MEDIFILE; drug information bulletin. (Supplement to: South African Pharmaceutical Journal (ISSN 0038-2558)) (Text in English) 1987. m. R.30. T P S Drug Information Centre, P.O. Box 31238, Braamfontein 2017, South Africa. FAX 27-11-3393819. Ed. Jackie van Schoor. abstr.; bibl. circ. 6,000. (looseleaf format) **Document type:** bulletin.
  Description: Provides the pharmacist with current, objective and accurate information on medicines.
  Refereed Serial

MEDIKAMENT & MEINUNG; Zeitschrift fuer Arzneimittel- und Gesundheitswesen. see *MEDICAL SCIENCES*

615.19 610 NR ISSN 0331-4782
MEDIPHARM. (Text in English) 1969. q. $130. Literamed Nigeria Ltd., Plot 45, Alausa, Oregun Village, P.M.B. 21068, Ikeja, Lagos, Nigeria. Ed. Yinka Lawal-Solarin. circ. 10,000.
  Description: Covers pharmaceutical specialties in Nigeria.

615 GW ISSN 0939-6292
MEDIZIN OHNE NEBENWIRKUNGEN. q. DM.74. M M V Medizin Verlag, Neumarkter Str. 18, 81673 Munich, Germany. TEL 089-43189648. FAX 089-43189633. **Document type:** academic/scholarly publication.

PHARMACY AND PHARMACOLOGY

615.2   GW   ISSN 0934-9170
CODEN: MEKOEK
MEDIZINISCH-PHARMAKOLOGISCHES KOMPENDIUM. 1985. irreg. Wissenschaftliche Verlagsgesellschaft mbH, Postfach 101061, 70009 Stuttgart, Germany. TEL 0711-2582-0. FAX 0711-2582-290. TELEX 723636-DAZ-D. **Indexed:** Biol.Abstr. (1988-). **Document type:** academic/scholarly publication.

615   JA   ISSN 0465-6105
CODEN: MSKNA9
MEIJI SEIKA KENKYU NENPO/MEIJI SEIKA KAISHA. SCIENTIFIC REPORTS. (Text in English, Japanese; summaries in English) 1959. a. Meiji Seika K.K., Yakuhin Sogo Kenkyujo - Meiji Seika Kaisha, Ltd., Pharmaceutical Research Center, 760, Morookacho, Kohoku-ku, Yokohama-shi, Kanagawa-ken 222, Japan.
—BLDSC (8198.800000); CASDDS.

615   JA   ISSN 0543-3975
MEIJI YAKKA DAIGAKU KENKYU KIYO/MEIJI COLLEGE OF PHARMACY. BULLETIN. (Text in English, Japanese; summaries in English) 1962. a. Meiji Yakka Daigaku, 22-1, Yatocho 1-chome, Tanashi-shi, Tokyo 188, Japan. **Indexed:** Chem.Abstr., INIS Atomind.
—BLDSC (2612.095000).

615   JA   ISSN 0911-9442
MEIJO DAIGAKU SENKOKA YAKUGAKU SENKO HOKOKUSHU. (Text in Japanese) 1975. a. Meijo Daigaku, Yakugakubu - Meijo University, Faculty of Pharmacy, 15, Yagotourayama, Tenpakucho, Tenpaku-ku, Nagoya-shi, Aichi-ken 468, Japan.

MEINE GESUNDHEIT "REISEAPOTHEKE". see *TRAVEL AND TOURISM*

616.97   JA   ISSN 0289-3371
CODEN: MYSHE9
MEN'EKI YAKURI SHINPOJUMU. (Text in English, Japanese) 1983. a. 4500 Yen. D M B Japan, 9-12, Roppongi 6-chome, Minato-ku, Tokyo 106, Japan.
—BLDSC (5678.442470); CASDDS.

METAL-BASED DRUGS. see *CHEMISTRY — Analytical Chemistry*

METHODOLOGICAL SURVEYS IN BIOANALYSIS OF DRUGS. see *BIOLOGY — Biological Chemistry*

615.19   SP   ISSN 0379-0355
CODEN: MFEPDX
METHODS AND FINDINGS IN EXPERIMENTAL AND CLINICAL PHARMACOLOGY. (Text in English) 1979. 10/yr. $450 (effective 1996). J.R. Prous, S.A. International Publishers, Apdo. de Correos 540, 08080 Barcelona, Spain. TEL 343-459-2220. FAX 343-458-1535. adv. contact: P. Blancafort. bk.rev.; index. circ. 3,000. (back issues avail.) **Indexed:** Biol.Abstr., Biotech.Abstr., Chem.Abstr., Curr.Adv.Cancer Res., Curr.Adv.Ecol.Sci., Curr.Cont., Dent.Ind., Excerp.Med., Ind.Med.Esp., Ind.Med., Ind.Sci.Rev., Sci.Cit.Ind. **Document type:** academic/scholarly publication.
—BLDSC (5746.620000); CASDDS; Faxon; Genuine Article; SWETS; UnCover. **CCC.**
Description: Forum for papers dealing with the methodology employed and the results obtained in the scientific assessment of drugs in animals and humans.

615.19   US   ISSN 0091-3030
QP905   CODEN: MTPHBO
METHODS IN PHARMACOLOGY. 1971. irreg., vol.7, 1993. price varies. Plenum Publishing Corp., 233 Spring St., New York, NY 10013-1578. TEL 212-620-8000. FAX 212-463-0742. TELEX 23-421139. Ed. A. Schwartz. (back issues avail.) **Document type:** monographic series.
—BLDSC (5748.204000); CASDDS.

615.7   NE   ISSN 0376-7396
RM302.5   CODEN: MSEFDQ
MEYLER'S SIDE EFFECTS OF DRUGS; the encyclopedia of adverse reactions. (Supplement avail.: Side Effects of Drugs Annual (ISSN 0378-6080)) (Text in English) 1956. irreg., 11th ed., 1988. fl.425 (effective 1992). Elsevier Science B.V., Books Division, P.O. Box 211, 1000 AE Amsterdam, Netherlands. TEL 31-20-4853911. FAX 31-20-4853705. TELEX 18582 ESPA NL. E-mail: nlinfo-f@elsevier.nl; usinfo-f@elsevier.com; forinfo-kyf04035@niftyserve.or.jp; Site addr.: http://www.elsevier.nl/. (Subscr. in U.S. and Canada to: Elsevier Science Inc., Box 882, Madison Sq. Sta., New York, NY 10159. TEL 212-989-5800) Ed. M.N.G. Dukes.
●Also available online. Vendor(s): Data-Star (SEDB), Knight-Ridder, Inc. (File no.70/SEDBASE), Ovid Technologies.
Also available on CD-ROM. Producer(s): SilverPlatter Information, Inc. (SEDBASE).
—CASDDS. **CCC.**
Formerly (until 1975): Side Effects of Drugs (ISSN 0583-1881)
Refereed Serial

615.1   US
MICHIGAN PHARMACIST. 1963. m. $40. Michigan Pharmacists Association, 815 N. Washington Ave., Lansing, MI 48906. TEL 517-484-1466. FAX 517-484-4893. Ed. Larry D. Wagenknecht. adv.: B&W page $580, color page $600; trim 7 1/4 x 9 3/4; adv. contact: Tanya M. Rungranont. bk.rev.; charts; illus.; stat. circ. 4,000. (also avail. in microform from UMI) **Indexed:** Med.Care Rev., Mich.Mag.Ind. **Document type:** trade publication.
—UMI.
Formerly: Journal Michigan Pharmacist (ISSN 1045-6481)
Refereed Serial

616.97   JA   ISSN 0388-4783
MINOPHAGEN MEDICAL REVIEW. (Text in Japanese) 1956. bi-m. Minofagen Seiyaku Honpo - Minophagen Pharmaceutical Co., 10-22, Akasaka 8-chome, Minato-ku, Tokyo 107, Japan.
—BLDSC (5810.550000).

615   JA   ISSN 0289-629X
MINOPHAGEN MEDICAL REVIEW. SUPPLEMENT. (Text in Japanese) 1968. irreg. Minofagen Seiyaku Honpo - Minophagen Pharmaceutical Co., 10-22, Akasaka 8-chome, Minato-ku, Tokyo 107, Japan.

615.19   IS
MIRKACHTON. (Text in Hebrew) 1987. q. Pharmaceutical Association of Israel, Pharmacies Branch, P.O. Box 566, Tel Aviv 65 112, Israel. TEL 03-615085.

615.1   US   ISSN 0026-6663
MISSOURI PHARMACIST. 1926. m. $25. Missouri Pharmaceutical Association, 410 Madison St., Jefferson City, MO 65101. TEL 314-636-7522. FAX 314-636-7485. Ed. Deedie K. Bedosky. adv.; bk.rev. circ. 1,200.
Description: Includes news items, continuing education articles and professional articles of interest to Missouri pharmacists.

516.1   IC   ISSN 1021-0075
MIXTURA; blad lyfjafraedinema. 1987. a. free. University of Iceland, Department of Pharmacy, IS-101 Reykjavik, Iceland. TEL 354-569-4462. FAX 354-552-1331. Ed.Bd. adv.; illus. circ. 4,000. (back issues avail.)

615   JA   ISSN 0913-2147
MIYAGIKEN YAKUJI JOHO/MIYAGI PREFECTURE DRUG INFORMATION. (Text in Japanese) 1982. s-a. Miyagiken Hoken Kankyobu - Miyagi Prefectural Government, Healthy Environment Division, 8-1, Honcho 3-chome, Aoba-ku, Sendai-shi, Miyagi-ken 980, Japan.

615   JA   ISSN 0917-6209
MIYAGIKEN YAKUJI JOHO YAKKYOKU YAKUTEN'YO/MIYAGI PREFECTURE DRUG INFORMATION FOR PHARMACY. (Text in Japanese) 1990. a. Miyagiken Hoken Kankyobu - Miyagi Prefectural Government, Healthy Environment Division, 8-1, Honcho 3-chome, Aoba-ku, Sendai-shi, Miyagi-ken 980, Japan.

615   US   ISSN 1044-0704
RS79
MODELL'S DRUGS IN CURRENT USE AND NEW DRUGS. 1955. a. price varies. Springer Publishing Company, 536 Broadway, New York, NY 10012-3955. TEL 212-431-4370. FAX 212-941-7842. Ed. Dr. Daniel Hussar. circ. 1,880. (also avail. in microform from UMI; back issues avail.; reprint service avail. from UMI) **Document type:** academic/scholarly publication.
Formerly: Drugs in Current Use and New Drugs (ISSN 0070-7392)

615.19   US   ISSN 0732-7218
RM301   CODEN: MMEPDE
MODERN METHODS IN PHARMACOLOGY. 1982. irreg., vol.5, 1990. price varies. John Wiley & Sons, Inc., Journals, 605 Third Ave., New York, NY 10158. TEL 212-475-7700. **Indexed:** Biol.Abstr., Chem.Abstr.
—BLDSC (5890.000200); CASDDS; Faxon. **CCC.**
Refereed Serial

615   US   ISSN 0098-6925
CODEN: MPTOD5
MODERN PHARMACOLOGY - TOXICOLOGY SERIES. 1973. irreg., vol.21, 1982. Marcel Dekker, Inc., 270 Madison Ave., New York, NY 10016. TEL 212-696-9000. FAX 212-658-4540. TELEX 421419. Eds. W. Bousquet, R.F. Palmer. illus. **Indexed:** Chem.Abstr. **Document type:** monographic series.
—CASDDS.
Formerly: Modern Pharmacology (ISSN 0092-0150)
Refereed Serial

MODERN PROBLEMS OF PHARMACOPSYCHIATRY. see *MEDICAL SCIENCES — Psychiatry And Neurology*

615.7   US   ISSN 0026-895X
QP901   CODEN: MOPMA3
MOLECULAR PHARMACOLOGY. m. $105 to individuals; institutions $230 (effective 1995). (American Society for Pharmacology & Experimental Therapeutics) Williams & Wilkins, 428 E. Preston St., Baltimore, MD 21202. TEL 410-528-4000; 800-638-6423. FAX 410-528-4312. TELEX 87669. Ed. Dr. Raymond Dingledine. adv.; index. circ. 1,712. (also avail. in microform from WWS; back issues avail.) **Indexed:** Biotech.Abstr., Chem.Abstr., Curr.Adv.Biochem., Curr.Adv.Cancer Res., Curr.Adv.Ecol.Sci., Curr.Adv.Genetics & Molec.Biol., Curr.Cont., Dent.Ind., Excerp.Med., Helminthol.Abstr., Ind.Med., Ind.Sci.Rev., Protozool.Abstr., Rev.Med.& Vet.Mycol. **Document type:** academic/scholarly publication.
—BLDSC (5900.818000); CASDDS; EMDOCS; Faxon; Genuine Article; SWETS; UnCover. **CCC.**
Description: Covers research on drug action and selective toxicity at the molecular level, for pharmacologists and biochemists.
Refereed Serial

615.1   FR   ISSN 0026-9689
MONITEUR DES PHARMACIES ET DES LABORATOIRES. 1946. w. 890 F. (foreign 926.50 F.) (effective 1994-95). Groupe Liaisons, 11 rue Godefroy Cavaigne, 75541 Paris Cedex 11, France. TEL 43-79-06-30. FAX 43-79-17-75. adv.; illus. circ. 35,800.

615   FR   ISSN 0993-9199
MONITEUR HOSPITALIER. 11/yr. 350 F. (foreign 585 F.) (effective 1994-95). Groupe Liaisons, 11 rue Godefroy Cavaignac, 75541 Paris Cedex 11, France. TEL 43-79-06-30. FAX 43-79-17-75. TELEX 211 351 F. Ed. Lawrence Flippone. circ. 3,500.

615   SP   ISSN 0463-1536
MONITOR DE LA FARMACIA Y DE LA TERAPEUTICA. 1895. m. (11/yr.). 3000 ptas. Centros Farmaceuticos Nacional S.A., Julian Camarillo, 37, 28037 Madrid, Spain. TEL 17754-43-84. FAX 1-754-56-59. Ed. Daniel Pacheco. adv.; bk.rev.; bibl. circ. 17,000. (also avail. in cards) **Indexed:** Biol.Abstr., I.P.A.
●Also available online.

MONTHLY PRESCRIBING REFERENCE. see *MEDICAL SCIENCES*

PHARMACY AND PHARMACOLOGY

615.1 US ISSN 8756-4483
N A B P NEWSLETTER. 1971. 10/yr. $25 to non-members. National Association of Boards of Pharmacy, 700 Busse Hwy., Park Ridge, IL 60068-2402. TEL 708-698-6227. Eds. Carmen Catizone, Janice Teplitz. abstr.; charts; illus.; stat.; index; circ. 1,800 (controlled). **Indexed:** I.P.A. **Document type:** newsletter.
●Also available online.
Formerly: N A B P Quarterly (ISSN 0027-5700)

615.328 US ISSN 1079-1108
N A C D S FEDERAL REPORT. bi-m. membership. National Association of Chain Drug Stores, Box 1417-D49, Alexandria, VA 22313-1417. TEL 703-549-3001. FAX 703-836-4869. Ed. David Lambert. circ. 400. **Document type:** newsletter.
Former titles: National Association of Chain Drug Stores. Legislative Newsletter; (until 1971): National Association of Chain Drug Stores. Legislative News Bulletin.

N A C D S LILLY DIGEST. (National Association of Chain Drug Stores) see BUSINESS AND ECONOMICS — Marketing And Purchasing

615 658 SA
N A P W NEWS/N V F G NUUS. (Text mainly in English, occasionally in Afrikaans) 1993. irreg. membership. National Association of Pharmaceutical Wholesalers - Nasionale Vereniging van Farmaseutiese Groothandelaars, P.O. Box 30857, Braamfontein 2017, South Africa. **Document type:** newsletter.

615.1 US ISSN 0027-5972
HD9666.1
N A R D JOURNAL. 1898. m. $50. National Association of Retail Druggists, 205 Daingerfield Rd., Alexandria, VA 22314. TEL 703-683-8200. FAX 703-683-3619. Ed. Todd Dankmyer. adv.; charts; illus.; tr.lit. circ. 30,000. **Indexed:** I.P.A., Search.
—UnCover.

615.1 US ISSN 0162-1602
HD9666.1
N A R D NEWSLETTER. 1970. s-m. $50. National Association of Retail Druggists, 205 Daingerfield Ave., Alexandria, VA 22314. TEL 703-683-8200. FAX 703-683-3619. Ed. Bob Appel. circ. 27,000. **Document type:** newsletter.

615.19 670 US ISSN 0890-6610
RS189
N D A PIPELINE. (New Drug Approval) 1981. a. $595. F-D-C Reports, Inc., 5550 Friendship Blvd., Ste. 1, Chevy Chase, MD 20815. TEL 301-657-9830. FAX 301-656-3094. Ed. Cindy Frederick. adv.: B&W page $1200; adv. contact: Richard Messmer. (back issues avail.) **Document type:** trade publication.
●Also available online.
Description: Contains a company-by-company compilation of Rx drug development activity in the U.S. throughout the past year - from new compounds in research to those that obtained FDA marketing approval.

615 UK
N P A SUPPLEMENT. 1921. m. membership. National Pharmaceutical Association, 38-42 St. Peters St., St. Albans, Herts, England. FAX 0727-840858. Ed. Colette McCreedy. index. circ. 10,500. (looseleaf format) **Document type:** bulletin.
Formerly: N P U Supplement.

615 US
N W D A EXECUTIVE NEWSLETTER. 1913. m. $100 to non-members. National Wholesale Druggists' Association, Box 2219, Reston, VA 22090. TEL 703-787-0000. FAX 703-787-6930. Ed. Lauren Asplen. circ. 2,300 (controlled). **Document type:** newsletter.
Description: Covers services and programs of NWDA, news of membership and industry trends. Includes some statistics on sales and growth on monthly basis.

615.1 US ISSN 0163-1586
N Y STATE PHARMACIST. 1926. bi-m. $25 (members $20). Pharmaceutical Society of the State of New York, Pine W. Plz. IV, Washington Ave. Ext., Albany, NY 12205-5221. TEL 518-869-6595. Ed. Anthony J. Conte. adv.; bk.rev.; illus.; mkt. circ. 2,000.
Formerly: New York State Pharmacist (ISSN 0028-7660)

615.19 JA ISSN 0369-5611
CODEN: NSDYAI
NAGOYA SHIRITSU DAIGAKU YAKUGAKUBU KENKYU NENPO/NAGOYA CITY UNIVERSITY. FACULTY OF PHARMACEUTICAL SCIENCE. ANNUAL REPORT. (Text in English and Japanese) 1953. a. free. Nagoya Shiritsu Daigaku, Yakugakubu, 3-1, Tanabe Dori, Mizuho-ku, Nagoya-shi, Aichi-ken 467, Japan. Ed.Bd. bibl. circ. 400. **Indexed:** Biol.Abstr., Chem.Abstr.
—BLDSC (1248.600000); CASDDS.

615 US ISSN 0077-3263
NATIONAL ASSOCIATION OF BOARDS OF PHARMACY. PROCEEDINGS. 1904. a. $15. National Association of Boards of Pharmacy, 700 Busse Hwy., Park Ridge, IL 60068-2402. TEL 708-698-6227. Ed. Carmen Catizone. index. circ. 300. **Indexed:** I.P.A. **Document type:** proceedings.
●Also available online.

NATIONAL ASSOCIATION OF CHAIN DRUG STORES. EXECUTIVE NEWSLETTER. see BUSINESS AND ECONOMICS — Management

615 US
NATIONAL ASSOCIATION OF PHARMACEUTICAL MANUFACTURERS. NEWS BULLETIN. 1960. m. free. National Association of Pharmaceutical Manufacturers, 320 Old Country Rd., Rm. 205, Garden City, NY 11530-1743. TEL 516-741-3699. FAX 516-741-3696. Ed. Robert S. Milanese. circ. 1,200. (looseleaf format) **Document type:** newsletter, bulletin.

615.1 US ISSN 0027-9897
NATIONAL PHARMACEUTICAL ASSOCIATION. JOURNAL. vol.17, 1970. 3/yr. $25 membership. National Pharmaceutical Association, Inc., c/o Texas Southern University, College of Pharmacy, 3100 Cleburne, Houston, TX 77004. TEL 713-527-7164. FAX 713-639-1091. Ed. Dr. Henry Lewis, III. adv. circ. 2,000. **Indexed:** I.P.A. **Document type:** academic/scholarly publication.
●Also available online.

615.1 JA ISSN 1340-3443
CODEN: NMEDEO
NATURAL MEDICINES. (Text in English and Japanese; summaries in English) 1947. q-a. 12000 Yen. Japanese Society of Pharmacognosy - Nihon Shoyaku Gakkai, c/o Business Center for Academic Societies, 5-16-9 Honkomagome, Bunkyo-ku, Tokyo 113, Japan. Ed. Hidezi Itokawa. adv.; bk.rev.; charts; illus.; cum.index. circ. 700. **Indexed:** Biol.Abstr., Chem.Abstr., Excerp.Med., Hort.Abstr., I.P.A., Rice Abstr., Seed Abstr.
—BLDSC (6040.735550); CASDDS; EMDOCS; UnCover. **CCC.**
Former titles (until 1994): Shoyukugaku Zasshi - Japanese Journal of Pharmacognosy (ISSN 0037-4377); (until 1952): Yakuyo Shokubutsu to Shoyaku (ISSN 0372-7831)

NATURAL TOXINS. see CHEMISTRY — Analytical Chemistry

615.1 GW ISSN 0028-1298
CODEN: NSAPCC
NAUNYN-SCHMIEDEBERG'S ARCHIVES OF PHARMACOLOGY. 1873. 12/yr. (in 2 vols., 6 nos./vol.). DM.1956($1421) (effective 1996). (Deutsche Gesellschaft fuer Pharmakologie und Toxikologie) Springer-Verlag, Heidelberger Platz 3, 14197 Berlin, Germany. TEL 030-8207-0. FAX 030-8214091. E-mail: orders@springer.de. (Subscr. in N. America to: Springer-Verlag New York, Inc., 44 Hartz Way, Secaucus, NJ 07096-2491. TEL 201-348-4033. FAX 201-348-4505) Ed. K. Stark. adv.; charts; illus. (also avail. in microform from UMI,PMC; back issues avail.; reprint service avail. from ISI) **Indexed:** Biol.Abstr., Chem.Abstr., Curr.Adv.Ecol.Sci., Curr.Chem.React., Curr.Cont., Dairy Sci.Abstr., Dent.Ind., Excerp.Med., Ind.Chem., Ind.Med., Ind.Sci.Rev., Mass Spectr.Bull. **Document type:** academic/scholarly publication.
—BLDSC (6060.200000); ADONIS; CASDDS; EMDOCS; Faxon; Genuine Article; SWETS; UMI; UnCover. **CCC.**
Formerly: Naunyn-Schmiedebergs Archiv fuer Pharmakologie und Experimentelle Pathologie.
Description: Original papers, ranging from reports on the molecular effects of drugs within the cell to observations of their effects on the whole organism. Focuses on pharmacology and toxicology.

615.1 US ISSN 0028-1891
NEBRASKA MORTAR AND PESTLE. 1937. m. $25 (effective 1993). Nebraska Pharmacists Association, Inc., 6221 S. 58th St., Ste. A, Lincoln, NE 68516-3679. TEL 402-420-1500. FAX 402-420-1406. Ed. Tom R. Dolan. adv.; charts; illus.; circ. 1,250 (controlled). **Document type:** trade publication.

615 NE
CODEN: TTGODB
NEDERLANDS TIJDSCHRIFT VOOR FARMACOTHERAPIE. 1976. bi-m. fl.100. Reed HealthCare (Subsidiary of: Reed Elsevier plc), P.O. Box 1126, 1000 BC Amsterdam, Netherlands. TEL 31-20-5153350. FAX 31-20-5153354. Ed. Mrs. M.F. Kooijmans-Coutinho. adv. contact: G.J.M. van den Akker. circ. 7,500. **Indexed:** Excerp.Med. **Document type:** trade publication.
—BLDSC (8813.799500); CASDDS; Genuine Article; SWETS.
Former titles (until 1995): Tijdschrift voor Geneesmiddel en Onderzoek (ISSN 0921-562X); (until 1984): Tijdschrift voor Geneesmiddelenonderzoek (ISSN 0166-2384); (until 1977): Medisch Magazine en T G O - J D R (ISSN 0923-6619)
Description: Informs general practitioners and pharmacists about relevant developments in the field of pharmacotherapy on a scientific and objective basis.
Refereed Serial

NEPAL. DEPARTMENT OF MEDICINAL PLANTS. ANNUAL REPORT. see BIOLOGY — Botany

615.19 NP ISSN 0253-8261
CODEN: JONPD6
NEPAL PHARMACEUTICAL ASSOCIATION. JOURNAL. (Text in English and Nepali) 1974. s-a. Rs.20($5) Nepal Pharmaceutical Association, 9-382, Bhedasingh, Kathmandu, Nepal. Ed. R.R. Prasad. adv.; bk.rev. circ. 500. **Indexed:** Chem.Abstr.
—CASDDS.
Description: Research articles on pharmacy, pharmaceuticals, medicinal plants and allied sciences.

615 GW ISSN 0724-567X
NEUE ARZNEIMITTEL. (Suppl. to Deutsche Apotheker Zeitung) 1953. m. DM.18 (free with subscr. to Deutsche Apotheker Zeitung). Deutscher Apotheker Verlag, Postfach 101061, 70009 Stuttgart, Germany. TEL 0711-2582-0. FAX 0711-2582290. Ed. Susanne Heinzl. **Indexed:** Chem.Abstr., Excerp.Med. **Document type:** trade publication.
—BLDSC (6077.237900). **CCC.**
Formerly: Neue Arzneimittel und Spezialitaeten (ISSN 0548-2674)

615.1 UK ISSN 0142-8233
NEUROPEPTIDES (SHEFFIELD). s-m. (diskette m.) £120 (diskette £115; both £175) (effective 1995). S U B I S, Mansion House, 19 Kingfield Rd., Sheffield S11 9AS, England. TEL 0114-2554433. FAX 0114-2554626. E-mail: admin@sheffac.demon.co.uk. (also avail. in diskette format) **Indexed:** Chem.Abstr., Curr.Adv.Ecol.Sci., Excerp.Med. **Document type:** abstracting/indexing.
—**CCC.**
Description: Current awareness service for researchers. Covers opioids, endorphins, neurotensin, cholecystokinin, TRH, VIP, neuropeptide Y and invertebrate peptides.

PHARMACY AND PHARMACOLOGY

615.1 UK ISSN 0028-3908
RM315 CODEN: NEPHBW
NEUROPHARMACOLOGY. 1962. m. £946($1505) (effective 1996). Elsevier Science Ltd., Pergamon, P.O. Box 800, Kidlington, Oxford OX5 1DX, England. TEL 44-1865-843000. FAX 44-1865-843010. E-mail: nlinfo-f@elsevier.nl; usinfo-f@elsevier.com; forinfo-kyf04035@niftyserve.or.jp; Site addr.: http://www.elsevier.nl/. (Subscr. in U.S. and Canada to: Elsevier Science, 660 White Plains Rd., Tarrytown, NY 10591-5153. TEL 914-524-9200. FAX 914-333-2444) Ed. G. Collingridge. adv.; bk.rev.; bibl.; charts; illus.; index. circ. 1,500. (also avail. in microfilm from UMI; reprint service avail. from UMI) **Indexed:** Biol.Abstr., Biotech.Abstr., Chem.Abstr., Curr.Adv.Ecol.Sci., Curr.Cont., Dent.Ind., Excerp.Med., Helminthol.Abstr., Ind.Med., Ind.Sci.Rev., Int.Aerosp.Abstr., Nutr.Abstr., Psychol.Abstr. (1970-). **Document type:** academic/scholarly publication.
—BLDSC (6081.517500); ADONIS; CASDDS; EMDOCS; Faxon; Genuine Article; SWETS; UMI; UnCover. **CCC.**
  Formerly: International Journal of Neuropharmacology.
  Description: Furthers the understanding of the mechanisms of drug actions on the nervous system.
  Refereed Serial

NEUROPSICOFARMACOLOGIA DEL COMPORTAMENTO. see *MEDICAL SCIENCES — Psychiatry And Neurology*

NEUROPSYCHOPHARMACOLOGY. see *MEDICAL SCIENCES — Psychiatry And Neurology*

615.1 NZ ISSN 0111-0020
CODEN: NEETEG
NEW ETHICALS. (Supplement avail.: New Ethicals Catalogue (ISSN 0110-9510)) 1963. m. NZ.$84.45 (foreign NZ.$172.45). Adis International Limited, Private Bag 65901, Mairangi Bay, Auckland 1010, New Zealand. TEL 64-9-479-8100. FAX 64-9-479-8066. Ed. Ian Millward. circ. 6,000.
—BLDSC (6084.125000).
  Description: Provides general practitioners, specialists, registrars with current, practical and independent information on the use of prescription drugs.

615.1 NZ ISSN 0110-9510
NEW ETHICALS CATALOGUE; the basis of a system of independent drug information. (Supplement to: New Ethicals (ISSN 0111-0020)) 1966. 3/yr. NZ.$68. Adis International Limited, Privet Bag 65901, Mairangi Bay, Auckland 10, New Zealnad. TEL 64-9-479-8100. FAX 64-9-479-8066. Ed. Jillian Sutherland. adv. circ. 6,000.
—CCC.

615.1 US ISSN 0028-5773
RS1
NEW JERSEY JOURNAL OF PHARMACY. 1928. 11/yr. $12. New Jersey Pharmaceuticists Association, 120 W. State St., Trenton, NJ 08608. TEL 609-394-5596. FAX 609-394-7806. Ed. Diana S. Herman. adv.; bk.rev.; illus. circ. 3,500. (also avail. in microfilm from UMI; reprint service avail. from UMI)
—BLDSC (6084.300000).

615 UK
NEW PRODUCT LAUNCH LETTER. 1976. s-m. £2500. IMSWORLD Publications Ltd., 7 Harewood Ave., London NW1 6JB, England. TEL 0171-393-5000. FAX 0171-393-5900. **Document type:** trade publication.
•Also available online. Vendor(s): Data-Star.
Also available on CD-ROM.
  Formerly (until 1990): New Product Card Index.

615.7 SZ ISSN 1011-6672
CODEN: NTLREE
NEW TRENDS IN LIPID MEDIATORS RESEARCH. 1988. irreg. price varies. S. Karger AG, Allschwilerstr. 10, P.O. Box, CH-4009 Basel, Switzerland. TEL 061-3061111. FAX 061-3061234. E-mail: Karger@Karger.ch. Ed. P. Braquet. **Document type:** academic/scholarly publication.
—BLDSC (6089.133000).
  Description: Describes recent advances in the field of lipid mediator research with special attention to platelet-activating factor and related lipids.
  Refereed Serial

615 616.8 IT ISSN 0393-5345
CODEN: NTCNEP
NEW TRENDS IN NEUROPHARMACOLOGY. (Text in English) 1987. q. L.60000($70) (effective 1992). (European Association for Clinical Neuropharmacology) C I C Edizioni Internazionali s.r.l., Via L. Spallanzani, 11, 00161 Rome, Italy. TEL 06-8412673. FAX 06-8845590. Ed. Prof. Battistin. adv.; bk.rev. (back issues avail.) **Indexed:** Excerp.Med.
—BLDSC (6089.127000).
  Description: Publishes new research and original papers. Includes research on new drugs in the field.

615 US ISSN 1080-1855
THE NEW YORK HEALTH SYSTEM PHARMACIST. 1981. m. membership. New York State Council of Hospital Pharmacists, 1070 Sibley Tower, Rochester, NY 14604-1072. TEL 716-546-7241. FAX 716-546-5141. Ed. J Edward Bell. adv. **Document type:** trade publication.
—BLDSC (6089.302500).
  Former titles (until 1994): New York State Council of Hospital Pharmacists. Newsletter (ISSN 1066-5617); (until 1992): New York State Journal of Pharmacy (ISSN 0279-8778); Which supersedes (in 1981): New York State Council of Hospital Pharmacists. Newsletter (ISSN 0199-6169)

615.329 US ISSN 0739-7062
NEW YORK STATE PHARMACIST - CENTURY II. 1927. q. $25. Pharmaceutical Society of the State of New York, Pine W. Plz. IV, Washington Ave Ext., Albany, NY 12205-5221. TEL 518-869-6595. Ed. Anthony J. Conte. adv. circ. 2,000.

615.1 NE ISSN 0927-0574
NIEUWE DROGIST. 1902. fortn. fl.97.50 (foreign fl.160). Keesing Nordvliert B.V., De Molen 82-86, 3995 AX Houten, Netherlands. TEL 31-3403-58585. FAX 31-3403-58500. Ed. A. van Andel. adv.; B&W page fl.3050, color page fl.5050; trim 230 x 297. bk.rev.; illus. circ. 6,200. **Indexed:** Key to Econ.Sci. **Document type:** trade publication.
  Formerly (until 1991): Drogist (ISSN 0012-6330)
  Description: Covers all aspects of the retail drug industry.

NIHON GAN YAKURI GAKKAI PUROGURAMU KOEN YOSHIUSU/JAPANESE SOCIETY FOR OCULAR PHARMACOLOGY. PROGRAM AND ABSTRACTS OF THE MEETING. see *MEDICAL SCIENCES — Abstracting, Bibliographies, Statistics*

615 JA ISSN 0914-0697
NIPPON BYOIN YAKUZAISHIKAI ZASSHI/JAPANESE SOCIETY OF HOSPITAL PHARMACISTS. JOURNAL. (Text in Japanese) m. 400 Yen per no. Nippon Byoin Yakuzaishikai, 12-15-304, Shibuya 2-chome, Shibuya-ku, Tokyo 150, Japan.
—BLDSC (4809.452000).

615.19 JA
NIPPON KAYAKU. ANNUAL REPORT. a. Nippon Kayaku Co., Tokyo Fujimi Bldg., 11-2, Fujimi 1-chome, Chiyoda-ku, Tokyo 102, Japan.

615 JA
NIPPON KAYAKU SOGO KENKYUJO NENPO/NIPPON KAYAKU RESEARCH LABORATORIES. ANNUAL REPORT. (Text in English, Japanese) 1984. a. Nippon Kayaku K.K., Iryo Jigyo Honbu Sogo Kenkyujo - Nippon Kayaku Co., Ltd., Pharmaceuticals Group, Research Laboratories, 31-12, Shimo 3-chome, Kita-ku, Tokyo 115, Japan.

615.328 CN
NON-PRESCRIPTION DRUG REFERENCE FOR HEALTH CARE PROFESSIONAL. quadrennial. Can.$140 (members Can.$100). Canadian Pharmaceutical Association, 1785 Alta Vista Dr., Ottawa, ON K1G 3Y6, Canada. TEL 613-523-7877. Ed. P. Carruthers-Czyzewski. **Document type:** directory.
•Also available on CD-ROM.
  Former titles: Self-Medication; Canadian Self-Medication.

615 US ISSN 1068-5316
NONPRESCRIPTION PHARMACEUTICALS AND NUTRITIONALS: THE TAN SHEET. 1939. w. $650. F-D-C Reports, Inc., 5550 Friendship Blvd., Ste. 1, Chevy Chase, MD 20815. TEL 301-657-9830. FAX 301-656-3094. Ed. Tula Michaelides. adv.: B&W page $2000; adv. contact: Richard Messmer. charts; illus.; stat.; tr.lit. (looseleaf format; back issues avail.; reprint service avail.) **Document type:** trade publication.
•Also available online. Vendor(s): Data-Star (FDCR), Lexis-Nexis.
—CCC.
  Supersedes in part (in 1993): Prescription and O T C Pharmaceuticals: The Pink Sheet (ISSN 0734-6514); Which was formerly (until 1982): F D C Reports. Ethical and O T C Pharmaceuticals (ISSN 0272-913X)
  Description: Provides in-depth coverage of nonprescription pharmaceuticals and dietary supplement-nutritionals.

615.1 NO ISSN 0802-8400
NORGES APOTEKERFORENINGS TIDSSKRIFT. 1893. 16/yr. NOK 400 (foreign NOK 450). Norges Apotekerforening, Generalsekretaeren, B.O. Box 5070, Majorstua, N-0301 Oslo, Norway. TEL 47-22-69-60-40. FAX 47-22-56-47-18. Ed. Ellen B. Wickstrand. adv.: B&W page NOK 4600, color page NOK 8800; trim 210 x 297. bk.rev.; charts; illus.; index. circ. 1,900. **Indexed:** Biol.Abstr., Chem.Abstr., I.P.A. **Document type:** bulletin.
  Formerly (until 1985): NAT. Norges Apotekerforenings Tidsskrift (ISSN 0332-8678)

615.1 NO ISSN 0029-1935
CODEN: NFTDAC
NORSK FARMACEUTISK TIDSSKRIFT. 1893. 16/yr. NOK 590. Norges Farmaceutiske Forening, Stenersgt. 4, 0184 Oslo 1, Norway. FAX 02-170960. Ed. Kari Bremer. adv.; bk.rev.; abstr.; charts; illus.; tr.lit.; index; circ. 2,415 (controlled). **Indexed:** I.P.A.

615.19 IT ISSN 0550-1156
NOTIZIARIO CHIMICO E FARMACEUTICO. 1970. m. (10/yr.). $200. Societa Editoriale Farmaceutica s.r.l., Via Ausonio, 12, 20123 Milan, Italy. TEL 02-89404545. FAX 02-89401168. Ed. M. Rucci. adv. contact: G.C. Lubner. bk.rev.; bibl. circ. 6,000. **Indexed:** I.P.A. **Document type:** newspaper.
•Also available online.
—BLDSC (6174.278000); SWETS.

615.1 IT ISSN 0029-439X
NOTIZIARIO MEDICO FARMACEUTICO. (Supplements annual director: Informatore Farmaceutico) 1950. m. included with Informatore Farmaceutico. Organizzazione Editoriale Medico-Farmaceutica, Via Edolo 42, Box 10434, 20125 Milan, Italy. TEL 2-675-051. FAX 2-67-50-52-02. (Dist. in U.S. by: Drug Intelligence & Clinical Pharmacy, Box 42435, Cincinnati, OH 45242) Ed. Dr. Lucio Marini. adv.: B&W page L.1240000, color page L.3700000; trim 180 x 260. circ. 19,799.
—SWETS.

615 610 382 PL ISSN 0209-3928
NOVOSTI FARMATSII I MEDITSINY/NEWS IN PHARMACOLOGY AND MEDICINE. (Text in Russian; summaries in English) 1967. q. (Osrodek Informacji Naukowej "Polfa") AGPOL - Polexportpress, Ul. Kierbedzia 4, 00-957 Warsaw, Poland. TEL 48-22-402391. Ed. Andrzej Werbeniec. adv.; bk.rev.; illus. circ. 30,000.
  Description: Covers all aspects of preparing, preserving, compounding and dispensing drugs.

615 636.08 PL ISSN 0860-3847
NOVOSTI VETERINARNOI FARMATSII I MEDITSINY. (Text in Russian) 1985. q. (Osrodek Informacji Naukowej "Polfa") AGPOL - Polexportpress, Ul. Kierbedzia 4, 00-957 Warsaw, Poland. TEL 48-22-402391. FAX 48-22-416061. Ed. Andrzej Werbeniec.
  Formerly (until 1986): Polfa: Novosti Farmatsii i Veterinarnoi Meditsiny (ISSN 0860-3154)

615 UK ISSN 1358-6327
NUMARK NEWS. 1973. bi-m. £75. Numark Ltd., Numark House, 5-6 Fairway Ct., Amber Close, Tamworth Business Park, Tamworth, Staffs B77 4RP, England. TEL 01827-69269. FAX 01827-62549. Ed. Val Pirie. circ. 700. **Document type:** trade publication.
  Formerly (until 1994): Numark Newsline.

PHARMACY AND PHARMACOLOGY

NURSES' DRUG ALERT. see *MEDICAL SCIENCES — Nurses And Nursing*

NURSING (YEAR) DRUG HANDBOOK. see *MEDICAL SCIENCES — Nurses And Nursing*

615 330.9   UK   ISSN 1350-1097
O T C BULLETIN. (Over the Counter), the business newsletter for Europe's consumer healthcare industry. 1993. 20/yr. £325 (outside Europe £345) (effective 1996). O T C Publications Ltd., 54 Creynolds Ln., Shirley, Solihull, W. Midlands B90 4ER, England. TEL 0121-733-8755. FAX 0121-733-8744. Ed. Deborah Wilkes. adv.: B&W page £1000, color page £1500; trim 210 x 297. bk.rev.; circ. 2,000 (paid). (back issues avail.) **Document type:** newsletter.
  Description: Contains news and information covering Europe's nonprescription medicine market.

615   UK   ISSN 0956-2559
O T C NEWS AND MARKET REPORT. (Over the Counter) 1988. 11/yr. Nicholas Hall & Co., 35 Alexandra St., Southend-on-Sea, Essex SS1 1BW, England. TEL 01702-431805. FAX 01702-430787. Ed. Wendy Birnie. adv. contact: Mark Turner. (back issues avail.) **Document type:** trade publication.
—SWETS.
  Description: Reports on OTC drug markets in Europe.

615.1   AU   ISSN 0029-8859
                    CODEN: OAZEAL
OESTERREICHISCHE APOTHEKER-ZEITUNG. 1946. fortn. S.1312.63. Oesterreichische Apotheker-Verlagsgesellschaft mbH, Spitalgasse 31, A-1094 Vienna, Austria. TEL 01-4023588. FAX 01-4085355. Ed. Gottfried Zimmermann. adv.; bk.rev.; abstr.; index. circ. 4,500. **Indexed:** Biotech.Abstr., Chem.Abstr., I.P.A. **Document type:** newspaper.
—CASDDS.
  Description: Information and networking for Austrian pharmacists.

615   SP   ISSN 0212-047X
OFFARM.* 1982. 12/yr. Haymarket, S.A., Travesera Gracia 17-21 5o 2o, 08022 Barcelona, Spain. TEL 3-237-22-66. FAX 3-237-66-88. Ed. Juan Mir Morato. circ. 18,000.

615.1   US   ISSN 0030-1027
OHIO PHARMACIST. 1952. m. $20. Ohio Pharmacists Association, 6037 Frantz Rd., Ste. 106, Dublin, OH 43017-3320. TEL 614-798-0037. Ed. Amy Bennett. adv.; illus. circ. 4,000. **Document type:** trade publication.

615   SZ
OPTIPHARM. m. Ave. de Chillon 90, Case Postale 1447, CH-1820 Montreux, Switzerland. TEL 021-9635161. FAX 021-9638679. Ed. Claude Hugonnaud. circ. 10,530. **Document type:** trade publication.

615   PO   ISSN 0872-7554
▼**ORDEM DOS FARMACEUTICOS. REVISTA.** 1994. q. Esc.2500 (foreign $24) (effective 1995). Ordem dos Farmaceuticos, R. da Sociedade Farmaceutica, 18, 1150 Lisboa, Portugal. TEL 351-1-521424. FAX 351-1-3524480. Ed. Dr. Carlos da Silveira. adv.; bk.rev. circ. 7,000. **Document type:** trade publication.
  Description: Presents current information on the society's activities and short articles of interest to the average pharmacist.

615   JA   ISSN 0387-480X
OSAKA UNIVERSITY. FACULTY OF PHARMACEUTICAL SCIENCES. MEMOIRS/OSAKA DAIGAKU YAKUGAKUBU KIYO. (Text in English) 1970. a. free. Osaka Daigaku, Yakugakubu - Osaka University, Faculty of Pharmaceutical Sciences, 1-6 Yamadaoka, Suita-shi, Osaka 565, Japan. FAX 06-877-4489. Ed. Tsutomu Nishihara. abstr. circ. 300.
  Description: Features the collection of abstracts of scientific papers published in the previous year by the faculty.

615.1   JA   ISSN 0030-669X
OTSUKA PHARMACEUTICAL FACTORY. JOURNAL/OTSUKA YAKUHO. (Text in Japanese) 1950. 11/yr. 2000 Yen. Otsuka Pharmaceutical Factory - Otsuka Seiyaku Kojo, 115 Tateiwa, Muya-cho, Naruto 772, Tokushima, Japan. Ed. M. Ohsaka. illus. circ. 61,500.

615   UK
OVER THE COUNTER. 10/yr. Sovereign Way, Tonbridge, Kent TN9 1RW, England. TEL 0732-364422. FAX 0732-361534. TELEX 95132-BENTON-G. Ed. John Skelton.

615   JA   ISSN 0300-8533
                    CODEN: OYYAA2
OYO YAKURI/PHARMACOMETRICS. (Text in Japanese or English) 1967. m. 10000 Yen($140) (effective 1995). Oyo Yakuri Kenkyukai - Japanese Society of Pharmacometrics, G.P.O. Box 180, Sendai 980-91, Japan. TEL 022-267-3810. FAX 022-222-0515. Ed. Dr. Hikaru Ozawa. adv.; bk.rev.; index. circ. 1,200. (back issues avail.) **Indexed:** Dairy Sci.Abstr., Excerp.Med. **Document type:** academic/scholarly publication.
—BLDSC (6447.085000); CASDDS; SWETS. **CCC.**
  Description: Covers pharmacodynamics, pharmacokinetics, and toxicity tests of new drugs.
  Refereed Serial

P A CER. (Pharmaceutical Advertising Council) see *ADVERTISING AND PUBLIC RELATIONS*

615   US   ISSN 1052-1372
                    CODEN: PPTTEK
P & T. (Pharmacy & Therapeutic); journal for formulary management. 1976. m. $105 to institutions outside the Americas; $83 to institutions in U.S (effective 1996). Excerpta Medica, Inc., Core Publishing Division (Subsidiary of: Reed Elsevier Medical group), 105 Raider Blvd., Belle Mead, NJ 08052. TEL 908-874-8550. FAX 908-874-0707. (Subscr. to: Box 3085, Princeton, NJ 08543-3085) adv. **Indexed:** Excerp.Med., I.P.A.
●Also available online.
—BLDSC (6327.163000); Faxon. **CCC.**
  Former titles (until Jul. 1990): Hospital Therapy (ISSN 0160-9459); Drug Therapy (Hospital Edition); Drug Therapy Hospital.
  Refereed Serial

615.1   US
                    CODEN: JPHTEU
P D A JOURNAL OF PHARMACEUTICAL SCIENCE AND TECHNOLOGY. (Supplements accompany some numbers) 1947. 6/yr. $70 (foreign $90). Parenteral Drug Association, Inc., 7500 Old Georgetown Rd., Ste. 620, Bethesda, MD 20814-6133. TEL 301-986-0293. FAX 301-986-0296. Ed. Dr. Joseph B. Schwartz. adv.; charts; illus.; index. circ. 7,200. (back issues avail.) **Indexed:** Biol.Abstr., Biotech.Abstr., Curr.Adv.Ecol.Sci., Excerp.Med., I.P.A., Ind.Med., Sugar Ind.Abstr. **Document type:** academic/scholarly publication.
●Also available online.
—CASDDS; Faxon; Genuine Article; SWETS.
  Former titles (until vol.48, no.5, 1994): Journal of Pharmaceutical Science and Technology (ISSN 1076-397X); (until vol.48, no.1, 1994): Journal of Parenteral Science and Technology (ISSN 0279-7976); (until 1981): Parenteral Drug Association. Journal (ISSN 0161-1933); (until vol.32, 1978): Parenteral Drug Association. Bulletin (ISSN 0048-2986)
  Description: Technical articles in the field of parenteral science and sterile products.

615.19   US
P D A LETTER. 1964. m. membership. Parenteral Drug Association, Inc., 7500 Old Georgetown Rd., Ste. 920, Bethesda, MD 20814-6133. TEL 301-986-0293. FAX 301-986-0296. circ. 6,400. **Document type:** newsletter.
  Description: Parenteral industry news and upcoming events, services and publications of the Parenteral Drug Association.

615   US
▼**P D R GENERICS.** (Physician's Desk Reference) 1995. a. $69395. Medical Economics Co., Inc., Five Paragon Dr., Montvale, NJ 07645-1742. TEL 201-358-7200; 800-442-6657. FAX 201-573-1045. charts; illus. **Document type:** directory.
  Description: Lists generic prescription drugs, giving indications and contraindications, price, identification information, reimbursement information, and cross-references with corresponding brand-name products.

615   GW   ISSN 0944-7032
P K A AKTUELL. (Supplement to: Deutsche Apotheker Zeitung) 1952. bi-m. DM.9 (free with subscr. to Deutsche Apotheker Zeitung). Deutscher Apotheker Verlag, Postfach 101061, 70009 Stuttgart, Germany. TEL 0711-2582-0. FAX 0711-2582290. Ed. Michael Schmidt. **Document type:** trade publication.
  Former titles: Apothekenhelferin Heute (ISSN 0939-3331); Apothekenhelferin (ISSN 0570-4723)
  Description: Aimed at enlightening pharmaceutical assistants.

615.7   AT   ISSN 0156-0433
P S. (Postscript) 1979. m. Aus.$95. Australian Pharmaceutical Publishing Co. Ltd., 40 Burwood Rd., Hawthorn, Vic. 3122, Australia. TEL 61-3-810-9800. FAX 61-3-819-1706. circ. 7,000. (back issues avail.) **Document type:** trade publication.

615   GW
P T A DIALOG. (Pharmazeutisch - Technische Assistentin) 1987. q. DM.20. (Beiersdorf AG) Industrie-Contact GmbH, Postfach 520262, 22592 Hamburg, Germany. TEL 040-89966617. FAX 040-8902641. Ed. Juergen Klimke. (back issues avail.) **Document type:** academic/scholarly publication.

615   GW   ISSN 0302-167X
                    CODEN: PTAHAF
P T A HEUTE. 1954. m. DM.48 (students DM.31.80). Deutscher Apotheker Verlag, Postfach 101061, 70009 Stuttgart, Germany. TEL 0711-2582-0. FAX 0711-2582290. Ed. Reinhild Berger. bk.rev. circ. 33,600. **Indexed:** Chem.Abstr. **Document type:** trade publication.
—SWETS.
  Formerly: Apothekerpraktikant und Pharmazeutisch-Technische Assistent.

615   GW   ISSN 0722-1029
                    CODEN: PTAED9
P T A IN DER APOTHEKE; Fachzeitschrift fuer pharmazeutisch-technische Assistenten. (Includes supplement: P T A - Repetitorium) m. DM.114.60 (students DM.93.60). Umschau Zeitschriftenverlag Breidenstein GmbH, Stuttgarter Str. 18-24, 60329 Frankfurt a.M., Germany. TEL 069-2600-0. FAX 069-2600-619. Ed. Julia Pflegel. adv.: B&W page DM.3600, color page DM.6300; trim 176 x 247; adv. contact: Barbara Eckert. circ. 10,210. **Document type:** academic/scholarly publication.
—BLDSC (6946.564250); CASDDS. **CCC.**
  Former titles: P T A in der Praktischen Pharmazie; P T A in Apotheke und Industrie.

615   GW   ISSN 0945-5566
                    CODEN: PZWIE4
P Z PRISMA; Pharmazeutische Zeitung - Materialen zur Weiterbildung. (Supplement to: Pharmazeutische Zeitung) 1983. q. DM.98. Bundesvereinigung Deutscher Apotheker) Govi Pharmazeutischer Verlag GmbH, Ginnheimerstr. 26, 65760 Eschborn, Germany. TEL 06196-928262. FAX 06196-928203. Ed. Dr. Axel Helmstaedter. adv. contact: Hans-Juergen Renn. **Indexed:** Biol.Abstr. (1990-). **Document type:** academic/scholarly publication.
—BLDSC (7163.530500); CASDDS. **CCC.**
  Former titles (until 1993): P Z Wissenschaft (ISSN 0935-5901); (until 1988): Pharmazeutische Zeitung. Scientific Edition (ISSN 0724-6315)

615   SP
PAGINAS DE PHARMACOLOGIA. 10/yr. Luzon S.A. de Ediciones, Virgen de la Alegria 9, 28027 Madrid, Spain. TEL 1-405-15-95. FAX 1-403-49-07.

615.19   PK   ISSN 1011-601X
                    CODEN: PJPSEN
PAKISTAN JOURNAL OF PHARMACEUTICAL SCIENCES. s-a. Rs.150($25) University of Karachi, Faculty of Pharmacy, Karachi 75270, Pakistan. Ed. Dr. S. Sabir Ali. **Indexed:** ExtraMED. **Document type:** academic/scholarly publication.
●Also available on CD-ROM.
—BLDSC (6341.690000); CASDDS.
  Description: Publishes short research papers and reviews in pharmaceutical chemistry, pharmaceutics, pharmacognosy, pharmacology, and related studies in toxicology.
  Refereed Serial

PHARMACY AND PHARMACOLOGY

615 PK ISSN 0255-7088
CODEN: PJPHEO
PAKISTAN JOURNAL OF PHARMACOLOGY. (Text in English) 1983. s-a. $50. University of Karachi, Department of Pharmacology, Karachi 75270, Pakistan. TEL 479001. Ed. S.I. Ahmad. **Document type:** academic/scholarly publication.
—CASDDS.

615 US
PALMETTO PHARMACIST.* m. $10. State Pharmaceutical Editorial Association, 223 W. Jackson Blvd., No. 1000, Chicago, IL 60606-6906. Ed. Sharon Fennell. adv. circ. 1,500.

615 FR
PARAPHARMEX. a. (updates 14/yr.). 490 F. (effective 1995). Societe d'Editions Medico-Pharmaceutiques (SEMP), 26 rue le Brun, 75013 Paris, France. TEL 1-43-37-83-50. FAX 43-31-94-11. circ. 3,400. (looseleaf format; also avail. in microfiche)
 Description: Contains references to cosmetics, perfumary and oral hygiene.

615.19 US ISSN 0736-0681
PARENTERAL DRUG ASSOCIATION. TECHNICAL INFORMATION BULLETIN. irreg., latest no.4. price varies. Parenteral Drug Association, Inc., 7500 Old Germantown Rd., Ste. 920, Bethesda, MD 20814-6133. TEL 301-986-0293. FAX 301-986-0296. **Document type:** monographic series.

615.19 US ISSN 0271-325X
PARENTERAL DRUG ASSOCIATION. TECHNICAL METHODS BULLETIN. 1980. irreg., latest no.3. price varies. Parenteral Drug Association, Inc., 7500 Old Germantown Rd., Ste. 920, Bethesda, MD 20814-6133. TEL 301-986-0293. FAX 301-986-0296. **Document type:** monographic series.

615.19 US ISSN 0277-3406
PARENTERAL DRUG ASSOCIATION. TECHNICAL REPORTS. 1978. irreg., latest no.21. $30 to non-members (members $15). Parenteral Drug Association, Inc., 7500 Old Germantown Rd., Ste. 920, Bethesda, MD 20814-6133. TEL 301-986-0293. FAX 301-986-0296. **Document type:** monographic series.
 Formerly (until 1981): Parenteral Drug Association. Technical Monograph (ISSN 0196-3619)

PARTICULATE SCIENCE AND TECHNOLOGY; an international journal. see ENGINEERING — Chemical Engineering

615.9 US
PATIENT DRUG FACTS. 1989. q. $75. Facts and Comparisons, 111 W. Port Plaza, Ste. 400, St. Louis, MO 63146-3098. TEL 800-223-0554. FAX 314-878-5563. (also avail. in diskette format)
 Formerly: Professional's Guide to Patient Drug Facts.
 Description: Drug information reference written in laymen's terms to aid health care professionals with the education and counseling of patients and drug therapy management.

615.1 US ISSN 0031-4633
PENNSYLVANIA PHARMACIST. 1926. m. $90 to non-members; members $45 (includes Pharmacy News and Review) (effective 1996). Pennsylvania Pharmaceutical Association, 508 N. Third St., Harrisburg, PA 17101-1199. TEL 717-234-6151. FAX 717-236-1618. Ed. Carmen A. DiCello. adv.; bk.rev.; illus.; tr.lit.; cum.index. circ. 2,500. **Document type:** trade publication.
—BLDSC (6421.748800).
 Description: Provides information on issues and concerns of interest to pharmacists.

615 NE ISSN 0928-2866
CODEN: PDDDEC
PERSPECTIVES IN DRUG DISCOVERY AND DESIGN. (Supplement to: Journal of Computer-Aided Molecular Design (ISSN 0920-654X)) (Text in English) 1993. 3/yr. fl.523($291) (effective 1995). E S C O M Science Publishers B.V., P.O. Box 214, 2300 AE Leiden, Netherlands. TEL 31-71-127052. FAX 31-71-121772. Ed.Bd. **Document type:** academic/scholarly publication.
—BLDSC (6428.141575); CASDDS; SWETS. **CCC.**
 Description: Publishes reviews of recent developments in drug design and discovery, covering specific disease entities, techniques, including computer-aided design, and therapeutic areas, such as immunosuppressants, antivirals or antiallergens.
 Refereed Serial

615 658 US
▼**PHARMA BUSINESS;** the international magazine of pharmaceutical business and marketing. 1995. 6/yr. $135. Engel Publishing Partners, 820 Bear Tavern Rd., W. Trenton, NJ 08628. TEL 609-530-0044. FAX 609-530-0207. **Document type:** trade publication.

615 SZ ISSN 0378-7958
PHARMA-FLASH. 1972. 8/yr. 35 SFr. (foreign 65 SFr.). Editions Medecine et Hygiene, Case Postale 456, CH-1211 Geneva 4, Switzerland. TEL 022-3469355. FAX 022-3475610. **Document type:** consumer publication.
—CCC.

615 JA ISSN 0285-4937
CODEN: PHAREX
PHARMA JAPAN; Japan drug industry news. (Text in English) 1960. w. 180000 Yen. Yakugyo Jiho Co. Ltd., 2-36 Kanda Jimbo-cho, Chiyoda-ku, Tokyo 101, Japan. TEL 03-265-7751. (Dist. in N. America by: F-D-C Reports, Inc., 5550 Friendship Blvd., Ste. One, Chevy Chase, MD 20815) pat.; stat.
—BLDSC (6441.881000); CASDDS.
 Formerly (until 1975): Pharmaceutical Daily News.
 Description: Focuses on matters of importance in the Japanese pharmaceutical and medical industries.

615 JA
PHARMA JAPAN YEARBOOK. (Text in English) a. 9000 Yen($88) Yakugyo Jiho Co., Ltd., 2-36 Kanda Jimbo-Cho, Chiyoda-ku, Tokyo 101, Japan. TEL 03-265-7751. (Dist. in N. America by: F-D-C Reports, Inc., 5550 Friendship Blvd., Ste. One, Chevy Chase, MD 20815)
 Former titles: Japan Drug Industry Review; (until 1976): Handbook of the Japan Drug Industry.
 Description: Explains trends in Japanese pharmaceutical and medical fields.

615 SZ ISSN 1010-5409
PHARMA KRITIK. 24/yr. Bergliweg 17, CH-9500 Wil, Switzerland. TEL 073-221818. FAX 073-238121. circ. 6,500.

PHARMA-MARKETING JOURNAL. see BUSINESS AND ECONOMICS — Marketing And Purchasing

615 UK
PHARMA MARKETLETTER.* 1974. w. £490. Marketletter (Publications) Ltd., 54-55 Wilton Rd., London SW1V 1DE, England. TEL 0171-828-7272. FAX 0171-828-0415. Ed. Barbara Obstoj. adv.: B&W page £990; trim 260 x 185; adv. contact: Robin Cardwell. index. (back issues avail.) **Indexed:** ABC. **Document type:** trade publication.
●Also available online. Vendor(s): Data-Star.
—CCC.
 Former titles (until 1994): Marketletter; IMS Pharmaceutical Marketletter (ISSN 0140-4288); Which incorporates: IMS Monitor Report (ISSN 0262-6756); Which was formerly: IMS Monitor Report: Europe (ISSN 0140-4741)

615 JA ISSN 0289-5803
PHARMA MEDICA. (Text in Japanese) 1983. m. 1545 Yen per no. Medkaru Rebyusha - Medical Review Co., Ltd., 7-3, Hiranomachi 1-chome, Chuo-ku, Osaka 541, Japan.
—BLDSC (6441.883000).

615 NE ISSN 0169-6882
PHARMA SELECTA. (Text in Dutch, English; summaries in English) 1985. bi-w. fl.125($110) Stichting Pharma Selecta, Postbus 127, 8430 Oosterwolde, Netherlands. TEL 31-5160-15908. Ed. H.J. Gebben. adv.; circ. 2,800 (controlled). (back issues avail.) **Document type:** newsletter.
 Description: Provides pharmacotherapy and drug information for hospital and community pharmacists.
 Refereed Serial

615 AU
PHARMA TIME; das unabhaengige Apothekerjournal. 1984. m. S.300. Pharma Time Verlag, Klostergasse 16, A-1180 Vienna, Austria. TEL 0222-4703238. FAX 0222-470978430. Ed. Hans Jakesz. adv.; bk.rev. circ. 8,000. **Document type:** trade publication.

615.1 II ISSN 0031-6849
CODEN: PHTIDW
PHARMA TIMES. (Text in English) 1969. m. $100. Indian Pharmaceutical Association, Kalina Santacruz East, Bombay 400098, India. Ed. A.K. Kapadia. adv.: B&W page Rs.3000, color page Rs.4500; trim 28 x 22. bk.rev.; pat. circ. 6,500. **Indexed:** I.P.A.
●Also available online.
—BLDSC (6441.890000); CASDDS.

615.19 GW ISSN 0933-0909
PHARMA UND WIR. 1986. bi-m. DM.10. Werkschriften-Verlag GmbH, Bachstr. 14, 69121 Heidelberg, Germany. TEL 06221-49064. FAX 06221-49066. circ. 55,000. **Document type:** bulletin.

615.1 CI ISSN 0031-6857
CODEN: PHAMBF
PHARMACA; casopis za farmakoterpiju. (Text in Serbo-Croatian and Slovenian; summaries in English) 1963. q. Udruzenje Organizacija Zdravstva Hrvatske, P.O. Box 878, Savska Cesta 41-VII, 41000 Zagreb, Croatia. Ed. Bozidar Vrhovac. bk.rev. circ. 3,500. **Indexed:** Biol.Abstr., Chem.Abstr., Excerp.Med.
—CASDDS; EMDOCS.

615.1 NE ISSN 0031-6865
CODEN: PAHEAA
PHARMACEUTICA ACTA HELVETIAE. (Text in English, French and German) 1926. bi-m. FL556($339) (effective 1996). (Societe Suisse de Pharmacie, SZ - Swiss Pharmaceutical Society) Elsevier Science B.V., P.O. Box 211, 1000 AE Amsterdam, Netherlands. TEL 31-20-4853911. FAX 31-20-4853598. TELEX 18582 ESPA NL. E-mail: nlinfo-f@elsevier.nl; usinfo-f@elsevier.com; forinfo-kyf04035@niftyserve.or.jp; Site addr.: http://www.elsevier.nl/. (Subscr. in U.S. and Canada to: Elsevier Science Inc., Box 882, Madison Sq. Sta., New York, NY 10159-0882. TEL 212-989-5800. FAX 212-633-3990) Ed. G. Folkers. adv.: B&W page fl.680, color page fl.1350; trim 180 x 255; adv. contact: W. van Cattenburch. abstr.; bibl.; charts; illus.; index. circ. 5,000. (also avail. in microform from UMI) **Indexed:** Anal.Abstr., Biol.Abstr., Biotech.Abstr., Chem.Abstr., Chem.Infd., Crop Physiol.Abstr., Curr.Adv.Ecol.Sci., Curr.Chem.React., Curr.Cont., Dairy Sci.Abstr., Dent.Ind., Excerp.Med., Helminthol.Abstr., Hort.Abstr., I.P.A., Ind.Chem., Ind.Med., Mass Spectr.Bull., Nutr.Abstr. **Document type:** academic/scholarly publication.
●Also available online.
—BLDSC (6442.000000); CASDDS; EMDOCS; Faxon; Genuine Article; SWETS. **CCC.**
 Description: Presents papers from all disciplines relating to pharmaceutical research, from drug discovery, modelling and biotechnology, to toxicology, drug delivery and metabolism, and clinical pharmacy practice.
 Refereed Serial

615 340 JA
PHARMACEUTICAL ADMINISTRATION IN JAPAN. (Text in English, Japanese) irreg., latest 6th ed. 14000 Yen($180) (Ministry of Health and Welfare, Pharmaceutical Affairs Bureau) Yakuji Nippo Ltd., 1, Kanda Izumicho, Chiyoda-ku, Tokyo 101, Japan. TEL 81-3-3862-2141. FAX 81-3-5821-8757. **Document type:** government publication.
 Description: Gives a broad description of the Japanese Government's recent steps in the pharmaceutical administration.

PHARMACY AND PHARMACOLOGY

PHARMACEUTICAL & COSMETIC REVIEW; devoted to the manufacture & marketing of medicines, toiletries, soaps, detergents in South Africa. see *BEAUTY CULTURE — Perfumes And Cosmetics*

PHARMACEUTICAL & MEDICAL PACKAGING NEWS. see *PACKAGING*

615 GW ISSN 0939-9488
CODEN: PPLEE3
PHARMACEUTICAL AND PHARMACOLOGICAL LETTERS. (Text in English) 1991. 6/yr. DM.360. Medpharm GmbH Scientific Publishers, Postfach 101061, 70009 Stuttgart, Germany. TEL 0711-2582-0. FAX 0711-2852-290. Ed. G. Franz. **Document type:** academic/scholarly publication.
—BLDSC (6442.760000); CASDDS; SWETS; UMI. CCC.
 Description: Topics covered include medical chemistry, molecular modelling, pharmacognosy, clinical applications of medicinal plants, pharmaceutics and biopharmaceutics, drug targeting, and toxicology.

PHARMACEUTICAL BIOTECHNOLOGY. see *BIOLOGY — Biotechnology*

330 615 UK ISSN 0956-0661
CODEN: PBNEEH
PHARMACEUTICAL BUSINESS NEWS; the executive newsletter for the pharmaceutical industry. 1983. s-m. £410($640) (overseas £465) (effective 1996). Financial Times Pharmaceuticals and Healthcare Publishing (Subsidiary of: Pearson Professional Ltd.), Maple House, 149 Tottenham Court Rd., London W1P 9LL, England. TEL 0171-896-2203. FAX 0171-896-2213. Ed. O. Glynn-Owen. adv. circ. 2,000. (also avail. in microform from UMI) **Document type:** newsletter.
—BLDSC (6443.245000); SWETS; UMI.
 Description: Analyzes and forecasts the pharmaceutical market worldwide.

615.19 US ISSN 0091-150X
RS402 CODEN: PCJOAU
PHARMACEUTICAL CHEMISTRY JOURNAL. English translation of: Khimiko-farmatsevticheskii Zhurnal (RU ISSN 0023-1134) 1967. m. $1260 (foreign $1475) (effective 1996). (Tsentr Khimii i Lekarstvernykh Sredstv, RU) Plenum Publishing Corp., Consultants Bureau, 233 Spring St., New York, NY 10013-1578. TEL 212-620-8468. FAX 212-463-0742. TELEX 23-421139. Ed. R.G. Glushkov. (also avail. in microform from UMI; microfilm from JSC; back issues avail.) **Indexed:** Biol.Abstr., Chem.Titles, Curr.Adv.Ecol.Sci., Int.Abstr.Biol.Sci. **Document type:** academic/scholarly publication.
—BLDSC (0416.770000); Faxon; SWETS; UMI. CCC.
 Refereed Serial

615 UK
PHARMACEUTICAL CODEX. 1907. quinquennial. £33. Royal Pharmaceutical Society of Great Britain, 1 Lambeth High St., London SE1 7JN, England. TEL 071-735-9141. FAX 071-735-7629. bibl.; charts; illus. circ. 20,000.

615 330.9 UK
▼**PHARMACEUTICAL COMPANIES ANALYSIS.** 1995. a. (plus m. updates). £595. M D I S Publications Ltd., MDIS House, City Fields Business Park, City Fields Way, Chichester, W. Sussex PO20 6FS, England. TEL 01243-533322. FAX 01243-533418. adv. contact: Helena Mancey. **Document type:** trade publication.
●Also available on CD-ROM.

615 330 UK
PHARMACEUTICAL COMPANY PROFILES. 1991. m. £10900 for full set of 110. IMSWORLD Publications Ltd., 7 Harewood Ave., London NW1 6JB, England. TEL 0171-393-5000. FAX 0171-393-5900. **Document type:** trade publication.
●Also available online.
Also available on CD-ROM.

615 338 US ISSN 1071-5096
PHARMACEUTICAL DAILY. 1993. d. $1097. Washington Business Information Inc., c/o Karen Harrington, 1117 North 19th St., Ste. 200, Arlington, VA 22209-1798. TEL 703-247-3434. Ed. Martha M. Canan.

615.19 US
PHARMACEUTICAL DIGEST.* 1991. s-a. Centcom, Ltd., 1599 Post Rd. E., Westport, CT 06880-5602. TEL 203-226-7131. FAX 203-454-9939. Ed. Joan Moynihan. adv. circ. 30,391.
 Description: Contains listings of literature and catalog descriptions.

PHARMACEUTICAL ENGINEERING. see *ENGINEERING*

615 US ISSN 0279-6570
RS1 CODEN: PHEXD2
PHARMACEUTICAL EXECUTIVE; a global business and marketing publication. 1981. m. $59 (foreign $117). Advanstar Communications, Inc. (Eugene), 859 Willamette St., Box 10460, Eugene, OR 97440-2460. TEL 503-343-1200. FAX 503-344-3514. (Subscr. to: 1 E. First St., Duluth, MN 55082. TEL 800-346-0085; Addr. in the U.K.: Advanstar House, Park West, Sealand Rd., Chester CH1 4RN, England. TEL 44-244-378888. FAX 44-244-380011) Ed. Wayne Koberstein. adv.: B&W page $2754; color page $3854. illus. circ. 15,000. (back issues avail.; reprint service avail.) **Indexed:** BPIA, Curr.Pack.Abstr., I.P.A., Telegen. **Document type:** trade publication.
●Also available online. Vendor(s): University Microfilms International.
—BLDSC (6443.680000); SWETS; UMI. CCC.
 Description: Designed to meet the management and marketing needs of professionals in the pharmaceutical industry. Covers the latest marketing techniques, industry trends, sales, promotional strategies, and the legal and regulatory issues influencing product development and management.

615.1 UK ISSN 0079-1393
RS61
PHARMACEUTICAL HISTORIAN. 1967. 4q. £4.60 (foreign £5). British Society for the History of Pharmacy, 36 York Pl., Edinburgh EH1 3HU, Scotland. Ed. Dr. J.G.L. Burnby.
—BLDSC (6443.700000).

615.1 UK ISSN 0031-6873
CODEN: PHJOAV
PHARMACEUTICAL JOURNAL. 1841. w. £64.50 (foreign £83). Royal Pharmaceutical Society of Great Britain, 1 Lambeth High St., London SE1 7JN, England. TEL 071-735-9141. FAX 071-735-7629. Ed. D. Simpson. adv.; bk.rev.; charts; tr.lit.; index. circ. 36,400. (also avail. in microform from PMC) **Indexed:** Abstr.Health Care Manage.Stud., Biol.Abstr., Biotech.Abstr., Chem.Abstr., Curr.Adv.Cancer Res., Curr.Adv.Ecol.Sci., Excerp.Med. (1994-), High.Educ.Curr.Aware.Bull., I.P.A., Ind.Vet., Protozool.Abstr., Sugar Ind.Abstr., Vet.Bull. **Document type:** academic/scholarly publication.
—BLDSC (6444.000000); CASDDS; EMDOCS; SWETS; UnCover.

615 RH
PHARMACEUTICAL JOURNAL OF ZIMBABWE. Running title: Zimbabwe Pharmaceutical Journal. bi-m. Z.$250 includes membership. Pharmaceutical Society of Zimbabwe, P.O. Box 1476, Harare, Zimbabwe. TEL 263-14-706967. FAX 263-14-706967. Ed. rtee Mithal. adv.: B&W page Z.$1200. circ. 350. **Document type:** academic/scholarly publication.

615 US
PHARMACEUTICAL: LATIN AMERICAN INDUSTRIAL REPORT. (Avail. for each of 22 Latin American countries) 1985. a. $435 per country report. Aquino Productions, Box 15760, Stamford, CT 06901. TEL 203-325-3138. Ed. Andres C. Aquino.

PHARMACEUTICAL LIBRARY BULLETIN/YAKUGAKU TOSHOKAN. see *LIBRARY AND INFORMATION SCIENCES*

PHARMACEUTICAL LITIGATION REPORTER; the national journal of record of pharmaceutical litigation. see *LAW — Civil Law*

PHARMACEUTICAL MANUFACTURERS OF JAPAN. see *BUSINESS AND ECONOMICS — Trade And Industrial Directories*

615 338 UK ISSN 0955-3894
CODEN: PMREEC
PHARMACEUTICAL MANUFACTURING REVIEW. q. £82.15($169.60) (foreign £106). Argus Business Media Ltd., Fuel and Metals Journals (Subsidiary of: Argus Press Group), Queensway House, 2 Queensway, Redhill, Surrey RH1 1QS, England. TEL 01737-768611. FAX 01737-761685. TELEX 948669 TOPJNL G. Ed. Tom Mulligan. **Document type:** trade publication.
—BLDSC (6444.037000).
 Description: Covers all aspects of pharmaceutical manufacturing, from raw materials to the packaged product, considering both management related topics and technological developments.

615 US ISSN 0149-0885
HD9666.3
PHARMACEUTICAL MARKETERS DIRECTORY. 1977. a. $155. C P S Communications, Inc., Directories Division, 7200 W. Camino Real, Ste. 215, Boca Raton, FL 33433. TEL 407-368-9301. FAX 407-368-7870. adv.; circ. 2,500 (paid). **Document type:** directory.
 Incorporates: Medical Products Marketers Directory.
 Description: Covers the entire healthcare field including names, titles, addresses, phone and FAX numbers for over 1,500 pharmaceutical and healthcare manufacturers, 300 advertising agencies, over 800 healthcare journals, as well as alternative media. Includes suppliers to the health care industry.

615 UK ISSN 0969-3963
PHARMACEUTICAL MARKETING. 1989. m. £48 (foreign £96). Ethical Publications Ltd., Vincent House, Vincent Ln., Dorking, Surrey RH4 3JD, England. TEL 01306-740777. FAX 01306-741069. Ed. Mark Barrowcliffe; Pub. Mark Savage. adv. contact: Zoe Almeida. circ. 6,300. **Document type:** trade publication.
—BLDSC (6444.038000).

615 610 UK ISSN 0265-0673
CODEN: PHMDEH
PHARMACEUTICAL MEDICINE (LONDON). 1985. q. £49($85) to individuals; institutions in the E.U £150 (N. America $225; elsewhere £150) (effective 1995). Chapman & Hall, Journals Department (Subsidiary of: International Thomson Publishing Group), 2-6 Boundary Row, London SE1 8HN, England. TEL 0171-865-0066. FAX 0171-522-9623. TELEX 290164 CHAPMA G. E-mail: journal@chall.mhs.compuserve.com. (Dist. by: International Thompson Publishing Services, Cheriton House, North Way, Andover, Hants. SP10 5BE, England. TEL 01264-342713. FAX 01264-342807; Subscr. in N. America to: Chapman & Hall, Journals Promotion Department, One Penn Plaza, 41st Fl., New York, NY 10119) Eds. J.C. Petrie; Robert N. Smith. adv. circ. 600. (also avail. in microform from UMI; reprint service avail.) **Indexed:** Excerp.Med. **Document type:** academic/scholarly publication.
—BLDSC (6444.051900); ADONIS; CASDDS; Faxon; SWETS; UMI. CCC.
 Description: Assesses new and old methods used to test drugs for clinical use.
 Refereed Serial

PHARMACEUTICAL MEDICINE (WORTHING); symposium proceedings. see *MEDICAL SCIENCES*

615.1 US ISSN 1071-894X
CODEN: PHNEEP
PHARMACEUTICAL NEWS. 4/yr. 73 ECU (effective 1996). Harwood Academic Publishers, c/o International Publishers Distributor, 820 Town Center Dr., Langhorne, PA 19047. TEL 215-750-2642; 800-545-8398. FAX 215-750-6343. (Subscr. to: International Publishers Distributor, P.O. Box 90, Reading, Berkshire, RG1 8JL, England. TEL 44-173-456-8316. FAX 44-173-456-8316) (back issues avail.) **Document type:** academic/scholarly publication.
—CASDDS.

615.19　　　　　US　　ISSN 1049-9156
　　　　　　　　　　CODEN: PLPREY
PHARMACEUTICAL PROCESSING. 1984. 12/yr. $40 (Canada $42.80; Mexico $40; elsewhere $60) (effective 1996). Gordon Publications, Inc., Part of Cahners Publishing Company, Division of Reed Elsevier Inc., 301 Gibraltar Dr., Box 650, Morris Plains, NJ 07950-0650. TEL 201-292-5100. FAX 201-898-9281. Ed. Michael Averbach. adv.; tr.lit. circ. 30,000.
—CCC.
　Formerly: Pharmaceutical and Cosmetic Equipment (ISSN 0895-2795)
　Description: Focuses on the processors and packagers of pharmaceuticals, biologicals, cosmetics and toiletry products.

615　　　　　　　US　　ISSN 0161-8415
PHARMACEUTICAL REPRESENTATIVE. 1971. m. $29.95 (Canada $39.95; elsewhere $49.95). McKnight Medical Communications (Subsidiary of: Medical Economics Publishing Co., Inc.), Two Northfield Plaza, Ste. 300, Northfield, IL 60093. TEL 708-441-3700. Ed. Laura Ramos. bk.rev.; abstr.; charts; illus.; stat.; tr.lit. circ. 28,000. (also avail. in microform from UMI) **Document type:** trade publication.
—UMI. **CCC.**
　Formerly: Pharmaceutical Salesman (ISSN 0048-3621)

615.19　　　　　US　　ISSN 0724-8741
　　　　　　　　　　CODEN: PHREEB
PHARMACEUTICAL RESEARCH. 1983. m. $575 (foreign $675) (effective 1996). (American Association of Pharmaceutical Scientists) Plenum Publishing Corp., 233 Spring St., New York, NY 10013-1578. TEL 212-620-8000. FAX 212-463-0742. TELEX 23-421139. Eds. Vincent H.L. Lee, Wolfgang Sadee. adv. (also avail. in microfilm from JSC; back issues avail.) **Indexed:** ASCA, Chem.Abstr., Curr.Adv.Ecol.Sci., Curr.Cont., Excerp.Med., Rev.Med.& Vet.Mycol., Sugar Ind.Abstr. **Document type:** academic/scholarly publication.
—BLDSC (6444.080000); ADONIS; CASDDS; Faxon; Genuine Article; SWETS; UMI; UnCover. **CCC.**
　Refereed Serial

615　　　　　　　UK　　ISSN 1351-6337
　　　　　　　　　　CODEN: PSCME3
PHARMACEUTICAL SCIENCE COMMUNICATIONS. 1991. bi-m. £175($295) to institutions (effective 1995). Rapid Communications of Oxford Ltd., The Old Malthouse, Paradise St., Oxford OX1 1LD, England. TEL 01865-790447. FAX 01865-244012. E-mail: rapidcom@vax.oxford.ac.uk. Ed. P.N. Shaw. **Indexed:** Excerp.Med. (1993-). **Document type:** academic/scholarly publication.
—ADONIS; CASDDS. **CCC.**
　Formerly (until 1994): Journal of Biopharmaceutical Sciences (ISSN 0957-7548)

615　　　　　　　UK　　ISSN 1356-6881
▼**PHARMACEUTICAL SCIENCES.** 1995. m. £198 (America and Japan $340; rest of world £220). Royal Pharmaceutical Society of Great Britain, 1 Lambeth High St., London SE1 7JN, England. TEL 0171-735-9141. FAX 0171-820-3917. Ed. Dr. J. Chamberlain. **Document type:** academic/scholarly publication.

615.1　　　　　　JA　　ISSN 0031-6903
　　　　　　　　　　CODEN: YKKZAJ
PHARMACEUTICAL SOCIETY OF JAPAN.
JOURNAL/YAKUGAKU ZASSHI. (Text in Japanese; contents page, summaries, captions in English) 1881. m. $90. Pharmaceutical Society of Japan - Nihon Yakugakkai, 12-15, Shibuya 2-chome, Shibuya-ku, Tokyo 150, Japan. Ed. Shoji Shibata. adv.; charts; illus.; index. circ. 2,800. (also avail. in microform from PMC) **Indexed:** Anal.Abstr., Biol.Abstr., Chem.Abstr., Crop Physiol.Abstr., Curr.Adv.Biochem., Curr.Adv.Ecol.Sci., Curr.Chem.React, Curr.Cont., Dairy Sci.Abstr., Excerp.Med., Food Sci.& Tech.Abstr., Forest.Abstr., Forest Prod.Abstr., Helminthol.Abstr., Hort.Abstr., I.P.A., Ind.Chem, Ind.Med., Mass Spectr.Bull., Nutr.Abstr.
●Also available online.
—BLDSC (4840.000000); CASDDS; EMDOCS; Faxon; Genuine Article; SWETS. **CCC.**

615　　　　　　　KO　　ISSN 0513-4242
　　　　　　　　　　CODEN: YAHOA3
PHARMACEUTICAL SOCIETY OF KOREA.
JOURNAL/YAKHAK HOEJI. (Text in Korean; summaries in English) 1948. bi-m. $30. Pharmaceutical Society of Korea, c/o College of Pharmacy, Seoul National University, Seoul 151-742, S. Korea. TEL 02-584-3257. FAX 02-521-1781. Ed. Young Choong Kim. bk.rev. circ. 1,300. (back issues avail.) **Indexed:** Biol.Abstr., Chem.Abstr., Excerp.Med. (until 1993), I.P.A., Ind.Med, INIS Atomind.
—BLDSC (4840.050000).

615　　　　　　　US　　ISSN 0147-8087
RS1　　　　　　　　　CODEN: PTECDN
PHARMACEUTICAL TECHNOLOGY. 1977. m. $59 (foreign $117). Advanstar Communications, Inc., 7500 Old Oak Blvd., Cleveland, OH 44130. TEL 216-826-2839. FAX 216-891-2726. (Subscr. to: 1 E. First St., Duluth, MN 55082. TEL 800-346-0085) Ed. B.K. Krewson. adv.; abstr.; charts; illus.; pat.; stat.; tr.lit. circ. 35,000. (back issues avail.) **Indexed:** Biotech.Abstr., Chem.Abstr., Curr.Pack.Abstr., Excerp.Med., I.P.A., Telegen. **Document type:** trade publication.
—BLDSC (6444.130000); CASDDS; Ei; Faxon; SWETS; UMI. **CCC.**
　Description: Offers practical hands-on information about the manufacture of pharmaceutical products, focusing on applied technology.
　Refereed Serial

615　　　　　　　UK
PHARMACEUTICAL TECHNOLOGY EUROPE - BIOPHARM. 1978; N.S. 1989. m. (11/yr.). $117 free to qualified persons in Europe (non-qualified persons in Europe £66; others £95) (effective 1996). Advanstar Communications, Advanstar House, Park West, Sealand Rd., Chester CH1 4RN, England. TEL 01244-378888. FAX 01244-370512. Ed. Rosemary Leyland; Pub. Fran Waldie. adv.; B&W page $4060; color page $5380; adv. contact: Clair Whitecross. charts; circ. 20,000 (controlled). (reprint service avail.) **Indexed:** Excerp.Med. **Document type:** trade publication.
—SWETS; UMI. **CCC.**
　Formerly (until 1994): Pharmaceutical Technology International (ISSN 0164-6826)
　Description: Targets the pharmaceutical industry in Western Europe; contains technical articles on the manufacturing of pharmaceuticals and biopharmaceuticals.
　Refereed Serial

615　　　　　　　UK　　ISSN 0963-6366
PHARMACEUTICAL TIMES. 1988. 11/yr. £60 (foreign £94). 75 Sheen Lane, E. Sheen, London SW14 8AD, England. TEL 0181-878-8566. FAX 0181-876-8834. Ed. Geoff Frew; Pub. Geoff Frew. adv. contact: Angela Fernandez. bk.rev. circ. 7,000. **Document type:** trade publication.
—BLDSC (6444.199000); SWETS.

PHARMACEUTICAL VENTURES. see BUSINESS AND ECONOMICS — Investments

615.1　　　　　　JA　　ISSN 0016-5980
　　　　　　　　　　CODEN: YAKUD5
PHARMACEUTICALS MONTHLY/GEKKAN YAKUJI. (Text in Japanese) 1959. m. 1200 Yen. (Pharmaceutical Research Association - Yakuji Kenkyukai) Yakugyo Jiho Co. Ltd., 2-36 Kanda Jimbo-cho, Chiyoda-ku, Tokyo 101, Japan. (Subscr. to: F-D-C Reports, Ste.1, 5550 Friendship Blvd., Chevy Chase, MD 20815) Ed. Shozo Takeda. adv.; bk.rev.; abstr.; index. circ. 14,400. **Indexed:** Chem.Abstr., I.P.A.
●Also available online.
—BLDSC (6444.390000); CASDDS.
　Description: Developments in medical treatment.

615.19　　　　　　BE
PHARMACEUTISCH TIJDSCHRIFT. (Text in Dutch) m. 217 av. d'Huart, 1950 Kraainem, Belgium. adv. circ. 3,200.

615.1　　　　　　NE　　ISSN 0031-6911
RS1.P53　　　　　　　CODEN: PHWEAW
PHARMACEUTISCH WEEKBLAD. (Includes bi-m. supplement: Pharmacy World and Science) 1864. w. fl.230 (effective 1994). Koninklijke Nederlandse Maatschappij ter Bevordering der Pharmacie - Royal Netherlands Pharmaceutical Society, P.O. Box 30460, Alexanderstraat 11, 2514 JL The Hague, Netherlands. TEL 31-70-3624111. FAX 31-70-3106530. Ed. H. Tel. adv.; bk.rev.; abstr.; charts; illus.; index; circ. 1,000 (paid); 4,000 (controlled). **Indexed:** Anal.Abstr., Biol.Abstr., Biotech.Abstr., Chem.Abstr, Crop Physiol.Abstr., Curr.Adv.Ecol.Sci., Excerp.Med., Forest Prod.Abstr., Hort.Abstr., I.P.A., Ind.Med., Key to Econ.Sci., Plant Grow.Reg.Abstr. **Document type:** academic/scholarly publication.
—BLDSC (6446.000000); CASDDS; EMDOCS; SWETS; UMI.
　Description: Practice oriented journal aimed at improving the scientific and professional practice by community, hospital, industrial and other pharmacists.

615　　　　　　　SA
PHARMACIAE. (Text in Afrikaans, English) 1985. q. Suid-Afrikaanse Aptekersraad - South African Pharmacy Council, Posbus 40040, Arcadia 0007, South Africa. illus.
　Formerly (until 1993): South African Pharmacy Council. Report.

615　　　　　　　FR　　ISSN 1246-9041
PHARMACIE PRATIQUE. 1993. m. (10/yr.). 300 F. Pharmacie Pratique, 48 bis, av. Kleber, 75116 Paris, France. TEL 47-55-06-06. FAX 47-55-69-41. TELEX 640 748. **Document type:** newspaper.

615.1　　　　　　FR　　ISSN 0031-6938
PHARMACIEN DE FRANCE; organe d'informations scientifiques et professionnelles. 1925. 20/yr. 60 F. Federation des Syndicats Pharmaceutiques de France, 13 rue Ballu, 75009 Paris, France. TEL 42-81-15-96. Ed. Paul Duchein. circ. 19,870. **Indexed:** Biol.Abstr., Chem.Abstr., I.P.A.
●Also available online.
—BLDSC (6446.175000).

615.8 658　　　　　FR　　ISSN 0768-9179
PHARMACIEN HOSPITALIER. 1966. q. 285 F. Syndicat des Pharmaciens Gerants, 31 rue du Terrage, 75010 Paris, France. TEL 42-06-23-25. FAX 42-09-09-10. adv. circ. 1,600.

615.1　　　　　　FR　　ISSN 0031-6954
PHARMACIEN RURAL.* 1953. 5/yr. Association de Pharmacie Rural, 24 rue Vintimille, 75009 Paris, France. TEL 48-74-64-26. FAX 45-26-13-37. Ed. Jean Calvet. adv.; bk.rev.; charts; illus.; rec.rev. circ. 6,500. **Indexed:** Chem.Abstr., I.P.A.
●Also available online.

615 658.8　　　　　UK
PHARMACIES AND DRUGSTORES: THE INTERNATIONAL MARKET. (Subseries of: Market Direction reports) a. £1595($3190) (effective 1996). Euromonitor, 60-61 Britton St., London EC1M 5NA, England. TEL 0171-251-8024. FAX 0171-608-3149. (Addr. in N. America: Euromonitor International, 122 S. Michigan Ave., Ste. 1200, Chicago, IL 60603. TEL 312-922-1115. FAX 312-922-1157) (looseleaf format) **Document type:** trade publication.
●Also available online. Vendor(s): Data-Star, Knight-Ridder, Inc.
　Description: Analyzes the market for drugstores and pharmacies for France, Germany, Italy, Spain, the U.K., the U.S., and Japan.

615.1　　　　　　CN
PHARMACIST NEWS. French edition: Actualite Pharmaceutique. 14/yr. Can.$38. Maclean-Hunter Ltd., Business Publication Division, Maclean-Hunter Bldg., 777 Bay St., Toronto, ON M5W 1A7, Canada. TEL 416-596-5950. Ed. Polly Thompson. adv.; illus. circ. 21,100 (16,600 English ed., 4,500 French ed.). (tabloid format; also avail. in microform from UMI) **Indexed:** Can.B.P.I., I.P.A. **Document type:** trade publication, newspaper.
●Also available online.
　Formerly (until 1993): Drug Merchandising (ISSN 0012-6586)
　Description: News about retail pharmacy and hospital and clinic-based pharmacists.

PHARMACY AND PHARMACOLOGY

615　　　　　　　US　　ISSN 0883-0371
PHARMACIST'S LETTER. 1985. m. $88. Therapeutic Research Center, 8834 Hildreth Ln., Box 8190, Stockton, CA 95208. TEL 209-931-2923. FAX 209-931-2929. Ed. Dr. Jeff. M. Jellin. index. (looseleaf format; back issues avail.) **Document type:** newsletter.
　　Description: Advises pharmacists on current drug therapy, including drug interactions, proper drug use, trends in therapy, new research findings, and new drugs.
　　Refereed Serial

615 338　　　　NZ　　ISSN 1170-7690
　　　　　　　　　　　　　CODEN: PARMEK
PHARMACOECONOMICS. 1992. m. $715 (effective 1996). Adis International Limited, Private Bag 65901, Mairangi Bay, Auckland 10, New Zealand. TEL 64-9-479-8100. FAX 64-9-479-8145. E-mail: pcl@topgun.adis.co.nz. (Subscr. addr. in US: Adis International Inc, Attn. Subscriptions Dept., Ste. F-10, 940 Town Center Dr., Langhorne, PA 19047. TEL 215-741-5229. FAX 215-741-5251) Ed. Richard Crampton. **Indexed:** Curr.Cont., Excerp.Med. (1995-), I.P.A., Sci.Cit.Ind. **Document type:** academic/scholarly publication.
　　—BLDSC (6446.246500); Genuine Article; SWETS. **CCC.**
　　Description: Promotes the development and study of health economics as applied to rational drug therapy.

615　　　　　　　UK　　ISSN 1053-8569
　　　　　　　　　　　　　CODEN: PDSAEA
PHARMACOEPIDEMIOLOGY AND DRUG SAFETY. 1992. bi-m. $375 (foreign $375) (effective 1996). John Wiley & Sons Ltd., Journals, Baffins Ln., Chichester, W. Sussex PO19 1UD, England. TEL 01243-779777. FAX 01243-776128. TELEX 86290 WIBOOK G. E-mail: subinfo@j.wiley.com. (Subscr. in the Americas to: John Wiley & Sons, Inc., 605 Third Ave., New York, NY 10158. TEL 212-850-6645. FAX 212-850-6021) Ed. Dr. Ronald Mann. circ. 493. (also avail. in microform from UMI; back issues avail.) **Indexed:** Excerp.Med. (1992-). **Document type:** academic/scholarly publication.
　　—BLDSC (6446.248000); CASDDS; SWETS; UMI. **CCC.**
　　Incorporates (1986-1995): Post Marketing Surveillance (ISSN 0269-2333)
　　Description: Provides an international forum for the communication and evaluation of data, methods and opinion in the emerging discipline of pharmacoepidemiology.
　　Refereed Serial

PHARMACOGENETICS. see *BIOLOGY — Genetics*

615.1　　　　　UK　　ISSN 1043-6618
RS122　　　　　　　　　CODEN: PHMREP
PHARMACOLOGICAL RESEARCH. 1969. m. £324 (effective 1996). (Italian Pharmacological Society) Academic Press Ltd. (Subsidiary of: Harcourt Brace & Company Ltd.), 24-28 Oval Rd., London NW1 7DX, England. TEL 44-171-267-4466. FAX 44-171-482-2293. TELEX 25775 ACPRES G. (Subscr. to: Harcourt Brace & Company Ltd., Foots Cray High St., Sidcup, Kent DA14 5HP, England. TEL 44-181-300-3322. FAX 44-181-309-0807) Ed.Bd. **Indexed:** Biol.Abstr., Chem.Abstr, Curr.Adv.Biochem., Curr.Adv.Ecol.Sci., Curr.Cont., Dairy Sci.Abstr., Excerp.Med., Helminthol.Abstr., Ind.Med., Ind.Vet., Nutr.Abstr., Risk Abstr., Vet.Bull. **Document type:** academic/scholarly publication.
　　—BLDSC (6446.550000); ADONIS; CASDDS; Faxon; Genuine Article; SWETS; UnCover. **CCC.**
　　Formerly: Pharmacological Research Communications (ISSN 0031-6989)
　　Description: Presents papers on basic and applied pharmacological research in both animals and man for specialist whose fileds of study vary widely within the discipline of pharmacology.

615.1　　　　　US　　ISSN 0031-6997
RS1　　　　　　　　　　CODEN: PAREAQ
PHARMACOLOGICAL REVIEWS. 1951. q. $60 to individuals; institutions $107 (effective 1995). (American Society for Pharmacology and Experimental Therapeutics) Williams & Wilkins, 428 E. Preston St., Baltimore, MD 21202. TEL 410-528-4000; 800-638-6423. FAX 410-528-4312. TELEX 87669. Ed. Robert E. Stitzel. adv.; bibl.; charts. circ. 2,277. (also avail. in microfilm from WWS) **Indexed:** Biotech.Abstr., Chem.Abstr., Curr.Adv.Ecol.Sci., Curr.Cont., Dent.Ind., Diar.Dis.Res., Excerp.Med., I.P.A., Ind.Med., Ind.Sci.Rev., Ind.Vet., Vet.Bull. **Document type:** academic/scholarly publication.
　　—BLDSC (6447.000000); CASDDS; EMDOCS; Faxon; Genuine Article; SWETS; UnCover. **CCC.**
　　Description: Contains review articles on topics of interest to pharmacologists, toxicologists and biochemists.
　　Refereed Serial

615.1　　　　　US　　ISSN 0031-7004
RM1　　　　　　　　　　CODEN: PHMCAA
PHARMACOLOGIST. 1959. q. $25 to non-members. American Society for Pharmacology and Experimental Therapeutics, 9650 Rockville Pike, Bethesda, MD 20814. Ed. Kay A. Croker. abstr.; charts; illus.; index. circ. 4,500. (also avail. in microform from UMI; back issues avail.; reprint service avail. from UMI) **Indexed:** Biol.Abstr., Biotech.Abstr., Chem.Abstr., Excerp.Med. **Document type:** trade publication.
　　—BLDSC (6447.050000); SWETS; UMI; UnCover.

615.1　　　　　SZ　　ISSN 0031-7012
RM1　　　　　　　　　　CODEN: PHMGBN
PHARMACOLOGY; international journal of experimental and clinical pharmacology. (Text in English) 1959. m. (2 vols./yr.). 604.80 SFr.($465.60) to individuals; institutions 1008 SFr.($776) (effective 1996). S. Karger AG, Allschwilerstr. 10, P.O. Box, CH-4009 Basel, Switzerland. TEL 061-3061111. FAX 061-3061234. E-mail: Karger@Karger.ch. Ed.Bd. adv.; abstr.; bibl.; charts; illus.; index. circ. 1,150. (also avail. in microfilm) **Indexed:** Biol.Abstr., Biotech.Abstr., Chem.Abstr., Curr.Adv.Ecol.Sci., Curr.Cont., Dent.Ind., Excerp.Med., Helminthol.Abstr., Ind.Med., Rev.Plant Path. **Document type:** academic/scholarly publication.
　　—BLDSC (6447.060000); CASDDS; EMDOCS; Faxon; Genuine Article; SWETS; UnCover. **CCC.**
　　Formerly: Medicina et Pharmacologia Experimentalis.
　　Refereed Serial

PHARMACOLOGY AND THE SKIN. see *MEDICAL SCIENCES — Dermatology And Venereology*

615　　　　　　　UK　　ISSN 0163-7258
RM1　　　　　　　　　　CODEN: PHTHDT
PHARMACOLOGY AND THERAPEUTICS; journal of the International Encyclopedia of Pharmacology and Therapeutics. 1975. m. $2265 to institutions (effective 1996). (International Union of Pharmacology) Elsevier Science Ltd., Pergamon, P.O. Box 800, Kidlington, Oxford OX5 1DX, England. TEL 44-1865-843000. FAX 44-1865-843010. E-mail: nlinfo-f@elsevier.nl; usinfo-f@elsevier.nl; forinfo-kyf04035@niftyserve.or.jp; Site addr.: http://www.elsevier.nl/. (Subscr. in U.S. and Canada to: Elsevier Science, 660 White Plains Rd., Tarrytown, NY 10591-5153. TEL 914-524-9200. FAX 914-333-2444) Ed. A. Sartorelli. adv.; bk.rev.; charts; illus.; stat.; index. (also avail. in microform from UMI; back issues avail) **Indexed:** Biol.Abstr., Biotech.Abstr., Chem.Abstr., Curr.Adv.Biochem., Curr.Adv.Cancer Res., Curr.Adv.Ecol.Sci., Curr.Adv.Genetics & Molec.Biol., Curr.Cont., Dent.Ind., Excerp.Med., Ind.Med., Ind.Sci.Rev., Med.& Surg.Dermat., Nutr.Abstr. **Document type:** academic/scholarly publication.
　　—BLDSC (6447.061800); ADONIS; CASDDS; Faxon; Genuine Article; SWETS; UMI; UnCover. **CCC.**
　　Formed by the Jan. 1979 merger of: Pharmacology and Therapeutics. Part A. Chemotherapy, Toxicology and Metabolic Inhibitors (ISSN 0362-5478); Pharmacology and Therapeutics. Part B. General and Systematic Pharmacology (ISSN 0306-039X); Pharmacology and Therapeutics. Part C. Clinical Pharmacology and Therapeutics (ISSN 0362-5486)
　　Description: Presents authoritative review articles covering recent developments in pharmacology, including chemotherapy, toxicology and clinical pharmacology.
　　Refereed Serial

615.9　　　　　DK　　ISSN 0901-9928
QP901　　　　　　　　CODEN: PHTOEH
PHARMACOLOGY & TOXICOLOGY. (Supplements avail.) (Text in English) 1944. 12/yr. DKK 1780 (incl. supplements) (effective 1996). (Nordic Pharmacological Society) Munksgaard International Publishers Ltd., 35 Noerre Soegade, P.O. Box 2148, DK-1016 Copenhagen K, Denmark. TEL 33-127030. FAX 33-129387. Ed. Jens Schou. bibl.; charts; illus.; index. circ. 1,200. (also avail. in microfilm from PMC; reprint service avail. from ISI) **Indexed:** ASCA, Biol.Abstr., Biotech.Abstr., C.I.S. Abstr., Chem.Abstr., Curr.Adv.Cell & Devel.Biol., Curr.Adv.Ecol.Sci., Curr.Cont., Dairy Sci.Abstr., Dent.Ind., Excerp.Med., Helminthol.Abstr., I.P.A., Ind.Med., Ind.Sci.Rev., Ind.Vet., Lab.Haz.Bull., NRN, Nutr.Abstr., Psychol.Abstr., Rev.Med.& Vet.Mycol., Sci.Cit.Ind., Sel.Water Res.Abstr., Vet.Bull. **Document type:** academic/scholarly publication.
　　—BLDSC (6447.070000); ADONIS; CASDDS; Faxon; Genuine Article; SWETS; UnCover. **CCC.**
　　Formerly: Acta Pharmacologica et Toxicologica (ISSN 0001-6683)
　　Refereed Serial

PHARMACOLOGY & TOXICOLOGY. SUPPLEMENTUM. see *ENVIRONMENTAL STUDIES — Toxicology And Environmental Safety*

PHARMACOLOGY, BIOCHEMISTRY AND BEHAVIOR. see *BIOLOGY — Biological Chemistry*

615　　　　　　　US　　ISSN 1060-4456
　　　　　　　　　　　　　CODEN: PCMME9
PHARMACOLOGY COMMUNICATIONS. 1992. 8/yr. (in 2 vols., 4 nos./vol.). 99 ECU per vol. (effective 1996). Harwood Academic Publishers, c/o International Publishers Distributor, 820 Town Center Dr., Langhorne, PA 19047. TEL 215-750-2642. FAX 215-750-6343. (Subscr. to: International Publishers Distributor, P.O. Box 90, Reading, Berkshire RG1 8JL, England. TEL 44-173-456-8316) (also avail. in microform) **Indexed:** Excerp.Med. (1993-). **Document type:** academic/scholarly publication.
　　—BLDSC (6447.078300); CASDDS; SWETS. **CCC.**
　　Description: Publishes original short research reports on all aspects of basic and clinical pharmacology.

615　　　　　　　GW
▼**PHARMACOLOGY OF CEREBRAL ISCHEMIA.** 1994. s-a. Medpharm GmbH Scientific Publishers, Postfach 101061, 70009 Stuttgart, Germany. TEL 0711-2582-0. FAX 0711-2582290. Eds. Josef Krieglstein, Heike Oberpichler-Schwenk. **Document type:** academic/scholarly publication.

615　　　　　　　US　　ISSN 0363-4655
PHARMACOPEIAL FORUM. 1975. bi-m. $310. United States Pharmacopeial Convention, Inc., 12601 Twinbrook Pkwy., Rockville, MD 20852. TEL 301-881-0666. **Indexed:** Curr.Cont., Sugar Ind.Abstr. **Document type:** directory.
　　—BLDSC (6447.087400); Genuine Article; SWETS.
　　Description: Presents proposed U.S.P. National Formulary revisions for public comment.

615　　　　　　　JA
THE PHARMACOPOEIA OF JAPAN. (Editions in English, Japanese) irreg., 12th ed., 1991. 49000 Yen($480) (Society of Japanese Pharmacopoeia) Yakuji Nippo, Ltd., 1, Kanda Izumicho, Chiyoda-ku, Tokyo 101, Japan. TEL 03-3862-2141. FAX 03-5821-8757. **Document type:** government publication.
　　Description: Contains general notices, general rules for preparation, general tests, processes and apparatus.

615　　　　　　　CC
PHARMACOPOEIA OF THE PEOPLE'S REPUBLIC OF CHINA. (Editions in Chinese, English) a. (Ministry of Public Health) People's Medical Publishing House, 10 Tianxili Lu, Beijing, People's Republic of China. (Dist. by: China Pharmaceutical Books Company, Rm. 1001-4 Champion Bldg., 287-291 Des Voeux Rd., Central, Hong Kong, Hong Kong) Ed.Bd.

PHARMACOPSYCHIATRY; clinical pharmacology, psychiatry, psychology, neurophysiology advances in theoretical and clinical research. see *MEDICAL SCIENCES — Psychiatry And Neurology*

PHARMACOPSYCHIATRY. SUPPLEMENT. see *MEDICAL SCIENCES — Psychiatry And Neurology*

615 330 NZ ISSN 1172-8299
▼**PHARMACORESOURCES**; world pharmacoeconomic news, views and practical application. 1994. s-m. $495. Adis International Limited, Private Bag 65901, Mairangi Bay, Auckland 10, New Zealand. TEL 64-9-479-8100. FAX 64-9-479-8145. E-mail: pcl@topgun.adis.co.nz. Ed. Tracey Langsdale. **Document type:** academic/scholarly publication.
—CCC.
Description: Provides brief, evaluated summaries of current pharmacoeconomic and outcomes research from the world biomedical literature.

615.19 US ISSN 0277-0008
CODEN: PHPYDQ
PHARMACOTHERAPY; journal of human pharmacology and drug therapy. 1981. bi-m. $95 (foreign $110) (effective 1996). (American College of Clinical Pharmacy) Pharmacotherapy Publications, Inc., New England Medical Center - Box 806, 750 Washington St., Boston, MA 02111. TEL 617-636-5390. FAX 617-636-5318. Ed. Richard T. Scheife; Pub. Richard T. Scheitz. adv.: B&W page $763; color $1761; trim 8 1/8 x 10 7/8. bk.rev.; charts; illus.; index; circ. 4,303 (paid); 309 (controlled). (also avail. in microfilm from UMI; back issues avail.; reprint service avail. from UMI) **Indexed:** Biol.Abstr., Chem.Abstr., Curr.Cont., Dent.Ind., Excerp.Med., Ind.Med., Kidney, Sugar Ind.Abstr. **Document type:** academic/scholarly publication.
—BLDSC (6447.089000); CASDDS; Faxon; Genuine Article; SWETS; UMI; UnCover. **CCC.**
Description: Publishes original articles of interest to physicians, pharmacists, and other health professionals with major interests in drug therapy or clinical drug research.
Refereed Serial

615.19 CN ISSN 0834-065X
PHARMACTUEL; la revue de la pratique pharmaceutique en etablissement e sante au Quebec. (Text in French) vol.19, 1986. bi-m. Can.$50 to non-members. Association des Pharmaciens des Etablissements de Sante du Quebec, 50 Cremazie Ouest, Bureau 505, Montreal, PQ H2P 2T2, Canada. TEL 514-381-7904. FAX 514-381-2781. Ed. Lucie Robitaille. adv. contact: Lucie Germain. circ. 1,800 (controlled). (back issues avail.) **Document type:** academic/scholarly publication.

615 US ISSN 1064-797X
RS122.5
PHARMACY CADENCE. 1992. a. $17.95 (effective through July 1996). P A S Pharmacy - Association Services, Box 6565, Athens, GA 30604. TEL 706-613-0100. FAX 706-613-0200. Ed. L. Michael Posey. circ. 2,000 (paid).
Description: Overview of pharmacy for students and others new to the profession in the U.S. and Canada.
Refereed Serial

615.9 001.64 CN
PHARMACY CLAIM STANDARD. biennial. Can.$25. Canadian Pharmaceutical Association, 1785 Alta Vista Dr., Ottawa, ON K1G 3Y6, Canada. TEL 613-523-7877. FAX 613-523-0445. **Document type:** trade publication.
Formerly: Electronic Claim Standard.

615.1 JA ISSN 0044-0043
PHARMACY COMPANION/YAKKYOKU NO TOMO. (Text in Japanese) 1953. m. 50 Yen. Yamanouchi Pharmaceutical Co. Ltd. - Yamanouchi Seiyaku K. K., 2-5 Nihonbashi Hon-cho, Chuo-ku, Tokyo 103, Japan. Ed. Nobuo Yamamuro. adv.; charts; illus.; tr.lit. circ. 20,000.

615.19 AT ISSN 1032-3279
PHARMACY GUILD OF AUSTRALIA. ANNUAL REPORT. 1975. a. Pharmacy Guild of Australia, P.O. Box 36, Deakin, A.C.T. 2600, Australia. TEL 06-281-0911. FAX 06-281-4745. circ. 5,500.
Formerly: Pharmacy Guild of Australia. National Report.

615.19 AT ISSN 0155-8595
PHARMACY GUILD OF AUSTRALIA. NATIONAL NEWSLETTER. 1976. irreg. free to members. Pharmacy Guild of Australia, P.O. Box 36, Deakin, A.C.T. 2600, Australia. TEL 06-281-0911. FAX 06-282-4745. Ed. Wal Williams. circ. 5,300. (back issues avail.) **Document type:** newsletter.

615.9 610.73 614.8 US ISSN 0739-9596
PHARMACY HEALTH-LINE. 1982. m. $50. Rx-Data-Pac Service, 8907 Terwilliger's Tr., Cincinnati, OH 45249. TEL 513-489-0943. Ed. I.H. Goodman. (looseleaf format; back issues avail.)

615.1 US ISSN 0031-7047
RS61 CODEN: PHHIB4
PHARMACY IN HISTORY. 1959. q. $50. American Institute of the History of Pharmacy, Pharmacy Bldg., Madison, WI 53706. TEL 608-262-5378. Ed. Gregory Higby. adv.; bk.rev.; bibl.; charts; illus.; index every 3 yrs. circ. 1,200. (also avail. in microfilm from UMI; reprint service avail. from UMI) **Indexed:** Amer.Hist.& Life, Hist.Abstr, I.P.A. **Document type:** academic/scholarly publication.
●Also available online.
—BLDSC (6447.350000); UMI; UnCover.

615.4 UK ISSN 1358-1538
CODEN: HPPRE8
PHARMACY IN PRACTICE. 1991. m. £55; newsstand price: £5. Medicon (UK) Ltd., The Quadrant, 118 London Rd., Kingston-upon-Thames, Surrey KT2 6QJ, England. TEL 0181-541-5666. FAX 0181-541-5450. Ed. Anthony Trice. **Indexed:** Excerp.Med. (1994-). **Document type:** academic/scholarly publication.
—BLDSC (6447.504000).
Formerly (until 1994): Hospital Pharmacy Practice (ISSN 0962-9734)

615.19 340 US ISSN 0149-1717
KF2915.P4
PHARMACY LAW DIGEST. 1965. a. (plus s-a. updates). $75. Facts and Comparisons, 111 W. Port Plaza, Ste. 400, St. Louis, MO 63146-3098. TEL 800-223-0554. FAX 314-878-5563. Ed.Bd. (looseleaf format)
Description: Information on controlled substances, pharmacy inspection, civil liability, pertinent court cases, business and drug control law, with emphasis on federal law.

615 SA ISSN 1015-1362
PHARMACY MANAGEMENT. 1980. 10/yr. R.75($80) (effective 1995). Medpharm Publications, P.O. Box 642, Irene 1675, South Africa. TEL 27-12-664-5738. FAX 27-12-664-6538. Ed. Oppel Greeff. adv. circ. 3,450.
Description: Contains management and clinical articles written by South African specialists.

410 US
PHARMACY MANAGEMENT QUARTERLY. 1981. q. $110 (foreign $132). Aspen Publishers, Inc., 200 Orchard Ridge Dr., Gaithersburg, MD 20878. TEL 301-417-7500. FAX 301-417-7550.
—UMI. **CCC.**
Formerly: Topics in Hospital Pharmacy Management (ISSN 0271-1206)

615.1 II ISSN 0031-7063
PHARMACY NEWS.* (Editions in English, Hindi, Punjabi, Urdu) 1962. m. Rs.8. (Punjab Pharmacists' Federation) Rajesh Publications, 1 Ansari Rd., Daryaganj, Dew Delhi 110 002, India. (Co-sponsors: All India Medical Practitioners' Association; All India Homeopathic League) Ed. Dr. Kuldip Bhatia. adv.; bk.rev.; illus.; pat.; circ. 12,000 (controlled). **Indexed:** I.P.A.
Incorporating: Modern Medical Practice.

PHARMACY NEWS; a consumer newsletter to advance awareness while saving time and money. see
MEDICAL SCIENCES — Dermatology And Venereology

615 US ISSN 8750-4790
PHARMACY NEWS AND REVIEW. m. $90 to non-members; members $45 (effective 1996). Pennsylvania Pharmaceutical Association, 508 N. Third St., Harrisburg, PA 17101-1199. TEL 717-234-6151; 800-582-4080. FAX 717-236-1618. **Document type:** newsletter.
Description: Covers current legal, administrative and medical issues affecting pharmacists.

615 CN ISSN 1199-2131
PHARMACY POST. 1993. m. Can.$42 (US Can.$52, elsewhere Can.$60). Thomson Healthcare Communications, 1120 Birchmount Rd., Ste. 200, Scarborough, ON M1K 5G4, Canada. TEL 416-750-8900. FAX 416-751-8126. Ed. Karen Welds; Pub. Robyn Brooking. circ. 12,636. (tabloid format)

615.1 CN ISSN 0829-2809
CODEN: PHRPEA
PHARMACY PRACTICE; the professional journal for Canada's pharmacists. 1985. 10/yr. Can.$37.45 (foreign $45). Thomson Healthcare Communications, 1120 Birchmount Rd., Ste. 200, Scarborough, ON M1K 5G4, Canada. TEL 416-750-8900. FAX 416-751-8126. Ed. Anne Bokma. adv.: B&W page Can.$2285. circ. 16,500.
—BLDSC (6447.506000).

615.1 US ISSN 0886-988X
PHARMACY PRACTICE NEWS. 1974. m. McMahon Group, 148 W. 24th St., 8th Fl., New York, NY 10011-1916. TEL 212-620-4600. FAX 212-620-5928. Ed. Sarah Tilyou. adv.; illus. circ. 24,577. **Indexed:** CINAHL, Excerp.Med., I.P.A. **Document type:** academic/scholarly publication.
●Also available online.
—UMI.
Former titles (until 1985): Intravenous Therapy News (ISSN 8750-3182); American Journal of Intravenous Therapy and Clinical Nutrition (ISSN 0195-0282); American Journal of Intravenous Therapy (ISSN 0161-3065); American Journal of I.V. Therapy (ISSN 0095-4012)

615 UK
PHARMACY PRODUCTS REVIEW. 1992. m. (11/yr.). £49 (foreign £59). Cosmetics Communications Ltd., 335 Linen Hall, 162-168 Regent St., London W1R 5TB, England. TEL 0171-434-1530. FAX 0171-437-0915. Ed. Sian Rees. adv. contact: Sally Ricketts. circ. 15,000. **Document type:** trade publication.

615 658 SA
PHARMACY RETAILER. m. Complete Publishing (Pty.) Ltd., P.O. Box 87745, Houghton 2041, South Africa. TEL 27-11-7892112. FAX 27-11-7895347. Ed. Roy Watson. adv. **Document type:** trade publication.

615.19 AT ISSN 0314-6316
PHARMACY REVIEW. 1976. a. Aus.$40. Pharmacy Guild of Australia, P.O. Box 36, Deakin, A.C.T. 2600, Australia. TEL 06-281-0911. FAX 06-282-4745. Ed. Wal Williams. circ. 5,200.
Description: Informs members about decisions relating to pharmacy in Australia.

615 378 US ISSN 0279-5272
PHARMACY STUDENT. vol.7, 1976. q. $25 to non-members. American Pharmaceutical Association, 2215 Constitution Ave., N.W., Washington, DC 20037. TEL 202-628-4410. Ed. Rick Harding. circ. 11,500.
—CCC.
Formerly (until vol.8, 1978): S A Ph A News.

615.1 US ISSN 0003-0627
RS1
PHARMACY TIMES; devoted to professional pharmacy, pharmacy economics, and prescription practice. 1935. m. $30 registered pharmacists and students $18; foreign $75. Romaine Pierson Publishers, Inc., 80 Shore Rd., Port Washington, NY 11050. TEL 516-883-6350. FAX 516-883-6609. Ed. Bruce Buckley; Pub. William J. Reynolds. adv. contact: Patricia Nolan. bk.rev.; abstr.; illus.; index. circ. 93,666. (also avail. in microfilm from UMI; back issues avail.; reprint service avail.) **Indexed:** Biol.Abstr., Chem.Abstr., I.P.A. **Document type:** trade publication.
●Also available online.
—BLDSC (6447.530000); UMI; UnCover. **CCC.**
Former titles (until 1969): American Professional Pharmacist (ISSN 0096-0349); Practical Druggist; Spatula.

615 US ISSN 1042-0991
PHARMACY TODAY. 1962. m. $50. American Pharmaceutical Association, 2215 Constitution Ave., N.W., Washington, DC 20037. TEL 202-628-4410. FAX 202-783-2351. Ed. Judy Blanchard. bibl.; illus.; circ. 40,000 (controlled).
—CCC.
Former titles: Pharmacy Weekly; A-Ph-Armacy Weekly (ISSN 0098-2814); A Ph A Newsletter (ISSN 0567-4069)
Description: Reports on current news and opinions, including pharmacotherapeutic, legislative and socioeconomic news.

PHARMACY AND PHARMACOLOGY

615 — UK — ISSN 0968-042X
PHARMACY TODAY. 1986. 9/yr. Miller Freeman Publishers Ltd., Sovereign Way, Tonbridge, Kent TN9 1RW, England. TEL 01732-364422. FAX 01732-361534. TELEX 95132 BENTON G. Ed. Jane Nichols. adv. contact: Richard Langrish. circ. 9,969 (controlled). **Document type:** trade publication.
Description: Contains articles of interest to managers of independent pharmacies.

615.1 — AT — ISSN 0031-7071
PHARMACY TRADE. 1967. m. Aus.$40. Reed Business Publishing Pty. Ltd. (Subsidiary of: Reed International PLC), 1-5 Railway St., Chatswood, N.S.W. 2067, Australia. TEL 02-372-5222. FAX 02-419-7599. Ed. B. Madden. adv.; illus. circ. 6,811. (tabloid format)

615 — US — ISSN 1075-2552
PHARMACY WEEK. 1992. w. free to qualified personnel. Pharmacy Week, 668 W. Washington Ave., Ste. 145, Madison, WI 53703. TEL 608-251-1112. FAX 608-251-1155. Pub. Paul Barnes. adv.: B&W page $2500, color page $3300; trim 8 1/2 x 11. circ. 11,500 (controlled). **Document type:** trade publication.
Description: For Hospital and home health care pharmacists. Covers drug information, computers, management and employment issues.

615.1 — US — ISSN 0191-6394
PHARMACY WEST. 1888. m. $18 (foreign $60). (Western Communications, Ltd.) E L F Publications, 333 W. Hampden Ave., Ste. 1050, Englewood, CO 80110-2340. TEL 303-761-8818. FAX 303-761-2440. Ed. Jennifer Lamb; Pubs. Judy Lane, Ron Quam. adv. contact: John Maginness. circ. 15,812. **Indexed:** I.P.A. **Document type:** trade publication.
●Also available online.
Formerly: West Coast - Rocky Mountain Druggist; Which was formed by the merger of: West Coast Druggist (ISSN 0043-3101); Rocky Mountain Druggist (ISSN 0035-757X)
Description: News and features on the pharmaceutical industry in the 13 Western states.

615 — NE — ISSN 0928-1231
CODEN: PWSCED
PHARMACY WORLD AND SCIENCE; a journal devoted to rational drug use. (Supplement to: Pharmaceutisch Weekblad (ISSN 0031-6911)) 1979. bi-m. fl.130 (effective 1994). Koninklijke Nederlandse Maatschappij ter Bevordering der Pharmacie - Royal Netherlands Pharmaceutical Society, P.O. Box 30460, Alexanderstraat 11, 2514 JL The Hague, Netherlands. TEL 31-70-3624111. FAX 31-70-3106530. (Co-sponsor: European Society of Clinical Pharmacy) Ed. J.H. Beijnen. adv.; circ. 2,000 (paid); 4,000 (controlled). **Indexed:** Excerp.Med. **Document type:** academic/scholarly publication.
—BLDSC (6447.541000); CASDDS; Faxon; Genuine Article; SWETS; UMI.
Formerly (until 1992): Pharmaceutisch Weekblad. Scientific Edition (ISSN 0167-6555)
Description: Provides a medium for the publication of articles within all fields of pharmaceutical sciences, with an emphasis on clinical pharmacy.

PHARMALERT. see DRUG ABUSE AND ALCOHOLISM

615.1 — US — ISSN 0048-3648
PHARMASCOPE; new products & investigational drugs. 1961. m. $575. Transpharma, Inc., 13072 Camino del Valle, Poway, CA 92064. Ed. Elvera R. Richardson. abstr.; bibl.; pat.; s-a. index. **Document type:** newsletter.

615 — FR — ISSN 0298-8550
PHARMASCOPE. 6/yr. Radigois Gauthiez Hervouet-des-Forges, 3 av. de Paris, 91150 Etampes, France. TEL 64-94-53-94. Ed. Jeanine Dufouil. circ. 15,000.

615.1 — GW — ISSN 0031-711X
CODEN: PHINAN
DIE PHARMAZEUTISCHE INDUSTRIE. (Text in English and German) 1939. m. DM.315. Editio Cantor, Postfach 1255, 88341 Aulendorf, Germany. TEL 07525-2060. FAX 07525-20680. Ed. Viktor Schramm. adv.; bk.rev.; abstr.; bibl.; charts; illus.; mkt.; pat.; tr.lit.; index. circ. 4,000. (reprint service avail. from IRC,ISI) **Indexed:** Biotech.Abstr., Chem.Abstr., Excerp.Med., I.P.A., Int.Packag.Abstr., Key to Econ.Sci., PROMT, Sugar Ind.Abstr.
●Also available online.
—BLDSC (6447.650000); CASDDS; EMDOCS; Faxon; Genuine Article; SWETS. CCC.

615.1 — GW — ISSN 0031-7128
RS1 — CODEN: PHMRAL
PHARMAZEUTISCHE RUNDSCHAU. 1968. m. DM.154.20 (foreign DM.178.20). (Bundesverband der Landesverbaende Deutscher Apotheker e.V.) P. Keppler Verlag GmbH und Co. KG, Industriestr. 2, 63150 Heusenstamm, Germany. TEL 06104-6060. FAX 06104-606117. Ed. Silvia Schmidtke. adv.; bk.rev. circ. 16,000. **Indexed:** Biol.Abstr., Excerp.Med. **Document type:** trade publication.
—CCC.
Description: Professional journal of pharmaceutical news and issues.

615.1 — GW — ISSN 0031-7136
CODEN: PHZIAP
PHARMAZEUTISCHE ZEITUNG. 1856. w. DM.192.40. (Bundesvereinigung Deutscher Apothekeverbaende) Govi Pharmazeutischer Verlag GmbH, Ginnheimerstr. 26, 65760 Eschborn, Germany. TEL 06196-928262. FAX 06196-928203. Ed. Dr. Hartmut Morck. adv.; bk.rev.; bibl.; charts; illus.; index. circ. 35,500. **Indexed:** Biotech.Abstr., Chem.Abstr., Chem.Infd., Excerp.Med., I.P.A. **Document type:** newspaper.
—BLDSC (6447.693000); CASDDS; EMDOCS; SWETS. CCC.

615.1 — GW — ISSN 0031-7144
RS1 — CODEN: PHARAT
DIE PHARMAZIE. (Text in English, German) 1946. m. DM.264 (foreign DM.360). Govi Pharmazeutischer Verlag GmbH, Ginnheimerstr. 26, 65760 Eschborn, Germany. TEL 06196-928262. FAX 06196-928203. E-mail: dingermann@em.uni-frankfurt.dbp.de. Eds. Dr. Peter Pflegel, Dr. Theodor Dingermann. adv. contact: Hans-Juergen Renn. bk.rev.; abstr.; bibl.; charts; illus.; index. circ. 1,800. (also avail. in microform from PMC) **Indexed:** Anal.Abstr., Biol.Abstr., Biotech.Abstr., Chem.Abstr., Chem.Infd., Curr.Adv.Ecol.Sci., Curr.Chem.React, Curr.Cont., Dairy Sci.Abstr., Dent.Ind., Excerp.Med., Forest.Abstr., Helminthol.Abstr., Herb.Abstr., Hort.Abstr., I.P.A., Ind.Chem, Ind.Med., Ind.Vet., Mass Spectr.Bull., Plant Grow.Reg.Abstr., Protozool.Abstr., Rev.Med.& Vet.Mycol., Seed Abstr. **Document type:** academic/scholarly publication.
●Also available online.
—BLDSC (6448.000000); CASDDS; EMDOCS; Faxon; Genuine Article; SWETS. CCC.
Refereed Serial

615.19 — GW — ISSN 0369-979X
CODEN: PHZHAM
PHARMAZIE HEUTE; Beilage der Deutschen Apotheker Zeitung zur Fortbildung. (Suppl. to: Deutscher Apotheker Zeitung) 1971. irreg. Deutscher Apotheker Verlag, Postfach 101061, 70009 Stuttgart, Germany. TEL 0711-2582-0. FAX 0711-2582290. **Indexed:** Chem.Abstr. **Document type:** trade publication.
—CASDDS; SWETS. CCC.

615 — GW — ISSN 0048-3664
CODEN: PHUZBI
PHARMAZIE IN UNSERER ZEIT. 1972. bi-m. DM.163($123) (effective 1996). (Deutsche Pharmazeutische Gesellschaft) V C H Verlagsgesellschaft mbH, Postfach 101161, 69451 Weinheim, Germany. TEL 06201-606-147. FAX 06201-606117. TELEX 465516-VCHWH-D. (US addr.: V C H Publishers Inc., 220 E. 23rd St., New York, NY, 10010-4606. TEL 212-683-8333) Ed. P. Pachaly. adv.; bk.rev. circ. 9,300. (reprint service avail. from ISI) **Indexed:** Biol.Abstr., Biotech.Abstr., Chem.Abstr., Excerp.Med., Ind.Med. **Document type:** academic/scholarly publication.
—BLDSC (6448.600000); CASDDS; EMDOCS; Faxon; SWETS. CCC.

615 — AU
PHARMIG INFO. 11/yr. Zieglergasse 5, A-1072 Vienna, Austria. TEL 01-5232956. FAX 01-52329519. TELEX 133710-PHARMA-A. Ed. Ruth Mayrhofer. circ. 4,000. **Document type:** trade publication.

615 — II — ISSN 0379-556X
CODEN: PMSDBB
PHARMSTUDENT. (Text in English) 1952. a. $8. Pharmaceutical Society, c/o Department of Pharmaceutics, Banaras Hindu University, Varanasi 221005, India. Ed. J.K. Pandit. adv. circ. 600. **Indexed:** Chem.Abstr.
—CASDDS.

615 — US — ISSN 1056-5671
CODEN: PPOFEL
PHASE III DRUG PROFILES;* international journal of pharmaceuticals in clinical trials. 1991. 10/yr. $325. BIOMEGA Corporation, 191 Waukegan Rd., Ste. 206, Northfield, IL 60093-2743. TEL 708-446-5511. FAX 708-446-5572. Ed. Donald L. Barbeau. index. (back issues avail.) **Indexed:** Excerp.Med. (1993-). **Document type:** academic/scholarly publication.
—BLDSC (6449.133000).
Description: Provides comprehensive information on drugs waiting approval by the FDA. Reviews the pharmacology, adverse effects, pharmacokinetics, dosage and administration, latest clinical data and anticipated cost for each drug.

615.1 — US — ISSN 0031-725X
PHILADELPHIA COLLEGE OF PHARMACY AND SCIENCE. BULLETIN. 1865. m. free to alumni. Philadelphia College of Pharmacy and Science, Woodland Ave. at 43rd St., Philadelphia, PA 19104. TEL 215-596-8800. Ed. Christine L. Bailey. illus. circ. 8,900. (reprint service avail. from UMI)

PHYSICIANS' DESK REFERENCE FOR NONPRESCRIPTION DRUGS. see MEDICAL SCIENCES

615 — US — ISSN 1043-3953
RM301.12
PHYSICIAN'S DRUG HANDBOOK. 1989. irreg., 6th edition, 1995. $29.95. Springhouse Corporation (Subsidiary of: Reed Elsevier Medical group plc.), 1111 Bethlehem Pike, Box 908, Springhouse, PA 19477. TEL 215-646-8700; 800-346-7844. FAX 215-646-4508. Pub. Minne Rose.

PHYSICIANS' GENRX; the official drug reference of FDA prescribing information and therapeutic equivalents. see MEDICAL SCIENCES

615.1 — FR — ISSN 0031-8876
CODEN: PHPHA6
PHYTIATRIE-PHYTOPHARMACIE. 4/yr. 80 F. (Societe Francaise de Phytiatrie et de Phytopharmacie) C.N.R.A., Route de St. Cyr, 78-Versailles, France. **Indexed:** Biotech.Abstr., Chem.Abstr., Field Crop Abstr., Helminthol.Abstr., Herb.Abstr., Hort.Abstr., Rev.Appl.Entomol., Rev.Plant Path., Soils & Fert.
—CASDDS.

615 — US
PILLS-A-GO-GO; journal of pills. 1991. 6/yr. $12 or exchange basis. Jim Hogshire, Ed. & Pub., 1202 E. Pike St., Seattle, WA 98122. TEL 206-328-1586. E-mail: 76130.2114@compuserve.com. adv. **Document type:** newsletter.
Description: Covers any issue having to do with pharmaceuticals, especially in pill form, including legal, medical, technical developments, news and essays on pill advertising and manufacture, lists of pills known to be taken by famous or notorious public figures.

615 GW ISSN 0032-0943
RS164 CODEN: PLMEAA
PLANTA MEDICA; journal of medicinal plant research. (Text in English, French and German) 1935. bi-m. DM.414. (Gesellschaft fuer Arzneipflanzenforschung) Georg Thieme Verlag, Ruedigerstr. 14, 70469 Stuttgart, Germany. TEL 0711-8931-0. FAX 0711-8931298. (Subscr. to: Postfach 104853, 70042 Stuttgart, Germany) Ed. Adolf Nahrstedt. adv.; bk.rev.; charts; illus.; tr.lit.; index. circ. 1,400. (also avail. in microfiche) Indexed: Apic.Abstr., Biol.Abstr., Biotech.Abstr., Chem.Abstr., Crop Physiol.Abstr., Curr.Adv.Ecol.Sci., Curr.Biotech.Abstr., Curr.Cont., Excerp.Med., Field Crop Abstr., Food Sci.& Tech.Abstr., Forest.Abstr., Forest Prod.Abstr., Helminthol.Abstr., Herb.Abstr., Hort.Abstr., I.P.A., Ind.Med., Ind.Vet., Mass Spectr.Bull., Ornam.Hort., Plant Grow.Reg.Abstr., Poult.Abstr., Protozool.Abstr., Rev.Med.& Vet.Mycol., Seed Abstr. **Document type:** academic/scholarly publication.
●Also available online.
—BLDSC (6524.100000); ADONIS; CASDDS; EMDOCS; Faxon; Genuine Article; SWETS; UMI; UnCover. **CCC.**

PODRAVKA; znanstveno-strucni casopis. see *AGRICULTURE*

615.1 PL ISSN 1230-6002
CODEN: PJPAE3
POLISH JOURNAL OF PHARMACOLOGY. (Text and summaries in English) 1949. bi-m. $150 (effective 1995). Polska Akademia Nauk, Instytut Farmakologii, Ul. Smetna 12, 31-343 Krakow, Poland. TEL 48-12-374022. FAX 48-12-374500. (Dist. by: Ars Polona-Ruch, Krakowskie Przedmiescie 7, Warsaw, Poland) Ed. Jerzy Vetulani. bk.rev.; charts; illus.; index. circ. 725. Indexed: Anal.Abstr., Biol.Abstr., Biotech.Abstr., Bull Signal., Chem.Abstr., Curr.Adv.Ecol.Sci., Curr.Chem.React, Curr.Cont., Excerp.Med., Helminthol.Abstr., I.P.A., Ind.Chem., Ind.Med., Int.Abstr.Biol.Sci., Ref.Zh. **Document type:** academic/scholarly publication.
●Also available online.
—BLDSC (6543.671450); CASDDS; Faxon; SWETS; UnCover.
Former titles (until 1992): Polish Journal of Pharmacology and Pharmacy (ISSN 0301-0244); (until 1973): Dissertationes Pharmaceuticae et Pharmacologicae (ISSN 0012-3870)
Description: Covers original experimental studies in the field of pharmacology in its broadest sense.

615 FR ISSN 0181-1169
PORPHYRE; revue professionnelle des preparatrices, preparateurs en pharmacie, collaborateurs de l'officine et candidats aux examens. 1949. m. 350 F. (foreign 387 F.) (effective 1994-95). Groupe Liaisons, 1 av. Edouard Belin, 92856 Reuil-Malmaison Cedex, France. TEL 1-41-29-99-35. FAX 1-41-29-97-05. Ed. Alain Rabelle. adv. contact: Frank Denis. bk.rev. circ. 14,641.

615.1 JA ISSN 0044-0035
PRACTICAL PHARMACY/YAKKYOKU. (Text in Japanese) 1950. m. 6000. Yen($17.) Nanzando Co., Ltd., 4-1-11 Yushima, Bunkyoku, Tokyo 113-91, Japan. Ed. Dr. Tootaroo Simizu. adv. circ. 15,000. Indexed: Chem.Abstr., I.P.A.
●Also available online.

615.1 US ISSN 0898-6738
RA975.5.P5
PRACTICE STANDARDS OF A S H P (YEAR). 1983. a. $25. American Society of Hospital Pharmacists, c/o Jean Rogers, Dir., Mkt. Svcs., 7272 Wisconsin Ave., Bethesda, MD 20814. TEL 301-657-4383. FAX 301-657-1251. circ. 15,000. **Document type:** academic/scholarly publication.
Description: Includes official statements, official guidelines, technical assistance bulletins, technical training program accreditation regulations and standards, residency accreditation regulations and standards.

615 FR ISSN 1153-0642
PRAXIPHARM. 210/yr. Compagnie Generale de Developpement, 11 rue Godefroy-Cavaignac, 75541 Paris Cedex 11, France. TEL 43-79-06-30. FAX 43-79-02-43. TELEX 211 351. Ed. Gilles Braud. circ. 20,000.

615.1 UK ISSN 0032-7611
CODEN: PRJOBY
PRESCRIBERS' JOURNAL. 1961. q. £12.20 (effective 1994). (Departments of Health and Social Security) H.M.S.O., 51 Nine Elms Ln., London SW8 5DR, England. TEL 071-873-0011. FAX 071-873-8463. (Subscr. to: H.M.S.O., P.O. Box 276, London SW8 5DT, England. TEL 071-873-9090. FAX 071-873-8200) Ed. Robyn Young. Indexed: Curr.Adv.Ecol.Sci., Excerp.Med., I.P.A. **Document type:** government publication.
●Also available online.
—BLDSC (6609.705000); EMDOCS; SWETS. **CCC.**

615 US ISSN 1073-7219
▼**PRESCRIBER'S LETTER.** 1994. m. $88. Therapeutic Research Center, 8834 Hildreth Ln., Box 8190, Stockton, CA 95208. TEL 209-931-2923. FAX 209-931-2929. Ed. Sandra Haley Counts; Pub. Dr. Jeff M. Jellin. index. (looseleaf format; back issues avail.) **Document type:** newsletter.
Description: Advises prescribing physicians on current drug therapy, including drug interactions, proper drug use, trends in therapy, new research findings, and new drugs.
Refereed Serial

615 US ISSN 1068-5324
CODEN: FRPBEK
PRESCRIPTION PHARMACEUTICALS AND BIOTECHNOLOGY: THE PINK SHEET. 1939. w. $790 (foreign $865). F-D-C Reports, Inc., 5550 Friendship Blvd., Ste. 1, Chevy Chase, MD 20815. TEL 301-657-9830. FAX 301-656-3094. Ed. Janet Aker. adv.; B&W page $2600; adv. contact: Richard Messmer. charts; illus.; stat.; tr.lit. (looseleaf format; back issues avail.; reprint service avail.) **Document type:** trade publication.
●Also available online. Vendor(s): Ovid Technologies (FDCR), Data-Star (FDCR), Knight-Ridder, Inc. (File no.187), Lexis-Nexis.
—**CCC.**
Supersedes in part (in 1993): Prescription and O T C Pharmaceuticals: The Pink Sheet (ISSN 0734-6514); Which was formerly (until 1982): F D C Reports. Ethical and O T C Pharmaceuticals (ISSN 0272-913X)
Description: Provides in-depth news and analysis about developments affecting prescription medicines.

615 FR ISSN 1167-7422
PRESCRIRE INTERNATIONAL. (Text in English) 1992. bi-m. 600 F. to individuals; institutions 1800 F. Association Mieux Prescrire, BP 459, 75527 Paris Cedex 11, France. TEL 47-00-94-45. FAX 48-07-87-32. Ed. Christophe Kopp; Philippe Schilliger. circ. 350. **Document type:** bulletin.
—BLDSC (6609.709200).
Description: For health professionals concerned with therapeutics and medical evaluation.
Refereed Serial

PREVENTION OF FOOD ADULTERATION CASES. see *LAW*

PREVISIONS GLISSANTES DETAILLEES EN PERSPECTIVES SECTORIELLES (VOL.22): PARACHIMIE. see *BUSINESS AND ECONOMICS — Economic Situation And Conditions*

615.7 US ISSN 1061-0359
PRIMARY CARE MEDICINE DRUG ALERTS. m. $59 (Canada $76; elsewhere $83) (effective 1996). M.J. Powers & Co., 65 Madison Ave., Morristown, NJ 07960-6088. TEL 201-898-1200. FAX 201-898-1201. Ed. John Roche. **Document type:** newsletter.
Incorporates: Women's Medicine Alerts; Formed by the Jan. 1992 merger of: Physicians Drug Alert & Drug Alerts for Internal Medicine.

PROBATUM EST; Informationen fuer den Arzt. see *MEDICAL SCIENCES*

PRODUCT ALERT. see *FOOD AND FOOD INDUSTRIES*

PRODUCT MANAGEMENT TODAY. see *BUSINESS AND ECONOMICS — Marketing And Purchasing*

615 340.5
PRODUCTS LIABILITY: PHARMACEUTICAL DRUG CASES. (Subseries of: Products Liabilities Series) 1988. irreg. (plus a. supplement). $95 (effective 1995). Shepard's - McGraw-Hill, Inc., Box 35300, Colorado Springs, CO 80935-3530. TEL 800-525-2474. Eds. Alexander E. Slaughter, Donald E. Vinson. **Document type:** trade publication.

615.7 SZ ISSN 1011-0267
CODEN: PBCPET
PROGRESS IN BASIC AND CLINICAL PHARMACOLOGY. (Text in English) 1988. irreg. price varies. S. Karger AG, Allschwilerstr. 10, P.O. Box, CH-4009 Basel, Switzerland. TEL 061-3061111. FAX 061-3061234. E-mail: Karger@Karger.ch. Ed.Bd. **Document type:** academic/scholarly publication.
—BLDSC (6865.955500); CASDDS. **CCC.**
Description: Designed to promote a rational approach to drug treatment.
Refereed Serial

615 SZ ISSN 0079-6085
CODEN: PBPHAW
PROGRESS IN BIOCHEMICAL PHARMACOLOGY. (Text in English) 1965. irreg., latest vol.24, 1990. price varies. S. Karger AG, Allschwilerstr. 10, P.O. Box, CH-4009 Basel, Switzerland. TEL 061-3061111. FAX 061-3061234. E-mail: Karger@Karger.ch. (US addr.: S. Karger Publishers, Inc., 26 W. Avon Rd., Box 529, Farmington, CT 06085) Ed. R. Paoletti. (reprint service avail. from ISI, back issues avail.) Indexed: Biol.Abstr., Chem.Abstr., Curr.Cont., Ind.Med. **Document type:** academic/scholarly publication.
—BLDSC (6865.960000); CASDDS. **CCC.**
Description: Volumes in this series consider drugs as the therapeutic agents and curative measures for dealing with various conditions of human health.
Refereed Serial

615 UK ISSN 0278-5846
RM315 CODEN: PNPPD7
PROGRESS IN NEURO-PSYCHOPHARMACOLOGY AND BIOLOGICAL PSYCHIATRY. 1977. 8/yr. $950 to institutions (effective 1996). Elsevier Science Ltd., Pergamon, P.O. Box 800, Kidlington, Oxford OX5 1DX, England. TEL 44-1865-843000. FAX 44-1865-843010. E-mail: nlinfo-f@elsevier.nl; usinfo-f@elsevier.com; forinfo-kyf04035@niftyserve.or.jp; Site addr.: http://www.elsevier.nl/. (Subscr. in U.S. and Canada to: Elsevier Science, 660 White Plains Rd., Tarrytown, NY 10591-5153. TEL 914-524-9200. FAX 914-333-2444) Eds. Corneille Radouco-Thomas, F. Garcin. bk.rev.; index. circ. 1,000. (also avail. in microfilm from UMI; back issues avail.) Indexed: Biol.Abstr., Chem.Abstr., Curr.Adv.Ecol.Sci., Curr.Cont., Dent.Ind., Excerp.Med., Ind.Med., Ind.Sci.Rev., Psychol.Abstr. (1977-). **Document type:** academic/scholarly publication.
—BLDSC (6870.380000); ADONIS; CASDDS; Faxon; Genuine Article; SWETS; UMI; UnCover. **CCC.**
Formerly: Progress in Neuro-Psychopharmacology (ISSN 0364-7722)
Refereed Serial

615 GW
PROGRESS IN PHARMACOLOGICAL RESEARCH. irreg., vol.2, 1993. Universitaetsverlag Ulm GmbH, Benzstr. 12, 89079 Ulm, Germany. TEL 0731-42086. FAX 0731-42087. Ed. B. Guth. **Document type:** monographic series.

615.19 UK ISSN 0268-8654
PROPRIETARY ARTICLES TRADE ASSOCIATION. PUBLICATION. 1986. a. £10. Sterling Publications Ltd., 86-88 Edgware Rd., London W2 2YW, England. Ed. Derek Bacon. circ. 10,000.

PROTEASES AND INHIBITORS. see *BIOLOGY — Biological Chemistry*

615.9 CN
PROVINCIAL DRUG BENEFIT PROGRAMS. s-a. Can.$275. Canadian Pharmaceutical Association, 1785 Alta Vista Dr., Ottawa, ON K1G 3Y6, Canada. TEL 613-523-7877. FAX 613-523-0445. **Document type:** trade publication.

615 US ISSN 0894-4873
PSYCHIATRY DRUG ALERTS. 1986. m. $59 to individuals (Canada $76; elsewhere $83); institutions $89 (effective 1996). M.J. Powers & Co., 65 Madison Ave., Morristown, NJ 07960-6088. TEL 201-898-1200. FAX 201-898-1201. Ed. Dory Greene. **Document type:** newsletter.

PHARMACY AND PHARMACOLOGY

615.1   GW   ISSN 0033-3158
RM315   CODEN: PSCHDL
PSYCHOPHARMACOLOGY. (Text mainly in English) 1959. 24/yr. (in 6 vols., 4 nos./vol.). DM.4200($3052) (effective 1996). Springer-Verlag, Heidelberger Platz 3, 14197 Berlin, Germany. TEL 030-8207-0. FAX 030-8214091. E-mail: orders@springer.de. (Subscr. in N. America to: Springer-Verlag New York, Inc., 44 Hartz Way, Secaucus, NJ 07096-2491. TEL 201-348-4033. FAX 201-348-4505) Eds. D. Casey, J. Gerlach. adv.; charts; illus. (also avail. in microform from UMI; back issues avail.; reprint service avail. from ISI) Indexed: Biol.Abstr., Biotech.Abstr., Chem.Abstr., Curr.Adv.Ecol.Sci., Curr.Cont., Excerp.Med., Ind.Med., Psychol.Abstr. (1965-). **Document type:** academic/scholarly publication.
—BLDSC (6946.546500); ADONIS; CASDDS; EMDOCS; Faxon; Genuine Article; SWETS; UMI; UnCover. **CCC.**
Formerly (until vol.47, 1976): Psychopharmacologia.
Description: Original research into the effects of drugs on behavior.

615   NE   ISSN 0167-9198
RC483   CODEN: PSYCEF
PSYCHOPHARMACOLOGY. 1983. irreg., vol.2, 1985. back issues avail. Elsevier Science B.V., Books Division, P.O. Box 211, 1000 AE Amsterdam, Netherlands. TEL 31-20-4853911. FAX 31-20-4853705. TELEX 18582 ESPA NL. E-mail: nlinfo-f@elsevier.nl; forinfo-kyf04035@niftyserve.or.jp; Site addr.: http://www.elsevier.nl/. (Subscr. in U.S. and Canada to: Elsevier Science Inc., Box 882, Madison Sq. Sta., New York, NY 10159. TEL 212-989-5800) Ed.Bd. (back issues avail.) Indexed: Chem.Abstr. **Document type:** monographic series.
—CASDDS.
Refereed Serial

615.1 150   US   ISSN 0048-5764
     CODEN: PSYBB9
PSYCHOPHARMACOLOGY BULLETIN. 1959. q. (plus special biennial no.) $21 (foreign $26.25) (effective 1995). U.S. Public Health Service, Alcohol, Drug Abuse and Mental Health Administration, 5600 Fishers Ln., Rockville, MD 20857. TEL 301-496-4000. (Subscr. to: Superintendent of Documents, U.S. Government Printing Office, Box 371954, Pittsburgh, PA 15250-7954. TEL 202-512-1800. FAX 202-512-2250) Ed.Bd. cum.index: 1969-1975. circ. 3,500. (also avail. in microform from MIM,UMI; back issues avail.; reprint service avail. from UMI) Indexed: Biol.Abstr., Biotech.Abstr., Chem.Abstr., Curr.Adv.Ecol.Sci., Excerp.Med., I.P.A., Ind.Med., Ind.U.S.Gov.Per., MEDOC, Psychol.Abstr. (1990-), Sci.Cit.Ind. **Document type:** government publication.
●Also available online. Vendor(s): National Library of Medicine.
—BLDSC (6946.549000); CASDDS; EMDOCS; Faxon; Genuine Article; SWETS; UMI; UnCover.
Description: Provides otherwise inaccessible information on ongoing psychgopharmacological research and alerts readers to places and proceedings of national and international meetings.

615   US
PSYCHOPHARMACOLOGY SUPPLEMENTA. 1984. irreg. price varies. Springer-Verlag, 175 Fifth Ave., New York, NY 10010. TEL 212-460-1500. FAX 212-473-6272. (Also: Berlin, Heidelberg, Tokyo and Vienna) (reprint service avail. from ISI) **Document type:** academic/scholarly publication.

615.1   US   ISSN 1068-5308
PSYCHOPHARMACOLOGY UPDATE. 1990. m. $109 to individuals (Canada $119; elsewhere $129); institutions $149 (Canada $159; elsewhere $169) (effective Jul. 1995). Manisses Communication Group, Inc., Box 9758, Providence, RI 02940-8758. TEL 401-831-6020. FAX 401-861-6370. Ed. Frank Tornatore.
Description: Advisory for mental health professionals on pharmaceutical developments.

615   GW   ISSN 0944-6877
▼**PSYCHOPHARMAKOTHERAPIE.** 1994. q. DM.36. Wissenschaftliche Verlagsgesellschaft mbH, Postfach 101061, 70009 Stuttgart, Germany. TEL 0711-2582-0. FAX 0711-2582290. Ed. Susanne Heinzl. **Document type:** academic/scholarly publication.
—BLDSC (6946.550600).

615   UK   ISSN 0954-3333
PULMONARY PHARMACOLOGY (SHEFFIELD). m. £75 (effective 1995). S U B I S, Mansion House, 19 Kingfield Rd., Sheffield S11 9AS, England. TEL 0114-2554433. FAX 0114-2554626. E-mail: admin@sheffac.demon.co.uk. **Document type:** abstracting/indexing.
—CCC.
Description: Current awareness service for researchers.

615.1   US   ISSN 0033-4529
PURDUE PHARMACIST. 1924. 3/yr. (Sep.-Jun.). free. Purdue University, School of Pharmacy, W. Lafayette, IN 47907. TEL 317-494-1363. Ed. Frank Murphy. adv.; cum.index: 1924-1935. circ. 6,000.
Description: Alumni news from the Purdue University School of Pharmacy.

615.1   PK   ISSN 0033-4790
Q I M P QUARTERLY. (Quick Index of Medical Preparations) 1963. q. Rs.100($25) Salma Plaza, Mir Karam Ali Talpur Rd., Saddar, Karachi 0306, Pakistan. Ed. Dr. A.H. Qureshi. adv. circ. 4,000.

615   US   ISSN 0163-2418
     CODEN: QUCRB6
QUALITY CONTROL REPORTS: THE GOLD SHEET. 1967. m. $280. F-D-C Reports, Inc., 5550 Friendship Blvd., Ste. One, Chevy Chase, MD 20815. TEL 301-657-9830. FAX 301-656-3094. Ed. Bill Paulson. (looseleaf format; also avail. in diskette format; back issues avail.; reprint service avail.) **Document type:** trade publication.
—BLDSC (7168.151500). **CCC.**
Description: Focuses on important changes in the FDA's policies for regulating good manufacturing practices for pharmaceutical companies and their suppliers.

615.19   GW   ISSN 0931-8771
RM301.42   CODEN: QSARDI
QUANTITATIVE STRUCTURE-ACTIVITY RELATIONSHIPS. (Text in English) 1982. bi-m. DM.896($674) (effective 1996). V C H Verlagsgesellschaft mbH, Postfach 101161, 69451 Weinheim, Germany. TEL 06201-606-147. FAX 06201-606117. TELEX 465516-VCHWH-D. (U.S. addr.: V C H Publishers Inc., 220 E. 23rd St., New York, NY, 10010-4606. TEL 212-683-8333) Eds. J.K. Seydel, Ferenc Darvas. adv. circ. 930. Indexed: Chem.Abstr., Curr.Adv.Ecol.Sci. **Document type:** academic/scholarly publication.
—BLDSC (7168.343000); CASDDS; Faxon; Genuine Article; SWETS. **CCC.**
Formerly (until 1986): Quantitative Structure-Activity Relationships in Pharmacology, Chemistry and Biology (ISSN 0722-3676)

615   FR   ISSN 0764-5104
QUOTIDIEN DU PHARMACIEN. 1985. 100/yr. 680 F. Societe d'Editions Scientifiques & Culturelles, 140 rue Jules-Guesde, 92593 Levallois Cedex, France. TEL 47307500. FAX 47307583. Ed. Jacques Gravier. circ. 21,000.

615   UK
R & D FOCUS. 1978. w. £3670 includes Drug News and Meetings Diary. IMSWORLD Publications Ltd., 7 Harewood Ave., London NW1 6JB, England. TEL 0171-393-5000. FAX 0171-393-5900. **Document type:** newsletter.
●Also available online. Vendor(s): Data-Star, Knight-Ridder, Inc.
Also available on CD-ROM.
Formerly: Drug License Opportunities.

615.19   US   ISSN 0748-6111
RADIOPHARMACY AND RADIOPHARMACOLOGY YEARBOOK SERIES. 1985. irreg., vol.3, 1988. Gordon & Breach Science Publishers, c/o International Publishers Distributor, 820 Town Center Dr., Langhorne, PA 19047. TEL 215-750-2642. FAX 215-750-6343. (Subscr. to: International Publishers Distributor, P.O. Box 90, Reading Berkshire RG1 8JL, England. TEL 44-173-456-8316) Ed. P.H. Cox. (also avail. in microform) **Document type:** monographic series.
—BLDSC (7240.017000).
Refereed Serial

615.1   SP   ISSN 0034-0618
     CODEN: ARAFAY
REAL ACADEMIA DE FARMACIA. ANALES. (Text in English, French and Spanish; summaries in English and French) 1932. q. 5000 ptas. (Latin America 5500 ptas; elsewhere 6000 ptas.). Real Academia de Farmacia, Calle de Farmacia 11, 28004 Madrid, Spain. TEL 915-31-03-07. FAX 91-531-03-06. Ed. Antonio Portoles. bk.rev.; bibl.; index. circ. 1,500. (back issues avail.) Indexed: Biol.Abstr., Bull.Signal., Chem.Abstr., Curr.Adv.Ecol.Sci., Excerp.Med., I.P.A., Ind.Med., Ind.SST, Ref.Zh.
—BLDSC (0882.000000); CASDDS; EMDOCS. **CCC.**

615   SP   ISSN 0375-9709
     CODEN: RRAFAH
REAL ACADEMIA DE FARMACIA DE BARCELONA. REVISTA. 1957. s-a. 500 ptas. Real Academia de Farmacia de Barcelona, 08071 Barcelona, Spain.
—CASDDS.

615   NE   ISSN 0048-6914
RECEPTARIUS; maanduitgave van de bedrijfsgroup gezondheidszorg. 1907. m. fl.60. Dienstenbond FNV, Houttuinlaan 3, 3447AN Woerden, Netherlands. TEL 03480-75922. (Subscr. to: Brain Communication, Postbus 1191, 1500AD Zaandam, Netherlands. FAX 075-312353) Ed. Guus van Betten. adv.; bk.rev. circ. 4,000. (back issues avail.)

338 615.1   US   ISSN 1072-1142
RED BOOK. (Supplement avail.: Red Book Update) 1897. a. $49.95 (foreign $75). Medical Economics, Five Paragon Dr., Montvale, NJ 07645. TEL 201-358-7200. FAX 201-307-0225. Ed. Harry C. Doherty. circ. 65,000. (also avail. in magnetic tape)
Formerly: Drug Topics Red Book (ISSN 0070-7376)
Description: Reference book for pharmacists; lists pricing and packaging information on more than 100,000 prescription and over-the-counter products, including forms, strength, size, N.D.C., and price. Includes reference section on hard-to-find information.

615.1   US
RED BOOK UPDATE. (Supplement to: Red Book) m. $99 (foreign $129). Medical Economics, Five Paragon Dr., Montvale, NJ 07645. TEL 201-358-7200. FAX 201-307-0225.
Formerly: Drug Topics Red Book Update (ISSN 0731-8596)
Description: Covers monthly price changes of prescription and over-the-counter drugs, pricing and packaging information on top volumekl products and newly introduced drugs.

615   UK   ISSN 0960-7889
REGULATORY AFFAIRS JOURNAL. 1990. m. £720 (outside Europe £780). Regulatory Affairs Journal Ltd., P.O. Box 59, Bagshot, Surrey GU19 5YZ, England. TEL 01276-476432. FAX 01276-475603. Ed. Robin Harman. adv. **Document type:** trade publication.
—BLDSC (7349.620000); SWETS.
Description: Provides comprehensive coverage of licensing of pharmaceuticals for governments and the pharmaceutical industry worldwide.

615   UK   ISSN 0969-4129
REGULATORY AFFAIRS JOURNAL. DEVICES. 1993. q. £395 (outside Europe £430). Regulatory Affairs Journal Ltd., P.O. Box 59, Bagshot, Surrey GU19 5YZ, England. TEL 01276-476432. FAX 01276-475603. Ed. Robin Harman. **Document type:** trade publication.
—BLDSC (7349.620500).
Description: Provides comprehensive coverage of regulations affecting medical devices for governments and the medical device industry worldwide.

REGULATORY TOXICOLOGY AND PHARMACOLOGY. see ENVIRONMENTAL STUDIES — Toxicology And Environmental Safety

RENIN, ANGIOTENSIN & KININS. see BIOLOGY — Physiology

PHARMACY AND PHARMACOLOGY

615.19 157.6 616.8   US   ISSN 1080-8388
RC563   CODEN: RCAAE3
RESEARCH COMMUNICATIONS IN ALCOHOL & SUBSTANCES OF ABUSE. 1980. q. $80 (foreign $90). P J D Publications Ltd., Box 966, Westbury, NY 11590. TEL 516-626-0550. FAX 516-626-5546. Ed. P.D. Wong. adv.; bk.rev.; abstr.; charts; illus.; index. (reprint service avail.) Indexed: Biol.Abstr., Chem.Abstr., Curr.Adv.Ecol.Sci., Curr.Cont., Excerp.Med. Document type: academic/scholarly publication.
—BLDSC (7736.630000); CASDDS; Genuine Article; UnCover. **CCC.**
 Formerly (until 1994): Research Communications in Substances of Abuse (ISSN 0193-0818)
 Description: Focuses on clinical and human aspects of all abused substances, including alcohol, drugs, and synthetic and natural substances.
 Refereed Serial

RESEARCH COMMUNICATIONS IN MOLECULAR PATHOLOGY AND PHARMACOLOGY. see *MEDICAL SCIENCES*

615.19   GW   ISSN 0179-8618
RESEARCH: THE BAYER SCIENTIFIC MAGAZINE. (Text in English) 1986. a. Bayer AG, Public Relations Department, Building W4, 51368 Leverkusen, Germany. TEL 0214-3081753. Ed. Dieter Porten. circ. 500,000. (back issues avail.) Document type: academic/scholarly publication.

615 616.2   SZ
▼**RESPIRATORY PHARMACOLOGY AND PHARMACOTHERAPY.** 1994. irreg. 148 SFr. Birkhaeuser Verlag, P.O. Box 133, CH-4010 Basel, Switzerland. TEL 061-2717400. FAX 061-2717666. (Dist. in N. America by: Springer-Verlag, Mercedes Distribution Center, 160 Imlay St., Brooklyn, NY 11231, USA) Eds. D. Raeburn, M. Giembycz. Document type: monographic series.

RESTORATIVE NEUROLOGY AND NEUROSCIENCE. see *MEDICAL SCIENCES — Psychiatry And Neurology*

615.1   GR   ISSN 1011-6583
CODEN: EKIEE
REVIEW OF CLINICAL PHARMACOLOGY AND PHARMACOKINETICS (INTERNATIONAL EDITION). Key Title: Epitheorese Klinikes Farmakologias kai Farmakokinetikes (International Edition). Greek edition (ISSN 1011-6575) (Text in English) 1987. 3/yr. Pharmakon Press, 20 Daskalaki St., 115 26 Athens, Greece. TEL 30-1-7778-101. Indexed: Excerp.Med. Document type: academic/scholarly publication.
—BLDSC (7788.985000); CASDDS.

REVIEWS OF ENVIRONMENTAL CONTAMINATION AND TOXICOLOGY. see *ENVIRONMENTAL STUDIES — Toxicology And Environmental Safety*

REVIEWS OF PHYSIOLOGY, BIOCHEMISTRY AND PHARMACOLOGY. see *BIOLOGY — Physiology*

615.1   BL   ISSN 0370-372X
CODEN: RBFAAH
REVISTA BRASILEIRA DE FARMACIA. (Text in Portuguese; summaries in English, Portuguese) 1920. q. $50. Associacao Brasileira de Farmaceuticos, Rua do Andradas 96-10 Andar, 20051-000 Rio de Janeiro, Brazil. FAX 55-21-2630791. Ed. Nuno Alvares Pereira. adv.; charts; illus.; stat. Document type: academic/scholarly publication.
—CASDDS.
 Former titles (until 1942): Associacao Brasileira de Farmaceuticos. Revista (ISSN 0370-3126); (until 1937): Associacao Brasileira de Farmaceuticos. Boletim (ISSN 0366-158X)
 Description: Original papers in pharmacology and chemistry.

615.1   CK   ISSN 0034-7418
RS402   CODEN: RCQFAQ
REVISTA COLOMBIANA DE CIENCIAS QUIMICO FARMACEUTICAS. (Text in Spanish; summaries in English) 1969. 2/yr. free. Universidad Nacional de Colombia, Departamento de Farmacia, Apdo. Aereo 14 490, Bogota, Colombia. Ed. Lucia A. de Garcia. illus. circ. 500. Indexed: Biol.Abstr., Chem.Abstr., Excerp.Med., I.P.A.
●Also available online.
—BLDSC (7851.401000); CASDDS.

615.1   CU   ISSN 0034-7515
CODEN: RCUFAC
REVISTA CUBANA DE FARMACIA. (Text in Spanish; summaries in English, Spanish) 1967. s-a. $28 in S. America; N. America $30; elsewhere $32. Ministerio de Salud Publica, Centro Nacional de Informacion de Ciencias Medicas, Calle E No. 452, e-19 y 21, Plaza de la Revolucion, Apdo. 6520, Havana, Cuba. TEL 809-32-5338. (Dist. by: Ediciones Cubana, Obispo No. 527, Apdo. 605, Havana, Cuba) Ed. Ana Dolores del Campo. abstr.; bibl.; charts; illus.; index. circ. 1,300. Indexed: Chem.Abstr., Excerp.Med., Hort.Abstr., I.P.A., Ind.Med., Seed Abstr., Weed Abstr.
●Also available online.
—BLDSC (7852.107000); CASDDS; EMDOCS.
 Description: Covers the fields of pharmacy, pharmacology and the drug industry.

615.1   BL   ISSN 0101-3793
CODEN: RCIFDN
REVISTA DE CIENCIAS FARMACEUTICAS. 1978. a. $30 or exchange basis. Universidade Estadual Paulista, Av. Vicente Ferreira 1278, Caixa Postal 603, 17515-901 Marilia SP, Brazil. TEL 0144-331844. FAX 0144-22-2504. TELEX 111-9016 UJME BR. charts; stat.; circ. controlled. Indexed: Anal.Abstr., Biol.Abstr., Chem.Abstr., Excerp.Med., I.P.A. Document type: academic/scholarly publication.
—BLDSC (7851.032500); CASDDS; EMDOCS.
 Formerly: Faculdade de Ciencias Farmaceuticas de Araraquara. Revista.
 Description: Original articles, notes and technical reviews on clinical cases in all areas of pharmacology.

615.9   SP   ISSN 0212-7113
CODEN: REVTE9
REVISTA DE TOXICOLOGIA. (Text in Spanish; summaries in English) 1983. 3/yr. 9000 ptas. to non-members (effective 1996). (Asociacion Espanola de Toxicologia) Springer-Verlag Iberica S.A., C. Provenca, 388, 1a, 08025 Barcelona, Spain. TEL 34-3-4570227. FAX 34-3-4571502. E-mail: barcelona@spint.compuserve.com. Ed. Dr. Eduardo de la Pena de Torres. adv.; B&W page 35000 ptas., color page 60000 ptas.; adv. contact: J. Arellano. bk.rev. circ. 800. Indexed: Excerp.Med.
—BLDSC (7873.150000); CASDDS.

615.1   AG   ISSN 0034-9496
CODEN: RFABAN
REVISTA FARMACEUTICA. 1858. 12/yr. (in 6 double issues). $20. Academia Argentina de Farmacia y Bioquimica, Junin 956, Buenos Aires 1113, Argentina. Ed. Alfredo Jose Bandoni. adv.; bk.rev.; bibl.; charts; illus. circ. 6,000. Indexed: Biol.Abstr., Biotech.Abstr., Chem.Abstr., I.P.A.
●Also available online.
—CASDDS.

615   PO   ISSN 0484-811X
CODEN: RPTFAU
REVISTA PORTUGUESA DE FARMACIA. (Text in Portuguese; summaries in English) 1951. q. Esc.6000 (foreign $60) (effective 1996). Ordem de Farmaceuticos, Rua da Sociedade Farmaceutica, No. 18, 1150 Lisbon, Portugal. TEL 351-1-3151104. FAX 351-1-3524480. Ed. Joao Silveira. adv.; bk.rev.; bibl.; charts; stat.; cum.index. circ. 7,000. Indexed: Apic.Abstr., Biol.Abstr., Biotech.Abstr., Chem.Abstr., I.P.A., Sugar Ind.Abstr. Document type: academic/scholarly publication.
●Also available online.
—BLDSC (7870.000000); CASDDS.
 Description: Presents original papers in pharmacy and pharmacology research.

615.1   FR   ISSN 0035-2349
REVUE D'HISTOIRE DE LA PHARMACIE. 1913. q. 550 F. (effective 1995). Societe d'Histoire de la Pharmacie, 4 Av. de l'Observatoire, 75270 Paris Cedex 06, France. Eds. Louis Cotinat, Pierre Julien. adv.; bk.rev.; abstr.; illus.; index, cum.index: 1913-1963, 1964-1983. circ. 1,400. Indexed: Bull.Signal., I.P.A. Document type: academic/scholarly publication.
—BLDSC (7919.900000).

REVUE DE MEDECINES ET PHARMACOPEES AFRICAINES. see *MEDICAL SCIENCES*

615   IT   ISSN 1120-379X
RICERCA & PRATICA. 1985. bi-m. L.247500($150) (effective 1996). (Istituto di Ricerche Farmacologiche Mario Negri) Pensiero Scientifico Editore s.r.l., Via Bradano 3-C, 00199 Rome, Italy. TEL 06-86207158. FAX 06-86207160. Ed. Daniele Coen. bibl.; index. circ. 3,000. Document type: academic/scholarly publication.
—BLDSC (7963.915000).

LA RIFORMA MEDICA; rivista quadrimestrale di farmacologia e terapia. see *MEDICAL SCIENCES*

615.9   IT   ISSN 0390-6019
CODEN: RTSCDD
RIVISTA DI TOSSICOLOGIA SPERIMENTALE E CLINICA. 1971. bi-m. L.66000 (foreign L.132000). (Centro Italiano Contro le Intossicazioni) Societa Editrice Universo, Via G.B. Morgagni 1, 00161 Rome, Italy. Ed. Enrico Malizia. Indexed: Biol.Abstr., Excerp.Med.
—CASDDS.
 Formerly (until 1975): Rivista di Clinica Tossicologica (ISSN 0390-6027)

615   GW
ROTE LISTE. 1935. a. DM.93.50. (Bundesverband der Pharmazeutischen Industrie e.V.) Editio Cantor, Baendelstockweg 20, 88326 Aulendorf, Germany. TEL 07525-2060. FAX 07525-20680. circ. 280,000.

ROYALTY RATE REPORT FOR THE PHARMACEUTICAL & BIOTECHNOLOGY INDUSTRIES. see *PATENTS, TRADEMARKS AND COPYRIGHTS*

615.19   US
RX UPDATE. 1990. m. free. Valley Forge Press, 1288 Valley Forge Rd., Box 1135, Valley Forge, PA 19482. TEL 610-935-3302; 800-9VF-PRES. FAX 610-935-3072. E-mail: vpfedit@aol.com. Ed. Beverly Hamill. bk.rev.; charts; illus.; circ. 60,000 (controlled).
 Formerly (until 1995): Pharmacy Update (ISSN 1055-9744)
 Description: Contains items of general interest to consultant, community, hospital, and retail pharmacists, including drug recalls, legislation, and news.

615   IT   ISSN 0081-0703
S.I.S.F. DOCUMENTI. 1965. irreg. price varies. Societa Italiana di Scienze Farmaceutiche, Via Giorgio Jan 18, 20129 Milan, Italy. TEL 39-2-29513303. FAX 39-2-29520179. Ed. Piero Sensi. Document type: monographic series.

615   JA
SAIKIN NO SHINYAKU/NEW DRUGS IN JAPAN. 1950. a. 4600 Yen (effective 1994). Yakuji Nippo, Ltd., 1 Kanda Izumicho, Chiyoda-ku, Tokyo 101, Japan. FAX 03-5821-8757. adv. circ. 20,000. (back issues avail.) Document type: government publication.
 Description: Description of old and new drugs marketed in Japan.

615.19   JA   ISSN 0080-6064
CODEN: SKKNAJ
SANKYO KENKYUSHO NEMPO/SANKYO RESEARCH LABORATORIES. ANNUAL REPORT. Key Title: Sankyo Kenkyujo Nenpo. (Text in English, Japanese; summaries in English) 1946. a. free. Sankyo Co., Ltd., Research Institute - Sankyo K.K. Sogo Kenkyujo, 1-2-58 Hiro-machi, Shinagawa-ku, Tokyo 140, Japan. TEL 03-492-3131. FAX 03-495-6734. Ed. Yoshihiko Baba. abstr.; circ. controlled. (reprint service avail. from UMI) Indexed: Biol.Abstr., Chem.Abstr.
—BLDSC (1430.050000); CASDDS.

615   US
SCHOOLS IN THE UNITED STATES AND CANADA OFFERING GRADUATE EDUCATION IN PHARMACOLOGY. 1963. biennial. free. American Society for Pharmacology and Experimental Therapeutics, 9650 Rockville Pike, Bethesda, MD 20814. Ed. Kay A. Croker. Document type: directory.

615   SZ   ISSN 0258-6983
SCHWEIZER HAUSAPOTHEKE.* 1930. m. Perpress Medien AG, Industriestr. 5, CH-3178 Bosingen, Switzerland. Ed. G. Haeuggi. circ. 274,134. Document type: trade publication.

PHARMACY AND PHARMACOLOGY

615.1   SZ   ISSN 0036-7508
CODEN: SAZTA8
SCHWEIZERISCHE APOTHEKER-ZEITUNG/JOURNAL SUISSE DE PHARMACIE/GIORNALE SVIZZERO DIE FARMACIA. 1862. s-m. 170 SFr. (foreign 200 SFr.). Schweizerischer Apothekerverein, Postfach, CH-3097 Bern-Liebefeld, Switzerland. TEL 031-9715858. FAX 031-9721569. Ed. Markus Kamber. adv.: B&W page 962 SFr., color page 2546 SFr.; trim 210 x 297. circ. 6,300. **Indexed:** Biol.Abstr., Biotech.Abstr., Chem.Abstr., Excerp.Med., I.P.A. **Document type:** trade publication.
—CASDDS; EMDOCS.

615.1   SZ   ISSN 0036-7567
SCHWEIZERISCHE DROGISTENZEITUNG. 1900. w. 85 SFr. Schweizerischer Drogistenverband, Postfach 924, CH-2501 Biel, Switzerland.

615.1   AU   ISSN 0036-8709
CODEN: SCPHA4
SCIENTIA PHARMACEUTICA. 1932. q. S.303. (Oesterreichische Apothekerkammer) Oesterreichische Apotheker-Verlagsgesellschaft mbH, Spitalgasse 31, A-1094 Vienna, Austria. TEL 01-4023588. FAX 01-4085355. Eds. Dr. Wolfgang Kubelka, Dr. Wilhelm Fleischhacker. adv.; bk.rev.; charts; index. circ. 800. **Indexed:** Anal.Abstr., Biol.Abstr., Biotech.Abstr., Chem.Abstr., Excerp.Med., I.P.A. **Document type:** academic/scholarly publication.
●Also available online.
—BLDSC (8173.000000); CASDDS; EMDOCS; SWETS.
Description: Covers all scientific aspects of pharmacy and related disciplines.

615   UK   ISSN 0143-7690
CODEN: SCRIDK
SCRIP - WORLD PHARMACEUTICAL NEWS. 1972. s-w. £440 (Europe £505; U.S. $980). P J B Publications Ltd., 18-20 Hill Rise, Richmond, Surrey TW10 6UA, England. TEL 0181-948-3262. FAX 0181-948-6866. TELEX 8951042. (In U.S. subscr. to: c/o Mary Dalia, Pharmabooks Ltd., 1775 Broadway, Ste. 511, New York, NY 10019. TEL 212-262-8230) Ed. Moira Dower. adv. contact: Robin Baker. bk.rev.; q. cum.index. circ. 9,000. **Indexed:** ABC, P.N.I. **Document type:** newsletter.
●Also available online. Vendor(s): Ovid Technologies (PHIN,PHIC,PHID), Data-Star (PHIND), Knight-Ridder, Inc.
—BLDSC (8211.859000); CASDDS; SWETS. **CCC.**
Description: Worldwide coverage of company news, product development and legislation for anyone working in or for the pharmaceutical industry.

615   UK
SCRIP'S ANTIBACTERIAL REPORT. irreg. £315($665) P J B Publications Ltd., 18-20 Hill Rise, Richmond, Surrey TW10 6UA, England. TEL 0181-948-3262. FAX 0181-332-8992. (Dist. in US by: PharmaBooks Ltd., 1775 Broadway, Ste. 511, New York, NY 10019. TEL 212-262-8230. FAX 212-262-8234) **Document type:** bulletin.

615.1   US   ISSN 0271-4078
RS403   CODEN: SMCCAS
SELECTED METHODS OF CLINICAL CHEMISTRY. 1953-1972; resumed 1977. irreg., vol.11, 1986. price varies. American Association for Clinical Chemistry, Inc., 2101 L St. N.W., Ste. 202, Washington, DC 20037-1526. TEL 800-892-1400. FAX 202-887-5093. index. **Indexed:** Biol.Abstr.
—**CCC.**
Supersedes (in 1977): Standard Methods of Clinical Chemistry (ISSN 0065-7115)

615   FI   ISSN 0049-0164
SEMINA. (Text in Finnish; summaries in Swedish) 1917. s-m. FIM 200. Suomen Farmasialiitto - Finnish Pharmacists' Association, Rautatielaisenkatu 6, 00520 Helsinki 52, Finland. FAX 0-1496354. Ed. Kirsti Bult. adv.; bk.rev. circ. 7,500. **Indexed:** Chem.Abstr.
—BLDSC (8239.000000).

SEMINARS IN HEMATOLOGY. see MEDICAL SCIENCES — Hematology

SEMINARS IN ONCOLOGY. see MEDICAL SCIENCES — Oncology

SEMINARS IN ONCOLOGY NURSING. see MEDICAL SCIENCES — Nurses And Nursing

615   FR
SEMPEX. 1959. a. (updates 34/yr.). 1310 F. (effective 1995). Societe d'Editions Medico-Pharmaceutiques (SEMP), 26 rue le Brun, 75013 Paris, France. TEL 1-43-37-83-50. FAX 43-31-94-11. circ. 4,900. (looseleaf format; also avail. in microfiche)
Formerly: Sempex Pharmaceutique (ISSN 0488-2644)
Description: Contains references to human and veterinary drugs; including French equivalents to foreign patent medicines and noncommercial products in France.

SHAANXI ZHONGYI XUEYUAN XUEBAO/SHAANXI INSTITUTE OF TRADITIONAL CHINESE MEDICINE. JOURNAL. see MEDICAL SCIENCES

SHANDONG YIYAO/SHANDONG MEDICAL JOURNAL. see MEDICAL SCIENCES

SHANGHAI ZHONGYIYAO ZAZHI/SHANGHAI JOURNAL OF TRADITIONAL CHINESE MEDICINE/REVUE DE MEDECINE TRADITIONNELLE CHINOISE/REVISTA DE MEDICINA TRADICIONAL CHINA DE SHANGHAI. see ALTERNATIVE MEDICINE

615   CC   ISSN 0253-9926
R97.7.C5   CODEN: SIYCDB
SHANXI YIYAO ZAZHI/SHANXI JOURNAL OF MEDICINE. (Text in Chinese) bi-m. Shanxi Sheng Weisheng-ting - Shanxi Provincial Bureau of Public Health, 23 Donghua Men, Taiyuan, Shanxi 030013, People's Republic of China. TEL 382791. Ed. Yang Fuhao.
—CASDDS.

615   CC   ISSN 1006-2858
CODEN: SYXUE3
SHENYANG YAOKE DAXUE XUEBAO/SHENYANG PHARMACEUTICAL UNIVERSITY. JOURNAL. (Text in Chinese) 1957. q. $30. Shenyang Yaoke Daxue, Xuebao Bianjibu, 103 Wenhua Rd., Shenyang, Liaoning 110015, People's Republic of China. TEL 3843711. Ed. Gu Xueqiu. adv.: page $300. circ. 2,200. **Indexed:** Sugar Ind.Abstr. **Document type:** academic/scholarly publication.
—BLDSC (4874.935300); CASDDS.
Formerly (until 1995): Shengyang Yaoxueyuan Xuebao - Shengyang College of Pharmacy. Journal (ISSN 1000-1727)
Description: Contains research reports on pharmaceutics, analysis, pharmaceutical chemistry, pharmacology, traditional Chinese medicine and synthesis of drugs.
Refereed Serial

615.7   NE   ISSN 0378-6080
RM302.5   CODEN: SEDAD8
SIDE EFFECTS OF DRUGS ANNUAL; a yearly critical survey of the world's literature on adverse reactions to drugs. (Supplement to: Meyler's Side Effects of Drugs (ISSN 0376-7396)) 1972. irreg., approx. a., vol.16, 1993. fl.325 (effective 1993). Elsevier Science B.V., Books Division, P.O. Box 211, 1000 AE Amsterdam, Netherlands. TEL 31-20-4853911. FAX 31-20-4853705. TELEX 18582 ESPA NL. E-mail: nlinfo-f@elsevier.nl; usinfo-f@elsevier.com; forinfo-kyf04035@niftyserve.or.jp; Site addr.: http://www.elsevier.nl/. (Subscr. in U.S. and Canada to: Elsevier Science Inc., Box 882, Madison Sq. Sta., New York, NY 10159. TEL 212-989-5800) Eds. M.N.G. Dukes, J.K. Aronson. **Indexed:** Biol.Abstr. **Document type:** academic/scholarly publication, monographic series.
●Also available online. Vendor(s): Data-Star (SEDB), Knight-Ridder, Inc. (File no.70/SEDBASE), Ovid Technologies.
Also available on CD-ROM. Producer(s): SilverPlatter Information, Inc. (SEDBASE).
—CASDDS. **CCC.**
Refereed Serial

615   SW   ISSN 0346-8453
SJUKHUSFARMACI. 1973. 4/yr. Apoteksbolaget, S-105 14 Stockholm, Sweden. Ed. Karin Bjoernsson.

615.7   SZ   ISSN 1011-0283
CODEN: SKPHEU
SKIN PHARMACOLOGY. (Text in English) 1988. bi-m. 266.40 SFr.($205.20) to individuals; institutions 444 SFr.($342) (effective 1996). (Skin Pharmacology Society) S. Karger AG, Allschwilerstr. 10, P.O. Box, CH-4009 Basel, Switzerland. TEL 061-3061111. FAX 061-30161234. E-mail: Karger@Karger.ch. Ed. F.H. Merk. bk.rev.; charts; illus.; index. (also avail. in microform from UMI) **Indexed:** Excerp.Med., Med.& Surg.Dermat. **Document type:** academic/scholarly publication.
—BLDSC (8295.935000); CASDDS; Faxon; Genuine Article; SWETS; UMI. **CCC.**
Incorporates (1985-1990): Bioengineering and the Skin (ISSN 0266-3082)
Refereed Serial

615.1   CK   ISSN 0037-8461
SOCIEDAD COLOMBIANA DE QUIMICOS FARMACEUTICOS. BOLETIN. 1961. m. free. Sociedad Colombiana de Quimicos Farmaceuticos, Seccional del Valle del Cauca, 415 Edificio Banco de La Repulica, Cali, Colombia. TEL 808336. adv.; charts. circ. 5,000.
Formerly: Colegio Colombiano de Quimicos Farmaceuticos. Boletin.

615.9 658   SP   ISSN 1130-8230
SOCIEDAD ESPANOLA DE FARMACIA HOSPITALARIA. BOLETIN INFORMATIVO. Cover title: Boletin Informativo - S E F H. q. 2650 ptas.($40) (effective 1995). Sociedad Espanola de Farmacia Hospitalaria, C. Echegaray, 13-3o, 28014 Madrid, Spain. TEL 34-1-4202798. Ed. Esteban Valverde Molina. circ. 1,700.
Formerly (until 1989): Asociacion Espanola de Farmaceuticos de Hospitales. Boletin Informativo (ISSN 1130-8222)

615.1   FR   ISSN 0037-9093
CODEN: BSPBAD
SOCIETE DE PHARMACIE DE BORDEAUX. BULLETIN. 1860. q. 150 F. Societe de Pharmacie de Bordeaux, c/o Faculte de Pharmacie, 3 place de la Victoire, 33076 Bordeaux Cedex, France. Ed. Jean Canellas. adv.; bk.rev.; abstr.; charts; index. circ. 900. **Indexed:** Biol.Abstr., Biotech.Abstr., Bull.Signal., Chem.Abstr., I.P.A.
—BLDSC (2747.500000); CASDDS.

615   FR
SOCIETE DE PHARMACIE DE LILLE. BULLETIN. 1946. q. 160 F. (Societe de Pharmacie) Universite de Lille, 3 rue du Professeur Laquese, Lille 1250-45, France. Ed.Bd. Various. **Indexed:** Biol.Abstr., Biotech.Abstr., Chem.Abstr., Excerp.Med., I.P.A., Nutr.Abstr.

615.1   FR   ISSN 0037-9107
CODEN: BTSLAV
SOCIETE DE PHARMACIE DE LYON. BULLETIN DES TRAVAUX.* 1957. q. 90 F. Publications Periodiques Specialisees, 17 Place Bellecour, 69002 Lyon, France. bibl.; charts; index. **Indexed:** Chem.Abstr., I.P.A.
—CASDDS.

615.1   FR   ISSN 0037-9131
CODEN: BPMSAS
SOCIETE DE PHARMACIE DE STRASBOURG. BULLETIN. 1955. s-a. 100 F. Societe de Pharmacie de Strasbourg, Faculte de Pharmacie, B.P. 24, 67401 Illkirch Cedex, France. Ed. Dr. Boymond. adv.; bk.rev.; charts; illus.; cum.index: 1955-1964, 1965-1973, 1974-1978. circ. 600. **Indexed:** Biol.Abstr., Chem.Abstr.
—CASDDS.

SOMATOSENSORY AND MOTOR RESEARCH. see BIOLOGY — Physiology

615.1   SA   ISSN 0038-2558
SOUTH AFRICAN PHARMACEUTICAL JOURNAL/SUID-AFRIKAANSE TYDSKRIF VIR APTEEKWESE. (Supplement avail.: Medifile (ISSN 1021-6987)) (Text and title in Afrikaans, English) 1934. m. R.86.50 (effective 1993). Pharmaceutical Society of South Africa - Aptekersvereniging van Suid-Afrika, P.O. Box 31360, Braamfontein, Johannesburg 2017, South Africa. TEL 27-11-339-1752. FAX 27-11-403-1309. Ed. Hayley Cameron. adv.; bk.rev.; charts; illus. circ. 5,931. **Indexed:** Biotech.Abstr., I.P.A., Ind.S.A.Per. **Document type:** trade publication.
●Also available online.

PHARMACY AND PHARMACOLOGY

615　　　　　SA　　ISSN 0038-2639
SOUTH AFRICAN RETAIL CHEMIST. (Text in English, occasionally in Afrikaans) 1951. m. R.80. George Warman Publications (Pty.) Ltd., P.O. Box 3847, Cape Town 8000, South Africa. TEL 27-21-245320. FAX 27-21-261332. Ed. Loren Kolevsohn. adv.; bk.rev.; illus. circ. 3,900. **Indexed:** I.P.A. **Document type:** trade publication.
Description: Information of interest to all retail pharmacies in South Africa.

615.1　　　　US　　ISSN 0192-5792
SOUTHERN PHARMACY JOURNAL. 1908. m. $18. 333 W. Hampden Ave., Ste. 1050, Englewood, CO 80010-2340. Ed. Jennifer Lamb. adv. contact: John Maginnes. bk.rev.; illus. circ. 20,000. (also avail. in microform from UMI; reprint service avail. from UMI) **Document type:** trade publication.
Formerly (until 1979): Southeastern Drug - Southern Pharmaceutical Journal (ISSN 0095-2354); Which was formed by the merger of: Southeastern Drug Journal (ISSN 0038-3651); Southern Pharmaceutical Journal (ISSN 0038-4410)
Description: Presents news and features of pharmacy activities in the southern United States.

615　　　　　CE
SRI LANKA PHARMACEUTICAL ASSOCIATION. QUARTERLY NEWSLETTER. q. Sri Lanka Pharmaceutical Association, c/o Dept. of Pharmacy, Faculty of Medicine, University of Sri Lanka, Colombo 8, Sri Lanka. **Document type:** newsletter.

615 614　　　　US
▼**STAT! (DAYTON)**; serving the greater Dayton medical and health care community. 1994. m. $25. Winkler Company, 435 Patterson Rd., Dayton, OH 45419. TEL 513-294-3662. FAX 513-294-8375. (Alt. addr.: Box 572, Dayton, OH 45409) Ed. Lance A. Winkler. adv.: page $412.75; trim 10 x 16 1/2. abstr.; circ. 7,200 (controlled). (tabloid format; back issues avail.) **Document type:** newspaper.
Description: Serves health care and medical professionals.

STEREOCHEMICAL TECHNOLOGY NEWS. see BIOLOGY — Biological Chemistry

STREET PHARMACOLOGIST. see DRUG ABUSE AND ALCOHOLISM

615　　　　　GW　　ISSN 0721-8672
STUDENT UND PRAKTIKANT; Forum fuer die Pharmazeutische Ausbildung. (Supplement to: Deutsche Apotheker Zeitung) 1982. q. Deutscher Apotheker Verlag, Postfach 101061, 70009 Stuttgart, Germany. TEL 0711-2582-0. FAX 0711-2582291. Ed. Reinhild Berger. adv.; bk.rev. **Document type:** trade publication.
—BLDSC (8480.100000).

SUBSTANCE ABUSE REPORT; twice-monthly newsletter covering all aspects of drug abuse: its prevention, detection and treatment. see DRUG ABUSE AND ALCOHOLISM

615　　　　　US
SUPER MARKET PHARMACY. 1992. m. Fairchild Fashion & Merchandising Group (Subsidiary of: Capital Cities - A B C, Inc.), 7 W. 34th St., New York, NY 10001. TEL 212-630-4199. FAX 212-630-4201. Ed. Tim Simmons. adv.: B&W or color page $4500; trim 11 x 14 3/4. circ. 11,000.

615.9 340　　US　　ISSN 0098-714X
SURVEY OF PHARMACY LAW. 1950. a. $20. National Association of Boards of Pharmacy, 700 Busse Hwy., Park Ridge, IL 60068-2402. TEL 708-698-6227. Ed. Carmen Catizone. stat.; charts. circ. 20,000.

615.1　　　　SW　　ISSN 0039-6524
　　　　　　　　　　CODEN: SFTIAE
SVENSK FARMACEVTISK TIDSKRIFT. 1897. 11/yr. SEK 370 in Sweden; Nordic countries SEK 500; elsewhere SEK 550; newsstand price: SEK 50. (Apotekarsocieteten) Swedish Pharmaceutical Press, P.O. Box 1136, S-111 81 Stockholm, Sweden. TEL 46-8-723-50-00. FAX 46-8-14-95-80. (Affiliate: Swedish Academy of Pharmaceutical Sciences) Ed. Thony Bjoerk. adv.: B&W page SEK 8500, color page SEK 16000; trim 180 x 270; adv. contact: Mats Lindkvist. bk.rev.; illus.; stat. circ. 7,600. pp./issue: 64. (also avail. in microfilm from UMI) **Indexed:** Biol.Abstr., Biotech.Abstr., Chem.Abstr., Excerp.Med., I.P.A., Ind.Med, PROMT. ●Also available online.
—CASDDS.

610　　　　　SZ　　ISSN 0082-0504
SWITZERLAND. BUNDESAMT FUER SOZIALVERSICHERUNG. SPEZIALITAETENLISTE - LISTE DES SPECIALITES - ELENCO DELLE SPECIALITA. 1955. s-a. 66 SFr. Bundesamt fuer Sozialversicherung, Effingerstr. 33, CH-3003 Bern, Switzerland. TEL 031-3229011. FAX 031-3227880. (Dist. by: Eidgenoessische Drucksachen- und Materialzentrale, CH-3000 Bern, Switzerland. TEL 031-3223908. FAX 031-9920023) circ. 12,000. (also avail. in microfilm) **Document type:** government publication.
Description: List of drugs being reimbursed by Swiss sickness funds.

615　　　　　US
T P A SPEEDLETTER. (Former name of issuing body: Texas Pharmaceutical Association) m. $15. Texas Pharmacy Association, 1624 E. Anderson Ln., Austin, TX 78752-1806. TEL 512-836-8350. FAX 512-836-0308. Ed. Paul F. Davis. bk.rev.; circ. 3,700 (paid). (back issues avail.) **Document type:** newsletter.
Description: Covers items of interest to pharmacists in managed care, institutional care, and home care, as well as consultants and manufacturers' representatives and all other specialty areas of pharmacy practice.

TAKEDA RESEARCH LABORATORIES. JOURNAL. see BIOLOGY

615 613　　　　DK　　ISSN 0107-1181
TAL OG DATA, MEDICIN OG SUNDHEDSVAESEN/FACTS, MEDICINE AND HEALTH CARE, DENMARK. (Text in Danish and English) 1976. a. free. Foreningen af Danske Medicinfabrikker, Stroedamvej 50 A, DK-2100 Copenhagen Oe, Denmark. TEL 45-39-27-00-88. FAX 45-32-27-00-50. illus. circ. 6,000.
Formerly: Tal og Data om Medicin.

615.9　　　　　FR
TAREX. 1969. a. (updates 4/yr.). 456.61 F. (effective 1995). Societe d'Editions Medico-Pharmaceutiques (SEMP), 26 rue Lebrun, 75013 Paris, France. TEL 1-43-37-83-50. FAX 43-31-94-11. adv.; bk.rev. (looseleaf format; also avail. in microfiche)

TARGET ORGAN TOXICOLOGY SERIES. see ENVIRONMENTAL STUDIES — Toxicology And Environmental Safety

TECHNOMARK REGISTER. CONTRACT RESEARCH ORGANISATIONS. see MEDICAL SCIENCES

615　　　　　IT
TEMA FARMACIA. m. (except July & Aug.). Utet Periodici Scientifici s.r.l., Via P. Giuria 20, 10125 Turin, Italy. TEL 39-2-29003555. FAX 39-2-6599049. Ed. Angelo Cambie. adv.: B&W page L.3740000, color page L.5600000; trim 185 x 246; adv. contact: Corrado Trevisan. circ. 16,311.

615.19　　　US　　ISSN 1047-0166
TENNESSEE PHARMACIST. 1965. m. membership. Tennessee Pharmacists Association, 226 Capitol Blvd., Ste. 810, Nashville, TN 37219. TEL 615-255-3528. Ed. Baeteena Black. adv. contact: Marsha Williams. bk.rev. circ. 2,500. **Document type:** trade publication.

615　　　　　US　　ISSN 0362-7926
　　　　　　　　　　CODEN: TXPDAE
TEXAS PHARMACY. (Former name of issuing body: Texas Pharmacy Association) 1879. m. $30 to non-members (foreign $60). Texas Pharmacy Association, Box 14709, Austin, TX 78761-4709. TEL 512-836-8350. FAX 512-836-0308. Ed. Paul F. Davis. adv. contact: Lori S. Alcala. bk.rev.; circ. 3,700 (paid). (back issues avail.) **Document type:** trade publication.
Description: Contains news of interest to pharmacists in all practices and covers new products and litigation. Provides drub profiles and offers practice and management tips.

THAI PHARMACEUTICAL DIRECTORY. see BUSINESS AND ECONOMICS — Trade And Industrial Directories

615　　　　　FR
THERA. 1984. a. 220 F. Societe d'Editions Medico-Pharmaceutiques (SEMP), 26 rue le Brun, 75013 Paris, France. TEL 1-43-37-83-50. FAX 1-43-31-94-11. circ. 24,400.
Supersedes (1944-1979): Formulaire Thera (ISSN 0071-7622)

615　　　　　US　　ISSN 0163-4356
RM301.5　　　　　　　CODEN: TDMODV
THERAPEUTIC DRUG MONITORING. 1979. bi-m. $203 to individuals(foreign $253); institutions $355 (foreign $438) (effective 1996); newsstand price: $75. Lippincott - Raven Publishers, 227 Washington Sq., Philadelphia, PA 19106. TEL 215-238-4200. Eds. Steven J. Soldin, Folke Sjoqvist. adv. contact: Phyllis Noyes. bk.rev.; illus.; index. circ. 2,500. (back issues avail.; reprint service avail. from UMI) **Indexed:** Anal.Abstr., ASCA, Biol.Abstr., Biotech.Abstr., Chem.Abstr., Curr.Adv.Ecol.Sci., Curr.Cont., Dent.Ind., Excerp.Med., Ind.Med., Kidney. **Document type:** academic/scholarly publication.
—BLDSC (8814.643000); CASDDS; Faxon; Genuine Article; SWETS; UMI; UnCover. **CCC.**
Refereed Serial

615　　　　　UK
THERAPEUTIC DRUGS. SUPPLEMENT. irreg., no.2, 1994. Churchill Livingstone Journals (Subsidiary of: Pearson Professional), Robert Stevenson House, 1-3 Baxter's Pl., Leith Walk, Edinburgh EH1 3AF, Scotland. TEL 0131-556-2424.
FAX 0131-459-1177. (U.S. subscr. to: Churchill Livingstone, 650 Ave. of the Americas, New York, NY 10011. TEL 212-206-5000) Ed. Sir Colin Dollery. **Document type:** academic/scholarly publication.

615.6　　　　SZ　　ISSN 0040-5930
THERAPEUTISCHE UMSCHAU; Monatsschrift fuer praktische Medizin. (Text in German; summaries in English and French) 1943. m. 105 SFr. (foreign 150 SFr.). Verlag Hans Huber, Laengassstr. 76, CH-3000 Bern 9, Switzerland. TEL 031-3004500. FAX 031-3004590. Ed. Prof. Dr. P. Weidmann. adv.; bk.rev.; abstr.; bibl.; charts; illus.; index. circ. 5,000. (also avail. in microform from PMC) **Indexed:** ASCA, Biol.Abstr., C.I.S. Abstr., Chem.Abstr., Curr.Cont., Dent.Ind., Excerp.Med., Helminthol.Abstr., Ind.Med. **Document type:** academic/scholarly publication.
—BLDSC (8814.696000); EMDOCS; Faxon; Genuine Article; SWETS. **CCC.**

610.9　　　　DK　　ISSN 0082-4003
THERIACA; samlinger til farmaciens og medicinens historie. (Text in Danish; summaries in English) 1956. irreg., no.29, 1994. price varies. Dansk Farmacihistorisk Selskab - Danish Society of the History of Pharmacy, Institut for Samfundsfarmaci, Universitetsparken 2, DK-2100 Copenhagen, Denmark. Ed. Poul R. Kruse.
—BLDSC (8814.770000).

615.1　　　　　US
THIRD PARTY RX. 1989. m. $50. National Association of Retail Druggists, 205 Daingerfield Rd., Alexandria, VA 22314. TEL 703-683-8200.
FAX 703-683-3619. Ed. Robert McCarthy. circ. 3,000.

PHARMACY AND PHARMACOLOGY

615 CC ISSN 0253-9896
R97.7.C5 CODEN: TIYADG
TIANJIN YIYAO/TIANJIN PHARMACY. (Text in Chinese) m. Tianjin Yixue Keji Qingbao Yanjiusuo - Tianjin Medical Science and Technology Information Institute, 131 Chengdu Dao, Tianjin 300050, People's Republic of China. TEL 311705. Ed. Zhang Yingfu.
—BLDSC (8820.510000); CASDDS.

615 SW ISSN 0348-0461
TIKAINFORMATION. 1968. 8/yr. Tika, P.O. Box 2, S-221 00 Lund, Sweden.

615 JA ISSN 0285-368X
CODEN: TTQUDB
TOKYO TANABE QUARTERLY. (Text in Japanese) 1967. q. free. Tokyo Tanabe Co., Ltd. - Tokyo Tanabe K.K., 2-7-3 Nihonbashi Hon-cho, Chuo-ku, Tokyo 103, Japan. adv.; bk.rev. circ. 20,000. **Indexed:** Chem.Abstr.
—CASDDS.

615.7 NE ISSN 0167-7101
RM1 CODEN: TMPHDK
TOPICS IN MOLECULAR PHARMACOLOGY. (Text in English) 1981. irreg., vol.4, 1987. price varies. Elsevier Science B.V., Books Division, P.O. Box 211, 1000 AE Amsterdam, Netherlands. TEL 31-20-4853911. FAX 31-20-4853705. TELEX 18582 ESPA NL.
E-mail: nlinfo-f@elsevier.nl; usinfo-f@elsevier.com; forinfo-kyf04035@niftyserve.or.jp; Site addr.: http://www.elsevier.nl/. (Subscr. in U.S. and Canada to: Elsevier Science Inc, Box 882, Madison Sq. Sta., New York, NY 10159. TEL 212-989-5800) (back issues avail.) **Document type:** monographic series.
—CASDDS. **CCC.**
Refereed Serial

TOXICOLOGICAL AND ENVIRONMENTAL CHEMISTRY. see ENVIRONMENTAL STUDIES — Toxicology And Environmental Safety

TOXICOLOGY; an international journal concerned with the effects of chemicals on living systems. see ENVIRONMENTAL STUDIES — Toxicology And Environmental Safety

TOXICOLOGY AND APPLIED PHARMACOLOGY; for those working in the fields of toxicology, pharmacology, biochemistry, nutrition, veterinary medicine. see ENVIRONMENTAL STUDIES — Toxicology And Environmental Safety

TOXICOLOGY AND INDUSTRIAL HEALTH; an international journal. see ENVIRONMENTAL STUDIES — Toxicology And Environmental Safety

TOXICOLOGY IN VITRO. see ENVIRONMENTAL STUDIES — Toxicology And Environmental Safety

TOXICOLOGY LETTERS; an international journal for the rapid publication of short reports on biochemical mechanisms of mammalian toxicity. see ENVIRONMENTAL STUDIES — Toxicology And Environmental Safety

TOXICOLOGY METHODS. see ENVIRONMENTAL STUDIES — Toxicology And Environmental Safety

615.9 UK ISSN 0041-0101
QP631 CODEN: TOXIA6
TOXICON; an international journal specialising in toxins. (Text in English, French, German and Spanish) 1962. m. £695($1106) (effective 1996). (International Society on Toxinology) Elsevier Science Ltd., Pergamon, P.O. Box 800, Kidlington, Oxford OX5 1DX, England. TEL 44-1865-843000. FAX 44-1865-843010.
E-mail: nlinfo-f@elsevier.nl; usinfo-f@elsevier.com; forinfo-kyf04035@niftyserve.or.jp; Site addr.: http://www.elsevier.nl/. (Subscr. in U.S. and Canada to: Elsevier Science, 660 White Plains Rd., Tarrytown, NY 10591-5153. TEL 914-524-9200. FAX 914-333-2444) Ed. Alan Harvey. adv.; bk.rev.; software rev.; abstr.; charts; illus.; index. circ. 1,000. (also avail. in microfilm from UMI) **Indexed:** Abstr.Hyg., Apic.Abstr., ASCA, Bio-Contr.News & Info., Biol.Abstr., Chem.Abstr., Crop Physiol.Abstr., Curr.Adv.Biochem., Curr.Adv.Ecol.Sci., Curr.Cont., Dairy Sci.Abstr., Deep Sea Res.& Oceanogr.Abstr., Diar.Dis.Res., Excerp.Med., Helminthol.Abstr., Herb.Abstr., Hort.Abstr., Ind.Med., Ind.Vet., Int.Aerosp.Abstr., Ocean.Abstr., Pig News & Info., Pollut.Abstr., Poult.Abstr., Rev.Appl.Entomol., Rev.Med.& Vet.Mycol., Small Anim.Abstr., Sport Fish.Abstr., Trop.Dis.Bull., Vet.Bull., Wild.Rev., Zoo.Rec. **Document type:** academic/scholarly publication.
—BLDSC (8873.050000); ADONIS; CASDDS; EMDOCS; Faxon; Genuine Article; SWETS; UMI; UnCover. **CCC.**
Description: Publishes original research on the chemical, pharmacological, zootoxicological and immunological properties of naturally occurring poisons, including clinical and therapeutic observations.
Refereed Serial

615.1 UK ISSN 0143-4241
TRANSMITTERS, RECEPTORS & SYNAPSES. 1980. s-m. (diskette m.). £130 (diskette £115; both £175) (effective 1995). S U B I S, Mansion House, 19 Kingfield Rd., Sheffield S11 9AS, England. TEL 0114-2554433. FAX 0114-2554626. E-mail: Admin@sheffac.demon.co.uk. (also avail. in diskette format) **Document type:** abstracting/indexing.
—**CCC.**
Description: Current awareness service for researchers. Covers synapses, neuromuscular junction, transmitters and neuromodulators.

TRANSPLANTATION PROCEEDINGS. see MEDICAL SCIENCES — Surgery

615 FR ISSN 0246-8476
TREBUCHET. 1980. 10/yr. Editions de la Balance, 36 rue Pasteur, 85000 La Roche sur Yon, France. TEL 52-13-71-40. FAX 51-05-16-03. Ed. J-P. Macouin. circ. 10,000.

615 UK ISSN 0165-6147
CODEN: TPHSDY
TRENDS IN PHARMACOLOGICAL SCIENCES. Library compendium: Trends in Pharmacological Sciences (Reference Edition) (ISSN 0167-7691) 1979. m. £386 to institutions; $614 to institutions (effective 1996). Elsevier Science Ltd., P.O. Box 800, Kidlington, Oxford OX5 1DX, England. TEL 44-1865-843000. FAX 44-1865-843010.
E-mail: nlinfo-f@elsevier.nl; usinfo-f@elsevier.com; forinfo-kyf04035@niftyserve.or.jp; Site addr.: http://www.elsevier.nl/. (Subscr. in U.S. and Canada to: Elsevier Science, 660 White Plains NY 10591-5153. TEL 914-524-9200. FAX 914-333-2444) (Co-sponsors: International Union of Pharmacology; International Union of Toxicology) Ed. Debbie Girdlestone. adv.; bk.rev.; bibl.; index. circ. 4,000. (also avail. in microform from UMI; back issues avail.; reprint service avail. from SWZ) **Indexed:** Biol.Abstr., Chem.Abstr., Curr.Adv.Biochem., Curr.Adv.Cancer Res., Curr.Adv.Ecol.Sci., Curr.Cont., Excerp.Med., I.P.A., Ind.Sci.Rev., Sci.Cit.Ind., Telegen. **Document type:** academic/scholarly publication.
—BLDSC (9049.675000); ADONIS; CASDDS; Faxon; Genuine Article; SWETS; UnCover. **CCC.**
Description: Covers the sciences of pharmacology and toxicology.
Refereed Serial

615 UK ISSN 0167-7691
TRENDS IN PHARMACOLOGICAL SCIENCES (REFERENCE EDITION). 1980. a. £345($514) includes m. Trends in Pharmacological Sciences (effective 1995). Elsevier Science Ltd., P.O. Box 800, Kidlington, Oxford OX5 1DX, England. TEL 44-1865-843000. FAX 44-1865-843010.
E-mail: nlinfo-f@elsevier.nl; usinfo-f@elsevier.com; forinfo-kyf04035@niftyserve.or.jp; Site addr.: http://www.elsevier.nl/. (Subscr. in U.S. and Canada to: Elsevier Science, 660 White Plains Rd., Tarrytown, NY 10591-5153. TEL 914-524-9200. FAX 914-333-2444) (Co-sponsors: International Union of Pharmacology; International Union of Toxicology) Ed. Debbie Girdlestone. (back issues avail.) **Document type:** academic/scholarly publication.
—**CCC.**
Description: Compendium of archival material from Trends in Pharmacological Sciences.
Refereed Serial

615 BL ISSN 0049-4631
TRIBUNA FARMACEUTICA. (Text in Portuguese; summaries in English, Portuguese) 1932. s-a. free or exchange basis. Universidade Federal do Parana, Faculdade de Farmacia, Rua Coronel Dulcidio 638, Caixa Postal 888, 80000 Curitiba, Parana, Brazil. FAX 041-2642243. TELEX 415100. Ed. Eduardo Augusto Moreira. adv.; bk.rev.; abstr.; bibl.; illus. circ. 500. **Indexed:** Biol.Abstr., Chem.Abstr., I.P.A.
●Also available online.

615 IT
TUTTOSALUTE. (Editions in German and Italian) 4/yr. Utet Periodici Scientifici s.r.l., Via P. Giuria 20, 10125 Turin, Italy. TEL 39-2-29003555. FAX 39-2-6599049. Ed. Romolo Saccomani. adv.: color page L.3000000; trim 180 x 245; adv. contact: Corrado Trevisan. circ. 42,117 (11,492 German ed.; 30,625 Italian ed.).

615 US ISSN 0090-6816
RS55 CODEN: UUDNDB
U S A N AND THE U S P DICTIONARY OF DRUG NAMES. (United States Adopted Names) 1963. a. $105. United States Pharmacopeial Convention, Inc., 12601 Twinbrook Pkwy., Rockville, MD 20852. TEL 301-881-0666.
—CASDDS.
Description: Lists more than 8,100 nonproprietary drug entries from the U.S., the U.K., and Japan.

615 US ISSN 0730-1324
U S P - D I UPDATE. 1980. m. United States Pharmacopoeia, 12601 Twinbrook Pkwy., Rockville, MD 20852. TEL 800-227-8772. FAX 301-816-8148.
Incorporates (1980-1990): U S P - D I Review (ISSN 1045-8301).

615 US ISSN 0740-4174
RM300
U S P - D I, VOLUME 1. DRUG INFORMATION FOR THE HEALTH CARE PROFESSIONAL. (Supplement avail.: U S P - D I Update (ISSN 0730-1324)) 1980. a. (plus m. Update). $119 (Canada $140; elsewhere $160). United States Pharmacopeia, 12601 Twinbrook Pkwy., Rockville, MD 20852. TEL 800-227-8772. FAX 301-816-8148. **Document type:** trade publication.
—BLDSC (9100.172100).
Supersedes in part (in 1983): United States Pharmacopeia Dispensing Information (ISSN 0276-5373)
Description: Contains infomation on both labeled and unlabeled U.S. and Canadian drug products.

615 US ISSN 0740-6916
RM300
U S P - D I, VOLUME 2. ADVICE FOR THE PATIENT; drug information in lay language. (Supplement avail.: U S P - D I Update (ISSN 0730-1324)) 1980. a. (plus m. Update). $59 (Canada $87; elsewhere $107) (includes Update). United States Pharmacopeia, 12601 Twinbrook Pkwy., Rockville, MD 20852. TEL 800-227-8772. FAX 301-816-8148. **Document type:** trade publication.
—BLDSC (9100.172100).
Supersedes in part (in 1983): United States Pharmacopeia Dispensing Information (ISSN 0276-5373)
Description: Contains information to educate and counsel patients on drug use, available dosage forms, side effects, and contraindications.

PHARMACY AND PHARMACOLOGY

615 340 US ISSN 1045-8298
RS131.2
U S P - D I, VOLUME 3. APPROVED DRUG PRODUCTS AND LEGAL REQUIREMENTS. (Supplement avail.: U S P - D I Update (ISSN 0730-1324)) 1989. a. $104 (Canada $130; elsewhere $150). United States Pharmacopeia, 12601 Twinbrook Pkwy., Rockville, MD 20852. TEL 800-227-8772.
FAX 301-816-8148. **Document type:** trade publication.
Description: Contains important therapeutic equivalence information, as well as selected federal and state requirements that affect the prescribing and dispensing of prescription drugs and controlled substances.

615.105 US ISSN 0148-4818
RS1
U S PHARMACIST. 1976. m. $30. Jobson Publishing, Inc., 100 Ave. of the Americas, New York, NY 10013-1678. TEL 212-274-7000; 800-852-9692. FAX 212-431-0500. (Subscr. to: US Pharmacist, Box 7632, Riverton, NJ 08077-7632. TEL 609-764-2675) Eds. Angele D'Angelo, Joseph Cupolo. adv. contact: Frank Bennicasa. index. circ. 103,000. (back issues avail.) **Indexed:** I.P.A. **Document type:** academic/scholarly publication.
●Also available online.
—BLDSC (9124.762000); Faxon; SWETS; UnCover. *Refereed Serial*

615 DK ISSN 0108-948X
RS67.D4
UNDERSOEGELSE OVER APOTEKERNES DRIFTSFORHOLD; regnskabsresultater fra apoteker. vol.9, 1944. a. DKK 75. Sundhedsstyrelsen, Amaliegade 13, 1012 Copenhagen K, Denmark. (Co-sponsor: Apotekerfonden)

615.1 US ISSN 0077-4235
U.S. FOOD AND DRUG ADMINISTRATION. NATIONAL DRUG CODE DIRECTORY. 1969. irreg. $76 includes supplements. Office of Public Affairs, 5600 Fisher's Ln., Rockville, MD 20857. TEL 202-783-3054. (Orders to: Superintendent of Documents, U.S. Government Printing Office, Box 371954, Pittsburgh, PA 15250-7954. TEL 202-783-3238. FAX 202-783-2250) **Document type:** government publication, directory.

615.11 US ISSN 0195-7996
RS141.2 CODEN: USPFDX
UNITED STATES PHARMACOPEIA - NATIONAL FORMULARY. 1820. every 5 yrs. $450 includes annual supplement. United States Pharmacopeial Convention, Inc., 12601 Twinbrook Pkwy., Rockville, MD 20852.
—BLDSC (9100.172000); CASDDS.
Formed by the 1980 merger of: National Formulary (ISSN 0084-6414); United States Pharmacopeia; Which was formerly titled: Pharmacopeia of the United States of America (ISSN 0079-1407)
Description: Compiles all the legally enforceable standards of strength, purity, packaging, labeling, and storage for drugs and excipients.

615.1 VE ISSN 0041-8307
CODEN: RFFVA6
UNIVERSIDAD CENTRAL DE VENEZUELA. FACULTAD DE FARMACIA. REVISTA. 1959. q. exchange. Universidad Central de Venezuela, Facultad de Farmacia, Apto. 40109, Nueva Granada, Ciudad Universitaria, las Chaguaramos, Caracas, Venezuela. Ed. Ivonne Gomez. bk.rev.; charts; illus.; index. circ. 1,000.
Indexed: Biol.Abstr., I.P.A.
—CASDDS.

615 SP ISSN 0067-4176
UNIVERSIDAD DE BARCELONA. FACULTAD DE FARMACIA. MEMORIA.* biennial. price varies. Universidad de Barcelona, Facultad de Farmacia, Av. Jose Antonio 585, Barcelona 7, Spain.

615 SP ISSN 0214-1442
UNIVERSIDAD DE SEVILLA. SERIE: FARMACIA. 1983. irreg., latest no.2. Universidad de Sevilla, Servicio de Publicaciones, Valparaiso 5, 41013 Seville, Spain. TEL 954-231958. FAX 954-232245.

615.19 574.192 PE ISSN 0377-4708
RS1
UNIVERSIDAD NACIONAL MAYOR DE SAN MARCOS. FACULTAD DE FARMACIA Y BIOQUIMICA. REVISTA. 1939. s-a. Universidad Nacional Mayor de San Marcos, Facultad de Farmacia y Bioquimica, Apdo. 1760, Lima, Peru. charts; illus.; stat. circ. 500. **Indexed:** Biol.Abstr. **Document type:** academic/scholarly publication.

615.1 PO ISSN 0378-9608
CODEN: BFFCDE
UNIVERSIDADE DE COIMBRA. FACULDADE DE FARMACIA. BOLETIM. (Text in Portuguese; summaries and keywords in English and French) 1976. s-a. Esc.2500 (foreign Esc.11000) or exchange basis (effective 1992). Universidade de Coimbra, Faculdade de Farmacia, Rua do Norte, 3000 Coimbra, Portugal. TEL 039-23681. FAX 039-27126. Ed.Bd. adv.; bibl.; charts; illus.; cum.index: 1976-1980. circ. 550. (back issues avail.) **Indexed:** Biol.Abstr., Bull.Signal., Chem.Abstr., I.P.A., Ref.Zh. **Document type:** academic/scholarly publication.
—CASDDS.
Supersedes: Universidade Coimbra. Faculdade de Farmacia. Edicao Didactica e Edicao Cientifica.
Description: Presents original papers in the pharmaceutical sciences.

615.19 BL ISSN 0370-4726
RS1 CODEN: RFBUBI
UNIVERSIDADE DE SAO PAULO. REVISTA DE FARMACIA E BIOQUIMICA. 1939. a. exchange basis. Universidade de Sao Paulo, Faculdade de Ciencias Farmaceuticas, C.P. 66083, 05389-970 Sao Paulo, Brazil. FAX 55-11-2128194. Ed. Andrejus Korolkovas. bk.rev. circ. 1,000. (back issues avail.) **Indexed:** Anal.Abstr., Chem.Abstr., Helminthol.Abstr., I.P.A., Nutr.Abstr. **Document type:** academic/scholarly publication.
●Also available online.
—BLDSC (7854.590000); CASDDS; UMI.
Formerly: Universidade de Sao Paulo. Faculdade de Farmacia e Bioquimica. Revista; Supersedes in part (in 1962): Universidade de Sao Paulo. Faculdade de Farmacia. Anais (ISSN 0365-2181)

615.329 547 BL ISSN 0080-0228
UNIVERSIDADE FEDERAL DE PERNAMBUCO. INSTITUTO DE ANTIBIOTICOS. REVISTA. (Text in Portuguese; summaries in English and Portuguese) 1958. irreg., vol.23, 1986. exchange basis. Universidade Federal de Pernambuco, Departamento de Antibioticos, Recife, Pernambuco, Brazil. TELEX 811267. bibl.; charts; illus. circ. 800. **Indexed:** Chem.Abstr. **Document type:** academic/scholarly publication.

615.1 BL ISSN 0041-8846
UNIVERSIDADE FEDERAL DE SANTA MARIA. FACULDADE DE FARMACIA E BIOQUIMICA. REVISTA.* s-a. Universidade Federal de Santa Maria, Faculdade de Farmacie e Bioquimica, Caixa Postal 124, Santa Maria R.G.S., Brazil. charts; illus.

615.1 XO ISSN 0041-9087
UNIVERSITAS COMENIANA. ACTA FACULTATIS PHARMACEUTICAE. (Text in English, German and Russian) 1958. irreg. exchange basis. Univerzita Komenskeho, Farmaceuticka Fakulta, Ustredna Kniznica, Odbojarov 10, 832 32 Bratislava, Slovakia. FAX 042-7060388. Ed. Milan Chalabala. charts; illus.; index. circ. 500. **Indexed:** Biol.Abstr., Chem.Abstr., I.P.A.
Formerly: Acta Facultatis Pharmaceuticae Bohemoslovenicae.

615 IR
UNIVERSITY OF TEHERAN. SCHOOL OF PHARMACY. JOURNAL/DANESHGAH-E TEHRAN. DANESHKADE-YE DARUSAZI. MAJALLEH. (Text in Persian; summaries in English) 1972. s-a. Rs.120. University of Teheran, Faculty of Pharmacy, Shahreza Ave., Teheran, Iran. Ed. Iraj Lalezari. adv.

615.1 US ISSN 0042-0441
RS1
UNLISTED DRUGS. 1949. m. $480. Pharmaco-Medical Documentation, Inc., Box 429, Chatham, NJ 07928. TEL 201-822-9200. FAX 201-765-0722. Ed. Rajka R. Anzlowar. adv.; bk.rev.; index, cum.index every 2 yrs. **Indexed:** Biol.Abstr., I.P.A.

615 US ISSN 8755-7142
RS1
UNLISTED DRUGS INDEX - GUIDE. irreg. (every 2-3/yrs.); latest 1992. $590. Pharmaco-Medical Documentation, Inc., Box 429, Chatham, NJ 07928. TEL 201-822-9200. FAX 201-765-0722.

616.6 615 US ISSN 1074-2921
▼**VACCINE WEEKLY.** 1994. w. $995. Charles W. Henderson, Ed. & Pub., Box 5528, Atlanta, GA 31107-0528. TEL 404-377-8895.
FAX 404-378-4511. TELEX 78-2661. (Subscr. to: Box 830409, Birmingham, AL 35283-0409. TEL 800-633-4931. FAX 205-995-1588) (also avail. in microform from UMI) **Document type:** newsletter. —UMI. **CCC.**
Description: Brings together relevant news and breakthroughs from interrelated topics ranging from therapeutic vaccines for AIDS, cancer, and other diseases, efficacy and safety trials, FDA regulations and approvals, prevention.

615.1 NO ISSN 0042-3351
VENEFICUS; farmasistudentenes tidsskrift. 1933. 8/yr. NOK 80($6) Studentforeningen Veneficus, Universitetets Farmasoeytiske Institutt, 0371 Oslo 3, Norway. Eds. Eli Neegard, Anegedde Dane. adv.; bk.rev.; charts; illus.; index. circ. 600. **Indexed:** Chem.Abstr., I.P.A.

VETERINARY AND HUMAN TOXICOLOGY. see *ENVIRONMENTAL STUDIES — Toxicology And Environmental Safety*

615.1 US ISSN 0042-6717
VIRGINIA PHARMACIST. 1917. m. $50. Virginia Pharmaceutical Association, 3119 West Clay St., Richmond, VA 23230. TEL 804-355-7941.
FAX 804-355-7991. Ed. John W. Hasty. adv.; bk.rev.; charts; illus.; mkt.; pat.; tr.lit. circ. 2,000. **Document type:** trade publication.

615.9 610.73 US ISSN 0739-9588
VITAL SIGNS PHARMACY SERVICES NEWSLETTER. 1978. m. $75. Rx-Data-Pac Service, 8907 Terwilliger's Tr., Cincinnati, OH 45249.
TEL 513-489-0943. Ed. Dr. I.H. Goodman. (looseleaf format; back issues avail.) **Document type:** newsletter.
Description: Hospital pharmacy-nursing newsletter with photocopy rights for facility. Helps meet JCAHO requirements for hospital staff continuing education.

615.328 JA ISSN 0913-1175
VITAMIN INFORMATION CENTER. NEWSLETTER. (Text in Japanese) 1981. bi-m. Bitamin Koho Senta, 2-3, Marunouchi 3-chome, Chiyoda-ku, Tokyo 100, Japan. **Document type:** newsletter.

615.328 GW ISSN 0930-4827
VITAMINE, MINERALSTOFFE, SPURENELEMENTE; in Medizin, Ernaehrung und Umwelt. 1986. q. DM.98. Hippokrates Verlag GmbH, Postfach 300504, 70445 Stuttgart, Germany. TEL 0711-8931-0. FAX 0711-8931453. Eds. K. Schmidt, W. Bayer. **Document type:** academic/scholarly publication.

615.328 JA ISSN 0006-386X
QP771 CODEN: BTMNA7
VITAMINS/BITAMIN. (Text in Japanese; summaries in English) 1948. m. $35. Japan Vitamin Society - Nippon Bitamin Gakkai, Nippon Itaria Kyoto Kaikan, 3rd Fl., 4 Ushinomiya-cho, Yoshida, Sakyo-ku, Kyoto 606, Japan. TEL 075-751-0314. Ed. Shyoichi Shimizu. **Indexed:** Biol.Abstr., Chem.Abstr., Dairy Sci.Abstr., Excerp.Med., Food Sci.& Tech.Abstr., INIS Atomind., INIS Atomind., Jap.Per.Ind., Nutr.Abstr. —BLDSC (9243.500000); CASDDS.

615.328 658.8 UK
VITAMINS AND DIETARY SUPPLEMENTS: THE INTERNATIONAL MARKET. (Subseries of: Market Direction reports) a. £1595($3190) (effective 1996). Euromonitor, 60-61 Britton St., London EC1M 5NA, England. TEL 0171-251-8024.
FAX 0171-608-3149. (Addr. in N. America: Euromonitor International, 122 S. Michigan Ave., Ste. 1200, Chicago, IL 60603. TEL 312-922-1115. FAX 312-922-1157) (looseleaf format) **Document type:** trade publication.
●Also available online. Vendor(s): Data-Star, Knight-Ridder, Inc.
Description: Analyzes the vitamin and dietary supplement market for France, Germany, Italy, Spain, the U.K., the U.S., and Japan.

PHARMACY AND PHARMACOLOGY

615.328 612.405   US   ISSN 0083-6729
QP801.V5   CODEN: VIHOAQ
VITAMINS AND HORMONES: ADVANCES IN RESEARCH AND APPLICATIONS. 1943. irreg., vol.47, 1993. Academic Press, Inc. (Subsidiary of: Harcourt Brace Jovanovich), 525 B St., Ste. 1900, San Diego, CA 92101-4495, TEL 619-231-0926. FAX 619-699-6715. (Subscr. to: Order Dept., 6277 Sea Harbor Dr., 4th Fl., Orlando, FL 32887. TEL 800-321-5068) Eds. G.D. Auerbach, Donald B. McCormick. index, cum.index: vols.1-5 (1943-1947), vols.6-10 (1948-1952), vols.11-15 (1953-1957). (reprint service avail. from ISI) **Indexed:** Anim.Breed.Abstr., Biol.Abstr., Biotech.Abstr., Chem.Abstr., Curr.Adv.Ecol.Sci., Dairy Sci.Abstr., Excerp.Med., Ind.Med., Nutr.Abstr., Vet.Bull. **Document type:** academic/scholarly publication.
—BLDSC (9244.000000); CASDDS; UnCover. **CCC.**
Refereed Serial

615.9   US   ISSN 0507-2379
VOICE OF THE PHARMACIST. 1946. q. $40. American College of Apothecaries, 205 Daingerfield Rd., Alexandria, VA 22314. TEL 703-684-8603. FAX 703-683-3619. Ed. D.C. Huffman, Jr. circ. 1,000. (looseleaf format) **Indexed:** I.P.A. **Document type:** newsletter.

VOJENSKE ZDRAVOTNICKE LISTY. see *MEDICAL SCIENCES*

VOJNOSANITETSKI PREGLED/MILITARY MEDICAL AND PHARMACEUTICAL REVIEW; casopis lekara i farmaceuta jugoslovenske narodne armije. see *MEDICAL SCIENCES*

W H O DRUG INFORMATION. (World Health Organization) see *PUBLIC HEALTH AND SAFETY*

615   JA   ISSN 0509-5832
WAKSMAN FOUNDATION OF JAPAN. REPORT. (Text in English) 1962. a. exchange basis. Waksman Foundation of Japan - Nihon Wakkusuman Zaidan, c/o Keio Daigaku Igakubu, 30-8 Daikyo-machi, Shinjuku-ku, Tokyo 106, Japan.

616   US   ISSN 0194-1291
KF3885.A15
WASHINGTON DRUG LETTER (WASHINGTON, 1979). 1969. w. $697. Washington Business Information, Inc., c/o Karen Harrington, 1117 N. 19th St., Arlington, VA 22209. TEL 703-247-3434. FAX 703-247-3421. Ed. John Briley. bk.rev. (looseleaf format) **Indexed:** P.N.I., Telegen. **Document type:** newsletter.
●Also available online. Vendor(s): Ovid Technologies (DIOG), Data-Star.
—**CCC.**
Former titles: Washington Drug and Device Letter (ISSN 0162-2994); Washington Drug Letter.

615   US   ISSN 0745-7413
THE WASHINGTON PHARMACIST. 1959. bi-m. $24 in U.S. (foreign $59). Washington State Pharmacists Association, 1501 Taylor Ave., S.W., Renton, WA 98055-3139. TEL 206-228-7171. FAX 206-277-3897. Ed. Rod Shafer. adv. contact: Sheri L. Ray. bk.rev. circ. 2,000. **Document type:** trade publication.
Formerly: Washington - Alaska Pharmacist.
Description: Focuses on current issues and challenges of the profession. Appeals to a broad spectrum of pharmacy professionals with articles about new products.

615.1   US   ISSN 0043-1893
                    CODEN: WPHRAR
WEEKLY PHARMACY REPORTS: THE GREEN SHEET. 1951. w. $65 (foreign $75). F-D-C Reports, Inc., 5550 Friendship Blvd., Ste. One, Chevy Chase, MD 20815. TEL 301-657-9830. FAX 301-656-3094. Ed. Michael Koppenheffer. (looseleaf format; back issues avail.; reprint service avail.) **Document type:** trade publication.
●Also available online. Vendor(s): Lexis-Nexis.
—**CCC.**
Description: News and information on the pharmacy profession and the pharmaceutical distribution system. Coverage of professional policy, pharmacy association activities, reimbursement issues, new drug introductions and pharmaceutical pricing and deals.

WEHRMEDIZIN UND WEHRPHARMAZIE. see *MEDICAL SCIENCES*

615.19   GW   ISSN 0171-4449
WER IST WAS IN DER DEUTSCHEN PHARMAZEUTISCHEN - INDUSTRIE. 1978. biennial. DM.225. B. Behr's Verlag GmbH, Averhoffstr. 10, 22085 Hamburg, Germany. **Document type:** directory.

615.19   NR   ISSN 0303-691X
                    CODEN: WAJPAS
WEST AFRICAN JOURNAL OF PHARMACOLOGY AND DRUG RESEARCH. 1974. biennial. $10.60. (West African Society for Pharmacology) Literamed Publications Nigeria, Ltd., Oregun Village, P.M.B. 21068, Ikeja, Nigeria. TEL 234-1-962512. FAX 234-1-961037. Pub. O.M. Lawal-Solarin. **Indexed:** Biol.Abstr., Chem.Abstr., Excerp.Med. (until 1993), Ind.Med. **Document type:** academic/scholarly publication.
—BLDSC (9298.735500); CASDDS.

615.1   CN   ISSN 0043-3829
WESTERN HORIZONS; a quarterly magazine for Western Canadian pharmacists. 1966. q. free. National Drug & Chemical Co. of Canada Ltd., Box 758, Winnipeg, Man., Canada. TEL 204-774-4511. Ed. T.H. Glenwright. adv. circ. 3,200. **Document type:** trade publication.

615.1   US   ISSN 0083-8969
                    CODEN: PWPSA8
WESTERN PHARMACOLOGY SOCIETY. PROCEEDINGS. 1958. a. $25 (effective 1995). Western Pharmacology Society, Inc., University of Arizona, Department of Pharmacology, College of Medicine, Tuscon, AZ 85724. TEL 602-626-7843. FAX 602-626-6883. E-mail: RJH@gas.uug.arizona.edu. Ed. Dr. Ryan J. Huxtable. circ. 500 (paid). (also avail. in microform from UMI; reprint service avail. from UMI) **Indexed:** Biol.Abstr., Chem.Abstr., Curr.Adv.Ecol.Sci., Curr.Cont., Dairy Sci.Abstr., Excerp.Med., Ind.Med., Nutr.Abstr. **Document type:** proceedings, academic/scholarly publication.
—BLDSC (6834.200000); CASDDS; EMDOCS; Faxon; Genuine Article; SWETS; UMI.
Refereed Serial

615.1   US
WHITE SHEET. 1967. m. free to pharmacists. Philips Roxane Laboratories, Inc., 330 Oak St., Columbus, OH 43216. TEL 614-228-5403. Ed. Richard E. Surface. bk.rev. circ. 25,000. (tabloid format)
Formerly (until 1977): Hospital Pharmacy (ISSN 0018-5779)

615   US   ISSN 0743-3778
HD9666.1
WHOLESALE DRUGS MAGAZINE. 1948. 10/yr. $30. E L F Publications, 333 W. Hampden Ave., Ste. 1050, Englewood, CO 80110-2340. TEL 303-761-8818. FAX 303-761-2440. Ed. ElRoy FitzSenry. adv. circ. 7,000. **Document type:** trade publication.
Description: Covers news as it affects the wholesale chain drug distribution.

615 574.192   UK   ISSN 0966-9094
WINDOW ON DRUG MONITORING. 1993. m. £50($90) The Royal Society of Chemistry, Thomas Graham House, Science Park, Milton Rd., Cambridge CB4 4WF, England. TEL 01223-420066. FAX 01223-423429. E-mail: rsc1@rsc.org. (Dist. by: Turpin Distribution Services Ltd., Blackhorse Rd., Letchworth, Herts. SG6 1HN, England. TEL 01462-672555. FAX 01462-480947) Ed. Judith Barnsley. abstr. **Document type:** academic/scholarly publication.
Description: Covers developments in the analysis of therapeutic drugs and drugs of abuse in biological tissues and fluids.

615.1   US   ISSN 0043-6585
WISCONSIN PHARMACIST. vol.40, 1971. m. $60. Wisconsin Pharmacists Association, 202 Price Pl., Madison, WI 53705. TEL 608-238-5515. FAX 608-238-5546. Ed. Christopher Decker. adv. circ. 1,800. **Indexed:** Chem.Abstr. **Document type:** trade publication.
—BLDSC (9325.850000).

615   UK   ISSN 0140-4806
WORLD DRUG MARKET MANUAL. 1975. a. £5100. IMSWORLD Publications Ltd., 7 Harewoood Ave., London NW1 6JB, England. TEL 0171-393-5000. FAX 0171-393-5900. TELEX 8954520. **Document type:** trade publication.
●Also available online.
Also available on CD-ROM.

615   US   ISSN 0276-2277
RM39
WORLD PHARMACEUTICAL DIRECTORY. irreg. (every 2-3 yrs.) $620. Pharmaco-Medical Documentation, Inc., Box 429, Chatham, NJ 07928. TEL 201-822-9200. FAX 201-765-0722. **Document type:** directory.

615.19   UK   ISSN 0966-7687
WORLD PHARMACEUTICALS REPORT. 1990. bi-w. £348($595) B N A International, Inc. (Subsidiary of: The Bureau of National Affairs, Inc.), Heron House, 10 Dean Farrar St., London SW1H ODX. TEL 0171-222-8831. FAX 0171-222-5550. (U.S. addr.: 1231 25th St., N.W., Washington, DC 20037. TEL 202-452-4200) Ed. Virginia A. Jackson. **Document type:** newsletter.
—SWETS. **CCC.**
Formerly: World Pharmaceutical Standards Review.
Description: Covers international regulatory, legislative and judicial news service within the pharmaceutical industry.

WORLDWIDE BIOTECH. see *BIOLOGY — Biotechnology*

615   CC   ISSN 1000-3843
RM300   CODEN: XYLIEU
XINYAO YU LINCHUANG/NEW DRUGS AND CLINICAL REMEDIES. (Text in Chinese; abstracts in English) 1982. bi-m. $60. Shanghai Yiyao Guanliju, Keji Qingbaosuo - Shanghai Pharmaceutical Administration Bureau, Information Institute, No. 50, Lane 532, Yuyuan Road, Shanghai 200040, People's Republic of China. TEL 86-21-2525690. FAX 86-21-2136256. (Subscr. to: China International Book Trading Corp., P.O. Box 339, Beijing 100044, P.R. China) (Co-sponsor: Chinese Pharmaceutical Association) Ed. Ding Guangsheng. adv.: page $1600; adv. contact: Yu Yaosong. circ. 30,000. **Document type:** academic/scholarly publication.
—CASDDS.
Description: Reflects the developments of drug research and clinical practice.

XINZHONGYI/NEW JOURNAL OF TRADITIONAL CHINESE MEDICINE. see *ALTERNATIVE MEDICINE*

615   KO
YAKUP SHINMOON/PHARMACEUTICAL NEWS. (Text in Korean) 1954. s-w. 42000 Won. Yakup Shinmoon, 100-1, 2-ka, Cheongpa-Dong, Yongsan-Ku, Seoul 140, S. Korea. TEL 02-718-1771. Ed. Seung-Joon Jin. adv. contact: Ki-Joo Ko. **Document type:** newspaper.

615   US   ISSN 0386-3603
                    CODEN: YACHDS
YAKURI TO CHIRYO/JAPANESE PHARMACOLOGY AND THERAPEUTICS. (Text in Japanese; summaries in English) 1973. m. Life Science Publishing Co. Ltd., 11-7 Nihonbashi, Kobuna-cho, Chuo-ku, Tokyo 103, Japan. TEL 3-3664-7750. **Indexed:** Chem.Abstr., Excerp.Med., INIS Atomind.
—BLDSC (4660.200000); CASDDS.

615   JA   ISSN 0910-5247
YAMAGUCHI UNIVERSITY. DRUG INFORMATION NEWS. (Text in Japanese) 1966. q. Yamaguchi Daigaku Igakubu, Fuzhoku Byoin D I Senta, 1144, Kogushi, Ube-shi, Yamaguchi-ken 755, Japan.

615   CC   ISSN 0254-1793
RS189   CODEN: YFZADL
YAOWU FENXI ZAZHI/JOURNAL OF PHARMACEUTICAL ANALYSIS. (Text in Chinese) bi-m. (Zhongguo Yaoxuehui - China Society of Pharmacology) Chinese Medical Association - Zhonghua Yixuehui, P.O. Box 2258, 42 Dongsi Xidajie, Beijing 100710, People's Republic of China. TEL 1-550394. Ed. Tu Guoshi. **Indexed:** Excerp.Med. (1993-), Hort.Abstr. **Document type:** academic/scholarly publication.
—BLDSC (3180.473000); CASDDS.
Refereed Serial

615   CC
YAOWU YU REN/MEDICINE AND MEN. (Text in Chinese) q. Zhongguo Yaoxuehui, Beijing Fenhui, 227, Donghuashi Dajie, Congwenmenwai, Beijing 100062, People's Republic of China. TEL 7013619. Ed. Zhang Qingya.

615.19 CC ISSN 0513-4870
RS1 CODEN: YHHPAL
YAOXUE XUEBAO/ACTA PHARMACEUTICA SINICA. (Text in Chinese) m. $3.50 per no. Guoji Shudian, Qikan Bu - China International Book Trading Corp., Chegongzhuang Xilu 21, P.O. Box 399, Beijing 100044, People's Republic of China. **Indexed:** Abstr.Hyg., Chem.Abstr., Crop Physiol.Abstr., Curr.Adv.Ecol.Sci., Hort.Abstr., I.P.A., Ind.Med., Seed Abstr.
—BLDSC (0646.500000); CASDDS.

615.1058 US ISSN 0084-3733
YEAR BOOK OF DRUG THERAPY. 1933. a. $66.95 (residents $35) (effective 1996). Mosby - Year Book, Inc., Continuity Division, 200 N. LaSalle, Chicago, IL 60601. TEL 312-726-9733. TELEX 312-726-6075. Eds. Drs. Louis Lasagna, Michael Weintraub. illus. **Indexed:** Curr.Adv.Ecol.Sci., Diar.Dis.Res.
●Also available online. Vendor(s): Ovid Technologies.
—BLDSC (9411.650000); SWETS.
Formerly: Year Book of General Therapeutics (ISSN 0270-3866)
Description: Presents abstracts and commentary of pertinent literature in over 900 scientific journals

615 CC
YIYAO GONGCHENG SHEJI. (Text in Chinese) bi-m. Guojia Yiyao Guanli-ju, Shanghai Yiyao Sheji-yuan - State Administration of Pharmacy, Shanghai Pharmacy Design Academy, 1856 Nanjing Donglu, Shanghai 200040, People's Republic of China. TEL 2584840. Ed. Lu Zhendong.

YOKOHAMA MEDICAL JOURNAL. see *MEDICAL SCIENCES*

YUNNAN ZHONGYI ZAZHI/YUNNAN JOURNAL OF TRADITIONAL CHINESE MEDICINE. see *ALTERNATIVE MEDICINE*

ZHEJIANG ZHONGYI XUEYUAN XUEBAO/ZHEJIANG TRADITIONAL CHINESE MEDICAL COLLEGE. JOURNAL. see *MEDICAL SCIENCES*

ZHEJIANG ZHONGYI ZAZHI/ZHEJIANG JOURNAL OF TRADITIONAL CHINESE MEDICINE. see *ALTERNATIVE MEDICINE*

615.328 615.89 CC
ZHONG CAO YAO/CHINESE HERBAL MEDICINE. (Text in Chinese) m. $0.80 per no. Guoji Shudian, Qikan Bu - China International Book Trading Corp., P.O. Box 399, Beijing 100044, People's Republic of China. **Indexed:** Chem.Abstr.

615 CC ISSN 1001-1528
ZHONG CHENG YAO/CHINESE TRADITIONAL PATENT MEDICINE. (Text in Chinese; some abstracts in English) 1978. m. Y24. Guojia Yiyao Guanli-ju, Zhong Cheng Yao Qingbao Zhongxin - State Pharmaceutical Administration, Chinese Traditional Patent Medicine Information Center, 324 Renmin Road, Shanghai 200002, People's Republic of China. TEL 3289639. (Dist. outside China by: Guoji Shudian - China International Book Trading Corp., P.O. Box 399, Beijing, P.R.C.) Ed. Zhang Yuanzhen. adv.; bk.rev. circ. 10,000. **Document type:** academic/scholarly publication, trade publication.
Description: Reports the recent research achievements in industry of Chinese patent medicine and introduces new products, dosage formulations, processes and new equipment used in this industry.

615.329 CC ISSN 1001-8689
CODEN: ZKZAEY
ZHONGGUO KANGSHENGSU ZAZHI/CHINESE JOURNAL OF ANTIBIOTICS. (Text in Chinese or English) bi-m. $90. Sichuan Kangjunsu Gongye Yanjiusuo - Sichuan Industrial Institute of Antibiotics, 9 Shanbanqiao Lu, Chengdu, Sichuan 610051, People's Republic of China. TEL 444641. TELEX 60111 SIIA CN. **Indexed:** Excerp.Med.
—BLDSC (3180.293500); CASDDS.

615 CC ISSN 1003-3734
ZHONGGUO XINYAO ZAZHI/CHINESE NEW DRUGS JOURNAL. (Text in Chinese) 1992. bi-m. Y9.60. Zhongguo Xinyao Zazhi, 78A, Dongsi Liutiao, Beijing 100007, People's Republic of China. TEL 403-5990. (Dist. by: China International Book Trading Corporation, Box 399, Beijing, People's Republic of China.) Ed. Yu Chuanlong.
—BLDSC (3181.030300).

615 CC ISSN 1001-0408
ZHONGGUO YAOFANG/JOURNAL OF CHINA PHARMACY. (Text in Chinese) bi-m. Y25.20. Chongqing Weishengjuliju, Chongqing Yiyao Guanliju - Chongqing Bureau of Public Health, Chongqi Bureau of Drug Administration, 44 Qingnian Lu, Chongqing, Sichuan 630010, People's Republic of China. TEL 41978. Ed. Chen Congyuan. **Document type:** academic/scholarly publication.
—BLDSC (4958.035000).

615.9 615.7 CC ISSN 0253-9756
RM1 CODEN: CYLPDN
ZHONGGUO YAOLI XUEBAO/ACTA PHARMACOLOGICA SINICA. (Text in Chinese, English) 1980. bi-m. $60. (Chinese Society of Pharmacology) Science Press, Marketing and Sales Department, 16 Donghuangchenggen Beijie, Beijing 100707, People's Republic of China. TEL 4010642. FAX 4012180. TELEX 210247-SPBJ-CN. adv. circ. 10,000. (reprint service avail. from ISI) **Indexed:** Biol.Abstr., Chem.Abstr., Curr.Cont., Excerp.Med., Ind.Med., Trop.Dis.Bull. **Document type:** academic/scholarly publication.
—BLDSC (0648.100000); CASDDS; Genuine Article; SWETS.
Description: Contains original articles on pharmacological and toxicological research, including the therapeutic effects, toxicities, metabolism, experimental uses and mechanisms of drugs, poisons, and biologically active substances.
Refereed Serial

615 CC ISSN 1001-1978
CODEN: ZYTOE
ZHONGGUO YAOLIXUE TONGBAO/CHINESE PHARMACOLOGICAL BULLETIN. (Text in Chinese) bi-m. Zhongguo Yaoli Xuehui - Chinese Society of Pharmacology, c/o Anhui Medical University, 21 Meishen Lu, Hefei 230032, People's Republic of China. TEL 336600. Ed. Xu Shuyun. **Indexed:** Excerp.Med. (1993-). **Document type:** academic/scholarly publication, bulletin.
—BLDSC (3181.046600).

ZHONGGUO YAOLIXUE YU DULIXUE ZAZHI/CHINESE JOURNAL OF PHARMACOLOGY AND TOXICOLOGY. see *ENVIRONMENTAL STUDIES — Toxicology And Environmental Safety*

615.19 CC ISSN 1001-2494
RS1 CODEN: ZYZAEU
ZHONGGUO YAOXUE ZAZHI/CHINESE PHARMACEUTICAL JOURNAL. (Text in Chinese; abstracts in English) m. Y5 per no. Zhongguo Yaoxuehui - Chinese Pharmaceutical Association, 42 Dongsi Xidajie, Beijing 100710, People's Republic of China. TEL 01-5133311. FAX 01-8354609. (Subscr. to: China International Book Trading Corp., P.O. Box 399, Beijing, P.R.C.) **Indexed:** Anal.Abstr., Apic.Abstr., Chem.Abstr., Excerp.Med. (1993-), ExtraMED. **Document type:** academic/scholarly publication.
●Also available on CD-ROM.
—BLDSC (3181.046000); CASDDS.
Formerly: Yaoxue Tongbao - Chinese Pharmaceutical Bulletin (ISSN 0512-7343)

615 CC
ZHONGGUO YIYAO/JOURNAL OF CHINESE PHARMACY. (Text in Chinese) q. $30. Guojia Yiyao Guanli-ju - State Pharmaceutical Administration, 841 Sichuan Beilu, Shanghai 200085, People's Republic of China. TEL 3250593. (Subscr. to: China National Publishing Industry Trading Corp., Shanghai Branch, 380 Bei Suzhou Lu, Shanghai, P.R.C.) Ed. Shi Heng.

615 CC ISSN 1001-8255
CODEN: ZYGZEA
ZHONGGUO YIYAO GONGYE ZAZHI/CHINESE JOURNAL OF PHARMACEUTICALS. (Text in Chinese) 1970. m. $36. Shanghai Yiyao Gongye Yanjiuyuan - Shanghai Institute of Pharmaceutical Industry, 1320 Beijing Xilu, Shanghai 200040, People's Republic of China. TEL 2479808. Ed. Wang Qizhuo. adv. contact: Li Yixin. bk.rev. circ. 6,200. **Document type:** academic/scholarly publication.
—BLDSC (3180.473500); CASDDS.
Formerly (until 1989): Yiyao Gongye (ISSN 0255-7223)

615 CC
▼**ZHONGGUO YIYAO SHANGQING ZONGLAN/CHINA PHARMACEUTICAL BUSINESS INFORMATION.** (Text in Chinese, English) 1994. s-a. $100. (Zhongguo Yiyao Shangye Xuehui - China Association of Pharmaceutical Commerce (CAPC)) Zhongguo Yiyao Zazhishe, No.27, Lane 842, Chengdu Rd., N., Shanghai 200003, People's Republic of China. TEL 86-21-358-9906.
Description: Covers sales trends and market quotations of Chinese and Western medicines, medical instruments and equipments, and other pharmaceutical commodities in China.

615 CC ISSN 1000-4971
R97.7.C5 CODEN: ZYIXEE
ZHONGGUO YIYAO XUEBAO/JOURNAL OF CHINESE PHARMACOLOGY. (Text in Chinese) bi-m. Zhonghua Quanguo Zhongyi Xuehui - All-China National Association of Chinese Medicine, A-4 Yinghualu, Hepingli Dongjie, Beijing 100029, People's Republic of China. TEL 4216650. Ed. Dong Jianhua.

615 CC ISSN 1001-5213
CODEN: ZYYAEP
ZHONGGUO YIYUAN YAOXUE ZAZHI/CHINESE JOURNAL OF HOSPITAL PHARMACY. (Text in Chinese) 1983. m. Zhongguo Yaoxuehui, 177 Shengli St., Hankou, Hubei 430014, People's Republic of China. (Dist. overseas by: China International Book Trading Corp., P.O. Box 399, Beijing, P.R. China)
—BLDSC (3180.352000); CASDDS.

615.328 615.89 CC
ZHONGYAO TONGBAO/CHINESE MEDICINE BULLETIN. (Text in Chinese) bi-m. $0.80 per no. (Association of Chinese Pharmacologists) Guoji Shudian, Qikan Bu - China International Book Trading Corp., Chegongzhuang Xilu 21, P.O. Box 399, Beijing 100044, People's Republic of China. **Indexed:** Chem.Abstr. **Document type:** bulletin.

615 CC ISSN 1001-859X
ZHONGYAO YAOLI YU LINCHUANG/PHARMACOLOGY AND CLINICS OF CHINESE MATERIA MEDICA. (Text in Chinese) 1985. bi-m. $20. Sichuan Sheng Zhongyao Yanjiusuo - Sichuan Institute of Chinese Materia Medica, Huangjiaoya, Chongqingshi Nan'an, Sichuan 630065, People's Republic of China. TEL 481615. **Document type:** bulletin, academic/scholarly publication.

ZHONGYI ZAZHI/JOURNAL OF TRADITIONAL CHINESE MEDICINE. see *ALTERNATIVE MEDICINE*

1199 NEWS. see *LABOR UNIONS*

PHARMACY AND PHARMACOLOGY — Abstracting, Bibliographies, Statistics

615.1 US ISSN 0065-8111
RS355
AMERICAN DRUG INDEX. 1950. a. $45 (effective 1995). Facts and Comparisons, 111 W. Port Plaza, Ste. 400, St. Louis, MO 63146-3098. TEL 800-223-0554. FAX 314-878-5563. Ed. Norman F. Billups. **Document type:** abstracting/indexing.
—CCC.
Description: Lists over 20,000 drug entries in dictionary style with cross-indexing of brands, generic and chemical names.

615 US ISSN 0898-4654
AMERICAN STATISTICAL ASSOCIATION. BIOPHARMACEUTICAL SECTION. PROCEEDINGS. a., 10th ed. $45 to non-members; members $30. American Statistical Association, 1429 Duke St., Alexandria, VA 22314-3402. TEL 703-684-1221. FAX 703-684-2037. **Indexed:** Curr.Ind.Stat. **Document type:** proceedings.
—BLDSC (6661.250000).

ATRIAL NATRIURETIC FACTORS. see *MEDICAL SCIENCES — Abstracting, Bibliographies, Statistics*

PHARMACY AND PHARMACOLOGY — ABSTRACTING, BIBLIOGRAPHIES, STATISTICS

615.19   US   ISSN 1051-3957
CODEN: CBUPEA
C A S BIOTECH UPDATES. SLOW-RELEASE PHARMACEUTICALS. 1991. s-w. $215 (effective Jan. 1995). Chemical Abstracts Service (Subsidiary of: American Chemical Society), 2540 Olentangy River Rd., Box 3012, Columbus, OH 43210-0012. TEL 614-447-3600. FAX 614-447-3713. TELEX 6842086. **Document type:** abstracting/indexing.
Description: Covers slow-release pharmaceutical dosage forms, including controlled- and sustained-release systems; newer dosage forms such as osmotic-release devices, transdermal systems, polymer conjugates, and other materials giving regulated drug release rates.

C A SELECTS. ANTIARRHYTHMICS. see *MEDICAL SCIENCES — Abstracting, Bibliographies, Statistics*

350   US   ISSN 0148-2459
CODEN: CSBADM
C A SELECTS. BETA-LACTAM ANTIBIOTICS. s-w. $220 to non-members; members $65 (effective 1996). Chemical Abstracts Service (Subsidiary of: American Chemical Society), 2540 Olentangy River Rd., Box 3012, Columbus, OH 43210-0012. TEL 614-447-3600. FAX 614-447-3713. TELEX 6842086. **Document type:** abstracting/indexing.
Description: Covers synthesis, biosynthesis, chemical reactivity, antimicrobial activity, pharmacodynamics, metabolism, toxicology, analysis, and formulation.

C A SELECTS. CALCIUM CHANNEL BLOCKERS. see *CHEMISTRY — Abstracting, Bibliographies, Statistics*

544.92 011   US   ISSN 1045-8530
CODEN: CSDTEM
C A SELECTS. DRUG ANALYSIS BIOLOGICAL FLUIDS & TISSUES. s-w. $220 to non-members; members $65 (effective 1996). Chemical Abstracts Service (Subsidiary of: American Chemical Society), 2540 Olentangy River Rd., Box 3012, Columbus, OH 43210-0012. TEL 614-447-3600. FAX 614-447-3713. TELEX 6842086. **Document type:** abstracting/indexing.
Description: Covers newly developed methods (gas chromatography, HPLC, mass spectrometry, immunoassay) for the analysis of drugs in biological fluids (blood, urine, saliva) and tissues (liver, lungs, kidneys).

615.9   US   ISSN 0162-7775
CODEN: CSDTDL
C A SELECTS. DRUG & COSMETIC TOXICITY. s-w. $220 to non-members; members $65 (effective 1996). Chemical Abstracts Service (Subsidiary of: American Chemical Society), 2540 Olentangy River Rd., Box 3012, Columbus, OH 43210-0012. TEL 614-447-3600. FAX 614-447-3713. TELEX 6842086. **Document type:** abstracting/indexing.
Description: Covers toxic manifestations of drugs, cosmetics, and ingredients of drug and cosmetic preparations, e.g., mutagenicity, teratogenicity, carcinogenicity, allergic potential; health hazards, side effects, and safety of drugs.

350   US   ISSN 1040-7162
CODEN: CSDSEJ
C A SELECTS. DRUG DELIVERY SYSTEMS & DOSAGE FORMS. 1989. s-w. $220 to non-members; members $65 (effective 1996). Chemical Abstracts Service (Subsidiary of: American Chemical Society), 2540 Olentangy River Rd., Box 3012, Columbus, OH 43210-0012. TEL 614-447-3600. FAX 614-447-3713. TELEX 6842086. **Document type:** abstracting/indexing.
Description: Covers pharmaceutical dosage forms, e.g., tablets, capsules, ointments; newer delivery systems and forms such as controlled-release devices, transdermal systems, ocular inserts, osmotic devices, antibody conjugates, and liposomes; properties, formulation, bioavailability, and pharmacokinetic studies of drugs from the delivery systems and dosage forms.

615.19   US   ISSN 1047-8205
CODEN: CSDIEN
C A SELECTS. DRUG INTERACTIONS. 1987. s-w. $220 to non-members; members $65 (effective 1996). Chemical Abstracts Service (Subsidiary of: American Chemical Society), 2540 Olentangy River Rd., Box 3012, Columbus, OH 43210-0012. TEL 614-447-3600. FAX 614-337-3713. TELEX 6842086. **Document type:** abstracting/indexing.
Formerly (until 1989): BIOSIS CAS Selects: Drug Interactions.
Description: Covers adverse, metabolic, and physicochemical drug interactions. Includes drug-drug, food-drug, and drug-alcohol interactions.

C A SELECTS. FOOD, DRUGS, & COSMETICS - LEGISLATIVE & REGULATORY ASPECTS. see *FOOD AND FOOD INDUSTRIES — Abstracting, Bibliographies, Statistics*

615   US   ISSN 0895-5875
CODEN: CSNAEF
C A SELECTS. NEW ANTIBIOTICS. 1988. s-w. $220 to non-members; members $65 (effective 1996). Chemical Abstracts Service (Subsidiary of: American Chemical Society), 2540 Olentangy River Rd., Box 3012, Columbus, OH 43210-0012. TEL 614-447-3600. FAX 614-447-3713. TELEX 6842086. **Document type:** abstracting/indexing.
Description: Covers production, isolation, characterization, structure determination, and antimicrobial activity of antibiotics, both natural and synthetic.

615.19   US   ISSN 0890-1902
CODEN: CPHAEW
C A SELECTS. PHARMACEUTICAL ANALYSIS. 1987. s-w. $220 to non-members; members $65 (effective 1996). Chemical Abstracts Service (Subsidiary of: American Chemical Society), 2540 Olentangy River Rd., Box 3012, Columbus, OH 43210-0012. TEL 614-447-3600. FAX 614-447-3713. TELEX 6842086. **Document type:** abstracting/indexing.
Description: Covers analysis of drugs in pure form or in pharmaceutical preparations.

615.19   US   ISSN 0890-1910
CODEN: CAPCE7
C A SELECTS. PHARMACEUTICAL CHEMISTRY (JOURNALS). 1987. s-w. $220 to non-members; members $65 (effective 1996). Chemical Abstracts Service (Subsidiary of: American Chemical Society), 2540 Olentangy River Rd., Box 3012, Columbus, OH 43210-0012. TEL 614-447-3600. FAX 614-447-3713. TELEX 6842086. **Document type:** abstracting/indexing.
Description: Covers all aspects of pharmaceutical chemistry: drug standards, pharmacopeias, formulations, prosthetic materials, surgical goods, and properties of pharmaceuticals.

615.19   US   ISSN 0890-1929
CODEN: CPCPEI
C A SELECTS. PHARMACEUTICAL CHEMISTRY (PATENTS). 1987. s-w. $220 to non-members; members $65 (effective 1996). Chemical Abstracts Service (Subsidiary of: American Chemical Society), 2540 Olentangy River Rd., Box 3012, Columbus, OH 43210-0012. TEL 614-447-3600. FAX 614-447-3713. TELEX 6842086. **Document type:** abstracting/indexing.
Description: Covers formulations, prosthetic materials, and surgical goods.

C A SELECTS. PSYCHOBIOCHEMISTRY. see *BIOLOGY — Abstracting, Bibliographies, Statistics*

615   US   ISSN 0160-9173
CODEN: CSBSDB
C A SELECTS. STEROIDS (BIOCHEMICAL ASPECTS). s-w. $220 to non-members; members $65 (effective 1996). Chemical Abstracts Service (Subsidiary of: American Chemical Society), 2540 Olentangy River Rd., Box 3012, Columbus, OH 43210-0012. TEL 614-447-3600. FAX 614-447-3713. TELEX 6842086. **Document type:** abstracting/indexing.
Description: Covers pharmacology, toxicology, general biochemistry, and nutritional uses of steroids.

C A SELECTS. STEROIDS (CHEMICAL ASPECTS). see *CHEMISTRY — Abstracting, Bibliographies, Statistics*

615 016   US   ISSN 0069-4770
CLIN-ALERT. 1962. 26/yr. $94.95 (foreign $99.95). Learned Information, Inc., 143 Old Marlton Pike, Medford, NJ 08055-8750. TEL 609-654-6266. FAX 609-654-4309. Ed. Ramona Scheible. q. cum.index. (looseleaf format; back issues avail.)
—CCC.
Description: Reference summaries of and conclusions about prescription drug reactions-interactions, for pharmacists, physicians, librarians, and lawyers.

CONTAMINATION CONTROL ABSTRACTS. see *ENGINEERING — Abstracting, Bibliographies, Statistics*

615   JA   ISSN 0385-6747
CONTENTS. (Text in Japanese) 1971. w. 103000 Yen. Japan Pharmaceutical Information Center - Nihon Iyaku Joho Senta, 3rd Fl., Nagai-Kinenkan, 2-12-15 Shibuya, Shibuya-ku, Tokyo 150, Japan. FAX 03-5466-1818. Ed. H. Miyake. circ. 900.
Document type: bibliography.
Description: Lists titles of medical and pharmaceutical journals.

CURRENT ADVANCES IN TOXICOLOGY. see *ENVIRONMENTAL STUDIES — Abstracting, Bibliographies, Statistics*

CURRENT BIBLIOGRAPHIES ON SCIENCE AND TECHNOLOGY: BIOLOGY, PHARMACY AND FOOD SCIENCE. see *BIOLOGY — Abstracting, Bibliographies, Statistics*

DRUG ABSTRACTS MONTHLY. see *DRUG ABUSE AND ALCOHOLISM — Abstracting, Bibliographies, Statistics*

DRUG ABUSE CURRENT AWARENESS BULLETIN. see *DRUG ABUSE AND ALCOHOLISM — Abstracting, Bibliographies, Statistics*

DRUG FILE UPDATE; a current awareness index to publications on drugs and doping in sport. see *SPORTS AND GAMES — Abstracting, Bibliographies, Statistics*

615 016   NE   ISSN 0927-2798
EXCERPTA MEDICA. SECTION 30: CLINICAL AND EXPERIMENTAL PHARMACOLOGY. 1948. 32/yr. fl.5480($3342) (effective 1996). Excerpta Medica (Subsidiary of: Elsevier Science B.V.), P.O. Box 548, 1000 AM Amsterdam, Netherlands. TEL 31-20-4853911. FAX 31-20-4853598. TELEX 18582 ESPA NL. (Dist. by: Elsevier Science Ireland Ltd., P.O. Box 85, Limerick, Ireland. TEL 353-61-471944. FAX 353-61-472144; Subscr. in U.S. and Canada to: Elsevier Science Inc., Box 882, Madison Sq. Sta., New York, NY 10159. TEL 212-989-5800. FAX 212-633-3990) Ed.Bd. adv.; index, cum.index. Indexed: Chem.Abstr. **Document type:** abstracting/indexing.
●Also available online. Vendor(s): Ovid Technologies, DIMDI, Data-Star, Knight-Ridder, Inc., JICST. Also available on CD-ROM. Producer(s): SilverPlatter Information, Inc.
—BLDSC (3835.824500). **CCC.**
Formerly (until 1992): Excerpta Medica. Section 30: Pharmacology (ISSN 0167-9643); **Supersedes:** Excerpta Medica. Section 30: Pharmacology and Toxicology (ISSN 0014-4347)
Description: Covers all aspects of experimental and clinical pharmacology, including pharmacokinetics, pharmacodynamics, methodology, mathematical models, and experimental studies on human organs, tissues and cells, and on the mechanisms of action of exogenous substances.

EXCERPTA MEDICA. SECTION 52: TOXICOLOGY. see *ENVIRONMENTAL STUDIES — Abstracting, Bibliographies, Statistics*

615   FR
FRANCE. SERVICE D'ETUDE DES STRATEGIES ET DES STATISTIQUES INDUSTRIELLES. RESULTATS MENSUELS DES ENQUETES DE BRANCHE. INDUSTRIE PHARMACEUTIQUE. m. 260 F. (foreign 310 F.)(effective 1991). Service d'Etude des Strategies et des Statistiques Industrielles (SESSI), 85 Bd. du Montparnasse, 75270 Paris Cedex 06, France. TEL 45-56-42-34. FAX 45-56-40-71. stat.
Description: Follows developments in the pharmaceutical industry through the performance of selected indicators.

PHARMACY AND PHARMACOLOGY — ABSTRACTING, BIBLIOGRAPHIES, STATISTICS

615.19　　　　　AT　　ISSN 0155-9885
GUILD DIGEST (YEAR). Key Title: Pharmacy Guild Digest. 1974. a. Aus.$100. Pharmacy Guild of Australia, P.O. Box 36, Deakin, A.C.T. 2600, Australia. TEL 06281-09111. FAX 06-282-4745. Ed. Vasken Demirian. index. circ. 5,500. (back issues avail.)
  Former titles: Community Pharmacy in Australia; Guild Digest.
  Description: Compares interfirm survey statistics on financial performance of pharmacies and some detail of drug usage and cost.

615.19　　　　　II
INDIAN CHEMICALS AND PHARMACEUTICALS STATISTICS. (Text in English) 1967. a. free. Ministry of Chemicals and Fertilizers, Economics and Statistics Division, New Delhi, India. stat.; circ. controlled. **Document type:** academic/scholarly publication.

615.1　　　　　NZ　　ISSN 0156-2703
INPHARMA; rapid alerts to news on drugs and drug therapy. 1975. w. $1725 (effective 1996). Adis International Limited, Private Bag 65901, Mairangi Bay, Auckland 10, New Zealand. TEL 64-9-479-8100. FAX 64-9-479-8145. E-mail: pcl@topgun.adis.co.nz. (Adis International Inc., Attn. Subscriptions Dept., Ste. F-10, 940 Town Center Dr., Langhorne, PA 19047. TEL 215-741-5229. FAX 215-741-5251) Ed. Mark Caldwell.
  ●Also available online. Vendor(s): Ovid Technologies (ADND,ADNC,ADNR,ADZZ).
  —Genuine Article; SWETS. **CCC.**
  Description: Provides brief evaluated summaries of all important pharmacological and therapeutic news from the world biomedical literature and from international meetings.

614　　　　　UN
INTERNATIONAL NARCOTICS CONTROL BOARD. STATISTICS ON PSYCHOTROPIC SUBSTANCES FOR (YEAR). (Text in English, French and Spanish) 1977. a. price varies. (International Narcotics Control Board - Organe International de Controle des Stupefiants) United Nations Publications, Room DC2-0853, New York, NY 10017. TEL 212-963-8302; 800-253-9646. FAX 212-963-3489. (Or: Vienna International Centre, P.O. Box 500, 1400 Vienna, Austria) (also avail. in microfiche from CIS) **Indexed:** IIS. **Document type:** academic/scholarly publication.
  Formerly: United Nations. International Narcotics Control Board. Statistics on Psychotropic Substances Furnished by Governments in Accordance with the Convention of 1971 on Psychotropic Substances (ISSN 0253-9403)

615 016　　　　　US　　ISSN 0020-8264
RS1　　　　　CODEN: IPMAAH
INTERNATIONAL PHARMACEUTICAL ABSTRACTS; key to the world's literature of pharmacy. 1964. s-m. $425 to non-members (foreign $450); members $100 (foreign $125). American Society of Hospital Pharmacists, c/o Jean Rogers, Dir., Mkt. Svcs., 7272 Wisconsin Ave., Bethesda, MD 20814. TEL 301-657-4383. FAX 301-657-1641. Ed. Dwight R. Tousignaut. index. circ. 2,000. (also avail. in microform from UMI; reprint service avail. from UMI; back issues avail.) **Indexed:** Anal.Abstr., JAMA. **Document type:** academic/scholarly publication, abstracting/indexing.
  ●Also available online. Vendor(s): Ovid Technologies (IPAB), DIMDI, Knight-Ridder, Inc. (File no.74), European Space Agency (File no.102/IPA), Lexis-Nexis, National Library of Medicine, University of Tsukuba.
  Also available on CD-ROM. Producer(s): SilverPlatter Information, Inc.
  —BLDSC (4544.924000); UMI. **CCC.**
  Description: Covers approximately 800 worldwide pharmaceutical, medical and health care publications.

615　　　　　JA
IYAKU TOKKYO SHOROKU/MEDICINE - PATENTS ABSTRACTS. (Text in Japanese) 1972. s-m. 250000 Yen. Aiaru Shuppan K.K. - Information Retrieval Publishing Co., Ltd., 50-15-101, Wada 3-chome, Suginami-ku, Tokyo 166, Japan.

615　　　　　JA　　ISSN 0385-0668
JAPAN PHARMACEUTICAL ABSTRACTS. (Text in English) 1975. m. 60000 Yen($810) Drug Business Research Co., Ltd. - Iyakuhin Sangyo Kenkyujo, 25-2, Koishikawa 1-chome, Bunkyo-ku, Tokyo 112, Japan. (Dist. by: Intercontinental Marketing Corp., I.P.O. Box 5056, Tokyo 100-31, Japan. TEL 81-3-3661-7458. FAX 81-3-3667-9646)
Document type: abstracting/indexing.

615.19　　　　　IS
M E D I C. (Monthly Ethical Drug Index Complication) (Text in English) 1971. 6/yr. $65. Shirol Publications Ltd., P.O. Box 2066, Herzlia, Israel. FAX 972-9-507604. Ed. S.H. Bergman. adv. circ. 7,000.

MEDICAL & PHARMACEUTICAL BIOTECHNOLOGY ABSTRACTS. see *MEDICAL SCIENCES — Abstracting, Bibliographies, Statistics*

615　　　　　JA
MEDICAL COMPANIES GUIDE TO JAPAN. (Text in English) 1987. irreg. 20000 Yen($167) Chemical Daily Co., Ltd., International Affairs, 3-16-8, Nihonbashi Hama-cho, Chuo-ku, Tokyo 103, Japan. TEL 03-3663-7932. FAX 03-3663-2530. TELEX 2422362 NIPPO J. **Document type:** directory.
  Formerly (until 1992): Japan Medical and Pharmaceutical Directory.
  Description: Lists pharmaceutical companies and those dealing with diagnostic agents and medical apparatuses with up-to-date information including company name, address, turnover, features, and main products.

615　　　　　US　　ISSN 0076-6518
MERCK INDEX: AN ENCYCLOPEDIA OF CHEMICALS AND DRUGS. 1889. irreg., 11th ed., 1989. $35. Merck Publishing Co., Attn: Merck Publishing, Box 2000, Rg 7-220, Rahway, NJ 07065. TEL 908-594-4600. Ed. Susan Budavari. **Document type:** monographic series.
  ●Also available online. Vendor(s): Ovid Technologies (MRCK), CISTI, Knight-Ridder, Inc., STN International, Telesystemes - Questel.

300 614.35　　　　　UN　　ISSN 1013-3453
HV5800
NARCOTIC DRUGS: ESTIMATED WORLD REQUIREMENTS FOR (YEAR). (Text in English, French and Spanish) a. $35. (International Narcotics Control Board - Organe International de Controle des Stupefiants) United Nations Publications, Room DC2-0853, New York, NY 10017. TEL 212-963-9302; 800-253-9646. FAX 212-963-3489. (Or Vienna International Centre, P.O. Box 500, 1400 Vienna, Austria) (also avail. in microfiche from CIS) **Indexed:** IIS.
  —BLDSC (6015.348290).
  Formed by the 1989 merger of: United Nations. International Narcotics Control Board. Statistics on Narcotics Drugs for (Year) (ISSN 1014-8817); Which was formerly: United Nations. International Narcotics Control Board. Statistics on Narcotic Drugs Furnished by Governments in Accordance with the International Treaties & United Nations. International Narcotics Control Board. Comparative Statement of Estimates and Statistics on Narcotic Drugs for (Year) (ISSN 0255-9374); Which was formerly: United Nations. International Narcotics Control Board. Comparative Statement of Estimates and Statistics on Narcotics Drugs Furnished by Governments in Accordance with the International Treaties & Estimated World Requirements of Narcotic Drugs (ISSN 0082-8335); United Nations. International Narcotics Control Board. Statistics on Narcotic Drugs Furnished by Governments in Accordance with the International Treaties; Which was formerly (until 1984): United Nations. International Narcotics Control Board. Statistics on Narcotic Drugs Furnished by Governments in Accordance with the International Treaties and Maximum Level of Opium Stocks (ISSN 0566-7658).

OXYTOCIN AND VASOPRESSIN. see *MEDICAL SCIENCES — Abstracting, Bibliographies, Statistics*

615 016　　　　　FR　　ISSN 1146-5301
P A S C A L. F 70: PHARMACOLOGIE. TRAITEMENTS MEDICAMENTEUX. (Printed format ceased Jan. 1995) (Text in English, French) 1961. 10/yr. Centre National de la Recherche Scientifique, Institut de l'Information Scientifique et Technique, 2 allee du Parc de Brabois, 54514 Vandoeuvre-Les-Nancy Cedex, France. TEL 83-50-46-00. FAX 83-50-46-50. adv. contact: Veronique Guinvarc'h. index, cum.index. (also avail. in microfiche) **Document type:** bibliography.
  ●Also available online. Vendor(s): European Space Agency (File no.14), Knight-Ridder, Inc. (File no.144), Telesystemes - Questel.
  Also available on CD-ROM.
  Former titles: P A S C A L Folio. F 70: Pharmacologie. Traitement Medicamenteux (ISSN 0761-1943); P A S C A L Folio. Part 70: Pharmacologie. Traitements Medicamenteux; Which superseded in part (in 1984): Bulletin Signaletique. Part 330: Sciences Pharmacologiques - Toxicologie (ISSN 0007-5442)

615.19　　　　　US
P M A STATISTICAL FACTBOOK; pharmaceuticals, in-vivo diagnostic. a. $21.50. Pharmaceutical Manufacturers Association, 1100 15th St., N.W., Washington, DC 20005. TEL 202-835-3400. FAX 202-835-3595. Ed.Bd. charts; stat. circ. 1,500. (looseleaf format) **Indexed:** SRI.
  Formerly: Prescription Drug Industry Fact Book.

615 016　　　　　US　　ISSN 0362-4439
P N I. (Pharmaceutical News Index) (Hard copy ceased 1984) 1975. w. U M I Company, 300 N. Zeeb Rd., Ann Arbor, MI 48106-1346. TEL 313-761-4700; 800-521-0600. FAX 313-761-1203. Ed. Paula McCoy. bibl. (also avail. in magnetic tape) **Document type:** abstracting/indexing.
  ●Also available online. Vendor(s): Ovid Technologies (PNII), Knight-Ridder, Inc. (File no.42), Orbit Search Service, STN International.

615　　　　　US　　ISSN 1043-5905
RS356
PHARMACEUTICAL ACTIVITIES INDEX - DIRECTORY. irreg. (every 3-4/yrs.) $570. Pharmaco-Medical Documentation, Inc., Box 429, Chatham, NJ 07928. TEL 201-822-9200. FAX 201-765-0722. **Document type:** directory.

615　　　　　US
PHARMACEUTICAL MANUFACTURERS ASSOCIATION. ANNUAL SURVEY REPORT. a. free. Pharmaceutical Manufacturers Association, 110 15th St., N.W., Washington, DC 20005. TEL 202-835-3400. FAX 202-835-3595. stat. **Indexed:** SRI.
  Description: Provides annual and historical statistical information on pharmaceutical industry sales and research.

PHILIPPINES INDEX OF MEDICAL SPECIALITIES. see *MEDICAL SCIENCES — Abstracting, Bibliographies, Statistics*

PRESS DIGEST. see *DRUG ABUSE AND ALCOHOLISM — Abstracting, Bibliographies, Statistics*

615　　　　　NZ　　ISSN 0114-9954
REACTIONS WEEKLY; rapid alerts to adverse drug experience. (Supplement avail.: Reactions Annual (ISSN 1172-6199)) 1979. 50/yr. $725 (effective 1996). Adis International Limited, Private Bag 65901, Mairangi Bay, Auckland 1010, New Zealand. TEL 64-9-479-8100. FAX 64-9-479-8145. E-mail: pcl@topgun.adis.co.nz. (Subscr. addr. in US: Adis International Inc., Subscriptions Dept., Ste. F-10, 940 Town Center Dr., Langhorne, PA 19047. TEL 215-741-5229. FAX 215-741-5251) Ed. Rosie Stather. bk.rev.; q. cum.index.
  ●Also available online. Vendor(s): Knight-Ridder, Inc.
  —SWETS. **CCC.**
  Formerly (until 1990): Reactions (ISSN 0157-7271)
  Description: Clinical information on adverse drug experiences reported in international medical journals.

PHARMACY AND PHARMACOLOGY — Computer Applications

615   RU   ISSN 0202-5132
REFERATIVNYI ZHURNAL. FARMAKOLOGIYA EFFEKTORNYKH SISTEM. KHIMIOTERAPEVTICHESKIE SREDSTVA. 1987. m. $234 (effective 1996). Vsesoyuznyi Institut Nauchno-Tekhnicheskoi Informatsii (VINITI), Baltiiskaya ul. 14, A-219 Moscow, Russia. (Subscr. to: Mezhdunarodnaya Kniga, Dimitrova ul. 39, 113095 Moscow, Russia) **Document type**: abstracting/indexing.

615   RU   ISSN 0134-580X
REFERATIVNYI ZHURNAL. FARMAKOLOGIYA. OBSHCHAYA FARMAKOLOGIYA NERVNOI SISTEMY. 1987. m. 78.20 Rub. (90.40 Rub. with index). Vsesoyuznyi Institut Nauchno-Tekhnicheskoi Informatsii (VINITI), Baltiiskaya ul. 14, A-219 Moscow, Russia. (Subscr. to: Mezhdunarodnaya Kniga, Dimitrova ul. 39, 113095 Moscow, Russia) **Document type**: abstracting/indexing.

615 016   RU   ISSN 0202-9162
REFERATIVNYI ZHURNAL. KLINICHESKAYA FARMAKOLOGIYA. 1979. m. $219 (effective 1996). Vsesoyuznyi Institut Nauchno-Tekhnicheskoi Informatsii (VINITI), Baltiiskaya ul. 14, Moscow A-219, Russia. (Subscr. to: Mezhdunarodnaya Kniga, Dimitrova ul. 39, 113095 Moscow, Russia) **Document type**: abstracting/indexing.

615.9 016   RU   ISSN 0202-9219
RA1190   CODEN: RZTODS
REFERATIVNYI ZHURNAL. TOKSIKOLOGIYA. 1958. m. $192 (effective 1996). Vsesoyuznyi Institut Nauchno-Tekhnicheskoi Informatsii (VINITI), Baltiiskaya ul. 14, Moscow A-219, Russia. (Subscr. to: Mezhdunarodnaya Kniga, Dimitrova ul. 39, 113095 Moscow, Russia) **Indexed**: Chem.Abstr. **Document type**: abstracting/indexing.
—CASDDS.

615.1 016   XR   ISSN 0034-2777
REFERATOVY VYBER Z LEKARENSTVI/ABSTRACTS OF PHARMACY. 1965. bi-m. 100 Kc. Narodni Lekarska Knihovna, Sokolska 31, 121 32 Prague 2, Czech Republic. TEL 2491-5775. FAX 2491-4625. Ed. Dr. Ivan Andel. bk.rev. circ. 500. **Document type**: abstracting/indexing.

615 368.4   CN   ISSN 1187-8991
HD7103.5.C2
SASKATCHEWAN HEALTH. PRESCRIPTION DRUG SERVICES BRANCH. ANNUAL STATISTICAL REPORT. (Supplement to: Saskatchewan Health. Annual Report) 1976. a. Saskatchewan Health, Prescription Drug Services Branch, 1100 - 2002 Victoria Ave., Regina, SK S4P 3V7, Canada. TEL 306-787-3317. FAX 306-787-8679. circ. 700. **Document type**: government publication.
Former titles (until 1991): Saskatchewan Health. Statistical Supplement to the Annual Report (ISSN 1182-218X); (until 1989): Saskatchewan. Prescription Drug Plan. Annual Report (ISSN 0707-0152).

615.9 016   RU   ISSN 0233-6588
SIGNAL'NAYA INFORMATSIYA. TOKSIKOLOGIYA LEKARSTVENNAYA. m. 6.40 Rub. Vsesoyuznyi Institut Nauchno-Tekhnicheskoi Informatsii (VINITI), Baltiiskaya ul. 14, Moscow A-219, Russia. (Subscr. to: Mezhdunarodnaya Kniga, Dimitrova ul. 39, 113095 Moscow, Russia) **Document type**: abstracting/indexing.
Formerly: Signal'naya Informatsiya. Toksikologiya (ISSN 0202-8514)

016 615.9   US   ISSN 0140-5365
RA1190
TOXICOLOGY ABSTRACTS. 1978. m. $795 (foreign $965). Cambridge Scientific Abstracts, 7200 Wisconsin Ave., 6th Fl., Bethesda, MD 20814. TEL 301-961-6750. FAX 301-961-6720. E-mail: market@csa.com. Ed.Bd; Pub. Ted Caris. adv.; bk.rev.; abstr.; index. (also avail. in magnetic tape; back issues avail.) **Indexed**: Cal.Tiss.Abstr., Chemorec.Abstr., Comput.& Info.Sys., Oncol.Abstr., Pollut.Abstr., World Surf.Coat. **Document type**: abstracting/indexing.
●Also available online. Vendor(s): Knight-Ridder, Inc. (File no.76/LIFE SCIENCES COLLECTION), STN International (LIFESCI).
Also available on CD-ROM. Producer(s): SilverPlatter Information, Inc.
—BLDSC (8873.037600).
Description: Covers all aspects of toxicology including substance abuse, radiation, and toxicity testing.

PHARMACY AND PHARMACOLOGY — Computer Applications

610 615 621.381   US   ISSN 0736-3893
COMPUTERTALK FOR THE PHARMACIST. 1981. bi-m. $45. ComputerTalk Associates, Inc., 482 Norristown Rd., Ste. 112, Blue Bell, PA 19422. TEL 610-825-7686. FAX 610-825-7641. Ed. Neil R. Bauman. adv. **Document type**: trade publication.
—UnCover.
Description: Offers practical advice to familiarize pharmacists with computers and computer applications. Short articles cover a broad range of topics.

610 615   US
COMPUTERTALK PHARMACY SYSTEMS BUYERS GUIDE. 1982. a. $25. ComputerTalk Associates, Inc., 482 Norristown Rd., Ste. 112, Blue Bell, PA 19422. TEL 610-825-7686. FAX 610-825-7641. Ed. Neil R. Bauman. adv. circ. 50,000. **Document type**: trade publication.
Formerly: ComputerTalk Directory of Pharmacy Systems (ISSN 0736-3877)
Description: A guide to available computer systems and services designed for pharmacy use. Information contained within product profiles written by vendors. Articles cover a range of topics on computers and applications.

TOXICOLOGY MODELING. see *ENVIRONMENTAL STUDIES — Computer Applications*

PHILATELY

769.569   DK   ISSN 0901-7003
A F A DANMARK, FAEROERNE, GROENLAND, DANSK VESTINDIEN FRIMAERKEKATALOG. Cover title: A F A Danmark Frimaerkekatalog. a. Aarhus Frimaerkehandel, Bruunsgade 42, 8000 Aarhus C, Denmark. FAX 45-86-199281. illus. **Document type**: catalog.

769.569   DK   ISSN 0901-6996
A F A DANMARK FIREBLOKKE. a. Aarhus Frimaerkehandel, Bruunsgade 42, 8000 Aarhus C, Denmark. FAX 45-86-199281. Ed. Lars Boes. illus. **Document type**: catalog.

769.5694   DK   ISSN 0901-6643
A F A OESTEUROPA FRIMAERKEKATALOG. Title varies: Oesteuropa Frimaerkekatalog. 1973. irreg. DKK 576 (for 2 vols.). Aarhus Frimaerkehandel, Bruunsgade 42, DK-8000 Aarhus C, Denmark. FAX 45-86-199281. illus. **Document type**: catalog.
Supersedes in part: A F A Europa Frimaerkekatalog.

769.569   DK   ISSN 0901-6635
A F A SKANDINAVIEN FRIMAERKEKATALOG. 1948. irreg. Aarhus Frimaerkehandel, Bruunsgade 42, DK-8000 Arhus C, Denmark. FAX 45-86-199281. illus. **Document type**: catalog.

769.569   DK   ISSN 0901-702X
A F A VESTEUROPA FRIMAERKEKATALOG. Title varies: Vesteuropa Frimaerkekatalog. 1974. a. DKK 596 (for 2 vols.). Aarhus Frimaerkehandel, Bruunsgade 42, 8000 Aarhus C, Denmark. TEL 45-86-12-52-88. FAX 45-86-199281. illus. **Document type**: catalog.
Supersedes in part: A F A Europa Frimaerkekatalog.

769.56   AG   ISSN 0001-1193
A F R A BOLETIN INFORMATIVO. 1939. bi-w. membership. Asociacion Filatelica de la Republica Argentina, Tucuman 672, 1 Piso, Depto. 2, 1049 Buenos Aires, Argentina. (Subscr. to: Casilla de Correo 1992, 1000 Buenos Aires, Argentina) Ed.Bd. adv.; bk.rev.
Former titles (until 1970): A F R A Boletin; Asociacion Filatelica de la Republica Argentina. Revista.

769.56   GW
A G M. 1974. 3/yr. DM.30 membership. Arbeitsgemeinschaft Malta im Bund Deutscher Philatelisten e.V., Suederstr. 66B, 24955 Harrislee, Germany. TEL 0461-71109. Ed. Peter C. Hansen. bk.rev. circ. 100. (back issues avail.) **Document type**: newsletter.
Formerly: G M Z.
Description: Reports and studies on the postal history of Malta for advanced philatelists.

769.56   US
A.S.D.A. NEWSLETTER. 1914. m. membership. American Stamp Dealers' Association, 3 School St., Ste. 205, Glen Cove, NY 11542. TEL 516-759-7000. Ed. Stefan J. Pinto. adv.; bk.rev.; tr.lit. circ. 2,500. **Document type**: newsletter.
Formerly: A.S.D.A. Bulletin.

796.56   GW   ISSN 0933-1409
A T M; der aktuelle Informationsdienst zum Thema Briefmarken-Automation. 1984. bi-w. DM.55. Verlag Brigitte Tast, Laaseweg 4, 31174 Schellerten, Germany. TEL 05123-4330. FAX 05123-2015. Ed. Hans-Juergen Tast. adv.; bk.rev. (looseleaf format; back issues avail.) **Document type**: trade publication.

769.56   US
ACROSS THE FENCE. m. Wisconsin Federation of Stamp Clubs, 1017 Chieftain Lookout, Madison, WI 53711. Ed. Howard Sherpe.

769.56   US
AERONAUTICA AND AIR LABEL COLLECTOR. 1943. q. $15 (foreign $20). Aeronautica & Air Label Collectors Club, Box 1239, Elgin, IL 60121-1239. TEL 708-468-0840. (Affiliate: Aerophilatelic Federation of the Americas) Ed. Don Thomas. adv.; bk.rev.; circ. controlled.
Description: Air transport catalog of the world.

769.56   UK   ISSN 0142-9868
AFRICA SINCE INDEPENDENCE STAMP CATALOGUE. 1980. irreg. (in 3 parts). price varies. Stanley Gibbons Publications Ltd., Unit 5 Parkside, Christchurch Rd., Ringwood, Hants. BH24 3SH, England. TEL 0425-472363. FAX 0425-470247. TELEX 41271-SGPPUB-G. **Document type**: catalog.

769.56   IT
AGENZIA STAMPA FILATELICA EUROPEA. Short title: A S F E. 1977. 11/yr. L.800000. Renato Russo, Ed. & Pub., Via Mascagni 31, 80128 Naples, Italy. TEL 39-81-5602346. FAX 39-81-5602321. adv.: B&W page L.800000. circ. 2,000.

769.56   US   ISSN 0739-0939
HE6187
AIRPOST JOURNAL. 1929. m. $20 (foreign $22). American Air Mail Society, Box 110, Mineola, NY 11501. TEL 516-746-5543. Ed. James W. Graue. adv.: B&W page $75; trim 5 1/2 x 8 1/2; adv. contact: Sanford Solarz. bk.rev.; illus. circ. 2,000. (tabloid format) **Indexed**: Stamp J.Ind. **Document type**: bulletin.
Description: Tells the history of air mail through stamps and covers.

ALAN SHAWN FEINSTEIN INSIDERS REPORT. see *BUSINESS AND ECONOMICS — Investments*

769.56   US
ALBUM PAGE.* 1960. m. $15. Oregon Stamp Society, Box 18165, Portland, OR 97218-0165. TEL 503-284-6770. Ed. Dr. Vance Terrall. adv. circ. 400.
Description: Philatelic and related articles.

769.56   UK
ALBUM TRACKING. m. £0.25 per issue. Grassglow Ltd., 14 Rosebery Ave., London EC1R 4TD, England. adv. circ. 35,000.

769.56   SP   ISSN 0401-3689
ALHAMBRA; revista filatelica internacional. 1950. m. 600 ptas.($10) Club International Alhambra, P.O. Box 109, Granada, Spain. Ed. F. del Darro. adv.; bk.rev.; bibl.; illus.; tr.lit. circ. 4,000. (back issues avail.) **Indexed**: Math.R.

769.56   US
AMERICAN PHILATELIC CONGRESS. CONGRESS BOOK. 1935. a. $20 to non-members; members $17.50. American Philatelic Congress, c/o Russell V. Skavaril, 222 E. Torrence Rd., Columbus, OH 43214-3834. Ed. Barbara Mueller. bk.rev.; charts, illus.; cum.index every 5 yrs. circ. 1,000.

769.56   US   ISSN 0003-0473
HE6187
AMERICAN PHILATELIST. 1887. m. $30 to non-members. American Philatelic Society, Inc., Box 8000, State College, PA 16803. TEL 814-237-3803. FAX 814-237-6128. Ed. William L. Welch, Jr. adv.; bk.rev.; illus.; index, cum.index: 1887-1986. circ. 57,000. **Indexed**: Art & Archaeol.Tech.Abstr. **Document type**: newsletter.
—Faxon; UnCover.

PHILATELY 5121

769.56 US ISSN 0163-1608
HJ5321.Z7
AMERICAN REVENUER. 1947. 10/yr. $18 to non-members (effective 1995). American Revenue Association, Box 56, Rockford, IA 50468-0056. TEL 515-756-3542. E-mail: KennethT4@aol.com. Ed. Kenneth Trettin. adv.; bk.rev.; illus.; index, cum.index; circ. 1,277 (paid). **Indexed:** Stamp J.Ind. **Document type:** bulletin.
—UnCover.
Description: Articles about and catalogue listings of tax stamps of the US and the world.

769.56 US
AMERICAN SOCIETY FOR NETHERLANDS PHILATELY. NEWSLETTER. 1975. q. $12 (foreign $14) includes the Journal. American Society for Netherlands Philately, W6428 Riverview Dr., Onalaska, WI 54650. TEL 608-781-8612. Ed. Frans H.A. Rummens. circ. 400. **Document type:** newsletter.

769.56 US
AMERICANA PHILATELIC NEWS. 1951. bi-m. $5. American Topical Association, Americana Unit, c/o June Bancroft, Sec.-Treas., Box 179, Washington, DC 20044-0179. TEL 202-387-4649. Ed. Melvin Morris. bk.rev. circ. 400. **Document type:** newsletter.
Description: News of stamps worldwide that have some relationship to the U.S. Official journal of Americana Unit.

769.56 FR
AMICALE PHILATELIQUE L'ANCRE. BULLETIN. 1976. q. Amicale Philatelique l'Ancre, 7 rue Dobre, 44100 Nantes, France. Ed.Bd. adv.; bk.rev. circ. 350. **Document type:** bulletin.

769.56 US
ANCHORAGE PHILATELIST. 1953. m. $10. Anchorage Philatelic Society, Inc., Box 10-2214, Anchorage, AK 99510. Ed. Eric Knapp. circ. 150. **Document type:** newsletter.

789.56 UK ISSN 0269-9249
THE ANGLO-BOER WAR PHILATELIST. 1958. q. £5 (overseas £8). Anglo-Boer War Philatelic Society, c/o Peter M. Prime, 56 Mount Way, Waverton, Ches. CH3 7QF, England. TEL 01224-336675. (Ed. addr.: 28 Oxford St., Burnham-on-Sea, Somers. TA8 1LQ, England) Ed. J.R. Stroud. adv. contact: J.R. Stroud. bk.rev. **Document type:** consumer publication.

APPRAISERS STANDARD; for collectors, auctioneers, dealers, etc. see ART

769.56 GW
ARBEITSGEMEINSCHAFT DEUTSCHE OSTGEBIETE. RUNDSCHREIBEN. 1959. q. DM.30. Arbeitsgemeinschaft Deutsche Ostgebiete, Tannenweg 11, 33098 Paderborn, Germany. Ed. Wolfhart Haacke.

769.56 GW
ARGE-SAAR. MITTEILUNGSBLATT. 1969. q. membership. Arbeits und Forschungsgemeinschaft, Dorfstr. 8, 66822 Lebach, Germany.

794
ARIZONA PHILATELIST. 1958. m. $4. Arizona Federation of Stamp Clubs, Inc., 25050 S. Drifter Dr., Sun Lakes, AZ 85248-7717. TEL 602-802-0822. Ed. Edward Leahr. bk.rev. circ. 275. **Document type:** newsletter.

ARTISTAMP NEWS. see ART

769.56 US
ASTROFAX. 1972. q. $6 (foreign $10). Astronomy Study Unit, c/o George Young, Box 632, Tewksbury, MA 01876. TEL 508-851-8283.
Description: Focuses on astronomy, astronomers, astrology and related subjects appearing on stamps and covers.

769.56 US
ASTROPHILE. 1957. bi-m. $12 membership. Space Topics Study Unit, Box 622678, Marathon Shores, FL 33052-2579. TEL 305-289-1847. Ed. Bernice Scholl. adv.; bk.rev.; circ. 1,000 (controlled).

769.56 SW
ATALAYA. 1974. 2/yr. $3. Christer Brunstrom, Ed. & Pub., Kungsgatan 23, S-032 45 Halmstad, Sweden. adv.; bk.rev.

769.56 AT ISSN 0155-8498
AUSTRALASIAN STAMP CATALOGUE. 1964. a. Aus.$16.95. Seven Seas Stamps Pty. Ltd., G.P.O. Box 3273, Sydney, N.S.W. 2001, Australia. Ed. David Foster. bk.rev.; illus. circ. 25,000. **Document type:** catalog.
Description: Illustrated and priced catalog of all Australian Commonwealth stamps and postal stationary. Includes Australian States and Australian Territories and Dependencies.

769.56 UK ISSN 0957-073X
AUSTRALIA CONCISE STAMP CATALOGUE. 1989. irreg. price varies. Stanley Gibbons Publications Ltd., Unit 5 Parkside, Christchurch Rd., Ringwood, Hants. BH24 3SH, England. TEL 0425-472363. FAX 0425-470247. TELEX 41271-SGPPUB-G. Ed. David Aggersberg. **Document type:** catalog.

769.56 AT
AUSTRALIAN COMMONWEALTH COLLECTORS CLUB OF NEW SOUTH WALES. BULLETIN. 1960. bi-m. Aus.$12. Australian Commonwealth Collectors Club of New South Wales, 1045 Canterbury Rd., Lakemba, N.S.W. 2195, Australia. Ed. N.J. Sheppard. bk.rev. circ. 500. **Document type:** bulletin.

760 AT
AUSTRALIAN STAMP BULLETIN. 1979. irreg. free. Australia Post Headquarters, Philatelic Group, G.P.O. Box 1777Q, Melbourne, Vic. 3001, Australia. TEL 03-204-7706. FAX 03-204-7744. (Subscr. to: Australian Stamp Bulletin, Locked Bag 8, S. Melbourne, Vic. 3205, Australia) Ed. John Tinney. bk.rev. circ. 350,000. **Document type:** bulletin.
Formerly: Philatelic Bulletin.

769.56 AT
AUSTRALIAN STAMP EXPLORER. 1977. q. free. Australia Post Headquarters, Philatelic Group, G.P.O. Box 1777Q, Melbourne, Vic. 3001, Australia. FAX 61-3-204-7744. Ed. Tina Lithgow. circ. 310,000. **Document type:** bulletin.
Formerly (until 1985): Junior Stamp Preview.
Description: Stamp collecting magazine for children.

769.56 UK ISSN 0142-9760
AUSTRIA & HUNGARY STAMP CATALOGUE. 1979. irreg. price varies. Stanley Gibbons Publications Ltd., Unit 5 Parkside, Christchurch Rd., Ringwood, Hants. BH24 3SH, England. TEL 0425-472363. FAX 0425-470247. TELEX 41271-SGPPUB-G. **Document type:** catalog.

769.56 AU ISSN 0005-0512
AUSTRIA-PHILATELIST; Oesterreichische Briefmarken-Zeitung. 1945. a. S.120. Verlag Adolf Kosel, Postfach 55, A-1095 Vienna, Austria. Ed. Leopold Sander. adv.; bk.rev. circ. 5,000.

769.56 UK ISSN 0140-2889
B A P I P BULLETIN. (Former name of issuing body: British Association of Palestine - Israel Philatelists) 1952. 3/yr. £10($20) Holyland Philatelic Society, 25 Sinclair Grove, London NW11 9JH, England. (Subscr. c/o: Mr. M. Lipczer, 94 Glenwood Gardens, Gants Hill, Ilford, Essex IG2 6XX, England) Ed. W. Barak. adv.; bk.rev.; cum.index. circ. 400. (back issues avail.) **Document type:** bulletin.

769.56 CN
B N A PORTRAITS. 1993. q. $20 to non-members. British North America Philatelic Society Ltd., Box 2788, Sta. D, Ottawa, ON K1P 5W8, Canada. TEL 613-990-2469. FAX 613-738-0877. Ed. Charles Verge. adv. contact: Henry Nerbonne. circ. 1,500. **Document type:** newsletter.

769.56 CN ISSN 0045-3129
HE6187
B N A TOPICS. 1943. 4/yr. Can.$24. British North America Philatelic Society Ltd., Box 10420, College Station, TX 77842. FAX 409-862-1256. E-mail: VLW8909@ZEUS.TAMU.EDU. Ed. V.L. Willson. adv. contact: Henry Narbonne. bk.rev. circ. 1,500. **Indexed:** Stamp J.Ind. **Document type:** academic/scholarly publication.
Description: Specialist philatelic journal featuring articles on stamps, postal history and related subjects of Canada and the provinces of Canada before their confederation.

769.56 UK ISSN 0953-8720
B W I STUDY CIRCLE BULLETIN. 1954. q. £7.50 in the U.K. and rest of Europe; elsewhere £10 (effective 1995). British West Indies Study Circle, 4 Hill Farm Close, Stafford, Staffs. ST17 9JE, England. Ed. Denis G.J. Charlesworth. adv.; bk.rev. circ. 350. **Indexed:** Stamp J.Ind. **Document type:** bulletin.

769.56 US
BADGER POSTAL HISTORY. 1947. q. membership. Wisconsin Postal History Society, c/o Frank Moertl, N95 W32259 County Line Rd., Hartland, WI 53029. TEL 414-499-3877. Ed. William B. Robinson. adv.: B&W page $30; trim 8 1/2 x 11. circ. 225.
Description: For postal history students and philatelists interested in the postal history of Wisconsin.

769.56 UK ISSN 0968-8153
BALE CATALOGUE OF ISRAEL POSTAGE STAMPS. 1969. a. $42.50. Michael H. Bale, Ed. & Pub., 41 High St., Ilfracombe, England. TEL 01271-862857. FAX 01271-867161. adv. circ. 1,700. **Document type:** catalog.
Former titles: Bale Catalogue of Palestine and Israel Stamps (ISSN 0305-4039); Bale Catalogue of Israel Stamps (ISSN 0067-3048)

769.56 UK ISSN 0142-9779
BALKANS STAMP CATALOGUE. 1980. irreg. price varies. Stanley Gibbons Publications Ltd., Unit 5 Parkside, Christchurch Rd., Ringwood, Hants. BH24 3SH, England. TEL 0425-472363. FAX 0425-470247. TELEX 41271-SGPPUB-G. **Document type:** catalog.

769.56 GW ISSN 0005-4364
BALLON KURIER. 1952. a. free. Pestalozzi Kinder- und Jugenddorf Wahlwies, 78333 Stockach, Germany. TEL 07771-8003-0. FAX 07771-800320. Ed. H.J. Scheer. adv.; illus. circ. 3,000. (looseleaf format) **Document type:** consumer publication.

769.56 US ISSN 0951-9955
BATON. 1968. 3/yr. $15. Philatelic Music Circle, Box 1781, Sequim, WA 98382. TEL 360-683-6373. Ed. Irene Lawford. (back issues avail.) **Document type:** bulletin.
Description: Provides information on music, fine art stamps and stamp auctions.

769.55 US ISSN 8756-5153
BAY PHIL. 1971. bi-m. $8. Friends of the Western Philatelic Library, Inc., Box 2219, Sunnyvale, CA 94087. Ed. Harold Short. bk.rev.; circ. 400 (paid). **Document type:** newsletter.

759.56 US
BELGIOPHILE. 1983. q. $7.50 membership (effective 1993). American-Belgian Philatelic Society, 25190 Canyon Dr., Carmel, CA 93923. TEL 408-624-7746. (Subscr. to: 621 Virginius Dr., Virginia Beach, VA 23452-4417) Ed. Harry W. Wilcke. adv.; bk.rev.; cum.index: 1983-1993. circ. 135. (looseleaf format; back issues avail.) **Document type:** bulletin.
Description: Covers philatelic matters of interest to persons from beginning to very advanced level.

769.56 US
BELIZE COLLECTOR. 1987. q. Belize Philatelic Society Circle, c/o Charles R. Gambill, 730 Collingswood, Corpus Christi, TX 78412.
Description: Focuses on all aspects of British Honduran and Belizean philately.

769.56 UK ISSN 0142-9787
BENELUX STAMP CATALOGUE. 1979. irreg. price varies. Stanley Gibbons Publications Ltd., Unit 5 Parkside, Christchurch Rd., Ringwood, Hants. BH24 3SH, England. TEL 0425-472363. FAX 0425-470247. TELEX 41271-SGPPUB-G. **Document type:** catalog.

769.56 US ISSN 1046-2813
BERMUDA POST. 1987. q. $22. Bermuda Collectors Society, c/o Thomas McMahon, 86 Nash Rd., Purdys, NY 10578. TEL 914-232-3088. FAX 203-798-9930. Ed. John Puzine. adv.; bk.rev.; cum.index. circ. 220. (back issues avail.) **Document type:** academic/scholarly publication.
Description: Covers the stamps and postal history of Bermuda.

PHILATELY

769.56 — SZ — ISSN 0005-9404
BERNER BRIEFMARKEN-ZEITUNG/JOURNAL PHILATELIQUE DE BERNE. (Text in French, German) 1908. 10/yr. (including two double nos.). 39 SFr. Zumstein und Cie, Postfach 1079, CH-3000 Bern 7, Switzerland. TEL 031-3120055. FAX 031-3122326. Ed. Max Hertsch. bk.rev.; illus. circ. 10,000. **Document type:** consumer publication.
Description: Stamp collectors magazine covering all countries of the world. Includes news, values, special issues, history, events and exhibitions, list of special collections, and list of new catalogs.

769.56 — IT
BOLLETTINO PREFILATELICO E STORICO-POSTALE. 1977. bi-m. L.25000. (Centro Studi Internazionale di Storia Postale) Benetton Editore, Via A. Da Bassano, 31, I-35100 Padua, Italy. adv.; bk.rev. **Document type:** bulletin.

789.56 — RH
BORDER POST. bi-m. Manicaland Philatelic Society, P.O. Box 684, Mutare, Zimbabwe. **Document type:** bulletin.

BRIEF AUS WAHLWIES; Mitteilungen aus dem Pestalozzi Kinder- und Jugenddorf. see *CHILDREN AND YOUTH — About*

769.56 — AU — ISSN 0007-0033
BRIEFMARKE. 1952. m. S.440. Verband Oesterreichischer Philatelisten-Vereine, Getreidemarkt 1, A-1060 Vienna, Austria. TEL 0222-5876469. FAX 0222-5877026. Ed. Richard Zimmerl. adv. contact: Walter Podlesak. bk.rev.; charts; illus.; mkt. circ. 7,000. **Document type:** newsletter.

769.56 — GW — ISSN 0933-968X
BRIEFMARKEN MAGAZIN. 1981. bi-m. E M S Verlag GmbH, Bientzlestr. 3, 70599 Stuttgart, Germany. TEL 0711-454098. FAX 0711-4570666. Ed. Wolfgang Erzinger. adv. contact: Christina Adelmann. circ. 15,000. (back issues avail.) **Document type:** consumer publication.
Formerly: *Jahrbuch der Philatelie.*

789.56 — GW — ISSN 0007-005X
BRIEFMARKEN POST. 1958. m. Philapress Verlag der Goettinger Tageblatt GmbH, Postfach 3042, 37020 Goettingen, Germany. TEL 0551-499050. FAX 0551-4990530. adv.: B&W page DM.1020, color page DM.3270; trim 176 x 122. circ. 27,800 (paid). **Document type:** consumer publication.

769.56 — GW — ISSN 0007-0041
BRIEFMARKEN-SPIEGEL; internationale Philatelie. 1961. m. DM.45.60 (foreign DM.66). Philapress Verlag der Goettinger Tageblatt GmbH, Postfach 3042, 37020 Goettingen, Germany. TEL 0551-49905-0. FAX 0551-4990530. Ed. Gerd Aschoff. adv.: B&W page DM.2060; trim 185 x 261; adv. contact: Irmgard Kessler-Winkelbach. bk.rev. circ. 41,000. **Document type:** bulletin.

769.56 — GW — ISSN 0171-1970
BRIEFMARKENWELT. 1978. 5/yr. DM.27.50. E M S Verlag GmbH, Bientzlestr. 3, 70599 Stuttgart, Germany. TEL 0711-454098. FAX 0711-4570666. Ed. Wolfgang Erzinger. adv.; bk.rev. circ. 85,000. (back issues avail.)

769.56 — CN — ISSN 0045-2890
HE6187
BRITISH CARIBBEAN PHILATELIC JOURNAL. 1961. q. $18 membership (effective 1995). British Caribbean Philatelic Study Group, Box 20145, Ottawa, ON K1N 9P4, Canada. TEL 613-789-4933. FAX 613-789-4280. Ed. Michel Forand. adv. contact: Charles E. Cwiakala. bk.rev.; charts; illus.; index. circ. 500. (back issues avail.) **Indexed:** Stamp J.Ind.
Description: Publishes research and information about the stamps and postal history of the British West Indies, British Honduras (Belize), British Guiana (Guyana) and Bermuda.

769.56 — NE — ISSN 0950-575X
BRITISH JOURNAL OF RUSSIAN PHILATELY. (Text in English; summaries occasionally in transliterated Russian) 1946. s-a. £10($15) (membership). Postbus 16636, 1001 RC Amsterdam, Netherlands. Ed. I.J. Steyn. bk.rev.; index; circ. 250 (controlled). **Indexed:** Stamp J.Ind.
Description: Specialist articles on the philately of present and past Russian territories.

769.56 — UK — ISSN 0953-8119
BRITISH PHILATELIC BULLETIN. 1963. m. £12.50. British Post Office, Royal Mail National, 12 Finsbury Sq., London EC2A 1NL, England. (Subscr. to: British Philatelic Bureau, 20 Brandon St., Edinburgh EH3 5TT, Scotland) Ed. John Holman. bk.rev.; charts; illus.; stat.; index. circ. 40,000. (back issues avail.) **Indexed:** Child.Lit.Abstr. **Document type:** bulletin.
—BLDSC (2336.320000).
Description: Covers a wide range of philatelic topics pertaining to the British post.

769.56 — UK
BRITISH PHILATELIC FEDERATION. CONGRESS HANDBOOK. a. $3. British Philatelic Federation Ltd., 107 Charterhouse St., London EC1M 6PT, England. TEL 071-251-5040. FAX 071-490-4253. Ed. Robert Seaman. adv.

789.56 — UK — ISSN 0955-923X
BRITISH POSTMARK BULLETIN. 1971. s-m. £10 (foreign £21.75). Royal Mail, 22 Finsbury Sq., London EC2A 1NL, England. (Subscr. to: British Philatelic Bureau, 20 Brandon St., Edinburgh EH3 5TT, Scotland. TEL 0131-550-8989) Ed. John Holman. bk.rev.; illus. circ. 2,000. **Document type:** bulletin.
Description: Provides details of forthcoming postmarks and background articles on postmarks of the past.

769.56 — UK
BRITISH POSTMARK SOCIETY. QUARTERLY BULLETIN. 1958. q. £7. British Postmark Society, c/o A.J. Howard, Secy., 21 Empress Way, Euxton, Chorley, Lancs. PR7 6QB, England. TEL 0257-269652. Ed. B.R. Reynolds. bk.rev. circ. 350. **Document type:** bulletin.

769.56 — FR
BULLETIN COLFRA. 1974. q. 160 F. Societe Philatelique Colfra, B.P. 628, 75367 Paris Cedex 08, France. bk.rev. circ. 160. **Document type:** bulletin.
Description: Postal and philatelic history of former French colonies and territories; study and research.

769.56 — US
C A C NEWSLETTER. 1981. q. $6 to non-members. American Philatelic Society, Chapter Activities Committee, Box 8000, State College, PA 16803. TEL 814-237-3803. FAX 814-237-6128. Ed. Diana Manchester. circ. 800. **Document type:** newsletter.
Description: Keeps chapters informed of official society news, new slide programs, events and programs of interest to chapters, and serves as a forum for the exchange of information among chapters.

769.56 — CN
C.A.F.I.P. BULLETIN. bi-m. Can.$35. Canadian Association for Israel Philately, 260 Adelaide St. E., P.O. Box 33, Toronto, ON M5A 1N0, Canada. TEL 416-635-1749. Ed. Joseph Berkovits. bk.rev.; abstr.; bibl.; illus. circ. 60. (back issues avail.) **Document type:** bulletin.

769.56 — US — ISSN 0746-2433
C O R O S CHRONICLE. 1948. bi-m. $7.50. Collectors of Religion on Stamps, 226 Robin Hood Rd., Mountainside, NJ 07092. Ed. Eileen E. Freeman. adv.; bk.rev. circ. 750.

769.56 — NZ — ISSN 1172-0166
CAMPBELL PATERSON NEWSLETTER; for collectors of New Zealand Stamps. 1949. m. NZ.$35. Campbell Paterson Ltd., P.O. Box 5555, Auckland 1, New Zealand. TEL 3793086. FAX 3793087. Ed. Warwick R. Paterson. bk.rev. circ. 2,000. **Document type:** newsletter.
—CCC.
Former titles (until 1992): *C.P. Newsletter Monthly* (ISSN 0112-8388); *Campbell Paterson Newsletter.*

769.56 — NZ
CAMPBELL PATERSON'S LOOSE-LEAF COLOUR CATALOGUE OF NEW ZEALAND STAMPS (SPECIALISED). 1950. a. NZ.$111.95. Campbell Paterson Ltd., P.O. Box 5555, Auckland 1, New Zealand. TEL 3793086. FAX 3793087. Ed. Campbell Paterson. **Document type:** catalog.
Description: Guide for collectors of New Zealand stamps from 1854 to the present day.

769.56 — US
CANADA AIR MAIL NOTES. (Published as part of *Jack Knight Air Log*) vol.15, 1973. q. $15 (foreign $20). American Air Mail Society, Jack Knight Air Mail Society, Box 1239, Elgin, IL 60121-1239. TEL 708-468-0840. (Co-sponsor: Canadian Air Mail Collectors Club) Ed. Richard K. Malott. adv.; bk.rev. (processed) **Document type:** bulletin.

769.56 — CN — ISSN 1195-0064
CANADIAN CONNECTION. 1987. q. Can.$10 (effective 1995 & 1996). Canadiana Study Unit, c/o John G. Peebles, Ed., P.O. Box 3262, Sta. A, London, ON N6A 4K3, Canada. E-mail: johnpeeb@village.ca. illus.; circ. 140 (paid). **Document type:** newsletter.

769.56 — CN — ISSN 0045-5253
CANADIAN PHILATELIST. 1950. bi-m. membership. (Royal Philatelic Society of Canada) Philaprint Ltd., Box 100, First Canadian Pl., Toronto, ON M5X 1B2, Canada. TEL 519-846-9954. Ed. Steve Thorning. adv.; bk.rev.; index; circ. 7,000 (controlled). **Indexed:** Can.B.P.I., CMI, Stamp J.Ind.

769.56 — CN — ISSN 0702-3154
CANADIAN STAMP NEWS. 1976. bi-w. Can.$24. Trajan Publishing Corp., 202-103 Lakeshore Rd., Catherines, ON L2N 2T6, Canada. TEL 905-646-7744. FAX 905-646-0995. Ed. Ellen Rodger. adv.: B&W page $795. bk.rev.; illus.; stat. circ. 10,424. **Indexed:** Can.B.P.I., CMI.

769.56 — JM
CARIBBEAN STAMP EXCHANGE AND PENPAL BULLETIN. 1983. bi-m. $4. Allen & Associates, P.O. Box 501, Kingston, Jamaica, W.I. Ed. Stewart Allen. tr.lit. circ. 600. (looseleaf format; back issues avail.)

769.56 — US — ISSN 0891-0758
CARTO-PHILATELIST. 1955. q. 15. c/o Miklos Pinther, Pres., 206 Grayson Pl., Teaneck, NJ 07666. FAX 201-836-5602. (Subscr. to: c/o C. Mugnier, Sect., Dept. of Civil Engineering, University of New Orleans, LA 70148) (Co-sponsors: American Topical Association; American Philatelic Society) Ed. Mark D. Larkin. adv.; bk.rev. circ. 210.
Description: News and articles on the science and art of map making and their depiction on postage stamps.

769.56 — UK — ISSN 0142-9876
CENTRAL AMERICA STAMP CATALOGUE. 1980. irreg. price varies. Stanley Gibbons Publications Ltd., Unit 5 Parkside, Christchurch Rd., Ringwood, Hants. BH24 3SH, England. TEL 0425-472363. FAX 0425-470247. TELEX 41271-SGPPUB-G. **Document type:** catalog.

769.56 — UK — ISSN 0142-9884
CENTRAL ASIA STAMP CATALOGUE. 1981. irreg. price varies. Stanley Gibbons Publications Ltd., Unit 5 Parkside, Christchurch Rd., Ringwood, Hants. BH24 3SH, England. TEL 0425-472363. FAX 0425-470247. TELEX 41271-SGPPUB-G. **Document type:** catalog.

769.56 — UK — ISSN 0142-5625
CHANNEL ISLANDS SPECIALISED CATALOGUE. 1979. irreg. price varies. Stanley Gibbons Publications Ltd., Unit 5 Parkside, Christchurch Rd., Ringwood, Hants. BH24 3SH, England. TEL 0425-472363. FAX 0425-470247. TELEX 41271-SGPPUB-G. **Document type:** catalog.

769.56 794.1 — US
CHESSTAMP REVIEW.* 1978. q. $7 (foreign $11). Chess on Stamps Study Unity, Box 9789, Midland, TX 79706-2739. Ed. Russ Ott. circ. 175. (back issues avail.)

769.56 — CL
CHILE FILATELICO. 1929. q. $5 per no. Almirante Simpson 75, Casilla 13245, Santiago, Chile. TEL 56-2-222-8036. Ed. Manuel de la Lastra B. circ. 750.

PHILATELY 5123

769.56 US ISSN 0885-9779
CHINA CLIPPER; remember the old, but know the new. 1936. bi-m. $15. China Stamp Society, Inc., c/o Clarence Springstead, 1529 Hickory Lane, Bettendorf, IA 52722. TEL 319-359-6765. FAX 405-794-1350. Ed. Donald R. Alexander. adv.; bk.rev. circ. 1,041. **Indexed:** Stamp J.Ind. **Document type:** academic/scholarly publication.
Description: Devoted to all aspects of Chinese philately. Contains studies and articles of interest, brief reports of new findings, inquiries and response, and data concerning new issues.

769.56 CC ISSN 1002-6789
CHINA PHILATELY; the bi-monthly magazine for stamp collectors. 1982. bi-m. $22 to individuals; institutions $34. All-China Philatelic Federation, 111 Nanzhugan Lane, Chaonei St., Beijing, People's Republic of China. FAX 86-1-513-9036. (Dist. outside China by: Guoji Shudian - China International Book Trading Corp., P.O. Box 399, Beijing, P.R.C.; Dist. in U.S. by: China Books & Periodicals, Inc., 2929 24th St., San Francisco, CA 94110. TEL 415-282-2994) Ed. Yin Xinzhang. adv.: B&W page $500, color page $1500. circ. 30,000. (back issues avail.)
Description: News of Chinese stamps, philatelic findings, trends in China and abroad, philatelic activities, and latest market values.

769.56 UK ISSN 0142-9892
CHINA STAMP CATALOGUE. 1979. irreg. price varies. Stanley Gibbons Publications Ltd., Unit 5 Parkside, Christchurch Rd., Ringwood, Hants. BH24 3SH, England. TEL 0425-472363. FAX 0425-470247. TELEX 41271-SGPPUB-G. **Document type:** catalog.

769.56 US
CHINA TRADER NEWSLETTER. 1980. q. $7.50. China Trader Supply, Box 630, Millbrook, NY 12545. Ed. Gene Klein. adv. circ. 200. **Document type:** newsletter.
Formerly: China.

769.56 US ISSN 0009-6008
HE6187
CHRONICLE OF U S CLASSIC POSTAL ISSUES. 1965. q. $24. U S Philatelic Classics Society, Inc., Briarwood, Lisbon, MD 21765. FAX 410-489-5318. Ed. Charles J. Peterson. adv. contact: Richard M. Wrona. bk.rev.; illus.; tr.lit. circ. 1,250. **Indexed:** Stamp J.Ind.

769.56 UK ISSN 0009-6911
CINDERELLA PHILATELIST. 1961. q. £10 to non-members. Cinderella Stamp Club, c/o L.N. Williams, 44 The Ridgeway, London NW11 8QS, England. adv.; bk.rev.; illus.; index; circ. 800 (controlled). **Indexed:** Stamp J.Ind.

769.56 US
CIVIL CENSORSHIP STUDY GROUP BULLETIN. 1973. q. $9. Civil Censorship Study Group, c/o L.D. Mayo, 4305 Wyandotte Dr., Indianapolis, IN 46220-5765. Eds. Regis Hoffman, A.R. Torrance. circ. 200. **Document type:** bulletin.

769.56 VE
CLUB FILATELICO DE CARACAS. GACETA MENSUAL. 1978-1981; resumed 1986. m. exchange basis. Club Filatelico de Caracas, Apartado 61.197, Caracas 1060-A, Venezuela. FAX 782-17-31. adv.; bk.rev. circ. 500.
Formerly (until no.80, 1981): Fila Nova; **Supersedes (1961-1978):** Club Filatelico de Caracas. Revista (ISSN 0529-9853)

769.56 PO ISSN 0009-9651
CLUBE FILATELICO DE PORTUGAL. BOLETIM. 1943. 4/yr. $10 (effective Jan. 1994). Clube Filatelico de Portugal, Av. Almirante Reis 70, 5 Dto., 1100 Lisbon, Portugal. TEL 351-1-8123936. Ed. Lages Cardoso. adv. contact: J. Dias Ferreira. bk.rev.; illus. circ. 5,000. **Document type:** bulletin.

769.56 913 US ISSN 0896-3533
CODEX FILATELICA. 1974. bi-m. $8 in U.S.; Canada and Mexico $9; elsewhere $20. Meso American Archeology Study Unit, Box 1442, Riverside, CA 92502. Ed. Chris L. Moser. bk.rev. circ. 95. **Document type:** newsletter.
Description: Newsletter for collectors of worldwide stamps that illustrate or relate to Pre-Columbian archeology.

769.56 UK ISSN 0264-679X
COLLECT BIRDS ON STAMPS. 1983. irreg. price varies. Stanley Gibbons Publications Ltd., Unit 5 Parkside, Christchurch Rd., Ringwood, Hants. BH24 3SH, England. TEL 0425-472363. FAX 0425-470247. TELEX 41271-SGPPUB-G. **Document type:** catalog.

769.56 UK ISSN 0069-5262
COLLECT BRITISH STAMPS. 1967. a. price varies. Stanley Gibbons Publications Ltd., Unit 5 Parkside, Christchurch Rd., Ringwood, Hants. BH24 3SH, England. TEL 0425-472363. FAX 0425-470247. TELEX 41271-SGPPUB-G. **Document type:** catalog.

769.56 UK
COLLECT MAMMALS ON STAMPS. 1986. irreg. price varies. Stanley Gibbons Publications Ltd., Unit 5 Parkside, Christchurch Rd., Ringwood, Hants. BH24 3SH, England. TEL 0425-472363. FAX 0425-470247. TELEX 41271-SGPPUB-G. Ed. David Aggersberg. **Document type:** consumer publication.

769.56 UK
COLLECT RAILWAYS ON STAMPS. 1986. irreg. price varies. Stanley Gibbons Publications Ltd., Unit 5 Parkside, Christchurch Rd., Ringwood, Hants. BH24 3SH, England. TEL 0425-472363. FAX 0425-470247. TELEX 41271-SGPPUB-G. Ed. David Aggersberg. **Document type:** consumer publication.

769.56 UK
COLLECT SHIPS ON STAMPS. 1989. irreg. price varies. Stanley Gibbons Publications Ltd., Unit 5 Parkside, Christchurch Rd., Ringwood, Hants. BH24 3SH, England. TEL 0425-472363. FAX 0425-470247. TELEX 41271-SGPPUB-G. Ed. David Aggersberg. **Document type:** consumer publication.

769.56 990 AT ISSN 0727-4211
COLLECTION OF AUSTRALIAN STAMPS. 1981. a. Aus.$54.95. Australia Post Headquarters, Philatelic Group, G.P.O. Box 1777Q, Melbourne, Vic. 3001, Australia. FAX 03-204-7744. (Subscr. to: Philatelic Bureau, G.P.O. Box 9988, Melbourne, Vic. 3001, Australia) illus. **Document type:** catalog.
Description: Features all Australian stamps and details of issue.

769.56 FR ISSN 0396-9096
COLLECTIONNEUR PHILATELISTE ET MARCOPHILE. 1969. q. membership. Cercle Lyonnais d'Etudes Philateliques et Marcophiles, 17 rue Colin, 34000 Montpellier, France. Ed. A. Camboulives. adv. circ. 500.

769.56 US ISSN 0010-0838
HE6187
COLLECTORS CLUB PHILATELIST. 1922. bi-m. $42 (effective 1995). Collectors Club, Inc., 22 E. 35th St., New York, NY 10016-0559. TEL 212-683-0559. FAX 2120-481-1269. Ed. E.E. Fricks. adv.; bk.rev.; abstr.; illus.; index, cum.index. circ. 1,500. **Indexed:** Stamp J.Ind. **Document type:** academic/scholarly publication.
Description: Covers philatelic subjects the world over, with emphasis on US.
Refereed Serial

769.56 US
COLLECTOR'S MARKETPLACE; buy, trade, sell. 1981. bi-m. $8.95. Box 25, Stewartsville, NJ 08886. TEL 908-479-4614. FAX 908-479-6158. Ed. Dorothy J. Graf. **Document type:** consumer publication.
Formerly (until 1986): Stamp Exchange.

769.56 IT ISSN 0010-1265
COLLEZIONISTA - ITALIA FILATELICA. 1945. m. L.72000. (Societa Culturale Opere Tipografiche) Giulio Bolaffi Editore s.r.l., Via Cavour 17-F, 10123 Turin, Italy. TEL 39-11-5625556. FAX 39-11-5620456. Ed. Alberto Bolaffi. adv.: B&W page L.2250000. bk.rev.; illus.; index. circ. 20,300.

769.56 US
COLUMBIAN (COLUMBUS). 1925. m. $8. Columbus Philatelic Club, Inc., Box 20582, Columbus, OH 43220-0582. FAX 614-457-5205. Ed. Diana Manchester. adv.; bk.rev.; circ. 145 (paid). **Document type:** newsletter.
Description: News, announcements, and articles of interest to the activities and members of the club, with lists of auction items.

769.56 US
COMMONWEALTH PHILATELY. 1980. bi-m. $7. Commonwealth International Philatelic Society, c/o Bill Scheuermann, Box 195, Minetto, NY 13115. TEL 315-343-5372. Ed. Ryan G. Lorenz. adv. circ. 125. **Indexed:** Stamp J.Ind.

769.56 IT ISSN 0393-1307
CRONACA FILATELICA; mensile di filatelia, storia postale, annulli e interi. 1970. m. L.66000 (Europe L.120000; elsewhere L.180000) (effective 1995). Eder s.r.l., Casella Postale 1065, 80100 Naples, Vomero, Italy. TEL 081-7611315. FAX 081-7611316. Ed. Carlo A. DeRosa. adv.: B&W page L.2100000, color page L.3600000; trim 185 x 259; adv. contact: Alf DeRosa. bk.rev. circ. 26,609.

769.56 US
CUBAN TOPICS. 1976. q. $5. Box 52-0002, Miami, FL 33152. Ed. Agustin J. Cantens. adv.; bk.rev. circ. 1,000.
Description: Covers articles and news about Cuban philately and postal history, and related field of collection.

769.56 US ISSN 0526-5843
THE CZECHOSLOVAK SPECIALIST. 1939. bi-m. $18. Society for Czechoslovak Philately, Inc., 2363 McCleary Dr., Chambersburg, PA 17201. TEL 717-263-5523. Ed. Mirko L. Vondra. adv. contact: Donna Lyons. bk.rev.; charts; illus.; cum. index 1939-1994. circ. 500. **Indexed:** Stamp J.Ind. **Document type:** consumer publication.
Description: Focuses on philatelic issues, particularly on Czech stamps. Also contains sales circuit updates and opinion.

769.56 UK ISSN 0142-9795
CZECHOSLOVAKIA & POLAND STAMP CATALOGUE. 1980. irreg. price varies. Stanley Gibbons Publications Ltd., Unit 5 Parkside, Christchurch Rd., Ringwood, Hants. BH24 3SH, England. TEL 0425-472363. FAX 0425-470247. TELEX 41271-SGPPUB-G. **Document type:** catalog.

769.56 UK ISSN 0142-3525
CZECHOUT. 1975. q. membership. Czechoslovak Philatelic Society of Great Britain, c/o Colin W. Spong, Ed., 70 Westlake Gardens, Worthing, W. Sussex BN13 1LF, England. TEL 01903-267803. bk.rev. circ. 300. **Document type:** bulletin.
Description: Disseminates and exchanges information on the philately of the Czech Republic and Slovakia.

769.56 GW ISSN 0011-4790
D B Z. (Deutsche Zeitung fuer Briefmarkenkunde) 1925. bi-w. DM.84. Deutsche Briefmarkenzeitung GmbH & Co. KG, Postfach 1363, 56373 Nassau, Germany. TEL 02604-970144. FAX 02604-970151. adv. contact: Michael Bowe. index; circ. 52,867. (back issues avail.) **Document type:** bulletin.

769.56 US ISSN 0882-0236
D O S S U JOURNAL. 1979. q. $3 (foreign $5). American Topical Association, Dogs on Stamps Study Unit, 3208 Hana Rd., Edison, NJ 08817-2552. TEL 908-248-1865. Ed. Morris Raskin. adv. circ. 275. **Document type:** newsletter.
Description: For philatelists interested in the collection and study of postal materials depicting dogs.

769.56 US
DAKOTA COLLECTOR. 1983. q. membership. North Dakota Postal History Society, Box 280, Maddock, ND 58348. Ed. Gordon Twedt. adv.: B&W page $20; trim 8 1/2 x 11. bk.rev. circ. 100. (back issues avail.)
Description: Publishes articles on various cancels and postal history of North and South Dakota.

769.36 DK ISSN 0903-2444
DANSK FILATELISTISK TIDSSKRIFT. 1934. 9/yr. DKK 150. Danmarks Filatelist Forbund, Fuglefaengervej 8, 3400 Hillerod, Denmark. TEL 45-42-26-98-54. FAX 45-42-26-98-54. Ed. Lennart Weber. adv.; bk.rev. circ. 8,000.

769.56 US
DAYTON STAMP CLUB. NEWSLETTER. vol.8, 1982. m. Dayton Stamp Club, Inc., Box 1574, Dayton, OH 45401. Ed. Martin Richardson. **Document type:** newsletter.

ULRICH'S INTERNATIONAL PERIODICALS DIRECTORY 1996

PHILATELY

737 769   GW   ISSN 0930-858X
DEUTSCHE BRIEFMARKEN - REVUE; SD - Sammlerdienst. 1949. m. DM.55 (foreign DM.71). (Fachblatt fuer Philatelie) P S B N - Verlagsgesellschaft mbH, Konkordiastr. 13, 40219 Duesseldorf, Germany. TEL 0211-394032. FAX 0211-3982225. Ed. Dieter Stein. adv.: B&W page DM.1375, color page DM.2700; trim 263 x 188; adv. contact: Hans Paikert. bk.rev.; illus. circ. 30,000. (back issues avail. **Document type:** consumer publication.

769.56   US
THE DISPATCHER (SAN FRANCISCO, 1950). 1950. bi-m. $5. Casey Jones Railroad Unit - A T A (Subsidiary of: American Topical Association), Box 31631, San Francisco, CA 94131. TEL 415-648-8057. Ed. Oliver C. Atchison. adv.; bk.rev.; illus. circ. 400. (looseleaf format) **Document type:** newsletter.
Formerly: American Topical Association. Casey Jones Railroad Unit. Newsletter.
Description: News and announcements pertaining to railroad-stamp collecting, with lists of recent and special issues.

769.56   FR   ISSN 1141-1341
DOCUMENTS PHILATELIQUES. 1959. q. 220 F. Academie de Philatelie de Paris, c/o J.P. Schroeder, 7 av. Beaucour, 75008 Paris, France. bk.rev.; illus. circ. 500. (tabloid format) **Document type:** bulletin.

769.56   US
E F O COLLECTOR. 1978. 6/yr. $16 (foreign $30). E F O Collectors Club, 1903 Village RD-W, Norwood, MA 02062-2516. TEL 800-236-2128. Ed. Cwo Jim McDevitt. adv.; bk.rev. circ. 350. (back issues avail.)

769.56   FR   ISSN 0012-9240
ECHO DE LA TIMBROLOGIE; revue mensuelle de philatelie. 1887. m. 103 F. 37 rue des Jacobins, 80036 Amiens, France. Ed. Jacques Gervais. adv.; bk.rev.; bibl.; illus.; mkt.; index.

769.56   CN   ISSN 0046-1318
EDMONTON STAMP CLUB BULLETIN. 1965. m. Can.$15. Edmonton Stamp Club, P.O. Box 399, Edmonton, AB, Canada. TEL 403-492-0473. FAX 403-492-7196. Ed. Keith R. Spencer. adv.; bk.rev. circ. 500. **Document type:** bulletin.

769.56   US
EESTI FILATELIST/ESTONIAN PHILATELIST. (Text in English, Estonian, German, Swedish) 1955. a. SEK 150($20) (Society of Estonian Philatelists in Sweden) Estonian Philatelic Society, c/o Rudolf Hamar, 31 Addison Terr., Old Tappan, NJ 07675. TEL 201-767-0535. FAX 212-643-1903. (Addr. in Sweden: c/o Teleskopgatan 18, Goteborg, Steden S-41518) Ed. Elmar Ojaste. circ. 700. (back issues avail.) **Document type:** bulletin.

769.56   US
EMERT'S STAMP QUARTERLY. q. $2. Buckingham Publications, Box 46, Buckingham, VA 23921.

769.56   GW
ERINNOPHILIE INTERNATIONAL. 1965. irreg. (3-4/yr.). DM.50. Erinnophilie International im Bund Deutscher Philatelisten e.V., c/o Herbert Geier, Postfach 1308, 96227 Staffelstein, Germany. TEL 09573-1870. (back issues avail.) **Document type:** consumer publication.

789.56 737   LU
EUROPHIL NEWS. (Text in Dutch, English, French, German) 1986. m. 650 Fr.($30) Europhil, 19 rue du Golf, 1638 Senningerberg, Luxembourg. TEL 352-34-04-69. Pub. Oege Weijs. adv.: B&W page 3000 Fr. circ. 1,000 (paid). **Document type:** newsletter.

769.56   GW
F I A S - REPORT; Mitteilungsblatt der Forschungsgemeinschaft Internationale Antwortscheine, Bundesarbeitsgemeinschaft im Bund Deutscher Philatelisten. 1972. s-a. DM.24. F I A S, c/o Horst Hoffmann, Ed., Schillerstr. 3, 29525 Uelzen, Germany. adv.; bk.rev. circ. 100. (back issues avail.)

769.56   US
EL FARO.* 1975. 4/yr. $8. Associated Collectors of El Salvador, c/o Robert A. Fisher, Ed., 28 Edgewood Dr., Granville, OH 43023-1076. adv.; circ. 100 (controlled). (processed) **Indexed:** Stamp J.Ind.
Formerly (until 1978): A C E S.

769.569   DK   ISSN 0900-1131
FAROE ISLANDS. POSTAGE STAMPS & POSTMARKS.* Variant title: Foeroyar. Postmarks and Postage Stamps. 1970. irreg. DKK 98. G F Frimaerker, Virum, Denmark.

769.56   GW
FEUERMELDER RUNDBRIEF. (Text in English and German) 1975. q. DM.45. Motiv-Arge Feuerwehr e.V., Buchenbergerstr. 26, 78112 St. Georgen, Germany. TEL 07724-6791. Ed. Hans-Ruediger Kohn. circ. 350. (looseleaf format) **Document type:** newsletter.

769.56   RM   ISSN 0428-3341
FILATELIA. (Text in Rumanian; summaries in English, French, German, Russian) 1958. m. $46. Federatia Filatelica Romana - Romanian Philatelic Federation, Strada Boteanu Nr.6, Bucharest 1, Rumania. (Subscr. to: Magazine "Filatelia", C.P. 1-870, 70100 Bucharest, Rumania) Ed. Aurelian Darnu. adv.; bk.rev.; bibl.; illus. circ. 12,000. (tabloid format)

769.56   CU   ISSN 0138-631X
FILATELIA CUBANA. (Text in Spanish; summaries in English, French) 3/yr. $10 in N. and S. America; Europe $12. (Federacion Filatelica Cubano) Ediciones Cubanas, Obispo No. 527, Apdo. 605, Havana, Cuba. illus.
Description: Contains articles on stamp history; critical studies of Cuban stamps; and information on the activities carried out by the Federation and stamp clubs in Cuba and abroad; for collectors of stamps and first-day issues.

769.56   IT   ISSN 0015-0940
FILATELIA ITALIANA. 1960. m. Via della Mercede 11, 00187 Rome, Italy. Ed. Michele Picardi. adv.; bk.rev.; illus.; index. circ. 37,500.

769.56   HU   ISSN 0133-168X
HE6187
FILATELIAI SZEMLE. m. $22.50. Pf. 4 H-1387, Budapest, Hungary. (Subscr. to: Kultura, Pf. 149 H-1389, Budapest, Hungary) Ed. Bela Milassin.

769.56
FILATELICO. m. Casella Postale 176, 95100 Catania, Italy. Ed. Luigi Musumarra.

769.56   XR   ISSN 0015-0959
FILATELIE. (Text in Czech or Slovak; summaries in English, French, German, Russian) 1950. s-m. 72 Kc.($63) (Svaz Ceskoslovenskych Filatelistu) Filatelie, spol. s r.o., Klimetska 6, 110 00 Prague 1, Czech Republic. (Dist. by: Artia, Ve Smeckach 30, 111 27 Prague 1, Czech Republic) Ed. Frantisek Benes. adv.; bk.rev.; illus. circ. 22,000.

769.56   CI   ISSN 0015-0967
FILATELIJA. (Text in Croatian; summary in English) 1940. irreg. (3-4/yr.). $4 per no. Hrvatski Filatelisticki Savez - Croatian Philatelic Union, Habdeliceva 2, 41000 Zagreb, Croatia. Ed. Nenad Nikolic. adv.; bk.rev.; illus.; index. circ. 4,000.

769.56   SW   ISSN 1100-0198
HE6187
FILATELISTEN (SKARA); svensk filatelistisk tidskrift. 1900. m. (10/yr.). SEK 260. Sveriges Filatelist-Foerbund, Klostergatan 15, S-532 30 Skara, Sweden. TEL 0511-12891. FAX 0511-12123. Ed. Goesta Karlsson. adv.; bk.rev.; index. circ. 13,600.
Incorporates: Frimaerksledaren; Formerly (until 1988): Svensk Filatelistisk Tidskrift (ISSN 0039-6532)

769.56   FI
FILATELISTI; stamp journal. (Text in Finnish and Swedish) 1950. 10/yr. FIM 180 (outside Scandinavia FIM 300). Suomen Filatelistiliitto r.y. - Philatelic Federation of Finland, Mannerheimintie 11 A, P.O. Box 257, FIN-00101 Helsinki, Finland. TEL 358-0-195-4078. FAX 358-0-195-4091. Eds. Pekka Taitto, Lauri Poropudas. adv.: B&W page FIM 1600; trim 186 x 256. bk.rev.; illus.; cum.index. circ. 6,000. (tabloid format) **Document type:** consumer publication.
Formerly (until 1991): Philatelia Fennica (ISSN 0355-502X)

769.56   RU   ISSN 0869-4478
FILATELIYA. 1966. m. $66 (effective 1996). (Rossiiskoe Obshchestvo Filatelistov - Russian Philatelic Society) Torgovyi Tsentr "Marka" - "Marka" Publishing and Trading Centre, Khlebny per. 8, 121069 Moscow, Russia. (Dist. by: B. Yakimanka 39, 117049 Moscow, Russia; Dist. in U.S. by: Victor Kamkin Inc., 4956 Boiling Brook Pkwy., Rockville, MD 20852. TEL 301-881-5973) Ed. J.G. Bekhterev. illus.; index. circ. 70,000.
Formerly: Filateliya S.S.S.R. (ISSN 0015-0983)

769.56   DR
FILOTELICO. 1977. bi-m. RD.$200($20) (Sociedad Filatelica Dominicana) Impresos de Calidad, Apartado 1930, Santo Domingo, Dominican Republic. Ed. Danilo A. Mueses. adv.; bk.rev. circ. 425. (back issues avail.) **Document type:** bulletin.

769.56   US   ISSN 0428-4836
FIRST DAYS. 1956. 8/yr. $20. American First Day Cover Society, Box 5424, Fairlawn, OH 44333. TEL 602-321-9206. Ed. Barry Newton. adv.: B&W page $148; trim 4 3/4 x 8. bk.rev.; illus.; index. circ. 4,000. **Indexed:** Stamp J.Ind. **Document type:** academic/scholarly publication.

769.56   UK   ISSN 0951-7561
FORCES POSTAL HISTORY SOCIETY. NEWSLETTER. 1952. q. membership. Forces Postal History Society, 48 Grange Bottom, Royston, Herts. SG8 9UQ, England. (Alt. addr.: 4 Springfield Ct., London SW19 7AJ, England) Ed. B. Ferguson; Pub. A.L. Kennedy. adv.; bk.rev. circ. 350. **Document type:** bulletin.

789.56   US   ISSN 1076-2612
FORERUNNERS. 1987. 3/yr. $20 includes membership. Philatelic Society for Greater Southern Africa, c/o William C. Brooks, Ed., Box 2698, San Bernardino, CA 92406-2698. TEL 909-882-3946. FAX 909-882-3946. adv.; bk.rev. circ. 200.
Description: Publishes scholarly articles, reviews and research efforts relating to southern African stamps.

769.56   GW
FORSCHUNGSGEMEINSCHAFT BERLIN. RUNDBRIEF. 1971. q. membership. Forschungsgemeinschaft Berlin, c/o Peter Koegel, Postfach 210724, 10507 Berlin, Germany. TEL 030-3452735. Eds. Klaus Janssen, Guenter Klein. circ. 140. (back issues avail.)
Description: Philatelic studies of Berlin.

769.56   UK   ISSN 0269-5006
FRANCE & COLONIES PHILATELIC SOCIETY OF GREAT BRITAIN. JOURNAL. 1951. q. £8 (rest of Europe £11; elsewhere £13) (effective 1996). France & Colonies Philatelic Society, 31 Wheatsheaf Close, Horsham, W. Sussex RH12 5TH, England. TEL 01280-815090. Ed. M.S. Tyler. adv. contact: M.S. Tyler. bk.rev.; circ. 400 (paid). **Document type:** newsletter.
Former titles: France and Colonies Philatelic Society. Bulletin; France and Colonies Philatelic Society. Newsletter; France and Colonies Philatelic Society. Journal.

769.56   UK   ISSN 0142-9809
FRANCE STAMP CATALOGUE. 1979. irreg. price varies. Stanley Gibbons Publications Ltd., Unit 5 Parkside, Christchurch Rd., Ringwood, Hants. BH24 3SH, England. TEL 0425-472363. FAX 0425-470247. TELEX 41271-SGPPUB-G. **Document type:** catalog.

769   IT
FRANCOBOLLI;* rivista mensile di filatelia. 1970. m. (11/yr.). L.25000($50) Sassone Editrice s.r.l., Via A. Vera, 19, 00142 Rome, Italy. Ed. Renato Russo. adv. circ. 10,000.

769.56   DK   ISSN 0108-4089
FRIMAERKENS VERDEN. 1982. m. DKK 57.50. Nordfrim, Kvindevadet 42, 5450 Otterup, Denmark. adv.; bk.rev.; illus.

769.56   DK   ISSN 0016-1438
FRIMAERKESAMLEREN. 1942. 7/yr. DKK 210($32) Birkemosevej 4, DK-2750 Ballerup, Denmark. TEL 44-97-71-71. FAX 44-97-71-71. Ed. Andreas Abitz. adv.; bk.rev. circ. 3,100.

769.56 737   NO   ISSN 0801-1869
FRIMERKER OG MYNTER. 1984. 3/yr. NOK 50. Alva Trading A-S, P.O. Box 889 Sentrum, N-0104 Oslo 1, Norway.

PHILATELY

769.56 US ISSN 0732-5517
FROM THE DRAGON'S DEN. 1969. 4/yr. membership. Ryukyu Philatelic Specialist Society, Box 172, Great Falls, VA 22066. Ed. Russ W. Carter. adv.; bk.rev.; charts; illus.; stat. circ. 350. (back issues avail.) **Indexed:** Stamp J.Ind.

769.56 UK ISSN 0430-8913
G B JOURNAL. (Great Britain) 1955. bi-m. £3.50 per issue. (Great Britain Philatelic Society) G B Philatelic Publications Ltd., Anso Corner Farm, Hempstead, Saffron Walden, Essex CB10 2NV, England. Eds. Mike Jackson, Harry Dagnall. adv.; bk.rev.; illus.; index. circ. 900.

769.56 US
G I P S. bi-m. membership. Government Imprinted Penalty Stationery Society, 10926 Annette Ave., Tampa, FL 33612.

769.56 IT ISSN 0016-5654
GAZZETTA FILATELICA. 1947. m. L.15000($15) Ercole Gloria s.r.l., Piazza Pio XI, No. 1, 20123 Milan, Italy. bk.rev. circ. 15,000.

769.56 US ISSN 0016-8823
GERMAN POSTAL SPECIALIST; a philatelic publication for stamp collectors specializing in Germany-related stamps. (Text in English) 1950. m. $18. Germany Philately Society, Inc., Box 779, Arnold, MD 21012. Ed. Rudolf E. Anders. adv.: B&W page $87. bk.rev.; charts; illus.; index, cum.index: vols.1-30; circ. 2,000 (paid). (also avail. in microfiche; back issues avail.) **Indexed:** Stamp J.Ind. **Document type:** academic/scholarly publication.
Description: Covers philately and postal history.

769.56 UK ISSN 0142-9817
GERMANY STAMP CATALOGUE. 1979. irreg. price varies. Stanley Gibbons Publications Ltd., Unit 5 Parkside, Christchurch Rd., Ringwood, Hants. BH24 3SH, England. TEL 0425-472363. FAX 0425-470247. TELEX 41271-SGPPUB-G. **Document type:** catalog.

769.56 UK ISSN 0016-9676
GIBBONS STAMP MONTHLY. (New Issue Supplement: Philatelic Discoveries) 1890. m. £19.20 (foreign £32). Stanley Gibbons Magazines Ltd., Unit 5 Parkside, Christchurch Rd., Ringwood, Hants. BH24 3SH, England. TEL 0425-472363. FAX 0425-470247. Ed. Hugh Jefferies. adv.; bk.rev.; illus.; mkt.; index; circ. 25,000 (paid). **Indexed:** Stamp J.Ind. **Document type:** consumer publication.

769.56 US ISSN 1060-0361
GLOBAL STAMP NEWS. 1990. m. $6.95. Brandewie Inc., 110 N. Ohio Ave., Box 97, Sidney, OH 45365. TEL 513-492-3183. FAX 513-492-6514. Ed. Jan Brandewie. adv.; illus.; circ. 20,000 (controlled).
Description: Covers worldwide stamp markets and collecting interests.

769.56 327 US ISSN 1070-3861
GLOBE UNION. 1976-1982; resumed 1988. q. $12 membership (foreign $19). Universal Postal Union Collectors, Box 607117, Orlando, FL 32860-7117. TEL 407-298-8308. E-mail: 75203.2717@CompuServe.com. (Co-sponsor: American Philatelic Society) Ed. Robert L. Malch. adv.: B&W page $20; adv. contact: Robert L. Malch. circ. 275 (paid). **Indexed:** Stamp J.Ind.
Formerly (until 1992): Universal Postal Union Collectors. Publication (ISSN 1041-8512)
Description: Fosters philatelic discussion and the study of postal history; examines postage stamps from all countries that commemorate the Universal Postal Union.

769.56 US
GREAT BRITAIN COLLECTORS CLUB. QUARTERLY NEWSLETTER. 1979. q. $15 (foreign $22). Frank J. Koch, Ed. & Pub., Box 309, Batavia, OH 45103-0309. TEL 513-634-4264. adv.; bk.rev. circ. 415. **Document type:** newsletter.
Formerly: Great Britain Correspondence Club. Quarterly Newsletter (ISSN 0887-6819)
Description: News, articles, and announcements pertaining to this stamp collection association.

769.56 UK
GREAT BRITAIN CONCISE STAMP CATALOGUE. 1986. a. £5.95. Stanley Gibbons Publications Ltd., Unit 5 Parkside, Christchurch Rd., Ringwood, Hants. BH24 3SH, England. TEL 0425-472363. FAX 0425-470247. TELEX 41271-SGPPUB-G. Ed. David Aggersberg. circ. 20,000. **Document type:** catalog.
Description: Contains facts aimed at the semi-advanced collector.

769.56 UK ISSN 0072-7229
GREAT BRITAIN SPECIALISED STAMP CATALOGUE. 1963. irreg. (in 5 vols.). price varies. Stanley Gibbons Publications Ltd., Unit 5 Parkside, Christchurch Rd., Ringwood, Hants. BH24 3SH, England. TEL 0425-472363. FAX 0425-470247. TELEX 41271-SGPPUB-G. index. **Document type:** catalog.

769.56 GT ISSN 0046-6549
HE6187
GUATEMALA FILATELICA. 1932. a. $6 membership. Asociacion Filatelica de Guatemala, Apdo. Postal 39, 01901 Guatemala City, Guatemala. Ed. Col. Romeo J. Routhier. adv.; bk.rev.; charts; illus.; stat. circ. 500.

769.56 US
HAITI PHILATELY. 1975. q. $12 (foreign $15). Haitian Philately Society, c/o Dr. Gerald L. Boarino, 834 Pierce St., Port Townsend, WA 98363. circ. 100. **Indexed:** Stamp J.Ind.

769.56 US
HAMILTON HANDBILL.* 1950. bi-w. Box 290 RR2, Jasper, FL 32052-9666. TEL 904-792-2218. Ed. Roger Ehlert. adv. circ. 2,000.

769.56 US
HANDBOOK OF INDIAN PHILATELY. 1970. irreg. $30. India Study Circle for Philately, c/o J. Warren, Box 70775, Washington, DC 20024. TEL 202-260-9464. Ed. Max Smith. illus. **Document type:** monographic series.
Description: Devoted to stamps and postal history of India.

383.2 US ISSN 0072-9981
HANDBOOK ON U S LUMINESCENT STAMPS. 1970. irreg. $6. Alfred G. Boerger, Ed. & Pub., Box 23822, Ft. Lauderdale, FL 33307. TEL 305-563-6590. adv.; circ. 3,000.

769.56 US
HAWAIIAN PHILATELIST. 1978. irreg. (approx. 6/yr.). $9.95. Los Angeles Stamp Company, c/o Gretchen H. Mitchell, Box 1387, Los Angeles, CA 90078. TEL 213-467-2215. bk.rev.

769.56 UK ISSN 0950-3102
HELLENIC PHILATELIC SOCIETY OF GREAT BRITAIN. BULLETIN. q. £1.50 per no. Hellenic Philatelic Society of Great Britain, 37 Alders View Dr., E. Grinstead, W. Sussex RH19 2DN, England. TEL 01342-326782. Ed. C. Ruffley. adv.; bk.rev. circ. 200. **Indexed:** Stamp J.Ind. **Document type:** bulletin.
Supersedes (in 1968): Hellenic Philatelic Society of Great Britain. Newsletter.

789.56 US
HIGGINS & GAGE WORLD POSTAL STATIONERY CATALOG. 1965. irreg. $280. Classic Philatelics, Box 5637, Huntington Beach, CA 92615. TEL 714-968-1717. FAX 714-968-6704. Ed. Mel Feiner. circ. 1,500. (looseleaf format) **Document type:** catalog.
Description: Lists alphabetically by country, governmental postal issues of postal stationery.

769.56 US
HOLLYWOOD PHILATELIST. 1968. m. membership. Hollywood Stamp Club, 4380 Casper Ct., Hollywood, FL 33021. Ed. Ben Wishnietsky. bk.rev. circ. 500. **Document type:** newsletter.

383 769.56 IS ISSN 0333-6875
HOLY LAND POSTAL HISTORY. (Text in English) 1979. q. $18. Society of the Postal History of Eretz-Israel, P.O. Box 10175, Jerusalem 91101, Israel. TEL 972-2-711719. Eds. E. Glassman, Z. Shimony. adv.; index. circ. 250. (back issues avail.) **Document type:** bulletin.

769.56 US ISSN 0019-1051
ICE CAP NEWS. 1955. q. $17. American Society of Polar Philatelists, c/o S.H. Jacobson, Box 945, Skokie, IL 60077. Ed. Arthur DuMont. adv.; bk.rev.; illus.; index, cum.index: vols.1-16, vols.17-25 in 1980. circ. 900. (back issues avail.) **Document type:** academic/scholarly publication, newsletter.

769.56 US
ILLINOIS POSTAL HISTORIAN. 1980. q. $12 to non-members. Illinois Postal History Society, Box 1513, Des Plaines, IL 60017. Ed. Leonard Piszkiewicz. adv.; bk.rev. circ. 225. **Document type:** academic/scholarly publication.
Description: Contains articles on postal history pertaining to Illinois cities, towns and personages

769.56 II
IND DAK; a journal in the English language devoted to philately & postal history. 1977. m. Rs.60($10) 190, Defence Colony, Indiranagar, Bangalore - 560 038, India. TEL 0812-542493. Ed. L.G. Shenoi. adv.; bk.rev. circ. 2,000. **Document type:** academic/scholarly publication.

769.56 UK ISSN 0952-7729
INDIA POST. 1967. q. £12. India Study Circle for Philately, 4 Lady Ln., Bingley, West Yorks. BD16 4AG, England. Ed. Max Smith. adv.; bk.rev.; cum.index every 3 yrs. circ. 700. **Indexed:** Stamp J.Ind. **Document type:** academic/scholarly publication.

769.56 US ISSN 0276-9573
INDO-CHINA PHILATELIST. 1970. bi-m. $15 membership. Society of Indo-China Philatelists, c/o George DeMeritte, Ed., Box 865, Largo, FL 34649-0865. TEL 813-584-0669. adv.; bk.rev. circ. 200. **Indexed:** Stamp J.Ind. **Document type:** newsletter.
Description: Provides information of interest to collectors specializing in Indo-China issues.

769.56 US ISSN 0884-8254
INFORMER (MERRYFIELD). 1947. q. $15 membership in the U.S. and Canada (foreign $16) (effective 1995). Society of Australasian Specialists - Oceania, Inc., Box 3386, Merryfield, VA 22116-3386. TEL 703-573-0317. (Subscr. to: Stuart Levin, Box 24764, San Jose, CA 95154-4764) Ed. Hugh Wynn. adv. contact: Joel L. Bromberg. bk.rev.; circ. 354 (paid). **Document type:** newsletter.
Description: Publishes original articles pertaining to Australasian postal history and stamp issues.

769.56 US ISSN 0892-9793
INTERLEAF. 1983. q. $10 (foreign $15). Booklet Collectors Club, c/o James Natale, Box 2461, Cinnaminson, NJ 08077-5461. Ed. Gerhard G. Korn. adv.; bk.rev. circ. 300. **Document type:** newsletter.
Description: Devoted to the study of worldwide booklets and booklet collecting, with emphasis on United States booklets.

INTERNATIONAL ART POST. see *ART*

769.56 SZ ISSN 0074-7343
INTERNATIONAL PHILATELIC FEDERATION. GENERAL ASSEMBLY. PROCES-VERBAL. 1973. a. free to members. International Philatelic Federation - Federation Internationale de Philatelie, Zollikerstr. 128, CH-8008 Zurich, Switzerland. FAX 01-3831446. Ed. Ms. M.L. Heiri. circ. 180. **Document type:** proceedings.

769.56 US
INTERNATIONAL PHILATELIC PRESS CLUB. REPORT TO MEMBERS. 1964. m. membership. International Philatelic Press Club, Inc., Box 114, Jamaica, NY 11419. Ed. Ernest A. Kehr. bk.rev. circ. 250. (looseleaf format) **Document type:** corporate report.

769.56 737 GW ISSN 0535-4455
INTERPHILA; international directory of philately and numismatics. (Text in English, French, German) 1963. a. DM.19.80. D B Z-Verlag, Feldstr. 6, P.O. Box 1363, 56377 Nassau, Germany. TEL 02604-701-0. circ. 6,000. **Document type:** directory.

PHILATELY

769.56 UK
IRAN PHILATELIC STUDY CIRCLE BULLETIN. 1966. 5/yr. £8. Iran Philatelic Study Circle, Flat 10, One Grand Ave., E. Sussex BN3 2LA, England. TEL 0273-777623. (Subscr. to: B. Lucas, Secretary, 99 Moseley Word Dr., Leeds LS16 7HS, England) Ed. P.A. Greenway. adv.; bk.rev. circ. 150. (looseleaf format) **Document type:** bulletin.
Formerly: Persian Study Circle Bulletin.

769.56 IE ISSN 0332-317X
IRISH STAMP NEWS. 1978. q. I£9.50($17) Ian Whyte Ltd., 30 Marlborough St., Dublin 1, Ireland. TEL 3531-8746161. FAX 3531-8746020. Ed. Ian W. Whyte. adv.; bk.rev.; illus. circ. 1,800. **Document type:** newsletter.

769.56 US ISSN 0161-0074
HE6187
ISRAEL PHILATELIST. 1948. m. $14 membership. Society of Israel Philatelists, 24355 Tunbridge Ln., Beachwood, OH 44122. TEL 216-292-3843. Ed. Oscar Stadtler. adv.; bk.rev. circ. 2,700. **Indexed:** Stamp J.Ind.

769.56 UK ISSN 0142-9825
HE6185.I7
ITALY & SWITZERLAND STAMP CATALOGUE. 1980. irreg. price varies. Stanley Gibbons Publications Ltd., Unit 5 Parkside, Christchurch Rd., Ringwood, Hants. BH24 3SH, England. TEL 0425-472363. FAX 0425-470247. TELEX 41271-SGPPUB-G. **Document type:** catalog.

769.56 US
JACK KNIGHT AIR LOG. 1943. q. $15 (foreign $20). American Air Mail Society, Jack Knight Air Mail Society, Box 1239, Elgin, IL 60121-1239. TEL 708-468-0840. Ed. Stephen Neulander. adv.; bk.rev.; bibl.; charts; illus.; stat. circ. 900. (back issues avail.)
Former titles: Jack Knight Air Log and A F A News; A F A News.
Description: For members, subscribers and friends interested in aero, astro, and specialized philately.

789.56 JM
JAMAICA PHILATELIC SOCIETY. NEWSLETTER. 1977. m. $10 for 2 yrs. (effective 1996). Jamaica Philatelic Society, c/o D.O. Uhlman, Treas., P.O. Box 201, Constant Spring P.O., Kingston 8, Jamaica, W.I. TEL 809-922-3790. FAX 809-968-7010. Ed. Ewan Cameron. circ. 50. **Document type:** newsletter.

769.56 UK ISSN 0142-9906
JAPAN & KOREA STAMP CATALOGUE. 1980. irreg. price varies. Stanley Gibbons Publications Ltd., Unit 5 Parkside, Christchurch Rd., Ringwood, Hants. BH24 3SH, England. TEL 0425-472363. FAX 0425-470247. TELEX 41271-SGPPUB-G. **Document type:** catalog.

769.56 US ISSN 0146-0994
HE6187
JAPANESE PHILATELY. 1946. bi-m. $11.50 to non-members; members $10. International Society for Japanese Philately, Inc., c/o James E. Jacobson, Office of the Publisher, 815 Springingsguth Rd., Schaumburg, IL 60193. TEL 708-844-2145. FAX 708-893-1430. (Subscr. to: Kenneth Kamholz, Sec., Box 1283, Haddonfield, NJ 08033) Ed. Robert M. Spaulding, Jr. adv.; bk.rev.; charts; illus.; index, cum.index. circ. 1,500. (also avail. in microfilm; back issues avail.) **Indexed:** Stamp J.Ind.
Description: Covers various aspects of the postal system and postal history of Japan.

769.56 CC ISSN 0529-0325
JI YOU. English edition: Chinese Philatelic Magazine. (Text in Chinese) m. (bi-m. English ed.) $35. Renmin Youdian Chubanshe - People's Post and Telecommunication Publishing House, Dong Chang'an Jie 27, Beijing 100740, People's Republic of China. TEL 8138139. (Dist. in US by: China Books & Periodicals, Inc., 2929 24th St., San Francisco, CA 94110) illus.

769.56 CC ISSN 1002-5898
JIYOU BOLAN/PHILATELY VISION. (Text in Chinese) 1987. bi-m. $18.50. Beijing Jiyou Xiehui - Beijing Philatelic Society, 5 Nanlishilu Toutiao, Fuxingmenwai, Beijing 100045, People's Republic of China. TEL 8011108. (Dist. in US by: China Books & Periodicals, Inc., 2929 24th St., San Francisco, CA 94110. TEL 415-282-2994) Ed. Wang Lu.

769.56 CC ISSN 1002-7750
JIYOU YANJIU/PHILATELY RESEARCH. (Text in Chinese) 1983. q. $16.20. Zhongguo Jiyou Chubanshe, Dong Chang'an Jie 27, Beijing, People's Republic of China. (Dist. in US by: China Books & Periodicals, Inc., 2929 24th St., San Francisco, CA 94110)
Description: Covers the study and collection of Chinese stamps. Includes the theory and practice of stamp collecting, and the history of stamps, stamp collecting, and postal services.

769.56 US
JOURNAL OF BRITISH COMMONWEALTH PHILATELY. 1992. q. $40. Arthur C. Hamm, 5301 Ridgefield Rd., Bethesda, MD 20816-3335. TEL 703-827-2718. adv. circ. 1,000. **Document type:** academic/scholarly publication.

768.56 UK ISSN 0951-8878
JOURNAL OF CHINESE PHILATELY. 1954. bi-m. membership. China Philatelic Society of London, 6B Richmond Parade, East Twickenham, Middlesex TW1 2ET, England. Ed. Roy W. Wright. adv.: B&W page £10. illus. circ. 600. (back issues avail.)
Formerly: China Section Bulletin.

769.56 US ISSN 0447-953X
HE6187
JOURNAL OF SPORTS PHILATELY. 1962. bi-m. $12 (foreign $24). Sports Philatelists International, c/o Margaret A. Jones, 5310 Lindenwood Ave., St.Louis, MO 63109-1758. TEL 314-352-0888. Ed. John La Porta. adv. contact: Stephen Rock. bk.rev.; illus.; stat.; index; circ. 500 (controlled). **Indexed:** Sportsearch (1977-). **Document type:** newsletter.

769.56 US
JUDAICA PHILATELIC JOURNAL. 1963. q. $10 (foreign $13.50). Judaica Historical Society, 2856 Grand Concourse, Bronx, NY 10458-2705. Ed. Oscar Stadtler. adv.; bk.rev. circ. 350.

769.56 GW ISSN 0022-6343
JUNGE SAMMLER; Zeitschrift fuer junge Briefmarkenfreunde. 1961. bi-m. DM.25. Deutsche Philatelisten Jugend e.V., Postfach 3968, 54229 Trier, Germany. Ed. Heinz Wenz. adv.; bk.rev.; illus. circ. 13,000. **Document type:** newsletter.

769.56 JA
KITTE SHUMI. vol.91, 1980. 12/yr. 42 Yen($20) Kitte Shumi-sha, 3-12-28 Mejiro, Toshima-ku, Tokyo, Japan.

769.56 UK ISSN 0964-7821
THE KIWI. bi-m. £10. New Zealand Society of Great Britain, 24 Irwin Rd., Guildford, Surrey GU2 5PP, England. TEL 01483-67185. FAX 01483-34676. Ed. Allan Berry. bk.rev.; index; circ. 350 (paid). (back issues avail.) **Document type:** newsletter.
Description: Covers the philately and postal history of New Zealand.
Refereed Serial

769.56 US
KOREAN PHILATELY. 1952. q. $25 membership (typically set in Aug.). Korea Stamp Society, Inc., c/o William A. Matthews, Secretary-Treasurer, Box 15306, Columbus, OH 43215. (Editorial addr.: Box 8142, St. Paul, MN 55108) Ed. Gary N. McLean. adv. circ. 200. **Indexed:** Stamp J.Ind.

769.56 059 KN ISSN 0452-5914
KOREAN STAMPS.* (Text in English) no.62, 1974. m. Philatelists Union of the Democratic People's Republic of Korea, Pyongyang, North Korea. charts; illus.

769.56 US
LAMBDA PHILATELIC JOURNAL. q. Gay - Lesbian History Stamp Club, Box 230940, Hartford, CT 06123-0940.
Description: Promotes, studies and collects worldwide philatelic material depicting gay history and awareness.

769.56 US
LATIN AMERICA PHILATELIST. 1960. q. $15 (foreign $20). American Air Mail Society, Jack Knight Air Mail Society, Box 1239, Elgin, IL 60121-1239. TEL 708-468-0840. circ. 1,000. (back issues avail.)
Formerly: Uruguay Philatelist.

769.56 CN
LATIN AMERICAN POST. 1976. q. $15. Latin American Philatelic Society, P.O. Box 6420, Hinton, AB T7V 1X7, Canada. TEL 403-865-2564. Ed. Piet Steen. adv.; bk.rev. circ. 250. (looseleaf format) **Indexed:** Stamp J.Ind.
Description: Studies Latin American philately and postal history.

769.56 US
LATVIAN COLLECTOR. 1974. 3/yr. $8.50. Box 5403, San Mateo, CA 94402. Ed. Maris Tirums. circ. 200. (back issues avail.)

769.56 US
LIBERIAN PHILATELIC SOCIETY JOURNAL. 1979. q. $15 (foreign $18). (Liberian Philatelic Society) Roy P. Mackal, Ed. & Pub., 9027 S. Oakley Ave., Chicago, IL 60620-6131. TEL 312-238-6516. adv. circ. 85. (back issues avail.)
Formerly (until Fall 1988): Liberian Philatelic Society Newsletter.
Description: Notes and articles on the activities and issues of interest to members of this stamp collector's association.

769.56 US
LILAC HINGE. m. membership. Inland Empire Philatelic Society, N. 10710 Nelson Rd., Spokane, WA 99218. Ed. Maude P. Wilson.

769.56 US ISSN 0161-6234
HE6187
LINN'S STAMP NEWS. 1928. w. $37. Amos Press Inc., Box 29, Sidney, OH 45365. TEL 513-498-0801. FAX 800-340-9501. Ed. Michael Laurence. adv.: B&W page $2116; trim 11 x 15. bk.rev.; charts; illus.; stat. circ. 70,000. (also avail. in microform from UMI) **Indexed:** Stamp J.Ind. **Document type:** consumer publication, newspaper.
—UMI.
Formerly: Linn's Weekly Stamp News (ISSN 0024-4104)
Description: Weekly news magazine for the philatelist and stamp dealer.

769.56 US
LITHUANIAN PHILATELIC SOCIETY OF NEW YORK. BULLETIN. 1954. q. $9. Lithuanian Philatelic Society of New York, c/o J.J. Norton, Ed., Box 432, Syosset, NY 11791. TEL 516-364-1279. circ. 200. (back issues avail.) **Document type:** bulletin.

769.56 UK ISSN 0024-6131
LONDON PHILATELIST. 1892. 10/yr. £36. Royal Philatelic Society, 41 Devonshire Place, London W1N 1PE, England. TEL 0171-486-1044. FAX 0171-486-0803. Ed. George E. Barker. adv.; bk.rev.; bibl.; illus.; index, cum.index: vols.1-77. circ. 1,700. (back issues avail.) **Indexed:** Stamp J.Ind. **Document type:** academic/scholarly publication.

769.56 383 UK ISSN 0969-8701
LONDON POSTAL HISTORY GROUP NOTEBOOK. 1971. 5/yr. £7. London Postal History Group, 64 Gordon Rd., Carshalton Beeches, Surrey SM5 3RE, England. Ed. Peter Forrestier Smith. bk.rev.; illus.; index. circ. 185. (back issues avail.) **Document type:** bulletin.

LONG ISLAND POSTAL HISTORIAN. see COMMUNICATIONS — Postal Affairs

769.56 US
LUNDY COLLECTORS CLUB PHILATELIC QUARTERLY. 1979. q. $12.50 (effective 1994). Lundy Collectors Club, 2021 Ridge Rd., Homewood, IL 60430. TEL 708-799-0880. Ed. Roger S. Cichorz. bk.rev. circ. 220.
Description: Disseminates information pertaining to the collecting and study of Lundy stamps, covers and postal history.

769.56 US ISSN 0739-0025
LUREN. 1969. m. $10. Scandinavian Philatelic Library of Southern California, Box 310, Claremont, CA 91711. TEL 909-626-1764. Ed. Paul Nelson. adv.; bk.rev.; index; circ. 250. **Document type:** newsletter.

769.56 US
M C S C C ON COVER. 1957. m. membership. Motor City Stamp and Cover Club, 22608 Poplar Ct., Hazel Park, MI 48030. TEL 313-546-0038. Ed. Robert Quintero. adv. circ. 150. **Document type:** newsletter.

769.56 US
MACHINE CANCEL FORUM.* 1974. m. free. 7 Hillside Rd., No. D, Greenbelt, MD 20770-1754. Eds. John R. McGee, John Koontz. bk.rev. circ. 300. (back issues avail.)

769.56 NZ ISSN 0542-0997
MAIL-COACH. 1964. bi-m. NZ.$30 (effective through Oct. 1996). Postal History Society of New Zealand, Inc., P.O. Box 59, Beachlands, New Zealand. TEL 64-9-5365201. FAX 64-9-5366690. Ed. J. Campbell. adv.; bk.rev. circ. 500. **Document type:** academic/scholarly publication.
—CCC.
   Description: Covers postal history of New Zealand and South Pacific.

769.56 UK ISSN 0951-5283
MAPLE LEAVES. 1946. 5/yr. £10.50 (effective Oct. 1994). Canadian Philatelic Society of Great Britain, c/o David F. Sessions, Ed., 99 Offington Ave., Worthing, W. Sussex BN14 9PR, England. TEL 01903-830266. (Subscr. to: c/o T. Almond, Secy., 2 Filbert Dr., Tilehurst, Reading RG3 5DZ, England) adv.: page £27; adv. contact: Brian Hargreaves. bk.rev.; circ. 500 (controlled).
   Description: Contains articles concerning philately and the postal history of British North America.

769.56 700 US
MASK LORE. 1990. q. $5 ($7.50 Canada; $10 elsewhere). Mask Study Unit of A.T.A., c/o Carolyn A. Weber, Ed., Box 2542, Oxnard, CA 93034. circ. 37. **Document type:** newsletter.
   Description: Contains articles about stamps that depict masks of all types; stamp illustrations; and news of general interest to the members.

769.56 US
MASSACHUSETTS SPY. 1975. bi-m. $7 (effective Jan. 1992). Massachusetts Postal Research Society, Box 202, North Abington, MA 02351. TEL 617-878-4446. Ed. Robert S. Borden. adv.; bk.rev., charts; illus.; stat.; cum.index: 1975-1991. circ. 90. (looseleaf format; back issues avail.)
   Description: Postal history research of Massachusetts.

769.56 US
MAXIMAPHILY.* 1980. q. $10. Maximum Card Study Unit, 3284 Winterberry Ln., Virginia Beach, VA 23456-5910. TEL 708-679-7356. Ed. Gary Denis. adv.; bk.rev.; illus. circ. 150. (looseleaf format)
   Description: For both advanced and beginning collectors; covers the collecting of maximum cards, which are picture postcards with a postage stamp of the same design affixed to and cancelled on the picture side.

769.56 US ISSN 0025-8857
HE6187
MEKEEL'S STAMP NEWS. 1891. w. $22.50. Philatelic Communications Corp., Box 5050, White Plains, NY 10602. TEL 914-997-7261; 800-635-3351. Ed. John F. Dunn; Pub. John F. Dunn. adv.; bk.rev.; illus.mkt. circ. 6,000. (tabloid format) **Document type:** newspaper.
   Description: Contains news and features for active stamp collectors.

789.56 US ISSN 1075-2226
MENELIK'S JOURNAL. 1985. q. $7.50 in US & Canada; elsewhere $8.50. Ethiopian Philatelic Society, c/o Floyd Heiser, 5710 S.E. Gamet Way, Milwaukie, OR 97267.
   Description: Focuses upon any and all philatelic matters related to Ethiopia.

769.56 US
MERCHANTVILLE STAMP CLUB. MONTHLY BULLETIN. 1932. m. $5. Merchantville Stamp Club, Box 2913, Cherry Hill, NJ 08034. Ed. Paul Schumacher. adv.; bk.rev. circ. 130.

769.56 US
MIASMA PHILATELIST.* 1979. q. membership. Malaria Philatelists International, Box 437, Polar, MT 59255-0437. Ed. Mike Birrer. adv.; bk.rev.; index. circ. 200.

769.56 GW ISSN 0076-7727
MICHEL-BRIEFMARKEN-KATALOGE. 1910. irreg. price varies. Schwaneberger Verlag GmbH, Muthmannstr. 4, 80939 Munich, Germany. **Document type:** catalog.

769.56 GW ISSN 0026-198X
MICHEL-RUNDSCHAU. 1957. 12/yr. DM.39.60. Schwaneberger Verlag GmbH, Muthmannstr. 4, 80939 Munich, Germany. Ed. Klaus Richnow. adv. contact: Hans Hohenester. bk.rev. circ. 62,000. **Document type:** bulletin.
—CCC.

769.56 US
MICHIANA PHILATELIST. vol.30, 1981. m. $5. Northern Indiana Philatelic Society, Box 393, Mishawaka, IN 46544. TEL 219-288-3751. Ed. Howard Wallace. bk.rev. circ. 120.

769.56 UK ISSN 0142-9914
MIDDLE EAST STAMP CATALOGUE. 1980. irreg. price varies. Stanley Gibbons Publications Ltd., Unit 5 Parkside, Christchurch Rd., Ringwood, Hants. BH24 3SH, England. TEL 0425-472363. FAX 0425-470247. TELEX 41271-SGPPUB-G. **Document type:** catalog.

769.56 NE ISSN 0026-3605
MIJN STOKPAARDJE; maandblad voor filatelisten. 1945. m. fl.66. B.V. Uitgeverij "de Postiljon", P.O. Box 15041, 3501 BA Utrecht, Netherlands. TEL 31–30-717988. Ed.Bd. adv.; bk.rev.; illus. circ. 10,000.

789.56 US ISSN 1075-5640
MILITARY POSTAL HISTORY SOCIETY BULLETIN. 1937. q. $10 includes membership. Military Postal History Society, c/o John Azarkevich, 1400 Altamore Ave., Ste. 111, Schenectady, NY 12303.

769.56 US ISSN 0890-2151
MITCHELL REPORT. m. $18.50. Los Angeles Stamp Company, c/o Gretchen H. Mitchell, Ed., Box 1387, Los Angeles, CA 90078. TEL 213-467-2215.

769.56 FR ISSN 0026-9387
MONDE DES PHILATELISTES; officiel de la philatelie. 1951. m. 250 F. (foreign 340 F.). Monde, 5 rue Antoine Bourdelle, 75015 Paris, France. TEL 40-65-25-25. (Subscr. to: Immeuble Sirius, 1 place Hubert-Beuve-Mery, 94852 Ivry-sur-Seine Cedex, France. TEL 49-60-32-90) Ed. M. Adalbert Vitalyos. adv.; charts; illus. circ. 48,568. **Document type:** newspaper.

769.56 US
MUSEUM POST RIDER. 1959. m. $25. Cardinal Spellman Philatelic Museum, Inc., 235 Wellesey St., Weston, MA 02193. TEL 617-894-6735. FAX 617-894-8056. Ed. T.G. Kudzma. adv.; bk.rev.; charts; illus. circ. 750. (back issues avail.) **Document type:** academic/scholarly publication, newsletter.

N J P H. (New Jersey Postal History Society Inc.) see COMMUNICATIONS — Postal Affairs

769.56 US
N Y EESTI FILATELISTIDE SELTSI BULLETAAN. 1971. s-a. $15 membership. Estonian Philatelic Society, 1912 Nugget Dr., Felton, CA 95018. Ed. Rudolf Hamar. circ. 300. (looseleaf format; back issues avail.)

769.56 GW
NAVICULA. 1959. bi-m. DM.40. S M S Navicula e.V., Fennstr. 34, 1000 Berlin 65, Germany. TEL 030-4624255. adv.; bk.rev. (back issues avail.) **Document type:** newsletter.

769.56 US
NETHERLANDS PHILATELY JOURNAL. 1975. q. $12 (foreign $14) includes Newsletter. American Society for Netherlands Philately, W6428 Riverview Dr., Onalaska, WI 54650. TEL 608-781-8612. Ed. Paul E. van Reyen. adv.; bk.rev. circ. 400. **Indexed:** Stamp J.Ind. **Document type:** bulletin.

769.56 US ISSN 0194-7753
NEW MEXICO PHILATELIST. 1948. bi-m. membership. New Mexico Philatelic Association, 1023 Rocky Point Ct., N.E., Albuquerque, NM 87123-1944. TEL 505-292-2539. Ed. Paul E. Tyler. charts; illus. circ. 325. (back issues avail.) **Document type:** newsletter.
   Description: Publishes articles of philatelic interest, including original and reprint, as well as Association notices concerning its business and events.

789.56 US ISSN 1073-0222
NEW STAMPS GAZETTE. 1992. bi-a. free to qualified personnel; others $2. Shield Stamp Company, Box 2977, Grand Central Sta., New York, NY 10163. TEL 212-629-7979. FAX 212-629-3350. Ed. Daniel Keren. circ. 15,000 (controlled). **Document type:** catalog.
   Description: Lists stamp collections available to collectors; contains some editorial material.

769.56 UK ISSN 1351-5608
NEW ZEALAND CONCISE STAMP CATALOGUE. 1990. irreg. price varies. Stanley Gibbon Publications Ltd., Unit 5 Parkside, Christchurch Rd., Ringwood, Hamps. BH24 3SH, England. TEL 0425-472363. FAX 0425-470247. Ed. David Aggersberg. **Document type:** catalog.

769.56 NZ ISSN 0112-5443
NEW ZEALAND STAMP COLLECTOR. 1919. q. NZ.$40. Royal Philatelic Society of New Zealand, Box 1269, Wellington, New Zealand. Ed. B.G. Vincent. adv.; bk.rev. circ. 1,500.
—CCC.

769.56 NZ ISSN 0028-8721
NEW ZEALAND STAMP MONTHLY. 1968. m. NZ.$9. Len Jury Ltd., P.O. Box 174, New Plymouth, New Zealand. bk.rev. circ. 2,000. (tabloid format)
—CCC.

769.56 US
NEWS OF HUNGARIAN PHILATELY. 1970. q. $12 membership (foreign $16). Society for Hungarian Philately, Box 1162, Samp-Mortar Sta., Fairfield, CT 06430. Ed. Csaba Kohalmi. bk.rev. circ. 250. **Indexed:** Stamp J.Ind.

769.56 US ISSN 0078-091X
NOBLE OFFICIAL CATALOG OF CANADA PRECANCELS.* 1923. irreg., 13th ed., 1981. $3. Gilbert W. Noble, Ed. & Pub., 1111 S. Lakemont Ave., Ste. 805, Winter Park, FL 32792. circ. 2,000. **Document type:** catalog.

769.56 US ISSN 0078-0928
NOBLE OFFICIAL CATALOG OF UNITED STATES BUREAU PRECANCELS.* 1926. irreg. $6. Gilbert W. Noble, Ed. & Pub., 1111 S. Lakemont Ave., Ste.805, Winter Park, FL 32792. circ. 1,000. **Document type:** catalog.

769.56 737 SW ISSN 0029-134X
NORDISK FILATELI. 1937. 9/yr. SEK 300 (effective 1995). Nordisk Filateli AB, P.O. Box 90, S-277 21 Kivik, Sweden. TEL 46-414-70230. FAX 46-414-70230. Ed. Morten Person. adv.; bk.rev. circ. 6,500.

769.56 DK ISSN 0903-3440
NORDISK FILATELISTISK TIDSSKRIFT. 1894. 4/yr. DKK 190. Koebenhavns Philatelist Klub, Postboks 3, DK-1001 Copenhagen K, Denmark. FAX 33-326632. Ed. Max Meedom. adv.; bk.rev. circ. 1,050.

769.56948 DK ISSN 0105-9106
NORDISK JULEMAERKE KATALOG; Nordic Christmas seal catalogue. (Text in Danish) 1974. biennial. DKK 195. Marielystvej 52, st., t.h., DK-2000 Frederiksberg, Denmark. TEL 45-31-74-44-22. Ed. Joergen Christoffersen. **Document type:** catalog.
   Formerly (until 1976): Julemaerke Katalog (ISSN 0904-907X)

769.56 NO ISSN 0332-8848
NORSK FILATELISTISK TIDSSKRIFT. Title varies: N F T. 1942. 10/yr. NOK 155($9) or membership in affiliated societies in Norway. Norsk Filatelistforbund, Postboks 2517, 7001 Trondheim, Norway. Ed. Tor Skauge. adv.; bk.rev.; illus.; stat.; index. circ. 7,600.

769.56 SA ISSN 1016-6734
O F S PHILATELIC MAGAZINE. 1951. m. R.60 membership. Orange Free State Philatelic Society, The Secretary, P.O. Box 702, Bloemfontein 9300, South Africa. FAX 27-51-366727. Ed. J.A. Van Beukering. adv.; bk.rev.; circ. 150 (paid). **Document type:** newsletter.

PHILATELY

769.56   UK   ISSN 0267-8071
O P A L JOURNAL. 1949. q. £8 (foreign £10). Oriental Philatelic Association of London, c/o Jeff Ertughrul, Ed., 62 Leopold Rd., E. Finchley, London N2 8BG, England. (Subscr. to: J.F. Cousins, 2 Blenheim Rd., Westbury Park, Bristol BS6 7JW, England) adv.; bk.rev. circ. 350. (back issues avail.) **Document type:** academic/scholarly publication.
    Description: Papers, informational articles, exchange listings, and historical sketches pertaining to stamp collectors of philately of the Ottoman Empire.

OFFICIALLY SEALED NOTES. see *COMMUNICATIONS — Postal Affairs*

769.56   US
OHIO POSTAL HISTORY JOURNAL. 1978. q. $10 includes membership. Ohio Postal History Society, Inc., 2707 Pickle Rd., Apt. 37, Oregon, OH 43616-3969. (Subscr. to: O P H S Secretary, Box 690042, Houston, TX 77269-0042) Ed. George J. Ball. adv.; bk.rev. circ. 300.

769.56   US
ORANGE COUNTY STAMP NEWS. 1931? m. membership. Orange County Philatelic Society, c/o Ron Weiner, Ed., 1020 W. Oakcrest, Brea, CA 92621-1829. adv. circ. 150.

769.56   US   ISSN 0892-5208
OREGON POSTAL HISTORY JOURNAL. 1981. q. $7.50. Oregon Postal History Society, Box 135, Lake Oswego, OR 97034. Ed. Leonard Lukens. bk.rev. circ. 100. (back issues avail.)

769.56   IT
OSSERVATORE FILATELICO. m. Piazza Italia 5, 20093 Cologno Monzese, Italy. Ed. Rolando Gianni.

769.56   US   ISSN 0737-0954
HE6185.C67
OXCART. 1960. q. $12. Society of Costa Rica Collectors, Box 8308, Wichita, KS 67208. Ed. Hal T. Edwards. adv.; bk.rev. circ. 275. **Indexed:** Stamp J.Ind. **Document type:** consumer publication.

769.56   CN   ISSN 0714-8305
P H S C JOURNAL. 1972. q. Can.$20 to non-members; members Can.$10. Philaprint Inc., 23 Queensbury Ave., Scarborough, ON M1N 2X8, Canada. TEL 416-691-1332. (Subscr. to: R.F. Narbonne, 216 Mailey Dr., Carleton Place, ON K7C 3X9, Canada) Ed. David Roberts. adv.; bk.rev.; illus. circ. 600. **Indexed:** Biol.Abstr., Stamp J.Ind.
    Former titles: Postal History Society of Canada. Journal (ISSN 0703-5365); Postal Histo-Mine.
    Description: Articles and research papers on all facets of postal history of Canada.

789.56   US   ISSN 1072-8732
P H S G NEWSLETTER. 1987. q. $14 membership (Canada $16; elsewhere $18). Pearl Harbor Study Group, c/o Larry R. Wendell, Jr., 104 E. Maple Ave., No.4, Ottumwa, IA 52501-2073. cum.index: 1987-1993; circ. 88 (paid). **Document type:** newsletter.
    Description: Covers all aspects of cover collecting with regard to the 1941 attack on Pearl Harbor, including WWII in the Pacific arena, aviation and shipping history, airmail covers of the Pacific PAA flights, history of Hawaii philately, wartime censorship of the mails, and more.

769.56   US   ISSN 1041-4894
P M C C BULLETIN. 1947. m. (11/yr.). $12.50. Post Mark Collectors Club, c/o David H. Proulx, 7629 Homestead Dr., Baldwinsville, NY 13027. TEL 315-638-0532. (Subscr. to: Robert J. Milligan, 23381 Greenleaf Blvd., Elkhart, IN 46514-4504) Ed. Kevin M. Tanzillo. adv.; illus. circ. 950. **Document type:** bulletin.
    Description: Articles on the hobby of postmark collecting. Covers current developments and historical information to aid collectors.

796.56   US
P M C C MEMBERSHIP ROSTER. 1947. triennial. membership. Post Mark Collectors Club, c/o David H. Proulx, 7629 Homestead Dr., Baldwinsville, NY 13027. TEL 315-638-0532. (Subscr. to: c/o Robert J. Milligan, 23381 Greenleaf Blvd., Elkhart, IN 46514-4504) circ. 1,500. **Document type:** directory.
    Description: Provides historic information on the club and its services. Lists names and addresses of members.

769.56   UK
P T S NEWS. 1947. bi-m. membership. Philatelic Traders Society Ltd., British Philatelic Centre, 107 Charterhouse St., London EC1M 6PT, England. TEL 0171-490-1005. FAX 0171-253-0414. Ed. Derek J. Yardley. adv.; bk.rev.; bibl.; circ. controlled. (tabloid format) **Document type:** newsletter.
    Formerly: P T S Journal (ISSN 0048-3729)

769.56   UK   ISSN 0306-0896
PACIFICA. 1962. q. £6($10) Pacific Islands Study Circle of Great Britain, 73 Neville Rd., Shirley, Solihull B90 2QN, England. Ed. B.A. Jones. adv.; bk.rev. circ. 450. (back issues avail.) **Indexed:** Stamp J.Ind.

769.56   US   ISSN 1055-8616
PAGE & PANEL JOURNAL OF THE AMERICAN SOCIETY FOR PHILATELIC PAGES AND PANELS. 1984. q. $15 membership. American Society for Philatelic Pages and Panels, 736 Colonial Blvd., Washington Twp., NJ 07675. (Alt. addr.: Box 475, Crosby, TX 77532) Ed. Ron Walenciak. adv.: B&W page $40. charts; illus.; index. circ. 800. (back issues avail.) **Document type:** newsletter.
    Formerly: U.S. Souvenir Page Society Bulletin.
    Description: Gathers and distributes information on all philatelic pages and panels, especially in U.S. souvenir pages and commemorative panels.

769.56   US
PANTOGRAPH OF POSTAL STATIONERY. bi-m. $6 to non-members. United Postal Stationery Society, Box 48, Redlands, CA 92373. **Indexed:** Stamp J.Ind.

769.56   US
PASTE-UP. vol.33, 1981. m. $5 includes membership. Cedar Rapids Stamp Club, Box 2554, Cedar Rapids, IA 52406. Ed. Jon White. circ. 50 (controlled).
    Description: Club meeting notices.

769.56   MY   ISSN 0126-6497
PEMUNGUT SETEM MALAYSIA/MALAYSIAN PHILATELIST. 1970. q. membership (M.$20). Philatelic Society of Malaysia, P.O. Box 10588 GPO, 50718 Kuala Lumpur, Malaysia. Ed. C. Nagarajah. adv.; bk.rev. circ. 800.

769.56   US
PENINSULAR PHILATELIST. 1951. q. $5 (effective 1994). Peninsular State Philatelic Society, Box 80946, Lansing, MI 48908. Ed. William C. Allen. adv.; bk.rev.; illus. circ. 175.
    Description: Provides data on the collecting scene in Michigan. Acts as a clearinghouse for stamp exhibition dates.

769.56   US   ISSN 8750-1627
PERFINS BULLETIN. 1945. m. $10 (Canada $13; elsewhere $15). Perfins Club, c/o John F. Lyding, Ed., Box 3342, Crofton, MD 21114-3342. adv.; bk.rev.; illus.; tr.lit. circ. 965. (looseleaf format) **Indexed:** Stamp J.Ind. **Document type:** bulletin.
    Description: Covers philatelic topics relating to the use of perforated initials as security markings on postage stamps.

769.56   US   ISSN 0279-3709
THE PETRO-PHILATELIST. 1974. q. $9 (foreign $11). Petroleum Philatelic Society International, 1740 S.W. 84 Ave., Hollywood, FL 33025-2127. Ed. Feitze Papa. adv.; circ. 225 (paid).
    Description: Covers topics of interest to collectors of petroleum-related postage stamps.

769.56   US
PHAROS (NORTHVILLE). 1973. m. $10 (foreign $15). Lighthouse Study Unit, 19735 Scenic Harbour Dr., Northville, MI 48167-1979. Ed. Gary M. Kurylo. bk.rev.; charts; illus.; stat. circ. 270. (looseleaf format; back issues avail.)
    Description: Presents lighthouses on stamps: covers, cancels and postmarks.

769.56   GW   ISSN 0940-7316
PHIL - FORUM. 1986. m. DM.44. Phil-Creativ GmbH, Postfach 10, 41364 Schwalmtal, Germany. TEL 02163-30777. FAX 02163-30003. Ed. W. Maassen. adv.; bk.rev. circ. 5,000. (back issues avail.) **Document type:** bulletin.
    Formerly (until 1991): A T M - Forum (ISSN 0932-5441)

769.56   GW
PHILA-LUPE; international advertiser for worldwide stamp exchange. (Text in English, German) 1982. 3/yr. DM.15($10) Phila-Lupe, Am Gerichtshaus 69, 45257 Essen, Germany. Ed. Rainer Volkenborn. adv. circ. 1,000. **Document type:** consumer publication.
    Description: Promotes exchange of stamps and information worldwide.

769.56 737   GW   ISSN 0720-2245
PHILA-REPORT; die Sammlerfreundliche Briefmarkenzeitung. 1980. m. DM.12($18) Allpress-Verlagsgesellschaft mbH & Co., 5410 Hoehr-Grenzhausen, P.O. Box 1452, Rheinstr. 41, Germany. Ed. Linus Wittich. circ. 22,000. (tabloid format)

769.56   US
PHILAGEMS INTERNATIONAL. 1976. q. $10 (foreign $15). Gems, Minerals & Jewelry Study Unit, c/o George Young, Box 632, Tewksbury, MA 01876. TEL 508-851-8283.
    Description: Focuses on gems, minerals, jewelry, fossils, mining and coin topics.

769.56   US
PHILAMATH; a journal of mathematical philately. 1979. q. $10 in N. America; elsewhere $13. American Topical Association, Mathematics Study Unit, c/o M. Strauss, 4209 88th St., Lubbock, TX 79423-2941. TEL 806-798-2688. (Subscr. to: 135 Witherspoon Ct., Athens, GA 30606) (Co-sponsor: American Philatelic Society) Ed. Randy Woodward. adv. circ. 125. (looseleaf format; back issues avail.) **Document type:** newsletter.

769.56   AT   ISSN 0725-2323
PHILAS NEWS. 1972. 4/yr. Aus.$5 (foreign Aus.$8) membership. Philatelic Association of New South Wales, P.O. Box A495, Sydney South, N.S.W. 2000, Australia. TEL 02-264-8406. bk.rev. circ. 500. **Document type:** newsletter.

769.56   US   ISSN 0739-6198
PHILATELI-GRAPHICS. 1976. q. $5 (foreign $8). Graphics Philately Association, Box 1513, Thousand Oaks, CA 91358. Ed. Joseph Sullivan. bk.rev.; illus.; index. cum.index: 1976-1982 in no.24. circ. 130. (back issues avail.) **Document type:** newsletter.
    Description: For people interested in printing and graphic arts of and on postage stamps and other philatelic items of the world.

769.56   US   ISSN 1041-2999
PHILATELIA CHIMICA ET PHYSICA. 1979. q. $8 (foreign $9). (Chemistry and Physics on Stamps Study Unit) C P O S S U, 13 Roxbury Dr., Athens, OH 45701. TEL 614-593-3729. Ed. D.G. Hendricker. bk.rev.; index. circ. 260. (back issues avail.)
    Formerly: Philatelia Chimica.

769.56   KE
PHILATELIC BULLETIN. (Text in English) 1977; N.S. 1979. q. free. Kenya Posts and Telecommunications Corporation, Kenya Stamp Bureau, P.O. Box 30368, Nairobi, Kenya. TEL 254-2-27401-2158. TELEX 22245 IJIR POSTS. circ. 3,000. **Document type:** bulletin.
    Description: Announces the issue and availability of special commemorative stamps from Kenya and provides ordering information.

769.56   US
PHILATELIC COMMUNICATOR. 1968. q. $10. American Philatelic Society, Writers Unit No. 30, 873 Carina Ln., Foster City, CA 94404-2866. (Subscr. to: 2501 Drexel St., Vienna, VA 22180) Ed. Mark A. Kellner; Pub. Joe F. Frye. adv.; bk.rev. circ. 850. **Document type:** newsletter.
    Formerly (until 1987): A.P.S. Writers Unit Number Thirty News Bulletin (ISSN 0147-3646)

769.56 658.048   US   ISSN 0892-032X
PHILATELIC EXHIBITOR. 1986. q. $15 membership. American Association of Philatelic Exhibitors, c/o Russell V. Skavaril, Exec.Sec., 222 E. Torrence Rd., Columbus, OH 43214. Ed. John Box 1125, Falls Church, VA 22041. TEL 703-820-5449) Ed. John M. Hotchner. adv.; bk.rev. circ. 1,300. (back issues avail.)
    Description: A forum for debate and information on philatelic exhibiting, judging, and exhibition administration. Offers encouragement to novices.

PHILATELY

769.56   UK   ISSN 0031-7381
THE PHILATELIC EXPORTER; world's greatest stamp trade journal. 1945. m. £23 (overseas £26.70). Philatelic Exporter, P.O. Box 137, Hatfield, Hertfordshire AL10 9DB, England. TEL 01707-266331. FAX 01707-274782. Ed. Graham R. Phillips. adv.; bk.rev.; bibl.; charts; illus.; stat.; tr.lit. circ. 3,000. **Document type:** trade publication.
    Incorporating: Coin and Note Dealer; Philatelic Trader.

796.56   US   ISSN 0196-5034
PHILATELIC FOUNDATION QUARTERLY. 1983. q. $50 contribution. Philatelic Foundation, 501 Fifth Ave., No. 1901, New York, NY 10017-6103. TEL 212-867-3699. FAX 212-867-3984. Ed. Harlan F. Stone. adv.; bk.rev.; charts; illus.; circ. 1,700 (controlled). (back issues avail.) **Document type:** newsletter.
    Formerly: Philatelic Foundation Bulletin.
    Description: Presents articles and opinions about the foundation's Expert Committee, its reference collections, research library, the educational programs, and its publications.

789.56 366   US
THE PHILATELIC FREEMASON. 1977. bi-m. $8 (outside N. America $14). (Masonic Study Unit) R A D Publishing Co., 59 Greenwood Rd, Andover, MA 01810. TEL 508-470-0583. Ed. Robert A. Domingue. cum.index: vols.1-17. circ. 280. (back issues avail.) **Document type:** newsletter.
    Description: Publishes articles concerning stamps and Masons, and information pertaining to a Masonic stamp collection.

793   US
PHILATELIC GUILD'S INVESTMENT NEWSLETTER. 1975. m. $10. Philatelic Guild, Box 798, Lakewood, NJ 08701.

769.56   US   ISSN 0270-1707
PHILATELIC LITERATURE REVIEW. 1942. q. $12 to individuals; institutions $30. American Philatelic Research Library, Box 8338, State College, PA 16803. TEL 814-237-3803. FAX 814-237-6128. Ed. William L. Welch Jr. adv.; bk.rev.; cum.index: 1942-1970. circ. 2,750. **Document type:** bulletin.

769.56   US   ISSN 0273-5598
PHILATELIC OBSERVER. 1963. bi-m. membership. Junior Philatelists of America, Inc., Box 850, Boalsburg, PA 16827-0850. Ed. Carey Sevier. adv.; bk.rev.; illus. circ. 1,000. **Document type:** newsletter.
    Description: Forum covering news on stamp collecting and other activities related to the J.P.A. Provides information to enhance the experience of youngsters in the hobby of stamp collecting.

769.56   US
PHILATELIC PROSPECTOR. m. $15 membership. Sacramento Philatelic Society, Box 13284, Sacramento, CA 95813. TEL 916-484-0490. Ed. John J. Pavalasky; Pub. Bob Short. bk.rev. circ. 315. **Document type:** newsletter.

769.56   UK   ISSN 0265-2641
PHILATELIC QUILL. 1982. q. £10 membership. Philatelic Writers Society, 138 Chastilian Rd., Dartford, Kent DA1 3LG, England. TEL 0322-270361. (Subscr. to: A.P. Berry, 24 Irwin Rd., Guildford, Surrey GU2 5PP, England. TEL 0483-67185) Ed. W.A. Page. bk.rev.; index. circ. 150. (back issues avail.) **Document type:** newsletter.

769.56   TR
PHILATELIC SOCIETY OF T & T BULLETIN. 1946. q. $10. Philatelic Society of Trinidad & Tobago, P.O. Box 596, Port-of-Spain, Trinidad & Tobago, W.I. TEL 809-622-1673. FAX 809-632-2759. Ed. John Chay. adv.; bk.rev. circ. 250. (processed) **Document type:** newsletter.
    Formerly: Trinidad Philatelic Society Bulletin.

769.56   NE   ISSN 0166-3437
PHILATELIE; Nederlandsch maandblad voor philatelie. 1922. 11/yr. fl.36 (Belgium 750 BEF; elsewhere fl.62.50). Stichting Nederlandsch Maandblad voor Philatelie, c/o S.W.D. Veenstra, Roeloefsstraat 31, 2596 VK The Hague, Netherlands. TEL 31-70-3280342. (Subscr. to: Box 5905, 3273 ZG Westmaas, Netherlands. TEL 31-1864-1776) Ed. A. Knikman. adv.; B&W page fl.1850, color page fl.2850; 191 x 275. bk.rev.; illus.; index. circ. 55,000.
    Formerly: Nederlandsch Maandblad voor Philatelie (ISSN 0028-2081)
    Description: Covers philately and postage stamps for the Dutch speaking regions.

769.56   GW
PHILATELIE. 1949. bi-m. membership. Bund Deutscher Philatelisten e.V., Mainzer Landstr. 221-223, 60327 Frankfurt a.M., Germany. FAX 02163-30003. Ed. Wolfgang Maassen. adv.; bk.rev. circ. 85,000.
    Formerly: Philatelie Bundesnachrichten.

769.56   FR   ISSN 0183-3634
PHILATELIE FRANCAISE. 1952. m. (11/yr.). 225 F. (foreign 295 F.). Federation des Societes Philateliques Francaises, 7 rue Saint-Lazare, 75009 Paris, France. TEL 42-85-50-25. FAX 44-63-01-39. Ed. Robert Deroy. adv.; bk.rev.; charts; illus.; index. circ. 20,000.

769.56   CN
PHILATELIE QUEBEC. (Text in French) 1969. 10/yr. Can.$30($35) (Federation Quebecoise de Philatelie) Editions Phibec Inc., 4545 ave. Pierre de Coubertin, C.P. 1000, Succ. M, Montreal, PQ H1V 3R2, Canada. TEL 514-252-3035. FAX 514-251-8038. Ed. F. Brisse. adv.; B&W page Can.$500, color page Can.$900. illus. circ. 3,500. **Indexed:** Pt.de Rep. (1983-).
    Formerly: Philatelie au Quebec (ISSN 0381-7547)

769.56   US
PHILATELION.* 1962. 10/yr. $25. Lions Philatelic Unit, 310 Forest Oaks Dr., St. Simons Island, GA 31522-2489. TEL 407-870-0022. Ed. Anton K. Dekom. adv. circ. 350. (looseleaf format; back issues avail.)

769.56   UK   ISSN 0260-6739
HE6187
PHILATELIST AND PHILATELIC JOURNAL OF GREAT BRITAIN. 1866. 4/yr. £12 (Europe £15; elsewhere £28). Premier House, Hinton Rd., Bournemouth BH1 2EF, England. TEL 01202-299277. FAX 01202-298303. Ed. Robson Lowe. adv. contact: Robson Lowe. bk.rev.; charts; illus.; mkt.; tr.lit.; index. circ. 3,500. (also avail. in microform from UMI; reprint service avail. from UMI) **Indexed:** Stamp J.Ind. **Document type:** trade publication. —UMI.
    Formed by the 1981 merger of: Philatelist (ISSN 0031-7373); P J G B (ISSN 0030-8048)
    Description: Describes famous collections and new discoveries.

769.56   AT   ISSN 0031-7403
PHILATELY FROM AUSTRALIA; a chronicle of Australasian stamps and their collectors. 1949. q. Aus.$7.50($12) Royal Philatelic Society of Victoria, Box 2071, Melbourne, Vic. 3001, Australia. Ed. H.L. Chisholm. adv.; bk.rev.; charts; illus.; index, cum.index: 1949-1958, 1959-1968. circ. 400. **Indexed:** Stamp J.Ind.

769.56   JA
PHILATELY IN JAPAN. (Text in English) 1977. q. 2000 Yen. Japan Philatelic Society Foundation, Box 1, Shinjuku, Tokyo 163-91, Japan. **Document type:** bulletin.

769.56   US
PHILATEX.* vol.86, 1982. m. free. San Antonio Philatelic Association, c/o Patricia Cote, 3807 E. Songbird Ln., San Antonio, TX 78229-2603. circ. 220.

769.56 794.1   FR
PHILEMAT. 1986. 4/yr. $20. 10 rue A. Pluchet, 92220 Bagneux, France. Ed. Claude Geiger. bk.rev.
    Description: Devoted to the collection of chess stamps and philately.

769.56   GR   ISSN 0031-8264
PHILOTELIA; bimonthly specialized philatelic magazine. (Text in English, French, Greek) 1924. bi-m. $25. Hellenic Philatelic Society, 57 Akademias St., 106 79 Athens, Greece. TEL 30-1-3621-125. Ed. J. Halvadjdopoulos. adv.; bk.rev.; abstr.; bibl.; charts; illus.; stat.; index, cum.index: 1924-1953; 1954-1973; 1974-1983; 1984-1993. circ. 1,000. (also avail. in microfiche) **Document type:** consumer publication.
    ●Also available online.

769.56   US   ISSN 0888-675X
PITCAIRN LOG. 1973. q. $10 membership. (Pitcairn Islands Study Group) Everett L. Parker, Ed. & Pub., Box 1306, Greenville, ME 04441-1306. TEL 207-695-3077. FAX 207-695-3780. adv.; bk.rev. circ. 500. **Indexed:** Stamp J.Ind. **Document type:** academic/scholarly publication.

769.56   AT   ISSN 0155-6215
POCKET AUSTRALIAN STAMP CATALOGUE. 1970. a. Aus.$7.95. Seven Seas Stamps Pty. Ltd., G.P.O. Box 3273, Sydney, N.S.W. 2001, Australia. Ed. D. Foster. illus. circ. 35,000. **Document type:** catalog.
    Description: Simplified catalog of Australian Commonwealth stamps issued from 1913 to the present. Includes current retail values for mint and used specimens.

769.56   US
POCONO MT. NEWS.* bi-m. membership. Pocono Mt. Philatelic Society, c/o Zellers, 350 Sproat Ave., Freedom, PA 15042.

769.56   DK   ISSN 0032-4418
POPULAER FILATELI. 1938. 10/yr. DKK 295($50) Aarhus Frimaerkehandel, Bruunsgade 42, 8000 Aarhus C, Denmark. FAX 45-86-19-92-81. Ed. Lars Boes. adv.; bk.rev.; illus.; mkt. circ. 3,500.

794   US   ISSN 0892-5178
PORTU-INFO. 1961. q. $10 (foreign $15). International Society for Portuguese Philately, Box 1916, Philadelphia, PA 19105. TEL 215-843-2106. FAX 215-204-1532. Ed. Stephen S. Washburne. adv.; bk.rev.; illus.; tr.lit.; index. circ. 450. **Indexed:** Stamp J.Ind.
    Description: Examines stamps and postal history of Portugal and ex-colonies.

769.56   UK   ISSN 0142-9833
PORTUGAL & SPAIN STAMP CATALOGUE. 1980. irreg. price varies. Stanley Gibbons Publications Ltd., Unit 5 Parkside, Christchurch Rd., Ringwood, Hants. BH24 3SH, England. TEL 0425-472363. FAX 0425-470247. TELEX 41271-SGPPUB-G. **Document type:** catalog.

769.56   US   ISSN 0164-6184
HE6204.U5
POSSESSIONS. 1978. q. $10. United States Possessions Philatelic Society, c/o W.T. Zuehlke, Sec.-Treas., 8100 Willow Steam Dr., Sandy, UT 84093. Ed. Gilbert N. Plass. adv.; bk.rev. circ. 600. **Indexed:** Stamp J.Ind.

POST- UND TELEKOMMUNIKATIONSGESCHICHTE. see COMMUNICATIONS — Postal Affairs

LA POSTA; a journal of American postal history. see COMMUNICATIONS — Postal Affairs

769.56   NZ
POSTAGE STAMPS OF NEW ZEALAND. irreg. Royal Philatelic Society of New Zealand, Box 1269, Wellington, New Zealand.

769.56   US
POSTAL ORDER NEWS. 1985. q. $10 (effective 1994). Postal Order Society, c/o Jack Harwood, Dir., Box 32015, Midtown Sta., Sarasota, FL 34239. TEL 813-924-0419. Ed. Mal Tedds. **Document type:** newsletter.

383.2   US
POSTAL SERVICE GUIDE TO U S STAMPS. 1927. a. $5.95. U.S. Postal Service, 475 L'Enfant Plaza West, S.W., Washington, DC 20260-6757. TEL 202-268-2000. (Orders to: Philatelic Sales Division, Box 449997, Kansas City, MO 64144-9997. TEL 816-455-4880)
    Former titles: United States Postage Stamps; (until 1970): Postage Stamps of the United States (ISSN 0079-4244)

PHILATELY

769.56 US
POSTAL STATIONERY STUDY GROUP.* q. Germany Philatelic Society, c/o Matchinegg, Ed., 2008 Ft. Stockton Dr., San Diego, CA 92103-1512.

769.56 BO
POSTALES DE BOLIVIA. 1971. q. free. Federacion Filatelica Boliviana, Apartado 4247, La Paz, Bolivia. Dir. Eugenio von Boeck. circ. 950. (tabloid format) **Document type:** bulletin.

769.56 US ISSN 0551-6897
POSTHORN; the bank of Scandinavian philatelic knowledge. 1943. q. $15. Scandinavian Collectors Club, 2316 Lakeview Dr., Fergus Falls, MN 56537-3903. TEL 901-452-8701. (Subscr. to: SCC, Exec. Sec., Box 125, Newark, DE 19715-0125) Ed. John Lindholm. adv.; bk.rev.; illus.; circ. 1,100 (controlled). **Indexed:** Stamp J.Ind. **Document type:** academic/scholarly publication.

769.56 GW
POSTILLON. 1954. 3/yr. DM.40. Bund Deutscher Philatelisten e.V., Arbeitsgemeinschaft Frankreich e.V., Tucholskyweg 5, 55127 Mainz, Germany. adv.; bk.rev. circ. 500.
Description: Covers philately of France, its French colonies and its offices abroad.

789.56 BE
DE POSTZEGEL. (Text in Dutch) 1938. 11/yr. 500 BEF (fl.30) (Europe 600 BEF; elsewhere 700 BEF). Koninklijke Vlaamse Bond van Postzegelverzamelaars v.z.w., Werfplein 6, B-8000 Brugge, Belgium. TEL 32-50-337047. Ed. Dirk Claeys. adv.; B&W page 6500 BEF. **Document type:** bulletin.
Description: Philatelic news from Belgium, the Netherlands and other countries.

769.56 US ISSN 0273-5415
HE6187
PRECANCEL FORUM. 1940. m. $17.50. Precancel Stamp Society Inc., Box 1134, Wichita, KS 67201-1134. Ed. Dilmond D. Postlewait. adv.; bk.rev.; charts; illus.; circ. 1,200 (paid). **Indexed:** Stamp J.Ind. **Document type:** newsletter.
Description: Covers activities of the society and its branch clubs. Includes articles on precancelled stamps and their collection.

769.56 US
PRECANCEL STAMP COLLECTOR. 1951. m. $15. National Association of Precancel Collectors, Inc., 84 W. National Dr., Newark, OH 43055-5358. (Co-sponsor: New Jersey Precancel Society) Ed. Glenn W. Dye. adv.; bk.rev.; circ. 7,000 (paid).
Description: Contains information on precanceled stamps.

769.56 UK ISSN 0140-8003
PRIVATE POST. 1977. a. £4. Cinderella Stamp Club, c/o L.N. Williams, Ed., 44 The Ridgeway, London NW11 8QS, England. bibl.; illus. circ. 600. (back issues avail.)

769.56 US ISSN 0162-7902
HE6185.G9
EL QUETZAL. 1949. q. $15 membership. International Society of Guatemala Collectors, c/o Michael Barie, Box 1445, Detroit, MI 48231. TEL 313-538-3865. Ed. Cecile Gruson. adv.; bk.rev. circ. 300. **Document type:** newsletter.
Description: Concerned with the philatelic history of Guatemala and other portions of Central America.

769.56 UK ISSN 0951-886X
RAILWAY PHILATELY. 1966. q. £6.50. Railway Philatelic Group, 4A Richmond Parade, E. Twickenham, Middx. TW1 1ET, England. Ed. R.W. Wright. adv.; bk.rev.; illus. circ. 500. **Document type:** newsletter.

769.56 629.4
RAPID NOTICE NEWS SERVICE. 1977. bi-m. $10. Space Philatelist International Society, Box 771, West Nyack, NY 10994. TEL 914-623-8149. FAX 914-591-6683. Ed. Scott Michaels. circ. 250. (looseleaf format; back issues avail.)

769.56 US
REPLY COUPON COLLECTOR. 1953. s-a. $15 for 2 yrs. International Society of Reply Coupon Collectors, Box 165, Somers, WI 53171-0165. TEL 414-552-8740. Ed. Allan Hauck. adv.; bk.rev.; illus.; circ. 75 (paid). (looseleaf format)
Description: Chronicles and studies all kinds of reply coupons issued by the various postal unions of the world.

RHODE ISLAND POSTAL HISTORY JOURNAL. see COMMUNICATIONS — Postal Affairs

769.56 RH
RHODESIA STAMP CATALOGUE. 1971. a. Z.$9.75. Zimbabwe Stamp Co. (Pvt.) Ltd., Box 200, Harare, Zimbabwe. Ed. D.G. Pollard. illus. circ. 7,000.

789.56 UK ISSN 0269-1574
RHODESIAN STUDY CIRCLE JOURNAL. 1948. q. £8. Rhodesian Study Circle, c/o Derek Lambert, Ed., 25 Carr Rd., Nelson, Lancashire BB9 7JZ, England. adv. contact: Keith Harrod. bk.rev. circ. 500. **Document type:** academic/scholarly publication.

769.56 US ISSN 0035-8363
ROSSICA SOCIETY OF RUSSIAN PHILATELY JOURNAL. 1929. s-a. $18 per no. Rossica Society of Russian Philately, Inc., c/o Kennedy Wilson, Ed., 7415 Venice St., Falls Church, VA 22043. adv.; bk.rev.; charts; illus.; index. circ. 350. (back issues avail.) **Indexed:** Numis.Lit., Stamp J.Ind. **Document type:** academic/scholarly publication.
Refereed Serial

769.56 NZ
ROYAL PHILATELIC SOCIETY OF NEW ZEALAND. ANNUAL REPORT. a. Royal Philatelic Society of New Zealand, Box 1269, Wellington, New Zealand. Eds. D.B. Tennant, B.G. Vincent. adv.

769.56 NZ
ROYAL PHILATELIC SOCIETY OF NEW ZEALAND. MONOGRAPH SERIES. biennial. price varies. Royal Philatelic Society of New Zealand, P.O. Box 1269, Wellington, New Zealand.

769.569883 UK ISSN 0953-3354
THE RUNNER POST. 1985. q. Bechuanalands & Botswana Society, c/o Mike George, Hon. Secy., P.O. Box 108, St. Albans, Herts AL1 3AD, England.

769.56 UK ISSN 0142-9841
HE6185.S652
RUSSIA STAMP CATALOGUE. 1981. irreg. price varies. Stanley Gibbons Publications Ltd., Unit 5 Parkside, Christchurch Rd., Ringwood, Hants. BH24 3SH, England. TEL 0425-472363. FAX 0425-470247. TELEX 41271-SGPPUB-G. **Document type:** catalog.

769.56 369.46 US ISSN 1066-6028
S O S S I JOURNAL.* 1951. m. $12.50 in N. America; elsewhere $15 (membership only). Scouts on Stamps Society International, 2320 Swallowtail Ln., Boise, ID 83706. TEL 208-338-9477. adv.; bk.rev. circ. 1,500. (looseleaf format)
Description: Presents a forum for those interested in collecting stamps and other philatelic material related to the Boy Scouts, Girl Scouts and girl guides of the world.

769.56 US
S O S SIGNAL. 1959. q. $5 membership. Stamps on Stamps Centenary Unit, c/o Boris Politziner, 2039 W. River Rd., Grand Island, NY 14072. TEL 716-773-5141. Ed. Robert Graves. circ. 100. **Document type:** newsletter.
Description: Focuses on stamp reproductions, from actual pictures of former stamps to simulations of stamps.

769.56 US
ST. HELENA AND DEPENDENCIES PHILATELIC SOCIETY NEWSLETTER. 1977. q. $10. St. Helena and Dependencies Philatelic Society, 222 E. Torrence Rd., Columbus, OH 43214. TEL 614-262-3046. Ed. Russell V. Skavaril. adv.; bk.rev. circ. 250. **Indexed:** Stamp J.Ind.

769.56 UK ISSN 0261-7226
SARAWAK JOURNAL. 1947. q. £6.50 membership. Sarawak Specialists' Society, 25 Cranedown, Lewes, E. Sussex BN7 3NA, England. TEL 0273-478676. (Subscr. to: David Brown, 112 Hall Bower Ln., Newsome, Huddersfield, W. Yorks. HD4 6RN, England) Ed. Brian J. Cave. adv.; bk.rev. circ. 337. **Indexed:** Ecol.Abstr., Geo.Abstr., IDA, Stamp J.Ind. **Document type:** bulletin.
Description: Covers philately and postal history of Sarawak, Brunei, northern Borneo and Labuan.

769.56 US ISSN 0048-9255
SCALPEL AND TONGS; medical philately. 1955. bi-m. membership. American Topical Association, Medical Subjects Unit, c/o Ranes Chakravorty, Ed., 5049 Cherokee Hills Dr., Salem, VA 24153-5848. TEL 703-380-2362. adv.; bk.rev. circ. 400. (also avail. in microform from UMI) **Indexed:** CWHM.

769.56 UK ISSN 0142-985X
SCANDINAVIA STAMP CATALOGUE. 1980. irreg. price varies. Stanley Gibbons Publications Ltd., Unit 5 Parkside, Christchurch Rd., Ringwood, Hants. BH24 3SH, England. TEL 0425-472363. FAX 0425-470247. TELEX 41271-SGPPUB-G. **Document type:** catalog.

769.56 US
SCANDINAVIAN PHILATELIC FOUNDATION. NEWSLETTER. 1980. s-a. $10 to members. Scandinavian Philatelic Foundation, Box 6716, Thousand Oaks, CA 91359. Ed. George B. Koplowitz. circ. 150. **Document type:** newsletter.
Description: Focuses on informing members of current projects in the field of translating Scandinavian area philatelic articles into English.

769.56 SZ
SCHWEIZER BRIEFMARKEN-ZEITUNG. 1889. 12/yr. 33 Fr. (Verband Schweizerischer Philatelistenvereine) Buri Druck AG, Eigerstr. 71, 3001 Berne, Switzerland. TEL 031-462323. FAX 031-455463. circ. 23,000.

769.56 US ISSN 0737-0741
HE6187
SCOTT STAMP MONTHLY; with catalogue update. 1920. m. $17.95. Scott Publishing Company (Subsidiary of: Amos Press, Inc.), 911 Vandemark Rd., Box 828, Sidney, OH 45365. TEL 513-498-0802. FAX 513-498-0808. Ed. Wayne Youngblood; Pub. Stuart Morrissey. adv.: B&W page $550; adv. contact: Bill Fay. bk.rev.; illus.; tr.lit.; circ. 23,000 (paid). (back issues avail.) **Document type:** consumer publication.
—UnCover.
Supersedes in part (until 1982): Scott's Monthly Stamp Journal; Which was formerly: Scott's Monthly Journal (ISSN 0036-9454)

769.56 UK ISSN 0080-8164
SCOTTISH POSTMARK GROUP. HANDBOOK.* 1962. irreg. price varies. Scottish Postmark Group, c/o David C. Jefferies, 11 Craigcrook Ave., Edinburgh EH4 3QE, Scotland.

769 UK
SCOTTISH STAMP NEWS. 1970. m. £3.50. Stanley K. Hunter, Ed. & Pub., 34, Gray Street, Glasgow G3 7TY, Scotland. adv.; bk.rev.; illus.; index. circ. 120.

SCOTT'S SPECIALIZED CATALOGUE OF U.S. STAMPS. 1923. a. $34. Scott Publishing Company, 911 Vandemark Rd., Box 828, Sidney, OH 45365. TEL 513-498-0802. FAX 513-498-0808. Ed. James Kloetzel; Pub. Stuart Morrissey. **Document type:** catalog.

SCOTT'S STANDARD POSTAGE STAMP CATALOGUE. 1867. a. (in 5 vols.). $34 per vol. Scott Publishing Company, 911 Vandemark Rd., Box 828, Sidney, OH 45365. TEL 513-498-0802. FAX 513-498-0808. Ed. James Kloetzel; Pub. Stuart Morrissey. **Document type:** catalog.

769.56 US
SCOUTS ON STAMPS OF THE WORLD. irreg., 8th ed., 1992. $31.50 includes subscr. to S O S S I Journal. Scouts on Stamps Society International, 2320 Swallowtail Ln., Boise, ID 83706. TEL 208-338-9477. Ed. Howard J. Kaplan. circ. 1,500.

PHILATELY

769.56 US
SEAL NEWS. 1946. bi-m. $8. Christmas Seal & Charity Stamp Society, c/o Richard E. Roberts, Box 39696, Minneapolis, MN 55439-0696. Ed. Joseph S. Wheeler, Sr. adv.; bk.rev.; illus.; index; circ. 390 (paid). (processed) **Document type:** newsletter.

769.56 US ISSN 0048-9891
SEAPOSTER. 1939. bi-m. $10. Maritime Postmark Society, c/o Thomas G. Hirschinger, Ed., 141 Gordon Ave., Wadsworth, OH 44281. bk.rev. circ. 200. (looseleaf format) **Document type:** newsletter.

SEMPRE PRONTO; mensario escotista. see *EDUCATION*

769.56 CC
SHANGHAI JIYOU/SHANGHAI PHILATELY. (Text in Chinese) bi-m. Shanghai Shi Jiyou Xiehui - Shanghai Association of Philately, No.13, Alley 155, Julu Lu, Shanghai 200020, People's Republic of China. TEL 3270365. Ed. Le Jinxiang.

769.56 CC
SHAONIAN JIYOU/JUVENILE PHILATELY. (Text in Chinese) 1983. m. $19.70. Zhongguo Jiyou Chubanshe, Dong Chang'an Jie 27, Beijing, People's Republic of China. (Dist. in US by: China Books & Periodicals, Inc., 2929 24th St., San Francisco, CA 94110. TEL 415-282-2994)
Description: Shows elementary and high school students the correct methods and purposes of stamp collecting, while encouraging their enthusiasm for learning and increasing their knowldge of the world.

769.56 SA
SOUTH AFRICA. PHILATELIC SERVICES AND INTERSAPA. PHILATELIC BULLETIN. (Text in Afrikaans, English) 1947. 44/yr. free. Philatelic Services and Intersapa, Private Bag X505, Pretoria 0001, South Africa. FAX 286025. circ. 67,000. **Document type:** bulletin.
Formerly: South Africa. Philatelic Services. Philatelic Bulletin (ISSN 0031-7349)
Description: News of forthcoming stamp issues, with technical and historical notes.

769.56 SA ISSN 0038-2566
SOUTH AFRICAN PHILATELIST. (Text mainly in English, occasionally in Afrikaans) 1923. bi-m. R.60($25) Philatelic Federation of Southern Africa, P.O. Box 2789, Cape Town 8000, South Africa. FAX 27-21-238763. Ed. Wilhelm Grutter. adv.; bk.rev.; bibl.; charts; illus.; mkt.; stat.; index. circ. 3,000. **Indexed:** Ind.S.A.Per., Stamp J.Ind. **Document type:** newsletter.
Description: Concerns the philately of southern Africa.

769.56 UK ISSN 0142-9922
SOUTH AMERICA STAMP CATALOGUE. 1980. irreg. price varies. Stanley Gibbons Publications Ltd., Unit 5 Parkside, Christchurch Rd., Ringwood, Hants. BH24 3SH, England. TEL 0425-472363. FAX 0425-470247. TELEX 41271-SGPPUB-G. **Document type:** catalog.

769.56 UK ISSN 0142-9930
SOUTH-EAST ASIA STAMP CATALOGUE. 1981. irreg. price varies. Stanley Gibbons Publications Ltd., Unit 5 Parkside, Christchurch Rd., Ringwood, Hants. BH24 3SH, England. TEL 0425-472363. FAX 0425-470247. TELEX 41271-SGPPUB-G. **Document type:** catalog.

769.56 US
STAMP AND COIN DIGEST. 1980. q. $1.50 per no. M & H Publications, 38 S. Madison Ave., Spring Valley, NY 10977. Ed. Martin R. Schranz.

769.56 UK
STAMP & COIN MART INTERNATIONAL. m. £17.50. Maze Media Ltd., Castle House, 97 High St., Colchester, Essex CO1 1TH, England. TEL 01206-792701. FAX 01206-795640. Ed. Steve Wright. adv. contact: Mandy Parker. **Document type:** consumer publication.

769.56 US ISSN 0273-7078
STAMP AUCTION NEWS; financial journal of the stamp market. 1963. m. $29. American Publishing Company of New York (Subsidiary of: H.L. Lindquist Publications), 85 Canisteo St., Hornell, NY 14843-1544. TEL 607-324-2212. FAX 607-324-1753. Ed. Denise Axtell. adv.
Description: Contains financial news and information relevant to the stamp market.

769.56 US ISSN 0277-3899
STAMP COLLECTOR. 1931. w. $34.88 (effective 1995). Box 10, Albany, OR 97321. TEL 503-928-3569. FAX 503-967-7672. Ed. Ken Palke; Pub. Jim Magruder. adv. contact: Mike Mathers. bk.rev.; circ. 18,000 (paid). (tabloid format; also avail. in microform) **Document type:** newspaper.
Formerly: Western Stamp Collector (ISSN 0043-4213)

769.56 II ISSN 0014-5467
STAMP DIGEST. (Text in English) 1969. m. Rs.40($20) (Philatelic Research Society) Stamp Digest Publications, P-70, C.I.T. 6M, Calcutta 700054, India. Ed. Bibhash Gupta. adv.; bk.rev.; charts; illus.; tr.lit. circ. 5,100. (tabloid format; also avail. in microfilm)

769.56 US
STAMP EXCHANGERS ANNUAL DIRECTORY. 1963. a. $16. Levine Publications, Box 9090, Trenton, NJ 08650. Ed. L. Jan Olssen. adv.; bk.rev.; charts; illus. circ. 1,703. **Document type:** directory.

769.56 UK ISSN 0038-9277
STAMP LOVER. 1908. 6/yr. $30 to non-members. National Philatelic Society, 107 Charterhouse St., London EC1M 6PT, England. TEL 0171-251-5040. Ed. Michael Furnell. adv.; bk.rev.; illus.; index, cum.index approx. every 10 yrs.; circ. 1,500 (controlled). **Indexed:** Stamp J.Ind. **Document type:** bulletin.

769.56 UK ISSN 0307-6679
STAMP MAGAZINE. m. £33.20. Link House Magazines Ltd., Link House, Dingwall Ave., Croydon, Surrey CR9 2TA, England. TEL 0181-686-2599. FAX 0181-760-0973. (Subscr. to: R F S, 120-126 Lavender Ave., Mitcham, Surrey CR4 3HP, England) Ed. Tom Hedley. adv.; bk.rev.; illus. **Indexed:** Stamp J.Ind. **Document type:** consumer publication.
Description: Provides information and news, technical guidance, a list of expositions, and a market catalog for the serious and avocational philatelist in the U.K.

769.56 UK ISSN 0953-5241
STAMP MAIL. 1946. m. £0.80 per issue. British Philatelic Federation Ltd., 107 Charterhouse St., London EC1M 6PT, England. TEL 071-251-5040. FAX 071-490-4253. Ed. David Sesslons. adv.; bk.rev. circ. 2,200. **Indexed:** Stamp J.Ind. —UMI.
Former titles (until 1988): Stamp News (ISSN 0265-8216); Stamp and Postal History News (ISSN 0261-1899); Incorporates: Philately (ISSN 0031-739X); Stamp Collecting (ISSN 0038-9269); Philatelic Magazine (ISSN 0261-3107); Stamp Collecting was formerly: Stamp Collecting Weekly; Former titles of Philatelic Magazine: Philatelic Magazine and Stamp Review; Philatelic Magazine (ISSN 0031-7357).

769.56 AT
STAMP NEWS. 1954. m. Aus.$63.95. Macquarie Print, 51-59 Wheelers Lane, Dubbo, N.S.W. 2830, Australia. TEL 068-859-478. FAX 068-844-443. Ed. B. Doherty. adv.; bk.rev. circ. 15,000.
Incorporates (1930-1991): Australian Stamp Monthly (ISSN 0005-0296); Former titles: Stamp News Australasia; Stamp News (ISSN 0038-9293)

769.56 US ISSN 0038-9315
HE6187
STAMP WHOLESALER; world's largest stamp dealer newspaper. 1936. 28/yr. $29.90. Van Dahl Publications, 520 E. First St., Box 706, Albany, OR 97321. TEL 503-928-3569. FAX 503-967-7262. Ed. Ed. Ken Palke; Pub. Jim Magruder. adv. contact: Mike Mathers. adv.; bk.rev.; illus.; circ. 5,000 (paid). **Document type:** newspaper, trade publication.
Description: Includes articles on business news items, how-to, mail order, auctions, storefront operations, the use of computers in the stamp business, and tax tips.

769.56 US ISSN 0038-9358
HE6187
STAMPS; the weekly magazine of philately. 1932. w. $23.50. American Publishing Company of New York (Subsidiary of: H.L. Lindquist Publications), 85 Canisteo St., Hornell, NY 14843. TEL 607-324-2212. FAX 607-324-1753. Ed. Denise M. Axtell. adv.: B&W page $780, color page $1030; trim 11 1/4 x 14. bk.rev.; illus.; mkt.; q. index. circ. 18,500. (also avail. in microform from UMI; reprint service avail. from UMI) **Indexed:** Mag.Ind., Stamp J.Ind. **Document type:** newspaper.
● Also available online. Vendor(s): University Microfilms International.
—UMI.

769.56 UK
STAMPS. 1980. m. Northern & Shell Publications, Northern & Shell Bldg., P.O. Box 381, Millharbour, London E14 9TW, England. TEL 44-171-987-5090. FAX 44-171-987-2160. Ed. Allan Dawell. adv.; bk.rev. circ. 25,000. **Indexed:** Mag.Ind.
Former titles (until 1990): Stamps and Printed Matters (ISSN 0956-1463); (until 1988): Stamps (ISSN 0955-0577); (until 1985): Stamps and Foreign Stamps (ISSN 0266-8084); Which was formed by the 1983 merger of: Stamps (ISSN 0143-7011); Foreign Stamps (ISSN 0263-3558)

769.56 II ISSN 0255-8254
STAMPS WORLD. (Text in English) 1979. q. Rs.16($24) 107-2 Amherst Street, Calcutta 700 009, India. Ed. Dipok Dey. circ. 1,015. (back issues avail.)

769.56 UK ISSN 0953-6027
STANLEY GIBBONS COLLECT CHANNEL ISLANDS AND ISLE OF MAN STAMPS. 1972. a. price varies. Stanley Gibbons Publications Ltd., Unit 5 Parkside, Christchurch Rd., Ringwood, Hants. BH24 3SH, England. TEL 0425-472363. FAX 0425-470247. TELEX 41271-SGPPUB-G. **Document type:** consumer publication.
Former titles (until 1986): Collect Channel Islands and Isle of Man Stamps (ISSN 0265-5608); Which was formed by the 1984 merger of: Collect Isle of Man Stamps (ISSN 0307-7098); Collect Channel Island Stamps (ISSN 0306-5103)

769.56 UK ISSN 0144-249X
HE6184.P65
STANLEY GIBBONS POSTCARD CATALOGUE. 1980. irreg. £5.95. Stanley Gibbons Publications Ltd., Unit 5 Parkside, Christchurch Rd., Ringwood, Hants. BH24 3SH, England. TEL 0425-472363. FAX 0425-470247. TELEX 41271-SGPPUB-G. **Document type:** catalog.

769.56 UK ISSN 0081-4210
STANLEY GIBBONS SIMPLIFIED CATALOGUE. STAMPS OF THE WORLD. (In 3 Volumes: Vol.1 Foreign Countries A-J; Vol.2 Foreign Countries K-Z; Vol.3 Commonwealth Countries) 1934; N.S. 1989. a. £15 each vol.1 & 2; £13 vol.3. Stanley Gibbons Publications Ltd., Unit 5 Parkside, Christchurch Rd., Ringwood, Hants. BH24 3SH, England. TEL 0425-472363. FAX 0425-470247. TELEX 412371-SGPPUB-G. illus. **Document type:** catalog.
Description: For the general and thematic stamp collector. The three volumes list over 260,000 stamps with 60,000 illustrations.

737 UK ISSN 0142-9752
HE6226
STANLEY GIBBONS STAMP CATALOGUE. PART 1: BRITISH COMMONWEALTH. 1865. a. £27. Stanley Gibbons Publications Ltd., Unit 5 Parkside, Christchurch Rd., Ringwood, Hants. BH24 3SH, England. TEL 0425-472363. FAX 0425-470247. TELEX 41271-SGPPUB-G. **Document type:** catalog.
Description: Covers Great Britain and the British Commonwealth countries.

769.56 US ISSN 0883-6760
THE STATE REVENUE NEWSLETTER. 1957. q. $10 membership. (State Revenue Society) Paragon Publishing Co. Inc., Box 45553, Tinker, OK 73145. (Alt. addr.: c/o R. Bilek, Pub., 1515 S. Highland, Arlington Heights, IL 60005) Ed. Peter Martin. adv.: B&W page $30; 7 1/2 x 10. bk.rev.; illus.; cum.index: 1957-1976. circ. 300. cols./p.: 3. (processed) **Document type:** newsletter.
Description: Provides current news, information, stamps, and related material used by states that show payment of various taxes.

PHILATELY

SUPERIOR COLLECTOR. see NUMISMATICS

769.56 US
SWEDEN RING TYPE STAMP STUDY UNIT. NEWSLETTER.* 1980. q. $3. Sweden Ring Type Study Unit, c/o James Burgeson, Ed., 920 W. Glenoaks, Ste. A207, Glendale, CA 91202-2757. bk.rev. circ. 75. **Document type:** newsletter.
Formerly: Sweden Ring Type Study Unit. Newsletter.

769.56 US
SYNCOPATED PERFS. 1930? irreg. (4-6/yr.). membership. Greater Cincinnati Philatelic Society, 6508 Craigland Ct., Cincinnati, OH 45230-2821. TEL 513-231-4208. E-mail: rmaifeld@tso.uc.edu. Ed. Douglas J. Newberry. adv. circ. 100. **Document type:** newsletter.

769.56 796.352 US
TEE TIME. 1987. q. $10. International Philatelic Golf Society, c/o Kevin Hadlock, 447 Skyline Dr., Orange, CT 06477. Ed. Stuart MacKenzie. adv. circ. 250.
Description: Focuses on all aspects of the game on stamps, including singles, errors, proofs, blocks, covers, and postal stationery.

769.56 US
TELL.* 1975. bi-m. $8. American Helvetia Philatelic Society, 707 Tam O'Shanter Blvd., Williamsburg, VA 23185. (Subscr. to: Richard T. Hall, Sec., Box 2425, Gaithersburg, MD 20879) Ed. Steve Turchik. adv.; bk.rev. circ. 550.
Formed by the merger of: Helvetia Alphorn & Helvetia Herald.

769.56 US ISSN 0893-2670
THE TEXAS PHILATELIST. 1963. bi-m. $10 membership. Texas Philatelic Association, Inc., 17209 Whippoorwill Trail, Leander, TX 78645-9734. TEL 512-267-4603. Ed. Jane King Fohn. adv. contact: Jane King Fohn. bk.rev.; circ. 600 (paid). **Document type:** newsletter.
Description: Provides members with articles on stamp collecting and assocation news and bulletins.

769.56 US ISSN 0198-7992
HE6185.T45
THAI PHILATELY. 1978. q. $12. Society for Thai Philately, Box 25644, Oklahoma City, OK 73125-0644. TEL 405-685-4405. Ed. Gary Van Cott. adv.; bk.rev.; index. circ. 150. (back issues avail.) **Indexed:** Stamp J.Ind. **Document type:** academic/scholarly publication, newsletter.
Description: Covers all aspects of the postage stamp and postal history of Thailand.

383 940.53 US
THIRD REICH STUDY GROUP BULLETIN. 1962. q. $17 membership (foreign $18). Third Reich Study Group, c/o Fred Williams, 10408 Avandale Ave., Charlotte, MA 28210. Ed. Myron Fox. bk.rev.; index. circ. 300. (looseleaf format; back issues avail.) **Document type:** academic/scholarly publication, bulletin.
Description: Covers postal history of Germany during 1933-1945 (Third Reich).

769.56 CC
TIANJIN JIYOU/TIANJIN PHILATELY. (Text in Chinese) 1983. q. Y1.10 per no. Tianjin Jiyou Xiehui - Tianjin Philately Association, 89 Jiefang Beilu, Tianjin 300041, People's Republic of China. TEL 314613. Ed. Jia Yingdong. adv. circ. 20,000.

769.56 FR ISSN 0995-6433
TIMBROLOISIRS. 1989. m. Timbropresse SA, 33 rue de Chazelles, 75850 Paris Cedex 17, France. TEL 47-66-02-13. FAX 47-66-11-34. adv.; B&W page 9000 F., color page 13000 F.; 148 x 210. **Document type:** consumer publication.

769.56 FR ISSN 0761-1358
TIMBROSCOPIE; le magazine de la philatelie active. 1984. m. 300 F. (foreign 370 F.). Timbropresse SA, 33 rue de Chazelles, 75850 Paris Cedex 17, France. TEL 47-66-02-13. FAX 47-66-11-34. adv.; B&W page 15000 F., color page 20000 F.; 210 x 297. cum.index; circ. 53,772 (controlled). (back issues avail.) **Document type:** consumer publication.

769.56 US
TIN CANNER. 1981. bi-m. $12 (effective 1995-1996). Tonga - Tin Can Mail Study Circle, Inc., 16500 S.E. First, No. 99, Vancouver, WA 98684. TEL 503-829-5508. Ed. Janet Klug. adv.; bk.rev.; illus.; index. circ. 180. (back issues avail.) **Document type:** newsletter.
Formerly: Philastannumy.
Description: Includes stamps and stationary related to Tong; contains articles and information about club activites.

769.56 US ISSN 0049-4135
TOPICAL STAMP HANDBOOKS. 1951. irreg., no.127, 1995. price varies. American Topical Association, Inc., Box 630, Johnstown, PA 15907. TEL 814-539-6301. Ed. Donald W. Smith.

769.56 US ISSN 0040-9332
HE6187
TOPICAL TIME. 1949. bi-m. $18. American Topical Association, Inc., Box 630, Johnstown, PA 15907. TEL 814-539-6301. Ed. Donald W. Smith. adv.; bk.rev.; charts; illus.; mkt.; cum.index: 1949-1959, then every 5 yrs. circ. 7,000. **Indexed:** Stamp J.Ind.
Description: Deals with topical interest areas.

796.56 US
TOPICAL WOMAN. 1979. q. $6 to members (foreign $8). Women on Stamps Study Unit, 515 Ocean Ave., No. 6085, Santa Monica, CA 90402. (Subscr. to: 259 Middle Rd., Falmouth, ME 04105-1225) Ed. Davida Kristy. index. circ. 100. (looseleaf format; back issues avail.) **Document type:** newsletter.
Description: Features biographies of women on stamps, women stamp designers and engravers, women's art on stamps, and lists of new issues.

769.56 US ISSN 0041-1175
HE6185.U5
TRANSIT POSTMARK COLLECTOR. 1950. 6/yr. $15007 membership. Mobile Post Office Society, c/o Douglas N. Clark, Ed., Box 51, Lexington, GA 30648. TEL 603-746-3828. (Subscr. to: Andrew Koval, Sec., Box 302, Bedford, IL 60499) adv.; bk.rev.; illus. circ. 650. (looseleaf format) **Document type:** newsletter.
Formerly: H P O Notes.

789.56 UK
THE TRANSVAAL PHILATELIST. 1965. q. Transvaal Study Circle, c/o Jeff Woolgar, 132 Bell St., Chatham, Kent ME4 6QH, England.

737 769.56 IT ISSN 0393-7534
TRIBUNA DEL COLLEZIONISTA; mensile culturale di attualita e cronaca filatelica e numismatica. 1975. m. L.60000($65) (foreign L.75000). Associazioni Filatelistiche, Via S. Nilo 4, 04024 Gaeta, Italy. TEL 39-771-460305. FAX 39-771-740176. Ed. Elena Conte; Pub. Tommasso Valente. adv.: B&W page L.800000, color page L.1200000; adv. contact: Tommaso Valente. bk.rev.; illus. circ. 12,000.

769.56 737 US ISSN 0882-1674
TRIDENT - VISNYK. Issued with: Ukranian Philatelist (ISSN 0198-6252) (Text mainly in English) q. (typically set triannually; effective 1995). Ukrainian Philatelic and Numismatic Society, Box 11184, Chicago, IL 60611-0184. Ed. Bohdan O. Pauk. adv. contact: Bohdan O. Pauk. **Document type:** newsletter.
Description: Ukrainian philatelic and numismatic news and events.

769.56 US ISSN 0148-673X
TRUMPETER. 1972. q. $22. Croatian Philatelic Society, 1512 Lancelot Rd., Borger, TX 79007-6341. TEL 806-273-7225. Ed. Eck Spahich. adv.: B&W page $50; trim 8 1/2 x 11. bk.rev.; illus.; tr.lit.; index. circ. 700. (processed; back issues avail.) **Indexed:** Stamp J.Ind.

769.56 US ISSN 0279-6139
U S C S LOG. 1932. m. $16. Universal Ship Cancellation Society, Box 981, Healdsburg, CA 95448. TEL 707-431-1109. Ed. Robert D. Rawlins. adv.; bk.rev. circ. 1,400. **Document type:** newsletter, bulletin.
Description: Dedicated to the collection and study of naval and maritime postal history.

769.56 US
U S CANCELLATION CLUB NEWS.* 1951. bi-m. $2.50. U S Cancellation Club, Box 286, Bonsall, CA 92003. adv.; bk.rev.; charts; stat.; illus.; cum.index: vols. 1-10. circ. 420.

760 US ISSN 0198-6252
HE6185.U45
UKRAINIAN PHILATELIST. (Text in English, Ukrainian) 1951. s-a. $20 (subscr. includes Trident-V isnyk) (typically set triannually; effective 1995). Ukrainian Philatelic and Numismatic Society, Box 11184, Chicago, IL 60611-0184. Ed. Ingert Kuzych. adv. contact: Bohdan O. Pauk. bk.rev. circ. 450. (reprint service avail. from UMI, ISI)
Formerly: Ukrayins'kyi Filatelist.
Description: Contains articles and studies on Ukrainian philately and numismatics.

760 UN
UNITED NATIONS POSTAL ADMINISTRATION PHILATELIC BULLETIN. 1993. 9/yr. United Nations Postal Administration, Box 5900, Grand Central Sta., New York, NY 10163-9992. **Document type:** bulletin.

769.56 US
U.S. TAX-STAMP REVIEW. 1978. bi-m. $10 membership. Interstate Cinderellans and Revenuers Educational Club, Box 9128, San Jose, CA 95157-9128. TEL 408-296-4171. Ed. Elbert S.A. Hubbard. adv.; bk.rev.; illus. circ. 100. **Document type:** newsletter.
Formerly (until 1995): I C A R Newsletter.
Description: Covers revenue and Cinderella stamps issued by the United States and its possessions. Promotes issuance of catalogs and listings.

794 US ISSN 0164-923X
HE6187
UNITED STATES SPECIALIST. 1930. m. $27 (effective 1995). Bureau Issues Association, Inc., 10725 John Price Rd., Charlotte, NC 28273. TEL 704-588-2636. FAX 704-588-2955. E-mail: rsine@cybernetics.net. Ed. Richard L. Sine. adv.; bk.rev.; illus. circ. 2,300. **Document type:** academic/scholarly publication.
Description: Promotes the study of United States stamps.

769.56 UK ISSN 0142-9949
UNITED STATES STAMP CATALOGUE. 1981. irreg. price varies. Stanley Gibbons Publications Ltd., Unit 5 Parkside, Christchurch Rd., Ringwood, Hants. BH24 3SH, England. TEL 0425-472363. FAX 0425-470247. TELEX 41271-SGPPUB-G. **Document type:** catalog.

769.56 UY ISSN 0042-1189
URUGUAY FILATELICO. 1928. 4/yr. $5. Club Filatelico del Uruguay, Box 518, Montevideo, Uruguay. Dir. Elias Casal Gari. illus.

789.56 IT ISSN 1120-6934
VACCARI MAGAZINE; rivista di informazione filatelica e storico postale. 1989. s-a. L.35000 (Europe L.45000; elsewhere L.60000). Edizioni Vaccari s.a.s., Via M. Buonarroti 46, 41058 Vignola (Mo), Italy. TEL 39-59-764106. FAX 39-59-760157. Ed. Paolo Vaccari. adv. contact: Valeria Vaccari. bk.rev. **Document type:** consumer publication.

769.56 SP
VALENCIA FILATELICA; cuadernos de filatelia. m. 250 ptas.($7) c/o Jose M. Gomis Segui, Ed., Box 912, Valencia 9, Spain. adv.; illus.

769.56 US
VATICAN NOTES. 1953. bi-m. $9. Vatican Philatelic Society, 3348 Clubhouse Rd., Virginia Beach, VA 23452. TEL 804-486-3614. Ed. William M. Wickert. adv.; bk.rev. circ. 600.

769.56 US ISSN 1053-9204
VERMONT PHILATELIST.* 1956. q. $5. Vermont Philatelic Society, 18 Fuller St., Montpelier, VT 05602. Ed. Morton Nash. adv.; bk.rev.; cum.index: nos.1-60; circ. controlled.

769.56 US
VIRGINIA PHILATELIC FORUM. 1974. q. $5. Virginia Philatelic Federation, Box 3486, College Station, Fredericksburg, VA 22402. Ed. James B. Gouger. adv.; bk.rev. circ. 1,000.

769.56 US
WAR COVER CLUB BULLETIN.* vol.21, 1981. q. $5. War Cover Club, 1400 Altamont Ave., No.110, Scenectady, NY 12303-2915. Ed. Chris Kulpinski. adv.; bk.rev. circ. 750. **Indexed:** Stamp J.Ind.

765.56   US   ISSN 1074-5890
WATERCRAFT PHILATELY. 1954. bi-m. $7 (effective July 1994). Robert L. Tessier, Ed. & Pub., Box 23092, Washington, DC 20026. TEL 703-671-6484. (Subscr. to: Robert P. Stuckert, 2750 Hwy.21, E. Paint Lick, KY 40461) Ed. Robert L. Tessier. adv.; bk.rev. circ. 350. (looseleaf format) **Document type:** newsletter.
   Description: Features histories of watercraft depicted on stamps.

769.56   GW
WELTRAUM PHILATELIE. (Text in German; summaries in English) 1976. bi-m. DM.40($25) Weltraum Philatelie e.V., Postfach 1211, 85632 Hoehenkirchen-Siegertsbrunn, Germany. TEL 089-60724849. Ed. P. Wilhelm. adv. circ. 600. (back issues avail.) **Document type:** bulletin.

769.56   US   ISSN 0510-2332
HE6185.U7
WESTERN EXPRESS; early western mails. 1950. q. $15. Western Cover Society, 1615 Rose St., Berkeley, CA 94703. TEL 415-569-2817. Ed. Alan Patera. adv.; bk.rev.; cum.index: 1950-1978. circ. 350. (back issues avail.)
—UnCover.

769.56   AU
WIENER KUNSTHANDEL. a. Landesgremium des Handels mit Gemaelden, Antiquitaeten und Kunstgegenstaeden sowie Briefmarken fuer Wien, Schwarzenbergpl. 14, A-1040 Vienna, Austria. TEL 657671.

WORLD COLLECTIONS NEWS; mensile di informazioni numismatiche e filateliche. see NUMISMATICS

769.56   US
WORLD POSTAL STATIONERY - NEW ISSUE REPORT. 1961. 3/yr. $10 (foreign $13). Classic Philatelics, Box 5637, Huntington Beach, CA 92615. TEL 714-968-1717. FAX 714-968-6704. Ed. Pat Feiner. circ. 250. **Document type:** newsletter.
   Former titles: New Issue Report; (until 1983): Entire Truth.
   Description: Lists of new postal stationery philatelic releases by governments of the world, with pricing in mint, first day of issue condition.

769.56   UK   ISSN 0043-9061
WORLD STAMPS.* 1966. m. 22s.($3.15) Solway Publications, 4 Buccleuch St., Dumfries, Scotland. Ed. Capt. K. Jahr. adv.; bk.rev.; charts; illus.; mkt.; tr.lit.; index. circ. 8,000.

769.56   UK   ISSN 0260-1265
HE6188
YEARBOOK AND PHILATELIC SOCIETIES' DIRECTORY. a. £7.50. British Philatelic Federation Ltd., 107 Charterhouse St., London EC1M 6PT, England. TEL 071-251-5040. FAX 071-490-4253. **Document type:** directory.

769.56   US
YUBA - SUTTER PHILATELIC SOCIETY. NEWSLETTER. vol.4, 1980. m. Yuba - Sutter Philatelic Society, 11222 Loma Rica Rd., Marysville, CA 95901. **Document type:** newsletter.

769.56   CN   ISSN 0843-7394
YULE LOG. 1969. bi-m. $10 (foreign $13) (effective 1995). Christmas Philatelic Club, 11 Rose Crescent, Stoney Creek, ON L8G 3W6, Canada. Ed. Kathy Ward. adv. contact: Glenn Vasbinder. bk.rev.; illus. circ. 420. **Document type:** newsletter.
   Description: Features articles on Christmas philately for collectors. Includes cancel and new issue reports and a 50 lot auction.

769.56   JA
YUSHU; philatelic magazine. m. 8800 Yen. Japan Philatelic Society Foundation, Box 1, Shinjuku-ku, Tokyo 163-91, Japan. **Indexed:** Chem.Abstr.

769.56   RH
ZIMBABWE STAMP CATALOGUE. a. Zimbabwe Stamp Co. (Pvt.) Ltd., Box 200, Harare, Zimbabwe. Ed. D.G. Pollard. **Document type:** catalog.

769.56   US
ZIP ME NEWS. m. $5. Zippy Collectors Club, Inc., 2021 W. 9th, Emporia, KS 66801.

769.56   US   ISSN 0363-6542
HE6185.U5
1869 TIMES. 1975. q. membership. U S 1869 Pictorial Research Associates, Inc., c/o Jonathan Rose, Ed., 30 Golf Rd., Pleasanton, CA 94566. adv.; bk.rev. circ. 300.

PHILATELY — Abstracting, Bibliographies, Statistics

769.56   NE   ISSN 0928-6594
P L N INTERNATIONAL; international philatelic literature news. (Text in English) 1970. 4/yr. fl.15($10) or 10 IRCs (effective 1995-1996). P L N International, c/o C. Nieuwland, Ed., Brandespad 14, 3067 EB Rotterdam, Netherlands. bk.rev. circ. 400. **Document type:** abstracting/indexing.
   Supersedes: Philabook International.
   Description: Information on new worldwide philatelic literature, with addresses of associations and publishers.

STAMPS, COINS, POSTCARDS & RELATED MATERIALS; a directory of periodicals. see NUMISMATICS — Abstracting, Bibliographies, Statistics

PHILOSOPHY

see also Religions and Theology

A I & SOCIETY; the journal of human-centered systems and machine intelligence. (Artificial Intelligence) see COMPUTERS — Artificial Intelligence

182.2   BL   ISSN 0001-1789
A LAMPADA. (Text in English, Portuguese and Spanish) 1931. q. free. Instituto Neo Pitagorico, P.O. Box 1047, Curitiba, Parana, Brazil. Ed.Bd. bk.rev.; abstr.; bibl. circ. 500.

100   US
A P A NEWSLETTERS. 2/yr. $20. American Philosophical Association, University of Delaware, Newark, DE 19716. TEL 302-831-1112. FAX 302-831-8690. E-mail: beller@brahms.udel.edu. circ. 6,000. **Document type:** newsletter.
   Formed by the merger of: A P A Newsletter on Philosophy and the Black Experience & A P A Newsletter on Philosophy and Medicine & A P A Newsletter on Philosophy and Law & A P A Newsletter on Teaching Philosophy & A P A Newsletter on Feminism and Philosophy; A P A Newsletter on Computer Use in Philosophy.

A R I E S. (Association pour la Recherche et l'Information sur l'Esoterisme) see PARAPSYCHOLOGY AND OCCULTISM

A U R A NEWSLETTER. (Association for Unity, Research and Awareness) see NEW AGE PUBLICATIONS

100 370   GW   ISSN 0065-0366
ABHANDLUNGEN ZUR PHILOSOPHIE, PSYCHOLOGIE UND PAEDAGOGIK. 1954. irregr., vol.231, 1992. price varies. Bouvier Verlag Herbert Grundmann, Am Hof 28, 53113 Bonn, Germany. TEL 0228-7290124. FAX 0228-7290179. **Document type:** monographic series.

100 340   MV
ACADEMIA DE STIINTE A REPUBLICA MOLDOVA. REVISTA FILOSOFIE SI DREPT/AKADEMIYA NAUK MOLDAVSKOI RESPUBLIKI. VOPROSY FILOSOFII I PRAVA. (Text in Rumanian, Russian) 1951. 3/yr. 3.60 Rub. Academia de Stiinte a Republica Moldova, Bd. Stefan cel Mare, 1, Kishinev 277001, Moldova. TEL 7-0422-261469. bk.rev. circ. 610. **Document type:** academic/scholarly publication.
—BLDSC (0073.765000).
   Formerly: Academia de Stiinte a R.S.S. Moldova. Buletinul. Filosofie, Drept, Studiul Artelor, Arhelogie (ISSN 0236-3062); Supersedes in part (in 1990): Akademiya Nauk Moldavskoi S.S.R. Izvestiya. Seriya Obshchestvennykh Nauk (ISSN 0321-1681)
   Description: Devoted to socio-philosophical, spiritual and political-legal problems.

ACME. see LITERATURE

100   GW   ISSN 0353-5150
B808.5.A1
ACTA ANALYTICA. (Text in English, German) s-a. DM.38. J.H. Roell, Wuerzburgerstr. 16, 97337 Dettelbach, Germany. TEL 09324-1429. Ed. Matjaz Potrc. **Document type:** academic/scholarly publication.

100   IT
ACTA PHILOSOPHICA (NAPLES). 1985. irregr., no.14, 1992. price varies. (Istituto Italiano per gli Studi Filosofici di Napoli) Edizioni Quattroventi, Via Dini 16, Casella Postale 156, 61029 Urbino, Italy. TEL 0722-2588. FAX 0722-320998.

100   IT   ISSN 1121-2179
ACTA PHILOSOPHICA (ROME); rivista internazionale di filosofia. 1992. s-a. L.45000($50) (Ateneo Romana della Santa Croce) Armando Editore s.r.l., Viale Trastevere 236, 00153 Rome, Italy. TEL 5806420. (Edit. addr.: Via S. Girolamo della Carita 64, 00186 Rome, Italy. TEL 6543752) Ed. Angel Rodriguez Luno. **Document type:** academic/scholarly publication.

100   FI   ISSN 0355-1792
B28.F5   CODEN: APFEDB
ACTA PHILOSOPHICA FENNICA. 1935. irregr., vol.51, 1991. Suomen Filosofinen Yhdistys - Philosophical Society of Finland, c/o Dept. of Philosophy, University of Helsinki, Unioninkatu 40, 00170 Helsinki 17, Finland. TEL 90-1911. FAX 90-1917627. **Indexed:** Math.R., Phil.Ind. **Document type:** monographic series.
—BLDSC (0648.300000). CCC.

100   SW   ISSN 0283-2380
ACTA PHILOSOPHICA GOTHOBURGENSIA. 1986. irregr., no.4, 1991. price varies. Acta Universitatis Gothoburgensis, P.O. Box 5096, S-402 22 Goeteborg, Sweden. Ed. Claes Aaberg. **Document type:** monographic series, academic/scholarly publication.

100 370   PL   ISSN 0208-6107
ACTA UNIVERSITATIS LODZIENSIS: FOLIA PHILOSOPHICA. (Text in Polish; summaries in various languages) 1955-1974; N.S. 1981. irregr. Wydawnictwo Uniwersytetu Lodzkiego, Ul. Jaracza 34, Lodz, Poland. TEL 331671. (Dist. by: Ars Polona-Ruch, Krakowskie Przedmiescie 7, Warsaw, Poland) Ed.Bd. **Indexed:** Bibl.Ling., Math.R. **Document type:** academic/scholarly publication.
—BLDSC (0585.208400).
   Supersedes in part: Uniwersytet Lodzki. Zeszyty Naukowe. Seria 1: Nauki Humanistyczno-Spoleczne (ISSN 0076-0358)
   Description: Contains work from the members of the philosophical faculty and papers presented at symposiums and conferences organized by the faculty on the history of philosophy during the 19th and 20th centuries. Covers philosophical anthropology, the ethics of ecology and aesthetics.

100   PL   ISSN 0208-564X
ACTA UNIVERSITATIS NICOLAI COPERNICI. FILOZOFIA. 1960. irregr. price varies. Uniwersytet Mikolaja Kopernika, Biblioteka Uniwersytecka, Ul. Gagarina 13, 87-100 Torun, Poland. TEL 233-52. TELEX 552382. (Dist. by Osrodek Rozpowszechniania Wydawnictw Naukowych PAN, Palac Kultury i Nauki, 00-901 Warsaw, Poland) **Document type:** academic/scholarly publication.
   Formerly: Uniwersytet Mikolaja Kopernika, Torun. Nauki Humanistyczno-Spoleczne. Filozofia (ISSN 0083-4475)

ACTA UNIVERSITATIS SZEGEDIENSIS DE ATTILA JOZSEF NOMINATAE. DISSERTATIONES SLAVICAE. SECTIO HISTORIAE LITTERARUM. see LITERATURE

100   HU   ISSN 0231-2670
ACTA UNIVERSITATIS SZEGEDIENSIS DE ATTILA JOZSEF NOMINATAE. SECTIO PHILOSOPHICA/FILOZOFIA. (Text in Hungarian; summaries in English, German and Russian) 1922. a. exchange basis. Attila Jozsef University, c/o E. Szabo, Exchange Librarian, Dugonics ter 13, P.O.B. 393, 6701 Szeged, Hungary. (Subscr. to: Kultura, Box 149, H-1389 Budapest, Hungary) Ed. Laszlo Horuczi. circ. 500. **Document type:** academic/scholarly publication.
   Supersedes (as of 1959): Acta Universitatis Szegediensis. Sectio Philosophica (ISSN 0586-3724)
   Description: Treats problems of philosophy linked with the teaching and research activity of the authors.

PHILOSOPHY

100   PL
ACTA UNIVERSITATIS WRATISLAVIENSIS. FILOZOFIA. (Text in English, German, Polish; summaries in English, German) 1992. irreg. price varies. (Uniwersytet Wroclawski) Wydawnictwo Uniwersytetu Wroclawskiego, Pl. Uniwersytecki 9-13, 50-137 Wroclaw, Poland. TEL 44-10-06. (Dist. by: Ksiagarnia Uniwersytetu Wroclawskiego, Pl. Uniwersytecki 9-13, 50-137 Wroclaw, Poland) Ed. Zdzislaw Kalita. circ. 300. **Document type:** academic/scholarly publication.

100 290   II
ADVENT. (Text in English) 1944. q. Rs.15($10) Sri Aurobindo Ashram Trust, Pondicherry 605002, India. Ed. Sameer Kanta Gupta. adv.; bk.rev.; illus. circ. 1,000. **Indexed:** CERDIC.

212.5   GW   ISSN 0001-9011
ADYAR; theosophische Zeitschrift. 1946. 3/yr. DM.19.50. Theosophische Gesellschaft Adyar in Deutschland e.V., Holbeinstr. 16, 28209 Bremen, Germany. TEL 0421-3498171. Ed. Gerda Hoefer. adv. contact: Hank Troemel. bk.rev. circ. 1,100. **Document type:** academic/scholarly publication.

100   ZR
AFRIQUE ET PHILOSOPHIE. (Text in French) 1976. a. 350 Fr.CFA. Facultes Catholiques de Kinshasa, Cercle Philosphique de Kinshasa, B.P. 1534, Kinshasa-Limete, Zaire. Ed. Ngwey Ngond'a Ndende. adv.; bk.rev. circ. 100.

110   NO   ISSN 0800-7136
AGORA. 1983. q. NOK 200. Agora, P.O. Box 1024 Blindern, N-0314 Oslo 3, Norway.

100 301   IT
AGORA (RAVENNA). irreg., latest no.16. price varies. Angelo Longo Editore, Via Paolo Costa 33, 48100 Ravenna, Italy. TEL 39-544-217026. FAX 39-544-217554. circ. 1,500. **Document type:** monographic series.
   Description: Studies on philosophy.

100   CL   ISSN 0568-3939
BH25
AISTHESIS; revista chilena de investigaciones esteticas. 1966. a. $6.50. Pontificia Universidad Catolica de Chile, Instituto de Estetica, Casilla 114-D, Santiago, Chile. Ed. Radoslav Ivelic. bibl.; cum.index. circ. 1,000. **Indexed:** Hisp.Amer.Per.Ind. (1970-).
   Description: Examines aesthetics and how it relates to art, literature, architecture and drama, with an emphasis on aesthetic criticism and research in Chile.

AKADEMIYA NAUK AZERBAIJANA. IZVESTIYA. SERIYA ISTORIYA, FILOSOFIYA I PRAVO. see *HISTORY*

100 340   TA
AKADEMIYA NAUK TAJIKISTANA. SERIYA: FILOSOFIYA I PRAVOVEDENIE. 1986. q. Akademiya Nauk Tajikistana, Pr. Rudaki 33, 734025 Dushanbe, Tajikistan.
   Formerly (until 1992): Akademiya Nauk Tadzhikskoi S.S.R. Seriaya: Filosofiya, Ekonomika, Pravovedenie (ISSN 0235-005X)

100   SZ   ISSN 0149-2004
B1
ALETHEIA; an international yearbook of philosophy. (Text in English, German) 1977. a. (Internationale Akademie fuer Philosophie, LH) Verlag Peter Lang AG, Jupiterstr. 15, CH-3000 Bern 15, Switzerland. TEL 031-9411122. FAX 031-9411131. TELEX 912651-PELA-CH. Ed. Josef Seifert. **Indexed:** Phil.Ind. **Document type:** academic/scholarly publication.
—BLDSC (0786.912000).

150   NE   ISSN 0002-5275
B8.D8
ALGEMEEN NEDERLANDS TIJDSCHRIFT VOOR WIJSBEGEERTE. (Text in Dutch; summaries in English) 1907. 4/yr. fl.85 (foreign fl.112.50) (effective 1994). Van Gorcum en Co. B.V., P.O. Box 43, 9400 AA Assen, Netherlands. TEL 31-5920-46846. FAX 31-5920-72064. Ed. Raymond Corbey. adv.; bk.rev.; bibl.; cum.index: vols.1-50 (1907-1958). circ. 1,100. **Indexed:** Lang.& Lang.Behav.Abstr., Phil.Ind. **Document type:** academic/scholarly publication.

100   GW   ISSN 0340-7969
ALLGEMEINE ZEITSCHRIFT FUER PHILOSOPHIE. 1976. 3/yr. DM.68. (Allgemeine Gesellschaft fuer Philosophie in Deutschland e.V.) Friedrich Frommann Verlag Guenther Holzboog, Koenig-Karl-Str. 27, 70372 Stuttgart, Germany. TEL 0711-9559690. FAX 0711-9559691. Ed. Tilman Borsche. **Indexed:** Bibl.Ling. **Document type:** academic/scholarly publication.
—SWETS.

ALMAS. see *RELIGIONS AND THEOLOGY*

149   US   ISSN 0516-9623
BL2747.3
AMERICAN ATHEIST; a journal of atheist news and thought. 1958. bi-m. $25. (American Atheist Library & Archives) American Atheist Press, Box 140195, Austin, TX 78714-0195. TEL 512-458-1244. FAX 512-467-9525. Ed. Robin Murray-O'Hair. adv.; bk.rev.; charts; illus.; stat.; tr.lit.; index. circ. 30,000. (back issues avail.) **Indexed:** Alt.Press Ind.
   Formerly: Poor Richard's Report (ISSN 0032-4310)
   Description: Provides an in-depth analysis of current state-church seperation violations. Explores atheist history and the effects of religion.

149   US
AMERICAN ATHEIST NEWSLETTER. 1959. m. membership. (American Atheist Library & Archives) American Atheist Press, Box 140195, Austin, TX 78714-0195. TEL 512-458-1244. FAX 512-467-9525. Eds. Jon Murray, Madalyn O'Hair. circ. 70,000.
   Former titles (until 1965): American Atheist Insiders' Newsletter; Poor Richard's Newsletter.
   Description: Keeps the Atheist community abreast of state-church separation violations and the latest religious financial schemes.

282 206   US   ISSN 0065-7638
B11
AMERICAN CATHOLIC PHILOSOPHICAL ASSOCIATION. PROCEEDINGS. 1926. a. $20. American Catholic Philosophical Association, The Catholic University of America, 403 Administration Bldg., Washington, DC 20064. TEL 202-319-5518. FAX 202-319-5518. E-mail: cua-acpa@cud.edu. Ed. Therese Anne Druart. adv.; cum.index: vols.1-63 (1926-1989). circ. 1,500. (also avail. in microfilm from UMI; reprint service avail.) **Indexed:** Arts & Hum.Cit.Ind., Cath.Ind., Curr.Cont., Phil.Ind. **Document type:** proceedings.
—BLDSC (6622.600000); UMI.

149.2   US   ISSN 1051-3558
AMERICAN CATHOLIC PHILOSOPHICAL QUARTERLY. 1927. q. $35. American Catholic Philosophical Association, Catholic Univ. of America, 403 Administration Bldg., Washington, DC 20064. TEL 202-319-5518. FAX 202-319-5047. E-mail: cua-acpa@cud.edu. Ed. Robert E. Wood. adv.; bk.rev.; tr.lit.; cum.index: vols.1-65 (1927-1991). circ. 1,800. (also avail. in microform from UMI; reprint service avail.; back issues avail.) **Indexed:** Arts & Hum.Cit.Ind., Cath.Ind., CERDIC, Curr.Cont., Mid.East: Abstr.& Ind., Phil.Ind., Psychol.Abstr. **Document type:** academic/scholarly publication.
—Faxon; Genuine Article; SWETS; UMI; UnCover.
   Formerly (until 1990): New Scholasticism (ISSN 0028-6621)

149 363.49   US
AMERICAN GAY & LESBIAN ATHEIST. 1983. m. $12. (American Gay Atheists, Inc.) American Atheist Press, Inc., Box 140195, Austin, TX 78714-0195. TEL 512-458-1255. FAX 713-862-3283. (Subscr. to: Box 66711, Houston, TX 77266-6711. TEL 713-862-3283) Ed. Don Sanders. adv.; bk.rev.; film rev.; bibl.; stat.; tr.lit. circ. 5,000. (also avail. in diskette format; back issues avail.)
   Formerly: American Gay Atheist.
   Description: Expresses thoughts and comments on news of concern to lesbian and gay atheists; includes state and church separation news, religious history; and covers contemporary issues.

AMERICAN JOURNAL OF THEOLOGY & PHILOSOPHY. see *RELIGIONS AND THEOLOGY*

AMERICAN LIVING PRESS. see *ART*

106   US   ISSN 0065-972X
B11
AMERICAN PHILOSOPHICAL ASSOCIATION. PROCEEDINGS AND ADDRESSES. 1927. 5/yr. $50. American Philosophical Association, c/o University of Delaware, Newark, DE 19716. TEL 302-831-1112. FAX 302-831-8690. E-mail: beller@brahms.udel.edu. Ed. Eric Hoffman. adv. circ. 8,000. (also avail. in microfilm from UMI; reprint service avail. from UMI) **Indexed:** Phil.Ind. **Document type:** proceedings.
—UMI.

100   US   ISSN 0003-0481
AMERICAN PHILOSOPHICAL QUARTERLY. 1964. q. $38 to individuals; institutions $148. Bowling Green State University, Philosophy Documentation Center, Bowling Green, OH 43403-0189. TEL 419-372-2419; 800-444-2419. FAX 419-372-6987. Ed. Nicholas Rescher. circ. 1,500. **Indexed:** Arts & Hum.Cit.Ind., Curr.Cont., Hum.Ind., Lang.& Lang.Behav.Abstr., Phil.Ind., RILM. **Document type:** academic/scholarly publication.
—BLDSC (0850.590000); Faxon; Genuine Article; SWETS; UnCover.

AMERICAN PHILOSOPHICAL SOCIETY. MEMOIRS. see *SCIENCES: COMPREHENSIVE WORKS*

AMERICAN PHILOSOPHICAL SOCIETY. PROCEEDINGS. see *HISTORY*

AMERICAN PHILOSOPHICAL SOCIETY. TRANSACTIONS. see *SCIENCES: COMPREHENSIVE WORKS*

106   US   ISSN 0065-9762
Q11   CODEN: YAPSAL
AMERICAN PHILOSOPHICAL SOCIETY. YEARBOOK. 1937. a. $15. American Philosophical Society, 104 S. Fifth St., Philadelphia, PA 19106. TEL 215-440-3400. Ed. Herman H. Goldstine. index. (also avail. in microform from UMI; reprint service avail. from UMI,ISI) **Indexed:** Amer.Hist.& Life, GeoRef., Hist.Abstr. **Document type:** directory.

211   US   ISSN 0003-0708
BL2700
AMERICAN RATIONALIST. 1956. bi-m. $10 (effective 1995). Rationalist Association, Inc., Box 994, St. Louis, MO 63188. Ed. Dr. Gordon Stein. adv.; bk.rev. circ. 1,500. (also avail. in microform from UMI; back issues avail.) **Document type:** consumer publication.
—UMI.
   Description: Concerns free thought, philosophy, critique of religion and theology, and the history of unbelief.

212.5   US   ISSN 0003-1402
AMERICAN THEOSOPHIST. 1912. bi-m. $30 membership (includes The Quest). Theosophical Society in America, 1926 N. Main St., Box 270, Wheaton, IL 60189-0270. TEL 708-668-1571. FAX 708-665-8791. Ed. William Metzger. bk.rev. circ. 5,000.

100   NE
AMERICAN UNIVERSITY PUBLICATIONS IN PHILOSOPHY. (Text in English) irreg. price varies. Kluwer Academic Publishers, Postbus 17, 3300 AA Dordrecht, Netherlands. TEL 31-78-392392. FAX 31-78-392254. TELEX 29245 KAPG NL. (Dist. by: Kluwer Academic Publishers Group, P.O. Box 322, 3300 AH Dordrecht, Netherlands. TEL 31-78-392392. FAX 31-78-546474; N. America dist. addr.: Box 358, Accord Sta., Hingham, MA 02018-0358. TEL 617-871-6600. FAX 617-871-6528) **Document type:** monographic series.

100   US   ISSN 0739-6392
AMERICAN UNIVERSITY STUDIES. SERIES 5. PHILOSOPHY. 1983. irreg. Peter Lang Publishing, Inc., 62 W. 45th St., 4th Fl., New York, NY 10036. TEL 212-302-6740. Ed. Christopher Myers. **Document type:** academic/scholarly publication, monographic series.

AMSTERDAM CLASSICAL MONOGRAPHS. see *CLASSICAL STUDIES*

100   NE
ANALECTA CARTESIANA. (Text in French) 1981. irreg. price varies. Quadratures, Postbus 6463, 1005 EL Amsterdam, Netherlands.
   Formerly: Collectanea Cartesiana.

PHILOSOPHY

100   NE   ISSN 0167-7276
ANALECTA HUSSERLIANA; yearbook of phenomenological research. (Text in English) 1971. irreg., vol.35, 1991. price varies. Kluwer Academic Publishers, Postbus 17, 3300 AA Dordrecht, Netherlands. TEL 31-78-392392. FAX 31-78-392254. TELEX 29245 KAPG NL. (Dist. by: Kluwer Academic Publishers Group, P.O. Box 322, 3300 AH Dordrecht, Netherlands. TEL 31-78-392392. FAX 31-78-546474; N. America dist. addr.: Box 358, Accord Sta., Hingham, MA 02018-0358. TEL 617-871-6600. FAX 617-871-6528) Ed. Anna-Teresa Tymieniecka. **Document type:** monographic series.
—BLDSC (0869.154000).
Refereed Serial

100   UK   ISSN 0003-2638
B1
ANALYSIS. 1933-1940; N.S. 1947. q. £23.50($50) (foreign £31) (effective 1996). Basil Blackwell Ltd., 108 Cowley Rd., Oxford OX4 1JF, England. TEL 0865 791100. FAX 0865-791347. TELEX 837022-OXBOOK-G. Ed. Peter Smith. adv.; index. circ. 1,350. (also avail. in microform; reprint service avail. from SWZ,UMI) **Indexed:** Arts & Hum.Cit.Ind., Br.Hum.Ind., Lang.& Lang.Behav.Abstr., Phil.Ind.
—BLDSC (0892.100000); Faxon; Genuine Article; SWETS; UMI; UnCover. **CCC**.

891   II
ANANDA ACHARYA UNIVERSAL SERIES. (Text in English) 1978. irreg. price varies. Vishveshvaranand Vedic Research Institute, P.O. Sadhu Ashram, Hoshiarpur 146021, Punjab, India.

100   BE
ANCIENT AND MEDIEVAL PHILOSOPHY. SERIES 1, PUBLICATIONS DE DE WULF-MANSION CENTRE. 1978. irreg., vol.14, 1993. Leuven University Press, Krakenstraat 3, B-3000 Leuven, Belgium. TEL 32-16-324175. FAX 32-16-323782. **Document type:** academic/scholarly publication.

100   BE
ANCIENT AND MEDIEVAL PHILOSOPHY. SERIES 2, HENRICI DE GANDAVO OPERA. 1979. irreg., vol.28, 1994. Leuven University Press, Krakenstraat 3, B-3000 Leuven, Belgium. TEL 32-16-324175. FAX 32-16-323782. **Document type:** academic/scholarly publication.

180 215   US   ISSN 0740-2007
ANCIENT PHILOSOPHY. 1980. 2/yr. $20 to individuals; institutions $45. Mathesis Publications, Inc., Department of Philosphy, Duquesne University, Pittsburgh, PA 15282. TEL 412-396-6500. Ed. Ronald M. Polansky. adv. contact: Ronald Polansky. bk.rev. circ. 600. (back issues avail.) **Indexed:** Phil.Ind. **Document type:** academic/scholarly publication.
—BLDSC (0900.325400); Faxon; SWETS; UnCover.
Description: Contains articles and reviews about classical philosophy and science.

ANFORA; revista cuatrimestral de literatura y filosofia. see *LITERATURE*

190 800 300   UK   ISSN 0969-725X
AP4
ANGELAKI. 1993. 3/yr. £12($24) to individuals (overseas £14); institutions £18 (overseas £20 ($33)). 44 Abbey Rd., Oxford OX2 0AE, England. TEL 44-865-793891. FAX 44-81-208-1641. Ed. Pelagia Goulimari. adv.: page £50; adv. contact: Gerard Greenway. bk.rev. circ. 400. (back issues avail.) **Document type:** academic/scholarly publication.
—BLDSC (0900.928000).
Description: Encourages critical engagement with philosophical, literary, and societal scientific theory.
Refereed Serial

100 282   VC   ISSN 1123-5772
BX800.A1
ANGELICUM; periodicum trimestre pontificae studiorum universitatis a Santo Thoma Aquinate in Urbe. (Text in English, French, German, Italian and Spanish) 1924. q. $50 (effective 1995). Pontificia Universita S. Tommaso d'Aquino, Largo Angelicum 1, 00184 Rome, Italy. TEL 06-67021. FAX 6790407. Ed. Stephen Krasic. bk.rev. circ. 80. **Indexed:** CERDIC, M.L.A., New Test.Abstr., Old Test.Abstr., Rel.& Theol.Abstr. (1979-). **Document type:** academic/scholarly publication.
Description: Scholarly articles on a variety of topics related to the Catholic faith.

ANHUI SHIDA XUEBAO (SHEHUI KEXUE BAN)/ANHUI NORMAL UNIVERSITY. JOURNAL (SOCIAL SCIENCE EDITION). see *SOCIAL SCIENCES: COMPREHENSIVE WORKS*

ANNALES D'ESTHETIQUE/CHRONIKA AISTHETIKIS. see *ART*

100 301   PL   ISSN 0137-2025
ANNALES UNIVERSITATIS MARIAE CURIE-SKLODOWSKA. SECTIO I. PHILOSOPHIA - SOCIOLOGIA. (Text in English or Polish; summaries in English, French, German) 1976. a. price varies. Uniwersytet Marii Curie-Sklodowskiej, Wydawnictwo, Pl. M. Curie-Skodowskiej 5, 20-031 Lublin, Poland. TEL 48-81-375304. FAX 48-81-336699. TELEX 0643223. Ed. Zdzislaw Cackowski. circ. 500. **Document type:** academic/scholarly publication.

ANNALS OF PURE AND APPLIED LOGIC. see *MATHEMATICS*

ANNUAL EDITIONS: BUSINESS ETHICS. see *BUSINESS AND ECONOMICS*

100   IT   ISSN 0394-1809
B4
ANNUARIO FILOSOFICO (YEAR). 1985. a. L.70000 (effective 1995). Ugo Mursia Editore S.p.A., Corso Unione Sovietica, 91, 10100 Turin, Italy. FAX 39-11-2041557. TELEX 325294. Ed. Giuseppe Riconda. bk.rev. circ. 1,000. **Document type:** academic/scholarly publication.

ANTHROPO-LOGIQUES. see *LINGUISTICS*

100   UK   ISSN 0269-3259
ANTHROPOSOPHY TODAY. 1986. 3/yr. £9 to non-members. Anthroposophical Society in Great Britain, 35 Park Rd., London NW1 6XT, England. TEL 44-71-723-4400. Eds. Eileen Lloyd, Susanne Mainzer. adv.; bk.rev. circ. 2,800. **Document type:** bulletin.
Former titles: Anthroposophical Review; Anthroposophical Quarterly.
Description: Covers Rudolf Steiner's anthroposophy and work arising from it in areas that include philosophy, science, education, medicine, and agriculture.

ANTICHITA CLASSICA E CRISTIANA. see *HISTORY*

149.3   IT   ISSN 0003-6145
ANTROPOSOFIA. 1947. 6/yr. L.40000 (effective Jan. 1994). Editrice Antroposofica S.r.l., Via Sangallo, 34, 20133 Milan, Italy. Ed.Bd. adv.; bk.rev. circ. 700.

100   SP   ISSN 0066-5215
B25   CODEN: ANFIEA
ANUARIO FILOSOFICO. 1968. 3/yr. 3975 ptas.($46) (Universidad de Navarra, Facultad de Filosofia y Letras) Servicio de Publicaciones de la Universidad de Navarra, S.A., Edificio Muga, Campus Universitario, 31080 Pamplona, Spain. TEL 948-25-27-00. Ed. Juan Cruz Cruz. adv.; bk.rev. **Indexed:** Phil.Ind.

100   CN   ISSN 0003-6390
APEIRON; a journal of ancient philosophy and science. 1966. q. Can.$65($47) to individuals; institutions Can.$103 ($78). (University of Alberta, Department of Philosophy) Academic Printing and Publishing, Box 4218, Edmonton, AB T6E 4T2, Canada. TEL 403-435-5898. FAX 403-435-5852. adv.; bk.rev. circ. 350. (processed; avail. on records) **Indexed:** INSPEC (1987-), Phil.Ind. **Document type:** academic/scholarly publication.
—BLDSC (1567.867200); Faxon; UnCover.

100 282   VC   ISSN 0003-7362
B765.T54
AQUINAS; rivista internazionale di filosofia. 1958. 3/yr. $65. Pontificia Universita Lateranense, Piazza S. Giovanni in Laterano 4, 00120 Vatican City (Rome), State of the Vatican City. Ed. Sanchez Sorondo. bk.rev. **Indexed:** M.L.A., Phil.Ind.
—BLDSC (1583.150000).

104   US   ISSN 0066-5614
AQUINAS LECTURE SERIES. 1937. a. $10. (Marquette University, Aristotelean Society) Marquette University Press, Box 1881, Milwaukee, WI 53201-1881. TEL 414-288-1564. Ed. Roland Teske, S.J. (back issues avail.; reprint service avail. from UMI) **Document type:** academic/scholarly publication.
Description: Annual lecture originating at Marquette University.

ARABIC SCIENCES AND PHILOSOPHY; a historical journal. see *SCIENCES: COMPREHENSIVE WORKS*

100   GW   ISSN 0003-8946
ARCHIV FUER BEGRIFFSGESCHICHTE; Bausteine zu einem historischen Woerterbuch der Philosophie. 1955. 2/yr. price varies. Bouvier Verlag Herbert Grundmann, Am Hof 28, 53113 Bonn, Germany. TEL 0228-7290124. FAX 0228-7290179. Ed. Karlfried Gruender. bk.rev. circ. 600. (reprint service avail. from SCH) **Indexed:** Phil.Ind. **Document type:** academic/scholarly publication.
—SWETS.

109   GW   ISSN 0003-9101
B3
ARCHIV FUER GESCHICHTE DER PHILOSOPHIE. vol.58, 1976. 3/yr. DM.216. Walter de Gruyter und Co., Genthiner Str. 13, 10785 Berlin, Germany. TEL 030-26005-0. FAX 030-26005251. TELEX 184027. (U.S. addr.: Walter de Gruyter, Inc., 200 Saw Mill River Rd., Hawthorne, NY 10532. TEL 914-747-0110) Eds. Dorothea Frede, Wolfgang Bartuschat. adv.; bk.rev.; index. **Indexed:** Arts & Hum.Cit.Ind., Curr.Cont., Ind.Bk.Rev.Hum., M.L.A., Phil.Ind. **Document type:** academic/scholarly publication.
—BLDSC (1612.060000); Faxon; Genuine Article; SWETS; UnCover. **CCC**.

170 300 340   GW   ISSN 0001-2343
ARCHIV FUER RECHTS- UND SOZIALPHILOSOPHIE/ARCHIVES DE PHILOSOPHIE DU DROIT ET DE PHILOSOPHIE SOCIALE/ARCHIVES FOR PHILOSOPHY OF LAW AND SOCIAL PHILOSOPHY. Short title: A R S P. (Supplement avail.) (Text in English, French, German, Spanish) 1907. q. DM.198. (Internationale Vereinigung fuer Rechts- und Sozialphilosophie) Franz Steiner Verlag Wiesbaden GmbH, Birkenwaldstr. 44, 70191 Stuttgart, Germany. TEL 0711-2582-0. FAX 0711-2582390. (Subscr. to: Postfach 101061, 70009 Stuttgart, Germany) Ed. Werner Maihofer. adv.; bk.rev.; cum.index. circ. 900. (back issues avail.; reprint service avail. from SCH) **Indexed:** Int.Polit.Sci.Abstr., Phil.Ind. **Document type:** academic/scholarly publication.
—SWETS; UnCover. **CCC**.

170 300 340   GW   ISSN 0341-079X
ARCHIV FUER RECHTS- UND SOZIALPHILOSOPHIE. BEIHEFTE. (Text in English, French, German) irreg., vol.64, 1995. price varies. (Internationale Vereinigung fuer Rechts- und Sozialphilosophie) Franz Steiner Verlag Wiesbaden GmbH, Birkenwaldstr. 44, 70191 Stuttgart, Germany. TEL 0711-2582-0. FAX 0711-2582390. (Subscr. to: Postfach 101061, 70009 Stuttgart, Germany) **Indexed:** Int.Polit.Sci.Abstr. **Document type:** monographic series.

100   GW   ISSN 0722-5679
ARCHIV FUER RECHTS UND SOZIALPHILOSOPHY. SUPPLEMENTA. irreg., vol.5, 1988. price varies. (Internationale Vereinigung fuer Rechts- und Sozialphilosophie) Franz Steiner Verlag Wiesbaden GmbH, Birkenwaldstr. 44, 70191 Stuttgart, Germany. TEL 0711-2582-0. FAX 0711-2582390. (Subscr. to: Postfach 101061, 70009 Stuttgart, Germany) **Document type:** monographic series.

180   FR   ISSN 0373-5478
B720
ARCHIVES D'HISTOIRE DOCTRINALE ET LITTERAIRE DU MOYEN AGE. (Text in English, French, German, Latin) 1926. a. price varies. Librairie Philosophique J. Vrin, 6 place de la Sorbonne, 75005 Paris, France. TEL 43-54-03-47. FAX 43-54-48-18. Ed.Bd. index. circ. 750. (also avail. in microfiche from IDC; back issues avail.) **Indexed:** M.L.A. **Document type:** academic/scholarly publication.

PHILOSOPHY

100 FR ISSN 0003-9632
B1
ARCHIVES DE PHILOSOPHIE; recherches et documentation. (Text in French; summaries in English, French) 1923. 4/yr. 385 F. (foreign 465 F.). Editons Beauchesne, 72 rue des Saints Peres, 75007 Paris, France. TEL 45-48-80-28. FAX 42-22-59-79. Ed. F. Marty. adv.; bk.rev.; abstr.; charts. circ. 800. **Indexed:** Arts & Hum.Cit.Ind., Curr.Cont., Int.Polit.Sci.Abstr., Phil.Ind.
—Faxon; SWETS.

100 NE ISSN 0066-6610
ARCHIVES INTERNATIONALES D'HISTOIRE DES IDEES/INTERNATIONAL ARCHIVES OF THE HISTORY OF IDEAS. (Text in English and French) 1963. irreg., vol.140, 1994. price varies. Kluwer Academic Publishers, Postbus 17, 3300 AA Dordrecht, Netherlands. TEL 31-78-392392. FAX 31-78-392254. TELEX 29245 KAPG NL. (Dist. by: Kluwer Academic Publishers Group, P.O. Box 322, 3300 AH Dordrecht, Netherlands. TEL 31-78-392392. FAX 31-78-546474; N. America dist. addr.: Box 358, Accord Sta., Hingham, MA 02018-0358. TEL 617-871-6600) Eds. P. Dibon, R. Popkin. **Document type:** monographic series.
—BLDSC (4536.110000).
Refereed Serial

100 IT ISSN 0004-0088
B4
ARCHIVIO DI FILOSOFIA. (Text in English, French, German or Italian) 1931. a. L.85000 (foreign L.120000) (effective 1995). (Universita degli Studi di Roma, Istituto di Studi Filosofici) Casa Editrice Dott. Antonio Milani, Via Jappelli 5-6, 35121 Padua, Italy. TEL 39-49-656677. FAX 39-49-8752900. Dir. Marco M. Olivetti. circ. 600. **Indexed:** CERDIC, Phil.Ind.
—SWETS.
Description: Publishes on themes of current international interest.

109 309 PL ISSN 0066-6874
ARCHIWUM HISTORII FILOZOFII I MYSLI SPOLECZNEJ. (Text in Polish; summaries in French, German, or Russian) 1954. a. price varies. Polska Akademia Nauk, Instytut Filozofii i Socjologii, Ul. Nowy Swiat 72, 00-330 Warsaw, Poland. Ed. Lech Szczucki.
Description: Studies the history of philosophy in Poland and throughout the world.

DAS ARGUMENT; Zeitschrift fuer Philosophie und Sozialwissenschaften. see *SOCIAL SCIENCES: COMPREHENSIVE WORKS*

100 NE ISSN 0920-427X
BC1 CODEN: ARGMEL
ARGUMENTATION; an international journal on reasoning. (Text in English) 1987. q. fl.378 to institutions; $242 to institutions in U.S. (effective 1996). (European Centre for the Study of Argumentation) Kluwer Academic Publishers, Postbus 17, 3300 AA Dordrecht, Netherlands. TEL 31-78-392392. FAX 31-78-392254. TELEX 29245 KAPG NL. E-mail: SERVICES@WKAP.NL. (Dist. by: Kluwer Academic Publishers Group, P.O. Box 322, 3300 AH Dordrecht, Netherlands. TEL 31-78-392392. FAX 31-78-546474; N. America dist. addr.: Box 358, Accord Sta., Hingham, MA 02018-0358. TEL 617-871-6600. FAX 617-871-6528) Ed.Bd. bk.rev. (also avail. in microform from UMI; back issues avail.; reprint service avail. from SWZ) **Indexed:** Bibl.Engl.Lang.& Lit., Commun.Abstr., Lang.& Lang.Behav.Abstr., Sociol.Abstr.
—BLDSC (1664.356100); Faxon; SWETS; UMI; UnCover. **CCC.**
Description: Covers all aspects of rhetoric and argumentation, ranging from literary rhetoric to linguistics, from theological arguments to legal reasoning.
Refereed Serial

100 PO ISSN 0871-7494
ARGUMENTO; revista quadrimestral de filosofia. 1991. 3/yr. Esc.1300($18) or exchange basis. Edicoes Cosmos, R. da Emenda, 111, 1o, 1200 Lisbon, Portugal. TEL 3422050. FAX 3478255. Ed. Antonio Marques. circ. 1,000.

100 UK
ARGUMENTS OF THE PHILOSOPHERS. irreg. price varies. Routledge, 11 New Fetter Ln., London EC4P 4EE, England. TEL 071-583-9855. FAX 071-583-4519. TELEX 263398-ROUT-G. (U.S. address: Routledge, Chapman & Hall Inc., 35 W. 35th St., New York, NY 10001-2291) **Document type:** academic/scholarly publication.
Description: Provides a contemporary assessment and history of the entire course of philosophical thought. Each book constitutes a detailed critical introduction to the work of a philosopher of major influence and significance.

ARISTOS. see *ART*

100 UK ISSN 0066-7374
ARISTOTELIAN SOCIETY. PROCEEDINGS. £33.50($62) (foreign £39.50) (effective 1996). (Aristotelian Society) Basil Blackwell Ltd., 108 Cowley Road, Oxford OX4 1JF, England. TEL 0865-791100. FAX 0865-791347. TELEX 837022-OXBOOK-G. (Subscr. to: Journals Department, Basil Blackwell, c/o Marston Book Services, P.O. Box 87, Oxford OX2 0DT, England) Ed. Dorothy Edgington. **Document type:** proceedings.
—BLDSC (6648.800000); SWETS; UnCover.

100 UK ISSN 0309-7013
B11
ARISTOTELIAN SOCIETY. PROCEEDINGS. SUPPLEMENTARY VOLUME. 1/yr. £34.50($64) (foreign £40.50) (effective 1996). (Aristotelian Society) Basil Blackwell Ltd., 108 Cowley Road, Oxford OX4 1JF, England. TEL 44-1865-791100. FAX 44-1865-791347. TELEX 837022-OXBOOK-G. (Subscr. to: Journals Department, Basil Blackwell, c/o Marston Book Services, P.O. Box 87, Oxford OX2 0DT, England) Ed. Dorothy Edgington. **Document type:** proceedings.
—BLDSC (8547.400000); UnCover.

ART AND PHILOSOPHY. see *ART*

100 CH
ASIAN JOURNAL OF PHILOSOPHY. (Text in English) 1988. 2/yr. $10 to individuals; institutions $12; students $5. c/o Tran Van Doan, Ed., National Taiwan University, Dept. of Philosophy, Roosevelt Rd., Sec. 4, Taipei, Taiwan 10764, Republic of China. TEL 035-317216. Ed.Bd. bk.rev.

100 950 UK ISSN 0955-2367
B5000
ASIAN PHILOSOPHY. 1991. 3/yr. £48 to individuals; institutions £158 (effective 1996). Carfax Publishing Co., P.O. Box 25, Abingdon, Oxon. OX14 3UE, England. TEL 01235-555335. FAX 01235-553559. (Subscr. in N. America to: Carfax Publishing Co., 875-81 Massachusetts Ave., Cambridge, MA 02139) Eds. Indira Mahalingam, Brian Carr. adv.; bk.rev.; index. (also avail. in microfiche; back issues avail.) **Indexed:** Per.Islam. (1991-). **Document type:** academic/scholarly publication.
—BLDSC (1742.715300); UMI; UnCover. **CCC.**
Description: Focuses on Indian, Chinese, Japanese, Buddhist, Persian, and Islamic philosophical traditions.
Refereed Serial

110 US
ASPECTS (PHILADELPHIA);* manual for personal development. 1989. m. free. Metaversal Productions, 6739 Regent St., Philadelphia, PA 19142-1640. TEL 215-726-9746. Ed. Lucy Zerr. **Document type:** academic/scholarly publication.
Description: A do-it-yourself manual for self-development and evaluation of consciousness-emphasis on metaphysics, libertarian philosophy and rock music.

144 360 FR ISSN 0153-6133
ASSOCIATION FRANCAISE DES AMIS D'ALBERT SCHWEITZER. CAHIERS. 1955. 4/yr. 130 F. Association Francaise des Amis d'Albert Schweitzer, 1 Quai St. Thomas, 67081 Strasbourg, France. Ed. Jean Christian. bk.rev.; bibl.; illus. circ. 2,750.

ASSOCIATION OF BRITISH THEOLOGICAL AND PHILOSOPHICAL LIBRARIES. BULLETIN. see *LIBRARY AND INFORMATION SCIENCES*

100 323.4 US
ASYNJUR. q. $2 per no. Box 567, Granville, OH 43023. Ed. Cheryl Newton.

108 GW ISSN 0938-5304
ATHENAEUMS MONOGRAFIEN. PHILOSOPHIE. 1947. irreg. price varies. Verlag Anton Hain GmbH, Savignystr. 53, 60325 Frankfurt a.M., Germany. Ed. Georgi Schischkoff. **Document type:** monographic series.
Formerly (until 1988): Monographien zur Philosophischen Forschung (ISSN 0344-340X)

ATTITUDE PROBLEM; multipurpose nonconformist rag. see *CHILDREN AND YOUTH — For*

100 US ISSN 0733-4311
B1
AUSLEGUNG; a journal of philosophy. 1973. s-a. $8 to individuals; institutions $12; students $6. (Graduate Association of Students in Philosophy) University of Kansas, Department of Philosophy, Lawrence, KS 66045. TEL 913-864-2700. Ed. Richard Michael Buck. adv. contact: Kirk Wolf. bk.rev.; charts. circ. 230. (back issues avail.; reprint service avail. from UMI) **Indexed:** Arts & Hum.Cit.Ind., Curr.Cont., Hum.Ind., Phil.Ind. **Document type:** academic/scholarly publication.
—BLDSC (1792.939000); Faxon; UnCover.

100 AT ISSN 0004-8402
B1
AUSTRALASIAN JOURNAL OF PHILOSOPHY. 1923. 4/yr. Aus.$40 (effective 1995). Australasian Association of Philosophy, Philosophy Dept., La Trobe University, Bundoora, Vic. 3083, Australia. TEL 61-3-4792424. FAX 61-3-4793639. E-mail: phiajp@lure.latrobe.edu.au. Ed. Robert Young. adv.; bk.rev.; abstr.; bibl.; index, cum.index every 10 yrs.; circ. 1,200 (paid). (also avail. in microform from JAI,MIM) **Indexed:** Amer.Hist.& Life, Arts & Hum.Cit.Ind., Aus.P.A.I.S., Curr.Cont., Hist.Abstr., Ind.Bk.Rev.Hum., Lang.& Lang.Behav.Abstr., Phil.Ind. **Document type:** academic/scholarly publication.
—BLDSC (1795.100000); Faxon; SWETS; UnCover.
Refereed Serial

AUSTRALASIAN STUDIES IN HISTORY AND PHILOSOPHY OF SCIENCE. see *SCIENCES: COMPREHENSIVE WORKS*

211 AT ISSN 1036-8191
AUSTRALIAN RATIONALIST. 1969. q. Aus.$25 to non-members. Rationalist Society of Australia, 42 Ruskin Ave., Croydon, Vic. 3136, Australia. TEL 03-723-2792. FAX 03-723-2792. Ed. Kate Oldaker. adv.; bk.rev.; film rev.; illus.
—UnCover.
Incorporates (1986-1990): News and Views; **Formed by the merger of:** Rationalist (ISSN 0034-0065); Australian Rationalist (ISSN 0005-0113)

100 IT ISSN 0005-0601
B4
AUT AUT; rivista di filosofia e di cultura. 1951. bi-m. L.65000 (foreign L.85000) (effective 1993). Nuova Italia Editrice S.p.A, Via Ernesto Codignola, 50018 Scandicci (FI), Italy. Dir. Pier Aldo Rovatti. adv.; index. **Indexed:** Curr.Cont., M.L.A.
—SWETS.

100 IT ISSN 1122-1151
AXIOMATHES. 1989. 3/yr. L.45000($42) to individuals (foreign L.65000); institutions L.65000($30) (foreign L.85000). (Centro Studi per la Filosofia Mitteleuropea) Il Poligrafo Casa Editrice, Turazza 19, 35128 Padua, Italy. Ed. Roberto Poli.
Formerly (until 1991): Centro Studi per la Filosofia Mitteleuropea. Quaderni (ISSN 1122-1550)

100 SP ISSN 0213-3563
B456.1
AZAFEA; estudios de historia de la filosofia hispanica. 1985. irreg., no.3, 1990. 2500 ptas. (effective 1995). Ediciones Universidad de Salamanca, Adpo. 325, 37080 Salamanca, Spain. TEL 34-23-294598. Dir. Laureano Robles Carcedo. **Document type:** academic/scholarly publication.

BACK TO GODHEAD; magazine of the Hare Krishna movement. see *RELIGIONS AND THEOLOGY — Hindu*

100 US
BALANCE. 1985. bi-m. $18. Balance Center, 359 Walden Green, Branford, CT 06405. TEL 203-481-6331. Ed. Donna Sommers. adv.: B&W page $900, color page $2000. circ. 10,000.
Description: Promotes holistic health.

PHILOSOPHY

BALSA DE LA MEDUSA. see ART

181   II
BASAVA JOURNAL. (Text in English) q. Rs.12. Basava Samiti, Sree Basaveshwara Rd., Sree Basaveshwara Circle, Bangalore 560 001, India. TEL 265505. Ed. B. Virupakshappa; Pub. R.C. Bhusnurmath. adv. contact: C.A. Jamkhandimath. **Document type:** academic/scholarly publication.
    Description: Devoted to the propogation of the message of Sri Basavesnwara and other Sharanas.

100   GW   ISSN 0941-9918
BASLER STUDIEN ZUR PHILOSOPHIE. 1992. irreg., vol.5, 1994. price varies. Francke Verlag GmbH, Postfach 2560, 72015 Tuebingen, Germany. TEL 07071-9797-0. FAX 07071-75288. Ed. Urs Thurnherr. **Document type:** monographic series.

BAZMAVEP. see HISTORY — History Of The Near East

THE BEACON (MIAMI). see NEW AGE PUBLICATIONS

100   US   ISSN 0005-7339
BEACON (NEW YORK). 1922. bi-m. $17. (Lucis Trust) Lucis Publishing Co., 113 University Pl., 11th Fl., Box 722, Cooper Sta., New York, NY 10276. TEL 212-982-8770. (European and British Commonwealth countries, except Canada, subscr. to: Lucis Press Ltd., 3 Whitehall Court, Suite 54, London, SW1A 2EF, England) Ed.Bd. bk.rev. circ. 5,000. (back issues avail.)
    Description: A forum for esotericists to contribute their visions, to share their experiences, and to develop their ideas about the evolution of humanity and the unfolding Plan for our world.

100 230   GW   ISSN 0067-5024
BEITRAEGE ZUR GESCHICHTE DER PHILOSOPHIE UND THEOLOGIE DES MITTELALTERS. NEUE FOLGE. 1894; N.S. 1970. irreg. price varies. Aschendorffsche Verlagsbuchhandlung, Soesterstr. 13, 48155 Muenster, Germany. TEL 0251-690-0. FAX 0251-690143. Eds. Ludwig Hoedl, Wolfgang Kluxen. **Document type:** monographic series.

107 370   GW   ISSN 0005-8157
BEITRAEGE ZUR PAEDAGOGISCHEN ARBEIT. 1956. q. membership. Gemeinschaft Evangelischer Erzieher in Baden, Blumenstr. 1, 76133 Karlshue, Germany. Ed. Rudolf Immig. bk.rev.; bibl. circ. 400.

181.4   II   ISSN 0006-0496
BHARATHA DARSHANA; the only magazine in Kannada devoted to the propagation of Mahabharatha, Ramayana and Bhagavatha. (Text in Kannada) 1957. m. Rs.20. Bharatha Darshana Prakashana, 163 Manjunatha Rd., II Block, Thyagarajanagar, Bangalore 560 028, India. TEL 605381. adv. circ. 13,000.

BHARATYA VIDYA. see ORIENTAL STUDIES

100 011   GW   ISSN 0173-1831
BIBLIOGRAPHIEN ZUR PHILOSOPHIE. (Text in English and German) 1979. irreg. price varies. Edition Gemini, Juelichstr. 7, 50354 Huerth-Efferen, Germany. TEL 02233-63550. FAX 02233-65866. Ed. Gernot Gabel. adv. circ. 200. (back issues avail.) **Document type:** monographic series.

100   BE   ISSN 0067-8430
BIBLIOTHEQUE PHILOSOPHIQUE DE LOUVAIN. (Text in French) 1947. a., vol.41, 1995. price varies. (Universite Catholique de Louvain) Editions Peeters s.p.r.l., Bondgenotenlaan 153, 3000 Leuven, Belgium. TEL 32-16-235170. FAX 32-16-228500. (back issues avail.) **Document type:** monographic series.

170 610 573.21   UK   ISSN 0269-9702
QH332
BIOETHICS. q. £81($171) (foreign £106) (effective 1996). Basil Blackwell Ltd., 108 Cowley Road, Oxford OX4 1JF, England. TEL 0865-791100. FAX 0865-791347. TELEX 837022-OXBOOK-G. Ed.Bd.
    —BLDSC (2072.119500); Faxon; Genuine Article; SWETS; UMI; UnCover. **CCC.**

BIOETHICS BULLETIN. see BIOLOGY

BIOETHICS YEARBOOK. see RELIGIONS AND THEOLOGY

BIOETICA. see BIOLOGY

BIOLOGY AND PHILOSOPHY. see BIOLOGY

BIOMEDICAL ETHICS REVIEWS. see MEDICAL SCIENCES

BIONEWS. see ENVIRONMENTAL STUDIES

BIOPOLITICS. see ENVIRONMENTAL STUDIES

BIOPOLITICS - THE BIO ENVIRONMENT. SYMPOSIUM PROCEEDINGS. see ENVIRONMENTAL STUDIES

BLOCH-ALMANACH. see LITERARY AND POLITICAL REVIEWS

100   NE
BOCHUMER STUDIEN ZUR PHILOSOPHIE. 1982. irreg., vol.22, 1994. price varies. John Benjamins Publishing Co., Amsteldijk 44, P.O. Box 75577, 1070 AN Amsterdam, Netherlands. TEL 31-20-6738156. FAX 31-20-6792956. (In N. America: Box 27519, Philadelphia, PA 19118-0519. TEL 215-836-1200. FAX 215-836-1204) Ed.Bd. **Document type:** monographic series.

BODYWORK SERIES. see NEW AGE PUBLICATIONS

100 200   US
BOLLINGEN SERIES. 1941. irreg. price varies. (Bollingen Foundation) Princeton University Press, 41 William St., Princeton, NJ 08540. TEL 609-258-4900. FAX 609-258-6305. E-mail: jhardy@pupress.princeton.edu. **Document type:** monographic series.

100   GW   ISSN 0344-1857
BONNER AKADEMISCHE REDEN. no.16, 1951. irreg., no.73, 1992. price varies. Bouvier Verlag Herbert Grundmann, Am Hof 28, 53113 Bonn, Germany. TEL 0228-7290124. FAX 0228-7290179. **Document type:** monographic series.

BOODSCHAP. see RELIGIONS AND THEOLOGY — Other Denominations And Sects

BOSTON STUDIES IN THE PHILOSOPHY OF SCIENCE; Boston colloquium for the philosophy of science. see SCIENCES: COMPREHENSIVE WORKS

BOSTON UNIVERSITY STUDIES IN PHILOSOPHY AND RELIGION. see RELIGIONS AND THEOLOGY

BREATH SERIES; a progression of pranayama practices. see NEW AGE PUBLICATIONS

101   GW
BRENNESSEL; Jahresschrift fuer Philosophie und verwandte Gebiete. 1974. a. Womm-Press, Mittelstr. 51, 32805 Horn - Bad Meinberg, Germany. Ed. H. Knauf. circ. 3,000.

100   GW   ISSN 0935-7009
B3212.Z7
BRENTANO STUDIEN. (Text in English and German) 1988. a. price varies. J.H. Roell, Wuerzburgerstr. 16, 97337 Dettelbach, Germany. TEL 09324-1429. Ed.Bd. **Document type:** academic/scholarly publication.

150 616.8   NE   ISSN 0924-0314
BRILL'S STUDIES IN EPISTEMOLOGY, PSYCHOLOGY AND PSYCHIATRY. 1989. irreg., vol.3, 1993. price varies. E.J. Brill, P.O. Box 9000, 2300 PA Leiden, Netherlands. TEL 31-71-5353500. FAX 31-71-5317532. TELEX 39296 BRILL NL. (In N. America: E.J. Brill, 24 Hudson St., Kinderhook, NY 12106. TEL 800-962-4406. FAX 518-758-1959) (back issues avail.) **Document type:** monographic series.
    Refereed Serial

100   UK   ISSN 0960-8788
B1
BRITISH JOURNAL FOR THE HISTORY OF PHILOSOPHY. 1993. s-a. £28 to individuals; institutions £36. Thoemmes Press, 11 Great George St., Bristol BS1 5RR, England. TEL 0117-929-1377. FAX 0117-922-1918. Ed. G.A. Rogers. adv. contact: Deborah Mann. bk.rev. circ. 400. **Indexed:** Amer.Hist.& Life (1993-), Hist.Abstr. (1993-). **Document type:** academic/scholarly publication.
    —BLDSC (2309.350000); SWETS.
    Description: Includes articles and reviews on the history of philosophy and related intellectual history from the ancient world through to the early decades of the twentieth century.

THE BRITISH JOURNAL FOR THE PHILOSOPHY OF SCIENCE. see SCIENCES: COMPREHENSIVE WORKS

THE BRITISH JOURNAL OF AESTHETICS. see ART

142.7   UK   ISSN 0007-1773
B829.5
BRITISH SOCIETY FOR PHENOMENOLOGY. JOURNAL. 1970. 3/yr. £30($54) to individuals; libraries £33 ($60). Haigh and Hochland Ltd., Precinct Centre, Oxford Rd., Manchester M13 9QA, England. TEL 0161-273-4156. FAX 0161-273-4340. Ed. Wolfe Mays; Pub. Steven Abraham. adv. contact: Steven Abraham. bk.rev.; bibl.; circ. 500 (paid). (reprint service avail. from ISI) **Indexed:** Abstr.Engl.Stud., Curr.Cont., Ind.Bk.Rev.Hum., Phil.Ind. **Document type:** academic/scholarly publication.
    —BLDSC (4719.223000); Faxon; Genuine Article; SWETS; UnCover.

109   UK   ISSN 0951-5151
BRITISH SOCIETY FOR THE HISTORY OF PHILOSOPHY NEWSLETTER. 1986. irreg. (2-3/yr.) membership. British Society for the History of Philosophy, University of York, Dept. of Philosophy, Heslington, York YO1 5DD, England. TEL 0904-430000. **Document type:** newsletter.

BUDDHA WORLD. see RELIGIONS AND THEOLOGY — Buddhist

THE BUDDHIST MONTHLY: VAJRA BODHI SEA/HAI TI PU KANG CHIN. see RELIGIONS AND THEOLOGY — Buddhist

180   BE   ISSN 0068-4023
B721
BULLETIN DE PHILOSOPHIE MEDIEVALE. (Text mainly in French; contributions in English, German, Italian, Spanish) 1959. a., vol.35, 1993. 1000 BEF (effective 1995). Societe Internationale pour l'Etude de la Philosophie Medievale, College Thomas More, 1 Chemin d'Aristote, B-1348 Louvain-la-Neuve, Belgium. TEL 32-10-474807. FAX 32-10-474807. E-mail: danhier@sofi.ucl.ac.be. (Non-member subscr. to: N.V. Brepols, Steenweg op Tielen 68, 2300 Turnhout, Belgium. TEL 32-14-402500. FAX 32-14-428022) Ed. J. Hamesse. adv. circ. 1,000. (back issues avail.) **Indexed:** Phil.Ind. **Document type:** academic/scholarly publication, bulletin.
    Formerly (until 1963): Societe Internationale pour l'Etude de la Philosophie Medievale. Bulletin.
    Description: Publishes articles and material of interest to those concentrating on the history of medieval philosophy.

174   US   ISSN 0277-2027
HF5387
BUSINESS & PROFESSIONAL ETHICS JOURNAL. 1981. q. $20 to individuals; institutions $75 (foreign $85) (effective 1995). Box 15017, Gainesville, FL 32604. TEL 904-392-2084. FAX 904-392-5577. Ed. Robert Baum. adv.; bk.rev.; circ. 800 (paid). (back issues avail.) **Indexed:** B.P.I., Eng.Ind., Phil.Ind., Soc.Sci.Ind. (until 1994). **Document type:** academic/scholarly publication.
    —BLDSC (2933.219000); Faxon; SWETS; UnCover.
    Description: Takes an interdisciplinary approach to the study and analysis of ethical issues that arise at the interface of business and the professions.
    Refereed Serial

BUSINESS ETHICS. see BUSINESS AND ECONOMICS

BUSINESS STRATEGY FOR THE BIO-ENVIRONMENT. see ENVIRONMENTAL STUDIES

100   US   ISSN 1049-9245
C P 2: COMMENTARIES - PHYSICAL AND PHILOSOPHIC. 1990. q. $25 (foreign $30). Cri-de-Coeur Press, 5070 Venida del Sol, Laguna Hills, CA 92653-1876. Ed. A.S. Iberall; Pub. A.S. Iberall.

100   FR   ISSN 1144-4924
CAHIERS DE PHILOSOPHIE POLITIQUE ET JURIDIQUE. irreg. Universite de Caen, Centre de Philosophie Politique et Juridique, 14032 Caen Cedex, France. Ed. S. Goyard-Fabre.
    Formerly: Cahiers de Philosophie Politique et Juridique de l'Universite de Caen (ISSN 0759-1810)

100 054   FR   ISSN 1163-0183
CAHIERS DU SENS. 1991. 3/yr. 100 F. Nouvel Athanor, 50 rue du Disque, 75645 Paris Cedex 13, France. TEL 45-70-83-84. FAX 45-43-73-91. circ. 250.

PHILOSOPHY

100   BE   ISSN 0008-0284
BF458
CAHIERS INTERNATIONAUX DE SYMBOLISME. 1962. 3/yr. 600 BEF to individuals (foreign 900 BEF); institutions and libraries 1200 BEF (foreign 1500 BEF). Universite de Mons - Hainaut, Centre Interdisciplinaire d'Etudes Philosophiques, 20 place du Parc, 7000 Mons, Belgium. TEL 32-65-335084. FAX 32-65-373054. Ed. Claire LeJeune. bk.rev. circ. 1,200. **Indexed:** Lang.& Lang.Behav.Abstr., M.L.A. **Document type:** academic/scholarly publication.
—Faxon.

100   FR   ISSN 0241-2799
CAHIERS PHILOSOPHIQUES. 1979. 4/yr. 142 F. (foreign 160 F.). (Ministere de l'Education) Centre National de Documentation Pedagogique, 29 rue de l'Ulm, 75230 Paris Cedex 05, France. (Subscr. to: CNDP-Abonnement, B.P. 7, 21 Square St. Charles, 75012 Paris, France) Ed. Jean-Louis Poirier. bk.rev.
Description: Articles and essays on all aspects of philosophical research and thought.

100   ZR   ISSN 0379-4105
CAHIERS PHILOSOPHIQUES AFRICAINS/AFRICAN PHILOSOPHICAL JOURNAL. (Text in French) 1972. irreg. Z.$80. (Universite Nationale du Zaire, Lubumbashi, Department de Philosophie) Presses Universitaires de Lubumbashi, B.P. 1825, Lubumbashi, Zaire. bk.rev. **Indexed:** CERDIC.

CAHIERS RATIONALISTES. see *SCIENCES: COMPREHENSIVE WORKS*

101   UK   ISSN 0950-6306
CAMBRIDGE STUDIES IN PHILOSOPHY. 1979. irreg. Cambridge University Press, Edinburgh Bldg., Shaftesbury Rd., Cambridge CB2 2RU, England. TEL 01223-312393. FAX 01223-315052. TELEX 817256. (N. American addr.: Cambridge University Press, 40 W. 20th St., New York, NY 10011. TEL 212-924-3900. FAX 212-691-3239) **Document type:** monographic series.

CANADIAN JOURNAL OF ITALIAN STUDIES. see *LITERATURE*

100   CN   ISSN 0045-5091
B1
CANADIAN JOURNAL OF PHILOSOPHY. (Text in English or French) 1971. q. plus a. supplement. Can.$25 to individuals (foreign US$25); institutions Can.$40 (foreign US$40); students Can.$15 (foreign US$15) (effective 1995). (Canadian Association for Publishing in Philosophy) University of Calgary Press, 2500 University Dr., N.W., Calgary, AB T2N 1N4, Canada. TEL 403-220-7578. FAX 403-282-0085. E-mail: 75003@ucdasvm1.admin.ucalgary.ca. Ed.Bd. adv.: page Can.$190 ($160). bk.rev.; index. circ. 1,200. (also avail. in microform) **Indexed:** Arts & Hum.Cit.Ind., Can.B.P.I., Can.Per.Ind., Can.Wom.Per.Ind., Curr.Cont., M.L.A., Phil.Ind. **Document type:** academic/scholarly publication.
—BLDSC (3033.900000); Faxon; Genuine Article; SWETS; UnCover. **CCC.**
Description: Publishes philosophical work of high quality in any field of philosophy.
Refereed Serial

100   CN   ISSN 0228-491X
B1
CANADIAN PHILOSOPHICAL REVIEWS/REVUE CANADIENNE DE COMPTES RENDUS EN PHILOSOPHIE. (Text in English and French) 1981. 6/yr. Can.$64($48) to individuals; institutions Can.$125 ($93). Academic Printing & Publishing, P.O. Box 4218, S. Edmonton, AB T6E 4T2, Canada. TEL 403-435-5898. FAX 403-435-5852. Ed. Roger Shiner. adv.; bk.rev. circ. 350. **Indexed:** Bk.Rev.Ind. (1989-), Can.Wom.Per.Ind., Child.Bk.Rev.Ind. (1989-), Phil.Ind. **Document type:** academic/scholarly publication.
—BLDSC (3043.820000); Faxon.
Description: Book review journal for recent work in philosophy.

212.5   CN   ISSN 0045-544X
CANADIAN THEOSOPHIST. 1920. bi-m. Can.$9 (foreign Can.$12). Theosophical Society in Canada, R.R. No.3, Burk's Falls, ON P0A 1C0, Canada. TEL 705-382-6012. Ed. S.L. Treloar. bk.rev.; index. circ. 300. **Document type:** bulletin.

CARNEGIE COUNCIL NEWSLETTER. see *POLITICAL SCIENCE — International Relations*

CATHOLIC THOUGHT FROM LUBLIN. see *RELIGIONS AND THEOLOGY — Roman Catholic*

108   US
CENTER FOR PHILOSOPHIC EXCHANGE. ANNUAL PROCEEDINGS. 1969. a. $15. Center for Philosophic Exchange, State University College at Brockport, Brockport, NY 14420. TEL 716-395-2493. Ed. Joseph Gilbert. circ. 300 (paid). **Document type:** proceedings.

149   US   ISSN 0360-618X
CENTER FOR PROCESS STUDIES. NEWSLETTER. Key Title: Newsletter of the Center for Process Studies. 1975. 3/yr. $10. School of Theology at Claremont, Center for Process Studies, 1325 N. College Ave., Claremont, CA 91711. TEL 909-621-5330. Ed. Olav B. Smith. circ. 650. (looseleaf format; back issues avail.) **Document type:** newsletter.
Description: Covers events and developments relating to the philosophy of Alfred North Whitehead for students and scholars of process philosophy.

CENTRAL CONFERENCE OF AMERICAN RABBIS. YEARBOOK. see *RELIGIONS AND THEOLOGY — Judaic*

174.280 600   DK   ISSN 0107-9786
R724
CENTRALE VIDENSKABSETISKE KOMITE. BERETNING/CENTRAL SCIENTIFIC - ETHICAL COMMITTEE OF DENMARK. REPORT. 1982. a. free. Undervisningsministeriet, Forskningsafdeling, H.C. Andersens Boulevard 40, DK-1553 Copenhagen V, Denmark. circ. 2,000.

141   GR   ISSN 1015-2563
CENTRE INTERNATIONAL D'ETUDES PLATONICIENNES ET ARISTOTELICIENNES. SERIE RECHERCHES. (Text in French) 1986. irreg., no.3, 1994. Evangelos Moutsopoulos, Ed. & Pub., 40 Ypsilantou St., 115 21 Athens, Greece. TEL 30-1-725-1212. FAX 30-1-722-7322. **Document type:** monographic series.
Description: Studies the philosophical legacies of Plato, Aristotle, and the Neoplatonists

CENTRE PROTESTANT D'ETUDES DE GENEVE. BULLETIN. see *RELIGIONS AND THEOLOGY — Protestant*

100   IT   ISSN 0392-7334
B3583
CENTRO DI STUDI VICHIANI. BOLLETTINO. 1971. a. L.50000. Bibliopolis, Via Arangio Ruiz 83, 80122 Naples, Italy. TEL (081) 664606. Dirs. Giuseppe Giarrizzo, Fulvio Tessitore. **Indexed:** Lang.& Lang.Behav.Abstr., M.L.A., Phil.Ind.
Description: Focuses on Gian Battista Vico's life and works and all the studies pertinent to the Neapolitan philosopher.

100   CE   ISSN 0577-4772
CEYLON RATIONALIST AMBASSADOR. (Text in English) 1967? a. Rs.5($1) Ceylon Rationalist Association, 89 Pamankada Ln., Colombo 6, Sri Lanka. Ed. Abraham T. Kovoor. circ. 3,000. (back issues avail.)

CHALCEDON REPORT. see *RELIGIONS AND THEOLOGY*

160   US   ISSN 0009-1774
B945.P44
CHARLES S. PEIRCE SOCIETY. TRANSACTIONS; a quarterly journal in American philosophy. 1965. 4/yr. $35 to individuals (foreign $38); institutions $60 (foreign $65). Charles S. Peirce Society, State University of New York at Buffalo, c/o Peter H. Hare, Dept. of Philosophy, Baldy Hall, Buffalo, NY 14260. TEL 716-636-2444. FAX 716-645-3825. Eds. Peter H. Hare, Richard S. Robin. adv.; bk.rev. circ. 600. **Indexed:** Arts & Hum.Cit.Ind., Ind.Bk.Rev.Hum., Phil.Ind. **Document type:** academic/scholarly publication.
—BLDSC (8912.377000); Faxon; Genuine Article; UnCover.

100   US   ISSN 0023-8627
B1
CHINESE STUDIES IN PHILOSOPHY; a journal of translations. 1967. q. $419 to institutions (foreign $472) (effective Jul. 1995). M.E. Sharpe, Inc., 80 Business Park Dr., Armonk, NY 10504. TEL 914-273-1800; 800-541-6563. FAX 914-273-2106. Ed. Chung-ying Cheng. adv.; index. (back issues avail.) **Indexed:** Arts & Hum.Cit.Ind., Curr.Cont., Phil.Ind. **Document type:** academic/scholarly publication.
—BLDSC (3181.122000); Faxon; Genuine Article; UMI; UnCover. **CCC.**
Refereed Serial

CHRISTIAN BIOETHICS; non-ecumenical studies in medical morality. see *MEDICAL SCIENCES*

CHUNG-KUO FO CHIAO. see *RELIGIONS AND THEOLOGY — Buddhist*

CINCINNATI JOURNAL OF MAGIC. see *PARAPSYCHOLOGY AND OCCULTISM*

CLASSICS IN THE HISTORY AND PHILOSOPHY OF SCIENCE. see *SCIENCES: COMPREHENSIVE WORKS*

CLINICAL MEDICAL ETHICS. see *MEDICAL SCIENCES*

100   UK   ISSN 0950-8864
B1
COGITO. 3/yr. £26 to individuals; institutions £132 (effective 1996). (Cogito Society) Carfax Publishing Co., P.O. Box 25, Abingdon, Oxon. OX14 3UE, England. TEL 01235-555335. FAX 01235-553559. (Subscr. in N. America to: Carfax Publishing Co., 875-81 Massachusetts Ave., Cambridge, MA 02139) Ed. Andrew Pyle. adv.; bk.rev. (also avail. in microfiche; back issues avail.) **Document type:** academic/scholarly publication.
—BLDSC (3292.868500); UMI; UnCover. **CCC.**
Description: Covers philosophy topics for students at the college level.
Refereed Serial

COGNITIVE DISSIDENTS. see *POLITICAL SCIENCE*

100   SP   ISSN 0069-5076
COLECCION FILOSOFICA. 1963. irreg., no.66, 1990. price varies. (Universidad de Navarra, Facultad de Filosofia y Letras) Ediciones Universidad de Navarra, S.A., Apdo. 396, 31080 Pamplona, Spain. TEL 94 825 6850.

181.45   US   ISSN 0164-1522
COLLABORATION. 1974. q. $20. Sri Aurobindo Association, 2288 Fulton St., Berkeley, CA 94704. TEL 510-848-1841. FAX 510-848-8531. Eds. Gordon Korstang, Lynda Lester. bk.rev.; bibl. circ. 250.
Incorporates (1970-1995): Nexus (Berkeley).
Description: Explores various yoga techniques and philosophies.

100   CN   ISSN 0824-9474
COLLECTION PHILOSOPHICA. 1972. irreg. price varies. University of Ottawa Press, 542 King Edward, Ottawa, ON K1N 6N5, Canada. TEL 613-564-2270. FAX 613-564-9284. Eds. Graeme Hunter, Daniele Letscha. **Document type:** monographic series.
Description: Books in English and French on various subjects in the field of philosophy.

COMMENTS & CRITICISMS. see *PSYCHOLOGY*

100 809   US   ISSN 0961-754X
COMMON KNOWLEDGE. 1992. 3/yr. £40($60) (effective 1996). Oxford University Press, Journals, 2001 Evans Rd., Cary, NC 27513. TEL 919-677-0977; 800-852-7323. FAX 919-677-1714. E-mail: jnlorders@oup-usa.org. (Subscr. outside N. America to: Oxford University Press, Journals, Walton St., Oxford OX2 6DF, England. TEL 44-1865-56767. FAX 44-1865-267773) Ed. Jeffrey Perl. adv.; bk.rev. circ. 1,050. (back issues avail.) **Indexed:** Amer.Hist.& Life (1992-), Hist.Abstr. (1992-). **Document type:** academic/scholarly publication.
—BLDSC (3339.239000); UMI; UnCover. **CCC.**
Description: Addresses the restructuring of traditional debates within intellectual communities.

100   UK   ISSN 0264-5211
COMMUNIQUE. 1988. 3/yr. £4.50. Sundial House Publications, Sundial House, Nevill Court, Tunbridge Wells, Kent TN4 8NJ, England.

140 190   IT   ISSN 1121-8444
CON-TRATTO; rivista di filosofia tomista e di filosofia contemporanea. 1992. s-a. L.35000 (foreign L.50000). (Centro di Studi Tomistici) Poligrafo Casa Editrice, Via Turazza 19, 35128 Padua, Italy. TEL 39-49-776986. FAX 39-49-772523. Eds. Emmanuele Morandi, Riccardo Panattoni.

100   GW   ISSN 0010-5155
CONCEPTUS; Zeitschrift fuer Philosophie. (Text in German; summaries in English and German) 1967. 2/yr. DM.48 (students DM.36). (Johannes Kepler Universitaet, Institut fuer Philosophie, AU) Academia Verlag GmbH, Postfach 1663, 53734 Sankt Augustin, Germany. TEL 02241-333349. FAX 02241-341528. Ed.Bd. adv.; bk.rev.; abstr.; bibl.; charts; index, cum.index. circ. 500. (reprint service avail. from KTO) **Indexed:** Math.R., Phil.Ind. **Document type:** academic/scholarly publication.
—SWETS.

100   AU   ISSN 0259-0670
CONCEPTUS-STUDIEN. 1984. irreg., no.8, 1991. price varies. Johannes Kepler Universitaet, Institut fuer Philosophie, A-4040 Linz-Auhof, Austria. Ed. Rainer Born. **Document type:** monographic series.

CONFERENCE ON EDITORIAL PROBLEMS: UNIVERSITY OF TORONTO. see *LITERATURE*

100   GW   ISSN 0589-4069
CONSCIENTIA. 1968. irreg., vol.18, 1990. price varies. Bouvier Verlag Herbert Grundmann, Am Hof 28, 53113 Bonn, Germany. TEL 0228-7290124. FAX 0228-7290179. Ed. Gerhard Funke. **Document type:** monographic series.

CONSTELLATIONS; an international journal of critical and democratic theory. see *POLITICAL SCIENCE*

100   US   ISSN 0895-0520
CONTEMPORARY EXISTENTIALISM. irreg., vol.4, 1992. Peter Lang Publishing, Inc., 62 W. 45th St., 4th Fl., New York, NY 10036. TEL 212-302-6740. FAX 212-302-7574. Ed. Howard K. Slaatte. **Document type:** academic/scholarly publication, monographic series.
—BLDSC (3425.181805).

100   US   ISSN 0732-4944
CONTEMPORARY PHILOSOPHY. 1966. bi-m. $30. Institute for Advanced Philosophic Research, Box 1373, Boulder, CO 80306. (Affiliate: Realia) bk.rev. circ. controlled.
—BLDSC (3425.198800); UnCover.
Formerly: Philosophic Research and Analysis (ISSN 0048-3907)

190   NE
CONTEMPORARY PHILOSOPHY. (Text in English, French) irreg. price varies. (Institut International de Philosophie, FR) Kluwer Academic Publishers, Postbus 17, 3300 AA Dordrecht, Netherlands. TEL 31-78-392392. FAX 31-78-392254. TELEX 29245 KAPG NL. (Dist. by: Kluwer Academic Publishers Group, P.O. Box 322, 3300 AH Dordrecht, Netherlands. TEL 31-78-392392. FAX 31-78-546474; N. America dist. addr.: Box 358, Accord Sta., Hingham, MA 02018-0358. TEL 617-871-6600. FAX 617-871-6528) (back issues avail.) **Document type:** monographic series.
Description: Publishes philosophical research in various world cultures.
Refereed Serial

100   US   ISSN 0084-926X
CONTRIBUTIONS IN PHILOSOPHY. 1968. irreg., no.50, 1992. price varies. Greenwood Press, Inc. (Subsidiary of: Greenwood Publishing Group Inc.), 88 Post Rd. W., Box 5007, Westport, CT 06881-5007. TEL 203-226-3571. FAX 203-222-1502.
—BLDSC (3461.110000).

140   NE   ISSN 0923-9545
CONTRIBUTIONS TO PHENOMENOLOGY. 1989. irreg., vol.18, 1993. price varies. Kluwer Academic Publishers, Postbus 17, 3300 AA Dordrecht, Netherlands. TEL 31-78-392392. FAX 31-78-392254. TELEX 29245 KAPG NL. (Dist. by: Kluwer Academic Publishers Group, P.O. Box 322, 3300 AH Dordrecht, Netherlands. TEL 31-78-392392. FAX 31-78-546474; N. America dist. addr.: Box 358, Accord Sta., Hingham, MA 02018-0358. TEL 617-871-6600. FAX 617-871-6528) **Document type:** monographic series.
—BLDSC (3461.108000).
Refereed Serial

140   IT   ISSN 0391-2418
IL CONTRIBUTO. 1976. q. L.25000($20) Editoriale B.M. Italiana, V. Pianciani 31-A4, 00185 Rome, Italy. TEL 06-6900483. Ed. Pietro Ciaravolo. adv.; bk.rev. circ. 1,000.

CORONA. see *LITERATURE*

CORPUS DEI PAPIRI FILOSOFICI GRECI E LATINI. STUDI E TESTI. see *CLASSICAL STUDIES*

108   IT   ISSN 0394-4360
CORPUS PHILOSOPHORUM MEDII AEVI. SERIE I. SUBSIDIA. 1980. irreg., no.8, 1993. price varies. Casa Editrice Leo S. Olschki, Casella Postale 66, 50100 Florence, Italy. TEL 39-55-6530684. FAX 39-55-6530214.

100   IT   ISSN 0394-4379
CORPUS PHILOSOPHORUM MEDII AEVI. SERIE II. TESTI E STUDI. 1980. irreg., no.12, 1993. price varies. Casa Editrice Leo S. Olschki, Casella Postale 66, 50100 Florence, Italy. TEL 055-6530684. FAX 055-6530214. **Document type:** monographic series.

144 360   US
COURIER (BOSTON). 1954. a. $15 membership. Albert Schweitzer Fellowship, 330 Brookline Ave., Boston, MA 02215. TEL 617-667-5111. FAX 617-667-7989. Ed. Maurice Loiselle. bk.rev. circ. 6,500. **Document type:** newspaper.
Description: Informs interested readers of the Schweitzer Fellowship's activities in support of "reverence for life".

CREATIVITY IN ACTION. see *BUSINESS AND ECONOMICS — Management*

345   US   ISSN 0731-129X
HV7231
CRIMINAL JUSTICE ETHICS. 1982. s-a. $15 to individuals (foreign $20); institutions $30 (foreign $35). Institute for Criminal Justice Ethics, John Jay College, 899 10th Ave., New York, NY 10019. TEL 212-237-8033. FAX 212-237-8901. Ed. John Kleinig. bk.rev. circ. 1,000. (also avail. in microform from UMI) **Indexed:** Abstr.Crim.& Pen., C.L.I., CJPI, Crim.Just.Abstr., Phil.Ind. **Document type:** academic/scholarly publication.
—BLDSC (3487.350100); Faxon; UMI; UnCover.

100   MX   ISSN 0011-1503
B1
CRITICA; revista hispanoamericana de filosofia. (Text in English, Spanish) 1967. 3/yr. Mex.$50($20) Universidad Nacional Autonoma de Mexico, Instituto de Investigaciones Filosoficas, Apdo. Postal 70-447, Mexico, D.F., Mexico. Ed.Bd. adv.; bk.rev.; index; circ. 1,000 (controlled). **Indexed:** Hisp.Amer.Per.Ind. (1970-1991), Phil.Ind.
—BLDSC (3487.394700); Genuine Article; UnCover.

100   PO   ISSN 0870-970X
CRITICA; revista do pensamento contemporaneo. 1987. s-a. Nucleo de Estudos Pragmaticos, c/o Joao Saagua, Dpto. de Filosofia, Univ. Nova de Lisboa, Av. de Berna 26-C, 1000 Lisbon, Portugal. Ed. Manuel Maria Carrilho.

100   US
CRITICAL PERSPECTIVES: A GUILFORD SERIES. irreg. (approx. 4/yr.). Guilford Publications, Inc., 72 Spring St., New York, NY 10012. TEL 212-431-9800; 800-365-7006. FAX 212-966-6708. Ed. Douglas Kellner. **Document type:** monographic series.
Description: Features the works of both established thinkers and the next generation of social, political and cultural critics, in the areas of poststructuralism, cultural studies, feminism, psychoanalysis, semiotics and Marxism.

CRITICAL REVIEW. see *LITERATURE*

100   MX   ISSN 0185-2604
CUADERNOS DE CRITICA. 1977. irreg., no.45, 1989. Universidad Nacional Autonoma de Mexico, Instituto de Investigaciones Filosoficas, Apdo. Postal 70-447, Mexico, D.F., Mexico. (Dist. by: Direccion General de Formento Editorial, Porto Alegre No. 260, San Andres Tetepilco, 094 4, Mexico, D.F., Mexico)

100   CK   ISSN 0120-8462
B1001
CUADERNOS DE FILOSOFIA LATINOAMERICANA. 1980. q. Col.2500 (Latin America $30, elsewhere $34). Universidad Santo Tomas, Cr. 9, no. 51-23, Santa Fe de Bogota, Colombia. Dir. Daniel Herrera Restrepo.

100 860   SP   ISSN 0210-749X
B4568.U54
CUADERNOS DE LA CATEDRA MIGUEL DE UNAMUNO. 1948. irreg., no.29, 1994. 3000 ptas. (effective 1995). Ediciones Universidad de Salamanca, Apdo. 325, 37080 Salamanca, Spain. TEL 34-23-294598. **Document type:** monographic series, academic/scholarly publication.

100   SP   ISSN 0210-4857
CUADERNOS SALMANTINOS DE FILOSOFIA. 1974. a. 3000 ptas.($47) Universidad Pontificia, Departamento de Ediciones y Publicaciones, Apdo. de Correos 541, 37080 Salamanca, Spain. TEL 923-21-51-40. FAX 923-21-34-50. Ed. Saturnino Alvarez Turienzo.

CULTURA, HISTORIA Y FILOSOFIA. see *HISTORY — History Of Europe*

190 306   UK   ISSN 0921-3740
GN357   CODEN: CUDYEH
CULTURAL DYNAMICS. 1989-1992; resumed 1994. 3/yr. £27 to individuals; institutions £85 (effective 1996). Sage Publications Ltd., 6 Bonhill St., London EC2A 4PU, England. TEL 0171-374-0645. FAX 0171-374-8741. E-mail: market@sageltd.co.uk. ED.Bd. adv.: B&W page £180; trim 185 x 110; adv. contact: Bernie Folan. (back issues avail.) **Indexed:** ASSIA, Sociol.Abstr. **Document type:** academic/scholarly publication.
—BLDSC (3491.662500); SWETS; UnCover. **CCC.**
Description: Committed to a relational and dynamic account of socio-cultural phenomena, thus explicitly resisting the conventional static models that have dominated much of the discourse of this area.
Refereed Serial

D W D NEWSLETTER. (Dying with Dignity) see *LAW*

101   IS   ISSN 0334-2336
DA'AT; Jewish philosophy and Kabbalah. (Text in English, French, Hebrew; summaries in English) 1978. s-a. $15 per no. (effective 1993). (Bar-Ilan University, Department of Philosophy) Bar-Ilan University Press, Ramat-Gan 52900, Israel. TEL 972-3-5318401. FAX 972-3-347601. TELEX 342290-BARIL-IL. Eds. Moshe Hallamish, E. Levinas. bk.rev.; bibl.; cum.index: vols.1-20 in vol.20. circ. 600. (back issues avail.) **Indexed:** Ind.Heb.Per. **Document type:** academic/scholarly publication.

100   SP   ISSN 1130-0507
DAIMON; revista de filosofia. (Text in English, French, German, Italian, Spanish) 1955-1986; resumed 1989. s-a. 2000 ptas.($25) Universidad de Murcia, Secretariado de Publicaciones e Intercambio Cientifico, Santo Cristo, 1, 30001 Murcia, Spain. TEL 34-68-363012. FAX 34-68-363414. Ed. Eduardo Bello. circ. 400. (back issues avail.) **Document type:** academic/scholarly publication, monographic series.
Formerly (until 1989): Universidad de Murcia. Anales de Filosofia (ISSN 0212-9698); **Supersedes in part (in 1983):** Universidad de Murcia. Filosofia y Letras. Anales (ISSN 0463-9863)
Description: One issue is monographic, the other publishes about 15 papers, 4 discussions, 6 critical notes and 15 reviews.
Refereed Serial

DALHOUSIE REVIEW; a Canadian journal of literature and opinion. see *LITERARY AND POLITICAL REVIEWS*

PHILOSOPHY

108 320   US
DANDELION. 1977. irreg., vol.20, 1987. $4.50 for 4 issues. Michael E. Coughlin, Ed. & Pub., 1985 Selby Ave., St. Paul, MN 55104. TEL 612-646-8917. adv.; bk.rev. circ. 400. (back issues avail.) **Indexed:** Can.Lit.Ind. **Document type:** academic/scholarly publication.
   Description: Focuses on philosophical anarchism; explores the movement through its history, its philosophy and personalities.

100   DK   ISSN 0070-2749
B1
DANISH YEARBOOK OF PHILOSOPHY. (Text in English) 1964. a. price varies. University of Copenhagen, Museum Tusculanum Press, Njalsgade 92, DK-2300 Copenhagen S, Denmark. TEL 45-35-32-91-09. FAX 45-35-32-91-13. (Dist. in U.S. and Canada by: Paul & Co., c/o P C S Data Processing, Inc., W. 31st St., New York, NY 10001. TEL 212-567-3730. FAX 212-971-7200) Ed.Bd. index. circ. 400. (reprint service avail. from ISI) **Indexed:** Curr.Cont., Phil.Ind. **Document type:** academic/scholarly publication.
•Also available on CD-ROM.
—BLDSC (3519.900000).
   Description: Articles by Danish philosophers on Danish or foreign philosophy. Often special issues or contributions from symposia

181.45   US   ISSN 0892-130X
BL624
DARSHAN. 1975. 12/yr. $86. Syda Foundation, Box 600, South Fallsburg, NY 12779. FAX 914-434-3276. Ed. Jane Johnson.
   Formerly (until 1986): Siddha Path (ISSN 0278-954X)

100   II   ISSN 0011-6734
B1
DARSHANA INTERNATIONAL; an international quarterly of philosophy, psychology, sociology, psychical research, religion and mysticism. (Text in English) 1961. q. Rs.150($40) Darashna International, Moradabad 244 001, India. TEL 23370. Ed. J.P. Atreya. adv.; bk.rev.; charts; illus.; index. circ. 500. **Indexed:** Curr.Cont., Phil.Ind. **Document type:** academic/scholarly publication.

DEGRES; revue de synthese a orientation semiologique. see LINGUISTICS

100   GW   ISSN 0943-9129
DIE DEUTSCHE VOLKSHOCHSCHULE; allgemeinverstaendliche Beitraege aus Wissenschaft, Kunst und Philosophie. 1978. bi-m. DM.60. 23845 Buehnsdorf, Germany. TEL 04550-1256. Ed. Nordfried Preisinger. bk.rev. circ. 1,000. **Document type:** academic/scholarly publication.

100   GW   ISSN 0012-1045
B3
DEUTSCHE ZEITSCHRIFT FUER PHILOSOPHIE. 1953. bi-m. DM.215 (students DM.125) (effective 1996). Akademie Verlag GmbH, Muehlenstr. 33-34, 13187 Berlin, Germany. TEL 030-47889348. FAX 030-47889357. Ed.Bd. adv.; bk.rev.; bibl.; index. (also avail. in microform from SWZ) **Indexed:** Arts & Hum.Cit.Ind., Curr.Cont., Lang.& Lang.Behav.Abstr., Phil.Ind., SSCI. **Document type:** academic/scholarly publication.
—BLDSC (3575.840000); Faxon; Genuine Article; SWETS.

DHARMA; a quarterly devoted to universal religion, righteousness & culture. see RELIGIONS AND THEOLOGY

DHARMA COMBAT; a magazine about spirituality, metaphysics, reality and other conspiracies. see RELIGIONS AND THEOLOGY

DIACRITICA. see LITERATURE

100   AT   ISSN 0084-9804
DIALECTIC. 1967. irreg. price varies. Newcastle University Philosophy Club, c/o Department of Philosophy, Univ. of Newcastle, N.S.W. 2308, Australia. TEL 61-49-215-186. FAX 61-49-216-928. E-mail: plden@cc.newcastle.edu.au. Ed.Bd. circ. 225. **Document type:** academic/scholarly publication.
   Description: Contains articles written by senior academis and, occasionally, postgraduate students, as well as by philosophers who work in other disciplines.

120   SZ   ISSN 0012-2017
B1
DIALECTICA; international journal of philosophy of knowledge. (Text in English, French and German) 1947. q. 70 SFr. to individuals; institutions 100 SFr. Societe Dialectica, P.O. Box 5907, CH-3001 Bern, Switzerland. Ed.Bd. adv.; bk.rev.; index. circ. 700. **Indexed:** Arts & Hum.Cit.Ind., Curr.Cont., Lang.& Lang.Behav.Abstr., Math.R., Phil.Ind., Risk Abstr., Sociol.Abstr. **Document type:** academic/scholarly publication.
—BLDSC (3579.700000); Faxon; SWETS; UnCover.

100   AG
DIALEKTICA; produccion intelectual estudiantil. 1992. s-a.? Instituto de Filosofia, 25 de Mayo 217, 2o piso, Buenos Aires, Argentina. **Document type:** academic/scholarly publication.

100 500   GW   ISSN 0939-5512
DIALEKTIK; enzyklopaedische Zeitschrift fuer Philosophie und Wissenschaften. 3/yr. DM.98. Felix Meiner Verlag GmbH, Richardstr. 47, 22081 Hamburg, Germany. TEL 040-29875641. FAX 040-2993614. Ed. Thomas Mies. **Document type:** academic/scholarly publication.

160   IT
DIALETTICA. irreg., latest vol.5. price varies. Edizioni Studium, Via Cassiodoro 14, 00193 Rome, Italy. **Document type:** monographic series.

100   IT   ISSN 0012-2084
DIALOGO; quaderni europei di dialogica. (Text in French, Italian and Spanish) 1957. L.1000. (Istituto Euromediterraneo di Scienze Umane della Citta-Studio di Urbino, Centro Studi Dialogici) A. Testa, Ed. & Pub., Via S. Isaia 67, Bologna, Italy.

100   IT
DIALOGO SULLA NATURA: PARADOSSO. 3/yr. L.51600. Pagvs Edizioni s.r.l., Via Curtatone, 10, Paese (Treviso), Italy. TEL 0422-950264. FAX 0422-951225. Ed. Margherita Petranzan.

100   PR   ISSN 0012-2122
B5
DIALOGOS. (Text in English or Spanish) 1964. s-a. $12 to individuals; institutions $16. Universidad de Puerto Rico, Departamento de Filosofia, Box 21572, U.P.R. Station, San Juan, PR 00931. TEL 809-764-0000 ext. 2072. FAX 809-764-5899. (Subscr. to: EDUPR, P.O. Box 23322, San Juan, PR 00931-3322. TEL 809-250-0615) Ed. Miguel A. Badia Cabrera. adv.; bk.rev.; bibl. circ. 800. **Indexed:** Hisp.Amer.Per.Ind. (1970-1994), Phil.Ind. **Document type:** academic/scholarly publication.
—BLDSC (3579.740000); UnCover.
   Description: Publishes philosophical articles.
   Refereed Serial

100   US   ISSN 0012-2246
B1
DIALOGUE (MILWAUKEE). 1956; N.S. 3/yr. $5. Phi Sigma Tau, Dept. of Philosophy, Marquette University, Milwaukee, WI 53233. TEL 414-288-6857. Ed. Thomas L. Prendergast. adv.; bk.rev.; bibl.; index. circ. 1,500. **Indexed:** Arts & Hum.Cit.Ind., Curr.Cont., Phil.Ind.
—BLDSC (3579.758000); UnCover.

100   PL   ISSN 0867-504X
DIALOGUE AND HUMANISM; the Polish philosophical quarterly. (Text in English) 1973. q. $24 to individuals; institutions $32. Uniwersytet Warszawski, Instytut Filozofii, Krakowskie Przedmiescie 3, 00-047 Warsaw, Poland. TEL 48-22-264567. FAX 48-22-267520. TELEX 815439 UW P. (Subscr. to: Ars Polona Ruch, Krakowskie Przedmiescie 7, 00-068 Warsaw, Poland) (Co-sponsor: Polska Akademia Nauk) Ed. Janusz Kuczynski. bibl. **Indexed:** Mid.East: Abstr.& Ind., Phil.Ind.
—BLDSC (3579.775215); Faxon; UnCover.
   Formerly (until 1991): Dialectics and Humanism (ISSN 0324-8275)

100   CN   ISSN 0012-2173
B1
DIALOGUE: CANADIAN PHILOSOPHICAL REVIEW/REVUE CANADIENNE DE PHILOSOPHIE. (Text in English, French) 1962. q. Can.$75 (foreign $80). (Canadian Philosophical Association) Wilfrid Laurier University Press, 75 University Ave. W., Waterloo, ON N2L 3C5, Canada. TEL 519-884-0710. FAX 519-725-1399. E-mail: press@mach1.wlu.ca. adv.; bk.rev.; cum.index: vols. 1-10. circ. 1,420. **Indexed:** Bk.Rev.Ind. (1989-), Child.Bk.Rev.Ind. (1989-), Curr.Cont., M.L.A., Phil.Ind. **Document type:** academic/scholarly publication.
—BLDSC (3579.755000); Faxon; Genuine Article; SWETS. CCC.
   Description: Covers the history of philosophy, metaphysics, epistemology, logic, philosophy of science, political philosophy, ethics, and the philosophy of religion.
   Refereed Serial

100   MX   ISSN 0419-0890
DIANOIA; anuario de filosofia. 1955. a. Universidad Nacional Autonoma de Mexico, Instituto de Investigaciones Filosoficas, Circuito Maestro Mano de la Cueva, Ciudad Universitaria, Coyoacan 04510, Mexico, D.F., Mexico. circ. 1,200. (back issues avail.) **Indexed:** Hisp.Amer.Per.Ind. (1970-1991), Phil.Ind.

DICTIONNAIRE PERMANENT: BIOETHIQUE ET BIOTECHNOLOGIES. see BIOLOGY — Biotechnology

100   SZ   ISSN 0070-4806
PQ1979
DIDEROT STUDIES. (Text in English and French) 1949. irreg., no.25, 1992. price varies. Librairie Droz S.A., 11, rue Massot, CH-1211 Geneva 12, Switzerland. TEL 022-3466666. FAX 022-3472391. Eds. Otis Fellows, Diana Guiragossian. bk.rev. **Indexed:** M.L.A. **Document type:** monographic series.
—CCC.

DIFFERENTIA; review of Italian thought. see LITERARY AND POLITICAL REVIEWS

DIJALEKTIKA/DIALECTICS; casopis za metodolosko filozofske probleme matematickih, prirodnih i tehnickih nauka. see SCIENCES: COMPREHENSIVE WORKS

100   GW   ISSN 0175-0135
DILTHEY-JAHRBUCH; fuer Philosophie und Geschichte der Geisteswissenschaften. (Text in English and German; summaries in German) 1983. a. price varies. Vandenhoeck und Ruprecht, Robert-Bosch-Breite 6, 37079 Goettingen, Germany. TEL 0551-6959-0. FAX 0551-695917. (Subscr. to: 37070 Goettingen, Germany) circ. 800. (back issues avail.) **Document type:** academic/scholarly publication.
—CCC.

DIOGENES (ENGLISH EDITION). see SOCIOLOGY

105 930   GR   ISSN 1010-7363
B1
DIOTIMA; epitheoresis philosophikes erevnes - revue de recherche philosophique - review of philosophical research. (Text in English, French) 1973. a. $45. (Hellenic Society for Philosophical Studies - Societe Hellenique d'Etudes Philosophiques) Evangelos Moutsopoulos, Ed. & Pub., 40 Ypsilantou St., 115 21 Athens, Greece. TEL 30-1-725-1212. FAX 30-1-722-7322. adv.; page $20; adv. contact: Evangelos Moutsopoulos. bk.rev.; index. circ. 400. (back issues avail.) **Indexed:** Phil.Ind. **Document type:** academic/scholarly publication, bibliography, proceedings.
   Description: Discusses the philosophy and history of art and values and the philosophy of history.
   Refereed Serial

100   US   ISSN 0070-508X
DIRECTORY OF AMERICAN PHILOSOPHERS. 1962. biennial, 17th ed., 1994. $109 (effective 1994). Bowling Green State University, Philosophy Documentation Center, Bowling Green, OH 43403-0189. TEL 419-372-2419; 800-444-2419. FAX 419-372-6987. Ed. Archie J. Bahm. circ. 1,000. **Document type:** directory.
   Description: Provides a comprehensive listing of philosophy faculty and the colleges and universities where philosophy is taught, with information on graduate programs, philosophy journals, publishers, centers, institutes and societies.

PHILOSOPHY

100　　　　　　　AG　ISSN 0327-2214
DISCURSO Y REALIDAD. 1985. 2/yr. Arg.$250000($25) Discurso y Realidad, 25 de Mayo 950, Block C, Piso 10-B, 4000 San Miguel de Tucuman, Argentina. Dir. Rolo Maris. bk.rev.

DISTANT DRUMS. see *RELIGIONS AND THEOLOGY*

DIVREI HA-AKADEMIA HA-LEUMIT HA-YISRAELIT LEMADAIM. see *HUMANITIES: COMPREHENSIVE WORKS*

DIVUS THOMAS; commentarium de philosophia et theologia. see *RELIGIONS AND THEOLOGY*

DOCTOR - PATIENT STUDIES. see *MEDICAL SCIENCES*

180　　　　　　　IT
DOCUMENTI E STUDI SULLA TRADIZIONE FILOSOFICA MEDIEVALE. 1990. s-a. L.100000 (effective Feb. 1994). Centro Italiano di Studi sull'Alto Medioevo, Palazzo Ancaiani, 06049 Spoleto, Italy. TEL 39-743-220418. FAX 39-743-223507. (Co-sponsor: Societa Internazionale per lo Studio del Medioevo Latino) Ed. Gian Carlo Garfagnini. Document type: academic/scholarly publication.

DONGBEI SHIDA XUEBAO (ZHEXUE SHEHUI KEXUE BAN)/NORTHEAST NORMAL UNIVERSITY. JOURNAL (PHILOSOPHY, SOCIAL SCIENCE EDITION). see *SOCIAL SCIENCES: COMPREHENSIVE WORKS*

100 301　　　　　　GW
DUISBURGER STUDIEN; Geistes- und Gesellschaftswissenschaften. 1979. s-a. Gilles & Francke Verlag, Blumenstr. 67-69, 47057 Duisburg, Germany. TEL 0203-355097. FAX 0203-355520. Ed.Bd. adv. contact: Barbara Francke. bk.rev. Document type: academic/scholarly publication.

181.4　　　　　NO　ISSN 0332-5792
DYADE. 1968. q. NOK 150. Dyade Forlag, P.O. Box 2559 Solli, N-0203 Oslo 2, Norway.
　Description: Publishes articles on art and culture in their broadest sense, psychology related to Acem-meditation and various philosophical issues.

E Z W - TEXTE; Informationen - Impulse - Arbeitstexte. (Evangelische Zentralstelle fuer Weltanschauungsfragen) see *RELIGIONS AND THEOLOGY*

EAST AND WEST SERIES; an interpreter of the life of the spirit. see *RELIGIONS AND THEOLOGY*

EASTERN BUDDHIST. see *RELIGIONS AND THEOLOGY — Buddhist*

212.5　　　　　US　ISSN 0046-1105
ECLECTIC THEOSOPHIST; following the Blavatsky and Point Loma traditions. 1971. q. $7 (foreign $10). Point Loma Publications, Inc., 3727 Charles St., Box 6507, San Diego, CA 92106. TEL 619-222-3291. Ed. Kenneth R. Small. bk.rev. circ. 800. (tabloid format; back issues avail.)
　Description: Publishes essays, studies fiction and poetry expressing the underlying unity of life. Serves as a forum for exponents of Theosophic insight, thought and practice.

ECONOMIES ET SOCIETES. SERIE M. PHILOSOPHIE - SCIENCES SOCIALES ECONOMIE. see *BUSINESS AND ECONOMICS — Economic Systems And Theories, Economic History*

ECUMENE; a journal of environment - culture - meaning. see *ENVIRONMENTAL STUDIES*

EDITIO; internationales Jahrbuch fuer Editionswissenschaft. see *LITERATURE*

100　　　　　　UK　ISSN 0142-3371
EFRYDIAU ATHRONYDDOL. (Text in Welsh) 1938. a. £3. University of Wales Press, 6 Gwennyth St., Cathays, Cardiff CF2 4YD, Wales. TEL 01222-231919. FAX 01222-230908. Eds. John Daniel, W.L. Gealey. bk.rev.; circ. 350 (paid). Document type: academic/scholarly publication.

100　　　　　　CN　ISSN 0707-2287
EIDOS; the Canadian graduate journal of philosophy. (Text in English and French) 1978. s-a. Can.$9 to students; institutions Can.$35; others Can.$18. University of Waterloo, Philosophy Graduate Student Association, Dept. of Philosophy, Waterloo, ON N2L 3G1, Canada. TEL 519-885-1211. Ed. Jason West. adv. contact: Alix Nalezinski. bk.rev. circ. 160. Indexed: Phil.Ind. Document type: academic/scholarly publication.
　Description: Provides a forum for academic discussion on philosophical themes to graduate students and recent Ph.D.s in Canada and abroad.
　Refereed Serial

EIGHTEENTH CENTURY: A CURRENT BIBLIOGRAPHY. see *BIBLIOGRAPHIES*

100　　　　　　NE
ELEMENTA. (Text in German) 1975. irreg., vol. 61, 1994. price varies. Editions Rodopi B.V., Keizersgracht 302-304, 1016 EX Amsterdam, Netherlands. TEL 31-20-6227507. FAX 31-20-6380948. E-mail: F.van.der.Zee@Rodopi.nl. (In N. America: 233 Peachtree St., N.E., Ste. 404, Atlanta, GA 30303-1504. TEL 800-225-3998. FAX 404-522-7116) Eds. Rudolph Berlinger, Wiebke Schrader. Document type: monographic series.

100　　　　　　IT　ISSN 0392-7342
B175.I7
ELENCHOS; rivista di studi sul pensiero antico. 1980. s-a. L.27000. (Centro di Studi sul Pensiero Antico) Biblipolis, Via Arangio Ruiz 83, 80122 Naples, Italy. TEL (081) 664606. Ed. Prof. Gabriele Gionnantoni.
　Description: Devoted exclusively to ancient philosophy.

EMERGING. see *NEW AGE PUBLICATIONS*

100　　　　　　US　ISSN 0883-6000
EMORY VICO STUDIES. 1987. irreg. Peter Lang Publishing, Inc., 62 W. 45th St., 4th Fl., New York, NY 10036. TEL 212-302-6740. Ed. Donald Verene. Document type: academic/scholarly publication, monographic series.

EMSHOCK LETTER. see *NEW AGE PUBLICATIONS*

100 954　　　　　US
ENLIGHTENMENT BOOK CLUB. 1982. bi-m. $50 (foreign $70). Intergalactice Lovetrance Civilization Center, Box 73, Harbor City, CA 90710-0073. Ed. Amanda Swamy. adv. contact: Prem Swamy. bk.rev.; bibl.; charts; illus.; stat. circ. 25. (also avail. in audio cassette; back issues avail.)
　Former titles: Lovetrance World & Aum Namo Narayanay; Lovetrance News.
　Description: Collection of inspirational wisdom, commentaries on Sanskrit scripture and literature, self-help and personal growth tips, bibliographies of saints and the true history of mankind.

100 614.7　　　　US　ISSN 0163-4275
GF80　　　　　　　　CODEN: ENETDD
ENVIRONMENTAL ETHICS; an interdisciplinary journal dedicated to the philosophical aspects of environmental problems. 1979. q. $40 (effective 1996). Environmental Philosophy, Inc., Department of Philosophy, University of North Texas, Box 13496, Denton, TX 76203-3496. TEL 817-565-2727. FAX 817-565-4448. Ed. Eugene C. Hargrove. adv.; bk.rev.; cum.index: 1979-1983 in vol.5, 1984-1988 in vol.10, 1979-1993 in vol.15. circ. 1,900. (also avail. in microform from UMI; reprint service avail. from UMI,WSH) Indexed: Curr.Cont., Ecol.Abstr., Energy Rev., Environ.Abstr. (1981-), Environ.Ind., Environ.Per.Bibl., Excerp.Med., Hum.Ind., Per.Islam. (1991-), Phil.Ind., Polit.Sci.Abstr., Rel.& Theol.Abstr. (1979-), Risk Abstr., Saf.Sci.Abstr., Sociol.Abstr., Sport Fish.Abstr., SSCI, Wild Life Rev., Wild.Rev., Zoo.Rec. Document type: academic/scholarly publication.
　—BLDSC (3791.465000); CIS; Faxon; Genuine Article; SWETS; UMI; UnCover. CCC.
　Description: Provides a forum for diverse interests and attitudes. Seeks to bring together the nonprofessional environmental philosophy tradition with the newly emerging professional interest in the subject.

121 501　　　　　IT　ISSN 0392-9760
EPISTEMOLOGIA; an Italian journal for the philosophy of science. (Special issues series avail.) (Text in English and Italian; occasionally in French) 1978. s-a. L.52000 (foreign L.78000) (effective 1994). Tilgher-Genova s.a.s., Via Assarotti 52, 16122 Genoa, Italy. TEL 10-8391140. FAX 10-870653. Ed. Evandro Agazzi. adv.; bk.rev.; index. (also avail. in microform) Document type: academic/scholarly publication.

100　　　　　　US
EPOCH (ADAIRSVILLE).* 6/yr. $10. Mandel Foundation Inc., 145 Ward Mt. Rd., Adairsville, GA 30103-9801. Indexed: Arts & Hum.Cit.Ind.

100　　　　　　SP　ISSN 0213-1668
ER. 1985. s-a. 1900 ptas. (Europe 3000 ptas.; elsewhere 3000 ptas.). Editorial Er, Apdo. 12345, 41085 Seville, Spain. TEL 954-22-69-63. circ. 1,400.

200　　　　　　US　ISSN 0276-2854
B785.E64
ERASMUS OF ROTTERDAM SOCIETY YEARBOOK. 1981. a. $40 to individuals; institutions $45. Erasmus of Rotterdam Society, University of Kentucky, Dept. of CLS, Lexington, KY 40506-0027. TEL 606-257-5710. FAX 606-323-1073. (Subscr. to: Richard A. Graham, 4201 Guilford Dr., College Park, MD 20740) Ed. Jane E. Phillips. bk.rev. circ. 600. Document type: academic/scholarly publication.
　Description: Contains articles on Erasmus, a scholar and humanist of Renaissance and Reformation, his contemporaries, and his intellectual milieu.
　Refereed Serial

100　　　　　　GW　ISSN 0179-163X
ERINNYEN; Zeitschrift fuer materialistische Ethik. 1985. a. DM.4. Verein zur Foerderung des Dialektischen Denkens e.V., Hertzstr. 39, 30827 Garbsen, Germany. TEL 05131-1623. Ed. Bodo Gassmann. adv.; bk.rev. circ. 700. (back issues avail.) Document type: academic/scholarly publication.
　Description: Examines materialistic-dialectic ethics and socialistic morals.

146　　　　　　NE　ISSN 0165-0106
B1　　　　　　　　　CODEN: ERKEDQ
ERKENNTNIS; an international journal of analytic philosophy. (Text in English) 1930. bi-m. fl.777 to institutions; $499 to institutions in U.S. (effective 1996). Kluwer Academic Publishers, Postbus 17, 3300 AA Dordrecht, Netherlands. TEL 31-78-392392. FAX 31-78-392254. TELEX 29245 KAPG NL. E-mail: SERVICES@WKAP.NL. (Dist. by: Kluwer Academic Publishers Group, P.O. Box 322, 3300 AH Dordrecht, Netherlands. TEL 31-78-392392. FAX 31-78-546474; N. America dist. addr.: Box 358, Accord Sta., Hingham, MA 02018-0358. TEL 617-871-6600. FAX 617-871-6528) Ed. Wolfgang Spohn. adv.; bk.rev. (also avail. in microform from UMI; reprint service avail. from SWZ) Indexed: Ind.Bk.Rev.Hum., Lang.& Lang.Behav.Abstr., Math.R., Phil.Ind., Sociol.Abstr. Document type: academic/scholarly publication.
　—SWETS; UMI; UnCover. CCC.
　Description: Publishes papers in philosophical disciplines associated with analytic philosophy, including epistemology, logic, philosophy of language, philosophy of science, practical philosophy and ethics.
　Refereed Serial

ESCRITOS. see *LITERATURE*

100　　　　　　EC
ESPACIOS; aportes al pensamiento critico contemporaneo. 1993. q. S/35000 (Latin America $30; US $40) (effective 1993). Centro de Investigaciones para el Desarrollo, P.O. Box 17-10-7169, Quito, Ecuador.

160　　　　　　AG　ISSN 0326-7946
ESPACIOS DE CRITICA Y PRODUCCION. 1984. s-a. Secretaria de Bienestar Estudiantil y Extension Universitaria, Facultad de Filosofia y Letra (UBA), Marcelo T. de Alvear 2230, 1 Piso, Buenos Aires, Argentina.

PHILOSOPHY

100   SP   ISSN 0014-0716
ESPIRITU. 1952. s-a. 3000 ptas. (Instituto Filosofico de Balmesiana) Editorial Balmes, S.A., Apdo. 1382, Duran y Bas 9, 08002 Barcelona, Spain. Ed. Juan Pegueroles. bk.rev.; cum.index: 1952-1977. circ. 300. Indexed: Amer.Hist.& Life, Bull.Signal., Hist.Abstr., Phil.Ind.

100   BE   ISSN 0071-1349
ESSAIS PHILOSOPHIQUES. no.5, 1950. irreg., latest 1992. price varies. (Institut Superieur de Philosophie) Editions Peeters s.p.r.l., Bondgenotenlaan 153, 3000 Leuven, Belgium. TEL 32-16-235170. FAX 32-16-228500. **Document type:** monographic series.
   Description: Monographs on different topics in philosophy by scholars of the institute.

100   133.91   IT
ESSERE. 1980. s-a. L.7500. Casa Editrice Psiche, Via Madama Cristina 70, Turin, Italy. TEL 011-6507058. Ed. Jean Klein.

100   IT   ISSN 1121-0036
ESTETICA (BOLOGNA). 1991. a. Societa Editrice Il Mulino, Strada Maggiore 37, 40125 Bologna, Italy. TEL 39-51-256011. FAX 39-51-256034. Ed. Stefano Zecchi. circ. 2,000.

ESTETIKA/AESTHETICS. see ART

100   SP   ISSN 0210-6086
B5
ESTUDIOS FILOSOFICOS; revista de investigacion y critica. 1952. 3/yr. 3700 ptas. (foreign 5000 ptas.) (effective 1993). Instituto Superior de Filosofia, Apdo. 586, 47080 Valladolid, Spain. TEL 983-35-66-99. FAX 983-34-34-09. Dir. D. Fernando Soria Heredia. adv.; bk.rev.; index. circ. 900. (back issues avail.) **Indexed:** Lang.& Lang.Behav.Abstr., Phil.Ind., Sociol.Abstr.
   —SWETS.

200   UK   ISSN 0014-1690
ETHICAL RECORD. 1895. m. (except Aug. & Dec.). £18. South Place Ethical Society, 25 Red Lion Sq., London WC1R 4RL, England. TEL 0171-831-7723. Ed. Norman Bacrac. bk.rev. circ. 750. (also avail. in microform from UMI; reprint service avail. from UMI) **Document type:** newsletter.
   —UMI.

170   US   ISSN 0273-2513
BJ1
ETHICS. (Subseries of: S I R S Social Issues (ISSN 0740-3127)) 1979. a. price varies; a. supplement $17. Social Issues Resources Series, Box 2348, Boca Raton, FL 33427-2348. TEL 407-994-0079; 800-232-7477. FAX 407-994-4704. (looseleaf format; also avail. in microfiche; back issues avail.; reprint service avail. from SCH) **Indexed:** Abstr.Crim.& Pen.
   Description: Reprints articles that probe the meaning and role of ethics in society.

300 320 340   US   ISSN 0014-1704
BJ1
ETHICS: AN INTERNATIONAL JOURNAL OF SOCIAL, POLITICAL AND LEGAL PHILOSOPHY. 1890. q. $29 to individuals; institutions $60; students $21. University of Chicago Press, Journals Division, 5720 S. Woodlawn Ave., Chicago, IL 60637. TEL 312-753-3347. FAX 312-753-0811. TELEX 25-4603. (Orders to: Box 37005, Chicago, IL 60637) Ed. Gerald Dworkin. adv.; bk.rev.; bibl.; index, cum.index: vols.1-75. circ. 3,300. (also avail. in microform from MIM,UMI,PMC; reprint service avail. from UMI,ISI,WSH) **Indexed:** A.B.C.Pol.Sci., Abstr.Bk.Rev.Curr.Leg.Per., Abstr.Crim.& Pen., Arts & Hum.Cit.Ind., Bk.Rev.Ind. (1977-), C.L.I., CERDIC, Chic.Per.Ind., Child.Bk.Rev.Ind. (1977-), Commun.Abstr., Curr.Cont., G.Soc.Sci.& Rel.Per.Lit., Ind.Bk.Rev.Hum., L.R.I., Lang.& Lang.Behav.Abstr., Phil.Ind., Soc.Sci.Ind., Sociol.Abstr., SSCI. **Document type:** academic/scholarly publication.
   —BLDSC (3814.650000); Faxon; Genuine Article; SWETS; UMI; UnCover. **CCC.**
   Refereed Serial

ETHICS AND INTERNATIONAL AFFAIRS (NEWSLETTER); a college-level curriculum development program. see *POLITICAL SCIENCE — International Relations*

215   US   ISSN 1071-3778
ETHICS AND MEDICS. 1976. m. $15 (foreign $18). Pope John XXIII Medical-Moral Research and Education Center, 186 Forbes Rd., Braintree, MA 02184. TEL 617-848-6965. FAX 617-849-1309. Ed. Albert S. Moraczewski. cum.index: 1976-1991; circ. 25,500 (paid). (back issues avail.) **Document type:** academic/scholarly publication, newsletter.
   Description: Catholic perspective on moral issues in the health and life sciences.
   Refereed Serial

100   US   ISSN 0897-0106
BJ1
ETHICS: EASIER SAID THAN DONE. 1988. q. $65 to institutions; members $40. Josephson Institute of Ethics, 4640 Admiralty Way, No. 1001, Marina del Rey, CA 90292-6610. TEL 310-306-1868. FAX 310-827-1864. Ed. Wes Hanson. bk.rev.; illus. circ. 5,000. (back issues avail.)
   —UnCover.

170 610   GW   ISSN 0935-7335
ETHIK IN DER MEDIZIN. 1989. 4/yr. DM.128($93) (effective 1996). Springer-Verlag, Heidelberger Platz 3, 14197 Berlin, Germany. TEL 030-8207-0. FAX 030-8214091. E-mail: orders@springer.de. (Subscr. in N. America to: Springer-Verlag New York, Inc., 44 Hartz Way, Secaucus, NJ 07096-2491. TEL 201-348-4033. FAX 201-348-4505) (also avail. in microform from UMI) **Document type:** academic/scholarly publication.
   —UMI. **CCC.**
   Description: Discusses ethical issues encountered in clinical medicine, research and development, and psychology.

174 658   US   ISSN 0895-5026
K5
ETHIKOS; examining ethical issues in business. 1987. s-m. $125 (Canada $135; elsewhere $145). Ethikos, Inc., 154 E. Boston Post Rd., Mamaroneck, NY 10543. TEL 914-381-7475. FAX 914-381-6947. Ed. Andrew W. Singer. adv. contact: Victoria Theodore. bk.rev. (also avail. in microform from UMI; back issues avail.) **Document type:** newsletter.
   —BLDSC (3814.675000); UMI. **CCC.**
   Description: Examines ethical issues in business with particular focus on corporate ethics programs, ombudsman offices, codes of conduct, and monitoring ethics.

170   FR   ISSN 1151-5104
ETHIQUE; la vie en question. 1991. q. 310 F. Societe Francaise de Reflexion Bioethique, 30 rue d'Auteuil, 75016 Paris, France. TEL 45-25-33-46. Ed. Dominique Folscheid; Pub. P. Dumont. adv. contact: Marie-Helene Congourdeau. bk.rev. circ. 1,200. **Document type:** academic/scholarly publication.
   Description: Studies ethics in relation to philosophy, biology, medicine, law, history and theology.

658 170 346   FR
▼**ETHIQUE DES AFFAIRES.** 1994. q. 385 F. (foreign 497 F.) (effective 1995). Editions E S K A, 27 rue Dunois, 75013 Paris, France. TEL 44-06-80-42. FAX 44-24-06-94. **Document type:** trade publication, academic/scholarly publication.
   Description: Covers all aspects of ethics in management, rendered in articles, conferences, and roundtables. Includes legal verdicts.

170   IT
ETHOS. q. Via F. Smaldone 5, 73100 Lecce, Italy. Ed. Salvatore Borgia.

100   AG   ISSN 0325-5387
ETHOS; revista de filosofia practica. 1973. a. $45. Instituto de Filosofia Practica, Viamonte 1596, 1055 Buenos Aires, Argentina. TEL 54-1-3713315. Ed. Julio Guido Soaje Ramos. adv. contact: Maria Lukac de Stier. bk.rev.; bibl. circ. 500. **Indexed:** SSCI. **Document type:** academic/scholarly publication.

100   CN   ISSN 0708-319X
ETIENNE GILSON SERIES. (Subseries: Etienne Gilson Lectures) 1979. irreg., vol.17, 1983. price varies. Pontifical Institute of Mediaeval Studies, 59 Queen's Park Crescent E., Toronto, ON M5S 2C4, Canada. TEL 416-926-7144. FAX 416-926-7258. (Dist. outside N. America and the U.K. by: N.V. Brepols, Steenweg op Tielen 68, 2300 Turnhout, Belgium. TEL 32-14-402500. FAX 32-14-428919) circ. 600. (back issues avail.) **Document type:** monographic series.
   —BLDSC (3816.125000).

100   FR   ISSN 0014-2166
ETUDES PHILOSOPHIQUES. 1926. q. 380 F. (foreign 430 F.) (effective 1996). Presses Universitaires de France, Departement des Revues, 14 Avenue du Bois-de-l'Epine, B.P.90, 91003 Evry Cedex, France. TEL 1-60-77-82-05. FAX 1-60-79-20-45. TELEX PUF 600 474 F. Ed.Bd. adv.; bk.rev.; charts; index. circ. 1,500. (also avail. in microform from UMI; reprint service avail. from KTO,UMI) **Indexed:** Arts & Hum.Cit.Ind., Curr.Cont., Ind.Bk.Rev.Hum., M.L.A., Phil.Ind., SSCI.
   —Faxon; Genuine Article; SWETS. **CCC.**
   Description: Each issue covers the essential ideas of a great philosophical thinker.

100 200   FR   ISSN 1155-2239
ETUDES SCHWEITZERIENNES; revue annuelle d'ethique, de theologie et de philosophie. 1990. a. (Association Francaise des Amis d'Albert Schweitzer) Editions Oberlin, 19 rue des Francs-Bourgeois, 67000 Strasbourg, France. Ed. Jean-Paul Sorg.

170   PL   ISSN 0014-2263
BJ8.P6
ETYKA. (Text in Polish; summaries in English and Russian) 1966. a. price varies. Polska Akademia Nauk, Instytut Filozofii i Socjologii, Nowy Swiat 72, 00-330 Warsaw, Poland. Ed. Barbara Skarga. bk.rev.; abstr. circ. 1,100. **Indexed:** Phil.Ind.

190   UK   ISSN 0966-8373
B1
EUROPEAN JOURNAL OF PHILOSOPHY. 1993. 3/yr. £99($149) (foreign £105) (effective 1996). Basil Blackwell Ltd., 108 Cowley Rd., Oxford OX4 1JF, England. TEL 44-1865-791100. FAX 44-1865-791347. (back issues avail.) **Document type:** academic/scholarly publication.
   —BLDSC (3829.734400); UMI. **CCC.**
   Refereed Serial

142.7   HU   ISSN 1215-5950
B1
EXISTENTIA; meleteesophias - philosophical papers - bolcseleti tanulmanyok. (Text in English, French, German, Greek, or Hungarian) 1991. 4/yr. (in 1 vol.). $40 (effective 1995). Societas Philosophia Classica, P.O. Box 554, 1374 Budapest 5, Hungary. TEL 36-62-21-611. FAX 36-62-10-894. Ed. Ferge Gabor.
   Description: Focuses on classical European thought, especially the doctrines of ancient Greek and Latin authors.

100 500   UK   ISSN 0261-1376
EXPLORATIONS IN KNOWLEDGE; an international journal in the philosophy of science. 1984. s-a. £12. Sombourne Press, 294 Leigh Rd., Chandlers Ford, Hants. SO5 3AU, England. TEL 01703-269687. Ed.Bd. adv.; bk.rev. circ. 500. **Document type:** academic/scholarly publication.
   —BLDSC (3842.207100); UnCover.
   Description: Covers philosophy of science, focusing on conceptual problems arising out of scientific research on the frontiers of knowledge. Subjects include the natural and human sciences as well as medical research, bioethics and cognitive studies.
   Refereed Serial

100   US   ISSN 1057-1035
EXTROPY; the journal of transhumanist thought. 1988. q. $18 to individuals (Canada & Mexico $22, elsewhere $24); institutions $40 (Canada & Mexico $45, elsewhere $60). Extropy Institute, 11860 Magnolia Ave., No. R, Riverside, CA 92503-4911. TEL 909-688-2323. Ed. Max More. adv.; bk.rev.; film rev.; bibl.; illus. circ. 2,500. (also avail. in diskette format) **Document type:** academic/scholarly publication, consumer publication.
   Description: Covers futurist philosophy, physical immortality, smart drugs, artificial intelligence and A-life, nanotechnology and others.

PHILOSOPHY

100 200 US ISSN 0739-7046
FAITH AND PHILOSOPHY. 1984. q. $25 to individuals (foreign $31); institutions $40 (foreign $46) (typically set in Jan.). Society of Christian Philosophers, Department of Philosophy, Asbury College, Wilmore, KY 40390. TEL 606-858-3511. Ed. Philip Quinn. adv.; bk.rev.; index. circ. 1,300. (also avail. in microform from UMI; back issues avail.) **Indexed:** Phil.Ind., Rel.& Theol.Abstr. (1987-), Rel.Ind.One. **Document type:** academic/scholarly publication.
—BLDSC (3865.511100); Faxon; UMI; UnCover.
   Formerly: Faith and Reason (Wilmore).

FARHANG. see *HUMANITIES: COMPREHENSIVE WORKS*

100 NE ISSN 0925-0166
FICHTE-STUDIEN. (Supplement avail. (ISSN 0927-3816)) 1991. irreg., vol.5, 1993. fl.75 per vol. (Johann Gotlieb Fichte Gesellschaft) Editions Rodopi B.V., Keizersgracht 302-304, 1016 EX Amsterdam, Netherlands. TEL 31-20-6227507. FAX 31-20-6380948. E-mail: F.van.der.Zee@Rodopi.nl. (In N. America: 233 Peachtree St. N.E., Ste. 404, Atlanta, GA 30303-1504. TEL 800-225-3998. FAX 404-522-7116) bk.rev. **Document type:** academic/scholarly publication, monograph series.
   Refereed Serial

193 NE ISSN 0927-3816
FICHTE-STUDIEN. SUPPLEMENTA. irreg., vol.4, 1994. price varies. (Johan Gotlieb Fichte Gesellschaft) Editions Rodopi B.V., Keizersgracht 302-304, 1016 EX Amsterdam, Netherlands. TEL 31-20-6227507. FAX 31-20-6380948. E-mail: F.van.der.Zee@Rodopi.nl. (In N. America: 233 Peachtree St. N.E., Ste. 404, Atlanta GA 30303-1504. TEL 800-225-3998. FAX 404-522-7116) **Document type:** academic/scholarly publication, monograph series.

100 AG ISSN 0325-805X
FILOSOFAR CRISTIANO. (Text in Portuguese or Spanish) 1974. s-a. $10. Asociacion Catolica Interamericana de Filosofia, Arturo M. Bas 366, 5000 Cordoba, Argentina. Ed. Alberto Caturelli. bk.rev. circ. 1,200.
   Formerly (until 1977): Asociacion Latino-Americana de Filosofos Catolicos. Boletin.

100 500 DK ISSN 0106-6668
FILOSOFI OG VIDENSKABSTEORI PAA ROSKILDE UNIVERSITETSCENTER. 1979. biennial. DKK 100. Roskilde Universitetscenter, Institut for Uddannelsesforskning, Medieforskning og Videnskabsteori Institut VII, P.O Box 260, DK-4000 Roskilde, Denmark. Ed. Arne Thing Mortensen. bk.rev. circ. 300. **Document type:** academic/scholarly publication.

100 IT ISSN 0015-1823
B4
FILOSOFIA. 1950. 3/yr. L.40000. Ugo Mursia Editore, Via Tadino, 29, 20124 Milan, Italy. Eds. Vittorio Mathieu, Marzio Pinottini. adv.; bk.rev.; bibl.; index, cum.index. (reprint service avail. from SCH) **Indexed:** Arts & Hum.Cit.Ind., Curr.Cont., Phil.Ind.
—SWETS.

100 IT ISSN 0392-9779
FILOSOFIA E SOCIETA. 1972. a. L.35000. Bibliotheca di Gabriele Chiusano, Largo Olgiata 15-106, 00123 Rome, Italy. Ed. Lido Chiusano.

294.54 IT
FILOSOFIA E TEOLOGIA. 1987. 3/yr. L.72000 to individuals; institutions L.94000; foreign L.120000 (effective 1993). Edizioni Scientifche Italiane S.p.A., Via Chiatamone 7, 80121 Naples, Italy. TEL 081-7645768. FAX 081-7646477.

110 IT ISSN 0392-9744
FILOSOFIA OGGI. (Text in Italian; occasionally in English, French, German, Spanish) 1978. q. L.80000($70) (effective 1994). Edizioni dell' Arcipelago s.a.s., Casella Postale 997, 16100 Genoa, Italy. TEL 010-27-22-431. adv.; bk.rev.; index. (also avail. in microform)

100 IT ISSN 0393-9936
FILOSOFIA OGGI. COLLANA. (Text in English, French, German, Italian, or Spanish) 1978. irreg. price varies. Edizioni dell' Arcipelago s.a.s., Casella Postale 997, 16100 Genoa, Italy. TEL 010-27-22-431. **Document type:** monograph series.

FILOSOFIA POLITICA. see *POLITICAL SCIENCE*

100 IT
FILOSOFIA PUBBLICA. 1989. irreg., no.7, 1993. price varies. Liguori Editore s.r.l., Via Mezzocannone, 19, 80134 Naples, Italy. TEL 081-5527139. Eds. S. Sebastiano Maffettone, Luciano Pellicani. **Document type:** monograph series.

100 XR ISSN 0015-1831
B8.C9
FILOSOFICKY CASOPIS/PHILOSOPHICAL REVIEW. (Text in Czech; summaries in various languages; table of contents in English, French, German, Russian) 1953. bi-m. $111.90. Ceska Akademie Ved, Filozoficky Ustav - Czech Academy of Sciences, Institute for Philosophy and Sociology, Jilska 1, 110 00 Prague 1, Czech Republic. TEL 42-2-4220992. FAX 42-2-4220257. (Dist. by: Artia Pegas, s.r.o. Ve Smeckach 30, 110 00 Prague 1, Czech Republic) Ed. Petr Horak. adv. contact: Olga Baranova. bk.rev.; bibl.; index. circ. 1,500. **Indexed:** Curr.Cont., Phil.Ind., Risk Abstr., SSCI.
—Genuine Article.
   Description: Examines all aspects of contemporary philosophy as well as history of philosophy.

198 SW ISSN 0348-7482
FILOSOFISK TIDSKRIFT. 1980. q. SEK 120. Stiftelsen Bokfoerlaget Thales, P.O. Box 50034, S-104 05 Stockholm, Sweden. TEL 46-8-717-94-86.

100 DK ISSN 0106-0449
FILOSOFISKE STUDIER. 1978. a. DKK 50. University of Copenhagen, Department of Education, Philosophy and Rhetoric, Njalsgade 80, DK-2300 Copenhagen S, Denmark. TEL 45-35-32-88-69. FAX 45-35-32-88-50. Ed.Bd. circ. 600. **Document type:** academic/scholarly publication.

100 KR ISSN 0235-7941
FILOSOFSKA I SOTSIOLOGICHESKA DUMKA; nauchno-teoreticheskii zhurnal. Russian edition: Filosofskaya i Sotsiologichnaya Mysl' (ISSN 0235-3512) (Text in Ukrainian; summaries in English) 1927. m. $125 (effective 1996). (Akademiya Nauk Ukrainy, Institut Filosofii) Vydavnitstvo Naukova Dumka, Vul. Tereshchinkivska 3, 252601 Kiev, Ukraine. TEL 044-224-4068. FAX 044-224-4068. (Dist. by: Mezhdunarodnaya Kniga, B. Yakimanka 39, 117049 Moscow, Russia; Dist. in U.S. by: Victor Kamkin Inc., Boiling Brook Pkwy., Rockville, MD 20852. TEL 301-881-5973. FAX 301-881-1637) Ed. Yu.D. Prilyuk. bibl. **Indexed:** M.L.A.
—BLDSC (0391.334700).
   Formerly (until 1989): Filosofska Dumka (ISSN 0130-5719)

197 KZ ISSN 0320-5452
B809.8
FILOSOFSKIE NAUKI (ALMA-ATA). 1971. irreg. 0.95 Rub. Kazakhskii Gosudarstvennyi Universitet, Ul. Lenina 18, Alma-Ata, Kazakhstan. bibl.

100 RU ISSN 0235-1188
B6
FILOSOFSKIE NAUKI (MOSCOW). 1958. bi-m. $75 (effective 1996). Izdatel'stvo Vysshaya Shkola, Neglinnaya ul. 29-14, Moscow, Russia. (Co-sponsor: Ministerstvo Vysshego i Srednego Spetsial'nogo Obrazovaniya) Ed. V.S. Gott. bk.rev.; bibl.; charts; illus.; stat. circ. 6,260. **Indexed:** Lang.& Lang.Behav.Abstr.
   Formerly (until 1987): Nauchnye Doklady Vysshei Shkoly (ISSN 0130-9749)

100 XO ISSN 0046-385X
FILOZOFIA/PHILOSOPHY. (Text in Slovak; summaries in German and Russian) 1946. bi-m. $20. (Slovenska Akademia Vied, Filozoficky Ustav) Veda, Publishing House of the Slovak Academy of Sciences, Klemensova 19, 814 30 Bratislava, Slovakia. (Dist. in Western countries by: John Benjamins B.V., Amsteldijk 44, Amsterdam (Z.), Netherlands) Ed. Vladimir Cirbes. **Indexed:** Bibl.Ling., Lang.& Lang.Behav.Abstr.
   Description: Offers original papers and articles from various spheres of philosophic creation.

100 PL
FILOZOFIA-LOGIKA. 1961. irreg., no.71, 1993. price varies. Adam Mickiewicz University Press, Nowowiejskiego 55, 61-734 Poznan, Poland. TEL 527-380. FAX 61-526425. TELEX 413260 UAM PL. Ed.Bd. bk.rev. circ. 600. **Document type:** academic/scholarly publication.
—BLDSC (9120.458000).
   Formerly: Uniwersytet im. Adama Mickiewicza w Poznaniu. Wydzial Filozoficzno-Historyczny. Prace. Seria Filozofia-Logika (ISSN 0083-4246)
   Description: Contains current research results of the university's scholars, their Ph.D. theses and monographs. Each volume contains the work of one author.

100 CI ISSN 0351-4706
B6
FILOZOFSKA ISTRAZIVANJA.* (Text in Serbo-Croatian) 1980. q. $10. Filozofski Fakultet, Djure Salaja 3, 41000 Zagreb, Croatia. Eds. Hotimir Burger, Ante Covic.
—BLDSC (3926.749800).

100 YU ISSN 0350-106X
FILOZOFSKE STUDIJE. 1975. a. $3 to individuals; institutions $5. Srpsko Filozofsko Drustvo - Philosophical Society of Serbia, Cika Ljubina 18-20, 11000 Belgrade, Serbia, Yugoslavia. TEL 11-638-104. Ed. Vladan Perisic.
   Description: Publishes collection of descriptive, analytical and critical studies in a wide areas of philosophy: metaphysics, ethics, epistemology, logic etc.

100 150 CI ISSN 0352-6798
B1
FILOZOFSKI FAKULTET - ZADAR. RAZDIO FILOZOFIJE, PSIHOLOGIJE, SOCIOLOGIJE I PEDAGOGIJE. RADOVI. (Text in Croatian, English; summaries in English) 1985. a. $20. Filozofski Fakultet u Zadru, Obala Marsala Tita, 2, 57000 Zadar, Croatia. TEL 057-436-623. TELEX 25-882. (Co-sponsor: Samoupravna Interesna Zajednica Znanosti SR Hrvatske) Ed. Katica Lackovic-Grgin. index, cum.index no.1-2. circ. 600. (back issues avail.) **Indexed:** Ling.Abstr.

FOLDGOMB. see *EARTH SCIENCES*

105 938 GR ISSN 1105-221X
FONDATION DE RECHERCHE ET D'EDITIONS DE PHILOSOPHIE NEOHELLENIQUE. SERIE RECHERCHES. (Text in French) 1980. irreg., no.3, 1994. (Fondation de Recherche et d'Editions de Philosophie Neohellenique) Evvengelos Moutsopoulos, Ed. & Pub., 40 Ypsilantou St., 115 21 Athens, Greece. TEL 30-1-725-1212. FAX 30-1-722-7322. **Document type:** monograph series, proceedings.
   Description: Explores the legacy of Platonic and Aristotelian thought in modern Greek history.

FOR A CHANGE; for moral re-armament. see *SOCIAL SCIENCES: COMPREHENSIVE WORKS*

100 001.3 GW ISSN 0933-6990
FORUM FUER INTERDISZIPLINAERE FORSCHUNG. (Text in English and German) 1988. s-a. DM.24. J.H. Roell, Wuerzburgerstr. 16, 97337 Dettelbach, Germany. TEL 09324-1429. Ed.Bd. **Document type:** academic/scholarly publication.

100 US
FORUM TODAY. 3/yr. $10. New Forum, 4176 Greystone, Yorba Linda, CA 92686. Ed. Judith A. Christie. adv.; illus.

100 UK ISSN 0262-8228
FRANCIS BACON RESEARCH TRUST JOURNAL; studies in ancient wisdom. 1981. irreg., latest 1988. price varies (typically set in Jan.). Francis Bacon Research Trust, Roses Farmhouse, Epwell Rd., Upper Tysoe, Warks. CV35 0TN, England. TEL 0129-568-8185. FAX 01295-680770. Ed. Peter Dawkins. **Document type:** academic/scholarly publication.
   Description: Discusses Francis Bacon's life, work, and teachings.

FRANCISCAN STUDIES. see *RELIGIONS AND THEOLOGY* — Roman Catholic

PHILOSOPHY

100 255 CK ISSN 0120-1468
BR7
FRANCISCANUM; revista de las ciencias del espiritu. 1959. 3/yr. Col.7500($25) (effective 1995) Col.$8500($27) (effective 1996). Universidad de San Buenaventura, Transversal 26, No. 172-08, Apdo. Aereo 52312, Bogota, D.E., Colombia. TEL 6775707. FAX 6773003. Ed. Adolfo Galeano A; Pub. Consuelo Lopez. adv.; bk.rev.; bibl.; index, cum.index: 1959-1983. circ. 3,000. **Document type:** academic/scholarly publication.
—BLDSC (4032.790000).
Description: Interdisciplinary studies of religion and philosophy.

100 US ISSN 0272-0701
BL2700
FREE INQUIRY. 1980. q. $28.50. Council for Democratic and Secular Humanism (CODESH Inc.), Box 664, Buffalo, NY 14226. TEL 716-636-1425. FAX 716-636-1733. Ed. Dr. Paul Kurtz. adv. contact: Timothy Madigan. bk.rev.; film rev.; illus.; cum.index: 1980-1986. circ. 23,000. (also avail. in microform from UMI; back issues avail.; reprint service avail. from UMI) **Indexed:** Curr.Lit.Fam.Plan., P.A.I.S., Phil.Ind. **Document type:** consumer publication.
●Also available online. Vendor(s): University Microfilms International.
—BLDSC (4033.321930); Faxon; UMI; UnCover.
Description: Deals with the separation of Church and State and secular humanism. Articles on religion, ethics and moral thought from a secular humanist viewpoint.
Refereed Serial

FREE LIFE. see POLITICAL SCIENCE

144 US
FREE MIND. bi-m. membership. American Humanist Association, 7 Harwood Dr., Box 1188, Amherst, NY 14226-7188. TEL 716-839-5080. FAX 716-839-5079. Ed. Bette Chambers. circ. 4,600. **Document type:** newsletter.
Description: Newsletter of the association providing membership with national, regional and chapter news.

100 US
FREE SPIRIT (BROOKLYN); a directory and journal of new realities. bi-m. $18. Paul English, Ed. & Pub., 107 Sterling Place, Brooklyn, NY 11217. TEL 718-638-3733. FAX 718-230-3459.
Description: Presents articles that illustrate the interconnection and interdependence of all things.

100 320 US
FREEDOM NETWORK NEWS. 1986. q. $20. International Society for Individual Liberty, 1800 Market St., San Francisco, CA 94102. TEL 415-864-0952. FAX 415-864-7506. Ed. Vincent H. Miller. circ. 3,000.
Description: Dedicated to building a free and peaceful world, respect for individual rights and liberties and an open and competitive economic system based on voluntary exchange and free trade.

100 UK ISSN 0016-0687
BL2700
FREETHINKER. 1881. m. £12 (overseas £25). 47 Bradlaugh House, 47 Theobald's Rd., London WC1X 8SP, England. TEL 0171-404-3126. Ed. Peter Brearey. bk.rev. circ. 1,500. (also avail. in microform) **Document type:** academic/scholarly publication.
Description: Devoted to topics of interest to humanists and secularists.

100 200 SZ ISSN 0016-0725
BR45
FREIBURGER ZEITSCHRIFT FUER PHILOSOPHIE UND THEOLOGIE. (Text in French and German) 1914. 2/yr. 60 SFr. (Institut fuer Oekumenische Studien) Editions Saint Paul, Perolles 42, CH-1700 Fribourg, Switzerland. bk.rev.; bibl.; index. circ. 600. **Indexed:** CERDIC, M.L.A., New Test.Abstr., Phil.Ind. **Document type:** academic/scholarly publication.
—Faxon.

100 301 335 GW ISSN 0067-5911
FREIE UNIVERSITAET BERLIN. OSTEUROPA-INSTITUT. PHILOSOPHISCHE UND SOZIOLOGISCHE VEROEFFENTLICHUNGEN. 1959. irreg., vol.28, 1994. price varies. (Freie Universitaet Berlin, Osteuropa-Institut) Harrassowitz Verlag, Taunusstr. 14, 65183 Wiesbaden, Germany. TEL 06121-530-0. FAX 06121-530570. TELEX 4186135. (Subscr. to: Postfach 2929, 65019 Wiesbaden, Germany) Ed.Bd. circ. 500. **Document type:** monographic series.

FREIRELIGIOESE RUNDSCHAU. see RELIGIONS AND THEOLOGY

FRIENDLY WAY. see RELIGIONS AND THEOLOGY — Buddhist

100 340 VE ISSN 1315-6268
▼**FRONESIS**; revista de filosofia juridica, social y politica. (Text in Spanish; abstracts in English, Spanish) 1994. s-a. (Universidad del Zulia, Instituto de Filosofia del Derecho) Ediluz, 4011 Maracaibo, Venezuela. TEL 58-61-424788. FAX 58-61-423913. Ed. Brigitte Bernard. **Document type:** academic/scholarly publication.
Refereed Serial

100 943 GW
G.W. LEIBNIZ: SAEMTLICHE SCHRIFTEN UND BRIEFE. (Text in English, French, German and Latin) 1950. irreg. Akademie Verlag GmbH, Muehlenstr. 33-34, 13187 Berlin, Germany. TEL 030-47889348. FAX 030-47889357. **Document type:** monographic series.
Description: Complete collection of Leibniz's work and correspondence.

GENRE HUMAN. see HUMANITIES: COMPREHENSIVE WORKS

GEORGETOWN JOURNAL OF LEGAL ETHICS. see LAW

GESHER. see RELIGIONS AND THEOLOGY — Judaic

100 IT ISSN 0017-0089
B4
GIORNALE CRITICO DELLA FILOSOFIA ITALIANA. (Text in English, French and Italian) 1920. 3/yr. L.130000. Casa Ed. Le Lettere, Costa S. Giorgio 28, Florence, Italy. (Dist. by: Licosa, Via Duca di Calabria 1-1, 50125 Florence, Italy) Ed. Eugenio Garin. bk.rev.; bibl.; index. circ. 800. **Indexed:** Arts & Hum.Cit.Ind., Curr.Cont., M.L.A.
—BLDSC (4177.600000); Faxon; SWETS.

110 IT ISSN 0017-0372
GIORNALE DI METAFISICA. 1946; N.S. 1979. 3/yr. L.65000 (foreign L.98000) (effective 1994). Tilgher-Genova s.a.s., Via Assarotti 52, 16122 Genoa, Italy. TEL 10-8391140. FAX 10-870653. Ed. Nunzio Incardona. index.

GIST. see RELIGIONS AND THEOLOGY

GLOBAL BIOETHICS; problemi di bioetica. see BIOLOGY

100 CN ISSN 0316-618X
GNOSIS; a journal of philosophic interest. (Text in English, French) 1973. a. Can.$3 to individuals; institutions Can.$5. Concordia University, Philosophy Department, 1455 de Maisonneuve Ouest, Montreal, PQ H3G 1M8, Canada. TEL 514-848-2500. adv.; bk.rev. circ. 150. **Indexed:** Phil.Ind. **Document type:** academic/scholarly publication.
—BLDSC (4196.576000).
Description: Publishes articles on various philosophical subjects, including metaphysics, epistemology, ethics, aesthetics, logic and philosphy of science.
Refereed Serial

100 CI ISSN 0352-3306
GODISNJAK ZA POVIJEST FILOZOFIJE. a. Sveuciliste u Zagrebu, Institut za Povijesne Znanosti, Odjel za Povijest Filozofije, Krcka 1, 41000 Zagreb, Croatia. TEL 041-511-841. Ed.Bd. circ. 800.

100 II
GOKULDAS SANSKRIT SERIES. (Text in English and Sanskrit) no.4, 1975. irreg., no.83, 1990. price varies. Chaukhambha Orientalia, Gokul Bhawan, K 37-109 Gopal Mandir Ln., Varanasi 221001, India.

100 NE ISSN 0165-9227
B20.6
GRAZER PHILOSOPHISCHE STUDIEN; internationale Zeitschrift fuer analytische Philosophie. 1975. s-a. price varies. Editions Rodopi B.V., Keizersgracht 302-304, 1016 EX Amsterdam, Netherlands. TEL 31-20-6227507. FAX 31-20-6380948. E-mail: F.van.der.Zee@Rodopi.nl. (In N. America: 233 Peachtree St. N.E., Ste. 404, Atlanta GA 30303-1504. TEL 800-225-3998. FAX 404-522-7116) Ed. Rudolf Haller. bk.rev. circ. 700. **Document type:** academic/scholarly publication.
—UnCover.
Description: Publishes original papers discussing topics in modern analytical philosophy.

GREEK ORTHODOX THEOLOGICAL REVIEW. see RELIGIONS AND THEOLOGY — Eastern Orthodox

GREGORIANUM. see RELIGIONS AND THEOLOGY — Roman Catholic

H E C FORUM; an interdisciplinary journal on hospitals' ethical and legal issues. (HealthCare Ethics Committee) see HOSPITALS

HANGZHOU SHIFAN XUEYUAN XUEBAO (SHEHUI KEXUE BAN)/HANGZHOU NORMAL COLLEGE. JOURNAL (SOCIAL SCIENCE EDITION). see SOCIAL SCIENCES: COMPREHENSIVE WORKS

HASTINGS CENTER REPORT. see MEDICAL SCIENCES

HEBEI DAXUE XUEBAO (SHEHUI ZHEXUE BAN)/HEBEI UNIVERSITY. JOURNAL (PHILOSOPHY & SOCIAL SCIENCES). see SOCIAL SCIENCES: COMPREHENSIVE WORKS

100 US
HEGEL SOCIETY OF AMERICA. PROCEEDINGS. 1968. irreg. price varies. State University of New York Press, State University Plaza, Albany, NY 12246. TEL 518-472-5000; 800-666-2211. FAX 518-472-5038. (Orders to: S U N Y Press, c/o C U P Services, Box 6525, Ithaca, NY 14851) Ed. Lois Patton; Pub. William Eastman. (back issues avail.) **Document type:** proceedings.
Refereed Serial

100 UK ISSN 0263-5232
B2900
HEGEL SOCIETY OF GREAT BRITAIN. BULLETIN. 1978. 2/yr. £8 to individuals (overseas $17); libraries £12 (overseas $24); students £6. Hegel Society of Great Britain, c/o Howard Williams, Department of International Politics, University College of Wales, Aberystwyth, Dyfed SY23 3DB, Wales. TEL 0970-622707. Ed. Robert Stern. adv.; bk.rev. circ. 300. **Document type:** academic/scholarly publication, bulletin.
—BLDSC (2554.350000); Faxon.
Description: Features articles and reviews on the philosopher G.W.F. Hegel.

190 GW ISSN 0073-1587
HEGEL - STUDIEN. 1955. irreg., vol.28, 1993. price varies. (Deutsche Forschungsgemeinschaft, Hegel Kommission) Bouvier Verlag Herbert Grundmann, Am Hof 28, 53113 Bonn, Germany. TEL 0228-7290124. FAX 0228-7290179. Eds. F. Nicolin, O. Poeggeler. **Indexed:** Arts & Hum.Cit.Ind., Curr.Cont. **Document type:** monographic series.
—SWETS.

140 GW ISSN 0440-5927
HEGEL - STUDIEN BEIHEFTE. 1964. irreg., latest no.34, 1992. free. Bouvier Verlag Herbert Grundmann, Am Hof 28, 53113 Bonn, Germany. TEL 0228-7290124. FAX 0228-7290179. Eds. F. Nicolini, O. Poeggeler. adv.; bk.rev. circ. 1,000. **Document type:** monographic series.
Formerly: Internationale Vereinigung zur Foerderung des Studiums der Hegelschen Philosophie. Veroeffentlichung.

100 GW ISSN 0885-4580
B3279.H49
HEIDEGGER STUDIES. 1985. a. DM.68. Duncker und Humblot GmbH, Postfach 410329, 12113 Berlin, Germany. TEL 030-7900060. FAX 030-79000631. Ed.Bd. adv.; bk.rev.; bibl. (back issues avail.) **Indexed:** Phil.Ind. **Document type:** academic/scholarly publication.
—BLDSC (4283.885000); Faxon.

HENOCH. see LINGUISTICS

PHILOSOPHY

190 378 US
HERMENAUT; the digest of heady philosophy. 1990. q. $10; newsstand price: $2.50. Shapely Mind Press, 3010 Hennepin Ave. S., No. 165, Minneapolis, MN 55408. TEL 612-870-4799. E-mail: Site addr.: www.pwainc.com/hermenaut. (Dist. by: Fine Print, 500 Pampa Dr., Austin, TX 78752) Ed. Joshua Glenn. adv.; page $100; adv. contact: John Cradock. bk.rev.; illus. circ. 5,000.
●Also available online.
   Description: Endeavors to bring difficult but important philosophical ideas to the general public, and at the same time uses philosophical categories and methods to study popular culture in a fun way.

100 US ISSN 1043-5735
HERMENEUTIC COMMENTARIES. irreg. Peter Lang Publishing, Inc., 62 W. 45th St., 4th Fl., New York, NY 10036. TEL 212-302-6740. FAX 212-302-7574. Ed. Pietro Pucci. **Document type:** academic/scholarly publication, monographic series.
   Description: Presents commentaries on classical texts with a strong emphasis on the hermeneutic, rather than on the historical, grammatical or stylistic aspects of the texts.

100 GW ISSN 0440-7563
HESTIA. 1960. biennial. price varies. Bouvier Verlag Herbert Grundmann, Am Hof 28, 53113 Bonn, Germany. TEL 0228-7290124. FAX 0228-7290179. **Document type:** monographic series.

HEYTHROP JOURNAL; a review of philosophy and theology. see *RELIGIONS AND THEOLOGY*

100 613 US ISSN 0891-6144
HIMALAYAN INSTITUTE QUARTERLY GUIDE. 1976. q. free. (Himalayan International Institute of Yoga Science and Philosophy) Himalayan Publishers, RR 1, Box 400, Honesdale, PA 18431. TEL 717-253-5551; 800-444-5772. TELEX 510 600 1805. Ed. Lawrence Clark. adv.; illus. circ. 35,000. **Document type:** bulletin.
   Former titles: Himalayan News; Himalayan (ISSN 0275-9802)
   Description: Guide to programs & other offerings.

HISTOIRE EPISTEMOLOGIE LANGAGE. see *LINGUISTICS*

HISTORIOGRAPHIA LINGUISTICA; international journal for the history of the language sciences. see *LINGUISTICS*

100 UK ISSN 0144-5340
BC1
HISTORY AND PHILOSOPHY OF LOGIC. 1980. q. £139($230) (effective 1996). Taylor & Francis Ltd., Rankine Rd., Basingstoke, Hants. RG24 8PR, England. TEL 44-1256-840366. FAX 44-1256-479438. TELEX 858540. E-mail: info@tandf.co.uk. (Subscr. in N. America to: Taylor & Francis Inc., 1900 Frost Rd., Ste. 101, Bristol, PA 19007-1598. TEL 800-821-8312. FAX 215-785-5515) Ed. Peter Simons. bk.rev. **Indexed:** Math.R. **Document type:** academic/scholarly publication.
   —BLDSC (4317.823000); Faxon; Genuine Article; SWETS; UnCover. **CCC**.
   Description: Concerned with general philosophical questions on logic: existential and ontological aspects, the relationship between classical and nonclassical logics, and the connections between logic and other fields of knowledge, such as mathematics, philosophy of science, epistemology, linguistics, psychology and computing.
   Refereed Serial

HISTORY AND PHILOSOPHY OF THE LIFE SCIENCES. see *BIOLOGY*

HISTORY AND THEORY; studies in the philosophy of history. see *HISTORY*

190.09 UK ISSN 0191-6599
D1
HISTORY OF EUROPEAN IDEAS. 1980. m. £445($708) (effective 1996). (International Society for the Study of European Ideas) Elsevier Science Ltd., Pergamon, P.O. Box 800, Kidlington, Oxford OX5 1DX, England. TEL 44-1865-843000. FAX 44-1865-843010. E-mail: nlinfo-f@elsevier.nl; usinfo-f@elsevier.com; forinfo-kyf04035@niftyserve.or.jp; Site addr.: http://www.elsevier.nl/. (Subscr. in U.S. and Canada to: Elsevier Science, 660 White Plains Rd., Tarrytown, NY 10591-5153. TEL 914-524-9200. FAX 914-333-2444) (Co-sponsor: European Cultural Foundation) Ed. Ezra Talmor, Sascha Talmor. adv.; bk.rev. (also avail. in microfilm from UMI; back issues avail.; reprint service avail. from UMI) **Indexed:** Amer.Hist.& Life, Arts & Hum.Cit.Ind., ASSIA, Curr.Cont., Hist.Abstr., Int.Polit.Sci.Abstr., Lang.& Lang.Behav.Abstr., Phil.Ind., Sociol.Abstr. **Document type:** academic/scholarly publication.
   —BLDSC (4318.138000); Faxon; Genuine Article; SWETS; UMI; UnCover. **CCC**.
   Description: Multidisciplinary journal covering the study of history of the cultural exchange between European nations, the influence of this exchange on the formation of European ideas and emergence of the idea of Europe.
   Refereed Serial

100 US ISSN 0740-0675
HISTORY OF PHILOSOPHY QUARTERLY. 1984. q. $38 to individuals; institutions $148. Bowling Green State University, Philosophy Documentation Center, Bowling Green, OH 43403-0189. TEL 419-372-2419; 800-444-2419. FAX 419-372-6987. Ed. Nicholas Rescher. circ. 500. **Indexed:** Phil.Ind. **Document type:** academic/scholarly publication.
   —BLDSC (4318.394500); Faxon; UnCover.

HISTORY OF POLITICAL THOUGHT; controversies in science & the humanities. see *POLITICAL SCIENCE*

HISTORY OF WOMEN PHILOSOPHERS. see *WOMEN'S STUDIES*

100 330.1 NE ISSN 0921-5891
HOBBES STUDIES. (Text in English, French, German) 1988. a. fl.70 (effective 1994). (Ben Gurion University of the Negev, IS) Van Gorcum en Co. B.V., P.O. Box 43, 9400 AA Assen, Netherlands. TEL 31-5920-46864. FAX 31-5920-72064. Ed. Timo Airaksinen. adv.; bk.rev. circ. 600. **Document type:** academic/scholarly publication.
   —BLDSC (4319.813000).

HOSPITAL ETHICS. see *HOSPITALS*

181.11 CH ISSN 0018-6937
HSIN JU CHIA/NEW CONFUCIANS. (Text in Chinese and English) 1967. m. $25. New Confucians Book Store, P.O. Box 22239, Taipei, Taiwan, Republic of China. Ed. Chien-Fu Chen. bk.rev.; index. circ. 1,000.
   Description: Religious essays devoted to Neo-Confucianism.

HUGINN AND MUNINN; interstellar messenger. see *PARAPSYCHOLOGY AND OCCULTISM*

170 SW ISSN 1101-0703
HUMAN-ETIK. 1979. bi-m. SEK 300 membership. Human - Etiska Foerbundet, P.O. box 108, S-694 23 Hallsberg, Sweden. TEL 46-582-105-82. FAX 46-582-105-82.
   Former titles (until 1989): H E F - Eko (ISSN 0283-152X); (until 1982): H E F - Nytt.
   Description: Focuses on different ethical questions from a non-religious perspective.

100 NE ISSN 0163-8548
B1 CODEN: HUSTDT
HUMAN STUDIES; a journal for philosophy and the social sciences. (Test in English) 1978. q. fl.408 to institutions; $261 to institutions in U.S. (effective 1996). Kluwer Academic Publishers, Postbus 17, 3300 AA Dordrecht, Netherlands. TEL 31-78-392392. FAX 31-78-392254. TELEX 29245 KAPG NL. E-mail: services@wkap.nl. (Dist. by: Kluwer Academic Publishing Group, P.O. Box 322, 3300 AH Dordrecht, Netherlands. TEL 31-78-392392. FAX 31-78-546474; N. America dist. addr.: Box 358, Accord Sta., Hingham, MA 02018-0358. TEL 617-871-6600. FAX 617-871-6528) Ed. George Psathas. adv.; bk.rev.; index. circ. 500. (also avail. in microform from UMI; back issues avail.; reprint service avail. from ISI,SWZ) **Indexed:** ASCA, Curr.Cont., IMFL, Lang.& Lang.Behav.Abstr., M.L.A., Phil.Ind., SSCI, Stud.Wom.Abstr. **Document type:** academic/scholarly publication.
   —BLDSC (4336.467000); Faxon; Genuine Article; SWETS; UMI; UnCover. **CCC**.
   Description: Provides a forums for discussion of issues relating to the dialogue between philosophy and the human sciences, such as the logic of inquiry, methodology, epistemology and fundamental issues.
   Refereed Serial

100 300 US ISSN 0733-5563
HUMANE STUDIES REVIEW. 1980. 3/yr. $5. (Institute for Humane Studies) George Mason University, 4084 University Dr., Ste. 101, Fairfax, VA 22030. TEL 703-934-6920. Ed. Brad Young. bk.rev.; bibl. circ. 8,000. (back issues avail.; reprint service avail.)
   Description: Covers themes relevant to the tradition of classical liberalism.

HUMANES LEBEN - HUMANES STERBEN. see *MEDICAL SCIENCES*

170 NE ISSN 0025-9489
HUMANIST. 1945. 9/yr. fl.42.50. Humanistisch Verbond, Postbus 114, 3500 AC Utrecht, Netherlands. TEL 31-30-318145. FAX 31-30-361704. adv.; bk.rev.; film rev.; play rev.; illus. circ. 18,000. **Indexed:** Acad.Ind., Mid.East: Abstr.& Ind. **Document type:** consumer publication.
   Formerly: Mens en Wereld.

100 US ISSN 0018-7399
B821.A1
HUMANIST. 1941. bi-m. $24.95. American Humanist Association, 7 Harwood Dr., Box 1188, Amherst, NY 14226-7188. TEL 716-839-5080. FAX 716-839-5079. Eds. Fred Edwards. adv.; bk.rev.; illus.; index. circ. 15,000. (also avail. in microform from UMI; back issues avail.; reprint service avail. from UMI) **Indexed:** Acad.Ind., Bk.Rev.Ind. (1978-), C.I.J.E., CERDIC, Chic.Per.Ind., Child.Bk.Rev.Ind. (1978-), Except.Child.Educ.Abstr., Film Lit.Ind. (1973-), Fut.Surv., Hum.Ind., Human Resour.Abstr., Lang.& Lang.Behav.Abstr., Mag.Ind., Media Rev.Dig., P.A.I.S., Per.Islam., Phil.Ind., PMR, R.G., SSCI.
●Also available online. Vendor(s): University Microfilms International.
   —BLDSC (4336.519000); Faxon; SWETS; UMI; UnCover.
   Description: Nontheistic, secular and naturalistic approach to broad areas of personal, scientific and philosophical concern.

170 NO ISSN 0801-6283
HUMANIST. 1975. 6/yr. Human - Etisk Forbund, P.O. Box 2870 Toeyen, N-608 Oslo 6, Norway.
   Formerly (until 1987): Human-Etikk (ISSN 0332-5970)
   Description: Contains articles, interviews and debates on outlook on life, morals, and faith.

PHILOSOPHY

144   CN   ISSN 0018-7402
HUMANIST IN CANADA. 1967. q. Can.$15 (foreign Can.$16) (effective 1995-96). Canadian Humanist Publications, P.O. Box 3769, Station C, Ottawa, ON K1Y 4J8, Canada. TEL 613-722-4652. FAX 613-749-8929. Pub. J.E. Piercy. adv.: B&W page $200; adv. contact: Dan Morrison. bk.rev.; abstr.; bibl.; charts; illus.; stat.; index, cum.index; circ. 1,500 (paid). (also avail. in microfilm from UMI; reprint service avail. from UMI) Indexed: Alt.Press Ind., Can.B.P.I., Can.Wom.Per.Ind., CMI. **Document type:** consumer publication.
—UMI.
   Formed by the merger of: Montreal Humanist; Victoria Humanist.
   Description: Discusses divergent views and topics covering a large spectrum of human interest from a non-religious perspective.

144   UK   ISSN 0953-1327
HUMANIST NEWS. 1965. bi-m. £15. British Humanist Association, 47 Thwobalds Rd., London WC1X 8SP, England. TEL 0171-430-0908. FAX 0171-430-1274. Ed. Donna Pickrell. adv.; bk.rev.; illus.; circ. 5,000 (paid). (looseleaf format) **Document type:** newsletter.
   Former titles: Humanist Newsletter; Humanist News (ISSN 0018-7410)
   Description: Examines moral issues from a nonreligious viewpoint.

144   US   ISSN 1054-9633
HUMANIST NEWS & VIEWS. 1986. m. $15. Humanist Association of Minneapolis and St. Paul, 4418 Josephine La., Robbinsdale, MN 55422-1328. TEL 612-537-1992. Ed. George Erickson; Pub. Dennis Griebenow. adv.; bk.rev. circ. 400. (also avail. in microfilm) **Document type:** newsletter.
   Description: Aims to promote a positive philosophy: a better life for all through education, democracy, free speech, reason, and science, without reliance on arbitrary dogmas, revelations and faiths.

144   II   ISSN 0018-7429
HUMANIST OUTLOOK. (Text in English) 1966. q. Rs.50($10) Indian Humanist Union, P.O. Box 448, New Delhi 110 001, India. TEL 011-371-8109. FAX 011-371-8109. Ed. Prakash Narain. adv.; bk.rev.; bibl. circ. 400.
   Description: Aims to promote human values through an ethics based on human perceptions examined in a spirit of free enquiry.

144   AT
HUMANIST POST. m. Aus.$4. Humanist Society of South Australia, Inc., 2 Almond Court, Vale Park, S.A. 5081, Australia.

HUMANIST VIEWPOINTS. see *POLITICAL SCIENCE — Civil Rights*

144   GW   ISSN 0046-824X
HUMANISTISCHE UNION. MITTEILUNGEN. no.49, 1971. q. membership. Humanistische Union e.V., Braeuhausstr. 2, 80331 Munich, Germany. TEL 089-226441. FAX 089-226442. Ed. Helga Killinger. adv.; bk.rev. circ. 3,200. **Document type:** newsletter.

HUMANITAS; strucni casopis studenata Univerziteta u Nisu. see *SOCIAL SCIENCES: COMPREHENSIVE WORKS*

HUMANITIES, CHRISTIANITY AND CULTURE. see *HUMANITIES: COMPREHENSIVE WORKS*

100   US   ISSN 0319-7336
B1450
HUME STUDIES. 1975. 2/yr. $15 to individuals (foreign $20); institutions $30 (foreign $35). Hume Society, 338 Orson Spencer Hall, University of Utah, Salt Lake City, UT 84112. TEL 801-581-8161. FAX 801-585-5195. E-mail: hume@cc.utah.edu. Eds. Don Garrett, William E. Morris. bk.rev.; circ. 250 (paid). (also avail. in microfilm; back issues avail.) Indexed: Amer.Hist.& Life, Hist.Abstr., Phil.Ind. **Document type:** academic/scholarly publication.
—BLDSC (4336.650000); Faxon; UnCover.
   Description: An interdisciplinary journal dedicated to publishing important work bearing on the thought of David Hume.
   Refereed Serial

100   US
HUNA WORK. 1948. q. $25. Huna Research, Inc., 126 Camellia Dr., Cape Girardeau, MO 63703-5722. TEL 314-334-3478. (And: 1760 Anna St., Cape Girardeau, MO 63701-4504) Ed. E. Otha Wingo. bk.rev. circ. 1,300. (back issues avail.)

190   NE   ISSN 0167-9848
B3279.H94   CODEN: HUSTEU
HUSSERL STUDIES. (Text in English and German) 1984. 3/yr. fl.322 to institutions; $207 to institutions in U.S. (effective 1996). Kluwer Academic Publishers, Postbus 17, 3300 AA Dordrecht, Netherlands. TEL 31-78-392392. FAX 31-78-392254. TELEX 29245 KAPG NL. E-mail: SERVICES@WAKP.NL. (Dist. by: Kluwer Academic Publishers Group, P.O. Box 322, 3300 AH Dordrecht, Netherlands. TEL 31-78-392392. FAX 31-78-546474; N. America dist. addr.: Box 358, Accord Sta., Hingham, MA 02018-0358. TEL 617-871-6600. FAX 617-871-6528) Eds. William R. McKenna, Karl Schuhmann. adv.; bk.rev. (also avail. in microform from UMI; back issues avail.; reprint service avail. from SWZ) Indexed: Arts & Hum.Cit.Ind., ASCA, Curr.Cont., Phil.Ind. **Document type:** academic/scholarly publication.
—Faxon; Genuine Article; SWETS; UMI; UnCover. **CCC.**
   Description: Emphasizes the relevance of Husserl's phenomenology for contemporary philosophy and the wider academic field.
   Refereed Serial

100   NE   ISSN 0439-9714
HUSSERLIANA. (Text in English, German) 1950. irreg., latest 1991. price varies. (Centre d'Archives Husserl, BE) Kluwer Academic Publishers, Postbus 17, 3300 AA Dordrecht, Netherlands. TEL 31-78-392392. FAX 31-78-392254. TELEX 29245 KAPG NL. (Dist. by: Kluwer Academic Publishers Group, P.O. Box 322, 3300 AH Dordrecht, Netherlands. TEL 31-78-392392. FAX 31-78-546474; N. America dist. addr.: Box 358, Accord Sta., Hingham, MA 02018-0358. TEL 617-871-6600) **Document type:** academic/scholarly publication, monograph series.
   Refereed Serial

100 323.4   US
HYPERBOREAN. 1990. bi-m. $11. Hyperborean Micropublishers, 2024 N. Manor Dr., Erie, PA 16505. TEL 814-456-6819. Ed. Richard Gaska. circ. 200. (also avail. in microfiche; back issues avail.)
   Description: Contains original and reprinted articles of interest to freethinkers, anarchists and libertarians.

HYPOMNEMATA; Untersuchungen zur Antike und zu ihrem Nachleben. see *CLASSICAL STUDIES*

170 628 610   UK
IAN RAMSEY CENTRE. PUBLICATIONS. no.2, 1989. irreg. Saint Cross College, University of Oxford, Ian Ramsey Centre, Environmental Ethics Working Party, St. Giles, Oxford OX1 3LZ, England. (Orders to: The Principal's Secretary, Westminster College, Oxford OX2 9AT, England) (Co-sponsor: University of Wales, College of Cardiff, Centre for Applied Statistics)
   Description: Studies ethical problems arising from scientific and medical research and practice; examines the underlying philosophical and theological issues.

100   US   ISSN 0046-8541
B823
IDEALISTIC STUDIES; international philosophical journal. 1971. 3/yr. $12 to individuals; libraries $25. c/o Walter E. Wright, Ed., Dept. of Philosophy, Clark University, Worcester, MA 01610. TEL 508-793-7414. adv.; bk.rev.; bibl.; index. circ. 600. Indexed: Arts & Hum.Cit.Ind., Curr.Cont., Phil.Ind.
—BLDSC (4362.382500); Faxon; Genuine Article; UnCover.

100   CK   ISSN 0120-0062
IDEAS Y VALORES. 1951. 3/yr. exchange basis. Universidad Nacional de Colombia, Departamento de Filosofia, Apdo. Aereo 14490, Ciudad Universitaria, Bogota, Colombia. TEL 2442794. Dir. Magdalena Holguin. bk.rev. circ. 1,500.
   Formerly: Ideas.
   Description: Includes articles on study and research in the field of philosophy.

121   US
IF LIFE, THEN ONE AMONG AT LEAST FOUR. 1975. m. $25. Horace Oliver, Jr., Ed. & Pub., Box 282, Palisades Park, NJ 07650-0282. TEL 201-947-3587. circ. 100.
   Description: Covers epistemology.

100   US   ISSN 0378-4789
B1
INDEPENDENT JOURNAL OF PHILOSOPHY/REVUE INDEPENDANTE DE PHILOSOPHIE. (Text in English, French, German) 1977. irreg. $22.50 to individuals; institutions $75 (effective 1995). George Elliott Tucker, Ed. & Pub., 87 Metacomet St., Belchertown, MA 01007-9795. adv.; bk.rev.; bibl. circ. 700. (back issues avail.) Indexed: Phil.Ind. **Document type:** academic/scholarly publication.
—UnCover.

100   II   ISSN 0019-4271
INDIAN ACADEMY OF PHILOSOPHY. JOURNAL. (Text in English) 1962. s-a. Rs.40($12) (effective since 1988). Indian Academy of Philosophy, Belgachia-Villa, Block F, Flat 8, Calcutta 37, India. Ed.Bd. bk.rev.; bibl.
—UnCover.

100   II   ISSN 0376-4109
INDIAN PHILOSOPHICAL ANNUAL. 1967. a. price varies. University of Madras, Radhakrishnan Institute for Advanced Study in Philosophy, Chepauk, Triplicane P.O., Madras 600 005, Tamil Nadu, India. TEL 91-44-568778. FAX 91-44-566693. TELEX 41 6376 UNOM IN. (And: Publications Division, University of Madras, Madras 600 005, India) Ed. T.S. Devadoss. circ. 300. (back issues avail.)
—BLDSC (4426.200000).
   Description: Publishes the proceedings of the institute's seminars and symposia. Contains a separate section for the publication of special articles.

100   II   ISSN 0376-415X
B130
INDIAN PHILOSOPHICAL QUARTERLY. 1973. q. $50 (effective 1994). University of Poona, Department of Philosophy, Ganeshkhind, Poona 411 007, India. TEL 336061. (Co-sponsor: Pratap Centre of Philosophy, Amalner) Ed. M.P. Marathe. adv.; bk.rev. circ. 800. Indexed: Curr.Cont., Ind.Bk.Rev.Hum., Phil.Ind. **Document type:** academic/scholarly publication.
—BLDSC (4426.300000).
   Supersedes: Philosophical Quarterly.

181.4   NE   ISSN 0924-8986
INDIAN THOUGHT. 1990. irreg., vol.5, 1993. price varies. E.J. Brill, P.O. Box 9000, 2300 PA Leiden, Netherlands. TEL 31-71-5353500. FAX 31-71-5317532. TELEX 39296 BRILL NL. (In N. America: E.J. Brill, 24 Hudson St., Kinderhook, NY 12106. TEL 800-962-4406. FAX 518-758-1959) Ed. Purusottama Billimoria. (back issues avail.) **Document type:** monographic series.
   Formerly (until 1992): Indian Thought and Culture (ISSN 0926-9703)
   Description: Scholarly studies of Indian philosophy, including analysis of Western philosophy from an Indian philosophical perspective.
   Refereed Serial

INDIVIDUAL LIBERTY. see *POLITICAL SCIENCE*

141.4   US   ISSN 0034-0030
INDIVIDUALIST.* 1968. m. $7.50. Society for Individual Liberty, Box 1147, Warminster, PA 18974. Ed. Jarret B. Wollstein. adv.; bk.rev.; film rev.; illus. circ. 2,000.
   Formerly: Rational Individualist.

INDO-IRANIAN JOURNAL. see *ORIENTAL STUDIES*

160   CN   ISSN 0824-2577
                     CODEN: INLOEA
INFORMAL LOGIC. 1978. 3/yr. Can.$30($30) to individuals; institutions Can.$50($50) (students Can.$15). Department of Philosophy, University of Windsor, Windsor, ON N9B 3P4, Canada. TEL 519-253-4232. FAX 519-973-7050. E-mail: infolog@uwindsor.ca. Eds. J.A. Blair, R.H. Johnson. adv. contact: Mark Letterl. bk.rev.; circ. 300 (controlled). (back issues avail.) **Document type:** academic/scholarly publication.
—BLDSC (4481.284000); UnCover. **CCC.**
   Description: Publishes articles which advance the dialectic in reasoning and argumentation in theory and practice.

PHILOSOPHY

100   **GW**
INFORMATION PHILOSOPHIE. 1972. bi-m. DM.54($39) Verlag Claudia Moser, Hauptstr. 42, 79540 Loerrach, Germany. TEL 07621-87125. Ed. Peter Moser. adv.; bk.rev. circ. 3,800. (reprint service avail.) **Document type:** academic/scholarly publication.

100   **IT**
INFORMAZIONE FILOSOFICA. bi-m. (5/yr.). L.45000 (students L.35000) (effective 1994). Istituto Lombardo per gli Studi Filosofici e Giuridici, Viale Monte Nero 68, 20135 Milan, Italy. TEL 02-55190714. FAX 02-5404319. (Co-sponsor: Istituto Italiano per gli Studi Filosofici) Ed. Riccardo Ruschi. (also avail. in diskette format)

100 300   **NO**   **ISSN 0020-174X**
INQUIRY; an interdisciplinary journal of philosophy. (Text in English) 1958. q. NOK 695 in Nordic countries; elsewhere $129 (effective 1996). Scandinavian University Press, P.O. Box 2959 Toeyen, N-0608 Oslo, Norway. TEL 47-22-57-54-00. FAX 47-22-57-53-53. (U.S. addr.: Scandinavian University Press, 200 Meachan Ave., Elmont, NY 11003. TEL 516-352-7300) Ed. Alastair Hannay. adv.; bk.rev.; index. circ. 1,000. (also avail. in microform from UMI; back issues avail.; reprint service avail. from ISI) **Indexed:** Amer.Hist.& Life, Arts & Hum.Cit.Ind., ASCA, Curr.Cont., Hist.Abstr., Ind.Bk.Rev.Hum., Int.Polit.Sci.Abstr., Lang.& Lang.Behav.Abstr., Med.Care Rev., Phil.Ind., Soc.Work Res.& Abstr., Soc.Work Res.& Abstr., Sociol.Abstr., SOPODA. **Document type:** academic/scholarly publication. —BLDSC (4516.200000); Faxon; Genuine Article; SWETS; UMI; UnCover. **CCC.**
    Description: Publishes scholarly articles, discussions and review discussions in all areas of philosophy.

INSTITUT INTERNATIONAL J. MARITAIN. NOTES ET DOCUMENTS; pour une recherche personnaliste - for a personalist approach. see POLITICAL SCIENCE

INSTITUT PIERRE BAYLE. STUDIES. see HISTORY — History Of Europe

100   **US**   **ISSN 1067-2478**
H1
INSTITUTE FOR PHILOSOPHY AND PUBLIC POLICY. REPORT. 1981. q. free. Institute for Philosophy and Public Policy, 3rd Fl., Van Munching Hall, University of Maryland, College Park, MD 20742. TEL 301-405-4753. FAX 301-314-9346. Ed. Arthur Evenchik. circ. 10,000. (back issues avail.) **Document type:** academic/scholarly publication.
    Description: Covers philosophical debate on current public policy choices.

INSTITUTE OF ASIAN STUDIES. JOURNAL. see SOCIOLOGY

INSTITUTO DE FILOSOFIA DEL DERECHO DR. JOSE MANUEL DELGADO OCANDO. BOLETIN. see LAW

INSTITUTO DE FILOSOFIA DEL DERECHO DR. JOSE MANUEL DELGADO OCANDO. REVISTA. see LAW

INSTITUTO DE FILOSOFIA DEL DERECHO DR. JOSE MANUEL DELGADO OCANDO. COLECCION DE CURSOS Y LECCIONES. see LAW

INSTITUTO DE FILOSOFIA DEL DERECHO DR. JOSE MANUEL DELGADO OCANDO. COLECCION DE MONOGRAFIAS. see LAW

INSTITUTO DE FILOSOFIA DEL DERECHO DR. JOSE MANUEL DELGADO OCANDO. CUADERNO DE TRABAJO. see LAW

100   **PO**
INSTITUTO NACIONAL DE INVESTIGACAO CIENTIFICA. TEXTOS CLASSICOS. irreg., no.11, 1981. (Instituto Nacional de Investigacao Cientifica, Centro de Linguistica) Universidade de Coimbra, Centro de Estudos Clasicos y Humanisticos, Faculdade de Letras, Coimbra, Portugal.

INTEGRAL. see MUSIC

100   **US**   **ISSN 0730-2355**
THE INTELLECTUAL ACTIVIST; an Objectivist review. 1979. bi-m. $24. T I A Publications, Inc., Box 262, Lincroft, NJ 07738-0262. TEL 908-842-6610. FAX 908-842-6381. E-mail: tia@osg.com. Ed. Robert W. Stubblefield. adv. contact: Robert W. Stubblefield. bk.rev.; circ. 5,000 (paid). (back issues avail.) **Document type:** academic/scholarly publication.
    Description: Contains articles that offer rational ideas on topics of philosophical significance.

INTERBEHAVIORIST; a quarterly newsletter of interbehavior psychology. see PSYCHOLOGY

100 800   **MR**
INTERDISCIPLINARITE ETUDES PHILOSOPHIQUES ET LITTERAIRES. N.S. 1977. s-a. DH.30 (students DH.15). Societe de Philosophie du Maroc, B.P. 25, Temara, Morocco. Ed. F. Jamai-Lahbabi. bk.rev. circ. 4,000.
    Formerly (until 1984): Etudes Philosophiques et Litteraires (ISSN 0531-1934)

160 401   **GW**   **ISSN 0945-9103**
INTEREST GROUP IN PURE AND APPLIED LOGICS. BULLETIN. 1993. irreg. (European Foundation for Logic, Language and Information, UK) Interest Group in Pure and Applied Logics, c/o Max-Planck-Institut fuer Informatik, Im Stadtwald, 66123 Saarbruecken, Germany. E-mail: igpl-request@doc.ic.ac.uk. (Editorial addr.: Department of Computing, Imperial College, 180 Queen's Gate, London SW7 2BZ, England. TEL 0171-225-8447. FAX 0171-581-8024) Ed. Dov M. Gabbay. **Document type:** academic/scholarly publication.
● Also available online.
—BLDSC (2556.255000).
    Description: Publishes papers in all areas of pure and applied logic, including pure logical systems, proof theory, nonclassical logics, nonmonotonic logics, numerical and uncertainty reasoning, logic and artificial intelligence, foundations of logic programming, logic and computation, logic and language, and logic engineering.
    Refereed Serial

212.5   **IS**
INTERNATIONAL ASSOCIATION FOR THE DEVELOPMENT OF CONSCIOUSNESS. INFORMATION BULLETIN. (Text in Hebrew) m. International Association for the Development of Consciousness, P.O. Box 4983, Haifa, Israel. TEL 04-642104.

INTERNATIONAL BIBLIOGRAPHY OF AUSTRIAN PHILOSOPHY/INTERNATIONALE BIBLIOGRAPHIE ZUR OESTERREICHISCHEN PHILOSOPHIE. see PHILOSOPHY — Abstracting, Bibliographies, Statistics

100   **US**   **ISSN 0074-4603**
B35
INTERNATIONAL DIRECTORY OF PHILOSOPHY AND PHILOSOPHERS. 1965. biennial, 8th ed., 1994. $99 (effective 1994). Bowling Green State University, Philosophy Documentation Center, Bowling Green, OH 43403-0189. TEL 419-372-2419; 800-444-2419. FAX 419-372-6987. Eds. Ramona Cormier, Richard H. Lineback. circ. 700. **Document type:** directory.
    Description: Covers philosophy in 119 countries, including philosophy departments, centers and institutes, societies, publishers and philosophy journals.

170   **NE**   **ISSN 0074-6258**
INTERNATIONAL HUMANIST AND ETHICAL UNION. PROCEEDINGS OF THE CONGRESS. 1952. irreg., 13th, 1993, Berlin. fl.30. International Humanist and Ethical Union, Nieuwegracht 69a, 3512 LG Utrecht, Netherlands. TEL 31-30-312155. FAX 31-30-364169. circ. 1,500. **Document type:** proceedings.

100   **UK**   **ISSN 0929-4589**
B821.A1
INTERNATIONAL HUMANIST NEWS. 1952. q. fl.30($15) International Humanist and Ethical Union, c/o Jim Herrick, Ed., 47 Theobald's Rd., London WC1X 8SP, England. TEL 0171-4301371. FAX 0171-4301271. (Subscr. to: International Humanist and Ethical Union, Nieuwegracht 69a. 3512 LG Utrecht, Netherlands. TEL 31-30-312155. FAX 31-20-364169) circ. 2,000. **Document type:** academic/scholarly publication.
    Former titles: International Humanist (ISSN 0925-1375); International Humanism (ISSN 0020-692X)

100   **FR**   **ISSN 0074-6525**
INTERNATIONAL INSTITUTE OF PHILOSOPHY. ACTES. (Proceedings published in host country) (Text in English, French or German) 1955. a. International Institute of Philosophy - Institut International de Philosophie, 8 rue Jean-Calvin, 75005 Paris, France. TEL 33-1-43-36-39-11. **Document type:** proceedings.

INTERNATIONAL JOURNAL FOR PHILOSOPHY OF RELIGION. see RELIGIONS AND THEOLOGY

770   **UK**   **ISSN 0967-2559**
B1
INTERNATIONAL JOURNAL OF PHILOSOPHICAL STUDIES. 1993. s-a. £28 (U.S. and Canada $45; rest of world £32) to individuals; institutions £55 (U.S. and Canada $85 rest of world £60). Routledge, 11 New Fetter Ln., London EC4P 4EE, England. TEL 0171-583-9855. FAX 0171-842-2298. E-mail: sample.journals@routledge.com. (Subscr. to: ITPS Ltd., Cheriton House, Andover, Hants SP10 5BE, England. TEL 01264-342919. FAX 01264-342807) Ed. Dermot Moran. adv.: page £150; trim 115 x 190. **Document type:** academic/scholarly publication.
—BLDSC (4542.454450); Faxon; SWETS. **CCC.**

198.0   **DK**   **ISSN 0108-3104**
B4370.A1
INTERNATIONAL KIERKEGAARD NEWSLETTER. 1979. a. free. Julia Watkin, Ed. & Pub., Stenagervej 15, DK-2900 Hellerup, Denmark. adv.; bk.rev. circ. 1,000. (back issues avail.) **Indexed:** Phil.Ind. **Document type:** academic/scholarly publication, newsletter.

100   **US**   **ISSN 0019-0365**
B1
INTERNATIONAL PHILOSOPHICAL QUARTERLY. 1961. q. $22 to individuals; institutions $35. Foundation for International Philosophical Exchange, Fordham University, Bronx, NY 10458. TEL 718-817-4776. FAX 718-817-4785. E-mail: IPQ@MURRAY.FORDHAM.EDU. Ed. Joseph W. Koterski, S.J. adv. contact: Sara Penella. bk.rev.; index; circ. 1,600 (paid). (also avail. in microform from UMI; reprint service avail. from UMI) **Indexed:** Amer.Bibl.Slavic & E.Eur.Stud., Arts & Hum.Cit.Ind., Bibl.Engl.Lang.& Lit., Bk.Rev.Ind. (1976-), Cath.Ind., Child.Bk.Rev.Ind. (1976-), Curr.Cont., Hum.Ind., Ind.Bk.Rev.Hum., Mid.East: Abstr.& Ind., Phil.Ind., SSCI. **Document type:** academic/scholarly publication. —BLDSC (4544.924800); Faxon; Genuine Article; SWETS; UMI; UnCover.
    Description: Scholarly research articles on contemporary creative, critical, and historical expression in the intercultural tradition of theistic, spiritualistic, and personalistic humanism.

100   **US**   **ISSN 0270-5664**
B1
INTERNATIONAL STUDIES IN PHILOSOPHY; an international journal of general philosophic inquiry. (Text occasionally in French, German or Italian) 1969. q. $35 to individuals; institutions $55. (State University of New York at Binghamton) Scholars Press, Box 15399, Atlanta, GA 30333-0399. TEL 404-727-2320. FAX 404-727-2348. (Subscr. to: Department of Philosophy, State University of New York at Binghamton, Binghamton, NY 13901) Eds. Leon Goldstein, Stephen Ross. bk.rev.; bibl. **Indexed:** Curr.Cont., Phil.Ind. **Document type:** academic/scholarly publication. —BLDSC (4549.794300); Faxon; Genuine Article; UnCover.
    Formerly: Studi Internazionali di Filosofia (ISSN 0039-2979)
    Description: Academic journal in philosophy.

PHILOSOPHY

215   UK   ISSN 0269-8595
INTERNATIONAL STUDIES IN THE PHILOSOPHY OF SCIENCE. 1987. 3/yr. £54 to individuals; institutions £154 (effective 1996). Carfax Publishing Co., P.O. Box 25, Abingdon, Oxon. OX14 3UE, England. TEL 01235-555335. FAX 01235-553559. (Subscr. in N. America to: Carfax Publishing Co., 875-81 Massachusetts Ave., Cambridge, MA 02139) Ed. W.H. Newton Smith. **Document type:** academic/scholarly publication.
—BLDSC (4549.794400); Faxon; SWETS; UMI. **CCC.**
Formerly: International Studies in the Philosophy of Science - the Dubrovnik Papers.
Description: Publishes articles by scholars of diverse nationalities on all aspects of the philosophy of science.
Refereed Serial

181.45 294.5   US   ISSN 0277-092X
B132.Y6
INTERNATIONAL YOGA GUIDE. 1962. m. $15 (foreign $26). Yoga Research Foundation, 6111 S.W. 74th Ave., Miami, FL 33143. TEL 305-666-2006. Ed. Swami Lalitananda; Pub. Swami Jyotirmayananda. circ. 2,500.
Description: Contains timeless articles on yoga, Vedanta, philosophy, and the scientific explanation of mysticism. Provides enlightened examination of religious scriptures of the world, especially Hinduism.

160   IT
INTERPRETAZIONI; collana di filosofia. irreg., latest vol.23. price varies. Edizioni Studium, Via Cassiodoro 14, 00193 Rome, Italy. Ed. Armando Rigobello. **Document type:** monograph series.

INTERVENTI CLASSENSI. see *ART*

100   PK   ISSN 0021-0773
BP80.I6
IQBAL REVIEW. Urdu edition: Iqbaliat. (Editions in Arabic, English, Persian, Turkish and Urdu) 1960. s-a. (English & Urdu eds.); a. (Arabic, Persian & Turkish eds.). $15 to institutions. Iqbal Academy Pakistan, 116 McLeod Rd., Lahore, Pakistan. TEL 92-42-7357214. FAX 92-42-381468. Ed. Dr. W. Quraishi. adv.; bk.rev. circ. 1,000. **Indexed:** M.L.A. **Document type:** academic/scholarly publication.
—BLDSC (4567.502000).
Description: Publishes research on the life, poetry and thought of the poet-philosopher Muhammad Iqbal, and disseminates his literary, political, philosophical and religious ideas.

100   UK   ISSN 0266-9080
IRISH PHILOSOPHICAL JOURNAL. 1984. a. £5 to individuals; institutions £15. c/o Dr. Bernard Cullen, Dept. of Scholastic Philosophy, Queen's University, Belfast BT7 1NN, N. Ireland. TEL 0232-245133. FAX 0232-247895.
—BLDSC (4574.642000).
Description: Covers all areas and orientations in philosophy, including the history of philosophy.

ISLAMIC PHILOSOPHY, THEOLOGY AND SCIENCE; texts and studies. see *RELIGIONS AND THEOLOGY — Islamic*

160 510   RU   ISSN 0302-9085
QA76
ISSLEDOVANIA PO TEORII ALGORIFMOV I MATEMATICHESKOI LOGIKE.* 1973. irreg. 1.12 Rub. Rossiiskaya Akademiya Nauk, Vychislitel'nyi Tsentr - Russian Academy of Sciences, Computer Center, Serpukhovskii raion, Pushchino, 142292 Moscow Oblast', Russia. TEL 3-24-08.

860 610   US   ISSN 0888-9201
R724
ISSUES: A CRITICAL EXAMINATION OF CONTEMPORARY ETHICAL ISSUES IN HEALTH CARE. 1986. bi-m. $125. 477 N. Lindbergh Blvd., St. Louis, MO 63141-7813. TEL 314-994-7910. FAX 314-994-7900. Ed. Dennis Brodeur. circ. 1,000. (back issues avail.) **Document type:** newsletter.
Description: Discusses current ethical concerns in the medical field.

174   NE   ISSN 0925-6733
ISSUES IN BUSINESS ETHICS. (Text in English) 1990. irreg., vol.5, 1993. price varies. Kluwer Academic Publishers, Postbus 17, 3300 AA Dordrecht, Netherlands. TEL 31-78-392392. FAX 31-78-392254. TELEX 29245 KAPG NL. (Dist. by: Kluwer Academic Publishers Group, P.O. Box 322, 3300 AH Dordrecht, Netherlands. TEL 31-78-392392. FAX 31-78-546474; N. America dist. addr.: Box 358, Accord Sta., Hingham, MA 02018-0358. TEL 617-871-6600. FAX 617-871-6528) **Document type:** monograph series.
—BLDSC (4584.139700).
Refereed Serial

100   IT
ISTITUTO UNIVERSITARIO ORIENTALE. DIPARTIMENTO DI FILOSOFIA E POLITICA. QUADERNI. 1987. irreg., no.11, 1992. price varies. Liguori Editore s.r.l., Via Mezzocannone, 19, 80134 Naples, Italy. TEL 081-5527139. Ed. Biagio DeGiovanni. **Document type:** monograph series.

294.54   IT   ISSN 0391-7509
ITALIA FRANCESCANA; rivista internazionale di cultura. (Text in English, Italian) 1926-1991; N.S. 1992. q. L.85000($125) Chiesa di S. Maria della Consolazione, Piazza della Consolazione, 84, 00186 Rome RM, Italy. TEL 06-6784654. FAX 06-6797338. Ed. P. Michelangelo Sabino Lattanzio. bk.rev. circ. 800. (back issues avail.) **Indexed:** M.L.A. **Document type:** academic/scholarly publication.

ITINERARIUM; revista quadrimestral de cultura. see *RELIGIONS AND THEOLOGY — Roman Catholic*

100 296   IS   ISSN 0021-3306
BJ52.5
IYYUN; Jerusalem philosophical quarterly. (2 nos. in English, 2 nos. in Hebrew) 1945. q. $24 to individuals ($15 for English issues only); institutions $27 ($18 for English issues only) (effective 1995). Hebrew University of Jerusalem, S.H. Bergman Centre for Philosophical Studies, Jerusalem 91905, Israel. TEL 972-2-883747. FAX 972-2-322545. TELEX 26458. E-mail: MSEVAS@pluto.mscc.huji.ac.il. (Co-sponsor: Jerusalem Philosophical Society) Ed. Eddy M. Zemach. bk.rev.; index. circ. 700. (back issues avail.) **Indexed:** Phil.Ind. **Document type:** academic/scholarly publication.
—Faxon; UnCover.

JAG. see *POLITICAL SCIENCE*

100   GW   ISSN 0946-9559
JAHRBUCH FUER HEGELFORSCHUNG. a. DM.48. Academia Verlag GmbH, Postfach 1663, 53734 Sankt Augustin, Germany. TEL 02241-333349. FAX 02241-341528. Ed. Helmut Schneider. **Document type:** monograph series.

JAPAN ASSOCIATION FOR PHILOSOPHY OF SCIENCE. ANNALS. see *SCIENCES: COMPREHENSIVE WORKS*

JERUSALEM STUDIES IN JEWISH THOUGHT. see *RELIGIONS AND THEOLOGY — Judaic*

100 300   CC   ISSN 1000-5072
AS452.C363
JINAN XUEBAO (ZHEXUE SHEHUI KEXUE BAN)/JINAN UNIVERSITY. JOURNAL (PHILOSOPHY & SOCIAL SCIENCES EDITION). (Text in Chinese; table of contents in English) 1979. q. Y6. Jinan Daxue, Xuebao Bianjibu - Jinan University, Journal Editorial Department, Rm. 216, 2nd Fl., Bldg. 75, Shipai, Guangzhou, Guangdong 510632, People's Republic of China. TEL 5516511. (Dist. outside China by: China International Book Trading Corp., P.O. Box 399, P.R. China) Eds. Jiang Shuzhuo, Yang Zengshu. adv.; bk.rev. circ. 3,000. **Document type:** academic/scholarly publication.
—UnCover.

JOBS FOR PHILOSOPHERS. see *OCCUPATIONS AND CAREERS*

JOURNAL FOR GENERAL PHILOSOPHY OF SCIENCE/ZEITSCHRIFT FUER ALLGEMEINE WISSENSCHAFTSTHEORIE. see *SCIENCES: COMPREHENSIVE WORKS*

212.5   US   ISSN 0090-2586
BF311   CODEN: JSCOA
JOURNAL FOR THE STUDY OF CONSCIOUSNESS.* 1974. s-a. $3. Linear & Circular Permutations, c/o Crane, 6 Harbor Way, Ste. 106, Santa Barbara, CA 93109-2300. Ed. Peter Crane. charts; illus.
Formerly: Nous Letter (ISSN 0276-0290)

JOURNAL FOR THE THEORY OF SOCIAL BEHAVIOUR. see *PSYCHOLOGY*

170 574 610   FR   ISSN 1145-0762
K10
JOURNAL INTERNATIONAL DE BIOETHIQUE/INTERNATIONAL JOURNAL OF BIOETHICS. q. 562 F. to individuals (foreign 703 F.); institutions 647 F. (foreign 809 F.) (effective 1995). Editions E S K A, 27 rue Dunois, 75013 Paris, France. TEL 44-06-80-42. FAX 44-24-06-94. Ed.Bd. **Document type:** academic/scholarly publication.
—BLDSC (4542.150500).
Supersedes in part (in 1990): Cahier de Droit et d'Ethique Medicale (ISSN 0997-7368)
Description: Provides an international review and data bank covering reproductive technology, organ transplants, and sophisticated techniques of reanimation and discusses how they have transformed birth, life, and death.

JOURNAL OF AESTHETIC EDUCATION. see *EDUCATION*

JOURNAL OF AESTHETICS AND ART CRITICISM. see *ART*

JOURNAL OF AFRICAN RELIGION AND PHILOSOPHY; a journal of religion and philosophy in Africa. see *RELIGIONS AND THEOLOGY*

174 333.7   CN   ISSN 1187-7863
BJ52.5   CODEN: JAETEC
JOURNAL OF AGRICULTURAL AND ENVIRONMENTAL ETHICS. 1988. s-a. Can.$35 to individuals (foreign Can.$38); institutions Can.$45 (foreign Can.$48); students Can.$18 (foreign Can.$21). Agricultural Institute of Canada, 907-151 Slater St., Ottawa, ON K1P 5H4, Canada. TEL 519-824-4120. FAX 519-837-9953. Eds. Frank Hurnick, Hugh Lehman. circ. 250. **Indexed:** Environ.Per.Bibl., Geo.Abstr., IDA, InterActions Bibl. (1988-). **Document type:** academic/scholarly publication.
—BLDSC (4919.999500); Genuine Article; UnCover. **CCC.**
Formerly (until 1991): Journal of Agricultural Ethics (ISSN 0893-4282)
Description: Concerned with ethical issues confronting agriculture, the environment and related disciplines.
Refereed Serial

100   UK   ISSN 0264-3758
B1
JOURNAL OF APPLIED PHILOSOPHY. 1984. 3/yr. £125($201) (foreign £125) (effective 1996). (Society of Applied Philosophy) Blackwell Publishers Ltd., 108 Cowley Rd., Oxford OX4 1JF, England. TEL 44-1865-791100. (Subscr. to: Marston Book Services, P.O. Box 87, Oxford, Oxford OX2 0DT, England. TEL 44-1865-791155. FAX 44-1865-791927) Eds. Brenda Almond, Stephen Clark. adv.; bk.rev.; index. (also avail. in microfiche; back issues avail.) **Indexed:** Phil.Ind., Stud.Wom.Abstr. **Document type:** academic/scholarly publication.
—BLDSC (4943.800000); Faxon; SWETS; UMI; UnCover. **CCC.**

JOURNAL OF BIBLICAL ETHICS IN MEDICINE. see *MEDICAL SCIENCES*

100   US   ISSN 0301-8121
B5230.A1
JOURNAL OF CHINESE PHILOSOPHY. (Text mainly in English) 1973. q. $83.25 to individuals; institutions $182. University of Hawaii at Manoa, Department of Philosophy, 2530 Dole St., Sakamaki Hall D301, Honolulu, HI 96822. TEL 808-956-6081. FAX 808-956-9228. E-mail: ccheng@uhunix.uhcc.hawaii.edu. Ed. Chung-Ying Cheng. adv. contact: Lin Yu Que. bk.rev. circ. 600. **Indexed:** Arts & Hum.Cit.Ind., Curr.Cont., M.L.A., Phil.Ind., SSCI. **Document type:** academic/scholarly publication.
—BLDSC (4958.140000); Genuine Article; SWETS; UnCover.

JOURNAL OF CONSCIOUSNESS STUDIES; controversies in science & the humanities. see *PSYCHOLOGY*

PHILOSOPHY

170   US   ISSN 1010-7304
BJ1
JOURNAL OF ETHICAL STUDIES. 1986. q. $50. International Association of Ethicists, Inc., 117 W. Harrison Bldg., Ste. I-104, 6th Fl., Chicago, IL 60605. TEL 800-423-3844. Ed. David Mrovka. adv.; bk.rev. (back issues avail.) **Document type:** academic/scholarly publication.
   Description: Case studies and articles of ethical interest.

JOURNAL OF ETHICS, LAW, AND AGING. see *GERONTOLOGY AND GERIATRICS*

JOURNAL OF GANDHIAN STUDIES. see *POLITICAL SCIENCE*

001 006   US   ISSN 1381-1231
▼**JOURNAL OF HEURISTICS.** 1995. q. fl.478 to institutions; $306 to institutions in U.S. (effective 1996). Kluwer Academic Publishers Boston, Box 358, Accord Sta., Hingham, MA 02018-0358. TEL 617-871-6600. FAX 617-871-6528. (Dist. outside N. America by: Kluwer Academic Publishers Group, P.O. Box 322, 3300 AH Dordrecht, Netherlands. TEL 31-78-392392. FAX 31-78-546474) Ed. Fred W. Glover. (back issues avail.) **Document type:** academic/scholarly publication.
   Description: Considers theoretical, empirical and experimental work relating to techniques for solving problems approximately.
   Refereed Serial

121 658.3 303.3   II
▼**JOURNAL OF HUMAN VALUES.** (Text in English) 1995. s-a. $35 to individuals; institutions $35 (effective Sep. 1995). (Indian Institute of Management, Management Centre for Human Values) Sage Periodicals India Pvt. Ltd., P.O. Box 4215, New Delhi 110 048, India. TEL 91-11-644-4958. FAX 91-11-647-2426. (Overseas subscr. to: Sage Publications Ltd., 6 Bonhill St., London EC2A 4PU, England. TEL 44-071-374-0645. FAX 44-071-374-8741; Overseas subscr. to: Sage Publications Ltd., 6 Bonhill St., London EC2A 4PU, England; In N. America: Sage Publications, Inc., Box 5084, Thousand Oaks, CA 91359. TEL 805-499-0721. FAX 805-499-0871) Ed. S.K. Chakraborty; Pub. Tejeshwar Singh. adv.: page Rs.1000; adv. contact: Sunanda Ghosh. circ. 600. (also avail. in microform from UMI; back issues avail.; reprint service avail.) **Document type:** academic/scholarly publication.
   Description: Provides an international forum for ideas, principles, and processes concerning the application of human values to organizations and institutions, as well as the world at large.
   Refereed Serial

211.3   US   ISSN 0899-7691
BP605.E84
JOURNAL OF HUMANISM & ETHICAL RELIGION. 1988. a. $10. American Ethical Union, National Leaders Council, 2 W. 64th St., New York, NY 10023. TEL 212-873-6500. Eds. Joseph Chuman, Arthur Dobrin. bk.rev. circ. 500. (back issues avail.) **Document type:** academic/scholarly publication.
   Description: Serves as a forum for communication between the academic and theological communities, including persons laying the theoretical groundwork for social change.

181   NE   ISSN 0022-1791
B130   CODEN: JIPHDI
JOURNAL OF INDIAN PHILOSOPHY. 1970. bi-m. fl.577 to institutions; $370 to institutions in U.S. (effective 1996). Kluwer Academic Publishers, Postbus 17, 3300 AA Dordrecht, Netherlands. TEL 31-78-392392. FAX 31-78-392254. TELEX 29245 KAPG NL. E-mail: SERVICES@WKAP.NL. (Dist. by: Kluwer Academic Publishers Group, P.O. Box 322, 3300 AH Dordrecht, Netherlands. TEL 31-78-392392. FAX 31-78-546474; N. America dist. addr.: Box 358, Accord Sta., Hingham, MA 02018-0358. TEL 617-871-6600. FAX 617-871-6528) Ed. Phyllis Granoff. adv.; bk.rev. (also avail. in microform from UMI; reprint service avail. from SWZ) **Indexed:** Arts & Hum.Cit.Ind., Bibl.Ling., Curr.Cont., M.L.A., Phil.Ind., Ref.Zh., Rel.Ind.One. **Document type:** academic/scholarly publication.
   —BLDSC (5005.325000); Genuine Article; SWETS; UMI; UnCover. **CCC.**
   Description: Publishes articles dealing with the work of Indian philosophers of the past as well as the creative researches of contemporary scholars.
   Refereed Serial

JOURNAL OF INFORMATION ETHICS. see *LIBRARY AND INFORMATION SCIENCES*

JOURNAL OF LOGIC, LANGUAGE AND INFORMATION. see *LINGUISTICS*

JOURNAL OF MEDICAL ETHICS. see *MEDICAL SCIENCES*

JOURNAL OF MEDICAL HUMANITIES. see *MEDICAL SCIENCES*

THE JOURNAL OF MEDICINE AND PHILOSOPHY; a forum for bioethics and philosophy of medicine. see *MEDICAL SCIENCES*

JOURNAL OF MIND AND BEHAVIOR. see *PSYCHOLOGY*

100   UK   ISSN 0305-7240
LC268   CODEN: JMEDFF
JOURNAL OF MORAL EDUCATION. 1971. q. £26 to individuals; institutions $98 (effective 1996). Carfax Publishing Co., P.O. Box 25, Abingdon, Oxon. OX14 3UE, England. TEL 01235-555335. FAX 01235-553559. (Subscr. in N. America to: Carfax Publishing Co., 875-91 Massachusetts Ave., Cambridge, MA 02139) Ed. Monica Taylor. adv.; bk.rev.; index, cum.index. (also avail. in microfiche; back issues avail.) **Indexed:** Adol.Ment.Hlth.Abstr., ASSIA, C.I.J.E., Cont.Pg.Educ., Curr.Cont., Educ.Ind., Educ.Tech.Abstr., High.Educ.Curr.Aware.Bull., Mult.Ed.Abstr., Phil.Ind., Psychol.Abstr., Sociol.Educ.Abstr., SOMA, Sp.Ed.Needs Abstr., SSCI, Stud.Wom.Abstr. **Document type:** academic/scholarly publication.
   —BLDSC (5020.950000); Faxon; Genuine Article; SWETS; UMI; UnCover. **CCC.**
   Refereed Serial

160   NE   ISSN 0022-3611
BC51   CODEN: JPLGA7
JOURNAL OF PHILOSOPHICAL LOGIC. (Text in English) 1972. bi-m. fl.587 to institutions; $377 to institutions in U.S. (effective 1996). (Association for Symbolic Logic) Kluwer Academic Publishers, Postbus 17, 3300 AA Dordrecht, Netherlands. TEL 31-78-392392. FAX 31-78-392254. TELEX 29245 KAPG NL. (Dist. by: Kluwer Academic Publishers Group, P.O. Box 322, 3300 AH Dordrecht, Netherlands. TEL 31-78-392392. FAX 31-78-546474; N. America dist. addr.: Box 358, Accord Sta., Hingham, MA 02018-0358. TEL 617-871-6600. FAX 617-871-6528) Eds. J. Michael Dunn, Terence Parsons. adv. (also avail. in microform from UMI; reprint service avail. from SWZ) **Indexed:** Arts & Hum.Cit.Ind., ASCA, Bibl.Ling., Curr.Cont., IBR, IBZ, Lang.& Lang.Behav.Abstr., M.L.A., Math R., Phil.Ind., Ref.Zh., Sociol.Abstr., SSCI, Zent.Math. **Document type:** academic/scholarly publication.
   —BLDSC (5034.400000); Faxon; Genuine Article; SWETS; UMI; UnCover. **CCC.**
   Refereed Serial

100   US   ISSN 1053-8364
B1
JOURNAL OF PHILOSOPHICAL RESEARCH; a bilingual journal of philosophy. (Text and summaries in English and French) 1976. a. $25 to individuals; institutions $60. Bowling Green State University, Philosophy Documentation Center, Bowling Green, OH 43403-0189. TEL 419-372-2419; 800-444-2419. FAX 419-372-6987. Ed. Panayot Butchvarov. circ. 600. **Indexed:** Phil.Ind. **Document type:** academic/scholarly publication.
   —BLDSC (5034.420000); UnCover.
   Formerly: Philosophy Research Archives (ISSN 0164-0771)
   Description: Publishes original papers in all branches of philosophy and from any philosophical orientation.
   Refereed Serial

100   US   ISSN 0022-362X
B1
JOURNAL OF PHILOSOPHY. 1904. m. $35 to individuals; libraries $65; students $20. Journal of Philosophy, Inc., 709 Philosophy Hall, Columbia University, New York, NY 10027. TEL 212-666-4419. Ed.Bd. adv.; bk.rev.; bibl.; index, cum.index: 1904-1953, 1954-1963, 1964-1988. circ. 4,500. (also avail. in microfilm from PMC; back issues avail.) **Indexed:** Amer.Hist.& Life, Arts & Hum.Cit.Ind., Bibl.Engl.Lang.& Lit., Bk.Rev.Dig., Bk.Rev.Ind. (1965-), Child.Bk.Rev.Ind. (1965-), Curr.Cont., Deep Sea Res.& Oceanogr.Abstr., Hist.Abstr., Hum.Ind., Ind.Bk.Rev.Hum., M.L.A., Math.R., Mid.East: Abstr.& Ind., Phil.Ind. **Document type:** academic/scholarly publication.
   —BLDSC (5034.500000); Faxon; Genuine Article; SWETS; UnCover. **CCC.**
   Description: Encourages the interchange of ideas, explores the relation between philosophy and special interests.

100   UK   ISSN 0309-8249
LB1025.2
JOURNAL OF PHILOSOPHY OF EDUCATION. 1966. 3/yr. £175($316) (foreign £196) (effective 1996). Basil Blackwell Ltd., 108 Cowley Rd., Oxford OX4 1JF, England. TEL 44-1865-791100. FAX 44-1865-791347. Ed. Richard Smith. adv. (also avail. in microfiche; back issues avail.) **Indexed:** C.I.J.E., Cont.Pg.Educ., Curr.Cont., Educ.Tech.Abstr., Mult.Ed.Abstr., Phil.Ind., Res.High.Educ.Abstr., Sociol.Educ.Abstr., SOMA, Sp.Ed.Needs Abstr., SSCI, Stud.Wom.Abstr., Tech.Educ.Abstr. **Document type:** academic/scholarly publication.
   —BLDSC (5034.510000); Faxon; SWETS; UnCover. **CCC.**
   Formerly: Philosophy of Education Society of Great Britain. Proceedings (ISSN 0048-3923)
   Refereed Serial

301 100   US   ISSN 0047-2786
H1
JOURNAL OF SOCIAL PHILOSOPHY. 1970. 3/yr. $25 to individuals (foreign $30); libraries $75 (foreign $80) (effective 1993). North American Society for Social Philosophy, c/o Peter A. French, Ed., University of South Florida, St. Petersburg Campus, Ethics Center, St. Petersburg, FL 33701-5016. TEL 813-553-3170. FAX 813-553-3169. E-mail: french@bayflash.st.pt.usf.edu. bk.rev. circ. 500. (also avail. in microform from UMI; reprint service avail. from UMI) **Indexed:** Phil.Ind., Polit.Sci.Abstr., Rel.Ind.One, Sage Fam.Stud.Abstr. **Document type:** academic/scholarly publication.
   —BLDSC (5064.775000); UMI; UnCover.
   Description: Interdisciplinary forum for political debate of moral, legal, political and social issues.

100   US   ISSN 0891-625X
B1
JOURNAL OF SPECULATIVE PHILOSOPHY. 1987. q. $25 to individuals (foreign $35); institutions $35 (foreign $45). Pennsylvania State University Press, 820 N. University Dr., Ste. C, University Park, PA 16802-1003. TEL 814-865-1327. FAX 814-863-1408. Eds. Carl R. Hausman, Douglas Anderson. (also avail. in microform from UMI; reprint service avail. from UMI,KTO) **Document type:** academic/scholarly publication.
   —BLDSC (5066.142000); Faxon; UMI; UnCover. **CCC.**
   Description: Covers trends in North American philosophy, offering systematic and interpretive essays about basic philosophical questions, and promoting constructive interaction between continental philosophy and American thought.
   Refereed Serial

PHILOSOPHY

164 510   US   ISSN 0022-4812
BC1   CODEN: JSYLA6
JOURNAL OF SYMBOLIC LOGIC. (Text in English, French, German) 1936. q. $210. Association for Symbolic Logic, Department of Mathematics, University of Illinois at Urbana-Champaign, 1409 W. Green St., Urbana, IL 61801. TEL 217-333-3410. FAX 217-333-9576. (Subscr. to: ASL, Journal Dept., UIP, 1325 S. Oak St., Champaign, IL 61820) Ed. Herbert B. Enderton. adv.; bk.rev.; bibl. circ. 2,500. (also avail. in microform from UMI,PMC) **Indexed:** Compumath, Curr.Cont., Hum.Ind., Ind.Bk.Rev.Hum., Ind.Sci.Rev., INSPEC, Math.R., Phil.Ind. **Document type:** academic/scholarly publication.
—BLDSC (5068.000000); Faxon; Genuine Article; SWETS; UnCover. **CCC.**

109   US   ISSN 0022-5053
B1
JOURNAL OF THE HISTORY OF PHILOSOPHY. (Text in various languages) 1963. q. $25 to individuals; $65 libraries. Journal of the History of Philosophy, Inc., Emory University, Dept. of Philosophy, Atlanta, GA 30322. TEL 404-329-6412. (Subscr. to: P.O. Box 24580, Los Angeles, CA 90024) (Co-sponsors: Claremont Colleges; Washington University-St. Louis; Stanford University; University of California) Ed. Rudolf Makkreel. adv. contact: Dennis Dugan. bk.rev.; charts; illus. circ. 1,600. (also avail. in microform from UMI; reprint service avail. from UMI) **Indexed:** Amer.Hist.& Life, Arts & Hum.Cit.Ind., Bibl.Engl.Lang.& Lit., Curr.Cont., Hist.Abstr., Hum.Ind., Phil.Ind. **Document type:** academic/scholarly publication.
—BLDSC (5001.500000); Faxon; SWETS; UMI; UnCover.
Description: Articles, notes and discussions on the history of Western philosophy.

JOURNAL OF THE PHILOSOPHY OF SPORT. see *SPORTS AND GAMES*

JOURNAL OF THOUGHT. see *SOCIAL SCIENCES: COMPREHENSIVE WORKS*

170   NE   ISSN 0022-5363
BD232   CODEN: JVINEP
THE JOURNAL OF VALUE INQUIRY. 1967. q. fl.458 to institutions; $293 to institutions in U.S. (effective 1996). Kluwer Academic Publishers, Postbus 17, 3300 AA Dordrecht, Netherlands. TEL 31-78-392392. FAX 31-78-392254. TELEX 29245 KAPG NL. E-mail: SERVICES@WKAP.NL. (Dist. by: Kluwer Academic Publishing Group, P.O. Box 322, 3300 AH Dordrecht, Netherlands. TEL 31-78-392392. FAX 31-78-546474; N, America dist. addr.: Box 358, Accord Sta., Hingham, MA 02018-0358. TEL 617-871-6600. FAX 617-871-6528) Ed. Robert Ginsberg. adv.; bk.rev.; index. (also avail. in microform from UMI; back issues avail.; reprint service avail. from SWZ) **Indexed:** Arts & Hum.Cit.Ind., ASCA, Curr.Cont., Ind.Bk.Rev.Hum., Phil.Ind. **Document type:** academic/scholarly publication.
—BLDSC (5072.260000); Faxon; Genuine Article; SWETS; UMI; UnCover. **CCC.**
Refereed Serial

JUKIC; zbornik radova. see *RELIGIONS AND THEOLOGY*

KABBALAH; newsletter of current research in Jewish mysticism. see *RELIGIONS AND THEOLOGY — Judaic*

100 800   AF
KABUL MOJALA. (Text in Pashtu) 1931. m. $5. Afghanistan Academy of Sciences, Sher Alikhan St., Kabul, Afghanistan. Ed. N.M. Saheem.

105   FR   ISSN 1148-9227
B2
KAIROS. 1972. a. 100 F. (effective 1994). (Universite de Toulouse II (le Mirail)) Presses Universitaires du Mirail, 56 rue du Taur, 31000 Toulouse, France. TEL 61-22-58-31. FAX 61-21-84-20. Ed. Jean-Marie Vaysse. (back issues avail.) **Document type:** academic/scholarly publication.
—BLDSC (5081.420000).
Formerly (until 1990): Philosophie (Toulouse) (ISSN 0182-7103)

KAMEN'; rivista semestrale di poesia e filosofia. see *LITERATURE — Poetry*

142.3   GW   ISSN 0022-8877
B2750
KANT STUDIEN. (Text in English, French and German) 1896. 4/yr. DM.175. (Kant-Gesellschaft) Walter de Gruyter und Co., Genthiner Str. 13, 10785 Berlin, Germany. TEL 030-26005-0. FAX 030-26005-251. TELEX 184027. (U.S. addr.: Walter de Gruyter, Inc., 200 Saw Mill River Rd., Hawthorne, NY 10532. TEL 914-747-0110) Eds. Gerhard Funke, Rudolf Malter. adv.; bk.rev.; abstr.; charts; index. circ. 1,000. **Indexed:** Arts & Hum.Cit.Ind., Curr.Cont., Ind.Bk.Rev.Hum., Phil.Ind. **Document type:** academic/scholarly publication.
—Faxon; Genuine Article; SWETS. **CCC.**

100   PH   ISSN 0116-7073
KARUNUNGAN. (Text in English) 1985. a. P.30($4.40) (De La Salle University, Philippine Academy of Philosophical Research) De La Salle University Press, 2401 Taft Ave., Manila, Philippines. TEL 2-59-48-32. FAX 632-521-9094. adv.; bk.rev. circ. 500. **Indexed:** Ind.Phil.Per. **Document type:** academic/scholarly publication.
Description: Publishes scholarly articles reflecting significant quantitative or qualitative research. Includes speeches, research reports, and "state of the art" papers.

100   PL
KATOLICKI UNIWERSYTET LUBELSKI. WYDZIAL FILOZOFICZNY. ROZPRAWY. (Text in Polish; summaries in English, French or German) 1957. irreg. price varies. Katolicki Uniwersytet Lubelski, Towarzystwo Naukowe, Ul. Gliniana 21, 20-616 Lublin, Poland. index. circ. 3,150.

KAYHAN ANDISHE. see *RELIGIONS AND THEOLOGY — Islamic*

491.6 944   FR   ISSN 0022-9792
KELTIA; organe de recherche d'un Celtisme moderne. (Supplement to: Bretagne Reelle) 1960. bi-m. 190 F. for 10 nos. J. Quatreboeufs, 22230 Merdrignac, Brittany, France. bk.rev.

KENNEDY INSTITUTE OF ETHICS. SCOPE NOTE. see *MEDICAL SCIENCES*

KENNEDY INSTITUTE OF ETHICS JOURNAL. see *MEDICAL SCIENCES*

KENNIS EN METHODE; tijdschrift voor wetenschapsfilosofie en methodologie. see *SCIENCES: COMPREHENSIVE WORKS*

KEXUE JISHU YU BIANZHENGFA/SCIENCE, TECHNOLOGY, AND DIALECTICS. see *SCIENCES: COMPREHENSIVE WORKS*

198.9   DK   ISSN 0075-6032
B4377
KIERKEGAARDIANA. (Text in English, French and German; summaries in English) 1955. a. DKK 200($25) (Soren Kierkegaard Selskabet - Soeren Kierkegaard Society) C.A. Reitzels Forlag, Noerregade 20, DK-1165 Copenhagen K, Denmark. (Co-sponsor: National Council of the Humanities) Ed.Bd. bk.rev. circ. 500. **Document type:** academic/scholarly publication.
—BLDSC (5095.135000).
Refereed Serial

100   US
KIERKEGAARD'S WRITINGS. 1978. irreg., no.20, 1991. price varies. Princeton University Press, 41 William St., Princeton, NJ 08540. TEL 609-258-4900. FAX 609-258-6305. E-mail: jhardy@pupress.princeton.edu. (reprint service avail. from UMI) **Document type:** monographic series.

100   US   ISSN 0023-1568
B1
KINESIS. 1968. s-a. $10 to individuals; institutions $15. (Graduate Students of S.I.U., Department of Philosophy) Southern Illinois University at Carbondale, Philosophy Department, Carbondale, IL 62901. TEL 618-536-6641. adv.; bk.rev. circ. 2,000. (also avail. in microform from UMI; reprint service avail. from UMI) **Indexed:** Can.Wom.Per.Ind., Phil.Ind.
—BLDSC (5096.030000); UMI; UnCover. **CCC.**
Formerly: Kinesis Report (ISSN 0193-1911)

100   AU   ISSN 0259-0743
KLAGENFURTER BEITRAEGE ZUR PHILOSOPHIE. (Supplement avail.) 1979. irreg. price varies. Philosophische Gesellschaft Klagenfurt, Universitaetsstr. 65-67, A-9022 Klagenfurt, Austria. Eds. Thomas Macho, Christof Subik. **Document type:** monographic series.

KNJIZEVNA KRITIKA; casopis za umetnicku, istorijsku i filosofsku kritiku. see *LITERATURE*

KNOWLEDGE AND POLICY; the international journal of knowledge transfer. see *SOCIAL SCIENCES: COMPREHENSIVE WORKS*

KOERS; bulletin vir Christelike wetenskap - bulletin for Christian scholarship. see *RELIGIONS AND THEOLOGY*

299.51   CC   ISSN 1002-2627
KONGZI YANJIU/STUDIES ON CONFUCIUS. (Text in Chinese) q. $16.50. Zhongguo Kongzi Jijinhui - China Confucius Foundation, Qufu Shifan Daxue, Qufu, Shandong 273165, People's Republic of China. TEL 411831. (Dist. in US by: China Books & Periodicals, Inc., 2929 24th St., San Francisco, CA 94110. TEL 415-282-2994) Ed. Xin Guanjie.

100 001.3   GW
KONKURSBUCH; Zeitschrift fuer Vernunftkritik. 1978. 2/yr. DM.15 per no. Konkursbuchverlag Claudia Gehrke, Postfach 1621, Garmerstr. 29, 72006 Tuebingen, Germany. TEL 07071-66551. FAX 07071-63539. Ed. Claudia Gehrke. (back issues avail.) **Document type:** academic/scholarly publication.

100   GW   ISSN 0454-448X
KOSMOSOPHIE. irreg., vol.7, 1992. price varies. (Paracelsus-Kommission) Franz Steiner Verlag Wiesbaden GmbH, Birkenwaldstr. 44, 70191 Stuttgart, Germany. TEL 0711-2582-0. FAX 0711-2582390. (Subscr. to: Postfach 101061, 70009 Stuttgart, Germany) Ed. Kurt Goldammer. **Document type:** monographic series.

100   NE   ISSN 0168-275X
KRISIS; tijdschrift voor filosofie. 1980. q. fl.60 to individuals; institutions fl.75; students fl.48 (effective 1995). Stichting Krisis, Kleine Gartmanplantsoen 10, 1017 RR Amsterdam, Netherlands. TEL 31-20-6233673. Ed.Bd. adv.; bk.rev. circ. 1,200. **Document type:** academic/scholarly publication.
—SWETS.

100   NE   ISSN 0924-5901
KRISIS-ONDERZOEK. 1989. s-a. fl.24.50. Stichting Krisis, Kleine Gartmanplantsoen 10, 1017 RR Amsterdam, Netherlands. TEL 31-20-6233673. **Document type:** monographic series.

100   AU   ISSN 1019-8288
KRITERION. (Text in English, German) 1991. 2/yr. S.60. Universitaet Salzburg, Institut fuer Philosophie, Franziskanergasse 1, A-5020 Salzburg, Austria. FAX 0662-8044214. E-mail: huermerwo@edvz.sbg.ac.at. Ed.Bd. adv.: page S.2000; adv. contact: D. Jahn. bk.rev.; circ. 500. (back issues avail.) **Document type:** academic/scholarly publication.

100   GW
KULTUR UND ERKENNTNIS. irreg., vol.10, 1993. price varies. (Heinrich-Heine-Universitaet Duesseldorf, Philosophische Fakultaet) Francke Verlag GmbH, Postfach 2560, 72015 Tuebingen, Germany. TEL 07071-9797-0. FAX 07071-75288. **Document type:** monographic series.

KULTURNI RADNIK. see *HUMANITIES: COMPREHENSIVE WORKS*

KUNGLIGA VITTERHETS HISTORIE OCH ANTIKVITETS AKADEMIEN. HANDLINGAR. FILOLOGISK-FILOSOFISKA SERIEN/ROYAL ACADEMY OF LETTERS, HISTORY AND ANTIQUITIES. PROCEEDINGS. PHILOLOGICAL-PHILOSOPHICAL SERIES. see *LINGUISTICS*

L I A S: SOURCES AND DOCUMENTS RELATING TO THE EARLY MODERN HISTORY OF IDEAS.. see *HISTORY*

100   IT
LACOONTE. 1990. irreg., no.2, 1993. price varies. Liguori Editore s.r.l., Via Mezzocannone 19, 80134 Naples, Italy. TEL 081-5527139. Ed. Umberto Carpi. **Document type:** monographic series.

LAST RIGHTS. see *MEDICAL SCIENCES*

200 100   CN   ISSN 0023-9054
BX802
LAVAL THEOLOGIQUE ET PHILOSOPHIQUE. Abbreviated title: L T P. (Text in English and French) 1945. 3/yr. Can.$25 to individuals; institutions Can.$32. Universite Laval, Faculte de Philosophie, Cite Universitaire, Quebec, PQ G1K 7P4, Canada. TEL 418-656-3816. FAX 418-656-7267. Ed. Lionel Ponton. bk.rev.; bibl.; index, cum.index. circ. 1,000. (also avail. in microfilm from BNQ) **Indexed:** Arts & Hum.Cit.Ind., Cath.Ind., CERDIC, Curr.Cont., New Test.Abstr., Old Test.Abstr., Phil.Ind., Pt.de Rep. (1983-), Rel.& Theol.Abstr. (1987-). **Document type:** academic/scholarly publication.
—BLDSC (5160.825000); Faxon; Genuine Article; SWETS; UMI.
Description: Offers an interdisciplinary review of theology and philosophy. Presents and discusses the main currents of thought that concern the history and contribution of both disciplines to modern times.
Refereed Serial

LAW & JUSTICE. see *LAW*

LAW AND PHILOSOPHY; an international journal for jurisprudence and legal philosophy. see *LAW*

LAW AND PHILOSOPHY LIBRARY. see *LAW*

100   UK   ISSN 0266-0598
LEIBNIZ NEWSLETTER. 1984. a. £2. c/o George MacDonald Ross, Dept. of Philosophy, The University, Leeds LS2 9JT, England. TEL 0532-333283.
Description: Reports on research and conferences on Leibniz, and on related 17th and 18th century topics and philosophers.

193   US   ISSN 1069-5192
B2550
LEIBNIZ SOCIETY REVIEW. 1991. a. free to members; institutions $20. Ohio State University, Philosophy Department, 1680 University Dr., Mansfield, OH 44906-1599. TEL 419-755-4354. FAX 419-755-4367.
E-mail: hartz, hartz.1@osu.edu. Ed. Glenn A. Hartz. bk.rev. circ. 150. **Indexed:** Phil.Ind.
Formerly (until 1993): Leibniz Society Newsletter & Review.
Description: Aspires to provide the community of Leignizscholars with up-to-date information about the international status of Leibniz studies.

LEICESTER LITERARY & PHILOSOPHICAL SOCIETY. TRANSACTIONS. see *LITERATURE*

LESBIAN ETHICS. see *HOMOSEXUALITY*

LETRAS DE DEUSTO. see *HUMANITIES: COMPREHENSIVE WORKS*

100   DK   ISSN 0106-8989
LIBER ACADEMIAE KIERKEGAARDIENSIS ANNUARIUS. (Text in Danish, English, German and Italian) 1980. irreg. DKK 122. C.A. Reitzels Forlag, Norregade 20, DK-1165 Copenhagen K, Denmark.

100   UK   ISSN 0267-7091
LIBERTARIAN ALLIANCE. PHILOSOPHICAL NOTES. 1985. irreg. £15($30) Libertarian Alliance, 25 Chapter Chambers, Esterbrooke St., London SW1P 4NN, England. TEL 0171-821-5502. FAX 0171-834-2031. E-mail: liberty@capital.demon.co.uk. Ed.Bd. adv.; bk.rev.; film rev.; bibl. circ. 1,000. (back issues avail.) **Document type:** monographic series.

LIBERTY (PORT TOWNSEND). see *LITERARY AND POLITICAL REVIEWS*

LIBRARY OF RELIGIOUS PHILOSOPHY. see *RELIGIONS AND THEOLOGY*

100 808   NE   ISSN 0929-6298
LIBRARY OF RHETORICS. (Text in English) 1993. irreg., vol.3, 1993. price varies. Kluwer Academic Publishers, Postbus 17, 3300 AA Dordrecht, Netherlands. TEL 31-78-392392. FAX 31-78-392254. (Dist. by: Kluwer Academic Publishers Group, P.O. Box 322, 3300 AH Dordrecht, Netherlands. TEL 31-78-392392. FAX 31-78-546474; N. America dist. addr.: Box 358, Accord Sta., Hingham, MA 02018-0358. TEL 617-871-6600. FAX 617-871-6528) (back issues avail.) **Document type:** monographic series.

100   SW   ISSN 0459-2603
LIBRARY OF THEORIA. (Text in English) 1955. irreg., no.16, 1985. price varies. Liber Forlag, S-205 10, Malmo, Sweden. Ed.Bd.

100   SP
LIBROS DE INICIACION FILOSOFICA. 1982. irreg., no.10, 1987. price varies. (Universidad de Navarra, Facultad de Filosofia y Letras) Ediciones Universidad de Navarra, S.A., Apdo. 396, 31080 Pamplona, Spain. TEL 94 825 6850.

LICHTENBERG-JAHRBUCH. see *BIOGRAPHY*

100 301   LI   ISSN 0235-7186
B8.L6
LIETUVOS MOKSLU AKADEMIJA. FILOSOFIJA, SOCIOLOGIJA. (Text in Lithuanian; summaries in English) 1955. 3/yr. $5 per issue. Leidykla Academia, A. Gostauto 12, 2600 Vilnius, Lithuania. Ed. J. Minkevicius. circ. 520. **Document type:** academic/scholarly publication.
—BLDSC (5208.806600).

100 500   US
LIFE IN ACTION MAGAZINE. 1975. bi-m. $12. (School of Natural Science Life in Action) Pioneer Press (Los Gatos), 25355 Spanish Ranch Rd., Los Gatos, CA 95030. TEL 408-353-4876. Ed. Philip Brown. bk.rev.; illus. circ. 650. **Document type:** academic/scholarly publication.

LIFGEISLAR; timarit um lifsamband vid adrar stjoernur. see *PARAPSYCHOLOGY AND OCCULTISM*

LIGHT OF CONSCIOUSNESS. see *NEW AGE PUBLICATIONS*

100   US   ISSN 0075-9554
LINDLEY LECTURE. 1961. a. $3.50. University of Kansas, Department of Philosophy, Lawrence, KS 66045. TEL 913-864-2700. Ed. A.C. Genova. circ. 600. **Document type:** monographic series.
—BLDSC (5221.030000).

LINGUA E STILE. see *LINGUISTICS*

LINGUISTICS AND PHILOSOPHY; a journal of natural language syntax, semantics, logic, pragmatics, and processing. see *LINGUISTICS*

LITERATURE AND THE SCIENCES OF MAN. see *LITERATURE*

100 200 575 600   US
LIVE AND LET LIVE. 1992. 4/yr. $3. James N. Dawson, Ed. & Pub., Box 613-B, Redwood Valley, CA 95470. TEL 707-485-7092. bk.rev. circ. 250. (back issues avail.) **Document type:** newsletter.
Description: Seeks to explore and develop a theory and strategy of fetal and animal rights from a libertarian - individualist framework.

THE LIVING LIGHT PHILOSOPHY. see *RELIGIONS AND THEOLOGY — Other Denominations And Sects*

LIVING PRAYER. see *RELIGIONS AND THEOLOGY*

100   UK   ISSN 0307-2606
B1250
LOCKE NEWSLETTER. (Text in English, French, German and Italian) 1970. a. £6($11) to individuals; institutions £8 ($14.50) (effective 1995). Roland Hall, Ed. & Pub., Department of Philosophy, University of York, Heslington, York YO1 5DD, England. TEL 0904-728408. adv.; bk.rev. circ. 600. **Indexed:** Phil.Ind. **Document type:** academic/scholarly publication.
—BLDSC (5290.300000).

100 808   NE   ISSN 0929-6298
LIBRARY OF RHETORICS

100   BE   ISSN 0024-5836
BC1   CODEN: LOANAM
LOGIQUE ET ANALYSE. (Text in Dutch, English, French, German) 1958. 4/yr. Nauwelaerts Printing Cy., Begaultlaan 17, B-3010 Wilsele, Belgium. Ed. J. Dopp. bk.rev.; bibl. circ. 1,000. **Indexed:** Lang.& Lang.Behav.Abstr., Math.R., Phil.Ind.
—Faxon; SWETS.
Description: Quarterly philosophical publication.

100   IT   ISSN 0024-5887
B4
LOGOS;* rivista di filosofia. 1969. 3/yr. L.6000. Libreria Scientifica Editrice, Corso Umberto I N. 38 e 40, 80138 Naples, Italy. Ed. Cleto Carbonara. (reprint service avail. from SCH) **Indexed:** Phil.Ind.

100   GW   ISSN 0941-9683
B3
LOGOS; Zeitschrift fuer systematische Philosophie. 1993. 4/yr. DM.98. Verlag J.C.B. Mohr (Paul Siebeck), Wilhelmstr. 18, 72074 Tuebingen, Germany. TEL 07071-923-0. FAX 07071-51104. TELEX 7262872-MOHR-D. (Subscr. to: Postfach 2040, 72010 Tuebingen, Germany) Eds. Michael Sukale, Hans Juergen Wendel. (reprint service avail. from SCH) **Document type:** academic/scholarly publication.

100 200   CN   ISSN 0828-184X
LONERGAN STUDIES NEWSLETTER. 1980. q. Can.$6($5) Lonergan Research Institute, 10 St. Mary St., Ste. 500, Toronto, ON M4Y 1P9, Canada. TEL 416-922-8374. FAX 416-921-1673. Ed. Fred Crowe. circ. 280. **Document type:** newsletter.
Description: Studies the works of Bernard Lonergan, provides information of related workshops, conferences, seminars and reports on other Lonergan institutes and centers around the world.

212.5   FR   ISSN 0024-6670
LOTUS BLEU; revue theosophique. vol.78, 1973. m. 240 F. Societe Theosophique de France, 4 Square Rapp, 75007 Paris, France. Ed. Francoise Caracostea. bk.rev.

100   BE
LOUVAIN PHILOSOPHICAL STUDIES. 1987. irreg., vol.9, 1995. Leuven University Press, Krakenstraat 3, B-3000 Leuven, Belgium. TEL 32-16-324175. FAX 32-16-323782. (back issues avail.) **Document type:** academic/scholarly publication.

LOVE; the journal of the human spirit. see *NEW AGE PUBLICATIONS*

LOVING BROTHERHOOD NEWSLETTER; a journal for personal and planetary transformation. see *HOMOSEXUALITY*

LUCA; casopis za filozofiju i sociologiju. see *SOCIOLOGY*

100   GW
LUDWIG FEUERBACH: GESAMMELTE WERKE. 1967. irreg., vol.19, 1993. Akademie Verlag GmbH, Muehlenstr. 33-34, 13187 Berlin, Germany. TEL 030-47889348. FAX 030-47889357. Ed. Werner Schuffenhauer. **Document type:** monographic series.

LUMEN. see *HISTORY*

100 410   CC   ISSN 1003-5044
LUOJI YU YUYAN XUEXI/LOGIC AND LANGUAGE STUDIES. (Text in Chinese) 1982. bi-m. Hebei Shifan Xueyuan, Zhengjiao Xi - Hebei Normal Institute, Department of Politics and Religion, Hongqi Dajie, Shijiazhuang, Hebei 050091, People's Republic of China.

MA'ARIF. see *RELIGIONS AND THEOLOGY — Islamic*

MACROBIOTICS TODAY. see *NUTRITION AND DIETETICS*

MAGICAL BLEND; a transformative journey. see *NEW AGE PUBLICATIONS*

PHILOSOPHY

100   HU   ISSN 0025-0090
MAGYAR FILOZOFIAI SZEMLE/HUNGARIAN PHILOSOPHICAL REVIEW. (Text in Hungarian; summaries in English, French, German and Russian) 1957. bi-m. $30. (Magyar Tudomanyos Akademia, Filozofiai Intezet) Aron Kiado, Szemere u. 1o, 1054 Budapest, Hungary. FAX 36-1-113-1793. (And: P.O. Box 487, 1447 Bucharest, Rumania) Ed. L.F. Lendvai. adv.; bk.rev.; index. **Indexed:** Lang.& Lang.Behav.Abstr., Phil.Ind.

MAHA BODHI; international Buddhist monthly. see *RELIGIONS AND THEOLOGY — Buddhist*

181   II   ISSN 0025-0414
MAHAJANMER LAGNA. (Text in Bengali) 1967. w. Rs.6. Sulekha Press, Arambagh, Hooghly, W. Bengal, India. Ed. Jay Krishna Mukherjee. adv.; bk.rev. circ. 1,000. (looseleaf format)

100   GW   ISSN 0076-2776
MAINZER PHILOSOPHISCHE FORSCHUNGEN. 1966. irreg., vol.35, 1990. price varies. Bouvier Verlag Herbert Grundmann, Am Hof 28, 53113 Bonn, Germany. TEL 0228-7290124. FAX 0228-7290179. Ed. Gerhard Funke. **Document type:** monographic series.
—BLDSC (5352.655000).

MAKING THE ROUNDS IN HEALTH, FAITH AND ETHICS. see *MEDICAL SCIENCES*

100   NE   ISSN 0025-1534
B1   CODEN: MWORE5
MAN AND WORLD; an international philosophical review. (Text in English, French and German) 1968. q. fl.353 to institutions; $226 to institutions in U.S. (effective 1996). Kluwer Academic Publishers, Postbus 17, 3300 AA Dordrecht, Netherlands. TEL 31-78-392392. FAX 31-78-392254. TELEX 29245 KAPG NL. E-mail: SERVICES@WKAP.NL. (Dist. by: Kluwer Academic Publishing Group, P.O. Box 322, 3300 AH Dordrecht, Netherlands. TEL 31-78-392392. FAX 31-78-546474; N. America dist. addr.: Box 358, Accord Sta., Hingham, MA 02018-0358. TEL 617-871-6600. FAX 617-871-6528) Ed.Bd. bk.rev.; bibl.; index. (also avail. in microform from UMI; reprint service avail. from SWZ) **Indexed:** Arts & Hum.Cit.Ind., ASCA, Curr.Cont., Int.Polit.Sci.Abstr., Phil.Ind. **Document type:** academic/scholarly publication.
—BLDSC (5358.012500); Faxon; Genuine Article; SWETS; UMI; UnCover. **CCC.**
Description: Provides a forum for dialogue on philosophical issues and fundamental philosophical problems, including both theoretical topics, practical problems, and philosophical concerns relating to the arts, science and religion.
Refereed Serial

106 806   UK   ISSN 0265-3575
                              CODEN: MPMLAQ
MANCHESTER MEMOIRS. 1785. a. £8.50. Manchester Literary and Philosophical Society, 14 Kennedy St., Manchester M2 4BY, England. FAX 061-228-3571. Ed. D. Wilson. bk.rev. circ. 800. (also avail. in microfilm from BHP) **Indexed:** Amer.Hist.& Life, Br.Hum.Ind., GeoRef., Hist.Abstr. **Document type:** academic/scholarly publication.
—BLDSC (5359.607000); CASDDS.
Formerly: Manchester Literary and Philosophical Society. Memoirs and Proceedings (ISSN 0076-3721)
Description: Devoted to the stimulation of public interest and appreciation of all forms of literature, science, arts, and public affairs.

160 121   BL   ISSN 0100-6045
B1
MANUSCRITO; revista internacional de filosofia. (Text in English, French, Portuguese, Spanish) 1977. s-a. $8 (foreign $15) to individuals; institutions $12 (foreign $20). Universidade Estadual de Campinas, Centro de Logica, Epistemologia e Historia da Ciencia - State University of Campinas, Center for Logic, Epistemology and History of Science, Caixa Postal 6133, Barao Geraldo, 13081-870 Campinas, SP, Brazil. TEL 0192-397374. FAX 0192-393269. TELEX 0191150. Eds. Marcelo Dascal, Michael Wrigley. adv.; bk.rev.; illus. circ. 700. **Indexed:** Phil.Ind. **Document type:** academic/scholarly publication.

MARKETING SIGNS; a newsletter at the crossroads of marketing, semiotics and consumer research. see *BUSINESS AND ECONOMICS — Marketing And Purchasing*

100   NE   ISSN 0924-4948
MARTINUS NIJHOFF PHILOSOPHY TEXTS. (Text in English) 1979. irreg. price varies. Kluwer Academic Publishers, Postbus 17, 3300 AA Dordrecht, Netherlands. TEL 31-78-392254. FAX 31-78-392254. TELEX 29245 KAPG NL. (Dist. by: Kluwer Academic Publishers Group, P.O. Box 322, 3300 AH Dordrecht, Netherlands. TEL 31-78-392392. FAX 31-78-546474; N. America dist. addr.: Box 358, Accord Sta., Hingham, MA 02018-0358. TEL 617-871-6600. FAX 617-871-6528) **Document type:** monographic series.

100   XR
MASARYKOVA UNIVERSITA. FILOZOFICKA FAKULTA. SBORNIK PRACI. B: RADA FILOZOFICKA. 1953. irreg. (approx. a). price varies. Masarykova Universita, Filozoficka Fakulta, A. Novaka 1, 660 88 Brno, Czech Republic. FAX 41-211241. bk.rev. **Document type:** proceedings.
Formerly: Universita J.E. Purkyne. Filozoficka Fakulta. Sbornik Praci. B: Rada Filozoficka (ISSN 0231-7664)
Description: Articles on ethics, aesthetics, logic and the history of philosophy.

MASTER OF LIFE. see *NEW AGE PUBLICATIONS*

180   US   ISSN 0076-5856
MEDIAEVAL PHILOSOPHICAL TEXTS IN TRANSLATION. 1942. a. price varies. Marquette University Press, Box 1881, Milwaukee, WI 53201-1881. TEL 414-288-1564. Ed. Roland Teske, S.J. (reprint service avail. from UMI) **Document type:** academic/scholarly publication.

100   PL   ISSN 0076-5880
MEDIAEVALIA PHILOSOPHICA POLONORUM. (Text in French or German) 1957. a. price varies. Polska Akademia Nauk, Instytut Filozofii i Socjologii, Ul. Nowy Swiat 72, 00-330 Warsaw, Poland. TEL 48-22-267181. Ed. W. Senko. **Indexed:** M.L.A. **Document type:** academic/scholarly publication.
—BLDSC (5525.295000).
Description: Dissertations on philosophical thought in the works of great philosophers, with commentaries.

MEDICAL ETHICS ADVISOR. see *MEDICAL SCIENCES*

180 370   US   ISSN 1057-0608
B721
MEDIEVAL PHILOSOPHY AND THEOLOGY. 1991. a. $29.95. University of Notre Dame Press, Notre Dame, IN 46556. TEL 219-631-6343. FAX 219-631-8148. (Orders to: 11030 S. Langley Ave., Chicago, IL 60628. TEL 800-621-2736. FAX 800-621-8476; Overseas orders to: Eurospan University Press Group, Order Dept., 3 Henrietta St., London WC2E 8LU, England) Ed. Mark D. Jordan. **Document type:** academic/scholarly publication.
—BLDSC (5534.266080).
Description: Provides a forum for ideas between disciplinary boundaries and among contrasting scholarly methodologies and traditions.

MEDIEVALIA ET HUMANISTICA; studies in medieval and renaissance culture. see *HISTORY — History Of Europe*

109   IT   ISSN 0391-2566
B720
MEDIOEVO; rivista di storia della filosofia medievale. 1975. irreg., no.17, 1991. price varies. (Universita degli Studi di Padova, Centro per Ricerche di Filosofia Medievale) Editrice Antenore, Via Rusca 15, Padua 35100, Italy. Ed.Bd.

100   CC
MEI YU SHIDAI. (Text in Chinese) m. Zhengzhou Daxue, Meixue Yanjiusuo - Zhengzhou University, Aesthetics Research Institute, No. 75, Daxue Lu, Zhengzhou, Henan 450052, People's Republic of China. TEL 771541. Ed. Zhang Heng.

MELITA THEOLOGICA. see *RELIGIONS AND THEOLOGY*

MERLEG; folyoiratok es konyvek szemleje. see *RELIGIONS AND THEOLOGY*

141 628   US
MESECHABE: THE JOURNAL OF SURREGIONALISM. 1988. 2/yr. $15 for 5 nos. Center for Gulf South History and Culture, Inc., 7725 Cohn St., New Orleans, LA 70118. TEL 504-861-8832. Eds. John Clark, Dennis Formento. circ. 1,000. **Document type:** newsletter.
Description: Explores philosophical issues concerning the ecology of the Mississippi River Basin.

100   AU   ISSN 1017-8279
MESOTES. 1991. q. S.560 (effective 1996). (Oesterreichische Gesellschaft fuer Philosophischen Ost-West-Dialog) Wilhelm Braumueller, Universitaets-Verlagsbuchhandlung GmbH, Servitengasse 5, A-1092 Vienna, Austria. TEL 01-3191159. FAX 01-3102805. index. (back issues avail.) **Document type:** academic/scholarly publication.

100   UK   ISSN 0026-1068
B1
METAPHILOSOPHY. 1970. q. £90($186) (foreign £111) (effective 1996). (Metaphilosophy Foundation, US) Basil Blackwell Ltd., 108 Cowley Rd., Oxford OX4 1JF, England. TEL 0865-791100. FAX 0865-791347. TELEX 837022-OXBOOK-G. Ed. Terrell Ward Bynum. adv.; bk.rev.; index. circ. 650. (reprint service avail. from SWZ) **Indexed:** Arts & Hum.Cit.Ind., Curr.Cont., Lang.& Lang.Behav.Abstr., Phil.Ind.
—BLDSC (5701.600000); Faxon; Genuine Article; SWETS; UMI; UnCover. **CCC.**

110   US
METAPHYSICAL FELLOWSHIP CHURCH. NEWSLETTER. m. free. Metaphysical Fellowship Church, 10591 Flower St., Stanton, CA 90680-2326. Ed. Yvonne Goodale. adv. contact: Yvonne Goodale. **Document type:** newsletter.

100   GW   ISSN 0327-0289
B5
METHEXIS; revista de filosofia antigua. 1988. a. DM.68. Academia Verlag GmbH, Postfach 1663, 53734 Sankt Augustin, Germany. TEL 02241-333349. FAX 02241-341528. (Subscr. in S. America to: Victoria Julia, C.C. 2059-Correo Central, RA-1000 Buenos Aires, Argentina) Ed. Conrado Eggers Lan. **Document type:** academic/scholarly publication.

018 200   US   ISSN 0736-7392
BD241
METHOD: JOURNAL OF LONERGAN STUDIES. 1983. s-a. $14 to individuals; institutions $25. Lonergan Institute at Boston College, Department of Philosophy, Carney Hall 216, Boston College, Chestnut Hill, MA 02167-3806. TEL 617-552-3845. Ed.Bd. bk.rev. circ. 300. (back issues avail.) **Indexed:** Phil.Ind. **Document type:** academic/scholarly publication.
—BLDSC (5745.601000).

100   CI   ISSN 0353-765X
METODICKI OGLEDI. (Text in Croatian; summaries in English) 1990. s-a. Hratsko Filozofsko Drustvo - Croatian Philosophical Society, Dure Salaja 3, 41000 Zagreb, Croatia. Ed. Milan Polic. circ. 600.
Description: Aims to foster a dialogue between philosophical and scientific approaches to education.

MIDWEST QUARTERLY; a journal of contemporary thought. see *HUMANITIES: COMPREHENSIVE WORKS*

100   US   ISSN 0363-6550
MIDWEST STUDIES IN PHILOSOPHY. 1976. irreg., vol.21, 1995. price varies. University of Notre Dame Press, Notre Dame, IN 46556. TEL 219-631-6346. FAX 219-631-8148. TELEX 62131650. (Orders to: 11030 S. Langley Ave., Chicago, IL 60628. TEL 800-621-2736. FAX 800-621-8476; Overseas orders to: Eurospan University Press Group, Order Dept., 3 Henrietta St., London WC2E 8LU, England) Ed.Bd. **Indexed:** Phil.Ind. **Document type:** academic/scholarly publication.
—BLDSC (5761.447600); SWETS; UnCover.
Description: Covers a single theme in philosophyy reflecting a wide range of views.

MILLTOWN STUDIES. see *RELIGIONS AND THEOLOGY*

100 150 UK ISSN 0026-4423
B1
MIND; a quarterly review of philosophy. 1876. q. £38($68) (effective 1996). (Mind Association) Oxford University Press, Oxford Journals, Walton St., Oxford OX2 6DP, England. TEL 01865-267907. FAX 01865-267773. TELEX 837330-OXPRES-G. E-mail: jnlorders@oup.co.uk. (U.S. subscr. to: Oxford University Press Inc., 2001 Evans Rd., Cary, NC 27513. TEL 919-677-0977. FAX 919-677-1714) Ed. Mark Sainsbury. adv. contact: Jane Parker. bk.rev.; index, cum.index. circ. 3,500. (also avail. in microform from UMI,PMC; reprint service avail. from KTO) **Indexed:** Amer.Hist.& Life, Arts & Hum.Cit.Ind., Br.Hum.Ind., Curr.Cont., Hist.Abstr., Hum.Ind., Ind.Bk.Rev.Hum., Lang.& Lang.Behav.Abstr., Math.R., Phil.Ind., SSCI. **Document type:** academic/scholarly publication.
—BLDSC (5775.500000); Faxon; Genuine Article; SWETS; UMI; UnCover. **CCC.**
Description: Expresses and gives direction to currents of thought in epistemology, the philosophy of language, metaphysics and philosophical psychology.

100 UK ISSN 0268-1064
P37 CODEN: MILAEB
MIND & LANGUAGE. 1986. q. £113($222) (foreign £138) (effective 1996). Basil Blackwell Ltd., 108 Cowley Rd., Oxford OX4 1JF, England. TEL 0865-791100. FAX 0865-791347. TELEX 837022-OXBOOK-G. Ed.Bd. adv.; bk.rev. (also avail. in microform; reprint service avail. from SWZ) **Indexed:** Art.Int.Abstr., Bibl.Ling., INSPEC (1988-), Psychol.Abstr. (1992-).
—BLDSC (5775.526400); Faxon; SWETS; UMI; UnCover. **CCC.**

100 500 US ISSN 0076-9258
Q175
MINNESOTA STUDIES IN THE PHILOSOPHY OF SCIENCE. 1956. irreg., vol.15, 1992. price varies. (Minnesota Center for Philosophy of Science) University of Minnesota Press, 111 Third Ave., S., Ste. 290, Minneapolis, MN 55401-2520. TEL 800-388-3863. FAX 612-627-1980. Ed.Bd. index. circ. 1,500. (reprint service avail. from UMI) **Indexed:** ASCA, SSCI. **Document type:** academic/scholarly publication.
—BLDSC (5810.465000). **CCC.**
Description: Essays drawn from research and conferences sponsored by the center.
Refereed Serial

MIRA; a monthly journal of Indian culture. see *LITERARY AND POLITICAL REVIEWS*

MISCELANEA COMILLAS; revista de teologia y ciencias humanas. see *RELIGIONS AND THEOLOGY*

MISCELLANEA FRANCESCANA; rivista trimestrale di scienze teologiche e di studi francescani. see *RELIGIONS AND THEOLOGY — Roman Catholic*

MITHILA INSTITUTE OF POST GRADUATE STUDIES AND RESEARCH IN SANSKRIT LEARNING. BULLETIN. see *LINGUISTICS*

MITZION TETZEH TORAH. M.T.T. see *RELIGIONS AND THEOLOGY — Judaic*

100 GW ISSN 0170-3013
MODERN GERMAN STUDIES. irreg., no.17, 1990. price varies. Bouvier Verlag Herbert Grundmann, Am Hof 28, 53113 Bonn, Germany. TEL 0228-7290124. FAX 0228-7290179. **Document type:** monographic series.
—BLDSC (5886.720000).

100 US ISSN 0026-8402
B1
MODERN SCHOOLMAN; a quarterly of philosophy. 1925. q. $26. Staint Louis University, 221 N. Grand, St. Louis, MO 63103. TEL 314-658-3149. Ed. William C. Charron. adv.; bk.rev. circ. 600. **Indexed:** Arts & Hum.Cit.Ind., Cath.Ind., CERDIC, Curr.Cont., Mid.East: Abstr.& Ind., Phil.Ind. **Document type:** academic/scholarly publication.
—BLDSC (5896.400000); Faxon; Genuine Article; SWETS; UnCover.
Description: Promotes historical research and critical analysis of philosophy of all periods: ancient, medieval, Renaissance and modern.
Refereed Serial

100 US ISSN 1051-127X
MOKSHA JOURNAL. (Text in English, Sanskrit) 1984. s-a. $8. Vajra Printing & Publishing of Yoga Anand Ashram, 49 Forrest Pl., Amityville, NY 11701. TEL 516-691-8475. Ed. Rocco LoBosco. circ. 500. (back issues avail.) **Document type:** academic/scholarly publication.

100 IT ISSN 0544-7526
MOMENTO; rivista di testimonianze e di dialogo. 1965. bi-m. Via Duccio di Boninsegna 25, Milan, Italy. Ed.Bd. abstr.

174.95 344 AT ISSN 1321-2753
MONASH BIOETHICS REVIEW. 1981. q. Aus.$42 to individuals; institutions Aus.$60. Monash University, Centre for Human Bioethics, Clayton, Vic. 3168, Australia. TEL 61-3-9054278. FAX 61-3-9053279. E-mail: john.mckie@arts.monash.edu.au. Ed. Helga Kuhse. circ. 1,000.
—BLDSC (5901.591450).
Description: Presents the study of the ethical, social and legal problems arising out of medical and biomedical research.

100 US ISSN 0026-9662
B1
MONIST; an international quarterly of general philosophical inquiry. 1890. q. $25 to individuals; institutions $48. Hegeler Institute, Box 600, La Salle, IL 61301. TEL 815-223-1500. FAX 815-223-4486. Ed. Barry Smith. adv.; bk.rev.; abstr. circ. 1,600. (back issues avail.; reprint service avail. from KTO) **Indexed:** Arts & Hum.Cit.Ind., Curr.Cont., Hum.Ind., Mid.East: Abstr.& Ind., Phil.Ind., SSCI. **Document type:** academic/scholarly publication.
—BLDSC (5908.600000); Faxon; Genuine Article; SWETS; UnCover.

100 170 FR ISSN 0026-9727
MONITEUR DU REGNE DE LA JUSTICE; journal bi-mensuel philanthropique et humanitaire, pour le relevement moral et social. (Editions in Dutch, English, French, Italian, Portuguese and Spanish) 1936. s-m. 25 F. Association les Amis de l'Homme, 22 rue David d'Angers, 75019 Paris, France. Ed. R. Cavin.

100 840 FR ISSN 0982-0191
MONITOIRES DU CYMBALUM PATAPHYSICUM. 1949. q. 211 F.($10) includes 2 monographs. College de Pataphysique, Courtaumont par Sermiers, 51500 Rilly la Montagne, France. Ed. Paul Gayot. illus.
Former titles (until 1986): Organographes du Cymbalum Pataphysicum (ISSN 0339-7203); (until 1975): Subsidia Pataphysica (ISSN 0039-4386); College de Pataphysique. Dossiers.

MONTESSORI NEWS. see *EDUCATION*

MORALITY AND THE MEANING OF LIFE. see *RELIGIONS AND THEOLOGY*

MORGENROTE. see *RELIGIONS AND THEOLOGY*

100 RU ISSN 0579-9465
B6
MOSKOVSKII UNIVERSITET. VESTNIK. SERIYA 8: FILOSOFIYA. 1946. bi-m. 13.50 Rub. Moskovskii Universitet, Ul. Gertsena 5-7, 103009 Moscow, Russia. bk.rev.; bibl.; index. **Indexed:** Rural Recreat.Tour.Abstr., World Agri.Econ.& Rural Sociol.Abstr. **Document type:** academic/scholarly publication.
Supersedes in part: Moskovskii Universitet. Vestnik. Seriya Ekonomika, Filosofiya (ISSN 0027-1365)

100 954 II ISSN 0027-1543
MOTHER INDIA; review of culture. (Text in English) 1949. m. Rs.80($18) Sri Aurobindo Ashram Trust, Pondicherry 605002, India. Ed. K.D. Sethna. adv.; bk.rev. circ. 1,050.

180 II ISSN 0027-2574
MOUNTAIN PATH. 1964. s-a. Rs.30($15) Sri Ramanasramam, Sri Ramanasramam, P.O., Tiruvannamali 606 603, India. TEL 04175-2491. Pub. V.S. Ramanan. adv.; bk.rev.; charts; illus.; index. circ. 5,000.
Description: Spiritual articles and poems devoted to Sri Bhagavan Ramana Maharshi.

100 GW ISSN 0077-1856
II
MUENCHNER UNIVERSITAETS-SCHRIFTEN. REIHE DER PHILOSOPHISCHEN FAKULTAET. 1965. irreg., latest vol.23. DM.48. Wilhelm Fink Verlag, Ohmstr. 5, 80802 Munich, Germany. TEL 089-348017. FAX 089-341378. **Document type:** monographic series.

100 DR
MUSEO DEL HOMBRE DOMINICANO. SERIE CONFERENCIAS PENSAMIENTO DOMINICANO. 1974. irreg. RD.$5. Museo del Hombre Dominicano, Calle Pedro Henriquez Urena, Santo Domingo, Dominican Republic.

100 DR
MUSEO DEL HOMBRE DOMINICANO. SERIE CONFERENCIAS SOBRE EL PENSAMIENTO DE PEDRO HENRIQUEZ URENA. irreg., no.2. RD.$5. Museo del Hombre Dominicano, Calle Pedro Henriquez Urena, Santo Domingo, Dominican Republic. TEL 687-3622.

MYSTICS QUARTERLY. see *RELIGIONS AND THEOLOGY*

294.54 II
NANDAN KANAN. (Text in Bengali) 1975. m. Rs.66 (foreign Rs.120). Adarsha Prakashani, Ma-Mahajnana Bishwa Kalyan Trust, Kharagpur 721 305, W.B., India. TEL 03222-661. circ. 10,000.

170 JA ISSN 0918-2209
NANZAN FORUM FOR SOCIAL ETHICS. (Text in Japanese) 1992. a. free. Nanzan University, Nanzan Institute for Social Ethics, 18 Yamazato-cho, Showa-ku, Nagoya-shi, Aichi-ken 466, Japan. TEL 052-832-3111. FAX 052-832-6157. **Document type:** academic/scholarly publication.

170 JA
▼**NANZAN INSTITUTE OF SOCIAL ETHICS MONOGRAPH SERIES**. (Text in Japanese) 1994. every 3 yrs. free. Nanzan University, Nanzan Institute for Social Ethics, 18 Yamazato-cho, Showa-ku, Nagoya-shi, Aichi-ken 466, Japan. TEL 052-832-3111. FAX 053-832-6157. **Document type:** monographic series.

100 UK
NATIONAL SECULAR SOCIETY. ANNUAL REPORT. 1867. a. membership. National Secular Society, 702 Holloway Rd., London N19 3NL, England. TEL 01-272-1266. Ed. T. Mullins.
Description: Contains a report of the Society's activities.

NATURAL LANGUAGE SEMANTICS; an international journal of semantics and its interfaces in grammar. see *LINGUISTICS*

215 291 US
NAZAN STUDIES IN RELIGION & CULTURE. 1982. irreg., no.15, 1991. price varies. University of California Press, 2120 Berkeley Way, Berkeley, CA 94720. TEL 510-642-4247. FAX 510-643-7127. (Orders to: California-Princeton Fulfillment Services, 1445 Lower Ewing Rd., Ewing, NJ 08618. TEL 800-777-4726. FAX 800-999-1958) (back issues avail.) **Document type:** monographic series.
Description: Examines Eastern and Western philosophical issues.
Refereed Serial

100 300 CC ISSN 1001-7623
NEI MENGGU SHIFAN DAXUE XUEBAO (ZHEXUE SHEHUI KEXUE HANWEN BAN)/INNER MONGOLIAN TEACHERS UNIVERSITY. JOURNAL (PHILOSOPHY & SOCIAL SCIENCE CHINESE EDITION). (Text in Chinese) 1983. q. Nei Menggu Shifan Daxue, Huhhot, Nei Menggu 010022, People's Republic of China. TEL 464444. **Document type:** academic/scholarly publication.
—UnCover.

100 500 RU ISSN 0301-5386
B67
NEKOTORYE FILOSOFSKIE VOPROSY SOVREMENNOGO ESTESTVOZNANIYA. 1973. irreg. 0.66 Rub. Sankt-Peterburgskii Universitet, Universitetskaya Nab. 7-9, St. Petersburg V-164, Russia. TEL 218-9788. TELEX 121481.

NEW AGE EXCHANGE; a magazine of contemporary metaphysical thought. see *NEW AGE PUBLICATIONS*

NEW ATHENAEUM/NEUES ATHENAEUM. see *LITERATURE*

PHILOSOPHY

NEW FRONTIER; magazine of transformation. see *NEW AGE PUBLICATIONS*

144   UK   ISSN 0306-512X
AP4
NEW HUMANIST. 1885. q. £15. Rationalist Press Association Ltd., Bradlaugh House, 47 Theobald's Rd., London WC1X 8SP, England. TEL 0171-430-1371. FAX 0171-430-1271. Ed. Jim Herrich. adv.; bk.rev. (also avail. in microform from UMI; reprint service avail. from UMI) Indexed: Br.Hum.Ind. **Document type:** bulletin.
—BLDSC (6084.246000); UMI.
Formerly: Humanist (ISSN 0018-7380)

100   UK   ISSN 0307-0980
NEW HUMANITY JOURNAL; journal for the creative individual - the free and independent thinker. 1975. bi-m. £29. New Humanity, 51a York Mansions, Prince of Wales Dr., London SW11 4BP, England. TEL 0171-622-4013. FAX 0171-498-0173. Ed. Johan Henri Quanjer. adv.; bk.rev. circ. 14,000. (back issues avail.) **Document type:** academic/scholarly publication.
—BLDSC (6084.246700).
Description: Integrates the disciplines of science, philosophy, politics, the arts, religion and the humanities to promote closer cooperation and understanding among them.

NEW PARADIGMS NEWSLETTER. see *SCIENCES: COMPREHENSIVE WORKS*

100   US   ISSN 1045-4500
NEW PERSPECTIVES IN PHILOSOPHICAL SCHOLARSHIP: TEXTS AND ISSUES. irreg. Peter Lang Publishing, Inc., 62 W. 45th St., 4th Fl., New York, NY 10036. TEL 212-302-6740. FAX 212-302-7574. Ed. James Duerlinger. **Document type:** academic/scholarly publication, monographic series.
Description: Seeks to integrate a range of different fields in philosophy which in the past have not often been combined.

100 230.94   US   ISSN 0028-6443
BX8701
THE NEW PHILOSOPHY. 1898. q. $8 to non-members. Swedenborg Scientific Association, Box 757, Bryn Athyn, PA 19009. TEL 215-947-2577. FAX 215-438-1056. Ed. Erland J. Brock. bk.rev.; cum.index every 3 yrs. circ. 450.
—UnCover.
Description: Articles address philosophical questions and topics that bear on the works of Emanuel Swedenborg.

100   US   ISSN 0093-4240
B1
NEW SCHOOL FOR SOCIAL RESEARCH. GRADUATE FACULTY PHILOSOPHY JOURNAL. (Text in English; contributions in French, German, Greek and Latin) 1971. s-a. $15 to individuals; institutions $35. New School for Social Research, Philosophy Department, 65 Fifth Ave., New York, NY 10003. TEL 212-229-5735. Ed. Robert Del Principe. adv.; bk.rev. circ. 1,000. (back issues avail.) Indexed: Phil.Ind. **Document type:** academic/scholarly publication.
—BLDSC (4206.827000); Faxon; UnCover.
Description: Promotes a scholarly forum exploring the diverse aspects of the history of philosophy and contemporary continental thought.

100   US   ISSN 0893-6005
NEW STUDIES IN AESTHETICS. (Text in English and other West European languages.) 1987. irreg., vol.2, 1988. Peter Lang Publishing, Inc., 62 W. 45th St., 4th Fl., New York, NY 10036. TEL 212-302-6740. Ed. Robert Ginsberg. **Document type:** academic/scholarly publication, monographic series.
—BLDSC (6088.773000).

109 160   NE
NEW SYNTHESE HISTORICAL LIBRARY; texts and studies in the history of logic and philosophy. 1969. irreg., vol.40, 1992. price varies. Kluwer Academic Publishers, Postbus 17, 3300 AA Dordrecht, Netherlands. TEL 31-78-392392. FAX 31-78-392254. TELEX 29245 KAPG NL. (Dist. by: Kluwer Academic Publishers Group, P.O. Box 322, 3300 AH Dordrecht, Netherlands. TEL 31-78-392392. FAX 31-78-546474; N. America dist. addr.: Box 358, Accord Sta., Hingham, MA 02018-0358. TEL 617-871-6600. FAX 617-871-6528) Ed.Bd. Indexed: Math.R. **Document type:** monographic series.
—CCC.
Formerly (until vol.37, 1990): Synthese Historical Library (ISSN 0082-111X)
Refereed Serial

100 200   US
NEW THOUGHT JOURNAL. 1992. q. $15 (effective 1995 & 1996). Box 700754, Tulsa, OK 74170. FAX 918-492-6237. (Dist. by: I P D, 674 Via de la Valle, Ste. 200, Solana Beach, 92075. TEL 619-481-5928) Ed. Edward Wincentsen. adv.; bk.rev. circ. 1,500. (back issues avail.)
Description: Contains poetry and articles on religion, philosophy and spirituality.

NEW TIMES (SEATTLE); enriching and changing lives since 1985. see *NEW AGE PUBLICATIONS*

100   US   ISSN 0733-9542
B3580.A1
NEW VICO STUDIES. 1983. a. $39.95. Humanities Press, 165 First Ave., Atlantic Highlands, NJ 07716-1289. TEL 908-872-1441. FAX 908-872-0717. Eds. Giorgio Tagliacozzo, Donald Phillip Verene. bk.rev. circ. 750. Indexed: Phil.Ind. **Document type:** academic/scholarly publication.
—Faxon.
Description: Includes articles, reviews, abstracts and notes reflecting the current state of the study of the thought of Giambattista Vico.

THE NEW WORLD. see *RELIGIONS AND THEOLOGY — Roman Catholic*

140   NZ   ISSN 0028-8632
NEW ZEALAND RATIONALIST AND HUMANIST; a journal on philosophy, science, religion, literature & society. 1927. q. NZ.$10. New Zealand Rationalist Association Inc., 64 Symonds St., Auckland 1, New Zealand. Ed. Bill Cooke. bk.rev. circ. 1,000. **Document type:** academic/scholarly publication.
—CCC.
Former titles (until 1964): New Zealand Rationalist; (until 1939): Truthseeker.

100   GW   ISSN 0342-1422
NIETZSCHE-STUDIEN; internationales Jahrbuch fuer die Nietzsche-Forschung. (Text in English and German) a. price varies. Walter de Gruyter und Co., Genthiner Str. 13, 10785 Berlin, Germany. TEL 030-26005-0. FAX 030-26005251. TELEX 184027. (U.S. addr.: Walter de Gruyter, Inc., 200 Saw Mill River Rd., Hawthorne, NY 10532) Indexed: Bibl.Ling., M.L.A., RILM. **Document type:** academic/scholarly publication.
—BLDSC (6110.950000).

NIGHTSUN; a journal of poetry, short-short fiction, and interviews. see *LITERATURE*

100   NE   ISSN 0924-4530
NIJHOFF INTERNATIONAL PHILOSOPHY SERIES. (Text in English) 1976. irreg., vol.47, 1993. price varies. Kluwer Academic Publishers, Postbus 17, 3300 AA Dordrecht, Netherlands. TEL 31-78-392392. FAX 31-78-392254. TELEX 29245 KAPG NL. (Dist. by: Kluwer Academic Publishers Group, P.O. Box 322, 3300 AH Dordrecht, Netherlands. TEL 31-78-392392. FAX 31-78-546474; N. America dist. addr.: Box 358, Accord Sta., Hingham, MA 02018-0358. TEL 617-871-6600. FAX 617-871-6528) Ed. Jan T.J. Srzednicki. Indexed: Math.R. **Document type:** monographic series.
—BLDSC (6113.172400).
Formerly (until 1989): Melbourne International Philosophy Series (ISSN 0924-493X)
Refereed Serial

NOOR AL-ISLAM; thiqafiyyah islamiyyah - islamic cultural magazine. see *RELIGIONS AND THEOLOGY — Islamic*

111   SW   ISSN 0284-7698
NORDISK ESTETISK TIDSKRIFT. (Text in Scandinavian languages and English) 1988. s-a. SEK 150. Nordiska Saellskapet foer Estetik, Uppsala Universitet, Institutionen foer Estetik, Stlottet, soedra taarnet, Inngang H, S-752 37 Uppsala, Sweden. TEL 46-18-18-15-82. FAX 46-18-18-15-89. Ed. Goeran Soerbom. **Document type:** academic/scholarly publication.

100 943   GW
NORDRHEIN-WESTFAELISCHE AKADEMIE DER WISSENSCHAFTEN. GEISTESWISSENSCHAFTEN VORTRAEGE. irreg. Westdeutscher Verlag GmbH (Leverkusen), Postfach 300944, 51338 Leverkusen, Germany. TEL 02171-44741. FAX 02171-48308. (back issues avail.) **Document type:** monographic series.
Formerly: Rheinisch-Westfaelische Akademie der Wissenschaften. Geisteswissenschaften Vortraege.

100   NO   ISSN 0029-1943
CODEN: NGGTAZ
NORSK FILOSOFISK TIDSSKRIFT/NORWEGIAN JOURNAL OF PHILOSOPHY. (Text in the Scandinavian languages) 1966. q. NOK 360 in Nordic countries; elsewhere $66 (effective 1996). Scandinavian University Press, P.O. Box 2959 Toeyen, N-0608 Oslo, Norway. TEL 47-22-57-54-00. FAX 47-22-57-53-53. (U.S. addr.: Scandinavian University Press, 200 Meacham Ave., Elmont, NY 11003. TEL 516-352-7300) Ed. Audun Oefsti. adv.; bk.rev.; bibl.; index. circ. 350.

NOTRE DAME JOURNAL OF FORMAL LOGIC. see *MATHEMATICS*

100   US   ISSN 0029-4624
B1
NOUS. 1967. 4/yr. $38 to individuals in N. America (elsewhere $50.50); institutions in N. America $81.50 (elsewhere $96). (Indiana University, Department of Philosophy) Blackwell Publishers, 238 Main St., Cambridge, MA 02142. TEL 617-547-7110. FAX 617-547-0789. Ed.Bd. adv.: page $365; trim 4 1/2 x 7 1/2. bk.rev.; index, cum.index. circ. 1,200. (also avail. in microfilm from UMI; back issues avail.) Indexed: Ind.Bk.Rev.Hum., Lang.& Lang.Behav.Abstr., Math.R., Phil.Ind. **Document type:** academic/scholarly publication.
—BLDSC (6176.310000); Faxon; Genuine Article; SWETS; UMI; UnCover. **CCC.**
Description: Publishes critical essays, brief discussions, and important results of philosophic research.

100   IT   ISSN 0392-2332
AS222.N775
NOUVELLES DE LA REPUBLIQUE DES LETTRES. 1981. s-a. L.50000($47) (foreign L.80000). (Istituto Italiano per gli Studi Filosofici) Prismi, Editrice Politecnica Napoli, Via F. Caracciolo 17, 80122 Naples, Italy. TEL 081-7612884. FAX 81-668339. Eds. Paul Dibon, Tullio Gregory. adv.; bk.rev. circ. 500. Indexed: M.L.A.
Description: Covers philosophy, science and art from the Renaissance and the Enlightenment periods.

NUDITARIAN. see *POLITICAL SCIENCE*

100   IT
NUOVA CIVILTA DELLE MACCHINE. 1983. q. L.50000 (foreign L.75000). E R I Edizioni R A I, Via Arsenale 41, 10121 Torin, Italy. TEL 011-8800. FAX 011-534732. Ed. Francesco Barone. bk.rev.

NUOVA CORRENTE; rivista di letteratura e filosofia. see *LITERATURE*

NUOVA UNIVERSALE STUDIUM. see *LITERATURE*

105   DK   ISSN 0107-7384
ODENSE UNIVERSITY STUDIES IN PHILOSOPHY. (Text in Danish and English) 1972. irreg. price varies. Odense University Press, Campusvej 55, DK-5230 Odense M, Denmark. TEL 66-157999. FAX 66-158126. (back issues avail.)

ODGOJ I SAMOUPRAVLJANJE. see *EDUCATION*

ODRA. see *LITERATURE*

PHILOSOPHY

100 SA ISSN 0256-0356
ODYSSEY; an adventure in more conscious living. 1977. 5/yr. R.30 (foreign R.40). Wellstead Association, The Wellstead, 1 Wellington Ave., Wynberg 7800, Cape Town, South Africa. TEL 021-797-8982. Ed. Rose de la Hunt. adv.: B&W page R.800, color page R.1600; trim 266 x 190. bk.rev.; tr.lit. circ. 6,000. (back issues avail.) **Indexed:** Ind.Child.Mag. **Document type:** consumer publication.
Description: Covers self-discovery, inspiration and transformation, philosophy, holistic health and nutrition, ecology, metaphysics, personal and spiritual growth and parapsychology.

OESTERREICHISCHE AKADEMIE DER WISSENSCHAFTEN. PHILOSOPHISCH-HISTORISCHE KLASSE. ANZEIGER. see HISTORY — History Of Europe

100 AU
OESTERREICHISCHEN KARL-JASPERS-GESELLSCHAFT. JAHRBUCH. irreg., no.5, 1992. varies. Universitaet Graz, Institut fuer Philosophie, Heinrichstr. 26, A-8010 Graz, Austria. Ed. Kurt Salamun. **Document type:** academic/scholarly publication.

ON COURSE; weekly inspiration for the inner journey. see NEW AGE PUBLICATIONS

190 940 NE
ON THE MAKING OF EUROPE. (Text in English) 1992. irreg., vol.2, 1993. price varies. Kok Pharos Publishing House, Postbus 5019, 8260 AG Kampen, Netherlands. TEL 31-5202-92565. FAX 31-5202-27331. (Dist. in U.S. and Canada by: Books International, Inc., Box 605, Herndon, VA 22070-0605. TEL 800-377-7192. FAX 703-689-0660) Ed. Jurjen Wiersma. (back issues avail.) **Document type:** monographic series.
Description: Discusses philosophical and ethical issues arising from the integration of Europe, with particular emphasis on studies of people and groups at the margins of the process.

ON WINGS. see WOMEN'S INTERESTS

OOMOTO. see RELIGIONS AND THEOLOGY — Other Denominations And Sects

100 200 US
OPINION. 1952. m. $10. (Gospel Truth Association) Opinion Publications, Box 681, Cape May Court House, NJ 08210-0681. Ed. James E. Kurtz. adv.: bk.rev.; illus.; tr.lit.; index; circ. 3,700 (controlled). (back issues avail.) **Document type:** academic/scholarly publication.
Description: Commentary on current events, with essays on philosophy, sociology, and theology.

144 US
OPOSSUM HOLLER TAROT;* an underground magazine. 1983. irreg. Larry Blazek, Ed. & Pub., RR 3 Box 109, Orleans, IN 47452-9649.

ORIENTIERUNG; katholische Blaetter fuer weltanschauliche Information. see RELIGIONS AND THEOLOGY — Roman Catholic

100 II
ORIYA-AUROVILIAN. (Text in English) 1972. q. Rs.18. Sri Aurobindo Sansktuti Sansad, Women's Wing, 39 Udyan Marg, Bhubaneswar, Orissa, India. Ed. Amar Singh. adv.; bk.rev.; illus. circ. 1,000. (reprint service avail.)

ORPHEUS; rivista di umanita classica e cristiana. see LITERATURE

OSHO TIMES INTERNATIONAL. see RELIGIONS AND THEOLOGY — Hindu

100 US ISSN 0030-7580
B2900
OWL OF MINERVA. 1969. s-a. $15 to individuals; institutions $25. Hegel Society of America, c/o Lawrence S. Stepelevich, Ed., Department of Philosophy, Villanova University, Villanova, PA 19085. TEL 215-519-4747. adv.; bk.rev.; bibl.; cum.index; circ. 620 (paid). (also avail. in microfilm) **Indexed:** Phil.Ind. **Document type:** academic/scholarly publication.
—BLDSC (6320.540000); Faxon; UnCover.
Description: Academic publication featuring articles, notes, and reports on Hegel, Hegelianism, and related subjects.

OXFORD CLASSICAL AND PHILOSOPHICAL MONOGRAPHS. see CLASSICAL STUDIES

OXFORD EDITIONS OF CUNEIFORM TEXTS. see ARCHAEOLOGY

OXFORD LITERARY REVIEW; critical analyses of literary, philosophical, political and psycho-analytic theory. see LITERATURE

100 US ISSN 0265-7651
B1
OXFORD STUDIES IN ANCIENT PHILOSOPHY. 1983. a. $69. Oxford University Press, 200 Madison Ave., New York, NY 10016. TEL 212-679-7600. FAX 212-725-2972. (Subscr. to: Oxford University Press, 2001 Evans Rd., Cary, NC 25713. TEL 919-677-0977) Ed. Julia Annas. **Document type:** academic/scholarly publication.
—BLDSC (6321.021800); Faxon; UnCover.
Refereed Serial

190 UK
P L I WARWICK JOURNAL OF PHILISOPHY. 1989. irreg. University of Warwick, Department of Philosophy, Coventry CV4 7AL, England. Ed. Joan Broadhurst. (back issues avail.) **Document type:** academic/scholarly publication.
Description: Concentrates on contemporary work coming from the European neo-Kantian and phenomological tradition.

P R O U T PRESS. (Progressive Utilization Theory) see GENERAL INTEREST PERIODICALS — United States

100 UK ISSN 0279-0750
AP2 CODEN: PPHQEJ
PACIFIC PHILOSOPHICAL QUARTERLY. 1920. q. £54($70) (foreign £60) (effective 1996). (University of Southern California, School of Philosophy, US) Basil Blackwell Ltd., 108 Cowley Rd., Oxford OX4 1JF, England. TEL 44-1865-791100. FAX 44-1865-791347. Ed.Bd. adv.; bibl.; index. circ. 850. (also avail. in microform from UMI; reprint service avail. from UMI; back issues avail.) **Indexed:** Arts & Hum.Cit.Ind., Bibl.Engl.Lang.& Lit., Curr.Cont., Hum.Ind., Phil.Ind., SSCI. **Document type:** academic/scholarly publication.
—BLDSC (6330.700000); Faxon; Genuine Article; UMI; UnCover. **CCC.**
Formerly (until vol.61, Jan. 1980): Personalist (ISSN 0031-5621)

PACIFICA; Australian theological studies. see RELIGIONS AND THEOLOGY

100 370 US ISSN 0190-1176
B1
PAIDEIA (BUFFALO). 1972. a. $10. State University of New York at Buffalo, Department of Foundational Studies, 1300 Elmwood Ave., Buffalo, NY 14222. TEL 716-878-4303. Ed. Albert Grande. adv.; bk.rev. circ. 1,000. **Indexed:** M.L.A.

100 CN ISSN 0838-4517
PAIDEUSIS. 1987. s-a. Can.$8 to non-members; members Can.$4; institutions Can.$12. Canadian Philosophy of Education Society, c/o Prof. Don Cochrane, Manag.Ed., University of Saskatchewan, Dept. of Educational Foundations, Saskatoon, SK S7N 0W0, Canada. FAX 306-966-8719. Ed. William Hare. bk.rev. circ. 125.
Description: Covers communication and interaction among philosophers of education in Canada.
Refereed Serial

100 PK ISSN 0078-8406
PAKISTAN PHILOSOPHICAL CONGRESS. PROCEEDINGS. (Text in English) 1954. a. $7. Pakistan Philosophical Congress, Department of Philosophy, University of the Punjab, New Campus, Lahore 20, Pakistan. Ed. Abdul Khaliq. circ. 900. **Document type:** proceedings.

100 PK ISSN 0552-914X
B1
PAKISTAN PHILOSOPHICAL JOURNAL. (Text in English) 1962. s-a. $7. Pakistan Philosophical Congress, Department of Philosophy, University of the Punjab, New Campus, Lahore 20, Pakistan. Ed. Abdul Khaliq. adv.; bk.rev.; bibl. circ. 1,000. **Indexed:** Phil.Ind.

113 291.14 US ISSN 0742-5368
PANTHEIST VISION. 1980. q. $15. Universal Pantheist Society, Box 265, Big Pine, CA 93513. TEL 209-739-8527. E-mail: visalian@aol.com. Ed. Harold J. Wood, Jr. bk.rev. (back issues avail.) **Document type:** newsletter.
Description: Espouses a way of life in opposition to anthropocentrism and in favor of reverence for the Earth, accepting nature as the ultimate context for human existence.

100 200 II
PARMARTH; religious monthly. (Text in Gujarati) 1953. m. Rs.110 (foreign Rs.250). Jai Hind Publications, Jai Hind Press Bldg., Babubhai Shah Marg, Rajkot 360 001, India. TEL 281-40513. FAX 281-48677. Ed. Y.N. Shah. adv. circ. 25,000.
Description: Promotes moral ethics of religion and philosophy.

PASHTO ACADEMY. MONTHLY JOURNAL. see LITERATURE

PATHWAY TO GOD; one God, one world, one humanity. see RELIGIONS AND THEOLOGY

100 641.1 US
PATHWAYS TO HEALTH. 1978. 4/yr. $25 donation. A.R.E. Medical Clinic, 4018 N. 40th St., Phoenix, AZ 85018. TEL 602-955-0551. Ed. Scott Grady. adv.; circ. 3,500 (controlled).
Description: Based on the Edgar Cayce readings, PTH includes holistic health tips, A.R.E. Clinic programs, educational activities and research projects, and Edgar Cayce insights on health.

170 US ISSN 0079-0249
PAUL ANTHONY BRICK LECTURES. 1960. irreg., no.10, 1993. price varies. University of Missouri Press, 2910 LeMone Blvd., Columbia, MO 65202. TEL 314-882-7641. FAX 314-884-4498. Ed. Beverly Jarrett. **Document type:** academic/scholarly publication.
Refereed Serial

104 US ISSN 0079-0257
PAUL CARUS LECTURES. 1925. irreg., no.18, 1994. price varies. (American Philosophical Association) Open Court Publishing Co., General Books (Subsidiary of: Carus Corporation), 315 Fifth St., Box 599, Peru, IL 61354. TEL 815-223-1500. index. (reprint service avail. from UMI) **Document type:** monographic series.

100 291 US ISSN 1059-2350
BP605.S73
PEARLS OF WISDOM. 1958. w. $45. (Church Universal and Triumphant) Summit Lighthouse, Box 5000, Corwin Springs, MT 59030-5000. TEL 406-848-7441. FAX 406-848-7441. Ed. Elizabeth Clare Prophet. circ. controlled. (also avail. in microfiche; back issues avail.)
Description: Disseminates the teachings and progressive revelation from the Ascended Masters delivered through their messengers, Mark L. and Elizabeth Clare Prophet, with insights and techniques to accelerate one's spiritual growth.

101 SP ISSN 0031-4749
B5
PENSAMIENTO; revista de investigacion e informacion filosofica. 1945. q. 4800 ptas.($45) (Europe $60; Latin America $65; US $70; Asia $75) (effective 1995). Centro Loyola de Estudios y Comunicacion Social, Pablo Aranda 3, 28006 Madrid, Spain. FAX 341-563-4073. bk.rev.; bibl.; index. **Indexed:** Phil.Ind.

PERMANENCIA. see RELIGIONS AND THEOLOGY

PERSATUAN PURE LIFE. ANNUAL REPORT. see SOCIAL SERVICES AND WELFARE

PERSISTENCE OF VISION. see MOTION PICTURES

PERSONA Y SOCIEDAD. see SOCIAL SCIENCES: COMPREHENSIVE WORKS

PHILOSOPHY

100 US ISSN 0889-065X
B828.5.A1
PERSONALIST FORUM. 1985. s-a. $10 to individuals; institutions $15 (effective Jan. 1991). Furman University, Department of Philosophy, Poinsett Hwy., Greenville, SC 29613. TEL 803-294-3139. FAX 803-294-3001. Ed. Thomas O. Buford. circ. 150.
●Also available online. Vendor(s): Knight-Ridder, Inc.
—CCC.
Description: Scholarly articles that address issues associated with being persons in this world, with reviews of philosophical works that are relevant to that theme.

100 200 CN ISSN 0847-0324
PERSPECTIVE. 1966. q. Can.$15($15) Institute for Christian Studies, 229 College St., Toronto, ON M5T 1R4, Canada. TEL 416-979-2331. FAX 416-979-2332. Ed. Robert E. VanderVennen. illus. circ. 6,000. (back issues avail.) **Document type:** newsletter.
Description: Promotes and provides information about the ICS and its work on the advancement of Christian scholarship.

PERSPECTIVE ON CONSCIOUSNESS & PSI RESEARCH. see NEW AGE PUBLICATIONS

100 GW
▼**PERSPECTIVES IN ANALYTICAL PHILOSOPHY.** 1994. irreg. price varies. Walter de Gruyter und Co., Genthiner Str. 13, 10785 Berlin, Germany. TEL 030-26005-0. FAX 030-26005251. (U.S. addr.: 200 Saw Mill River Rd., Hawthorne, NY 10532. TEL 914-747-0110) Eds. Georg Meggle, Ulla Wessels. **Document type:** monographic series.

100 NE ISSN 0171-1288
B3
PERSPEKTIVEN DER PHILOSOPHIE. NEUES JAHRBUCH. (Text in English, German) 1975. a., vol.19, 1993. fl.115($67.50) Editions Rodopi B.V., Keizersgracht 302-304, 1016 Amsterdam, Netherlands. TEL 31-20-6227507. FAX 31-20-6380948. E-mail: F.van.der.Zee@Rodopi.nl. (In N. America: 233 Peachtree St. N.E., Atlanta GA 30303-1504. TEL 800-225-3998. FAX 404-522-7116) Ed.Bd. adv.; bk.rev. circ. 500. **Document type:** academic/scholarly publication.

142 NE ISSN 0079-1350
PHAENOMENOLOGICA. (Text in English, French, German) 1958. irreg., vol.129, 1993. price varies. (Centre d'Archives Husserl, BE) Kluwer Academic Publishers, Postbus 17, 3300 AA Dordrecht, Netherlands. TEL 31-78-392392. FAX 31-78-392254. TELEX 29245 KAPG NL. (Dist. by: Kluwer Academic Publishers Group, P.O. Box 322, 3300 AH Dordrecht, Netherlands. TEL 31-78-392392. FAX 31-78-546474; N. America dist. addr.: Box 358, Accord Sta., Hingham, MA 02018-0358. TEL 617-871-6600. FAX 617-871-6528) Ed. S. Ysseling. **Indexed:** Rel.Ind.Two. **Document type:** monographic series.
Refereed Serial

142.7 GW
PHAENOMENOLOGISCHE FORSCHUNGEN/PHENOMENOLOGICAL STUDIES. 1975. s-a. (Deutsche Gesellschaft fuer Phaenomenologische Forschung) Karl Alber GmbH, Hermann Herder Str. 4, 79104 Freiburg, Germany. Ed. Ernst Wolfgang Orth. bibl.

100 US
PHENOMENA.* 4/yr. $10. P O M Project Newsletter, 612 Camino Verde, South Pasadena, CA 91030-4140. Ed. Robert Stowell. illus.

PHENOMENEWS; exploring human potential, holistic health and living. see NEW AGE PUBLICATIONS

100 US ISSN 0885-3886
B829.5
PHENOMENOLOGICAL INQUIRY; a review of philosophical ideas and trends. (Text mainly in English; occasionally in French, German) 1976. a. $30 to individuals (outside N. America $35). World Phenomenology Institute, 348 Payson Rd., Belmont, MA 02178. TEL 617-489-3696. FAX 617-489-3696. Ed. Anna-Teresa Tymieniecka. adv.; bk.rev.; bibl. circ. 1,000. (back issues avail.) **Document type:** academic/scholarly publication.
—SWETS; UnCover.
Formerly (until 1985): Phenomenology Information Bulletin (ISSN 0278-8322)

100 200 US
PHENOMENOLOGICAL THEOLOGY. irreg. Peter Lang Publishing, Inc., 62 W. 45th St., 4th Fl., New York, NY 10036. TEL 212-302-6740. FAX 212-302-7574. Ed. Stephen W. Laycock. **Document type:** academic/scholarly publication, monographic series.

100 US
PHIL FACTS. 1984. s-a. free. Bowling Green State University, Philosophy Documentation Center, Bowling Green, OH 43403-0189. TEL 419-372-2419; 800-444-2419. FAX 419-372-6987. Ed. Lori Fells. **Document type:** newsletter.
Description: Contains news, announcements and information on philosophical activities.

100 410 IT
PHILO (:) LOGICA; rassegna di analisi linguistica ed ironia culturale. Issued with: Centro Studi Archivio Barocco. Bollettino. 1992. s-a.? L.30000 (effective 1994). Universita di Parma, Centro Studi Archivio Barocco, Via Universita 12, 43100 Parma, Italy. TEL 0521-200542. FAX 0521-208170. Eds. Marzio Pieri, Lorenzo Pozzi. **Document type:** academic/scholarly publication.

PHILOLOGOS/SCHOLAR. see CLASSICAL STUDIES

100 UK ISSN 0967-6074
PHILOSOPHER. 1913. 2/yr. £1.50 to non-members. Philosophical Society, 92 Worple Rd., Wimbledon, London SW19, England. adv.; bk.rev.
Description: Covers the study of philosophy for the general public.

100 US
PHILOSOPHER OF CREATIVITY MONOGRAPH SERIES. 1984. irreg. price varies. Foundation for Philosophy of Creativity, Inc., c/o Larry Cobb, Dept. of Government, Slippery Rock University, Slippery Rock, PA 16057. TEL 412-794-2938. (Subscr. to: University Press of America, 4720 Boston Way, Lanham, MD 20706. TEL 301-459-3366) Ed. John C. Thomas. (back issues avail.) **Document type:** monographic series.
Description: For researchers at all levels. Explores the nature and structure of creativity.

190 BE ISSN 0079-1660
PHILOSOPHES CONTEMPORAINS. 1948. irreg. price varies. Universite Catholique de Louvain, Institut Superieur de Philosophie, 1 chemin d'Aristote, B-1348 Louvain-la-Neuve, Belgium. TEL 016-48-81-02. FAX 016-48-14-86. **Document type:** monographic series.

180 BE ISSN 0079-1679
PHILOSOPHES MEDIEVAUX. 1948. irreg., no.31, 1994. price varies. Editions Peeters s.p.r.l., Bondgenotenlaan 153, 3000 Leuven, Belgium. TEL 32-16-235170. FAX 32-16-228500. **Document type:** academic/scholarly publication.

100 AG ISSN 0031-8000
PHILOSOPHIA. 1944. s-a. exchange basis. Universidad Nacional de Cuyo, Instituto de Filosofia, Facultad de Filosofia y Letras, Parque General San Martin, Mendoza, Argentina. **Indexed:** Arts & Hum.Cit.Ind.

100 IS ISSN 0048-3893
PHILOSOPHIA; philosophical quarterly of Israel. 1971. q. $21 to individuals; institutions $28 (effective 1992). (Bar-Ilan University, Department of Philosophy) Bar-Ilan University Press, Ramat Gan 52900, Israel. Ed. Asa Kasher. adv.; bk.rev.; bibl.; charts. circ. 600. **Indexed:** Curr.Cont., Phil.Ind. **Document type:** academic/scholarly publication.
—BLDSC (6461.492000); Faxon; Genuine Article; UnCover.

105 GR
PHILOSOPHIA. (Text in English, French, German, or Greek) 1971. a. $40. Academy of Athens, Research Center for Greek Philosophy - Kentron Erevnis tis Hellenikes Philosophias, 14 Anagnostopoulou, 106 73 Athens, Greece. TEL 30-1-3600-140. Ed. E. Moutsopoulos. bk.rev. circ. 1,000. (back issues avail.) **Indexed:** Bull.Signal., Phil.Ind. **Document type:** academic/scholarly publication.
Description: Includes articles about philosophy, the history of philosophy, and the philosophy of right, of literature, and aesthetics.

100 DK ISSN 0108-1632
PHILOSOPHIA; tidsskrift for filosofi. (Text in Danish, Norwegian, Swedish) 1977. q. DKK 200 to individuals; institutions DKK 275. Filosofisk Forening i Aarhus, Institut for Filosofi, Aarhus Universitet, 8000 Aarhus C, Denmark. Ed. Lone Kalstrup. adv.; bk.rev. circ. 500.
Formerly: Philosophia Aarhusiensis (ISSN 0556-0136)

180 NE ISSN 0079-1687
PHILOSOPHIA ANTIQUA. 1946. irreg., vol.65, 1995. price varies. E.J. Brill, P.O. Box 9000, 2300 PA Leiden, Netherlands. TEL 31-71-5353500. FAX 31-71-5317532. TELEX 39296 BRILL NL. (In N. America: E.J. Brill, 24 Hudson St., Kinderhook, NY 12106. TEL 800-962-4406. FAX 518-758-1959) (back issues avail.) **Document type:** monographic series.
Description: Scholarly monographs on topics in ancient philosophy.
Refereed Serial

510.01 CN ISSN 0031-8019
QA9 CODEN: PHMAB5
PHILOSOPHIA MATHEMATICA; philosophy of mathematics, its learning, and its application. (Text in English, French) 1964-1981 (vol.18); 2nd series 1986-1991 (vol.6); 3rd series 1993. s-a. $29 to individuals; institutions $60 (effective 1993). (Canadian Society for History and Philosophy of Mathematics - Societe Canadienne d'Histoire et de Philosophie des Mathematiques) University of Toronto Press, Journals Department, 5201 Dufferin St., Downsview, ON M3H 5T8, Canada. TEL 416-667-7838. FAX 416-667-7881. Ed. Robert Thomas. adv.; bk.rev.; index. circ. 500. (back issues avail.) **Indexed:** Math.R., Phil.Ind., Zent.Math. **Document type:** academic/scholarly publication.
—BLDSC (6461.500000); Faxon; UnCover.
Description: Philosophical study in the nature of mathematics.
Refereed Serial

530 146 GW ISSN 0031-8027
B3
PHILOSOPHIA NATURALIS; Archiv fuer Naturphilosophie und die philosophischen Grenzgebiete der exakten Wissenschaften und Wissenschaftsgeschichte. 1950. s-a. DM.158. Vittorio Klostermann, Frauenlobstr. 22, 60487 Frankfurt a.M., Germany. TEL 069-774011. FAX 069-708038. adv.; bk.rev.; bibl.; index. circ. 1,000. **Indexed:** Math.R., Phil.Ind. **Document type:** academic/scholarly publication.
—SWETS; UnCover.

185 US ISSN 1195-8553
▼**PHILOSOPHIA PERENNIS.** 1994. s-a. $40 membership; libraries $50 (effective 1995-1996). Society for Aristotelian Sudies, c/o Robert Augros, Treas., Box 1643, St. Anselm College, 100 St. Anselm Dr., Manchester, NH 03102. TEL 603-641-7065. Ed. Gerard Campbell. bk.rev.; circ. 160 (paid). **Document type:** academic/scholarly publication.
Refereed Serial

294.54 NE ISSN 0031-8035
BX9401
PHILOSOPHIA REFORMATA. (Summaries in several languages) 1936. s-a. fl.60 to individuals (effective 1995-1996). Stichting voor Reformatorische Wijsbegeerte, Postbus 368, 3500 AJ Utrecht, Netherlands. TEL 31-30-342030. Ed. J. van der Hoeven. bk.rev.; bibl. circ. 800. **Indexed:** CERDIC, Phil.Ind. **Document type:** academic/scholarly publication.
Description: Addresses issues facing Calvinist philosophy.

100 NE
PHILOSOPHIA RELIGIONIS. irreg., vol.27, 1993. price varies. Van Gorcum en Co. B.V., P.O. Box 43, 9400 AA Assen, Netherlands. TEL 31-5920-46846. FAX 31-5920-72064. **Document type:** monographic series.

100 NE
PHILOSOPHIA SPINOZAE PERENNIS. 1976. irreg., no.9, 1994. price varies. Van Gorcum en Co. B.V., P.O. Box 43, 9400 AA Assen, Netherlands. TEL 31-5920-46846. FAX 31-5920-72064. Ed. H. de Dijn. bibl.; index. **Document type:** monographic series.

100		II
PHILOSOPHICA. (Text in Bengali or English) q. Rs.10. Shankar Basu, 50b Haldarpara Rd., Calcutta 700026, India.

100	BE	ISSN 0379-8402
B63		

PHILOSOPHICA. (Text in Dutch, English, French and German) 1963. s-a. 600 BEF. Rijksuniversiteit Gent, Department of Philosophy, Rozier 44, B-9000 Ghent, Belgium. Ed. Diderik Batens. adv.; bk.rev. circ. 350. Indexed: Phil.Ind. **Document type:** academic/scholarly publication.
—BLDSC (6461.635000).
Formerly (until 1974): Studia Philosophica Gandensia (ISSN 0081-6833)
Description: Journal of philosophical inquiry. Each volume is devoted to a current issue in epistemology, philosophy of science, ethics, or social philosophy.

180		NE

PHILOSOPHICA. (Text in English) 1983. irreg., vol.4, 1992. J.C. Gieben, Nieuwe Herengracht 35, 1011 RM Amsterdam, Netherlands. TEL 31-20-6275170. FAX 31-20-6275170. (Dist. in N. America by: John Benjamins Publishing Co., Box 27519, Philadelphia, PA 19118-0519. TEL 215-836-1200. FAX 215-836-1204) (back issues avail.) **Document type:** monographic series.

100 016	UK	ISSN 0031-8051
Z7127		

PHILOSOPHICAL BOOKS. 1960. q. £75($155) (foreign £96) (effective 1996). Basil Blackwell Ltd., 108 Cowley Rd., Oxford OX4 1JF, England. TEL 0865-791100. FAX 0865-791100. TELEX 837022-OXBOOK-G. Ed. Anthony Ellis. adv.; bk.rev. circ. 850. (reprint service avail. from SWZ) **Indexed:** Arts & Hum.Cit.Ind., Curr.Cont., Ind.Bk.Rev.Hum., Phil.Ind.
—BLDSC (6461.640000); Faxon; SWETS; UMI. **CCC.**

100	US	ISSN 0031-806X
B1		

PHILOSOPHICAL FORUM. 1942. q. $15 to individuals (foreign $19); institutions $60 (foreign $64). Philosophical Forum, Inc., c/o Baruch College, Box 239, 17 Lexington Ave., NY 10010. TEL 212-387-1682. Ed. Marx W. Wartofsky. adv.; bibl.; index. circ. 2,000. (back issues avail.) **Indexed:** Curr.Cont., Int.Polit.Sci.Abstr., Phil.Ind. **Document type:** academic/scholarly publication.
●Also available online. Vendor(s): Ovid Technologies.
—BLDSC (6461.700000); Faxon; Genuine Article; UnCover.

105	GR	ISSN 1105-235X

PHILOSOPHICAL INQUIRY. 1978. q. $40. Aristotelian University, P.O. Box 84, Thessaloniki, Greece. TEL 30-31-992-519. Ed. D.Z. Andriopoulos; Pub. D.Z. Andriopoulos. adv. contact: Helen Andriopoulos. bk.rev.; bibl. circ. 1,300. (back issues avail.) **Document type:** academic/scholarly publication.
Description: Examines Ancient Greek philosophy, theory of knowledge - epistemology, aesthetics, ethics, philosophy of language, and philosophy of literature.
Refereed Serial

100	UK	ISSN 0190-0536
B1		

PHILOSOPHICAL INVESTIGATIONS. 1978. q. £85($182) (foreign £113) (effective 1996). Basil Blackwell Ltd., 108 Cowley Rd., Oxford OX4 1JF, England. TEL 0865-791100. FAX 0865-791347. TELEX 837022-OXBOOK-G. Ed. D.Z. Phillips. adv.; bk.rev.; index. circ. 650. (back issues avail.; reprint service avail. from SWZ) **Indexed:** Arts & Hum.Cit.Ind., Curr.Cont., Phil.Ind.
—BLDSC (6461.780000); Faxon; Genuine Article; SWETS; UMI. **CCC.**

100	SA	ISSN 0556-8641

PHILOSOPHICAL PAPERS. (Text in English) 1972. 3/yr. R.60($18) to individuals; institutions R.150($55); students R.25($11) (effective 1995). c/o Dept. of Philosophy, University of the Witwatersrand, Private Bag 3, Wits 2050, South Africa. TEL 716-2890. FAX 403-1174.
E-mail: 103philp@muse.arts.wits.ac.za. Ed. Michael Pendlebury. adv. circ. 450. (back issues avail.) **Indexed:** Ind.S.A.Per., Phil.Ind. **Document type:** academic/scholarly publication.
—BLDSC (6462.200000).
Description: An international journal of philosophy in the broad analytical tradition.

190		NE

▼**PHILOSOPHICAL PROBLEMS TODAY/PROBLEMES PHILOSOPHIQUES D'AUJOURD'HUI.** (Text in English, French) 1994. irreg. price varies. (Institut International de Philosophie, FR) Kluwer Academic Publishers, Postbus 17, 3300 AA Dordrecht, Netherlands. TEL 31-78-392392. FAX 31-78-392254. TELEX 29245 KAPG NL. (Dist. by: Kluwer Academic Publishers Group, P.O. Box 322, 3300 AH Dordrecht, Netherlands. TEL 31-78-392392. FAX 31-78-546474; N. America dist. addr.: Box 358, Accord Sta., Hingham, MA 02018-0358. TEL 617-871-6600. FAX 617-871-6528) Ed. Guttorm Floistad. **Document type:** monographic series.
Description: Publishes extensive discussions of topical philosophical problems.
Refereed Serial

PHILOSOPHICAL PSYCHOLOGY. see PSYCHOLOGY

100	UK	ISSN 0031-8094
B1		

PHILOSOPHICAL QUARTERLY. 1950. q. £62($134) (foreign £83) (effective 1996). (University of St. Andrews, Scots Philosophical Club) Basil Blackwell Ltd., 108 Cowley Rd., Oxford OX4 1JF, England. TEL 0865 791100. FAX 0865-791347. TELEX 837022-OXBOOK-G. Ed.Bd. adv.; bk.rev.; bibl.; index. circ. 1,600. (also avail. in microform from UMI; reprint service avail. from SWZ,UMI) **Indexed:** Arts & Hum.Cit.Ind., Br.Hum.Ind., Curr.Cont., Hum.Ind., Ind.Bk.Rev.Hum., Lang.& Lang.Behav.Abstr., M.L.A., Phil.Ind, SSCI.
—BLDSC (6462.300000); Faxon; Genuine Article; SWETS; UMI; UnCover. **CCC.**

100		CH

PHILOSOPHICAL RESEARCH. 1982-1987; resumed 1992. a. $20 per no. Soochow University, Philosophy Department - Tung Wu Ta Hsueh Che Hsueh Hsi, Wai Shuang Hsi, Shih Lin, Taipei, Taiwan, Republic of China. FAX 8829310. bk.rev.
Formerly (until 1992): Chuanxi Lu (ISSN 1010-0725)

100	US	ISSN 0031-8108
B1		

PHILOSOPHICAL REVIEW. 1892. q. $54 (foreign $60) (effective 1996). Cornell University, Sage School of Philosophy, 327 Goldwin Smith Hall, Ithaca, NY 14853. TEL 607-255-6817. FAX 607-255-1454. Ed. Terence Irwin. adv.; bk.rev.; bibl.; index. circ. 3,000. (also avail. in microform from MIM,UMI,PMC; reprint service avail. from UMI) **Indexed:** Arts & Hum.Cit.Ind., Bk.Rev.Ind. (1965-), Child.Bk.Rev.Ind. (1965-), Curr.Cont., Deep Sea Res.& Oceanogr.Abstr., Hum.Ind., Ind.Bk.Rev.Hum., Lang.& Lang.Behav.Abstr., M.L.A., Phil.Ind., SSCI. **Document type:** academic/scholarly publication.
—BLDSC (6462.700000); Faxon; Genuine Article; SWETS; UMI.

190	NE	ISSN 0031-8116
B21		CODEN: PLSDA3

PHILOSOPHICAL STUDIES; an international journal for philosophy in the analytic tradition. 1950. m. fl.1214 to institutions; $742 to institutions in U.S. (effective 1996). Kluwer Academic Publishers, Postbus 17, 3300 AA Dordrecht, Netherlands. TEL 31-78-392392. FAX 31-78-392254. TELEX 29245 KAPG NL. E-mail: SERVICES@WKAP.NL. (Dist. by: Kluwer Academic Publishers Group, P.O. Box 322, 3300 AH Dordrecht, Netherlands. TEL 31-78-392392. FAX 31-78-546474; N. America dist. addr.: Box 358, Accord Sta., Hingham, MA 02018-0358. TEL 617-871-6600. FAX 617-871-6528) Eds. Keith Lehrer, Stewart Cohen. adv.; bk.rev. (also avail. in microform from UMI; reprint service avail. from SWZ) **Indexed:** Arts & Hum.Cit.Ind., ASCA, Bull.Signal., Cath.Ind., Curr.Cont., IBR, IBZ, Ind.Bk.Rev.Hum., Lang.& Lang.Behav.Abstr., M.L.A., Math.R., Phil.Ind., Sociol.Abstr., SSCI. **Document type:** academic/scholarly publication.
—BLDSC (6462.900000); Faxon; Genuine Article; SWETS; UMI; UnCover. **CCC.**
Description: Publishes work in analytical philosophy, particularly in epistemology, philosophical logic, the philosophy of language and ethics.
Refereed Serial

100 300	NE	ISSN 0928-9518

PHILOSOPHICAL STUDIES IN CONTEMPORARY CULTURE. (Text in English) 1992. irreg., vol.2, 1994. price varies. Kluwer Academic Publishers, Postbus 17, 3300 AA Dordrecht, Netherlands. TEL 31-78-392392. FAX 31-78-392254. (Dist. by: Kluwer Academic Publishers Group, P.O. Box 322, 3300 AH Dordrecht, Netherlands. TEL 31-78-392392. FAX 31-78-546474; N. America dist. addr.: Box 358, Accord Sta., Hingham, MA 02018-0358. TEL 617-871-6600. FAX 617-871-6528) Ed. H. Tristam Engelhardt, Jr. **Document type:** monographic series.

100	NE	ISSN 0921-8599

PHILOSOPHICAL STUDIES SERIES. 1974. irreg. price varies. Kluwer Academic Publishers, Postbus 17, 3300 AA Dordrecht, Netherlands. TEL 31-78-392392. FAX 31-78-392254. TELEX 29245 KAPG NL. (Dist. by: Kluwer Academic Publishers Group, P.O. Box 322, 3300 AH Dordrecht, Netherlands. TEL 31-78-392392. FAX 31-78-546474; N. America dist. addr.: Box 358, Accord Sta., Hingham, MA 02018-0358. TEL 617-871-6600. FAX 617-871-6528) Eds. Wilfrid Sellars, Keith Lehrer. **Indexed:** Math.R. **Document type:** monographic series.
—BLDSC (6462.937000).
Formerly (until 1987): Philosophical Studies Series in Philosophy (ISSN 0169-7323)
Refereed Serial

100	US	ISSN 0276-2080
B1		

PHILOSOPHICAL TOPICS. 1970. 2/yr. $25 to individuals; institutions $45. University of Arkansas Press, 201 Ozark Ave., Fayetteville, AR 72701. FAX 501-575-6044. Ed. Christopher Hill. adv. circ. 750. (reprint service avail. from ISI) **Indexed:** Arts & Hum.Cit.Ind., Curr.Cont., Phil.Ind., SSCI. **Document type:** academic/scholarly publication.
—BLDSC (6462.947000); Faxon; UnCover.
Formerly: Southwestern Journal of Philosophy (ISSN 0038-481X)

100	FR	ISSN 0294-1805

PHILOSOPHIE (PARIS). 1984. q. 188 F. (foreign 226 F.). Editions de Minuit, 7 rue Bernard-Palissy, 75006 Paris, France. TEL 44-39-39-20. FAX 45-44-82-36. Ed. Claude Romano. bk.rev. **Document type:** academic/scholarly publication.
—SWETS.
Description: Presents current philosophic works in the Anglo-Saxon world, original French works and interpretations of classical texts.

100	FR	ISSN 0760-9620

PHILOSOPHIE IMAGINAIRE. 1985. s-a. Editions de L'Eclat, Combas, F-30250 Sommieres, France. TEL 66-77-87-63.

PHILOSOPHIE POLITIQUE; revue internationale de philosophie politique. see POLITICAL SCIENCE

PHILOSOPHY

100   NE   ISSN 0927-4405
PHILOSOPHIE & REPRAESENTATION/PHILOSOPHY & REPRESENTATION. (Text in German) 1992. irreg. Editions Rodopi B.V., Keizersgracht 302-304, 1016 EX Amsterdam, Netherlands. TEL 31-20-6227507. FAX 31-20-6380948. E-mail: F.van.der.Zee@Rodopi.nl. (In N. America: 233 Peachtree St., N.E., Ste. 404, Atlanta, GA 30303-1504. TEL 800-225-3998. FAX 404-522-7116) **Document type:** monographic series.

181   GW   ISSN 0233-089X
PHILOSOPHIEHISTORISCHE TEXTE. 1955. irreg. price varies. Akademie Verlag GmbH, Muehlenstr. 33-34, 13187 Berlin, Germany. TEL 030-47889348. FAX 030-47889357. **Document type:** monographic series.
     Formerly: Philosophische Studientexte (ISSN 0079-1717)

100 305.4   GW   ISSN 0936-7586
HQ1190
DIE PHILOSOPHIN; Forum fuer feministische Theorie und Philosophie. 1990. s-a. DM.30. Edition Diskord, Schwarzlocher Str. 104-b, 72070 Tuebingen, Germany. TEL 07071-40102. FAX 07071-44710. Eds. Astrid Deuber-Mankowsky, Ursula Konnertz. adv.; bk.rev. circ. 1,200. **Document type:** academic/scholarly publication.

100   CN   ISSN 0316-2923
B2
PHILOSOPHIQUES. 1974. s-a. Can.$40 (foreign Can.$45). Editions Fides, 165 rue Deslaurier, Ville St. Laurent, PQ H4N 2S4, Canada. TEL 514-745-4290. **Indexed:** Phil.Ind., Pt.de Rep. (1983-).
     —BLDSC (6464.059500); Faxon.

100   GW   ISSN 0175-6508
PHILOSOPHISCHE ABHANDLUNGEN. irreg., vol.63, 1995. price varies. Vittorio Klostermann, Frauenlobstr. 22, 60487 Frankfurt a.M., Germany. TEL 069-9708160. FAX 069-708038. (Subscr. to: Postfach 900601, 60446 Frankfurt a.M., Germany) **Indexed:** Math.R. **Document type:** monographic series.

100   GW   ISSN 0031-8159
B3
PHILOSOPHISCHE RUNDSCHAU. 1953. q. DM.132 (students DM.66). Verlag J.C.B. Mohr (Paul Siebeck), Wilhelmstr 18, 72074 Tuebingen, Germany. TEL 07071-923-0. FAX 07071-51104. TELEX 7262872-MOHR-D. (Subscr. to: Postfach 2040, 72010 Tuebingen, Germany) Eds. R. Bubner, B. Waldenfels. adv.; bk.rev.; cum.index. **Indexed:** Arts & Hum.Cit.Ind., Curr.Cont., Phil.Ind. **Document type:** academic/scholarly publication.
     —Faxon; Genuine Article; SWETS. **CCC.**
     Description: Philosophical journal that follows international philosophical publications, outlines trends, examines schools and research programs.

100   GW   ISSN 0175-9574
PHILOSOPHISCHE TEXTE UND STUDIEN. irreg., vol.38, 1993. price varies. Georg Olms Verlag, Hagentorwall 7, 31134 Hildesheim, Germany. TEL 05121-1501-0. FAX 05121-150150. (U.S. subscr. to: 111 W. 57th St., New York, NY 10019. TEL 212-757-5237) **Document type:** monographic series.

100   GW   ISSN 0031-8175
PHILOSOPHISCHER LITERATURANZEIGER. 1949. 4/yr. DM.148. Vittorio Klostermann GmbH, Frauenlobstr. 22, 60487 Frankfurt a.M., Germany. TEL 069-774011. FAX 069-708038. (Subscr. to: Postfach 900601, 60446 Frankfurt a.M., Germany) Ed.Bd. adv.; bk.rev.; abstr.; bibl.; index. circ. 700. **Document type:** academic/scholarly publication.
     —SWETS.
     Description: Includes elaborate reports of new books in philosophy and related fields, published in German and other languages. Also includes comparative philosophical essays.

100   GW   ISSN 0031-8183
B3
PHILOSOPHISCHES JAHRBUCH. 1888. a. DM.94. (Goerres-Gesellschaft) Karl Alber GmbH, Hermann-Herder-Str.4, 79104 Freiburg, Germany. Ed.Bd. bk.rev.; abstr.; bibl. circ. 800. (reprint service avail. from KTO,SCH) **Indexed:** Arts & Hum.Cit.Ind., Curr.Cont., Ind.Bk.Rev.Hum., Phil.Ind., RILM.
     —BLDSC (6464.470000); Faxon; Genuine Article; SWETS. **CCC.**

100   UK   ISSN 0031-8191
B1
PHILOSOPHY. (Two supplements avail.) 1925. q. £116($204) (effective 1996). (Royal Institute of Philosophy) Cambridge University Press, Edinburgh Bldg., Shaftesbury Rd., Cambridge CB2 2RU, England. TEL 01223-312393. FAX 01223-315052. TELEX 851817256. (N. American addr.: Cambridge University Press, Journals Dept., 40 W. 20th St., New York, NY 10011. TEL 212-924-3900. FAX 212-691-3239) Ed. Anthony O'Hear. adv.; bk.rev.; index. (also avail. in microform from UMI; back issues avail.) **Indexed:** Abstr.Crim.& Pen., Br.Hum.Ind., Curr.Cont., Deep Sea Res.& Oceanogr.Abstr., Hum.Ind., Ind.Bk.Rev.Hum., Mid.East: Abstr.& Ind., Phil.Ind., Psychol.Abstr, SSCI. **Document type:** academic/scholarly publication.
     —BLDSC (6464.500000); Faxon; Genuine Article; SWETS; UMI; UnCover. **CCC.**
     Description: Contains significant articles in the field of philosophy; also serves the philosophical interests of specialists in other fields and those of the general reader.

PHILOSOPHY AND ARTIFICIAL INTELLIGENCE. see COMPUTERS — Artificial Intelligence

100 370   NE   ISSN 0923-9065
PHILOSOPHY AND EDUCATION. (Text in English) 1988. irreg., vol.4, 1992. price varies. Kluwer Academic Publishers, Postbus 17, 3300 AA Dordrecht, Netherlands. TEL 31-78-392392. FAX 31-78-392254. TELEX 29245 KAPG NL. (Dist. by: Kluwer Academic Publishers Group, P.O. Box 322, 3300 AH Dordrecht, Netherlands. TEL 31-78-392392. FAX 31-78-546474; N. America dist. addr.: Box 358, Accord Sta., Hingham, MA 02018-0358. TEL 617-871-6600. FAX 617-871-6528) **Document type:** monographic series.
     Refereed Serial

100 800   US   ISSN 0190-0013
PN2   CODEN: PHILEL
PHILOSOPHY AND LITERATURE. 1976. s-a. $22 to individuals (foreign $27.50); institutions $43 (foreign $48.50). (Whitman College) Johns Hopkins University Press, Journals Publishing Division, 2715 N. Charles St., Baltimore, MD 21218. TEL 410-516-6987. FAX 410-516-6968. Ed. Denis Dutton. adv. contact: Tara Dorai-Berry. bk.rev.; bibl. circ. 1,100. (back issues avail.) **Indexed:** Abstr.Engl.Stud., Amer.Bibl.Slavic & E.Eur.Stud., Amer.Hum.Ind., Arts & Hum.Cit.Ind., Bibl.Engl.Lang.& Lit., Can.Rev.Comp.Lit., Curr.Cont., Ind.Bk.Rev.Hum., LCR, M.L.A., Phil.Ind. **Document type:** academic/scholarly publication.
     —BLDSC (6464.570000); Faxon; Genuine Article; SWETS; UMI; UnCover. **CCC.**
     Description: Addresses fresh perspectives to two modes on inquiry through its effective interdisciplinary approach to the study of major literary and philosophical texts.

100 610   NE   ISSN 0376-7418
     CODEN: PHIMDN
PHILOSOPHY AND MEDICINE. (Text in English) 1975. irreg, vol.47, 1994. price varies. Kluwer Academic Publishers, Postbus 17, 3300 AA Dordrecht, Netherlands. TEL 31-78-392392. FAX 31-78-392254. TELEX 29245 KAPG NL. (Dist. by: Kluwer Academic Publishers Group, P.O. Box 322, 3300 AH Dordrecht, Netherlands. TEL 31-78-392392. FAX 31-78-546474; N. America dist. addr.: Box 358, Accord Sta., Hingham, MA 02018-0358. TEL 617-871-6600. FAX 617-871-6528) Eds. H. Tristram Engelhardt Jr., Stuart F. Spicker. **Indexed:** Biol.Abstr. **Document type:** monographic series.
     —BLDSC (6464.580000); Faxon; SWETS.
     Refereed Serial

100 142.7   US   ISSN 0031-8205
B1   CODEN: PPHRAI
PHILOSOPHY AND PHENOMENOLOGICAL RESEARCH. 1940. q. $20 to individuals (foreign $24); institutions $55 (foreign $59 (effective 1996). International Phenomenological Society, Brown University, Box 1947, Providence, RI 02912. TEL 401-863-3215. FAX 401-863-2719. E-mail: ppr@brownvm.brown.edu. Ed. Ernest Sosa. adv. contact: Suzanne Bertrand. bk.rev. (also avail. in microform from UMI) **Indexed:** Amer.Bibl.Slavic & E.Eur.Stud., Arts & Hum.Cit.Ind., Curr.Cont., Hum.Ind., Ind.Bk.Rev.Hum., Lang.& Lang.Behav.Abstr., M.L.A., Mid.East: Abstr.& Ind., Phil.Ind., Psychol.Abstr., SSCI. **Document type:** academic/scholarly publication.
     —BLDSC (6464.600000); Faxon; SWETS; UMI; UnCover.
     Refereed Serial

100 290   NE   ISSN 0924-7904
PHILOSOPHY AND RELIGION; a comparative yearbook. Key Title: Philosophy and Religion (Leiden). (Text in English) 1989. irreg., vol.3, 1993. price varies. E.J. Brill, P.O. Box 9000, 2300 PA Leiden, Netherlands. TEL 31-71-5353500. FAX 31-71-5317532. TELEX 39296 BRILL NL. (In N. America: E.J. Brill, 24 Hudson St., Kinderhook, NY 12106. TEL 800-962-4406. FAX 518-758-1959) Eds. Shlomo Biderman, Ben-Ami Scharfstein. (back issues avail.) **Document type:** monographic series.
     —BLDSC (6464.680000).
     Description: Scholarly contributions on topics in comparative religion and philosophy.
     Refereed Serial

100 808   US   ISSN 0031-8213
B1
PHILOSOPHY AND RHETORIC. 1968. q. $25 to individuals (foreign $32.50); institutions $37.50 (foreign $45). Pennsylvania State University Press, 820 N. University Dr., Ste. C, University Park, PA 16802-1003. TEL 814-865-1327. FAX 814-863-1408. Ed.Bd. adv.; bk.rev.; bibl.; index. circ. 750. (also avail. in microform from UMI; reprint service avail. from UMI) **Indexed:** Abstr.Engl.Stud., Arts & Hum.Cit.Ind., Curr.Cont., IJCS (1968-), Ind.Bk.Rev.Hum., M.L.A., Phil.Ind. **Document type:** academic/scholarly publication.
     —BLDSC (6464.800000); Faxon; Genuine Article; SWETS; UMI; UnCover. **CCC.**
     Refereed Serial

PHILOSOPHY AND TECHNOLOGY. see TECHNOLOGY: COMPREHENSIVE WORKS

180 370   US   ISSN 0890-2461
PHILOSOPHY & THEOLOGY; Marquette University quarterly. 1986. q. $25 (foreign $30). Marquette University Press, Box 1881, Milwaukee, WI 53201-1881. TEL 414-288-1564. Ed. Phillip Rossi. (also avail. in diskette format) **Document type:** academic/scholarly publication.
     —BLDSC (6464.822000).

100   US   ISSN 0031-8221
B1
PHILOSOPHY EAST AND WEST; a quarterly of comparative philosophy. 1951. q. $31 to individuals; institutions $40. University of Hawaii Press, Journals Department, 2840 Kolowalu St., Honolulu, HI 96822. TEL 808-956-8833. FAX 808-988-6052. E-mail: rtames@uhnix.uhcc.hawaii.edu. Ed. Roger T. Ames. adv.; bk.rev.; index. circ. 1,550. (also avail. in microform from UMI; back issues avail.; reprint service avail. from ISI,SCH,UMI) **Indexed:** Arts & Hum.Cit.Ind., Curr.Cont., Hum.Ind., Ind.Bk.Rev.Hum., Lang.& Lang.Behav.Abstr., M.L.A., Mid.East: Abstr.& Ind., Phil.Ind., Rel.& Theol.Abstr. (1968-), Sociol.Abstr. **Document type:** academic/scholarly publication.
     —BLDSC (6464.850000); Faxon; Genuine Article; SWETS; UnCover.
     Description: Focuses on comparative and Asian philosophy.
     Refereed Serial

149.2 155   US   ISSN 0743-3417
PHILOSOPHY FOR CHILDREN NEWSLETTER. 1984. q. $8. Texas Wesleyan College, School of Education, Ft. Worth, TX 76105. TEL 817-531-4957. Ed. Ron Reed.

500 100   US   ISSN 0277-2434
Q174
PHILOSOPHY IN SCIENCE. 1983. irreg., vol.56 1995. $48 (effective 1995). Pachart Publishing House, 1130 San Lucas Cir., Tucson, AZ 85704. FAX 602-297-4797. (Subscr. to: Order Dept., Box 35549, Tucson, AZ 85740) Dir. A.G. Pacholczyk. bk.rev. (back issues avail.) **Document type:** academic/scholarly publication.
—Faxon.
  Description: Provides a forum for the articulation of philosophical issues arising within the sciences.

100   UK   ISSN 0961-5970
PHILOSOPHY NOW. 1991. q. £2.50 per no. 226 Bramford Rd., Ipswich IP1 4AS, England. TEL 01473-240185. E-mail: ricatphilnow@delphi.com. (Dist. by: Diamond Magazine Distribution Ltd., Unit 1, Burgess Rd., Ivyhouse Ln., Hastings, E. Sussex TN35 4NR, England. TEL 01424-430422; Dist. in US by: Ubiquity Distributors Inc., 607 Degaw St., Brooklyn, NY 11217) Ed. Richard Lewis. adv. contact: Sue Roberts. **Document type:** academic/scholarly publication.
—BLDSC (6464.956500).

100 301   NE   ISSN 0922-6001
PHILOSOPHY OF HISTORY AND CULTURE. 1988. irreg., vol.14, 1994. price varies. E.J. Brill, P.O. Box 9000, 2300 PA Leiden, Netherlands. TEL 31-71-5353500. FAX 31-71-5317532. TELEX 39296 BRILL NL. (In N. America: E.J. Brill, 24 Hudson St., Kinderhook, NY 12106. TEL 800-962-4406. FAX 518-758-1959) Ed. Michael Krauz. (back issues avail.) **Document type:** monographic series.
—BLDSC (6464.950500).
  Refereed Serial

PHILOSOPHY OF SCIENCE. see *SCIENCES: COMPREHENSIVE WORKS*

PHILOSOPHY OF THE SOCIAL SCIENCES. see *SOCIAL SCIENCES: COMPREHENSIVE WORKS*

100   US   ISSN 0031-8256
B1
PHILOSOPHY TODAY. 1957. q. $21 (foreign $25). DePaul University, 2320 N. Kenmore Ave., Chicago, IL 60614-3214. TEL 312-325-7276. FAX 312-362-5811. Ed. David Pellauer. adv.; bk.rev.; index. circ. 1,180. (also avail. in microform from UMI; back issues avail.; reprint service avail. from UMI) **Indexed:** Arts & Hum.Cit.Ind., Cath.Ind., Curr.Cont., Hum.Ind., Phil.Ind. **Document type:** academic/scholarly publication.
—BLDSC (6465.090000); Faxon; Genuine Article; SWETS; UMI; UnCover.

180   NE   ISSN 0031-8868
B1
PHRONESIS; a journal for ancient philosophy. (Text in English, French, German, Italian) 1956. 3/yr. fl.105 (foreign fl.130) (effective 1994). Van Gorcum en Co. B.V., P.O. Box 43, 9400 AA Assen, Netherlands. TEL 31-5920-46864. FAX 31-5920-72064. Ed. Bob Sharples. adv.; bk.rev.; index. circ. 1,100. (reprint service avail. from SWZ) **Indexed:** Arts & Hum.Cit.Ind., Bibl.Ling., Curr.Cont., Ind.Bk.Rev.Hum., Phil.Ind. **Document type:** academic/scholarly publication.
—Faxon; Genuine Article; SWETS; UnCover.

215 610 509   US
PITTSBURGH SERIES IN PHILOSOPHY & HISTORY OF SCIENCE. 1982. irreg., no.14, 1992. price varies. University of California Press, 2120 Berkeley Way, Berkeley, CA 94720. TEL 510-642-4247. FAX 510-643-7127. (Orders to: California-Princeton Fulfillment Services, 1445 Lower Ferry Rd., Ewing, NJ 08618. TEL 800-777-4726. FAX 800-999-1958) (back issues avail.) **Document type:** monographic series.
  Description: Examines philosophical issues in the history of medical and physical sciences.
  Refereed Serial

170   US
POYNTER CENTER NEWSLETTER. 1986. 2/yr. free. Poynter Center for the Study of Ethics and American Institutions, 410 N. Park Ave., Bloomington, IN 47405. TEL 812-855-0261. FAX 812-855-3315. Ed. Judith A. Granbois. bk.rev. circ. 1,200. **Document type:** newsletter.
  Description: Reports center activities and projects.

190   NE   ISSN 0303-8157
        CODEN: PSSHEY
POZNAN STUDIES IN THE PHILOSOPHY OF THE SCIENCES AND THE HUMANITIES. (Text in English) 1975. irreg., vol.37, 1994. price varies. (Adam Mickiewics University, PL) Editions Rodopi B.V., Keizersgracht 302-304, 1016 EX Amsterdam, Netherlands. TEL 31-20-6227507. FAX 31-20-6380948. E-mail: F.van.der.Zee@Rodopi.nl. (In N. America: 233 Peachtree St. N.E., Ste. 404, Atlanta, GA 30303-1504. TEL 800-225-3998. FAX 404-522-7116) Ed. Jerzy Brzezinski. adv.; bk.rev. (back issues avail.) **Indexed:** Phil.Ind. **Document type:** monographic series.
—BLDSC (6579.127000).
  Refereed Serial

100   PL   ISSN 0079-4635
POZNANSKIE TOWARZYSTWO PRZYJACIOL NAUK. KOMISJA FILOZOFICZNA. PRACE. (Text in German, Polish; summaries in English, French, German, Russian) 1921. irreg., vol.18, 1995. price varies. Poznanskie Towarzystwo Przyjaciol Nauk, Komisja Filozoficzna, Ul. Mielzynskiego 27-29, 61-725 Poznan, Poland. **Document type:** monographic series.

PRABUDDHA BHARATA/AWAKENED INDIA. see *RELIGIONS AND THEOLOGY* — *Hindu*

PRAGMATICS AND DISCOURSE ANALYSIS. see *LINGUISTICS*

100   PL   ISSN 0079-4872
PRAKSEOLOGIA. (Text in Polish; summaries in English) 1962. q. $46. Polska Akademia Nauk, Instytut Filozofii i Socjologii, Zaklad Prakseologii i Naukoznawstwa, Ul. Nowy Swiat 72, Palac Staszica, 00-330 Warsaw, Poland. TEL 48-22-265231. FAX 48-22-267181. Ed. Wojciech Gasparski. bk.rev.; bibl.; charts. **Document type:** academic/scholarly publication.
  Description: Covers philosophical, theoretical, and methodological topics of efficient action.

181.45   US   ISSN 0149-953X
PRANA YOGA LIFE. 1977. irreg. $3. Prana Yoga Ashram, Box 1037, Berkeley, CA 94701. TEL 415-549-2911. Ed. Swami Vignanananda. adv.; bk.rev.; illus. circ. 1,500. (back issues avail.)

100   US   ISSN 0138-0311
BD450
PRAXIOLOGY; the international annual of practical philosophy and methodology. 1980. a. price varies. Transaction Publishers, Transaction Periodicals Consortium, Department 3092, Rutgers University, New Brunswick, NJ 08903. TEL 908-445-2280. FAX 908-445-3138. (Dist. by: Transaction Publishers, Department PR205, Rutgers University, New Brunswick, NJ 08903; In the U.K. by: Transaction Publishers (UK), Plymbridge Distributors, Ltd., Estover Plymouth PL6 7P2, England) Ed. Wojciech W. Gasparski. **Document type:** academic/scholarly publication.

100   CR
PRAXIS. 1975. q. exchange basis. Universidad Nacional, Departamento de Filosofia, c/o Jack Wilson-Pacheco, Coordinacion de Publicaciones y Canje, Centro de Documentacion e Informacion en Filosofia, Heredia, Costa Rica. Ed.Bd. bibl.; charts; illus.; stat. circ. 1,000.

105   BL   ISSN 0103-2283
PRESENCA FILOSOFICA. (Text in Portuguese and French; occasionally in English) 1974. irreg. $25. Sociedade Brasileira de Filosofos Catolicos, Rua Benjamin Constant 23-420, 20241 Rio de Janeiro, RJ, Brazil. Ed. Prof. Tarcisio Meirelles Padilha. bibl. circ. 2,000.

100   FR   ISSN 1166-9993
PRESENCE DE GABRIEL MARCEL. 1978. a. 100 F. Association Presence de Gabriel Marcel, 85 bd. de Port-Royal, 75013 Paris, France. **Document type:** bulletin.
  Formerly (until 1991): Presence de Gabriel Marcel. Cahier (ISSN 0294-6491)

PRESSE-INTER. see *NEW AGE PUBLICATIONS*

100   CI   ISSN 0350-2791
PRILOZI ZA ISTRAZIVANJE HRVATSKE FILOZOFSKE BASTINE. (Text in Croatian, Greek, Latin; summaries in English, French, German and Italian) 1975. s-a. $8. Sveuciliste u Zagrebu, Institut za Povijesne Znanosti, Odjel za Povijest Filozofije, Krcka 1, 41000 Zagreb, Croatia. TEL 041 511-841. Ed. Damir Barbaric. bk.rev. circ. 800. (back issues avail.)

142.7   NE   ISSN 0924-1965
PRIMARY SOURCES IN PHENOMENOLOGY. (Text in English) 1987. irreg. price varies. Kluwer Academic Publishers, Postbus 17, 3300 AA Dordrecht, Netherlands. TEL 31-78-392392. FAX 31-78-392254. TELEX 29245 KAPG NL. (Dist. by: Kluwer Academic Publishers Group, P.O. Box 322, 3300 AH Dordrecht, Netherlands. TEL 31-78-392392. FAX 31-78-546474; N. America dist. addr.: Box 358, Accord Sta., Hingham, MA 02018-0358. TEL 617-871-6600. FAX 617-871-6528) **Document type:** monographic series.
—BLDSC (6612.913150).
  Refereed Serial

PRINCIPIA CYBERNETICA NEWSLETTER. see *COMPUTERS* — *Cybernetics*

100 001.3   GW
PROBLEMATA. 1971. irreg. price varies. Friedrich Frommann Verlag Guenther Holzboog, Koenig-Karl-Str. 27, 70372 Stuttgart, Germany. TEL 0711-9559690. FAX 0711-9559691. Ed. Guenther Holzboog. **Indexed:** Math.R. **Document type:** monographic series.

160   RM
PROBLEME DE LOGICA. 1969. irreg., vol.9, 1986. (Academia Romana) Editura Academiei Romane, Calea Victoriei 125, 79717 Bucharest, Rumania. (Subscr. to: Artexim, Str. Piata Scinteii 1, P.O. Box 33-16, 70055 Bucharest, Rumania) Eds. Crizantema Joja, Calin Candiescu.

149.946   GW   ISSN 0933-4483
PROBLEME DER SEMIOTIK. 1984. irreg., no.17, 1994. DM.86. Stauffenburg Verlag, Postfach 2567, 72015 Tuebingen, Germany. TEL 07071-78091. FAX 07071-75288. Ed. Sven Sager. **Document type:** monographic series.

100   US   ISSN 0898-0136
PROBLEMS IN CONTEMPORARY PHILOSOPHY. 1986. irreg., latest no.33. $39.95 per no. Edwin Mellen Press, 415 Ridge St., Box 450, Lewiston, NY 14092. TEL 716-754-2788. FAX 716-754-4056. **Document type:** monographic series.
—BLDSC (6617.879700).

192   US   ISSN 0360-6503
BD372
PROCESS STUDIES. 1971. q. $20 to individuals (foreign $27); institutions $30 (foreign $37). School of Theology at Claremont, Center for Process Studies, 1325 N. College Ave., Claremont, CA 91711. TEL 909-621-5330. Ed. Lewis S. Ford. adv. contact: Laurel J. Huff. bk.rev.; abstr. circ. 1,000. (also avail. in microform from UMI; back issues avail.; reprint service avail. from ISI,UMI) **Indexed:** Arts & Hum.Cit.Ind., CERDIC, Curr.Cont., Phil.Ind., Rel.& Theol.Abstr. (1973-), Rel.Ind.One, Rel.Per. **Document type:** academic/scholarly publication.
—BLDSC (6849.990700); Faxon; Genuine Article; SWETS; UMI; UnCover.
  Description: Covers the process philosophy of Alfred North Whitehead, and its application to other philosophies and other fields, including aesthetics, mathematics, physics, biology, cosmology, history of religion, social science, and literary criticism.

174   US   ISSN 1063-6579
BJ1725
PROFESSIONAL ETHICS; a multidisciplinary journal. 1992. q. $20 to individuals; institutions $50 (foreign $60) (effective 1995). Box 15017, Gainesville, FL 32604. TEL 904-392-2084. FAX 904-392-5575. Ed. Robert J. Baum. adv.; bk.rev. circ. 700. (back issues avail.; reprint service avail. from WSH) **Indexed:** Bus.Ind., Phil.Ind., Soc.Sci.Ind. **Document type:** academic/scholarly publication.
—BLDSC (6858.750000); SWETS; UnCover.
  Description: Interdisciplinary forum for the discussion and analysis of ethical issues that arise in the practice of the professions and in professional organizations.
  Refereed Serial

PHILOSOPHY

170 US ISSN 1045-8808
PROFESSIONAL ETHICS REPORT. 1988. q. free. American Association for the Advancement of Science, 1333 H St., N.W., Washington, DC 20005. TEL 202-326-6600. FAX 202-289-4950. Ed. Mark S. Frankel. bk.rev.; cum.index: 1988-1991, 1992-1993. circ. 1,750. (back issues avail.) **Document type:** newsletter.
  Description: Provides a forum for the exchange of information on professional ethics issues that affect a wide range of professions, especially scientists and engineers.

190 NE ISSN 0924-1930
PROFILES; an international series on contemporary philosophers and logicians. 1979. irreg. price varies. Kluwer Academic Publishers, Postbus 17, 3300 AA Dordrecht, Netherlands. TEL 31-78-392392. FAX 31-78-392254. TELEX 29245 KAPG NL. (Dist. by: Kluwer Academic Publishers Group, P.O. Box 322, 3300 AH Dordrecht, Netherlands. TEL 31-78-392392. FAX 31-78-546474; N. America dist. addr.: Box 358, Accord Sta., Hingham, MA 02018-0358. TEL 617-871-6600. FAX 617-871-6528) Eds. R.J. Bogdan, I. Niiniluoto. bibl.; index. (back issues avail.) **Document type:** monographic series.
  —CCC.
  Refereed Serial

PROGRESS (MEDFORD). see *RELIGIONS AND THEOLOGY*

100 MX ISSN 0186-7377
PROMETEO;* revista latinoamericana de filosofia. 1984. 3/yr. Mex.$400($20) Universidad de Guadalajara, Facultad de Filosofia y Letras, Apdo. Postal 2393, Guadalajara, Jalisco, Mexico. Ed. Luis Govea.

PROPHETIC VOICES; an international literary journal. see *LITERATURE*

100 IT ISSN 0033-1791
PROTEUS; revista di filosofia. 1970. 3/yr. L.4000. Corso Vitt. Emanuele 39, 00186 Rome, Italy. Ed. Pietro Prini. bk.rev.

PROTOSOZIOLOGIE. see *SOCIOLOGY*

100 IT
PUBBLICAZIONI DI VERIFICHE. irreg. price varies. Verifiche, Casella Postale 269, 38 100 Trento, Italy.
  Description: Focuses on philosophy.

100 US ISSN 0887-0373
H96
PUBLIC AFFAIRS QUARTERLY. 1987. q. $38 to individuals; institutions $132. Bowling Green State University, Philosophy Documentation Center, Bowling Green, OH 43403-0189. TEL 419-372-2419; 800-444-2419. FAX 419-372-6987. Ed. Nicholas Rescher. **Indexed:** Phil.Ind. **Document type:** academic/scholarly publication.
  —BLDSC (6962.765000); Faxon; UnCover.

PUBLICATIONS IN MEDIEVAL STUDIES. see *HISTORY — History Of Europe*

Q J I. (Quarterly Journal of Ideology) see *POLITICAL SCIENCE*

QIU ZHI/SEEK KNOWLEDGE. see *POLITICAL SCIENCE*

100 IT
QUADERNI DI FILOSOFIA. 1978. irreg., no.3, 1980. price varies. (Universita degli Studi di Palermo, Istituto di Filosofia) Editrice Italo-Latino-Americana Palma, Via B. Castiglia 6, 90141 Palermo, Italy. Ed.Bd.

100 IT
QUADERNI DI VERIFICHE. irreg. price varies. Verifiche, Casella Postale 269, 38100 Trento, Italy. Ed. Franco Chiereghin. bibl.
  Description: Focuses on philosophy.

144 300 IT
QUADERNI SARDI DI FILOSOFIA E SCIENZE UMANE. vol.3, 1979. irreg., no.15-16, 1987. L.5000($15) Libreria Dessi, Largo Cavallotti 17, 07100 Sassari, Italy. TEL 079-231673. Ed.Bd.

100 121 FR
QUE FAIRE DE L'ECONOMIE. 1973. q. 110 F. David Kaisergruber, 77 bis rue Legendre, 75017 Paris, France.
  Formerly (until 1981): Dialectiques.

100 NE ISSN 1011-226X
B1
QUEST; philosophical discussions. (Text in English, French) 1987. s-a. $15 to individuals in Africa (elsewhere $25); institutions in Africa $20 (elsewhere $35). (University of Zambia, Department of Philosophy, ZA) Quest, P.O. Box 9114, 9703 LC Groningen, Netherlands. TEL 31-50-636154. FAX 31-50-636160. Ed. P. Boele van Hensbroek. adv.; bk.rev. circ. 200. (back issues avail.) **Indexed:** Documentatieblad. **Document type:** academic/scholarly publication.
  —Faxon.
  Description: Endeavors to act as a channel of expression for African thinkers; reflects on the radical transformations taking place. Intended to serve professionals and students of philosophy and intellectuals in other disciplines.
  Refereed Serial

THE QUEST (WHEATON). see *NEW AGE PUBLICATIONS*

340 UK ISSN 0300-211X
B1 CODEN: RAPHEH
RADICAL PHILOSOPHY; journal of socialist feminist philosophy. 1972. 6/yr. $69 to individuals; institutions $69. Radical Philosophy Ltd., c/o Jean Grimshaw, North View, Dundry Lane, Dundry, Bristol BS18 8JG, England. TEL 01272-642986. (Subscr. to: Central Books, 99 Wallis Rd., London E9 5LN, England. TEL 0171-986-4854) adv. contact: Peter Osborne. bk.rev.; illus. circ. 2,000. **Indexed:** Br.Hum.Ind., Left Ind. (1986-), Phil.Ind., Stud.Wom.Abstr. **Document type:** academic/scholarly publication.
  —BLDSC (7228.095000); Faxon; SWETS; UnCover.
  Refereed Serial

306 US ISSN 1047-8302
HN1
RADICAL PHILOSOPHY REVIEW OF BOOKS. 1990. 2/yr. $5 to individuals; institutions $15. Radical Philosophy Association, 1443 Gorsuch Ave., Baltimore, MD 21218. **Indexed:** Alt.Press Ind. **Document type:** academic/scholarly publication.

100 IT
RAGION PRATICA. 1993. s-a. Edizioni Anabasi S.p.a., Via San Giovanni sul Muro 4, 20121 Milan, Italy. Ed. Riccardo Guastini.

RAINBOW RAY FOCUS. see *NEW AGE PUBLICATIONS*

211 FR ISSN 0033-9075
RAISON PRESENTE. 1968. q. 260 F. Nouvelles Editions Rationalistes, 14 rue de l'Ecole Polytechnique, 75005 Paris, France. Ed. Jean-Paul Thomas. bk.rev.; film rev. **Indexed:** Lang.& Lang.Behav.Abstr.
  —BLDSC (7253.221000).

294.54 200 IT
RASSEGNA DI LETTERATURA TOMISTICA. (Text mainly in French and Italian) 1966. a. L.80000($80) (Pontificia Universita S. Tommaso D'Aquino, VC) Herder Editrice e Libreria s.r.l., Piazza Montecitori, 120, 00186 Rome, Italy. TEL 67-94-628. FAX 678-47-51. (Co-sponsor: Domenicane Italiane) Ed. C. Vansteenkiste. bk.rev. (back issues avail.) **Document type:** academic/scholarly publication.
  Formerly: Bulletin Thomiste.
  Description: Features critical reviews and notices about the work, thought, and influence of Thomas Aquinas.

100 UK ISSN 0034-0006
B1
RATIO. 1957. 3/yr. £84($174) (foreign £108) (effective 1996). Basil Blackwell Ltd., 108 Cowley Rd., Oxford OX1 1JF, England. TEL 0865-791100. FAX 0865-791347. TELEX 837022-OXBOOK-G. Ed. Edward Craig. adv.; index. circ. 700. (reprint service avail. from SWZ) **Indexed:** Arts & Hum.Cit.Ind., Br.Hum.Ind., Curr.Cont., Lang.& Lang.Behav.Abstr., Math.R., Phil.Ind., SSCI.
  —BLDSC (7295.400000); Genuine Article; SWETS; UMI; UnCover. CCC.

100 SZ ISSN 0253-3294
RATIO HUMANA. 1975. q. Schweizerische Vereinigung fuer Humanismus, Hohlegasse 6, Postfach 10, CH-8612 Uster, Switzerland. TEL 01-9403850. Ed. Albert Anderes. **Document type:** academic/scholarly publication.

RATIO JURIS; an international journal of jurisprudence and philosophy law. see *LAW*

211 AT ISSN 0156-7594
THE RATIONALIST NEWS. 1966. q. $8. Rationalist Association of New South Wales, 58 Regent, Chippendale, N.S.W. 2008, Australia. Ed. Peter Hanna. bk.rev. circ. 1,000.

100 US ISSN 0744-432X
RAYS FROM THE ROSE CROSS. 1915. bi-m. $15 (foreign $21). Rosicrucian Fellowship, 2222 Mission Ave., Box 713, Oceanside, CA 92054. TEL 619-757-6600. FAX 619-721-3806. Ed. Charles Weber. bk.rev.; index. circ. 3,500.

100 US ISSN 0882-6196
READING PLUS. 1986. irreg. Peter Lang Publishing, Inc., 62 W. 45th St., 4th Fl., New York, NY 10036. TEL 212-302-6740. Ed. Mary Ann Caws. **Document type:** academic/scholarly publication, monographic series.

RECHERCHES AUGUSTINIENNES. see *RELIGIONS AND THEOLOGY*

294.54 572 ZR
RECHERCHES PHILOSOPHIQUES AFRICAINES. (Text in English, French) 1977. a. $5. Faculte Catholique de Kinshasa, Faculte de Philosophie, B.P. 1534, Kinshasa-Limete, Zaire. Ed. Ngwey Ngondia N. adv.; bk.rev. circ. 1,500.
  Formerly (until 1977): Recherches Philosophiques Africaines. Collection.

RECONSTRUCTIONISM TODAY. see *RELIGIONS AND THEOLOGY — Judaic*

REFORMED REVIEW. see *RELIGIONS AND THEOLOGY — Protestant*

REKENSCHAP; humanistisch tijdschrift voor wetenschap en cultuur. see *LITERARY AND POLITICAL REVIEWS*

RELIGIOUS HUMANISM; a quarterly journal of religious and ethical humanism. see *RELIGIONS AND THEOLOGY — Other Denominations And Sects*

189 BE
RENCONTRES DE PHILOSOPHIE MEDIEVALE. (Text in French) 1991. a. price varies. (Societe Internationale pour l'Etude de la Philosophie Medievale) N.V. Brepols, Steenweg op Tielen 68, 2300 Turnhout, Belgium. TEL 32-14-402500. FAX 32-14-428919. (back issues avail.) **Document type:** academic/scholarly publication, proceedings.

RENCONTRES INTERNATIONALES DE GENEVE. see *SOCIAL SCIENCES: COMPREHENSIVE WORKS*

100 300 CH ISSN 1018-189X
RENWEN JI SHEHUI KEXUE JIKAN/JOURNAL OF SOCIAL SCIENCES AND PHILOSOPHY. (Text in Chinese, English) 1988. s-a. free. Academia Sinica, Sun Yat-Sen Institute for Social Sciences and Philosophy, Nankang, Taipei 11529, Taiwan, Republic of China. TEL 886-2-782-1693. FAX 886-2-785-4160. Ed. Wen-shien Peng. circ. 1,000.
  Description: Publishes contributions in the fields of philosophy, political science, history, economics, social studies and law.
  Refereed Serial

REPORTS ON MATHEMATICAL LOGIC. see *MATHEMATICS*

170 340   UK   ISSN 1356-4765
▼RES PUBLICA; a journal of legal and social philosophy. 1995. s-a. £40 (effective 1995). (U.K. Association for Legal and Social Philosophy) Deborah Charles Publications, 173 Mather Ave., Liverpool L18 6JZ, England. TEL 0151-724-2500. FAX 0151-721-0371. (Dist. in the U.S. by: Wm. W. Gaunt & Sons, Inc., 3011 Gulf Dr., Holmes Beach, FL 34217-2199. TEL 813-778-5211. FAX 813-778-5252) Ed. B. Brecher. **Document type:** academic/scholarly publication.
 Description: Takes an interdisciplinary approach to the philosophical analysis of moral, social, and legal issues.
 Refereed Serial

100   US   ISSN 0085-5553
B829.5
RESEARCH IN PHENOMENOLOGY. 1971. a. $39.95 to individuals; institutions $49.95. Humanities Press, 165 First Ave., Atlantic Highlands, NJ 07716-1289. TEL 908-872-1441. FAX 908-872-0717. Ed. John Sallis. adv.; bk.rev. circ. 1,000. (back issues avail.) **Indexed:** Hum.Ind., Phil.Ind. **Document type:** academic/scholarly publication.
 —BLDSC (7755.073000); Faxon; Genuine Article; UMI; UnCover.
 Description: Dedicated to encouraging original, creative phenomenological research; to furthering the interpretative and critical study of the writings of major phenomenological philosophers; and, to providing in-depth reviews of current work in phenomenology.

100 601   US   ISSN 0161-7249
T14
RESEARCH IN PHILOSOPHY AND TECHNOLOGY. (Supplement avail.: Jacques Ellul: A Comprehensive Bibliography) 1978. a. $63.50 to institutions. (Society for Philosophy and Technology) J A I Press Inc., 55 Old Post Rd., No. 2, Box 1678, Greenwich, CT 06836-1678. TEL 203-661-7602. Eds. Paul T. Durbin, Carl Mitcham. bibl.
 —BLDSC (7755.074000); Faxon; UnCover.
 Refereed Serial

100   II
RESEARCH JOURNAL OF PHILOSOPHY.* (Text in English) 1966. s-a. Rs.10.($4) Ranchi University, Ranchi 1, Bihar, India. Ed. R.S. Srivastava. bk.rev.

RESEARCH NOTES AND MEMORANDA OF APPLIED GEOMETRY FOR PREVENIENT NATURAL PHILOSOPHY. see *MATHEMATICS*

170   BE   ISSN 0773-1213
RESEAUX; revue interdisciplinaire de philosophie morale et politique. 1965. 3/yr. 600 BEF to individuals (foreign 900 BEF); institutions and libraries 1200 BEF (foreign 1500 BEF) (effective 1994). Universite de Mons - Hainaut, Centre Interdisciplinaire d'Etudes Philosophiques, 20 Place du Parc, B-7000 Mons, Belgium. TEL 32-65-335084. FAX 32-65-373054. Ed. Claire LeJeune. bk.rev.; bibl. **Indexed:** Lang.& Lang.Behav.Abstr. **Document type:** academic/scholarly publication.
 Formerly: Revue Universitaire de Science Morale (ISSN 0035-435X)

THE RESHAPING OF PSYCHOANALYSIS; from Sigmund Freud to Ernest Becker. see *PSYCHOLOGY*

RESURGENCE; journal of the ecological and spiritual culture. see *POLITICAL SCIENCE*

REVELATIONS OF AWARENESS; the cosmic newsletter. see *NEW AGE PUBLICATIONS*

330   II   ISSN 0258-1701
H1
REVIEW JOURNAL OF PHILOSOPHY AND SOCIAL SCIENCE. (Text in English) biennial. Rs.70($10) Anu Books, Shivaji Rd, Meerut 25001, India. (Editorial office: Dr. Michael V. Belok, College of Education, Arizona State University, Tempe, AZ 85281) Ed. Michael V. Belok.

110   US   ISSN 0034-6632
B1
REVIEW OF METAPHYSICS; a philosophical quarterly. 1947. q. $28 to individuals; institutions $45; students, retirees $18 (effective 1996). Philosophy Education Society, Inc., Catholic University of America, Washington, DC 20064. TEL 202-635-8778. FAX 202-319-4731. Ed. Jude P. Dougherty. adv.; bk.rev.; abstr.; bibl.; index, cum.index: 1947-1967; circ. 2,300 (paid). (tabloid format; also avail. in microform from UMI; reprint service avail. from UMI) **Indexed:** Amer.Bibl.Slavic & E.Eur.Stud., Arts & Hum.Cit.Ind., Bk.Rev.Ind. (1965-), CERDIC, Child.Bk.Rev.Ind. (1965-), Curr.Cont., Hum.Ind., Ind.Bk.Rev.Hum., Lang.& Lang.Behav.Abstr., Phil.Ind., SSCI. **Document type:** academic/scholarly publication.
 —BLDSC (7793.070000); Faxon; Genuine Article; SWETS; UMI; UnCover.
 Description: Promotes persistent, resolute inquiries into root questions, and technically competent, definitive contributions to philosophical knowledge.

100   US   ISSN 0899-9937
REVISIONING PHILOSOPHY. irreg. Peter Lang Publishing, Inc., 62 W. 45th St., 4th Fl., New York, NY 10036. TEL 212-302-6740. FAX 212-302-7574. Ed. David Appelbaum. **Document type:** academic/scholarly publication, monographic series.

170
REVISIONS (NOTRE DAME). 1981. irreg., vol.13, 1995. price varies. University of Notre Dame Press, Notre Dame, IN 46556. TEL 219-631-6346. FAX 219-631-8148. (Orders to: 11030 S. Langley Ave., Chicago, IL 60628. TEL 800-621-2736. FAX 800-621-8476; Overseas orders to: Eurospan University Press Group, Order Dept., 3 Henrietta St., London WC2E 8LU, England) Eds. Stanley Hauerwas, Alasdair MacIntyre. **Document type:** academic/scholarly publication.

100   SP   ISSN 0212-8780
B5
REVISTA CANARIA DE FILOSOFIA Y CIENCIA SOCIAL. 1983. a. $15 to individuals; institutions $20. Universidad de La Laguna, Facultad de Filosofia y Ciencias de la Educacion. Seccion de Filosofia, Secretariado de Publicaciones, San Agustin, 30, 38201 La Laguna-Tenerife, Islas Canarias, Spain. TEL 922-25-81-27. adv.
 Description: Theoretical and empirical research in philosophy and social sciences.

100   CL   ISSN 0034-8236
REVISTA DE FILOSOFIA. 1949. s-a. $10. Universidad de Chile, Departamento de Filosofia, Facultad de Filosofia y Humanidades, Avda. Igancio Carrera Pinto 1025, Santiago de Chile, Chile. Dir. Jorge Estrella Avila. bk.rev. circ. 500.

100   CR   ISSN 0034-8252
B5   CODEN: RFURE5
REVISTA DE FILOSOFIA. 1958. s-a. Col.750($20) Editorial de la Universidad de Costa Rica, Apartado 75-2060, Ciudad Universitaria Rodrigo Facio, 2050 San Pedro de Montes de Oca, San Jose, Costa Rica. TEL 506-25-3133. FAX 506-24-9367. TELEX UNICORI 2544. Dir. Rafael A. Herra. bk.rev.; index. circ. 750. (also avail. in microfilm from OMN; back issues avail.) **Indexed:** Hisp.Amer.Per.Ind. (1970-1994). **Document type:** academic/scholarly publication.

100   VE   ISSN 0798-1171
REVISTA DE FILOSOFIA. 1974. s-a. Bs.344.10($11.63) Universidad del Zulia, Centro de Estudios Filosoficos, Facultad de Humanidades y Educacion, Edif. Viyaluz, Av. 4 esq. Calle 74, 8o piso, Maracaibo, Zulia, Venezuela. TEL 78246. Dir. Angelo Munoz Garcia. bibl.
 Supersedes (after no.1) (1974): Centro de Estudios Filosoficos. Boletin.

100   MX   ISSN 0185-3481
B5
REVISTA DE FILOSOFIA. 1968. 3/yr. Mex.$42($30) (effective 1995). Universidad Iberoamericana, Departamento de Filosofia, Prol. Paseo de la Reforma 880, Lomas de Santa Fe, 01210 Mexico, D.F., Mexico. TEL 5-570-20-74. FAX 5-726-90-48. Ed. Jose Ruben Sanabria. bk.rev. circ. 750. **Indexed:** Phil.Ind. **Document type:** academic/scholarly publication.
 Description: Includes works in philosophy written by professors at the university and others.

PHILOSOPHY   5161

110   BL
REVISTA DE FILOSOFIA E CIENCIAS HUMANAS. s-a.? Universidade Federal da Bahia, Faculdade de Filosofia e Ciencias Humanas, Rua Sao Lazaro 197, Federacao, 40000 Salvador, Bahia, Brazil. TEL 071-247-2978. **Document type:** academic/scholarly publication.

100   RM   ISSN 0034-8260
B8.R8
REVISTA DE FILOSOFIE/REVUE DE PHILOSOPHIE. (Text in Rumanian; summaries in French and Russian) 1954. 6/yr. 180 lei($51) (Academia Romana) Editura Academiei Romane, Calea Victoriei 125, 79717 Bucharest, Rumania. (Dist. by: Rompresfilatelia, Calea Grivitei 64-66, P.O. Box 12-201, 78104 Bucharest, Rumania) Ed. Alexandru Surdu. bk.rev.; index. **Indexed:** Phil.Ind.
 —BLDSC (7854.690000).

REVISTA ESTUDIOS; revista trimestral publicada por los frailes de la orden de la merced. see *RELIGIONS AND THEOLOGY*

100   AG   ISSN 0325-0725
B5
REVISTA LATINOAMERICANA DE FILOSOFIA. (Text in Spanish, Portuguese; summaries in English) 1975. 2/yr. $22 to individuals; institutions $32 (effective 1995). Centro de Investigaciones Filosoficas, Casilla de Correo 5379, 1000 Buenos Aires, Argentina. TEL 5401-787-0533. (U.S. address: Box 1192, Birmingham, AL 35201) Ed.Bd. bk.rev. circ. 500. **Indexed:** Phil.Ind.
 —BLDSC (7863.430000).
 Description: Presents unpublished works by Latinamerican philosophers.

100   CL   ISSN 0716-1913
REVISTA PHILOSOPHICA. 1978. a. $40. (Universidad Catolica de Valparaiso, Instituto de Filosofia) Ediciones Universitarias de Valparaiso, Casilla 1415, Valparaiso, Chile. TEL 56-32-252900. FAX 56-32-238768. TELEX 230389 UCVAL CL. Ed. Juan Antonio Widow. bk.rev. circ. 300. **Document type:** academic/scholarly publication.
 Formerly: Philosophica.

100   PO   ISSN 0870-5283
REVISTA PORTUGUESA DE FILOSOFIA. (Supplemento Bibliografico issued s-a.) 1945. q. $60. Universidade Catolica Portuguesa, Braga, Faculdade de Filosofia, Praca da Faculdade, 1, 4719 Braga Codex, Portugal. TEL 23-25041. FAX 23-610655. bk.rev.; bibl.; index, cum.index: 1945-1994. **Indexed:** M.L.A., Phil.Ind. **Document type:** academic/scholarly publication.

100 056   VE   ISSN 1013-2368
B5
REVISTA VENEZOLANA DE FILOSOFIA. 1973. s-a. $10 per no. (or exchange basis). Universidad Simon Bolivar, Departamento de Filosofia, Apdo. 80659, Caracas, Venezuela. (Co-sponsor: Sociedad Venezolana de Filosofia) Ed. Javier Sasso; Pub. Alberto Rosales. bk.rev. **Indexed:** Phil.Ind. **Document type:** academic/scholarly publication.

111.85   FR   ISSN 0035-2292
REVUE D'ESTHETIQUE. 1945. 2/yr. 500 F. (foreign 500F) (effective 1996). Editions Jean Michel Place, 12 rue Pierre et Marie Curie, 75005 Paris, France. TEL 33-1-46-33-05-11. FAX 33-1-46-34-52-65. (Subscr. to: Centrale des Revues (CDR), 11 rue Gossin, 92543 Montrouge Cedex, France) (Co-sponsor: Societe Francaise d'Esthetique) Ed.Bd. bk.rev.; bibl.; charts; illus.; index. **Indexed:** Artbibl., Artbibl.Mod., M.L.A.
 —SWETS.

110 190   FR   ISSN 0035-1571
B2
REVUE DE METAPHYSIQUE ET DE MORALE. 1893. q. 56 ECU($68) Armand Colin (Subsidiary of: Masson), 103 bd. Saint-Michel, 75005 Paris, France. TEL 1-46-34-19-12. FAX 1-43-26-96-38. TELEX 201 269 F. Ed.Bd. adv.; bk.rev.; bibl. circ. 1,700. (also avail. in microfiche from IDC; reprint service avail. from KTO,SCH) **Indexed:** Arts & Hum.Cit.Ind., Curr.Cont., M.L.A., Phil.Ind. **Document type:** academic/scholarly publication.
 —BLDSC (7933.200000); Faxon; SWETS.

PHILOSOPHY

100   FR   ISSN 0035-1776
D1
REVUE DE SYNTHESE. 1900. q. 300 F. (Centre International de Synthese) Editions Albin Michel, 12 rue Colbert, 75002 Paris, France. TEL 1-42-97-50-68. FAX 1-42-97-46-46. Ed. Dominique Bourel. bk.rev.; bibl.; index. circ. 1,000. **Indexed:** Amer.Hist.& Life, Hist.Abstr.
—SWETS.

REVUE DE THEOLOGIE ET DE PHILOSOPHIE. see *RELIGIONS AND THEOLOGY*

REVUE DE THEOLOGIE ET DE PHILOSOPHIE. CAHIERS. see *RELIGIONS AND THEOLOGY*

215   FR   ISSN 0751-5804
AS162
REVUE DES SCIENCES MORALES ET POLITIQUES. 4/yr. 640 F. (Academie des Sciences Morales et Politiques) Gauthier-Villars, 15 rue Gossin, 92543 Montrouge Cedex, France. TEL 33-1-40-92-65-00. FAX 33-1-40-92-65-97. TELEX 634 916 F. (Subscr. to: Centrale des Revues, 11 rue Gossin, 92543 Montrouge Cedex, France. TEL 33-1-46-56-52-66) Ed. B. Chenot. circ. 600.
—SWETS. **CCC.**
Description: Presents the proceedings of the Academie des Sciences Morales et Politiques- an account of discussions on the major ideas which mark our present time.

100 200   FR   ISSN 0035-2209
REVUE DES SCIENCES PHILOSOPHIQUES ET THEOLOGIQUES. 1907. q. 590 F.($127) (Faculte de Philosophie et de Theologie de Saulchoir) Librairie Philosophique J. Vrin, 6 Place de la Sorbonne, 75005 Paris, France. TEL 1-43-54-03-47. FAX 43-54-48-18. Ed. R.P. Bernard Quelquejeu. bk.rev.; index. circ. 1,475. **Indexed:** Arts & Hum.Cit.Ind., CERDIC, M.L.A., New Test.Abstr., Old Test.Abstr., Phil.Ind., Rel.& Theol.Abstr. (1979-), Rel.Ind.One, Rel.Per.
—Faxon; SWETS.

REVUE DU M A U S S. (Mouvement Anti-Utilitariste dans les Science Sociales) see *SOCIOLOGY*

100   BE   ISSN 0048-8143
B1
REVUE INTERNATIONALE DE PHILOSOPHIE. (Text in English and French) 1938. q. 2000 BEF. Universa - Wetteren, Rue Hoender 24, 9200 Wetteren, Belgium. adv.; bk.rev. (also avail. in microfiche from IDC; reprint service avail. from ISI/SCH) **Indexed:** Arts & Hum.Cit.Ind., Curr.Cont., Ind.Bk.Rev.Hum., Lang.& Lang.Behav.Abstr., Math.R., Phil.Ind. **Document type:** academic/scholarly publication.
—BLDSC (7925.119000); Faxon; Genuine Article; SWETS; UnCover.

294.54   ZR
REVUE PHILOSOPHIQUE DE KINSHASA. (Text in French and English) 1983. a. $70. Faculte Catholique de Kinshasa, Faculte de Philosophie et Religions Africaines, B.P. 1534, Kinshasa-Limite, Zaire. Ed. Ngwey Ngond'a N. adv.; bk.rev. circ. 1,500. **Indexed:** P.L.E.S.A.

100   FR   ISSN 0035-3833
B2
REVUE PHILOSOPHIQUE DE LA FRANCE ET DE L'ETRANGER. 1876. q. 420 F. (foreign 480 F.) (effective 1996). Presses Universitaires de France, Departement des Revues, 14 av. du Bois-de-l'Epine, B.P.90, 91003 Evry Cedex, France. TEL 1-60-77-82-05. FAX 1-60-79-20-45. TELEX PUF 600 474 F. Dir. Yvon Bres. bk.rev.; abstr.; bibl.; index. (reprint service avail. from KTO) **Indexed:** Arts & Hum.Cit.Ind., Curr.Cont., Ind.Bk.Rev.Hum., Int.Polit.Sci.Abstr., Phil.Ind.
—Faxon; Genuine Article. **CCC.**

100   BE   ISSN 0035-3841
REVUE PHILOSOPHIQUE DE LOUVAIN. (Supplement avail.: Repertoire Bibliographique de la Philosophie) (Text in.French; summaries in English) 1894. q. 2000 BEF (effective 1995). (Universite Catholique de Louvain, Institut Superieur de Philosophie) Editions Peeters s.p.r.l., Bondgenotenlaan 153, 3000 Leuven, Belgium. TEL 32-16-235170. FAX 32-16-228500. (Co-sponsor: Fondation Universitaire Belge) Ed. Claude Troisfontaines. adv.; bk.rev.; bibl.; index. circ. 1,400. **Indexed:** Arts & Hum.Cit.Ind., Cath.Ind., M.L.A., Phil.Ind. **Document type:** academic/scholarly publication.
—Faxon; SWETS.
Formerly: Revue Neo-Scolastique.
Description: Review of the international philosophical movement by scholars of the Institute and others as well.

100 160 300   RM   ISSN 1220-5400
B1
REVUE ROUMAINE DE PHILOSOPHIE. 1953. 4/yr. 140 lei($52) (Academia Romana) Editura Academiei Romane, Calea Victoriei 125, 79717 Bucharest, Rumania. (Dist. by: Rompresfilatelia, Calea Grivitei 64-66, P.O. Box 12-201, 78104 Bucharest, Rumania)
Former titles (until 1991): Revue Roumaine de Philosophie et Logique (ISSN 1220-5486); (until 1990): Revue Roumaine des Sciences Sociales. Serie de Philosophie et Logique (ISSN 0035-4031); Which superseded in part (in 1964): Revue des Sciences Sociales (ISSN 0484-8640).

REVUE THOMISTE; revue doctrinale de theologie et de philosophie. see *RELIGIONS AND THEOLOGY*

100   US   ISSN 0277-3945
PN171.4
RHETORIC SOCIETY QUARTERLY. 1968. q. $10 to institutions. Rhetoric Society of America, c/o Department of Philosophy, St. Cloud State University, St. Cloud, MN 56301. TEL 612-255-2234. Ed. George E. Yoos. adv.; bk.rev.; bibl.; cum.index. circ. 700. **Indexed:** M.L.A.
—BLDSC (7960.610000); Faxon; UnCover.
Formerly: Rhetoric Society Newsletter.

RICERCHE STORICHE SALESIANE; rivista semestrale di storia religiosa e civile. see *RELIGIONS AND THEOLOGY — Roman Catholic*

100 700   IT   ISSN 0035-6212
RIVISTA DI ESTETICA. (Text in English, French and Italian) 1956-1973; N.S. 1979. 3/yr. L.76000 (Europe L.96000; elsewhere L.120000) (effective 1995). Rosenberg & Sellier, Via Andrea Doria 14, 10123 Turin, Italy. TEL 39-11-8127820. FAX 39-11-8127744. Ed. Gianni Vattimo. adv.; bk.rev.; abstr.; index. circ. 1,500. (back issues avail.) **Indexed:** Artbibl.Mod., M.L.A.
—Faxon; SWETS.
Description: Covers topics related to estetics, word vs. case, rhetoric, philosophy, poetry and anthropology.

100   IT   ISSN 0035-6239
RIVISTA DI FILOSOFIA. 1909. 3/yr. L.120000. Societa Editrice Il Mulino, Strada Maggiore, 37, 40125 Bologna, Italy. TEL 39-51-256011. FAX 39-51-256034. Ed. Pietro Rossi. adv.; bk.rev.; bibl.; index. circ. 1,500. (back issues avail.) **Indexed:** Phil.Ind.
—Faxon; SWETS.

149.2   IT   ISSN 0035-6247
B4
RIVISTA DI FILOSOFIA NEOSCOLASTICA. 1909. q. L.87000 (foreign L.147000 ($110)) (effective 1996). (Universita Cattolica del Sacro Cuore) Vita e Pensiero, Largo Gemelli 1, 20123 Milan, Italy. TEL 39-2-72342310. FAX 39-2-72342260. TELEX 321033 UCATMI 1. Ed. Adriano Bausola. adv.; B&W page L.2500000. bk.rev.; bibl. **Indexed:** Phil.Ind. **Document type:** academic/scholarly publication.
—Faxon; SWETS.
Description: Covers various areas in philosophy.

RIVISTA DI PSICOLOGIA DELL'ARTE. see *ART*

109   IT   ISSN 0393-2516
B4
RIVISTA DI STORIA DELLA FILOSOFIA. 1946; N.S. 1950. q. L.80000 (foreign L.110000) (effective 1993). Franco Angeli Editore, Viale Monza 106, 20127 Milan, Italy. TEL 02-28-27-651. Ed. Mario Dal Pra. adv.; bk.rev.; abstr.; bibl.; index. circ. 1,000. (back issues avail.) **Indexed:** Arts & Hum.Cit.Ind., Curr.Cont. **Document type:** academic/scholarly publication.
—Faxon; SWETS.
Formerly (until 1984): Rivista Critica di Storia della Filosofia (ISSN 0035-581X); (until 1950): Rivista di Storia della Filosofia (ISSN 0393-2508).

RIVISTA INTERNAZIONALE DI FILOSOFIA DEL DIRITTO. see *LAW*

100   IT   ISSN 0035-7030
RIVISTA ROSMINIANA DI FILOSOFIA E DI CULTURA. (Text in English, French, Italian, Spanish) 1906; N.S. 1967. q. L.50000 (foreign L.60000). (Centro Internazionale di Studi Rosminiani) Edizioni Rosminiane Sodalitas s.a.s., Corso Umberto 1st, 15, 28049 Stresa (Novara), Italy. TEL 0323-30091. FAX 0323-31623. Ed. P. Paolo Ottonello. adv.; bk.rev.; bibl.; index. circ. 600. **Indexed:** Lang.& Lang.Behav.Abstr. **Document type:** academic/scholarly publication.

100 300   PL   ISSN 0035-7685
B31   CODEN: RFLZBF
ROCZNIKI FILOZOFICZNE. (In four parts: 1. Metaphysics, Logic, History of Philosophy; 2. Philosophy of Morals, Philosophy of Religion; 3. Natural Philosophy; 4. Psychology) (Text in Polish; summaries in English, French, German) 1948. irreg.? price varies. Katolicki Uniwersytet Lubelski, Towarzystwo Naukowe, Ul. Gliniana 21, 20-616 Lublin, Poland. bk.rev.; index. circ. 720. **Indexed:** Psychol.Abstr.

100   NE   ISSN 0925-8639
RODOPI PHILOSOPHICAL STUDIES. 1993. irreg. price varies. Editions Rodopi B.V., Keizersgracht 302-304, 1016 EX Amsterdam, Netherlands. TEL 31-20-6227507. FAX 31-20-6380948. E-mail: F.van.der.Zee@Rodopi.nl. (In N. America: 233 Peachtree St., N.E., Ste. 404, Atlanta, GA 30303-1504. TEL 800-225-3998. FAX 404-522-7116) Ed. Ernest Sosa. **Document type:** monographic series.
Description: Publishes South American studies of philosophy.

100 200   US   ISSN 1072-9380
THE ROLL; magazine of the Schola Contemplationis. 1984. q. $12. Scholar Contemplationis, 3425 Forest Ln., Pfafftown, NC 27040-9545. TEL 919-924-4980. Ed. James Somerville. adv.; bk.rev.; illus.; circ. 550 (controlled). (back issues avail.) **Document type:** academic/scholarly publication.
Description: Examines philosophical and religious questions and topics through a liberal perspective for the informed reader.

366.4 135.43   US   ISSN 0035-8266
ROSACRUZ. (Text in Spanish) 1947. bi-m. $9. Supreme Grand Lodge of AMORC, Inc., Rosicrucian Park, San Jose, CA 95191-0001. TEL 408-287-9171. Ed. Laura Torres. illus.; circ. 17,000 (controlled). (tabloid format)
Description: Explores mysticism and philosophy.

366.4 135.43   US   ISSN 0035-8339
BF1623.R7
ROSICRUCIAN DIGEST. 1915. q. $12. Rosicrucian Order, AMORC, Rosicrucian Park, 1342 Naglee Ave., San Jose, CA 95191. TEL 408-947-3600. FAX 408-947-3677. Ed. Robin M. Thompson. bk.rev. circ. 45,000.
—Faxon; UnCover.

100   NE   ISSN 0923-0114
ROYAL INSTITUTE OF PHILOSOPHY CONFERENCE. (Text in English) 1979. irreg. price varies. Kluwer Academic Publishers, Postbus 17, 3300 AA Dordrecht, Netherlands. TEL 31-78-392392. FAX 31-78-392254. TELEX 29245 KAPG NL. (Dist. by: Kluwer Academic Publishers Group, P.O. Box 322, 3300 AH Dordrecht, Netherlands. TEL 31-78-392392. FAX 31-78-546474; N. America dist. addr.: Box 358, Accord Sta., Hingham, MA 02018-0358. TEL 617-871-6600. FAX 617-871-6528) **Document type:** proceedings.
Refereed Serial

100 PL ISSN 0035-9599
RUCH FILOZOFICZNY. (Text mainly in Polish; some in English, German) 1911. q. $32 (effective 1995). Polskie Towarzystwo Filozoficzne - Polish Philosophical Society, c/o Uniwersitet im. Mikolaja Kopernika, Katedra Logiki, Fosa Staromiejska 3, 87-100 Torun, Poland. TEL 48-22-265231. Ed. Leon Gumanski. bk.rev.; abstr.; bibl.; index; circ. 530 (controlled). **Document type:** academic/scholarly publication.
   Description: Philosophy and history of philosophy including logic and methodology.

100 FR
RUE DESCARTES. 3/yr. 300 F. (foreign 360 F.). (College International de Philosophie) Editions Albin Michel, 22 rue Huyghens, 75014 Paris, France. TEL 42-79-10-00. Ed.Bd.

100 US ISSN 1052-7729
B1649.R94
RUSSELL SOCIETY NEWS. 1974. q. $35 membership. Bertrand Russell Society, Inc., 1965 Winding Hills Rd., Ste. 1304, Davenport, IA 52807. TEL 312-286-0676. Ed. Dennis Darland. bk.rev.; cum.index: 1974-1990. circ. 325. (looseleaf format; back issues avail.) **Document type:** newsletter.

026 CN ISSN 0036-0163
B1649 .R94
RUSSELL: THE JOURNAL OF THE BERTRAND RUSSELL ARCHIVES. 1971. s-a. Can.$16 to individuals; institutions Can.$28. McMaster University Library Press, Mills Memorial Library, Hamilton, ON L8S 4L6, Canada. TEL 416-525-9140. FAX 416-546-0625. E-mail: blackwk@mcmaster.ca. Ed. Kenneth Blackwell. adv.; bk.rev.; bibl. circ. 500. **Indexed:** Arts & Hum.Cit.Ind., Curr.Cont., Ind.Bk.Rev.Hum., Phil.Ind.
   —BLDSC (8052.660000); Faxon; Genuine Article; UnCover.
   Description: Articles and reviews about Bertrand Russell.

100 US ISSN 1061-1967
B1
RUSSIAN STUDIES IN PHILOSOPHY; a journal of translations from Soviet scholarly sources. 1962. q. $419 to institutions (foreign $472) (effective Jul. 1995). M.E. Sharpe, Inc., 80 Business Park Dr., Armonk, NY 10504. TEL 914-273-1800; 800-541-6563. FAX 914-273-2106. Ed. James P. Scanlan. adv.; index. (back issues avail.) **Indexed:** Arts & Hum.Cit.Ind., ASCA, Curr.Cont., Phil.Ind., SSCI. **Document type:** academic/scholarly publication.
   —BLDSC (8052.931200); Faxon; Genuine Article; SWETS; UMI; UnCover. CCC.
   Formerly: Soviet Studies in Philosophy (ISSN 0038-5883)
   Refereed Serial

S E R IN ACTION NEWSLETTER. (Society for Educational Reconstruction) see EDUCATION

SAINT BONAVENTURE UNIVERSITY. FRANCISCAN INSTITUTE. PHILOSOPHY SERIES. see RELIGIONS AND THEOLOGY — Roman Catholic

100 200 US ISSN 1059-8375
ST. WILLIBRORD STUDIES IN PHILOSOPHY AND RELIGION. 1991. irreg., no.3, 1995. price varies. Borgo Press, St. Willibrord's Press, Box 2845, San Bernardino, CA 92406. TEL 909-884-5813. FAX 909-888-4942. Ed. Karl Pruter. **Document type:** monographic series.
   Description: Features studies on all aspects of Christianity, including histories, treatises, and manuals.

294 II ISSN 0036-3316
SAIVA SIDDHANTA. (Text in English) 1966. q. Rs.15 (foreign $5). Saiva Siddhantha Peru Manram, 4, Venkatesa Agraharam Salai I Fl., Mylapore, Madras 600004, India. Ed. G.M. Muthuswamy. adv.; bk.rev.; abstr.; index. circ. 500.
   Description: Siddhanta philosophy, religion, and literature.

SALESIANUM. see RELIGIONS AND THEOLOGY — Roman Catholic

100 920 AU ISSN 0259-0794
SALZBURGER BEITRAEGE ZUR PARACELSUSFORSCHUNG. 1960. irreg., no.27, 1990. price varies. (Internationale Paracelsus-Gesellschaft) Oesterreicher Kunst- und Kulturverlag, Postfach 17, A-1016 Vienna, Austria. **Document type:** monographic series.

100 AU ISSN 0080-5696
B23
SALZBURGER JAHRBUCH FUER PHILOSOPHIE. 1957. a. price varies. Universitaetsverlag Anton Pustet, Bergstr. 12, A-5020 Salzburg, Austria. TEL 0662-87350755. FAX 0662-87350758. **Indexed:** Phil.Ind. **Document type:** academic/scholarly publication.

100 AU ISSN 0080-5726
SALZBURGER STUDIEN ZUR PHILOSOPHIE. 1962. irreg. price varies. Universitaetsverlag Anton Pustet, Bergstr. 12, A-5020 Salzburg, Austria. TEL 0662-87350755. FAX 0662-87350758. **Document type:** academic/scholarly publication.

100 200 AG ISSN 0036-4703
SAPIENTIA. (Text in Spanish) 1946. s-a. $70. Universidad Catolica Argentina, Facultad de Filosofia y Letras, Bme. Mitre 1869, 1039 Buenos Aires, Argentina. Ed. Octavio Derisi. adv.; bk.rev.; bibl.; charts; illus.; index, cum.index: 1946-1992. circ. 1,100. (also avail. in microfilm from UMI; reprint service avail. from UMI) **Indexed:** Cath.Ind., Hisp.Amer.Per.Ind. (1970-), Phil.Ind., Rel.& Theol.Abstr. **Document type:** academic/scholarly publication.
   —UMI.

100 200 IT ISSN 0036-4711
SAPIENZA; rivista internazionale di filosofia e di teologia. 1948. q. L.50000($34) (effective 1995). (Dominican Fathers) Editrice Domenicana Italiana, Via Luigi Palmieri, 19, 80133 Naples, Italy. TEL 081-459-003. (Ed. addr.: Vicoletto S. Pietro a Maiella 4, 80134 Naples, Italy) Ed. Michele Miele. adv.; bk.rev.; abstr.; bibl.; index. circ. 500. **Indexed:** CERDIC, M.L.A., New Test.Abstr., Old Test.Abstr., Phil.Ind.

181.45 US
SAT SANDESH;* the message of the masters. 1968. m. $20. Sawan Kirpal Publications, 19384 Smoots Rd., Bowling Green, VA 22427. Ed. Arthur Stein. bk.rev. circ. 1,800.
   Description: The teachings of Sant Rajinder Singh of India and earlier spiritual mentors of Sant Mat tradition, also known as Science of Spirituality.

100 IT ISSN 1122-1852
SCHERIA. 1992. 3/yr. (Circulo G. Sadoul di Ischia) Valentino Editore, Via Michele Mazzella, 47, 80077 Ischia, Italy. TEL 081-984056. (Ed. addr.: Via Osservatorio 2, 80077 Ischia Porto (Na), Italy. TEL 081-992117. FAX 081-981298) (Co-sponsor: Istituto Italiano per gli Studi Filosofici) Ed. Edoardo Malagoli.

100 GW ISSN 0080-6935
SCHOPENHAUER-JAHRBUCH. a. DM.48. (Schopenhauer Gesellschaft e.V.) Verlag Koenigshausen et Neumann GmbH, Leistenstr. 3, 97082 Wuerzburg, Germany. bk.rev. circ. 1,912. (reprint service avail. from KTO) **Indexed:** Phil.Ind. **Document type:** academic/scholarly publication.
   Description: Articles on Schopenhauer's philosophy.

190 NE ISSN 0925-2657
SCHRIFTENREIHE ZUR PHILOSOPHIE KARL L. POPPERS UND DES KRITISCHEN RATIONALISMUS. 1991. irreg., vol.4, 1993. price varies. Editions Rodopi B.V., Keizersgracht 302-304, 1016 EX Amsterdam, Netherlands. TEL 31-20-6227507. FAX 31-20-6380948. E-mail: F.van.der.Zee@Rodopi.nl. (In N. America: 233 Peachtree St. N.E., Ste. 404, Atlanta, GA 30303-1504. TEL 800-225-3998. FAX 404-522-7116) Ed. Kurt Salamun. **Document type:** monographic series.

SCIENCE AND CHRISTIAN BELIEF. see RELIGIONS AND THEOLOGY

SCIENCE AND ENGINEERING ETHICS. see SCIENCES: COMPREHENSIVE WORKS

SCIENCE AND PHILOSOPHY. see SCIENCES: COMPREHENSIVE WORKS

200 CN ISSN 0316-5345
BR3
SCIENCE ET ESPRIT. 1948. 3/yr. Can.$20. Editions Fides, 165 Deslauriers, Ville St-Laurent, PQ H4N 2S4, Canada. TEL 514-745-4290. bk.rev.; index. circ. 375. **Indexed:** CERDIC, M.L.A., New Test.Abstr., Old Test.Abstr., Pt.de Rep. (1983-), Rel.Ind.One, Rel.Per.
   —BLDSC (8142.920000); SWETS.

SCIENCE OF MIND MAGAZINE. see RELIGIONS AND THEOLOGY — Other Denominations And Sects

SCIENCE OF SCIENCE; an international journal of studies on scientific reasoning and scientific enterprise. see SCIENCES: COMPREHENSIVE WORKS

SCUOLA NORMALE SUPERIORE DI PISA. ANNALI. CLASSE DI LETTERE E FILOSOFIA. see HUMANITIES: COMPREHENSIVE WORKS

100 NR ISSN 0048-9964
SECOND ORDER; an African journal of philosophy. 1972. s-a. $50. Obafemi Awolowo University Press, Ltd., Periodicals Department, Ile-Ife, Osun State, Nigeria. Ed. O.S. Eyey. adv.; bk.rev.; bibl. circ. 500. **Indexed:** Lang.& Lang.Behav.Abstr., Phil.Ind. **Document type:** academic/scholarly publication.

100 II ISSN 0049-0008
SECULARIST. (Text in English) 1971. 6/yr. Rs.30($7) Indian Secular Society, 850-8A Shivajinagar, Pune 411 004, Maharashtra, India. TEL 345246. Ed. V.K. Sinha. adv.; bk.rev. circ. 400. **Document type:** newsletter.
   —UnCover.
   Description: Committed to secular human values and their promotion in Indian society. Seeks to combat religious obscurantism and to educate public opinion.

100 US
SEEDS OF UNFOLDING; spiritual ideas for daily living. 1982. q. $10 (foreign $15). Cafh Foundation, Inc., 1510 Whitehill Rd., Yorktown Heights, NY 10598. TEL 212-724-4260. FAX 914-962-5732. (Subscr. to: 168 W. Kerley Rd., Tivoli, NY 10598) Ed. Carol Cooper. bk.rev.; film rev. (back issues avail.)

100 IT ISSN 1121-6530
SEGNI E COMPRENSIONE. 1987. q. L.34000 (foreign L.68000). (Universita degli Studi di Lecce, Dipartimento di Filosofia) Capone Editore s.r.l., Via Caprarica, 35, 73020 Cavallino (Lecce), Italy. TEL 0832-611877. FAX 0832-612618. Ed. Giovanni Invitto.

SEIKYO TIMES. see RELIGIONS AND THEOLOGY — Buddhist

100 GW ISSN 0939-0952
SELBSTORGANISATION. JAHRBUCH FUER KOMPLEXITAET IN DEN NATUR-, SOZIAL- UND GEISTESWISSENSCHAFTEN. 1990. a. Duncker und Humblot GmbH, Postfach 410329, 12113 Berlin, Germany. TEL 030-7900060. FAX 030-79000631. Ed. U. Niedersen. **Document type:** academic/scholarly publication.

SELF & SOCIETY; European journal of humanistic psychology. see PSYCHOLOGY

181.45 UK ISSN 0037-1556
SELF-KNOWLEDGE; a yoga quarterly devoted to spiritual thought and practice. 1950. q. £8 (foreign £9). Shanti Sadan Centre of Adhyatma Yoga, 29 Chepstow Villas, London W11 3DR, England. TEL 0171-727-7846. FAX 0171-792-9817. Ed.Bd. bk.rev. circ. 250. **Document type:** bulletin.
   Description: A quarterly journal devoted to spiritual thought and practice, mastery of the mind, meditation.

SELF-REALIZATION. see RELIGIONS AND THEOLOGY

100 GW ISSN 0170-219X
SEMIOSIS; internationale Zeitschrift fuer Semiotik und Aesthetik. (Text in English, French, German, Italian; summaries in English) 1976. q. (Vereinigung fuer Wissenschaftliche Semiotik) Agis Verlag GmbH, Ooser Luisenstr. 23, Postfach 2220, 76532 Baden-Baden, Germany. FAX 07221-66810. Ed. Elisabeth Walther. adv.; bk.rev.; index. (back issues avail.) **Indexed:** Bibl.Ling.

SEMIOTEXT(E). see LITERARY AND POLITICAL REVIEWS

SEMIOTIC REVIEW OF BOOKS. see *HUMANITIES: COMPREHENSIVE WORKS*

SEMIOTISCH PERSPECTIEF. see *LINGUISTICS*

SEMIQUASI REVIEW. see *LITERATURE — Poetry*

212.5   TU
SEVGI DUNYASI. 1963. m. P.T.6000($12) Sevgi Yayinlari Tic. Ltd. Sti., Aydede Cad. 4-5, Taksim, Istanbul, Turkey. (Dist. by: Sevgi Dunyasi, P.K.140, Serkeci-Istanbul, Turkey) Ed. Refet Kayserilioglu. circ. 5,000. (back issues avail.)
 Description: Explores spiritualism and moral issues.

SHARE IT; international journal for celebrating & sharing who we really are. see *NEW AGE PUBLICATIONS*

SHAW; the annual of Bernard Shaw Studies. see *LITERATURE*

SHREE HARI KATHA/GOSPEL OF GOD. see *RELIGIONS AND THEOLOGY — Hindu*

100 320   BL   ISSN 0103-4332
H8
SINTESE. (Text in Portuguese; summaries in English) 1959. q. Cr.$20($30) (effective 1995). (Centro de Estudos Superiores da Companhia de Jesus, Faculdade de Filosofia) Edicoes Loyola, Rua 1822, 347, 04216-000 Sao Paulo SP, Brazil. TEL 031-441-0233. FAX 031-441-7227. (Edit. addr.: Av. Dr. Cristiano Guimaraes 2127, 31720-300 Belo Horizonte MG, Brazil. TEL 55-31-4410233. FAX 55-31-4417227) Eds. Danilo Mondoni, Henrique C.L. Vaz; Pub. Gabriel Galache. adv. contact: Vicente Pedro Carvalho. bk.rev.; abstr.; bibl.; cum.index: vols.1-17 (1974-1990). circ. 1,800. (back issues avail.) **Indexed:** CERDIC. **Document type:** academic/scholarly publication.
 Formerly: Sintese Politica, Economica e Social (ISSN 0037-5772)
 Description: Publishes textx by contemporary philosophers which are of real interest and quality, with a view to enriching the national philosophical culture.

100   IT   ISSN 0037-5888
SISTEMATICA; rivista di filosofia e di filologia. 1968. q. L.20000. Edizioni Pergamena s.a.s., Viale Ezio 7, 20149 Milan, Italy. Dir. Giovanni Giraldi. bk.rev.

SISTEMI INTELLIGENTI; rivista quadrimestrale di scienze cognitive e intelligenza artificiale. see *PSYCHOLOGY*

100   GW   ISSN 1105-1582
SKEPSIS. 1990. 2/yr. DM.54. Academia Verlag GmbH, Postfach 1663, 53734 Sankt Augustin, Germany. TEL 02241-333349. FAX 02241-341528. Eds. L.C. Bargeliotes, N. Chronis. **Document type:** academic/scholarly publication.

110   II
SKEPTICS INDIA. (Text in English) 1991. m. newsstand price: Rs.6. H. 5, Shakarpur, Opp. Sanjay Park, New Delhi 110 092, India. Ed. Gulshan Mahajan. circ. 18,585.

100 301 320   XV   ISSN 0353-4510
HX8   CODEN: FIVEFV
SLOVENSKA AKADEMIJA ZNANOSTI IN UMETNOSTI. FILOZOFSKI VESTNIK/ACTA PHILOSOPHICA. Key Title: Filozofski Vestnik. (Text in English, Slovenian) 1980. s-a. $18 to individuals; institutions $36. Slovenska Akademija Znanosti in Umetnosti, Novi Trg 3, 61000 Ljubljana, Slovenia. TEL 386-61-1256068. FAX 386-61-1255253. E-mail: fi@zrc-sasu.si. (Subscr. to: Cankarjeba Zalozba, Trg Osvoboditve 7, 61000 Ljubljana, Slovenia) Ed. Vojislav Likar. bk.rev. circ. 800. (back issues avail.) **Indexed:** Arts & Hum.Cit.Ind., Bull.Signal., Curr.Cont.
 Formerly: Institut za Marksisticne Studije. Vestnik (ISSN 0351-6881)

100 300   UK   ISSN 0269-1728
BD175
SOCIAL EPISTEMOLOGY; a journal of knowledge, culture and policy. 1987. q. £133($220) (effective 1996). Taylor & Francis Ltd., Rankine Rd., Basingstoke, Hants. RG24 8PR, England. TEL 44-1256-840366. FAX 44-1256-479438. TELEX 858540. E-mail: info@tandf.co.uk. (Subscr. in. N. America to: Taylor & Francis Inc., 1900 Frost Rd., Ste. 101, Bristol, PA 19007-1598. TEL 800-821-8312. FAX 215-785-5515) Ed. Steve Fuller. circ. 171. **Document type:** academic/scholarly publication.
 —BLDSC (8318.087500); SWETS; UnCover. **CCC.**
 Description: Devoted to research explorations in the social structure of knowledge, and establishing a forum for philosophical and sociological inquiry.
 Refereed Serial

100   UK   ISSN 0265-0525
H61
SOCIAL PHILOSOPHY AND POLICY. 1983. s-a. £54($80) (effective 1996). Cambridge University Press, Edinburgh Bldg., Shaftesbury Rd., Cambridge CB2 2RU, England. TEL 01223-312393. FAX 01223-315052. TELEX 851817256. (N. American addr.: Cambridge University Press, Journals Dept., 40 W. 20th St., New York, NY 10011. TEL 212-924-3900. FAX 212-691-3239) Ed. Ellen Frankel Paul. adv. circ. 1,000. (back issues avail.; reprint service avail. from SWZ) **Indexed:** ASCA, ASSIA, Int.Polit.Sci.Abstr., Lang.& Lang.Behav.Abstr., Phil.Ind. **Document type:** academic/scholarly publication.
 —BLDSC (8318.129000); Faxon; Genuine Article; SWETS; UMI; UnCover. **CCC.**
 Description: Takes an interdisciplinary approach to the philosophical underpinnings of enduring social policy debates.

170   US   ISSN 0883-9395
BJ1725
SOCIAL RESPONSIBILITY: BUSINESS, JOURNALISM, LAW, MEDICINE. 1975. a. Washington and Lee University, Social Responsibility: Business, Journalism, Law, Medicine, Lexington, VA 24450. TEL 703-463-8786. FAX 703-463-8045. E-mail: lhodges@wlu.edu. Ed. Louis W. Hodges. circ. 10,000. (also avail. in microfilm from WSH,PMC; reprint service avail. from WSH) **Indexed:** C.L.I., L.R.I., Leg.Per. **Document type:** academic/scholarly publication.
 —UnCover.
 Formerly (until 1984): Social Responsibility: Journalism, Law, Medicine (ISSN 0732-9938)

100   US   ISSN 0037-802X
H1
SOCIAL THEORY AND PRACTICE; an international and interdisciplinary journal of social philosophy. 1970. 3/yr. $15 to individuals; libraries $36 (effective 1996). Florida State University, Department of Philosophy, 153 Dodd Hall, Tallahassee, FL 32306-1054. TEL 904-644-0224. FAX 904-644-3832. E-mail: journals@mailer.fsu.edu. Ed. Russell Dancy. adv.: B&W page $75; adv. contact: Roxane Fletcher. bk.rev. circ. 600. (also avail. in microfilm from UMI; reprint service avail. from UMI) **Indexed:** A.B.C.Pol.Sci., Abstr.Crim.& Pen., Amer.Hist.& Life, ASSIA, Hist.Abstr., Int.Polit.Sci.Abstr., Lang.& Lang.Behav.Abstr., Mid.East: Abstr.& Ind., Phil.Ind., Soc.Sci.Ind., Sociol.Abstr., SSCI. **Document type:** academic/scholarly publication.
 —BLDSC (8318.217800); Faxon; SWETS; UMI; UnCover.

100   US   ISSN 1042-6833
SOCIETE AMERICAINE DE PHILOSOPHIE DE LANGUE FRANCAISE. BULLETIN. (Text in English, French) 1989. s-a. $15. Societe Americaine de Philosophie de Langue Francaise, c/o Northern Illinois University, 5 Moraine Terr., DeKalb, IL 60115. TEL 815-753-6463. FAX 815-753-6302. Ed. Colette V. Michael. (back issues avail.) **Indexed:** Phil.Ind. **Document type:** academic/scholarly publication.
 Description: Facilitates exchange among international scholars of French language, literature, and philosophy.
 Refereed Serial

100   FR   ISSN 0037-9352
B12
SOCIETE FRANCAISE DE PHILOSOPHIE. BULLETIN. 1901. 4/yr. 30 ECU($38) (typically set in Jan.). Armand Colin (Subsidiary of: Masson), 103 bd. Saint-Michel, 75005 Paris, France. TEL 1-46-34-19-12. FAX 1-43-26-96-38. TELEX 201 269 F. bk.rev. circ. 1,000. (back issues avail.; reprint service avail. from SCH) **Indexed:** Phil.Ind. —Faxon. **CCC.**

SOEKAREN; tidskrift foer livsfraagor. see *PARAPSYCHOLOGY AND OCCULTISM*

750   AT   ISSN 0038-1527
BL1
SOPHIA; a journal for philosophical theology and cross-cultural philosophy of religion. 1962. 2/yr. Aus.$12.50($15) (effective 1995 & 1996). School of Social Inquiry, Faculty of Arts, Deakin University, Geelong, Vic. 3217, Australia. TEL 61-3-344-4778. FAX 61-3-344-4280. E-mail: zsophia@ariel.its.unimelb.edu.au. Ed. Purushottama Bilimoria. tr.lit. circ. 201. (also avail. in microform from UMI) **Indexed:** Aus.P.A.I.S., CERDIC, M.L.A., Phil.Ind. **Document type:** academic/scholarly publication.
 —BLDSC (8328.180000); UMI; UnCover.
 Description: Covers the broad spectrum of philosophy of religion, including cross-cultural philosophy of religion, feminist theology, and eco-theology.
 Refereed Serial

100   PH   ISSN 0115-8988
SOPHIA; journal of philosophy. (Text in English) 1971. a. P.30($3.20) (De La Salle University, Department of Philosophy) De La Salle University Press, 2401 Taft Ave., Manila, Philippines. TEL 2-59-48-32. FAX 632-521-9094. adv.; bk.rev. circ. 300. **Indexed:** Ind.Phil.Per.
 Description: Publishes scholarly articles reflecting significant quantitative or qualitative research in philosophy. Includes speeches, research reports, and "state of the art" papers.

170 330   US
SOUNDINGS (NOTRE DAME); a series of books on ethics, economics and business. 1987. irreg., latest vol.3. price varies. University of Notre Dame Press, Notre Dame, IN 46556. TEL 219-631-6346. FAX 219-631-8148. (Orders to: 11030 S. Langley Ave., Chicago, IL 60628. TEL 800-621-2736. FAX 800-621-8476; Overseas orders to: Eurospan University Press Group, Order Dept., 3 Henrietta St., London WC2E 8LU, England) Ed. Thomas Donaldson. **Document type:** academic/scholarly publication.

100   SA   ISSN 0258-0136
                                  CODEN: SAJPEM
SOUTH AFRICAN JOURNAL OF PHILOSOPHY. (Text and summaries in English) 1982. q. R.90. (Philosophical Society of Southern Africa) Foundation for Education, Science & Technology, P.O. Box 1758, Pretoria 0001, South Africa. TEL 27-12-322-6422. FAX 27-12-320-7803. Ed. A.A. van Niekerk. adv. contact: A.A. van Niekerk. circ. 550. **Indexed:** Biol.Abstr., Curr.Cont., Ind.S.A.Per., Phil.Ind. **Document type:** academic/scholarly publication.
 —Genuine Article. **CCC.**
 Description: Publishes original contributions in the field of philosophy.
 Refereed Serial

100   US   ISSN 0038-4283
B1
SOUTHERN JOURNAL OF PHILOSOPHY. (Supplement avail.) 1963. q. $20 to individuals (foreign $21); institutions $30 (foreign $31); students $10 (foreign $11) (effective 1996). University of Memphis, Department of Philosophy, Memphis, TN 38152. TEL 901-678-2669. FAX 901-678-4365. E-mail: itanner@cc.memphis.edu. Ed. Nancy D. Simco. adv. contact: Leigh Tanner. bk.rev.; index. circ. 1,000. (also avail. in microform from UMI; back issues avail.; reprint service avail. from UMI) **Indexed:** Arts & Hum.Cit.Ind., Curr.Cont., Phil.Ind. **Document type:** academic/scholarly publication.
 —BLDSC (8354.280000); Faxon; Genuine Article; SWETS; UMI; UnCover.
 Description: Serves a forum for the scholarly discussion of philosophical issues.

100 US ISSN 0897-2346
B1
SOUTHWEST PHILOSOPHY REVIEW. JOURNAL. 1937. s-a. $30 membership. Southwestern Philosophical Society, c/o Westminster College, Philosophy Department, Fulton, MO 65251-1299. TEL 314-592-1277. FAX 314-642-6356. E-mail: jswindlr@micro.wcmo.edu. (Co-sponsor: Westminster College) Ed. James K. Swindler. bk.rev.; circ. 250 (paid). (processed) **Document type:** academic/scholarly publication.
 Formerly (until 1984): Southwestern Philosophical Society. Newsletter (ISSN 0038-4925)
 Description: Consists of papers from the annual meeting of the society in one issue and refereed papers and reviews in the other. Seeks submissions on any philosophical topic from any perspective.
 Refereed Serial

SOUTHWESTERN JOURNAL OF THEOLOGY. see *RELIGIONS AND THEOLOGY*

SOVIETICA. PUBLICATIONS AND MONOGRAPHS. see *HISTORY — History Of Europe*

100 GW ISSN 0178-1367
SOZIALPHILOSOPHISCHE STUDIEN. 1984. irreg., vol.5. DM.68. Wilhelm Fink Verlag, Ohmstr. 5, 80802 Munich, Germany. TEL 089-348017. FAX 089-341378. **Document type:** monographic series.

100 GW
SPECULA. 1978. irreg. price varies. Friedrich Frommann Verlag Guenther Holzboog, Koenig-Karl-Str. 27, 70372 Stuttgart, Germany. TEL 0711-9559690. FAX 0711-9559691. Ed. Guenther Holzboog. **Document type:** monographic series.

SPELING. see *RELIGIONS AND THEOLOGY*

THE SPIRITUAL HEALER; journal of spiritual healing and philosophy. see *NEW AGE PUBLICATIONS*

100 IT ISSN 0038-7649
SPIRITUALITA; rassegna di cultura varia. 1956. q. L.3000. Sodalizio Internazionale di Spiritualita Alpina, Ordine del Cardo, Eremo San Salvatore, Casorezzo, 20010 Milan, Italy. Ed. Sandro Prada. illus.

SSU YU YEN/THOUGHT AND WORDS; journal of the humanities and social sciences. see *HUMANITIES: COMPREHENSIVE WORKS*

100 US
STILL WATERS NEWSLETTER. 1977. q. $5 suggested donation. Still Waters Foundation, Inc., 615 Stafford Ln., Pensacola, FL 32506. TEL 904-455-9511. Ed. John E. Pepper. bk.rev.; circ. 2,000 (controlled).
 Former titles: Still Waters Presents; Still Waters Digest.

101 SW ISSN 0491-0877
STOCKHOLM STUDIES IN PHILOSOPHY. (Subseries of Acta Universitatis Stockholmiensis) (Text in English) 1957. irreg. price varies. (Stockholms Universitet) A W I International AB, P.O. Box 4627, S-116 91 Stockholm, Sweden. TEL 468-640-8800. FAX 468-641-1180. Eds. Harald Ofstad, Anders Wedberg. (back issues avail.)
 —BLDSC (8465.680000).

STRATEGIES (LOS ANGELES); a journal of theory, culture and politics. see *POLITICAL SCIENCE — International Relations*

215 AG ISSN 0049-2353
BX805
STROMATA; antigua ciencia y fe. 1944. q. (in two issues). $25 in Latin America; elsewhere $30 (effective 1992). (Universidad del Salvador, Facultades de Filosofia y Teologia) Asociacion Civil Facultades Loyola, C.C. 10, Avda. Mitre 3226, 1663 San Miguel, Argentina. FAX 54-1-664-6442. E-mail: stromata@bibusv.edu.ar. Ed. Jorge R. Seibold; Pub. Diego Fares. adv.; bk.rev.; abstr.; bibl.; cum.index: 1944-1981. circ. 1,000. **Indexed:** Bull.Signal., Hisp.Amer.Per.Ind. (1970-1993), New Test.Abstr., Old Test.Abstr., Phil.Ind. **Document type:** academic/scholarly publication.

100 320 IT ISSN 1122-5599
STUDI CRITICI; rivista di etica, filosofia e politica. 1991. s-a. L.30000 (foreign L.60000). (Associazione Giovanni Amendola) Flavio Pagano Editore, Piazza S. Domenico Maggiore 9, Monumentale Palazzo S. Severo, 80134 Naples, Italy. TEL 081-5528782. FAX 081-5528783. Ed. Ernesto Paolozzi. bk.rev.

STUDI CRITICI SULLE SCIENZE. see *SCIENCES: COMPREHENSIVE WORKS*

100 IT
STUDI EUROPEI. 1993. a. (Dipartimento di Studi sulla Storia del Pensiero Europeo "Michele Federico Sciacca) Casa Editrice Leo S. Olschki, Viuzzio del Pozzetto, 50126 Florence, Italy. TEL 39-55-6530684. FAX 39-55-6530214. Ed. Maria Adelaide Raschini.

100 IT ISSN 0081-6310
STUDIA ARISTOTELICA. 1958. irreg., no.12, 1986. price varies. (Universita degli Studi di Padova) Editrice Antenore, Via G. Rusca 15, 35100 Padua, Italy.

100 NE ISSN 0921-9919
STUDIA CARTESIANA. (Text in English and French) 1979. irreg. price varies. Quadratures, Postbus 6463, 1005 EL Amsterdam, Netherlands. Ed.Bd. bk.rev.

100 500 GW ISSN 0039-3185
B2550 CODEN: STLBBI
STUDIA LEIBNITIANA; Zeitschrift fuer Geschichte der Philosophie und der Wissenschaften. (Text in English, German) 1969. s-a. DM.128 (supplements individually priced). (Gottfried-Wilhelm-Leibniz Gesellschaft e.V.) Franz Steiner Verlag Wiesbaden GmbH, Birkenwaldstr. 44, 70191 Stuttgart, Germany. TEL 0711-2582-0. FAX 0711-2582390. (Subscr. to: Postfach 101061, 70009 Stuttgart, Germany) Ed.Bd. adv.; bk.rev. circ. 450. (back issues avail.) **Indexed:** Arts & Hum.Cit.Ind., Curr.Cont., Math.R., Phil.Ind.
 —Faxon; Genuine Article; SWETS; UnCover. **CCC.**

100 GW ISSN 0341-0765
STUDIA LEIBNITIANA. SONDERHEFTE. (Text in English and German) irreg., vol.24, 1995. price varies. (Gottfried Wilhelm Leibniz Gesellschaft, Hannover) Franz Steiner Verlag Wiesbaden GmbH, Birkenwaldstr. 44, 70191 Stuttgart, Germany. TEL 0711-2582-0. FAX 0711-2582390. (Subscr. to: Postfach 101061, 70009 Stuttgart, Germany) Ed.Bd. **Indexed:** Math.R. **Document type:** monographic series.

100 GW ISSN 0303-5980
B2550
STUDIA LEIBNITIANA. SUPPLEMENTA. (Text in English, French, and German) irreg., vol.30, 1995. price varies. (Gottfried Wilhelm Leibniz Gesellschaft, Hannover) Franz Steiner Verlag Wiesbaden GmbH, Birkenwaldstr. 44, 70191 Stuttgart, Germany. TEL 0711-2582-0. FAX 0711-2582390. (Subscr. to: Postfach 101061, 70009 Stuttgart, Germany) Ed.Bd. **Indexed:** Math.R. **Document type:** monographic series.

160 NE ISSN 0039-3215
CODEN: SLOGAP
STUDIA LOGICA; an international journal for symbolic logic. (Text in English) 1953. bi-m. fl.607 to institutions; $389 to institutions in U.S. (effective 1996). (Polska Akademia Nauk, Instytut Filozofii i Socjologii, PL - Polish Academy of Sciences, Institute of Philosophy and Sociology) Kluwer Academic Publishers, Postbus 17, 3300 AA Dordrecht, Netherlands. TEL 31-78-392392. FAX 31-78-392254. TELEX 29245 KAPG NL. E-mail: SERVICES@WKAP.NL. (Dist. by: Kluwer Academic Publishers Group, P.O. Box 322, 3300 AH Dordrecht, Netherlands. TEL 31-78-392392. FAX 31-78-546474; N. America dist. addr.: Box 358, Accord Sta., Hingham, MA 02018-0358. FAX 617-871-6528) Ed. Ryszard Wojcicki. bk.rev.; charts; index. (also avail. in microform from UMI; reprint service avail. from SWZ) **Indexed:** Bibl.Ling., Biol.Abstr., Eng.Ind., Geo.Abstr., INSPEC (1992-), Lang.& Lang.Behav.Abstr., Math.R., Phil.Ind., Ref.Zh., Sociol.Abstr., Zent.Math. **Document type:** academic/scholarly publication.
 —BLDSC (8482.975000); Faxon; SWETS; UMI; UnCover. **CCC.**
 Description: Papers on all technical issues of contemporary logic, logical systems, their semantics, methodology and application of logic in linguistics, mathematics and other sciences.
 Refereed Serial

189 PL ISSN 0039-3231
STUDIA MEDIEWISTYCZNE. (Text in English, German, Latin and Polish) 1959. s-a. Polska Akademia Nauk, Instytut Filozofii i Socjologii, Ul. Nowy Swiat 72, 00-330 Warsaw, Poland. TEL 48-22-267181. Ed. Z. Kuksewicz. **Indexed:** M.L.A. **Document type:** academic/scholarly publication.

110 PL ISSN 0039-324X
STUDIA METODOLOGICZNE. DISSERTATIONES METHODOLOGICAE. 1965. s-a. price varies. Adam Mickiewicz University Press, Nowowiejskiego 55, 61-734 Poznan, Poland. TEL 527-380. FAX 61-526425. TELEX 413260 UAMPL. Eds. Jerzy Kmita, Jerzy Topolski. bk.rev.; bibl.; index. circ. 380. **Document type:** academic/scholarly publication.
 —BLDSC (8483.056000).
 Description: Research papers in Polish, summaries in English, prepared by sociologists, philosophers, historians, psychologists, linguists and others.

291.42 808.8 US ISSN 0161-7222
BL625
STUDIA MYSTICA. 1978. a. $29.95. (Skidmore University) Edwin Mellen Press, 415 Ridge St., Box 450, Lewiston, NY 14092. TEL 716-754-2788. FAX 716-754-4056. Eds. Robert Boenig, Kate Greenspan. adv.; bk.rev.; film rev.; play rev.; illus. circ. 500. (back issues avail.; reprint service avail. from ISI) **Indexed:** Arts & Hum.Cit.Ind., Curr.Cont., M.L.A., Rel.& Theol.Abstr. (1990-), Rel.Ind.One. **Document type:** academic/scholarly publication.
 —BLDSC (8483.075000); Faxon; UMI; UnCover.
 Description: Scholarly articles, poetry, prose fiction, essays, reviews, and other art forms pertaining to mystical experience.

STUDIA PATAVINA; rivista di scienze religiose. see *RELIGIONS AND THEOLOGY*

100 SZ
STUDIA PHILOSOPHICA. (Text in French and German) 1981. irreg., vol.51, 1992. price varies. Paul Haupt AG, Falkenplatz 14, CH-3001 Bern, Switzerland. TEL 031-3012345. FAX 031-3014669. Eds. Dr Helmut Holzhey, Dr. Jean-Pierre Leyvraz. **Document type:** monographic series.

100 500 GW ISSN 0179-3896
STUDIA SPINOZANA; an international & interdisciplinary series. (Each issue has distinctive title and theme) 1985. a. DM.48($24.80) Verlag Koenigshausen und Neumann GmbH, Postfach 6007, 97010 Wuerzburg, Germany. TEL 0931-76401. FAX 0931-83620. (Dist. in U.S. by: Dr. Douglas J. Den Uyl, Bellarmine College, Newburg Rd., Louisville, KY 40205) Ed.Bd. adv.; bk.rev. circ. 1,000. **Document type:** academic/scholarly publication.
 Description: Articles on all aspects of Spinoza's philosophy, including its cultural and intellectual background and influence.

PHILOSOPHY

100   RM   ISSN 0578-5480
B8.R8
STUDIA UNIVERSITATIS "BABES-BOLYAI". PHILOSOPHIA.
(Text in English, French, German, Rumanian) 1958. s-a. exchange basis. Universitatea "Babes-Bolyai", Biblioteca Centrala Universitara, Str. Clinicilor 2, Cluj-Napoca 3400, Rumania. TEL 36-64-197092. FAX 36-64-197633. Ed. I. Haiduc. bk.rev.; cum.index: 1956-1963, 1964-1970. **Document type:** academic/scholarly publication.
—BLDSC (8482.309600).
Incorporates (in 1975): Studia Universitatis Babes-Bolyai. Psychologia-Pedagogia (ISSN 0578-5502); Studia Universitatis Babes-Bolyai. Sociologia.

100   GW   ISSN 0585-5802
STUDIEN UND MATERIALEN ZUR GESCHICHTE DER PHILOSOPHIE. irreg., vol.36, 1994. Georg Olms Verlag, Hagentorwall 7, 31134 Hildesheim, Germany. TEL 05121-1501-0. FAX 05121-150150. (U.S. subscr. to: 111 W. 57th St., New York, NY 10019. TEL 212-757-5237) Eds. Gerhard Funke, Rudolf Malter. **Document type:** monographic series.

189   NE   ISSN 0169-8028
STUDIEN UND TEXTE ZUR GEISTESGESCHICHTE DES MITTELALTERS. (Text in English, German) 1950. irreg., vol.44, 1994. price varies. E.J. Brill, P.O. Box 9000, 2300 PA Leiden, Netherlands. TEL 31-71-5353500. FAX 31-71-5317532. TELEX 39296 BRILL NL. (In N. America: E.J. Brill, 24 Hudson St., Kinderhook, NY 12106. TEL 800-962-4406. FAX 518-758-1959) Ed. A. Zimmermann. (back issues avail.) **Document type:** monographic series.
Description: Scholarly studies on medieval European philosophical texts and issues in the history of philosophy, theology and science in the medieval European world.
Refereed Serial

100   NE   ISSN 0921-9129
STUDIEN ZUR ANTIKEN PHILOSOPHIE. 1971. irreg., vol.14, 1987. price varies. John Benjamins Publishing Co., Amsteldijk 44, P.O. Box 75577, 1070 AN Amsterdam, Netherlands. TEL 31-20-6738156. FAX 31-20-6792956. (In N. America: Box 27519, Philadelphia, PA 19118-0519. TEL 215-836-1200. FAX 215-836-1204) (back issues avail.) **Document type:** monographic series.
Description: Monographs in classical philology confined to the interpretation of ancient philosophical texts contributing to interdisciplinary discussion between philologists and philosophers.

100   GW   ISSN 0340-5958
STUDIEN ZUR FRANZOESISCHEN PHILOSOPHIE DES ZWANZIGSTEN JAHRHUNDERTS. irreg., vol.12, 1986. price varies. Bouvier Verlag Herbert Grundmann, Am Hof 28, 53113 Bonn, Germany. TEL 0228-7290124. FAX 0228-7290179. Eds. V.V. Berning, H.R. Schlette. **Document type:** monographic series.

100   NE
▼**STUDIEN ZUR INTERKULTURELLEN PHILOSOPHIE.** (Text in German) 1994. irreg. price varies. Editions Rodopi B.V., Keizersgracht 302-304, 1016 EX Amsterdam, Netherlands. TEL 31-20-6227507. FAX 31-20-6380948. E-mail: F.van.der.Zee@Rodopi.nl. (In N. America: 233 Peachtree St., N.E., Ste. 404, Atlanta, GA 30303-1504. TEL 800-225-3998. FAX 404-522-7116) **Document type:** monographic series.

100   NE   ISSN 0167-4102
STUDIEN ZUR OESTERREICHISCHEN PHILOSOPHIE. (Supplement avail.: International Bibliography of Austrian Philosophy (ISSN 0923-3342)) (Text in English and German) 1979. irreg., vol.21, 1994. price varies. Editions Rodopi B.V., Keizersgracht 302-304, 1016 EX Amsterdam, Netherlands. TEL 31-20-6227507. FAX 31-20-6380948. E-mail: F.van.der.Zee@Rodopi.nl. (In N. America: 233 Peachtree St. N.E., Ste. 404, Atlanta GA 30303-1504. TEL 800-225-3998. FAX 404-522-7116) Ed. Rudolf Haller. (back issues avail.) **Document type:** monographic series.

109   GW   ISSN 0171-7278
STUDIEN ZUR PHILOSOPHIE DES 18. JAHRHUNDERTS. 1976. irreg., no.5, 1995. price varies. Peter Lang GmbH Europaeischer Verlag der Wissenschaften, Eschborner Landstr. 42-50, 60489 Frankfurt a.M., Germany. TEL 069-7807050. FAX 069-785893. **Document type:** monographic series.

189 940   NE   ISSN 0169-9857
STUDIEN ZUR PROBLEMGESCHICHTE DER ANTIKEN UND MITTELALTERLICHEN PHILOSOPHIE. 1966. irreg., vol. 12, 1989. price varies. E.J. Brill, P.O. Box 9000, 2300 PA Leiden, Netherlands. TEL 31-71-5353500. FAX 31-71-5317532. TELEX 39296 BRILL NL. (In N. America: E.J. Brill, 24 Hudson St., Kinderhook, NY 12106. TEL 800-962-4406. FAX 518-758-1959) (back issues avail.) **Document type:** monographic series.
Description: Scholarly discussions of historical and textual aspects of classical and medieval European philosophy.
Refereed Serial

111 701   SW   ISSN 1100-035X
STUDIES IN AESTHETICS. (Text in English, Swedish) 1988. irreg. price varies. Lund University Press, P.O. Box 141, S-221 00 Lund, Sweden. TEL 46-46-31-20-00. FAX 46-46-30-53-38. E-mail: Order@Studli.se. Ed. G. Hermeren. **Document type:** academic/scholarly publication.
—BLDSC (8488.933000).

100   US
STUDIES IN ASIAN THOUGHT AND RELIGION. 1983. irreg., latest no.16. $49.95 per no. Edwin Mellen Press, 415 Ridge St., Box 450, Lewiston, NY 14092. TEL 716-754-2788. FAX 716-754-4056. **Document type:** monographic series.

170 266   UK   ISSN 0953-9468
STUDIES IN CHRISTIAN ETHICS. 1988. 2/yr. £19.95 (U.S. $39.95; elsewhere £21.95). T & T Clark, 59 George St., Edinburgh EH2 2LQ, Scotland. TEL 0131-225-4703. FAX 0131-220-4260. Ed. Rev. R. Franklin. adv.; bk.rev. circ. 500. **Document type:** academic/scholarly publication.
—BLDSC (8489.904000).
Description: Each issue examines an important theme in contemporary Christian ethics with contributions from major moral theologians.

STUDIES IN COGNITIVE SYSTEMS. see *PSYCHOLOGY*

100   US   ISSN 0893-6919
STUDIES IN CONTEMPORARY CONTINENTAL PHILOSOPHY. irreg. Peter Lang Publishing, Inc., 62 W. 45th St., 4th Fl., New York, NY 10036. TEL 212-302-6740. FAX 212-302-7574. Ed. Galen A. Johnson. **Document type:** academic/scholarly publication, monographic series.
Description: Provides a forum for English-language authors of monographs in contemporary continental philosophy.

108   US
STUDIES IN CONTEMPORARY GERMAN SOCIAL THOUGHT. irreg. (2-5/yr.) M I T Press, Book Division, 55 Hayward St., Cambridge, MA 02142. TEL 617-253-5242. Ed. Thomas McCarthy. **Document type:** academic/scholarly publication.

STUDIES IN EAST EUROPEAN THOUGHT. see *POLITICAL SCIENCE*

STUDIES IN HISTORY AND PHILOSOPHY OF SCIENCE. see *SCIENCES: COMPREHENSIVE WORKS*

STUDIES IN HISTORY AND PHILOSOPHY OF SCIENCE PART B: STUDIES IN HISTORY AND PHILOSOPHY OF MODERN PHYSICS. see *PHYSICS*

STUDIES IN LANGUAGE. see *LINGUISTICS*

STUDIES IN LINGUISTICS AND PHILOSOPHY. see *PSYCHOLOGY*

STUDIES IN LOGIC AND COMPUTATION. see *MATHEMATICS*

STUDIES IN LOGIC AND THE FOUNDATIONS OF MATHEMATICS. see *MATHEMATICS*

STUDIES IN MARXISM. see *POLITICAL SCIENCE*

100 200   US   ISSN 0899-4897
STUDIES IN MORAL PHILOSOPHY. irreg. Peter Lang Publishing, Inc., 62 W. 45th St., 4th Fl., New York, NY 10036. TEL 212-302-6740. FAX 212-302-7574. Ed. John Kekes. **Document type:** academic/scholarly publication, monographic series.
Description: Focuses on the nature of good lives, character and its development, virtues and vices.

100   US
STUDIES IN MORAL, POLITICAL, AND LEGAL PHILOSOPHY. irreg. price varies. Princeton University Press, 41 William St., Princeton, NJ 08540. TEL 609-258-4900. FAX 609-258-6305. E-mail: jhardy@pupress.princeton.edu. Ed. Marshall Cohen. **Document type:** monographic series.

STUDIES IN PHILOSOPHICAL THEOLOGY. see *RELIGIONS AND THEOLOGY*

100   SW   ISSN 1100-4290
STUDIES IN PHILOSOPHY. (Text in English, Swedish) 1989. irreg. price varies. Lund University Press, P.O. Box 141, S-221 00 Lund, Sweden. TEL 46-46-31-20-00. FAX 46-46-30-53-38. E-mail: Order@Studli.se. Eds. B. Hansson, G. Hermeren. **Document type:** academic/scholarly publication.

STUDIES IN PHILOSOPHY AND EDUCATION; an international quarterly. see *EDUCATION*

100 200   NE
STUDIES IN PHILOSOPHY AND RELIGION. (Text in English) irreg. price varies. Kluwer Academic Publishers, Postbus 17, 3300 AA Dordrecht, Netherlands. TEL 31-78-392392. FAX 31-78-392254. TELEX 29245 KAPG NL. (Dist. by: Kluwer Academic Publishers Group, P.O. Box 322, 3300 AH Dordrecht, Netherlands. TEL 31-78-392392. FAX 31-78-546474; N. America dist. addr.: Box 358, Accord Sta., Hingham, MA 02018-0358. TEL 617-871-6600. FAX 617-871-6528) **Document type:** monographic series.
Refereed Serial

100   US   ISSN 0585-6965
B21
STUDIES IN PHILOSOPHY & THE HISTORY OF PHILOSOPHY. 1961. irreg., vol.23, 1991. price varies. Catholic University of America Press, 620 Michigan Ave., N.E., Washington, DC 20064. TEL 202-319-5052. FAX 202-319-5082. (Subscr. to: Box 4852, Hampden Sta., Baltimore, MD 21211. TEL 410-516-6953) Ed. Jude P. Dougherty. (reprint service avail. from UMI) **Indexed:** Phil.Ind.
—BLDSC (8491.220400).

109   NE   ISSN 0927-5088
STUDIES IN THE HISTORY OF IDEAS IN THE LOW COUNTRIES. 1993. irreg., vol.2, 1994. price varies. Editions Rodopi B.V., Keizersgracht 302-304, 1016 EX Amsterdam, Netherlands. TEL 31-20-6227507. FAX 31-20-6380948. E-mail: F.van.der.Zee@Rodopi.nl. (In N. America: 233 Peachtree St., N.E., Ste. 404, Atlanta, GA 30303-1504. TEL 800-225-3998. FAX 404-522-7116) **Document type:** academic/scholarly publication, monographic series.

109   US
STUDIES IN THE HISTORY OF PHILOSOPHY. vol.5, 1987. irreg., latest no.36. $49.95 per no. Edwin Mellen Press, 415 Ridge St., Box 450, Lewiston, NY 14092. TEL 716-754-2788. FAX 716-754-4056. **Document type:** monographic series.

181 954 294   NE   ISSN 0167-4161
STUDIES OF CLASSICAL INDIA. 1978. irreg., vol.13, 1992. price varies. Kluwer Academic Publishers, Postbus 17, 3300 AA Dordrecht, Netherlands. TEL 31-78-392392. FAX 31-78-392254. TELEX 29245 KAPG NL. (Dist. by: Kluwer Academic Publishers Group, P.O. Box 322, 3300 AH Dordrecht, Netherlands. TEL 31-78-392392. FAX 31-78-546474; N. America dist. addr.: Box 358, Accord Sta., Hingham, MA 02018-0358. TEL 617-871-6600. FAX 617-871-6528) Eds. B.K. Matilal, J.M. Masson. **Document type:** monographic series.
Refereed Serial

100   CC   ISSN 1005-8273
STUDIES ON MAO ZEDONG AND DENG XIAOPING THEORIES. (Text in Chinese) 1980. bi-m. Y21. Shanghai Shehui Kexueyuan, Zhexue Yanjiusuo - Shanghai Academy of Social Sciences, Institute of Philosophy, No.7, Alley 622, Huaihai Zhonglu, Shanghai 200020, People's Republic of China. TEL 3271170. FAX 3270004. Ed. Wang Miaoyang. adv.; bk.rev. **Document type:** academic/scholarly publication.
   Formerly (until Apr. 1994): Mao Zedong Zhexue Sixiang Yanjiu - Studies in Mao Zedong's Philosophical Thought.
   Description: Introduces and reviews main contemporary philosophy.

294.54   II
SUDHI SAHITYA; a bilingual literary monthly. (Text in Bengali, English) 1977. m. Rs.100. Adarsha Prakashani, Ma-Mahajnana Bishwa Kalyan Trust, Kharagpur 721 305, India. TEL 03222-661. circ. 17,000.

100   US   ISSN 0562-6048
BP500
SUNRISE; theosophic perspectives. 1951. bi-m. $9 (foreign $12). (Theosophical Society) Theosophical University Press, Box C, Pasadena, CA 91109-7107. TEL 818-798-3378. FAX 818-798-4749. Ed. Grace F. Knoche. bk.rev.; illus. (back issues avail.) **Document type:** academic/scholarly publication.
   Description: Published articles on scientific, religious, and philosophic themes in the light of ancient and modern theosophy. Includes interviews and reports on significant trends.

SUPPORTIVE LIFESTYLES NEWS. see *NEW AGE PUBLICATIONS*

100   FR
SURFACES (PARIS, 1978). 1978. irreg. Editions Jean-Michel Place, 12 rue Pierre et Marie Curie, 75005 Paris, France. Dir. Peter Hoy.

SUZHOU DAXUE XUEBAO (ZHEXUE SHEHUI KEXUE BAN)/SUZHOU UNIVERSITY. JOURNAL (PHILOSOPHY AND SOCIAL SCIENCES). see *SOCIAL SCIENCES: COMPREHENSIVE WORKS*

180   IT
SYMBOLON; studi e testi di filosofia antica e medievale. 1984. irreg., no.7, 1989. price varies. L'Erma di Bretschneider, Via Cassiodoro 19, 00193 Rome, Italy. TEL 06-687-41-27. FAX 06-687-41-29. Ed. Francesco Romano.

501   NE   ISSN 0039-7857
AP1   CODEN: SYNTAE
SYNTHESE; an international journal for epistemology, methodology and philosophy of science. 1936. m. fl.1514 to institutions; $922 to institutions in U.S. (effective 1996). Kluwer Academic Publishers, Postbus 17, 3300 AA Dordrecht, Netherlands. TEL 31-78-392392. FAX 31-78-392254. TELEX 29245 KAPG NL. E-mail: SERVICES@WKAP.NL. (Dist. by: Kluwer Academic Publishers Group, P.O. Box 322, 3300 AH Dordrecht, Netherlands. TEL 31-78-392392. FAX 31-78-546474; N. America dist. addr.: Box 358, Accord Sta., Hingham, MA 02018-0358. TEL 617-871-6600. FAX 617-871-6528) Ed. Jaakko Hintikka. adv.; bk.rev. (also avail. in microform from UMI; reprint service avail. from SWZ) **Indexed:** Arts & Hum.Cit.Ind., ASCA, Bibl.Ling., Curr.Cont., IBR, IBZ, Ind.Bk.Rev.Hum., Lang.& Lang.Behav.Abstr., Math.R., Phil.Ind., Ref.Zh., Sociol.Abstr., SSCI, Zent.Math. **Document type:** academic/scholarly publication.
   —BLDSC (8586.750000); Faxon; Genuine Article; SWETS; UMI; UnCover. **CCC.**
   Description: Publishes articles on the theory of knowledge, the general methodological problems of science, including related issues such as the role of mathematics, statistics and logic in science, and relevant aspects of the history and sociology of science.
   Refereed Serial

109   NE   ISSN 0166-6991
SYNTHESE LIBRARY; monographs on epistemology, logic, methodology, philosophy of science and of knowledge, and the mathematical methods of social and behavioral sciences. 1959. irreg., vol.229, 1993. price varies. Kluwer Academic Publishers, Postbus 17, 3300 AA Dordrecht, Netherlands. TEL 31-78-392392. FAX 31-78-392254. TELEX 29245 KAPG NL. (Dist. by: Kluwer Academic Publishers Group, P.O. Box 322, 3300 AH Dordrecht, Netherlands. TEL 31-78-392392. FAX 31-78-546474; N. America dist. addr.: Box 358, Accord Sta., Hingham, MA 02018-0358. TEL 617-871-6600. FAX 617-871-6528) Ed. J. Hintikka. **Indexed:** Math.R. **Document type:** monographic series.
   —BLDSC (8586.757000).
   Refereed Serial

100   US   ISSN 0271-2482
T A T JOURNAL. 1977. a. T A T Foundation, Box 236, Bellaire, OH 43906. Ed. Louis Khourey. adv.; bk.rev.; illus. (back issues avail.)

TABONA; revista de prehistoria y de arqueologia y filologia clasicas. see *ARCHAEOLOGY*

TAKING SIDES: CLASHING VIEWS ON CONTROVERSIAL BIOETHICAL ISSUES. see *MEDICAL SCIENCES*

TAKING SIDES: CLASHING VIEWS ON CONTROVERSIAL ISSUES IN BUSINESS ETHICS AND SOCIETY. see *BUSINESS AND ECONOMICS*

100   US   ISSN 0275-7656
BD232
TANNER LECTURES ON HUMAN VALUES. 1980. a. price varies. University of Utah Press, 101 University Services Bldg., Salt Lake City, UT 84112. TEL 801-581-6771. Ed. Grethe B. Peterson. **Document type:** academic/scholarly publication.
   —BLDSC (8602.573000).

TAROT NETWORK NEWS. see *NEW AGE PUBLICATIONS*

AL-TAWHID; a quarterly journal of Islamic thought and culture. see *RELIGIONS AND THEOLOGY* — *Islamic*

107   US   ISSN 0145-5788
B52
TEACHING PHILOSOPHY. 1975. q. $26 to individuals; institutions $63. Bowling Green State University, Philosophy Documentation Center, Bowling Green, OH 43403-0189. TEL 419-372-2419; 800-444-2419. FAX 419-372-6987. Ed. Arnold Wilson. adv.; bk.rev.; film rev. circ. 1,150. (back issues avail.) **Indexed:** Cont.Pg.Educ., Media Rev.Dig., Phil.Ind., RILA. **Document type:** academic/scholarly publication.
   —BLDSC (8614.298000); Faxon; SWETS; UnCover. **CCC.**
   Description: Provides a forum for the exchange and evaluation of ideas, information and materials concerning the teaching of philosophy.

TEILHARD REVIEW - A JOURNAL FOR BRIDGING SCIENCE AND RELIGION. see *RELIGIONS AND THEOLOGY*

TEKHNEMA; journal of philosophy and technology. see *POLITICAL SCIENCE*

TEL QUEL; litterature - philosophie - science - politique. see *SCIENCES: COMPREHENSIVE WORKS*

100 800   US
TELICOM. 1975. 10/yr. $35. International Society for Philosophical Enquiry, 10741 Moorpark St., Ste. 19, North Hollywood, CA 91602-2737. Ed. Rich Kapnick. adv. contact: Rich Kapnick. bk.rev. circ. 750. (back issues avail.)
   Description: Expository writing by those in the 99.9 percentile of high intelligence. Restricted to authors who are members.

100   US   ISSN 0090-6514
H1
TELOS; a quarterly journal of critical thoughts. 1968. q. $32 to individuals; institutions $80. Telos Press Ltd., 431 E. 12th St., New York, NY 10009. TEL 212-228-6479. FAX 212-228-6379. Ed. Paul Piccone. adv.; bk.rev. circ. 4,500. (also avail. in microform from UMI; back issues avail.; reprint service avail. from UMI) **Indexed:** Alt.Press Ind., Amer.Bibl.Slavic & E.Eur.Stud., HR Rep., Int.Polit.Sci.Abstr., Lang.& Lang.Behav.Abstr., Left Ind. (1982-), Mid.East: Abstr.& Ind., Phil.Ind., Sociol.Abstr. **Document type:** academic/scholarly publication.
   —BLDSC (8789.350000); Faxon; SWETS; UMI; UnCover.

TEME. see *SOCIOLOGY*

THE TEMPTATION OF SAINT ANTHONY. see *LITERATURE*

101   SP   ISSN 0210-1602
B5
TEOREMA. 1971. q. 600($10) Universidad de Valencia, Departamento de Logica y Filosofia de Ciencia, Facultad de Filosofia y Ciencias de la Educacion, Apdo. No. 61159, 28080 Madrid, Spain. Ed.Bd. adv.; bk.rev.; bibl.; charts. **Indexed:** Math.R., Phil.Ind.

100   IT   ISSN 1122-1259
TEORIA; rivista di filosofia. (Text in English and Italian) 1981. s-a. $15. Editrice Tecnico-Scientifica, Piazza Torricelli, 4, 56100 Pisa, Italy. Eds. Vittorio Sainati, Renzo Raggiunti. adv.; bk.rev. circ. 1,000. **Document type:** academic/scholarly publication.

100   IT
TEORIE E OGGETTI SERIE ROSSA. 1978. irreg., no.31, 1993. price varies. Liguori Editore s.r.l., Via Mezzacannone, 19, 80134 Naples, Italy. TEL 081-5527139. Ed. Roberto Esposito. **Document type:** monographic series.
   Supersedes in part: Teorie e Oggetti (ISSN 0392-2154)

100   YU   ISSN 0351-2274
B6
TEORJA. 1957. q. $12 to individuals; institutions $18. Srpsko Filozofsko Drustvo - Philosophical Society of Serbia, Cika Ljubina 18-20, 11000 Belgrade, Serbia, Yugoslavia. TEL 11-638-104. Ed. Milorad Stupar. bk.rev. circ. 1,750. **Indexed:** Lang.& Lang.Behav.Abstr.
   Formerly (until 1975): Filozofija (ISSN 0015-1866)
   Description: Publishes articles in all general areas of philosophy.

THEMATA. see *EDUCATION*

THEOLOGIA 21. see *RELIGIONS AND THEOLOGY*

THEOLOGIE UND PHILOSOPHIE. see *RELIGIONS AND THEOLOGY*

THEOLOGY AND MEDICINE. see *RELIGIONS AND THEOLOGY*

THEORETICAL MEDICINE; an international journal for the philosophy and methodology of medical research and practice. see *MEDICAL SCIENCES*

100   SW   ISSN 0040-5825
B1   CODEN: THRAA5
THEORIA; a Swedish journal of philosophy. (Text in English) 1935. 3/yr. SEK 150($30) Theoria, Filosofiska Institutionen, Kungshuset i Lundagaard, S-223 50 Lund, Sweden. Ed.Bd. bk.rev.; bibl. **Indexed:** Bibl.Engl.Lang.& Lit., Curr.Cont., Math.R., Psychol.Abstr., RILM, SSCI. **Document type:** academic/scholarly publication.
   —Faxon; SWETS; UnCover.

PHILOSOPHY

100　　　　　SP　　　ISSN 0495-4548
THEORIA. 1952. 3/yr. 5500 ptas.($50) to individuals; institutions 7500 ptas.($65) (effective 1996). Centro de Analisis, Logica e Informatica Juridica, Universidad del Pais Vasco, Servicio Editorial, Apdo. 1397, 48080 Bilbao, Spain. TEL 34-43-291725. FAX 34-43-4801314. E-mail: theoria@sf.ehu.es. Ed. Miguel Sanchez-Mazas. adv.; bk.rev.; cum.index: nos.1-20. circ. 700. **Document type:** academic/scholarly publication.
　Description: Covers logic, history and philosophy of science, philosophy of language, and cognitive science.
　Refereed Serial

THEORY AND DECISION; an international journal for methods and models in the social and decision sciences. see *SOCIAL SCIENCES: COMPREHENSIVE WORKS*

THEORY AND DECISION LIBRARY. SERIES A: PHILOSOPHY AND METHODOLOGY OF THE SOCIAL SCIENCES. see *SOCIAL SCIENCES: COMPREHENSIVE WORKS*

299.934　　　NE　　　ISSN 0040-5868
THEOSOFIA; brotherhood, problems of society, religion and occult research. 1897. bi-m. fl.30. Theosofische Vereniging in Nederland, Tolstraat 154, NL 1074 VM Amsterdam, Netherlands. TEL 31-20-6765672. FAX 31-20-6757657. Ed. A. Ritsema. adv.; bk.rev.; index. circ. 1,200.

212.5　　　　　　　NE
THEOSOFISCH FORUM. 1951. m. (11/yr.). fl.17.50. Theosofische Stichting H.P. Blavatsky - H.P. Blavatsky Theosophical Society, Hortensiastr. 20, Capelle a-d IJssel, Netherlands. Ed. H.A. Kruytbosch. bk.rev. circ. 300.
　Former titles (until 1979): Levende Gedachten (ISSN 0047-4444); Theosofisch Forum.

THEOSOPHICAL HISTORY; a quarterly journal of research. see *HISTORY*

299.934　　　UK　　　ISSN 0040-5876
THEOSOPHICAL JOURNAL. 1960. bi-m. £4 to non-members. Theosophical Society in England, 50 Gloucester Place, London W1H 3HJ, England. adv.; bk.rev. circ. 2,000.

212.5　　　　　II　　　ISSN 0040-5884
BP500
THEOSOPHICAL MOVEMENT; a magazine devoted to the living of the higher life. (Text in English) 1930. m. Rs.30($12) Theosophy Company (India) Private Ltd., 40 New Marine Lines, Bombay 400 020, India. Ed. Manek Dastur; Pub. Gopal G. Thakur. index.

299.934　　　II　　　ISSN 0040-5892
THEOSOPHIST. 1879. m. $10 in N. America & Japan; U.K. & S. Africa £5. (Theosophical Society) Theosophical Publishing House, Adyar, Madras 600 020, India. TEL 91-44-4911338. FAX 91-44-4915552. (US subscr. to: Theosophical Publishing House, P.O. Box 270. Wheaton, IL 60188) Ed. Radha Burnier. adv.; bk.rev.; s-a. index. circ. 2,500.

212.5 100　　US　　　ISSN 0040-5906
THEOSOPHY; devoted to the theosophical movement and the brotherhood of humanity, the study of occult science and philosophy and Aryan literature. 1912. m. $10. Theosophy Co., 245 W. 33rd St., Los Angeles, CA 90007. TEL 213-748-7244. (And: 347 E. 72nd St., New York, NY 10021) Ed.Bd. bk.rev.; index. circ. 800.

100　　　　　US　　　ISSN 0190-3330
B105.C45
THINKING; the journal of philosophy for children. 1979. q. $25 to individuals; institutions $40 (effective Jan. 1992). Institute for the Advancement of Philosophy for Children, Montclair State University, Upper Montclair, NJ 07043. TEL 201-655-4277. FAX 201-655-5455. Ed. Matthew Lipman. bk.rev.; charts; illus.; index. circ. 700. (back issues avail.) **Indexed:** ERIC, Phil.Ind. **Document type:** academic/scholarly publication.
　—BLDSC (8820.134000); Faxon.

THINKING & REASONING. see *PSYCHOLOGY*

THOMIST; a speculative quarterly review of theology and philosophy. see *RELIGIONS AND THEOLOGY — Roman Catholic*

100　　　　　US
THE THOUGHT (ORANGE). 1981. m. $11 (foreign $28) (effective until Mar. 1994). Philosophers Guild Publications, Box 3092, Orange, CA 92665. adv.; bk.rev. circ. 750.
　Description: Explores the worlds of philosophy, libertarian anarchism, and various concerns such as prison reform, the environment, native American rights, and current events.

100　　　　　US
THOUGHTLINE. 1954. 12/yr. $25. Arcana Workshops, Box 506, Manhattan Beach, CA 90266-0506. TEL 213-379-9990. Ed. Tom Carney. circ. 3,000. **Document type:** academic/scholarly publication.

THOUGHTS FOR ALL SEASONS; the magazine of epigrams. see *LITERATURE*

THRESHOLDS QUARTERLY. see *NEW AGE PUBLICATIONS*

212.5　　　　　SW　　　ISSN 0284-4427
TIDLOES VISDOM. 1961. q. SEK 100. Theosophical Society in Sweden, Karlaplan 5 B, S-114 60 Stockholm, Sweden. Ed.Bd. bk.rev. circ. 600.
　Formerly (until 1987): Teosofi i Norden (ISSN 0040-3628)

100　　　　　BE　　　ISSN 0040-750X
TIJDSCHRIFT VOOR FILOSOFIE. (Supplement: International Philosophical Bibliography) (Text in Dutch, English, French, German) 1939. q. 3000 BEF in EUrope; elsewhere $110 (effective 1996). Tijdschrift voor Filosofie V.Z.W., Kardinaal Mercierplein 2, B-3000 Leuven, Belgium. TEL 32-16-326326. Ed. H. De Dijn. bk.rev.; bibl.; index, cum.index every 25 yrs. circ. 1,300. **Indexed:** Arts & Hum.Cit.Ind., Curr.Cont., Lang.& Lang.Behav.Abstr., Phil.Ind., SSCI. **Document type:** academic/scholarly publication, bibliography.
　—Faxon; Genuine Article; SWETS.

TIJDSCHRIFT VOOR GENEESKUNDE EN ETHIEK. see *MEDICAL SCIENCES*

105　　　　　US　　　ISSN 1051-0362
TOPICS IN PHILOSOPHY. 1975. irreg., vol.6, 1988. price varies. University of California Press, 2120 Berkeley Way, Berkeley, CA 94720. TEL 510-642-4247. FAX 510-643-7127. (Orders to: California-Princeton Fulfillment Services, 1445 Lower Ferry Rd., Ewing, NJ 08618. TEL 800-777-4726. FAX 800-999-1958) **Document type:** monographic series.
　Refereed Serial

150　　　　　NE　　　ISSN 0167-7411
B1　　　　　　　CODEN: TOPODL
TOPOI; an international review of philosophy. (Text in English) 1982. s-a. fl.340 to institutions; $218 to institutions in U.S. (effective 1996). Kluwer Academic Publishers, Postbus 17, 3300 AA Dordrecht, Netherlands. TEL 31-78-392392. FAX 31-78-392254. TELEX 29245 KAPG NL. E-mail: SERVICES@WKAP.NL. (Dist. by: Kluwer Academic Publishers Group, P.O. Box 322, 3300 AH Dordrecht, Netherlands. TEL 31-78-392392. FAX 31-78-546474; N. America dist. addr.: Box 358, Accord Sta., Hingham, MA 02018-0358. TEL 617-871-6600) Ed. Ermanno Bencivenga. adv.; bk.rev.; index. (also avail. in microform from UMI; back issues avail.; reprint service avail. from SWZ) **Indexed:** Arts & Hum.Cit.Ind., ASCA, Curr.Cont., Math.R., Phil.Ind. **Document type:** academic/scholarly publication.
　—BLDSC (8867.499800); Faxon; Genuine Article; UMI; UnCover. CCC.
　Description: Publishes articles, reviews and discussions of philosophy and the history of philosophy.
　Refereed Serial

TRADITION (NEW YORK); a journal of Orthodox Jewish thought. see *RELIGIONS AND THEOLOGY — Judaic*

100　　　　　BL　　　ISSN 0101-3173
B5　　　　　　　CODEN: TFACDH
TRANS - FORM - ACAO; revista de filosofia. (Text in Portuguese; summaries in English and Portuguese) 1974-1975; resumed 1980. a. $30 or exchange basis. Universidade Estadual Paulista, Av. Vicente Ferreira 1278, Caixa Postal 603, 17515-901 Marilia SP, Brazil. TEL 0144-33-1844. FAX 0144-22-2504. TELEX 111 9016 UJME BR. bk.rev.; charts. circ. 1,000. (back issues avail.) **Indexed:** Hisp.Amer.Per.Ind. (1989-), Phil.Ind. **Document type:** academic/scholarly publication.
　Description: Interdisciplinary approach to the study of philosophy.

TRANSFORMERS NOTEBOOK. see *DRUG ABUSE AND ALCOHOLISM*

TRANSILVANIA. see *RELIGIONS AND THEOLOGY*

TRENDS IN HEALTH CARE, LAW & ETHICS; a journal of contemporary issues in health care. see *MEDICAL SCIENCES*

100 284　　　US　　　ISSN 1044-6532
TRINITY REVIEW. 1979. m. free. Trinity Foundation, Box 1666, Hobbs, NM 88241-1666. TEL 505-392-7274. Ed. John W. Robbins; Pub. John W. Robbins. bk.rev.; circ. 3,000 (controlled). (back issues avail.) **Document type:** newsletter.
　Description: Contains essays in philosophy and theology.

TRUMPETER; journal of ecosophy. see *ENVIRONMENTAL STUDIES*

100　　　　　US
TRUTH IN ACTION. q. Seicho-No-Ie Truth of Life Movement, 14527 S. Vermont Ave., Gardena, CA 90247. TEL 213-323-8486.

100　　　　　US
TRUTH OF LIFE. 12/yr. $11. Seicho-No-Ie Truth of Life Movement, 14527 S. Vermont Ave., Gardena, CA 90247. TEL 313-371-2494. Ed. Masayo Tsuruta. illus.

100　　　　　US　　　ISSN 0041-3712
BL2700
TRUTH SEEKER. 1873. q. $20 (foreign $35) (effective 1995). Truth Seeker Co., Inc., 16935 W. Bernardo Dr., Ste. 103, San Diego, CA 92117. TEL 619-676-0430; 800-321-9054. FAX 619-676-0433. Ed. Bonnie Lange; Pub. Bonnie Lange. adv.; B&W page $500; adv. contact: Marti Kranzberg. bk.rev. circ. 10,000. **Document type:** academic/scholarly publication.
　●Also available online.
　Description: Deals with intellectual liberation and civil liberties; focuses on religious and political issues.

450　　　　　CN　　　ISSN 0315-3002
U R A M NEWSLETTER. 1972. biennial. membership. International Society for the Study of Human Ideas on Ultimate Reality and Meaning, Regis College, 15 St. Mary St., Toronto, ON M4Y 2R5, Canada. TEL 905-839-3858. FAX 905-839-3387. E-mail: jperry@epas.utoronto.ca. Ed. Tibor Horvath; Pub. William Addley. circ. 500. (back issues avail.) **Document type:** academic/scholarly publication.
　Description: Disseminates information to members and the general public concerning the activities of the International Society for URAM.

100 200   CN   ISSN 0709-549X
BD331
ULTIMATE REALITY AND MEANING; interdisciplinary studies in the philosophy of understanding. 1978. q. Can.$30 to individuals; institutions Can.$48. (International Society for the Study of Human Ideas on Ultimate Reality and Meaning) University of Toronto Press, Journals Department, 5201 Dufferin St., Downsview, ON M3H 5T8, Canada. TEL 416-667-7781. FAX 416-667-7881. E-mail: jperry@epas.utoronto.ca. (U.S. addr.): 340 Nagel Dr., Cheektowaga, NY 14225) Ed. John F. Perry. bibl. circ. 500. **Indexed:** Amer.Bibl.Slavic & E.Eur.Stud., Arts & Hum.Cit.Ind., G.Soc.Sci.& Rel.Per.Lit., Lang.& Lang.Behav.Abstr., Phil.Ind., Rel.& Theol.Abstr. (1981-), Rel.Ind.One. **Document type:** academic/scholarly publication.
—BLDSC (9082.780500); Genuine Article; UnCover.
  Supersedes: Institute for Encyclopedia of Human Ideas on Ultimate Reality and Meaning. Newsletter.
  Description: Publishes studies dealing with facts, things, ideas, axioms, persons, and values which people throughout history have considered ultimate, or as horizons, or as supreme value.
  Refereed Serial

UNARIUS LIGHT JOURNAL. see *NEW AGE PUBLICATIONS*

UNIVERSAL PROUTIST. see *NEW AGE PUBLICATIONS*

100   II   ISSN 0041-8218
UNIVERSALIST. 1968. irreg. (2-4/yr.) Rs.15.($2) (World Jnana Sadhak Society) Jnana Sadhak Publishing House, Babupara-Mishralodge, Jalpaiguri 735101, West Bengal, India. Eds. Rajkishore Mollenhauer, B. Mollenhauer. bk.rev.

UNIVERSIDAD COMPLUTENSE DE MADRID. REVISTA. see *LITERATURE*

100   CK   ISSN 0120-1492
UNIVERSIDAD DE CALDAS. FACULTAD DE FILOSOFIA. REVISTA. (Text in Spanish; summaries in English) 1980. q. Col.$5000($6) Universidad de Caldas, Facultad de Filosofia, Apdo. 275, Manizales, Caldas, Colombia. TEL 57968857022. FAX 968-862520. Ed. Roberto Velez-Correa. bk.rev. circ. 1,000. **Document type:** academic/scholarly publication.

100   SP   ISSN 0008-7750
B5
UNIVERSIDAD DE GRANADA. CATEDRA FRANCISCO SUAREZ. ANALES. 1961. a. price varies. Universidad de Granada, Departamento de Filosofia del Derecho, Servicio de Publicaciones, Antiguo Colegio Maximo, Campus de Cartuja, 18071 Granada, Spain. TEL 34-58-243930. FAX 34-58-242827. Dir. Nicolas M. Lopez Calera. circ. 1,000. **Document type:** academic/scholarly publication.

100   UY   ISSN 0258-1841
UNIVERSIDAD DE LA REPUBLICA. FACULTAD DE HUMANIDADES Y CIENCIAS. REVISTA. SERIE FILOSOFIA. irreg. exchange basis. Universidad de la Republica, Facultad de Humanidades y Ciencias, Seccion Revista, Tristan Narvaja 1674, Montevideo, Uruguay. Dir. Beatriz Martinez Osorio.
  Supersedes in part: Universidad de la Republica. Facultad de Humanidades y Ciencias. Revista.

110   SP   ISSN 0580-8650
BD115
UNIVERSIDAD DE MADRID. SEMINARIO DE METAFISICA. ANALES. 1966. a. 1000 ptas. Universidad Complutense de Madrid, Departamento de Filosofia I, Metafisica y Teoria del Conocimiento, Servicio de Publicaciones, Madrid, Spain. TEL 91-499-6500. Ed. Sergio Rabade Romeo. adv.; bk.rev.; bibl. circ. 500. **Indexed:** Phil.Ind. **Document type:** academic/scholarly publication.

100 001.3   SP
UNIVERSIDAD DE SEVILLA. SERIE: FILOSOFIA Y LETRAS. 1967. irreg., latest no.121. price varies. Universidad de Sevilla, Servicio de Publicaciones, Valparaiso 5, 41013 Seville, Spain. TEL 954-231958. FAX 954-232245. **Indexed:** Amer.Hist.& Life, Biol.Abstr., Hist.Abstr.
  Former titles: Universidad Hispalense. Anales. Serie: Filosofia y Letras (ISSN 0210-7678); (until 1969): Universidad Hispalense. Anales. Series: Filosofia y Letras, Derecho, Medicina, Ciencias y Veterinaria (ISSN 0041-8552)

100 460   MX   ISSN 0185-2558
UNIVERSIDAD NACIONAL AUTONOMA DE MEXICO. INSTITUTO DE INVESTIGACIONES FILOSOFICAS. CUADERNOS. 1959. irreg., no.50, 1989. Universidad Nacional Autonoma de Mexico, Instituto de Investigaciones Filosoficas, Apdo. Postal 70-447, Mexico, D.F., Mexico. (Dist. by: Direccion General de Fomento Editorial, Porto Alegre No. 260, San Andres Tetepilco, 09440 Mexico, D.F., Mexico) circ. 2,000.

UNIVERSIDAD PONTIFICIA COMILLAS DE MADRID. PUBLICACIONES. SERIE 1: ESTUDIOS. see *RELIGIONS AND THEOLOGY*

100   IT   ISSN 0390-0614
UNIVERSITA DEGLI STUDI DI LECCE. BOLLETTINO DI STORIA DELLA FILOSOFIA. 1973. a. free. Universita degli Studi di Lecce, Facolta di Lettere e Filosofia, Via V.M. Stampacchia, 73100 Lecce, Italy. TEL 0832-406709. FAX 0832-4061. Ed. Giovanni Papuli.
  Description: Covers the history of philosophy. Includes lessons, seminars, reports, group studies, documents and news.

UNIVERSITA DEGLI STUDI DI PADOVA. FACOLTA DI LETTERE E FILOSOFIA. OPUSCOLI ACCADEMICI. see *LITERATURE*

UNIVERSITA DEGLI STUDI DI PADOVA. FACOLTA DI LETTERE E FILOSOFIA. PUBBLICAZIONI. see *LITERATURE*

UNIVERSITA DEGLI STUDI DI SIENA. FACOLTA DI LETTERE E FILOSOFIA. ANNALI. see *LITERATURE*

100   IT   ISSN 0394-5073
UNIVERSITA DI FIRENZE. DIPARTIMENTO DI FILOSOFIA. ANNALI. 1979. a. price varies. Casa Editrice Leo S. Olschki, Casella Postale 66, 50100 Florence, Italy. TEL 39-55-6530684. FAX 39-55-6530214. Ed. A. Ingegno. circ. 1,000. (back issues avail.) **Document type:** academic/scholarly publication.
  Formerly (until 1984): Universita degli Studi di Firenze. Istituto di Filosofia. Annali.

UNIVERSITA DI MESSINA. FACOLTA DI MAGISTERO. NUOVI ANNALI. see *HUMANITIES: COMPREHENSIVE WORKS*

UNIVERSITA DI NAPOLI. FACOLTA DI LETTERE E FILOSOFIA. ANNALI. see *HISTORY*

UNIVERSITA DI PERUGIA. CENTRO PER IL COLLEGAMENTO DEGLI STUDI MEDIEVALI E UMANISTICI. BIBLIOTECA. see *HISTORY — History Of Europe*

UNIVERSITA DI PERUGIA. CENTRO PER IL COLLEGAMENTO DEGLI STUDI MEDIEVALI E UMANISTICI. QUADERNI. see *HISTORY — History Of Europe*

100   IT   ISSN 1122-0759
UNIVERSITA DI SIENA. DIPARTIMENTO DI FILOSOFIA. PUBBLICAZIONI. 1981. irreg. price varies. Casa Editrice Leo S. Olschki, Casella Postale 66, 50100 Florence, Italy. TEL 39-55-6530684. FAX 39-55-6530214. **Document type:** monographic series.

100   RM   ISSN 0379-7856
AS345.A1
UNIVERSITATEA "AL. I. CUZA" DIN IASI. ANALELE STIINTIFICE. SECTIUNEA 3B: FILOZOFIE. (Text in English, French, Rumanian) s-a. 35 lei. Universitatea "Al. I. Cuza" din Iasi, Calea M. Eminescu 11, Jassy, Rumania. (Subscr. to: ILEXIM, Str. 13 Decembrie Nr. 3, P.O. Box 136-137, Bucharest, Rumania) Ed. Petru Ioan. circ. 550.
  Formerly: Universitatea "Al. I. Cuza" din Iasi. Analele Stiintifice. Sectiunea 3b: Stiinte Filozofice (ISSN 0075-353X)
  Description: Works on philosophy, history of philosophy, logic and epistemology, sociology, ethics and pedagogy.

100 940 340   RM
UNIVERSITATEA BUCURESTI. ANALELE. FILOZOFIE. ISTORIE. DREPT. a. $10. Universitatea Bucuresti, Bd. Gh. Gheorghiu-Dej Nr. G4, Bucharest, Rumania.

100   BE   ISSN 0076-1273
UNIVERSITE CATHOLIQUE DE LOUVAIN. INSTITUT SUPERIEUR DE PHILOSOPHIE. COURS PUBLIES. 1952. irreg. price varies. Universite Catholique de Louvain, Institut Superieur de Philosophie, 1 chemin d'Aristote, B-1348 Louvain-la-Neuve, Belgium. TEL 016-48-81-02. FAX 016-48-14-86. **Document type:** academic/scholarly publication.
  Formerly (until 1964): Universite Catholique de Louvain. Institut Superieur de Philosophie. Cours de Philosophie (ISSN 0773-1345)

084   FR
UNIVERSITE DE BESANCON. CENTRE DE DOCUMENTATION ET DE BIBLIOGRAPHIE PHILOSOPHIQUES. TRAVAUX. 1973. irreg. (Universite de Besancon, Centre de Documentation et de Bibliographie Philosophiques) Societe d'Edition les Belles Lettres, 95, Boulevard Raspail, 75006 Paris, France. TEL 1-45485826. FAX 1-45485860. illus.

100   FR   ISSN 0771-4963
UNIVERSITE LIBRE DE BRUXELLES. INSTITUT DE PHILOSOPHIE. ANNALES. 1969. a. price varies. (Institut de Philosophie) Librairie Philosophique J. Vrin, 6 place de la Sorbonne, 75005 Paris, France. FAX 43-54-48-18. bk.rev.; bibl. circ. 1,000.

UNIVERSITY OF KANSAS. CENTER FOR EAST ASIAN STUDIES. INTERNATIONAL STUDIES: EAST ASIAN SERIES. REFERENCE SERIES. see *HISTORY — History Of Asia*

UNIVERSITY OF KANSAS. CENTER FOR EAST ASIAN STUDIES. INTERNATIONAL STUDIES: EAST ASIAN SERIES. RESEARCH SERIES. see *HISTORY — History Of Asia*

160   PL   ISSN 0138-0680
UNIVERSITY OF LODZ. DEPARTMENT OF LOGIC. BULLETIN OF THE SECTION OF LOGIC. (Text in English) 1972. q. Uniwersytet Lodzki, Wydzial Logiki - University of Lodz, Department of Logic, Ul. Matejki 34a, 90-237 Lodz, Poland. Ed. Grzegorz Malinowski.
  Formerly (until 1992): Polish Academy of Sciences. Institute of Philosophy and Sociology. Section of Logic. Bulletin.

180   II   ISSN 0076-2253
UNIVERSITY OF MADRAS. PHILOSOPHICAL SERIES.* irreg. University of Madras, c/o Director, Publications Division, Madras 600005, Tamil Nadu, India. TEL 91-44-568778. FAX 91-44-566693.

UNIVERSITY OF NOTRE DAME. STUDIES IN THE PHILOSOPHY OF RELIGION. see *RELIGIONS AND THEOLOGY*

105   SL
UNIVERSITY OF SIERRA LEONE. FOURAH BAY COLLEGE. PHILOSOPHICAL SOCIETY. JOURNAL. 1977. a. University of Sierra Leone, Fourah Bay College, Philosophical Society, Freetown, Sierra Leone.

501   NE   ISSN 0929-6417
UNIVERSITY OF WESTERN ONTARIO SERIES IN PHILOSOPHY OF SCIENCE. Variant title: Western Ontario Series. 1972. irreg., latest 1991. price varies. Kluwer Academic Publishers, 3300 AA Dordrecht, Netherlands. TEL 31-78-392392. FAX 31-78-392254. TELEX 29245 KAPG NL. (Dist. by: Kluwer Academic Publishers Group, P.O. Box 322, 3300 AH Dordrecht, Netherlands. TEL 31-78-392392. FAX 31-78-546474; N. America dist. addr.: Box 358, Accord Sta., Hingham, MA 02018-0358. TEL 617-871-6600) Ed. R.E. Butts. **Document type:** monographic series.
  Refereed Serial

UNIVERZITA KOMENSKEHO. FILOZOFICKA FAKULTA. ZBORNIK: GRAECOLATINA ET ORIENTALIA. see *CLASSICAL STUDIES*

100   XO   ISSN 0083-4181
B26
UNIVERZITA KOMENSKEHO. FILOZOFICKA FAKULTA. ZBORNIK: PHILOSOPHICA. (Text in Czech or Slovak; summaries in German and Russian) 1960. a. exchange basis. Univerzita Komenskeho, Filozoficka Fakulta, c/o Ustredna Kniznica Filozofickej Fakulty, Gondova 2, 818 01 Bratislava, Slovakia. Ed. M. Zigo. circ. 700. **Document type:** academic/scholarly publication.
  Incorporates: Univerzita Komeskeho. Ustav Marxismu-Leninizmu. Zbornik: Marxistiska Filozofia.

PHILOSOPHY

100 301   PL   ISSN 0208-4694
B63
UNIWERSYTET GDANSKI. WYDZIAL HUMANISTYCZNY. ZESZYTY NAUKOWE. FILOZOFIA I SOCJOLOGIA. (Text in Polish; summaries in English and Russian) 1965. irreg., latest no.16. price varies. Uniwersytet Gdanski, Wydzial Humanistyczny, c/o Biblioteka Glowna, Ul. Armii Krajowej 110, 81-824 Sopot, Poland. TEL 51-0061. TELEX 051-2247 BMOR PL. (Dist. by: Ars Polona-Ruch, Krakowskie Przedmiescie 7, Warsaw, Poland) **Document type:** academic/scholarly publication.
  Former titles (until 1974): Wyzsza Szkola Pedagogiczna. Gdanskie Zeszyty Humanistyczne. Filozofia i Socjologia (ISSN 0208-4686); (until 1970): Wyzsza Szkola Pedagogiczna. Gdanskie Zeszyty Humanistyczne. Filozofia (ISSN 0072-0453)
  Description: Covers the history of philosophy, methodology, and philosophical anthropology. Examines the theory of knowledge, historical and dialectical materialism, and the philosophical and anxiological problems of natural science.

100   PL   ISSN 0208-5437
H8
UNIWERSYTET SLASKI W KATOWICACH. PRACE NAUKOWE. PRACE Z NAUK SPOLECZNYCH. FOLIA PHILOSOPHICA. (Text in Polish; summaries in English and Russian) 1975. irreg. price varies. Wydawnictwo Uniwersytetu Slaskiego, Ul. Bankowa 12B, 40-007 Katowice, Poland. TEL 59-69-15. FAX 48-32-599-605. TELEX 315594 USKTL. (Dist. by: CHZ Ars Polona, P.O. Box 1001, 00-950 Warsaw, Poland) **Document type:** academic/scholarly publication.
  Description: Studies on philosophy.

110   US
UPPER TRIAD. 1974. bi-m. free. Upper Triad Association, Inc., Box 2050, Germantown, MD 20875. TEL 301-916-2933. Ed. Peter Hamilton. bk.rev.; circ. 2,000 (controlled).

100   UK   ISSN 0953-8208
UTILITAS. 1978. s-a. £27.50 to individuals (outside the E.U. £29.75 ($49.75)); institutions £55 (outside the E.U. £59.50 ($99.50)) (effective 1996). (Bentham Project, London) Edinburgh University Press, 22 George Sq., Edinburgh EH8 9LF, Scotland. TEL 44-131-650-6207. FAX 44-131-662-0053. Ed. Fred Rosen. adv. contact: Kathryn MacLean. bk.rev. circ. 900. **Document type:** academic/scholarly publication.
  —BLDSC (9135.376700); SWETS; UMI; UnCover. CCC.
  Formed by the 1988 merger of: Bentham Newsletter (ISSN 0141-190X); Mill Newsletter.
  Description: Covers all aspects of utilitarian thought and its historical context.

121.8   NE
VALUE INQUIRY BOOK SERIES. Abbreviated title: V I B S. (Text in English) 1993. irreg., vol.12, 1994. price varies. Editions Rodopi B.V., Keizersgracht 302-304, 1016 EX Amsterdam, Netherlands. TEL 31-20-6227507. FAX 31-20-6380948. E-mail: F.van.der.Zee@Rodopi.nl. (In N. America: 233 Peachtree St., N.E., Ste. 404, Atlanta, GA 30303-1504. TEL 800-225-3998. FAX 404-522-7116) Ed. Alan Ginsberg. (back issues avail.) **Document type:** monographic series.

VEDANTA KESARI. see RELIGIONS AND THEOLOGY — Hindu

VEDIC LIGHT. see RELIGIONS AND THEOLOGY — Hindu

500 974   US   ISSN 0893-4851
K26
VERA LEX; historical & philosophical study of natural law and right. 1980. s-a. $15 to individuals; institutions $30 (effective 1994). Pace University, Buchsbaum House, Pleasantville, NY 10570-2799. TEL 914-773-3309. FAX 914-773-3541. (Co-sponsor: Natural Law Society) Ed. Virginia Black. adv.; bk.rev.; bibl.; illus.; cum.index every 5 yrs. circ. 425. (back issues avail.) **Document type:** academic/scholarly publication.
  Description: Attempts to strengthen the current revived interest in the discussion of natural and positive law and advance its historical and philosophical research.
  Refereed Serial

100 200   SP   ISSN 0042-3718
BX3601
VERDAD Y VIDA; revista de las ciencias del espiritu. 1943. q. 4000 ptas.($65) (effective 1995). Franciscanos Espanoles, Joaquin Costa 36, 28002 Madrid, Spain. TEL 34-1-5619900. FAX 34-1-5613990. adv.; bk.rev.; bibl.; index. circ. 550. **Indexed:** CERDIC, M.L.A.

100   IT   ISSN 0391-4186
B4
VERIFICHE; rivista trimestrale di scienze umane. 1972. q. L.30000. (Associazione Trentina di Scienze Umane) Verifiche, Casella Postale 269, 38100 Trento, Italy. Ed. Mario Rigoni. adv.; bk.rev.; bibl. circ. 500. (back issues avail.) **Indexed:** Amer.Hist.& Life, Arts & Hum.Cit.Ind., Hist.Abstr.
  —Genuine Article.
  Description: Focuses on literary philosophy.

374   AT
VICTORIAN HUMANIST. 1961. m. (10/yr.). Aus.$18. Humanist Society of Victoria, P.O. Box 1555P, Melbourne, Vic. 3001, Australia. Ed. Rosslyn Ives. bk.rev. circ. 100. (back issues avail.) **Document type:** newsletter.
  Description: Activities, decisions and policies of the committee, reports of public meetings, and humanist ethics.

190   NE   ISSN 0929-6328
VIENNA CIRCLE INSTITUTE YEARBOOK. (Text in English) 1993. a. fl.185 (effective 1995). (Institut 'Wiener Kreis' - Vienna Circle Institute) Kluwer Academic Publishers, Postbus 17, 3300 AA Dordrecht, Netherlands. TEL 31-78-392392. FAX 31-78-392254. TELEX 29245 KAPG NL. (Dist. by: Kluwer Academic Publishers Group, P.O. Box 322, 3300 AH Dordrecht, Netherlands. TEL 31-78-392392. FAX 31-78-546474; N. America dist. addr.: Box 358, Accord Sta., Hingham, MA 02018-0358. TEL 617-871-6600. FAX 617-871-6528) Ed. Friedrich Stadler. **Document type:** proceedings.
  —BLDSC (9235.585600).

VIEWS FROM OFF CENTER. see NEW AGE PUBLICATIONS

100   II   ISSN 0505-7523
VISHVA JYOTI. (Text in Hindi) 1952. m. Rs.30. Vishveshvaranand Vedic Research Institute, P.O. Sadhu Ashram, Hoshiarpur 146021, Punjab, India. Ed. Veda Prakasha.
  Description: Covers Hindu philosophy and Indian culture.

100   II   ISSN 0042-7187
VISVA - BHARATI JOURNAL OF PHILOSOPHY. (Text in English) 1964. s-a. Rs.25($8) Visva-Bharati, Department of Philosophy and Religion, P.O. Santiniketan, Dist. Birbhum, Pin 731 235, India. TEL 03463-52751. FAX 03463-52672. TELEX 203 201 RABI IN. Ed. Rita Gupta. bk.rev. circ. 500. **Indexed:** Ind.Per.Lit. **Document type:** academic/scholarly publication.
  —UnCover.

VIVARIUM; an international journal for the philosophy and intellectual life of the Middle Ages and Renaissance. see HISTORY

DE VLAAMSE GIDS. see LITERARY AND POLITICAL REVIEWS

100   RU   ISSN 0042-8744
VOPROSY FILOSOFII. (Text in Russian; summaries in English) 1947. m. $138 (effective 1996). (Rossiiskaya Akademiya Nauk, Institut Filosofii) Izdatel'stvo Pressa, Ul. Pravdy, 24, Moscow 125047, Russia. (Dist. by: Mezhdunarodnaya Kniga, Moscow, G-200, Russia; Dist. in U.S. by: Victor Kamkin Inc., 4956 Boiling Brook Pkwy, Rockville, MD 20852. TEL 301-881-5973) Ed. I.T. Frolov. adv.; bk.rev.; bibl.; index. circ. 37,000. (also avail. in microform) **Indexed:** Amer.Hist.& Life, Arts & Hum.Cit.Ind., Biol.Abstr., Curr.Cont., Curr.Dig.Sov.Press, Hist.Abstr., Int.Polit.Sci.Abstr., Lang.& Lang.Behav.Abstr., Math.R., Psychol.Abstr.
  —BLDSC (0045.130000); Genuine Article. CCC.

100   GW   ISSN 0940-9394
WEGE OHNE DOGMA. 1973. m. DM.26.40. (Bund Freireligioeser Gemeinden Deutschlands) Freireligioese Verlagsbuchhandlung, L10, 4-6, 68161 Mannheim, Germany. Ed. Ortrun Lenz. adv.; bk.rev.; index. circ. 6,000. **Indexed:** Acad.Ind.
  Formerly (until 1992): Humanist; **Supersedes:** Freigeistige Aktion (ISSN 0016-0830)

WEST COAST LIBERTARIAN. see LITERARY AND POLITICAL REVIEWS

100   AU   ISSN 0083-999X
B31
WIENER JAHRBUCH FUER PHILOSOPHIE. 1968. a. price varies. Wilhelm Braumueller, Universitaets Verlagsbuchhandlung GmbH, Servitengasse 5, A-1092 Vienna, Austria. TEL 01-3191159. FAX 01-3102805. Ed. Erich Heintel. bk.rev.; index. circ. 500. **Document type:** academic/scholarly publication.

181.4 954   AU   ISSN 0084-0084
DS2
WIENER ZEITSCHRIFT FUER DIE KUNDE SUEDASIENS UND ARCHIV FUER INDISCHE PHILOSPHIE. 1957. a. S.490. (Oesterreichische Akademie der Wissenschaften, Kommission fuer Sprachen und Kulturen Suedasiens) Verlag der Oesterreichischen Akademie der Wissenschaften, Dr. Ignatz-Seipel-Platz 2, A-1010 Vienna, Austria. FAX 0222-5139541. (Co-sponsor: Universitaet Wien. Indologisches Institut) Ed. G. Oberhammer. **Indexed:** Bibl.Ling., Numis.Lit.
  —UnCover.
  Former titles (until 1969): Wiener Zeitschrift fuer die Kunde Sued- und Ostasiens; Archiv fuer Indische Philosophie.

100 300 500   NE-   ISSN 0043-5414
WIJSGERIG PERSPECTIEF OP MAATSCHAPPIJ EN WETENSCHAP/PHILOSOPHICAL PERSPECTIVES ON SOCIETY AND SCIENCE. 1960. bi-m. fl.56 to individuals (foreign fl.67.50) (effective 1994). Uitgeverij Boom, P.O. Box 400, 7940 AK Meppel, Netherlands. TEL 31-5220-57012. FAX 31-5220-53864. Ed.Bd. adv.; bk.rev. circ. 1,900. **Document type:** academic/scholarly publication.
  —SWETS.

100   GW   ISSN 0175-6486
WISSENSCHAFT UND GEGENWART. GEISTESWISSENSCHAFTLICHE REIHE. irreg., no.66, 1990. price varies. Vittorio Klostermann, Frauenlobstr. 22, 60487 Frankfurt a.M., Germany. TEL 069-9708160. FAX 069-708038. (Subscr. to: Postfach 900601, 60446 Frankfurt a.M., Germany) **Document type:** monographic series.

190   GW   ISSN 0943-5727
▼**WITTGENSTEIN STUDIES.** (Text in English, German) 1995. s-a. DM.98($71) (effective 1996). Springer-Verlag, Heidelberger Platz 3, 14197 Berlin, Germany. TEL 030-8207-1. FAX 030-8241091. (Subscr. in N. America to: Springer-Verlag New York, Inc., 44 Hartz Way, Secaucus, NJ 07096-2491. TEL 201-348-4033. FAX 201-348-4505) (diskette format) **Document type:** academic/scholarly publication.
  Description: Devoted exclusively to the work and influence of Ludwig Wittgenstein.

WOMEN'S ELECTORAL LOBBY (W.A.) BROADSHEET. see SOCIAL SCIENCES: COMPREHENSIVE WORKS

574   US
WOODBRIDGE LECTURES, COLUMBIA UNIVERSITY. no.4, 1972. irreg., no.12, 1987. Columbia University Press, 562 W. 113th St., New York, NY 10025. TEL 212-666-1000.

181 891   II   ISSN 0084-1242
WOOLNER INDOLOGICAL SERIES. (Text in English, Hindi and Sanskrit) 1960. irreg., vol.21, 1976. price varies. Vishveshvaranand Vedic Research Institute, P. O. Sadhu Ashram, Hoshiarpur 146021, Punjab, India. Ed. S. Bhaskaran Nair.

PHILOSOPHY — ABSTRACTING, BIBLIOGRAPHIES, STATISTICS

100   US   ISSN 0260-4027
B1   CODEN: WOFUDM
WORLD FUTURES; the journal of general evolution. 1962. 12/yr. (in 3 vols., 4 nos./vol.). 126 ECU per vol. (effective 1996). Gordon and Breach Science Publishers, c/o International Publishers Distributor, 820 Town Center Dr., Langhorne, PA 19047. TEL 215-750-2642. FAX 215-750-6343. (Subscr. to: International Publishers Distributor, P.O. Box 90, Reading, Berkshire RG1 8JL, England. TEL 44-173-456-8316) Ed. Ervin Laszlo. adv.; bk.rev.; bibl.; illus.; index. (also avail. in microform from MIM) **Indexed:** Curr.Cont., Fut.Surv., Hum.Ind., Lang.& Lang.Behav.Abstr., SSCI.
—BLDSC (9356.025750); Faxon; UnCover. **CCC.**
Formerly: Philosophy Forum (ISSN 0031-823X)
Refereed Serial

WORLD ORDER; a Baha'i magazine. see *RELIGIONS AND THEOLOGY — Other Denominations And Sects*

WORLD TRIBUNE. see *RELIGIONS AND THEOLOGY — Buddhist*

709   PL   ISSN 0208-497X
WYDZIAL FILOLOGICZNO-FILOZOFICZNY. PRACE. (Text in Polish; summaries in English, French, German) 1948. irreg., vol.34, no.1, 1992. price varies. Towarzystwo Naukowe w Toruniu, Ul. Wysoka 16, 87-100 Torun, Poland. TEL 48-56-23941. TELEX 552388 FSBH PL. Ed. Marian Szarmach. circ. 300. **Document type:** monographic series.
—BLDSC (6588.800150).

100   PL
WYZSZA SZKOLA PEDAGOGICZNA IM. KOMISJI EDUKACJI NARODOWEJ W KRAKOWIE. ROCZNIK NAUKOWO-DYDAKTYCZNY. PRACE FILOZOFICZNE. 1972. irreg., no.5, 1990. price varies. Wydawnictwo Naukowe W S P, Ul. Karmelicka 41, 31-128 Krakow, Poland. TEL 33-78-20. (Co-sponsor: Ministerstwo Edukacji Narodowej)

100   PL   ISSN 0867-3594
WYZSZA SZKOLA PEDAGOGICZNA IM. KOMISJI EDUKACJI NARODOWEJ W KRAKOWIE. ROCZNIK NAUKOWO-DYDAKTYCZNY. PRACE FIZYCZNE. 1972. irreg., no.5, 1990. price varies. Wydawnictwo Naukowe W S P, Ul. Karmelicka 41, 31-128 Krakow, Poland. TEL 33-78-20. (Co-sponsor: Ministerstwo Edukacji Narodowej)

181.45 294.54   DK   ISSN 0044-0485
YOGA; tidsskrift for universel religion. English edition: Yoga; magazine for the universal religion (ISSN 0107-7414) 1957. 3/yr. DKK 90($10) (typically set in Apr.). Narayanananda Universal Yoga Trust, N.U. Yoga Ashrama, Gylling, DK-8300 Odder, Denmark. TEL 45-86-55-17-00. FAX 45-86-55-17-88. Ed. Swami Adwaitananda. adv.; bk.rev.; index. circ. 1,000.
Formerly (until 1960): Yoga Maanedsblad (ISSN 0512-8056)

181.45 294.54   II   ISSN 0970-1737
YOGA AND TOTAL HEALTH. (Text in English and Sanskrit) 1933. m. Rs.100($15) Yoga Institute, Prabhat Colony, Santa Cruz East, Bombay 400 055, India. TEL 22-6122185. Ed. Jayadeva Yogendra. adv.; bk.rev.; abstr.; bibl.; charts; illus. circ. 15,000. (back issues avail.) **Document type:** academic/scholarly publication.
Formerly: Yoga Institute. Journal (ISSN 0044-0493)
Description: Contains articles on Yoga education, therapy, and mind-body-spirit connection.

YOGA INTERNATIONAL. see *NEW AGE PUBLICATIONS*

181.45 613.7   UK
YOGA LIFE. 1961. 2/yr. $10. Sivananda Yoga Vedanta Centre, 51 Felsham Rd., London SW15 1AZ, England. TEL 0181-780-0160. FAX 0181-780-0128. Ed. Swami Saradananda. bk.rev. circ. 40,000. **Document type:** bulletin.
Former titles: International Sivananda Yoga Life and Yoga Vacations (ISSN 0708-076X); International Yoga Life and Yoga Vacations (ISSN 0381-9043)

181.45 294.54   II   ISSN 0044-0507
YOGA - MIMAMSA; quarterly journal devoted to scientific-philosophico-literary research in yoga. (Text in English, Sanskrit; summaries in English) 1924. q. Rs.300. Kaivalyadhama Institution, Lonavla 410 403, District Poona, Maharashtra, India. TEL 02114-73039. Ed. R.S. Bhogal. adv.; bk.rev.; charts; illus.; stat. circ. 1,500. **Document type:** academic/scholarly publication.

181.45   II
YOGA SUDHA. (Text in English) m. Rs.25($15) Vivekananda Kendra Yogas, 1531, 17th Main, 2A Cross, Iind Phase, J.P. Nagar, Bangalore 560 078, India. TEL 645108. Ed. H.R. Nagendra; Pub. S.R. Krishnamurthy.

YOKOHAMA KOKURITSU DAIGAKU JINBUN KIYO DAI-1-RUI, TETSUGAKU, SHAKAI KAGAKU/YOKOHAMA NATIONAL UNIVERSITY. HUMANITIES. SECTION 1: PHILOSOPHY AND SOCIAL SCIENCES. see *SOCIAL SCIENCES: COMPREHENSIVE WORKS*

100   GW   ISSN 0044-2186
N9
ZEITSCHRIFT FUER AESTHETIK UND ALLGEMEINE KUNSTWISSENSCHAFT. (Text in English, French and German) 1906. s-a. DM.65. Bouvier Verlag Herbert Grundmann, Am Hof 28, 53113 Bonn, Germany. TEL 0228-7290124. FAX 0228-7290179. Ed.Bd. bk.rev. circ. 600. (also avail. in microfiche from BHP) **Indexed:** Artbibl.Mod., Curr.Cont., RILA. **Document type:** academic/scholarly publication.
—SWETS.
Formerly: Jahrbuch fuer Aesthetik.

100 371.3   GW
ZEITSCHRIFT FUER DIDAKTIK DER PHILOSOPHIE. 1979. q. DM.49. Schroedel Schulbuchverlag GmbH, Hildesheimer Str. 202-206, 30519 Hannover, Germany. TEL 0511-8388-0. TELEX 9-23527-HSVHAD. (Subscr. to: Oeding Druck GmbH, Wilhelmstr. 1, 3300 Braunschweig, Germany) circ. 1,800.

100   AU   ISSN 0044-2763
ZEITSCHRIFT FUER GANZHEITSFORSCHUNG. 1957. q. S.200($20) Gesellschaft fuer Ganzheitsforschung, Augasse 2-6, A-1090 Vienna, Austria. TEL 0222-313364531. FAX 0222-31336727. Ed. Hubert Verhonig. adv. contact: Hubert Verhonig. bk.rev.; charts; illus.; index. circ. 500. **Document type:** academic/scholarly publication.
—BLDSC (9462.230000).

ZEITSCHRIFT FUER KATHOLISCHE THEOLOGIE. see *RELIGIONS AND THEOLOGY — Roman Catholic*

ZEITSCHRIFT FUER MEDIZINISCHE ETHIK. see *MEDICAL SCIENCES*

100   GW   ISSN 0044-3301
B3
ZEITSCHRIFT FUER PHILOSOPHISCHE FORSCHUNG. 1947. 4/yr. DM.178. Vittorio Klostermann, Frauenlobstr. 22, 60487 Frankfurt a.M., Germany. TEL 069-774011. FAX 069-708038. Eds. H.M. Baumgartner, O. Hoeffe. adv.; bk.rev.; bibl.; cum.index every 10 yrs. circ. 1,200. **Indexed:** Arts & Hum.Cit.Ind., Curr.Cont., Ind.Bk.Rev.Hum., Phil.Ind. **Document type:** academic/scholarly publication.
—BLDSC (9480.500000); Faxon; SWETS.

101   GW   ISSN 0514-2733
ZEITSCHRIFT FUER PHILOSOPHISCHE FORSCHUNG. BEIHEFTE. 1950. irreg., no.43, 1984. price varies. Verlag Anton Hain GmbH, Savignystr. 53, 60325 Frankfurt a.M., Germany. Eds. H.M. Baumgartner, O. Hoeffe.

100   GW   ISSN 0945-7232
ZEITSCHRIFT FUER PHILOSOPHISCHE PRAXIS. s-a. DM.24. (Gesellschaft fuer Philosophische Praxis) Academia Verlag GmbH, Postfach 1663, 53734 Sankt Augustin, Germany. TEL 02241-333349. FAX 02241-341528. Ed.Bd. **Document type:** academic/scholarly publication.

149.946   GW   ISSN 0170-6241
P99   CODEN: ZESEE3
ZEITSCHRIFT FUER SEMIOTIK. 1979. q. DM.96. Stauffenburg Verlag, Postfach 2567, 72015 Tuebingen, Germany. TEL 07071-78091. FAX 07071-75288. Ed. Roland Posner. adv.; bk.rev. **Indexed:** Arts & Hum.Cit.Ind., Bibl.Ling.; Curr.Cont.; RILM. **Document type:** newsletter.
—SWETS; UnCover.

100   CC
ZHEXUE DONGTAI. (Text in Chinese) m. Zhongguo Shehui Kexueyuan, Zhexue Yanjiusuo - Chinese Academy of Social Sciences, Institute of Philosophy, No.5, Jianguomennei Dajie, Beijing 1000732, People's Republic of China. TEL 5137954. Ed. Ren Junming.

100   CC
ZHEXUE LUNCONG. (Text in Chinese) bi-m. Zhongguo Shehui Kexueyuan, Zhexue Yanjiusuo - Chinese Academy of Social Sciences, Institute of Philosophy, No.5, Jianguomennei Dajie, Beijing 1000732, People's Republic of China. TEL 5137954. Ed. Li Shubai.

100   CC   ISSN 1000-0216
ZHEXUE YANJIU/PHILOSOPHICAL RESEARCH. (Text in Chinese, table of contents in English) 1955. m. Y42($33.80) Chinese Academy of Social Sciences, Institute of Philosophy, 5 Jianguo Mennei Dajie, Beijing 100732, People's Republic of China. TEL 861-513-7954. FAX 861-5137826. (Dist. outside China by: China International Book Trade Corp., P.O. Box 399, Beijing, P.R.C.; Dist. in US by: China Books & Periodicals, Inc., 2929 24th St., San Francisco, CA 94110. TEL 415-282-2994) Eds. Yang Shen, Chen Yunquan. adv.; bk.rev. **Document type:** academic/scholarly publication.
—BLDSC (6462.650000); UnCover.

100   CC   ISSN 1001-2710
ZHEXUE YUANLI. (Subseries of: Fuyin Baokan Ziliao) (Text in Chinese) m. Y155.65. Zhongguo Renmin Daxue, Shubao Ziliao Zhongxin - China People's University, Book & Newspaper Information Center, No.3 Zhang Zizhong Rd., P.O. Box 1122, Beijing 100007, People's Republic of China. TEL 86-10-4015080. index.
Description: Reprints papers and articles on philosophical principles.

ZHONGGUO QINGNIAN/CHINESE YOUTH. see *CHILDREN AND YOUTH — For*

100 299.51   CC
ZHONGGUO ZHEXUESHI YANJIU. (Text in Chinese; table of contents in English) s-a. Y4.60($13.20) (Zhongguo Zhexueshi Xuehui) Shehui Kexue Zazhishe, A-158 Gulou Xidajie, Beijing 100720, People's Republic of China. (Dist. in US by: China Books & Periodicals, Inc., 2929 24th St., San Francisco, CA 94110. TEL 415-282-2994)
Description: Publishes research on the history of Chinese philosophy.

ZNAK. see *RELIGIONS AND THEOLOGY*

ZUR DEBATTE. see *RELIGIONS AND THEOLOGY — Roman Catholic*

057.8   PL   ISSN 0044-5584
BX806.P6
ZYCIE I MYSL/LIFE AND THOUGHT. (Text in Polish; summaries in French) 1950. m. 150 Zl.($8.10) Instytut Wydawniczy "Pax", Ul. Chocimska 8-10, 00-791 Warsaw, Poland. (Dist. by: Ars Polona-Ruch, Krakowskie Przedmiescie 7, Warsaw, Poland) Ed. Anna Borowska. bk.rev.; film rev.; bibl.; charts; illus.; index. circ. 8,000. **Indexed:** Amer.Hist.& Life, CERDIC, Hist.Abstr., New Test.Abstr.

144   US
▼**1650 - 1850: IDEAS, AESTHETICS AND INQUIRIES.** 1994. a. $52.50. (Abrahams Magazines Service) A M S Press, Inc., 56 E. 13th St., New York, NY 10003. TEL 212-777-4700. FAX 212-995-5413. **Document type:** academic/scholarly publication.

PHILOSOPHY — Abstracting, Bibliographies, Statistics

ABSTRACTS OF BULGARIAN SCIENTIFIC LITERATURE. PHILOSOPHY, SOCIOLOGY, SCIENCE OF SCIENCES, PSYCHOLOGY AND PEDAGOGICS. see *EDUCATION — Abstracting, Bibliographies, Statistics*

PHOTOGRAPHY

100 200 016 SP ISSN 0211-4143
ACTUALIDAD BIBLIOGRAFICA DE FILOSOFIA Y TEOLOGIA; selecciones de libros. 1964. s-a. 2500 ptas.($25) Instituto de Teologia Fundamental, Facultad de Teologia de Catalunya, Llaseres 30, Sant Cugat del Valles, Barcelona, Spain. TEL 93-301-23-50. (Subscr. to: Selecciones de Teologia, Roger de Lluria 13, 08010 Barcelona, Spain) Ed. Josep Boada. adv.; bk.rev.; abstr.; bibl.; index. circ. 700. **Indexed:** Amer.Hist.& Life, CERDIC, Hist.Abstr.
  Formerly: Selecciones de Libros (ISSN 0037-1181)

100 016 VC ISSN 0084-7836
BIBLIOGRAPHIA INTERNATIONALIS SPIRITUALITATIS. (Text in various languages; summaries in Latin) 1966. a. L.115000 (effective 1996). (Pontificio Istituto di Spiritualita) Edizioni del Teresianum, Piazza S. Pancrazio 5-A, 00152 Rome, Italy. TEL 39-6-58540250. FAX 39-6-58540300. Ed. Juan Luis Astigarraga. circ. 650. **Document type:** bibliography.

100 016 FR ISSN 0006-1352
Z7127
BIBLIOGRAPHIE DE LA PHILOSOPHIE/BIBLIOGRAPHY OF PHILOSOPHY. (Text in English, French, German, Italian, Spanish) 1937. q. 600 F.($131) International Institute of Philosophy, 8 Rue Jean-Calvin, 75006 Paris, France. TEL 1-43-36-39-11. FAX 1-43-54-03-47. (Subscr. to: Librairie Philosophique J. Vrin, 6 Place de la Sorbonne, 75005 Paris, France) adv.; bk.rev.; bibl.; index. circ. 1,100. (back issues avail.)
  Description: Reviews and analyzes recent books in philosophy from all over the world.

100 US ISSN 0742-6887
BIBLIOGRAPHIES AND INDEXES IN PHILOSOPHY. 1985. irreg. price varies. Greenwood Press, Inc. (Subsidiary of: Greenwood Publishing Group Inc.), 88 Post Rd. W., Box 5007, Westport, CT 06881-5007. TEL 203-226-3571. FAX 203-222-1502.

300 016 IT ISSN 0006-6621
BOLLETTINO BIBLIOGRAFICO PER LE SCIENZE MORALI E SOCIALE.* (Supplement to de Homme) 1968. q. L.2500($5) Universita degli Studi di Roma, Istituto di Filosofia, Rome, Italy. Ed. G.G. Sansoni. adv.; bibl.

300 100 016 FR ISSN 1157-3694
Z7127
F R A N C I S. 519: PHILOSOPHIE. (Printed format ceased Jan. 1995) 1947. q. Centre National de la Recherche Scientifique, Institut de l'Information Scientifique et Technique, 2 allee du Parc de Brabois, 54514 Vandoeuvre-les-Nancy Cedex, France. TEL 83-50-46-00. FAX 83-50-46-50. adv. contact: Veronique Guinvarc'h. index, cum.index. **Document type:** bibliography.
  ●Also available online. Vendor(s): Telesystemes - Questel.
  Also available on CD-ROM.
  Formerly: Bulletin Signaletique. Part 519: Philosophie (ISSN 0007-554X)

215 RU
FILOSOFIYA: OTECHESTVENNAYA I ZARUBEZHNAYA LITERATURA; referativnyi zhurnal. 1992. q. $65. Rossiiskaya Akademiya Nauk, Institut Nauchnoi Informatsii po Obshchestvennym Naukam, Ul. Krasikova 28-21, 117418 Moscow V-418, Russia. Ed. A.I. Panchenko. **Document type:** abstracting/indexing.
  Formed by the merger of (1973-1992): Obshchestvennye Nauki v S.S.S.R. Filosofskie Nauki (ISSN 0202-2052); (1972-1992): Obshchestvennye Nauki za Rubezhom. Filosofiya; Which superseded in part: Obshchestvennye Nauki za Rubezhom. Filosofiya i Sotsiologiya (ISSN 0132-7356)

100 SP ISSN 1130-9105
Z7127
INDICE ESPANOL DE HUMANIDADES. SERIES D: PHILOSOPHY. 1979. a. 8800 ptas. or exchange basis (effective 1995). Centro de Informacion y Documentacion Cientifica (Cindoc), Pinar 25, 3, 28006 Madrid, Spain. TEL 34-1-4112220. FAX 34-1-5645069. E-mail: bib___isoc@bib.csic.es. adv. contact: Angel Villagra. (also avail. in diskette format)
  ●Also available online.
  Also available on CD-ROM.
  Formerly: Indice Espanol de Ciencias Sociales. Series F: Philosophy; Which superseded in part (in 1982): Indice Espanol de Ciencias Sociales (ISSN 0211-1373)

190 NE ISSN 0923-3342
INTERNATIONAL BIBLIOGRAPHY OF AUSTRIAN PHILOSOPHY/INTERNATIONALE BIBLIOGRAPHIE ZUR OESTERREICHISCHEN PHILOSOPHIE. Key Title: Studien zur Oesterreichischen Philosophie. Supplement. (Text in English, German) 1986. a., vol.6, 1993. price varies. Editions Rodopi B.V., Keizersgracht 302-304, 1016 EX Amsterdam, Netherlands. TEL 31-20-6227507. FAX 31-20-6380948. E-mail: F.van.der.Zee@Rodopi.nl. (In N. America: 233 Peachtree St., N.E., Ste. 404, Atlanta, GA 30303-1504. TEL 800-225-3998. FAX 404-522-7116) index. (back issues avail.) **Document type:** bibliography.
  Description: Covers philosophy, psychology, and the history of science. Includes articles on notable Austrian philosophers, information on libraries and other institutions of information and documentation.

100 GW ISSN 0722-7329
KATALOG PHILOSOPHIE. 1965. a. DM.35.80. Buchwerbung in Berlin GmbH, Luetzowstr. 105-106, 10785 Berlin, Germany. adv. **Document type:** bibliography.
  Formerly: Jahreskatalog Philosophie (ISSN 0075-2916)
  Description: Bibliography of each year's new titles in philosophy.

NEW TITLES IN BIOETHICS. see *MEDICAL SCIENCES — Abstracting, Bibliographies, Statistics*

100 301 011 RU
NOVAYA LITERATURA PO SOTSIAL'NYM I GUMANITARNYM NAUKAM. FILOSOFIYA I SOTSIOLOGIYA; bibliograficheskii ukazatel' 1992. m. $91. Rossiyskaya Akademiya Nauk, Institut Nauchnoi Informatsii po Obshchestvennym Naukam, Ul. Krasikova 28-21, 117418 Moscow V-418, Russia. Ed. B.P. Ginsburg. **Document type:** bibliography.
  Formed by the merger of (1947-1992): Novaya Inostrannaya Literatura po Obshchestvennym Naukam. Filosofiya i Sotsiologiya (ISSN 0134-2851); (1946-1992): Novaya Sovetskaya Literatura po Obshchestvennym Naukam. Filosofskie Nauki (ISSN 0134-2789)

100 016 US ISSN 0031-7993
Z7127 CODEN: PHIXA
PHILOSOPHER'S INDEX; an international index to philosophical periodicals and books. (Text in English, French, German, Italian, Spanish and Portuguese) 1967. q. (with a. cumulation). $52 to individuals; institutions $174; cumulation $181 (effective 1994). Bowling Green State University, Philosophy Documentation Center, Bowling Green, OH 43403-0189. TEL 419-372-2419; 800-444-2419. FAX 419-372-6987. E-mail: PHILDOC@OPIE.BGSU.EDU. Ed. Richard H. Lineback. adv.; bk.rev.; index, cum.index. circ. 1,150. **Document type:** abstracting/indexing.
  ●Also available online. Vendor(s): Knight-Ridder, Inc. (File no.57).
  Also available on CD-ROM.
  —BLDSC (6461.480000).
  Description: Subject and author index to philosophy articles, books, contributions to anthologies from more than 40 countries.

100 016 BE ISSN 0034-4567
Z7127
REPERTOIRE BIBLIOGRAPHIQUE DE LA PHILOSOPHIE/INTERNATIONAL PHILOSOPHICAL BIBLIOGRAPHY/BIBLIOGRAFISCH REPERTORIUM VAN DE WIJSBEGEERTE. (Supplement to: Revue Philosophique de Louvain (ISSN 0035-3841)) (Text in language of authors; introductions in Dutch, English, French, German, Italian, Spanish) 1949. q. 1750 BEF (effective 1995). (Universite Catholique de Louvain, Institut Superieur de Philosophie) Editions Peeters s.p.r.l., Bondgenotenlaan 153, 3000 Leuven, Belgium. TEL 32-16-235170. FAX 32-16-228500. (Co-sponsor: Institut International de Philosophie) Eds. Claude Troisfontaines. bk.rev.; bibl.; index. circ. 1,800. (back issues avail.) **Indexed:** Phil.Ind. **Document type:** academic/scholarly publication, bibliography.
  Description: International bibliography on works, articles and reviews of philosophy.

100 FR ISSN 0080-4789
RUDOLF STEINER PUBLICATIONS. 1963. irreg. Librairie Fischbacher, 33 Rue de Seine, 75006 Paris, France. TEL 43-26-84-87. FAX 43-26-48-87.

600 ISSN 0739-0971
TRANET; transnational network for appropriate alternative technologies. 1976. bi-m. $30 to individuals; libraries $50; institutions $150 (effective 1996). Tranet, Inc., Box 567, Rangeley, ME 04970. TEL 207-864-2252. FAX 207-864-2252. E-mail: tranet@igc.apc.org. Ed. William N. Ellis; Pub. Peter Thibeault. bk.rev.; circ. 2,000 (paid). (looseleaf format; back issues avail.) **Document type:** abstracting/indexing, directory.
  Description: Abstracts articles, books, and papers and discusses people active in the Gaian Cutural Transition. Seeks to further an understanding and respect for the Earth and the indigenous cultural traditions that foster it.

PHOTOGRAPHY

see also Motion Pictures

A D A MAGAZINE. (Art, Design, Architecture) see *ARCHITECTURE*

770 UK
A F A E P AWARDS. 1984. a. £30. (Association of Photographers) Reed Information Services (Subsidiary of: Reed Elsevier group), Windsor Court, E. Grinstead House, E. Grinstead, W. Sussex RH19 1XA, England. TEL 01342-335832. FAX 01342-335948. TELEX 95127-INFSER-G. Ed. Valerie May. adv. (back issues avail.) **Document type:** bulletin.
  Description: Shows award winning photographs from the members of the association.

770 IT ISSN 1120-205X
A F T; rivista di storia e fotografia. (Text in Italian; abstracts in English) 1985. 2/yr. L.20000 (foreign L.35000) (effective 1995). Archivio Fotografico Toscano, Via Ricasoli, 7, 50047 Prato, Italy. TEL 39-574-616011. FAX 39-574-616018. (Subscr. to: Opuslibri, Via della Torretta, No. 16, 50137 Florence, Italy. TEL 39-55-660833) Ed. Sauro Lusini. bk.rev. circ. 800.
  Description: Covers research about photography, the study of history of photography, and the preservation, restoration, and cataloguing of photographs.

770 US
A P N Y NEWSLETTER. 1989. 6/yr. free. Advertising Photographers of New York, 27 W. 20th St., Rm. 601, New York, NY 10011. TEL 212-807-0399. FAX 212-727-8120. Ed. Michael O'Connor. adv.; bk.rev.; circ. 1,000 (controlled). **Document type:** newsletter.
  Formerly: A P A Magazine (ISSN 1046-4522)
  Description: Addresses the business and aesthetic concerns of the professional photographer.

770 070.49 DK ISSN 0109-4440
AARETS PRESSEFOTO. a. DKK 10. Pressefotografforbundet, Gammel Strand 46, 1202 Copenhagen K, Denmark.

ACOUSTICAL IMAGING. see *PHYSICS — Sound*

PHOTOGRAPHY

770   UK
ACTUALITIES. 1988. a. $17. 152 Narrow St., London E14 8BP, England.

778 069   SW   ISSN 1102-5565
ADOMUS. 1985. irreg. Svenska Museifoereningen, P.O. Box 4715, S-116 92 Stockholm, Sweden.
Formerly (until 1989): Adomus-nytt.

ADVANCED IMAGING. see COMMUNICATIONS — Computer Applications

AERIAL ARCHAEOLOGY. see ARCHAEOLOGY

778.5   US   ISSN 0300-7472
TR640
AFTERIMAGE. 1972. m. (10/yr.). $30 to individuals (foreign $35); institutions $40 (foreign $45). Visual Studies Workshop, 31 Prince St., Rochester, NY 14607. TEL 716-442-8676. Ed. Grant H. Kester. bk.rev.; film rev.; illus.; index. circ. 6,000. (tabloid format; also avail. in microform from UMI; reprint service avail. from UMI) **Indexed:** Artbibl.Mod., Bk.Rev.Ind. (1984-), Child.Bk.Rev.Ind. (1984-), Film Lit.Ind. (1974-), Int.Ind.Film Per., Intl.Ind.TV, RILA. **Document type:** academic/scholarly publication.
—BLDSC (0735.632000); Ei; Faxon; UMI.
Description: Presents independent critical commentary on issues in media arts, including scholarly research, in-depth reviews, investigative journalism, and interviews.

770   SP
AGFOVAL. q. free. Agrupacio Fotografica Valenciana, Maestro Clave 10, 1o, 2a, Apdo. 1575, 46001 Valencia, Spain. TEL 34-6-3512520. Ed. J. Collado Martinez. circ. 1,000. **Document type:** bulletin.

770   SP
AGRUPACION FOTOGRAFICA DE NAVARRA. BOLETIN MENSUAL. 12/yr. Agrupacion Fotografica de Navarra, Zapateria 42, 2o Dcha., 31001 Pamplona, Spain. TEL 48-22-23-58. Ed. J.L. Larrion Torres.

AILERON; a literary journal. see LITERATURE — Poetry

770   GW   ISSN 0944-4017
AKTIVE FOTOGRAFIE. bi-m. DM.36 (foreign DM.42) (effective 1995). Verlag fuer Technik und Handwerk GmbH, Robert-Bosch-Str. 4, 76532 Baden-Baden, Germany. TEL 07221-5087-0. FAX 07221-508752. Ed. Thomas Maschke. adv. **Document type:** consumer publication.
Formerly: Amateurfotografie (ISSN 0174-2361)

ALBUM, LETRAS Y ARTES. see ART

ALBUM OF VISUALIZATION. see PHYSICS — Optics

ALLTAG; die Sensationen des Gewoehnlichen. see LITERATURE

770   IT   ISSN 0393-9758
ALMANACCO DI FOTOGRAFARE. 1968. q. L.33000 (foreign L.60000). Cesco Ciapanna Editore S.p.A., Via Lipari 8, 00141 Rome, Italy. TEL 39-6-87183441. FAX 39-6-87183995. Ed. Cesco Ciapanna. adv.: page L.4400000. circ. 75,000.

770   IT
ALMANACCO FOTOGRAFICO. 1978. q. L.10000 per no. Editrice Progresso s.r.l., Viale Piceno 14, 20129 Milan, Italy. TEL 39-2-70002222. FAX 39-2-713030. Ed. Paolo Namias. adv. circ. 25,000.
Formerly: Annuario Fotografico.

770   DK   ISSN 0908-3316
ALT OM FOTO & VIDEO. 1966. m. (11/yr.). DKK 330. Steen Soerensen, P.O. Box 239, DK-9900 Frederikshavn, Denmark. Ed. Finn Nesgaard. adv.; illus. circ. 6,886.
Formed in the 1993 merger of: Alt om Foto & Fotokino & Foto, Film & Video; (until 1983): Foto og Smalfilm.

770   UK   ISSN 0002-6840
TR1
AMATEUR PHOTOGRAPHER. 1884. w. £137; newsstand price: £1.30. I P C Magazines, Specialist Magazine Group (Subsidiary of: Reed Elsevier group), King's Reach Tower, Stamford St., London SE1 9LS, England. TEL 071-261-5100. FAX 0444-440619. TELEX 892084 REEDBP G. (Dist. by: Quadrant Subscription Services, Oakfield House, Perrymount Rd., Haywards Heath, W. Sussex RH16 3DH, England. TEL 0444-440421) Ed. Keith Wilson. adv.; bk.rev.; illus.; s-a. index. circ. 73,704. (also avail. in microform from UMI) **Indexed:** Chem.Abstr. **Document type:** consumer publication.
—UMI. CCC.
Description: Covers photo technique, equipment reviews, news and features.

AMERICAN CINEMATOGRAPHER; international journal of motion picture production techniques. see MOTION PICTURES

770   US   ISSN 1046-8986
TR1
AMERICAN PHOTO. 1978. bi-m. $19.90. Hachette Magazines, Inc., 1633 Broadway, 45th Fl., New York, NY 10019. TEL 212-767-6000. (Subscr. to: Box 52616, Boulder, CO 80322) Ed. David Schonauer. adv.: B&W page $11300, color page $18000; adv. contact: Arlene Weinberg. bk.rev. circ. 250,000. **Indexed:** Access (1980-), Artbibl.Mod., Mag.Ind., P.M.I., PMR.
—BLDSC (0850.597000); Faxon; UMI; UnCover.
Formerly (until 1990): American Photographer (ISSN 0161-6854)

770   US
AMERICAN PHOTOGRAPHERS; * an illustrated who's who among leading contemporary Americans. 1988. irreg. $39.95. American References Publishing Corp., 2210 N. Burling St., Chicago, IL 60614-3712. Ed. Les Krantz. illus.
Description: Presents profiles of more than 1000 American photographers. Contains phone numbers, specialties, shooting situations and career overviews. Includes a list of stock photography houses, an alphabetical index with cross-references by subject and situation, and several hundred photographs.

770   US   ISSN 0097-577X
TR1
AMERICAN PHOTOGRAPHY. 1907. a. $60 (effective 1993). Fadner Media Enterprises, 5 E. 16th St., New York, NY 10003-3112. TEL 212-647-0874. FAX 212-691-6609. (Dist. by: Watson Guptil, 1695 Oak St., Lakewood, NJ 08701. TEL 908-363-5679) Ed. Edward Booth-Clibborn. illus. circ. 4,000. (back issues avail.) **Document type:** monographic series.
Incorporates (1939-1941): Photo Techniques (ISSN 0097-5893); (1921-1932): Photo-Era Magazine (ISSN 0097-5885)
Description: Publishes outstanding photographs by US and Canadian photographers.

770   US   ISSN 0744-5784
TR820
AMERICAN SOCIETY OF MEDIA PHOTOGRAPHERS. BULLETIN. 1944. m. membership only. American Society of Media Photographers, 14 Washington Rd., Ste. 502, Princeton Junction, NJ 08550-1033. TEL 609-799-8300. FAX 609-799-2233. Ed. Peter Skinner. adv. contact: Peter Skinner. bk.rev. circ. 7,000. **Document type:** bulletin.
Formerly: American Society of Magazine Photographers. Bulletin (ISSN 0361-9168)
Description: Provides information pertaining to the business of professional photography. Published for the members of ASMP, a trade association.

ANHUI HUABAO/ANHUI PICTORIAL. see GENERAL INTEREST PERIODICALS — China

770   BL
ANUARIO BRASILEIRO DE OTICA CINE FOTO SOM. * 1971. a. Alpha Empresa de Divulagacao e Cultura Ltda., P. Don Gastao Liberal Pinto 27, CEP 04534 Sao Paulo SP, Brazil. TEL 881-1402. Ed. Sergio Salles. circ. 260,000.

770   US   ISSN 0003-6420
TR1
APERTURE. 1952. q. $40 (effective Feb. 1991). Aperture Foundation, Inc., 20 E. 23rd St., New York, NY 10010. TEL 212-505-5555. FAX 212-979-7759. TELEX 857718. Ed. Melissa Harris. adv.: B&W page $2500, color page $3300; 9 9/16 x 11 3/8. bk.rev.; bibl.; illus.; cum.index: vols.1-6 in 1958. circ. 17,000. (also avail. in microfilm from UMI; reprint service avail. from UMI) **Indexed:** Art Ind., Artbibl.Mod., Arts & Hum.Cit.Ind., Curr.Cont.
—BLDSC (1567.880000); SWETS; UMI; UnCover.
Description: Devoted to photography as art, contains illustrated profiles of photographers or thematic material.

770   SP   ISSN 0212-5900
AQUI IMAGEN. 1983. 4/yr. Plaza de Santa Ana 1, 28012 Madrid, Spain. TEL 1-532-62-09. Ed. Alberto Murias. circ. 5,000.

770   US   ISSN 0735-5572
TR640
ARCHIVE (TUCSON). 1976. a. $25. University of Arizona, Center for Creative Photography, Tucson, AZ 85721. TEL 602-621-7968. FAX 602-621-9444. Ed. Nancy Solomon. circ. 1,100 (paid). **Indexed:** Artbibl.Mod. **Document type:** academic/scholarly publication.
Formerly (until 1981): Center for Creative Photography.
Description: Presents materials from the collection of photographs, negatives and manuscripts in the center's archives.

771   GW   ISSN 0932-3333
ART BUYER'S HANDBOOK; Fotografen Journal. 1988. a. DM.120. Verlag Design und Technik GmbH, A.-Paul-Weber-Str. 5, 21493 Schretstaken, Germany. circ. 12,000.
Description: Directed to art directors and art buyers; showcases work from professional photographers.

ART CALENDAR. see ART

770   FR
ART ET IMAGE. 1949. 5/yr. 250 F. Musee Francais de la Photographie, 28 ter, rue Gassendi, 75014 Paris, France. TEL 43-22-11-72. (Co-sponsor: Photo-Club du Val de Bievre) Ed. Andre Fage. adv.; bk.rev. circ. 1,000.

ART NEW ZEALAND. see ART

770   SP   ISSN 0514-9193
ARTE FOTOGRAFICO. 1952. m. 10000 ptas. Ediarte S.A., Santo Angel 76, 28043 Madrid, Spain. TEL 34-1-3886533. FAX 34-1-7597584. Dir. Antonio Casello. adv.; bk.rev.; illus. circ. 25,000.

ARTIBUS ET HISTORIAE; international journal for visual arts. see ART

ARTISTIC TRAVELER; architecture & travel with art & photography. see TRAVEL AND TOURISM

770   JA   ISSN 0044-9148
ASAHI CAMERA. (Text in Japanese) 1926. m. $158.50. Asahi Shimbun Publishing Co., 3-2, Tsukiji 5-chome, Chuo-ku, Tokyo 104-11, Japan. (Subscr. to: Japan Publications Trading Co., Ltd., Box 5030, Tokyo International, Tokyo, Japan) Ed. Masami Fujisawa. adv.; bk.rev. circ. 200,000. **Indexed:** JTA.

770   AT
AUSTRALIA CAMERA CRAFT PHOTOGRAPHER'S HANDBOOK. 1981. a. Aus.$7.95. Horwitz Publications Pty. Ltd., 55 Chandos St., St. Leonards, N.S.W. 2065, Australia. Ed. Bill Harrington. **Document type:** consumer publication.

770   AT   ISSN 0158-2658
AUSTRALIAN CAMERA CRAFT. 1979. m. Aus.$42 (foreign Aus.$55). Horwitz Publications Pty. Ltd., 55 Chandos St., St. Leonards, N.W.S. 2065, Australia. (Subscr. to: P.O. Box 5555, St. Leonards, N.W.S., 2065, Australia) Ed. Bill Harrngton. circ. 16,000. (back issues avail.) **Document type:** consumer publication.
—CCC.
Description: Popular magazine for photography enthusiasts.

PHOTOGRAPHY

770   AT   ISSN 0004-9964
AUSTRALIAN PHOTOGRAPHY. 1950. m. Aus.$51 (foreign Aus.$137) (effective Feb. 1995). Yaffa Publishing Group, 17-21 Bellevue St., Surry Hills, N.S.W. 2010, Australia. TEL 61-2-281-2333. FAX 61-2-281-2750. Ed. Steven Packer. adv.: B&W page Aus.$1370, color page Aus.$1960; trim 273 x 210. bk.rev.; charts; illus.; tr.lit. circ. 10,492. **Indexed:** Pinpointer. **Document type:** consumer publication.
    Description: Serves the enthusiast interested in cameras, craft, tools and techniques of photography.

770   AT   ISSN 1321-6376
AUSTRALIAN PHOTOGRAPHY PHOTO-DIRECTORY. 1951. a. Aus.$6.95. Yaffa Publishing Group, 17-21 Bellevue St., Surry Hills, N.S.W. 2010, Australia. TEL 61-2-281-2333. FAX 61-2-281-2750. adv.: B&W page Aus.$1370, color page Aus.$1960; trim 273 x 210. bk.rev. **Document type:** directory.
    Formerly: Australian Photography Directory (ISSN 0816-3669)
    Description: Directory of photographic goods available on the local market.

770   UK   ISSN 0269-2023
B A P L A DIRECTORY. a. £10. British Association of Picture Libraries and Agencies, 13 Woodberry Crescent, London N10 1PJ, England. TEL 0181-444-9713. FAX 0181-883-9215. **Document type:** directory.

770   UK   ISSN 0269-7742
B A P L A JOURNAL. 1985. s-a. £15 for 2 yrs. British Association of Picture Libraries and Agencies, 13 Woodberry Crescent, London N10 1PJ, England. TEL 0181-444-7913. FAX 0181-883-9215. Ed. Brian Shuel. adv. contact: Simon Shuel. bk.rev. circ. 3,000. **Document type:** trade publication.
—BLDSC (1863.127000).
    Description: Covers British photo libraries and agencies, how they work, who they are, details concerned with running libraries.

770   UK
B P I - THE BUSINESS OF PHOTOGRAPHY & IMAGING. m. Market Link House, Tye Green, Elsenham, Bishops Stratford, Herts. CM22 6DY, England. TEL 0279-647555. FAX 0279-815300. Ed. Lisa Foster; Pub. Michael Garside. adv. contact: Andy Rice. circ. 6,500 (controlled). **Document type:** trade publication.
    Formerly: B P I News.

770   NE
BELICHT; foto en filmblad voor de amateurfotograaf. m. fl.47.50. Uitgeverij C P S B.V., Postbus 301, 7400 AA Deventer, Netherlands. adv.; bk.rev. circ. 16,000.

770   US
BELLA PHOTO GLAMOUR ART. 1993. q. $50 (foreign $60). Aquino Productions, Box 15760, Stamford, CT 06901-0760. TEL 203-967-9952. FAX 203-359-1546. Ed. Elaine Hallgren. adv.: B&W page $1000, color page $1500; trim 8 3/8 x 10 7/8. circ. 16,500. **Document type:** trade publication.
    Description: Features a collection of artistic glamour photographs, unusual expressions, striking images, avant gard tableaux, spellbinding renderings.

770   AU   ISSN 0005-8947
DAS BERGMANN-ECHO. 1958. bi-m. free. (Bergmann-Kameradschaft 137. Inf. Div.) Sepp Sattelberger, Editor, Postanschrift A-3252, Petzenkirchen, Austria.

770   US
BLACK'S PHOTO GUIDE: CHICAGO.* 1993. s-a. $124.95. Black's Guide, Inc., 818 W. Diamond Ave., Ste. 300, Gaithersburg, MD 20878-1417. **Document type:** directory.

770   US   ISSN 1068-1647
BLIND SPOT. 1993. s-a. $24. Lexington Photo Labs., Inc., 49 W. 23rd St., New York, NY 10010. adv.; illus.

770 910.4   US
BLUE BOOK: THE DIRECTORY OF GEOGRAPHIC, TRAVEL & DESTINATION STOCK PHOTOGRAPHY. biennial. $30. A G Editions, Inc., 41 Union Sq., W., Ste. 523, New York, NY 10003-3208. TEL 212-929-0959. FAX 212-924-4796. **Document type:** directory.

BLUE PITCHER; a biannual magazine of poetry and photography. see LITERATURE — Poetry

770   GW   ISSN 0932-7231
BRENNPUNKT; Magazin fuer Photographie. 1984. q. DM.18. Edition Dibue, Waghaeuseler Str. 8, 10715 Berlin, Germany. TEL 030-8533527. Ed. Dietmar Buehrer.

770   UK   ISSN 0007-1196 CODEN: BRJFAM
BRITISH JOURNAL OF PHOTOGRAPHY; technical, professional, scientific. (Supplements avail.: Photo (Year) (ISSN 1354-7011); British Journal of Photography Services Guide (ISSN 0969-3580)) 1854. w. £45.50. Bouverie Publishing Company Ltd., 147-151 Temple Chambers, Temple Ave., London EC47 0DT, England. TEL 0171-583-3030. FAX 0171-583-4068. Ed. Revel Golden. adv.; bk.rev.; charts; illus.; stat.; index. circ. 11,500. (also avail. in microfilm from WMP) **Indexed:** Artbibl.Mod., Br.Tech.Ind., Chem.Abstr., INSPEC (1971-), Photo.Abstr., Print.Abstr. **Document type:** trade publication.
—BLDSC (2317.000000); CASDDS; SWETS; UnCover.

770   UK   ISSN 0969-3580
BRITISH JOURNAL OF PHOTOGRAPHY SERVICES GUIDE. (Supplement to: British Journal of Photography (ISSN 0007-1196)) 1990. a.? Bouverie Publishing Company Ltd., 147-151 Temple Chambers, Temple Ave., London EC47 0DT, England. TEL 0171-583-3030. FAX 0171-583-4068.

771 658.8   UK
BUSINESS RATIO REPORT: PHOTOGRAPHIC EQUIPMENT AND PROCESSORS; an industry sector analysis. 1980. a. I C C Business Ratios Ltd. (Subsidiary of: I C C Information Group), Field House, Hampton, Mddx. TW12 1BR, England. TEL 0181-783-7940. FAX 0181-783-1940. charts; stat. **Document type:** trade publication.
    Former titles (until 1991): Business Ratio Report: Photographic Equipment and Processing (ISSN 0954-6731); (until 1987): Business Ratio Report: The Photographic Industry (ISSN 0261-9369)

770   UK   ISSN 0961-0863
BUYING CAMERAS. 1990. m. £31.20 (foreign £47.85) (effective 1995-1996). E M A P - Apex, Tower House, Sovereign Park, Lathkill St., Market Harborough, Leics. LE16 9EF, England. TEL 01858-468811. FAX 01858-432164. adv. **Document type:** consumer publication.

C MAGAZINE; the magazine of contemporary art. see ART

770   FR   ISSN 0294-4081
CAHIERS DE LA PHOTOGRAPHIE. 1981. q. 385 F. (foreign 450 F.). Association de Critique Contemporaire en Photographie, c/o Gilles Mora, Lascledes, Brax, 47310 Laplume, France. TEL 53-96-78-28. FAX 53-98-21-89. bk.rev. (back issues avail.) **Indexed:** Artbibl.Mod.

770   US   ISSN 0883-489X
TR197
CAMERA. Variant title: Orion Camera Blue Book. 1985. a. Orion Research Corp., 14555 N. Scottsdale Rd., Ste. 330, Scottsdale, AZ 85254.
    Formerly: Camera Reference Guide (ISSN 0740-1647)

770   US   ISSN 1056-8484
TR287
CAMERA & DARKROOM PHOTOGRAPHY. Key Title: Camera & Darkroom. 1979. 12/yr. $24.95 (foreign $34.95). Larry Flynt Publications, Inc., 9171 Wilshire Blvd., Ste. 300, Beverly Hills, CA 90210. TEL 310-858-7100. FAX 310-274-7985. (Subscr. to: Box 16928, N. Hollywood, CA 91615) Ed. Ana Jones. illus.; stat.; index. circ. 75,000. (also avail. in microfilm from UMI; back issues avail.; reprint service avail. from UMI) **Indexed:** Art & Archaeol.Tech.Abstr., Graph.Arts Lit.Abstr., Ind.How To Do It (1979-), P.M.I. **Document type:** consumer publication.
—UMI; UnCover.
    Formerly Until 1990): Darkroom Photography (ISSN 0163-9250)

770   AU   ISSN 1015-1915
TR1
CAMERA AUSTRIA. (Text in English, German) 1980. q. S.520. Forum Stadtpark, Stadtpark 1, A-8010 Graz, Austria. TEL 0316-827734. FAX 0316-8253696. Ed. Christine Frisinghelli; Pub. Manfred Willmann. adv.: B&W page S.13200, color page S.20000; trim 210 x 295; adv. contact: Christine Frisinghelli. bk.rev. circ. 3,000. **Document type:** consumer publication.
—BLDSC (3016.061890).
    Description: Presents artistic and theoretical work in and about photography.

770 028.5   CN   ISSN 0008-2090
CAMERA CANADA. 1969. q. Can.$16 to non-members. National Association for Photographic Art, Inc., 31858 Hopedale Ave., Clearbrook, BC V2T 2G7, Canada. TEL 604-855-4848. Ed. Marilyn McEwen. adv.: B&W page $500, color page $900; trim 8 1/4 x 11. bk.rev. circ. 4,000. **Indexed:** Artbibl.Mod., Can.B.P.I., Can.Per.Ind., CMI.

770   FR   ISSN 0765-9849
TR1
CAMERA INTERNATIONAL. 1984. q. 320 F. (foreign 400 F.). 51 rue de l'Amiral Mouchez, 75013 Paris, France. TEL 45-65-46-00. TELEX 202 548 F. (Subscr. to: 99 rue d'Amsterdam, 75008 Paris, France. TEL 42-80-68-55) Ed. Gabriel Bauret.
—BLDSC (3016.113000).

770   NZ   ISSN 0114-264X
CAMERA NEW ZEALAND. 1953. bi-m. NZ.$33.75. Photographic Society of New Zealand, P.O. Box 51-365, Pakuranga Auckland, New Zealand. TEL 64-9-576-923. Ed. John E.A. Reece. adv.; bk.rev.; illus.; index. circ. 2,000. **Document type:** newsletter.
    Former titles: Camera (ISSN 0110-3989); New Zealand Camera (ISSN 0048-0118)
    Description: Promotes all forms of photography both within New Zealand and overseas.

770   JA   ISSN 0008-2082
CAMERART/KAMERA ATO; all the news about cameras and photography. (Text in English) 1958. m. $52.50. Intercontinental Marketing Corp., I.P.O. Box 5056, Tokyo 100-30, Japan. TEL 81-3-3661-7458. FAX 81-3-3667-9646. Ed. Kunika Todoriki. adv.; bk.rev.; illus.; index. circ. 18,000.
—UnCover.

CAMERART PHOTO TRADE DIRECTORY. see BUSINESS AND ECONOMICS — Trade And Industrial Directories

770 700   US
CAMERAWORK; a journal of photographic arts. 1984. s-a. $35. S F Camerawork, 70 12th St., San Francisco, CA 94103-1242. TEL 415-621-1001. adv. contact: Beth Goldberg. bk.rev. circ. 2,500. (tabloid format) **Document type:** academic/scholarly publication.
    Formerly: S F Camerawork Quarterly.
    Description: Presents new writing and reproductions of artists' work that reflect contemporary issues in the photographic arts.

770   JA
CAPA; active camera magazine. (Text in Japanese) 1981. m. 4200 Yen. Gakken Co. Ltd., 40-5, 4-chome, Kamiikedai, Ohta-ku, Tokyo 145, Japan. Ed. Shonosuke Abe.

CAPE ROCK; a journal of poetry. see LITERATURE — Poetry

CHAMPAIGN COUNTY HISTORICAL ARCHIVES HISTORICAL PUBLICATIONS SERIES. see HISTORY — History Of North And South America

770   FR   ISSN 0396-8235
CHASSEUR D'IMAGES. 1976. 10/yr. 260 F. Editions Jibena, La Petite Motte, 86100 Senille, France. TEL 49-85-49-85. FAX 49-85-49-99. Ed. Roman Loaec; Pub. Guy Hachette. adv. contact: Guy-Michel Cogne. illus. circ. 105,000. **Document type:** consumer publication.
—CCC.

CHICAGO RENAISSANCE. see LITERATURE

PHOTOGRAPHY

770 SI ISSN 0009-6954
CINE NEWS. vol.11, 1970. m. free. Singapore Cine Club, 42 Branksome Rd., Singapore 1543, Singapore. Ed. Paul Gomez. adv.; illus. circ. 1,500.

770 GW ISSN 0343-3102
COLOR FOTO. 1971. m. DM.96; newsstand price: DM.9. Vereinigte Motor-Verlage GmbH und Co. KG, Leuschnerstr. 1, 70174 Stuttgart, Germany. TEL 0711-18201. FAX 0711-1821756. Ed. Michael Tafelmaier; Pub. Uwe Hagen. adv.: B&W page DM.11640, color page DM.19788; trim 185 x 248; adv. contact: Peter Heyde. circ. 73,562. **Document type**: consumer publication.
  Formerly (until 1976): Color Foto Journal (ISSN 0343-3099)

COLOR RESEARCH AND APPLICATION. see *ENGINEERING — Chemical Engineering*

771 US
COLORGRAM. m. membership only. (Association of Professional Color Laboratories) Photo Marketing Association International, 3000 Picture Pl., Jackson, MI 49201. TEL 517-788-8100. FAX 517-788-8371. circ. 1,050. (back issues avail.) **Document type**: trade publication.

770 US ISSN 0145-899X
TR640
COMBINATIONS; a journal of photography. 1977. q. $12 to individuals; institutions $14. Mary Ann Lynch, Ed. & Pub., Middle Grove Rd., Greenfield Center, NY 12833. TEL 518-584-4612. adv.; bk.rev. circ. 1,500.

770 US
  CODEN: INPHA5
THE COMMERCIAL IMAGE. 1952. m. $60. P T N Publishing Corp., 445 Broad Hollow Rd., Ste. 21, Melville, NY 11747-4722. TEL 516-845-2700. FAX 516-845-7109. Ed. Steven Shaw. adv.; bk.rev.; bibl.; illus.; index. circ. 45,000. **Indexed**: A.S.& T.Ind., Art & Archaeol.Tech.Abstr., Chem.Abstr., Curr.Cont., Eng.Ind., Graph.Arts Lit.Abstr., Ind.How To Do It (1970-), Ind.Sci.Rev., INSPEC, Ocean.Abstr., Pollut.Abstr. **Document type**: trade publication.
  —Ei; SWETS; UMI; UnCover.
  Formerly (until 1995): Industrial Photography (ISSN 0019-8595)
  Description: Tools and techniques for image-makers in business and industry.

770 JA
COMMERCIAL PHOTO. 1980. 12/yr. $300. Intercontinental Marketing Corp., P.O. Box 5056, Tokyo 100-31, Japan. TEL 81-3-3661-7458. FAX 81-3-3667-9646.

778 AT ISSN 1037-6992
COMMERCIAL PHOTOGRAPHY. 1962. bi-m. Aus.$27.60 (foreign Aus.$79) (effective Feb. 1995). Yaffa Publishing Group, 17-21 Bellevue St., Surry Hills, N.S.W. 2010, Australia. TEL 61-2-281-2333. FAX 61-2-281-2750. Ed. Andrew Pegler. adv.: B&W page Aus.$1100, color Aus.$1655; trim 297 x 210. bk.rev.; illus. circ. 2,935. (reprint service avail. from UMI) **Document type**: trade publication.
  —BLDSC (3337.104000).
  Former titles: Industrial and Commercial Photography (ISSN 0313-4393); Industrial Photography and Commercial Camera (ISSN 0019-8609)
  Description: Features insights into creativity, studio management, new techniques and equipment.

770 US
CONCEPTUAL PEOPLE PHOTOGRAPHY. 1988. a. $22.95. Watson - Guptill Publications, 1515 Broadway, New York, NY 10036. TEL 212-764-7300. (Subscr. to: 1695 Oak St., Lakewood, NJ 08701. TEL 800-451-1741. FAX 908-363-0338) illus. **Document type**: trade publication.
  Description: Presents examples and ideas of innovative commercial photography of persons.

770 US
CONCEPTUAL STILL LIFE PHOTOGRAPHY. 1989. a. $22.95. Watson - Guptill Publications, 1515 Broadway, New York, NY 10036. TEL 212-764-7300. (Subscr. to: 1685 Oak St., Lakewood, NJ 08701. TEL 800-451-1741. FAX 908-363-0338) illus. **Document type**: trade publication.
  Description: Presents examples of and ideas for innovative commercial still-life photography.

770 UK
CONTEMPORARY PHOTOGRAPHERS.* 1982. quinquennial. $70. St. James Press, 2-6 Boundary Row, London SE1 8HO, England. TEL 212-674-5151. Ed.Bd.

770 070.49 340 SW ISSN 1102-4038
COPYRIGHT; tidskrift foer press- och dokumentaerfotografi. 1991. q. SEK 100 (effective 1991). Copyright, c/o P. Widing, Carl Larssonsg. 6A, S-412 72 Goeteborg, Sweden.

CORPORATE SHOWCASE; photography, illustration & graphic design. see *ART*

778.315 FR ISSN 0396-5791
COURRIER DE LA MICROCOPIE. (Text in French) 1976. m. 1050 F. Micro Journal, 11 rue de Provence, 75009 Paris, France. Ed. Jean-Jacques Maleval. adv.; bk.rev. circ. 1,000.

770 UK ISSN 0011-0876
TR640
CREATIVE CAMERA. 1968. bi-m. $50 to individuals; institutions $70. C C Publishing, 5 Hoxton Sq., London N1 6NU, England. TEL 0171-713-0671. Ed. David Brittain. adv.; bk.rev.; illus. circ. 7,500. **Indexed**: Artbibl.Mod. **Document type**: academic/scholarly publication.
  —Faxon; SWETS; UnCover.
  Formerly: Camera Owner.
  Description: Contains news about photo-based artwork with news, reviews, portfolios, and features by influential writers.

CREATIVE SOURCE. see *ADVERTISING AND PUBLIC RELATIONS*

CREATIVE SOURCE AUSTRALIA; the wizards of Oz. see *ARTS AND HANDICRAFTS*

770 700 US
D B C C PHOTOGRAPHIC SOCIETY. NEWSLETTER. 1978. q. free. Dayton Beach Community College, Photo Society, 1200 Volusia Ave., Box 1111, Dayton Beach, FL 32014. TEL 904-254-3057. Ed. Ed Davenport. adv.; bk.rev. circ. 2,750.

770 DK ISSN 0901-7453
DANSK FOTOGRAFI. a. DKK 70. Selskabet for Dansk Fotografi - Society of Danish Photography, Kommenhaven 19, DK-2730 Herlev, Denmark. Ed. Fredde Hansen. adv. circ. 1,000.
  Formerly (until 1982): Selskabet for Dansk Fotografi - Aarskatalog (ISSN 0107-0363)

770 DK ISSN 0901-1668
DANSK FOTOGRAFISK TIDSSKRIFT. 1879. 4/yr. DKK 150. Dansk Fotografisk Forening, Bornholmsgade 1, DK-1266 Copenhagen K, Denmark. TEL 45-33-12-00-90. FAX 45-33-93-26-01. Ed. Keld Nielsen. adv.; bk.rev. circ. 850. **Indexed**: Photo.Ind.
  Formerly (until 1903): Beretninger fra Dansk Fotografisk Forening.

331.881 770 DK ISSN 0107-7112
DANSK GRAFIA. 1981. 26/yr. DKK 250. Grafisk Forbund, Grafisk Forbundshus, Lygten 16, DK-2400 Copenhagen NV, Denmark. FAX 45-35-82-02-07. Ed. Soeren Hoej. adv.; bk.rev.; illus. circ. 32,000.
  Former titles (until 1993): Medieforbundet Fotografisk Landsforbund. Medlemsavisen (ISSN 0905-1376); (until 1989): F L's Medlevsavis (ISSN 0107-7104)

770 US ISSN 0195-3850
TR287
DARKROOM & CREATIVE CAMERA TECHNIQUES. 1979. bi-m. $18.95. Preston Publications, Inc., 7800 N. Merrimac Ave., Niles, IL 60714. TEL 708-965-0566. FAX 708-965-7639. (Subscr. to: Box 585, Mt. Morris, IL 61054) Ed. Michael Johnson. adv.: B&W page $2375, color page $3655. bk.rev.; charts; illus.; stat. circ. 33,200. (back issues avail.) **Indexed**: Ind.How To Do It (1979-). —BLDSC (3533.740500); Faxon.
  Formerly: Darkroom Techniques.
  Description: Discusses photographic and darkroom equipment procedures and techniques for serious amateurs and professionals.

770 CC ISSN 0494-4372
DAZHONG SHEYING/POPULAR PHOTOGRAPHY. (Text in Chinese). m. $72.80. (Zhongguo Sheyingjia Xiehui - China Photographers' Association) Dazhong Sheying Zazhishe, 61 Hongxing Hutong, Dongdan, Beijing 100705, People's Republic of China. TEL 557378. (Dist. in US by: China Books & Periodicals, Inc., 2929 24th St., San Francisco, CA 94110. TEL 415-282-2994)

770 JA
DEJA-VU; a photography quarterly. (Text in Japanese) 1992. q. $110. Photo - Planete Co., Ltd., 3-21-14-402 Higashi, Shibuya-ku, Tokyo 150, Japan. Ed. Iizawa Kohtaro. adv.; illus.
  Description: Each issue focuses on one or two influential contemporary photographers.

DESIGN QUARTERLY. see *ARCHITECTURE*

DESIGNERS DIGEST; magazin fuer Gestaltung und Technik. see *ART*

770 SP ISSN 0212-8187
DIORAMA. 1984. 10/yr. 3500 ptas. (foreign 6425 ptas.) (effective 1995 & 1996). Ed. Alcocer de Castro, S.A., Tembleque 96, bajo C, 28024 Madrid, Spain. TEL 34-1-7192413. FAX 34-1-7192494. Ed. Jose Alcocer Saez. **Document type**: consumer publication.

DIRECT STOCK. see *ART*

DIRECTORY OF CONSUMER ELECTRONICS (YEAR); includes: photography, major appliance retailers & distributors. see *BUSINESS AND ECONOMICS — Trade And Industrial Directories*

770 FR ISSN 0419-5361
DOCUMENTATION PHOTOGRAPHIQUE. (Includes Dossiers and Cahiers de Diapositives) 1947. 6/yr. 530 F. (Europe 650 F., elsewhere 810 F.). Documentation Francaise, 29-31 Quai Voltaire, 75344 Paris Cedex 07, France. TEL 1-40-15-70-00. FAX 40-15-72-30. TELEX 215 666 DOCFRAN. (Subscr. to: 124 rue Henri Barbusse, 93308 Aubervilliers Cedex, France. TEL 48-39-56-00. FAX 48-39-56-01) bibl.; illus. circ. 15,000. (also avail. in microfiche from DFR) **Document type**: government publication.
  Description: Treats the themes of history and geography through a photographic view.

770 US ISSN 0896-0976
ELECTRONIC PHOTOGRAPHY NEWS. 1986. m. $90 (foreign $112). Photofinishing News, Inc., 10915 Bonita Beach Rd., Bonita Springs, FL 33923. TEL 813-992-4421. FAX 813-992-6328. Eds. Don Franz, John Larish. bk.rev.; charts; stat. circ. 400. (back issues avail.) **Document type**: newsletter, trade publication.

770 JA ISSN 0011-8478
ELECTROPHOTOGRAPHY/DENSHI SHASHINGAKKAISHI. (Text in Japanese; summaries in English) 1959. q. 8000 Yen. Society of Electrophotography of Japan - Denshi Shashin Gakkai, c/o Tokyo Institute of Polytechnics, 2-9-5 Honcho, Nakano-ku, Tokyo 164, Japan. TEL 03-3373-9576. FAX 03-3372-4414. Ed. Masaaki Yokoyama. adv.; charts; illus. circ. 1,500. **Indexed**: Chem.Abstr., INSPEC, JCT, JTA, Photo.Abstr.

770 UK
EUROPEAN PHOTOGRAPHY. 1981. a. £25. D & AD European Illustration, Nash House, 12 Carlton House Terrace, London SW1Y 5AH, England. Ed. Edward Booth-Clibborn. **Indexed**: Artbibl.Mod., Artbibl.

PHOTOGRAPHY

770   GW   ISSN 0172-7028
TR640
EUROPEAN PHOTOGRAPHY. (Text in English and German) 1980. s-a. DM.60 in Europe; elsewhere $40. Postfach 3043, 37020 Goettingen, Germany. TEL 0551-24820. FAX 0551-25224. Ed. Andreas Mueller-Pohle; Pub. Andreas Mueller-Pohle. adv. contact: Bernd Neubauer529. bk.rev.; bibl.; cum.index. circ. 4,800. (back issues avail.) Document type: consumer publication.
—Faxon.
   Description: International art magazine for contemporary photography and new media.

770.5   US   ISSN 0098-8863
TR1
EXPOSURE (DALLAS). 1963. s-a. $35 to institutions (foreign $50). Society for Photographic Education, Box 222116, Dallas, TX 75222-2116. TEL 817-273-2845. FAX 817-273-2846. Ed. Patricia Johnston. adv.: page $500; adv. contact: Blake Farley. bk.rev.; illus. circ. 1,700. (back issues avail.) Indexed: Artbibl.Mod., RILA. Document type: academic/scholarly publication.
—BLDSC (3843.374500); Faxon; UnCover.
   Description: Blends scholarly insight, historical perspective, critical dialogue, and educational issues of the study of photography.
   Refereed Serial

770 778.53   UK   ISSN 0950-737X
EYEPIECE. 1980. bi-m. £20 (overseas £35) (effective 1996). Guild of British Camera Technicians, 5-11 Taunton Rd., Metropolitan Centre, Greenford, Mddx. UB6 8UQ, England. TEL 0181-578-9243. FAX 0181-575-5972. Eds. Charles Hewitt, Kerry Ann Burrows. bk.rev. circ. 6,000. Indexed: Film Lit.Ind. (1985-). Document type: trade publication.

770 384.55   SP   ISSN 0214-2244
F V - FOTO VIDEO ACTUALIDAD. 1988. m. 5800 ptas. (Europe 11600 ptas.; elsewhere 14200 ptas.). Omnicon, S.A., Hierro, 9 3A - 7, 28045 Madrid, Spain. TEL 34-1-5278249. FAX 34-1-5281348. Dir. Juan M. Varela. adv.; bk.rev. circ. 25,000.
   Description: Covers all that pertains to Spanish photography and video. Informs on new techniques, products and applications.

770   BE
FEDERATION NATIONALE DES PHOTOGRAPHES PROFESSIONNELS PROFESSIONNELLE. REPORT MAGAZINE. bi-m. Federation Nationale des Photographes Professionnels Professionnelle, Rue des Boers 52A, B-1040 Brussels, Belgium.

770   UK
FINANCIAL SURVEY. COMPANY DATA FOR SUCCESS: PHOTOGRAPHIC EQUIPMENT MANUFACTURERS & DISTRIBUTORS. a. I C C Financial Surveys Ltd., Field House, 72 Oldfield Rd., Hampton, Mddx. TW12 2HQ, England. TEL 081-783-0977. FAX 081-783-1940. charts; stat. Document type: trade publication.
   Formerly (until 1991): Financial Survey Company Directory. Photographic Equipment Manufacturers and Distributors (ISSN 0951-7065)

770   SA   ISSN 0015-3494
FLASH. 1956. m. R.5. Pretoria Photographic Society, P.O. Box 3611, Pretoria 0001, South Africa. circ. 150.

770   NE   ISSN 0015-4997
                     CODEN: FOCUAL
FOCUS; maandblad voor fotografie en visuele communicatie. 1914. 11/yr. fl.99.50. Uitgeverij Focus, Postbus 15435, 1001 MK Amsterdam, Netherlands. TEL 31-20-6264353. FAX 31-20-6236049. adv.; bk.rev.; film rev.; illus.; index. circ. 23,500. Document type: trade publication.
—SWETS.

770   IE   ISSN 0790-4940
FOCUS.* 1979. irreg. Irish Professional Photographers Association, c/o 74 Stringhill Ave., Blackrock, Dublin, Ireland. Ed. Edward Moss. adv.; bk.rev.; illus. circ. 300.

770   NE   ISSN 0015-8682
FOTO; universeel tijdschrift voor fotografie. 1946. 10/yr. fl.93. Uitgeverij Foto, Postbus 3, 3830 AV Leusden, Netherlands. TEL 31-33-947200. FAX 31-33-652251. Ed. W. Broekman. adv.; bk.rev.; abstr.; illus.; index. circ. 15,500. Indexed: Excerp.Med., Photo.Abstr. Document type: consumer publication.
—SWETS.

770   HU   ISSN 0427-0576
FOTO. 1954. m. $30.50. Lapkiado Vallalat, Lenin korut 9-11, 1073 Budapest, Hungary. TEL 222-408. (Subscr. to: Kultura, Box 149, H-1389 Budapest, Hungary) adv.; illus.

770 778.59   SW
FOTO. 1992. m. SEK 410; newsstand price: SEK 39. Aller Specialtidningar AB, S-251 85 Helsingborg, Sweden. TEL 46-42-17-35-00. FAX 46-42-17-37-90. ED. Jan Almloef. adv.: B&W page SEK 19500, color page SEK 25500; trim 185 x 260; adv. contact: Lars Eric Brolin. circ. 31,900. cols./p.: 4; pp./issue: 108.
   Former titles: Aktuell Fotografi och Foto (ISSN 1103-0690); Formed by the merger of (1989-1992): Foto och Video (ISSN 1100-4673); (1972-1992): Aktuell Fotografi (ISSN 0345-0511)

770   DK   ISSN 0046-4775
FOTO-AVISEN.* 1962. q. DKK 12($2.) Foto-Avisen, Kallestrupvej 99, DK-9632 Moldrup, Denmark. TEL 06-69-20-41. FAX 86-69-19-21. Ed. Per Soerensen. adv.; bk.rev.

770   BL
FOTO - CINE. 1946. 6/yr. Foto - Cine Clube Bandeirante, Rua Jose Getulio 442, Caixa Postal 8861, CEP 01509 Sao Paulo SP, Brazil. Ed. Roberto B. Macedo. circ. 15,000.

770   SP
FOTO GALAXIS. (Text in English and Spanish) irreg. Galaxis, S.A., Zamora 46-48, Barcelona, Spain. illus.

FOTO-KINO REVIJA; jugoslovenski casopis za fotografijui amaterski film. see *MOTION PICTURES*

770   NE
FOTO MARKT; vakblad voor de foto-detailhandel, foto-snelservice, foto-vaklabs en vakfotografen. 1992. 11/yr. fl.65($50) (effective 1995). Foto Markt B.V., Postbus 27, 5427 ZG Boekel, Netherlands. TEL 31-4922-2505. Ed. Harry Putter. adv. contact: Harry Putter. bk.rev.; illus. circ. 5,600. Document type: trade publication.

770   IO   ISSN 0852-596X
FOTO MEDIA. 1990. m. $34.80. PT. Elex Media Komputindo, Jalan Palmerah Selatan 22, 6th Floor, Jakarta 10270, Indonesia. TEL 021-5483008. FAX 021-5486085. TELEX 46327 KOMPAS JKT. Agus Tjahjono W. circ. 10,000.

770   IT   ISSN 0015-8720
FOTO-NOTIZIARIO. 1946. w. free. Mediaspazio, Via M. Melloni, 17, 20129 Milan, Italy. TEL 02-718341. FAX 02-714067. Ed. Luciano Scattolin. adv.: color page L.3500000; adv. contact: Gisella Scatiolin. illus. circ. 14,000. Document type: trade publication.
   Description: Covers professional photography, videography and imaging. For professional photographers, photo shops and photofinishers.

770   AU
FOTO OBJEKTIV. 6/yr. Z B Verlag, Marschallplatz 23-1-21, A-1125 Vienna, Austria. TEL 01-8040474. FAX 01-8044439. Ed. G.K. Buchberger. circ. 14,200.

770   GW   ISSN 0943-1993
FOTO UND LABOR. 1980. 6/yr. DM.54; newsstand price: DM.10. Vereinigte Motor-Verlage GmbH und Co. KG, Leuschnerstr. 1, 70174 Stuttgart, Germany. TEL 0711-18201. FAX 0711-1821156. Ed. Michael Tafelmaier; Pub. Uwe Hagen. adv.: B&W page DM.8300, color page DM.14525; trim 185 x 248; adv. contact: Peter Michael Heyde. bk.rev. circ. 29,233. (back issues avail.) Document type: consumer publication.

770   SP
FOTO - VENTAS. 1978. 16/yr. 7500 ptas. Fopren S.L., Caspe 54 5o, 08010 Barcelona, Spain. TEL 93-301-28-89. FAX 93-412-53-75. Ed. Francisco Torres. adv.; circ. 5,000 (controlled). Document type: consumer publication.

770   BE   ISSN 0777-3625
FOTO VIDEO AUDIO NEWS. French edition: Photo Video Audio News (ISSN 0777-3641) (Text in Dutch) 1984. bi-m. free to qualified personnel. Mema N.V., Wielewaalstraat 20, B-2610 Wilrijk, Belgium. TEL 32-3-4480827. FAX 32-3-4480832. Ed. Piet Germeys. adv.: B&W page 36000 BEF, color page 60000 BEF; trim 210 x 297; adv. contact: Piet Germeys. illus.; circ. 6,000 (controlled). Document type: trade publication.
   Former titles (until 1989): Foto Film Video News (ISSN 0777-3617); Foto-Contact (ISSN 0772-5795)
   Description: Covers news and business developments of interest to all branches of the photo, video and audio trade, including retailers, film processors and photofinishing labs, photographers, manufacturers and importers.

770   NE   ISSN 0165-1692
FOTO VISIE; vakblad voor de fotodetailhandel, minilabs, etc. 1971. 11/yr. fl.69.50 (in Belgium 1250 BEF; elsewhere fl.133) (effective 1995). Blauw Media Fototijdschriften B.V., Postbus 1043, 3600 BA Maarsen, Netherlands. TEL 31-3465-74040. FAX 31-3465-76056. Ed. Johan Elzenga. adv.: B&W page fl.1795, color fl.4290; trim 215 x 285; adv. contact: Gerie Jansen. abstr.; illus.; mkt.; stat. circ. 5,100. Document type: trade publication.

770   AG   ISSN 0015-8771
FOTOCAMARA CON POPULAR PHOTOGRAPHY.* 1938. m. $5. (International Federation of Photographic Art, SZ) Editora Publicitaria S.A.C.I.F., Andreas Weichselbraun, Sec. Gen., Liechtensteinstr. 13, A - 1090 Vienna, Austria. Ed. Hector Y. Faita. illus.

770   IT
FOTOCINE 80. 1980. m. L.50000 (Europe L.90000; elsewhere L.100000). Societa Foto Editrice s.r.l., Via Giuseppe Ricciardi 28, 80142 Naples, Italy. TEL 39-81-2844228. FAX 39-81-5537522. Ed. Ettore Bernabo Silorata. adv.: B&W page L.2200000, color page L.3400000.

770   CN   ISSN 0318-7500
FOTOFLASH. vol.14, 1981. 4/yr. membership only. National Association for Photographic Art, c/o Bruce A. Blackburn, Pub. Mgr., 23 Latham Ave., Scarborough, Ont. M1N 1M7, Canada. circ. 2,800.

770   GW   ISSN 0720-5260
TR15
FOTOGESCHICHTE; Beitraege zur Geschichte und Aesthetik der Fotografie. 1981. q. DM.110 (foreign DM.122). Jonas Verlag, Weidenhaeuserstr. 88, 35037 Marburg, Germany. TEL 06421-25132. Ed. Timm Starl. bk.rev.; index. circ. 550. Document type: academic/scholarly publication.

770   TU   ISSN 1018-7901
FOTOGRAF. (Text in Turkish; contents page in English) 1978. 6/yr. TL.60000($36) Ankara Fotograf Sanatcilari Dernigli - Association of Fine Art Photographers of Ankara, PK 649 Kizilay, 06425 Ankara, Turkey. TEL 93-12-2300409. FAX 90-312-2294566. Ed. Tanju Akdeniz. adv.: B&W page $700; trim 200 x 270; adv. contact: Ms Mehtap Yildiz. bk.rev.; illus.; index. circ. 3,500.
   Description: Publishes profiles of photographers and their work, articles on art and photography, news and technical articles addressing recent advances in film or equipment.

777   IT
FOTOGRAFARE. 1967. m. L.50000 (foreign L.75000). Cesco Ciapanna Editore S.p.A., Via Lipari 8, 00141 Rome, Italy. TEL 39-6-87183441. FAX 39-6-87183995. Ed. Cesco Ciapanna. adv.: B&W page L.5700000, color page L.10000000. bk.rev. circ. 80,000.
   Formerly: Fotografare Novita.

770   SP
FOTOGRAFIA ACTUAL. 1989. 10/yr. 6000 ptas. (Europe 8500 ptas.; America $75; Canada $85; elsewhere 9500 ptas. ($83)) (effective 1996). Artual Ediciones S.L., C. Consell de Cent, 83, Entl. 3a, 08015 Barcelona, Spain. TEL 34-3-4264661. FAX 34-3-4269236. Ed. Francs Gori. adv.: B&W page 180000 ptas., color page 210000 ptas.; 245 x 330; adv. contact: Concepcion Alarcon. bk.rev. circ. 16,000. Document type: consumer publication.
   Formerly: Fotografia.

PHOTOGRAPHY

770   IT
FOTOGRAFIAMO. 1984. s-a. L.10000 per no. Societa Foto Editrice s.r.l., Via Giuseppe Ricciardi 28, 80142 Naples, Italy. TEL 39-81-5537518. FAX 39-81-5537522. adv.: B&W page L.1500000, color page L.2000000.

770   XR   ISSN 1211-0019
TR1
FOTOGRAFIE/PHOTOGRAPHY. (Text in Czech or Slovak; summaries in English, German, Russian) 1946. m. 24 Kc. (Spolecnost Pratel Fotografie) Ringier C.R., a.s., Domazlicka 3, 130 00 Prague 3, Czech Republic. TEL 42-2-6842658. FAX 42-2-6852660. Ed. Daniela Mrazkova. adv.; bk.rev.; charts; illus.; index. circ. 57,000.
—BLDSC (4024.592000).
Formerly: Ceskoslovenska Fotografie (ISSN 0009-0549)

770   GW   ISSN 0935-414X
FOTOGRAFIE DRAUSSEN; Erleben aus erster Hand. 1969. bi-m. DM.51 (foreign DM.56.20). Verlag Tecklenborg, Lindenstr. 4, 48565 Steinfurt, Germany. TEL 02552-3933. Ed. Hubert Tecklenborg. adv.; bk.rev.
Formerly: Tier und Naturfotografie.

770   SW   ISSN 0284-7035
FOTOGRAFISK TIDSKRIFT. Variant title: F. (Text in Swedish; summaries in English) 1888. 6/yr. SEK 350. Svenska Fotografernas Foerbund - Swedish Professional Photographers Association, Gotgatan 48, S-118 26 Stockholm, Sweden. TEL 46-8-6-418472. FAX 46-8-6406988. Ed. Goesta Flemming. adv.; bk.rev.; charts; illus.; tr.lit.; index. circ. 7,000. **Indexed:** Chem.Abstr.
Former titles (until 1988): Svensk Fotografisk Tidskrift (ISSN 0039-6540); (until 1916): Svenska Fotografen.

770   RU   ISSN 0869-4648
TR1
FOTOGRAFIYA. 1926. bi-m. $63 (effective 1996). M. Lubyanka 16, Tsentr, 101878 GSP Moscow, Russia. TEL 095-925-1014. FAX 095-200-4237. TELEX 411421 PERO SU. (Dist. in U.S. by: Victor Kamkin Inc., 4956 Boiling Brook Pkwy., Rockville, MD 20852. TEL 301-881-5973) Ed. G. Chudakov. adv.; bk.rev.; illus.; index. circ. 79,500. **Indexed:** Artbibl.Mod., Chem.Abstr., World Bibl.Soc.Sec.
—BLDSC (0391.788495).
Formerly (until 1992): Sovetskoe Foto (ISSN 0371-4284)

770   IT
FOTOGRAFO. 1992. m. L.55000 (foreign L.105000). Fotografo s.r.l., Via G.B. Pergolesi 8, 20124 Milan, Italy. TEL 39-2-66715150. FAX 39-2-66715171. Ed. Edo Prando; Pub. Gaetano Manti. adv.: color page L.7000000; adv. contact: Stafano Spagnolo. circ. 48,143. **Document type:** consumer publication.

770   NE   ISSN 0015-8852
FOTOHANDEL; vakblad voor de gfotohandel. 1929. 11/yr. fl.60. Uitgeverij Foto, Postbus 3, 3830 AV Leusden, Netherlands. TEL 31-33-947200. FAX 31-33-952251. Ed. F.D. Withoff. adv.; bk.rev.; abstr.; illus.; stat.; index. circ. 3,800. **Document type:** trade publication.

770   SZ
FOTOHEFT. m. Verlag Novapress, Schlagbaumstr. 6, Postfach 365, CH-8201 Schaffhausen, Switzerland. TEL 053-250003. FAX 053-254977. Ed. Joseph Neumann. circ. 20,000.

770   GW   ISSN 0015-8712
FOTOMAGAZIN. 1949. m. DM.86.40 (foreign DM.96). Ringier Verlag GmbH, Gustav-Heinemann-Ring 212, 81739 Munich, Germany. TEL 089-638180. FAX 089-63818100. Ed. Rainer Thiele. adv.: color page DM.19950. bk.rev.; illus.; index. circ. 77,568. **Document type:** consumer publication.

770 621.389   AG   ISSN 0325-7150
FOTOMUNDO. 1966. m. Ediciones Fotograficas Argentina S.A., Maipu 671, piso 5, 1006 Buenos Aires, Argentina. TEL 322-2006. Ed. Silvia Mangialardi. adv.; bk.rev.; illus. circ. 10,000. (back issues avail.)

770   HU   ISSN 0532-3010
TR640
FOTOMUVESZET. (Text in Hungarian; summaries in English) 1966. q. $26.50. (Magyar Fotomuveszek Szovetsege) Lapkiado Vallalat, Lenin korut 9-11, 1073 Budapest, Hungary. TEL 222-408. (Subscr. to: Kultura, Box 149, H-1389 Budapest, Hungary) Ed. Tamas Fener. circ. 3,500. **Indexed:** Lang.& Lang.Behav.Abstr.

770 791.43   VE   ISSN 0015-8895
FOTON; fotografia, cine y sonida (photography, amateur movie and sound). 1965. m. Bs.200($30) M.G. Ediciones Especializadas, S.A., Av. Maturin, No. 15, Urb. Los Cedros, El Bosque, Caracas 1050, Venezuela. Ed. Montserrat Giol. adv. circ. 4,500.

770   SW   ISSN 0015-8909
FOTONYHETERNA. 1961. 10/yr. SEK 398. P.O. Box 5111, 102 43 Stockholm, Sweden. Ed. Bjoern Sandels. adv.; bk.rev.; charts; illus.; mkt.; pat.; tr.lit. circ. 5,000.
Incorporating: Scandinavian Journal of Photography and Film.

770   IT
FOTOPRATICA IMMAGINI. 1968. bi-m. L.70000. Societa Editrice Fotografica, Via Ciro Menotti, 11, 20129 Milan, Italy. TEL 39-2-730162. FAX 39-2-714495. TELEX 320665 GIBI. (Subscr. to: Messaggerie Internazionali s.r.l., Via Rogoredo 55, Milan, Italy) Ed. Giambattista Bonato. adv.: B&W page L.3500000, color page L.6000000. bk.rev. circ. 50,000.
Formerly: Fotopratica.
Description: Covers photography, technical aspects, cultural events and more.

770   IT   ISSN 1121-726X
FOTOPRO. 1987. m. L.80000 (foreign L.150000). Editrice Reflex s.r.l., Via Di Villa Severini 54, 00191 Rome, Italy. TEL 39-6-3278595. FAX 39-6-3295648. adv.: B&W page L.2600000, color page L.4600000. circ. 18,000.
Formerly: Pro (ISSN 1120-4079)

770   NE   ISSN 0169-183X
FOTOPROF; zakenmagazine voor de professionele fotobranche. 1980. bi-m. newsstand price: fl.11.50. Business Publishers, Postbus 121, 5000 AC Tilburg, Netherlands. TEL 31-13-438220. FAX 31-13-430955. adv. contact: J.F.F.M. Maaskamp. **Document type:** trade publication.

770   CU
FOTOTECNICA. q. $8 in N. America; S. America $10; Europe $12; elsewhere $14. (Union de Periodistas de Cuba, Secretariado Ejecutivo) Ediciones Cubanas, Obispo No. 527, Apdo. 605, Havana, Cuba. illus.

770   GW   ISSN 0340-6644
FOTOWIRTSCHAFT; unabhaengiges Wirtschaftsmagazin der Fotobranche fuer Industrie, Handel, Handwerk. 1950. m. DM.132 (foreign DM.139.80). Ringier Verlag GmbH, Gustav-Heinemann-Ring 212, 81739 Munich, Germany. TEL 089-63818-0. FAX 089-63818100. Ed. Franz Raith. adv.: color page DM.6470. charts; illus.; mkt.; pat.; stat.; index. circ. 1,994. **Indexed:** Photo.Abstr. **Document type:** trade publication.
—SWETS.
Formerly: Fotohaendler (ISSN 0015-8844)

770   FR
FRANCE - PHOTOGRAPHIE. bi-m. 140 F. Federation Photographique, 9 rue Faraday, 75017 Paris, France. FAX 47-63-65-44. Ed. Jean Lamouret. adv.; bk.rev. circ. 5,000.

FREE-LANCE WRITING & PHOTOGRAPHY. see *JOURNALISM*

FREELANCE WRITER'S REPORT. see *JOURNALISM*

FUJIAN HUABAO/FUJIAN PICTORIAL. see *GENERAL INTEREST PERIODICALS — China*

GADNEY'S GUIDES TO INTERNATIONAL CONTESTS, FESTIVALS & GRANTS IN FILM & VIDEO, PHOTOGRAPHY, TV-RADIO BROADCASTING, WRITING & JOURNALISM. see *COMMUNICATIONS*

770   CC   ISSN 1000-3231
TR692   CODEN: GKKHE9
GANGUANG KEXUE YU GUANGHUAXUE/PHOTOGRAPHIC SCIENCE AND PHOTOCHEMISTRY. (Text in Chinese; summaries in English) 1983. q. $80.40. (Chinese Academy of Sciences, Institute of Photographic Chemistry) Science Press, Marketing and Sales Department, 16 Donghuangchenggen North St., Beijing 100717, People's Republic of China. TEL 4010642. FAX 4019810. (Co-sponsor: Chinese Society of Photographic Science and Engineering (CSPSE)) Ed. Ren Xinmin. adv. circ. 11,000. **Document type:** academic/scholarly publication.
—BLDSC (6471.800000); CASDDS.
Description: Covers photochemical imaging systems, exposure and development mechanisms, image structure and evaluation, sensitometry of photographic materials, organic photochemistry, photochemistry of polymers, photobiochemistry, photoelectrochemistry at interface, and photocatalysis.
Refereed Serial

GANSU HUABAO/GANSU PICTORIAL. see *GENERAL INTEREST PERIODICALS — China*

770   IT   ISSN 0393-0785
GAZZETTA DELLA FOTOGRAFIA. 1923. m. Via Principe Granatelli 96, 90139 Palermo, Italy. Ed. Franco Randazzo.

778   US
GEORGE EASTMAN HOUSE - INTERNATIONAL MUSEUM OF PHOTOGRAPHY AND FILM. ANNUAL REPORT. a. membership. George Eastman House - International Museum of Photography and Film, 900 East Ave., Rochester, NY 14607. TEL 716-271-3361. FAX 716-271-3970. **Document type:** corporate report.

770   US
TR1
GEORGE EASTMAN HOUSE - INTERNATIONAL MUSEUM OF PHOTOGRAPHY AND FILM. NEWSLETTER. 1952. bi-m. membership. George Eastman House - International Museum of Photography and Film, 900 East Ave., Rochester, NY 14607-2298. TEL 716-271-3361. FAX 716-271-3970. Ed. Karen Kahler-Jensen. circ. 3,800. **Document type:** newsletter.
Formerly: International Museum of Photography at George Eastman House. Newsletter (ISSN 1055-3886)

770 659   SZ   ISSN 1016-0507
TR690.A1
GRAPHIS PHOTO; international annual of photography. (Text in English, French, German) 1966. a. 123 Fr.($69) B. Martin Pedersen Graphis Press Corp, Dufourstr. 107, CH-8008 Zurich, Switzerland. (Dist. in the U.S. by: Watson-Guptill Publications, 1695 Oak St., Lakewood, NJ 08701. TEL 800-451-1741. FAX 908-363-0338) Ed. B. Martin Pedersen. index. circ. 12,500.
—BLDSC (4212.529250).
Formerly: Photographis (ISSN 0079-1830)

GRAPHIS POSTERS; international annual of poster art. see *ART*

770   SA   ISSN 1021-9161
GREAT PHOTO & VIDEO. 1991. m. Promedia Publications, P.O. Box 255, Silverton 0127, South Africa. adv.; illus. **Document type:** consumer publication.
Formerly (until 1993): Great Photography and Video (ISSN 1017-2335)

770   US
GREEN BOOK (NEW YORK); the directory of natural history and general stock photography. biennial. $30 (free to qualified personnel). A G Editions, Inc., 41 Union Sq., W., Ste. 523, New York, NY 10003-3208. TEL 212-929-0959. FAX 212-924-4796. Ed. Ann Guilfoyle. **Document type:** directory.
Description: Directory of photo sources for editorial photo buyers. Features description of stock files and cross-referenced natural history, general stock and geographic indexes.

GUANGDONG HUABAO/GUANGDONG PICTORIAL. see *GENERAL INTEREST PERIODICALS — China*

5178 PHOTOGRAPHY

770   US   ISSN 0889-8235
GUILFOYLE REPORT. 8/yr. $125. A G Editions, Inc., 41 Union Sq., Ste. 523, New York, NY 10003-3208. TEL 212-929-0959. FAX 212-924-4796. Ed. Ann Guilfoyle. **Document type:** newsletter, trade publication.
   Description: For natural history photographers. Identifies buyers and their photo needs; discusses equipment, pricing, and professional practices.

770   GR   ISSN 1011-1638
HELLENIC PHOTOGRAPHY SELECTIONS. (Text in English, Greek) 1989. q. Dr.4000($24) (Hellenic Centre of Photography) Moressopoulos & Associates, Ltd., 19 Iperidou, 105 58 Athens, Greece. TEL 30-1-323-4217. FAX 30-1-323-2082. (Subscr. to: P.O. Box 30 501, 100 33 Athens, Greece) Ed. Stavros Moressopoulos. adv. circ. 7,000. (back issues avail.) **Document type:** monographic series.
   Description: Photographic art magazine presenting eight contemporary Greek photographers in each issue. Includes essays and information on events.

HENAN HUABAO. see GENERAL INTEREST PERIODICALS — China

770   UK   ISSN 0308-7298
TR15
HISTORY OF PHOTOGRAPHY; an international journal. 1976. q. £105($175) (effective 1996). Taylor & Francis Ltd., Rankine Rd., Basingstoke, Hants. RG24 8PR, England. TEL 44-1256-840366. FAX 44-1256-479438. TELEX 858540. E-mail: info@tandf.co.uk. (Subscr. in N. America to: Taylor & Francis Inc., 1900 Frost Rd., Ste. 101, Bristol, PA 19007-1598. TEL 800-821-8312. FAX 215-785-5515) Ed. M.L. Weaver. adv.; bk.rev. Indexed: Artbibl., Arts & Hum.Cit.Ind., Avery Ind.Archit.Per., Curr.Cont., RILA. **Document type:** academic/scholarly publication.
   —BLDSC (4318.395000); Faxon; Genuine Article; SWETS; UnCover. **CCC.**
   Description: Devoted to the history and early development of this graphic art form. Covers the earliest uses of photography in exploration, science and war, lives of notable practitioners and inventors; the influence of photography on painting and sculpture; history of photojournalism; and the preservation and restoration of old photographs.
   Refereed Serial

HORIZONTES (PATERSON). see LITERATURE

770   UK   ISSN 0959-6933
TR690
HOTSHOE INTERNATIONAL; the magazine for today's professional photographer. 1980. q. £19.50($52.50) Creative Magazines Ltd., 35 Britannia Row, London N1 8QH, England. TEL 0171-226-1739. FAX 0171-226-1540. Ed. Tim Rich; Pub. Robert T. Prior. adv.: page £945; trim 297 x 210; adv. contact: Robert T. Prior. bk.rev.; software rev.; illus. circ. 6,000. (back issues avail.) Indexed: DAAI. **Document type:** trade publication.
   Formerly: Hot Shoe (ISSN 0260-5783)
   Description: Directed to the advertising, design, and corporate photographer.

770   FR
I R I S. (International Research for Image Selection) q. free. 7 place Saint-Sulpice, 75006 Paris, France. TEL 43-25-33-33. FAX 43-25-88-88.

770   AT   ISSN 0728-5701
IMAGE. 1964. bi-m. Aus.$24 (foreign Aus.$30). Australian Photographic Society, Inc., P.O. Box 53, Hackett, A.C.T. 2602, Australia. TEL 06-2574814. Ed. Max Leonard. adv.; bk.rev. circ. 1,200.
   Description: Contains photographs, articles about photography and society news and information.

770   SA
IMAGE. (Text in Afrikaanns and English) m. (except Dec.). Photographic Society of Southern Africa, P.O. Box 370, Edenvale 1610, South Africa. adv.

770   UK
IMAGE (LONDON). 1969. m. £24 (foreign £40). Association of Fashion, Advertising & Editorial Photographers, 9-10 Domingo St., London EC1Y 0TA, England. TEL 071-608-1441. FAX 071-253-3007. Ed. Jackie Kelley. adv.; bk.rev. circ. 2,500.

770   US   ISSN 0536-5465
TR1
IMAGE (ROCHESTER, 1952); journal of photography and motion pictures. 1952. 2/yr. $40 membership (foreign $50). George Eastman House - International Museum of Photography and Film, 900 East Ave., Rochester, NY 14607. TEL 716-271-3361. FAX 716-271-3970. Ed. Marianne Fulton. illus. circ. 3,000. (back issues avail.) Indexed: Art.Ind., Film Lit.Ind. (1987-). **Document type:** academic/scholarly publication.
   —Faxon; Genuine Article; UMI; UnCover.
   Description: Presents scholarly essays and reproductions covering the scsience, history and art of photography and film.

770   US   ISSN 0893-1925
IMAGING ON CAMPUS. 1987. 6/yr. Executive Business Media, Inc., 825 Old Country Rd., Box 1500, Westbury, NY 11590. TEL 516-334-3030. Ed. Barry Tenenbaum. adv. circ. 85,000.

770   II
INDIAN JOURNAL OF MEDICAL PHOTOGRAPHY. (Text in English) 1965. q. Rs.6. Biological Photographic Association, Indian Chapter, 10-D Medical Enclave, Patiala, Punjab, India.

770   II
INDIAN JOURNAL OF PHOTOGRAPHY. (Text in English) 1966. m. 6-12-A Band Stand Area, Delhi 110009, India. Ed. Raj Monga. adv.; bk.rev. circ. 5,000.

770 700   GW   ISSN 0947-8418
▼**INFOFAX: FOTOGRAFIE.** 1994. fortn. Verlag Brigitte Tast, Laaseweg 4, 31174 Schellerten, Germany. TEL 05123-4330. FAX 05123-2015. Ed. Hans-Juergen Tast. bk.rev. (looseleaf format; back issues avail.) **Document type:** bulletin.

770   GW   ISSN 0019-0179
INPHO. 1962. fortn. DM.172. (Bundesverband des Deutschen Fototechhandels e.V.) G F W Verlag GmbH, Volmerswertherstr. 20, 40221 Duesseldorf, Germany. TEL 0211-39009-0. Ed. Volker Storck. adv.; bk.rev.; illus.; stat. circ. 7,000. **Document type:** trade publication.
   —SWETS.

770   AU   ISSN 0020-1707
INPHO OESTERREICH. 1967. m. S.308. (Oesterreichischer Fotohaendlerverband) Verlag die Galerie GmbH, Linke Wienzeile 36, A-1060 Vienna, Austria. TEL 0222-587-1078. FAX 0222-587-5524. Ed. Walter Kristof. adv.; bk.rev.; illus. circ. 2,000.

770   GW   ISSN 0174-6944
INSTANT. 1978. irreg. DM.120 per 12 issues. Trust Corporate Culture, Hanauer Landstr. 139-145, 60314 Frankfurt a.M., Germany. FAX 069-40578599. Eds. Franz Aumueller, Thomas Feicht. adv.; bk.rev. circ. 20,000. (back issues avail.) **Document type:** consumer publication.

771   UK   ISSN 0260-9363
INSTANT RECORD. 1980. 3/yr. free to qualified personnel. Polaroid (U.K.) Ltd., Ashley Rd., St. Albans, Herts. AL1 5PR, England. TEL 01727-78209. FAX 01727-69335. TELEX 263246. Ed. Pat Wallace. illus. circ. 25,000.

778.3   US   ISSN 1063-7478
TR661
INTERNATIONAL ASSOCIATION OF PANORAMIC PHOTOGRAPHERS. bi-m. International Association of Panoramic Photographers, 1739 Limewood La., Orlando, FL 32818.

770   GW   ISSN 0939-8619
INTERNATIONAL CONTACT - PHOTO, VIDEO, LAB TECHNOLOGY; independent journal for the international photographic market. 1982. bi-m. $44. C.A.T. Verlag, Freiligrathring 18-20, 40832 Ratingen, Germany. TEL 02102-26096. FAX 02102-21892. Ed. Thomas Bloemer. adv.; bk.rev.; charts; stat. circ. 8,700. (back issues avail.) **Document type:** trade publication.

770   US   ISSN 0020-8299
INTERNATIONAL PHOTOGRAPHER. 1929. m. $24 (foreign $50). c/o Local 659, 7715 Sunset Blvd., Ste. 300, Hollywood, CA 90046. TEL 213-876-0160. FAX 213-876-6383. (Subscr. to: International Photographer, Box 931659, Los Angeles, CA 90046-1659) Ed. George Dibie. adv.: B&W page $1691, color page $2584; trim 7 x 10. bk.rev.; bibl.; illus. circ. 11,500. Indexed: Chem.Abstr. **Document type:** trade publication.
   Description: Written by professionals for professionals, covering cinematography and video techniques.

770 778.53   BL   ISSN 0103-0132
IRIS; a revista que e a sua imagem. Variant title: IrisFoto. 1947. m. Cr.$78000($65) Editora Iris Ltda., Rua Jacucaim 67, Caixa Postal 1704, 04563-020 Sao Paulo, SP, Brazil. TEL 531-1299. FAX 531-1627. Ed. Silvia H. de Azevedo Marques Pilz. adv.; bk.rev. circ. 120,000.

ISLAND (LANTZVILLE). see LITERATURE

770   IT   ISSN 0535-9031
ITALIA; rivista di documentazione fotografica. 1953. q. L.20000 (foreign L.24000). Redazione Vita Italiana, Via Po, 14-16-A, 00198 Rome, Italy. TEL 4745506.

771   JA   ISSN 0021-4345
JAPAN CAMERA TRADE NEWS; monthly information on photographic products, optical instruments and accessories. (Text in English) 1950. m. $130. Genyosha Publications, Inc., 8-7, Shibuya 2-chome, Shibuya-ku, Tokyo 150, Japan. TEL 03-3407-7521. FAX 03-3407-7902. Ed. K. Eda. adv.; bk.rev.; illus.; stat. circ. 9,234. (tabloid format)

JINRI SHENGHUO/TODAY'S LIFE. see GENERAL INTEREST PERIODICALS — China

THE JOURNAL (COLUMBUS). see LITERATURE

JOURNAL OF BIOLOGICAL PHOTOGRAPHY. see BIOLOGY

614.19   US
JOURNAL OF EVIDENCE PHOTOGRAPHY. Variant title: E P I C Journal. 1968. s-a. Evidence Photographers International Council, 600 Main St., Honesdale, PA 18431. TEL 717-253-5450. FAX 717-253-5011. Ed. Kris Ammerman-Scofield. adv.: page $250. circ. 2,500. (also avail. in microform from UMI; reprint service avail. from UMI)
   Description: Features articles advancing knowledge in the field of forensic photography.

770 620   US   ISSN 1062-3701
TR1   CODEN: JIMTE6
JOURNAL OF IMAGING SCIENCE AND TECHNOLOGY. 1950. bi-m. $120 (foreign $135). Society for Imaging Science and Technology, 7003 Kilworth Ln., Springfield, VA 22151. TEL 703-642-9090. FAX 703-642-9094. Ed. Vivian K. Walworth. adv.; bk.rev.; abstr.; bibl.; charts; illus.; pat.; stat.; tr.lit.; index. circ. 3,500. (also avail. in microform from UMI; reprint service avail. from UMI) Indexed: Art & Archaeol.Tech.Abstr., ASCA, Chem.Abstr., Curr.Cont., INSPEC, Print.Abstr.
   —BLDSC (5004.556900); CASDDS; Ei; Faxon; Genuine Article; SWETS; UMI; UnCover. **CCC.**
   Formed by the 1991 merger of: Journal of Imaging Technology (ISSN 0747-3583); (1985-1991): Journal of Imaging Science (ISSN 8750-9237); Which was formerly (until 1984): Photographic Science and Engineering (ISSN 0031-8760); (until 1983): Journal of Applied Photographic Engineering (ISSN 0098-7298); (until 1957): Photographic Engineering (ISSN 0554-1085)
   Description: Covers a broad range of research, development, and applications in imaging.
   Refereed Serial

PHOTOGRAPHY 5179

740 US ISSN 0863-0453
TR280 CODEN: JIRMEA
JOURNAL OF INFORMATION RECORDING MATERIALS.
(Text in English and German; summaries in English, German, Russian) 1973. bi-m. 116 ECU (effective 1996). (Photochemisches Kombinat Wolfen) Gordon & Breach Science Publishers, c/o International Publishers Distributor, 820 Town Center Dr., Langhorne, PA 19047. TEL 215-750-2642. FAX 215-750-6343. (Subscr. to: International Publishers Distributor, P.O. Box 90, Reading, Berkshire RG1 8JL, England. TEL 44-173-456-8316) Ed. K. Stopperka. adv.; bk.rev.; charts; illus.; index. **Indexed:** Chem.Abstr., Curr.Cont., INIS Atomind., INSPEC, Phys.Ber.
— BLDSC (5006.772500); CASDDS. **CCC.**
Formerly: Journal fuer Signalaufzeichnungsmaterialien (ISSN 0323-598X)

778.315 JA ISSN 0287-6655
JOURNAL OF MICROGRAPHICS/MAIKURO SHASHIN.*
(Text in Japanese) 1962. m. 3600 Yen($65) Japan Microphotography Association - Nihon Maikuro Shashin Kyokai, 2nd Ohkouchi Bldg., 1-9-15 Kaji-Machi, Chiyoda-Ku, Tokyo 101, Japan. Ed. Tokuchika Ochiai. adv.; charts; illus.; mkt.; stat.; cum.index. circ. 3,500. (also avail. in microfiche)
Formerly: Journal of Micrography (ISSN 0026-2811)

JOURNAL OF PHOTOCHEMISTRY AND PHOTOBIOLOGY, A: CHEMISTRY; an international journal devoted to the study of the quantitative and qualitative aspects of photochemistry and energy transfer. see *CHEMISTRY — Physical Chemistry*

770 UK ISSN 0022-3638
TR1 CODEN: JPTSAF
JOURNAL OF PHOTOGRAPHIC SCIENCE. 1953. bi-m. £84 (foreign £94). The Barn, Whitehall, Near Middle Marwood, Barnstaple, N. Devon EX31 4EQ, England. TEL 01271-72482. FAX 01271-24716. Ed. Michael Austin. adv. contact: R. Green. bk.rev.; bibl.; charts; illus.; index. circ. 2,000. **Indexed:** Art & Archaeol.Tech.Abstr., Br.Tech.Ind., Cadscan, Chem.Abstr., Curr.Cont., Deep Sea Res.& Oceanogr.Abstr., Graph.Arts Lit.Abstr., Ind.Sci.Rev., INIS Atomind., INSPEC, Lead Abstr., Photo.Abstr., Print.Abstr., Zincscan. **Document type:** academic/scholarly publication.
— BLDSC (5035.000000); CASDDS; Ei; Faxon; Genuine Article; SWETS; UnCover.
Description: Features original papers in physics and chemistry on photographic processes, and on the technology of imaging systems and their applications.
Refereed Serial

JUMP CUT; a review of contemporary media. see *MOTION PICTURES*

770 FI ISSN 0022-8133
KAMERALEHTI. 1950. 11/yr. FIM 395. Kameraseura r.y., Malminrinne 1 B 31, FIN-Helsinki, Finland. FAX -358-0-694-0077. Ed. Pekka Punkari. adv.; bk.rev.; index. circ. 13,029.

KARTOGRAPHISCHE NACHRICHTEN. see *GEOGRAPHY*

770 UK ISSN 1352-6588
KEY NOTE REPORT: CAMERAS & CAMCORDERS. Variant title: Cameras & Camcorders. irreg. £185. Key Note Publications Ltd., Field House, 72 Oldfield Rd., Hampton, Middlesex TW12 2HQ, England. TEL 0181-783-0755. FAX 0181-783-1720. **Document type:** trade publication.
• Also available online.
Also available on CD-ROM.
— BLDSC (3016.178800).

770 UK
▼**KEY NOTE REPORT: PHOTOGRAPHIC SERVICES.** Variant title: Photographic Services. 1995. irreg. £185. Key Note Publications Ltd., Field House, 72 Oldfield Rd., Hampton, Middlesex TW12 2HQ, England. TEL 0181-783-0755. FAX 0181-783-1720. Ed. Anthony Doyle. **Document type:** trade publication.
• Also available online.
Also available on CD-ROM.

770 338.025 US ISSN 1067-9839
TR690.4
KLIK! SHOWCASE PHOTOGRAPHY. 1977. a. $45. American Showcase Inc., 915 Broadway, 14th Fl., New York, NY 10010. TEL 212-637-6600. FAX 212-673-9795. (Dist. in the U.S. by: Watson-Guptill Publications, 1695 Oak St., Lakewood, NJ 08701. TEL 1-800-451-1741. FAX 908-363-0338; Overseas & Canada: Rotovision S.A., Route Suisse 9, CH-1295 Mies, Switzerland. TEL 41-22755-3055)
Formerly: American Showcase Photography (ISSN 0278-8314); Supersedes in part (in 1982): American Showcase (ISSN 0742-6100)
Description: With more than 1,200 images in award-winning four-color reproduction, KSP provides visual solutions for every conceivable creative challenge. Also includes names and addresses for more than 10,000 photographers, reps, stock photo agencies and film-photo support services, arranged topically and by region for easy access.

KRONIKA; casopis za Slovensko krajevno zgodovino. see *HISTORY — History Of Europe*

LAKE SUPERIOR MAGAZINE. see *HISTORY — History Of North And South America*

770 GW ISSN 0024-0621
TR1
LEICA-FOTOGRAFIE INTERNATIONAL; Zeitschrift der Kleinbildfotografie. French edition (ISSN 0174-0261); English edition (ISSN 0174-0253) (Editions in English, French and German) 1949. 8/yr. DM.57.60. (Leica Camera GmbH) Umschau Zeitschriftenverlag Breidenstein GmbH, Stuttgarterstr. 18-24, 60329 Frankfurt a.M., Germany. TEL 069-2600-0. FAX 069-2600619. Ed. Heiner Henninges. adv.; B&W page DM.5135, color page DM.8987; adv. contact: Barbara Eckert. bk.rev.; bibl.; charts; illus.; index. circ. 18,500. (back issues avail.) **Indexed:** Chem.Abstr. **Document type:** consumer publication.
— CCC.

770 IE
LENS. 1925. bi-m. membership. Photographic Society of Ireland, 38-39 Parnell Sq., Dublin, Ireland. Ed. Joseph Webb. adv. circ. 600.

770 US
LIGHT AND SHADE. 1916. 9/yr. $40. Pictorial Photographers of America, 299 W. 12 St., New York, NY 10014. Ed. Sylvia Mavis. bk.rev. circ. 100. (looseleaf format; back issues avail.) **Document type:** newsletter.

LIGHTWORKS; illuminating thresholds of new art. see *ART*

770 US ISSN 1049-4812
LINKED RING LETTER. 1990. q. $15 (foreign $30). Consultant Press, Ltd., 163 Amsterdam Ave., No.201, New York, NY 10023. TEL 212-838-8640. FAX 212-873-7065. Ed. Robert S. Persky. adv. contact: Lesli Li. bk.rev. circ. 25,000. **Document type:** newsletter.
Description: For photographers who exhibit and sell fine art photography.

770 MX ISSN 0188-8005
TR640
LUNA CORNEA. q. Mex.$100 (foreign $50). Consejo Nacional para la Cultura y las Artes, Av. Revolucion 1500, Col. Guadalupe Inn, 01020 Mexico DF, Mexico. Ed. Patricia Gola; Pub. Pablo Ortiz Monasterio.

770 791.43 GW ISSN 0941-7818
M F M FOTOTECHNIK. 1953. m. DM.97.80 (foreign DM.133.80). (Deutsches Institut fuer Normung e.V., Fachnormenausschuss Bild und Film) A.G.T. Verlag Thum GmbH, Postfach 109, 71601 Ludwigsburg, Germany. TEL 07141-223156. FAX 07141-223131. Ed. Wolfgang J. Schaezler. circ. 8,067. **Document type:** consumer publication.
— SWETS.
Formerly: M F M - Moderne Fototechnik (ISSN 0024-8142)
Description: Covers all fields of applied photographic, film and AV technology.

770 PL ISSN 0324-8453
MAGAZYN FOTOGRAFICZNY FOTO. Variant title: Foto. 1953. m. $33. P.O. Box 29, 02-363 Warsaw, Poland. TEL 48-22-659-7419. (Dist. by: Ars Polona-Ruch, Krakowskie Przedmiescie 7, Warsaw, Poland) Ed. Pawel Kazimierczak. adv.; bk.rev.; abstr.; illus.; index. circ. 30,000.
— BLDSC (4024.440000).
Formerly: Fotografia (ISSN 0015-8801)

770 UK
MASTER PIECE. British Amateur Photographers Association, 110 Weston St., Sheffield, S. Yorks. S3 7NQ, England. TEL 0742-724726. FAX 0742-739478. adv.; bk.rev.; film rev.; charts; illus. (back issues avail.)
Description: Covers all aspects of photography including theory and practice, as well as membership news, schedule of competitions, various activities, and merchandising campaigns.

770 GW ISSN 0945-0335
MEDIEN UND SCHULPRAXIS. 1993. q. DM.22. (Bundesgremium fuer Schulphotographie) Juenger Verlag, Schumannstr. 161, 63069 Offenbach a.M., Germany. TEL 069-840003-0. TELEX 4152889-JUED. Ed. M. Huschner. adv.; bk.rev.; illus. circ. 5,000.
Formed by the merger of (1981-1992): SchulPraxis (ISSN 0720-8634); (1988-1992): Medien Aktiv (ISSN 0936-9767); Which was formerly (1962-1988): Kamera und Schule (ISSN 0022-8109); SchulPraxis was formed by the merger of (1974-1980): Schul- und Unterrichts Organisation (ISSN 0342-7714) & (1968-1980): Neue Unterrichtspraxis (ISSN 0342-9865).

778.35 FR ISSN 0076-6364
MEMOIRES DE PHOTO-INTERPRETATION. 1963. irreg., no.7, 1970. price varies. (Ecole Pratique des Hautes Etudes) Librairie Touzot, 38 rue Saint Sulpice, 75278 Paris Cedex 06, France. **Indexed:** GeoRef.

778.315 UK
MICROGRAPHICS AND OPTICAL STORAGE BUYER'S GUIDE. 1981. a. £10. G.G. Baker & Associates, c/o Alan Armstrong & Assoc. Ltd., 72 Park Rd., London NW1 4SH, England. adv.; illus. circ. 1,000.
Formerly: Micrographics Year Book (ISSN 0260-7069)

MIDLAND REVIEW. see *LITERATURE*

770 US
MINI LAB FOCUS. m. membership only. Photo Marketing Association International, 3000 Picture Pl., Jackson, MI 49201. TEL 517-788-8100. FAX 517-788-8371. circ. 3,800. (back issues avail.) **Document type:** trade publication.

771 US ISSN 1052-4142
MINILAB DEVELOPMENTS. 1986. bi-m. free. International Minilab Association, Inc., 2627 Grimsley St., Greensboro, NC 27403. TEL 919-854-8088. FAX 919-854-8566. Ed. Bess Lewis; Pub. Roger McManus. adv. contact: Susan Smoot. circ. 15,466. **Document type:** trade publication.
Description: Focuses on how to maintain and build the success of the minilab (on-site retail photofinishing outlet) industry.

771 UK ISSN 0968-6312
MINILAB DEVELOPMENTS. 1993. bi-m. £24.95. Professional & Trade Publications Ltd., 46 Ford End, Woodford Green, Essex IG8 0EG, England. TEL 0181-506-1011. Ed. Stephen Webb. adv.; B&W page £1024, color page £1318; trim 297 x 207; adv. contact: Barry Wadsworth-Smith. bk.rev.; circ. 5,000. (back issues avail.) **Document type:** trade publication.

770 UK
MINOLTA IMAGE. q. Maxwell Lane, Kelso, Roxburghshire TD5 7BB, England. TEL 0573-26032. FAX 0573-26000. Ed. D. Kilpatrick. circ. 13,000.

MINZU HUABAO/NATIONALITY PICTORIAL. see *ETHNIC INTERESTS*

THE MONOCACY VALLEY REVIEW. see *LITERATURE*

5180 PHOTOGRAPHY

770   NE
MONOGRAFIEEN VAN NEDERLANDSE FOTOGRAFEN. 1993. irreg. (Prins Bernhard Fonds) Fragment Uitgeverij, Lindengracht 168, 1015 KL Amsterdam, Netherlands. TEL 31-20-6267133. FAX 31-20-6207989. **Document type:** monographic series.
    Description: Publishes studies devoted to the work of notable Dutch photographers.

770 791.4   DK   ISSN 0904-2334
TR640
MUSEET FOR FOTOKUNST. KATALOG; kvartaltidsskrift for fotografi - quarterly magazine for photography. (Text in Danish, English) 1988. q. DKK 275($47) to individuals; institutions DKK 300 or $50. (Museet for Fotokunst) Forlaget Brandts Klaedefabrik, Brandts Passage 37 & 43, DK-5000 Odense C, Denmark. TEL 45-66137816. FAX 45-66137310. E-mail: mffkmffk@inet.uni-c.dk. (Co-sponsor: Brandts Klaedefabrik) Eds. Henning Hansen, Finn Thrane. adv. contact: Henning Hansen. bk.rev.; illus.; index. circ. 1,800. (back issues avail.). **Document type:** academic/scholarly publication, catalog, newsletter.
    Description: Features portfolios, critical and biographical essays, reviews, calendars of exhibitions and events.

771   US
N A P E T NEWS. q. membership only. (National Association of Photo Equipment Technicians) Photo Marketing Association International, 3000 Picture Pl., Jackson, MI 49201. TEL 517-788-8100. FAX 517-788-8371. circ. 700. (back issues avail.) **Document type:** trade publication.

770   US
N T I S ALERTS: PHOTOGRAPHY & RECORDING DEVICES. w. $140 (outside N. America $195). U.S. National Technical Information Service, 5285 Port Royal Rd., Springfield, VA 22161. TEL 703-487-4650. FAX 703-321-8547. TELEX 64617. bibl. **Document type:** abstracting/indexing, government publication.

770   UK   ISSN 0956-9502
NATURE PHOTOGRAPHY;* animals plants landscapes. a. Fountain Press Ltd., Queensborough House 2, Claremont Rd., Surbiton, Surrey KT6 4QU, England.
    Description: International coverage of nature photographers' works.

770   UK   ISSN 0143-036X
TR505
NEW MAGIC LANTERN JOURNAL. 1978. irreg. £2.50 per issue. Magic Lantern Society of Great Britain, 61 Desford Rd., Newbold Verdon, Leicester LE9 9LG, England. TEL 01455-823952. Ed. David Robinson. adv. contact: John Finney. bk.rev.; illus. circ. 500. Indexed: Film Lit.Ind. (1991-). **Document type:** academic/scholarly publication.
    Description: Covers magic lantern and lantern slide related materials.

NEW ORLEANS REVIEW. see *LITERATURE*

NEW VIRGINIA REVIEW. see *LITERATURE*

770   NZ   ISSN 0114-4154
NEW ZEALAND PHOTOGRAPHY. 1988. m. Colour Workshop Ltd., P.O. Box 34-355 Birkenhead, Auckland 10, New Zealand. TEL 09-418-2502.

770   US   ISSN 0199-2422
TR820
NEWS PHOTOGRAPHER; dedicated to the service and advancement of news photography. 1946. m. $28 (foreign $44). National Press Photographers Association, Inc., 1446 Conneaut Ave., Bowling Green, OH 43402-2145. TEL 419-352-8175. FAX 419-354-5435. Ed. James Gordon. adv.: B&W page $1567, color page $2775; 8 1/4 x 11. bk.rev.; illus. circ. 11,500. (also avail. in microform from UMI; back issues avail.) Indexed: Graph.Arts Lit.Abstr. **Document type:** trade publication.
    ●Also available online. Vendor(s): University Microfilms International.
    —Faxon; UMI; UnCover.
    Formerly (until 1974): National Press Photographer (ISSN 0027-9935)
    Description: Presents articles, interviews, profiles, history, and news relating to still and television news photography. Discusses new products and related issues such as electronic imaging.

770   NE   ISSN 0927-8311
NIEUWSBRIEF NEDERLANDS FOTOARCHIEF. 1991. 3/yr. free. Nederlands Fotoarchief - Netherlands Photo Archives, Witte de Withstraat 63, 3012 BN Rotterdam, Netherlands. TEL 31-10-2330788. FAX 31-10-2140375. illus. **Document type:** newsletter.
    Description: News and information relating to the holdings of the archives (about 40 photographers), and other topics relating to the history of Dutch photography.

NIHON SHASHIN SOKURYO GAKKAI. GAKUJUTSU KOENKAI HAPPYO RONBUNSHU. see *GEOGRAPHY*

770   AT   ISSN 1038-9423
NOT ONLY BLACK AND WHITE. bi-m. $168. Studio Magazines Pty. Ltd., Level 3, 101-111 William St., Sydney, N.S.W. 2011, Australia. TEL 02-360-1422. FAX 02-360-9723. **Document type:** consumer publication.

770   CN   ISSN 0848-9807
NOUVEAU PHOTO SELECTION. (Text in French) 1981. 8/yr. Can.$23($33) (foreign $38). Apex Publications Inc., 185 rue St. Paul, Quebec, PQ G1K 3W2, Canada. TEL 418-692-2110. FAX 418-692-3392. Ed. Jacques Thibault; Pub. Curtis J. Sommerville. adv.: B&W page $2240, color page $3115; adv. contact: Denis Beaumont. bk.rev.; cum.index: 1981-1984. circ. 18,500. (back issues avail.)
    Formerly: Photo Selection (ISSN 0226-9708)

770 778.5   SP   ISSN 0210-8801
NUEVA LENTE; publicacion mensual de fotografia y cine. 1971. m. 2250 ptas. Miguel J. Goni Fernandez, Ed. & Pub., Ardemans 64, Madrid, Spain. circ. 10,000 (controlled).

770   US   ISSN 0887-5855
NUEVA LUZ. (Text in English, Spanish) 1984. 2/yr. $25 (foreign $35) to individuals; institutions $40 (foreign $45) (effective 1995). En Foco, Inc., 32 E. Kingsbridge Rd., Bronx, NY 10468. TEL 718-584-7718. Ed. Charles Biasiny. adv. contact: Miriam Romais. circ. 5,000. (back issues avail.) **Document type:** consumer publication.
    Description: Publishes portfolios of work by minority American photographers.

OASIS; mensile di natura, ecologia, fotografia e viaggi. see *CONSERVATION*

770   DK   ISSN 0107-6329
OBJEKTIV. 1976. 4/yr. $40. Dansk Fotohistorisk Selskab, c/o Flemming Berendt, Teglgaardsvej 308, 3050 Humlebaek, Denmark. adv.; bk.rev.; illus. circ. 400.

770 778.53   NO
OBJEKTIVET. q. NOK 405. Oslo Kamera Klubb, Postboks 5231, Majorstua, 0303 Oslo 3, Norway. adv.; bk.rev.

770   AU   ISSN 0048-1459
OESTERREICHISCHE FOTO-ZEITUNG;* fachblatt fuer Lichtbildner. 1952. m. S.180. Zeitungsverlag Kuhn und Co. GmbH, Kutschkergasse 42, A-1180 Vienna, Austria. Ed. Hans Hamann. adv.; bk.rev.; charts; illus.; tr.lit. circ. 4,000.

686.2 778.1   GW   ISSN 0030-0594
OFFSETPRAXIS; Europaeische Fachzeitschrift fuer Offset-, Kleinoffset-Druck, Reprofotographie und Fotosatz. 1958. m. (except Aug.) DM.90 (foreign DM.102). Fachschriften Verlag GmbH, Hoehenstr. 17, 70736 Fellbach, Germany. TEL 0711-5206-256. FAX 0711-5281424. Ed. Ottmar Strebel. **Document type:** trade publication.
    Description: Industry news about printing: type and printing technology, graphics, events and meetings.

770   US
ON COLLECTING PHOTOGRAPHS. 1983. every 5 yrs. $5. Association of International Photography Art Dealers, 1609 Connecticut Ave., N.W., Ste. 200, Washington, DC 20009. TEL 202-986-0105. FAX 202-986-0448. bibl.
    Description: A brief guide for beginning collectors.

OSNOVAC. see *ART*

770   US   ISSN 1058-7756
TR659.5
OUTDOOR & TRAVEL PHOTOGRAPHY. 1988. q. $3.95 per no. Harris Publications, Inc., 1115 Broadway, 8th fl., New York, NY 10010. TEL 212-807-7100. FAX 212-627-4678. circ. 62,321.
    Description: For the amateur photographer whose interests include travel and the great outdoors.

770   US   ISSN 0890-5304
OUTDOOR PHOTOGRAPHER. 1985. 10/yr. $21.95. Werner Publishing Corporation, 12121 Wilshire Blvd., Ste. 1220, Los Angeles, CA 90025-1175. TEL 310-820-1500. FAX 310-826-5008. adv.: B&W page $8440, color page $11740. circ. 200,000. **Document type:** consumer publication.
    —UnCover.

770   US   ISSN 0030-8277
P S A JOURNAL. 1934. m. $40 membership. Photographic Society of America, Inc., 3000 United Founders Blvd., No. 103, Oklahoma City, OK 73112-3940. TEL 405-843-1437. FAX 405-843-1438. E-mail: 74521,2414@compuserve.com. Ed. Dennis J. Ramsey. adv.: B&W page $1185, color page 2185; trim 8 1/2 x 11. abstr.; illus.; index; circ. 6,756 (paid). (also avail. in microform from UMI; reprint service avail. from UMI) Indexed: Bus.Ind., Chem.Abstr., Graph.Arts Lit.Abstr., Mag.Ind., Tr.& Indus.Ind. **Document type:** consumer publication.
    —Faxon; SWETS; UMI; UnCover.
    Description: Promotes the arts and sciences of photography in all its forms.

771   US   ISSN 1053-8968
P T N. (Includes P T N Master Buying Guide and Directory) 1937. 24/yr. $25. P T N Publishing Corp., 445 Broad Hollow Rd., Ste. 21, Melville, NY 11747-4722. TEL 516-845-2700. FAX 516-845-7109. adv.; bk.rev.; illus.; tr.lit. circ. 14,000. **Document type:** trade publication.
    Former titles (until 1989): Photographic Video Trade News (ISSN 1054-0601); (until 1987): Photographic Trade News (ISSN 0031-8779)

770   US
P T N MASTER BUYING GUIDE & DIRECTORY. (Photographic Trade News); main entrance to the retail photographic market. 1937. a. included with subscr. to Photographic Trade News. P T N Publishing Corp., 445 Broad Hollow Rd., Ste. 21, Melville, NY 11747-4722. TEL 516-845-2700. FAX 516-845-7109. Ed. Bill Schiffner. adv.; illus.; circ. 10,000 (controlled). **Document type:** directory.

770 301.412   US
P W P NEWSLETTER. 1984. bi-m. $25 in NYC; outside NYC $15. Professional Women Photographers, c/o Photographics Unlimited, 17 W. 17th St., New York, NY 10011-5510. Ed. Meryl Meisler. adv.; bk.rev. circ. 500. **Document type:** newspaper.
    Supersedes: P W P Times.

PALATINATE. see *LITERATURE*

770   NE   ISSN 0167-9104
PERSPEKTIEF; quarterly for photography. (Text in Dutch and English) 1980. 2/yr. fl.90 for 4 issues (Europe $58; elsewhere $68) (effective 1995-1996). Stichting Perspektief Magazine, Sint Jobsweg 30, 3024 EJ Rotterdam, Netherlands. TEL 31-10-4765208. FAX 31-10-4769069. E-mail: paradox@knoware.nl. (Co-publisher: Voetnoot Publishers) Ed. Bas Vroege. adv.: B&W page fl.1500; trim 240 x 285. bk.rev.; bibl.; illus.; stat. circ. 3,000. Indexed: Artbibl.Mod.
    —SWETS.
    Description: Publishes articles concerning creative photography, theoretical issues and portfolios.

770   US   ISSN 0199-4913
PETERSEN'S PHOTOGRAPHIC. 1971. m. $19.94. Petersen Publishing Co., 6420 Wilshire Blvd., Los Angeles, CA 90048. TEL 213-782-2000; 800-800-3686. FAX 213-782-2465. (Subscr. to: Box 50004, Boulder, CO 80323) Ed. Jenni Bidner. adv.: B&W page $7575, color page $12880. bk.rev.; charts; illus.; stat.; index. circ. 209,000. (also avail. in microform from UMI; back issues avail.) **Indexed:** Bk.Rev.Ind. (1978-), Child.Bk.Rev.Ind. (1978-), Consum.Ind., Ind.How To Do It (1978-), Mag.Ind., P.M.I., R.G. **Document type:** consumer publication.
●Also available online. Vendor(s): Knight-Ridder, Inc. —BLDSC (6430.165000); Faxon; SWETS; UMI; UnCover.
Former titles (until 1979): Petersen's PhotoGraphic Magazine (ISSN 0048-3583); Photographic Quarterly.

770   FR   ISSN 0151-783X
PHOT'ARGUS (EDITION PROFESSIONNELLE). 1965. 8/yr. 330 F. Editions V.M., 116 bd. Malesherbes, 75017 Paris, France. TEL 42-27-25-44. FAX 47-66-57-74. Ed. Jean-Paul Chantry. adv.; illus.

770   FR
PHOTO. 1960. 8/yr. 200 F. (foreign 375 F.) (effective 1995). Publications Filipacchi, 63 Champs-Elysees, 75306 Paris, France. TEL 40-74-70-00. TELEX 651 294. (Subscr. to: 99 rue d'Amsterdam, 75008 Paris, France. TEL 42-80-68-55) Ed. Michel Decron. illus. circ. 191,908. **Document type:** consumer publication.

770   UK   ISSN 1354-7011
TR1
PHOTO (YEAR). (Supplement to: British Journal of Photography (ISSN 0007-1196)) 1964. a. £19.95. (Kodak) Bouverie Publishing Company Ltd., 147-151 Temple Chambers, Temple Ave., London EC47 0DT, England. TEL 0171-583-3030. FAX 0171-583-4068. Ed. C. Dickie. adv.; index. circ. 4,000. (also avail. in microfilm from WMP) **Document type:** trade publication.
Formerly (until 1992): British Journal of Photography Annual (ISSN 0068-2217)

771 778.59   AT   ISSN 1036-384X
PHOTO & VIDEO RETAILER. 1951. m. Aus.$42 (foreign Aus.$115)(effective Feb. 1995). Yaffa Publishing Group, 17-21 Bellevue St., Surry Hills, N.S.W. 2010, Australia. TEL 02-281-2333. FAX 02-281-2750. Ed. Margaret Brown. adv.: B&W page Aus.$1050, color page Aus.$1620; trim 297 x 210. illus. circ. 2,379. **Document type:** trade publication.
Former titles (until 1991): Photo Retailer (ISSN 0816-1909); (until 1985): Photo Trade News (ISSN 0031-8590)
Description: Source of product information for the photo-finishing trade and the camcorder-video market.

770   UK   ISSN 0956-8719
PHOTO ANSWERS. 1964. m. £24 (foreign £38.20) (effective 1995-1996). E M A P - Apex, Tower House, Sovereign Park, Lathkill St., Market Harborough, Leics. LE16 9EF, England. TEL 01858-468811. FAX 01858-432164. adv.; bk.rev.; charts; illus.; index. circ. 67,694. (also avail. in microform from UMI) **Document type:** consumer publication.
Incorporates: Camera (ISSN 0144-1248); Creative Photography; Camera User; S L R Photography (ISSN 0269-1272); Which was formerly: S L R Camera (ISSN 0036-1631)

770 791.43   SZ
PHOTO-CINE-EXPERT (1979); la revue suisse au service des photographes et cineastes. 1940. 9/yr. 55 Fr. Editions Jean Spinatsch SA, 13, route de Bellebouche, CH-1246 Corsier-Geneva, Switzerland. Ed. Jean Spinatsch. adv.; bk.rev.; illus. circ. 8,500.
Former titles: Nouveau Photo-Cine-Expert; Photo-Cine-Expert (ISSN 0031-8450)

770   US   ISSN 1075-4466
TR147
PHOTO COMPETITION U S A; a cute magazine for amateur photographers. 1992. q. $16 (outside U.S. $25) (effective 1995). 3900 Ford Rd., No. 18Q, Philadelphia, PA 19131-2047. TEL 215-878-1307. Ed. Allan K. Marshall. adv.: B&W or color page $3100; trim 8 3/8 x 10 7/8; adv. contact: Allan K. Marshall. bk.rev.; illus.; circ. 35,000 (paid). **Document type:** consumer publication.
Description: Publishes prizewinning photographs from amateurs all over the world, and general and non-technical articles on photography. Sponsors 5 competitions (general, thematic, photo-essay, art and cover-girl) in each issue.

770   US   ISSN 0888-5680
TR640
PHOTO DESIGN. 1984. bi-m. $42. B P I Communications, Inc. (New York), 1515 Broadway, New York, NY 10036. TEL 212-764-7300; 800-344-7119. FAX 212-944-1710. circ. 28,000. —UMI.
Description: For creative professionals, advertising, editorial and corporate communications.

770   GW
PHOTO DESIGN UND TECHNIK. 1986. 12/yr. Verlag Design und Technik GmbH, A.-Paul-Weber-Str. 5, 21493 Schretstaken, Germany. circ. 25,000. (back issues avail.)

770   CN   ISSN 0843-6029
PHOTO DIGEST. 1990. 8/yr. Can.$23($28) (foreign $38). Apex Publishers Inc. (Toronto), Toronto-Dominion Centre, Ste. 2550, P.O. Box 77, Toronto, ON M5K 1E7, Canada. TEL 416-287-6357. FAX 416-287-6359. E-mail: 76743,3210@compuserve.com. Ed. Jacques Thibault. adv.: B&W page Can.$4520, color page Can.$6295; adv. contact: Denis Beaumont. circ. 39,500. **Document type:** consumer publication.

770   US
PHOTO DISTRICT NEWS. 1980. m. $36 (Canada $76; elsewhere $111). B P I Communications, Inc. (New York), 1515 Broadway, New York, NY 10036. TEL 212-764-7300; 800-344-7119. FAX 212-944-1719. circ. 20,000 (controlled). **Document type:** trade publication.
Description: Educates and informs the reader on all phases of professional photography.

770   FR
PHOTO ECHOS. 21/yr. Editions du Gaillard, 29 rue de la Fontaine-au-Roi, 75011 Paris, France. TEL 43-38-99-77. FAX 43-38-50-13. circ. 7,000.

771   US   ISSN 1060-4936
TR1   CODEN: PELIE6
PHOTO ELECTRONIC IMAGING; the magazine for photographic, electronic imaging & graphics professionals. 1958. m. $18 (Canada $28; elsewhere $45). Professional Photography of America, 57 Forsyth St., N.W., Ste. 1600, Atlanta, GA 30303. Ed. Kim Brody; Pub. Andrew Foster. adv.: B&W page $4950; adv. contact: Donna McMahon. bk.rev.; charts; illus.; tr.lit.; index. circ. 48,000. (also avail. in microform from UMI; reprint service avail.) **Indexed:** Art & Archaeol.Tech.Abstr., Graph.Arts Lit.Abstr., Ind.How To Do It (1971-), PROMT. **Document type:** trade publication.
—SWETS; UMI; UnCover.
Former titles (until 1991): Photomethods (ISSN 0146-0153); (until 1974): Photomethods for Industry (ISSN 0030-8110)

PHOTO INTERPRETATION; images aeriennes et spatiales. see *GEOGRAPHY*

770   IT
PHOTO ITALIA. m. L.115000 in Europe; America L.160000. Publimedia Societa Editrice, Corso Venezia 18, 20121 Milan, Italy. TEL 02-77521. FAX 02-781068. Ed. Francesco Buffa di Perrero. adv. circ. 75,000.
Formerly: Photo Italiana.

771   US   ISSN 0884-9528
PHOTO-LAB INDEX; cumulative formulary of standard recommended photographic procedures. 1939. a. (q. updates) $69 ($30 for supplements; foreign $33). Morgan & Morgan Inc., 145 Palisade St., Dobbs Ferry, NY 10522. TEL 914-693-0023. FAX 914-693-1572. Ed. Liliane Morgan. charts; index, cum.index. circ. 8,000. (looseleaf format)

771 658   US   ISSN 0164-4769
TR287
PHOTO LAB MANAGEMENT. 1979. m. $15. P L M Publishing, 1312 Lincoln Blvd., Box 1700, Santa Monica, CA 90406. TEL 310-451-1344. FAX 310-395-9058. Ed. Carolyn Ryan. adv.: B&W page $2880, color page $3900. bibl.; charts; illus.; stat.; tr.lit. circ. 18,150. (back issues avail.) **Document type:** trade publication.

770   US
PHOTO LETTER.* 1980. s-a. $10. Texas Photographic Society, Box 650170, Austin, TX 78765-0170. TEL 512-471-1976. Ed. Julie Newton. adv.; bk.rev. circ. 2,000.

770   CN   ISSN 0700-3021
PHOTO LIFE. 1976. 8/yr. Can.$19.95 (foreign $28.64). Camar Publications Ltd., 130 Spy Court, Markham, ON L3R 5H6, Canada. TEL 416-485-8440. FAX 416-475-9246. Ed. Jerry Kobalenko. adv.: B&W page $5175, color page $6950. bk.rev. circ. 36,000. **Indexed:** Can.B.P.I., CMI. **Document type:** consumer publication.
—Faxon.
Description: Features Canadian news, reviews of the latest equipment, tips and portfolios.

770   IT
PHOTO MADE IN ITALY. (Text in English) 1981. 4/yr. free. Mediaspazio, Via M. Melloni 17, 20129 Milan, Italy. TEL 39-2-718341. FAX 39-2-714067. Ed. Luciano Scattolin. adv.: color page L.4500000. circ. 9,000. **Document type:** trade publication.

771   US   ISSN 0031-8531
TR1
PHOTO MARKETING. 1924. m. membership only. Photo Marketing Association International, 3000 Picture Pl., Jackson, MI 49201. TEL 517-788-8100. FAX 517-788-8371. illus. circ. 22,500. (back issues avail.) **Indexed:** PROMT. **Document type:** trade publication.
—SWETS.

771   US
PHOTO MARKETING NEWSLINE. s-m. membership only. Photo Marketing Association International, 3000 Picture Pl., Jackson, MI 49201. TEL 517-788-8100. FAX 517-788-8371. circ. 13,400. (back issues avail.) **Document type:** trade publication.

770   US
PHOTO MERCHANDISING. m. 3004 Glenview Rd., Wilmette, IL 60091. TEL 708-256-6067. FAX 708-441-2264. Ed. Saran Hirscaman.

770   US   ISSN 0888-1138
PHOTO METRO MAGAZINE. 1982. 10/yr. $20. Photo Metro Magazine, 17 Tehama St., San Francisco, CA 94105-3109. TEL 415-243-9917. FAX 415-243-9919. E-mail: photometro@designlink.com. Ed. Henry Brimmer; Pub. Henry Brimmer. adv. contact: Erich Muller. circ. 15,000. **Document type:** consumer publication.

771   CN   ISSN 1188-5955
PHOTO RETAILER. 1992. 10/yr. Apex Publications Inc., 185 St. Paul, Quebec, PQ G1K 3W2, Canada. TEL 416-287-6357. FAX 416-287-6359. Ed. Don Long. adv.: B&W page Can.$1245, color page Can.$1735; trim 8 1/4 x 10 7/8; adv. contact: Denis Beaumont. circ. 6,058. **Document type:** trade publication.

770   US
THE PHOTO REVIEW. 1976. q. $28 (Canada $35; Europe & S. America $42; Australia $50) (effective 1995). Photo Review, 301 Hill Ave., Langhorne, PA 19047. TEL 215-757-8921. Ed. Stephen Perloff. adv.; bk.rev.; illus. circ. 2,500.
Formerly: Philadelphia Photo Review (ISSN 0363-6488)
Description: Contains critical reviews of exhibitions, essays, interviews, portfolios of photography and industry news.

PHOTOGRAPHY

770 US
PHOTO REVIEW NEWSLETTER. 1976. 8/yr. $25 includes Photo Review. Photo Review, 301 Hill Ave., Langhorne, PA 19047. Ed. Stephen Perloff. bk.rev. circ. 2,000. (back issues avail.) **Document type:** newsletter.
  Formerly: Philadelphia Photo Review Newsletter.
  Description: Photography exhibition listings for New York, Philadelphia, Baltimore, Washington, Pittsburgh; news and exhibition opportunities.

770 GW
PHOTO TECHNIK INTERNATIONAL. (Editions in English, German) 1954. bi-m. Rupert-Mayer-Str. 45, 81379 Munich, Germany. TEL 089-7231992. FAX 089-72492250. (U.S. subscr. to: H P Marketing Corp., 16 Chapin Road, Pine Brook, NJ 07058) Ed. Hans-Eberhard Hess; Pub. Hildrun Kerkmann. adv. contact: Gabriele Arndt. bk.rev.; charts; illus.; mkt.; tr.lit. circ. 26,748. Indexed: Photo.Abstr. **Document type:** consumer publication.
  —CCC.
  Formerly: International Photo Technik (ISSN 0020-8280).

770 BE ISSN 0777-3641
PHOTO VIDEO AUDIO NEWS. Dutch edition: Foto Video Audio News (ISSN 0777-3625) (Text in French) 1984. bi-m. free to qualified personnel. Mema N.V., Wielewaalstraat 20, B-2610 Wilrijk, Belgium. TEL 32-3-4480827. FAX 32-3-4480832. Ed. Piet Germeys. adv.: B&W page 36000 BEF, color page 60000 BEF; trim 210 x 297; adv. contact: Piet Germeys. illus.; circ. 6,000 (controlled). **Document type:** trade publication.
  Former titles (until 1989): Photo Film Video News (ISSN 0777-3633); Photo-Contact (ISSN 0772-5809)
  Description: Covers news and business developments of interest to all branches of the photo, video and audio trade, including retailers, film processing and photofinishing labs, photographers, manufacturers and importers.

770 SZ
PHOTO VIDEO EXPERT. 9/yr. Bellebouche 13, CH-1246 Corsier, Switzerland. TEL 022-7511653. FAX 022-7511871. Ed. Jean Spinatsch. circ. 7,500.

770 FR ISSN 0152-4119
PHOTO WORK. 1978. 4/yr. 126 rue des 3 Epis Katzenthal, 68230 Turckheim, France. TEL 89-27-26-48. FAX 89-27-37-27. Ed. Rene Ansel. circ. 10,000. **Document type:** academic/scholarly publication, consumer publication.

770 SZ
PHOTOAMATEUR. 6/yr. Postfach 870, CH-1212 Grand-Lancy, Switzerland. TEL 022-7944340. FAX 022-7944284. circ. 3,000.

770 US ISSN 0885-4270
PHOTOBULLETIN. Daily edition (ISSN 1054-0598) 1985. w. (d. also avail.). $540 ($660 for d. service). PhotoSource International, Pine Lake Farm, Osceola, WI 54020. TEL 715-248-3800. FAX 715-248-7394. TELEX 6511892053. Ed. Lori Johnson. circ. 227. **Document type:** newsletter.
  ●Also available online. Vendor(s): NewsNet (PB26).

770 US ISSN 1054-0598
PHOTOBULLETIN DAILY. Weekly edition (ISSN 0885-4270) 1992. d. $660. PhotoSource International, Pine Lake Farm, Osceola, WI 54020. TEL 715-248-3800. FAX 715-248-7394. Ed. Lori Johnson. circ. controlled. **Document type:** newsletter.
  ●Also available online.
  Description: Information resource for photographers and photobuyers.

770 AT ISSN 0811-0859
PHOTOFILE. 1982. 3/yr. Aus.$30 to individuals; institutions Aus.$40; foreign Aus.$50. Australian Centre for Photography, 257 Oxford St., Paddington, N.S.W. 2021, Australia. TEL 61-2-331-6253. FAX 61-2-331-6887. Ed. Jo Holder. adv.: B&W page $415; trim 215 x 160. bk.rev. circ. 5,000. (back issues avail.) **Document type:** academic/scholarly publication.
  Description: Covers photomedia in Australasia including new techniques in film, video and still photography.

770 US ISSN 0889-2393
PHOTOFINISHING NEWS LETTER. 1983. bi-w. $100 (foreign $125) (effective 1993). Photofinishing News, Inc., 10915 Bonita Beach Rd., Bonita Springs, FL 33923. TEL 813-992-4421. FAX 813-992-6328. Ed. Don Franz. bk.rev.; stat. circ. 500. (back issues avail.) **Document type:** newsletter.

770 US
PHOTOFOLIO; photography collectors' newsletter. 1979. q. $20. Photocollect, 740 West End Ave., New York, NY 10025. Ed. Alan Klotz. bk.rev. circ. 500. (back issues avail.)

PHOTOGRAMMETRIC ENGINEERING AND REMOTE SENSING. see GEOGRAPHY

PHOTOGRAMMETRIC RECORD. see GEOGRAPHY

770 AU
DER PHOTOGRAPH. 11/yr. (Landesinnung der Fotografen fuer Wien) Verlag fuer Photographische Literatur A. Barylli, Opernring 6, A-1010 Vienna, Austria. TEL 01-5128712. FAX 01-5137833. Ed. Andreas Barylli. adv.: B&W page S.9000; trim 185 x 265. circ. 2,600. **Document type:** trade publication.

790.132 332.67 US ISSN 0271-0838
PHOTOGRAPH COLLECTOR; for collectors, curators and dealers. 1980. m. $125. Consultant Press, Ltd., 163 Amsterdam Ave., No.201, New York, NY 10023. TEL 212-838-8640. FAX 212-873-7065. Ed. Robert S. Persky. adv. contact: Lesli Li. bk.rev. circ. 1,000. (looseleaf format; back issues avail.) **Document type:** newsletter.
  Description: For curators, dealers and collectors. Covers all aspects of collecting and selling collectible photographs. Provides information and news on dealer and collector activity, seminars, trade fairs, auctions, court cases.

770 US
PHOTOGRAPH COLLECTOR'S RESOURCE DIRECTORY. 1983. biennial. $24.95. Consultant Press, Ltd., 163 Amsterdam Ave., No.201, New York, NY 10023. TEL 212-838-8640. FAX 212-873-7065. Ed. Robert S. Persky. adv. contact: Lesli Li. **Document type:** directory.
  Description: Listing of galleries, museums and non-profit institutions that either exhibit, collect, or sell fine art photography. Additional sections list auction houses, photography publications, associations and organizations.

770 FR ISSN 0369-9560
PHOTOGRAPHE. 10/yr. 265 F. (foreign 440 F.). 103 bd. St. Michel, 75005 Paris, France. TEL 43-29-40-90. FAX 43-29-14-05. TELEX 204 012 CINEFRA. Ed. Bernard Perrine. adv. circ. 10,511. Indexed: Pt.de Rep.
  Description: Magazine for photography professionals in France.

770 UK ISSN 0031-8698
PHOTOGRAPHER. 1922. m. £33. (British Institute of Professional Photography) Icon Publications Ltd., Maxwell Ln., Kelso, Roxburyshire TD5 7BB, England. TEL 01573-226032. FAX 01573-226000. Ed. Christopher Wordsworth. adv.; bk.rev.; charts; film rev.; illus. circ. 10,266. **Document type:** trade publication.
  Formerly: Institute of Incorporated Photographers Record.
  Description: Magazine for professional photographers.

770 US ISSN 0194-5467
TR1
PHOTOGRAPHER'S FORUM. 1978. q. $12. Serbin Communications, Inc., 511 Olive St., Santa Barbara, CA 93101. Ed. Glen R. Serbin. adv.; bk.rev. circ. 12,000.
  —UnCover.
  Formerly: Student Forum.

770 US ISSN 0147-247X
TR12
PHOTOGRAPHER'S MARKET. 1979. a. $23.99. F & W Publications, Inc., 1507 Dana Ave., Cincinnati, OH 45207. TEL 513-531-2222. Ed. Michael Willins.
  —BLDSC (6468.870000).
  Description: Lists 2500 places to sell publicity, product, editorial, scenic, portrait, fashion, wildlife, audiovisual, sports and travel photos.

770 GR ISSN 0259-7349
PHOTOGRAPHIA. 1977. bi-m. Dr.4,000($24) Moressopoulos & Associates Ltd., 19 Iperidou, 105 58 Athens, Greece. TEL 30-1-323-4217. FAX 30-1-323-2082. (Subscr. to: P.O. Box 30 564, 100 33 Athens, Greece) Ed. Stavros Moressopoulos. adv.; bk.rev. circ. 15,000. (back issues avail.) **Document type:** consumer publication.
  Description: Photographic trade magazine for amateur photography.

770 GR
PHOTOGRAPHIA NEWS LINE. 1992. m. Dr.3600($18) Moressopoulos & Associates S.A., 19 Iperidou, 105 58 Athens, Greece. TEL 30-1-323-4217. FAX 30-1-323-2082. Ed. Spyros Papageorgiou. adv. (back issues avail.) **Document type:** newsletter.
  Description: Covers news, trends, and developments in photography and business information of interest to sales representatives, wholesalers, and distributors.

770 GR
PHOTOGRAPHIA PRO. 1992. q. Dr.3000($15) Moressopoulos & Associates Ltd., 19 Iperidou, 105 58 Athens, Greece. TEL 30-1-323-4217. FAX 30-1-323-2082. Ed. Spyros Papageorgiou. adv.; bk.rev. circ. 6,000. (back issues avail.) **Document type:** trade publication.
  Description: Photographic trade magazine for professional photography.

770 US ISSN 1053-7031
TR6.5
PHOTOGRAPHIC ART MARKET: AUCTION PRICES (YEAR). 1981. a. $49.95. Consultant Press, Ltd., 163 Amsterdam Ave., No.201, New York, NY 10023. TEL 212-838-8640. FAX 212-873-7065. Ed. Robert S. Persky. adv. contact: Lesli Li. circ. 1,000.
  Formerly: Photographic Art Market Auction Price Results and Analysis.
  Description: For collectors, dealers, curators, and appraisers for buying, selling, appraising, valuing a donation, insuring, or filing an insurance claim.

770 900 CN ISSN 0704-0024
PHOTOGRAPHIC CANADIANA. 1974. 5/yr. Can.$24($24) Photographic Historical Society of Canada, 1712 Avenue Rd., Box 54620, Toronto, ON M5M 4N5, Canada. TEL 416-662-0433. Ed. Everett Roseborough. bk.rev.; index; circ. 300 (paid). (back issues avail.) **Document type:** academic/scholarly publication.
  Description: Provides information on images, photographers, and hardware with an emphasis on Canadian content and perspective.

770 UK ISSN 0031-8736
TR1
PHOTOGRAPHIC JOURNAL. 1853. m. £53 (foreign £58). Royal Photographic Society of Great Britain, Acorn House, 74-94 Cherry Orchard Dr., Croydon CR0 6BA, England. TEL 081-681-8339. FAX 081-681-1880. Ed. Roy Green. adv.; bk.rev.; bibl.; charts; illus.; circ. 10,000 (controlled). (also avail. in microform from UMI; reprint service avail. from UMI) Indexed: Artbibl.Mod., Br.Tech.Ind., Chem.Abstr., Graph.Arts Lit.Abstr., World Surf.Coat.
  —BLDSC (6471.000000); Faxon; SWETS; UnCover.

771 US ISSN 0031-8744
PHOTOGRAPHIC PROCESSING. 1964. m. $40 (free to qualified personnel). P T N Publishing Corp., 445 Broad Hollow Rd., Ste. 21, Melville, NY 11747-4722. TEL 516-845-2700. FAX 516-845-7109. adv.; bk.rev.; charts; illus.; stat. circ. 20,025. Indexed: Graph.Arts Lit.Abstr. **Document type:** trade publication.
  —SWETS.

770 US
PHOTOGRAPHIC RESOURCE CENTER. NEWSLETTER. 1979. 9/yr. $30 membership. Photographic Resource Center, Boston University, 602 Commonwealth Ave., Boston, MA 02215-2503. TEL 617-353-0700. adv.; bk.rev. circ. 2,500. **Document type:** newsletter.

PHOTOGRAPHY

770 US
PHOTOGRAPHICA. 1969. 4/yr. $30 (foreign $40). American Photographic Historical Society, 1150 Sixth Ave., 3rd Fl., New York, NY 10036-2701. TEL 212-575-0483. Ed. George Gilbert. adv.; bk.rev.; illus.; circ. 500 (controlled). (also avail. in microform from WMP) **Document type:** bulletin.
Former titles (until 1987): Photograhica Journal; Photographica (ISSN 0090-2063)
Description: News and information on early photography.

770 SZ
PHOTOGRAPHIE. m. Verlag Novapress, Schlagbaumstr. 6, Postfach 365, CH-8201 Schaffhausen, Switzerland. TEL 053-250003. FAX 053-254977. Ed. Petra Olschewski. circ. 21,000.

770 FR
PHOTOGRAPHIE; l'information economique des professionnels photo-video. 10/yr. 425 F. (foreign 540 F.) E M P P S, 103 bd. Saint-Michel, 75005 Paris, France. TEL 43-29-40-90. FAX 43-29-14-05. TELEX 204 012. (Subscr. to: 90 rue de Flandre, 75947 Paris Cedex 19, France. TEL 44-89-44-89) Ed. Jean-Jacques Cagnart. adv. contact: Daniel Fallet. index. circ. 10,200. **Document type:** consumer publication.

770 BE ISSN 0777-3374
PHOTOGRAPHIE OUVERTE. 1979. bi-m. 400 BEF (foreign 1000 BEF). Musee de la Photographie, Ave. Paul Pastur 11, 6032 Charleroi - Mont-sur-Marchienne, Belgium. TEL 32-71435810. FAX 32-71-364645. Ed. Georges Vercheval. adv.; bk.rev. **Document type:** bulletin, newsletter.
Description: News of the museum's activities, exhibitions and collections, and information on notable exhibitions and festivals in Belgium and other countries.

770 US
PHOTOGRAPHY. 1990. q. $250. Devin - Adair Publishers, Inc., 6 N. Water St., Greenwich, CT 06830. TEL 203-531-7755. FAX 203-622-6688. Ed. W. Dows; Pub. Roger Greene. adv.; bk.rev.; circ. 4,800 (controlled). **Document type:** newsletter, bulletin.
Description: Covers new books on photography, reviews of exhibitions, photographers, photo reproduction, illustrations, auction results, gallery openings and international exhibits.

770 CN
PHOTOGRAPHY AT OPEN SPACE MONOGRAPHS. 1976. irreg. price varies. Photography at Open Space, 510 Fort St., Victoria, BC V8W 1E6, Canada. bk.rev. circ. 500.

770 JA
PHOTOGRAPHY IN JAPAN. (Text in Japanese) 1953. m. 200 Yen. Photographic Society of Japan - Nihon Shashin Kyokai, JCII Bldg., 1st Fl., 25, Ichiban-cho, Chiyoda-ku, Tokyo, Japan. FAX 03-5276-3586. Ed. Hatsuo Akiyama. adv.; bk.rev. circ. 1,000.

770 US ISSN 1040-0346
PHOTOGRAPHY IN NEW YORK. 1988. bi-m. $18 (Canada $25; elsewhere $30). Photography in New York, Inc., 64 W. 89th St., New York, NY 10024. TEL 212-787-0401. FAX 212-799-3054. Ed. Bill Mindlin. adv.; bk.rev. circ. 8,000. (back issues avail.)
Description: Presents a listing of gallery and museum exhibitions, dealers, and booksellers, as well as information about auctions, classes and workshops. Includes a calendar of events.

770 CN
PHOTOGRAPHY MONOGRAPH SERIES. 1978. irreg. Photography at Open Space, 510 Fort St., Victoria, BC V8W 1E6, Canada. circ. 600. **Document type:** monographic series.

770 US
PHOTOGRAPHY QUARTERLY; journal for photography and related arts. 1979. q. $25 (Canada and Mexico $40; elsewhere $45). Center for Photography at Woodstock, 59 Tinker St., Woodstock, NY 12498-9984. TEL 914-679-9957. Ed. Kathleen Kenyon. adv. contact: Lawrence Lewis. bk.rev. circ. 10,000. **Document type:** trade publication.
Formerly: Center Quarterly (ISSN 0890-4634)
Description: Contains articles on contemporary artists and diverse aesthetic concerns.

770 US
THE PHOTOGRAPHY SHOW. (year) membership directory and illustrated catalogue. a. $25. Association of International Photography Art Dealers, 1609 Connecticut Ave., N.W., Ste. 200, Washington, DC 20009. TEL 202-986-0105. FAX 202-986-0448. adv. contact: Mary Jane Appel. illus.; index. circ. 5,000. (back issues avail.) **Document type:** catalog, directory.
Description: Catalogs the association's annual event and lists members. Includes index of photographs represented by membership.

770 658.8 UK
PHOTOGRAPHY: THE INTERNATIONAL MARKET. (Subseries of: Market Direction reports) a. £1595($3190) (effective 1996). Euromonitor, 60-61 Britton St., London EC1M 5NA, England. TEL 0171-251-8024. FAX 0171-608-3149. (Addr. in N. America: Euromonitor International, 122 S. Michigan Ave., Ste. 1200, Chicago, IL 60603. TEL 312-922-1115. FAX 312-922-1157) (looseleaf format) **Document type:** trade publication.
●Also available online. **Vendor(s):** Data-Star, Knight-Ridder, Inc.
Description: Analyzes the market for camera equipment and accessories and film for France, Germany, Italy, Spain, the U.K., the U.S., and Japan.

770 UK ISSN 0079-1865
PHOTOGRAPHY YEAR BOOK.* 1937. a. £35. Fountain Press, Queeensborough House, 2 Claremont Rd., Surbotin, Surrey KT6 4QU, England. Ed. John Sanders. adv.
—BLDSC (6474.280000).

770 US ISSN 1047-661X
TR1
PHOTOINFO. 1989. q. PhotoInfo, Bailey Hill Box BCD, Bisbee, AZ 85603.

770 070.49 US ISSN 0893-5610
TR820
PHOTOJOURNALIST (NEWARK). 1969. a. $5.20. New Jersey Press Photographers Association, c/o New Jersey Newsphotos, Airport International Plaza, Rt. 1, Newark, NJ 07114. TEL 201-242-1111. Ed. Ray Fisk. adv. circ. 500.

770 US
PHOTOKINA NEWS. a. P T N Publishing Corp., 445 Broad Hollow Rd., Ste. 21, Melville, NY 11747-4722. TEL 516-845-2700. FAX 516-845-7109. circ. 30,000.

770 US ISSN 0190-1400
PHOTOLETTER. 1976. m. $110. PhotoSource International, Pine Lake Farm, Osceola, WI 54020. TEL 715-248-3800. FAX 715-248-7394. TELEX 6511892053. Ed. Lynette Layer. adv.; bk.rev.; tr.lit.; charts; index. circ. 1,850. (looseleaf format; back issues avail.) **Document type:** newsletter.
●Also available online. **Vendor(s):** NewsNet (PB12).
—CCC.

PHOTOMAGAZINE; magazine des photographes et cineastes amateurs. see *MOTION PICTURES*

770 US ISSN 0885-4262
PHOTOMARKET; PhotoSource International. 1984. s-m. $360. PhotoSource International, Pine Lake Farm, Osceola, WI 54020. TEL 715-248-3800. FAX 715-248-7394. TELEX 6511892053. Ed. Lori Johnson. index. circ. 595. (back issues avail.)
●Also available online. **Vendor(s):** NewsNet (PB17).
Description: Lists specific photographic needs of middle-range magazine and book publishers.

770 UK ISSN 1359-2769
PHOTON. 1989. q. £23.40 (foreign £36) (effective Jun. 1995). Icon Publications Ltd., Maxwell Ln., Kelso, Roxburghshire TD5 7BB, England. TEL 01573-226032. FAX 01573-226000. Ed. David Kilpatrick. adv.; bk.rev.; illus. circ. 10,000.
●Also available online.
Formerly (until Jun. 1995): Photo Pro (ISSN 0956-2745)

770 US
PHOTOPAPER. 1982. s-a. membership. Silver Eye Center for Photography, 1015 E. Carson St., Pittsburgh, PA 15203. TEL 412-431-1810. Ed. Marc Silverman. adv.: B&W page $400; trim 8 x 10 1/2; adv. contact: Jody Guy. bk.rev. circ. 2,000.
Description: Treats the aesthetic, political, social, and historical issues of photography for high-school to graduate school photographers.

770 US ISSN 1049-8974
PHOTOPRO. 1990. bi-m. $11.97. Patch Communications, 5211 S. Washington Ave., Titusville, FL 32780. TEL 407-268-5010. FAX 407-267-7216. Ed. David Brooks. adv.: B&W page $2995. circ. 45,000.
Description: Contains technical information and creative approaches for commercial, portrait, wedding, outdoor and other working professional photographers. Includes reports on lighting tests.

770 BE
PHOTOSCOOP; foto - video / photo - video. (Editions in Dutch, French) 1979; N.S. 1994. q. 300 BEF. Eder Editions, 1, Golden Hope, 1620 Drogenbos, Belgium. TEL 32-2-3782127. FAX 32-2-3783729. Ed. Raymond Naumann; Pub. Alain Mathieu. adv.: B&W page 63000 BEF, color page 74500 BEF. bk.rev.; illus. circ. 13,000. **Document type:** consumer publication.
Formerly (until Apr. 1994): Pictorial Magazine.

770 SP ISSN 0211-7029
PHOTOVISION. (Text in English, Spanish) 1981. 2/yr. 3000 ptas. (foreign $38) (effective 1995). Arte y Proyectos Editoriales, S.L., Apdo. 164, 41710 Utrera (Seville), Spain. TEL 95-486-28-95. Ed. Joan Fontcuberta; Pub. Ignacio Gonzalez. adv.; index every 6 nos. circ. 13,000. **Document type:** monographic series.
Description: Devoted to creative photography. Issues deal with historical and contemporary themes. Presents the work of international photographers and writers.
Refereed Serial

770 AT ISSN 0727-3959
PHOTOWORLD.* 1978. m. Aus.$2.95. Australian Hi-Fi & Specialist Magazines Group Pty. Ltd., P.O. Box 341, Mona Vale, N.S.W. 2103, Australia. TEL 02 913-1444. FAX 913-2342. Ed. Don Norris. adv. circ. 16,000.
Formerly: Photographic World.
Description: News about photographic equipment and technique travel plus photography.

770 US
PICTORIALIST. 1941. m. membership. Photo Pictorialists of Milwaukee, Inc., c/o Ed. Ronald M. Buege, 2909 S. 101 St., West Allis, WI 53227. circ. 75. (looseleaf format)

778.1 US
PICTURE PERFECT. 1990. bi-m. $24 (foreign $36). Aquino Productions, One Bank St., Ste. 201, Box 15760, Stamford, CT 06901-0760. TEL 203-967-9952. FAX 203-359-1546. Ed. Andres C. Aquino. adv.: B&W page $1400, color page $2800. circ. 51,000.
Description: For photographers and fashion buyers, and video, TV and film producers. Covers the creative aspects of fashion photography.

770 US ISSN 1066-2189
PICTURE THIS!; simple tips for better photos. q. $8.95 for ten issues to non-members. Pappas Communications Group, Inc., 771 Boston Poast Rd. E., Ste. 181, Marlborough, MA 01752. TEL 508-229-2550. FAX 508-229-2551. (And: 204E N. El Camino Real, Ste. 545, Encinitas, CA 92024, U.S.A.. TEL 619-633-1850. FAX 619-633-1390) Ed. Craig Patchett; Pub. Lee H. Pappas. adv. contact: Jane Holt Siedenburg. illus.

PIG IRON; the annual thematic anthology of contemporary literature. see *LITERATURE*

770 UK
PIXEL VIDEO & PHOTOGRAPHY. 37/yr. 36 Stoke Fields, Guildford, Surrey GU1 4LS, England. TEL 0483-505351. FAX 0483-505364. Ed. Dennis Taylor. circ. 3,000.

PHOTOGRAPHY

770 US ISSN 0032-4582
TR1
POPULAR PHOTOGRAPHY. 1937. m. $19.94 (foreign $27.94). Hachette Magazines, Inc., 1633 Broadway, New York, NY 10019. TEL 212-767-6000. (Subscr. to: Box 54912, Boulder, CO 80322. TEL 800-876-6636) Ed. Jason Schneider. adv.: B&W page $44880, color page $57920. bk.rev.; charts; illus.; mkt.; index. circ. 450,000. (also avail. in microform from UMI; reprint service avail. from UMI) **Indexed:** Acad.Ind., Art & Archaeol.Tech.Abstr., Artbibl.Mod., Bk.Rev.Ind. (1989-), Chem.Abstr., Child.Bk.Rev.Ind. (1989-), Consum.Ind., Film Lit.Ind. (1973-), Gdlns., Graph.Arts Lit.Abstr., Ind.How To Do It (1966-), Mag.Ind., P.M.I., PMR, R.G., TOM.
● Also available online. Vendor(s): Knight-Ridder, Inc., University Microfilms International.
—Faxon; UMI; UnCover.
Formerly (until 1955): Photography.

770 UK ISSN 0032-6445
PRACTICAL PHOTOGRAPHY. (Supplement avail.: Practical Video Photography (ISSN 0267-8462)) m. £26.40 (foreign £50.30) (effective 1995-1996). E M A P - Apex, Tower House, Sovereign Park, Lathkill St., Market Harborough, Leics. LE16 9EF, England. TEL 01858-468811. FAX 01858-432164. adv.; bk.rev.; charts; illus. circ. 101,000.
—BLDSC (6595.405000). **CCC.**
Formerly (until 1959): Popular Photography (British Edition).

770 DK ISSN 0908-9810
PRAKTISK FOTO. 1955. s-a. Specialbladsforlaget ApS, Finsensvej 80, DK-2000 Frederiksberg, Denmark. TEL 45-38-88-22-22. FAX 45-38-88-30-38. Ed. Finn Nesgaard. adv. contact: Joergen Hansen. circ. 30,000. **Document type:** consumer publication.
Formerly (until 1993): Kamera (ISSN 0022-8095)

PRESIDENT AND PLANNER. see *LAW — Civil Law*

770 US
PRICE GUIDE TO WALLACE NUTTING PICTURES. 1980. irreg., 4th ed., 1991. $14.95. Diamond Press, Box 2458, Doylestown, PA 18901. TEL 215-345-6094. FAX 215-345-6692. Pres. Michael Ivankouich.

PRINTSHOP. see *PRINTING*

770 UK ISSN 0144-509X
PROFESSIONAL PHOTOGRAPHER. 1961. m. £31.50. E M A P Vision Ltd., 19 Scarbrook Rd., Croydon, Surrey CR9 1QH, England. TEL 081-760-9690. FAX 081-681-1672. TELEX 946665. Ed. David Warr. adv.; bk.rev.; illus.; index. circ. 7,315. (also avail. in microform from UMI; reprint service avail. from UMI) **Indexed:** Agri.Eng.Abstr.
—BLDSC (6864.135000); SWETS; UMI. **CCC.**
Formerly: Industrial and Commercial Photographer (ISSN 0019-784X)

770 US ISSN 0033-0167
TR690
PROFESSIONAL PHOTOGRAPHER. 1907. m. $24.50. (Professional Photographers of America) P P A Publications and Events, Inc., 57 Forsyth St., N.W., No. 1600, Atlanta, GA 30303-2206. TEL 708-299-8161. FAX 708-299-1975. Ed. Alfred DeBat. adv.: B&W page $2515. bk.rev.; charts; illus.; index; circ. 31,000 (paid). (also avail. in microform from UMI; reprint service avail.) **Indexed:** Graph.Arts Lit.Abstr., Ind.How To Do It (1990-). **Document type:** trade publication.
—UMI; UnCover.
Formerly: National Photographer.

PROFESSIONAL PHOTOGRAPHER DIRECTORY AND BUYER'S GUIDE. see *BUSINESS AND ECONOMICS — Trade And Industrial Directories*

770 US
PROFESSIONAL PHOTOGRAPHIC EQUIPMENT DIRECTORY AND BUYING GUIDE. 1975. a. $20. P T N Publishing Corp., 445 Broad Hollow Rd., Ste. 21, Melville, NY 11747-4722. TEL 516-845-2700. FAX 516-845-7109. adv.; illus. **Document type:** directory.

770 AT ISSN 0159-8880
PROFESSIONAL PHOTOGRAPHY IN AUSTRALIA. 1949. m. Aus.$59 (foreign Aus.$69). Horwitz Publications Pty. Ltd., 55 Chandos St., St. Leonards, N.S.W. 2065, Australia. Ed. Paul Burrows. adv.; bk.rev. circ. 6,000. (back issues avail.) **Document type:** trade publication.
—CCC.
Formerly: I.A.P. Professional Photography in Australia (ISSN 0046-9742)
Description: News and views for professional photographers.

770 NE ISSN 0168-9991
PROFESSIONELE FOTOGRAFIE; vakblad voor fotografie en imaging. Key Title: X. Cover title: P - F. 1983. 9/yr. fl.116.75. P-F Publishing B.V., Postbus 318, 2280 AH Rijswijk, Netherlands. TEL 31-70-3941007. FAX 31-70-3938382. circ. 9,000. **Document type:** trade publication.
Incorporates (1991-1993): Professional Imaging (ISSN 0928-3846); Incorporates (1983-1984): F (Amsterdam) (ISSN 0168-0994)

770 791.4 GW ISSN 0721-9725
PROFIFOTO; magazine for professional photography and electronic imaging. 1969. bi-m. DM.75. (Arbeitskreis Werbe-, Mode- und Industriefotographie) G F W Verlag GmbH, Volmerswertherstr. 20, 40221 Duesseldorf, Germany. TEL 0211-39009-0. Ed. T. Gerwers. adv.; bk.rev.; illus.; tr.lit. circ. 17,000. **Document type:** trade publication.
Formerly: Fachkontakt (ISSN 0721-9709)

770 SA ISSN 0033-0329
PROFOTO. (Text in English, occasional articles in Afrikaans) 1964. bi-m. membership. South African Institute of Photographers, P.O. Box 18813, Hillbrow 2038, South Africa. Ed. J. J. Wessel. adv.; illus.; tr.lit.; circ. 650 (controlled).

770 IT ISSN 0033-0868
PROGRESSO FOTOGRAFICO. 1894. m. L.92000. Editrice Progresso s.r.l., Viale Piceno, 14, 20129 Milan, Italy. TEL 39-2-70002222. FAX 39-2-713030. adv.: B&W page L.4000000, color page L.6000000. bk.rev.; illus.; index. circ. 20,000. **Indexed:** Artbibl.Mod., Chem.Abstr. **Document type:** consumer publication.

RAILROAD PRESS. see *HOBBIES*

770 US ISSN 0033-9202
RANGEFINDER. 1952. m. $18. Rangefinder Publishing Co., Inc., 1312 Lincoln Blvd., Box 1703, Santa Monica, CA 90406. TEL 310-451-8506. FAX 310-395-9058. Ed. Karre Marino; Pub. Steve Sheanin. adv.: B&W page $6130, color page $7230; adv. contact: Jerry Goldstein. bk.rev.; index. circ. 50,500. **Indexed:** Graph.Arts Lit.Abstr., Ind.How To Do It (1990-), P.M.I. **Document type:** trade publication.

770 US ISSN 0891-5326
RE: VIEW. 1978. bi-m. membership. Friends of Photography, 250 Fourth St., San Francisco, CA 94103. TEL 415-495-7000. Ed. Michael Read. bk.rev.; illus. circ. 8,000. **Document type:** newsletter.
Formerly (until 1987): Friends of Photography. Newsletter (ISSN 0163-9552)
Description: Contains information about the field of creative photography and activities of the organization.

770 IT ISSN 0393-473X
REFLEX. 1980. m. L.55000. Editrice Reflex s.r.l., Via di Villa Severini 54, 00191 Rome, Italy. TEL 39-6-36308595. FAX 39-6-32-95-648. Ed. Giulio Forti. adv.: B&W page L.4500000, color page L.8100000. circ. 45,000.

771 IT
REFLEX FOTO MARKET. 1984. 3/yr. Editrice Reflex s.r.l., Via DiVilla Severini 54, 00101 Rome, Italy. TEL 39-6-36308595. Ed. Giulio Forti. adv.: B&W page L.1900000. circ. 45,000.

770 CC ISSN 1002-7211
RENXIANG SHEYING/PORTRAIT PHOTOGRAPHY. (Text in Chinese) 1983. bi-m. (Shangye-bu, Yinshi Fuwu-ju - Ministry of Commerce, Food Service Bureau) Renxiang Sheying Zazhishe, 45 Fuxingmennei Dajie, Beijing 100801, People's Republic of China. TEL 6011012. (Dist. overseas by: China Book Import & Export Corp., 16 Gongti Donglu, Chaoyang District, Beijing, P.R. China. TEL 5068031) Ed. Ji Yunbiao. adv. contact: Mu Xiuzhen. circ. 100,000.
Description: Studies the photographic techniques, and introduces cameras and other related euipments.

778.1 NE ISSN 0168-6542
REPEAT. 1972. q. (Genootschap voor Dokumentreproduktie) Drukkerij Veldwijk, Waddinxveen, Netherlands. Ed. A. Van Der Schee. bibl.; charts; illus.
—SWETS.
Formerly: Reproduktie (ISSN 0166-4905)

REPORTAGE; the international magazine of photojournalism. see *JOURNALISM*

REPRO BULLETIN. see *PRINTING*

778.315 FR ISSN 0245-3355
REPRODUIRE. 1981. m. 910 F. C I P Publication, 40 rue St. Anne, 75002 Paris, France. FAX 33-1-42-96-37-08. Ed. Christian Thiebaut. adv.; bk.rev. circ. 5,000.

778.1 GW
DER REPROGRAF. 1913. 5/yr. DM.100. Fachverband Reprografie e.V. Deutschland, An den Drei Steinen 23, 60435 Frankfurt a.M., Germany. TEL 069-541073. FAX 069-541016. Ed. Achim Carius. adv.: B&W page DM.1345, color page DM.2835. bk.rev. circ. 1,500. **Document type:** bulletin.

770 384.55 SP
REVISTA FOTO. 1983. 12/yr. 7000 ptas. (Europe 14000 ptas., elsewhere 16000 ptas.) (effective 1995). Revista Foto, S.L., Real, 22, 28230 Las Rozas (Madrid), Spain. TEL 34-1-636-79-48. FAX 34-1-636-16-65. Ed. Manuel Lopez. adv.: B&W page 218000 ptas., color page 320000 ptas.; 285 x 210. bk.rev. circ. 24,000. **Document type:** trade publication.
Formerly: Foto Professional (ISSN 0211-9552)
Description: Covers photography and video.

770 US
S P F E NEWSLETTER. m. membership only. (Society of Photo Finishing Engineers) Photo Marketing Association International, 3000 Picture Pl., Jackson, MI 49201. TEL 517-788-8100. FAX 517-788-8371. circ. 1,000. (back issues avail.) **Document type:** newsletter.

770 620 001.644
535 US
S P S E ANNUAL CONFERENCE. PAPER SUMMARIES (YEAR). (Former name of issuing body: Society of Photographic Scientists & Engineers) no.42, 1989. a. $35. Society for Imaging Science and Technology, 7003 Kilworth Ln., Springfield, VA 22151. TEL 703-642-9090. FAX 703-642-9094. **Document type:** proceedings.
Formerly: S P S E's Annual Conference. Paper Summaries.

770 330 US
SALES COUNTER. m. membership only. (Society for Photographic Counselors) Photo Marketing Association International, 3000 Picture Pl., Jackson, MI 49201. TEL 517-788-8100. FAX 517-788-8371. circ. 1,300. (back issues avail.) **Document type:** trade publication.

779 JA
SANGAKU SHASHIN NENKAN. 1974. Yama-Kei (Publishers) Co., Ltd., 1-1-33 Shiba Daimon, Minato-ku, Tokyo 105, Japan.

770 371.2 US
SCHOOL PHOTOGRAPHER. m. membership only. (Professional School Photographers of America) Photo Marketing Association International, 3000 Picture Pl., Jackson, MI 49201. TEL 517-788-8100. FAX 517-788-8371. circ. 1,000. (back issues avail.) **Document type:** trade publication.

PHOTOGRAPHY

770   GW
SCHWARZWEISS. 1991. 3/yr. DM.22 per no. Umschau Zeitschriftenverlag Breidenstein GmbH, Stuttgarterstr. 18-24, 60329 Frankfurt a.M., Germany. TEL 069-2600-0. FAX 069-2600619. Ed. Heiner Henninges. adv.: B&W page DM.6300, color page DM.11025; trim 185 x 245; adv. contact: Barbara Eckert. **Document type:** consumer publication.

770   SZ   ISSN 0036-7737
SCHWEIZERISCHE PHOTORUNDSCHAU. 1938. s-m. 69 Fr. Schweizerischer Photographenverband, Postfach 17, 3930 Visp, Switzerland. (Co-sponsor: Schweizerischer Photohandlerverband) Ed. O. Ruppen. adv.; bk.rev.; illus. circ. 2,500. **Indexed:** Chem.Abstr.

770   US   ISSN 1063-4088
TR1   CODEN: SAPHES
SCIENTIFIC AND APPLIED PHOTOGRAPHY. English translation of: Zhurnal Nauchnoi i Prikladnoi Fotografii i Kinematografii (UR ISSN 0044-4561) 6/yr. (in 1 vol.; 6 nos./vol.). 459 ECU (effective 1996). Gordon & Breach Science Publishers, c/o International Publishers Distributor, 820 Town Center Dr., Langhorne, PA 19047. TEL 215-750-2642. FAX 215-750-6343. (Subscr. to: International Publishers Distributor, P.O. Box 90, Reading, Berkshire RG1 8JL, England. TEL 44-173-456-8316) Ed. M.V. Alfimov. index. (also avail. in microform; back issues avail.) —CCC.
Formerly: Scientific and Applied Photography and Cinematography (ISSN 0734-1504)
Refereed Serial

770   UK   ISSN 0269-1787
SCOTTISH PHOTOGRAPHY BULLETIN. 1986. s-a. £12 to individuals; institutions £27. Scottish Society for the History of Photography, c/o National Library of Scotland, Department of Printed Books, George IV Bridge, Edinburgh EH1 1EW, Scotland. TEL 0131-226-4531. Ed. Richard Ovenden. adv.; bk.rev. circ. 200. **Document type:** academic/scholarly publication.
Description: Provides a forum for critical debate on issues relating to historical and contemporary photography in Scotland.

SCREEN DIGEST. see COMMUNICATIONS — Television And Cable

770   IT
SCUOLA DI FOTOGRAFIA.* 1980. m. L.30000 (free to photography stores). Curcio Periodici S.p.A., Via IV Novembre 149, 00187 Rome, Italy. Ed. Rosanna Falconi. adv. circ. 143,000.

SHANGHAI PICTORIAL. see GENERAL INTEREST PERIODICALS — China

770   CC   ISSN 1002-6770
SHEYING SHIJIE/PHOTOGRAPHY WORLD. (Text in Chinese) 1982? m. $51.20. Sheying Shijie Zazhishe, 57 Xuanwumen Xidajie, Beijing 100803, People's Republic of China. TEL 3074453. (Dist. in US by: China Books & Periodicals, Inc., 2929 24th St., San Francisco, CA 94110. TEL 415-282-2994) Ed. Liu Xinning.

770   CC
SHEYING ZHI YOU/PHOTOGRAPHY FANS. (Text in Chinese) bi-m. Zhongguo Sheyingjia Xiehui, Guangdong Fenhui, No. 23, Siheng Lu, Dongshan Xihepu, Guangzhou, Guangdong 510080, People's Republic of China. TEL 765607. Ed. Meng Shan.

770   CH   ISSN 1019-9608
SHEYINGJIA ZAZHI/PHOTOGRAPHERS INTERNATIONAL. (Text in Chinese, English) 1992. bi-m. NT.$2200 (foreign $103). Photographers International, Rm. 1015, 10F, No. 61 Chungking S. Rd., Sec. 1, Taipei, Taiwan, Republic of China. TEL 02-3751552. FAX 02-3317679. (Subscr. to: Box 39-1265, Taipei Post Office, Taiwan, Republic of China) Ed. Huan I-Jong. adv. contact: Winnie Chang. **Document type:** monographic series.

770 006.6   US   ISSN 1058-2789
TR1
SHOOTER'S RAG; the practical gazette for silver & didgital photographers. 1992. bi-m. $16 (foreign $20). Havelin Communications, Inc., 7000 Roswell Rd. NE, No. 290, Atlanta, GA 30328-2391. TEL 404-392-1013; 800-PHO-TO25. FAX 404-392-0127. Ed. Michael F. Havelin. adv. contact: Tom Williams. bk.rev. circ. 2,000. **Document type:** trade publication.
Description: How-to magazine aimed at high-end amateurs through professional photographers. Seeks to help solve problems and get people started with digital imaging.

770   US   ISSN 1048-793X
TR640
SHOTS. 1986. q. $18 membership. D. Price, Ed. & Pub., Box 109, Joseph, OR 97846. adv. circ. 1,600. **Document type:** newspaper.
Description: Fine-art photography for people worldwide.

770   US   ISSN 0895-321X
TR197
SHUTTERBUG. (Annual Buying Guide avail. (ISSN 1074-5378)) 1971. m. $19.95. Patch Communications, 5211 S. Washington Ave., Titusville, FL 32780. TEL 407-268-5010. FAX 407-267-7216. Ed. Christi Ashby. adv.: B&W page $1895. bk.rev. circ. 120,000. **Indexed:** Ind.How To Do It (1992-).
Formerly: Shutterbug Ads.
Description: Photo equipment magazine for advanced amateur and professional photographers. Features articles on camera systems and techniques, including test reports, user reviews and accessory updates.

SKRIEN. see MOTION PICTURES

SLIPSTREAM (NIAGARA FALLS). see LITERATURE — Poetry

770.5   US   ISSN 0748-6413
SOCIETY FOR PHOTOGRAPHIC EDUCATION. QUARTERLY NEWSLETTER. q. $55 membership (includes Exposure). Society for Photographic Education, Box 22216, Dallas, TX 75222-2116. TEL 817-273-2845. FAX 817-273-2846. **Document type:** newsletter.
Description: Provides a network for communicating member concerns and for sharing information about society business and future events.

770   US
SOCIETY OF PHOTOGRAPHER AND ARTIST REPRESENTATIVES. MEMBER DIRECTORY. irreg. Society of Photographer and Artist Representatives, 60 E. 42nd St., No.1166, New York, NY 10165-0006. TEL 212-779-7464. **Document type:** directory.

770 700   US
SOCIETY OF PHOTOGRAPHER AND ARTIST REPRESENTATIVES. NEWSLETTER. q. membership only. Society of Photographer and Artist Representatives, 60 E. 42nd St., No. 1166, New York, NY 10165-0006. TEL 212-779-7464. circ. (controlled). **Document type:** newsletter.

770   JA   ISSN 0369-5662
CODEN: NSGKAP
SOCIETY OF PHOTOGRAPHIC SCIENCE AND TECHNOLOGY OF JAPAN. JOURNAL/NIHON SHASHIN GAKKAI EIBUNGO. 1935. q. 1000 Yen per no. to non-members. Society of Photographic Science and Technology of Japan - Nihon Shashin Gakkai, c/o Tokyo College of Photography, 2-9-5 Honcho, Nakano-ku, Tokyo 164, Japan. FAX 03-3299-5887. Ed. Eiichi Ashikawa. adv.; bk.rev.; bibl.; charts; illus.; stat.; index. circ. 1,500. **Indexed:** INSPEC (1984-). **Document type:** academic/scholarly publication.
—BLDSC (4894.850000); CASDDS.
Incorporates (in 1974): Society of Photographic Science and Technology of Japan. Bulletin (ISSN 0038-0059); Which then was previously (1951-1970): Society of Scientific Photography in Japan. Bulletin (ISSN 0366-3582)

SOUTHEAST ASIA MICROFILMS NEWSLETTER. see HISTORY — History Of Asia

770   US   ISSN 0038-4070
SOUTHERN EXPOSURE (TALLADEGA). 1950. q. membership. Southeastern Professional Photographers Association, Inc., Box 355, Talladega, AL 35160. TEL 205-362-3485. FAX 205-362-3485. Eds. Van & MaryLee Blankenship. adv.; bk.rev. circ. 5,200. **Indexed:** Access. **Document type:** trade publication.

770   US
SPECIALTY LAB UPDATE. m. membership only. Photo Marketing Association International, 3000 Picture Pl., Jackson, MI 49201. TEL 517-788-8100. FAX 517-788-8371. circ. 2,300. (back issues avail.) **Document type:** trade publication.
Description: For commercial, private and in-house photographic labs of the association.

770 370   US   ISSN 1049-0450
SPOT. 1983. 3/yr. $15. Houston Center for Photography, 1441 W. Alabama, Houston, TX 77006. TEL 713-529-4755. FAX 713-529-9248. Ed. Karen Allen. adv.: B&W page $995. bk.rev. circ. 2,000.
Formerly: Image.
Description: Serves the photographic community as a resource for educational exchange through feature articles, profiles, and exhibitions.

770   US   ISSN 0191-4030
TR780
STEREO WORLD. 1974. bi-m. $26 (foreign $38) (effective 1995-1996). National Stereoscopic Association, Inc., Box 14801, Columbus, OH 43214. Ed. John Dennis. adv.: B&W page $160. bk.rev.; circ. 3,600 (paid). **Document type:** bulletin.
Description: Magazine of stereophotography - everything from the study of and collecting historical stereographs to modern 3-D techniques.

770   US   ISSN 0081-5586
STILL: YALE PHOTOGRAPHY ANNUAL. 1970. irreg., no.3, 1973. price varies. (Yale University, School of Art and Architecture) Yale University Press, Box 209040, New Haven, CT 06520. TEL 203-436-0308. (Dist. by: George Wittenborn, Inc., 1018 Madison Ave., New York, N.Y. 10021)

770   US   ISSN 0897-6287
STOCK PHOTO DESKBOOK. 1977. a. $43.95. Photographic Arts Center, Ltd., 163 Amsterdam Ave., Ste. 201, New York, NY 10023. TEL 212-838-8640. FAX 212-873-7065. **Document type:** directory.
Formerly (until 1989): Stock Photo and Assignment Stock Book (ISSN 0146-5961)
Description: Lists the names and addresses of U.S. and foreign stock houses, private, government, and museum sources, freelance picture researchers, CD-ROM producers, and professional associations.

770   GW
STOCK PHOTO FEES IN EUROPE. (Editions in English, German) 1993. a. Presse Informations Agentur GmbH, Stefanienstr. 25, 76530 Baden-Baden, Germany. TEL 07221-25348. FAX 07221-26821. Ed. Dieter Brinzer. **Document type:** directory.

771   US   ISSN 0746-0996
STUDIO PHOTOGRAPHY. 1964. m. $40 (free to qualified personnel). P T N Publishing Corp., 445 Broad Hollow Rd., Ste. 21, Melville, NY 11747-4722. TEL 516-845-2700. FAX 516-845-7109. adv.: page $3990. bk.rev.; illus. circ. 50,050. **Indexed:** Graph.Arts Lit.Abstr. **Document type:** trade publication.
Formerly: Photographic Business and Product News (ISSN 0031-8728)

TAUCHEN; internationales Unterwasser-Magazin. see SPORTS AND GAMES

770   IT
▼**TECHNOPHOTO NEW.** 1994. bi-m. TechnoGroup, Via Marco Aurelio 8, 20127 Milan, Italy. TEL 39-2-26112544. FAX 39-2-26140115. Ed. M.D. Zanini Vallin. adv.: B&W page L.2300000, color page L.3300000; adv. contact: Daniela LoSardo. circ. 15,200. **Document type:** consumer publication.

PHOTOGRAPHY

770   UK
TEN.8 PHOTO PAPERBACK. 1979. q. £29.95 to individuals (foreign £34.45); institutions £39.95 (foreign £44.45). Ten.8 Ltd., 9 Key Hill Drive, Hockley, Birmingham B18 5NY, England. TEL 021-554-2237. FAX 021-554-5970. Ed. Derek Bishton. adv.; bk.rev. circ. 2,500. (back issues avail.) Indexed: Artbibl.Mod.
—BLDSC (8790.332000).
   Formerly: Ten.8 International Photography Magazine (ISSN 0142-9663)
   Description: Presents cultural and theoretical debate on issues involving photography, image-making and technology.

TEN THOUSAND WORDS!. see *MOTION PICTURES*

770   US
TEST PHOTOGRAPHERS IN NEW YORK CITY. 1988. a. $12.95. Peter Glenn Publications, Inc., 42 W. 38th St., Ste. 802, New York, NY 10018. TEL 212-869-2020. FAX 212-869-3287. Ed. Gregory James; Pub. Chip Brill. adv. contact: Michael Henry. circ. 2,000. **Document type:** directory.
   Description: Presents a working list of photographers who take pictures of aspiring models. How and where to contact these specialty photographers.

770   US
TODAY'S PHOTOGRAPHER MAGAZINE. 1984. bi-m. $17.70. (International Freelance Photographer's Organization) American Image, Inc., 6495 Shallowford Rd., Lewisville, NC 27023. TEL 910-945-9867. FAX 910-945-3711. Ed. Vonda Blackburn; Pub. Jack Gallimore. adv.: B&W page $2992, color page $4631; trim 8 1/4 x 10 7/8; adv. contact: Bill Kaprelian. circ. 89,663. **Document type:** consumer publication.
   Formerly: International Photographer (Lewisville).

770   791.43   IT   ISSN 0041-4395
TUTTI FOTOGRAFI. 1969. m. L.80000. Editrice Progresso s.r.l., Viale Piceno 14, 20129 Milan, Italy. TEL 39-2-70002222. FAX 39-2-713030. adv.: B&W page L.7000000, color page L.10000000. bk.rev.; illus.; index. circ. 33,000.

770   IS
TZEILUM MIKTZOEI/PROFESSIONAL PHOTOGRAPHY. (Text in Hebrew; table of contents and summaries in English) 1985. q. $30 (outside Israel $60). (Union of Professional Photographers in Israel) Studio 19 Productions Ltd., P.O. Box 26177, Tel Aviv 61261, Israel. TEL 972-3-5251470. FAX 972-3-5251469. Ed. Ilan Aharon. adv. contact: Avi Kalian. bk.rev. circ. 5,000.
   Description: Covers technical and creative aspects of visual communication with emphasis on international items of interest to the working professional photographer.

770   778   US   ISSN 1046-9311
TR593
ULTRAHIGH SPEED AND HIGH SPEED PHOTOGRAPHY, PHOTONICS, AND VIDEOGRAPHY. 1983. a. International Society for Optical Engineering (SPIE), Society of Photo-Optical Instrumentation Engineers, Box 10, Bellingham, WA 98227-0010.
   Formerly (until 1989): High Speed Photography, Videography, and Photonics (ISSN 1044-436X)

770   US   ISSN 0163-7916
TR1
UNTITLED. 1972. 2/yr. $60 (includes subscr. to: Re:View). Friends of Photography, 250 Fourth St., San Francisco, CA 94103. TEL 415-495-7000. Ed. Michael Read. illus. circ. 8,000. (back issues avail.) **Document type:** monographic series.
—BLDSC (9121.327400).
   Description: Individual issues are monographs on the work of specific photographers or photographic themes.

770   FI   ISSN 0355-1466
VALOKUVA/FINNISH PHOTOGRAPHY. (Text in English, Finnish; summaries in English) 1949. 8/yr. FIM 250 in Finland and Scandinavia; elsewhere FIM 350. (Suomen Valokuvajarjestojen Keskusliitto Finnfoto - Central Association of Finnish Photographic Organizations) Postvalokuva Oy, Korkeavuorenkatu 2 b F 72, SF-00140 Helsinki, Finland. TEL 358-0-663-433. FAX 358-0-662-422. Eds. Kati Lintonen, Aino Martikainen. adv.: B&W page FIM 4200, color page FIM 7700; trim 210 x 297; adv. contact: Kati Lintonen. bk.rev.; illus. circ. 4,000.
   Formerly (until 1971): Valokuvaaja.
   Description: Aims to improve the position of photography and photographers, as well as to promote the development of photographic art. Articles deal mainly with the photograph, photographic research and the presentation of photographers' work.

770   FI   ISSN 0356-8075
VALOKUVAUKSEN VUOSIKIRJA/FINNISH PHOTOGRAPHIC YEARBOOK/FINSK FOTOGRAFISK ARSBOK. (Text in English, Finnish and Swedish) 1972. a. Fmk.120($30) Suomen Valokuvataiteen Museon Saatio - Foundation of the Photographic Museum of Finland, P.O. Box 596, FIN-00101 Helsinki 10, Finland. TEL 358-0-685-1033. FAX 358-0693-1576. Ed. Ritva Tahtinen. adv.; illus. circ. 4,000.

770   384.5   IT
VIDEO ALMANACCO. 1978. s-a. L.10000. Editrice Progresso s.r.l., Viale Piceno 14, 20129 Milan, Italy. TEL 39-2-70002222. FAX 39-2-713030. Ed. Paolo Namias. adv.: B&W page L.3600000, color page L.6000000. circ. 25,000.
   Formerly: Annuario Video.

770   384.55   UK   ISSN 0956-5337
VIDEO CAMERA; your camcorder monthly. 1989. m. £25($40) I P C Magazines, Specialist Magazine Group (Subsidiary of: Reed Elsevier group), King's Reach Tower, Stamford St., London SE1 9LS, England. TEL 0171-261-5876. FAX 0171-261-6050. TELEX 892084 REEDBP G. (Dist. by: Quadrant Subscription Services, Oakfield House, Perrymount Rd., Haywards Heath, W. Sussex RH16 3DH, England. TEL 01444-440421; U.S. subscr. to: Reed Business Publishing, 205 E. 42nd St., New York, NY 10017) Ed. Chris George. adv.: B&W page £805; color page £3160; adv. contact: Tim Sandford, Mickaela Jones. circ. 23,950. (back issues avail.) **Document type:** consumer publication.
   Description: Contains camcorder reviews, video techniques, and news on video technology.

770   US   ISSN 1066-6958
TR1
VIEW CAMERA. 1988. bi-m. $25. 2774 Harkness St., Sacramento, CA 95818-3060. TEL 916-441-2557. FAX 916-441-7407. Ed. Lizabeth A. Johnson; Pub. Steve Simmons. adv.: B&W page $1025, color page $1575; trim 8 1/2 x 11. bk.rev.; illus. circ. 13,500.

770   700   US
VIEWFINDER JOURNAL OF FOCAL POINT GALLERY. 1982. a. $35 membership (effective 1995 & 1996). Focal Point Press, 321 City Island Ave., New York, NY 10464. TEL 718-885-1403. Ed. Ron Terner. circ. 3,000. (back issues avail.) **Document type:** catalog.
   Description: Prints of artwork from and promotional information on the gallery, located in City Island, New York.

770   US   ISSN 0743-8044
VIEWS (BOSTON); the New England journal of photography. 1977-1993; resumed vol.14, no.3, 1994. 3/yr. $30 membership (includes PRC newsletter). Photographic Resource Center, Boston University, 602 Commonwealth Ave., Boston, MA 02215. TEL 617-353-0700. FAX 617-353-1662. Ed.Bd. adv.; bk.rev.; bibl.; illus. circ. 4,000.
   Description: Critical and theoretical forum addressing a broad range of issues pertaining to photography, with reviews of noteworthy exhibitions and profiles of photographers.

VISUAL RESOURCES; an international journal of documentation. see *ART*

VYTVARNICTVO, FOTOGRAFIA, FILM; mesacnik pre zaujmovu umelecku cinnost. see *ART*

770   US
THE WEDDING PHOTOGRAPHER. 1978. m. $75 membership. (Wedding & Portrait Photographers International) Rangefinder Publishing Co., Inc., 1312 Lincoln Blvd., Box 2003, Santa Monica, CA 90406. TEL 310-451-0090. FAX 310-395-9058. Ed. Marquita Thomas. circ. 3,000. (back issues avail.) **Document type:** newsletter.
   Formerly: Wedding Photographers International.
   Description: Provides information on running a wedding photography studio, how-to techniques, business management, and continuing education. Publishes print competition winners.

770   US   ISSN 0738-8039
WESTERN PHOTOGRAPHER.* 1960. m. $22. Bear With Me Productions Inc., 2031 E. Via Burton, Ste. C, Anaheim, CA 92806-1202. TEL 619-463-1711. Ed. S.T. Bear. circ. 7,000.
   Description: Where and how to take photos.

WESTWIND (LOS ANGELES); U C L A's journal of the arts. see *ART*

770   UK   ISSN 0263-9106
WHICH CAMERA?. 1981. bi-m. £27.80. Evro Publishing Co., 60 Waldgrave Rd., Teddington, Middx. TW11 8LG, England. TEL 081-943-5000. FAX 081-843-5871. TELEX 8952440-HAYMRT-G. Ed. Stuart Watt. adv.; illus. circ. 8,000. **Document type:** consumer publication.
   Description: Camera and camcorder buyer's guide, with test results and ratings.

770   UK
WIDESCREEN INTERNATIONAL. 1964. bi-m. £35. Widescreen Centre, 48 Dorset St., London W1H 3FH, England. TEL 0171-935-2580. FAX 0171-486-1272. Ed. Tony Shapps. adv.; bk.rev.; film rev. circ. 5,000. (back issues avail.) **Document type:** consumer publication.
   Formerly: Widescreen.
   Description: Panoramic photography, 3-D, stereoscopic, multi-channel sound, multi-projector set-ups.

770   US   ISSN 0084-103X
WOLFMAN REPORT ON THE PHOTOGRAPHIC INDUSTRY IN THE UNITED STATES. 1958. a. $135. Hachette Magazines, Inc., 1633 Broadway, 45th Fl., New York, NY 10009. TEL 212-767-6000. Ed. Lydia Wolfman. adv. circ. 9,000.

770   US   ISSN 0197-3444
S494.5.A25
WORKSHOP ON COLOR AERIAL PHOTOGRAPHY IN THE PLANT SCIENCES. PROCEEDINGS. biennial. $90 to non-members; members $45. American Society for Photogrammetry and Remote Sensing, 5410 Grosvenor Ln., Ste. 210, Bethesda, MD 20814-2160. TEL 301-493-0290. FAX 301-493-0208.
—BLDSC (3320.620000).

WRITERS' AND PHOTOGRAPHERS' MARKETING GUIDE; DIRECTORY OF AUSTRALIAN AND NEW ZEALAND LITERARY AND PHOTO MARKETS. see *PUBLISHING AND BOOK TRADE*

XEROX DISCLOSURE JOURNAL. see *PATENTS, TRADEMARKS AND COPYRIGHTS*

770   CC
XIANDAI SHEYING/INPHOTO. (Text in Chinese) 1984221. q. $16. Shenzhen Shi Wenlian - Shengzhen Writers and Artists Federation, 2nd Fl., No. 13 Guiyuan Rd., Shenzhen, Guangdong 518001, People's Republic of China. TEL 86-755-586168. FAX 86-755-586168. Ed. Li Mei. adv.; bk.rev. circ. 4,000.
   Description: Features fine art photographs by both Chinese and foreign photographers. Also includes critics.

770   IS
YIDIOT LETZALAM. (Text in Hebrew) bi-m. Association of Photographers and Cameramen, 16 Zemenhoff St., Tel Aviv 64 373, Israel. TEL 03-280895.

770   CC   ISSN 1001-0270
YINGXIANG JISHU. (Text in Chinese) q. Quanguo Qinggong Ganguang Cailiao Keji Qingbao-zhan, 20 Dongting Lu, Hexi Qu, Tianjin 300220, People's Republic of China. TEL 840654. Ed. Wei Zhengeng.

771 UK
YOU AND YOUR CAMERA. 1979. w. £0.70 per no. Eaglemoss Publications Ltd., 7 Cromwell Rd., London SW7 2HR, England. Ed. Jack Schofield. adv. circ. 53,024.

770 CC
ZHAOXIANGJI/CAMERAS. (Text in Chinese) bi-m. Hangzhou Zhaoxiangji Jixie Yanjiusuo, 94 Xixi Lu (W. Brook Rd.), Hangzhou, Zhejiang 310013, People's Republic of China. TEL 521014. Ed. Wang Zhenkui.

770 CC
ZHONGGUO SHEYING/CHINESE PHOTOGRAPHY. (Text in Chinese) bi-m. $64.40. (Zhongguo Sheyingjia Xiehui - Chinese Photographers Association) Zhongguo Sheying Zazhishe, 61 Hongxing Hutong, Dongdan, Beijing 1007 5, People's Republic of China. TEL 552277. (Dist. in US by: China Books & Periodicals, Inc., 2929 24th St., San Francisco, CA 94110. TEL 415-282-2994) Ed. Liu Bang.

770 RU ISSN 0869-6144
TR1 CODEN: ZNPFEK
ZHURNAL NAUCHNOI I PRIKLADNOI FOTOGRAFII. 1956. bi-m. $96 (effective 1996). (Rossiiskaya Akademiya Nauk, Institut Khimicheskoi Fiziki im. N.N. Semenova) Izdatel'stvo Nauka, 90 Profsoyuznaya ul., 117864 Moscow, Russia. TEL 095-336-0266. FAX 095-420-2220. (Dist. by: Mezhdunarodnaya Kniga, B. Yakimanka 39, 117049 Moscow, Russia; Dist. in U.S. by: Victor Kamkin Inc., 4956 Boiling Brook Pkwy., Rockville, MD 20852. TEL 301-881-5973. FAX 301-881-1637) Ed. M.V. Alfimov. bibl.; charts; illus.; index. circ. 70,290.
Indexed: Chem.Abstr.; Curr.Cont.; INSPEC (197201989).
—BLDSC (0060.999000); CASDDS; Genuine Article. **CCC.**
Formerly (until 1992): Zhurnal Nauchnoi i Prikladnoi Fotografii Kinematografii (ISSN 0044-4561)

770 IT ISSN 0393-4330
ZOOM. (Text in English) 1980. bi-m. $49.90. Editrice Progresso s.r.l., Viale Piceno 14, 20129 Milan, Italy. TEL 39-2-70002222. FAX 39-2-713030. adv.; B&W page L.6000000, color page L.7000000. bk.rev.; illus.; index. circ. 10,000.

770 SZ
ZOOM. 24/yr. Postfach 7622, CH-3001 Bern, Switzerland. TEL 031-453291. FAX 031-460980. Ed. Ursula Ganz-Blaettler. circ. 5,000.

770 SP
40 POR 50. 4/yr. Argentina 8 bajo, 15011 La Coruna, Spain. TEL 81-27-27-29.

770 US
2029 MAGAZIN. 1985. a. DM.79($44) 8191 Mannix Dr., Los Angeles, CA 90046. TEL 213-654-1263. FAX 213-654-1263. Ed. Peter Schulz Foersten. adv. circ. 30,000. (back issues avail.) **Document type:** consumer publication.

PHOTOGRAPHY — Abstracting, Bibliographies, Statistics

770 SZ
ART DIRECTORS' INDEX TO PHOTOGRAPHERS. (In 2 vols.: vol.1: Europe; vol.2: The Americas, Asia and Australasia) (Text in English, French, German, Spanish) 1976. a. $135 (for both vols.). Rotovision S.A., Route Suisse 9, CH-1295 Mies, Switzerland. TEL 022-7553055. FAX 022-7554072. (Dist in the U.S. by: Watson-Guptill Publications, 1695 Oak St., Lakewood, NJ 08701. TEL 800-451-1741. FAX 908-363-0338) illus. **Document type:** abstracting/indexing.
Description: Displays trend-setting commercial photography from around the world.

770 FR
FRANCE. SERVICE D'ETUDE DES STRATEGIES ET DES STATISTIQUES INDUSTRIELLES. RESULTATS TRIMESTRIELS DES ENQUETES DE BRANCHE. LABOS PHOTOGRAPHIQUES ET CINEMATOGRAPHIQUES. q. 180 F. (foreign 210 F.)(effective 1991). Service d'Etude des Strategies et des Statistiques Industrielles (SESSI), 85 Bd. du Montparnasse, 75270 Paris Cedex 06, France. TEL 45-56-42-34. FAX 45-56-40-71. stat.
Description: Provides detailed industry-wide performance statistics for comparative evaluations.

770 016 UK ISSN 0896-100X
TR1
IMAGING ABSTRACTS. 1921. 6/yr. £300($460) (effective 1994). (Royal Photographic Society of Great Britain, Imaging Science and Technology Group) Pira International, Randalls Rd., Leatherhead, Surrey KT22 7RU, England. TEL 0372-376161. FAX 0372-360104. Eds. P. Ellis, D.M.A. Roberts. index, cum.index. circ. 250. (also avail. in microfiche from PMC; microform from UMI; back issues avail.) **Document type:** abstracting/indexing.
●Also available online. Vendor(s): Orbit Search Service (IMAB).
—BLDSC (4368.996450).
Formerly: Photographic Abstracts (ISSN 0031-8701)
Description: Offers comprehensive coverage of the literature of imaging and photographic science and technology. Over 100 periodicals, as well as patents and other publications are scanned for relevant data on every aspect of the industry.
Refereed Serial

770 US
INTERNATIONAL PHOTO PROCESSING INDUSTRY REPORT. 1983. a. $900. Photofinishing News, Inc., 10915 Bonia Beach Rd., Bonita Springs, FL 33923. TEL 813-992-4421. FAX 813-992-6328. **Document type:** trade publication.
Description: Statistical review of the worldwide photo processing market.

770 016 RU ISSN 0370-8063
REFERATIVNYI ZHURNAL. FOTOKINOTEKHNIKA. 1957. m. (effective 1996). Vsesoyuznyi Institut Nauchno-Tekhnicheskoi Informatsii (VINITI), Baltiiskaya ul., 14, Moscow A-219, Russia. (Subscr. to: Mezhdunarodnaya Kniga, Dimitrova ul. 39, 113095 Moscow, Russia) **Document type:** abstracting/indexing.

770 316.8 SA
SOUTH AFRICA. CENTRAL STATISTICAL SERVICE. CENSUS OF SOCIAL, RECREATIONAL AND PERSONAL SERVICES - PHOTOGRAPHIC STUDIOS. (Report No. 95-02-01) irreg., latest 1988. R.4.40 (foreign R.4.80). Central Statistical Service - Sentrale Statistiekdiens, Private Bag X44, Pretoria 0001, South Africa. TEL 27-12-310-8911. FAX 27-12-310-8500. (Orders to: Government Printing Works, Private Bag X85, Pretoria 0001, South Africa) **Document type:** government publication.

PHOTOGRAPHY — Computer Applications

770.285 GW ISSN 0937-101X
IMAGE-SCENE; Zeitschrift fuer elektronische Fotografie und digitale Bildverarbeitung. 1977. 6/yr. DM.72. Verlag Peter Walz, Jaegerstr. 2, 16567 Muehlenbeck, Germany. TEL 033056-8730. FAX 033056-87399. Ed.Bd. adv.; bk.rev. circ. 8,000. **Document type:** trade publication.

770.285 GW
3 D-MAGAZIN; das internationale Magazin fuer die 3. Dimension. 1992. 4/yr. DM.70; newsstand price: DM.13.50. Bode Verlag, Postfach 405, 45716 Haltern, Germany. TEL 02364-16107. FAX 02364-169273. E-mail: 3d-magazin@stereo.stgt.sub.org. Ed. Franz Weiland; Pub. Rainer Bode. adv. contact: Doris Bode. **Document type:** consumer publication.
Description: Features up-to-date information on all aspects of three-dimensional imaging.

PHYSICAL CHEMISTRY

see Chemistry–Physical Chemistry

PHYSICAL FITNESS AND HYGIENE

see also Medical Sciences; Nutrition and Dietetics; Public Health and Safety; Sports and Games

A C H A ACTION. (American College Health Association) see *EDUCATION — Higher Education*

A C H P E R HEALTHY LIFESTYLES JOURNAL. (Australian Council for Health, Physical Education and Recreation Inc.) see *EDUCATION*

A S H SMOKING AND HEALTH REVIEW. (Action on Smoking & Health) see *LAW*

613.7 US
A V A CHECKPOINT. 1980. m. membership only. American Volkssport Association, Phoenix Sq., Ste. 101, 1001 Pat Booker Rd., Universal City, TX 78148. TEL 210-659-2112. FAX 210-659-1212. Ed. Sandra Ward. circ. 600. **Document type:** newsletter.
Formerly: A V A Newsletter.
Description: To inform clubs of AVA business.

613.7 330 US ISSN 1067-1714
A W H P ACTION. 1975. bi-m. free to members. Association for Worksite Health Promotion, 60 Revere Dr., Ste. 500, Northbrook, IL 60062-1577. TEL 708-480-9574. FAX 708-480-9282. Ed. Coleen Cronin. adv.; circ. 3,000 (controlled).
Indexed: Sportsearch (1983-).
Formerly: A F B Action (ISSN 0891-7450)

ACTA MEDICA ET SOCIOLOGICA. see *SOCIOLOGY*

613.7 612.67 US
ACTIVE AMERICAN. 1990. q. Russ Moore and Associates Inc., 4151 Knob Dr., St. Paul, MN 55122. TEL 612-452-0571. FAX 612-454-5791. Ed. Diane Steen. adv. circ. 150,000.
Description: For the mature adult who wants to take an active part in achieving and maintaining good health.

613.7 AT ISSN 1321-1609
ACTIVE AND HEALTHY; the ACHPER magazine for physical educators, health educators and fitness leaders. q. Aus.$32 (foreign Aus.$39) (effective 1996). Australian Council for Health, Physical Education and Recreation Inc., P.O. Box 304, Hindmarsh, S.A. 5007, Australia. TEL 61-8-340-3388. FAX 61-8-340-3399. (back issues avail.)
Formed by the 1994 merger of: Physical Education Teacher Newsletter & Health and Fitness Newsletter (ISSN 0814-754X) & Health Education and Lifestyle Promotion Newsletter; Which was formerly (until 1991): Health Education and Lifestyle Project Newsletter.
Description: Aims to improve the health and life-styles of Australians by the dissemination of classroom ideas, teaching strategies and trends for fitness, health and physical education.

ADAPTED PHYSICAL ACTIVITY QUARTERLY. see *EDUCATION — Special Education And Rehabilitation*

330 613 US ISSN 0731-2199
RA410.A1
ADVANCES IN HEALTH ECONOMICS AND HEALTH SERVICES RESEARCH. 1979. a. $63.50 to institutions. J A I Press Inc., 55 Old Post Rd., No. 2, Box 1678, Greenwich, CT 06836-1678. TEL 203-661-7602. Eds. Richard M. Scheffler, Louis F. Rossiter. **Indexed:** Abstr.Health Care Manage.Stud.
—BLDSC (0709.008000); Faxon; SWETS; UnCover. **CCC.**
Formerly (until 1981): Research in Health Economics (ISSN 0197-0690)
Refereed Serial

ADVANCES IN HEALTH EDUCATION: CURRENT RESEARCH. see *EDUCATION — Teaching Methods And Curriculum*

613.7 649 US ISSN 0888-9287
RJ133
ADVANCES IN MOTOR DEVELOPMENT RESEARCH. 1987. a. $37.50. A M S Press, Inc., 56 E. 13th St., New York, NY 10003. TEL 212-777-4700. FAX 212-995-5413. Eds. Jane E. Clark, James H. Humphrey. bk.rev.; index. (back issues avail.)
—Faxon.
Description: Original research and review in the study of motor development.
Refereed Serial

613.7 US
AEROBIC BEAT. 1984. bi-m. $25. 7985 Santa Monica Blvd., Ste. 109, Los Angeles, CA 90046-5186. TEL 310-659-2503. FAX 213-655-5223. Eds. Ken Alan, Randy Sills. adv.; bk.rev.; music rev. **Document type:** newsletter.
Description: Designed to help in the location of the latest and most appropriate music for aerobic workouts, jogging, step training and other fitness activities done with music.

PHYSICAL FITNESS AND HYGIENE

AICHI KYOIKU DAIGAKU TAIIKU KYOSHITSU KENKYU KIYO/AICHI UNIVERSITY OF EDUCATION. BULLETIN OF THE PHYSICAL EDUCATION AND SPORT RESEARCH. see *EDUCATION*

AIDS EDUCATION AND PREVENTION; an interdisciplinary journal. see *MEDICAL SCIENCES — Communicable Diseases*

613   CN   ISSN 0228-586X
CODEN: ACOLEL
ALIVE; Canadian journal of health and nutrition. 1975. 12/yr. Can.$24.50. Canadian Health Reform Products Ltd., 7436 Fraser Park Dr., Burnaby, B.C. V5J 5B9, Canada. TEL 604-435-1919. FAX 604-435-4888. (Subscr. addr.: P.O. Box 80055, Burnaby, B.C. V5J 3X5, Canada) Ed. Rhody Lake; Pub. Siegfried Gursche. adv. contact: Siegfried Gursche. bk.rev. circ. 170,000. **Indexed:** Mid.East: Abstr.& Ind. **Document type:** consumer publication.

613.7 790   US   ISSN 0273-8023
ALLIANCE UPDATE. 1970. 6/yr. $45 to institutions. American Alliance for Health, Physical Education, Recreation, and Dance, 1900 Association Dr., Reston, VA 22091. TEL 703-476-3400. FAX 703-476-9527. circ. 32,000. (tabloid format; reprint service avail. from UMI) **Indexed:** Sportsearch. **Document type:** trade publication.
 Former titles: A A H P E R D Update; A A H P E R Update.
 Description: Provides news of activitews and programs of A A H P E R D.

613.7   US   ISSN 1054-7711
TT950
ALLURE. 1991. m. $15. Conde Nast Publications Inc., Allure Magazine, 360 Madison Ave., New York, NY 10017. TEL 212-880-5550. (Subscr. to: Box 53598, Boulder, CO 80322. TEL 800-678-1825) Ed. Linda Wells. circ. 697,690. (also avail. in microform from UMI)
 —UMI.
 Description: Covers fitness, health, beauty and fashion.

613.194   US
AMERICAN ASSOCIATION FOR NUDE RECREATION. BULLETIN. m. $3 per no. American Association for Nude Recreation, 1703 N. Main St., Kissimmee, FL 34744-3396. Ed. Arne Eriksen.
 Formerly: American Sunbathing Association. Bulletin (ISSN 0279-8158)

AMERICAN BABY; for expectant and new parents. see *CHILDREN AND YOUTH — About*

613.7   US   ISSN 0893-5238
CODEN: AAFIEL
AMERICAN FITNESS. 1983. 6/yr. $27. Aerobics and Fitness Association of America, 15250 Ventura Blvd., Ste. 310, Sherman Oaks, CA 91403. TEL 818-905-0040. Ed. Peg Jordan, R.N. adv.; bk.rev. circ. 30,000. (also avail. in microform from UMI) **Indexed:** Phys.Ed.Ind., Sportsearch (1987-). **Document type:** trade publication.
 ●Also available online. Vendor(s): Knight-Ridder, Inc. (File no.149), University Microfilms International.
 —BLDSC (0815.220000); UMI.
 Supersedes (in 1987): Aerobics and Fitness (ISSN 0749-8942); **Formerly (until 1984):** Aerobics and Fitness Association of America. Journal.
 Description: Provides news and information concerning health and fitness via aerobics.

613.7   US   ISSN 0730-7004
RA773   CODEN: AMHEEZ
AMERICAN HEALTH; fitness of body and mind. 1982. 10/yr. $17.97 (foreign $26). Reader's Digest Association, Inc. (New York), 28 West 23rd St., New York, NY 10010. TEL 212-366-8900. FAX 212-366-8760. (Subscr. to: Box 3017, Harlan, IA 51537) Ed. Carey Winfrey; Pub. Susan Buckley. adv.; bk.rev.; circ. 800,000 (paid). **Indexed:** CHNI, CINAHL, Hlth.Ind., Phys.Ed.Ind. **Document type:** consumer publication.
 —BLDSC (0816.575000); Faxon; SWETS; UnCover.
 Description: Research-based consumer magazine on health, fitness, medicine and nutrition.

AMERICAN HIKER. see *SPORTS AND GAMES — Outdoor Life*

AMERICAN JOURNAL OF HEALTH PROMOTION. see *PUBLIC HEALTH AND SAFETY*

613.194   US
AMERICAN NUDIST RESEARCH LIBRARY NEWSLETTER. 1980. s-a. membership. American Nudist Research Library, 2950 Sun Cove Dr., Kissimmee, FL 34746. Ed. Lyda Hadley. circ. 400. (looseleaf format) **Document type:** newsletter.

613.7   US   ISSN 0748-7444
THE AMERICAN WANDERER. 1978. bi-m. $15. American Volkssport Association, Phoenix Sq., Ste. 101, 1001 Pat Booker Rd., Universal City, TX 78148. TEL 210-659-2112. FAX 210-659-1212. Ed. Sandra Ward. adv. contact: Jacklyn Hess. circ. 7,000. **Document type:** newspaper.
 Description: Covers Association news, national office news, health and fitness articles and international fitness events. Offers chartered club list, upcoming events, and list of award recipients.

AMIS DE LA RADIESTHESIE. see *PARAPSYCHOLOGY AND OCCULTISM*

ANDERS LEBEN. see *GARDENING AND HORTICULTURE*

613   US   ISSN 0278-4653
RA773
ANNUAL EDITIONS: HEALTH. 1975. a. $12.95. Dushkin Publishing Group, Sluice Dock, Guilford, CT 06437-9989. TEL 203-453-4351. FAX 203-453-6000. Ed. Rick Yarian; Pub. Ian Nielsen. illus. **Document type:** academic/scholarly publication.
 Former titles (1980-1981): Readings in Health (ISSN 0730-8930); Annual Editions: Readings in Health (ISSN 0360-9766)
 Refereed Serial

ANNUAL EDITIONS: NUTRITION. see *NUTRITION AND DIETETICS*

613.7 647.94   IT
ANNUARIO PROFESSIONALE DELLE TERME E DEI CENTRI DI BENESSERE. 1992. a. Ediman s.r.l., Corso San Gottardo 39, 20136 Milan, Italy. TEL 39-2-58103791. FAX 39-2-58103789. Ed. Marco Biamonti. adv.: B&W page L.3300000, color page L.5000000. **Document type:** trade publication.

613   II   ISSN 0003-6498
APKA SWASTHYA. (Text in Hindi) 1953. m. Rs.361. Indian Medical Association, I.M.A. House, Indraprastha Marg, New Delhi 110002, India. (Subscr. to: Apka Swasthya, I.M.A. Building, C. 7-31 Chet Ganj, Varanasi 1, India) Ed.Bd. circ. 3,500.

613.7 640.73   US
AQUA INDUSTRY GUIDE. 1979. a. $48. A B Publications, 1846 Hoffman St., Madison, WI 53704. TEL 608-249-0186. FAX 608-249-1153. Ed.Shawn Gahagan. adv. contact: Brad Zaugg. circ. 14,000. **Document type:** trade publication.
 Former titles: Aqua Buyers Guide; Spa and Sauna Buyers Guide.

ARENA; laekemedel, sjukvaard, samhaelle. see *PHARMACY AND PHARMACOLOGY*

613.7 610   II   ISSN 0253-682X
CODEN: AROGD8
AROGYA; a journal of health sciences. (Text in English) 1975. s-a. free. Kasturba Medical College Trust, Manipal, Department of Clinical Biochemistry, Editor - Arogyal, Manipal - 576 119, India. TEL 20060. Ed. Sudhakar S. Nayak. adv.; bk.rev.; circ. 1,000 (controlled). **Indexed:** Chem.Abstr., Food Sci.& Tech.Abstr., INIS Atomind., Rev.Med.& Vet.Mycol.
 —CASDDS.

613.7   II
AROGYA SANJEEVANI. (Text in Hindi) 1990. m.? Pioneer Book Co. Pvt. Ltd., C-14, Royal Industrial Estate, 5-B, Naigaum Cross Rd., Wadala, Bombay 31, India. Ed. Vaidya Swati Govilkar. adv.: B&W page Rs.6000, color page Rs.12000; trim 230 x 170. circ. 82,261.

613.7   CH   ISSN 1015-1990
ASIAN JOURNAL OF PHYSICAL EDUCATION. 1978. q. No.3, Lane 153, Section 2, Cahng An East Rd., Taipei, Taiwan, Republic of China. **Indexed:** Sportsearch (1978-).
 —BLDSC (1742.560000).

613   GW   ISSN 0341-3403
ATEM UND MENSCH;* Zeitschrift fuer Atempflege - Massage - Entspannung - moderne Gymnastik. 1959. q. DM.14. Helfer-Verlag, E. Schuabe, Basler Str. 2, 6380 Bad Homburg, Germany. Eds. Dr. K.O. Kuppe, Guenther Braunger. bk.rev.; illus. circ. 5,000.
 Supersedes (1962-1975): Atem (ISSN 0004-6477)

613.7   US
AUSTIN HEALTH & FITNESS. 1988. m. $10. Metro Publishing, Box 2534, Cedar Park, TX 78630. TEL 512-918-8190. FAX 512-331-9271. Ed. Rhonda Cloos. adv.; circ. 50,000 (controlled). **Document type:** consumer publication.

613.194   AT   ISSN 1034-3431
AUSTRALIAN SUN & HEALTH. 1983. q. Aus.$22. Leslie J. Hotchkin, Ed. & Pub., P.O. Box 5601, M-C Gold Coast, Qld. 4217, Australia. TEL 61-75-73-3138. (back issues avail.) **Document type:** consumer publication.
 Description: Lists locations for people who are at ease with nudity.

613.7   CN   ISSN 1201-6144
▼**AVANTE.** (Text in English, French) 1995. 3/yr. Can.$65 (foreign Can.$83). Canadian Association for Health, Physical Education, Recreation and Dance, Place R. Tait McKenzie, 1600 James Naismith Dr., Gloucester, ON K1B 5N4, Canada. TEL 613-748-5622. FAX 613-748-5737. E-mail: andrea.grantham@cdnsport.ca. Ed.Bd; Pub. Andrea Grantham. **Document type:** academic/scholarly publication.
 Description: Designed to stimulate and communicate Canadian research and critical thought on issues pertaining to health, physical education and recreation.
 Refereed Serial

613.7   SW   ISSN 1100-3839
B & K SPORTS MAGAZINE. 1981. 11/yr. SEK 318; newsstand price: SEK 39.50. B & K Sports Magazine AB, Box 45026, S-104 30 Stockholm, Sweden. TEL 46-8-34-77-00. FAX 46-8-34-63-33. Ed. Ove Rytter. adv.: B&W page SEK 12776, color page SEK 17226; trim 185 x 275; adv. contact: Johan Lindgren. circ. 24,600. cols./p.: 3; pp./issue: 84.

B B A - BIOENERGETICS. (Biochimica et Biophysica Acta) see *BIOLOGY — Biophysics*

BABY AGE. see *CHILDREN AND YOUTH — About*

613.7   US   ISSN 1046-2783
BACK TO HEALTH MAGAZINE;* your guide to relief recovery and well-being. 1988. m. $17.55. 795 St. Albans Dr., Boca Raton, FL 33486-1522. Ed. Herbert Siegel. adv.; bk.rev. circ. 200,000. (back issues avail.)
 Formerly: Backpain.
 Description: Directed towards men and women over 40 years old. Covers pain relief, proper diet, exercise and mental health.

613.7   GW   ISSN 0171-0591
DAS BAD. m. DM.91. Ebert Verlag GmbH, Blankenseer Str. 6-8, 23562 Luebeck, Germany. TEL 0451-501011. FAX 04509-2241. **Document type:** bulletin.

613.194   US
BARE IN MIND.* 1972. 12/yr. $12. Leisure Publications (Perris), Box 368, Perris, CA 92370-0368. Ed. Thelma Manning. adv.; bk.rev. circ. 2,700. (tabloid format)
 Description: Focuses on nudism.

613.7   GW   ISSN 0176-8700
BETRIFFT SPORT. 1979. 6/yr. DM.73.80. Meyer und Meyer Verlag GmbH, Von-Coels-Str. 390, 52080 Aachen, Germany. TEL 0241-556033. FAX 0241-558281. Ed.Bd. circ. 2,000. (looseleaf format; back issues avail.) **Document type:** trade publication.
 Description: Magazine for exercise and dance instructors. Practical directions for rhythm and music, body movement and learning a sport.

PHYSICAL FITNESS AND HYGIENE

613   LH   ISSN 0006-0429
BEWUSSTER LEBEN; Zeitschrift fuer positive Lebens- und Arbeitsgestaltung, gesunde Ernaehrung und natuerliche Lebensweise. 1935. m. 48 Fr. Leben Verlag AG, FL-9490 Vaduz, Liechtenstein. TEL 075-20977. adv.; bk.rev.; bibl.; charts; illus. circ. 25,000.
    Formerly: Leben.

612.76   US
BEYOND P E. (Physical Education) 1991. bi-m. $18. 105 Lexington Ave., No. 8B, New York, NY 10016. TEL 212-779-0294. FAX 212-779-1526. Ed. Ronald L. Dobrin. adv.; circ. 80,000 (controlled). (back issues avail.) Document type: consumer publication.
    Formerly (until 1993): New York Bodies.
    Description: Covers topics in bodybuilding, fitness and health for the urban man and woman, including aerobics, yoga, nutrition, massage and healing.

613.7   IR   ISSN 0252-5356
BIHDASHT-I JAHAN. (Text in Persian) 1983. 3/yr. IRI.1000 per no. Markaz-i Nashr-i Danishgahi - Iran University Press, 85 Park Ave., Dr. Bihishti Ave., P.O. Box 15875-4748, Tehran, Iran. TEL 98-21-8713232. FAX 98-21-8861749. TELEX 213636-8-D5000. Ed. Dr. F. Adibzadeh. circ. 6,000. Document type: academic/scholarly publication.
    Description: Covers issues relating to health and hygiene in Iran.

613.7   GW
BIO SPEZIAL MAGAZIN. 1984. bi-m. DM.42. Bio Ritter GmbH, Monatshauserstr. 8, 82327 Tutzing, Germany. TEL 08158-8021. FAX 08158-7142. Ed. Monica Ritter. adv. contact: Barbara Hellemann. circ. 60,000. (back issues avail.) Document type: consumer publication.
    Description: Contains information on achieving health through natural means and procedures.

613   GW   ISSN 0006-3487
BIONOMICA. 1950. bi-m. DM.20. (Bionomica-Gemeinschaft e.V.) Bionomica Verlag, Duesseldorferstr. 9-11, 68219 Mannheim, Germany. TEL 0621-895061. FAX 0621-814962. Ed. Ewald Koenemann. adv.; bk.rev. Document type: bulletin.

613.7 646.7   BL   ISSN 0104-1533
BOA FORMA. 1988. m. $85. Editora Azul, S.A., Av. Nacoes Unidas, 5777, 05479-900 Sao Paulo SP, Brazil. TEL 11-816-7866. FAX 11-813-9115. (Subscr. to: Rua do Curtume 769, 0565-900 Sao Paulo SP, Brazil. TEL 011-823-9100) Ed. Jorge de Souza. adv.: color page $11000; 208 x 274. charts; illus. circ. 63,000. Document type: consumer publication.
    Description: Probes current health and fitness issues for all ages.

BODY & BEAUTY CARE. see BEAUTY CULTURE

BODY BULLETIN NEWSLETTER. see OCCUPATIONAL HEALTH AND SAFETY

613.7   US   ISSN 1066-3797
BODYWISE. 1992. bi-m. $15.24. Prestige Publications, Inc., 4151 Knob Dr., St. Paul, MN 55122-1876. TEL 800-728-3213. FAX 612-454-5791. Ed. Carla Waldemar; Pub. Russ Moore. adv. contact: Don Beeson. circ. 160,000 (paid). Document type: consumer publication.

613.7   CU   ISSN 0138-6565
BOLETIN CIENTIFICO-TECNICO I N D E R - CUBA. 1965. q. Instituto Nacional de Deportes, Educacion Fisica y Recreacion, Centre de Documentacion e Informacion, Havana, Cuba. Indexed: Sportsearch (1976-). Document type: bulletin.

613.194   UK   ISSN 0264-0406
BRITISH NATURISM. 1964. q. $12. Central Council for British Naturism, Assurance House, 30-32 Wycliffe Rd., Northampton NN1 5JF, England. TEL 01604-20361. FAX 01604-230176. adv.; illus.; circ. 11,000 (controlled).

613.7   PR   ISSN 0896-2642
BUENA SALUD. (Text in Spanish) 1987. m. $22 (foreign $37) (effective 1995). (Interamerican College of Physicians and Surgeons) Casiano Communications Inc., 1700 Fernandez Juncos Ave., San Juan, PR 00909-2999. TEL 809-728-3000. FAX 809-728-7325. Ed. Ivonne Longueira. adv.: B&W page $2845, color page $4080; trim 8 1/8 x 10 3/4. circ. 70,000. Document type: consumer publication.
    Description: Covers health and fitness for families and individuals.

613.7 613.2   ZA
BWINO: HEALTH CARE NEWS. 1981. bi-m. free. Ministry of Health, Health Education Unit, P.O. Box 32669, Lusaka, Zambia. circ. 6,000. Document type: government publication, newsletter.

C C B C NEWSLETTER. (Council of Community Blood Centers) see MEDICAL SCIENCES — Hematology

C P H A HEALTH DIGEST. (Canadian Public Health Association) see PUBLIC HEALTH AND SAFETY

CAHIERS DE LA PUERICULTRICE. see CHILDREN AND YOUTH — About

613.7   CN   ISSN 1201-2319
CANADIAN ASSOCIATION FOR HEALTH, PHYSICAL EDUCATION, RECREATION AND DANCE. JOURNAL. Short title: C A H P E R D Journal. (Text in English, French) 1933. q. Can.$65. Canadian Association for Health, Physical Education, Recreation and Dance, Place R. Tait McKenzie, 1600 James Naismith Dr., Gloucester, ON K1B 5N4, Canada. TEL 613-748-5622. FAX 613-748-5737. Ed. Andrea Grantham. adv.; bk.rev.; illus. circ. 2,200. (processed; also avail. in microfilm from MML) Indexed: Can.Per.Ind., CMI, Sportsearch (1952-). Document type: academic/scholarly publication.
—BLDSC (4722.300000); Faxon; UnCover. CCC.
    Former titles: Canadian Association for Health, Physical Education and Recreation. Journal (ISSN 0834-1915); C A H P E R Journal (ISSN 0226-5478)

613.7   CN   ISSN 1187-0818
CANADIAN INTRAMURAL RECREATION ASSOCIATION. BULLETIN; the voice of intramurals in Canada. (Text in English and French) 1977. bi-m. Can.$40. Canadian Intramural Recreation Association - Association Canadienne de Loisirs Intramuros, 1600 James Naismith Dr., Ste. 601, Gloucester, ON K1B 5N4, Canada. TEL 613-748-5639. FAX 613-748-5737. Ed. Suzanne Bray. bk.rev.; abstr.; illus. circ. 1,500. Document type: bulletin.
    Description: Contains ideas, information and hands-on practical and user-friendly information on intramurals for practitioners and participants.

CANADIAN JOURNAL OF DIABETES CARE. see MEDICAL SCIENCES — Endocrinology

CAPITAL SPORTS FOCUS. see SPORTS AND GAMES

616.1   US   ISSN 0194-2557
CARDIAC ALERT. 1979. m. $39. Phillips Publishing, Inc., Consumer Publishing, 7811 Montrose Rd., Potomac, MD 20854. TEL 301-340-2100. FAX 301-424-7034. Ed. Dr. Jorge C. Rios. index.
—CCC.

CATALYST (MARIETTA); a publication resource of New Age newsletters, book reviews, personals, holistic health, UFO's and psychic connections. see NEW AGE PUBLICATIONS

CHEMECOLOGY; covering health, safety and the environment. see ENVIRONMENTAL STUDIES

613.7 612.3   US
CHICAGO HEALTHCARE.* m. Syncom, Inc., Box 2847, Glen Ellyn, IL 60138-2847. TEL 708-858-1980. FAX 708-858-0440. Ed. Herb Hillabrand. circ. 10,000. Document type: trade publication.

613.7   US
CHICAGO RUNNER MAGAZINE. 1992. q. (Chicago Area Runners Association) Eliot Wineberg, Ed. & Pub., 7840 W. Lincoln Ave., Skokie, IL 60077. TEL 708-675-0200. FAX 708-675-2903. adv.: B&W page $2730, color page $3230; trim 8 1/2 x 11. circ. 45,000. Document type: consumer publication.

CHILD MAGAZINE'S GUIDE TO HAVING A BABY. see CHILDREN AND YOUTH — About

CHILDREN IN THE TROPICS. see CHILDREN AND YOUTH — About

CLINICAL JOURNAL OF SPORT MEDICINE. see MEDICAL SCIENCES — Sports Medicine

CLUB BUSINESS INTERNATIONAL. see BUSINESS AND ECONOMICS — Small Business

613.7   US   ISSN 0747-8283
CLUB INDUSTRY MAGAZINE.* 1984. m. $68 (foreign $125). 1300 Virginia Dr., Fl. 400, Fort Washington, PA 19034. TEL 508-872-2021. Ed. Margie Mararian. circ. 30,000.
—UMI.

613.7 616.12   FR   ISSN 0335-5306
COEUR ET SANTE. (Includes special numbers) 1974. bi-m. 100 F. (Federation Francaise de Cardiologie) Edicardio, 50 rue de Rocher, 75008 Paris, France. TEL 44-90-83-67. FAX 42-93-38-97. Ed. Guy Malherbe; Pub. Armand Schaller. adv. Document type: newspaper.

613.7 155.937   US
CONNECTICUT HOSPICE NEWSLETTER; making today count. 1979. s-a. free. Connecticut Hospice Inc., 61 Burban Dr., Branford, CT 06405. TEL 203-481-6231. FAX 203-483-9539. circ. 50,000.
    Description: Provides information related to timely medical issues as they impact hospice care; includes features about hospice services.

CONNELLY REPORT. see NUTRITION AND DIETETICS

613   UK
CONSULTANT. q. free. Hospital Consultants and Specialists Association, No. One Kingsclere Rd., Overton, Basingstoke, Hampshire RG25 3JP, England. TEL 0265-771777. FAX 0265-770999. adv. circ. 7,000. Indexed: Bus.Ind., Hospit.Ind., Tr.& Indus.Ind.

613.7   US   ISSN 1058-0832
    CODEN: CREHEI
CONSUMER REPORTS ON HEALTH. 1989. m. $24 (foreign $30). Consumers Union of the United States, Inc., 101 Truman Ave., Yonkers, NY 10703-1057. TEL 914-378-2000. FAX 914-378-2906. (Subscr. to: Box 56356, Boulder, CO 80322-6356) Ed. Michael Leff. circ. 40,000. Indexed: CINAHL.
    ●Also available online. Vendor(s): Knight-Ridder, Inc. (File no.646).
—BLDSC (3424.551000).
    Formerly: Consumer Reports Health Letter (ISSN 1044-3193)
    Description: Provides current information to help you make wise decisions about the health care services and products you and your family need.

CONTACT QUARTERLY; a vehicle for moving ideas. see DANCE

613.7   JA
CONTEMPORARY HEALTH DIGEST. (Text in Japanese) 1986. a. Snow Brand Milk Products Co., Ltd., Health & Nutrition Institute - Yukijirushi Nyugyo K.K. Kenko Seikatsu Kenkyujo, 13, Honshiocho, Shinjuku-ku, Tokyo 160, Japan.

613.7   US
COORDINATOR (ST. PAUL). q. $10. National Association of Health Unit Clerks-Coordinators, 1821 University Ave., Ste. 162-S, St. Paul, MN 55104. Ed. Lupe Gutierrez. circ. 2,350. (looseleaf format) Document type: newsletter.
    Description: Information for health unit coordinators.

613.7   IT
CORRERE. 1981. m. L.52000 (foreign L.86000). Editoriale Sport Italia, Via Masaccio 12, 20149 Milan, Italy. TEL 39-2-4815396. FAX 39-2-4690907. Ed. Antonio Brazzit. adv.: B&W page L.4500000, color page L.6750000. circ. 50,000.

613.7   SP   ISSN 1130-4421
CUERPOMENTE. 1990. m. 4950 ptas. (foreign 8700 ptas.). Oasis, S.L., Taquigraf Garriga 10, 08014 Barcelona, Spain. TEL 34-3-4193888. FAX 34-3-4197588. circ. 45,000.

5190 PHYSICAL FITNESS AND HYGIENE

613 790.1   SP
CURATE REGENERATE. 12/yr. Cuatro Caminos 27 y Jaime Cancer 33, 080222 Barcelona, Spain. TEL 85-23-65-10.

613.7   US
CURRENT AWARENESS IN HEALTH EDUCATION. m. $24. U.S. Bureau of Health Education, Department of Health and Human Services, Washington, DC 20201. TEL 202-655-4000. (Subscr. to: Supt. of Documents, Washington, DC 20402)
●Also available online. Vendor(s): Ovid Technologies.

371.37 375   US   ISSN 0199-820X
CURRENT HEALTH 1; the beginning guide to health education. 1974. m. (Sep.-May). $27.95 (effective 1995-1996). Weekly Reader Corporation, 245 Long Hill Rd., Box 2791, Middletown, CT 06457. TEL 800-446-3355. FAX 609-786-3360. (Subscr. to: 3000 Cindel Dr., Delran, NJ 08075-9291) Ed. Sandra Maccarone; Pub. Richard J. Le Brasseur. charts; illus.; circ. 169,654 (paid). (also avail. in microform from UMI; reprint service avail. from UMI) Indexed: Ind.Child.Mag., Jun.High.Mag.Abstr., Mag.Ind., PMR, R.G.
—UMI; UnCover.
Description: Presents current information on all aspects of health and well-being. For grades 4-6.

613.7 371.3   US   ISSN 0163-156X
CURRENT HEALTH 2; the continuing guide to health education. m. (Sep.-May). $27.95 (effective 1996) (includes Human Sexuality Supplement). Weekly Reader Corporation, 245 Long Hill Rd., Box 2791, Middletown, CT 06457-9291. TEL 800-446-3355. FAX 609-786-3360. (Subscr. to: 3000 Cindel Dr., Delran, NJ 08075) Ed. Sandra Maccarone; Pub. Richard J. Le Brasseur. circ. 248,722 (paid). Indexed: Acad.Ind., Hlth.Ind., Jun.High.Mag.Abstr.
●Also available online. Vendor(s): University Microfilms International.
Also available on CD-ROM. Producer(s): University Microfilms International.
—Faxon; UMI; UnCover.
Description: For grades 7-12. Contains current information on all aspects of health and well-being.

613.7   US   ISSN 1055-1352
CURRENT ISSUES IN EXERCISE SCIENCE. 1991. q. Human Kinetics Publishers, Inc., Box 5076, Champaign, IL 61825-5076. TEL 217-351-5076; 800-747-4457. FAX 217-351-2674. Ed. Julia Anderson. adv. contact: Michele Watson. Document type: monographic series.
—BLDSC (3499.068500).
Description: Reports on hot topics of interest in exercise science.

CURRENT TOPICS IN BIOENERGETICS. see BIOLOGY — Biophysics

613.7   US
DALLAS RECOVERY.* m. 4644 Amesbury Dr., Apt. 220, Dallas, TX 75206-4818. TEL 214-521-8318. Ed. Bruce Lanahan.

613.7   CC   ISSN 1002-574X
DAZHONG JIANKANG/ORDINARY PEOPLE'S HEALTH. (Text in Chinese) 1985. m. Jiankang Baoshe - Health Journal Publishing, 11 Shuangsi, Jiu Gulou Dajie, Beijing 100009, People's Republic of China. TEL 4015114. Ed. Li Zhimin.

DEATH. see PSYCHOLOGY

DEMETER-BLAETTER. see FOOD AND FOOD INDUSTRIES

613   GW   ISSN 0343-3838
DER DEUTSCHE BADEBETRIEB. Short title: D D B. 1909. m. DM.109. (Verband Deutscher Badebetriebe e.V.) Ebert Verlag GmbH, Blankenseer Str. 6-8, 23562 Luebeck, Germany. TEL 0451-501011. FAX 04509-2241. Ed. Hans Juergen Ebert. circ. 14,400. Document type: trade publication.
Formerly: Kurbad; Which incorporated: Bad.

DIABETES DIALOGUE. see MEDICAL SCIENCES — Endocrinology

613.7   US   ISSN 1048-8391
DIET & HEALTH MAGAZINE. 1989. q. $4.95 per no. Blockbuster Periodicals, Inc., 2131 Hollywood Blvd., Hollywood, FL 33020. TEL 305-925-5242. Ed. Barbara Newman. circ. 65,000.
Incorporates: Diet and Health Series.
Description: For adults interested in health, nutrition, weight loss, and healthy living.

613.7 610   IT
DIMENSIONE SALUTE. m. L.35000. Valentini Editore s.r.l., Via Fabio Fulzi 19, 20124 Milan, Italy. TEL 02-6696471. TELEX 330299 VALEDI I. Ed. Aldo Quinto Lazzari.

DIRECTORY OF U.S. INTERNATIONAL HEALTH ORGANIZATIONS. see MEDICAL SCIENCES

610   DK   ISSN 0904-2369
DIT LAEGEMAGASIN. (Supplement to: Laegemagasinet (ISSN 0902-1787)) 1987. bi-m. DKK 160. Forlaget John Vaboe A-S, Emiliekildevej 35, DK-2930 Klampenborg, Denmark. TEL 45-39-90-80-00. FAX 45-39-90-82-80. Ed. Jannie P. Helle. adv. contact: Kirsten Waaben.
Formerly: Patientmagasinet (ISSN 0902-1795)

613.7   CC
DONGFANG QIGONG/ORIENTAL QIGONG. (Text in Chinese) bi-m. Beijing Qigong Yanjiuhui - Beijing Qigong Research Society, Gongren Tiyuguan-nei (Inside Beijing Workers Gym), Beijing 100027, Poeple's Republic of China. TEL 592961. Ed. Xu Yixing.

613.7   IT
DOSSIER SALUTE. 1993. m.? Editrend s.r.l., Via Torino 51, 20123 Milan, Italy. TEL 39-2-2023007. FAX 39-2-8690449. Ed. Virgilio Degiovanni. bibl.; illus. Document type: consumer publication.

EATING WELL; the magazine of food & health. see FOOD AND FOOD INDUSTRIES

EDUCACION MEDICA Y SALUD. see EDUCATION — Guides To Schools And Colleges

613   IT
EDUCAZIONE SANITARIA E PROMOZIONE DELLA SALUTE. (Text in Italian; summaries in English and French) 1978. q. L.195000($130) (effective 1996). (Centro Sperimentale per l'Educazione Sanitaria) Pensiero Scientifico Editore s.r.l., Via Bradano 3-C, 00199 Rome, Italy. TEL 06-86207158. FAX 06-86207160. Ed. M.A. Modolo. bk.rev.; bibl.; index. circ. 900. Document type: academic/scholarly publication.
Formerly: Educazione Sanitaria e Medicina Preventiva (ISSN 0391-6200); Supersedes (1956-1977): Educazione Sanitaria (ISSN 0013-2098)

613.7   HU   ISSN 0073-4004
EGESZSEGNEUELES; educatio sanitaria. 1959. bi-m. $29.50 (effective 1993). Ifsusagi Lap- es Konyvkiado Vallalat, Revay u. 16, 1374 Budapest, Hungary. TEL 361-113-7038. (Subscr. to: Kultura, P.O.B. 149, 1398 Budapest 62, Hungary) Ed. Simon Tamas. bk.rev. circ. 4,300. Document type: newspaper.

613   GW   ISSN 0944-3746
ELAN. 1955. m. DM.44. Urban and Vogel, Lindwurmstr. 95, 80337 Munich, Germany. TEL 089-53292-0. FAX 089-53292100. circ. 100,000. Document type: consumer publication.
—CCC.
Formerly: Deine Gesundheit (ISSN 0415-1798)

ELYSIUM: JOURNAL OF THE SENSES. see NEW AGE PUBLICATIONS

410   US   ISSN 0199-6304
EMPLOYEE HEALTH AND FITNESS; the executive update on health improvement programs. 1979. m. $219. American Health Consultants, Inc., Six Piedmont Center, Ste. 400, Atlanta, GA 30305. TEL 404-262-7436; 800-688-2421. FAX 800-284-3291. Ed. Steve Lewis. bk.rev. circ. 820. (also avail. in microfilm from UMI; back issues avail.; reprint service avail. from UMI) Indexed: Sportsearch (1980-). Document type: newsletter.
●Also available online. Vendor(s): Lexis-Nexis.
—CCC.

613.7 368   BE   ISSN 0013-6964
EN MARCHE; journal bimensuel d'information pour les beneficiaires des soins de sante. 1948. s-m. 550 Fr. Alliance Nationale des Mutualites Chretiennes, 121 rue de la Loi, B-1040 Brussels, Belgium. TEL 02-237-46-27. FAX 02-237-33-00. Ed. H. Peemans-Poullet. adv.; bk.rev.; charts; illus.; stat. circ. 430,000. (tabloid format)
Description: Discusses various aspects of health and relevant fields, such as insurance.

ENFANT EN MILIEU TROPICAL. see CHILDREN AND YOUTH — About

ENVIRONMENTAL HEALTH MONTHLY. see ENVIRONMENTAL STUDIES

DIE ERSATZKASSE. see SOCIAL SERVICES AND WELFARE

613.7   MP
ERUUL MEND/HEALTH. (Text in Mongolian) 1959. q. 160 tugrik. Ministry of Health, Ulan Bator, Mongolia. TEL 976-1-321307. FAX 976-1-321278. TELEX 247 MINHE MH. Ed. T. Ochirkhuu. circ. 25,000.

613.7   CH
EVERGREEN MONTHLY. (Text in Chinese) 1983. m. 2 Pa Teh Rd., 11th Floor, Sec.3, Taipei, Taiwan, Republic of China. TEL 02-7731665. FAX 02-7416838. circ. 140,000.
Description: Introduces health care knowledge.

613   US   ISSN 1048-2954
GV201
EXECUTIVE EDGE. 1970. m. $69.95 (foreign $79.95); renewal $59.95 (foreign $69.95). Select Press, Box 37, Corte Madera, CA 94925. TEL 415-924-1612. Ed. Rick Crandall. bk.rev.; circ. 46,131. circ. 9,000 (paid). (back issues avail.) Indexed: Sportsearch. Document type: newsletter.
—CCC.
Former titles (until 1990): Executive Fitness (ISSN 0889-6739); (until 1986): Executive Fitness Newsletter (ISSN 0014-4525)
Description: Offers health tips for the busy executive trying to stay in shape; with topical articles on exercise, diet and stress-reducing techniques.

613.7   HK
EXECUTIVE FITNESS NEWSLETTER. s-m. $48. Asia Letter Group, Hennessy Rd., P.O. Box 20036, Hennessy Rd. Post Office, Hong Kong. Document type: newsletter.
Formerly: Executive Fitness.

614   US
EXECUTIVE HEALTH'S GOOD HEALTH REPORT. 1963. m. (plus 1 bonus issue). $34 in US; Canada, Mexico $40; elsewhere $58. Executive Health, 383 Route 46 W., Fairfield, NJ 07004-2402. TEL 201-575-3507. Ed. Deborah Hauss; Pub. Daniel Glassman. adv. contact: Mark Sheridan. bk.rev.; index. circ. 15,000. (also avail. in microfilm from UMI; microfiche from UMI; back issues avail.; reprint service avail. from UMI) Indexed: Consum.Ind., Hlth.Ind., Sportsearch. Document type: newsletter.
—UMI.
Former titles (until June 1991): Executive Health Report (ISSN 0882-2131); Executive Health.
Description: Disseminates information on health issues, plus regular features including nutrition and exercise.

613.9   US
EXER-SAFETY NEWS.* 1980. q. $25. Exer-Safety Association, 3536 N. Econlockhatchee Trl., Orlando, FL 32817-1612. TEL 216-562-8280. Ed. Sharon Foy. adv.; bk.rev. circ. 6,000.
Description: Information on safe practices in exercise to music classes.

613.7   US   ISSN 0882-4657
EXERCISE FOR MEN ONLY. bi-m. $33.15. Chelo Publishing Inc., Empire State Bldg., 350 Fifth Ave., New York, NY 10118. TEL 212-947-4322. FAX 212-563-4774. Document type: consumer publication.

613.7 641.1   US   ISSN 0748-3155
QP301
EXERCISE PHYSIOLOGY: CURRENT SELECTED RESEARCH. 1985. a. $45. A M S Press, Inc., 56 E. 13th St., New York, NY 10003. TEL 212-777-4700. FAX 212-995-5413. Eds. Charles O. Dotson, James H. Humphrey. index. (back issues avail.)
—BLDSC (3836.235900).
Description: Research articles on various topics of exercise science and sports medicine.

EXERCISE STANDARDS AND MALPRACTICE REPORTER. see LAW

PHYSICAL FITNESS AND HYGIENE

613.7 612.3 US ISSN 0895-2906
EXTENDED CARE PRODUCT NEWS. 1987. bi-m. free. Heath Management Publications, Inc., 550 American Rd., King of Prussia, PA 19406-1441. TEL 215-337-4466. FAX 215-337-0890. Ed. Peter Norris. adv.: B&W page $3540, color page $4790. circ. 42,036.

613.7 US
▼**FABIO'S HEALTHY BODIES MAGAZINE.*** 1994. bi-m. $16.60; newsstand price: $2.95. Sting Ray Publishing, Box 96004, Inwood, NY 11096-0004. TEL 516-593-2632. Ed. Steve Raimondi; Pub. Steve Raimondi. adv.: B&W page $4080. circ. 100,000 (paid). Document type: consumer publication.

613.7 CH
FAMILIES MONTHLY. (Text in Chinese) 1976. m. 2 Pa Teh Rd., 11th Floor, Sec.3, Taipei, Taiwan, Republic of China. TEL 02-7731665. FAX 02-7416838. circ. 155,000.
  Description: Covers family life.

613.7 US
FAMILY PROGRAMMER. m. free. Bodylog Inc., 34 Maple Ave., Box 8, Armonk, NY 10504.
  Formerly (until 1983): T I Source and Logo News.
  Description: Information about the Step-In-Time fitness test and health and fitness awareness.

613.7 US
FEELING GREAT. 1984. m. $15.97. 45 W. 34th St., Rm. 407, New York, NY 10001. TEL 212-239-0855. Ed. Tim Moriarty. adv. circ. 250,000.

613.7 US ISSN 0888-4162
FEMALE BODYBUILDING AND WEIGHT TRAINING. Variant title: Female Bodybuilding. 1986. bi-m. $17.99. Starlog Group, Inc., 475 Park Ave., S., 8th Fl., New York, NY 10016. TEL 212-689-2830. FAX 212-889-7933. Document type: consumer publication.

FIRST-TIME PARENTS. see *CHILDREN AND YOUTH — About*

FIRST YEAR OF LIFE; a guide to your baby's growth and development month by month. see *CHILDREN AND YOUTH — About*

613.7 790.1 GW
▼**FIT FOR FUN.** 1994. m. DM.54; newsstand price: DM.5. Verlagsgruppe Milchstrasse, Milchstr. 1, 20148 Hamburg, Germany. TEL 040-44198-0. FAX 040-458519. adv. Document type: consumer publication.

613.7 617.1 US
FIT FOR THE NATION. irreg. American College of Sports Medicine, Box 1440, Indianapolis, IN 46206-1440. TEL 317-637-9200. FAX 317-634-7817. Document type: newsletter.
  Description: Covers issues on health care reform and activities of the Health and Science Policy network.

613 UK ISSN 0266-5212
FITNESS. 1982. m. £10.80. Goodhead Publications Ltd., 27 Murdock Rd., Bicester, Oxon. OX6 7RG, England. adv. circ. 40,000.
  Formerly (until 1984): Health and Fitness (Bicester) (ISSN 0264-2549)

613.7 SZ
FITNESS. 10/yr. Buechler & Co. AG, Hardeggstr. 27, 8049 Zurich, Switzerland.

613.7 US ISSN 1060-9237
GV482
FITNESS; mind body spirit. m. (10/yr.) $17 (foreign $32). Gruner & Jahr U.S.A. Publishing, 685 Third Ave., New York, NY 10017. TEL 212-878-8700; 800-888-1181. Ed. Rona Cherry; Pub. Margery Gladstone. adv. contact: Mary Morgan. circ. 500,000. Document type: consumer publication.
  Formerly (until 1992): Family Circle's Fitness Now.
  Description: Covers beauty and fashion, health, fitness and wellness for women.

613.7 CN ISSN 0820-6163
FITNESS BULLETIN. 1978. m. $30 (effective 1995 & 1996). (Fitness Institute) Steen Publishing, RR 1, Cheltenham, ON L0P 1C0, Canada. TEL 905-838-0943. FAX 905-838-0948. Ed. David Steen. bk.rev. circ. 4,000. (back issues avail.) Document type: newsletter.
  Formerly (until 1982): Fitness Institute Bulletin (ISSN 0826-4341)
  Description: Contains health and fitness news, and instructive articles for subscribers and institute members.

613.7 658 US ISSN 0882-0481
FITNESS MANAGEMENT. 12/yr. $24. Leisure Publications, Inc., 3923 W. 6th St., Los Angeles, CA 90020. TEL 213-385-3926. FAX 213-383-1152. Ed. Edward Pitts. circ. 23,000. (back issues avail.) Indexed: Sportsearch (1991-). Document type: trade publication.
  —BLDSC (3948.229200); UnCover.
  Description: For owners and managers of athletic and health facilities.

613.7 US ISSN 1054-674X
FITNESS PLUS. 1990. bi-m. $35.35. Focus Publishing Ltd., 28 W. 25th St., 7th Fl., New York, NY 10010. TEL 212-647-0222. Ed. Russ Oliver. adv. circ. 250,000.
  Description: Covers health, nutrition, weight training, exercise, dieting, fitness fashions.

613.7 US
▼**FITNESS SPECTRUM SERIES.** 1994. irreg. (2-3/yr.). $14.95 (Canada $19.95) per no. Human Kinetics Publishers, Inc., Box 5076, Champaign, IL 61825-5076. TEL 800-747-4457. FAX 217-351-1549.

613 BU ISSN 0861-6485
CODEN: KUFIAT
FIZIKALNA, KURORTNA I REKHABILITATSIONNA MEDITSINA/JOURNAL OF PHYSICAL, HEALTH RESORT AND REHABILITATION MEDICINE. (Text in Bulgarian; summaries in English, Russian) q. 10 lv. (Ministerstvo na Narodnoto Zdrave) Izdatelstvo Meditsina i Fizkultura, 11 Pl. Slaveikov, 1080 Sofia, Bulgaria. (Distr. by: Hemus, 6 Rouski Blvd., 1000 Sofia, Bulgaria) (Co-sponsor: Nauchno Druzhestvo po Kurortologija, Fizioterapija i Rehabilitacija) Ed. St. Bankov. circ. 850. Indexed: Abstr.Bulg.Sci.Med.Lit., Excerp.Med. (until 1993).
  —CASDDS.
  Formerly (until 1992): Kurortologija i Fizioterapija (ISSN 0368-7066)

FOCUS ON FEDERAL EMPLOYEE HEALTH AND ASSISTANCE. see *OCCUPATIONAL HEALTH AND SAFETY*

FODOR'S HEALTHY ESCAPES. see *TRAVEL AND TOURISM*

FOOD AND FITNESS. see *FOOD AND FOOD INDUSTRIES*

613.7 646.7 IT
FORMA IN MODO NATURALE. m. L.50000 (foreign L.80000). Alberto Peruzzi Editore, Via E. Marelli 165, 20099 Sesto San Giovanni (MI), Italy. TEL 02-242021.

A FRIEND INDEED; for women in the prime of life/pour les femmes dans la force de l'age. see *WOMEN'S INTERESTS*

FRONTIERS OF HEALTH SERVICES MANAGEMENT. see *HOSPITALS*

613 FR ISSN 0995-6301
GAZETTE OFFICIELLE DU THERMALISME.* 1988. bi-m. 250 F. Office des Nouvelles Internationales, Agence de Presse, 16 rue de l'Estrapade, 75005 Paris, France. TEL 59-30-03-28. (Co-sponsor: Federation Thermale et Climatique Francaise) Ed. Nicole Belval.

GENEESKUNDE EN SPORT. see *MEDICAL SCIENCES — Sports Medicine*

GESICHERTES LEBEN. see *SOCIAL SERVICES AND WELFARE*

613 GW ISSN 0016-9234
GESUND LEBEN. 1952. 12/yr. DM.24.80. Verlag M. und H. Schaper GmbH, Kalandstr. 4, 31061 Alfeld, Germany. TEL 05181-8009-0. FAX 05181-8009-33. (Subscr. to: Postfach 1642, 31046 Alfeld, Germany) Ed. Arnim Sagaster. adv.; charts; illus. circ. 60,000. Document type: bulletin.
  —CCC.

613 GW ISSN 0016-9250
GESUNDES LEBEN; Medizinalpolitische Rundschau, Zeitschrift fuer natuerliche Lebensordnung. 1924. m. DM.30. Praxiswissen und Fachfortbildungs Gesellschaft mgH, Stresemannstr. 7, 37269 Eschwege, Germany. Ed. Hermann Forschepiepe. adv.; bk.rev.; tr.lit. circ. 5,000.
  —BLDSC (4163.900000).

613 GW ISSN 0016-9269
GESUNDHEIT. 1949. bi-m. DM.9. Agis Verlag GmbH, Ooser Luisenstr. 23, Postfach 2220, 76532 Baden-Baden, Germany. FAX 07221-66810. adv.; bk.rev.; illus. circ. 3,400,000. (also avail. in microform from UMI)
  Former titles: Gesundheit in Betrieb und Familie; Gesundheit.

613.7 AU
GEWICHTHEBER. 1954. 10/yr. S.300. Oesterreichischer Gewichtheberverband, Postfach 22, A-1172 Vienna, Austria. TEL 01-7497067. FAX 01-7497062. Ed. Gerhard Peya. (also avail. in diskette format) Document type: bulletin.
  Formerly: Kraftsportmagazin Gewichtheben.

614 RU ISSN 0016-9900
CODEN: GISAAA
GIGIENA I SANITARIYA/HYGIENE AND SANITATION. 1922. m. $96 (effective 1996). Izdatel'stvo Meditsina, Petroverigskii pereulok 6-8, 101000 Moscow, Russia. (Dist. by: Mezhdunarodnaya Kniga, B. Yakimanka 39, 117049 Moscow, Russia. TEL 7-095-2384600. FAX 7-095-2384634) Ed. V.P. Sinitsyna. adv.: E.I./Kosmodemyanskaya. bk.rev.; bibl.; index. (tabloid format) Indexed: Abstr.Hyg., Anal.Abstr., Biol.Abstr., C.I.S. Abstr., Chem.Abstr., Dairy Sci.Abstr., Dent.Ind., Field Crop Abstr., Food Sci.& Tech.Abstr., Ind.Med., Ind.Vet., INIS Atomind., Int.Aerosp.Abstr., Irr.& Drain.Abstr., Nutr.Abstr., Packag.Sci.Tech., Pollut.Abstr., Potato Abstr., Soils & Fert., Soyabean Abstr., Trop.Dis.Bull., Vet.Bull., W.R.C.Inf., World Bibl.Soc.Sec.
  —BLDSC (0048.000000); CASDDS; SWETS. CCC.
  Description: Publishes papers on all the branches of hygienic science and sanitary practice.

613.7 617.1 US
GOAL POST. q. American College of Sports Medicine, Box 1440, Indianapolis, IN 46206-1440. TEL 317-637-9200. FAX 317-634-7817. Document type: newsletter.
  Description: Contains information and updates on Healthy People 2000 health objectives and the activities of the HP2000 Program.

613.194 CN
GOING NATURAL. q. Can.$30. Federation of Canadian Naturists, P.O. Box 186, Islington, ON M9A 4X2, Canada.
  Description: Reports on naturist resorts, beaches, travel, events and all aspects of the naturist lifestyle.

GOOD NEIGHBOR. see *SOCIAL SERVICES AND WELFARE*

GREAT ACTIVITIES NEWSPAPER; an elementary physical education publication. see *EDUCATION*

613.7 612.3 US
GREAT BODY. 1989. bi-m. $2.95 per no. Harris Publications, Inc., 1115 Broadway, 8th fl., New York, NY 10010. TEL 212-807-7100. Ed. Mary Greenberg. adv. circ. 30,000.
  Description: Provides information on healthy eating and dieting, as well as work-out routines and fitness programs to improve health and stamina.

613.194 UK
GROVE. 1949. 3/yr. £10($20) Naturist Foundation, Naturist Headquarters, Orpington, Kent BR5 4ET, England. Ed. Christine Ashford. adv.; bk.rev. circ. 750. Document type: bulletin.
  Description: Information on facilities for naturist recreation in Great Britain and elsewhere.

PHYSICAL FITNESS AND HYGIENE

614 US
H E F NEWS. 1977. q. $15. Health Education Foundation, Inc., 2600 Virginia Ave., N.W., Ste. 502, Washington, DC 20037. TEL 202-338-3501. Ed. Marion Donovan Chafetz. circ. 900. (looseleaf format) **Document type:** newsletter.
Description: Provides information and perspectives on health behavior and lifestyle, written in layperson language.

613.7 US
H E - XTRA. bi-m. $100 membership. Association for the Advancement of Health Education, 1900 Association Dr., Reston, VA 22091. TEL 703-476-3438. FAX 703-476-6638. Ed. Linda Moore. adv. contact: Linda Moore. **Document type:** newsletter.
Description: The mission of AAHE is to advance health by encouraging, supporting, and assisting health professionals concerned with health promotion through education and other systematic strategies.

H V A CURRENT AWARENESS BULLETIN. (Health Visitors' Association) see *MEDICAL SCIENCES — Nurses And Nursing*

HAELSOKURIREN; tidningen om haelsa och egenvaard. see *PHARMACY AND PHARMACOLOGY*

613.7 HT
HAITI SANTE. 1980. q. $7. Centre D'Hygiene Familiale, 10, 1ere Impasse Lavand, Box 430, Port-au-Prince, Haiti. Ed. Ary Bordes. circ. 4,000.

HANDBOOK OF PSYCHOLOGY AND HEALTH SERIES. see *PSYCHOLOGY*

051 US ISSN 1052-1577
RC81.A1 CODEN: HHLEET
HARVARD HEALTH LETTER; a publication for the general readership, designed to provide accurate and timely health information. 1975. m. $24 (Canada $30; elsewhere $39) (effective 1994). (Harvard Medical School) Harvard Health Publications Group, 164 Longwood Ave., Boston, MA 02115. TEL 617-432-1485. FAX 617-432-1506. E-mail: jrudin@warren.med.edu. (Subscr. to: Box 420300, Palm Coast, FL 32142-0300. TEL 800-829-9045) Ed. Patricia Thomas. index; circ. 300,000 (paid). (back issues avail.) **Indexed:** Biol.Dig., CHNI, CINAHL, Hlth.Ind., Mag.Ind., Sportsearch. **Document type:** newsletter.
●Also available online. Vendor(s): Information Access Co.
—BLDSC (4267.127000); CASDDS.
Formerly: Harvard Medical School Health Letter (ISSN 0161-7486)
Description: Interprets timely health information for the general reader in layman's terms.

613.7 US ISSN 0899-4420
HEALING CURRENTS. 1976. q. $20 (foreign $24). Whole Health Institute, 4817 N. County Rd. 29, Loveland, CO 80538. TEL 303-679-4306. Ed. Kathy Bassett. bk.rev. circ. 1,500.
Formerly (until 1988): Crosstalk (ISSN 0899-4757)

613 II ISSN 0017-8861
HEALTH; devoted to healthful living. (Text in English) 1923. m. Rs.60 (foreign Rs.360) (effective 1992). Professional Publications Ltd., P.O. Box 2, Satya Sai Nagar, Madurai 625 003, Tamil Nadu, India. TEL 0452-600001. FAX 0452-601602. Pub. R. Lakshmipathy. adv.; B&W page Rs.1100, color page Rs.2000; trim 200 x 125. circ. 11,872. (reprint service avail. from UMI)

613 US ISSN 1059-938X
RA773
HEALTH (SAN FRANCISCO). 1969. 7/yr. $24. Heath Publishing Group (Subsidiary of: Time Publishing Ventures, Inc.), 301 Howard St., 18th Fl., San Francisco, CA 94105. TEL 415-512-9100. (Subscr. to: Box 56892, Boulder, CO 80322-6892. TEL 800-274-2522) Ed. Eric Schrier. adv.; bk.rev.; charts; illus.; stat. circ. 900,000. (also avail. in microform from UMI; reprint service avail. from UMI) **Indexed:** Acad.Ind., Biol.Abstr., Biol.Dig., C.I.N.L., Can.Per.Ind., CHNI, Curr.Lit.Fam.Plan., Gen.Sci.Ind., Hlth.Ind., Mag.Ind., Phys.Ed.Ind., PMR, R.G., Sportsearch, TOM. **Document type:** consumer publication.
●Also available online. Vendor(s): University Microfilms International.
—Faxon; SWETS; UMI; UnCover. **CCC.**
Formed by the merger of (1990-1992): In Health (ISSN 1047-0549); (1969-1991): Health (New York) (ISSN 0279-3547); Which was formerly (until 1981): Family Health (ISSN 0014-7249); Which incorporated (1950-1976): Today's Health (ISSN 0040-8514)
Description: Features a wide range of articles on how to maintian good health, including nutrition and physical fitness.

613.7 344 US ISSN 0897-3598
KF3821.A15
HEALTH ADVOCATE. 1971. 4/yr. $30. National Health Law Program, 2639 S. La Cienega Blvd., Los Angeles, CA 90034. TEL 310-204-6010. FAX 310-204-0891. Ed. L.M. Lavin. bk.rev. circ. 2,300. **Indexed:** Med. Care Rev.
Former titles (until 1982): N H E L P Health Advocate (ISSN 0272-7102); (until 1980): Health Law Newsletter (ISSN 0160-7227)
Description: Covers legal aspects of current health care issues, including Medicaid, substance abuse treatment, HIV, managed care and more.

613.194 UK ISSN 0017-8888
HEALTH AND EFFICIENCY. (Text in English, French, German) 1899. 12/yr. (plus q., s-a. eds.). $45. Peenhill Ltd., 28 Charles Sq., Pitfield St., London N1 6HT, England. TEL 071-253-4037. FAX 071-253-0539. Ed. Kate Sturdy. adv.; bk.rev.; illus. circ. 130,000. **Document type:** newsletter.
Description: News, views and reflections on the nudist and naturist scene, including areas where nudity and naked living are accepted.

HEALTH & ENVIRONMENT DIGEST. see *ENVIRONMENTAL STUDIES*

613.7 US
HEALTH & FITNESS; magazine for healthy, sound living. Short title: H F. 1989. q. Blockbuster Periodicals, Inc., 2131 Hollywood Blvd., Hollywood, FL 33020. TEL 305-925-5242. Ed. Barbara Newman. circ. 30,000.
Incorporates: Health Series.
Description: Probes current health and fitness issues for all ages.

613.7 UK
HEALTH AND FITNESS (LONDON). 1984. m. £23.40 (Europe £33.60; rest of world £52.71). Nexus Media Ltd., Nexus House, Azalea Dr., Swanley, Kent BR8 8HY. TEL 01322-660070. FAX 01322-667633. Ed. Sharon Walker. adv. contact: Pippa Sillitoe. circ. 49,000. **Document type:** consumer publication.
—BLDSC (4274.811500).
Formerly: Fitness.

613 UK ISSN 0265-2021
HEALTH AND HEALING. 1982. 6/yr. £1.50. Churches' Council for Health and Healing, St. Marylebone Parish Church, Marylebone Rd., London NW1 5LT, England. TEL 071-486-9644. Ed. David Goodacre. bk.rev. circ. 3,000.
Description: To serve Christians who care and heal, to share ideas and information, and to explore the churches' theological and spiritual role in health and healing.

613 US
HEALTH & HEALING. (Supplement avail.) 1991. m. $39.95 (effective 1992). Phillips Publishing, Inc., Consumer Publishing, 7811 Montrose Rd., Potomac, MD 20854. TEL 800-777-5005. FAX 301-424-7034. Ed. Dr. Julian Whitaker. (looseleaf format) **Document type:** newsletter.

613.7 610 US ISSN 1066-1786
RA773
HEALTH & MEDICAL YEAR BOOK. 1982. a. $22.95. 866 Third Ave., 11th Fl., New York, NY 10022-6221. Ed. Richard Hantula; Pub. P.F. Collier. index.
Formerly: Health and Medical Horizon (ISSN 0734-5003)
Description: Summarizes latest medical breakthroughs, research advances, and good health practices.

613.7 664 II
HEALTH & NUTRITION. (Text in English) 1989. m. newsstand price: Rs.20. Magna Publishing Company Ltd., Magna House, 100E Old Prabhadevi Rd., Prabhadevi, Bombay 400 025, India. TEL 91-22-4362270. FAX 91-22-4306523. TELEX 11-73288 MAG IN. Ed. Nirmala Ferrao. adv.: B&W page Rs.22200, color page Rs.44400; trim 267 x 203; adv. contact: Carol Daver. circ. 74,720.

HEALTH AND PHYSICAL EDUCATION/HOKEN TAIIKU KYOSHITSU. see *EDUCATION*

613.7 US ISSN 0898-3569
HEALTH & YOU. 1985. q. $10. Health Ink Inc., 1 Executive Dr., Moorestown, NJ 08057. TEL 609-778-0011. FAX 609-778-4422. Ed. Pat McGuire; Pub. Lou Antosh. circ. 700,000. (back issues avail.) **Indexed:** CINAHL. **Document type:** consumer publication.
Description: General health and wellness publication for consumers covering fitness, nutrition, and prevention.

HEALTH CARE STRATEGIC MANAGEMENT; the newsletter for hospital strategists. see *HOSPITALS*

HEALTH COUNTER NEWS. see *NUTRITION AND DIETETICS*

HEALTH DIET & NUTRITION. see *NUTRITION AND DIETETICS*

613 UK ISSN 0017-8969
RA421
HEALTH EDUCATION JOURNAL. 1943. q. £25 to individuals; institutions £35. Health Education Authority, Hamilton House, Marbledon Pl., London WC1H 9TX, England. (Subscr. to: Royal Society of Medicine Press Ltd., 1 Wimpole St., London W1M 8AE, England. TEL 0171-290-2900. FAX 0171-290-2929) Ed. M. Whitehead. adv.; bk.rev.; index. circ. 3,000. (also avail. in microform from UMI; reprint service avail. from UMI) **Indexed:** Abstr.Hyg., ASSIA, Cont.Pg.Educ., Curr.Adv.Ecol.Sci., Diar.Dis.Res., Educ.Tech.Abstr., Excerp.Med., Res.High.Educ.Abstr., SSCI, Stud.Wom.Abstr., Tech.Educ.Abstr., Trop.Dis.Bull. **Document type:** academic/scholarly publication.
—BLDSC (4275.000000); Faxon; SWETS; UMI; UnCover.

613.7 US
HEALTH HANDBOOK.* 1982. s-a. $.99 per no. Compendium Systems Corp., 75 Holly Hill Ln., 3rd Fl., Greenwich, CT 06830-6098. TEL 310-286-0988. FAX 310-286-1293. adv.: B&W page $6540, color page $8000; trim 8 1/8 x 10 3/4. circ. 847,108 (paid).

613.7 US ISSN 0898-1728
HEALTH JOURNAL; the magazine of America's leading HMOs. 1988. q. free to qualified personnel. Madison Publishing, 263 Summer St., Boston, MA 02210. TEL 617-428-4600. FAX 617-428-4626. Ed. Cary Barbor. adv. contact: Sara Van Beckum. circ. 1,108,229 (controlled). **Description:** Combines local HMO news and information with articles on health and fitness. *Refereed Serial*

HEALTH LAW DIGEST. see *LAW*

HEALTH LAW JOURNAL. see *LAW*

HEALTH LAW JOURNAL OF OHIO. see *LAW*

PHYSICAL FITNESS AND HYGIENE

301.1 150 613.7   US
HEALTH MASTER. 1983. s-a. $1. Conscious Living Foundation, Inc., Box 9, Drain, OR 97435. TEL 503-836-2358. FAX 503-836-2930. Ed. Tim Lowenstein. adv.; bk.rev. circ. 80,000. (back issues avail.) **Document type:** newsletter, catalog.
    Former titles: Stress Master; Gentle Places and Quiet Spaces.
    Description: Health & wellness improvement through biofeedback, stress management, relaxation, communications skills, diet, exercise and more.

630   CN   ISSN 1188-9500
HEALTH NATURALLY. 1992. 6/yr. Can.$12 (foreign Can.$18). Health Naturally Publications Inc., P.O. Box 149, R.R. No. 1, Nobel, ON P0G 1G0, Canada. TEL 705-342-1360. FAX 705-342-9552. Ed. David Rowland. adv.; bk.rev. circ. B&W page Can.$2890, color page Can.$3680; trim 8 1/8 x 10 7/8; adv. contact: Nancy Ludwig. circ. 50,297. **Document type:** consumer publication.

HEALTH NEWS NATURALLY. see *NUTRITION AND DIETETICS*

613.7   US
HEALTH OF THE REP NEWSLETTER. m. (United Association Manufacturers' Representatives) Keith Kittrell & Associates, Inc., P.O. Box 986, Dana Point, CA 92629. TEL 714-240-4966. Ed. Karen K. Mazzola. **Document type:** newsletter.
    Description: Covers the world of manufacturing.

HEALTH PHYSICS; the radiation protection journal. see *MEDICAL SCIENCES*

613.7   US
HEALTH POLICY SERIES. 1981. irreg. Marcel Dekker, Inc., 270 Madison Ave., New York, NY 10016. TEL 212-696-9000. FAX 212-685-4540. TELEX 421419. (Subscr. to: Box 5017, Monticello, NY 12701) Ed. Milton I. Roemer. **Indexed:** Med.Care Rev. **Document type:** monographic series.

HEALTH SCIENCE; living in harmony with nature. see *NUTRITION AND DIETETICS*

613.7   US
HEALTH SHOPPER. q. Swanson Health Products, 1318 39th St., N.W., Box 2803, Fargo, ND 58102. TEL 800-437-4148. adv.
    Description: Provides current health information; covers nutrition and diets.

HEALTH, SOCIETY AND CULTURE. see *SOCIOLOGY*

613.7   US   ISSN 0147-0353
RA421   CODEN: HEVAEC
HEALTH VALUES; the journal of health behavior, education & promotion. 1977. bi-m. $64 to individuals (Canada $74; elsewhere $94); institutions $99 (Canada $109; elsewhere $129) (effective August 1995). P N G Publications, Box 4593, Star City, WV 26504-4593. TEL 304-293-4699. FAX 304-293-4693. Ed. Elbert D. Glover. adv. contact: Penny N. Glover. bk.rev.; index; circ. 2,000 (paid). (also avail. in microform from UMI; reprint service avail. from UMI) **Indexed:** CHNI, CINAHL, NRN, Phys.Ed.Ind., Psychol.Abstr. (1990-). **Document type:** academic/scholarly publication.
    —BLDSC (4275.243000); Faxon; UMI; UnCover.
    Description: Seeks to provide a comprehensive understanding of the relationships among personal behavior, social structure and health, and to disseminate knowledge of major behavioral science principles and strategies to assist in designing and implementing programs to prevent disease and promote health.
    Refereed Serial

HEALTH WATCH. see *NUTRITION AND DIETETICS*

HEALTHCARE MANAGEMENT TEAM LETTER. see *BUSINESS AND ECONOMICS — Management*

613.7   US
HEALTHCARE MARKETING AND MANAGEMENT REPORT.* m. Box 432152, Miami, FL 33243-2152. TEL 305-252-7757. FAX 305-252-7741. Ed. Pete Silver.

613.7   US   ISSN 0741-9368
HEALTHCARE MARKETING REPORT. m. H M R Publication Group, Box 76002, Atlanta, GA 30358-1002. TEL 404-457-6105. FAX 404-457-0049. Ed. Beverly Seitz. circ. 1,900.

613.7 612.3   US
HEALTHCARE NEW ORLEANS. m. CityBusiness - New Orleans Publishing Group, 111 Veterans Blvd., Rm. 1810, Metairie, LA 70005. TEL 504-834-9292. FAX 504-837-2258. Ed. Brian Ettinger. circ. 25,000 (controlled). **Document type:** trade publication.
    Description: Contains articles of interest to local healthcare professionals.

613.7   US
HEALTHCARE U S A. m. S T L Publishing, Box 146571, Chicago, IL 60614. TEL 312-929-7398. FAX 312-929-5733. adv.: B&W page $3950, color page $4950. **Document type:** consumer publication.

613.7   US   ISSN 8756-453X
HEALTHLINES. 1982. m. $15. University of Michigan, Fitness Research Center, 401 Washtenaw Ave., Ann Arbor, MI 48109-2214. TEL 313-763-2462. FAX 313-763-2206. Ed. Marilyn Pearce Edington. bk.rev. circ. 5,000. (also avail. in diskette format) **Document type:** newsletter.

613.7   US   ISSN 1051-8770
RC81.A1
HEALTHWISE HANDBOOK. 1976. irreg. Doubleday & Company, Inc., 501 Franklin Ave., Garden City, NY 11530.

613   JA
HEALTHY FAMILY. (Text in Japanese) 1976. bi-m. 3420 Yen. Shufu-to-Seikatsusha Ltd., 5-7, 3-chome, Kyobashi, Chuo-ku, Tokyo 104, Japan. Ed. Kyoshi Inoue.

HEALTHY KIDS. see *CHILDREN AND YOUTH — About*

613.7 612.3   US
HEALTHY TIMES. bi-m. Vitamin Shoppe, 4700 Westside Ave., North Bergen, NJ 07047. TEL 800-223-1216. FAX 201-866-9513. Ed. Helen Howard.

HELAN MEDICAL MAGAZINE. see *MEDICAL SCIENCES*

613   DK   ISSN 0018-0149
HELSE; familiens laegemagasin. 1955. m. DKK 140. (Almindelige Danske Laegeforening) Helse - Familiens Laegemagasin, Classensgade 36, DK-2100 Copenhagen Oe, Denmark. TEL 45-35-26-79-00. FAX 45-35-26-87-60. Ed. Leif Hansgaard, Kirsten Engel. adv. contact: Bjarne Hedegaard. circ. 240,000.

HERA; Binghamton's women's newspaper. see *WOMEN'S INTERESTS*

613   II   ISSN 0018-0491
HERALD OF HEALTH. (Text in English) 1909. m. Rs.60 foreign $6 (typically set in Apr.). (Seventh-day Adventists) Oriental Watchman Publishing House, Box 35, Poona 411001, India. TELEX 145 358 SUD IN. Ed. C.B. Hammond. adv.; bk.rev.; illus.; stat. circ. 36,000.

613.7   MX
HERCULES MODERNO. 1980. fortn. Mex.$150($80) (Federacion Internacional de Fisioconstructores (IFBB)) Editormex Mexicano, S.A., Avda. Rodolfo Gaona, Edif. 82-B-203, Lomas de Sotelo, 11200 Mexico D.F., Mexico. TEL 557-07-92. FAX 525-395-65-64. Ed. Javier Barrigo. adv.; illus. circ. 45,000.
    Description: Covers bodybuilding, nutrition, kinesiology, training, psychology and health.

613   UK   ISSN 0018-0696
HERE'S HEALTH; a monthly guide to health, nutrition, natural food and natural therapy. 1956. m. £22.80 (foreign £33.10) (effective 1995-1996). E M A P - Elan, 20 Orange St., London WC2H 7ED, England. TEL 0171-957-8383. FAX 0171-930-5728. (Subscr. to: Tower Publishing Services Ltd., Tower House, Sovereign Park, Lathkill St., Market Harborough, Leics. LE16 9EF, England. TEL 01858-468811. FAX 01858-432164) Ed. Simon Martin. adv.; bk.rev.; illus. **Document type:** consumer publication.
    —CCC.
    Incorporates: Health for All (ISSN 0017-8985)
    Description: Covers nutrition and alternative medicine.

HIMALAYAN INSTITUTE QUARTERLY GUIDE. see *PHILOSOPHY*

HIMAN CHIRYO KENKYUKAI KOENSHU/JAPANESE SOCIETY FOR OBESITY THERAPY. PROCEEDINGS. see *NUTRITION AND DIETETICS*

HOCHSCHULSPORT. see *SPORTS AND GAMES*

613   JA   ISSN 0018-3342
HOKEN NO KAGAKU/HEALTH CARE. (Text in Japanese) 1959. m. 10200 Yen. (Health Science Research Association - Hoken Kagaku Kenkyukai) Kyorin Shoin, 4-2-1 Yushima, Tokyo 113, Japan. Ed. Fusao Akiyama. index. circ. 710.

HOKKAIDO KYOIKU DAIGAKU KIYO. DAI-2-BU, C. KATEI, TAIIKU- HEN/HOKKAIDO UNIVERSITY OF EDUCATION. JOURNAL. SECTION 2 C. HOME ECONOMICS, TEACHER TRAINING FOR SCHOOL HEALTH AND PHYSICAL EDUCATION. see *HOME ECONOMICS*

613.7   US
▼**HOME GYM AND FITNESS.** 1994. q. $14.95; newsstand price: $2.95. Century Publishing Co., 990 Grove St., Evanston, IL 60201-4370. TEL 708-491-6440. Ed. Noah Lieberman; Pub. Jerry Croft. adv.: B&W page $4020. circ. 175,000 (paid). **Document type:** consumer publication.

613.7   US   ISSN 1078-2389
HOME HEALTH LINE; the home care industry's national independent newsletter. 1975. w. (48/yr.). $399. 11300 Rockville Pike, Ste. 1100, Rockville, MD 20852-3030. TEL 301-816-8950. FAX 301-816-8945. Ed. Lisa Mann. adv. contact: Terry Gray. index. circ. 2,800. (back issues avail.) **Document type:** newsletter.

HOME HEALTHCARE NURSE. see *MEDICAL SCIENCES*

301.16 613.7   US   ISSN 0891-3374
HOPE HEALTH LETTER. 1978. m. $19.80. (Hope Heart Institute) International Health Awareness Center Inc., 350 E. Michigan Ave., Ste. 301, Kalamazoo, MI 49007-3851. TEL 616-343-0770. Ed. Carol Garzona. illus. (looseleaf format) **Document type:** newsletter.
    Formerly (until 1986): Hope Newsletter.
    Description: Covers many subjects on health including smoking, stress management, diet, self-care, cost-containment. Written for all levels.

613.7 790.1   PO
HORIZONTE; revista de educacao fisica e desporto. 1984. bi-m. Livros Horizonte, Lda., Rua das Chagas, 17, 1121 Lisbon Codex, Portugal. TEL 1-3466917. FAX 1-3426921.

613.7 658   US
HOSPITAL HEALTH SCENE; journal of wellness and good health care. 1987. q. free. Hackettstown Community Hospital, 651 Willow Grove St., Hackettstown, NJ 07840. TEL 908-852-5100. FAX 908-850-6822. Ed. Bill Weber. circ. 58,000. (tabloid format) **Document type:** consumer publication.
    Description: Contains articles on ways to achieve a healthier life and includes news of Hackettstown Community Hospital events and services.

HOSPITAL REVENUE REPORT. see *BUSINESS AND ECONOMICS — Marketing And Purchasing*

HOW ON EARTH!; youth supporting compassionate, ecologically sound living. see *NUTRITION AND DIETETICS*

HUMAN MOVEMENT SCIENCE; journal devoted to pure and applied research on human movement. see *MEDICAL SCIENCES*

613.7 306.7   US   ISSN 0196-061X
HUMAN SEXUALITY SUPPLEMENT. (Supplement to: Current Health 2 (ISSN 0163-156X)) m. (Sep.-May.). $7.95. Weekly Reader Corporation, 245 Long Hill Rd., Middletown, CT 06457. TEL 800-446-3355. FAX 609-786-3360. Ed. Sandra Maccarone; Pub. Richard J. Le Brasseur.
    Description: Contains current information on the sexual aspects of health and well-being.

PHYSICAL FITNESS AND HYGIENE

613   XR   ISSN 1210-7840
CODEN: CEHYAN
HYGIENA; casopis pro ochranu a podporu zdravi. (Text in Czech or Slovak; summaries in English and Russian) 1955. 10/yr. $62.60. (Ceska Lekarska Spolecnost J.E. Purkyne - Czech Medical Society) Nakladateske Stredisko C L S J.E. Purkyne, Sokolska 31, 120 26 Prague 2, Czech Republic.
FAX 42-2-202788. (Dist. by: Artia Pegas Press, Ve Smeckach 30, 111 27 Prague 1, Czech Republic) Eds. J. Lener, L. Aghnova. adv.; bk.rev.; bibl.; charts; illus. circ. 1,150. **Indexed:** Abstr.Hyg., Biol.Abstr., C.I.S. Abstr., Cadscan, Chem.Abstr., Dairy Sci.Abstr., Dent.Ind., Ergon.Abstr., Excerp.Med., INIS Atomind., Lead Abstr., Protozool.Abstr., Rev.Med.& Vet.Mycol., Trop.Dis.Bull., Zincscan.
—BLDSC (4352.236200); CASDDS. **CCC**.
Formerly (until 1994): Ceskoslovenska Hugiena (ISSN 0009-0573)

613.7   US
HYGIENIC COMMUNITY NETWORK NEWS. 1980. bi-m. $8. Hygienic Community Network, Box 277, Boulder Creek, CA 95006. Ed. Helen Jean Story. bk.rev.; circ. 150 (paid). **Document type:** newsletter.
Description: For people in the Natural Hygiene movement who are interested in forming cooperative communities dedicated to healthful living.

613   UK   ISSN 0018-8263
HYGIENIST. 1959. q. £10.50($22) British Natural Hygiene Society, c/o Shalimar, Harold Grove, Frinton-on-Sea, Essex, England. TEL 0255-672823. Ed. Keki R. Sidhwa. bk.rev. circ. 300. (processed) **Document type:** trade publication.

I A P N H NEWSLETTER. (International Association of Professional Natural Hygienists) see *NUTRITION AND DIETETICS*

613.7   US
I C H P E R CONGRESS PROCEEDINGS. 1958. biennial. price varies. International Council on Health, Physical Education and Recreation, 1900 Association Dr., Reston, VA 22091. TEL 703-476-3462. FAX 703-476-9527. **Indexed:** Sportsearch.
Formerly: I C H P E R Congress Reports (ISSN 0074-4417)
Description: Covers physical fitness.

613.7   US   ISSN 1073-7952
I D E A FITNESS MANAGER NEWSLETTER. 10/yr. membership. I D E A International Association of Fitness Professionals, 6190 Cornerstone Court E., Ste. 204, San Diego, CA 92121-3773. TEL 619-535-8979; 800-999-4332. Ed. Patricia Ryan. circ. 3,000. **Document type:** newsletter.
Description: Offers fitness business owners, program directors and managers information needed to build business, support staff and be effective administrators.

613.7   US   ISSN 1068-087X
I D E A PERSONAL TRAINER. 9/yr. I D E A International Association of Fitness Professionals, 6190 Cornerstone Court E., Ste. 204, San Diego, CA 92121-3773. TEL 619-535-8979; 800-999-4332. Ed. Patricia Ryan. circ. 10,000. **Document type:** trade publication.
Description: Enables trainers to operate successful businesses, plan prudent exercise programs and motivate clients to pursue a healthy lifestyle.

613.7   US   ISSN 1040-8126
RA781.15
I D E A TODAY. 1984. 10/yr. membership. I D E A International Association of Fitness Professionals, 6190 Cornerstone Court E., Ste. 204, San Diego, CA 92121-3773. TEL 619-535-8979. Ed. Mary Monroe. bk.rev. B&W page $1662, color page $2660; 7 1/4 x 10. bk.rev. circ. 22,000. (back issues avail.) **Indexed:** Phys.Ed.Ind., Sportsearch (1988-).
—BLDSC (4362.372500).
Formerly: Dance Exercise Today (ISSN 0882-1399)
Description: Covers exercise science, research and teaching skills, motivation and communication skills, programming, nutrition and weight loss, business operations and marketing and association news for exercise instructors, personal trainers and business operators.

613.7   DK   ISSN 0902-1620
I FORM. 1987. m. DKK 486; newsstand price: DKK 36.50. Bonniers Specialmagasiner A-S, Strandboulevarden 130, DK-2100 Copenhagen OE, Denmark. TEL 45-39-28-55-00.
FAX 45-39-29-01-99. Ed. Jens Henneberg. adv.: page DKK 22250; trim 185 x 250; adv. contact: Helen E. Larsen. circ. 56,664. (back issues avail.) **Document type:** consumer publication.

613   IT   ISSN 0019-1655
CODEN: IGMPAX
IGIENE MODERNA; rivista di igiene, microbiologia, epidemiologia. (Text in English, Italian, Spanish) 1908. m. L.150000($180) (effective 1994). European Journal of Epidemiology Publishers, S.r.l., Via Zandonai, 11, 00194 Rome (Pratti), Italy. TEL 06-36309593. FAX 06-3290343. TELEX 611330 UCATRO. Ed. Dr. Giovanni Fadda. adv. contact: Cristina Del Monte. bk.rev.; abstr.; charts; illus.; index. **Indexed:** Abstr.Hyg., Biol.Abstr., C.I.S. Abstr., Chem.Abstr., Curr.Adv.Ecol.Sci., Excerp.Med., Ind.Med., Nutr.Abstr., Rev.Med.& Vet.Mycol., Trop.Dis.Bull., Vet.Bull.
—BLDSC (4363.440000); CASDDS; EMDOCS.
Description: Covers the Italian Society of Hygiene, Preventive Medicine and Public Health; includes microbiology and epidemiology.

613   CN   ISSN 0848-1733
IN TOUCH (GLOUCESTER). (Text in English, French) 1974. 3/yr. membership. Canadian Association for Health, Physical Education, Recreation and Dance, Place R. Tait McKenzie, 1600 James Naismith Dr., Gloucester, ON K1B 5N4, Canada.
TEL 613-748-5622. FAX 613-748-5737. Ed. Debbie Vanderburgh. circ. 1,300. (back issues avail.) **Document type:** newsletter.
Former titles (until 1989): C A H P E R Keeps In Touch (ISSN 0829-1055); C A H P E R News (ISSN 0318-1960)

613.7   II
INDIAN SOCIETY OF HEALTH ADMINISTRATORS. PROCEEDINGS. a. Indian Society of Health Administrators, 104 (15-37) Cambridge Road Cross, Ulsoor, Bangalore 560 008, India. TEL 574297.

613.7   FR
INFORMATIONS U F O L E P-U S E P. 1945. m. (10/yr.). 45 F. Union Francaise des Oeuvres Laiques d'Education Physique, 3 rue Recamier, 75341 Paris, France. adv.; bk.rev. circ. 104,000.

INSTITUTE OF HEALTH EDUCATION. JOURNAL. see *EDUCATION*

INTERMEDICA POST. see *BUSINESS AND ECONOMICS — International Development And Assistance*

613.7   US   ISSN 1046-3380
GV201
INTERNATIONAL COUNCIL FOR HEALTH, PHYSICAL EDUCATION AND RECREATION. JOURNAL. q. International Council for Health, Physical Education and Recreation - Conseil International pour l'Hygiene de l'Education et de la Recreation, 1900 Association Dr., Reston, VA 22091. TEL 703-476-3462. FAX 703-476-9527. Ed. Dulian Stein. **Indexed:** Sportsearch (1988-).
—Faxon; UnCover.

INTERNATIONAL JOURNAL OF OBESITY. see *NUTRITION AND DIETETICS*

INTERNATIONAL JOURNAL OF PHYSICAL EDUCATION/INTERNATIONALE ZEITSCHRIFT FUER SPORTPAEDAGOGIK. see *EDUCATION — Teaching Methods And Curriculum*

613.7   NE
INTERNATIONAL NATURIST INFORMATION CENTER NEWSLETTER. (Text in English) 1984. 3/yr. $7 (effective 1995-1996). International Naturist Information Center, P.O. Box 2082, 2800 BE Gouda, Netherlands. TEL 31-1820-30998. Ed. R. Broekstra. **Document type:** newsletter.
Description: Reports on naturist activities worldwide, including travel updates, news of nude beaches and resorts, and difficulties encountered. Also includes names and addresses of people wishing to correspond.

613   GW   ISSN 0178-7764
INTERNATIONALES SAUNA - ARCHIV. 1952. q. DM.30. (Deutscher Sauna - Bund e.V.) Sauna Matti GmbH, Kavalleriestr. 9, 33602 Bielefeld, Germany. TEL 0521-178134. Ed. Dr. Werner Fritzsche. adv.; bk.rev.; abstr.; charts; stat. circ. 3,000.
—**CCC**.
Formerly: Sauna Nachrichten mit Sauna Archiv (ISSN 0036-5033)

613   US   ISSN 0047-1496
IRONMAN.* 1936. m. $29.95. IronMan Publishing, 1701 Ives Ave., Oxnard, CA 93033-1866. TEL 213-822-2844. FAX 213-823-2614. Ed. Peary Rader. adv.; charts; illus.; tr.lit.

ISOKINETICS AND EXERCISE SCIENCE. see *MEDICAL SCIENCES — Sports Medicine*

IT'S OKAY!. see *PSYCHOLOGY*

613   JA   ISSN 0021-5082
CODEN: NEZAAQ
JAPANESE JOURNAL OF HYGIENE/NIHON EISEIGAKU ZASSHI. (Text in English or Japanese; abstracts in English) 1946. bi-m. 4500 Yen (foreign 6500 Yen). Japanese Society for Hygiene - Nihon Eisei Gakkai, c/o Dept. of Hygiene and Preventive Medicine, Faculty of Medicine, University of Tokyo, 7-3-1 Hongo, Bunkyo-ku, Tokyo 113, Japan.
FAX 81-3-5684-2297. Ed. K. Morimoto. adv. circ. 2,700. **Indexed:** C.I.S.Abstr., Excerp.Med., Food Sci.& Tech.Abstr., Helminthol.Abstr., Ind.Med., Nutr.Abstr. **Document type:** academic/scholarly publication.
—BLDSC (4655.300000); CASDDS; EMDOCS; UnCover.

610 613.7   JA   ISSN 0039-906X
JAPANESE JOURNAL OF PHYSICAL FITNESS AND SPORTS MEDICINE. (Text in English, Japanese) 1950. bi-m. 12000 Yen. Japanese Society of Physical Fitness and Sports Medicine, 3-25-8 Nishi-Shibashi, Minato-ku, Tokyo 105, Japan. (Dist. by: Business Center for Academic Societies Japan, 5-16-9 Honkomagome, Bunkyo-ku, Tokyo 113, Japan. TEL 03-5814-5811) Ed. Masahisa Usami. circ. 2,540. **Indexed:** Excerp.Med., Nutr.Abstr. **Document type:** academic/scholarly publication.
—BLDSC (4657.420000).
Formerly: Japanese Journal of Physical Fitness. **Refereed Serial**

613.7   US
JENNY CRAIG'S YOUR BODY, YOUR HEALTH. 1990. 4/yr. $2.95 per no. Hachette Magazines, Inc., Hachette Custom Publishing, 1633 Broadway, New York, NY 10019. TEL 212-767-6797.
FAX 212-921-0705. Ed. Margo Gilman. adv.; bk.rev. circ. 800,000.
Formerly (until 1992): Woman's Day (Year) Guide to Your Body, Your Health.
Description: Covers nutrition, diets, exercise, cholesterol, walking, beauty and good health.

613.7 796.1 296.7   US   ISSN 1077-4823
JEWISH SPORTS & FITNESS.* irreg.? Jewish Sports Congress, P.O. Box 234549, Great Neck, NY 11023-4549. TEL 516-482-5550.
FAX 516-482-5583. Ed. Mike Cohen. film rev.; play rev.; abstr.; charts; illus.; stat.; tr.lit.; circ. 250,000 (controlled). (tabloid format) **Document type:** bulletin.

JEWISH VEGETARIAN. see *NUTRITION AND DIETETICS*

613.7   US   ISSN 1002-8803
JIAN YU MEI/FITNESS AND BEAUTY. (Text in Chinese) 1980. bi-m. $24.50. China Books & Periodicals, Inc., 2929 24th St., San Francisco, CA 94110. TEL 415-282-2994. FAX 415-282-0994.

613.7   CC   ISSN 1002-297X
JIANKANG/HEALTH. (Text in Chinese) 1980. m. Y12. Beijing Jiankang Jiaoyusuo - Beijing Health Education Institute, 20 Hepingli Beijie, Beijing 100013, People's Republic of China. TEL 4215827. Ed. Feng Ailan. adv. circ. 100,000.

613   US
JIANKANG BAO/HEALTH NEWS. (Text in Chinese) 6/w. $210.20. China Books & Periodicals, Inc., 2929 24th St., San Francisco, CA 94110.
TEL 415-282-2994. FAX 415-282-0994. **Document type:** newspaper.

PHYSICAL FITNESS AND HYGIENE

613.7 CC ISSN 1003-000X
JIANKANG GUWEN/HEALTH CONSULTANT. (Text in Chinese) 1980. bi-m. Renmin Tiyu Chubanshe - People's Sports Publishing House, 8 Tiyuguan Lu, Chongwen Qu, Beijing 100061, People's Republic of China. TEL 5112466. FAX 7016129. Ed. Zeng Fusheng.

613.7 028.5 CC ISSN 1002-3089
JIANKANG SHAONIAN HUABAO/HEALTHY CHILDREN'S PICTORIAL. (Text in Chinese) 1985. bi-m. Beijing Jiankang Jiaoyusuo - Beijing Health Education Institute, 20 Hepingli Beijie, Beijing 100013, People's Republic of China. TEL 4215827. Ed. Feng Ailan.

613.7 CC
JIANKANG TIANDI/HEALTH WORLD. (Text in Chinese) bi-m. Hebei Fangyi Zhan - Hebei Epidemic Prevention Station, 18 Hongqi Lu, Baoding, Hebei 071000, People's Republic of China. TEL 24911. Ed. Zhang Furui.

613.7 CC ISSN 1002-8714
JIANKANG ZHI YOU/FRIEND OF HEALTH. (Text in Chinese) 1985. bi-m. Xin Tiyu Zazhishe, 8 Tiyuguan Lu, Chongwen-qu, Beijing 100061, People's Republic of China. TEL 757161. Ed. Cao Yan.

613.7 US ISSN 8750-8915
JOE WEIDER'S FLEX. 1983. m. $29.97. Weider Publications, 21100 Erwin St., Woodland Hills, CA 91367. TEL 818-884-6800. FAX 818-704-5734. Ed. Jerry Kindela; Pub. Joe Weider. adv. circ. 153,134. (also avail. in microform from UMI) **Document type:** consumer publication.
—UMI; UnCover.
Description: Discusses bodybuilding and nutrition.

613.7 US ISSN 0893-4460
GV481
JOE WEIDER'S MEN'S FITNESS. 1985. m. $21.97. Weider Publications, 21100 Erwin St., Woodland Hills, CA 91367. TEL 818-884-6800. FAX 818-704-5734. Ed. Peter Sikowitz; Pub. Joe Weider. adv.; bk.rev. circ. 250,000. (also avail. in microform from UMI) **Indexed:** Phys.Ed.Ind., Sports Per.Ind. **Document type:** consumer publication.
—UMI; UnCover.
Formerly (until 1987): Joe Weider's Sports Fitness (ISSN 0885-0763)
Description: Discusses health and nutrition for active men.

613.7 US ISSN 0744-5105
GV481
JOE WEIDER'S MUSCLE & FITNESS. m. $35. Weider Publications, 21100 Erwin St., Woodland Hills, CA 91367. TEL 818-884-6800; 800-998-0731. FAX 818-704-5734. Ed. Tom Deters; Pub. Joe Weider. adv. circ. 525,000. **Indexed:** Hlth.Ind., Phys.Ed.Ind., Sportsearch (1981-). **Document type:** consumer publication.
—UMI; UnCover.
Formerly: Joe Weider's Muscle.
Description: Discusses physical fitness, health and nutrition.

613.7 301.412 US ISSN 0744-5121
JOE WEIDER'S SHAPE; the best information available for your body, mind, spirit and beauty. 1981. m. $19.97. Weider Publications, 21100 Erwin St., Woodland Hills, CA 91367. TEL 818-884-6800; 800-998-0731. FAX 818-704-5734. Ed. Barbara Harris; Pub. Joe Weider. adv.; bk.rev. circ. 900,000. (also avail. in microform from UMI) **Indexed:** Hlth.Ind., Phys.Ed.Ind., Sportsearch (1983-). **Document type:** consumer publication.
—UMI; UnCover.
Description: Discusses health and nutrition for the active woman.

613.7 MX
JOE WEIDER'S SHAPE MEXICO; mujer sana de mente y cuerpo. 1988. m. Mex.$90($65) Consorcio Sayrols, Miel y Pesado 126, Col. del Valle, 03100 Mexico D.F., Mexico. TEL 525-543-4991. FAX 525-523-7045. Ed. Diana de Ramery. circ. 75,000. **Document type:** consumer publication.
Description: Covers physical fitness, aerobics, diets, and fashion for women.

JOGGING; loepartidningen. see SPORTS AND GAMES

JOGGING - LE GRANDE CORSA. see SPORTS AND GAMES

JOSAI DAIGAKU KENKYU NENPO. SHIZEN KAGAKU HEN/JOSAI UNIVERSITY BULLETIN OF LIBERAL ARTS. NATURAL SCIENCE, HEALTH AND PHYSICAL EDUCATION. see HUMANITIES: COMPREHENSIVE WORKS

JOURNAL OF AGING AND PHYSICAL ACTIVITY. see GERONTOLOGY AND GERIATRICS

613 US ISSN 0744-8481
RA564.5
JOURNAL OF AMERICAN COLLEGE HEALTH. 1952. bi-m. $49 to individuals; institutions $85. (American College Health Association) Heldref Publications, 1319 Eighteenth St., N.W., Washington, DC 20036-1802. TEL 202-296-6267. FAX 202-296-5149. (Co-sponsor: Helen Dwight Reid Educational Foundation) Ed. Martha Wedemen. adv. contact: Raymond Rallo. bk.rev.; charts; illus.; index. circ. 2,000. (also avail. in microform; reprint service avail.) **Indexed:** ASSIA, Biol.Abstr., C.I.J.E., C.I.S.Abstr., Chem.Abstr., CINAHL, Curr.Lit.Fam.Plan., Educ.Ind., Excerp.Med., Hosp.Lit.Ind., Ind.Med., Phys.Ed.Ind., Psychol.Abstr. (1971-). **Document type:** academic/scholarly publication.
● Also available on CD-ROM. Producer(s): University Microfilms International.
—BLDSC (4927.231000); Faxon; SWETS; UMI; UnCover. **CCC.**
Formerly (until 1982): American College Health Association. Journal (ISSN 0002-7944);
Incorporates: American College Health Association. Proceedings.
Refereed Serial

JOURNAL OF BIOENERGETICS AND BIOMEMBRANES. see BIOLOGY — Biophysics

JOURNAL OF COMPARATIVE PHYSICAL AND EDUCATION SPORT. see SPORTS AND GAMES

613 610 US ISSN 1044-2790
JOURNAL OF HEALTH & HEALING. 1975. q. $10. Wildwood Lifestyle Center & Hospital, Box 129, Wildwood, GA 30757-0129. TEL 404-820-1493. FAX 706-820-1474. Ed. Dr. Marjorie Baldwin. adv.; charts; illus.; index. circ. 10,000. (back issues avail.) **Document type:** academic/scholarly publication.

613.7 200 US ISSN 0885-4726
BV4335
JOURNAL OF HEALTH CARE CHAPLAINCY. 1987. s-a. $85 (foreign $119) (effective Mar. 1995). Haworth Press, Inc., 10 Alice St., Binghamton, NY 13904. TEL 607-722-5857; 800-342-9678. FAX 607-722-1424. Ed. Rev. O. Ray Fitzgerald. adv.; bk.rev. circ. 282. (also avail. in microfiche from UMI; reprint service avail. from HAW) **Indexed:** Curr.Cont., IMFL, Ind.Med.
—Haworth.
Description: Promotes both foundational and applied interdisciplinary research related to chaplaincy as practiced in community hospitals, medical centers, nursing homes, and other health care institutions.
Refereed Serial

JOURNAL OF HEALTH CARE MARKETING. see BUSINESS AND ECONOMICS — Marketing And Purchasing

JOURNAL OF HEALTH EDUCATION. see EDUCATION — Teaching Methods And Curriculum

JOURNAL OF HEALTH SCIENCE. see NUTRITION AND DIETETICS

JOURNAL OF PHYSICAL EDUCATION, RECREATION AND DANCE. see EDUCATION — Teaching Methods And Curriculum

JOURNAL OF SEX EDUCATION AND THERAPY. see EDUCATION

JOURNAL OF SPORTS MEDICINE AND PHYSICAL FITNESS. see MEDICAL SCIENCES — Sports Medicine

JOURNAL OF STRENGTH AND CONDITIONING RESEARCH. see MEDICAL SCIENCES — Sports Medicine

K A H P E R D JOURNAL. (Kentucky Association for Health, Physical Education, Recreation and Dance) see EDUCATION

613.7 GW ISSN 0932-1055
K K H JOURNAL. 1940. q. Kaufmaennische Krankenkasse - K K K H, Hauptverwaltung, Hindenburgstr. 43-45, 30175 Hannover, Germany. TEL 0511-2802-0. FAX 0511-2802-232. TELEX 9230924. Ed.Bd. bk.rev. circ. 1,000,000. **Document type:** bulletin.

KENKO KYOIKU/PUBLIC HEALTH EDUCATION. see PUBLIC HEALTH AND SAFETY

613 JA ISSN 0022-9946
KENKO NA KURASHI/LONGER AND HEALTHIER LIFE. (Text in Japanese) 1965. m. 1800 Yen($5) Kenko na Kurashi no Kai, 1-2, 5-chome, Hongo, Bunkyo-ku, Tokyo 113, Japan. Ed. Toshiko Yamamoto. bk.rev.; illus. circ. 3,000.

613 SZ ISSN 0023-2246
KNEIPP.* 1939. m. (Schweizer Kneippverband) Kuenzler Bachmann AG, Postfach 1162, CH-9001 St. Gallen, Switzerland. Ed. Hedy Pueschel. adv. circ. 16,500.

613 GW ISSN 0023-2254
KNEIPP BLAETTER. 1891. m. Kneipp Verlag GmbH, Adolf-Scholz-Allee 6-8, 86825 Bad Woerishofen, Germany. TEL 08247-3002160. FAX 08247-3002199. Ed. Norbert Kraemer. adv. contact: Walter Kostenbader. bk.rev.; illus. circ. 111,631. **Document type:** consumer publication.

613.7 GW ISSN 0323-4916
KOERPERERZIEHUNG; Fachzeitschrift fuer Sportlehrer, Trainer und Uebungsleiter im Kinder- und Jugendsport. 1951. 11/yr. DM.60.50. Paedagogischer Zeitschriftenverlag, Postfach 269, 10107 Berlin, Germany. TEL 030-20343431. FAX 030-20343432. circ. 4,000. **Document type:** academic/scholarly publication.

613 FI ISSN 0787-9385
KOTILAAKARI. 1889. m. FIM 288. Yhtyneet Kuvalehdet Oy, Maistraatinportti 1, FIN-00240 Helsinki, Finland. TEL 358-0-156-6524. FAX 358-0-156-6505. TELEX 121364. Ed. Tarja Hurme. adv.; B&W page FIM 11400, color page FIM 16700. illus. circ. 58,580.
Former titles (until 1978): T H Kotilaakari (ISSN 0355-1903); Terveydenhoitolehti (ISSN 0040-3903)

613 AU
LEBENSSCHUTZ; Der stille Weg. 1949. 4/yr. S.180 (foreign S.270). (Verein fuer Lebenskunde) Anna Pichler Verlag, Marchettigasse 6, A-1060 Vienna, Austria. TEL 01-5971652. FAX 01-5970984. Ed. Anna Maria Pichler. adv. contact: Heinz Lasta. bk.rev.; illus. circ. 5,200. **Document type:** academic/scholarly publication.
Formerly: Glueckliche Leben-der Stille Weg (ISSN 0017-1395)

LEHRHILFEN FUER DEN SPORTUNTERRICHT. see EDUCATION — Teaching Methods And Curriculum

613 US ISSN 0024-1288
TX341
LET'S LIVE. 1933. m. $19.95. Hilltopper Inc., 320 N. Larchmont Blvd., 3rd Fl., Box 74908, Los Angeles, CA 90004. TEL 213-469-3901. FAX 213-469-9597. Ed. Patty Padilla Gallagher; Pub. Judith Vodrey. adv.; bk.rev. circ. 1,200,000. (also avail. in microform from UMI; reprint service avail. from UMI) **Indexed:** Hlth.Ind. **Document type:** consumer publication.
—UMI.
Description: Publishes articles on holistic and alternative medicine, homeopathy and naturopathy.

613.7 HK
LIFE AND HEALTH. (Text in Chinese) 1976. m. HK.$440 (effective 1994). Life and Health Centre Ltd., Rm. G28, Seven Seas Shopping Centre, No. 121, King's Rd., North Point, Hong Kong. TEL 5703185. FAX 8063417. Ed. Doris Lee. adv. circ. 36,000. (back issues avail.)

613.7 CN ISSN 1182-0489
LIFELINES (SASKATOON). 1989. irreg. Can.$15. (Saskatchewan Health Educators Association) Saskatchewan Teachers' Federation, P.O. Box 1108, Saskatoon, SK S7K 3N3, Canada. Ed. Eunice Cameron. **Document type:** monographic series.

LIFELINES (TORONTO); the voice of Toronto's vegetarian community. see NUTRITION AND DIETETICS

PHYSICAL FITNESS AND HYGIENE

613.7   FI   ISSN 0355-7073
LIIKUNTAKASVATUS. 1934. 5/yr. Fmk.90. Suomen Liikunnanopettajain Liitto, Rautatielaisenk 6, 00520 Helsinki, Finland. TEL 90-15021. Ed. Jussi Luukko. adv.; bk.rev. circ. 2,200.

613   US
LIVEWELL.* 1988. m. $2.50 per no. 4353 E. 119th Way, Denver, CO 80233-1738. TEL 303-292-3343. Ed. Pam Avery. adv. circ. 150,000.
   Description: Focuses on heart attacks, cancer, lung disease, and strokes; discusses prevention and aftercare.

LIVING FIT; a guide to fitness at any age. see *WOMEN'S HEALTH*

613.7   US
LIVING WELL. a. $1.95. Hearst Magazines, Living Well, 250 W. 55th St., New York, NY 10019. TEL 212-649-4203. FAX 212-977-9825.

613.7   US   ISSN 0890-4189
GV510.U5
LOOKING FIT. 1986. m. $40. Virgo Publishing, Inc., 13402 N. Scottsdale Rd., Ste. B-185, Scottsdale, AZ 85254. TEL 602-483-0014.

613.7 613.2   SW   ISSN 0346-6280
MAA BRA; specialtidningen foer kropp & sjael. 1976. 12/yr. SEK 330. Aller Specialtidninger AB, Helsingborg, Landskronavaegen 23, S-251 85 Helsingborg, Sweden. FAX 46-8-667-34-39. Ed. Inger Ridstroem. adv.: B&W page SEK 20500, color page SEK 24000. circ. 90,500. cols./p.: 4.

613   JA
MAINICHI LIFE. (Text in Japanese) 1970. m. 4200 Yen. Mainichi Newspapers, 1-1-1, Hitotsubashi, Chiyoda-ku, Tokyo 100-51, Japan. TEL 03-3212-0321. FAX 03-3211-8895. TELEX 22324. Ed. Yasuo Miyazawa.

MARIE CLAIRE HEALTH & BEAUTY. see *BEAUTY CULTURE*

615.82 371.42   US   ISSN 1066-9337
MASSAGE AND BODYWORK QUARTERLY. 1988. q. $9.95. Associated Bodywork and Massage Professionals, 28677 Buffalo Park Rd., Evergreen, CO 80439-7347. TEL 303-647-8478. FAX 303-674-0859. Ed. Valerie K. Cass. adv. contact: Connie Gilbertson. circ. 17,000. **Document type:** consumer publication, trade publication.
   Formerly: Associated Bodywork and Massage Professionals News (ISSN 1053-458X)
   Description: Aims to educate and inform massage and bodywork practitioners, as well as the general public, on various forms of massage-bodywork techniques. Assists in building successful careers.

613   US   ISSN 1045-4268
MASSAGE MAGAZINE; keeping those who touch - in touch. 1985. bi-m. $22. Noah Publishing Company, Box 1500, Davis, CA 95617-1500. TEL 916-757-6033. FAX 916-757-6041. adv.; bk.rev.; film rev.; bibl.; illus.; stat. circ. 45,000. (back issues avail.) **Document type:** trade publication.
   Former titles: Massage and Healing Arts Magazine; Massage and Bodywork Magazine.
   Description: International information resource for the massage and bodywork industry. Articles include interviews with leaders and innovators in the field, practical columns on business and technique, and a resource directory of schools and learning centers.

613   US   ISSN 0895-0814
MASSAGE THERAPY JOURNAL. 1946. q. $20 (effective 1995). American Massage Therapy Association, 820 Davis St., No. 100, Evanston, IL 60201-4444. TEL 708-864-0123. FAX 708-864-1178. (Adv. addr.: 3221 N. Main St., Rockford, IL 61103. TEL 815-877-8407. FAX 815-877-8413) Ed. Rafael Tuburan. adv. contact: Judy Buroker. bk.rev.; tr.lit.; circ. 32,000 (paid). (back issues avail.; reprint service avail.)
   Formerly (until 1962): Massage Journal.
   Description: Covers techniques, research, case histories, anecdotes, business advice, legislative updates, philosophical reflections, poems and reviews relating to massage therapy theory and practice.

MEDECINE DU SPORT. see *MEDICAL SCIENCES — Sports Medicine*

MEDECINE ET HYGIENE. see *MEDICAL SCIENCES*

MEDICAL AND HEALTH ANNUAL. see *MEDICAL SCIENCES*

613   US   ISSN 0749-9973
R118.4.U6
MEDICAL & HEALTH INFORMATION DIRECTORY. 1978. triennial. $485 for 3 vol. set. Gale Research Inc., P.O. Box 33477, Detroit, MI 48283-9852. TEL 800-877-4253. FAX 313-961-6083. TELEX TWX 810-221-7086. Ed. Karen Backus.
   Description: Guide to medical and health information in the U.S.

613.7   US
MEDICAL UPDATE; a monthly medical newsletter. 1976. m. $15 (effective thru 1996). Benjamin Franklin Literary and Medical Society, Inc., Medical Education and Research Foundation, Box 567, 1100 Waterway Blvd., Indianapolis, IN 46202. FAX 317-684-8094. Ed.Bd. circ. 21,000. **Indexed:** CHNI, Hlth.Ind. **Document type:** newsletter.
   Description: Covers all areas of health, nutrition and fitness.

613.7   US   ISSN 0188-2384
MEDIX. (Text in Spanish) 1989. m. Editorial America, S.A., Vanidades Continental Bldg., 6355 N.W. 36th St., Virginia Gardens, FL 33166. TEL 305-871-6400. Dir. Mirtha Forest. adv. **Document type:** consumer publication.
   Description: Covers general health and medicine.

613   GW   ISSN 0179-0404
MEDIZIN HEUTE; Gesundheit fuer die ganze Familie. 1950. m. DM.36 (students DM.27). Deutscher Aerzte-Verlag GmbH, Postfach 400265, 50832 Cologne, Germany. TEL 02234-7011-0. FAX 02234-7011444. Ed. Johann Friedrich Jeurink. adv.; bk.rev.; illus. circ. 244,333. **Document type:** trade publication.

MELPOMENE JOURNAL; a journal for women's health research. see *WOMEN'S HEALTH*

613.7   US   ISSN 1043-8475
MEMPHIS HEALTH CARE NEWS. fortn. Mid-South Communications, Inc., 88 Union, Rm. 200, Memphis, TN 38103-5100. TEL 901-526-2007. FAX 901-526-5240. Ed. Deborah DuBois. circ. 12,601. **Document type:** trade publication.
—CCC.

MEN'S CONFIDENTIAL NEWSLETTER; health, sex and fitness news for men. see *MEN'S HEALTH*

613.7 790   US   ISSN 1059-9169
MEN'S EXERCISE. bi-m. $17.75. Pumpkin Press, Inc., Empire State Bldg., 350 Fifth Ave., Ste. 3323, New York, NY 10118. TEL 212-947-4322. FAX 212-563-4774. Ed. Steve Downs; Pub. Cheh N. Low. adv. contact: Roger Barnet. **Document type:** consumer publication.

613   US   ISSN 0164-1336
RA440.A1
MICHIGAN HEALTH EDUCATOR. 1976. bi-m. $7.50. Michigan Health Educator Company, 2843 Hilton Rd., Ferndale, MI 48220. Ed. E. Dewey Little. adv.; bk.rev.; index. circ. 10,200. (back issues avail.)

MICHIGAN RUNNER. see *SPORTS AND GAMES — Outdoor Life*

613.7   IT
MISSIONE SALUTE. 1988. bi-m. L.30000. Provincia Lombardo Veneta dei Camilliani d'Italia, Via F. Nava 31, 20159 Milan, Italy. TEL 39-2-69516156. FAX 39-2-6883291. Ed. P. Domenico Fantin. adv.: B&W page L.2500000, color page L.3500000. circ. 20,000.

MON BEBE. see *CHILDREN AND YOUTH — About*

MONKEYSHINES ON HEALTH AND SCIENCE. see *CHILDREN AND YOUTH — For*

MOTHERING. see *WOMEN'S HEALTH*

613.7   GW   ISSN 0170-5792
MOTORIK. q. DM.56 (students DM.52). Verlag Karl Hofmann, Postfach 1360, 73603 Schorndorf, Germany. TEL 07181-402-0. FAX 07181-402111. Ed. Klaus Fischer. circ. 3,500. **Indexed:** Sportsearch (1981-). **Document type:** bulletin.
—CCC.

613.7   US
MUSCLE & HEALTH. 1993. 2/yr. Rodale Press, Inc., 33 Minor St., Emmaus, PA 18098. TEL 610-967-5171. Ed. Mark Bricklin. adv. **Document type:** consumer publication.
   Description: Covers health and fitness issues for an educated male audience.

613.7   US
MUSCLE MEDIA 2000. bi-m. newsstand price: $4.50. Mile High Publishing, 400 Corporate Circle, Ste. J, Golden, CO 80401. **Document type:** consumer publication.

613   US   ISSN 0047-8407
MUSCLE TRAINING ILLUSTRATED. 1965. 9/yr. $22. Muscle Man Inc., 219-10 S. Conduit Ave., Springfield Gardens, NY 11413. TEL 718-258-3900. Ed. Dan Lurie. adv.; charts; illus.; stat. circ. 100,000. **Indexed:** Sportsearch.

613 796.41   US
MUSCULAR DEVELOPMENT FITNESS & HEALTH. 1964. m. $29.95. Advanced Research Press, Inc., 2120 Smithtown Ave., Ronkonkoma, NY 11779. TEL 516-467-3140. FAX 516-471-1241. Ed. Alan Paul; Pub. Steve Blechman. adv. contact: Roy Ulin. charts; illus.; tr.lit.; circ. 120,000 (paid). **Indexed:** Phys.Ed.Ind., Sportsearch. **Document type:** consumer publication.
—UnCover.
   Formerly: Muscular Development (ISSN 0047-8415)
   Description: Comprehensive coverage of bodybuilding, sports nutrition, muscular development and strength training.

613.194   US   ISSN 1075-735X
THE N (NUDE & NATURAL) NEWSLETTER. 1992. m. $15 (effective Sep. 1994). Naturist Society, Box 132, Oshkosh, WI 54902. TEL 414-426-5009. FAX 414-231-9977. (Co-sponsors: Naturist Action Committee; Naturist Education Foundation) Ed. Pat O'Brien. (back issues avail.) **Document type:** newsletter.
   Description: Covers public policy and legal issues relating to public nudity, including breast feeding and skinny dipping.

613.194   US   ISSN 1070-9835
GV450
N: NUDE AND NATURAL. 1981. q. $25. Naturist Society, Box 132, Oshkosh, WI 54902. TEL 414-426-5009. FAX 414-231-9977. Ed. Lee Baxandall. adv.; bk.rev.; film rev.; play rev.; cum.index. circ. 20,000. (back issues avail.) **Document type:** consumer publication.
   Formerly: Clothed with the Sun (ISSN 0883-4326)
   Description: Journal of clothes-optional living.

NACHRICHTEN AUS DER AERZTLICHEN MISSION. see *RELIGIONS AND THEOLOGY*

613.7   US
NATIONAL STRENGTH & CONDITIONING ASSOCIATION BULLETIN. irreg. membership. National Strength & Conditioning Association, 530 Communication Cir., Ste. 204, Colorado Springs, CO 80905. **Indexed:** Sportsearch (1986-). **Document type:** bulletin, newsletter.

613.7   GW   ISSN 0934-3407
NATUERLICH. 1988. 6/yr. DM.57. A T Fachverlag GmbH, Postfach 500180, 70331 Stuttgart, Germany. TEL 0711-952951-0. FAX 0711-952951-99. Ed. Michael Flatzek. illus. circ. 40,000. **Document type:** consumer publication.

613   MX
NATURA; tu salud en la naturaleza. m. Editorial Posada, S.A., Oculistas No. 43, Col. El Sifon, 09400 Mexico, D.F., Mexico. illus.

613.7   US   ISSN 1071-555X
NATURAL BODYBUILDING AND FITNESS. 1988. q. $10.92. Chelo Publishing Inc., Empire State Bldg., 350 Fifth Ave., New York, NY 10118. TEL 212-947-4322. FAX 212-563-4774. **Document type:** consumer publication.
   Formerly (until 1993): Natural Physique (ISSN 1044-6583)

NATURAL HEALTH; the guide to well-being. see *ALTERNATIVE MEDICINE*

PHYSICAL FITNESS AND HYGIENE 5197

NATURAL HEALTH. see NUTRITION AND DIETETICS

613 US ISSN 0028-0704
NATURAL HEALTH WORLD.* 1961. m. $7.50. Naturopath Publishing Co., 141 N. Steelhammer Dr., Silverton, OR 97381-1821. TEL 206-695-0213. Ed. Robert W. Noble. adv.; bk.rev.; stat.; tr.lit. circ. 3,600. (tabloid format)

613.194 US ISSN 1076-3295
NATURALLY. 1982. q. $19.95. Events Unlimited, Box 317, New Foundland, NJ 07435. TEL 201-697-8313. Ed. Bernard J. Loibl. adv.; bk.rev. circ. 30,000. (back issues avail.) **Indexed:** Arts & Hum.Cit.Ind. **Document type:** consumer publication.
  Formerly (until 1990): Event (Pequannock).
  Description: Leisure magazine for nudists; includes information on travel, resorts, and nude beaches.

613.194 NE ISSN 0028-0968
NATURISME. 1961. 5/yr. fl.37($19) Stichting Naturistische Uitgaven - Dutch Federation of Naturist Organisations, Postbus 783, 3500 AT Utrecht, Netherlands. TEL 31-30-328810. FAX 31-30-332957. Ed. Bertus Boivin. adv.; bk.rev.; illus. circ. 37,500.

613.194 IT ISSN 0392-4173
NATURISMO; rivista naturista e umanitaria. 1972. s-a. free. Via I. Mitterer 5 (Villa Laura), 39042 Bressanone (BZ), Italy. TEL 39-472-801359. Ed. Daniele Agnoli. bk.rev. circ. 1,500.
  Description: Covers gymnosophy, the philosophy of nudism, and nature and the unconscious being.

613.7 US ISSN 0895-0911
NATURIST LIFE INTERNATIONAL. 1987. q. $20. Naturist Life International, Inc., Box 300, Troy, VT 05868-0300. Ed. Jim C. Cunningham. circ. 1,300 (paid). (back issues avail.)
  Description: Family-oriented magazine promoting clothing-optional living.

613.7 641.1 US
NAUTILUS (INDEPENDENCE). 1979-1983; resumed 1992. bi-m. $11.95. Nautilus, 709 Power House Dr., Ste. 708, Independence, VA 24348. TEL 703-773-2881. FAX 703-773-3306. adv. contact: Becky Gray. bk.rev. circ. 150,000.
  Formerly (until 1983): Nautilus Magazine (ISSN 0278-3118)

NEBRASKA JOURNAL. see EDUCATION

613.7 AA
NENA DHE FEMIJA. 3/yr. Ministria e Shendetesise - Ministry of Health, Tirana, Albania. TELEX 4205.

613.7 XO
NEPEGESZEG. (Text in Hungarian) m. $18. (Czechoslovak Red Cross) Obzor, Spitalska 35, 815 85 Bratislava, Slovakia.

613 GW
NEUE GESUNDHEIT. 1974. bi-m. Klambt Verlag GmbH, Im Neudeck 1, 67346 Speyer, Germany. TEL 06232-310-0. FAX 06232-310292. Ed. Ruth Fena. adv. contact: Klaus Fortmann. circ. 140,000. **Document type:** consumer publication.
  Formerly: Alles fuer ihre Gesundheit.

NEW BEGINNINGS (FRANKLIN PARK); every baby is a new beginning. see CHILDREN AND YOUTH — About

613.7 US ISSN 0732-4782
NEW BODY. 1982. bi-m. G C R Publishing Group, Inc., 1700 Broadway, 34th Fl., New York, NY 10019. TEL 212-541-7100. Ed. Nayda Rhondon. adv. circ. 90,000.

613.7 US
NEW BODY DIET AND EXERCISE. 5/yr. G C R Publishing Group, Inc., 1700 Broadway, 34th Fl., New York, NY 10019. TEL 212-541-7100.

613.7 US ISSN 1048-6224
GV245
NEW DIRECTIONS IN PHYSICAL EDUCATION. 1990. a. Human Kinetics Publishers, Inc., Box 5076, Champaign, IL 61825-5076. TEL 217-351-5076. FAX 217-351-3674. adv. contact: Michele Watson.

NEW LIFE; for those who want to make a change. see NEW AGE PUBLICATIONS

613.7 US
NEW LIVING. 1991. m. $12.95. Christine Lynn Harvey, Ed. & Pub., Box 1519, Stony Brook, NY 11790. TEL 516-981-7232. FAX 516-585-4606. adv.; B&W page $1295. bk.rev. circ. 50,000. **Document type:** newspaper.

NEW OHIO JOURNAL. see ENVIRONMENTAL STUDIES

613.7 US
NEWSLETTER FOR PEOPLE WITH LACTOSE INTOLERANCE AND MILK ALLERGY. 1987. bi-m. $28.50 (effective 1996). Commercial Writing and Design, P.O. Box 3129, Ann Arbor, MI 48106-3129. TEL 313-572-9134. Ed. Jane Zukin. bk.rev. circ. 1,000. (reprint service avail.) **Document type:** newsletter.
  Description: Provides information, support, and recipes for those with lactose intolerance or milk protein allergy.

613 II ISSN 0029-070X
NISARG ANE AROGYA. (Text in Gujarati) 1966. m. Rs.3. S.A. Pandit, Ed. & Pub., Arya Kanya Gurukul, Rajwadi, Porbandar, India. adv.; bk.rev. circ. 600.

613.7 US
NORTHWEST HEALTH. 1958. bi-m. $12. Group Health Cooperative, 521 Wall St., Seattle, WA 98121. TEL 206-448-5999. FAX 206-448-4271. E-mail: nwhealth@accgw.ghc.org. adv.; B&W page $3123, color page $4721; trim 8 1/8 x 10 7/8; adv. contact: Jennifer Loflin. bk.rev. circ. 187,622. **Document type:** consumer publication.
  Formerly: View (Seattle) (ISSN 0504-264X)
  Description: Covers health and fitness life-styles for western Washington State.

NUDITARIAN. see POLITICAL SCIENCE

NUTRITION AND HEALTH. see NUTRITION AND DIETETICS

OBESITY RESEARCH. see MEDICAL SCIENCES

OCCUPATIONAL HEALTH; a journal for the occupational health team. see MEDICAL SCIENCES — Nurses And Nursing

OESTERREICHISCHES JUGENDROTKREUZ. ARBEITSBLAETTER. see SOCIAL SERVICES AND WELFARE

ON THE LEVEL. see SOCIOLOGY

613.7 CN ISSN 1180-7563
ON THE MOVE. q. Can.$20. (Saskatchewan Physical Education Association) Saskatchewan Teachers' Federation, Box 1108, Saskatoon, Sask. S7K 3N3, Canada. TEL 306-373-1660. Ed. Shannon Pritchard. **Document type:** bulletin.

ONTARIO WRESTLER MAGAZINE. see SPORTS AND GAMES

613.7 IT ISSN 1121-3264
OPTIMA SALUTE. 1990. m. (10/yr.). L.25000. Editoriale Optima s.r.l., Largo Augusto 8, 20122 Milan, Italy. TEL 39-2-76017397. FAX 39-2-76014959. Ed. Giacomo Casarotto. adv.: B&W page L.9450000, color page L.14000000. circ. 245,000. **Document type:** consumer publication.

OREGON DISTANCE RUNNER. see SPORTS AND GAMES

ORTOPEDICI E SANITARI. see MEDICAL SCIENCES — Orthopedics And Traumatology

OSAKA JOSHI DAIGAKU KIYO. KISO RIGAKU HEN, TAIIKUGAKU HEN/OSAKA WOMEN'S UNIVERSITY. BULLETIN. SERIES OF NATURAL SCIENCE, PHYSICAL EDUCATION. see SCIENCES: COMPREHENSIVE WORKS

PALAESTRA; the forum of sport, physical education and recreation for the disabled. see HANDICAPPED

613 PL ISSN 0035-7715
CODEN: RPZHAW
PANSTWOWY ZAKLAD HIGIENY. ROCZNIKI. Short title: Roczniki P Z H. (Text in Polish; summaries in English and Russian) 1950. q. $132. Ul. Chocimska 24, 00-791 Warsaw, Poland. TEL 48-22-494051. FAX 49-22-497484. TELEX 816712. (Dist. by: Ars Polona-Ruch, Krakowskie Przedmiescie 7, Warsaw, Poland) Ed. K. Cwiek-Ludwicka. bk.rev.; abstr.; charts; illus.; stat.; index. **Indexed:** Biol.Abstr., Chem.Abstr., Dent.Ind., Excerp.Med., Ind.Med., Nutr.Abstr., Rev.Med.& Vet.Mycol. **Document type:** academic/scholarly publication.
  —BLDSC (8006.000000); CASDDS; EMDOCS.

613.7 US
PATHWAY TO HEALTH. 1992. q? free. Morristown Memorial Hospital, Department of Public Relations, 100 Madison Ave., Box 1956, Morristown, NJ 07962-9967. Ed. Lisa Blumert. **Document type:** newsletter.
  Description: Describes services offered by the hospital and offers health tips.

PATHWAYS TO HEALTH. see PHILOSOPHY

613.7 US
PATIENT'S DIGEST. 1983. s-a. Patient's Digest, Inc., 627 Greenwich St., New York, NY 10014. TEL 212-741-2111. adv.; tr.lit. (reprint service avail.)

PELIZZA'S POSITIVE PRINCIPLES FOR BETTER LIVING. see PSYCHOLOGY

613.7 617.1 US ISSN 0738-7857
PERSONAL FITNESS. 1983. m. $67. (Personal Fitness Consultants) Cromwell - Sloan Publishing Company, 63 Vine Rd., Stamford, CT 06905-2012. TEL 203-323-6839. Ed. Paul Sloan. bk.rev.; abstr.; charts; illus. circ. 32,000. (back issues avail.)

613.7 US
PERSONAL FITNESS AND WEIGHT LOSS; a complete guide. 1990. q. Russ Moore and Associates Inc., 4151 Knob Dr., St. Paul, MN 55122. TEL 612-452-0571. FAX 612-454-5791. Ed. Diane Steen. adv. circ. 108,500.

PHYSICAL EDUCATION DIGEST. see SPORTS AND GAMES

PHYSICAL EDUCATION PROVINCIAL SPECIALIST ASSOCIATION. NEWSLETTER. see EDUCATION — Teaching Methods And Curriculum

615.8 GW ISSN 0031-9392
PHYSIOTHERAPIE. 1909. m. DM.109. (Verband Deutscher Badebetriebe e.V.) Ebert Verlag GmbH, Blankenseer Str. 6-8, 23562 Luebeck, Germany. TEL 0451-501011. FAX 04509-2241. Ed. Hans Juergen Ebert. adv.; bk.rev.; charts; index. circ. 9,500. **Document type:** bulletin.
  Formerly: Fachblatt der Physikalischen Therapie.

613.7 US ISSN 1059-8073
PILLSBURY FAST AND HEALTHY MAGAZINE. 1992. bi-m. $14.95. Pillsbury Company, 200 S. Sixth St., Minneapolis, MN 55402. TEL 612-330-4475. FAX 612-330-4875. Ed. Diane Anderson. adv.; B&W page $5040; adv. contact: Nancy Jones. circ. 210,000. **Document type:** consumer publication.
  Description: Food and lifestyle magazine focusing on low-fat, quick-to-make recipes and articles on well-being.

613.7 US
PLEASURE QUEST;* your success guide to sensual adventures & romance. 1989. q. $12. Health & Wealth Guardian, Ltd., 462 S. Gilbert Rd., Mesa, AZ 85204. TEL 602-829-8888. FAX 602-835-5741. Ed. Phillip Fry. circ. 25,000.
  Description: Promotes health methods for relieving stress, with how-to tips on leisure activities from love and romance to gourmet cooking and games.

POOLWAYS; the magazine of outdoor living (year). see SPORTS AND GAMES

POWER SPORT. see SPORTS AND GAMES

PHYSICAL FITNESS AND HYGIENE

613.7 362.4 GW ISSN 0170-060X
PRAXIS DER PSYCHOMOTORIK. 1976. q. DM.56. Verlag Modernes Lernen - Dortmund, Borgmann KG, Hohe Str. 39, 44139 Dortmund, Germany. TEL 0231-128008. FAX 0231-125640. Ed. Dieter Borgmann. adv.; bk.rev.; abstr.; charts; illus.; index. circ. 3,000. (back issues avail.) Document type: academic/scholarly publication.
 Description: Deals with the importance of movement in a child's education and development. Covers dance, sport, play, and the physically handicapped.

613 US
PRESIDENT'S COUNCIL OF PHYSICAL FITNESS & SPORTS. NEWSLETTER. 1965. 6/yr. free. U.S. Department of Health and Human Services, President's Council on Physical Fitness & Sports, Public Health Service, 701 Pennsylvania Ave., N.W., Ste. 250, Washington, DC 20004. TEL 202-272-3430. (Subscr. to: Superintendent of Documents, U.S. Government Printing Office, Box 371954, Pittsburgh, PA 15250-7954. TEL 202-783-3238. FAX 202-512-2233) Ed. Phil Wiethorn. circ. 10,000. **Indexed:** Sportsearch (1964-). **Document type:** government publication, newsletter.

613 US ISSN 0032-8006
RA421 CODEN: PRVEAT
PREVENTION; the magazine for better health. 1950. m. $21.97 (Canada $26.97; elsewhere $31.97). Rodale Press, Inc., 33 E. Minor St., Emmaus, PA 18098. TEL 610-967-5171; 800-441-7761. TELEX 847338. Ed. Mark Bricklin. adv.; bk.rev.; illus.; index. circ. 3,427,803. (also avail. in microform from UMI; reprint service avail. from UMI) **Indexed:** CHNI, Environ.Per.Bibl., Hlth.Ind., Jun.High.Mag.Abstr., Mag.Ind., PMR. **Document type:** consumer publication.
 •Also available online. Vendor(s): University Microfilms International.
 —Faxon; Genuine Article; SWETS; UMI; UnCover. **CCC.**
 Description: Reports on new developments in nutrition, preventive medicine, fitness, natural living and drugless therapies; emphasis on practicality and self-improvement.

314 FR ISSN 0247-6800
PREVENTION SANTE. 1981. m. 210 F. Hachette Filipacchi Publications, 6 rue Ancelle, 92525 Neuilly sur Seine Cedex, France. TEL 40-88-72-59. FAX 40-88-72-62. (Subscr. to: 90 rue de Flandre, 75947 Paris Cedex 19, France. TEL 40-34-35-00) **Document type:** consumer publication.

613.7 US
PREVENTION WEIGHT LOSS. a. $3.25. Rodale Press, 33 E. Minor St., Emmaus, PA 18098. TEL 215-967-8639. FAX 215-967-8963. adv. **Document type:** consumer publication.

613.7 US
▼ **PRIME FITNESS & HEALTH.** 1994. m. $12.97 for 6 issues; newsstand price: $2.95. Weider Publications, 2110 Erwin St., Woodland Hills, CA 91367. TEL 818-884-6800. FAX 818-704-5734. Ed. Tom Deters. adv. contact: Bob Washburn. **Document type:** consumer publication.
 Description: Provides a guide to the total well-being of men over 35.

PRIME TIMES MAGAZINE. see *CONSUMER EDUCATION AND PROTECTION*

PROGRESS IN OBESITY RESEARCH (YEAR). see *MEDICAL SCIENCES*

PROMOTION ET EDUCATION; international journal of health education. see *PUBLIC HEALTH AND SAFETY*

PROPHYWAYS. see *MEDICAL SCIENCES — Dentistry*

PSYCHOLOGY AND SOCIOLOGY OF SPORT: CURRENT SELECTED RESEARCH. see *PSYCHOLOGY*

PUERTO RICO. DEPARTMENT OF HEALTH. BOLETIN ESTADISTICO. see *PUBLIC HEALTH AND SAFETY — Abstracting, Bibliographies, Statistics*

PUERTO RICO. DEPARTMENT OF HEALTH. INFORME DE RECURSOS HUMANOS DE LA SALUD. see *MEDICAL SCIENCES*

PUERTO RICO. DEPARTMENT OF HEALTH. INFORME ESTADISTICO DE FACILIDADES DE SALUD. see *HOSPITALS*

PUNJAB MEDICAL JOURNAL. see *MEDICAL SCIENCES*

613.7 CC ISSN 1000-825X
QIGONG. (Text in Chinese) m. Zhejiang Sheng Zhongyiyao Yanjiusuo - Zhejiang Provincial Institute of Traditional Medicine, 26 Tianmushan Lu, Hangzhou, Zhejiang 310007, People's Republic of China. TEL 882214. Ed. Lu Zheng.

613.7 CC ISSN 1000-0895
RM727.C54
QIGONG YU KEXUE/QIGONG AND SCIENCE. (Text in Chinese) m. Y12. (Guangdongsheng Qigong Kexue Yanjiu Xiehui - Guangdong Qigong Science Research Association) Qigong yu Kexue Zazhishe, P.O. Box 343, Guangzhou, Guangdong 510030, People's Republic of China. (Dist. overseas by: Jiangsu Publications Import & Export Corp., 56 Gao Yun Ling, Nanjing, Jiangsu, P.R.C.)
 Description: Presents different theories and practice of different schools of qigong in China and abroad. Introduces the applications of this deep-breathing excercise to medical treatment, sports and education.

613.7 CC
QINGCHUN YU JIANKANG/YOUTH AND HEALTH. (Text in Chinese) 1985. m Y.7.20. (Shanghai Shi Weisheng Jiaoyu-guan - Shanghai Health Education Institute) Qingchun yu Jiankang Zazhishe, 394 Zhoushan Lu, Shanghai 200082, People's Republic of China. TEL 5460177. Ed. Hu Jinhua. circ. 200,000.

R S G; vakblad voor training, onderwijs en wetenschap. (Richting - Sport-Gericht) see *SPORTS AND GAMES*

RADIANCE; the magazine for large women. see *WOMEN'S INTERESTS*

613 GW ISSN 0722-9062
RATGEBER AUS DER APOTHEKE. 1922. s-m. free. Gebr. Storck GmbH, Bebelstr. 102, 46049 Oberhausen, Germany. bk.rev.; illus. circ. 400,000.
 Formerly: Ratgeber fuer Kranke und Gesunde (ISSN 0033-9997)

RECREATION CANADA. see *LEISURE AND RECREATION*

RECRUITMENT DIRECTIONS. see *OCCUPATIONS AND CAREERS*

613.7 370 US ISSN 0270-1367
GV201 CODEN: RQESD4
RESEARCH QUARTERLY FOR EXERCISE AND SPORT. 1930. q. $100 to institutions. American Alliance for Health, Physical Education, Recreation, and Dance, 1900 Association Dr., Reston, VA 22091. TEL 703-476-3400. FAX 703-476-9527. Ed. Maureen Weiss. adv.; bibl.; charts; illus.; index, cum.index every 10 yrs.: 1930-1969 (in 4 vols.). circ. 10,000. (also avail. in microform (ISSN 0364-9857) from UMI; microform from PMC; reprint service avail. from ISI,UMI) **Indexed:** Biol.Abstr., C.I.J.E., Curr.Cont., Educ.Ind., Ergon.Abstr., Excerp.Med., Phys.Ed.Ind., Psychol.Abstr., Sportsearch (1980-), SSCI. **Document type:** academic/scholarly publication.
 •Also available online. Vendor(s): University Microfilms International.
 —BLDSC (7759.172000); Faxon; SWETS; UMI; UnCover.
 Formerly (until 1980): American Alliance for Health, Physical Education and Recreation. Research Quarterly (ISSN 0034-5377)
 Description: Includes research articles in the art and science of human movement that lead to the development of theory or the application of new techniques.

REVISTA CUBANA DE HIGIENE Y EPIDEMIOLOGIA. see *PUBLIC HEALTH AND SAFETY*

613 610 RM ISSN 0019-1620
RA523.R8 CODEN: IGIBA5
REVISTA DE IGIENA, BACTERIOLOGIE, VIRUSOLOGIE, PARAZITOLOGIE, PNEUMOFTIZIOLOGIE. IGIENA. (Text in Rumanian; summaries in English, French, German, Russian) 1952. 4/yr. $20. Uniunea Societatilor de Stiinte Medicale din Republica Socialista Rumania, Str. Progresului No. 8, Bucharest, Rumania. (Subscr. to: ILEXIM, Str. 13 Decembrie Nr. 3, P.O. Box 136-137, Bucharest, Rumania) Ed.Bd. adv.; bk.rev.; abstr.; bibl.; charts; illus. **Indexed:** Biol.Abstr., Chem.Abstr., Nutr.Abstr.

613.7 SP ISSN 0213-3016
REVISTA DE LA SALUD. 1985. m. Saned, S.A., Paseo de la Habana 202-bis, 28036 Madrid, Spain. TEL 1-3594092. Ed. Carmen Marino. circ. 135,000.

613 IT ISSN 0035-6921
RA421 CODEN: RIIGAV
RIVISTA ITALIANA D'IGIENE. (Text in Italian; summaries in English and Italian) vol.25, 1965. bi-m. L.100000 (foreign L.120000) (effective 1996). Nistri-Lischi Editori, Via XIV Maggio 28, 56123 Pisa, Italy. TEL 39-50-563371. FAX 39-50-562726. Ed. Giuseppe Armani. adv. contact: Giuseppe Caroli. bibl.; charts; illus.; stat.; index. **Indexed:** Abstr.Hyg., Biol.Abstr., Chem.Abstr., Excerp.Med., Nutr.Abstr., Trop.Dis.Bull. **Document type:** academic/scholarly publication.
 —CASDDS.

ROBERT WOOD JOHNSON FOUNDATION. ANNUAL REPORT. see *MEDICAL SCIENCES*

613.7 US ISSN 0735-570X
THE RODALE REPORT. 1982. m. Rodale Press, Inc., 33 E. Minor St., Emmaus, PA 18098. TEL 610-967-5171. FAX 610-967-3044. Ed. Sid Kirchheimer. **Document type:** newsletter.

RODALE'S FITNESS SWIMMER. see *SPORTS AND GAMES*

RODALE'S HEALTHY WOMAN. see *WOMEN'S HEALTH*

613.7 US ISSN 1072-7345
RA776.5
RODALE'S HEART & SOUL. 1993. 2/yr. $11.97. Rodale Press, Inc., 33 E. Minor St., Emmaus, PA 18098. TEL 610-967-5171. Ed. Reginald Ware. circ. 210,000. **Document type:** consumer publication.
 —UMI.
 Description: Covers health and fitness concerns of African-Americans.

ROYAL SOCIETY OF HEALTH JOURNAL. see *SOCIAL SERVICES AND WELFARE*

613.7 612.3 US ISSN 0898-5162
RUNNING & FITNEWS. 1983. m. $25 to members; health professionals $40. American Running and Fitness Association, 4405 East-West Hwy., Ste. 405, Bethesda, MD 20814. TEL 301-913-9517. FAX 301-913-9520. Ed. Trevor Smith. bk.rev.; charts; index; circ. 15,000 (paid); 20,000 (controlled). (back issues avail.) **Indexed:** Sportsearch (1984-).
 Former titles (until 1984): Running and Fitness; Jogger (ISSN 0164-694X)
 Description: Dedicated to helping recreational athletes get the most from their exercise program by providing information on excercise, nutrition, training, sports medicine, injury prevention and long term health.

301.4 612 US ISSN 0091-3995
HQ1
S I E C U S REPORT. 1972. bi-m. contribution. Sex Information and Education Council of the U S, 130 W. 42nd St., Ste. 350, New York, NY 10036. TEL 212-819-9770. FAX 212-819-9776. Dore Hollander. adv.; bk.rev.; film rev.; bibl. circ. 3,500. (also avail. in microfilm; back issues avail.; reprint service avail. from ISI,UMI) **Indexed:** Curr.Lit.Fam.Plan., Educ.Ind., IMFL. **Document type:** academic/scholarly publication.
 —BLDSC (8271.970000); UMI; UnCover.
 Formerly: S I E C U S Newsletter (ISSN 0036-150X)
 Description: Covers all aspects of human sexuality, including AIDS.

S T A P S. (Sciences et Techniques des Activites Physiques et Sportives) see *MEDICAL SCIENCES — Sports Medicine*

613.17 US
ST. PATRICK HOSPITAL MESSENGER. 1979. m. free. St. Patrick Hospital, 500 W. Broadway, Missoula, MT 59802. TEL 406-543-7271. FAX 406-543-6836. Ed. JoAnn Hoven. circ. 6,000. (back issues avail.)
 Description: Health issues forum for consumers.

613.7 US
ST. RAPHAEL'S BETTER HEALTH. 1978. bi-m. $11. Institute for Better Health, 1384 Chapel St., New Haven, CT 06511. TEL 203-789-4089. Ed. Paul J. Taylor. adv.; bk.rev. circ. 120,000.

SALUD PARA TODOS. see *CHILDREN AND YOUTH — For*

613　　　　　IT　　ISSN 1120-446X
SALVE. 1977. m. L.52800. Rizzoli Editore-Corriere della Sera, Via A. Rizzoli 2, 20132 Milan, Italy. TEL 39-2-2588. Ed. Antonio Vellani. adv.: page L.22350000; adv. contact: Flavio Biondi. circ. 132,923.

613.7 613.2　　CN　　ISSN 0832-6770
SANTE. 1984. 10/yr. Can.$19.50. Editions du Feu Vert, Inc., 5148 St. Laurent Blvd., Montreal, PQ H2T 1R8, Canada. TEL 514-273-9773. FAX 514-273-9268. Ed. Lucie Desaulniers. adv. circ. 37,874. Indexed: Pt.de Rep. (1989-). **Document type:** consumer publication.

SATSANG. see *AGRICULTURE*

613　　　　　BL　　ISSN 0104-1568
SAUDE!; e vital! 1983. m. $50. Editora Azul, S.A., Av. Nacoes Unidas, 5777, 05479-900 Sao Paulo, SP, Brazil. TEL 11-816-7866. FAX 11-813-9115. (Subscr. to: Rua do Curtume 769, 05065-900 Sao Paulo SP, Brazil. TEL 011-823-9100) Ed. Lana Nowikow. adv.: color page $7700; 135 x 190. charts; illus. circ. 75,000. **Document type:** consumer publication.
　Description: For active, health-conscious readers. Contains information on the world of health, nutrition and related fields.

613.7　　　　US　　ISSN 0036-6382
GV561
SCHOLASTIC COACH. 1931. 10/yr. $14.95. Scholastic Inc., 555 Broadway, New York, NY 10012-3999. TEL 212-343-6100. Ed. Herman L. Masin. adv.; bk.rev.; film rev.; illus.; index. circ. 42,000. (also avail. in microform from UMI; back issues avail.; reprint service avail. from UMI,KTO) **Indexed:** Acad.Ind., Educ.Ind., Phys.Ed.Ind., Sports Per.Ind., Sportsearch (1976-). **Document type:** trade publication.
　—BLDSC (8092.541000); Faxon; SWETS; UMI; UnCover.
　Incorporates (1921-198?): Athletic Journal (ISSN 0004-6655)
　Description: Aimed at school gymnastics coaches.

SCRIPPS CLINIC PERSONAL HEALTH LETTER. see *MEDICAL SCIENCES*

613.7　　　　GW　　ISSN 0344-872X
DER SCHWIMMEISTER. 1975. m. DM.91. Ebert Verlag GmbH, Blankenseer Str. 6-8, 23562 Luebeck, Germany. TEL 0451-501011. FAX 04509-2241. **Document type:** bulletin.

614.8　　　　US　　ISSN 1068-1930
SEARCH FOR HEALTH. m. U.S. National Institutes of Health, News Branch, Bldg. 31, Rm. 28-10, Bethesda, MD 20892. TEL 301-496-2535. Ed. Helen Ou.

SEKRETY MLODOSCI I URODY. see *BEAUTY CULTURE*

613　　　　　FR　　ISSN 0037-153X
SELF.* 1966. m. (11/yr.). 25 F. S A F P, 68 Colmar-Ingersheim, France. Ed. Marcel Rouet. adv.; bk.rev.; film rev.; illus.

SENIOR SPORTS NEWS. see *SPORTS AND GAMES*

SHAOLIN YU TAIJI. see *SPORTS AND GAMES*

613.972　　　JA　　ISSN 0037-4113
SHONI HOKEN KENKYU/JOURNAL OF CHILD HEALTH. (Text in Japanese) 1933. bi-m. Nihon Shoni Hoken Kenkyukai - Japanese Society of Child Health, 1-12, Katamachi, Shinjuku-ku, Tokyo 160, Japan. bk.rev.; stat.; index.

SICHERHEITSBEAUFTRAGTER; Zeitschrift fuer Unfallverhuetung und Arbeitssicherheit. see *BUSINESS AND ECONOMICS — Labor And Industrial Relations*

SICHERHEITSINGENIEUR; Zeitschrift fuer Arbeitssicherheit. see *BUSINESS AND ECONOMICS — Labor And Industrial Relations*

SILENT SPORTS; mid-America's aerobic recreational sports magazine. see *SPORTS AND GAMES*

613.7　　　　US　　ISSN 1055-5552
SLIM FAST MAGAZINE. 1991. q. $1.95 per no. Welsh Publishing Group, Inc., 300 Madison Ave., New York, NY 10017. TEL 212-687-0680. FAX 212-986-1849. Ed. Margot Gilman. **Document type:** consumer publication.

SLIMMING. see *NUTRITION AND DIETETICS*

613　　　　　US
SMOKING AND HEALTH NEWSLETTER.* 1965. q. free. National Interagency Council on Smoking and Health, 7320 Greenville Ave., Dallas, TX 75231. TEL 214-750-5359. Dir. Robert E. Wallace. circ. 10,000. (processed)

SOCCER NEWS. see *SPORTS AND GAMES — Ball Games*

613.7　　　　JA
SOKAI. (Text in Japanese) 1974. m. Kodansha Ltd., 12-21 Otowa 2-chome, Bunkyo-ku, Tokyo 112, Japan. TEL 03-3811-4071. FAX 03-3818-2247. TELEX J34509 KODANSHA. Ed. Masaaki Kajiyama. circ. 250,000. **Document type:** consumer publication.

SOKOL POLSKI/POLISH FALCON. see *CLUBS*

613　　　　　US　　ISSN 0147-5231
SOMATICS; magazine-journal of the mind body arts and sciences. 1976. s-a. $20 to individuals (Canada $24; Europe $28; elsewhere $30); institutions $25 (Canada $29; Europe $33; elsewhere $35) (effective 1995-1996). Novato Institute for Somatic Research and Training, 1516 Grant Avenue, Ste. 212, Novato, CA 94945. TEL 415-897-0336. Ed. Eleanor Criswell Hanna. adv.; bk.rev. circ. 1,300. (back issues avail.) **Indexed:** Psychol.Abstr., Sociol.Abstr.
　Description: Publishes articles for professionals and laypersons in the mind/body field. Covers issues relating to holistic health care, fitness, movement, dance, psychology and philosophy.

613　　　　　US
SORENSON HEALTH AND FITNESS BULLETIN. 1991. 6/yr. $19.95. National Institute of Fitness, 202 N. Snow Canyon Rd., Box 938, Ivins, UT 84738. TEL 801-673-4905; 800-944-3488. Ed. Marc Sorenson.
　Description: Covers recent news and research in nutrition, health and fitness for a general audience.

613.7 910.09　　US
SPA FINDER. 1987. a. $4.95. Spa Finders - Travel Arrangements Ltd., 91 Fifth Ave., New York, NY 10003-3039. TEL 212-924-6800. FAX 212-924-7240. adv.: B&W page $7200, color page $8200; trim 8 1/2 x 10 3/4. maps. circ. 100,000.
　Description: Contains information on the world's great spas and fitness resorts for health, fitness and beauty enthusiasts.

613.7　　　　US
SPA SPECS; resources for health and well-being. 1990. bi-m. $59. Spa Specs International, 21548 Hyde Rd., Sonoma, CA 95476. TEL 707-939-0101. Ed. Eva M. Jensch; Pub. Eva M. Jensch. adv. circ. 1,200. (tabloid format; back issues avail.) **Document type:** newsletter.
　Description: Covers trends in preventative medicine, health and fitness, nutrition, body work, and beauty.

613.7　　　　GW　　ISSN 0171-6298
SPIRIDON LAUFMAGAZIN. 1975. m. DM.60. Spiridon Verlags GmbH, Dorfstr. 18a, 40699 Erkrath, Germany. TEL 0211-726364. FAX 0211-786823. Ed. Manfred Steffny. adv. contact: Jens Steinhaeuser. bk.rev.; illus.; index. circ. 17,000. (back issues avail.) **Document type:** consumer publication.

SPLASH! (COLORADO SPRINGS). see *SPORTS AND GAMES*

SPOKANE WOMAN. see *WOMEN'S INTERESTS*

613　　　　　UK　　ISSN 0266-8963
SPORT & FITNESS.* 1892. m. £25($45) Sport & Fitness Ltd., P.O. Box 10, Sunbury, Middlesex TW16 5PZ, England. TEL 01-891-6885. Ed. Edward Hankey. circ. 27,000. (back issues avail.) **Indexed:** Sportsearch (1984-).
　Incorporates: Health and Strength (ISSN 0017-890X)

SPORT AND RECREATION INFORMATION GROUP BULLETIN. see *SPORTS AND GAMES*

SPORT & MEDICINA. see *MEDICAL SCIENCES — Sports Medicine*

SPORT SCENE; focus on youth programs. see *SPORTS AND GAMES*

SPORT SPECIAL - CONDITION; die Zeitschrift fuer Lauf- und Ausdauersport. see *SPORTS AND GAMES*

796.41　　　　IT
SPORTMAN. 1973. bi-m. L.42000 (foreign L.65000). Edizioni Sportman, Strada Francesca 42, 24040 Zingonia (BG), Italy. TEL 39-35-884646. FAX 39-35-885332. Ed. Franco Fassi; Pub. Nadia Fassi. adv.: B&W page L.1600000, color page L.2700000; adv. contact: Giuseppe Ranica. **Document type:** consumer publication.
　Description: Covers bodybuilding and fitness for men and women.

SPORTPARADE. see *EDUCATION — Special Education And Rehabilitation*

SPORTS MEDICINE BULLETIN. see *MEDICAL SCIENCES — Sports Medicine*

SPORTS MEDICINE IN PRIMARY CARE. see *MEDICAL SCIENCES — Sports Medicine*

613.7　　　　IT
STAR BENE. 1978. m. L.54000 (foreign L.64800). Arnoldo Mondadori Editore S.p.A., Casella Postale 1833, 20101 Milan, Italy. TEL 39-2-75421. Ed. Gabriele Zappa. adv.: page L.23800000. circ. 177,000.

613.7 790.1　　XO　　ISSN 0139-7052
START.* 1956. w. (Czechoslovak Union of Physical Education) Sport, Vajnorska Cesta 100-a, 832-58 Bratislava, Slovakia. Ed. Matej Szecher. circ. 81,000.

613.7　　　　US　　ISSN 1073-6840
GV514
STRENGTH & CONDITIONING. Abbreviated title: S & C. 1978. bi-m. membership. (National Strength & Conditioning Association) Human Kinetics Publishers, Inc., Box 5076, Champaign, IL 61825-5076. TEL 217-351-5076. FAX 217-351-2674. Ed. Harvey Newton. adv. contact: Pamela Anderson. bk.rev. circ. 10,000. **Indexed:** Phys.Ed.Ind., Sportsearch (1981-). **Document type:** trade publication.
　—BLDSC (8474.119900); Faxon; Genuine Article; SWETS; UMI; UnCover. **CCC.**
　Former titles (until 1994): N S C A Journal (ISSN 1073-2721); (until 1992): National Strength and Conditioning Journal (ISSN 0744-0049); (until 1981): National Strength Coaches Association Journal (ISSN 0199-610X)
　Description: Focuses on resistance training, conditioning, sports science and medicine and current issues in strength and conditioning.

613.7 362　　US　　ISSN 0891-849X
STUDIES IN HEALTH AND HUMAN SERVICES. 1983. irreg., latest no.23. $49.95 per no. Edwin Mellen Press, 415 Ridge St., Box 450, Lewiston, NY 14092. TEL 716-754-2788. FAX 716-754-4056. **Document type:** monographic series.
　—BLDSC (8490.627900).

613.7 790.1　　FI　　ISSN 0356-1070
STUDIES IN SPORT, PHYSICAL EDUCATION AND HEALTH. (Text in English and Finnish) 1971. irreg., no.9, 1976. exchange basis. Jyvaskylan Yliopisto - University of Jyvaskyla, Publications Center, PL 35, 40100 Jyvaskyla 10, Finland. TEL 941-601-371. FAX 603-371. TELEX 28219 JYK SF. Eds. Juhani Kirjonen, Harri Suominen. circ. 450. **Document type:** monographic series.

PHYSICAL FITNESS AND HYGIENE

612.044 790.072　SA　ISSN 0379-9069
SUID-AFRIKAANSE TYDSKRIF VIR NAVORSING IN SPORT, LIGGAAMLIKE OPVOEDKUNDE EN ONTSPANNING/SOUTH AFRICAN JOURNAL FOR RESEARCH IN SPORT, PHYSICAL EDUCATION AND RECREATION. (Text in Afrikaans, English; summaries in English) 1978. s-a. R.40 (effective 1993). Southern African Federation for Movement and Leisure Sciences, P.O. Box 13206, Clubview 0014, South Africa. TEL 27-12-6633290. FAX 27-12-6633294. Ed. B.C. Andrews. bk.rev. circ. 600. (back issues avail.) **Indexed:** Sportsearch (1980-). **Document type:** academic/scholarly publication.
—BLDSC (8053.668500).
　Description: Aimed at scientists involved in the areas of physical fitness, sport, sports medicine, movement education and recreation.

613　II　ISSN 0039-4882
SUKH DATTA. (Text in Punjabi) 1966. m. Rs.2.($0.75) Narula Dwakhana, Maisewan, Amritsar, India. Ed. Sundersinch Narula. adv.; bk.rev. circ. 4,000.

613　DK　ISSN 0039-5366
SUNDHEDSBLADET; hjemmets raadgiver. 1881. 6/yr. DKK 126. Dansk Bogforlag, Box 770, Boerstenbindervej 4, DK-5230 Odense M, Denmark. TEL 45-66-15-88-43. FAX 45-66-15-57-43. Ed. Aage Andersen. adv.; bk.rev.; illus.; index. circ. 40,000.

613　NO　ISSN 0332-7434
SUNNHETSBLADET. 1881. m. (11/yr.). NOK 248. Norsk Bokforlag A-S, Olaf Helsets vei 8, Oslo 6, Norway. TEL 22-28-52-20. FAX 22-29-85-11. Ed. Bjoern D. Kendel. adv. contact: Egil Johansen. bk.rev./ circ. 14,408 (controlled).
—CCC.

SWIMMING POOLS TODAY. see SPORTS AND GAMES — Outdoor Life

613.7　US
SYRACUSE HEALTH & FITNESS. m. Box 270, Baldwinsville, NY 13027. TEL 315-635-3921. Ed. Dave Grieves.

613.7　US　ISSN 0889-0846
T A H P E R D JOURNAL. 1954. 3/yr. $32 to individuals; institutions $40. Texas Association for Health, Physical Education, Recreation and Dance, 6300 La Calma Dr., No. 100, Austin, TX 78752. TEL 512-459-1299. FAX 512-459-1290. Ed. Quentin A. Christian. adv. contact: Brom Hoban. circ. 4,000. **Indexed:** Sportsearch (1983-). **Document type:** academic/scholarly publication.
　Refereed Serial

613.7 613.2　US
T O P S NEWS. 1949. m. membership. Take Off Pounds Sensibly, Inc., 4575 S. Fifth St., Box 07360, Milwaukee, WI 53207-0360. TEL 414-482-4620. Ed. Kathleen Davis. circ. 303,692. (back issues avail.)
　Description: News and features about weight-control and nutrition. Covers activities of the organization.

613.85　FR
TABAC ET SANTE; tabagisme. 1970. q. 50 F. (Comite National Contre le Tabagisme) Nouvelles Editions Touristiques et Artistiques, 19 rue Bergere, 75009 Paris, France. Ed. J.P. Lejard. adv.; bk.rev. circ. 3,000.

T'AI CHI; the leading international magazine of T'ai Chi Ch'uan. see ORIENTAL STUDIES

TAIIKU NO KAGAKU/JOURNAL OF HEALTH, PHYSICAL EDUCATION AND RECREATION. see EDUCATION — Teaching Methods And Curriculum

TAL OG DATA, MEDICIN OG SUNDHEDSVAESEN/FACTS, MEDICINE AND HEALTH CARE, DENMARK. see PHARMACY AND PHARMACOLOGY

TEACHING ELEMENTARY PHYSICAL EDUCATION. see EDUCATION — Teaching Methods And Curriculum

613.7　US
TEAM S P I NEWS. m. membership. National Spa & Pool Institute, 2111 Eisenhower Ave., Alexandria, VA 22314. TEL 703-838-0083. Ed. Barbara Brady. circ. 4,300.

613.7　US　ISSN 0890-1597
TENNESSEE JOURNAL OF HEALTH, PHYSICAL EDUCATION, RECREATION AND DANCE. 196? s-a. Tennessee Association of Health, Physical Education, Recreation and Dance, Peabody College of Vanderbilt University, Box 513, Nashville, TN 37203. **Indexed:** Phys.Ed.Ind., Sportsearch.

TERMALISMO - BALNEARIOS. see HEATING, PLUMBING AND REFRIGERATION

613.7　IT
TERME EUROPA; mensile si turismo, salute, bellezza e vacanze - benessere. 1991. m. (10/yr.). L.40000 (foreign L.70000). Gestione Periodici Riuniti, Residenza Mestieri, Milano Due, 20090 Segrate (MI), Italy. TEL 39-2-26413274. FAX 39-2-26413409. Ed. Giorgio Pozzani. adv.: B&W page L.3200000, color page L.5300000; trim 210 x 275; adv. contact: Marco Zulberti. circ. 73,000. (back issues avail.) **Document type:** consumer publication.
　Description: Deals with spas, health and tourism, with medical information about hydrological and spa treatments.

613　FI　ISSN 0040-3911
TERVEYS. 1937. m. FIM 270. (Suomen Adventtikirkko - Finland Union of Seventh-Day Adventists Church) Kirjatoimi Publishing House, PL 94, 33101 Tampere 10, Finland. FAX 358-31-600454. Ed. Birgitta Salo. adv. contact: Heimo Lempinen. charts; illus.; index. circ. 18,000. **Document type:** newsletter.

615.5　US　ISSN 0040-5914
　　　　　　　　CODEN: TRJOED
THERAPEUTIC RECREATION JOURNAL. 1967. q. $46 (foreign $52). (National Therapeutic Recreation Society) National Recreation and Park Association, 2775 S. Quincy St., No. 300, Arlington, VA 22206. TEL 703-820-4940. FAX 703-671-6772. Eds. Michael Mabin, Mark Searle. adv.; bk.rev. circ. 4,000. (also avail. in microform from UMI; back issues avail.) **Indexed:** Phys.Ed.Ind., Sportsearch (1973-).
—BLDSC (8814.672100); Faxon; UMI; UnCover.

613.7　US
TO YOU YOUR HEALTH!; the magazine of healing and hope. 1989. m. free. 371 Bay Ridge Parkway, Brooklyn, NY 11209. TEL 718-921-3131. Ed. Bernice Stock. adv.; illus.

TOKYO JIKEIKAI IKA DAIGAKU TAIRYOKU IGAKU KENKYUSHITSU NENPO/JIKEI UNIVERSITY. SCHOOL OF MEDICINE. ANNUAL REPORT OF LABORATORY SPORTS MEDICINE. see MEDICAL SCIENCES — Sports Medicine

613.7　IT
TOP SALUTE. 1993. m. (10/yr.). L.40000 (foreign L.100000). Alberto Peruzzo Editore s.r.l., Via E. Marelli 165, 20099 Sesto San Giovanni (MI), Italy. TEL 39-2-242021. Ed. Nadia Gelmi. adv.: B&W page L.6000000, color page L.7000000. **Document type:** consumer publication.

613.7 615.53　US
TOUCH FOR HEALTH.* 1982. q. $30 (subsc. includes Touch for Health Journal). Touch for Health Foundation, 7625 Hayvenhurst Ave., No. 45, Van uys, CA 91406-1700. TEL 818-794-1181. adv.; bk.rev. circ. 2,000.
　Description: Collection of papers on health presented at annual meeting.

613.7　GW
TRIATHLON MAGAZIN. 1985. bi-m. DM.24. Spiridon Verlags GmbH, Dorfstr. 18a, 40699 Erkrath, Germany. TEL 0211-726364. FAX 0211-786823. Ed. Manfred Steffny. adv. contact: Jens Steinhaeuser. bk.rev.; index. circ. 4,000. (back issues avail.) **Document type:** consumer publication.

TSPORT; impianti sportivi e ricreativi, piscine, fitness e arredo urbano. see SPORTS AND GAMES

613.7　UK　ISSN 0957-0616
ULTRA-FIT. 1989. bi-m. £18. Ultra-Fit Publications, Champions Yard, Causeway, Penzance TR18 2SP, England. TEL 0736-50204. FAX 0736-68587. Ed. Mark McKeon. circ. 30,000. (back issues avail.)

613.7　AT　ISSN 1321-1536
ULTRA-FIT AUSTRALIA. 1985. bi-m. Aus.$44. Australian Workout Publications, P.O. Box 266, Etham, Vic. 3095, Australia. TEL 61-3-439-2828. FAX 61-3-439-2605. Ed. Mark McKeon. adv.: B&W page Aus.$1200, color Aus.$2000; trim 202 x 213. circ. 25,000. (back issues avail.) **Document type:** consumer publication.
　Former titles (until 1991): Australian Fitness and Training Magazine (ISSN 1031-4105); (until 1987): Australian Workout (ISSN 0815-6980)
　Description: For people interested in health, sports and fitness.

613.7 612.3　US　ISSN 0739-4217
UNIVERSITY OF TEXAS LIFETIME HEALTH LETTER. 1972. 12/yr. $24. 7000 Fannin St., Houston, TX 77030. TEL 713-792-4265. FAX 713-794-4738. Ed. Joe Sigler. circ. 70,000. **Indexed:** CINAHL.
　Formerly (until 1989): Health Letter.
　Description: Articles on health habits people can practice to improve the quality of their physical and mental lives.

613.7　MX　ISSN 0188-395X
UNO MISMO; sensibilidad conciencia compromiso. 1990. m. Editorial Samra, S.A. de C.V., Lucio Blanco 435, Azcapotzalco, 02400 Mexico DF, Mexico.
　Description: Covers the enrichment of the body, mind and spirit.

613.7 790.1　US　ISSN 0739-4586
V A H P E R D JOURNAL. 1978. s.a. $20 (effective Sep. 1993). Virginia Association for Health, Physical Education and Dance, c/o Dr. Robert Davis, Virginia Commonwealth Univ., 817 W. Franklin St., Richmond, VA 23284. TEL 804-395-2539. FAX 804-395-2568. Ed. Dr. Maria Theresa Wessel. circ. 1,000. (back issues avail.) **Indexed:** Sportsearch (1979-).

613.7　FI　ISSN 0789-0095
VALMENNUS & KUNTO. 1978. 8/yr. FIM 240. Juoksija-lehti, Kuparitie 10 A, FIN-00440 Helsinki, Finland. Ed. Antero Kujala. circ. 9,584.

VEGETARIAN VOICE. see NUTRITION AND DIETETICS

613　US　ISSN 0749-3509
R773
VIBRANT LIFE; a Christian guide to total health. 1904. bi-m. $12.95. Review and Herald Publishing Association, 55 W. Oak Ridge Dr., Hagerstown, MD 21740. TEL 301-791-7000. Ed. Barbara Jackson-Hall. adv.; bk.rev.; abstr.; charts; illus.; index. circ. 37,000. (reprint service avail. from UMI) **Indexed:** C.I.N.L., CCR, Hlth.Ind.
—Faxon; UMI.
　Former titles: Your Life and Health (ISSN 0279-2680); Life and Health (ISSN 0024-3035)

613.7　AG
VIDA FELIZ. 1899. m. $15.50. (Iglesia Adventista del Septimo Dia) Asociacion Casa Editora Sudamericana, Avda. San Martin 4555, 1602 Florida, Buenos Aires, Argentina. TEL 0541-760-2426. FAX 0541-7618455. TELEX 24646 AR (GRACES). Ed. Ricardo Bentancur. illus. circ. 30,000.

613　FR　ISSN 0986-0754
LA VIE CLAIRE. 1946. m. (10/yr.). 90 F. La Vie Claire, 70 Av. Republique, 94700 Maisons-Alfort, France. Ed. Marie-Pierre Vaur. adv.; bk.rev.; stat. circ. 30,000.

613　FR　ISSN 0042-5524
VIE ET SANTE. 1890. m. 250 F. Editions Vie et Sante, 60 av. Emile Zola, 77192 Dammarie les Lys Cedex, France. FAX 64-87-00-66. Ed. Marc Geurra. adv.; bk.rev.; circ. 40,000 (controlled). **Indexed:** ExtraMED, Pt.de Rep. (1979-).
●Also available on CD-ROM.

613.7　US　ISSN 0886-6554
VIM & VIGOR; America's family health magazine. 1985. q. $7. McMurry Publishing, 8805 N. 23rd Ave., No. 400, Phoenix, AZ 85021. FAX 602-395-5853. Ed. Fred Petrovsky. adv.; bk.rev.; tr.lit.; circ. 950,000 (controlled). (back issues avail.)
　Description: Directed to health-conscious people who are interested in a variety of health issues including diagnosis, treatment, diet, fitness, and exercise.

VISIONARY. see MEDICAL SCIENCES — Ophthalmology And Optometry

PHYSICAL FITNESS AND HYGIENE

613   IT   ISSN 0042-7268
VITA E SALUTE; rivista mensile di medicina preventiva. 1952. m. L.55000 (effective 1996). Edizioni A.D.V., Via Chiantigiana, 30, Falciani, 50023 Impruneta, (FI), Italy. TEL 39-55-2326291. Ed. Bruno Rimoldi. adv: color page L.7000000. bk.rev.; charts; illus.; index. circ. 40,000.

613   GW   ISSN 0507-1747
VITAL; das Magazin fuer modernes Leben. 1970. m. Jahreszeiten Verlag GmbH, Possmoorweg 5, 22301 Hamburg, Germany. TEL 040-27170. FAX 040-27172056. Ed. Karsten Flohr. adv. contact: Simone Zolling. circ. 388,193. **Document type:** consumer publication.
    Formerly: Vital Gesundheit, Freizeit, Lebensfreude.

613   US   ISSN 1074-5831
VITALITY. 1987. m. $12.99. Vitality, Inc., 8080 N. Central, LB 78, Dallas, TX 75206. TEL 214-691-1480. Ed. Barbara Floria. adv.; bk.rev.; circ. 1,500,000 (controlled).
    Description: Credible source features about diet, fitness, parenting, and personal finance.

VITALITY. see *NUTRITION AND DIETETICS*

VITASANA. see *NUTRITION AND DIETETICS*

613.7   IT
VIVA. 1985. bi-m. L.35000. Valentini Editore s.r.l., Via Fabio Filzi 41, 20124 Milan, Italy. TEL 39-2-66804467. FAX 39-2-6887740. TELEX 330299 VALEDI I. Ed. Pietro Paolo Valentini. adv.: B&W page L.1700000, color page L.3500000. circ. 24,000. **Document type:** consumer publication.

613.7 646.7   IT
VIVERSANI E BELLI; settimanale di salute e bellezza. 1992. w. L.70000 (foreign L.132000). D.E. Didieffe s.r.l., Via Boschetti 6, 20121 Milan, Italy. TEL 39-2-618331. FAX 39-2-66015851. Eds. Nicola De Feo, Sergio Del Duca. adv.: color page L.28200000. circ. 333,892. **Document type:** consumer publication.

613   SP
VIVIR CON SALUD; la revista decana del naturismo espanol. 1953. 5/yr. 4000 ptas.($50) (effective 1994). Ediciones CEDEL, C. Mallorca 257, Apartado 5326, 08008 Barcelona, Spain. TEL 343-215-6039. FAX 343-215-6088. Ed. Jose Avila. adv.; bk.rev.; bibl.; illus.; tr.mk.; index. circ. 5,000. (back issues avail.) **Document type:** consumer publication.
    Formerly: Vivir (ISSN 0042-7578)

613.7   FI   ISSN 0780-1122
VOI HYVIN. 6/yr. FIM 274. A-Lehdet Oy, Hitsaajankatu 7, SF-00810 Helsinki, Finland. FAX 0-786-858. Ed. Marikka Burton. circ. 57,525. **Document type:** consumer publication.
    Description: Devoted to well-being and self development.

613   GW   ISSN 0042-8493
VOLKSGESUNDHEIT; Monatzeitschrift fuer gesundes Leben und naturgemaesse Heilverfahren. 1924. m. DM.32. Helfer-Verlag E. Schwabe, PF 1645, 6380 Bad Homburg, Germany. Ed. Emil Schwabe. adv.; abstr.; illus.

WALKING! JOURNAL; the art, science and sport of walking. see *SPORTS AND GAMES — Outdoor Life*

613.7   US   ISSN 1042-2102
GV199
WALKING MAGAZINE. 1986. 6/yr. $14.95 (foreign $20.95). Cowles Magazines, Inc. (Subsidiary of: Cowles Media Company), 6405 Flank Dr., Box 8200, Harrisburg, PA 17105-8200. TEL 717-657-9555; 800-435-9610. FAX 717-657-9526. Ed. Seth Bauer. adv.; bk.rev.; circ. 500,000 (paid). **Document type:** consumer publication.
—CCC.
    Description: Contains information for recreational and fitness walkers. Focuses on health, fitness, nutrition, travel, and equipment.

613   JA
WATASHI NO KENKO/MY HEALTH. (Text in Japanese) 1976. m. 8520 Yen. Shufunotomo Co. Ltd., 2-9 Kanda Surugadai, Chiyoda-ku, Tokyo 101, Japan. Ed. Yoshitaka Kujime. adv.; bk.rev. circ. 200,000. **Document type:** consumer publication.

WEIGHT WATCHERS MAGAZINE. see *NUTRITION AND DIETETICS*

613.7   UK   ISSN 0309-8095
WEIGHT WATCHERS MAGAZINE. 1977. bi-m. £4.80. (Weight Watchers (U.K.) Ltd.) Gat Publishing, 141-143 Drury Lane, London WC2B 5TS, England. Ed. Harriet Cross. adv.; bk.rev. circ. 128,443.
    Indexed: Hlth.Ind.

613.7   US
WEIGHTLIFTING U S A. 1983. bi-m. $20. U S Weightlifting Federation, One Olympic Plaza, Colorado Springs, CO 80909-5764. TEL 719-578-4508. FAX 719-578-4741. Ed. John Halpin. adv.; bk.rev. circ. 2,700. (back issues avail.) **Document type:** newsletter.
    Description: Covers US weightlifting, coaching, health and fitness, sports medicine, and local, national, and international competition results.

613.7 613.2   AT
WELL BEING MAGAZINE; personal and planetary healing. 1984. q. Aus.$66 (foreign). Wellspring Publishers P-L, 1-187A Avenue Rd., Mosman, N.S.W. 2088, Australia. TEL 61-2-969-7122. FAX 61-2-968-2489. Ed. Barbara McGregor. adv.; bk.rev. circ. 30,000. (back issues avail.)
    Formerly: Australian Well Being (ISSN 0812-8227)

613.7 612.3   US   ISSN 0748-9234
RA773   CODEN: UCWLE9
WELLNESS LETTER; the newsletter of nutrition, fitness, and stress management. 1984. m. $24. Health Letter Associates, Box 412, Prince St. Sta., New York, NY 10012. TEL 212-505-2255; 800-829-9170. FAX 212-505-5462. (Subscr. to: Box 420148, Palm Coast, FL 32142; Alt addr.: 48 Shattuck Sq., Berkeley, CA 94704) Ed. Michael Golden. illus. circ. 500,000. (back issues avail.) **Indexed:** CINAHL, Hlth.Ind. **Document type:** newsletter.
  •Also available online. Vendor(s): University Microfilms International.
  —Faxon. **CCC.**
    Description: Provides information for physicians, nutritionists, and other professionals in the health care field; focuses on staying well rather than coping with illness.

613   UK   ISSN 0957-1728
WHICH? WAY TO HEALTH. 1983. bi-m. £31 membership. Consumers' Association Ltd., 2 Marylebone Rd., London NW1 4DF, England. TEL 0171-830-6000. FAX 0171-830-6220. (Subscr. to: Consumers' Association Ltd., P.O. Box 44, Hertford SG14 1SH, England. TEL 01992-822800) Ed. David P.S. Dickinson. bk.rev.; cum.index; circ. 71,000 (paid).
  •Also available online.
  —BLDSC (9310.904000).
    Formerly (until Sep. 1988): Self Health (ISSN 0265-5497)
    Description: Independent food and health magazine for the lay person. Features and information on self-care and on major illnesses, health promotion and provisions in Britain; independent testing of health products and services, and information on nutrition.

WHOLE LIFE TIMES. see *NEW AGE PUBLICATIONS*

613.7   US
WILDWOOD NEWS; journal of health and healing. q. $10. Wildwood Lifestyle Center & Hospital, Box 129, Wildwood, GA 30757-0129. **Document type:** newsletter.
    Description: Promotes the preventative medicine practiced at the Wildwood Lifestyle Center and Hospital, including hydrotherapy, hiking, and diet consciousness.

613.7   US   ISSN 0043-5856
WINGED FOOT. 1892. m. $24. New York Athletic Club, 180 Central Park South, New York, NY 10019. TEL 212-247-5100. Ed. Fred Jarvis. adv.; bk.rev.; illus. circ. 8,400.

WISCONSIN IN MOTION. see *SPORTS AND GAMES*

WOMAN'S DAY 101 WAYS TO LOSE WEIGHT AND STAY HEALTHY. see *NUTRITION AND DIETETICS*

613.7 618.082   US   ISSN 1068-0594
WOMEN'S EXERCISE. 1993. bi-m. $17.75. Chelo Publishing Inc., Empire State Bldg., 50 Fifth Ave., New York, NY 10118. TEL 212-947-4322. FAX 212-563-4774. **Document type:** consumer publication.

WOMEN'S SPORTS EXPERIENCE. see *SPORTS AND GAMES*

WORLD BOOK HEALTH AND MEDICAL ANNUAL. see *ENCYCLOPEDIAS AND GENERAL ALMANACS*

THE WORLD OF A S P. see *SPORTS AND GAMES*

613   US   ISSN 0161-7672
RA1242.T6
WORLD SMOKING & HEALTH. 1976. 3/yr. free. American Cancer Society, Inc., 1599 Clifton Rd., N.E., Atlanta, GA 30329. TEL 404-329-7936. FAX 404-325-2217. Ed. Jerie Jordan. charts; illus.; stat. circ. 16,000.
  —BLDSC (9360.031000); Faxon.

WUSHU JIANSHEN/HEALTH THROUGH MARTIAL ARTS. see *SPORTS AND GAMES*

WYCHOWANIE FIZYCZNE I HIGIENA SZKOLNA. see *EDUCATION — Teaching Methods And Curriculum*

WYCHOWANIE FIZYCZNE I SPORT. STUDIA I MATERIALY. see *EDUCATION — Teaching Methods And Curriculum*

613.7   PL   ISSN 0860-8075
WYCHOWANIE FIZYCZNE I ZDROWOTNE. 5/yr. (Ministerstwo Edukacji Narodowej) Wydawnictwa Szkolne i Pedagogiczne, Pl. Dabrowskiego 8, 00-950 Warsaw, Poland. FAX 48-22-268971. (Dist. by: Ars Polona, Krakowskie Przedmiescie 7, 00-068 Warsaw, Poland) Ed. Tadeusz Maszczak. circ. 4,000.
    Description: For teachers of physical education, doctors and nurses working in schools with healthy and disabled students.

613.7   CC   ISSN 1001-747X
XI'AN TIYU XUEYUAN XUEBAO/XI'AN INSTITUTE OF PHYSICAL EDUCATION. JOURNAL. (Text in Chinese) 1984. q. Y12. Xi'an Tiyu Xueyuan - Xi'an Institute of Physical Education, Lingyuan Lu, Xi'an, Shaanxi 710068, People's Republic of China. TEL 5262327. (Co-sponsor: Xinwen Chubanshu) Ed. Zhao Yuting. circ. 600. **Document type:** academic/scholarly publication.
    Description: Covers the latest achievement, technology and experiment of teaching, training and scientific research in physical education. Also includes news in China and abroad.

613.7 790.1   CN
Y M C A WEEKLY NEWS (VANCOUVER, BC). w. Vancouver Downtown Young Men's Christian Association, 955 Burrard St., Vancouver, B.C. V6Z 1Y2, Canada. TEL 604-681-0221. Ed. Terry Connolly. circ. 1,000.

613.7   GR
YGIA KAI OMORPHIA/HEALTH AND BEAUTY. 1979. bi-m. Dr.44000($50) I C O International, 3A Barbanou St., P.O. Box 190.25, 117 10 Athens, Greece. TEL 30-1-9017-806. FAX 30-1-9016-663. Ed. Dimitrios E. Tsirimocos. adv.: B&W page DM.3000, color page DM.3200; 230 x 305. bk.rev. circ. 15,000. (back issues avail.) **Document type:** consumer publication.
    Description: Covers beauty, cosmetics, hair dressing, fashion, diet, health, gymnastics, dance, and aesthetics.

YOGA AND TOTAL HEALTH. see *PHILOSOPHY*

YOGA JOURNAL; for health and conscious living. see *NEW AGE PUBLICATIONS*

YOGA LIFE. see *PHILOSOPHY*

613.7   US   ISSN 0191-3298
B132.Y6
YOGA RESEARCH. 1978. a. Yoga Research Society, 251 S. 12th St., Philadelphia, PA 19107. **Document type:** bulletin.

PHYSICAL FITNESS AND HYGIENE — ABSTRACTING, BIBLIOGRAPHIES, STATISTICS

613.7 US ISSN 0279-9324
RA773
YOUR HEALTH & FITNESS. 1980. q. $16.50. General Learning Corporation, Health Communications Group, 60 Revere Dr., Northbrook, IL 60062-1563. TEL 708-205-3000. FAX 708-564-8197. Ed. Carol Lezak; Pub. Julio Abreu. adv. contact: Mark Collins. bibl. circ. 800,000. **Document type:** consumer publication.
 Description: Contains general health, fitness and safety articles for the layman. Includes recipes.
 Refereed Serial

613.7 US ISSN 1040-7057
YOUR PERSONAL BEST NEWSLETTER. 1989. m. $18. Rodale Press, Inc., 33 E. Minor St., Emmaus, PA 18098. TEL 610-967-5171. TELEX 847338. **Document type:** newsletter.
 Description: Gives tips, advice and information about harnessing your mind to improve your emotions and your health.

613 XO ISSN 0044-1953
ZDRAVIE; popularno-zdravotnicky casopis moderneho cloveka. m. $35. Slovensky Cerveny Kriz, Ruzova Dolina 27, 824 65 Bratislava, Slovakia. (Dist. by: Slovart, Gottwaldovo nam. 48, 805 32 Bratislava, Slovakia) Ed. Juraj Bogdan. adv.; bk.rev.; illus. circ. 80,000.
 Formerly: Zdravie Ludu.

ZDROWIE, URODA I ZYCIE. see *BEAUTY CULTURE*

613.7 CC
ZHONG LAO NIAN BAOJIAN. (Text in Chinese) bi-m. Zhongri Youhao Yiyuan - Sino-Japanese Friendship Hospital, Hepingli Beikou, Beijing 100029, People's Republic of China. TEL 4221122. Ed. Ma Xiuye.

613.7 CC ISSN 1000-8268
ZHONGGUO QIGONG. (Text in Chinese) 1986. m. $120. Hebei Beidaihe Qigong Kangfu Yiyuan, 198 Dongjing Lu, Beidaihe-qu, Qinhuandao, Hebei 066100, People's Republic of China. TEL 0335441257. (Co-sponsor: Zhongguo Qigong Keyan Hui) Ed. Liu Jing Ping. adv. circ. 70,000.

613.7 CC ISSN 0529-5548
R97.7.C5
ZHONGJI YIKAN. (Text in Chinese) m. $2.70. Renmin Weisheng Chubanshe, 10 Tiantan Xili, Beijing 100050, People's Republic of China. TEL 7015802. Ed. Liu Yiqing. circ. 110,000. **Document type:** academic/scholarly publication.

PHYSICAL FITNESS AND HYGIENE — Abstracting, Bibliographies, Statistics

016 613.85 US ISSN 0067-7361
RA1242.T6
BIBLIOGRAPHY ON SMOKING AND HEALTH. (Subseries of: Public Health Service Bibliography Series; reprint service avail. from CIS) 1967. a. free. U.S. Centers for Disease Control, National Center for Chronic Disease Prevention and Health Promotion, Office on Smoking and Health, 4770 Buford Hwy., N.E., MS K-50, Atlanta, GA 30341-3724.
TEL 404-488-5705; 800-CDC-1311.
FAX 404-488-5939. (Orders to: Superintendent of Documents, U.S. Government Printing Office, Box 371954, Pittsburgh, PA 15250-7954. TEL 202-512-1800. FAX 202-512-2250; Or: Bernan, 4611-F Assembly Dr., Lanham, MD 20706. TEL 301-459-7666. FAX 301-459-0056) index; circ. controlled. (also avail. in microfiche from CIS) **Indexed:** Amer.Stat.Ind. (1979-), MEDOC. **Document type:** bibliography, government publication.
 Supersedes (in 1989): Smoking and Health Bulletin (ISSN 0081-0363); Which was formerly: Smoking and Health Bibliographical Bulletin.
 Description: Lists articles pertaining to the prevention and cessation of tobacco use and the protection of nonsmokers.

BRITISH JOURNAL OF PHYSICAL EDUCATION. see *EDUCATION — Teaching Methods And Curriculum*

BRITISH JOURNAL OF PHYSICAL EDUCATION. RESEARCH SUPPLEMENT. see *EDUCATION — Teaching Methods And Curriculum*

FITNESS IN AMERICA. see *SPORTS AND GAMES — Abstracting, Bibliographies, Statistics*

613.7 011 GW ISSN 0932-2884
GESUNDHEITSFOERDERUNG. (Text in English or German) 1987. irreg. DM.13 per no. Landesinstitut fuer den Oeffentlichen Gesundheitsdienst des Landes Nordrhein-Westfalen, Westerfelderstr. 35-37, 33611 Bielefeld, Germany. TEL 0521-8007-O. (Subscr. to: Postfach 201012, 33548 Bielefeld, Germany) bk.rev. circ. 350. **Document type:** abstracting/indexing.

HAWAII. DEPARTMENT OF HEALTH. RESEARCH AND STATISTICS OFFICE. R & S REPORT. see *POPULATION STUDIES — Abstracting, Bibliographies, Statistics*

613.7 790 370 US ISSN 0090-5119
HEALTH, PHYSICAL EDUCATION AND RECREATION MICROFORM PUBLICATIONS BULLETIN.* 1949. s-a. $10. Microform Publications, University of Oregon, Eugene, OR 97403-1243. TEL 503-346-4117. FAX 503-346-2814. TELEX 510-597-0354-EUG. Ed. Gwen Steigelman. cum.index: 1949-1991. circ. 2,630. (also avail. in microfiche)
 Formerly: Health, Physical Education, and Recreation Microcard Bulletin (ISSN 0017-906X)
 Description: Lists titles and descriptions of theses and dissertations in the fields of physical education, sport sciences, health, dance, and recreational studies.

613.194 CN ISSN 0840-6529
RA645.C34
HEALTH REPORTS. q. Can.$104($125) (foreign $146). Statistics Canada, Publications Division, Ottawa, ON K1A 0T6, Canada. TEL 613-951-7277; 800-267-6677. FAX 613-951-1584.
—BLDSC (4275.106250). **CCC.**
 Description: Presents the most frequently requested health information in Canada.

K I H A S A BULLETIN. (Korean Institute for Health and Social Affairs) see *SOCIAL SERVICES AND WELFARE*

MEDICAL ABSTRACTS NEWSLETTER; your direct pipeline to the latest breakthroughs in health care. see *MEDICAL SCIENCES — Abstracting, Bibliographies, Statistics*

MINNESOTA SPORTS. see *SPORTS AND GAMES*

613 016 US
N T I S ALERTS: HEALTH CARE. w. $135 (foreign $195). U.S. National Technical Information Service, 5285 Port Royal Rd., Springfield, VA 22161. TEL 703-487-4630. FAX 703-321-8547. TELEX 64617. index. (back issues avail.)
 Former titles: Abstract Newsletter: Health Care; Abstract Newsletter: Health Planning and Health Services Research; Weekly Abstract Newsletter: Health Planning and Health Services Research; Weekly Government Abstracts. Health Planning and Health Services Research (ISSN 0199-9974); Weekly Government Abstracts. Health Planning (ISSN 0017-9086)

613.7 016 US ISSN 0191-9202
GV201
PHYSICAL EDUCATION INDEX. 1978. q. $175. Ben Oak Publishing Company, Box 474, Cape Girardeau, MO 63702-0474. TEL 314-334-8789. Ed. Ronald F. Kirby; Pub. Ronald F. Kirby. bk.rev.; index. (back issues avail.)
 Description: Subject index to health, physical education, recreation, dance, sports, and sports medicine literature in over 180 journals.

SOZIALMEDIZIN. see *MEDICAL SCIENCES — Abstracting, Bibliographies, Statistics*

613 011 US ISSN 0161-603X
HV5825
U.S. NATIONAL INSTITUTE ON DRUG ABUSE. STATISTICAL SERIES D. DATA FROM THE CLIENT ORIENTED DATA ACQUISITION PROCESS. QUARTERLY REPORT. PROVISIONAL DATA. 1973-1979; resumed 1982. q. U.S. National Institute on Drug Abuse, 5600 Fishers Ln., Rm. 111, Rockville, MD 20857. TEL 301-443-6637. charts; stat. **Indexed:** Amer.Stat.Ind.
 Formerly: U.S. National Institute on Drug Abuse. Statistical Series D. Client Oriented Data Acquisition Process. Quarterly Report (ISSN 0145-1065)

PHYSICAL MEDICINE AND REHABILITATION

see *Medical Sciences–Physical Medicine and Rehabilitation*

PHYSICALLY IMPAIRED

see *Handicapped–Physically Impaired*

PHYSICS

see also *Physics–Computer Applications; Physics–Electricity; Physics–Heat; Physics–Mechanics; Physics–Nuclear Physics; Physics–Optics; Physics–Sound*

A C O NEWSLETTER. (American College of Orgonomy) see *MEDICAL SCIENCES — Psychiatry And Neurology*

A I A A - A S M E JOINT FLUID MECHANICS, PLASMA DYNAMICS, AND LASER CONFERENCE. PROCEEDINGS. (American Institute of Aeronautics and Astronautics, Inc.) see *ENGINEERING — Mechanical Engineering*

530 US ISSN 1058-8132
QC1 CODEN: ANWSEN
A P S NEWS. 1992. m. $140 (foreign $160) (effective 1996). American Physical Society, One Physics Ellipse, College Park, MD 20740-3844.
TEL 301-209-3200. (Subscr. to: A P S Subscriber Service, c/o American Institute of Physics, 500 Sunnyside Blvd., Woodbury, NY 11797-2999. TEL 516-576-2270) **Document type:** newsletter.
—Faxon; SWETS. **CCC.**

530 510 600 MV
  CODEN: IZFMBL
ACADEMIA DE STIINTE A REPUBLICA MOLDOVA. BULETINUL. FIZICA SI TEHNICA. (Text in Rumanian, Russian) 1951. 3/yr. 6.60 Rub. Academia de Stiinte a Republica Moldova - Akademiya Nauk Moldavskoi Respubliki, Bd. Stefan cel Mare, 1, Kishinev 277001, Moldova. **Indexed:** Chem.Abstr., INIS Atomind., Math.R., Met.Abstr., World Alum.Abstr.
—BLDSC (0073.770000); CASDDS.
 Formerly (until 1989): Academia de Stiinte a R.S.S. Moldova. Buletinul. Fizica si Tehnika (ISSN 0236-3097); *Supersedes in part* (in 1968): Akademiya Nauk Moldovskoi S.S.R. Izvestiya. Seriya Fiziko-Tekhnicheskikh i Matematicheskikh Nauk (ISSN 0321-169X)

530 CH ISSN 0304-5293
QC1 CODEN: RIPSD3
ACADEMIA SINICA. INSTITUTE OF PHYSICS. ANNUAL REPORT/CHUNG YANG YEN CHIU YUAN WU LI HSUEH YEN CHIU SO NIEN PAO. 1970. a. exchange basis. Academia Sinica, Institute of Physics - Chung Yang Yen Chiu Yuan Wu Li Hsueh Yen Chiu So, Nankang, Taipei Hsien, Taiwan 11529, Republic of China. FAX 02-783-4187. Ed. E.K. Lin. bk.rev. circ. 500. **Indexed:** Biol.Abstr., Chem.Abstr., INSPEC (1978-), Met.Abstr., Meteor.& Geoastrophys.Abstr., World Alum.Abstr.
—CASDDS.

530 II ISSN 0253-7257
  CODEN: JSOIDI
ACOUSTICAL SOCIETY OF INDIA. JOURNAL. 1973. q. Rs.40($25) Acoustical Society of India, Osmania University, Department of Physics, Hyderabad 500 007, India. Ed. S.K. Kor. circ. 300. **Indexed:** Chem.Abstr., INSPEC.
—BLDSC (4675.800000); CASDDS.

530 II ISSN 0253-732X
QC1 CODEN: ACIPD2
ACTA CIENCIA INDICA. PHYSICS. (Text in English) 1974. q. Rs.150($80) (Society for the Progress of Science) Pragati Prakashan, c/o K.K. Mittal, Business Manager, Box 62, Meerut 250001, India. Ed. V.P. Kudesia. adv.; bk.rev.; bibl.; charts. circ. 1,000. **Indexed:** Chem.Abstr., INSPEC (1984-), Math.R.
—BLDSC (0611.373000); CASDDS.
 Supersedes in part (in 1979): Acta Ciencia Indica (ISSN 0379-5411)

530   PL   ISSN 0209-3316
ACTA MAGNETICA. (Text and summaries in English) 1983. a., vol.9, 1992. $6. (Adam Mickiewicz University, Institute of Physics) Adam Mickiewicz University Press, Nowowiejskiego 55, 61-734 Poznan, Poland. TEL 527-380. TELEX 413260 UAM PL. Ed. Leon Kowalewski. circ. 280. (back issues avail.) **Document type:** academic/scholarly publication.
—BLDSC (0629.730000).
  Description: Covers all aspects of physics.

ACTA MATHEMATICA SCIENTIA. see *MATHEMATICS*

530   HU   ISSN 0231-4428
QC3   CODEN: APHUE2
ACTA PHYSICA HUNGARICA. (Text in English, French, German, Russian) 1951. 8/yr. (in 2 vols., 4 nos./vol.). $84 (effective 1992). (Magyar Tudomanyos Akademia) Akademiai Kiado, Publishing House of the Hungarian Academy of Sciences, P.O. Box 245, H-1519 Budapest, Hungary. TEL 181-2134. FAX 166-6466. TELEX 22-6228 AKNYO H. Ed. Istvan Kovacs. adv.; bk.rev.; bibl.; charts; illus.; index. **Indexed:** ASCA, Cadscan, Chem.Abstr., Curr.Cont., Ind.Sci.Rev., INIS Atomind., INSPEC (1983-), Int.Aerosp.Abstr., Lead Abstr., Math.R., Met.Abstr., Phys.Ber., Risk Abstr., Sci.Cit.Ind., Zincscan.
—BLDSC (0649.075000); CASDDS; Ei; UnCover. CCC.
  Formerly (until 1982): Academiae Scientiarum Hungaricae. Acta Physica (ISSN 0001-6705); Superseded in part (1946-1949): Hungarica Acta Chimica (ISSN 0367-634X).
  Description: Publishes original papers in the sphere of theoretical and experimental physics, including classical and quantum physics, elementary particles and fields, nuclear physics, atomic and molecular physics, optics, acoustics, thermodynamics, etc.

530   PL   ISSN 0587-4246
QC1   CODEN: ATPLB6
ACTA PHYSICA POLONICA. SERIES A: GENERAL PHYSICS, PHYSICS OF CONDENSED MATTER, OPTICS AND QUANTUM ELECTRONICS, ATOMIC AND MOLECULAR PHYSICS, APPLIED PHYSICS. (Text in various languages) 1932. m. $205 (effective 1995). Polska Akademia Nauk, Instytut Fizyki, Al. Lotnikow 32-46, 02-668 Warsaw, Poland. (Dist. by: Ars Polona, Krakowskie Przedmiescie 7, 00-068 Warsaw, Poland) Ed. Jerzy Prochorow. bibl.; charts; illus.; index. circ. 1,130. (also avail. in microfiche from BHP) **Indexed:** ASCA, Biwk.Pap.Rad.Chem.& Photochem., Cadscan, Ceram.Abstr., Chem.Abstr., Ind.Sci.Rev., INIS Atomind., INSPEC (1970-), Lead Abstr., Math.R., Met.Abstr., Sci.Cit.Ind., World Alum.Abstr., Zincscan. **Document type:** academic/scholarly publication.
—BLDSC (0650.050000); CASDDS; Ei; Faxon; Genuine Article; SWETS; UnCover. CCC.
  Supersedes in part: Acta Physica Polonica (ISSN 0001-673X)

530   PL   ISSN 0587-4254
QC770   CODEN: APOBBB
ACTA PHYSICA POLONICA. SERIES B: ELEMENTARY PARTICLE PHYSICS, NUCLEAR PHYSICS, STATISTICAL PHYSICS, THEORY OF RELATIVITY, FIELD THEORY. (Text in English) 1932. m. $150 (effective 1995). Uniwersytet Jagiellonski, Instytut Fizyki - Jagellonian University, Institute of Physics, Reymonta 4, 30-059 Krakow, Poland. TEL 48-12-336377. TELEX 322723IFUJ PL. E-mail: acta@if.uj.edu.pl. (Dist. by: Ars Polona, Krakowskie Przedmiescie 7, 00-068 Warsaw, Poland) (Co-sponsor: Polskie Towarzystwo Fizyczne) Ed. Andrzej Staruszkiewicz. bk.rev.; index. (back issues avail.) **Indexed:** ASCA, Cadscan, Chem.Abstr., Ind.Sci.Rev., INIS Atomind., INSPEC (1970-), Lead Abstr., Math.R., Met.Abstr., Ref.Zh., Sci.Cit.Ind., World Alum.Abstr., Zincscan. **Document type:** academic/scholarly publication.
—BLDSC (0650.060000); CASDDS; Faxon; Genuine Article; SWETS. CCC.
  Supersedes in part: Acta Physica Polonica (ISSN 0001-673X)
  Refereed Serial

530   CC   ISSN 1004-423X
CODEN: APHSEU
ACTA PHYSICA SINICA (OVERSEAS EDITION). Chinese edition: Wuli Xuebao (ISSN 1000-3290) (Text in English) 1992. m. $248 to individuals (foreign $308); institutions $372 (foreign $432). (Chinese Physical Society) Science Press, Marketing and Sales Department, 16 Donghuangchenggen North St., Beijing 100717, People's Republic of China. TEL 4010642. FAX 4019810. (Overseas dist. by: Science Press New York, Ltd., 84-04 58th Ave., Elmhurst, NY 11373. TEL 718-476-0238. FAX 718-476-0273) Ed. Huang Zuqia. **Indexed:** INSPEC (1993-). **Document type:** academic/scholarly publication.
—BLDSC (0650.520000); CASDDS.
  Description: Features the latest developments in all fields of physics in China.

530   XO   ISSN 0323-0465
QC1   CODEN: APSVCO
ACTA PHYSICA SLOVACA. (Text in English; summaries in English and Russian) vol.23, 1973. bi-m. $16. Slovenska Akademia Vied, Fyzikalny Ustav, Dubravska cesta 9, 842 28 Bratislava, Slovakia. (Dist. by: Slovart, Nam. Slobody 6, 817 64 Bratislava, Slovakia) Ed. Mikulas Blazek. bk.rev.; abstr.; bibl.; charts; illus. **Indexed:** ASCA, Cadscan, Chem.Abstr., Curr.Cont., Ind.Sci.Rev., INIS Atomind., INSPEC (1973-), Lead Abstr., Math.R., Met.Abstr., Phys.Ber., Sci.Cit.Ind., World Alum.Abstr., Zincscan.
—BLDSC (0650.630000); CASDDS; Faxon; UnCover.
  Description: Publishes original scientific and special works from all areas of physics, especially physics of solid substances, nuclear and subnuclear physics, as well as borderline areas such as biophysics and physical electronics.

ACTA UNIVERSITATIS CAROLINE: MATHEMATICA ET PHYSICA. see *MATHEMATICS*

530 540   HU   ISSN 0365-7930
CODEN: APDBAN
ACTA UNIVERSITATIS DEBRECENIENSIS. SERIES PHYSICA ET CHIMICA. Variant title: Acta Physica et Chimica Debrecina. (Text in English, German, Russian) 1962. irreg., vol.28, 1994. Kossuth Lajos Tudomanyegyetem, Egyetem Ter 1, 4010 Debrecen 10, Hungary. Ed. R. Gaspar. **Indexed:** Chem.Abstr.
—BLDSC (0649.052000).
  Superseded in part (in 1962): Acta Universitatis Debreceniensis (ISSN 0365-7817).

530 370   PL   ISSN 0208-6190
QC1   CODEN: ALFPDG
ACTA UNIVERSITATIS LODZIENSIS: FOLIA PHYSICA. (Text in Polish; summaries in various languages) 1955-1974; N.S. 1981. s-a. Wydawnictwo Uniwersytetu Lodzkiego, Ul. Jaracza 34, Lodz, Poland. TEL 331671. (Dist by: Ars Polona-Ruch, Krakowskie Przedmiescie 7, Warsaw, Poland) **Document type:** academic/scholarly publication.
—BLDSC (0585.208500); CASDDS.
  Supersedes in part: Uniwersytet Lodzki. Zeszyty Naukowe. Seria 2: Nauki Matematyczno-Przyrodnicze (ISSN 0076-0366)
  Description: Publishes original papers which advance the understanding of theoretical and experimental physics.

530 540   HU   ISSN 0001-6721
CODEN: AUSHAF
ACTA UNIVERSITATIS SZEGEDIENSIS DE ATTILA JOZSEF NOMINATAE. ACTA PHYSICA ET CHEMICA. (Text in English, German, Russian) 1928; N.S. 1955. s-a. exchange basis. Attila Jozsef University, c/o E. Szabo, Exchange Librarian, Dugonics ter 13, P.O.B. 393, Szeged H-6701, Hungary. (Subscr. to: Kultura, Box 149, H-1389 Budapest, Hungary) Ed. Miklos I. Ban. bibl.; charts; illus. circ. 400. **Indexed:** Biol.Abstr., Chem.Abstr., Curr.Cont., INSPEC (1968-1990), Ref.Zh.
—CASDDS.
  Description: Journal of physics and chemistry focusing on luminescence and various problems of organic and physical chemistry.

ADSORPTION. see *ENGINEERING — Chemical Engineering*

530   SI
ADVANCED SERIES IN APPLIED PHYSICS. (Text in English) 1988. irreg., vol.2, 1990. price varies. World Scientific Publishing Co. Pte. Ltd., Farrer Rd., P.O. Box 128, Singapore 9128, Singapore. TEL 3825663. FAX 3825919. TELEX RS 28561 WSPC. (UK addr.: 73 Lynton Mead, Totteridge, London N20 8DH, England. TEL 44-81-4462461; US addr.: 1060 Main St., River Edge, NJ 07661. TEL 800-227-7562) **Document type:** monographic series.

530 510   SI   ISSN 0218-0340
ADVANCED SERIES IN MATHEMATICAL PHYSICS. (Text in English) 1987. irreg., vol.15, 1992. price varies. World Scientific Publishing Co. Pte. Ltd., Farrer Rd., P.O. Box 128, Singapore 9128, Singapore. TEL 3825663. FAX 3825919. TELEX RS 28561 WSPC. (UK addr.: 73 Lynton Mead, Totteridge, London N20 8DH, England. TEL 44-81-4462461; US addr.: 1060 Main St., Ste. 1B, NJ 07661. TEL 800-227-7562) **Document type:** monographic series.

530   SI
ADVANCED SERIES IN NONLINEAR DYNAMICS. (Text in English) 1991. irreg., latest vol.3. price varies. World Scientific Publishing Co. Pte. Ltd., Farrer Rd., P.O. Box 128, Singapore 9128, Singapore. TEL 3825663. FAX 3825919. TELEX RS 28561 WSPC. (UK addr.: 73 Lynton Mead, Totteridge, London N20 8DH, England. TEL 44-81-4463356; US addr.: 1060 Main St., River Edge, NJ 07661. TEL 800-227-7562) Ed. R.S. MacKay. **Document type:** monographic series.

530   SI   ISSN 0218-0324
CODEN: ASDPEM
ADVANCED SERIES ON DIRECTIONS IN HIGH ENERGY PHYSICS. (Text in English) 1988. irreg., vol.12, 1993. price varies. World Scientific Publishing Co. Pte. Ltd., Farrer Rd., P.O. Box 128, Singapore 9128, Singapore. TEL 3825663. FAX 3825919. TELEX RS 28561 WSPC. (UK addr.: 73 Lynton Mead, Totteridge, London N20 8DH, England. TEL 44-81-4462461; US addr.: 1060 Main St., River Edge, NJ 07661. TEL 800-227-7562) **Document type:** monographic series.
—BLDSC (0696.927340); CASDDS.

530   US
ADVANCES IN AEROSOL PHYSICS. irreg., vol.7, 1973. price varies. John Wiley & Sons Ltd., 605 Third Ave., New York, NY 10016. TEL 212-850-6000. FAX 212-850-6088. Ed. V.A. Fedoseev. **Document type:** academic/scholarly publication.

530 541.3   US   ISSN 0065-2385
QD453   CODEN: ADCPAA
ADVANCES IN CHEMICAL PHYSICS. 1958. irreg., latest no.85. price varies. John Wiley & Sons, Inc., 605 Third Ave., New York, NY 10158-0012. TEL 212-850-6000. FAX 212-850-6099. TELEX 12-7063. Ed. I. Prigogine. **Indexed:** Biol.Abstr., Chem.Abstr., Deep Sea Res.& Oceanogr.Abstr., Ind.Sci.Rev., Mass Spectr.Bull., Sci.Cit.Ind. **Document type:** monographic series.
—BLDSC (0703.550000); CASDDS; Faxon; SWETS; UnCover. CCC.
Refereed Serial

ADVANCES IN COLLOID AND INTERFACE SCIENCE; an international journal devoted to experimental and theoretical developments in interfacial and colloidal phenomena and their implications in biology, chemistry, physics and technology. see *CHEMISTRY — Physical Chemistry*

530   SI
ADVANCES IN DISORDERED SEMICONDUCTORS. (Text in English) 1989. irreg., vol. 3, 1992. price varies. World Scientific Publishing Co. Pte. Ltd., Farrer Rd., P.O. Box 128, Singapore 9128, Singapore. TEL 3825663. FAX 3825919. TELEX RS 28561 WSPC. (UK addr.: 73 Lynton Mead, Totteridge, London N20 8DH, England. TEL 44-81-4462461; US addr.: 1060 Main St., River Edge, NJ 07661. TEL 800-227-7562) Ed. H. Fritzsche. **Document type:** monographic series.

ADVANCES IN ELECTRONICS AND ELECTRON PHYSICS. see *ENGINEERING — Electrical Engineering*

PHYSICS

538
QC762
US   ISSN 1057-2732
CODEN: AMORE7
ADVANCES IN MAGNETIC AND OPTICAL RESONANCE.
1965. irreg., vol.17, 1992. Academic Press, Inc., 525 B St., Ste. 1900, San Diego, CA 92101-4495. TEL 619-231-0926. FAX 619-699-6715. (Subscr. to: Order Dept., 6277 Sea Harbor Dr., 4th Fl., Orlando, FL 32887. TEL 800-321-5068) Ed. W. Warren. index. (reprint service avail. from ISI) **Indexed:** Ind.Sci.Rev., INSPEC, Sci.Cit.Ind.
—BLDSC (0709.334000); Faxon; SWETS; UnCover. **CCC.**
  Formerly (until 1990): Advances in Magnetic Resonance (ISSN 0065-2873)
  Refereed Serial

ADVANCES IN MAGNETIC RESONANCE IMAGING. see *COMPUTERS — Computer Graphics*

ADVANCES IN MICROWAVES. see *ENGINEERING — Electrical Engineering*

530
QD461
US   ISSN 1057-8951
CODEN: AMETEV
ADVANCES IN MOLECULAR ELECTRONIC STRUCTURE THEORY. 1990. a. J A I Press Inc., 55 Old Post Rd., No. 2, Box 1678, Greenwich, CT 06836-1678. TEL 203-661-7602.
—CASDDS.

530
QC1
UK   ISSN 0001-8732
CODEN: ADPHAR
ADVANCES IN PHYSICS. 1952. bi-m. £358($590) (effective 1996). Taylor & Francis Ltd., Rankine Rd., Basingstoke, Hants. RG24 8PR, England. TEL 44-1256-840366. FAX 44-1256-479438. TELEX 858540. E-mail: info@tandf.co.uk. (Subscr. in N. America to: Taylor & Francis Inc., 1900 Frost Rd., Ste. 101, Bristol, PA 19007-1598. TEL 800-821-5800. FAX 215-785-5515) Ed. D. Sherrington. adv.; charts. circ. 1,200. (also avail. in microform) **Indexed:** Br.Tech.Ind., Chem.Abstr., Curr.Cont., GeoRef., Ind.Med., Ind.Sci.Rev., INIS Atomind., INSPEC (1968-), Mass Spectr.Bull., Math.R., Met.Abstr., Phys.Ber., Sci.Cit.Ind., World Alum.Abstr. **Document type:** academic/scholarly publication.
—BLDSC (0710.000000); CASDDS; Ei; Faxon; Genuine Article; SWETS; UnCover. **CCC.**
  Description: Aims to meet the need for review papers in the major branches of condensed-matter physics.
  Refereed Serial

530   NE
ADVANCES IN SOLID STATE TECHNOLOGY. 1985. irreg. price varies. Kluwer Academic Publishers, Postbus 17, 3300 AA Dordrecht, Netherlands. TEL 31-78-392392. FAX 31-78-392254. TELEX 29245 KAPG NL. (Dist. by: Kluwer Academic Publishers Group, P.O. Box 322, 3300 AH Dordrecht, Netherlands. TEL 31-78-392392. FAX 31-78-546474; N. America dist. addr.: Box 358, Accord Sta., Hingham, MA 02018-0358. TEL 617-871-6600) **Document type:** monographic series.
  Refereed Serial

530   PL   ISSN 0208-8940
AKADEMIA ROLNICZA, POZNAN. ROCZNIKI. FIZYKA, CHEMIA. (Text in English, Polish; summaries in English, Polish, Russian) 1976. irreg. price varies. Wydawnictwo Akademii Rolniczej w Poznaniu, Ul. Witosa 45, 60-667 Poznan, Poland. TEL 48-61-487809. FAX 48-61-487802. **Indexed:** Bibl.Agri. **Document type:** academic/scholarly publication.
  Description: Deals with the influence of ultrasound and ultraviolet radiation on biological preparations, and spectrophotometric research on purified plant products.

AKADEMIE DER WISSENSCHAFTEN IN GOETTINGEN. ABHANDLUNGEN. MATHEMATISCH-PHYSIKALISCHE KLASSE. DRITTE FOLGE. see *MATHEMATICS*

AKADEMIE DER WISSENSCHAFTEN IN GOETTINGEN. NACHRICHTEN 2. MATHEMATISCH-PHYSIKALISCHE KLASSE. see *MATHEMATICS*

530   AI
CODEN: IAAFA3
AKADEMIYA NAUK ARMENII. IZVESTIYA. SERIYA FIZIKA/HAYASTANI HANRAPETUTIAN GITUTSUNNERI AZGAIN ACADEMIAY TEGEKAGIR PHIZIKA. English translation: Journal of Contemporary Physics (US ISSN 1068-3372) (Text Armenian, Russian) 1966. bi-m. Akademiya Nauk Armenii, Pr. Marshala Bagramayana, 24, 375019 Erevan, Armenia. TEL 78852-524580. FAX 78852-151087. TELEX 243344. E-mail: gayane@arminco.com. Ed. Vladimir M. Aroutounian. charts; illus.; index. circ. 820. **Indexed:** Chem.Abstr., INIS Atomind., INSPEC (1992-), Math.R., Met.Abstr., Phys.Ber., Sel.Water Res.Abstr. **Document type:** academic/scholarly publication, proceedings.
—CASDDS.
  Formerly: Akademiya Nauk Armyanskoi S.S.R. Izvestiya. Seriya Fizika (ISSN 0002-3035)

AKADEMIYA NAUK AZERBAIJANA. DOKLADY. see *MATHEMATICS*

530 510   AJ
CODEN: IAFMAF
AKADEMIYA NAUK AZERBAIJANA. IZVESTIYA. SERIYA FIZIKO-TEKHNICHESKIKH I MATEMATICHESKIKH NAUK. (Text in Azerbaijani and Russian) 1958. bi-m. 22.50 Rub. Izdatel'stvo Elm, Ul. Narimanova, 37, 370073 Baku, Azerbaijan. (Subscr. to: Mezhdunarodnaya Kniga, Moscow, G-200, Russia) Ed. A. Guseinov. charts; illus.; index. circ. 990. **Indexed:** Chem.Abstr., INIS Atomind., INSPEC, Math.R., Met.Abstr., Phys.Ber.
—CASDDS. **CCC.**
  Formerly: Akademiya Nauk Azerbaidzhanskoi S.S.R. Izvestiya. Seriya Fiziko-Tekhnicheskikh i Matematicheskikh Nauk (ISSN 0002-3108)

530 510   KZ
Q4
CODEN: IAKFBK
AKADEMIYA NAUK KAZAKHSTANA. IZVESTIYA. SERIYA FIZIKO-MATEMATICHESKAYA. 1963. bi-m. $16.20. Gylym, Ul. Pushkina 111-113, 480100 Alma-Ata, Kazakhstan. TEL 3272-611877. charts; index. **Indexed:** Chem.Abstr., INIS Atomind., Math.R.
—CASDDS.
  Formerly (until 1992): Akademiya Nauk Kazakhskoi S.S.R. Izvestiya. Seriya Fiziko-Matematicheskaya (ISSN 0002-3191)

530 510   KG
CODEN: INKSAD
AKADEMIYA NAUK RESPUBLIKI KYRGYZSTAN. IZVESTIYA. FIZIKO-TEKHNICHESKIE I MATEMATICHESKIE NAUKI. (Text in Russian) 1955. bi-m. Izdatel'stvo Ilim, Leninsky pr. 265 A, 720071 Bishkek, Kyrgyzstan. Ed. P.I. Chalov.
—CASDDS.
  Formerly (until 1991): Akademiya Nauk Kirgizskoi S.S.R. Izvestiya. Fiziko-tekhnicheskie i Matematicheskie Nauki (ISSN 0235-0076); Which supersedes in part (in 1985): Akademiya Nauk Kirgizskoi S.S.R. Izvestiya (ISSN 0002-3221)

AKADEMIYA NAUK TAJIKISTANA. DOKLADY. see *MATHEMATICS*

530 510 551   TA
Q60
CODEN: IANNES
AKADEMIYA NAUK TAJIKISTANA. IZVESTIYA. OTDELENIE FIZIKO-MATEMATICHESKIKH I GEOLOGO-KHIMICHESKIKH NAUK. (Text in Russian) 1967. q. 12.40 Rub. Akademiya Nauk Tajikistana, Pr. Rudaki 33, 734025 Dushanbe, Tajikistan. TEL 22-50-83. charts; illus. **Indexed:** INIS Atomind., Math.R.
—CASDDS.
  Formerly (until 1992): Akademiya Nauk Tadzhikskoi S.S.R. Izvestiya. Otdelenie Fiziko-Matematicheskikh i Geologo-Khimicheskikh Nauk (ISSN 0002-3485)

530 551   TK
QC1
CODEN: ITUFAW
AKADEMIYA NAUK TURKMENISTANA. IZVESTIYA. SERIYA FIZIKO-TEKHNICHESKIKH, KHIMICHESKIKH I GEOLOGICHESKIKH NAUK. 1960. bi-m. $15 (effective Jan. 1992). Akademiya Nauk Turkmenistana, Ul. Gogolya, 15, 744000 Ashkhabad, Turkmenistan. charts; illus.; index. circ. 500. **Indexed:** Biol.Abstr., Chem.Abstr., Ind.Vet., INIS Atomind., Math.R., Met.Abstr., World Alum.Abstr.
—CASDDS. **CCC.**
  Formerly (until 1992): Akademiya Nauk Turkmenskoi S.S.R. Izvestiya. Seriya Fiziko-Tekhnicheskikh, Khimicheskikh i Geologicheskikh Nauk (ISSN 0002-3507)

530 510   KR
CODEN: DNNADO
AKADEMIYA NAUK UKRAINY. DOPOVIDI; naukovi zhurnal. (Text in Russian; summaries in English) 1991. m. $376. Vidavnitstvo Naukova Dumka, Vul. Tereshchenkivska 3, 252601 Kiev, Ukraine. TEL 044-224-40-68. FAX 044-224-70-60. Ed. V.P. Kukhar. bk.rev.; bibl.; charts; illus.; index. circ. 252,601. (tabloid format) **Indexed:** Biol.Abstr., Chem.Abstr., Comput.Rev., Helminthol.Abstr., INIS Atomind., INSPEC, Met.Abstr., Phys.Ber., World Alum.Abstr.
—CASDDS. **CCC.**
  Formerly (until 1992): Akademiya Nauk Ukraisnkoi S.S.R. Doklady (ISSN 0868-8044); Formed by the merger of (1979-1991): Akademiya Nauk Ukrainskoi S.S.R. Doklady. Seriya A. Fiziko-matematicheskie i Tekhnicheskie Nauki (ISSN 0201-8446); (1979-1991): Akademiya Nauk Ukrainskoi S.S.R. Doklady. Seriya B. Geologicheskie, Khimicheskie i Biologicheskie Nauki (ISSN 0201-8454)

530 510   UZ
CODEN: IUZFAU
AKADEMIYA NAUK UZBEKISTANA. IZVESTIYA. SERIYA FIZIKO-MATEMATICHESKIKH NAUK. (Text in Russian) 1957. bi-m. 11.10 Rub. Izdatel'stvo Fan, Ul. Gogolya 70, k. 105, 700000 Tashkent, Uzbekistan. **Indexed:** Chem.Abstr., INIS Atomind., Math.R., Met.Abstr., World Alum.Abstr.
—CASDDS.
  Formerly: Akademiya Nauk Uzbekskoi S.S.R. Izvestiya. Seriya Fiziko-Matematicheskikh Nauk (ISSN 0131-8012)

530 510   BW
QC1
CODEN: VBSFA5
AKADEMIYA NAVUK BELARUSI. VESTSI. SERIYA FIZIKA-MATEMATYCHNYKH NAVUK. (Text in Russian; summaries in English) 1965. bi-m. 19.80 Rub. Vydavetstvo Navuka i Tekhnika, Zhodzinskaya, 18, 220067 Minsk 67, Belarus. TEL 39-55-17. FAX 252494. TELEX 252277 NAUKA. Ed. L.N. Kuselevskii. bibl.; charts; illus.; index. circ. 540. **Indexed:** Math.R.
—CASDDS.
  Formerly (until 1992): Akademiya Navuk Belarusskai S.S.R. Vestsi. Seriya Fizika-Matematychnykh Navuk (ISSN 0002-3574)
  Description: Presents papers on general and theoretical physics, including optics, main branches of mathematics, and computer science.

530   BW
CODEN: VABFAF
AKADEMIYA NAVUK BELARUSI. VESTSI. SERIYA FIZIKA-TEKHNICHNYKH NAVUK. (Text in Russian; summaries in English) 1956. q. 13.20 Rub. Vydavetstvo Navuka i Tekhnika, Zhodzinskaya, 18, 220067 Minsk, Belarus. TEL 0172-637618. Ed. S.A. Astapchik. bibl.; charts; illus.; index. circ. 530. **Indexed:** Chem.Abstr. **Document type:** academic/scholarly publication.
—CASDDS.
  Formerly (until 1992): Akademiya Navuk Belarusskai S.S.R. Vestsi. Seriya Fizika-Tekhnichnykh Navuk (ISSN 0002-3566)
  Description: Presents papers on the heavy machinery industry, reliability and longevity of machines, physics of strength and plasticity, applied physics, pressure and thermal treatment of metals and other materials.

ALKALMAZOTT MATEMATIKAI LAPOK. see *MATHEMATICS*

AMERICAN CRYSTALLOGRAPHIC ASSOCIATION. PROGRAM & ABSTRACTS. see *CHEMISTRY — Crystallography*

PHYSICS

530 US ISSN 0148-5857
QC9.U5
AMERICAN INSTITUTE OF PHYSICS. CENTER FOR HISTORY OF PHYSICS. NEWSLETTER. 1964. s-a. free. American Institute of Physics, Center for History of Physics, One Physics Ellipse, College Park, MD 20740. TEL 301-209-3165. E-mail: chp@aip.org. Site addr.: http://aip.org/aip/histctr/f94tc.html. Ed. Spencer Weart. bibl.; cum.index. circ. 6,000. (back issues avail.) **Document type:** newsletter.
●Also available online.
—CCC.
Former titles (until 1972): American Institute of Physics. Center for History and Philosophy of Physics. Newsletter (ISSN 0008-9060); (until 1966): American Institute of Physics. Newsletter (ISSN 0569-5708)
Description: Scholarly publication for historians of science, archivists, physicists.

530 375 US ISSN 0002-9505
CODEN: AJPIAS
AMERICAN JOURNAL OF PHYSICS. 1933. m. $253 (foreign $263) (effective Sep. 1996). American Association of Physics Teachers, One Physics Ellipse, College Park, MD 20740-3845. TEL 301-209-3333. FAX 301-209-0845. Ed. R. Romer. adv.; bk.rev.; illus.; index, cum.index: vols.1-20 (1933-1952), vols.21-30 (1953-1963), vols.31-40 (1963-1972). (also avail. in microform from AIP; back issues avail.) **Indexed:** A.S.& T.Ind., Abstr.Bull.Inst.Pap.Chem., Bibl.Ind., C.I.J.E., C.P.I., Cadscan, Chem.Abstr., Curr.Cont., Deep Sea Res.& Oceanogr.Abstr., Eng.Ind., Gen.Phys.Adv.Abstr., Gen.Sci.Ind., High.Educ.Curr.Aware.Bull., Ind.Sci.Rev., INIS Atomind., INSPEC (1968-), Lead Abstr., Mass Spectr.Bull., Math.R., Met.Abstr., Phys.Ber., Res.High.Educ.Abstr., Risk Abstr., Sci.Cit.Ind., Zincscan.
—BLDSC (0833.000000); CASDDS; Ei; Faxon; Genuine Article; SWETS; UnCover. **CCC.**
Formerly (until 1940): American Physics Teacher (ISSN 0096-0322)
Refereed Serial

530 US ISSN 0003-0503
QC1 CODEN: BAPSA6
AMERICAN PHYSICAL SOCIETY. BULLETIN. 1956. irreg. $380 (foreign $400) (effective 1996). American Physical Society, One Physics Ellipse, College Park, MD 20740-3844. TEL 301-209-3202. (Subscr. to: APS Subscriber Service, c/o American Institute of Physics, 500 Sunnyside Blvd., Woodbury, NY 11797-2999. TEL 516-576-2270) Ed. B. Ripin. abstr.; index. (also avail. in microfilm from AIP) **Indexed:** Biol.Abstr., Chem.Abstr., Curr.Pack.Abstr., Mass Spectr.Bull., Phys.Ber. **Document type:** bulletin.
—BLDSC (2391.000000); Ei; SWETS; UnCover. **CCC.**

530 SP ISSN 1133-0376
QC1 CODEN: AFBIDZ
ANALES DE FISICA. (Text and summaries in English, French, German, Spanish) 1903. q. $120. Real Sociedad Espanola de Fisica, Facultad de Fisica y Quimica, Ciudad Universitaria, 28040 Madrid, Spain. TEL 91-394-43-59. Ed. Manuel Tello Leon. adv.; bk.rev.; bibl.; charts; illus.; index. **Indexed:** Chem.Abstr., Dairy Sci.Abstr., INSPEC (1970-), Met.Abstr. **Document type:** academic/scholarly publication.
—BLDSC (0889.106000); CASDDS; SWETS. **CCC.**
Formed by the 1993 merger of: Anales de Fisica. Seria A. Fenomenos e Interacciones (ISSN 0211-6243) & Anales de Fisica. Seria B. Aplicaciones. Metodos e Instrumentos (ISSN 0211-6251); Both supersedes in part (in 1980): Anales de Fisica (ISSN 0365-4818); Which was formerly (until 1967): Real Sociedad Espanola de Fisica y Quimica. Anales. Serie A: Fisica (ISSN 0034-0871); Which supersedes in part (in 1948): Anales de Fisica y Quimica (ISSN 0365-2351).

530 GW ISSN 0003-3804
CODEN: ANPYA2
ANNALEN DER PHYSIK. (Text in English, German) 1790. 8/yr. DM.620 (foreign DM.632). Huethig GmbH, Postfach 102869, 69018 Heidelberg, Germany. TEL 06221-489261.
FAX 06221-489205. Ed. B. Muehlschlegel. adv.: B&W page DM.650; trim 131 x 240; adv. contact: Micheline Cohen. charts; illus.; index. **Indexed:** Cadscan, Chem.Abstr., Eng.Ind., INIS Atomind., INSPEC (1968-), Lead Abstr., Math.R., Met.Abstr., Sci.Cit.Ind., Zincscan. **Document type:** academic/scholarly publication.
—BLDSC (0912.000000); CASDDS; Ei; Faxon; Genuine Article; SWETS; UMI; UnCover. **CCC.**
Description: Offers a forum covering the entire field of experimental, computational, applied, and theoretical physics.

530 FR ISSN 0003-4169
QC1 CODEN: ANPHAJ
ANNALES DE PHYSIQUE. (Text and summaries in English, French) 6/yr. 2300 F. (effective 1996). Editions de Physique, Z.I. de Courtaboeuf, B.P. 112, 91944 Les Ulis Cedex, France. TEL 69-07-36-88. FAX 69-28-84-91. TELEX 602 321 F. Ed. C. Boisson. bk.rev.; illus.; index. circ. 1,150. (also avail. in microfilm from PMC; reprint service avail. from ISI) **Indexed:** Cadscan, Chem.Abstr., Deep Sea Res.& Oceanogr.Abstr., Eng.Ind., Ind.Sci.Rev., INIS Atomind., INSPEC (1968-), Lead Abstr., Math.R., Met.Abstr., World Alum.Abstr., Zincscan. **Document type:** academic/scholarly publication.
—BLDSC (0993.000000); CASDDS; Ei; Faxon; Genuine Article; SWETS; UnCover. **CCC.**
Description: Covers the basics of atomic and molecular physics, condensed matter, nuclear physics and astrophysics.

530 PL ISSN 0137-6861
QC1 CODEN: AUMADZ
ANNALES UNIVERSITATIS MARIAE CURIE-SKLODOWSKA. SECTIO AAA. PHYSICA. (Text in English, French, Polish; summaries in English, Polish) 1978. a. price varies. Uniwersytet Marii Curie-Sklodowskiej, Wydawnictwo, Pl. M. Curie-Sklodowskiej 5, 20-031 Lublin, Poland. TEL 48-81-375304.
FAX 48-81-336699. TELEX 0643223. Ed. Jan Sielewiesiuk. circ. 575. **Indexed:** Chem.Abstr., INIS Atomind. **Document type:** academic/scholarly publication.
—BLDSC (0956.007000); CASDDS.
Supersedes in part (in 1979): Annales Universitatis Mariae Curie-Sklodowska. Section AA. Physica et Chemica (ISSN 0137-1819)

530 US ISSN 0003-4916
QC1 CODEN: APNYA6
ANNALS OF PHYSICS. 1957. 16/yr. $1872 (foreign $2160) (effective 1996). Academic Press, Inc., Journal Division, 525 B St., Ste. 1900, San Diego, CA 92101-4495. TEL 619-230-1840.
FAX 619-699-6800. (Subscr. to: Box 620000, Orlando, FL 32891-8340. TEL 800-543-9534) Ed. Herman Feshbach. adv.; charts; index. (back issues avail.) **Indexed:** Cadscan, Chem.Abstr., Deep Sea Res.& Oceanogr.Abstr., Eng.Ind., Ind.Sci.Rev., INIS Atomind., INSPEC (1968-), Int.Aerosp.Abstr., Lead Abstr., Math.R., Met. Abstr., Phys.Ber., Sci.Cit.Ind., Zincscan. **Document type:** academic/scholarly publication.
—BLDSC (1043.500000); CASDDS; Ei; Faxon; Genuine Article; SWETS; UMI; UnCover. **CCC.**
Description: Presents original work in all areas of basic physics research. Publishes papers on particular topics spanning theory, methodology, and applications.
Refereed Serial

ANNUAL REVIEW OF ASTRONOMY AND ASTROPHYSICS.
see *ASTRONOMY*

531.14 US
ANNUAL SUMMARY OF PROGRESS IN GRAVITATION SCIENCES. 1974. a. membership. (Ensanian Physicochemical Institute) Minas Ensanian Corporation, Box 98, Eldred, PA 16731.
TEL 814-225-3296. Ed. Minas Ensanian. adv.; bk.rev.; abstr.; bibl.; charts; illus.; pat.; stat.; circ. 100 (controlled).

530 US ISSN 1051-0303
APERIODICITY AND ORDER. 1988. irreg. vol.3, 1989. Academic Press, Inc., 525 B St., Ste. 1900, San Diego, CA 92101-4495. TEL 619-231-6616.
FAX 619-699-6715. (Subscr. to: Order Dept., 6277 Sea Harbor Dr., 4th Fl., Orlando, FL 32887. TEL 800-321-5068) (back issues avail.)
—BLDSC (1567.873000).
Refereed Serial

530 AU ISSN 0937-9347
QC762 CODEN: APMREI
APPLIED MAGNETIC RESONANCE. 1990. 8/yr. (in 2 vols., 4 nos./vol.). DM.1112($808) (effective 1996). (Russian Academy of Sciences, Kazan Physical - Technical Institute, RU) Springer-Verlag, Sachsenplatz 4-6, Postfach 89, A-1201 Vienna, Austria. TEL 0222-3302415. FAX 0222-3302426. (Subscr. in N. America to: Springer-Verlag New York, Inc., 44 Hartz Way, Secaucus, NJ 07096-2491. TEL 201-348-4033) (Co-sponsor: Department of General Physics and Astronomy) Ed. K.M. Salikhov. **Indexed:** INSPEC (1992-). **Document type:** academic/scholarly publication.
—BLDSC (1573.500000); CASDDS; Ei; Genuine Article; UMI. **CCC.**
Description: Provides an international forum for the application of magnetic resonance in physics, chemistry, biology, medicine, geochemistry, ecology, engineering, and related fields. Emphasizes new applications of the technique, and new experimental methods.

621 530 GW ISSN 0947-8396
QC1 CODEN: APSFDB
APPLIED PHYSICS. A: MATERIALS SCIENCE & PROCESSING. (Text in English) 1973. 12/yr. (in 2 vols., 6 nos./vol.). DM.2300($1671) (effective 1996). (Deutsche Physikalische Gesellschaft - German Physical Society) Springer-Verlag, Heidelberger Platz 3, 14197 Berlin, Germany. TEL 030-8207-0. FAX 030-8214091. E-mail: orders@springer.de. (Subscr. in N. America to: Springer-Verlag New York, Inc., 44 Hartz Way, Secaucus, NJ 07096-2491. TEL 201-348-4033. FAX 201-348-4505) Ed. H.K.V. Lotsch. adv.; abstr.; charts; illus.; index. (also avail. in microform from UMI; reprint service avail. from ISI) **Indexed:** C.I.S. Abstr., Cadscan, Chem.Abstr., Curr.Cont., INIS Atomind., INSPEC (1981-), Int.Aerosp.Abstr., Int.Sci.Rev., Lead Abstr., Mass Spectr.Bull., Met.Abstr., Phys.Ber., Sci.Cit.Ind., World Alum.Abstr., Zincscan. **Document type:** academic/scholarly publication.
—CASDDS; Ei; Faxon; Genuine Article; UMI; UnCover. **CCC.**
Former titles: Aplied Physics A: Solids and Surfaces (ISSN 0721-7250); Supersedes in part (in 1981): Applied Physics (ISSN 0340-3793); Which superseded: Zeitschrift fuer Angewandte Physik (ISSN 0044-2283)
Description: Covers primarily the condensed state, including surface science and engineering.

621 530 GW ISSN 0946-2171
CODEN: APBOEM
APPLIED PHYSICS. B: LASERS AND OPTICS. (Text in English) 12/yr. (in 2 vols., 6 nos./vol.). DM.2300($1671) (effective 1996). (Deutsche Physikalische Gesellschaft) Springer-Verlag, Heidelberger Platz 3, 14197 Berlin, Germany. TEL 030-8207-0. FAX 030-8214091. E-mail: orders@springer.de. (Subscr. in N. America to: Springer-Verlag New York, Inc., 44 Hartz Way, Secaucus, NJ 07096-2491. TEL 201-348-4033. FAX 201-348-4505) Ed. H.K.V. Lotsch. adv. (also avail. in microform from UMI) **Indexed:** Biwk.Pap.Rad.Chem.& Photochem., Chem.Abstr., Eng.Ind., Ind.Sci.Rev., INIS Atomind., INSPEC (1973-), Mass Spectr.Bull., Met.Abstr., Sci.Cit.Ind., World Alum.Abstr. **Document type:** academic/scholarly publication.
—BLDSC (1576.375000); CASDDS; Ei; Faxon; Genuine Article; SWETS; UMI; UnCover. **CCC.**
Formerly: Applied Physics. B: Photophysics and Laser Chemistry (ISSN 0721-7269); Supersedes in part (in 1981): Applied Physics (ISSN 0340-3793)

530 620 US ISSN 0066-5509
APPLIED PHYSICS AND ENGINEERING. (Text in English) 1967. irreg., no.12, 1976. price varies. Springer-Verlag, 175 Fifth Ave., New York, NY 10010. TEL 212-460-1500. FAX 212-473-6272. (Also: Berlin, Heidelberg, Tokyo and Vienna) (reprint service avail. from ISI) **Document type:** academic/scholarly publication.

PHYSICS

621 530   US   ISSN 0003-6951
QC1   CODEN: APPLAB
APPLIED PHYSICS LETTERS. 1962. w. $1315 (foreign $1455) (effective 1996). American Institute of Physics, One Physics Ellipse, College Park, MD 20740-3843. TEL 301-209-3000. (Subscr. to: AIP Member and Subscriber Service, 500 Sunnyside Blvd., Woodbury, NY 11797-2999. TEL 516-576-2270. FAX 516-349-9704) Ed. Nghi Q. Lam. adv.: B&W page $350, color $850. charts; illus.; index, cum.index: 1977-1981, 1982-1986. (also avail. in microfiche from AIP; back issues avail.) **Indexed:** Anal.Abstr., Br.Ceram.Abstr., C.P.I., Cadscan, Ceram.Abstr., Chem.Abstr., Curr.Cont., Eng.Ind., Gen.Phys.Adv.Abstr., GeoRef., Ind.Sci.Rev., INIS Atomind., INSPEC (1968-), Lead Abstr., Mass Spectr.Bull., Met.Abstr., Phys.Ber., Sci.Cit.Ind., World Alum.Abstr., Zincscan. **Document type:** academic/scholarly publication.
●Also available online. Vendor(s): OCLC.
Also available on CD-ROM.
—BLDSC (1576.400000); CASDDS; Ei; Faxon; Genuine Article; SWETS; UMI; UnCover. **CCC.**
   Description: Concise up to date reports of new findings in applied physics. Includes coverage of experimental and theoretical research in condensed matter, semiconductors, superconductivity, optics, solid state lasers, nonlinear optics, surfaces, thin films, materials and device properties.

APPLIED SOLID STATE SCIENCE; advances in materials and device research. see ENGINEERING — Electrical Engineering

ARAB GULF JOURNAL OF SCIENTIFIC RESEARCH. see SCIENCES: COMPREHENSIVE WORKS

ARKHIMEDES. see MATHEMATICS

ASTRONOMY AND ASTROPHYSICS; a European journal. see ASTRONOMY

THE ASTRONOMY AND ASTROPHYSICS REVIEW. see ASTRONOMY

ASTROPARTICLE PHYSICS. see ASTRONOMY

ASTROPHYSICAL JOURNAL; an international review of astronomy and astronomical physics. see ASTRONOMY

ASTROPHYSICAL JOURNAL. SUPPLEMENT SERIES. see ASTRONOMY

ASTROPHYSICAL LETTERS AND COMMUNICATIONS. see ASTRONOMY

ASTROPHYSICS. see ASTRONOMY

ASTROPHYSICS AND SPACE SCIENCE; an international journal of cosmic physics. see ASTRONOMY

ASTROPHYSICS AND SPACE SCIENCE LIBRARY; a series of books on the developments of space science and of general astronomy and astrophysics published in connection with the journal Space Science Reviews. see ASTRONOMY

ATELIERS. see CHILDREN AND YOUTH — For

AURORAL OBSERVATORY. MAGNETIC OBSERVATIONS. see ASTRONOMY

AUSTRALASIAN PHYSICAL & ENGINEERING SCIENCES IN MEDICINE. see MEDICAL SCIENCES — Experimental Medicine, Laboratory Technique

530   AT   ISSN 1036-3831
QC1   CODEN: ANZPET
AUSTRALIAN & NEW ZEALAND PHYSICIST. 1964. m. Aus.$50 (foreign Aus.$62). 14 Ridley St., Turner, A.C.T. 2601, Australia. TEL 062491563. FAX 062491563. (Subscr. to: Australian & New Zealand Physicist, P.O. Box 391, Dickson, A.C.T. 2601, Australia) Ed. Jak Kelly. adv. contact: Judith Nikolesky. bk.rev.; charts; illus. circ. 3,000. **Indexed:** Aus.Educ.Ind., Sci.Ind., Chem.Abstr., INIS Atomind., INSPEC (1983-). **Document type:** academic/scholarly publication.
—CASDDS; Ei; Faxon.
   Formerly: Australian Physicist (ISSN 0004-9972)
   Description: Information on physics for the professional for research and teaching purposes.

530   AT   ISSN 0004-9506
QC1   CODEN: AUJPAS
AUSTRALIAN JOURNAL OF PHYSICS. 1948. bi-m. Aus.$320($320) (effective 1996). C.S.I.R.O., 314 Albert St., E. Melbourne, Vic. 3002, Australia. TEL 61-3-94187333. FAX 61-3-94194096. Ed. R.P. Robertson. adv.; bibl.; charts; illus.; index. circ. 750. (also avail. in microform from UMI; back issues avail.) **Indexed:** AESIS, Appl.Mech.Rev., Cadscan, Chem.Abstr., Comput.Rev., Curr.Cont., Eng.Ind., GeoRef., Ind.Sci.Rev., INIS Atomind., INSPEC (1968-), Lead Abstr., Mass Spectr.Bull., Math.R., Met.Abstr., Meteor.& Geoastrophys.Abstr., Phys.Ber., Sci.Cit.Ind., World Alum.Abstr., World Text.Abstr., Zincscan. **Document type:** academic/scholarly publication.
—BLDSC (1811.000000); CASDDS; Ei; Faxon; Genuine Article; SWETS; UMI; UnCover. **CCC.**
   Description: Covers all aspects of physics ranging from elementary particles and fields to astronomy and astrophysics.

530   AT
AUSTRALIAN NATIONAL UNIVERSITY. RESEARCH SCHOOL OF PHYSICAL SCIENCES AND ENGINEERING. ANNUAL REPORT. 1972. a. Australian National University, Institute of Advanced Studies, Canberra, A.C.T. 0200, Australia. FAX 61-62-495457. Ed. E. Weigold. circ. 600. **Document type:** academic/scholarly publication.
   Formerly: Australian National University. Research School of Physical Sciences. Annual Report (ISSN 0155-624X)

530   AT   ISSN 0084-7518
AUSTRALIAN NATIONAL UNIVERSITY, CANBERRA. RESEARCH SCHOOL OF PHYSICAL SCIENCES AND ENGINEERING. RESEARCH PAPER. irreg. Aus.$10 per no. Australian National University, Research School of Physical Sciences and Engineering, Energy Research Centre, Canberra, A.C.T. 0200, Australia. **Indexed:** AESIS.
   Formerly: Australian National University, Canberra. Research School of Physical Sciences. Research Paper.

B W K; Zeitschrift des Vereins Deutscher Ingenieure fuer Energietechnik und Energiewirtschaft. (Brennstoff-Waerme-Kraft) see ENERGY

BEAM MODIFICATION OF MATERIALS. see PHYSICS — Optics

BEIKOKU TOKKYO SHOROKU. DORYOKU, DORYOKU KIKAI, BUTSURYU, BUNPAI, RYUTAI NO TORIATSUKAI HEN/U.S. PATENT ABSTRACTS. POWER, POWER MACHINE, PHYSICAL DISTRIBUTION, DISTRIBUTION, LIQUID HANDLING. see PATENTS, TRADEMARKS AND COPYRIGHTS — Abstracting, Bibliographies, Statistics

530   PL   ISSN 0137-5059
BIBLIOTEKA FIZYKI. 1974. irreg., vol.14, 1991. Wydawnictwo Naukowe P W N, Ul. Miodowa 10, 00-251 Warsaw, Poland. TEL 48-22-312738. FAX 48-22-267163. TELEX 813763 PWN PL.

BIOELECTROMAGNETICS SOCIETY NEWSLETTER. see BIOLOGY — Biophysics

530 574   UK   ISSN 0966-9051
R857.O6   CODEN: BOIME9
BIOIMAGING. 1993. q. £55($129) to individuals; institutions £127 ($254) (effective 1996). (Institute of Physics) I O P Publishing Ltd., Techno House, Redcliffe Way, Bristol, Avon. BS1 6NX, England. TEL 017-929-7481. FAX 0117-929-4318. TELEX 449149 INSTP G. (U.S. subscr. to: American Institute of Physics, Subscriber Services, 500 Sunnyside Blvd., Woodbury, NY 11797-2900. TEL 516-349-7800) Ed. T. Jovin. index. circ. 83. (also avail. in microfiche) **Indexed:** Excerp.Med. (1994-). **Document type:** academic/scholarly publication.
—BLDSC (2072.339000); CASDDS.
   Description: Covers original research and innovative developments in the field of biological imaging.

538.36 574.192   US   ISSN 0192-6020
                                     CODEN: BMGRDB
BIOLOGICAL MAGNETIC RESONANCE. 1978. irreg., vol.13, 1993. price varies. Plenum Publishing Corp., 233 Spring St., New York, NY 10013-1578. TEL 212-620-8000. FAX 212-463-0742. TELEX 23-421139. Eds. L.J. Berliner, J. Reuben. (back issues avail.) **Document type:** monographic series.
—BLDSC (2076.550000); CASDDS. **CCC.**
   Refereed Serial

BIOMASS BULLETIN. see ENERGY

BIPOLAR - BICMOS CIRCUITS AND TECHNOLOGY MEETING. PROCEEDINGS. see ELECTRONICS

530   BL   ISSN 0103-9733
QC1   CODEN: BJPHE6
BRAZILIAN JOURNAL OF PHYSICS. (Text in English) 1971. q. $50. Sociedade Brasileira de Fisica, Universidade de Sao Paulo, Instituto de Fisica, Caixa Postal 20553, 01000 Sao Paulo, Brazil. TEL 81-271-0111. FAX 081-2710359. Ed. Cid B. de Araujo. charts. circ. 1,700. **Indexed:** Chem.Abstr., INSPEC (1971-), Int.Aerosp.Abstr. **Document type:** academic/scholarly publication.
—BLDSC (2277.419550); CASDDS; UnCover.
   Formerly (until 1992): Revista Brasileira de Fisica (ISSN 0374-4922)
   Description: Original research work and review articles in physics.
   Refereed Serial

530   BU   ISSN 0323-9217
QC1   CODEN: BJPHD5
BULGARIAN JOURNAL OF PHYSICS/BOLGARSKII FIZICHESKII ZHURNAL (Text in English; summaries in Russian) 1974. bi-m. 2.70 lv. per no. (Bulgarska Akademiia na Naukite) Publishing House of the Bulgarian Academy of Sciences, Acad. G. Bonchev St., Bldg. 6, 1113 Sofia, Bulgaria. (Dist. by: Hemus, 6, Rouski Blvd., 1000 Sofia, Bulgaria) Ed. A. Datseff. illus.; bibl.; charts. circ. 520. (reprint service avail. from IRC) **Indexed:** BSL Math., Chem.Abstr, INIS Atomind., INSPEC (1974-), Int.Aerosp.Abstr., Math.R., Met.Abstr., Phys.Ber., World Alum.Abstr.
—CASDDS. **CCC.**
   Formed by the merger of: Bulgarska Akademiia na Naukite. Fizicheskii Institut. Izvestiia; Bulgarska Akademiia na Naukite. Institut po Elektronika. Izvestiia.

540 530   US   ISSN 0163-559X
QC762   CODEN: BUMRDT
BULLETIN OF MAGNETIC RESONANCE. 1979. q. $35 to individuals; libraries $50; members $18. International Society of Magnetic Resonance, c/o University of California, San Diego, 9500 Gilman Dr., La Jolla, CA 92093-0342. Ed. J. Howard Bradbury. **Document type:** bulletin, academic/scholarly publication.
—BLDSC (2866.400000); CASDDS; Ei; Faxon; SWETS.

530   II   ISSN 0970-6569
QC1
BULLETIN OF PURE & APPLIED SCIENCES. SECTION D: PHYSICS. 1982. 2/yr. Rs.50($9) to individuals; institutions Rs.100($14). Dr. A.K. Sharma, Ed. & Pub., 140 (RPS) D.D.A. Flat, Mansarovar Park, Shahdara, New Delhi 110032, India. TEL 011-2117408. adv.; bk.rev. circ. 300. **Document type:** academic/scholarly publication.
—CCC.

530   JA   ISSN 0525-2997
QC173.28   CODEN: BUSKB2
BUSSEI KENKYU/MATERIAL SCIENCE STUDY. (Text in English, Japanese; summaries in Japanese) 1963. m. 19200 Yen (effective Apr. 1994). Bussei Kenkyu Kankokai, c/o Kyoto Daigaku Yukawa Kinenkan, Kitashirakawa Oiwake-cho, Sakyo-ku, Kyoto 606, Japan. TEL 075-722-3540. FAX 075-722-6339. Ed. Masatoshi Murase. circ. 400. **Indexed:** Chem.Ahstr., INIS Atomind., Jap.Per.Ind. **Document type:** academic/scholarly publication.
   Refereed Serial

530   JA   ISSN 0385-9843
QC176.A1   CODEN: BUDADZ
BUSSEIKEN DAYORI/INSTITUTE FOR SOLID STATE PHYSICS. NEWS. (Text in English, Japanese) 1957. bi-m. University of Tokyo, Institute for Solid State Physics - Tokyo Daigaku Bussei Kenkyujo, 22-1, Roppongi 7-chome, Minato-ku, Tokyo 106, Japan. —CASDDS.

530   JA   ISSN 0029-0181
                                     CODEN: NBGSAW
BUTSURI. Variant title: Nihon Butsuri Gakkaishi. (Text in Japanese) 1946. m. 28000 Yen. Physical Society of Japan - Nihon Butsuri Gakkai, Rm. 211, Kikai Shinko Bldg., 3-5-8 Shiba Koen, Minato-ku, Tokyo 105, Japan. Ed. H. Ezawa. adv.; bk.rev.; advr.; bibl.; charts; illus. circ. 19,000. **Indexed:** GeoRef., JTA.
—BLDSC (2935.200000); CASDDS.
   Description: Publishes original papers in all fields of physics.

530 370   JA   ISSN 0385-6992
BUTSURI KYOIKU/PHYSICS EDUCATION SOCIETY OF JAPAN. JOURNAL. (Text in Japanese) 1953. q. Physics Education Society of Japan - Nihon Butsuri Kyoiku Gakkai, P.O. Box 29, Koishikawa Yubbinkyoku, Tokyo 112, Japan.

530   JA   ISSN 0912-4446
BUTSURIGAKUSHI/JOURNAL FOR THE HISTORY OF PHYSICS. (Text in Japanese) 1986. biennial. Butsurigakushi Kenkyukai - Study Group of the History of Physics, Yokohama Kokuritsu Daigaku, Kyoikugakubu Fujimura Kenkyushitsu, 156 Tokiwadai, Hodogaya-ku, Yokohama-shi, Kanagawa-ken 240, Japan.

C R C HANDBOOK OF CHEMISTRY AND PHYSICS. see *CHEMISTRY*

530   UK
▼**CAMBRIDGE LECTURE NOTES IN PHYSICS.** 1994. irreg., no.4. University of Cambridge, The Pitt Bldg., Trumpington St., Cambridge CB2 1RP, England. TEL 01223-315052. (Subscr. in US to: 40 W. 20th St., New York, NY 10011-4211) Eds. P. Goddard, J. Yeomans. **Document type:** monographic series.
Refereed Serial

CAMBRIDGE MONOGRAPHS ON ATOMIC, MOLECULAR AND CHEMICAL PHYSICS. see *CHEMISTRY — Physical Chemistry*

**530 510   UK   ISSN 0269-8242
CODEN: CMMPED**
CAMBRIDGE MONOGRAPHS ON MATHEMATICAL PHYSICS. 1973. irreg., latest 1987. price varies. Cambridge University Press, Edinburgh Bldg., Shaftesbury Rd., Cambridge CB2 2RU, England. TEL 01223-312393. FAX 01223-315052. TELEX 851817256. (N. American addr.: Cambridge University Press, Journals Dept., 40 W. 20th St., New York, NY 10011. TEL 212-924-3900. FAX 212-691-3239) Ed.Bd. **Indexed:** INSPEC, Math.R., Phys.Ber. **Document type:** monographic series.

530   UK   ISSN 0965-6200
CAMBRIDGE MONOGRAPHS ON PARTICLE PHYSICS, NUCLEAR PHYSICS AND COSMOLOGY. 1992. irreg. Cambridge University Press, Edinburgh Bldg., Shaftesbury Rd., Cambridge CB2 2RU, England. TEL 01223-312393. FAX 01223-315052. TELEX 851817256. (N. American addr.: Cambridge University Press, Journals Dept., 40 W. 20th St., New York, NY 10011. TEL 212-924-3900. FAX 212-691-3239) Eds. T. Ericson, P.V. Landshoff. **Document type:** monographic series.
—BLDSC (3015.965600).

530   UK
CAMBRIDGE MONOGRAPHS ON PHYSICS. irreg. price varies. Cambridge University Press, Edinburgh Bldg., Shaftesbury Rd., Cambridge CB2 2RU, England. TEL 01223-312393. FAX 01223-315052. TELEX 851817256. (N. American addr.: Cambridge University Press, Journals Dept., 40 W. 20th St., New York, NY 10011. TEL 212-924-3900. FAX 212-691-3239) Ed.Bd. **Indexed:** INSPEC. **Document type:** monographic series.

CAMBRIDGE PHILOSOPHICAL SOCIETY. MATHEMATICAL PROCEEDINGS. see *MATHEMATICS*

530   UK   ISSN 0964-6752
CAMBRIDGE SOLID STATE SCIENCE SERIES. 1979. irreg. price varies. Cambridge University Press, Edinburgh Bldg., Shaftesbury Rd., Cambridge CB2 2RU, England. TEL 01223-312393. FAX 01223-315052. TELEX 851817256. (N. American addr.: Cambridge University Press, Journals Dept., 40 W. 20th St., New York, NY 10011. TEL 212-924-3900. FAX 212-691-3239) Ed.Bd. **Document type:** monographic series.

538   UK   ISSN 0964-0312
CAMBRIDGE STUDIES IN MAGNETISM. 1991. irreg. Cambridge University Press, Edinburgh Bldg., Shaftesbury Rd., Cambridge CB2 2RU, England. TEL 01223-312393. FAX 01223-315052. TELEX 1817256. (N. American addr.: Cambridge University Press, 40 W. 20th St., New York, NY 10011. TEL 212-924-3900. FAX 212-691-3239) **Document type:** monographic series.
—BLDSC (3015.994450).

**530   CN   ISSN 0008-4204
QC1   CODEN: CJPHAD**
CANADIAN JOURNAL OF PHYSICS/JOURNAL CANADIEN DE PHYSIQUE. (Text mainly in English, occasionally in French) 1929. m. Can.$94 to individuals (foreign $96); institutions Can.$296 (foreign $296) (effective 1995). National Research Council of Canada, Research Journals, Ottawa, ON K1A 0R6, Canada. TEL 613-993-9084. FAX 613-952-7656. Ed. Donald .D. Betts. adv.: B&W page Can.$600; trim 8 1/2 x 11; adv. contact: Hoda Jabbour. bibl.; illus.; index. circ. 1,100. (also avail. in microform from UMI,PMC; back issues avail.; reprint service avail. from UMI) **Indexed:** Abstr.Bull.Inst.Pap.Chem., Biol.Abstr., Bull.Signal, Bull.Thermodyn.& Thermochem., Cadscan, Chem.Abstr., Curr.Cont., Dairy Sci.Abstr., Deep Sea Res.& Oceanogr.Abstr., Eng.Ind., Ind.Sci.Rev., INIS Atomind., INSPEC (1968-), Int.Aerosp.Abstr., Lead Abstr., Mass Spectr.Bull., Math.R., Met.Abstr., Meteor.& Geoastrophys.Abstr., Nucl.Sci.Abstr., Nutr.Abstr., Petrol.Abstr., Phys.Ber., RAPRA, Sci.Cit.Ind., World Alum.Abstr., World Text.Abstr., Zincscan. **Document type:** academic/scholarly publication.
—BLDSC (3034.000000); CASDDS; Ei; Faxon; Genuine Article; SWETS; UMI; UnCover. **CCC**.
Refereed Serial

**530   US   ISSN 1054-1500
Q172.5.C45   CODEN: CHAOEH**
CHAOS; an interdisciplinary journal of nonlinear science. 1991. q. $350 (Canada $360; elsewhere $370) (effective 1996). American Institute of Physics, One Physics Ellipse, College Park, MD 20740-3843. TEL 301-209-3000. (Subscr. to: AIP Member and Subscriber Services, 500 Sunnyside Blvd., Woodbury, NY 11797-2999. TEL 516-576-2270. FAX 516-349-9705) Ed. David K. Campbell. **Indexed:** INSPEC (1991-). **Document type:** academic/scholarly publication.
—BLDSC (3129.715000); CASDDS; SWETS; UnCover. **CCC**.
Description: International journal features research articles, brief reports, and solicited technical reviews from physics, mathematics, engineering, chemistry, biology and other disciplines in which nonlinear phenomena play an important role.
Refereed Serial

CHEMICAL PHYSICS; a journal devoted to the experimental and theoretical research involving problems of both a chemical and a physical nature. see *CHEMISTRY — Physical Chemistry*

CHEMICAL PHYSICS OF SOLID SURFACES. see *CHEMISTRY — Physical Chemistry*

**530 541.3   US   ISSN 1074-1550
QD450   CODEN: SJCPDF**
CHEMICAL PHYSICS REPORTS. English translation of: Khimicheskaya Fizika. 24/yr. (in 2 vols., 12 nos./vol.). 666 ECU per vol. (effective 1996). Gordon and Breach Science Publishers, c/o International Publishers Distributor, 820 Town Center Dr., Langhorne, PA 19047. TEL 215-750-2642. FAX 215-750-6343. (Subsc. to: International Publishers Distributor, P.O. Box 90, Reading, Berkshire RG1 8JL, England. TEL 44-173-456-8316. FAX 44-173-456-8316) Ed. V.I. Goldansky. index. (also avail. in microform) **Document type:** academic/scholarly publication.
—BLDSC (0410.440000). **CCC**.
Formerly (until 1994): Soviet Journal of Chemical Physics (ISSN 0733-2831)
Description: Publishes original and review papers on recent progress in areas of physics relevant to chemical conversions.
Refereed Serial

CHEMICAL SOCIETY OF JAPAN. SYMPOSIUM ON PHYSICAL AND CHEMICAL ASPECTS OF ULTRASOUND. PROCEEDINGS/ONPA NO BUSSEI TO KAGAKU TORONKAI KOEN RONBUNSHU. see *CHEMISTRY*

530 540   NE   ISSN 0927-5878
CHEMICAL THERMODYNAMICS. (Text in English) 1992. irreg. Elsevier Science B.V., Books Division, P.O. Box 211, 1000 AE Amsterdam, Netherlands. TEL 31-20-4853911. FAX 31-20-4853705. TELEX 18582 ESPA NL. E-mail: nlinfo-f@elsevier.nl; usinfo-f@elsevier.com; forinfo-kyf04035@niftyserve.or.jp; Site addr.: http://www.elsevier.nl/. (Subscr. in U.S. and Canada to: Elsevier Science Inc., Box 882, Madison Sq. Sta., New York, NY 10159. TEL 212-989-5800) **Document type:** monographic series.
Refereed Serial

530   US   ISSN 0069-3294
CHICAGO LECTURES IN PHYSICS. 1963. irreg., vol.7, 1984. price varies. University of Chicago Press, 5801 S. Ellis Ave., Chicago, IL 60637. TEL 312-702-7899. (reprint service avail. from UMI,ISI)
Refereed Serial

**530   US   ISSN 0256-307X
CODEN: CPLEEU**
CHINESE PHYSICS LETTERS/ZHONGGUO WULI KUAIBAO. 1984. m. $415 (effective 1996). Allerton Press, Inc., 150 Fifth Ave., New York, NY 10011. TEL 212-924-3950. FAX 212-463-9684. Ed. Gan Zizhao. adv.; abstr.; bibl.; illus. circ. 3,000. **Indexed:** INIS Atomind., INSPEC (1984-). **Document type:** academic/scholarly publication.
—BLDSC (3181.048400); CASDDS; Faxon; UnCover. **CCC**.
Description: Provides information on work in progress in all areas of physics, particularly nuclear physics, fundamental areas of phenomenology, condensed matter physics, geophysics, astronomy and astrophysics.
Refereed Serial

**530   UK   ISSN 0264-9381
QC178   CODEN: CQGRDG**
CLASSICAL AND QUANTUM GRAVITY. 1984. m. £882($1817) (effective 1996). (Institute of Physics) I O P Publishing Ltd., Techno House, Redcliffe Way, Bristol, Avon BS1 6NX, England. TEL 0117-929-7481. FAX 0117-929-4318. TELEX 449149 INSTP G. (U.S. subscr. to: American Institute of Physics, Member and Subscriber Services, 500 Sunnyside Blvd., Woodbury, NY 11797-2900) Ed. G.W. Gibbons. index. (also avail. in microfiche; microfilm from AIP; back issues avail.) **Indexed:** ASCA, Curr.Cont., Ind.Sci.Rev., INIS Atomind., INSPEC (1984-), Int.Aerosp.Abstr., Math.R. **Document type:** academic/scholarly publication.
—BLDSC (3274.534200); CASDDS; Ei; Faxon; Genuine Article; SWETS; UnCover. **CCC**.
Description: Discusses the geometry of fluid theories, supergravity and cosmology.

530 620.1   NE   ISSN 0922-7725
COHESION AND STRUCTURE. (Text in English) 1988. irreg., vol.3, 1991. Elsevier Science B.V., Books Division, P.O. Box 211, 1000 AE Amsterdam, Netherlands. TEL 31-20-4853911. FAX 31-20-4853705. TELEX 18582 ESPA NL. E-mail: nlinfo-f@elsevier.nl; usinfo-f@elsevier.com; forinfo-kyf04035@niftyserve.or.jp; Site addr.: http://www.elsevier.nl/. (Subscr. in U.S. and Canada to: Elsevier Science Inc., Box 882, Madison Sq. Sta., New York, NY 10159. TEL 212-989-5800) (back issues avail.) **Document type:** monographic series.
—BLDSC (3292.898100).
Refereed Serial

**530 510 540 610   FI   ISSN 0788-5717
Q60   CODEN: CPMCCET**
COMMENTATIONES PHYSICO-MATHEMATICAE ET CHEMICO-MEDICAE. (Text in English) 1923. irreg. price varies. Societas Scientiarum Fennica - Finnish Society of Sciences and Letters, Marieg 5, FIN-00170 Helsinki, Finland. TEL 358-0-633-005. FAX 358-0-661-065. Ed. Erik Spring. charts; illus.; index. circ. 600. **Indexed:** Bull.Signal., Chem.Abstr., Curr.Cont., Deep Sea Res.& Oceanogr.Abstr., Ind.Sci.Rev., INIS Atomind., INSPEC (1992-), Phys.Ber., Ref.Zh., Sci.Cit.Ind., Zent.Math. **Document type:** academic/scholarly publication.
—BLDSC (3336.006000); CASDDS; UnCover.
Formerly: Commentationes Physico-Mathematicae (ISSN 0069-6609)

COMMENTS ON ASTROPHYSICS. see *ASTRONOMY*

PHYSICS

530.41 US ISSN 0885-4483
QC176.A1 CODEN: CCMPEB
COMMENTS ON CONDENSED MATTER PHYSICS. 1968. 12/yr. (in 2 vols., 6 nos./vol.) 177 ECU per vol. (effective 1996). Gordon and Breach Science Publishers, c/o International Publishers Distributor, 820 Town Center Dr., Langhorne, PA 19047. TEL 215-750-2642. FAX 215-750-6343. (Subscr. to: International Publishers Distributor, P.O. Box 90, Reading, Berkshire RG1 8JL, England. TEL 44-173-456-8316) Ed. Douglas Mills. adv. (also avail. in microform) **Indexed:** Chem.Abstr., INSPEC (1986-), Mass Spectr.Bull., Met.Abstr., Phys.Ber., World Alum.Abstr.
—BLDSC (3336.027500); CASDDS; Faxon; SWETS; UnCover. **CCC.**
Formerly: Comments on Solid State Physics (ISSN 0308-1206)

COMMENTS ON PLASMA PHYSICS AND CONTROLLED FUSION. see *PHYSICS — Nuclear Physics*

530 510 GW ISSN 0010-3616
QC20 CODEN: CMPHAY
COMMUNICATIONS IN MATHEMATICAL PHYSICS. (Text in English) 1965. 24/yr. (in 8 vols., 3 nos./vol.). DM.6096($4430) (effective 1996). Springer-Verlag, Heidelberger Platz 3, 14197 Berlin, Germany. TEL 030-8207-0. FAX 030-8214091. E-mail: orders@springer.de. (Subscr. in N. America to: Springer-Verlag New York, Inc., 44 Hartz Way, Secaucus, NJ 07096-2491. TEL 201-348-4033. FAX 201-348-4505) Ed. A. Jaffe. adv.; bibl.; charts; illus.; index. (also avail. in microform from UMI; back issues avail.; reprint service avail. from ISI) **Indexed:** Compumath, Curr.Cont., Ind.Sci.Rev., INIS Atomind., INSPEC (1968-), Math.R., Phys.Ber., Sci.Cit.Ind. **Document type:** academic/scholarly publication.
—BLDSC (3361.100000); Faxon; Genuine Article; SWETS; UMI; UnCover. **CCC.**
Description: Features physics papers with mathematical content. Covers a broad spectrum of topics, from classical to quantum physics.

530 CC ISSN 0253-6102
QC19.2 CODEN: CTPHDI
COMMUNICATIONS IN THEORETICAL PHYSICS/LILUN WULI. (Text in English) 1981. 8/yr. (in 2 vols.). 978 SFr. (effective 1996). (Academia Sinica, Institute of Theoretical Physics, CC) Baltzer Science Publishers B.V., Asterweg 1A, 1031 HL Amsterdam, Netherlands. TEL 31-20-6370061. FAX 31-20-6323651. (Subscr. in N. America to: Baltzer Science Publishers, Box 8577, Red Bank, NJ 07701-8577) (Co-publisher: International Academic Publishers, CC) Ed. Ho Tsohsiu. **Indexed:** INSPEC (1982-). **Document type:** academic/scholarly publication.
—BLDSC (3363.458000); CASDDS; Ei; Faxon; Genuine Article.
Description: Covers multifarious aspects of theoretical research in physics, such as atomic and molecular physics, condensed matter and statistical physics, plasma and fluid theory, nuclear theory, particle physics, and quantum field theory.
Refereed Serial

530 NE ISSN 0927-6440
COMPOSITE INTERFACES. (Text in English) 1992. bi-m. DM.570 (effective 1996). V S P, P.O. Box 346, 3700 AH Zeist, Netherlands. TEL 31-30-6925790. FAX 31-30-6932081. E-mail: 100341.2372@compuserve.com. Ed. H. Ishida. (back issues avail.) **Indexed:** Intl.Polym.Sci.& Tech., RAPRA. **Document type:** academic/scholarly publication.
—BLDSC (3364.959520); Ei.
Description: Publishes scientific and engineering research on composite interfaces and interphase structures, including studies of chemistry, physical properties, mechanical properties, molecular structures, as well as theoretical concerns.
Refereed Serial

COMPUTATIONAL MATHEMATICS AND MATHEMATICAL PHYSICS. see *MATHEMATICS*

CONCEPTS IN MAGNETIC RESONANCE; an educational quarterly. see *MEDICAL SCIENCES — Radiology And Nuclear Medicine*

530 548 US ISSN 0893-861X
QC173.4.C65 CODEN: CMTHEO
CONDENSED MATTER THEORIES. 1986. irreg., vol.8, 1993. price varies. Plenum Publishing Corp., 233 Spring St., New York, NY 10013-1578. TEL 212-620-8000. FAX 212-463-0742. TELEX 23-421139. Ed. F.B. Malik. (back issues avail.) **Document type:** proceedings.
—BLDSC (3405.710000); CASDDS.
Description: Covers new theoretical developments in solid-state physics of condensed matter.
Refereed Serial

530 US ISSN 0272-2488
CONTEMPORARY CONCEPTS IN PHYSICS. 1981. irreg., vol.8, 1994. Harwood Academic Publishers, 820 Town Center Dr., Langhorne, PA 19047. TEL 215-750-2642. FAX 215-750-6343. (UK subscr. to: Box 90 Reading, Berkshire RG1 8JL, England. TEL 0734-560-080) Ed. Herman Feshbach. (microform) **Indexed:** Math.R. **Document type:** monographic series.
—BLDSC (3425.177500).
Refereed Serial

530 UK ISSN 0010-7514
QC1 CODEN: CTPHAF
CONTEMPORARY PHYSICS. 1959. bi-m. £227($375) (effective 1996). Taylor & Francis Ltd., Rankine Rd., Basingstoke, Hants. RG24 8PR, England. TEL 44-1256-840366. FAX 44-1256-479438. TELEX 858540. E-mail: info@tandf.co.uk. (Subscr. in N. America to: Taylor & Francis Inc., 1900 Frost Rd., Ste. 101, Bristol, PA 19007-1598. TEL 800-821-8312. FAX 215-785-5515) Ed. P.L. Knight. adv.; bk.rev.; bibl.; charts; illus.; index. (also avail. in microform from MIM,PMC) **Indexed:** Chem.Abstr., Curr.Cont., Excerp.Med., Gen.Sci.Ind., Ind.Sci.Rev., INIS Atomind., INSPEC, Int.Aerosp.Abstr., Mass Spectr.Bull., Met.Abstr., Phys.Ber., Sci.Cit.Ind., World Alum.Abstr. **Document type:** academic/scholarly publication.
—BLDSC (3425.200000); CASDDS; Ei; Faxon; Genuine Article; SWETS; UnCover. **CCC.**
Description: Presents articles on important developments in physics that can be read and understood by anyone with an interest in and fundamental grasp of physics.
Refereed Serial

530 US
CONTEMPORARY PHYSICS. 1986. irreg. price varies. Springer-Verlag, 175 Fifth Ave., New York, NY 10010. TEL 212-460-1500. FAX 212-473-6272. (Also: Berlin, Heidelberg, Tokyo, Vienna) (reprint service avail. from ISI) **Indexed:** Gen.Sci.Ind. **Document type:** academic/scholarly publication.

530 US ISSN 1043-3996
CONTEMPORARY TOPICS IN PURE AND APPLIED CONDENSED MATTER SCIENCE. irreg. Gordon and Breach Science Publishers, c/o International Publishers Distributor, 820 Town Center Dr., Langhorne, PA 19047. TEL 215-750-2642. FAX 215-750-6343. (Subscr. to: International Publishers Distributor, P.O. Box 90, Reading, RG1 8JL, England. TEL 44-173-456-8316) Ed. R.R. Hasiguti. **Document type:** monographic series.
—BLDSC (3425.314200).
Refereed Serial

530.44 GW ISSN 0863-1042
QC717.6 CODEN: CPPHEP
CONTRIBUTIONS TO PLASMA PHYSICS. (Text in English, French, German) 1961. bi-m. DM.213 to individuals; institutions DM.998 (effective 1996). Akademie Verlag GmbH, Muehlenstr. 33-34, 13187 Berlin, Germany. TEL 030-47889348. FAX 030-47889357. (U.S. subscr. to: VCH Publishers Inc., 303 N.W. 12th Ave., Deerfield Beach, FL 33442-1788) Ed.Bd. illus.; index. **Indexed:** ASCA, Chem.Abstr., Curr.Cont., INSPEC, Int.Aerosp.Abstr., Math.R., Phys.Ber., Sci.Cit.Ind. **Document type:** academic/scholarly publication.
—BLDSC (3461.116000); CASDDS; Ei; Faxon; Genuine Article; UnCover. **CCC.**
Formerly: Beitraege aus der Plasmaphysik (ISSN 0005-8025)

530 UK ISSN 0143-926X
COSMATOM. 1973. irreg., latest vol.8, 1995. £36 (foreign £60). Cosmatom (Publishers and Booksellers), Five-Dimensional Space-Time-Mass, P.O. Box 12, Worthing, Sussex BN14 7HD, England. Ed. Ian McGrimmon. bibl.; charts. circ. 1,000. (back issues avail.) **Indexed:** Chem.Abstr., Ref.Zh. **Document type:** academic/scholarly publication.
—BLDSC (3477.173000).

530.41 US ISSN 1040-8436
QC176.A1 CODEN: CCRSDA
CRITICAL REVIEWS IN SOLID STATE & MATERIALS SCIENCES. 1970. bi-m. $80 to individuals; institutions $285. C R C Press, Inc., 2000 Corporate Blvd., N.W., Boca Raton, FL 33431. TEL 407-994-0555; 800-272-7737. FAX 407-998-9784. TELEX 568689-CRC PRESS. Ed. Dr. Joseph E. Greene. bibl.; charts; illus. circ. 570. (back issues avail.) **Indexed:** Biol.Abstr., Chem.Abstr., Ind.Sci.Rev., INIS Atomind., INSPEC, Mass Spectr.Bull., Sci.Cit.Ind. **Document type:** academic/scholarly publication.
—BLDSC (3487.482000); CASDDS; Ei; Faxon; Genuine Article; SWETS; UnCover. **CCC.**
Former titles: C R C Critical Reviews in Solid State and Materials Sciences (ISSN 0161-1593); C R C Critical Reviews in Solid State Sciences (ISSN 0011-085X)
Description: Reviews articles in theoretical and experimental solid state materials science including new and emerging areas in a variety of disciplines.

530 US ISSN 0045-9348
CURRENT PHYSICS MICROFORM. 1972. m. American Institute of Physics, One Physics Ellipse, College Park, MD 20740-3843. TEL 301-209-3000. (Subscr. to: Member and Subscriber Service, 500 Sunnyside Blvd., Woodbury, NY 11797-2999. TEL 516-576-2270) index, cum.index. (microfilm) **Indexed:** C.P.I. **Document type:** bulletin.

530 NE ISSN 0922-503X
CURRENT PHYSICS - SOURCES AND COMMENTS. (Text in English) 1988. irreg., vol.10, 1993. price varies. Elsevier Science B.V., Books Division, P.O. Box 211, 1000 Amsterdam, Netherlands. TEL 31-20-4853911. FAX 31-20-4853705. TELEX 18582 ESPA NL. E-mail: nlinfo-f@elsevier.nl; usinfo-f@elsevier.com; forinfo-kyf04035@niftyserve.or.jp; Site addr.: http://www.elsevier.nl/. (Subscr. in U.S. and Canada to: Elsevier Science Inc., Box 882, Madison Sq. Sta., New York, NY 10159. TEL 212-989-5800) (back issues avail.) **Indexed:** INSPEC. **Document type:** monographic series.
Refereed Serial

530 US ISSN 0732-4383
QC1
CURRENT TOPICS IN CHINESE SCIENCE. SECTION A: PHYSICS. 1982. irreg., vol.3, 1985. Gordon & Breach Science Publishers, c/o International Publishers Distributor, 820 Town Center Dr., Langhorne, PA 19047. TEL 215-750-2642. FAX 215-750-6343. (Subscr. to: International Publishers Distributor, P.O. Box 90, Reading Berkshire RG1 8JL, England. TEL 44-173-456-8316) (also avail. in microform) **Indexed:** Biol.Abstr. **Document type:** monographic series.
Refereed Serial

530 NE ISSN 0165-1854
TA403 CODEN: CTMSD2
CURRENT TOPICS IN MATERIALS SCIENCE. 1977. irreg., vol.12, 1985. price varies. Elsevier Science B.V., Books Division, P.O. Box 211, 1006 AE Amsterdam, Netherlands. TEL 31-20-4853911. FAX 31-20-4853705. TELEX 18582 ESPA NL. E-mail: nlinfo-f@elsevier.nl; usinfo-f@elsevier.com; forinfo-kyf04035@niftyserve.or.jp; Site addr.: http://www.elsevier.nl/. (Subscr. in U.S. and Canada to: Elsevier Science Inc., Box 882, Madison Sq. Sta., New York, NY 10159. TEL 212-989-5800) Ed. E. Kaldis. **Indexed:** Cadscan, Chem.Abstr., INSPEC, Lead Abstr., Zincscan. **Document type:** monographic series.
—CASDDS. **CCC.**
Refereed Serial

PHYSICS

530   US   ISSN 0011-4626
QC1   CODEN: CZYPAO
CZECHOSLOVAK JOURNAL OF PHYSICS; europhysics journal. (Text in English, French, German; summaries in English) 1952. m. $795 (foreign $930) (effective 1996). (Czech Academy of Sciences, Institute of Physics, XR) Plenum Publishing Corp., 233 Spring St., New York, NY 10013-1578. TEL 212-620-8000. FAX 212-463-0742. TELEX 23-421139. (Co-publisher: Academia, CS) Ed. V. Petrzilka. abstr.; bibl.; charts; illus.; index. circ. 1,450. (back issues avail.) **Indexed:** Appl.Mech.Rev., Biol.Abstr., Cadscan, Chem.Abstr., Curr.Cont., Ind.Sci.Rev., INIS Atomind., INSPEC, Int.Aerosp.Abstr., Lead Abstr., Math.R., Met.Abstr., Phys.Ber., Ref.Zh., Sci.Cit.Ind., World Alum.Abstr., Zincscan. **Document type:** academic/scholarly publication.
—BLDSC (3508.000000); CASDDS; Ei; Faxon; Genuine Article; SWETS; UMI; UnCover. CCC.
   Formerly (until 1971): Czechoslovak Journal of Physics. Section B.
   Description: Publishes original research contributions in all branches of physics.
   Refereed Serial

530 540   US   ISSN 0177-7823
                 CODEN: PCEREI
DAHLEM WORKSHOP REPORTS. PHYSICAL, CHEMICAL, AND EARTH SCIENCES RESEARCH REPORT. Key Title: Physical, Chemical, and Earth Sciences Research Report. 1975-1982; resumed 1984. irreg. price varies. Springer-Verlag, 175 Fifth Ave., New York, NY 10010. TEL 212-460-1500.
FAX 212-473-6272. (Also: Berlin, Heidelberg, Tokyo and Vienna) **Document type:** monographic series.
—BLDSC (6475.298000); CASDDS.
   Formerly (until 1982): Dahlem Workshop Reports. Physical and Chemical Sciences Research Report (ISSN 0340-8116)

DELTA; matematyczno-fizyczno-astronomiczny miesiecznik popularny. see *MATHEMATICS*

530   DK
DENMARK. RISOE NATIONAL LABORATORY. PHYSICS DEPARTMENT. ANNUAL PROGRESS REPORT. 1970. a. DKK 48.80. Risoe National Laboratory, Box 49, DK-4000 Roskilde, Denmark. FAX 45-46-75-56-27. TELEX 43 116. (Subscr. to: G.E.C. Gad, Vimmelskaftet 32, DK-1161 Copenhagen K, Denmark)
   Formerly: Denmark. Forsoeganslaeg Risoe. Fysikafdelingen. Annual Progress Report (ISSN 0107-8348)

530   GW   ISSN 0420-0195
DEUTSCHE PHYSIKALISCHE GESELLSCHAFT. VERHANDLUNGEN. (Text and summaries in English and German) 1966. irreg. (5-10/yr.). membership. (Deutsche Physikalische Gesellschaft e.V.) Physik-Verlag GmbH, Postfach 1260-1280, 69469 Weinheim, Germany. TEL 06201-602-0.
FAX 06201-602-328. (U.S. addr.: V C H Publishers, Inc., 220 E. 23rd St., New York, NY 10010-4606) Ed. V. Haeselbarth. adv. circ. controlled. **Document type:** monographic series.
—BLDSC (9163.360000).

530 621.3   US   ISSN 1053-7465
DEVELOPMENTS IN NANOTECHNOLOGY. 1991. irreg., latest vol.2. price varies. Gordon and Breach Science Publishers, c/o International Publishers Distributor, 820 Town Center Dr., Langhorne, PA 19047.
TEL 215-750-2642. FAX 215-750-6343. (Subscr. to: International Publishers Distributor, P.O. Box 90, Reading, Berkshire RG1 8JL, England. TEL 44-173-456-8316) Ed. D. Bowen. **Document type:** monographic series.
   Refereed Serial

530   US   ISSN 1051-9084
TP873.5.D5   CODEN: DDSTE3
DIAMOND DEPOSITIONS; science and technology. 1990. m. $177 (foreign $207) (effective 1996). Superconductivity Publications, Sunset Plaza, 828 Livingston Ave., North Brunswick, NJ 08902-2356. TEL 908-846-2002. FAX 908-846-2050. E-mail: 74130,650@compuserve.com. Ed. C. Jim Russell; Pub. C. Jim Russell. adv.: B&W page $500; adv. contact: Kathy Kleppin. bk.rev.; charts; illus.; pat.; stat.; index. (back issues avail.)
—BLDSC (3579.835500).
   Description: Covers low-pressure, high-pressure, and temperature synthesis of diamond, diamondlike, and related materials. Includes applications, patent abstracts, market assessments, technical meeting highlights, and funding worldwide.
   Refereed Serial

DIAMOND FILMS AND TECHNOLOGY. see *ENGINEERING — Mechanical Engineering*

530   US   ISSN 1073-7316
▼**DIAMOND INDUSTRY WEEK.** 1994. w. (48/yr.). $377 (effective 1995-1996). Superconductivity Publications, 828 Livingston Ave, North Brunswick, NJ 08902-2356. TEL 908-846-2002.
FAX 908-846-2050. E-mail: 74130,650@compuserve.com. Ed. C. Jim Russell; Pub. C. Jim Russell. adv. contact: Kathy Kleppin. pat. (back issues avail.) **Document type:** trade publication.
   Description: Covers all aspects of industrial diamonds and related materials. Includes news of business and technical developments, as well as government contract announcements and awards.

530   JA
DIGESTS OF ANNUAL CONFERENCE ON MAGNETICS IN JAPAN/NIHON OYO JIKI GAKKAI GAKUJUTSU KOEN GAIYOSHU. (Text in English, Japanese) a. 5000 Yen. Magnetics Society of Japan - Nihon Oyo Jiki Gakkai, 2-8, Toranomon 1-chome, Minato-ku, Tokyo 105, Japan.

DIMENSIO. see *MATHEMATICS*

530   SI   ISSN 0217-9148
DIRECTIONS IN CHAOS. (Text in English) 1990. irreg., vol. 5, 1991. price varies. World Scientific Publishing Co. Pte. Ltd., Farrer Rd., P.O. Box 128, Singapore 9128, Singapore. TEL 3825663. FAX 3825919. TELEX RS 28561 WSPC. (UK addr.: 73 Lynton Mead, Totteridge, London N20 8DH, England. TEL 44-81-4462461; US addr.: 1060 Main St., Ste. 1B, River Edge, NJ 07661. TEL 800-227-7562)

DIRECTORY OF PHYSICS & ASTRONOMY STAFF (YEAR). see *EDUCATION — Higher Education*

530 548   NE
DISLOCATIONS IN SOLIDS. 1978. irreg., vol.9, 1992. price varies. Elsevier Science B.V., Books Division, P.O. Box 211, 1000 AE Amsterdam, Netherlands. TEL 31-20-4853911. FAX 31-20-4853705. TELEX 18582 ESPA NL.
E-mail: nlinfo-f@elsevier.nl; usinfo-f@elsevier.com; forinfo-kyf04035@niftyserve.or.jp; Site addr.: http://www.elsevier.nl/. (Subscr. in U.S. and Canada to: Elsevier Science Inc., Box 882, Madison Sq. Sta., New York, NY 10159. TEL 212-989-5800) Ed. F.R.N. Nabarro. **Document type:** monographic series.
   Refereed Serial

530 620   UK   ISSN 0967-1846
QA76.9.D5   CODEN: DSENEK
DISTRIBUTED SYSTEMS ENGINEERING. 1993. q. £101($204) (effective 1996). (Institute of Physics) I O P Publishing Ltd., Techno House, Redcliffe Way, Bristol, Avon BS1 6NS, England.
TEL 0117-929-7481. FAX 0117-929-4318. (U.S. subscr. to: American Institute of Physics, 500 Sunnyside Blvd., Woodbury, NY 11797-2900. TEL 516-349-7800) (Co-sponsors: British Computer Society; Institution of Electrical Engineers) Ed. D. Hutchiison. adv.; bk.rev.; index. (also avail. in microfiche) **Indexed:** INSPEC (1993-).
—BLDSC (3602.672000).
   Description: Covers integration of processing, storage, and communication subsystems within an overall parallel processing.

DOMINION ASTROPHYSICAL OBSERVATORY, VICTORIA. PUBLICATIONS. see *ASTRONOMY*

530   IE   ISSN 0070-7414
               CODEN: CDIAAH
DUBLIN INSTITUTE FOR ADVANCED STUDIES. COMMUNICATIONS. SERIES A. 1943. irreg. no.28, 1984. price varies. Dublin Institute for Advanced Studies, 10 Burlington Rd., Dublin 4, Ireland. TEL 680748. FAX 680561. **Indexed:** Deep Sea Res.& Oceanogr.Abstr., INSPEC (1968-), Math.R., Phys.Ber.

DYES AND PIGMENTS. see *CHEMISTRY*

ECLETICA QUIMICA; serie quimica. see *CHEMISTRY*

639.2   ER   ISSN 1018-7650
              CODEN: ETFMB3
EESTI TEADUSTE AKADEEMIA. TOIMETISED. FUUSIKA. MATEMAATIKA/ESTONIAN ACADEMY OF SCIENCES. PROCEEDINGS. PHYSICS. MATHEMATICS. (Text and summaries in English, Estonian, Russian) 1956. q. $60 (effective 1993). Teaduste Akadeemia Kirjastus, Estonia pst.7, EE-0100 Tallinn, Estonia. (Subscr. to: Akateeminen Kirjakauppa 128 SF, 00101 Helsinki, Finland; or to: Bibliotekstjanst AB 200, S22100 Lund, Sweden) Ed.Bd. charts; illus.; index. circ. 500. **Indexed:** Chem.Abstr., GeoRef., INIS Atomind., INSPEC (1968-), Met.Abstr., World Alum.Abstr. **Document type:** academic/scholarly publication.
—CASDDS.
   Formerly (until 1990): Akademiya Nauk Estonskoi S.S.R. Izvestiya. Fizika. Matematika (ISSN 0367-1429)

530   UA   ISSN 1110-0214
EGYPTIAN JOURNAL OF PHYSICS. (Text in English; summaries in English and Arabic) 1970. s-a. $57 (effective 1996). (Egyptian Physical Society, Research Department) National Information and Documentation Centre (NIDOC), Tahrir St., Dokki, Awqaf P.O., Cairo, Egypt. TEL 20-2-701696. Ed. M. El-Nady. abstr.; charts. circ. 1,000. (reprint service avail. from IRC) **Indexed:** Chem.Abstr., Mass Spectr.Bull., Phys.Ber. **Document type:** academic/scholarly publication.

621.3819   JA   ISSN 0389-214X
EIZO JOHO MEDIKARU/IMAGE TECHNOLOGY & INFORMATION DISPLAY, MEDICAL. (Text in Japanese; summaries in English, Japanese) 1969. m. 21800 Yen. Sangyo Kaihatsu Kiko K.K., 1-1, Kanda Izumicho, Chiyoda-ku, Tokyo 101, Japan.
TEL 03-3861-7051. FAX 03-5687-7744. Ed. Tsuneyoshi Sakamaki; Pub. Hiroshi Wakebe. circ. 15,000. **Indexed:** INIS Atomind. **Document type:** academic/scholarly publication.
—BLDSC (4368.994300).
   Description: Covers diagnostic imaging in medicine.

ELECTROMAGNETIC FIELD LITIGATION REPORTER. see *ENERGY — Electrical Energy*

537.5   NE   ISSN 0929-5054
ELECTROMAGNETIC WAVES. (Text in English) 1992. irreg. price varies. Elsevier Science B.V., Books Division, P.O. Box 211, 1000 AE Amsterdam, Netherlands. TEL 31-20-4853911.
FAX 31-20-4853705.
E-mail: nlinfo-f@elsevier.nl; usinfo-f@elsevier.com; forinfo-kyf04035@niftyserve.or.jp; Site addr.: http://www.elsevier.nl/. (Subscr. in U.S. and Canada to: Elsevier Science Inc., Box 882, Madison Sq. Sta., New York, NY 10159-0882. TEL 212-989-5800. FAX 212-633-3680) **Document type:** monographic series.
—BLDSC (3699.555000).
   Description: Publishes comprehensive review articles on aspects of fundamental physics and research in electromagnetic wave phenomena in a wide range of materials.
   Refereed Serial

ELEKTRONENMIKROSKOPIE. see *BIOLOGY — Microscopy*

ENCYCLOPEDIA OF PHYSICAL SCIENCE & TECHNOLOGY YEARBOOK. see *SCIENCES: COMPREHENSIVE WORKS*

ENERGY SOURCES; journal of extraction, conversion, & the environment. see *ENERGY*

ENERGY TODAY. see *ENERGY*

PHYSICS

530 541.3   US   ISSN 0013-8533
ENSANIAN PHYSICOCHEMICAL INSTITUTE. JOURNAL.
1969. q. membership. Ensanian Physicochemical Institute, Box 98, Eldred, PA 16731. TEL 814-225-3296. Ed. Minas Ensanian. bk.rev.; abstr.; bibl.; charts; illus.; pat.; index, cum.index. circ. 250. (processed)

530   DK   ISSN 0106-407X
ENVIRONMENTAL RADIOACTIVITY IN DENMARK. 1961. a. free. Risoe National Laboratory, P.O. Box 49, DK-4000 Roskilde, Denmark. illus. **Document type:** academic/scholarly publication.
Formerly: Environmental Radioactivity at Risoe.

530   DK   ISSN 0108-0962
ENVIRONMENTAL RADIOACTIVITY IN GREENLAND. 1962. a. DKK 48.80. G.E.C. GAD, Dansk og Udenlandsk Boghandel Aktieselskab, Vimmelskaftet 32, 1161 Copenhagen K, Denmark. illus.

530   DK   ISSN 0107-9069
ENVIRONMENTAL RADIOACTIVITY IN THE FAROES. 1962. a. DKK 48.80. G.E.C. GAD, Dansk og Udenlandsk Boghandel Aktieselskab, Vimmelskaftet 32, 1161 Copenhagen K, Denmark.

ETTORE MAJORANA INTERNATIONAL SCIENCE SERIES. PHYSICAL SCIENCES. see *SCIENCES: COMPREHENSIVE WORKS*

530   UK   ISSN 0143-0807
QC1   CODEN: EJPHD4
EUROPEAN JOURNAL OF PHYSICS. 1980. bi-m. £224($461) (effective 1996). (Institute of Physics) I O P Publishing Ltd., Techno House, Redcliffe Way, Bristol, Avon BS1 6NX, England. TEL 01272 297481. FAX 01272-294318. TELEX 449149 INSTP G. (U.S. subscr. to: American Institute of Physics, Member and Subscriber Services, 500 Sunnyside Blvd., Woodbury, NY 11797-2900. TEL 516-349-7800) (Co-sponsor: European Physical Society) Ed. B. Pippard. bk.rev.; bibl.; illus.; charts; index. circ. 571. (also avail. in microfiche from AIP; microfilm from AIP; back issues avail.) **Indexed:** Chem.Abstr., INIS Atomind., INSPEC, Math.R., Phys.Ber. **Document type:** academic/scholarly publication.
—BLDSC (3829.735000); CASDDS; Ei; Faxon; SWETS; UnCover.
Description: Publishes educational and scholarly studies in physics and closely related sciences at the university level.

530   FR   ISSN 0295-5075
QC1   CODEN: EULEEJ
EUROPHYSICS LETTERS. (Text and summaries in English, French, German, Russian) 1986. s-m. 1820 SFr. or 7735 F. (effective 1996). Editions de Physique, Zone Industrielle de Courtaboeuf, B.P. 112, 91944 Les Ulis Cedex, France. TEL 69-07-36-88. FAX 69-28-84-91. TELEX 602 321 F. Ed. W. Buckel. circ. 1,500. (back issues avail.) **Indexed:** INIS Atomind., INSPEC (1986-).
—BLDSC (3830.419000); CASDDS; Ei; Faxon; Genuine Article; SWETS; UnCover. **CCC.**
Description: New ideas, experimental methods, theoretical treatments and results of interest to the physics community.

530   SZ   ISSN 0531-7479
   CODEN: EUPNAS
EUROPHYSICS NEWS. 1969. bi-m. 135 SFr. European Physical Society, P.O. Box 69, CH-1213 Petit Lancy 2, Switzerland. Ed. P.G. Boswell. adv. circ. 26,700. **Indexed:** INIS Atomind., INSPEC. **Document type:** academic/scholarly publication, newsletter.
—BLDSC (3830.420000); CASDDS; Faxon; SWETS.
Formerly: Europhysics Review.

530   GW   ISSN 0014-4924
   CODEN: EXPPAL
EXPERIMENTELLE TECHNIK DER PHYSIK/EXPERIMENTAL TECHNIQUE OF PHYSICS; zeitschrift fuer die gesamte theoretische und experimentelle physikalische Grundlagenforschung zur naturwissenschaftlichen und technischen Nutzung. 1953. bi-m. DM.130.20. VEB Deutscher Verlag der Wissenschaften, Johannes-Dieckmann-Str. 10, 1080 Berlin, Germany. Ed.Bd. adv.; bk.rev.; charts; illus.; index. **Indexed:** Appl.Mech.Rev., Chem.Abstr., INIS Atomind., INSPEC, Met.Abstr.
—CASDDS; UnCover.

EXPLORING (SAN FRANCISCO). see *SCIENCES: COMPREHENSIVE WORKS*

F G M NEWS. (Functionally Gradient Materials) see *TECHNOLOGY: COMPREHENSIVE WORKS*

F & S. (Filtrieren und Separieren) see *CHEMISTRY*

530   US   ISSN 0015-0193
QC595   CODEN: FEROA8
FERROELECTRICS. 1973. 48/yr. (in 12 monthly vols., 4 nos./vol.) 347 ECU per vol. (effective 1996). Gordon and Breach Science Publishers, c/o International Publishers Distributor, 820 Town Center Dr., Langhorne, PA 19047. TEL 215-750-2642. FAX 215-750-6343. (Subscr. to: International Publishers Distributor, P.O. Box 90, Reading, Berkshire RG1 8JL, England. TEL 44-173-456-8316) Ed. George W. Taylor. adv.; bk.rev.; index. (also avail. in microform) **Indexed:** Cadscan, Chem.Abstr., Curr.Cont., Eng.Ind., Ind.Sci.Rev., INSPEC, Lead Abstr., Met.Abstr., Phys.Ber., Sci.Cit.Ind., World Alum.Abstr., Zincscan. **Document type:** academic/scholarly publication.
—BLDSC (3908.400000); CASDDS; Faxon; SWETS; UnCover. **CCC.**
Description: Publishes experimental, theoretical, and applied papers aimed at understanding ferroelectrics and related materials.
Refereed Serial

530   AU   ISSN 0177-7963
   CODEN: FBSYEQ
FEW-BODY SYSTEMS. ACTA PHYSICA AUSTRIACA. NEW SERIES. (Supplementum avail. (ISSN 0177-8811)) (Text in English) 1947; N.S. 1986. 8/yr. (in 2 vols., 4 nos./vol.). DM.832($604) (effective 1996). Springer-Verlag, Sachsenplatz 4-6, Postfach 89, A-1201 Vienna, Austria. TEL 0222-3302415. FAX 0222-3302426. (Subscr. in N. America to: Springer-Verlag New York, Inc., 44 Hartz Way, Secaucus, NJ 07096-2491. TEL 201-348-4033. FAX 201-348-4505) Eds. H. Mitter, W. Plessas. adv.; bk.rev.; charts; illus.; index. (also avail. in microform from UMI; reprint service avail. from ISI) **Indexed:** ASCA, Cadscan, Chem.Abstr., Curr.Cont., Ind.Sci.Rev., INIS Atomind., INSPEC (1968-), Lead Abstr., Math.R., Met.Abstr., Phys.Ber., Sci.Cit.Ind., Zincscan. **Document type:** academic/scholarly publication.
—CASDDS; Faxon; Genuine Article; SWETS; UMI; UnCover. **CCC.**
Formerly: Acta Physica Austriaca (ISSN 0001-6713).

530   AU   ISSN 0177-8811
   CODEN: FBSSE8
FEW-BODY SYSTEMS. SUPPLEMENTUM. 1965; N.S. 1986. irreg. price varies. Springer-Verlag, Sachsenplatz 4-6, Postfach 89, Sachsenplatz 4-6, A-1201 Vienna, Austria. TEL 0222-3302415. FAX 0222-3302426. (N. American subscr. to: Journal Fulfillment Services, Box 2485, Secaucus, NJ 07096-2491. TEL 800-777-2491; Also: Berlin, Heidelberg, New York and Tokyo) (also avail. in microform from UMI; reprint service avail. from ISI) **Indexed:** INSPEC (1981-1985), Math.R. **Document type:** academic/scholarly publication.
—BLDSC (3914.145100); CASDDS; UMI. **CCC.**
Formerly (until no.27, 1985): Acta Physica Austriaca. Supplement (ISSN 0065-1559)

530   RU
FILOSOFIYA I FIZIKA. 1972. 0.75 Rub. Voronezhskii Gosudarstvennyi Universitet, Universitetskaya Ploshchad, 1, Voronezh, Russia.

530.15   AG   ISSN 0326-7512
FISICA. 1985. 2/yr. $4 per no. (effective 1995). Zagier & Urruty Publicaciones, P.O. Box 94, Sucursal 19, 1419 Buenos Aires, Argentina. TEL 541-572-1050. FAX 541-572-5766. (U.S. addr.: Box 526806, Miami, FL 33152-6806) Ed. Sergio Zagier. adv.; B&W page $400. bk.rev. circ. 1,500. **Document type:** academic/scholarly publication.
Description: Includes articles on history, philosophy, tools and more.

530   IT
FISICA. 1987. irreg., no.3, 1993. price varies. Liguori Editore s.r.l., Via Mezzocannone, 19, 80134 Naples, Italy. TEL 081-5527139. Ed. Vittorio Silvestrini. **Document type:** monographic series.

530   CI   ISSN 1330-0008
QC1   CODEN: FIZAE4
FIZIKA A; a journal of experimental and theoretical physics. (Supplements avail.) (Text in English) 1969. q. $60. Croatian Physical Society, Bijenicka c.54, 41000 Zagreb, Croatia. FAX 38-41-425-497. Ed. K. Ilakovac. circ. 700. **Indexed:** Chem.Abstr., INSPEC, Int.Aerosp.Abstr., Phys.Ber.
—BLDSC (3949.110000); CASDDS; UnCover.
Supersedes in part (in 1992): Fizika (ISSN 0015-3206)
Description: Publishes results of original experimental or theoretical research work on atomic and colecular physics, condensed matter physics, and plasma physics.

530   CI   ISSN 1330-0016
QC1   CODEN: FIZBE7
FIZIKA B; a journal of experimental and theoretical physics. (Text in English) 1969. q. $60. Croatian Physical Society, Bijenicka c.54, 41000 Zagreb, Croatia. Ed. K. Ilakovac.
—BLDSC (3949.120000); CASDDS; UnCover.
Supersedes in part (in 1992): Fizika (ISSN 0015-3206)
Description: Publishes results of original experimental or theoretical research work on general and nuclear physics.

530   KR   ISSN 0206-3638
   CODEN: FMSIDK
FIZIKA MNOGOCHASTICHNYKH SISTEM; respublikanskii mezhvedomstvennyi sbornik nauchnykh trudov. 1975. s-a. (Akademiya Nauk Ukrainy, Institut Teoreticheskoi Fiziki) Vidavnitstvo Naukova Dumka, Vul. Tereshchenkivska 3, 252601 Kiev, Ukraine. TEL 044-224-4068. FAX 044-224-7060. (Dist. by: Mezhdunarodnaya Kniga, B. Yakimanka 39, 117049 Moscow, Russia) Ed. A.S. Dawydov. **Indexed:** Chem.Abstr.
—CASDDS.
Formerly (until 1982): Fizika Molekul (ISSN 0131-176X)

530.44   RU   ISSN 0134-5052
QC7176   CODEN: FIPLDK
FIZIKA PLAZMY. English translation: Plasma Physics Reports (US ISSN 1063-780X) 1975. m. 57.90 Rub. (Rossiiskaya Akademiya Nauk) Izdatel'stvo Nauka, Mezhdunarodnyi Otdel, Profsoyuznaya, 90, 117864 Moscow, Russia. TEL 234-05-84. (Dist. by: Mezhdunarodnaya Kniga, ul. Dimitrova D.39, 113095 Moscow, Russia) Ed. V.D. Shafranov. illus. **Indexed:** Chem.Abstr., INIS Atomind., INSPEC. **Document type:** academic/scholarly publication.
—CASDDS.

530   RU   ISSN 0367-3294
QC176.A1   CODEN: FTVTAC
FIZIKA TVERDOGO TELA. English translation: Physics of the Solid State (US ISSN 1063-7834) 1959. m. $434 (effective 1996). (Rossiiskaya Akademiya Nauk) Izdatel'stvo Nauka, S.-Peterburgskoe Otdelenie, Mendeleevskaya liniya, 1, 199034 St. Petersburg B-34, Russia. Ed. S.N. Zhurkov. charts; illus.; index. (tabloid format) **Indexed:** Cadscan, Ceram.Abstr., Chem.Abstr., Curr.Cont., Ind.Sci.Rev., INIS Atomind., INSPEC, Lead Abstr., Met.Abstr., Sci.Cit.Ind., World Alum.Abstr., Zincscan. **Document type:** academic/scholarly publication.
—CASDDS; Ei; Genuine Article.

530   HU   ISSN 0015-3257
   CODEN: FISZA6
FIZIKAI SZEMLE. 1891. m. $35.50. (Eotvos Lorand Fizikai Tarsulat) Lapkiado Vallalat, Lenin korut 9-11, 1073 Budapest 7, Hungary. (Subscr. to: Kultura, Box 149, H-1389 Budapest, Hungary) Ed. Gy. Marx. charts; index. **Indexed:** Chem.Abstr, INIS Atomind., INSPEC, Risk Abstr.
—CASDDS.

530 510   BU   ISSN 0015-3265
   CODEN: FMBMAC
FIZIKO-MATEMATICHESKO SPISANIE. (Contents page in English and Russian) 1959? q. 5.70 lv.($7) (Bulgarska Akademiia na Naukite, Fizicheski i Matematicheski Institut) Publishing House of the Bulgarian Academy of Sciences, Acad. G. Bonchev St., Bldg. 6, 1113 Sofia, Bulgaria. (Dist. by: Hemus, 6, Rouski Blvd., 1000 Sofia, Bulgaria) Ed. L. Iliev. bk.rev.; bibl.; illus.; index, cum.index: vols.1-10, 1968. circ. 780. (reprint service avail. from IRC) **Indexed:** Chem.Abstr., Math.R., Ref.Zh.
—CASDDS.

PHYSICS

530 PL ISSN 0554-825X
CODEN: UPMFAS
FIZYKA. 1961. irreg., no.69, 1993. price varies. Adam Mickiewicz University Press, Nowowiejskiego 55, 61-734 Poznan, Poland. TEL 527-380. FAX 61-525425. TELEX 412360 UAMPL. circ. 330. Document type: academic/scholarly publication.
—BLDSC (9120.460000); CASDDS.
Formerly: Uniwersytet im. Adama Mickiewicza w Poznaniu. Wydzial Matematyki, Fizyki i Chemii. Seria Fizyka.
Description: Contains current physics research results, Ph.D. theses, and monographs of the university's scholars. Each volume contains the work of one author.

530 PL ISSN 0426-3383
CODEN: FISZD9
FIZYKA W SZKOLE. 1955. bi-m. $12. (Ministerstwo Edukacji Narodowej) Wydawnictwa Szkolne i Pedagogiczne, Pl. Dabrowskiego 8, 00-950 Warsaw, Poland. TEL 48-22-261327. FAX 48-22-268971. (Dist. by: Ars Polona, Krakowskie Przedmiescie 7, Warsaw, Poland) Ed. Zygmunt Przeniczny. circ. 7,200.
—CASDDS.
Description: Publishes articles on the theory and practice of teaching physics and astronomy, with discussions of school syllabi and research methodology in physics. Provides information on the latest developments in modern physics, astrophysics and technology, and presents new concepts in teaching physics.

530 XR
CODEN: FFSPER
FOLIA FACULTATIS SCIENTIARUM NATURALIUM UNIVERSITATIS MASARYKIANAE BRUNENSIS: PHYSICA. 1960. a. price varies. Masarykova Universita, Prirodovedecka Fakulta - Masaryk University, Faculty of Sciences, Kotlarska 2, 611 37 Brno, Czech Republic. Indexed: INSPEC. Document type: monographic series.
—CASDDS.
Formerly: Folia Facultatis Scientiarum Naturalium Universitatis Purkynianae Brunensis: Physica (ISSN 0323-0287)

530 FR ISSN 0182-4295
CODEN: AFLBDU
FONDATION LOUIS DE BROGLIE. ANNALES. (Text and summaries in English, French) 1975. q. 400 F. to individuals (foreign 500 F.); institutions 500 F. (foreign 600 F.). Fondation Louis de Broglie, 23 Quai de Conti, 75006 Paris, France. TEL 40-46-05-54. FAX 40-51-08-65. Eds. Daniel Fargue, Michel Karatchentzeff. adv. contact: Michel Cazin. bk.rev. circ. 600. (back issues avail.) Indexed: INIS Atomind., INSPEC (1981-). Document type: academic/scholarly publication.
—Ei; UnCover.
Description: Journal of theoretical physics, primarily intended for the publication of lectures given at the foundation's seminars. Also presents articles on wave mechanics, the foundation of microphysics, wave and quantum mechanics.

530 GW ISSN 0015-8208
QC1 CODEN: FPYKA6
FORTSCHRITTE DER PHYSIK/PROGRESS OF PHYSICS. (Text in English) 1953. 8/yr. DM.215 to individuals; institutions DM.880 (effective 1996). Akademie Verlag GmbH, Muehlenstr. 33-34, 13187 Berlin, Germany. TEL 030-47889348. FAX 030-47889357. (U.S. subscr. to: VCH Publishers Inc., 303 N.W. 12th Ave., Deerfield Beach, FL 33442-1788) Ed. F. Kaschluhn. adv.; charts; illus.; index. (also avail. in microfilm from BHP) Indexed: Chem.Abstr., Curr.Cont., Ind.Sci.Rev., INIS Atomind., INSPEC, Math.R., Met.Abstr., Phys.Ber., Sci.Cit.Ind. Document type: academic/scholarly publication.
—BLDSC (6873.458200); CASDDS; Faxon; Genuine Article; SWETS; UnCover. **CCC.**

530 US ISSN 0015-9018
QC1 CODEN: FNDPA4
FOUNDATIONS OF PHYSICS; an international journal devoted to the conceptual and fundamental theories of modern physics, biophysics, and cosmology. 1970. m. $915 (foreign $1070) (effective 1996). Plenum Publishing Corp., 233 Spring St., New York, NY 10013-1578. TEL 212-620-8000. FAX 212-463-0742. TELEX 23-421139. Ed. Alwyn van der Merwe. adv. (also avail. in microfilm from JSC) Indexed: Cadscan, Curr.Cont., Ind.Sci.Rev., INIS Atomind., INSPEC, Lead Abstr., Math.R., Phys.Ber., Ref.Zh., Sci.Cit.Ind., Zincscan. Document type: academic/scholarly publication.
—BLDSC (4025.400000); Ei; Faxon; Genuine Article; SWETS; UMI; UnCover. **CCC.**
Refereed Serial

530 US ISSN 0894-9875
QC1 CODEN: FPLEET
FOUNDATIONS OF PHYSICS LETTERS. 1988. bi-m. $345 (foreign $405) (effective 1996). Plenum Publishing Corp., 233 Spring St., New York, NY 10013-1578. TEL 212-620-8000. FAX 212-463-0742. TELEX 23-421139. Ed. Alwyn van der Merwe. adv. (also avail. in microfilm from JSC; back issues avail.) Indexed: INSPEC (1988-). Document type: academic/scholarly publication.
—BLDSC (4025.405000); Ei; Faxon; Genuine Article; SWETS; UMI; UnCover. **CCC.**
Refereed Serial

530 NO ISSN 0015-9247
CODEN: FYVDAX
FRA FYSIKKENS VERDEN. 1939. q. NOK 100 (effective 1995). Universitetet i Oslo - Fysisk Institutt, P.O. Box 1048 Blindern, N-0316 Oslo, Norway. TEL 47-22-85-64-28. FAX 47-22-85-64-22. E-mail: finn.ingebretsen @fys.uio.no. Eds. Oeivin Holter, F. Ingebretsen. adv. contact: Kari Maaseide. bk.rev.; charts; illus.; index. circ. 1,600. Indexed: Chem.Abstr., INIS Atomind., INSPEC. Document type: academic/scholarly publication.
—BLDSC (4029.950000); CASDDS. **CCC.**
Refereed Serial

530 510 UK ISSN 0016-0032
T1 CODEN: JFINAB
FRANKLIN INSTITUTE. JOURNAL. Key Title: Journal of the Franklin Institute. 1826. bi-m. £505($803) (effective 1996). Elsevier Science Ltd., Pergamon, P.O. Box 800, Kidlington, Oxford OX5 1DX, England. TEL 44-1865-843000. FAX 44-1865-843010. E-mail: nlinfo-f@elsevier.nl; usinfo-f@elsevier.com; forinfo-kyf04035@niftyserve.or.jp; Site addr.: http://www.elsevier.nl/. (Subscr. in U.S. and Canada to: Elsevier Science, 660 White Plains Rd., Tarrytown, NY 10591-5153. TEL 914-524-9200. FAX 914-333-2444) Ed. Martin A. Pomerantz. adv.; bk.rev.; charts; illus.; stat.; s-a. index, cum.index every 10 yrs.; vols.1-280 (1826-1965) in 8 vols. circ. 1,500. (also avail. in microfiche from MIM; microfilm from UMI; microform from PMC; back issues avail.) Indexed: A.S.& T.Ind., Appl.Mech.Rev., Biol.Abstr., Chem.Eng.Abstr., Comput.Abstr., Curr.Cont., Cyb.Abstr., Deep Sea Res.& Oceanogr.Abstr., Eng.Ind., GeoRef., INSPEC, Int.Aerosp.Abstr., Math R., Met.Abstr., Petrol.Abstr., Photo.Abstr., Plant Breed.Abstr., Psychol.Abstr., Sh.& Vib.Dig., T.C.E.A., World Surf.Coat. Document type: academic/scholarly publication.
—BLDSC (4755.000000); CASDDS; Ei; Faxon; Genuine Article; SWETS; UMI; UnCover. **CCC.**
Description: Multidisciplinary journal publishing papers on all aspects of pure and applied mathematics and physical sciences.
Refereed Serial

530 US ISSN 0429-7725
CODEN: FRPHAY
FRONTIERS IN PHYSICS. 1961. irreg., no.79, 1989. price varies. Benjamin-Cummings Publishing Co., Inc. (Subsidiary of: Addison-Wesley Publishing Co.), 1 Jacob Way, Reading, MA 01867. TELEX 94-9416. Ed. Richard W. Mixter. Indexed: INSPEC, Math.R.

530 NE ISSN 0168-1222
FUNDAMENTAL THEORIES OF PHYSICS; an international series of monographs on the fundamental theories of physics: their clarification, development and application. 1982. irreg., vol.56, 1993. price varies. Kluwer Academic Publishers, Postbus 17, 3300 AH Dordrecht, Netherlands. TEL 31-78-392392. FAX 31-78-392254. TELEX 29245 KAPG NL. (Dist. by: Kluwer Academic Publishers Group, P.O. Box 322, 3300 AH Dordrecht, Netherlands. TEL 31-78-392392. FAX 31-78-546474; N. America dist. addr.: Box 358, Accord Sta., Hingham, MA 02018-0358. TEL 617-871-6600. FAX 617-871-6528) Ed. Alwyn van der Merwe. Indexed: INSPEC. Document type: monographic series.
—BLDSC (4056.086000).
Refereed Serial

FUNDAMENTALS OF COSMIC PHYSICS. see *ASTRONOMY*

530 DK ISSN 0109-6664
FYSIKTIPS. 1976. irreg. DKK 31.70. Danmarks Fysik og Kemilaererforening, Dyrlaege Jurgensens Gade 11, 3740 Svaneke, Denmark. TEL 01-603540. illus.
Formerly: Gode Gamle Fysiktips.

530 FR ISSN 0761-3369
G A P H Y O R. BASE DE DONNEES. (Gaz - Physique - Orsay) (Printed format ceased Jan. 1995) 1978. q. Centre National de la Recherche Scientifique, Institut de l'Information Scientifique et Technique, 2 allee du Parc de Brabois, 54514 Vandoeuvre-Les-Nancy Cedex, France. TEL 83-50-46-00. FAX 83-50-46-50. (Co-sponsor: Laboratoire de Physique des Gaz et des Plasmas) Ed. J.L. Delcroix. adv. contact: Veronique Guinvarc'h. (also avail. in microfiche) Document type: bibliography.
●Also available online. Vendor(s): European Space Agency (File no.14), Knight-Ridder, Inc. (File no.144), Telesystemes - Questel.
Also available on CD-ROM.
Former titles: Bulletin Signaletique. Part 166: G A P H Y O R. Base de Donnees; Bulletin Signaletique. Part 166: G A P H Y O R. Atomes, Molecules, Gaz Neutres et Ionises (ISSN 0399-1571)

530 US ISSN 1047-4811
CODEN: GAELEN
GALILEAN ELECTRODYNAMICS. 1990. bi-m. $35 to individuals; corporations $70; organizations $140. Howard C. Hayden, Ed. & Pub., Box 545, Storrs, CT 06268-0545. TEL 203-486-0436. FAX 203-429-7775. bk.rev. circ. 570. Indexed: INSPEC (1990-). Document type: academic/scholarly publication.
—BLDSC (4067.445000).
Description: Publishes scientific papers based on experimental evidence.

GAUSS - GESELLSCHAFT. MITTEILUNGEN. see *ASTRONOMY*

530 US ISSN 0001-7701
QC173.6 CODEN: GRGVA8
GENERAL RELATIVITY AND GRAVITATION. 1970. m. $725 (foreign $850) (effective 1996). (International Committee on General Relativity and Gravitation) Plenum Publishing Corp., 233 Spring St., New York, NY 10013-1578. TEL 212-620-8000. FAX 212-463-0742. TELEX 23-421139. Ed. A. Held. adv.; bk.rev.; charts. (also avail. in microfilm from JSC; back issues avail.) Indexed: Curr.Cont., Ind.Sci.Rev., INSPEC, Int.Aerosp.Abstr., Math.R., Phys.Ber., Ref.Zh., Sci.Cit.Ind., Zent.Math. Document type: academic/scholarly publication.
—BLDSC (4109.650000); Ei; Faxon; Genuine Article; SWETS; UMI; UnCover. **CCC.**
Refereed Serial

530 IT ISSN 0017-0283
CODEN: GFSIAD
GIORNALE DI FISICA. 1956. q. $50 to non-members; members $45 (effective 1931). (Societa Italiana di Fisica) Editrice Compositori s.r.l., Via Stalingrado 97-2, 40128 Bologna, Italy. TEL 51-327811. Ed. Carlo Castagnoli. circ. 1,500. (tabloid format) Indexed: Chem.Abstr., INSPEC (1983-).
—CASDDS; UMI.

GRADUATE PROGRAMS: PHYSICS, ASTRONOMY, AND RELATED FIELDS (YEAR). see *EDUCATION* — *Higher Education*

PHYSICS

530 US ISSN 0938-037X
GRADUATE TEXTS IN CONTEMPORARY PHYSICS. 1986. irreg. price varies. Springer-Verlag, 175 Fifth Ave., New York, NY 10010. TEL 212-460-1500. FAX 212-473-6272. (Also: Berlin, Heidelberg, Tokyo and Vienna) (reprint service avail. from ISI) **Document type:** monographic series.

HACETTEPE FEN VE MUHENDISLIK BILIMLERI DERGISI. SERI C: KIMYA, FIZIK VE MUHENDISLIK/HACETTEPE BULLETIN OF NATURAL SCIENCES AND ENGINEERING. SERIES C: CHEMISTRY, PHYSICS AND ENGINEERING. see *SCIENCES: COMPREHENSIVE WORKS*

530 US ISSN 0162-5519
QC793.5.H322 CODEN: HAJODX
HADRONIC JOURNAL. (Supplement avail. (ISSN 0882-5394)) 1978. bi-m. $250. Hadronic Press, Inc., 35246 U.S. N 131, Palm Harbor, FL 34683. Ed. R.M. Santilli. adv. circ. 1,000. **Indexed:** Chem.Abstr., Curr.Cont., Ind.Sci.Rev., INIS Atomind., INSPEC (1978-), Math.R., Phys.Ber., Sci.Cit.Ind. **Document type:** academic/scholarly publication.
—BLDSC (4237.700000); CASDDS; Faxon; SWETS; UnCover.

530 US ISSN 0882-5394
QC793.5.H32 CODEN: HJSUEO
HADRONIC JOURNAL. SUPPLEMENT. 1985. 4/yr. $150. Hadronic Press, Inc., 35246 U.S N 131, Palm Harbor, FL 34683. Ed. R.M. Santilli. adv. circ. 1,000. **Indexed:** Chem.Abstr., Curr.Cont., INIS Atomind., INSPEC (1985-), Math.R., Phys.Ber., Sci.Cit.Ind. **Document type:** academic/scholarly publication.
—BLDSC (4237.701000); CASDDS.

530 JA
HAKUMAKU HYOMEN BUTSURI SEMINA/JAPAN SOCIETY OF APPLIED PHYSICS. THIN FILM AND SURFACE PHYSICS SEMINAR. (Text in English, Japanese; summaries in English) 1970. a. 4000 Yen. Japan Society of Applied Physics - Oyo Butsuri Gakkai, 12-3, Kudan Kita 1-chome, Chiyoda-ku, Tokyo 102, Japan.

530.44 NE ISSN 0169-2852
HANDBOOK OF PLASMA PHYSICS. 1983. irreg., vol.3, 1991. Elsevier Science B.V., Books Division, P.O. Box 211, 1000 AE Amsterdam, Netherlands. TEL 31-20-4853911. FAX 31-20-4853705. TELEX 18582 ESPA NL. E-mail: nlinfo-f@elsevier.nl; usinfo-f@elsevier.com; forinfo-kyf04035@niftyserve.or.jp; Site addr.: http://www.elsevier.nl/. (Subscr. in U.S. and Canada to: Elsevier Science Inc., Box 882, Madison Sq. Sta., New York, NY 10159. TEL 212-989-5800) Eds. M.N. Rosenbluth, R.Z Sagdeer. **Indexed:** INSPEC. **Document type:** monographic series.
Refereed Serial

HANDBOOK ON FERROMAGNETIC MATERIALS. see *METALLURGY*

HANDBOOK ON SYNCHROTRON RADIATION. see *INSTRUMENTS*

530.1 669 NE ISSN 0168-1273
HANDBOOK ON THE PHYSICS AND CHEMISTRY OF RARE EARTHS. 1978. irreg., vol.17, 1993. price varies. Elsevier Science B.V., Books Division, P.O. Box 211, 1000 AE Amsterdam, Netherlands. TEL 31-20-4853911. FAX 31-20-4853705. TELEX 18582 ESPA NL. E-mail: nlinfo-f@elsevier.nl; usinfo-f@elsevier.com; forinfo-kyf04035@niftyserve.or.jp; Site addr.: http://www.elsevier.nl/. (Subscr. in U.S. and Canada to: Elsevier Science Inc., Box 882, Madison Sq. Sta., New York, NY 10159. TEL 212-989-5800) Eds. K.A. Gschneidner, L. Eyring. cum.index: vols.1-15 in 1993. (back issues avail.) **Indexed:** INSPEC. **Document type:** monographic series.
—BLDSC (4250.962700).
Description: Publishes original reviews of technological advances and research relating to the lanthanide series of rare earth metals, related alloys and compounds, and applications of these elements in all industries.
Refereed Serial

530 540 NE
HANDBOOK ON THE PHYSICS AND CHEMISTRY OF THE ACTINIDES. 1984. irreg., vol.6, 1991. price varies. Elsevier Science B.V., Books Division, P.O. Box 211, 1000 AE Amsterdam, Netherlands. TEL 31-20-4853911. FAX 31-20-4853705. TELEX 18582 ESPA NL. E-mail: nlinfo-f@elsevier.nl; usinfo-f@elsevier.com; forinfo-kyf04035@niftyserve.or.jp; Site addr.: http://www.elsevier.nl/. (Subscr. in U.S. and Canada to: Elsevier Science Inc., Box 882, Madison Sq. Sta., New York, NY 10159. TEL 212-989-5800) **Document type:** monographic series.
Refereed Serial

530 SZ ISSN 0018-0238
QC1 CODEN: HPACAK
HELVETICA PHYSICA ACTA. Short title: H P A. (Text in English, French, German and Italian) 1928. 8/yr. 730.90 SFr. (foreign 747 SFr.). (Schweizerischen Physikalischen Gesellschaft - Swiss Society of Physics) Birkhaeuser Verlag, P.O. Box 133, CH-4010 Basel, Switzerland. TEL 061-2717400. FAX 061-2717666. (Dist. in N. America by: Springer-Verlag, Mercedes Distribution Center, 160 Imlay St., Brooklyn, NY 11231, USA) Ed. O. Piguet. adv.; bk.rev.; charts; illus.; pat.; index. (also avail. in microfilm from UMI,PMC) **Indexed:** Chem.Abstr., Curr.Cont., Ind.Sci.Rev., INIS Atomind., INSPEC, Mass Spectr.Bull., Math.R., Met.Abstr., Phys.Ber., Sci.Cit.Ind. **Document type:** academic/scholarly publication.
—BLDSC (4288.000000); CASDDS; Ei; Faxon; Genuine Article; SWETS; UMI; UnCover. **CCC.**

537 540 669 US ISSN 1048-1141
HIGH - TC UPDATE. 1987. s-m. free. Iowa State University, Ames Laboratory, A219 Physics, Ames, IA 50011-3020. TEL 515-294-3877. FAX 515-294-1134. (Co-sponsor: U.S. Department of Energy, Office of Basic Energy Sciences) Ed. Dr. Sreeparna Mitra. bk.rev. circ. 2,700. (back issues avail.) **Document type:** newsletter.
●Also available online.
Description: Covers high-temperature superconductors. Provides analysis section, list of preprints, coming events, information resources and services.

530 GW ISSN 0073-2850
HOCHSCHULBUECHER FUER PHYSIK. 1953. irreg. price varies. VEB Deutscher Verlag der Wissenschaften, Postfach 1216, 1080 Berlin, Germany. Eds. Robert Rompe, Ernst Schmutzer.

HOKKAIDO KYOIKU DAIGAKU KIYO. DAI-2-BU, A. SUGAKU, BUTSURI, KAGAKU, KOGAKU-HEN/HOKKAIDO UNIVERSITY OF EDUCATION. JOURNAL. SECTION 2 A. MATHEMATICS, PHYSICS, CHEMISTRY, ENGINEERING. see *MATHEMATICS*

HOSHASEN KAGAKU TORONKAI KOEN YOSHISHU/PROCEEDINGS OF SYMPOSIUM ON RADIATION CHEMISTRY. see *CHEMISTRY — Physical Chemistry*

530 NE ISSN 0924-8099
LES HOUCHES SUMMER SCHOOL PROCEEDINGS. Key Title: Houches (Amsterdam). (Text in English and French) 1951. irreg, vol.47, 1993. price varies. (Ecole d'Ete de Physique Theorique, Les Houches) Elsevier Science B.V., Books Division, P.O. Box 211, 1000 AE Amsterdam, Netherlands. TEL 31-20-4853911. FAX 31-20-4853705. TELEX 18582 ESPA NL. E-mail: nlinfo-f@elsevier.nl; usinfo-f@elsevier.com; forinfo-kyf04035@niftyserve.or.jp; Site addr.: http://www.elsevier.nl/. (Subscr. in U.S. and Canada to: Elsevier Science Inc., Box 882, Madison Sq. Sta., New York, NY 10159. TEL 212-989-5800) **Indexed:** INSPEC. **Document type:** monographic series, proceedings.
—BLDSC (5183.565000).
Formerly: Ecole d'Ete de Physique Theorique. Les Houches.
Refereed Serial

530 540 CC
HUAXUE WULI XUEBAO/JOURNAL OF CHEMICAL PHYSICS.* (Text in Chinese) bi-m. Zhongguo Kexue Jishu Daxue - Chinese University of Science and Technology, c/o Lou Nanquan, Ed., 96 Jinzhai Lu, Hefei, Anhui 230026, People's Republic of China. TEL 331134. Ed. Lou Nanquan. **Document type:** academic/scholarly publication.

530 HU ISSN 0133-5502
HUNGARIAN ACADEMY OF SCIENCES. CENTRAL RESEARCH INSTITUTE FOR PHYSICS. YEARBOOK/MAGYAR TUDOMANYOS AKADEMIA. KOZPONTI FIZIKAI KUTATO INTEZET. EVKONYV. (Text in English) 1971. s-a. avail. on exchange basis only. Magyar Tudomanyos Akademia, Kozponti Fizikai Kutato Intezet, P.O. Box 76, 1325 Budapest, Hungary. Ed. T. Dolinszky. circ. 1,400. **Indexed:** Chem.Abstr.

530 JA ISSN 0388-5321
CODEN: HYKAET
HYOMEN KAGAKU/SURFACE SCIENCE SOCIETY OF JAPAN. JOURNAL. (Text in Japanese; summaries in English) 1980. m. 3500 Yen per no. Nihon Hyomen Kagakukai - Surface Science Society of Japan, 40-13-402, Hongo 2-chome, Bunkyo-ku, Tokyo 113, Japan. Ed. Y. Iwasawa. **Document type:** academic/scholarly publication.
—BLDSC (4904.473000); CASDDS.

530 540 JA
HYOMEN KAGAKU KISO KOZA/TEXTBOOK OF LECTURES ON SURFACE SCIENCE. (Text in Japanese) a. Nihon Hyomen Kagakukai - Surface Science Society of Japan, 40-13-402, Hongo 2-chome, Bunkyo-ku, Tokyo 113, Japan. **Document type:** academic/scholarly publication.

530 540 JA
HYOMEN KAGAKU KOEN TAIKAI KOEN YOSHISHU/SURFACE SCIENCE SOCIETY OF JAPAN. ABSTRACTS OF MEETINGS. (Text in Japanese) 1982. a. Nihon Hyomen Kagakukai - Surface Science Society of Japan, 40-13-402, Hongo 2-chome, Bunkyo-ku, Tokyo 113, Japan. **Document type:** academic/scholarly publication.

530 540 JA
HYOMEN KAGAKU SEMINA/TEXTBOOK OF SEMINAR ON SURFACE SCIENCE. (Text in Japanese) a. Nihon Hyomen Kagakukai - Surface Science Society of Japan, 40-13-402, Hongo 2-chome, Bunkyo-ku, Tokyo 113, Japan. **Document type:** academic/scholarly publication.

530 NE ISSN 0304-3843
QC762 CODEN: HYINDN
HYPERFINE INTERACTIONS. 1975. 28/yr. (in 7 vols., 4 nos./vol.). 2387 SFr. (effective 1996). Baltzer Science Publishers B.V., Asterweg 1A, 1031 HL Amsterdam, Netherlands. TEL 31-20-6370061. FAX 31-20-6323651. E-mail: publish@baltzer.nl. (Subscr. in N. America to: Baltzer Science Publishers, Box 8577, Red Bank, NJ 07701-8577) Eds. H. de Waard, G. Langouche. adv. **Indexed:** Cadscan, Chem.Abstr., Curr.Cont., Ind.Sci.Rev., INIS Atomind., INSPEC (1983-), Lead Abstr., Phys.Ber., Sci.Cit.Ind., Zincscan. **Document type:** academic/scholarly publication.
—BLDSC (4352.625000); CASDDS; Ei; Faxon; Genuine Article; SWETS. **CCC.**
Incorporates (1987-1992): Muon Catalyzed Fusion (ISSN 0259-9805)

530 SI ISSN 0218-0243
I C T P SERIES IN THEORETICAL PHYSICS. (Text in English) 1984. irreg., vol. 8, 1992. price varies. (International Atomic Energy Agency, International Centre for Theoretical Physics) World Scientific Publishing Co. Pte. Ltd., Farrer Rd., P.O. Box 128, Singapore 9128, Singapore. TEL 3825663. FAX 3825919. TELEX RS 28561 WSPC. (UK addr.: 73 Lynton Mead, Totteridge, London N20 8DH, England. TEL 44-81-4462461; US addr.: 1060 Main St., Ste. 1B, River Edge, NJ 07661. TEL 800-227-7562) **Document type:** monographic series.
—BLDSC (4362.200300).

I E E E MICROWAVE AND GUIDED WAVE LETTERS. see *ENGINEERING — Electrical Engineering*

I E E E PARTICLE ACCELERATOR CONFERENCE. PROCEEDINGS. see *ENGINEERING — Electrical Engineering*

I E E E TRANSACTIONS ON APPLIED SUPERCONDUCTIVITY. see *ELECTRONICS*

530.44	US	ISSN 0093-3813
TA2001		CODEN: ITPSBD

I E E E TRANSACTIONS ON PLASMA SCIENCE. 1973. bi-m. $265 to non-members (effective 1996). (I E E E, Nuclear and Plasma Sciences Society) Institute of Electrical and Electronics Engineers, Inc., 345 E. 47th St., New York, NY 10017-2394. TEL 908-981-0060. FAX 908-981-9667. (Subscr. to: Box 1331, 445 Hoes Lane, Piscataway, NJ 08855-1331) Ed. Steven J. Gitomer. bk.rev.; index. (also avail. in microform) **Indexed:** Chem.Abstr., Curr.Cont., Eng.Ind., Ind.Sci.Rev., INIS Atomind., INSPEC, Int.Aerosp.Abstr., Math.R., Phys.Ber., Sci.Cit.Ind.
—BLDSC (4363.212000); CASDDS; Ei; Faxon; Genuine Article; SWETS; UMI; UnCover. **CCC.**

I F S NEWSLETTER. (Institute for Fusion Studies) see *ENERGY — Nuclear Energy*

530	II	ISSN 0019-5480
Q1		CODEN: IJPYAS

INDIAN JOURNAL OF PHYSICS AND PROCEEDINGS OF THE INDIAN ASSOCIATION FOR THE CULTIVATION OF SCIENCE. (Issued in two parts: Part A: Condensed Matter, Nuclear Physics, Particle Physics; Part B: Atmospheric and Space Physics, Atomic and Molecular Physics, General Physics, Optics and Spectroscopy, Plasma Physics, Relativity and Cosmology.) (Text in English) 1926. m. Rs.800($350) to non-members; members Rs. 50. Indian Association for the Cultivation of Science, 2A & 2B Raja Subodh Chandra Mallick Road, Jadavpur, Calcutta 700 032, India. TEL 91-33-473-4971. FAX 91-33-473-2805. TELEX 021-5501 IACS IN. Ed.Bd. adv.; bk.rev.; bibl.; charts; illus.; index. circ. 800. (also avail. in microform from PMC; back issues avail.) **Indexed:** Biol.Abstr., Cadscan, Ceram.Abstr., Chem.Abstr., INIS Atomind., INSPEC, Int.Aerosp.Abstr., Lead Abstr., Math.R., Met.Abstr., Sci.Cit.Ind., World Alum.Abstr., Zincscan. **Document type:** academic/scholarly publication.
—BLDSC (4419.910000); Ei; Faxon; SWETS; UnCover.

Description: Review articles and papers on research, as well as proceedings of national and international symposia, including annual endowment lectures.

530	II	ISSN 0019-5596
QC1		CODEN: IJOPAU

INDIAN JOURNAL OF PURE & APPLIED PHYSICS. (Text in English) 1963. m. Rs.400($200) (Council of Scientific and Industrial Research, Publications & Information Directorate) Scientific Publishers, P.O. Box 91, 5A, New Pali Rd., Jodhpur 342 001, India. TEL 0291-33323. (Co-sponsor: Indian National Science Academy) Ed. K.S. Rangarajan. bibl.; charts; illus.; index. circ. 1,200. (back issues avail.) **Indexed:** Anal.Abstr., Appl.Mech.Rev., Biol.Abstr., Cadscan, Ceram.Abstr., Chem.Abstr., Curr.Cont., Ind.Sci.Rev., INIS Atomind., INSPEC, Lead Abstr., Mass Spectr.Bull., Math.R., Met.Abstr., Phys.Ber., Sci.Cit.Ind., World Alum.Abstr., World Text.Abstr., Zincscan. **Document type:** academic/scholarly publication.
—BLDSC (4420.700000); CASDDS; Faxon; Genuine Article; SWETS; UnCover.

530	II	ISSN 0019-5693
QC1		CODEN: IJTPAL

INDIAN JOURNAL OF THEORETICAL PHYSICS. (Text in Bengali and English) 1953. q. Rs.1000($50) (effective 1995). Institute of Theoretical Physics, Bignan Kutir, 4-1 Mohan Bagan Lane, Calcutta 700004, India. Ed.Bd. bk.rev. (back issues avail.) **Indexed:** Appl.Mech.Rev., Chem.Abstr., INIS Atomind., INSPEC, Math.R., Phys.Ber. **Document type:** academic/scholarly publication.
—BLDSC (4421.500000); CASDDS.

553.5	II	ISSN 0970-2334
		CODEN: BIVSES

INDIAN VACUUM SOCIETY. BULLETIN. (Text in English) 1970. q. Rs.100 to individuals; libraries Rs.250; foreign $100. Indian Vacuum Society, c/o Technical Physics & Prototype Engineering Division, Bhabha Atomic Research Centre, Bombay 400 085, India. TEL 022-5573060. Ed. R. Vijayaraghvan. adv.; bk.rev.; circ. 700 (controlled). (back issues avail.) **Indexed:** INIS Atomind., INSPEC (1986-1992). **Document type:** bulletin.
—BLDSC (2564.140000).
Formerly: V A C News (ISSN 0254-7848)

INSTITUT HENRI POINCARE. ANNALES: ANALYSE NON LINEAIRE. see *MATHEMATICS*

530	FR	ISSN 0246-0211
QC19.2		CODEN: AIPTEO

INSTITUT HENRI POINCARE. ANNALES: PHYSIQUE THEORIQUE. (Text in English, French) 1930. 8/yr. 2000 F. Gauthier-Villars, 15 rue Gossin, 92543 Montrouge Cedex, France. TEL 33-1-40-92-65-00. FAX 33-1-40-92-65-97. TELEX 634 916 F. (Subscr. to: Centrale des Revues, 11 rue Gossin, 92543 Montrouge Cedex, France. TEL 33-1-46-56-52-66) Ed. P. Collet. adv. circ. 800. (also avail. in microfilm from UMI; reprint service avail. from KTO) **Indexed:** Chem.Abstr., Curr.Cont., INIS Atomind., INSPEC (1968-), Math.R., Sci.Cit.Ind., Zent.Math. **Document type:** academic/scholarly publication.
—CASDDS; Genuine Article; SWETS; UnCover. **CCC.**
Formerly (until 1983): Institut Henri Poincare. Annales. Section A: Physique Theorique (ISSN 0020-2339); Which supersedes in part: Institut Henri Poincare. Annales (ISSN 0365-320X)

Description: Covers all aspects of theoretical and mathematical physics and those areas of pure and applied mathematics that have relevance to physics.

INSTITUT ROYAL METEOROLOGIQUE DE BELGIQUE. BULLETIN MENSUEL: OBSERVATIONS IONOSPHERIQUES ET DU RAYONNEMENT COSMIQUE/KONINKLIJK METEOROLOGISCH INSTITUUT VAN BELGIE. MAANDBULLETIN: WAARNEMINGEN DE DE IONOSFEER EN DE KOSMISCHE STRALING. see *METEOROLOGY*

INSTITUTE OF MATHEMATICAL SCIENCES, MADRAS. REPORTS. see *MATHEMATICS*

530 540	JA	ISSN 0020-3092
QC1		CODEN: SPIPAG

INSTITUTE OF PHYSICAL AND CHEMICAL RESEARCH. SCIENTIFIC PAPERS. (Text and summaries in English) 1922. irreg. Rikagaku Kenkyujo - Institute of Physical and Chemical Research, 2-1 Hirosawa, Wako-shi, Saitama-ken 351-01, Japan. TEL 0484-621111. FAX 0484-621554. Ed. Minoru Oda. abstr.; charts; illus.; index. circ. 1,000. **Indexed:** Appl.Mech.Rev., Chem.Abstr., Deep Sea Res.& Oceanogr.Abstr., Eng.Ind., INIS Atomind., INSPEC (1968-), JCT, JTA, Met.Abstr., Nucl.Sci.Abstr., World Alum.Abstr.
—CASDDS; UnCover.
Formerly: Journal of the Scientific Research Institute.

530		RM

INSTITUTUL DE SUBINGINERI ORADEA. LUCRARI STIINTIFICE: SERIA FIZICA. (Text in Rumanian, occasionally in English or French; summaries in Rumanian, French or German) 1967. a. Institutul de Subingineri Oradea, Calea Armatei Rosii Nr. 5, 3700 Oradea, Rumania.
Formerly: Institutul Pedagogic Oradea. Lucrari Stiintifice: Seria Fizica; which continues in part (in 1973): Institutul Pedagogic Oradea. Lucrari Stiintifice: Seria Matematica, Fizica, Chimie; which superseded (in 1971): Institutul Pedagogic Oradea. Lucrari Stiintifice: Seria A and Seria B; which was formerly (until 1969): Institutul Pedagogic Oradea. Lucrari Stiintifice.

INSTITUTUL POLITEHNIC DIN IASI. BULETINUL. SECTIA I: MATEMATICA, MECANICA, FIZICA. see *MATHEMATICS*

INTERFACE SCIENCE. see *CHEMISTRY — Physical Chemistry*

530	UN	ISSN 0304-7091
QC1.I6285		

INTERNATIONAL CENTRE FOR THEORETICAL PHYSICS. ANNUAL REPORT. 1964. a. free. International Atomic Energy Agency, International Centre for Theoretical Physics, Strada Costiera 11, P.O. Box 586, 34100 Trieste, Italy. TEL 40-22-40111. FAX 40-22-4163. TELEX 460302 ICTP I. E-mail: sci-info@ictp.trieste.it. circ. 450.
Formerly (until 1965): International Centre for Theoretical Physics. Report (ISSN 0538-5415)

INTERNATIONAL JOURNAL OF HEAT AND MASS TRANSFER. see *ENGINEERING — Mechanical Engineering*

INTERNATIONAL JOURNAL OF HYDROGEN ENERGY. see *ENERGY*

530	US	ISSN 0899-9457
TK8315		CODEN: IJITEG

INTERNATIONAL JOURNAL OF IMAGING SYSTEMS AND TECHNOLOGY. 1989. q. $260 to institutions (foreign $322) (effective 1996). John Wiley & Sons, Inc., Journals, 605 Third Ave., New York, NY 10158-0012. TEL 212-850-6000. FAX 212-850-6021. TELEX 12-7063. E-mail: SUBINFO@JWILEY.COM. (Subscr. outside the Americas to: John Wiley & Sons Ltd., Baffins Ln., Chichester, W. Sussex PO19 1UD, England. TEL 44-1243-779777. FAX 44-1243-776128) Ed.Bd. (also avail. in microform from UMI; back issues avail.) **Indexed:** Geo.Abstr., INSPEC (1989-). **Document type:** academic/scholarly publication.
—BLDSC (4542.299000); Ei; Faxon; SWETS; UMI. **CCC.**

Description: Covers current information pertinent to engineers and specialists working with imaging technology.
Refereed Serial

INTERNATIONAL JOURNAL OF MATHEMATICS AND MATHEMATICAL SCIENCES. see *MATHEMATICS*

530	SI	ISSN 0217-751X
QC793		CODEN: IMPAEF

INTERNATIONAL JOURNAL OF MODERN PHYSICS A. 1986. 32/yr. $855 to individuals & institutions of developing countries; institutions of developed countries $ 1710. World Scientific Publishing Co. Pte. Ltd., Farrer Rd., P.O. Box 128, Singapore 9128, Singapore. TEL 3825663. FAX 3825919. TELEX RS-28561-WSPC. (UK addr.: 73 Lynton Mead, Totteridge, London N20 8DH, England. TEL 44-81-4462461; US addr.: 1060 Main St., Ste. 1B, River Edge, NJ 07661. TEL 800-227-7562) circ. 500. (back issues avail.) **Indexed:** Curr.Cont., INIS Atomind., INSPEC (1987-). **Document type:** academic/scholarly publication.
—BLDSC (4542.365200); CASDDS; Ei; Faxon; Genuine Article; SWETS; UnCover. **CCC.**

Description: Covers particle and field physics, nuclear physics, gravitation and cosmology.

530	SI	ISSN 0217-9792
QC173.4.C65		CODEN: IJPBEV

INTERNATIONAL JOURNAL OF MODERN PHYSICS B. (Text in English) 1987. 28/yr. $580 to individuals & institutions of developing countries; institutions of developed countries $1200. World Scientific Publishing Co. Pte. Ltd., Farrer Rd., P.O. Box 128, Singapore 9128, Singapore. TEL 3825663. FAX 3825919. TELEX RS-28561-WSPC. (European addr.: 73 Lynton Mead, Totteridge, London N20 8DH, England. TEL 44-81-4462461; US addr.: 1060 Main St., Ste. 1B, River Edge, NJ 07661. TEL 800-227-7562) circ. 300. (back issues avail.) **Indexed:** INSPEC (1987-). **Document type:** academic/scholarly publication.
—BLDSC (4542.365210); CASDDS; Ei; Faxon; Genuine Article; SWETS. **CCC.**

Description: Review and research articles on condensed matter, statistical and applied physics at graduate and post-graduate levels.

530 500	SI	ISSN 0129-1831
QC52		CODEN: IJMPEO

INTERNATIONAL JOURNAL OF MODERN PHYSICS C: PHYSICS AND COMPUTERS. 1990. bi-m. $160 to individuals & institutions of developing countries; institutions of developed countries $350. World Scientific Publishing Co. Pte. Ltd., Farrer Rd., P.O. Box 128, Singapore 9128, Singapore. TEL 3825663. FAX 3825919. TELEX RS-28561-WSPC. (European addr.: 73 Lynton Mead, Totteridge, London N20 8DH, England. TEL 44-81-4462461; US addr.: 1060 Main St., Ste. 1B, River Edge, NJ 07661. TEL 800-227-7562) Ed.Bd. **Indexed:** INSPEC (1990-). **Document type:** academic/scholarly publication.
—BLDSC (4542.365220); Ei; Genuine Article; SWETS. **CCC.**

Description: Publishes both review and research articles on the use of computers to advance knowledge in the physical sciences and the use of physical analogies in computation.

PHYSICS

530   SI   ISSN 0218-2718
QB460   CODEN: IMPDEO
INTERNATIONAL JOURNAL OF MODERN PHYSICS D: GRAVITATION, ASTROPHYSICS AND COSMOLOGY. 1992. q. $195 to developed countries; developing countries $100. World Scientific Publishing Co. Pte. Ltd., Farrer Rd., P.O. Box 128, Singapore 9128, Singapore. TEL 3825663. FAX 3825919. TELEX RS-28561-WSPC. (U.K. addr.: 73 Lynton Mead, Totteridge, London N20 8DH, England. TEL 44-181-4462461; U.S. addr.: 1060 Main St., Ste. 1B, River Edge, NJ 07661. TEL 800-277-7562) Ed. Fang Li Zhi. **Indexed:** INSPEC (1992-). **Document type:** academic/scholarly publication.
—BLDSC (4542.365230); Genuine Article; SWETS.
   Description: Features research and review articles on theoretical, observational, and experimental findings in the fields of gravitation, astrophysics and cosmology.

INTERNATIONAL JOURNAL OF MULTIPHASE FLOW. see ENGINEERING — Mechanical Engineering

INTERNATIONAL JOURNAL OF RADIATION BIOLOGY. see MEDICAL SCIENCES — Oncology

530   US   ISSN 0020-7748
QC1   CODEN: IJTPBM
INTERNATIONAL JOURNAL OF THEORETICAL PHYSICS. 1968. m. $745 (foreign $870) (effective 1996). Plenum Publishing Corp., 233 Spring St., New York, NY 10013-1578. TEL 212-620-8000. FAX 212-463-0742. TELEX 23-421139. Ed. David Finkelstein. adv.; bk.rev.; abstr.; bibl.; charts. (also avail. in microfilm from JSC; back issues avail.) **Indexed:** Chem.Abstr., Curr.Cont., Ind.Sci.Rev., INIS Atomind., INSPEC, Math.R., Phys.Ber., Ref.Zh., Sci.Cit.Ind. **Document type:** academic/scholarly publication.
—BLDSC (4542.695000); CASDDS; Ei; Faxon; Genuine Article; SWETS; UMI; UnCover. **CCC.**
   Refereed Serial

538   US
   CODEN: DICODA
INTERNATIONAL MAGNETICS CONFERENCE. DIGESTS OF THE INTERMAG CONFERENCE. a. price varies. (I E E E, Magnetics Society) Institute of Electrical and Electronics Engineers, Inc., 345 E. 47th St., New York, NY 10017-2394. TEL 212-705-7900. FAX 212-705-7682. (Subscr. to: Box 1331, 445 Hoes Ln., Piscataway, NJ 08855-1331)
—CASDDS; UMI.
   Former titles: Abstracts of the Intermag Conference; International Magnetics Conference. Digest (ISSN 0074-6843)
   Description: Covers all areas of basic science, applied science and engineering as they pertain to magnetism.

INTERNATIONAL MONOGRAPHS ON ADVANCED MATHEMATICS AND PHYSICS. see MATHEMATICS

530   NE   ISSN 0074-784X
   CODEN: PIPFA7
INTERNATIONAL SCHOOL OF PHYSICS "ENRICO FERMI". PROCEEDINGS. Variant title: Enrico Fermi International School of Physics. 1953. irreg., vol.123, 1994. (Societa Italiana di Fisica, IT - Italian Physical Society) Elsevier Science B.V., Books Division, P.O. Box 211, 100 AE Amsterdam, Netherlands. TEL 31-20-4853911. FAX 31-20-4853705. TELEX 18582 ESPA NL. E-mail: nlinfo-f@elsevier.nl; usinfo-f@elsevier.com; forinfo-kyf04035@niftyserve.or.jp; Site addr.: http://www.elsevier.nl/. (Subscr. in U.S. and Canada to: Elsevier Science Inc., Box 882, Madison Sq. Sta., New York, NY 10159-0882. TEL 212-989-5800) (reprint service avail. from ISI) **Indexed:** Chem.Abstr., INSPEC, Math.R. **Document type:** monographic series, proceedings.
—BLDSC (6733.900000); CASDDS.
   Former titles: Scuola Internazionale di Fisica "Enrico Fermi". Rendiconti, Corso (ISSN 0375-7595); (until 1960): Scuola Internazionale di Fisica "Enrico Fermi". Rendiconti (ISSN 0370-7253); **Supersedes:** International School of Physics "Ettore Majorana". Proceedings (ISSN 0074-7858)
   Description: Collects papers presented at conferences during sessions of the international summer school, covering specialized topics in physics, including classical and quantum physics, condensed matter, mathematical physics, and other related areas.
   Refereed Serial

530   IT
INTERNATIONAL SCHOOL OF PLASMA PHYSICS PIERO CALDIROLA. PROCEEDINGS. (Text in English) 1987. irreg., no.14, 1993. price varies. Editrice Compositori s.r.l., Via Stalingrado 97-2, 40128 Bologna, Italy. TEL 51-327811. FAX 51-327877. **Document type:** proceedings.

530   US   ISSN 0950-5563
   CODEN: IMPHAW
INTERNATIONAL SERIES OF MONOGRAPHS ON PHYSICS. 1930. irreg. price varies. Oxford University Press, 200 Madison Ave., New York, NY 10016. TEL 212-679-7300. Ed.Bd. **Indexed:** INSPEC, Math.R. **Document type:** monographic series.
—BLDSC (4549.260650).
   Refereed Serial

533.5   US   ISSN 0020-9066
INTERNATIONAL UNION FOR VACUUM SCIENCE, TECHNIQUE AND APPLICATIONS. NEWS BULLETIN. (Text in English, French, German) 1959. q. $20. International Union for Vacuum Science Technique and Applications, c/o Dr. Theodore E. Madey, Rutgers University, P.O. Box 849, Piscataway, NJ 08855. Ed. J. Lyn Provo. adv.; bk.rev. circ. 250.

IOWA AGRICULTURE AND HOME ECONOMICS EXPERIMENT STATION. RESEARCH BULLETIN. see AGRICULTURE

ISOTOPE NEWS. see BIOLOGY — Biological Chemistry

ISOTOPENPRAXIS. see CHEMISTRY

530   IS   ISSN 0309-8710
   CODEN: AIPSDK
ISRAEL PHYSICAL SOCIETY. ANNALS; conference proceedings. (Text in English) 1977. a. price varies. Israel Physical Society, P.O. Box 16105, Jerusalem 91160, Israel. (Dist. in U.S. by: American Institute of Physics, 335 E. 45 St., New York, NY 10017) (Co-publishers: American Institute of Physics, US; Institute of Physics, UK) Ed.Bd. circ. 600 (paid). (back issues avail., reprint service avail. from ISI) **Indexed:** Chem.Abstr., INSPEC (1980-), Math.R., Phys.Ber. **Document type:** academic/scholarly publication, proceedings.
—BLDSC (1028.320000); CASDDS. **CCC.**

ISTANBUL UNIVERSITESI FEN FAKULTESI ASTRONOMI VE FIZIK DERGISI/ISTANBUL UNIVERSITY FACULTY OF SCIENCE JOURNAL OF ASTRONOMY AND PHYSICS. see ASTRONOMY

530   RU   ISSN 0021-3411
   CODEN: IVUFAC
IZVESTIYA VYSSHIKH UCHEBNYKH ZAVEDENII. SERIYA FIZIKA. English translation: Russian Physics Journal (US ISSN 1064-8887) (Text in Russian; contents page in English) 1957. m. $184 (effective 1996). (Vysshie Uchebnye Zavedeniya) Tomskii Universitet, Prospekt Lenina, 36, Tomsk-10, Russia. Ed. V.N. Detinko. charts; illus.; index, cum.index: 1957-1967. circ. 2,200. **Indexed:** Cadscan, Chem.Abstr., Curr.Cont., Ind.Sci.Rev., INIS Atomind., INSPEC, Lead Abstr., Phys.Ber., Ref.Zh., Sci.Cit.Ind., Zincscan.
—BLDSC (0077.900000); CASDDS; Genuine Article. **CCC.**

530 621.38   RU   ISSN 0021-3462
QC 661   CODEN: IVYRAY
IZVESTIYA VYSSHIKH UCHEBNYKH ZAVEDENII. SERIYA RADIOFIZIKA. English translation: Radiophysics and Quantum Electronics (US ISSN 0033-8443) (Text in Russian; summaries in English) 1958. m. $278 (effective 1996). (Vysshie Uchebnye Zavedeniya) Izdatel'stvo Vysshaya Shkola, Neglinnaya ul. 29-14, Moscow, Russia. (Co-sponsor: Ministerstvo Vysshego i Srednego Spetsial'nogo Obrazovaniya) Ed. V.L. Ginzburg. charts; illus.; index. (tabloid format) **Indexed:** Chem.Abstr., Curr.Cont., INIS Atomind., INSPEC, Phys.Ber., Ref.Zh., Risk Abstr., Sci.Cit.Ind.
—BLDSC (0077.760000); CASDDS; Genuine Article. **CCC.**

J A M P NEWS. (Japanese Association of Medical Physics) see MEDICAL SCIENCES

530   US   ISSN 0021-3640
   CODEN: JTPLA2
J E T P LETTERS. English translation of: Pis'ma v Zhurnal Eksperimental'noi i Teoreticheskoi Fiziki. 1965. s-m. $1280 (foreign $1315) (effective 1996). American Institute of Physics, One Physics Ellipse, College Park, MD 20740-3843. TEL 301-209-3000. (Subscr. to: AIP Member and Subscriber Services, 500 Sunnyside Blvd., Woodbury, NY 11797-2999. TEL 516-576-2270) Ed. S.J. Amoretty. (also avail. in microfilm; back issues avail.) **Indexed:** Appl.Mech.Rev., C.P.I., Cadscan, Curr.Cont., Gen.Phys.Adv.Abstr., INIS Atomind., INSPEC, Int.Aerosp.Abstr., Lead Abstr., Mass Spectr.Bull., Met.Abstr., Phys.Ber., Sci.Cit.Ind., World Alum.Abstr., Zincscan. **Document type:** academic/scholarly publication.
—BLDSC (0412.741000); Ei; Faxon; Genuine Article; SWETS; UnCover. **CCC.**
   Description: Timely, topical short papers, emphasizing fundamental theoretical and experimental reserach in all fields of physics.

530   JA   ISSN 0914-9090
   CODEN: JJSEEW
J J A P SERIES. (Text in English) 1988. a. Japanese Journal of Applied Physics, Publication Office - Oyo Butsurigaku Obunshi Kankokai, 24-8, Shinbashi 4-chome, Minato-ku, Tokyo 105, Japan.
—CASDDS.

JAPAN SOCIETY FOR TECHNOLOGY OF PLASTICITY. JOURNAL/SOSEI TO KAKO. see TECHNOLOGY: COMPREHENSIVE WORKS

530   JA
JAPAN SOCIETY OF APPLIED PHYSICS. THIN FILM AND SURFACE PHYSICS DIVISION. NEWSLETTER. (Text in Japanese) bi-m. Japan Society of Applied Physics, Thin Film and Surface Physics Division - Oyo Butsuri Gakkai Hakumaku Hyomen Butsuri Bunkakai, 12-3, Kudan Kita 1-chome, Chiyoda-ku, Tokyo 102, Japan.

621 530   JA   ISSN 0021-4922
TA4   CODEN: JJAPA5
JAPANESE JOURNAL OF APPLIED PHYSICS. (Issued in 2 parts - Part 1: regular papers and short notes; Part 2: letters.) (Text in English) 1962. m. (Part 1); s-m. (Part 2). $1580. Daini Toyokaiji Bldg., 4-24-8 Shinbashi, Minato-ku, Tokyo 105, Japan. FAX 81-3-3667-9646. (Dist. by: Intercontinental Marketing Corp., I.P.O. Box 5056, Tokyo 100-30, Japan. TEL 81-3-3661-7458) (Co-sponsors: Japan Society of Applied Physics, Physical Society of Japan) Eds. Ryoichi Ito, Seiichi Kagoshima. index. circ. 3,900. (also avail. in microform; reprint service avail. from UMI) **Indexed:** Apic.Abstr., Art & Archaeol.Tech.Abstr., Bull.Signal., Cadscan, Ceram.Abstr., Chem.Abstr., Curr.Cont., Eng.Ind., GeoRef., Ind.Sci.Rev., INIS Atomind., INSPEC, Int.Aerosp.Abstr., JCT, JTA, Lead Abstr., Mass Spectr.Bull., Met.Abstr., Phys.Ber., Sci.Cit.Ind., World Alum.Abstr., Zincscan. **Document type:** academic/scholarly publication.
—CASDDS; Ei; Faxon; Genuine Article; SWETS; UMI; UnCover.
   Description: Research papers in the field of applied physics.

JIKI KYOMEI IGAKKAI PUROGURAMU/SOCIETY OF MAGNETIC RESONANCE IN MEDICINE. PROCEEDINGS OF ANNUAL CONFERENCE. see MEDICAL SCIENCES — Radiology And Nuclear Medicine

JIKI KYOMEI TO IGAKU/MAGNETIC RESONANCE IN MEDICINE. see MEDICAL SCIENCES — Radiology And Nuclear Medicine

530   JA   ISSN 0913-7785
JINRUI DOTAI GAKKAI KAIHO/HUMAN ERGOLOGY SOCIETY. NEWSLETTER. (Text in Japanese) 1970. 3/yr. Jinrui Dotai Gakkai Kaiho - Human Ergology Society, Rodo Kagaku Kenkyujo, 8-14 Sugao 2-chome, Miyamae-ku, Kawasaki-shi, Kanagawa-ken 213, Japan. **Document type:** newsletter.
   Description: Contains news of the organization.

530 621 US ISSN 0270-5214
TA1 CODEN: JHADDQ
JOHNS HOPKINS A P L TECHNICAL DIGEST. 1980. q. free. Johns Hopkins University, Applied Physics Laboratory, Johns Hopkins Rd., Laurel, MD 20723. TEL 301-953-5625. Ed. Kishin Moorjani. bk.rev.; charts; illus.; circ. 5,000 (controlled). **Indexed:** ASCA, Chem.Abstr., Curr.Cont., Deep Sea Res.& Oceanogr.Abstr., Eng.Ind., INSPEC (1968-1977, 1980-), Int.Aerosp.Abstr., Meteor.& Geoastrophys.Abstr., Ocean.Abstr. **Document type:** academic/scholarly publication.
—BLDSC (4671.530000); CASDDS; Ei; Faxon; Genuine Article; UnCover.
Formerly: A P L Technical Digest (ISSN 0001-2211)
Refereed Serial

530 SP
JORNADAS SOBRE TECNICAS DE NEUTRONES. 1991. irreg. 3100 ptas. Universidad de Cantabria, Servicio de Publicaciones, Avda. de los Castros, s-n, 39005 Santander, Spain.

530 FR ISSN 1155-4304
QC1 CODEN: JPGCE8
JOURNAL DE PHYSIQUE I. (Text and summaries in English, French, German, Russian) 1872. m. 3950 F. (effective 1996). Editions de Physique, 7 av. du Hoggar, Z.I. de Courtaboeuf, B.P. 112, 91944 Les Ulis Cedex A, France. TEL 69-07-36-88. FAX 69-28-84-91. TELEX 602 321 F. Ed. D. Jerome. bk.rev.; index. circ. 1,500. (also avail. in microfiche from BHP,PMC; back issues avail.) **Indexed:** Cadscan, Chem.Abstr., Deep Sea Res.& Oceanogr.Abstr., Ind.Sci.Rev., INIS Atomind., INSPEC, Int.Aerosp.Abstr., Lead Abstr., Mass Spectr.Bull., Math.R., Met.Abstr., Phys.Ber., Sci.Cit.Ind., World Alum.Abstr., Zincscan.
—BLDSC (5040.211000); CASDDS; Ei; Faxon; Genuine Article; SWETS; UnCover. **CCC.**
Formerly: Journal de Physique (ISSN 0302-0738)
Description: Original articles in theoretical and experimental research.

530 FR ISSN 1155-4312
QC1 CODEN: JPAHER
JOURNAL DE PHYSIQUE II. m. 4250 F. (effective 1996). Editions de Physique, 7 av. du Hoggar, Z.I. de Courtaboeuf, B.P. 112, 91944 Les Ulis Cedex A, France. TEL 69-07-36-88. FAX 69-28-84-91. TELEX 602 321 F. **Indexed:** INSPEC (1991-).
—BLDSC (5040.212000); CASDDS; Ei; Faxon; Genuine Article; SWETS; UnCover. **CCC.**

621 530 FR ISSN 1155-4320
QC1 CODEN: JPAIEU
JOURNAL DE PHYSIQUE III. (Supplement to the Journal de Physique I) (Text in English, French) 1966. m. 4950 F. (effective 1996). Editions de Physique, 7 av. du Hoggar, Z.I. de Courtaboeuf, B.P. 112, 91944 Les Ulis Cedex A, France. TEL 69-07-36-88. FAX 69-28-84-91. TELEX 602 321 F. Ed. F. Rioux-Damidau. bk.rev.; charts; illus.; index. circ. 3,500. (back issues avail.) **Indexed:** Cadscan, Chem.Abstr., Curr.Cont., GeoRef., INSPEC, Lead Abstr., Mass Spectr.Bull., Met.Abstr., Phys.Ber., World Alum.Abstr., Zincscan.
—BLDSC (5040.213000); CASDDS; Ei; Faxon; Genuine Article; SWETS; UnCover. **CCC.**
Formerly: Revue de Physique Appliquee (ISSN 0035-1687)
Description: Articles on original measurements relative to known phenomena or experimental methods in physics.

530 FR ISSN 1155-4339
QC1 CODEN: JPICEI
JOURNAL DE PHYSIQUE IV. 1991. irreg. 5450 F. (effective 1996). Editions de Physique, 7 av. du Hoggar, Z.I. de Courtaboeuf, B.P. 112, 91944 Les Ulis Cedex A, France. TEL 69-07-36-88. FAX 69-28-84-91. TELEX 602 321 F. **Indexed:** Chem.Abstr., INSPEC (1991-). **Document type:** proceedings.
—BLDSC (5040.214000); CASDDS; Ei; Faxon; Genuine Article; SWETS; UnCover. **CCC.**
Description: Publishes international conference proceedings.

668.3 US ISSN 0021-8464
QC183 CODEN: JADNAJ
JOURNAL OF ADHESION. 1969. 16/yr. (in 4 vols., 4 nos./vol.). 355 ECU per vol. (effective 1996). Gordon and Breach Science Publishers, c/o International Publishers Distributor, 820 Town Center Dr., Langhorne, PA 19047. TEL 215-750-2642. FAX 215-750-6343. (Subscr. to: International Publishers Distributor, P.O. Box 90, Reading, Berkshire RG1 8JL, England. TEL 44-173-456-8316) Ed. Louis H. Sharpe. adv.; bk.rev.; charts; illus.; index. (also avail. in microform) **Indexed:** Abstr.Bull.Inst.Pap.Chem., Appl.Mech.Rev., Chem.Abstr., Curr.Cont., Ind.Sci.Rev., INSPEC, Intl.Polym.Sci.& Tech., ISMEC, RAPRA, Sci.Cit.Ind., Text.Tech.Dig., World Surf.Coat. **Document type:** academic/scholarly publication.
—BLDSC (4918.935000); CASDDS; Faxon; SWETS; UnCover. **CCC.**
Description: For the technical community concerned with the development of an understanding of the phenomenon of adhesion and its practical applications.
Refereed Serial

JOURNAL OF ALLOYS AND COMPOUNDS; an interdisciplinary journal of materials science and solid-state chemistry and physics. see *METALLURGY*

JOURNAL OF APPLIED MECHANICS AND TECHNICAL PHYSICS. see *ENGINEERING — Engineering Mechanics And Materials*

530 540 US ISSN 0021-8979
QC1 CODEN: JAPIAU
JOURNAL OF APPLIED PHYSICS. 1931. s-m. $2045 (foreign $2130) (effective 1996). American Institute of Physics, One Physics Ellipse, College Park, MD 20740-3843. TEL 301-209-3000. (Subscr. to: AIP Member and Subscriber Services, 500 Sunnyside Blvd., Woodbury, NY 11797-2999. TEL 516-576-2270. FAX 516-349-9704) Ed. Steve J. Rothman. charts; illus.; index. (also avail. in microfiche from AIP; microform from AIP; back issues avail.) **Indexed:** A.S.& T.Ind., Abstr.Bull.Inst.Pap.Chem., Appl.Mech.Rev., Br.Ceram.Abstr., C.P.I., Cadscan, Ceram.Abstr., Chem.Abstr., Curr.Cont., Deep Sea Res.& Oceanogr.Abstr., Eng.Ind., Fluidex, Gen.Phys.Adv.Abstr., Geotech.Abstr., Ind.Sci.Rev., INIS Atomind., INSPEC, Int.Aerosp.Abstr., Lead Abstr., Mass Spectr.Bull., Math.R., Met.Abstr., Petrol.Abstr., RAPRA, Sci.Cit.Ind., World Alum.Abstr., World Text.Abstr., Zincscan. **Document type:** academic/scholarly publication.
—BLDSC (4944.000000); CASDDS; Ei; Faxon; Genuine Article; SWETS; UnCover. **CCC.**
Description: Publishes results of original physics research with applications to other fields.

JOURNAL OF BIOLOGICAL PHYSICS; an international journal for the formulation and application of physical and mathematical models in the biological sciences. see *BIOLOGY — Biophysics*

530 541.3 US ISSN 0021-9606
QD1 CODEN: JCPSA6
JOURNAL OF CHEMICAL PHYSICS. 1931. w. $2980 (foreign $3240) (effective 1996). American Institute of Physics, One Physics Ellipse, College park, MD 20740-3843. TEL 301-209-3000. FAX 516-349-9704. (Subscr. to: AIP Member and Subscriber Services, 500 Sunnyside Blvd., Woodbury, NY 11797-2999. TEL 516-576-2270. FAX 516-349-9704) Ed. J.C. Light. charts; illus.; index. (also avail. in microfiche; microfilm; back issues avail.) **Indexed:** Abstr.Bull.Inst.Pap.Chem., Appl.Mech.Rev., Biol.Abstr., Biwk.Pap.Rad.Chem.& Photochem., Br.Ceram.Abstr., Bull.Thermodyn.& Thermochem., C.P.I., Chem.Abstr., Chem.Eng.Abstr., Chem.Infd., Curr.Cont., E&P Hlth. (1993-), Eng.Ind., Gas Process.& Ppl. (1993-), Gen.Phys.Adv.Abstr., Ind.Sci.Rev., INIS Atomind., INSPEC, Int.Aerosp.Abstr., Mass Spectr.Bull., Math.R., Met.Abstr., Off.Tech. (1993-), Petrol.Abstr. (1961-1971, 1977-), Phys.Ber., RAPRA, Sci.Cit.Ind., T.C.E.A. **Document type:** academic/scholarly publication.
●Also available on CD-ROM.
—BLDSC (4957.000000); CASDDS; Ei; Faxon; Genuine Article; PADDS; SWETS; UnCover. **CCC.**
Description: Publishe original research at the interface between physics and chemistry.
Refereed Serial

530 US ISSN 1068-3372
QC1 CODEN: JCOPEU
JOURNAL OF CONTEMPORARY PHYSICS. English translation of: Akademiya Nauk Armenii. Izvestiya. Seriya Fizika. 1984. bi-m. $720 (effective 1996). (Armenian Academy of Sciences, Al) Allerton Press, Inc., 150 Fifth Ave., New York, NY 10011. TEL 212-924-3950. FAX 212-463-9684. Ed. V.M. Arutyunyan. **Indexed:** INSPEC (1992-). **Document type:** academic/scholarly publication.
—BLDSC (0414.260000). **CCC.**
Formerly: Soviet Journal of Contemporary Physics (ISSN 8755-4585)

JOURNAL OF DYNAMICAL AND CONTROL SYSTEMS. see *ENGINEERING — Industrial Engineering*

530 NE ISSN 0920-5071
QC660.5 CODEN: JEWAE5
JOURNAL OF ELECTROMAGNETIC WAVES AND APPLICATIONS. (Text in English) 1987. m. DM.1450 (effective 1996). V S P, P.O. Box 346, 3700 AH Zeist, Netherlands. TEL 31-30-6925790. FAX 31-30-6932081. E-mail: 100341.2372@compuserve.com. Ed. J.A. Kong. adv. (back issues avail.) **Indexed:** INSPEC (1988-). **Document type:** academic/scholarly publication.
—BLDSC (4974.850000); Ei; Faxon; SWETS; UnCover.
Description: Original papers and review articles on new theories, methodology, and computational results about electromagnetic wave theory and its various applications.
Refereed Serial

530 US
JOURNAL OF ELECTROTOPOGRAPHY. 1981. s-a. free. (Ensanian Physiochemical Institute) Electrotopograph Corporation, Box 98, Eldred, PA 16731. TEL 814-225-3296. Ed. Minas Ensanian. bk.rev.; bibl.; charts; illus.; circ. 1,000 (controlled).
Refereed Serial

530 US ISSN 0737-0652
TP270.A1 CODEN: JOEMDK
JOURNAL OF ENERGETIC MATERIALS. 1983. 5/yr. $250 (foreign $260). Dowden, Brodman & Devine, Inc., Box 188, Stroudsburg, PA 18360. Ed. Paul L. Marinkas. abstr.; bibl.; charts. **Indexed:** Chem.Abstr.
—BLDSC (4978.240000); CASDDS; Ei; Faxon; SWETS.

JOURNAL OF ENGINEERING PHYSICS AND THERMOPHYSICS. see *ENGINEERING*

530 US ISSN 1063-7761
QC1 CODEN: JTPHES
JOURNAL OF EXPERIMENTAL AND THEORETICAL PHYSICS. English translation of: Zhurnal Eksperimental'noi i Teoreticheskoi Fiziki (RU ISSN 0044-4510). 1955. m. $2615 (foreign $2670) (effective 1996). (Russian Academy of Sciences, RU) American Institute of Physics, One Physics Ellipse, College Park, MD 20740-3843. TEL 301-209-3000. Eds. M. Damashek, D.L. Book. charts; illus.; index. (also avail. in microform from AIP; back issues avail.) **Indexed:** Appl.Mech.Rev., C.P.I., Eng.Ind., Gen.Phys.Adv.Abstr., INSPEC, Mass Spectr.Bull., Math.R., Met.Abstr., Phys.Ber., World Alum.Abstr. **Document type:** academic/scholarly publication.
—BLDSC (0414.500000); Faxon; SWETS; UnCover. **CCC.**
Formerly: Soviet Physics - J E T P (ISSN 0038-5646)
Description: Offers basic research results in experimental and theoretical physics.

JOURNAL OF FLUID MECHANICS. see *ENGINEERING — Hydraulic Engineering*

JOURNAL OF GEOMETRY AND PHYSICS. see *MATHEMATICS*

530 US ISSN 1070-2458
QC20.7.G76
JOURNAL OF GROUP THEORY IN PHYSICS. 1993. q. $315 (effective 1996). Nova Science Publishers, Inc., 6080 Jericho Tpke., Ste. 207, Commack, NY 11725-2808. TEL 516-499-3103. FAX 516-499-3146. E-mail: novasci1@ao.com. **Document type:** academic/scholarly publication.

JOURNAL OF HARD MATERIALS. see *ENGINEERING — Engineering Mechanics And Materials*

PHYSICS

530   CC   ISSN 1001-6058
JOURNAL OF HYDRODYNAMICS. Chinese Edition: Shuidong Lixue Yanjiu yu Jinzhan (ISSN 1000-4874) (Text in English) q. $120 (effective 1996). (Zhongguo Chuanbo Kexue Yanjiu Zhongxin, Shanghai Fenbu) China Ocean Press, International Department, Haimao Dalou, 1 Fuxingmenwai Dajie, Beijing 100860, People's Republic of China. TEL 8032211. FAX 8033515. TELEX 22536 NBO CN. Ed.Bd.
    Description: Provides up-to-date information about various aspects of hydrodynamic research especially in China, including theoretical, experimental and computational techniques plus field measurement.
    Refereed Serial

530   US   ISSN 0022-2348
QD380   CODEN: JMAPBR
JOURNAL OF MACROMOLECULAR SCIENCE: PART B - PHYSICS. 1967. q. $317.50 to individuals; institutions $635. Marcel Dekker Journals, 270 Madison Ave., New York, NY 10016. TEL 212-696-9000. FAX 212-685-4540. TELEX 421419 MARDEEK. (Subscr. to: Box 5017, Monticello, NY 12701) Ed. Phillip M. Geil. adv. (also avail. in microform from RPI) **Indexed:** Chem.Abstr., Curr.Cont., Ind.Sci.Rev., INIS Atomind., INSPEC, Intl.Polym.Sci.& Tech., RAPRA, Sci.Cit.Ind. **Document type:** academic/scholarly publication.
—BLDSC (5010.770000); CASDDS; Ei; Faxon; Genuine Article; SWETS; UMI; UnCover. **CCC.**
    Supersedes in part: Journal of Macromolecular Chemistry (ISSN 0449-2730)
    Refereed Serial

538.3   US   ISSN 1064-1858
QP519.9.N83   CODEN: JMRAE2
JOURNAL OF MAGNETIC RESONANCE - SERIES A. 1969. m. $1178 (foreign $1398) (effective 1996). Academic Press, Inc., Journal Division, 525 B St., Ste. 1900, San Diego, CA 92101-4495. TEL 619-230-1840. FAX 619-699-6800. (Subscr. to: Box 620000, Orlando, FL 32891-8340. TEL 800-543-9534) Ed. Wallace S. Brey, Jr. adv.; abstr.; bibl.; charts; illus.; index. (back issues avail.) **Indexed:** Abstr.Bull.Inst.Pap.Chem., Biwk.Pap.Rad.Chem.& Photochem., Cadscan, Chem.Abstr., Curr.Cont., Ind.Sci.Rev., INIS Atomind., INSPEC, Lead Abstr., Sci.Cit.Ind., Zincscan. **Document type:** academic/scholarly publication.
—BLDSC (5010.791500); ADONIS; CASDDS; Ei; Faxon; Genuine Article; SWETS; UnCover. **CCC.**
    Supersedes in part (in 1992): Journal of Magnetic Resonance (ISSN 0022-2364)
    Description: Provides current information on the theory, techniques, methods of spectral analysis and interpretation, spectral correlations, and results of magnetic resonance spectroscopy.
    Refereed Serial

538.3   US   ISSN 1064-1866
RC78.7.N83   CODEN: JMRBE5
JOURNAL OF MAGNETIC RESONANCE - SERIES B. 1969. m. $515 (foreign $616) (effective 1996). Academic Press, Inc., Journal Division, 525 B St., Ste. 1900, San Diego, CA 92101-4495. TEL 619-230-1840. FAX 619-699-6800. (Subscr. to: Box 620000, Orlando, FL 32891-8340. TEL 800-543-9534) Ed. Wallace Brey. **Indexed:** Ind.Med. (1994-), INSPEC (1993-). **Document type:** academic/scholarly publication.
—BLDSC (5010.792000); ADONIS; CASDDS; Faxon; Genuine Article; SWETS; UnCover. **CCC.**
    Supersedes in part (in 1992): Journal of Magnetic Resonance (ISSN 0022-2364)

538   NE   ISSN 0304-8853
QC750   CODEN: JMMMDC
JOURNAL OF MAGNETISM AND MAGNETIC MATERIALS. 1976. 39/yr. fl.7358($4487) (effective 1996). (European Physical Society) North-Holland (Subsidiary of: Elsevier Science B.V.), P.O. Box 211, 1000 AE Amsterdam, Netherlands. TEL 31-20-4853911. FAX 31-20-4853598. TELEX 18582 ESPA NL. (Subscr. in U.S. and Canada to: Elsevier Science Inc., Box 882, Madison Sq. Sta., New York, NY 10159. TEL 212-989-5800. FAX 212-633-3990) Ed. A.J. Freeman. adv.; charts; cum.index. circ. 800. (also avail. in microform from UMI; back issues avail.) **Indexed:** Cadscan, Chem.Abstr., Curr.Cont., GeoRef., Ind.Sci.Rev., INIS Atomind., INSPEC, Lead Abstr., Met.Abstr., Phys.Ber., Sci.Cit.Ind., World Alum.Abstr., Zincscan. **Document type:** academic/scholarly publication.
—BLDSC (5010.793000); CASDDS; Ei; Faxon; Genuine Article; SWETS; UnCover. **CCC.**
    Description: Covers the whole spectrum of topics from basic magnetism to the technology and applications of magnetic materials and magnetic recording.
    Refereed Serial

JOURNAL OF MATERIALS RESEARCH. see ENGINEERING — Engineering Mechanics And Materials

JOURNAL OF MATHEMATICAL AND PHYSICAL SCIENCES. see MATHEMATICS

500   US   ISSN 0022-2488
QC20   CODEN: JMAPAQ
JOURNAL OF MATHEMATICAL PHYSICS. 1960. m. $1440 (foreign $1525) (effective 1996). American Institute of Physics, One Physics Ellipse, College Park, MD 20740-3843. TEL 301-209-3000. (Subscr. to: AIP Member and Subscriber Services, 500 Sunnyside Blvd., Woodbury, NY 11797-2999. TEL 516-576-2270. FAX 516-349-9704) Ed. R.G. Newton. abstr.; bibl.; charts. (also avail. in microfiche; microform from PMC; back issues avail.) **Indexed:** C.P.I., Chem.Abstr, Compumath, Curr.Cont., Eng.Ind., Gen.Phys.Adv.Abstr., Ind.Sci.Rev., INIS Atomind., INSPEC, Int.Aerosp.Abstr., Math.R., Phys.Ber., Sci.Cit.Ind. **Document type:** academic/scholarly publication.
—BLDSC (5012.400000); CASDDS; Ei; Faxon; Genuine Article; SWETS; UnCover. **CCC.**
    Description: Published original research covering developments in the mathematical formulation of physical theories, mathematical methods for the solution of physical problems, and mathematical ideas suitable for physical applications.
    Refereed Serial

JOURNAL OF MATHEMATICAL SCIENCES. see MATHEMATICS

JOURNAL OF NATURAL SCIENCES AND MATHEMATICS. see SCIENCES: COMPREHENSIVE WORKS

530 541   NE   ISSN 0022-3093
TP845   CODEN: JNCSBJ
JOURNAL OF NON-CRYSTALLINE SOLIDS; a journal on the physical, chemical and structural properties of glasses, amorphous semiconductors and metals, including the liquid state. 1969. 48/yr. fl.7632($4654) (effective 1996). North-Holland (Subsidiary of: Elsevier Science B.V.), P.O. Box 211, 1000 AE Amsterdam, Netherlands. TEL 31-20-4853911. FAX 31-20-4853598. TELEX 18582 ESPA NL. (Subscr. in U.S. and Canada to: Elsevier Science Inc., Box 882, Madison Sq. Sta., New York, NY 10159. TEL 212-989-5800. FAX 212-633-3990) Ed. R.A. Weeks. adv.; bk.rev.; charts; illus.; stat.; cum.index. (also avail. in microform from UMI; back issues avail.; reprint service avail. from ISI,SWZ) **Indexed:** Cadscan, Ceram.Abstr., Chem.Abstr., Curr.Cont., Ind.Sci.Rev., INIS Atomind., INSPEC, Int.Aerosp.Abstr., Lead Abstr., Mass Spectr.Bull., Met.Abstr., Phys.Ber., Psychol.Abstr., World Alum.Abstr., Zincscan. **Document type:** academic/scholarly publication.
—BLDSC (5022.830000); CASDDS; Ei; Faxon; Genuine Article; SWETS; UnCover. **CCC.**
    Description: Publishes review articles, research papers, on oxide and non-oxide glasses, amorphous semiconductors, non-crystalline films such as those prepared by vapor-deposition, glass ceramics and glassy composites.
    Refereed Serial

530   US   ISSN 0938-8974
QC20.7.N6   CODEN: JNSCEK
JOURNAL OF NONLINEAR SCIENCE. (Electronic supplement avail.: Nonlinear Science Today (ISSN 0938-9008)) 1991. bi-m. $331 (includes Nonlinear Science Today) (effective 1996). Springer-Verlag, Journals, 175 Fifth Ave., New York, NY 10010. TEL 212-460-1500. FAX 212-473-6272. (N. American subscr. to: Journal Fulfillment Services, Box 2485, Secaucus, NJ 07096-2491. TEL 800-777-4643; Subscr. outside N. America: Heidelberger Platz 3, 1000 Berlin 33, Germany. TEL 030-8207-1. FAX 030-8214091) Eds. Stephen R. Wiggins, E.A. Kuznetsov. (reprint service avail.) **Indexed:** Compumath, Curr.Cont., Sci.Cit.Ind. **Document type:** academic/scholarly publication.
—BLDSC (5022.839000); Ei; Genuine Article; SWETS; UMI; UnCover. **CCC.**
    Description: Publishes research papers that augment the fundamental ways that humans analyze, describe, and predict aspects of the nonlinear world.
    Refereed Serial

JOURNAL OF ORGONOMY. see MEDICAL SCIENCES — Psychiatry And Neurology

JOURNAL OF PHYSICAL AND CHEMICAL REFERENCE DATA. see CHEMISTRY

JOURNAL OF PHYSICAL AND CHEMICAL REFERENCE DATA. MONOGRAPH. see CHEMISTRY

530   UK   ISSN 0305-4470
QC1   CODEN: JPHAC5
JOURNAL OF PHYSICS A: MATHEMATICAL AND GENERAL. 1968. s-m. £1565($3224) (effective 1996). (Institute of Physics) I O P Publishing Ltd., Techno House, Redcliffe Way, Bristol, Avon BS1 6NX, England. TEL 0117-929-7481. FAX 0117-929-4318. TELEX 449149 INSTP G. (U.S. subscr. to: American Institute of Physics, Member and Subscriber Service, 500 Sunnyside Blvd. Woodbury, NY 11797-2900. TEL 516-349-7800) Ed. J. Zinn-Justin. bibl.; charts; illus.; index. circ. 1,003. (also avail. in microfiche from AIP; microfilm from AIP; back issues avail.) **Indexed:** Appl.Mech.Rev., Br.Ceram.Abstr., Chem.Abstr., Curr.Cont., Deep Sea Res.& Oceanogr.Abstr., Eng.Ind., Ind.Sci.Rev., INIS Atomind., INSPEC, Int.Aerosp.Abstr., Math.R., Phys.Ber. **Document type:** academic/scholarly publication.
—BLDSC (5036.237300); CASDDS; Ei; Faxon; Genuine Article; SWETS; UnCover. **CCC.**
    Former titles: Journal of Physics A: Mathematical, Nuclear and General (ISSN 0301-0015); Journal of Physics (ISSN 0022-3689); Physical Society. Proceedings.
    Description: Examines classical mechanics, chaotic systems, statistical physics, and thermodynamics.

530 540   UK   ISSN 0022-3697
QC176.A1   CODEN: JPCSAW
THE JOURNAL OF PHYSICS AND CHEMISTRY OF SOLIDS. (Text in English, French and German) 1956. m. £1350($2147) (effective 1996). Elsevier Science Ltd., Pergamon, P.O. Box 800, Kidlington, Oxford OX5 1DX, England. TEL 44-1865-843000. FAX 44-1865-843010.
E-mail: nlinfo-f@elsevier.nl; usinfo-f@elsevier.com; forinfo-kyf04035@niftyserve.or.jp; Site addr.: http://www.elsevier.nl/. (Subscr. in U.S. and Canada to: Elsevier Science, 660 White Plains Rd., Tarrytown, NY 10591-5153. TEL 914-524-9200. FAX 914-333-2444) Ed. D.E. Cox. adv.: B&W page $550, color page $1350. bk.rev. circ. 2,300. (also avail. in microfiche from MIM; microfilm from UMI; back issues avail.) **Indexed:** Appl.Mech.Rev., Br.Ceram.Abstr., Bull.Thermodyn.& Thermochem., Cadscan, Chem.Abstr., GeoRef., Ind.Sci.Rev., INIS Atomind., INSPEC, Lead Abstr., Mass Spectr.Bull., Met.Abstr., Phys.Ber., World Alum.Abstr., Zincscan. **Document type:** academic/scholarly publication.
—BLDSC (5036.500000); CASDDS; Ei; Faxon; Genuine Article; SWETS; UMI; UnCover. **CCC.**
    Description: Covers all aspects of the fundamental physics and chemistry of the solid state.
    Refereed Serial

530.41 UK ISSN 0953-4075
QC770 CODEN: JPAPEH
JOURNAL OF PHYSICS B: ATOMIC, MOLECULAR AND OPTICAL PHYSICS. 1968. s-m. £1287($2651) (effective 1996). (Institute of Physics) I O P Publishing Ltd., Techno House, Redcliffe Way, Bristol, Avon BS1 6NX, England. TEL 0117-929-7481. FAX 0117-929-4318. TELEX 449149 INSTP G. (U.S. subscr. to: American Institute of Physics, Member and Subscriber Services, 500 Sunnyside Blvd, Woodbury, NY 11797-2900. TEL 516-349-7800) Ed. J.P. Connerade. bibl.; illus.; charts; index. circ. 993. (also avail. in microfiche from AIP; microfilm from AIP; back issues avail.) **Indexed:** Appl.Mech.Rev., Br.Ceram.Abstr., Bull.Thermodyn.& Thermochem., Cadscan, Chem.Abstr., Curr.Cont., Eng.Ind., Ind.Sci.Rev., INIS Atomind., INSPEC, Int.Aerosp.Abstr., Lead Abstr., Mass Spectr.Bull., Math.R., Met.Abstr., Phys.Ber., Zincscan. **Document type:** academic/scholarly publication.
—BLDSC (5036.238400); CASDDS; Ei; Faxon; Genuine Article; SWETS; UnCover. **CCC.**
Former titles: Journal of Physics B: Atomic and Molecular Physics (ISSN 0022-3700); Physical Society. Proceedings.

530.41 UK ISSN 0953-8984
QC173.4.C65 CODEN: JCOMEL
JOURNAL OF PHYSICS: CONDENSED MATTER. 1968. w. (50/yr.). £2586($5328) (effective 1996). (Institute of Physics) I O P Publishing Ltd., Techno House, Redcliffe Way, Bristol, Avon BS1 6NX, England. TEL 0117-929-7481. FAX 0117-929-4318. TELEX 449149 INSTP G. (U.S. subscr. to: American Institute of Physics, Member and Subscriber Services, 500 Sunnyside Blvd., Woodbury, NY 11797-2900. TEL 516-349-7800) Ed. D.L. Weaire. bibl.; charts; illus.; index. circ. 1,123. (also avail. in microfiche from AIP; microfilm from AIP; back issues avail.) **Indexed:** Appl.Mech.Rev., Br.Ceram.Abstr., Cadscan, Chem.Abstr., Curr.Cont., Eng.Ind., GeoRef., Ind.Sci.Rev., INIS Atomind., INSPEC, Lead Abstr., Mass Spectr.Bull., Math.R., Met.Abstr., Phys.Ber., World Alum.Abstr., Zincscan. **Document type:** academic/scholarly publication.
—BLDSC (5036.800000); CASDDS; Ei; Faxon; Genuine Article; SWETS; UnCover. **CCC.**
Formed by the 1989 merger of: Journal of Physics F: Metal Physics (ISSN 0305-4608); Journal of Physics C: Solid State Physics (ISSN 0022-3719); Which was formerly: Physical Society. Proceedings.
Description: Reports experimental and theoretical studies of the structural, thermal, mechanical, electrical, magnetic and optical properties of condensed matter, including crystals, quasicrystals and liquid crystals; amorphous and polymeric materials, alloys and metalic materials; liquids.

530 621 UK ISSN 0022-3727
QC1 CODEN: JPAPBE
JOURNAL OF PHYSICS D: APPLIED PHYSICS. 1968. m. £695($1432) (effective 1996). (Institute of Physics) I O P Publishing Ltd., Techno House, Redcliffe Way, Bristol, Avon BS1 6NX, England. TEL 0117-929-7481. FAX 0117-929-4318. TELEX 449149 INSTP G. (U.S. subscr. to: American Institute of Physics, Member and Subscriber Services, 500 Sunnyside Blvd., Woodbury, NY 11797-2900. TEL 516-349-7800) Ed. S.B. Palmer. bibl.; charts; illus.; index. circ. 1,217. (also avail. in microfiche from AIP; microfilm from AIP; back issues avail.) **Indexed:** A.S.& T.Ind., Abstr.Bull.Inst.Pap.Chem., Anal.Abstr., Biol.Abstr., Br.Ceram.Abstr., Br.Tech.Ind., C.I.S. Abstr., Cadscan, Chem.Abstr., Curr.Cont., Deep Sea Res.& Oceanogr.Abstr., Eng.Ind., Fluidex, GeoRef., Ind.Sci.Rev., INIS Atomind., INSPEC, Intl.Polym.Sci.& Tech., Lead Abstr., Mass Spectr.Bull., Met.Abstr., RAPRA, RAPRA, World Alum.Abstr., World Text.Abstr., Zincscan. **Document type:** academic/scholarly publication.
—BLDSC (5036.240000); CASDDS; Ei; Faxon; Genuine Article; SWETS; UnCover. **CCC.**
Formerly: British Journal of Applied Physics.
Description: Explores the theoretical and experimental aspects of physics, as applied to interdisciplinary science, engineering or industry.

JOURNAL OF PHYSICS G: NUCLEAR AND PARTICLE PHYSICS. see PHYSICS — Nuclear Physics

530 620 TU ISSN 1013-7815
JOURNAL OF PHYSICS ENGINEERING/FIZIK MUHENDISLIGI DERGISI. 1977. q. T M M O B Chamber of Turkish Physics Engineering, Konur Sokak 4, Kat 3, Yenisehir, 06450 Ankara, Turkey. TEL 4-188-83-96.

530.44 UK ISSN 0022-3778
QC718 CODEN: JPLPBZ
JOURNAL OF PLASMA PHYSICS. 1967. bi-m. £324($610) (effective 1996). Cambridge University Press, Edinburgh Bldg., Shaftesbury Rd., Cambridge CB2 2RU, England. TEL 01223-312393. FAX 01223-315052. TELEX 851817256. (N. American addr.: Cambridge University Press, Journals Dept., 40 W. 20th St., New York, NY 10011. TEL 212-924-3900. FAX 212-691-3239) Ed. Dr. J.P. Dougherty. adv.; bk.rev.; bibl.; charts; index. (also avail. in microform from UMI; back issues avail.; reprint service avail. from SWZ) **Indexed:** Appl.Mech.Rev., Chem.Abstr., Curr.Cont., Ind.Sci.Rev., INIS Atomind., INSPEC, Int.Aerosp.Abstr., Phys.Ber., Solid St.Abstr. **Document type:** academic/scholarly publication.
—BLDSC (5040.550000); CASDDS; Ei; Faxon; Genuine Article; SWETS; UMI; UnCover. **CCC.**
Description: Features primary research articles in plasma physics, both theoretical and experimental, and its applications to fusion, laboratory plasmas and communications devices.

JOURNAL OF RUSSIAN LASER RESEARCH. see ENGINEERING

JOURNAL OF SOL-GEL SCIENCE AND TECHNOLOGY. see ENGINEERING — Engineering Mechanics And Materials

530 US ISSN 0022-4715
QC175 CODEN: JSTPSB
JOURNAL OF STATISTICAL PHYSICS. 1969. 24/yr. $1575 (foreign $1845) (effective 1996). Plenum Publishing Corp., 233 Spring St., New York, NY 10013-1578. TEL 212-620-8000. FAX 212-463-0742. TELEX 23-421139. Ed. Joel L. Lebowitz. adv. (also avail. in microfilm from JSC; back issues avail.) **Indexed:** Appl.Mech.Rev., Compumath, Comput.Abstr., Curr.Cont., Eng.Ind., Ind.Sci.Rev., INIS Atomind., INSPEC, Math.R., Nucl.Sci.Abstr., Phys.Ber., Ref.Zh., Sci.Res.Abstr., Solid.St.Abstr. **Document type:** academic/scholarly publication.
—BLDSC (5066.840000); Ei; Faxon; Genuine Article; SWETS; UMI; UnCover. **CCC.**
Refereed Serial

530 US ISSN 0896-1107
QC611.9 CODEN: JOUSEH
JOURNAL OF SUPERCONDUCTIVITY. 1988. bi-m. $325 (foreign $380) (effective 1996). Plenum Publishing Corp., 233 Spring St., New York, NY 10013-1578. TEL 212-620-8000. FAX 212-463-0742. TELEX 23-421139. Ed.Bd. adv. (also avail. in microfilm from JSC; back issues avail.) **Indexed:** Energy Info.Abstr., INSPEC (1988-). **Document type:** academic/scholarly publication.
—BLDSC (5067.118000); CASDDS; Ei; Faxon; Genuine Article; SWETS; UMI; UnCover. **CCC.**
Description: Forum for the publication of original articles on all aspects of the science and technology of superconductivity.
Refereed Serial

530 548 US ISSN 1063-4576
TA418.45
JOURNAL OF SUPERHARD MATERIALS. English translation of: Sverkhtverdye Materialy (RU ISSN 0203-3119) 1983. bi-m. $895 (effective 1996). (Akademiya Nauk Ukrainy, Otdelenie Fiziko-Tekhnicheskikh Materialov, KR) Allerton Press, Inc., 150 Fifth Ave., New York, NY 10011. TEL 212-924-3950. FAX 212-463-9684. Ed. P.S. Kislyi. **Indexed:** Eng.Ind., Met.Abstr., World Alum.Abstr. **Document type:** academic/scholarly publication.
—BLDSC (0415.380000); Faxon. **CCC.**
Formerly: Soviet Journal of Superhard Materials (ISSN 0739-8425)

530 IR ISSN 0378-1046
CODEN: JESPCS
JOURNAL OF THE EARTH AND SPACE PHYSICS. (Text and summaries in English, Farsi, French, German) 1972. s-a. University of Teheran, Institute of Geophysics, Amirabad-e Shomali Ave., Teheran 14394, Iran. Ed. Bahram Akasheh. adv.; charts; stat. **Indexed:** Abstr.J.Earthq.Eng., GeoRef. **Document type:** academic/scholarly publication.

530 US ISSN 0887-8722
TL900 CODEN: JTHTEO
JOURNAL OF THERMOPHYSICS AND HEAT TRANSFER; devoted to thermophysics and heat transfer. 1987. q. $220 to non-members (foreign $260); members $36 (foreign $56). American Institute of Aeronautics and Astronautics, Inc., 370 L'Enfant Promenade, S.W., Washington, DC 20024. TEL 202-646-7400. Ed. Alfred L. Crosbie. charts; illus.; index. circ. 1,000. (also avail. in microform; reprint service avail. from UMI) **Indexed:** Appl.Mech.Rev. **Document type:** academic/scholarly publication.
—BLDSC (5069.099300); CASDDS; Ei; Faxon; Genuine Article; SWETS; UnCover. **CCC.**
Description: Advancement of the science and technology of thermophysics and heat transfer through the dissemination of original research papers disclosing new technical knowledge and exploratory developments and applications based on new knowledge.
Refereed Serial

530 US ISSN 0731-3764
JOURNAL OF UNDERGRADUATE RESEARCH IN PHYSICS. 1982. s-a. $5 to individuals (foreign $7); institutions $10 (foreign $12) (effective 1995-96). (American Institute of Physics) Guilford College, Department of Physics, Guilford, NC 27410. TEL 910-316-2279. FAX 910-316-2951. E-mail: adelbergerre@rascal.guilford.edu. (Co-sponsor: Society of Physics Students) Ed. Rexford E. Adelberger. bk.rev.; charts; circ. 5,000 (paid). **Document type:** academic/scholarly publication.
—Faxon; UnCover.
Description: Devoted to research work done by undergraduate students in physics and related fields.
Refereed Serial

533.5 US ISSN 0734-2101
TJ940 CODEN: JVTAD6
JOURNAL OF VACUUM SCIENCE AND TECHNOLOGY. PART A. VACUUM, SURFACES AND FILMS. 1964. 6/yr. $530 (foreign $574). (American Vacuum Society) American Institute of Physics, One Physics Ellipse, College Park, MD 20740-3843. TEL 301-209-3000. Ed. G. Lucovsky. adv.; bk.rev.; charts; illus.; index. (also avail. in microform from UMI; back issues avail.) **Indexed:** C.P.I., Cadscan, Chem.Abstr., Curr.Cont., Eng.Ind., Gen.Phys.Adv.Abstr., Ind.Sci.Rev., INIS Atomind., INSPEC (1968-), Int.Aerosp.Abstr., Int.Packag.Abstr., Lead Abstr., Mass Spectr.Bull., Met.Abstr., Phys.Ber., World Alum.Abstr., Zincscan. **Document type:** academic/scholarly publication.
●Also available on CD-ROM.
—BLDSC (5072.210100); CASDDS; Ei; Faxon; Genuine Article; SWETS; UnCover. **CCC.**
Supersedes in part: Journal of Vacuum Science and Technology (ISSN 0022-5355)
Refereed Serial

533.5 US ISSN 1071-1023
TJ940 CODEN: JVTBD9
JOURNAL OF VACUUM SCIENCE AND TECHNOLOGY. PART B. MICROELECTRONICS AND NANOMETER STRUCTURES. 1964. 6/yr. $430 (foreign $474). (American Vacuum Society) American Institute of Physics, One Physics Ellipse, College Park, MD 20740-3843. TEL 301-209-3000. Ed. G.E. McGuire. adv.; bk.rev.; charts; illus.; index. (also avail. in microform from AIP,UMI; back issues avail.) **Indexed:** Cadscan, INIS Atomind., INSPEC (1968-), Lead Abstr., Mass Spectr.Bull., Met.Abstr., Zincscan. **Document type:** academic/scholarly publication.
●Also available on CD-ROM.
—BLDSC (5072.210150); CASDDS; Ei; Faxon; Genuine Article; SWETS.
Formerly: Journal of Vacuum Science and Technology. Part B. Microelectronics Processing and Phenomena (ISSN 0734-211X); Which superseded in part: Journal of Vacuum Science and Technology (ISSN 0022-5355)
Refereed Serial

PHYSICS

530 620 US ISSN 0895-3996
QC480.8 CODEN: JXSTE5
JOURNAL OF X-RAY SCIENCE AND TECHNOLOGY. 1988. q. $140 (foreign $155) (effective 1996). Academic Press, Inc., Journal Division, 525 B St., Ste. 1900, San Diego, CA 92101-4495. TEL 619-230-1840. FAX 619-699-6800. (Subscr. to: Box 620000, Orlando, FL 32891-8340. TEL 800-543-9534) Ed. Larry Knight. (back issues avail.) Indexed: INSPEC (1990-). **Document type:** academic/scholarly publication.
—BLDSC (5072.705000); Ei; Faxon; SWETS; UnCover. **CCC**.
  Description: Articles on recent developments in x-ray sources: synchrotons, and x-ray lasers; x-ray image formation; x-ray spectroscopy; and x-ray physics.
  Refereed Serial

530 MY ISSN 0128-0333
CODEN: JFMAEU
JURNAL FIZIK MALAYSIA. (Text in English) 1980. q. $80 to libraries; individuals $40. Malaysian Institute of Physics, c/o Physics Department, University of Malaysia, 59100 Kuala Lumpur, Malaysia. TEL 603-7594385. FAX 603-7561521. TELEX 39845-MA-UNIMAL. Ed. C.S. Wong. circ. 500. (back issues avail.) Indexed: Chem.Abstr., INIS Atomind., INSPEC (1984-). **Document type:** academic/scholarly publication.
—BLDSC (5075.600500); CASDDS.

530 JA
K E K ANNUAL REPORT. (Text in English) 1971. a. National Laboratory for High Energy Physics - Koenerugi Butsurigaku Kenkyujo, 1-1, Oho, Tsukuba-shi, Ibaraki-ken 305, Japan. TEL 0298-64-1171. FAX 0298-64-4604. TELEX 3652434 KEKOHO J. E-mail: library@kekvax.kek.jp. Indexed: INIS Atomind. **Document type:** government publication.

530 JA
K E K PREPRINT. (Text in English) 1971. irreg. National Laboratory for High Energy Physics - Koenerugi Butsurigaku Kenkyujo, 1-1, Oho, Tsukuba-shi, Ibaraki-ken 305, Japan. TEL 0298-64-1171. FAX 0298-64-4604. TELEX 3652534 KEKOHO J. E-mail: library@kekvax.kek.jp.

530 JA
K E K PROCEEDINGS. (Text in English or Japanese) 1991. irreg. National Laboratory for High Energy Physics - Koenerugi Butsurigaku Kenkyujo, 1-1, Oho, Tsukuba-shi, Ibaraki-ken 305, Japan. TEL 0298-64-1171. FAX 0298-64-4604. TELEX 3652534 KEKOHO J. E-mail: library@kekvax.kek.jp. **Document type:** proceedings.

530 JA
K E K PROGRESS REPORT. (Text in English) 1983. irreg. National Laboratory for High Energy Physics - Koenerugi Butsurigaku Kenkyujo, 1-1, Oho, Tsukuba-shi, Ibaraki-ken 305, Japan. TEL 0298-64-1171. FAX 0298-64-4604. TELEX 3652534 KEKOHO J. E-mail: library@kekvax.kek.jp. **Document type:** government publication.

530 JA
K E K REPORT. (Text in English or Japanese) 1971. irreg. National Laboratory for High Energy Physics - Koenerugi Butsurigaku Kenkyujo, 1-1, Oho, Tsukuba-shi, Ibaraki-ken 305, Japan. TEL 0298-64-1171. FAX 0298-64-4604. TELEX 3652534 KEKOHO J. E-mail: library@kekvax.kek.jp. **Document type:** government publication.

530 540 JA
KAGAKU KOENKAI KOEN YOSHI. (Text in Japanese) 1978. a. Rikagaku Kenkyujo - Institute of Physical and Chemical Research, 2-1 Hirosawa, Wako-shi, Saitama-ken 351-01, Japan. TEL 0484-621111. FAX 0484-621554.

KAGOSHIMA DAIGAKU RIGAKUBU KIYO. SUGAKU, BUTSURIGAKU, KAGAKU/KAGOSHIMA UNIVERSITY. FACULTY OF SCIENCE. REPORTS. MATHEMATICS, PHYSICS, CHEMISTRY. see *SCIENCES: COMPREHENSIVE WORKS*

KEISHA KINO ZAIRYO SHINPOJUMU KOENSHU/SYMPOSIUM OF FUNCTIONALLY GRADIENT MATERIALS FORUM. PROCEEDINGS. see *TECHNOLOGY: COMPREHENSIVE WORKS*

KINEMATICS AND PHYSICS OF CELESTIAL BODIES. see *ASTRONOMY*

530 JA ISSN 0918-8088
KOBAYASHI RIGAKU KENKYUJO REPOTO/KOBAYASHI INSTITUTE OF PHYSICAL RESEARCH. ANNUAL REPORT. (Text in English, Japanese) 1989. a. Kobayashi Rigaku Kenkyujo - Kobayashi Institute of Physical Research, 20-41, Higashimoto-machi 3-chome, Kokubunji-shi, Tokyo 185, Japan.

530 JA
KOBAYASHI RIKEN NYUSU/KOBAYASHI INSTITUTE OF PHYSICAL RESEARCH. NEWS. (Text in Japanese) 1983. q. Kobayashi Rigaku Kenkyujo - Kobayashi Institute of Physical Research, 20-41, Higashimoto-machi 3-chome, Kokubunji-shi, Tokyo 185, Japan.

530 JA ISSN 0389-0260
KOCHI UNIVERSITY. FACULTY OF SCIENCE. MEMOIRS. SERIES B, PHYSICS. (Text in English) 1980. a. Kochi University, Faculty of Science - Kochi Daigaku Rigakubu, 5-1, Akebonocho 2-chome, Kochi-shi, Kochi-ken 780, Japan. **Document type:** academic/scholarly publication.
—BLDSC (5597.832000).

KOLLOIDNYI ZHURNAL; journal of physico-chemistry of surface phenomena and dispersed systems. see *CHEMISTRY — Physical Chemistry*

KONGELIGE DANSKE VIDENSKABERNES SELSKAB. MATEMATISK - FYSISKE MEDDELELSER. see *MATHEMATICS*

KONSORYU/JAPANESE JOURNAL OF MULTIPHASE FLOW. see *ENGINEERING — Mechanical Engineering*

KONSORYU SHINPOJUMU KOEN RONBUNSHU/SYMPOSIUM ON MULTIPHASE FLOW. PROCEEDINGS. see *ENGINEERING — Mechanical Engineering*

KUMAMOTO JOURNAL OF MATHEMATICS. see *MATHEMATICS*

530 JA ISSN 0303-4070
QC1 CODEN: PRKUBN
KUMAMOTO UNIVERSITY. DEPARTMENT OF PHYSICS. PHYSICS REPORTS. 1973. biennial. free. Kumamoto Daigaku, Rigakubu Butsuri Kyoshitsu - Kumamoto University, Faculty of Science, Department of Physics, 39-1, Kurokami 2-chome, Kumamoto-shi, Kumamoto-ken 860, Japan. circ. 400. Indexed: Chem.Abstr., GeoRef., Math.R.
—BLDSC (6478.886000); CASDDS.
  Description: Presents technical research reports in physics from the university.

KVANTOVAYA ELEKTRONIKA; respublikanskii mezhvedomstvennyi sbornik nauchnykh trudov. see *ENGINEERING — Electrical Engineering*

530.44 JA
KYOTO UNIVERSITY. PLASMA PHYSICS LABORATORY. ANNUAL REVIEW. (Text in English) 1978. a. Kyoto University, Plasma Physics Laboratory, Gokasho, Uji-shi, Kyoto 611, Japan.

530.44 JA
KYOTO UNIVERSITY. PLASMA PHYSICS LABORATORY. RESEARCH REPORT. (Text in English) irreg. Kyoto University, Plasma Physics Laboratory - Kyoto Daigaku Heriotoron Kaku Yugo Kenkyu Senta, Goka-sho, Uji-shi, Kyoto 611, Japan.

530 548 US ISSN 0075-787X
LANDOLT-BOERNSTEIN, ZAHLENWERTE UND FUNKTIONEN AUS NATURWISSENSCHAFTEN UND TECHNIK. NEUE SERIE. GROUP 3: CRYSTAL PHYSICS. 1966. irreg. price varies. Springer-Verlag, 175 Fifth Ave., New York, NY 10010. TEL 212-460-1500. FAX 212-473-6272. (Also: Berlin, Heidelberg, Tokyo and Vienna) Ed. K.H. Hellwege. (reprint service avail. from ISI) **Document type:** academic/scholarly publication.
—CCC.

530 600 LV ISSN 0868-8257
TA4 CODEN: LJPSED
LATVIJAS FIZIKAS UN TEHNISKO ZINATNU ZURNALS/LATVIAN JOURNAL OF PHYSICS AND TECHNICAL SCIENCES. 1964. bi-m. 0.50 Ls. per no. to individuals; institutions 5 Ls. (effective 1995). Latvijas Zinatnu Akademijas, Fizikalas Energetikas Instituts, Aizkraukles iela, 21, Riga LV-1006, Latvia. TEL 371-2-552011. FAX 371-2-8820339. E-mail: fei@sun.lza.lv. Ed. Ju. Ekmanis. adv.; illus.; index. circ. 600. Indexed: INSPEC, Met.Abstr., World Alum.Abstr. **Document type:** academic/scholarly publication.
—BLDSC (0095.405000); CASDDS. **CCC**.
  Former titles: Latvijas Zinatnu Akademijas. Fisikas un Tehnisko Zinatnu Serija; Akademiya Nauk Latviiskoi S.S.R. Izvestiya. Seriya Fizicheskikh i Tkhnicheskikh Nauk (ISSN 0321-1673)
  Description: Covers solid state physics, energetics, themophysics, and gas thermodynamics.

LAWRENCE BERKELEY LABORATORY. CATALOG OF RESEARCH PROJECTS. see *SCIENCES: COMPREHENSIVE WORKS*

530 US ISSN 1068-3356
QC1 CODEN: BLPIEN
LEBEDEV PHYSICS INSTITUTE. BULLETIN. English translation of: Kratkie Soobshcheniya po Fizike (RU ISSN 0455-0595) 1974. m. $850 (effective 1996). (Russian Academy of Sciences, Institute of Physics - P.N. Lebedeva, RU) Allerton Press, Inc., 150 Fifth Ave., New York, NY 10011. TEL 212-924-3950. FAX 212-463-9684. Ed. N.G. Basov. index. Indexed: INSPEC (1974-), Phys.Ber. **Document type:** academic/scholarly publication.
—BLDSC (0409.280000); Ei; Faxon; SWETS. **CCC**.
  Formerly: Soviet Physics - Lebedev Institute Reports (ISSN 0364-2321)

530 US ISSN 0075-8450
CODEN: LNPHA4
LECTURE NOTES IN PHYSICS. 1969. irreg. price varies. Springer-Verlag, 175 Fifth Ave., New York, NY 10010. TEL 212-460-1500. FAX 212-473-6272. (Also: Berlin, Heidelberg, Tokyo and Vienna) (reprint service avail. from ISI) Indexed: Chem.Abstr., Ind.Sci.Rev., INSPEC, Phys.Ber. **Document type:** monographic series.
—BLDSC (5180.350000); CASDDS; Ei. **CCC**.

530 SI ISSN 0218-026X
LECTURE NOTES IN PHYSICS. (Text in English) 1985. irreg., vol. 53, 1993. price varies. World Scientific Publishing Co. Pte. Ltd., Farrer Rd., P.O. Box 128, Singapore 9128, Singapore. TEL 3825663. FAX 3825919. TELEX RS 28561 WSPC. (UK addr.: 73 Lynton Mead, Totteridge, London N20 8DH, England. TEL 44-81-4462461; US addr.: 1060 Main St., River Edge, NJ 07661. TEL 800-227-7562) **Document type:** monographic series.
—BLDSC (9360.003000).

530.1 NE ISSN 0377-9017
QC19.2 CODEN: LMPHDY
LETTERS IN MATHEMATICAL PHYSICS; a journal for the rapid dissemination of short contributions in the field of mathematical physics. Short title: L M P. 1975. m. fl.1212 to institutions; $739 to institutions in U.S. (effective 1996). Kluwer Academic Publishers, Postbus 17, 3300 AA Dordrecht, Netherlands. TEL 31-78-392392. FAX 31-78-392254. TELEX 29245 KAPG NL. E-mail: SERVICES@WKAP.NL. (Dist. by: Kluwer Academic Publishers Group, P.O. Box 322, 3300 AH Dordrecht, Netherlands. TEL 31-78-392392. FAX 31-78-546474; N. America dist. addr.: Box 358, Accord Sta., Hingham, MA 02018-0358. TEL 617-871-6600. FAX 617-871-6528) Ed. J.C. Cortet. adv. (also avail. in microform from UMI; reprint service avail. from SWZ) Indexed: ASCA, Astron.& Astrophys.Abstr., Chem.Abstr., Compumath, Curr.Cont., IBR, IBZ, Ind.Sci.Rev., INIS Atomind., INSPEC, Math.R., Phys.Ber., Ref.Zh., Sci.Cit.Ind., Zent.Math.
—BLDSC (5185.170154); CASDDS; Ei; Faxon; Genuine Article; SWETS; UMI; UnCover. **CCC**.
  Description: Covers the most recent developments in mathematical physics.
  Refereed Serial

530 BE
LEUVEN NOTES IN MATHEMATICAL AND THEORETICAL PHYSICS. SERIES A, MATHEMATICAL PHYSICS. 1989. irreg., vol.2, 1990. Leuven University Press, Krakenstraat 3, B-3000 Leuven, Belgium. TEL 32-16-324175. FAX 32-16-323782. **Document type:** academic/scholarly publication.

PHYSICS

530   BE
LEUVEN NOTES IN MATHEMATICAL AND THEORETICAL PHYSICS. SERIES B, THEORETICAL PARTICLE PHYSICS. 1990. irreg., vol.4, 1991. Leuven University Press, Krakenstraat 3, B-3000 Leuven, Belgium. TEL 32-16-324175. FAX 32-16-323782. **Document type:** academic/scholarly publication.

LICHTENBERG-JAHRBUCH. see BIOGRAPHY

530   LI
QC1
                    CODEN: LFRMA7
LIETUVOS FIZIKOS ZHURNALAS/LITOVSKII FIZICHESKII ZHURNAL. English translation: Lithuanian Physics Journal (US ISSN 1047-4064) (Text in English, Russian; summaries in English, Lithuanian, Russian) 1961. bi-m. $120 (effective thru 1996). (Akademiya Nauk Litvy, Institut Fiziki - Lithuanian Academy of Sciences, Institute of Physics) Leidykla Fisica, A. Gostauto 11, 2600 Vilnius, Lithuania. TEL 370-2-619-402. FAX 370-2-618-464. E-mail: shilcika@uj.pfi.lt. Ed. Algirdas Shileika. bibl.; charts; illus. circ. 600. **Indexed:** Chem.Abstr., INIS Atomind., INSPEC, World Alum.Abstr. **Document type:** academic/scholarly publication.
—CASDDS.
    Formerly (until 1993): Litovskii Fizicheskii Sbornik (ISSN 0024-2969)
    Description: Deals with semiconductor physics, spectroscopy and laser radiation.
    Refereed Serial

530   US   ISSN 1047-4064
QC1   **CODEN: LPJOED**
LITHUANIAN PHYSICS JOURNAL. English translation of: Lietuvos Fizikos Zhurnalas. 1974. bi-m. $860 (effective 1996). (Akademiya Nauk Litvy, Institut Fiziki, LI) Allerton Press, Inc., 150 Fifth Ave., New York, NY 10011. TEL 212-924-3950. FAX 212-463-9684. Ed. A. Sileika. **Indexed:** INSPEC, Math.R., Phys.Ber. **Document type:** academic/scholarly publication.
—BLDSC (0415.596000); Faxon. **CCC.**
    Formerly (until 1989): Soviet Physics - Collection (ISSN 0363-7891)

M M I PRESS POLYMER MONOGRAPH SERIES. see MATHEMATICS

M M I PRESS SYMPOSIUM SERIES. see MATHEMATICS

538.3   US   ISSN 1055-6273
M R (SAN FRANCISCO); the news magazine of magnetic resonance. 1991. q. $60. Miller Freeman, Inc., 600 Harrison St., San Francisco, CA 94107. TEL 415-905-2200. FAX 415-905-2233. Ed. Peter Ogle. adv. circ. 20,000.
    Description: Covers magnetic resonance imaging in detail.

M R NYUMON KOZA TEKISUTO/BEGINNER'S TEXTBOOK OF MAGNETIC RESONANCE IN MEDICINE. (Magnetic Resonance) see MEDICAL SCIENCES — Radiology And Nuclear Medicine

M R RINSHO KOZA TEKISUTO/TEXTBOOK OF CLINICAL MEDICINE ON MAGNETIC RESONANCE. (Magnetic Resonance) see MEDICAL SCIENCES — Radiology And Nuclear Medicine

M R S BULLETIN. (Materials Research Society) see ENGINEERING — Engineering Mechanics And Materials

530 621.3   US   ISSN 1055-6915
TP156.M26   **CODEN: MELSE3**
MAGNETIC AND ELECTRICAL SEPARATION. 4/yr. (in 1 vol., 4 nos./vol.). 131 ECU (effective 1996). Gordon & Breach Science Publishers, c/o International Publishers Distributor, 820 Town Center Dr., Langhorne, PA 19047. TEL 215-750-2642. FAX 215-750-6343. (Subscr. to: International Publishers Distributor, P.O. Box 90, Reading, Berkshire RG1 8JL, England. TEL 44-173-456-8316). Eds. Jan Svoboda, F.J. Friedlander. index. (also avail. in microform) **Indexed:** Met.Abstr.
—BLDSC (5335.900000); CASDDS. **CCC.**
    Formerly (until vol.3): Magnetic Separation News (ISSN 0731-3632)
    Refereed Serial

MAGNETIC RESONANCE IN MEDICINE. see MEDICAL SCIENCES — Radiology And Nuclear Medicine

538.3   US   ISSN 0097-7330
QC762   **CODEN: MRSRBL**
MAGNETIC RESONANCE REVIEW. 1972. 4/yr. (in 1 vol., 4 nos./vol.). 293 ECU (effective 1996). Gordon and Breach Science Publishers, c/o International Publishers Distributor, 820 Town Center Dr., Langhorne, PA 19047. TEL 215-750-2642. FAX 215-750-6343. (Subscr. to: International Publishers Distributor, P.O. Box 90, Reading, Berkshire RG1 8JL, England. TEL 44-173-456-8316) Ed. Charles P. Poole, Jr. adv.; bk.rev.; index. (also avail. in microform) **Indexed:** Chem.Abstr., INSPEC, Met.Abstr.
—BLDSC (5337.800000); CASDDS; Faxon; UnCover. **CCC.**
    Description: Surveys all the magnetic resonance literature so that researchers in the field can rely upon it as a prime source of reference material.
    Refereed Serial

530   JA   ISSN 0285-0192
QC750   **CODEN: NOJGD3**
MAGNETICS SOCIETY OF JAPAN. JOURNAL/NIHON OYO JIKI GAKKAISHI. (Text in English, Japanese) 1977. 5/yr. 2000 Yen per no. Magnetics Society of Japan - Nihon Oyo Jiki Gakkai, 2-8, Toranomon 1-chome, Minato-ku, Tokyo 105, Japan. **Indexed:** Chem.Abstr., INIS Atomind.
—BLDSC (4819.180000); CASDDS.

530   JA
MAGNETICS SOCIETY OF JAPAN. PAPERS OF TECHNICAL MEETING/NIHON OYO JIKI GAKKAI KENKYUKAI SHIRYO. (Text in Japanese; summaries in English) irreg. Magnetics Society of Japan - Nihon Oyo Jiki Gakkai, 2-8, Toranomon 1-chome, Minato-ku, Tokyo 105, Japan.

530 520   IR   ISSN 0254-9611
MAJALLAH-I FIZIK/IRANIAN JOURNAL OF PHYSICS. (Text in Persian; table of contents in English) 1983. q. IRI.3400 (Middle East £23; Europe £25; elsewhere £30). Markaz-i Nashr-i Danishgahi - Iran University Press, 85 Park Ave., Dr. Bihishti Ave., P.O. Box 15875-4748, Tehran, Iran. TEL 98-21-8713232. FAX 98-21-8861749. TELEX 213636-8-D5300. Ed. R. Mansouri. bk.rev. circ. 4,000. **Indexed:** INIS Atomind. **Document type:** academic/scholarly publication.
    Description: Aims to maintain personal communication among Farsi speaking physicists. Deals with educational and cultural aspects of physics. Reports on the most recent developments in fundamental and applied physics.

530   XR
MASARYK UNIVERSITY. FACULTY OF SCIENCES. SCRIPTA PHYSICA/SCRIPTA FACULTATIS SCIENTIARUM NATURALIUM UNIVERSITATIS MASARYKIANAE BRUNENSIS: PHYSICA. (Text in English, French, German, Russian) a. price varies. Masarykova Universita, Prirodovedecka Fakulta - Masaryk University, Faculty of Sciences, Kotlarska 2, 611 37 Brno, Czech Republic. **Indexed:** INSPEC. **Document type:** academic/scholarly publication.
    Formerly: Scripta Facultatis Scientiarum Naturalium Universitatis Purkynianae Brunensis: Physica (ISSN 0231-6129)

MASS SPECTROMETRY. see CHEMISTRY

MATEMATICHESKAYA FIZIKA I FUNKTSIONAL'NYI ANALIZ. see MATHEMATICS

MATEMATIKA, FYZIKA, INFORMATIKA. see EDUCATION

530   NE   ISSN 0167-577X
TA401   **CODEN: MLETDJ**
MATERIALS LETTERS; an interdisciplinary journal affiliated with the Materials Research Society devoted to the rapid publication of short communications on the science, applications and processing of materials. (Text in English) 1982. 18/yr. fl.1416($863) (effective 1996). (Materials Research Society) North-Holland (Subsidiary of: Elsevier Science B.V.), P.O. Box 211, 1000 AE Amsterdam, Netherlands. TEL 31-20-4853911. FAX 31-20-4853598. TELEX 18582 ESPA NL. (Subscr. in U.S. and Canada to: Elsevier Science Inc., Box 882, Madison Sq. Sta., New York, NY 10159. TEL 212-989-5800. FAX 212-633-3990) Ed.Bd. (also avail. in microform from UMI; back issues avail.) **Indexed:** Ceram.Abstr., Chem.Abstr., INIS Atomind., INSPEC, Int.Aerosp.Abstr., Met.Abstr., Phys.Ber., World Alum.Abstr. **Document type:** academic/scholarly publication.
—BLDSC (5396.002000); CASDDS; Ei; Faxon; Genuine Article; SWETS; UnCover. **CCC.**
    Description: Covers the entire spectrum of materials science, from solid state physics to materials technology.
    Refereed Serial

530   NE   ISSN 0167-790X
                   CODEN: MPTPD8
MATERIALS PROCESSING: THEORY AND PRACTICES. 1980. irreg., vol.9, 1991. price varies. Elsevier Science B.V., Books Division, P.O. Box 211, 1000 AE Amsterdam, Netherlands. TEL 31-20-4853911. FAX 31-20-4853705. TELEX 18582 ESPA NL. E-mail: nlinfo-f@elsevier.nl; usinfo-f@elsevier.com; forinfo-kyf04035@niftyserve.or.jp; Site addr.: http://www.elsevier.nl/. (Subscr. in U.S. and Canada to: Elsevier Science Inc., Box 882, Madison Sq. Sta., NY 10159. TEL 212-989-5800) Ed. F.F.Y. Wang. **Indexed:** INSPEC. **Document type:** monographic series.
—CASDDS. **CCC.**
    Refereed Serial

530 540 620   US   ISSN 0272-9172
                   CODEN: MRSPDH
MATERIALS RESEARCH SOCIETY SYMPOSIUM PROCEEDINGS. 1981. irreg. (approx. 50/yr.), no.418, 1995. price varies. Materials Research Society, 9800 McKnight Rd., Pittsburgh, PA 15237. TEL 412-367-3012. FAX 412-367-4373. (reprint service avail. from UMI) **Indexed:** Anthropol.Lit., Chem.Abstr., INIS Atomind., INSPEC, Phys.Ber. **Document type:** proceedings.
—BLDSC (5396.412000); CASDDS; Ei; SWETS; UMI. **CCC.**

MATERIALS SCIENCE AND ENGINEERING R: REPORTS. see ENGINEERING — Engineering Mechanics And Materials

530 541.3   SZ   ISSN 0255-5476
TA401.3   **CODEN: MSFOEP**
MATERIALS SCIENCE FORUM. 1984. 30/yr. $2580. Trans Tech Publications, Trottenstr. 20, CH-8037 Zurich, Switzerland. FAX 01-2721092. Ed.Bd. circ. 800. **Indexed:** Chem.Abstr., INIS Atomind., INSPEC, Met.Abstr. **Document type:** academic/scholarly publication.
—BLDSC (5396.435700); CASDDS; Ei; SWETS; UnCover.
    Incorporates (in 1992): Crystal Properties and Preparation; Diffusion and Defect Monograph Series; Which was formerly: Diffusion Monograph Series.

MATHEMATICAL AND PHYSICAL SOCIETY OF EGYPT. PROCEEDINGS. see MATHEMATICS

MATHEMATICAL PHYSICS AND APPLIED MATHEMATICS. see MATHEMATICS

5220 PHYSICS

530 510 US
QC19.2
MATHEMATICAL PHYSICS REVIEWS. vol.2, 1981. a. 151 ECU (effective 1996). Harwood Academic Publishers, c/o International Publishers Distributor, 820 Town Center Dr., Langhorne, PA 19047. TEL 215-750-2642. FAX 215-750-6343. (Subscr. to: International Publishers Distributor, P.O. Box 90, Reading, Berkshire RG1 8JL, England. TEL 44-173-456-8316) Ed. S.P. Norikov. index. (also avail. in microform; back issues avail.) **Indexed:** INSPEC. **Document type:** academic/scholarly publication.
—CCC.
Formerly (until vol.10): Soviet Scientific Reviews. Section C: Mathematical Physics Reviews (ISSN 0143-0416)
Refereed Serial

530 510 NE ISSN 0921-3767
MATHEMATICAL PHYSICS STUDIES. (Supplementary series to: Letters in Mathematical Physics (ISSN 0377-9017)) 1977. irreg., vol.16, 1993. price varies. Kluwer Academic Publishers, Postbus 17, 3300 AA Dordrecht, Netherlands. TEL 31-78-392392. FAX 31-78-392254. TELEX 29245 KAPG NL. (Dist. by: Kluwer Academic Publishers Group, P.O. Box 322, 3300 AH Dordrecht, Netherlands. TEL 31-78-392392. FAX 31-78-546474; N. America dist. addr.: Box 358, Accord Sta., Hingham, MA 02018-0358. TEL 617-871-6600. FAX 617-871-6528) Ed.Bd. **Indexed:** INSPEC, Math.R. **Document type:** monographic series.
—Faxon.
Refereed Serial

530 US ISSN 1081-2865
▼**MATHEMATICS AND MECHANICS OF SOLIDS.** Announced for publication in 1996. q. $65 to individuals; institutions $250 (effective 1996). Sage Publications, Inc., Sage Science Press, 2455 Teller Rd., Thousand Oaks, CA 91320. TEL 805-499-0721. FAX 805-499-0871. Ed.Bd. **Document type:** academic/scholarly publication.
Description: Publishes original research that elucidates the mechanical behavior of solids, with particular emphasis on mathematical principles.
Refereed Serial

MATHEMATISCHE SEMESTERBERICHTE; zur Foerderung der Mathematik in Unterricht und Kultur. see MATHEMATICS

MEASUREMENT. see METROLOGY AND STANDARDIZATION

MEASUREMENT SCIENCE AND TECHNOLOGY. see INSTRUMENTS

MECHANICS AND PHYSICS OF DISCRETE SYSTEMS. see ENGINEERING — Mechanical Engineering

MEDICAL PHYSICS. see MEDICAL SCIENCES

MEDICAL PHYSICS SERIES. see MEDICAL SCIENCES

530 JA ISSN 0910-0717
CODEN: MUKKDH
MEIDAI UCHUSAN KENKYUSHITSU KIJI/NAGOYA UNIVERSITY. SOLAR-TERRESTRIAL ENVIRONMENT LABORATORY. COSMIC RAY SECTION. PROCEEDINGS. (Text in Japanese) 1947. irreg. (1-2/yr.). exchange basis. Nagoya University, Solar-Terrestrial Environment Laboratory, Cosmic Ray Section, Chikusa-ku, Nagoya-shi, Aichi-ken 464-01, Japan. FAX 52-782-4992. Ed. Y. Muraki. cum.index: 1947-1993. **Indexed:** Chem.Abstr., INSPEC (1992-), JTA. **Document type:** proceedings.
—CASDDS.

MEISEI DAIGAKU KENKYU KIYO. RIKOGAKUBU/MEISEI UNIVERSITY. RESEARCH BULLETIN. PHYSICAL SCIENCES AND ENGINEERING. see ENGINEERING

METHODEN UND VERFAHREN DER MATHEMATISCHEN PHYSIK. see MATHEMATICS

530 US ISSN 0076-695X
CODEN: MEEPAN
METHODS OF EXPERIMENTAL PHYSICS. 1959. irreg., vol.27, 1988. Academic Press, Inc., 525 B St., Ste. 1900, San Diego, CA 92101-4495. TEL 619-231-0926. FAX 619-699-6715. (Subscr. to: Order Dept., 6277 Sea Harbor Dr., 4th Fl., Orlando, FL 32887. TEL 800-321-5068) Eds. Robert Celotta, Juah Levine. (reprint service avail. from ISI) **Indexed:** Chem.Abstr., INSPEC, Phys.Ber.
—BLDSC (5748.067000); CASDDS. **CCC.**
Refereed Serial

METHODS OF SURFACE CHARACTERIZATION. see CHEMISTRY — Electrochemistry

MICROBEAM ANALYSIS. see CHEMISTRY — Analytical Chemistry

530 JA
MICROPROCESS CONFERENCE. DIGEST OF PAPERS. (Text in English) 1988. a. Japan Society of Applied Physics - Oyo Butsuri Gakkai, 12-3, Kudan Kita 1-chome, Chiyoda-ku, Tokyo 102, Japan.

530 UK ISSN 0965-0393
TA407 CODEN: MSMEEU
MODELLING & SIMULATION IN MATERIALS SCIENCE AND ENGINEERING. 1992. q. £204($420) (effective 1996). (Institute of Physics) I O P Publishing Ltd., Techno House, Redcliffe Way, Bristol, Avon BS1 6NX, England. TEL 0117-929-7481. FAX 0117-929-4318. TELEX 449149 INSTP G. (U.S. subscr. to: American Institute of Physics, Subscriber Services, 500 Sunnyside Blvd., Woodbury, NY 11797-2900. TEL 516-349-7800) Ed. M.I. Baskes. index. circ. 129. (also avail. in microfiche) **Indexed:** INSPEC (1992-). **Document type:** academic/scholarly publication.
—BLDSC (5883.531980); CASDDS; Ei; Genuine Article; SWETS. **CCC.**
Description: Covers the whole range of methods and applications of modeling and simulation in materials science and engineering.

530.4 NE ISSN 0167-7837
CODEN: MPCSDY
MODERN PROBLEMS IN CONDENSED MATTER SCIENCES. (Text in English) 1982. irreg., vol.35, 1992. price varies. Elsevier Science B.V., Books Division, P.O. Box 211, 1000 AE Amsterdam, Netherlands. TEL 31-20-4853911. FAX 31-20-4853705. TELEX 18582 ESPA NL. E-mail: nlinfo-f@elsevier.nl; usinfo-f@elsevier.com; forinfo-kyf04035@niftyserve.or.jp; Site addr.: http://www.elsevier.nl/. (Subscr. in U.S. and Canada to: Elsevier Science Inc., Box 882, Madison Sq. Sta., New York, NY 10159. TEL 212-989-5800) Eds. V.M. Agranovich, A.A. Maraudin. (back issues avail.) **Indexed:** INSPEC. **Document type:** monographic series.
Refereed Serial

MOLECULAR PHYSICS. see CHEMISTRY — Physical Chemistry

MONOGRAPHS IN CRYOGENICS. see ENGINEERING

MONOGRAPHS IN PHYSICAL MEASUREMENT. see ENGINEERING

530 540 US ISSN 0969-3386
MONOGRAPHS ON THE PHYSICS AND CHEMISTRY OF MATERIALS. irreg. price varies. Oxford University Press, 200 Madison Ave., New York, NY 10016. TEL 212-679-7300. Ed.Bd. **Indexed:** INSPEC. **Document type:** monographic series.
Refereed Serial

530 US ISSN 0960-0175
QC1 CODEN: JMPSEC
MOSCOW PHYSICAL SOCIETY. JOURNAL. Short title: J M P S. 1991. q. $325. Allerton Press, Inc., 150 Fifth Ave., New York, NY 10011. TEL 212-924-3950. FAX 212-463-9684. Ed. L.V. Keldysh. index. (also avail. in microfiche; microform; back issues avail.) **Indexed:** INSPEC (1991-). **Document type:** academic/scholarly publication.
—BLDSC (4828.372000); CASDDS; UnCover. **CCC.**
Description: Subjects include: mathematical and general physics, classical phenomenology, non-linear phenomena, plasma physics, optics and spectroscopy, condensed matter physics, high energy physics, field theory, and general relativity.
Refereed Serial

530 US ISSN 0027-1349
Q4 CODEN: MUPBAC
MOSCOW UNIVERSITY PHYSICS BULLETIN. English translation of: Moskovskii Universitet. Vestnik. Seriya 3: Fizika, Astronomiya (RU ISSN 0579-9392) 1966. bi-m. $855 (effective 1996). (Moskovskii Universitet, RU) Allerton Press, Inc., 150 Fifth Ave., New York, NY 10011. TEL 212-924-3950. FAX 212-463-9684. Ed. V.I. Trukhin. bk.rev.; charts; illus.; index. **Indexed:** INSPEC (1979-), Math.R. **Document type:** academic/scholarly publication.
—BLDSC (0416.240000); Faxon; UnCover. **CCC.**

530 520 RU ISSN 0579-9392
CODEN: VMUFAO
MOSKOVSKII UNIVERSITET. VESTNIK. SERIYA 3: FIZIKA, ASTRONOMIYA. English translation: Moscow University Physics Bulletin (US ISSN 0027-1349) (Contents page in English) bi-m. $85 (effective 1996). Moskovskii Universitet, Ul. Gertsena 5-7, 103009 Moscow, Russia. bk.rev.; bibl.; index. **Indexed:** Chem.Abstr., Int.Aerosp.Abstr., Math.R., Met.Abstr., Meteor.& Geoastrophys.Abstr., Phys.Ber., World Alum.Abstr. **Document type:** academic/scholarly publication.
—BLDSC (0032.450000); CASDDS; Genuine Article. **CCC.**
Supersedes in part (in 1960): Moskovskii Universitet. Vestnik. Seriya Matematiki, Mekhaniki, Astronomii, Fiziki, Khimii (ISSN 0579-9376)

530 US ISSN 0258-1221
CODEN: NASBD3
N A T O ADVANCED SCIENCE INSTITUTES SERIES B: PHYSICS. irreg., vol.337, 1995. (North Atlantic Treaty Organization, Scientific Affairs Division, BE) Plenum Publishing Corp., 233 Spring St., New York, NY 10013. TEL 212-620-8000. FAX 212-463-0742. TELEX 23-421139. (back issues avail.) **Indexed:** INSPEC, Meteor.& Geoastrophys.Abstr. **Document type:** monographic series, proceedings.
●Also available online. Vendor(s): European Space Agency (File no.128).
—BLDSC (6033.648710); CASDDS; Ei. **CCC.**
Description: Proceedings of NATO sponsored conferences in physics.
Refereed Serial

533.5 NE ISSN 0169-9431
CODEN: NDVTBN
N E V A C BLAD/DUTCH VACUUM SOCIETY. JOURNAL. 1963. 4/yr. fl.50. Nederlandse Vacuumvereniging - Dutch Vacuum Society, c/o FOM - Institute for Atomic and Molecular Physics, Kruislaan 407, 1098 SJ Amsterdam, Netherlands. TEL 31-20-6081234. FAX 31-20-6684106. Ed. Elias Vlieg. adv.; bk.rev.; charts; illus.; pat. circ. 450. **Indexed:** Chem.Abstr., INSPEC. **Document type:** academic/scholarly publication, newsletter.
—CASDDS; SWETS.
Formerly: Nederlands Tijdschrift voor Vacuumtechniek - Dutch Journal of Vacuum Technology (ISSN 0047-9233)
Description: Studies vacuum technology and its applications.

539.7 NE
N I K H E F. K BULLETIN. (Text in English) 1976. irreg., no.15, 1990. Nationaal Instituut voor Kernfysica en Hoge-Energiefysica, Sectie-K - Institute for Physics Research, Postbus 41882, 1009 AJ Amsterdam, Netherlands. TEL 31-20-5922000. illus. circ. 150. **Document type:** bulletin.
Formerly: I K O Newsletter.

530 NE
N I K H E F ANNUAL REPORT. 1946. a. Nationaal Instituut voor Kernfysica en Hoge-Energiefysica, Sectie-K - National Institute for Nuclear Physics Research, Section K, Postbus 41882, 1009 AJ Amsterdam, Netherlands. TEL 31-20-5922000. circ. 650. **Document type:** corporate report.
Former titles: National Instituut voor Kernfysica en Hoge-Energiefysica; Instituut voor Kernphysisch Onderzoek. Annual Report.

530   JA   ISSN 0914-5613
CODEN: MNIRDD
N I P R SYMPOSIUM ON UPPER ATMOSPHERE PHYSICS. PROCEEDINGS. (Text in English) 1988. a., no.7, 1994. exchange basis. National Institute of Polar Research - Kokuritsu Kyokuchi Kenkyujo, Library, 9-10, Kaga 1-chome, Itabashi-ku, Tokyo 173, Japan. TEL 03-3962-2214. FAX 03-3962-2225. TELEX 272-3515 POLRSCJ. Ed. Takeo Hirasawa. circ. 1,000. **Indexed:** Geo.Abstr., GeoRef., Meteor.& Geoastrophys.Abstr. **Document type:** proceedings.
—BLDSC (6848.270620); CASDDS.
    Supersedes in part (in 1987): National Institute of Polar Research. Memoirs. Special Issue (ISSN 0386-0744); Which was formerly (1967-1972): Japanese Antarctic Research Expedition Scientific Reports. Special Issue (ISSN 0386-5452)
Refereed Serial

530   UK   ISSN 0143-1536
N P L NEWS. 1900. irreg. (1-2/yr.). free. National Physical Laboratory, Teddington, Middx. TW11 0LW, England. TEL 0181-943-6055. FAX 0181-943-2155. Ed. H.C. Fuller. circ. 6,000. **Indexed:** INSPEC (1985-). **Document type:** newsletter.
—BLDSC (6180.510000). CCC.

530   II   ISSN 0027-6898
N P L TECHNICAL BULLETIN. (Text in English) 1966. q. free. (National Physical Laboratory) S.K. Joshi, Ed. & Pub., Dr. K.S. Krishnan Rd., New Delhi 110012, India. TEL 91-11-5741441. FAX 91-11-5752678. TELEX 031-77099 NPL IN. adv.; charts; illus.; pat.; stat. circ. 1,000. (also avail. in record)

530.44   JA   ISSN 0547-1567
QC718
NAGOYA UNIVERSITY. INSTITUTE OF PLASMA PHYSICS. ANNUAL REVIEW/NAGOYA DAIGAKU PURAZUMA KENKYUJO NENPO. (Text in English) 1960. a. exchange basis. Nagoya University, Plasma Science Center - Nagoya Daigaku Purazuma Kagaku Senta, Furo-cho, Chikusa-ku, Nagoya-shi 464, Japan. **Indexed:** INIS Atomind.

530   US   ISSN 1073-7294
▼**NANONEWS.** 1995. bi-m. $97 (outside N. America $117) (effective 1996). Superconductivity Publications, 828 Livingston Ave., North Brunswick, NJ 08902-2356. TEL 908-846-2002. FAX 908-846-2050. E-mail: 74130.650@compuserve.com. Ed. C. Jim Russell; Pub. C. Jim Russell. adv.; B&W page $500; adv. contact: Kathy Kleppin. pat. (back issues avail.)
    Description: Covers a broad range of future technologies, including nanoprocessing, nanofabrication, nanocomposite materials and nanostructured materials, nanoscale analytical instruments and micromachines, and many forms of nanobiology.
Refereed Serial

530 621.3   UK   ISSN 0957-4484
T174.7   CODEN: NNOTER
NANOTECHNOLOGY. 1990. q. £193($398) (effective 1996). (Institute of Physics) I O P Publishing Ltd., Techno House, Redcliffe Way, Bristol BS1 6NX, England. TEL 0117-929-7481. FAX 0117-929-4318. TELEX 449149 INSTP G. (U.S. subscr. to: American Institute of Physics, Member and Subscriber Services, 500 Sunnyside Blvd., Woodbury, NY 11797-2900. TEL 516-349-7800) Ed. E. Clayton Teague. index. circ. 305. (also avail. in microfiche; microform; back issues avail.) **Indexed:** INSPEC (1990-). **Document type:** academic/scholarly publication.
—BLDSC (6015.335540); CASDDS; Ei; Genuine Article; SWETS. **CCC.**
    Description: Aims to promote the dissemination of research and improve understanding among the engineering, fabrications, optics, electronics, materials science, biology, and medical communities.
Refereed Serial

530   US   ISSN 1073-7308
▼**NANOWEEK.** 1995. s-m. $277 (effective 1996). Superconductivity Publications, 828 Livingston Ave., North Brunswick, NJ 08902-2356. TEL 908-846-2002. FAX 908-846-2050. E-mail: 74130.650@compuserve.com. Ed. C. Jim Russell; Pub. C. Jim Russell. adv. contact: Kathy Kleppin. pat. (back issues avail.) **Document type:** newsletter.
    Description: Covers the emerging technologies of nanofabrication, nanoprocessing, nanomaterials, and nanobiology.

NATIONAL ACADEMY OF SCIENCES, INDIA. PROCEEDINGS. SECTION A. PHYSICAL SCIENCES. see *SCIENCES: COMPREHENSIVE WORKS*

530   JA   ISSN 0917-1185
NATIONAL INSTITUTE FOR FUSION SCIENCE. ANNUAL REPORT. (Text in English) a. National Institute for Fusion Science - Kaku Yugo Kagaku Kenkyujo, Furocho, Chikusa-ku, Nagoya-shi, Aichi-ken 464-01, Japan. Ed. Kazuo Toi. **Document type:** academic/scholarly publication.
—BLDSC (1364.685000).

530   JA   ISSN 0915-6348
CODEN: RNPSE5
NATIONAL INSTITUTE FOR FUSION SCIENCE. RESEARCH REPORT. (Text in English) irreg. National Institute for Fusion Science, Research Information Center, Nagoya 464-01, Japan. Ed. T. Toi. **Indexed:** INSPEC.
—BLDSC (7762.722437); CASDDS.

539.76 621.48   ISSN 0915-6356
NATIONAL INSTITUTE FOR FUSION SCIENCE. RESEARCH REPORT. TECH SERIES. Key Title: Research Report N I F S. TECH Series. (Text in Japanese) 1990. irreg. National Institute for Fusion Science, Research Information Center, Nagoya 464-01, Japan. Ed. T. Toi.
—BLDSC (7762.722440).

NATIONAL INSTITUTE OF STANDARDS AND TECHNOLOGY. JOURNAL OF RESEARCH. see *METROLOGY AND STANDARDIZATION*

530   JA
NATIONAL LABORATORY FOR HIGH ENERGY PHYSICS. MONTHLY BULLETIN/KOENERUGIKEN GEPPO. (Text in Japanese) 1972. m. National Laboratory for High Energy Physics - Koenerugi Butsurigaku Kenkyujo, 1-1, Oho, Tsukuba-shi, Ibaraki-ken 305, Japan. TEL 0298-64-1171. **Document type:** government publication.

NATIONAL TECHNICAL REPORT. see *ENGINEERING — Electrical Engineering*

530 371   GW
NATURWISSENSCHAFTEN IM UNTERRICHT PHYSIK; Beitraege zu seinen fachlichen, methodischen und didaktischen Problemen. 1967. 5/yr. DM.75.80 (foreign DM.80.80). Erhard Friedrich Verlag GmbH, Im Brande 17, 30926 Seelze, Germany. TEL 0511-40004-0. FAX 0511-4000444. (Subscr. to: Postfach 100150, 30917 Seelze, Germany) index, cum.index. circ. 3,000. (processed) **Document type:** academic/scholarly publication.
    Formerly (until 1990): Physikunterricht (ISSN 0031-9295)

530.07   NE
NEDERLANDSE CENTRALE ORGANISATIE VOOR TOEGEPAST - NATUURWETENSCHAPPELIJK ONDERZOEK. TECHNISCH - PHYSISCHE DIENST. ANNUAL REPORT. (Text in English) 1946. a. free. Nederlandse Centrale Organisatie voor Toegepast - Natuurwetenschappelijk Onderzoek, Technisch - Physische Dienst, Stieltjesweg 1, Delft, Netherlands. Ed.Bd. circ. 2,700.

NEW TECHNOLOGY JAPAN. see *MACHINERY*

530   UN   ISSN 0077-8907
NEW TRENDS IN PHYSICS TEACHING. (Text in English and French) 1968. irreg., latest no.6. price varies. Unesco, 7-9 Place de Fontenoy, 75700 Paris, France. TEL 45-77-16-10. (Dist. in U.S. by: Unipub, 4611-F Assembly Dr., Lanham, MD 20706-4391)

530   UN
NEWS FROM I C T P. 1984. q. International Atomic Energy Agency, International Centre for Theoretical Physics, Strada Costiera 11, P.O. Box 586, 34100 Trieste, Italy. TEL 40-22-40111. FAX 40-22-4163. TELEX 460392 ICTP I. E-mail: sci-info@ictp.trieste.it. **Document type:** newsletter.

530   NE
NIELS BOHR - COLLECTED WORKS. 1972. irreg., vol.9, 1986. price varies. Elsevier Science B.V., Books Division, P.O. Box 211, 1000 AE Amsterdam, Netherlands. TEL 31-20-4853911. FAX 31-20-4853705. TELEX 18582 ESPA NL. E-mail: nlinfo@elsevier.nl; usinfo-f@elsevier.com; forinfo-kyf04035@niftyserve.or.jp; Site addr.: http://www.elsevier.nl/. (Subscr. in U.S. and Canada to: Elsevier Science Inc., Box 882, Madison Sq. Sta., New York, NY 10159. TEL 212-989-5800) Ed. L. Rosenfeld. **Document type:** monographic series.
Refereed Serial

530   JA
NIHON BUTSURI GAKKAI BUNKAKAI KOEN GAIYOSHU/PHYSICAL SOCIETY OF JAPAN. SECTIONAL MEETING. ABSTRACTS. (Text in English, Japanese) 1952. s-a. Nihon Butsuri Gakkai - Physical Society of Japan, Kikai Shinko Bldg., Rm. 211, Shiba Koen 3-5-8, Minato-ku, Tokyo 105, Japan. FAX 80-3-3432-0997. Dir. Mariko Takabatake. **Document type:** abstracting/indexing.

530   JA
NIHON BUTSURI GAKKAI NENKAI KOEN GAIYOSHU/PHYSICAL SOCIETY OF JAPAN. ANNUAL MEETING. ABSTRACTS. (Text in English, Japanese) a. 9200 Yen (effective 1995). Nihon Butsuri Gakkai - Physical Society of Japan, Kikai Shinko Bldg., Rm. 211, Shiba Koen 3-5-8, Minato-ku, Tokyo 105, Japan. FAX 81-3-3432-0997. Dir. Mariko Takabatake. **Document type:** abstracting/indexing.

540 530   JA   ISSN 0287-864X
NIHON RIKAGAKU KYOKAI. KENKYU KIYO. (Text in Japanese) 1968. a. 1500 Yen. Nihon Rikagaku Kyokai - Japan Society of Physics and Chemistry Education, 11-2-206 Sugamo 1-chome, Toshima-ku, Tokyo 170, Japan. circ. 800. **Document type:** bulletin.
    Description: Research bulletin of the society.

539   JA   ISSN 0388-0125
QC976.A3
NIIGATA AIRGLOW OBSERVATORY. BULLETIN. (Text in English) 1972. a. exchange basis. Niigata Daigaku, Rigakubu, Fuzoku Chokoso Taikiko Kansokujo - Niigata University, Faculty of Science, Niigata Airglow Observatory, 8050 Igarashi Nino-cho, Niigata-shi, Niigata-ken 950-21, Japan.

530 540   JA   ISSN 0286-7125
CODEN: NIRID7
NIIGATA RIKAGAKU/JOURNAL OF PHYSICS AND CHEMISTRY OF NIIGATA. (Text in Japanese) a. Niigata-ken Rikagaku Gijutsu Shokuin Kyogikai, Niigata-ken Eisei Kogai Kenkyujo, 314-1 Sowa, Niigata-shi, Niigata-ken 950-21, Japan. abstr. **Indexed:** Chem.Abstr.
—CASDDS.
    Description: Contains original articles, reviews, commentary, and news.

530   JA   ISSN 0371-2699
NIIGATA UNIVERSITY. FACULTY OF SCIENCE. SCIENCE REPORTS. SERIES B: PHYSICS. (Text in European languages) 1964. irreg. exchange basis. Niigata Daigaku, Rigakubu - Niigata University, Faculty of Science, 8050 Igarashi Nino-cho, Niigata-shi 950-21, Japan.

530   PL   ISSN 0044-1597
QA935   CODEN: NLVBAO
NONLINEAR VIBRATIONS PROBLEMS/ZAGADNIENIA DRGAN NIELINIOWYCH. (Text in English; summaries in Polish, Russian) 1960. irreg., vol.25, 1992. price varies. (Polska Akademia Nauk, Instytut Podstawowych Problemow Techniki) Wydawnictwo Naukowe P W N, Ul. Miodowa 10, 00-251 Warsaw, Poland. TEL 48-22-312738. FAX 48-22-267163. TELEX 813763 PWN PL. Ed. Z. Wesolowski. abstr.; bibl.; charts; illus.; index. circ. 300. **Indexed:** Appl.Mech.Rev., INSPEC.
—BLDSC (6117.320000).

NONLINEARITY. see *MATHEMATICS*

PHYSICS

530   NE   ISSN 0927-5029
NORTH-HOLLAND DELTA SERIES. (Text in English) 1989. irreg., vol.16, 1993. price varies. Elsevier Science B.V., Books Division, P.O. Box 211, 1000 AE Amsterdam, Netherlands. TEL 31-20-4853911. FAX 31-20-4853705. TELEX 18582 ESPA NL. E-mail: nlinfo-f@elsevier.nl; usinfo-f@elsevier.com; forinfo-kyf04035@niftyserve.or.jp; Site addr.: http://www.elsevier.nl/. (Subscr. in U.S. and Canada to: Elsevier Science Inc., Box 882, Madison Sq. Sta., New York, NY 10159. TEL 212-989-5800) (back issues avail.) **Document type:** monographic series.
Refereed Serial

530   NE   ISSN 0925-5818
NORTH-HOLLAND PERSONAL LIBRARY. (Text in English) 1985. irreg., latest 1992. price varies. Elsevier Science B.V., Books Division, P.O. Box 211, 1000 AE Amsterdam, Netherlands. TEL 31-20-4853911. FAX 31-20-4853705. TELEX 18582 ESPA NL. E-mail: nlinfo-f@elsevier.nl; usinfo-f@elsevier.com; forinfo-kyf04035@niftyserve.or.jp; Site addr.: http://www.elsevier.nl/. (Subscr. in U.S. and Canada to: Elsevier Science Inc., Box 882, Madison Sq. Sta., New York, NY 10159. TEL 212-989-5800) (back issues avail.) **Document type:** monographic series.
Refereed Serial

NOTES ON NUMERICAL FLUID MECHANICS. see *ENGINEERING — Hydraulic Engineering*

NUCLEAR FUSION/FUSION NUCLEAIRE; journal of plasma physics and thermonuclear fusion. see *PHYSICS — Nuclear Physics*

530   IT   ISSN 0393-4578
CODEN: FITEDJ
IL NUOVO SAGGIATORE. 1958. bi-m. $60 to non-members (effective 1994). Editrice Compositori s.r.l., Via Salingrado 97-2, 40128 Bologna, Italy. TEL 51-327811. Ed. Pio Picchi.
—CASDDS; Faxon; UMI.
Incorporates (1978-1990): Fisica e Tecnologia (ISSN 0391-9757); Formerly (until 1984): Societa Italiana di Fisica. Bollettino (ISSN 0037-8801)

530   US   ISSN 0078-6322
CODEN: SFPTDU
ORGANIZATION OF AMERICAN STATES. DEPARTMENT OF SCIENTIFIC AFFAIRS. SERIE DE FISICA: MONOGRAFIAS. (Subseries of: Coleccion de Monografias Cientificas) (Text in Spanish) 1965. irreg., no.13, 1979. $3.50 per no. Organization of American States, 1889 F St., N.W., Washington, DC 20006. TEL 703-941-1617. circ. 3,000. **Document type:** monographic series.

ORGONOMIC FUNCTIONALISM. see *MEDICAL SCIENCES — Psychiatry And Neurology*

530   JA   ISSN 0918-1156
OSAKA DAIGAKU KYOKUGEN BUSSHITSU KENKYU SENTA HOKOKUSHO/OSAKA UNIVERSITY. RESEARCH CENTER FOR EXTREME MATERIALS. REPORT. (Text in English, Japanese; summaries in English) 1990. a. Osaka Daigaku, Kyokugen Bussitsu Kenkyu Senta - Osaka University, Research Center for Extreme Materials, 1-1, Machikaneyama-machi, Toyonaka-shi, Osaka 560, Japan.

OSTRAVSKE UNIVERSITY. PRIRODOVEDECKA FAKULTA. SBORNIK PRACI. RADA A: MATEMATIKA, FYZIKA. see *MATHEMATICS*

OTTAWA R & D REPORT. see *ENGINEERING*

530   JA   ISSN 0369-8009
QC1   **CODEN: OYBSA9**
OYO BUTSURI/APPLIED PHYSICS. (Text in Japanese; summaries in English, Japanese) 1932. m. 1500 Yen per no. Japan Society of Applied Physics - Oyo Butsuri Gakkai, 12-3, Kudan Kita 1-chome, Chiyoda-ku, Tokyo 102, Japan. **Indexed:** Chem.Abstr., INIS Atomind., INSPEC, Jap.Per.Ind.
—BLDSC (6321.086000); CASDDS.

P-H'ATOM; popular physics magazine. see *CHILDREN AND YOUTH — For*

538.3   RU   ISSN 0202-2257
PARAMAGNITNYI REZONANS. irreg. 0.58 Rub. per no. Kazanskii Universitet, Ul. Lenina, 4-5, Kazan, Russia. illus. **Indexed:** Chem.Abstr.
—BLDSC (0129.143000).

530   JA   ISSN 0911-4815
PARITI/PARITY. (Text in Japanese) 1985. m. 1200 Yen per no. Maruzen Co., Ltd., 3-10, Nihonbashi 2-chome, Chuo-ku, Tokyo 103, Japan.

530   JA   ISSN 0913-137X
PARITI. BESSATSU SHIRIZU/PARITY. SPECIAL ISSUE. (Text in Japanese) 1986. irreg. 2800 Yen per no. Maruzen Co., Ltd., 3-10, Nihonbashi 2-chome, Chuo-ku, Tokyo 103, Japan.

530   GW   ISSN 0934-0866
TA418.78   **CODEN: PPCHEZ**
PARTICLE & PARTICLE SYSTEMS CHARACTERIZATION; an international journal devoted to the measure and description of particle and bulk properties in dispersed systems. (Text in English) 1983. bi-m. DM.610($459) (effective 1996). V C H Verlagsgesellschaft mbH, Postfach 101161, 69451 Weinheim, Germany. TEL 06201-606-147. FAX 06201-606117. TELEX 465516-VCHWH-D. (U.S. addr.: V C H Publishers Inc., 220 E. 23rd St., New York, NY 10010-4606. TEL 212-683-8333) Ed.Bd. adv. contact: R. Roth. bk.rev. circ. 650. **Indexed:** INSPEC (1988-). **Document type:** academic/scholarly publication.
—BLDSC (6407.310000); CASDDS; Ei; Faxon; Genuine Article; SWETS; UnCover. **CCC.**
Formerly: Particle Characterization (ISSN 0176-2265)

530   US   ISSN 1043-6790
QC793   **CODEN: PARWEG**
PARTICLE WORLD. 1991. 6/yr. 48 ECU per vol. (effective 1996). Gordon and Breach Science Publishers, c/o International Publishers Distributor, 820 Town Center Dr., Langhorne, PA 19047. TEL 215-750-2642. FAX 215-750-6343. (Subscr. to: International Publishers Distributor, P.O. Box 90, Reading, Berkshire RG1 8JL, England. TEL 44-173-456-8316) Ed. Robert Klapisch. (also avail. in microform) **Indexed:** INSPEC (1989-).
—BLDSC (6407.432000); Faxon; SWETS. **CCC.**
Refereed Serial

530   HU   ISSN 1216-0563
CODEN: PPNSEL
PERIODICA POLYTECHNICA. PHYSICS AND NUCLEAR SCIENCES. (Text in English) 1993. s-a. $8. Budapesti Muszaki Egyetem - Technical University of Budapest, 1521 Budapest, Hungary. TEL 36-1-4631105. FAX 36-1-166-6808. TELEX 22-5931 MUEGY H. E-mail: perpol@tuo.bme.hu. (Subscr. to: Kultura, P.O. Box 149, 1389 Budapest 62, Hungary) Ed. P. Zagyvai. bk.rev. circ. 400. **Indexed:** INSPEC (1993-). **Document type:** academic/scholarly publication.
—BLDSC (6425.520000); CASDDS; Ei.
Refereed Serial

530   US   ISSN 0260-4280
QC1
PERSPECTIVE OF PHYSICS. 1976. irreg., latest vol.4. price varies. Gordon & Breach Science Publishers, c/o International Publishers Distributor, 820 Town Center Dr., Langhorne, PA 19047. TEL 215-750-2642. FAX 215-750-6343. (Subscr. to: International Publishers Distributor, P.O. Box 90, Reading, Berks. RG1 8JL, England. TEL 44-173-456-8316) Eds. R. Peierls, H. Massey. **Document type:** monographic series.
Refereed Serial

530   NE   ISSN 0923-1749
PERSPECTIVES IN CONDENSED MATTER PHYSICS. (Text in English) 1989. irreg., vol.7, 1993. price varies. Kluwer Academic Publishers, Postbus 17, 3300 AA Dordrecht, Netherlands. TEL 31-78-392392. FAX 31-78-392254. TELEX 29245 KAPG NL. (Dist. by: Kluwer Academic Publishers Group, P.O. Box 322, 3300 AH Dordrecht, Netherlands. TEL 31-78-392392. FAX 31-78-546474; N. America dist. addr.: Box 358, Accord Sta., Hingham, MA 02018-0358. TEL 617-871-6600. FAX 617-871-6528) **Document type:** monographic series.
Refereed Serial

530   US   ISSN 1054-4143
PERSPECTIVES IN PHYSICS. 1988. irreg., vol.3, 1989. Academic Press, Inc., 525 B St., Ste. 1900, San Diego, CA 92101-4495. TEL 619-231-6616. FAX 619-699-6715. (Subscr. to: Order Dept., 66277 Sea Harbor Dr., 4th Fl., Orlando, FL 32887. TEL 800-321-5068) Ed.Bd.
Refereed Serial

530   NE   ISSN 0169-3050
PHASE TRANSITION PHENOMENA. (Text in English) 1978. irreg., vol.3, 1990. price varies. Elsevier Science B.V., Books Division, P.O. Box 211, 1000 AE Amsterdam, Netherlands. TEL 31-20-4853911. FAX 31-20-4853705. TELEX 18582 ESPA NL. E-mail: nlinfo-f@elsevier.nl; usinfo-f@elsevier.com; forinfo-kyf04035@niftyserve.or.jp; Site addr.: http://www.elsevier.nl/. (Subscr. in U.S. and Canada to: Elsevier Science Inc., Box 882, Madison Sq. Sta., New York, NY 10159. TEL 212-989-5800) **Indexed:** INSPEC. **Document type:** monographic series.
Refereed Serial

530   US   ISSN 0141-1594
QC176.8.P45   **CODEN: PHTRDP**
PHASE TRANSITIONS; a multinational journal. 1979. 8/yr. (in 2 vols.; 4 nos./vol.). 196 ECU per vol. (effective 1996). Gordon and Breach Science Publishers, c/o International Publishers Distributor, 820 Town Center Dr., Langhorne, PA 19047. TEL 215-750-2642. FAX 215-750-6343. (Subscr. to: International Publishers Distributor, P.O. Box 90, Reading, Berkshire RG1 8JL, England. TEL 44-173-456-8316) Ed. A.M. Glazer. adv.; bk.rev.; charts; illus. (also avail. in microform) **Indexed:** Cadscan, Chem.Abstr., INSPEC, Lead Abstr., Met.Abstr., Phys.Ber., World Alum.Abstr., Zincscan.
—BLDSC (6449.155000); CASDDS; Faxon; SWETS; UnCover. **CCC.**
Refereed Serial

530   UK   ISSN 0141-8610
QC173.4.C65   **CODEN: PMAADG**
PHILOSOPHICAL MAGAZINE A: PHYSICS OF CONDENSED MATTER, DEFECTS AND MECHANICAL PROPERTIES. 1798. m. £806($1330) (effective 1996) (includes Part B). Taylor & Francis Ltd., Rankine Rd., Basingstoke, Hants. RG24 8PR, England. TEL 44-1256-840366. FAX 44-1256-479438. TELEX 858540. E-mail: info@tandf.co.uk. (Subscr. in N. America to: Taylor & Francis Inc., 1900 Frost Rd., Ste. 101, Bristol, PA 19007-1598. TEL 800-821-8312. FAX 215-785-5515) Ed. E.A. Davis. adv.; bibl.; charts; illus.; index. (also avail. in microform from PMC) **Indexed:** Appl.Mech.Rev., Br.Ceram.Abstr., Br.Tech.Ind., Cadscan, Ceram.Abstr., Chem.Abstr., Curr.Cont., Deep Sea Res.& Oceanogr.Abstr., Eng.Ind., GeoRef., INSPEC (1968-), Lead Abstr., Math.R., Met.Abstr., Phys.Ber., World Alum.Abstr., Zincscan. **Document type:** academic/scholarly publication.
—BLDSC (6462.060000); CASDDS; Ei; Faxon; Genuine Article; SWETS; UnCover. **CCC.**
Supersedes in part (in 1978): Philosophical Magazine (ISSN 0031-8086)
Description: Contains information on experimental, theoretical and applied mechanics and physics of condensed matter.
Refereed Serial

530   UK   ISSN 0958-6644
QC173.4.C65   **CODEN: PMABDJ**
PHILOSOPHICAL MAGAZINE B: PHYSICS OF CONDENSED MATTER, STRUCTURAL, ELECTRONIC, OPTICAL, AND MAGNETIC PROPERTIES. 1798. m. £806($1330) (effective 1996) (includes Part A). Taylor & Francis Ltd., Rankine Rd., Basingstoke, Hants. RG24 8PR, England. TEL 44-1256-840366. FAX 44-1256-479438. E-mail: info@tandf.co.uk. (Subscr. in N. America to: Taylor & Francis Inc., 1900 Frost Rd., Ste. 101, Bristol, PA 19007-1598. TEL 800-821-8312. FAX 215-785-5515) adv.; bibl.; charts; illus.; index. (also avail. in microform from PMC) **Indexed:** INSPEC (1968-). **Document type:** academic/scholarly publication.
—BLDSC (6462.110000); CASDDS; Faxon; Genuine Article; SWETS; UnCover. **CCC.**
Formerly (until 1986): Philosophical Magazine B: Physics of Condensed Matter, Electronic, Optical and Magnetic Properties (ISSN 0141-8637); Which supersedes in part (in 1978): Philosophical Magazine (ISSN 0031-8086)

PHYSICS

530 UK ISSN 0950-0839
QC173.4.C65 CODEN: PMLEEG
PHILOSOPHICAL MAGAZINE LETTERS. (Text and summaries in English, French, German) 1987. m. £221($365) (effective 1996). Taylor & Francis Ltd., Rankine Rd., Basingstoke, Hants. RG24 8PR, England. TEL 44-1256-840366. FAX 44-1256-479438. TELEX 858540. E-mail: info@tandf.co.uk. (Subscr. in N. America to: Taylor & Francis Inc., 1900 Frost Rd., Ste. 101, Bristol, PA 19007-1598. TEL 800-821-8312. FAX 215-785-5515) Ed. E.A. Davis. index. circ. 1,500. (also avail. in microfiche; back issues avail.) **Indexed:** INSPEC (1987-). **Document type:** academic/scholarly publication.
—BLDSC (6462.120000); CASDDS; Ei; Faxon; Genuine Article; SWETS; UnCover. **CCC.**
Refereed Serial

530 CN ISSN 0710-0140
PHYS 13 NEWS. 1971. 4/yr. Can.$5. University of Waterloo, Department of Physics, Waterloo, ON N2L 3G1, Canada. TEL 519-885-1211. FAX 519-746-8115. Ed. Phil Eastman; Pub. Jim Leslie. adv.; B&W page $300. bk.rev. circ. 4,000. **Document type:** newsletter.
Description: Items of interest to high school and first-year university physics students and teachers.

530 NE ISSN 0378-4371
QC1 CODEN: PHYADX
PHYSICA A - STATISTICAL AND THEORETICAL PHYSICS. (Text in English, French and German) 1934. 48/yr. fl.5580($3403) (effective 1996). (European Physical Society) North-Holland (Subsidiary of: Elsevier Science B.V.), P.O. Box 211, 1000 AE Amsterdam, Netherlands. TEL 31-20-4853911. FAX 31-20-4853598. TELEX 18582 ESPA NL. (Subscr. in U.S. and Canada to: Elsevier Science Inc., Box 882, Madison Sq. Sta., New York, NY 10159. TEL 212-989-5800. FAX 212-633-3990) Eds. H.W. Capel, I. Oppenheim. charts; index. (also avail. in microform from UMI; back issues avail.) **Indexed:** Appl.Mech.Rev., Cadscan, Chem.Abstr., Compumath, Deep Sea Res.& Oceanogr.Abstr., INSPEC (1968-), Lead Abstr., Mass Spectr.Bull., Math.R., Met.Abstr., Phys.Ber., Zincscan. **Document type:** academic/scholarly publication.
—BLDSC (6475.010000); CASDDS; Ei; Faxon; Genuine Article; SWETS; UnCover. **CCC.**
Supersedes in part (in 1975): Physica (ISSN 0031-8914).
Description: Contains papers in all fields of statistical and general theoretical physics.
Refereed Serial

531 621.3 NE ISSN 0921-4526
QC1 CODEN: PHYBE3
PHYSICA B - PHYSICS OF CONDENSED MATTER. (Text in English) 1934. 56/yr. fl.6045($3686) (effective 1996). (European Physical Society) North-Holland (Subsidiary of: Elsevier Science B.V.), P.O. Box 211, 1000 AE Amsterdam, Netherlands. TEL 31-20-4853911. FAX 31-20-4853598. TELEX 18582 ESPA NL. (Subscr. in U.S. and Canada to: Elsevier Science Inc., Box 882, Madison Sq. Sta., New York, NY 10159. TEL 212-989-5800. FAX 212-633-3990) Ed.Bd. (also avail. in microform from UMI; back issues avail.) **Indexed:** Eng.Ind., INSPEC (1975-). **Document type:** academic/scholarly publication.
—BLDSC (6475.015000); CASDDS; Ei; Faxon; Genuine Article; SWETS; UnCover. **CCC.**
Supersedes in part (in 1988): Physica B en C (ISSN 0378-4363); Which supersedes in part (in 1975): Physica (ISSN 0031-8914).
Description: Discusses solid state and low-temperature physics as well as fundamental research on novel materials.
Refereed Serial

530 621.3 NE ISSN 0921-4534
QC611.9 CODEN: PHYCE6
PHYSICA C - SUPERCONDUCTIVITY. (Text in English) 1934. 76/yr. fl.8835($5388) (effective 1996). (European Physical Society) North-Holland (Subsidiary of: Elsevier Science B.V.), P.O. Box 211, 1000 AE Amsterdam, Netherlands. TEL 31-20-4853911. FAX 31-20-4853598. TELEX 18582 ESPA NL. (Subscr. in U.S. and Canada to: Elsevier Science Inc., Box 882, Madison Sq. Sta., New York, NY 10159. TEL 212-989-5800. FAX 212-633-3990) Ed. M.B. Brodsky. illus.; tr.lit.; index. (also avail. in microform from UMI; back issues avail.) **Indexed:** Eng.Ind., INSPEC (1975-). **Document type:** academic/scholarly publication.
—BLDSC (6475.025000); CASDDS; Ei; Faxon; Genuine Article; SWETS; UnCover. **CCC.**
Supersedes in part (in 1988): Physica B en C (ISSN 0378-4363); Which supersedes in part (1975): Physica (ISSN 0031-8914)
Description: Covers all aspects of superconductivity research: fundamental work, materials engineering and applications.
Refereed Serial

531 621.3 NE ISSN 0167-2789
QC1 CODEN: PDNPDT
PHYSICA D - NONLINEAR PHENOMENA. (Text in English) 1980. 40/yr. fl.4650($2836) (effective 1996). (European Physical Society) North-Holland (Subsidiary of: Elsevier Science B.V.), P.O. Box 211, 1000 AE Amsterdam, Netherlands. TEL 31-20-4853911. FAX 31-20-4853598. TELEX 18582 ESPA NL. (Subscr. in U.S. and Canada to: Elsevier Science Inc., Box 882, Madison Sq. Sta., New York, NY 10159. TEL 212-989-5800. FAX 212-633-3990) Eds. H. Flaschka, F.H. Busse. (also avail. in microform from UMI; back issues avail.) **Indexed:** Comput.Rev., Eng.Ind., INSPEC (1980-), Math.R. **Document type:** academic/scholarly publication.
—BLDSC (6475.030000); CASDDS; Ei; Faxon; Genuine Article; SWETS; UnCover. **CCC.**
Description: Explores research of theoretical physicists working in statistical mechanics, plasma physics, hydrodynamics, and solid state physics as well as mathematics.
Refereed Serial

PHYSICA MEDICA. see *MEDICAL SCIENCES*

530 SW ISSN 0031-8949
QC1 CODEN: PHSTBO
PHYSICA SCRIPTA; a monthly international journal for experimental and theoretical physics. (Supplement avail.) (Text in English) 1970. a. SEK 4725 in the Nordic countries; U.S, Canada, Mexico $900; elsewhere DM.1575 (includes Physica Scripta Topical Issues). Kungliga Vetenskapsakademien - Royal Swedish Academy of Sciences, P.O. Box 50005, S-104 05 Stockholm, Sweden. (Co-sponsors: Academies of Sciences and Physical Societies of Denmark, Finland, Iceland, Norway and Sweden) Ed. Anders Barany. charts; stat.; index. circ. 650. (back issues avail.) **Indexed:** Appl.Mech.Rev., Cadscan, Chem.Abstr., Curr.Cont., GeoRef., INSPEC, Int.Aerosp.Abstr., Lead Abstr., Mass Spectr.Bull., Math.R., Met.Abstr., Phys.Ber., World Alum.Abstr., Zincscan.
—BLDSC (6475.150000); CASDDS; Ei; Faxon; SWETS; UnCover. **CCC.**
Incorporates: Physica Norvegica (ISSN 0031-8930) & Physica Fennica (ISSN 0031-8922)

530 SW ISSN 0281-1847
QC1 CODEN: PHSTBO
PHYSICA SCRIPTA TOPICAL ISSUES. (Supplement to: Physica Scripta) 1982. irreg. Kungliga Vetenskapsakademien - Royal Swedish Academy of Sciences, P.O. Box 50005, S-104 05 Stockholm, Sweden. Ed. Aasa von Krusenstjerna. **Indexed:** INSPEC (1987-).
—BLDSC (6475.151000); CASDDS; Ei; Genuine Article; UnCover. **CCC.**

530.41 GW ISSN 0031-8965
QC176.A1 CODEN: PSSABA
PHYSICA STATUS SOLIDI (A). APPLIED RESEARCH. (Text in English) 1970. 12/yr. (in 6 vols., 2 nos./vol.). DM.345 to individuals; institutions DM.2900 (effective 1996). Akademie Verlag GmbH, Muehlenstr. 33-34, 13187 Berlin, Germany. TEL 030-47889348. FAX 030-47889357. (U.S. subscr. to: V C H Publishers, Inc., 303 N.W. 12th Ave., Deerfield Beach, FL 33442-1788) Ed. E. Gutsche. charts; illus.; index. **Indexed:** Cadscan, Chem.Abstr., Curr.Cont., GeoRef., INSPEC, Lead Abstr., Mass Spectr.Bull., Met.Abstr., Phys.Ber., Soils & Fert., World Alum.Abstr., Zincscan. **Document type:** academic/scholarly publication.
—BLDSC (6475.220000); CASDDS; Ei; Faxon; Genuine Article; SWETS; UnCover. **CCC.**

530.41 GW ISSN 0370-1972
QC176.A1 CODEN: PSSBBD
PHYSICA STATUS SOLIDI (B). BASIC RESEARCH. (Text in English) 1961. 12/yr. (in 6 vols., 2 nos./vol.). DM.345 to individuals; institutions DM.2900 (effective 1996). Akademie Verlag GmbH, Muehlenstr. 33-34, 13187 Berlin, Germany. TEL 030-47889348. FAX 030-47889357. (U.S. subscr. to VCH Publishers, Inc., 303 N.W. 12th Ave., Deerfield Beach, FL 33442-1788) Ed. E. Gutsche. abstr.; bibl.; charts; illus.; index. **Indexed:** Cadscan, Chem.Abstr., Curr.Cont., Eng.Ind., INSPEC, Lead Abstr., Mass Spectr.Bull., Met.Abstr., World Alum.Abstr., Zincscan. **Document type:** academic/scholarly publication.
—BLDSC (6475.230000); CASDDS; Faxon; Genuine Article; SWETS; UnCover. **CCC.**

530.07 II
PHYSICAL RESEARCH LABORATORY, AHMEDABAD: ANNUAL REPORT. (Text in English) 1954. a. Physical Research Laboratory, Ahmedabad-9, India. TELEX 0121-6397 PRL IN. Ed. Dr. Purobi Chakrabarty. illus. circ. 250.

530 US ISSN 1050-2947
QC1 CODEN: PLRAAN
PHYSICAL REVIEW A. 1970. m. $1320 (foreign $1370) (effective 1996). American Physical Society, One Physics Ellipse, College Park, MD 20740-3844. TEL 301-209-3202. (Subscr. to: APS Subscriber Service, c/o American Institute of Physics, 500 Sunnyside Blvd., Woodbury, NY 11797-2999. TEL 516-579-2270) Ed. B. Crasemann. bibl.; illus.; s-a. index. (also avail. in microfiche from BHP; microform from AIP; back issues avail.) **Indexed:** Appl.Mech.Rev., C.P.I., Cadscan, Chem.Abstr., Curr.Cont., Eng.Ind., INSPEC, Int.Aerosp.Abstr., Lead Abstr., Mass Spectr.Bull., Math.R., Met.Abstr., Phys.Ber., Zincscan. **Document type:** academic/scholarly publication.
—BLDSC (6476.020000); CASDDS; Ei; Faxon; Genuine Article; SWETS; UnCover. **CCC.**
Formerly (until 1989): Physical Review A (General Physics) (ISSN 0556-2791); Which supersedes in part (1893-1969): Physical Review (ISSN 0031-899X)
Refereed Serial

530 US ISSN 0163-1829
QC176.A1 CODEN: PRBMDO
PHYSICAL REVIEW B (CONDENSED MATTER). 1970. 48/yr. (4/m.). $3830 (foreign $4020) (effective 1996). American Physical Society, One Physics Ellipse, College Park, MD 20740-3844. TEL 301-209-3202. (Subscr. to: APS Subscriber Service, c/o American Institute of Physics, 500 Sunnyside Blvd., Woodbury, NY 11797-2999. TEL 516-576-2270) Ed. P.D. Adams. bibl.; illus.; s-a. index. (also avail. in microform from AIP; back issues avail.) **Indexed:** Abstr.Bull.Inst.Pap.Chem., Appl.Mech.Rev., C.P.I., Cadscan, Ceram.Abstr., Chem.Abstr., Curr.Cont., Eng.Ind., GeoRef., INSPEC, Int.Aerosp.Abstr., Lead Abstr., Mass Spectr.Bull., Math.R., Met.Abstr., Phys.Ber., World Alum.Abstr., Zincscan. **Document type:** academic/scholarly publication.
—BLDSC (6476.050000); CASDDS; Ei; Faxon; Genuine Article; SWETS; UnCover. **CCC.**
Formerly (until Jul. 1978): Physical Review B (Solid State) (ISSN 0556-2805); Supersedes in part (1893-1969): Physical Review (ISSN 0031-899X)
Refereed Serial

PHYSICS

530   US   ISSN 1063-651X
QC174.7   CODEN: PLEEE8
PHYSICAL REVIEW E (STATISTICAL PHYSICS, PLASMAS, FLUIDS, AND RELATED INTERDISCIPLINARY TOPICS). 1993. m. $1120 (foreign $1170) (effective 1996). American Physical Society, One Physics Ellipse, College Park, MD 20740-3844. TEL 301-209-3000. (Subscr. to: APS Subscriber Services, c/o American Institute of Physics, 500 Sunnyside Blvd., Woodbury, NY 11797-2999. TEL 516-576-2270) Ed. I. Oppenheimer. (also avail. in microform from UMI) **Indexed:** INSPEC (1993-). **Document type:** academic/scholarly publication.
—BLDSC (6476.070500); CASDDS; Ei; Faxon; Genuine Article; SWETS; UnCover. **CCC.**

530   US   ISSN 0031-9007
QC1   CODEN: PRLTAO
PHYSICAL REVIEW LETTERS. 1958. w. $1820 (foreign $1890) (effective 1996). American Physical Society, One Physics Ellipse, College Park, MD 20740-3844. TEL 301-209-3202. (Subscr. to: APS Subscriber Service, c/o American Institute of Physics, 500 Sunnyside Blvd., Woodbury, NY 11797-2999. TEL 516-576-2270) Ed.Bd. abstr.; index, cum.index: 1956-1976. (also avail. in microform from AIP; back issues avail.) **Indexed:** Appl.Mech.Rev., C.P.I., Cadscan, Chem.Abstr., Curr.Cont., Eng.Ind., GeoRef., INSPEC, Int.Aerosp.Abstr., Lead Abstr., Mass Spectr.Bull., Math.R., Met.Abstr., Phys.Ber., World Alum.Abstr., Zincscan. **Document type:** academic/scholarly publication.
●Also available online. Vendor(s): OCLC.
—BLDSC (6476.200000); CASDDS; Ei; Faxon; Genuine Article; SWETS; UnCover. **CCC.**
Refereed Serial

530   NE   ISSN 0921-318X
PHYSICAL SCIENCES DATA. 1978. irreg., vol.43, 1991. price varies. Elsevier Science B.V., Books Division, P.O. Box 211, 1000 AE Amsterdam, Netherlands. TEL 31-20-4853911. FAX 31-20-4853705. TELEX 18582 ESPA NL.
E-mail: nlinfo-f@elsevier.nl; usinfo-f@elsevier.com; forinfo-kyf04035@niftyserve.or.jp; Site addr.: http://www.elsevier.nl/. (Subscr. in U.S. and Canada to: Elsevier Science Inc., Box 882, Madison Sq. Sta., New York, NY 10159. TEL 212-989-5800)
Indexed: INSPEC. **Document type:** monographic series.
—BLDSC (6476.267000).
Refereed Serial

530   JA   ISSN 0031-9015
QC1   CODEN: JUPSAU
PHYSICAL SOCIETY OF JAPAN. JOURNAL. (Supplement avail.) (Text in English) 1946. m. 75000 Yen in Asia; N. America & Australasia 89400 Yen; elsewhere 94200 Yen. Physical Society of Japan - Nihon Butsuri Gakkai, Rm. 211 Kikai Shinko Bldg., 3-5-8 Shiba Koen, Minato-ku, Tokyo 105, Japan. FAX 81-3-3432-0997. Ed. A. Kawabata. abstr.; charts; illus.; index, cum.index. circ. 2,600. (also avail. in microfiche from PMC; back issues avail.) **Indexed:** Appl.Mech.Rev., Chem.Abstr., Curr.Cont., GeoRef., INIS Atomind., INSPEC, Int.Aerosp.Abstr., JCT, JTA, Mass Spectr.Bull., Math.R., Met.Abstr., Phys.Ber., World Alum.Abstr.
—BLDSC (4842.000000); CASDDS; Ei; Faxon; Genuine Article; SWETS; UnCover.
Formerly: Physico-Mathematical Society of Japan. Proceedings (ISSN 0370-1239)
Description: Devoted to the publication of original papers in all fields of physics. Intended to secure prompt publication of important new discoveries in physics.

530   JA   ISSN 0375-9598
PHYSICAL SOCIETY OF JAPAN. JOURNAL. SUPPLEMENT. irreg. price varies. Physical Society of Japan - Nihon Butsuri Gakkai, Rm. 211, Kikai Shinko Bldg., 3-5-8 Shiba Koen, Minato-ku, Tokyo 105, Japan.
—BLDSC (4842.010000).

530   US   ISSN 0276-8925
PHYSICS: A SERIES OF MONOGRAPHS & TRACTS. 1981. irreg. $88. Harwood Academic Publishers, c/o International Publishers Distributor, 820 Town Center Dr., Langhorne, PA 19047. TEL 215-750-2642. FAX 215-750-6343. (Subscr. to: International Publishers Distributor, Box 90, Reading, Berkshire RG1 8JL, England. TEL 44-173-456-8316) Ed. P.B. Burt. bk.rev. (microform) **Document type:** monographic series.
Formerly: Quantum Mechanics and Nonlinear Waves.
Refereed Serial

530   XO   ISSN 0139-9861
   CODEN: PHAPDQ
PHYSICS AND APPLICATIONS. (Text in English) a. price varies. (Slovenska Akademia Vied) Veda, Publishing House of the Slovak Academy of Sciences, Klemensova 19, 814 30 Bratislava, Slovakia. (Dist. by: Slovart, Nam. Slobody 6, 817 64 Bratislava, Slovakia) Ed. Mikulas Blazek. **Indexed:** Chem.Abstr.
—CASDDS.
Formerly: High Energy Particle Physics.

PHYSICS AND CHEMISTRY IN SPACE. see *CHEMISTRY*

PHYSICS AND CHEMISTRY OF MATERIALS TREATMENT. see *ENGINEERING — Engineering Mechanics And Materials*

530   US   ISSN 1049-4162
PHYSICS AND SOCIETY. 1972. q. $10 (free to members). American Physical Society, Forum on Physics and Society, 1 Physics Ellipse, College Park, MD 20740-3842. Ed. Art Hobson. bk.rev. circ. 4,500. **Document type:** academic/scholarly publication, newsletter.
—Faxon.
Formerly: Forum on Physics and Society. Newsletter (ISSN 1049-4170)
Description: Presents letters, articles, reviews, news, and comment on the relations of physics to society.

PHYSICS, CHEMISTRY AND MECHANICS OF SURFACES. see *ENGINEERING — Mechanical Engineering*

530   RU   ISSN 1063-7753
QC1   CODEN: PHDOE5
PHYSICS - DOKLADY. English translation of: Rossiiskaya Akademiya Nauk. Doklady. 1956. m. $1570 (foreign $1590) (effective 1996). (Rossiiskaya Akademiya Nauk) Maik Nauka, Mezhdunarodnyi Otdel, Profsoyuznaya, 90, 117864 Moscow, Russia. (Subscr. to: American Institute of Physics, Member and Subscriber Services, 500 Sunnyside Blvd., Woodbury, NY 11797-2999, U.S.A.. TEL 516-576-2280. FAX 516-349-9707) Ed. V.A. Kabanov. index. (also avail. in microform from AIP; back issues avail.) **Indexed:** Appl.Mech.Rev., C.P.I., Gen.Phys.Adv.Abstr., INSPEC (1968-), Mass Spectr.Bull., Math.R., Phys.Ber. **Document type:** academic/scholarly publication.
—BLDSC (0416.828000); Ei; Faxon; SWETS; UnCover. **CCC.**
Formerly: Soviet Physics - Doklady (ISSN 0038-5689)
Description: Contains research in general physics and all subspecialities.

530.07 370   UK   ISSN 0031-9120
QC30   CODEN: PHEDA7
PHYSICS EDUCATION. 1966. bi-m. £114($235) (effective 1996). (Institute of Physics) I O P Publishing Ltd., Techno House, Redcliffe Way, Bristol, Avon BS1 6NX, England. TEL 0117-929-7481. FAX 0117-929-4318. TELEX 449149 INSTP G. (U.S. subscr. to: American Institute of Physics, Member and Subscriber Services, 500 Sunnyside Blvd., Woodbury, NY 11797-2900. TEL 516-349-7800) Ed. J. Avison. adv.; bk.rev.; film rev.; charts; illus.; index. circ. 1,116. (also avail. in microfiche from AIP; microfilm from AIP; back issues avail.) **Indexed:** C.I.J.E., Chem.Abstr., Cont.Pg.Educ., Educ.Tech.Abstr., High.Educ.Curr.Aware.Bull., INSPEC, Phys.Ber., Res.High.Educ.Abstr., Stud.Wom.Abstr. **Document type:** academic/scholarly publication.
—BLDSC (6478.530000); CASDDS; Ei; Faxon; SWETS; UnCover. **CCC.**
Description: Provides reliable treatments of difficult subjects and clear explanations of new and established concepts in physics to aid in the teaching of physics to students 16 to 21 years old.
Refereed Serial

530   II   ISSN 0970-5953
   CODEN: PHEDEB
PHYSICS EDUCATION. (Text and summaries in English) 1984. q. Rs.120($40) per no. (University Grants Commission) New Age International Pvt. Ltd., Journals Division, 4835-24 Ansari Rd., Daryaganj, New Delhi 110 002, India. TEL 3276802. Ed. Arun S. Nigavekar. adv.; bk.rev.; illus. circ. 1,000. **Indexed:** C.I.J.E., Educ.Tech.Abstr., ERIC, INSPEC (1987-), Tech.Educ.Abstr. **Document type:** academic/scholarly publication.
—BLDSC (6478.530500).
Description: Contains articles on physics. Aims to inform Indian audiences in academic areas of science.
Refereed Serial

530   CN   ISSN 0836-1398
   CODEN: PHESEM
PHYSICS ESSAYS. 1988. q. Can.$58 to individuals; institutions Can.$115; students Can.$32. Advanced Laser and Fusion Technology, Inc., c/o Ken Charbonneau, Publ. Service, 289 Champlain, Hull, PQ J8X 3S3, Canada. TEL 416-667-7781. (U.S. address: 340 Nagel Dr., Cheektowaga, NY 14225) Ed. E. Panarella. circ. 200. (back issues avail.) **Indexed:** INSPEC (1990-).
—BLDSC (6478.560000); CASDDS; Ei; Faxon; Genuine Article; UnCover. **CCC.**

530   CN   ISSN 0031-9147
PHYSICS IN CANADA/PHYSIQUE AU CANADA. (Text in English, French) 1944. 6/yr. Can.$37.20($34.75) (foreign $39) (effective 1996). Canadian Association of Physicists, 151 Slater St., Ste. 903, Ottawa, ON K1P 5H3, Canada. TEL 613-237-3392. FAX 613-238-1677. Ed. J.S.C. McKee. adv. contact: F.M. Ford. bk.rev.; charts; illus.; index. circ. 2,000. (also avail. in microfilm from UMI; reprint service avail. from MML)
—Faxon.
Supersedes in part: Canadian Association of Physicists. Annual Report.
Refereed Serial

530   US   ISSN 0160-3353
QC1
PHYSICS NEWS. 1970. a. free. American Institute of Physics, One Physics Ellipse, College Park, MD 20740-3843. TEL 301-209-3000. (Subscr. to: AIP Member and Subscriber Services, 500 Sunnyside Blvd., Woodbury, NY 11797-2999. TEL 516-576-2270) Ed. Philip Shewe. (back issues avail.) **Indexed:** PMR. **Document type:** academic/scholarly publication.
Formerly (until 1975): Physics (ISSN 0092-8437)

530   II   ISSN 0253-7583
QC1   CODEN: PNEWD7
PHYSICS NEWS. (Text in English) 1970. q. Rs.40($25) Indian Physics Association, T.I.F.R., Bombay 400 005, India. FAX 2205560750. TELEX 011-71017 BARC IN. (Subscr. address: Editor, Physics News, Tata Institute of Fundamental Research, Homi Bhabha Rd., Bombay 400005, India) Ed. S.V. Lawande. adv.; bk.rev.; charts; illus, stat.; index. circ. 3,200. (back issues avail.) **Indexed:** Chem.Abstr.
—BLDSC (6478.872000); CASDDS.

530.44   US   ISSN 1070-6631
QC150   CODEN: PHFLE6
PHYSICS OF FLUIDS. 1958. m. $1275 (foreign $1340) (effective 1996). American Institute of Physics, One Physics Ellipse, College Park, MD 20740-3843. TEL 301-209-3000. (Subscr. to: AIP Member and Subscriber Services, 500 Sunnyside Blvd., Woodbury, NY 11797-2999. TEL 516-576-2270. FAX 516-349-9704) (Co-sponsor: American Physical Society) Eds. Andreas Acrivos, Joel Koplik. (also avail. in microform from AIP) **Indexed:** Geo.Abstr., Geol.Abstr., INSPEC (1994-). **Document type:** academic/scholarly publication.
—BLDSC (6478.600000); CASDDS; Ei; Faxon; Genuine Article; SWETS; UnCover. **CCC.**
Formerly: Physics of Fluids A: Fluid Dynamics (ISSN 0899-8213); Which superseded in part (in 1989): Physics of Fluids (ISSN 0031-9171)
Description: Devoted to original contributions to the physics of fluids covering kinetic theory, statistical mechanics, structure and general physics of gases, liquids, and other fluids, as well as certain basic aspects of physics of fluids bordering geophysics, astrophysics, biophysics, and other fields of science.
Refereed Serial

PHYSICS OF METALS. see *METALLURGY*

530.44   US   ISSN 1070-664X
QC717.6   CODEN: PHPAEN
PHYSICS OF PLASMAS. 1958. m. $1525 (foreign $1595) (effective 1996). American Institute of Physics, One Physics Ellipse, College Park, MD 20740-3843. TEL 301-209-3000. (Subscr. to: AIP Member and Subscriber Services, 500 Sunnyside Blvd., Woodbury, NY 11797-2999. TEL 516-576-2270. FAX 516-349-9704) (Co-sponsor: American Physical Society) Ed. R.C. Davidson. (also avail. in microform from AIP) **Indexed:** INSPEC (1994-). **Document type:** academic/scholarly publication.
—BLDSC (6478.879000); CASDDS; Ei; Faxon; Genuine Article; SWETS; UnCover. **CCC.**
    Formerly: Physics of Fluids B: Plasma Physics (ISSN 0899-8221); Which superseded in part (in 1989): Physics of Fluids (ISSN 0031-9171)
    Description: Devoted to original contributions to and reviews of the physics of plasma, including magneto-fluid mechanics, kinetic theory and statistical mechanics of fully and partially ionized gases.
    Refereed Serial

530.41   US   ISSN 1063-7834
QC176   CODEN: PSOSED
PHYSICS OF THE SOLID STATE. English translation of: Fizika Tverdogo Tela (RU ISSN 0367-3294) 1959. m. $2730 (foreign $2775) (effective 1996). (Rossiiskaya Akademiya Nauk, RU) American Institute of Physics, One Physics Ellipse, College Park, MD 20740-3843. TEL 301-209-3000. Eds. L.V. Azaroff, James Anderson. bibl.; charts; illus.; index. (also avail. in microform from AIP; back issues avail.) **Indexed:** C.P.I., Eng.Ind., Gen.Phys.Adv.Abstr., INSPEC, Math.R., Met.Abstr., Phys.Ber., World Alum.Abstr. **Document type:** academic/scholarly publication.
—BLDSC (0416.866000); Faxon; SWETS. **CCC.**
    Formerly: Soviet Physics - Solid State.

---

530   US   ISSN 0079-1970
QC176.A1   CODEN: PYTFA3
PHYSICS OF THIN FILMS; ADVANCES IN RESEARCH AND DEVELOPMENT. 1963. irreg., vol.17, 1993. Academic Press, Inc., 525 B St., Ste. 1900, San Diego, CA 92101-4495. TEL 619-231-0926. FAX 619-699-6715. (Subscr. to: Order Dept., 6277 Sea Harbor Dr., 4th Fl., Orlando, FL 32887. TEL 800-321-5068) Ed. George Haas. index. (reprint service avail. from ISI) **Indexed:** Chem.Abstr., INSPEC.
—BLDSC (6478.950000); CASDDS; Faxon; UnCover. **CCC.**
    Refereed Serial

---

530   NE   ISSN 0370-1573
QC1   CODEN: PRPLCM
PHYSICS REPORTS; a review section of Physics Letters. 1971. 78/yr. fl.5252($3203) (effective 1996). North-Holland (Subsidiary of: Elsevier Science B.V.), P.O. Box 211, 1000 AE Amsterdam, Netherlands. TEL 31-20-4853911. FAX 31-20-4853598. TELEX 18582 ESPA NL. (Subscr. in U.S. and Canada to: Elsevier Science Inc., Box 882, Madison Sq. Sta., New York, NY 10159. TEL 212-989-5800. FAX 212-633-3990) Ed.Bd. (also avail. in microform from UMI; back issues avail.) **Indexed:** Chem.Abstr., Curr.Cont., Ind.Sci.Rev., INSPEC (1971-), Int.Aerosp.Abstr., Mass Spectr.Bull., Math.R., Phys.Ber. **Document type:** academic/scholarly publication.
—BLDSC (6478.885000); CASDDS; Ei; Faxon; Genuine Article; SWETS; UnCover. **CCC.**
    Incorporates: Case Studies in Atomic Physics (ISSN 0300-4503)
    Description: Short review articles on recent developments in all fields of physics, including particle and field physics, nuclear, molecular, plasma and condensed matter physics, geophysics, interdisciplinary papers, and applications.
    Refereed Serial

---

530   NE
PHYSICS REPORTS REPRINTS BOOK SERIES. 1974. irreg., vol.5, 1982. price varies. Elsevier Science B.V., Books Division, P.O. Box 211, 1000 AE Amsterdam, Netherlands. TEL 31-20-4853911. FAX 31-20-4853705. TELEX 18582 ESPA NL. E-mail: nlinfo-f@elsevier.nl; usinfo-f@elsevier.com; forinfo-kyf04035@niftyserve.or.jp; Site addr.: http://www.elsevier.nl/. (Subscr. in U.S. and Canada to: Elsevier Science Inc., Box 882, Madison Sq. Sta., New York, NY 10159. TEL 212-989-5800) **Indexed:** INSPEC. **Document type:** monographic series.
    Refereed Serial

---

530   UK   ISSN 0959-8472
PHYSICS REVIEW. 1991. 5/yr. (Sept.-May). £19.95 (rest of Europe £29; elsewhere £34) (effective 1996). Philip Allan Publishers Ltd., Market Pl., Deddington, Oxon. OX15 0SE, England. TEL 01869-338652. FAX 01869-338803. adv. contact: Ceri Jenkins.

---

530   US
QC1   CODEN: SSRPDH
PHYSICS REVIEWS. vol.4, 1982. q. 151 ECU (effective 1996). Harwood Academic Publishers, c/o International Publishers Distributor, 820 Town Center Dr., Langhorne, PA 19047. TEL 215-750-2642. FAX 215-750-6343. (Subscr. to: International Publishers Distributor, P.O. Box 90, Reading, Berkshire RG1 8JL, England. TEL 44-173-456-8316) Ed. I.M. Khalatnikov. index. (also avail. in microform; back issues avail.) **Indexed:** INSPEC. **Document type:** academic/scholarly publication.
—CASDDS. **CCC.**
    Formerly (until vol.18): Soviet Scientific Reviews. Section A: Physics Reviews (ISSN 0143-0394)
    Refereed Serial

---

530 370   US   ISSN 0031-921X
QC30   CODEN: PHTEAH
PHYSICS TEACHER. 1963. 9/yr. $147 (foreign $157) (effective Sep. 1995). American Association of Physics Teachers, One Physics Ellipse, College Park, MD 20740-3845. TEL 301-345-4200. Ed. C. Swartz. adv.: B&W page $550, color page $1080. bk.rev.; film rev.; charts; illus.; index. (also avail. in microform from AIP; back issues avail.; reprint service avail. from UMI) **Indexed:** C.I.J.E., C.P.I., Chem.Abstr., Cont.Pg.Educ., Curr.Cont., Educ.Ind., Gen.Sci.Ind., INSPEC, Phys.Ber.
—BLDSC (6478.900000); CASDDS; Ei; Faxon; SWETS; UMI; UnCover.

---

530   II
PHYSICS TEACHER. (Text in English) 1958. q. Rs.80($50) Indian Physical Society, 2-3 Raja Subodh Mallik Rd., Calcutta 700032, India. TEL 91-033-4734971. FAX 91-033-4732805. TELEX 021-5501 IACS IN. E-mail: msspag@iacs.ernet.in. Ed.Bd. adv.; bk.rev. circ. 600. **Indexed:** C.I.J.E., Educ.Ind.

---

530   US   ISSN 0031-9228
QC1   CODEN: PHTOAD
PHYSICS TODAY. 1948. m. $147 (foreign $175) (effective 1996). American Institute of Physics, One Physics Ellipse, College Park, MD 20740-3843. TEL 301-209-3000. (Subscr. to: AIP Member and Subscriber Services, 500 Sunnyside Blvd., Woodbury, NY 11797-2999. TEL 516-576-2270) Ed. S.G. Benka. adv.: B&W page $4650, color page $5600. bk.rev.; bibl.; charts; illus.; stat.; index. circ. 119,000. (also avail. in microform from AIP; back issues avail.) **Indexed:** A.S.& T.Ind., Acad.Ind., Appl.Mech.Rev., Art & Archaeol.Tech.Abstr., C.I.J.E., C.P.I., Cadscan, Chem.Abstr., Curr.Cont., Curr.Pack.Abstr., Deep Sea Res.& Oceanogr.Abstr., Energy Info.Abstr., Eng.Ind., Excerp.Med., Gen.Sci.Ind., Geo.Abstr., Geol.Abstr., GeoRef., Graph.Arts Lit.Abstr., INSPEC, Int.Aerosp.Abstr., Lead Abstr., Mag.Ind., Mass Spectr.Bull., Phys.Ber., R.G., TOM, Zincscan. **Document type:** academic/scholarly publication.
—BLDSC (6479.000000); CASDDS; Ei; Faxon; Genuine Article; SWETS; UnCover. **CCC.**
    Refereed Serial

---

530   UK   ISSN 1063-7869
QC1   CODEN: PHUSEY
PHYSICS - USPEKHI. English translation of: Uspekhi Fizicheskikh Nauk (RU ISSN 0042-1294) 1958. m. $1125 includes archival CD-ROM (effective 1996). (Russian Academy of Sciences, RU) Turpin Distribution Services Ltd., Blackhorse Rd., Letchworth, Herts. SG6 1HN, England. TEL 44-1462-672555. FAX 44-1462-489047. Ed. G.M. Volkoff. bibl.; charts; index. (also avail. in microform from AIP; back issues avail.) **Indexed:** C.P.I., GeoRef., INSPEC, Mass Spectr.Bull., Math.R., Met.Abstr., Phys.Ber. **Document type:** academic/scholarly publication.
    ●Also available on CD-ROM.
—BLDSC (0416.867000); Faxon; SWETS; UnCover. **CCC.**
    Formerly: Soviet Physics - Uspekhi (ISSN 0038-5670)

---

530   UK   ISSN 0953-8585
QC1   CODEN: PHWOEW
PHYSICS WORLD. 1950. m. £97($175) (effective 1996). (Institute of Physics) I O P Publishing Ltd., Techno House, Redcliffe Way, Bristol, Avon BS1 6NX, England. TEL 0117-929-7481. FAX 0117-929-4318. TELEX 449149 INSTP G. E-mail: magsmktg@ioppublishing.co.uk. (Subscr. to: I O P Circulation Centre, WDIS Ltd., Publishing House, Victoria Rd., Ruislip, Mddx. HA4 0SX, England. TEL 0181-845-8545. FAX 0181-845-7696; U.S. subscr. to: American Institute of Physics, Member and Subscriber Services, 500 Sunnyside Blvd., Woodbury, NY 11797-2900. TEL 516-349-7800) Ed. P. Campbell. adv.; bk.rev.; charts; illus.; index. (also avail. in microfiche; microfilm from AIP; back issues avail.) **Indexed:** AESIS, Agri.Eng.Abstr., Br.Tech.Ind., Chem.Abstr., Excerp.Med., INSPEC, Phys.Ber., Res.High.Educ.Abstr. **Document type:** academic/scholarly publication.
—BLDSC (6479.200000); CASDDS; Ei; Faxon; Genuine Article; SWETS; UnCover. **CCC.**
    Formerly (until 1988): Physics Bulletin (ISSN 0031-9112); **Incorporates:** Physics in Technology (ISSN 0305-4624)
    Description: For all physicists: those in industry, government, education or academia, pure or applied physics, in engineering or business.

---

530   GW   ISSN 0344-8401
                             CODEN: PHDADU
PHYSIK DATEN. 1975. irreg. Fachinformationszentrum Karlsruhe, Gesellschaft fuer Wissenschaftlich-Technische Information mbH, 76344 Eggenstein-Leopoldshafen, Germany. TEL 07247-808333. FAX 07247-808135. TELEX 724710-FIZKA. **Indexed:** INSPEC (1981-). **Document type:** monographic series.
—BLDSC (6478.522500); CASDDS.

---

530 370   GW   ISSN 0031-9244
PHYSIK IN DER SCHULE. 1963. 11/yr. DM.60.50. Paedagogischer Zeitschriftenverlag, Postfach 269, 10107 Berlin, Germany. TEL 030-20343431. FAX 030-20343432. Ed. Ursula Jablko. adv.; bk.rev.; abstr, illus, stat.; index. **Document type:** academic/scholarly publication.
—SWETS.

---

530   GW   ISSN 0031-9252
QC1   CODEN: PHUZAH
PHYSIK IN UNSERER ZEIT. 1969. bi-m. DM.163($123) (effective 1996). V C H Verlagsgesellschaft mbH, Postfach 101161, 69451 Weinheim, Germany. TEL 06201-606-147. FAX 06201-606117. TELEX 465516-VCHWH-D. (US addr.: V C H Publishers Inc., 220 E. 23rd St., New York, NY 10010-4606. TEL 212-683-8333) Eds. T. Buehrke, B. Kramer. adv.; bk.rev.; charts; illus.; index. circ. 7,600. (also avail. in microform from VCl; reprint service avail. from ISI) **Indexed:** Chem.Abstr., Phys.Ber. **Document type:** academic/scholarly publication.
—CASDDS; SWETS. **CCC.**

PHYSIK UND DIDAKTIK. see *EDUCATION — Teaching Methods And Curriculum*

---

530   GW   ISSN 0079-1997
PHYSIKALISCH-CHEMISCHE TRENN- UND MESSMETHODEN. 1960. irreg. price varies. VEB Deutscher Verlag der Wissenschaften, Postfach 1216, 1080 Berlin, Germany. Ed. Erich Krell.

530	GW	ISSN 0031-9279
		CODEN: PHBLAG

PHYSIKALISCHE BLAETTER. 1944. m. DM.358($269) (effective 1996). (Deutsche Physikalische Gesellschaft) V C H Verlagsgesellschaft mbH, Postfach 101161, 69451 Weinheim, Germany. TEL 06201-606-147. FAX 06201-606117. TELEX 465516-VCHWH-D. (US addr.: V C H Publishers Inc., 220 E. 23rd St., New York, NY 10010-4606. TEL 212-683-8333) Ed. E. Dreisigacker. adv.; bk.rev.; abstr.; charts; illus.; index. circ. 26,000. (also avail. in microfilm from VCI; reprint service avail. from ISI) **Indexed:** Chem.Abstr., Excerp.Med., INSPEC, Met.Abstr., Phys.Ber. **Document type:** academic/scholarly publication.
—BLDSC (6481.000000); CASDDS; Faxon; SWETS; UnCover. **CCC.**

PHYSIOLOGICAL MEASUREMENT. see *MEDICAL SCIENCES*

PLASMA CHEMISTRY & PLASMA PROCESSING. see *ENGINEERING — Chemical Engineering*

530	US	ISSN 1051-9998
TA2001		CODEN: PDOPEZ

PLASMA DEVICES AND OPERATIONS. 1991. 4/yr. 151 ECU (effective 1996). Gordon and Breach Science Publishers, c/o International Publishers Directory, 820 Town Center Dr., Langhorne, PA 19046. TEL 215-750-2642. FAX 215-750-6343. (Subscr. to: International Publishers Directory, P.O. Box 90, Reading, Berkshire RG1 8JL, England. TEL 44-173-456-8316) Ed. V.A. Glukhikh. (also avail. in microform)
—BLDSC (6528.400000); CASDDS. **CCC.**
Description: Covers plasma technology, engineering, and applications; plasma source and pulsed plasma devices; plasma accelerators and pulsed plasma heating systems.
Refereed Serial

530.44	UK	ISSN 0741-3335
QC770		CODEN: PPCFET

PLASMA PHYSICS AND CONTROLLED FUSION. (Contains a section of English translations of Atomnaya Energiya) (Text and summaries in English, French and German) 1959. m. £764($1573) (effective 1996). (Institute of Physics) I O P Publishing Ltd., Techno House, Redcliffe Way, Bristol BS1 6NX, England. TEL 0117-929-7481. FAX 0117-929-4318. TELEX 449149 INSTP G. (U.S. subscr. to: American Institute of Physics, Member and Subscriber Services, 500 Sunnyside Blvd., Woodbury, NY 11797-2900. TEL 516-349-7800) Ed. P. Scott. adv.; bk.rev.; bibl.; illus.; index. circ. 363. (also avail. in microform from MIM,UMI; reprint service avail. from UMI) **Indexed:** A.S.& T.Ind., Appl.Mech.Rev., ASCA, Chem.Abstr., Curr.Cont., Eng.Ind., INSPEC. **Document type:** academic/scholarly publication.
—BLDSC (6528.720000); CASDDS; Ei; Faxon; Genuine Article; SWETS; UMI; UnCover. **CCC.**
Formerly: Plasma Physics (ISSN 0032-1028)
Description: Publishes research covering all aspects of plasma physics and controlled nuclear fusion, as well as the plasma physics of highly ionized gases, high-temperature, collective processes, and other fusion-oriented research.
Refereed Serial

530.44	RU	ISSN 1063-780X
QC717.6		CODEN: PPHREM

PLASMA PHYSICS REPORTS. English translation of: Fizika Plazmy (RU ISSN 0134-5052) 1975. m. $1845 (foreign $1870) (effective 1996). (Rossiiskaya Akademiya Nauk) Maik Nauka, Mezhdunarodnyi Otdel, Profsoyuznaya 90, 117864 Moscow, Russia. (Subscr. to: American Institute of Physics, Member and Subscriber Services, 500 Sunnyside Blvd., Woodbury, NY 11797-2999, U.S.A.. TEL 516-576-2270. FAX 516-349-9707) Ed. David L. Book. abstr.; bibl.; charts; illus.; index. (also avail. in microform from AIP; back issues avail.) **Indexed:** Gen.Phys.Adv.Abstr., INSPEC, Int.Aerosp.Abstr., Phys.Ber. **Document type:** academic/scholarly publication.
—BLDSC (0416.900500); Faxon; SWETS; UnCover. **CCC.**
Formerly: Soviet Journal of Plasma Physics (ISSN 0360-0343)

530	UK	ISSN 0963-0252
QC717.6		CODEN: PSTEEU

PLASMA SOURCES SCIENCE AND TECHNOLOGY. 1992. q. £178($367) (effective 1996). (Institute of Physics) I O P Publishing Ltd., Techno House, Redcliffe Way, Bristol, Avon BS1 6NX, England. TEL 0117-929-7481. FAX 0117-929-4318. TELEX 449149 INSTP G. (U.S. subscr. to: American Institute of Physics, Member and Subscriber Services, 500 Sunnyside Blvd., Woodbury, NY 11797-2900. TEL 516-349-7800) Ed. Noah Hershkowitz. circ. 144. **Indexed:** INSPEC (1992-). **Document type:** academic/scholarly publication.
—BLDSC (6528.782150); Ei; SWETS. **CCC.**
Description: Publishes papers on nonfusion plasma sources that operate at all ranges of pressure and density.
Refereed Serial

530 621.3	NE	

PLASMA TECHNOLOGY. (Text in English) 1985. irreg., vol.4, 1992. price varies. Elsevier Science B.V., Books Division, P.O. Box 211, 1000 AE Amsterdam, Netherlands. TEL 31-20-4853911. FAX 31-20-4853705. TELEX 18582 ESPA NL. E-mail: nlinfo-f@elsevier.nl; usinfo-f@elsevier.com; forinfo-kyf04035@niftyserve.or.jp; Site addr.: http://www.elsevier.nl/. (Subscr. in U.S. and Canada to: Elsevier Science Inc., Box 882, Madison Sq. Sta., New York, NY 10159. TEL 212-989-5800) (back issues avail.) **Document type:** monographic series.
Refereed Serial

POLISH ACADEMY OF SCIENCES. BULLETIN. MATHEMATICAL SCIENCES. see *MATHEMATICS*

530	PL	ISSN 0072-0364

POLITECHNIKA GDANSKA. ZESZYTY NAUKOWE. FIZYKA. (Text in English and Polish; summaries in Russian and one Western European language) 1967. irreg. price varies. Politechnika Gdanska, Ul. G. Narutowicza 11-12, 80-952 Gdansk 6, Poland. (Dist. by: Osrodek Rozpowszechniania Wydawnictw Naukowych PAN, Palac Kultury i Nauki, 00-901 Warsaw, Poland) bibl.; charts; illus. **Document type:** academic/scholarly publication.

530	PL	ISSN 0137-2564
QC1		CODEN: ZNPFDJ

POLITECHNIKA LODZKA. ZESZYTY NAUKOWE. FIZYKA. (Text in Polish; summaries in English and Russian) 1973. irreg. price varies. Wydawnictwo Politechniki Lodzkiej, Ul. Wolczanska 223, 93-005 Lodz, Poland. (Dist. by: Ars Polona-Ruch, Krakowskie Przedmiescie 7, Warsaw, Poland) Ed. Cecylia Malinowska-Adamska. circ. 186. **Indexed:** Chem.Abstr., INSPEC (1979-). **Document type:** academic/scholarly publication.
—BLDSC (9512.310700); CASDDS.
Description: Articles on technical physics.

POLITECHNIKA SLASKA. ZESZYTY NAUKOWE. MATEMATYKA - FIZYKA. see *MATHEMATICS*

530	PL	ISSN 0324-8380
		CODEN: PIFWA8

POLITECHNIKA WARSZAWSKA. INSTYTUT FIZYKI. PRACE. (Text in English, Polish and Russian) 1967. irreg., no.41, 1993. price varies. Politechnika Warszawska, Instytut Fizyki, c/o Biblioteka Glowna, Pl. Politechniki 1, 00-661 Warsaw, Poland. TEL 48-2-6211370. Ed. Waclaw Jakubowski. **Indexed:** Chem.Abstr. **Document type:** academic/scholarly publication.
—CASDDS.

621	PL	ISSN 0137-625X

POLITECHNIKA WROCLAWSKA. INSTYTUT FIZYKI. PRACE NAUKOWE. KONFERENCJE. 1977. irreg., no.4, 1988. price varies. Wydawnictwo Politechniki Wroclawskiej, Wybrzeze Wyspianskiego 27, 50-370 Wroclaw, Poland. FAX 22-36-64. TELEX 712559 PWRPL. (Dist. by: Ars Polona-Ruch, Krakowskie Przedmiescie 7, Warsaw, Poland) **Indexed:** INSPEC. **Document type:** proceedings.

621 530	PL	ISSN 0370-0828
QC1		CODEN: PIFWDB

POLITECHNIKA WROCLAWSKA. INSTYTUT FIZYKI. PRACE NAUKOWE. MONOGRAFIE. (Text in Polish; summaries in English and Russian) 1972. irreg., no.19, 1991. price varies. Wydawnictwo Politechniki Wroclawskiej, Wybrzeze Wyspianskiego 27, 50-370 Wroclaw, Poland. FAX 22-36-64. TELEX 712559 PWRPL. (Dist. by: Ars Polona-Ruch, Krakowskie Przedmiescie 7, Warsaw, Poland) **Indexed:** INSPEC. **Document type:** monographic series.

621	PL	ISSN 0324-9697
QC1		CODEN: PIFWDB

POLITECHNIKA WROCLAWSKA. INSTYTUT FIZYKI. PRACE NAUKOWE. STUDIA I MATERIALY. (Text in Polish; summaries in English and Russian) 1969. irreg., no.7, 1976. price varies. (Instytut Fizyki) Wydawnictwo Politechniki Wroclawskiej, Wybrzeze Wyspianskiego 27, 50-370 Wroclaw, Poland. FAX 22-26-64. TELEX 712559 PWRPL. (Dist. by: Ars Polona-Ruch, Krakowskie Przedmiescie 7, Warsaw, Poland) **Indexed:** Chem.Abstr. **Document type:** academic/scholarly publication.
—CASDDS.

POLITECHNIKA WROCLAWSKA. INSTYTUT MATEMATYKI. PRACE NAUKOWE. STUDIA I MATERIALY. see *MATHEMATICS*

530	PO	ISSN 0048-4903
		CODEN: POPYA4

PORTUGALIAE PHYSICA. (Text and summaries in English and French) 1943-1975; resumed 1979. s-a. $24 to individuals; libraries $60. Sociedade Portuguesa de Fisica, Laboratorio de Fisica, Praca Gomes Teixeira, 4000 Porto, Portugal. TEL 2-325937. Ed. J.M. Machado da Silva. circ. 950. **Indexed:** Chem.Abstr., INSPEC, Math.R., Phys.Ber.

534	PL	ISSN 0032-5430
QC1		CODEN: PSTFAT

POSTEPY FIZYKI. (Text in Polish; summaries in English) 1953. bi-m. $25.30. Polskie Towarzystwo Fizyczne, Zarzad Glowny, Ul. Hoza 69, 00-681 Warsaw, Poland. (Dist. by: Ars Polona, Krakowskie Przedmiescie 7, 00-068 Warsaw, Poland) Ed. A. Sobiczewski. illus. circ. 2,230. **Indexed:** Chem.Abstr., INSPEC, Phys.Ber.
—CASDDS.

530 510	PL	ISSN 0137-8996
QC584		CODEN: FDRSBE

POZNANSKIE TOWARZYSTWO PRZYJACIOL NAUK. KOMISJA MATEMATYCZNO-PRZYRODNICZA. PRACE. (Text in Polish; summaries in English and French) 1921. irreg., vol.11, 1979. price varies. Poznanskie Towarzystwo Przyjaciol Nauk, Komicja Matematyczno-Przyrodnicza, Ul. Mielzynskiego 27-29, 61-725 Poznan, Poland. (Dist by: Ars Polona-Ruch, Krakowskie Przedmiescie 7, Warsaw, Poland) **Indexed:** Chem.Abstr. **Document type:** monographic series.
—BLDSC (3949.660000); CASDDS.

530	II	ISSN 0304-4289
QC1		CODEN: PRAMCI

PRAMANA; journal of physics. (Text in English) 1973. m. Rs.100($200) (effective 1996). Indian Academy of Sciences, C.V. Raman Avenue, P.B. No. 8005, Bangalore 560 080, India. TEL 91-80-3342546. FAX 91-80-3346094. TELEX 0845-2178-ACAD-IN. Ed. R. Nityananda. illus.; s-a. index. circ. 1,000. (also avail. in microform from UMI; back issues avail.; reprint service avail. from ISI,UMI) **Indexed:** Appl.Mech.Rev., Chem.Abstr., Curr.Cont., GeoRef., INSPEC (1973-), Met.Abstr., Phys.Ber., Sci.Cit.Ind., World Alum.Abstr. **Document type:** academic/scholarly publication.
—BLDSC (6601.300000); CASDDS; Ei; Faxon; Genuine Article; SWETS; UnCover.

530 370	GW	ISSN 0177-8374

PRAXIS DER NATURWISSENSCHAFTEN. PHYSIK. 8/yr. DM.112 (foreign DM.124). Aulis-Verlag Deubner und Co. KG, Antwerpener Str. 6-12, 50672 Cologne, Germany. TEL 0221-951454-0. FAX 0221-518443. adv.; bk.rev.; abstr.; illus. **Indexed:** Chem.Abstr., Phys.Ber. **Document type:** academic/scholarly publication.
—BLDSC (6603.175900). **CCC.**
Formerly (until 1980): Praxis der Naturwissenschaften. Physik im Unterricht der Schulen (ISSN 0342-8729)

530	US	ISSN 0079-5216

PRINCETON SERIES IN PHYSICS. 1971. irreg. price varies. Princeton University Press, 41 William St., Princeton, NJ 08540. TEL 609-258-4900. FAX 609-258-6305. E-mail: jhardy@pupress.princeton.edu. Eds. A.S. Wightman, J.J. Hopfield. (reprint service avail. from UMI) **Indexed:** INSPEC, Math.R. **Document type:** monographic series.
Refereed Serial

530 551.5   RU   ISSN 0552-2056
QC880   CODEN: PFATAL
PROBLEMY FIZIKI ATMOSFERY. 1963. irreg. 1.50 Rub. per no. Sankt-Peterburgskii Universitet, Universitetskaya Nab. 7-9, St. Petersburg V-164, Russia. circ. 1,000. **Indexed:** Chem.Abstr., GeoRef. —BLDSC (0133.860000); CASDDS.

PROCESS TECHNOLOGY PROCEEDINGS. see ENGINEERING — Industrial Engineering

530   SI
PROGRESS IN HIGH TEMPERATURE SUPERCONDUCTIVITY. (Text in English) 1987. irreg., vol. 33, 1992. price varies. World Scientific Publishing Co. Pte. Ltd., Farrer Rd., P.O. Box 128, Singapore 9128, Singapore. TEL 3825663. FAX 3825919. TELEX RS 28561 WSPC. (UK addr.: 73 Lynton Mead, Totteridge, London N20 8DH, England. TEL 44-81-4463356; US addr.: 1060 Main St., Ste. 1B, River Edge, NJ 07661. TEL 800-227-7562) **Indexed:** INSPEC. **Document type:** monographic series.

530   UK   ISSN 0079-6816
QD506   CODEN: PSSFBP
PROGRESS IN SURFACE SCIENCE; an international review journal. 1971. m. £525($835) (effective 1996). Elsevier Science Ltd., Pergamon, P.O. Box 800, Kidlington, Oxford OX5 1DX, England. TEL 44-1865-843000. FAX 44-1865-843010. E-mail: nlinfo-f@elsevier.nl; usinfo-f@elsevier.com; forinfo-kyf04035@niftyserve.or.jp; Site addr.: http://www.elsevier.nl/. (Subscr. in U.S. and Canada to: Elsevier Science, 660 White Plains Rd., Tarrytown, NY 10591-5153. TEL 914-524-9200. FAX 914-333-2444) Ed. Sydney G. Davison. (also avail. in microfilm from UMI) **Indexed:** Chem.Abstr., Curr.Cont., INSPEC, Mass Spectr.Bull., Met.Abstr., Phys.Ber., World Alum.Abstr. **Document type:** academic/scholarly publication.
—BLDSC (6924.575000); CASDDS; Ei; Faxon; Genuine Article; SWETS; UMI; UnCover. **CCC.**
Description: Publishes review articles from all disciplines where surfaces and interfaces play an important role.
Refereed Serial

530   JA   ISSN 0033-068X
QC1   CODEN: PTPKAV
PROGRESS OF THEORETICAL PHYSICS/RIRON BUTSURIGAKU NO SHINPO. (Supplement avail.) (Text in English; summaries in European languages) 1946. m. 75000 Yen (effective 1993). Yukawa Institute for Theoretical Physics, c/o Publication Office, Yukawa Hall, Kyoto University, Kitashirakawa Oiwake-cho, Sakyo-ku, Kyoto 606-01, Japan. FAX 075-722-6339. (Co-sponsor: Physical Society of Japan) index, cum.index every 5 yrs. circ. 1,900. (also avail. in microfilm from PMC; microfiche from PMC) **Indexed:** ASCA, Chem.Abstr., GeoRef., INSPEC, JCT, JTA, Math.R., Met.Abstr., Phys.Ber. **Document type:** academic/scholarly publication.
—BLDSC (6924.600000); CASDDS; Faxon; Genuine Article; SWETS; UnCover. **CCC.**
Description: Publishes papers in such areas as particles and fields, nuclear physics, solid state physics, statistical physics, astrophysics and cosmology.

530   JA   ISSN 0375-9687
CODEN: PTPSAL
PROGRESS OF THEORETICAL PHYSICS. SUPPLEMENT. (Text in English) 1955. irreg. (approx. 4/yr.). Yukawa Institute for Theoretical Physics, c/o Publication Office, Yukawa Hall, Kyoto University, Kitashirakawa Oiwake-cho, Sakyo-ku, Kyoto 606-01, Japan. FAX 75-722-6339. (Co-sponsor: Physical Society of Japan) Ed.Bd. **Document type:** academic/scholarly publication.
—BLDSC (6924.601000); CASDDS; Faxon; SWETS; UnCover.
Description: Covers the developments in various fields of fundamental physics.

PSYCHOTRONIC VIDEO. see COMMUNICATIONS — Video

530.44 621.381   JA
PURAZUMA PUROSESHINGU KENKYUKAI PUROSHIDINGUSU/PLASMA PROCESSING. (Text in English, Japanese; summaries in English) a. Oyo Butsuri Gakkai, Purazuma Erekutoronikusu Kenkyukai - Japan Society of Applied Physics, Research Group of Plasma Electronics, Waseda Daigaku Rikogakubu, 4-1, Okubo 3-chome, Shinjuku-ku, Tokyo 160, Japan. **Document type:** academic/scholarly publication.

QUANTUM ELECTRONICS. see ENGINEERING — Electrical Engineering

RADIATION CHEMISTRY/HOSHASEN KAGAKU. see CHEMISTRY

RADIOISOTOPES. see BIOLOGY — Biological Chemistry

620.1 519.2   NE   ISSN 0925-5850
RANDOM MATERIALS AND PROCESSES. (Text in English) 1990. irreg., vol.5, 1994. price varies. Elsevier Science B.V., Books Division, P.O. Box 211, 1000 AE Amsterdam, Netherlands. TEL 31-20-4853911. FAX 31-20-4853705. TELEX 18582 ESPA NL. E-mail: nlinfo-f@elsevier.nl; usinfo-f@elsevier.com; forinfo-kyf04035@niftyserve.or.jp; Site addr.: http://www.elsevier.nl/. (Subscr. in U.S. and Canada to: Elsevier Science Inc., Box 882, Madison Sq. Sta., New York, NY 10159. TEL 212-989-5800) Eds. H.E. Stanley, E. Guyon. (back issues avail.) **Document type:** monographic series.
Refereed Serial

RAUM UND ZEIT; die Neue Dimension der Wissenschaft. see MEDICAL SCIENCES

530   US   ISSN 1060-6823
CODEN: RCHAE4
RECEPTORS AND CHANNELS. 1993. q. 99 ECU (effective 1996). Harwood Academic Publishers, c/o International Publishers Distributor, 820 Town Center Dr., Langhorne, PA 19047. TEL 215-750-2642. FAX 215-750-6343. (Subscr. to: International Publishers Distributor, P.O. Box 90, Reading, Berkshire RG1 8JL, England. TEL 44-173-456-8316) (also avail. in microform) **Indexed:** Excerp.Med. (1994-), Ind.Med. (1994-). **Document type:** academic/scholarly publication.
—BLDSC (7305.277000); CASDDS; SWETS. **CCC.**
Description: Publishes research on receptors and ion channels and related signalling elements.

530.1   UK   ISSN 0034-4877
QC19.2   CODEN: RMHPBE
REPORTS ON MATHEMATICAL PHYSICS. 1975. bi-m. £400($636) (effective 1996). (Nicolaus Copernicus University, Institute of Physics, PL) Elsevier Science Ltd., Pergamon, P.O. Box 800, Kidlington, Oxford OX5 1DX, England. TEL 44-1865-843000. FAX 44-1865-843010. E-mail: nlinfo-f@elsevier.nl; usinfo-f@elsevier.com; forinfo-kyf04035@niftyserve.or.jp; Site addr.: http://www.elsevier.nl/. (Subscr. in U.S. and Canada to: Elsevier Science, 660 White Plains Rd., Tarrytown, NY 10591-5153. TEL 914-524-9200. FAX 914-333-2444) (Co-publisher: Polish Scientific Publishers) Ed. Roman S. Ingarden. adv.: B&W page $550, color page $1350. (also avail. in microform) **Indexed:** INSPEC (1970-). **Document type:** academic/scholarly publication.
—BLDSC (7660.510000); CASDDS; Faxon; SWETS; UMI; UnCover. **CCC.**
Description: Publishes papers in theoretical physics presenting a rigorous mathematical approach to problems of quantum and classical mechanics and field theories, relativity and gravitation, statistical physics and mathematical foundations of physical theories.
Refereed Serial

530   UK   ISSN 0034-4885
QC3   CODEN: RPPHAG
REPORTS ON PROGRESS IN PHYSICS. 1934. m. £666($1373) (effective 1996). (Institute of Physics) I O P Publishing Ltd., Techno House, Redcliffe Way, Bristol, Avon BS1 6NX, England. TEL 0117-929-7481. FAX 0117-929-4318. TELEX 449149 INSTP G. (U.S. subscr. to: American Institute of Physics, Member and Subscriber Services, 500 Sunnyside Blvd., Woodbury, NY 11797-2900. TEL 516-349-7800) Ed. M. Hart. bibl.; charts; illus.; cum.index. circ. 877. (also avail. in microfiche from AIP; microfilm from AIP) **Indexed:** Appl.Mech.Rev., Art & Archaeol.Tech.Abstr., Br.Ceram.Abstr., Cadscan, Chem.Abstr., Curr.Cont., Deep Sea Res.& Oceanogr.Abstr., GeoRef., INSPEC, Int.Aerosp.Abstr., Lead Abstr., Mass Spectr.Bull., Math.R., Met.Abstr., Phys.Ber., World Alum.Abstr., Zincscan. **Document type:** academic/scholarly publication.
—BLDSC (7665.500000); CASDDS; Faxon; Genuine Article; SWETS; UnCover. **CCC.**
Description: Provides a foundation of reviews for all research libraries and an overview of physics for other libraries.
Refereed Serial

530 547   JA   ISSN 0486-4476
QD471
REPORTS ON PROGRESS IN POLYMER PHYSICS IN JAPAN. (Text in English) 1958. a. 6000 Yen. (Research Group of Polymer Physics in Japan - Kobunshi Butsuri Nenpo Kankokai) Association for Science Document Information - Gakujutsu Bunken Fukyukai, Tokyo Kogyo Daigaku, 2-12, Ookayama, Meguro-ku, Tokyo 152, Japan.
—BLDSC (7665.520000).

REPUBLIC OF CHINA. NATIONAL SCIENCE COUNCIL. PROCEEDINGS. PART A: PHYSICAL SCIENCE AND ENGINEERING. see ENGINEERING

RESEARCH INSTITUTE FOR MATHEMATICAL SCIENCES. PUBLICATIONS/KYOTO DAIGAKU SURI KAISEKI KENKYUJO KIYO. see MATHEMATICS

530   SI   ISSN 0129-055X
QC19.2   CODEN: RMPHEX
REVIEWS IN MATHEMATICAL PHYSICS; a journal for survey and expository articles in the field of mathematical physics. (Text in English) 1989. bi-m. $380 to institutions of developed countries; individuals & developing countries $182. World Scientific Publishing Co. Pte. Ltd., Farrer Rd., P.O. Box 128, Singapore 9128, Singapore. TEL 3825663. FAX 3825919. TELEX RS-28561-WSPC. (US addr.: 1060 Main St., Ste. 1B, River Edge, NJ 07661. TEL 800-227-7562; European addr.: 73 Lynton Mead, Totteridge, London N20 8DH, England. TEL 44-81-4462461) Ed. Huzihiro Araki. circ. 150. (back issues avail.) **Indexed:** INSPEC (1989-). **Document type:** academic/scholarly publication.
—BLDSC (7791.700000); Faxon; Genuine Article; SWETS; UnCover. **CCC.**
Description: Contains survey and expository articles in mathematical physics.

REVIEWS OF GEOPHYSICS. see EARTH SCIENCES — Geophysics

539   US   ISSN 0034-6861
QC1   CODEN: RMPHAT
REVIEWS OF MODERN PHYSICS. 1929. q. $340 (foreign $350) (effective 1996). American Physical Society, One Physics Ellipse, College Park, MD 20740-3844. TEL 301-209-3202. (Subscr. to: APS Subscriber Service, c/o American Institute of Physics, 500 Sunnyside Blvd., Woodbury, NY 11797-2299. TEL 516-576-2270) Ed. George Bertsch. bibl.; illus.; cum.index. vols. 1-27 (1929-1955); vols.28-45 (1956-1973); vols.46-53 (1974-1981). (also avail. in microform from AIP,MIM; back issues avail.; reprint service avail.) **Indexed:** Appl.Mech.Rev., Biol.Abstr., C.P.I., Chem.Abstr., Deep Sea Res.& Oceanogr.Abstr., Excerp.Med., GeoRef., Ind.Med., INSPEC, Int.Aerosp.Abstr., Mass Spectr.Bull., Math.R., Met.Abstr., Phys.Ber. **Document type:** academic/scholarly publication.
—BLDSC (7793.300000); CASDDS; Ei; Faxon; Genuine Article; SWETS; UnCover. **CCC.**
Refereed Serial

PHYSICS

530.44   US   ISSN 0080-2050
QC718   CODEN: RPLPAK
REVIEWS OF PLASMA PHYSICS. 1965. irreg., vol.18, 1993. price varies. Plenum Publishing Corp., Consultants Bureau, 233 Spring St., New York, NY 10013-1578. TEL 212-620-8000. FAX 212-463-0742. TELEX 23-421139. Ed. M.A. Leontovich. (back issues avail.) **Document type:** monographic series.
—BLDSC (7794.050000); Faxon.
Description: English translations of research originally published in Russian.
Refereed Serial

530   CU   ISSN 0253-9268
               CODEN: RECFD7
REVISTA CUBANA DE FISICA. (Text in Spanish; summaries in English and Spanish) 1981. 3/yr. C.$4.50($24) in N. America; S. America $25; Europe $26. (Universidad de La Habana, Direccion de Informacion Cientifica y Tecnica) Ediciones Cubanas, Obispo No. 527, Apdo. 605, Havana, Cuba. (back issues avail.)
—CASDDS.

530.15   AG   ISSN 0080-2360
QA1
REVISTA DE MATEMATICA Y FISICA TEORICA. SERIE A. (Text in Spanish, French, German, Italian and English; summaries in English) 1940. a. $15. Universidad Nacional de Tucuman, Facultad de Ciencias Exactas y Tecnologia, Avda. Independencia 1800, Tucuman, Argentina. FAX 81311462. TELEX 61249-FDCET-AR. Eds. Raul Luccioni, Constantino Grosse. bk.rev.; index. circ. 250. **Indexed:** Math.R., Zent.Math.

530   SP   ISSN 0213-862X
REVISTA ESPANOLA DE FISICA. 1987. q. 5300 ptas.($60) Real Sociedad Espanola de Fisica, Fac. de Fisica, Univ. Complutense, Ciudad Universitaria, 28040 Madrid, Spain. Ed. Antonio F. Ranada. **Document type:** academic/scholarly publication.
Description: Addresses the community of physicists.

530   MX   ISSN 0035-001X
QC1   CODEN: RMXFAT
REVISTA MEXICANA DE FISICA. (Supplements avail.) (Text and summaries in English and Spanish) 1952. 6/yr. Mex.$100($100) (effective 1996). Sociedad Mexicana de Fisica, A.C., Apdo. 70-348, 04511 Mexico, D.F., Mexico. TEL 525-622-4848. E-mail: smf@hp.fciencias.unam. Ed. Shahen Hacyan. bibl.; charts; illus.; index. circ. 1,500. **Indexed:** Astron.& Astrophys.Abstr., Bull.Signal., Chem.Abstr., Curr.Cont., INIS Atomind., INSPEC (1968-), Math.R., Nucl.Sci.Abstr., Phys.Ber., Sci.Cit.Ind. **Document type:** academic/scholarly publication.
—BLDSC (7866.300000); CASDDS; Genuine Article; UnCover.
Description: Original papers in physics: research, education, instrumentation, history and philosophy; letters and review articles.
Refereed Serial

531.11   NE   ISSN 0169-3107
RHEOLOGY SERIES. (Text in English) 1984. irreg., vol.4, 1993. price varies. Elsevier Science B.V., Books Division, P.O. Box 211, 1000 AE Amsterdam, Netherlands. TEL 31-20-4853911. FAX 31-20-4853705. TELEX 18582 ESPA NL. E-mail: nlinfo-f@elsevier.nl; usinfo-f@elsevier.com; forinfo-kyf04035@niftyserve.or.jp; Site addr.: http://www.elsevier.nl/. (Subscr. in U.S. and Canada to: Elsevier Science Inc., Box 882, Madison Sq. Sta., New York, NY 10159) Ed. K. Walters. (back issues avail.) **Indexed:** INSPEC. **Document type:** monographic series.
—BLDSC (7960.590000).

530   JA   ISSN 0913-543X
RIGAKU JOURNAL. (Text in English) 1984. s-a. Rigaku Denki K.K. - Rigaku Corp., 3-9-12 Matsubara-cho, Akishima-shi, Tokyo 196, Japan. TEL 0425-45-8139. FAX 0425-46-7090. Ed. Tomohiko Watanabe. **Document type:** academic/scholarly publication.
—BLDSC (7970.680500).

RIGAKKAISHI/JOURNAL OF PHYSICS, CHEMISTRY AND EARTH SCIENCE. see *SCIENCES: COMPREHENSIVE WORKS*

530 540   JA   ISSN 0020-3084
               CODEN: RKKHAO
RIKAGAKU KENKYUJO HOKOKU/INSTITUTE OF PHYSICAL AND CHEMICAL RESEARCH. REPORTS. (Text in Japanese; summaries in English) 1922. irreg. Rikagaku Kenkyujo - Institute of Physical and Chemical Research, 2-1 Hirosawa, Wako-shi, Saitama-ken 351-01, Japan. TEL 0484-621111. FAX 0484-621554. Ed. Minoru Oda. abstr.; charts; illus.; index. circ. 800. **Indexed:** Appl.Mech.Rev., Chem.Abstr., Eng.Ind., INIS Atomind., INSPEC, Jap.Per.Ind., JTA, Met.Abstr., Nucl.Sci.Abstr., World Alum.Abstr.
—CASDDS.
Formerly: Scientific Research Institute. Reports.

530   RM   ISSN 1221-146X
QC1   CODEN: RJPHEC
ROMANIAN JOURNAL OF PHYSICS. (Text in English, French) 1956. 10/yr. 400 lei($90) (Academia Romana) Editura Academiei Romane, Str. 13, Septembrie 11, Sect. 5, Bucharest, Rumania. TEL 40-1-6807040. (Dist. by: Rompresfilatelia, Calea Grivitei 64-66, P.O. Box 12-201, 78104 Bucharest, Rumania) Ed. A. Sandulescu. adv. contact: A. Calboreanu. bk.rev.; charts; illus.; index. circ. 600. **Indexed:** Bull.Signal., Cadscan, Ceram.Abstr., Chem.Abstr., Curr.Cont., INSPEC, Lead Abstr., Math.R., Met.Abstr., Nucl.Sci.Abstr., Phys.Ber., Ref.Zh., Zincscan. **Document type:** academic/scholarly publication.
—BLDSC (8019.638950); CASDDS.
Formerly (until 1992): Revue Roumaine de Physique (ISSN 0035-4090)
Description: Includes papers and short notes in all fields of physics.
Refereed Serial

530 551.46   RU
ROSSIISKAYA AKADEMIYA NAUK. INSTITUT OBSHCHEI FIZIKI. TRUDY.* English translation: Russian Academy of Sciences. Institute of General Physics. Proceedings. 1986. irreg. 15 Rub. Ul. Vavilova 38, 117942 Moscow, Russia. TEL 135-2366. (Subscr. to: Akademkniga, B. Cherkasskij per. 2-10, 103624 Moscow, Russia) Ed. A.M. Prokhorov. adv.
Formerly: Akademiya Nauk S.S.S.R. Institut Obshchei Fiziki. Trudy (ISSN 1011-0399)

ROYAL IRISH ACADEMY. PROCEEDINGS. SECTION A: MATHEMATICAL AND PHYSICAL SCIENCES. see *MATHEMATICS*

ROYAL NETHERLANDS ACADEMY OF SCIENCES. PROCEEDINGS; biological, chemical, geological, physical and medical sciences. see *SCIENCES: COMPREHENSIVE WORKS*

530 620   UK   ISSN 0962-8428
Q41   CODEN: PTRMAD
ROYAL SOCIETY OF LONDON. PHILOSOPHICAL TRANSACTIONS. SERIES A. PHYSICAL SCIENCES AND ENGINEERING. 1665. m. £490 in Europe; U.S. and Canada £524. Royal Society of London, 6 Carlton House Terrace, London SW1Y 5AG, England. TEL 0171-839-5561. FAX 0171-976-1837. Ed. F.T. Smith. adv. contact: Peter Cooper. circ. 865. (also avail. in microform from PMC; microfiche from IDC; reprint service avail. from ISI,KTO) **Indexed:** Acid Rain Abstr., Acid Rain Ind., Appl.Mech.Rev., Biol.Abstr., Br.Archaeol.Abstr., Br.Geol.Lit., Chem.Abstr., Energy Info.Abstr., Eng.Ind., Environ.Abstr., Fluidex, Geo.Abstr., Geol.Abstr., GeoRef., INSPEC, Mass Spectr.Bull., Math.R., Met.Abstr., Nutr.Abstr., Petrol.Abstr., Soils & Fert., Vet.Bull. **Document type:** academic/scholarly publication.
—BLDSC (6463.000000); CASDDS; Ei; Faxon; Genuine Article; SWETS; UnCover. **CCC.**
Formerly: Royal Society of London. Philosophical Transactions. Series A. Mathematical and Physical Sciences (ISSN 0080-4614)
Description: Original papers on mathematical, physical, engineering, and earth sciences.
Refereed Serial

RUSSIAN ACADEMY OF SCIENCE. LEBEDEV PHYSICS INSTITUTE. PROCEEDINGS. see *PHYSICS — Optics*

530   US   ISSN 1062-8738
QC1   CODEN: BRSPEX
RUSSIAN ACADEMY OF SCIENCES. BULLETIN. PHYSICS. English translation of: Rossiiskaya Akademiya Nauk. Izvestiya. Seriya Fizicheskaya. (Supplement avail.) m. $1565 (effective 1996). (Rossiiskaya Akademiya Nauk, RU) Allerton Press, Inc., 150 Fifth Ave., New York, NY 10011. TEL 212-924-3950. FAX 212-463-9684. Ed. A.V. Gaponov-Grekhov. **Indexed:** INSPEC (1992-). **Document type:** academic/scholarly publication.
—BLDSC (0409.350000); Ei; Faxon; SWETS; UnCover. **CCC.**
Formerly: Academy of Sciences of the U S S R. Bulletin. Physical Series (ISSN 0001-432X)

RUSSIAN ACADEMY OF SCIENCES. COLLOID JOURNAL. see *CHEMISTRY — Physical Chemistry*

530 551.46   US
RUSSIAN ACADEMY OF SCIENCES. INSTITUTE OF GENERAL PHYSICS. PROCEEDINGS. English translation of: Rossiiskaya Akademiya Nauk. Institut Obshchei Fiziki. Trudy. 1987. irreg., no.16, 1990. price varies. (Rossiiskaya Akademiya Nauk, Institut Obshchei Fiziki, RU - Russian Academy of Sciences, Institute of General Physics) Nova Science Publishers, Inc., 6080 Jericho Tpke. Ste. 207, Commack, NY 11725-2808. TEL 516-499-3103. **Indexed:** INSPEC. **Document type:** proceedings.
Formerly: Academy of Sciences of the U S S R. Institute of General Physics. Proceedings (ISSN 0895-8823)
Description: Compilation of advanced physics research.
Refereed Serial

530 621   US   ISSN 1051-8053
TJ265   CODEN: RJETER
RUSSIAN JOURNAL OF ENGINEERING THERMOPHYSICS. 1991. 4/yr. $275 (effective 1996). (Rossiiskaya Akademiya Nauk, Sibirskoe Otdelenie, Institut Teplophysiki, RU) Begell House Inc., 79 Madison Ave., New York, NY 10016-7892. TEL 212-725-1999. FAX 212-213-8368. E-mail: 74353.2052@compuserve.com. Eds. V.E. Nakoryakov, E.N. Ganic. (also avail. in microform from UMI; back issues avail.) **Document type:** academic/scholarly publication.
—BLDSC (8052.709700); CASDDS.
Description: Publishes original English language articles on work conducted at major research institutions in Russia.
Refereed Serial

530 510   US   ISSN 1061-9208
QC19.2   CODEN: RJMPEL
RUSSIAN JOURNAL OF MATHEMATICAL PHYSICS. 1993. q. $404 (foreign $466) (effective 1996). John Wiley & Sons, Inc., Journals, 605 Third Ave., New York, NY 10158. TEL 212-850-6645. FAX 212-850-6021. TELEX 12-7063. E-mail: SUBINFO@JWILEY.COM. (Subscr. outside the Americas to: John Wiley & Sons Ltd., Baffins Ln., Chichester, W. Sussex PO19 1UD, England. TEL 44-1243-779777. FAX 44-1243-776128) (also avail. in microform from UMI; back issues avail.) **Document type:** academic/scholarly publication.
—BLDSC (8052.713200).
Refereed Serial

530   US   ISSN 1064-8887
QC1   CODEN: RPJOEB
RUSSIAN PHYSICS JOURNAL. English translation of: Izvestiya Vysshikh Uchebnykh Zavedenii. Seriya Fizika (RU ISSN 0021-3411) 1965. m. $1395 (foreign $1630) (effective 1996). (Vysshie Uchebnye Zavedeniya, RU) Plenum Publishing Corp., Consultants Bureau, 233 Spring St., New York, NY 10013-1578. TEL 212-620-8468. FAX 212-463-0742. TELEX 23-421139. Ed. V.N. Detinko. (also avail. in microfilm from JSC; back issues avail.) **Indexed:** Appl. Mech.Rev., Chem.Titles, Eng.Ind., INSPEC (1992-), Math.R., Solid St.Abstr. **Document type:** academic/scholarly publication.
—BLDSC (0420.778500); Faxon; SWETS; UMI; UnCover. **CCC.**
Formerly (until 1993): Soviet Physics Journal (ISSN 0038-5697)
Refereed Serial

RYUTAI RIKIGAKU KOENKAI KOENSHU/PROCEEDINGS OF THE SYMPOSIUM ON FLUID MECHANICS. see *ENGINEERING — Hydraulic Engineering*

SAGA DAIGAKU RIKOGAKUBU SHUHO/SAGA UNIVERSITY. FACULTY OF SCIENCE AND ENGINEERING. REPORTS. see *ENGINEERING*

SAITAMA MATHEMATICAL JOURNAL. see *MATHEMATICS*

530 540   RU
AS262   CODEN: VLUFBI
SANKT-PETERBURGSKII UNIVERSITET. VESTNIK. SERIYA FIZIKA I KHIMIYA. (Text in Russian; summaries in English) 1946. q. 18.60 Rub. Sankt-Peterburgskii Universitet, Universitetskaya Nab., 7-9, St. Petersburg V-164, Russia. (Subscr. to: Mezhdunarodnaya Kniga, Dimitrova ul. 39, Moscow, G-200, Russia) Ed. S.P. Merkur'ev. bk.rev.; charts; illus.; index. circ. 1,340. (also avail. in microfiche from BHP) Indexed: Chem.Abstr., Math.R. Document type: academic/scholarly publication.
—CASDDS; UMI.
    Formerly (until 1992): Leningradskii Universitet. Vestnik. Seriya Fizika i Khimiya (ISSN 0024-0826)

SCIEN TECH/SAGA DAIGAKU RIKOGAKUBU KOHO. see *ENGINEERING*

530   UK
SCOPE (YORK). 1951. q. membership. Institute of Physical Sciences in Medicine, P.O. Box 303, York YO1 2WR, England. TEL 0904-610821. Ed. Christine Tonge. adv.; bk.rev. circ. 1,500.
    Formerly: H P A Bulletin (Hospital Physicists Association).

SCUOLA NORMALE SUPERIORE DI PISA. ANNALI. CLASSE DI SCIENZE. see *MATHEMATICS*

530   JA
SEIDENKI GAKKAI KOEN RONBUNSHU/INSTITUTE OF ELECTROSTATICS JAPAN. PROCEEDINGS OF ANNUAL MEETING. (Text in English, Japanese; summaries in English) a. 6000 Yen. Seidenki Gakkai - Institute of Electrostatics Japan, 1-3, Hongo 4-chome, Bunkyo-ku, Tokyo 113, Japan. TEL 81-3-3815-4173. Document type: proceedings.

530   JA   ISSN 0386-2550
QC570
SEIDENKI GAKKAISHI/INSTITUTE OF ELECTROSTATICS JAPAN. JOURNAL. (Text in English, Japanese; summaries in English) 1977. bi-m. 3000 Yen per no. Seidenki Gakkai - Institute of Electrostatics Japan, 1-3, Hongo 4-chome, Bunkyo-ku, Tokyo 113, Japan. TEL 81-3-3815-4173. Ed. Tada Etal. Indexed: Jap.Per.Ind. Document type: academic/scholarly publication.
—BLDSC (6715.240000).

SELECTA MATHEMATICA. see *MATHEMATICS*

530   NE   ISSN 0080-8636
        CODEN: STSSB2
SELECTED TOPICS IN SOLID STATE PHYSICS. (Text in English) 1962. irreg., vol.18, 1986. price varies. Elsevier Science B.V., Books Division, P.O. Box 211, 1000 AE Amsterdam, Netherlands. TEL 31-20-4853911. FAX 31-20-4853705. TELEX 18582 ESPA NL. E-mail: nlinfo-f@elsevier.nl; usinfo-f@elsevier.com; forinfo-kyf04035@niftyserve.or.jp; Site addr.: http://www.elsevier.nl/. (Subscr. in U.S. and Canada to: Elsevier Science Inc., Box 882, Madison Sq. Sta., New York, NY 10159. TEL 212-989-5800) Ed. E.P. Wohlfarth. Indexed: INSPEC. Document type: monographic series.
    Supersedes: Series of Monographs on Selected Topics in Solid State Physics (ISSN 0582-8104)
    Refereed Serial

530   US
▼**SELECTED TOPICS IN SUPERCONDUCTIVITY.** 1994. irreg., vol.2, 1994. price varies. Plenum Publishing Corp., 233 Spring St., New York, NY 10013-1578. TEL 212-620-8000. FAX 212-463-0742. TELEX 23-421139. Ed. Stu Wolf. (back issues avail.) Document type: monographic series.
    Description: Discusses contemporary issues in the science and technology of superconductivity, including applications and techniques of current interest.
    Refereed Serial

537.622   US   ISSN 1063-7826
QC612.S4   CODEN: SMICES
SEMICONDUCTORS. English translation of: Fizika i Tekhnika Poluprovodnikov (RU ISSN 0015-3222) 1967. m. $2465 (foreign $2505) (effective 1996). (Russian Academy of Sciences, St. Petersburg Division, AC) American Institute of Physics, One Physics Ellipse, College Park, MD 20740-3843. TEL 301-209-3000. Ed. S. Amoretty. index. (also avail. in microform from AIP; back issues avail.) Indexed: ASCA, C.P.I., Eng.Ind., Gen.Phys.Adv.Abstr., INSPEC, Met.Abstr., Phys.Ber., World Alum.Abstr. Document type: academic/scholarly publication.
—BLDSC (0420.805800); Faxon; Genuine Article; SWETS; UnCover. **CCC**.
    Formerly: Soviet Physics - Semiconductors (ISSN 0038-5700)

SENSOR TECHNOLOGY; a monthly intelligence service. see *COMPUTERS — Cybernetics*

530   JA   ISSN 0914-4935
        CODEN: SENMER
SENSORS AND MATERIALS. (Text in English) 1989. bi-m. $250. M Y U, Scientific Publishing Division, 2-32-3 Sendagi, Bunkyo-ku, Tokyo 113, Japan. Ed. T. Nakamura. Indexed: INSPEC (1993-). Document type: academic/scholarly publication.
—BLDSC (8241.785400); CASDDS.

SERIE DI MATEMATICA E FISICA. TESTI. see *MATHEMATICS*

530   SI
SERIES IN MODERN CONDENSED MATTER PHYSICS. (Text in English) 1991. irreg., vol.4, 1992. price varies. World Scientific Publishing Co. Pte. Ltd., Farrer Rd., P.O. Box 128, Singapore 9128, Singapore. TEL 3825663. FAX 3825919. TELEX RS 28561 WSPC. (UK addr.: 73 Lynton Mead, Totteridge, London N20 8DH, England. TEL 44-81-4462461; US addr.: 1060 Main St., River Edge, NJ 07661. TEL 800-227-7562) Document type: monographic series.

530   SI   ISSN 0218-0332
SERIES ON DIRECTIONS IN CONDENSED MATTER PHYSICS. (Text in English) 1986. irreg., vol.11, 1991. price varies. World Scientific Publishing Co. Pte. Ltd., Farrer Rd., P.O. Box 128, Singapore 9128, Singapore. TEL 3825663. FAX 3825919. TELEX RS 28561 WSPC. (UK addr.: 73 Lynton Mead, Totteridge, London N20 8DH, England. TEL 44-81-4462461; US addr.: 1060 Main St., River Edge, NJ 07661. TEL 800-227-7562) Document type: monographic series.
—BLDSC (9360.006000).

530 621.3   US   ISSN 0955-9019
SERIES ON SEMICONDUCTOR SCIENCE AND TECHNOLOGY. 1989. irreg. price varies. Oxford University Press, 200 Madison Ave., New York, NY 10016. TEL 212-679-7300. Document type: monographic series.
—BLDSC (8250.202280).

SEVERO-KAVKAZSKII NAUCHNYI TSENTR VYSSHEI SHKOLY. ESTESTVENNYE NAUKI. IZVESTIYA/NORTH-CAUCASUS SCIENTIFIC CENTER OF HIGH SCHOOL. NATURAL SCIENCES. NEWS. see *MATHEMATICS*

530   JA   ISSN 0559-8516
        CODEN: SHINAM
SHINKU/VACUUM SOCIETY OF JAPAN. JOURNAL. (Text in Japanese; summaries in English) 1958. m. 1300 Yen per no. Nihon Shinku Kyokai - Vacuum Society of Japan, 5-22, Shiba Koen 3-chome, Minato-ku, Tokyo 105, Japan.
—BLDSC (4912.350000); CASDDS.

530   JA
SHINKU NI KANSURU RENGO KOENKAI KOEN YOKOSHU/PREPRINTS OF THE JOINT SYMPOSIA ON VACUUM. (Text in Japanese) 1960. a. membership. Nihon Shinku Kyokai - Vacuum Society of Japan, 5-22, Shiba Koen 3-chome, Minato-ku, Tokyo 105, Japan.

530 510   JA   ISSN 0368-4571
TS1300   CODEN: JTSFAX
SHINSHU UNIVERSITY. FACULTY OF TEXTILE SCIENCE AND TECHNOLOGY. JOURNAL. SERIES F: PHYSICS AND MATHEMATICS. (Text in European languages; summaries in English) 1962-1992 (no.10). irreg. exchange basis. Shinshu University, Faculty of Textile Science and Technology - Shinshu Daigaku Sen'igakubu, 15-1 Tokida 3-chome, Ueda-shi, Nagano-ken 386, Japan.

SHUXUE WULI XUEBAO. see *MATHEMATICS*

530   IT   ISSN 1122-1437
SOCIETA ITALIANA DI FISICA. ATTI DI CONFERENZE/ITALIAN PHYSICAL SOCIETY. CONFERENCE PROCEEDINGS. 1985. irreg., vol.44, 1993. price varies. Editrice Compositori s.r.l., Via Stalingrado 97-2, 40128 Bologna, Italy. TEL 51-327811. Document type: proceedings.
—BLDSC (3409.770700).

530   IT
SOCIETA ITALIANA DI FISICA. CONGRESSO NAZIONALE.* a. Societa Italiana di Fisica, Dipartimento di Biologia, Via L. degli Andalo 2, 40124 Bologna, Italy.

530 539.7   IT   ISSN 0369-3546
        CODEN: NCIAAT
SOCIETA ITALIANA DI FISICA. NUOVO CIMENTO A; nuclei, particles and fields. (Text in English, French, German; summaries in English, Italian, Russian) 1855. m. $880 to non-members; members $710 (effective 1994). Editrice Compositori s.r.l., Via Stalingrado 97-2, 40128 Bologna, Italy. TEL 051-327811. Ed. Renato Angelo Ricci. Indexed: Chem.Abstr., Curr.Cont., INSPEC (1968-), Mass Spectr.Bull., Phys.Ber. Document type: academic/scholarly publication.
—BLDSC (6185.100000); Genuine Article; SWETS; UnCover. **CCC**.
    Supersedes in part in 1965: Nuovo Cimento (ISSN 0029-6341)
    Description: Covers physics of elementary particles and includes articles in the field of nuclear physics.

530 520   IT   ISSN 0369-3554
        CODEN: NIFBAP
SOCIETA ITALIANA DI FISICA. NUOVO CIMENTO B; general physics, relativity, astronomy and mathematical physics and methods. (Text in English, French, German; summaries in English, Italian, Russian) 1855. m. $620 to non-members; members $510 (effective 1994). Editrice Compositori s.r.l., Via Stalingrado 97-2, 40128 Bologna, Italy. TEL 051-327811. Ed. Renato Angelo Ricci. Indexed: Chem.Abstr., Curr.Cont., INSPEC (1968-), Phys.Ber., Ref.Zh. Document type: academic/scholarly publication.
—BLDSC (6185.200000); Genuine Article; SWETS; UnCover. **CCC**.
    Supersedes in part in 1965: Nuovo Cimento (ISSN 0029-6341)
    Description: Covers general topics in classical areas of phenomenology. Includes plasma and electric discharges, fundamental astronomy and astrophysics.

530 551   IT   ISSN 0390-5551
        CODEN: NIFCAS
SOCIETA ITALIANA DI FISICA. NUOVO CIMENTO C; geophysics and space physics. (Text in English, French, German; summaries in English, Italian, Russian) 1978. bi-m. $310 to non-members; members $245 (effective 1994). Editrice Compositori s.r.l., Via Stalingrado 97-2, 40128 Bologna, Italy. TEL 051-327811. Ed. Renato Angelo Ricci. Indexed: Chem.Abstr., INSPEC, Meteor.& Geoastrophys.Abstr.
—BLDSC (6185.250000); CASDDS; Faxon; Genuine Article; SWETS; UMI; UnCover. **CCC**.
    Description: Covers geophysics and space physics.

PHYSICS

530   IT   ISSN 0392-6737
CODEN: NCSDDN
SOCIETA ITALIANA DI FISICA. NUOVO CIMENTO D; condensed matter, atomic, molecular and chemical physics, fluids, plasmas, biophysics. (Text in English, French, German; summaries in English, Italian Russian) 1982. m. $530 to non-members; members $420 (effective 1994). Editrice Compositori s.r.l., Via Stalingrado 97-2, 40128 Bologna, Italy. TEL 051-327811. Ed. Renato Angelo Ricci. index. circ. 700. (back issues avail.) **Indexed:** Chem.Abstr., INSPEC, Met.Abstr.
—BLDSC (6185.260000); CASDDS; Ei; Faxon; Genuine Article; SWETS; UMI. **CCC.**
Description: Covers atomic and molecular physics; structure, mechanical, thermal properties; electronic structure, electric, magnetical and optical properties.

530   IT   ISSN 0393-697X
CODEN: RNUCAC
SOCIETA ITALIANA DI FISICA. RIVISTA DEL NUOVO CIMENTO. (Text in English) 1969. m. $340 to non-members; members $265 (effective 1994). (Societa Italiana di Fisica) Editrice Compositori s.r.l., Via Stalingrado 97-2, 40128 Bologna, Italy. TEL 51-327811. Ed. R.A. Ricci. charts. **Indexed:** Appl.Mech.Rev., Chem.Abstr., Curr.Cont., INSPEC (1969-), Math.R., Ref.Zh. **Document type:** academic/scholarly publication.
—BLDSC (7991.500000); CASDDS; Faxon; Genuine Article; SWETS; UMI; UnCover. **CCC.**
Formerly (until 1971): Rivista del Nuovo Cimento (ISSN 0035-5917)
Description: Review of original articles of general arguments in physics.

530   FR   ISSN 0081-1076
SOCIETE FRANCAISE DE PHYSIQUE. ANNUAIRE. 1913. biennial. 360 F. Societe Francaise de Physique, 33 rue Croulebarbe, 75013 Paris, France.

530   FR   ISSN 0037-9360
CODEN: BFPYAP
SOCIETE FRANCAISE DE PHYSIQUE. BULLETIN. (Includes supplements) 1881. 5/yr. 250 F. Societe Francaise de Physique, 33 rue Croulebarbe, 75013 Paris, France. TEL 47-07-32-98. FAX 43-31-74-26. Ed. Pierre Radvanyi. charts; illus.; stat. **Indexed:** Chem.Abstr. **Document type:** bulletin.
—CASDDS.
Description: Lists all congresses to take place as well as all relevant information about them.

533.5   FR
SOCIETE FRANCAISE DU VIDE. PROCEEDINGS. Issued with: Le Vide: Science, Technique et Applications. (Text in English, French) irreg. 3200 F. (foreign 3400 F.) (includes subscr. to: Le Vide: Science, Technique et Applications). Societe Francaise du Vide, 19 rue du Renard, 75004 Paris, France. TEL 42-78-15-82. FAX 42-78-63-20. **Document type:** proceedings.
Description: Presents proceedings from conferences in the subject.

SOCIETE NATIONALE DES SCIENCES NATURELLES ET MATHEMATIQUES DE CHERBOURG. MEMOIRES. see *SCIENCES: COMPREHENSIVE WORKS*

SOLAR-GEOPHYSICAL DATA. PART 1 - PROMPT REPORTS. see *ASTRONOMY*

SOLAR-GEOPHYSICAL DATA: PART 2 - COMPREHENSIVE REPORTS. see *ASTRONOMY*

SOLAR PHYSICS; a journal for solar and solar-stellar research and the study of solar terrestrial physics. see *ASTRONOMY*

SOLAR SYSTEM RESEARCH. see *ASTRONOMY*

530.41   UK   ISSN 0038-1098
QC176.A1   CODEN: SSCOA4
SOLID STATE COMMUNICATIONS; an international journal. 1963. 48/yr. £1463($2327) (effective 1996). Elsevier Science Ltd., Pergamon, P.O. Box 800, Kidlington, Oxford OX5 1DX, England. TEL 44-1865-843000. FAX 44-1865-843010. E-mail: nlinfo-f@elsevier.nl; usinfo-f@elsevier.com; forinfo-kyf04035@niftyserve.or.jp; Site addr.: http://www.elsevier.nl/. (Subscr. in U.S. and Canada to: Elsevier Science, 660 White Plains Rd., Tarrytown, NY 10591-5153. TEL 914-524-9200. FAX 914-333-2444) Ed. Manuel Cardona. adv.: B&W page $550, color page $1350. bk.rev.; charts; illus.; index. circ. 2,000. (also avail. in microfiche from MIM; microfilm from UMI; back issues avail.) **Indexed:** Appl.Mech.Rev., ASCA, Chem.Abstr., Curr.Cont., Eng.Ind., GeoRef., INSPEC, Mass Spectr.Bull., Met.Abstr., Phys.Ber., World Alum.Abstr. **Document type:** academic/scholarly publication.
—BLDSC (8327.378000); CASDDS; Ei; Faxon; Genuine Article; SWETS; UMI; UnCover. **CCC.**
Description: Original experimental and theoretical research on the physical and chemical properties of solids and condensed systems.
Refereed Serial

530   NE   ISSN 0167-2738
QC176.A1   CODEN: SSIOD3
SOLID STATE IONICS; diffusion and reactions. (Text in English) 1980. 40/yr. fl.4140($2525) (effective 1996). North-Holland (Subsidiary of: Elsevier Science B.V.), P.O. Box 211, 1000 AE Amsterdam, Netherlands. TEL 31-20-4853911. FAX 31-20-4853598. TELEX 18582 ESPA NL. (Subscr. in U.S. and Canada to: Elsevier Science Inc., Box 882, Madison Sq. Sta., New York, NY 10159. TEL 212-989-5800. FAX 212-633-3990) Ed. M.S. Whittingham. adv.; index. (also avail. in microform from UMI; back issues avail.) **Indexed:** ASCA, Chem.Abstr., Curr.Cont., INSPEC (1986-), Met.Abstr., Phys.Ber., World Alum.Abstr. **Document type:** academic/scholarly publication.
—BLDSC (8327.386000); CASDDS; Ei; Faxon; Genuine Article; SWETS; UnCover. **CCC.**
Incorporates (1985-1989): Reactivity of Solids (ISSN 0168-7336)
Description: Devoted to the physics, chemistry and materials science of diffusion in mass transport and reactivity of solids.
Refereed Serial

530   US   ISSN 0081-1947
QC173   CODEN: SSPHAE
SOLID STATE PHYSICS: ADVANCES IN RESEARCH AND APPLICATIONS. 1955. irreg., vol.46, 1992. Academic Press, Inc., 525 B St., Ste. 1900, San Diego, CA 92101-4495. TEL 619-231-0926. FAX 619-699-6715. (Subscr. to: Order Dept., 6277 Sea Harbor Dr., 4th Fl., Orlando, FL 32887. TEL 800-321-5068) Ed.Bd. index, cum.index: vols.1-11 (1955-1960). (reprint service avail. from ISI) **Indexed:** ASCA, GeoRef., INSPEC.
—BLDSC (8327.400000); CASDDS; Faxon; SWETS; UnCover. **CCC.**
Refereed Serial

530   US   ISSN 0275-7796
SOVIET SCIENTIFIC REVIEWS SUPPLEMENT SERIES. SECTION A: PHYSICS. irreg., latest vol.2. price varies. Harwood Academic Publishers, c/o International Publishers Distributor, 820 Town Center Dr., Langhorne, PA 19047. TEL 215-750-2642. FAX 215-750-6343. (Subscr. to: International Publishers Distributor, Box 90, Reading, Berkshire RG1 8JL, England. TEL 44-173-456-8316) Ed. I.M. Khalatnikov. (also avail. in microform) **Document type:** monographic series.

530   US   ISSN 0930-8989
CODEN: SPPPEL
SPRINGER PROCEEDINGS IN PHYSICS. 1984. irreg. price varies. Springer-Verlag, 175 Fifth Ave., New York, NY 10010. TEL 212-460-1500. FAX 212-473-6272. (Also: Berlin, Heidelberg, Tokyo and Vienna) (reprint service avail. from ISI) **Indexed:** INSPEC. **Document type:** proceedings.
—BLDSC (8424.726500); CASDDS; Faxon. **CCC.**

530 541.3   US   ISSN 0172-6218
CODEN: SSCPDA
SPRINGER SERIES IN CHEMICAL PHYSICS. 1978. irreg. price varies. Springer-Verlag, 175 Fifth Ave., New York, NY 10010. TEL 212-460-1500. FAX 212-473-6272. (Also: Berlin, Heidelberg, Tokyo and Vienna) Ed.Bd. (reprint service avail. from ISI) **Indexed:** Biol.Abstr., Chem.Abstr., INSPEC, Phys.Ber. **Document type:** monographic series.
—BLDSC (8424.755000); CASDDS; Ei. **CCC.**

530   US   ISSN 0933-033X
CODEN: SSMSE2
SPRINGER SERIES IN MATERIALS SCIENCES. 1986. irreg., vol.27, 1994. price varies. Springer-Verlag, 175 Fifth Ave., New York, NY 10010. TEL 212-460-1500. FAX 212-473-6272. (Also: Berlin, Heidelberg, Tokyo and Vienna) (reprint service avail. from ISI) **Document type:** monographic series.
—BLDSC (8424.766600); CASDDS.

530   US   ISSN 0171-1873
CODEN: SSSSDV
SPRINGER SERIES IN SOLID STATE SCIENCES. 1978. irreg. price varies. Springer-Verlag, 175 Fifth Ave., New York, NY 10010. TEL 212-460-1500. FAX 212-473-6272. (Also: Berlin, Heidelberg, Tokyo and Vienna) Ed.Bd. (reprint service avail. from ISI) **Indexed:** Chem.Abstr., INSPEC, Phys.Ber. **Document type:** monographic series.
—BLDSC (8424.775000); CASDDS. **CCC.**

530   US   ISSN 0931-5195
CODEN: SSSSEW
SPRINGER SERIES IN SURFACE SCIENCES. 1986. irreg. price varies. Springer-Verlag, 175 Fifth Ave., New York, NY 10010. TEL 212-460-1500. FAX 212-473-6272. (Also: Berlin, Heidelberg, Tokyo and Vienna) (reprint service avail. from ISI) **Indexed:** INSPEC. **Document type:** monographic series.
—BLDSC (8424.777200); CASDDS. **CCC.**

539   US   ISSN 0081-3869
CODEN: STPHBM
SPRINGER TRACTS IN MODERN PHYSICS. 1964. irreg. price varies. Springer-Verlag, 175 Fifth Ave., New York, NY 10010. TEL 212-460-1500. FAX 212-473-6272. (Also: Berlin, Heidelberg, Tokyo and Vienna) (reprint service avail. from ISI) **Indexed:** ASCA, INSPEC, Phys.Ber. **Document type:** monographic series.
—BLDSC (8424.800000); CASDDS.
Continues: Ergebnisse der Exacten Naturwissenschaften.

STAATLICHE MATHEMATISCH-PHYSIKALISCHE SALONS, DRESDEN. VEROEFFENTLICHUNGEN. see *MATHEMATICS*

530 540   NE
STRUCTURE AND DYNAMICS OF MOLECULAR SYSTEMS. (Text in English) irreg. price varies. Kluwer Academic Publishers, Postbus 17, 3300 AA Dordrecht, Netherlands. TEL 31-78-392392. FAX 31-78-392254. TELEX 29245 KAPG NL. (Dist. by: Kluwer Academic Publishers Group, P.O. Box 322, 3300 AH Dordrecht, Netherlands. TEL 31-78-392392. FAX 31-78-546474; N. America dist. addr.: Box 358, Accord Sta., Hingham, MA 02018-0358. TEL 617-871-6600. FAX 617-871-6528) **Document type:** monographic series.

530   RM   ISSN 0258-8730
QC1   CODEN: SBBPAJ
STUDIA UNIVERSITATIS "BABES-BOLYAI". PHYSICA. (Text in English, French, German, Rumanian) 1959. s-a. exchange basis. Universitatea "Babes-Bolyai", Biblioteca Centrala Universitara, Str. Clinicilor Nr. 2, Cluj-Napoca 3400, Rumania. TEL 36-64-197092. FAX 36-64-197633. Ed. I. Haiduc. **Indexed:** Chem.Abstr., Math.R. **Document type:** academic/scholarly publication.
—BLDSC (8482.309800).

STUDIES IN APPLIED MATHEMATICS (CAMBRIDGE). see *MATHEMATICS*

530 US ISSN 0270-4730
CODEN: SEPHDL
STUDIES IN HIGH ENERGY PHYSICS SERIES. irreg., latest vol.6. price varies. Harwood Academic Publishers, c/o International Publishers Distributor, 820 Town Center Dr., Langhorne, PA 19047. TEL 215-750-2642. FAX 215-750-6343. (Subscr. to: International Publishers Distributor, Box 90, Reading, Berkshire RG1 8JL, England. TEL 44-173-456-8316) Ed. M. Charap. (also avail. in microform) **Document type:** monographic series.
—CASDDS.
Refereed Serial

530.9 UK ISSN 1355-2198
STUDIES IN HISTORY AND PHILOSOPHY OF SCIENCE PART B: STUDIES IN HISTORY AND PHILOSOPHY OF MODERN PHYSICS. vol.26, 1995. q. £160($255) (effective 1996). Elsevier Science Ltd., Pergamon, P.O. Box 800, Kidlington, Oxford OX5 1DX, England. TEL 44-1865-843000. FAX 44-1865-843010. E-mail: nlinfo-f@elsevier.nl; usinfo-f@elsevier.com; forinfo-kyf04035@niftyserve.or.jp; Site addr.: http://www.elsevier.nl/. (Subscr. in U.S. and Canada to: Elsevier Science, 660 White Plains Rd., Tarrytown, NY 10591-5153. TEL 914-524-9200. FAX 914-333-2444) (also avail. in microform from UMI; back issues avail.) **Document type:** academic/scholarly publication.
—SWETS.
Refereed Serial

530.1 NE ISSN 0925-8582
STUDIES IN MATHEMATICAL PHYSICS. (Text in English) 1990. irreg., vol.5, 1992. price varies. Elsevier Science B.V., Books Division, P.O. Box 211, 1000 AE Amsterdam, Netherlands. TEL 31-20-4853911. FAX 31-20-4853705. TELEX 18582 ESPA NL. E-mail: nlinfo-f@elsevier.nl; usinfo-f@elsevier.com; forinfo-kyf04035@niftyserve.or.jp; Site addr.: http://www.elsevier.nl/. (Subscr. in U.S. and Canada to: Elsevier Science Inc., Box 882, Madison Sq. Sta., New York, NY 10159. TEL 212-989-5800) (back issues avail.) **Document type:** monographic series.
—BLDSC (8491.049000).
Refereed Serial

530 RM ISSN 0039-3940
QC1 CODEN: SCEFAB
STUDII SI CERCETARI DE FIZICA. 1950. 10/yr. 350 lei($75) (Academia Romana) Editura Academiei Romane, Calea Victoriei 125, 79717 Bucharest, Rumania. (Dist. by: Rompresfilatelia, Calea Grivitei 64-66, P.O. Box 12-201, 78104 Bucharest, Rumania) Ed. Ioan Ursu. bk.rev.; illus.; index. **Indexed:** Chem.Abstr., INSPEC, Int.Aerosp.Abstr., Math.R., Met.Abstr., Phys.Ber.
—CASDDS.

530 US ISSN 8756-4475
CODEN: SUSEE4
SUBNUCLEAR SERIES. 1963. irreg., vol.29, 1992. price varies. Plenum Publishing Corp., 233 Spring St., New York, NY 10013-1578. TEL 212-620-8000. FAX 212-463-0742. TELEX 23-421139. Ed. Antonino Zichichi. (back issues avail.) **Indexed:** INSPEC. **Document type:** proceedings.
—CASDDS.
Refereed Serial

530 510 KN ISSN 0371-0688
QA1 CODEN: SKMOAW
SUHAK KWA MULLI. Variant title: Soohak Kwa Moolli. (Text in Korean) 1957. q. Korean Academy of Sciences, Physics and Mathematics Committee, Pyongyang, N. Korea.
—CASDDS.

530 US ISSN 1055-5773
QC787.P7
SUPER COLLIDER NEWS. 1990. m. $247. Atlantic Information Services, Inc., 1050 17th St. N.W., Ste. 480, Washington, DC 20036. TEL 202-775-9008. FAX 202-331-9542. Ed. C. David Chaffee.
—CCC.
Description: News and analytical reports on the SSC and related technologies.

530 US ISSN 0897-2427
SUPERCONDUCTIVITY NEWS. 1987. w. (48/yr., plus m. technical issues and q. patent issues). $237 to academic institutions (outside N. America $287); others $297 (outside N. America $347) (effective 1996). Superconductivity Publications, 828 Livingston Ave., North Brunswick, NJ 08902-2356. TEL 908-846-2002. FAX 908-846-2050. E-mail: 74130.650@compuserve.com. Ed. C. Jim Russell; Pub. C. Jim Russell. adv.: B&W page $300; adv. contact: Kathy Kleppin. illus.; pat. (back issues avail.) **Document type:** trade publication.
Description: Covers topics in superconductivity and magnetic resonance imaging, both business and research and development news.

600 530 RU ISSN 0235-8964
QC611.9 CODEN: SPCUE5
SUPERCONDUCTIVITY: PHYSICS, CHEMISTRY, TECHNOLOGY. 1988. m. $920 (foreign $950). Kurchatov Institute of Atomic Energy, Moscow, Russia. TEL 7-095-196-6957. **Indexed:** INSPEC (1993-). **Document type:** academic/scholarly publication.
—BLDSC (0425.895000); CASDDS; Ei; UnCover. CCC.
Description: Covers Russian research in the area of superconductivity.

530 540 620 UK ISSN 0953-2048
QC611.9 CODEN: SUSTEF
SUPERCONDUCTOR SCIENCE & TECHNOLOGY. 1988. m. £325($670) (effective 1996). (Institute of Physics) I O P Publishing Ltd., Techno House, Redcliffe Way, Bristol, Avon BS1 6NX, England. TEL 0117-929-7481. FAX 0117-929-4318. TELEX 449149 INSTP G. (U.S. subscr. to: American Institute of Physics, Member and Subscriber Services, 500 Sunnyside Blvd., Woodbury, NY 11797-2900. TEL 516-349-7800) Ed. D. Dew-Hughes. circ. 623. (also avail. in microform from AIP) **Indexed:** Energy Info.Abstr., INSPEC (1988-). **Document type:** academic/scholarly publication.
—BLDSC (8547.075500); CASDDS; Ei; Faxon; Genuine Article; SWETS; UnCover. CCC.
Description: Provides a forum for chemists, physicists, materials scientists, and electronics and electrical engineers involved in any aspect of the science and technology of superconductors, both conventional and the new ceramic materials.

530 US ISSN 0894-7635
SUPERCONDUCTOR WEEK; the newsletter of record in the field of superconductivity. 1987. w. (40/yr.). $364. Atlantic Information Services, Inc., 1050 17th St., N.W., Ste. 480, Washington, DC 20036. TEL 202-775-9008. FAX 202-331-9542. Ed. David Chaffee.
• Also available online. Vendor(s): Data-Star, Knight-Ridder, Inc., NewsNet.
—BLDSC (8547.077550); Faxon; SWETS.
Description: Covers research, development and applications in high and low temperature superconductivity.

SUPERLATTICES AND MICROSTRUCTURES. see CHEMISTRY

530.44 JA
SUPESU PURAZUMA KENKYUKAI. (Text in English and Japanese) 1970. a. Institute of Space and Astronautical Science, Space Plasma Study Group - Uchu Kagaku Kenkyujo, Supesu Purazuma Kenkyukai, 1-1, Yoshinodai 3-chome, Sagamihara-shi, Kanagawa-ken 229, Japan.

539 UK ISSN 0968-5677
QD380 CODEN: SUSCFX
▼**SUPRAMOLECULAR SCIENCE.** 1994. q. £150($239) (effective 1996). Butterworth - Heinemann, Part of the Reed Elsevier group, Linacre House, Jordan Hill, Oxford OX2 8DP, England. TEL 0865-310366. FAX 0865-310398. (Subscr. to: Elsevier Science Ltd., P.O. Box 800, Kidlington, Oxford OX5 1DX, England. TEL 44-865-843010. FAX 44-865-843010; Subscr. in U.S. and Canada to: Elsevier Science, 660 White Plains Rd., Tarrytown, NY 10591-5153. TEL 914-524-9200. FAX 914-333-2444) Ed.Bd. (also avail. in microform from UMI; back issues avail.) **Document type:** academic/scholarly publication.
—BLDSC (8547.638690); CASDDS; Ei; UMI; UnCover.
Refereed Serial

541.345 NE ISSN 0039-6028
QD506 CODEN: SUSCAS
SURFACE SCIENCE; a journal devoted to the physics and chemistry of interfaces. (Includes section: Surface Science Letters (ISSN 0167-2584)) (Text in English, French or German; summaries in English) 1964. 72/yr. fl.12960($7903) (effective 1996). North-Holland (Subsidiary of: Elsevier Science B.V.), P.O. Box 211, 1000 AE Amsterdam, Netherlands. TEL 31-20-4853911. FAX 31-20-4853598. TELEX 18582 ESPA NL. (Subscr. in U.S. and Canada to: Elsevier Science Inc., Box 882, Madison Sq. Sta., New York, NY 10159. TEL 212-989-5800. FAX 212-633-3990) Ed. Harry C. Gatos. adv.; bk.rev.; bibl.; charts; illus.; index. (also avail. in microform from UMI; back issues avail.) **Indexed:** ASCA, Br.Ceram.Abstr., Chem.Abstr., Curr.Cont., INSPEC (1968-), Int.Aerosp.Abstr., Mass Spectr.Bull., Met.Abstr., Phys.Ber., World Alum.Abstr. **Document type:** academic/scholarly publication.
—BLDSC (8547.950000); CASDDS; Ei; Faxon; Genuine Article; SWETS; UnCover. CCC.
Description: Deals with theoretical and experimental studies in the physics and chemistry of surfaces.
Refereed Serial

SURFACE SCIENCE LETTERS. see PHYSICS — Abstracting, Bibliographies, Statistics

530 NE ISSN 0167-5729
QC173.4.S94 CODEN: SSREDI
SURFACE SCIENCE REPORTS; a review journal. (Text in English) 1981. 24/yr. fl.1305($796) (effective 1996). North-Holland (Subsidiary of: Elsevier Science B.V.), P.O. Box 211, 1000 AE Amsterdam, Netherlands. TEL 31-20-4853911. FAX 31-20-4853598. TELEX 18582 ESPA NL. (Subscr. in U.S. and Canada to: Elsevier Science Inc., Box 882, Madison Sq. Sta., New York, NY 10159. TEL 212-989-5800. FAX 212-633-3990) Ed. A.V. Oostrom. adv. (also avail. in microform from UMI; back issues avail.; reprint service avail. from SWZ) **Indexed:** Chem.Abstr., INSPEC (1981-), Met.Abstr., Phys.Ber., World Alum.Abstr. **Document type:** academic/scholarly publication.
—BLDSC (8547.950530); CASDDS; Ei; Faxon; Genuine Article; SWETS; UnCover. CCC.
Description: Contains papers on the properties of surfaces and interfaces of metals, semiconductors and insulators with emphasis on fundamental aspects of solid and liquid interfaces, their atomic and electronic structure.
Refereed Serial

530 US ISSN 1055-5269
QC173.4.S94 CODEN: SSSPEN
SURFACE SCIENCE SPECTRA; an international journal devoted to archiving surface science spectra of technological and scientific interest. 1991. q. $987 (Canada $997; elsewhere $1007). (American Vacuum Society) American Institute of Physics, One Physics Ellipse, College Park, MD 20740-3843. TEL 301-209-3000. (Subscr. to: AIP Member and Subscriber Services, 500 Sunnyside Blvd., Woodbury, NY 11797-2999. TEL 516-576-2270) Ed. C.B. Bryson. index. **Indexed:** INSPEC (1992-). **Document type:** academic/scholarly publication.
—CASDDS.
Description: Publishes complete records of original surface spectroscopic data.

530 US ISSN 0142-2413
QC793 CODEN: SHEPDB
SURVEYS IN HIGH ENERGY PHYSICS; an international journal. 1980. 12/yr. (in 2 vols., 6 nos./vol.). 151 ECU per vol. (effective 1996). Harwood Academic Publishers, c/o International Publishers Distributor, 820 Town Center Dr., Langhorne, PA 19047. TEL 215-750-2642. FAX 215-750-6343. (Subscr. to: International Publishers Distributor, P.O. Box 90, Reading, Berkshire RG1 8JL, England. TEL 44-173-456-8316) Eds. A.B. Kaidalov, M.I. Vysotsky. bk.rev.; charts; illus. (also avail. in microfiche; microfilm; back issues avail.) **Indexed:** Chem.Abstr., INSPEC.
—CASDDS; Faxon; UnCover. CCC.
Refereed Serial

530 SW
SWEDISH INSTITUTE OF SPACE PHYSICS. UPPSALA DIVISION. SCIENTIFIC REPORTS. 1977. irreg. price varies. Swedish Institute of Space Physics, Uppsala Division, S-755 91 Uppsala, Sweden. TEL 46-18-40 30 00. **Document type:** monographic series.
Formerly: Uppsala Ionospheric Observatory. Scientific Reports (ISSN 0349-2699)

PHYSICS

530   SW
SWEDISH INSTITUTE OF SPACE PHYSICS. UPPSALA DIVISION. TECHNICAL REPORTS. 1978. irreg. price varies. Swedish Institute of Space Physics, Uppsala Division, S-755 91 Uppsala, Sweden. TEL 46-18-40 30 00. **Document type:** monographic series.
  Formerly: Uppsala Ionospheric Observatory. Technical Reports (ISSN 0349-2680)

SYNTHETIC METALS; an international journal integrating research and applications on intercalation compounds of graphite, transition metal compounds, and quasi-one-dimensional conductors. see *ENGINEERING — Engineering Mechanics And Materials*

530   US   ISSN 1063-7842
QC1   CODEN: TPHEX
TECHNICAL PHYSICS. English translation of: Zhurnal Tekhnicheskoi Fiziki (RU ISSN 0044-4642) 1956. m. $2390 (foreign $2420) (effective 1996). (Russian Academy of Science, St. Petersburg Division, RU) American Institute of Physics, One Physics Ellipse, College Park, MD 20740-3843. TEL 301-209-3000. Ed. S. Torstveit. bibl.; charts; illus.; index. (also avail. in microform from AIP; back issues avail.) **Indexed:** Appl.Mech.Rev., C.P.I., Eng.Ind., Gen.Phys.Adv.Abstr., INSPEC, Int.Aerosp.Abstr., Mass Spectr.Bull., Math.R., Met.Abstr., Phys.Ber. **Document type:** academic/scholarly publication.
  —BLDSC (0425.899600); Ei; Faxon; SWETS; UnCover. **CCC.**
  Formerly: Soviet Physics - Technical Physics (ISSN 0038-5662)
  Description: Simultaneous translation of Russian workd in applied physics, especially on instrumentation and measurement techniques. Particular emphasis is on plasma physics.

530.05   US   ISSN 1063-7850
QC1   CODEN: TPLEED
TECHNICAL PHYSICS LETTERS. English translation of: Pis'ma v Zhurnal Tekhnicheskoi Fiziki. 1975. m. $1515 (foreign $1545) (effective 1996). American Institute of Physics, One Physics Ellipse, College Park, MD 20740-3843. TEL 301-209-3000. Ed. J.R. Anderson. bibl.; charts; illus.; index. (also avail. in microform from AIP; back issues avail.) **Indexed:** Gen.Phys.Adv.Abstr., INSPEC, Int.Aerosp.Abstr., Mass Spectr.Bull., Phys.Ber. **Document type:** academic/scholarly publication.
  —BLDSC (0425.899800); Ei; Faxon; SWETS; UnCover. **CCC.**
  Formerly: Soviet Technical Physics Letters (ISSN 0360-120X)
  Description: Rapid publication on developments in theoretical and experimental physics with potential technological applications.

530   US   ISSN 0308-5392
CODEN: TEPHDW
TECHNIQUES OF PHYSICS. 1973. irreg., vol.13, 1990. Academic Press, Inc., 525 B St., Ste. 1900, San Diego, CA 92101-4495. TEL 619-231-0926. FAX 619-699-6715. (Subscr. to: Order Dept., 6277 Sea Harbor Dr., 4th Fl., Orlando, FL 32887. TEL 800-321-5068) Eds. N.H. March, H.N. Daglish. (reprint service avail. from ISI) **Indexed:** INSPEC. **Document type:** academic/scholarly publication.
  Refereed Serial

530   NE
TECHNISCH FYSISCHE DIENST T N O - T H. JAARVERSLAG. (Toegepast - Natuurwetenschappelijk Onderzoek) (Text in Dutch; summaries in English) 1946. a. free. Technisch Fysische Dienst T N O - T H - T N O Institute of Applied Physics, Stieltjesweg 1, P.O. Box 155, Delft, Netherlands. Ed.Bd. illus. circ. 2,500.

530   US   ISSN 0082-2590
TECHNISCHE PHYSIK IN EINZELDARSTELLUNGEN. 1948. irreg. price varies. Springer-Verlag, 175 Fifth Ave., New York, NY 10010. TEL 212-460-1500. (Also: Berlin, Heidelberg, Tokyo and Vienna) (reprint service avail. from ISI) **Document type:** monographic series.

530 620   YU   ISSN 0350-0594
QC1   CODEN: TEFIDJ
TEHNICKA FIZIKA/JOURNAL OF ENGINEERING PHYSICS. (Text in English, German, Russian; summaries in Serbo-Croatian) 1964. a. Univerzitet u Beogradu, Tehnicki Fakultet, Zavod za Fiziku, Ruzveltova 1a, 11000 Belgrade, Serbia, Yugoslavia. Ed. Jordan Pop-Jordanov. bk.rev. circ. 1,000. **Indexed:** Chem.Abstr., INSPEC (1976-), Math.R., Ref.Zh. **Document type:** academic/scholarly publication.
  —CASDDS.
  Formerly: Zavod za Fiziku. Radovi (ISSN 0522-8557)

530   IS
TEHUDA/RESONANCE; physics teacher's journal. (Text in Hebrew) 1972. 3/yr. $16. Weizman Institute of Science, Department of Science Teaching, Rehovot 76100, Israel. TEL 972-8-342981. FAX 972-8-344174. E-mail: ntgoldri@weizmann.weizmann.ac.il. (Dist. by: Gestelit, P.O. Box 2088, Hayotsek St., Haifa 31020, Israel) Ed. Hanna Goldring. adv.; bk.rev.; illus. circ. 200. (back issues avail.) **Indexed:** Ind.Heb.Per. **Document type:** academic/scholarly publication.
  Refereed Serial

TEKSTER FRA I M F U F A. (Institut for Studiet af Matematik og Fysik samt deres Funktioner i Undervisning Forskning og Anvendelse) see *MATHEMATICS*

536   RU   ISSN 0040-3644
CODEN: TVYTAP
TEPLOFIZIKA VYSOKIKH TEMPERATUR. English translation: High Temperature (US ISSN 0018-151X) 1963. bi-m. $192 (effective 1996). (Rossiiskaya Akademiya Nauk, Otdelenie Fiziko-tekhnicheskikh Problem Energetiki) Izdatel'stvo Nauka, Mezhdunarodnyi Otdel, Profsoyuznaya, 90, 117864 Moscow, Russia. Ed. V.M. Batenin. bk.rev.; bibl.; index. (tabloid format) **Indexed:** Bull.Thermodyn.& Thermochem., Chem.Abstr., INSPEC, Met.Abstr., World Alum.Abstr. **Document type:** academic/scholarly publication.
  —BLDSC (0178.850000); CASDDS. **CCC.**

530   GW   ISSN 0233-0911
CODEN: TTPHE2
TEUBNER-TEXTE ZUR PHYSIK. 1984. a. B.G. Teubner Verlagsgesellschaft mbH, Johannisgasse 16, 04103 Leipzig, Germany. TEL 216860. Ed.Bd. **Document type:** academic/scholarly publication.
  —BLDSC (8798.289000); CASDDS.

530   US   ISSN 0172-5998
TEXTS AND MONOGRAPHS IN PHYSICS. 1976. irreg. price varies. Springer-Verlag, 175 Fifth Ave., New York, NY 10010. TEL 212-460-1500. (And Berlin, Heidelberg, Tokyo and Vienna) Ed. W. Beiglboeck. (reprint service avail. from ISI) **Indexed:** INSPEC, Math.R. **Document type:** monographic series, academic/scholarly publication.

530 510   US   ISSN 0040-5779
QC20   CODEN: TMPHAH
THEORETICAL AND MATHEMATICAL PHYSICS. English translation of: Teoreticheskaya i Matematicheskaya Fizika (RU ISSN 0564-6162) 1969. m. $1295 (foreign $1515) (effective 1996). (Russian Academy of Sciences, RU) Plenum Publishing Corp., Consultants Bureau, 233 Spring St., New York, NY 10013-1578. TEL 212-620-8468. FAX 212-463-0742. TELEX 23-421139. Ed. A.A. Logunov. (also avail. in microfilm from JSC; back issues avail.) **Indexed:** Appl.Mech.Rev., Compumath, Curr.Cont., INSPEC (1972-), Math.R., Sci.Res.Abstr., Zent.Math. **Document type:** academic/scholarly publication.
  —BLDSC (0426.250000); Faxon; Genuine Article; SWETS; UMI; UnCover. **CCC.**
  Refereed Serial

530   NO   ISSN 0803-4222
CODEN: TPSTEP
THEORETICAL PHYSICS SEMINAR IN TRONDHEIM. (Text in English) 1953. fortn. exchange basis. (Norges Tekniske Hoegskole, Gruppe for Teoretisk Fysikk) University of Trondheim, Theoretical Physics Seminar in Trondheim, N-7034 Trondheim, Norway. TEL 47-7-593646. FAX 47-7-593372. TELEX 55637. circ. 160. **Indexed:** INSPEC (1973-), Ref.Zh. **Document type:** academic/scholarly publication.
  —BLDSC (8814.564000); CASDDS. **CCC.**
  Formerly (until 1990): Arkiv for det Fysiske Seminar i Trondheim (ISSN 0365-2459)

530.425   NE   ISSN 0924-6118
THEORY AND APPLICATIONS OF TRANSPORT IN POROUS MEDIA. 1987. irreg., vol.4, 1989. price varies. Kluwer Academic Publishers, Postbus 17, 3300 AA Dordrecht, Netherlands. TEL 31-78-392392. FAX 31-78-392254. TELEX 29245 KAPG NL. (Dist. by: Kluwer Academic Publishers Group, P.O. Box 322, 3300 AH Dordrecht, Netherlands. TEL 31-78-392392. FAX 31-78-546474; N. America dist. addr.: Box 358, Accord Sta., Hingham, MA 02018-0358. TEL 617-871-6600. FAX 617-871-6528) **Document type:** monographic series.
  —BLDSC (8814.626200).
  Refereed Serial

530 620.11   US
▼**THIN FILM - DIAMOND TECHNOLOGY NEWS.** 1995. m. $325. Business Communications Co., Inc. (Norwalk), 25 Van Zant St., Ste. 13, Norwalk, CT 06855. TEL 203-853-4266. FAX 203-853-0348. Ed. Robert Moran. **Document type:** newsletter.

530   NE   ISSN 0168-2075
THIN FILMS SCIENCE AND TECHNOLOGY. (Text in English) 1980. irreg., vol.7, 1990. price varies. Elsevier Science B.V., Books Division, P.O. Box 211, 1000 AE Amsterdam, Netherlands. TEL 31-20-4853911. FAX 31-20-4853705. TELEX 18582 ESPA NL. E-mail: nlinfo-f@elsevier.nl; usinfo-f@elsevier.com; forinfo-kyf04035@niftyserve.or.jp; Site addr.: http://www.elsevier.nl/. (Subscr. in U.S. and Canada to: Elsevier Science Inc., Box 882, Madison Sq. Sta., New York, NY 10159. TEL 212-989-5800) Ed. G. Siddall. (back issues avail.) **Document type:** monographic series.
  Refereed Serial

541.345   SZ   ISSN 0040-6090
TK7871.15.F5   CODEN: THSFAP
THIN SOLID FILMS; an international journal on the science and technology of condensed matter films. (Text in English) 1968. 40/yr. 8200 SFr.($6722) (effective 1996). Elsevier Science S.A., P.O. Box 564, CH-1001 Lausanne 1, Switzerland. TEL 41-21-3207381. FAX 41-21-3235444. TELEX 450620-ELSA-CH. (Subscr. in U.S. and Canada to: Elsevier Science Inc., Box 882, Madison Sq. Sta., New York, NY 10159. TEL 212-989-5800. FAX 212-633-3990) Ed. J.E. Greene. adv.; bk.rev.; bibl.; illus.; index. (also avail. in microform from UMI) **Indexed:** ASCA, Chem.Abstr., Curr.Cont., Eng.Ind., INSPEC (1969-), Int.Aerosp.Abstr., Mass Spectr.Bull., Met.Abstr., Phys.Ber., Sci.Cit.Ind., World Alum.Abstr. **Document type:** academic/scholarly publication.
  —BLDSC (8820.120000); CASDDS; Ei; EMDOCS; Faxon; Genuine Article; SWETS; UnCover. **CCC.**
  Description: Serves scientists and engineers working in the fields of thin-film synthesis, characterization, and applications.
  Refereed Serial

TIANTI WULI XUEBAO/ACTA ASTROPHYSICA SINICA. see *ASTRONOMY*

530   JA   ISSN 0916-2860
TOHOKU DAIGAKU RYUTAI KAGAKU KENKYUJO HOKOKU/TOHOKU UNIVERSITY. INSTITUTE OF FLUID SCIENCE. MEMOIRS. (Text in Japanese) 1949. a. Tohoku Daigaku, Ryutai Kagaku Kenkyujo - Tohoku University, Institute of Fluid Science, 1-1, Katahira 2-chome, Aoba-ku, Sendai-shi, Miyagi-ken 980, Japan.
  —BLDSC (5619.527000).

530   JA   ISSN 0916-2879
TA357   CODEN: RIFUES
TOHOKU UNIVERSITY. INSTITUTE OF FLUID SCIENCE. REPORTS. (Text in English) 1990. a. Tohoku University, Institute of Fluid Science - Tohoku Daigaku Ryutai Kagaku Kenkyujo, 1-1, Katakira 2-chome, Aoba-ku, Sendai-shi, Miyagi-ken 980, Japan.

PHYSICS

530 540   JA   ISSN 0040-8808
Q77.T55   CODEN: SRTAA6
TOHOKU UNIVERSITY. SCIENCE REPORTS OF THE RESEARCH INSTITUTES. SERIES A: PHYSICS, CHEMISTRY, AND METALLURGY/TOHOKU DAIGAKU KENKYUJO HOKOKU. A-SHU: BUTSURIGAKU, KAGAKU, YAKINGAKU. (Text in English) 1949. s-a. exchange basis. Tohoku Daigaku, Kenkyujo Rengokai - Tohoku University, Association of the Research Institutes, 4-1 Seiryo-machi, Aoba-ku, Sendai-shi, Miyagi-ken 980, Japan. FAX 022-264-7984. Ed. Hiroyasu Fujimori. charts; illus.; index, cum.index every 10 yrs. circ. 1,250. (also avail. in microform from PMC) Indexed: ASCA, Cadscan, Chem.Abstr., Curr.Cont., Eng.Ind., INIS Atomind., INSPEC, JCT, JTA, Lead Abstr., Met.Abstr., Sci.Cit.Ind., World Alum.Abstr., Zincscan.
—BLDSC (8156.545000); CASDDS; Genuine Article; UnCover.

530 540 520   JA   ISSN 0388-5607
Q77   CODEN: SRTAD9
TOHOKU UNIVERSITY. SCIENCE REPORTS. SERIES 8: PHYSICS AND ASTRONOMY.* (Text in English, French, German) 1911. q. exchange basis. Tohoku Daigaku, Rigakubu - Tohoku University, Faculty of Science, Aoba, Aramaki, Sendai-shi, Miyagi-ken 980, Japan. Eds. M. Tanaka, K. Takabuka. charts; illus.; stat.; index. circ. 800. (also avail. in microform from PMC) Indexed: Chem.Abstr., INIS Atomind., INSPEC, Math.R., Met.Abstr., World Alum.Abstr.
—BLDSC (8159.501000); CASDDS.
Supersedes (in 1980): Tohoku University. Science Reports. Series 1: Physics, Chemistry, Astronomy (ISSN 0040-8778)

530   JA   ISSN 0910-0709
TOKYO DAIGAKU RIGAKUBU BUTSURIGAKU KYOSHITSU NENJI KENKYU HOKOKU/UNIVERSITY OF TOKYO. FACULTY OF SCIENCE. DEPARTMENT OF PHYSICS. ANNUAL REPORT. (Text in English, Japanese) 1966. a. Tokyo Daigaku, Rigakubu, Butsurigaku Kyoshitsu, 3-1, Hongo 7-chome, Bunkyo-ku, Tokyo 113, Japan. Document type: bulletin.

530 621   US   ISSN 0303-4216
CODEN: TAPHD4
TOPICS IN APPLIED PHYSICS. 1974. irreg. price varies. Springer-Verlag, 175 Fifth Ave., New York, NY 10010. TEL 212-460-1500. FAX 212-473-6272. (Also: Berlin, Heidelberg, Tokyo and Vienna) (reprint service avail. from ISI) Indexed: ASCA, Biol.Abstr., INSPEC, Phys.Ber. Document type: monographic series.
—BLDSC (8867.420000); CASDDS; Ei; Genuine Article. CCC.

530   US   ISSN 0342-6793
CODEN: TCPHDI
TOPICS IN CURRENT PHYSICS. 1976. irreg. price varies. Springer-Verlag, 175 Fifth Ave., New York, NY 10010. TEL 212-460-1500. FAX 212-473-6272. (Also: Berlin, Heidelberg, Tokyo and Vienna) (reprint service avail. from ISI) Indexed: Chem.Abstr, INSPEC, Phys.Ber. Document type: monographic series.
—BLDSC (8867.437000); CASDDS; Genuine Article. CCC.

530 500   US   ISSN 0740-7564
TOTH-MAATIAN REVIEW; a journal for criticism and dissident opinion. 1982. irreg. $20 to individuals (foreign $25); institutions $50 (foreign $55). Toth-Maatian Press, 3101 20th St., Lubbock, TX 79410. TEL 806-797-2788. Ed. Harold Willis Milnes. bk.rev. circ. 250. (back issues avail.) Document type: academic/scholarly publication.

530 540   JA   ISSN 0372-039X
CODEN: TOKHA6
TOYODA KENKYU HOKOKU/TOYODA PHYSICAL AND CHEMICAL RESEARCH INSTITUTE. REPORTS. (Text in Japanese; summaries in English) 1942. a. Toyoda Rikagaku Kenkyujo - Toyoda Physical and Chemical Research Institute, 41-1, Yokomichi, Nagakute, Nagakute-cho, Aichi-gun, Aichi-ken 480-11, Japan. abstr. Indexed: Chem.Abstr., INIS Atomind., Jap.Per.Ind.

530   FR   ISSN 0765-0019
TK5102.5
TRAITEMENT DU SIGNAL; signal, image, parole. (Text and summaries in English and French) 1964. bi-m. (with 2 special nos.). 770 F. (outside Europe 930 F.). Groupe de Recherche et d'Etude de Traitement du Signal et des Images (GRETSI), B.P. 46, 38402 Saint-Martin d'Heres, France. TEL 76-82-62-74. FAX 76-82-63-84. E-mail: malbos@cephag.observ-gr.fr. (Dist. by: Centrale des Revues, 11 rue Gossin, 92543 Montrouge Cedex, France. TEL 46-56-52-66) Ed. Jean-Louis Lacoume. adv.: page 3800 F; 180 x 270; adv. contact: Jeanne Malbos. bk.rev.; bibl.; illus.; index. circ. 700. (back issues avail.) Indexed: INSPEC, Math.R.
—BLDSC (8883.767000); Ei; Faxon; SWETS.
Formerly: Revue du Cethedec (ISSN 0035-2535)
Description: Focuses on the scientific aspects of new scientific and technical results.
Refereed Serial

TRANSPORT IN POROUS MEDIA. see *CHEMISTRY*

530.13   US   ISSN 0041-1450
QC175.2   CODEN: TTSPB4
TRANSPORT THEORY AND STATISTICAL PHYSICS. 1971. 9/yr. $447.50 to individuals; institutions $895. Marcel Dekker Journals, 270 Madison Ave., New York, NY 10016. TEL 212-696-9000. FAX 212-685-4540. TELEX 421419 MARDEEK. (Subscr. to: Box 5017, Monticello, NY 12701) Ed. Paul Nelson. adv. (also avail. in microform from RPI) Indexed: Chem.Abstr., Curr.Cont., INSPEC, Math.R., Phys.Ber. Document type: academic/scholarly publication.
—BLDSC (9025.965000); CASDDS; Faxon; SWETS; UMI; UnCover. CCC.
Refereed Serial

TRIBOLOGY SERIES. see *ENGINEERING — Mechanical Engineering*

530   US
TRIESTE NOTES IN PHYSICS. 1986. irreg. price varies. Springer-Verlag, 175 Fifth Ave., New York, NY 10010. TEL 212-460-1500. FAX 212-473-6272. (Also: Berlin, Heidelberg, Tokyo and Vienna) (reprint service avail. from ISI) Document type: monographic series.
Refereed Serial

530   JA   ISSN 0915-5317
QC1
TSUKUBA DAIGAKU BUTSURIGAKUKEI NENJI KENKYU HOKOKU/UNIVERSITY OF TSUKUBA. INSTITUTE OF PHYSICS. ANNUAL REPORT. (Text in Japanese) 1988. a. Tsukuba Daigaku, Butsurigakukei - University of Tsukuba. Institute of Physics, 1-1, Tennodai 1-chome, Tsukuba-shi, Ibaraki-ken 305, Japan.

530   TU   ISSN 1300-0101
CODEN: TJPHEY
TURKISH JOURNAL OF PHYSICS. (Text and summaries in English) m. $300 (effective 1995 & 1996). Scientific and Technical Research Council of Turkey - TUBITAK - Turkiye Bilimsel ve Teknik Arastirma Kurumu, Ataturk Bulvari, No. 221, Kavaklidere, 06100 Ankara, Turkey. TEL 90-312-4685300. FAX 90-312-4271336. TELEX 43186 BTAK TR. Ed. Cengiz Yalcin. Indexed: Geo.Abstr., Geol.Abstr., INSPEC (1984-). Document type: academic/scholarly publication.
—CASDDS; UnCover.
Former titles (until 1994): Doga Turkish Journal of Physics (ISSN 1010-7630); Doga Turkish Journal of Physics and Astrophysics; **Supersedes in part (in 1986):** Doga Bilim Dergisi. Serie A: Basic Sciences.
Refereed Serial

530   UK   ISSN 0960-6068
UKRAINIAN JOURNAL OF PHYSICS. 1956. m. £385($640) (Ukrainian Academy of Sciences, KR) Riecansky Science Publishing Co., 7 Meadow Walk, Great Abington, Cambridge CB1 6AZ, England. TEL 0223-893295. FAX 0223-893295. Ed. A.G. Sitenko. Indexed: INSPEC (1991-).
—BLDSC (0428.920000).

530   KR   ISSN 0202-3628
CODEN: UFIZAW
UKRAINSKII FIZICHESKII ZHURNAL; nauchnyi zhurnal. Ukrainian edition: Ukrainskii Fizichnii Zhurnal (ISSN 0372-400X) (Text in Russian) 1956. m. $275. (Akademiya Nauk Ukrainy, Otdelenie Fiziki i Astronomii) Vydavnitstvo Naukova Dumka, Vul. Tereshchenkivska 3, 252601 Kiev, Ukraine. TEL 044-224-4068. FAX 044-224-7060. (Dist. in U.S. by: Victor Kamkin Inc., 4956 Boiling Brook Pkwy., Rockville, MD 20852. TEL 301-881-5973. FAX 301-881-1637) Ed. A.A. Smirnov. charts; illus.; index. circ. 1,000. Indexed: Chem.Abstr., INSPEC, Int.Aerosp.Abstr., Math.R., Met.Abstr., Phys.Ber.

530   II   ISSN 0970-9150
CODEN: SPSCEV
ULTRA SCIENTIST OF PHYSICAL SCIENCES. (Text in English) 1989. s-a. Rs.75($20) to individuals; institutions Rs.350($50). P.O. Box 93, G.P.O., Bhopal 462 001, India. Ed. A.H. Ansari. adv.: page Rs.2000. Document type: academic/scholarly publication.
—BLDSC (9082.780623); CASDDS.
Description: Publishes original research papers in pure and applied physical sciences.
Refereed Serial

ULTRASONIC IMAGING; an international journal. see *MEDICAL SCIENCES — Radiology And Nuclear Medicine*

UNION MATEMATICA ARGENTINA. REVISTA. see *MATHEMATICS*

UNIVERSITA DEGLI STUDI DI MODENA. SEMINARIO MATEMATICO E FISICO. ATTI. see *MATHEMATICS*

530   RM   ISSN 0041-9141
QC1   CODEN: AUZFAA
UNIVERSITATEA "AL. I. CUZA" DIN IASI. ANALELE STIINTIFICE. SECTIUNEA 1B: FIZICA. (Text in English, French, German or Russian) 1955. a. 35 lei. Universitatea "Al. I. Cuza" din Iasi, Calea M. Eminescu 11, Jassy, Rumania. (Subscr. to: ILEXIM, Str. 13 Decembrie Nr. 3, P.O. Box 136-137, Bucharest, Rumania) Ed. M. Sandulovici. bk.rev.; abstr.; charts; illus. circ. 250. Indexed: Chem.Abstr., INIS Atomind., INSPEC (1968-), Math.R.
—BLDSC (0869.614000); CASDDS.
Description: Review articles, original papers, short notes and book reviews on physics.

UNIVERSITATEA DIN CRAIOVA. ANALE. SERIA: MATEMATICA, FIZICA-CHIMIE. see *MATHEMATICS*

530 540   RM   ISSN 0257-7488
CODEN: AUTFDH
UNIVERSITATEA DIN TIMISOARA. ANALELE. STIINTE FIZICE. 1963. s-a. $10. Universitatea din Timisoara, Facultatea de Stiinte ale Naturii, Bd. Vasile Pirvan Nr. 4, Timisoara, Rumania. (Dist. by: ILEXIM, Str. 13 Decembrie Nr. 3, Box 136-137, Bucharest, Rumania) Ed. Nicolae Avram.
—BLDSC (0869.566200); CASDDS.
Formerly (until vol.22, 1982): Universitatea din Timisoara. Analele. Stiinte Fizico-Chimice (ISSN 0082-4453)

530   RM
UNIVERSITATEA DIN TIMISOARA. FACULTATEA DE FIZICA. PUBLICATIONS. irreg. Universitatea din Timisoara, Facultatea de Fizica, Bd. Vasile Parvan Nr. 4, 1900 Timisoara, Rumania.
Formerly (until 1989): Universitatea din Timisoara. Facultatea de Stiinte ale Naturii. Sectia Fizica. Publications.

UNIVERSITATEA POLITEHNICA BUCURESTI. BULETIN STIINTIFIC. MATEMATICA APLICATA SI FISICA/POLYTECHNICAL UNIVERSITY OF BUCHAREST. SCIENTIFIC BULLETIN. APPLIED MATHEMATICS AND PHYSICS. see *MATHEMATICS*

UNIVERSITATEA TRANSILVANIA DIN BRASOV. BULETINUL. SERIA C. MATEMATICA, FIZICA, CHIMIE/TRANSYLVANIA UNIVERSITY OF BRASOV. BULLETIN. SERIES C. MATHEMATICS, PHYSICS, CHEMISTRY. see *MATHEMATICS*

UNIVERSITEXTS. see *MATHEMATICS*

PHYSICS

530 520 CN
UNIVERSITY OF BRITISH COLUMBIA, PHYSICS SOCIETY. JOURNAL. 1960. a. Can.$3 to non-members. University of British Columbia, Physics Society, Dept. of Physics, 6224 Agriculture Rd., Vancouver, B.C. V6T 2A6, Canada. TEL 604-228-2211. Ed. Aaron Drake. adv. circ. 150. (back issues avail.)
Description: Review of papers from undergraduates in physics, astronomy, and geophysics.

530 DK ISSN 0908-617X
CODEN: RCPLD8
UNIVERSITY OF COPENHAGEN. NIELS BOHR INSTITUTE, OERSTED LABORATORY. REPORT. (Text in English) 1972. irreg. free. Copenhagen University, Niels Bohr Institute (APG), Oersted Laboratory, Universitetsparken 5, DK-2100 Copenhagen OE, Denmark. TEL 45-35-32-04-00. FAX 45-35-32-04-60. E-mail: job@fys.kw.dk. Ed. Bjarne Andresen. circ. 100. **Document type:** academic/scholarly publication.
—BLDSC (7620.907150); CASDDS.
Former titles (until 1994): University of Copenhagen. Physics Laboratory. Report (ISSN 0902-9419); (until 1986): University of Copenhagen. Physics Laboratory II (ISSN 0106-7222)
Description: Preprints of papers to be published in scientific journals.

530 FI
UNIVERSITY OF JYVASKYLA. DEPARTMENT OF PHYSICS. PREPRINTS. 1969. irreg. (5-6/yr.). exchange basis. University of Jyvaskyla, Department of Physics, PL 35, SF-40351 Jyvaskyla, Finland. FAX 358-41-602351. Ed. Soili Leskinen. circ. 130. (processed) **Document type:** academic/scholarly publication.
—BLDSC (7761.472000).
Formerly (until 1984): Jyvaskylan Yliopisto. Department of Physics. Research Report (ISSN 0075-465X)

UNIVERSITY OF OSAKA PREFECTURE. RESEARCH INSTITUTE FOR ADVANCED SCIENCE AND TECHNOLOGY. ANNUAL REPORT/OSAKA-FURITSU-DAIGAKU FUZOKUKENKYUSHO NENPO. see ENVIRONMENTAL STUDIES

530 PP ISSN 0085-4735
UNIVERSITY OF PAPUA NEW GUINEA. DEPARTMENT OF PHYSICS. TECHNICAL PAPER. 1968. irreg. free. University of Papua New Guinea, Department of Physics, P.O. Box 4820, University P.O., Papua New Guinea. circ. 75.

530 JA ISSN 0082-4798
QC176
UNIVERSITY OF TOKYO. INSTITUTE FOR SOLID STATE PHYSICS. TECHNICAL REPORT. SERIES A. (Text in English) 1959. irreg. University of Tokyo, Institute for Solid State Physics - Tokyo Daigaku Bussei Kenkyujo, 7-22-1 Roppongi, Minato-ku, Tokyo 106, Japan. Indexed: INIS Atomind. **Document type:** academic/scholarly publication.
—BLDSC (8715.930000).
Description: Reprints articles published in scientific journals.

530 JA ISSN 0082-4801
UNIVERSITY OF TOKYO. INSTITUTE FOR SOLID STATE PHYSICS. TECHNICAL REPORT. SERIES B. (Text in English) 1960. irreg. University of Tokyo, Institute for Solid State Physics - Tokyo Daigaku Bussei Kenkyujo, 7-22-1 Roppongi, Minato-ku, Tokyo 106, Japan. **Document type:** academic/scholarly publication.
—BLDSC (8715.931000).
Description: Original papers and other data not intended for publication elsewhere.

530 JA ISSN 0917-754X
UNIVERSITY OF TOKYO. INTERNATIONAL CENTER FOR ELEMENTARY PARTICLE PHYSICS. Variant title: U T - I C E P P. (Text in English) irreg. University of Tokyo, International Center for Elementary Particle Physics - Tokyo Daigaku Soryushi Butsuri Kokusai Kenkyu Senta, 3-1, Hongo 7-chome, Bunkyo-ku, Tokyo 113, Japan.

530 613.7 PL ISSN 0208-4872
UNIWERSYTET GDANSKI. WYDZIAL MATEMATYKI, FIZYKI I CHEMII. ZESZYTY NAUKOWE. PROBLEMY DYDAKTYKI FIZYKI. (Text in Polish; summaries in English and Russian) 1974. irreg., latest no.8. price varies. Uniwersytet Gdanski, Wydzial Matematyki, Fizyki i Chemii, c/o Biblioteka Glowna, Ul. Armii Krajowej 110, 81-824 Sopot, Poland. TEL 51-0061. TELEX 051-2247 BMOR PL. (Dist. by: Ars Polona-Ruch, Krakowskie Przedmiescie 7, 00-680 Warsaw, Poland) Ed. Kazimierz Badziag. circ. 250. **Document type:** academic/scholarly publication.
—BLDSC (9512.436300).
Description: Reports on research work and methodology of physics didactics, proposals and discussion, school practicum, and descriptions of teaching physics in the world.

530 PL ISSN 0867-7719
UNIWERSYTET JAGIELLONSKI. ZESZYTY NAUKOWE. FOLIA PHYSICA. (Text in English and Polish; summaries in English and Russian) 1963. irreg. price varies. Uniwersytet Jagiellonski, Ul. Golebia 24, 31-007 Krakow, Poland. (Dist. by: Ars Polona, Krakowskie Przedmiescie 7, 00-068 Warsaw, Poland) Ed. Bronislaw Sredniawa. circ. 470. **Indexed:** Math.R.
Formerly (until 1991): Uniwersytet Jagiellonski. Zeszyty Naukowe. Prace Fizyczne (ISSN 0083-4335)

530 RU ISSN 0042-1294
QC1 CODEN: UFNAAG
USPEKHI FIZICHESKIKH NAUK. English translation: Physics - Uspekhi (UK ISSN 1063-7869) 1918. m. $283 (effective 1996). (Rossiyskaya Akademiya Nauk) Izdatel'stvo Nauka, Mezhdonarodnyi Otdel, Profsoyuznaya, 90, 117864 Moscow, Russia. bk.rev.; bibl.; charts; illus.; index. circ. 5,000. **Indexed:** Chem.Abstr., Curr.Cont., GeoRef., Ind.Med., INSPEC, Int.Aerosp.Abstr., Math.R., Met.Abstr., Phys.Ber., World Alum.Abstr. **Document type:** academic/scholarly publication.
—BLDSC (0387.000000); CASDDS; Genuine Article. **CCC.**

533.5 016 UK ISSN 0042-207X
QC166 CODEN: VACUAV
VACUUM; surface engineering, surface instrumentation & vacuum technology. 1951. m. £745($1185) (effective 1996). (British Vacuum Council) Elsevier Science Ltd., Pergamon, P.O. Box 800, Kidlington, Oxford OX5 1DX, England. TEL 44-1865-843000. FAX 44-1865-843010. E-mail: nlinfo-f@elsevier.nl; usinfo-f@elsevier.com; forinfo-kyf04035@niftyserve.or.jp; Site addr.: http://www.elsevier.nl/. (Subscr. in U.S. and Canada to: Elsevier Science, 660 White Plains Rd., Tarrytown, NY 10591-5153. TEL 914-524-9200. FAX 914-333-2444) Ed.Bd. adv.: B&W page $550, color page $1350. bk.rev.; abstr.; illus.; index. circ. 1,500. (also avail. in microfilm from UMI) **Indexed:** A.S.& T.Ind., Anal.Abstr., Art & Archaeol.Tech.Abstr., Br.Tech.Ind., Chem.Abstr., Curr.Cont., Eng.Ind., Fluidex, INSPEC, ISMEC, Mass Spectr.Bull., Met.Abstr., Phys.Ber., World Alum.Abstr. **Document type:** academic/scholarly publication.
—BLDSC (9139.000000); CASDDS; Ei; Faxon; Genuine Article; SWETS; UMI; UnCover. **CCC.**
Description: Covers all theoretical, methodological, experimental and applied aspects of vacuum science and technology, including instrumentation and developments in related disciplines.
Refereed Serial

533.5 621.55 GW
CODEN: VAPREN
VAKUUM IN FORSCHUNG UND PRAXIS. (Text in German; summaries in English, French, German) 1951. q. DM.220($165) (effective 1996). V C H Verlagsgesellschaft mbH, Postfach 101161, 69451 Weinheim, Germany. TEL 06201-606-147. FAX 06201-606-117. TELEX 465516-VCHWH-D. (US addr.: V C H Publishers Inc., 220 E. 23rd St., New York, NY 10010-4606. TEL 212-683-8333) Ed. J. Scherle. adv.; bk.rev.; charts; illus.; index, cum.index every 20 yrs. circ. 3,350. **Indexed:** Chem.Abstr., Eng.Ind., INSPEC, Met.Abstr., World Alum.Abstr. **Document type:** academic/scholarly publication.
—CASDDS; Ei. **CCC.**
Former titles: Vakuum in der Praxis (ISSN 0934-9758); Vakuum-Technik (ISSN 0042-2266)

533.5 XV ISSN 0351-9716
VAKUUMIST; the voice of the Slovenian Vacuum Society. (Text in Serbo-Croatian, Slovenian; occasionally in English) 1981. irreg. (2-3/yr.). $10. Drustvo za Vakuumsko Tehniko Slovenije - Slovenian Society for Vacuum Technique, Teslova 30, 61000 Ljubljana, Slovenia. TEL 061-263-461. FAX 061-263-098. TELEX 31629. Ed. Andrej Pregelj. adv.; cum.index. circ. 250. (looseleaf format; back issues avail.)

533.5 FR
QC166 CODEN: VCMIDS
LE VIDE: SCIENCE, TECHNIQUE ET APPLICATIONS. (Supplement avail.: Comptes Rendus des Travaux des Congres et Colloques) (Text and summaries in English, French) 1946. 5/yr. 840 F. (foreign 975 F.); with supplementary proceedings 3200 F. (foreign 3400 F.). Societe Francaise du Vide, 19 rue du Renard, 75004 Paris, France. TEL 42-78-15-82. FAX 42-78-63-20. Ed. Dominique Celier. adv. contact: Dominique Celier. bk.rev.; bibl.; abstr.; charts; illus.; index. circ. 4,000. (also avail. in microform from UMI) **Indexed:** Chem.Abstr., Curr.Cont., Eng.Ind., INSPEC, Met.Abstr. **Document type:** trade publication, monographic series.
—BLDSC (9233.110000); CASDDS; Ei; Genuine Article; SWETS; UMI.
Former titles (until Jan. 1995): Vide, les Couches Minces (ISSN 0223-4335); (until 1979): Vide (ISSN 0042-5281)
Description: Presents scientific papers, technical texts, news and new products in the field of vacuum technology, list of next conferences in the field, presentation of laboratories, employment information.
Refereed Serial

530 RU ISSN 0301-6919
VOPROSY FIZIKI TVERDOGO TELA. irreg. 2.30 Rub. Chelyabinskii Gosudarstvennyi Pedagogicheskii Institut, Chelyabinsk, Russia. illus.

530 NE ISSN 0165-2125
QA927 CODEN: WAMOD9
WAVE MOTION; an international journal reporting research on wave phenomena. (Text in English) 1979. 8/yr. fl.992($605) (effective 1996). North-Holland (Subsidiary of: Elsevier Science B.V.), P.O. Box 211, 1000 AE Amsterdam, Netherlands. TEL 31-20-4853911. FAX 31-20-4853598. TELEX 18582 ESPA NL. (Subscr. in U.S. and Canada to: Elsevier Science Inc., Box 882, Madison Sq. Sta., New York, NY 10159. TEL 212-989-5800. FAX 212-633-3990) Ed. J.D. Achenbach. adv.; bibl.; illus.; index, cum.index. (also avail. in microform from UMI; back issues avail.) **Indexed:** Appl.Mech.Rev., Curr.Cont., Eng.Ind., INSPEC (1979-), Int.Aerosp.Abstr., Math.R., Phys.Ber., Sci.Cit.Ind., Sh.& Vib.Dig. **Document type:** academic/scholarly publication.
—BLDSC (9280.765000); Ei; Faxon; Genuine Article; SWETS; UnCover. **CCC.**
Description: Publishes articles on analytical, numerical and experimental methods.
Refereed Serial

530 UK ISSN 0959-7174
QC669 CODEN: WRMEEV
WAVES IN RANDOM MEDIA. 1991. q. £190($391) (effective 1996). (Institute of Physics) I O P Publishing Ltd., Techno House, Redcliffe Way, Bristol BS1 6NX, England. TEL 0117-929-7481. FAX 0117-929-4318. TELEX 449149 INSTP G. (U.S. subscr. to: American Institute of Physics, Member and Subscriber Services, 500 Sunnyside Blvd., Woodbury, NY 11797-2900. TEL 516-349-7800) Ed. A. Ishimaru. circ. 511. (also avail. in microform; microfiche) **Indexed:** INSPEC (1991-). **Document type:** academic/scholarly publication.
—BLDSC (9280.775800); Ei; Faxon; Genuine Article; SWETS.
Description: Provides a forum for papers on new and original theory in wave propagation and scattering in random media, as well as experimental or numerical studies demonstrating basic principles and theories.

PHYSICS

530 540 SI
WORLD SCIENTIFIC SERIES IN CONTEMPORARY CHEMICAL PHYSICS. (Text in English) irreg., no.3, 1993. World Scientific Publishing Co. Pte. Ltd., Farrer Rd., P.O. Box 128, Singapore 9128, Singapore. TEL 3825663. FAX 3825919. TELEX RS 28561 WSPC. (UK addr.: 73 Lynton Mead, Totteridge, London N20 8DH, England. TEL 44-81-4462461; US addr.: Ste. 1B, 1060 Main St., River Edge, NJ 07661. TEL 800-227-7562)

530 SI
WORLD SCIENTIFIC SERIES IN 20TH CENTURY PHYSICS. (Text in English) irreg., no.7, 1994. World Scientific Publishing Co. Pte. Ltd., Farrer Rd., P.O. Box 128, Singapore 9128, Singapore. TEL 3825663. FAX 3825919. TELEX RS-28561-WSPC. (US addr.: 1060 Main St., Ste. 1B, River Edge, NJ 07661. TEL 800-227-7562; UK addr.: 73 Lynton Mead, Totteridge, London N20 8DH, England. TEL 44-81-4462461)

530 CC ISSN 0379-4148
CODEN: WULIAL
WULI/PHYSICS. (Text in Chinese) 1951. m. $128.40. (Zhongguo Wuli Xuehui - Chinese Physical Society) Science Press, Marketing and Sales Department, 16 Donghuangchenggen North St., Beijing 100717, People's Republic of China. TEL 4010642. FAX 4019810. adv.; bk.rev. circ. 21,000. **Indexed:** INSPEC (1978-). **Document type:** academic/scholarly publication.
—BLDSC (9365.190000); CASDDS.
Description: Introduces modern physics in simple language. Reports on developments in new branches of physics, new theories, phenomena, materials, experimental techniques and methods, and the application of physics in economic construction in China.
Refereed Serial

530 371.3 CC ISSN 1002-0748
WULI JIAOXUE/PHYSICS TEACHING. (Text in Chinese) 1978. m. Y36 (effective 1994). Huadong Shifan Daxue, Wuli Xi - East China Normal University, Department of Physics, 3663 Zhongshan Beilu, Shanghai 200062, People's Republic of China. TEL 2577577. FAX 2570590. TELEX 33328 ECNU CN. (Dist. in US by: China Books & Periodicals, Inc., 2929 24th St., San Francisco, CA 94110. TEL 415-282-2994) (Co-sponsor: Zhongguo Wuli Xuehui - Chinese Physical Society) Ed. Mi Zihong. adv.; bk.rev.; index. circ. 40,000. (back issues avail.) **Document type:** academic/scholarly publication.
Description: Covers teaching material and teaching methods, and suggests physics problems and experiments. Includes information on teaching abroad, new developments in physics, and observations on physics in daily life.

530 CC
WULI SHIYAN/PHYSICS EXPERIMENTS. (Text in Chinese) bi-m. Dongbei Shifan Daxue - Northeast Normal University, 110, Stalin Street, Changchun, Jilin 130024, People's Republic of China. TEL 882320. Ed. Yu Fuchun.

530 CC ISSN 0509-4038
WULI TONGBAO/PHYSICS BULLETIN. (Text in Chinese) 1982. m. Y24 (foreign $24) (effective 1996). Hebei Sheng Wuli Xuehui - Physics Society of Hebei Province, Hebei Daxue - Hebei University, 1 Hezuo Lu, Baoding, Hebei 071002, People's Republic of China. TEL 5025052. (Co-sponsor: Hebei University) Ed. Wu Zuren. circ. 10,000.

530 CC ISSN 1000-3290
QC1 CODEN: WLHPAR
WULI XUEBAO. Overseas edition: Acta Physica Sinica (ISSN 1004-423X) English translation: Journal of Chinese Physics (US ISSN 1044-8357) (Text in Chinese; summaries in English) 1933. m. $188.40. (Zhongguo Wuli Xuehui - Chinese Physical Society) Science Press, Marketing and Sales Department, Donghuangchenggen North St., Beijing 100717, People's Republic of China. TEL 4010642. FAX 4019810. adv. circ. 11,000. **Indexed:** Corros.Abstr., INIS Atomind., Math.R., Met.Abstr., Phys.Ber., World Alum.Abstr. **Document type:** academic/scholarly publication.
—BLDSC (0650.500000); CASDDS.
Description: Covers physics research in mainland China, including surface physics, excitation, and amorphous physics.
Refereed Serial

530 PL ISSN 0078-5385
QC1 CODEN: ZNWFBI
WYŻSZA SZKOŁA PEDAGOGICZNA, OPOLE. ZESZYTY NAUKOWE. SERIA A. FIZYKA. (Text in Polish; summaries in English) 1963. irreg., vol.25, 1991. price varies; available on exchange. Wyższa Szkoła Pedagogiczna, Opole, Oleska 48, 45-951 Opole, Poland. TEL 48-77-383-87. (Dist. by: Ars Polona-Ruch, Krakowskie Przedmieście 7, Warsaw, Poland) Eds. Danuta Tokar, Bożena Pedzisz. circ. 300. **Indexed:** Chem.Abstr., Math.R. **Document type:** academic/scholarly publication.
—BLDSC (9512.478970); CASDDS.

530 CC ISSN 1001-0610
QC1 CODEN: XWZHEF
XIANDAI WULI ZHISHI/MODERN PHYSICS. (Text in Chinese) 1976. bi-m. $18.60. Science Press, Marketing and Sales Department, 16 Donghuangchenggen North St., Beijing 100717, People's Republic of China. TEL 4010642. FAX 4019810. adv. circ. 10,000. **Document type:** academic/scholarly publication.
Formerly: Gaoneng Wuli - High Energy Physics.

ZEITSCHRIFT FUER ANGEWANDTE MATHEMATIK UND PHYSIK/JOURNAL OF APPLIED MATHEMATICS AND PHYSICS/JOURNAL DES MATHEMATIQUES ET DE PHYSIQUE APPLIQUEES. see *MATHEMATICS*

530 541.3 523.01 GW ISSN 0932-0784
QC1 CODEN: ZNASEI
ZEITSCHRIFT FUER NATURFORSCHUNG. SECTION A: PHYSICAL SCIENCES. (Text in English) 1946. m. DM.692. Verlag der Zeitschrift fuer Naturforschung, Postfach 2645, 72016 Tuebingen, Germany. TEL 07071-31555. FAX 07071-360571. Ed. T. Littmann. adv.; bk.rev.; charts; illus.; index. circ. 800. **Indexed:** Bull.Thermodyn.& Thermochem., Chem.Abstr., Chem.Infd., Curr.Cont., Deep Sea Res.& Oceanogr.Abstr., Excerpt.Med., GeoRef., Helminthol.Abstr., INSPEC, Int.Aerosp.Abstr., Mass Spectr.Bull., Math.R., Met.Abstr., Phys.Ber. **Document type:** academic/scholarly publication.
—BLDSC (9474.000000); CASDDS; Ei; Faxon; Genuine Article; SWETS; UnCover. **CCC.**
Former titles: Zeitschrift fuer Naturforschung. Section A: Physics, Physical Chemistry, Cosmic Physics (ISSN 0340-4811); Zeitschrift fuer Naturforschung. Ausgabe A (ISSN 0044-3166)
Refereed Serial

ZEITSCHRIFT FUER PHYSIK A. HADRONS AND NUCLEI. see *PHYSICS — Nuclear Physics*

536.44 GW ISSN 0722-3277
CODEN: ZPCMDN
ZEITSCHRIFT FUER PHYSIK B: CONDENSED MATTER. (Text in English) vols.13-14, 1971. 12/yr. (in 3 vols., 4 nos./vol.). DM.2742($1992) (effective 1996). Springer-Verlag, Heidelberger Platz 3, 14197 Berlin, Germany. TEL 030-8207-0. FAX 030-8214091. E-mail: orders@springer.de. (Subscr. in N. America to: Springer-Verlag New York, Inc., 44 Hartz Way, Secaucus, NJ 07096-2491. TEL 201-348-4033. FAX 201-348-4505) Eds. S. Grossman, F. Steglich. (also avail. in microform from UMI,PMC; back issues avail.; reprint service avail. from ISI) **Indexed:** Chem.Abstr., Curr.Cont., INSPEC (1968-), Math.R., Met.Abstr., Phys.Ber., World Alum.Abstr. **Document type:** academic/scholarly publication.
—BLDSC (9481.020000); CASDDS; Ei; Faxon; Genuine Article; SWETS; UMI; UnCover. **CCC.**
Former titles (until 1981): Zeitschrift fuer Physik B (Condensed Matter and Quanta) (ISSN 0340-224X); (until 1975): Physik der Kondensierten Materie - Physique de la Matiere Condensee - Physics of Condensed Matter (ISSN 0031-9236).
Description: Papers on the physical properties of crystalline, disordered, and amorphous solids, and on classical and quantum liquids.

530 GW CODEN: ZPCFD2
QC1
ZEITSCHRIFT FUER PHYSIK C: PARTICLES AND FIELDS. (Text in English) 1979. 16/yr. (in 4 vols., 4 nos./vol.). DM.4440($3226) (effective 1996). Springer-Verlag, Heidelberger Platz 3, 14197 Berlin, Germany. TEL 030-8207-0. FAX 030-8214091. E-mail: orders@springer.de. (Subscr. in N. America to: Springer-Verlag New York, Inc., 44 Hartz Way, Secaucus, NJ 07096-2491. TEL 201-348-4033. FAX 201-348-4505) Ed. G. Kramer. adv. (also avail. in microform from UMI,PMC; reprint service avail. from ISI) **Indexed:** Chem.Abstr., Curr.Cont., INSPEC, Math.R., Phys.Ber. **Document type:** academic/scholarly publication.
—BLDSC (9481.100000); CASDDS; Ei; Genuine Article; SWETS; UMI; UnCover. **CCC.**
Formerly: Zeitschrift fuer Physik. Section C: Particles and Fields (ISSN 0170-9739)
Description: Covers experimental and theoretical particle physics.

530 GW ISSN 0178-7683
QC170 CODEN: ZDACE2
ZEITSCHRIFT FUER PHYSIK D: ATOMS, MOLECULES AND CLUSTERS. (Text in English) 1986. 16/yr. (in 4 vols., 4 nos./vol.). DM.1710($1242) (effective 1996). Springer-Verlag, Heidelberger Platz 3, 14197 Berlin, Germany. TEL 030-8207-0. FAX 030-8214091. (Subscr. in N. America to: Springer-Verlag New York, Inc., 44 Hartz Way, Secaucus, NJ 07096-2491. TEL 201-348-4033. FAX 201-348-4505) Ed. I.V. Hertel. adv. circ. 700. (back issues avail.) **Indexed:** Curr.Cont., INSPEC (1986-). **Document type:** academic/scholarly publication.
—BLDSC (9481.100500); CASDDS; Ei; Faxon; Genuine Article; SWETS; UMI; UnCover. **CCC.**
Description: Encompasses the entire field of atomic, molecular, cluster, and chemical physics.

ZHONGXUESHENG SHU-LI-HUA (GAOZHONG BAN). see *EDUCATION — Teaching Methods And Curriculum*

530 375 CC
ZHONGXUESHENG WULI YUANDI/PHYSICS FOR MIDDLE SCHOOL STUDENTS. (Text in Chinese) bi-m. Y2.50. Fujian Society of Physics, Physics Department, Fuzhou University, Fuzhou, Fujian 350002, People's Republic of China. TEL 710845. (Dist. overseas by: Jiangsu Publications Import & Export Corp., 56 Gao Yun Ling, Nanjing, Jiangsu, P.R.C.) Ed. Qiu Jinzhang.

530 RU ISSN 0044-4510
QC1 CODEN: ZETFA7
ZHURNAL EKSPERIMENTAL'NOI I TEORETICHESKOI FIZIKI. English translation: Journal of Experimental and Theoretical Physics (US ISSN 1063-7761) (Text in Russian; summaries in English) 1931. m. $605 (effective 1996). (Rossiiskaya Akademiya Nauk) Izdatel'stvo Nauka, Mezhdunarodnayi Otdel, Profsoyznaya, 90, 117864 Moscow, Russia. TEL 234-05-84. Ed. A.S. Borovik-Romanov. charts; illus.; index. circ. 2,700. (also avail. in microform from PMC) **Indexed:** Chem.Abstr., Curr.Cont., Eng.Ind., INSPEC, Math.R., Met.Abstr., Phys.Ber., World Alum.Abstr. **Document type:** academic/scholarly publication.
—BLDSC (0068.000000); CASDDS; Genuine Article. **CCC.**

530 RU ISSN 0044-4642
QC1 CODEN: ZTEFA3
ZHURNAL TEKHNICHESKOI FIZIKI. English translation: Technical Physics (US ISSN 1063-7842) 1931. m. $348 (effective 1996). (Rossiiskaya Akademiya Nauk, S.-Peterburgskoe Otdelenie) Izdatel'stvo Nauka, Mezhdunarodnyi Otdel, Profsoyuznaya, 90, 117864 Moscow, Russia. TEL 234-05-84. Ed. B.P. Konstantinov. charts; illus.; index. circ. 4,000. **Indexed:** Appl.Mech.Rev., Chem.Abstr., Curr.Cont., Eng.Ind., INSPEC, Met.Abstr., Phys.Ber., World Alum.Abstr. **Document type:** academic/scholarly publication.
—BLDSC (0066.000000); CASDDS; Genuine Article. **CCC.**

ZHURNAL VYCHISLITEL'NOI MATEMATIKI I MATEMATICHESKOI FIZIKI. see *MATHEMATICS*

PHYSICS — Abstracting, Bibliographies, Statistics

534 016   UK   ISSN 0001-4974
CODEN: ACOABJ
ACOUSTICS ABSTRACTS. 1967. m. £273 u.K. and Europe; rest of world £284. Multi-Science Publishing Co. Ltd., 107 High St., Brentwood, Essex CM14 4RX, England. TEL 01277-224632.
FAX 01277-223453. (U.S. subscr. to: Box 176, Avenel, NJ 07001) Ed. D.G. Cottingham. abstr.; index. **Indexed:** Fluidex. **Document type:** abstracting/indexing.
—BLDSC (0578.695000). **CCC.**
   Formerly: Acoustics and Ultrasonics Abstracts.
   Description: Treats all aspects of acoustics: solid, liquid and gaseous state acoustics; acoustic diagnostic techniques; acoustics measurements; ultrasonic applications, vibration, shock and noise.

539.7 614 016   UK   ISSN 0305-7615
RA569   CODEN: AHPAES
APPLIED HEALTH PHYSICS ABSTRACTS AND NOTES. 1974. q. £160($330) (effective 1995). Nuclear Technology Publishing, P.O. Box 7, Ashford, Kent TN23 1YW, England. TEL 01233-641683.
FAX 01233-610021. Ed. E.P. Goldfinch. adv. contact: L. Richmond. circ. 1,000. (back issues avail.) **Document type:** abstracting/indexing.
   Description: An international abstracts journal in applied health physics covering radiation dosimetry, measurement techniques, radiation effects and applications.

ASTRONOMY AND ASTROPHYSICS ABSTRACTS. see ASTRONOMY — Abstracting, Bibliographies, Statistics

681 016   HU   ISSN 0231-0643
AUTOMATIZALASI, SZAMITASTECHNIKAI ES MERESTECHNIKAI SZAKIRODALMI TAJEKOZTATO/AUTOMATION, COMPUTING, COMPUTERS & MEASUREMENT ABSTRACTS. 1948. m. 9700 Ft. Orszagos Muszaki Informacios Kozpont es Konyvtar (O.M.I.K.K.) - National Technical Information Centre and Library, Muzeum u. 17, P.O. Box 12, 1428 Budapest, Hungary. (Subscr. to: Kultura, P.O. Box 149, 1389 Budapest, Hungary) Ed. Pal Konyves Toth. abstr.; index. circ. 420.
   Supersedes: Muszaki Lapszemle. Fizika, Meres- es Muszertechnika, Automatika - Technical Abstracts. Physics, Measurement and Instrument Technology, Automation (ISSN 0027-500X)

535   US   ISSN 0195-4911
CODEN: CAASDD
C A SELECTS. ATOMIC SPECTROSCOPY. s-w. $220 to non-members; members $65 (effective 1996). Chemical Abstracts Service (Subsidiary of: American Chemical Society), 2540 Olentangy River Rd., Box 3012, Columbus, OH 43210-0012.
TEL 614-447-3600. FAX 614-447-3713. TELEX 6842086. **Document type:** abstracting/indexing.
   Description: Covers atomic absorption, emission, and fluorescence in optical regions, i.e., infared, visible, and ultraviolet; applications in spectrochemical analysis.

535   US   ISSN 0146-4450
CODEN: CSESDN
C A SELECTS. ELECTRON & AUGER SPECTROSCOPY. s-w. $220 to non-members; members $65 (effective 1996). Chemical Abstracts Service (Subsidiary of: American Chemical Society), 2540 Olentangy River Rd., Box 3012, Columbus, OH 43210-0012.
TEL 614-447-3600. FAX 614-447-3713. TELEX 6842086. **Document type:** abstracting/indexing.
   Description: Covers x-ray photoelectron, photoexcitation, and photoemission spectroscopy.

535   US   ISSN 0890-1872
CODEN: CSOCEQ
C A SELECTS. FIBER OPTICS AND OPTICAL COMMUNICATION. 1987. s-w. $220 to non-members; members $65 (effective 1996). Chemical Abstracts Service (Subsidiary of: American Chemical Society), 2540 Olentangy River Rd., Box 3012, Columbus, OH 43210. TEL 614-447-3600. FAX 614-447-3713. TELEX 6842086. **Document type:** abstracting/indexing.
   Description: Covers materials used for fiber optics and optical communications.

535   US   ISSN 0190-9428
CODEN: CSIADN
C A SELECTS. INFRARED SPECTROSCOPY (ORGANIC ASPECTS). s-w. $220 to non-members; members $65 (effective 1996). Chemical Abstracts Service (Subsidiary of: American Chemical Society), 2540 Olentangy River Rd., Box 3012, Columbus, OH 43210-0012. TEL 614-337-3600.
FAX 614-447-3713. TELEX 6842086. **Document type:** abstracting/indexing.
   Description: Covers organic, macromolecular, and biochemical aspects of infrared spectroscopy; spectroscopic characterization of substances.

535   US   ISSN 0190-9436
CODEN: CISAD3
C A SELECTS. INFRARED SPECTROSCOPY (PHYSICOCHEMICAL ASPECTS). s-w. $220 to non-members; members $65 (effective 1996). Chemical Abstracts Service (Subsidiary of: American Chemical Society), 2540 Olentangy River Rd., Box 3012, Columbus, OH 43210-0012.
TEL 614-447-3600. FAX 614-447-3713. TELEX 6842086. **Document type:** abstracting/indexing.
   Description: Covers applied and physicochemical aspects of infrared spectroscopy; infrared lasers; infrared spectroscopic determination of organic and inorganic substances.

C A SELECTS. MASS SPECTROMETRY. see CHEMISTRY — Abstracting, Bibliographies, Statistics

535   US   ISSN 0895-5867
CODEN: CSNMEH
C A SELECTS. NONLINEAR OPTICAL MATERIALS. 1988. s-w. $220 to non-members; members $65 (effective 1996). Chemical Abstracts Service (Subsidiary of: American Chemical Society), 2540 Olentangy River Rd., Box 3012, Columbus, OH 43210-0012. TEL 614-447-3600.
FAX 614-447-3713. TELEX 6842086. **Document type:** abstracting/indexing.
   Description: Covers materials with nonlinear optical properties; applications of these materials in optical communications, laser, waveguides, electrooptical devices, and photoelectric devices.

535   US   ISSN 0195-5063
CODEN: COPMDW
C A SELECTS. OPTICAL AND PHOTOSENSITIVE MATERIALS. s-w. $220 to non-members; members $65 (effective 1996). Chemical Abstracts Service (Subsidiary of: American Chemical Society), 2540 Olentangy River Rd., Box 3012, Columbus, OH 43210-0012. TEL 614-447-3600.
FAX 614-447-3713. TELEX 6842086. **Document type:** abstracting/indexing.
   Description: Covers light absorbing, transmitting, and reflective materials: films, coatings, glasses, fibers, mirrors, polarizers, solar collectors.

C A SELECTS. THERMAL ANALYSIS. see CHEMISTRY — Abstracting, Bibliographies, Statistics

C A SELECTS. ULTRAVIOLET & VISIBLE SPECTROSCOPY. see CHEMISTRY — Abstracting, Bibliographies, Statistics

535   US   ISSN 0162-7872
CODEN: CSXSDG
C A SELECTS. X-RAY ANALYSIS & SPECTROSCOPY. s-w. $220 to non-members; members $65 (effective 1996). Chemical Abstracts Service (Subsidiary of: American Chemical Society), 2540 Olentangy River Rd., Box 3012, Columbus, OH 43210-0012.
TEL 614-447-3600. FAX 614-447-3713. TELEX 6842086. **Document type:** abstracting/indexing.
   Description: Covers x-ray techniques in chemical analysis, e.g. electron microprobe.

539.7 016   UN   ISSN 1011-2545
C I N D A; an index to the literature on microscopic neutron data. (Text in English) 1965. a. price varies. International Atomic Energy Agency, Wagramerstr. 5, P.O. Box 100, A-1400 Vienna, Austria.
TEL 43-1-209-2360. FAX 43-1-209-5302. E-mail: fossett@adp01.iaea.or.at. (Dist. by: Unipub, 4611-F Assembly Dr., Lanham, MD 20706-4391) (Co-sponsors U.S.A. National Nuclear Data Center; Russian Nuclear Data Centre; N.E.A. Databank; IAEA Nuclear Data Section) circ. 1,500 (paid). **Document type:** bibliography.
•Also available online.
—BLDSC (3198.630000).

530 016   JA   ISSN 0011-3336
CURRENT BIBLIOGRAPHY ON SCIENCE AND TECHNOLOGY: PURE AND APPLIED PHYSICS/KAGAKU GIJUTSU BUNKEN SOKUHO. BUTSURI, OYOBUTSURI-HEN. (Text in Japanese) 1959. s-m. $2620. Japan Information Center of Science and Technology - Nihon Kagaku Gijutsu Joho Senta, 5-3, Yonbancho, Chiyoda-ku, Tokyo 102, Japan.
TEL 03-5214-8413. FAX 03-5214-8410. index. circ. 500. **Document type:** bibliography.
•Also available online. Vendor(s): JICST.

CURRENT CONTENTS: PHYSICAL, CHEMICAL & EARTH SCIENCES. see CHEMISTRY — Abstracting, Bibliographies, Statistics

530 016 520   UK   ISSN 0011-3786
QC5.5   CODEN: CPPHAL
CURRENT PAPERS IN PHYSICS; containing about 78,000 titles of research articles from the world's physics journals. 1966. fortn. £300 (effective 1996). INSPEC, I.E.E., Michael Faraday House, Six Hills Way, Stevenage, Herts. SG1 2AY, England. TEL 01438-313311. FAX 01438-742840. TELEX 825578 IEESTV G. E-mail: inspec@ieee.org.
(Subscr. to: Publication Sales Dept., P.O. Box 96, Stevenage, Herts. SG1 2SD, England; U.S. addr.: INSPEC/IEEE, Box 1331, 445 Hoes Ln., Piscataway, NJ 08855-1331. TEL 908-562-5549. FAX 908-562-8737) **Indexed:** Fluidex. **Document type:** abstracting/indexing.
—CASDDS. **CCC.**

530 016   US   ISSN 0098-9819
Z7143
CURRENT PHYSICS INDEX. 1975. q. $1190 (effective 1996). American Institute of Physics, One Physics Ellipse, College Park, MD 20740-3843.
TEL 301-209-3000. (Subscr. to: AIP Member and Subscriber Services, 500 Sunnyside Blvd., Woodbury, NY 11797-2999. TEL 516-576-2270. FAX 516-349-9704) bibl.; cum.index. (back issues avail.) **Document type:** abstracting/indexing.
•Also available online.
—BLDSC (3501.282000). **CCC.**

ENERGIAIPARI ES ENERGIAGAZDALKODASI TAJEKOZTATO/POWER ENGINEERING ABSTRACTS. see ENERGY — Abstracting, Bibliographies, Statistics

539.7   US
ENVIRONMENTAL AND SITING. (Subseries of: Nuclear Regulatory Commission Guides) irreg. price varies. (Nuclear Regulatory Commission) U.S. National Technical Information Service, 5825 Port Royal Rd., Springfield, VA 22161. TEL 703-487-4630.

539.7 016   SZ   ISSN 0304-2871
EUROPEAN ORGANIZATION FOR NUCLEAR RESEARCH. LIST OF SCIENTIFIC PUBLICATIONS/CONSEIL EUROPEEN POUR LA RECHERCHE NUCLEAIRE. LISTE DES PUBLICATIONS SCIENTIFIQUES. 1955. irreg. free. C E R N - European Laboratory for Particle Physics, CH-1211 Geneva 23, Switzerland.
Document type: academic/scholarly publication.
   Former titles: European Organization for Nuclear Research. Repertoire des Communications Scientifiques - Index of Scientific Publications (ISSN 0423-7781); European Organization for Nuclear Research. Repertoire des Publications Scientifiques - Index of Scientific Publications.

530   SZ   ISSN 0378-2271
CODEN: ECABDW
EUROPHYSICS CONFERENCE ABSTRACTS. irreg. (8-10/yr.). 360 SFr. European Physical Society, P.O. Box 69, CH-1213 Petit Lancy 2, Switzerland.
Indexed: Phys.Ber. **Document type:** abstracting/indexing.
—BLDSC (3830.415000).

F R A N C I S. 731: ECONOMIE DE L'ENERGIE. see ENERGY — Abstracting, Bibliographies, Statistics

FACHBUCHVERZEICHNIS MATHEMATIK - PHYSIK (YEAR). see MATHEMATICS — Abstracting, Bibliographies, Statistics

539.7   US
FUELS AND MATERIALS FACILITIES. (Subseries of: Nuclear Regulatory Commission Guides) irreg. price varies. (Nuclear Regulatory Commission) U.S. National Technical Information Service, 5825 Port Royal Rd., Springfield, VA 22161.
TEL 703-487-4630.

PHYSICS — ABSTRACTING, BIBLIOGRAPHIES, STATISTICS

539.7 US
GENERAL. (Subseries of: Nuclear Regulatory Commission Guides) irreg. price varies. (Nuclear Regulatory Commission) U.S. National Technical Information Service, 5825 Port Royal Rd., Springfield, VA 22161. TEL 703-487-4630.

530 US ISSN 0749-4823
CODEN: GPAAE7
GENERAL PHYSICS ADVANCE ABSTRACTS. 1985. s-m. $730 (foreign $765) (effective 1996). American Institute of Physics, One Physics Ellipse, College Park, MD 20740-3843. TEL 301-209-3000. (Subscr. to: Member and Subscriber Service, 500 Sunnyside Blvd., Woodbury, NY 11797-2999. TEL 516-576-2270. FAX 516-349-9704) **Document type:** abstracting/indexing.
—CCC.

539.7 JA
GENSHIRYOKU ANZEN KENKYU SOGO HAPPYOKAI KOEN YOSHISHU/ABSTRACTS OF MEETING ON NUCLEAR SAFETY RESEARCH. (Text in Japanese) a. Genshiryoku Anzen Kenkyu - Nuclear Safety Research Association, 2-2, Uchisaiwaicho 1-chome, Chiyoda-ku, Tokyo 100, Japan.

539.76 016 GW ISSN 0018-1447
HIGH ENERGY PHYSICS INDEX/HOCHENERGIEPHYSIK-INDEX. (Text in English; contents pages in English and German) 1963. fortn. DM.460 (subscr. includes Thesaurus). (Deutsches Elektronen-Synchrotron (DESY)) Fachinformationszentrum Karlsruhe, Gesellschaft fuer wissenschaftlich-technische Information mbH, 76344 Eggenstein-Leopoldshafen, Germany. TEL 07247-808333. FAX 07247-808135. TELEX 724710-FIZKA. adv.; bk.rev.; index. circ. 160. **Document type:** abstracting/indexing.
Description: Index of articles, books, reports, conference proceedings on high energy physics.

539.2 JA
HOSHASEN RIYO KENKYU SEIKA HOKOKUKAI KOEN YOSHI/ABSTRACTS OF RESEARCH RESULTS OF RADIATION UTILIZATION. (Text in Japanese) a. Nihon Genshiryoku Kenkyujo, Takasaki Kenkyujo - Japan Atomic Energy Research Institute, Takasaki Radiation Chemistry Research Establishment, 1233, Watanukimachi, Takasaki-shi, Gunma-ken 370-12, Japan.

539.7 016 UN ISSN 0004-7139
Z7144.N8 CODEN: INAXAC
I N I S ATOMINDEX. (Text in English; summaries in English, French, Russian or Spanish) 1970. s-m. S.6900 incl. indexes. International Atomic Energy Agency, Wagramerstrasse 5, Box 100, A-1400 Vienna, Austria. TEL 43-1-209-2360. FAX 43-1-209-5302. E-mail: fossett@adp01.iaea.or.at. (Dist. in U.S. by: Unipub, 4611-F Assembly Dr., Lanham, MD 20706-4391) bibl.; s-a. index. circ. 1,650. (also avail. in microfilm from PMC) Indexed: Anal.Abstr., Chem.Abstr., Mass Spectr.Bull. **Document type:** abstracting/indexing.
●Also available online. Vendor(s): BELINDIS, CISTI, European Space Agency (File no.28/INIS), STN International (ENERGY).
Also available on CD-ROM. Producer(s): SilverPlatter Information, Inc. (INIS).
—BLDSC (4513.900000).
Incorporates (as of June 1976): Nuclear Science Abstracts (United States Energy Research and Development Administration) (ISSN 0029-5612)

INSPEC LIST OF JOURNALS AND OTHER SERIAL SOURCES. see ENGINEERING — Abstracting, Bibliographies, Statistics

539.7 JA
J A I F ANNUAL CONFERENCE ABSTRACTS. (Text in English) 1968. a. Japan Atomic Industrial Forum - Nihon Genshiryoku Sangyo Kaigi, 1-13, Shinbashi 1-chome, Minato-ku, Tokyo 105, Japan.

535.58 016 US ISSN 0022-0264
TK7871.3
JOURNAL OF CURRENT LASER ABSTRACTS. 1964. m. $450 (foreign $470) (effective 1994). PennWell Publishing Co. (Nashua), 10 Tara Blvd., 5th Fl., Nashua, NH 03062-2801. TEL 603-891-9177. FAX 603-891-0539. bk.rev.; abstr.; bibl.; charts; illus.; pat.; index. circ. 300. (back issues avail.) **Document type:** abstracting/indexing.
—BLDSC (4965.900000).
Description: Coverage of more than 1,000 source publications, concerning lasers and laser applications, including periodicals, conference proceedings, government reports, patents.

530 668.4 UK ISSN 0950-4753
KEY ABSTRACTS - ADVANCED MATERIALS. 1987. m. £110 (effective 1996). INSPEC, I.E.E., Michael Faraday House, Six Hills Way, Stevenage, Herts. SG1 2AY, England. TEL 01438-313311. FAX 01438-742840. TELEX 825578 IEESTV G. E-mail: inspec@iee.org.uk. (Subscr. to: Publication Sales Dept., P.O. Box 96, Stevenage, Herts. SG1 2SD, England; U.S. addr.: INSPEC/IEEE, Box 1331, 445 Hoes Ln., Piscataway, NJ 08855-1331. TEL 908-562-5549. FAX 908-562-8737) index. **Document type:** abstracting/indexing.
Description: Covers the preparation, structure, properties and testing of ceramics, refractories, composite materials, polymers and glasses and porous materials.

536.7 UK ISSN 0953-1262
KEY ABSTRACTS - HIGH-TEMPERATURE SUPERCONDUCTORS. 1989. m. £110 (effective 1996). INSPEC, I.E.E., Michael Faraday House, Six Hills Way, Stevenage, Herts SG1 2AY, England. TEL 01438-313311. FAX 01438-742840. TELEX 825578 IEESTV G. E-mail: inspec@iee.org.uk. (Subscr. to: Publication Sales Dept., P.O. Box 96, Stevenage, Herts. SG1 2SD, England; U.S. addr.: INSPEC/IEEE, Box 1331, 445 Hoes Ln., Piscataway, NJ 08855-1331. TEL 908-562-5549. FAX 908-562-8737) Ed. John Deaves. **Document type:** abstracting/indexing.
—CCC.

621.38 535 UK ISSN 0950-4826
KEY ABSTRACTS - OPTOELECTRONICS. 1987. m. £110 (effective 1996). INSPEC, I.E.E., Michael Faraday House, Six Hills Way, Stevenage, Herts. SG1 2AY, England. TEL 01438-313311. FAX 01438-742840. TELEX 825578 IEESTV G. E-mail: inspec@iee.org.uk. (Subscr. to: Publication Sales Dept., P.O. Box 96, Stevenage, Herts. SG1 2SD, England; U.S. addr.: INPSEC/IEEE, Box 1331, 445 Hoes Ln., Piscataway, NJ 08855-1331. TEL 908-562-5549. FAX 908-562-8737) index. **Document type:** abstracting/indexing.
Description: Covers fiberoptics, integrated optoelectronics, electro-optic devices, lasers and their applications, nonlinear optics, and holography.

539.7 US
MATERIALS AND PLANT PROTECTION. (Subseries of: Nuclear Regulatory Commission Guides) irreg. price varies. (Nuclear Regulatory Commission) U.S. National Technical Information Service, 5825 Port Royal Rd., Springfield, VA 22161. TEL 703-487-4630.

539.7 US
N R C DOCKET MICROFICHE. m. $2200 per no. in U.S., Canada, Mexico; elsewhere $2900. (Nuclear Regulatory Commission) U.S. National Technical Information Service, 5825 Port Royal Rd., Springfield, VA 22161. TEL 703-487-4630. (microfiche)
Description: Concerns testing, licensing, and operation of nuclear power reactors.

530 016 US
N T I S ALERTS: PHYSICS. w. $140 (foreign $195). U.S. National Technical Information Service, 5285 Port Royal Rd., Springfield, VA 22161. TEL 703-487-4630. FAX 703-321-8547. TELEX 64617. index. (back issues avail.) **Document type:** abstracting/indexing.
Former titles: Abstract Newsletter: Physics (ISSN 0163-1446); Weekly Abstract Newsletter: Physics; Weekly Government Abstracts. Physics.

536 JA
NETSU SOKUTEI TORONKAI KOEN YOSHISHU/ABSTRACTS OF JAPANESE CALORIMETRY CONFERENCE. (Text in English, Japanese) 1965. a. Nihon Netsu Sokutei Gakkai - Japan Society of Calorimetry and Thermal Analysis, Cosmos Hongo ldg., 8F, 4-1-4 Hongo, Bunkyo-ku, Tokyo 113, Japan. **Document type:** abstracting/indexing.

535.84 JA
NIHON BUNKO GAKKAI SHINPOJUMU KOEN YOSHISHU/SPECTROSCOPICAL SOCIETY OF JAPAN. ABSTRACTS OF SYMPOSIA. (Text in English, Japanese) 4/yr. Nihon Bunko Gakkai - Spectroscopical Society of Japan, 1-13, Kanda Awajicho, Chiyoda-ku, Tokyo 101, Japan. **Document type:** abstracting/indexing.

532 JA
NIHON REOROJI GAKKAI NENKAI KOEN YOKOSHU/ABSTRACTS OF ANNUAL MEETING ON RHEOLOGY. (Text in Japanese) 1974. a. Nihon Reoroji Gakkai - Society of Rheology, Japan, 1-101, Yoshida Izumidonocho, Sakyo-ku, Kyoto 606, Japan. **Document type:** abstracting/indexing.

539.7 US
NUCLEAR REGULATORY COMMISSION GUIDES. (Series of: Power Reactors, Research and Test Reactors, Fuels and Materials Facilities, Environmental and Siting, Materials and Plant Protection, Products, Transportation, Occupational Health, and General) irreg. price varies. (Nuclear Regulatory Commission) U.S. National Technical Information Service, 5825 Port Royal Rd., Springfield, VA 22161. TEL 703-487-4630.
Description: Information on the methods of implementing specific parts of the Commission regulations. Describes techniques used by the NRC in evaluating specific problems and provides guidance to applicants who are involved with nuclear reactors.

535 JA
OYO SUPEKUTOROMETORI TOKYO TORONKAI KOEN YOSHISHU/ABSTRACTS OF PAPERS PRESENTED AT THE TOKYO SYMPOSIA ON THE APPLIED SPECTROMETRY. (Text in Japanese) 1965. a. Oyo Butsuri Gakkai - Japan Society of Applied Physics, 12-3, Kudan Kita 1-chome, Chiyoda-ku, Tokyo 102, Japan. **Document type:** abstracting/indexing.

530 016 FR ISSN 1146-531X
P A S C A L E 11: PHYSIQUE ATOMIQUE ET MOLECULAIRE. PLASMAS. (Printed format ceased Jan. 1995) (Text in French, English) 1984. 10/yr. Centre National de la Recherche Scientifique, Institut de l'Information Scientifique et Technique, 2 allee du Parc de Brabois, 54514 Vandoeuvre-Les-Nancy Cedex, France. TEL 83-50-46-00. FAX 83-50-46-50. adv. contact: Veronique Guinvarc'h. index, cum.index. (also avail. in microfiche) **Document type:** bibliography.
●Also available online. Vendor(s): European Space Agency (File no.14), Knight-Ridder, Inc. (File no.144), Telesystemes - Questel.
Also available on CD-ROM.
Former titles: P A S C A L Explore. E 11: Physique Atomique et Moleculaire. Plasmas (ISSN 0761-1951); P A S C A L Part 11: Physique Atomique et Moleculaire. Plasmas; Supersedes: Bulletin Signaletique. Part 165: Atomes et Molecules. Plasmas (ISSN 0398-9968); Bulletin Signaletique. Part 165: Atomes et Molecules. Physiques des Fluides et Plasmas (ISSN 0301-3359); Bulletin Signaletique. Part 165: Physique Atomique et Moleculaire. Physique des Fluides et des Plasmas; Which supersedes in part: Bulletin Signaletique. Part 160: Structure de la Matiere I (ISSN 0007-537X).

PHYSICS — ABSTRACTING, BIBLIOGRAPHIES, STATISTICS

530 016   FR   ISSN 1146-5328
P A S C A L. E 12: ETAT CONDENSE. (Printed format ceased Jan. 1995) (Text in English, French) 1984. 10/yr. Centre National de la Recherche Scientifique, Institut de l'Information Scientifique et Technique, 2 allee du Parc de Brabois, 54514 Vandoeuvre-Les-Nancy Cedex, France. TEL 83-50-46-00. FAX 83-50-46-50. adv. contact: Veronique Guinvarc'h. abstr.; index, cum.index. (also avail. in microfiche) **Document type:** bibliography.
●Also available online. Vendor(s): European Space Agency (File no.14), Knight-Ridder, Inc. (File no.144), Telesystemes - Questel.
Also available on CD-ROM.
—**CCC.**
    Former titles: P A S C A L Explore. E 12: Etat Condense (ISSN 0761-196X); P A S C A L Explore. Part 12: Etat Condense; Supersedes (1961-1984): Bulletin Signaletique. Part 160: Physique de l'Etat Condense (ISSN 0301-3332); Which supersedes in part: Bulletin Signaletique. Part 160: Structure de la Matiere I (ISSN 0007-537X)

535 011   FR   ISSN 1146-5360
P A S C A L. E 27: METHODES DE FORMATION ET TRAITEMENT DES IMAGES. (Print format ceased Jan. 1995) (Text in English, French) 1984. 10/yr. Centre National de la Recherche Scientifique, Institut de l'Information Scientifique et Technique, 2 allee du Parc de Brabois, 54514 Vandoeuvre-les-Nancy Cedex, France. TEL 83-50-46-00. FAX 83-50-46-50. adv. contact: Veronique Guinvarc'h. (also avail. in microfiche) **Document type:** bibliography.
●Also available online. Vendor(s): European Space Agency (File no.14), Knight-Ridder, Inc. (File no.144), Telesystemes - Questel.
Also available on CD-ROM.
    Former titles: P A S C A L Explore. Part 27: Methodes de Formation et Traitement des Images; Supersedes in part (1961-1984): Bulletin Signaletique. Part 130: Physique Mathematique, Optique, Acoustique, Mecanique, Chaleur (ISSN 0397-7757)

P A S C A L. E 32: METROLOGIE ET APPAREILLAGE EN PHYSIQUE ET PHYSICOCHIMIE. see *METROLOGY AND STANDARDIZATION — Abstracting, Bibliographies, Statistics*

530 016   FR   ISSN 1146-5107
P A S C A L. F 10: MECANIQUE, ACOUSTIQUE ET TRANSFERT DE CHALEUR. (Printed format ceased Jan. 1995) (Text in English, French) 1984. 10/yr. Centre National de la Recherche Scientifique, Institut de l'Information Scientifique et Technique, 2 allee du Parc de Brabois, 54514 Vandoeuvre-Les-Nancy Cedex, France. TEL 83-50-46-00. FAX 83-50-46-50. Ed. Claude Patou. adv. contact: Veronique Guinvarc'h. abstr.; index, cum.index. (also avail. in microfiche) **Document type:** bibliography.
●Also available online. Vendor(s): European Space Agency (File no.14), Knight-Ridder, Inc. (File no.144), Telesystemes - Questel.
Also available on CD-ROM.
    Former titles: P A S C A L Folio. F 10: Mecanique et Acoustique et Transfert de Chaleur; P A S C A L Folio. F 10: Mecanique et Acoustique (ISSN 0761-1730); Supersedes in part (1961-1984): Bulletin Signaletique. Part 130: Physique Mathematique, Optique, Acoustique, Mecanique, Chaleur (ISSN 0397-7757); Which was formerly: Bulletin Signaletique. Part 130: Physique (ISSN 0007-5345); Supersedes: Bulletin Signaletique. Part 891: Industries Mecaniques (ISSN 0223-4246); Which supersedes in part: Bulletin Signaletique. Part 890: Industries Mecaniques - Batiment - Travaux Public - Transports (ISSN 0398-995X); Formerly: P A S C A L Folio. Part 10: Mecanique et Acoustique.

536 016   FR   ISSN 1146-5042
P A S C A L. T 230: ENERGIE. (Printed format ceased Jan. 1995) (Text in English, French) 1984. 10/yr. Centre National de la Recherche Scientifique, Institut de l'Information Scientifique et Technique, 2 allee du Parc de Brabois, 54514 Vandoeuvre-Les-Nancy Cedex, France. TEL 83-50-46-00. FAX 83-50-46-50. adv. contact: Veronique Guinvarc'h. abstr.; index, cum.index. (also avail. in microfiche) **Document type:** bibliography.
●Also available online. Vendor(s): European Space Agency (File no.14), Knight-Ridder, Inc. (File no.144), Telesystemes - Questel.
Also available on CD-ROM.
    Former titles: P A S C A L Thema. T 230: Energie (ISSN 0761-1668); P A S C A L Thema. Part 230: Energie; Which superseded: Bulletin Signaletique. Part 730: Combustibles. Energie (ISSN 0007-5647)

530 016   US   ISSN 0048-4024
CODEN: PRVABI
PHYSICAL REVIEW ABSTRACTS. 1970. s-m. $400 (foreign $420). American Physical Society, One Physics Ellipse, College Park, MD 20740-3844. TEL 301-209-3202. (Subscr. to: APS Subscriber Service, c/o American Institute of Physics, 500 Sunnyside Blvd., Woodbury, NY 111797-2799. TEL 516-576-2270) Ed. R. Terwilliger. abstr. **Document type:** academic/scholarly publication.
—**CCC.**
Refereed Serial

530 016   US   ISSN 0094-0003
QC1   CODEN: PRPIEF
PHYSICAL REVIEW - INDEX. a. $100 (foreign $105) (effective 1996). American Physical Society, One Physics Ellipse, College Park, MD 20740-3844. TEL 301-209-3202. (Subscr. to: APS Subscriber Serivce, c/o AIP, 500 Sunnyside Blvd., Voodbury, NY 11797-2799. TEL 516-576-2270) Ed.Bd. (also avail. in microfiche from AIP) **Document type:** abstracting/indexing.

530 016   UK   ISSN 0036-8091
QC1   CODEN: PYASAF
PHYSICS ABSTRACTS. Alternative title: INSPEC. Section A. Represents: Science Abstracts. Section A. 1898. s-m. £1950 (effective 1996). INSPEC, I.E.E., Michael Faraday House, Six Hills Way, Stevenage, Herts. SG1 2AY, England. TEL 01438-313311. FAX 01438-742840. TELEX 825578 IEESTV G. E-mail: inspec@iee.org.uk. (Subscr. to: Publication Sales Dept., P.O. Box 96, Stevenage, Herts. SG1 2SD, England; U.S. addr.: INSPEC/IEEE, Box 1331, 445 Hoes Ln., Piscataway, NJ 08855-1331. TEL 908-562-5549. FAX 908-562-8757) adv.; abstr.; index, cum. index every 4 yrs. **Indexed:** Br.Ceram.Abstr., Chem.Abstr., Mass Spectr.Bull. **Document type:** abstracting/indexing.
●Also available online. Vendor(s): CEDOCAR, Data-Star, European Space Agency, FIZ Technik, Knight-Ridder, Inc., Orbit Search Service, STN International.
Also available on CD-ROM. Producer(s): University Microfilms International.
—BLDSC (6477.000000); CASDDS; UnCover. **CCC.**
    Description: Covers recently published primary research in all areas of physics, including particle, nuclear, atomic, molecular, fluid, plasma and solid-state physics, biophysics, geophysics, astrophysics, measurement, and instrumentation.

539.7   US   ISSN 0360-6309
POWER REACTORS. (Subseries of: Nuclear Regulatory Commission Guides) irreg. price varies. (Nuclear Regulatory Commission) U.S. National Technical Information Service, 5825 Port Royal Rd., Springfield, VA 22161. TEL 703-487-4630.

539.7   US
PRODUCTS. (Subseries of: Nuclear Regulatory Commission Guides) irreg. price varies. (Nuclear Regulatory Commission) U.S. National Technical Information Service, 5825 Port Royal Rd., Springfield, VA 22161. TEL 703-487-4630.

016.5392   US
RADIATION RESEARCH SOCIETY. ANNUAL MEETING. 1952. a., 42nd, 1994, Nashville. membership. Radiation Research Society, 2021 Spring Rd., Ste. 600, Oak Brook, IL 60521. TEL 708-571-2881. FAX 708-571-7837. (Co-sponsor: North American Hyperthermia Society) Ed. R.J.M. Fry. **Document type:** proceedings.
    Formerly (until 1994): Radiation Research Society. Annual Meeting. Abstracts of Papers.

530 016   RU   ISSN 0034-2343
CODEN: RZFZAM
REFERATIVNYI ZHURNAL. FIZIKA. 1954. m. 551 Rub. (800 Rub. including index). Vsesoyuznyi Institut Nauchno-Tekhnicheskoi Informatsii (VINITI), Baltiiskaya ul., 14, Moscow A-219, Russia. (Subscr. to: Mezhdunarodnaya Kniga, Dimitrova ul. 39, 113095 Moscow, Russia) (also avail. in microfiche from BHP) **Indexed:** Chem.Abstr. **Document type:** abstracting/indexing.
—BLDSC (0149.000000); CASDDS. **CCC.**

535   RU   ISSN 0234-9647
REFERATIVNYI ZHURNAL. VOLOKONNO-OPTICHESKIE SYSTEMY. 1987. m. $182 (effective 1996). Vsesoyuznyi Institut Nauchno-Tekhnicheskoi Informatsii (VINITI), Baltiiskaya ul. 14, Moscow A-219, Russia. **Document type:** abstracting/indexing.

621.483 016   RU   ISSN 0034-2653
REFERATIVNYI ZHURNAL. YADERNYE REAKTORY. 1958. m. 32 Rub. (32.40 Rub. including index). Vsesoyuznyi Institut Nauchno-Tekhnicheskoi Informatsii (VINITI), Baltiiskaya ul., 14, Moscow A-219, Russia. (Subscr. to: Mezhdunarodnaya Kniga, Dimitrova ul. 39, Moscow G-200, Russia) **Indexed:** Chem.Abstr. **Document type:** abstracting/indexing.

530 016   US   ISSN 0735-0791
TK7870
RELIABILITY PHYSICS. Represents: International Reliability Physics Symposium. Proceedings. a. (I E E E, Electron Devices Society and Reliability Society) Institute of Electrical and Electronics Engineers, Inc., 345 E. 47th St., New York, NY 10017-2394. TEL 212-705-7900. FAX 212-705-7682. (Subscr. to: Box 1331, 445 Hoes Ln., Piscataway, NJ 08855-1331) **Indexed:** Chem.Abstr.
—BLDSC (7356.423000); Faxon; UMI. **CCC.**
    Former titles: Reliability Physics Symposium. Proceedings; Reliability Physics Symposium. Presentation Abstracts; Reliability Physics Symposium Abstracts (ISSN 0080-0821)
    Description: Focuses on device reliability as the dominating influence in the development of new VLSI technologies and circuit designs.
Refereed Serial

531   JA
REOROJI TORONKAI KOEN YOSHISHU/ABSTRACTS OF SYMPOSIUM ON RHEOLOGY. (Text in English, Japanese) 1952. a. Nihon Reoroji Gakkai - Society of Rheology, Japan, 1-101, Yoshida Izumidonocho, Sakyo-ku, Kyoto 606, Japan. **Document type:** abstracting/indexing.

539.7   US
RESEARCH AND TEST REACTORS. (Subseries of: Nuclear Regulatory Commission Guides) irreg. price varies. (Nuclear Regulatory Commission) U.S. National Technical Information Service, 5825 Port Royal Rd., Springfield, VA 22161. TEL 703-487-4630.

535   JA   ISSN 0913-6355
REZA GAKKAI GAKUJUTSU KOENKAI NENJI TAIKAI KOEN YOKOSHU/LASER SOCIETY OF JAPAN. ANNUAL MEETING. DIGEST OF TECHNICAL PAPERS. (Text in English, Japanese) 1981. a. Reza Gakkai - Laser Society of Japan, 2-6, Yamadaoka, Suita-shi, Osaka 565, Japan.

535   JA
REZA KAGAKU/ABSTRACTS OF RIKEN SYMPOSIUM ON LASER SCIENCE. (Text in English, Japanese) a. Rikagaku Kenkyujo, Reza Kagaku Kenkyu Gurupu - Institute of Physical and Chemical Research, Laser Science Group, 2-1, Hirosawa, Wako-shi, Saitama-ken 351-01, Japan. **Document type:** abstracting/indexing.

PHYSICS — ABSTRACTING, BIBLIOGRAPHIES, STATISTICS

532 540 016   UK   ISSN 0035-452X
QC189   CODEN: RHABA3
RHEOLOGY ABSTRACTS. 1958. 4/yr. £255($380) (effective 1995). (British Society of Rheology) Elsevier Science Ltd., Pergamon, P.O. Box 800, Kidlington, Oxford OX5 1DX, England. TEL 44-1865-843000. FAX 44-1865-843010. E-mail: nlinfo-f@elsevier.nl; usinfo-f@elsevier.com; forinfo-kyf04035@niftyserve.or.jp; Site addr.: http://www.elsevier.nl/. (Subscr. in U.S. and Canada to: Elsevier Science, 660 White Plains Rd., Tarrytown, NY 10591-5153. TEL 914-524-9200. FAX 914-333-2444) Ed. G.R. Browney. adv.: B&W page $550, color page $1350. bk.rev. circ. 1,300. (also avail. in microfilm from UMI; back issues avail.) Indexed: Biol.Abstr., Br.Ceram.Abstr., RAPRA. **Document type:** abstracting/indexing.
—BLDSC (7960.500000); UMI. **CCC.**
Description: Covers all papers describing work within the science of rheology, the study of deformation and flow.

530 540   JA
RIKAGAKU KENKYUJO KENKYU HAPPYO RONBUN MOKUROKU/INSTITUTE OF PHYSICAL AND CHEMICAL RESEARCH. LIST OF PAPERS. (Text in English and Japanese) 1982. a. Rikagaku Kenkyujo - Institute of Physical and Chemical Research, 2-1 Hirosawa, Wako-shi, Saitama-ken 351-01, Japan. TEL 0484-621111. FAX 0484-621554. abstr.

530 540   JA   ISSN 0557-0220
OC1
RIKAGAKU KENKYUJO KENKYU NENPO/I P C R. ANNUAL REPORTS OF RESEARCH ACTIVITIES. (Text in Japanese) 1964. a. Rikagaku Kenkyujo - Institute of Physical and Chemical Research, 2-1 Hirosawa, Wako-shi, Saitama-ken 351-01, Japan. TEL 0484-621111. FAX 0484-621554. Indexed: INIS Atomind.

530 540   JA   ISSN 0916-619X
RIKAGAKU KENKYUJO NYUSU/RIKEN NEWS. (Text in Japanese) 1968. m. Rikagaku Kenkyujo - Institute of Physical and Chemical Research, 2-1 Hirosawa, Wako-shi, Saitama-ken 351-01, Japan. TEL 0484-621111. FAX 0484-621554.
Description: Contains information on current researches.

535.84 016   UK   ISSN 0036-1178
S D C BULLETIN. 1963. irreg. £5. Scientific Documentation Centre Ltd., Halbeath House, Dunfermline, Fife KY12 0TZ, Scotland. Ed. P.S. Davison. bk.rev.; bibl.; index.
Formerly: Spectra Index and S D C Bulletin.

535   US   ISSN 1055-6885
Z7144.O6
S P I E PUBLICATIONS INDEX. 1991. a.? International Society for Optical Engineering (SPIE), Box 10, Bellington, WA 98227-0010.

530 016   US
SEARCHABLE PHYSICS INFORMATION NOTICES. 1970. s-m. American Institute of Physics, One Physics Ellipse, College Park, MD 20740-3843. TEL 301-209-3000. (Subscr. to: AIP Member and Subscriber Services, 500 Sunnyside Blvd., Woodbury, NY 11797-2999. TEL 516-576-2270) abstr.; bibl. (magnetic tape) **Document type:** academic/scholarly publication.
●Also available online. Vendor(s): Knight-Ridder, Inc. (File no.62/SPIN).

534 016   RU   ISSN 0320-3123
SIGNAL'NAYA INFORMATSIYA. AKUSTIKA. 1973. s-m. 27.80 Rub. Vsesoyuznyi Institut Nauchno-Tekhnicheskoi Informatsii (VINITI), Baltiiskaya ul. 14, Moscow A-219, Russia. **Document type:** abstracting/indexing.

539.7 016   RU   ISSN 0203-5545
SIGNAL'NAYA INFORMATSIYA. ATOMNOE YADRO. 1970. s-m. 52.60 Rub. Vsesoyuznyi Institut Nauchno-Tekhnicheskoi Informatsii (VINITI), Baltiiskaya ul. 14, Moscow A-219, Russia. (Subscr. to: Mezhdunarodnaya Kniga, Dimitrova ul. 39, 113095 Moscow, Russia) **Document type:** abstracting/indexing.

530 016   RU   ISSN 0135-0870
SIGNAL'NAYA INFORMATSIYA. ATOMY I MOLEKULY. 1973. s-m. 37.80 Rub. Vsesoyuznyi Institut Nauchno-Tekhnicheskoi Informatsii (VINITI), Baltiiskaya ul. 14, Moscow A-219, Russia. (Subscr. to: Mezhdunarodnaya Kniga, Dimitrova ul. 39, 113095 Moscow, Russia) **Document type:** abstracting/indexing.

530 016   RU   ISSN 0320-3182
SIGNAL'NAYA INFORMATSIYA. CHASTITSY I POLYA. 1969. s-m. 52.50 Rub. Vsesoyuznyi Institut Nauchno-Tekhnicheskoi Informatsii (VINITI), Baltiiskaya ul. 14, Moscow A-219, Russia. **Document type:** abstracting/indexing.

530 016   RU   ISSN 0320-3166
SIGNAL'NAYA INFORMATSIYA. ELEKTRICHESKIE SVOISTVA TVERDYKH TEL. 1972. s-m. 55.60 Rub. Vsesoyuznyi Institut Nauchno-Tekhnicheskoi Informatsii (VINITI), Baltiiskaya ul. 14, Moscow A-219, Russia. **Document type:** abstracting/indexing.

539.7 016   RU   ISSN 0320-314X
SIGNAL'NAYA INFORMATSIYA. FIZIKA YADERNYKH REAKTOROV. 1970. s-m. 23.60 Rub. Vsesoyuznyi Institut Nauchno-Tekhnicheskoi Informatsii (VINITI), Baltiiskaya ul. 14, Moscow A-219, Russia. **Document type:** abstracting/indexing.

536.7 016   RU   ISSN 0135-0889
SIGNAL'NAYA INFORMATSIYA. GAZY I ZHIDKOSTI. TERMODINAMIKA I STATISTICHESKAYA FIZIKA. 1973. s-m. 48.50 Rub. Vsesoyuznyi Institut Nauchno-Tekhnicheskoi Informatsii (VINITI), Baltiiskaya ul. 14, Moscow A-219, Russia. (Subscr. to: Mezhdunarodnaya Kniga, Dimitrova ul. 39, 113095 Moscow, Russia) **Document type:** abstracting/indexing.

530 016   RU   ISSN 0136-0612
SIGNAL'NAYA INFORMATSIYA. MAGNITNYE SVOISTVA TVERDYKH TEL. 1972. s-m. 24 Rub. Vsesoyuznyi Institut Nauchno-Tekhnicheskoi Informatsii (VINITI), Baltiiskaya ul. 14, Moscow A-219, Russia. (Subscr. to: Mezhdunarodnaya Kniga, Dimitrova ul. 39, 113095 Moscow, Russia) **Document type:** abstracting/indexing.

535 016   RU   ISSN 0203-5553
SIGNAL'NAYA INFORMATSIYA. NELINEINAYA OPTIKA I KVANTOVAYA ELEKTRONIKA. 1973. s-m. 46.20 Rub. Vsesoyuznyi Institut Nauchno-Tekhnicheskoi Informatsii (VINITI), Baltiiskaya ul. 14, Moscow A-219, Russia. (Subscr. to: Mezhdunarodnaya Kniga, Dimitrova ul. 39, 113095 Moscow, Russia) **Document type:** abstracting/indexing.

535 016   RU   ISSN 0135-0897
SIGNAL'NAYA INFORMATSIYA. OPTIKA. 1973. s-m. 67.80 Rub. Vsesoyuznyi Institut Nauchno-Tekhnicheskoi Informatsii (VINITI), Baltiiskaya ul. 14, Moscow A-219, Russia. (Subscr. to: Mezhdunarodnaya Kniga, Dimitrova ul. 39, 113095 Moscow, Russia) **Document type:** abstracting/indexing.

530 016   RU   ISSN 0208-0656
SIGNAL'NAYA INFORMATSIYA. POVERKHNOST'. 1982. s-m. 47.40 Rub. Vsesoyuznyi Institut Nauchno-Tekhnicheskoi Informatsii (VINITI), Baltiiskaya ul. 14, Moscow A-219, Russia. **Document type:** abstracting/indexing.

530 016   RU   ISSN 0203-5561
SIGNAL'NAYA INFORMATSIYA. STRUKTURA I DINAMIKA RESHETKI TVERDYKH TEL. 1972. s-m. 50.40 Rub. Vsesoyuznyi Institut Nauchno-Tekhnicheskoi Informatsii (VINITI), Baltiiskaya ul. 14, Moscow A-219, Russia. Eds. B.B. Kadomtsev, A.M. Afanas'ev. **Document type:** abstracting/indexing.

531 016   US   ISSN 0896-5900
TK7800   CODEN: SSABER
SOLID STATE AND SUPERCONDUCTIVITY ABSTRACTS. 1957. bi-m. $995 (foreign $1195). Cambridge Scientific Abstracts, 7200 Wisconsin Ave., 6th Fl., Bethesda, MD 20814. TEL 301-961-6750. FAX 301-961-6720. E-mail: market@csa.com. (Co-publisher: Engineering Information, Inc.) Ed. Evelyn Beck; Pub. Ted Caris. adv.; bk.rev.; abstr.; bibl.; index, cum.index. (also avail. in magnetic tape; back issues avail.) Indexed: Cal.Tiss.Abstr., Chem.Abstr., Chemorec.Abstr., Oncol.Abstr. **Document type:** abstracting/indexing.
●Also available online. Vendor(s): STN International (SOLIDSTATE).
Former titles: Solid State Abstracts Journal; Solid State Abstracts (ISSN 0038-108X); Incorporates: Science Research Abstracts Journal. Laser and Electro-Optic Reviews, Quantum Electronics, Unconventional Energy Sources; Science Research Abstracts Journal. Superconductivity, Magnetohydrodynamics and Plasma, Theoretical Physics (ISSN 0361-3321); Which was formerly: Science Research Abstracts, Part A. MHD and Plasma, Superconductivity and Research, and Theoretical Physics; Which incorporated: Theoretical Physics Journal (ISSN 0049-3678).
Description: Covers theory, development and application of solid state materials, with emphasis on superconductivity.

530   NE   ISSN 0167-2584
SURFACE SCIENCE LETTERS. Issued with: Surface Science (ISSN 0039-6028) 1980. 24/yr. North-Holland (Subsidiary of: Elsevier Science B.V.), P.O. Box 211, 1000 AE Amsterdam, Netherlands. TEL 31-20-4853911. FAX 31-20-4853598. TELEX 18582 ESPA NL. (Subscr. in U.S. and Canada to: Elsevier Science Inc., Box 882, Madison Sq. Sta., New York, NY 10159. TEL 212-989-5800. FAX 212-633-3990) Ed. Harry C. Gatos. (also avail. in microform from UMI; back issues avail.) **Document type:** academic/scholarly publication, abstracting/indexing.
—CCC.
Description: Current awareness service for scientists concerned with the physics and chemistry of surfaces; includes letters and abstracts of primary research papers.

530 016   UK   ISSN 0049-2639
QC157
SURFACE WAVE ABSTRACTS. 1971. q. £128 u.K. and Europe; rest of world £137. Multi-Science Publishing Co. Ltd., 107 High St., Brentwood, Essex CM14 4RX, England. TEL 01277-224632. FAX 01277-223453. (U.S. subscr. to: Box 176, Avenel, NJ 07001) Ed. J.J. Aspinall. bk.rev.; abstr.; bibl.; index. **Document type:** abstracting/indexing.
—CCC.
Description: Covers the study of acoustic surface waves in applied physics and engineering.

539.7   US
TRANSPORTATION (SPRINGFIELD). (Subseries of: Nuclear Regulatory Commission Guides) irreg. price varies. (Nuclear Regulatory Commission) U.S. National Technical Information Service, 5825 Port Royal Rd., Springfield, VA 22161. TEL 703-487-4630. Indexed: Energy Info.Abstr., Environ.Abstr.

530   NE   ISSN 0022-8141
UNIVERSITY OF LEIDEN. KAMERLINGH ONNES LABORATORY. COMMUNICATIONS. (Text in English; occasionally in French and German) 1885. a. free. Rijksuniversiteit te Leiden, Kamerlingh Onnes Laboratory, Nieuwsteeg 18, 2311 SB Leiden, Netherlands. TEL (071)275643. FAX 071-275819. TELEX 39058-ASTRO-NL. Ed. M. Durieux. charts, illus. circ. 450. (also avail. in microform from PMC) Indexed: INSPEC.
—BLDSC (3354.000000).
Description: Contains abstracts and references to the original journals of all papers published by physicists in the Kamerlingh Onnes Laboratory.

535.84   CC   ISSN 1004-8073
ZHONGGUO GUANGXUE YU YINGYONG GUANGXUE WENZHAI/CHINESE OPTICS AND APPLIED OPTICS ABSTRACTS. (Text in Chinese) 1985. bi-m. Y54 (effective 1995). Chinese Academy of Science, Changchun Institute of Optical Precision Machinary, Changchun Guangxue Jingmi Jixie Yanjiusuo, 112, Stalin Street, Changchun, Jilin 130022, People's Republic of China. TEL 684692. FAX 682346. Ed. Wang Jiaqi. **Document type:** abstracting/indexing.

PHYSICS — Computer Applications

530   CC   ISSN 1000-8802
ZHONGGUO WULI WENZHAI/CHINESE PHYSICS ABSTRACTS. 1986. bi-m. $90. Zhongguo Kexueyuan, Wenxian Qingbao Zhongxin - Chinese Academy of Sciences, Documentation Information Center, 8 Kexueyuan Nanlu, Zhongguancun, Beijing 100080, People's Republic of China.
TEL 256-1452. FAX 256-6846. Ed. Liu Zaili. circ. 2,000. **Document type:** abstracting/indexing.

PHYSICS — Computer Applications

APPLIED COMPUTATIONAL ELECTROMAGNETICS SOCIETY JOURNAL. see *PHYSICS — Electricity*

APPLIED COMPUTATIONAL ELECTROMAGNETICS SOCIETY NEWSLETTER. see *PHYSICS — Electricity*

534   NE
COMPUTATIONAL ACOUSTICS. Represents: I M A C S Symposium on Computational Acoustics. Proceedings. (Text in English) 1986. irreg., 2nd, 1989, Princeton. price varies. (International Association for Mathematics and Computers in Simulation) Elsevier Science B.V., Books Division, P.O. Box 211, 1000 AE Amsterdam, Netherlands.
TEL 31-20-4853911. FAX 31-20-4853705. E-mail: nlinfo-f@elsevier.nl; usinfo-f@elsevier.com; forinfo-kyf04035@niftyserve.or.jp; Site addr.: http://www.elsevier.nl/. (Subscr. in U.S. and Canada to: Elsevier Science Inc., Box 882, Madison Sq. Sta., New York, NY 10159-0882. TEL 212-989-5800. FAX 212-633-3680) Ed. D. Lee. (back issues avail.) **Document type:** proceedings.
Refereed Serial

COMPUTATIONAL MECHANICS ADVANCES. see *MATHEMATICS — Computer Applications*

530.285   NE   ISSN 0010-4655
QC52   CODEN: CPHCBZ
COMPUTER PHYSICS COMMUNICATIONS; an international journal and program library for computational physics and computer programs in physics. (Text in English) 1969. 21/yr. fl.5320($3244) (effective 1996). North-Holland (Subsidiary of: Elsevier Science B.V.), P.O. Box 211, 1000 AE Amsterdam, Netherlands.
TEL 31-20-4853911. FAX 31-20-4853598. TELEX 18582 ESPA NL. (Subscr. in U.S. and Canada to: Elsevier Science Inc., Box 882, Madison Sq. Sta., New York, NY 10159. TEL 212-989-5800. FAX 212-633-3990) Ed. P.G. Burke. adv.: bk.rev.; software rev.; charts; index. (also avail. in microform from UMI; back issues avail.) **Indexed:** Chem.Abstr., Compumath, Comput.Rev., Curr.Cont., Cyb.Abstr., Ind.Sci.Rev., INIS Atomind., INSPEC (1969-), Math.R., Phys.Ber., Risk Abstr., Sci.Cit.Ind. **Document type:** academic/scholarly publication.
—BLDSC (3394.150000); CASDDS; Ei; Faxon; Genuine Article; SWETS; UnCover. CCC.
Refereed Serial

530   GW   ISSN 0179-2792
COMPUTER THEORETIKUM UND PRAKTIKUM FUER PHYSIKER. 1985. irreg., no.5, 1990. DM.18. Fachinformationszentrum Karlsruhe, Gesellschaft fuer Wissenschaftlich-Technische Information mbH, 76344 Eggenstein-Leopoldshafen, Germany.
TEL 07247-808333. FAX 07247-808135. TELEX 724710-FIZKA. **Document type:** monographic series.

001.6 621.38   US   ISSN 0894-1866
QC52   CODEN: CPHYE2
COMPUTERS IN PHYSICS. 1987. 6/yr. $275 (foreign $295) (effective 1996). American Institute of Physics, One Physics Ellipse, College Park, MD 20740-3843. TEL 301-209-3000. (Subscr. to: 500 Sunnyside Blvd., Woodbury, NY 11797. TEL 516-576-2270) Ed. Lewis H. Holmes. adv.; B&W page $1075, color page $1825. charts; illus.; stat.; tr.lit. (also avail. in microfilm from AIP; back issues avail.) **Indexed:** Comput.Abstr., INIS Atomind., INSPEC (1987-), Oper.Res.Manage.Sci., Qual.Contr.Appl.Stat. **Document type:** academic/scholarly publication.
—BLDSC (3394.931350); Ei; Faxon; SWETS; UnCover. CCC.
Description: News, features, and archival articles on computers in science, teaching and research.
Refereed Serial

530   US   ISSN 0021-9991
QC20   CODEN: JCTPAH
JOURNAL OF COMPUTATIONAL PHYSICS. 1966. 14/yr. $1698 (foreign $2023) (effective 1996). Academic Press, Inc., Journal Division, 525 B St., Ste. 1900, San Diego, CA 92101-4495. TEL 619-230-1840. FAX 619-699-6800. (Subscr. to: Box 620000, Orlando, FL 32891-8340. TEL 800-543-9534) Ed. Philip L. Rowe. adv.; abstr.; charts; illus.; index. (back issues avail.) **Indexed:** Appl.Mech.Rev., BMT, Chem.Abstr., Compumath, Curr.Cont., Excerp.Med., GeoRef., Ind.Sci.Rev., INIS Atomind., INSPEC, Int.Aerosp.Abstr., Math.R., Phys.Ber., Sci.Cit.Ind., W.R.C.Inf. **Document type:** academic/scholarly publication.
—BLDSC (4963.500000); CASDDS; Ei; Faxon; Genuine Article; SWETS; UnCover. CCC.
Description: Covers the computational aspects of physical problems.
Refereed Serial

530   US   ISSN 0172-5726
SPRINGER SERIES IN COMPUTATIONAL PHYSICS. 1977. irreg. price varies. Springer-Verlag, 175 Fifth Ave., New York, NY 10010. TEL 212-460-1500. FAX 212-473-6272. (Also: Berlin, Heidelberg, Tokyo and Vienna) Ed. H. Cabannes. (reprint service avail. from ISI) **Indexed:** INSPEC, Math.R. **Document type:** monographic series.

530.285   SW   ISSN 0284-172X
SWEDISH INSTITUTE OF SPACE PHYSICS. SOFTWARE REPORT. (Text in English) 1977. irreg. price varies (free to qualified institutions, libraries and personnel). Swedish Institute of Space Physics, Box 812, S-98128 Kiruna, Sweden.
TEL 46-980-79000. FAX 46-980-79050. TELEX 8754-IRF-S. (back issues avail.) **Document type:** academic/scholarly publication.
Formerly: Kiruna Geophysical Institute. Software Report (ISSN 0349-2664)
Description: Monographs on computer software.

WINDOWS ON ACOUSTICS. see *PHYSICS — Sound*

PHYSICS — Electricity

ADVANCES IN ELECTROMAGNETIC FIELDS IN LIVING SYSTEMS. see *BIOLOGY — Bioengineering*

537 530   US   ISSN 1054-4887
QC759.6   CODEN: JCSOED
APPLIED COMPUTATIONAL ELECTROMAGNETICS SOCIETY JOURNAL. Abbreviated title: A C E S Journal. 1986. 3/yr. $65 to individuals (foreign $68); institutions $115. Applied Computational Electromagnetics Society, Inc., c/o Prof. Richard W. Adler, Naval Postgraduate School, Code EC-AB, 833 Dyer Rd., Rm. 437, Monterey, CA 93943. TEL 408-646-1111. FAX 408-649-0300. Ed. Duncan Baker. adv.; index, cum.index: 1986-1991. circ. 600. (back issues avail.; reprint service avail.) **Indexed:** Eng.Ind., INSPEC (1990-).
—BLDSC (1571.936900); Ei.
Description: Methods of computer analysis of electromagnetic problems.
Refereed Serial

537 530   US   ISSN 1056-9170
APPLIED COMPUTATIONAL ELECTROMAGNETICS SOCIETY NEWSLETTER. Abbreviated title: A C E S Newsletter. 1986. 3/yr. $65 to individuals (foreign $68); institutions $115. Applied Computational Electromagnetics Society, Inc., c/o Prof. Richard W. Adler, Naval Postgraduate School, Code EC-AB, 833 Dyer Rd., Rm. 437, Monterey, CA 93943. TEL 408-646-1111. FAX 408-649-0300. Ed. Ray Perez. adv. circ. 600. (back issues avail.; reprint service avail.) **Indexed:** Eng.Ind., INSPEC.
—BLDSC (6106.338950).
Refereed Serial

L'ARTISAN ELECTRICIEN ELECTRONICIEN. see *ELECTRONICS*

BEIKOKU TOKKYO SHOROKU. DENKI HEN/U.S. PATENT ABSTRACTS. ELECTRICITY. see *PATENTS, TRADEMARKS AND COPYRIGHTS — Abstracting, Bibliographies, Statistics*

CHUGOKU CHIHO DENRYOKU KISHO GAIHO/CHUGOKU DISTRICT. REPORT OF THE POWER AND WEATHER. see *METEOROLOGY*

537   JA
DENKI NO KAGAKKAN NENPO/ELECTRIC SCIENCE MUSEUM. ANNUAL REPORT. (Text in Japanese) a. Chubu Denryoku K.K., Denki no Kagakukan - Chubu Electric Power Co., Inc., Electric Science Museum, 2-5, Sakae 2-chome, Naka-ku, Nagoya-shi, Aichiken 460, Japan. **Document type:** corporate report.

DENRYOKU TO KISHO/POWER AND WEATHER COORDINATING COMMITTEE. ANNUAL REPORT. see *METEOROLOGY*

537   GW   ISSN 0938-6440
E M V - E S D. 1990. 4/yr. V P Verlagsgesellschaft mbH, Plapphalde 5, 71083 Herrenberg, Germany. TEL 07032-6061. FAX 07032-26940. adv.; B&W page DM.5170, color page DM.7120; trim 182 x 262. circ. 15,100. **Document type:** academic/scholarly publication.
Description: Covers all aspects of electromagnetic compatability and the effects of electrostatic discharge.

537   US   ISSN 1042-7481
KF2125.A15
ELECTRICITY YEARBOOK. 1989. a. Executive Enterprises, Inc., 22 W. 21st St., New York, NY 10010-6904.

ELSEVIER STUDIES IN APPLIED ELECTROMAGNETICS IN MATERIALS. see *ENGINEERING — Electrical Engineering*

537   US   ISSN 1043-3716
EXTRAORDINARY SCIENCE. q. $30 membership (includes monthly bulletin). International Tesla Society, Inc, Box 5636, Colorado Springs, CO 80931-5636. TEL 719-475-0918. FAX 719-475-0582. **Document type:** academic/scholarly publication.
Description: Examines the work of Nikola Tesla and his contributions to high-energy physics.

537   JA   ISSN 0911-8713
HODEN KENKYU/JAPAN RESEARCH GROUP OF ELECTRICAL DISCHARGES. JOURNAL. (Text in Japanese) 1958. irreg. Hoden Kenkyu Gurupu - Japan Research Group of Electrical Discharges, Seikei Daigaku Kogakubu, Denki Denshi Kogakka, 3-1, Kitamachi 3-chome, Kichijoji, Musashino-shi, Tokyo 180, Japan.

537   US
INTERNATIONAL TESLA SOCIETY. BULLETIN. m. $30 membership (also includes Extraordinary Science). International Tesla Society, Inc., Box 5636, Colorado Springs, CO 80931. TEL 719-475-0918. FAX 719-475-0582. Ed. Steven R. Elswick.
Description: Keeps members up to date on news of the society, news of chapters, and events or items of interest.

537   UK
KEY NOTE REPORT: DRY BATTERIES. Variant title: Dry Batteries. irreg. £185. Key Note Publications Ltd., Field House, 72 Oldfield Rd., Hampton, Middlesex TW12 2HQ, England. TEL 0181-783-0755. FAX 0181-783-1720. **Document type:** trade publication.
●Also available online.
Also available on CD-ROM.

KOATSU TORONKAI KOEN YOSHISHU/HIGH PRESSURE CONFERENCE OF JAPAN. PROGRAMME AND ABSTRACTS OF PAPERS. see *ENGINEERING*

KOATSURYOKU NO KAGAKU TO GIJUTSU/REVIEW OF HIGH PRESSURE SCIENCE AND TECHNOLOGY. see *ENGINEERING*

KOMPASS PROFESSIONNEL. ELECTRICITE, ELECTRONIQUE, INFORMATIQUE. see *BUSINESS AND ECONOMICS — Trade And Industrial Directories*

537   JA
KYOYUDENTAI OYO KAIGI KOEN YOKOSHU/ABSTRACTS OF THE MEETING ON FERROELECTRIC MATERIALS AND THEIR APPLICATIONS. (Text in Japanese) 1977. a. Kyoyudentai Oyo Kaigi Un'ei Iinkai - Organizing Committee of the Meeting on Ferroelectric Materials and Their Applications, Kyoto Daigaku Kogakubu, Denshi Kogaku Kyoshitsu, Yoshida Honmachi, Sakyo-ku, Kyoto-shi, Kyoto 606, Japan. **Document type:** abstracting/indexing.

537   JA   ISSN 0386-0884
N G K REBYU/N G K REVIEW. (Text in Japanese; summaries in English) 1976. a. Nippon Gaishi K.K. - N G K Insulators, Ltd., 2-56, Suda-cho, Mizuho-ku, Nagoya-shi, Aichi-ken 467, Japan.
Formed by the merger of (1975-1976): N G K Denki Nyusu (ISSN 0386-0876); (1969-1976): Gaishi Rebyu (ISSN 0386-0868); Which was formerly (1952-1963): Nichigai Rebyu (ISSN 0549-155X)

537   JA   ISSN 0386-5843
N G K REVIEW. OVERSEAS EDITION. (Text in English) 1977. a. Nippon Gaishi K.K. - N G K Insulators, Ltd., 2-56, Suda-cho, Mizuho-ku, Nagoya-shi, Aichi-ken 467, Japan.

NIHON KOATSURYOKU GAKKAI GAKUJUTSU KOENKAI KOEN YOSHI/JAPAN SOCIETY OF HIGH PRESSURE SCIENCE AND TECHNOLOGY. TEXT OF SYMPOSIUM. see *ENGINEERING*

NIHON TAIKI DENKI GAKKAI KAIHO/SOCIETY OF ATMOSPHERIC ELECTRICITY OF JAPAN. JOURNAL. see *METEOROLOGY*

POLITECHNIKA WARSZAWSKA. PRACE NAUKOWE. ELEKTRYKA. see *ENGINEERING — Electrical Engineering*

RADIO SCIENCE. see *EARTH SCIENCES — Geophysics*

RESEARCH LETTERS ON ATMOSPHERIC ELECTRICITY. see *METEOROLOGY*

537   SZ   ISSN 0924-4247
TK7881.2   CODEN: SAAPEB
SENSORS AND ACTUATORS: A PHYSICAL; an international journal devoted to research and development of physical and chemical transducers. (Text in English) 1981. 18/yr. 2070 SFr.($1697) (effective 1996). Elsevier Science S.A., P.O. Box 564, CH-1001 Lausanne 1, Switzerland. TEL 41-21-3207381. FAX 41-21-3235444. TELEX 450620-ELSA-CH. (Subscr. in U.S. and Canada to: Elsevier Science Inc., Box 882, Madison Sq. Sta., New York, NY 10159. TEL 212-989-5800. FAX 212-633-3990) Ed. S. Middelhoek. (also avail. in microform from UMI) **Indexed:** ASCA, CAD CAM Abstr., Chem.Abstr., Cyb.Abstr., Energy Ind., Energy Info.Abstr., Fluidex, INSPEC, Int.Aerosp.Abstr., Robomat., Telegen. **Document type:** academic/scholarly publication.
—BLDSC (8241.785200); CASDDS; Ei; Faxon; Genuine Article; SWETS; UnCover. **CCC.**
Supersedes in part (in 1990): Sensors and Actuators (ISSN 0250-6874)
Description: Covers all aspects of research and development of solid-state devices for transducing physical signals.
Refereed Serial

537 530   GW   ISSN 0931-7260
CODEN: SSEPEL
SPRINGER SERIES IN ELECTRONICS AND PHOTONICS. 1977. irreg. price varies. Springer-Verlag, Heidelberger Platz 3, 14197 Berlin, Germany. TEL 030-8207-1. FAX 030-8214091. Ed. Walter Engl. (reprint service avail. from ISI) **Indexed:** Chem.Abstr., INSPEC. **Document type:** monographic series.
—BLDSC (8424.759000); CASDDS.
Formerly (until 1986): Springer Series in Electrophysics (ISSN 0172-5734)

537 621.3   JA   ISSN 0387-4990
TOKYO DAIGAKU CHOKOATSU DENSHI KENBIKYOSHITSU NENPO/UNIVERSITY OF TOKYO. ANNUAL REPORT OF HIGH VOLTAGE ELECTRON MICROSCOPE. (Text in English, Japanese) 1976. a. Tokyo Daigaku, Kogakubu Sogo Shikenjo Chokoatsu Denshi Kenbikyoshitsu - University of Tokyo, Engineering Research Institute, High Voltage Electron Microscopy Laboratory, 11-16, Yayoi 2-chome, Bunkyo-ku, Tokyo 113, Japan.

PHYSICS — Heat

536   US
A I A A - A S M E THERMOPHYSICS AND HEAT TRANSFER CONFERENCE. PROCEEDINGS. irreg., 4th, 1986, Boston. $40 to non-members; members $20. American Institute of Aeronautics and Astronautics, Inc., 370 L'Enfant Promenade S.W., Washington, DC 20024. TEL 202-646-7400. **Document type:** proceedings.

621.59 536.56   US   ISSN 0065-2482
TP490   CODEN: ACYEAC
ADVANCES IN CRYOGENIC ENGINEERING. Represents: Cryogenic Engineering Conference Proceedings. Even-numbered vols. represent: International Cryogenic Materials Conferences. 1960. irreg., vol.40, 1995. price varies. Plenum Publishing Corp., 233 Spring St., New York, NY 10013-1578. TEL 212-620-8000. FAX 212-463-0742. TELEX 23-421139. Ed.Bd. **Indexed:** Chem.Abstr., Energy Info.Abstr., INIS Atomind., INSPEC. **Document type:** proceedings.
—BLDSC (0704.200000); CASDDS; Ei; Faxon; SWETS. **CCC.**
Refereed Serial

536.2   US   ISSN 0065-2717
QC320.A1   CODEN: AHTRAR
ADVANCES IN HEAT TRANSFER. (Supplements avail.) 1964. irreg., vol.23, 1993. Academic Press, Inc., 525 B St., Ste. 1900, San Diego, CA 92101-4495. TEL 619-231-0926. FAX 619-699-6715. (Subscr. to: Order Dept., 6277 Sea Harbor Dr., 4th Fl., Orlando, Fl 32887. TEL 800-321-5068) Eds. James P. Hartnett, Thomas F. Irvine, Jr. index. (reprint service avail. from ISI) **Indexed:** Appl.Mech.Rev., Deep Sea Res.& Oceanogr.Abstr., GeoRef., INIS Atomind., INSPEC.
—BLDSC (0709.010000); CASDDS; Faxon; SWETS; UnCover. **CCC.**
Refereed Serial

536   UK   ISSN 1359-4311
TJ260   CODEN: HRSCEQ
APPLIED THERMAL ENGINEERING. 1980. m. £490($780) (effective 1996). Elsevier Science Ltd., Pergamon, P.O. Box 800, Kidlington, Oxford OX5 1DX, England. TEL 44-1865-843000. FAX 44-1865-843010.
E-mail: nlinfo-f@elsevier.nl; usinfo-f@elsevier.com; forinfo-kyf04035@niftyserve.or.jp; Site addr.: http://www.elsevier.nl/. (Subscr. in U.S. and Canada to: Elsevier Science, 660 White Plains Rd., Tarrytown, NY 10591-5153. TEL 914-524-9200. FAX 914-333-2444) Ed. David Reay. (also avail. in microfilm from UMI; reprint service avail. from UMI) **Indexed:** Appl.Mech.Rev., Br.Tech.Ind., Chem.Abstr., Chem.Eng.Abstr., Energy Ind., Energy Info.Abstr., Environ.Abstr., Fluidex, Foul.Prev.Res.Dig., INIS Atomind., INSPEC (1988-), Met.Abstr., T.C.E.A., World Alum.Abstr. **Document type:** academic/scholarly publication.
—BLDSC (4276.090700); CASDDS; Ei; Faxon; Genuine Article; SWETS; UnCover. **CCC.**
Former titles (until vol.16): Heat Recovery Systems & C H P (Combined Heat & Power) (ISSN 0890-4332); (until 1983?): Journal of Heat Recovery Systems (ISSN 0198-7593)
Description: Reports developments and research in energy recovery from prime movers, overall system performance, and applications, including district heating, system viability, and economics.
Refereed Serial

536 541.3   PL
CODEN: ATERD5
ARCHIVES OF THERMODYNAMICS. (Text in English; summaries in Polish, Russian) 1980. q. $52. (Polska Akademia Nauk, Komitet Termodynamiki i Spalania) Wydawnictwo Naukowe P W N - Polish Scientific Publishers P W N Ltd., Ul. Miodowa 10, 00-251 Warsaw, Poland. TEL 48-22-260207. FAX 48-22-267163. (Dist. by: Ars Polona, Krakowskie Przedmiescie 7, 00-068 Warsaw, Poland) Ed. Wieslaw Gogol.
—CASDDS.
Formerly (until 1991): Archiwum Termodynamiki (ISSN 0208-418X)
Description: Includes papers on thermodynamics, heat and mass transfer.

BOLLETTINO TERMOMECCANICA. see *ENGINEERING — Mechanical Engineering*

536   UK   ISSN 0963-1623
CAMBRIDGE STUDIES IN LOW-TEMPERATURE PHYSICS. 1989. irreg. Cambridge University Press, Edinburgh Bldg., Shaftesbury Rd., Cambridge CB2 2RU, England. TEL 01223-312393. FAX 01223-315052. TELEX 817256. (N. American addr.: Cambridge University Press, 40 W. 20th St., New York, Ny 10011. TEL 212-924-3900. FAX 212-691-3239) **Document type:** monographic series.
—BLDSC (3015.994400).

621.59   US
COLD FACTS. 1985. q. $50 (foreign $65). Cryogenic Society of America, c/o Huget Advertising, Inc., 1033 South Blvd., Ste. 13, Oak Park, IL 60302. TEL 708-383-6220. FAX 708-383-9337. Ed. Laurie Huget. adv. contact: Mike Samec. bk.rev.; circ. 350 (paid); 2,000 (controlled). (back issues avail.)
Description: For those interested in all applications of low-temperatures (cryogenics).

COMITE INTERNATIONAL DES POIDS ET MESURES. COMITE CONSULTATIF DE THERMOMETRIE. RAPPORTS ET ANNEXES. see *METROLOGY AND STANDARDIZATION*

536.7   GW   ISSN 0935-1175
CODEN: CMETEJ
CONTINUUM MECHANICS AND THERMODYNAMICS; models and analysis of complex materials. (Text in English) 4/yr. DM.628($456) (effective 1996). Springer-Verlag, Heidelberger Platz 3, 14197 Berlin, Germany. TEL 030-8207-0. FAX 030-8214091. E-mail: orders@springer.de. (N. American subscr. to: Springer-Verlag New York, Inc., 44 Hartz Way, Secaucus, NJ 07096-2491. TEL 201-348-4033. FAX 201-348-4505) (also avail. in microform from UMI) **Indexed:** Curr.Cont., INIS Atomind., INSPEC (1989-), Math.R., Zent.Math. **Document type:** academic/scholarly publication.
—BLDSC (3425.730000); CASDDS; Faxon; Genuine Article; SWETS; UMI; UnCover. **CCC.**
Description: Provides information on observed phenomena and presents models that are based on principles of mechanics, thermodynamics and statistical thermodynamics.

CRYOGAS INTERNATIONAL; the source of timely and relevant information for the industrial gas and cryogenics industries. see *ENGINEERING — Mechanical Engineering*

536.56   UK   ISSN 0011-2275
TP480   CODEN: CRYOAX
CRYOGENICS; the international journal of low temperature engineering & research. 1960. m. £675($1074) (effective 1996). Butterworth-Heinemann, Part of the Reed Elsevier group, Linacre House, Jordan Hill, Oxford OX2 8DP, England. TEL 0865-310366. FAX 0865-310898. TELEX 83111 BHPOXF G. (Subscr. to: Elsevier Science Ltd., P.O. Box 800, Kidlington, Oxford OX5 1DX, England. TEL 44-865-843000. FAX 44-865-843010; Subscr. in U.S. and Canada to: Elsevier Science, 660 White Plains Rd., Tarrytown, NY 10591-5153. TEL 914-524-9200. FAX 914-333-2444) Ed.Bd. adv.; bk.rev.; abstr.; bibl.; illus.; index. (also avail. in microform from UMI; back issues avail.) **Indexed:** A.S.& T.Ind., Appl.Mech.Rev., Biol.Abstr., Br.Tech.Ind., Chem.Abstr., Chem.Eng.Abstr., Curr.Cont., Eng.Ind., Fuel & Energy Abstr., Gas Abstr., Ind.Sci.Rev., INIS Atomind., INSPEC, Met.Abstr., Phys.Ber., Sci.Cit.Ind., T.C.E.A., World Alum.Abstr. **Document type:** academic/scholarly publication.
—BLDSC (3490.150000); CASDDS; Ei; Faxon; Genuine Article; SWETS; UMI; UnCover. **CCC.**
Description: Provides international coverage of cryoengineering, cryoplastics and low-temperature engineering and research.
Refereed Serial

536.56 621.59   SZ
CRYOPHYSICS NEWSLETTER. 1967. s-a. 80 SFr. Cryophysics S.A., 39 rue Rothschild, CH-1202 Geneva, Switzerland. TEL 022-7329520. FAX 022-7385246. TELEX 412450-CRYO-CH. Ed. K.A. Geiger. adv. contact: A. Monier. circ. 7,000. **Document type:** newsletter.

536.56   CC   ISSN 1000-3258
CODEN: DWXUES
DIWEN WULI XUEBAO. (Text in Chinese; summaries in English) 1978. bi-m. $88.20. (Zhongguo Kexue Jishu Daxue - University of Science and Technology of China) Science Press, Marketing and Sales Department, 16 Donghuangchenggen North St., Beijing 100717, People's Republic of China. TEL 4010642. FAX 4019810. Ed. Yao Xixian. adv. circ. 6,000. **Indexed:** Chem.Abstr., INSPEC. **Document type:** academic/scholarly publication.
—BLDSC (3180.368000); CASDDS.
Formerly: Acta Physica Temperaturae Humilis Sinica: Cryophysics (ISSN 0253-3634)
Description: Publishes research papers in physics from China and the world. Topics include low-temperature physics and technology, and superconductors.
Refereed Serial

PHYSICS — HEAT

536   US   ISSN 0891-6152
TJ260   CODEN: EXHTEV
EXPERIMENTAL HEAT TRANSFER; an international journal. q. £135($222) (effective 1996). Taylor & Francis Inc., 1900 Frost Rd., Ste. 101, Bristol, PA 19007-1598. TEL 215-785-5800; 800-821-8312. FAX 215-785-5515. (Subscr. in Europe to: Taylor & Francis Ltd., Rankine Rd., Basingstoke, Hants. RG24 8PR, England. TEL 44-1256-840366. FAX 44-1256-479438) Ed.Bd. (also avail. in microform from UMI; back issues avail.; reprint service avail. from UMI) **Indexed:** Energy Info.Abstr., INSPEC (1990-). **Document type:** academic/scholarly publication.
—BLDSC (3839.350000); CASDDS; Ei; Faxon; SWETS; UnCover. **CCC.**
    Description: Presents research on measurement techniques and the results of experimental studies in heat and mass transfer and related fluid flows.
    Refereed Serial

536.56   KR   ISSN 0132-6414
QC278   CODEN: FNTEDK
FIZIKA NIZKIKH TEMPERATUR/LOW TEMPERATURE PHYSICS; vsesoiuznyi nauchnyi zhurnal. English translation: Low Temperature Physics (US ISSN 1063-777X) (Text in Russian; summaries in English) 1975. m. $260 (effective 1996). (Akademiya Nauk Ukrainy, Otdelenie Fiziki i Astronomii) Vidavnitstvo Naukova Dumka, Vul. Tereshchenkivska 3, 252601 Kiev, Ukrainie. TEL 32-10-17. Ed. B.I. Verkin. illus. **Indexed:** Cadscan, Chem.Abstr., Curr.Cont., Ind.Sci.Rev., INIS Atomind., INSPEC, Lead Abstr., Phys.Ber., Sci.Cit.Ind., Zincscan. **Document type:** academic/scholarly publication.
—BLDSC (0389.833000); CASDDS; Ei; Genuine Article. **CCC.**

536.7   CC   ISSN 0253-231X
QC310.15   CODEN: KCJPDF
GONGCHENG RE-WULI XUEBAO. English translation: Chinese Journal of Engineering Thermophysics (US ISSN 1043-8033) (Text in Chinese) 1980. q. $8 per no. (Chinese Society of Engineering Thermophysics - Zhongguo Gongcheng Re-Wuli Xuehui) Science Press, Marketing and Sales Department, 16 Donghuangchenggen North St., Beijing 100717, People's Republic of China. TEL 4010642. FAX 4012180. TELEX 210247-SPBJ-CN. (US office: Science Press New York, 63-117 Alderton St., Rego Park, NY 11374. TEL 718-459-4638) adv. circ. 6,000. **Indexed:** Chem.Abstr., Fluidex.
—BLDSC (4979.240000); CASDDS
    Description: Publishes original papers on engineering thermodynamics, aerothermodynamics of heat engines, heat and mass transfer, combustion, thermophysical properties of matter, and techniques related to thermophysical property measurement and experimentation.
    Refereed Serial

536.4 532   GW   ISSN 0947-7411
TJ260
HEAT AND MASS TRANSFER. (Text in English or German) 1968. 6/yr. DM.1138($827) (effective 1996). Springer-Verlag, Heidelberger Platz 3, 14197 Berlin, Germany. TEL 030-2807-0. FAX 030-8214091. E-mail: orders@springer.de. (Subscr. in N. America to: Springer-Verlag New York, Inc., 44 Hartz Way, Secaucus, NJ 07096-2491. TEL 201-348-4033. FAX 201-348-4505) Ed.Bd. adv.; bibl.; charts; illus. (also avail. in microform from UMI; back issues avail.; reprint service avail. from ISI) **Indexed:** Chem.Abstr., Eng.Ind., INSPEC (1968-), Petrol.Abstr., T.C.E.A. **Document type:** academic/scholarly publication.
—BLDSC (9261.837000); CASDDS; Ei; Genuine Article; UMI; UnCover. **CCC.**
    Formerly: Waerme- und Stoffuebertragung (ISSN 0042-9929)
    Description: Experimental and theoretical research on the problems of heat and mass transfer.

HEAT TRANSFER - JAPANESE RESEARCH. see
ENGINEERING — Mechanical Engineering

HEAT TRANSFER RESEARCH. see *ENGINEERING — Mechanical Engineering*

536   US   ISSN 1057-9737
TN672
HEAT TREATMENT YEARBOOK. a. $325. A S M International, Materials Information, Materials Park, OH 44073. TEL 216-338-5151. FAX 216-338-4634. TELEX 980-619. (UK addr.: Institute of Materials, Materials Information, 1 Carlton House Terr., London SW1Y 5DB, England. TEL 071-839-4071) **Document type:** abstracting/indexing, bibliography.

536.57   RU   ISSN 0018-151X
QC276   CODEN: HITEA4
HIGH TEMPERATURE. English translation of: Teplofizika Vysokikh Temperatur (RU ISSN 0040-3644) 1963. bi-m. $1345 (foreign $1575) (effective 1996). (Russian Academy of Sciences) Interperiodica, Staromonetnyi Per., 22, Moscow 109180, Russia. TEL 7-095-231-2164. FAX 7-095-233-5590. (Dist. by: Plenum Publishing Corp., 233 Spring St., New York, NY 10013-1578. TEL 212-620-8468. FAX 212-463-0742) (Co-publisher: Maik Nauka) Ed. V.M. Batenin. (also avail. in microfilm from JSC; back issues avail.) **Indexed:** Appl.Mech.Rev., Chem.Eng.Abstr., Chem.Titles, Curr.Cont., Energy Res.Abstr., Eng.Ind., INIS Atomind., INSPEC (1968-), Sci.Res.Abstr., Solid St.Abstr., T.C.E.A. **Document type:** academic/scholarly publication.
—BLDSC (0412.087000); CASDDS; Faxon; Genuine Article; SWETS; UMI; UnCover. **CCC.**
    Formerly: High Temperature Physics.
    Refereed Serial

536 620 540   UK   ISSN 0018-1544
QC276   CODEN: HTHPAK
HIGH TEMPERATURES - HIGH PRESSURES. (Text in English, French, German) 1969. bi-m. £420 (effective 1996). Pion Ltd., 207 Brondesbury Park, London NW2 5JN, England. TEL 0181-459-0069. FAX 0181-451-6454. E-mail: dales@pion.demon.co.uk. Ed. R. Taylor. bk.rev.; index. **Indexed:** Chem.Abstr., Eng.Ind., INIS Atomind., INSPEC, Met.Abstr., Mineral.Abstr., Phys.Ber., World Alum.Abstr. **Document type:** academic/scholarly publication, proceedings.
—BLDSC (4307.369500); CASDDS; Ei; Faxon; SWETS; UnCover.
    Description: Devoted primarily to experimental and theoretical study matter under extreme thermal and mechanical conditions. Includes proceedings of European Conference on Thermophysical Properties.
    Refereed Serial

536.56   JA   ISSN 0073-2931
QC1   CODEN: CLTSBD
HOKKAIDO UNIVERSITY. INSTITUTE OF LOW TEMPERATURE SCIENCE. CONTRIBUTIONS. SERIES A. PHYSICAL SCIENCE. (Text in English) 1954. irreg. exchange basis. Hokkaido University, Institute of Low Temperature Science, North 19, West 8, Kita-ku, Sapporo 060, Japan. FAX 011-706-7142. TELEX 932261 ILTSHU J. **Indexed:** INSPEC (1971-). **Document type:** academic/scholarly publication.
—BLDSC (3447.001000).
    Supersedes in part (in 1960): Contributions from the Institute of Low Temperature Science (ISSN 0376-1924)

I E E E SEMICONDUCTOR THERMAL AND TEMPERATURE MEASUREMENT SYMPOSIUM. PROCEEDINGS. see
ENGINEERING — Electrical Engineering

536   II   ISSN 0379-0479
    CODEN: IJCRDD
INDIAN JOURNAL OF CRYOGENICS; an international quarterly journal of basic and applied low temperatures. 1976. q. $50. Indian Cryogenics Council, Jadavpur University, P.B. No. 17005, Calcutta 700 032, India. (Co-sponsor: Advanced Centre of Cryogenic Research Calcutta) Ed. A. Bose. adv.: page $150. bk.rev.; abstr.; bibl. circ. 300. (back issues avail.) **Indexed:** Chem.Abstr., INSPEC, Met.Abstr., Phys.Ber., Sci.Cit.Ind., World Alum.Abstr.
—CASDDS.
    Formerly: National Symposia on Cryogenics. Proceedings.
    Description: Reviews, research papers, short communications on cryogenics and allied subjects.

536.56   US   ISSN 0538-7051
INTERNATIONAL CRYOGENICS MONOGRAPH SERIES. 1964. irreg., latest 1994. price varies. Plenum Publishing Corp., 233 Spring St., New York, NY 10013-1578. TEL 212-620-8000. FAX 212-463-0742. TELEX 23-421139. Eds. K. Timmerhaus, A.F. Clark. **Document type:** monographic series.
    Refereed Serial

536 621   US   ISSN 0142-727X
TJ260   CODEN: IJHFD2
INTERNATIONAL JOURNAL OF HEAT AND FLUID FLOW. 1971; N.S. 1979. bi-m. $570 to institutions (effective 1996). Butterworth - Heinemann, Part of the Reed Elsevier group, 313 Washington St., Newton, MA 02158. TEL 617-928-2500; 800-366-2665. FAX 617-928-2610. TELEX 880052. (Subscr. to: Elsevier Science Inc., Box 882, Madison Sq. Sta., New York, NY 10159-0882. TEL 212-989-5800. FAX 212-633-3990) Ed.Bd. adv.; bk.rev.; abstr.; bibl.; charts; illus.; stat.; index. (also avail. in microform from UMI; back issues avail.) **Indexed:** Appl.Mech.Rev., Chem.Abstr., Chem.Eng.Abstr., Curr.Cont, Fluidex, Foul.Prev.Res.Dig., INSPEC (1973-), Int.Build.Serv.Abstr., ISMEC, Phys.Ber., T.C.E.A. **Document type:** academic/scholarly publication.
—BLDSC (4542.279000); CASDDS; Ei; Faxon; Genuine Article; SWETS; UMI; UnCover. **CCC.**
    Formerly (until 1979): Heat and Fluid Flow (ISSN 0046-7138)
    Description: Experimental aspects of engineering thermodynamics, heat transfer and fluid dynamics relevant to industrial applications. Includes energy use and conversion.
    Refereed Serial

536 669   US   ISSN 1061-3862
TA401   CODEN: ISHSE3
INTERNATIONAL JOURNAL OF SELF-PROPAGATING HIGH-TEMPERATURE SYNTHESIS. 1992. q. $365 (effective 1996). Allerton Press, Inc., 150 Fifth Ave., New York, NY 10011. TEL 212-924-3950. FAX 212-463-9684. Ed. Alexander G. Merzhanov. **Indexed:** INSPEC (1992-). **Document type:** academic/scholarly publication.
—BLDSC (4542.544650); CASDDS. **CCC.**
    Description: For materials scientists, physical and chemical engineers and metallurgists. Covers the new technology of "SHS," the unique process for the production of advanced materials based on solid-state combustion utilizing internally generated chemical energy.

536   US   ISSN 0195-928X
QC192   CODEN: IJTHDY
INTERNATIONAL JOURNAL OF THERMOPHYSICS. 1980. bi-m. $645 (foreign $755) (effective 1996). Plenum Publishing Corp., 233 Spring St., New York, NY 10013-1578. TEL 212-620-8000. FAX 212-463-0742. TELEX 23-421139. Ed. Ared Cezairliyan. adv. (also avail. in microfilm from JSC; back issues avail.) **Indexed:** Br.Ceram.Abstr., Chem.Abstr., Curr.Cont., Eng.Ind., INIS Atomind., INSPEC, Met.Abstr., Phys.Ber., World Alum.Abstr. **Document type:** academic/scholarly publication.
—BLDSC (4542.695200); CASDDS; Ei; Faxon; Genuine Article; SWETS; UMI; UnCover. **CCC.**
    Refereed Serial

536   RU   ISSN 0202-8247
ITOGI NAUKI I TEKHNIKI: TEPLO- I MASSOOBMEN. irreg., vol.9, 1989. price varies. Vsesoyuznyi Institut Nauchno-Tekhnicheskoi Informatsii (VINITI), Ul. Usievicha 20-A, 125219 Moscow A-219, Russia. (Subscr. to: Mezhdunarodnaya Kniga, Moscow 121200, Russia)
—BLDSC (0178.600000).

JOURNAL OF ENERGY, HEAT AND MASS TRANSFER. see
ENERGY

JOURNAL OF FLOW VISUALIZATION AND IMAGE PROCESSING. see *ENGINEERING — Mechanical Engineering*

PHYSICS — HEAT

536.56 US ISSN 0022-2291
QC278 CODEN: JLTPAC
JOURNAL OF LOW TEMPERATURE PHYSICS. 1969. 24/yr. $1075 (foreign $1260) (effective 1996). Plenum Publishing Corp., 233 Spring St., New York, NY 10013-1578. TEL 212-620-8000. FAX 212-463-0742. TELEX 23-421139. Eds. Horst Meyer, Frank Pobell. adv. (also avail. in microfilm from JSC; back issues avail.) **Indexed:** Appl.Mech.Rev., Bull.Thermodyn.& Thermochem., Cadscan, Chem.Abstr., Curr.Cont., Eng.Ind., Ind.Sci.Rev., INIS Atomind., INSPEC, Lead Abstr., Met.Abstr., Nucl.Sci.Abstr., Phys.Ber., Sci.Cit.Ind, World Alum.Abstr., Zincscan. **Document type:** academic/scholarly publication.
—BLDSC (5010.570000); CASDDS; Ei; Faxon; Genuine Article; SWETS; UMI; UnCover. **CCC.**
   Description: Covers developments in the science of cryogenics.
   Refereed Serial

536.7 US
TK2970
JOURNAL OF MAGNETOHYDRODYNAMICS AND PLASMA RESEARCH; an international journal. 1988. q. $365 (effective 1996). Nova Science Publishers, Inc., 6080 Jericho Tpke., Ste. 207, Commack, NY 11725-2808. TEL 516-499-3103. FAX 516-499-3146. E-mail: novasci1@aol.com. (also avail. in microform from UMI; back issues avail.; reprint service avail. from UMI) **Indexed:** INIS Atomind. **Document type:** academic/scholarly publication.
—CASDDS. **CCC.**
   Formerly: Magnetohydrodynamics (ISSN 0891-9801)
   Description: Covers MHD applications and related technologies.
   Refereed Serial

536 GW ISSN 0340-0204
QC318.I7 CODEN: JNETDY
JOURNAL OF NON-EQUILIBRIUM THERMODYNAMICS. (Text in English) 1976. 4/yr. DM.765. Walter de Gruyter und Co., Genthiner Str. 13, 10785 Berlin, Germany. TEL 030-26005-0. FAX 030-26005251. TELEX 184027. (U.S. addr.: Walter de Gruyter, Inc., 200 Saw Mill River Rd., Hawthorne, NY 10532. TEL 914-747-0110) **Indexed:** Appl.Mech.Rev., Chem.Abstr., Curr.Cont., Ind.Sci.Rev., INIS Atomind., INSPEC, Phys.Ber. **Document type:** academic/scholarly publication.
—BLDSC (5022.837000); CASDDS; Ei; Faxon; Genuine Article; SWETS; UnCover. **CCC.**

536.7 CC ISSN 1003-2169
CODEN: JTSCES
JOURNAL OF THERMAL SCIENCE/REKEXUE XUEBAO; international journal of thermal and fluid sciences. (Text in English) 1992. q. $120 to individuals (foreign $140); institutions $195 (foreign $215). (Chinese Academy of Sciences, Institute of Engineering Thermophysics) Science Press, Marketing and Sales Department, 16 Donghuangchenggen North St., Beijing 100717, People's Republic of China. TEL 4010642. FAX 4019810. (Overseas dist by: Science Press New York, Ltd., 84-04 58th Ave, Elmhurst, NY 11373. TEL 718-476-0238) **Document type:** academic/scholarly publication.
—CASDDS.
   Description: Publishes original papers on experimental, numerical and theoretical investigations in the major areas of thermal and fluid sciences.
   Refereed Serial

536 US ISSN 1059-9630
TS653 CODEN: JTTEE5
JOURNAL OF THERMAL SPRAY TECHNOLOGY. 1992. q. $261. A S M International, Materials Information, Materials Park, OH 44073-0002. TEL 216-338-5151. FAX 216-338-4634. TELEX 98-0619 ASMINT. Ed. Christopher C. Berndt. adv.; bk.rev.; abstr.; bibl.; charts; illus.; pat.; stat.; tr.lit.; index. (also avail. in microfilm; microfiche; Braille; record; video cassette) **Indexed:** Chem.Abstr., Curr.Cont., Eng.Ind., Eng.Mat.Abstr., World Alum.Abstr. **Document type:** academic/scholarly publication.
—BLDSC (5069.098700); CASDDS; Ei; Genuine Article; SWETS; UMI. **CCC.**
   Description: Covers the latest research, product, equipment and process developments in thermal spray technology; applications; problem-solving; literature; patents; technical case studies.
   Refereed Serial

536 JA ISSN 0387-1096
CODEN: KGAKDH
KOON GAKKAISHI/HIGH TEMPERATURE SOCIETY. JOURNAL. (Text in Japanese; summaries in English) 1975. bi-m. Kook Gakkai - High Temperature Society, Osaka Daigaku, Yosetsu Kogaku Kenkyujo, 11-1 Mihogaoka, Ibaraki-shi, Osaka 567, Japan. **Indexed:** Chem.Abstr., INIS Atomind., Jap.Per.Ind.
—BLDSC (4758.095000); CASDDS.

536.56 US ISSN 1063-777X
QC278 CODEN: LTPHEG
LOW TEMPERATURE PHYSICS. English translation of: Fizika Nizkikh Temperatur (KR ISSN 0132-6414) 1975. m. $1980 (foreign $2010) (effective 1996). (Verkin Physicotechnical Trust of Low Temperature Physics (Kharkov), KR) American Institute of Physics, One Physics Ellipse, College Park, MD 20740-3843. TEL 301-209-3000. (Subscr. to: AIP Member and Subscriber Services, 500 Sunnyside Blvd., Woodbury, NY 11797-2999. TEL 516-576-2270) Ed. R.T. Beyer. adv.; bibl.; charts; illus.; index. (also avail. in microform from AIP; back issues avail.) **Indexed:** C.P.I., Gen.Phys.Adv.Abstr., INSPEC (1975-), Phys.Ber. **Document type:** academic/scholarly publication.
—BLDSC (0415.598000); Faxon; SWETS; UnCover. **CCC.**
   Formerly: Soviet Journal of Low Temperature Physics (ISSN 0360-0335)
   Description: Publishes results of experimental and theoretical studies at low - meinly liquid nelium - temperatures.

536.56 JA ISSN 0385-3683
QC277.9
LOW TEMPERATURE SCIENCE. SERIES A. DATA REPORT. (Text in Japanese; abstracts in English) 1969. a. exchange basis. Hokkaido University, Institute of Lower Temperature Science, North 19, West 8, Kita-ku, Sapporo 060, Japan. FAX 011-716-5698. TELEX 932261 ILTSHU J.
—BLDSC (3535.345000).

536.56 JA ISSN 0439-3538
QC277.9 CODEN: TEKAAH
LOW TEMPERATURE SCIENCE. SERIES A. PHYSICAL SCIENCE. (Until vol.10, 1956, Series A and B issued in one vol.) (Text in Japanese; summaries in English) 1952. a. exchange basis. Hokkaido University, Institute of Low Temperature Science, North 19, West 8, Kita-ku, Sapporo 060, Japan. FAX 011-706-7142. TELEX 932261 ILTSHU J. Ed. Eizi Akitaya. circ. 600. **Indexed:** Deep Sea Res.& Oceanogr.Abstr., INSPEC, JTA, Meteor.& Geoastrophys.Abstr. **Document type:** academic/scholarly publication.
—BLDSC (5297.000000).

536 JA ISSN 0913-946X
CODEN: NEBUE4
NETSU BUSSEI/JAPAN JOURNAL OF THERMOPHYSICAL PROPERTIES. (Text in Japanese; summaries in English, Japanese) 1987. q. 1000 Yen per no. Nihon Netsu Bussei Gakkai - Japan Society of Thermophysical Properties, Dept. of Mechanical Engineering, Nagaoka University of Technology, 1603-1 Kamitomioka-cho, Nagaoka-shi, Niigata-ken 940, Japan. TEL 81-258-46-6000. FAX 81-258-46-6972.
—BLDSC (4648.332000); CASDDS.
   Refereed Serial

536 JA ISSN 0386-2615
QD79.T38 CODEN: NESOD2
NETSU SOKUTEI/CALORIMETRY AND THERMAL ANALYSIS. (Text in English, Japanese) 1974. q. Nihon Netsu Sokutei Gakkai - Japan Society of Calorimetry and Thermal Analysis, Cosmos Hongo Bldg., 8F, 4-1-4 Hongo, Bunkyo-ku, Tokyo 113, Japan. **Indexed:** Chem.Abstr., INIS Atomind., INSPEC (1985-).
—CASDDS.

NETSU SOKUTEI TORONKAI KOEN YOSHISHU/ABSTRACTS OF JAPANESE CALORIMETRY CONFERENCE. see *PHYSICS — Abstracting, Bibliographies, Statistics*

536 JA
NETSU SOKUTEI WAKUSHOPPU/CALORIMETRY AND THERMAL ANALYSIS WORKSHOP. (Text in English, Japanese; summaries in English) irreg. Nihon Netsu Sokutei Gakkai - Japan Society of Calorimetry and Thermal Analysis, Cosmos Hongo Bldg., 8F, 4-1-4 Hongo, Bunkyo-ku, Tokyo 113, Japan.

536 624 JA ISSN 1340-3354
NIHON NETSU RYUTAI KOGAKKAI RONBUNSHU/JAPAN SOCIETY OF HEAT AND FLUID ENGINEERING. TRANSACTIONS. (Text in English, Japanese; summaries in English) 1986. a. Nihon Netsu Ryutai Kogakkai - Japan Society of Heat and Fluid Engineering, Nihon Daigaku Seisan Sogakubu Suri Kogakka, 2-1, Izumicho 1-chome, Narashino-shi, Chiba-ken 273, Japan.

536 535 600 JA ISSN 0916-7900
CODEN: NSGKET
NIHON SEKIGAISEN GAKKAISHI/JAPAN SOCIETY OF INFRARED SCIENCE AND TECHNOLOGY. JOURNAL. (Text in Japanese) 1976. a. 5000 Yen. Nihon Sekigaisen Gakkai, Nihon Gakkai Jimu Senta, 16-9, Honkomagome 5-chome, Bunkyo-ku, Tokyo 113, Japan. TEL 03-5814-5801. FAX 03-5814-5820. Ed. Y. Itakura. adv. contact: Y Tsunawaki. circ. 1,000. **Indexed:** INIS Atomind., INSPEC (1991-).
—BLDSC (4807.520000); CASDDS.
   Formerly (until 1991): Sekigaisen Gijutsu - Infrared Society of Japan. Proceedings (ISSN 0386-8044)
   Description: Contains original papers and reviews on infrared science and technology.
   Refereed Serial

536 JA ISSN 0387-4419
OSAKA DAIGAKU TEION SENTA DAYORI/OSAKA UNIVERSITY. LOW TEMPERATURE CENTER. NEWS. (Text in Japanese) 1973. q. Osaka Daigaku, Teion Senta, 2-1, Yamadaoka, Suita-shi, Osaka 565, Japan. TEL 81-6-879-7985. FAX 81-6-879-7986. E-mail: momose@ele.eng.osaka-u.ac.jp. Ed. Kazuo Murase. **Document type:** newsletter.

PETROCHEMICAL EQUIPMENT. see *ENGINEERING — Chemical Engineering*

PHYSICA B - PHYSICS OF CONDENSED MATTER. see *PHYSICS*

536.56 NE ISSN 0079-6417
QC277.9 CODEN: PLTPAA
PROGRESS IN LOW TEMPERATURE PHYSICS. 1955. irreg., vol.13, 1991. price varies. Elsevier Science B.V., Books Division, P.O. Box 211, 1000 AE Amsterdam, Netherlands. TEL 31-20-4853911. FAX 31-20-4853705. TELEX 18582 ESPA NL. E-mail: nlinfo-f@elsevier.nl; usinfo-f@elsevier.com; forinfo-kyf04035@niftyserve.or.jp; Site addr.: http://www.elsevier.nl/. (Subscr. in U.S. and Canada to: Elsevier Science Inc., Box 882, Madison Sq. Sta., New York, NY 10159. TEL 212-989-5800) Ed. D.F. Brewer. **Indexed:** INSPEC. **Document type:** monographic series.
—BLDSC (6868.700000); CASDDS. **CCC.**
   Description: Discusses various aspects of cryogenics.
   Refereed Serial

REVUE INTERNATIONALE DES HAUTES TEMPERATURES ET DES REFRACTAIRES. see *CHEMISTRY — Physical Chemistry*

536.7 US ISSN 0869-8643
▼**RUSSIAN JOURNAL OF THERMOPHYSICS & AEROMECHANICS**. English translation of: Teplofizika i Aeromekhanika (RU ISSN 0869-8635) 1995. q. $270 (effective 1996). (Rossiiskaya Akademiya Nauk, Sibirskoe Otdelenie, Institut Teplofiziki, RU) Begell House Inc., 79 Madison Ave., New York, NY 10016-7892. TEL 212-725-1999. FAX 212-213-8368. E-mail: 74353.2052@compuserve.com. Ed.Bd. **Document type:** academic/scholarly publication.
   Description: Publishes articles of both theoretical and applied nature, studies on numerical and theoretical simulation, experimental data, and new engineering principles.

536 JA ISSN 0916-6971
CODEN: SNSSEVe
SHIN NETSU SOKUTEI NO SHINPO/PROGRESS IN CALORIMETRY AND THERMAL ANALYSIS. NEW SERIES. (Text in English, Japanese; summaries in English) 1990. a. 8000 Yen. (Nihon Netsu Sokutei Gakkai - Society of Calorimetry and Thermal Analysis, Japan) Riaraizusha - Realize, Inc., 16-13, Yushima 2-chome, Bunkyo-ku, Tokyo 113, Japan.
—BLDSC (8256.754000); CASDDS.

STUDIES OF HIGH TEMPERATURE SUPERCONDUCTORS. see *CHEMISTRY — Electrochemistry*

PHYSICS — MECHANICS

536.56 621.59   JA   ISSN 0389-2441
CODEN: CRYEB4
TEION KOGAKU/CRYOGENIC ENGINEERING. (Text in Japanese; summaries in English) 1966. bi-m. Teion Kogakkai - Cryogenic Society of Japan, Teion Kogaku Kyokai, 12-8-302, Hongo 6-chome, Bunkyo-ku, Tokyo 113, Japan. **Indexed:** Chem.Abstr., INIS Atomind.
—CASDDS.

536.56 621.59   JA   ISSN 0919-5998
TEION KOGAKU CHODENDO GAKKAI KOEN GAIYOSHU/MEETING ON CRYOGENICS AND SUPERCONDUCTIVITY. (Text in English, Japanese) s-a. Teion Kogakkai - Cryogenic Society of Japan, Teion Kogaku Kyokai, 12-8-302, Hongo 6-chome, Bunkyo-ku, Tokyo 113, Japan.
Formerly (until 1991): Teion Kogaku Chodendo Gakkai Yokoshu.

536   LV   ISSN 0320-6475
TEPLOPROVODNOST' I DIFFUZIYA. 1969. irreg. Politehniskais Instituts, Riga, Kalku 1, Riga 226355, Latvia. illus.

THERMODYNAMICS AT TEXAS A & M. see
CHEMISTRY — Physical Chemistry

536   JA   ISSN 0911-1743
THERMOPHYSICAL PROPERTIES/NIHON NETSU BUSSEI SHINPOJUMU KOEN RONBUNSHU. (Text in English, Japanese; summaries in English) 1980. a. 4000 Yen. Nihon Netsu Bussei Gakkai - Japan Society of Thermophysical Properties, Nagaoka Gijutsu Kagaku Daigaku, Kikaikei, 1603 Kamitomioka-cho, Nagaoka-shi, Niigata-ken 940-21, Japan. TEL 81-258-46-6000. FAX 81-258-46-6972. Ed. Tsutomu Yamamura.
—BLDSC (8814.889000).
Refereed Serial

536.56   JA
TOKYO DAIGAKU TEOIN SENTA DAYORI/UNIVERSITY OF TOKYO. CRYOGENIC CENTER. REPORT. (Text in Japanese) 1966. 2/yr. free. Tokyo Daigaku, Teion Senta - University of Tokyo, Cryogenic Center, 11-16, Yayoi 2-chome, Bunkyo-ku, Tokyo 113, Japan. TEL 03-3812-2111. FAX 03-3815-8389. Ed. Seiich Kagoshima. circ. 500 (controlled). **Document type:** academic/scholarly publication.
Refereed Serial

TRATAMIENTOS TERMICOS. see METALLURGY

532 536   KR   ISSN 0320-8702
TP480   CODEN: VGTSDJ
VOPROSY GIDRODINAMIKI I TEPLOOBMENA V KRIOGENNYKH SISTEMAKH. 1970. irreg. (Akademiya Nauk Ukrainy, Fiziko-Tekhnicheskii Institut Nizkikh Temperatur) Vidavnitstvo Naukova Dumka, Vul. Tereshchenkivska 3, 252601 Kiev, Ukraine. TEL 044-224-4068. FAX 044-224-7060. illus.

PHYSICS — Mechanics

A I A A - A S M E THERMOPHYSICS AND HEAT TRANSFER CONFERENCE. PROCEEDINGS. (American Institute of Aeronautics and Astronautics, Inc.) see
PHYSICS — Heat

ACTA MECHANICA. see ENGINEERING — Mechanical Engineering

ACTA MECHANICA. SUPPLEMENTUM. see
ENGINEERING — Mechanical Engineering

531   CC   ISSN 0567-7718
QA801   CODEN: AMSNEF
ACTA MECHANICA SINICA. Chinese edition: Lixue Xuebao (ISSN 0459-1879) (Text in English) 1985. q. $365. (Chinese Society of Theoretical and Applied Mechanics) Science Press, Marketing and Sales Department, 16 Donghuangchenggen North St., Beijing 100717, People's Republic of China. TEL 4010642. FAX 4012180. TELEX 210247-SPBJ-CN. (US office: Science Press New York, Ltd., 84-04 58th Ave., Elmhurst, NY 11373. TEL 718-476-0238; Exclusively dist. outside P.R. China by: Allerton Press, Inc., 150 Fifth Ave., New York, NY 10011. TEL 212-924-3950. FAX 212-463-9684) (Co-publisher: Allerton Press, Inc.) Ed. Hwang Kehchih. adv. circ. 6,000. **Indexed:** INSPEC (1992-).
—BLDSC (0632.600000). **CCC.**
Description: Covers all branches of mechanics. Includes research treatises, experimental technology and methods, brief accounts of research work, studies on the history of mechanics, and academic discussions.
Refereed Serial

ACTA TECHNICA C S A V. see ENGINEERING

530 620.1   US   ISSN 0065-2156
TA350   CODEN: AAMCAY
ADVANCES IN APPLIED MECHANICS. (Supplements avail.: Rarefied Gas Dynamics) 1948. irreg., vol.30, 1993. Academic Press, Inc., 525 B St., Ste. 1900, San Diego, CA 92101-4495. TEL 619-231-0926. FAX 619-699-6715. (Subscr. to: Order Dept., 6277 Sea Harbor Dr., 4th Fl., Orlando, FL 32887. TEL 800-321-5068) Eds. Theodore Wie, John Hutchinson. index. (reprint service avail. from ISI) **Indexed:** Appl.Mech.Rev., Deep Sea Res.& Oceanogr.Abstr., Ind.Sci.Rev., INSPEC, Math.R., Sci.Cit.Ind.
—BLDSC (0699.000000); Ei; Faxon; SWETS. **CCC.**
Refereed Serial

531   US   ISSN 0272-0434
TA418.7   CODEN: AMPSDE
ADVANCES IN THE MECHANICS AND PHYSICS OF SURFACES SERIES. 1981. irreg., vol.3, 1986. price varies. Harwood Academic Publishers, c/o International Publishers Distributor, 820 Town Center Dr., Langhorne, PA 19047. TEL 215-750-2642. FAX 215-750-6343. (Subscr.to: International Publishers Distributor, P.O. Box 90, Reading, Berkshire RG1 8JL, England. TEL 44-173-456-8316) Eds. R.M. Latanision, T.E. Fischer. (also avail. in microform) **Indexed:** INSPEC. **Document type:** monographic series.
—CASDDS.
Refereed Serial

532   US   ISSN 0066-4189
QC145   CODEN: ARVFA3
ANNUAL REVIEW OF FLUID MECHANICS. 1969. a. $47 (foreign $52) (effective Jan. 1995). Annual Reviews Inc., 4139 El Camino Way, Box 10139, Palo Alto, CA 94303-0139. TEL 415-493-4400; 800-523-8635. FAX 415-855-9815. E-mail: annrevu@class.org. Eds. Milton Van Dyke, John L. Lumley. bibl.; charts; illus.; index, cum.index. (also avail. in microfilm from UMI; back issues avail.; reprint service avail.) **Indexed:** Appl.Mech.Rev., Biol.Abstr., Chem.Abstr., Curr.Adv.Ecol.Sci., Curr.Cont., Deep Sea Res.& Oceanogr.Abstr., Fluidex, GeoRef., Ind.Sci.Rev., INSPEC, Int.Aerosp.Abstr., M.M.R.I., Nucl.Sci.Abstr., Ocean.Abstr., Phys.Ber., Sci.Cit.Ind., Sel.Water Res.Abstr., T.C.E.A. **Document type:** academic/scholarly publication.
—BLDSC (1522.540000); Ei; Faxon; Genuine Article; SWETS; UMI; UnCover. **CCC.**
Description: Original critical reviews on the significant primary literature and current developments in fluid mechanics.

APPLIED MATHEMATICS AND MECHANICS; an international series of monographs. see
MATHEMATICS

APPLIED MATHEMATICS AND MECHANICS. see
MATHEMATICS

621 531   PL   ISSN 0373-2029
TA350   CODEN: AVMHBR
ARCHIVES OF MECHANICS. (Text in English) 1974? bi-m. $168. (Polska Akademia Nauk, Instytut Podstawowych Problemow Techniki) Wydawnictwo Naukowe P W N, Miodowa 10, 00-251 Warsaw, Poland. TEL 48-22-312738. FAX 48-22-267163. TELEX 813763 PWN PL. Ed. M. Sokolowski. abstr.; bibl.; charts; illus. circ. 790. **Indexed:** Appl.Mech.Rev., Chem.Abstr., Chem.Eng.Abstr., Curr.Cont., Excerp.Med., Geotech.Abstr., Ind.Sci.Rev., INSPEC (1973-), ISMEC, Math.R., Phys.Ber., Ref.Zh., Sci.Cit.Ind., T.C.E.A.
—BLDSC (1637.470000); CASDDS; Ei; SWETS; UnCover.
Formerly: Archiwum Mechaniki Stosowanej (ISSN 0004-0800)

BAUPHYSIK. see BUILDING AND CONSTRUCTION

531   BU   ISSN 0204-7594
BIOMEKHANIKA/BIOMECHANICS. (Text in Bulgarian and Russian; summaries in English and Russian) 1974. irreg. 2 Iv. per no. (Bulgarska Akademiia na Naukite, Tsentralna Laboratoriia po Biomekhanika) Publishing House of the Bulgarian Academy of Sciences, Acad. G. Bonchev St., Bldg. 6, 1113 Sofia, Bulgaria. (Dist. by: Hemus, 6, Rouski Blvd., 1000 Sofia, Bulgaria) Ed. G. Brankov. bibl.; illus. circ. 470. (reprint service avail. from IRC) **Indexed:** Biol.Abstr., BSL Math.
—BLDSC (0017.985000).

532   UK   ISSN 0045-3145
CODEN: BBRHAO
BRITISH SOCIETY OF RHEOLOGY. BULLETIN. 1940. q. £20 (free to members). British Society of Rheology, c/o Mrs. C.A. Moules, 27 Alexander Rd., Stotfold, Hitchin, Herts. SG5 4NA, England. Ed. P.F.G. Banfill. adv. circ. 600. (tabloid format) **Indexed:** INSPEC, Rheol.Abstr. **Document type:** bulletin.
—BLDSC (2426.000000).
Description: Contains reports on conferences and other Society activities, review articles on rheological topics, information on future meetings and general notes and news.

531 510   UK   ISSN 0960-2933
CAMBRIDGE MONOGRAPHS ON MECHANICS AND APPLIED MATHEMATICS. irreg. price varies. Cambridge University Press, Edinburgh Bldg., Shaftesbury Rd., Cambridge CB2 2RU, England. TEL 01223-312393. FAX 01223-315052. TELEX 851817256. (N. American addr.: Cambridge University Press, Journals Dept., 40 W. 20th St., New York, NY 10011. TEL 212-924-3900. FAX 212-691-3239) Ed.Bd. **Indexed:** Math.R. **Document type:** monographic series.

533   RU   ISSN 0302-6086
QA930   CODEN: CMRGA7
CHISLENNYE METODY V DINAMIKE RAZREZHENNYKH GAZOV. 1973. irreg. 0.73 Rub. (Akademiya Nauk S.S.S.R., Laboratoriya Teorii Protsessov Perenosa) Izdatel'stvo Nauka, 90 Profsoyuznaya ul., 117864 Moscow, Russia. TEL 234-05-84. illus. **Indexed:** Chem.Abstr.
—CASDDS.

CLOSED LOOP; the magazine of testing and simulation technology. see ENGINEERING — Engineering Mechanics And Materials

CONTINUUM MECHANICS AND THERMODYNAMICS; models and analysis of complex materials. see
PHYSICS — Heat

531   PL
CODEN: CZTEAY
CZASOPISMO TECHNICZNE. SERIA M: MECHANIKA. (Contents page in 4 languages) 1877. irreg. 4 Zl. Politechnika Krakowska, Ul. Warszawska 24, 31-155 Krakow, Poland. TEL 48-12-374289. FAX 48-12-335773. TELEX 322468 PK PL. bk.rev.; charts; illus.; index. circ. 12,000. **Document type:** academic/scholarly publication.
—CASDDS.
Supersedes in part: Czasopismo Techniczne (ISSN 0011-4561); Which was formerly (until 1883): Dzwignia (ISSN 1230-2791).

D C A M M REPORT. (Danish Center for Applied Mathematics and Mechanics) see MATHEMATICS

PHYSICS — MECHANICS

531 621   KR   ISSN 0419-1544
              CODEN: DNPRAE
DINAMIKA I PROCHNOST' MASHIN. 1965. irreg.
Kharkivskyi Politekhnichnyi Instytut, Ul. Frunze, 21,
Kharkov 310002, Ukraine.
—BLDSC (0053.250000).

531 621   KR   ISSN 0419-8719
              CODEN: DVSGBJ
DVIGATELI VNUTRENNEGO SGORANIYA. 1965. irreg.
Kharkivskyi Politekhnichnyi Instytut, Ul. Frunze, 21,
Kharkov 310002, Ukraine.
—CASDDS.

531   NE
DYNAMICAL PROPERTIES OF SOLIDS. 1974. irreg.,
vol.6, 1990. price varies. Elsevier Science B.V.,
Books Division, P.O. Box 211, 1000 AE Amsterdam,
Netherlands. TEL 31-20-4853911.
FAX 31-20-4853705. TELEX 18582 ESPA NL.
E-mail: nlinfo-f@elsevier.nl; usinfo-f@elsevier.com;
forinfo-kyf04035@niftyserve.or.jp; Site addr.:
http://www.elsevier.nl/. (Subscr. in U.S. and Canada
to: Elsevier Science Inc., Box 882, Madison Sq. Sta.,
New York, NY 10159. TEL 212-989-5800) (back
issues avail.)
Refereed Serial

533   SZ   ISSN 0084-5744
**EIDGENOESSISCHE TECHNISCHE HOCHSCHULE
ZUERICH. MITTEILUNGEN. AERODYNAMIK.** (Text in
English, French and German) no.9, 1949. irreg.,
no.32, 1963. price varies. E T H Zurich, Ramistr.
101, 8092 Zurich, Switzerland.

531 621   KR   ISSN 0424-9844
              CODEN: ENMABS
ENERGETICHESKOE MASHINOSTROENIE. 1966. irreg.
Kharkivskyi Politekhnichnyi Instytut, Ul. Frunze, 21,
Kharkov 310002, Ukraine.
—BLDSC (0399.365000); CASDDS.

EUROPEAN JOURNAL OF MECHANICAL ENGINEERING.
see *ENGINEERING — Mechanical Engineering*

531   FR   ISSN 0997-7538
QA801   CODEN: EJASEV
EUROPEAN JOURNAL OF MECHANICS A - SOLIDS. (Text
in English) 1977. 6/yr. 2030 F. (A and B combined
3300 F.). Gauthier-Villars, 15 rue Gossin, 92543
Montrouge Cedex, France. TEL 33-1-40-92-65-00.
FAX 33-1-40-92-65-97. TELEX 634 916 F.
(Subscr. to: Centrale des Revues, 11 rue Gossin,
92543 Montrouge Cedex, France. TEL
33-1-46-56-52-66) Ed. J. Lemaitre. adv. circ.
1,600. (also avail. in microform from UMI; reprint
service avail. from UMI) **Indexed:** Appl.Mech.Rev.,
Curr.Cont., Excerp.Med., Ind.Sci.Rev., INIS Atomind.,
INSPEC, Int.Aerosp.Abstr., Math.R., Sci.Cit.Ind., Sh.&
Vib.Dig. **Document type:** academic/scholarly
publication.
—BLDSC (3829.731300); CASDDS; Ei; Faxon;
Genuine Article; SWETS; UnCover. **CCC.**
 Supersedes in part: Journal de Mecanique
Theorique et Appliquee (ISSN 0750-7240); Which
was formed by the merger of: Journal de Mecanique
(ISSN 0021-7832); Journal de Mecanique Appliquee
(ISSN 0399-0842)

531   FR   ISSN 0997-7546
QA901   CODEN: EJBFEV
EUROPEAN JOURNAL OF MECHANICS B - FLUIDS. 1977.
6/yr. 1820 F. (A and B combined 3300 F.).
Gauthier-Villars, 15 rue Gossin, 92543 Montrouge
Cedex, France. TEL 33-1-40-92-65-00.
FAX 33-1-40-92-65-97. TELEX 634 916 F.
(Subscr. to: Centrale des Revues, 11 rue Gossin,
92543 Montrouge Cedex, France. TEL
33-1-46-56-52-66) Eds. H.H. Fernholz, G. Iooss.
adv. circ. 1,600. **Indexed:** Appl.Mech.Rev., Curr.Cont.,
INSPEC, Math.R. **Document type:** academic/scholarly
publication.
—BLDSC (3829.731310); CASDDS; Ei; Faxon;
Genuine Article; SWETS; UnCover. **CCC.**
 Supersedes in part: Journal de Mecanique
Theorique et Appliquee (ISSN 0750-7240); Which
was formed by the merger of: Journal de Mecanique
(ISSN 0021-7832) & Journal de Mecanique
Appliquee (ISSN 0399-0842)

532   US
F P S MEMBERSHIP DIRECTORY AND ANNUAL REPORT.
1991. a. $100 to non-members. Fluid Power
Society, 2433 N. Mayfair Rd., Ste. 111, Milwaukee,
WI 53226. TEL 414-257-0910.
FAX 414-257-4092. adv. contact: Juli Kwakenat.
circ. 3,000 (controlled). **Document type:** directory.
 Description: Provides a list of members and their
certifications, information on the society and its
activities, rosters of Chapters and members, lists of
board and committee members, and annual financial
information.

531   RU   ISSN 0130-5611
FIZICHESKAYA MEKHANIKA. 1974. irreg. vol.3, 1978.
1.80 Rub. per no. Sankt-Peterburgskii Universitet,
Universitetskaya Nab. 7-9, St. Petersburg V-164,
Russia. abstr.; bibl.; charts. circ. 2,000. **Indexed:**
Chem.Abstr.
—BLDSC (0390.780000).

**FIZIKO-KHIMICHESKA MEKHANIKA/PHYSICO-CHEMICAL
MECHANICS.** see *CHEMISTRY — Physical Chemistry*

532   US
FLUID CONTROLS INSTITUTE. NEWS & VIEWS. 1965. q.
Fluid Controls Institute, 1300 Sumner Ave.,
Cleveland, OH 44115. TEL 216-241-7333. circ.
450. **Document type:** newsletter.

532 620   US   ISSN 0015-4628
TA357   CODEN: FLDYAH
FLUID DYNAMICS. English translation of: Rossiiskaya
Akademiya Nauk. Izvestiya. Mekhanika Zhidkosti i
Gaza. 1966. bi-m. $1375 (foreign $1610)
(effective 1996). (Russian Academy of Sciences,
RU) Plenum Publishing Corp., Consultants Bureau,
233 Spring St., New York, NY 10013-1578.
TEL 212-620-8468. FAX 212-463-0742. TELEX
23-421139. Ed. G.G. Chernyi. bk.rev. (also avail. in
microfilm from JSC; back issues avail.) **Indexed:**
Appl.Mech.Rev., Chem.Eng.Abstr., Energy Res.Abstr.,
Eng.Ind., INIS Atomind., INSPEC, ISMEC, Math.R.,
Phys.Ber., T.C.E.A., Zent.Math. **Document type:**
academic/scholarly publication.
—BLDSC (0411.753000); Ei; Faxon; SWETS; UMI;
UnCover. **CCC.**
 Description: Focuses on rheology.
Refereed Serial

532   PL   ISSN 0137-6462
QA911
FLUID DYNAMICS TRANSACTIONS. (Text in English)
irreg., vol.14, 1989. price varies. (Polska Akademia
Nauk, Instytut Podstawowych Problemow Techniki)
Wydawnictwo Naukowe P W N, Miodowa 10,
00-251 Warsaw, Poland. TEL 48-22-312738.
FAX 48-22-267163. TELEX 813763 PWN PL.
Ed.Bd. circ. 250.
—BLDSC (3961.670000).

531 620.1   NE   ISSN 0926-5112
FLUID MECHANICS AND ITS APPLICATIONS. (Text in
English) 1990. irreg., vol.19, 1993. price varies.
Kluwer Academic Publishers, Postbus 17, 3300 AA
Dordrecht, Netherlands. TEL 31-78-392392.
FAX 31-78-392254. (Dist. by: Kluwer Academic
Publishers Group, P.O. Box 322, 3300 AH
Dordrecht, Netherlands. TEL 31-78-392392. FAX
31-78-546474; N. America dist. addr.: Box 358,
Accord Sta., Hingham, MA 02018-0358. TEL
617-871-6600. FAX 617-871-6528) **Document
type:** monographic series.
—BLDSC (3962.039000).
Refereed Serial

532   US   ISSN 0260-4353
              CODEN: FMAGDQ
**FLUID MECHANICS OF ASTROPHYSICS AND
GEOPHYSICS.** 1981. irreg., vol.6, 1989. Gordon &
Breach Science Publishers, c/o International
Publishers Distributor, 820 Town Center Dr.,
Langhorne, PA 19047. TEL 215-750-2642.
FAX 215-750-6343. (Subscr. to: International
Publishers Distributor, P.O. Box 90, Reading,
Berkshire RG1 8JL, England. TEL
44-173-456-8316) Ed. P. Roberts. **Indexed:**
INSPEC. **Document type:** monographic series.
—BLDSC (3962.040000); CASDDS.
Refereed Serial

**FLUID POWER CERTIFICATION BOARD. CERTIFICATION
DIRECTORY;** accredited fluid power educational
institutions and instructors and certified fluid power
mechanics, technicians, specialists and engineers.
see *BUSINESS AND ECONOMICS — Trade And
Industrial Directories*

FONDATION LOUIS DE BROGLIE. ANNALES. see *PHYSICS*

G A M M MITTEILUNGEN. (Gesellschaft fuer
Angewandte Mathematik und Mechanik) see
MATHEMATICS

531 621   KR   ISSN 0130-1152
GIDRAVLICHESKIE MASHINY. 1967. irreg. Kharkivskyi
Politekhnichnyi Instytut, Ul. Frunze, 21, Kharkov
310002, Ukraine.
—BLDSC (0048.320000).

531   KR   ISSN 0367-4088
              CODEN: GDMKBA
GIDROMEKHANIKA; respublikanskii mezhvedomstvennyi
sbornik nauchnykh trudov. (Text in Russian) 1965.
s-a. (Akademiya Nauk Ukrainy, Institut
Gidrodinamiki) Vidavnitstvo Naukova Dumka, Vul.
Tereshchenkivska 3, 252601 Kiev, Ukraine.
TEL 044-224-4068. FAX 044-224-7060. (Dist. by:
Mezhdunarodnaya Kniga, B. Yakimanka 39,
117049 Moscow, Russia) Ed. A.J. Oleynik. **Indexed:**
INSPEC, Math.R.
—BLDSC (0048.750000); CASDDS. **CCC.**

531   CC   ISSN 0254-7805
GUTI LIXUE XUEBAO. (Editions in Chinese, English) q.
Zhongguo Lixue Xuehui - China Mechanics Society,
Huazhong Ligong Daxue, Yujiashan, Wuchang-qu,
Wuhan, Hubei 430074, People's Republic of China.
TEL 701154. Eds. Luo Zudao, Du Qinghua. **Indexed:**
INSPEC (1980-).
—BLDSC (0632.610000).

531   JA
**HAKAI RIKIGAKU SHINPOJUMU KOEN
RONBUNSHU/SYMPOSIUM ON FRACTURE AND
FRACTURE MECHANICS. PROCEEDINGS.** (Text in
Japanese; summaries in English) irreg. Society of
Materials Science, Japan - Nihon Zairyo Gakkai,
1-101, Yoshida Izumidonocho, Sakyo-ku, Kyoto-shi,
Kyoto 606, Japan. TEL 075-761-5321.
FAX 075-761-5325. **Document type:** proceedings.

HEAT AND MASS TRANSFER. see *PHYSICS — Heat*

531   US   ISSN 0895-7959
QC280   CODEN: HPRSEL
HIGH PRESSURE RESEARCH. 1988. 12/yr. (in 2 vols.,
6 nos./vol.). 121 ECU per vol. (effective 1996).
Gordon & Breach Science Publishers, c/o
International Publishers Distributor, 820 Town
Center Dr., Langhorne, PA 19047.
TEL 215-750-2642. FAX 215-750-6343. (Subscr.
to: International Publishers Distributor, P.O. Box 90,
Reading, Berkshire RG1 8JL, England. TEL
44-173-456-8316) Ed. Marvin Ross. (also avail. in
microform)
—BLDSC (4307.355650); Faxon. **CCC.**
 Description: Dedicated solely to research in high
pressure science and technology. Provides a forum
for experimental and theoretical advances.
Refereed Serial

INDUSTRIAL MATHEMATICS. see *MATHEMATICS*

**INSTITUTUL POLITEHNIC DIN IASI. BULETINUL. SECTIA I:
MATEMATICA, MECANICA, FIZICA.** see *MATHEMATICS*

531   US   ISSN 1071-6769
TA416.5.U6
**INTERNATIONAL DIRECTORY OF TESTING
LABORATORIES.** a. $69 to non-members; members
$62. American Society for Testing & Materials,
1916 Race St., Philadelphia, PA 19103.
TEL 215-299-5400. FAX 215-977-9679. **Document
type:** directory.
—BLDSC (4539.688950). **CCC.**
 Formerly (until 1992): Directory of Testing
Laboratories (ISSN 0895-7886)

PHYSICS — MECHANICS

531   US   ISSN 1061-8562
QA911   CODEN: IJCFEC
INTERNATIONAL JOURNAL OF COMPUTATIONAL FLUID DYNAMICS. 1993. q. 99 ECU (effective 1996). Gordon & Breach Science Publishers, c/o International Publishers Distributor, 820 Town Center Dr., Langhorne, PA 19047. TEL 215-750-2642. FAX 215-750-6343. (Subscr. to: International Publishers Distributor, P.O. Box 90, Reading, Berkshire RG1 8JL, England. TEL 44-173-456-8316) Ed. Wagdi G. Habashi. **Document type:** academic/scholarly publication.
—CCC.
    Description: Publishes advances in the field of fluid dynamics for the aeronautics, astronautics, astrophysics, environmental, hydrodynamics, and power and process fields.

531   620.1   UK   ISSN 0020-7683
TA349   CODEN: IJSOAD
INTERNATIONAL JOURNAL OF SOLIDS AND STRUCTURES. 1965. 30/yr. £2050($3260) (effective 1996). Elsevier Science Ltd., Pergamon, P.O. Box 800, Kidlington, Oxford OX5 1DX, England. TEL 44-1865-843000. FAX 44-1865-843010. E-mail: nlinfo-f@elsevier.nl; usinfo-f@elsevier.com; forinfo-kyf04035@niftyserve.or.jp; Site addr.: http://www.elsevier.nl/. (Subscr. in U.S. and Canada to: Elsevier Science, 660 White Plains Rd., Tarrytown, NY 10591-5153. TEL 914-524-9200. FAX 914-333-2444) Ed. Charles Steele. adv.; charts; illus. circ. 1,400. (also avail. in microform from UMI; reprint service avail. from UMI). **Indexed:** Abstr.J.Earthq.Eng., Appl.Mech.Rev., Chem.Abstr., Curr.Cont., Eng.Ind., Geotech.Abstr., Ind.Sci.Rev., INSPEC, Int.Aerosp.Abstr., Intl.Civil Eng.Abstr., ISMEC, J.of Ferroc., Math.R., Met.Abstr., Phys.Ber., Sci.Cit.Ind., Sh.& Vib.Dig., Soft.Abstr.Eng., World Alum.Abstr. **Document type:** academic/scholarly publication.
—BLDSC (4542.650000); Ei; Faxon; Genuine Article; SWETS; UMI; UnCover. **CCC.**
    Description: Original research on the mechanics of solids and structures as a field of applied science and engineering.
Refereed Serial

681 621.38 535   XR   ISSN 0447-6441
TS500   CODEN: JMKOA5
JEMNA MECHANIKA A OPTIKA/FINE MECHANICS AND OPTICS.* (Text in Czech; summaries in English, German and Russian) 1956. m. $58.30. (Ceska Academie Ved, Fizikalni Ustav) Agentura LINA, Mimonska 632, 190 00 Prague 9, Czech Republic. (Dist. by: Artia, Ve Smeckach 30, 111 27 Prague 1, Czech Republic) (Co-sponsor: International Society for Optical Engineering) Ed. Jaroslav Nevrala. charts; illus. circ. 1,650. **Indexed:** C.I.S. Abstr., INSPEC.
—BLDSC (4663.500000).

JOURNAL OF ACOUSTIC EMISSION. see *PHYSICS — Sound*

JOURNAL OF FLOW VISUALIZATION AND IMAGE PROCESSING. see *ENGINEERING — Mechanical Engineering*

JOURNAL OF FLUID CONTROL; applications and research on fluid control, hydraulics and pneumatics, instrumentation, and fluidics. see *ENGINEERING — Mechanical Engineering*

531   NE   ISSN 0377-0257
QA901   CODEN: JNFMDI
JOURNAL OF NON-NEWTONIAN FLUID MECHANICS. (Text in English) 1976. 18/yr. fl.3060($1866) (effective 1996). Elsevier Science B.V., P.O. Box 211, 1000 AE Amsterdam, Netherlands. TEL 31-20-4853911. FAX 31-20-4853598. TELEX 18582 ESPA NL. E-mail: nlinfo-f@elsevier.nl; usinfo-f@elsevier.com; forinfo-kyf04035@niftyserve.or.jp; Site addr.: http://www.elsevier.nl/. (Subscr. in U.S. and Canada to: Elsevier Science Inc., Box 882, Madison Sq. Sta., New York, NY 10159. TEL 212-989-5800. FAX 212-633-3990) Ed. K. Walters. adv.; bk.rev.; index. (also avail. in microform from UMI; reprint service avail. from SWZ) **Indexed:** Appl.Ecol.Abstr., Appl.Mech.Rev., Chem.Abstr., Chem.Eng.Abstr., Curr.Cont., E&P Hlth. (1993-), Eng.Ind., Eng.Mat.Abstr., Fluidex, Gas Process.& Ppl. (1993-), Ind.Sci.Rev., INSPEC, Off.Tech. (1993-), Petrol.Abstr. (1986-), Phys.Ber., Rheol.Abstr., T.C.E.A. **Document type:** academic/scholarly publication.
—BLDSC (5022.842000); CASDDS; Ei; Faxon; Genuine Article; PADDS; SWETS; UnCover. **CCC.**
    Description: For those working on basic rheological science and applications.
Refereed Serial

532   US   ISSN 0148-6055
QC189   CODEN: JORHD2
JOURNAL OF RHEOLOGY. 1957. bi-m. $375 (Canada & Mexico $435) (effective 1996). (Society of Rheology) American Institute of Physics, One Physics Ellipse, College Park, MD 20740-3843. TEL 301-209-3000. (Subscr. to: AIP Member and Subscriber Service, 500 Sunnyside Blvd., Woodbury, NY 119797-2999. TEL 516-576-2270. FAX 516-349-9704) Ed. Arthur B. Metzner. adv. circ. 1,900. (also avail. in microform from UMI; back issues avail.; reprint service avail. from UMI) **Indexed:** API Abstr., Appl.Mech.Rev., Chem.Abstr., Curr.Cont., Eng.Ind., Ind.Sci.Rev., INIS Atomind., INSPEC (1971-), Intl.Polym.Sci.& Tech., RAPRA, Sci.Cit.Ind. **Document type:** academic/scholarly publication.
—BLDSC (5052.051000); CASDDS; Ei; Faxon; Genuine Article; SWETS; UnCover. **CCC.**
    Formerly: Society of Rheology. Transactions (ISSN 0038-0032)
Refereed Serial

531 620.1   UK   ISSN 0022-5096
TA350   CODEN: JMPSA8
JOURNAL OF THE MECHANICS AND PHYSICS OF SOLIDS. 1952. m. £1075($1710) (effective 1996). Elsevier Science Ltd., Pergamon, P.O. Box 800, Kidlington, Oxford OX5 1DX, England. TEL 44-1865-843000. FAX 44-1865-843010. E-mail: nlinfo-f@elsevier.nl; usinfo-f@elsevier.com; forinfo-kyf04035@niftyserve.or.jp; Site addr.: http://www.elsevier.nl/. (Subscr. in U.S. and Canada to: Elsevier Science, 660 White Plains Rd., Tarrytown, NY 10591-5153. TEL 914-524-9200. FAX 914-333-2444) Eds. B. Freund, J.R. Willis. adv.: B&W page $550, color page $1350. bk.rev.; charts; illus.; index. circ. 1,500. (also avail. in microfilm from UMI; back issues avail.) **Indexed:** Agri.Eng.Abstr., Appl.Mech.Rev., Cadscan, Chem.Abstr., Eng.Ind., Geotech.Abstr., Ind.Sci.Rev., INIS Atomind., INSPEC, ISMEC, Lead Abstr., Math.R., Met.Abstr., Sh.& Vib.Dig., World Alum.Abstr., Zincscan. **Document type:** academic/scholarly publication.
—BLDSC (5016.000000); CASDDS; Ei; Faxon; Genuine Article; SWETS; UMI; UnCover. **CCC.**
    Description: Research, theory and practice on the properties of construction materials, from the fields of mathematics, engineering, materials science, and physics.
Refereed Serial

531   JA
KEISAN RIKIGAKU SHINPOJUMU HOBUNSHU/SYMPOSIUM ON COMPUTATIONAL MECHANICS. (Text in English, Japanese) 1987. a. Union of Japanese Scientists and Engineers - Nihon Kagaku Gijutsu Renmei, 5-10-11, Sendagaya, Shibuya-ku, Tokyo 151, Japan. **Document type:** proceedings.

531   CC   ISSN 0258-1825
QA930
KONGQI DONGLIXUE XUEBAO. (Text in Chinese) q. Y20 (effective 1996). Zhongguo Kongqi Dongli Yanjiu yu Fazhan Zhongxin - China Aerodynamics R & D Center (CARDC), P.O. Box 211, Mianyang, Sichuan 621000, People's Republic of China. TEL 0816-332490. Ed. Zhuang Fenggan. **Document type:** academic/scholarly publication.
Refereed Serial

531   JA   ISSN 0454-4544
KOTAI BUTSURI/SOLID STATE PHYSICS. 1966. m. 2000 Yen per no. Agne Gijutsu Center, Kitamura Bldg., 5-1-25 Minamiaoyama, Minato-ku, Tokyo 107, Japan. **Indexed:** Chem.Abstr., INIS Atomind., INSPEC, JTA.
—BLDSC (8327.410000).

531   JA
KYUSHU UNIVERSITY. TANDEM ACCELERATOR LABORATORY. REPORT. (Text in English) 1980. irreg. Kyushu University, Faculty of Science, Tandem Accelerator Laboratory - Kyushu Daigaku Rigakubu Tandemu Kasoku Jikkenshitsu, 10-1 Hakozaki 6-chome, Higashi-ku, Fukuoka-shi, Fukuoka-ken 812, Japan.

LATIN AMERICAN APPLIED RESEARCH. see *CHEMISTRY*

531   CC   ISSN 1000-0992
LIXUE JINZHAN/ADVANCES IN MECHANICS. (Text in Chinese) 1971. q. $18.92. Zhongguo Kexueyuan, Lixue Yanjiusuo - Chinese Academy of Sciences, Institute of Mechanics, 15 Zhongguancun Lu, Beijing 100080, People's Republic of China. TEL 2554108. FAX 86-1-2561284. TELEX 222554 MEHAS CN. (Dist. outside China by: Guoji Shudian - China International Book Trading Corp., P.O. Box 399, Beijing, P.R.C.. TEL 8413063) Ed. Tan Haosheng.
Refereed Serial

531   CC   ISSN 0459-1879
TA349   CODEN: LHHPAE
LIXUE XUEBAO. English edition: Acta Mechanica Sinica (ISSN 0567-7718) (Text in Chinese; summaries in English) 1957. bi-m. $103.20. (Chinese Society of Theoretical and Applied Mechanics) Science Press, Marketing and Sales Department, 16 Donghuangchenggen North St., Beijing 100717, People's Republic of China. TEL 4010642. FAX 4019810. adv. circ. 11,000. **Indexed:** Chem.Abstr., INSPEC (1978-), Math.R. **Document type:** academic/scholarly publication.
—BLDSC (0632.500000); CASDDS.
    Description: Publishes original theses on mechanics and its branches, including research treatises, experimental technology and methodology, brief accounts of research work, studies on the history of mechanics, and academic discussions.
Refereed Serial

LIXUE YU SHIJIAN/MECHANICS AND PRACTICE. see *ENGINEERING — Mechanical Engineering*

MANUFACTURING REVIEW. see *TECHNOLOGY: COMPREHENSIVE WORKS*

MATHEMATICAL RESEARCH. see *MATHEMATICS*

533   GW   ISSN 0374-1257
TL507
MAX-PLANCK-INSTITUT FUER STROEMUNGSFORSCHUNG. MITTEILUNGEN. 1950. irreg., no.112, 1993. price varies. Max-Planck-Institut fuer Stroemungsforschung, Bunsenstr. 10, 37073 Goettingen, Germany. FAX 0551-7092704. Ed. E.A. Mueller. bk.rev. circ. 300. **Indexed:** Appl.Mech.Rev. **Document type:** monographic series.
—BLDSC (5859.000000).
    Formerly: Mitteilungen aus dem Max-Planck-Institut fuer Stroemungsforschung und der Aerodynamischen Versuchsanstalt (ISSN 0076-5678)

PHYSICS — MECHANICS

531 620.1 NE ISSN 0025-6455
QA801 CODEN: MECCB9
MECCANICA. (Text in English) 1966. bi-m. fl.623 to institutions; $400 to institutions in U.S. (effective 1996). (Associazione Italiana per Meccanica Teoretica ed Applicata, IT - Italian Association for Theoretical and Applied Mechanics) Kluwer Academic Publishers, Postbus 17, 3300 AA Dordrecht, Netherlands. TEL 31-78-392392. FAX 31-78-392254. TELEX 29245 KAPG NL. E-mail: SERVICES@WKAP.NL. (Dist. by: Kluwer Academic Publishers Group, P.O. Box 322, 3300 AH Dordrecht, Netherlands. TEL 31-78-392392. FAX 31-78-546474; N. America dist. addr.: Box 358, Accord Sta., Hingham, MA 02018-0358. TEL 617-871-6600. FAX 617-871-6528) Ed. Giuliano Augusti. adv.; charts; illus.; index. (also avail. in microform from UMI; back issues avail.) **Indexed:** Appl.Mech.Rev., Chem.Abstr., Fluidex, Geo.Abstr., IDA, INIS Atomind., INSPEC (1968-), Int.Aerosp.Abstr., ISMEC, Sh.& Vib.Dig., Zent.Math. **Document type:** academic/scholarly publication.
—BLDSC (5415.770000); Ei; UMI; UnCover. **CCC.**
Refereed Serial

531 IT ISSN 1121-2047
MECCANICA OGGI. m. (11/yr.). L.53900 (foreign L.107800). Gruppo Editoriale Jackson S.p.A., Via M. Gorki 69, 20092 Cinisello B. (MI), Italy. TEL 39-2-66034289. FAX 39-2-66034238. Ed. Giuseppe Grassi. adv.: B&W page L.2000000, color page L.2700000; 210 x 297. circ. 9,958 (paid); 10,329 (controlled).
Description: Examines the whole metalworking production process.

531 510 US ISSN 0076-5783
TA349
MECHANICS. 1970. 10/yr. $15. American Academy of Mechanics, c/o John Dundurs, Ed., Department of Civil Engineering, Northwestern University, Evanston, IL 60201. TEL 312-491-4034. adv.; bk.rev. circ. 1,300.

MECHANICS AND MATHEMATICAL METHODS - SERIES OF HANDBOOKS. see *MATHEMATICS*

531 US ISSN 0025-6544
TJ1 CODEN: MESOBN
MECHANICS OF SOLIDS. English translation of: Rossiiskaya Akademiya Nauk. Izvestiya. Mekhanika Tverdogo Tela. 1965. bi-m. $1005 (effective 1996). (Russian Academy of Sciences, RU) Allerton Press, Inc., 150 Fifth Ave., New York, NY 10011. TEL 212-924-3950. FAX 212-463-9684. bk.rev.; abstr.; charts; illus.; index. **Indexed:** Appl.Mech.Rev., INSPEC, Math.R. **Document type:** academic/scholarly publication.
—BLDSC (0415.850000); Faxon; SWETS; UnCover. **CCC.**
Description: Provides reports on research being conducted at leading Russian institutions for advanced studies in applied and theoretical mechanics.

MECHANIKA TEORETYCZNA I STOSOWANA; journal of theoretical and applied mechanics. see *ENGINEERING — Engineering Mechanics And Materials*

531 KR ISSN 0321-1975
MEKHANIKA TVERDOGO TELA; respublikanskii mezhvedomstvennyi sbornik nauchnykh trudov. (Text in Russian) 1969. a. (Akademiya Nauk Ukrainy, Institut Prikladnoi Matematiki i Mekhaniki) Izdatel'stvo Naukova Dumka, c/o Yu.A. Khramov, Dir, Ul. Repina, 3, Kiev 252 601, Ukraine. (Subscr. to: Mezhdunarodnaya Kniga, Dimitrova ul. 39, Moscow, 200, Russia) Ed. P.V. Kharlamov. **Indexed:** INSPEC, Math.R., Met.Abstr., World Alum.Abstr. **Document type:** academic/scholarly publication.
—BLDSC (0114.530000). **CCC.**

531 CC ISSN 1004-0595
CODEN: MAXUE7
MOCAXUE XUEBAO/TRIBOLOGY. (Text in Chinese) q. $56.80. Science Press, Marketing and Sales Department, 16 Donghuangchenggen North St., Beijing 100717, People's Republic of China. TEL 4010642. FAX 4019810. **Document type:** academic/scholarly publication.
—BLDSC (9050.216900); CASDDS.

531 US ISSN 0027-1330
CODEN: MUVMB8
MOSCOW UNIVERSITY MECHANICS BULLETIN. English translation in part of: Moskovskii Universitet. Vestnik. Seriya 1: Matematika i Mekhanika (RU ISSN 0579-9368) 1966. bi-m. $815 (effective 1996). (Moskovskii Universitet, RU) Allerton Press, Inc., 150 Fifth Ave., New York, NY 10011. TEL 212-924-3950. FAX 212-463-9684. Ed. O.B. Lupanov. bk.rev.; abstr.; bibl.; charts; illus.; index. **Indexed:** Appl.Mech.Rev. **Document type:** academic/scholarly publication.
—BLDSC (0416.239500); UnCover. **CCC.**
Description: Presents articles on a variety of aspects of mechanics, with emphasis on the analytical and approximated analytical methods of current research being conducted.

MOSKOVSKII UNIVERSITET. VESTNIK. SERIYA 1: MATEMATIKA I MEKHANIKA. see *MATHEMATICS*

531 US ISSN 0889-3934
MOTION;* guide to electronic motion control. 1985. bi-m. $36. (International Motion Control Association) Motion Corporation, P.O. Box 21730, Carson City, NV 89721. TEL 702-885-1500. FAX 702-246-9222. Ed. Sandra Falk. adv. circ. 33,000. **Indexed:** Energy Info.Abstr.
Description: Covers industrial and aerospace-related electronic motion control.

531 US ISSN 1053-4644
TJ214.5
MOTION CONTROL; the magazine for motion control applications and technology. 1990. q. $30 (foreign $50). I S A Services, Inc., 67 Alexander Dr., Box 12277, Research Triangle Park, NC 27709. TEL 919-549-8411. FAX 919-549-8288. TELEX 802540 ISA DURM. Ed. George R. Davis. adv. contact: Richard Simpson. circ. 25,000. (back issues avail.) **Document type:** trade publication.
—CCC.
Description: Covers new and developing techniques and the practical applications of new and existing technologies for motion control; includes sections on industry news and new products.

NAGARE/JAPAN SOCIETY OF FLUID MECHANICS. JOURNAL. see *ENGINEERING — Hydraulic Engineering*

NIHON REOROJI GAKKAI NENKAI KOEN YOKOSHU/ABSTRACTS OF ANNUAL MEETING ON RHEOLOGY. see *PHYSICS — Abstracting, Bibliographies, Statistics*

532 JA ISSN 0387-1533
QC189 CODEN: NRGADP
NIHON REOROJI GAKKAISHI/SOCIETY OF RHEOLOGY, JAPAN. JOURNAL. (Text in English, Japanese; summaries in English) 1973. q. 2000 Yen per no. Nihon Reoroji Gakkai - Society of Rheology, Japan, 1-101, Yoshida Izumidonocho, Sakyo-ku, Kyoto 606, Japan. **Indexed:** Chem.Abstr., Jap.Per.Ind.
—BLDSC (4896.860000); CASDDS.

P A S C A L F 10: MECANIQUE, ACOUSTIQUE ET TRANSFERT DE CHALEUR. see *PHYSICS — Abstracting, Bibliographies, Statistics*

P M T F. (Prikladnaya Mekhanika i Tekhnicheskaya Fizika) see *ENGINEERING — Mechanical Engineering*

532 540 US ISSN 0031-9104
QD541 CODEN: PCLQAC
PHYSICS AND CHEMISTRY OF LIQUIDS. 1968. 8/yr. (in 2 vols., 4 nos./vol.). 293 ECU per vol. (effective 1996). Gordon and Breach Science Publishers, c/o International Publishers Distributor, 820 Town Center Dr., Langhorne, PA 19047. TEL 215-750-2642. FAX 215-750-6343. (Subscr. to: International Publishers Distributor, P.O. Box 90, Reading, Berkshire RG1 8JL, England. TEL 44-173-456-8316) Ed. Norman H. March. adv. (also avail. in microform from MIM) **Indexed:** Appl.Mech.Rev., Chem.Abstr., Curr.Cont., INSPEC, Phys.Ber.
—BLDSC (6478.200000); CASDDS; Faxon; SWETS; UnCover. **CCC.**
Refereed Serial

530 541.2 NE ISSN 0924-6339
CODEN: PMLSEO
PHYSICS AND CHEMISTRY OF MATERIALS WITH LOW-DIMENSIONAL STRUCTURES. (Text in English) 1976. irreg., vol.17, 1994. price varies. Kluwer Academic Publishers, Postbus 17, 3300 AA Dordrecht, Netherlands. TEL 31-78-392392. FAX 31-78-392254. TELEX 29245 KAPG NL. (Dist. by: Kluwer Academic Publishers Group, P.O. Box 322, 3300 AH Dordrecht. TEL 31-78-392392. FAX 31-78-546474; N. America dist. addr.: Box 358, Accord Sta., Hingham, MA 02018-0358. TEL 617-871-6600. FAX 617-871-6528) Ed. E. Mooser. **Indexed:** Chem.Abstr. **Document type:** monographic series.
—BLDSC (6478.215030); CASDDS.
Formed by the 1989 merger of: Physics and Chemistry of Materials with Low-Dimensional Structures. Series C: Molecular Structures (ISSN 0924-459X); Physics and Chemistry of Materials with Low-Dimensional Structures. Series B: Quasi-One-Dimensional Structures (ISSN 0924-4581); Physics and Chemistry of Materials with Low-Dimensional Structures. Series A: Layered Structures (ISSN 0924-4573); Which was formerly (until 1986): Physics and Chemistry of Materials with Layered Structures (ISSN 0378-1917)
Refereed Serial

531 PL ISSN 0372-9486
POLITECHNIKA KRAKOWSKA. ZESZYTY NAUKOWE. MECHANIKA. (Text in Polish; summaries in English, French, German, Russian) 1956. irreg. price varies. Politechnika Krakowska, Ul. Warszawska 24, 31-155 Krakow, Poland. TEL 48-12-374289. TELEX 322468 PK PL. bibl.; charts; illus. circ. 200. **Indexed:** Math.R. **Document type:** academic/scholarly publication.

531 621 PL ISSN 0079-4538
TJ145
POLITECHNIKA POZNANSKA. ZESZYTY NAUKOWE. MECHANIKA. (Text in Polish; summaries in English) 1958. irreg. price varies. Politechnika Poznanska, Pl. Curie-Sklodowskiej 5, Poznan, Poland. Ed. Zenon Ignaszak. circ. 150. **Document type:** academic/scholarly publication.
Description: Research notes and information covering all fields of design, manufacturing and exploitation of machinery in mechanical engineering.

POLITECHNIKA WROCLAWSKA. INSTYTUT MATERIALOZNAWSTWA I MECHANIKI TECHNICZNEJ. PRACE NAUKOWE. KONFERENCJE. see *ENGINEERING — Mechanical Engineering*

531 PL ISSN 0324-9565
POLITECHNIKA WROCLAWSKA. INSTYTUT MATERIALOZNAWSTWA I MECHANIKI TECHNICZNEJ. PRACE NAUKOWE. MONOGRAFIE. (Text in Polish; summaries in English and Russian) 1969. irreg., no.20, 1990. price varies. Wydawnictwo Politechniki Wroclawskiej, Wybrzeze Wyspianskiego 27, 50-370 Wroclaw, Poland. FAX 22-36-64. TELEX 712559 PWRPL. (Dist. by: Ars Polona-Ruch, Krakowskie Przedmiescie 7, Warsaw, Poland) **Document type:** monographic series.
—BLDSC (6590.520000); Ei.

531 PL ISSN 0370-0917
TA401 CODEN: PNMMAE
POLITECHNIKA WROCLAWSKA. INSTYTUT MATERIALOZNAWSTWA I MECHANIKI TECHNICZNEJ. PRACE NAUKOWE. STUDIA I MATERIALY. (Text in Polish; summaries in English and Russian) 1970. irreg., no.28, 1991. price varies. (Politechnika Wroclawska) Wydawnictwo Politechniki Wroclawskiej, Wybrzeze Wyspianskiego 27, 50-370 Wroclaw, Poland. FAX 22-36-64. TELEX 712559 PWRPL. (Dist. by: Ars Polona-Ruch, Krakowskie Przedmiescie 7, Warsaw, Poland) **Indexed:** Chem.Abstr. **Document type:** academic/scholarly publication.
—CASDDS.

621.3 PL ISSN 0324-9395
POLITECHNIKA WROCLAWSKA. INSTYTUT TECHNIKI CIEPLNEJ I MECHANIKI PLYNOW. PRACE NAUKOWE. KONFERENCJE. (Text in Polish and English) 1974. irreg., no.7, 1988. price varies. (Instytut Techniki Cieplnej i Mechaniki Plynow) Wydawnictwo Politechniki Wroclawskiej, Wybrzeze Wyspianskiego 27, 50-370 Wroclaw, Poland. FAX 22-36-64. TELEX 712559 PWRPL. (Dist. by: Ars Polona-Ruch, Krakowskie Przedmiescie 7, Warsaw, Poland) circ. 575.

PHYSICS — MECHANICS

621.3   PL   ISSN 0324-9387
POLITECHNIKA WROCLAWSKA. INSTYTUT TECHNIKI CIEPLNEJ I MECHANIKI PLYNOW. PRACE NAUKOWE. MONOGRAFIE. (Text in Polish; summaries in English and Russian) 1970. irreg., no.21, 1992. price varies. (Politechnika Wroclawska) Wydawnictwo Politechniki Wroclawskiej, Wybrzeze Wyspianskiego 27, 50-370 Wroclaw, Poland. FAX 22-36-64. TELEX 712559 PWRPL. (Dist. by: Ars Polona-Ruch, Krakowskie Przedmiescie 7, Warsaw, Poland) **Document type:** monographic series.
—Ei.

621.3   PL   ISSN 0324-9409
POLITECHNIKA WROCLAWSKA. INSTYTUT TECHNIKI CIEPLNEJ I MECHANIKI PLYNOW. PRACE NAUKOWE. STUDIA I MATERIALY. (Text in Polish; summaries in English and Russian) 1970. irreg., no.13, 1987. price varies. Wydawnictwo Politechniki Wroclawskiej, Wybrzeze Wyspianskiego 27, 50-370 Wroclaw, Poland. FAX 22-36-64. TELEX 712559 PWRPL. (Dist. by: Ars Polona-Ruch, Krakowskie Przedmiescie 7, Warsaw, Poland) **Document type:** academic/scholarly publication.
—BLDSC (6590.720000).

531 620.1   PL   ISSN 0079-3337
POLSKA AKADEMIA NAUK. ODDZIAL W KRAKOWIE. KOMISJA MECHANIKI STOSOWANEJ. PRACE: MECHANIKA. (Text in English and Polish; summaries in English and Russian) 1966. irreg., no.15, 1991. price varies. Polska Akademia Nauk, Oddzial w Krakowie, Komisja Mechaniki Stosowanej, Ul. Slawkowska 17, 31-016 Krakow, Poland. TEL 48-12-224853. FAX 48-12-222791. Ed. Edward Maciag. **Document type:** monographic series.
Formerly: Polska Akademia Nauk. Komisja Nauk Technicznych. Prace.
Description: Presents selections from Master's theses from the Metallurgical and Mining Academy, and Technical University in Cracow.

671   RU
PRIKLADNAYA MEKHANIKA I PRIBOROSTROENIE. 1973. irreg. 1.07 Rub. Sankt-Peterburgskii Universitet, Universitetskaya Nab. 7-9, St. Petersburg V-164, Russia. TEL 218-9788. illus.

PROBLEMY ISTORII MATEMATIKI I MEKHANIKI. see MATHEMATICS

531   CC   ISSN 1001-1641
QIDONG SHIYAN YU CELIANG KONGZHI/AERODYNAMIC EXPERIMENT AND MEASUREMENT AND CONTROL. (Text in Chinese) q. Y15 (effective 1996). Zhongguo Kongqi Dongli Yanjiu yu Fazhan Zhongxin - China Aerodynamics R & D Center (CARDC), P.O. Box 211, Mianyang, Sichuan 621000, People's Republic of China. TEL 0816-22490. Ed. Le Jialin. **Document type:** academic/scholarly publication.
Refereed Serial

RANRYU SHINPOJUMU KOEN RONBUNSHU/PROCEEDINGS OF SYMPOSIUM ON TURBULENCE. see ENGINEERING — Hydraulic Engineering

REOROJI TORONKAI KOEN YOSHISHU/ABSTRACTS OF SYMPOSIUM ON RHEOLOGY. see PHYSICS — Abstracting, Bibliographies, Statistics

531 621   KR   ISSN 0370-808X
CODEN: RZITAJ
REZANIE I INSTRUMENT. 1970. irreg. Kharkivskyi Politekhnichnyi Instytut, Ul. Frunze, 21, Kharkov 310002, Ukraine.
—CASDDS.

532   GW   ISSN 0035-4511
QC189   CODEN: RHEAAK
RHEOLOGICA ACTA. (Text and summaries in English, German) 1958. bi-m. DM.1296($941) (effective 1996). Dr. Dietrich Steinkopff Verlag, Saalbaustr. 12, 64283 Darmstadt, Germany. TEL 06151-1745-0. FAX 06151-174510. (Subscr. to: Postfach 111442, 64229 Darmstadt, Germany) Ed. H. Winter. adv.; bk.rev.; charts. circ. 2,000. (also avail. in microform from UMI) **Indexed:** API Abstr., Appl.Mech.Rev., Chem.Abstr., Chem.Eng.Abstr., Curr.Cont., Dairy Sci.Abstr., Food Sci.& Tech.Abstr., Geotech.Abstr., INSPEC (1968-), Intl.Polym.Sci.& Tech., Math.R., Petrol.Abstr., RAPRA, RAPRA, T.C.E.A., World Surf.Coat. **Document type:** academic/scholarly publication.
—BLDSC (7960.300000); CASDDS; Ei; Faxon; Genuine Article; SWETS; UMI; UnCover. CCC.

532   GW   ISSN 0939-5059
CODEN: RHEOEW
RHEOLOGY (YEAR); Fliessverhalten steuern. (Text in English, German) 1991. q. DM.156 (foreign DM.168). Vincentz Verlag, Schiffgraben 43, 30175 Hannover, Germany. TEL 0511-9909851. FAX 0511-9909899. (Subscr. to: Postfach 6247, 30062 Hannover, Germany) Ed. E. Dewald. adv.: B&W page DM.3020, color page DM.5690; trim 250 x 175. circ. 3,320. **Document type:** academic/scholarly publication.
—BLDSC (7960.480000); CASDDS; Ei.

532   US   ISSN 0035-4538
RHEOLOGY BULLETIN. 1937. irreg. membership. Society of Rheology, Center for Composite Materials, University of Delaware, Newark, DE 19716. TEL 302-451-2328. Ed. A.B. Metzner.

RUSSIAN ACADEMY OF SCIENCE. LEBEDEV PHYSICS INSTITUTE. PROCEEDINGS. see PHYSICS — Optics

531   US   ISSN 1061-7566
TA349   CODEN: RJCMEU
RUSSIAN JOURNAL OF COMPUTATIONAL MECHANICS. 1993. q. $040 (foreign $395) (effective 1996). John Wiley & Sons, Inc., Journals, 605 Third Ave., New York, NY 10158. TEL 212-850-6645. FAX 212-850-6021. TELEX 12-7063. E-mail: SUBINFO@JWILEY.COM. (Subscr. outside the Americas to: John Wiley & Sons Ltd., Baffins Ln., Chichester, W. Sussex PO19 1UD, England. TEL 44-1243-779777. FAX 44-1243-776128) (also avail. in microform from UMI; back issues avail.) **Document type:** academic/scholarly publication.
Refereed Serial

531   US   ISSN 1068-8005
QA801
ST. PETERSBURG UNIVERSITY MECHANICS BULLETIN. English translation of the mechanics section of: Sankt-Peterburgskii Universitet. Vestnik. Seriya: Matematika, Mekhanika i Astonomiya. 1984. q. $570 (effective 1996). (St. Petersburg University, RU) Allerton Press, Inc., 150 Fifth Ave., New York, NY 10011. TEL 212-924-3950. FAX 212-463-9684. Ed. L.A. Verbitskaya. **Document type:** academic/scholarly publication.
—BLDSC (0425.847000). CCC.
Formerly: Leningrad University Mechanics Bulletin (ISSN 0883-623X)

531   GW   ISSN 0933-8047
SEIBT OBERFLAECHENTECHNIK. (Text in English, French, German) 1988. a. DM.32. Seibt Verlag GmbH, Leopoldstr. 208, 80804 Munich, Germany. TEL 089-360903-0. FAX 089-364317. circ. 8,000. **Document type:** directory.
●Also available online. Vendor(s): GBI. Also available on CD-ROM.

531   SI   ISSN 0218-0235
SERIES IN THEORETICAL & APPLIED MECHANICS. (Text in English) 1986. irreg., vol.11, 1990. price varies. World Scientific Publishing Co. Pte. Ltd., Farrer Rd., P.O. Box 128, Singapore 9128, Singapore. TEL 3825663. FAX 3825919. TELEX RS 28561 WSPC. (UK addr.: 73 Lynton Mead, Totteridge, London N20 8DH, England. TEL 44-81-4462461; US addr.: 1060 Main St., River Edge, NJ 07661. TEL 300-227-7562) Ed. R.K.T. Hsieh. **Document type:** monographic series.
—BLDSC (8250.202780).

531   SI   ISSN 0218-0111
SERIES ON ADVANCES IN STATISTICAL MECHANICS. (Text in English) 1985. irreg., vol.7, 1991. price varies. World Scientific Publishing Co. Pte. Ltd., Farrer Rd., P.O. Box 128, Singapore 9128, Singapore. TEL 3825663. FAX 3826919. TELEX RS 28561 WSPC. (UK addr.: 73 Lynton Mead, Totteridge, London N20 8DH, England. TEL 44-81-4462461; US addr.: 1060 Main St., River Edge, NJ 07661. TEL 300-227-7562) Ed. M. Rasetti. **Document type:** monographic series.
—BLDSC (8250.149000).

531   CC
CODEN: SHLIDP
SHANGHAI JOURNAL OF MECHANICS. (Text in Chinese) 1980. q. $10 (effective through 1995). Shanghai Lixue Xuehui - Shanghai Society of Mechanics, Tongji University, 1239 Siping Road, Shanghai 200092, People's Republic of China. TEL 5455080. FAX 5458965. (Co-sponsor: Tongji University) Ed. Wang Rongchang. bk.rev. circ. 1,000. **Document type:** academic/scholarly publication.
—CASDDS.
Formerly (until 1992): Shanghai Lixue (ISSN 0254-0053)

531   CC   ISSN 1001-4888
SHIYAN LIXUE/EXPERIMENTAL MECHANICS. (Text in Chinese) q. Zhongguo Lixue Xuehui - Chinese Mechanics Society, Zhongguo Keji Daxue, 96 Jinzhai Lu, Hefei, Anhui 230026, People's Republic of China. TEL 331134. Ed. Jia Youquan.

531   GW   ISSN 0938-1287
CODEN: SHWAEN
SHOCK WAVES. (Text in English) 1990. 6/yr. DM.418($303) (effective 1996). Springer-Verlag, Heidelberger Platz 3, 14197 Berlin. TEL 030-8207-0. FAX 030-8214091. E-mail: orders@springer.de. (Subscr. in N. America to: Springer-Verlag New York, Inc., 44 Hartz Way, Secaucus, NJ 07096-2491. TEL 201-348-4033. FAX 201-348-4505) Ed. I.I. Glass. **Indexed:** INSPEC (1991-). **Document type:** academic/scholarly publication.
—BLDSC (8267.485400); Faxon; SWETS; UMI. CCC.
Description: Emphasizes both theoretical and experimental research on shock-wave phenomena in gases, liquids, solids, and two-phase media.

620.1 531   NE   ISSN 0925-0042
SOLID MECHANICS AND ITS APPLICATIONS. (Text in English) 1990. irreg., vol.20, 1993. price varies. Kluwer Academic Publishers, Postbus 17, 3300 AA Dordrecht, Netherlands. TEL 31-78-392392. FAX 31-78-392245. TELEX 29245 KAPG NL. (Dist by: Kluwer Academic Publishers Group, P.O. Box 322, 3300 AH Dordrecht, Netherlands. TEL 31-78-392392. FAX 31-78-546474; N. America dist. addr.: Box 358, Accord Sta., Hingham, MA 02018-0358. TEL 617-871-6600. FAX 617-871-6528) bibl. (back issues avail.) **Document type:** monographic series.
—BLDSC (8327.352000).
Refereed Serial

531   US   ISSN 1076-4046
STANFORD SYNCHROTRON RADIATION LABORATORY. ACTIVITY REPORT. a. Stanford University, Stanford Synchrotron Radiation Laboratory, Box 4349, MS-69, Stanford, CA 94309. TEL 415-926-4000. Eds. Katherine Cantwell, Lisa Dunn. **Document type:** corporate report.

531   NE   ISSN 0922-5382
STUDIES IN APPLIED MECHANICS. 1979. irreg., vol.36, 1994. price varies. Elsevier Science B.V., Books Division, P.O. Box 211, 1000 AE Amsterdam, Netherlands. TEL 31-20-4853911. FAX 31-20-4853705. TELEX 18582 ESPA NL. E-mail: nlinfo-f@elsevier.nl; usinfo-f@elsevier.com; forinfo-kyf04035@niftyserve.or.jp; Site addr.: http://www.elsevier.nl/. (Subscr. in U.S. and Canada to: Elsevier Science Inc., Box 882, Madison Sq. Sta., New York, NY 10159. TEL 212-989-5800) **Indexed:** INSPEC. **Document type:** monographic series.
—BLDSC (8489.480500).
Refereed Serial

531   NE   ISSN 0081-8542
QC175   CODEN: SSTMBG
STUDIES IN STATISTICAL MECHANICS. 1962. irreg., vol.14, 1988. price varies. Elsevier Science B.V., Books Division, P.O. Box 211, 1000 AE Amsterdam, Netherlands. TEL 31-20-4853911. FAX 31-20-4853705. TELEX 18582 ESPA NL. E-mail: nlinfo-f@elsevier.nl; usinfo-f@elsevier.com; forinfo-kyf04035@niftyserve.or.jp; Site addr.: http://www.elsevier.nl/. (Subscr. in U.S. and Canada to: Elsevier Science Inc., Box 882, Madison Sq. Sta., New York, NY 10159. TEL 212-989-5800) Eds. E.W. Montroll, J.L. Lebowitz. **Indexed:** INSPEC. **Document type:** monographic series.
—CASDDS.
Refereed Serial

PHYSICS — NUCLEAR PHYSICS

531 NE ISSN 0167-2991
CODEN: SSCTDM
STUDIES IN SURFACE SCIENCE AND CATALYSIS. (Text in English) 1976. irreg., vol.80, 1993. price varies. Elsevier Science B.V., Books Division, P.O. Box 211, 1000 AE Amsterdam, Netherlands. TEL 31-20-4853911. FAX 31-20-4853705. TELEX 18582 ESPA NL.
E-mail: nlinfo-f@elsevier.nl; usinfo-f@elsevier.com; forinfo-kyf04035@niftyserve.or.jp; Site addr.: http://www.elsevier.nl/. (Subscr. in U.S. and Canada to: Elsevier Science Inc., Box 882, Madison Sq. Sta., New York, NY 10159. TEL 212-989-5800) Ed. B. Delmon, J.T. Yates. (back issues avail.) **Indexed:** INSPEC. **Document type:** monographic series.
—BLDSC (8491.783000); CASDDS; Genuine Article. **CCC.**
Refereed Serial

532 US ISSN 0082-0849
SYMPOSIUM ON NAVAL HYDRODYNAMICS. PROCEEDINGS. 1956. biennial. price varies. U.S. Department of the Navy, Office of Naval Research, 800 North Quincy, Arlington, VA 22217. TEL 202-545-6700.

T & A M REPORT. (Department of Theoretical and Applied Mechanics) see *ENGINEERING — Engineering Mechanics And Materials*

531 CU ISSN 0138-8800
T4
TECNICA POPULAR. 1975. bi-m. $10 in N. America; S. America $13; Europe $15; elsewhere $21. Ministerio de la Industria Sidero Mecanica, 36 A No. 712th 7ma y 42, Playa, Havana, Cuba. TELEX 512160. (Dist. by: Ediciones Cubanas, Obispo No. 527, Apdo. 605, Havana, Cuba) circ. 5,000.

531 621 KR ISSN 0321-4419
TEORIYA MEKHANIZMOV I MASHIN. 1966. irreg. Kharkivskyi Politekhnichnyi Instytut, Ul. Frunze, 21, Kharkov 310002, Ukraine.
—BLDSC (0178.250000).

TEST ENGINEERING & MANAGEMENT. see *AERONAUTICS AND SPACE FLIGHT*

531 NE ISSN 0167-8442
CODEN: TAFME4
THEORETICAL AND APPLIED FRACTURE MECHANICS; an international journal devoted to research in the theoretical and experimental aspects of material damage. (In 2 parts: Fracture Mechanics Technology; Mechanics and Physics of Fracture) 1984. bi-m. fl.960($585) (effective 1996). Elsevier Science B.V., P.O. Box 211, 1000 AE Amsterdam, Netherlands. TEL 31-20-4853911. FAX 31-20-4853598. TELEX 18582 ESPA NL.
E-mail: nlinfo-f@elsevier.nl; usinfo-f@elsevier.com; forinfo-kyf04035@niftyserve.or.jp; Site addr.: http://www.elsevier.nl/. (Subscr. in U.S. and Canada to: Elsevier Science Inc., Box 882, Madison Sq. Sta., New York, NY 10159. TEL 212-989-5800. FAX 212-633-3990) Ed. G.C. Sih. (also avail. in microform from UMI) **Indexed:** Appl.Mech.Rev., Geol.Abstr., INSPEC (1984-), Met.Abstr. **Document type:** academic/scholarly publication.
—BLDSC (8814.551850); CASDDS; Ei; Faxon; Genuine Article; SWETS. **CCC.**
Description: Part one emphasizes material characterization techniques and translation of specimen data to design. Part two publishes original research on material damage leading to crack growth or fracture in materials such as metal alloys, polymers, composites, rocks, ceramics and related substances.
Refereed Serial

531 JA ISSN 0285-6042
THEORETICAL AND APPLIED MECHANICS. (Text in English) 1953. a. 20000 Yen. (Science Council of Japan, Japan National Committee for Theoretical and Applied Mechanics - Nihon Gakujutsu Kaigi, Rikigaku Kenkyu Renraku Iinkai) Hokusensha Publishing Co., 3-4-3-503 Iidabashi, Chiyoda-ku, Tokyo 102, Japan.
—BLDSC (8814.552200); Ei.

532 GW ISSN 0935-4964
QA911 CODEN: TCFDEP
THEORETICAL AND COMPUTATIONAL FLUID DYNAMICS. (Text in English) 1989. bi-m. DM.798($579) (effective 1996). Springer-Verlag, Heidelberger Platz 3, 14197 Berlin, Germany. TEL 030-8207-0. FAX 030-8214091. E-mail: orders@springer.de. (Subscr. in N. America to: Springer-Verlag New York, Inc., 44 Hartz Way, Secaucus, NJ 07096-2491. TEL 201-348-4033. FAX 201-348-4505) Ed. M.Y. Hussaini. (also avail. in microform from UMI) **Indexed:** Curr.Cont., INSPEC (1990-), Zent.Math. **Document type:** academic/scholarly publication.
—BLDSC (8814.552280); CASDDS; Faxon; Genuine Article; SWETS; UMI; UnCover. **CCC.**
Description: Presents original research in theoretical and computational fluid dynamics aimed at elucidating flow physics.

VOPROSY GIDRODINAMIKI I TEPLOOBMENA V KRIOGENNYKH SISTEMAKH. see *PHYSICS — Heat*

531 621 CC ISSN 1000-6915
YANSHI LIXUE YU GONGCHENG XUEBAO/JOURNAL OF ROCK MECHANICS AND ENGINEERING. (Text in Chinese) 1982. q. $40. (Chinese Academy of Sciences, Institute of Geophysics) Zhongguo Yanshi Lixue yu Gongcheng Xuehui, No. A-11, Datun Lu, Dewai, Beijing 100101, People's Republic of China. Ed. Yu Xuefu. circ. 1,000. **Document type:** academic/scholarly publication.
Description: Covers new ideas and latest developments in the field of rock engineering in China.
Refereed Serial

531 CC ISSN 1000-7598
YANTU LIXUE/ROCK AND SOIL MECHANICS. (Text in Chinese) q. Zhongguo Kexueyuan, Wuhan Yantu Lixue Yanjiusuo - Chinese Academy of Sciences, Wuhan Institute of Rock and Soil Mechanics, Xiaohongshan, Wuhan, Hubei 430071, People's Republic of China. TEL 813712. (Dist. outside China by: Guoji Shudian - China International Book Trading Corp., P.O. Box 399, Beijing, P.R.C.) Ed. Yuan Jianxin.
—BLDSC (8001.443000).
Refereed Serial

YINGYONG SHUXUE YU LIXUE. see *MATHEMATICS*

531 CC ISSN 1000-3835
ZHENDONG YU CHONGJI/VIBRATION AND SHOCK. (Text in Chinese) q. Zhongguo Zhendong Gongcheng Xuehui - Chinese Vibration Engineering Society, 121 Nanjiang Lu, Shanghai 200011, People's Republic of China. TEL 3774325. Ed. Huang Wenhu.

PHYSICS — Nuclear Physics

539.7 US ISSN 0272-5088
CODEN: ASRGDU
ACCELERATORS AND STORAGE RINGS SERIES. irreg., latest vol.6. price varies. Harwood Academic Publishers, c/o International Publishers Distributor, 820 Town Center Dr., Langhorne, PA 19047. TEL 215-750-2642. FAX 215-750-6343. (Subscr. to: International Publishers Distributor, Box 90, Reading, Berkshire RG1 8JL, England. TEL 44-173-456-8316) Eds. J.P. Blewett, F.T. Cole. (also avail. in microform) **Document type:** academic/scholarly publication.
—CASDDS.
Refereed Serial

539.7 FI ISSN 0355-2721
QC1 CODEN: APSSDG
ACTA POLYTECHNICA SCANDINAVICA. APPLIED PHYSICS SERIES. (Text and summaries in English) irreg. (4-5/yr.) FIM 450. Teknillisten Tieteiden Akatemia - Finnish Academy of Technology, Tekniikantie 12, FIN-02150 Espoo, Finland. Ed. Mauri Luukkala. index, cum.index: 1958-1991. circ. 500. (also avail. in microform from UMI; back issues avail.; reprint service avail. from UMI) **Indexed:** ASCA, Cadscan, Chem.Abstr., Curr.Cont., INIS Atomind., INSPEC (1981-), Intl.Civil Eng.Abstr., Lead Abstr., Met.Abstr., Soft.Abstr.Eng., World Alum.Abstr., Zincscan. **Document type:** monographic series.
—BLDSC (0661.252000); CASDDS; Genuine Article; UMI; UnCover.
Formerly: Acta Polytechnica Scandinavica. Physics Including Nucleonics Series (ISSN 0001-6888)
Description: Presents research results in physical engineering and technical physics.

539 US ISSN 1049-250X
QC173 CODEN: AAMPE9
ADVANCES IN ATOMIC, MOLECULAR AND OPTICAL PHYSICS. 1965. irreg., vol.35, 1993. Academic Press, Inc., 525 B St., Ste. 1900, San Diego, CA 92101-4495. TEL 619-231-0926. FAX 619-699-6715. (Subscr. to: Order Dept., 6277 Sea Harbor Dr., 4th Fl., Orlando, FL 32887. TEL 800-321-5068) Eds. D.R. Bates, Immanueal Estermann. index. (reprint service avail. from ISI) **Indexed:** Chem.Abstr., Ind.Sci.Rev., INIS Atomind., INSPEC, Mass Spectr.Bull., Phys.Ber., Sci.Cit.Ind.
—BLDSC (0699.810000); CASDDS; Faxon; UnCover. **CCC.**
Formerly: Advances in Atomic and Molecular Physics (ISSN 0065-2199)

539 US ISSN 0065-2970
QC173 CODEN: ANUPBZ
ADVANCES IN NUCLEAR PHYSICS. 1968. irreg., vol.21, 1994. price varies. Plenum Publishing Corp., 233 Spring St., New York, NY 10013-1578. TEL 212-620-8000. FAX 212-463-0742. TELEX 23-421139. Eds. J.W. Negele, E. Vogt. **Indexed:** ASCA, Ind.Sci.Rev., INIS Atomind., INSPEC, Phys.Ber., Sci.Cit.Ind. **Document type:** monographic series.
—CASDDS; Genuine Article. **CCC.**
Refereed Serial

539.7 621.48 US ISSN 0065-2989
TK9001 CODEN: ANUTAC
ADVANCES IN NUCLEAR SCIENCE AND TECHNOLOGY. 1962. irreg., vol.22, 1991. Plenum Publishing Corp., 233 Spring St., New York, NY 10013-1578. TEL 212-620-8047. Eds. E.J. Henley, H. Kouts. index. **Indexed:** Chem.Abstr., INIS Atomind., INSPEC. **Document type:** monographic series.
—BLDSC (0709.500000); CASDDS; Faxon. **CCC.**
Refereed Serial

539 US ISSN 0163-8998
QC770 CODEN: ARPSDF
ANNUAL REVIEW OF NUCLEAR AND PARTICLE SCIENCE. 1951. a. $62 (foreign $67) (effective Jan. 1995). Annual Reviews Inc., 4139 El Camino Way, Box 10139, Palo Alto, CA 94303-0139. TEL 415-493-4400; 800-523-8635. FAX 415-855-9815. E-mail: annrevu@class.org. Ed. Chris Quigg. bibl.; index, cum.index. (also avail. in microfilm from UMI; back issues avail.; reprint service avail.) **Indexed:** Biol.Abstr., Cadscan, Chem.Abstr., Curr.Cont., Energy Info.Abstr., Environ.Abstr., GeoRef., Ind.Sci.Rev., INIS Atomind., INSPEC, Lead Abstr., M.M.R.I., Nucl.Sci.Abstr., Phys.Ber., Sci.Cit.Ind., Zincscan. **Document type:** academic/scholarly publication.
—BLDSC (1523.900000); CASDDS; Ei; Faxon; Genuine Article; SWETS; UMI; UnCover. **CCC.**
Formerly (until 1978): Annual Review of Nuclear Science (ISSN 0066-4243)
Description: Original critical reviews of the significant primary literature and current developments in nuclear and particle science.

PHYSICS — NUCLEAR PHYSICS

539 616   UK   ISSN 0969-8043
QC770   CODEN: ARISEF
APPLIED RADIATION AND ISOTOPES; including data, instrumentation and methods for use in agriculture, industry and medicine. (Text in English, French, German, Russian) 1956. m. £794($1263) (effective 1996). Elsevier Science Ltd., Pergamon, P.O. Box 800, Kidlington, Oxford OX5 1DX. TEL 44-1865-843000. FAX 44-1865-843010. E-mail: nlinfo-f@elsevier.nl; usinfo-f@elsevier.com; forinfo-kyf04035@niftyserve.or.jp; Site addr.: http://www.elsevier.nl/. (Subscr. in U.S. and Canada to: Elsevier Science, 660 White Plains Rd., Tarrytown, NY 10591-5153. TEL 914-524-9200. FAX 914-333-2444) Ed. H. Seligman, W.L. McLaughlin. adv.: B&W page $550, color page $1350. bk.rev.; charts; illus.; index. circ. 2,000. (also avail. in microfilm from UMI; reprint service avail. from UMI) **Indexed**: Anal.Abstr., Biol.Abstr., Biotech.Abstr., Biwk.Pap.Rad.Chem.& Photochem., Chem.Abstr., Curr.Adv.Ecol.Sci., Curr.Cont., Dairy Sci.Abstr., Deep Sea Res.& Oceanogr.Abstr., Excerp.Med., Food Sci.& Tech.Abstr., Ind.Med., Ind.Sci.Rev., Ind.Vet., INIS Atomind., INSPEC (1986-), Mass Spectr.Bull., Nutr.Abstr., Ocean.Abstr., Pollut.Abstr., Sci.Cit.Ind., Sel.Water Res.Abstr., Soils & Fert., Vet.Bull. **Document type**: academic/scholarly publication.
—BLDSC (1576.565000); ADONIS; CASDDS; Ei; Faxon; Genuine Article; SWETS; UMI; UnCover. **CCC**.
    Former titles (until 1993): International Journal of Radiation Applications and Instrumentation. Part A: Applied Radiation and Isotopes (ISSN 0883-2889); (until 1985): International Journal of Applied Radiation and Isotopes (ISSN 0020-708X)
    Description: Publishes papers relating to the production, measurement and application of radionuclides and radiation in all branches of science and technology.
Refereed Serial

539.7   US   ISSN 0893-4908
ARCHIVES OF SOVIET SCIENCE SERIES: PHYSICAL SCIENCES SECTION. irreg. Harwood Academic Publishers, c/o International Publishers Distributor, 820 Town Center Dr., Langhorne, PA 19047. TEL 215-750-2642. FAX 215-750-6343. (Subscr.to: International Publishers Distributor PO Box 90,Reading, Berkshire RG1 8JL, England. TEL 44-173-456-8316) Eds. G.B. Abdullaev, T.D. Dzhafarov. (also avail. in microform)
Refereed Serial

539.7   JA
ATOMIC COLLISION RESEARCH IN JAPAN. PROGRESS REPORT. (Text and summaries in English) 1971. a. 3000 Yen($20) Society for Atomic Collision Research - Genshi Shototsu Kenkyu Kyokai, Jochi Daigaku Rikogakubu, Butsurigakka Genshi Butsurigaku Kenkyushitsu, 7-1 Kioicho, Chiyoda-ku, Tokyo 102, Japan. FAX 81-3-3238-3341. Ed. Y. Awaya. circ. 500. (back issues avail.)

539   US   ISSN 0092-640X
QC173   CODEN: ADNDAT
ATOMIC DATA AND NUCLEAR DATA TABLES; a journal devoted to compilations of experimental and theoretical results in atomic physics. 1969. bi-m. $497 (foreign $578) (effective 1996). Academic Press, Inc., Journal Division, 525 B. St., Ste. 1900, San Diego, CA 92101-4495. TEL 619-230-1840. FAX 619-699-6800. (Subscr. to: Box 620000, Orlando, FL 32891-8340. TEL 800-543-9534) Ed. Angela Li-Scholz. abstr.; bibl.; charts; illus.; stat.; index; circ. controlled. (back issues avail.) **Indexed**: Chem.Abstr., Excerp.Med., Ind.Sci.Rev., INIS Atomind., INSPEC (1973-), Phys.Ber., Sci.Cit.Ind. **Document type**: academic/scholarly publication.
—BLDSC (1769.375000); CASDDS; Faxon; Genuine Article; SWETS. **CCC**.
    Formed by the merger of: Atomic Data (ISSN 0004-7082); Nuclear Data Tables (ISSN 0090-0214); Which supersedes in part: Nuclear Data (ISSN 0029-5477)
    Description: Presents compilations of experimental and theoretical information in atomic physics, nuclear physics, and closely related fields.
Refereed Serial

539.7   NE
ATOMIC ENERGY LEVELS AND GROTRIAN DIAGRAMS. 1976. irreg., vol.4, 1982. price varies. Elsevier Science B.V., Books Division, P.O. Box 211, 1000 AE Amsterdam, Netherlands. TEL 31-20-4853911. FAX 31-20-4853705. TELEX 18582 ESPA NL. E-mail: nlinfo-f@elsevier.nl; usinfo-f@elsevier.com; forinfo-kyf04035@niftyserve.or.jp; Site addr.: http://www.elsevier.nl/. (Subscr. in U.S. and Canada to: Elsevier Science Inc., Box 882, Madison Sq. Sta., New York, NY 10159. TEL 212-989-5800) Eds. S. Bashkin, J.O. Stoner. **Document type**: monographic series.
Refereed Serial

539.7   JA
BEIKOKU GENSHIRYOKU JOHO/NUCLEAR ACTIVITY NEWS IN U.S.A.. (Text in Japanese) 197. s-m. membership. Genshiryoku Anzen Kenkyu Kyokai - Nuclear Safety Research Association, 2-2, Uchisaiwai-cho 1-chome, Choyoda-ku, Tokyo 100, Japan.

539   II
BHABHA ATOMIC RESEARCH CENTRE. NUCLEAR PHYSICS DIVISION. ANNUAL REPORT. 1971. a. $5. Bhabha Atomic Research Centre, Trombay, Bombay 400085, India. circ. controlled. **Indexed**: Chem.Abstr., Nucl.Sci.Abstr.

539.2   JA   ISSN 0385-0560
QC172   CODEN: BURTDQ
BUNSHIKEN RETAZU/INSTITUTE FOR MOLECULAR SCIENCE. LETTERS. (Text in English, Japanese) 1976. s-a. Okazaki National Research Institutes, Institute for Molecular Science - Okazaki Kokuritsu Kyodo Kenkyu Kiko Bunshi Kagaku Kenkyujo, 38, Saigonaka, Myodaiji-cho, Okazaki-shi, Aichi-ken 444, Japan.
—CASDDS.

539.7   SZ   ISSN 0304-288X
QC770   CODEN: CECOA2
C E R N COURIER. French edition: Courrier C E R N (ISSN 0374-2288) (Former name of issuing body: Conseil Europeen pour la Recherche Nucleaire) (Text in English) 1959. m. (10/yr.) free. C E R N - European Laboratory for Particle Physics, CH-1211 Geneva 23, Switzerland. Ed. Gordon Fraser. adv.; bibl.; charts; illus. circ. 25,000. **Indexed**: INIS Atomind., INSPEC (1981-). **Document type**: academic/scholarly publication.
—Faxon; UnCover.

539.7   SZ   ISSN 0366-5690
   CODEN: CEHEAV
C E R N - H E R A REPORTS. (Former name of issuing body: Conseil Europeen pour la Recherche Nucleaire) 1969. irreg. free. C E R N - European Laboratory for Particle Physics, CH-1211 Geneva 23, Switzerland. (also avail. in microfiche) **Indexed**: INIS Atomind, INSPEC. **Document type**: academic/scholarly publication.
—CASDDS.

539.7   SZ   ISSN 0007-8328
   CODEN: CERNA6
C E R N REPORTS. (Former name of issuing body: Conseil Europeen pour la Recherche Nucleaire) 1955. irreg. free. C E R N - European Laboratory for Particle Physics, CH-1211 Geneva 23, Switzerland. **Indexed**: Chem.Abstr., INIS Atomind., INSPEC. **Document type**: academic/scholarly publication.
—BLDSC (3120.110000); CASDDS.

539.7   SZ   ISSN 0531-4283
C E R N SCHOOL OF PHYSICS. PROCEEDINGS. (Former name of issuing body: Conseil Europeen pour la Recherche Nucleaire) 1962. a. free. C E R N - European Laboratory for Particle Physics, CH-1211 Geneva 23, Switzerland. circ. 3,500. **Indexed**: INIS Atomind., INSPEC. **Document type**: proceedings.

539.7   JA
CHODENDO ENERUGI CHOZO KENKYUKAI/SUPERCONDUCTING MAGNETIC ENERGY STORAGE. (Text in Japanese) 1986. s-a. Chodendo Enerugi Chozo Kenkyukai - Research Association of Superconducting Magnetic Energy Storage, 9-9, Tokodai 5-chome, Tsukuba-shi, Ibaraki-ken 300-26, Japan.

539.7   JA
CHODENDO ENERUGI CHOZO KENKYUKAI KENKYU HOKOKUSHO/RESEARCH ASSOCIATION OF SUPERCONDUCTING MAGNETIC ENERGY STORAGE. RESEARCH REPORT. (Text in Japanese) 1986. a. Chodendo Enerugi Chozo Kenkyukai - Research Association of Superconducting Magnetic Energy Storage, 9-9, Tokodai 5-chome, Tsukuba-shi, Ibaraki-ken 300-26, Japan.

539.7   JA   ISSN 1340-3818
CHODENDO KAGAKU KENKYU SENTA HOKOKU/RESEARCH INSTITUTE OF SUPERCONDUCTIVITY. ANNUAL REPORT. (Text in English, Japanese; summaries in English) 1984; N.S. 1994. a. Kyushu Daigaku, Kogakubu, Fuzoku Chodendo Kagaku Kenkyu Senta - Kyushu University, Faculty of Engineering, Research Institute of Superconductivity, 10-1, Hakozaki 6-chome, Higashi-ku, Fukuoka-shi, Fukuoka-ken 812, Japan. TEL 092-632-2438. FAX 092-651-7399. Ed. K. Funatei. **Indexed**: Chem.Abstr. **Document type**: academic/scholarly publication.
—BLDSC (1410.855000).
    Formerly (until 1994): Chodendo Magunetto Kenkyu Senta Hokoku - Research Institute for Superconducting Magnets. Annual Report (ISSN 0914-6318)

539   US   ISSN 0010-2687
QC770   CODEN: CAMPBS
COMMENTS ON ATOMIC AND MOLECULAR PHYSICS. 1969. 6/yr. (in 1 vol./yr.). 177 ECU per vol. to individuals (effective 1996). Gordon and Breach Science Publishers, c/o International Publishers Distributor, 820 Town Center Dr., Langhorne, PA 19047. TEL 215-750-2642. FAX 215-750-6343. (Subscr. to: International Publishers Distributor, P.O. Box 90, Reading, Berkshire RG1 8JL, England. TEL 44-173-456-8316) Ed. H. Henry Stroke. adv. (also avail. in microform) **Indexed**: Chem.Abstr., Curr.Cont., INIS Atomind., INSPEC (1969-), Mass Spectr.Bull., Phys.Ber. **Document type**: academic/scholarly publication.
—BLDSC (3336.027000); CASDDS; Ei; Faxon; SWETS; UnCover. **CCC**.

539   US   ISSN 0010-2709
   CODEN: CNPPAV
COMMENTS ON NUCLEAR AND PARTICLE PHYSICS. 1967. 12/yr. (in 2 vols., 6 nos./vol.). 177 ECU per vol. (effective 1996). Gordon and Breach Science Publishers, c/o International Publishers Distributor, 820 Town Center Dr., Langhorne, PA 19047. TEL 215-750-2642. FAX 215-750-6343. (Subscr. to: International Publishers Distributor, P.O. Box 90, Reading, Berkshire RG1 8JL, England. TEL 44-173-456-8316) Ed. William Marciano. adv. (also avail. in microform) **Indexed**: Chem.Abstr., INIS Atomind., INSPEC (1968-), Phys.Ber.
—BLDSC (3336.030000); CASDDS; Faxon; SWETS; UnCover. **CCC**.

539.7 530.44   US   ISSN 0374-2806
QC717.6   CODEN: CPCFBJ
COMMENTS ON PLASMA PHYSICS AND CONTROLLED FUSION. 6/yr. 177 ECU (effective 1996). Gordon and Breach Science Publishers, c/o International Publishers Disributor, 820 Town Center Dr., Langhorne, PA 19047. TEL 215-750-2642. FAX 215-750-6343. (Subscr. to: International Publishers Distributor, P.O. Box 90, Reading, Berkshire RG1 8JL, England. TEL 44-173-456-8316) Ed. Burton D. Fried. adv. (also avail. in microform) **Indexed**: Chem.Abstr., INIS Atomind., INSPEC (1972-), Phys.Ber.
—BLDSC (3336.035000); CASDDS; Faxon; SWETS; UnCover. **CCC**.

EGYPTIAN JOURNAL OF RADIATION SCIENCES & APPLICATIONS. see *MEDICAL SCIENCES — Radiology And Nuclear Medicine*

PHYSICS — NUCLEAR PHYSICS

539.7   US   ISSN 0379-4229
TK9001   CODEN: EARRDF
EUROPEAN APPLIED RESEARCH REPORTS: NUCLEAR SCIENCE AND TECHNOLOGY SECTION. 1979. a. 517 ECU (effective 1993). Harwood Academic Publishers, c/o International Publishers Distributor, 820 Town Center Dr., Langhorne, PA 19047. TEL 215-750-2642. FAX 215-750-6343. (Subscr. to : International Publishers Distributor,PO Box 90, Reading, Berkshire, RG1 8JL England. TEL 44-173-456-8316) (Co-sponsor: Commission of the European Communities) Ed. K.K. Appleyard. (also avail. in microform; back issues avail.) **Indexed:** CAD CAM Abstr., Chem.Abstr., INSPEC, Met.Abstr. —CASDDS. **CCC.**
Refereed Serial

539.7   US   ISSN 0273-2998
EUROPEAN APPLIED RESEARCH REPORTS SPECIAL TOPICS SERIES. irreg., latest vol.12. price varies. Harwood Academic Publishers, c/o International Publishers Distributor, 820 Town Center Dr., Langhorne, PA 19047. TEL 215-750-2642. FAX 215-750-6343. (Subscr. to : International Publishers Distributor, PO Box 90, Reading, Berkshire, RG1 8JL England. TEL 44-173-456-8316) (also avail. in microform) **Document type:** monographic series.
Refereed Serial

539.764   SZ
EUROPEAN CONFERENCE ON CONTROLLED FUSION AND PLASMA PHYSICS. PROCEEDINGS. (Text in English) 14th, 1981. a. 320 SFr. European Physical Society, P.O. Box 69, CH-1213 Petit-Lancy 2, Switzerland. Ed.Bd. **Document type:** proceedings.

EXCERPTA MEDICA. SECTION 23: NUCLEAR MEDICINE. see *MEDICAL SCIENCES — Abstracting, Bibliographies, Statistics*

539.7   CC   ISSN 0254-3052
QC793   CODEN: KNWLD9
GAONENG WULI YU HE WULI. English translation: High Energy Physics and Nuclear Physics (US ISSN 0899-9996) (Text in Chinese; summaries in English) 1977. m. $182.70. (Chinese Society of High Energy Physics - Zhongguo Gaoneng Wuli Xuehui) Science Press, Marketing and Sales Department, 16 Donghuangchenggen North St., Beijing 100717, People's Republic of China. TEL 4010642. FAX 4109810. adv. circ. 6,000. **Indexed:** Chem.Abstr., INSPEC, Math.R., Met.Abstr., World Alum.Abstr. **Document type:** academic/scholarly publication.
—BLDSC (4307.301800); CASDDS.
Description: Covers physics research in China, including quantum field theory and particle physics.
Refereed Serial

GENSHI NENRYO SAIKURU SHISETSU KANKYO HOSHASENTO JIZEN CHOSA HOKOKUSHO/REPORT OF ENVIRONMENTAL RADIOLOGY OF NUCLEAR FUEL CYCLE FACILITIES. see *ENVIRONMENTAL STUDIES*

539.2   JA   ISSN 0912-4063
GENSHI SHOTOTSU SAKYURA/SOCIETY FOR ATOMIC COLLISION RESEARCH. CIRCULAR. (Text in Japanese) 1968. bi-m. Genshi Shototsu Kenkyu - Society for Atomic Collision Research, Jochi Daigaku Rikogakubu, Butsurigakka Genshi Butsurigaku Kenkyushitsu, 7-1, Kioicho, Chiyoda-ku, Tokyo 102, Japan.

539.7   JA   ISSN 0915-4418
GENSHIRO JIKKENJO DAYORI/RESEARCH REACTOR INSTITUTE. NEWS. (Text in Japanese) 1988. q. free. Kyoto Daigaku, Genshiro Jikkenjo - Kyoto University, Research Reactor Institute, Kumatori-cho, Sennan-gun, Osaka 590-04, Japan. TEL 81-724-52-0901. FAX 81-724-53-0360. E-mail: shiroya@kuca.rri.kyoto-u.ac.jp. Dir. Seiji Shiroya. **Document type:** newsletter.

539.7   JA
GENSHIRYOKU ANZEN HAKUSHO/WHITE PAPER OF NUCLEAR SAFETY. (Text in Japanese) 1981. a. 3480 Yen. (Sorifu Genshiryoku Anzen Iikai - Prime Minister's Office, Nuclear Safety Commission) Okurasho Insatsukyoku - Ministry of Finance, Printing Bureau, 2-4, Toranomon 2-chome, Minato-ku, Tokyo 105, Japan. (Subscr. to: Government Publications Service Center, 2-1, 1-chome, Kasumigaseki, Chiyoda-ku, Tokyo, Japan) **Document type:** government publication.

539.7   JA   ISSN 0387-9674
GENSHIRYOKU ANZEN IINKAI GEPPO/NUCLEAR SAFETY COMMISSION. MONTHLY REPORT. (Text in Japanese) 1978. m. 700 Yen per no. (Kagaku Gijutsucho, Genshiryoku Anzenkyoku - Science and Technology Agency, Nuclear Safety Bureau) Okurasho Insatsukyoku - Ministry of Finance, Printing Bureau, 2-4, Toranomon 2-chome, Minato-ku, Tokyo 105, Japan.

GENSHIRYOKU ANZEN KENKYU SOGO HAPPYOKAI KOEN YOSHISHU/ABSTRACTS OF MEETING ON NUCLEAR SAFETY RESEARCH. see *PHYSICS — Abstracting, Bibliographies, Statistics*

539.7   JA
GENSHIRYOKU ANZEN KENKYU SOGO HAPPYOKAI YOKOSHU/PREPRINTS OF MEETING ON NUCLEAR SAFETY RESEARCH. (Text in Japanese) a. Genshiryoku Anzen Kenkyu Kyokai - Nuclear Safety Research Association, 2-2, Uchisaiwaicho 1-chome, Chiyoda-ku, Tokyo 100, Japan.

539.7   JA
GENSHIRYOKU ANZEN NENPO/ANNUAL REPORT OF NUCLEAR SAFETY. (Text in Japanese) 1981. a. Sorifu Genshiryoku Anzen Iikai - Prime Minister's Office, Nuclear Safety Commission, 6-1, Nagatacho 1-chome, Chiyoda-ku, Tokyo 100, Japan.

539.7   JA
GENSHIRYOKU ANZENSEI KENKYU NO GENJO/PROGRESS OF NUCLEAR SAFETY RESEARCH. (Text in Japanese) 1973. a. Nihon Genshiryoku Kenkyujo, Anzen Shiken Kenkyu Senta - Japan Atomic Energy Research Institute, Nuclear Safety Research Center, 2-4, Shirane, Shirakata, Tokaimura, Naka-gun, Ibaraki-ken 319-11, Japan.

539.7   CC   ISSN 1003-9988
          CODEN: HEDOEW
HE WULI DONGTAI/TRENDS IN NUCLEAR PHYSICS. (Text in Chinese; abstracts in English) 1984. q. $30. (Zhongguo Kexueyuan, Jindai Wuli Yanjiusuo - Chinese Academy of Sciences, Institute of Modern Physics) He Wuli Dongtai Bianjibu, P.O. Box 31, Lanzhou, Gansu 730000, People's Republic of China. TEL 0931-28961. FAX 0931-8881100. TELEX 72153 IMP AS CN. Ed. Wu Enjiu. circ. 2,000. **Document type:** academic/scholarly publication.
—CASDDS.
Description: Features new developments in the field of nuclear physics.
Refereed Serial

539.7   JA
HERIKARUKEI NO TOJIKOME/CONFINEMENT OF HELICAL SYSTEM. (Text in English, Japanese) irreg. Kyoto University, Plasma Physics Laboratory - Kyoto Daigaku Heriotoron Kaku Yugo Kenkyu Senta, Gokasho, Uji-shi, Kyoto 611, Japan.

539.7   US   ISSN 0899-9996
QC793
HIGH ENERGY PHYSICS AND NUCLEAR PHYSICS. English translation of: Gaoneng Wuli yu He Wuli (CC ISSN 0254-3052) 1988. q. $455 (effective 1996). (Chinese Society of High Energy Physics, CC - Zhongguo Gaoneng Wuli Xuehui) Allerton Press, Inc., 150 Fifth Ave., New York, NY 10011. TEL 212-924-3950. FAX 212-463-9684. Ed. Xian Dingchang. (back issues avail.) **Indexed:** INSPEC (1987-). **Document type:** academic/scholarly publication.
—CCC.
Description: Covers physics research in China, including quantum field theory, and particle physics.
Refereed Serial

539.7   JA   ISSN 0914-9287
HOSHAKO/SYNCHROTRON RADIATION. (Text in Japanese; summaries in English, Japanese) 1988. q. 2000 Yen per no. Nihon Hoshako Gakkai - Japanese Society for Synchrotron Radiation Research, c/o Aionikusu K.K., 3-4, Koishikawa 2-chome, Bunkyo-ku, Tokyo 112, Japan. **Indexed:** INIS Atomind.
—BLDSC (4809.518100).

539.7   JA
HOSHAKO SHINPOJUMU YOKOSHU/JAPANESE SOCIETY FOR SYNCHROTRON RADIATION RESEARCH. PREPRINTS OF SYMPOSIUM. (Text in Japanese; summaries in English) 1990. a. 2000 Yen. Nihon Hoshako Gakkai - Japanese Society for Synchrotron Radiation Research, c/o Aionikusu K.K., 3-4, Koishikawa 2-chome, Bunkyo-ku, Tokyo 112, Japan.

539.2   JA   ISSN 0285-3604
          CODEN: HOSHDJ
HOSHASEN/IONIZING RADIATION. (Text in English, Japanese; summaries in English) 1974. 3/yr. 4000 Yen membership. Oyo Butsuri Gakkai Hoshasen Bunkakai - Japan Society of Applied Physics, 1-12-3, Kudan Kita, Chiyada-ku, Tokyo 102, Japan. adv. **Document type:** academic/scholarly publication.
—CASDDS.

539.2   JA   ISSN 0912-5116
HOSHASEN JIKKENJO DAYORI/RADIATION LABORATORY NEWS. (Text in Japanese) 1985. s-a. Osaka Daigaku, Sangyo Kagaku Kenkyujo, Fuzoku Hoshasen Jikkenjo - Osaka University, Institute of Science and Industrial Research, Radiation Laboratory, 8-1, Mihogaoka, Ibaraki-shi, Osaka 567, Japan.

539.2   JA
HOSHASEN KANRISHITSU NENPO/RADIOLOGICAL HEALTH OFFICE. ANNUAL REPORT. (Text in Japanese) 1965. a. Tokyo Daigaku, Genshiryoku Kenkyu Sogo Senta, Hoshasen Kanrishitsu - University of Tokyo, Research Center for Nuclear Science and Technology, Radiological Health Office, 11-16, Yayoi 2-chome, Bunkyo-ku, Tokyo 113, Japan.

539.2   JA
HOSHASEN PUROSESU KOKUSAI KAIGI SANKA CHOSADAN HOKOKUSHO/INTERNATIONAL MEETING ON RADIATION PROCESSING. RESEARCH REPORTS. (Text in Japanese) a. Nihon Genshiryoku Sangyo Kaigi - Japan Atomic Industrial Forum, 1-13, Shinbashi 1-chome, Minato-ku, Tokyo 105, Japan.

HOSHASEN RIYO KENKYU SEIKA HOKOKUKAI KOEN YOSHI/ABSTRACTS OF RESEARCH RESULTS OF RADIATION UTILIZATION. see *PHYSICS — Abstracting, Bibliographies, Statistics*

539.2   JA
HOSHASEN RIYO KENKYUKAI HOKOKUKAI/STUDY MEETING OF UTILIZATION OF RADIATION. (Text in Japanese) a. Nihon Genshiryoku Sangyo Kaigi - Japan Atomic Industrial Forum, 1-13, Shinbashi 1-chome, Minato-ku, Tokyo 105, Japan.

539.2   JA
HOSHASEN RIYO KENKYUKAI HOKOKUSHO, AISOTOPU RIYO GURUPU/RESEARCH REPORT OF UTILIZATION OF RADIATION BY ISOTOPE USER'S GROUP. (Text in Japanese) a. Nihon Genshiryoku Sangyo Kaigi - Japan Atomic Industrial Forum, 1-13, Shinbashi 1-chome, Minato-ku, Tokyo 105, Japan.

539.2   JA
HOSHASEN RIYO KENKYUKAI HOKOKUSHO, SHOSHA RIYO GURUPU/RESEARCH REPORT OF UTILIZATION OF RADIATION BY IRRADIATION THERAPY GROUP. (Text in Japanese) a. Nihon Genshiryoku Sangyo Kaigi - Japan Atomic Industrial Forum, 1-13, Shinbashi 1-chome, Minato-ku, Tokyo 105, Japan.

539.2   JA   ISSN 0286-8873
HOSHASEN TO SANGYO/RADIATION AND INDUSTRIES. (Text in Japanese) 1976. 3/yr. 620 Yen per no. Hoshasen Shosha Shinko Kyokai - Irradiation Development Association, Nihon Genshiryoku Kenkyujo Takasaki Kenkyujo, 1233, Watanukimachi, Takasaki-shi, Gunma-ken 370-12, Japan.

I S T E C JOURNAL. (International Superconductivity Technology Center) see *ELECTRONICS*

539.7   FR   ISSN 0399-127X
INSTITUT DES SCIENCES NUCLEAIRES GRENOBLE. RAPPORT D'ACTIVITE. (Text in French; summaries in English) 1982. biennial. free. Institut des Sciences Nucleaires Grenoble, 53 av. des Martyrs, 38026 Grenoble Cedex, France. TEL 76-28-40-00. FAX 76-28-40-04. circ. 500. (back issues avail.) **Indexed:** INIS Atomind. **Document type:** corporate report.
Formerly (until 1981): Universite Scientifique et Medical de Grenoble. Institut des Sciences Nucleaires. Rapport Annuel (ISSN 0399-1261)

PHYSICS — NUCLEAR PHYSICS

539.2   JA
INSTITUTE FOR MOLECULAR SCIENCE. ANNUAL REVIEW. (Text in English) 1978. a. Okazaki National Research Institutes, Institute for Molecular Science - Okazaki Kokuritsu Kyodo Kenkyu Kiko Bunshi Kagaku Kenkyujo, 38, Saigonaka, Myodaiji-cho, Okazaki-shi, Aichi-ken 444, Japan.

538.2   JA
INSTITUTE FOR MOLECULAR SCIENCE. COMPUTER CENTER REPORT/OKAZAKI KOKURITSU KYODO KENKYU KIKO BUNSHI KAGAKU KENKYUJO DENSHI KEISANKI SENTA REPOTO. (Text in English, Japanese) 1980. a. Okazaki National Research Institutes, Institute for Molecular Science, Computer Center, 38, Saigo Naka, Myodaiji-cho, Okazaki-shi, Aichi-ken 444, Japan.

539.722   II   ISSN 0074-3046
INTERNATIONAL CONFERENCE ON COSMIC RAYS. (PROCEEDINGS). 1984. biennial, 18th, 1983, India. $120. Tata Institute of Fundamental Research, c/o Prof. P.V. Ramana Murthy, Colaba, Bombay 5, India. adv.; bk.rev.

539.75   US
INTERNATIONAL CONFERENCE ON THE PHYSICS OF ELECTRONIC AND ATOMIC COLLISIONS. ABSTRACTS OF CONTRIBUTED PAPERS AND INVITED PAPERS. Variant titles: Electronic and Atomic Collisions. Physics of Electronic and Atomic Collisions. (Publisher varies for each conference; 7th, 10th-15th published by North-Holland) 1958. irreg., 15th, 1987, Brighton. $150. International Union of Pure and Applied Physics, Commission on Atomic and Molecular Physics and Spectroscopy, c/o Norman Bardsley, Sec., L-296, Box 800, Livermore, CA 94550. TEL 510-422-1100. (Dist. by: Elsevier Science B.V., P.O. Box 211, 1000 AE Amsterdam, Netherlands. TEL 020-5803911; Subscr. in U.S. and Canada to: Elsevier Science Inc., Box 882, Madison Sq. Sta., New York, NY 10159. TEL 212-989-5800) circ. 1,500. **Indexed:** INSPEC. **Document type:** proceedings.
Formerly: International Conference on the Physics of Electronic and Atomic Collisions. Papers (ISSN 0074-333X)

539.7   SI   ISSN 0218-3013
QC770   CODEN: IMPEER
INTERNATIONAL JOURNAL OF MODERN PHYSICS E: REPORT ON NUCLEAR PHYSICS. 1992. q. $100 for developing countries; developed countries $195. World Scientific Publishing Co. Pte. Ltd., Farrer Rd., P.O. Box 128, Singapore 9128, Singapore. TEL 3825663. FAX 3825919. TELEX RS-28561-WSPC. (U.K. addr.: 73 Lynton Mead, Totteridge, London N20 8DH, England. TEL 44-181-4462461; U.S. addr.: 1060 Main St., River Edge, NJ 07661. TEL 800-227-7562) Ed. Walter Greiner. **Indexed:** INSPEC (1992-). **Document type:** academic/scholarly publication.
—BLDSC (4542.365240); SWETS.
Description: Publishes research papers as well as review articles both in theoretical and experimental nuclear physics, including articles devoted to the interface between particle and nuclear and between astrophysics and nuclear physics.

539.7 643   SI   ISSN 0129-0835
QD96.X2   CODEN: IJPXET
INTERNATIONAL JOURNAL OF P I X E. (Particle-Induced X-ray Emission) (Text in English) 1990. q. $115 to individuals; institutions of developing countries $160, of developed countries $250. World Scientific Publishing Co. Pte. Ltd., Farrer Rd., P.O. Box 128, Singapore 9128, Singapore. TEL 3825663. FAX 3825919. TELEX RS-28561-WSPC. (UK addr.: 73 Lynton Mead, London N20 8DH, England. TEL 44-81-4462461; US addr.: 1060 Main St., Ste. 1B, River Edge, NJ 07661. TEL 800-227-7562) Ed. S. Morita. **Document type:** academic/scholarly publication.
—BLDSC (4542.467300); CASDDS. **CCC.**
Description: Publishes original papers and reviews in various aspects of particle-induced X-ray emission (PIXE).

574 530 618   UK   ISSN 0360-3016
RC271.R3   CODEN: IOBPD3
INTERNATIONAL JOURNAL OF RADIATION: ONCOLOGY - BIOLOGY - PHYSICS. 1976. 15/yr. $1850 to institutions (effective 1996). Elsevier Science Ltd., Pergamon, P.O. Box 800, Kidlington, Oxford OX5 1DX, England. TEL 44-1865-843000. FAX 44-1865-843010. E-mail: nlinfo-f@elsevier.nl; usinfo-f@elsevier.com; forinfo-kyf04035@niftyserve.or.jp; Site addr.: http://www.elsevier.nl/. (Subscr. in U.S. and Canada to: Elsevier Science, 660 White Plains Rd., Tarrytown, NY 10591-5153. TEL 914-524-9200. FAX 914-333-2444) Ed. Dr. Philip Rubin. circ. 4,000. (also avail. in microfilm from UMI; reprint service avail. from UMI) **Indexed:** Abstr.Health Care Manage.Stud., Biol.Abstr., Biwk.Pap.Rad.Chem.& Photochem., Chem.Abstr., Curr.Adv.Cancer Res., Curr.Adv.Genetics & Molec.Biol., Curr.Cont., Dairy Sci.Abstr., Dent.Ind., Excerp.Med., Helminthol.Abstr., Ind.Med., Ind.Sci.Rev., INIS Atomind., INSPEC, Med.& Surg.Dermat., Risk Abstr., Sci.Cit.Ind. **Document type:** academic/scholarly publication.
—BLDSC (4542.523000); CASDDS; Ei; Faxon; Genuine Article; SWETS; UMI; UnCover. **CCC.**
Refereed Serial

539.7   SI   ISSN 0217-9474
CODEN: IRNPEH
INTERNATIONAL REVIEW OF NUCLEAR PHYSICS. (Text in English) 1984. irreg., vol.7, 1991. price varies. World Scientific Publishing Co. Pte. Ltd., Farrer Rd., P.O. Box 128, Singapore 9128, Singapore. TEL 3825663. FAX 3825919. TELEX RS 28561 WSPC. (UK addr.: 73 Lynton Mead, Totteridge, London N20 8DH, England. TEL 44-81-4462461; US addr.: 1060 Main St., Ste. 1B, River Edge, NJ 07661. TEL 800-227-7562) Ed. T.T.S. Kuo.
Indexed: INSPEC. **Document type:** monographic series.
—BLDSC (4547.410000); CASDDS.

J A I F ANNUAL CONFERENCE ABSTRACTS. (Japan Atomic Industrial Forum) see *PHYSICS — Abstracting, Bibliographies, Statistics*

621.48   NE   ISSN 0022-3115
TK9185.A1   CODEN: JNUMAM
JOURNAL OF NUCLEAR MATERIALS; materials aspects of fission and fusion. (Text in English, French, German) 1959. 36/yr. fl.6912($4215) (effective 1996). North-Holland (Subsidiary of: Elsevier Science B.V.), P.O. Box 211, 1000 AE Amsterdam, Netherlands. TEL 31-20-4853911. FAX 31-20-4853598. TELEX 18582 ESPA NL. (Subscr. in U.S. and Canada to: Elsevier Science Inc., Box 882, Madison Sq. Sta., New York, NY 10159. TEL 212-989-5800. FAX 212-633-3990) Ed. L.K. Mansur. adv.; bk.rev.; charts; illus.; cum.index. (also avail. in microform from UMI; back issues avail.) **Indexed:** Appl.Mech.Rev., Bull.Thermodyn.& Thermochem., Cadscan, Chem.Abstr., Curr.Cont., Energy Info.Abstr., Eng.Ind., Fuel & Energy Abstr., Ind.Sci.Rev., INIS Atomind., INSPEC (1968-), Lead Abstr., Met.Abstr., Phys.Ber., World Alum.Abstr., Zincscan. **Document type:** academic/scholarly publication.
—BLDSC (5023.200000); CASDDS; Ei; Faxon; Genuine Article; SWETS; UnCover. **CCC.**
Description: Publishes papers covering the field of materials research related to nuclear science and technology.
Refereed Serial

539 621.48   JA   ISSN 0022-3131
CODEN: JNSTAX
JOURNAL OF NUCLEAR SCIENCE AND TECHNOLOGY/NIHON GENSHIRYOKU GAKKAI OBUN RONBUNSHI. (Text in English) 1964. m. 18000 Yen($150) Atomic Energy Society of Japan - Nihon Genshiryoku Gakkai, 1-1-13, Shinbashi, Minato-ku, Tokyo 105, Japan. TEL 03-3508-1261. FAX 03-3581-6128. Ed. Hiroshi Sekimoto. adv.; abstr.; charts; illus.; index. circ. 1,500. (also avail. in microform; reprint service avail.) **Indexed:** Biwk.Pap.Rad.Chem.& Photochem., CAD CAM Abstr., Chem.Abstr., Crop Physiol.Abstr., Curr.Cont., Energy Info.Abstr., Environ.Abstr., Environ.Per.Bibl., Excerp.Med., Fluidex, Ind.Sci.Rev., INIS Atomind, INSPEC, JTA, Met.Abstr., Sci.Cit.Ind., World Alum.Abstr. **Document type:** academic/scholarly publication.
—BLDSC (5023.500000); CASDDS; CIS; Ei; Faxon; Genuine Article; SWETS; UMI; UnCover. **CCC.**

539.7   UK   ISSN 0954-3899
QC770   CODEN: JPGPED
JOURNAL OF PHYSICS G: NUCLEAR AND PARTICLE PHYSICS. 1975. m. £867($1786) (effective 1996). (Institute of Physics) I O P Publishing Ltd., Techno House, Redcliffe Way, Bristol, Avon BS1 6NX, England. TEL 0117-929-7481. FAX 0117-929-4318. TELEX 449149 INSTP G. (U.S. subscr. to: American Institute of Physics, Member and Subscriber Services, 500 Sunnyside Blvd., Woodbury, NY 11797-2900. TEL 516-349-7800) Ed. P. Paul. bibl.; charts; illus.; index. circ. 745. (also avail. in microfiche from AIP; microfilm from AIP; back issues avail.) **Indexed:** Cadscan, Chem.Abstr., Curr.Cont., Ind.Sci.Rev., INIS Atomind., INSPEC, Lead Abstr., Math.R., Phys.Ber., Zincscan. **Document type:** academic/scholarly publication.
—BLDSC (5036.219000); CASDDS; Faxon; Genuine Article; UnCover. **CCC.**
Formerly: Journal of Physics G: Nuclear Physics (ISSN 0305-4616)
Description: Explores theoretical and experimental topics in the physics of elementary particles and fluids, intermediate energy and cosmic rays.

539.735   DK   ISSN 0909-0495
▼**JOURNAL OF SYNCHROTRON RADIATION.** (Text in English) 1994. bi-m. DKK 2750 (with Journal of Applied Crystallography, DKK 3535) (effective 1996). (International Union of Crystallography) Munksgaard International Publishers Ltd., 35 Noerre Soegade, P.O. Box 1248, DK-1016 Copenhagen K, Denmark. TEL 45-33-12-70-30. FAX 45-33-12-93-87. E-mail: fsub@mail.munksgaard.dk.

539.7   JA
KAKU YUGO KENKYU KAIHATSU NO GENJO/STATUS OF NUCLEAR FUSION RESEARCH AND DEVELOPMENT. (Text in Japanese) 1975. a. Nihon Genshiryoku Kenkyujo, Naka Kenkyujo - Japan Atomic Energy Research Institute, Naka Fusion Research Establishment, 801, Mukoyama, Naka-machi, Naka-gun, Ibaraki-ken 311-01, Japan.

539.7   JA
KAKU YUGO RENGO KOENKAI YOKOSHU/PREPRINTS OF JOINT CONFERENCE ON NUCLEAR FUSION. (Text in Japanese) 1978. a. Purazuma Kaku Yugo Gakkai - Japan Society of Plasma Science and Nuclear Fusion Research, 20-29, Nishiki 2-chome, Naka-ku, Nagoya-shi, Aichi-ken 460, Japan.

539.7   JA   ISSN 0915-6704
KAKU YUUGOU KAGAKU KENKYUSHO NYUSU/NATIONAL INSTITUTE FOR FUSION SCIENCE. NEWS. (Text in Japanese) 1989. m. free. Kaku Yuugou Kagaku Kenkyusho - National Institute for Fusion Science, Furocho, Chikusa-ku, Nagoya-shi, Aichi-ken 464-01, Japan. TEL 81-52-789-4551. FAX 81-52-789-4200. TELEX 0447-3691 NIFSJ. circ. 2,650 (controlled). **Document type:** newsletter.

539.7   JA   ISSN 0385-2105
QC770   CODEN: TLNRBV
KAKURIKEN KENKYU HOKOKU/LABORATORY OF NUCLEAR SCIENCE. RESEARCH REPORT. (Text in English, Japanese) 1968. s-a. Tohoku Daigaku, Rigakubu, Fuzoku Genshikaku Rigaku Kenkyu Shisetsu - Tohoku University, Faculty of Science, Laboratory of Nuclear Science, 2-1, Minamine 1-chome, Taihaku-ku, Sendai-shi, Miyagi-ken 982, Japan.
—BLDSC (7762.430000); CASDDS.

KYUSHU UNIVERSITY. RESEARCH INSTITUTE FOR APPLIED MECHANICS. BULLETIN/KYUSHU DAIGAKU OYORIKIGAKU KENKYUSHO SHOHO. see *ENGINEERING — Engineering Mechanics And Materials*

KYUSHU UNIVERSITY. RESEARCH INSTITUTE FOR APPLIED MECHANICS. REPORTS/OYORIKIGAKU KENKYUSHO OBUN HOKOKU. see *ENGINEERING — Engineering Mechanics And Materials*

539 US ISSN 0075-7888
LANDOLT-BOERNSTEIN, ZAHLENWERTE UND FUNKTIONEN AUS NATURWISSENSCHAFTEN UND TECHNIK. NEUE SERIE. GROUP 1: NUCLEAR PHYSICS/LANDOLT-BOERNSTEIN NUMERICAL DATA AND FUNCTIONAL RELATIONSHIPS IN SCIENCE AND TECHNOLOGY. NEW SERIES. 1961. irreg. price varies. Springer-Verlag, 175 Fifth Ave., New York, NY 10010. TEL 212-460-1500. FAX 212-473-6272. (Also: Berlin, Heidelberg, Tokyo and Vienna) (reprint service avail. from ISI) **Document type:** academic/scholarly publication.

539 US ISSN 0075-7918
LANDOLT-BOERNSTEIN, ZAHLENWERTE UND FUNKTIONEN AUS NATURWISSENSCHAFTEN UND TECHNIK. NEUE SERIE. GROUP 2: ATOMIC PHYSICS. 1965. irreg. price varies. Springer-Verlag, 175 Fifth Ave., New York, NY 10010. TEL 212-460-1500. FAX 212-473-6272. (Also: Berlin, Heidelberg, Tokyo and Vienna) (reprint service avail. from ISI) **Document type:** academic/scholarly publication.

543.0877 UK ISSN 1352-8661
CODEN: MRBMEQ
MAGNETIC RESONANCE MATERIALS IN PHYSICS, BIOLOGY AND MEDICINE. 1993. q. £59($95) to individuals; institutions in the E.U. £125 (N. America $200; elsewhere £140) (effective 1995). Chapman & Hall, Journals Department (Subsidiary of: International Thomson Publishing Group), 2-6 Boundary Row, London SE1 8HN, England. TEL 0171-856-0066. FAX 0171-522-9623. TELEX 290164 CHAPMA G. E-mail: journal@chahall.mhs.compuserve.com. (Subscr. to: International Thomson Publishing Services Ltd., Cheriton House, North Way, Andover, Hants. SP10 5BE, England. TEL 01264-342713. FAX 01264-342807; Subscr. in N. America to: Chapman & Hall, Journals Promotion Department, One Penn Plaza, 41st Fl., New York, NY 10119. TEL 212-564-1060. FAX 212-564-1505) Eds. Axel Haase, Dieter Matthaei. adv.; bk.rev. (reprint service avail.) **Indexed:** Chem.Abstr., Excerp.Med. (1994-), INSPEC (1993-). **Document type:** academic/scholarly publication.
—BLDSC (5334.854000); CASDDS; Genuine Article.
Formerly (until 1995): Magma (ISSN 0968-5243); Which was previously announced as: Magma Magnetic Resonance Materials.
Description: Presents the latest research, development, and application of techniques in magnetic resonance imaging and spectroscopy
Refereed Serial

539.7 US
MICHIGAN STATE UNIVERSITY. NATIONAL SUPERCONDUCTING CYCLOTRON LABORATORY (PUBLICATION). no.21, 1964. irreg., no.700, 1989. Michigan State University, Superconducting Cyclotron Laboratory, E. Lansing, MI 48824-1321. TEL 517-355-9671. circ. 300. **Document type:** monographic series.
Formerly: Michigan State University. Department of Physics. Cyclotron Project (Publication) (ISSN 0076-8146)

539.7 SI ISSN 0217-7323
QC770 CODEN: MPLAEQ
MODERN PHYSICS LETTER A. 1986. 40/yr. $1089 to institutions of developed countries; individuals & developing countries $545. World Scientific Publishing Co. Pte. Ltd., Farrer Rd., P.O. Box 128, Singapore 9128, Singapore. TEL 3825663. FAX 3825919. TELEX RS-28561-WSPC. (UK addr.: 73 Lynton Mead, Totteridge, London N20 8DH, England. TEL 44-81-4462461; US addr.: 1060 Main St., Ste. 1B, River Edge, NJ 07661. TEL 800-227-7562) Ed.Bd. circ. 550. (back issues avail.) **Indexed:** INSPEC (1987-).
—BLDSC (5890.835000); CASDDS; Ei; Faxon; Genuine Article; SWETS; UnCover. **CCC.**
Description: Contains research papers covering current research development in particle and field physics, nuclear physics, cosmology and gravitation.

539.7 SI ISSN 0217-9849
QC173.4.C65 CODEN: MPLBET
MODERN PHYSICS LETTER B. (Text in English) 1987. 30/yr. $1020 to institutions of developed countries; individuals & developing countries $510. World Scientific Publishing Co. Pte. Ltd., Farrer Rd., P.O. Box 128, Singapore 9128, Singapore. TEL 3825663. FAX 3825919. TELEX RS-28561-WSPC. (US addr.: 1060 Main St., Ste. 1B, River Edge, NJ 07661. TEL 800-227-7562; European addr.: 73 Lynton Mead, Totteridge, London N20 8DH, England. TEL 44-81-4462461) Ed.Bd. circ. 350. (back issues avail.) **Indexed:** INSPEC (1987-). **Document type:** academic/scholarly publication.
—BLDSC (5890.835100); CASDDS; Ei; Faxon; SWETS; UnCover. **CCC.**
Description: Covers condensed matter physics, statistical physics and applied physics at the post-graduate level.

MUTATION BREEDING REVIEW. see *AGRICULTURE — Crop Production And Soil*

539.7 US ISSN 0170-5989
QC490 CODEN: NBPPD3
N M R. (Nuclear Magnetic Resonance); basic principles and progress. (Text mainly in English; occasionally in German) 1969. irreg., no.28, 1992. price varies. Springer-Verlag, 175 Fifth Ave., New York, NY 10010. TEL 212-460-1500. FAX 212-473-6272. (Also: Berlin, Heidelberg, Tokyo and Vienna) Ed. E. Fluck. illus. (reprint service avail. from ISI) **Document type:** academic/scholarly publication.
—CASDDS; Faxon. **CCC.**
Supersedes: N M R Basic Principles and Progress (ISSN 0078-088X)

539.764 JA ISSN 0915-7522
NAGOYA UNIVERSITY. PLASMA SCIENCE CENTER. (Text in English) 1989. irreg. Nagoya University, Plasma Science Center - Nagoya Daigaku Purazuma Kagaku Senta, Furo-cho, Chikusa-ku, Nagoya-shi, Aichi-ken 464-01, Japan.
—BLDSC (6015.144000).

539.76 JA ISSN 0915-6364
NATIONAL INSTITUTE FOR FUSION SCIENCE. RESEARCH REPORT. DATA SERIES. Key Title: Research Report N I F S - Data Series. (Text in English) 1990. irreg. National Institute for Fusion Science - Kaku Yugo Kagaku Kenkyujo, Furo-cho, Chikusa-ku, Nagoya-shi, Aichi-ken 464-01, Japan. **Indexed:** INSPEC.
—BLDSC (7762.722434).

539.76 JA ISSN 0915-6372
NATIONAL INSTITUTE FOR FUSION SCIENCE. RESEARCH REPORT. MEMO SERIES. Key Title: Research Report N I F S - Memo Series. (Text in Japanese; summaries in English, Japanese) 1991. irreg. National Institute for Fusion Science - Kaku Yugo Kagaku Kenkyujo, Furo-cho, Chikusa-ku, Nagoya-shi, Aichi-ken 464-01, Japan. Ed. Kazuo Toi. **Document type:** academic/scholarly publication.
—BLDSC (7762.722436).

539.7 US ISSN 1044-8632
QC793.5.N462 CODEN: NTNEEJ
NEUTRON NEWS. 1989. 4/yr. 73 ECU (effective 1996). Gordon and Breach Science Publishers, c/o International Publishers Distributor, 820 Town Center Dr., Langhorne, PA 19047. TEL 215-750-2642. FAX 215-750-6343. (Subscr. to: International Publishers Distributor, P.O. Box 90, Reading, Berkshire RG1 8JL, England. TEL 44-173-456-8316) (also avail. in microform)
—BLDSC (6081.605500). **CCC.**
Refereed Serial

539.2 JA
NIHON AISOTOPU HOSHASEN SOGO KAIGI HOBUNSHU/JAPAN CONFERENCE ON RADIATION AND RADIOISOTOPES. PROCEEDINGS. (Text in English, Japanese; summaries in English) 1956. biennial. Nihon Genshiryoku Sangyo Kaigi - Japan Atomic Industrial Forum, 1-13, Shinbashi 1-chome, Minato-ku, Tokyo 105, Japan. **Document type:** proceedings.

539.7 JA ISSN 0915-5244
NIHON HOSHAKO GAKKAI NENKAI YOKOSHU/JAPANESE SOCIETY OF SYNCHROTRON RADIATION RESEARCH. PREPRINTS OF ANNUAL MEETING. (Text in English, Japanese) 1988. a. Nihon Hoshako Gakkai - Japanese Society of Synchrotron Radiation Research, c/o Aionikusu K.K., 3-4, Koishikawa 2-chome, Bunkyo-ku, Tokyo 112, Japan.

539.7 530.44 UN ISSN 0029-5515
QC791 CODEN: NUFUAU
NUCLEAR FUSION/FUSION NUCLEAIRE; journal of plasma physics and thermonuclear fusion. (Text and summaries in English) 1960. m. S.9000($900) International Atomic Energy Agency, Wagramerstr. 5, P.O. Box 100, A-1400 Vienna, Austria. TEL 43-1-209-2630. FAX 43-1-209-5302. E-mail: fossett@adp01.iaea.or.at. (Dist. in U.S. by: Unipub, 4611-F Assembly Dr., Lanham, MD 20706-4391) Ed. C. Bobeldijk. bk.rev.; abstr.; bibl.; charts; illus.; index; circ. 1,100 (paid). (also avail. in microform from UMI; reprint service avail. from UMI) **Indexed:** Appl.Mech.Rev., Chem.Abstr., Curr.Cont., Eng.Ind., Ind.Sci.Rev., INIS Atomind., INSPEC, Phys.Ber. **Document type:** academic/scholarly publication.
—BLDSC (6180.760000); CASDDS; Ei; Faxon; Genuine Article; SWETS; UnCover.

539 NE ISSN 0168-9002
QC785.5 CODEN: NIMAER
NUCLEAR INSTRUMENTS & METHODS IN PHYSICS RESEARCH. SECTION A. ACCELERATORS, SPECTROMETERS, DETECTORS, AND ASSOCIATED EQUIPMENT. (Text in English, French and German; summaries in English) 1957. 51/yr. fl.11968($7298) (effective 1996). North-Holland (Subsidiary of: Elsevier Science B.V.), P.O. Box 211, 1000 AE Amsterdam, Netherlands. TEL 31-20-4853911. FAX 31-20-4853598. TELEX 18582 ESPA NL. (Subscr. in U.S. and Canada to: Elsevier Science Inc., Box 882, Madison Sq. Sta., New York, NY 10159. TEL 212-989-5800. FAX 212-633-3990) Ed. K. Siegbahn. adv.; bk.rev.; index. (also avail. in microform from UMI; back issues avail.) **Indexed:** Acid Rain Abstr., Acid Rain Ind., Art & Archaeol.Tech.Abstr., Cadscan, Chem.Abstr., Comput.Abstr., Energy Ind., Energy Info.Abstr., Eng.Ind., Excerp.Med., GeoRef., Ind.Sci.Rev., INSPEC, Int.Aerosp.Abstr., Lead Abstr., Mass Spectr.Bull., Nucl.Sci.Abstr., Phys.Ber., Zincscan. **Document type:** academic/scholarly publication.
—BLDSC (6180.861300); CASDDS; Ei; Faxon; Genuine Article; SWETS; UnCover. **CCC.**
Supersedes in part (in 1984): Nuclear Instruments and Methods in Physics Research (ISSN 0167-5087); Formerly: Nuclear Instruments and Methods (ISSN 0029-554X)
Description: Publishes papers on particle accelerators and other devices producing and measuring nuclear radiations.
Refereed Serial

539.7 NE ISSN 0168-583X
QC785.5 CODEN: NIMBEU
NUCLEAR INSTRUMENTS & METHODS IN PHYSICS RESEARCH. SECTION B. BEAM INTERACTIONS WITH MATERIALS AND ATOMS. 1957. 52/yr. fl.9724($5930) (effective 1996). North-Holland (Subsidiary of: Elsevier Science B.V.), P.O. Box 211, 1000 AE Amsterdam, Netherlands. TEL 31-20-4853911. FAX 31-20-4853598. TELEX 18582 ESPA NL. (Subscr. in U.S. and Canada to: Elsevier Science Inc., Box 882, Madison Sq. Sta., New York, NY 10159. TEL 212-989-5800. FAX 212-633-3990) Ed. K. Siegbahn. (also avail. in microform from UMI; back issues avail.) **Indexed:** Acid Rain Abstr., Acid Rain Ind., Comput.Abstr., INSPEC (1984-), Mass Spectr.Bull. **Document type:** academic/scholarly publication.
—BLDSC (6180.861320); CASDDS; Ei; Faxon; Genuine Article; SWETS; UnCover. **CCC.**
Supersedes in part (in 1984): Nuclear Instruments and Methods in Physics Research (ISSN 0167-5087); Formerly: Nuclear Instruments and Methods (ISSN 0029-554X)
Description: Covers all aspects of the interaction of energetic beams with atoms, molecules and aggregate forms of matter.
Refereed Serial

NUCLEAR MEDICINE AND BIOLOGY. see *MEDICAL SCIENCES — Radiology And Nuclear Medicine*

PHYSICS — NUCLEAR PHYSICS

539.7 US ISSN 1061-9127
QC770
NUCLEAR PHYSICS NEWS. 1990. 4/yr. 48 ECU (effective 1996). (Nuclear Physics European Collaboration Committee) Gordon and Breach Science Publishers, c/o International Publishers Distributor, 820 Town Center Dr., Langhorne, PA 19046. TEL 215-750-2642. FAX 215-750-6343. (Subscr. to: International Publishers Distributor, P.O. Box 90, Reading, Berkshire RG1 8JL, England. TEL 44-173-456-8316) (also avail. in microform)
—BLDSC (6182.340000). **CCC.**
 Formerly (until 1991): European Nuclear Physics News (ISSN 1050-6896)
 Refereed Serial

539 NE ISSN 0375-9474
QC173 CODEN: NUPABL
NUCLEAR PHYSICS, SECTION A; devoted to the experimental and theoretical study of the fundamental constituents of matter and their interactions. (Text in English, French and German) 1956. 64/yr. fl.10512($6410) (effective 1996). North-Holland (Subsidiary of: Elsevier Science B.V.), P.O. Box 211, 1000 AE Amsterdam, Netherlands. TEL 31-20-4853911. FAX 31-20-4853598. TELEX 18582 ESPA NL. (Subscr. in U.S. and Canada to: Elsevier Science Inc., Box 882, Madison Sq. Sta., New York, NY 10159. TEL 212-989-5800. FAX 212-633-3990) Ed. G.E. Brown. adv.; bk.rev.; charts; index. (also avail. in microform from UMI; back issues avail.) **Indexed:** Cadscan, Chem.Abstr., Curr.Cont., Ind.Sci.Rev., INSPEC, Lead Abstr., Math.R., Met.Abstr., Phys.Ber., Zincscan. **Document type:** academic/scholarly publication.
—BLDSC (6182.010000); CASDDS; Ei; Faxon; Genuine Article; SWETS; UnCover. **CCC.**
 Supersedes in part (in 1967): Nuclear Physics (ISSN 0029-5582)
 Description: Covers the domain of general nuclear physics together with intermediate energy and heavy-ion physics, and astrophysics.
 Refereed Serial

539 NE ISSN 0550-3213
QC173 CODEN: NUPBBO
NUCLEAR PHYSICS, SECTION B; a journal devoted to the experimental and theoretical study of the fundamental constituents of matter and their interactions. (Proceedings supplement avail. (ISSN 0920-5632)) 1956. 75/yr. fl.16250($9909) (effective 1996). North-Holland (Subsidiary of: Elsevier Science B.V.), P.O. Box 211, 1000 AE Amsterdam, Netherlands. TEL 31-20-4853911. FAX 31-20-4853598. TELEX 18582 ESPA NL. (Subscr. in U.S. and Canada to: Elsevier Science Inc., Box 882, Madison Sq. Sta., New York, NY 10159. TEL 212-989-5800. FAX 212-633-3990) Ed. B.G. Altarelli. index. (also avail. in microform from UMI; back issues avail.) **Indexed:** Chem.Abstr., Curr.Cont., Ind.Sci.Rev., INSPEC, Math.R., Phys.Ber. **Document type:** academic/scholarly publication.
—BLDSC (6182.020000); CASDDS; Ei; Faxon; Genuine Article; SWETS; UnCover. **CCC.**
 Supersedes in part (in 1967): Nuclear Physics (ISSN 0029-5582)
 Description: Focuses on the domain of high energy physics and quantum field theory, and includes sections on cosmology, astrophysics and gravitation, computer simulations in physics and methods in theoretical physics.
 Refereed Serial

539.7 NE ISSN 0920-5632
QC770 CODEN: NPBSE7
NUCLEAR PHYSICS, SECTION B, PROCEEDINGS SUPPLEMENTS. (Supplement to: Nuclear Physics, Section B (ISSN 0550-3213)) 1987. 21/yr. fl.2541($1550) (effective 1996). North-Holland (Subsidiary of: Elsevier Science B.V.), P.O. Box 211, 1000 AE Amsterdam, Netherlands. TEL 31-20-4853911. FAX 31-20-4853598. TELEX 18582 ESPA NL. (Subscr. in U.S. and Canada to: Elsevier Science Inc., Box 882, Madison Sq. Sta., New York, NY 10159. TEL 212-989-5800. FAX 212-633-3990) Ed. B.G. Altarelli. index. (also avail. in microform from UMI; back issues avail.) **Indexed:** INSPEC (1987-). **Document type:** academic/scholarly publication, proceedings.
—BLDSC (6182.050000); CASDDS; SWETS. **CCC.**
 Description: Proceedings of large international conferences and specialized meetings in the field of high energy physics, covering developments in experimental and particle theory physics, hadronic physics, cosmology, astrophysics and gravitation, field theory, and statistical systems.
 Refereed Serial

539.7 CC ISSN 1001-8042
 CODEN: NSETEC
NUCLEAR SCIENCE AND TECHNIQUES. Chinese edition: He Jishu (ISSN 0253-3219) (Text in English) 1990. q. $70 to individuals (foreign $90); institutions $138 (foreign $158). (Chinese Academy of Sciences) Science Press, Marketing and Sales Department, 16 Donghuangchenggen North St., Beijing 100717, People's Republic of China. TEL 4010642. FAX 4019810. (Overseas dist. by: Science Press New York, Ltd., 84-04 58th Ave., Elmhurst, NY 11373. TEL 718-476-0238. FAX 718-476-0273) **Indexed:** INSPEC (1990-). **Document type:** academic/scholarly publication.
—BLDSC (6183.157000); CASDDS.
 Description: Covers the application of nuclear techniques in various fields, such as archaeology, geology, environmental science, radiochemistry and radiation chemistry.
 Refereed Serial

539.7 US
 CODEN: NSAPDD
NUCLEAR SCIENCE APPLICATIONS - SECTION B: IN DEPTH REVIEWS. (Included with section A) 1981. a. 167 ECU (effective 1993). Harwood Academic Publishers, c/o International Publishers Distributor, 820 Town Center Dr., Langhorne, PA 19047. TEL 215-750-2642. FAX 215-750-6343. (Subscr. to: International Publishers Distributor, PO Box 90, Reading, Berkshire, RG1 8JL, England. TEL 44-173-456-8316) Ed. Alexander Zucker. adv.; bk.rev. (also avail. in microfilm; microfiche; back issues avail.) **Indexed:** INSPEC.
—BLDSC (6183.165000); CASDDS. **CCC.**
 Supersedes in part: Nuclear Science Applications (ISSN 0191-1686)
 Refereed Serial

539.7 JA
 CODEN: NSIJAW
NUCLEAR SCIENCE INFORMATION OF JAPAN. ORAL PRESENTATION. (Text in English) 1961. 4/yr. exchange basis. Japan Atomic Energy Research Institute - Nippon Genshiryoku Kenkyusho, Tokai-mura, Naka-gun, Ibaraki 319-11, Japan. TEL 81-292-82-5376. FAX 81-292-82-6718. Ed. Nobuaki Hiramatsu. pat.; index. circ. 645. **Document type:** bibliography.
—CASDDS.
 Formerly (until Jan. 1987): Nuclear Science Information of Japan (ISSN 0029-5620); **Supersedes (in 1970):** Nuclear Science Abstracts of Japan (ISSN 0550-3248)
 Description: Provides bibliographic information on oral presentations at major conferences and meetings in the field of nuclear science and technology in Japan.

539 CH ISSN 0029-5647
 CODEN: HTKHAB
NUCLEAR SCIENCE JOURNAL. Key Title: Hezi Kexue. (Text in Chinese, English) 1957. bi-m. free. Chung Hua Nuclear Society, 67, Lane 144, Keelung Rd., Section 4, Taipei, Taiwan 107, Republic of China. (Editorial addr.: 1000 Wen-Hua Rd., Chia-An Village, Lung-Tan, Taiwan 325, Republic of China. TEL 03-471-1400. FAX 03-471-1404) Ed. Chao-Yie Yang. bk.rev. circ. 300. **Indexed:** Energy Rev., Environ.Per.Bibl., INSPEC (1982-), Nucl.Sci.Abstr. **Document type:** academic/scholarly publication.
—BLDSC (6183.300000); CASDDS; Ei; Faxon.
 Description: International medium for the publication of original studies, technical notes and review articles in the field of peaceful use of nuclear energy and technology.

539.7 US ISSN 0250-4375
 CODEN: NSRSD5
NUCLEAR SCIENCE RESEARCH CONFERENCE SERIES. irreg., latest vol.16. Harwood Academic Publishers, c/o International Publishers Distributor, 820 Town Center Dr., Langhorne, PA 19047. TEL 215-750-2642. FAX 215-750-6343. TELEX 236745 GOPUB UR. (Subscr. to: International Publishers Distributor, PO Box 90, Reading, Berkshire, RG1 8JL, England. TEL 44-173-456-8316) Ed. A. Zucker. (also avail. in microform) **Indexed:** INSPEC.
—CASDDS.
 Refereed Serial

539 621.48 US ISSN 0029-5450
TK9001 CODEN: NUTYBB
NUCLEAR TECHNOLOGY; applications for nuclear science, nuclear engineering and related arts. 1965. m. $455. American Nuclear Society, 555 N. Kensington Ave., La Grange Park, IL 60525. TEL 708-352-6611. (Co-sponsor: European Nuclear Society) Ed. William Vogelsang. bk.rev.; charts; illus.; stat.; index. circ. 1,300. (reprint service avail.) **Indexed:** A.S.& T.Ind., Art & Archaeol.Tech.Abstr., Biol.Abstr., CAD CAM Abstr., Cadscan, Chem.Abstr., Curr.Cont., Energy Info.Abstr., Eng.Ind., Environ.Abstr., Fuel & Energy Abstr., Ind.Sci.Rev., INSPEC, Lead Abstr., Met.Abstr., Risk Abstr., World Alum.Abstr., Zincscan. **Document type:** academic/scholarly publication.
—BLDSC (6183.520000); CASDDS; Ei; Faxon; Genuine Article; SWETS; UnCover. **CCC.**
 Formerly: Nuclear Applications and Technology.

OAK RIDGE NATIONAL LABORATORY REVIEW. see *ENERGY*

539.7 JA ISSN 0919-3952
 CODEN: ODCEEX
OSAKA DAIGAKU CHODENDO EREKUTORONIKUSU KENKYU SENTA HOKOKU/OSAKA UNIVERSITY. RESEARCH CENTER FOR SUPERCONDUCTING MATERIALS AND ELECTRONICS. ANNUAL PROGRESS REPORT. (Text in Japanese; summaries in English) 1981. a. Osaka Daigaku, Chodendo Erekutoronikusu Kenkyu Senta, 2-1, Yamada Oka, Suita-shi, Osaka 565, Japan.
—CASDDS.
 Formerly (until 1990): Osaka Daigaku Chodendo Kogaku Jikken Senta Hokoku - Osaka University. Laboratory for Applied Superconductivity. Annual Progress Report.

539 JA ISSN 0473-4580
OSAKA UNIVERSITY. LABORATORY OF NUCLEAR STUDIES. ANNUAL REPORT. (Text in English) 1962. a. exchange basis. Osaka University, Laboratory of Nuclear Studies - Osaka Daigaku Rigakubu Genshikaku Kenkyu Shisetsu, 1-1 Machikanayama-cho, Toyonaka-shi, Osaka 560, Japan. FAX 06-855-6664. Ed. Kenji Katori. circ. 1,200. **Document type:** academic/scholarly publication.

539.1 US ISSN 0956-9545
OXFORD SERIES ON NEUTRON SCATTERING IN CONDENSED MATTER. irreg. price varies. Oxford University Press, 200 Madison Ave., New York, NY 10016. TEL 212-679-7300. **Document type:** monographic series.
—BLDSC (6321.019700).

P A S C A L. E 11: PHYSIQUE ATOMIQUE ET MOLECULAIRE. PLASMAS. see *PHYSICS — Abstracting, Bibliographies, Statistics*

539.7 US ISSN 0031-2460
QC787.P3 CODEN: PLACBD
PARTICLE ACCELERATORS. (Text in English, French and German) 1969. 12/yr. (in 3 vols., 4 nos./vol.). 283 ECU per vol. (effective 1996). Gordon and Breach Science Publishers, c/o International Publishers Distributor, 820 Town Center Dr., Langhorne, PA 19047. TEL 215-750-2642. FAX 215-7850-6343. (Subscr. to: International Publishers Distributor, P.O. Box 90, Reading, Berkshire RG1 8JL, England. TEL 44-173-456-8316) Ed. Eberhard Keil. adv.; bk.rev.; charts; illus.; index. (also avail. in microform from MIM) **Indexed:** Chem.Abstr., Curr.Cont., Eng.Ind., INSPEC, Phys.Ber.
—BLDSC (6407.250000); CASDDS; Faxon; SWETS; UnCover. **CCC.**
 Refereed Serial

539 PH ISSN 0079-1490
QC770 CODEN: PNUJAB
PHILIPPINES NUCLEAR JOURNAL. 1966. a. $20. Philippine Nuclear Research Institute, Commonwealth Ave., Diliman, Quezon City, Philippines. FAX 951646. TELEX 66804 PNRI PN. Ed. Alumanda M. de la Rosa. circ. 500. **Indexed:** Biol.Abstr., Ind.Phil.Per. **Document type:** government publication.

PHYSICS — NUCLEAR PHYSICS

539.2   JA   ISSN 0912-1803
PHOTON FACTORY ACTIVITY REPORT. (Text in English) 1983. a. National Laboratory for High Energy Physics, Photon Factory - Koenerugi Butsurigaku Kenkyujo Hoshako Jikken Shisetsu, 1-1, Oho, Tsukuba-shi, Ibaraki-ken 305, Japan. **Document type:** government publication.

539.2   JA   ISSN 0916-0604
PHOTON FACTORY NEWS. (Text in Japanese) 1983. q. National Laboratory for High Energy Physics, Photon Factory - Koenerugi Butsurigaku Kenkyujo Hoshako Jikken Shisetsu, 1-1, Oho, Tsukuba-shi, Ibaraki-ken 305, Japan. **Document type:** newsletter.

539.7   US   ISSN 0556-2813
QC770   CODEN: PRVCAN
PHYSICAL REVIEW C (NUCLEAR PHYSICS). 1970. m. $1050 (foreign $1065) (effective 1996). American Physical Society, One Physics Ellipse, College Park, MD 20740-3843. TEL 301-209-3000. (Subscr. to: APS Subscriber Service, c/o American Institute of Physics, 500 Sunnyside Blvd., Woodbury, NY 11797-2999. TEL 516-576-2270) Ed. S.M. Austin. bibl.; illus.; s-a. index. (also avail. in microform from AIP; back issues avail.) **Indexed:** Appl.Mech.Rev., C.P.I., Cadscan, Chem.Abstr., Curr.Cont., Eng.Ind., INSPEC, Lead Abstr., Math.R., Met.Abstr., Nucl.Sci.Abstr., Phys.Ber., Zincscan. **Document type:** academic/scholarly publication.
—BLDSC (6476.060000); CASDDS; Faxon; Genuine Article; SWETS; UnCover. **CCC.**
Supersedes in part (1893-1969): Physical Review.
Refereed Serial

539.7   US   ISSN 0556-2821
QC721   CODEN: PRVDAQ
PHYSICAL REVIEW D (PARTICLES AND FIELDS). 1970. 24/yr. $1900 (foreign $1965) (effective 1996). American Physical Society, One Physics Ellipse, College Park, MD 20740-3843. TEL 301-209-3000. (Subscr. to: APS Subscriber Service, c/o American Institute of Physics, 400 Sunnyside Blvd., Woodbury, NY 11797-2999. TEL 516-576-2270) Ed. L. Brown. bibl.; illus.; s-a. index. (also avail. in microform from AIP; back issues avail.) **Indexed:** Appl.Mech.Rev., C.P.I., Chem.Abstr., Curr.Cont., Eng.Ind., INSPEC (1991-), Int.Aerosp.Abstr., Math.R., Met.Abstr., Nucl.Sci.Abstr., Phys.Ber. **Document type:** academic/scholarly publication.
—BLDSC (6476.070000); CASDDS; Ei; Faxon; Genuine Article; SWETS; UnCover. **CCC.**
Supersedes in part (1893-1969): Physical Review.

539.7   NE   ISSN 0375-9601
QC1   CODEN: PYLAAG
PHYSICS LETTERS. SECTION A: GENERAL, ATOMIC AND SOLID STATE PHYSICS. Key Title: Physics Letters A. 1962. 78/yr. fl.5252($3203) (effective 1996). North-Holland (Subsidiary of: Elsevier Science B.V.), P.O. Box 211, 1000 AE Amsterdam, Netherlands. TEL 31-20-4853911. FAX 31-20-4853598. TELEX 18582 ESPA NL. (Subscr. in U.S. and Canada to: Elsevier Science Inc., Box 882, Madison Sq. Sta., New York, NY 10159. TEL 212-989-5800. FAX 212-633-3990) Ed.Bd. (also avail. in microform from UMI; back issues avail.) **Indexed:** Cadscan, Chem.Abstr., Curr.Cont., Deep Sea Res.& Oceanogr.Abstr., INSPEC (1968-), Lead Abstr., Mass Spectr.Bull., Math.R., Met.Abstr., Phys.Ber., World Alum.Abstr., Zincscan. **Document type:** academic/scholarly publication.
—BLDSC (6478.761000); CASDDS; Ei; Faxon; Genuine Article; SWETS; UnCover. **CCC.**
Supersedes in part (in 1967): Physics Letters (ISSN 0031-9163)
Description: Covers all fields of physics excluding nuclear and particle physics.
Refereed Serial

539.7   NE   ISSN 0370-2693
QC1   CODEN: PYLBAJ
PHYSICS LETTERS. SECTION B: NUCLEAR, ELEMENTARY PARTICLE AND HIGH-ENERGY PHYSICS. Key Title: Physics Letters B. 1962. 100/yr. fl.10100($6159) (effective 1996). North-Holland (Subsidiary of: Elsevier Science B.V.), P.O. Box 211, 1000 AE Amsterdam, Netherlands. TEL 31-20-4853911. FAX 31-20-4853598. TELEX 18582 ESPA NL. (Subscr. in U.S. and Canada to: Elsevier Science Inc., Box 882, Madison Sq. Sta., New York, NY 10159. TEL 212-989-5800. FAX 212-633-3990) Ed.Bd. (also avail. in microform from UMI; back issues avail.) **Indexed:** Cadscan, Chem.Abstr., Curr.Cont., Deep Sea Res.& Oceanogr.Abstr., INSPEC (1968-), Lead Abstr., Mass Spectr.Bull., Math.R., Phys.Ber., Zincscan. **Document type:** academic/scholarly publication.
—BLDSC (6478.762000); CASDDS; Ei; Faxon; Genuine Article; SWETS; UnCover. **CCC.**
Supersedes in part (in 1967): Physics Letters (ISSN 0031-9163)
Description: Presents new results in nuclear and particle physics.
Refereed Serial

539   RU   ISSN 1063-7788
QC770   CODEN: PANUEO
PHYSICS OF ATOMIC NUCLEI. English translation of: Yadernaya Fizika (RU ISSN 0044-0027) 1965. m. $2735 (foreign $2780) (effective 1996). (Rossiiskaya Akademiya Nauk) Maik Nauka, Mezhdunarodnyi Otdel, Profsoyuznaya, 90, 117864 Moscow, Russia. (Subscr. to: American Institute of Physics, Member and Subscriber Services, 500 Sunnyside Blvd., Woodbury, NY 11797-2999, U.S.A. TEL 516-576-2270. FAX 516-349-9707) Ed. Yu. G. Abov. charts; stat. (also avail. in microform from AIP; back issues avail.) **Indexed:** ASCA, C.P.I., Curr.Cont., Gen.Phys.Adv.Abstr., INSPEC, Math.R., Phys.Ber. **Document type:** academic/scholarly publication.
—BLDSC (0416.826000); Faxon; Genuine Article; SWETS; UnCover. **CCC.**
Formerly: Soviet Journal of Nuclear Physics (ISSN 0038-5506)

539.7   US   ISSN 1063-7796
QC793   CODEN: PPNUER
PHYSICS OF PARTICLES AND NUCLEI. English translation of: Fizika Elementarnykh Chastits i Atomnogo Yadra. vol.3, 1972. bi-m. $1495 (foreign $1515) (effective 1996). American Institute of Physics, One Physics Ellipse, College Park, MD 20740-3843. TEL 301-209-3000. (Subscr. to: AIP Member and Subscriber Services, 500 Sunnyside Blvd., Woodbury, NY 11797-2999. TEL 516-576-2270) Ed. N.M. Queen. bibl.; charts; illus.; index. (also avail. in microform from AIP; back issues avail.) **Indexed:** C.P.I., Gen.Phys.Adv.Abstr., INSPEC, Math.R., Phys.Ber. **Document type:** academic/scholarly publication.
—BLDSC (0416.863000); Faxon; SWETS; UnCover. **CCC.**
Formerly: Soviet Journal of Particles and Nuclei (ISSN 0090-4759)
Description: Contains articles or experimental and theoretical research in high-energy and nuclear physics and related instrumentation.
Refereed Serial

PROGRESS IN NUCLEAR MAGNETIC RESONANCE SPECTROSCOPY. see CHEMISTRY — *Analytical Chemistry*

539.7   UK   ISSN 0146-6410
QC770   CODEN: PPNPDB
PROGRESS IN PARTICLE AND NUCLEAR PHYSICS. 1977. s-a. £524($834) (effective 1996). Elsevier Science Ltd., Pergamon, P.O. Box 800, Kidlington, Oxford OX5 1DX, England. TEL 44-1865-843000. FAX 44-1865-843010.
E-mail: nlinfo-f@elsevier.nl; usinfo-f@elsevier.com; forinfo-kyf04035@niftyserve.or.jp; Site addr.: http://www.elsevier.nl/. (Subscr. in U.S. and Canada to: Elsevier Science, 660 White Plains Rd., Tarrytown, NY 10591-5153. TEL 914-524-9200. FAX 914-333-2444) Ed. Amand Faessler. index. (also avail. in microfilm from UMI) **Indexed:** Chem.Abstr., INSPEC, Phys.Ber. **Document type:** academic/scholarly publication, monographic series.
—BLDSC (6872.400000); CASDDS; Faxon; Genuine Article; SWETS; UMI. **CCC.**
Supersedes (1950-1976): Progress in Nuclear Physics (ISSN 0079-659X)
Description: Publishes reviews of new developments in nuclear and particle physics, with emphasis on the interface between the two fields.
Refereed Serial

539.764   JA   ISSN 0916-4316
PURAZUMA KAGAKU SENTA NYUSU/NAGOYA UNIVERSITY. PLASMA SCIENCE CENTER NEWS. (Text in Japanese) 1989. m. Nagoya University, Plasma Science Center - Nagoya Daigaku Purazuma Kagaku Senta, Furo-cho, Shikusa-ku, Nagoya-shi, Aichi-ken 464-01, Japan.

539.764   JA
PURAZUMA KAKU YUGO GAKKAI NENKAI YOKAI YOKOSHU/JAPAN SOCIETY OF PLASMA SCIENCES AND NUCLEAR FUSION RESEARCH. PREPRINTS OF ANNUAL MEETING. (Text in English, Japanese) 1984. a. 1500 Yen. Purazuma Kaku Yugo Gakkai - Japan Society of Plasma Sciences and Nuclear Fusion Research, 20-29, Nishiki 2-chome, Naka-ku, Nagoya-shi, Aichi-ken 460, Japan.

539.7   JA   ISSN 0918-7928
CODEN: PKYGE5
PURAZUMA KAKU YUGO GAKKAISHI/JOURNAL OF PLASMA AND FUSION RESEARCH. (Text in English, Japanese; summaries in English) 1958. m. 1300 Yen per no. Purazuma Kaku Yugo Gakkai - Japan Society of Plasma Science and Nuclear Fusion Research, 20-29, Nishiki 2-chome, Naka-ku, Nagoya-shi, Aichi-ken 460, Japan. **Indexed:** Chem.Abstr., INIS Atomind., Jap.Per.Ind.
—BLDSC (5040.548000); CASDDS.
Formerly (until Feb. 1993): Kaku Yugo Kenkyu - Nuclear Fusion (ISSN 0451-2375)

539.7   JA
R C N P ANNUAL REPORT. (Text and summaries in English) 1976. a. Research Center for Nuclear Physics, Osaka University, 10-1 Mihogaoka, Ibarakishi Osaka 567, Japan. TEL 81-6-877-5111. FAX 81-6-877-9412. TELEX 5286-214 RCNP J. Ed. Toru Suzuki. (back issues avail.).

539.9   US   ISSN 1042-0150
QD601.A1   CODEN: REDSEI
RADIATION EFFECTS AND DEFECTS IN SOLIDS. 1969. q. 283 ECU (effective 1996). Gordon & Breach Science Publishers, c/o International Publishers Distributor, 820 Town Center Dr., Langhorne, PA 19047. TEL 215-750-2642. FAX 215-750-6343. (Subscr. to: International Publishers Distributor, P.O. Box 90, Reading, Berkshire RG1 8JL, England. TEL 44-173-456-8316) Ed. Jochen Biersack. (also avail. in microform) **Indexed:** INSPEC (1989-). **Document type:** academic/scholarly publication.
—BLDSC (7227.957100); CASDDS; Faxon; SWETS. **CCC.**
Formed by the 1989 merger of: Radiation Effects (ISSN 0033-7579); Crystal Lattice Defects and Amorphous Materials (ISSN 0732-8699); Which was formerly (until 1982): Crystal Lattice Defects (ISSN 0011-2305)
Refereed Serial

PHYSICS — NUCLEAR PHYSICS

539.7 UK ISSN 1350-4487
QC787.N78 CODEN: RMEAEP
RADIATION MEASUREMENTS. 1977. bi-m. £447($711) (effective 1996). Elsevier Science Ltd., Pergamon, P.O. Box 800, Kidlington, Oxford OX5 1DX, England. TEL 44-1865-843000. FAX 44-1865-843010. E-mail: nlinfo-f@elsevier.nl; usinfo-f@elsevier.com; forinfo-ky04035@niftyserve.or.jp; Site addr.: http://www.elsevier.nl/. (Subscr. in U.S. and Canada to: Elsevier Science, 660 White Plains Rd., Tarrytown, NY 10591-5153. TEL 914-524-9200. FAX 914-333-2444) Eds. E.V. Benton, S.A. Durrani. adv.: B&W page $550, color page $1350. index. circ. 1,000. (also avail. in microfilm from UMI; back issues avail.) **Indexed:** ASCA, Biol.Abstr., Chem.Abstr., Curr.Cont., GeoRef., Ind.Sci.Rev., INSPEC (1982-), Phys.Ber. **Document type:** academic/scholarly publication.
—BLDSC (7227.973000); ADONIS; CASDDS; Ei; Faxon; Genuine Article; SWETS; UMI; UnCover. **CCC.**
Former titles (until 1994): Nuclear Tracks and Radiation Measurements (ISSN 0969-8078); (until 1993): International Journal of Radiation Applications and Instrumentation. Part D: Nuclear Tracks and Radiation Measurements; (until 1985): Nuclear Tracks and Radiation Measurements (ISSN 0735-245X); (until 1981): Nuclear Tracks (ISSN 0191-278X); (until 1978): Nuclear Track Detection (ISSN 0145-224X); Nuclear Tracks in Solids.
Description: Publishes the latest developments in the field of radiation measurement, emphasizing nuclear tracks, thermoluminescence, space radiation and related phenomena.
Refereed Serial

539 541 UK ISSN 0969-806X
QD601.A1 CODEN: RPCHDM
RADIATION PHYSICS AND CHEMISTRY. (Text in English, French, German, Russian) 1969. m. £592($942) (effective 1996). Elsevier Science Ltd., Pergamon, The Boulevard, Langford Ln., Kidlington, Oxford OX5 1GB, England. TEL 44-1865-843000. FAX 44-1865-843010. E-mail: nlinfo-f@elsevier.nl; usinfo-f@elsevier.com; forinfo-kyf04035@niftyserve.or.jp; Site addr.: http://www.elsevier.nl/. (Subscr. in U.S. and Canada to: Elsevier Science, 660 White Plains Rd., Tarrytown, NY 10591-5153. TEL 914-524-9200. FAX 914-333-2444) Ed. A. Miller, J. Hubbell. adv. contact: Paul Titcombe. bk.rev. circ. 1,050. (also avail. in microfilm from UMI; back issues avail.) **Indexed:** Chem.Abstr., Curr.Cont., Excerp.Med., INSPEC, Mass Spectr.Bull., Rice Abstr. **Document type:** academic/scholarly publication.
—BLDSC (7227.984000); ADONIS; CASDDS; Ei; Faxon; Genuine Article; SWETS; UMI. **CCC.**
Former titles (until 1993): International Journal of Radiation Applications and Instrumentation. Part C: Radiation Physics and Chemistry; (until 1985): Radiation Physics and Chemistry (ISSN 0146-5724)
Description: Publishes papers dealing with the interaction of ionizing radiation with matter, the resultant physical and chemical changes, and the mechanisms involved, as well as papers dealing with applications and techniques.
Refereed Serial

614 UK ISSN 0144-8420
R905 CODEN: RPDODE
RADIATION PROTECTION DOSIMETRY. 1981. 24/yr. (in 6 vols.) £550($1190) (effective 1995). Nuclear Technology Publishing, P.O. Box 7, Ashford, Kent TN23 1JW, England. TEL 01233-641683. FAX 01233-610021. Ed. E.P. Goldfinch. adv. contact: L. Richmond. bk.rev. circ. 1,000. (back issues avail.) **Indexed:** ASCA, Chem.Abstr., Energy Ind., Energy Info.Abstr., Environ.Abstr., INIS Atomind, INSPEC, Risk Abstr. **Document type:** academic/scholarly publication.
—BLDSC (7227.993000); CASDDS; Genuine Article; SWETS.
Description: International coverage of biological aspects, physical concepts, external and internal dosimetry and monitoring, environmental and workplace monitoring as well as dosimetry monitoring related to the protection of patients.

RADIATION PROTECTION MANAGEMENT; the journal of applied health physics. see *OCCUPATIONAL HEALTH AND SAFETY*

615.842 US ISSN 0033-7587
QC770 CODEN: RAREAE
RADIATION RESEARCH; an international journal. 1954. m. $560 (foreign $648). Kluge Carden Jennings, 853 W. Main St., Charlottesville, VA 22903. Ed. R.J.M. Fry. bibl.; charts; illus.; index. (back issues avail.) **Indexed:** Biol.Abstr., Chem.Abstr., Curr.Adv.Biochem., Curr.Adv.Cancer Res., Curr.Adv.Ecol.Sci., Curr.Adv.Genetics & Molec.Biol., Curr.Cont., Dairy Sci.Abstr., Deep Sea Res.& Oceanogr.Abstr., Dent.Ind., Energy Rev., Environ.Per.Bibl. (1974-), Excerp.Med., Helminthol.Abstr., Ind.Med., Ind.Vet., INSPEC, Kidney, Mass Spectr.Bull., Nutr.Abstr., Ocean.Abstr., Pollut.Abstr., Risk Abstr., Vet.Bull. **Document type:** academic/scholarly publication.
—BLDSC (7228.000000); CASDDS; Ei; EMDOCS; Faxon; Genuine Article; SWETS; UnCover. **CCC.**
Description: Publishes original articles on the physical, chemical, and biological effects of radiation and on related subjects in the areas of physics, chemistry, biology, and medicine.
Refereed Serial

RADIATION RESEARCH SOCIETY. ANNUAL MEETING. see *PHYSICS — Abstracting, Bibliographies, Statistics*

539 JA ISSN 0289-842X
RIKEN. ACCELERATOR PROGRESS REPORT. (Text in English) 1967. a. 5000 Yen. Rikagaku Kenkyujo, Saikurotoron Kenkyushitsu - Institute of Physical and Chemical Research, Cyclotron Laboratory, 2-1 Hirosawa, Wako-shi, Saitama-ken 351-01, Japan. FAX 0484-62-1554. TELEX 02962818-RIKEN-J.
Former titles: I P C R Accelerator Progress Report; I P C R Cyclotron Progress Report.

539 JA
RIKEN - A F - N P. (Text in English) 1970. irreg. Rikagaku Kenkyujo, Saikurotoron Kenkyushitsu - Institute of Physical and Chemical Research, Cyclotron Laboratory, 2-1 Hirosawa, Wako-shi, Saitama-ken 351-01, Japan. FAX 0484-62-1554. TELEX 02962818-RIKEN-J.
Former titles: Riken. Cyclotron Report; I P C R Cyclotron Report.

539.7 JA
RIKOGAKU NI OKERU DOI GENSO KENKYU HAPPYOKAI YOSHISHU/ANNUAL MEETING ON RADIOISOTOPES IN THE PHYSICAL SCIENCES AND INDUSTRIES. (Text in Japanese) 1964. a. Oyo Butsuri Gakkai - Japan Society of Applied Physics, 12-3, Kudan Kita 1-chome, Chiyoda-ku, Tokyo 102, Japan.

530 RM
ROMANIAN PHYSICAL SOCIETY. NATIONAL CONFERENCE FOR PHYSICS. ABSTRACTS. a. free. Institutul de Fizica Atomica, P.O. Box MG-6, Bucharest-Magurele, Rumania. TEL 40-1-6807040. FAX 40-1-6122247. (Co-sponsor: Romanian Physical Society) **Document type:** proceedings.
Formerly (until 1990): Institutul de Fizica Atomica. Sesiunea Stiintifica Anuala de Comunicari; Program si Rezumate.
Refereed Serial

539.2 JA ISSN 0917-432X
CODEN: SKGJEP
S R KAGAKU GIJUTSU JOHO/S R SCIENCE AND TECHNOLOGY INFORMATION. (Text in Japanese) 1991. m. Kokido Hihari Kagaku Kenkyu Senta - Japan Synchrotron Radiation Research Institute, 9-1, Minatojma Nakamachi 6-chome, Chuo-ku, Kobe-shi, Hyoyo-ken 650, Japan. TEL 078-302-6751. FAX 078-302-6618.
—BLDSC (8425.053165).

539.76 JA ISSN 0371-1838
CODEN: SOKEAK
SORYUSHIRON KENKYU/STUDY OF ELEMENTARY PARTICLES. (Text in English, Japanese) 1948. m. 9600 Yen (effective till Mar. 1996). (Soryushiron Gurupu - Research Group on the Theory of Particle and Nuclear Physics) Soryushiron Kenkyu Henshubu, c/o Yukawa Hall, Kyoto University, Kyoto 606-01, Japan. TEL 075-722-3540. FAX 075-722-6339. E-mail: sokened@jpnyitp.bitnet. Ed. Masafumi Fukuma. circ. 550. **Document type:** academic/scholarly publication.
—CASDDS.

539.2 JA
SPRING EITO NYUSU/JAPAN SYNCHROTRON RADIATION RESEARCH INSTITUTE. NEWS. (Text in Japanese) 1989. q. Kokido Hihari Kagaku Kenkyu Senta - Japan Synchrotron Radiation Research Institute, 9-1, Minatojima Nakamachi 6-chome, Chuo-ku, Kobe-shi, Hyogo-ken 650, Japan. **Document type:** academic/scholarly publication.

539.2 JA
SYNCHROTRON RADIATION LABORATORY. ACTIVITY REPORT. (Text in English) a. University of Tokyo, Institute for Solid State Physics - Tokyo Daigaku Bussei Kenkyujo, 22-1, Roppongi 7-chome, Minato-ku, Tokyo 106, Japan.

539.7 US ISSN 0894-0886
SYNCHROTRON RADIATION NEWS. 6/yr. 73 ECU (effective 1996). Gordon & Breach Science Publishers, c/o International Publishers Distributor, 820 Town Center Dr., Langhorne, PA 19047. TEL 215-750-2642. FAX 215-750-6343. (Subscr. to: International Publishers Distributor, P.O. Box 90, Reading, Berkshire RG1 8JL, England. TEL 44-173-456-8316) (also avail. in microform)
—BLDSC (8585.886500). **CCC.**
Refereed Serial

539 CN
T R I U M F ANNUAL REPORT SCIENTIFIC ACTIVITIES. (Tri-University Meson Facility) 1967. a. free. T R I U M F, 4004 Wesbrook Mall, Vancouver, BC V6T 2A3, Canada. TEL 604-222-1047. FAX 604-222-1074. Ed. Jana Thomson. **Indexed:** Nucl.Sci.Abstr.
Formerly (until 1980): T R I U M F Annual Report (ISSN 0082-6367)

539 CN
T R I U M F FINANCIAL AND ADMINISTRATIVE ANNUAL REPORT. (Tri-University Meson Facility) 1980. a. free. T R I U M F, 4004 Wesbrook Mall, Vancouver, BC V6T 2A3, Canada. TEL 604-222-1047. FAX 604-222-1074. Ed. Michael LaBrooy.

TAIKI HOSHANO KANSOKU SEISEKI/BULLETIN OF ATMOSPHERIC RADIOACTIVITY. see *METEOROLOGY*

539.7 630 JA ISSN 0916-8621
CODEN: TNDHE2
TOKYO NOGYO DAIGAKU AISOTOPU SENTA KENKYU HOKOKU/TOKYO UNIVERSITY OF AGRICULTURE. ISOTOPE CENTER. BULLETIN. (Text in English, Japanese; summaries in English) 1980. irreg. Tokyo Nogyo Daigaku, Aisotopu Senta, 1-1 Sakuragaoka 1-chome, Setagaya-ku, Tokyo 156, Japan. **Document type:** bulletin.
—CASDDS.

539.735 JA ISSN 0911-5730
QC787.S9
U V S O R ACTIVITY REPORT. (Ultraviolet Synchrotron Orbital Radiation Facility) (Text in English) 1984. a. Okazaki National Research Institutes, Institute for Molecular Science - Okazaki Kokuritsu Kyodo Kenkyu Kiko, Bunshi Kagaku Kenkyujo, 38, Saigonaka, Myodaijicho, Okazaki-shi, Aichi-ken 444, Japan.

539.2 JA
UCHU HOSHASEN SHINPOJUMU/SYMPOSIUM ON COSMIC RADIATION. (Text in Japanese) 1972. a. Institute of Space and Astronautical Science - Uchu Kagaku Kenkyujo, 1-1, Yoshinodai 3-chome, Sagamihara-shi, Kanagawa-ken 229, Japan.

539 FR
UNIVERSITE DE NANTES. LABORATOIRE DE PHYSIQUE NUCLEAIRE. RAPPORT INTERNE. irreg. Universite de Nantes, Laboratoire de Physique Nucleaire, 2 rue de la Houssiniere, 44072 Nantes Cedex 03, France.
Formerly: Universite de Nantes. Laboratoire de Spectroscopie Nucleaire.

539 JA ISSN 0365-5075
UNIVERSITY OF TOKYO. INSTITUTE FOR NUCLEAR STUDY. ANNUAL REPORT. (Text in English) 1960. a. exchange basis. University of Tokyo, Institute for Nuclear Study - Tokyo Daigaku Genshikaku Kenkyujo, 2-1, Midori-cho 3-chome, Tanashi-shi, Tokyo 188, Japan. abstr.

PHYSICS — OPTICS

539 JA ISSN 0495-7814
UNIVERSITY OF TOKYO. INSTITUTE FOR NUCLEAR STUDY. INS-J. (Text in English) 1957. a. exchange basis. University of Tokyo, Institute for Nuclear Study - Tokyo Daigaku Genshikaku Kenkyusho, 3-2-1 Midori-cho, Tanashi-shi, Tokyo 188, Japan. **Indexed:** Chem.Abstr.

539 JA
UNIVERSITY OF TOKYO. INSTITUTE FOR NUCLEAR STUDY. INS-PH. (Text in Japanese) 1969. irreg. exchange basis. University of Tokyo, Institute for Nuclear Study - Tokyo Daigaku Genshikaku Kenkyusho, 3-2-1 Midori-cho Tanashi-shi, Tokyo 188, Japan.

539 JA ISSN 0563-7848
UNIVERSITY OF TOKYO. INSTITUTE FOR NUCLEAR STUDY. INS-PT. (Text in Japanese; summaries in English) 1957. irreg. exchange basis. University of Tokyo, Institute for Nuclear Study - Tokyo Daigaku Genshikaku Kenkyusho, 3-2-1 Midori-cho Tanashi-shi, Tokyo 188, Japan.

539 JA
UNIVERSITY OF TOKYO. INSTITUTE FOR NUCLEAR STUDY. INS-TCH. (Text in Japanese; summaries in English) 1967. irreg. exchange basis. University of Tokyo, Institute for Nuclear Study - Tokyo Daigaku Genshikaku Kenkyusho, 3-2-1 Midori-cho Tanashi-shi, Tokyo 188, Japan.

539 JA
UNIVERSITY OF TOKYO. INSTITUTE FOR NUCLEAR STUDY. INS-TEC. (Text in Japanese; summaries in English) 1971. irreg. exchange basis. University of Tokyo, Institute for Nuclear Study - Tokyo Daigaku Genshikaku Kenkyusho, 3-2-1 Midori-cho Tanashi-shi, Tokyo 188, Japan.

539 JA ISSN 0563-7872
UNIVERSITY OF TOKYO. INSTITUTE FOR NUCLEAR STUDY. INS-TH. (Text in Japanese; summaries in English) 1954. irreg. exchange basis. University of Tokyo, Institute for Nuclear Study - Tokyo Daigaku Genshikaku Kenkyusho, 3-2-1 Midori-cho Tanashi-shi, Tokyo 188, Japan.

539 JA ISSN 0563-7880
UNIVERSITY OF TOKYO. INSTITUTE FOR NUCLEAR STUDY. INS-TL. (Text in Japanese; summaries in English) 1954. irreg. exchange basis. University of Tokyo, Institute for Nuclear Study - Tokyo Daigaku Genshikaku Kenkyusho, 3-2-1 Midori-cho Tanashi-shi, Tokyo 188, Japan. **Indexed:** Chem.Abstr.

539 JA
UNIVERSITY OF TOKYO. INSTITUTE FOR NUCLEAR STUDY. INS-TS. (Text in Japanese; summaries in English) 1967. irreg. exchange basis. University of Tokyo, Institute for Nuclear Study - Tokyo Daigaku Genshikaku Kenkyusho, 3-2-1 Midori-cho Tanashi-shi, Tokyo 188, Japan.

539 JA ISSN 0495-7822
CODEN: INSUAP
UNIVERSITY OF TOKYO. INSTITUTE FOR NUCLEAR STUDY. REPORT. (Text in English) 1959. irreg. exchange basis. University of Tokyo, Institute for Nuclear Study - Tokyo Daigaku Genshikaku Kenkyusho, 3-2-1 Midori-cho, Tanashi-shi, Tokyo 188, Japan. **Indexed:** Chem.Abstr., INIS Atomind., INSPEC.
—CASDDS.

539 RU ISSN 0044-0027
CODEN: IDFZA7
YADERNAYA FIZIKA. English translation: Physics of Atomic Nuclei (US ISSN 1063-7788) 1965. m. $528 (effective 1996). (Rossiiskaya Akademiya Nauk) Izdatel'stvo Nauka, Mezhdunarodnyi Otdel, Profsoyuznaya, 90, 117864 Moscow, Russia. TEL 238-4321. charts; index. circ. 1,000. (tabloid format) **Indexed:** Chem.Abstr., INSPEC (1968-), Phys.Ber. **Document type:** academic/scholarly publication.
—BLDSC (0399.780000); CASDDS.

539.7 JA ISSN 0917-0731
YUKAI/NUCLEAR FUSION SCIENCE SOCIETY. NEWS. (Text in Japanese) 1990. 10/yr. Kaku Yugo Kagaku Kenkyukai - Nuclear Fusion Science Society. 14-12, Higashisakura 1-chome, Higashi-ku, Nagoya-shi, Aichi-ken 461, Japan. TEL 81-52-953-9846. **Document type:** newsletter.

539.7 GW ISSN 0939-7922
QC1 CODEN: ZPAHEX
ZEITSCHRIFT FUER PHYSIK A. HADRONS AND NUCLEI. (Text in English and German; summaries in English) 1920. 12/yr. (in 3 vols., 4 nos./vol.). DM.2262($1643) (effective 1996). (Deutsche Physikalische Gesellschaft) Springer-Verlag, Heidelberger Platz 3, 14197 Berlin, Germany. TEL 030-8207-0. FAX 030-8214091. E-mail: orders@springer.de. (Subscr. in N. America to: Springer-Verlag New York, Inc., 44 Hartz Way, Secaucus, NJ 07096-2491. TEL 201-348-4033. FAX 201-348-4505) Ed. B. Povh. adv.; charts; illus. (also avail. in microform from UMI,PMC; reprint service avail. from ISI) **Indexed:** Chem.Abstr., Curr.Cont., INSPEC (1968-), Mass Spectr.Bull., Math.R., Phys.Ber. **Document type:** academic/scholarly publication.
—BLDSC (9481.015000); CASDDS; Faxon; Genuine Article; SWETS; UMI; UnCover. **CCC.**
Former titles (until 1991): Zeitschrift fuer Physik. Section A. Atomic Nuclei (ISSN 0930-1151); (until 1986): Zeitschrift fuer Physik. Section A: Atoms and Nuclei (ISSN 0340-2193); Zeitschrift fuer Physik (ISSN 0044-3328)
Description: Devoted to original research in experimental and theoretical physics on hadron and nuclear structure.

PHYSICS — Optics

ADVANCED MATERIALS FOR OPTICS AND ELECTRONICS.
see CHEMISTRY — Electrochemistry

535 US ISSN 1058-4382
CODEN: AMLUEZ
ADVANCES IN MULTIDIMENSIONAL LUMINESCENCE. 1991. a. J A I Press Inc., 55 Old Post Rd., No. 2, Box 1678, Greenwich, CT 06836-1678. TEL 203-661-7602.
—BLDSC (0709.453700); CASDDS.

535.84 SI ISSN 0218-0227
ADVANCES IN MULTIPHOTON PROCESSES AND SPECTROSCOPY. (Text in English) 1984. irreg., latest vol. 9. price varies. World Scientific Publishing Co. Pte. Ltd., Farrer Rd., P.O. Box 128, Singapore 9128, Singapore. TEL 3825663. FAX 3825919. TELEX RS 28561 WSPC. (UK addr.: 57 Shelton St., Covent Garden, London WC2H 9HE. TEL 44-171-836-0888; US addr.: 1060 Main St., River Edge, NJ 07661. TEL 800-227-7562) Ed. S.H. Lin. **Document type:** monographic series.

578 535 US ISSN 0065-3012
QH201 CODEN: AOEMAK
ADVANCES IN OPTICAL AND ELECTRON MICROSCOPY. 1966. irreg., vol.12, 1991. Academic Press, Inc., 525 B St., Ste. 1900, San Diego, CA 92101-4495. TEL 619-699-6715. FAX 619-231-6616. (Subscr. to: Order Dept., 6277 Sea Harbor Dr., 4th Fl., Orlando, FL 32887. TEL 800-321-5068) Eds. V.E. Cosslett, R. Barer. (back issues avail.) **Indexed:** Biol.Abstr., Curr.Adv.Ecol.Sci., GeoRef, INSPEC.
—BLDSC (0709.553000); CASDDS; Faxon.
Refereed Serial

535 JA ISSN 0919-4630
ALBUM OF VISUALIZATION. (Text in Japanese; summaries in English) 1984. a. 1000 Yen. Kashika Joho Gakkai - Visualization Society of Japan, 16-13, Hyakunin-cho 2-chome, Shinjuku-ku, Tokyo 169, Japan. TEL 81-3-3364-1762. FAX 81-3-3364-3919. Ed. Junta Doi. circ. 500. **Document type:** academic/scholarly publication.
Formerly: Nagare no Kashika Shashinshu - Photographic Journal of Flow Visualization (ISSN 0914-3408)

535.84 547 US ISSN 1044-0305
QD96.M3 CODEN: JAMSEF
AMERICAN SOCIETY FOR MASS SPECTROMETRY. JOURNAL. Key Title: Journal of the American Society for Mass Spectrometry. 1990. m. $349 to institutions in U.S.; $437 to institutions outside the Americas (effective 1996). Elsevier Science Inc., 655 Ave. of the Americas, New York, NY 10010. TEL 212-989-5800. FAX 212-633-3990. TELEX 420643 AEP UI. (Subscr. to: Box 882, Madison Sq. Sta., New York, NY 10159-0882) Ed. Michael L. Gross. **Indexed:** Chem.Abstr., Curr.Cont., Energy Info.Abstr., Eng.Mat.Abstr., Environ.Abstr., INSPEC (1990-), Sci.Cit.Ind., World Alum.Abstr. **Document type:** academic/scholarly publication.
—BLDSC (4692.920000); CASDDS; Ei; Faxon; Genuine Article; SWETS; UnCover. **CCC.**
Description: Covers the fundamentals and applications of mass spectrometry. Principal focus is on research papers that present new and significant findings in all fields of scientific inquiry in which mass spectrometry can play a role.
Refereed Serial

535 US ISSN 0066-4103
QC490 CODEN: NMRPAJ
ANNUAL REPORTS ON N M R SPECTROSCOPY. 1968. a., vol.26, 1993. Academic Press, Inc., 525 B St., Ste. 1900, San Diego, CA 92101-4495. TEL 619-231-0926. FAX 619-699-6715. (Subscr. to: Order Dept., 6277 Sea Harbor Dr., 4th Fl., Orlando, FL 32887. TEL 800-321-5068) Ed. G.A. Webb. (reprint service avail. from ISI) **Indexed:** Chem.Abstr.
—BLDSC (1513.400000); CASDDS; Ei; SWETS.
Formerly (until 1970): Annual Review of N M R Spectroscopy (ISSN 0066-4235)
Refereed Serial

535 620 US ISSN 1042-4687
TJ212.2
APPLICATIONS OF DIGITAL IMAGE PROCESSING. (Subseries of: Society of Photo-optical Instrumentation Engineers (ISSN 0361-0748); International Society for Optical Engineering. Proceedings (ISSN 0277-786X)) 1977. a. International Society for Optical Engineering (SPIE), Society of Photo-Optical Instrumentation Engineers, Box 10, 1022 19th St., Bellingham, WA 98227-0010. TEL 206-676-3290. FAX 206-647-1445.
—CCC.
Description: Theoretical approaches, specialized architectures, image coding, medical and various industrial applications.

535 US ISSN 0003-6935
QC350 CODEN: APOPAI
APPLIED OPTICS. 1962. 36/yr. (3/m.). $1220. Optical Society of America, Inc., 2010 Massachusetts Ave., N.W., Washington, DC 20036-1023. TEL 202-223-8130. Ed. William T. Rhodes. adv.: B&W page $1120, color page $1350; 8 1/4 x 11 1/4. bk.rev.; charts; illus.; pat.; cum.index: vols.1-12. circ. 7,000. (also avail. in microfiche; microform) **Indexed:** A.I.Abstr., A.S.& T.Ind., Abstr.Bull.Inst.Pap.Chem., Agri.Eng.Abstr., C.P.I., CAD CAM Abstr., Cadscan, Ceram.Abstr., Chem.Abstr., Comput.Abstr., Curr.Cont., Deep Sea Res.& Oceanogr.Abstr., Eng.Ind., Excerp.Med., Fluidex, Geo.Abstr., Geol.Abstr., GeoRef., Graph.Arts Lit.Abstr., Ind.Sci.Rev., INIS Atomind., INSPEC (1968-), Lead Abstr., Met.Abstr., Meteor.& Geoastrophys.Abstr., Phys.Ber., Sci.Cit.Ind., Zincscan. **Document type:** academic/scholarly publication.
—BLDSC (1576.250000); CASDDS; Ei; Faxon; Genuine Article; SWETS; UnCover. **CCC.**
Description: Articles cover the applications of facts, principles, and methods of optics. For applied physicists, space scientists and astronomers, information processing scientists, and optical, electrical and mechanical engineers.

PHYSICS — OPTICS

540 535.84 US ISSN 0003-7028
QD71 CODEN: APSPA4
APPLIED SPECTROSCOPY.* 1946. 12/yr. $275 (Canada & Mexico $315; elsewhere $355) (effective 1996). Society for Applied Spectroscopy, 201B Broadway St., Frederick, MD 21701. TEL 301-694-8122. FAX 301-694-6860. Ed. William G. Fateley. adv.; bk.rev.; bibl.; charts; illus.; tr.lit.; index. circ. 7,000. (also avail. in microform from SAS; back issues avail.; reprint service avail. from KTO) **Indexed:** Abstr.Bull.Inst.Pap.Chem., AESIS, Anal.Abstr., Art & Archaeol.Tech.Abstr., Biol.Abstr., Br.Ceram.Abstr., Cadscan, Chem.Abstr., Curr.Cont., Deep Sea Res.& Oceanogr.Abstr., Eng.Ind., Excerp.Med., GeoRef., Ind.Sci.Rev., INIS Atomind., INSPEC (1968-), Intl.Polym.Sci.& Tech., Lead Abstr., Mass Spectr.Bull., Met.Abstr., Numis.Lit., RAPRA, Sci.Cit.Ind., Sel.Water Res.Abstr., W.R.C.Inf., World Alum.Abstr., World Surf.Coat., Zincscan. **Document type:** academic/scholarly publication.
—BLDSC (1579.000000); CASDDS; Ei; Faxon; Genuine Article; SWETS; UnCover. **CCC**.
Refereed Serial

535.84 US ISSN 0570-4928
QC450 CODEN: APSRBB
APPLIED SPECTROSCOPY REVIEWS; an international journal of principles, methods, and applications. 1964. 4/yr. $435. Marcel Dekker Journals, 270 Madison Ave., New York, NY 10016. TEL 212-696-9000. FAX 212-685-4540. TELEX 421419. (Subscr. to: Box 5017, Monticello, NY 12701) Ed. Edward G. Brame, Jr. adv. contact: Eridania Perez. charts; stat. (also avail. in microform from RPI) **Indexed:** Cadscan, Chem.Abstr., Curr.Cont., Eng.Ind., GeoRef., Ind.Sci.Rev., INSPEC (1971-), Lead Abstr., Sci.Cit.Ind., Zincscan. **Document type:** academic/scholarly publication.
—CASDDS; Ei; Faxon; Genuine Article; SWETS; UMI; UnCover. **CCC**.
Description: Provides information on principles, methods and applications of spectroscopy for the researcher and also presents discussions that relate physical concepts to chemical applications.
Refereed Serial

535.58 NE ISSN 0921-8637
 CODEN: BMOME3
BEAM MODIFICATION OF MATERIALS. 1984. irreg., vol.3, 1989. price varies. Elsevier Science B.V., Books Division, P.O. Box 211, 1000 AE Amsterdam, Netherlands. TEL 31-20-4853911. FAX 31-20-4853705. TELEX 18582 ESPA NL. E-mail: nlinfo-f@elsevier.nl; usinfo-f@elsevier.com; forinfo-kyf04035@niftyserve.or.jp; Site addr.: http://www.elsevier.nl/. (Subscr. in U.S. and Canada to: Elsevier Science Inc., Box 882, Madison Sq. Sta., New York, NY 10159. TEL 212-989-5800) (reprint service avail. from ISI) **Document type:** monographic series.
—CASDDS.
Refereed Serial

535 CC ISSN 1000-4556
 CODEN: BOZAE2
BOPUXUE ZAZHI/CHINESE JOURNAL OF MAGNETIC RESONANCE. (Text in Chinese, English) 1983. q. $60. Zhongguo Kexueyuan, Wuhan Wuli Yanjiusuo - Chinese Academy of Sciences, Wuhan Institute of Physics, P.O. Box 71010, Xiaohongshan, Wuchang-qu, Wuhan, Hubei 430071, People's Republic of China. TEL 86-27-7822544. FAX 86-27-7825291. Ed. Ye Chaohui. adv.: B&W page $500; adv. contact: Qianwai Sun. circ. 600 (paid) (paid); 200 (controlled). **Document type:** academic/scholarly publication.
—CASDDS.
Description: Covers new techniques and applications in magnetic resonance spectroscopy.

535 JA
BUNKAKAI NIHON KOGAKKAI SAMA SEMINA RONBUNSHU/OPTICAL SOCIETY OF JAPAN. PROCEEDINGS OF THE SUMMER SEMINAR. (Text in English, Japanese; summaries in English) a. Japan Society of Applied Physics, Optical Society of Japan - Oyo Butsuri Gakkai Bunkakai Nihon Kogakkai, 12-3, Kudan Kita 1-chome, Chiyoda-ku, Tokyo 102, Japan. **Document type:** proceedings.

535 617.7 658.8 UK ISSN 0261-9172
BUSINESS RATIO REPORT: OPTICAL INDUSTRY; an industry sector analysis. 1980. a. I C C Business Ratios Ltd., Freepost, Field House, Hampton, Mddx. TW12 1BR, England. TEL 081-783-0977. FAX 081-783-1940. charts; stat. **Document type:** trade publication.
—BLDSC (6273.197500).

535 UK ISSN 0959-6208
 CODEN: CSMOEI
CAMBRIDGE STUDIES IN MODERN OPTICS. 1983. irreg. Cambridge University Press, Edinburgh Bldg., Shaftesbury Rd., Cambridge CB2 2RU, England. TEL 01223-312393. FAX 01223-315052. TELEX 817256. (N. American edition.: Cambridge University Press, 40 W. 20th St., New York, NY 1011. TEL 212-924-3900. FAX 212-691-3239) **Document type:** monographic series.
—BLDSC (3015.995380); CASDDS.

535.84 544.6 CN ISSN 1183-7306
QC451 CODEN: CJSPEM
CANADIAN JOURNAL OF APPLIED SPECTROSCOPY. (Text in English, French) 1963. q. Can.$150. (Spectroscopy Society of Canada) Polyscience Publications Inc., 44 Seize Arpents, P.O. Box 148, Morin Heights, PQ J0R 1H0, Canada. TEL 514-226-5870. FAX 514-226-5866. Ed. I. Butler. adv.; bk.rev.; charts; illus.; index. circ. 1,500. (reprint service avail. from UMI) **Indexed:** Abstr.Bull.Inst.Pap.Chem., Anal.Abstr., Biol.Abstr., Cadscan, Chem.Abstr., Curr.Cont., GeoRef., Ind.Sci.Rev., INIS Atomind., INSPEC (1990-), Lead Abstr., Mass Spectr.Bull., Met.Abstr., Sci.Cit.Ind., World Alum.Abstr., Zincscan. **Document type:** academic/scholarly publication.
—BLDSC (3028.580000); CASDDS; Ei; Faxon; Genuine Article; SWETS; UMI; UnCover. **CCC**.
Formerly (until June 1990): Canadian Journal of Spectroscopy (ISSN 0045-5105); **Supersedes:** Canadian Spectroscopy (ISSN 0008-5057)
Description: For all branches of fundamental and applied spectroscopy.

535 US ISSN 0890-9903
TA1570 CODEN: CJIWER
CHINESE JOURNAL OF INFRARED AND MILLIMETER WAVES. English translation of: Hongwai Yanjiu, Ser. A (CC ISSN 0258-7114) 1987. bi-m. $495 (effective 1996). (Optical Society of China, CC) Allerton Press, Inc., 150 Fifth Ave., New York, NY 10011. TEL 212-924-3950. FAX 212-463-9684. Ed. Tang Dingyuan. **Document type:** academic/scholarly publication.
—UnCover. **CCC**.

535.58 CC ISSN 1004-2822
CHINESE JOURNAL OF LASERS. Chinese edition: Zhongguo Jiguang (ISSN 0258-7025) (Text in English) bi-m. $158. (Chinese Optical Society) Science Press, Marketing and Sales Department, 16 Donghuangchenggen North St., Beijing 100717, People's Republic of China. (Overseas subscr. to: Optical Society of America, 2010 Massachusetts Ave., N.W., Washington, DC 20036. TEL 202-223-8130. FAX 202-223-1096) Ed. Xingli Tang. **Indexed:** INSPEC (1983-). **Document type:** academic/scholarly publication.
—BLDSC (3180.367100). **CCC**.
Description: Contains research papers in the field of laser science and electro-optics.
Refereed Serial

535 640 JA
COLOR. (Text in Japanese) 1969. q. Japan Color Research Institute - Nihon Shikisai Kenkyujo, 1-19, Nishiazabu 3-chome, Minato-ku, Tokyo 106, Japan.

COLOURAMA; colour-light-art research. see *ART*

COMITE INTERNATIONAL DES POIDS ET MESURES. COMITE CONSULTATIF DE PHOTOMETRIE ET RADIOMETRIE. (RAPPORT ET ANNEXES). see *METROLOGY AND STANDARDIZATION*

535 DK ISSN 0901-4632
D O P S NYT. 1986. q. DKK 230($35) Dansk Optisk Selskab, Bldg. 309, DK-2800 Lyngby, Denmark. TEL 45-42-88-16-11. FAX 45-45-93-16-69. TELEX 37529-DTHDIA-DK. Ed. Torben Skettrup. adv.; bk.rev. circ. 500. (back issues avail.) **Indexed:** INSPEC (1986-). **Document type:** academic/scholarly publication.
—BLDSC (3619.501000).

535 SZ ISSN 0084-5752
EIDGENOESSISCHE TECHNISCHE HOCHSCHULE ZUERICH. MITTEILUNGEN. PHOTOELASTIZITAET. 1943. irreg., no.19, 1993. free. E T H Zentrum, CH-8092 Zurich, Switzerland. **Document type:** proceedings.

535.58 621.329 UK ISSN 0013-4589
 CODEN: EOPTA4
ELECTRO OPTICS. 6/yr. £90 (foreign £95). Milton Publishing Co. Ltd., 5 Tranquil Passage, Blackheath, London SE3 0BY, England. TEL 081-297-1097. FAX 081-297-1098. Ed. David Whiffen. adv.; tr.lit. circ. 16,000. (back issues avail.) **Indexed:** Ind.Sci.Rev., INSPEC. **Document type:** trade publication.
—SWETS.
Incorporates: Laser Review.
Description: News regarding lasers, optoelectronics, fiber optics, sensors, imaging displays and optics.

535.58 UK ISSN 0261-5657
ELECTRO OPTICS NEWSLETTER. 1981. m. £125. Milton Publishing Co. Ltd., 5 Tranquil Passage, Blackheath, London SE3 0BY, England. TEL 081-297-1097. FAX 081-297-1098. Ed. David Whiffen. **Document type:** newsletter.

ELECTRON MICROSCOPY SOCIETY OF SOUTHERN AFRICA. PROCEEDINGS/ELEKTRON - MIKROSKOPIEVERENIGING VAN SUIDELIKE AFRIKA. VERRIGTINGS. see *BIOLOGY — Microscopy*

ELECTRONIC MATERIALS AND PROCESSING. see *ELECTRONICS*

535 SP ISSN 0210-9891
 CODEN: EOCTDA
ESCUELA DE OPTICA CUANTICA. CURSOS. 1978. a. price varies. Sociedad Espanola de Optica, Serrano 121, 28006 Madrid, Spain.
—CASDDS.

F UND M, FEINWERKTECHNIK MIKROTECHNIK MESSTECHNIK; Zeitschrift fuer Elektronik, Optik, Feinmechanik und Mikrotechnik in Geraetebau und Messtechnik. see *ENGINEERING*

535.84 CC ISSN 1000-7032
QC476.4
FAGUANG XUEBAO/CHINESE JOURNAL OF LUMINESCENCE. (Text in Chinese; abstracts in Chinese, English) 1980. q. $40 (effective through 1995). (Chinese Physical Society, Luminescence Branch) Changchun Institute of Physics - Changchun Wuli Yanjiusuo, 13, Xinmin St., Changchun, Jilin 130021, People's Republic of China. TEL 0431-552215. FAX 0431-555378. (Subscr. to: Chinese Journal of Luminescence Editorial Board, P.O. Box 1035, Changchun 130021, P.R. China) Ed. Xu Xurong. circ. 1,000. **Document type:** academic/scholarly publication.
Description: Covers physics of luminescence, optical properties of solids, laser spectroscopy, light emitting devices, optoelectronics and photonics.

535 GW ISSN 0014-7680
TP890
DIE FARBE; Zeitschrift fuer alle Zweige der Farbenlehre und ihre Anwendung. (Text in English, French and German) 1952. a. DM.385.50 (foreign DM.388.80). Muster-Schmidt Verlag, Brauweg 36a, 37073 Goettingen, Germany. TEL 0551-71741. FAX 0551-7702774. Ed. Prof. H. Terstiege. adv. contact: Eva-Maria Gerhardy. bk.rev.; charts; illus.; index. circ. 600. **Indexed:** Chem.Abstr., World Surf.Coat. **Document type:** academic/scholarly publication.
—BLDSC (3868.000000); SWETS. **CCC**.

535 US ISSN 0146-8030
TA1800 CODEN: FOIOD2
FIBER AND INTEGRATED OPTICS; a journal stressing components, systems, and future trends. 1977. q. £132($217) (effective 1996). Taylor & Francis Inc., 1900 Frost Rd., Ste. 101, Bristol, PA 19007. TEL 215-785-5800; 800-821-8312. FAX 215-785-5515. (Subscr. in Europe to: Taylor & Francis Ltd., Rankine Rd., Basingstoke, Hants. RG24 8PR, England. TEL 44-1256-840366. FAX 44-1256-479438) Ed. Henri Hodara. adv.; abstr.; index. **Indexed**: Chem.Abstr., Curr.Cont., Eng.Ind., INSPEC, J.Curr.Laser Abstr., Phys.Ber., Sci.Res.Abstr. **Document type**: academic/scholarly publication. —BLDSC (3914.620000); CASDDS; Ei; Faxon; Genuine Article; SWETS; UnCover. **CCC**.
Description: Focuses on fiberoptic developments and in-depth surveys. Achieves a balance between scientific developments in integrated optics, systems, manufacturing and applications of optical fibers, and articles on economics and market trends.
Refereed Serial

535.58 US ISSN 1044-4378
TA1800
FIBER OPTIC AND LASER SENSORS. 1983. a. International Society for Optical Engineering (SPIE), Box 10, 1000 20th St., Bellingham, WA 98227-0010.

535 US ISSN 1051-1946
FIBER OPTIC SENSOR AND SYSTEMS; monthly newsletter on worldwide developments in fiber optic sensors and systems. Short title: F O S S. m. $545 (foreign $595). Information Gatekeepers, Inc., 214 Harvard Ave., Boston, MA 02134. TEL 617-232-3111. FAX 617-734-8562. Ed. Paul Polishuk. (looseleaf format; back issues avail.) **Document type**: newsletter.
—**CCC**.
Description: Covers optics applications to sensors, technology, applications, markets, patents, products, and business developments.

FIBER OPTICS NEWS. see *COMMUNICATIONS*

621.36 658.8 US ISSN 0748-9358
FIBEROPTICS MARKETING INTELLIGENCE. 1980. bi-w. $375 in the US; Canada and Mexico $385; elsewhere 395. K M I Corporation, America's Cup Ave., 31 Bridge St., Newport, RI 02840. TEL 401-849-6771. FAX 401-847-5866. Ed. Richard R. Mack; Pub. John N. Kessler. (looseleaf format) **Document type**: newsletter.

535.58 UK ISSN 0264-7249
FIBRE OPTICS NEWSLETTER. 1983. m. £125. Milton Publishing Co. Ltd., 5 Tranquil Passage, Blackheath, London SE3 0BY, England. TEL 081-297-1097. FAX 081-297-1098. Ed. David Whiffen. **Document type**: newsletter.

535 IT ISSN 0015-606X
QC350 CODEN: AFDGA2
FONDAZIONE GIORGIO RONCHI. ATTI. (Text in English, French, German, Italian) 1946. bi-m. L.240000 (foreign L.250000). Fondazione Giorgio Ronchi, Via S. Felice a Ema, 20, 50125 Florence, Italy. TEL 055-2320844. Ed. Laura Ronchi-Abbozzo. adv.; bk.rev.; charts; illus.; index, cum.index every 5 yrs: vols.1-28 (1946-1973). circ. 1,000. **Indexed**: Chem.Abstr., Excerp.Med., INSPEC (1976-), Ophthal.Lit., Psychol.Abstr.
—CASDDS.

FOTEC FIBER OPTIC TESTING NEWS; from the fiber optic test equipment company. see *COMMUNICATIONS*

535 CC
GUANG DE SHIJIE/WORLD OF LIGHT. (Text in Chinese) bi-m. Zhongguo Guang Xuehui, Zhejiang Daxue, Zheda Lu, Hangzhou, Zhejiang 310027, People's Republic of China. TEL 572244. Ed. Tang Jinfa.

535.58 CC ISSN 1005-0086
GUANGDIANZI - JIGUANG/OPTRONICS - LASERS. (Text in Chinese) 1990. bi-m. Y21($29.27) Tianjin Daxue, Jidian Fenxiao - Tianjin University, College of Mechanical & Electronic Engineering, 47, Yingjian Rd., Yangliuqing, Tianjin 300380, People's Republic of China. TEL 86-22-7390978. (Dist. outside China by: China International Book Trading Corporation, P.O. Box 399, Beijing, P.R.C.) Ed. Enxu Ba. adv. contact: Wang Meilin. **Document type**: academic/scholarly publication.
—BLDSC (6276.620000).
Description: Covers opt-electronic integration & fiber application techniques, opt-electr information processing, optical computing & optical neural network, laser medicine, laser biology, and laser applications.

535.84 CC ISSN 1000-0593
CODEN: GYGFED
GUANGPUXUE YU GUANGPU FENXI/SPECTROSCOPY AND SPECTRAL ANALYSIS. (Text in Chinese; abstracts in English) 1981. bi-m. $25 (effective 1996). (Zhongguo Guangxue Xuehui - China Optics Society) Beijing University Publishing Press, Haidian-qu, Beijing 100871, People's Republic of China. TEL 86-10-2182998. FAX 86-10-2181051. Ed. Yao Yuankai. adv.: page $150; adv. contact: Qiang Huang. film rev.; software rev.; abstr.; bibl.; illus. circ. 4,000. (reprint service avail.) **Document type**: academic/scholarly publication.
—BLDSC (8411.114400); CASDDS.
Description: Covers laser spectroscopy measurements, molecular spectroscopy, atomic emission spectrometry, coupled plasma, X-ray fluorescence spectrometry, instrumentation and physics-optics.
Refereed Serial

GUANGXIAN YU DIANLAN/OPTICAL FIBRE AND CABLE. see *ENGINEERING — Electrical Engineering*

535 CC ISSN 0253-2239
QC350 CODEN: GUXUDC
GUANGXUE XUEBAO/ACTA OPTICA SINICA. (Text in Chinese) m. $158.40. (Zhongguo Guangxue Xuehui - China Optics Society) Science Press, Marketing and Sales Department, 16 Donghuangchenggen North St., Beijing 100717, People's Republic of China. TEL 4010642. FAX 4019810. Ed. Wang Runwen. **Document type**: academic/scholarly publication.
—BLDSC (0641.790000); CASDDS.

GUANGXUE YIQI/OPTICAL INSTRUMENTS. see *INSTRUMENTS*

535.58 CC
GUOWAI JIGUANG/FOREIGN LASERS. (Text in Chinese) 1964. m. Y36. Zhongguo Kexueyuan - Shanghai Institute of Optics and Fine Mechanics, P.O. Box 800-211, Shanghai 201800, People's Republic of China. TEL 86-21-9534890. FAX 86-21-9528885. TELEX 30902 SIOFM CN. (Co-sponsor: China Optics Society) Ed. Deng Ximing. circ. 1,000. **Document type**: academic/scholarly publication.

HAKIM FASHION EYEWEAR MAGAZINE. see *CLOTHING TRADE — Fashions*

535 CC ISSN 1001-8891
HONGWAI JISHU/INFRARED TECHNOLOGY. (Text in Chinese) 1979. bi-m. Y3.50 per no. Kunming Wuli Yanjiusuo - Kunming Institute of Physics, P.O. Box 500, Kunming, Yunnan 650223, People's Republic of China. (Dist. outside China by: China International Book Trading Corp., P.O. Box 399, Beijing 100044, P.R. China) Ed. Su Junhong.
—BLDSC (4499.513000).

535 CC ISSN 1001-9014
CODEN: HHXUEZ
HONGWAI YU HAOMIBO XUEBAO/JOURNAL OF INFRARED AND MILLIMETER WAVES. (Text in Chinese) 1982. bi-m. $79.20 (effective 1993). (Zhongguo Guangxue Xuehui (Shanghai) - Chinese Optical Society) Science Press, Marketing and Sales Department, 16 Donghuangchengen North St., Beijing 100717, People's Republic of China. Ed. Tang Dingyuan. **Indexed**: INSPEC (1991-). **Document type**: academic/scholarly publication.
—CASDDS.
Formerly (until 1991): Hongwai Yanjiu (ISSN 1001-9464)

535.58
I E E E INTERNATIONAL SEMICONDUCTOR LASER CONFERENCE. CONFERENCE DIGEST. 1967. biennial. price varies. (I E E E, Laser and Electro-Optics Society) Institute of Electrical and Electronics Engineers, Inc., 345 E. 47th St., New York, NY 10017-2394. TEL 212-705-7900. FAX 212-705-6782. (Subscr. to: 445 Hoes Ln., Box 1331, Piscataway, NJ 08855-1331) **Indexed**: INSPEC.
Formerly (until 1982): I E E E Semiconductor Laser Conference.
Description: Covers all aspects of semiconductor injection laser technology.

I E E E JOURNAL OF QUANTUM ELECTRONICS. see *ELECTRONICS*

535.58 US ISSN 1041-1135
CODEN: IPTLEL
I E E E PHOTONICS TECHNOLOGY LETTERS. 1989. m. $325 to non-members (effective 1996). Institute of Electrical and Electronics Engineers, Inc., 345 E. 47th St., New York, NY 10017-2394. FAX 908-981-9667. (Subscr. to: 445 Hoes Lane, Box 1331, Piscataway, NJ 08855-1331. TEL 908-981-0060) Ed. Paul Shumate. (also avail. in microform from UMI,EEE) **Indexed**: INSPEC (1989-). —BLDSC (4363.013500); Ei; Faxon; Genuine Article; SWETS; UMI. **CCC**.
Description: Publishes original research relevant to photonics technology; laser and electrooptic technology, laser physics and systems, and photonic - lightwave components and applications.

535 621.38 UK ISSN 1350-2433
TA1750 CODEN: IPOPE8
I E E PROCEEDINGS - OPTOELECTRONICS. (Institution of Electrical Engineers) Online edition (ISSN 1359-7078) (Subseries of: I E E Proceedings) 1985. bi-m. £370 (effective 1996). I.E.E., Michael Faraday House, Six Hills Way, Stevenage, Herts. SG1 2AY, England. TEL 01438-313311. FAX 01438-742840. TELEX 825578 IEEESTV G. E-mail: inspec@iee.org.uk. (Subscr. to: Publication Sales Dept., P.O. Box 96, Stevenage, Herts. SG1 2SD, England; U.S. addr.: INSPEC/IEEE, Box 1331, 445 Hoes Ln., Piscataway, NJ 08855-1331. TEL 908-562-5549. FAX 908-562-8737) Ed. Gill Wheeler. circ. 2,000. **Indexed**: A.S.& T.Ind., Br.Tech.Ind., INSPEC. **Document type**: proceedings.
●Also available online.
—BLDSC (4362.751950); CASDDS; Ei; Faxon; Genuine Article; SWETS; UMI; UnCover. **CCC**.
Formerly: I E E Proceedings J (Optoelectronics) (ISSN 0267-3932)
Description: Covers displays, guided optical waves, and integrated optics; holography; light sources, optical modulation and multiplexing, nonlinear optics and optical computing; optical amplifiers; communication systems, fibers and fiber sensors, cables and connectors, information theory and materials; photodetectors and optical receivers. Also includes theory, development, and application of lasers.

530 UK ISSN 0969-6008
IMAGE PROCESSING; capture management and analysis. bi-m. £36 (non-E.C. nations £50). European Technology Publishing, Preston Barn, Preston Ln., Ramsbury, Malborough, Wilts. SN8 2HF, England. TEL 01632-21096. FAX 01672-20789. E-mail: 100071.3167@compuserve.com. Ed. John Haig. adv.: B&W page £1365; color page £1834; trim 300 x 229; adv. contact: Hilary Turnbull. circ. 12,000. (back issues avail.) **Indexed**: Info.Media & Tech., INSPEC (1989-). **Document type**: trade publication.
—BLDSC (4368.992580); SWETS.
Description: Covers such image-processing topics as machine vision, microscopy, remote sensing, medical imaging, multimedia, phototypesetting, and graphic design applications.

535 660 US ISSN 0941-4185
TA1671
INDUSTRIAL LASER BUYERS GUIDE. 1986-1991; resumed 199? a. $225 (foreign $265). PennWell Publishing Co. (Nashua), 10 Tara Blvd., 5th Fl., Nashua, NH 03062-2801. TEL 603-891-0123. Ed. David Belforte. **Document type**: trade publication.
—BLDSC (4457.531920). **CCC**.
Formerly (until 1991): Industrial Laser Annual Handbook (ISSN 0886-0106)

PHYSICS — OPTICS

621.329 US ISSN 0888-935X
INDUSTRIAL LASER REVIEW. 1986. m. $225 (foreign $265) (effective 1994). PennWell Publishing Co. (Nashua), 10 Tara Blvd., 5th Fl., Nashua, NH 03062-2801. TEL 603-891-9177. FAX 603-891-0539. Ed. David Belforte. **Document type:** trade publication.
—BLDSC (4457.531950); SWETS. **CCC**.
Description: Links users, manufacturers, and suppliers of industrial lasers. Coverage includes production-line laser news, actual applications, new systems and products, technical and economic analyses, market trends, and exclusive conference reports.

535 FR ISSN 0758-5756
INFORM'OPTIQUE; revue de liaison bimestrielle entre les professionnels de l'optique. 1971. bi-m. 440 F. Societe Inform' Optique, 3 rue de Seguier, 75006 Paris, France. TEL 43-26-55-06. FAX 46-33-95-92. Ed. Julien Uzzan. adv. circ. 5,500.

535 UK ISSN 1350-4495
QC457 CODEN: IPTEEY
INFRARED PHYSICS AND ENGINEERING. 1961. 7/yr. fl.1578($962) (effective 1996). Elsevier Science Ltd., Pergamon, P.O. Box 800, Kidlington, Oxford OX5 1DX, England. TEL 44-1865-843000. FAX 44-1865-843010. E-mail: nlinfo-f@elsevier.nl; usinfo-f@elsevier.com; forinfo-kyf04035@niftyserve.or.jp; Site addr.: http://www.elsevier.nl/. (Subscr. in U.S. and Canada to: Elsevier Science, 660 White Plains Rd., Tarrytown, NY 10591-5153. TEL 914-524-9200. FAX 914-333-2444) Ed. T.S. Moss. adv.: B&W page $550, color page $1350. bk.rev.; illus.; index. circ. 1,400. (also avail. in microfilm from UMI; back issues avail.; reprint service avail. from UMI) **Indexed:** Cadscan, Chem.Abstr., Curr.Cont., Eng.Ind., Ind.Sci.Rev., INIS Atomind., INSPEC, Int.Aerosp.Abstr., Lead Abstr., Met.Abstr., Phys.Ber., Sci.Cit.Ind., World Alum.Abstr., Zincscan. **Document type:** academic/scholarly publication.
—BLDSC (4499.410000); CASDDS; Ei; Faxon; Genuine Article; SWETS; UMI; UnCover. **CCC**.
Formerly (until 1994): Infrared Physics (ISSN 0020-0891)
Description: Covers detectors, solid state photoconductors, multi-element and image tubes, optical materials and systems, polarizers, filters, infrared properties of solids, liquids, and gases, and all types of lasers.
Refereed Serial

535 SP ISSN 0304-9957
INSTITUTO DE OPTICA "DAZA DE VALDES". PUBLICACION. 1947. irreg. price varies. Instituto de Optica "Daza de Valdes", Serrano, 121, 28006 Madrid, Spain. TEL 91-5616800. FAX 91-5645557.

535 GW ISSN 0940-0117
INTERFERENZEN. (Text in English, German) 1990. q. DM.40. Deutsche Gesellschaft fuer Holografie e.V., Postfach 1722, 49007 Osnabrueck, Germany. TEL 0541-7102199. FAX 0541-7102189. Ed. Vito Orazem. **Document type:** bulletin.
—BLDSC (4533.473500).

535 621.3 US
INTERNATIONAL CONFERENCE ON INFRARED AND MILLIMETER WAVES. CONFERENCE DIGEST. (Published by other organizations when held outside of U.S.) 1974. a. price varies. (I E E E, Microwave Theory and Techniques Society) Institute of Electrical and Electronics Engineers, Inc., 345 E. 47th St., New York, NY 10017-2394. TEL 212-705-7900. FAX 212-705-7682. (Subscr. to: 445 Hoes Lane, Box 1331, Piscataway, NJ 0885-1331) Ed. Kenneth J. Button.
Former titles: International Conference on Infrared and Millimeter Waves and Their Applications. Conference Digest; International Conference on Submillimeter Waves and Their Applications. Conference Digest.
Description: Discusses materials measurement and techniques, submillimeter waves, free electron lasers and gyrotron.

535.58 US ISSN 0190-4132
TA1673 CODEN: PICLDV
INTERNATIONAL CONFERENCE ON LASERS. PROCEEDINGS (YEAR). Key Title: Proceedings of the International Conference on Lasers (Year). Variant title: Lasers (Year). 1979. a. $160 (for 1996 edition). (Society for Optical & Quantum Electronics) S T S Press, Box 245, McLean, VA 22101. TEL 703-642-5835. FAX 703-642-5838. TELEX 892320. Eds. V.J. Cochran, T.A. Goldman. circ. 300 (controlled). **Indexed:** Chem.Abstr, INSPEC. **Document type:** proceedings.
—BLDSC (6844.715000); CASDDS. **CCC**.

535 US ISSN 0195-9271
TA1570 CODEN: IJIWDO
INTERNATIONAL JOURNAL OF INFRARED AND MILLIMETER WAVES. 1980. m. $545 (foreign $640) (effective 1996). Plenum Publishing Corp., 233 Spring St., New York, NY 10013-1578. TEL 212-620-8000. FAX 212-463-0742. TELEX 23-421139. Ed. Kenneth J. Button. adv.; illus. (also avail. in microfilm from JSC; back issues avail.) **Indexed:** Chem.Abstr., Curr.Cont., Eng.Ind., Ind.Sci.Rev., INIS Atomind., INSPEC, Int.Aerosp.Abstr., Phys.Ber., Sci.Cit.Ind. **Document type:** academic/scholarly publication.
—BLDSC (4542.305000); CASDDS; Ei; Faxon; Genuine Article; SWETS; UMI; UnCover. **CCC**.
Refereed Serial

535.84 NE ISSN 0168-1176
QC454 CODEN: IJMPDN
INTERNATIONAL JOURNAL OF MASS SPECTROMETRY AND ION PROCESSES. (Text in English, French and German) 1968. 33/yr. fl.4895($2985) (effective 1996). Elsevier Science B.V., P.O. Box 211, 1000 AE Amsterdam, Netherlands. TEL 31-20-4853911. FAX 31-20-4853598. TELEX 18582 ESPA NL. E-mail: nlinfo-f@elsevier.nl; usinfo-f@elsevier.com; forinfo-kyf04035@niftyserve.or.jp; Site addr.: http://www.elsevier.nl/. (Subscr. in U.S. and Canada to: Elsevier Science Inc., Box 882, Madison Sq. Sta., New York, NY 10159-0882. TEL 212-989-5800. FAX 212-633-3990) Ed.Bd. adv.; bk.rev.; charts; index. (also avail. in microform from UMI) **Indexed:** Anal.Abstr., Biwk.Pap.Rad.Chem.& Photochem., Chem.Abstr., Curr.Cont., Deep Sea Res.& Oceanogr.Abstr., Excerp.Med., INSPEC (1908-), Int.Aerosp.Abstr., Mass Spectr.Bull., Phys.Ber., Sci.Cit.Ind. **Document type:** academic/scholarly publication.
—BLDSC (4542.335000); ADONIS; CASDDS; Ei; Faxon; Genuine Article; SWETS; UnCover. **CCC**.
Formerly (until 1983): International Journal of Mass Spectrometry and Ion Physics (ISSN 0020-7381)
Description: Contains papers dealing with fundamental aspects of mass spectrometry and ion processes, and the application of mass spectrometric techniques to specific problems in chemistry and physics.
Refereed Serial

535 UK ISSN 0952-5432
TA1750 CODEN: IJOOEV
INTERNATIONAL JOURNAL OF OPTOELECTRONICS. bi-m. £224($370) (effective 1996). Taylor & Francis Ltd., Rankine Rd., Basingstoke, Hants RG24 8PR, England. TEL 44-1256-840366. FAX 44-1256-479438. TELEX 858540. E-mail: info@tandf.co.uk. (Subscr. in N. America to: Taylor & Francis Inc., 1900 Frost Rd., Ste. 101, Bristol, PA 19007-1598. TEL 800-821-8312. FAX 215-785-5515) Ed.Bd. **Indexed:** INSPEC (1988-). **Document type:** academic/scholarly publication.
—BLDSC (4542.429300); Ei; Faxon; Genuine Article; SWETS. **CCC**.
Formerly: International Journal of Optical Sensors.
Description: Disseminates information on optical fibers and optical sensors. Covers detectors, transmission systems, attenuators, amplifiers, couplers, and frequency and mode changers.
Refereed Serial

INTERNATIONAL SOCIETY ON OPTICS WITHIN LIFE SCIENCES. SERIES (PROCEEDINGS). see BIOLOGY

535 HU ISSN 0237-2215
INTERNATIONAL SYMPOSIUM OF THE TECHNICAL COMMITTEE ON PHOTON-DETECTORS. (Text in English) 1980. irreg., 15th, 1995. $41. International Measurement Confederation (IMEKO), P.O. Box 457, 1371 Budapest, Hungary. Ed. J. Schanda. circ. 150. (also avail. in microfiche; back issues avail.) **Indexed:** Chem.Abstr. **Document type:** proceedings.

535 US ISSN 0731-2911
QC495
INTER-SOCIETY COLOR COUNCIL NEWS. 1933. bi-m. membership. Inter-Society Color Council, c/o Danny C. Rich, Sec., Datacolor Int'l, 5 Princess Rd., Lawrenceville, NJ 08648. TEL 609-895-7427. FAX 609-895-7461. (Edit. addr.: 3782 Bonny Rigg Trail, Roswell, GA 30075. TEL 404-587-5120) Ed. Michael A. Hammel. bk.rev.; film rev.; charts; illus.; pat.; stat.; index. circ. 1,000. (processed) **Indexed:** Graph.Arts Lit.Abstr.
—BLDSC (4557.444800).
Formerly: Inter-Society Color Council Newsletter (ISSN 0300-7588)

530 JA ISSN 0916-3492
J A S C O REPORT. (Text in Japanese) 1989. m. 200 Yen per no. Japan Spectroscopic Corporation - Nihon Bunko Kogyo K.K., 2967-5, Ishikawa-machi, Hachioji-shi, Tokyo 192, Japan.
—BLDSC (4663.141800).
Formed by the merger of (1982-1989): I R Report (ISSN 0911-6478); (1979-1989): L C Family (ISSN 0389-5270); Which was formerly (1963-1979): J A S C O Report (ISSN 0389-5262)

535 681.1 GW ISSN 0075-272X
Q185
JAHRBUCH FUER OPTIK UND FEINMECHANIK. 1954. a. DM.64. Fachverlag Schiele und Schoen GmbH, Markgrafenstr. 11, 10969 Berlin, Germany. TEL 030-253752-0. FAX 030-2517248. Ed. W.-D. Prenzel. adv. circ. 3,000. **Document type:** academic/scholarly publication.
—CCC.

535 JA ISSN 0389-6625
CODEN: KOGAD5
JAPANESE JOURNAL OF OPTICS/KOGAKU. (Text in English, Japanese; summaries in English) 1972. m. 800 Yen per no. Japan Society of Applied Physics, Optical Society of Japan - Oyo Butsuri Gakkai Bunkakai Nihon Kogakkai, 12-3, Kudan Kita 1-chome, Chiyoda-ku, Tokyo 102, Japan.
—BLDSC (4656.780000); CASDDS.

JEMNA MECHANIKA A OPTIKA/FINE MECHANICS AND OPTICS. see PHYSICS — Mechanics

535.84 544.6 US ISSN 0021-9037
QD95 CODEN: JASYAP
JOURNAL OF APPLIED SPECTROSCOPY. English translation of: Zhurnal Prikladnoi Spektroskopii (RU ISSN 0514-7506) 1965. m. $1375 (foreign $1610) (effective 1996). Plenum Publishing Corp., Consultants Bureau, 233 Spring St., New York, NY 10013-1578. TEL 212-620-8468. FAX 212-463-0742. TELEX 23-421139. Ed. N.A. Borisevich. (also avail. in microfilm from JSC; back issues avail.) **Indexed:** Appl.Mech.Rev., Chem.Titles, Eng.Ind., INIS Atomind., INSPEC (1970-), Phys.Ber., Sci.Res.Abstr., Solid St.Abstr. **Document type:** academic/scholarly publication.
—BLDSC (0414.200000); Ei; Faxon; SWETS; UMI; UnCover. **CCC**.
Refereed Serial

535.84 NE ISSN 0368-2048
QC454.E4 CODEN: JESRAW
JOURNAL OF ELECTRON SPECTROSCOPY AND RELATED PHENOMENA; an international journal devoted to all aspects of electron spectroscopy - including theoretical studies and other spectroscopic measurements of relevance to the field of electron spectroscopy. (Text in English, French and German) 1972. 21/yr. fl.2940($1793) (effective 1996). Elsevier Science B.V., P.O. Box 211, 1000 AE Amsterdam, Netherlands. TEL 31-20-4853911. FAX 31-20-4853598. TELEX 18582 ESPA NL. E-mail: nlinfo-f@elsevier.nl; usinfo-f@elsevier.com; forinfo-kyf04035@niftyserve.or.jp; Site addr.: http://www.elsevier.nl/. (Subscr. in U.S. and Canada to: Elsevier Science Inc., Box 882, Madison Sq. Sta. New York, NY 10159-0882. TEL 212-989-5800. FAX 212-633-3990) Ed.Bd. adv.; bk.rev.; charts; illus.; index. (also avail. in microform from UMI) **Indexed:** Chem.Abstr., Curr.Cont., Ind.Sci.Rev., INIS Atomind., INSPEC, Mass Spectr.Bull., Phys.Ber., Sci.Cit.Ind. **Document type:** academic/scholarly publication.
—BLDSC (4974.900000); CASDDS; Ei; Faxon; Genuine Article; SWETS; UnCover. **CCC**.
Refereed Serial

535.84 US ISSN 1017-9909
TA1632 CODEN: JEIME5
JOURNAL OF ELECTRONIC IMAGING. 1992. q. $40 to individual non-members (foreign $60); institutions $100 (foreign $120). International Society for Optical Engineering (SPIE), Box 10, Bellingham, WA 98227. TEL 206-676-3290. FAX 206-647-1445. (Co-sponsor: I S & T - Society for Imaging Science and Technology) Ed. Paul G. Roetling. adv.; bk.rev.; abstr.; charts; illus.; index. circ. 3,000. **Indexed:** INSPEC (1992-). **Document type:** academic/scholarly publication.
—BLDSC (4974.940000); Ei; SWETS. **CCC.**
   Description: Covers all aspects of electronic imaging applications.

621.329 UK ISSN 1042-346X
TA1671 CODEN: JLAPEN
JOURNAL OF LASER APPLICATIONS. 1976. q. £110 to institutions in the E.U. (N. America $159; elsewhere £125) (effective 1995). (Laser Institute of America, US) Chapman & Hall, Journals Department (Subsidiary of: International Thomson Publishing Group), 2-6 Boundary Row, London SE1 8HN, England. TEL 0171-865-0066. FAX 0171-522-9623. TELEX 290164 CHAPMA G. E-mail: journal@chall.mhs.compuserve.com. (Dist. by: International Thomson Publishing Services Ltd., Cheriton House, North Way, Andover, Hants. SP10 5BE, England. TEL 01264-342713. FAX 01264-342807; N. American subscr. to: Chapman & Hall, Journals Promotion Department, One Penn Plaza, 41st Fl., New York, NY 10119. TEL 212-564-1060. FAX 212-564-1505) Ed. Sidey S. Charschan. adv.; bk.rev.; abstr.; bibl.; charts; illus.; index. circ. 5,000. (back issues avail.; reprint service avail.) **Document type:** academic/scholarly publication.
—BLDSC (5010.103000); CASDDS; Ei; Genuine Article; SWETS; UnCover. **CCC.**
   Formerly (until 1988): Topics of Laser Applications. **Description:** Publishes basic and applied papers dealing with the diverse laser-electro-optics applications of laser-electro-optics.
   Refereed Serial

535 JA ISSN 0387-8805
CODEN: JLEVDQ
JOURNAL OF LIGHT & VISUAL ENVIRONMENT. (Text in English) 1977. 4/yr. Illuminating Engineering Institute of Japan - Shomei Gakkai, 1-7-1 Yurako-cho, 1-chome, Chiyoda-ku, Tokyo 100, Japan. Ed. Yasuyuki Otani. **Indexed:** Chem.Abstr., INSPEC (1984-). **Document type:** academic/scholarly publication.
—CASDDS. **CCC.**

535 US ISSN 0733-8724
TA1501 CODEN: JLTEDG
JOURNAL OF LIGHTWAVE TECHNOLOGY. 1983. m. $550 to non-members (effective 1996). Institute of Electrical and Electronics Engineers, Inc., 345 E. 47th St., New York, NY 10017-2394. TEL 908-981-0060. FAX 908-981-9667. (Subscr. to: Box 1331, 445 Hoes Lane, Piscataway, NJ 08855-1331) (Co-publisher: Optical Society of America) Ed. Donald Keck. (also avail. in microform) **Indexed:** ASCA, CAD CAM Abstr., Chem.Abstr., Ind.Sci.Rev., INIS Atomind., INSPEC (1983-), Int.Aerosp.Abstr., Sci.Cit.Ind., Tel.Abstr.
—BLDSC (5010.474000); CASDDS; Ei; Faxon; Genuine Article; SWETS; UMI; UnCover. **CCC.**
   Description: Original papers reporting theoretical and-or experimental results which advance the technological base of guided-wave technology.
   Refereed Serial

535 NE ISSN 0022-2313
QC476.4 CODEN: JLUMA8
JOURNAL OF LUMINESCENCE; an interdisciplinary journal of research on excited state processes in condensed matter. (Text in English, French, German; summaries in English) 1970. 24/yr. fl.2256($1376) (effective 1996). North-Holland (Subsidiary of: Elsevier Science B.V.), P.O. Box 211, 1000 AE Amsterdam, Netherlands. TEL 31-20-4853911. FAX 31-20-4853598. TELEX 18582 ESPA NL. (Subscr. in U.S. and Canada to: Elsevier Science Inc., Box 882, Madison Sq. Sta., New York, NY 10159. TEL 212-989-5800. FAX 212-633-3990) Ed. R.S. Meltzer. adv.; bk.rev.; bibl.; charts; illus.; index, cum.index. (also avail. in microform from UMI; back issues avail.) **Indexed:** Biol.Abstr., Biwk.Pap.Rad.Chem.& Photochem., Cadscan, Chem.Abstr., Curr.Cont., Eng.Ind., GeoRef., Ind.Sci.Rev., INIS Atomind., INSPEC (1970-), Lead Abstr., Phys.Ber., Sci.Cit.Ind., Zincscan. **Document type:** academic/scholarly publication.
—BLDSC (5010.650000); CASDDS; Ei; Faxon; Genuine Article; SWETS; UnCover. **CCC.**
   Description: Provides a means of communication between scientists in different disciplines who share a common interest in the electronic excited state of molecular, ionic and covalent system, whether crystalline, amorphous, or liquid.
   Refereed Serial

535 UK ISSN 0950-0340
QC350 CODEN: JMOPEW
JOURNAL OF MODERN OPTICS. 1954. m. £842($1390) (effective 1996). Taylor & Francis Ltd., Rankine Rd., Basingstoke, Hants. RG24 8PR, England. TEL 44-1256-840366. FAX 44-1256-479438. TELEX 858540. E-mail: info tandf.co.uk. (Subscr. in N. America to: Taylor & Francis Inc., 1900 Frost Rd., Ste. 101, Bristol, PA 19007-1598. TEL 800-821-8312. FAX 215-785-5515) Eds. P.L. Knight, R.W. Boyd. adv.; bk.rev.; illus.; index. (also avail. in microform) **Indexed:** Chem.Abstr., Curr.Cont., Excerp.Med., Ind.Med., INSPEC, Math.R., Phys.Ber. **Document type:** academic/scholarly publication.
—BLDSC (5020.686000); CASDDS; Ei; Faxon; Genuine Article; SWETS; UnCover. **CCC.**
   Formerly: Optica Acta: International Journal of Optics (ISSN 0030-3909)
   Description: Aims to cover both the fundamental and applied aspects of contemporary research worldwide on such topics as nonlinear and quantum optics; laser physics, coherence and speckle; optical fibres and thin films; integrated optics and electro-optics; and optical design and testing.
   Refereed Serial

535.84 544.6 US ISSN 0022-2852
QC451 CODEN: JMOSA3
JOURNAL OF MOLECULAR SPECTROSCOPY. 1957. m. $1498 (foreign $1710) (effective 1996). Academic Press, Inc., Journal Division, 525 B St., Ste. 1900, San Diego, CA 92101-4495. TEL 619-230-1840. FAX 619-699-6800. (Subscr. to: Box 620000, Orlando, FL 32891-8340. TEL 800-543-9534) Ed. K. Narahari Rao. adv.; bibl.; charts; illus.; index. (back issues avail.) **Indexed:** Abstr.Bull.Inst.Pap.Chem., Biol.Abstr., Bull.Thermodyn.& Thermochem., Chem.Abstr., Curr.Adv.Ecol.Sci., Curr.Cont., Ind.Sci.Rev., INIS Atomind., INSPEC, Int.Aerosp.Abstr., Phys.Ber., Sci.Cit.Ind. **Document type:** academic/scholarly publication.
—BLDSC (5020.750000); CASDDS; Ei; Faxon; Genuine Article; SWETS; UnCover. **CCC.**
   Description: Presents experimental and theoretical articles on all subjects relevant to molecular spectroscopy and its modern applications.
   Refereed Serial

535 SI
QC446.15
JOURNAL OF NONLINEAR OPTICAL PHYSICS & MATERIALS. (Text in English) 1992. q. $170 to individuals and institutions of developing countries; institutions of developed countries $348. World Scientific Publishing Co. Pte. Ltd., Farrer Rd., P.O. Box 128, Singapore 9128, Singapore. TEL 3825663. FAX 3825919. TELEX RS 28561 WSPC. (U.K. addr.: 73 Lynton Mead, Totteridge, London N20 8DH, England. TEL 44-181-4462461; U.S. addr.: 1060 Main St., Ste. 1B, River Edge, NJ 07661. TEL 800-227-7562) Ed. Iam-Choon Khoo. **Indexed:** INSPEC (1992-). **Document type:** academic/scholarly publication.
—CASDDS; Faxon; SWETS; UnCover. **CCC.**
   Formerly (until Jan. 1995): International Journal of Nonlinear Optical Physics (ISSN 0218-1991)
   Description: Covers research and development in nonlinear interactions of light with matter, including fundamental nonlinear optical processes, novel nonlinear material properties, guided waves and solutions, intense field phenomena, and their applications in laser and coherent lightwave amplification, guiding, switching, modulation, communication and information processing.

535 US ISSN 1070-9762
TS510 CODEN: JOTEE4
JOURNAL OF OPTICAL TECHNOLOGY. English translation of: Opticheskii Zhurnal. 1966. m. $1345 to non-members. (Opticheskii Institut im. S.I. Vavilova (S.-Peterburg), RU) Optical Society of America, Inc., 2010 Massachusetts Ave., N.W., Washington, DC 20036-1023. TEL 202-223-8130. FAX 202-223-1096. Ed. William Manthey. (also avail. in microform; back issues avail.) **Indexed:** ASCA, C.P.I., Curr.Cont., Eng.Ind., Gen.Phys.Adv.Abstr., INSPEC (1968-), Int.Aerosp.Abstr., Phys.Ber., Risk Abstr. **Document type:** academic/scholarly publication.
—BLDSC (0415.219000); Ei; Faxon; Genuine Article; SWETS; UnCover. **CCC.**
   Formerly (until vol.61, no.1, 1994): Soviet Journal of Optical Technology (ISSN 0038-5514)
   Description: Reports the theoretical and experimental research concerning many phases of optical, space and astronomical engineering.

535 FR ISSN 0150-536X
QC350 CODEN: JOOPDB
JOURNAL OF OPTICS/NOUVELLE REVUE D'OPTIQUE. (Text in English, French; summaries in English, French) 1970. bi-m. 1512 F. (foreign 1796 F.) (effective 1996). Masson - Periodiques, Villa Laromiguiere, 75005 Paris, France. TEL 1-40-46-62-00. FAX 1-40-46-62-01. Ed. A.C. Boccara. adv.; bk.rev. circ. 750. (reprint service avail. from ISI) **Indexed:** Chem.Abstr., Curr.Cont., Excerp.Med., Fluidex, GeoRef., INIS Atomind., INSPEC. **Document type:** academic/scholarly publication.
—BLDSC (5026.365000); CASDDS; Ei; Faxon; Genuine Article; SWETS; UMI. **CCC.**
   Former titles (1973-1976): Nouvelle Revue d'Optique (ISSN 0335-7368); (1970-1972): Nouvelle Revue d'Optique Appliquee (ISSN 0029-4780)

535 II ISSN 0970-0374
JOURNAL OF OPTICS. (Text in English) 1972. q. Rs.500($50) Optical Society of India, c/o Dept. of Applied Physics, University of Calcutta, 92 Acharya Prafulla Chandra Rd., Calcutta 700 009, India. Ed. A.K. Ghosh. adv.; bk.rev.; index. circ. 600. (also avail. in microform from UMI; back issues avail. from UMI) **Indexed:** CAD CAM Abstr., Chem.Abstr., Curr.Cont., Ind.Sci.Rev., INSPEC, Int.Aerosp.Abstr. **Document type:** academic/scholarly publication.
—BLDSC (5026.360000).

535 534 US
JOURNAL OF OPTICS RESEARCH. 1990. q. $315 (effective 1996). Nova Science Publishers, Inc., 6080 Jericho Tpke., Ste. 207, Commack, NY 11725-2808. TEL 516-499-3103. E-mail: novasci1@aol.com. **Document type:** academic/scholarly publication.
—UnCover.
   Formerly: Optical and Acoustical Review (ISSN 1050-3315)

PHYSICS — OPTICS

535.84   UK   ISSN 0022-4073
QC451   CODEN: JQSRAE
JOURNAL OF QUANTITATIVE SPECTROSCOPY AND RADIATIVE TRANSFER. (Text in English, French, German or Russian) 1961. m. £1341($2133) (effective 1996). Elsevier Science Ltd., Pergamon, P.O. Box 800, Kidlington, Oxford OX5 1DX, England. TEL 44-1865-843000. FAX 44-1865-843010. E-mail: nlinfo-f@elsevier.nl; usinfo-f@elsevier.com; forinfo-kyf04035@niftyserve.or.jp; Site addr.: http://www.elsevier.nl/. (Subscr. in U.S. and Canada to: Elsevier Science, 660 White Plains Rd., Tarrytown, NY 10591-5153. TEL 914-524-9200. FAX 914-333-2444) Ed. P. Varanasi. adv.: B&W page $550, color page $1350. bk.rev.; charts; illus.; index. circ. 1,200. (also avail. in microfilm from UMI; back issues avail.) **Indexed:** Appl.Mech.Rev., Biol.Abstr., Cadscan, Chem.Abstr., Curr.Cont., Excerp.Med., Ind.Sci.Rev., INIS Atomind., INSPEC, Int.Aerosp.Abstr., Lead Abstr., Mass Spectr.Bull., Phys.Ber., Zincscan. **Document type:** academic/scholarly publication.
—BLDSC (5043.700000); CASDDS; Ei; Faxon; Genuine Article; SWETS; UMI; UnCover. **CCC.**
Description: Covers spectral line shapes and widths, quantitative spectroscopic techniques for environmental studies, radiant energy emissions for plasmas and spectroscopic studies involving lasers.
Refereed Serial

535   JA   ISSN 0916-4731
KASHIKA JOHO/VISUALIZATION SOCIETY OF JAPAN. JOURNAL. (Text in English, Japanese) 1981. q. 12500 Yen. Kashika Joho Gakkai - Visualization Society of Japan, 16-13, Hyakunin-cho 2-chome, Shinjuku-ku, Tokyo 169, Japan. TEL 81-3-3364-1762. FAX 81-3-3364-3919. Ed. Yuko Oshima. circ. 1,800. **Indexed:** INIS Atomind.
—BLDSC (4912.557000).

535 770 791.4   HU   ISSN 0023-0480
TR845   CODEN: KEHTAS
KEP- ES HANGTECHNIKA. (Text in Hungarian; summaries in English, German and Russian) 1955. bi-m. $26. (Optikai, Akusztikai es Filmtechnikai Egyesulet) Lapkiado Vallalat, Lenin korut 9-11, 1073 Budapest 7, Hungary. TEL 222-408. (Subscr. to: Kultura, Box 149, H-1389 Budapest, Hungary) adv.; charts; illus. circ. 900. **Indexed:** INSPEC, Photo.Abstr.
—CASDDS.

KEY ABSTRACTS - OPTOELECTRONICS. see PHYSICS — Abstracting, Bibliographies, Statistics

535   JA   ISSN 0910-9854
KODANSEIGAKU RONBUNSHU/JAPAN SOCIETY FOR PHOTOELASTICITY. PROCEEDINGS. (Text in Japanese) 1979. a. Nihon Kodansei Gakkai - Japan Society for Photoelasticity, Nihon Gakkai Jimu Senta, 16-9, Honkomagome 5-chome, Bunkyo-ku, Tokyo 113, Japan. **Document type:** proceedings.

535   JA
KOGAKU GO GAKKAI KANSAI SHIBU RENGO KOENKAI YOKOSHU/KANSAI BRANCHES FIVE SOCIETIES ON OPTICS. JOINT CONVENTION RECORD. (Text in Japanese) a. Kogaku Go Gakkai Kansai Shibu, c/o Shomei Gakkai Kansai Shibu, Chuo Denki Kurabu, 1-25, Dojima Hama 2-chome, Kita-ku, Osaka 530, Japan.

L D & A. (Lighting Design & Application) see ENGINEERING — Electrical Engineering

535   UK   ISSN 0263-0346
QC689.5.L37   CODEN: LPBEDA
LASER AND PARTICLE BEAMS; pulse power & high energy densities. 1983. q. £194($359) (effective 1996). Cambridge University Press, Edinburgh Bldg., Shaftesbury Rd., Cambridge CB2 2RU, England. TEL 01223-312393. FAX 01223-315052. TELEX 851817256. (N. American addr.: Cambridge University Press, Journals Dept., 40 W. 20th St., New York, NY 10011. TEL 212-924-3900. FAX 212-691-3239) Ed. George Miley. adv.: bk.rev. (back issues avail. reprint service avail. from SWZ) **Indexed:** Chem.Abstr., Curr.Cont., Energy Info.Abstr., INIS Atomind., INSPEC (1983-), Phys.Ber., Sci.Cit.Ind. **Document type:** academic/scholarly publication.
—BLDSC (5156.518800); CASDDS; Ei; Faxon; Genuine Article; SWETS; UMI; UnCover. **CCC.**
Description: Provides a forum for physicists and engineers to pool the findings of their research on the generation of high-intensity laser and particle beams and their interaction with matter.

LASER AND TECHNOLOGY; clinical and experimental. see MEDICAL SCIENCES — Experimental Medicine, Laboratory Technique

535.58 621.329   IT
LASER APPLICAZIONI INDUSTRIALI, TECNOLOGIE, MERCATI. 1991. 5/yr. L.74900 (foreign L.145800) (includes Mecanica Oggi). Gruppo Editoriale Jackson S.p.A., Via M. Gorki 69, 20092 Cinisello B. (MI), Italy. TEL 39-2-660341. FAX 39-2-66034238. Ed. Giuseppe Grassi. adv.: B&W page L.2000000, color page L.2700000; 210 x 297. circ. 6,000 (controlled).
Description: Covers all aspects of industrial usage, application and technology of lasers.

535.58   US   ISSN 0278-6273
QD701   CODEN: LSCHDB
LASER CHEMISTRY. 6/yr. 207 ECU (effective 1996). Harwood Academic Publishers, c/o International Publishers Distributor, 820 Town Center Dr., Langhorne, PA 19047. TEL 215-750-2642. FAX 215-750-6343. (Subscr. to: International Publishers Distributor PO Box 90, Reading,Berkshire, RG1 8JL, England. TEL 44-173-456-8316) Ed. R. Vetter. adv. (also avail. in microform) **Indexed:** Chem.Abstr., INSPEC, Mass Spectr.Bull.
—BLDSC (5156.527000); CASDDS; Faxon; SWETS. **CCC.**
Refereed Serial

535.58 621.329   US   ISSN 1043-8092
TA1501   CODEN: LFWOE8
LASER FOCUS WORLD; the magazine of electro-optics technology. 1964. m. $149 (foreign $219). PennWell Publishing Co. (Nashua), 10 Tara Blvd., 5th Fl., Nashua, NH 03062-2801. TEL 603-891-0123. FAX 603-891-0574. Ed. Jeffrey N. Bairstow. adv. circ. 64,000. (also avail. in microform from UMI) **Indexed:** A.S.& T.Ind., Abstr.Bull.Inst.Pap.Chem., CAD CAM Abstr. (until 1992), Chem.Abstr., Curr.Cont., Eng.Ind., INIS Atomind., INSPEC, Robomat. (until 1992).
—BLDSC (5156.530610); CASDDS; Ei; Faxon; Genuine Article; SWETS; UMI; UnCover. **CCC.**
Former titles: Laser Focus (ISSN 8755-1853); Laser Focus Including Electro-Optics Magazine (ISSN 0740-2511); (1981-1983): Laser Focus with Fiberoptic Technology (ISSN 0275-1399); (until vol.17, no.3, 1981): Laser Focus with Fiberoptic Communications (ISSN 0190-1451); (until vol.14, 1978): Laser Focus (ISSN 0023-8589); Incorporates (1969-1983): Electro-Optics (ISSN 0745-5003); Which was formerly titled: Electro-Optical Systems Design (ISSN 0424-8457).
Description: Covers basic electro-optical devices and systems for OEM design engineers, technical managers, scientists, and researchers.

535.58 658.8   US
LASER FOCUS WORLD BUYERS' GUIDE. 1964. a. $85 (foreign $110). PennWell Publishing Co. (Nashua), 10 Tara Blvd., 5th Fl., Nashua, NH 03062-2801. TEL 603-891-0123. FAX 603-891-0574. adv. circ. 50,000. **Document type:** directory.
—**CCC.**
Former titles: Laser Focus - Electro Optics Buyers' Guide (ISSN 8755-1616); Laser Focus Buyers' Guide (ISSN 0075-8027); (until 1970): Laser Marketers' and Buyers' Guide.

535.3 621.36   NE   ISSN 0921-8564
LASER HANDBOOK. (Text in English) 1972. irreg., vol.6, 1990. price varies. Elsevier Science B.V., Books Division, P.O. Box 211, 1000 AE Amsterdam, Netherlands. TEL 31-20-4853911. FAX 31-20-4853705. TELEX 18582 ESPA NL. E-mail: nlinfo@elsevier.nl; usinfo-f@elsevier.com; forinfo-kyf04035@niftyserve.or.jp; Site addr.: http://www.elsevier.nl/. (Subscr. in U.S. and Canada to: Elsevier Science Inc., Box 882, Madison Sq. Sta., New York, NY 10159. TEL 212-989-5800) (back issues avail.) **Document type:** monographic series.
Refereed Serial

621.36   CC
LASER JOURNAL. (Text in Chinese) bi-m. Y4 per no. Chongqing Shi Guangxue Jixie Yanjiusuo, Editorial Board of Laser Journal, 35 Yuzhou Rd., Shiqiaopu, Chongqing, Sichuan 630041, People's Republic of China. TEL 811450. (Dist. outside China by: China National Publishing Industry Trading Corp., P.O. Box 782, Beijing, P.R. China) Ed. Yang Keda. **Indexed:** Eng.Ind.
Description: Publishes papers on laser techniques and their applications in industry, medicine and science.

535.58   RU   ISSN 1054-660X
QC685   CODEN: LAPHEJ
LASER PHYSICS; the new international journal covering theoretical and experimental laser research and application. (English translation of Russian title) 1991. 6/yr. $542 in U.S. and Canada (elsewhere $601) (effective 1995). (Russian Academy of Sciences, Institute of General Physics) Interperiodica, Ul. Profsoyuznaya 90, Moscow 117864, Russia. TEL 7-095-3360066. FAX 7-095-3360666. (Subscr. to: Interperiodica, Box 1831, Birmingham, AL 35201-1831. TEL 205-995-1567. FAX 205-995-1588) Ed. Alexander M. Prokhorov. **Indexed:** INSPEC (1991-). **Document type:** academic/scholarly publication.
—BLDSC (5156.606000); CASDDS.
Description: Covers the whole range of questions of modern laser physics and quantum electronics, emphasizing physical effects in various media (solid, gaseous, liquid) leading to the generation of laser radiation.

535.58   GW   ISSN 0937-7069
TA1671   CODEN: LASPEO
LASER PRAXIS; Forum fuer industrielle Laser-Anwendungen. m. Carl Hanser Verlag, Kolbergerstr. 22, 81679 Munich, Germany. TEL 089-998300. FAX 089-984809. (Subscr. to: Postfach 860420, 81631 Munich, Germany) Ed. C. Treffert. adv. contact: Guenther Steidl. circ. 29,000. **Indexed:** INSPEC (1990-). **Document type:** trade publication.
—BLDSC (5156.607700); Ei.

535.58 621.329   US   ISSN 0023-8600
LASER REPORT; the market outlook in lasers and opto-electronics. 1965. 24/yr. $330 (foreign $350) (effective 1994). PennWell Publishing Co. (Nashua), 10 Tara Blvd., 5th Fl., Nashua, NH 03062-2801. TEL 603-891-0123. FAX 603-891-0574. Ed. David Kales. circ. 400. **Indexed:** PROMT.
—**CCC.**
Formerly: Laser Focus Mid-Month Report.
Description: Covers business news and market trends in laser equipment and systems.

535.58   US   ISSN 0899-2711
LASER SCIENCE AND TECHNOLOGY. irreg., latest vol.17. Harwood Academic Publishers, c/o International Publishers Distributor, 820 Town Center Dr., Langhorne, PA 19047. TEL 215-750-2642. FAX 215-750-6343. (Subscr. to: International Publishers Distributor, PO Box 90, Reading, Berkshire, RG1 8JL, England. TEL 44-173-456-8316) Ed. V.S. Letokhov. (also avail. in microform)
—BLDSC (5156.635000).
Refereed Serial

535.58   US
LASER TECH BRIEFS. 1993. q. $75. Associated Business Publications, 41 E. 42nd St., Ste. 921, New York, NY 10017. TEL 212-490-3999. FAX 212-986-7864. Ed. Joseph Pramberger. adv.: B&W page $3100. circ. 40,000. **Document type:** academic/scholarly publication, trade publication.
Description: Contains short reports describing the latest photonics inventions and technologies developed by NASA and other major federal agencies under government's R&D budget. Covers laser components and systems, electro-optics, fiber optics and imaging technology, as well as new commercial products and company profiles.

535.58 621.329   GW   ISSN 0722-9003
TA1671   CODEN: LAOPD3
LASER UND OPTOELEKTRONIK. (Text in German; contents page in English) 1969. 6/yr. DM.170. A T Fachverlag GmbH, Postfach 500180, 70331 Stuttgart, Germany. TEL 0711-952951-0. FAX 0711-952951-99. Ed. Uwe Brinkmann. circ. 5,610. **Indexed:** INIS Atomind., INSPEC. **Document type:** academic/scholarly publication.
—BLDSC (5156.656000); Ei; SWETS. **CCC.**
Former titles: Laser und Elektro-Optik; Laser (ISSN 0023-8554).

535.58 537.5 US ISSN 0892-9947
TA1671 CODEN: LAOPE4
LASERS & OPTRONICS. 1982. m. (13/yr.). $60.50 (Canada $64.74; Mexico $60.50; elsewhere $77) (effective 1996). Gordon Publications, Inc., Part of Cahners Publishing Company, Division of Reed Elsevier Inc., 301 Gibraltar Dr., Box 650, Morris Plains, NJ 07950-0650. TEL 201-292-5100. FAX 201-898-9281. Ed. Robert Clark. adv.; bk.rev.; charts; illus.; pat.; index. circ. 60,000. (tabloid format; also avail. in microform from UMI; back issues avail.) **Indexed:** INSPEC, Met.Abstr., World Alum.Abstr.
—BLDSC (5156.672000); Ei; Faxon; UMI; UnCover. **CCC.**
 Formerly: Laser and Applications (ISSN 0733-303X)
 Description: Serves the laser, optic and electro-optics market, primarily manufacturers and users of systems, subsystems and components.
 Refereed Serial

535.58 537.5 US
LASERS & OPTRONICS TECHNOLOGY AND INDUSTRY REFERENCE MANUAL. a. $99 (Canada $111.82; elsewhere $104.50). Gordon Publications, Inc., Part of Cahners Publishing Company, Division of Reed Elsevier Inc., 301 Gibraltar Dr., Box 650, Morris Plains, NJ 07950-0650. TEL 201-292-5100. FAX 201-898-9281.

621.329 US ISSN 0898-1507
TA367.5 CODEN: LAENEG
LASERS IN ENGINEERING. 1991. 4/yr. 131 ECU (effective 1996). Gordon and Breach Science Publishers, c/o International Publishers Distributor, 820 Town Center Dr., Langhorne, PA 19047. TEL 215-750-2642. FAX 215-750-6343. (Subscr. to: International Publishers Distributor, P.O. Box 90, Reading, Berkshire RG1 8JL, England. TEL 44-173-456-8316) Ed. B.L. Mordike. (also avail. in microform)
—BLDSC (5156.674000); CASDDS. **CCC.**
 Description: Publishes research and reviews on the use of lasers in sensors or measuring devices and as integral parts of production assemblies.
 Refereed Serial

LASERS IN MEDICAL SCIENCE. see *MEDICAL SCIENCES*

LASERS IN SURGERY AND MEDICINE. see *MEDICAL SCIENCES — Surgery*

535 574 US ISSN 0886-0467
CODEN: LLSCES
LASERS IN THE LIFE SCIENCES. 1986. 4/yr. (in 1 vol., 4 nos./vol.). 131 ECU (effective 1996). Harwood Academic Publishers, c/o International Publishers Distributor, 820 Town Center Dr., Langhorne, PA 19047. TEL 215-750-2642. FAX 215-750-6343. (Subscr. to: International Publishers Distributor, PO Box, Reading, Berkshire, RG1 8JL, England. TEL 44-173-456-8316) Ed. Myron Wolbarsht. (also avail. in microform) **Indexed:** INSPEC (1986-).
—BLDSC (5156.680500); Faxon; SWETS; UnCover. **CCC.**
 Refereed Serial

LIETUVOS FIZIKOS ZHURNALAS/LITOVSKII FIZICHESKII ZHURNAL. see *PHYSICS*

535 620 US ISSN 1068-9761
TK4310
LIGHT & ENGINEERING. English translation of: Svetotekhnika (RU ISSN 0039-7067) 1993. q. $75 to individuals; institutions $160. Allerton Press, Inc., 150 Fifth Ave., New York, NY 10011. TEL 212-924-3950. FAX 212-463-9684. Ed. Julian Aizenberg. **Document type:** academic/scholarly publication.
—**CCC.**
 Description: Covers developments and trends in lighting research, technology and applications.

LITHUANIAN PHYSICS JOURNAL. see *PHYSICS*

LYS; miljoe-design-teknik. see *ENGINEERING — Electrical Engineering*

535.84 US ISSN 0277-7037
QC454.M3 CODEN: MSRVD3
MASS SPECTROMETRY REVIEWS. 1982. bi-m. $396 (foreign $489) (effective 1996). John Wiley & Sons, Inc., Journals, 605 Third Ave., New York, NY 10158. TEL 212-850-6645. FAX 212-850-6021. TELEX 12-7063. E-mail: SUBINFO@JWILEY.COM. (Subscr. outside the Americas to: John Wiley & Sons Ltd., Baffins Ln., Chichester, W. Sussex PO19 1UD, England. TEL 44-1243-779777. FAX 44-1243-776128) Ed. Nicco N.M. Nibbering. circ. 500. (also avail. in microform from UMI; back issues avail.) **Indexed:** AESIS, Biol.Abstr., Chem.Abstr., Ind.Sci.Rev., Mass Spectr.Bull., Sci.Cit.Ind. **Document type:** academic/scholarly publication.
—BLDSC (5388.250000); ADONIS; CASDDS; Ei; Faxon; Genuine Article; SWETS; UMI; UnCover. **CCC.**
 Description: Publishes current research on mass spectrometry instrumentation and application in chemistry, biology, environmental science, medicine, agriculture, engineering and physics.
 Refereed Serial

535.58 610 US
MEDICAL LASER REPORT. (Supplement avail.: Buyers' Guide) 1986. 12/yr. $320 (foreign $340) (effective 1994). PennWell Publishing Co. (Nashua), 10 Tara Blvd., 5th Fl., Nashua, NH 03062-2801. TEL 603-891-0123. FAX 603-891-0574. Ed. David Kales. circ. 700.
 Formerly: Medical Laser Industrial Report.
 Description: Features news and reports about trends and developments in the medical laser business. Includes information on new technologies, market opportunites, product trends, and relevant FDA decisions.

535.38 FR ISSN 0990-7939
MEMOIRES OPTIQUES ET SYSTEMES; le journal de la gestion electronique de documents et du multimedia. 1982. 10/yr. 860 F. Arca Editions, B.P. 303, 56008 Vannes Cedex, France. TEL 97-47-83-06. FAX 97-47-49-46. Ed. Francis Pelletier. bk.rev. circ. 4,000. **Indexed:** Info.Media & Tech.
 Formerly: Memoires Optiques (ISSN 0755-432X)

578 537.534 FR ISSN 1154-2799
QH212.E4 CODEN: MMMIEY
MICROSCOPY MICROANALYSIS MICROSTRUCTURES. (Text in English, French, German) 1976. bi-m. 1650 F. (effective 1996). Societe Francaise de Microscopie Electronique, Case 243, Universite Paris VI, 4 place Jussieu, 75252 Paris Cedex 05, France. TEL 46-70-28-44. FAX 46-70-88-46. (Subscr. to: Les Editions de Physique, Av. du Hoggar, Zone Industrielle de Courtaboeuf, B.P. 112, 91944 Les Ulis Cedex, France.) (Co-sponsor: Centre National de la Recherche Scientifique) Ed. Christian Colliex. adv.; bk.rev.; abstr.; bibl.; charts; illus.; index. circ. 500. **Indexed:** Biol.Abstr., Chem.Abstr., Ind.Sci.Rev., INIS Atomind., INSPEC, Met.Abstr., Sci.Cit.Ind., World Alum.Abstr.
—BLDSC (5760.600800); CASDDS; Faxon; Genuine Article; SWETS. **CCC.**
 Formerly (until 1989): Journal de Microscopie et de Spectroscopie Electroniques (ISSN 0395-9279); **Supersedes in part:** Journal de Microscopie (ISSN 0021-7921)
 Description: Presents original manuscripts dealing with developments in all aspects of microscopy and microanalysis and with their use in materials science.

502.8 US
MICROSCOPY SOCIETY OF AMERICA. DIRECTORY. 1987. biennial. $40 to members; corporate membership $350; student membership $10. Microscopy Society of America, Box M.S.A, Woods Hole, MA 02543. TEL 800-538-3672. FAX 508-548-9053. circ. 5,000. **Document type:** directory.
 Description: Listing of Microscopy Society of America members.

621.381 681 US ISSN 0895-2477
TK7876 CODEN: MOTLEO
MICROWAVE & OPTICAL TECHNOLOGY LETTERS. 18/yr. $558 (foreign $837) (effective 1996). John Wiley & Sons, Inc., Journals, 605 Third Ave., New York, NY 10158. TEL 212-850-6645. FAX 212-850-6021. TELEX 12-7063. E-mail: SUBINFO@JWILEY.COM. (Subscr. outside the Americas to: John Wiley & Sons Ltd., Baffins Ln., Chichester, W. Sussex PO19 1UD, England. TEL 44-1243-779777. FAX 44-1243-776128) (also avail. in microform from UMI; back issues avail.) **Document type:** academic/scholarly publication.
—BLDSC (5761.071500); Ei; Faxon; Genuine Article; SWETS; UMI; UnCover. **CCC.**
 Refereed Serial

535 629.892 US ISSN 1018-9149
TJ211.415
MOBILE ROBOTS. 1986. a. International Society for Optical Engineering (SPIE), Box 10, 1000 20th St., Bellingham, WA 98227-0010.
—UnCover.

535 US ISSN 0163-9587
CODEN: MERJD5
MOESSBAUER EFFECT REFERENCE AND DATA JOURNAL. 1978. m. (except Jul.-Aug.). $560 (effective 1995). University of North Carolina at Asheville, Mossbauer Effect Data Center, Asheville, NC 28804-3299. TEL 704-251-6617. FAX 704-251-6002. Ed. John G. Stevens; Pub. John G. Stevens. adv. contact: Christine R. Boss. bk.rev.; abstr.; bibl.; index. circ. 200. (also avail. in magnetic tape; back issues avail.) **Document type:** bibliography.

535 US ISSN 1058-7268
QC446.15 CODEN: MCLOEB
MOLECULAR CRYSTALS AND LIQUID CRYSTALS SCIENCE AND TECHNOLOGY. SECTION B: NONLINEAR OPTICS. 1966. 12/yr. (in 3 vols., 4 nos./vol.). 118 ECU per vol. (effective 1996). Gordon and Breach Science Publishers, c/o International Publishers Distributor, 820 Town Center Dr., Langhorne, PA 19047. TEL 215-750-2642. FAX 215-750-6343. (Subscr. to: International Publishers Distributor, P.O. Box 90, Reading, Berkshire RG1 8JL, England. TEL 44-173-456-8316) Ed. M.M. Labes. (also avail. in microform)
—BLDSC (5900.817000); CASDDS; Faxon; UnCover. **CCC.**
 Formerly: Nonlinear Optics (ISSN 1053-3729); **Supersedes in part (in 1991):** Molecular Crystals and Liquid Crystals Incorporating Nonlinear Optics (ISSN 1044-1859); Which was formerly (until 1987): Molecular Crystals and Liquid Crystals (ISSN 0026-8941); Incorporates (in 1982): Nonlinear Optics; Formerly (until 1969): Molecular Crystals (ISSN 0369-1152)
 Description: Covers four main areas of the development of applications of nonlinear optical materials to practical devices: principles, materials, phenomena and devices.
 Refereed Serial

535 US ISSN 1058-7284
CODEN: DIMTD7
MOLECULAR CRYSTALS AND LIQUID CRYSTALS SCIENCE AND TECHNOLOGY. SECTION D: DISPLAY AND IMAGING. 1985. 6/yr. (in 1 vol., 6 nos./vol.). 177 ECU (effective 1996). Gordon & Breach Science Publishers, c/o International Publishers Distributor, 820 Town Center Dr., Langhorne, PA 19047. TEL 215-750-2642. FAX 215-750-6343. (Subscr. to: International Publishers Distributor, P.O. Box 90, Reading Berkshire RG1 8JL, England. TEL 44-173-456-8316) Ed. M.M. Labes. (also avail. in microform) **Indexed:** INSPEC (1985-).
—**CCC.**
 Formerly (until 1991): Display and Imaging Technology (ISSN 0733-2386)
 Refereed Serial

535.58 US
MUSEUM OF HOLOGRAPHY. DIRECTORY & BUYERS' GUIDE.* 1979. irreg. Museum of Holography, Information Services, 399 Knollwood Rd., White Plains, NY 10603-1900. Eds. M. Tanko, S. Bains. adv.
 Formerly: Holography Directory.

PHYSICS — OPTICS

535 578   JA   ISSN 0913-5510
MYU. (Text in Japanese) 1987. s-a. Meisei Daigaku, Kobunkaino Bunseki Denshi Kenbikyo Senta - Meisei University, High Resolution Analytical Electron Microscopy Research Center, 1-1, Hodokubo 2-chome, Hino-shi, Tokyo 191, Japan. **Document type:** academic/scholarly publication.

535.58   US   ISSN 0145-319X
TL521.3.T4
N A S A TECH BRIEFS. 1963. m. $75 free to libraries and aerospace engineers. (U.S. National Aeronautical and Space Administration, Center for Aerospace Information, Technology Transfer Office) Associated Business Publications, 317 Madison Ave., Ste. 921, New York, NY 10017. TEL 212-490-3999. FAX 212-986-7864. (Subscr. to: N.A.S.A. Center for Aerospace Information, Technology Transfer Office, 800 Elkridge Landing Rd., Linthicum Hghts., MD 21090-2934. TEL 310-321-0390. FAX 301-621-0134) **Document type:** government publication, bulletin.
—Faxon; SWETS. **CCC.**
Formerly (until 1976): N A S A Tech Brief (ISSN 0096-7491)

578 535   JA
NAGOYA DAIGAKU DENSHI KOGAKU KENKYU NO AYUMI/PROGRESS IN ELECTRON OPTICS RESEARCH. (Text in English, Japanese) 1973. a. free. Nagoya Daigaku, Hyakuman Boruto Denshi Kenbikyo Kenkyushitsu - Nagoya University, 1000KV Electron Microscopy Laboratory, Furo-cho, Chikusa-ku, Nagoya-shi, Aichi-ken 464, Japan. TEL 81-52-789-3154. FAX 81-52-789-3155. Ed. Michio Iseki. circ. 500. **Document type:** academic/scholarly publication, newsletter.

535.84   JA
NIHON BUNKO GAKKAI. KAKI SEMINA/SPECTROSCOPICAL SOCIETY OF JAPAN. SUMMER SEMINAR. (Text in Japanese) a. Nihon Bunko Gakkai - Spectroscopical Society of Japan, 1-13, Kanda Awaji-cho, Chiyoda-ku, Tokyo 101, Japan.

NIHON BUNKO GAKKAI SHINPOJUMU KOEN YOSHISHU/SPECTROSCOPICAL SOCIETY OF JAPAN. ABSTRACTS OF SYMPOSIA. see *PHYSICS — Abstracting, Bibliographies, Statistics*

535   JA
NIHON KODANSEI GAKKAI KAIHO/JAPAN SOCIETY FOR PHOTOELASTICITY. JOURNAL. (Text in Japanese) 1980. 3/yr. Nihon Kodansei Gakkai - Japan Society of Photoelasticity, Nihon Gakkai Jimu Senta, 16-9, Honkomagome 5-chome, Bunkyo-ky, Tokyo 113, Japan.

535   JA   ISSN 0910-9862
NIHON KODANSEI GAKKAI KENKYU HAPPYO KOENKAI KOEN RONBUNSHU/PROCEEDINGS OF THE SYMPOSIUM ON PHOTOELASTICITY. (Text in Japanese) 1980. a. Nihon Kodansei Gakkai - Japan Society for Photoelasticity, Nihon Gakkai Jimu Senta, 16-9, Honkomagome 5-chome, Bunkyo-ky, Tokyo 113, Japan. **Document type:** proceedings.

NIHON SEKIGAISEN GAKKAISHI/JAPAN SOCIETY OF INFRARED SCIENCE AND TECHNOLOGY. JOURNAL. see *PHYSICS — Heat*

535   JA
NIHON SHIKISAI GAKKAI NYUZU/C S A J NEWS. (Text in Japanese) bi-m. Nihon Shikisai Gakkai - Color Science Association of Japan, Tokyo Kasei Gakuin, 22, Sanban-cho, Choyoda-ku, Tokyo 102, Japan.

535   JA   ISSN 0389-9357
NIHON SHIKISAI GAKKAISHI/COLOR SCIENCE ASSOCIATION OF JAPAN. JOURNAL. (Text in Japanese; summaries in English, Japanese) 1972. 3/yr. 2000 Yen per no. Nihon Shikisai Gakkai - Color Science Association of Japan, Tokyo Kasei Gakuin, 22, Sanban-cho, Chiyoda-ku, Tokyo 102, Japan.

331   US   ISSN 1048-6879
TA1501
O E REPORTS. (Optical Engineering) 1984. m. $25 in N. America; elsewhere $35. International Society for Optical Engineering (S.P.I.E.), 1000 20th St., Box 10, Bellingham, WA 98227-0010.
TEL 206-676-3290. FAX 206-647-1445. TELEX 46-7053. E-mail: oer@mom.spie.org. Ed. Robert E. Fischer. adv.: B&W page $2435, color page $3075; 11 1/2 x 17; adv. contact: Bonnie Peterson. circ. 30,000. (tabloid format; back issues avail.) **Document type:** newspaper.
●Also available online.
—BLDSC (6235.248110). **CCC.**
Formerly: S P I E Optical Engineering Reports (ISSN 0741-5931)
Description: Contains technical articles, and interviews with recognized industry leaders in optical and optoelectronic applied science and engineering, as well as industry news, technology advances, forthcoming symposia, new publications and a comprehensive employment section.

535 600 011   US
O S A ANNUAL MEETING DIGEST. a. $75 (effective 1993). Optical Society of America, Inc., 2010 Massachusetts Ave., N.W., Washington, DC 20036. TEL 202-223-8130. FAX 202-223-1096. **Document type:** academic/scholarly publication.
Formerly: O S A Annual Meeting Proceedings.

OPHTHALMIC AND PHYSIOLOGICAL OPTICS. see *MEDICAL SCIENCES — Ophthalmology And Optometry*

535   PL   ISSN 0078-5466
QC350   CODEN: OPAPBZ
OPTICA APPLICATA. (Text in English; summaries in Russian) 1971. q. price varies. (Politechnika Wroclawska) Wydawnictwo Politechniki Wroclawskiej, Wybrzeze Wyspianskiego 27, 50-370 Wroclaw, Poland. FAX 22-36-64. TELEX 712559 PWRPL. (Dist. by: Ars Polona-Ruch, Krakowskie Przedmiescie 7, Warsaw, Poland) Ed. Miron Gaj. circ. 350. **Indexed:** Cadscan, Chem.Abstr., INSPEC, Lead Abstr., Phys.Ber., Zincscan.
—BLDSC (6273.050000); CASDDS; Ei; Genuine Article; UMI.
Description: Papers on diffraction theory, quantum optics, holography, scientific photography and technology of manufacturing optical elements.

535   SP   ISSN 0030-3917
QC350   CODEN: OPAPAY
OPTICA PURA Y APLICADA. (Text in English, French, Spanish; summaries in English, Spanish) 1968. 3/yr. 4500 ptas.($45) (effective 1993). Instituto de Optica "Daza de Valdes", Serrano 121, 28006 Madrid, Spain. TEL 91-5616800.
FAX 91-5645557. TELEX 42182. Ed. Antonio Corrons. adv.: bk.rev.; index, cum.index. circ. 1,000. (also avail. in microfilm; back issues avail.) **Indexed:** Art & Archaeol.Tech.Abstr., Chem.Abstr., Ind.SST, INSPEC, Phys.Ber.
—CASDDS. **CCC.**

535   US   ISSN 0091-3286
TR692.5   CODEN: OPEGAR
OPTICAL ENGINEERING. 1962. m. $170 (foreign $210). International Society for Optical Engineering (SPIE), Box 10, 1000 20th St., Bellingham, WA 98227-0010. TEL 206-676-3290.
FAX 206-647-1445. TELEX 46-7053. Ed. Brian Thompson. adv.: B&W page $925; 8 1/2 x 11. bk.rev.; abstr.; charts; illus.; tr.lit.; index, cum.index: vols.1-23 in 1985. circ. 12,900. (also avail. in microform) **Indexed:** A.S.& T.Ind., Chem.Abstr., Curr.Cont., Eng.Ind., Excerp.Med., INSPEC, Int.Aerosp.Abstr., Phys.Ber., Risk Abstr., Sci.Cit.Ind. **Document type:** academic/scholarly publication.
—BLDSC (6273.180000); CASDDS; Ei; Faxon; Genuine Article; SWETS; UMI; UnCover. **CCC.**
Formerly: S P I E Journal (ISSN 0036-1860)
Description: Covers engineering, design, production and applications of optical, electro-optical, fiberoptic, laser as well as photographic components and systems.

535   US
OPTICAL ENGINEERING SERIES. 1982. irreg., vol.47, 1995. price varies. Marcel Dekker, Inc., 270 Madison Ave., New York, NY 10016.
TEL 212-696-9000. FAX 212-685-4540. TELEX 421419.

621.36   US   ISSN 1068-5200
OPTICAL FIBER TECHNOLOGY; materials, devices & systems. q. $184 (foreign $222) (effective 1996). Academic Press, Inc., Journal Division, 525 B St., Ste. 1900, San Diego, CA 92101-4495.
TEL 619-699-6715. FAX 619-231-6616. Ed.Bd.
Document type: academic/scholarly publication.
—BLDSC (6273.184700). **CCC.**
Refereed Serial

535   NE   ISSN 0925-3467
                           CODEN: OMATET
OPTICAL MATERIALS. 1991. 8/yr. fl.808($493) (effective 1996). North-Holland (Subsidiary of: Elsevier Science B.V.), P.O. Box 211, 1000 AE Amsterdam, Netherlands. TEL 31-20-4853911. FAX 31-20-4853598. TELEX 18582 ESPA NL. (Subscr. in U.S. and Canada to: Elsevier Science Inc., Box 882, Madison Sq. Sta., New York, NY 10159. TEL 212-989-5800. FAX 212-633-3990) Ed. R.C. Powell. (also avail. in microform from UMI; back issues avail.) **Indexed:** INSPEC (1992-). **Document type:** academic/scholarly publication.
—BLDSC (6273.328000); CASDDS; Ei; Genuine Article; SWETS; UnCover. **CCC.**
Description: Publishes original papers and review articles on the design, synthesis, characterization and applications of optical materials; focuses on materials systems, optical phenomena in materials, and devices.
Refereed Serial

535   US   ISSN 1045-6570
OPTICAL MATERIALS AND ENGINEERING NEWS. 1990. m. $350. Business Communications Co., Inc. (Norwalk), 25 Van Zant St., Norwalk, CT 06855. TEL 203-853-4266. FAX 203-853-0348. TELEX 6502934929 WUI. Ed. Richard Hilton.
●Also available online. Vendor(s): Data-Star, Knight-Ridder, Inc., NewsNet (RD37).
Description: Provides information on who's doing what, developing technology, commercialization, business and economic trends, new applications, and contracts.

535   US   ISSN 1060-992X
TK7895.M4   CODEN: OMNNE8
OPTICAL MEMORY & NEURAL NETWORKS. 1992. q. $280 (effective 1996). Allerton Press, Inc., 150 Fifth Ave., New York, NY 10011.
TEL 212-924-3950. FAX 212-463-9684. Ed. Andrei L. Mikealian. **Indexed:** INSPEC (1992-). **Document type:** academic/scholarly publication.
—BLDSC (6273.328900). **CCC.**
Description: Covers the fundamental principles of optical memory, including mechanisms of optical information recording and physical characteristics of photosensitive materials and structures. Includes applied research directed at the realization of optical memory systems for data storage and processing.

621.381 535   US   ISSN 8755-1195
TK7895.M4
OPTICAL MEMORY REPORT.* a. $1995. Rothchild Consultants Inc., 2140 Shattuck Ave., Berkeley, CA 94704-1210.
—CCC.
Description: Covers all products and companies in the optical technology sector.
Refereed Serial

535 621   US   ISSN 0078-5482
OPTICAL PHYSICS AND ENGINEERING. 1967. irreg., latest 1981. price varies. Plenum Publishing Corp., 233 Spring St., New York, NY 10013-1578. TEL 212-620-8000. FAX 212-463-0742. Ed. William L. Wolfe. **Document type:** monographic series.
Refereed Serial

535   JA   ISSN 1340-6000
▼**OPTICAL REVIEW.** (Text in English) 1994. bi-m. 30000 Yen. Optical Society of Japan, Kudan-Kita Bldg. 5F, 1-12-3, Kudan-Kita, Chiyoda-ku, Tokyo 102, Japan. (Subscr. to: Japan Publications Trading Co., Ltd., P.O. Box 5030, Tokyo International 100-31, Japan. TEL 81-3-3292-0410) Ed. Ryoichi Ito.
—BLDSC (6273.369000).

PHYSICS — OPTICS

535 US ISSN 0740-3232
QC350 CODEN: JOAOD6
OPTICAL SOCIETY OF AMERICA. JOURNAL PART A. 1917. 12/yr. $655. Optical Society of America, Inc., 2010 Massachusetts Ave., N.W., Washington, DC 20036-1023. TEL 202-223-8130. Ed. B.E.A. Saleh. bk.rev.; bibl.; illus.; index, cum.index: vols.1-63, 1917-1973. circ. 9,782. (also avail. in microform; back issues avail.) **Indexed:** A.S.& T.Ind., Abstr.Bull.Inst.Pap.Chem., Appl.Mech.Rev., Biol.Abstr., Br.Ceram.Abstr., C.P.I., Chem.Abstr., Curr.Cont., Deep Sea Res.& Oceanogr.Abstr., Eng.Ind., Ergon.Abstr., GeoRef., Graph.Arts Lit.Abstr., Ind.Med., INIS Atomind., INSPEC (1968-), Int.Aerosp.Abstr., Mass Spectr.Bull., Math.R., Met.Abstr., Meteor.& Geoastrophys.Abstr., Phys.Ber., Psychol.Abstr. (1929-). **Document type:** academic/scholarly publication.
—BLDSC (4837.010100); CASDDS; Ei; Faxon; Genuine Article; SWETS. **CCC.**
 Supersedes in part: Optical Society of America. Journal (ISSN 0030-3941)
 Description: Basic research on optical phenomena. Includes atmospheric, physiological and statistical optics; image processing; scattering and coherence theory, machine and color vision; design and diffraction.
 Refereed Serial

535 US ISSN 0740-3224
QC392 CODEN: JOBPDE
OPTICAL SOCIETY OF AMERICA. JOURNAL PART B. 1917. 12/yr. $685. Optical Society of America, Inc., 2010 Massachusetts Ave., N.W., Washington, DC 20036-1023. TEL 202-223-8130. Ed. P.F. Liao. bk.rev.; bibl.; illus.; index, cum.index: vols.1-63, 1917-1973. circ. 9,782. (also avail. in microform; back issues avail.) **Indexed:** A.S.& T.Ind., Appl.Mech.Rev., Biol.Abstr., C.P.I., CAD CAM Abstr., Chem.Abstr., Curr.Cont., Deep Sea Res.& Oceanogr.Abstr., Eng.Ind., GeoRef., Graph.Arts Lit.Abstr., INIS Atomind., INSPEC (1968-), Mass Spectr.Bull., Math.R., Met.Abstr., Meteor.& Geoastrophys.Abstr., Phys.Ber., Psychol.Abstr. **Document type:** academic/scholarly publication.
—BLDSC (4837.010110); CASDDS; Ei; Faxon; Genuine Article; SWETS; UnCover. **CCC.**
 Supersedes in part: Optical Society of America. Journal (ISSN 0030-3941)
 Refereed Serial

535 621.3 NE ISSN 0927-5479
OPTICAL WAVE SCIENCES AND TECHNOLOGY. (Text in English) 1991. irreg., vol.2, 1992. price varies. Elsevier Science B.V., Books Division, P.O. Box 211, 1000 AE Amsterdam, Netherlands. TEL 31-20-4853911. FAX 31-20-4853705. TELEX 18582 ESPA NL. E-mail: nlinfo-f@elsevier.nl; usinfo-f@elsevier.com; forinfo-kyf04035@niftyserve.or.jp; Site addr.: http://www.elsevier.nl/. (Subscr. in U.S. and Canada to: Elsevier Science Inc., Box 882, Madison Sq. Sta., New York, NY 10159. TEL 212-989-5800) **Document type:** monographic series.
—BLDSC (6273.389500).
 Refereed Serial

535 RU
QC350 CODEN: OPMPAQ
OPTICHESKII ZHURNAL. English translation: Journal of Optical Technology (US ISSN 1070-9762) 1931. m. $27.60. Opticheskii Institut im. S.I. Vavilova (S.-Peterburg), Birzhevaya Liniya 4, 199034 St. Petersburg, Russia. Ed. M.M. Miroshnikov. index. **Indexed:** Biol.Abstr., Chem.Abstr., INSPEC. **Document type:** academic/scholarly publication.
—CASDDS.
 Formerly: Optiko-Mekhanicheskaya Promyshlennost' (ISSN 0030-4042)

535.58 621.39 UK ISSN 0030-3992
QC350 CODEN: OLTCAS
OPTICS AND LASER TECHNOLOGY. 1968. 8/yr. £350($557) (effective 1996). Butterworth-Heinemann, Part of the Reed Elsevier group, Linacre House, Jordan Hill, Oxford OX2 8DP, England. TEL 0865-310366. FAX 0865-310898. TELEX 83111 BHPOXF G. (Subscr. to: Elsevier Science Ltd., P.O. Box 800, Kidlington, Oxford OX5 1DX, England. TEL 44-865-843000. FAX 44-865-843010; Subscr. in U.S. and Canada to: Elsevier Science, 660 White Plains Rd., Trrytown, NY 10591-5153. TEL 914-524-9200. FAX 914-333-2444) Ed. Marja Vukovojac. adv.; bk.rev.; charts; illus.; pat.; index. (also avail. in microform from UMI; back issues avail.) **Indexed:** Br.Tech.Ind., Chem.Abstr., Curr.Cont., Eng.Ind., Excerp.Med., Fluidex, INSPEC, ISMEC, Phys.Ber., Risk Abstr., Sociol.Educ.Abstr. **Document type:** academic/scholarly publication.
—BLDSC (6273.440000); CASDDS; Ei; Faxon; Genuine Article; SWETS; UMI; UnCover. **CCC.**
 Formerly: Optics Technology.
 Description: Discusses developments in products and techniques in the field.
 Refereed Serial

535.58 621.39 UK ISSN 0143-8166
CODEN: OLENDN
OPTICS AND LASERS IN ENGINEERING. 1980. m. £475($756) (effective 1996). Elsevier Science Ltd., P.O. Box 800, Kidlington, Oxford OX5 1DX, England. TEL 44-1865-843000. FAX 44-1865-843010. E-mail: nlinfo-f@elsevier.nl; usinfo-f@elsevier.com; forinfo-kyf04035@niftyserve.or.jp; Site addr.: http://www.elsevier.nl/. (Subscr. in U.S. and Canada to: Elsevier Science, 660 White Plains Rd., Tarrytown, NY 10591-5153. TEL 914-524-9200. FAX 914-333-2444) Eds. F.-P. Chiang, G.T. Reid. adv.; bk.rev.; charts; illus.; index. (also avail. in microform from UMI; back issues avail.) **Indexed:** Appl.Mech.Rev., Curr.Cont., Eng.Ind., INSPEC (1980-), Int.Aerosp.Abstr., Met.Abstr., Photo.Abstr., Phys.Ber., Sci.Cit.Ind., World Alum.Abstr. **Document type:** academic/scholarly publication.
—BLDSC (6273.443000); Ei; Faxon; Genuine Article; SWETS; UnCover. **CCC.**
 Description: Provides a forum for interchange of information on developments and applications of optical techniques and laser technology in engineering.
 Refereed Serial

535 US ISSN 1047-6938
TA1501 CODEN: OPPHEL
OPTICS & PHOTONICS NEWS. 1975. m. $99. Optical Society of America, Inc., 2010 Massachusetts Ave. N.W., Washington, DC 20036. TEL 202-223-8130. Ed. Andrea Pendleton. adv.: B&W page $1250; color page $1770; trim 8 1/4 x 11 1/4. circ. 13,000. **Indexed:** Abstr.Bull.Inst.Pap.Chem., Graph.Arts Lit.Abstr., INSPEC (1990-), Phys.Ber.
—BLDSC (6273.450000); Ei; Faxon; SWETS; UnCover. **CCC.**
 Formerly (until 1990): Optics News (ISSN 0098-907X)
 Description: For scientists, engineers and business executives. Articles and papers on optics research and industry trends.

535.84 US ISSN 0030-400X
QC350 CODEN: OPSUA3
OPTICS AND SPECTROSCOPY. English translation of: Optika i Spektroskopiya (RU ISSN 0030-4034) 1959. m. $1425. Optical Society of America, Inc., 2010 Massachusetts Ave., N.W., Washington, DC 20036-1023. TEL 202-223-8130. FAX 202-223-1096. (Co-sponsor: Russian Academy of Sciences) Ed. P.R. Wakeling. bk.rev.; bibl.; charts; illus.; tr.lit.; s-a. index. (also avail. in microform; back issues avail.) **Indexed:** Abstr.Bull.Inst.Pap.Chem., Appl.Mech.Rev., Br.Ceram.Abstr., C.P.I., Curr.Cont., Eng.Ind., Gen.Phys.Adv.Abstr., INSPEC (1968-), Mass Spectr.Bull., Met.Abstr., Phys.Ber. **Document type:** academic/scholarly publication.
—BLDSC (0416.650000); Ei; Faxon; SWETS; UnCover. **CCC.**
 Description: Soviet research in optical phenomena ranging from molecular and atomic spectroscopy of gases through solid-state phenomena to physical optics.
 Refereed Serial

535 US ISSN 0078-5504
OPTICS AND SPECTROSCOPY. SUPPLEMENT. (English translation of Russian language editions) 1966. irreg., no.4, 1970. $25. Optical Society of America, Inc., 2010 Massachusetts Ave., N.W., Washington, DC 20036-1023. TEL 202-223-8130. FAX 202-223-1096. **Document type:** bulletin.

535 NE ISSN 0030-4018
QC350 CODEN: OPCOB8
OPTICS COMMUNICATIONS; a journal devoted to the rapid publication of contributions in the field of optics and interaction of light with matter. (Text in English, French, German; summaries in English) 1969. 66/yr. fl.5159($3146) (effective 1996). North-Holland (Subsidiary of: Elsevier Science B.V.), P.O. Box 211, 1000 AE Amsterdam, Netherlands. TEL 31-20-4853911. FAX 31-20-4853598. TELEX 18582 ESPA NL. (Subscr. in U.S. and Canada to: Elsevier Science Inc., Box 882, Madison Sq. Sta., New York, NY 10159. TEL 212-989-5800. FAX 212-633-3990) Ed. F. Abeles. adv.; illus.; index. (also avail. in microform from UMI; back issues avail.; reprint service avail. from SWZ) **Indexed:** CAD CAM Abstr., Chem.Abstr., Curr.Cont., Eng.Ind., INSPEC, Int.Aerosp.Abstr., Phys.Ber. **Document type:** academic/scholarly publication.
—BLDSC (6273.600000); CASDDS; Ei; Faxon; Genuine Article; SWETS; UnCover. **CCC.**
 Description: Covers all fields of fundamental research in optics, both theoretical and experimental.
 Refereed Serial

535 US ISSN 1018-9157
TA1632
OPTICS, ILLUMINATION, AND IMAGE SENSING FOR MACHINE VISION. 1986. a. International Society of Optical Engineering (SPIE), Box 10, 1000, 20th St., Bellingham, WA 98227-0010.

535 US ISSN 0146-9592
QC350 CODEN: OPLEDP
OPTICS LETTERS. 1977. s-m. $700. Optical Society of America, Inc., 2010 Massachusetts Ave., N.W., Washington, DC 20036-1023. TEL 202-223-8130. Ed. P.W.E. Smith. (also avail. in microfiche; microfilm; back issues avail.) **Indexed:** Cadscan, Chem.Abstr., Curr.Cont., Excerp.Med., Graph.Arts Lit.Abstr., INSPEC (1977-), Int.Aerosp.Abstr., Lead Abstr., Phys.Ber., Zincscan. **Document type:** academic/scholarly publication.
—BLDSC (6273.650000); CASDDS; Ei; Faxon; Genuine Article; SWETS; UnCover. **CCC.**
 Description: Disseminates new, important results in all branches of optics research.

535 621.3 US ISSN 1076-5700
▼**OPTICS REPORT.** 1994. m. $730 (effective 1995). Avelon Corporation, 20540 E. Arrow Hwy, Ste. N4, Covina, CA 91724. TEL 818-332-7822. FAX 818-915-0714. E-mail: avelon@cerfnet.com. Pub. Randy Schroeter. charts; pat.; stat. (back issues avail.) **Document type:** newsletter.
 Supersedes: Laser Bulletin (ISSN 1074-715X)
 Description: Covers advances in laser design and application, business news, market trends and new patents related to laser components, systems, and laser-based processes.

535 GW ISSN 0030-4026
QC350 CODEN: OTIKAJ
OPTIK; international journal for light and electron optics. (Text in English and German) 1946. m. (3 vols./yr.) DM.406 per vol. (Deutsche Gesellschaft fuer Elektronenmikroskopie e.V.) Wissenschaftliche Verlagsgesellschaft mbH, Postfach 101061, 70009 Stuttgart, Germany. TEL 0711-2582-0. FAX 0711-2582-290. TELEX 723636-DAZ-D. (Co-sponsor: Deutsche Gesellschaft fuer angewandte Optik e.V.) Ed. Theo Tschudi. adv.; bk.rev.; bibl.; illus.; index. circ. 1,000. **Indexed:** Chem.Abstr., Curr.Cont., Eng.Ind., Geo.Abstr., INSPEC, Math.R., Met.Abstr., Phys.Ber. **Document type:** academic/scholarly publication.
—BLDSC (6274.000000); CASDDS; Ei; Faxon; Genuine Article; SWETS; UnCover. **CCC.**

PHYSICS — OPTICS

535   RU   ISSN 1019-9942
QC974.5
OPTIKA ATMOSFERY I OKEANA. English edition: Atmospheric and Oceanic Optics. 1970. m. $750 (Canada $765; elsewhere $785). Russian Academy of Sciences, Institute of Atmospheric Optics, Akademicheskii Prospect 1, Tomsk 634055, Russia. TEL 7-3822259303. (Dist. by: Mezhdunarodnaya Kniga, B. Yakimanka 39, 117049 Moscow, Russia) Ed. V.R. Zuev.
Formerly (until 1992): Optika Atmosfery (ISSN 0235-277X)

535.84   RU   ISSN 0030-4034
QC476.5   CODEN: OPSPAM
OPTIKA I SPEKTROSKOPIYA. English translation: Optics and Spectroscopy (US ISSN 0030-400X) 1956. m. $372 (effective 1996). (Rossiiskaya Akademiya Nauk, S.-Peterburgskoe Otdelenie) Izdatel'stvo Nauka, Mezhdunarodnyi Otdel, Profsoyuznaya, 90, 117864 Moscow, Russia. (Dist. by: Mezhdunarodnaya Kniga, ul. Dimitrova D.39, 113095 Moscow, Russia) Ed. P.P. Feofilov. charts; illus.; index, cum.index every 5 yrs. circ. 2,600. (also avail. in microfiche from BHP) **Indexed:** Chem.Abstr., GeoRef., INSPEC.
—BLDSC (0128.000000); CASDDS; Genuine Article. **CCC.**

OPTO. see ELECTRONICS

621.36   UK   ISSN 0966-9809
CODEN: OLEEEV
OPTO & LASER EUROPE. Short title: O L E. 1992. 10/yr. £82($148) (effective 1996). (Institute of Physics) I O P Publishing Ltd., Techno House, Redcliffe Way, Bristol, Avon BS1 6NX, England. TEL 0117-929-7481. FAX 0117-929-4318. TELEX 449149 INSTP G. E-mail: magsmktg@ioppublishing.co.uk. (Subscr. to: I O P Circulation Centre, WDIA Ltd., Publishing House, Victoria Rd., Ruislip, Mddx. HA4 OSX, England. TEL 0181-845-8545. FAX 0181-845-7696; U.S. Subscr. to: American Institute of Physics, Subscriber Services, 500 Sunnyside Blvd., Woodbury 11797-2900. TEL 516-349-7800) Ed. J. Bell. adv.: B&W page $3075, color page $4530; trim 8 x 10 3/4. circ. 25,000. (also avail. in microfiche) **Indexed:** INSPEC (1993-). **Document type:** academic/scholarly publication.
—BLDSC (6275.449300).
Formerly: Opto and Laser Products.
Description: Provides news, commentary, features, and user applications

OPTOMAGAZINE. see MEDICAL SCIENCES — Ophthalmology And Optometry

535.58 621.3   JA   ISSN 0286-9659
CODEN: OPUTDD
OPUTORONIKUSU/OPTRONICS. (Text in Japanese) 1982. m. $230. Oputoronikususha - Optronics Co., Ltd., Sunken Bldg., 5-5 Shin-Ogawa-machi, Shinjuku-ku, Tokyo, Japan. TEL 03-3269-3550. FAX 03-3269-2551. Ed. Takashi Kawajiri; Pub. Naoki Ueno. adv. contact: Tetsuo Ohsawa. circ. 12,000. **Indexed:** Chem.Abstr. **Document type:** trade publication.
—BLDSC (6276.600000); CASDDS.

OYO SUPEKUTOROMETORI TOKYO TORONKAI KOEN YOSHISHU/ABSTRACTS OF PAPERS PRESENTED AT THE TOKYO SYMPOSIA ON THE APPLIED SPECTROMETRY. see PHYSICS — Abstracting, Bibliographies, Statistics

535 621.381   US   ISSN 1067-5345
TA1501   CODEN: PHOPET
PHOTONICS AND OPTOELECTRONICS. 1992. q. $260 (effective 1996). Allerton Press, Inc., 150 Fifth Ave., New York, NY 10011. TEL 212-924-3950. FAX 212-463-9684. Ed. Yuri V. Gulyaev. **Indexed:** INSPEC (1993-). **Document type:** academic/scholarly publication.
—BLDSC (6474.315900); CASDDS. **CCC.**
Description: Covers fundamental principles of photonic switching and optoelectronic transducing, including properties of the acousto-, electro- and magneto-optic effects and relevant material characteristics of both uniform materials and for investigating optical ones.

535   US   ISSN 1044-1425
TS511.U6
PHOTONICS DIRECTORY. 1954. a. $96.50 (foreign $111.50). Laurin Publishing Co., Inc., Box 4949, Berkshire Common, Pittsfield, MA 01202-4949. TEL 413-499-0514. FAX 413-442-3180. adv. circ. 25,000. **Document type:** directory.
—UnCover.
Former titles: Photonics Industry and Systems Purchasing Directory; Optical Industry and Systems Purchasing Directory (ISSN 0191-0647); **Supersedes** (1963-1978): Optical Industry and Systems Directory (ISSN 0078-5474)
Description: Four volume buyers' guide and reference for the photonics industry.

535 544.6   US   ISSN 0731-1230
TS510   CODEN: PHSAD3
PHOTONICS SPECTRA. 1967. m. $98 (foreign $123). Laurin Publishing Co., Inc., Box 4949, Berkshire Common, Pittsfield, MA 01202-4949. TEL 413-499-0514. FAX 413-442-3180. index; circ. 85,000 (controlled). **Indexed:** Appl.Mech.Rev., CAD CAM Abstr., Chem.Abstr., Curr.Cont., Eng.Ind., GeoRef., Graph.Arts Lit.Abstr., INSPEC, Met.Abstr., PROMT, Tel.Abstr., World Alum.Abstr.
—BLDSC (6474.317000); CASDDS; Ei; Faxon; Genuine Article; SWETS; UMI.
Formerly (until 1982): Optical Spectra (ISSN 0030-395X)
Description: Presents news and technical and business information of worldwide developments in the photonics industry.

PLASTIC OPTICAL FIBER. see COMMUNICATIONS

535   NE   ISSN 0079-6638
QC351   CODEN: POPTAN
PROGRESS IN OPTICS. 1961. irreg., vol.33, 1994. price varies. Elsevier Science B.V., Books Division, P.O. Box 211, 1000 AE Amsterdam, Netherlands. TEL 31-20-4853911. FAX 31-20-4853705. TELEX 18582 ESPA NL. E-mail: nlinfo-f@elsevier.nl; usinfo-f@elsevier.com; forinfo-kyf04035@niftyserve.or.jp; Site addr.: http://www.elsevier.nl/. (Subscr. in U.S. and Canada to: Elsevier Science Inc., Box 882, Madison Sq. Sta., New York, NY 10159. TEL 212-989-5800) Ed. E. Wolf. index, cum.index: vols.1-32 in vol.32. **Indexed:** ASCA, Deep Sea Res.& Oceanogr.Abstr., INSPEC, Phys.Ber. **Document type:** monographic series.
—BLDSC (6871.700000); CASDDS; Ei; Faxon; Genuine Article; UnCover. **CCC.**
Refereed Serial

535   UK   ISSN 0963-9659
QC350   CODEN: PAOAE3
PURE AND APPLIED OPTICS. Variant title: European Optical Society. Journal. Part A. 1992. bi-m. £195($394) (effective 1996). (Institute of Physics) I O P Publishing Ltd., Techno House, Redcliffe Way, Bristol BS1 6NX, England. TEL 0117-929-7481. FAX 0117-929-4318. TELEX 449149 INSTP G. (Subscr. to: I O P Circulation Centre, Readerlink, Audit House, 260 Field End Rd., Eastcote, Ruislip, Mddx. HA4 9LT, England. TEL 0181-868-4499. FAX 0181-428-3117; U.S. subscr. to: American Institute of Physics, 500 Sunnyside Blvd., Woodbury, NY 11797-2900. TEL 516-349-7800) Ed. M. Bertolotti. index. circ. 112. (also avail. in microfiche) **Indexed:** INSPEC (1992-). **Document type:** academic/scholarly publication.
—BLDSC (7161.459500); CASDDS; SWETS. **CCC.**
Description: Covers all aspects of modern and classical optics.

535   UK   ISSN 1355-5111
QC446.15   CODEN: QUSOEC
QUANTUM AND SEMICLASSICAL OPTICS. Variant title: European Optical Society. Journal. Part B. 1989. bi-m. £225($452) (effective 1996). (European Optical Society) I O P Publishing Ltd., Techno House, Redcliffe Way, Bristol BS1 6NX, England. TEL 0117-928-7481. FAX 0117-929-4318. TELEX 449149 INSTP G. (U.S. addr.: American Institute of Physics, Member and Subscriber Services, 500 Sunnyside Blvd., Woodbury, NY 11797-2999. TEL 516-576-2200) Ed. P. Mandel. circ. 234. (also avail. in microform; microfiche; back issues avail.) **Indexed:** INSPEC (1989-). **Document type:** academic/scholarly publication.
—CASDDS; Ei; Faxon; Genuine Article; UnCover. **CCC.**
Formerly (until 1995): Quantum Optics (ISSN 0954-8998)
Description: Devoted to optical phenomena that require (for descriptive purposes) the quantum theory.

535.84 301.16   UK   ISSN 0951-4198
QD96.M3   CODEN: RCMSEF
RAPID COMMUNICATIONS IN MASS SPECTROMETRY. 1987. 15/yr. £1395 (foreign $1395) (effective 1996). John Wiley & Sons Ltd., Journals, Baffins Ln., Chichester, W. Sussex PO19 1UD, England. TEL 01243-779777. FAX 01243-776128. TELEX 86290 WIBOOK G. (Subscr. in the Americas to: John Wiley & Sons, Inc., 605 Third Ave., New York, NY 10158. TEL 212-850-6645. FAX 212-850-6021) Ed. John H. Beynon. (also avail. in microform from UMI; back issues avail.; reprint service avail. from SWZ) **Indexed:** INSPEC (1990-). **Document type:** academic/scholarly publication.
—BLDSC (7254.440000); CASDDS; Ei; Faxon; Genuine Article; SWETS; UMI; UnCover. **CCC.**
Description: Publishes preliminary accounts of recent research in mass spectrometry.
Refereed Serial

REFERATIVNYI ZHURNAL. VOLOKONNO-OPTICHESKIE SYSTEMY. see PHYSICS — Abstracting, Bibliographies, Statistics

535   UK
REMOTE IMAGING GROUP JOURNAL. q. Remote Imaging Group, Thornlea, Fishergate, Sutton St. James, Spalding, Lincs. PE12 OEZ, England. TEL 01945-85353. Ed. James Brown. **Document type:** bulletin.
Formerly (until 1993): Remote Imaging Group Newsletter.

525   JA
RESEARCH COMMITTEE FOR GRAPHIC SIMULATION AND VISUALIZATION OF MULTIPHASE FLOW. PROCEEDINGS. (Text in English, Japanese) 1988. 4/yr. Japan Society of Multiphase Flow, Research Committee for Graphic Simulation and Visualization of Multiphase Flow - Nihon Konsoryu Gakkai Konsoryu no Gurafikku Shimyureshon to Kashika ni Kansuru Kenkyukai, Tsukuba Daigaku Kozo Kogakukei, Matsui Kenkyushitsu, 1-1, Tennodai 1-chome, Tsukuba-shi, Ibaraki-ken 305, Japan. **Document type:** proceedings.

REZA GAKKAI GAKUJUTSU KOENKAI NENJI TAIKAI KOEN YOKOSHU/LASER SOCIETY OF JAPAN. ANNUAL MEETING. DIGEST OF TECHNICAL PAPERS. see PHYSICS — Abstracting, Bibliographies, Statistics

535   JA
REZA GAKKAI KENKYUKAI HOKOKU; Laser Society of Japan. Reports on Topical Meeting. (Text in Japanese) 5/yr. Reza Gakkai - Laser Society of Japan, 2-6, Yamadaoka, Suita-shi, Osaka 565, Japan.

535   JA
REZA GIJUTSU SOGO KENKYUJO JIGYO HOKOKUSHO/INSTITUTE FOR LASER TECHNOLOGY. REPORT. (Text in Japanese) a. Reza Gijutsu Sogo Kenkyujo - Institute for Laser Technology, Osaka Kagaku Gijutsu Senta Biru, 8-4, Utsubohonmachi 1-chome, Nishi-ku, Osaka-shi, Osaka 550.

535   JA
REZA GIJUTSU SOGO KENKYUJO NENPO/INSTITUTE FOR LASER TECHNOLOGY. ANNUAL PROGRESS REPORT. (Text in English, Japanese; summaries in English) a. Reza Gijutsu Sogo Kenkyujo - Institute for Laser Technology, Osaka Kagaku Gijutsu Senta Biru, 8-4, Utsubohonmachi 1-chome, Nishi-ku, Osaka 550, Japan.

REZA KAGAKU/ABSTRACTS OF RIKEN SYMPOSIUM ON LASER SCIENCE. see PHYSICS — Abstracting, Bibliographies, Statistics

535   JA   ISSN 0289-8411
CODEN: RKAKDK
REZA KAGAKU KENKYU/I P C R LASER SCIENCE PROGRESS REPORT. (Text in Japanese; summaries in English) 1979. a. Rikagaku Kenkyujo - Institute of Physical and Chemical Research, 2-1, Hirosawa, Wako-shi, Saitama-ken 351-01, Japan. **Indexed:** Chem.Abstr., INIS Atomind.
—BLDSC (5156.637000); CASDDS.

535   JA
REZA KAGAKU KENKYUKAI KOENSHU/PROCEEDINGS OF THE LASER SCIENCE PROGRESS. (Text in Japanese) 1989. a. Kansai Daigaku, Kogyo Gijutsu Kenkyujo - Kansai University, Research Institute of Industrial Technology, 3-35, Yamatecho 3-chome, Suita-shi, Osaka 564, Japan. **Document type:** proceedings.

535 JA ISSN 0387-0200
  CODEN: REKEDA
REZA KENKYU/REVIEW OF LASER ENGINEERING. (Text in English, Japanese; summaries in English) 1973. m. 1500 Yen per no. Reza Gakkai - Laser Society of Japan, 2-6, Yamadaoka, Suita-shi, Osaka 565, Japan. **Indexed:** Chem.Abstr., INIS Atomind., INSPEC, Jap.Per.Ind.
  —BLDSC (7791.160000); CASDDS.

535 JA ISSN 0914-9805
REZA KUROSU/LASER CROSS. (Text in Japanese) 1988. m. Reza Gijutsu Sogo Kenkyujo - Institute for Laser Technology, Osaka Kagaku Gijutsu Senta Biru, 8-4, Utsubohon-machi 1-chome, Nishi-ku, Osaka-shi, Osaka 550.

535 JA ISSN 0913-1361
REZA KYOKAI UINTA SEMINA/JAPAN SOCIETY OF LASER TECHNOLOGY. WINTER SEMINAR. (Text in Japanese) a. Reza Kyokai - Japan Society of Laser Technology, Chuo Daigaku Rikogakubu Seimitsu Kikai Kogakka, Kawasumi Kenkyushitsu, P.O. Box 27, Koishikawa Yubinkyoku, Bunkyo-ku, Tokyo 112, Japan.

535 JA ISSN 0916-7277
REZA KYOKAISHI/LASER. (Text in Japanese) 1974. bi-m. Reza Kyokai - Japan Society of Laser Technology, Chuo Daigaku Rikogakubu Seimitsu Kikai Kogakka, Kawasumi Kenkyushitsu, P.O. Box 27, Koishikawa Yubinkyoku, Bunkyo-ku, Tokyo 112, Japan.

535 JA
REZA NO KISO TO SONO OYO. (Text in Japanese) a. Reza Gakkai - Laser Society of Japan, 2-6, Yamadaoka, Suita-shi, Osaka 565, Japan.

535 US
RUSSIAN ACADEMY OF SCIENCE. LEBEDEV PHYSICS INSTITUTE. PROCEEDINGS. irreg., latest 1993. price varies. Nova Science Publishers, Inc., 6080 Jericho Tpke., Ste. 207, Commack, NY 11725-2808. TEL 516-499-3103. (back issues avail.) **Document type:** proceedings.
  —BLDSC (0420.402000).
  Former titles: Academy of Science of the U S S R. Lebedev Physics Institute. Proceedings (ISSN 0896-8462); (until 1987): P.N. Lebedev Physics Institute. Proceedings - Trudy (ISSN 0568-5508)
  Description: Compilations of advanced physics research.
  Refereed Serial

535 US ISSN 1058-045X
TA1542
S P I E HOLOGRAPHICS INTERNATIONAL DIRECTORY AND RESOURCE GUIDE. 1991. biennial. $50 to non-members; members $35. International Society for Optical Engineering (SPIE), Box 10, Bellingham, WA 98227-0010. TEL 206-676-3290. FAX 206-647-1445. E-mail: SPIE@MOM.SPIE.ORG. adv.; bk.rev.; circ. 1,000 (paid). **Document type:** directory.
  Description: Contains comprehensive listings of over 2,000 people-companies in 57 countries active in holography. Includes review articles on advances in holography in technical display research, art holographic interferometry, commercial displays, holographic optical elements.

S P I E PUBLICATIONS INDEX. see *PHYSICS — Abstracting, Bibliographies, Statistics*

S P S E ANNUAL CONFERENCE. PAPER SUMMARIES (YEAR). (Society for Imaging Science and Technology) see *PHOTOGRAPHY*

SCANNING MICROSCOPY; an international journal of scanning electron microscopy, related techniques, and applications. see *BIOLOGY — Microscopy*

535 CC ISSN 1000-8713
QD79.C4   CODEN: SEPUER
SE PU/CHINESE JOURNAL OF CHROMATOGRAPHY. (Text in Chinese) 1984. bi-m. $70. Zhongguo Kexueyuan, Dalian Huaxue Wuli Yanjiusuo - Chinese Academy of Sciences, Dalian Institute of Chemical Physics, 161 Zhongshan Lu, Dalian, Liaoning 116012, People's Republic of China. TEL 3631841. (Dist. by: China National Publishing Industry Trading Corporation, P.O. Box 782, Beijing, P.R. China) Ed. Lu Peichang. adv.: B&W page $450, color page $500; trim 220 x 145. circ. 5,000. **Document type:** academic/scholarly publication.
  —BLDSC (3180.299800); CASDDS.
  Description: Contains review articles, research papers on theories and experiments in the field of chromatography.

535 621.3 US
SENSORS SERIES. irreg. (Institute of Physics) I O P Publishing Ltd., Techno House, Redcliffe Way, Bristol, Avon BS1 6NX, England. TEL 0272-297481. FAX 0272-294318. (U.S. addr.: The Public Ledger Bldg., Ste. 1035, Independence Sq., Philadelphia, PA 19106. TEL 215-627-0880. FAX 215-627-0879) Ed. B.E. Jones. **Document type:** monographic series.

535 JA ISSN 0915-1079
SENTAN GIJUTSU KOENKAI/LECTURE ON ADVANCED LASER TECHNOLOGY. (Text in Japanese) 1988. irreg. 2000 Yen per no. Reza Gijutsu Sogo Kenkyujo - Institute for Laser Technology, Osaka Kagaku Gijutsu Senta Biru, 8-4, Utsubohon-machi 1-chome, Nishi-ku, Osaka 550, Japan.

535 SI
SERIES ON OPTICS AND PHOTONICS. (Text in English) 1989. irreg., vol.3, 1991. price varies. World Scientific Publishing Co. Pte. Ltd., Farrer Rd., P.O. Box 128, Singapore 9128, Singapore. TEL 3825663. FAX 3825919. TELEX RS 28561 WSPC. (UK addr.: 73 Lynton Mead, Totteridge, London N20 8DH, England. TEL 44-81-4462461; US addr.: 1060 Main St., River Edge, NJ 07661. TEL 800-227-7562) Ed. S.L. Chin. **Document type:** monographic series.

535 540 JA
SHIKISAI KOGAKU KONFARENSU RONBUNSHU/PROCEEDINGS OF JOINT CONFERENCE ON COLOR TECHNOLOGY. (Text in Japanese; summaries in English) 1984. a. Shikisai Kogaku Konfarensu Jikko Iinkai - Committee of Joint Conference on Color Technology, 12-14, Hamamatsucho 2-chome, Minato-ku, Tokyo 105, Japan. **Document type:** proceedings.

SPECTROCHIMICA ACTA. PART A: MOLECULAR SPECTROSCOPY. see *CHEMISTRY — Analytical Chemistry*

SPECTROCHIMICA ACTA. PART B: ATOMIC SPECTROSCOPY. see *CHEMISTRY — Analytical Chemistry*

SPECTROSCOPIC PROPERTIES OF INORGANIC & ORGANOMETALLIC COMPOUNDS. see *CHEMISTRY*

535 JA
SPECTROSCOPICAL SOCIETY OF JAPAN. ABSTRACTS OF THE MEETING/NIHON BUNKO GAKKAI KOEN YOSHISHU. (Text in English, Japanese) irreg. Spectroscopical Society of Japan - Nihon Bunko Gakkai, 1-13, Kanda Awajicho, Chiyoda-ku, Tokyo 101, Japan. **Document type:** abstracting/indexing.

535.84 JA ISSN 0038-7002
  CODEN: BUKKAT
SPECTROSCOPICAL SOCIETY OF JAPAN. JOURNAL/BUNKO KENKYU. (Text in Japanese; summaries in English) 1951. bi-m. $36. Spectroscopical Society of Japan - Nihon Bunko Gakkai, Clean Bldg., 1-13 Kanda Awajicho, Chiyoda-ku, Tokyo 101, Japan. adv.; bk.rev.; bibl.; charts; illus.; index. circ. 2,000. **Indexed:** Anal.Abstr., Chem.Abstr., INIS Atomind., INSPEC, JTA.
  —BLDSC (4902.500000); CASDDS.

PHYSICS — OPTICS 5267

535 543 US ISSN 0887-6703
QC450 CODEN: SPECET
SPECTROSCOPY. 1985. 9/yr. $59 (foreign $117); free to qualified personnel. Advanstar Communications, Inc., 7500 Old Oak Blvd., Cleveland, OH 44130. TEL 216-826-2839. FAX 216-891-2726. (Subscr. to: 1 E. First St., Duluth, MN 55082. TEL 800-346-0085) Ed. Linda Crabtree. adv.; charts; illus.; stat.; tr.lit. circ. 30,000. (back issues avail.) **Indexed:** Excerp.Med., Telegen. **Document type:** trade publication.
  —BLDSC (8411.113900); CASDDS; Ei; Faxon; SWETS; UMI. **CCC.**
  Description: Concise research and applications articles for users and buyers of all types of spectroscopic equipment and related accessories. Combines practical information with principles of modern science for analysts in industrial, academic, and government laboratories.

535.84 US ISSN 0038-7010
QD95 CODEN: SPLEBX
SPECTROSCOPY LETTERS; an international journal for rapid communication. 1968. 8/yr. $397.50 to individuals; institutions $795. Marcel Dekker Journals, 270 Madison Ave., New York, NY 10016. TEL 212-696-9000. FAX 212-685-4540. TELEX 421419 MARDEEK. (Subscr. to: Box 5017, Montecello, NY 12701) Ed. J.W. Robinson. adv.; charts. (also avail. in microform from RPI) **Indexed:** Anal.Abstr., ASCA, Ceram.Abstr., Chem.Abstr., Curr.Cont., Excerp.Med., GeoRef., INSPEC, Mass Spectr.Bull. **Document type:** academic/scholarly publication.
  —BLDSC (8411.120000); CASDDS; Ei; Faxon; Genuine Article; SWETS; UMI; UnCover. **CCC.**
  Refereed Serial

621.39 681 IS
SPECTRUM. (Text in Hebrew) 1991. bi-m. Tzavta Publishing, P.O. Box 18287, Tel Aviv 61181, Israel. TEL 3-5622076. FAX 3-5618549. Ed. Y. Elyada. adv.; bk.rev.; circ. 4,000 (controlled).
  Description: Covers advances in optical engineering, laser applications, and general photonics.

535 US ISSN 0490-4176
  CODEN: SPSKDK
SPEX SPEAKER. 1955. q. Spex Industries Inc., 3880 Park Ave., Edison, NJ 08820. TEL 201-549-7144. FAX 201-549-5125. Ed. Ray Kaminski. adv.; charts; stat. circ. 15,000. **Indexed:** GeoRef.
  —CASDDS.

535 US ISSN 0342-4111
  CODEN: SSOSDB
SPRINGER SERIES IN OPTICAL SCIENCES. 1976. irreg. price varies. Springer-Verlag, 175 Fifth Ave., New York, NY 10010. TEL 212-460-1500. FAX 212-473-6272. (Also: Berlin, Heidelberg, Tokyo and Vienna) (reprint service avail. from ISI) **Indexed:** Chem.Abstr, INSPEC, Phys.Ber. **Document type:** monographic series.
  —BLDSC (8424.770000); CASDDS. **CCC.**

535 540 JA ISSN 0562-4096
STUDIES OF COLOR/SHIKISAI KENKYU. (Text in Japanese; summaries in English) 1954. s-a. Japan Color Research Institute - Nihon Shikisai Kenkyujo, 1-19, Nishiazabu 3-chome, Minato-ku, Tokyo 106, Japan.

TECHNIQUES IN VISIBLE AND ULTRAVIOLET SPECTROMETRY. see *CHEMISTRY — Analytical Chemistry*

535 RU ISSN 0566-3911
  CODEN: USFOA7
USPEKHI FOTONIKI. 1969. irreg. 1.83 Rub. per no. Sankt-Peterburgskii Universitet, Universitetskaya Nab. 7-9, St. Petersburg V-164, Russia. abstr.; bibl. circ. 705. **Indexed:** Chem.Abstr.
  —BLDSC (0387.500000).

PHYSICS — SOUND

535.84   UK   ISSN 0049-8246
QC481   CODEN: XRSPAX
X R S - X-RAY SPECTROMETRY; an international journal. 1972. bi-m. $995 (foreign $995) (effective 1996). John Wiley & Sons Ltd., Journals, Baffins Ln., Chichester, W. Sussex PO19 1UD, England. TEL 01243-779777. FAX 01243-776128. TELEX 86290 WIBOOK G. (Subscr. in the Americas to: John Wiley & Sons, Inc., 605 Third Ave., New York, NY 10158. TEL 212-850-6645. FAX 212-850-6021) Ed. John V. Gilfrich. adv.; bk.rev.; bibl.; illus.; tr.lit. circ. 587. (also avail. in microform from UMI; back issues avail.; reprint service avail. from SWZ) **Indexed:** AESIS, Br.Ceram.Abstr., Chem.Abstr., Curr.Cont., INSPEC. **Document type:** academic/scholarly publication.
—BLDSC (9365.780000); CASDDS; Ei; Faxon; Genuine Article; SWETS; UMI; UnCover. **CCC.**
Description: Covers advances in techniques, methods and equipment, news and events, and provides a platform for the discussion of more sophisticated X-ray analytical methods.
Refereed Serial

535.58   CC   ISSN 1000-372X
YINGYONG JIGUANG/APPLIED LASERS. (Text in Chinese) 1981. bi-m. $25 (effective 1996). (Shanghai Jiguang Jishu Yanjiusuo - Shanghai Laser Technology Institute) Shanghai Scientific and Technical Publishers, 450 Ruijin Er Rd., Shanghai 200020, People's Republic of China. (Subscr. to: Yingyong Jiguang Bianjibu, 770 Yishan Rd., Shanghai 200233, People's Republic of China. TEL 86-21-4700560. FAX 86-21-4700037) Ed. Shao Ziwen. adv.: page $300; adv. contact: Lin Qingbai. circ. 3,000.
—BLDSC (1573.240000).

535   GW   ISSN 0941-7567
                 CODEN: ZIJREP
ZEISS INFORMATION WITH JENA REVIEW. (Editions in English, German) 1953. irreg. free. Carl Zeiss Jena GmbH, Carl-Zeiss-Str. 1, 07740 Jena, Germany. TEL 03641-642770. FAX 03641-642941. Eds. Gudrun Vogel, Hansjoachim Hinkelmann. charts; illus.; index. circ. 70,000. **Indexed:** Biol.Abstr., C.R.I.Abstr., C.R.I.Curr.Cont., Chem.Abstr., INSPEC, Met.Abstr., World Alum.Abstr. **Document type:** trade publication.
—BLDSC (9440.295000); CASDDS; UnCover. **CCC.**
Formed by merger of (1953-1991): Zeiss Information (ISSN 0044-2054); (1956-1991): Jena Review (ISSN 0448-9497)

ZHONGGUO GUANGXUE YU YINGYONG GUANGXUE WENZHAI/CHINESE OPTICS AND APPLIED OPTICS ABSTRACTS. see *PHYSICS — Abstracting, Bibliographies, Statistics*

535.58   CC   ISSN 0258-7025
                 CODEN: ZHJIDO
ZHONGGUO JIGUANG. English edition: Chinese Journal of Lasers (ISSN 1004-2822) (Text in Chinese) m. $100.80. (Zhongguo Guangxue Xuehui - Chinese Optical Society) Science Press, Marketing and Sales Department, 16 Donghuangchenggen North St., Beijing 100717, People's Republic of China. TEL 4010642. FAX 4019810. **Indexed:** Chem.Abstr. **Document type:** academic/scholarly publication.
—BLDSC (3180.366000); CASDDS.

PHYSICS — Sound

see also *Sound Recording and Reproduction*

534 621.3   US
A S S P WORKSHOP ON SPECTRUM ESTIMATION AND MODELING. 1981. a. price varies. (I E E E, Acoustics, Speech and Signal Processing Society) Institute of Electrical and Electronics Engineers, Inc., 345 E. 47th St., New York, NY 10017-2394. TEL 212-705-7900. FAX 212-705-7682. (Subscr. to: 445 Hoes Ln., Box 1331, Piscataway, NJ 08855-1331) **Indexed:** INSPEC.
Former titles: A S S P Spectrum Estimation Workshop; A S S P Workshop on Spectral Estimation.

534 774   US   ISSN 0270-5117
QC244.5   CODEN: ACIGD9
ACOUSTICAL IMAGING. Represents: International Symposium on Acoustical Holography and Imaging. Proceedings. 1969. irreg., vol.20, 1994. price varies. Plenum Publishing Corp., 233 Spring St., New York, NY 10013-1578. TEL 212-620-8000. FAX 212-463-0742. TELEX 23-421139. **Indexed:** Biol.Abstr., Chem.Abstr., INSPEC. **Document type:** proceedings.
—BLDSC (0578.692000); CASDDS. **CCC.**
Former titles: Acoustical Imaging: Recent Advances in Visualization and Characterization; (until 1977): Acoustical Holography (ISSN 0065-0870)
Refereed Serial

534   RU   ISSN 1063-7710
QC221   CODEN: AOUSEK
ACOUSTICAL PHYSICS. English translation of: Akusticheskii Zhurnal (RU ISSN 0320-7919) 1955. bi-m. $1055 (foreign $1075) (effective 1996). (Rossiiskaya Akademiya Nauk) Maik Nauka, Mezhdunarodnyi Otdel, Profsoyuznaya, 90, 117864 Moscow, Russia. (Subscr. to: American Institute of Physics, Member and Subscriber Services, 500 Sunnyside Blvd., Woodbury, NY 11797-2999, U.S.A. TEL 516-576-2270. FAX 516-349-9704) bibl.; charts; illus.; index. (also avail. in microform from AIP; back issues avail.) **Indexed:** Appl.Mech.Rev., ASCA, C.P.I., Curr.Cont., Deep Sea Res.& Oceanogr.Abstr., Eng.Ind., Excerp.Med., Gen.Phys.Adv.Abstr., INSPEC (1994-), Int.Aerosp.Abstr., Math.R., Noise Pollut.Publ.Abstr., Nucl.Sci.Abstr., Phys.Ber., Pollut.Abstr. **Document type:** academic/scholarly publication.
—BLDSC (0404.570000); Faxon; Genuine Article; SWETS; UnCover. **CCC.**
Formerly: Soviet Physics - Acoustics (ISSN 0038-562X)

534   US   ISSN 0001-4966
                 CODEN: JASMAN
ACOUSTICAL SOCIETY OF AMERICA. JOURNAL. 1929. m. $900 (effective 1996). American Institute of Physics, One Physics Ellipse, College Park, MD 20740-3843. TEL 301-209-3100. (Subscr. to: AIP Member and Subscriber Service, 500 Sunnyside Blvd., Woodbury, NY 11797-2999. TEL 516-576-2270) Ed. Daniel W. Martin. abstr.; illus.; pat.; index. cum.index: vols.1-94, 1929-1993. (also avail. in microform from AIP; back issues avail.) **Indexed:** A.S.& T.Ind., Abstr.Bull.Inst.Pap.Chem., Abstr.J.Earthq.Eng., Agri.Eng.Abstr., Appl.Mech.Rev., Bibl.Ling., Biol.Abstr., C.P.I., Cadscan, Chem.Abstr., Child Devel.Abstr., Curr.Cont., Deep Sea Res.& Oceanogr.Abstr., Dent.Ind., Energy Ind., Energy Info.Abstr., Eng.Ind., Environ.Abstr., Ergon.Abstr., Excerp.Med., Fluidex, Gen.Phys.Adv.Abstr., Geo.Abstr., Geo.Ref., Geol.Abstr., HRIS, Ind.Med., INIS Atomind., INSPEC (1970-), Int.Aerosp.Abstr., ISMEC, Lead Abstr., Ling.Abstr., Math.R., Meteor.& Geoastrophys.Abstr., NBA, Noise Pollut.Publ.Abstr., Ocean.Abstr., Petrol.Abstr., Phys.Ber., Pollut.Abstr., Psychol.Abstr. (1930-), Sh.& Vib.Dig., Sport Fish.Abstr., Wild.Rev., Zincscan, Zoo.Rec. **Document type:** academic/scholarly publication.
—BLDSC (4675.000000); CASDDS; Ei; Faxon; Genuine Article; SWETS; UnCover. **CCC.**
Description: Covers all phases of research and engineering of interest to acoustical scientists and engineers.
Refereed Serial

534   JA   ISSN 0388-2861
                 CODEN: JASED2
ACOUSTICAL SOCIETY OF JAPAN. JOURNAL. Japanese edition: Nihon Onkyo Gakkaishi (ISSN 0369-4232) (Text in English) 1980. bi-m. 1545 Yen per no. Acoustical Society of Japan - Nihon Onkyo Gakkai, Ikeda Bldg., 7-7, Yoyogi 2-chome, Shibuya-ku, Tokyo 151, Japan. TEL 81-3-3379-1200. FAX 81-3-3379-1456227. Ed. Eiichi Miyasaka. adv. contact: Sadaoki Furui. bk.rev. circ. 4,000. **Indexed:** Eng.Ind., INIS Atomind., INSPEC (1980-). **Document type:** academic/scholarly publication.
—BLDSC (4676.050000); Ei; Faxon; SWETS.
Description: Contains technical papers, and news of the Society.
Refereed Serial

534   UK   ISSN 0308-437X
                 CODEN: ACOBEP
ACOUSTICS BULLETIN. 1974. bi-m. £36. Institute of Acoustics, P.O. Box 320, St. Albans, Herts. AL1 1PZ, England. TEL 01727-848195. FAX 01727-850553. (Editorial addr.: 11 Colwyn Close, Yalety, Camberly, Surrey GU17 7QH, England. TEL 01252-871298) Ed. J.W. Tyler. adv. contact: Keith Rose. bk.rev. circ. 1,900. **Indexed:** INSPEC (1990-). **Document type:** academic/scholarly publication, bulletin.
—BLDSC (0578.697300); Ei.
Description: Written for research establishments covering all aspects of acoustics including aerodynamic noise, the environment, speech, underwater vibrations, and more.

534   UK   ISSN 0140-1599
                 CODEN: ACLEDI
ACOUSTICS LETTERS. 1977. m. £89($169) (effective 1995). Parjon Information Services, P.O. Box 144, Haywards Heath, Sussex RH16 2YX, England. Ed. Dr. J. Scott; Pub. J. Parry. bk.rev. **Indexed:** Appl.Mech.Rev., Chem.Abstr., Deep Sea Res.& Oceanogr.Abstr., INSPEC (1979-). **Document type:** academic/scholarly publication.
—BLDSC (0578.697400); CASDDS; Ei; Faxon; UnCover. **CCC.**
Description: Short papers on all aspects of acoustics.
Refereed Serial

534   FR   ISSN 1022-4793
ACTA ACUSTICA. (Text in English, French, German) bi-m. 2450 F. (European Acoustics Association) Editions de Physique, B.P. 112, 7, Av. du Hoggar, Zone Industrielle de Courtaboeuf, 91944 Les Ulis Cedex, France. TEL 69-07-36-88. FAX 69-28-84-91. TELEX 602 321 F. bk.rev.; charts; illus. **Indexed:** INSPEC (1993-).
—BLDSC (0587.150000); Faxon. **CCC.**
Supersedes: Journal d'Acoustique (ISSN 0988-4319)
Description: Forum for research in acoustics, including musical acoustics, hearing, physics and ultrasonics.
Refereed Serial

534   GW   ISSN 0001-7884
QC221   CODEN: ACUSAY
ACUSTICA; Internationale Akustische Zeitschrift - International Journal on Acoustics. (Text in English, French and German) 1936. bim. DM.672. (Deutsche Physikalische Gesellschaft) S. Hirzel Verlag, Postfach 101061, 70009 Stuttgart, Germany. TEL 0711-2582-0. FAX 0711-2582290. (Co-sponsor: Groupement des Acousticiens de Langue Francaise) Ed. V. Mellert. adv.; bk.rev.; illus.; index. circ. 1,500. **Indexed:** C.I.S. Abstr., Chem.Abstr., Curr.Cont., Deep Sea Res.& Oceanogr.Abstr., Energy Ind., Energy Info.Abstr., Eng.Ind., Environ.Abstr., Ergon.Abstr., Excerp.Med., Ind.Sci.Rev., INSPEC (1968-), Intl.Civil Eng.Abstr., Lang.& Lang.Behav.Abstr., Math.R., RILM, Sci.Cit.Ind., Sh.& Vib.Dig., Soft.Abstr.Eng. **Document type:** academic/scholarly publication.
—BLDSC (0678.000000); CASDDS; Ei; Faxon; Genuine Article; SWETS; UnCover. **CCC.**
Formerly (until 1951): Akustische Zeitschrift.

ADVANCES IN ACOUSTIC MICROSCOPY. see *BIOLOGY — Microscopy*

534   JA
AKOSUTIKKU EMISSHON SOGO KONFARENSU RONBUNSHU/NATIONAL CONFERENCE ON ACOUSTIC EMISSION. PROCEEDINGS. (Text in Japanese) 1977. biennial. 7000 Yen. Nihon Hihakai Kensa Kyokai - Japanese Society for Non-Destructive Inspection, Natsume No. 5 Bldg., 4th Fl., 67 Kanda-Sakumagashi, Chiyoda-ku, Tkyo 101, Japan. TEL 81-3-5821-5105. FAX 81-3-3863-6524. Ed. Teruo Kishi. adv. **Document type:** proceedings.

PHYSICS — SOUND

534 RU ISSN 0320-7919
QC221 CODEN: AKZHAE
AKUSTICHESKII ZHURNAL. English translation: Acoustical Physics (US ISSN 1063-7710) (Text in Russian; contents page in English) 1955. bi-m. $192 (effective 1996). (Rossiiskaya Akademiya Nauk) Izdatel'stvo Nauka, Mezhdunarodnyi Otdel, Profsoyuznaya, 90, 117864 Moscow, Russia. (Dist. by: Mezhdunarodnaya Kniga, ul. Dimitrova D.39, 113095 Moscow, Russia) Ed. Z.M. Zamshev. bk.rev.; bibl.; charts; illus.; index. circ. 2,180. **Indexed:** Biol.Abstr., Chem.Abstr., Deep Sea Res.& Oceanogr.Abstr., Eng.Ind., INIS Atomind., INSPEC (1968-), Math.R. **Document type:** academic/scholarly publication.
—CASDDS. **CCC.**

534 PL ISSN 0554-8039
AKUSTYKA. 1972. irreg., latest no.9. price varies. Adam Mickiewicz University Press, Nowowiejskiego 55, 61-734 Poznan, Poland. TEL 527-380. TELEX 413260 UAMPL. **Document type:** academic/scholarly publication.
Formerly: Uniwersytet im. Adama Mickiewicza w Poznaniu. Wydzial Matematyki, Fizyki i Chemii. Prace. Seria Akustyka.

534 UK ISSN 0003-682X
TA365 CODEN: AACOBL
APPLIED ACOUSTICS. (Text in English, French, German) 1968. m. £595($947) (effective 1996). Elsevier Science Ltd., P.O. Box 800, Kidlington, Oxford OX5 1DX, England. TEL 44-1865-843000. FAX 44-1865-843010. E-mail: nlinfo-f@elsevier.nl; usinfo-f@elsevier.com; forinfo-kyf04035@niftyserve.or.jp; Site addr.: http://www.elsevier.nl/. (Subscr. in U.S. and Canada to: Elsevier Science, 660 White Plains Rd., Tarrytown, NY 10591-5153. TEL 914-524-9200. FAX 914-333-2444) Ed. P. Lord. adv.; bk.rev.; illus.; index. (also avail. in microform from UMI; back issues avail.) **Indexed:** Agri.Eng.Abstr., B.C.I.R.A., BMT, C.I.S. Abstr., CAD CAM Abstr., Curr.Cont., DSH Abstr., Environ.Abstr., Excerp.Med., Fluidex, INSPEC (1969-), Noise Pollut.Publ.Abstr., Ocean.Abstr., Phys.Ber., Pollut.Abstr., Sci.Cit.Ind., Sh.& Vib.Dig. **Document type:** academic/scholarly publication.
—BLDSC (1571.400000); Ei; Faxon; Genuine Article; SWETS; UnCover. **CCC.**
Description: For those concerned with the design of buildings, measurements and control of industrial noise and vibration, transportation noise, hearing, the understanding of the acoustics of musical instruments, the propagation of sound through the atmosphere and under water.
Refereed Serial

534 PL ISSN 0137-5075
QC221 CODEN: AACODN
ARCHIVES OF ACOUSTICS. (Text in English) 1976. q. $120. (Polska Akademia Nauk, Komitet Akustyki) Wydawnictwo Naukowe P W N, Miodowa 10, 00-251 Warsaw, Poland. TEL 48-22-312738. FAX 48-22-267163. TELEX 813763 PWN PL. Ed. J. Molecki. abstr.; bibl.; illus. circ. 360. **Indexed:** Appl.Mech.Rev., INSPEC (1978-), Noise Pollut.Publ.Abstr., Phys.Ber.
—BLDSC (1630.800000); CASDDS.

534 GW ISSN 0171-4147
AUDIO. 1977. m. DM.90; newsstand price: DM.8.50. Vereinigte Motor-Verlage GmbH und Co. KG, Leuschnerstr. 1, 70174 Stuttgart, Germany. TEL 0711-18201. FAX 0711-1821669. Ed. Ulrich Smyrek; Pub. Uwe Hagen. adv.: B&W page DM.8200, color page DM.15170; trim 185 x 248; adv. contact: Rolf Priesmann. bk.rev.; index. circ. 68,739. (back issues avail.) **Indexed:** A.S.& T.Ind., Consum.Ind., Ind.Sci.Rev. **Document type:** consumer publication.

534 GW ISSN 0172-8261
CODEN: AUKADP
AUDIOLOGISCH AKUSTIK/AUDIOLOGICAL ACOUSTICS. (Text in English and German) 1962. 4/yr. DM.68. Median Verlag GmbH, Postfach 103964, 69029 Heidelberg, Germany. TEL 06221-25731. FAX 06221-25020. Ed.Bd. adv.; bk.rev.; bibl.; charts; illus.; index. circ. 2,300. **Indexed:** Excerp.Med., INSPEC (1982-), NBA. **Document type:** academic/scholarly publication.
—BLDSC (1789.060000).
Formerly: Zeitschrift fuer Hoergeraete Akustik (ISSN 0044-2860)

534 AT ISSN 0157-1532
AUSTRALIAN JOURNAL OF AUDIOLOGY. 1979. s-a. Aus.$30 to individuals (foreign Aus.$45); institutions Aus.$55 (foreign Aus.$80). (Audiological Society of Australia) Australian Academic Press Pty. Ltd., 32 Jeays St., Bown Hills, Qld. 4006, Australia. **Indexed:** Biol.Abstr., Excerp.Med., INSPEC (1982-), Noise Pollut.Publ.Abstr.
—UnCover.
Description: Publishes original, scientific articles on all aspects of Audiology.

534 UK ISSN 0952-4622
CODEN: BIOAE7
BIOACOUSTICS; the international journal of animal sound and its recording. 1988. q. £89($179) (British Library National Sound Archive) A B Academic Publishers, P.O. Box 42, Bicester, Oxon. OX6 7NW, England. TEL 0869-320949. Ed. Peter K. McGregor. **Indexed:** Ecol.Abstr., Psychol.Abstr. (1988-), Sport Fish.Abstr., Wild.Rev., Zoo.Rec. **Document type:** academic/scholarly publication.
—BLDSC (2066.679000); Faxon; UnCover.
Description: Collects research papers and articles on all aspects of wildlife recording.

534 720 UK ISSN 1351-010X
▼**BUILDING ACOUSTICS.** 1994. q. £80($132) Multi-Science Publishing Co. Ltd., 107 High St., Brentwood, Essex CM14 4RX, England. TEL 01277-224632. FAX 01277-223453. (U.S. subscr. to: Box 176, Avenel, NJ 07001) Eds. B.M. Gibbs, D.J. Oldham. **Document type:** academic/scholarly publication.
—BLDSC (2359.320500).
Description: Provides a forum for scientists and engineers concerned with research and development for acoustic enhancement and noise control in buildings.

BUILDING PERFORMANCE NEWS. see *BUILDING AND CONSTRUCTION*

534 CN ISSN 0711-6659
CODEN: CAACDX
CANADIAN ACOUSTICS/ACOUSTIQUE CANADIENNE. (Text in English and French) 1973. q. Can.$35. Canadian Acoustical Association, P.O. Box 1351, Sta. F, Toronto, ON M4Y 2V9, Canada. TEL 613-993-0102. FAX 613-954-5984. (Subscr. to: T. Nightingale, Secy., P.O. Box 74068, Ottawa, ON K1M 2H9, Canada. TEL 613-993-0102) Ed. Murray Hodgson. adv. contact: Chris Hugh. bk.rev.; charts. circ. 500. (back issues avail.) **Indexed:** Acoust.Abstr., Ind.Hyg.Dig., INSPEC (1982-). **Document type:** academic/scholarly publication.
—BLDSC (3016.476000); Faxon.
Formerly (until Jan. 1982): Acoustics and Noise Control in Canada.

534 CC ISSN 0217-9776
CHINESE JOURNAL OF ACOUSTICS. Chinese edition: Shengxue Xuebao. (Text in English) 1982. q. $295. (Academia Sinica, Institute of Acoustics) Science Press, Marketing and Sales Department, 16 Donghuangchenggen North St., Beijing 100717, People's Republic of China. TEL 4010642. FAX 4019810. (US office: 84-04 58th Ave., Elmhurst, NY 11373. TEL 718-476-0238; Exclusively dist. outside P.R. China by: Allerton Press, Inc., 150 Fifth Ave., New York, NY 10011. TEL 212-924-3950. FAX 212-463-9684) (Co-publisher: Allerton Press, Inc.) Ed. Ma Dayou. adv. circ. 6,000. (also avail. in microform; back issues avail.) **Document type:** academic/scholarly publication.
—Faxon. **CCC.**
Description: Covers acoustical research in China, including physical acoustics, underwater sound, and electroacoustics.
Refereed Serial

534 JA
CONFERENCE ON SOLID STATE DEVICES & MATERIALS. EXTENDED ABSTRACTS. (Text in English) 1969. a. 35000 Yen($420) (Japan Butsuri Gakkai, Kotai Soshi Zairyo Konfarensu - Japan Society of Applied Physics, Solid State Devices and Materials) Business Center for Academic Societies Japan, 5-16-9 Honkomagome, Bunkyo-ku, Tokyo 113, Japan. TEL 03-5814-5811. FAX 03-5814-5822. (Dist. by: Intercontinental Marketing Corp., I.P.O. Box 5056, Tokyo 100-30, Japan. TEL 81-3-3661-7458. FAX 81-3-3667-9646) **Document type:** abstracting/indexing.

534 DK ISSN 0105-2853
DANMARKS TEKNISKE HOEJSKOLE. LABORATORIET FOR AKUSTIK. PUBLIKATION. irreg. price varies. Danmarks Tekniske Hoejskole, Laboratoriet for Akustik, Bygn 352, 2800 Lyngby, Denmark. illus.

534 DK
DELTA AKUSTIK & VIBRATION. 1975. irreg. price varies. Lydteknisk Institut, Akademiet for de Tekniske Videnskaber - Danish Acoustical Institute, Building 356, Akademivej, DK-2800 Lyngby, Denmark. TEL 45-931211. FAX 45-931990. illus.
Former titles: Lydteknisk Institut. Rapport (ISSN 0109-3673); (until 1983): Lydteknisk Laboratorium. Rapport (ISSN 0105-614X)

FREQUENCY CONTROL SYMPOSIUM. see *ELECTRONICS*

534 US
HEMI - SYNC JOURNAL. 1983. q. $25. The Monroe Institute, Rte. 1, Box 175, Faber, VA 22938. TEL 804-361-1252. FAX 804-361-1237. Ed. Shirley N. Bliley. circ. 3,000. (back issues avail.) **Document type:** academic/scholarly publication.
Formerly: Breakthrough (Faber).
Description: Covers research in and applications of the Hemi-Sync sound technology in various professional arenas.

534 GW ISSN 0933-1980
HOERAKUSTIK. 1965. m. DM.192. Median Verlag GmbH, Postfach 103964, 69029 Heidelberg, Germany. TEL 06221-25731. FAX 06221-25020. circ. 2,300. **Document type:** trade publication.
Formerly: Hoergeraete-Akustiker (ISSN 0178-4536).

534 US ISSN 1053-5888
TK5981 CODEN: ISPRE6
I E E E - SIGNAL PROCESSING MAGAZINE. Represents: I E E E Acoustics, Speech and Signal Processing Magazine. 1984. q. $80 to non-members (effective 1996). (I E E E, Acoustics, Speech, and Signal Processing Society) Institute of Electrical and Electronics Engineers, Inc., 345 E. 47th St., New York, NY 10017. TEL 908-981-0060. FAX 908-981-9667. (Subscr. to: Box 1331, 445 Hoes Lane, Piscataway, NJ 08855-1331) Ed. Gregory Wakefield. (also avail. in microform) **Indexed:** A.I.Abstr., INSPEC.
—BLDSC (4363.066520); Ei; Faxon; SWETS; UMI; UnCover. **CCC.**
Formerly: I E E E - A S S P Magazine (ISSN 0740-7467)
Description: Features tutorials of a light technical nature. Provides news and notes on conferences, workshops, seminars and lectures.

534 US ISSN 0885-3010
QC244 CODEN: ITUCER
I E E E TRANSACTIONS ON ULTRASONICS, FERROELECTRICS AND FREQUENCY CONTROL. 1954. bi-m. $230 to non-members (effective 1996). (I E E E, Ultrasonics, Ferroelectrics and Frequency Control Society) Institute of Electrical and Electronics Engineers, Inc., 345 E. 47th St., New York, NY 10017-2394. TEL 908-981-0060. FAX 908-981-9667. (Subscr. to: Box 1331, 445 Hoes Lane, Piscataway, NJ 08855-1331) Ed. William D. O'Brien. bk.rev.; abstr.; illus.; index. (also avail. in microform) **Indexed:** A.S.& T.Ind., Chem.Abstr., Comput.Lit.Ind., Curr.Cont., Deep Sea Res.& Oceanogr.Abstr., Eng.Ind., Excerp.Med., Ind.Sci.Rev., INIS Atomind., INSPEC, Int.Aerosp.Abstr., Math.R., Sci.Cit.Ind.
—BLDSC (4363.227500); CASDDS; Ei; Faxon; Genuine Article; SWETS; UMI; UnCover. **CCC.**
Former titles: I E E E Transactions on Sonics and Ultrasonics (ISSN 0018-9537); I E E E Transactions on Ultrasonics Engineering; I R E Transactions on Ultrasonics Engineering; I R E Professional Group on Ultrasonics Engineering. Transactions.
Description: Discusses theory, design and application in generation, transmission and detection of bulk and surface mechanical waves.

534 UK
I S V R MEMORANDUM. irreg., no.740, 1994. University of Southampton, Institute of Sound and Vibration Research, Southampton SO9 5NH, England. **Document type:** monographic series.

PHYSICS — SOUND

534 UK
INSTITUTE OF ACOUSTICS. PROCEEDINGS. 1979. a. Institute of Acoustics, Environmental Noise Group, Agriculture House, 5 Holywell St, St. Albans, Herts. AL1 1EU, England. TEL 01727-848195. FAX 01727-850553. abstr. **Document type:** proceedings.
 Description: Presents research on various topics in applied acoustics.

534 JA ISSN 0386-8761
INSTITUTE OF NOISE CONTROL ENGINEERING. JOURNAL. (Text in Japanese) 1972. s-m. 16100 Yen (effective 1993). Institute of Noise Control Engineering (INCE), c/o Kobayashi Institute of Physical Research, 3-20-41 Higashimoto-machi, Kokubunji-shi, Tokyo 185, Japan. TEL 0423-25-1652. FAX 0423-27-3847. Ed. N. Imaizumi. adv. **Document type:** bibliography.

534 US
INTERNATIONAL AUDIO REVIEW. Abbreviated title: I A R. 1978? q. $28 (foreign $38). Institute for Audio Research, Box 4271, Berkeley, CA 94704-0271. Ed. J. Peter Moncrieff.
 Description: Review of audio products on an international scale.

534 CN ISSN 0074-400X
INTERNATIONAL CONFERENCE ON ACOUSTICS. REPORTS. 1953. irreg., 11th. 1983, Paris, France. International Commission on Acoustics, c/o Dr. E.A.W. Shaw, Division de Physique, Conseil National de Recherches, Ottawa, Ont. K1A 0R6, Canada. TEL 613-966-5845.
 —**CCC**.

534 UK ISSN 0969-9112
▼**INTERNATIONAL JOURNAL OF ACTIVE CONTROL.** 1994. q. £80($132) Multi-Science Publishing Co. Ltd., 107 High St., Brentwood, Essex CM14 4RX, England. TEL 01277-224632. FAX 01277-223453. (U.S. subscr. to: Box 176, Avenel, NJ 07001) Eds. J. Tichy, H.G. Leventhall. **Document type:** academic/scholarly publication.
 —BLDSC (4541.535000).
 Description: Provides information on technical progress in active control of sound and vibration.

534 US ISSN 0730-0050
TA418.84 CODEN: JACEDO
JOURNAL OF ACOUSTIC EMISSION. 1982. q. $96 (effective 1994). Acoustic Emission Group, 308 Westwood Blvd., Box 364, Los Angeles, CA 90024-1647. TEL 310-825-5233. FAX 818-368-8309. Ed. Kanji Ono. adv.; bk.rev.; circ. 300 (paid). **Indexed:** Chem.Abstr., INIS Atomind., INSPEC, Met.Abstr. **Document type:** academic/scholarly publication.
 —BLDSC (4918.922000); CASDDS; Ei; Faxon; SWETS; UnCover.
 Description: Covers science and technology of acoustic emission for researchers and applications engineers.

534 UK ISSN 0263-0923
JOURNAL OF LOW FREQUENCY NOISE & VIBRATION. 1982. 4/yr. £98 u.K. and Europe; rest of world £105. Multi-Science Publishing Co. Ltd., 107 High St., Brentwood, Essex CM14 4RX, England. TEL 01277-224632. FAX 01277-223453. (U.S. subscr. to: Box 176, Avenel, NJ 07001) Ed. H.G. Leventhall. **Indexed:** Agri.Eng.Abstr., INSPEC, Noise Pollut.Publ.Abstr. **Document type:** academic/scholarly publication.
 —BLDSC (5010.565000); Faxon; SWETS. **CCC**.
 Description: Discusses low frequency noise and vibration, their effects on man, animals, the environment, and active and passive methods of control.

JOURNAL OF OPTICS RESEARCH. see *PHYSICS — Optics*

534 300 II ISSN 0256-4637
JOURNAL OF PURE AND APPLIED ULTRASONICS. 1979. q. $100 (effective Jan. 1992). Ultrasonics Society of India, c/o Ultrasonic Section, National Physical Laboratory, Hillside Rd., New Delhi 110012, India. TEL 91-11-5781736. FAX 91-11-5752678. TELEX 03177099. Ed. V.N. Bindal. adv.; bk.rev.; index. circ. 300. (back issues avail.) **Indexed:** INSPEC. **Document type:** academic/scholarly publication.
 —BLDSC (5043.682000).
 Refereed Serial

534 UK ISSN 0022-460X
QC221 CODEN: JSVIAG
JOURNAL OF SOUND AND VIBRATION. 1964. 50/yr. £2 (effective 1996). Academic Press Ltd. (Subsidiary of: Harcourt Brace & Company Ltd.), 24-28 Oval Rd., London NW1, England. TEL 44-171-267-4466. FAX 44-171-482-2293. TELEX 25775 ACPRES G. (Subscr. to: Harcourt Brace & Company Ltd., Foots Cray High St., Sidcup, Kent DA14 5HP, England. TEL 44-181-300-3322. FAX 44-181-309-0807) Ed. P.E. Doak. adv.; bk.rev.; bibl.; charts; illus.; index. circ. 1,500. **Indexed:** Abstr.J.Earthq.Eng., Appl.Mech.Rev., Biol.Abstr., BMT, Br.Rail.Bd., Br.Tech.Ind., C.I.S. Abstr., Curr.Cont., Deep Sea Res.& Oceanogr.Abstr., Eng.Ind., Ergon.Abstr., Excerp.Med., Fluidex, Fuel & Energy Abstr., HRIS, Ind.Sci.Rev., INIS Atomind., INSPEC, Int.Aerosp.Abstr., ISMEC, Math.R., Noise Pollut.Publ.Abstr., Ocean.Abstr., Phys.Ber., Pollut.Abstr., Sh.& Vib.Dig. **Document type:** academic/scholarly publication.
 —BLDSC (5065.850000); Ei; Faxon; Genuine Article; SWETS; UnCover. **CCC**.
 Description: Examines experimental and theoretical work concerning all aspects of sound vibration.

530 PL ISSN 0324-8313
TA355 CODEN: JTPHDR
JOURNAL OF TECHNICAL PHYSICS. (Text in English) 1959. q. $120. (Polska Akademia Nauk, Instytut Podstawowych Problemow Techniki) Wydawnictwo Naukowe P W N, Miodowa 10, 00-251 Warsaw, Poland. Ed. Czeslaw Rymarz. abstr.; charts; illus. circ. 600. **Indexed:** Appl.Mech.Rev., Chem.Abstr., INIS Atomind., INSPEC, Math.R., Phys.Ber., Ref.Zh.
 —BLDSC (5068.291000); CASDDS; Ei; Faxon; UnCover. **CCC**.
 Formerly (until 1975): Proceedings of Vibrations Problems (ISSN 0032-9576)

JOURNAL OF ULTRASOUND IN MEDICINE. see *MEDICAL SCIENCES — Radiology And Nuclear Medicine*

534 US ISSN 1077-5463
▼**JOURNAL OF VIBRATION AND CONTROL.** (Abbreviated title: J V C) 1995. q. $64 to individuals; institutions $210 (effective 1996). Sage Publications, Inc., Sage Science Press, 2455 Teller Rd., Thousand Oaks, CA 91320. TEL 805-499-0721. FAX 805-499-0871. Ed. Ali H. Nayfeh. adv.; charts; illus. (back issues avail.) **Document type:** academic/scholarly publication.
 Description: Encompasses all linear and nonlinear vibration phenomena occurring in mechanical, structural, aeronautical, materials, oceanographic, electrical, control, chemical, biological, electromagnetic, and environmental fields.
 Refereed Serial

534 551.46 JA ISSN 0916-5835
KAIYO ONKYO GAKKAISHI. English edition: Marine Acoustics Society of Japan. Journal (ISSN 0285-4120) (Text in Japanese) 1974. q. Marine Acoustics Society of Japan - Kaiyo Onkyo Gakkai, Nihon Odio Kyokai, 14-34, Jingumae 1-chome, Shibuya-ku, Tokyo 150, Japan.

534 JA
KENKYU JOSEI JIGYO JOSEI KENKYU SEIKA HOKOKU GAIYO/SOUND TECHNOLOGY PROMOTION FOUNDATION. RESEARCH REPORT. (Text in Japanese) a. Saundo Gijutsu Shinko Zaidan - Sound Technology Promotion Foundation, 36-4, Yoyogi 1-chome, Shibuya-ku, Tokyo 151, Japan.

534 551.46 JA ISSN 0285-4120
MARINE ACOUSTICS SOCIETY OF JAPAN. JOURNAL. Japanese edition: Kaiyo Onkyo Gakkaishi (ISSN 0916-5835) (Text in English) 1977. irreg. Marine Acoustics Society of Japan - Kaiyo Onkyo Gakkai, Nihon Odio Kyokai, 14-34, Jingumae 1-chome, Shibuya-ku, Tokyo 150, Japan.

534 551.46 JA
MARINE ACOUSTICS SOCIETY OF JAPAN. PROCEEDINGS OF THE MEETING/KAIYO ONKYO GAKKAI KENKYU HAPPYOKAI KOEN RONBUNSHU. (Text in Japanese) 1985. a. Marine Acoustics Society of Japan - Kaiyo Onkyo Gakkai, Nihon Odio Kyokai, 14-34, Jingumae 1-chome, Shibuya-ku, Tokyo 150, Japan. **Document type:** proceedings.

534 US
N C A C NEWSLETTER. 1970. q. membership. National Council of Acoustical Consultants, 66 Morris Ave., Ste. 1A, Springfield, NJ 07081-1409. TEL 201-564-5859. FAX 201-564-7480. Ed. Jerry Lilly. circ. 500. **Document type:** newsletter.

534 JA
NIHON ONKYO GAKKAI KENKYU HAPPYOKAI KOEN RONBUNSHU/ACOUSTICAL SOCIETY OF JAPAN. REPORT OF THE MEETING. (Text in Japanese) 1952. s-a. Nihon Onkyo Gakkai - Acoustical Society of Japan, 7-7, Yoyogi 2-chome, Shibuya-ku, Tokyo 151, Japan.

534 JA ISSN 0369-4232
CODEN: NIOGAH
NIHON ONKYO GAKKAISHI. English edition: Acoustical Society of Japan. Journal (ISSN 0388-2861) (Text in Japanese) 1936. m. 1500 Yen. Nihon Onkyo Gakkai - Acoustical Society of Japan, 7-7, Yoyogi 2-chome, Shibuya-ku, Tokyo 151, Japan. **Indexed:** INIS Atomind., INSPEC (1970-), Jap.Per.Ind.
 —BLDSC (4676.000000).

534 UK ISSN 0950-8163
NOISE & VIBRATION IN INDUSTRY. 1986. 4/yr. £98 u.K. and Europe; rest of world £105. Multi-Science Publishing Co. Ltd., 107 High St., Brentwood, Essex CM14 4RX, England. TEL 01277-224632. FAX 01277-223453. (U.S. subscr. to: Box 176, Avenel, NJ 07001) **Document type:** academic/scholarly publication.
 —BLDSC (6115.857000).
 Formerly: Noise and Vibration for Works Managers.
 Description: Covers regulations governing noise at work.

534 UK ISSN 0957-4565
TD891 CODEN: NVWOE6
NOISE AND VIBRATION WORLDWIDE. 1969. m. (11/yr.). £134($241) (effective 1996). (Institute of Physics) I O P Publishing Ltd., Techno House, Redcliffe Way, Bristol, Avon BS1 6NX, England. TEL 01272-297481. FAX 01272-294318. (Subscr. to: I O P Circulation Centre, WDIS Ltd. Publishing House, Victoria Rd., Ruislip, Mddx. HA4 0SX, England. TEL 0181-845-8545. FAX 0181-845-7696; U.S. subscr. to: American Institute of Physics, Subscriber Services, 500 Sunnyside Blvd., Woodbury, NY 11791-2900. TEL 516-349-7800) Ed. Susan Traill. adv.; bk.rev.; charts; illus.; tr.lit.; index. circ. 700. **Indexed:** BMT, C.I.S. Abstr., Cadscan., Excerp.Med., Fluidex, Fuel & Energy Abstr., INSPEC, Lead Abstr., Zincscan. **Document type:** academic/scholarly publication.
 —BLDSC (6115.865000); Ei; Faxon; SWETS. **CCC**.
 Former titles (until 1989): Noise and Vibration Control - Worldwide (ISSN 0143-6481); Noise Control, Vibration Isolation; Noise Control, Vibration and Insulation (ISSN 0309-8230); Noise Control and Vibration Reduction.
 Description: Devoted to the engineering discipline of noise control and vibration reduction.

534 JA ISSN 0912-7283
ONGAKU ONKYO KENKYUKAI SHIRYO/ACOUSTICAL SOCIETY OF JAPAN. TRANSACTIONS OF COMMITTEE MEETING ON MUSIC ACOUSTICS. (Text in English, Japanese) 1982. irreg. Nihon Onkyo Gakkai - Acoustical Society of Japan, 7-7, Yoyogi 2-chome, Shibuya-ku, Tokyo 151, Japan.

534 UK ISSN 1355-7718
▼**ORGANISED SOUND.** (Includes cumulation on CD-ROM) Announced for publication in 1996. 3/yr. £63($98) (effective 1996). Cambridge University Press, Edinburgh Bldg., Shaftesbury Rd., Cambridge CB2 2RU, England. TEL 44-1223-312393. FAX 44-1223-315052. (In N. America: Cambridge University Press, Journals Dept., 40 W. 20th St., New York, NY 10011-4211. TEL 212-924-3900. FAX 212-691-3239) **Document type:** academic/scholarly publication.
 ●Also available on CD-ROM.

534 US ISSN 0079-1873
PHYSICAL ACOUSTICS: PRINCIPLES AND METHODS. 1964. irreg., vol.22, 1992. Academic Press, Inc., 525 B St., Ste. 1900, San Diego, CA 92101-4495. TEL 619-231-0926. FAX 619-699-6715. (Subscr. to: Order Dept., 6277 Sea Harbor Dr., 4th Fl., Orlando, FL 32887. TEL 800-321-5068) Eds. R. Thurston, A. Pierce. (reprint service avail. from ISI) **Indexed:** Appl.Mech.Rev., Ind.Sci.Rev.
 Refereed Serial

POLITECHNIKA WROCLAWSKA. INSTYTUT TELEKOMUNIKACJI I AKUSTYKI. PRACE NAUKOWE. KONFERENCJE. see *COMMUNICATIONS — Telephone And Telegraph*

POLITECHNIKA WROCLAWSKA. INSTYTUT TELEKOMUNIKACJI I AKUSTYKI. PRACE NAUKOWE. MONOGRAFIE. see *COMMUNICATIONS — Telephone And Telegraph*

POLITECHNIKA WROCLAWSKA. INSTYTUT TELEKOMUNIKACJI I AKUSTYKI. PRACE NAUKOWE. STUDIA I MATERIALY. see *COMMUNICATIONS — Telephone And Telegraph*

534   RU   ISSN 0202-2354
QC670
PROBLEMY DIFRAKTSII I RASPROSTRANENIYA VOLN/PROBLEMS OF DIFFRACTION AND SPREADING OF WAVES. 1962. irreg. 1.69 Rub. per no. Sankt-Peterburgskii Universitet, Universitetskaya Nab. 7-9, St. Petersburg V-164, Russia. abstr.; bibl. circ. 900.
—BLDSC (0133.260000).

534   JA
PROGRESS IN ACOUSTIC EMISSION. (Text in English) biennial. 15000 Yen. Nihon Hihakai Kensa Kyokai - Japanese Society for Non-Destructive Inspection, Natsume No. 5 Bldg., 4th Fl., 67 Kanda-Sakumagashi, Chiyoda-ku, Tokyo 101, Japan. TEL 81-3-5821-5105. FAX 81-3-3863-6524. Ed. Teruo Kishi.

534   KR   ISSN 0485-8972
CODEN: RTKHAJ
RADIOTEKHNIKA (KHARKOV). 1965. q. price varies. (Khar'kovskii Institut Radioelektroniki) Izdatel'stvo Vysshaya Shkola, Khar'kovskoe Otdelenie, Universitetskaya 16, 310003 Kharkov, Ukraine. Ed. A. Tereshchenko. abstr.; charts. circ. 1,000. **Indexed:** Int.Aerosp.Abstr.
—BLDSC (0138.200000); CASDDS. **CCC.**
Description: Presents articles dealing with the results of theoretical and experimental research in the fields of radio engineering devices and systems of radio measurements, electro-dynamics and electronics of microwaves.

534.55   SP   ISSN 0210-3680
REVISTA DE ACUSTICA. (Text and summaries in English and Spanish) 1970. q. 7000 ptas.($10) Sociedad Espanola de Acustica - Spanish Society of Acoustics, Serrano 144, 28006 Madrid, Spain. TEL 261-88-06. TELEX 4117651. Ed. Antonio Calvo-Manzano. adv.; bk.rev.; bibl. circ. 1,000. (tabloid format; also avail. in microfilm) **Indexed:** Ind.SST.

534.55   UK   ISSN 0048-8828
RUSSIAN ULTRASONICS. 1971. bi-m. £200 u.K. and Europe; rest of world £210. Multi-Science Publishing Co. Ltd., 107 High St., Brentwood, Essex CM14 4RX, England. TEL 01277-224632. FAX 01277-223453. (U.S. subscr. to: Box 176, Avenel, NJ 07001) bibl.; charts; illus.; index. **Document type:** academic/scholarly publication.
—BLDSC (8053.040000); Ei; Faxon. **CCC.**

534   CC   ISSN 1000-3630
SHENGXUE JISHU/TECHNICAL ACOUSTICS. (Text in Chinese) 1982. q. $16. Chinese Academy of Sciences, Shanghai Acoustics Society, Shanghai Acoustics Laboratory, 456 Xiaomuqiao Road, Shanghai 200032, People's Republic of China. TEL 8621-4048159. FAX 8621-4374915. (Dist. overseas by: China National Publishing Service Trading Co., P.O. Box 782, Beijing, P.R. China) (Co-sponsor: Tongji University, Institute of Acoustics) Eds. Feng Shaosong, Wei Mo'an. adv.; bk.rev. **Document type:** academic/scholarly publication.
Description: Covers ultrasonics, bio-medical ultrasonics, underwater sound, architectural acoustics, audio engineering, noise control, physiological and psychological acoustics.

534   CC
QC221   CODEN: SHGHAS
SHENGXUE XUEBAO. English edition: Chinese Journal of Acoustics (ISSN 0217-9776) (Text in Chinese; summaries in English) 1964. bi-m. $103.20. (Acoustical Society of China) Science Press, Marketing and Sales Department, 16 Donghuangchenggen North St., Beijing 100717, People's Republic of China. TEL 4010642. FAX 4019810. adv. circ. 6,000. **Indexed:** INSPEC (1981-), Math.R., Phys.Ber. **Document type:** academic/scholarly publication.
—BLDSC (0587.200000); CASDDS.
Formerly: Acta Acustica (ISSN 0371-0025)
Description: Contains original papers and brief communications on acoustical research in mainland China and abroad, including physical acoustics, underwater sound, electroacoustics, and manufacture of instruments.
Refereed Serial

534.5 620.11   US   ISSN 1070-9622
TA355   CODEN: SHVIE8
▼**SHOCK AND VIBRATION.** 1994. bi-m. $228 (foreign $321) (effective 1996). John Wiley & Sons, Inc., Journals, 605 Third Ave., New York, NY 10158. TEL 212-850-6645. FAX 212-850-6021. TELEX 12-7063. E-mail: SUBINFO@JWILEY.COM. (Subscr. outside the Americas to: John Wiley & Sons Ltd., Baffin Ln., Chichester, W. Sussex PO19 1UD, England. TEL 44-1243-779777. FAX 44-1243-776128) (also avail. in microform from UMI; back issues avail.) **Document type:** academic/scholarly publication.
—BLDSC (8267.457000).
Refereed Serial

534   UK   ISSN 0964-1726
TA418.9.S62   CODEN: SMSTER
SMART MATERIALS AND STRUCTURES. 1992. q. £195($394) (effective 1996). (Institute of Physics) I O P Publishing Ltd., Techno House, Redcliffe Way, Bristol, Avon BS1 6NX, England. TEL 0117-929-7481. FAX 0117-929-4318. TELEX 449149 INSTP G. (U.S. subscr. to: American Institute of Physics, Subscriber Services, 500 Sunnyside Blvd., Woodbury, NY 11797-2900. TEL 516-349-7800) Ed R.O. Claus. index. circ. 178. (also avail. in microfiche) **Indexed:** INSPEC (1992-), Intl.Polym.Sci.& Tech., RAPRA. **Document type:** academic/scholarly publication.
—BLDSC (8310.193520); CASDDS; Ei; Faxon; Genuine Article; SWETS. **CCC.**
Description: Covers technical advance of smart materials and structures systems from acoustic to electromagnetic fields.

534   UK
SONAR TRANSDUCERS CONFERENCE. PROCEEDINGS. a. Institute of Acoustics, Underwater Acoustics Group, Agriculture House, 5 Holywell Hill, St. Albans, Herts. AL1 1EU, England. TEL 01727-848195. FAX 01727-850553. abstr. **Document type:** proceedings.
Description: Presents new research on such topics as applications of composite materials in sonar equipment, designs for extreme depths, finite- and boundary-element analysis, flextensional transducers, hydrophones, and very wide bandwidth sources.

534   SZ   ISSN 0258-9141
TK7881.7   CODEN: SRTEEM
SOUND. 1978. 10/yr. 65 SFr. A T Zeitschriftenverlag, Bahnhofstr. 39-43, CH-5001 Aarau, Switzerland. TEL 064-266161. FAX 064-266213. Ed. Fernando Palencias. adv. Ed. Moritz Eggenschwiler. circ. 11,747. **Document type:** academic/scholarly publication.
—BLDSC (8330.375000).
Formerly: Electronic Sound and R T E (ISSN 1013-7831); Formed by merger of: Electronic Sound (ISSN 0254-4350); R T E (ISSN 0254-4369)

534   CN   ISSN 0847-1223
ML3790
SOUND RECORDING. 1984. Can.$24($29) (foreign $34). Statistics Canada, Publication Sales, Ottawa, ON K1A OT6, Canada. TEL 613-951-7277. FAX 613-951-1584. Ed. Kathryn Banner. **Document type:** government publication.
Formerly (until 1991): Sound Recording Preliminiary Statistics (ISSN 0830-8373)
Description: Provides details on all aspects of the sound recording survey, a census of all record and label companies in Canada.

534   SA   ISSN 0259-0638
   CODEN: JSAIEH
SOUTH AFRICAN ACOUSTICS INSTITUTE. JOURNAL. 1987. a. South African Acoustics Institute, P.O. Box 912169, Silverton 0127, South Africa. **Indexed:** INSPEC (1987-). **Document type:** academic/scholarly publication.
—BLDSC (4899.800000).

534   DK   ISSN 0105-3027
TECHNICAL UNIVERSITY OF DENMARK. ACOUSTICS LABORATORY REPORT. no.34, 1982. irreg. price varies. Danmarks Tekniske Hoejskole, Laboratoriet for Akustik, Bygning 352, 2800 Lyngby, Denmark. illus. **Indexed:** Concr.Abstr.
Description: Contains research and thesis reports in acoustics.

534   LI   ISSN 0369-6367
ULTRAGARSAS/ULTRASOUND. (Text in Russian; summaries in English and Lithuanian) 1969. a. price varies. Kaunas Technological University, Donelaicio 73, 3006 Kaunas, Lithuania. (Co-sponsor: Lithuanian Ministry of Culture and Education) Ed. V. Domarkas. circ. 500. **Document type:** academic/scholarly publication.
—BLDSC (0122.639000).
Description: Covers theoretical and practical problems of ultrasonic interferometry and spectroscopy, quantum and molecular acoustics and medical diagnosis.

534   UK   ISSN 0041-624X
TA367   CODEN: ULTRA3
ULTRASONICS; the world's leading journal covering the science & technology of ultrasound. 1963. 11/yr. fl.1272; $776 (effective 1996). Butterworth - Heinemann, Part of the Reed Elsevier group, Linacre House, Jordan Hill, Oxford OX2 8DP, England. TEL 0865-310366. FAX 0865-310898. TELEX 83111 BHPOXF G. (Subscr. to: Elsevier Science Ltd., P.O. Box 800, Kidlington, Oxford OX5 1DX, England. TEL 44-865-843000. FAX 44-865-843010); Subscr. in U.S. and Canada to: Elsevier Science, 660 White Plains Rd., Tarrytown, NY 10591-5153. TEL 914-524-9200. FAX 914-333-2444) adv.; bk.rev.; abstr.; bibl.; illus.; index. (also avail. in microform from UMI; back issues avail.) **Indexed:** A.S.& T.Ind., Abstr.Bull.Inst.Pap.Chem., Appl.Mech.Rev., B.C.I.R.A., Biol.Abstr., Br.Rail.Bd., Br.Tech.Ind., C.I.S. Abstr., Chem.Abstr., Curr.Adv.Ecol.Sci., Curr.Cont., Excerp.Med., Fluidex, HRIS, Ind.Med., INSPEC (1968-), Int.Aerosp.Abstr., Met.Abstr., PROMT, World Alum.Abstr. **Document type:** academic/scholarly publication.
—BLDSC (9082.796000); CASDDS; Ei; Faxon; Genuine Article; SWETS; UMI; UnCover. **CCC.**
Description: Covers the field of ultrasonics and its applications: transducers, nondestructive testing, signal processing.
Refereed Serial

534 541.3   UK   ISSN 1350-4177
QD801   CODEN: ULSOER
▼**ULTRASONICS SONOCHEMISTRY.** 1994. 3/yr. fl.323($197) (effective 1996). Butterworth - Heinemann, Part of the Reed Elsevier group, Linacre House, Jordan Hill, Oxford OX2 8DP, England. TEL 0865-310366. FAX 0865-310398. (Subscr. to: Elsevier Science Ltd., P.O. Box 800, Kidlington, Oxford OX5 1DX, England. TEL 44-865-843000. FAX 44-865-843010; Subscr. in U.S. and Canada to: Elsevier Science, 660 White Plains Rd., Tarrytown, NY 10591-5153. TEL 914-524-9200. FAX 914-333-2444) Ed.Bd; Pub. Diane Cogan. adv. contact: Mark Butler. (also avail. in microfilm from UMI; back issues avail.) **Document type:** academic/scholarly publication.
—BLDSC (9082.805000); CASDDS; Ei; SWETS; UMI.
Refereed Serial

620.2 534   US   ISSN 0090-5607
TA367   CODEN: ULSPDT
ULTRASONICS SYMPOSIUM. PROCEEDINGS. Key Title: Proceedings - Ultrasonics Symposium. a. price varies. (I E E E, Ultrasonics, Ferroelectrics, and Frequency Control Society) Institute of Electrical and Electronics Engineers, Inc., 345 E. 47th St., New York, NY 10017-2394. TEL 212-705-7900. FAX 212-705-7682. (Subscr. to: Box 1331, 445 Hoes Ln., Piscataway, NJ 08855-1331) **Indexed:** Chem.Abstr, INSPEC.
—CASDDS; UMI. **CCC.**
Description: Discoveries, recent advances, new devices, new techniques and application in all areas of sound.

PHYSIOLOGY

ULTRASOUND IN MEDICINE & BIOLOGY. see *BIOLOGY*

WIDESCREEN INTERNATIONAL. see *PHOTOGRAPHY*

534   UK
WINDOWS ON ACOUSTICS. bi-m. AcSoft, 6 Church Ln., Cheddington, Leignton Buzzard, Beds. LU7 0RU, England. TEL 01296-662852.
FAX 01296-661400. software rev.; illus. **Document type:** newsletter.
    Description: Reviews software used in acoustic applications and research.

YEAR BOOK OF ULTRASOUND. see *MEDICAL SCIENCES — Radiology And Nuclear Medicine*

534   CC   ISSN 1000-310X
YINGYONG SHENGXUE/APPLIED ACOUSTICS. (Text in Chinese) 1981. bi-m. $74.80. (Zhongguo Shengxue Xuehui - Chinese Acoustics Society) Science Press, Marketing and Sales Department, 16 Donghuangchenggen North St., Beijing 100717, People's Republic of China. TEL 4010642.
FAX 4019810. adv. circ. 11,000. **Document type:** academic/scholarly publication.
    Description: Aims to present concrete applications of acoustics in various branches of China's economy. Popularizes basic knowledge of acoustics and reports on academic developments in China and other countries.
    Refereed Serial

534   GW   ISSN 0174-1098
TD891
ZEITSCHRIFT FUER LAERMBEKAEMPFUNG. 1954. 6/yr. DM.238($172) (effective 1996). (Deutscher Arbeitsring fuer Laermbekaempfung e.V.) Springer-Verlag, Heidelberger Platz 3, 14197 Berlin, Germany. TEL 030-8207-0. FAX 030-8214091.
E-mail: orders@springer.de. (Subscr. in N. America to: Springer-Verlag New York, Inc., 44 Hartz Way, Secaucus, NJ 07096-2491. TEL 201-348-4033.
FAX 201-348-4505) Ed.Bd. adv.; bk.rev.; abstr.; charts; illus.; tr.lit. (also avail. in microform from UMI; reprint service avail. from ISI) **Indexed:** Dok.Str., Excerp.Med. **Document type:** academic/scholarly publication.
—BLDSC (9468.750000); Faxon; SWETS; UMI. **CCC.**
    Formerly: Kampf dem Laerm (ISSN 0022-8249)

PHYSIOLOGY

see Biology–Physiology

PLASTICS

668.44   US
A S E P NEWS AND VIEWS. 1967. q. membership. American Society of Electroplated Plastics, 1767 Business Center Dr., Ste. 302, Reston, VA 22090-5332. TEL 202-371-1323.
FAX 202-371-1090. TELEX 292046 IMGUR. Ed. David W. Barrack. adv. circ. 500. **Document type:** newsletter.
    Formerly: A S E P Electroplater.

668.4   CK
ACOPLASTICOS. 1957. a. Asociacion Colombiana de Industrias Plasticas Acoplasticos, Carrera 10a, No. 27-27, Interior 134 Of. 901 (Edificio Bachue), Apdo. 29844, Bogota, Colombia. adv.

668.4   UK   ISSN 0306-3747
ADDITIVES FOR POLYMERS; an international newsletter. 1971. m. £370($589) (effective 1996). Elsevier Science Ltd., P.O. Box 800, Kidlington, Oxford OX5 1DX, England. TEL 44-1865-843000.
FAX 44-1865-843010. E-mail: nlinfo-f@elsevier.nl; usinfo-f@elsevier.com;
forinfo-kyf04035@niftyserve.or.jp; Site addr.: http://www.elsevier.nl/. (Subscr. in U.S. and Canada to: Elsevier Science, 660 White Plains Rd., Tarrytown, NY 10591-5153. TEL 914-524-9200.
FAX 914-333-2444) Ed. J.A. Shelton. bk.rev.; index. (also avail. in microform from UMI) **Document type:** newsletter.
—SWETS. **CCC.**
    Description: Summarizes information on new products and materials (including patents), new manufacturing techniques and processes, and new applications. Also industry and market news and the strategies of key players in this sector.

668.4   UK   ISSN 0260-4450
TP968   CODEN: ADHED5
ADHESION. (Represents: Papers Presented at the Annual Conference on Adhesion and Adhesives, City University, London) 1977. irreg., approx a., vol.15, 1991. Elsevier Science Ltd., Books Division, P.O. Box 800, Kidlington, Oxford OX5 1DX, England. TEL 44-1865-843000. FAX 44-1865-843010.
E-mail: nlinfo-f@elsevier.nl; usinfo-f@elsevier.com; forinfo-kyf04035@niftyserve.or.jp; Site addr.: http://www.elsevier.nl/. (Subscr. in U.S. and Canada to: Elsevier Science, 660 White Plains Rd., Tarrytown, NY 10591-5153. TEL 914-524-9200) Ed. K.W. Allen. charts; illus.; index. **Indexed:** Art & Archaeol.Tech.Abstr., Chem.Abstr. **Document type:** proceedings.
—CASDDS. **CCC.**
    Refereed Serial

668.4   JA   ISSN 0037-0495
CODEN: STHKAO
ADHESION AND ADHESIVES/SETCHAKU. (Text in Japanese) 1957. m. 7800 Yen. High Polymer Publishing Association - Kobunshi Kankokai, Chiekoin-Sagaru, Marutamachi, Kamikyoku, Kyoto 602, Japan. Ed. Hitoshi Okuda. adv.; charts; illus. **Indexed:** Chem.Abstr.
—BLDSC (0680.810000); CASDDS.

ADHESIVE TRENDS. see *RUBBER*

668.4 666   UK   ISSN 0951-953X
ADVANCED COMPOSITES BULLETIN; an international newsletter. 1987. m. £287($457) (effective 1996). Elsevier Science Ltd., P.O. Box 800, Kidlington, Oxford OX5 1DX, England. TEL 44-1865-843000.
FAX 44-1865-843010. E-mail: nlinfo-f@elsevier.nl; usinfo-f@elsevier.com;
forinfo-kyf04035@niftyserve.or.jp; Site addr.: http://www.elsevier.nl/. (Subscr. in U.S. and Canada to: Elsevier Science, 660 White Plains Rd., Tarrytown, NY 10591-5153. TEL 914-524-9200.
FAX 914-333-2444) Ed. Paul Hogg. bk.rev.; abstr.; charts; illus.; pat. (also avail. in microform from UMI; back issues avail.) **Indexed:** Intl.Polym.Sci.& Tech., RAPRA. **Document type:** newsletter.
●Also available online. Vendor(s): Data-Star (PTBN), Knight-Ridder, Inc. (File no.636).
—BLDSC (0696.838500); SWETS. **CCC.**
    Description: Contains information on new materials, applications, processing and company news. Reports on technological and business opportunities in composites industry.

668.4   UK   ISSN 0963-6935
ADVANCED COMPOSITES LETTERS. 1992. bi-m. £140($235) elsewhere £145 (effective 1996). Woodhead Publishing Ltd., Abington Hall, Abington, Cambridge CB1 6AH, England.
TEL 01223-891358. FAX 01223-893694. (Subscr. to: Turpin Distribution Services Ltd., Blackhorse Rd., Letchworth, Herts. SG6 1HN, England. TEL 01462-672555. FAX 01462-480947) Ed. Costas Galiotis; Pub. Martin Woodhead. **Indexed:** Intl.Polym.Sci.& Tech., RAPRA. **Document type:** academic/scholarly publication.
—BLDSC (0696.839200).
    Description: Covers the selection, design, processing and manufacture of fiber reinforced materials.
    Refereed Serial

668.4   UK   ISSN 0952-9691
ADVANCED COMPOSITES MANUFACTURING CENTRE NEWSLETTER. 1987. irreg. (approx. 2/yr.). free to qualified personnel. Advanced Composites Manufacturing Centre, University of Plymouth, School of Manufacturing, Materials and Mechanical Engineering, Drake Circus, Plymouth, Devon PL4 8AA, England. TEL 01752-232650.
FAX 01752-232638. Ed. John Summerscales. adv.; bk.rev.; circ. 4,600 (controlled). **Document type:** newsletter.
—BLDSC (0578.675200).
    Description: Reports progress in the manufacture of fiber reinforced composite plastics.

668.4   US   ISSN 0730-6679
TP1101   CODEN: APTYD5
ADVANCES IN POLYMER TECHNOLOGY. q. $476 (foreign $538) (effective 1996). (Polymer Processing Institute) John Wiley & Sons, Inc., Journals, 605 Third Ave., New York, NY 10158-0012. TEL 212-850-6645.
FAX 212-850-6021. TELEX 12-7063. E-mail: SUBINFO@JWILEY.COM. (Subscr. outside the Americas to: John Wiley & Sons Ltd., Baffins Ln., Chichester, W. Sussex PO19 1UD, England. TEL 44-1243-779777. FAX 44-1243-776128) Ed. Marino Xanthos. adv.; charts; illus.; pat.; stat. circ. 300. (also avail. in microform from UMI; back issues avail.) **Indexed:** Eng.Ind., Intl.Polym.Sci. & Tech., RAPRA. **Document type:** academic/scholarly publication.
—BLDSC (0710.610000); CASDDS; Ei; Faxon; Genuine Article; SWETS; UMI; UnCover. **CCC.**
    Formerly: Advances in Plastics Technology (ISSN 0272-9504)
    Description: Features articles, technical papers and the latest news on plastics technology, processing, and physics. Focuses on materials developments, new processing techniques, and materials and processes involving new fields such as plastics in solar energy.
    Refereed Serial

ADVANCES IN URETHANE SCIENCE AND TECHNOLOGY. see *CHEMISTRY — Organic Chemistry*

668.4 630   US   ISSN 1073-1776
AGRI-PLASTICS REPORT. 1985. bi-m. $50. American Society for Plasticulture, Box 860238, St. Augustine, FL 32086. TEL 904-829-0754.
FAX 904-829-0755. Ed. H. Carl Hoefer, Jr. circ. 275. (looseleaf format; back issues avail.) **Document type:** academic/scholarly publication.
    Description: Agricultural research on yield enhancement and earliness of vegetable crops and flowers through the use of agricultural plastic products.

ANNUAL BOOK OF A S T M STANDARDS. VOLUME 04.09. WOOD. see *ENGINEERING — Engineering Mechanics And Materials*

ANNUAL BOOK OF A S T M STANDARDS. VOLUME 08.01. PLASTICS (1): C 177 TO D 1600. see *ENGINEERING — Engineering Mechanics And Materials*

ANNUAL BOOK OF A S T M STANDARDS. VOLUME 08.02. PLASTICS (2): D 1601 TO D 3099. see *ENGINEERING — Engineering Mechanics And Materials*

ANNUAL BOOK OF A S T M STANDARDS. VOLUME 08.04. PLASTIC PIPE AND BUILDING PRODUCTS. see *ENGINEERING — Engineering Mechanics And Materials*

668.4   BL
ANUARIO BRASILEIRO DO PLASTICO. a. Editora Quimica e Derivados Ltda., Rua Dr. Gabriel dos Santos, 55, Santa Cecilia, CEP 01231-900 Sao Paulo, SP, Brazil. TEL 55-11-826-6899.
FAX 55-11-825-8192. TELEX 11-21801. Ed. Emanoel Fairbanks.

668.4   MX
ANUARIO LATINOAMERICANO DE LOS PLASTICOS. 1973. a. $25. Anuarios Latinoamericanos, S.A. de C.V., Colima No. 436, Piso 2, Mexico 7, DF, Mexico. Ed. Roberto J. Marquez. adv. circ. 7,000.
    Formerly: Directorio Nacional de la Industria de los Plasticos y Proveedores (Year).

668.4   UK   ISSN 0966-1867
ASIAN PLASTICS NEWS. 1988. q. $85. E M A P Maclaren Ltd., 19 Scarbrook Rd., Croydon, Surrey CR9 1QH, England. TEL 0181-688-7788.
FAX 0181-668-8375. Ed. Philippa Hutchinson. adv.; circ. 9,877. (back issues avail.) **Indexed:** Intl.Polym.Sci.& Tech., RAPRA.
    Description: Focuses on the processing technology, raw materials and machinery hardware used in Asia and often sourced in Europe.

ASSOCIATION FRANCAISE DES INGENIEURS ET CADRES DU CAOUTCHOUC ET DES PLASTIQUES. ANNUAIRE. see *RUBBER*

BAUEN MIT KUNSTSTOFFEN. see *BUILDING AND CONSTRUCTION*

PLASTICS

BIOMEDICAL MATERIALS; an international newsletter. see *MEDICAL SCIENCES*

668.4 678.2 UK ISSN 0307-6164
HD9661.G7
BRITISH PLASTICS AND RUBBER MAGAZINE. 1977. m. £90 (effective Jan. 1994). M C M Publishing Ltd., 37 Nelson Rd., Caterham, Surrey CR3 5PP, England. Ed. Ken Grace. adv.; bk.rev.; charts; illus.; tr.lit. circ. 12,239. Indexed: Br.Tech.Ind., Cadscan, Excerp.Med., INIS Atomind., Int.Packag.Abstr., Intl.Polym.Sci.& Tech., Key to Econ.Sci., Lead Abstr., PROMT, RAPRA, Text.Tech.Dig., Zincscan. **Document type**: trade publication.
—BLDSC (2337.300000); Ei; SWETS. **CCC**.
Incorporates: Polymer Age.
Description: For managers in polymer processing companies.

BUSINESS RATIO REPORT: PLASTICS PACKAGING; an industry sector analysis. see *PACKAGING*

668.4 658.8 UK ISSN 0261-9393
BUSINESS RATIO REPORT: PLASTICS PROCESSORS; an industry sector analysis. 1974. a. I C C Business Ratios Ltd., Freepost, Field House, Hampton, Mddx. TW1 1BR, England. TEL 081-783-0977. FAX 081-783-1940. charts; stat. **Document type**: trade publication.
—BLDSC (6536.990000).

668.4 CN ISSN 0008-4778
CODEN: CNPLAJ
CANADIAN PLASTICS. 1943. 8/yr. Can.$48.15($55) (foreign $85). Southam Magazine Group, 1450 Don Mills Rd., Don Mills, ON M3B 2X7, Canada. TEL 416-445-6641. FAX 416-442-2213. Ed. Michael Shelley. adv.: B&W page $2600, color page $3695; adv. contact: Marlene Dempster. bk.rev.; charts; illus.; stat.; tr.lit. circ. 10,170. (also avail. in microfilm from PMC) Indexed: Can.B.P.I., Can.Per.Ind., Chem.Abstr., Intl.Polym.Sci.& Tech., Key to Econ.Sci., PROMT, RAPRA.
—BLDSC (3044.000000); CASDDS; Faxon; SWETS; UMI. **CCC**.
Description: Provides plastics processors and end users with information on developments in plastics markets and technology, as they affect Canada.

668.4 CN ISSN 0068-9459
CANADIAN PLASTICS DIRECTORY AND BUYER'S GUIDE. 1959. a. Can.$69.55 (foreign $65). Southam Magazine Group, 1450 Don Mills Rd., Don Mills, ON M3B 2X7, Canada. TEL 416-445-6641. FAX 416-442-2261. Ed. Michael Shelley. **Document type**: directory, trade publication.
Description: Lists processors and products, suppliers of raw material, machinery and equipment, mold, tool and die makers, services and associations.

CAOUTCHOUCS ET PLASTIQUES; l'information economique et technique de la profession. see *RUBBER*

668.4 677 UK ISSN 0268-0491
CARBON & HIGH PERFORMANCE FIBRES DIRECTORY AND DATABOOK. 1981. biennial. £85($104.95) (paperback edition). Chapman & Hall, 2-6 Boundary Row, London SE1 8HN, England. TEL 0171-865-0066. FAX 0171-522-9623. TELEX 290164 CHAPMA G. E-mail: journal@chall.mhs.compuserve.com. (Dist. by: International Thomson Publishing Services Ltd., Cheriton House, North Way, Andover, Hants., SP10 5BE, England. TEL 01264-342713. FAX 01264-342807; N. American orders to: Chapman & Hall, One Penn Plaza, 41st Fl., New York, NY 10019. TEL 212-564-1060. FAX 212-564-1505) adv. (back issues avail.) **Document type**: directory.

668.4 US
CARD MANUFACTURERS. 1990. bi-m. $110. (International Card Manufacturers Association) C M A Publications, Creative Marketing Alliance, Inc., 40 Washington Rd., Princeton Junction, NJ 08550. TEL 609-799-4900. FAX 609-799-7032. Ed. Mary Kay Metcalf. illus.; tr.lit. circ. 1,000. **Document type**: trade publication.
Formerly: Transaction Times.
Description: Supports, promotes and encourages the success and growth of companies and organizations that participate in the plastic card industry - including manufacturers, industry suppliers and service providers.

668.4 660.284 UK ISSN 0262-4893
TP1183.F6 CODEN: CELPDJ
CELLULAR POLYMERS. 1982. 6/yr. £220 (foreign £240). R A P R A Technology Ltd., Shawbury, Shrewsbury, Shrops. SY4 4NR, England. TEL 01939-250383. FAX 01939-251118. TELEX 35134. Ed. J.M. Buist. adv.; bk.rev.; illus. (back issues avail.) Indexed: Curr.Cont., Intl.Polym.Sci.& Tech., RAPRA, Sci.Cit.Ind. **Document type**: academic/scholarly publication.
—BLDSC (3097.935000); CASDDS; Ei; Faxon; SWETS.
Description: Covers developments over the full range of foam polymers, from elastomeric material to rigid plastics. Papers are included on the polymers, additives and manufacturing processes used in the industry and on the properties and applications of the finished products.
Refereed Serial

CHEMICALS & POLYMERS NEWS. see *PETROLEUM AND GAS*

668.4 HK ISSN 1021-1330
CHINA PLASTIC AND RUBBER JOURNAL/ZHONGGUO CUOLIAO XIANGJIAO; a plastic and rubber journal for P.R. China. (Text in Chinese; table of content in Chinese, English) 1982. q. HK.$194($45) for Asia; elsewhere $50. (Ministry of Light Industry, Institute of Plastics Processing and Application, CC) Adsale Publishing Company, 14-F, Devon House, Taikoo Place, 979 King's Rd., Quarry Bay, Hong Kong. TEL 852-2811-8897. FAX 852-2516-5119. (Subscr. to: P.O. Box 20032, Hennessy Rd., Hong Kong) Ed. Alfred Wong. adv. circ. 16,500. (back issues avail.)
Description: Information on foreign advanced technology and market trends in the plastic and rubber industries for readers in the PRC.

668.4 UK
COMPOSITE CONGRESS PAPERS. 1958. biennial. £120. British Plastics Federation, 6 Bath Pl., Rivington St., London EC2A 3JE, England. TEL 0171-457-5000. FAX 0171-457-5045. circ. 1,000. **Document type**: trade publication.
Former titles: Reinforced Plastics Congress (ISSN 0306-3607) & International Reinforced Plastics Conference. Papers and Proceedings. (ISSN 0074-7661)

668.4 678.2 FR ISSN 0754-0876
CODEN: PRFTDV
COMPOSITES. 1963. 6/yr. 2850 F. 65 rue de Prony, 75854 Paris Cedex 17, France. TEL 44-01-1642. FAX 47-63-57-39. TELEX 641 636 F INPLAST. Ed. J. Marechal. circ. 4,000.
—BLDSC (3365.510000); CASDDS.
Formerly (until 1983): Plastiques Renforces, Fibres de Verre Textile (ISSN 0240-9917)

668.4 US ISSN 0888-1227
THE COMPOSITES AND ADHESIVES NEWSLETTER. 1984. q. $150 (foreign $170). T - C Press (Subsidiary of: Technology Conferences), Box 36006, Los Angeles, CA 90036-0006. TEL 213-938-6923. Ed. George Epstein. adv. contact: Irene Stone. bk.rev.; circ. 150 (paid). (back issues avail.) Indexed: Intl.Polym.Sci.& Tech., RAPRA. **Document type**: newsletter.
●Also available online. Vendor(s): Data-Star, Knight-Ridder, Inc..
—BLDSC (3365.515000). **CCC**.
Description: Covers composite and adhesive materials. Includes information on new applications, alerts or problems to avoid, technology developments, as well as industry news about companies, schools, and professional societies.

668.4 US
COMPOSITES FABRICATION. 1986. m. $36 (effective until Spr. 1995). Composites Fabricators Association, 1735 N. Lynn St., Ste. 950, Arlington, VA 22209-2022. TEL 703-524-3332. FAX 703-524-2303. Ed. Nola Kende. adv.: B&W page $990, color page $1720; trim 8 1/2 x 11; adv. contact: Karin Brandvold. circ. 5,000. **Document type**: trade publication.
Formerly (until May 1994): Fabrication News.

668.4 GW ISSN 0936-0352
DEUTSCHES KUNSTSTOFF-INSTITUT. MITTEILUNGEN. 1964. s-a. free. Deutsches Kunststoff-Institut, Schlossgartenstr. 6, 64289 Darmstadt, Germany. TEL 06151-162105. FAX 06151-292855. **Document type**: newsletter.
Description: Research results and coming events at the German Plastics Institute.

DIRECTORY OF U S AND CANADIAN SCRAP PLASTICS PROCESSORS AND BUYERS. see *BUSINESS AND ECONOMICS — Trade And Industrial Directories*

E P E. (European Production Engineering) see *ENGINEERING — Mechanical Engineering*

668.4 UK ISSN 0952-6900
TP1101 CODEN: ENPLEB
ENGINEERING PLASTICS. 1974. bi-m. £220 (foreign £240). R A P R A Technology Ltd., Shawbury, Shrewsbury, Shrops. SY4 4NR, England. TEL 01939-250383. FAX 01939-251118. TELEX 35134. Ed. Tony Whelan. Indexed: Intl.Polym.Sci.& Tech., RAPRA. **Document type**: academic/scholarly publication.
—BLDSC (3766.329000); Ei; Faxon; Genuine Article; SWETS.
Description: Emphasis on practical information on the materials, properties, processing and application of engineering polymers.
Refereed Serial

ENVIRONEWS. see *ENVIRONMENTAL STUDIES*

668.4 678.2 US
EPIC INNOVATOR. 1988. q. $1.50 (effective through 1996). Edison Polymer Innovation Corporation, 10235 Brecksville Rd., Ste. 100, Cleveland, OH 44141-3207. TEL 216-838-5015. FAX 216-838-1567. Ed. J. James Asbeck. circ. 9,000. **Document type**: newsletter.
Description: Covers research and development on plastics, rubber, coating and adhesives, materials, products and processes.

668.4 GW
EUROPAEISCHER WIRTSCHAFTSDIENST. KUNSTSTOFF-DIENST. 1926. w. DM.780. E U W I D - Europaeischer Wirtschaftsdienst GmbH, Bleichstr. 20-22, 76593 Gernsbach, Germany. TEL 07224-9397-0. FAX 07224-939750. TELEX 78915-DBV-D. Ed. Monika Bender. circ. 1,080. **Document type**: trade publication.

668.4 UK ISSN 0959-3861
EUROPEAN PLASTICS DIRECTORY. 1989. a. £80 (foreign £90). R A P R A Technology Ltd., Shawbury, Shrewsbury, Shropshire SY4 4NR, England. TEL 01939-250383. FAX 01939-251118. **Document type**: directory.

668.4 UK ISSN 0306-3534
TP1101 CODEN: EUPNBT
EUROPEAN PLASTICS NEWS. 1929. m. $170. E M A P Maclaren Ltd., 19 Scarbrook Rd., Croydon, Surrey CR9 1HQ, England. TEL 0181-688-7788. FAX 0181-688-8375. Ed. Kevin O'Toole. adv.; bk.rev.; charts; illus.; tr.mk.; circ. 24,051 (controlled). (also avail. in microform from UMI,PMC; back issues avail.; reprint service avail. from UMI) Indexed: A.S.& T.Ind., BMT, Br.Ceram.Abstr., Br.Tech.Ind., C.I.S. Abstr., Cadscan, Chem.Abstr., Eng.Ind., Int.Packag.Abstr., Intl.Polym.Sci.& Tech., Key to Econ.Sci., Lead Abstr., Packag.Sci.Tech., RAPRA, Zincscan. **Document type**: trade publication.
—BLDSC (3829.787000); CASDDS; Ei; Genuine Article; SWETS; UMI; UnCover.
Formerly: Europlastics; **Incorporates**: British Plastics (ISSN 0007-1625)
Description: Coverage of developments and events within Europe's plastics industry.

FIRE & FLAMMABILITY BULLETIN; an international newsletter. see *FIRE PREVENTION*

FOOD, COSMETICS AND DRUGS PACKAGING; an international newsletter. see *PACKAGING*

668.4 FR ISSN 0985-0503
TA418.9.C6
FRANCE COMPOSITES. (Text in English, French, German) 1988. a. 286 F. C E P P Publications, 25 Rue Dagorno, 75012 Paris, France. TEL 43-47-30-20. FAX 43-46-58-18. Ed.Bd. adv.; bk.rev. circ. 10,000.
Description: Contains important working tools for entreprises dealing with composites materials.

668.4 FR ISSN 0071-9056
FRANCE PLASTIQUES. 1949. a. 610 F. C E P P Publications, 25 Rue Dagorno, 75012 Paris, France. TEL 43-47-30-20. FAX 43-46-58-18. Ed. Martine Clavel. adv. circ. 5,000.

5274 PLASTICS

668.4   GW
GENAU. m. Bundesverband des Holz- und Kunstoffverarbeitende Industrie, Abraham-Lincoln-Str. 32, 65189 Wiesbaden, Germany.

668.4   JA   ISSN 0387-0936
CODEN: GOSJBC
GOSEI JUSHI/PLASTICS. (Text in Japanese) 1947. m. 12875 Yen. Nihon Gosei Jushi Gijutsu Kyokai - Japan Society of Plastics Technology, 10-18 Ginza 2-chome, Chuo-ku, Tokyo 104, Japan. TEL 81-3-3542-0261. FAX 81-3-3543-0619.
—BLDSC (6531.008000); CASDDS.

668.4   MX
GUIA DE LA INDUSTRIA: HULE, PLASTICOS Y RESINAS/RUBBER, PLASTICS AND RESINS GUIDE. (Text in English, Spanish) 1964. a. $80. Informatica Cosmos, S.A. de C.V., Calz. del Hueso 334-A1, Col. Ex-Hacienda Coapa, 14300 Mexico D.F., Mexico. TEL 525-677-4868. FAX 525-679-35-75. (Schnell Publishing Company, Inc.. TEL 212-248-4177. FAX 212-248-4903) Ed. Raul Macazaga. adv.: B&W page $1000; trim 211 x 274; adv. contact: Mary Christen. circ. 5,000. **Document type:** directory.
Former titles: Hule, Plasticos y Resinas (Annual); Plasticos y Resinas (Annual).
Description: Lists over 1200 suppliers of raw materials, machinery and services. Lists 2400 products, services and materials. Indexes 1300 rubber and plastics items manufacturers in the country.

668.4   AG
GUIA DEL PLASTICO. 1952. 6/yr. Camara Argentina de la Industria Plastica, Jeronimo Salguero 1939, 1425 Buenos Aires, Argentina. TEL 826-5480. circ. 5,000.

668.4   SZ   ISSN 0073-0084
HANDBUCH DER INTERNATIONALEN KUNSTSTOFFINDUSTRIE/INTERNATIONAL PLASTICS DIRECTORY/MANUEL INTERNATIONAL DES PLASTIQUES. (Text and index in English, French and German) 1958. every 10 yrs. 300 SFr. Verlag fuer Internationale Wirtschaftsliteratur GmbH, Box 30, CH-8047 Zurich, Switzerland. FAX 01-4010545. Ed. Walter Hirt. index.

668.4   UK
HIGH FREQUENCY WELDER. 1987. bi-m. membership. Federation of High Frequency Welders, 66 East St., Ashburton, Devon TQ13 7AX, England. TEL 01803-873599. FAX 01803-873167. Ed. Alison Ainsworth. adv. contact: Alison Ainsworth. circ. 1,500. **Document type:** trade publication.
Description: Covers all aspects of high-frequency welding and other relevant information.

668.4   US
HIGH-PERFORMANCE COMPOSITE; design and manufacturing solutions for industry. 1993. bi-m. free to qualified personnel. 1900 Wazee St., Ste. 309, Denver, CO 80202. TEL 303-292-4080. FAX 302-292-4181. Ed. Judith Hazen. circ. controlled. **Document type:** trade publication.

668.4   UK   ISSN 0264-7753
HIGH PERFORMANCE PLASTICS; an international bulletin. 1983. m. £298($474) (effective 1996). (Rubber and Plastics Research Association of Great Britain) Elsevier Science Ltd., P.O. Box 800, Kidlington, Oxford OX5 1DX, England. TEL 44-1865-843000. FAX 44-1865-843010. E-mail: nlinfo-f@elsevier.nl; usinfo-f@elsevier.com; forinfo-kyf04035@niftyserve.or.jp; Site avail.: http://www.elsevier.nl/. (Subscr. in U.S. and Canada to: Elsevier Science, 660 White Plains Rd., Tarrytown, NY 10591-5153. TEL 914-524-9200. FAX 914-333-2444) Ed. I. Guy. bk.rev.; illus.; stat. (back issues avail.) **Indexed:** Intl.Polym.Sci.& Tech., RAPRA. **Document type:** trade publication, bulletin, newsletter.
●Also available online. Vendor(s): Data-Star, Knight-Ridder, Inc..
—BLDSC (4307.338650); SWETS. **CCC.**

668.4   II
HINDUSTAN LATEX. VARSHIKA RIPORTA/HINDUSTAN LATEX. ANNUAL REPORTS. (Text in English, Hindi) 11th ed., 1976. a. Varikkat House, TC 4-485, Kowdiar, Trivandrum 695003, India. stat.

HULE MEXICANO Y PLASTICOS; revista tecnica industrial. see *RUBBER*

668.4   UK
I A L PLASTICS YEARBOOK. 1987. irreg., latest 1993. £150. I A L Consultants, 314-316 Harbour Yard, Chelsea Harbour, London SW10 0XD, England. TEL 0171-376-3676. FAX 0171-376-8281.
Document type: trade publication.
Formerly: Plastics Euro-Guide.
Description: Presents statistics and information about West European plastic raw materials manufacturers and markets.

668.4   US
I A P D MAGAZINE; the voice of plastics distribution. (Former name of issuing body: National Association of Plastics Distributors) 1986. bi-m. $50 to non-members. International Association of Plastics Distributors, 4707 College Blvd., Ste. 105, Leawood, KS 66211-1611. TEL 913-345-1005. FAX 913-345-1006. Ed. Carol Wagner. adv.: B&W page $2490; adv. contact: Janet Thill. circ. 8,000.
Document type: trade publication.
Formerly: N A P D Magazine.

I E E E CONFERENCE OF ELECTRICAL ENGINEERING PROBLEMS IN THE RUBBER AND PLASTICS INDUSTRIES. CONFERENCE RECORD. see *RUBBER*

668.4   UK   ISSN 0261-5487
I R P I: INTERNATIONAL REINFORCED PLASTICS INDUSTRY. 1981. bi-m. £12($60) Channel Publications, Loudwater House, London Rd., Loudwater, High Wycombe HP10 9TL, England. TEL 44-494-436111. Ed. D. Pamington. adv.: B&W page $1404, color page $1854; trim 8 1/2 x 11 5/8. bk.rev.; illus. circ. 6,442.
—BLDSC (4545.805000).

INDIAN RUBBER & PLASTICS AGE. see *RUBBER*

INFORMATIONS DU CAOUTCHOUC ET DES PLASTIQUES. see *RUBBER*

668.4 678   FR
INFORMATIONS OFFICIELLE DES PLASTIQUES ET DU CAOUTCHOUC. 3/yr. 32 rue Saint-Marc, 75002 Paris, France. TEL 42-60-83-92. FAX 46-28-36-10. TELEX 220 064. circ. 4,900.

668.4   US   ISSN 1071-362X
INJECTION MOLDING. 1993. m. free to qualified personnel. 3400 E. Bayaud Ave., Ste. 230, Denver, CO 80209. TEL 303-321-2322. FAX 303-321-3552. Ed. Suzy Witzler; Pub. T. Peter Sullivan. circ. 35,000 (controlled). **Document type:** trade publication.

INTERNATIONAL BOTTLER AND PACKER. see *BEVERAGES*

668.4   UK   ISSN 0143-7496
CODEN: IJAADK
INTERNATIONAL JOURNAL OF ADHESION AND ADHESIVES. 1980. q. £260($414) (effective 1996). Butterworth - Heinemann, Part of the Reed Elsevier group, Linacre House, Jordan Hill, Oxford OX2 8DP, England. TEL 01865-310366. FAX 01865-310898. TELEX 83111 BHPOXF G. (Subscr. to: Elsevier Science Ltd., P.O. Box 800, Kidlington, Oxford OX5 1DX, England. TEL 44-1865-846000. FAX 44-1865-843010; Subscr. in U.S. and Canada to: Elsevier Science, 660 White Plains Rd., Tarrytown, NY 10591-5153. TEL 914-5524-9200. FAX 914-333-2444) Ed. Diane Cogan. adv.; bk.rev.; abstr.; bibl.; charts; illus.; stat.; index. (also avail. in microform from UMI; back issues avail.) **Indexed:** Abstr.Bull.Inst.Pap.Chem., Appl.Mech.Rev., Chem.Abstr., Eng.Ind., HRIS, Int.Aerosp.Abstr., Int.Packag.Abstr., Intl.Polym.Sci.& Tech., Met.Abstr., RAPRA, World Alum.Abstr., World Surf.Coat. **Document type:** academic/scholarly publication.
—BLDSC (4541.560000); CASDDS; Ei; Faxon; Genuine Article; SWETS; UMI; UnCover. **CCC.**
Description: Covers design of joints, stress analysis, surface preparation, dynamic properties, manufacturing technology, and industrial and academic developments in sealants and adhesives.
Refereed Serial

668.4   II
INTERNATIONAL PLASTICS ENGINEERING & TECHNOLOGY. s-a. $50. New Age International Pvt. Ltd., Journals Division, 4835-24, Ansari Rd., Daryaganj, New Delhi 110 002, India. TEL 91-11-3267996. FAX 91-11-3267437.

668.4   GW   ISSN 0930-777X
TP1080   CODEN: IPPREJ
INTERNATIONAL POLYMER PROCESSING. (Text in English) 1986. q. DM.396.80. (Polymer Processing Society) Carl Hanser Verlag, Kolbergerstr. 22, 81679 Munich, Germany. TEL 089-998300. FAX 089-984809. (Subscr. to: Postfach 860420, 81631 Munich, Germany) Ed.Bd. adv.; bk.rev.; charts; illus. circ. 2,000. **Indexed:** Intl.Polym.Sci.& Tech., RAPRA. **Document type:** trade publication.
—BLDSC (4544.965800); CASDDS; Ei; Faxon; Genuine Article; SWETS. **CCC.**
Description: Publishes articles on the science of processing thermoplastics, thermosets, elastomers and fibers.

668.4 540   UK   ISSN 0307-174X
QD380
INTERNATIONAL POLYMER SCIENCE AND TECHNOLOGY. 1974. m. £750 (foreign £750). R A P R A Technology Ltd., Shawbury, Shrewsbury, Shrops. SY4 4NR, England. TEL 01939-250383. FAX 01939-251118. TELEX 35134. abstr. circ. 350. (back issues avail.) **Indexed:** Art & Archaeol.Tech.Abstr., Excerp.Med., Fluidex, Intl.Polym.Sci.& Tech., RAPRA, World Surf.Coat. **Document type:** academic/scholarly publication.
—BLDSC (4544.965900); Ei; SWETS; UnCover.
Description: Contains English translations of papers selected from eight foreign rubber and plastics journals, primarily Russian, Japanese, Hungarian and Czech.

668.4   II   ISSN 0047-0899
INTERNATIONAL PRESS CUTTING SERVICE: MODERN PLASTICS AND ENGINEERING. 1967. w. $65. International Press Cutting Service, Box 63, Allahabad 211001, India. Ed. N. Khanna. bk.rev.; index. circ. 1,200. (processed)

668.4 547   US   ISSN 0147-0671
TP1180.P8   CODEN: IPURD9
INTERNATIONAL PROGRESS IN URETHANES. 1977. irreg. price varies. Technomic Publishing Co., Inc., 851 New Holland Ave., Box 3535, Lancaster, PA 17604. TEL 717-291-5609. FAX 717-295-4538. TELEX 230 753656 (TECHNOMIC UD). Ed.Bd. **Indexed:** Chem.Abstr. **Document type:** monographic series.
—BLDSC (4544.990000); CASDDS; Ei. **CCC.**
Refereed Serial

668.4   UK   ISSN 1352-2248
INTERNATIONAL STATUS REPORT ON PLASTICS INDUSTRY WORLDWIDE. a. £75. British Plastics Federation, 6 Bath Pl., Rivington St., London EC2A 3JE, England. TEL 0171-457-5000. FAX 0171-457-5045. **Document type:** trade publication.

668.4   IT   ISSN 0392-3800
CODEN: INPLDK
INTERPLASTICS. 1978. bi-m. L.50000 (foreign L.150000) (effective 1995). Tecniche Nuove s.p.a., Via C. Menotti 14, 20129 Milan, Italy. TEL 02-75701. FAX 02-7610351. adv.: B&W page L.1620000, color page L.2490000; trim 185 x 266. circ. 6,373.
Description: Essays for those in the plastics field.

668.4   IT
ITALIAN PLASTICS QUALITY TRADE. 2/yr. C I D A Editrice Stampa Periodica, Viale Certosa 238, 20156 Milan, Italy. TEL 2-30-85-141. FAX 2-308-8503. Ed. Franco Pigozzi.

668.4   SZ
JAHRBUCH KUNSTSTOFFE: SYNTHETICS; Jahrbuch fuer Herstellung, Verarbeitung und Anwendung von Kunststoffen und neuen Werkstoffen. (Text in German) 1965. a. 25 SFr. Vogt-Schild AG, Zuchwilerstr. 21, CH-4501 Solothurn 1, Switzerland. TEL 065-247247. FAX 065-247235. Eds. Alfred Widmer, Marianne Flury. adv.: B&W page 2340 SFr., color page 3440 SFr.; trim 185 x 260; adv. contact: Hansruedi Spiri. bk.rev. circ. 6,000. (tabloid format) **Document type:** trade publication.
Formerly: Jahrbuch Kunststoffe: Plastics.

PLASTICS

668.4   JA   ISSN 0021-4582
TP986.A1   CODEN: JPLAAN
JAPAN PLASTICS AGE. (Includes Japan Plastics Industry Annual) (Text in English) 1963. bi-m. 13000 Yen($60) Plastics Age Co. Ltd., Okochi Bldg., 1-10-6 Kaji-cho, Chiyoda-ku, Tokyo 101, Japan. Ed. Eiichi Asayama. circ. 23,000. (also avail. in microform from UMI; reprint service avail. from UMI) **Indexed:** Chem.Abstr., JTA, PROMT.
—CASDDS; UMI.

JOURNAL OF ADHESION. see *PHYSICS*

668.4   NE   ISSN 0169-4243
TP967   CODEN: JATEE8
JOURNAL OF ADHESION SCIENCE AND TECHNOLOGY. (Text in English) 1987. m. DM.1370 (effective 1996). V S P, P.O. Box 346, 3700 AH Zeist, Netherlands. TEL 31-30-6925790. FAX 31-30-6932081. E-mail: 100341.2372@compuserve.com. Eds. K.L Mittal, W.J. Van Ooij. adv.; bk.rev.; index. (back issues avail.) **Indexed:** INSPEC (1988-), Intl.Polym.Sci.& Tech., RAPRA. **Document type:** academic/scholarly publication.
—BLDSC (4918.936000); CASDDS; Ei; Faxon; SWETS; UnCover.
Description: Covers theoretical and basic aspects of adhesion science and its applications in all areas of technology.
Refereed Serial

668.4   US   ISSN 0885-3282
R856.A1   CODEN: JBAPEL
JOURNAL OF BIOMATERIALS APPLICATIONS. 1986. q. $285. Technomic Publishing Co., Inc., 851 New Holland Ave, Box 3535, Lancaster, PA 17604. TEL 717-291-5609. FAX 717-295-4538. TELEX 230-753565 (TECHNOMIC UD). Ed. Michael Szycher. circ. 175. (back issues avail.) **Document type:** academic/scholarly publication.
—BLDSC (4953.515000); CASDDS; Ei; Faxon; Genuine Article; SWETS; UMI. **CCC.**
Refereed Serial

668.44   US   ISSN 0021-955X
TP1183.F6   CODEN: JCUPAM
JOURNAL OF CELLULAR PLASTICS. 1965. bi-m. $185. Technomic Publishing Co., Inc., 851 New Holland Ave., Box 3535, Lancaster, PA 17604. TEL 717-291-5609. FAX 717-295-4538. TELEX 230-753565 (TECHNOMIC UD). Ed. Sidney H. Metzger, Jr. adv.; bk.rev.; charts; illus.; pat.; stat.; index. circ. 500. (also avail. in microform from UMI; reprint service avail. from UMI) **Indexed:** Appl.Mech.Rev., Chem.Abstr., Eng.Ind., Int.Packag.Abstr., Intl.Polym.Sci.& Tech., RAPRA. **Document type:** academic/scholarly publication.
—BLDSC (4955.050000); CASDDS; Ei; Faxon; Genuine Article; SWETS; UMI; UnCover. **CCC.**
Refereed Serial

JOURNAL OF COATED FABRICS. see *TEXTILE INDUSTRIES AND FABRICS*

668.4   US   ISSN 0095-2443
TA455.P5   CODEN: JEPLAX
JOURNAL OF ELASTOMERS AND PLASTICS. 1969. q. $215. Technomic Publishing Co. Inc., 851 New Holland Ave., Box 3535, Lancaster, PA 17604. TEL 717-291-5609. FAX 717-295-4538. TELEX 230 753565 (TECHNOMIC UD). Ed. H.A. Aglan. adv.; bk.rev.; charts; stat.; index. circ. 350. (also avail. in microform from UMI; reprint service avail. from UMI) **Indexed:** Appl.Mech.Rev., Chem.Abstr., Curr.Cont., Eng.Ind., Intl.Polym.Sci.& Tech., RAPRA. **Document type:** academic/scholarly publication.
—BLDSC (4973.289000); CASDDS; Ei; Faxon; Genuine Article; SWETS; UMI; UnCover. **CCC.**
Formerly: Journal of Elastoplastics. (ISSN 0022-071X)
Refereed Serial

668.4   US   ISSN 8756-0879
    CODEN: JPFSEH
JOURNAL OF PLASTIC FILM AND SHEETING. 1985. q. $280. Technomic Publishing Co., Inc., 851 New Holland Ave., Box 3535, Lancaster, PA 07604. TEL 717-291-5609. FAX 717-295-4538. TELEX 230 753565 (TECHNOMIC UD). Ed. James P. Harrington. abstr.; bibl.; illus. circ. 400. **Indexed:** Intl.Polym.Sci.& Tech., RAPRA. **Document type:** academic/scholarly publication.
—BLDSC (5040.695000); CASDDS; Ei; Faxon; Genuine Article; SWETS; UMI. **CCC.**

JOURNAL OF REINFORCED PLASTICS & COMPOSITES. see *ENGINEERING — Engineering Mechanics And Materials*

668.4   US   ISSN 0892-7057
TA418.9.C6   CODEN: JTMAEQ
JOURNAL OF THERMOPLASTIC COMPOSITE MATERIALS. 1988. q. $240. Technomic Publishing Co., Inc., 851 New Holland Ave., Box 3535, Lancaster, PA 17604. TEL 717-291-5609. FAX 717-295-4538. TELEX 230 753565 (TECHNOMIC UD). Ed. John W. Gillespie. index. circ. 300. (back issues avail.) **Indexed:** Intl.Polym.Sci.& Tech., RAPRA. **Document type:** academic/scholarly publication.
—BLDSC (5069.099400); CASDDS; Ei; Faxon; Genuine Article; SWETS; UMI; UnCover. **CCC.**
Refereed Serial

668.4   US   ISSN 0193-7197
TP1180.V48   CODEN: JVTEDI
JOURNAL OF VINYL TECHNOLOGY. 1979. q. $125 (foreign $140). Society of Plastics Engineers, Inc., 14 Fairfield Dr., Brookfield, CT 06804-0403. TEL 203-775-0471. FAX 203-775-8490. TELEX 643-712. Ed. Robert P. Braddicks, Jr. charts; illus.; index. circ. 535. (back issues avail.) **Indexed:** Intl.Polym.Sci.& Tech., RAPRA. **Document type:** academic/scholarly publication.
—CASDDS; Ei; Faxon; Genuine Article; UMI; UnCover. **CCC.**
Refereed Serial

668.4   GW   ISSN 0451-1646
K MITTEILUNGEN. 1950. m. membership. Gesamtverband Kunststoffverarbeitende Industrie e.V., Froschgfort 16, 56410 Montabaur, Germany. FAX 02602-4308. Ed. Reinhard Ackermann. adv.; bk.rev.; abstr.; bibl.; stat.; circ. controlled. **Document type:** newsletter.

668.4   GW   ISSN 0177-0608
K: PLASTIC UND KAUTSCHUK ZEITUNG. 1969. fortn. DM.129. Giesel Verlag fuer Publizitaet GmbH, Stuttgarterstr. 18-24, 60329 Frankfurt a.M., Germany. TEL 069-2600-0. FAX 069-2600609. Ed. H. Rupprecht. adv.; bk.rev.; illus.; stat.; index. circ. 16,000. **Document type:** trade publication.

668.4 658.8   UK
KEY NOTE REPORT: PLASTICS PROCESSING. Variant title: Plastics Processing. 3rd ed., 1987. irreg. £185. Key Note Publications Ltd., Field House, 72 Oldfield Rd., Hampton, Middlesex TW12 2HQ, England. TEL 0181-783-0755. FAX 0181-783-1720. **Document type:** trade publication.
●Also available online.
Also available on CD-ROM.
Description: Overview of the plastics processing industry including industry structure, market size and trends, and processing techniques.

668.4   RU   ISSN 0023-1118
    CODEN: KVLKA4
KHIMICHESKIE VOLOKNA. 1959. bi-m. $85 (effective 1996). Izdatel'stvo Khimiya, Novaya Pl. 10, Moscow K-12, Russia. bk.rev.; bibl.; index. **Indexed:** Abstr.Bull.Inst.Pap.Chem., Chem.Abstr, INIS Atomind., Text.Tech.Dig., World Text.Abstr.
—BLDSC (0393.300000); CASDDS.

668.4 540   GW   ISSN 0943-1454
TP967   CODEN: ADHAES
KLEBEN & DICHTEN; Klebstoffe, Dichtstoffe, Geraete- und Anlagentechnik, Anwendungen. 1957. 10/yr. DM.320 (effective 1996). Friedr. Vieweg und Sohn Verlagsgesellschaft mbH, Postfach 1546, 65005 Wiesbaden, Germany. TEL 0611-534389. FAX 0611-534430. Ed. Traude Wuest. adv.; bk.rev.; abstr.; bibl.; charts; illus.; mkt.; pat.; index. circ. 4,700. **Indexed:** Abstr.Bull.Inst.Pap.Chem., Art & Archaeol.Tech.Abstr., Chem.Abstr., Curr.Leather Lit., Eng.Ind., Excerp.Med., INIS Atomind., Int.Packag.Abstr., Intl.Polym.Sci.& Tech., Packag.Sci.Tech., RAPRA, World Surf.Coat. **Document type:** trade publication.
—CASDDS; Ei; SWETS. **CCC.**
Formerly: Adhaesion (ISSN 0001-8198)

KLOECKNER WERKE HEUTE: Maschinenbau, Kunststoff Verarbeitung. see *METALLURGY*

KOMPASS PROFESSIONNEL. CHIMIE, PLASTIQUES, CAOUTCHOUC, PRODUITS MINERAUX. see *BUSINESS AND ECONOMICS — Trade And Industrial Directories*

KOMPASS SELECT EXPORT. RUBBER INDUSTRY, PLASTICS INDUSTRY. see *RUBBER*

668.4   NE   ISSN 0167-9597
    CODEN: KRUBDV
KUNSTSTOF EN RUBBER; monthly review on plastics. 1948. m. fl.170. Kunststof en Rubber Instituut, Schoemakerstraat 97, Postbus 6031, 2600 JA Delft, Netherlands. Ed. J.L. Hey. adv.; bk.rev.; abstr.; charts; illus.; tr.lit. circ. 2,000. **Indexed:** Chem.Abstr., Eng.Ind., Excerp.Med., RAPRA.
—BLDSC (5130.795000); CASDDS; Ei; SWETS.
Formerly: Plastica (ISSN 0032-1095)

668.4   NE   ISSN 0925-5648
KUNSTSTOF MAGAZINE. m. fl.126 (effective 1992). (Nederlandse Federatie voor Kunstoffen - Netherlands Plastics Federation) Misset (Subsidiary of: Reed Elsevier plc), Postbus 4, 7000 BA Doetinchem, Netherlands. TEL 31-8340-49911. FAX 31-8340-43839. adv.: B&W page fl.2550; trim 215 x 285; adv. contact: Cor van Nek. illus. circ. 5,500. **Document type:** trade publication.

668.4   GW   ISSN 0075-7276
DIE KUNSTSTOFF-INDUSTRIE UND IHRE HELFER. 1952. a. $51. Industrieschau-Verlagsgesellschaft mbH, Postfach 100262, 64202 Darmstadt, Germany. TEL 06151-3892-0. FAX 06151-33164. (U.S. subscr. to: Western Hemisphere Publishing Corp., Box 847, Hillsboro, OR 97123-0847. TEL 503-640-3736. FAX 503-640-2748) Ed. Margit Selka. circ. 11,000. **Document type:** directory.
●Also available online.
Also available on CD-ROM.

668.4   GW   ISSN 0047-3766
TP1101   CODEN: KUNJD7
KUNSTSTOFF JOURNAL. 1967. 6/yr. DM.124 (Europe DM.142; overseas DM.172). Verlag Moderne Industrie, Justus-von-Liebig-Str. 1, 86899 Landsberg, Germany. TEL 08191-125-0. FAX 08191-125483. Ed. Wolfgang Kluigauf. adv.: B&W page DM.5160; trim 257 x 178; adv. contact: Claus Mayer. bk.rev. circ. 14,574. **Indexed:** Intl.Polym.Sci.& Tech., RAPRA. **Document type:** trade publication.
—**CCC.**

668.4   GW
KUNSTSTOFF-MAGAZIN; Kennziffer-Fachzeitschrift mit Elastomer-Forum und Recycling-Kolleg. (Text in English and German) 1962. 7/yr. free. Verlag Hoppenstedt GmbH, Havelstr. 9, 64295 Darmstadt, Germany. TEL 06151-380-0. FAX 06151-380-360. Ed. Siegfried Heimlich. adv. circ. 12,700. **Document type:** trade publication.
Former titles: Kunststoff-Magazin-Prodoc (ISSN 0941-8520); Prodoc-Kunststoff-Magazin (ISSN 0936-6113); Prodoc-Kunststoff-Technik (ISSN 0170-0820)

668.4   GW   ISSN 0941-0384
KUNSTSTOFF- UND KAUTSCHUK-PRODUKTE. 1982. a. DM.25. Verlag Hoppenstedt GmbH, Havelstr. 9, 64295 Darmstadt, Germany. TEL 06151-380-0. FAX 06151-38-360. Ed. Ingrid Bode. index. circ. 10,000. **Document type:** bulletin.
Formerly (until 1991): Kunststoff-Produkte (ISSN 0937-423X)

668.4   GW   ISSN 0172-6374
TP1101   CODEN: KUNSDY
KUNSTSTOFFBERATER. 1955. m. DM.151. Giesel Verlag fuer Publizitaet GmbH, Stuttgarterstr. 18-24, 60329 Frankfurt a.M., Germany. TEL 069-2600-0. FAX 069-2600609. Ed. H. Rupprecht. adv.; bk.rev.; illus.; mkt.; index. circ. 6,200. (also avail. in microform from UMI; reprint service avail. from UMI) **Indexed:** C.I.S. Abstr., Chem.Abstr., Excerp.Med., INSPEC, Int.Packag.Abstr., Intl.Polym.Sci.& Tech., Packag.Sci.Tech., PROMT, RAPRA. **Document type:** trade publication.
—CASDDS; SWETS; UMI. **CCC.**
Formerly: Kunststoffberater, -Rundschau, -Technik (ISSN 0340-8442); **Incorporates:** Kunststoff Rundschau (ISSN 0023-5555); Kunststofftechnik (ISSN 0023-5601)

PLASTICS

668.4   GW   ISSN 0023-5563
TP986.A1   CODEN: KUNSAV
KUNSTSTOFFE; Organ deutscher Kunststoff-Fachverbaende. English edition: Kunststoffe - Plast Europe (ISSN 0945-0084) 1911. m. DM.266.40. Carl Hanser Verlag, Kolbergerstr. 22, 81679 Munich, Germany. TEL 089-998300. FAX 089-984809. (Subscr. to: Postfach 860420, 81631 Munich, Germany) Ed.Bd. adv.; bk.rev.; charts; illus.; mkt.; pat.; tr.lit.; index. circ. 12,400. (also avail. in microform from PMC) **Indexed:** Anal.Abstr., C.I.S. Abstr., Chem.Abstr., Eng.Ind., Excerp.Med., INIS Atomind., Intl.Polym.Sci.& Tech., Key to Econ.Sci., Packag.Sci.Tech., RAPRA, World Surf.Coat. **Document type:** trade publication.
—CASDDS; SWETS; UnCover. **CCC.**

668.4   GW   ISSN 0075-7292
KUNSTSTOFFE IM LEBENSMITTELVERKEHR. 1962. irreg., no.43, 1994. DM.61. (Bundesgesundheitsamt, Kunststoff-Kommission) Carl Heymanns Verlag KG, Luxemburgerstr. 449, 50939 Cologne, Germany. TEL 0221-46010-0. FAX 0221-4601069. **Document type:** government publication.
—BLDSC (5131.025000).

668.4   GW   ISSN 0945-0084
KUNSTSTOFFE - PLAST EUROPE. German edition: Kunststoffe (ISSN 0023-5563) (Text in English, German) m. DM.351. Carl Hanser Verlag, Kolbergerstr. 22, 81679 Munich, Germany. TEL 089-998300. FAX 089-984809. (Subscr. to: Postfach 860420, 81631 Munich, Germany) **Indexed:** Curr.Cont., Int.Packag.Abstr., Intl.Polym.Sci.& Tech., PROMT, RAPRA. **Document type:** trade publication.
—BLDSC (5131.027000); Ei; Genuine Article; SWETS. **CCC.**
Formerly (until 1993): Kunststoffe - German Plastics (ISSN 0723-0192)

668.4   SZ   ISSN 1021-0601
TP986.A1   CODEN: KUSYEA
KUNSTSTOFFE - SYNTHETICS; Fachzeitschrift fuer Herstellung, Verarbeitung und Anwendung von Kunststoffen und neuen Werkstoffen. (Text in German) 1953. m. 85 SFr. (foreign 105 SFr.). Vogt-Schild AG, Zuchwilerstr. 21, CH-4501 Solothurn, Switzerland. TEL 065-247247. FAX 065-247235. Eds. Alfred Widmer, Marianne Flury. adv.: B&W page 2340 SFr., color page 3440 SFr.; trim 185 x 260; adv. contact: Hansruedi Spiri. bk.rev.; illus.; index. circ. 7,300. (tabloid format) **Indexed:** Chem.Abstr., Eng.Ind., Excerp.Med., Intl.Polym.Sci.& Tech., Key to Econ.Sci., Met.Abstr., RAPRA, World Alum.Abstr. **Document type:** trade publication.
—BLDSC (5131.060000); CASDDS; SWETS. **CCC.**
Formerly (until 1992): Kunststoffe - Plastics (ISSN 0023-5598)

LIQUID CRYSTALS; an international journal in the field of anisotropic fluids. see CHEMISTRY — Crystallography

668.4   IT   ISSN 0394-3453
MACPLAS; rivista mensile per l'industria delle materie plastiche e della goma. (Includes q. English edition: Macplas International) 1976. m. L.140000 (free to qualified personnel) (foreign L.210000). Promaplast S.r.l., Centro Commerciale Milanofiori, Palazzo F-2, 20090 Assago Milan, Italy. TEL 39-2-57512700. FAX 39-2-57512490. TELEX 341378 ASPLAS. Ed. Gino Delvecchio. adv.: B&W page L.1950000, color page L.2600000; trim 192 x 254. circ. 11,500. **Indexed:** Intl.Polym.Sci.& Tech., RAPRA. **Document type:** trade publication.
—BLDSC (5330.393700).
Description: Covers the plastics and rubber industries.

668.4   IT
MACPLAS INTERNATIONAL (CHINESE EDITION). s-a. Promaplast s.r.l., Centro Commerciale Milanofiori, Palazzo F-2, 20090 Assago (MI), Italy. TEL 39-2-57512700. FAX 39-2-57512490. adv.: B&W page L.3100000; trim 192 x 254. circ. 7,000. **Document type:** trade publication.
Description: Covers the plastics and rubber industries.

668.4   IT
MACPLAS INTERNATIONAL (ENGLISH EDITION); technical magazine for the plastics and rubber industry. 1976. q. L.100000 (foreign L.150000). Promaplast S.r.l., Centro Commerciale Milanofiori, Palazzo F-2, 20090 Assago Milan, Italy. TEL 39-2-57512700. FAX 39-2-57512490. TELEX 341378 ASPLAS. Ed. Gino Delvecchio. adv.: B&W page L.2950000; trim 192 x 254. circ. 21,000. (back issues avail.) **Document type:** trade publication.

668.4   IT
MACPLAS INTERNATIONAL (SPANISH EDITION); revista tecnica para la industria de materias plasticas y del caucho. s-a. Promaplast s.r.l., Centro Commerciale Milanofiori, Palazzo F-2, 20090 Assago (MI), Italy. TEL 39-2-57512700. FAX 39-2-57512490. adv.: B&W page L.2050000; trim 192 x 254. circ. 6,000. **Document type:** trade publication.

668.4   RM   ISSN 0025-5289
     CODEN: MPLAAM
MATERIALE PLASTICE. Title varies slightly: Revista Materiale Plastice. (Text in Rumanian; summaries in English, French, German, Russian) 1964. q. 15000 lei($60) Chiminform Data S.A., Calea Plevnei 139, 77131 Bucharest, Rumania. FAX 3-1231-60. TELEX 10307 CHINF. Ed. Nelia Mihaila. adv. contact: Paul Zugravescu. bk.rev.; abstr.; bibl.; charts; illus.; pat.; stat.; index. circ. 1,000. **Indexed:** C.I.S. Abstr., Chem.Abstr., Inform.Sci.Abstr., Intl.Polym.Sci.& Tech., RAPRA. **Document type:** academic/scholarly publication.
—BLDSC (5393.670000); CASDDS; Genuine Article; UMI.

MATERIALS AND MANUFACTURE. see ENGINEERING — Mechanical Engineering

MATERIALS TECHNOLOGY. see METALLURGY

668.4   IT   ISSN 0025-5459
TP1101   CODEN: MPELAK
MATERIE PLASTICHE ED ELASTOMERI. (Text mainly in Italian; occasionally in English, French or German; summaries in English, Italian) 1934. m. (11/yr.). O.Ve.S.T. s.r.l., Via S. d'Orsenigo 22, 20139 Rome, Italy. TEL 39-2-5469174. FAX 39-2-55185263. Ed. Carlo Latorre; Pub. Ugone Carutti. adv.: B&W page L.1400000, color page L.1900000. bk.rev.; abstr.; bibl.; charts; illus.; pat.; stat. circ. 6,000. **Indexed:** Chem.Abstr., Eng.Ind., Intl.Polym.Sci.& Tech., PROMT, RAPRA.
—BLDSC (5399.010000).

668.4   GW
MEISTERBETRIEB. q. Landesverband Holz- und Kunststoffverarbeitendem Handwerk, Leihgesterner Weg 20, 35392 Giessen, Germany.

METALLIZED PLASTICS; fundamental and applied aspects. see CHEMISTRY — Electrochemistry

668.4   US   ISSN 0026-8275
TP986.A1   CODEN: MOPLAY
MODERN PLASTICS. International edition (ISSN 0026-8283) 1925. m. $41.75 (Canada $46; elsewhere $225). McGraw-Hill, Inc., 1221 Ave. of the Americas, New York, NY 10020. TEL 212-512-6245. FAX 212-512-6111. (Subscr. to: Box 605, Hightstown, NJ 08520) Ed. Keith Kreisher. adv.; bk.rev.; abstr.; illus.; pat.; tr.lit.; index. circ. 75,227 (55,727 U.S. ed., 19,500 international ed.). (also avail. in microform from UMI) **Indexed:** A.S.& T.Ind., ABI Inform., Abstr.Bull.Inst.Pap.Chem., Art & Archaeol.Tech.Abstr., Bus.Ind., Chem.Abstr., Curr.Pack.Abstr., Eng.Ind., Ind.Sci.Rev., Intl.Polym.Sci.& Tech., PROMT, RAPRA, SRI, Text.Tech.Dig., Tr.& Indus.Ind. **Document type:** academic/scholarly publication.
●Also available online. Vendor(s): Knight-Ridder, Inc (MP), Dow Jones News Retrieval (MP), Lexis-Nexis (MODPLA), NewsNet (CH23).
—BLDSC (5891.000000); CASDDS; Ei; Faxon; Genuine Article; SWETS; UMI; UnCover. **CCC.**
Description: Provides analysis and assessment of significant developments in materials, processes, design and markets.

660.2   US   ISSN 0085-3518
MODERN PLASTICS ENCYCLOPEDIA. (Special October issue of: Modern Plastics) 1925. a. $57 or included with subscr. to Modern Plastics. McGraw-Hill, Inc., 1221 Ave. of the Americas, New York, NY 10020. TEL 212-512-6241. FAX 212-512-6111. Ed. Robert J. Martino. adv. circ. 48,700.
—BLDSC (5891.005000). **CCC.**

668.4   US   ISSN 0026-8283
MODERN PLASTICS INTERNATIONAL. (International edition of Modern Plastics) (Text in English) 1971. m. $175 in Europe and Japan; elsewhere $115. McGraw-Hill, Inc., 1221 Ave. of the Americas, New York, NY 10020. TEL 212-512-6241. FAX 212-512-6111. (Subscr. in Europe to: 50 av. de la Gare, Lausanne, Switzerland. FAX 021-272-919) Ed. Dennis Brownbill. adv.; bk.rev.; index. circ. 19,500. (also avail. in microform from UMI) **Indexed:** Br.Ceram.Abstr., Cadscan, Int.Packag.Abstr., Intl.Polym.Sci.& Tech., Key to Econ.Sci., Lead Abstr., Packag.Sci.Tech., PROMT, RAPRA, W.R.C.Inf., Zincscan.
—BLDSC (5892.200000); Ei; Faxon; SWETS; UMI. **CCC.**

668.4   JA
MOLDERS. 1961. m. 3600 Yen($20) Japan Plastics Journal Ltd - Nihon Parasuchikkusu Shinposha, Kimura Bldg., 38 Minami-Sumiya-cho, Minami-ku, Osaka 552, Japan. Ed. Toshiyuki Shimogaito. adv.; bk.rev.; abstr.; illus. circ. 20,000.

668.4   HU   ISSN 0027-2914
     CODEN: MUGUAO
MUANYAG ES GUMI/PLASTICS AND RUBBER. (Text in Hungarian; summaries in English, French, German, Russian) 1964. m. $33. (Gepipari Tudomanyos Egyesulet) Lapkiado Vallalat, Lenin korut 9-11, 1073 Budapest 7, Hungary. TEL 222-408. (Subscr. to: Kultura, Box 149, H-1389 Budapest, Hungary) (Co-sponsor: Magyar Kemikusok Egyesulete) Eds. S. Odon Gal, Hugo Macskasy. adv.; bk.rev.; bibl.; charts; illus.; mkt.; index. circ. 1,700. **Indexed:** Chem.Abstr., Hung.Build.Bull., Intl.Polym.Sci.& Tech., RAPRA, RAPRA, Ref.Zh.
—BLDSC (5980.910000); CASDDS; Ei.

668.4   FI   ISSN 0788-8430
MUOVI - PLAST. 1990. 8/yr. FIM 350 (foreign FIM 430). Muoviyhdistys ry - Finnish Plastics Association, Mariankatu 26 B 6, FIN-00110 Helsinki, Finland. TEL 358-0-135-1200. FAX 358-0-135-5601. Ed. Hannele Heikkila. adv.: B&W page FIM 4100, color page FIM 7700; trim 185 x 270. bk.rev. circ. 1,600. **Document type:** bulletin.
Formerly (until 1989): Muoviyhdistys Tiedottaa.

668.4 678.2   NE   ISSN 0165-7089
N V R - INFORMATIEF. 1940. 11/yr. fl.165 (effective 1996). Nederlandse Vereniging van Rubber- en Kunststoffabrikanten, P.O. Box 418, 2260 AK Leidschendam, Netherlands. TEL 31-70-3177243. FAX 31-70-3177412. circ. 300. **Document type:** bulletin.
Description: Covers news and information of interest to rubber and plastics manufacturers.

668.4 630   US   ISSN 1073-1768
NATIONAL AGRICULTURAL PLASTICS CONGRESS. PROCEEDINGS. 1960. irreg., vol.25, 1994. $68. American Society for Plasticulture, c/o H. Carl Hoefer, Jr., Exec. Sec., Box 860238, St. Augustine, FL 32086. TEL 904-829-0754. FAX 904-829-0755. circ. 350. **Document type:** academic/scholarly publication, proceedings.
Formerly: National Agricultural Plastics Association. Proceedings.
Description: University research on effect of agricultural plastics on crop production.

668.4   JA
NEW MATERIALS DEVELOPED IN JAPAN (YEAR). 1984. irreg., latest 1991. $1250. Toray Research Center, Inc., (Subsidiary of: Toray Industries, Ltd.), 3-1-8 Nihonbashi - Muromachi, Chuo-ku, Tokyo 103, Japan. TEL 81-3-3245-5895. FAX 81-3-3245-5789. TELEX J22623 TRC JA. **Description:** Includes information on 379 new materials developed in Japan from April 1987 to March 1991.

NEW TECHNOLOGY JAPAN. see MACHINERY

668.4   JA   ISSN 0029-0351
NIHON PURASUCHIKKUSU SHINPO/JAPAN PLASTICS JOURNAL. (Text in Japanese) 1949. 4/m. 6000 Yen($40) Japan Plastics Journal Ltd. - Nihon Purasuchikkusu Shinpo-sha, Kimura Bldg., 38 Minamisumiya-cho, Minami-ku, Osaka 552, Japan. Ed. Toshiyuki Shimogaito. adv.; bk.rev.; charts; illus.; pat.; stat.; tr.lit.; index. circ. 20,000.

668.3   JA   ISSN 0916-4812
TP967   CODEN: NSEGE7
NIHON SETCHAKU GAKKAISHI/ADHESION. (Text in English, Japanese) 1965. m. Nihon Setchaku Gakkai - Adhesion Society of Japan, Koa Nipponbashi 203, 4-2-20 Nipponbashi, Naniwa-ku, Osaka 556, Japan. Ed. Kazumune Nakao. adv.; bk.rev.; abstr.; charts; illus.; pat.; index. **Indexed:** JTA.
—BLDSC (4676.300000); CASDDS. **CCC.**
     Formerly (until 1990): Nihon Setchaku Kyokaishi (ISSN 0001-8201)

668.4   NO   ISSN 0332-6136
NORSK PLAST. 1968. 8/yr. NOK 185. Teknisk Presse A.S, Hovfaret 17, P.O. Box 235 Skoeyen, N-0212 Oslo 2, Norway. TEL 47-2-52-10-40. FAX 47-2-50-66-48. Ed. Ragnar Brekke. adv. circ. 7,136.

668.4   US
NORTH CAROLINA PLASTICS INDUSTRY DIRECTORY. quinquennial. $30. North Carolina State University, School of Engineering, Industrial Extension Service, Box 7902, Raleigh, NC 27695-7902. TEL 919-515-2358. Ed. W. Paul Cowgill. **Document type:** directory.
     Formerly (until 1993): North Carolina Plastics Processor and Producers.

668.4   AG   ISSN 0325-0407
NOTICIERO DEL PLASTICO - ELASTOMEROS. 1959. m. Aus.$300($300) Editorial Tecnica Siglo XXI, S.A., Talcahuano 374-1p. B, 1013 Buenos Aires, Argentina. TEL 452348. Ed. Guillermo Oliveti. adv.; bk.rev.; bibl.; stat. circ. 6,000. (tabloid format; back issues avail.) **Indexed:** PROMT.
     Description: Covers plastics and rubber, machines, technology, design, analysis of markets, tests, events and reports.

668.4   AU
         CODEN: OKZSAV
OESTERREICHISCHE KUNSTSTOFF ZEITSCHRIFT. 1970. bi-m. S.573. (Gesellschaft zur Foerderung der Kunststofftechnik) Verlag Lorenz, Ebendorferstr. 10, A-1010 Vienna, Austria. TEL 0222-426695. FAX 0222-438693. Ed. Robert Hillisch. adv.; bk.rev.; illus.; pat.; stat. circ. 2,000. **Indexed:** Chem.Abstr. **Document type:** trade publication.
—BLDSC (6307.850000); CASDDS.
     Formerly: Oesterreichische Kunststoff Zeitung (ISSN 0029-926X)

668.4   US
OXYCHEM NEWSBRIEFS. 1930. q. free. Occidental Chemical Corp., Durez Division, 528 Walck Rd., N. Tonawanda, NY 14120. TEL 716-696-6000. adv. circ. 6,000.
     Former titles: Durez Molder Newsbriefs; Durez Molder (ISSN 0012-7264)

668.4   US
P M - U S A THE GREEN SHEET. 1972. m. $25. Marketing Handbooks, Inc., 7094 Skyline Dr., Delray Beach, FL 33446-2212. TEL 407-498-7660. FAX 407-495-5278. adv.; B&W page $1500; trim 7 x 10. circ. 7,800. **Document type:** trade publication.
     Description: For the plastics, packaging and rubber processing industries.

668.4   MX
PANORAMA PLASTICO; la revista mexicana del plastico. 1984. m. Mex.$84000($95) Editorial Corso, S.A. de C.V., Insurgentes Sur No. 594-502, Col. del Valle, 03100 Mexico, D.F., Mexico. TEL 669-30-87. FAX 523-22-03. Ed. Carlos Moreno. bk.rev. circ. 10,000. (back issues avail.)
     Description: Provides technical information on the plastics industry in Mexico.

PAPER, FILM AND FOIL CONVERTER. see *PACKAGING*

668.4   FR   ISSN 0031-4803
PENSEZ PLASTIQUES.* (Text in English, French and German) 1954. m. (plus q. and s-a. editions). 38 F. Editions de Berne et Cie, 11 bd. des Batignolles, 75008 Paris, France. Ed. J.S. de Berne. adv.; charts; illus. **Indexed:** Chem.Abstr., RAPRA.

668.4   IT   ISSN 0391-7401
         CODEN: PLATDW
PLAST; rivista delle materie plastiche. (Text in Italian; summaries in English) 1969. m. L.64000. E R I S S.p.A., Via Tellini, 2, 20155 Milan, Italy. TEL 2-331-033-05. FAX 2-331-042-45. Ed. Aldo Rotta. adv.; B&W page L.1800000, color page L.2400000; trim 175 x 255. bk.rev.; abstr.; bibl.; charts; illus.; pat.; stat. circ. 7,326. **Indexed:** Chem.Abstr.
—CASDDS.

668.4   DK   ISSN 0107-2943
         CODEN: PLPSD2
PLAST EMBALLAGE SCANDINAVIA.* Issued with: Plast Panorama Scandinavia (ISSN 0106-1720) 1979. 10/yr. DKK 550. Dansk Bladforlag ApS, Hellerupvej 78, DK-2900 Hellerup, Denmark. TEL 35-378055. FAX 35-373639. Ed. Sven Vollertzen. adv. circ. 6,324.

668.4   DK   ISSN 0106-1720
         CODEN: PLPSD2
PLAST PANORAMA SCANDINAVIA. 1950. 10/yr. DKK 550. (Association of Danish Plastics Industries) Teknisk Forlag A-S, Skelbaekgade 4, DK-1780 Copenhagen V, Denmark. TEL 45-31-21-68-01. FAX 45-31-21-04-01. (Co-sponsor: Plastic Industry's Employers' Association) Ed. Erik Buhl. adv.; B&W page DKK 9670, color page DKK 15670; trim 277 x 191. circ. 4,447 (controlled). **Indexed:** Int.Packag.Abstr.
—BLDSC (6528.791000); CASDDS.
     Formerly: Plastic (ISSN 0032-1044)
     Description: Provides information about plastic raw materials, products and production methods for the industries processing and using plastics in Scandinavia.

668.4   SP   ISSN 1131-7515
PLAST 21. 10/yr. $100. Mazustegui 21, 3a y 4a planta, 48006 Bilbao, Spain. TEL 4-415-90-22. FAX 4-416-27-43.

668.4   SW
PLASTER. 1969. biennial. SEK 160. Plast- och Kemibranchen, P.O. Box 105, S-101 22 Stockholm, Sweden. FAX 46-8-411-45-26.

668.4 678.2   SW   ISSN 0347-8262
PLASTFORUM SCANDINAVIA. 1970. 10/yr. SEK 450 (effective Jan. 1994). Indufa Foerlag AB, P.O. Box 601, S-251 06 Haelsingborg, Sweden. TEL 46-42-19-99-00. FAX 46-42-19-99-19. Ed. Hans Widen. adv.; B&W page SEK 15100; trim 185 x 265; adv. contact: Beth Holmkvist. bk.rev. circ. 5,000. **Document type:** trade publication.
     Formerly (until 1977): Plastforum (ISSN 0048-4369)
     Description: Focuses on plastics and rubber converting industry as well as end-use industries.

668.4   MX
PLASTI-NOTICIAS. 1972. m. Publi-News Latinoamericana, S.A.C.V., Colima 436, piso 2, Mexico 7 D.F., Mexico. Ed. Roberto J. Marquez. adv.; circ. controlled.

668.4   US
PLASTIC BUSINESS NEWS. s-m. Washington Business Information, 1117 N. 19th St., Rm. 200, Arlington, VA 22209. TEL 703-247-3434.
     Description: Covers plastics industry developments.

668.4   UK
PLASTIC INDUSTRY DIRECTORY. irreg. E M A P Vision Ltd., Maclaren House, 19 Scarbrook Rd., Croydon CR9 1QH, England. TEL 081-760-9690. FAX 081-681-1672. TELEX 946665.
     Description: Guide to the plastics industry.

PLASTICHEM. see *ENGINEERING — Chemical Engineering*

668.4   BL   ISSN 0102-1931
PLASTICO MODERNO. 1971. m. Cr.$52($26) (effective Mar. 1995). Editora Quimica e Derivados Ltda., Rua Dr. Gabriel dos Santos, 55, Santa Cecilia, CEP 01231-900 Sao Paulo, SP, Brazil. TEL 55-11-826-6899. FAX 55-11-8258192. TELEX 11-21801. Ed. Emanoel Fairbanks. adv.; bk.rev.; charts; illus. circ. 12,000. (back issues avail.) **Document type:** trade publication.
     Description: Deals with the Brazilian plastics industry, its producers, manufacturers and customers. Also covers the rubber industry, new materials and processing, technology and application.

668.4   AG
PLASTICOS. 1948. bi-m. $50. Camara Argentina del Libro - Argentine Book Association, Avda. Belgrano 1580, 6 Piso, 1093 Buenos Aires, Argentina. Ed. Hugo Brik. adv.; bk.rev.; abstr.; charts; illus.; mkt.; stat.; tr.lit. circ. 10,000. **Indexed:** Chem.Abstr.
     Former titles: Sip-Plastinoticias; Plasticos (ISSN 0032-1125)

668.4   BL   ISSN 0032-1133
HD9661.B7   CODEN: PLRVBJ
PLASTICOS EM REVISTA. 1962. m. Cr.$2700($300) Plasticos em Revista Editora Ltda., Rua Piaui 1164, Casas 7 e 8, 01241-000 Sao Paulo, SP, Brazil. FAX 55-11-66-0496. TELEX 11-24711 LRDL BR. Ed. Helio Helman; Pub. Helio Helman. adv. contact: Beatriz de Mello Helman. bk.rev.; abstr.; charts; illus.; mkt.; stat.; tr.lit. circ. 10,000. **Indexed:** Chem.Abstr., Packag.Sci.Tech.
—BLDSC (6530.250000); CASDDS.

660   US   ISSN 0192-1789
PLASTICS. 1974. bi-m. $15 to qualified personnel; others $20. Western Plastics News Inc., 1704 Colorado Ave., Santa Monica, CA 90404-3410. TEL 213-829-4876. Ed. Aida Pavletich. adv.; bk.rev. circ. 20,000.
     Formerly: Western Plastics.

660   JA   ISSN 0551-0503
         CODEN: PUEJDH
PLASTICS AGE/PURASUCHIKKUSU EJI. (Includes: Plastics Age Encyclopedia) (Text in Japanese; summaries in English) 1954. m. 16.000 Yen. Plastics Age Co., Ltd. - Purasuchikkuse Eji K. K., Okochi Bldg., 1-10-6 Kajicho, Chiyoda-ku, Tokyo 101, Japan. Ed. Eiichi Asayama. adv.; bk.rev.; stat. circ. 27,000.
—BLDSC (6531.300000); CASDDS.

668.4 678.2   UK   ISSN 0032-1168
HD9661.A1
PLASTICS AND RUBBER WEEKLY. 1964. w. £73. E M A P Maclaren Ltd., 19 Scarbrook Rd., Croydon, Surrey CR9 1QH, England. TEL 0181-760-9690. FAX 0181-681-1672. TELEX 946665. Ed. G. Sommer. adv.; illus.; mkt.; pat.; stat.; tr.mk.; circ. 20,584 (controlled). (also avail. in microfilm from UMI; reprint service avail. from UMI) **Indexed:** Chem.Abstr., Fluidex, Int.Packag.Abstr., Intl.Polym.Sci.& Tech., PROMT, RAPRA, World Surf.Coat., World Text.Abstr. **Document type:** trade publication.
—BLDSC (6531.460000); UMI. **CCC.**
     Description: For the plastics and rubber industries.

668.4   US   ISSN 0734-1784
PLASTICS BUSINESS NEWS; and major market indicators report. 1982. fortn. $327 in U.S. & Canada. Market Search, Inc., 2727 Holland Sylvania Rd., Ste. A, Toledo, OH 43615. TEL 419-535-7899. FAX 419-535-1243. Ed. James R. Best.
●Also available online. Vendor(s): NewsNet (CH17).
—BLDSC (6532.010000).
     Description: News and information on trends, new product development, alternate uses of plastic materials, acquisitions and mergers, as well as production and distribution processes.

PLASTICS

668.4 US ISSN 0148-9119
TP1101 CODEN: PLCODR
PLASTICS COMPOUNDING; for resin producers, formulators and compounders. 1977. 6/yr. $40. Advanstar Communications, Inc., 7500 Old Oak Blvd., Cleveland, OH 44130. TEL 216-826-2839. FAX 216-891-2726. (Subscr. to: 131 W. First St., Duluth, MN 55802. TEL 800-346-0085) Ed. Mary C. McMurrer. adv.; bk.rev. circ. 16,500. (also avail. in microform from UMI; back issues avail.; reprint service avail.) **Indexed:** Chem.Abstr., Curr.Pack.Abstr., Intl.Polym.Sci.& Tech., PROMT, RAPRA. **Document type:** trade publication.
—CASDDS; Ei; Faxon; SWETS; UMI. **CCC.**
Description: Discusses resin production, compounding and formulating techniques, polymer materials and applications.

668.4 US
PLASTICS COMPOUNDING REDBOOK. 1981. a. $40. Advanstar Communications, Inc., 7500 Old Oak Blvd., Cleveland, OH 44130. TEL 216-826-2839. FAX 216-891-2726. (Subscr. to: 131 W. First St., Duluth, MN 55802. TEL 800-346-0085) Ed. Mary C. McMurrer. adv.; charts; illus. circ. 16,500. (back issues avail.) **Document type:** directory, trade publication.
Description: Buyers' guide for additives, modifiers, reinforcements; test and compounding equipment; services.

668.4 US
PLASTICS CONFERENCE PROCEEDINGS (YEAR). 1976. a. Business Communications Co., Inc. (Norwalk), 25 Van Zant St., Norwalk, CT 06855. TEL 203-853-4266. FAX 203-853-0348. TELEX 6502934929 WUI. Ed. Louis Naturman. circ. 1,000. (also avail. in microfilm; microfiche; back issues avail.) **Document type:** proceedings.
Formerly: Conference on Contingency Planning for Plastics. Proceedings.

668.4 US ISSN 1045-0769
TA455.P5
PLASTICS D.A.T.A. DIGEST; thermoplastics and thermosets. 1980. a. $245. D.A.T.A. Business Publishing (Subsidiary of: Information Handling Services), 15 Inverness Way E., Box 6510, Englewood, CO 80155-6510. TEL 800-477-4666. FAX 303-799-4082. TELEX 4322083 IHS UI. Ed. Paul Magin. adv. contact: Kevin Asbjornson.
● Also available on CD-ROM.
Formerly: Plastics D.A.T.A. Book.
Description: Reference guide covering 23 technical parameters on over 18,500 plastics, thermoplastics and thermosets from more than 230 manufacturers.

668.4 US
THE PLASTICS DISTRIBUTOR & FABRICATOR MAGAZINE. 1980. bi-m. free to qualified personnel ($50 outside U.S. & Canada). P M D Publishing Inc., 2701 N. Pulaski Rd., Chicago, IL 60639-2119. TEL 312-235-3800. FAX 312-235-7204. Ed. Harry Greenwald. adv.; circ. 20,150 (controlled). **Document type:** trade publication.
Formerly: Plastics Distributor.
Description: For plastic distributors, fabricators and equipment manufacturers.

668.4 US ISSN 0091-9578
TP1101 CODEN: PLEGBB
PLASTICS ENGINEERING. 1945. m. $50 (foreign $70). Society of Plastics Engineers, Inc., 14 Fairfield Dr., Brookfield, CT 06804-0403. TEL 203-775-0471. FAX 203-775-8490. TELEX 743-712. Ed. Roger Ferris. adv.; B&W page $2900. bk.rev.; charts; illus.; pat.; stat.; index. circ. 35,000. (also avail. in microfilm from UMI; reprint service avail. from UMI) **Indexed:** A.S.& T.Ind., Abstr.Bull.Inst.Pap.Chem., C.I.S. Abstr., Chem.Abstr., Curr.Cont., Curr.Pack.Abstr., Eng.Ind., Excerp.Med., INSPEC, Int.Packag.Abstr., Intl.Polym.Sci. & Tech., Packag.Sci.Tech., PROMT, RAPRA, Text.Tech.Dig. **Document type:** trade publication.
—BLDSC (6532.310000); CASDDS; Ei; Faxon; Genuine Article; SWETS; UMI; UnCover. **CCC.**
Formerly: S P E Journal (ISSN 0036-1844)

668.4 US ISSN 1040-2527
CODEN: PLENEZ
PLASTICS ENGINEERING SERIES. 1981. irreg., vol.27, 1993. price varies. Marcel Dekker, Inc., 270 Madison Av., New York, NY 10016. TEL 212-696-9000. FAX 212-685-4540. TELEX 421419.
—BLDSC (6532.314000); CASDDS.
Refereed Serial

668.4 US ISSN 0554-2952
PLASTICS FOCUS; an interpretive news report. 1969. 25/yr. $270 in N. America; elsewhere $310 (effective 1996). Plastics Connection, Inc., Box 814, Amherst, MA 01004. TEL 413-549-5020. FAX 413-549-9955. Ed. Michael L. Barins. **Document type:** newsletter.
Description: Covers pricing, technical developments and market news for managers in the plastic resin, machinery and processing businesses.

PLASTICS IN BUILDING CONSTRUCTION. see BUILDING AND CONSTRUCTION

668.4 JA ISSN 0032-1206
PLASTICS INDUSTRY NEWS, JAPAN. (Text in English) 1955. m. $120. Institute of Polymer Industry, Inc. - Porima Kogyo Kenkyujo, C.P.O. Box 1176, Tokyo 100-91, Japan. TEL 03-3211-7739. FAX 03-3211-7730. Ed. S. Miyamoto. adv.; bk.rev.; mkt.; pat.; tr.lit.; cum.index every 10 yrs. circ. 10,450. (also avail. in microfilm from UMI; reprint service avail. from UMI) **Indexed:** Chem.Abstr., Intl.Polym.Sci.& Tech., JTA, RAPRA. **Document type:** trade publication.
—BLDSC (6532.600000); Ei; UMI.

668.4 CN ISSN 1197-6020
PLASTICS INDUSTRY REFERENCE GUIDE & SOURCEBOOK. 1993. a. Kenilworth Publishing Inc., 80 W. Beaver Creek, Ste. 18, Richmond Hill, ON L4B 1H3, Canada. TEL 905-771-7333. FAX 905-771-7336. Ed. Edward Mason. adv.; B&W page Can.$1450, color page Can.$2200; trim 8 1/8 x 10 3/4; adv. contact: Jim Meecham. circ. 1,000.

668.4 GW ISSN 0944-1395
PLASTICS INFORMATION EUROPE. (Text in English) fortn. DM.360. Kunststoff Information Verlagsgesellschaft mbH, Saalburgstr. 157, 61350 Bad Homburg, Germany. TEL 06172-32007. FAX 06172-304178. Ed. Helmut Hertsch.
—BLDSC (6532.702000).
Formerly (until 1993): Plastics Industry Europe (ISSN 0268-8247)

668 US
PLASTICS: LATIN AMERICAN INDUSTRIAL REPORT. (Avail. for each of 22 Latin American countries) 1985. a. $435 per country report. Aquino Productions, Box 15760, Stamford, CT 06901. TEL 203-325-3138. Ed. Andres C. Aquino.

668.4 US
PLASTICS MOLDING TECHNOLOGY. 1991. m. $160 to non-members (foreign $180); members $130 (foreign $145) (effective 1996). A S M International, Materials Information, Materials Park, OH 44073. TEL 216-338-5151. FAX 216-338-4634. TELEX 980-619. E-mail: DBarthel@po.ASM-Intl.org. (UK addr.: Institute of Materials, Materials Information, 1 Carlton House Terr., London SW1Y 5DB, England. TEL 071-839-4071) **Document type:** abstracting/indexing.
Formerly: Plastics - Composites Molding Digest.
Description: Selection of plastics and composites molding information published in Engineered Materials Abstracts and the Materials Business Information series.

668.4 II ISSN 0971-3689
PLASTICS NEWS. 1960. m. Rs.300. All India Plastics Manufacturers Association, A-52, Street No. 1, M.I.D.C., Marol, Andheri (East), Bombay 400 093, India. TEL 8217324. FAX 8216390. Ed. Shri Vijay V. Merchant. adv.; B&W page Rs.2500; trim 230 x 180. bk.rev. circ. 3,000.
Description: Contains news and the latest developments in the Indian plastics industry.

678 US ISSN 1042-802X
HD9661.A1
PLASTICS NEWS. 1989. w. $55. Crain Communications Inc. (Akron), 1725 Merriman Rd., Akron, OH 44313-3185. TEL 216-836-9180. FAX 216-836-1005. (Subscr. to: 965 E. Jefferson Ave., Detroit, MI 48207-3187. TEL 800-678-9595) Ed. Robert Grace. adv.; B&W page $7550, color page $9620. circ. 60,148. **Indexed:** Intl.Polym.Sci.& Tech., RAPRA. **Document type:** trade publication.
—BLDSC (6535.695000); UMI. **CCC.**
Description: Identifies and connects the manufacturers and suppliers. Covers financial moves, plant closings, acquisitions, process developments, new machinery and price indexing.

668.4 AT
PLASTICS NEWS INTERNATIONAL. (Quarterly supplement avail.: Plastics South East Assia Pacific) 1950. m. Aus.$55. (Plastics and Chemical Industry Association, Plastics Sector) Editors Desk Pty. Ltd., Box 546, Mount Eliza, Vic. 3930, Australia. TEL 61-3-9775-2139. FAX 61-3-9787-6105. Ed. Mike Kettle. adv.; bk.rev.; circ. 2,100 (paid). **Indexed:** Aus.Rd.Ind., Intl.Polym.Sci.& Tech., RAPRA, W.R.C.Inf. **Document type:** trade publication.
Formerly (until May 1989): Plastics News.
Description: Designed to inform plastics industry about developments of plastics resins and their applications, including the machinery and equipment offered for sale to plastics processors.

668.4 CN
PLASTICS PROGRESS. 1990. q. for employees only. Novacor Chemicals Ltd., Box 2535, Sta. M, Calgary, AB T2P 2N6, Canada. TEL 403-750-3951. FAX 403-750-3941. Ed. Brenda Bramhill. circ. 3,500.

604.6 668.4 US ISSN 1046-2201
HD9661.U6
PLASTICS RECYCLING AS A FUTURE BUSINESS OPPORTUNITY. 1986. a. (Plastics Institute of America, Technology Exchange Program) Technomic Publishing Co., Inc., 851 New Holland Ave., Box 3535, Lancaster, PA 17604. TEL 717-295-4538. FAX 717-295-4538. TELEX 230 753565 (TECHNOMIC UD). **Document type:** monographic series.

PLASTICS RECYCLING UPDATE. see ENVIRONMENTAL STUDIES — Waste Management

668.4 678.2 UK ISSN 0959-8111
TP1101 CODEN: PRPAEP
PLASTICS, RUBBER & COMPOSITES PROCESSING AND APPLICATIONS. 1981. 10/yr. (in 2 vols., 5 nos./vol.). £410($611) (effective 1995). (Plastics and Rubber Institute) Elsevier Science Ltd., P.O. Box 800, Kidlington, Oxford OX5 1DX, England. TEL 44-1865-843000. FAX 44-1865-843010. E-mail: nlinfo-f@elsevier.nl; usinfo-f@elsevier.com; forinfo-kyf04035@niftyserve.or.jp; Site addr.: http://www.elsevier.nl/. (Subscr. in U.S. and Canada to: Elsevier Science, 660 White Plains Rd., Tarrytown, NY 10591-5153. TEL 914-524-9200. FAX 914-333-2444) Ed. N.G. McCrum. adv.; bk.rev.; illus.; index. (also avail. in microform from UMI; back issues avail.) **Indexed:** Br.Tech.Ind., Chem.Abstr., Chem.Eng.Abstr., Curr.Cont., Curr.Pack.Abstr., Eng.Ind., Food Sci.& Tech.Abstr., HRIS, INSPEC, Intl.Polym.Sci.& Tech., Ocean.Abstr., Pollut.Abstr., RAPRA, Sci.Cit.Ind., T.C.E.A., Text.Tech.Dig., W.R.C.Inf. **Document type:** academic/scholarly publication, trade publication.
—BLDSC (6537.187000); CASDDS; Ei; Genuine Article; SWETS. **CCC.**
Formerly (until 1991): Plastics and Rubber Processing and Applications (ISSN 0144-6045)
Description: Provides an international forum for the presentation of the science and technology involved in the plastics and rubber industries.
Refereed Serial

668.4 SA ISSN 0048-4385
PLASTICS SOUTHERN AFRICA. Abbreviated title: P S A. (Text in English) 1971. m. R.140. (Plastics Institute of South Africa) George Warman Publications (Pty.) Ltd., P.O. Box 3847, Cape Town 8000, South Africa. TEL 27-21-245320. FAX 27-21-261332. Ed. Martin Wells. adv.; bk.rev.; illus.; tr.lit. circ. 2,000. **Indexed:** Ind.S.A.Per., Intl.Polym.Sci.& Tech., RAPRA. **Document type:** trade publication.
Description: Technical journal covering the plastics industry.

668.4 SA
PLASTICS SOUTHERN AFRICA BUYERS GUIDE. (Text in English) 1990. a. R.110. George Warman Publications (Pty.) Ltd., P.O. Box 3847, Cape Town 8000, South Africa. TEL 27-21-245320. FAX 27-21-261332. Ed. Martin Wells. **Document type:** trade publication.
Description: Guide for buyers of machinery for the plastics industry.

PLASTICS

668.4 — US — ISSN 0032-1257
TP1101 — CODEN: PLTEAB
PLASTICS TECHNOLOGY; machinery/materials systems for maximum productivity. 1955. 13/yr. free to qualified personnel; $69 in US; Canada $79; elsewhere $180. Bill Communications, Inc., 355 Park Ave. S., 5th Fl., New York, NY 10010-1706. TEL 212-592-6570. FAX 212-592-6579. Ed. Matthew H. Naitove. adv.; bk.rev.; abstr.; charts; illus.; pat.; tr.lit.; index; circ. 47,000 (controlled). (reprint service avail. from UMI) **Indexed:** A.S.& T.Ind., Chem.Abstr., Excerp.Med., Int.Packag.Abstr., Intl.Polym.Sci.& Tech., Packag.Sci.Tech., PROMT, RAPRA, RAPRA.
—BLDSC (6537.300000); CASDDS; Ei; Faxon; Genuine Article; SWETS; UMI; UnCover. **CCC**.
Description: For plastics manufacturers.

668.4 — US
PLASTICS TECHNOLOGY. PLASTICS MANUFACTURING HANDBOOK AND BUYERS' GUIDE.* 1967. a. included in subscr. to Plastics Technology. Bill Communications, Inc., 355 Park Ave. S., 3rd Fl., New York, NY 10010-1706. TEL 212-592-6200. Ed. Matthew H. Naitove. adv.; charts; illus.; tr.lit.; index. circ. 40,000. (reprint service avail. from UMI)

668.4 — US — ISSN 1044-9663
PLASTICS WEEK. w. $530 (foreign $580). McGraw-Hill, Inc., Chemicals & Plastics Information Services, 1220 Ave. of the Americas, 43rd Fl., New York, NY 10020. TEL 212-512-6779. FAX 212-512-2989. (Subscr. to: McGraw-Hill, Inc., P.O. Box 632, Hightstown, NJ 08520. TEL 609-426-7116) Ed. Peter R. Savage. **Document type:** newsletter.
Incorporates (in Dec., 1992): Plastics and Environment (ISSN 1051-0567)
Description: Covers recycling, source reduction, environmental strategies, and other major plastics industry issues.

668.4 — US — ISSN 0032-1273
TP1101 — CODEN: PLAWA4
PLASTICS WORLD. 1942. 12/yr. $74.95 (Canada $112.30; Mexico $104.95; elsewhere $134.95). P T N Publishing Corp., 445 Broad Hollow Rd., Ste. 21, Melville, NY 11747-4722. TEL 516-845-2700. Ed. Mike McEnaney. adv.; bk.rev.; illus.; stat.; tr.lit. circ. 51,400. (also avail. in microform; reprint service avail. from UMI) **Indexed:** A.S.& T.Ind., B.P.I, Bus.Ind., Chem.Abstr., Int.Packag.Abstr., Intl.Polym.Sci.& Tech., Key to Econ.Sci., PROMT, RAPRA, Text.Tech.Dig., Tr.& Indus.Ind. **Document type:** trade publication.
—BLDSC (6537.500000); CASDDS; Ei; Faxon; Genuine Article; SWETS; UMI; UnCover. **CCC**.
Incorporates: Plastics Industry (ISSN 0096-9168)
Description: For processors and designers involved in buying and specifying plastics materials, additives and processing equipment.

668.4 — US — ISSN 1041-0821
PLASTICSBRIEF: DESIGN & MATERIALS NEWSLETTER. w. $249. Market Search, Inc., 2727 Holland Sylvania Rd., Ste. A, Toledo, OH 43615. TEL 419-535-7899. FAX 419-535-1243. Ed. James R. Best.
Former titles: Plastics Brief. Design and Materials Edition (ISSN 0745-0133); Plastic Product Design (ISSN 0194-8466)

668.4 — US — ISSN 1041-0813
PLASTICSBRIEF: EXTRUSION & BLOW MOLDING NEWSLETTER. w. $249. Market Search, Inc., 2727 Holland Sylvania Rd., Ste. A, Toledo, OH 43615. TEL 419-535-7899. FAX 419-535-1243. Ed. James R. Best.
Former titles: Plastics Brief. Extrusion and Blow Molding Edition (ISSN 0745-0141); Extrusion and Blow Molding News Brief (ISSN 0194-8482)

668.4 — US — ISSN 1041-0791
PLASTICSBRIEF: INJECTION MOLDING NEWSLETTER. w. $249. Market Search, Inc., 2727 Holland Sylvania Rd., Ste. A, Toledo, OH 43615. TEL 419-535-7899. FAX 419-535-1243. Ed. James R. Best.
Former titles: Plastics Brief. Injection Molding Edition (ISSN 0745-015X); Injection Molding News Brief (ISSN 0300-7545)

668.4 — US — ISSN 0744-5296
PLASTICSBRIEF: REINFORCED PLASTIC EDITION. w. $249. Market Search, Inc., 2727 Holland Sylvania Rd., Ste. A, Toledo, OH 43615. TEL 419-535-7899. FAX 419-535-1243. Ed. James R. Best.

668.4 — US — ISSN 1041-083X
PLASTICSBRIEF: THERMOPLASTICS MARKETING NEWSLETTER. 1972. w. $249. Market Search, Inc., 2727 Holland Sylvania Rd., Ste. A, Toledo, OH 43615. TEL 419-535-7899. FAX 419-535-1243. Ed. James R. Best. index. circ. 400.
Former titles: Plastics Brief: Marketing Edition (ISSN 0745-0168); Plastics Marketing News Brief (ISSN 0194-8474)
Description: News on sales opportunities and competitive intelligence for the industry, targeted toward executives.

668.4 630 — FR — ISSN 0257-9022
PLASTICULTURE; les plastiques dans l'agriculture - plastics in agriculture and horticulture - los plasticos en la agricultura - kunststoffe im landbau. (Text in English and French; abstracts in German, Spanish) 1968. q. 400 F. (foreign 480 F.) (effective 1996). International Committee of Plastics in Agriculture, 65 rue de Prony, 75854 Paris Cedex 17, France. TEL 44-01-16-49. FAX 44-01-16-55. (Dist. in US by: American Society for Plasticulture (ASP), c/o H. Carl Hoefer, Jr., Box 860238, St. Augustine, FL 32086.. TEL 904-829-1667) Ed. Jean-Claude Garnaud. adv.; bk.rev.; illus. circ. 1,000. **Indexed:** Agri.Eng.Abstr., Hort.Abstr., Intl.Polym.Sci.& Tech., Irr.& Drain.Abstr., Ornam.Hort., RAPRA. **Document type:** academic/scholarly publication.
—BLDSC (6537.550000).

668.4 678.4 — YU — ISSN 0351-8787
CODEN: PLGUDV
PLASTIKA I GUMA. (Text in Serbo-Croatian; summaries in English) 1982. q. $50. Savez Hemicara i Tehnologa Jugoslavije, Kneza Milosa 9, P.O. Box 187, 11001 Belgrade, Yugoslavia. Ed. Milenko Trbovic. adv.; bk.rev. circ. 1,000. **Indexed:** Chem.Abstr., Ref.Zh.
—BLDSC (6537.555000); CASDDS.

668.4 — NO — ISSN 0801-6747
PLASTINDUSTRIEN. 1935. m. NOK 260. Selvig Publishing AS, Plastindustrien, P.O. Box 9070 Groenland, N-0133 Oslo, Norway. Ed. Tove Gjerdrum. adv.; bk.rev.; charts; illus.; stat.; index. circ. 3,457. **Indexed:** Chem.Abstr.
Formerly: Plastnytt (ISSN 0032-1311)

668.4 — FR — ISSN 0180-9237
PLASTIQUES FLASH. 1965. 10/yr. 150 F. Societe Europeenne de Presse et d'Edition, 78 route de la Reine, 92100 Boulogne, France. TEL 46-04-78-26. FAX 46-04-24-76. Ed. Jack Marchal. circ. 7,500. **Indexed:** Intl.Polym.Sci.& Tech., RAPRA.
—BLDSC (6537.581000).
Description: Contains information on state-of-the-art robotics equipment and machines used in the plastics manufacturing industry.

668.4 — FR — ISSN 0032-1303
TP986.A1 — CODEN: PMELAW
PLASTIQUES MODERNES ET ELASTOMERES. 1948. m. 520 F. (foreign 590 F.). Societe de Publications Specialisees, 142 rue Montmartre, 75002 Paris, France. TEL 40-26-83-21. FAX 40-39-97-52. TELEX 220 528 F. Ed. Benedite Topuz. adv.; charts; illus.; mkt.; cum.index. circ. 6,644. **Indexed:** C.I.S. Abstr., Intl.Polym.Sci.& Tech., PROMT, RAPRA.
—BLDSC (6537.620000); CASDDS; Ei; SWETS. **CCC**.
Incorporates: Plastiques Informations (ISSN 0032-129X); **Formerly:** Industrie des Plastiques Moderne et Elastomeres.

668.4 — GW — ISSN 0032-1338
TP986.A1 — CODEN: PLARAN
PLASTVERARBEITER; kunststoffanwendung und -verarbeitung. 1950. m. DM.288 (foreign DM.306). Huethig GmbH, Postfach 102869, 69018 Heidelberg, Germany. TEL 06221-489349. FAX 06221-489242. TELEX 5215498-HUEM-D. Eds. Bernhard Liesch, Alexander Buechler. adv.; B&W page DM.4650; trim 210 x 297; adv. contact: Ludger Aulich. bk.rev.; illus.; index; circ. 11,532. **Indexed:** Art & Archaeol.Tech.Abstr., C.I.S. Abstr., Chem.Abstr., Eng.Ind., Excerp.Med., Int.Packag.Abstr., Intl.Polym.Sci.& Tech., Packag.Sci.Tech., RAPRA. **Document type:** trade publication.
—BLDSC (6537.750000); CASDDS; Ei; SWETS.
Description: For plastics processors and users, machinery and appliance constructors, and raw material manufacturers.

668.4 678.2 — CI — ISSN 0351-1871
CODEN: PLMRDI
POLIMERI; Jugoslavenski casopis za plastiku i gumu. 1980. bi-m. $100. Drustvo Plasticara i Gumaraca, Garicgradska 6, 41001 Zagreb, Croatia. TEL 041-388-132. FAX 041-422-936. TELEX 22167. Ed. Barbara Rastovic. adv.; bk.rev. circ. 1,000. **Indexed:** Chem.Abstr., Intl.Polym.Sci.& Tech., RAPRA, Ref.Zh.
—BLDSC (6543.380600); CASDDS; Ei.

668.4 — PL — ISSN 0370-0879
POLITECHNIKA WROCLAWSKA. INSTYTUT TECHNOLOGII ORGANICZNEJ I TWORZYW SZTUCZNYCH. PRACE NAUKOWE. STUDIA I MATERIALY. (Text in Polish; summaries in English and Russian) 1971. irreg., no.17, 1977. price varies. Wydawnictwo Politechniki Wroclawskiej, Wybrzeze Wyspianskiego 27, 50-370 Wroclaw, Poland. FAX 22-36-64. TEL 712559 PWRPL. (Dist. by: Ars Polona-Ruch, Krakowskie Przedmiescie 7, Warsaw, Poland) **Indexed:** Chem.Abstr. **Document type:** academic/scholarly publication.

668.4 — US — ISSN 0272-8397
TA418.9.C6 — CODEN: PCOMDI
POLYMER COMPOSITES. 1980. bi-m. $200 (foreign $220). Society of Plastics Engineers, Inc., 14 Fairfield Dr., Brookfield, CT 06804-0304. TEL 203-775-0471. FAX 203-775-8490. TELEX 643-712. Ed. Roger Porter. charts; illus.; index. circ. 1,000. (back issues avail.) **Indexed:** Cadscan, Chem.Abstr., Eng.Ind., INSPEC, Int.Aerosp.Abstr., Intl.Polym.Sci.& Tech., Lead Abstr., RAPRA, Zincscan. **Document type:** academic/scholarly publication.
—BLDSC (6547.704300); CASDDS; Ei; Faxon; Genuine Article; SWETS; UMI; UnCover. **CCC**.

POLYMER DEGRADATION AND STABILITY. see CHEMISTRY — Organic Chemistry

POLYMER FRIENDS FOR RUBBER, PLASTICS AND FIBER/PORIMA NO TOMO. see RUBBER

668.42 — UK — ISSN 0959-8103
TP1101 — CODEN: PLYIEI
POLYMER INTERNATIONAL. 1969. m. $875 (foreign $875) (effective 1996). John Wiley & Sons Ltd., Journals, Baffins Ln., Chichester, W. Sussex PO19 1UD, England. TEL 01243-779777. FAX 01243-776128. (Subscr. in the Americas to: John Wiley & Sons, Inc., 605 Third Ave., New York, NY 10518. TEL 212-850-6645. FAX 212-850-6021) Ed. J.F. Kennedy. adv.; bk.rev.; charts; illus.; index. circ. 379. (also avail. in microform from UMI; back issues avail.) **Indexed:** Anal.Abstr., Br.Tech.Ind., Chem.Abstr., Chem.Eng.Abstr., Curr.Cont., Curr.Pack.Abstr., Dairy Sci.Abstr., Excerp.Med., INSPEC (1969-1989), Intl.Polym.Sci.& Tech., RAPRA, T.C.E.A., W.R.C.Inf., World Surf.Coat., World Text.Abstr. **Document type:** academic/scholarly publication.
—BLDSC (6547.706750); CASDDS; Ei; Faxon; Genuine Article; SWETS. **CCC**.
Formerly (until 1987): British Polymer Journal (ISSN 0007-1641)
Description: Reports original research and advances in all branches of macromolecular science and technology, including polymer chemistry and physics, biopolymers and industrial polymer science. Refereed Serial

POLYMER RECYCLING. see ENVIRONMENTAL STUDIES — Waste Management

668.4 547 — UK — ISSN 0142-9418
TA455.P58 — CODEN: POTEDZ
POLYMER TESTING. 1980. bi-m. £355($565) (effective 1996). Elsevier Science Ltd., P.O. Box 800, Kidlington, OX5 1DX, England. TEL 44-1865-843000. FAX 44-1865-843010. E-mail: nlinfo-f@elsevier.nl; usinfo-f@elsevier.com; forinfo-kyf04035@niftyserve.or.jp; Site addr.: http://www.elsevier.nl/. (Subscr. in U.S. and Canada to: Elsevier Science, 660 White Plains Rd., Tarrytown, NY 10591-5153. TEL 914-524-9200. FAX 914-333-2444) Ed. R. Brown. adv.; bk.rev.; illus.; index. (also avail. in microform from UMI; back issues avail.) **Indexed:** Chem.Abstr., Curr.Cont., Eng.Ind., INSPEC, Intl.Polym.Sci.& Tech., Met.Abstr., RAPRA, Sci.Cit.Ind. **Document type:** academic/scholarly publication.
—BLDSC (6547.740500); CASDDS; Ei; Faxon; Genuine Article; SWETS; UnCover. **CCC**.
Description: Provides a forum for developments in the testing of polymers and polymeric products. Refereed Serial

PLASTICS

POLYMERIC MATERIALS SCIENCE AND ENGINEERING. see *CHEMISTRY — Organic Chemistry*

668.4 UK ISSN 0967-3911
TA418.9.C6 CODEN: PPOCEC
POLYMERS AND POLYMER COMPOSITES. 1988. bi-m. £220 (foreign £240). R A P R A Technology Ltd., Shawbury, Shrewsbury, Shrops. SY4 4NR, England. TEL 01939-250383. FAX 01939-251118. TELEX 35134. Ed. G. Pritchard. abstr.; bibl.; charts; illus.; stat. (back issues avail.) **Indexed:** Intl.Polym.Sci.& Tech., RAPRA. **Document type:** academic/scholarly publication
—BLDSC (6547.742310); CASDDS; Ei; Faxon; SWETS.
Formerly (until 1993): Composite Polymers (ISSN 0952-6919)
Description: For engineers, scientists and designers working with polymeric organic matrix composite materials, particularly those needing original papers for research, material specification, sales or end-use purposes.
Refereed Serial

668.4 678.2 UK ISSN 0268-9812
POLYMERS AND RUBBER ASIA. 1985. bi-m. £65. S K C Communications Ltd., Southfields, South View Rd., Wadhurst, E. Sussex TN5 6TP, England. TEL 01892-784099. FAX 01892-784089. Eds. Tim Knight, Neil Riley; Pub. Tim Ornellas. adv.; B&W page £1820, color page £2600; trim 254 x 181. bk.rev. circ. 11,905. **Indexed:** Intl.Polym.Sci.& Tech., RAPRA. **Document type:** trade publication.
—BLDSC (6547.742322).
Description: Presents technical information for the processors of plastics and rubber in the Pacific Rim area.

668.4 540 UK ISSN 1042-7147
TP1080 CODEN: PADTE5
POLYMERS FOR ADVANCED TECHNOLOGIES. 1990. m. $995 (foreign $995) (effective 1996). John Wiley & Sons Ltd., Journals, Baffins Ln., Chichester, W. Sussex PO19 1UD, England. TEL 01243-779777. FAX 01243-776128. TELEX 86290 WIBOOK G. (Subscr. in the Americas to: John Wiley & Sons, Inc., 605 Third Ave., New York, NY 10158. TEL 212-850-6645. FAX 212-850-6021) Ed. M. Lewin. circ. 163. (also avail. in microform from UMI; back issues avail.) **Indexed:** Intl.Polym.Sci.& Tech., RAPRA. **Document type:** academic/scholarly publication.
—BLDSC (6547.742200); CASDDS; Ei; Faxon; Genuine Article; SWETS; UMI. **CCC.**
Description: Focuses on the interest of scientists and engineers from academia and industry who are participating in new areas of polymer research and development related to advanced technologies.

668.4 US ISSN 0171-709X
POLYMERS - PROPERTIES AND APPLICATIONS. 1952. irreg. price varies. Springer-Verlag, 175 Fifth Ave., New York, NY 10010. TEL 212-460-1500. FAX 212-473-6272. (Also: Berlin, Heidelberg, Tokyo and Vienna) Ed. K.A. Wolf. (reprint service avail. from ISI) **Indexed:** INSPEC. **Document type:** monographic series.
Formerly (until vol.15, 1970): Chemie, Physik und Technologie der Kunststoffe in Einzeldarstellungen (ISSN 0069-3073)

668.4 II ISSN 0253-7303
CODEN: POPLD2
POPULAR PLASTICS. 1955. m. Rs.250($100) Colour Publications Pvt. Ltd., 126-A Dhuruwadi, Off Dr. Nariman Rd., Bombay 400 025, India. TEL 430-9318. TELEX 71242 CEPE IN. Ed. R.V. Raghavan. adv.; bk.rev.; abstr.; charts; illus. circ. 10,375. (also avail. in microfilm from UMI; reprint service avail. from UMI) **Indexed:** Chem.Abstr.
—CASDDS; UMI.
Former titles: Popular Plastics and Rubber; (until 1979, vol. 24): Popular Plastics (ISSN 0032-4604)

PREVISIONS GLISSANTES DETAILLEES EN PERSPECTIVES SECTORIELLES (VOL.23): TRANSFORMATION DU CAOUTCHOUC ET DES MATIERES PLASTIQUES. see *BUSINESS AND ECONOMICS — Economic Situation And Conditions*

PROGRESS IN RUBBER AND PLASTICS TECHNOLOGY. see *RUBBER*

668.4 JA ISSN 0289-4556
PURASUCHIKKU SEIKEI GIJUTSU/PLASTIC MOLDING TECHNOLOGY. (Text in Japanese) 1984. m. 1000 Yen per no. Shiguma Publishing Co., Ltd., 15-8-203, Sakuragaokacho, Shibuya-ku, Tokyo 150, Japan.
—BLDSC (7160.449000).

R A P R A NEW TRADE NAMES IN THE RUBBER AND PLASTICS INDUSTRIES. (Rubber and Plastics Research Association of Great Britain) see *RUBBER*

668.4 678.2 658.5 UK ISSN 0140-041X
R A P R A NEWS. 1977. q. free. R A P R A Technology Ltd., Shawbury, Shrewsbury, Shrops. SY4 4NR, England. TEL 01939-250383. FAX 01939-251118. TELEX 35134. Ed. Sharon Lloyd. illus.; stat.; tr.lit. circ. 7,000. (back issues avail.) **Indexed:** Intl.Polym.Sci.& Tech., RAPRA. **Document type:** newsletter.

668.4 660 UK ISSN 0966-9698
RADNEWS. q. £65. Paint Research Association, 8 Waldegrave Rd., Teddington, Mddsx. TW11 8LD, England. TEL 081-977-4427. FAX 081-943-4705. **Document type:** bulletin.
Description: Provides information on the radiation curing industry.

RAW MATERIALS FOR PIGMENTS, FILLERS AND EXTENDERS. see *CERAMICS, GLASS AND POTTERY*

668.4 660 UK ISSN 0144-6266
RECENT ADVANCES IN CROSSLINKING & CURING. 1980. 6/yr. £190. Paint Research Association, 8 Waldegrave Rd., Teddington, Middlesex TW11 8LD, England. TEL 081-977-4427. FAX 081-943-4705. Ed. H. Warson. circ. 70. **Document type:** trade publication.

668.4 614 US ISSN 1065-1896
REGULATORY UPDATE; government regulations related to plastics industry. 1983. m. $95. Lewis B. Weisfeld, Ed. & Pub., 1 Franklin Town Blvd., Ste. 1204, Philadelphia, PA 19103. TEL 215-567-7235. FAX 215-567-7235. E-mail: 76674.1441@CompuServe.com. (back issues avail.) **Document type:** newsletter.
●Also available online.
Description: Covers regulatory (Federal Register) and legislative updates in public health and safety and environmental developments affecting the plastics industry.

668.4 UK ISSN 0034-3617
TA455.P55
REINFORCED PLASTICS. 1956. m. £90($144) (effective 1996). Elsevier Science Ltd., P.O. Box 800, Kidlington, Oxford OX5 1DX, England. TEL 44-1865-843000. FAX 44-1865-843010. E-mail: nlinfo-f@elsevier.nl; usinfo-f@elsevier.com; forinfo-kyf04035@niftyserve.or.jp; Site addr.: http://www.elsevier.nl/. (Subscr. in U.S. and Canada to: Elsevier Science, 660 White Plains Rd., Tarrytown, NY 10591-5153. TEL 914-524-9200. FAX 914-333-2444) Ed. Amanda Weaver. adv.; bk.rev.; charts; illus.; tr.lit.; index. circ. 3,000. **Indexed:** BMT, Br.Tech.Ind., Chem.Abstr., Intl.Polym.Sci.& Tech., PROMT, RAPRA. **Document type:** trade publication.
—BLDSC (7351.200000); Ei; Faxon; SWETS. **CCC.**
Description: For those involved in the polymer-based composites industry.

668.4 SP ISSN 0034-8708
TP986.A1 CODEN: RPMOAM
REVISTA DE PLASTICOS MODERNOS. 1950. m. $30. Instituto de Ciencia y Tecnologia de Polimeros, Juan de la Cierva 3, 28006 Madrid, Spain. TEL 91-261-34-41. FAX 91-5644853. (Co-sponsor: Consejo Superior de Investigaciones Cientificas) Ed. O. Laguna Castellanos. adv.; bk.rev.; charts; illus.; pat. circ. 5,000. **Indexed:** Art & Archaeol.Tech.Abstr., Chem.Abstr., Ind.SST, Intl.Polym.Sci.& Tech., RAPRA, World Surf.Coat. **Document type:** trade publication.
—BLDSC (7869.810000); CASDDS; Ei; SWETS. **CCC.**

RUBBER AND PLASTICS DIGEST. see *RUBBER*

RUBBER & PLASTICS NEWS; the rubber industry's international newspaper. see *RUBBER*

RUBBER & PLASTICS NEWS II. see *RUBBER*

RUBBER RESEARCH INSTITUTE OF SRI LANKA. JOURNAL. see *RUBBER*

RUBBER SOUTHERN AFRICA. see *RUBBER*

RUBBICANA-EUROPE (YEAR). see *RUBBER*

668.4 US
S P I MEMBERSHIP DIRECTORY AND BUYER'S GUIDE. 1937. a. $270 to non-members; members $90. Society of the Plastics Industry, Inc., 1275 "K" St., N.W., Washington, DC 20005. TEL 202-371-5200. FAX 202-408-0736. Ed. Diana D. Wright. circ. 3,000. (back issues avail.) **Document type:** directory.
Description: Lists SPI member companies and their products and services.

SEALANTS; the professional's guide. see *RUBBER*

668.4 JA ISSN 0915-4027
CODEN: SIKAE4
SEIKEI KAKOU/JAPAN SOCIETY OF POLYMER PROCESSING. JOURNAL. (Text in English, Japanese) 1989. bi-m. (Purasuchikku Seikei Kako Gakkai - Japan Society of Polymer Processing) Shiguma Shuppan - Sigma Publishing Co., Ltd., 15-8-203, Sakuragaoka-cho, Shibuya-ku, Tokyo 150, Japan. TEL 03-3477-0336. FAX 03-3477-2710.
—BLDSC (8219.724000); CASDDS.

668.4 IT
SELEPLAST. 12/yr. Editrice Stampa Periodica, Viale Certosa 238, 20156 Milan, Italy. TEL 2-308-51-41. FAX 2-30-88-503. Ed. Franco Pigozzi. circ. 9,500.

668
SELF-ADHESIVE MATERIALS AND MARKETS BULLETIN. 10/yr. £185($315) (outside Europe £330). Data Transcripts Ltd., P.O. Box 14, Dorking, Surrey RH5 4YN, England. TEL 01306-884473. Ed. Robert A. Higham. **Document type:** newsletter.

668.4 US
SOCIETY OF PLASTICS ENGINEERS. ANNUAL TECHNICAL CONFERENCE (ANTEC). PROCEEDINGS. a. $135 to non-members; members $135; institutions $160. Society of Plastics Engineers, Inc., 14 Fairfield Dr., Brookfield, CT 06804-0403. TEL 203-775-0471. FAX 203-775-8490. TELEX 643-712. **Document type:** proceedings.

660 US ISSN 0195-4288
SOCIETY OF PLASTICS ENGINEERS. MONOGRAPHS. 1973. irreg., unnumbered, latest 1992. price varies. John Wiley & Sons, Inc., 605 Third Ave., New York, NY 10158. TEL 212-850-6000. FAX 212-850-6088. TELEX 12-7063. **Document type:** monographic series.

668.4 US
SOCIETY OF THE PLASTICS INDUSTRY. REINFORCED PLASTICS COMPOSITES INSTITUTE. ANNUAL TECHNICAL CONFERENCE. PREPRINT. 1946. a. $10. Society of the Plastics Industry, Composites Institute, 355 Lexington Ave., New York, NY 10017. TEL 212-351-5410. FAX 212-370-1731. Ed. J. McDermott. circ. 3,000. **Indexed:** Chem.Abstr.
Formerly: Society of the Plastics Industry. Reinforced Plastics Composites Institute. Annual Technical Conference. Proceedings.

668.4 US
SOCIETY OF THE PLASTICS INDUSTRY. URETHANE DIVISION. CONFERENCE PROCEEDINGS. 1979. irreg. price varies. Technomic Publishing Co., Inc., 851 New Holland Ave., Box 3535, Lancaster, PA 17604. TEL 717-291-5609. FAX 717-295-4538. TELEX 230 753565 (TECHNOMIC UD). **Document type:** proceedings.
Refereed Serial

STUDIES IN POLYMER SCIENCE. see *CHEMISTRY*

668.4 HK ISSN 1023-0246
SUJIAO KEJI/PLASTICS TECHNOLOGY. (Text in Chinese, English) 1991? bi-m. B & I Publication Co., Ltd., 18-F, First Pacific Bank Centre, 51-57 Gloucester Rd., Wanchai, Hong Kong. TEL 852-865-2633. FAX 852-866-1770. **Indexed:** Intl.Polym.Sci.& Tech., RAPRA. **Document type:** trade publication.
Description: Covers the plastics processing industry.

668.4   CC
SUOLIAO/PLASTICS. (Text in Chinese, English) bi-m. Beijing Plastics Research Institute, 47, Jiu Gu Lou Street, Beijing 100009, People's Republic of China. TEL 441734. TELEX 22470 BFTCC CN. (Dist. overseas by: Guoji Shudian - China International Book Trading Corp., P.O. Box 339, Beijing, P.R.C.) Ed. Zhao Yiming.

TECHNICAL TEXTILES INTERNATIONAL. see *TEXTILE INDUSTRIES AND FABRICS*

668.4   US   ISSN 0120-7644
TECNOLOGIA DEL PLASTICO.* 1985. bi-m. Carvajal International, Inc., 901 Ponce de Leon Blvd., Ste. 901, Coral Gables, FL 33134-3073. TEL 305-448-6875. FAX 305-448-9942. Ed. Miguel Garzon. circ. 10,308.

UMFORMTECHNIK. see *METALLURGY*

UNION DES INDUSTRIES ET DE LA DISTRIBUTION DES PLASTIQUES ET DU CAOUTCHOUC. GUIDE. see *BUSINESS AND ECONOMICS — Trade And Industrial Directories*

UNIVERSITATEA POLITEHNICA BUCURESTI. BULETIN STIINTIFIC. CHIMIE SI STIINTA MATERIALELOR/POLYTECHNICAL UNIVERSITY OF BUCHAREST. SCIENTIFIC BULLETIN. CHEMISTRY AND MATERIALS SCIENCE. see *CHEMISTRY*

668.4   US   ISSN 0149-1342
TP1180.P8   CODEN: URABB
URETHANE ABSTRACTS. 1971. m. $205. Technomic Publishing Co., Inc., 851 New Holland Ave., Box 3535, Lancaster, PA 17604. TEL 717-291-5609. FAX 717-295-4538. TELEX 230 753565 (TECHNOMIC UD). Ed. John W. DeGroot, Jr. circ. 175. **Document type:** abstracting/indexing.
—UMI. **CCC.**
Refereed Serial

668.4 660.284   US   ISSN 0049-5700
TP1180.P8
URETHANE PLASTICS AND PRODUCTS. 1971. m. $195. Technomic Publishing Co., Inc., 851 New Holland Ave., Box 3535, Lancaster, PA 17604. TEL 717-291-5609. FAX 717-295-4538. TELEX 230 753565 (TECHNOMIC UD). Ed. Michael Margotta. bk.rev.; charts; illus. circ. 160. (looseleaf format) Indexed: Intl.Polym.Sci.& Tech.; PROMT, RAPRA. **Document type:** academic/scholarly publication.
—BLDSC (9124.140000); UMI. **CCC.**

668.4 698   IT
VERNICIATURA E FINITURA DEI PLASTICI. 1986. bi-m. L.90000 (free within Italy). Rivista del Colore s.r.l., Via degli Imbriani 10, 20158 Milan, Italy. Ed. Danilo O. Malvolti. adv.; bk.rev.; abstr.; tr.lit.; index. circ. 3,000.

PLASTICS — Abstracting, Bibliographies, Statistics

668.4   US
BIBLIOGRAPHY OF TECHNICAL RESOURCES ON PLASTICS IN THE 90'S. a. free. Society of Manufacturing Engineers, Plastics Molders and Manufacturers Group, One SME Dr., Box 930, Dearborn, MI 48121. TEL 313-271-1500. FAX 313-240-8255. TELEX 297742 SME UR (VIA RCA). **Document type:** bibliography.

668.4   US   ISSN 0734-869X
    CODEN: CAFPEU
C A SELECTS. FIBER-REINFORCED PLASTICS. s-w. $220 to non-members; members $65 (effective 1996). Chemical Abstracts Service (Subsidiary of: American Chemical Society), 2540 Olentangy River Rd., Box 3012, Columbus, OH 43210-0012. TEL 614-447-3600. FAX 614-447-3713. TELEX 6842086. **Document type:** abstracting/indexing.
Description: Covers properties, processing, use of thermoplastics and thermosetting resins reinforced by natural or synthetic fibers.

668.4   US   ISSN 0734-8673
    CODEN: CANPE2
C A SELECTS. NEW PLASTICS. s-w. $220 to non-members; members $65 (effective 1996). Chemical Abstracts Service (Subsidiary of: American Chemical Society), 2540 Olentangy River Rd., Box 3012, Columbus, OH 43210-0012. TEL 614-447-3600. FAX 614-447-3713. TELEX 6842086. **Document type:** abstracting/indexing.
Description: Covers newly synthesized or newly reported thermoplastic and thermosetting resins.

668.4   US   ISSN 0195-511X
    CODEN: CSPFD5
C A SELECTS. PLASTIC FILMS. s-w. $220 to non-members; members $65 (effective 1996). Chemical Abstracts Service (Subsidiary of: American Chemical Society), 2540 Olentangy River Rd., Box 3012, Columbus, OH 43210-0012. TEL 614-447-3600. FAX 614-447-3713. TELEX 6842086. **Document type:** abstracting/indexing.
Description: Covers manufacture, properties, fabrication, and applications of polymeric films.

668.4   US   ISSN 0734-8681
    CODEN: CAADE3
C A SELECTS. PLASTICS ADDITIVES. s-w. $220 to non-members; members $65 (effective 1996). Chemical Abstracts Service (Subsidiary of: American Chemical Society), 2540 Olentangy River Rd., Box 3012, Columbus, OH 43210-0012. TEL 614-447-3600. FAX 614-447-3713. TELEX 6842086. **Document type:** abstracting/indexing.
Description: Covers materials added to thermoplastic and thermosetting resins to modify properties; plasticizers, inert and reinforcing fillers, pigments, heat and light stabilizers, antioxidants, blowing agents.

668.4   US   ISSN 0275-7125
    CODEN: CPFUDD
C A SELECTS. PLASTICS FABRICATION & USES. s-w. $220 to non-members; members $65 (effective 1996). Chemical Abstracts Service (Subsidiary of: American Chemical Society), 2540 Olentangy River Rd., Box 3012, Columbus, OH 43210-0012. TEL 614-447-3600. FAX 614-447-3713. TELEX 6842086. **Document type:** abstracting/indexing.
Description: Covers processes of chemical or chemical engineering interest for fabricating polymers or compositions containing them.

668.4   US   ISSN 0275-7133
    CODEN: CSPPDZ
C A SELECTS. PLASTICS MANUFACTURE & PROCESSING. s-w. $220 to non-members; members $65 (effective 1996). Chemical Abstracts Service (Subsidiary of: American Chemical Society), 2540 Olentangy River Rd., Box 3012, Columbus, OH 43210-0012. TEL 614-447-3600. FAX 614-447-3713. TELEX 6842086. **Document type:** abstracting/indexing.
Description: Covers manufacture, testing, compounding, and processing of polymeric materials for use as resins or unsupported films; natural resins of industrial interest; additives for plastics and resins, e.g. crosslinking agents, plasticizers, fillers, foaming agents, pigments.

668.4 667.6   US   ISSN 0891-1886
C P I DIGEST. (Chemical Process Industries); key to world literature serving the coatings, plastics, fibers, adhesives, and related industries. 1974. m. $297. C P I Information Services, 2117 Cherokee Pkwy., Louisville, KY 40204. TEL 502-456-6288. FAX 502-454-4808. Ed. George S. Mattingly. adv. contact: Jeanne Phillips. abstr.; pat. circ. 850. (back issues avail.; reprint service avail. from CPI) **Document type:** academic/scholarly publication.
—**CCC.**
Formerly: Coatings Adlibra (ISSN 0146-9290)

668.4   US   ISSN 1049-1341
C2C ABSTRACTS: JAPAN - PLASTICS.* 1990. m. $200. Scan C2C, 1001 Pennsylvaia Ave., N.W., No.1300, Washington, DC 20024-2505. TEL 800-525-3865. FAX 202-863-3855. **Document type:** abstracting/indexing.
●Also available online. Vendor(s): Data-Star (JPTC), Knight-Ridder, Inc. (File no.582), European Space Agency (File no.241), Orbit Search Service (JTEC). Also available on CD-ROM. Producer(s): Knight-Ridder, Inc..
Description: Contains English abstracts of articles in Japanese scientific, business, and technical journals. Covers plastics, the plastics industry, processing, instrumentation, molding and extrusion.

011   GW   ISSN 0932-7754
D K I LITERATUR-SCHNELLDIENST KUNSTSTOFFE KAUTSCHUK FASERN. 1955. m. DM.2160. Deutsches Kunststoff-Institut, Schlossgartenstr. 6, 64289 Darmstadt, Germany. TEL 06151-162106. FAX 06151-292855. (Affiliate: Forschungsgesellschaft Kunststoffe e.V. Darmstadt) adv. circ. 150. (also avail. in diskette format; back issues avail.) **Document type:** abstracting/indexing.
●Also available online. Vendor(s): FIZ Technik, STN International.
—**CCC.**
Formerly: Literatur-Schnelldienst Kunststoffe und Kautschuk (ISSN 0024-4651)
Description: Abstract journal in the field of science and technology of polymer material (plastics, rubber and fiber materials).

668.4 016   US   ISSN 0013-7154
HD9661.A1   CODEN: TEUMA
END-USE MARKETS FOR PLASTICS. Variant title: Trends in End-Use Markets for Plastics. (Former name of issuing body: Springborn Laboratories, Inc.) 1968. m. $550 (Europe and S. America $585; elsewhere $595) (effective 1996). Springborn Materials Science Corp., 30 Springborn Ctr., Enfield, CT 06082. TEL 203-749-8371. FAX 203-749-8234. Ed. Cherie P. Henselder. charts; stat.; index; circ. 400 (paid). Indexed: Intl.Polym.Sci.& Tech., RAPRA. **Document type:** abstracting/indexing.
Description: Provides abstracts of articles on new plastics applications, end use market performance and growth potential, plastics penetration into market segments, and current events that may influence the plastics and allied chemicals industries.

668.4   FR
FRANCE. SERVICE D'ETUDE DES STRATEGIES ET DES STATISTIQUES INDUSTRIELLES. RESULTATS TRIMESTRIELS DES ENQUETES DE BRANCHE. TRANSFORMATION DES MATIERES PLASTIQUES. q. 180 F. (foreign 210 F.)(effective 1991). Service d'Etude des Strategies et des Statistiques Industrielles (SESSI), 85 Bd. du Montparnasse, 75270 Paris Cedex 06, France. TEL 45-56-42-34. FAX 45-56-40-71. stat.
Description: Provides detailed industry-wide performance statistics for comparative evaluations.

KEY ABSTRACTS - ADVANCED MATERIALS. see *PHYSICS — Abstracting, Bibliographies, Statistics*

668.4   US   ISSN 1066-7717
MARO POLYMER NOTES.* 1985. m. $895. Maro Communications, Box 37019, Tucson, AZ 85740-7019. TEL 602-322-5739. Ed. Roger D. Corneliussen. circ. 400.
—**CCC.**
Formerly (until 1987): Drexel Polymer Notes (ISSN 8756-4572)
Description: Contains abstracts on polymers: plastics, paints, coatings, rubber, elastomers, films, biomedical materials.
Refereed Serial

668.4 330   UK   ISSN 0956-1234
NONWOVENS ABSTRACTS. 1989. m. $504. Pira International, Randalls Rd., Leatherhead, Surrey KT22 7RU, England. TEL 0372-376161. FAX 0372-360104. Ed. Mark Englund; Pub. Marie Rushton. (back issues avail.) **Document type:** abstracting/indexing.
●Also available online. Vendor(s): Data-Star, Knight-Ridder, Inc., Orbit Search Service, STN International. Also available on CD-ROM. Producer(s): Knight-Ridder, Inc..
—**CCC.**

P A S C A L F 24: POLYMERES - PEINTURES - BOIS. see *CHEMISTRY — Abstracting, Bibliographies, Statistics*

PLASTICS — COMPUTER APPLICATIONS

668.4 338   US
POLYMERS, CERAMICS, COMPOSITE ALERT. (Part of: Materials Business Information Series) 1985. m. $285 (foreign $310); Metals Abstracts subscribers $180 (foreign $200). A S M International, Materials Information, Materials Park, OH 44073. TEL 216-338-5151. FAX 216-338-4634. TELEX 980-619. (UK Addr.: Institute of Materials, Materials Information, 1 Carlton House Terr., London SW1Y 5DB, England. TEL 071-839-4071) Ed.Bd. **Document type:** abstracting/indexing.
●Also available online. Vendor(s): CEDOCAR, CISTI, Data-Star (MBUS), Knight-Ridder, Inc. (File no.269), European Space Agency (File no.111), Orbit Search Service (MABU), STN International (MATBUS). Also available on CD-ROM. Producer(s): Knight-Ridder, Inc..
Description: International coverage of business developments for the engineered materials industries.

R A P R A ABSTRACTS. (Rubber and Plastics Research Association of Great Britain) see *RUBBER — Abstracting, Bibliographies, Statistics*

R A P R A ABSTRACTS - C D - R O M. (Rubber and Plastics Research Association of Great Britain) see *RUBBER — Abstracting, Bibliographies, Statistics*

668.4 678.2   UK   ISSN 0889-3144
TA455.P58   CODEN: RRVREQ
R A P R A REVIEW REPORTS; current developments in polymeric materials technology and engineering. 1988. m. £420 (foreign £470). (Rubber and Plastics Research Association of Great Britain, UK) R A P R A Technology Ltd., Shawbury, Shrewsbury, Shrops. SY4 4ND, England. TEL 01939-250383. FAX 01939-251118. TELEX 35134. Ed. Rebecca Dolbey. (also avail. in microform; back issues avail.) **Indexed:** Intl.Polym.Sci.& Tech., RAPRA. **Document type:** abstracting/indexing.
—BLDSC (7291.760000); CASDDS; SWETS; UMI. **CCC**.
Description: Covers recent advances within specific fields of plastics, rubber and composite materials technology.
Refereed Serial

URBAN WILDLIFE MANAGER'S NOTEBOOK. see *BIOLOGY*

PLASTICS — Computer Applications

668.4   US   ISSN 1052-0643
QD381.9.M3   CODEN: CPOSEJ
COMPUTATIONAL POLYMER SCIENCE. 1992. q. $190. Polymer Research Associates, Inc., 9200 Montgomery Rd., Ste. 23B, Cincinnati, OH 45242. TEL 513-891-7030. FAX 513-891-5867. Ed. James Mark. bk.rev.; software rev. **Document type:** academic/scholarly publication.
—BLDSC (3390.622000); CASDDS; Ei; Genuine Article; SWETS. **CCC**.
Refereed Serial

POETRY

see *Literature–Poetry*

POLITICAL SCIENCE

see also *Political Science–Civil Rights; Political Science–International Relations; Public Administration*

324.248907   DK   ISSN 0107-4628
A B AS BIBLIOGRAFISKE SERIE. 1973. irreg. Noerrebrogade 66 D, DK-2200 Copenhagen N, Denmark. TEL 45-35-36-15-22. FAX 45-35-36-32-22. Ed. Gerd Callesen. circ. 700. **Document type:** newsletter.
Description: Bibliographies of the Danish labor movement, its publishing houses, and foreign language material on the Danish labor movement.

322.4 947   US   ISSN 0001-0545
DK272.5
A B N CORRESPONDENCE. 1950. bi-m. $27. American Friends of the Anti-Bolshevik Bloc of Nations, 136 Second Ave., New York. Ed. Mrs. Slava Stetsko. bk.rev.; illus. circ. 6,000. **Indexed:** Mid.East: Abstr.& Ind.

329.3 330 370
531.64   US   ISSN 0896-3134
E740
A D A TODAY; a newsletter for liberal activists. 1947. 4/yr. $20 to non-members. Americans for Democratic Action, 1625 K St. N.W., Ste. 210, Washington, DC 20006. TEL 202-785-5980. FAX 202-785-5969. E-mail: 73311.2221@compuserve.com. Eds. Valerie Dulk, Emy Isaacs. circ. 60,000. (also avail. in microform from MIM,KTO) **Document type:** newsletter.
Formerly: A D A World (ISSN 0001-0871)
Description: Political and governmental news and commentary from liberal viewpoint, including congressional voting records and ratings.

329.3   US
A D ACTION NEWS AND NOTES. 1989. w. $20. Americans for Democratic Action, 1625 K St. N.W., Ste. 210, Washington, DC 20006. TEL 202-785-5980. E-mail: 73311.2221@compuserve.com. Eds. Amy Isaacs, Valerie Dulk. **Document type:** newsletter.
Description: Reports on congressional action.

320 300   GW   ISSN 0930-8199
A F B INFO. (Text in English, German) 1986. s-a. free. Arbeitsstelle Friedensforschung Bonn - Information Unit Peace Research Bonn, Beethovenallee 4, 53173 Bonn, Germany. TEL 0228-356032. FAX 0228-356050. E-mail: afbipra@iz-bonn.gesis.d.400de. Ed. Regine Mehl. circ. 3,000. (back issues avail.) **Document type:** newsletter.

320   US   ISSN 0893-293X
A L F NEWSLETTER. 1976. q. $10. Association of Libertarian Feminists, Box 20252, London Terrace Post Office, New York, NY 10011. Ed. Joan Kennedy Taylor. bk.rev. circ. 300. **Document type:** newsletter.
Description: Discusses the women's movement, the contemporary political scene, individual rights aimed at feminists and women in general.

320.532   CU
A N J U P E C. q. Asociacion Nacional de Jubilados y Pensionados de Comunicaciones, Oquendo No. 751, La Habana 3, Havana, Cuba.

320 920   US
A P S A BIOGRAPHICAL DIRECTORY. (Supplement: Trennial Directory of Members) irreg., 7th, 1988. $20 to non-members; members $15. American Political Science Association, 1527 New Hampshire Ave, N.W., Washington, DC 20036. TEL 202-483-2512. FAX 202-483-2657. **Document type:** directory.
Description: Contains names, addresses, current position, institutional affiliation, highest degree, fields of specialization, and honors and publications, of APSA individual members.

320.07   US
A P S A DIRECTORY OF POLITICAL SCIENCE DEPARTMENT CHAIRPERSONS. 1972. a. $20. American Political Science Association, 1527 New Hampshire Ave., N.W., Washington, DC 20036. TEL 202-483-2512. FAX 202-483-2657. circ. 1,000. **Document type:** directory.
Former titles: A P S A Directory of Department Chairpersons (ISSN 0196-5255); A P S A Directory of Department Chairmen (ISSN 0092-8658)
Description: Lists all four-year colleges and universities in the United States with departments of political science giving current chair names, e-mail addresses, department address, fax, and phone number.

320 350   AT   ISSN 0725-2390
A P S A NEWSLETTER. 1980. 6/yr. Aus.$20 (effective 1996). Australasian Political Studies Association, Dept. of Goverment, Queensland University, St. Lucia, Qld. 4067, Australia. TEL 61-7-365-2635. FAX 61-7-365-1388. E-mail: gtdgow@mailbox.uq.oz.au. Ed. David Gow. adv.; bk.rev. circ. 460. **Document type:** newsletter.
Description: Aims to keep members up-to-date with what is happening in political science.

320   US
JA28
A P S A SURVEY OF POLITICAL SCIENCE DEPARTMENTS. 1971. a. $20. American Political Science Association, 1527 New Hampshire Ave., N.W., Washington, DC 20036. TEL 202-483-2512. FAX 202-483-2657. stat. circ. 800. **Indexed:** SRI. **Document type:** monographic series.
Formerly: A P S A Departmental Services Program Survey of Departments (ISSN 0094-7954)
Description: Report of extensive questionnaire sent to 4-year institutions offering political science. Includes salary information and enrollment trends.

335.83   IT   ISSN 0044-5592
HX821
A - RIVISTA ANARCHICA. 1971. m. L.40000 (foreign L.60000). Editrice A Coop. a.r.l., Casella Postale 17120, 20170 Milan, Italy. TEL 02-2896627. Ed.Bd. bk.rev.; illus. circ. 8,500. (back issues avail.)
Description: Features articles that cover political events and ideas concerning the anarchist movement worldwide.

A S E A N BRIEFING. (Association of Southeast Asian Nations) see *BUSINESS AND ECONOMICS — Economic Situation And Conditions*

ABHAYADUTA. see *GENERAL INTEREST PERIODICALS — India*

ABRAHAM LINCOLN ASSOCIATION. JOURNAL. see *HISTORY*

320 300   VE
ACADEMIA DE CIENCIAS POLITICAS Y SOCIALES. BOLETIN.* 1937. irreg. Academia de Ciencias Politicas y Sociales, Bolsa a San Francisco, Palacio de las Academias, Caracas 1010, Venezuela. bibl.

320   AG
ACADEMIA NACIONAL DE CIENCIAS MORALES Y POLITICAS. ANALES. 1972. a. Academia Nacional de Ciencias Morales y Politicas, Avda. Alvear 1711-P.B. (1014), Buenos Aires, Argentina.

329.9   PO   ISSN 0871-102X
ACCAO SOCIALISTA. 1976. w. Socialist Party, Rua Sacadura Cabral 26, Dafundo, 1495 Lisbon, Portugal. TEL 01-4197705. Dir. Jose Manuel Vilaca.

ACTA FACULTATIS POLITICO-JURIDICAE UNIVERSITATIS SCIENTIARUM BUDAPESTIENSIS DE ROLANDO EOTVOS NOMINATAE. see *LAW*

320   NE   ISSN 0001-6810
ACTA POLITICA; tijdschrift voor politicologie. (Text in Dutch, English) 1966. 4/yr. fl.106 to individuals (foreign fl.148); institutions fl.172 (foreign fl.185) (effective 1994). (Nederlandse Kring voor Wetenschap der Politiek) Uitgeverij Boom, P.O. Box 400, 7940 AK Meppel, Netherlands. TEL 31-5220-57012. FAX 31-5220-53864. adv.; bk.rev.; charts. circ. 750. **Indexed:** A.B.C.Pol.Sci., Amer.Hist.& Life (until 1993), E.I., Hist.Abstr. (until 1993), Int.Polit.Sci.Abstr., Lang.& Lang.Behav.Abstr., Mid.East: Abstr.& Ind. **Document type:** academic/scholarly publication.
—BLDSC (0658.700000); SWETS; UnCover.

ACTA UNIVERSITATIS DE ATTILA JOZSEF NOMINATAE. ACTA IURIDICA ET POLITICA. see *LAW*

320   PL   ISSN 0137-6667
ACTA UNIVERSITATIS NICOLAI COPERNICI. NAUKI POLITYCZNE. 1967. irreg. price varies. Uniwersytet Mikolaja Kopernika, Biblioteka Uniwersytecka, Ul. Gagarina 13, 87-100 Torun, Poland. TEL 233-52. TELEX 552382. (Dist. by: Osrodek Rozpowszechniania Wydawnictw Naukowych PAN, Palac Kultury i Nauki, 00-901 Warsaw, Poland)

POLITICAL SCIENCE

320.531   HU   ISSN 0230-3558
DE1
ACTA UNIVERSITATIS SZEGEDIENSIS DE ATTILA JOZSEF NOMINATAE. SECTIO SCIENTIAE SOCIALISMI. (Supplement avail.: Tudomanyos Szocialismi (ISSN 0563-0657)) (Text in Hungarian, Russian; summaries in French, German and Russian) 1961. a. exchange basis. Attila Jozsef University, c/o E. Szabo, Exchange Librarian, Dugonics ter 13, P.O.B. 393, 6701 Szeged, Hungary. (Subscr. to: Kultura, Box 149, H-1389 Budapest, Hungary) Ed. Laszlo J. Nagy. circ. 300.
Description: Recent and contemporary history of Hungarian and world ideology, politics, society and economy linked with workers' and liberation movements and Marxism-Leninism.

327   PL   ISSN 0867-7409
ACTA UNIVERSITATIS WRATISLAVIENSIS. POLITOLOGIA. (Text in Polish; summaries in English or German) 1991. irreg. price varies. (Uniwersytet Wroclawski) Wydawnictwo Uniwersytetu Wroclawskiego, Pl. Uniwersytecki 9-13, 50-137 Wroclaw, Poland. TEL 44-10-06. (Dist. by: Ksiagarnia Uniwersytetu Wroclawskiego, Pl. Uniwersytecki 9-13, 50-137 Wroclaw, Poland) Ed. Andrzej W. Jablonski. circ. 300. **Document type:** academic/scholarly publication.

ACTA UNIVERSITATIS WRATISLAVIENSIS. PRAWO. see POLITICAL SCIENCE — Civil Rights

ACTA UNIVERSITATIS WRATISLAVIENSIS. STUDIA NAD FASZYZMEM I ZBRODNIAMI HITLEROWSKIMI. see HISTORY — History Of Europe

320.52   FR   ISSN 1166-3286
HC271
L'ACTION FRANCAISE. 1947. w. 780 F. S N I E P, 10 rue Croix des Petits Champs, 75001 Paris, France. TEL 1-40-39-92-06. Ed. Pierre Pujo. adv.; bk.rev. (tabloid format)
Formerly (until 1992): Aspects de la France (ISSN 0223-5773); Which incorporated: Cahiers d'Action Francaise; Which was formerly: Action Francaise Etudiante; Which superseded: A.F. Universite (ISSN 0001-1231)

322.4   CN   ISSN 0001-7469
ACTION NATIONALE. 1917. 10/yr. Can.$35. Ligue d'Action Nationale, 82 ouest, rue Sherbrooke, Montreal, Que. H2X 1X3, Canada. TEL 514-845-8533. FAX 514-844-6369. Ed. Gerard Turcotte. adv.; bk.rev.; index. circ. 2,000. **Indexed:** Amer.Hist.& Life, Can.B.P.I., Can.Per.Ind., Hist.Abstr., Pt.de Rep. (1979-).

320.9   DM   ISSN 0044-6106
ACTION POPULAIRE. 1964. 3/wk. 2160 Fr.CFA($25.) c/o Julian Aza, Ed., Boite Postale 215, Cotonou, Benin.

258   SZ   ISSN 0001-7507
ACTION SOCIALE. s-m. 12 Fr. Organisations Chretiennes-Sociales, Rue de l'Abbe Bovet 6, 1700 Fribourg, Switzerland.

320 800   US   ISSN 1074-2360
ACTIVE VOICE; of the people, by the people, for the people. 1988. m. $10 (Canada & Mexico $12; elsewhere $25). Active Communication Inc., Box 394, Berea, OH 44017. TEL 216-243-2189. FAX 216-362-6553. Ed. Ron McEntee. adv.: page $600. **Document type:** newspaper.

320   AG   ISSN 0327-6058
F2849.2
ACTUALIZACION POLITICA. 1991. m.? Fundacion Integracion Americana, Callao 420, 6o A, 1022 Buenos Aires, Argentina. TEL 49-1182. Ed. Mario A. Balzan.
Description: Provides political, economic, cultural and social analysis and information.

320.531 330.1   FR   ISSN 0994-4524
ACTUEL MARX. s-a. 290 F. (foreign 340 F.) (effective 1996). Presses Universitaires de France, Departement des Revues, 14 av. du Bois-de-l'Epine, 91003 Evry Cedex, France. TEL 1-60-77-82-05. FAX 1-60-79-20-45. TELEX PUF 600 474 F. Dirs. Jacques Bidet, Jacques Texier.
Description: Covers the philosophical, economic, historical, social science and literary aspects of Marxism.

320   IS   ISSN 0334-5831
HC415.25.A1
ADAM CHOFSHE/FREE MAN; free economy and society. (Text in Hebrew) 1984. bi-m. $15. P.O. Box 33180, Tel Aviv, Israel. Ed. Jacob Resler. adv.; bk.rev. circ. 1,000.

350 338   CK   ISSN 0120-3754
JA5
ADMINISTRACION Y DESARROLLO. 1962. s-a. Col.4000. Escuela Superior de Administracion Publica, Centro de Investigaciones en Administracion Publica, Diagonal 40 No. 46A-37, Bogota, Colombia. TEL 2224700. FAX 2224356. Ed. Julio Roballo Lozano. adv.; bk.rev.; bibl.; charts; stat. circ. 2,000.

320 350   US   ISSN 0738-3401
ADMINISTRATION AND POLICY JOURNAL. 1981-1983. m. $6.50. Rider College, Institute for Policy Research, Box 6400, Lawrenceville, NJ 08648. TEL 609-896-5357. Ed.Bd. bk.rev. circ. 400. **Indexed:** Educ.Admin.Abstr.
Formerly (until 1983): Administrative Comments and Letters.

320 350   TS
ADMINISTRATION AND POLITICAL SCIENCES REVIEW/MAJALLAT AL-ULUM AL-IDARIYYAH WAL-SIYASIYYAH.* (Text in Arabic, English) 1985. a. exchange basis. United Arab Emirates University, Faculty of Administration and Political Sciences, P.O. Box 15551, Al-Ain, United Arab Emirates. TEL 637833. TELEX 33521 JAMEAH. circ. 500.
Description: Publishes research papers on topics in administration and political science.

ADMINISTRATION & SOCIETY. see PUBLIC ADMINISTRATION

328 973   US
ADVANCE LOCATOR FOR CAPITOL HILL. Variant title: C.S.D. Advance Locator. 1963. a. $30. Staff Directories Ltd., Box 62, Mt. Vernon, VA 22121. TEL 703-739-0900. FAX 703-739-0234. Ed. Wayne Walker; Pub. Ann L. Brownson. (also avail. in diskette format) **Document type:** directory.
●Also available on CD-ROM.
Description: Provides updates on members of Congress, staffs, titles, addresses, district offices and phone number.

322.4   US
ADVOCATE (PANHANDLE). 1986. bi-m. $5. Peace Farm, HCR2 Box 25, Panhandle, TX 79068. TEL 806-335-1715. Ed. Mavis Belisle. adv.; bk.rev.; circ. 450 (paid); 400 (controlled). (back issues avail.) **Document type:** newsletter.
Description: Anti-nuclear and anti-war activist news and views. Aims to create an environment for peace through peaceful means, to assert that peace can exist only where there is justice, and to develop an ecological model for nonviolent social change.

320   US
ADVOCATE'S ADVOCATE.* 1988. m. $25. Advocacy Institute, 1707 L St., N.W., Ste. 400, Washington, DC 20036-4201. TEL 202-659-8475. FAX 202-659-8484. Ed. Stan Cohen. bk.rev. circ. 500. (back issues avail.)
Formerly: GiantKilling.
Description: Covers lobbying, using the media, and public policy advocacy.

AELDRE DANSKE TINGBOEGER. see HISTORY — History Of Europe

AFRICA ANALYSIS; fortnightly bulletin on financial and political trends. see BUSINESS AND ECONOMICS — Economic Situation And Conditions

960   UK   ISSN 0044-6483
DT1
AFRICA CONFIDENTIAL. 1960. 25/yr. £180($468) (foreign £242) (effective 1996). Basil Blackwell Ltd., 108 Cowley Rd., Oxford OX4 1JF, England. TEL 44-1865-791100. FAX 44-1865-791347. Ed. Patrick Smith. index. circ. 3,500. (back issues avail.) **Indexed:** Curr.Cont.M.E., Key to Econ.Sci. **Document type:** newsletter.
—BLDSC (0732.153000). **CCC.**
Description: Covers political and economic analysis of African countries.

320   NP   ISSN 8755-5034
AFRICA INTERNATIONAL. (Text in English) 1983. a. $100. Siveast Consultants, Inc., USA, P.O. Box 8510, Kathmandu, Nepal. (UK subscr. to: Dr. Ramasastry, c/o Overseas Customer Service, Midland Bank Blc., Poultry and Princes St., London EC2, England) Ed. C.V. Ramasastry. adv.; bk.rev. circ. controlled. (looseleaf format) **Document type:** academic/scholarly publication.

960   II   ISSN 0044-6491
AFRICA LETTER. 1971. w. Rs.520($100.) K.K. Roy (Private) Ltd., 55 Gariahat Rd., P.O. Box 10210, Calcutta 700 019, India. Ed. Dr. K.K. Roy. circ. 1,180. (also avail. in microfilm)

960   US
DT1
AFRICA NEWS ONLINE. 1973. s-m. Africa News Service, Inc., Box 3851, Durham, NC 27702. TEL 919-286-0747. FAX 919-286-2614. Ed. Reed Kramerl. adv.; bk.rev.; s-a. index. (back issues avail.; reprint service avail.) **Indexed:** Alt.Press Ind., HR Rep. (1985-1986).
●Available only online. Vendor(s): NewsNet.
—UMI.
Formerly: Africa News (ISSN 0191-6521)
Description: Addresses movements for improving society on the African continent. Liberation struggles, reform efforts and solidarity drives are all covered.

960   II   ISSN 0001-9828
DT1
AFRICA QUARTERLY; a journal of African affairs. (Text in English) 1961. q. Rs.100($40) Indian Council for Cultural Relations, Azad Bhavan, Indraprastha Estate, New Delhi 110002, India. Ed. Sh.T.G. Ramamurthi; Pub. Niranjan Desai. adv.; bk.rev.; index. circ. 1,900. (also avail. in microform from UMI; reprint service avail. from UMI) **Indexed:** A.B.C.Pol.Sci., Amer.Hist.& Life, ASSIA, Curr.Cont.Africa, Hist.Abstr., Int.Polit.Sci.Abstr., Mid.East: Abstr.& Ind., P.A.I.S.
—BLDSC (0732.170000); UMI; UnCover.

960   UK   ISSN 0001-9844
AFRICA RESEARCH BULLETIN. SERIES A: POLITICAL, SOCIAL AND CULTURAL. 1964. m. £253($459) (foreign £285) (effective 1996). Basil Blackwell Ltd., 108 Cowley Road, Oxford OX4 1JF, England. TEL 44-1865-791100. FAX 44-1865-791347. Ed. P. Adams. **Indexed:** Curr.Cont.Africa. **Document type:** academic/scholarly publication.
—SWETS; UMI. **CCC.**

AFRICA REVIEW. see BUSINESS AND ECONOMICS — Economic Situation And Conditions

960 330.9   UK   ISSN 0065-3896
DT351
AFRICA SOUTH OF THE SAHARA (YEAR). 1971. a. $310. Europa Publications, 18 Bedford Sq., London WC1B 3JN, England. TEL 0171-580-8236. FAX 0171-636-1664. TELEX 21540 EUROPA G. **Document type:** academic/scholarly publication, directory.
—BLDSC (0732.188000). **CCC.**
Description: Follows a general introduction, essays on African affairs and a section covering regional organizations. Includes separate chapters on each of the countries. Supplies the latest facts and figures and directory material.

960   US   ISSN 0001-9887
DT1
AFRICA TODAY. 1954. q. $25 to individuals (foreign $33); institutions $60 (foreign $68) (effective 1996). Lynne Reinner Publishers, 1800 30th St., Ste. 314, Boulder, CO 80301. TEL 303-444-6684. FAX 303-444-0824. E-mail: afrtoday@du.edu. Ed. Jendayi Frazer. adv. contact: Erik Hansen. bk.rev.; bibl.; index; circ. 1,627 (controlled). (also avail. in microform from UMI; back issues avail.) **Indexed:** A.B.C.Pol.Sci., Acad.Ind., Amer.Hist.& Life, Bk.Rev.Ind. (1980-), CERDIC, Child.Bk.Rev.Ind. (1980-), Curr.Cont.Africa, Curr.Cont., Documentatieblad, Hist.Abstr., HR Rep. (1984-), IDA, M.L.A., Mid.East: Abstr.& Ind., P.A.I.S., Per.Islam. (1992-), Polit.Sci.Abstr., Refug.Abstr., Soc.Sci.Ind. **Document type:** academic/scholarly publication.
●Also available online. Vendor(s): University Microfilms International.
—BLDSC (0732.190000); Faxon; Genuine Article; SWETS; UMI; UnCover.
Description: Examines issues affecting contemporary Africa, with emphasis on politics and economics.

POLITICAL SCIENCE

960 UK ISSN 0001-9909
DT1
AFRICAN AFFAIRS. 1901. q. £63($118) (effective 1996). (Royal African Society) Oxford University Press, Oxford Journals, Walton St., Oxford OX2 6DP, England. TEL 01865-56767. FAX 01865-56646. TELEX 837330-OXPRES-G. E-mail: jnlorders@oup.co.uk. (U.S. subscr. to: Oxford University Press Inc., 2001 Evans Rd., Cary, NC 27513. TEL 919-677-0977. FAX 919-677-1714) Ed. Peter Woodward. adv. contact: Jane Parker. bk.rev.; bibl.; index. circ. 1,650. (also avail. in microform; reprint service avail. from KTO) **Indexed:** A.B.C.Pol.Sci., A.I.C.P., Abstr.Anthropol., Abstr.Rural Dev.Trop., Agroforest.Abstr., Amer.Hist.& Life, ASSIA, Br.Hum.Ind., Curr.Cont.Africa, Curr.Cont., Documentatieblad, Geo.Abstr., Hist.Abstr., Hum.Ind., IDA, Int.Lab.Doc., Int.Polit.Sci.Abstr., Lang.& Lang.Behav.Abstr., Peace Res.Abstr., Polit.Sci.Abstr., Ref.Sour., Refug.Abstr., Rural Devel.Abstr., Rural Recreat.Tour.Abstr., SSCI, World Agri.Econ.& Rural Sociol.Abstr. **Document type:** academic/scholarly publication.
—BLDSC (0732.300000); Faxon; Genuine Article; SWETS; UMI; UnCover. **CCC.**
 Description: Provides a forum for the discussion of African writing by both African and non-African writers.

320.96 SA ISSN 1024-3194
▼**AFRICAN AGENDA.** 1995. m. R.55 ($25 in SADC; rest of Africa $30; Europe £35; N. America $70; elsewhere $100). (Third World Network) Africa South & East Publications Trust, P.O. Box 94154, Yeoville 2143, South Africa. TEL 27-11-4871596. FAX 27-11-648-0907. E-mail: afagend@iaccess.za. Ed. Gwen Ansell. adv.; illus.
 Description: Covers national, regional and international development issues and trends affecting the African continent.

320 SW
AFRICAN CLARION. 1972. 6/yr. $15. Box 4037, 422 04 Hisings Backa, Sweden. Ed. T.H. Mudzingwa.
 Description: Covers African studies.

320.532 960 SA ISSN 0001-9976
HX3
AFRICAN COMMUNIST. 1959. q. R.20($24) (£12). (South African Communist Party) Inkululeko Publications, P.O. Box 1027, Johannesburg 2000, South Africa. TEL 27-11-3393644. FAX 27-11-3396880. Ed.Bd. adv.; bk.rev.; stat.; cum.index: 1959-1988. circ. 10,000. (also avail. in microform from UMI) **Indexed:** Curr.Cont.Africa, Documentatieblad.
—BLDSC (0732.390000); SWETS; UMI; UnCover.
 Description: Serves as a forum for Marxist-Leninist thought by the South African Communist Party.

960 II ISSN 0002-0133
AFRICAN RECORDER; fortnightly digest of events in Africa with index. (Text in English) 1962. fortn. $136. Asian Recorder & Publications (Private) Ltd., A-126, Niti Bagh, New Delhi 110 049, India. TEL 011-652622. FAX 011-6862857. TELEX 031-73137 KRAK IN. Ed. A.K.B. Menon. charts; index every 3 mos. and annually.
 Description: Culled from newspapers of many African countries and of the leading newspapers of the world. Provides news events taking place in Africa.

960 TZ ISSN 0856-0056
AFRICAN REVIEW; a journal of African politics, development and international affairs. 1971. s-a. Sh.35. University of Dar es Salaam, Department of Political Science, P.O. Box 35042, Dar es Salaam, Tanzania. TEL 255-51-43130. FAX 255-51-43395. Ed. Charles Gasarasi. adv.; bk.rev. circ. 1,000. (back issues avail.) **Indexed:** A.B.C.Pol.Sci. (until 1992), Amer.Hist.& Life, Documentatieblad, Hist.Abstr., Int.Polit.Sci.Abstr., P.L.E.S.A., Rural Recreat.Tour.Abstr., World Agri.Econ.& Rural Sociol.Abstr. **Document type:** academic/scholarly publication.
—UnCover.
 Formerly: African Political Review (ISSN 0002-0117).

AFRICAN STUDIES; a biannual journal devoted to the study of African anthropology, history, sociology, literature and languages. see ANTHROPOLOGY

320 SA ISSN 0304-615X
AFRICANUS; journal of development alternatives. (Text in English) 1972. 2/yr. R.8 (overseas $3.42) (effective 1996). University of South Africa, Department of Development Administration, P.O. Box 392, Pretoria 0001, South Africa. TEL 27-12-429-6813. FAX 27-12-429-3221. TELEX 350068. Ed. J.C.N. Mentz. adv.; bk.rev.; charts; stat. circ. 660. (also avail. in microfiche; back issues avail.) **Indexed:** Curr.Cont.Africa, Documentatieblad, Ind.S.A.Per. **Document type:** academic/scholarly publication.
 Description: Publishes articles, research reports, reviews and bibliographies on subjects relating to development problems and strategies in the Third World.

320 330.9 301 GW ISSN 0002-0397
DT1
AFRIKA SPECTRUM; Zeitschrift fuer gegenwartsbezogene Afrikaforschung. (Text in English, French, German; summaries in English, French) 1966. 3/yr. DM.90. Institut fuer Afrika-Kunde, Neuer Jungfernstieg 21, 20354 Hamburg, Germany. TEL 040-3562523. FAX 040-3562511. Ed. Dirk Kohnert. adv.; bk.rev.; bibl.; charts; index. circ. 500. **Indexed:** Curr.Cont.Africa, Documentatieblad, IDA, Int.Lab.Doc., Int.Polit.Sci.Abstr., Key to Econ.Sci., P.A.I.S.For.Lang.Ind., P.A.I.S., Rural Devel.Abstr., Rural Ext.Educ.& Tr.Abstr., Rural Recreat.Tour.Abstr., World Agri.Econ.& Rural Sociol.Abstr. **Document type:** academic/scholarly publication.
—BLDSC (0735.268000).
 Description: Contemporary problems and developments in Africa.

960 SG ISSN 0002-0524
AFRIQUE MON PAYS.* no.27, 1969. m. B.P. 2469, Dakar, Senegal. Ed. Madani N'Diaya. adv.; charts; illus.

AFRIQUE NOIRE POLITIQUE ET ECONOMIQUE. see BUSINESS AND ECONOMICS — Economic Situation And Conditions

320.531 US ISSN 0739-4853
HX1
AGAINST THE CURRENT. 1979; N.S. 1986. bi-m. $20 to individuals; institutions $25. 7012 Michigan Ave., Detroit, MI 48210. TEL 313-841-0161. FAX 313-841-8884. Center for Changes. adv.; bk.rev. circ. 2,500. (also avail. in microform from UMI) **Indexed:** Alt.Press Ind., Chic.Per.Ind., Left Ind. (1990-).
—BLDSC (0735.826000).
 Supersedes: Changes (Detroit) (ISSN 0746-5335); Formerly (until 1984): Changes Socialist Monthly.
 Description: Contains discussions of movements for social and political change, and commentary from a socialist and feminist viewpoint with special emphasis on labor.

320 FR ISSN 0242-3782
AGENCE TELEGRAPHIQUE JUIVE. BULLETIN. (Text in French) 1970. d. 250 F. Jewish Telegraph Agency, 14 rue Georges Berger, 75017 Paris, France. Ed. Adam Loss.

320 BO ISSN 0252-8444
AGENCIA DE NOTICIAS FIDES. NOTAS. 1972. w. $200. Agencia de Noticias Fides, Casilla 5782, La Paz, Bolivia. TEL 591-2-365152. FAX 591-2-365153. TELEX 3236 FIDES BV. Ed. Jose Gramunt. circ. 1,200. **Document type:** newsletter.
 Description: Political and economic analysis of Bolivia.

AGIR. see SOCIOLOGY

AGRICULTURAL WORKING PEOPLE OF KOREA. see AGRICULTURE

956.9 LE ISSN 0002-3981
AHAD.* 1949. w. $50. Dar-al Kifah, Box 1462, Beirut, Lebanon. Ed. Riad Taha. adv. circ. 5,000.

320 SA
AIDA PARKER NEWSLETTER. (Text in English) 1983. m. R.80($80) Aida Parker Newsletter Pty. Ltd., P.O. Box 91059, Auckland Park 2006, Johannesburg, South Africa. TEL 27-11-726-6856. FAX 27-11-726-5537. Ed. Aida Parker. bk.rev. circ. 6,000. **Document type:** newsletter.
 Description: Analysis and perspectives on Southern African affairs.

320.532 AI
AJACK. 1923. m. 3 Rub. Pr. Ordzhonikidze 2, 375023 Erevan, Armenia. TEL 52-89-93. Ed. Aram S. Simonyan. bk.rev.; abstr.; bibl.; charts; illus.; stat. circ. 12,000.
 Formerly (until 1991): Leninyan Ugiov (ISSN 0130-8114).

320.5 SW ISSN 0348-4688
AKTINFORM; aktiv information - oberoende nationell publikation foer information och analys. 1969. q. SEK 35 (effective 1991). Arbetsgrupp Aktinform, P.O. Box 17113, S-200 10 Malmoe, Sweden.

320 GW ISSN 0939-3099
AKTUELLE OSTINFORMATIONEN. 1969. s-a. DM.9. Gesamteuropaeisches Studienwerk Vlotho e.V., Suedfeldstr. 2-4, 32591 Vlotho, Germany. TEL 05733-2258. FAX 05733-18804. bk.rev. circ. 2,000. **Document type:** newspaper.

320.531 YU
HX365.5
AKTUELNA PITANJA SOCIJALIZMA. English edition: Socialist Thought and Practice (ISSN 0583-7200); German edition: Sozialistische Theorie und Praxis (ISSN 0350-476X); Italian edition: Questioni Attuali del Socialismo (ISSN 0351-0107); Russian edition: Sotsialisticheskaya Mysl' i Praktika (ISSN 0350-4751); Spanish edition: Cuestiones Actuales del Socialismo (ISSN 0350-8846) (Arabic edition (ISSN 0350-5413); French edition: Questions Actuelles de Socialisme (ISSN 0033-6351)) (Text in Serbo-Croatian) 1961. m. $30. Komunist, Trg Marksa i Engelsa 11, 11000 Belgrade, Yugoslavia. TEL 11-632-569. Ed. Branko Prnjat. bk.rev. **Indexed:** Int.Polit.Sci.Abstr., Key to Econ.Sci., Mid.East Abstr.& Ind.
 Description: Contains both original articles and material reprinted from other publications dealing with theoretical problems of socialist development in Yugoslavia; reviews the activities of organizations of the self-management socialist system; reviews world events and the international activity of Yugoslavia.

320.531 NO ISSN 0332-7426
AKTUELT PERSPEKTIV. 1979. 48/yr. NOK 200. Norske Arbeiderparti - Norwegian Labour Party, P.B. 8824, Youngstorget, N-0028 Oslo 1, Norway. Ed. Johs Skeide Larsen. bk.rev.; bibl. circ. 17,000.
 Formed by the merger of (1964-1978): Sosialistisk Perspektiv (ISSN 0049-1330); (1952-1978): Tillitsmannen (ISSN 0332-866X)
 Description: Traces the origins of the Norwegian Labour Party.

320 US
ALABAMA LIBERTY. 1979. bi-m. $10. Alabama Libertarian Party, Box 11209, Montgomery, AL 36111-0209. TEL 205-265-1770. Ed. Mike Cobb. illus. circ. 1,000. (back issues avail.) **Document type:** newsletter.

320 VE
ALARMA. 1977. fortn. Torre de la Prensa, Plaza del Panteon, Apdo. 2976, Caracas 101, Venezuela. Dir. Jose Campos Suarez. circ. 65,150.

322.4 FR
ALBANIAN RESISTANCE. vol.25, 1978. irreg. National Democratic Committee for a Free Albania, 18 bis rue Brunel, 75017 Paris, France. (processed)
 Description: Informs readers of the state of the Albanian struggle for independence.

325 FR ISSN 0002-5313
ALGERIEN EN EUROPE. 1968. bi-m. 60 F. Centre Algerien de Documentation et d'Information, 3 rue Joseph Sansboeuf, 75008 Paris, France. Ed. G. Abdelkrim. adv.; bk.rev.; bibl.; charts. (tabloid format)

329.3 301.4157 US
ALICE REPORTS. 1972. m. $30. Alice B. Toklas Lesbian & Gay Democratic Club, Box 422698, San Francisco, CA 94142-2698. TEL 415-522-3809. circ. 800. **Document type:** newsletter.

320 II
ALL INDIA CONGRESS COMMITTEE. CONGRESS BULLETIN. 1972. m. All India Congress Committee, Publications Department, 5 Dr. Rajendra Prasad Rd., New Delhi 110001, India. Ed. N. Balakrishnan.

POLITICAL SCIENCE

320 US
ALL THE WAY. 1987. m. $12. Nationalist Movement, Box 2000, Learned, MS 39154. TEL 601-885-2288. Ed. Richard Barrett. bk.rev. (also avail. in microfilm; back issues avail.)
Description: News, current events and American political issues from a nationalist perspective.

ALLAM- ES JOGTUDOMANY/POLITICAL SCIENCE AND JURISPRUDENCE. see *LAW*

320 RM
ALLIANCE FOR PEACE IN RUMANIA. INFORMATION BULLETIN. (Text in English) 1962. q. free. Alliance for Peace in Rumania, 29 Biserica Amzei St., 70172 Bucharest 29, Rumania. TEL 118948. charts; illus.
Formerly (until vol.3, 1989): National Committee for the Defence of Peace in the Socialist Republic of Rumania. Information Bulletin (ISSN 0547-5090)
Description: Discusses economic progress, industry, agricultural development, security, disarmament and human rights.

329.9 UK ISSN 0002-6085
ALLIANCE NEWS. 1971. m. 30p. per no. Alliance Party of Northern Ireland, 88 University St., Belfast BT7 1HE, Northern Ireland. TEL 44-232-324274. FAX 44-232-333147. Ed. David Ford. adv.; bk.rev.; charts; illus. circ. 9,000. Document type: newspaper.
Formerly: Alliance (ISSN 0044-734X)

320 CU
ALMA MATER. m. $20 in N. America; S. America $26; Europe $29; others $41. (Editorial Abril) Ediciones Cubanas, Obispo No. 527, Apdo. 605, Havana, Cuba.

328.73 US ISSN 0362-076X
JK1012
ALMANAC OF AMERICAN POLITICS.* 1972. irreg., latest 1994. $48.95 (hardcover $59.95) (effective 1994). National Journal, Inc. (Subsidiary of: Times Mirror Company), 1501 M St., N.W., Ste. 300, Washington, DC 20005. TEL 202-739-8400. FAX 202-833-8069. (Subscr. to: Box 46909, St. Louis, MO 63146-9719. TEL 800-356-4838) Eds. Michael Barone, Grant Ujifusa.
Description: Provides comprehensive information on the American political scene, at the state and federal levels.

328 US ISSN 1047-0999
JK1083
ALMANAC OF THE UNELECTED; staff of the U.S. Congress. 1988. a. $250. Almanac Publishing, Inc., 1156 15th St., N.W., Ste. 525, Washington, DC 20005. TEL 202-296-2297.

320 SG ISSN 0850-0622
JF60
ALTERNATIVE DEMOCRATIQUE; dans le Tiers Monde. s-a. Centre d'Etudes et de Recherches sur la Democratie Pluraliste dans le Tiers Monde, B.P. 12092 Dakar (Colobane), Ave. Bourguiba, Villa no. 2565 Dakar, Senegal. TEL 221-24-47-81. FAX 221-25-29-36. Ed.Bd.

071 US
ALTERNATIVE TIMES. 1990. m. $12. Timeless Publications, Box 7134, Tyler, TX 75711-7134. TEL 214-597-7973. Ed. James Dixon. adv. circ. 3,000. Document type: newspaper.

320 355 BO
ALTOS ESTUDIOS. 1989. a. Bol.$10. Centro de Diplomados en Altos Estudios Nacionales, Av. Mcal. Santa Cruz 1364, Edif. "La Primera", piso 13, Bloque B, Casilla 5899, La Paz, Bolivia. TEL 358459. Ed. Hugo A. Castrillo Mercado. bk.rev. circ. 1,400. Document type: bulletin.
Description: Promotes the works, studies and projects of the schools graduates.

968 NE ISSN 0166-0373
AMANDLA; tijdschrift over zuidelijk Afrika. (Text in Dutch) 1971. 6/yr. fl.20 (effective 1995). Stichting Amandla, Oudezijds Achterburgwal 173, 1012 DJ Amsterdam, Netherlands. TEL 31-20-6232229. FAX 31-20-6270441. TELEX 17125. (Co-sponsors: Komitee Zuidelijk Afrika, Werkgroep Kairos) Ed.Bd. adv.; bk.rev.; bibl.; charts; illus. circ. 9,000. Document type: bulletin.
Formerly (until 1977): Angola Bulletin (ISSN 0044-8281)
Description: Political and cultural coverage of Southern Africa.

320 AG ISSN 0326-422X
K1
AMBIENTE Y RECURSOS NATURALES; revista de derecho, politica y administracion. q. Fundacion Ambiente y Recursos Naturales, Monroe 2142, 1428 Buenos Aires, Argentina. TEL 541-781-9171. E-mail: farn-cds@wamani.apc.org. Ed. Pedro Tarak.

320 330.9 AG ISSN 0327-1161
F1415
AMERICA LATINA - INTERNACIONAL. 1993. s-a. Arg.$35 (foreign $60). (Facultad Latinoamericana de Ciencias Sociales, Area de Relaciones Internacionales) Mino y Davila Editores, Federico Lacroze 2097, Casilla 145, Suc. 26, 1426 Buenos Aires, Argentina. TEL 54-1-7710978. FAX 54-1-7756937. Eds. Roberto Bouzas, Roberto Russell.

324 US ISSN 0065-678X
JK1967
AMERICA VOTES; handbook of contemporary American election statistics. 1956. biennial. $110. Congressional Quarterly Inc., 1414 22nd St., N.W., Washington, DC 20037. TEL 202-887-8500. FAX 202-728-1863. Eds. Richard M. Scammon, Alice V. McGillivray. Indexed: SRI.
Description: Contents include most recent election results for senator, representative and governor by ward, county, town and congressional district; most recent state-by-state primary results; state-by-state presidential election totals since 1920; and presidential primary totals since 1972.

320 300 US ISSN 0002-7162
H1 CODEN: AAYPA
AMERICAN ACADEMY OF POLITICAL AND SOCIAL SCIENCE. ANNALS. 1891. bi-m. $74 in hardcover to individuals (paperback $51); institutions $229 (paperback $197) (effective 1996). Sage Publications, Inc., 2455 Teller Rd., Thousand Oaks, CA 91320. TEL 805-499-0721. FAX 805-499-0871. E-mail: libraries@sagepub.com. (Overseas subscr. to: Sage Publications Ltd., 6 Bonhill St., London EC2A 4PU, England) Ed. Richard D. Lambert. adv.; bk.rev.; charts; cum.index every 5 yrs. circ. 4,800. (also avail. in microfilm from KTO,PMC; microfiche from IDC; back issues avail.; reprint service avail. from KTO) Indexed: A.B.C.Pol.Sci., Acad.Ind., Amer.Bibl.Slavic & E.Eur.Stud., Amer.Hist.& Life, Bibl.Engl.Lang.& Lit., Bk.Rev.Ind. (1965-), Br.Archaeol.Abstr., Child.Bk.Rev.Ind. (1965-), Commun.Abstr., Comput.Rev., Curr.Cont., Fut.Surv., Hist.Abstr., IDA, Int.Lab.Doc., Int.Polit.Sci.Abstr., Key to Econ.Sci., Lang.& Lang.Behav.Abstr., Mag.Ind., Mid.East: Abstr.& Ind., P.A.I.S., Peace Res.Abstr., Pers.Lit., Polit.Sci.Abstr., R.G., Sage Fam.Stud.Abstr., Sage Urb.Stud.Abstr., Soc.Sci.Ind., SSCI. Document type: academic/scholarly publication.
—BLDSC (1018.800000); Faxon; SWETS; UMI; UnCover. CCC.
Description: Directed to practitioners, students and researchers. Looks at health care, social care, rehabilitation, the aging of intelligence, and the lives of older people and the changing social roles.

970 US ISSN 0569-2245
AMERICAN ASSEMBLY. REPORT. (Title varies with topics of American Assembly.) 1951. 2/yr. free. American Assembly, Columbia University, 475 Riverside Dr., New York, NY 10115-0456. TEL 212-870-3500. FAX 212-870-3555. circ. 25,000. Document type: proceedings.
Supersedes in part: American Assembly (Background Papers and Final Report) (ISSN 0065-6976)

AMERICAN COUNCIL FOR JUDAISM. SPECIAL INTEREST REPORT; a digest of news items and articles in the area of the council's interest. see *RELIGIONS AND THEOLOGY — Judaic*

320 300 US ISSN 1047-3572
D839 CODEN: AEETE9
AMERICAN ENTERPRISE. 1978. bi-m. $29 to individuals; corporations $56. American Enterprise Institute for Public Policy Research, 1150 17th St., N.W., Washington, DC 20036. TEL 202-862-5800. FAX 202-862-7178. TELEX 671-1239. (Subscr. to: Box 6827, Syracuse, NY 13217-7940) Ed. Karlyn Bowman. adv.: B&W page $2000, color page $2700; 8 1/2 x 11; adv. contact: Ashley H. Cooper. charts; stat. circ. 15,000. (also avail. in microfiche) Indexed: A.B.C.Pol.Sci., Int.Polit.Sci.Abstr., Mag.Ind., Mid.East: Abstr.& Ind., P.A.I.S., Soc.Sci.Ind., SRI (until 1990). Document type: academic/scholarly publication.
●Also available online. Vendor(s): University Microfilms International.
—BLDSC (0813.848000); Faxon; SWETS; UMI; UnCover.
Formerly (until 1990): Public Opinion (Washington) (ISSN 0149-9157)
Description: Contains articles in economics, foreign policy, law, social policy, regulation, politics, public opinion, and media.

322.4 US
AMERICAN INDEPENDENT. 1974. m. $15 (includes California Statesman publications). William K. Shearer, Ed. & Pub., 8158 Palm St., Lemon Grove, CA 91945. TEL 619-460-4484. circ. 800. Document type: newsletter.
Description: Contains current and historical information about the American Independent Party.

320 US ISSN 0092-5853
JA1
AMERICAN JOURNAL OF POLITICAL SCIENCE. Key Title: Abbreviated title: A J P S. 1950. q. $30 to individuals; institutions $69 (effective 1995). (Midwest Political Science Association) University of Wisconsin Press, Journal Division, 114 N. Murray St., Madison, WI 53715. TEL 608-262-5839. FAX 512-262-7560. Ed. Kenneth J. Meier. adv.: page $250; 4 1/2 x 7 1/2. charts; stat.; index. circ. 3,500. (also avail. in microform from KTO,UMI; reprint service avail. from KTO,SCH,KTO) Indexed: A.B.C.Pol.Sci., Abstr.Crim.& Pen., Amer.Hist.& Life, Bibl.Ind., Curr.Cont., Hist.Abstr., Int.Polit.Sci.Abstr., Lang.& Lang.Behav.Abstr., Mid.East: Abstr.& Ind., Mult.Ed.Abstr., P.A.I.S., Polit.Sci.Abstr., PSI, Sage Pub.Admin.Abstr., Sage Urb.Stud.Abstr., Soc.Sci.Ind., SSCI, Stud.Wom.Abstr. Document type: academic/scholarly publication.
—BLDSC (0834.300000); Faxon; Genuine Article; SWETS; UMI; UnCover. CCC.
Formerly: Midwest Journal of Political Science (ISSN 0026-3397)
Description: Presents academic research in American politics and international methodology.

320 US ISSN 1045-3679
JK1118
AMERICAN LOBBYISTS DIRECTORY. 1990. a. Gale Research Inc., 835 Penobscot Bldg., Detroit, MI 48226-4094. TEL 313-961-2242. FAX 313-961-6083. TELEX 810-221-7086. Document type: directory.

323.4 US
AMERICAN PATRIOT (SCOTTSDALE). 1948. q. $15. Harry T. Everingham, Ed. & Pub., Box A, Scottsdale, AZ 85252. TEL 602-941-0144. adv.; bk.rev. circ. 20,000. (tabloid format)
Formerly (until 1976, vol.29, no.6): Free Enterprise (ISSN 0016-0342)

320 US
AMERICAN POLITICAL PARTIES AND ELECTION SERIES. 1980. irreg. price varies. Praeger Publishers (Subsidiary of: Greenwood Publishing Group Inc.), 88 Post Rd. W., Box 5007, Westport, CT 06881-5007. TEL 203-226-3571. FAX 203-222-1502. Document type: monographic series.

320 US ISSN 8755-562X
JK1
AMERICAN POLITICAL REPORT. 1971. bi-w. $195. American Political Research Corp., 7316 Wisconsin Ave., Bethesda, MD 20814. TEL 301-654-4990. FAX 301-656-0822. Ed. Kevin P. Phillips. circ. 1,400. Document type: academic/scholarly publication, government publication, newsletter.
Description: Covers American politics, polls, elections, and political economics.

POLITICAL SCIENCE

320   US   ISSN 0003-0554
JA1
AMERICAN POLITICAL SCIENCE REVIEW. 1906. q. membership. American Political Science Association, 1527 New Hampshire Ave., N.W., Washington, DC 20036. TEL 202-483-2512. FAX 202-483-2657. Ed. Bingham Powell. adv.: page $720. bk.rev.; charts; illus.; index, cum.index. circ. 20,000. (also avail. in microform from MIM,PMC,UMI) **Indexed:** A.B.C.Pol.Sci., Abstr.Bk.Rev.Curr.Leg.Per., Abstr.Crim.& Pen., Acad.Ind., Amer.Hist.& Life, Bibl.Engl.Lang.& Lit., Biog.Ind., Bk.Rev.Dig., Bk.Rev.Ind. (1965-), CERDIC, Chic.Per.Ind., Child.Bk.Rev.Ind. (1965-), Commun.Abstr., Curr.Cont., Fut.Surv., Hist.Abstr., INSPEC, Int.Polit.Sci.Abstr., Int.Polit.Sci.Abstr., J.of Econ.Lit., Mid.East: Abstr.& Ind., Pers.Lit., Polit.Sci.Abstr., R.G., Ref.Sour., Soc.Sci.Ind., Soc.Work Res.& Abstr. **Document type:** trade publication.
●Also available online. Vendor(s): University Microfilms International.
—BLDSC (0851.500000); Faxon; Genuine Article; SWETS; UMI; UnCover. **CCC**.
Description: Publishes scholarly articles in political science.
Refereed Serial

320.9   US   ISSN 0044-7803
JK1
AMERICAN POLITICS QUARTERLY. 1973. q. $54 to individuals; institutions $174 (effective Sep. 1995). Sage Publications, Inc., 2455 Teller Rd., Thousand Oaks, CA 91320. TEL 805-499-0721. FAX 805-499-0871. E-mail: libraries@sagepub.com. (Overseas subscr. to: Sage Publications Ltd., 6 Bonhill St., London EC2A 4PU, England; Sage Publications India, Pvt. Ltd., P.O. Box 4215, New Delhi 110 048, India) Ed. James C. Garland. adv.; bk.rev.; charts; index. circ. 1,250. (back issues avail.; reprint service avail.) **Indexed:** A.B.C.Pol.Sci., Amer.Hist.& Life, Commun.Abstr., Curr.Cont., Hist.Abstr., Int.Polit.Sci.Abstr., Mid.East: Abstr.& Ind., P.A.I.S., Polit.Sci.Abstr., Sage Pub.Admin.Abstr., Sage Urb.Stud.Abstr., Soc.Sci.Ind. (1994-), Sociol.Educ.Abstr., SSCI. **Document type:** academic/scholarly publication.
—BLDSC (0851.600000); Faxon; Genuine Article; SWETS; UMI; UnCover. **CCC**.
Description: Promotes basic research in all areas of American political behavior, including urban, state, and national policies, as well as pressing social problems requiring political solutions.

320   US   ISSN 1049-7285
E838   CODEN: APROEY
AMERICAN PROSPECT; a journal for the liberal imagination. 1990. q. $25 to individuals; public libraries $40; universities $60. New Prospect, Inc., Box 383080, Cambridge, MA 02238-3080. TEL 617-547-2950. FAX 617-547-3896. Eds. Robert Kuttner, Paul Starr. adv.: B&W page $525. bk.rev. circ. 12,000. (also avail. in microform from UMI) **Indexed:** J.of Econ.Lit., P.A.I.S., Sage Pub.Admin.Abstr., Soc.Sci.Ind. (1994-), Sociol.Abstr. **Document type:** academic/scholarly publication.
—BLDSC (0853.330000); Faxon; UMI; UnCover.

AMERICAN REVIEW. see HISTORY — History Of North And South America

320   US
AMERICAN REVIEW OF POLITICS. 1980. q. $15. (University of Central Arkansas, Department of Political Science) University of Central Arkansas Press, Conway, AR 72032. TEL 501-450-5686. Ed. Gary Wekkin. circ. 300. **Document type:** academic/scholarly publication.
Formerly (until 1992): Midsouth Political Science Journal (ISSN 1051-5054)

973   US   ISSN 0003-1593
AMERICA'S FUTURE; a monthly review of news, books and public affairs. 1959. m. $10 (free to public and school libraries). Americas Future, Inc., Westfall Professional Plaza, Box 1625, Milford, PA 18337-2625. TEL 717-296-2800. FAX 717-296-2811. Eds. Allan C. Brownfeld, Philip C. Clarke; Pub. Robert Morris. bk.rev.; index. circ. 8,000. (also avail. in microfilm; back issues avail.) **Document type:** newsletter.

AMERICAS REVIEW. see BUSINESS AND ECONOMICS — Economic Situation And Conditions

322.4   CY
AMMOCHOSTOS. (Text in Greek) w. 44 Egnatias, Plati, Eylenya, Nicosia, Cyprus. TEL 02-352918. Ed. Niko Falas. circ. 2,800.
Description: Right-wing political review reflecting the voice of "Famagusta" refugees.

AMUDIM; bulletin of the religious kibbutzim. see BUSINESS AND ECONOMICS — Cooperatives

AN PHOBLACHT/REPUBLICAN NEWS. see GENERAL INTEREST PERIODICALS — Ireland

320 300   AG   ISSN 0327-0297
JA5
ANALES DE CIENCIAS POLITICAS Y SOCIALES. 1950. s-a. free or exchange basis. Universidad Nacional de Cuyo, Facultad de Ciencias Politicas y Sociales, Biblioteca, Casilla de Correos 217, 5500 Mendoza, Argentina. TEL 54-61-234393. FAX 54-61-381347. Ed. Isaac Francisco Gutierrez. adv. contact: Carlos Finochio. bk.rev.; charts; stat. **Document type:** bulletin.
Formerly (until 1987): Boletin de Ciencias Politicas y Sociales (ISSN 0045-2394)

320   PE   ISSN 0252-8851
ANALISIS; cuadernos de investigacion. 1977. 2/yr. S/750($12) to individuals; institutions $20. Apdo. 11093, Correo Santa Beatriz, Lima 14, Peru. Ed. Ernesto Yepes. adv.; bk.rev. circ. 5,000.

320   CK
ANALYSIS POLITICO. 1987. 3/yr. Col.$8000 (N. America $54; elsewhere $60) to individuals; institutions Col.$10000 (N. America $66; elsewhere $72). Universidad Nacional de Colombia, Instituto de Estudios Politicos y Relaciones Internacionales, Apdo. Aereo No. 14490, Ciudad Universitaria, Bogota, Colombia. TEL 2697118. FAX 2684489. Ed. William Ramirez Tobon.

335.83   IT   ISSN 0390-0886
ANARCHISMO. 1975. m. Edizioni Anarchismo, Casella Postale 61, 95100 Catania, Italy. Ed. Alfredo M. Bonanno. bk.rev. circ. 4,000.

320 301   UK   ISSN 0967-3393
ANARCHIST STUDIES. 1993. 2/yr. £16($30) to individuals; institutions £32($55). White Horse Press, 10 High St., Knapwell, Cambridge CB3 8NR, England. TEL 01954-267527. (Subscr. to: 1 Strond, Isle of Harris PA83 3UD, Scotland. TEL 01859-520204) Eds. Thomas Cahill, Sharif Gemier. circ. 500. **Document type:** academic/scholarly publication.
—CCC.
Description: Concerned with all aspects of anarchist research and theory, with the primary focus on contemporary developments in anarchism.
Refereed Serial

320   US   ISSN 1044-1387
ANARCHY; a journal of desire armed. 1980. q. $12 to individuals; libraries $18. BAL Press, Box 2647, Stuy. Sta., New York, NY 10009. TEL 212-332-9660. E-mail: anarchy@panix.com. Ed. Tad Kepley. adv. contact: Alex Trotter. bk.rev. circ. 7,500. **Indexed:** Alt.Press Ind. **Document type:** consumer publication.

335   SW   ISSN 1101-2897
ANARKISTISK TIDSKRIFT. 1990. q. SEK 130 (effective 1991). Foereningen Anarkistisk Tidskrift, Bokhandeln Info, Hornsg. 151, S-117 34 Stockholm, Sweden.

328 900   BE   ISSN 0066-1589
ANCIENS PAYS ET ASSEMBLEES D'ETATS. (Text in language of contributor) 1950. irreg. price varies. (International Committee of Historical Sciences, Commission for the History of State Assemblies) U. G. A., Stijn Streuvelslaan 73, B-8501 Heule-Kortrijk, Belgium. TEL 32-56-363211. FAX 32-56-356096. TELEX 85579.

320   SG
ANDE SOPI. 1977. m. Mouvement Democratique Populaire, Dakar, Senegal. Ed. Mamadou Dia.

THE ANDERSON MONITOR - BUSINESS & POLITICS. see BUSINESS AND ECONOMICS

329   TZ
ANGOLA IN ARMS.* 1972. m. S.10($4) Departamento de Informacao e Propaganda do Comite Central, MPLA - Partido do Trabalho, Luanda, Tanzania. illus.

320 960   SG   ISSN 0066-2364
ANNEE POLITIQUE AFRICAINE. 1964. a. 17.500 Fr.CFA. Societe Africaine d'Edition, B.P. 1877, Dakar, Senegal. (And 32, rue de l'Echiquier, Paris, France) Ed.Bd.
Formed by the 1981 merger of: Annee Politique Africaine; Economie Africaine.

320   FR   ISSN 0764-8138
ANNEE POLITIQUE, ECONOMIQUE ET SOCIALE. 1876; N.S. 1944. a. 475 F. Editions du Moniteur, 17 rue d'Uzes, 75002 Paris, France. FAX 40-41-94-95. TELEX UPRESSE 680876F. Ed. Jean-Marc Pilpoul. (reprint service avail. from SCH)
Formerly: Annee Politique (ISSN 0066-2356)

320   SZ   ISSN 0066-2372
HC397
ANNEE POLITIQUE SUISSE/SCHWEIZERISCHE POLITIK. (Text in French, German) 1965. a. 45 SFr. Universitaet Bern, Institut fuer Politikwissenschaft - Universite de Berne, Institut de Science Politique, Lerchenweg 36, CH-3000 Bern 9, Switzerland. TEL 031-6318331. FAX 031-6318590. Ed. Hans Hirter. index. circ. 1,500. **Document type:** academic/scholarly publication.
Description: Complete review and analysis of all political events and developments in Swiss politics.

320   CN   ISSN 0706-1021
F1059.7.F83
ANNUAIRE FRANCO-ONTARIEN. 1978. a. Can.$6.95. Centre Franco-Ontarien de Ressources Pedagogiques, 290 rue Dupuis, Vanier, PQ K1L 1A2, Canada. TEL 613-747-1553. FAX 613-747-0866. Ed. Bernadette LaRochelle. (also avail. in diskette format) **Document type:** directory.
Formerly: Bottin des Organismes Franco-Ontariens (ISSN 0707-3356)

320   SZ   ISSN 0066-3727
JA34
ANNUAIRE SUISSE DE SCIENCE POLITIQUE/SCHWEIZERISCHES JAHRBUCH FUER POLITISCHE WISSENSCHAFT/SWISS POLITICAL SCIENCE YEARBOOK. (Text in English, French and German) 1961. a. price varies. (Forschungsstelle fuer Politische Wissenschaft) Paul Haupt AG, Falkenplatz 14, CH-3001 Bern, Switzerland. TEL 031-3012345. FAX 031-3014669. **Indexed:** A.B.C.Pol.Sci., Amer.Hist.& Life, Hist.Abstr., Int.Polit.Sci.Abstr. **Document type:** monographic series.
—CCC.

320.4   US
ANNUAL EDITIONS: AMERICAN GOVERNMENT. 1971. a. $12.95. Dushkin Publishing Group, Sluice Dock, Guilford, CT 06437-9989. TEL 203-453-4351. FAX 203-453-6000. Ed. Bruce Steinbrickner; Pub. Ian Nielsen. illus. **Document type:** academic/scholarly publication.
Formerly: Annual Editions: Readings in American Government (ISSN 0090-547X)
Refereed Serial

320   US   ISSN 1052-0678
F1034.2
ANNUAL EDITIONS: CANADIAN POLITICS. 1990. a. $12.95. Dushkin Publishing Group, Sluice Dock, Guilford, CT 06437-9989. TEL 203-453-4351. FAX 203-453-6000. Eds. Gregory Mahler, Roman R. March; Pub. Ian Nielsen. illus. **Document type:** academic/scholarly publication.
Refereed Serial

320   US   ISSN 0741-7233
JF37
ANNUAL EDITIONS: COMPARATIVE POLITICS. 1983. a. $12.95. Dushkin Publishing Group, Sluice Dock, Guilford, CT 06437-9989. TEL 203-453-4351. FAX 203-453-6000. Ed. Christian Soe; Pub. Ian Nielsen. illus. **Document type:** academic/scholarly publication.
Refereed Serial

ANNUAL EDITIONS: WORLD POLITICS. see POLITICAL SCIENCE — International Relations

POLITICAL SCIENCE

320   UK   ISSN 0066-4057
D2
THE ANNUAL REGISTER (YEAR); a record of world events. 1758. a. £89. Longman Group UK Ltd., Westgate House, The High, Harlow, Essex CM20 1YR, England. TEL 0279-442601. FAX 0279-444501. (Dist. in U.S. and Canada by: Gale Research Inc., 10 Penobscot Bldg., Detroit, MI 48226. TEL 313-961-2242) Ed. H.V. Hodson. index. (also avail. in microform from PMC) **Document type:** directory.

ANNUAL REPORT ON PRIVATIZATION. see *PUBLIC ADMINISTRATION*

320   US   ISSN 0748-8599
JA1
ANNUAL REVIEW OF POLITICAL SCIENCE. 1986. irreg., vol.3, 1990. price varies. Ablex Publishing Corporation, 355 Chestnut St., Norwood, NJ 07648. TEL 201-767-8450. FAX 201-767-6717. TELEX 135-393. Ed. Samuel Long. **Document type:** academic/scholarly publication.
—BLDSC (1528.120000).

ANNUAL THIRD WORLD CONFERENCE PROCEEDINGS. see *HISTORY*

320   AG
ANOCERO. 1985. w. Editorial Ano Cero, Libertad 936, 5-D, 1012 Buenos Aires, Argentina.

320   GR
ANTI; independent fortnightly political review. (Text in English) 1972. fortn. $60. 60 Dimocharous St., 115 21 Athens, Greece. TEL 30-1-723-2713. FAX 30-1-722-6107. Ed. Ilias Kanelis; Pub. Christos G. Papontsakis. adv. contact: Tassia Roumpou. bk.rev.; index. circ. 30,000. (back issues avail.) **Document type:** academic/scholarly publication.
Refereed Serial

ANUARIO DE DERECHO PENAL Y CIENCIAS PENALES. see *LAW*

322.4   CR
APORTES. 1980. m. Col.550($45) Editorial Aportes para la Educacion, S.A., Apdo. 103-1009 Fecosa, San Jose, Costa Rica. TEL 21-13-20. Ed. Melvin Jimenez. adv.; bk.rev.; film rev.; play rev.; illus.; cum.index 1980-1988. circ. 2,600. (back issues avail.)

320.9   FR   ISSN 0003-7176
JA11
APRES - DEMAIN; journal mensuel de documentation politique. 1957. m. 220 F. (foreign 330 F.). Ligue des Droits de l'Homme, 27 rue Jean Dolent, 75014 Paris, France. TEL 47-05-14-01. Ed. Francoise Seligmann. adv.; bk.rev.; abstr.; bibl.; index, cum.index. circ. 8,000. (back issues avail.) **Indexed:** P.A.I.S.For.Lang.Ind.
—BLDSC (1581.600000).
Description: For those who want to understand and those who must explain the world's political, economic and social problems.

AQUI. see *SOCIOLOGY*

320   UK   ISSN 0196-3538
DS63.1
ARAB-ASIAN AFFAIRS. 1975. 10/yr. £100($175) World Reports Ltd., 108 Horseferry Rd., Westminster, London SW1P 2EF, England. TEL 071-222-3826. FAX 071-233-0185. (U.S. subscr. to: World Reports Ltd., 280 Madison Ave., Ste. 1209, New York, NY 10016-0802. TEL 212-599-4560) Ed. Christopher Story. (back issues avail.)
—BLDSC (1583.224040).
Formerly: Afro-Asian Affairs.
Description: Covers developments in the Middle East.

320   LE
THE ARAB WORLD. (Text in English) 1985. s-m. $1500. Dar Naaman lith-Thaqafah, P.O. Box 567, Jounieh, Lebanon. TEL 961-9-935096. Ed. Naji Naaman. index.
Description: Covers political and economic developments in the Arab world.

329   IS   ISSN 0334-4622
ARACHIM/VALUES; a magazine of problems of peace and socialism. Key Title: Rkym. (Text in Hebrew) 1969. bi-m. $8. Communist Party of Israel, P.O. Box 26205, Tel Aviv, Israel. Ed. Wolf Ehrlich.

ARAUCO DOCUMENTOS. see *ETHNIC INTERESTS*

320.531   GW   ISSN 0943-402X
ARBEITERSTIMME; Zeitschrift fuer marxistische Theorie und Praxis. 1971. q. DM.25($15) Gruppe Arbeiterstimme, Postfach 910307, 90261 Nuernberg, Germany. Ed. Thomas Gradl. adv.; bk.rev. circ. 2,000. (also avail. in microfilm from KTO; back issues avail.) **Document type:** academic/scholarly publication.

324.248907   DK   ISSN 0900-2723
ARBEJDERBEVAEGELSENS BIBLIOTEK OG ARKIV. AARSSKRIFT. 1985. a. Arbejderbevaegelsens Bibliotek og Arkiv, Noerrebrogade 66 D, DK-2200 Copenhagen N, Denmark. TEL 45-35-36-15-22. FAX 45-35-36-32-22. Ed. Henning Grelle. circ. 4,500. **Document type:** newsletter.
Description: Contains short articles on Danish labor history and on the work of the institution.

320.9 330   GW   ISSN 0003-8865
ARCHIV DER GEGENWART; die weltweite Dokumentation fuer Politik und Wirtschaft. 1931. fortn. DM.460. Siegler & Co. Verlag fuer Zeitarchive GmbH, Einsteinstr. 10, 53757 Sankt Augustin, Germany. TEL 02241-3164-0. FAX 02241-316436. Ed.Bd. abstr.; charts; stat.; index. circ. 1,700. (also avail. in microfilm from NRP) **Document type:** directory.
Description: Detailed information on current world politics and economics; record of world events based on a variety of international sources.

320   FR
ARCHIVES PARLEMENTAIRES DE 1787 A 1860. (Text in French) irreg. C N R S Editions, 20-22 rue St. Amand, 75015 Paris, France. TEL 45-33-16-00. FAX 45-33-92-13. TELEX 200 356 F. adv.; bk.rev.; index; circ. 1,500 (controlled). (also avail. in microform from BHP)

320   IT   ISSN 0390-0916
DG576
ARCHIVIO TRIMESTRALE; rassegna storica di studi sul movimento republicano. 1975. q. L.25000. Istituto di Studi per la Storia del Movimento Repubblicano, Via Tomacelli 146, 00186 Rome, Italy. Ed. Graziantonio Panunzio. adv.; bk.rev. circ. 7,500.

320   MP
ARDYN TOR/PEOPLE'S STATE. 1950. bi-m. People's Great Hural, Ulan Bator, Mongolia.

320 327   CI   ISSN 0402-9283
ARENA; informativni drustveno politicki ilustrirani tjednik. 1959. w. $122. Vjesnik, Avenija Bratstva i Jedinstva 4, 41000 Zagreb, Croatia. TEL 666-666. FAX 041-3411-777. TELEX 21121 VSK ZG. Ed. Stevo Maodus. **Indexed:** E.I., Polit.Sci.Abstr.

320.531   AT   ISSN 1320-6567
ARENA JOURNAL. 1963. 2/yr. Aus.$16 to individuals; institutions Aus.$25. Arena Printing and Publications Pty. Ltd., P.O. Box 18, N. Carlton, Vic. 3054, Australia. TEL 61-3-416-0232. FAX 61-3-415-1301. Ed.Bd. adv.; bk.rev. circ. 900. (tabloid format) **Indexed:** Alt.Press Ind., Aus.Educ.Ind., Aus.P.A.I.S., Polit.Sci.Abstr. **Document type:** academic/scholarly publication.
—BLDSC (1664.071000). CCC.
Former titles (until 1993): Arena Magazine; (until 1992): Arena (ISSN 0004-0932)
Description: Includes analyses of interpretive and technical intellectual practices and their relation to the reconstruction of social processes.
Refereed Serial

320   IT   ISSN 0392-6176
ARENGO; mensile di formazione politica. 1974. m. L.15000. Democrazia Ecumenica Mondialista., Via XXIV Maggio 81-D, 87100 Cosenza, Italy. TEL 0984-412651. Dir. Pietro De Franco. adv.
Description: Looks at political issues throughout Italy as well as other countries.

ARGENTINE LETTER. see *BUSINESS AND ECONOMICS — Economic Situation And Conditions*

320.531   IT   ISSN 0391-6677
HN490.R3
ARGOMENTI RADICALI. 1977. bi-m. L.15000. Edizioni il Formichiere s.r.l., Via del Lauro 3, 20121 Milan, Italy. Ed. Massimo Teodori. circ. 7,000.

323.4   SW   ISSN 0004-1149
ARGUMENT FOER FRIHET OCH RAETT. 1965. irreg. SEK 4. P.O. Box 414, S-126 04 Haegersten, Sweden. Ed. Svante Hjertstrand. bk.rev. circ. 40,000.

ARIZONA CAPITOL TIMES. see *PUBLIC ADMINISTRATION*

ARKANSAS POLITICAL REPORT. see *PUBLIC ADMINISTRATION*

320.9 355   CN
▼**ARMED CONFLICTS REPORT.** 1994. a. price varies. (Canadian Council of Churches) Project Ploughshares, Conrad Grebel College, Waterloo, ON N2L 3G6, Canada. TEL 519-888-6541. FAX 519-885-0014. E-mail: plough@watservl.uwaterloo.ca. Ed.Bd. charts; maps.
Description: Lists the world's major armed conflicts; includes introductory essays, maps, descriptions of each major conflict and accompanying photos, graphs and tables.

ARMED FORCES AND SOCIETY; an interdisciplinary journal on military institutions, civil-military relations, arms control and peacekeeping, and conflict management. see *MILITARY*

ARMENIAN INTERNATIONAL MAGAZINE. see *ETHNIC INTERESTS*

320   US   ISSN 0196-125X
JX1974
ARMS CONTROL TODAY. 1972. m. $40 to individuals; institutions $50. Arms Control Association, 1726 M St., N.W., Ste. 201, Washington, DC 20036-4504. TEL 202-463-8270. FAX 202-463-8273. E-mail: armscontrol@ig.apc.org. Ed. John J. Schulz. adv.; bk.rev. circ. 4,000. (also avail. in microform from UMI) **Indexed:** Abstr.Mil.Bibl., D M & T, P.A.I.S., PROMT. **Document type:** academic/scholarly publication.
●Also available online. **Vendor(s):** University Microfilms International.
—BLDSC (1683.097100); Faxon; SWETS; UMI; UnCover.
Description: Covers nuclear and conventional arms control issues with timely editorials, interviews, and feature articles by experts in the field.

ASIA & PACIFIC REVIEW. see *BUSINESS AND ECONOMICS — Economic Situation And Conditions*

320 950   CH   ISSN 1015-0153
ASIAN BULLETIN. 1976. m. NT.$250($7) (Asian Pacific Anti-Communist League - Republic of China) A P A C L Publications, 100 Hengyang Rd., 8th Fl., Taipei, Taiwan, Republic of China. Ed. Martin L. Lasater.

ASIAN JOURNAL OF PUBLIC ADMINISTRATION. see *PUBLIC ADMINISTRATION*

320 327   KO   ISSN 0258-9184
ASIAN PERSPECTIVE; biannual journal of regional & international affairs. 1977. s-a. 12000 Won($24) Kyungnam University, Institute for Far Eastern Studies, 28-42 Samchung-dong, Chongro-gu, Seoul 110-230, S. Korea. TEL 82-2-735-3200. FAX 82-2-735-4359. TELEX KIFES K26834. Ed. Manwoo Lee. adv.; bk.rev.; cum.index. circ. 2,000. (back issues avail.; reprint service avail.) **Indexed:** Asian-Pac.Econ.Lit., E.I. **Document type:** academic/scholarly publication.
—BLDSC (1742.708000); UnCover.

POLITICAL SCIENCE

950   US   ISSN 0004-4687
DS1
ASIAN SURVEY. 1961. m. $52 to individuals; institutions $104; students $29 (effective 1996). (University of California at Berkeley, Institute of East Asian Studies) University of California Press, Journals Division, 2120 Berkeley Way, Berkeley, CA 94720. TEL 510-643-7154. FAX 510-642-9917. Ed.Bd. adv.; bibl. circ. 2,800. (also avail. in microform from UMI; back issues avail.; reprint service avail. from KTO) **Indexed:** A.B.C.Pol.Sci., Abstr.Anthropol., Acad.Ind., Amer.Bibl.Slavic & E.Eur.Stud., Amer.Hist.& Life, Asian-Pac.Econ.Lit., Curr.Cont., E.I., Geo.Abstr., Hist.Abstr., IDA, Int.Lab.Doc., Int.Polit.Sci.Abstr., Key to Econ.Sci., Mid.East: Abstr.& Ind., P.A.I.S., Polit.Sci.Abstr., Rural Recreat.Tour.Abstr., Sage Pub.Admin.Abstr., Sage Urb.Stud.Abstr., Soc.Sci.Ind., SSCI, World Agri.Econ.& Rural Sociol.Abstr. **Document type:** academic/scholarly publication.
● Also available online. Vendor(s): University Microfilms International.
—BLDSC (1742.750000); Faxon; Genuine Article; SWETS; UMI; UnCover. **CCC.**
Description: Provides detailed commentary on political, economic, and social developments in Asia. *Refereed Serial*

956   LE   ISSN 0004-5012
ASSAYAD. (Text in Arabic) 1943. w. $300. Dar Assayad S.A.L., P.O. Box 1038, Hazmieh, Beirut, Lebanon. FAX 961-1-456373. (UK addr.: c/o Contact PR & Mgt. (UK) Ltd, 3 Park Pl., 12 Lawn Ln., London SW8, England. TEL 071-582-2220) Ed. Issam Freiha. adv. contact: Salim Zreik. circ. 89,775. (tabloid format) **Document type:** consumer publication.

ASSOCIATION OF COLLEGE AND RESEARCH LIBRARIES. LAW AND POLITICAL SCIENCE SECTION NEWS. see *LAW*

ASSOCIATION SENEGALAISE POUR L'ETUDE DU QUATERNAIRE AFRICAIN. BULLETIN DE LIAISON. see *HISTORY — History Of Africa*

322   IT   ISSN 0004-5985
ASSOCIAZIONE NAZIONALE EX INTERNATI. BOLLETTINO UFFICIALE. 1949. bi-m. membership. Associazione Nazionale Ex Internati, Via 20 Settembre 27-B, Rome 00187, Italy. Ed. Dr. Carlo De Luca. adv.; illus. circ. 50,000.

320   FR
ASTROLABE;* revue de philosophie politique. bi-m. 50 F. S E P I C, 185 rue de Solignac, 87000 Limoges, France. Ed. Philippe Liard.

322.4   FR   ISSN 0339-9958
AUJOURD'HUI L'AFRIQUE. 1975. q. 120 F. (foreign 150 F.) Association Francaise d'Amitie et de Solidarite avec les Peuples d'Afrique, 35 rue G. Lauriau, 93100 Montreuil, France. TEL 1-48-58-71-20. Ed. Francis Arzalier. adv. contact: Pierre Kaldor. bk.rev.
Formerly: Association Francaise d'Amitie et de Solidarite avec les Peuples d'Afrique. Bulletin d'Information (ISSN 0335-0290)

320 350   US   ISSN 1063-0368
AUSTIN REPORT. 1947. w. $28. Report Publications, Inc., Box 12368, Austin, TX 78711. TEL 512-478-5663. Ed. Bill Kidd. circ. 1,150.
Description: Covers Texas legislative and political activity.

329.07   AT   ISSN 0311-3264
AUSTRALASIAN SPARTACIST. 1972. bi-m. Aus.$5 (foreign Aus.$7). Spartacist A N Z Publishing Co., G.P.O. Box 3473, Sydney, N.S.W. 2001, Australia. TEL 02-281-2181. FAX 02-281-2185.
Formerly: Revolutionary Communist Bulletin.

320   II
AUSTRALIA & PACIFIC ISLANDS LETTER. (Text in English) 1981. m. Rs.488($96) K.K. Roy (Private) Ltd., 55 Gariahat Rd., P.O. Box 10210, Calcutta 700 019, India. Ed. Dr. K.K. Roy.

320   UK   ISSN 1036-1146
JQ3995.A1
AUSTRALIAN JOURNAL OF POLITICAL SCIENCE. 1966. 3/yr. £40($60) to individuals; institutions £80($130) (effective 1996). (Australasian Political Studies Association (Canberra)) Carfax Publishing Co., P.O. Box 25, Abingdon, Oxon. OX14 3UE, England. TEL 44-1235-555335. FAX 44-1235-553559. (N. American subscr. to: Carfax Publishing Co., 875-81 Massachusetts Ave., Cambridge, MA 02139) Ed. Ian McAllister. bk.rev.; bibl.; charts; stat. circ. 800. (also avail. in microfilm from UMI; reprint service avail. from UMI) **Indexed:** A.B.C.Pol.Sci., Amer.Hist.& Life, Aus.P.A.I.S., Curr.Cont., Hist.Abstr., Int.Polit.Sci.Abstr., Polit.Sci.Abstr., So.Pac.Per.Ind., SSCI. **Document type:** academic/scholarly publication.
—BLDSC (1811.140000); Genuine Article; UMI; UnCover.
Formerly: Politics (ISSN 0032-3268)

320 900   AT   ISSN 0004-9522
DU80
AUSTRALIAN JOURNAL OF POLITICS AND HISTORY. 1955. 3/yr. Aus.$58 to individuals; institutions & libraries Aus.$60 (effective 1996). University of Queensland Press, P.O. Box 42, St. Lucia, Qld. 4067, Australia. TEL 61-7-3652452. FAX 61-7-3651988. Ed. John Moses. adv.; bk.rev.; charts; tr.lit.; index. circ. 1,000. (also avail. in microfilm from UMI; reprint service avail. from KTO,SCH) **Indexed:** A.B.C.Pol.Sci., Amer.Hist.& Life, Arts & Hum.Cit.Ind., Asian-Pac.Econ.Lit., Aus.P.A.I.S., Br.Hum.Ind., Curr.Cont., E.I., Gdlns., Hist.Abstr., Int.Polit.Sci.Abstr., Mid.East: Abstr.& Ind., P.A.I.S., So.Pac.Per.Ind., SSCI. **Document type:** academic/scholarly publication.
—BLDSC (1811.150000); Faxon; Genuine Article; SWETS; UnCover.

320.531   AT   ISSN 0310-8252
AUSTRALIAN MARXIST REVIEW. 1972. q. Aus.$13.60. Socialist Party of Australia, 65 Campbell St., Surry Hills, N.S.W. 2010, Australia. FAX 61-2-281-5795. Ed. P.D. Symon. bibl. circ. 2,500.

320   AT
AUSTRALIAN NATIONAL UNIVERSITY, CANBERRA. RESEARCH SCHOOL OF SOCIAL SCIENCES. DEPARTMENT OF POLITICAL SCIENCE. OCCASIONAL PAPERS. 1965. irreg., no.19, 1986. price varies. Australian National University, Research School of Social Sciences, Department of Political Science, P.O. Box 4, Canberra, A.C.T. 2600, Australia. FAX 062-571893. TELEX AA 2694 SOPAC. (Dist. in U.S. by: International Scholarly Book Services, Box 4347, Portland, OR 97208) circ. 625.
Formerly: Australian National University, Canberra. Department of Political Science. Occasional Paper. (ISSN 0067-2033)

320   AT   ISSN 0005-0091
DU80
AUSTRALIAN QUARTERLY. 1929. q. Aus.$50 (foreign Aus.$60). Australian Institute of Political Science, 72 Bathurst St., Sydney, N.S.W. 2000, Australia. TEL 02-264-8923. FAX 02-267-7900. Eds. Damian Grace, Ian March. adv.; bk.rev.; index, cum.index: 1954-1963, 1964-1968, 1969-1978. circ. 1,500. (reprint service avail. from KTO) **Indexed:** A.B.C.Pol.Sci., AESIS, Amer.Hist.& Life, ASSIA, Aus.P.A.I.S., Curr.Cont., Gdlns., Geo.Abstr., Hist.Abstr., Int.Polit.Sci.Abstr., Mid.East: Abstr.& Ind., Res.High.Educ.Abstr., SSCI. **Document type:** academic/scholarly publication.
—BLDSC (1818.450000); Faxon; UnCover.
Description: Publishes original manuscripts dealing with economic, political, social, philosophical, historical and scientific matters which have a bearing on the contemporary Australian scene.

AUTONOMIE LOCALI E SERVIZI SOCIALI; vademecum a schede. see *SOCIAL SERVICES AND WELFARE*

329.9   NQ
AVANCE. 1972. w. Partido Comunista de Nicaragua, Cuidad Jardin 0-30, Apdo. 4231, Managua JR, Nicaragua. TEL 2-43750. circ. 20,000.

329.9   PO   ISSN 0870-1865
AVANTE. w. Communist Party, Rua Soeiro Pereira Gomes, 1699 Lisbon, Portugal. TEL 01-769725. Dir. A. Dias Lourenco da Silva.

320   AG
▼**AVISPA.** 1994. m. Arg.$3 per no. Centro de Estudios Union para la Nueva Mayoria, Estados Unidos 943, 1101 Buenos Aires, C.F., Argentina. FAX 54-1-273164. Dir. Rosendo M. Fraga.

320.9   II   ISSN 0005-2515
AZAD MAZDUR; Hindi weekly. (Text in Hindi) 1953. w. Rs.10. G.P. Koushal, Ed. & Pub., Tripti Bhavan, Station Rd., Jusalai, Jamshedpur 831006, India. adv.; bk.rev.; film rev.; play rev.; bibl. circ. 5,000.

327 950 960   RU   ISSN 0005-2574
AZIYA I AFRIKA SEGODNYA. 1947. m. $49. (Rossiiskaya Akademiya Nauk, Institut Narodov Azii) Izdatel'sto Nauka, 90 Profsoyuznaya, 117864 Moscow, Russia. TEL 095-336-0266. FAX 095-420-2220. (Dist. by: Mezhdunarodnaya Kniga, B. Yakimanka 39, 117049 Moscow, Russia; Dist. in U.S. by: Victor Kamkin Inc., 4956 Boiling Brook Pkwy., Rockville, MD 20852. TEL 301-881-5973. FAX 301-881-1637) (Co-sponsor: Institut Afriki) Ed. G.F. Kim. index. **Indexed:** Amer.Hist.& Life (until 1990), Curr.Cont.Africa, E.I., Hist.Abstr. (until 1990).

320   LE
AZTAG SHAPATORIAG-TROSHAG. 1969. w. $24. Ste. Aztag S.A.R.L., Salim Bustany St., Beirut, Lebanon. (Dist. in U.S. by: Haig Gakavian, 9417 Curren Rd., Silver Spring, MD 20901) Ed. Sarkis Zeitlian.

320   GW
B D V NACHRICHTEN. 1952. q. DM.36. Bund der Vertriebenen Landesverband Baden-Wuerttemberg e.V., Schlossstr. 92, 70176 Stuttgart, Germany. TEL 0711-625277. FAX 0711-610162. bk.rev. **Document type:** bulletin.

B M A NEWS REVIEW. (British Medical Association) see *MEDICAL SCIENCES*

BABYFISH LOST ITS MOMMA. see *LITERATURE — Poetry*

947   GW   ISSN 0005-4526
BALTISCHE BRIEFE. 1948. m. DM.75.55. Verlag Baltische Briefe Wolf J. von Kleist GmbH, Deefkamp 13, 22927 Grosshansdorf, Germany. TEL 04102-61112. FAX 04102-65388. adv.; bk.rev.; bibl.; illus. circ. 5,900. (tabloid format)

320.532   IT   ISSN 1122-519X
BANDIERA ROSSA. 1951. m. L.30000 (foreign L.35000) (effective 1993). Associazione Politico-Culturale Quarta Internazionale, Via B. Varchi 3, 20158 Milan, Italy. TEL 39-2-3760027. FAX 39-2-39320935. Ed. Sergio D'Amia; Pub. Antonio Moscato.

BANGLADESH NEWS. see *ETHNIC INTERESTS*

320   BG
BANGLADESH POLITICAL STUDIES. (Text in English and Bengali) 1978. a. Tk.50($10) (£5). University of Chittagong, Department of Political Science, Chittagong, Bangladesh. TEL 414393. Ed. Muhammad A. Hakim. adv.; bk.rev. circ. 1,000.

322.4   NQ   ISSN 0254-802X
F1528
BARRICADA INTERNACIONAL. English edition (ISSN 1013-9567) (German edition avail.) 1981. m. $35 for English ed.; Spanish ed. 4000 ptas.; German ed. DM.48. Editorial El Amanecer, Apdo. 4461, Managua, Nicaragua. TEL 784933. FAX 673941. TELEX 2017 BARR. (For English ed. subscr. to: Box 410150, San Francisco, CA 94141-0150, TEL 415-621-8981; For German ed.: Verlag Im Hof, Wiesenweg 19, D-5300 Bonn, Germany, TEL 0228-626326, FAX 0228-627277; For Spanish ed.: Apdo. 23296, 08080 Barcelona, Spain, TEL 93-421-8392, FAX 93-421-9033) Ed. Carlos Fernando Chamorro. adv.; bk.rev. circ. 15,000. (also avail. in microform from UMI)
Description: Covers socio-economic, political and cultural news and analysis, with emphasis on Nicaragua and Central America.

320.9   IT   ISSN 0005-6111
BASILICATA; rassegna di politica e cronache meridionali. 1954. m. L.20000. Basilicata Editrice, Via Ridola 20, Casella Postale 70, Matera 75100, Italy. Ed. Leonardo Sacco. adv.; bk.rev.; film rev.; play rev.; abstr.; bibl.; charts; illus.; stat.; circ. 10,000 (controlled).

POLITICAL SCIENCE

956.940 296   US
BATNUA. 1970. bi-m. $5. Habonim Dror Labor Zionist Youth, 27 W. 20th St., 9th Fl., New York, NY 10011. TEL 212-255-1796. Ed. Charles Boxbaum. circ. 2,500. (also avail. in microfilm from AJP)
Formerly: Bagolah (ISSN 0005-3929)
Description: Forum for discussing relevant Zionist issues and internal Habonim Dror Labor Camp Zionist Youth issues and events.

332.4   PN
BAYANO. fortn. Partido del Pueblo de Panama, Calle 1a, Perejil, Panama City, Panama. Dir. Efrain Reyes Medina.

320   GW
BAYERISCHER MONATSSPIEGEL. 1964. bi-m. DM.25. Bayerischer Monatsspiegel Verlag GmbH, Postfach 221123, 80501 Munich, Germany. TEL 089-167235. FAX 089-168700. Ed. Freda von Stackelberg; Pub. Gerhard Treutlein. adv. contact: Karl-Heinz Feuerlein. bk.rev.; bibl. circ. 20,000. **Document type:** bulletin.

320   CC
BEIJING ZHIBU SHENGHUO. (Text in Chinese) m. Zhonggong Beijing Shiwei, 53, Xibianmennei Dajie, Beijing 100053, People's Republic of China. TEL 3017333. Ed. Cheng Manzhen.

320   GW   ISSN 0522-6643
BEITRAEGE ZUR GESCHICHTE DES PARLEMENTARISMUS UND DER POLITISCHEN PARTEIEN. 1952. irreg., vol.98, 1993. price varies. Droste Verlag GmbH, 40196 Duesseldorf, Germany. TEL 0211-5052604. FAX 0211-5052671. **Document type:** monographic series.

320   GW   ISSN 0582-0421
BEITRAEGE ZUR POLITISCHEN WISSENSCHAFT. 1967. irreg., vol.68, 1993. DM.128. Duncker und Humblot GmbH, Postfach 410329, 12113 Berlin, Germany. TEL 030-790006-0. FAX 030-79000631. Eds. Werner Suess, Gehard Becher. **Document type:** monographic series.

BEITRAEGE ZUR ZEITGESCHICHTE. see HISTORY

320   NE   ISSN 0165-1625
BELEID EN MAATSCHAPPIJ. 6/yr. (plus supplement). fl.102 to individuals (foreign fl.134.50); institutions fl.173 (foreign fl.183.50) (effective 1994). Uitgeverij Boom, P.O. Box 400, 7940 AK Meppel, Netherlands. TEL 31-5220-57012. FAX 31-5220-53864. circ. 1,000. **Indexed:** ELLIS, Key to Econ.Sci.
—SWETS.

320   BH
BELIZE TIMES. 1956. w. People's United Party, P.O. Box 506, 3 Queen St., Belize City, Belize. TEL 2-45757. Ed. Amalia Mai. circ. 5,000. **Document type:** newspaper.

966.9   NR
BENDEL STATE GAZETTE. 1964. w. £N9.50($11) Ministry of Home Affairs and Information, Printing and Stationery Division, P.M.B. 1099, Benin City, Nigeria. charts; stat. circ. 4,500.
Formerly: Midwestern Nigeria Gazette (ISSN 0026-3494)

BENGAL: PAST AND PRESENT. see HISTORY — History Of Asia

320   US   ISSN 0067-5717
BENJAMIN F. FAIRLESS LECTURES. 1964. a. (Carnegie - Mellon University) Columbia University Press, 562 W. 113th St., New York, NY 10025. TEL 212-666-1000. **Document type:** monographic series.

300 011   IT   ISSN 0006-1654
BIBLIOTECA DELLA LIBERTA. 1964. q. L.60000 (foreign L.80000) (effective 1993). (Centro di Ricerca e Documentazione Luigi Einaudi) Franco Angeli Editore, Viale Monza, 106, 20127 Milan, Italy. TEL 39-2-2895762. FAX 39-11-7495796. Ed. G. Zincone. adv.: page L.800000. bk.rev.; film rev.; play rev.; bibl.; illus.; index. circ. 7,000. **Indexed:** Int.Polit.Sci.Abstr.

320 943.8   PL   ISSN 0138-094X
BIBLIOTEKA POLONIJNA/POLONIA LIBRARY. 1960. irreg., vol.27, 1992. price varies. (Polska Akademia Nauk, Komitet Badania Polonii Zagranicznej) Ossolineum, Publishing House of the Polish Academy of Sciences, Rynek 9, 50-106 Wroclaw, Poland. TEL 48-71-386-25. FAX 48-71-448-103. TELEX 0712771 OSS PL. Ed. Hieronim Kubiak. **Document type:** monographic series.
Formerly (until 1977): Problemy Polonii Zagranicznej (ISSN 0079-5798)

BILANS HEBDOMADAIRES. see BUSINESS AND ECONOMICS

BILL OF RIGHTS IN ACTION. see LAW — Constitutional Law

328 305.896   US   ISSN 0895-1780
BLACK CONGRESSIONAL MONITOR; reporting on activities of the US Congress and executive departments and agencies; initiatives of particular interest and benefit to African Americans and by African American members of Congress. 1987. fortn. $45 (effective Jan. 1994). Len Mor Publications, Box 75035, Washington, DC 20013. TEL 202-488-8879. FAX 202-554-3116. Ed. Lenora Moragne. adv. contact: Nora Champion. **Document type:** newsletter.
Description: Available grant awards, contract and subcontract opportunities; public notices; proposed and final rules and regulations; public policy documents, and other government publications; and coverage of bills and resolutions introduced, hearings held, congressional comments made by African-Americans in the U.S. Congress.

320   UK   ISSN 0045-2157
BLACK FLAG; anarchist monthly. 1970. m. £18 to individuals; institutions £30. Black Flag, BM-Hurricane, London WC1 3XX, England. Ed. L. Mitchell. bk.rev.; abstr.; bibl.; charts; illus.; pat.; stat.; tr.lit. circ. 4,000. (back issues avail.)

320   US   ISSN 0891-9631
BLACK POLITICAL STUDIES. 1993. irreg., no.5, 1994. Borgo Press, Box 2845, San Bernardino, CA 92406. TEL 909-884-5813. FAX 909-888-4942. Ed. Hanes Walton, Jr.
Description: Monographs on Black politics and political figures, in North America and throughout the world.

320.57   US
BLACK ROSE. 4/yr. $8 to individuals; institutions $16. Box 1075, Boston, MA 02103. bk.rev. circ. 800. **Indexed:** Alt.Press. Ind.

BLACK SCHOLAR; journal of Black studies and research. see ETHNIC INTERESTS

943 327   GW   ISSN 0006-4416
D839
BLAETTER FUER DEUTSCHE UND INTERNATIONALE POLITIK. 1956. m. DM.109.80 (foreign DM.126). Blaetter Verlagsgesellschaft mbH, Bertha-von-Suttner-Platz 6, 53111 Bonn, Germany. TEL 0228-650133. FAX 0228-650251. Ed.Bd. adv.; bk.rev.; bibl.; stat.; index. circ. 18,000. (reprint service avail. from SCH) **Indexed:** ELLIS, INIS Atomind., P.A.I.S.For.Lang.Ind. **Document type:** academic/scholarly publication.
—CCC.

320.5   SW   ISSN 0345-1631
BOHUS LAENS FOLKBLAD. 1947. bi-m. SEK 100 (effective 1995). Frisinnade Unions-partiet, Bua 6186, Dr Resmarks vaeg, S-440 80 Elloes, Sweden. Ed. Sven A. Lundehaell.

322.4   US
BOLCHEVIQUE. (Text in Spanish) 1980. m. $20. October Publications, 3309 1-2 Mission St., San Francisco, CA 94110. TEL 415-695-0340. circ. 2,500.

320   MX   ISSN 0186-0461
BOLETIN DE POLITICA INFORMATICA. 1982. m. free or exchange basis. Instituto Nacional de Estadistica, Geografia e Informatica, Secretaria de Programacion y Presupuesto, Prol. Heroe de Nacozari 2301 Sur, Puerta 11, Acceso, 20270 Aguascalientes, Ags., Mexico. TEL 49-18-19-48. FAX 491-807-39. circ. 700.

324   CR   ISSN 1020-0940
BOLETIN ELECTORAL LATINOAMERICANO. 1989. s-a. $15. Instituto Interamericano de Derechos Humanos, Apdo. Postal 100 81, 1000 San Jose, Costa Rica. TEL 506-234-04-04.
FAX 506-234-09-55. Ed. Daniel Zovatto. circ. 1,000. (back issues avail.) **Document type:** bulletin.
Description: Analyzes the electoral processes in the region. Contains official results.

320.532   IT   ISSN 0392-3886
IL BOLSCEVICO. 1969. w. L.60000. Editoriale il Girasole, C.P. 477, 50100 Florence, Italy. TEL 055-2347272. Ed. Monica Martenghi. **Document type:** newspaper.
Description: Covers the Italian Marxist-Leninist party.

320 972   US
BORDER ISSUES AND PUBLIC POLICY. RESEARCH PAPERS. 1982. irreg., no.29, Jan. 1994. $5 per no. University of Texas at El Paso, Center for Inter-American and Border Studies, Publications Program, c/o Gloria Macias, Man. Ed., El Paso, TX 79968-0002. TEL 915-747-5274. FAX 915-747-5574. E-mail: AVVM%UTEP@UTEPVM.UTEP.edu. (back issues avail.) **Document type:** monographic series.
Description: Examines economics, labor, politics and migration patterns.

320 972   US
BORDER PERSPECTIVES. RESEARCH PAPERS. 1983. irreg., latest no.13, Jul. 1994. $5 per no. University of Texas at El Paso, Center for Inter-American and Border Studies, Publications Program, c/o Gloria Macias, Man. Ed., El Paso, TX 79968-0002. TEL 915-747-5274. FAX 915-747-5574. E-mail: AVVM%UTEP@UTEPVM.UTEP.edu. **Document type:** monographic series.

BORGO REFERENCE GUIDES. see HISTORY

320   IT   ISSN 0391-6723
BOZZE. 1978. q. L.40000 (foreign L.60000) (effective 1994). Edizioni Dedalo s.r.l., Casella Postale 362, 70100 Bari, Italy. TEL 080-5311413. FAX 080-5311414. (Edit. addr.: Piazza Campitelli 2, 00186 Rome, Italy. TEL 06-6781002) Dir. Raniero La Valle. circ. 9,000.
Description: Covers current political topics, such as the defense of peace, equality and freedom.

BRAZIL REPORT. see BUSINESS AND ECONOMICS — Economic Situation And Conditions

329.82   US   ISSN 1073-2519
HQ75
BREAKTHROUGH (SAN FRANCISCO). 1977. 3/yr. $10 for 4 nos. to individuals (foreign $15). (Prairie Fire Organizing Committee) John Brown Education Fund, Box 14422, San Francisco, CA 94114. bk.rev.; illus. circ. 3,500. (back issues avail.) **Indexed:** Alt.Press Ind.
Description: Provides original articles, interviews and selected reprints analyzing international and domestic issues of concern to the left and progressive movements.

320.531   SZ
BRECHE. 1969. bi-m. 55 F. Parti Socialiste Ouvrier, 11 rue de la Borde, CH-1018 Lausanne, Switzerland. TEL 021-362616. FAX 021-362732. Ed. C.A. Udry. bk.rev.; bibl.; illus.; cum.index: nos.1-100. circ. 3,500. (tabloid format) **Document type:** newspaper.

944   FR   ISSN 0006-9647
BRETAGNE REELLE; tribune libre-la voix du pays gallo. (Includes semi-annual supplement: An Nerzh) 1954. s-m. 650 F. J. Quatreboeufs, 22230 Merdrignac, Brittany, France. bk.rev.

320   CN   ISSN 0703-8968
BRIARPATCH. 1973. 10/yr. Can.$24.61 (foreign Can.$34.61) to individuals; institutions Can.$35.31 (foreign Can.$45.31). Briarpatch Society, 2138 McIntyre St., Regina, SK S4P 2R7, Canada. TEL 306-525-2949. FAX 306-565-3430. Ed. George Martin Manz. adv.: B&W page $350. bk.rev. circ. 2,000. (also avail. in microform from MML) **Indexed:** Alt.Press Ind., Can.B.P.I. **Document type:** consumer publication.
Description: Covers issues related to labor, the environment, peace, native people, and provincial and national politics, from a leftist perspective.

POLITICAL SCIENCE

320 330.9   TU
BRIEFING. (Text in English) 1974. w. $460 (effective 1995-1996). Turk Ekonomik Basin Ajansi, Bestekar Sokak 59-3, 06680 Kavaklidere - Ankara, Turkey. TEL 90-312-4685376. FAX 90-312-4684114. TELEX 43204 FTEB TR. Ed. Yavuz Tolun. adv. contact: Melek Tolun. bk.rev.; charts; stat. circ. 1,000.
    Description: Provides political and economic analysis, forecasts and independent commentary on developments in Turkey's domestic and foreign policy and economic affairs.

THE BRITISH EAST - WEST JOURNAL. see *GENERAL INTEREST PERIODICALS — Russia*

320   UK   ISSN 0007-1234
BRITISH JOURNAL OF POLITICAL SCIENCE. 1971. q. £89($159) (effective 1996). Cambridge University Press, Edinburgh Bldg., Shaftesbury Rd., Cambridge CB2 2RU, England. TEL 01223-312393. FAX 01223-315052. TELEX 851817256. (N. American addr.: Cambridge University Press, Journals Dept., 40 W. 20th St., New York, NY 10011. TEL 212-924-3900. FAX 212-691-3239) Eds. David Sanders, Albert Weale. adv.; charts; index. (also avail. in microform from UMI; back issues avail.; reprint service avail. from SWZ) **Indexed:** A.B.C.Pol.Sci., Amer.Hist.& Life, ASCA, ASSIA, Curr.Cont., ELLIS, Hist.Abstr., Int.Polit.Sci.Abstr., Int.Polit.Sci.Abstr., Mid.East: Abstr.& Ind., Mult.Ed.Abstr., P.A.I.S., Rural Recreat.Tour.Abstr., Sage Pub.Admin.Abstr., Soc.Sci.Ind., SSCI, Stud.Wom.Abstr., World Agri.Econ.& Rural Sociol.Abstr. **Document type:** academic/scholarly publication.
    —BLDSC (2319.600000); Faxon; Genuine Article; SWETS; UMI; UnCover. **CCC.**

BRITISH LIBRARY. ORIENTAL AND INDIA OFFICE COLLECTIONS. REVIEW. see *ORIENTAL STUDIES*

320 378.83   US
BROADSIDE. 1980. bi-m. $18 (free to college students). College Republican National Committee, 450 Maple Ave. E., Ste. 308, Vienna, VA 22180. TEL 703-319-9221. FAX 703-319-0203. Ed. Bill Spadea. adv. contact: Paul S. Teller. bk.rev. circ. 25,000. **Document type:** newspaper.
    Former titles (until 1994): College Republican; C R Report.
    Description: Dedicated to informing and mobilizing young conservatives on college campuses.

BUDGET AND THE REGION; a regional analysis of the President's budget request. see *PUBLIC ADMINISTRATION*

943   GW   ISSN 0007-3121
DER BUERGER IM STAAT. 1951. q. (Landeszentrale fuer Politische Bildung) W. Kohlhammer GmbH, Hessbruehlstr. 69, 70565 Stuttgart, Germany. TEL 0711-7863-1. FAX 0711-7863263. Ed. H.G. Wehling. bk.rev.; abstr.; bibl.; stat.; index. circ. 36,000. **Indexed:** INIS Atomind. **Document type:** bulletin.

BUERGERRECHTE & POLIZEI. see *CRIMINOLOGY AND LAW ENFORCEMENT*

322.4   GW
BUKO KAMPAGNE STOPPT DEN RUESTUNGSEXPORT. RUNDBRIEF. 1984. irreg. Verein zur Foerderung Entwicklungspaedagogischer Zusammenarbeit e.V., Buchtstr. 14-15, 28195 Bremen, Germany. TEL 0421-326045. illus. **Document type:** newsletter.

BULGARSKI DNEVNIK/BULGARIAN DIARY. see *HISTORY — History Of Europe*

320 330 300   FR   ISSN 0007-4071
Z7163
BULLETIN ANALYTIQUE DE DOCUMENTATION POLITIQUE, ECONOMIQUE ET SOCIALE CONTEMPORAINE. 1946. m. 430 F. to individuals (foreign 485 F.); institutions 845 F. (foreign 940 F.). (Fondation Nationale des Sciences Politiques) Presses de la Fondation Nationale des Sciences Politiques, 44 rue du Four, 75006 Paris, France. TEL 44-39-39-60. FAX 1-45-48-04-41. Ed. Nicole Richard. index. circ. 1,700. (reprint service avail. from SCH) **Indexed:** P.A.I.S.For.Lang.Ind., Popul.Ind.
    —CCC.

960   FR   ISSN 0045-3501
DT348
BULLETIN DE L'AFRIQUE NOIRE. (Includes special nos.) 1956. w. 5400 F. I C Publications, 10 rue Vineuse, 75116 Paris Cedex 16, France. TEL 44-30-81-00. FAX 44-30-81-11. Ed.Bd. adv.; charts; stat. **Indexed:** Curr.Cont.Africa, P.A.I.S.For.Lang.Ind., Rural Devel.Abstr., Rural Recreat.Tour.Abstr., World Agri.Econ. & Rural Sociol.Abstr.

320   FR   ISSN 0766-5849
BULLETIN QUOTIDIEN; quotidien d'information documentation et prospective. d. 29300 F. (foreign 30600 F.). Societe Generale de Presse et d'Editions, 13 av. de l'Opera, 75001 Paris, France. TEL 40-15-17-89. FAX 40-15-17-15. TELEX SOGPRESS230023. Ed. Etienne Lacour; Pub. Marianne Berard-Quelin.
    —CCC.

DER BUND. see *ETHNIC INTERESTS*

320   GW   ISSN 0933-2731
BUNDESTAG REPORT. 1987. 10/yr. free. (Deutscher Bundestag) Osang Verlag GmbH Bonn, Am Roemerlager 2, 53117 Bonn, Germany. TEL 0228-678383. FAX 0228-679631. (Subscr. to: Deutscher Bundestag, Bundeshaus, 5300 Bonn 1, Germany) circ. 60,000. (back issues avail.)
    Description: Information about German Parliament and its politics.

320 371.3   GW   ISSN 0435-7604
JN3966
BUNDESZENTRALE FUER POLITISCHE BILDUNG. SCHRIFTENREIHE. (Supplement avail.: Daten Report (ISSN 0175-4173)) 1964. irreg. Bundeszentrale fuer Politische Bildung, Berliner Freiheit 7, 53111 Bonn, Germany. TEL 0228-515279. FAX 0228-515113. **Document type:** monographic series.

BUSINESS CENTRAL EUROPE. see *BUSINESS AND ECONOMICS*

BUSQUEDA. see *BUSINESS AND ECONOMICS — Economic Situation And Conditions*

BYERS ELECTION LAW. see *LAW*

322.4   UK   ISSN 0142-7113
C A A T NEWSLETTER. 1974. bi-m. £15 to individuals; institutions £25 (effective 1995). Campaign Against Arms Trade, 11 Goodwin St., London N4 3HQ, England. TEL 0171-281-0297. FAX 0171-281-4369. Ed.Bd. bk.rev. circ. 4,000. **Document type:** newsletter.
    Description: Watchdog publication monitoring arms trade.

320   NE   ISSN 0168-6690
C D A KRANT. 1984. 9/yr. membership. Christen Democratisch Appel (CDA), Dr. Kuyperstraat 5, 2514 BA The Hague, Netherlands. TEL 31-70-3424840. FAX 31-70-3643417. adv. **Document type:** bulletin.
    —SWETS.

320   NE   ISSN 0924-2260
C D ACTUEEL. 1980. 20/yr. fl.56. Christen Democratisch Appel (CDA), Dr. Kuyperstraat 5, 2514 BA The Hague, Netherlands. TEL 31-70-3424840. FAX 31-70-3643417. TELEX 31050. Ed.Bd. adv.; illus. circ. 10,000. **Document type:** consumer publication.
    —SWETS.
    Former titles (until 1989): C D A Actueel (ISSN 0920-3559); (until 1986): C D Actueel (ISSN 0168-2091)

329   BE
C D - INFO. (Text in Dutch, English, French, German, Hungarian, Italian, Polish, Russian, Spanish) 1964. 4/yr. Christian Democrat International, 16 rue de la Victoire, Boite 1, B-1060 Brussels, Belgium. TEL 32-2-537-13-22. FAX 32-2-537-93-48. **Document type:** newsletter.
    Former titles: Christian Democrat International. Information Bulletin; Christian Democratic World Union. Information Bulletin; (until 1972): International Christian Democratic Study and Documentation Center. Bulletin International (ISSN 0538-5520)

320   GW
C D U GERLINGEN INFORM. 1983. bi-m. (Christlich Demokratische Union) C D U Gerlingen, c/o Rainer Wieland, Ed., Vesoulerstr. 3, 70839 Gerlingen, Germany. circ. 250. **Document type:** bulletin.

340 300   UA   ISSN 0752-4412
DT43
C E D E J EGYPTE - MONDE ARABE; droit, economie, societe. (Text in French) 1990. 4/yr. £E50 (in Europe 300 F.; elsewhere 400 F.). Centre d'Etudes et de Documentation Economique, Juridique et Sociale, 14 Sharia Gameyet al-Nisr, Mohandessin, Cairo, Egypt. TEL 3611932. FAX 3493518. TELEX 93088 CEFEC UN. Ed. Philippe Fargues. adv.; bk.rev. circ. 1,000.
    —BLDSC (3664.223000).
    Formed by the 1989 merger of: Revue de la Presse Egyptienne & C E D E J Departement des Sciences Sociales. Bulletin (ISSN 0255-755X); **Formerly:** Centre de Documentation d'Etudes Juridiques, Economiques et Sociales. Bulletin (ISSN 0251-3668)
    Description: Covers politics, the social and human sciences in Egypt and the Middle East.
    Refereed Serial

320   CU
C I A C SINTESIS INFORMATIVA. 1978. bi-m. free. W P C Information Center for the Americas and the Caribbean, Linea No. 556, Vedado, Havana, Cuba. TEL 809 32-0506. FAX 53-7-338212.
    Description: Promotes materials on peace issues and against military build-up.

329.6   US
C I D. 1980. bi-m. donations. Cuba Independiente y Democratica, 10021 S.W. 37th Terr., Miami, FL 33165. TEL 305-551-8484. FAX 305-559-9365. Ed. Huber Matos, Jr. circ. 30,000. (tabloid format; back issues avail.) **Document type:** newspaper.
    Description: For members and exiled Cubans in general.

321   SZ
C I R A BULLETIN. (Text in English, French, German, Italian, Spanish) 1957. s-a. 20 SFr. Centre International de Recherches sur l'Anarchisme, Av. de Beaumont 24, CH-1012 Lausanne, Switzerland. bk.rev.; bibl. circ. 1,000. **Document type:** bulletin.

320 350   US
C J WEEKLY. (California Journal) 1984. w. $295. Information for Public Affairs, Inc., 2101 K St., Sacramento, CA 95816. TEL 916-444-2840. bk.rev. circ. 550. **Document type:** newsletter.
    Formerly (until 1993): California Journal Newsfile.
    Description: Insider information on people and organizations in California politics and government.

320   SA
C O D E S R I A BOOK SERIES. irreg. (Council for the Development of Economic and Social Research in Africa (CODESRIA), SG) Skotaville Publishers, P.O. Box 32483, Braamfontein 2017, South Africa. (Dist. outside Africa by: African Books Collective Ltd., The Jam Factory, 27 Park End St., Oxford OX1 1HU, England. TEL 0865-726686. FAX 0865-793298) **Document type:** monographic series.

320   US   ISSN 0194-0856
C P P A X NEWSLETTER. 1962. 5/yr. $5. Citizens for Participation in Political Action, 25 West St., 4th Fl., Boston, MA 02111. TEL 617-426-3040. Ed. Sarah Browning. circ. 5,000. **Document type:** newsletter.
    Description: Covers reform oriented topics in Massachusetts such as world peace, social justice, economic democracy, and open government.

320   US
C Q ALMANAC. a. $215. Congressional Quarterly Inc., 1414 22nd St., N.W., Washington, DC 20037. TEL 800-638-1710. FAX 202-887-6706.
    Description: Key bills and amendments explained; laws passed; roll-call votes cast by every member.

POLITICAL SCIENCE

320.9 US ISSN 1056-2036
H35 CODEN: CQREEX
C Q RESEARCHER. 1923. 4/m. $299. Congressional Quarterly Inc., 1414 22nd St., N.W., Washington, DC 20037. TEL 800-432-2250. FAX 202-728-1863. Ed. Sandra Stencil. bk.rev.; charts; index. (also avail. in microform from UMI,MIM; reprint service avail. from UMI) **Indexed:** Acad.Ind., Adol.Ment.Hlth.Abstr., INIS Atomind., Mid.East: Abstr.& Ind., Noise Pollut.Publ.Abstr., P.A.I.S., Vert.File Ind.
—BLDSC (3486.410000); Faxon; UMI; UnCover.
CCC.
Former titles (until 1991): Congressional Quarterly's Editorial Research Reports (ISSN 1057-0926); (until 1987): Editorial Research Reports (ISSN 0013-0958)

320 US
C Q RESEARCHER BOUND VOLUME. a. $137. Congressional Quarterly Inc., 1414 22nd St., N.W., Washington, DC 20037. TEL 800-638-1710. FAX 202-887-6706. indes. (reprint service avail.)
Formerly: E R R Bound Volume.
Description: Editorial research reports.

320 US ISSN 0899-0352
C S I S PANEL REPORTS. 1982. irreg. $215. Center for Strategic & International Studies, 1800 K St., N.W., Ste. 400, Washington, DC 20006. TEL 202-775-3119. Ed. Tracy Sutton-Masters.
Document type: academic/scholarly publication, monographic series.

C S P: CRITICAL SOCIAL POLICY; a journal of socialist theory and practice in social welfare. see *SOCIAL SERVICES AND WELFARE*

CADERNOS DO C.E.A.S.. see *SOCIOLOGY*

CAHIERS AFRICAINS/AFRIKA STUDIES. see *HISTORY — History Of Africa*

CAHIERS D'ETUDE ET DE RECHERCHE. see *BUSINESS AND ECONOMICS — Economic Systems And Theories, Economic History*

320.532 FR
CAHIERS D'HISTOIRE (PARIS). 1966. q. 250 F. (foreign 500 F.). Institut des Recherches Marxistes, 64 bd. Auguste Blanqui, 75013 Paris, France. Ed. Roger Bourderon. adv.; bk.rev. circ. 3,000. **Indexed:** Amer.Hist.& Life, Hist.Abstr.
—BLDSC (2948.978000).
Former titles: Institut de Recherches Marxistes. Cahiers d'Histoire (ISSN 0246-9731); Institut Maurice Thorez. Cahiers d'Histoire (ISSN 0020-2363)

320.5 FR ISSN 0007-9839
CAHIERS DE LA RECONCILIATION. 1923. q. 120 F. (Europe 135 F., elsewhere 150 F.). Mouvement International de la Reconciliation, 114 rue de Vaugirard, 75006 Paris, France.
TEL 1-45-44-39-42. FAX 1-45-44-39-42. Ed. Christian Renoux; Pub. Francois Jourdan. bk.rev. circ. 1,800. **Indexed:** CERDIC.

320.532 FR ISSN 0008-0136
HX5
CAHIERS DU COMMUNISME. 1924. m. (11/yr.). 350 F. (foreign 445 F.). Parti Communiste Francais, Comite National, 2, Place du Colonel Fabien, 75019 Paris, France. TEL 40-40-13-04. Ed. Marie-George Buffet. bk.rev.; illus.; index. (reprint service avail. from KTO) **Indexed:** P.A.I.S.For.Lang.Ind.
—Faxon; SWETS.

CAHIERS DU MONDE RUSSE ET SOVIETIQUE. see *HISTORY — History Of Europe*

320.531 BE ISSN 0591-0633
CAHIERS MARXISTES. 1969? m. 700 Fr. Fondation Joseph Jacquemotte, 20 Ave. de Stalingrad, 1000 Brussels, Belgium. Ed. Rosine Lewin. adv.; bk.rev. circ. 2,000.

320 FR ISSN 0068-5194
CAHIERS NEPALAIS. 1969. irreg. price varies. (Centre National de la Recherche Scientifique) C N R S Editions, 20-22 rue St. Amand, 75015 Paris, France. TEL 45-33-16-00. FAX 45-33-92-13. TELEX 200 356 F. adv.; bk.rev.; index; circ. 1,500 (controlled).

320 300 ZR ISSN 0304-2707
HC591.C6
CAHIERS ZAIROIS D'ETUDES POLITIQUES ET SOCIALES. 1973. q. Universite de Lumbashi, Faculte des Sciences Socials, Politiques et Administratives, B.P. 1825, Lumbashi, Zaire. bibl. **Indexed:** Amer.Hist.& Life, Hist.Abstr.

320 350 II ISSN 0970-406X
CALCUTTA JOURNAL OF POLITICAL STUDIES. (Text in English) 1980. s-a. Rps.18($3) University of Calcutta, Department of Political Science, Asutosh Bldg., Calcutta 700073, India. Ed. A. Mukherjee. adv.; bk.rev. circ. 1,000. (back issues avail.) **Indexed:** Int.Polit.Sci.Abstr.

327 II ISSN 0045-3862
CALCUTTAN. (Text in English) 1960. s-a. Rs.12($8.) Indo-American Society, 2B, Mona Lisa, 17 Camac St., Calcutta 700017, India. Ed. P.N. Mookerji. adv.; illus. circ. 550.
Description: Cultural, scientific and economic developments in India and the U.S.A.

320.531 UK ISSN 0262-723X
CALDER VOICE; Calderdale's socialist journal. 1977. m. £1.80. Independent Labour Publications, c/o A. Graham, 4 Upper Gaukroger, Sowerby New Rd., Sowerby Bridge, W. Yorkshire, England. illus.

320 US ISSN 0279-0246
THE CALIFORNIA EYE. bi-w. $150 (effective 1994). The Political Animal Co., 1000 W. Sunset Blvd., 2nd Fl., Los Angeles, CA 90012-2197. TEL 213-276-9223. FAX 213-276-9224. Ed. Bill Homer; Pub. Bill Homer. **Document type:** newsletter.
Description: Covers news and issues in California politics and government.

320 US ISSN 0084-8271
JK8701
CALIFORNIA GOVERNMENT & POLITICS ANNUAL. 1970. a. $7.95. California Journal Press (Subsidiary of: Information for Public Affairs, Inc.), 2101 K St., Sacramento, CA 95816. TEL 916-444-2840. Ed. Thomas R. Hoeber, Charles Price. circ. 6,000. (also avail. in microfilm)
Description: Reprints from California Journal. Analysis of state government and politics organized for student use.

353 US ISSN 0008-1205
JK8701
CALIFORNIA JOURNAL; the monthly analysis of state government and politics. 1970. m. $34.95 to individuals; educational and governmental institutions and libraries $59 (includes index); corporations and associations $95. Information for Public Affairs, Inc., 2101 K St., Sacramento, CA 95816. TEL 916-444-2840. Ed. Richard Zeiger. adv.: B&W page $2400, color page $3150; 8 1/2 x 11. charts; stat.; index. circ. 15,000. (also avail. in microfilm) **Indexed:** Cal.Per.Ind. (1984-), P.A.I.S., Sage Pub.Admin.Abstr., Sage Urb.Stud.Abstr. **Document type:** bulletin.
—UnCover.
Description: Analysis of government and politics.

320 350 US ISSN 0195-6175
CALIFORNIA POLITICAL WEEK; calpeek. 1979. w. $90. California Political Week, Inc., Box 1468, Beverly Hills, CA 90213. TEL 310-659-0205.
FAX 310-657-4340. Ed. Dick Rosengarten; Pub. Dick Rosengarten. adv. circ. 3,000. **Document type:** newsletter.
Description: California and western U.S. state and local government and political developments and trends.

320 US ISSN 1051-032X
CALIFORNIA SERIES ON SOCIAL CHOICE & POLITICAL ECONOMY. 1981. irreg., vol.24, 1993. price varies. University of California Press, 2120 Berkeley Way, Berkeley, CA 94720. TEL 510-643-7127.
FAX 510-643-7127. (Orders to: California-Princeton Fulfillment Services, 1445 Lower Ferry Rd., Ewing, NJ 08618. TEL 800-777-4726. FAX 800-999-1958) Ed.Bd. (back issues avail.)
Document type: monographic series.
—BLDSC (3015.288000).
Description: Discusses a wide variety of sociopolitical issues.
Refereed Serial

322.4 US
CALIFORNIA STATESMAN. 1962. m. $15 (included in subscr. to American Independent). William K. Shearer, Ed. & Pub., 8158 Palm St., Lemon Grove, CA 91945. TEL 619-460-4480. circ. 800.
Document type: newsletter.
Description: Contains commentary on California state and national issues.

322.4 US
CALIFORNIA STATESMAN'S FOREIGN POLICY REVIEW. 1972. m. $15 (included in subscr. to American Independent). William K. Shearer, Ed. & Pub., 8158 Palm St., Lemon Grove, CA 91945.
TEL 619-460-4480. circ. 800. **Document type:** newsletter.
Description: Commentary about foreign policy issues.

322.4 US
CALIFORNIA STATESMAN'S LEGISLATIVE SURVEY. 1965. m. $15 (included in subscr. to American Independent). William K. Shearer, Ed. & Pub., 8158 Palm St., Lemon Grove, CA 91945.
TEL 619-460-4480. circ. 800. **Document type:** newsletter.
Description: Covers the national and Californian political scene.

320.531 II ISSN 0008-1728
CALL. (Text in English) vol.22, 1970-1971. m. Rs.6. Revolutionary Socialist Party, 780 Ballimaran, Delhi 6, India. Ed. Tridib Chaudhuri.

320 PE
CAMBIO Y DESARROLLO; revista del pensamiento social and democratico. 1991. s-a. Instituto de Investigaciones, Avda. Dos de Mayo 1890, San Isidro, Lima, Peru. TEL 417955. FAX 429411. Ed. Jose Manuel Mejia.

320 UK ISSN 0575-6871
CAMBRIDGE STUDIES IN THE HISTORY AND THEORY OF POLITICS. 1967. irreg. price varies. Cambridge University Press, Edinburgh Bldg., Shaftesbury Rd., Cambridge CB2 2RU, England.
TEL 01223-312393. FAX 01223-315052. TELEX 851817256. (N. American addr.: Cambridge University Press, Journals Dept., 40 W. 20th St., New York, NY 10011. TEL 212-924-3900. FAX 212-691-3239) Ed.Bd. **Document type:** monographic series.

320 UY
CAMINOS. 1991. m.? 2500 N$ per no. Pando 2694, Montevideo, Uruguay. Ed. Omar Rovira.

320 330 US ISSN 0884-8351
KF4920.Z95
CAMPAIGN FINANCE LAW. 1981. biennial. $40. (U.S. Library of Congress, Congressional Research Service, American Law Division) National Clearing House on Education Administration, c/o Superintendent of Documents, Box 371954, Pittsburgh, PA 15250. (Dist. by: GPO, Superintendent of Documents, Washington, DC 20402) **Document type:** government publication.

320 US
CAMPAIGN GUIDE FOR CONGRESSIONAL CANDIDATE AND COMMITTEES. irreg. Federal Election Commission, Washington, DC 20463.
TEL 202-219-3420; 800-424-9530.
Description: Helps House and Senate candidate committees to comply with the federal campaign finance laws.

320 US
CAMPAIGN GUIDE FOR CORPORATIONS AND LABOR ORGANIZATIONS. irreg. Federal Election Commission, Washington, DC 20463. TEL 202-219-3420; 800-424-9530.
Description: Helps segregated funds, political action committees, labor organizations and corporations comply with federal campaign finance law.

320 US
CAMPAIGN GUIDE FOR NONCONNECTED COMMITTEES. irreg. Federal Election Commission, Washington, DC 20463. TEL 202-219-3420; 800-424-9530.
Description: Helps independent political committees to comply with federal election campaign finance laws.

POLITICAL SCIENCE

320 US
CAMPAIGN GUIDE FOR POLITICAL PARTY COMMITTEES.
irreg. Federal Election Commission, Washington, DC 20463. TEL 202-219-3420; 800-424-9530.
Formerly: Campaign Guide for Party Committees.
Description: Helps political party committees to comply with federal election campaign finance laws.

322.4 US
CAMPAIGN REPORT - JOBS WITH PEACE CAMPAIGN.*
4/yr. $15. 750 N. 18th St., Milwaukee, WI 53223-2109. TEL 617-338-5783.
Description: Objective is peace conversion from weapons and military-based jobs to employment producing goods for civilian use.

320.52 UK ISSN 0266-6065
CAMPAIGNER. 1989. s-a. British Conservative Party, 32 Smith Sq., London SW1P 3HH, England. TEL 71-222-9000. Ed. Paul S. Gray. adv. circ. 30,000.
Description: Examines current affairs issues of international importance.

320 US ISSN 0197-0771
JK1976
CAMPAIGNS AND ELECTIONS. 1980. 10/yr. $29.95. Campaigns and Elections, 1511 K St., N.W., Ste. 1020, Washington, DC 20005.
TEL 202-638-7788. Ed. Ron Faucheux; Pub. Ron Faucheux. adv.: B&W page $4225, color page $5250; trim 8 1/4 x 10 7/8; adv. contact: Peter Dunn. bk.rev.; charts; illus.; stat. circ. 64,000. (also avail. in microform from UMI; back issues avail.; reprint service avail. from UMI) **Indexed:** Int.Polit.Sci.Abstr., P.A.I.S. **Document type:** trade publication.
●Also available online. Vendor(s): University Microfilms International.
—BLDSC (3016.345000); Faxon; SWETS; UMI; UnCover. **CCC.**
Description: For political professionals; includes news, views and how-to's for modern campaigns.

CANADA. PRIVACY COMMISSIONER. ANNUAL REPORT.
see COMPUTERS — Computer Security

320 915.406 CN ISSN 0846-9547
E92
CANADA. SPECIAL COMMITTEE ON INDIAN SELF-GOVERNMENT. PROCEEDINGS. MINUTES. 1982. irreg.? Canadian Publications Centre, Supply and Services Canada, Hull, Que. K1A O59, Canada.
Former titles: Canada. Special Committee on Indian Self-Government. Proceedings and Evidence. Minutes (ISSN 0826-3051); Canada. Standing Committee on Indian Affairs and Northern Development. Sub-Committee on Indian Self-Government. Proceedings and Evidence. Minutes (ISSN 0826-3043)

320 CN ISSN 0827-0708
JL27
CANADA: THE STATE OF THE FEDERATION. (Text in English, French) 1985. a. Can.$20. Institute of Intergovernmental Relations, Queen's University, Kingston, ON K7L 3N6, Canada.
TEL 603-545-2080. FAX 603-545-6868. Eds. Douglas M. Brown, Robert Young. circ. 800. (back issues avail.) **Indexed:** Ind.Can.L.P.L. **Document type:** academic/scholarly publication.
Description: Studies fiscal federalism, constitutional reform, federal-provincial relations, the global economy, comparative federalism.
Refereed Serial

971 CN ISSN 0008-3402
AP5
CANADIAN DIMENSION; an independent journal of socialist opinion. 1963. 6/yr. Can.$24.50 to individuals; institutions Can.$35 (effective Jan. 1991). Dimension Publishing Inc., 228 Notre Dame Ave., Ste. 707, Winnipeg, MB R3B 1N7, Canada. TEL 204-957-1519. FAX 204-943-4617. E-mail: INFO@CANADIANDIMENSION.MB.CA. Ed.Bd. adv.: B&W page $350; 8 x 10 1/2; adv. contact: Michelle Torres. bk.rev.; illus.; index. circ. 3,200. (also avail. in microfiche from UMI,MML) **Indexed:** Alt.Press Ind., Amer.Hist.& Life, Can.B.P.I., Can.Per.Ind., Can.Wom.Per.Ind., CMI, Hist.Abstr., Mag.Ind., Mid.East: Abstr.& Ind. **Document type:** consumer publication.
—BLDSC (3021.170000); Faxon. **CCC.**

320 301 CN ISSN 0380-9420
JA4
CANADIAN JOURNAL OF POLITICAL & SOCIAL THEORY/REVUE CANADIENNE DE THEORIE POLITIQUE ET SOCIALE. (Not avail. in printed format. Not published in 1992) (Text in English, French) 1977. 2/yr. Can.$25 individuals; libraries Can.$35. Concordia University, 1455 de Maisonneuve West, Montreal, PQ H3G 1M8, Canada.
TEL 514-841-2112. FAX 514-848-3494. Eds. Arthur and Marilouise Kroker. adv.; bk.rev.; film rev.; index. circ. 2,000. (diskette format; microform from UMI; back issues avail.) **Indexed:** A.B.C.Pol.Sci. (until 1989), Alt.Press Ind., Can.Per.Ind., Can.Wom.Per.Ind., CMI, Film Lit.Ind. (1989-), Int.Polit.Sci.Abstr., Lang.& Lang.Behav.Abstr., Polit.Sci.Abstr., Sociol.Abstr. **Document type:** academic/scholarly publication.
●Also available online.
—UMI; UnCover.
Description: Internationally oriented, focusing on theory, technology and culture from a critical and feminist perspective.
Refereed Serial

320 CN ISSN 0008-4239
CANADIAN JOURNAL OF POLITICAL SCIENCE/REVUE CANADIENNE DE SCIENCE POLITIQUE. (Text in English, French) 1968. q. Can.$65 to non-members (O.E.C.D. nations $85; elsewhere $65). Canadian Political Science Association - Association Canadienne de Science Politique, 1 Stewart St., Ste. 205, Ottawa, ON K1N 6H7, Canada.
TEL 613-564-4026. FAX 613-230-2746. E-mail: cpscc@acadvm1.uottawa.ca. (Dist. by: Wilfrid Laurier University Press, Waterloo, ON N2L 3C5, Canada. TEL 519-884-0710. FAX 519-725-1399) (Co-sponsor: Societe Quebecoise de Science Politique) Ed.Bd. adv.: B&W page Can.$400. bk.rev.; index. circ. 3,000. (also avail. in microfiche from UMI; microfilm from PMC) **Indexed:** A.B.C.Pol.Sci., Amer.Bibl.Slavic & E.Eur.Stud., Amer.Hist.& Life, ASSIA, Can.B.P.I., Can.Per.Ind., Can.Wom.Per.Ind., CMI, Commun.Abstr., Curr.Cont., Geo.Abstr., Hist.Abstr., Ind.Can.L.P.L., Int.Polit.Sci.Abstr., Lang.& Lang.Behav.Abstr., Mid.East: Abstr.& Ind., P.A.I.S.For.Lang.Ind., P.A.I.S., Peace Res.Abstr., Polit.Sci.Abstr., Pt.de Rep. (1979-), Soc.Sci.Ind., SSCI. **Document type:** academic/scholarly publication.
—BLDSC (3034.600000); Faxon; Genuine Article; SWETS; UnCover. **CCC.**
Supersedes in part (in 1967): Canadian Journal of Economics and Political Science.
Description: Crosses the range of subfields in political science.
Refereed Serial

328 US ISSN 0315-6168
CANADIAN PARLIAMENTARY GUIDE (YEAR)/GUIDE PARLEMENTAIRE CANADIEN. (Text in English, French) 1867. a. Can.$59.95. Gale Research Inc., 835 Penobscot Bldg., Detroit, MI 48226.
TEL 313-961-2242. FAX 313-961-7086. TELEX 810-221-7086. Ed. Kathryn O'Handley. stat.
Document type: government publication.
Description: Contains general, biographical and electoral information for members of the House of Commons, Senate, Privy Council and each of the provincial and territorial legislatures.

320 CN
CANADIAN POLITICAL SCIENCE ASSOCIATION. ANNUAL MEETING/ASSOCIATION CANADIENNE DE SCIENCE POLITIQUE. CONGRES ANNUEL. (Text in English, French) 1980. a. Can.$75. Canadian Political Science Association - Association Canadienne de Science Politique, 1 Stewart St., Ste. 205, Ottawa, ON K1N 6H7, Canada. TEL 613-564-4026.
FAX 613-230-2746. E-mail: cpscc@acadvm1.uottawa.ca. circ. 75. **Document type:** proceedings.

320 CN ISSN 0319-6461
CANADIAN POLITICAL SCIENCE ASSOCIATION. BULLETIN. (Text in English, French) 1971. s-a. Can.$15. Canadian Political Science Association - Association Canadienne de Science Politique, 1 Stewart St., Ste. 205, Ottawa, ON K1N 6H7, Canada. TEL 613-564-4026. FAX 613-230-2746. E-mail: cpscc@acadvm1.uottawa.ca. adv.: B&W page Can.$300; adv. contact: Michelle Hopkins. circ. 1,200. **Document type:** newsletter.
Description: Includes news from the departments, articles on a broad range of subjects, listings of conferences and events of interest to political scientists.

CANADIAN REVIEW OF AMERICAN STUDIES. see HISTORY — History Of North And South America

CANADIAN SPEECHES: ISSUES OF THE DAY. see BUSINESS AND ECONOMICS

956.940 296.7 CN
CANADIAN ZIONIST NEWSLETTER. (Text in English, French, Hebrew) 1934. 3/yr. Canadian Zionist Federation, 5250 Decarie Blvd., Blvd. 550, Montreal, PQ H3X 2H9, Canada. TEL 514-486-9526.
FAX 514-483-6392. adv.; bk.rev. circ. 3,000.
Document type: newsletter, bulletin.
Formerly: Canadian Zionist (ISSN 0008-5383)

CAPITAL AND CLASS. see BUSINESS AND ECONOMICS — Economic Systems And Theories, Economic History

350 US ISSN 0891-9836
CAPITAL JOURNAL. w. during state legislative session. Business Council of New York State, Inc., 152 Washington Ave., Albany, NY 12210.
TEL 518-465-7511. **Document type:** newsletter.
Description: Newsletter about New York State government action affecting business.

320 US ISSN 0898-6916
F192.3
CAPITAL SOURCE.* s-a. $24.95 per no. National Journal, Inc. (Subsidiary of: Times Mirror Company), 1501 M St., N.W., Ste. 300, Washington, DC 20005. TEL 202-739-8400. FAX 202-833-8069. adv.
—BLDSC (3050.669230); SWETS.
Description: Telephone directory of the Washington power structure. Includes government officials, trade associations, interest groups, political consultants and news media.

320 333.7 US ISSN 1045-5752
HD75.6 CODEN: CNSOED
CAPITALISM, NATURE, SOCIALISM; a journal of socialist ecology. 1989. 4/yr. $22 (foreign $37) to individuals; institutions $65 (foreign $80) (effective 1995). Guilford Publications, Inc., 72 Spring St., 4th Fl., New York, NY 10012. TEL 212-431-9800.
FAX 212-966-6708. Ed. James O'Connor; Pub. Robert Matloff. adv. contact: Marian Robinson. circ. 1,000. (reprint service avail. from UMI) **Indexed:** Alt.Press Ind., Environ.Per.Bibl. (1989-), Left Ind. (1989-).
—BLDSC (3050.669720); UMI. **CCC.**

CARIBBEAN & CENTRAL AMERICA REPORT. see BUSINESS AND ECONOMICS — Economic Situation And Conditions

320 BL ISSN 0103-958X
CARTA; informe de distribuicao restrita do Senador Darcy Ribeiro. 1991. a.? Gabinete do Senador Darcy Ribeiro, Senado Federal, Anexo II, Gabinete 21, 70160 Brasilia D.F., Brazil. TEL 061-311-4229.
FAX 061-3217333. TELEX 061-1357.

CARTHAGE; Tunisian quarterly review. see HISTORY — History Of Africa

CASOPIS MATICE MORAVSKE. see HISTORY — History Of Europe

CATHOLIC WORKER. see RELIGIONS AND THEOLOGY — Roman Catholic

320 US ISSN 0273-3072
H1
CATO JOURNAL; an interdisciplinary journal of public policy analysis. 1981. 3/yr. $24 to individuals; institutions $50. Cato Institute, 1000 Massachusetts Ave., N.W., Washington, DC 20001-5403. TEL 202-842-0200.
FAX 202-842-3490. Ed. James A. Dorn. adv. circ. 3,200. (back issues avail.; reprint service avail. from WSH) **Indexed:** A.B.C.Pol.Sci., ABI Inform., Amer.Hist.& Life, C.L.I., Curr.Cont., Environ.Abstr., Hist.Abstr., INIS Atomind., Int.Polit.Sci.Abstr., J.of Econ.Lit., Leg.Per., P.A.I.S., SSCI.
●Also available online. Vendor(s): University Microfilms International.
—BLDSC (3093.272000); CIS; Faxon; Genuine Article; SWETS; UMI; UnCover.

CENTER FOR EUROPEAN STUDIES WORKING PAPER SERIES. see HISTORY — History Of Europe

POLITICAL SCIENCE 5293

320   US
CENTER FOR STRATEGIC AND INTERNATIONAL STUDIES. SIGNIFICANT ISSUES SERIES. 1979. 9/yr. $85. Center for Strategic and International Studies, 1800 K St. N.W., Ste. 400, Washington, DC 20006. TEL 202-775-3119. FAX 202-775-3199. Ed. Roberta Howard. **Document type:** academic/scholarly publication, monographic series.
—BLDSC (8276.305000).
    Formerly: Georgetown University Center for Strategic and International Studies. Significant Issues Series (ISSN 0736-7163)

320   US
CENTER FOR THE STUDY OF THE PRESIDENCY. ANNUAL REPORT. a. Center for the Study of the Presidency, 208 E. 75th St., New York, NY 10021. TEL 212-249-1200. FAX 212-628-9503. (reprint service avail. from UMI) **Document type:** corporate report.

320   US
CENTER FOR THE STUDY OF THE PRESIDENCY. PROCEEDINGS. 1971. irreg., vol.6, 1989. membership. Center for the Study of the Presidency, 208 E. 75th St., New York, NY 10021. TEL 212-249-1200. FAX 212-628-9503. Ed. R. Gordon Hoxie. circ. 11,000. (also avail. in microform from UMI; reprint service avail. from UMI) **Indexed:** Abstr.Mil.Bibl., Amer.Hist.& Life (1989-), Hist.Abstr. (1989-). **Document type:** monographic series.

956.940 296   RH   ISSN 0008-9184
CENTRAL AFRICAN ZIONIST DIGEST. 1958. m. free. Central African Zionist Organisation, Box 1162, Bulawayo, Zimbabwe. Ed. Barney Katz. illus.

320 330   GT   ISSN 0254-2471
HC141.A1
CENTRAL AMERICA REPORT. (Text in English) 1974. w. $219. Inforpress Centroamericana, 11 Ave. 16-60, Zona 2, Apdo. 2823, Guatemala City, Guatemala. TEL 530681. **Indexed:** HR Rep. **Document type:** newspaper, bulletin.
    Description: Contains information and analysis on the economic and political events in Belize, Guatemala, El Salvador, Honduras, Nicaragua, Costa Rica and Panama.

CENTRAL AMERICA REPORT. see *RELIGIONS AND THEOLOGY*

820   US   ISSN 1053-413X
CENTRAL AMERICA REPORTER. 1981. m. $5 to individuals; institutions $25. Central America Solidarity Association, Central America Education Fund, 1151 Massachusetts Ave., Cambridge, MA 02138-5201. TEL 617-492-8699. circ. 10,000.
    Formerly (until 1988): Central American Monitor.

958.008   UK   ISSN 0966-3452
DK845
CENTRAL ASIA BRIEF. Arabic edition: Al-Muslimun fi Asiya al-Wusta. 1985. 6/yr. £6 to individuals (foreign £9); institutions £12 (foreign £15). Islamic Foundation, Markfield Dawah Centre, Ratby Lane, Markfield, Leicester LE67 9RN, England. TEL 0530-244944. FAX 0530-244946. Ed. Mr. Karim. **Indexed:** Per.Islam. (1991-). **Document type:** academic/scholarly publication, newsletter.
    Formerly (until 1992): Soviet Muslims Brief (ISSN 0950-9739)
    Description: Examines Central Asian affairs. Provides information from Central Asian sources.

330 320   US   ISSN 1062-2314
DK859.5
CENTRAL ASIA MONITOR. 1992. bi-m. $60 to individuals; institutions $96 (effective 1995 & 1996). Institute for Democratic Development, R.R. 2, Box 6880, Fair Haven, VT 05743. TEL 802-537-4361. FAX 802-537-4362. Ed. Valery Chaldze. adv.: page $150; adv. contact: Valery Chaldze. bk.rev.; stat.; index. (back issues avail.) **Indexed:** Per.Islam. **Document type:** academic/scholarly publication.
    Description: Covers Kazakhstan, Kyrgyzstan, Tajikistan, Turkmenistan, Uzbekistan.
    Refereed Serial

320 950   UK   ISSN 0263-4937
DS327
CENTRAL ASIAN SURVEY. 1982. q. £40 to individuals; institutions £186 (effective 1996). (Society for Central Asian Studies) Carfax Publishing Co., P.O. Box 25, Abingdon, Oxon. OX14 3UE, England. TEL 01235-555335. FAX 01235-553559. (Subscr. in N. America to: Carfax Publishing Co., 875-81 Massachusetts Ave., Cambridge, MA 02139) Ed. Marie Broxup. (back issues avail.) **Indexed:** Abstr.Musl.Rel., Amer.Hist.& Life, Curr.Cont., Hist.Abstr., Int.Polit.Sci.Abstr. **Document type:** academic/scholarly publication.
—BLDSC (3105.960000); Faxon; SWETS; UMI; UnCover. **CCC.**
    Description: Publishes research in the history, politics, cultures and economics of the Turkic peoples of the Central Asian region (from western Anatolia to western China, including the republics of former Soviet Central Asia) sharing a common ethnic, cultural, linguistic and religious heritage.
    Refereed Serial

320   BU   ISSN 0861-038X
CENTRAL COMMITTEE OF THE BULGARIAN COMMUNIST PARTY. INFORMATION BULLETIN. Bulgarian edition (ISSN 0861-0355); Russian edition (ISSN 0861-0363); Spanish edition (ISSN 0861-0371) (Text in English) 1946. m. 40.80 lv. (Bulgarian ed. 12 lv.). Central Committee of the Bulgarian Communist Party, 2, Dondoukov Blvd., 1000 Sofia, Bulgaria. (Subscr. to: RP - 2A, Klokotnitza St., 1202 Sofia, Bulgaria) Ed. Emil Markov. index. circ. 11,100 (1,800 Eng. ed.; 6,300 Bulg. ed.; 1,700 Russ. ed.; 1,300 Sp. ed.).

320 330.9   US
CENTRAL INTELLIGENCE AGENCY. MONOGRAPHS. (In 7 subseries avail.: All Communist Countries; All Countries; All International Countries; China; Commonwealth of Independent States; Maps Only) irreg. price varies. U.S. National Technical Information Service, 5825 Port Royal Rd., Springfield, VA 22161. TEL 703-487-4630. **Document type:** government publication.
    Description: Presents the political, statistical, economic, and military conditions.

320 330.9   US
CENTRAL INTELLIGENCE AGENCY. MONOGRAPHS. ALL COMMUNIST COUNTRIES REPORTS. (Subseries of: Central Intelligence Agency. Monographs.) irreg. price varies. U.S. National Technical Information Service, 5825 Port Royal Rd., Springfield, VA 22161. TEL 703-487-4630.
    Description: Presents the political, economic, statistical, and military conditions.

320 330.9   US
CENTRAL INTELLIGENCE AGENCY. MONOGRAPHS. ALL COUNTRIES REPORTS. (Subseries of: Central Intelligence Agency. Monographs) irreg. price varies. U.S. National Technical Information Service, 5825 Port Royal Rd., Springfield, VA 22161. TEL 703-487-4630.
    Description: Brings out the political, economic, statistical, and military conditions.

320 330.9   US
CENTRAL INTELLIGENCE AGENCY. MONOGRAPHS. ALL INTERNATIONAL COUNTRIES REPORTS. (Subseries of: Central Intelligence Agency. Monographs) irreg. price varies. U.S. National Technical Information Service, 5825 Port Royal Rd., Springfield, VA 22161. TEL 703-487-4630. **Document type:** government publication.
    Formerly (until 1992): Central Intelligence Agency. Monographs. All Non-Communist Country Reports.
    Description: Reports on the political, economic, statistical, and military conditions.

320 330.9   US
CENTRAL INTELLIGENCE AGENCY. MONOGRAPHS. CHINA REPORTS. (Subseries of: Central Intelligence Agency. Monographs) irreg. price varies. U.S. National Technical Information Service, 5825 Port Royal Rd., Springfield, VA 22161. TEL 703-487-4630.
    Description: Covers the political, economic, statistical, and military conditions.

327 365.64   US
CENTRAL INTELLIGENCE AGENCY. MONOGRAPHS. COMMONWEALTH OF INDEPENDENT STATES REPORT. (Subseries of: Central Intelligence Agency. Monographs) irreg. price varies. U.S. National Technical Information Service, 5825 Port Royal Rd., Springfield, VA 22161. TEL 703-487-4630. **Document type:** government publication.
    Formerly (until 1992): Central Intelligence Agency. Monographs. U.S.S.R. Reports.
    Description: Details the political, economic, statistical, and military conditions.

320 330.9   US
CENTRAL INTELLIGENCE AGENCY. MONOGRAPHS. MAPS ONLY. (Subseries of: Central Intelligence Agency. Monographs) irreg. price varies. U.S. National Technical Information Service, 5825 Port Royal Rd., Springfield, VA 22161. TEL 703-487-4630.
    Description: Provides visual information on political, economic, statistical, and military conditions.

CENTRE D'HISTOIRE CONTEMPORAINE DU LANGUEDOC-ROUSSILLON. BULLETIN. see *HISTORY — History Of Europe*

CENTRE FOR DEVELOPMENT RESEARCH. PUBLICATIONS. see *AGRICULTURE*

320   UK   ISSN 0577-1935
CENTREPOINT. 1974. 3/yr. free. Christian Centre Party, 157 Vicarage Rd., London E10 5DU, England. TEL 0181-539-3876. Ed. Ronald King; Pub. Ronald King. bk.rev.; circ. controlled.

320   PR
CENTRO DE ESTUDIOS DE LA REALIDAD PUERTORRIQUENA. CUADERNOS. no.5, 1982. irreg. Ediciones Huracan, Inc., Avda. Gonzalez 1003, Santa Rica, Rio Piedras, PR 00925.

CENTRO DE ESTUDIOS PUBLICOS. DOCUMENTO DE TRABAJO. see *BUSINESS AND ECONOMICS — Economic Situation And Conditions*

CERCLE FUSTEC DE COULANGES. DOCUMENTS. see *HISTORY — History Of Europe*

CHAIN REACTION. see *ENVIRONMENTAL STUDIES*

CHALCEDON REPORT. see *RELIGIONS AND THEOLOGY*

320.532   US   ISSN 0009-1049
E838
CHALLENGE (NEW YORK); the Revolutionary Communist newspaper. Monthly French edition: Defi. (Includes monthly supplement Desafio) (Text in English and Spanish) 1964. w. $15 to individuals; institutions $35. Progressive Labor Party, 231 W. 29th St., No. 501, New York, NY 10001. TEL 212-282-9000. Ed. Luis Castro. illus. circ. 10,000. (also avail. in microform from UMI) **Indexed:** Alt.Press Ind., BPIA, Fut.Surv. **Document type:** newspaper.
—UMI.

320   II
CHANDIGARH POST. (Text in English) 1972. w. Rs.12. H. No. 2017 Sector 15-C, Chandigarh 160017, India. Ed. Surrinder Khullar. adv.; illus.
    Description: News and current affairs.

320   UK   ISSN 0968-7866
CHARTIST. no.141, 1993. q. £8 to individuals; institutions £18. Chartist Publications, 18 Southcote Rd., London N19 5BJ, England. **Indexed:** Alt.Press Ind.

320 951   GW   ISSN 0341-6631
DS701
CHINA AKTUELL. (English-language supplement: China Monthly Data) 1972. m. DM.156 (foreign DM.171; students DM.60). Institut fuer Asienkunde - Institute of Asian Affairs Hamburg, Rothenbaumchaussee 32, 20148 Hamburg, Germany. TEL 040-443001-03. FAX 040-4107945. **Indexed:** Key to Econ.Sci. **Document type:** academic/scholarly publication.
—SWETS.

POLITICAL SCIENCE

951 310   US   ISSN 0190-602X
DS779.15
CHINA FACTS AND FIGURES ANNUAL. 1978. a. $75. Academic International Press, Box 1111, Gulf Breeze, FL 32562-1111. (back issues avail.)
Document type: academic/scholarly publication.
 Description: Accululates annually all basic and statistical information about the Peaple Public of China.

THE CHINA JOURNAL. see *ORIENTAL STUDIES*

CHINA NEWS ANALYSIS. see *GENERAL INTEREST PERIODICALS — China*

951 327   UK   ISSN 0045-6764
CHINA NOW. 1970. 4/yr. £12 to individuals (foreign £18); institutions £25 (foreign £30). Society for Anglo-Chinese Understanding Ltd., 109 Promenade, Cheltenham, Glos. GL50 1NW, England. TEL 01242-226625. Ed. John Hilary. adv.: B&W page £150; trim 260 x 190; adv. contact: Jean Penders. bk.rev.; index. circ. 800. **Document type:** academic/scholarly publication.
—BLDSC (3180.214000).

320 301 355   US   ISSN 0891-351X
CHINA REPORT: POLITICAL, SOCIOLOGICAL, AND MILITARY AFFAIRS. irreg. (approx. 90/yr.). $5 per no. U.S. Joint Publications Research Service, Box 12507, Arlington, VA 22209. TEL 703-487-4630. (Dist. by: NTIS, Springfield, VA 22161)

CHINESE LAW AND GOVERNMENT; a journal of translations. see *LAW*

320   NE   ISSN 0167-9155
CHRISTEN DEMOCRATISCHE VERKENNINGEN. 1971. m. fl.70.25 (students fl.45). C D A Wetenschappelijk Instituut, Dr. Kuyperstraat 5, 2514 BA The Hague, Netherlands. TEL 31-70-3424870. FAX 31-70-3643417. Ed. Th. B.F.M. Brinkel. adv.; bk.rev.; index. circ. 3,000.
—BLDSC (3181.774000); SWETS.
 Supersedes: Socialisme en Democratie (ISSN 0037-8135) & Politiek Perspectief (ISSN 0166-8196); Which was formerly: Politiek (ISSN 0032-3330)

320.5   US   ISSN 0195-9387
CHRISTIAN ANTI-COMMUNISM CRUSADE. NEWSLETTER. Variant title: C.A.C.C. Newsletter. 1958. m. contributions. Christian Anti-Communism Crusade, 227 E. 6th St., Box 890, Long Beach, CA 90801-0890. TEL 310-437-0941. FAX 310-432-2074. Ed. Fred Schwarz. bk.rev.; rec.rev. circ. 30,000. (also avail. in microform from UMI) **Document type:** newsletter.
—UMI.

CHRISTIAN BEACON. see *RELIGIONS AND THEOLOGY — Protestant*

320.531   UK   ISSN 0009-5648
HX51
CHRISTIAN SOCIALIST. 1960. q. £2. Christian Socialist Movement, 133 Shepherdess Walk, London N1 7QA, England. TEL 44-71-253-6301. Ed.Bd. adv.; bk.rev. circ. 1,300. (also avail. in microfilm from KTO) **Document type:** newsletter.
 Formerly: C S M News.
 Description: Forum for debate between Christians of all denominations on issues of peace and social justice.

CHRISTIAN STATESMAN. see *RELIGIONS AND THEOLOGY*

CHRISTLICHE DEMOKRATIE; Vierteljahresschrift fuer Zeitgeschichte, Sozial-, Kultur- und Wirtschaftsgeschichte. see *HISTORY — History Of Europe*

CHRONICLE OF LATIN AMERICAN ECONOMIC AFFAIRS. see *BUSINESS AND ECONOMICS — Economic Situation And Conditions*

320   SZ   ISSN 0302-2498
JF501
CHRONICLE OF PARLIAMENTARY ELECTIONS AND DEVELOPMENTS. (Editions in English, French) 1966. a. 35 SFr. Inter-Parliamentary Union, Place du Petit-Saconnex, CH-1211 Geneva 19, Switzerland. TEL 022-7344150. FAX 022-7333141. TELEX 414217-IPU-CH. **Document type:** bulletin.
—BLDSC (3186.281000).
 Formerly (until vol.12, 1978): Chronicle of Parliamentary Elections (ISSN 0074-1043)

CHRONIQUE JUDICIAIRE D'HAITI; revue juridique et culturelle Haitienne. see *LAW*

320.532 951   CH   ISSN 1015-9355
CHUNG KUNG YEN CHIU/STUDIES ON CHINESE COMMUNISM. Key Title: Zhonggong Yanjiu. (Text in Chinese; contents page in English) 1967. m. NT.$1000($35) Institute for the Study of Chinese Communist Problems, P.O. Box 351, Taipei, Taiwan, Republic of China. TEL 7089780. FAX 3259915. Ed.Bd; Pub. Weng Yen-Ching. index. circ. 1,800. **Document type:** academic/scholarly publication.
 Formerly: Fei Ch'ing Yen Chiu (ISSN 0014-9667)

320.532 951   CH   ISSN 1013-2716
DS779.15
CHUNG-KUO TA-LU YEN-CHIU/MAINLAND CHINA STUDIES. Key Title: Zhongguo Dalu Yanjiu. (Text in Chinese) 1958. m. $53. Institute of International Relations, 64 Wan Shou Rd., Mucha, Taipei, Taiwan, Republic of China. TEL 02-939-4921. Ed. Szu-Yin Ho. index. circ. 5,000. (also avail. in microform from UMI; reprint service avail. from ISI,UMI)
—UMI; UnCover.
 Formerly (until 1985): Fei Ch'ing Yueh Pao - Chinese Communist Affairs Monthly (ISSN 0014-9675)

CHURCH & STATE. see *RELIGIONS AND THEOLOGY*

320   IE   ISSN 0332-3625
CHURCH & STATE; a magazine of Irish secularist opinion. q. I£6. P.O. Box 159, Cork, Ireland. Ed. Angela Clifford. **Document type:** bulletin.
 Description: Aims to assist in the growth of a powerful secular and liberal opinion in Ireland.

CINEMA POLITIQUE; dans la perspective d'une vie passionnante. see *MOTION PICTURES*

CIRCOLO ROSSELLI. QUADERNI. see *CLUBS*

320   FR   ISSN 0756-3205
CITE; revue de la nouvelle citoyennete. 1982. 4/yr. 150 F. Societe Nationale Presse Francaise, 17 rue des Petits Champs, 75001 Paris, France. TEL 42-97-42-57. Ed. Bertrand Renouvin. circ. 3,000. (back issues avail.)

320   CN   ISSN 1181-4357
CITOYEN.* 1941. w. Can.$13. Groupe Hebcor, Inc., 4545 Frontenad St., Quebec, Que. H2H 2R7, Canada. TEL 819-879-5409. Ed. Roger Laliberte. adv. circ. 4,600. (tabloid format)

320   US   ISSN 1060-8540
F128.55
THE CITY JOURNAL. 1990. q. $24. Manhattan Institute, Inc., 52 Vanderbilt Ave., New York, NY 10017-3808. TEL 212-599-7000. FAX 212-599-3494. Ed. Lawrence Mone. circ. 10,000 (paid); 2,000 (controlled). **Indexed:** Abstr.Crim.& Pen. **Document type:** consumer publication.
—BLDSC (3268.365000); UnCover.
 Formerly (until 1992): N Y (ISSN 1057-3607)
 Description: Covers politics and culture.

355   US   ISSN 0045-7035
CIVIL AFFAIRS JOURNAL & NEWSLETTER. 1949. bi-m. $10. Civil Affairs Association, 416 Eisner St., Silver Spring, MD 20901. TEL 301-564-0854. bk.rev.; illus. circ. 2,600. **Document type:** newsletter.
 Formerly: Military Government Journal and Newsletter (ISSN 0026-3990)

CIVILIAN CONGRESS; includes a directory of persons holding executive branch-military office in Congress contrary to constitutional prohibition (Art.1, Sec.6, Cl.2) of concurrent office-holding. see *LAW*

327   NE   ISSN 0030-3283
AP15
CIVIS MUNDI. 1962. q. fl.44.50 to individuals (foreign fl.49); institutions fl.58; students fl.40 (effective 1994). Stichting Civis Mundi, Akkerwindestraat 23, 3051 LA Rotterdam, Netherlands. TEL 31-10-4182580. FAX 31-10-4525332. Ed. S.W. Couwenberg. adv. contact: Ms A.L. van der Bree. bk.rev.; bibl.; index; circ. 1,000 (paid). **Indexed:** Key To Econ.Sci. **Document type:** academic/scholarly publication.
—SWETS.
 Formerly: Oost-West.
 Description: Covers political culture and philosophy.

320   IT   ISSN 0009-8191
H7
CIVITAS; periodico di studi politici. (Text in Italian; summaries in English, French, German, Serbo-Croatian, Spanish) 1919. m. L.25000. Edizioni Civitas, Via Tirso 92, 00198 Rome, Italy. TEL 06-8555651. Ed. Paolo E. Taviani. adv.; bk.rev.; charts; stat.; index. circ. 8,580. **Indexed:** Amer.Hist.& Life, Hist.Abstr., Int.Polit.Sci.Abstr.

320   II
CLARITY; newsman's newsweekly. (Text in English) 1974. w. Rs.100. Writers Foundation Charitable Trust, Barrack No. 3,2-3, Adarsh Nagar, Prabhadevi, Bombay 400 025, India. Ed. S.B. Kolpe. adv.; bk.rev.; illus. circ. 5,000.

320.532   FR   ISSN 1162-096X
CLARTE.* 1947. 6/yr. Union des Etudiants Communistes de France, 19 rue Victor Hugo, 93170 Bagnolet, France. adv.; illus.
 Former titles (until 1991): Nouveau Clarte (ISSN 0242-0090); (until 1965): Clarte (ISSN 0412-7242)

320.532   SW   ISSN 0345-2085
CLARTE. 1924. q. SEK 150. Svenska Clartefoerbundet, Torsten Alms gata 19, S-126 51 Haegersten, Sweden. TEL 46-8-19-13-58. E-mail: clarte@nn.apc.org. Eds. Olle Josephson, Hans Isaksson.
 Description: Publishes analysis and debate on social, scientific and cultural questions.

320.531   NO
CLASS STRUGGLE. (Text in English) 1969. d. NOK 150. Workers Communist Party (Marxist-Leninist) of Norway, P.O. Box 83 Bryn, 0611 Oslo 6, Norway. Ed. S. Allern. adv.; bk.rev. circ. 8,000. (back issues avail.)

320   SZ   ISSN 0069-4533
CLASSIQUES DE LA PENSEE POLITIQUE. 1965. irreg., no.15, 1995. price varies. Librairie Droz S.A., 11, rue Massot, CH-1211 Geneva 12, Switzerland. TEL 022-3466666. FAX 022-3472391. circ. 1,000. **Document type:** academic/scholarly publication.
—CCC.

320   US
CLAUSTROPHOBIA (COLUMBUS); breaking through barriers to freedom and liberty. m. $10 (foreign $15). 400 N. High St., Ste. 137, Columbus, OH 43215. Eds. Dena L. Bruedigam, Michael D. Campbell.
 Description: Discusses what is wrong with the governing of our nations.

320   CU
CLAVE. q. $7 in N. America; S. America and Europe $8; others $9. (Ministerio de Cultura) Ediciones Cubanas, Obispo No. 527, Apdo. 605, Havana, Cuba.

320   AG
CLAVES PARA INTERPRETAR LOS HECHOS. 1984. m. Editorial Claves, Riombamba 212, Buenos Aires, Argentina. Ed. Juan Carlos Cerutti.

320.531   NE   ISSN 0929-5100
CLINCH. 1974. 6/yr. fl.20 to non-members. Jonge Socialisten in de Partij van de Arbeid, Nicolaas Witsenkade 30, 1017 ZT Amsterdam, Netherlands. TEL 31-20-5512452. FAX 31-20-5512330. Ed.Bd. adv.; bk.rev.; illus.; stat. circ. 13,000.
 Formerly (until Mar. 1993): Linksaf (ISSN 0167-093X); **Supersedes:** Opinie (ISSN 0030-3771); Which was formerly: Kapitalist; Paraat.

POLITICAL SCIENCE

320.531   GW
COCHISE; Zeitung des sozialistischen Schuelerbundes Berlin. 1986. q. Sozialistischen Schuelerbundes Berlin, Muellerstr. 163, 1000 Berlin 65, Germany. TEL 030-4792132.

320   GW   ISSN 0932-3473
CODE; das andere deutsche Nachrichtenmagazin. 1974. m. DM.105. Verlag Diagnosen, Untere Burghalde 51, 71229 Leonberg, Germany. TEL 07152-26011. Ed. Ekkehard Franke-Gricksch. adv. circ. 30,000. **Document type:** consumer publication.

COEXISTENCE; a review of East-West and development issues. see SOCIAL SCIENCES: COMPREHENSIVE WORKS

COGITATIONS ON LAW AND GOVERNMENT. see LAW

320 100   US
COGNITIVE DISSIDENTS. 1987. irreg. (2-3/yr.). 4223 Cottage Circle, Ste. 4, Las Vegas, NV 89119. TEL 702-735-4433. FAX 702-733-3979. E-mail: 70402.3124@compuserve.com. Ed. Scott A. Kjar. circ. 700. (back issues avail.) **Document type:** newsletter.
   Description: Provides a free perspective on politics, philosophy, economics, religion and human nature.

320   BL
COLECAO CAMINHOS BRASILEIROS. irreg. Edicoes Tiempo Brasileiro Ltda, Rua Gago Coutinho 61, C.P. 16099, ZC-01 Laranjeiras, Rio de Janeiro, Brazil. Dir. Carlos Chagas Filho.

320   BL
COLECAO TENDENCIAS. irreg., vol.3, 1982. Edicoes Graal Ltda., Rua Hermenegildo de Barroa, 31-A, 20241 Gloria, Rio de Janeiro RJ, Brazil.

320 330   PO
COLECCAO HORIZONTE UNIVERSITARIO. no.30, 1982. irreg., no.56, 1991. Livros Horizonte, Lda., Rua das Chagas, 17, 1121 Lisbon Codex, Portugal. TEL 1-3466917. FAX 1-3426921.

320   UY
COLECCION CIEN TEMAS BASICOS.* no.18, 1976. irreg. Editorial Medina s.r.l., Tristan Naruaja 1547, Montevideo, Uruguay.

320   CR
COLECCION CUADERNOS C E D A L. 1974. irreg. Centro de Estudios C E D A L, Apdo. 874, San Jose, Costa Rica. Ed. Alberto Baeza Flores.

320   ES
COLECCION DEBATE. 1983. irreg. (Universidad Centroamericana Jose Simeon Canas) U C A Editores, Autopista Sur, Jardines de Guadalupe, Apdo. Postal 01-575, San Salvador, El Salvador. Ed. Rodolfo Cardenal. circ. 1,200.

320   DR
COLECCION ESTUDIOS POLITICOS. irreg. Publicaciones O N A P, Edif. de Oficinas Gubernamentales, Av. Mexico esq. Leopoldo Navarro, Santo Domingo, Dominican Republic. circ. 750.

320   SP
COLECCION IBERICA. 1976. irreg. Editorial Anagrama, S.A., Calle Pedro de la Creu, 58, 08034 Barcelona, Spain.

320   VE
COLECCION MONOGRAFIAS POLITICAS.* 1978. irreg. Editorial Juridica Venezolana, Edif. Galipan, Av. Francisco de Miranda, Piso 3, Apdo. 17598, Caracas 1015-A, Venezuela.

320   SP
COLECCION VIERA Y CLAVIJO. 1982. a. Universidad de la Laguna, Cabildo Insular de Gran Canaria, Secretariado de Publicaciones, San Agustin, 30, 38201 La Laguna-Tenerife, Islas Canarias, Spain. TEL 922-25-81-27.

320   US
COLONIE HI-LITER. 1974. s-a. free to residents. Town of Colonie, 747 Downing St., Schenectady, NY 12309. TEL 518-783-2700. Ed. Robert E. Keating. circ. 38,000.
   Formerly: Colonie Quarterly.

320   US
COLORADO STATESMAN. 1898. w. $39. Box 18129, Denver, CO 80218. TEL 303-827-8600. Ed. Jody Strogoff. **Document type:** newspaper.
   Description: Covers all levels of Colorado politics.

320.9   PK   ISSN 0010-2121
COMBAT; an independent news weekly. (Text in English) 1969. w. Rs.24. 81-82 Farid Chambers, Abdullah Haroon Rd., Karachi 3, Pakistan. Ed. Yunus Said. adv.

COMISION ECONOMICA PARA AMERICA LATINA Y EL CARIBE. SERIE REFORMAS DE POLITICA PUBLICA. see BUSINESS AND ECONOMICS — Economic Situation And Conditions

322.4   CK
COMITE DE ACCION INTERAMERICANA DE COLOMBIA. BOLETIN. irreg. Comite de Accion Interamericana de Colombia, Cra. 7 No.32-33, Of. 1601, Apdo. Aereo 10598, Bogota, Colombia.

320   US
COMMITTEE TO RESTORE THE CONSTITUTION. BULLETIN. 1965. m. $25 membership. Committee to Restore the Constitution, Box 986, Ft. Collins, CO 80522. TEL 303-484-2575. Ed. Archibald E. Roberts. **Document type:** bulletin.
   Description: Reveals hidden facts behind the national crisis. Explains constitutional authority to halt economic-political exploitation. Incorporates model procedures for county and state action to restore interest-free money, defend - preserve freedom of person and property.

320   US   ISSN 0271-9592
JK1
COMMON CAUSE MAGAZINE; people, power and politics in Washington. 1980. q. $20 (effective 1995 & 1996). Common Cause, 2030 M St., N.W., Washington, DC 20036. TEL 202-833-1200. FAX 202-659-3716. Ed. Vicki Kemper. circ. 200,000. Indexed: Acad.Ind., Environ.Abstr., P.A.I.S., PSI. **Document type:** consumer publication.
   ●Also available online. Vendor(s): Lexis-Nexis, University Microfilms International.
   —Genuine Article; UMI; UnCover.
   Supersedes: Frontline (Washington); In Common (ISSN 0196-6677)
   Description: Investigative political reporting.

341.1 100   UK   ISSN 0010-3276
COMMON LIFE.* a newsletter on reconciliation, non-violence, peace and spiritual communism. 1951. q. free. Vedanta Movement, Batheaston Villa, Batheaston, Bath, England. Ed. Swami Avyaktanananda.

320 330   AT   ISSN 0810-7947
COMMON SENSE. 1981. irreg. Common Sense Publications, 1 Schneider Rd., Rosevale, Qld. 4340, Australia. TEL 074-640-533. Ed. Mr. Viv Forbes. circ. 800.
   Description: Political and economic commentary from free market perspective.

COMMON SENSE. see BUSINESS AND ECONOMICS — Economic Systems And Theories, Economic History

320.5   UK
COMMON WEALTH JOURNAL. 1966. 4/yr. 50p. Common Wealth, c/o W.J. Taylor, 107 Pilton St., Pilton, Barnstaple, Devon, England. Ed. J.C. Banks. bk.rev. circ. 1,000. (processed)
   Former titles: Common Wealth; Libertarian (ISSN 0024-2004)

COMMONWEALTH. see LITERARY AND POLITICAL REVIEWS

320   SW   ISSN 0283-2925
COMMUNIDAD. (Text in Spanish) 1977. q. SEK 130($25) Centrum foer Kooperativa Studier och Verkamhetet, P.O. Box 15128, S-10465 Stockholm, Sweden. FAX 46-8-6445985. Ed. Ruben G. Prieto. bk.rev. circ. 2,500. (back issues avail.)

329.9   FR   ISSN 2209-7007
COMMUNISME; revue d'histoire, de sociologie et de science politique. (Summaries in English, French) 1982. 3/yr. 220 F. Editions l'Age d'Homme, 5 rue Ferou, 75006 Paris, France. Ed. Stephane Courtois. bk.rev. circ. 700.

320.532   UK   ISSN 0967-067X
HX1
COMMUNIST AND POST-COMMUNIST STUDIES. 1962. q. £132($210) (effective 1996). Butterworth - Heinemann, Part of the Reed Elsevier group, Linacre House, Jordan Hill, Oxford OX2 8DP, England. TEL 01865-310366. FAX 01865-310898. TELEX 83111 BHPOXF G. (Subscr. to: Elsevier Science Ltd., P.O. Box 800, Kidlington, Oxford OX5 1DX, England. TEL 44-1865-843000. FAX 44-1865-843010; Subscr. in U.S. and Canada to: Elsevier Science, 660 White Plains Rd., Tarrytown, NY 10591-5153. TEL 914-524-9200. FAX 914-333-2444) Ed. Andrzej Korbonski. adv.; bk.rev.; index, cum.index: vols.1-10 (1968-1977). (also avail. in microform from UMI; back issues avail.) Indexed: A.B.C.Pol.Sci., Amer.Bibl.Slavic & E.Eur.Stud., Amer.Hist.& Life, ASCA, Curr.Cont., Hist.Abstr., Int.Polit.Sci.Abstr., Mid.East: Abstr.& Ind., P.A.I.S., Polit.Sci.Abstr., Soc.Sci.Ind., SSCI. **Document type:** academic/scholarly publication.
   —BLDSC (3363.547700); Faxon; Genuine Article; SWETS; UMI; UnCover. CCC.
   Former titles (until 1992): Studies in Comparative Communism (ISSN 0039-3592); (until 1968): Communist Affairs (ISSN 0588-8174)
   Description: Provides research, probes the origins of the malaise and evaluates the reforms and likelihood of their success.
   Refereed Serial

COMMUNIST ECONOMIES AND ECONOMIC TRANSFORMATION. see BUSINESS AND ECONOMICS — Economic Systems And Theories, Economic History

320.532   UK   ISSN 0950-2416
COMMUNIST REVIEW; theoretical and discussion journal. 1988. 3/yr. £5. Communist Party of Britain, 3 Ardleigh Rd., London N1 4HS, England. TEL 0171-275-8162. Ed. Ron Bellamy. adv. circ. 2,000. (also avail. in microfilm from WMP; back issues avail.)

320.3   US   ISSN 0010-4140
JA3
COMPARATIVE POLITICAL STUDIES. 1968. q. $54 to individuals; institutions $182 (effective Sep. 1995). Sage Publications, Inc., 2455 Teller Rd., Thousand Oaks, CA 91320. TEL 805-499-0721. FAX 805-499-0871. E-mail: libraries@sagepub.com. (Overseas subsr. to: Sage Publications Ltd., 6 Bonhill St., London EC2A 4PU, England; Sage Publications India Pvt. Ltd., P.O. Box 4215, New Delhi 110 048, India) Ed. James A. Caporaso. adv.; bk.rev.; bibl.; charts; stat.; index. circ. 1,650. (also avail. in microform from UMI; back issues avail.; reprint service avail.) Indexed: A.B.C.Pol.Sci., Abstr.Crim.& Pen., Amer.Bibl.Slavic & E.Eur.Stud., Amer.Hist.& Life, ASSIA, Commun.Abstr., Curr.Cont., Geo.Abstr., Hist.Abstr., Int.Polit.Sci.Abstr., Mid.East: Abstr.& Ind., P.A.I.S., Per.Islam. (1991-), Polit.Sci.Abstr., Rural Recreat.Tour.Abstr., Soc.Sci.Ind., Sociol.Abstr., Sociol.Educ.Abstr., SSCI, Stud.Wom.Abstr., World Agri.Econ.& Rural Sociol.Abstr. **Document type:** academic/scholarly publication.
   —BLDSC (3363.795000); Faxon; Genuine Article; SWETS; UMI; UnCover. CCC.
   Description: Publishes theoretical and empirical research articles by scholars engaged in comparative, cross-national studies.

320.3   US   ISSN 0010-4159
JA3
COMPARATIVE POLITICS. 1968. q. $30 to individuals (foreign $37.50); institutions $55 (foreign $63.50). City University of New York, Political Science Program, 33 W. 42nd St., New York, NY 10036. TEL 212-642-2377. (Subscr. to: Boyd Printing Co., 49 Sheridan Ave. P.O. Box 1413, Albany, NY 12210-1413. TEL 518-436-9686) Ed. Dankwart A. Rustow. adv. contact: Larry Peterson. bk.rev.; charts; index. circ. 2,000. (also avail. in microform from MIM,UMI; back issues avail.; reprint service avail. from UMI) Indexed: A.B.C.Pol.Sci., Acad.Ind., Amer.Bibl.Slavic & E.Eur.Stud., Amer.Hist.& Life, Curr.Cont., Hist.Abstr., Int.Polit.Sci.Abstr., Mid.East: Abstr.& Ind., P.A.I.S., Polit.Sci.Abstr., Rural Recreat.Tour.Abstr., Sage Pub.Admin.Abstr., Soc.Sci.Ind., SSCI, World Agri.Econ.& Rural Sociol.Abstr. **Document type:** academic/scholarly publication.
   —BLDSC (3363.797000); Faxon; SWETS; UMI; UnCover.
   Refereed Serial

POLITICAL SCIENCE

320 US ISSN 1047-1006
JK2403
COMPARATIVE STATE POLITICS. vol.9, 1988. bi-m. $12.50. Illinois Legislative Studies Center, Sangamon State University, Springfield, IL 62794-9243. TEL 217-786-6574. Ed. David H. Everson. bk.rev.; index. circ. 375. **Indexed:** P.A.I.S.
—Faxon; UnCover.
 Formerly (until 1989): Comparative State Politics Newsletter (ISSN 0273-1347)
 Description: Covers political events nationwide, focusing on state governments. Analyzes election results, and provides highlights of legislative works.

320 US ISSN 0149-5933
JX1 CODEN: COSTDY
COMPARATIVE STRATEGY; an international journal. 1978. q. £88($145) (effective 1996). Taylor & Francis Inc., 1900 Frost Rd., Ste. 101, Bristol, PA 19007. TEL 215-785-5800; 800-821-8312. FAX 215-785-5515. (Subscr. in Europe to: Taylor & Francis Ltd., Rankine Rd., Basingstoke, Hants. RG24 8PR, England. TEL 44-1256-840366. FAX 44-1256-479438) Ed. Keith B. Payne. adv.; bk.rev.; abstr.; index. **Indexed:** Abstr.Mil.Bibl., Amer.Bibl.Slavic & E.Eur.Stud., Curr.Cont., Int.Polit.Sci.Abstr., P.A.I.S., Peace Res.Abstr., Polit.Sci.Abstr., Soc.Sci.Ind. (1994-), SSCI. **Document type:** academic/scholarly publication.
—BLDSC (3363.830000); Faxon; Genuine Article; SWETS; UnCover. **CCC.**
 Description: Focuses on American strategic thought and the influence of history and ideas on the strategic interactions between the West and the former Soviet Union.
 Refereed Serial

320.9 US ISSN 1058-0247
 CODEN: CINREU
COMPETITIVE INTELLIGENCE REVIEW. q. $112 (foreign $174) (effective 1996). (Society of Competitive Intelligence Professionals) John Wiley & Sons, Inc., Journals, 605 Third Ave., New York, NY 10158. TEL 212-850-6645. FAX 212-850-6021. TELEX 12-7063. E-mail: SUBINFO@JWILEY.COM. (Subscr. outside the Americas to: John Wiley & Sons Ltd., Baffins Ln., Chichester, W. Sussex PO19 1UD, England. TEL 44-1243-779777. FAX 44-1243-776128) (also avail. in microform from UMI; back issues avail.) **Document type:** academic/scholarly publication.
 Formerly (until 1990): Competitive Intelligencer (ISSN 1040-9645)
 Refereed Serial

320 AG
COMPROMISO POLITICO Y SOCIAL. 1984. m. Ediciones Compromiso, Mendes de Andes 33-35, Buenos Aires, Argentina. Ed. Miguel Angel Marcos.

COMUNI D'EUROPA. see *PUBLIC ADMINISTRATION — Municipal Government*

320.532 IT ISSN 0393-6740
COMUNISMO. 1979. s-a. L.10000($10) Partito Comunista Internazionale, Casella Postale 1157, 50100 Florence, Italy. Ed. Livio Vallillo. circ. 1,000. (back issues avail.)

320 GT
CONCERTACION. m. Presidencia de la Republica de Guatemala, Secretaria de Relaciones Publicas, Guatemala City, Guatemala.

320 AG
CONCIENCIA NACIONAL. 1991. m.? Arg.$15000 per no. Corrientes 1250 6o B, 1043 Buenos Aires, Argentina. TEL 35-1861. Ed. Alberto Guerberof.

320 US ISSN 0738-8942
JX1291
CONFLICT MANAGEMENT AND PEACE SCIENCE. 1974. irreg., vol.13, no.2, 1994. $25 per vol. Peace Science Society (International), Department of Political Science, Box 6000, State University of New York at Binghamton, Binghamton, NY 13902-6000. FAX 607-777-2675. Ed. Stuart A. Bremer. bk.rev. circ. 1,000. (back issues avail.; reprint service avail. from SCH) **Indexed:** A.B.C.Pol.Sci., Amer.Hist.& Life, Curr.Cont., Hist.Abstr., Mid.East: Abstr.& Ind., P.A.I.S., Polit.Sci.Abstr., SSCI. **Document type:** academic/scholarly publication.
—BLDSC (3410.654000); Faxon; Genuine Article; UnCover.
 Formerly (until 1981): Journal of Peace Science (ISSN 0094-3738)

322.4 AG
CONFRONTACION; de ideas para una nueva sociedad. 1986. q. Avda. Belgrano 1787, piso 2, 1093 Buenos Aires, Argentina. TEL 45-4756. Dir. Julian Lemoine.

CONGRESS. see *PUBLIC ADMINISTRATION*

320 350 US ISSN 1047-1324
KF49
CONGRESS AND THE NATION. 1965. every 4 yrs. $199.95. Congressional Quarterly Inc., 1414 22nd St., N.W., Washington, DC 20037. TEL 202-887-8500. FAX 202-887-6706.
 Description: Covers summary of Reagan's first term and important congressional decisions between 1981 and 1984. Description of legislative issues summarize key activities for each year.

320 970 US ISSN 0734-3469
JK1041
CONGRESS AND THE PRESIDENCY. 1972. s-a. $15 individuals (foreign $25); institutions $22 (foreign $32). American University, Center for Congressional and Presidential Studies, Washington, DC 20016. TEL 202-885-6250. FAX 202-885-1037. Eds. Susan Hammond, Darrell West. adv. contact: Pam Horner. bk.rev.; abstr.; bibl.; illus. circ. 650. (also avail. in microform from UMI) **Indexed:** A.B.C.Pol.Sci., Amer.Hist.& Life, Hist.Abstr., Int.Polit.Sci.Abstr., P.A.I.S., Polit.Sci.Abstr., SSCI. **Document type:** academic/scholarly publication.
—BLDSC (3415.828000); Faxon; Genuine Article; UMI; UnCover.
 Former titles (until 1981): Congressional Studies (ISSN 0194-4053); (until 1978): Capitol Studies (ISSN 0045-5687)

320 US ISSN 0193-4627
KF1.C65
CONGRESS IN PRINT; the weekly catalog of congressional documents. 1969. 48/yr. $198. Congressional Quarterly Inc., 1414 22 St., N.W., Washington, DC 20037. TEL 800-432-2250. FAX 202-728-1863. Ed. Victoria A. Needham. (looseleaf format) **Document type:** newsletter, catalog.
 ●Also available online.
 Incorporates (in Sept. 1985): Checklist of Congressional Hearings and Committee Prints (ISSN 0195-3761); Formerly (1954-19??): Checklist of Congressional Hearings (ISSN 0009-2096)
 Description: A weekly list of committee prints, hearing reports and other congressional documents printed by the Government Printing Office.

329.9 II ISSN 0376-5776
JQ298.I5
CONGRESS MARCHES AHEAD. (Text in English) 1970. irreg. price varies. All India Congress Committee, Publications Department, 5 Dr. Rajendra Prasad Rd., New Delhi 110001, India.

973 328 US ISSN 0010-5899
JK1
CONGRESSIONAL DIGEST. 1921. 10/yr. $35.95. Congressional Digest Corp., 3231 P St., N.W., Washington, DC 20007. TEL 202-333-7332; 800-637-9915. FAX 202-625-6670. Ed. Sarah Orrick; Pub. Page B. Robinson. index, cum.index: 1921-1993. (also avail. in microform; back issues avail.) **Indexed:** Acad.Ind., Adol.Ment.Hlth.Abstr., Curr.Cont., Energy Rev., Mag.Ind., Mid.East: Abstr.& Ind., P.A.I.S., PMR, PSI, R.G., Soc.Sci.Ind., TOM.
—BLDSC (3415.950000); Faxon; SWETS; UnCover.
 Description: Features the major issues and controversies in the Congress, pro and con.

973 328 US ISSN 0010-5902
CONGRESSIONAL MONITOR; daily listing of all scheduled Congressional committee hearings, with witnesses. Variant titles: Congressional Daily Monitor. Daily Congressional Monitor. 1965. d. (plus w. supplements). $1349. Congressional Quarterly Inc., 1414 22nd St., N.W., Washington, DC 20037. TEL 800-432-2250. FAX 202-728-1863. Ed. Brian Nutting. **Indexed:** Polit.Sci.Abstr. **Document type:** newsletter.
 ●Also available online.
 —CCC.
  Incorporating: Congress Daily.
 Description: Provides schedule of congressional action, including the agenda for congressional hearings and witness lists.

973 328 US ISSN 0010-5910
JK1
CONGRESSIONAL QUARTERLY SERVICE. WEEKLY REPORT. (Includes annual almanac) 1945. w. $1349. Congressional Quarterly Inc., 1414 22nd St., N.W., Washington, DC 20037. TEL 800-432-2250. FAX 202-728-1863. Ed. Robert W. Merry. charts; index every 90 days and annually. circ. 11,000. (also avail. in microform from UMI,MIM; reprint service avail. from UMI) **Indexed:** Acad.Ind., Bank.Lit.Ind., Mid.East: Abstr.& Ind., Noise Pollut.Publ.Abstr., P.A.I.S.
 ●Also available online.
 —BLDSC (3415.960000); SWETS; UMI; UnCover. **CCC.**
 Description: Provides detailed reports on all major legislative action, the president's legislative proposals, statements and major speeches and analyses of the Supreme Court's decisions. Includes coverage of political and lobbying activities.

320 US ISSN 0191-1473
JK1
CONGRESSIONAL ROLL CALL (YEAR); a chronology and analysis of votes in the House and Senate. 1972. a. $29.95 (paperback). Congressional Quarterly Inc., 1414 22nd St., N.W., Washington, DC 20037. TEL 202-887-8500. FAX 202-887-6706. charts. (back issues avail.; reprint service avail. from UMI)
 Description: Shows every roll-call vote for all members of Congress for that year. Also shows votes on critical issues, each member's party unity, presidential support and voting record.

973 350 US ISSN 0069-8938
CONGRESSIONAL STAFF DIRECTORY. 1959. s-a. $79. Staff Directories Ltd., Box 62, Mount Vernon, VA 22121. TEL 703-739-0900. FAX 703-739-0234. Ed. Wayne Walker; Pub. Ann L. Brownson. index. (also avail. in diskette format) **Document type:** directory.
 ●Also available on CD-ROM.
 Description: Lists members of Congress, committees, and 16,999 staff, including more than 3,400 biographies of congressional members and their Capitol and district office staff.

320 370 574 US
CONNECTIONS (DAYTON). 1961. a. free. Charles F. Kettering Foundation, 200 Commons Rd., Dayton, OH 45459-2799. circ. 10,000. **Document type:** newsletter.
 Former titles: Kettering Report; Charles F. Kettering Foundation. Annual Report (ISSN 0069-2735)

320 CN ISSN 0708-9422
CONNEXIONS DIGEST; a social change sourcebook. 1976. q. Can.$15.50. Connexions Information Sharing Services, Box 158, Sta. D, Toronto, ON M6P 3J8, Canada. TEL 416-537-3949. Ed. Ulli Diemer. adv.; bk.rev.; abstr.; bibl.; illus.; index. circ. 1,200. (back issues avail.) **Indexed:** HR Rep.
 Description: Acts as a networking medium, improving the exchange of ideas, strategies and resources among grass roots groups in Canada.

322.4 HO
CONSEJO CENTRAL EJECUTIVO DEL PARTIDO LIBERAL DE HONDURAS. MEMORIA. irreg. Partido Liberal, Consejo Central Ejecutivo, Tegucigalpa, Honduras.

CONSERVATION VOTER. see *ENVIRONMENTAL STUDIES*

320 US ISSN 0888-1359
CONSERVATIVE CHRONICLE. 1975. w. $42. Hampton Publishing Company, 9 Second St. N.W., Box 29, Hampton, IA 50441. TEL 515-456-2585. FAX 515-456-2587. (Subscr. to: Box 11297, Des Moines, IA 50309) Ed. Joseph P. Roth. adv. contact: Jerry O'Rourke. circ. 74,162 (paid). (tabloid format) **Document type:** newspaper.

320 301 US ISSN 1047-5990
H53.U5 CODEN: CORWE5
CONSERVATIVE REVIEW. 1990. bi-m. $28 to individuals; institutions $56. 1307 Dolley Madison Blvd., Rm. 203, McLean, VA 22101. TEL 703-893-7302. FAX 703-893-7273. Ed. Frederic N. Smith. bk.rev.; circ. 1,000 (paid). **Document type:** academic/scholarly publication.
—Faxon; UMI.
 Description: Current national and international affairs.

POLITICAL SCIENCE

320 **CN**
A CONSTANT THREAT. 1989. s-a. $8 to individuals; institutions $15. Box 84001, Trafalgar Postal Outlet, Oakville, Ont. L6H 5V7, Canada. adv.: B&W page $50; trim 8 1/2 x 11. circ. 500.
Formerly: Artists for Cultural Terrorism.

320 929 **US** **ISSN 0270-532X**
THE CONSTANTIAN. 1970. 4/yr. $12 to non-members (foreign $15). Constantian Society, 123 Orr Rd., Pittsburgh, PA 15241-2219. TEL 412-831-8750. Ed. Randall J. Dicks. adv.; bk.rev.; charts; illus.; stat. circ. 550. Document type: newsletter.
Description: Features articles and essays on current and historical topics regarding royalty and monarchy throughout the world, biographical sketches, analysis, genealogical information, and reports on current developments and trends.

320 100 **UK** **ISSN 1351-0487**
B809.8
CONSTELLATIONS; an international journal of critical and democratic theory. 1981. 3/yr. £107($208) (foreign £132) (effective 1996). Basil Blackwell Ltd., 108 Cowley Rd., Oxford OX4 1JF, England. TEL 44-865-791100. FAX 44-865-791347. TELEX 837022-OXBOOK-G. (Subscr. to: P.O. Box 87, Oxford OX2 0DT, England. TEL 44-865-791155. FAX 44-865-791927; In N. America: Blackwell Publishers, 238 Main St., Cambridge, MA 02142. TEL 617-547-7110. FAX 617-547-0789) Eds. Seyla Banhabib, Andrew Arato. adv.; bk.rev. (reprint service avail. from SWZ,UMI) Indexed: Alt.Press Ind., Lang.& Lang.Behav.Abstr., Left Ind. (1986-), Phil.Ind. Document type: academic/scholarly publication.
—BLDSC (3420.346000); Faxon; UMI; UnCover. CCC.
Former titles (until 1994): Praxis International (ISSN 0260-8448)

320 **US** **ISSN 1046-0896**
K3
CONSTITUTION (NEW YORK). 1988. q. $25. Foundation for the United States Constitution, 1271 Ave. of the Americas, New York, NY 10020. Ed. John A. Meyers. circ. 50,000.
—Faxon; UnCover.
Description: Devoted to the US Constitution and how it influences history and our lives.

CONSTITUTIONAL POLITICAL ECONOMY. see *LAW — Constitutional Law*

CONSUMING INTEREST. see *CONSUMER EDUCATION AND PROTECTION*

324.271 **CN**
CONTACT (OTTAWA, 1981).* 1981. q. Progressive Conservative Party of Canada, P C Canada Fund, 275 Slater St., 6th Fl., Ottawa, ON K1P 5H9, Canada. TEL 613-238-6111.

320 **FR**
CONTACTS (PARIS). bi-m. free. (Rassemblemnt pour la Republique, Jeunes du Rassemblement) Etape Communications, 123 rue de Lille, 75340 Paris Cedex 07, France. Eds. Valentin Ferry, Lilian Soubranne.

CONTEMPORARY CHINA PAPERS. see *HISTORY — History Of Asia*

943.8 **PL** **ISSN 0010-7522**
DK4010
CONTEMPORARY POLAND. German edition: Polens Gegenwart. French edition: Pologne Contemporaine. (Text in English) 1967. s-m. $15. Polska Agencja Interpress, Ul. Bagatela 12, 00-585 Warsaw, Poland. Indexed: Key to Econ.Sci.

CONTEMPORARY RECORD; the journal of contemporary British history. see *HISTORY — History Of Europe*

320 **UK** **ISSN 0958-4935**
CONTEMPORARY SOUTH ASIA. 1992. 3/yr. £42 to individuals; institutions £148 (effective 1996). Carfax Publishing Co., P.O. Box 25, Abingdon, Oxon. OX14 3UE, England. TEL 01235-555335. FAX 01235-553559. (Subscr. in N. America to: Carfax Publishing Co., 875-81 Massachusetts Ave., Cambridge, MA 02139) Eds. Gowher Rizvi, Robert Cassen. (also avail. in microfiche; back issues avail.) Indexed: Geo.Abstr., IDA, Int.Polit.Sci.Abstr. Document type: academic/scholarly publication.
—BLDSC (3425.305300); SWETS; UMI; UnCover. CCC.
Description: Presents research and analysis of contemporary policy issues as well as historical articles on southeastern Asia.
Refereed Serial

320 959 **SI** **ISSN 0129-797X**
DS520
CONTEMPORARY SOUTHEAST ASIA; a quarterly journal of international and strategic affairs. (Text in English) 1979. 4/yr. $29 to individuals (Europe & N. America $35); institutions $25 (Europe & N. America $44). Institute of Southeast Asian Studies, Heng Mui Keng Terrace, Off Pasir Panjang Rd., Singapore 0511, Singapore. TEL 7780955. FAX 7781735. TELEX RS 37068 ISEAS. E-mail: pubsunit@merlion.iseas.ac.sg. Ed.Bd. bk.rev.; bibl.; index, cum.index. (also avail. in microform from UMI; back issues avail.; reprint service avail. from SCH) Indexed: Asian-Pac.Econ.Lit., E.I., Int.Polit.Sci.Abstr., Mid.East: Abstr.& Ind., P.A.I.S., Per.Islam. (1991-), Rural Recreat.Tour.Abstr., World Agri.Econ.& Rural Sociol.Abstr. Document type: academic/scholarly publication.
—BLDSC (3425.305500); SWETS; UMI; UnCover.
Description: Specializes in the politics, international relations, and security-related issues of Southeast Asia and its wider geostrategic environment.

320 **US**
CONTINUING INQUIRY. 1976. m. $24. Penn Jones Publications, Inc., Rt. 6, Box 356, Watahachie, TX 75165. Ed. Penn Jones. bk.rev. circ. 300.

329.11 **SW** **ISSN 0347-6472**
CONTRA; oberoende borgerlig tidskrift. 1975. bi-m. SEK 145 (effective 1990). Stiftelsen Contra, P.O. Box 8052, S-104 20 Stockholm, Sweden. TEL 46-8-654-95-52. FAX 46-8-65248-99. Ed. Tommy Hansson. adv.; bk.rev.
Formerly (until 1975, vol.4): Progressiv Information.
Description: Devoted to freedom and human rights, free market economy and Western democratic ideals.

320.531 **IT**
LA CONTRADDIZIONE; bimestrale di marxismo. 1987. bi-m. L.35000 (foreign L.50000). Associazione Culturale Marxista Contraddizione, C.P. 11-188 Montesacro, 00141 Rome, Italy.
TEL 39-6-8185693. FAX 39-6-87190070. bk.rev. circ. 700. (also avail. in diskette format) Document type: academic/scholarly publication.
Description: Forum on Marxism that looks at theoretical problems in the structure of economics, society and history, from an analytical rather than an ideological point of view.

CONTREPOINT. see *LITERARY AND POLITICAL REVIEWS*

320 **US** **ISSN 0147-1066**
CONTRIBUTIONS IN POLITICAL SCIENCE. 1978. irreg., no.306. 1992. price varies. Greenwood Press, Inc. (Subsidiary of: Greenwood Publishing Group Inc.), 88 Post Rd. W., Box 5007, Westport, CT 06881-5007. TEL 203-226-3571. FAX 203-222-1502. Ed. Bernard K. Johnpoll.
—BLDSC (3461.120000).

CONTRIBUTIONS TO POLITICAL ECONOMY. see *BUSINESS AND ECONOMICS — Economic Situation And Conditions*

320 **CK** **ISSN 0120-4165**
CONTROVERSIA. 1972. irreg. Col.$8000($50) Centro de Investigacion y Educacion Popular, Carrera 5, No.33A-08, Apdo. Aereo 25916, Bogota, Colombia. TEL 2858977. Ed. Alejandro Angulo. stat. circ. 2,000. (also avail. in microfiche)
Formerly (until 1975): Anali C I A S.

320 **BL**
CONVIVIUM; investigacao e cultura. 1961. bi-m. $30. Sociedade Brasileira de Cultura, Alameda Eduardo Prado 705, C.P. 30004, 01218 Sao Paulo, Brazil. Ed. Gumercindo Rocha Dorea. adv.; bk.rev.; bibl. circ. 3,500. Indexed: Hisp.Amer.Per.Ind. (1970-), Phil.Ind.
Description: Political philosophy and cultural problems of Brazil.

320 **US**
COOK POLITICAL REPORT. 1984. 12/yr. $295. Cook and Company, 900 Second St. N.E., Ste. 107, Washington, DC 20002. TEL 202-289-1625. FAX 202-289-0454. Ed. Charles E. Cook, Jr. circ. 800. Document type: newsletter.
●Also available online.
Formerly: National Political Review.
Description: Non-partisan analysis of congressional, gubernatorial and presidential elections as well as political trends.

329.9 **UK** **ISSN 0956-4640**
JN1129.C8
CO-OPERATORS' PLATFORM. 1965. bi-m. £6. Co-operative Party, Victory House, 10-14 Leicester Sq., London WC2H 7QH, England.
TEL 0171-439-0123. FAX 0171-439-3434. Ed. Jean Whitehead. bk.rev.; charts; illus.; stat. circ. 24,000. (tabloid format) Document type: newspaper.
Formerly (until 1989): Platform (London) (ISSN 0032-1370)
Description: Contains news of the Co-operative Party

CORNELL JOURNAL OF LAW AND PUBLIC POLICY. see *LAW*

320 910.09 **IT**
CORRIERE DEL MEZZOGIORNO; il tridente. (Text in English, French, German, Spanish) 1967. w. L.300000($215) Via Ascoli, 43-M (Villa Cotti), Casella Postale 33, 71100 Foggia, Italy.
TEL 39-881-688890. FAX 39-881-678984. Ed. Lorenzo Vittorio Vasco. adv.: page $4375. illus.; charts. circ. 7,000.

329.9 **IT**
CORRIERE DELL'ADDA. 1860. fortn. L.10000($10) Partito Liberale Italiano, Sezione di Lodi, Corso V. Emanuele 21, 20075 Lodi, Italy. Ed. Vitaliano Peduzzi. adv.; bk.rev.; film rev.; play rev. circ. 4,000. (tabloid format; back issues avail.)

322.4 **IT**
COSCIENZA DEL CITTADINO. w. Via Madonna di Loreto 4, 00015 Monterotondo, Rome, Italy. Ed. Domenico Moreschi.

251 320 301 **IT** **ISSN 0390-1750**
COSTAROSSA; rivista subalpinia di studi politici e sociali. 1973. q. L.4000. Circulo Culturale Costa Rossa, Via Roma 55, Cuneo, Italy. Ed. Sergio Fenoglio. adv.; bk.rev.; illus. circ. 2,500.

338 **EI** **ISSN 0252-0958**
D1050
COUNCIL OF EUROPE FORUM. French edition (ISSN 0251-320X); German edition (ISSN 0252-0966) (Editions in English, French, German, Italian) 1959; N.S. 1990. 4/yr. 160 F.($32) Council of Europe, Publications Section, 67075 Strasbourg Cedex, France. TEL 88-41-20-00. FAX 88-41-27-81. TELEX 870 943 EUR F. (Subscr. to: Societe Mereau, 27 rue de Rome, 75008 Paris, France; Dist. in U.S. by: Manhattan Publishing Co., Box 650, Croton-on-Hudson, N.Y. 10520) Ed. Gustaves Bemtgen. bk.rev. circ. 120,000. Indexed: Excerp.Med.
—BLDSC (4024.083600); Faxon; UnCover.
Supersedes (since 1977, no. 32): Education and Culture (ISSN 0013-1229); Forward in Europe (ISSN 0015-8631)
Description: Provides detailed information on the Council of Europe's activities.

303.6 **US**
▼**COUNTER TERRORISM CHRONICLE.** 1995. bi-m. free. Muslim Public Affairs Council, 3010 Wilshire Blvd., Ste. 217, Los Angeles, CA 90010.
TEL 213-383-3443. FAX 213-383-9674. Ed. Salan Al-Marayati. circ. 3,000. Document type: newsletter.
Description: Tracks terrorism and encourages constructive dialogue to deal with the issue.

POLITICAL SCIENCE

320   US   ISSN 0196-2809
G1
COUNTRIES OF THE WORLD AND THEIR LEADERS YEARBOOK. (In 2 vols.) 1974. a. $160 (supplement $78) (effective 1993). Gale Research Inc., 835 Penobscot Bldg., Detroit, MI 48226. TEL 313-961-2242. FAX 313-961-6083. TELEX 810-221-7086. Ed. Frank E. Bair. —BLDSC (3481.520000).
   Formerly: Countries of the World.
   Description: Annual reference on countries worldwide with a guide to their leadership.

320 330.9   US
COUNTRY FORECAST. ALGERIA. q. £370($715) Economist Intelligence Unit, 111 W. 57th St., New York, NY 10019. TEL 212-554-0600; 800-938-4685. FAX 212-586-1182. TELEX 175567. (UK addr.: Economist Intelligence Unit Ltd., Subscriptions Dept., P.O. Box 200, Harold Hill, Romford, Essex RM3 8UX, England. TEL 44-1708-381-444. FAX 44-1708-371-850)
   ●Also available online. Vendor(s): Knight-Ridder, Inc., Lexis-Nexis.
   Formerly (until 1992): Global Forecasting Service. Algeria (ISSN 0966-8969)
   Description: Focuses on the key factors affecting Algeria's political and economic outlook and its business environment over the next five years.

320 330.9   US
COUNTRY FORECAST. ARGENTINA. q. £370($715) Economist Intelligence Unit, 111 W. 57th St., New York, NY 10019. TEL 212-554-0600; 800-938-4685. FAX 212-586-1182. TELEX 175567. (UK addr.: Economist Intelligence Unit Ltd., Subscriptions Dept., P.O. Box 200, Harold Hill, Romford, Essex RM3 8UX, England. TEL 44-1708-381-444. FAX 44-1708-371-850)
   ●Also available online. Vendor(s): Knight-Ridder, Inc., Lexis-Nexis.
   Formerly (until 1992): Global Forecasting Service. Argentina (ISSN 0966-8977)
   Description: Focuses on the key factors affecting Argentina's political and economic outlook and its business environment over the next five years.

320 330.9   US
COUNTRY FORECAST. ASIA - PACIFIC. (Text in English) 1977. q. £370($715) Economist Intelligence Unit, 111 W. 57th St., New York, NY 10019. TEL 212-554-0600; 800-938-4685. FAX 212-586-1182. TELEX 175567. (UK addr.: Economist Intelligence Unit Ltd., Subscriptions Dept., P.O. Box 200, Harold Hill, Romford, Essex RM3 8UX, England. TEL 44-1708-381-444. FAX 44-1708-371-850) Ed. John Ip. (looseleaf format; back issues avail.)
   ●Also available online. Vendor(s): Knight-Ridder, Inc.
   Former titles: Business International Forecasting. Asia - Pacific; (until 1992): Global Forecasting Service. Asia - Pacific (ISSN 0966-8713); Asia - Pacific Forecasting Study.
   Description: Focuses on the key factors affecting the region's political and economic outlook and its business environment over the next five years.

320 330.9   US
COUNTRY FORECAST. AUSTRALIA. q. £360($695) Economist Intelligence Unit, 111 W. 57th St., New York, NY 10019. TEL 212-554-0600; 800-938-4685. FAX 212-586-1182. TELEX 175567. (UK addr.: Economist Intelligence Unit Ltd., Subscriptions Dept., P.O. Box 200, Harold Hill, Romford, Essex RM3 8UX, England. TEL 44-1708-381-444. FAX 44-1708-371-850)
   ●Also available online. Vendor(s): Knight-Ridder, Inc., Lexis-Nexis.
   Formerly (until 1992): Global Forecasting Service. Australia (ISSN 0966-8942)
   Description: Focuses on the key factors affecting Australia's political and economic outlook and its business environment over the next five years.

320 330.9   US
COUNTRY FORECAST. AUSTRIA. q. £370($715) Economist Intelligence Unit, 111 W. 57th St., New York, NY 10019. TEL 212-554-0600; 800-938-4685. FAX 212-586-1182. TELEX 175567. (UK addr.: Economist Intelligence Unit Ltd., Subscriptions Dept., P.O. Box 200, Harold Hill, Romford, Essex RM3 8UX, England. TEL 44-1708-381-444. FAX 44-1708-371-850)
   ●Also available online. Vendor(s): Knight-Ridder, Inc., Lexis-Nexis.
   Formerly (until 1992): Global Forecasting Service. Austria (ISSN 0966-8950)
   Description: Focuses on the key factors affecting Austria's political and economic outlook and its business environment over the next five years.

320 330.9   US
COUNTRY FORECAST. BELGIUM. q. £370($715) Economist Intelligence Unit, 111 W. 57th St., New York, NY 10019. TEL 212-554-0600; 800-938-4685. FAX 212-586-1182. TELEX 175567. (UK addr.: Economist Intelligence Unit Ltd., Subscriptions Dept., P.O. Box 200, Harold Hill, Romford, Essex RM3 8UX, England. TEL 44-1708-381-444. FAX 44-1708-371-850)
   ●Also available online. Vendor(s): Knight-Ridder, Inc., Lexis-Nexis.
   Formerly (until 1992): Global Forecasting Service. Belgium.
   Description: Focuses on the key factors affecting Belgium's political and economic outlook and its business environment over the next five years.

320 330.9   US
COUNTRY FORECAST. BRAZIL. q. £370($715) Economist Intelligence Unit, 111 W. 57th St., New York, NY 10019. TEL 212-554-0600; 800-938-4685. FAX 212-586-1182. TELEX 175567. (UK addr.: Economist Intelligence Unit Ltd., Subscriptions Dept., P.O. Box 200, Harold Hill, Romford, Essex RM3 8UX, England. TEL 44-1708-381-444. FAX 44-1708-371-850)
   ●Also available online. Vendor(s): Knight-Ridder, Inc., Lexis-Nexis.
   Formerly (until 1992): Global Forecasting Service. Brazil.
   Description: Focuses on the key factors affecting Brazil's political and economic outlook and its business environment over the next five years.

320 330.9   US
COUNTRY FORECAST. BULGARIA. q. £370($715) Economist Intelligence Unit, 111 W. 57th St., New York, NY 10019. TEL 212-554-0600; 800-938-4685. FAX 212-586-1182. TELEX 175567. (UK addr.: Economist Intelligence Unit Ltd., Subscriptions Dept., P.O. Box 200, Harold Hill, Romford, Essex RM3 8UX, England. TEL 44-1708-381-444. FAX 44-1708-371-850)
   ●Also available online. Vendor(s): Knight-Ridder, Inc., Lexis-Nexis.
   Formerly (until 1992): Global Forecasting Service. Bulgaria.
   Description: Focuses on the key factors affecting Bulgaria's political and economic outlook and its business environment over the next five years.

320 330.9   US
COUNTRY FORECAST. CANADA. q. £370($715) Economist Intelligence Unit, 111 W. 57th St., New York, NY 10019. TEL 212-554-0600; 800-938-4685. FAX 212-586-1182. TELEX 175567. (UK addr.: Economist Intelligence Unit Ltd., Subscriptions Dept., P.O. Box 200, Harold Hill, Romford, Essex RM3 8UX, England. TEL 44-1708-381-444. FAX 44-1708-371-850)
   ●Also available online. Vendor(s): Knight-Ridder, Inc., Lexis-Nexis.
   Formerly (until 1992): Global Forecasting Service. Canada.
   Description: Focuses on the key factors affecting Canada's political and economic outlook and its business environment over the next five years.

320 330.9   US
COUNTRY FORECAST. CHILE. q. £370($715) Economist Intelligence Unit, 111 W. 57th St., New York, NY 10019. TEL 212-554-0600; 800-938-4685. FAX 212-586-1182. TELEX 175567. (UK addr.: Economist Intelligence Unit Ltd., Subscriptions Dept., P.O. Box 200, Harold Hill, Romford, Essex RM3 8UX, England. TEL 44-1708-371-850)
   ●Also available online. Vendor(s): Knight-Ridder, Inc., Lexis-Nexis.
   Formerly (until 1992): Global Forecasting Service. Chile.
   Description: Focuses on the key factors affecting Chile's political and economic outlook and its business environment over the next five years.

320 330.9   US
COUNTRY FORECAST. CHINA. q. £370($715) Economist Intelligence Unit, 111 W. 57th St., New York, NY 10019. TEL 212-554-0600; 800-938-4685. FAX 212-586-1182. TELEX 175567. (UK addr.: Economist Intelligence Unit Ltd., Subscriptions Dept., P.O. Box 200, Harold Hill, Romford, Essex RM3 8UX, England. TEL 44-1708-381-444. FAX 44-1708-371-850)
   ●Also available online. Vendor(s): Knight-Ridder, Inc., Lexis-Nexis.
   Formerly (until 1992): Global Forecasting Service. China (ISSN 0966-9493)
   Description: Focuses on the key factors affecting China's political and economic outlook and its business environment over the next five years.

320 330.9   US
COUNTRY FORECAST. COLOMBIA. q. £370($715) Economist Intelligence Unit, 111 W. 57th St., New York, NY 10019. TEL 212-554-0600; 800-938-4685. FAX 212-586-1182. TELEX 175567. (UK addr.: Economist Intelligence Unit Ltd., Subscriptions Dept., P.O. Box 200, Harold Hill, Romford, Essex RM3 8UX, England. TEL 44-1708-381-444. FAX 44-1708-371-850)
   ●Also available online. Vendor(s): Knight-Ridder, Inc., Lexis-Nexis.
   Formerly (until 1992): Global Forecasting Service. Colombia.
   Description: Focuses on the key factors affecting Colombia's political and economic outlook and its business environment over the next five years.

320 330.9   US
COUNTRY FORECAST. CZECH REPUBLIC. q. £370($715) Economist Intelligence Unit, 111 W. 57th St., New York, NY 10019. TEL 212-554-0600; 800-938-4685. FAX 212-586-1182. TELEX 175567. (UK addr.: Economist Intelligence Unit Ltd., Subscriptions Dept., P.O. Box 200, Harold Hill, Romford, Essex RM3 8UX, England. TEL 44-1708-381-444. FAX 44-1708-371-850)
   ●Also available online. Vendor(s): Knight-Ridder, Inc., Lexis-Nexis.
   Description: Focuses on the key factors affecting Czech Republic's political and economic outlook and its business environment over the next five years.

320 330.9   US
COUNTRY FORECAST. DENMARK. q. £370($715) Economist Intelligence Unit, 111 W. 57th St., New York, NY 10019. TEL 212-554-0600; 800-938-4685. FAX 212-586-1182. TELEX 175567. (UK addr.: Economist Intelligence Unit Ltd., Subscriptions Dept., P.O. Box 200, Harold Hill, Romford, Essex RM3 8UX, England. TEL 44-1708-381-444. FAX 44-1708-371-850)
   ●Also available online. Vendor(s): Knight-Ridder, Inc., Lexis-Nexis.
   Formerly (until 1992): Global Forecasting Service. Denmark (ISSN 0966-9485)
   Description: Focuses on the key factors affecting Denmark's political and economic outlook and its business environment over the next five years.

320 330.9   US
COUNTRY FORECAST. EASTERN EUROPE AND THE FORMER SOVIET UNION. q. £370($715) Economist Intelligence Unit, 111 W. 57th St., New York, NY 10019. TEL 212-554-0600; 800-938-4685. FAX 212-486-1182. TELEX 175567. (U.K. addr.: Economist Intelligence Unit Ltd., Subscriptions Dept., P.O. Box 200, Harold Hill, Romford, Essex RM3 8UX, England. TEL 44-1708-381444. FAX 44-1708-371850)
   Description: Focuses on the key factors affecting the covered areas' political and economic outlook and their business environment over the next five years.

POLITICAL SCIENCE

320 330.9 US
COUNTRY FORECAST. ECUADOR. q. £370($715) Economist Intelligence Unit, 111 W. 57th St., New York, NY 10019. TEL 212-554-0600; 800-938-4685. FAX 212-586-1182. TELEX 175567. (UK addr.: Economist Intelligence Unit Ltd., Subscriptions Dept., P.O. Box 200, Harold Hill, Romford, Essex RM3 8UX, England. TEL 44-1708-381-444. FAX 44-1708-371-850)
●Also available online. Vendor(s): Knight-Ridder, Inc., Lexis-Nexis.
Formerly (until 1992): Global Forecasting Service. Ecuador (ISSN 0966-9515)
Description: Focuses on the key factors affecting Ecuador's political and economic outlook and its business environment over the next five years.

320 330.9 US
COUNTRY FORECAST. EGYPT. q. £370($715) Economist Intelligence Unit, 111 W. 57th St., New York, NY 10019. TEL 212-554-0600; 800-938-4685. FAX 212-586-1182. TELEX 175567. (UK addr.: Economist Intelligence Unit Ltd., Subscriptions Dept., P.O. Box 200, Harold Hill, Romford, Essex RM3 8UX, England. TEL 44-1708-381-444. FAX 44-1708-371-850)
●Also available online. Vendor(s): Knight-Ridder, Inc., Lexis-Nexis.
Formerly (until 1992): Global Forecasting Service. Egypt (ISSN 0966-9507)
Description: Focuses on the key factors affecting Egypt's political and economic outlook and its business environment over the next five years.

320 330.9 US
COUNTRY FORECAST. EUROPE. q. £370($715) Economist Intelligence Unit, 111 W. 57th St., New York, NY 10019. TEL 212-554-0600; 800-938-4685. FAX 212-586-1182. TELEX 175567. (UK addr.: Economist Intelligence Unit Ltd., Subscriptions Dept., P.O. Box 200, Harold Hill, Romford, Essex RM3 8UX, England. TEL 44-1708-381-444. FAX 44-1708-371-850)
●Also available online. Vendor(s): Knight-Ridder, Inc., Lexis-Nexis.
Formerly (until 1992): Global Forecasting Service. Europe.
Description: Focuses on the key factors affecting the region's political and economic outlook and its business environment over the next five years.

320 330.9 US
COUNTRY FORECAST. FINLAND. q. £370($715) Economist Intelligence Unit, 111 W. 57th St., New York, NY 10019. TEL 212-554-0600; 800-938-4685. FAX 212-586-1182. TELEX 175567. (UK addr.: Economist Intelligence Unit Ltd., Subscriptions Dept., P.O. Box 200, Harold Hill, Romford, Essex RM3 8UX, England. TEL 44-1708-381-444. FAX 44-1708-371-850)
●Also available online. Vendor(s): Knight-Ridder, Inc., Lexis-Nexis.
Formerly (until 1992): Global Forecasting Service. Finland (ISSN 0966-9523)
Description: Focuses on the key factors affecting Finland's political and economic outlook and its business environment over the next five years.

320 330.9 US
COUNTRY FORECAST. FRANCE. q. £370($715) Economist Intelligence Unit, 111 W. 57th St., New York, NY 10019. TEL 212-554-0600; 800-938-4685. FAX 212-586-1182. TELEX 175567. (UK addr.: Economist Intelligence Unit Ltd., Subscriptions Dept., P.O. Box 200, Harold Hill, Romford, Essex RM3 8UX, England. TEL 44-1708-381-444. FAX 44-1708-371-850)
●Also available online. Vendor(s): Knight-Ridder, Inc., Lexis-Nexis.
Formerly (until 1992): Global Forecasting Service. France (ISSN 0966-9531)
Description: Focuses on the key factors affecting France's political and economic outlook and its business environment over the next five years.

320 330.9 US
COUNTRY FORECAST. GERMANY. q. £370($715) Economist Intelligence Unit, 111 W. 57th St., New York, NY 10019. TEL 212-554-0600; 800-938-4685. FAX 212-586-1182. TELEX 175567. (UK addr.: Economist Intelligence Unit Ltd., Subscriptions Dept., P.O. Box 200, Harold Hill, Romford, Essex RM3 8UX, England. TEL 44-1708-381-444. FAX 44-1708-271-850)
●Also available online. Vendor(s): Knight-Ridder, Inc., Lexis-Nexis.
Formerly (until 1992): Global Forecasting Service. Germany.
Description: Focuses on the key factors affecting Germany's political and economic outlook and its business environment over the next five years.

320 330.9 US ISSN 0967-358X
COUNTRY FORECAST. GLOBAL OUTLOOK. q. Economist Intelligence Unit, 111 W. 57th St., New York, NY 10019. TEL 212-554-0600; 800-938-4685. FAX 212-586-1182. TELEX 175567. (U.K. addr.: Economist Intelligence Unit Ltd., Subscriptions Dept., P.O. Box 200, Harold Hill, Romford, Essex RM3 8UX, England. TEL 44-1708-381-444. FAX 44-1708-371-850)
●Also available online.

320 330.9 US
COUNTRY FORECAST. GREECE. q. £370($715) Economist Intelligence Unit, 111 W. 57th St., New York, NY 10019. TEL 212-554-0600; 800-938-4685. FAX 212-586-1182. TELEX 175567. (UK addr.: Economist Intelligence Unit Ltd., Subscriptions Dept., P.O. Box 200, Harold Hill, Romford, Essex RM3 8UX, England. TEL 44-1708-381-444. FAX 44-1708-371-850)
●Also available online. Vendor(s): Knight-Ridder, Inc., Lexis-Nexis.
Formerly (until 1992): Global Forecasting Service. Greece (ISSN 0966-954X)
Description: Focuses on the key factors affecting Greece's political and economic outlook and its business environment over the next five years.

320 330.9 US
COUNTRY FORECAST. HONG KONG. q. £370($715) Economist Intelligence Unit, 111 W. 57th St., New York, NY 10019. TEL 212-554-0600; 800-938-4685. FAX 212-586-1182. TELEX 175567. (UK addr.: Economist Intelligence Unit Ltd., Subscriptions Dept., P.O. Box 200, Harold Hill, Romford, Essex RM3 8UX, England. TEL 44-1708-381-444. FAX 44-1708-371-850)
●Also available online. Vendor(s): Knight-Ridder, Inc., Lexis-Nexis.
Formerly (until 1992): Global Forecasting Service. Hong Kong (ISSN 0966-8748)
Description: Focuses on the key factors affecting Hong Kong's political and economic outlook and its business environment over the next five years.

320 330.9 US
COUNTRY FORECAST. HUNGARY. q. £370($715) Economist Intelligence Unit, 111 W. 57th St., New York, NY 10019. TEL 212-554-0600; 800-958-4685. FAX 212-586-1182. TELEX 175567. (UK addr.: Economist Intelligence Unit Ltd., Subscriptions Dept., P.O. Box 200, Harold Hill, Romford, Essex RM3 8UX, England. TEL 44-1708-381-444. FAX 44-1708-371-850)
●Also available online. Vendor(s): Knight-Ridder, Inc., Lexis-Nexis.
Formerly (until 1992): Global Forecasting Service. Hungary (ISSN 0966-8810)
Description: Focuses on the key factors affecting Hungary's political and economic outlook and its business environment over the next five years.

320 330.9 US
COUNTRY FORECAST. INDIA. q. £370($715) Economist Intelligence Unit, 111 W. 57th St., New York, NY 10019. TEL 212-554-0600; 800-938-4685. FAX 212-586-1182. TELEX 175567. (UK addr.: Economist Intelligence Unit Ltd., Subscriptions Dept., P.O. Box 200, Harold Hill, Romford, Essex RM3 8UX, England. TEL 44-1708-381-444. FAX 44-1708-371-850)
●Also available online. Vendor(s): Knight-Ridder, Inc., Lexis-Nexis.
Formerly (until 1992): Global Forecasting Service. India (ISSN 0966-8829)
Description: Focuses on the key factors affecting India's political and economic outlook and its business environment over the next five years.

320 330.9 US
COUNTRY FORECAST. INDONESIA. q. £360($695) Economist Intelligence Unit, 111 W. 57th St., New York, NY 10019. TEL 212-554-0600; 800-938-4685. FAX 212-586-1182. TELEX 175567. (UK addr.: Economist Intelligence Unit Ltd., Subscriptions Dept., P.O. Box 200, Harold Hill, Romford, Essex RM3 8UX, England. TEL 44-1708-381-444. FAX 44-1708-371-850)
●Also available online. Vendor(s): Knight-Ridder, Inc., Lexis-Nexis.
Formerly (until 1992): Global Forecasting Service. Indonesia (ISSN 0966-9426)
Description: Focuses on the key factors affecting Indonesia's political and economic outlook and its business environment over the next five years.

320 330.9 US
COUNTRY FORECAST. IRAN. q. £370($715) Economist Intelligence Unit, 111 W. 57th St., New York, NY 10019. TEL 212-554-0600; 800-938-4685. FAX 212-486-1182. TELEX 175567. (UK addr.: Economist Intelligence Unit Ltd., Subscriptions Dept., P.O. Box 200, Harold Hill, Romford, Essex RM3 8UX, England. TEL 44-1708-381-444. FAX 44-1708-371-850)
●Also available online. Vendor(s): Knight-Ridder, Inc., Lexis-Nexis.
Formerly (until 1992): Global Forecasting Service. Iran (ISSN 0966-9566)
Description: Focuses on the key factors affecting Iran's political and economic outlook and its business environment over the next five years.

332 330.9 US
COUNTRY FORECAST. IRAQ. q. £370($715) Economist Intelligence Unit, 111 W. 57th St., New York, NY 10019. TEL 212-554-0600; 800-938-4685. FAX 212-586-1182. TELEX 175567. (UK addr.: Economist Intelligence Unit Ltd., Subscriptions Dept., P.O. Box 200, Harold Hill, Romford, Essex RM3 8UX, England. TEL 44-1708-381-444. FAX 44-1708-371-850)
●Also available online. Vendor(s): Knight-Ridder, Inc., Lexis-Nexis.
Formerly (until 1992): Global Forecasting Service. Iraq (ISSN 0966-9434)
Description: Focuses on the key factors affecting Iraq's political and economic outlook and its business environment over the next five years.

320 330.9 US
COUNTRY FORECAST. IRELAND. q. £370($715) Economist Intelligence Unit, 111 W. 57th St., New York, NY 10019. TEL 212-554-0600; 800-938-4685. FAX 212-586-1182. TELEX 175567. (UK addr.: Economist Intelligence Unit Ltd., Subscriptions Dept., P.O. Box 200, Harold Hill, Romford, Essex RM3 8UX, England. TEL 44-1708-381-444. FAX 44-1708-371-850)
●Also available online. Vendor(s): Knight-Ridder, Inc., Lexis-Nexis.
Formerly (until 1992): Global Forecasting Service. Ireland (ISSN 0966-8837)
Description: Focuses on the key factors affecting Ireland's political and economic outlook and its business environment over the next five years.

320 330.9 US
COUNTRY FORECAST. ITALY. q. £370($715) Economist Intelligence Unit, 111 W. 57th St., New York, NY 10019. TEL 212-554-0600; 800-938-4685. FAX 212-9586-1182. TELEX 175567. (UK addr.: Economist Intelligence Unit Ltd., Subscriptions Dept., P.O. Box 200, Harold Hill, Romford, Essex RM3 8UX, England. TEL 44-1708-381-444. FAX 44-1708-371-850)
●Also available online. Vendor(s): Knight-Ridder, Inc., Lexis-Nexis.
Formerly (until 1992): Global Forecasting Service. Italy (ISSN 0966-8845)
Description: Focuses on the key factors affecting Italy's political and economic outlook and its business environment over the next five years.

POLITICAL SCIENCE

320 330.9   US
COUNTRY FORECAST. JAPAN. q. £370($715). Economist Intelligence Unit, 111 W. 57th St., New York, NY 10019. TEL 212-554-0600; 800-938-4685. FAX 212-586-1182. TELEX 175567. (UK addr.: Economist Intelligence Unit Ltd., Subscriptions Dept., P.O. Box 200, Harold Hill, Romford, Essex RM3 8UX, England. TEL 44-1708-381-444. FAX 44-1708-371-850)
●Also available online. Vendor(s): Knight-Ridder, Inc., Lexis-Nexis.
   Formerly (until 1992): Global Forecasting Service. Japan (ISSN 0966-8853)
   Description: Focuses on the key factors affecting Japan's political and economic outlook and its business environment over the next five years.

320 330.9   US
COUNTRY FORECAST. LATIN AMERICA. q. price varies. Economist Intelligence Unit, 111 W. 57th St., New York, NY 10019. TEL 212-554-0600; 800-938-4685. FAX 212-586-1182. TELEX 175567. (UK addr.: Economist Intelligence Unit Ltd., Subscriptions Dept., P.O. Box 200, Harold Hill, Romford, Essex RM3 8UX, England. TEL 44-1708-381-444. FAX 44-1708-371-850)
●Also available online. Vendor(s): Knight-Ridder, Inc., Lexis-Nexis.
   Formerly (until 1992): Global Forecasting Service. Latin America.
   Description: Focuses on the key factors affecting the region's political and economic outlook and its business environment over the next five years.

320 330.9   US
COUNTRY FORECAST. MALAYSIA. q. £370($715). Economist Intelligence Unit, 111 W. 57th St., New York, NY 10019. TEL 212-554-0600; 800-938-4685. FAX 212-586-1182. TELEX 175567. (UK addr.: Economist Intelligence Unit Ltd., Subscriptions Dept., P.O. Box 200, Harold Hill, Romford, Essex RM3 8UX, England. TEL 44-1708-381-444. FAX 44-1708-371-850)
●Also available online. Vendor(s): Knight-Ridder, Inc., Lexis-Nexis.
   Formerly (until 1992): Global Forecasting Service. Malaysia (ISSN 0966-9442)
   Description: Focuses on the key factors affecting Malaysia's political and economic outlook and its business environment over the next five years.

320 330.9   US
COUNTRY FORECAST. MEXICO. q. £370($715). Economist Intelligence Unit, 111 W. 57th St., New York, NY 10019. TEL 212-554-0600; 800-938-4685. FAX 212-586-1182. TELEX 175567. (UK addr.: Economist Intelligence Unit Ltd., Subscriptions Dept., P.O. Box 200, Harold Hill, Romford, Essex RM3 8UX, England. TEL 44-1708-381-444. FAX 44-1708-371-850)
●Also available online. Vendor(s): Knight-Ridder, Inc., Lexis-Nexis.
   Formerly (until 1992): Global Forecasting Service. Mexico (ISSN 0966-9469)
   Description: Focuses on the key factors affecting Mexico's political and economic outlook and its business environment over the next five years.

320 330.9   US
COUNTRY FORECAST. MIDDLE EAST AND NORTH AFRICA. q. price varies. Economist Intelligence Unit, 111 W. 57th St., New York, NY 10019. TEL 212-554-0600; 800-938-4685. FAX 212-586-1182. TELEX 175567. (UK addr.: Economist Intelligence Unit Ltd., Subscriptions Dept., P.O. Box 200, Harold Hill, Romford, Essex RM3 9UX, England. TEL 44-1708-381-444. FAX 44-1708-371-850)
●Also available online. Vendor(s): Knight-Ridder, Inc., Lexis-Nexis.
   Former titles: Country Forecast. Middle East and Africa; (until 1992): Global Forecasting Service. Middle East and Africa.
   Description: Focuses on the key factors affecting the region's political and economic outlook and its business environment over the next five years.

320 330.9   US
COUNTRY FORECAST. NETHERLANDS. q. £370($715). Economist Intelligence Unit, 111 W. 57th St., New York, NY 10019. TEL 212-544-0600; 800-938-4685. FAX 212-586-1182. TELEX 175567. (UK addr.: Economist Intelligence Unit Ltd., Subscriptions Dept., P.O. Box 200, Harold Hill, Romford, Essex RM3 8UX, England. TEL 44-1708-381-444. FAX 44-1708-371-850)
●Also available online. Vendor(s): Knight-Ridder, Inc., Lexis-Nexis.
   Formerly (until 1992): Global Forecasting Service. Netherlands (ISSN 0966-8861)
   Description: Focuses on the key factors affecting the Netherland's political and economic outlook and its business environment over the next five years.

320 330.9   US
COUNTRY FORECAST. NEW ZEALAND. q. £370($715). Economist Intelligence Unit, 111 W. 57th St., New York, NY 10019. TEL 212-554-0600; 800-938-4685. FAX 212-586-1182. TELEX 175567. (UK addr.: Economist Intelligence Unit Ltd., Subscriptions Dept., P.O. Box 200, Harold Hill, Romford, Essex RM3 8UX, England. TEL 44-1708-381-444. FAX 44-1708-371-850)
●Also available online. Vendor(s): Knight-Ridder, Inc., Lexis-Nexis.
   Formerly (until 1992): Global Forecasting Service. New Zealand.
   Description: Focuses on the key factors affecting New Zealand's political and economic outlook and its business environment over the next five years.

320 330.9   US
COUNTRY FORECAST. NIGERIA. q. £370($715). Economist Intelligence Unit, 111 W. 57th St., New York, NY 10019. TEL 212-554-0600; 800-938-4685. FAX 212-586-1182. TELEX 175567. (UK addr.: Economist Intelligence Unit Ltd., Subscriptions Dept., P.O. Box 200, Harold Hill, Romford, Essex RM3 8UX, England. TEL 44-1708-381-444. FAX 44-1708-371-850)
●Also available online. Vendor(s): Knight-Ridder, Inc., Lexis-Nexis.
   Formerly (until 1992): Global Forecasting Service. Nigeria (ISSN 0966-887X)
   Description: Focuses on the key factors affecting Nigeria's political and economic outlook and its business environment over the next five years.

320 330.9   US
COUNTRY FORECAST. NORWAY. q. £370($715). Economist Intelligence Unit, 111 W. 57th St., New York, NY 10019. TEL 212-544-0600; 800-938-4685. FAX 212-586-1182. TELEX 175567. (UK addr.: Economist Intelligence Unit Ltd., Subscriptions Dept., P.O. Box 200, Harold Hill, Romford, Essex RM3 8UX, England. TEL 44-1708-381-444. FAX 44-1708-371-850)
●Also available online. Vendor(s): Knight-Ridder, Inc., Lexis-Nexis.
   Formerly (until 1992): Global Forecasting Service. Norway (ISSN 0966-9450)
   Description: Focuses on the key factors affecting Norway's political and economic outlook and its business environment over the next five years.

320 330.9   US
COUNTRY FORECAST. PAKISTAN. q. £370($715). Economist Intelligence Unit, 111 W. 57th St., New York, NY 10019. TEL 212-554-0600; 800-938-4685. FAX 212-586-1182. TELEX 175567. (UK addr.: Economist Intelligence Unit Ltd., Subscriptions Dept., P.O. Box 200, Harold Hill, Romford, Essex RM3 8UX, England. TEL 44-1708-381-444. FAX 44-1708-371-1182)
●Also available online. Vendor(s): Knight-Ridder, Inc., Lexis-Nexis.
   Formerly (until 1992): Global Forecasting Service. Pakistan (ISSN 0966-8888)
   Description: Focuses on the key factors affecting Pakistan's political and economic outlook and its business environment over the next five years.

320 330.9   US
COUNTRY FORECAST. PERU. q. £370($715). Economist Intelligence Unit, 111 W. 57th St., New York, NY 10019. TEL 212-554-0600; 800-938-4685. FAX 212-586-1182. TELEX 175567. (UK addr.: Economist Intelligence Unit Ltd., Subscriptions Dept., P.O. Box 200, Harold Hill, Romford, Essex RM3 8UX, England. TEL 44-1708-381-444. FAX 44-1708-371-850)
●Also available online. Vendor(s): Knight-Ridder, Inc., Lexis-Nexis.
   Formerly (until 1992): Global Forecasting Service. Peru (ISSN 0966-9477)
   Description: Focuses on the key factors affecting Peru's political and economic outlook and its business environment over the next five years.

320 330.9   US
COUNTRY FORECAST. PHILIPPINES. q. £370($715). Economist Intelligence Unit, 111 W. 57th St., New York, NY 10019. TEL 212-554-0600; 800-938-4685. FAX 212-586-1182. TELEX 175567. (UK addr.: Economist Intelligence Unit Ltd., Subscriptions Dept., P.O. Box 200, Harold Hill, Romford, Essex RM3 8UX, England. TEL 44-1708-381-444. FAX 44-1708-371-850)
●Also available online. Vendor(s): Knight-Ridder, Inc., Lexis-Nexis.
   Formerly (until 1992): Global Forecasting Service. Philippines (ISSN 0966-8896)
   Description: Focuses on the key factors affecting the Philippines' political and economic outlook and its business environment over the next five years.

320 330.9   US
COUNTRY FORECAST. POLAND. q. £370($715). Economist Intelligence Unit, 111 W. 57th St., New York, NY 10019. TEL 212-554-0600; 800-938-1182. FAX 212-586-1182. TELEX 175567. (UK addr.: Economist Intelligence Unit Ltd., Subscriptions Dept., P.O. Box 200, Harold Hill, Romford, Essex RM3 8UX, England. TEL 44-1708-381-444. FAX 44-1708-371-850)
●Also available online. Vendor(s): Knight-Ridder, Inc., Lexis-Nexis.
   Formerly (until 1992): Global Forecasting Service. Poland (ISSN 0966-890X)
   Description: Focuses on the key factors affecting Poland's political and economic outlook and its business environment over the next five years.

320 330.9   US
COUNTRY FORECAST. PORTUGAL. q. £370($715). Economist Intelligence Unit, 111 W. 57th St., New York, NY 10019. TEL 212-554-0600; 800-938-4685. FAX 212-586-1182. TELEX 175567. (UK addr.: Economist Intelligence Unit Ltd., Subscriptions Dept., P.O. Box 200, Harold Hill, Romford, Essex RM3 8UX, England. TEL 44-1708-381-444. FAX 44-1708-371-850)
●Also available online. Vendor(s): Knight-Ridder, Inc., Lexis-Nexis.
   Formerly (until 1992): Global Forecasting Service. Portugal (ISSN 0966-8721)
   Description: Focuses on the key factors affecting Portugal's political and economic outlook and its business environment over the next five years.

320 330.9   US
COUNTRY FORECAST. ROMANIA. q. £370($715). Economist Intelligence Unit, 111 W. 57th St., New York, NY 10019. TEL 212-554-0600; 800-938-4685. FAX 212-586-1182. TELEX 175567. (UK addr.: Economist Intelligence Unit Ltd., Subscriptions Dept., P.O. Box 200, Harold Hill, Romford, Essex RM3 8UX, England. TEL 44-1708-381-444. FAX 44-1708-371-850)
●Also available online. Vendor(s): Knight-Ridder, Inc., Lexis-Nexis.
   Formerly (until 1992): Global Forecasting Service. Romania (ISSN 0966-8918)
   Description: Focuses on the key factors affecting Romania's political and economic outlook and its business environment over the next five years.

POLITICAL SCIENCE 5301

320 330.9 US
COUNTRY FORECAST. RUSSIA. q. £370($715)
Economist Intelligence Unit, 111 W. 57th St., New York, NY 10019. TEL 212-554-0600; 800-938-4685. FAX 212-586-1182. TELEX 175567. (UK addr.: Economist Intelligence Unit Ltd., Subscriptions Dept., P.O. Box 200, Harold Hill, Romford, Essex RM3 8UX, England. TEL 44-1708-381-444. FAX 44-1708-371-850)
●Also available online. Vendor(s): Knight-Ridder, Inc., Lexis-Nexis.
Former titles: Country Forecast. Commonwealth of Independent States; (until 1992): Global Forecasting Service. Commonwealth of Independent States; Global Forecasting Service. U S S R.
Description: Focuses on the key factors affecting Russia's political and economic outlook and its business environment over the next five years.

320 330.9 US
COUNTRY FORECAST. SAUDI ARABIA. q. £370($715)
Economist Intelligence Unit, 111 W. 57th St., New York, NY 10019. TEL 212-554-0600; 800-938-4685. FAX 212-586-1182. TELEX 175567. (UK addr.: Economist Intelligence Unit Ltd., Subscriptions Dept., P.O. Box 200, Harold Hill, Romford, Essex RM3 8UX, England. TEL 44-1708-381-444. FAX 44-1708-371-850)
●Also available online. Vendor(s): Knight-Ridder, Inc., Lexis-Nexis.
Formerly (until 1992): Global Forecasting Service. Saudi Arabia (ISSN 0966-873X)
Description: Focuses on the key factors affecting Saudi Arabia's political and economic outlook and its business environment over the next five years.

320 330.9 US
COUNTRY FORECAST. SINGAPORE. q. £370($715)
Economist Intelligence Unit, 111 W. 57th St., New York, NY 10019. TEL 212-554-0600; 800-938-4685. FAX 212-586-1182. TELEX 175567. (UK addr.: Economist Intelligence Unit Ltd., Subscriptions Dept., P.O. Box 154, Dartford, Kent DA1 1QB, England. TEL 44-1708-381-444. FAX 44-1708-371-850)
●Also available online. Vendor(s): Knight-Ridder, Inc., Lexis-Nexis.
Formerly (until 1992): Global Forecasting Service. Singapore (ISSN 0966-8926)
Description: Focuses on the key factors affecting Singapore's political and economic outlook and its business environment over the next five years.

320 330.9 US
COUNTRY FORECAST. SOUTH AFRICA. q. £370($715)
Economist Intelligence Unit, 111 W. 57th St., New York, NY 10019. TEL 212-554-0600; 800-938-4685. FAX 212-586-1182. TELEX 175567. (UK addr.: Economist Intelligence Unit Ltd., Subscriptions Dept., P.O. Box 200, Harold Hill, Romford, Essex RM3 8UX, England. TEL 44-1708-381-444. FAX 44-1708-371-850)
●Also available online. Vendor(s): Knight-Ridder, Inc., Lexis-Nexis.
Formerly (until 1992): Global Forecasting Service. South Africa (ISSN 0966-8683)
Description: Focuses on the key factors affecting South Africa's political and economic outlook and its business environment over the next five years.

320 330.9 US
COUNTRY FORECAST. SOUTH KOREA. q. £370($715)
Economist Intelligence Unit, 111 W. 57th St., New York, NY 10019. TEL 212-554-0600; 800-938-4685. FAX 212-586-1182. TELEX 175567. (UK addr.: Economist Intelligence Unit Ltd., Subscriptions Dept., P.O. Box 200, Harold Hill, Romford, Essex RM3 8UX, England. TEL 44-1708-381-444. FAX 44-1708-371-850)
●Also available online. Vendor(s): Knight-Ridder, Inc., Lexis-Nexis.
Formerly (until 1992): Global Forecasting Service. South Korea (ISSN 0966-8675)
Description: Focuses on the key factors affecting South Korea's political and economic outlook and its business environment over the next five years.

320 330.9 US
COUNTRY FORECAST. SPAIN. q. £370($715)
Economist Intelligence Unit, 111 W. 57th St., New York, NY 10019. TEL 212-554-0600; 800-938-4685. FAX 212-586-1182. TELEX 175567. (UK addr.: Economist Intelligence Unit Ltd., Subscriptions Dept., P.O. Box 200, Harold Hill, Romford, Essex RM3 8UX, England. TEL 44-1708-381-444. FAX 44-1708-371-850)
●Also available online. Vendor(s): Knight-Ridder, Inc., Lexis-Nexis.
Formerly (until 1992): Global Forecasting Service. Spain (ISSN 0966-8659)
Description: Focuses on the key factors affecting Spain's political and economic outlook and its business environment over the next five years.

320 330.9 US
COUNTRY FORECAST. SRI LANKA. q. £370($715)
Economist Intelligence Unit, 111 W. 57th St., New York, NY 10019. TEL 212-554-0600; 800-938-4685. FAX 212-586-1182. TELEX 175567. (UK addr.: Economist Intelligence Unit Ltd., Subscriptions Dept., P.O. Box 200, Harold Hill, Romford, Essex RM3 8UX, England. TEL 44-1708-381-444. FAX 44-1708-371-850)
●Also available online. Vendor(s): Knight-Ridder, Inc., Lexis-Nexis.
Formerly (until 1992): Global Forecasting Service. Sri Lanka (ISSN 0966-8691)
Description: Focuses on the key factors affecting Sri Lanka's political and economic outlook and its business environment over the next five years.

320 330.9 US ISSN 1356-4013
▼**COUNTRY FORECAST. SUB-SAHARAN AFRICA.** 1994. q. £370($715) Economist Intelligence Unit, 111 W. 57th St., New York, NY 10019. TEL 212-554-0600; 800-938-4685. FAX 212-486-1182. TELEX 175567. (U.K. addr.: Economist Intelligence Unit Ltd., Subscriptions Dept., P.O. Box 200, Harold Hill, Romford, Essex RM3 8UX, England. TEL 44-1708-381444. FAX 44-1708-371850)
Description: Focuses on the key factors affecting Sub-Saharan Africa's political and economic outlook and its business environment over the next five years.

320 330.9 US
COUNTRY FORECAST. SWEDEN. q. £370($715)
Economist Intelligence Unit, 111 W. 57th St., New York, NY 10019. TEL 212-554-0600; 800-938-4685. FAX 212-586-1182. TELEX 175567. (UK addr.: Economist Intelligence Unit Ltd., Subscriptions Dept., P.O. Box 200, Harold Hill, Romford, Essex RM3 8UX, England. TEL 44-1708-381-444. FAX 44-1708-371-850)
●Also available online. Vendor(s): Knight-Ridder, Inc., Lexis-Nexis.
Formerly (until 1992): Global Forecasting Service. Sweden (ISSN 0966-8667)
Description: Focuses on the key factors affecting Sweden's political and economic outlook and its business environment over the next five years.

320 330.9 US
COUNTRY FORECAST. SWITZERLAND. q. £370($715)
Economist Intelligence Unit, 111 W. 57th St., New York, NY 10019. TEL 212-554-0600; 800-938-4685. FAX 212-586-1182. TELEX 175567. (UK addr.: Economist Intelligence Unit Ltd., Subscriptions Dept., P.O. Box 200, Harold Hill, Romford, Essex RM3 8UX, England. TEL 44-1708-381-444. FAX 44-1708-371-850)
●Also available online. Vendor(s): Knight-Ridder, Inc., Lexis-Nexis.
Formerly (until 1992): Global Forecasting Service. Switzerland (ISSN 0966-8934)
Description: Focuses on the key factors affecting Switzerland's political and economic outlook and its business environment over the next five years.

320 330.9 US
COUNTRY FORECAST. TAIWAN. q. £370($715)
Economist Intelligence Unit, 111 W. 57th St., New York, NY 10019. TEL 212-554-0600; 800-938-4685. FAX 212-586-1182. TELEX 175567. (UK addr.: Economist Intelligence Unit Ltd., Subscriptions Dept., P.O. Box 200, Harold Hill, Romford, Essex RM3 8UX, England. TEL 44-1708-381-444. FAX 44-1708-371-850)
●Also available online. Vendor(s): Knight-Ridder, Inc., Lexis-Nexis.
Formerly (until 1992): Global Forecasting Service. Taiwan (ISSN 0966-8640)
Description: Focuses on the key factors affecting Taiwan's political and economic outlook and its business environment over the next five years.

320 330.9 US
COUNTRY FORECAST. THAILAND. q. £370($715)
Economist Intelligence Unit, 111 W. 57th St., New York, NY 10019. TEL 212-554-0600; 800-938-4685. FAX 212-586-1182. TELEX 175567. (UK addr.: Economist Intelligence Unit Ltd., Subscriptions Dept., P.O. Box 200, Harold Hill, Romford, Essex RM3 8UX, England. TEL 44-1708-381-444. FAX 44-1708-371-850)
●Also available online. Vendor(s): Knight-Ridder, Inc., Lexis-Nexis.
Formerly (until 1992): Global Forecasting Service. Thailand (ISSN 0966-8624)
Description: Focuses on the key factors affecting Thailand's political and economic outlook and its business environment over the next five years.

320 330.9 US
COUNTRY FORECAST. TURKEY. q. £370($715)
Economist Intelligence Unit, 111 W. 57th St., New York, NY 10019. TEL 212-554-0600; 800-938-4685. FAX 212-586-1182. TELEX 175567. (UK addr.: Economist Intelligence Unit Ltd., Subscriptions Dept., P.O. Box 200, Harold Hill, Romford, Essex RM3 8UX, England. TEL 44-1708-381-444. FAX 44-1708-371-850)
●Also available online. Vendor(s): Knight-Ridder, Inc., Lexis-Nexis.
Formerly (until 1992): Global Forecasting Service. Turkey (ISSN 0966-8632)
Description: Focuses on the key factors affecting Turkey's political and economic outlook and its business environment over the next five years.

320 330.9 US
COUNTRY FORECAST. UNITED KINGDOM. q. £370($715) Economist Intelligence Unit, 111 W. 57th St., New York, NY 10019. TEL 212-554-0600; 800-938-4685. FAX 212-586-1182. TELEX 175567. (UK addr.: Economist Intelligence Unit Ltd., Subscriptions Dept., P.O. Box 200, Harold Hill, Romford, Essex RM3 8UX, England. TEL 44-1708-381-444. FAX 44-1708-371-850)
●Also available online. Vendor(s): Knight-Ridder, Inc., Lexis-Nexis.
Formerly (until 1992): Global Forecasting Service. United Kingdom.
Description: Focuses on the key factors affecting the United Kingdom's political and economic outlook and its business environment over the next five years.

320 330.9 US
COUNTRY FORECAST. UNITED STATES OF AMERICA. q. £370($715) Economist Intelligence Unit, 111 W. 57th St., New York, NY 10019. TEL 212-554-0600; 800-938-4685. FAX 212-586-1182. TELEX 175567. (UK addr.: Economist Intelligence Unit Ltd., Subscriptions Dept., P.O. Box 200, Harold Hill, Romford, Essex RM3 8UX, England. TEL 44-1708-381-444. FAX 44-1708-371-850)
●Also available online. Vendor(s): Knight-Ridder, Inc., Lexis-Nexis.
Formerly (until 1992): Global Forecasting Service. United States of America.
Description: Focuses on the key factors affecting USA's political and economic outlook and its business environment over the next five years.

POLITICAL SCIENCE

320 330.9   US
COUNTRY FORECAST. VENEZUELA. q. £370($715) Economist Intelligence Unit, 111 W. 57th St., New York, NY 10019. TEL 212-554-0600; 800-938-4685. FAX 212-586-1182. TELEX 175567. (UK addr.: Economist Intelligence Unit Ltd., Subscriptions Dept., P.O. Box 200, Harold Hill, Romford, Essex RM3 8UX, England. TEL 44-1708-381-444. FAX 44-17-8-371-850)
●Also available online. Vendor(s): Knight-Ridder, Inc., Lexis-Nexis.
   Formerly (until 1992): Global Forecasting Service. Venezuela (ISSN 0966-9574)
   Description: Focuses on the key factors affecting Venezuela's political and economic outlook and its business environment over the next five years.

320 330.9   US
COUNTRY FORECASTS (NEW YORK). (Covers 55 countries) q. £370($715) Economist Intelligence Unit, 111 W. 57th St., New York, NY 10019. TEL 212-554-0600; 800-938-4685. FAX 212-586-1182. TELEX 175567. (UK addr.: Economist Intelligence Unit Ltd., Subscriptions Dept., P.O. Box 200, Harold Hill, Romford, Essex RM3 8UX, England. TEL 44-1708-381-444. FAX 44-1708-371-850)
●Also available online. Vendor(s): Knight-Ridder, Inc., Lexis-Nexis.
Also available on CD-ROM.
   Formerly (until 1992): Global Forecasting Services.
   Description: Forecasts the political, economic and business trends in 55 countries for the next five years.

332 382   US   ISSN 1041-3553
HC10
COUNTRY FORECASTS (SYRACUSE). 1985. s-a. $545 (effective 1995). Political Risk Services, Box 248, E. Syracuse, NY 13057-0248. TEL 315-431-0511. FAX 315-431-0200. Eds. William D. Coplin, Michael K. O'Leary. (also avail. in diskette format; back issues avail.)
●Also available online. Vendor(s): Data-Star (FSRI), Knight-Ridder, Inc., Information Access Co., NewsNet (IT933).
—CCC.
   Incorporates (1981-1988): Political Climate for International Business (ISSN 0887-7637); (1986-1988): Political Risk Database (ISSN 0890-4928); (1986-1988): Country Database (ISSN 0890-4952); Former titles (until 1988): Country Facts (ISSN 0889-5007); Country Data Quarterly.
   Description: Contains rankings and data for 100 countries on political, economic, and social variables; methods of data-gathering and forecasting; and assumptions underlying the forecasts.

320 330.9   US   ISSN 0269-6053
COUNTRY PROFILE. ALGERIA; annual survey of political and economic background. 1952. a. £95($145) Economist Intelligence Unit, 111 W. 57th St., New York, NY 10019. TEL 212-554-0600; 800-938-4685. FAX 212-586-1182. TELEX 175567. (UK addr.: Economist Intelligence Unit Ltd., Subscriptions Dept., P.O. Box 200, Harold Hill, Romford, Essex RM3 8UX, England. TEL 44-1708-381-444. FAX 44-1708-371-850) stat. (also avail. in microform from UMI)
●Also available online. Vendor(s): Knight-Ridder, Inc., Lexis-Nexis.
—BLDSC (3481.893010).

320 330.9   US
HC965.A1
COUNTRY PROFILE. ANGOLA; annual survey of political and economic background. 1952. a. £95($145) Economist Intelligence Unit, 111 W. 57th St., New York, NY 10019. TEL 212-554-0600; 800-938-4685. FAX 212-586-1182. TELEX 175567. (UK addr.: Economist Intelligence Unit Ltd., Subscriptions Dept., P.O. Box 200, Harold Hill, Romford, Essex RM3 8UX, England. TEL 44-1708-381-444. FAX 44-1708-371-850) illus.; stat. (also avail. in microform from UMI)
●Also available online. Vendor(s): Knight-Ridder, Inc., Lexis-Nexis.
   Supersedes in part (in 1993): Country Profile. Angola, Sao Tome and Principe (ISSN 0269-7092)

320 330.9   US   ISSN 0269-4468
HC171
COUNTRY PROFILE. ARGENTINA; annual survey of political and economic background. 1952. a. £95($145) Economist Intelligence Unit, 111 W. 57th St., New York, NY 10019. TEL 212-554-0600; 800-938-4685. FAX 212-586-1182. TELEX 175567. (UK addr.: Economist Intelligence Unit Ltd., Subscriptions Dept., P.O. Box 200, Harold Hill, Romford, Essex RM3 8UX, England. TEL 44-1708-381-444. FAX 44-1708-371-850) stat. (also avail. in microform from UMI)
●Also available online. Vendor(s): Knight-Ridder, Inc., Lexis-Nexis.
—BLDSC (3481.893090); UMI.

320 330.9   US   ISSN 0269-4476
COUNTRY PROFILE. AUSTRALIA; annual survey of political and economic background. 1952. a. £95($145) Economist Intelligence Unit, 111 W. 57th St., New York, NY 10019. TEL 212-554-0600; 800-938-4685. FAX 212-586-1182. TELEX 175567. (UK addr.: Economist Intelligence Unit Ltd., Subscriptions Dept., P.O. Box 200, Harold Hill, Romford, Essex RM3 8UX, England. TEL 44-1708-381-444. FAX 44-1708-371-850) stat. (also avail. in microform from UMI)
●Also available online. Vendor(s): Knight-Ridder, Inc., Lexis-Nexis.
—BLDSC (3481.893130).

320 330.9   US   ISSN 0269-4484
HC261
COUNTRY PROFILE. AUSTRIA; annual survey of political and economic background. 1952. a. £95($145) Economist Intelligence Unit, 111 W. 57th St., New York, NY 10019. TEL 212-554-0600; 800-938-4685. FAX 212-586-1182. TELEX 175567. (UK addr.: Economist Intelligence Unit Ltd., Subscriptions Dept., P.O. Box 200, Harold Hill, Romford, Essex RM3 8UX, England. TEL 44-1708-381-444. FAX 44-1708-371-850) stat. (also avail. in microform from UMI)
●Also available online. Vendor(s): Knight-Ridder, Inc., Lexis-Nexis.
—BLDSC (3481.893170).

320 330.9   US   ISSN 0269-7335
HC415.38.A1
COUNTRY PROFILE. BAHRAIN, QATAR; annual survey of political and economic background. 1952. a. £95($145) Economist Intelligence Unit, 111 W. 57th St., New York, NY 10019. TEL 212-554-0600; 800-938-4685. FAX 212-586-1182. TELEX 175567. (UK addr.: Economist Intelligence Unit Ltd., Subscriptions Dept., P.O. Box 200, Harold Hill, Romford, Essex RM3 8UX, England. TEL 44-1708-381-444. FAX 44-1708-371-850) stat. (also avail. in microform from UMI)
●Also available online. Vendor(s): Knight-Ridder, Inc., Lexis-Nexis.
—UMI.

320 330.9   US   ISSN 0969-6253
COUNTRY PROFILE. BALTIC REPUBLICS: LITHUANIA, LATVIA, ESTONIA; annual survey of political and economic background. 1952. a. £95($145) Economist Intelligence Unit, 111 W. 57th St., New York, NY 10019. TEL 212-554-0600; 800-938-4685. FAX 212-586-1182. TELEX 175567. (UK addr.: Economist Intelligence Unit Ltd., Subscriptions Dept., P.O. Box 200, Harold Hill, Romford, Essex RM3 8UX, England. TEL 44-1708-381-444. FAX 44-1708-371-850) illus.; stat. (also avail. in microform from UMI)
●Also available online. Vendor(s): Knight-Ridder, Inc., Lexis-Nexis.
—BLDSC (3481.893230).
   Supersedes in part (1991-1993): Country Profile. Commonwealth of Independent States; Which was formerly (until 1990): Country Profile. U S S R.

320 330.9   US   ISSN 0269-8145
COUNTRY PROFILE. BANGLADESH; annual survey of political and economic background. 1952. a. £95($145) Economist Intelligence Unit, 111 W. 57th St., New York, NY 10019. TEL 212-554-0600; 800-938-4685. FAX 212-586-1182. TELEX 175567. (UK addr.: Economist Intelligence Unit Ltd., Subscriptions Dept., P.O. Box 200, Harold Hill, Romford, Essex RM3 8UX, England. TEL 44-1708-381-444. FAX 44-1708-371-850) stat. (also avail. in microform from UMI)
●Also available online. Vendor(s): Knight-Ridder, Inc., Lexis-Nexis.
—BLDSC (3481.893250).

320 330.9   US   ISSN 0269-4352
HC311
COUNTRY PROFILE. BELGIUM, LUXEMBOURG; annual survey of political and economic background. 1952. a. £95($145) Economist Intelligence Unit, 111 W. 57th St., New York, NY 10019. TEL 212-554-0600; 800-938-4685. FAX 212-586-1182. TELEX 175567. (UK addr.: Economist Intelligence Unit Ltd., Subscriptions Dept., P.O. Box 200, Harold Hill, Romford, Essex RM3 8UX, England. TEL 44-1708-381-444. FAX 44-1708-371-850) stat. (also avail. in microform from UMI)
●Also available online. Vendor(s): Knight-Ridder, Inc., Lexis-Nexis.
—BLDSC (3481.893290); UMI.

320 330.9   US   ISSN 0269-4514
COUNTRY PROFILE. BELIZE, BAHAMAS, BERMUDA; annual survey of political and economic background. 1952. a. £95($145) Economist Intelligence Unit, 111 W. 57th St., New York, NY 10019. TEL 212-554-0600; 800-938-4685. FAX 212-586-1182. TELEX 175567. (UK addr.: Economist Intelligence Unit Ltd., Subscriptions Dept., P.O. Box 200, Harold Hill, Romford, Essex RM3 8UX, England. TEL 44-1708-381-444. FAX 44-1708-371-850) stat. (also avail. in microform from UMI)
●Also available online. Vendor(s): Knight-Ridder, Inc., Lexis-Nexis.
—BLDSC (3481.893310).

320 330.9   US   ISSN 0269-5952
COUNTRY PROFILE. BOLIVIA; annual survey of political and economic background. 1952. a. £95($145) Economist Intelligence Unit, 111 W. 57th St., New York, NY 10019. TEL 212-554-0600; 800-938-4685. FAX 212-586-1181. TELEX 175567. (UK addr.: Economist Intelligence Unit Ltd., Subscriptions Dept., P.O. Box 200, Harold Hill, Romford, Essex RM3 8UX, England. TEL 44-1708-381-444. FAX 44-1708-371-850) illus.; stat. (also avail. in microform from UMI)
●Also available online. Vendor(s): Knight-Ridder, Inc., Lexis-Nexis.
—BLDSC (3481.893315).

320 330.9   US
COUNTRY PROFILE. BOSNIA-HERCEGOVINA, CROATIA, SLOVENIA; annual survey of political and economic background. 1952. a. £95($145) Economist Intelligence Unit, 111 W. 57th St., New York, NY 10019. TEL 212-554-0600; 800-938-4685. FAX 212-586-1182. TELEX 175567. (UK addr.: Economist Intelligence Unit Ltd., Subscriptions Dept., P.O. Box 200, Harold Hill, Romford, Essex RM3 8UX, England. TEL 44-1708-381-444. FAX 44-1708-371-850) illus.; stat. (also avail. in microform from UMI)
●Also available online. Vendor(s): Knight-Ridder, Inc., Lexis-Nexis.
   Supersedes in part (in 1993): Country Profile. Yugoslavia (ISSN 0269-803X)

320 330.9   US
COUNTRY PROFILE. BOTSWANA, LESOTHO; annual survey of political and economic background. 1952. a. £95($145) Economist Intelligence Unit, 111 W. 57th St., New York, NY 10019. TEL 212-554-0600; 800-938-4685. FAX 212-586-1182. TELEX 175567. (UK addr.: Economist Intelligence Unit Ltd., Subscriptions Dept., P.O. Box 200, Harold Hill, Romford, Essex RM3 8UX, England. TEL 44-1708-381-444. FAX 44-1708-371-850) illus.; stat. (also avail. in microform from UMI)
●Also available online. Vendor(s): Knight-Ridder, Inc., Lexis-Nexis.
   Supersedes in part (in 1993): Country Profile. Botswana, Lesotho, Swaziland (ISSN 0269-7394)

POLITICAL SCIENCE

320 330.9   US   ISSN 0269-4492
HC186
COUNTRY PROFILE. BRAZIL; annual survey of political and economic background. 1952. a. £95($145) Economist Intelligence Unit, 111 W. 57th St., New York, NY 10019. TEL 212-554-0600; 800-938-4685. FAX 212-586-1182. TELEX 175567. (UK addr.: Economist Intelligence Unit Ltd., Subscriptions Dept., P.O. Box 200, Harold Hill, Romford, Essex RM3 8UX, England. TEL 44-1708-381-444. FAX 44-1708-371-850) stat. (also avail. in microform from UMI)
●Also available online. Vendor(s): Knight-Ridder, Inc., Lexis-Nexis.
—BLDSC (3481.893330); UMI.

320 330.9   US   ISSN 0269-6398
HC403.A1
COUNTRY PROFILE. BULGARIA, ALBANIA; annual survey of political and economic background. 1952. a. £95($145) Economist Intelligence Unit, 111 W. 57th St., New York, NY 10019. TEL 212-554-0600; 800-938-4685. FAX 212-586-1182. TELEX 175567. (UK addr.: Economist Intelligence Unit Ltd., Subscriptions Dept., P.O. Box 200, Harold Hill, Romford, Essex RM3 8UX, England. TEL 44-1708-381-444. FAX 44-1708-371-850) illus.; stat. (also avail. in microform from UMI)
●Also available online. Vendor(s): Knight-Ridder, Inc., Lexis-Nexis.
—UMI.

320 330.9   US   ISSN 0269-7963
COUNTRY PROFILE. CAMEROON, CENTRAL AFRICAN REPUBLIC, CHAD; annual survey of political and economic background. 1952. a. £95($145) Economist Intelligence Unit, 111 W. 57th St., New York, NY 10019. TEL 212-554-0600; 800-938-4685. FAX 212-586-1182. TELEX 175567. (UK addr.: Economist Intelligence Unit Ltd., Subscriptions Dept., P.O. Box 200, Harold Hill, Romford, Essex RM3 8UX, England. TEL 44-1708-381-444. FAX 44-1708-371-850) illus.; stat. (also avail. in microform from UMI)
●Also available online. Vendor(s): Knight-Ridder, Inc., Lexis-Nexis.
—BLDSC (3481.893350).

320 330.9   US   ISSN 0269-4379
HC111
COUNTRY PROFILE. CANADA; annual survey of political and economic background. 1952. a. £95($145) Economist Intelligence Unit, 111 W. 57th St., New York, NY 10019. TEL 212-554-0600; 800-938-4685. FAX 212-586-1182. TELEX 175567. (UK addr.: Economist Intelligence Unit Ltd., Subscriptions Dept., P.O. Box 200, Harold Hill, Romford, Essex RM3 8UX, England. TEL 44-1708-381-444. FAX 44-1708-371-850) stat. (also avail. in microform from UMI)
●Also available online. Vendor(s): Knight-Ridder, Inc., Lexis-Nexis.
—BLDSC (3481.893410); UMI.

320 330.9   US   ISSN 0269-5081
HC191
COUNTRY PROFILE. CHILE; annual survey of political and economic background. 1952. a. £95($145) Economist Intelligence Unit, 111 W. 57th St., New York, NY 10019. TEL 212-554-0600; 800-938-4685. FAX 212-586-1182. TELEX 175567. (UK addr.: Economist Intelligence Unit Ltd., Subscriptions Dept., P.O. Box 200, Harold Hill, Romford, Essex RM3 8UX, England. TEL 44-1708-381-444. FAX 44-1708-371-850) stat. (also avail. in microform from UMI)
●Also available online. Vendor(s): Knight-Ridder, Inc., Lexis-Nexis.
—BLDSC (3481.893450); UMI.

320 330.9   US   ISSN 1352-089X
HC426
COUNTRY PROFILE. CHINA, MONGOLIA; annual survey of political and economic background. 1952. a. £95($145) Economist Intelligence Unit, 111 W. 57th St., New York, NY 10019. TEL 212-554-0600; 800-938-4685. FAX 212-586-1182. TELEX 175567. (UK addr.: Economist Intelligence Unit Ltd., Subscriptions Dept., P.O. Box 200, Harold Hill, Romford, Essex RM3 8UX, England. TEL 44-1708-381-444. FAX 44-1708-371-850) illus.; stat. (also avail. in microfilm; microform from UMI)
●Also available online. Vendor(s): Knight-Ridder, Inc., Lexis-Nexis.
—BLDSC (3481.893480).
     Supersedes in part (in 1993): Country Profile. China, North Korea (ISSN 0269-509X)

320 330.9   US   ISSN 0269-5103
HC196
COUNTRY PROFILE. COLOMBIA; annual survey of political and economic background. 1952. a. £95($145) Economist Intelligence Unit, 111 W. 57th St., New York, NY 10019. TEL 212-554-0600; 800-938-4685. FAX 212-586-1182. TELEX 175567. (UK addr.: Economist Intelligence Unit Ltd., Subscriptions Dept., P.O. Box 200, Harold Hill, Romford, Essex RM3 8UX, England. TEL 44-1708-381-444. FAX 44-1708-371-850) stat. (also avail. in microform from UMI)
●Also available online. Vendor(s): Knight-Ridder, Inc., Lexis-Nexis.
—BLDSC (3481.893530); UMI.

320 330.9   US
HC980.A1
COUNTRY PROFILE. CONGO, SAO TOME AND PRINCIPE, GUINEA-BISSAU, CAPE VERDE; annual survey of political and economic background. 1952. a. £95($145) Economist Intelligence Unit, 111 W. 57th St., New York, NY 10019. TEL 212-554-0600; 800-938-4685. FAX 212-586-1182. TELEX 175567. (UK addr.: Economist Intelligence Unit Ltd., Subscriptions Dept., P.O. Box 200, Harold Hill, Romford, Essex RM3 8UX, England. TEL 44-1708-381-444. FAX 44-1708-371-850) illus.; stat. (also avail. in microform from UMI)
●Also available online. Vendor(s): Knight-Ridder, Inc., Lexis-Nexis.
—UMI.
     Formed by the 1993 merger of: Country Profile. Congo (ISSN 0269-6363); part of (1952-1993): Country Profile. Angola, Sao Tome and Principe (ISSN 0269-7092); part of (1952-1993): Country Profile. The Gambia, Guinea-Bissau, Cape Verde.

320 330.9   US   ISSN 1351-9042
HC141.A1
COUNTRY PROFILE. COSTA RICA, PANAMA; annual survey of political and economic background. 1952. a. £95($145) Economist Intelligence Unit, 111 W. 57th St., New York, NY 10019. TEL 212-554-0600; 800-938-4685. FAX 212-586-1182. TELEX 175567. (UK addr.: Economist Intelligence Unit Ltd., Subscriptions Dept., P.O. Box 200, Harold Hill, Romford, Essex RM3 8UX, England. TEL 44-1708-381-444. FAX 44-1708-371-850) illus.; stat. (also avail. in microform from UMI)
●Also available online. Vendor(s): Knight-Ridder, Inc., Lexis-Nexis.
—BLDSC (3481.895050).
     Supersedes in part (in 1993): Country Profile. Nicaragua, Costa Rica, Panama (ISSN 0269-4409)

320 330.9   US
COUNTRY PROFILE. COTE D'IVOIRE, MALI; annual survey of political and economic background. 1952. a. £95($145) Economist Intelligence Unit, 111 W. 57th St., New York, NY 10019. TEL 212-554-0600; 800-938-4685. FAX 212-586-1182. TELEX 175567. (UK addr.: Economist Intelligence Unit Ltd., Subscriptions Dept., P.O. Box 200, Harold Hill, Romford, Essex RM3 8UX, England. TEL 44-1708-381-444. FAX 44-1708-371-850) stat. (also avail. in microform from UMI)
●Also available online. Vendor(s): Knight-Ridder, Inc., Lexis-Nexis.
     Formed by the 1993 merger of: Country Profile. Cote d'Ivoire (ISSN 0269-7068); part of: Country Profile. Guinea, Mali, Mauritania (ISSN 0269-4417)

320 330.9   US   ISSN 0269-5111
HC152.5.A1
COUNTRY PROFILE. CUBA; annual survey of political and economic background. 1952. a. £95($145) Economist Intelligence Unit, 111 W. 57th St., New York, NY 10019. TEL 212-554-0600; 800-938-4685. FAX 212-586-1182. TELEX 175567. (UK addr.: Economist Intelligence Unit Ltd., Subscriptions Dept., P.O. Box 200, Harold Hill, Romford, Essex RM3 8UX, England. TEL 44-1707-381-444. FAX 44-1708-371-850) illus.; stat. (also avail. in microform from UMI)
●Also available online. Vendor(s): Knight-Ridder, Inc., Lexis-Nexis.
—BLDSC (3481.893610); UMI.

320 330.9   US   ISSN 1351-9085
HC415.2.A1
COUNTRY PROFILE. CYPRUS, MALTA; annual survey of political and economic background. 1993. a. £95($145) Economist Intelligence Unit, 111 W. 57th St., New York, NY 10019. TEL 212-554-0600; 800-938-4685. FAX 212-9586-1182. TELEX 175567. (UK addr.: Economist Intelligence Unit Ltd., Subscriptions Dept., P.O. Box 200, Harold Hill, Romford, Essex RM3 8UX, England. TEL 44-1708-381-444. FAX 44-1708-371-850) illus.; stat. (also avail. in microform from UMI)
●Also available online. Vendor(s): Knight-Ridder, Inc., Lexis-Nexis.
     Formed by the 1993 merger of: Country Profile. Malta (ISSN 0269-8137); part of (1952-1992): Country Profile. Lebanon, Cyprus (ISSN 0269-7351)

320 330.9   US   ISSN 1351-9093
COUNTRY PROFILE. CZECH REPUBLIC AND SLOVAKIA; annual survey of political and economic background. 1952. a. £95($145) Economist Intelligence Unit, 111 W. 57th St., New York, NY 10019. TEL 212-554-0600; 800-938-4685. FAX 212-586-1182. TELEX 175567. (UK addr.: Economist Intelligence Unit Ltd., Subscriptions Dept., P.O. Box 200, Harold Hill, Romford, Essex RM3 8UX, England. TEL 44-1708-381-444. FAX 44-1708-371-850) illus.; stat. (also avail. in microform from UMI)
●Also available online. Vendor(s): Knight-Ridder, Inc., Lexis-Nexis.
     Formerly (until 1993): Country Profile. Czechoslovakia (ISSN 0269-8048)

320 330.9   US   ISSN 0269-5138
HC351
COUNTRY PROFILE. DENMARK, ICELAND; annual survey of political and economic background. 1952. a. £95($145) Economist Intelligence Unit, 111 W. 57th St., New York, NY 10019. TEL 212-554-0600; 800-938-4685. FAX 212-586-1182. TELEX 175567. (UK addr.: Economist Intelligence Unit Ltd., Subscriptions Dept., P.O. Box 200, Harold Hill, Romford, Essex RM3 8UX, England. TEL 44-1708-381-444. FAX 44-1708-371-850) stat. (also avail. in microform from UMI)
●Also available online. Vendor(s): Knight-Ridder, Inc., Lexis-Nexis.
—BLDSC (3481.893690); UMI.

320 330.9   US   ISSN 0269-512X
HC153.5.A1
COUNTRY PROFILE. DOMINICAN REPUBLIC, HAITI, PUERTO RICO; annual survey of political and economic background. 1952. a. £95($145) Economist Intelligence Unit, 111 W. 57th St., New York, NY 10019. TEL 212-554-0600; 800-938-4685. FAX 212-586-1182. TELEX 175567. (UK addr.: Economist Intelligence Unit Ltd., Subscriptions Dept., P.O. Box 200, Harold Hill, Romford, Essex RM3 8UX, England. TEL 44-1708-381-444. FAX 44-1708-371-850) illus.; stat. (also avail. in microform from UMI)
●Also available online. Vendor(s): Knight-Ridder, Inc., Lexis-Nexis.
—BLDSC (3481.893710); UMI.

POLITICAL SCIENCE

320 330.9 US ISSN 0269-7971
HC201
COUNTRY PROFILE. ECUADOR; annual survey of political and economic background. 1952. a. £95($145) Economist Intelligence Unit, 111 W. 57th St., New York, NY 10019. TEL 212-554-0600; 800-938-4685. FAX 212-586-1182. TELEX 175567. (UK addr.: Economist Intelligence Unit Ltd., Subscriptions Dept., P.O. Box 200, Harold Hill, Romford, Essex RM3 8UX, England. TEL 44-1708-381-444. FAX 44-1708-371-850) stat. (also avail. in microform from UMI)
●Also available online. Vendor(s): Knight-Ridder, Inc., Lexis-Nexis.
—BLDSC (3481.897810); UMI.

320 330.9 US ISSN 0269-5227
HC830.A1
COUNTRY PROFILE. EGYPT; annual survey of political and economic background. 1952. a. £95($145) Economist Intelligence Unit, 111 W. 57th St., New York, NY 10019. TEL 212-554-0600; 800-938-4685. FAX 212-586-1182. TELEX 175567. (UK addr.: Economist Intelligence Unit Ltd., Subscriptions Dept., P.O. Box 200, Harold Hill, Romford, Essex RM3 8UX, England. TEL 44-1708-381-444. FAX 44-1708-371-850) stat. (also avail. in microform from UMI)
●Also available online. Vendor(s): Knight-Ridder, Inc., Lexis-Nexis.
—BLDSC (3481.893810); UMI.

320 330.9 US ISSN 0269-7084
COUNTRY PROFILE. ETHIOPIA, SOMALIA, DIJBOUTI; annual survey of political and economic background. 1952. a. £95($145) Economist Intelligence Unit, 111 W. 57th St., New York, NY 10019. TEL 212-554-0600; 800-938-4685. FAX 212-586-1182. TELEX 175567. (UK addr.: Economist Intelligence Unit Ltd., Subscriptions Dept., P.O. Box 200, Harold Hill, Romford, Essex RM3 8UX, England. TEL 44-1708-381-444. FAX 44-1708-371-850) stat. (also avail. in microform from UMI)
●Also available online. Vendor(s): Knight-Ridder, Inc., Lexis-Nexis.

320 330.9 US ISSN 0269-5332
HC340.2.A1
COUNTRY PROFILE. FINLAND; annual survey of political and economic background. 1952. a. £95($145) Economist Intelligence Unit, 111 W. 57th St., New York, NY 10019. TEL 212-554-0600. FAX 212-586-1182. TELEX 175567. (UK addr.: Economist Intelligence Unit Ltd., Subscriptions Dept., P.O. Box 200, Harold Hill, Romford, Essex, RM3 8UX, England. TEL 44-1708-381-444. FAX 44-1708-371-850) stat. (also avail. in microform from UMI)
●Also available online. Vendor(s): Knight-Ridder, Inc., Lexis-Nexis.
—BLDSC (3481.893850); UMI.

320 330.9 US ISSN 0269-5340
HC271
COUNTRY PROFILE. FRANCE; annual survey of political and economic background. 1952. a. £95($145) Economist Intelligence Unit, 111 W. 57th St., New York, NY 10019. TEL 212-554-0600; 800-938-4685. FAX 212-586-1182. TELEX 175567. (UK addr.: Economist Intelligence Unit Ltd., Subscriptions Dept., P.O. Box 200, Harold Hill, Romford, Essex RM3 8UX, England. TEL 44-1708-381-444. FAX 44-1708-371-850) stat. (also avail. in microform from UMI)
●Also available online. Vendor(s): Knight-Ridder, Inc., Lexis-Nexis.
—BLDSC (3481.893870); UMI.

320 330.9 US ISSN 0269-6371
HC975.A1
COUNTRY PROFILE. GABON, EQUATORIAL GUINEA; annual survey of political and economic background. 1952. a. £95($145) Economist Intelligence Unit, 111 W. 57th St., New York, NY 10019. TEL 212-554-0600; 800-938-4685. FAX 212-586-1182. TELEX 175567. (UK addr.: Economist Intelligence Unit Ltd., Subscriptions Dept., P.O. Box 200, Harold Hill, Romford, Essex RM3 8UX, England. TEL 44-1708-381-444. FAX 44-1708-371-850) stat. (also avail. in microform from UMI)
●Also available online. Vendor(s): Knight-Ridder, Inc., Lexis-Nexis.
—BLDSC (3481.893890); UMI.

320 330.9 US ISSN 0969-6245
COUNTRY PROFILE. GEORGIA, ARMENIA, AZERBAIJAN, CENTRAL ASIAN REPUBLICS; annual survey of political and economic background. 1952. a. £95($145) Economist Intelligence Unit, 111 W. 57th St., New York, NY 10019. TEL 212-554-0600; 800-938-4685. FAX 212-586-1182. TELEX 175567. (UK addr.: Economist Intelligence Unit Ltd., Subscriptions Dept., P.O. Box 200, Harold Hill, Romford, Essex RM3 8UX, England. TEL 44-1708-381-444. FAX 44-1708-371-850) stat. (also avail. in microform from UMI)
●Also available online. Vendor(s): Knight-Ridder, Inc., Lexis-Nexis.
Supersedes in part (1991-1992): Country Profile. Commonwealth of Independent States; Which was formerly (until 1990): Country Profile. U S S R.

320 330.9 US ISSN 0264-4495
COUNTRY PROFILE. GERMANY; annual survey of political and economic background. 1952. q. £95($145) Economist Intelligence Unit, 111 W. 57th St., New York, NY 10019. TEL 212-554-0600; 800-938-4685. FAX 212-586-1182. TELEX 175567. (UK addr.: Economist Intelligence Unit Ltd., Subscriptions Dept., P.O. Bix 200, Harold Hill, Romford, Essex RM3 8UX, England. TEL 44-1708-381-444. FAX 44-1708-371-850) stat. (also avail. in microform from UMI)
●Also available online. Vendor(s): Knight-Ridder, Inc., Lexis-Nexis.

320 330.9 US ISSN 0269-4549
HC1060.A1
COUNTRY PROFILE. GHANA; annual survey of political and economic background. 1952. a. £95($145) Economist Intelligence Unit, 111 W. 57th St., New York, NY 10019. TEL 212-554-0600; 800-938-4685. FAX 212-586-1182. TELEX 175567. (UK addr.: Economist Intelligence Unit Ltd., Subscriptions Dept., P.O. Box 200, Harold Hill, Romford, Essex RM3 8UX, England. TEL 44-1708-381-444. FAX 44-1708-371-850) stat. (also avail. in microform from UMI)
●Also available online. Vendor(s): Knight-Ridder, Inc., Lexis-Nexis.
—UMI.

320 330.9 US ISSN 0269-5367
HC291
COUNTRY PROFILE. GREECE; annual survey of political and economic background. 1952. a. £95($145) Economist Intelligence Unit, 111 W. 57th St., New York, NY 10019. TEL 212-554-0600; 800-938-4685. FAX 212-586-1182. TELEX 175567. (UK addr.: Economist Intelligence Unit Ltd., Subscriptions Dept., P.O. Box 200, Harold Hill, Romford, Essex RM3 8UX, England. TEL 44-1708-381-444. FAX 44-1708-371-850) stat. (also avail. in microform from UMI)
●Also available online. Vendor(s): Knight-Ridder, Inc., Lexis-Nexis.
—BLDSC (3481.893970); UMI.

320 330.9 US ISSN 1351-9050
HC141
COUNTRY PROFILE. GUATEMALA, EL SALVADOR; annual survey of political and economic background. 1952. a. £95($145) Economist Intelligence Unit, 111 W. 57th St., New York, NY 10019. TEL 212-554-0600; 800-938-4685. FAX 212-586-1182. TELEX 175567. (UK addr.: Economist Intelligence Unit Ltd., Subscriptions Dept., P.O. Box 200, Harold Hill, Romford, Essex RM3 8UX, England. TEL 44-1708-381-444. FAX 44-1708-371-850) illus.; stat. (also avail. in microform from UMI)
●Also available online. Vendor(s): Knight-Ridder, Inc., Lexis-Nexis.
Supersedes in part (in 1993): Country Profile. Guatemala, El Salvador, Honduras (ISSN 0269-4387)

320 330.9 US ISSN 1350-7710
HC1030.A1
COUNTRY PROFILE. GUINEA, SIERRA LEONA, LIBERIA; annual survey of political and economic background. 1952. a. £95($145) Economist Intelligence Unit, 111 W. 57th St., New York, NY 10019. TEL 212-554-0600; 800-938-4685. FAX 212-586-1182. TELEX 175567. (UK addr.: Economist Intelligence Unit Ltd., Subscriptions Dept., P.O. Box 200, Harold Hill, Romford, Essex RM3 8UX, England. TEL 44-1708-381-444. FAX 44-1708-371-850) illus.; stat. (also avail. in microform from UMI)
●Also available online. Vendor(s): Knight-Ridder, Inc., Lexis-Nexis.
—BLDSC (3481.894060).
Formed by the 1993 merger of: Country Profile. Sierra Leone, Liberia (ISSN 0269-5057); part of: Country Profile. Guinea, Mali, Mauritania (ISSN 0269-4417)

320 330.9 US
HC206
COUNTRY PROFILE. GUYANA, WINDWARD AND LEEWARD ISLANDS; annual survey of political and economic background. 1952. a. £95($145) Economist Intelligence Unit, 111 W. 57th St., New York, NY 10019. TEL 212-554-0600; 800-938-4685. FAX 212-586-1182. TELEX 175567. (UK addr.: Economist Intelligence Unit Ltd., Subscriptions Dept., P.O. Box 200, Harold Hill, Romford, Essex RM3 8UX, England. TEL 44-1708-381-444. FAX 44-1708-371-850) illus.; stat. (also avail. in microform from UMI)
●Also available online. Vendor(s): Knight-Ridder, Inc., Lexis-Nexis.
Supersedes in part (in 1993): Country Profile. Guyana, Barbados, Windward and Leeward Islands (ISSN 0269-8110)

320 330.9 US ISSN 0269-7319
COUNTRY PROFILE. HONG KONG, MACAU; annual survey of political and economic background. 1952. a. £95($145) Economist Intelligence Unit, 111 W. 57th St., New York, NY 10019. TEL 212-554-0600; 800-938-4685. FAX 212-586-1182. TELEX 175567. (UK addr.: Economist Intelligence Unit Ltd., Subscriptions Dept., P.O. Box 200, Harold Hill, Romford, Essex RM3 8UX, England. TEL 44-1708-381-444. FAX 44-1708-371-850) stat. (also avail. in microform from UMI)
●Also available online. Vendor(s): Knight-Ridder, Inc., Lexis-Nexis.
—BLDSC (3481.894090).

320 330.9 US
COUNTRY PROFILE. HUNGARY; annual survey of political and economic background. 1952. a. £95($145) Economist Intelligence Unit, 111 W. 57th St., New York, NY 10019. TEL 212-554-0600; 800-938-4685. FAX 212-586-1182. TELEX 175567. (UK addr.: Economist Intelligence Unit Ltd., Subscriptions Dept., P.O. Box 200, Harold Hill, Romford, Essex RM3 8UX, England. TEL 44-1708-381-444. FAX 44-1708-371-850) stat. (also avail. in microform from UMI)
●Also available online. Vendor(s): Knight-Ridder, Inc., Lexis-Nexis.

320 330.9 US ISSN 0269-5359
HC435.2.A1
COUNTRY PROFILE. INDIA, NEPAL; annual survey of political and economic background. 1952. a. £95($145) Economist Intelligence Unit, 111 W. 57th St., New York, NY 10019. TEL 212-554-0600; 800-938-4685. FAX 212-586-1182. TELEX 175567. (UK addr.: Economist Intelligence Unit Ltd., Subscriptions Dept., P.O. Box 200, Harold Hill, Romford, Essex RM3 8UK, England. TEL 44-1708-381-444. FAX 44-1708-371-850) stat. (also avail. in microform from UMI)
●Also available online. Vendor(s): Knight-Ridder, Inc., Lexis-Nexis.
—BLDSC (3481.894170); UMI.

320 330.9 US ISSN 0269-6622
HC441.A1
COUNTRY PROFILE. INDOCHINA: VIETNAM, LAOS, CAMBODIA; annual survey of political and economic background. 1952. a. £95($145) Economist Intelligence Unit, 111 W. 57th St., New York, NY 10019. TEL 212-554-0600; 800-938-4685. FAX 212-586-1182. TELEX 175567. (UK addr.: Economist Intelligence Unit Ltd., Subscriptions Dept., P.O. Box 200, Harold Hill, Romford, Essex RM3 8UX, England. TEL 44-1708-381-444. FAX 44-1708-371-850) stat. (also avail. in microform from UMI)
●Also available online. Vendor(s): Knight-Ridder, Inc., Lexis-Nexis.
—BLDSC (3481.894190); UMI.

320 330.9 US ISSN 0269-5375
HC446
COUNTRY PROFILE. INDONESIA; annual survey of political and economic background. 1952. a. £95($145) Economist Intelligence Unit, 111 W. 57th St., New York, NY 10019. TEL 212-554-0600; 800-938-4685. FAX 212-586-1182. TELEX 175567. (UK addr.: Economist Intelligence Unit Ltd., Subscriptions Dept., P.O. Box 200, Harold Hill, Romford, Essex RM3 8UX, England. TEL 44-1708-381-444. FAX 44-1708-371-850) stat. (also avail. in microform from UMI)
●Also available online. Vendor(s): Knight-Ridder, Inc., Lexis-Nexis.
—BLDSC (3481.894210); UMI.

320 330.9 US ISSN 0269-5960
HC471
COUNTRY PROFILE. IRAN; annual survey of political and economic background. 1952. a. £95($145) Economist Intelligence Unit, 111 W. 57th St., New York, NY 10003-1658. TEL 212-554-0600; 800-938-4685. FAX 212-586-1182. TELEX 175567. (UK addr.: Economist Intelligence Unit Ltd., Subscriptions Dept., P.O. Box 200, Harold Hill, Romford, Essex RM3 8UX, England. TEL 44-1708-381-444. FAX 44-1708-371-850) stat. (also avail. in microform from UMI)
●Also available online. Vendor(s): Knight-Ridder, Inc., Lexis-Nexis.
—BLDSC (3481.894250); UMI.

320 330.9 US ISSN 0269-4395
HC415.4.A1
COUNTRY PROFILE. IRAQ; annual survey of political and economic background. 1952. a. £95($145) Economist Intelligence Unit, 111 W. 57th St., New York, NY 10019. TEL 212-554-0600; 800-938-4685. FAX 212-586-1182. TELEX 175567. (UK addr.: Economist Intelligence Unit Ltd., Subscriptions Dept., P.O. Box 200, Harold Hill, Romford, Essex RM3 8UX, England. TEL 44-1708-381-444. FAX 44-1708-371-850) stat. (also avail. in microform from UMI)
●Also available online. Vendor(s): Knight-Ridder, Inc., Lexis-Nexis.
—BLDSC (3481.894290); UMI.

320 330.9 US ISSN 0269-5324
HC260.5.A1
COUNTRY PROFILE. IRELAND; annual survey of political and economic background. 1952. a. £95($145) Economist Intelligence Unit, 111 W. 57th St., New York, NY 10019. TEL 212-554-0600; 800-938-4685. FAX 212-586-1182. TELEX 175567. (UK addr.: Economist Intelligence Unit Ltd., Subscriptions Dept., P.O. Box 200, Harold Hill, Romford, Essex RM3 8UX, England. TEL 44-1708-381-444. FAX 44-1708-371-850) stat. (also avail. in microform from UMI)
●Also available online. Vendor(s): Knight-Ridder, Inc., Lexis-Nexis.
—BLDSC (3481.894330); UMI.

320 330.9 US ISSN 0269-5383
COUNTRY PROFILE. ISRAEL; annual survey of political and economic background. 1952. a. £95($145) Economist Intelligence Unit, 111 W. 57th St., New York, NY 10019. TEL 212-554-0600; 800-938-4685. FAX 212-586-1182. TELEX 175567. (UK addr.: Economist Intelligence Unit Ltd., Subscriptions Dept., P.O. Box 200, Harold Hill, Romford, Essex RM3 8UX, England. TEL 44-1708-381-444. FAX 44-1708-371-850) stat. (also avail. in microform from UMI)
●Also available online. Vendor(s): Knight-Ridder, Inc., Lexis-Nexis.

320 330.9 US ISSN 0269-5391
HC301
COUNTRY PROFILE. ITALY; annual survey of political and economic background. 1952. a. £95($145) Economist Intelligence Unit, 111 W. 57th St., New York, NY 10019. TEL 212-554-0600; 800-938-4685. FAX 212-586-1182. TELEX 175567. (UK addr.: Economist Intelligence Unit Ltd., Subscriptions Dept., P.O. Box 200, Harold Hill, Romford, Essex RM3 8UX, England. TEL 44-1708-381-444. FAX 44-1708-371-850) stat. (also avail. in microform from UMI)
●Also available online. Vendor(s): Knight-Ridder, Inc., Lexis-Nexis.
—BLDSC (3481.894410); UMI.

332 330.9 US ISSN 1351-4164
HC154.A1
COUNTRY PROFILE. JAMAICA, BARBADOS; annual survey of political and economic background. 1952. a. £95($145) Economist Intelligence Unit, 111 W. 57th St., New York, NY 10019. TEL 212-554-0600; 800-938-4685. FAX 212-586-1182. TELEX 175567. (UK addr.: Economist Intelligence Unit Ltd., Subscriptions Dept., P.O. Box 200, Harold Hill, Romford, Essex RM3 8UX, England. TEL 44-1708-381-444. FAX 44-1708-371-850) illus.; stat. (also avail. in microform from UMI)
●Also available online. Vendor(s): Knight-Ridder, Inc., Lexis-Nexis.
Formed by the 1993 merger of: Country Profile. Jamaica (ISSN 0269-4506); part of (1952-1992): Country Profile. Guyana, Barbados, Windward and Leeward Islands (ISSN 0269-8110)

320 330.9 US ISSN 0269-5405
HC461
COUNTRY PROFILE. JAPAN; annual survey of political and economic background. 1952. a. £95($145) Economist Intelligence Unit, 111 W. 57th St., New York, NY 10019. TEL 212-554-0600; 800-938-4685. FAX 212-586-1182. TELEX 175567. (UK addr.: Economist Intelligence Unit Ltd., Subscriptions Dept., P.O. Box 200, Harold Hill, Romford, Essex RM3 8UX, England. TEL 44-1708-381-444. FAX 44-1708-371-850) stat. (also avail. in microform from UMI)
●Also available online. Vendor(s): Knight-Ridder, Inc., Lexis-Nexis.
—UMI.

320 330.9 US ISSN 0269-8072
HC415.26.A1
COUNTRY PROFILE. JORDAN; annual survey of political and economic background. 1952. a. £95($145) Economist Intelligence Unit, 111 W. 57th St., New York, NY 10019. TEL 212-554-0600; 800-938-4685. FAX 212-586-1182. TELEX 175567. (UK addr.: Economist Intelligence Unit Ltd., Subscriptions Dept., P.O. Box 200, Harold Hill, Romford, Essex RM3 8UX, England. TEL 44-1708-381-444. FAX 44-1708-371-850) stat. (also avail. in microform from UMI)
●Also available online. Vendor(s): Knight-Ridder, Inc., Lexis-Nexis.
—BLDSC (3481.894570); UMI.

320 330.9 US ISSN 0269-4530
HC865.A1
COUNTRY PROFILE. KENYA; annual survey of political and economic background. 1952. q. £95($145) Economist Intelligence Unit, 111 W. 57th St., New York, NY 10019. TEL 212-554-0600; 800-938-4685. FAX 212-586-1192. TELEX 175567. (UK addr.: Economist Intelligence Unit Ltd., Subscriptions Dept., P.O. Box 200, Harold Hill, Romford, Essex RM3 8UX, England. TEL 44-1708-381-444. FAX 44-1708-371-850) stat. (also avail. in microform from UMI)
●Also available online. Vendor(s): Knight-Ridder, Inc., Lexis-Nexis.
—BLDSC (3481.894610); UMI.

320 330.9 US ISSN 0269-7327
HC415.39.A1
COUNTRY PROFILE. KUWAIT; annual survey of political and economic background. 1952. a. £95($145) Economist Intelligence Unit, 111 W. 57th St., New York, NY 10019. TEL 212-554-0600; 800-938-4685. FAX 212-586-1182. TELEX 175567. (UK addr.: Economist Intelligence Unit Ltd., Subscriptions Dept., P.O. Box 200, Harold Hill, Romford, Essex RM3 8UX, England. TEL 44-1708-381-444. FAX 44-1708-371-850) stat. (also avail. in microform from UMI)
●Also available online. Vendor(s): Knight-Ridder, Inc., Lexis-Nexis.
—BLDSC (3481.894690); UMI.

320 330.9 US
HC415.24.A1
COUNTRY PROFILE. LEBANON; annual survey of political and economic background. 1952. a. £95($145) Economist Intelligence Unit, 111 W. 57th St., New York, NY 10019. TEL 212-554-0600; 800-938-4685. FAX 212-586-1182. TELEX 175567. (UK addr.: Economist Intelligence Unit Ltd., Subscriptions Dept., P.O. Box 200, Harold Hill, Romford, Essex RM3 8UX, England. TEL 44-1708-381-444. FAX 44-1708-371-850) illus.; stat. (also avail. in microform from UMI)
●Also available online. Vendor(s): Knight-Ridder, Inc., Lexis-Nexis.
Supersedes in part (in 1993): Country Profile. Lebanon, Cyprus (ISSN 0269-7351)

320 330.9 US ISSN 0269-6347
HC825.A1
COUNTRY PROFILE. LIBYA; annual survey of political and economic background. 1952. a. £95($145) Economist Intelligence Unit, 111 W. 57th St., New York, NY 10019. TEL 212-554-0600; 800-938-4685. FAX 212-586-1182. TELEX 175567. (UK addr.: Economist Intelligence Unit Ltd., Subscriptions Dept., P.O. Box 200, Harold Hill, Romford, Essex RM3 8UX, England. TEL 44-1708-381-444. FAX 44-1708-371-850) stat. (also avail. in microform from UMI)
●Also available online. Vendor(s): Knight-Ridder, Inc., Lexis-Nexis.
—BLDSC (3481.894770); UMI.

320 330.9 US
COUNTRY PROFILE. MACEDONIA, SERBIA-MONTENEGRO; annual survey of political and economic background. 1952. a. £95($145) Economist Intelligence Unit, 111 W. 57th St., New York, NY 10019. TEL 212-554-0600; 800-938-4685. FAX 212-586-1182. TELEX 175567. (UK addr.: Economist Intelligence Unit Ltd., Subscriptions Dept., P.O. Box 200, Harold Hill, Romford, Essex RM3 8UX, England. TEL 44-1708-381-444. FAX 44-1708-371-850) illus.; stat. (also avail. in microform from UMI)
●Also available online. Vendor(s): Knight-Ridder, Inc., Lexis-Nexis.
Supersedes in part (in 1993): Country Profile. Yugoslavia (ISSN 0269-803X)

320 330.9 US ISSN 1351-8747
COUNTRY PROFILE. MADAGASCAR; annual survey of political and economic background. 1952. a. £95($145) Economist Intelligence Unit, 111 W. 57th St., New York, NY 10019. TEL 212-554-0600; 800-938-4685. FAX 212-586-1182. TELEX 175567. (UK addr.: Economist Intelligence Unit Ltd., Subscriptions Dept., P.O. Box 200, Harold Hill, Romford, Essex RM3 8UX, England. TEL 44-1708-381-444. FAX 44-1708-371-850) illus.; stat. (also avail. in microform from UMI)
●Also available online. Vendor(s): Knight-Ridder, Inc., Lexis-Nexis.
—BLDSC (3481.894800).
Supersedes in part (in 1993): Country Profile. Madagascar, Comoros (ISSN 0269-736X)

POLITICAL SCIENCE

320 330.9   US   ISSN 0269-4522
HC935.A1
COUNTRY PROFILE. MALAWI; annual survey of political and economic background. 1952. a. £95($145) Economist Intelligence Unit, 111 W. 57th St., New York, NY 10019. TEL 212-554-0600; 800-938-4685. FAX 212-586-1182. TELEX 175567. (UK addr.: Economist Intelligence Unit Ltd., Subscriptions Dept., P.O. Box 200, Harold Hill, Romford, Essex RM4 8UX, England. TEL 44-1708-381-444. FAX 44-1708-371-850) illus.; stat. (also avail. in microform from UMI)
●Also available online. Vendor(s): Knight-Ridder, Inc., Lexis-Nexis.
—BLDSC (3481.894830); UMI.

320 330.9   US   ISSN 0269-5588
HC445.5.A1
COUNTRY PROFILE. MALAYSIA, BRUNEI; annual survey of political and economic background. 1952. a. £95($145) Economist Intelligence Unit, 111 W. 57th St., New York, NY 10019. TEL 212-554-0600; 800-938-4685. FAX 212-586-1182. TELEX 175567. (UK addr.: Economist Intelligence Unit Ltd., Subscriptions Dept., P.O. Box 200, Harold Hill, Romford, Essex RM3 8UX, England. TEL 44-1708-381-444. FAX 44-1708-371-850) illus.; stat. (also avail. in microform from UMI)
●Also available online. Vendor(s): Knight-Ridder, Inc., Lexis-Nexis.
—BLDSC (3481.894850); UMI.

320 330.9   US   ISSN 0269-7378
HC895.A1
COUNTRY PROFILE. MAURITIUS, SEYCHELLES; annual survey of political and economic background. 1986. a. £95($145) Economist Intelligence Unit, 111 W. 57th St., New York, NY 10019. TEL 212-544-0600; 800-938-4685. FAX 212-586-1182. TELEX 175567. (UK addr.: Economist Intelligence Unit Ltd., Subscriptions Dept., P.O. Box 200, Harold Hill, Romford, Essex RM3 8UX, England. TEL 44-1708-381-444. FAX 44-1708-371-850) illus.; stat. (also avail. in microform from UMI)
●Also available online. Vendor(s): Knight-Ridder, Inc., Lexis-Nexis.
—BLDSC (3481.894870); UMI.
Formerly: Quarterly Economic Review of Mauritius, Seychelles.

320 330.9   US   ISSN 0269-5596
HC131
COUNTRY PROFILE. MEXICO; annual survey of political and economic background. 1952. a. £95($145) Economist Intelligence Unit, 111 W. 57th St., New York, NY 10019. TEL 212-554-0600; 800-928-4685. FAX 212-586-1182. TELEX 175567. (UK addr.: Economist Intelligence Unit Ltd., Subscriptions Dept., P.O. Box 200, Harold Hill, Romford, Essex RM3 8UX, England. TEL 44-1708-381-444. FAX 44-1708-371-850) stat. (also avail. in microform from UMI)
●Also available online. Vendor(s): Knight-Ridder, Inc., Lexis-Nexis.
—BLDSC (3481.894890); UMI.

320 330.9   US   ISSN 0269-6614
COUNTRY PROFILE. MOROCCO; annual survey of political and economic background. 1952. a. £95($145) Economist Intelligence Unit, 111 W. 57th St., New York, NY 10019. TEL 212-554-0600; 800-938-4685. FAX 212-586-1182. TELEX 175567. (UK addr.: Economist Intelligence Unit Ltd., Subscriptions Dept., P.O. Box 200, Harold Hill, Romford, Essex RM3 8UX, England. TEL 44-1708-381-444. FAX 44-1708-371-850) stat. (also avail. in microform from UMI)
●Also available online. Vendor(s): Knight-Ridder, Inc., Lexis-Nexis.
—BLDSC (3481.894910).

320 330.9   US   ISSN 0269-7017
HC890.A1
COUNTRY PROFILE. MOZAMBIQUE; annual survey of political and economic background. 1952. a. £95($145) Economist Intelligence Unit, 111 W. 57th St., New York, NY 10019. TEL 212-554-0600; 800-938-4685. FAX 212-586-1182. TELEX 175567. (UK addr.: Economist Intelligence Unit Ltd., Subscriptions Dept., P.O. Box 200, Harold Hill, Romford, Essex RM3 8UX, England. TEL 44-1708-381-444. FAX 44-1708-371-850) illus.; stat. (also avail. in microform from UMI)
●Also available online. Vendor(s): Knight-Ridder, Inc., Lexis-Nexis.
—BLDSC (3481.894930); UMI.

320 330.9   US
COUNTRY PROFILE. NAMIBIA, SWAZILAND; annual survey of political and economic background. 1952. a. £95($145) Economist Intelligence Unit, 111 W. 57th St., New York, NY 10019. TEL 212-554-0600; 800-938-4685. FAX 212-586-1182. TELEX 175567. (UK addr.: Economist Intelligence Unit Ltd., Subscriptions Dept., P.O. Box 200, Harold Hill, Romford, Essex RM3 8UX, England. TEL 44-1708-381-444. FAX 44-1708-371-850) illus.; stat. (also avail. in microform from UMI) **Document type:** trade publication.
●Also available online. Vendor(s): Knight-Ridder, Inc., Lexis-Nexis.
—UMI.
Formed by the 1993 merger of: Country Profile. Namibia (ISSN 0269-7386); part of (1952-1993): Country Profile. Botswana, Lesotho, Swaziland (ISSN 0269-7394).

320 330.9   US   ISSN 0264-4886
COUNTRY PROFILE. NETHERLANDS; annual survey of political and economic background. 1952. a. £95($145) Economist Intelligence Unit, 111 W. 57th St., New York, NY 10019. TEL 212-554-0600; 800-938-5685. FAX 212-586-1182. TELEX 175567. (UK addr.: Economist Intelligence Unit Ltd., Subscriptions Dept., P.O. Box 200, Harold Hill, Romford, Essex RM3 8UX, England. TEL 44-1708-381-444. FAX 44-1708-371-850) stat. (also avail. in microform from UMI)
●Also available online. Vendor(s): Knight-Ridder, Inc., Lexis-Nexis.

320 330.9   US   ISSN 0269-5618
COUNTRY PROFILE. NEW ZEALAND; annual survey of political and economic background. 1952. a. £95($145) Economist Intelligence Unit, 111 W. 57th St., New York, NY 10019. TEL 212-554-0600; 800-948-4685. FAX 212-586-1182. TELEX 175567. (UK addr.: Economist Intelligence Unit Ltd., Subscriptions Dept., P.O. Box 200, Harold Hill, Romford, Essex RM3 8UX, England. TEL 44-1708-381-444. FAX 44-1708-371-850) stat. (also avail. in microform from UMI)
●Also available online. Vendor(s): Knight-Ridder, Inc., Lexis-Nexis.

320 330.9   US   ISSN 1351-9077
HC146.A1
COUNTRY PROFILE. NICARAGUA, HONDURAS; annual survey of political and economic background. 1952. a. £95($145) Economist Intelligence Unit, 111 W. 57th St., New York, NY 10019. TEL 212-554-0600; 800-938-4685. FAX 212-586-1182. TELEX 175567. (UK addr.: Economist Intelligence Unit Ltd., Subscriptions Dept., P.O. Box 200, Harold Hill, Romford, Essex RM3 8UX, England. TEL 44-1708-381-444. FAX 44-1708-371-850) illus.; stat. (also avail. in microform from UMI)
●Also available online. Vendor(s): Knight-Ridder, Inc., Lexis-Nexis.
—BLDSC (3481.895100).
Formed by the 1993 merger of part of: Country Profile. Nicaragua, Costa Rica, Panama (ISSN 0269-4409); part of: Country Profile. Guatemala, El Salvador, Honduras (ISSN 0269-4387)

320 330.9   US   ISSN 0269-8064
HC1020.A1
COUNTRY PROFILE. NIGER, BURKINA FASO; annual survey of political and economic background. 1952. a. £95($145) Economist Intelligence Unit, 111 W. 57th St., New York, NY 10019. TEL 212-554-0600; 800-938-4685. FAX 212-586-1182. TELEX 175567. (UK addr.: Economist Intelligence Unit Ltd., Subscriptions Dept., P.O. Box 200, Harold Hill, Romford, Essex RM3 8UX, England. TEL 44-1708-381-444. FAX 44-1708-371-850) illus.; stat. (also avail. in microform from UMI)
●Also available online. Vendor(s): Knight-Ridder, Inc., Lexis-Nexis.

320 330.9   US   ISSN 0269-6339
HC1055.A1
COUNTRY PROFILE. NIGERIA; annual survey of political and economic background. 1952. a. £95($145) Economist Intelligence Unit, 111 W. 57th St., New York, NY 10019. TEL 212-554-0600; 800-938-4685. FAX 212-586-1182. TELEX 175567. (UK addr.: Economist Intelligence Unit Ltd., Subscriptions Dept., P.O. Box 200, Harold Hill, Romford, Essex RM3 8UX, England. TEL 44-1708-381-444. FAX 44-1708-371-850) stat. (also avail. in microform from UMI)
●Also available online. Vendor(s): Knight-Ridder, Inc., Lexis-Nexis.
—BLDSC (3481.895130); UMI.

320 330.9   US   ISSN 0269-5626
COUNTRY PROFILE. NORWAY; annual survey of political and economic background. 1952. a. £95($145) Economist Intelligence Unit, 111 W. 57th St., New York, NY 10019. TEL 212-554-0600; 800-938-4685. FAX 212-586-1182. TELEX 175567. (UK addr.: Economist Intelligence Unit Ltd., Subscriptions Dept., P.O. Box 200, Harold Hill, Romford, Essex RM3 8UX, England. TEL 44-1708-381-444. FAX 44-1708-371-850) stat. (also avail. in microform from UMI)
●Also available online. Vendor(s): Knight-Ridder, Inc., Lexis-Nexis.
—BLDSC (3481.895170).

320 330.9   US   ISSN 0269-7343
HC415.35.A1
COUNTRY PROFILE. OMAN, YEMEN; annual survey of political and economic background. 1952. a. £95($145) Economist Intelligence Unit, 111 W. 57th St., New York, NY 10019. TEL 212-554-0600; 800-938-4685. FAX 212-586-1182. TELEX 175567. (UK addr.: Economist Intelligence Unit Ltd., Subscriptions Dept., P.O. Box 200, Romford, Essex RM3 8UX, England. TEL 44-1708-381-444. FAX 44-1708-371-850) stat. (also avail. in microform from UMI)
●Also available online. Vendor(s): Knight-Ridder, Inc., Lexis-Nexis.
—BLDSC (3481.895188).

320 330.9   US   ISSN 0269-8080
HC681.A1
COUNTRY PROFILE. PACIFIC ISLANDS: FIJI, SOLOMON ISLANDS, WESTERN SAMOA, VANUATU, TONGA; annual survey of political and economic background. 1952. a. £95($145) Economist Intelligence Unit, 111 W. 57th St., New York, NY 10019. TEL 212-554-0600; 800-938-4685. FAX 212-586-1182. TELEX 175567. (UK addr.: Economist Intelligence Unit Ltd., Subscriptions Dept., P.O. Box 200, Harold Hill, Romford, Essex RM3 8UX, England. TEL 44-1708-381-444. FAX 44-1708-371-850) illus.; stat.
●Also available online. Vendor(s): Knight-Ridder, Inc., Lexis-Nexis.

320 330.9   US   ISSN 0269-5634
HC440.5.A1
COUNTRY PROFILE. PAKISTAN, AFGHANISTAN; annual survey of political and economic background. 1952. a. £95($145) Economist Intelligence Unit, 111 W. 57th St., New York, NY 10019. TEL 212-554-0600; 800-938-4685. FAX 212-586-1182. TELEX 175567. (UK addr.: Economist Intelligence Unit Ltd., Subscriptions Dept., P.O. Box 200, Harold Hill, Romford, Essex RM3 8UX, England. TEL 44-1708-381-444. FAX 44-1708-371-850) stat. (also avail. in microform from UMI)
●Also available online. Vendor(s): Knight-Ridder, Inc., Lexis-Nexis.
—BLDSC (3481.895250); UMI.

POLITICAL SCIENCE 5307

320 330.9 US ISSN 0269-8099
HC683.5.A1
COUNTRY PROFILE. PAPUA NEW GUINEA; annual survey of political and economic background. 1952. a. £33($145) Economist Intelligence Unit, 111 W. 57th St., New York, NY 10019. TEL 212-554-0600; 800-938-4685. FAX 212-586-1182. TELEX 175567. (UK addr.: Economist Intelligence Unit Ltd., Subscriptions Dept., P.O. Box 200, Harold Hill, Romford, Essex RM3 8UX, England. TEL 44-1708-381-444. FAX 44-1708-371-850) illus.; stat. (also avail. in microform from UMI)
●Also available online. Vendor(s): Knight-Ridder, Inc., Lexis-Nexis.
—BLDSC (3481.895270); UMI.

320 330.9 US ISSN 0269-5944
COUNTRY PROFILE. PERU; annual survey of political and economic background. 1952. a. £95($145) Economist Intelligence Unit, 111 W. 57th St., New York, NY 10019. TEL 212-554-0600; 800-938-4685. FAX 212-586-1182. TELEX 175567. (UK addr.: Economist Intelligence Unit Ltd., Subscriptions Dept., P.O. Box 200, Harold Hill, Romford, Essex RM3 8UX, England. TEL 44-1708-381-444. FAX 44-1708-371-850) illus.; stat. (also avail. in microform from UMI)
●Also available online. Vendor(s): Knight-Ridder, Inc., Lexis-Nexis.
—BLDSC (3481.895290).

320 330.9 US ISSN 0269-5979
HC451
COUNTRY PROFILE. PHILIPPINES; annual survey of political and economic background. 1952. a. £95($145) Economist Intelligence Unit, 111 W. 57th St., New York, NY 10019. TEL 212-554-0600; 800-938-4685. FAX 212-586-1182. TELEX 175567. (UK addr.: Economist Intelligence Unit Ltd., Subscriptions Dept., P.O. Box 200, Harold Hill, Romford, Essex RM3 8UX, England. TEL 44-1708-381-444. FAX 44-1708-371-850) stat. (also avail. in microform from UMI)
●Also available online. Vendor(s): Knight-Ridder, Inc., Lexis-Nexis.
—BLDSC (3481.895330); UMI.

320 330.1 US ISSN 0269-5219
HC340.3.A1
COUNTRY PROFILE. POLAND; annual survey of political and economic background. 1952. a. £95($145) Economist Intelligence Unit, 111 W. 57th St., New York, NY 10019. TEL 212-554-0600; 800-938-4685. FAX 212-586-1182. TELEX 175567. (UK addr.: Economist Intelligence Unit Ltd., Subscriptions Dept., P.O. Box 200, Harold Hill, Romford, Essex RM3 8UX, England. TEL 44-1708-381-444. FAX 44-1708-371-850) stat. (also avail. in microform from UMI)
●Also available online. Vendor(s): Knight-Ridder, Inc., Lexis-Nexis.
—BLDSC (3481.895370); UMI.

320 330.9 US ISSN 0269-5987
HC391
COUNTRY PROFILE. PORTUGAL; annual survey of political and economic background. 1952. a. £95($145) Economist Intelligence Unit, 111 W. 57th St., New York, NY 10019. TEL 212-554-0600; 800-938-4685. FAX 212-586-1182. TELEX 275567. (UK addr.: Economist Intelligence Unit Ltd., Subscriptions Dept., P.O. Box 200, Harold Hill, Romford, Essex RM3 8UX, England. TEL 44-1708-381-444. FAX 44-1708-371-850) stat. (also avail. in microform from UMI)
●Also available online. Vendor(s): Knight-Ridder, Inc., Lexis-Nexis.
—UMI.

320 330.9 US ISSN 0269-638X
COUNTRY PROFILE. ROMANIA; annual survey of political and economic background. 1952. a. £95($145) Economist Intelligence Unit, 111 W. 57th St., New York, NY 10003-1658. TEL 212-554-0600; 800-938-4685. FAX 212-596-1182. TELEX 175567. (UK addr.: Economist Intelligence Unit Ltd., Subscriptions Dept., P.O. Box 200, Harold Hill, Romford, Essex RM3 8UX, England. TEL 44-1708-381-444. FAX 44-1708-371-850) illus.; stat. (also avail. in microform from UMI)
●Also available online. Vendor(s): Knight-Ridder, Inc., Lexis-Nexis.

320 330.9 US ISSN 0969-627X
COUNTRY PROFILE. RUSSIA; annual survey of political and economic background. 1952. a. £95($145) Economist Intelligence Unit, 111 W. 57th St., New York, NY 10019. TEL 212-554-0600; 800-938-4685. FAX 212-586-1182. TELEX 175567. (UK addr.: Economist Intelligence Unit Ltd., Subscriptions Dept., P.O. Box 200, Harold Hill, Romford, Essex RM3 8UX, England. TEL 44-1708-381-444. FAX 44-1708-371-850) illus.; stat. (also avail. in microform from UMI)
●Also available online. Vendor(s): Knight-Ridder, Inc., Lexis-Nexis.
—BLDSC (3481.895470).
Supersedes in part (1991-1992): Country Profile. Commonwealth of Independent States; Which was formerly (until 1990): Country Profile. U S S R.

320 330.9 US ISSN 1352-0873
HC955.A1
COUNTRY PROFILE. RWANDA, BURUNDI; annual survey of political and economic background. 1952. a. £95($145) Economist Intelligence Unit, 111 W. 57th St., New York, NY 10019. TEL 212-554-0600; 800-938-4685. FAX 212-586-1182. TELEX 175567. (UK addr.: Economist Intelligence Unit Ltd., Subscriptions Dept., P.O. Box 200, Harold Hill, Romford, Essex, RM3 8UX, England. TEL 44-1708-381-444. FAX 44-1708-371-850) illus.; stat. (also avail. in microform from UMI)
●Also available online. Vendor(s): Knight-Ridder, Inc., Lexis-Nexis.
Supersedes in part (in 1993): Country Profile. Zaire, Rwanda, Burundi (ISSN 0269-6320)

320 330.9 US ISSN 0269-6355
HC415.33.A1C67
COUNTRY PROFILE. SAUDI ARABIA; annual survey of political and economic background. 1952. a. £95($145) Economist Intelligence Unit, 111 W. 57th St., New York, NY 10019. TEL 212-544-0600; 800-938-4685. FAX 212-586-1182. TELEX 175567. (UK addr.: Economist Intelliegnce Unit Ltd., Subscriptions Dept., P.O. Box 200, Harold Hill, Romford, Essex RM3 8UX, England. TEL 44-1708-381-444. FAX 44-1708-371-850) stat. (also avail. in microform from UMI)
●Also available online. Vendor(s): Knight-Ridder, Inc., Lexis-Nexis.
—BLDSC (3481.895490); UMI.

320 330.9 US ISSN 0269-6037
HC1045.A1
COUNTRY PROFILE. SENEGAL; annual survey of political and economic background. 1952. a. £95($145) Economist Intelligence Unit, 111 W. 57th St., New York, NY 10019. TEL 212-554-0600; 800-938-4685. FAX 212-586-1182. TELEX 175567. (UK addr.: Economist Intelligence Unit Ltd., Subscriptions Dept., P.O. Box 200, Harold Hill, Romford, Essex RM3 8UX, England. TEL 44-1708-381-444. FAX 44-1708-371-850) stat. (also avail. in microform from UMI)
●Also available online. Vendor(s): Knight-Ridder, Inc., Lexis-Nexis.
—BLDSC (3481.895510).

320 330.9 US ISSN 0269-7041
HC445.8.A1
COUNTRY PROFILE. SINGAPORE; annual survey of political and economic background. 1952. a. £95($145) Economist Intelligence Unit, 111 W. 57th St., New York, NY 10019. TEL 212-544-0600; 800-938-4685. FAX 212-586-1182. TELEX 175567. (UK addr.: Economist Intelligence Unit Ltd., Subscriptions Dept., P.O. Box 200, Harold Hill, Romford, Essex RM3 8UX, England. TEL 44-1708-381-444. FAX 44-1708-371-850) stat. (also avail. in microform from UMI)
●Also available online. Vendor(s): Knight-Ridder, Inc., Lexis-Nexis.
—BLDSC (3481.895570); UMI.

320 330.9 US ISSN 0269-8153
HC905.A1
COUNTRY PROFILE. SOUTH AFRICA; annual survey of political and economic background. 1952. a. £95($145) Economist Intelligence Unit, 111 W. 57th St., New York, NY 10019. TEL 212-554-0600; 800-938-4685. FAX 212-586-1182. TELEX 175567. (UK addr.: Economist Intelligence Unit Ltd., Subscriptions Dept., P.O. Box 200, Harold Hill, Romford, Essex RM3 8UX, England. TEL 44-1708-381-444. FAX 44-1708-371-850) stat. (also avail. in microform from UMI)
●Also available online. Vendor(s): Knight-Ridder, Inc., Lexis-Nexis.
—BLDSC (3481.895610); UMI.

320 330.9 US ISSN 1351-4431
COUNTRY PROFILE. SOUTH KOREA, NORTH KOREA; annual survey of political and economic background. 1952. a. £95($145) Economist Intelligence Unit, 111 W. 57th St., New York, NY 10019. TEL 212-554-0600; 800-938-4685. FAX 212-586-1182. TELEX 175567. (UK addr.: Economist Intelligence Unit Ltd., Subscriptions Dept., P.O. Box 200, Harold Hill, Romford, Essex RM3 8UX, England. TEL 44-1708-381-444. FAX 44-1708-371-850) illus.; stat. (also avail. in microform from UMI)
●Also available online. Vendor(s): Knight-Ridder, Inc., Lexis-Nexis.
Formed by the 1993 merger of: Country Profile. South Korea (ISSN 0269-7955); part of (1952-1993): Country Profile. China, North Korea (ISSN 0269-509X)

320 330.9 US ISSN 0269-5995
HC381
COUNTRY PROFILE. SPAIN; annual survey of political and economic background. 1952. a. £95($145) Economist Intelligence Unit, 111 W. 57th St., New York, NY 10019. TEL 212-554-0600; 800-938-4685. FAX 212-586-1182. TELEX 175567. (UK addr.: Economist Intelligence Unit Ltd., Subscriptions Dept., P.O. Box 200, Harold Hill, Romford, Essex RM3 8UX, England. TEL 44-1708-381-444. FAX 44-1708-371-850) stat. (also avail. in microform from UMI)
●Also available online. Vendor(s): Knight-Ridder, Inc., Lexis-Nexis.
—UMI.

320 330.9 US ISSN 0269-5073
HC424.A1
COUNTRY PROFILE. SRI LANKA; annual survey of political and economic background. 1952. a. £95($145) Economist Intelligence Unit, 111 W. 57th St., New York, NY 10019. TEL 212-554-0600; 800-938-4685. FAX 212-586-1182. TELEX 175567. (UK addr.: Economist Intelligence Unit Ltd., Subscriptions Dept., P.O. Box 154, Dartford, Kent DA1 1QB, England. TEL 44-1708-381-444. FAX 44-1708-371-850) stat. (also avail. in microform from UMI)
●Also available online. Vendor(s): Knight-Ridder, Inc., Lexis-Nexis.
—BLDSC (3481.895730); UMI.

320 330.9 US ISSN 0269-705X
HC835.A1
COUNTRY PROFILE. SUDAN; annual survey of political and economic background. 1952. a. £95($145) Economist Intelligence Unit, 111 W. 57th St., New York, NY 10019. TEL 212-554-0600; 800-938-4685. FAX 212-586-1182. TELEX 175567. (UK addr.: Economist Intelligence Unit Ltd., Subscriptions Dept., P.O. Box 200, Harold Hill, Romford, Essex RM3 8UX, England. TEL 44-1708-381-444. FAX 44-1708-371-850) stat. (also avail. in microform from UMI)
●Also available online. Vendor(s): Knight-Ridder, Inc., Lexis-Nexis.
—BLDSC (3481.895770); UMI.

POLITICAL SCIENCE

320 330.9　　　US　　ISSN 0269-6002
HC371
COUNTRY PROFILE. SWEDEN; annual survey of political and economic background. 1952. a. £95($145) Economist Intelligence Unit, 111 W. 57th St., New York, NY 10019. TEL 212-554-0600; 800-938-4685. FAX 212-586-1182. TELEX 175567. (UK addr.: Economist Intelligence Unit Ltd., Subscriptions Dept., P.O. Box 200, Harold Hill, Romford, Essex RM3 8UX, England. TEL 44-1708-381-444. FAX 44-1708-371-850) stat. (also avail. in microform from UMI)
●Also available online. Vendor(s): Knight-Ridder, Inc., Lexis-Nexis.
—UMI.

320 330.9　　　US　　ISSN 0269-6010
HC395
COUNTRY PROFILE. SWITZERLAND; annual survey of political and economic background. 1952. a. £95($145) Economist Intelligence Unit, 111 W. 57th St., New York, NY 10019. TEL 212-554-0600; 800-938-4685. FAX 212-9586-1182. TELEX 175567. (UK addr.: Economist Intelligence Unit Ltd., Subscriptions Dept., P.O. Box 200, Harold Hill, Romford, Essex RM3 8UX, England. TEL 44-1708-381-444. FAX 44-1708-371-850) stat. (also avail. in microform from UMI)
●Also available online. Vendor(s): Knight-Ridder, Inc., Lexis-Nexis.
—BLDSC (3481.895850); UMI.

320 330.9　　　US　　ISSN 0269-6045
HC415.23.A1
COUNTRY PROFILE. SYRIA; annual survey of political and economic background. 1952. a. £95($145) Economist Intelligence Unit, 111 W. 57th St., New York, NY 10019. TEL 212-554-0600; 800-938-4685. FAX 212-586-1182. TELEX 175567. (UK addr.: Economist Intelligence Unit Ltd., Subscriptions Dept., P.O. Box 200, Harold Hill, Romford, Essex RM3 8UX, England. TEL 44-1708-381-444. FAX 44-1708-371-850) stat. (also avail. in microform from UMI)
●Also available online. Vendor(s): Knight-Ridder, Inc., Lexis-Nexis.
—BLDSC (3481.895890); UMI.

320 330.9　　　US　　ISSN 0269-7025
HC430.5.A1
COUNTRY PROFILE. TAIWAN; annual survey of political and economic background. 1952. a. £95($145) Economist Intelligence Unit, 111 W. 57th St., New York, NY 10019. TEL 212-554-0600; 800-938-4685. FAX 212-586-1182. TELEX 175567. (UK addr.: Economist Intelligence Unit Ltd., Subscriptions Dept., P.O. Box 200, Harold Hill, Romford, Essex RM3 8UX, England. TEL 44-1708-381-444. FAX 44-1708-371-850) stat. (also avail. in microform from UMI)
●Also available online. Vendor(s): Knight-Ridder, Inc., Lexis-Nexis.
—UMI.

320 330.9　　　US　　ISSN 1351-9034
HC885.A1
COUNTRY PROFILE. TANZANIA, COMOROS; annual survey of political and economic background. 1952. a. £95($145) Economist Intelligence Unit, 111 W. 57th St., New York, NY 10019. TEL 212-554-0600; 800-938-4685. FAX 212-586-1182. TELEX 175567. (UK addr.: Economist Intelligence Unit Ltd., Subscriptions Dept., P.O. Box 200, Harold Hill, Romford, Essex RM3 8UX, England. TEL 44-1708-381-444. FAX 44-1708-371-850) illus.; stat. (also avail. in microform from UMI)
●Also available online. Vendor(s): Knight-Ridder, Inc., Lexis-Nexis.
Formed by the 1993 merger of: Country Profile. Tanzania (ISSN 0269-6630); part of: Country Profile. Madagascar, Comoros (ISSN 0269-736X)

320 330.9　　　US
HC445.A1
COUNTRY PROFILE. THAILAND, MYANMAR; annual survey of political and economic background. 1952. a. £95($145) Economist Intelligence Unit, 111 W. 57th St., New York, NY 10019. TEL 212-554-0600; 800-938-4685. FAX 212-586-1192. TELEX 175567. (UK addr.: Economist Intelligence Unit Ltd., Subscriptions Dept., P.O. Box 200, Harold Hill, Romford, Essex RM3 8UX, England. TEL 44-1708-381-444. FAX 44-1708-371-850) illus.; stat. (also avail. in microform from UMI)
●Also available online. Vendor(s): Knight-Ridder, Inc., Lexis-Nexis.
Formerly (until 1993): Country Profile. Thailand, Burma (ISSN 0269-5065)

320 330.9　　　US　　ISSN 1352-0938
HC1070.A1
COUNTRY PROFILE. THE GAMBIA, MAURITANIA; annual survey of political and economic background. 1952. a. £95($145) Economist Intelligence Unit, 111 W. 57th St., New York, NY 10019. TEL 212-554-0600; 800-938-4685. FAX 212-586-1182. TELEX 175567. (Economist Intelligence Unit Ltd., Subscriptions Dept., P.O. Box 200, Romford, Essex RM3 8UX, England. TEL 44-1708-381-444. FAX 44-1708-371-850) illus.; stat. (also avail. in microform from UMI)
●Also available online. Vendor(s): Knight-Ridder, Inc., Lexis-Nexis.
—UMI.
Formed by the 1993 merger of part of: Country Profile. The Gambia, Guinea-Bissau, Cape Verde; part of: Country Profile. Guinea, Mali, Mauritania (ISSN 0269-4417)

320 330.9　　　US　　ISSN 0269-8056
HC1015.A1
COUNTRY PROFILE. TOGO, BENIN; annual survey of political and economic background. 1952. a. £95($145) Economist Intelligence Unit, 111 W. 57th St., New York, NY 10019. TEL 212-554-0600; 800-938-4685. FAX 212-586-1182. TELEX 175567. (UK addr.: Economist Intelligence Unit Ltd., Subscriptions Dept., P.O. Box 200, Harold Hill, Romford, Essex RM3 8UX, England. TEL 44-1708-381-444. FAX 44-1708-371-850) illus.; stat. (also avail. in microform from UMI)
●Also available online. Vendor(s): Knight-Ridder, Inc., Lexis-Nexis.
—BLDSC (3481.896050); UMI.

320 330.9　　　US
COUNTRY PROFILE. TRINIDAD AND TOBAGO, SURINAME, NETHERLANDS ANTILLES, ARUBA; annual survey of political and economic background. 1952. a. £95($145) Economist Intelligence Unit, 111 W. 57th St., New York, NY 10019. TEL 212-554-0600; 800-938-4685. FAX 212-586-1182. TELEX 175567. (UK addr.: Economist Intelligence Unit Ltd., Subscriptions Dept., P.O. Box 200, Harold Hill, Romford, Essex RM3 8UX, England. TEL 44-1708-381-444. FAX 44-1708-371-850) illus.; stat. (also avail. in microform from UMI)
●Also available online. Vendor(s): Knight-Ridder, Inc., Lexis-Nexis.
Formed by the 1993 merger of: Country Profile. Trinidad and Tobago (ISSN 0269-8102); part of (1952-1993): Country Profile. Venezuela, Suriname, Netherlands Antilles, Aruba (ISSN 0269-607X)

320 330.9　　　US　　ISSN 0269-8129
HC820.A1
COUNTRY PROFILE. TUNISIA; annual survey of political and economic background. 1952. a. £95($145) Economist Intelligence Unit, 111 W. 57th St., New York, NY 10019. TEL 212-554-0600; 800-938-4685. FAX 212-586-1182. TELEX 175567. (UK addr.: Economist Intelligence Unit Ltd., Subscriptions Dept., P.O. Box 200, Harold Hill, Romford, Essex RM3 8UX, England. TEL 44-1708-381-444. FAX 44-1708-371-850) illus.; stat. (also avail. in microform from UMI)
●Also available online. Vendor(s): Knight-Ridder, Inc., Lexis-Nexis.
—BLDSC (3481.896130); UMI.

320 330.9　　　US
COUNTRY PROFILE. TURKEY; annual survey of political and economic background. 1952. a. £95($145) Economist Intelligence Unit, 111 W. 57th St., New York, NY 10019. TEL 212-554-0600; 800-938-4685. FAX 212-586-1182. TELEX 175567. (UK addr.: Economist Intelligence Unit Ltd., Subscriptions Dept., P.O. Box 200, Harold Hill, Romford, Essex RM3 8UX, England. TEL 44-1708-381-444. FAX 44-1708-371-850) illus.; stat. (also avail. in microform from UMI)
●Also available online. Vendor(s): Knight-Ridder, Inc., Lexis-Nexis.

320 330.9　　　US　　ISSN 0269-7076
COUNTRY PROFILE. UGANDA; annual survey of political and economic background. 1952. a. £95($145) Economist Intelligence Unit, 111 W. 57th St., New York, NY 10019. TEL 212-554-0600; 800-938-4685. FAX 212-586-1182. TELEX 175567. (UK addr.: Economist Intelligence Unit Ltd., Subscriptions Dept., P.O. Box 200, Harold Hill, Romford, Essex RM3 8UX, England. TEL 44-1708-381-444. FAX 44-1708-371-850) illus.; stat. (also avail. in microform from UMI)
●Also available online. Vendor(s): Knight-Ridder, Inc., Lexis-Nexis.
—BLDSC (3481.896210).

320 330.9　　　US　　ISSN 0969-6261
COUNTRY PROFILE. UKRAINE, BELARUS, MOLDOVA; annual survey of political and economic background. 1952. a. £95($145) Economist Intelligence Unit, 111 W. 57th St., New York, NY 10019. TEL 212-554-0600; 800-938-4685. FAX 212-586-1182. TELEX 175567. (UK addr.: Economist Intelligence Unit Ltd., Subscriptions Dept., P.O. Box 200, Harold Hill, Romford, Essex RM3 8UX, England. TEL 44-1708-381-444. FAX 44-1708-371-850) illus.; stat. (also avail. in microform from UMI)
●Also available online. Vendor(s): Knight-Ridder, Inc., Lexis-Nexis.
—BLDSC (3481.896240).
Supersedes in part (1991-1992): Country Profile. Commonwealth of Independent States; Which was formerly (until 1990): Country Profile. U S S R.

320 330.9　　　US　　ISSN 0269-6606
HC415.36.A1
COUNTRY PROFILE. UNITED ARAB EMIRATES; annual survey of political and economic background. 1952. a. £95($145) Economist Intelligence Unit, 111 W. 57th St., New York, NY 10019. TEL 212-554-0600; 800-938-4685. FAX 212-586-1182. TELEX 175567. (UK addr.: Economist Intelligence Unit Ltd., Subscriptions Dept., P.O. Box 200, Harold Hill, Romford, Essex RM3 8UX, England. TEL 44-1708-381-444. FAX 44-1708-371-850) illus.; stat. (also avail. in microform from UMI)
●Also available online. Vendor(s): Knight-Ridder, Inc., Lexis-Nexis.
—BLDSC (3481.896250); UMI.

320 330.9　　　US　　ISSN 0269-798X
HC251
COUNTRY PROFILE. UNITED KINGDOM; annual survey of political and economic background. 1952. a. £95($145) Economist Intelligence Unit, 111 W. 57th St., New York, NY 10019. TEL 212-554-0600; 800-938-4685. FAX 212-586-1182. TELEX 175567. (UK addr.: Economist Intelligence Unit Ltd., Subscriptions Dept., P.O. Box 200, Harold Hill, Romford, Essex RM3 8UX, England. TEL 44-1708-381-444. FAX 44-1708-371-850) illus.; stat. (also avail. in microform from UMI)
●Also available online. Vendor(s): Knight-Ridder, Inc., Lexis-Nexis.
—BLDSC (3481.896290); UMI.

320 330.9　　　US　　ISSN 0269-8005
HC101
COUNTRY PROFILE. UNITED STATES OF AMERICA; annual survey of political and economic background. 1952. a. £95($145) Economist Intelligence Unit, 111 W. 57th St., New York, NY 10019. TEL 212-554-0600; 800-938-4685. FAX 212-586-1182. TELEX 175567. (UK addr.: Economist Intelligence Unit Ltd., Subscriptions Dept., P.O. Box 200, Harold Hill, Romford, Essex, RM3 8UX, England. TEL 44-1708-381-444. FAX 44-1708-371-850) illus.; stat.
●Also available online. Vendor(s): Knight-Ridder, Inc., Lexis-Nexis.
—BLDSC (3481.896370); UMI.

POLITICAL SCIENCE

320 330.9   US   ISSN 0269-7998
COUNTRY PROFILE. URUGUAY, PARAGUAY; annual survey of political and economic background. 1952. a. £95($145) Economist Intelligence Unit, 111 W. 57th St., New York, NY 10019. TEL 212-554-0600; 800-938-4685. FAX 212-586-1182. TELEX 175567. (UK addr.: Economist Intelligence Unit Ltd., Subscriptions Dept., P.O. Box 200, Harold Hill, Romford, Essex, RM3 8UX, England. TEL 44-1708-381-444. FAX 44-1708-371-850) illus.; stat. (also avail. in microform from UMI)
●Also available online. Vendor(s): Knight-Ridder, Inc., Lexis-Nexis.
—BLDSC (3481.896330).

320 330.9   US
COUNTRY PROFILE. VENEZUELA; annual survey of political and economic background. 1952. a. £95($145) Economist Intelligence Unit, 111 W. 57th St., New York, NY 10003-1658. TEL 212-554-0600; 800-938-4685. FAX 212-586-1182. TELEX 175567. (UK addr.: Economist Intelligence Unit Ltd., Subscriptions Dept., P.O. Box 200, Harold Hill, Romford, Essex, RM3 8UX, England. TEL 44-1708-381-444. FAX 44-1708-371-850) illus.; stat. (also avail. in microform from UMI)
●Also available online. Vendor(s): Knight-Ridder, Inc., Lexis-Nexis.
Supersedes in part (in 1993): Country Profile. Venezuela, Suriname, Netherlands Antilles, Aruba (ISSN 0269-607X)

320 330.9   US   ISSN 1352-0881
COUNTRY PROFILE. ZAIRE; annual survey of political and economic background. 1952. a. £95($145) Economist Intelligence Unit, 111 W. 57th St., New York, NY 10019. TEL 212-554-0600; 800-938-4685. FAX 212-586-1182. TELEX 175567. (UK addr.: Economist Intelligence Unit Ltd., Subscriptions Dept., P.O. Box 200, Harold Hill, Romford, Essex RM3 8UX, England. TEL 44-1708-381-444. FAX 44-1708-371-850) illus.; stat. (also avail. in microform from UMI)
●Also available online. Vendor(s): Knight-Ridder, Inc., Lexis-Nexis.
Supersedes in part (in 1993): Country Profile. Zaire, Rwanda, Burundi (ISSN 0269-6320)

320 330.9   US   ISSN 0269-7300
COUNTRY PROFILE. ZAMBIA; annual survey of political and economic background. 1952. a. £95($145) Economist Intelligence Unit, 111 W. 57th St., New York, NY 10019. TEL 212-554-0600; 800-938-4685. FAX 212-586-1182. TELEX 175567. (UK addr.: Economist Intelligence Unit Ltd., Subscriptions Dept., P.O. Box 200, Harold Hill, Romford, Essex RM3 8UX, England. TEL 44-1708-381-444. FAX 44-1708-371-850) illus.; stat. (also avail. in microform from UMI)
●Also available online. Vendor(s): Knight-Ridder, Inc., Lexis-Nexis.
—BLDSC (3481.896610).

320 301.9   US   ISSN 0269-4360
HC910.A1
COUNTRY PROFILE. ZIMBABWE; annual survey of political and economic background. 1952. a. £95($145) Economist Intelligence Unit, 111 W. 57th St., New York, NY 10019. TEL 212-554-0600; 800-938-4685. FAX 212-586-1182. TELEX 175567. (UK addr.: Economist Intelligence Unit Ltd., Subscriptions Dept., P.O. Box 200, Harold Hill, Romford, Essex RM3 8UX, England. TEL 44-1708-381-444. FAX 44-1708-371-850) illus.; stat. (also avail. in microform from UMI)
●Also available online. Vendor(s): Knight-Ridder, Inc., Lexis-Nexis.
—BLDSC (3481.896650); UMI.

332 330.9   US   ISSN 0161-5475
COUNTRY PROFILES; annual survey of political and economic background. (Series consists of 115 vols. covering developments in 180 countries) 1952. a. £95($145) per vol. Economist Intelligence Unit, 111 W. 57th St., New York, NY 10019. TEL 212-554-0600; 800-938-4685. FAX 212-586-1182. TELEX 175567. (UK addr.: Economist Intelligence Unit Ltd., Subscriptions Dept., P.O. Bxo 200, Harold Hill, Romford, Essex RM3 8UX, England. TEL 44-1708-381-444. FAX 44-1708-371-850) illus.; stat.
●Also available online. Vendor(s): Knight-Ridder, Inc., Lexis-Nexis.

COUNTRY REPORT. ALGERIA; analysis of economic and political trends every quarter. see BUSINESS AND ECONOMICS — Economic Situation And Conditions

COUNTRY REPORT. ANGOLA; analysis of economic and political trends every quarter. see BUSINESS AND ECONOMICS — Economic Situation And Conditions

COUNTRY REPORT. ARGENTINA; analysis of economic and political trends every quarter. see BUSINESS AND ECONOMICS — Economic Situation And Conditions

COUNTRY REPORT. AUSTRALIA; analysis of economic and political trends every quarter. see BUSINESS AND ECONOMICS — Economic Situation And Conditions

COUNTRY REPORT. AUSTRIA; analysis of economic and political trends every quarter. see BUSINESS AND ECONOMICS — Economic Situation And Conditions

COUNTRY REPORT. BAHRAIN, QATAR; analysis of economic and political trends every quarter. see BUSINESS AND ECONOMICS — Economic Situation And Conditions

COUNTRY REPORT. BALTIC REPUBLICS: LITHUANIA, LATVIA, ESTONIA; analysis of economic and political trends every quarter. see BUSINESS AND ECONOMICS — Economic Situation And Conditions

COUNTRY REPORT BANGLADESH; analysis of economic and political trends every quarter. see BUSINESS AND ECONOMICS — Economic Situation And Conditions

COUNTRY REPORT. BELARUS, MOLDOVA; analysis of economic and political trends every quarter. see BUSINESS AND ECONOMICS — Economic Situation And Conditions

COUNTRY REPORT. BELGIUM, LUXEMBOURG; analysis of economic and political trends every quarter. see BUSINESS AND ECONOMICS — Economic Situation And Conditions

COUNTRY REPORT. BOLIVIA; analysis of economic and political trends every quarter. see BUSINESS AND ECONOMICS — Economic Situation And Conditions

COUNTRY REPORT. BOSNIA-HERCEGOVINA, CROATIA, MACEDONIA, SERBIA-MONTENEGRO, SLOVENIA; analysis of economic and political trends every quarter. see BUSINESS AND ECONOMICS — Economic Situation And Conditions

COUNTRY REPORT. BOTSWANA, LESOTHO; analysis of economic and political trends every quarter. see BUSINESS AND ECONOMICS — Economic Situation And Conditions

COUNTRY REPORT. BRAZIL; analysis of economic and political trends every quarter. see BUSINESS AND ECONOMICS — Economic Situation And Conditions

COUNTRY REPORT. BULGARIA, ALBANIA; analysis of economic and political trends every quarter. see BUSINESS AND ECONOMICS — Economic Situation And Conditions

COUNTRY REPORT. CAMEROON, C.A.R., CHAD; analysis of economic and political trends every quarter. see BUSINESS AND ECONOMICS — Economic Situation And Conditions

COUNTRY REPORT. CANADA; analysis of economic and political trends every quarter. see BUSINESS AND ECONOMICS — Economic Situation And Conditions

COUNTRY REPORT. CENTRAL ASIAN REPUBLICS, KAZAKHSTAN; analysis of economic and political trends every quarter. see BUSINESS AND ECONOMICS — Economic Situation And Conditions

COUNTRY REPORT. CHILE; analysis of economic and political trends every quarter. see BUSINESS AND ECONOMICS — Economic Situation And Conditions

COUNTRY REPORT. CHINA, MONGOLIA; analysis of economic and political trends every quarter. see BUSINESS AND ECONOMICS — Economic Situation And Conditions

COUNTRY REPORT. COLOMBIA; analysis of economic and political trends every quarter. see BUSINESS AND ECONOMICS — Economic Situation And Conditions

COUNTRY REPORT. CONGO, SAO TOME AND PRINCIPE, GUINEA-BISSAU, CAPE VERDE; analysis of economic and political trends every quarter. see BUSINESS AND ECONOMICS — Economic Situation And Conditions

COUNTRY REPORT. COSTA RICA, PANAMA; analysis of economic and political trends every quarter. see BUSINESS AND ECONOMICS — Economic Situation And Conditions

COUNTRY REPORT. COTE D'IVOIRE, MALI; analysis of economic and political trends every quarter. see BUSINESS AND ECONOMICS — Economic Situation And Conditions

COUNTRY REPORT. CUBA, DOMINICAN REPUBLIC, HAITI, PUERTO RICO; analysis of economic and political trends every quarter. see BUSINESS AND ECONOMICS — Economic Situation And Conditions

COUNTRY REPORT. CYPRUS, MALTA; analysis of economic and political trends every quarter. see BUSINESS AND ECONOMICS — Economic Situation And Conditions

COUNTRY REPORT. CZECH REPUBLIC, SLOVAKIA; analysis of economic and political trends every quarter. see BUSINESS AND ECONOMICS — Economic Situation And Conditions

COUNTRY REPORT. DENMARK, ICELAND; analysis of economic and political trends every quarter. see BUSINESS AND ECONOMICS — Economic Situation And Conditions

COUNTRY REPORT. ECUADOR; analysis of economic and political trends every quarter. see BUSINESS AND ECONOMICS — Economic Situation And Conditions

COUNTRY REPORT. EGYPT; analysis of economic and political trends every quarter. see BUSINESS AND ECONOMICS — Economic Situation And Conditions

COUNTRY REPORT. ETHIOPIA, ERITREA, SOMALIA, DJIBOUTI; analysis of economic and political trends every quarter. see BUSINESS AND ECONOMICS — Economic Situation And Conditions

COUNTRY REPORT. FINLAND; analysis of economic and political trends every quarter. see BUSINESS AND ECONOMICS — Economic Situation And Conditions

COUNTRY REPORT. FRANCE; analysis of economic and political trends every quarter. see BUSINESS AND ECONOMICS — Economic Situation And Conditions

COUNTRY REPORT. GABON, EQUATORIAL GUINEA; analysis of economic and political trends every quarter. see BUSINESS AND ECONOMICS — Economic Situation And Conditions

COUNTRY REPORT. GERMANY; analysis of economic and political trends every quarter. see BUSINESS AND ECONOMICS — Economic Situation And Conditions

COUNTRY REPORT. GHANA; analysis of economic and political trends every quarter. see BUSINESS AND ECONOMICS — Economic Situation And Conditions

COUNTRY REPORT. GREECE; analysis of economic and political trends every quarter. see BUSINESS AND ECONOMICS — Economic Situation And Conditions

COUNTRY REPORT. GUATEMALA, EL SALVADOR; analysis of economic and political trends every quarter. see BUSINESS AND ECONOMICS — Economic Situation And Conditions

COUNTRY REPORT. GUINEA, SIERRA LEONE, LIBERIA; analysis of economic and political trends every quarter. see BUSINESS AND ECONOMICS — Economic Situation And Conditions

COUNTRY REPORT. HONG KONG, MACAU; analysis of economic and political trends every quarter. see BUSINESS AND ECONOMICS — Economic Situation And Conditions

COUNTRY REPORT. HUNGARY; analysis of economic and political trends every quarter. see BUSINESS AND ECONOMICS — Economic Situation And Conditions

POLITICAL SCIENCE

COUNTRY REPORT. INDIA, NEPAL. see *BUSINESS AND ECONOMICS — Economic Situation And Conditions*

COUNTRY REPORT. INDOCHINA: MYANMAR, LAOS, CAMBODIA; analysis of economic and political trends every quarter. see *BUSINESS AND ECONOMICS — Economic Situation And Conditions*

COUNTRY REPORT. INDONESIA; analysis of economic and political trends every quarter. see *BUSINESS AND ECONOMICS — Economic Situation And Conditions*

COUNTRY REPORT. IRAN; analysis of economic and political trends every quarter. see *BUSINESS AND ECONOMICS — Economic Situation And Conditions*

COUNTRY REPORT. IRAQ; analysis of economic and political trends every quarter. see *BUSINESS AND ECONOMICS — Economic Situation And Conditions*

COUNTRY REPORT. IRELAND; analysis of economic and political trends every quarter. see *BUSINESS AND ECONOMICS — Economic Situation And Conditions*

COUNTRY REPORT. ISRAEL, THE OCCUPIED TERRITORIES; analysis of economic and political trends every quarter. see *BUSINESS AND ECONOMICS — Economic Situation And Conditions*

COUNTRY REPORT. ITALY; analysis of economic and political trends every quarter. see *BUSINESS AND ECONOMICS — Economic Situation And Conditions*

COUNTRY REPORT. JAMAICA, BELIZE, BAHAMAS, BERMUDA, BARBADOS; analysis of economic and political trends every quarter. see *BUSINESS AND ECONOMICS — Economic Situation And Conditions*

COUNTRY REPORT. JAPAN; analysis of economic and political trends every quarter. see *BUSINESS AND ECONOMICS — Economic Situation And Conditions*

COUNTRY REPORT. JORDAN; analysis of economic and political trends every quarter. see *BUSINESS AND ECONOMICS — Economic Situation And Conditions*

COUNTRY REPORT. KENYA; analysis of economic and political trends every quarter. see *BUSINESS AND ECONOMICS — Economic Situation And Conditions*

COUNTRY REPORT. KUWAIT; analysis of economic and political trends every quarter. see *BUSINESS AND ECONOMICS — Economic Situation And Conditions*

COUNTRY REPORT. LEBANON; analysis of economic and political trends every quarter. see *BUSINESS AND ECONOMICS — Economic Situation And Conditions*

COUNTRY REPORT. LIBYA; analysis of economic and political trends every quarter. see *BUSINESS AND ECONOMICS — Economic Situation And Conditions*

COUNTRY REPORT. MALAYSIA, BRUNEI; analysis of economic and political trends every quarter. see *BUSINESS AND ECONOMICS — Economic Situation And Conditions*

COUNTRY REPORT. MAURITIUS, MADAGASCAR, SEYCHELLES; analysis of economic and political trends every quarter. see *BUSINESS AND ECONOMICS — Economic Situation And Conditions*

COUNTRY REPORT. MEXICO; analysis of economic and political trends every quarter. see *BUSINESS AND ECONOMICS — Economic Situation And Conditions*

COUNTRY REPORT. MOROCCO; analysis of economic and political trends every quarter. see *BUSINESS AND ECONOMICS — Economic Situation And Conditions*

COUNTRY REPORT. MOZAMBIQUE, MALAWI; analysis of economic and political trends every quarter. see *BUSINESS AND ECONOMICS — Economic Situation And Conditions*

COUNTRY REPORT. NAMIBIA, SWAZILAND; analysis of economic and political trends every quarter. see *BUSINESS AND ECONOMICS — Economic Situation And Conditions*

COUNTRY REPORT. NETHERLANDS; analysis of economic and political trends every quarter. see *BUSINESS AND ECONOMICS — Economic Situation And Conditions*

COUNTRY REPORT. NEW ZEALAND; analysis of economic and political trends every quarter. see *BUSINESS AND ECONOMICS — Economic Situation And Conditions*

COUNTRY REPORT. NICARAGUA, HONDURAS; analysis of economic and political trends every quarter. see *BUSINESS AND ECONOMICS — Economic Situation And Conditions*

COUNTRY REPORT. NIGERIA; analysis of economic and political trends every quarter. see *BUSINESS AND ECONOMICS — Economic Situation And Conditions*

COUNTRY REPORT. NORWAY; analysis of economic and political trends every quarter. see *BUSINESS AND ECONOMICS — Economic Situation And Conditions*

COUNTRY REPORT. OMAN, YEMEN; analysis of economic and political trends every quarter. see *BUSINESS AND ECONOMICS — Economic Situation And Conditions*

COUNTRY REPORT. PACIFIC ISLANDS: PAPUA NEW GUINEA, FIJI, SOLOMON ISLANDS, WESTERN SAMOA, VANUATU, TONGA; analysis of economic and political trends every quarter. see *BUSINESS AND ECONOMICS — Economic Situation And Conditions*

COUNTRY REPORT. PAKISTAN, AFGHANISTAN; analysis of economic and political trends every quarter. see *BUSINESS AND ECONOMICS — Economic Situation And Conditions*

COUNTRY REPORT. PERU; analysis of economic and political trends every quarter. see *BUSINESS AND ECONOMICS — Economic Situation And Conditions*

COUNTRY REPORT. PHILIPPINES; analysis of economic and political trends every quarter. see *BUSINESS AND ECONOMICS — Economic Situation And Conditions*

COUNTRY REPORT. POLAND; analysis of economic and political trends every quarter. see *BUSINESS AND ECONOMICS — Economic Situation And Conditions*

COUNTRY REPORT. PORTUGAL; analysis of economic and political trends every quarter. see *BUSINESS AND ECONOMICS — Economic Situation And Conditions*

COUNTRY REPORT. ROMANIA; analysis of economic and political trends every quarter. see *BUSINESS AND ECONOMICS — Economic Situation And Conditions*

COUNTRY REPORT. RUSSIA; analysis of economic and political trends every quarter. see *BUSINESS AND ECONOMICS — Economic Situation And Conditions*

COUNTRY REPORT. SAUDI ARABIA; analysis of economic and political trends every quarter. see *BUSINESS AND ECONOMICS — Economic Situation And Conditions*

COUNTRY REPORT. SENEGAL, THE GAMBIA, MAURITANIA; analysis of economic and political trends every quarter. see *BUSINESS AND ECONOMICS — Economic Situation And Conditions*

COUNTRY REPORT. SINGAPORE; analysis of economic and political trends every quarter. see *BUSINESS AND ECONOMICS — Economic Situation And Conditions*

COUNTRY REPORT. SOUTH AFRICA; analysis of economic and political trends every quarter. see *BUSINESS AND ECONOMICS — Economic Situation And Conditions*

COUNTRY REPORT. SOUTH KOREA, NORTH KOREA; analysis of economic and political trends every quarter. see *BUSINESS AND ECONOMICS — Economic Situation And Conditions*

COUNTRY REPORT. SPAIN; analysis of economic and political trends every quarter. see *BUSINESS AND ECONOMICS — Economic Situation And Conditions*

COUNTRY REPORT. SRI LANKA; analysis of economic and political trends every quarter. see *BUSINESS AND ECONOMICS — Economic Situation And Conditions*

COUNTRY REPORT. SUDAN; analysis of economic and political trends every quarter. see *BUSINESS AND ECONOMICS — Economic Situation And Conditions*

COUNTRY REPORT. SWEDEN; analysis of economic and political trends every quarter. see *BUSINESS AND ECONOMICS — Economic Situation And Conditions*

COUNTRY REPORT. SWITZERLAND; analysis of economic and political trends every quarter. see *BUSINESS AND ECONOMICS — Economic Situation And Conditions*

COUNTRY REPORT. SYRIA; analysis of economic and political trends every quarter. see *BUSINESS AND ECONOMICS — Economic Situation And Conditions*

COUNTRY REPORT. TAIWAN; analysis of economic and political trends every quarter. see *BUSINESS AND ECONOMICS — Economic Situation And Conditions*

COUNTRY REPORT. TANZANIA, COMOROS; analysis of economic and political trends every quarter. see *BUSINESS AND ECONOMICS — Economic Situation And Conditions*

COUNTRY REPORT. THAILAND; analysis of economic and political trends every quarter. see *BUSINESS AND ECONOMICS — Economic Situation And Conditions*

COUNTRY REPORT. TOGO, NIGER, BENIN, BURKINA FASO; analysis of economic and political trends every quarter. see *BUSINESS AND ECONOMICS — Economic Situation And Conditions*

COUNTRY REPORT. TRINIDAD & TOBAGO, GUYANA, WINDWARD & LEEWARD ISLANDS, SURINAME, NETHERLANDS ANTILLES, ARUBA; analysis of economic and political trends every quarter. see *BUSINESS AND ECONOMICS — Economic Situation And Conditions*

COUNTRY REPORT. TUNISIA; analysis of economic and political trends every quarter. see *BUSINESS AND ECONOMICS — Economic Situation And Conditions*

COUNTRY REPORT. TURKEY; analysis of economic and political trends every quarter. see *BUSINESS AND ECONOMICS — Economic Situation And Conditions*

COUNTRY REPORT. UGANDA, RWANDA, BURUNDI; analysis of economic and political trends every quarter. see *BUSINESS AND ECONOMICS — Economic Situation And Conditions*

COUNTRY REPORT. UKRAINE; analysis of economic and political trends every quarter. see *BUSINESS AND ECONOMICS — Economic Situation And Conditions*

COUNTRY REPORT. UNITED ARAB EMIRATES; analysis of economic and political trends every quarter. see *BUSINESS AND ECONOMICS — Economic Situation And Conditions*

COUNTRY REPORT. UNITED KINGDOM; analysis of economic and political trends every quarter. see *BUSINESS AND ECONOMICS — Economic Situation And Conditions*

COUNTRY REPORT. UNITED STATES OF AMERICA; analysis of economic and political trends every quarter. see *BUSINESS AND ECONOMICS — Economic Situation And Conditions*

COUNTRY REPORT. URUGUAY, PARAGUAY; analysis of economic and political trends every quarter. see *BUSINESS AND ECONOMICS — Economic Situation And Conditions*

COUNTRY REPORT. VENEZUELA; analysis of economic and political trends every quarter. see *BUSINESS AND ECONOMICS — Economic Situation And Conditions*

COUNTRY REPORT. VIETNAM; analysis of economic and political trends every quarter. see *BUSINESS AND ECONOMICS — Economic Situation And Conditions*

COUNTRY REPORT. ZAMBIA, ZAIRE; analysis of economic and political trends every quarter. see *BUSINESS AND ECONOMICS — Economic Situation And Conditions*

COUNTRY REPORT. ZIMBABWE; analysis of economic and political trends every quarter. see *BUSINESS AND ECONOMICS — Economic Situation And Conditions*

COUNTRY REPORTS; analysis of economic and political trends every quarter. see *BUSINESS AND ECONOMICS — Economic Situation And Conditions*

POLITICAL SCIENCE

COURRIER DES PAYS DE L'EST. see *BUSINESS AND ECONOMICS*

959.7   VN   ISSN 0045-8902
COURRIER DU VIETNAM. (Editions in English, French, Russian) 1964. m. $10.70. 46 Tran Hung Dao, Hanoi, Socialist Republic of Vietnam. Ed.Bd. adv.; bk.rev.; charts; illus. (tabloid format)

341.1   FR   ISSN 0011-0574
COURRIER EUROPEEN.* 1952. m. 4 F. Organisation Francaise du Mouvement Europeen, 24 rue Feydeau, 75 Paris (2e), France. Dir. Raymond Andrieu.

320   BE   ISSN 0776-944X
COURRIER HEBDOMADAIRE. 1959. w. (40/yr.). 9500 BEF (foreign 11000 BEF) (effective 1995). Centre de Recherche et d'Information Socio-Politiques (CRISP), Rue du Congres 35, 1000 Brussels, Belgium. TEL 31-2-2183226. **Indexed:** ELLIS, Int.Lab.Doc.

320   US   ISSN 1067-7232
JK468.I6
COVERTACTION QUARTERLY. Variant title: Covert Action Quarterly. 1978. q. $22 to individuals; institutions $27. CovertAction Publications, Inc., 1500 Massachusetts Ave., N.W., Ste. 732, Washington, DC 20005. TEL 202-331-9763. FAX 202-331-9751. E-mail: caq@igc.apc.org. Eds. Terry Allen, Phillip Smith. bk.rev.; cum.index: 1978-1982; 1982-1986. circ. 11,000. (also avail. in microform from UMI; reprint service avail. from UMI; back issues avail.) **Indexed:** Alt.Press Ind., HR Rep.
—BLDSC (3486.109500); UMI.
Formerly (until 1993): Covert Action Information Bulletin (ISSN 0275-309X)
Description: In-depth international coverage, investigating and documenting wherever the hands of Western intelligence services can be found and exposed.

320   CU
CRITERIOS; teoria literaria, estetica y cultural. q. $4 in N. America; S. America $12; Europe $17. (Ministerio de Cultura) Ediciones Cubanas, Obispo No. 527, Apdo. 605, Havana, Cuba.

320   IT   ISSN 0390-0657
CRITICA DEL DIRITTO; stato e conflitto de classe. 1974. 3/yr. L.80000. Sapere 2000 S.r.l., Via Filippo Turati 48, 00185 Rome, Italy. TEL 06-730 776. Ed. Angelo Ruggieri. bk.rev.; bibl.

320.532   ISSN 0011-152X
CRITICA MARXISTA/MARXIST CRITICISM. 1963. bi-m. L.50000 (L.71000 foreign). Editori Riuniti, Via dei Polacchi 41, 00186 Rome, Italy. TEL 39-6-6711319. FAX 39-6-8416096. TELEX EDIRIU I 625292. Ed. E. A. Zanardo. adv.= page L.600000. bibl.; charts; index. circ. 12,000. **Indexed:** Int.Polit.Sci.Abstr.
—SWETS.

320.531   IT   ISSN 0011-1538
CRITICA SOCIALE; rivista del socialismo fondata da Filippo Turati. 1891. m. Societa Editrice dell Critica Sociale s.r.l., Via Olmetto 5, 20123 Milan, Italy. TEL 39-2-86450005. FAX 39-2-86453373. Dir. Pier-Vittorio Scotti. adv.: B&W page L.2000000, color page L.3000000. bk.rev.

320   IT
CRITICA UMBRA.* no.16, 1976. m. L.2000. Piazza Fanti, 1, Citta di Castello (Pg), Italy. bk.rev.

614   US   ISSN 0194-1909
CRITICAL ISSUES. 1979. irreg. price varies. Heritage Foundation, 214 Massachusetts Ave., N.E., Washington, DC 20002. TEL 202-546-4400. FAX 202-546-8328. **Document type:** monographic series.
●Also available online. Vendor(s): Lexis-Nexis.

320.531   UK   ISSN 0301-7605
DK246
CRITIQUE; a journal of Soviet studies & socialist theory. 1973. s-a. £8($16) to individuals; institutions £20($40). Glasgow Caledonian University, Department of Economics, Cowcaddens Rd., Glasgow G4 0BA, Scotland. TEL 041-331-3312. Ed. Hillel Ticktin. adv.; bk.rev.; cum.index: vols.1-6, 7-12, 13-21. circ. 5,000. (back issues avail.) **Indexed:** Alt.Press Ind., Amer.Hist.& Life (until 1990), Arts & Hum.Cit.Ind., Hist.Abstr. (until 1990). **Document type:** academic/scholarly publication.
—BLDSC (3487.489200); Faxon; SWETS.

CRITIQUE COMMUNISTE. see *LITERARY AND POLITICAL REVIEWS*

320.531   FR   ISSN 0045-9089
CRITIQUE SOCIALISTE.* 1970. bi-m. 100 F. (Parti Socialiste Unifie) Editions Syros, 9 bis, rue Abel-Lovelacque, 75013 Paris, France. Ed. Roger Cerat.

340   AG
CRONICA DOCUMENTAL DE LAS MALVINAS. w. Editorial Redaccion S.A., Bartolome Mitre 1970, Buenos Aires, Argentina. Eds. Hugo Gambini, Emiliana Lopez Saavedra.

329.9   US   ISSN 1051-0575
HN90.R3
CROSS ROADS; contemporary political analysis & lett dialogue. 1990. m. $26 to individuals; institutions $40. Institute for Social and Economic Studies, Box 2809, Oakland, CA 94609. TEL 415-843-7495. FAX 510-843-5877. E-mail: crossroads@igc.apc.org. Ed. Max Elbaum. adv. contact: Sushawn Robb. bk.rev. circ. 3,000. **Indexed:** Alt.Press Ind.
Formed by the merger of (1984-1989): Frontline (Oakland) (ISSN 0738-4769) & North Star Review.
Description: Activist articles, analysis, interviews, and editorials on current events in the national-international political, social, and economic arena which have an impact on racial-sexual equality and the prospects for peace.

CROSSCURRENTS. see *SOCIOLOGY*

320.5   MX   ISSN 0011-2208
CRUZADO; si lo leyo en el cruzado es veridico. 1961. d. Mex.$500($24) Roberto Murillo Rocha, Ed. & Pub., Manuel Ocaranza 13 B., Uruapan, Michoacan, Mexico. adv. circ. 9,500.

320   AG
CUADERNOS DE ESTUDIOS LATINOAMERICANOS. no.2, 1974. irreg. Universidad Nacional del Nordeste, Instituto de Letras, Resistencia, Chaco, Argentina. Dir. Alfredo Veirave.

CUADERNOS DE NUESTRA AMERICA. see *LITERARY AND POLITICAL REVIEWS*

320   UY
CUADERNOS DEL 26. bi-m. Movimiento 26 de Marzo, Rivera 2572 bis, Montevideo, Uruguay.

320   MX
CUADERNOS POLITECNICAS; ciencia y cultura. 1973. bi-m. Mex.$60($5) Instituto Politecnico Nacional, Comision de Operacion y Fomento de Actividades Academicas, Tolsa y Tresquerras 27, Mexico 1 D.F., Mexico. circ. 6,000.

320   CU   ISSN 1013-6207
CUBA. MINISTERIO DE CULTURA. CARTELERA. w. Ministerio de Cultura, 4 No. 251 esq. a 11, Vedado, Havana, Cuba.

972.91   CU   ISSN 0011-2593
CUBA INTERNACIONAL. (Editions in Russian, Spanish) 1969. m. $34 in S. America; N. America $36; elsewhere $42. Ediciones Cubanas, Obispo No. 527, Aptdo. 605, Havana, Cuba. TEL 7-32-9353. Dir. Jesus Hernandez. charts; illus. circ. 30,000.
—Faxon.

320 016   US   ISSN 0361-4441
F1751
CUBAN STUDIES/ESTUDIOS CUBANOS; scholarly multidisciplinary annual book publication devoted entirely to Cuba. (As of 1986, subseries of Pitt Latin American Series) (Text in English or Spanish) 1970. a. price varies. (Center for Latin American Studies) University of Pittsburgh Press, 127 N. Bellefield Ave., Pittsburgh, PA 15260. TEL 800-666-2211. FAX 412-624-7380. adv.; bk.rev.; abstr.; bibl. circ. 750. (back issues avail.) **Indexed:** A.B.C.Pol.Sci., Amer.Bibl.Slavic & E.Eur.Stud., Amer.Hist.& Life, Hisp.Amer.Per.Ind. (1971-), Hist.Abstr., IDA, Int.Polit.Sci.Abstr. **Document type:** academic/scholarly publication.
—BLDSC (3490.858000); UnCover.
Formerly: Cuban Studies Newsletter - Boletin de Estudios Cubanos (ISSN 0011-2631)

972.91   US
CUBATIMES.* 1974. 6/yr. $12 to individuals; $24 to institutions. Cuba Resource Center, 11-A Seventh Ave., Brooklyn, NY 11200. Ed.Bd. adv.; bk.rev.; bibl.; charts. circ. 450. (back issues avail.) **Indexed:** Alt.Press Ind., Left Ind.
Former titles: Cuba Review (ISSN 0147-8869); C R C Newsletter.

320 300   AG
CULTURA NACIONAL; revista bimestrale de politica y ciencias sociales. bi-m. Cnel. Zelaya 1438, Lanus Oeste, Provincia de Buenos Aires, Argentina. Ed. Eduardo Varela.

CULTURAL POLICY. see *POLITICAL SCIENCE — International Relations*

322   AG
CUMPA. 1986. s-m. Hechos S.A., Florida 716 3, Buenos Aires, Argentina. TEL 392-8529.

320   PK
CURRENT. (Text in English) 1975. w. Rs.65. Sheika Bldg., Faiz Mohd Fatehali Rd., P.O. Box 789, Karachi, Pakistan. Ed. M.T. Bokhari. illus. **Indexed:** G.Soc.Sci.& Rel.Per.Lit.

CURRENT (WASHINGTON, 1960); significant new material from all sources on the frontier problems of today. see *EDUCATION*

320   SX
CURRENT EVENTS IN NAMIBIA. (Text in English) 1974. q. South West Africa People's Organization, P.O. Box 1071, Windhoek, Namibia. TEL 38364. FAX 32368. TELEX 724.

320.9 909   US   ISSN 0011-3530
D410
CURRENT HISTORY; the monthly magazine of world affairs. 1914. m. (9/yr.) $32. Current History, Inc., 4225 Main St., Philadelphia, PA 19127. TEL 215-482-4464. FAX 215-482-9197. E-mail: christory@aol.com. Ed. William W. Finan, Jr; Pub. Daniel Mark Redmond. bk.rev.; index; circ. 24,560 (paid). (also avail. in microform from UMI) **Indexed:** A.B.C.Pol.Sci., Acad.Ind., Amer.Bibl.Slavic & E.Eur.Stud., Amer.Hist.& Life (until 1992), Asian-Pac.Econ.Lit., Bk.Rev.Ind. (1965-), Can.B.P.I., Child.Bk.Rev.Ind. (1965-), Curr.Cont., Hist.Abstr. (until 1992), IDA, Mag.Ind., Mid.East: Abstr.& Ind., P.A.I.S., Per.Islam. (1992-), PMR, Polit.Sci.Abstr., R.G., Rural Ext.Educ.& Tr.Abstr., Rural Recreat.Tour.Abstr., SSCI, TOM, World Agri.Econ.& Rural Sociol.Abstr. **Document type:** academic/scholarly publication.
●Also available online. Vendor(s): Ovid Technologies, Knight-Ridder, Inc..
Also available on CD-ROM.
—BLDSC (3497.500000); Faxon; Genuine Article; SWETS; UMI; UnCover.

320 330.9   US   ISSN 1057-2309
D2009
CURRENT POLITICS AND ECONOMICS OF EUROPE. 1991. q. $250 (effective 1996). Nova Science Publishers, Inc., 6080 Jericho Tpke., Ste.207, Commack, NY 11725-2808. TEL 516-499-3103. E-mail: novasci1@aol.com. **Document type:** academic/scholarly publication.
Description: Focuses on the momentous changes in Europe, spanning the entire spectrum of contemporary politics and economics.

320 330.9   US   ISSN 1056-7593
HC462.9
CURRENT POLITICS AND ECONOMICS OF JAPAN. 1991. q. $145 (effective 1996). Nova Science Publishers, Inc., 6080 Jericho Tpke., Ste. 207, Commack, NY 11725-2808. TEL 516-499-3109. FAX 516-499-3146. E-mail: novasci1@aol.com. **Document type:** academic/scholarly publication.

320   US
CURRENT POLITICS AND ECONOMICS OF THE UNITED STATES. 1993. q. $115 (effective 1996). Nova Science Publishers, Inc., 6080 Jericho Tpke., Ste. 207, Commack, NY 11725-2808. TEL 516-499-3103. E-mail: novasci1@aol.com. **Document type:** academic/scholarly publication.

POLITICAL SCIENCE

327   US   ISSN 0192-6802
D839   CODEN: CWOLED
CURRENT WORLD LEADERS; almanac & international issues. (Issued in two parts: The Almanac, 3/yr., and International Issues) 1957. 6/yr. $190 to individuals and public libraries; others $245. International Academy at Santa Barbara, 800 Garden St., Ste. D, Santa Barbara, CA 93101. TEL 805-965-5010; 800-530-2682. FAX 805-965-6071. E-mail: iasb@igc.org. Ed. Thomas S. Garrison. stat.; index; cum.index. circ. 2,000. (also avail. in microform from UMI; back issues avail.; reprint service avail. from UMI) Indexed: Geo.Abstr., IDA, Int.Polit.Sci.Abstr., Per.Islam. **Document type**: academic/scholarly publication. —UMI; UnCover. **CCC**.
     Formed by the merger of: Almanac of Current World Leaders (ISSN 0002-6255); Current World Leaders - Biography and News (ISSN 0002-6263); Current World Leaders - Speeches, Reports and Position Papers (ISSN 0092-1386)
     Description: Lists current key officials of independent states, colonies, dependent territories, international organizations and alliances. Also lists current population, population growth rates, area, major cities, natural resources, land use, agriculture, religions, ethnic groups, languages, gross domestic product, and membership in international organizations and alliances for each country.

D D R STUDIEN/EAST GERMAN STUDIES. see *HISTORY*

320   IS
D I A.* (Decisions, Issues and Alternatives) (Text in English) 1975. m. $12. University Publishing Projects Ltd., 28 Hanatziv St., Tel Aviv, Israel. Ed. Shlomo Einstein. illus.

320   US
D P F NEWS NOTES. q. $10. Disciples Peace Fellowship, Box 1986, Indianapolis, IN 46206. TEL 317-353-1491. FAX 317-352-8294. Ed. A. Garnett Day. circ. 2,200. **Document type**: newsletter.

320   II   ISSN 0971-4391
D R D O NEWSLETTER. 1981. bi-m. (Ministry of Defence, Defence Scientific Information & Documentation Centre) Defence Research & Development Organization, Metcalfe House, New Delhi 110 054, India. TEL 011-2932252. FAX 011-2919151. E-mail: pubs@desidoc.ernet.in. Ed. S.S. Murthy. circ. 1,900 (controlled). **Document type**: government publication, newsletter.
     Description: Highlights the achievements of DRDO, its politics, future plans and other scientific administrative and cultural activities.

320   DK   ISSN 0905-5525
D S U'EREN. 1920. 10/yr. membership. Danmarks Socialdemokratiske Ungdom, Landsforbundet, Torveporten 2-5, 2500 Valby, Denmark. FAX 36-44-02-55. Eds. Allan Pagh Kristensen, Brian Jacobsen. adv.; bk.rev.; illus. circ. 12,000.
     Former titles (until 1989): En Tern. Informations og Debatblad (ISSN 0109-6397) & D S U -Nyt (ISSN 0109-6389)
     Description: Focuses on Danish and international politics as seen through the eyes of young Danish Social Democrats.

320   VN   ISSN 1022-8829
DAI DOAN KET/GREAT UNITY. 1977. w. Viet-Nam Fatherland Front, 66 Ba Trieu, Hanoi, Socialist Republic of Vietnam. TEL 62420. (Alt. addr.: 176 Vo Thi Sau St., Ho Chi Minh City, Hanoi, Vietnam) Ed. Nguyen Ngoc Thach.

DANCERS FOR DISARMAMENT NEWSLETTER. see *DANCE*

DANDELION. see *PHILOSOPHY*

320   CC   ISSN 1002-9702
DANG JIAN/PARTY CONSTRUCTION. (Text in Chinese) 1988. m. Y16.80 (effective 1994). (Xuanchuan Bu - Ministry of Propaganda) Dang Jian Zazhishe, A1 Nan Xinhua Jie, Beijing 100051, People's Republic of China. TEL 301-7964. Ed. Song Shizhong. adv. contact: hu Pengguang. bk.rev. **Document type**: government publication.

329.9 378   US   ISSN 1002-4816
DANGXIAO LUNTAN/C C P PARTY SCHOOL MAGAZINE. (Text in Chinese) 1988. m. $41.30. (Zhongguo Gongchandang, CC - Chinese Communist Party) China Books & Periodicals, Inc., 2929 24th St., San Francisco, CA 94110. TEL 415-282-2994. FAX 415-282-0994.

320   CC
DAODE YU WENMING/MORALITY AND CIVILIZATION. (Text in Chinese) bi-m. Tianjin Shi Shehui Kexueyuan, 7 Yingshui Dao, Nankai-qu, Tianjin 300191, People's Republic of China. TEL 344047. Ed. Li Qi.

DAWN TRAIN. see *LITERARY AND POLITICAL REVIEWS*

320   UK
UA10
DEFENSE & FOREIGN AFFAIRS STRATEGIC POLICY; the international journal of national management and national security management. 1972. m. £60($120) International Media Corporation Ltd., 175 Piccadilly, Ste. 1A, London W1V 9DB, England. TEL 071-491-2044. FAX 071-409-1923. Ed. Gregory R. Copley. adv.; bk.rev. circ. 9,559. (back issues avail.) Indexed: Air Un.Lib.Ind., DM & T, PROMT. **Document type**: trade publication.
●Also available online. Vendor(s): Lexis-Nexis. —SWETS.
     Formerly (until 1990): Defense and Foreign Affairs (ISSN 0277-4933)
     Description: Contains reports of U.S. and Soviet policies, arms transfer and price tables and in-depth strategic analysis, power tables.

320   US   ISSN 1061-6845
UB251.U5
DEFENSE INTELLIGENCE JOURNAL. 1992. s-a. $35 to individuals; institutions $45. Joint Military Intelligence College Foundation, 6723 Whittier Ave., Ste. 303 A, McLean, VA 22101. TEL 703-790-1428. FAX 703-790-0264. Ed. William H.J. Manthrope, Jr. bk.rev. circ. 1,000. **Document type**: academic/scholarly publication. —BLDSC (3546.218200).
     Description: Provides a forum for analytic essays on topics of importance to defense intelligence and national security professionals and scholars.

320.532   RU   ISSN 0869-4729
JN6598.V7
DELOVAYA ZHIZN'. 1919. m. $69. Izdatel'stvo Stavropolskaya Pravda, Ul. Spartaka 10, Stavropol, Russia. (Dist. in U.S. by: Victor Kamkin Inc., 4956 Boiling Brook Pkwy, Rockville, MD 20852. TEL 301-881-5973) Ed. M.I. Chaldeev. bk.rev.; bibl. Indexed: Curr.Dig.Sov.Press.
     Formerly (until 1991): Partiinaya Zhizn' (ISSN 0132-0734)

320   UY
DEMOCRACIA. 1981. w. (Partido Nacional) Editorial por la Patria S.A., Colonia 1308, Montevideo, Uruguay. Ed. Alberto Zumaran.

329.3   ES
DEMOCRACIA. 1990? m.? Instituto Salvadoreno de Estudios Politicos, 1a Calle Poniente No. 3549, Col. Escalon, Apdo. Postal 2687, San Salvador, El Salvador. TEL 98-1908. illus. **Document type**: academic/scholarly publication.

320 360   BL
DEMOCRACIA NA TERRA. bi-m. Cr.$5000($30) to individuals; institutions Cr.$8500 ($60). Instituto Brasileiro de Analises Sociais e Economicas, Rua Vicente de Sousa, 29, 22251-007 Botafogo RJ, Brazil. TEL 286-6161. (Co-sponsor: Campanha Nacional pela Reforma Agraria) **Document type**: bulletin.
     Supersedes (in 1991): C N R A Informa.

329.3   US
DEMOCRACY IN THE WORLD. 1986. irreg. price varies. Praeger Publishers (Subsidiary of: Greenwood Publishing Group Inc.), 88 Post Rd. W., Box 5007, Westport, CT 06881-5007. TEL 203-226-3571. FAX 203-222-1502. **Document type**: monographic series.

329.9   SA
DEMOCRAT. (Text in Afrikaans, English) 1971. 5/yr. free to members. Democratic Party - Demokratiese Party, 501 Ruskin House, 2 Roeland St., Cape Town 8001, South Africa. TEL 27-21-451431. FAX 27-21-4615276. Ed.Bd. adv.; bk.rev.; illus. circ. 60,000. (tabloid format) **Document type**: newsletter.
     Former titles (until Mar. 1989): Progress; Newsline; Deurbraak (ISSN 0033-0582); Which was formed by the merger of: Party's Afrikaans Magazine; (1967-1970): Progress.

329.9   SG
LE DEMOCRATE.* 1974. m. 4500 Fr.CFA. Parti Democratique Senegalais, 5 bd. Dial Diop, Dakar, Senegal. illus.

320   US   ISSN 0164-3207
DEMOCRATIC LEFT.* 1972. bi-m. $8 to individuals; institutions $15. Democratic Socialists of America, 180 Varick St., 12th Fl., New York, NY 10014-4606. TEL 212-962-0390. Ed. Michael Lighty. adv.; bk.rev.; bibl.; illus. circ. 5,500. (also avail. in microform; back issues avail.) Indexed: Alt.Press Ind.
—Faxon.
     Formerly: Newsletter of the Democratic Left.
     Description: Features organizational affairs, views of rank-and-file activists are also heard in this effective alliance of grassroots and national organizers.

329.3   US
DEMOCRATIC VIEWPOINT.* 1978. bi-m. $5. Democratic National Committee, 430 S. Capitol St., S.E., Washington, DC 20003. TEL 202-863-8000.

320   II   ISSN 0301-9047
DEMOCRATIC WORLD; political and economic analysis. (Text in English) 1972. w. Rs.16($6) M. Gulab Singh & Sons (P). Ltd., 6 Bahadur Shah Zafar Marg, New Delhi 1, India. Ed. Thomas P. Matthai. adv.; bk.rev. circ. 3,000.
     Formerly: Parliamentary Studies (ISSN 0048-3001)

321.8   FR   ISSN 0011-8222
DEMOCRATIE MODERNE; l'hebdomadaire des democrates sociaux. 1967. w. 200 F. (Centre des Democrates Sociaux) Societe Editions et Publicite France-Etranger, 133 bis, rue de l'Universite, 75007 Paris, France. FAX 45-55-94-62. Ed. Stephane Lafertey.

329.9   SA
DEMOKRATIA. (Text in Afrikaans, English) 1989. every 6 wks. free to qualified personnel. Democratic Party - Demokratiese Party, 501 Ruskin House, 2 Roeland St., Cape Town 8001, South Africa. TEL 27-21-451431. FAX 27-21-4615276. circ. 4,000. **Document type**: newsletter.

329.3   RU
DEMOKRATICHESKAYA GAZETA. 1990. m. 0.50 Rub. per issue. Demokraticheskaya Partiya Rossii, Ul. Koroleva 8, Korpus 2, pod'ezd 3, 129515 Moscow, Russia. Ed. Ivan Podshivalov. circ. 50,000. **Document type**: newspaper.

350   UK
DEMOS. PAPERS. 1993. irreg. price varies. Demos, 120 Wilton Rd., London SW1V 1GZ, England. TEL 0171-828-6321. FAX 0171-630-9271. **Document type**: monographic series.
     Description: Seeks radical solutions to long-term problems.

320   GW   ISSN 0934-3040
DEUTSCHE STIMME; Nationaldemokratische Zeitung. 1976. m. DM.42 (foreign DM.52). Deutsche Stimme Verlagsgesellschaft mbH, Roetestr. 4, 70197 Stuttgart, Germany. TEL 0711-610605. FAX 0711-611716. Ed.Bd. adv. contact: Guenter Dedlert. bk.rev. circ. 6,000. **Document type**: newspaper.

943   GW   ISSN 0723-4295
DEUTSCHE UMSCHAU.* 1954. m. (Bund der Vertriebene) Osmipress GmbH, Bismarckstr. 90, 40210 Duesseldorf, Germany. Ed. Hanns Kraus. adv. contact: Rudolf Wollner. bk.rev.; illus.; stat. circ. 80,000. **Document type**: bulletin.
     Formerly: Heimatwacht.

POLITICAL SCIENCE 5313

943   GW   ISSN 0012-1428
DD261
DEUTSCHLAND ARCHIV; Zeitschrift fuer das vereinigte Deutschland. 1968. m. DM.70. Verlag Wissenschaft und Politik Claus-Peter von Nottbeck, Salierring 14, 50677 Cologne, Germany. Ed. Ilse Spittmann. adv.; bk.rev.; charts; index. circ. 9,000. Indexed: Amer.Hist.& Life, CERDIC, Hist.Abstr., P.A.I.S.For.Lang.Ind. **Document type:** academic/scholarly publication.
—Faxon.

943   GW   ISSN 0012-1436
DEUTSCHLAND-BERICHTE.* (Text in English, German and Hebrew) 1965. m. free. Birkemweg 14, 5300 Bonn 1, Germany. Ed. Rolf Vogel. bk.rev.; index. circ. 6,000.

320   GW   ISSN 0012-141X
DEUTSCHLAND-MAGAZIN. 1969. m. DM.50. (Deutschland Stiftung e.V.) Verlag Deutschland Magazin, Koenigstr. 42, 83254 Breitbrunn, Germany. TEL 08051-3041. FAX 08051-62497. Ed. Hans-Juergen Mahlitz. adv.; bk.rev.; charts; illus. circ. 30,000. **Document type:** bulletin.

320   UK   ISSN 0961-5431
DEVELOPMENTS IN POLITICS. 1990. a. £39.50. Causeway Press Ltd., P.O. Box 13, Ormskirk, Lancs. L39 5HP, England. TEL 01695-576048. FAX 01695-570714. Ed. Steve Lancaster. circ. 800. **Document type:** academic/scholarly publication.
—BLDSC (3579.086250).

DIALECTICAL ANTHROPOLOGY; an independent international journal in the critical tradition committed to the transformation of our society and the humane union of theory and practice. *see* ANTHROPOLOGY

329.9   RU   ISSN 0236-0942
DK266.A2   CODEN: DIALEQ
DIALOG. (Former name of issuing body: Kommunisticheskaya Partiya Sovetskogo Soyuza, Tsentral'nyi Komitet) 1990. m. $79 (effective 1996). Izdatel'stvo Pressa, Ul. Pravdy, 24, Moscow 125047, Russia. (Dist. in U.S. by: Victor Kamkin Inc., Boiling Brook Pkwy, Rockville, MD 20852. TEL 301-881-5973) Ed. N.Y. Klepach. circ. 1,862,000. (also avail. in microform) **Indexed:** Curr.Dig.Sov.Press.
Formed by the merger of (1956-1990): Agitator (ISSN 0320-7161) & Politicheskoe Obrazovanie (ISSN 0235-327X); **Formerly:** Politicheskoe Samoobrazovanie (ISSN 0132-070X)

320   IT
DIALOGO (JESI). m. Piazza Indipendenza 2, 60035 Jesi, Italy. Ed. Bruno Bravetti.

DIALOGO SOCIAL. *see* SOCIOLOGY

320   GO
DIALOGUE. 1969. m. Parti Democratique Gabonais, B.P. 213, Libreville, Gabon. Ed. Eloie Chambrien. circ. 3,000.

DIANA (MARCIANISE); rassegna di politica e di cultura. *see* LITERARY AND POLITICAL REVIEWS

322.4   IT
IL DIBATTITO FEDERALISTA. 1972. m. L.20000. Sezione Gioventu Federalista Europea, Vicolo Tre Re 1, 27100 Pavia, Italy. Ed. Luigi V. Majocchi. bk.rev. circ. 1,000.
Supersedes (as of 1984): Federalismo Militante.

320   UK
A DICTIONARY OF MODERN POLITICS. 1985. irreg. $80. Europa Publications, 18 Bedford Sq., London WC1B 3JN, England. TEL 0171-580-8236. FAX 0171-636-1664. TELEX 51464 EUROPA G.
Description: Provides a comprehensive guide to the ideology and terminology of the world of politics.

320   GW   ISSN 0932-6162
DIESSEITS; Zeitschrift fur Aufklaerung und Humanismus. 1987. q. DM.20. Humanistischer Verband Deutschlands, Hobrechtstr. 8, 12043 Berlin, Germany. TEL 030-6139040. FAX 030-61390450. Ed. Christian John. bk.rev. circ. 5,000. (back issues avail.) **Document type:** bulletin.

322.4   FR   ISSN 0247-9065
DIFFERENCES; magazine contre le racisme pour l'amitie entre les peuple. 1981. m. 240 F. (foreign 300 F.). Mouvement contre le Racisme et pour l'Amitie entre les Peuples (MRAP), 89 rue Oberkampf, 75543 Paris Cedex 11, France. TEL 1-48-06-88-00. FAX 1-48-06-88-01. Ed. Cherifa Benabdessadok. adv.: B&W page 10000 F. bk.rev. circ. 15,000. **Indexed:** HR Rep.
Description: Current information and comments on racial-ethnic conflicts and various forms of action to suppress racism (law, education, mutual understanding).

320   KO
DIPLOMACY; international magazine. (Text in English) 1975. m. $60. Diplomacy Co., Rm. 906, Samduck Bldg., 131 Da-dong, Choong-ku, Seoul, S. Korea. TEL 777-3370-4906. FAX 773-8862. Ed. Kim Suk-won. adv. circ. 30,000. (reprint service avail.)
Description: Promotes diplomatic relations through non-governmental diplomacy.

320   LE   ISSN 0417-5190
DS41
DIRASAT ARABIYAT/ARAB STUDIES; majallat fikriyat iqtisdiyat ijtimaiyat. (Text in Arabic) 1964. m. $75. Dar at-Tali'at, P.O. Box 111813, Beirut, Lebanon. TELEX INTCO 20376 LE. Ed. J. Safir. adv.; bk.rev. circ. 6,500.

329.9   FR   ISSN 0046-032X
DIRE;* nouvelle revue de la gauche socialiste. 1968. 4/yr. F S G T, 14-16 rue Scandicci, 93508 Pantin Cedex, France. Ed. Jean-Louis Pain. circ. 3,500.

972.9   CU   ISSN 0046-0338
DIRECT FROM CUBA. (Text in English) 1969. s-m. $108. Prensa Latina Agencia Informativa Latinoamericana, Calle 23 No. 201, Havana 4, Cuba. illus. circ. controlled. (also avail. in microform from UMI; reprint service avail. from UMI) **Indexed:** Alt.Press Ind.
—UMI.

354   BU
DIRECTORY OF KEY BULGARIAN GOVERNMENT AND PARTY OFFICIALS. (Monthly supplement avail.) a. 42 lv. Bulgarska Telegrafna Agentsia, Blvd. Tzarigradsko Shosse 49, 1040 Sofia, Bulgaria. TEL 359-2-8461.
Description: Includes state agencies, institutions, organizations.

320   US   ISSN 0884-5859
JA28
DIRECTORY OF UNDERGRADUATE POLITICAL SCIENCE FACULTY (YEAR). 1984. triennial. $35 to non-members; members $20. American Political Science Association, 1527 New Hampshire Ave., N.W., Washington, DC 20036. TEL 202-483-2512. FAX 202-483-2657. Ed. Patricia Spellman. circ. 2,000. **Document type:** directory.
Description: Lists in alphabetical order undergraduate deperpments offering political science with name, address, phone numbers, and names and specializations of faculty members.

322.4   FR   ISSN 0294-8281
HD28
DIRIGEANT; magazine trimestriel du centre des jeunes dirigeants d'entreprise. 1968. q. 350 F. 13 rue Duroc, 75007 Paris, France. TEL 1-47-83-42-28. FAX 1-42-73-32-90. TELEX 200 298 F CJDETAP. Ed. Jacques Chaize. adv.; bk.rev.; illus. circ. 5,000.

322.4   UN   ISSN 0257-1897
DISARMAMENT NEWSLETTER. (Editions in English, French, Russian, Spanish) 1983. q. free. United Nations, Department of Disarmament Affairs, Room S-3150 F, New York, NY 10017. TEL 212-963-5597. circ. 28,000 English and Russian eds., 15,000 French and Spanish eds.

322.4   UN   ISSN 0259-3629
JX1974
DISARMAMENT TIMES. 1978. 6/yr. $15. United Nations, Non-Govermental Organizations Committee on Disarmament, 777 United Nations Plaza, New York, NY 10017. TEL 212-304-0222. Ed. Jim Wurst. bk.rev. circ. 5,000. (tabloid format)

320   IT   ISSN 0416-0371
DISCUSSIONE. 1953. w. L.40000. Edizioni Cinque Lune S.p.A., Piazza delle Cinque Lune 113, 00186 Rome, Italy. TEL 39-6-6792110. FAX 39-6-6878893. Ed.Bd. adv.: page L.7500000. circ. 33,000.

320.9 051   US   ISSN 0012-3846
HX1
DISSENT (NEW YORK). 1954. q. $22 to individuals; institutions $30. Foundation for the Study of Independent Social Ideas, Inc., 521 Fifth Ave., New York, NY 10017. TEL 212-687-0890. Ed. Michael Walzer. adv.; bk.rev.; cum.index every 2 yrs. circ. 9,000. (also avail. in microform from UMI; reprint service avail. from KTO) **Indexed:** A.B.C.Pol.Sci., Acad.Ind., Alt.Press Ind., Amer.Hist.& Life, Bk.Rev.Ind. (1965-), Child.Bk.Rev.Ind. (1965-), Film Lit.Ind. (1973-), Fut.Surv., Hist.Abstr., Int.Polit.Sci.Abstr., Lang.& Lang.Behav.Abstr., Left Ind. (1982-), P.A.I.S., Per.Islam. (1991-), Soc.Sci.Ind. **Document type:** academic/scholarly publication.
—BLDSC (3598.900000); Faxon; SWETS; UMI; UnCover.
Description: Covers politics and culture.

AL-DJEICH; revue de l'Armee Nationale Populare. *see* MILITARY

340   PO
DOCUMENTACO E DIREITO COMPARADO. (Supplement to: Portugal. Ministerio da Justica. Boletin) (Text in French and Portuguese) 1980. q. Esc.4000($26) Ministerio da Justica, Gabinete de Gestao Financeira, Praca do Comercio, 1100 Lisbon, Portugal. circ. 6,000. **Indexed:** ELLIS.
Description: Deals with common market law, international organizations and legal developments concerning human rights.

320   FR
DOCUMENTS ET INFORMATIONS PARLEMENTAIRES; revue hebdomadaire d'information et de documentation sur la vie politique et parlementaire en France. w. 4600 F. (foreign 4880 F.). Societe Generale de Presse et d'Editions, 13 av. de l'Opera, 75001 Paris, France. TEL 40-15-17-89. FAX 40-15-17-15. TELEX SOGPRES 230023.

320   UK   ISSN 0070-7007
JN500
DOD'S PARLIAMENTARY COMPANION. 1832. a. £75 (outside UK £90) (effective 1995). Dod's Parliamentary Companion Ltd., Hurst Green, E. Sussex TN19 7PX, England. TEL 01932-860288. Ed. Michael Bedford. bk.rev.; index. circ. 5,000.
—BLDSC (3614.300000). CCC.
Description: Complete guide to who's who in UK politics and government. Includes over 7,000 contacts and information.

052   PK   ISSN 0012-4907
DOGAR'S GENERAL KNOWLEDGE DIGEST. Variant title: General Knowledge Digest. (Text in English) vol.4, 1970. m. Rs.70. Dogar Bros., Santnagar, Lahore, Pakistan. Ed. Haji Wali Muhammad Dogar.

320 940   GW   ISSN 0070-7031
DD257.4
DOKUMENTE ZUR DEUTSCHLANDPOLITIK. (In five series) 1961. irreg., vol.5, no.2, 1987. price varies. Bundesminister des Inneren, Postfach 170290, 5300 Bonn 1, Germany. Eds. Karl Dietrich Bracher, Hans-Adolf Jacobsen.

320 940   GW   ISSN 0341-3276
DOKUMENTE ZUR DEUTSCHLANDPOLITIK. BEIHEFTE. 1975. irreg., vol.7, 1985. price varies. Bundesminister des Inneren, Postfach 170290, 5300 Bonn 1, Germany. Eds. K.D. Bracher, H.A. Jacobsen.

320   DQ
DOMINICA OFFICIAL GAZETTE. 1877. w. EC$18 (foreign EC$45). (House of Assembly) Government Printery, Roseau, Dominica, W.I. adv. circ. 600. (also avail. in microfilm from UMI)

DOMOVA POKLADNICA. *see* LITERATURE

320   US
DON BELL REPORTS.* bi-w. $40. 544 Ferguson Ln., W. Palm Beach, FL 33415-3527. Ed. Don Bell.
Description: Discusses historical and topical issues pertaining to US domestic policy.

POLITICAL SCIENCE

940   AU   ISSN 0012-5415
DB443
DER DONAURAUM. 1956. 4/yr. S.390. (Institut fuer den Donauraum und Mitteleuropa) Boehlau Verlag GmbH & Co.KG., Sachsenplatz 4-6, Postfach 87, A-1201 Vienna, Austria. TEL 0222-3302427. FAX 0222-3302432. adv.; bk.rev.; bibl. circ. 1,000. **Indexed:** Amer.Hist.& Life, CERDIC, Hist.Abstr., Int.Polit.Sci.Abstr. **Document type:** academic/scholarly publication.
   Description: Provides results of research work in the fields of culture, economy, history, politics and law in Central Europe and the Danubian region.

338   EI
DOSSIER EUROPA. 1955. s-a. free. Commissione Europea, Rappresentanza in Italia, Via Poli 29, 00187 Rome, Italy. TEL 06-699-1160. FAX 06-472-2163. TELEX 610184. Ed. Luciano Angelino. adv.; bk.rev.; charts; illus.; stat.; index; circ. 5,000 (controlled).
   Formerly (until 1987): Comunita Europee (ISSN 0010-5058)

DROIT/AL-HAQQ. see *LAW*

DRUM (AMHERST); black literary experience. see *LITERATURE*

320.531   US   ISSN 0741-0263
DYNAMIC. 1983. q. $4 to individuals; institutions $10 (for 6 issues). Young Communist League USA, 235 W. 23rd St., 5th Fl., New York, NY 10011. FAX 212-645-5436. Ed. Jason Rabinowitz. adv.; bk.rev. circ. 30,000.
   Formerly (until May 1983): Young Worker.
   Description: Covers current events, student rights, culture, international affairs, etc. - from a left perspective.

320   GW   ISSN 0343-6667
E G MAGAZIN. (Europaeische Gemeinschaft) 1976. m. (10/yr.). DM.54. (Kommission der Europaeischen Gemeinschaften) Nomos Verlagsgesellschaft mbH und Co. KG, Waldseestr. 3-5, 76530 Baden-Baden, Germany. TEL 07221-21040. FAX 07221-210427. TELEX 05193354. (Subscr. to: Postfach 610, 76484 Baden-Baden, Germany) Ed.Bd. **Indexed:** INIS Atomind. **Document type:** bulletin.

300   FR   ISSN 0421-4226
E S O P E. (Etudes Sociales-Politiques, Economiques) 1953. bi-m. 240 F. Societe d'Editions Generales et de Documentation (SEGEDO), 6 Villa Bosquet, 75007 Paris, France. circ. 3,000.
—BLDSC (3811.300000).

320   UG
EAST AFRICA ANALYSIS; economic - political updates in East Africa. (Text in English) 1992. fortn. $105 to individuals; institutions $130. P.O. Box 9948, Kampala, Uganda. FAX 256-41-245580. Eds. Gerald Mwaita, John Kateeba. bk.rev.; circ. 25,000 (paid). **Document type:** newspaper.
   Description: Provides a forum for the popular discussion of economic and political issues in Uganda, Kenya, and Tanzania.

EAST EUROPE & THE REPUBLICS: A POLITICAL RISK ANNUAL. see *BUSINESS AND ECONOMICS — Economic Situation And Conditions*

EAST EUROPE & THE REPUBLICS: A WEEKLY BUSINESS RISK ALERT. see *BUSINESS AND ECONOMICS — Economic Situation And Conditions*

320 301   US
EAST EUROPE REPORT. irreg. (approx. 200/yr.) $7 per no. (foreign $14 per no.). U.S. Joint Publications Research Service, Box 10257, Arlington, VA 22209. TEL 703-487-4630. (Orders to: NTIS, Springfield, VA 22161)

320 947   US   ISSN 0888-3254
JN96.A2
EAST EUROPEAN POLITICS & SOCIETIES. Abbreviated title: E E P S. 1987. 3/yr. $58 (foreign $63) (effective 1996). (Joint Committee on Eastern Europe) University of California Press, Journals Division, 2120 Berkeley Way, Berkeley, CA 94720. TEL 510-643-7154. FAX 510-642-9917. Ed. Ivo Banac. adv. circ. 1,200. (also avail. in microform from UMI; back issues avail.) **Indexed:** A.B.C.Pol.Sci., Curr.Cont., Int.Polit.Sci.Abstr., Per.Islam, Soc.Sci.Ind. (1994-), SSCI. **Document type:** academic/scholarly publication.
—BLDSC (3646.317000); Faxon; Genuine Article; SWETS; UMI; UnCover. **CCC.**
   Description: Examines the social, political, and economic issues in Eastern Europe.
Refereed Serial

320 330.9   UK
EASTERN EUROPE AND THE COMMONWEALTH OF INDEPENDENT STATES (YEAR). 1991. biennial. $390. Europa Publications, 18 Bedford Sq., London WC1B 3JN, England. TEL 0171-580-8236. FAX 0171-636-1664. TELEX 21540 EUROPA G. **Document type:** academic/scholarly publication.
—BLDSC (3646.593270).
   Formerly (until 1991): Eastern Europe and the U S S R (Year) (ISSN 0962-1040)
   Description: Contains information on the region as a whole is followed by separate chapters on the countries and states in the area.

320.9 947   UK   ISSN 0950-7450
                            CODEN: EENWE5
EASTERN EUROPE NEWSLETTER. (Annual country reports avail. for: Albania, Bulgaria, Croatia, Czech Republic, Hungary, Poland, Serbia and Montenegro, Slovakia, Ukraine) 1987. fortn. (25/yr.), £245 (rest of Europe $500; elsewhere $510); with Russia Briefing £410 (rest of Europe $810; elsewhere $830) (effective 1995). E E N Ltd., 70 Bassein Park Rd., London W12 9RS, England. TEL 0181-743-2829. FAX 0181-743-8637. Ed. Charles Meynell. index; circ. 1,000 (paid). (back issues avail.) **Document type:** newsletter.
   Description: Analyzes political and economic events in Eastern Europe.

320.9 947   UK
EASTERN EUROPE NEWSLETTER - BRIEFING. ALBANIA; a general briefing. a. £12($20) (for subscribers to Eastern Europe Newsletter or Russia Briefing only). E E N Ltd., 70 Bassein Park Rd., London W12 9RZ, England. TEL 0181-743-2829. FAX 0181-743-8637. Ed. Charles Meynell. **Document type:** newsletter.
   Description: Provides a political and economic overview of the year's events in Albania.

320.9 947   UK
EASTERN EUROPE NEWSLETTER - BRIEFING. BULGARIA; a general briefing. a. £12($20) (for subscribers to Eastern Europe Newsletter or Russia Briefing only). E E N Ltd., 70 Bassein Park Rd., London W12 9RZ, England. TEL 0181-743-2829. FAX 0181-743-8637. Ed. Charles Meynell. **Document type:** newsletter.
   Description: Provides a political and economic overview of the year's events in Bulgaria.

320.9 947   UK
EASTERN EUROPE NEWSLETTER - BRIEFING. CROATIA; a general briefing. a. £12($20) (for subscribers to Eastern Europe Newsletter or Russia Briefing only). E E N Ltd., 70 Bassein Park Rd., London W12 9RZ, England. TEL 0181-743-2829. FAX 0181-743-8637. Ed. Charles Meynell. **Document type:** newsletter.
   Description: Provides an overview of the year's political and economic developments in Croatia.

320.9 947   UK
EASTERN EUROPE NEWSLETTER - BRIEFING. CZECH REPUBLIC; a general briefing. a. £12($20) (for subscribers to Eastern Europe Newsletter or Russia Briefing only). E E N Ltd., 70 Bassein Park Rd., London W12 9RZ, England. TEL 0181-743-2829. FAX 0181-743-8637. Ed. Charles Meynell. **Document type:** newsletter.
   Description: Provides an overview of the year's political and economic events in the Czech Republic.

320.9 947   UK
EASTERN EUROPE NEWSLETTER - BRIEFING. HUNGARY; a general briefing. a. £12($20) (for subscribers to Eastern Europe Newsletter or Russia Briefing). E E N Ltd., 70 Bassein Park Rd., London W12 9RZ, England. TEL 0181-743-2829. FAX 0181-743-8637. Ed. Charles Meynell. **Document type:** newsletter.
   Description: Reviews the year's political and economic events in Hungary.

320.9 943.8   UK
EASTERN EUROPE NEWSLETTER - BRIEFING. POLAND; a general briefing. a. £12($20) (for subscribers to Eastern Europe Newsletter or Russia Briefing only). E N Ltd., 70 Bassein Park Rd., London W12 (RZ, England. TEL 0181-743-2829. FAX 0181-743-8637. Ed. Charles Meynell. **Document type:** newsletter.
   Description: Reviews the year's political and economic events in Poland.

320.9 947   UK
EASTERN EUROPE NEWSLETTER - BRIEFING. ROMANIA; a general briefing. a. £12($20) (for subscribers to Eastern Europe Newsletter or Russia Briefing only). E N Ltd., 70 Bassein Park Rd., London W12 9RZ, England. TEL 0181-743-2829. FAX 0181-743-8637. Ed. Charles Meynell. **Document type:** newsletter.
   Description: Reviews the year's political and economic developments in Rumania.

320.9 947   UK
EASTERN EUROPE NEWSLETTER - BRIEFING. SERBIA - MONTENEGRO; a general briefing. a. £12($20) (for subscribers to Eastern Europe Newsletter or Russia Briefing only). E N Ltd., 70 Bassein Park Rd., London W12 9RZ, England. TEL 0181-743-2829. FAX 0181-743-8637. Ed. Charles Meynell. **Document type:** newsletter.
   Description: Provides an overview of the year's political and economic developments in Serbia and Montenegro.

320.9 947   UK
EASTERN EUROPE NEWSLETTER - BRIEFING. SLOVAKIA; a general briefing. a. £12($20) for subscribers to Eastern Europe Newsletter or Russia Briefing only. E N Ltd., 70 Bassein Park Rd., London W12 9RZ, England. TEL 0181-743-2829. FAX 0181-743-8637. Ed. Charles Meynell. **Document type:** newsletter.
   Description: Reviews the year's political and economic events in Slovakia.

320.9 947   UK
EASTERN EUROPE NEWSLETTER - BRIEFING. SLOVENIA; a general briefing. a. £12($20) (for subscribers to Eastern Europe Newsletter or Russia Briefing only). E N Ltd., 70 Bassein Park Rd., London W12 9RZ, England. TEL 0181-743-2829. FAX 0181-743-8637. Ed. Charles Meynell. **Document type:** newsletter.
   Description: Provides a political and economic overview of the year's major events in Slovenia.

320.9 947   UK
EASTERN EUROPE NEWSLETTER - BRIEFING. UKRAINE; a general briefing. a. £12($20) (for subscribers to Eastern Europe Newsletter or Russia Briefing only). E N Ltd., 70 Bassein Park Rd., London W12 9RZ, England. TEL 0181-743-2829. FAX 0181-743-8637. Ed. Charles Meynell. **Document type:** newsletter.
   Description: Reviews the year's political and economic developments in the Ukraine.

960   UV   ISSN 0046-1032
ECCLAIRE.* no.28, 1972. bi-m. Mouvement de Liberation Nationale, B.P. 606, Ouagadougou, Burkina Faso. Ed. Hyacinthe Sandwidi.

320   US
ECO SOCIALIST REVIEW. 1986. q. $10. Chicago Democratic Socialists of America, 1608 N. Milwaukee, Ste. 403, Chicago, IL 60647. TEL 312-394-0327. FAX 312-702-0090. Ed. J. Hughes. adv. contact: J. Hughes. circ. 800. (back issues avail.) **Document type:** newsletter.
   Description: To network green leftists and socialists, and to develop the intellectual and strategic agenda for eco-socialists.

ECOLE ET LA NATION-ACTUALITES. see *EDUCATION*

POLITICAL SCIENCE

ECONOMIC AFFAIRS. see *BUSINESS AND ECONOMICS*

320 330   UK   ISSN 0143-831X
HD5650
ECONOMIC AND INDUSTRIAL DEMOCRACY; an international journal. 1980. 4/yr. £42 to individuals; institutions £143 (effective 1996). (Arbetslivscentrum, SW - The Swedish Center for Working Life) Sage Publications Ltd., 6 Bonhill St., London EC2A 4PU, England. TEL 0171-374-0645. FAX 0171-374-8741. E-mail: market@sageltd.co.uk. Ed. Rudolf Meidner. adv.: B&W page £180; trim 170 x 100; adv. contact: Bernie Folan. bk.rev. Indexed: ABI Inform, Account.& Data Proc.Abstr., BPIA, Bus.Ind., Cont.Pg.Manage., Curr.Cont., Human Resour.Abstr., IBZ, Int.Lab.Doc., Int.Polit.Sci.Abstr., Intl.Bibl.S.S.Econ., J.of Econ.Lit., Manage.Cont., Polit.Sci.Abstr., Sociol.Abstr., SSCI, Stud.Wom.Abstr., Work Rel.Abstr. **Document type:** academic/scholarly publication.
—BLDSC (3651.466000); Faxon; SWETS; UMI; UnCover.
Description: Covers all aspects of industrial democracy, from the practical problems of democratic management to wide-ranging social, political and economic analysis.
Refereed Serial

ECONOMIC AND POLITICAL WEEKLY; a journal of current economic and political affairs. see *BUSINESS AND ECONOMICS*

320 330.1   UK   ISSN 1350-1070
ECONOMIC INTELLIGENCE REVIEW. 10/yr. £97($195) (overseas £129) (effective 1995). Intelligence International Ltd., The Stoneyhill Centre, Brimpsfield, Glos. GL4 8LF, England. TEL 01452-864764. FAX 01452-864848. Ed. R.H. Buttery. **Document type:** academic/scholarly publication.
Description: Reviews international economic intelligence and features reports on major economic trends, country forecasts, investment briefings, and science and energy reports.

ECONOMICS & POLITICS. see *BUSINESS AND ECONOMICS — Economic Systems And Theories, Economic History*

320.531   FR   ISSN 0424-3218
HB3
ECONOMIE ET POLITIQUE; revue Marxiste d'economie. 1954. bi-m. 320 F. (foreign 480 F.). 2 place du Colonel Fabiene, 75019 Paris, France. TEL 40-40-13-49. Ed. Yves Dimicoli. bibl. **Indexed:** P.A.I.S.For.Lang.Ind.
—BLDSC (3657.800000); SWETS.

ECONOMY AND SOCIETY. see *SOCIAL SCIENCES: COMPREHENSIVE WORKS*

320 330   AG   ISSN 0326-7180
ECOS DE A L A D I. 1982. m. Asociacion Latinoamericana de Integracion, Cangallo 1515, 10 Piso, Buenos Aires, Argentina.

320   EC   ISSN 1012-1498
ECUADOR DEBATE. 1982. 3/yr. $18. C A A P, Apdo. Postal 17-15-173-B, Quito, Ecuador. TEL 523-262. FAX 593-2-568-452. E-mail: FRHON@CAAP.ORG.EC. Ed. Juan Carlos Ribadeneira. bk.rev. circ. 1,500. **Document type:** academic/scholarly publication.
Description: Each issue offers a discussion of current political issues, a central theme concerning a major structural problem, an agrarian section and analyses of social issues.

EDUCATION AND URBAN SOCIETY. see *EDUCATION*

EDUCATION LINKS. see *EDUCATION*

L'EGYPTE CONTEMPORAINE. see *BUSINESS AND ECONOMICS — Abstracting, Bibliographies, Statistics*

324.2   II   ISSN 0971-2291
ELECTION ARCHIVES AND INTERNATIONAL POLITICS. (Text in English) 1970. bi-m. $120. (Institute for Electoral Studies) Election Archives, 101, 22-75 West Punjabi Bagh, New Delhi 110 026, India. TEL 594160. FAX 5454155. Ed. Shiv Lal. adv.; bk.rev. circ. 1,000. (also avail. in microfilm from UMI; reprint service avail. from UMI) **Document type:** academic/scholarly publication.
Former titles: Election Archives Updating International Encyclopedia of Politics and Laws; Election Archives and International Electoral Politics and Law; Which was formed by the merger of: Election Archives (ISSN 0046-1644); International Electoral Politics and Law.
Description: Discusses international parlimentary politics, constitutional laws, political party systems and psephology.

320   UK   ISSN 0261-3794
JF1001
ELECTORAL STUDIES. 1982. q. £244($388) (effective 1996). Butterworth - Heinemann, Part of the Reed Elsevier group, Linacre House, Jordan Hill, Oxford OX2 8DP, England. TEL 0865-310366. FAX 0865-310898. TELEX 83111 BHPOXF G. (Subscr. to: Elsevier Science Ltd., P.O. Box 800, Kidlington, Oxford OX5 1DX, England. TEL 44-1865-843000. FAX 44-1865-843010; Subscr. in U.S. and Canada to: Elsevier Science, 660 White Plains Rd., Tarrytown, NY 10591-5153. TEL 914-524-9200. FAX 914-333-2444) Eds. David Butler, Bo Sarlvik. bk.rev.; index. (also avail. in microform from UMI; back issues avail.) Indexed: A.B.C.Pol.Sci., Amer.Hist.& Life (until 1993), Geo.Abstr., Hist.Abstr. (until 1993), IDA, Int.Polit.Sci.Abstr., P.A.I.S., Polit.Sci.Abstr., SSCI. **Document type:** academic/scholarly publication.
—BLDSC (3670.890000); Faxon; Genuine Article; SWETS; UMI; UnCover. CCC.
Description: Focuses on the behavior of voters, the effect of electoral systems, and the rules pertaining to elections. Aimed at historians, sociologists, political scientists, economists, geographers, lawyers, game theorists, and statisticians.
Refereed Serial

220.5   GW   ISSN 0177-2430
ELEMENTE DER METAPOLITIK ZUR EUROPAEISCHEN NEUGEBURT. 1986. a. (plus 2 special issues). DM.25 (Europe DM.30; overseas DM.35). Thule-Seminar e.V., Postfach 410347, 34065 Kassel, Germany. FAX 0561-405129. Ed. Pierre Krebs. adv.: B&W page DM.600; trim 210 x 167. circ. 5,000. (back issues avail.) **Document type:** academic/scholarly publication.
Formerly (until 1990): Elemente zur Metapolitik (ISSN 0178-7659)

EMBASSY OF SWITZERLAND BULLETIN. see *SCIENCES: COMPREHENSIVE WORKS*

320 350   US   ISSN 0747-0711
JK3401
EMPIRE STATE REPORT; the magazine of politics and public policy in New York State. 1982. m. $39. Empire State Report Magazine, Inc., 4 Central Ave., 3rd Fl., Albany, NY 12210. TEL 518-465-5502. FAX 518-465-9822. Ed. Jeff Plungis. adv. contact: David Bulmer. bk.rev.; bibl. circ. 10,000. (also avail. in microfilm) Indexed: P.A.I.S. **Document type:** consumer publication.
—UMI.
Former titles: Empire State Report Weekly; Empire State Report (ISSN 0363-7190)

329.3   NQ
EN MARCHA. m. C.$2. Partido Conservador Democrata de Nicaragua, Cine Cabrera 2, Apdo. 725, Managua, Nicaragua.

320   US
ENCYCLOPEDIC DICTIONARY OF AMERICAN GOVERNMENT. irreg., 3rd ed., 1985. $14.95. Dushkin Publishing Group, Sluice Dock, Guilford, CT 06437-9989. TEL 203-453-4351. FAX 203-453-6000. Pub. Rick Connelly. illus.

956 960   UA   ISSN 0013-7146
DT107.83
ENCYCLOPEDIE POLITIQUE ARABE. DOCUMENTS ET NOTES.* s-a. P.T.100. Centre de Documentation et de Recherches, Administration de l'Information, 22 rue Talaat Harb, Cairo, Egypt.

320 972   MX
ENFOPRENSA.* (Text in English, Dutch, French, Spanish) 1982. w. $50. Agencia Centroamericana de Noticias Enfoprensa, Apdo. Postal 32-124, Mexico, D.F. 06470, Mexico. TEL 5927398. circ. 2,000.

ENIGMA; revista de literatura policiaca. see *LITERARY AND POLITICAL REVIEWS*

ENLIGHTENMENT AND DISSENT. see *HISTORY*

320.9   II   ISSN 0013-8517
ENQUIRY. (Text in English) vol.3, 1969. 3/yr. Rs.6. (Enquiry Association) New Age Press, 15C University Rd., Delhi 7, India. Ed. Bipan Chandra. adv.; bk.rev.; bibl.

ENSAIOS F E E. (Fundacao de Economia e Estatistica) see *BUSINESS AND ECONOMICS — Economic Systems And Theories, Economic History*

329.3   RU
EPOKHA. 1989. w.? Sotsial Demokraticheskaya Partiya R.S.F.S.R., Pr. Suslova, d.36, Korpus 7, kv.25, 198215 St. Petersburg, Russia. TEL 255-84-95. Ed. Vadim Lifshitz. **Document type:** newspaper.
Formerly (until 1990): E S D E K.

320   RM   ISSN 0379-3710
ERA SOCIALISTA.* 1920. s-m. 120 lei($46) Partidul Comunist Roman, Comitetul Central, c/o Rompresfilatelia, Calea Grivitei 64-66, P.O. Box 12-201, Bucharest, Rumania. Ed.Bd. illus. circ. 50,000.
Formerly (until 1972): Lupta de Clasa.

ESCUELA NACIONAL DE INTELIGENCIA. REVISTA. see *MILITARY*

320   HU   ISSN 0865-0810
HM7
ESELY. 1989. bi-m. Hilscher Reszo Szocialpolitikai Alapitvany, Ludovika ter. 2, 1083 Budapest 7, Hungary.

320   CN
F1053.2
L'ESPOIR. (Text in French) 1977. irreg. Can.$20 for 4 nos. 522 rue Trudeau, LaSalle, Que. H8R 3C4, Canada. TEL 514-367-1516. Dir. Luc Potvin. bk.rev. circ. 1,000. (back issues avail.) Indexed: Pt.de Rep.
Formerly: Revue Independantiste (ISSN 0702-8571)

320.531   SZ   ISSN 0014-0732
L'ESPOIR DU MONDE. 1908. q. 10 SFr. Socialistes Chretiens de Langue Francaise, c/o Georges Cuendet, Gd-Vennes 3c, CH-1010 Lausanne, Switzerland. Ed. J.-F. Martin. bk.rev. circ. 400. **Document type:** bulletin.
Formerly: Socialiste Chretien.

320   GW
ESPRESSO. 1985. q. Junge Union Main-Taunus, Hattersheimerstr. 46, 65719 Hofheim, Germany. TEL 06192-25093. FAX 06192-8715. Ed. Marc Bockholt. adv.; bk.rev.; film rev.; play rev. circ. 1,200. (back issues avail.)

320   GW
ESPRIT;* the German political and society magazine. 1969. m. DM.54($24) Heinz Moeller-Verlag, c/o S P S, Karl-Maud-Str. 2, 5400 Koblenz, Germany. Ed. Heinz Moeller. adv.; bk.rev.; bibl.; illus. circ. 60,000. Indexed: Arts & Hum.Cit.Ind.
Formerly: Bonn Journal.

320.5   UK
ESSEX PAPERS IN POLITICS AND GOVERNMENT; a sub-series in ideology and discourse analysis. no.2, 1992. irreg. University of Essex, Department of Government, Colchester, Essex CO4 3SQ, England. TEL 01206-872757. **Document type:** monographic series.

320   FR   ISSN 0014-1062
ESSOR DU COMMINGES. 1966. q. 50 F. Association pour l'Avenir du Comminges et du Saint Gaudinois, La Serre d'Estadens, 31160 Aspet Cedex 1361, France. Dir. Jean-Paul Buffelan-Lanore.

POLITICAL SCIENCE

320   HC161   PE   ISSN 0014-1429
ESTUDIOS ANDINOS. 1970. 3/yr. $9. Universidad de Pacifica, Centro de Investigacion, Avda. Salverry 2020, Lima 11, Peru. bk.rev.; bibl. **Indexed:** Amer.Hist.& Life, Hisp.Amer.Per.Ind. (1970-1983), Hist.Abstr.

320   AG   ISSN 0302-2420
ESTUDIOS INTERDISCIPLINARIOS.* 1973. q. Centro de Estudios Politicos, San Nicolas 66, Cordoba, Argentina. Ed. Bd.

320   CL   ISSN 0716-1468
ESTUDIOS NORTEAMERICANOS. 1984. q. Esc.1000($10) Universidad de Chile, Instituto de Ciencia Politica, Belgrado 11, Casilla 258, Santiago, Chile. Ed. Hernan Rodriquez Fisse.

327.05 350   MX   ISSN 0185-1616
JA5   CODEN: ESPOFM
ESTUDIOS POLITICOS. 1975. q. $90 (effective 1995). Universidad Nacional Autonoma de Mexico, Facultad de Ciencias Politicas y Sociales, Coordinacion de Ciencias Politicas y Coordinacion de Administracion Publica, Ciudad Universitaria, 04510 Mexico D.F., Mexico. Eds. Hector Zamitiz, Erika Boring. circ. 1,000. **Indexed:** Amer.Hist.& Life, Hist.Abstr., Int.Polit.Sci.Abstr., P.A.I.S.For.Lang.Ind.

320   SP
ESTUDIOS POLITICOS. 4/yr. $44. (Centro de Estudios Constitucionales) Edisa, Lopez de Hoyos, 141, 28002 Madrid, Spain. TEL 415-97-12.

320 300   PO   ISSN 0014-1623
ESTUDOS POLITICOS E SOCIAIS. (Text in English, French and Portuguese) 1963. q. $3.60. Instituto Superior de Ciencias Sociais e Politicas, Rua da Junqueira 86, 1399 Lisbon, Portugal. Ed. Dir. Prof. Adriano Moreira. adv.; bk.rev.; bibl.; charts; illus.; index. circ. 1,500. (tabloid format) **Indexed:** Lang.& Lang.Behav.Abstr.

320 200   US
ETHICS AND PUBLIC POLICY CENTER NEWSLETTER. 1982. q. contribution. Ethics and Public Policy Center, 1015 15th St., N.W., Ste. 900, Washington, DC 20005. TEL 202-682-1200. FAX 202-408-0632. Ed. Jacqui Stark. circ. 15,000. **Document type:** newsletter.
    Description: Reports on activities of the Center, a non-partisan organization that conducts a program of research, writing, publications, and conferences to encourage debate on domestic and foreign policy issues among religious, academic, political, and other leaders. Special interest in positions of religious bodies on public policy questions.

329.3   SG
ETHIOPIQUE.* 1974. m. Parti Democratique Senegalais, 5 bd Dial Diop, Dakar, Senegal.

ETHIOPIQUES. see *HISTORY — History Of Africa*

329.9   GP   ISSN 0755-2947
ETINCELLE. w. 119 rue Vatable, 97110 Pointe-a-Pitre, Guadeloupe. TELEX 919419. Ed. Raymond Baron. circ. 5,000.

059.915 320   IR   ISSN 1017-4141
ETTELA'AT-E SIYASSI EQTESADI; mahnameh siyassi ve eqtesadi. (Text in Persian, contents page in English) 1987. bi-m. IRI.6000 (foreign IRI.9000; N. America $63) (effective 1994). Ettela'at Publications, P.O. Box 11365-9365, Khayyam Ave., Tehran 11144, Iran. TEL 98-21-328460. FAX 3111223. TELEX 212336. Ed. Mahdi Besharat. bk.rev.; illus. circ. 50,000. **Document type:** academic/scholarly publication.
    Description: Publishes analytical and critical articles addressing Iranian domestic policies and issues, and international political and economic developments.

320   VN   ISSN 0531-206X
ETUDES VIETNAMIENNES. English edition: Vietnamese Studies (ISSN 0085-7823) (Text in French) 1964. q. $24 (effective 1994). G I O I Publishers - Foreign Languages Publishing House, 46 Tran Hung Dao, Hanoi, Socialist Republic of Vietnam. TEL 84-4-253841. FAX 84-4-262996. Ed. Mai Ly Quang. charts; illus. **Indexed:** Amer.Hist.& Life (1994-), Hist.Abstr. (1994-). **Document type:** academic/scholarly publication.

916.75   ZR   ISSN 0301-9209
DT658
ETUDES ZAIROISES. 1961. q. K.85 per no. Institut National d'Etudes Politiques, B.P. 2307, Kinshasa, Zaire. bibl.
    Supersedes: Etudes Congolaises (ISSN 0425-4805)

EUROPA ETHNICA; Vierteljahresschrift fuer Nationalitaetenfragen. see *ETHNIC INTERESTS*

940   AU   ISSN 0014-2522
EUROPA-KORRESPONDENZ; Monatsinformationen. 1954. m. S.70($6) Gesellschaft zur Foerderung der Unabhaengigen Presse, Favoritenstr. 56, A-1040 Vienna, Austria. Ed. Wilhelm Landig. bk.rev. circ. 1,500. (processed)

EUROPE - ASIA STUDIES. see *BUSINESS AND ECONOMICS*

EUROPE-MAGAZINE. see *LITERARY AND POLITICAL REVIEWS*

329.9   UK   ISSN 0309-474X
EUROPEAN BULLETIN AND PRESS. (Text in English, French, German and Polish) 1963. s-a. $3.60. Central European Federalists, 39 Stanwick Mansions, Stanwick Rd., London W.14, England. Ed. A.J. Jez-Cydzik. adv.; bk.rev.; charts; illus. circ. 5,000.

355   UK   ISSN 0961-7906
EUROPEAN DEFENCE AND STRATEGIC STUDIES ANNUAL (YEAR). 1991. a. (Institute for European Defence & Strategic Studies & the Authors) Adamantine Press Ltd., Richmond Bridge House, 417-21 Richmond Rd., Twickenham TW1 2EX, England. Ed. Gerald Frost.
    —BLDSC (3829.688870).

THE EUROPEAN JOURNAL OF DEVELOPMENT RESEARCH. see *BUSINESS AND ECONOMICS — International Development And Assistance*

EUROPEAN JOURNAL OF POLITICAL ECONOMY. see *BUSINESS AND ECONOMICS — Macroeconomics*

320   NE   ISSN 0304-4130
JA88.E9   CODEN: EJPRDY
EUROPEAN JOURNAL OF POLITICAL RESEARCH. (Text in English) 1973. 8/yr. fl.756 to institutions; $485 to institutions in U.S. (effective 1996). (European Consortium for Political Research) Kluwer Academic Publishers, Postbus 17, 3300 AA Dordrecht, Netherlands. TEL 31-78-392392. FAX 31-78-392254. TELEX 29245 KAPG NL. E-mail: SERVICES@WKAP.NL. (Dist by: Kluwer Academic Publishers Group, P.O. Box 322, 3300 AH Dordrecht, Netherlands. TEL 31-78-392392. FAX 31-78-546474; N. America dist. addr.: Box 358, Accord Sta., Hingham, MA 02018-0358. TEL 617-871-6600. FAX 617-871-6528) Eds. Mogens Pederson, Derek Urwin. adv.; bk.rev.; index. (also avail. in microform from UMI; reprint service avail. from SWZ) **Indexed:** A.B.C.Pol.Sci., Abstr.Crim.& Pen., Amer.Hist.& Life, ASCA, ASSIA, Commun.Abstr., Curr.Cont., Hist.Abstr., Int.Polit.Sci.Abstr., Lang.& Lang.Behav.Abstr., Mid.East: Abstr.& Ind., Polit.Sci.Abstr., Risk Abstr., Sociol.Educ.Abstr., SSCI, Stud.Wom.Abstr. **Document type:** academic/scholarly publication.
    —BLDSC (3829.737000); Faxon; Genuine Article; SWETS; UMI; UnCover. **CCC.**
    Refereed Serial

EUROPEAN MONOGRAPHS. see *LAW — International Law*

329.3   EI
EUROPEAN PARLIAMENT. CHRISTIAN-DEMOCRATIC GROUP. REPORT ON THE ACTIVITIES; group of the European People's Party. a. European Parliament, Secretariat, L-2929 Luxembourg, Luxembourg. FAX 43-70-09.

320   EI   ISSN 0259-2290
D1058
EUROPEAN POLITICAL COOPERATION DOCUMENTATION BULLETIN. a. $45. Office for Official Publications of the European Communities, L-2985 Luxembourg, Luxembourg. (Dist. in the U.S. by: Unipub, 4611-F Assembly Dr., Lanham, MD 20706-4391. TEL 800-274-4888. FAX 301-459-0056)
    —BLDSC (3829.788400).

320.9   US   ISSN 0014-3650
EVANS-NOVAK POLITICAL REPORT; what's happening...who's ahead...in politics today. (Includes special reports) 1967. bi-w. $247 (foreign $330) (effective 1994). Eagle Publishing, A Phillips Publishing International Company, 422 First St., S.E., Washington, DC 20003. TEL 202-546-5005. FAX 202-546-8759. circ. 2,000. **Document type:** newsletter.
    —CCC.
    Description: In-depth analysis of current political and economic developments.

320   MX
EXAMEN; una publicacion por la democracia. 1972. m. Mex.$60000($65) (effective Jan. 1993). Partido Revolucionario Institucional, Insurgentes Norte, No.59, Col. Buenavista, 06359 Mexico, D.F., Mexico. TEL 535-82-31. FAX 525-566-8417. adv.; bk.rev.; bibl.; illus.; stat. circ. 15,000.
    Formerly (until 1989): Linea.

320 360   US
EXCHANGE PROJECT. 1984. 3/yr. Peace Development Fund, Exchange Project, 44 N. Prospect St., Box 270, Amherst, MA 01004. TEL 413-256-8306. Ed. Elizabeth Rankin. circ. 1,800. **Document type:** newsletter.
    Description: Covers topics relating to grassroots organizing for social change.

320   US   ISSN 0273-6314
HF1410
EXECUTIVE INTELLIGENCE REVIEW.* Short title: E I R 1974. w. $396. E I R News Service, Box 17390, Washington, DC 20041. TEL 202-544-7022. FAX 703-771-3099. Ed. Nora Hamerman. adv.; bk.rev. circ. 14,000.
    —BLDSC (3836.219500); UnCover.
    Description: Review of economics, science, politics and culture.

320   US   ISSN 0046-2926
JA1
EXPERIMENTAL STUDY OF POLITICS.* 1971. 3/yr. $12. c/o Marilyn Dantico, Ed., Arizona State University West, Office of Vice Probos for Academic Affairs, 4701 W. Thunderbird, Box 37100, Phoenix, AZ 85069-7100. TEL 602-543-4504. bk.rev. (also avail. in microform from UMI; reprint service avail. from UMI)

329.9   GW   ISSN 0343-5121
EXPRESS (OFFENBACH); Zeitung fuer sozialistische Betriebs-und Gewerkschaftsarbeit. 1962. m. DM.64. (Sozialistiches Buero) Verlag 2000 GmbH, Bleichstr. 5-7, 63065 Offenbach, Germany. TEL 069-885006. adv.; bk.rev.; illus. **Document type:** bulletin.

320 055.1   IT
EXPRESSION; trimestrale di attualita cultura e politica. q. Rusconi Editori S.p.A., Viale Sarca 235, 20126 Milan, Italy. TEL 02-6619-1. FAX 02-6619-2737. adv.: B&W or color page L.35000000. circ. 272,865.
    Description: For American Express card holders.

320   US   ISSN 1071-4340
EXTENSIONS. 1982. 4/yr. free. University of Oklahoma, Carl Albert Center, 630 Parrington Oval, Rm. 101, Norman, OK 73019-0375. TEL 405-325-6372. FAX 405-325-6419. Ed. Danney Goble. adv.; bk.rev. circ. 10,000. **Document type:** academic/scholarly publication.
    Description: Provides analysis and commentary on the U.S. Congress and on representative government in general.

EXTRA! see *JOURNALISM*

320 947   US
F B I S REPORT: CENTRAL EURASIA. 3/wk. $525 in N. America; microfiche $230 (foreign $1050). (U.S. Foreign Broadcast Information Service) U.S. National Technical Information Service, 5285 Port Royal Rd., Springfield, VA 22161. TEL 703-487-4600. FAX 703-321-8547. TELEX 64617. (also avail. in microfiche)
    Formerly (until 1992): U.S. Foreign Broadcast Information Service. Daily Reports: Soviet Union (ISSN 0565-5560)

F C I B COUNTRY CREDIT REPORT. (Finance, Credit and International Business - National Association of Credit Management) see *BUSINESS AND ECONOMICS — Banking And Finance*

POLITICAL SCIENCE

F C I B - N A C M. MINUTES OF ROUND TABLE CONFERENCE. (Finance, Credit and International Business - National Association of Credit Management) see BUSINESS AND ECONOMICS — Banking And Finance

328 364 360 US ISSN 0071-9560
F C L ACTION ALERTS. 1955. irreg. price varies. Friends Committee on Legislation of California, 926 J St., Rm. 707, Sacramento, CA 95814. TEL 916-443-3734. Ed. Doug Thompson. circ. 750. **Document type:** bulletin.
  Formerly: F C L Action.
  Description: Urges contact of legislators to express opinions on bills relating to human services, peace, welfare, prison and parole, low-income housing and the death penalty.

320 US ISSN 0532-7091
F C L NEWSLETTER. 1952. 10/yr. $20. Friends Committee on Legislation of California, 926 J St., Rm. 707, Sacramento, CA 95814. TEL 916-443-3734. Ed. Doug Thompson. circ. 3,800. **Document type:** newsletter.
  Description: Informs readers of state legislation and related matters regarding social issues, including criminal justice, human services, and peace.

322.1 200 US ISSN 0014-5734
F C N L WASHINGTON NEWSLETTER. 1943. m. (11/yr.). $35 donation. Friends Committee on National Legislation, 245 Second St., N.E., Washington, DC 20002. TEL 202-547-6000. FAX 202-547-6019. E-mail: fcnl@igc.apc.org. Ed. Ruth Flower. circ. 8,000. (also avail. in microform from UMI; reprint service avail. from UMI) **Indexed:** HR Rep. **Document type:** newsletter.
  —UMI.
  Description: Public policy and issues of interest to Quakers and others.

320 330 AT
FABIAN NEWSLETTER. 1960. bi-m. Aus.$50 (effective 1993). Australian Fabian Society, P.O. Box 2707X, Melbourne, Vic. 3001, Australia. TEL 03-388-2309. Ed. Tony Robinson. bk.rev. circ. 1,500. **Document type:** newsletter.

320 UK
FABIAN PAMPHLETS. 1884. bi-m. £24($35) Fabian Society, 11 Dartmouth St., London SW1H 9BN, England. TEL 0171-222-8877. FAX 0171-976-7153. circ. 5,500. (reprint service avail. from KTO)
  Formerly: Fabian Tract (ISSN 0307-7535)

320.531 UK
HX3
FABIAN REVIEW. 1891. bi-m. £24($35) Fabian Society, 11 Dartmouth St., London SW1H 9BN, England. TEL 0171-222-8877. FAX 0171-976-7153. Ed. S. Pollard. adv.; bk.rev. circ. 5,000. (reprint service avail. from KTO) **Document type:** academic/scholarly publication.
  Formerly: Fabian News (ISSN 0014-6196)
  Description: Explores issues that pertain to Britain's Labour movement.

320 UK ISSN 0071-3570
FABIAN SOCIETY. ANNUAL REPORT. 1891. a. £3.50($5.50) Fabian Society, 11 Dartmouth St., London, SW1H 9BN, England. TEL 0171-222-8877. FAX 0171-976-7153. (reprint service avail. from KTO) **Document type:** corporate report.
  Formerly: Annual Report on Work of Fabian Society.

320.9 US ISSN 0014-651X
FACT FINDER. 1942. fortn. $30. Harry T. Everingham, Ed. & Pub., Box A, Scottsdale, AZ 85252. TEL 602-947-4466. circ. 12,000. **Document type:** newsletter.

320 EI
FACT SHEETS ON THE EUROPEAN PARLIAMENT. every 30 mos. 17.50 ECU. European Parliament, Directorate General for Research, L-2929 Luxembourg, Luxembourg.

FACTS ON FILE WORLD NEWS DIGEST WITH INDEX. see HISTORY

320 BL
FACULDADE DE FILOSOFIA, CIENCIAS E LETRAS DE ARARAQUARA. CADEIRA DE POLITICA. BOLETIM. 1968. m. Faculdade de Filosofia, Ciencias e Letras de Araraquara, Cadeira de Politica, Praca Santos Dumont, Caixa Postal 174, Araraquara, Brazil. bk.rev.; bibl.

340 PE
FAENA. q. S/200. Instituto de Promocion y Educacion Popular, Av. Pardo 130, Chimbote, Peru. Ed. Roberto Lopez Linares.

320 330.9 UK ISSN 0071-3791
DS1
FAR EAST AND AUSTRALASIA (YEAR). 1969. a. $375. Europa Publications, 18 Bedford Sq., London WC1B 3JN, England. TEL 0171-580-8236. FAX 0171-636-1664. TELEX 21540 EUROPA G. **Document type:** academic/scholarly publication.
  —BLDSC (3865.785000).
  Description: Contains information on the region as a whole is followed by separate chapters on each of the countries and territories; these include general and statistical surveys, and directories of the government, diplomatic corps, political parties, communications, finance, trade and industry, tourism, and nuclear energy.

320 IT ISSN 0393-4195
LA FAVILLA. 1984. m. free. Gruppo Aziendale Repubblicano Ferrovieri, Via Generale Baldissera, 42-8, 33100 Udine, Italy. TEL 0432-505320. FAX 0432-505320. Ed. Giorgio Bellini. bk.rev. circ. 4,500.

320 US
FEDERAL ELECTION COMMISSION RECORD. Variant title: F E C Record. 1975. m. free. U.S. Federal Election Commission, Washington, DC 20463. TEL 202-219-3420. Ed. Louise D. Wides. abstr.; charts; index. circ. 12,000. (looseleaf format; also avail. in microfilm) **Indexed:** Ind.U.S.Gov.Per. **Document type:** government publication.
  Description: Reports on all F.E.C. actions such as summary of advisory opinions, litigation, compliance, and provides data on reporting requirements.

320 US ISSN 0195-749X
KF5406.A15
FEDERAL REGULATORY DIRECTORY. quadrennial, 7th ed. $139.95. Congressional Quarterly Inc., 1414 22nd St., N.W., Washington, DC 20037. TEL 202-887-8500. FAX 202-887-6706. **Document type:** directory.
  Description: Describes over 100 federal regulatory bodies, including the laws and regulations they enforce. Includes names, addresses and phone numbers of key personnel; organization charts; appendix with texts of major regulatory laws.

FEDERAL STAFF DIRECTORY. see PUBLIC ADMINISTRATION

320 US ISSN 0194-2840
JC355
FEDERALISM REPORT. 1971. q. membership. Temple University, Center for the Study of Federalism, 1616 Walnut St., Rm. 507, Philadelphia, PA 19103. TEL 215-787-1480. FAX 215-787-7784. E-mail: B2026R@TEMPLE.VM.edu. Ed. Daniel J. Elazar; Pub. Kimberly J. Robinson. adv. contact: Kimberly J. Robinson. bk.rev. circ. 1,700. (back issues avail.) **Document type:** newsletter.
  Former titles: C S F Notebook; C F S Notebook.
  Description: Provides reports on research, publications, and conference activities of the Center for the Study of Federalism.

320.9 IT ISSN 0393-1358
FEDERALIST; a political review. Italian edition: Federalista (ISSN 0392-1042) (Text in English) 1959. q. $35 in Europe; elsewhere $50 (effective 1994). E D I F, Via Porta Pertusi 6, 27100 Pavia, Italy. TEL 39-382-20092. FAX 39-382-303784. Ed. Mario Albertini. adv.; bk.rev. circ. 3,000. **Indexed:** ELLIS.
  —BLDSC (3901.948530).

320 US ISSN 0014-9810
JX1901
FELLOWSHIP. 1934. bi-m. $15 (foreign $23) or membership. Fellowship of Reconciliation, 521 N. Broadway, Box 271, Nyack, NY 10960. TEL 914-358-4601. FAX 914-358-4924. TELEX 152-243-432. E-mail: fornatl@igc.org. Ed. Richard L. Deats. adv. contact: Ruth Taylor. bk.rev.; film rev.; illus.; index. circ. 8,000. (also avail. in microform from UMI; reprint service avail. from UMI) **Indexed:** HR Rep. (1986-), P.A.I.S, Peace Res.Abstr, Rehabil.Lit. **Document type:** academic/scholarly publication.
  —UMI.
  Description: Covers interfaith peacemaking and nonviolence, domestic and international issues. Refereed Serial

329.9 CC
FENDOU/STRUGGLE. (Text in Chinese) m. Y1 per no. (Zhongguo Gongchandang, Heilongjiang Sheng-Wei - Chinese Communist Party, Heilongjiang Provincial Committee) Fendou Zazhishe, 62 Huayuan Jie, Nangang Qu, Harbin, Heilongjiang 150001, People's Republic of China. TEL 37784. illus.

335.83 FR ISSN 0015-041X
FEUILLE ANARCHISTE. no.12, 1970. q. 5 F. 122 Ave. de Choisy, Paris (13e), France. bk.rev.

320 UK ISSN 0143-5426
FIGHT RACISM! FIGHT IMPERIALISM!; newspaper of the revolutionary communist group. 1979. s-m. £9.50 (Europe £12.50; rest of world £18). Larkin Publications, B.C.M. Box 5909, London WC1N 3XX, England. Ed. David Reed. adv. contact: Carol Brickley. bk.rev. circ. 7,000. **Document type:** newspaper.
  Description: Focuses on anti-imperialist movements in South Africa, Ireland, Cuba, Kurdistan, and Turkey from a communist perspective. Also takes issue with racism and incarceration.

320 NE
FILIPPIJNENBULLETIN. 1975. bi-m. fl.25. Filippijnengroep Nederland, Korte Janstraat 2A, 3512 GN Utrecht, Netherlands. TEL 31-30-319323. FAX 31-30-321379. Ed.Bd. adv.; bk.rev. circ. 1,000.

332.4 BL ISSN 0103-1880
FILOSOFIA POLITICA. 1985. 2/yr. L & P M Editores Ltda., Rua Nova Iorque, 306, 90.000 Porto Alegre, Rio Grande do Sul, Brazil. Ed. Bd.

320 901 IT ISSN 0394-7297
FILOSOFIA POLITICA. 1987. 3/yr. L.120000. Societa Editrice Il Mulino, Strada Maggiore, 37, 40125 Bologna, Italy. TEL 39-51-256011. FAX 39-51-256034. Ed. Nicola Matteucci. adv.; index. circ. 1,000. (back issues avail.)

FIN DE SIGLO. see GENERAL INTEREST PERIODICALS — Argentina

FINANCIAL TIMES (FRANKFURT EDITION). see BUSINESS AND ECONOMICS — Banking And Finance

FINANCIAL TIMES (LONDON, 1888). see BUSINESS AND ECONOMICS — Banking And Finance

FINANCIAL TIMES (NORTH AMERICAN EDITION). see BUSINESS AND ECONOMICS — Banking And Finance

320 052 IE
FINE GAEL NEWS. 1978. 6/yr. free. Fine Gael Party, Fine Gael Press Rooms, Leinster House, Dublin 2, Ireland. TEL 01-6789030. FAX 01-6763658. Ed. Mary Cummins. adv.; bk.rev.; illus.; circ. 10,000 (controlled). **Document type:** newsletter.
  Former titles (until 1984): New Democrat (Dublin) (ISSN 0790-1267); (until 1983): National Democrat.

FINLAND; books and publications in politics, political history and international relations. see HISTORY — History Of Europe

322.4 US ISSN 0015-2722
FIRING LINE. 1952. m. $7. American Legion, National Americanism Commission, Box 1055, Indianapolis, IN 46204. TEL 317-635-8411. Ed.Bd. index. circ. 8,500. **Document type:** newsletter.

POLITICAL SCIENCE

329.15   SW   ISSN 0345-3375
FJAERDE INTERNATIONALEN; socialistiska partiets teoretiska tidskrift. 1959. q. SEK 80 (effective 1990). Kommunistiska Arbetarfoerbundet, (Dist. by: Bokhandeln Roeda Rummet, P.O. Box 3077, S-400 Goeteborg, Sweden)

320.9   FR   ISSN 0015-3516
FLASH ACTUALITE. 1961. w. 6500 F. Agence Transcontinentale de Presse, 28 rue Navarin, 75009 Paris, France. TEL 45-26-02-75. FAX 33-1-40-16-09-51. TELEX 281 342. adv. circ. 260.
    Incorporating: Politique Interieure; Coulisse Diplomatique (ISSN 0010-986X)

320.531   FR   ISSN 0768-7028
FLASH ALTERNATIVE. 1969. w. 80 F. (Parti Pour une Alternative Communiste) Presse d'Aujourd'hui, B.P. 90, 75962 Paris Cedex 20, France. Ed. M. Cuisinier. bk.rev.
    Former titles (until 1982): Pont Flash; P C M L-Flash (ISSN 0754-2143)

320   BD
FLASH-INFOR;* bulletin quotidien d'information. (Text in French) no.539, 1972. m. Departement de la Presse, 6 Ave. de la Poste, B. P. 1400, Bujumbura, Burundi.

FLINDERS JOURNAL OF HISTORY AND POLITICS. see HISTORY — History Of Australasia And Other Areas

320   US
FLORENCE ASTONISHER.* 1988. irreg. Florence County Libertarian Party, 551 Wellington Ave., Reading, PA 19609-2313. Ed. John T. Harllee. adv.; bk.rev. circ. 500. (looseleaf format)

320 330.960   GW   ISSN 0947-9368
▼**FOCUS AFRIKA;** I A K Diskussionsbeitraege. 1994. irreg. price varies. Institut fuer Afrika-Kunde, Neuer Jungfernstieg 21, 20354 Hamburg, Germany. TEL 040-3562523. FAX 040-3562511. Eds. Andreas Mehler, Ulf Engel. **Document type:** academic/scholarly publication, monographic series.

FOERSVAR I NUTID. see MILITARY

320 301.412   SW   ISSN 0349-7623
FOKUS; tidning foer centerpartiet och centerkvinnorna. 1910. m. SEK 60. Centerpartiets Riksorganisation, Bergsgatan 7 B, P.O. Box 22107, 104 22 Stockholm, Sweden. TEL 08-617-38-00. FAX 46-6-526440. Ed. Lennart Svensson. adv.: B&W page SEK 28500, color page SEK 35150; trim 250 x 370; adv. contact: Haakan Hofgren. circ. 130,000. (also avail. in audio cassette)
    Former titles (1952-1981): Svensk Politik (ISSN 0346-220X); Budkavle till Sveriges Kvinnor (ISSN 0345-1194)

320   NO
FOLKETS FRAMTID. 1946. w. NOK 350; newsstand price: NOK 8. P.O. Box 453 Sentrum, N-0104 Oslo, Norway. TEL 47-22-41-14-30. FAX 47-22-33-62-50. Ed. Odd Hagen. adv.: B & W page NOK 10000, color page NOK 14725. bk.rev. circ. 8,861. **Document type:** newspaper.

320 910   IT   ISSN 1122-3960
FONDAZIONE GUARASCI. BOLLETTINO MENSILE D'INFORMAZIONE. 1986. m. Fondazione Guarasci, Via Idria, No.26, 87100 Cosenza, Italy. TEL 0984-25145. Ed. Antonlivio Perfetti.
    Description: Forum covering regional social and political issues.

320   US
FOOD FIRST NEWS & VIEWS. 1978. 4/yr. $30 (effective 1992). Institute for Food & Development Policy, 398 60th St., Oakland, CA 94618-1212. TEL 510-654-4400. FAX 510-654-4551. Ed. Kathleen McClung. bk.rev. circ. 20,000. **Document type:** newsletter, trade publication.
    Formerly: Food First News (ISSN 0749-9825)

320   DK   ISSN 0907-1296
FOQUS. 1984. bi-m. membership. Kristeligt Folkeparti, Bernhard Bangs Alle 23, 2000 Frederiksberg, Denmark. TEL 00945-38885152. FAX 00945-38883115. Ed. Christel Kirk Brubacher. adv.; illus. circ. 7,500.
    Formerly (until Nov. 1991): Q - Avisen (ISSN 0109-887X)

FOREIGN POLICY (WASHINGTON). see POLITICAL SCIENCE — International Relations

320 320   UK   ISSN 0532-1328
D839
FOREIGN REPORT; the private intelligence behind the news. 1946. w. £99($265) (rest of Europe £130; elsewhere £160) (effective May 1993). Economist Newspaper, 25 St. James' St., London SW1A 1HG, England. TEL 071-839-7000. FAX 071-839-2968. TELEX 927809. (All subscr. to: International Subscr. Services, P.O. 14, Harold Hill, Romford, Essex RM3 8EQ, England. TEL 0708-381555. FAX 0708-381211; U.S. addr.: 11 W. 57th St., New York, NY 10019)
    —CCC.
    Description: Reports on political and business developments around the world.

320.532 054.1   FR   ISSN 0242-3332
LA FORGE. 1979. s-m. 200 F. Parti Communiste des Ouvriers de France, c/o Pierrel Christian, 15 Cite Popincourt, 75011 Paris, France. TEL 48-05-30-14. FAX 43-55-04-84. adv.; bk.rev. circ. 3,000.
    Description: Marxist-leninist perspective on national and international political situation, with special emphasis on French colonies.

FORME DELL'UTOPIA. see HISTORY

320 970   US   ISSN 1070-0374
THE FORMER PRESIDENTS QUARTERLY; a focus on our current retired presidents of the United States. 1993. q. $12. R H L Enterprises, Box 6443, Fullerton, CA 92634. TEL 714-738-4386. Ed. Robert H. Lewandowski. bk.rev. (back issues avail.) **Document type:** newsletter.
    Description: Reports on the activities of retired U.S. presidents, including notable speeches, overseas travel, articles and books they have written or agreed to write.

320.531 300   GW   ISSN 0933-9361
                               CODEN: FNSBE7
FORSCHUNGSJOURNAL NEUE SOZIALE BEWEGUNGEN. 1988. q. DM.54 (students DM.40.50) (effective 1996). Westdeutscher Verlag GmbH, Postfach 1546, 65005 Wiesbaden, Germany. TEL 0611-534389. FAX 0611-534430. Ed.Bd. circ. 800. **Document type:** academic/scholarly publication.

FORUM DER AG SPAK. see SOCIAL SCIENCES: COMPREHENSIVE WORKS

329.15   SW   ISSN 1100-0627
FORUM FOER REVOLUTIONAER ANALYS OCH DEBATT. 1986. q. SEK 90 (effective 1991). Forum foer Revolutionaer Analys & Debatt, c/o Isaksson, Sandeslaett 50, S-424 36 Angered, Sweden.

320 340   IO   ISSN 0215-8280
FORUM KEADILAN/MAJALAH HUKUM DAN DEMOKRASI. (Text in Indonesian) bi-w. Rps.3750 per no. P.T. Keadilan, Kebayoran Center No. 12a-14, Jl. Kabayoran Baru - Velbak, Jakarta Selatan 12240, Indonesia. TEL 021-7510734. FAX 021-7206620. TELEX 62797-IA. (Singapore addr.: Media Link, 1 Sophia Rd., No.04-26, Peace Centre, Singapore 0922. TEL 65-3361725; Japan addr.: Raira Enterprise Co., Ltd., 1-6-8-402, Shimoocgiai, Shinjuku-ku, Tokyo 161, Japan. TEL 03-3360-9171) Ed. Karni Ilyas. adv.: B&W page $789.50, color page $1842; trim 190 x 257. circ. 70,000.
    Description: Publishes articles on law and democracy.

320   GW
FORUM LIBERAL; liberale Zeitung. 1972. 8/yr. DM.4. Wirtschafts- und Sozialpolitik Verlag, Sternstr. 44, 40479 Duesseldorf, Germany. TEL 02132-73057. FAX 02132-8769. Ed. Klaus Golombek. adv.; bk.rev. circ. 50,000. (back issues avail.) **Document type:** newspaper.

330 370 614.7 320   GW   ISSN 0724-9780
FORUM LOCCUM. 1982. 4/yr. DM.21.50. Evangelische Akademie Loccum, c/o Beate Blatz, 31547 Rehburg-Loccum, Germany. TEL 05766-810. FAX 05766-81188. TELEX 17576610. bibl.; illus.; cum.index: 1982-1984. circ. 2,000. (back issues avail.) **Document type:** newsletter.
    Description: Protestant publication discussing religion, Church, human ethics, humanities and social science. Includes activities of the Protestant Academies.

FORUM POLITISCHE BILDUNG. see EDUCATION — Teaching Methods And Curriculum

320.531   US   ISSN 1076-9412
FORWARD MOTION; a magazine of socialist ideas and action. 1982. 5/yr. $15. (Center for Democratic Alternatives) Forward Motion, Box 150311, Brooklyn, NY 11215-0311. TEL 718-789-2551. E-mail: fmlink@igc.apc.org. Ed. Martha Cameron. bk.rev.; music rev.; video rev.; illus. circ. 1,000. (back issues avail.) **Indexed:** Alt.Press Ind. **Document type:** consumer publication.
    ●Also available online.
    Description: Socialist magazine covering the struggles of oppressed nationalities, oppressed groups, and the working class.

320.5   SW   ISSN 0345-3618
FOSTERLAENDSK ENAD UNGDOM; organ foer Frisinnade Unions-Partiets ungfylking, Nordisk Ungdom. 1957. q. Frisinnade Unions-Partiet (FUP), Bua 6186, Dr Resmarks Vaeg, S-440 80 Elloes, Sweden.

FOURTH WORLD REVIEW; for small nations, small communities, and the human spirit. see LITERARY AND POLITICAL REVIEWS

323.4   GW   ISSN 0015-928X
FRAGEN DER FREIHEIT; Schriftenreihe fuer Ordnungsfragen der Wirtschaft des Staates und des kulturellen Lebens. 1957. bi-m. DM.48. Seminar fuer Freiheitliche Ordnung e.V., Badstrasse 35, 73087 Boll, Germany. TEL 07164-3573. circ. 1,500.

320.9   FR   ISSN 0046-4910
FRANCE FORUM. 1957. 4/yr. 120 F. 133 bis, rue de l'Universite, 75007 Paris, France. TEL 45-55-10-10. FAX 45-51-89-53. Ed. Rene Plantade. adv.; bk.rev.; film rev.; illus. circ. 3,500. **Indexed:** P.A.I.S.For.Lang.Ind. **Document type:** academic/scholarly publication.

329.3   IV
FRATERNITE - HEBDO. w. Parti Democratique de la Cote d'Ivoire, 01 B.P. 1212, Abidjan 01, Ivory Coast. TEL 21-29-15. Ed. Guy Pierre Nouama.

329.3   IV
FRATERNITE - MATIN. 1964. d. Parti Democratique de la Cote d'Ivoire, Blvd. du General de Gaulle, 01 B.P. 1807, Abidjan 01, Ivory Coast. TEL 21-27-27. TELEX 23718. Ed. Auguste Miremont. circ. 80,000. **Document type:** newspaper.
    Description: Official journal of record for government activities.

320   GW   ISSN 0016-0202
FRAU UND POLITIK. 1954. 6/yr. DM.20. (Christlich-Demokratische Union (CDU), Frauen-Union) Union-Betriebs-Gesellschaft mbH, Friedrich-Ebert-Allee 73-75, 53113 Bonn, Germany. TEL 0228-234091. adv.; bk.rev.; charts; illus.; stat.; index. circ. 2,700. **Document type:** bulletin.

FREE ASSOCIATIONS; psychoanalysis, groups, politics, culture. see PSYCHOLOGY

322.4 100 301   UK   ISSN 0260-5112
FREE LIFE. 1979. q. £10($20) Libertarian Alliance, 25 Chapter Chambers, Esterbrooke St., London SW1P 4NN, England. TEL 0171-821-5502. FAX 0171-834-2031. E-mail: liberty@xapital.demon.co.uk. Ed. Sean Gabb. adv.; bk.rev.; film rev.; bibl. circ. 1,000. (also avail. in microfiche; back issues avail.) **Document type:** academic/scholarly publication.
    —BLDSC (4033.324500).

052   UK
FREE RADICAL. 1991. 6/yr. £5 to non-members. Liberal Democrat Youth and Students of England and Wales, 4 Cowley St., London SW1P 3NB, England. TEL 0171-222-7999. FAX 0171-799-2170. Ed. Louise Fish. adv. contact: Louise Fish. circ. 2,500. **Document type:** newsletter.
    Former titles (until 1991): Young Liberal News; Y L Newsletter.

950 322.4   JA   ISSN 0021-6984
FREE WORLD/JIYU SEKAI;* liberty & responsibility. 1964. m. 1300. Yen($3.30) Free Asia Association, Rm. 323, Yaesu Bldg., 2-6 Marunouchi, Chiyoda-ku, Tokyo, Japan. Ed. Kattsundo Jono. circ. 10,000.

POLITICAL SCIENCE

323.4 UK ISSN 0016-0504
HX821
FREEDOM; anarchist fortnightly. 1886. fortn. £18 to individuals (foreign £18); institutions £22 (foreign £25) (effective 1992). Freedom Press, 84-B Whitechapel, High St., London E1 7QX, England. TEL 071-247-9249. Ed.Bd. bk.rev. circ. 2,000. (also avail. in microform from RPI) **Document type:** newspaper.
Description: Focuses on political science from an anarchist perspective.

322.4 KO
FREEDOM DIGEST. (Text in English) 1967. q. $20. (World League for Freedom and Democracy) World Freedom Center Press, World Freedom Center, Changchung-dong San 5-19, Chung-gu, Seoul, S. Korea. TEL 02-235-0823. FAX 02-236-7059. TELEX TOWER-K28246. Ed. Dr. Woo Jae-Seung. adv. contact: Sun-Kyong Kang. bk.rev.; abstr.; charts; illus.; stat. circ. 2,000. **Document type:** academic/scholarly publication.
Formerly (until 1982): W A C L Bulletin (ISSN 0042-9449)
Description: Covers political philosophy: problems of communism and democracy and human rights.

323.4 II ISSN 0016-0547
FREEDOM FIRST; journal of liberal ideas. (Text in English) 1952. q. Rs.50($10) Indian Committee for Cultural Freedom, 3rd Fl., Army & Navy Bldg., 148, Mahatma Gandhi Rd., Bombay 400001, India. TEL 9122-2843416. FAX 9122-2610596. Ed. S.V. Raju. adv.; bk.rev. circ. 2,000. (also avail. in microfilm from UMI; reprint service avail. from UMI) **Document type:** newsletter.

320.531 US
FREEDOM NETWORK. m. 3242 N. Pulaski Rd., Chicago, IL 60641.

FREEDOM NETWORK NEWS. see PHILOSOPHY

FREEDOM SOCIALIST; voice of revolutionary feminism. see WOMEN'S INTERESTS

FREEDOMWAYS; a quarterly review of the Freedom Movement. see ETHNIC INTERESTS

323.4 330 US ISSN 0016-0652
AP2
FREEMAN; ideas on liberty. 1950. m. $30 (foreign $45). Foundation for Economic Education, Inc., 30 S. Broadway, Irvington-on-Hudson, NY 10533. TEL 914-591-7230. FAX 914-591-8910. Ed. Beth Hoffman. bk.rev.; index. circ. 32,000. (also avail. in microform from UMI; back issues avail.; reprint service avail. from UMI) **Indexed:** Amer.Hist.& Life, Hist.Abstr., Ind.Free Per., P.A.I.S., Polit.Sci.Abstr.
●Also available online.
—BLDSC (4033.365000); Faxon; UMI; UnCover.

FREIE LEHRERSTIMME. see EDUCATION

323.4 GW ISSN 0016-0768
FREIE PRESSE-KORRESPONDENZ. 1953. m. DM.24. Verband der Freien Presse e.V., Postfach 440208, 8000 Munich 44, Germany. Ed. Stefan Marinoff. adv.; bk.rev. circ. 2,000.

FREIE UNIVERSITAET BERLIN. OSTEUROPA-INSTITUT. BERICHTE. see HUMANITIES: COMPREHENSIVE WORKS

FREIE UNIVERSITAET BERLIN. OSTEUROPA-INSTITUT. ERZIEHUNGSWISSENSCHAFTLICHE VEROEFFENTLICHUNGEN. see EDUCATION

FREIE UNIVERSITAET BERLIN. OSTEUROPA-INSTITUT. PHILOSOPHISCHE UND SOZIOLOGISCHE VEROEFFENTLICHUNGEN. see PHILOSOPHY

320 AU
FREIHEITLICHER PRESSEDIENST. 1953. s-w. Die Freiheitlichen, Kaerntnerstr. 28, A-1010 Vienna, Austria. TEL 01-5123535. FAX 01-5123277. circ. 180. (looseleaf format) **Document type:** bulletin.

320 US ISSN 0882-1267
DC417
FRENCH POLITICS & SOCIETY. q. $32 to individuals (foreign $40); institutions $44 (foreign $52). Harvard University, Minda de Gunzburg Center for European Studies, 27 Kirkland St., Cambridge, MA 02138-2043. TEL 617-495-4303. FAX 617-495-8509. Eds. Stanley Hoffmann, George Ross. bk.rev. (back issues avail.) **Indexed:** Int.Polit.Abstr., Polit.Sci.Abstr. **Document type:** academic/scholarly publication.
—BLDSC (4034.405000); UnCover.
Description: Provides current information on developments in contemporary France.

FREUNDSCHAFT/FRIENDSHIP; democratic monthly. see ETHNIC INTERESTS

322.4 GW
FRIEDEN. 1981. a. DM.12. Lamuv Verlag GmbH, Nikolaikirchhof 7, 37073 Goettingen, Germany. TEL 0551-44024. FAX 0551-41392. Eds. Alwin Meyer, Karl-Klaus Rabe. circ. 8,000. (back issues avail.) **Document type:** newsletter.

320 GW ISSN 0942-2587
FRIEDEN UND ABRUESTUNG. 1982. q. DM.30. Initiative fuer Frieden e.V., Stralsunder Weg 50, 53119 Bonn, Germany. TEL 0228-664442. FAX 0228-665843. Ed. Wolfgang Biermann. adv.; bk.rev. circ. 2,000. **Document type:** bulletin.

322.4 GW ISSN 0179-7131
FRIEDENSFORUM; Rundbrief der Friedensbewegung. 1983. bi-m. DM.25. Foerdereverein Frieden, Romerstr. 88, 53111 Bonn, Germany. TEL 0228-692904. FAX 0228-692906. circ. 4,000. **Document type:** bulletin.

323.4 SW ISSN 0016-142X
FRIHET. Variant title: Tidningen Frihet. 1917. m. SEK 120($17) Sveriges Socialdemokratiska Ungdomsfoerbund - Social Democratic Youth of Sweden, P.O. Box 11544, 100 61 Stockholm, Sweden. TEL 46-8-714-48-00. TELEX 15547-SSU-S. Eds. Jonas Helling, Helena Norman. adv. contact: Lennart Enblom. bk.rev.; illus.; play rev.; index; circ. 32,500 (controlled).
Description: For young people interested in politics. Deals with cultural trends and social phenomena with emphasis on young people's point of view.

320.12 SW ISSN 0345-3693
FRIHETSFACKLAN; frihet - sanning - raettvisa. 1965. m. SEK 5 per no. Frisinnade Unions-Partiet, Bua 6186, Dr Resmarks Vaeg, S-440 80 Elloes, Sweden. Ed. Sven A. Undehaell. illus.

320.5 SW ISSN 0345-3723
FRISINNAD TIDSKRIFT. 1936. 10/yr. SEK 80 (effective 1990). Frisinnad Tidskrift, N. Schoen, P.O. Box 20, S-532 21 Skara, Sweden.
Former titles (until 1938): Frisinnad Tidskrift, Vaest Sverige; (until 1936): Vaest-Sverige.

320.9 II ISSN 0016-2094
FRONTIER. (Text in English) 1968. w. $50. Germinal Publications Pvt. Ltd., 61 Mott Lane, Calcutta 700 013, India. Ed. Timir Basu. adv.; bk.rev. circ. 5,800.

320 CC ISSN 0427-7112
FUDAO YUAN. (Text in Chinese) m. Zhongguo Qingnian Chubanshe, Qikan Bu - China Youth Press, No. 21, Dongsi 12 Tiao, Beijing 100708, People's Republic of China. TEL 442125. Ed. Miu Li.

320.9 SP ISSN 0016-2477
AP60
FUERZA NUEVA. 1967. w. 2200 ptas. Nunez de Balboa, 31, Madrid 1, Spain. Dir. Pedro Rodrigo Martinez. adv.; bk.rev.

320 AG
FUNDACION ECUMENICA DE CUYO. BOLETIN DE DOCUMENTACION. 1979. bi-m. Arg.$70($10) Fundacion Ecumenica de Cuyo, Pedernera 1291, Guaymallen, Mendoza, Argentina. (Subscr. to: Libros Dialogo, 9 de Julio 718, 5500 Mendoza, Argentina) Dir. Maria Teresa Brachetta.

G A N P A C BRIEF. (German-American National Political Action Committee) see ETHNIC INTERESTS

320.9 US ISSN 1051-2616
HM261.A1
GALLUP POLL MONTHLY. 1965. m. $70 to non-profit institutions; others $100; foreign $110 (effective Jan. 1994). Gallup Poll News Service, 47 Hulfish St., Box 628, Princeton, NJ 08542. TEL 609-924-9600. FAX 609-683-9256. Ed. Leslie C. McAneny. adv.; charts; illus.; stat.; index. circ. 1,300. (processed) **Indexed:** P.A.I.S., Polit.Sci.Abstr., PROMT, SRI. **Document type:** academic/scholarly publication.
●Also available online.
—Faxon; UnCover.
Former titles (until Dec. 1989): Gallup Report (ISSN 0731-6143); Gallup Opinion Index (ISSN 0016-4194); Gallup Political Index.

GARIBALDI. see LITERARY AND POLITICAL REVIEWS

320 US ISSN 0745-6468
HN90.P8
GARTH ANALYSIS; research by Penn & Schoen Associates. 1982. bi-m. $295. Penn and Schoen Associates, Inc., 245 E. 92nd St., New York, NY 10028. TEL 212-534-4000. Ed. Jeffrey Toobin. stat. circ. 200. (also avail. in microform from UMI)

320.531 CN ISSN 1183-2053
LA GAUCHE. (Text in French) 1983. 10/yr. Can.$10($10) to individuals; institutions Can.$25($25). C.P. 5152 Succ. N, Montreal, Que. H2X 3N2, Canada. TEL 514-845-6797. Ed. Francois Moreau. bk.rev. circ. 3,000. (back issues avail.)
Formerly (until 1991): Gauche Socialiste.

GAY VOTE. see HOMOSEXUALITY

320 330.9 IT
GAZZETTA ITALO-SVIZZERA. 1973. w. L.15000 (foreign L.30000). U.R.E., Via Marraioli 3 25, 82030 Castelvenere (Benevento), Italy. TEL 0824-940751. Ed. Ugo Ragozzino. adv.: B&W page L.1080000. **Document type:** newspaper.

320.531 JA ISSN 0435-1754
GEKKAN SHAKAITO. m. 600 Yen per no. Social Democratic Party of Japan - Nihon Shakaito, 1-8-1 Nagata-cho, Chiyoda-ku, Tokyo, Japan. FAX 81-03-3580-0691. illus. **Document type:** trade publication.

320 296 AU ISSN 0021-2334
DIE GEMEINDE. 1958. m. S.300. Israelitische Kultusgemeinde Wien, Seitenstetteng. 4, A-1010 Vienna, Austria. FAX 0222-5334516. TELEX 136298-ISKUL-A. Ed. Karl Pfeifer. adv.; bk.rev.; illus. circ. 6,000.

GENTE MESE; mensile di politica, attualita, cultura. see GENERAL INTEREST PERIODICALS — Italy

GEOGRAPHIC AND GLOBAL ISSUES REPORT. see GEOGRAPHY

320 US
▼**GEORGE.** 1995. bi-m. newsstand price: $2.95. Hachette Filipacchi Magazines, 1633 Broadway, 41st Fl., New York, NY 10019. TEL 212-767-6000. FAX 212-767-5622. Eds. John Kennedy, Eric Etheridge; Pub. Eleanor Carmody. adv. contact: Judy Hom. illus. **Document type:** consumer publication.
Description: Non-partisan coverage of politics in American life, with a focus on politics as entertainment and the intersection of politics in everyday life.

320 US
GEORGIA BEAT. 1986. 22/yr. $90. Joe Sports Associates, Inc., 21 Finch Trail, Atlanta, GA 30308. TEL 404-873-3728. FAX 404-874-8512. Ed. Joe Sports. circ. 1,000.
Description: Inside report of people and politics of Georgia.

POLITICAL SCIENCE

320 US ISSN 1045-0300
DD1
GERMAN POLITICS & SOCIETY. 1983. q. $35 to individuals (foreign $42); institutions $55 (foreign $62). University of California at Berkeley, German Center, 247 Moses Hall, Berkeley, CA 94720. TEL 510-642-4508. FAX 510-643-5996. E-mail: gps@uclink2.berkeley.edu. Ed. Andrei S. Markovits. adv. contact: Patricia M. La Hay. bk.rev. (back issues avail.) **Document type:** academic/scholarly publication.
—BLDSC (4162.150700); Faxon; UnCover.
Formerly (until 1986): German Studies Newsletter (ISSN 0882-7079)
Description: Focuses on developments in contemporary Germany.
Refereed Serial

GERMAN STUDIES REVIEW. see *HISTORY — History Of Europe*

GESCHICHTE, POLITIK UND IHRE DIDAKTIK. see *HISTORY — History Of Europe*

322 AU ISSN 0016-9099
HN401
GESELLSCHAFT UND POLITIK; Zeitschrift fuer soziales und wirtschafliches Engagement. 1965. q. S.200. Institut fuer Sozialpolitik und Sozialreform (Dr. Karl Kummer-Institut), Ebendorferstr. 6-4, A-1010 Vienna, Austria. Ed. Josef Steurer. adv.; bk.rev.; charts; stat. circ. 1,500. (tabloid format)

322 GW ISSN 0016-9102
GESELLSCHAFTSPOLITISCHE KOMMENTARE. 1954. s-m. DM.84. Postfach 102, 54614 Schoenecken, Germany. TEL 06553-92110. FAX 06553-92113. Ed. Leo Schuetze; Pub. Leo Schuetze. bk.rev.; index. circ. 5,500. (looseleaf format) **Document type:** newsletter.

320.532 GW ISSN 0945-4403
GESELLSCHAFTSREFORM JETZT!. 1969. m. DM.25 (foreign DM.30). Edition Wissenschaft Kultur und Politik, Postfach 110262, 10832 Berlin, Germany. TEL 030-2318490. FAX 030-2728236. Ed. Paul Schulz. **Document type:** bulletin.
Former titles (until 1993): Marxismus Heute (ISSN 0934-649X); Arbeiterstimme.

GHANA DIGEST. see *GENERAL INTEREST PERIODICALS — Ghana*

966.7 US ISSN 0016-9579
GHANA NEWS. 1970. m. free. Embassy of Ghana, Information Section, 3512 International Dr. N.W., Washington, DC 20003-3035. TEL 202-686-4520. illus. circ. 8,000.

320.9 330 IT ISSN 0017-0186
GIORNALE DEL MEZZOGIORNO; economico-politico. 1947. w. L.60000 (foreign L.150000). Vito Bianco, Ed. & Pub., Via Messina, 31, 00198 Rome, Italy. TEL 39-6-8554962. FAX 39-6-8844703. adv.; B&W page L.3744000. bk.rev.; charts; illus.; mkt.; tr.lit. **Document type:** newspaper.
Description: An economic, political, independent weekly newspaper.

GIUSTIZIA NUOVA. see *LAW*

320 SW ISSN 0346-5942
GOETEBORG STUDIES IN POLITICS. irreg. price varies. (Goeteborgs Universitet, Statsvetenskapliga Institutionen) Liber Laeromedel, Gleerup, Skaane, Sweden. Eds. Bo Saerlvik, Lars Stroemberg.
—BLDSC (4201.980000).
Formerly: Studier i Politik - Studies in Politics (ISSN 0081-7422)

300 II ISSN 0436-1326
GOKHALE INSTITUTE MIMEOGRAPH SERIES. 1968. irreg. price varies. Gokhale Institute of Politics and Economics, Pune 411 004, India. TEL 0212-344287.

320 330 II ISSN 0072-4912
GOKHALE INSTITUTE OF POLITICS AND ECONOMICS. STUDIES. (Text in English) 1931. irreg., no.72, 1991. price varies. Gokhale Institute of Politics and Economics, Pune 411004, India. TEL 0212-344287.

GOOD GOVERNMENT; a journal of political, social & economic comment. see *BUSINESS AND ECONOMICS — Economic Systems And Theories, Economic History*

320 US ISSN 0952-1895
JA1.A1
GOVERNANCE; an international journal of policy and administration. 1987. 4/yr. $66 to individuals in N. America (elsewhere $75.50); institutions $134 in N. America (elsewhere $149). Blackwell Publishers, 238 Main St., Cambridge, MA 02142. TEL 617-547-7110. FAX 617-547-0789. Ed.Bd. adv.: page $260; trim 4 1/2 x 7 1/2. circ. 700. **Indexed:** Int.Polit.Sci.Abstr.
—BLDSC (4203.819600); Faxon; SWETS; UMI. CCC.
Description: Provides a forum for work in the field of international executive politics, primarily from a comparative perspective.

320 US ISSN 1058-1774
GOVERNMENT (BOCA RATON). (Subseries of: S I R S Global Perspectives (ISSN 1058-1731)) 1991. a. $80. Social Issues Resources Series, Box 2348, Boca Raton, FL 33427-2348. TEL 407-994-0079; 800-232-7477. FAX 407-994-4704. (looseleaf format; also avail. in microfiche; back issues avail.)
Description: Reprints 70 articles examining sociopolitical affairs worldwide.

320 350 UK ISSN 0017-257X
JA8
GOVERNMENT AND OPPOSITION. 1965. q. $70 to individuals; institutions $99. London School of Economics and Political Science, Houghton St., London WC2, England. TEL 0171-405-5991. FAX 0171-242-0392. Ed. Ghita Ionescu. adv. contact: Rosalind Jones. bk.rev.; abstr.; cum.index: vols.1-5, 6-10; circ. 1,500 (paid). **Indexed:** A.B.C.Pol.Sci., Amer.Hist.& Life, Br.Hum.Ind., ELLIS, Hist.Abstr., Int.Polit.Sci.Abstr., Mid.East: Abstr.& Ind., P.A.I.S., Polit.Sci.Abstr., Soc.Sci.Ind., SSCI. **Document type:** academic/scholarly publication.
—BLDSC (4203.900000); Faxon; SWETS; UnCover.
Refereed Serial

320 US
GOVERNORS' BULLETIN. 1967. bi-w. $50. National Governors' Association, 444 North Capitol St., N.W., Ste. 250, Washington, DC 20001. TEL 202-624-5330. Ed. Gary Enos. circ. 3,400. **Document type:** bulletin.
Former titles: Governors' Weekly Bulletin (ISSN 0888-8647); Capital Ideas; Governors' Bulletin.
Description: Features latest information on Governors' initiatives and policies, giving readers an insider's perspective on opportunities and problems faced by state governors.

320.532 CU ISSN 0864-4632
GRANMA INTERNACIONAL (PORTUGUESE EDITION). 1984. w. $40. Comite Central del Partido Comunista de Cuba - Central Committee of the Communist Party of Cuba, Ave. General Suarez y Territorial, Plaza de la Revolucion, 10699 Havana 6, Cuba. TEL 70-8218. TELEX 0511-355. Ed. Gabriel Molina Franchossi. circ. 5,000.

320.532 CU ISSN 0864-4616
GRANMA INTERNACIONAL (SPANISH EDITION); resumen semanal. 1966. w. $40. Comite Central del Partido Comunista de Cuba - Central Committee of the Communist Party of Cuba, Ave. General Suarez y Territorial, Plaza de la Revolucion, 10699 Havana 6, Cuba. TEL 70-8218. TELEX 0511-355. Ed. Gabriel Molina Franchossi. circ. 25,000.

320.532 CU ISSN 0864-4624
GRANMA INTERNACIONAL (ENGLISH EDITION); weekly review. 1966. w. $40. Comite Central del Partido Comunista de Cuba - Central Committee of the Communist Party of Cuba, Av. Suarez y Territorial, Plaza de la Revolucion, 10699 Havana 6, Cuba. TEL 70-8218. TELEX 511221. (Subscr. to: Granma, Apdo. 6260, Havana 6, Cuba. TEL 70-771-432) Ed. Gabriel Molina Franchossi. adv.; bk.rev.; charts; illus. circ. 23,000. (also avail. in microform from UMI) **Indexed:** Alt.Press Ind. **Document type:** newspaper.

320.532 CU ISSN 0864-4640
GRANMA INTERNATIONAL (FRENCH EDITION); resume hebdomaire. 1966. w. $40. Comite Central del Partido Comunista de Cuba - Central Committee of the Communist Party of Cuba. Av. General Suarez y Territorial, Plaza de la Revolucion, 10699 Havana 6, Cuba. TEL 70-8218. TELEX 0511-355. Ed. Gabriel Molina Franchossi. circ. 10,000.

320 US
GRASS ROOTS CAMPAIGNING. 1979. m. $36. Campaign Consultants, Box 7281, Little Rock, AR 72217. TEL 501-225-3996. Ed. Jerry L. Russell. bk.rev. circ. 375. (looseleaf format; back issues avail.) **Document type:** newsletter.
Description: Covers political campaign techniques, philosophy, and psychology.

328.42 UK ISSN 0309-8826
J301
GREAT BRITAIN. HOUSE OF COMMONS. PARLIAMENTARY DEBATES. Key Title: Parliamentary Debates, Hansard. House of Commons Official Report. Weekly edition (ISSN 0261-8303) d. £1275. H.M.S.O., P.O. Box 276, London SW8 5DT, England. (Dist. by: UNIPUB, 4611-F Assembly Dr., Lantham, MD 20706-4391. TEL 301-459-7666) index. (also avail. in microfiche from BHP) **Document type:** government publication.
Description: Transcripts of the oral arguments presented in the House of Commons.

328.42 UK ISSN 0309-8834
GREAT BRITAIN. HOUSE OF LORDS. PARLIAMENTARY DEBATES. Key Title: Parliamentary Debates, Hansard. House of Lords Official Report. Weekly edition (ISSN 0261-8311) d. H.M.S.O., P.O. Box 276, London SW8 5DT, England. TEL 071-873-0011. FAX 071-873-8463. index. (also avail. in microfiche from BHP) **Document type:** government publication.

320 800 301 US ISSN 0270-7497
GREAT ISSUES OF THE DAY. 1981. irreg., no.7, 1994 (approx. 2/yr.). price varies. Borgo Press, Box 2845, San Bernardino, CA 92406. TEL 909-884-5813. FAX 909-888-4942. Ed. Jeffrey M. Elliot.
Description: Discussion on vital topics of the day, by leading academics, professionals, writers, and government officials.

322.4 614.7 UK ISSN 0957-5170
GREEN ANARCHIST; global anarchist 'zine. 1984. irreg. (approx. 4/yr.). £9.50. BCM 1715, London WC1N 3XX, England. adv.; bk.rev.; illus. circ. 2,500. (tabloid format) **Document type:** newspaper.

320 US ISSN 1066-9671
JA75.8
GREEN PERSPECTIVES. 1986. irreg. $12 for 10 issues. Box 111, Burlington, VT 05402. E-mail: bookchin@ipc.apc.org. Pub. Janet Biehl. bk.rev. circ. 500. **Document type:** newsletter.
Description: Covers social ecology, green politics and democracy.

GREEN WORLD. see *ENVIRONMENTAL STUDIES*

322.4 613.1 UK
GREENPEACE NEWSLETTER. 1971. q. free to supporters. Greenpeace (London), 5 Caledonian Rd., London N1, England. Ed.Bd. bk.rev. circ. 750. (processed) **Document type:** academic/scholarly publication.

324 US ISSN 1062-9726
GREENWOOD HISTORICAL ENCYCLOPEDIA OF THE WORLD'S POLITICAL PARTIES. 1982. irreg. price varies. Greenwood Press, Inc. (Subsidiary of: Greenwood Publishing Group Inc.), 88 Post Rd., W., Box 5007, Westport, CT 06881-5007. TEL 203-226-3571. FAX 203-222-1502. **Document type:** academic/scholarly publication.
Formerly: Greenwood Encyclopedia of the World's Political Parties.

320 US
GREYZONE; newsletter of Twin Cities anarchists. bi-m. Back Room Anarchist Books, Box 10854, Minneapolis, MN 55458-3854. TEL 612-870-7008.

320.5 IE ISSN 0017-4254
GRILLE; Irish Christian left. 1969. bi-m. 10s. 14 Kinvara Rd., Dublin 9, Ireland. Eds. John Feeney, William Ledwich. bk.rev.; bibl.

320.5 333.7 SW ISSN 1100-0872
GROENSAKEN. 1988. bi-m. SEK 130 membership (effective 1991). Miljoepartiet De Groene, P.O. Box 1244, S-221 05 Lund, Sweden.

POLITICAL SCIENCE

322 US ISSN 0017-4742
E838
GROUP RESEARCH REPORT.* 1962. m. $40. Group Research, Inc., 2000 M St., N.W., Ste. 400, Washington, DC 20036-3307. Ed. Wesley McCune. bk.rev.; illus.; index.
 Description: News and announcements pertaining to the political bloc of right-wing activists and intellectuals.

322.44 GP ISSN 0757-7907
F2066
GUADELOUPE 2000 MAGAZINE. 1970. fortn. Residence Massabielle, 97110 Pointe-a-Pitre, Guadeloupe. Ed. Edouard Boulogne. circ. 4,000.
 Formerly (until 1982): Guadeloupe 2000 (ISSN 0757-7893)

320.531 AT
GUARDIAN. w. Aus.$88. Socialist Party of Australia, 65 Campbell St., Surry Hills, N.S.W. 2010, Australia. FAX 61-2-281-5795. Ed. Anna Pha. **Document type:** newspaper.
 Formerly: Socialist.

GUARDIAN (LEXINGTON). see LAW

351 US
JK1
GUIDE TO CURRENT AMERICAN GOVERNMENT; a survey of recent significant developments in national government and politics. s-a. $15.95. Congressional Quarterly Inc., 1414 22nd St., N.W., Washington, DC 20037. TEL 202-887-8500. FAX 202-887-6706. index.
 —BLDSC (3486.370000).
 Former titles (until 1991): Current American Government (ISSN 0196-612X); (until 1970): C Q Guide to Current American Government (ISSN 0007-8956)
 Description: Topics and articles of current political, legislative or judicial interest.

320 US ISSN 1069-5354
E839.5
GUIDE TO POLITICAL VIDEOS. 1993. s-a. $30 to individuals; institutions $55 (effective 1995). Pacifica Communications, Box 4426, Santa Barbara, CA 93140-4426. TEL 805-965-5873. **Document type:** directory.
 Description: Features about 350 listings covering the politics of the environment, foreign policy, gay and lesbian issues, health care, the peace movement, and women's issues. Includes a synopsis of each video and full bibliographic and ordering information.

320.5 US ISSN 0894-4547
HX81
GUIDE TO THE AMERICAN LEFT. 1979. a. $19.95. Laird Wilcox. Ed. & Pub., Box 2047, Olathe, KS 66061. TEL 913-829-0609. FAX 913-829-0609. bibl. circ. 700. **Indexed:** P.A.I.S., Vert.File Ind. **Document type:** bibliography, directory.
 Former titles: Directory of the American Left (ISSN 0733-9623); (until 1970): Guide to the American Left (ISSN 0017-5315)
 Description: Lists 1,400 left-wing organizations and serials with a bibliography.

320 US ISSN 8756-0216
HS2321
GUIDE TO THE AMERICAN RIGHT; directory and bibliography. 1978. a. $19.95. Laird Wilcox, Ed. & Pub., Box 2047, Olathe, KS 66061. TEL 913-829-0609. FAX 913-829-0609. circ. 1,800. **Indexed:** P.A.I.S., Vert.File Ind. **Document type:** bibliography, directory.
 Formerly: Directory of the American Right.
 Description: Lists 1,500 right-wing organizations and serials. Includes a bibliography.

988 GY
GUYANA INFORMATION BULLETIN. 1964. m. free. People's Progressive Party, Freedom House, 41 Robb St., Georgetown, Guyana. Ed. Janet Jagan. circ. 1,000. (processed) **Indexed:** HR Rep.
 Former titles (until 1979): Overseas Mirror; (until 1978): Guyana Information Bulletin (ISSN 0017-5862)

988.1 GY ISSN 0046-6654
GUYANA JOURNAL.* 1970. q. Ministry of External Affairs, Carmichael St., Georgetown, Guyana. Ed. L. Searwar. illus.

370 355 320 GW
H S F K STANDPUNKTE - FRIEDENSFORSCHUNG AKTUELL. 1981. q. free. Hessische Stiftung Friedens- und Konfliktforschung, Leimenrode 29, 60322 Frankfurt a.M., Germany. TEL 069-9591040. FAX 069-558481. Ed. Eva von Hase-Mihalik. circ. 4,000. (back issues avail.) **Document type:** academic/scholarly publication.
 Formerly: Friedensforschung Aktuell (ISSN 0930-830X)
 Description: Articles and essays on current topics of peace and foreign policy, as well as peace research and peace movements.

320 SA
H S R C CENTRE FOR CONSTITUTIONAL ANALYSIS. irreg. Human Sciences Research Council, Centre for Constitutional Analysis, Private Bag X41, Pretoria 0001, South Africa. Ed. Dr. Bertus de Villiers. circ. 500. **Document type:** newsletter.
 Description: Covers constitutional matters.

HADASSAH MAGAZINE. see ETHNIC INTERESTS

320 IS
AL-HAHOMA. 1913. m. free. Hashomar Hatzair Israel, 7 Bezalel Yaffe St., Tel Aviv 65204, Israel. TEL 972-3-291161. FAX 972-3-202601. Ed Roy Peled. circ. 5,000 (controlled).
 Description: Covers issues in education, Zionism, Middle Eastern politics, and others issues of interest to members of the political youth movement.

320 PK
HALAT O AFKAR. (Text in Urdu) w. Independent Newspapers Corp. Pvt. Ltd., Printing House, I.I. Chundrigar Rd., P.O. Box 52, Karachi (Sindh) 74200, Pakistan. TEL 92-21-2637111. FAX 92-21-2636066.

320 330.9 GW ISSN 0947-4900
HAMBURG AFRICAN STUDIES/ETUDES AFRICAINES HAMBOURGEOISES. (Text in English or French) 1993. irreg. price varies. Institut fuer Afrika-Kunde, Neuer Jungfernstieg 21, 20354 Hamburg, Germany. TEL 040-3562523. FAX 040-3562511. circ. 300. **Document type:** monographic series.
 Description: Contemporary problems and developments in Africa.

327 SI
HAMMER.* (Text in English) 1972. m. $2.60. Workers' Party, Ste. 602, Colombo Ct., Singapore 0617, Singapore. illus.

320 MY ISSN 0127-4147
AL-HARAKAH. parti Islam se-Malaysia. 1973. 2/w. M.0.70 per no. Islamic Party of Malaysia, 28A Jalan Pahang Barat, Off Jalan Pahang, 53000 Kuala Lumpur, Malaysia. TEL 603-4213343. FAX 603-4212422. Ed.Bd. adv.; bk.rev.; circ. 50,000 (controlled).
 Formerly (until 1987): Berita Pas.
 Description: Provides news about the Islamic Party of Malaysia.

HARVARD JOURNAL OF HISPANIC POLICY. see ETHNIC INTERESTS

320 US ISSN 0090-1032
JK1
HARVARD POLITICAL REVIEW. 1972. q. $15 in U.S. and Canada; elsewhere $30. Institute of Politics, Student Advisory Committee, 79 John F. Kennedy St., Cambridge, MA 02138. TEL 617-495-1360. FAX 617-495-1364. Ed. John Turner. adv. contact: Raj Inamdar. bk.rev.; illus. circ. 12,000. **Document type:** academic/scholarly publication.

320.532 II
HAYAT.* (Text in Urdu) 1970. w. Ajoy Bhavan, Kutla Road, New Delhi, India. illus.

320 NP
HEADS OF STATE AND CHIEF EXECUTIVES' AWARD. 1980. a. $350. Siveast Consultants, Inc., USA, P.O. Box 8510, Kathmandu, Nepal. adv.; bk.rev.
 Description: Lists prominent politicians and chief executives who distinguished themselves and contributed to the cause of humanity and world at large.

320 JA ISSN 0385-0749
JX1903
HEIWA KENKYU/PEACE STUDIES. (Text in Japanese) 1976. a. 2,800 Yen. (Nihon Heiwa Gakkai - Peace Studies Association of Japan) Waseda Daigaku Shuppanbu - Wasedu University Press, 1-103 Totsuka-machi, Shinjuku-ku, Tokyo 169, Japan. TEL 03-3203-1551. FAX 03-3207-0406. bk.rev. circ. 1,500.

320 301 NE
HELLING.* 1978. q. fl.52. (Stichting Instituut voor Politiek en Sociaal Onderzoek) Leeuwenbergh B.V., Postbus 139, 2170 AC Sassenheim, Netherlands. (Dist. by: I P S O, c/o Pegasus, Leidsestraat 25, 1017 NT, Amsterdam, Netherlands) Ed. Paul Streumer. adv.; bk.rev. circ. 1,200.
 Formed by the merger of (1978-1987): Socialisties Perspektief (ISSN 0166-8390); (1980-1987): Komma (ISSN 0167-4463)

320 CK
HERALDO DE CALDAS. w. Col.2 per no. Editorial Sigma - Pereira, Carrera 23, no. 20-59, Manizales, Colombia. Ed. Alberto Trujillo Escobar. adv.; illus. (tabloid format)

320 US
HERITAGE FOUNDATION. ISSUE BULLETINS. 1977. irreg., no.205, 1995. $125 includes Backgrounder and Backgrounder Update; newsstand price: $3.50. Heritage Foundation, 214 Massachusetts Ave., N.E., Washington, DC 20002. TEL 202-546-4400. FAX 202-546-8328. (back issues avail.)
 •Also available online. Vendor(s): Lexis-Nexis.

323.44 US ISSN 1069-7268
HETERODOXY; articles and animadversions on political correctness and other follies. 1992. 12/yr. $25. Center for the Study of Popular Culture, 12400 Ventura Blvd., Ste. 304, Studio City, CA 91604. TEL 310-843-3692; 800-752-6562. FAX 310-843-3699. Eds. Peter Collier, David Horowitz. adv. contact: David Horowitz. (back issues avail.)
 Description: Covers freedom of speech issues in academia.

954.96 330.9 NP ISSN 1012-9804
HC430.6.Z7
HIMAL; Himalayan magazine. 1988. bi-m. Rs.220 to individuals (S. Asia $12; Europe DM.50; in U.S. $22.50; Canada $27.50); institutions Rs.600 (S. Asia $25; Europe DM.70; in U.S. $35); newsstand price: Rs.40 ($4.75 in U.S.). Himal Associates, P.O. Box 42, Lalitpur 44702, Nepal. TEL 977-1-523845. FAX 977-1-521013. E-mail: himal@mosnepal.ernet.in. (Subscr. in U.S. to: Himal, Box 470758, San Francisco, CA 94147. TEL 800-203-8600; Subscr. in Europe to: Durga Press (Himal), Luitpoldstr. 20, 82211 Herrsching, Germany) Ed. Kanak Mani Dixit. adv. contact: Kiran Shrestha. bk.rev.; abstr.; illus.; index, cum.index on diskette. circ. 7,200. **Document type:** consumer publication.
 Description: Covers political, social and cultural issues and news pertaining to the Himalayan regions, including Nepal, Sikkim, Bhutan, India, Tibet and Tibetans in exile. Also covers recent publications on the region.

950 II ISSN 0018-1900
HIMMAT/COURAGE; Asia's new voice. (Text in English) 1964. w. Rs.30($25) Himmat Publications Trust, 501 Arun Chambers, Tardeo Road, Bombay 400034, India. Ed. Kalpana Sharma. adv.; bk.rev.; charts; illus. circ. 10,000.

322.4 GW ISSN 0722-8252
HIMMEL & ERDE; international revue. 1981. irreg. Verlag Roter Funke, Goethestr. 22, 28203 Bremen, Germany. Ed. Klaus Mecking. (back issues avail.)

HISPO. see HISTORY — History Of Europe

HISTORIA ECONOMICA. see BUSINESS AND ECONOMICS — Economic Situation And Conditions

HISTORIC DOCUMENTS. see HISTORY — History Of North And South America

POLITICAL SCIENCE

320 900   US
HISTORIC WORLD LEADERS. (In 5 vols.: Vol.1 Western Europe, Vol.2 Eastern Europe, Vol.3 Asia and Australia, Vol.4 Africa, Middle East, Vol.5 United States, Canada, and South and Latin America) 21st ed., 1993. irreg. $225 ($49.95 per vol.) (effective 1993). Gale Research Inc., 835 Penobscot Bldg., Detroit, MI 48226. TEL 313-961-2242. FAX 313-961-6083. Ed. Anne Commire.

943.7 320 301   XO   ISSN 0441-8026
HISTORICA CARPATICA.* 196? irreg. price varies. (Vychodoslovenske Muzeum v Kosicach) Vychodoslovenske Vydavatel'stvo v Kosiciach, Alejova 3, 040-11 Kosice, Slovakia.

HISTORICAL METHODS. see *HISTORY*

HISTORICAL SOCIAL RESEARCH/HISTORISCHE SOZIALFORSCHUNG. see *HISTORY — History Of Europe*

HISTORICKY OBZOR; casopis pro vyuku dejepisu a popularizaci historie. see *HISTORY — History Of Europe*

DAS HISTORISCH-POLITISCHE BUCH; Ein Wegweiser durch das Schrifttum. see *HISTORY*

HISTORISCH-POLITISCHE MITTEILUNGEN; Archiv fuer Christlich-Demokratische Politik. see *HISTORY*

320 900   UK   ISSN 0143-781X
JA8
HISTORY OF POLITICAL THOUGHT; controversies in science & the humanities. 1980. q. £29($56) to individuals (foreign £32); institutions £57.75 (foreign £68.75 ($120)) (effective 1996). Imprint Academic, P.O. Box 1, Thorverton, Exeter, Devon EX 5YX, England. TEL 01392-841600. E-mail: keith@imprint.co.uk. Eds. Janet Coleman, Iain Hampshire-Monk; Pub. Keith Sutherland. adv.: page £100 ($170); adv. contact: Sandra Good. bk.rev.; bibl.; circ. 900 (paid). (back issues avail.) **Indexed:** A.B.C.Pol.Sci., Amer.Hist.& Life, Arts & Hum.Cit.Ind., Curr.Cont., Hist.Abstr., Int.Polit.Sci.Abstr., Phil.Ind., Polit.Sci.Abstr. **Document type:** academic/scholarly publication.
—BLDSC (4318.405000); Faxon; SWETS; UnCover.
  Description: Takes a multidisciplinary approach to the historical study of political ideas and associated methodological problems.
  Refereed Serial

HISTORY WORKSHOP JOURNAL; a journal of socialist historians. see *HISTORY*

HITOTSUBASHI JOURNAL OF LAW AND POLITICS. see *LAW*

HOGAKU/JOURNAL OF LAW AND POLITICAL SCIENCE. see *LAW*

HOGAKU KENKYU/JOURNAL OF LAW, POLITICS, AND SOCIOLOGY. see *LAW*

HOKOUK. see *LAW*

HOMME LIBRE; fils de la terre. see *PSYCHOLOGY*

320 350   US
HOTLINE (FALLS CHURCH).* 1987. d. price varies. American Political Network, Inc., 3129 Mount Vernon Ave., Alexandria, VA 22305-2640. TEL 703-237-5130. Ed. Will Salatin.
●Also available online. Vendor(s): NewsNet (PO01).
  Description: Coverage of American politics, focusing on gubernatorial, Senate and House races.

320   UK   ISSN 0957-0136
HOUSMANS PEACE DIARY & WORLD PEACE DIRECTORY. 1954. a. £6($12) Housmans Bookshop Ltd., 5 Caledonian Rd., Kings Cross, London N1 9DX, England. TEL 0171-837-4473. FAX 0171-278-4444. E-mail: worldpeace@bn.apc.org. Ed. Albert Beale. adv. circ. 8,000. (also avail. in diskette format; back issues avail.) **Document type:** directory.
  Description: Provides up-to-date listings and information of 2,000 national and international organizations in more than 140 countries in the fields of peace campaigning, human rights, and environmental issues.

057.8   CN   ISSN 0702-3855
F1035.C7
HRVATSKI PUT/CROATIAN WAY. (Text occasionally in English) 1962. m. Can.$36. Croatian-Canadian Society, 34 Southport St., Ste. 88510, Toronto, ON M6S 3N0, Canada. TEL 416-979-5341. FAX 416-621-4819. Ed. Rudi Tomic. adv.; bk.rev.; illus. circ. 3,000.
  Formerly: Nas Put - Our Way (ISSN 0027-8092)
  Description: Covers world affairs and Croatian national culture and political activity throughout the world.

320 342   CH
HSIEN CHENG SSU CH'AO. (Text in Chinese) q. (Kuo Min Ta Hui, Hsien Cheng Yen T'ao Wei Yuan Hui - National People's Council, Committee for the Discussion of Constitutional Government) Hsien Cheng Ssu Ch'ao Magazine House, No. 1, Hsiushan St., Taipei, Taiwan, Republic of China. TEL 02-311-4066.
  Description: Investigates systems of government and political theories, centering on the concept and reality of Constitutional rule. Includes translations.

320   UK   ISSN 0142-7377
HULL PAPERS IN POLITICS. 1978. irreg. price varies. University of Hull, Department of Politics, Hull HU6 7RX, England. Ed. Philip Norton.

320.9   US   ISSN 0018-7194
D410
HUMAN EVENTS; the national conservative weekly. 1944. w. $69.95. Eagle Publishing, A Phillips Publishing International Company, 422 First St., S.E., Washington, DC 20003. TEL 202-546-0856. FAX 202-546-9579. Ed. Thomas S. Winter. adv.; bk.rev.; illus.; index. circ. 40,000. (tabloid format; also avail. in microform from UMI; microfiche from BHP,KTO; reprint service avail. from UMI) **Indexed:** Bk.Rev.Ind. (1977-), Child.Bk.Rev.Ind. (1977-). **Document type:** consumer publication.
—UMI. **CCC.**

HUMAN RESOURCES ABSTRACTS; an international information service. see *SOCIOLOGY — Abstracting, Bibliographies, Statistics*

320   GW
HUMANE GESELLSCHAFT. 1972. q. Junge Union Baden-Wuerttemberg, Hohenheimerstr. 9, 70184 Stuttgart, Germany. TEL 0711-2104353. adv.; bk.rev.; film rev.; play rev.; bibl.; illus.; stat. circ. 20,000.

I C P S R BULLETIN. (Inter-University Consortium for Political and Social Research) see *SOCIAL SCIENCES: COMPREHENSIVE WORKS*

I F M - S E I BULLETIN. (International Falcon Movement - Socialist Educational International) see *EDUCATION*

I LAISVE/TOWARD FREEDOM; Lithuanian magazine of politics. see *ETHNIC INTERESTS*

320   GW   ISSN 0177-6657
I N P R E K O R R. (Internationale Pressekorrespondenz) 1971. m. DM.50 (foreign DM.65). (Vereinigtes Sekretariat der IV. Internationale) Neuer Kurs GmbH, Dasselstr. 75-77, 50674 Cologne, Germany. Ed.Bd. adv.; bk.rev.; index. circ. 1,000. (back issues avail.) **Document type:** newsletter.
  Description: Presents issues of interest for working people, feminist movements, international solidarity groups, and those interested in socialist movements and Marxist theory.

300 320   II   ISSN 0019-0403
I P S S BULLETIN. (Text in English) vol.4, 1969. Rs.10. Institute of Political and Social Studies, 357-1C Prince Anwar Shah Rd., Calcutta 31, India. Ed. K.K. Sinha.

I S H I OCCASIONAL PAPERS IN SOCIAL CHANGE. (Institute for the Study of Human Issues) see *SOCIOLOGY*

320.531   AU
I U S Y NEWSLETTER. 1971. irreg. free. International Union of Socialist Youth, Neustiftgasse, A-1070 Vienna, Austria. TEL 431-931267. FAX 431-523124385. TELEX 75312469 SJOE. Ed. Ricard Torrell. bk.rev.; illus. circ. 1,500.
  Former titles (until 1985): I U S Y Bulletin; I U S Y Survey (ISSN 0019-0888)

I W K. (Internationale Wissenschaftliche Korrespondenz zur Geschichte der Deutschen Arbeiterbewegung) see *LABOR UNIONS*

IBYKUS; Zeitschrift fuer Poesie, Wissenschaft und Staatskunst. see *LITERATURE — Poetry*

320.9   NO   ISSN 0046-8517
IDE; magazine for Christian democratic debate. 1967. q. NOK 100 prices typically set in January. Valo Forlag A-S, Postboks 478, Sentrum, 0105 Oslo 1, Norway. TEL 47-22-41-11-80. Ed. Johannes Morken. bk.rev.; bibl.; illus. circ. 1,100.
—**CCC.**

320   DK   ISSN 0107-1149
IDE POLITIK. 1971. 36/yr. DKK 270. Kristeligt Folkeparti, Bernhard Bangs Alle 23, 2000 Frederiksberg, Denmark. TEL 00945-38881024. FAX 00945-38883115. Ed. Christel Kirk Brubacher. bk.rev.; illus. circ. 3,600.

320   IT
IDEA LIBERALE. 1959. bi-m. L.20000. Edizioni Pergamena s.a.s., Viale Ezio 7, 20149 Milan, Italy. Dir. Giovanni Giraldi.

IDENTITIES. see *ETHNIC INTERESTS*

320   PE   ISSN 1019-455X
IDEOLOGIA Y POLITICA. 1973. irreg., no.7, 1990. price varies. (Instituto de Estudios Peruanos) I E P Ediciones, Horacio Urteaga 694, Lima 11, Peru. TEL 51-14-323070. FAX 51-14-324981. E-mail: postmaster@iep.org.pe.

320 990   US   ISSN 1075-9328
IF YUH INT'RESTED - TOTAL CARIBBEAN NEWS. 1993. m. $25 (Canada Can.$30); newsstand price: $3. T C N Publishing, Box 1226, Bothell, WA 98041-1226. TEL 206-485-7944; 800-484-9704. Ed. Anthony Maillard. adv. contact: Anthony Maillard. music rev. circ. 500. **Document type:** consumer publication.
  Description: Covers political, economic, social, and cultural news of the Caribbean. Seeks to keep expatriots well informed of events in their native countries.

320.5   DK   ISSN 0107-5276
IKKEVOLD (LANGESKOV); tidsskrift for antimilitarisme og fredsarbejde. 1933. 4/yr. Kr.95. Aldrig Mere Krig, Hoegh-Guldbergsgade 59 st., DK-8000 Aarhus C, Denmark. Ed. Steen Nielsen. adv.; bk.rev.; bibl.; illus. circ. 1,300.

320   US   ISSN 0738-9663
ILLINOIS ISSUES; a magazine of government and politics. 1975. m. $35.95 (foreign $94.95). Sangamon State University, Springfield, IL 62794-9243. TEL 217-786-6084. (Subscr. to: Box 251, Mt. Morris, IL 61054) (Co-sponsor: University of Illinois) Ed. Peggy Boyer Long. adv.: B&W page $998, color page $1448. bk.rev. circ. 6,000. **Indexed:** P.A.I.S., Urb.Aff.Abstr.
—UnCover.
  Description: Covers political and governmental issues affecting Illinois.

329   US
ILLINOIS LIBERTARIAN. 1975. m. $15. Libertarian Party of Illinois, 1602 Colonial Parkway, Inverness, IL 60057. TEL 708-776-8090. FAX 708-475-3776. Ed. Ken Prazak. adv.; bk.rev. circ. 1,000.
  Description: Newsletter of articles, letters, book reviews, editorials, announcements, and directories of interest to support the platform of the Libertarian Party.

324.6   US   ISSN 1041-1283
ILLINOIS VOTER. 1820. q. $8. League of Women Voters of Illinois, 332 S. Michigan Ave., Ste. 1142, Chicago, IL 60604. TEL 312-939-5935. FAX 312-939-6887. Ed. Cynthia Scott. adv. contact: Cynthia Scott. illus. (tabloid format; back issues avail.) **Document type:** newsletter.

374 320   GW   ISSN 0721-2097
IM GESPRAECH. 1971. q. DM.16. (Institut fuer Begabtenfoerderung) Ernst Knoth GmbH, Postfach 226, 49303 Melle, Germany. TEL 05422-2895. FAX 05422-43038. Ed. Felix Becker. circ. 5,000. **Document type:** bulletin.

IMMIGRATION WATCH. see *POPULATION STUDIES*

IMPACT; Asian magazine for human transformation. see SOCIAL SCIENCES: COMPREHENSIVE WORKS

IN DE WAAGSCHAAL. see RELIGIONS AND THEOLOGY

320.531 US ISSN 0160-5992
AP2
IN THESE TIMES. 1976. 26/yr. $35.95. Institute for Public Affairs, 2040 N. Milwaukee Ave., 2nd Fl., Chicago, IL 60647-4002. TEL 312-472-5700. FAX 312-772-4180. Ed. James Weinstein. bk.rev.; illus. circ. 35,000. (also avail. in microfilm from UMI; back issues avail.; reprint service avail. from UMI) Indexed: Alt.Press Ind., Chic.Per.Ind., HR Rep., Left Ind. (1982-).
—UMI; UnCover.
Description: Presents a leftist viewpoint; however, with frequent discussions of strategies for the Democratic Party. It is strong on its labor and women's movement coverage; less strong on the international front.

INCHIESTA. see SOCIAL SERVICES AND WELFARE

INCITE INFORMATION; inquiry and commentary. see JOURNALISM

L'INCONTRO DELLE GENTI; rivista di scienze lettere ed arte. see ART

320 301 800 IT
INDAGINI E PROSPETTIVE. irreg., latest no.19. price varies. Angelo Longo Editore, Via Paolo Costa 33, 48100 Ravenna, Italy. TEL 39-544-217026. FAX 39-544-217554. **Document type:** monographic series.

INDEPENDENT NATIONAL EDITION; a monthly journal for thoughtful Canadians. see ENVIRONMENTAL STUDIES

320 US
INDEPENDENT POLITICAL ACTION BULLETIN. q. $12. National Committee for Independent Political Action, Box 170610, Brooklyn, NY 11217-0610. TEL 718-643-9603. Eds. Ted Glick, Maryellen Kluxen. circ. 1,000. **Document type:** bulletin.
Formerly (until 1992): National Committee for Independent Political Action. Discussion Bulletin.
Description: Reports on developments in progressive politics in the U.S.

954 US ISSN 0019-4212
INDIA NEWS. 1962. fortn. 15. India Information Service, Embassy of India, 2107 Massachusetts Ave., N.W., Washington, DC 20008. TEL 202-265-5050. FAX 202-939-7027. Ed. Dayakar Ratakonda. bk.rev.; illus. circ. 15,000. (also avail. in microform) Indexed: P.A.I.S. **Document type:** newspaper.

320 300 II
INDIAN INSTITUTE OF PUBLIC OPINION. MONTHLY PUBLIC OPINION SURVEYS. (Text in English) 1955. m. Rs.400($80) Indian Institute of Public Opinion Private Ltd., 2-A National Insurance Bldg., Parliament St., Box 288, New Delhi 110001, India. Ed. E.P.W. da Costa. charts; stat.
Description: Highlights survey results on socio-economic and political affairs by a variety of demographic variables.

320 II ISSN 0019-5510
JA26
INDIAN JOURNAL OF POLITICAL SCIENCE. (Text in English) 1937. q. $65. Indian Political Science Association, Nagarjuna University, Dept. of Political Science & Public Administration, Guntur 522 510, A.P., India. TEL 0863-23225. Ed. C.V. Raghavulu. adv.; bk.rev. circ. 2,000. (also avail. in microform from UMI; reprint service avail. from UMI) Indexed: A.B.C.Pol.Sci., Amer.Hist.& Life, ASSIA, Hist.Abstr., Int.Polit.Sci.Abstr. **Document type:** academic/scholarly publication.
—Faxon; UnCover.

320 II ISSN 0303-9951
JA26
INDIAN JOURNAL OF POLITICS. 1967. q. Rs.100($35) (effective 1991). Aligarh Muslim University, Department of Political Science, Aligarh 202 002, Uttar Pradesh, India. Ed. A.S. Usmani. adv.; bk.rev. circ. 1,000. (also avail. in microform; reprint service avail. from ISI) Indexed: Amer.Hist.& Life, Curr.Cont., Hist.Abstr., Ind.Per.Lit., Int.Polit.Sci.Abstr., Sociol.Abstr.
—UnCover. CCC.

320 990 AT ISSN 1037-7131
INDIAN OCEAN CENTRE FOR PEACE STUDIES. BRIEFING PAPERS. irreg. price varies. Indian Ocean Centre for Peace Studies, University of Western Australia, Nedlands, W.A. 6009, Australia. FAX 09-380-1074. Ed. Kenneth McPherson. **Document type:** academic/scholarly publication.

320 990 AT ISSN 1039-0871
INDIAN OCEAN CENTRE FOR PEACE STUDIES. OCCASIONAL PAPERS AND MONOGRAPHS. irreg. price varies. Indian Ocean Centre for Peace Studies, University of Western Australia, Nedlands, W.A. 6009, Australia. FAX 09-380-1074. Ed. Kenneth McPherson. **Document type:** academic/scholarly publication.
Formed by the merger of: Indian Ocean Centre for Peace Studies. Monographs & Indian Ocean Centre for Peace Studies. Occasional Papers (ISSN 1037-7123)

320 990 AT ISSN 1031-2331
DS331
INDIAN OCEAN REVIEW. (Text in English and French) 1980. q. Aus.$30 to individuals; institutions Aus.$40. Indian Ocean Centre for Peace Studies, University of Western Australia, Nedlands, W.A. 6009, Australia. FAX 09-380-1074. Ed. Kenneth McPherson. bk.rev.; illus.; charts. circ. 900. (back issues avail.) **Document type:** academic/scholarly publication.
—UnCover.
Formerly: Indian Ocean Newsletter (ISSN 0728-4330)
Description: Multi-disciplinary publication centered upon issues concerning the Indian Ocean region.

INDIAN SCHOOL OF POLITICAL ECONOMY. JOURNAL. see BUSINESS AND ECONOMICS

INDIANA CENTER ON GLOBAL CHANGE AND WORLD PEACE. OCCASIONAL PAPER SERIES. see ENVIRONMENTAL STUDIES

323.4 100 US
INDIVIDUAL LIBERTY. 1970. m. $10. Society for Individual Liberty, Box 1147, Warminster, PA 18974. TEL 215-365-7389. Eds. David Walter, Donald Ernsperger. adv.; bk.rev. circ. 1,700. (processed)
Formerly: S I L News (ISSN 0036-1550)
Description: Monthly newsletter of the Society for Individual Liberty, a Pennsylvania-based group of the Libertarian Party. Addresses Constitutional concerns and news of the Libertarian Party.

INDIVIDUALIST. see PHILOSOPHY

954 GW ISSN 0019-719X
DS401
INDO-ASIA; fuer Politik, Kultur und Wirtschaft Indiens und Suedost Asiens. (Text in German; occasionally in English) 1959. 4/yr. DM.71.20. (Deutsch-Indische Gesellschaft) Burg-Verlag, 74343 Sachsenheim, Germany. TEL 07147-6091. FAX 07147-12447. Ed. Gisela Bonn. adv.; bk.rev.; charts; illus.; index. circ. 2,500. Indexed: P.A.I.S.For.Lang.Ind. **Document type:** academic/scholarly publication.

327 II ISSN 0042-9740
INDO-IRAN JOURNAL. (Text in English and Persian) 1969. q. Rs.7($1) Indo-Iran Society, Tilak Marg, New Delhi 110001, India. Ed. H. Kardoosh. illus.

INDONESIA LETTER. see BUSINESS AND ECONOMICS — Economic Situation And Conditions

959.8 IO ISSN 0304-2170
INDONESIAN QUARTERLY. (Text in English) 1972. 3/m. $50 in Asia, Pacific; N. America $70; elsewhere $60. Centre for Strategic and International Studies, Jalan Tanah Abang III-27, Jakarta 10160, Indonesia. TEL 3865532-5. FAX 021-375317. TELEX 45164-CENTRE-IA. Ed. Daniel Setyawan. adv.; bk.rev.; bibl.; charts. circ. 3,000. **Indexed:** Abstr.Mil.Bibl., Asian-Pac.Econ.Lit., E.I., Polit.Sci.Abstr., Rice Abstr. **Document type:** academic/scholarly publication.
—BLDSC (4438.045000).

INFORMACION POLITICA Y ECONOMICA. see BUSINESS AND ECONOMICS — Economic Situation And Conditions

INFORMATION FUER ORMESHEIM. see PUBLIC ADMINISTRATION — Municipal Government

320 371.3 GW ISSN 0046-9408
INFORMATIONEN ZUR POLITISCHEN BILDUNG/INFORMATION FOR CIVIC EDUCATION. 1952. 4/yr. free. Bundeszentrale fuer Politische Bildung, Berliner Freiheit 7, 53111 Bonn, Germany. TEL 0228-515229. FAX 0228-515113. Ed. Juergen Faulenbach. bk.rev. circ. 1,150,000.
Indexed: Amer.Hist.& Life, Hist.Abstr. **Document type:** academic/scholarly publication.
—BLDSC (4496.478300).
Description: Devoted to the study and teaching of political science in Germany. Includes bibliography and list of educational materials.

328 FR ISSN 0010-6623
INFORMATIONS CONSTITUTIONNELLES ET PARLEMENTAIRES/CONSTITUTIONAL AND PARLIAMENTARY INFORMATION. (Editions in English, French) 1948. s-a. 40 SFr. (effective 1996). (Union Interparlementaire, SZ - Inter-Parliamentary Union) Association des Secretaires Generaux des Parlements - Association of Secretaries General of Parliaments, c/o Vincent Tocanne, Assemble Nationale, 75005 Paris, France. adv.; index. circ. 1,500. **Indexed:** P.A.I.S.
—UnCover.

INFORME LATINOAMERICANO. see BUSINESS AND ECONOMICS — Economic Situation And Conditions

340 PE
INFORMES. no.8, 1982. irreg. Instituto de Promocion y Educacion Popular, Av. Pardo 130, Chimbote, Peru.

320 332 GT ISSN 0252-8754
HC141.A1
INFORPRESS CENTROAMERICANA. 1972. w. $439. Inforpress Centroamericana, 11 Ave. 16-60, Zona 2, Guatemala City, Guatemala. TEL 530681. charts. (back issues avail.) **Document type:** newspaper, bulletin.
Description: Contains information and analysis on the economic and political events in Belize, Guatemala, El Salvador, Honduras, Nicaragua, Costa Rica and Panama.

INKWEL. see WOMEN'S INTERESTS

INSIDE ALABAMA POLITICS. see PUBLIC ADMINISTRATION

994 AT ISSN 0046-9629
INSIDE CANBERRA. 1948. w. Aus.$345. Australian Press Services Pty., Ltd., P.O. Box E 160, Queen Victoria Terrace, A.C.T. 2600, Australia. Ed. R. D. Chalmers. **Document type:** newsletter.

320.958 UK ISSN 1352-4100
▼**INSIDE CENTRAL ASIA**; a weekly roundup of media reports covered by B B C Monitoring. 1994. w. £435 (rest of Europe £455; elsewhere £475) (effective 1996). B B C Monitoring, Caversham Park, Reading, Berks. RG4 8TZ, England. TEL 01734-469289. FAX 01734-463823. TELEX 848318. E-mail: 1004321,2524@compuserve.com. Ed. Bob Eggington. **Document type:** trade publication.
Description: Offers insight into the economic and political trends of central Asian nations.

INSIDE MICHIGAN POLITICS. see PUBLIC ADMINISTRATION

320 SP
INSTITUCIONES EUROPEAS. 3/yr. $40. (Centro de Estudios Constitucionales) Edisa, Lopez Hoyos, 141, 28002 Madrid, Spain. TEL 415-97-12.

INSTITUT DES HAUTES ETUDES DE L'AMERIQUE LATINE. COLLECTION DES TRAVAUX ET MEMOIRES. see HUMANITIES: COMPREHENSIVE WORKS

INSTITUT DES RECHERCHES MARXISTES. ISSUES. see BUSINESS AND ECONOMICS

INSTITUT DES RECHERCHES MARXISTES. RECHERCHES INTERNATIONALES. see POLITICAL SCIENCE — International Relations

320 330.9 GW ISSN 0945-3601
INSTITUT FUER AFRIKA-KUNDE. ARBEITEN. 1974. irreg. Institut fuer Afrika-Kunde, Neuer Jungfernstieg 21, 20354 Hamburg, Germany. TEL 040-3562523. FAX 040-3562511. circ. 250. **Document type:** monographic series.

POLITICAL SCIENCE

320 100   IT   ISSN 0393-6503
INSTITUT INTERNATIONAL J. MARITAIN. NOTES ET DOCUMENTS; pour une recherche personnaliste - for a personalist approach. 1975. q. £30 (effective 1994). Institut International Jacques Maritain, Via Quintino Sella, 33, 00187 Rome, Italy. TEL 39-6-4874336. FAX 39-6-4825188. Ed. Gianfranco Martini. adv.; bk.rev.; circ. 2,000 (controlled). **Document type:** academic/scholarly publication.
—Faxon.

INSTITUT PO ISTORIIA NA B S P. IZVESTIIA. see HISTORY — History Of Europe

INSTITUTE FOR SOCIAL RESEARCH NEWSLETTER. see SOCIAL SERVICES AND WELFARE

330 301   US   ISSN 0364-0779
HV95   CODEN: JISSDW
INSTITUTE FOR SOCIOECONOMIC STUDIES. JOURNAL. Key Title: Journal of the Institute for Socioeconomic Studies. 1976. q. Institute for Socioeconomic Studies, Airport Rd., White Plains, NY 10604. TEL 914-428-7400. Ed. B.A. Rittersporn, Jr. circ. 17,500. (also avail. in microfiche from WSH,PMC; microfilm from WSH,PMC) **Indexed:** ASSIA, BPIA, CLOA, Fut.Surv.; Med.Care Rev., Mid.East: Abstr.& Ind., P.A.I.S., Sage Pub.Admin.Abstr.
—UMI.

323.4   US
INSTITUTE FOR THE STUDY OF GENOCIDE NEWSLETTER. 1988. s-a. $30 to individuals; institutions $20. Institute for the Study of Genocide, 899 Tenth Ave., Rm. 621, New York, NY 10019. TEL 617-354-2785. FAX 617-491-8076. Ed. Helen Fein. bk.rev. circ. 1,000. **Document type:** newsletter, monographic series.

INSTITUTE OF DEVELOPING ECONOMIES. LIBRARY BULLETIN/AJIA KEIZAI SHIRYO-GEPPO. see LIBRARY AND INFORMATION SCIENCES

INSTITUTE OF URBAN STUDIES. see HOUSING AND URBAN PLANNING

320   AG   ISSN 0074-0063
INSTITUTO DE CIENCIA POLITICA RAFAEL BIELSA. ANUARIO. 1968. a. Arg.$75($8) Universidad Nacional de Rosario, Instituto de Ciencia Politica Rafael Bielsa, Facultad de Ciencia Politica y Relaciones Internacionales, Division Publicaciones, Cordoba 2020, Rosario, Argentina. Ed. Alberto Dominguez.

320   PE
INSTITUTO PERUANO DE POLEMOLOGIA. 1986. s-a. free. Instituto Peruano de Polemologia, Apdo. Postal 2284, Lima 1, Peru. Ed. Luis Callegari Botteri. circ. 2,000.

320.9   UK
INTELLIGENCE DIGEST - A REVIEW OF WORLD AFFAIRS; international political, economic and strategic intelligence. 1938. w. (45/yr.). £97($197) (overseas £117) (effective 1995): Intelligence International Ltd., The Stoneyhill Centre, Brimpsfield, Glos. GL4 8LF, England. TEL 01452-864764. FAX 01452-864848. Ed. J.K.C. de Courcy. bk.rev. **Document type:** academic/scholarly publication.
—UMI.
Former titles: Intelligence Digest (Cheltenham); Intelligence Digest Political and Strategic Review; Intelligence Digest World Report; Intelligence Digest (ISSN 0020-4900); Intelligence Digest Weekly Review (ISSN 0307-188X); Weekly Review (ISSN 0043-1915).

320.5   AT   ISSN 0047-0406
INTELLIGENCE SURVEY. 1953. m. Aus.$6. Australian League of Rights, 273 Little Collins St., Melbourne, Victoria 3001, Australia. Ed. Eric D. Butler. circ. 2,000. (tabloid format)

323.44   US
INTER AMERICAN PRESS ASSOCIATION. FREEDOM OF THE PRESS ANNUAL REPORT. a. membership. Inter American Press Association, 2911 N.W. 39th St., Miami, FL 33142. TEL 305-634-2465. FAX 305-635-2272.
Formerly: Inter American Press Association. Committee on Freedom on the Press. Report (ISSN 0579-6695)

INTERESSE; soziale Information. see SOCIAL SERVICES AND WELFARE

320   US   ISSN 0362-8507
JK325
INTERGOVERNMENTAL PERSPECTIVE. 1975. q. free. U.S. Advisory Commission on Intergovernmental Relations, 800 K St., N.W., Ste. 450-S., Washington, DC 20575. TEL 202-653-5640. bk.rev.; charts; illus. circ. 20,000. (also avail. in microform from UMI; microfiche from CIS; reprint service avail. from CIS,UMI) **Indexed:** Amer.Stat.Ind. (1983-), Ind.U.S.Gov.Per., Int.Polit.Sci.Abstr. **Document type:** government publication.
—BLDSC (4533.520300); Faxon; UMI; UnCover.
Description: Current issues in federal and state local relations.

320   UK   ISSN 0960-1503
THE INTERNATIONAL (LONDON, 1990). 1990. q. £26 for 6 issues. Workers International to Rebuild the Fourth International, P.O. Box 735, London SW8 1YB, England. TEL 0171-582-8882. FAX 0171-582-8834. Eds. Bob Archer, Bridget Leach. adv. contact: Jill Oxley. bk.rev. circ. 500. (also avail. in microform from UMI) **Document type:** bulletin.

INTERNATIONAL COUNTRY RISK GUIDE. see BUSINESS AND ECONOMICS — Economic Situation And Conditions

INTERNATIONAL JOURNAL OF CONFLICT MANAGEMENT. see BUSINESS AND ECONOMICS — Management

INTERNATIONAL JOURNAL OF GAME THEORY. see MATHEMATICS

INTERNATIONAL JOURNAL OF GROUP TENSIONS. see PSYCHOLOGY

320   US   ISSN 0885-0607
UB250
INTERNATIONAL JOURNAL OF INTELLIGENCE AND COUNTERINTELLIGENCE. 1986. q. $75. Intel Publishing Group, Inc., Box 188, Stroudsburg, PA 18360. Ed. F. Reese Brown.
—BLDSC (4542.310300).

341   US   ISSN 0891-1916
JA1.A1
INTERNATIONAL JOURNAL OF POLITICAL ECONOMY; a journal of translations. 1971. q. $495 to institutions (foreign $560) (effective Jul. 1995). M.E. Sharpe, Inc., 80 Business Park Dr., Armonk, NY 10504. TEL 914-273-1800; 800-541-6563. FAX 914-273-2106. Ed. Paul Mattick, Jr. adv.; index. (back issues avail.) **Indexed:** Amer.Hist.& Life, Curr.Cont., Hist.Abstr., Int.Polit.Sci.Abstr., Mid.East: Abstr.& Ind., Polit.Sci.Abstr., SSCI. **Document type:** academic/scholarly publication.
—BLDSC (4542.470900); Faxon; SWETS; UMI; UnCover. **CCC.**
Former titles (until 1987): International Journal of Politics (ISSN 0012-8783); Eastern European Studies in Law and Government.
Refereed Serial

INTERNATIONAL JOURNAL OF PUBLIC OPINION RESEARCH. see SOCIAL SCIENCES: COMPREHENSIVE WORKS

INTERNATIONAL JOURNAL OF PUNJAB STUDIES. see SOCIAL SCIENCES: COMPREHENSIVE WORKS

320 338.91   US   ISSN 8755-8335
HF1410
INTERNATIONAL POLITICAL ECONOMY YEARBOOK. 1985. a. price varies. Lynne Rienner Publishers, 1800 30th St., Ste. 314, Boulder, CO 80301. TEL 303-444-6684. FAX 303-444-0824. **Document type:** monographic series.
—BLDSC (4544.958500).

320   IE
INTERNATIONAL POLITICAL SCIENCE ASSOCIATION. WORLD CONGRESS. 1951. triennial, 12th, 1982 Rio de Janeiro; 13th, 1985 Paris; 14th, 1988 Washington; 15th, 1991, Buenos Aires. price varies. International Political Science Association, c/o University College Dublin, Department of Politics, Belfield, Dublin 4, Ireland. TEL 01-7068182. FAX 01-7061171. E-mail: ipsa@ollamh.ucd.ie. (also avail. in microfiche)
Formerly: International Political Science Association. World Conference. Proceedings (ISSN 0074-7467)

INTERNATIONAL REVIEW OF THIRD WORLD CULTURE AND ISSUES. see HUMANITIES: COMPREHENSIVE WORKS

329.9   UK
INTERNATIONAL SOCIALISM. 1961. q. £12($20) to individuals; institutions £20($33). Socialist Workers Party, P.O. Box 82, London E3 3HL, England. TEL 071-538-1626. FAX 071-538-0018. Ed. John Rees. adv.; bk.rev. circ. 7,000. (also avail. in microfiche) **Indexed:** Acad.Ind., Alt.Press Ind., ASCA, Curr.Cont. **Document type:** bulletin.
—BLDSC (4549.525000).
Former titles: Socialist Worker Review; Socialist Review (ISSN 0141-2442); (until 1978): International Socialism (ISSN 0020-8736)

320.531   US   ISSN 0020-8744
HX1
INTERNATIONAL SOCIALIST REVIEW. (Supplement to: The Militant (ISSN 0026-3885)) 1928. m. $45 includes The Militant. 408 Printing and Publishing Co., 410 West St., New York, NY 10014. TEL 212-243-6392. Ed. George Fyson. circ. 10,000. (also avail. in microfilm from BHP) **Document type:** newspaper.

320 327   IT   ISSN 0393-2729
D839
INTERNATIONAL SPECTATOR. (Text in English) 1966. q. L.80000. (Istituto Affari Internazionali) Casa Editrice Fratelli Palombi, Via dei Gracchi 181-185, 00192 Rome, Italy. TEL 39-6-3214150. FAX 39-6-3214752. Ed. Gianni Bonvicini. adv. circ. 1,500. **Indexed:** E.I., Int.Polit.Sci.Abstr.
—BLDSC (4549.626500).
Description: Forum covering internal politics.

320   FR   ISSN 0294-2925
INTERNATIONAL VIEWPOINT. French edition: Inprecor. (Text in English) 1982. m. 330 Fr. (foreign US $60). Presse-Edition-Communication Internationale (PECI), B.P. 85, 75522 Paris Cedex 11, France. TEL 43-79-29-60. FAX 43-79-29-61. E-mail: inprecor@igc.apc.org. Ed. Jan Malewski; Pub. Jan Malewski. adv. contact: Jan Malewski. bk.rev.; charts, illus. stat.; index. circ. 1,500. (back issues avail.) **Indexed:** Alt.Press Ind. **Document type:** consumer publication.
Description: News and analysis under the auspices of the United Secretariat of the Fourth International. Likely to be of interest to activists in socialist, worker's and Third World solidarity movements.

324.1 331   US   ISSN 1068-6576
HX1
INTERNATIONAL WORKERS BULLETIN. 1964. w. $48. (Workers League) Labor Publications, 25905 Greenfield, Oak Park, MI 48037. TEL 313-967-2924. FAX 313-967-3023. (Subscr. to: Box 706, Southfield, MI 48086. TEL 313-967-2924) Ed. Barry Porster. bk.rev.; film rev. (tabloid format; back issues avail.) **Document type:** bulletin.
Former titles (until 1993): Workers League (U.S.). Central Committee. Bulletin (ISSN 0279-0165); (until 1973): Workers League (U.S.) - Bulletin (ISSN 0894-3028); (until 1968): Bulletin of International Socialism (ISSN 0007-4934)
Description: Deals with political, historical, scientific and cultural issues of significance to the working class. Places special emphasis on international politico-economic developments.

INTERNATIONAL YEAR BOOK AND STATESMEN'S WHO'S WHO. see BIOGRAPHY

320   GW   ISSN 0936-5184
INTERNATIONALE BEZIEHUNGEN. 1989. irreg., vol.5, 1994. price varies. Franz Steiner Verlag Wiesbaden GmbH, Birkenwaldstr. 44, 70191 Stuttgart, Germany. TEL 0711-2582-0. FAX 0711-2582390. (Subscr. to: Postfach 101061, 70009 Stuttgart, Germany) **Document type:** monographic series.

320   GW   ISSN 0933-9884
INTERNATIONALE DIREKTINVESTIONEN. (Subseries of: H W W A - Report (ISSN 0179-2253)) 1975. irreg. (H W W A - Institut fuer Wirtschaftsforschung, Hamburg) Verlag Weltarchiv, Neuer Jungfernstieg 21, 20347 Hamburg, Germany. TEL 040-3562354. FAX 040-351900.

320.5　　　　　SW　　ISSN 0345-5467
INTERNATIONALEN. 1971. w. SEK 170 (effective 1991). Socialistiska Partiet, Sektion av Fjaerde Internationalen, P.O. Box 235, S-126 02 Haegersten, Sweden.
Formerly (until 1974): Mullvaden.

329.9　　　　　AU　　ISSN 0020-9473
INTERNATIONALES FREIES WORT. 1964. q. S.25 (foreign S.36). Bund Demokratischer Sozialisten, Gussriegelstr. 50, A-1100 Wien, Austria. TEL 0222-6487293. (U.S. subscr. to: World Socialist Party, Box 405, Boston, MA 02272) Ed. Friedrich Vogt. adv.; bk.rev. circ. 2,000. **Document type:** bulletin.
Formerly: Wiener Freie Wort - W F W.

320.5　　　　　SW　　ISSN 0283-2372
INTERNATIONELL REVOLUTION. 1980. bi-m. Internationell Revolution, P.O. Box 21106, S-100 31 Stockholm, Sweden.

320　　　　　SZ　　ISSN 0579-8337
INTER-PARLIAMENTARY UNION. SERIES: "REPORTS AND DOCUMENTS". 1965. irreg., no.22, 1994. price varies. Inter-Parliamentary Union, Place du Petit-Saconnex, CH-1211 Geneva 19, Switzerland. TEL 022-7344150. FAX 022-7333141. TELEX 414217-IPU-CH. **Document type:** monographic series.

320　　　　　US　　ISSN 0020-9635
JA26
INTERPRETATION (FLUSHING); a journal of political philosophy. 1970. 3/yr. $25 to individuals; institutions $40; students $16. Queens College, Flushing, NY 11367-1597. TEL 718-997-5542. Ed. Hilail Gildin; Pub. Leonard Grey. bk.rev. circ. 1,000. **Indexed:** Biol.Abstr., Bk.Rev.Ind., CERDIC, Chr.Per.Ind., Curr.Cont., G.Soc.Sci.& Rel.Per.Lit., M.L.A., Mid.East: Abstr.& Ind., New Test.Abstr., Old Test.Abstr., Phil.Ind., Rel.Ind.One. **Document type:** academic/scholarly publication.
● Also available online. Vendor(s): University Microfilms International.
—BLDSC (4557.347200); Faxon; SWETS.
Refereed Serial

320　　　　　US　　ISSN 0074-1078
INTER-UNIVERSITY CONSORTIUM FOR POLITICAL AND SOCIAL RESEARCH. ANNUAL REPORT. 1963. a. free. Inter-University Consortium for Political and Social Research, Box 1248, Ann Arbor, MI 48106. TEL 313-764-2570. FAX 313-764-8041. **Document type:** corporate report.
Description: Report of finances, data collections released, major activities, funding, member organizations, council, and staff of computerized social science data archives.

INVESTIGATOR (BAY CITY). see *HISTORY — History Of North And South America*

329.81　　　　　US　　ISSN 1046-4425
IOWA IDEA. 1978. q. $5 donation. Iowa Socialist Party, State Committee, Box 924, Iowa City, IA 52244. TEL 515-243-3577. E-mail: kkubby@blue.weeg.uiowa.edu. Ed. Aric West. bk.rev. circ. 2,000. (tabloid format; back issues avail.) **Document type:** newsletter.
Description: Studies the ideas of this democratic socialist feminist organization working for social change through education, direct action and electoral politics.

320　　　　　IR
IRAN PRESS DIGEST (POLITICAL). w. Iran Press Digest Establishment, Hafiz Ave., 4 Kuchh Hurtab, P.O. Box 11365-5551, Teheran, Iran. TEL 016-668114. TELEX 212300.

320　　　　　CE
IRANAMA. 1964. w. 5 Gunasena Mawatha, Colombo 12, Sri Lanka. TEL 1-23864.

320　　　　　UK
IRELAND AGENDA. 1980. 5/yr. £5 (foreign £10). Labour Committee on Ireland, c/o L.C.I. BM Box 5355, London WC1N 3XX, England. TEL 0171-249-3626. E-mail: 100544.3665@compuserve.com. Ed. Kate Foley. adv.; bk.rev.; illus. circ. 1,000. **Document type:** newsletter.
Formerly: Labour and Ireland (ISSN 0260-6615).
Description: News and opinion within British labor movement, advocating withdrawal from Ireland.

IRISH AMERICA MAGAZINE. see *ETHNIC INTERESTS*

320　　　　　IE
IRISH PEOPLE. 1973. w. £20. (Sinn Fein the Workers' Party) Repsol Publications, 30 Gardiner Pl., Dublin 1, Ireland. Ed. John Gallagher. adv. circ. 26,000.

329.9　　　　　IE　　ISSN 0790-7672
IRISH POLITICAL REVIEW. 1986. m. I£12. Reform Society, 2 Corrig Rd., Dalkey, Co. Dublin, Ireland. bk.rev. circ. 1,000. **Document type:** bulletin.
Description: Covers current affairs and political commentary and analysis in Ireland and the rest of the world.

320　　　　　IE　　ISSN 0790-7184
JN1400
IRISH POLITICAL STUDIES. 1986. a. I£15 to individuals; institutions I£22. Political Studies Association of Ireland, College of Humanities, University of Limerick, Limerick, Ireland. TEL 061-202280. FAX 061-338170. Eds. V. Geoghegan, R. English. bk.rev. circ. 500. **Indexed:** Int.Polit.Sci.Abstr. **Document type:** academic/scholarly publication.
—BLDSC (4574.650700).
Description: Contains articles and information on, or related to, Irish politics, including extensive data section and bibliography.

IRISH VOICE. see *ETHNIC INTERESTS*

IRODALOM - SZOCIALIZMUS. see *LITERATURE*

ISLAM ET SOCIETES AU SUD DU SAHARA. see *HISTORY — History Of Africa*

320 297　　　　　NP　　ISSN 8755-8912
ISLAM INTERNATIONAL. 1986. s-a. $150. Siveast Consultants, Inc., USA, c/o P.O. Box 8510, Kathmandu, Nepal. (UK subscr. to: Dr. Ramasastry, c/o Overseas Customer Service, Midland Bank Blc., Poultry and Princes St., London EC 2, England) Ed. C.V. Ramasastry. adv.; bk.rev.; circ. 20(controlled). (looseleaf format; reprint service avail.) **Document type:** academic/scholarly publication.

320　　　　　UK　　ISSN 0969-4234
ISLAMIC AFFAIRS ANALYST. m. £148($297) (overseas £198) (effective 1995). Intelligence International Ltd., 17 Rodney Rd., Cheltenham, Glos. GL50 1HX, England. TEL 01452-864764. FAX 01452-564848. Ed. J.K.C. de Courcy. **Document type:** academic/scholarly publication.
Description: Reports on political, economic, and strategic developments throughout the Islamic world.

956.940 296　　　　　DK　　ISSN 0021-194X
ISRAEL. 1948. q. DKK 90. Dansk Zionist Forbund, Ny Kongensgade 6, 1472 Copenhagen K, Denmark. FAX 45-33-91-00-91. Ed. Hans Henrik Fafner. adv.; bk.rev.; illus. circ. 3,000.
Description: Covers events in Israel and the Middle East as well as events of interest to Jews elsewhere.

956.94 328　　　　　IS　　ISSN 0012-4249
ISRAEL. KNESSET. DIVREI HA-KNESSET. (Text in Hebrew) 1948. w. Knesset, Jerusalem, Israel. Ed. Gideon Greif.

956.940 327 296.7　　US　　ISSN 0021-2083
DS101
ISRAEL HORIZONS; the socialist Zionist journal. 1952. q. $15. Americans for Progressive Israel, 224 W. 35th St., Ste. 403, New York, NY 10001. Ed. Ralph Seliger. adv.; bk.rev.; film rev.; charts; illus.; index. circ. 2,000. **Indexed:** HR Rep., Left Ind. (1986-), Mid.East: Abstr.& Ind., P.A.I.S.
Description: Deals with the Israeli left and the peace camp in Israel, Israeli culture and life, the world Jewish community, and questions confronting socialism.

ISRAEL STUDIES. see *SOCIAL SCIENCES: COMPREHENSIVE WORKS*

320　　　　　GW　　ISSN 0175-7024
ISRAEL UND PALAESTINA; Zeitschrift fuer Dialog. 1984. q. DM.50. (Deutsch-Israelischer Arbeitskreis fuer Frieden im Nahen Osten) Haag & Herchen GmbH, Fichardstr. 30, 60320 Frankfurt a.M., Germany. TEL 069-550911. FAX 06323-2195. Ed. Christian Sterzing. adv.; bk.rev. circ. 500. (back issues avail.) **Document type:** bulletin.

320　　　　　IS
ISRAELI DEMOCRACY (HEBREW EDITION). q. free. Israel Democracy Institute, P.O. Box 4702, Jerusalem 91040, Israel. FAX 02-635319.

320　　　　　IT
ISTITUTO GRAMSCI PIEMONTESE. MATERIALI.* vol.2, 1976. irreg. (Istituto Gramsci Piemontese) T. Musolini Editore, Via Rubiana 47, 10139 Turin, Italy.

ITALIA CONTEMPORANEA. see *HISTORY — History Of Europe*

322.4　　　　　IT
ITALIA DEL POPOLO. 1981. w. L.15000. Via del Corso 504, Rome, Italy. Ed. Mauro Mita. bk.rev. circ. 10,000.

320 055.1　　　　　IT
ITALIA VIVA; mensile politico. 1971. m. L.15000($10) (effective Jan. 1995). Via Milano 37 (UD), 33037 Pasian di Prato, Italy. TEL 0432-699055. Ed. Antonio Bottega. bk.rev. circ. 1,500. **Document type:** newspaper.

320.532　　　　　IT　　ISSN 0391-5581
JN5657.C635
ITALIAN COMMUNISTS; foreign bulletin of the P C I. (Text in English, French, German, Spanish) q. free. Partito Comunista Italiano, Foreign Section, Via delle Botteghe Oscure, 4, Rome 00186, Italy. TEL 06-6711. Dir. Bernardino Bernardini. bk.rev. circ. 4,500.
Description: Compares the philosophy of the Italian communist party with Italy's other political parties. Reviews the politics of Italy and the problems that face its foreign policies, and outlines the international activities of the PCI.

ITALIAN POLITICS; a review. see *BUSINESS AND ECONOMICS*

320　　　　　IS
IYUNIM B'BIKORET HAMEDINA. (Text in Hebrew) 1962. a. State Comptrollers Office, P.O. Box 1081, Jerusalem 91 010, Israel. FAX 972-2-384978. Ed. B. Geist. bk.rev. circ. 1,000. **Document type:** government publication.

IZVESTIYA NA DARZHAVNITE ARKHIVI. see *HISTORY — History Of Europe*

320　　　　　SA
IZWI LABASEBENZI SERIES. irreg. Skotaville Publishers, P.O. Box 32483, Braamfontein 2017, South Africa. (Dist. outside Africa by: African Books Collective Ltd., The Jam Factory, 27 Park End St., Oxford OX1 1HU, England. TEL 0865-726686. FAX 0865-793298) **Document type:** monographic series.

320 350　　　　　US　　ISSN 0888-8957
JK1342
J C P S CONGRESSIONAL DISTRICT FACT BOOK. a. Joint Center for Political Studies, Inc., 1090 Vermont Ave., N.W., Ste. 1100, Washington, DC 20005-4905. TEL 202-626-3500.

355　　　　　IS
J C S S STUDIES. (Text in English) irreg., no.24, 1994. price varies. (Tel Aviv University, Jaffee Center for Strategic Studies) Jerusalem Post, P.O. Box 81, Jerusalem 91000, Israel. TEL 972-3-420200. FAX 972-2-537527. (U.S. subscr. to: 211 E. 43rd St., Ste 601, New York, NY 10017) Ed. Joseph Alpher. circ. 1,500. **Document type:** academic/scholarly publication, monographic series.
Formerly (until 1985): J C S S Papers.
Description: Covers strategic subjects in Middle East politics, military, economy, and international relations.

J P I - JUGEND PRESSE INFORMATIONEN. see *CHILDREN AND YOUTH — For*

J T A COMMUNITY NEWS REPORTER. (Jewish Telegraphic Agency) see *ETHNIC INTERESTS*

POLITICAL SCIENCE

296.7 US ISSN 0021-3772
DS101
J T A DAILY NEWS BULLETIN. 1922. d. (except Sat. & Sun.). $295. Jewish Telegraphic Agency, 330 Seventh Ave, 11th Fl., New York, NY 10001. TEL 212-643-1890. FAX 212-643-8498. TELEX 126978. Ed. Mark Joffe. circ. 2,500. (also avail. in microfilm from AJP)
Description: Daily chronicle of international events affecting Jews and Jewish communities.

296.7 US ISSN 0021-6763
J T A WEEKLY NEWS DIGEST. 1935. w. $100. Jewish Telegraphic Agency, 330 Seventh Ave., 11th Fl., New York, NY 10001. TEL 212-643-1890. FAX 212-643-8498. TELEX 126978. Ed. Mark Joffe. circ. 7,000. (also avail. in microfilm from AJP)
Description: Weekly summary of international events of concern to and affecting Jews and Jewish communities.

051 US ISSN 0021-390X
JAG.* 1962. irreg. (9-10/yr.). free. Jag, Inc., 101 Hillside Dr., W., Oelwein, IA 50662-2640. TEL 319-283-3491. FAX 319-283-3926. Ed. Dr. R.S. Jaggard. bk.rev. circ. 1,000. (processed; back issues avail.) **Indexed:** C.L.I., Leg.Per. **Document type:** newsletter.
Description: Covers politics as it relates to medicine.

JAHRBUCH DER POLITIK UND WIRTSCHAFT IN NORDRHEIN-WESTFALEN. see BUSINESS AND ECONOMICS

320 LE
JAMHOUR - AL-JADID.* 1936. w. £L150($50) c/o Farid Abu Shahla, P.O. Box 1834, Beirut, Lebanon.

328.54 II ISSN 0448-2433
JQ620.K35
JAMMU AND KASHMIR. LEGISLATIVE COUNCIL. COMMITTEE ON PRIVILEGES. REPORT. (Text in English) irreg. Legislative Council, Committee on Privileges, Srinagar, Jammu and Kashmir, India.

059.94 II ISSN 0021-4205
JANA SANGH PATRIKA.* (Text in Malayalam) 1967. s-m. Rs.6. Bharatiya Janasangh Kerala Pradesh, M.G. Road, Cochin 11, India. Ed. P. Narayanan. circ. controlled.

320 CE
JANAKAVI. (Text in Sinhala) fortn. 47 Jayantha Weerasekera Mawatha, Colombo 10, Sri Lanka. Ed. Karunaratne Amerasinghe.

320.531 II ISSN 0021-4213
JANAMAN; a spokesman for democratic socialism. (Text and summaries in Hindi) 1969. w. Rs.15. U. Shukla, Ed. & Pub., 107 Gopalganj, Sagar, Madhya Pradesh, India. adv.; bk.rev.

320.531 II ISSN 0021-4221
DS401
JANATA. (Text in English) 1946. w. $40. Janata Trust, c/o G.G. Parikh, National House, 6 Tulloch Rd., Bombay 1, India. Ed. H.K. Paranjabe. adv. circ. 6,000.

320 GW ISSN 0944-3800
JAPAN. bi-m. DM.135 (foreign DM.144; students DM.80). Institut fuer Asienkunde - Institute of Asian Affairs, Rothenbaumchaussee 32, 20148 Hamburg, Germany. TEL 040-443001. FAX 040-4107945. **Document type:** academic/scholarly publication.

952 US ISSN 1051-1776
JAPAN POLITICAL RESEARCH; an annual review. 1969. a. $7 (foreign $8). Brigham Young University, Political Science Department, 745 SWKT, Provo, UT 84602. TEL 801-378-3303. FAX 801-378-5730. Ed. Lee W. Farnsworth. bk.rev.; bibl. circ. 200. (tabloid format; back issues avail.) **Document type:** newsletter.
Formerly (until 1990): Newsletter of Research on Japanese Politics (ISSN 0160-1164)

JAPAN REPORT (ARLINGTON). see BUSINESS AND ECONOMICS — Economic Situation And Conditions

320.532 JA ISSN 0007-4683
JAPANESE COMMUNIST PARTY. CENTRAL COMMITTEE. BULLETIN: INFORMATION FOR ABROAD. (Text in English, French, Spanish) 1961. irreg. $60. Japanese Communist Party, Sendagaya 4-26-7, Shibuya-ku, Tokyo, Japan. TEL 03-5474-8420. FAX 03-3746-0767. E-mail: CXG00373@niftyserve.or.jp. illus.

320 330.9 CK ISSN 0021-5562
JAVERIANA. 1934. m. (Feb.-Nov.). Col.28500($50) (effective 1995). Compania de Jesus de Colombia, Carrera 23 no. 39-69, Apdo. Aereo 24773, Bogota, Colombia. Ed. Javier Sanin. adv.; bk.rev.; bibl.; index. circ. 8,000. (also avail. in microform from UMI) **Indexed:** Hisp.Amer.Per.Ind. (1989-).
Description: Studies important current themes of national and international interest in Latin America.

320.532 296 US ISSN 0021-6305
DS101
JEWISH AFFAIRS. 1970. bi-m. $7.50. Communist Party, U S A, 235 W. 23rd St., 7th Fl., New York, NY 10011. TEL 212-989-4994. Ed. Herbert Aptheker. adv.; bk.rev.; bibl. circ. 1,500. (also avail. in microfilm from AJP)

JEWISH DEFENSE LEAGUE ITON. see ETHNIC INTERESTS

320.55 956.940 US ISSN 0021-6453
296.7
DS149
JEWISH FRONTIER.* 1934. bi-m. $15. Labor Zionist Letters, Inc., 275 7th Ave., Rm. 17R, New York, NY 10001-6776. Ed. Nahum Guttman. adv.; bk.rev.; film rev. circ. 12,500. (also avail. in microfilm from UMI; reprint service avail. from UMI) **Indexed:** G.Soc.Sci.& Rel.Per.Lit., Ind.Bk.Rev.Hum., Ind.Jew.Per., P.A.I.S.
—UMI; UnCover.

320 296 IS ISSN 0792-335X
DS140 CODEN: JPRVEI
JEWISH POLITICAL STUDIES REVIEW. 1989. 2/yr. $24 to individuals; institutions $38. Jerusalem Center for Public Affairs, 13 Tel Hai St., Jerusalem 92107, Israel. TEL 972-2-619281. FAX 972-2-619112. (U.S. subscr. to: Center for Jewish Community Studies, 1616 Walnut St., Ste. 1513, Philadelphia, PA 19103. TEL 215-204-1459. FAX 215-204-7784) **Indexed:** Int.Polit.Sci.Abstr.
Document type: academic/scholarly publication.
Description: Studies Jewish political institutions and behavior, Jewish political thought and Jewish public affairs.

323.1 US ISSN 0047-200X
JEWISH RADICAL. 1969. 3/yr. $5 to individuals; $10 to organizations. Radical Jewish Union, 300 Eshleman Hall, University of Calif., Berkeley, CA 94720. TEL 415-642-6000. Ed.Bd. circ. 6,000. (also avail. in microfilm from AJP)

JIHOCESKY SBORNIK HISTORICKY. see HISTORY — History Of Europe

JOHNS HOPKINS UNIVERSITY STUDIES IN HISTORICAL AND POLITICAL SCIENCE. see HISTORY

320 US
JOINT CENTER FOR POLITICAL STUDIES. NEW AND RECENT BOOKS. s-a. (Joint Center for Political Studies, Inc.) University Press of America, 4720 Boston Way, Ste. A, Lanham, MD 20706. TEL 301-459-3366. **Document type:** bibliography.

320 KN
JOKOOK TONGIL. (Text in Korean) 1961. m. Committee for the Peaceful Unification of Korea, Kangan 1 Dong, Youth Avenue, Sonkyo District, Pyongyang, N. Korea. Ed. Li Myong Gyu. circ. 70,000.

JOURNAL OF CHURCH AND STATE. see RELIGIONS AND THEOLOGY

338 UK ISSN 0021-9886
HC241
JOURNAL OF COMMON MARKET STUDIES. 1962. q. £148($280) (foreign £179) (effective 1996). Basil Blackwell Ltd., 108 Cowley Rd., Oxford OX4 1JF, England. TEL 0865-791100. FAX 0865-791347. TELEX 837022-OXBOOK-G. Ed. Peter Robson. adv.; bk.rev. circ. 1,400. (also avail. in microfilm from RRI; reprint service avail. from RRI,UMI,WSH) **Indexed:** A.B.C.Pol.Sci, ABI Inform, Asian-Pac.Econ.Lit., ASSIA, B.P.I, BPIA, Br.Hum.Ind., Bus.Ind., C.L.I., C.R.E.J., Cont.Pg.Manage., Curr.Cont., ELLIS, Euro.LJI, Hist.Abstr. (until 1993), Int.Lab.Doc., Int.Polit.Sci.Abstr., J.of Econ.Lit., Key to Econ.Sci., Leg.Per., LJI, Manage.Cont., Mgmt.& Market.Abstr., P.A.I.S., Rural Recreat.Tour.Abstr., SCIMP (1978-), Soc.Sci.Ind., SSCI, Tr.& Indus.Ind., World Agri.Econ.& Rural Sociol.Abstr., World Bank.Abstr. **Document type:** academic/scholarly publication.
—BLDSC (4961.200000); Faxon; Genuine Article; SWETS; UMI; UnCover. **CCC.**

328 II ISSN 0022-0043
JQ201
JOURNAL OF CONSTITUTIONAL & PARLIAMENTARY STUDIES. (Text in English) 1967. q. Rs.100($20) Institute of Constitutional and Parliamentary Studies, 18-21 Vithalbhai Patel House, Rafi Marg, New Delhi 110001, India. Ed. Phul Chand. circ. 1,000. (also avail. in microfilm from UMI; reprint service avail. from UMI) **Indexed:** A.B.C.Pol.Sci., Ind.Per.Lit., Int.Polit.Sci.Abstr.
—UMI.

JOURNAL OF CONTEMPORARY HISTORY. see HISTORY

329.3 US ISSN 1045-5736
JF1051
JOURNAL OF DEMOCRACY. 1990. q. $26 to individuals; institutions $55. (National Endowment for Democracy) Johns Hopkins University Press, Journals Publishing Division, 2715 N. Charles St., Baltimore, MD 21218. TEL 410-516-6987. FAX 410-516-6968. Eds. Larry Diamond, Marc F. Plattner. adv. contact: Tara Dorai-Berry. bk.rev. circ. 819. **Indexed:** A.B.C.Pol.Sci., HR Rep. (1990-), Int.Polit.Sci.Abstr., Polit.Sci.Abstr., Soc.Sci.Ind. (1994-). **Document type:** academic/scholarly publication.
—BLDSC (4968.250000); Faxon; SWETS; UnCover. **CCC.**
Description: Scholarly journal devoted to the study of democracy and democratic institutions worldwide.

JOURNAL OF DEVELOPING AREAS. see BUSINESS AND ECONOMICS — International Development And Assistance

JOURNAL OF DEVELOPMENT STUDIES. see BUSINESS AND ECONOMICS — International Development And Assistance

320 KO
JOURNAL OF EAST AND WEST STUDIES/TONGSO YONGU. (Text in English) 1972. s-a. $20. Yonsei University, Institute of East and West Studies, 134 Shinchon-Dong, Seodaemoon-gu, Seoul, S. Korea. FAX 02-393-9027. TELEX K29127. Ed. Ku-Hyun Jung. adv.; bk.rev. circ. 700.
Description: Publishes articles in all disciplines pertinent to East-West and North-South problems in the field of social sciences.

320 US
JOURNAL OF FREEDOM. 1984. bi-m. Box 158, Fayette, IA 52142.

320 100 II ISSN 0970-9908
DS481.G3
JOURNAL OF GANDHIAN STUDIES. (Text in English) 1973. q. $30. Institute of Gandhian Thought and Peace Studies, University of Allahabad, Gandhi Bhawan, Allahabad, India. TEL 54900. Ed. J.S. Mathur. adv.; bk.rev.; bibl. circ. 500. **Indexed:** Amer.Hist.& Life, Hist.Abstr.
Description: Encourages objective study of Gandhi's non-violent methods.

320 II ISSN 0251-3056
JOURNAL OF GOVERNMENT AND POLITICAL STUDIES. (Text in English) 1977. s-a. Rs.10($3) Punjabi University, Department of Political Science, Patiala 147002, India. Ed. Manorama Kohli. bk.rev. **Document type:** academic/scholarly publication.

JOURNAL OF HEALTH POLITICS, POLICY AND LAW. see MEDICAL SCIENCES

POLITICAL SCIENCE

320 340 GW ISSN 0932-4569
H5
JOURNAL OF INSTITUTIONAL AND THEORETICAL ECONOMICS. 1844. q. DM.312. Verlag J.C.B. Mohr (Paul Siebeck), Wilhelmstr. 18, 72074 Tuebingen, Germany. TEL 07071-923-0. FAX 07071-51104. TELEX 7262872-MOHR-D. (Subscr. to: Postfach 2040, 72010 Tuebingen, Germany) Ed. Rudolf Richter. adv.; bk.rev.; charts; index. **Indexed:** C.R.E.J., ELLIS, Int.Polit.Sci.Abstr., J.of Econ.Lit., Key to Econ.Sci., P.A.I.S., P.A.I.S.For.Lang.Ind., SCIMP (1991-). **Document type:** academic/scholarly publication.
—BLDSC (5007.506000); Faxon; Genuine Article; SWETS; UnCover. **CCC.**
Formerly: Zeitschrift fuer die Gesamte Staatswissenschaft (ISSN 0044-2550)
Description: Covers political economy and modern institutional economics.

JOURNAL OF INTERNATIONAL DEVELOPMENT: POLICY, ECONOMICS, & INTERNATIONAL RELATIONS. see SOCIAL SCIENCES: COMPREHENSIVE WORKS

THE JOURNAL OF ISRAELI HISTORY; studies in Zionism and statehood. see HISTORY — History Of The Near East

JOURNAL OF LATIN AMERICAN STUDIES. see HISTORY — History Of North And South America

JOURNAL OF LAW AND POLITICS/HO-SEI KENKYU. see LAW

320 960 UK ISSN 0022-278X
DT1
JOURNAL OF MODERN AFRICAN STUDIES. 1963. q. £84($149) (effective 1996). Cambridge University Press, Edinburgh Bldg., Shaftesbury Rd., Cambridge CB2 2RU, England. TEL 01223-312393. FAX 01223-315052. TELEX 851817256. (N. American addr.: Cambridge University Press, Journals Dept., 40 W. 20th St., New York, NY 10011. TEL 212-924-3900. FAX 212-691-3239) Ed. David Kimble. adv.; bk.rev.; bibl.; index. (also avail. in microform from UMI; back issues avail.; reprint service avail. from SWZ) **Indexed:** A.B.C.Pol.Sci., Abstr.Anthropol., Acad.Ind., Amer.Hist.& Life, Br.Hum.Ind., C.R.E.J., CERDIC, Curr.Cont., Curr.Cont.Africa, Documentatieblad, G.Soc.Sci.& Rel.Per.Lit., Geo.Abstr., Hist.Abstr., HR Rep. (1971-), IDA, Int.Lab.Doc., Int.Polit.Sci.Abstr., Lang.& Lang.Behav.Ind., M.L.A., Mid.East: Abstr.& Ind., Numis.Lit., P.A.I.S., Polit.Sci.Abstr., Rice Abstr., Rural Devel.Abstr., Rural Recreat.Tour.Abstr., Sage Fam.Stud.Abstr., Soc.Sci.Ind., SSCI, World Agri.Econ.& Rural Sociol.Abstr. **Document type:** academic/scholarly publication.
—BLDSC (5020.600000); Faxon; Genuine Article; SWETS; UMI; UnCover. **CCC.**
Description: Covers the politics, economics and related aspects of contemporary Africa.

320 US
JOURNAL OF PEACE & JUSTICE STUDIES. 1989. s-a. $15 to individuals (foreign $20); institutions $30 (foreign $35). Villanova University, Center for Peace and Justice Education, Villanova, PA 19085. Ed. W. Werpehowski, Barbara Wall. adv.; bk.rev. **Document type:** academic/scholarly publication.
Description: Covers a variety of disciplines, including but not limited to philosophy, theology, social and political theory, and public policy, all from a primarily Judeo-Christian intellectual perspective.

JOURNAL OF POLICY ANALYSIS AND MANAGEMENT. see PUBLIC ADMINISTRATION

320 US ISSN 0161-8938
H1
JOURNAL OF POLICY MODELING; a social science forum of world issues. 1979. bi-m. $310 to institutions in U.S.; $354 to institutions outside the Americas (effective 1996). (Society for Policy Modeling) Elsevier Science Inc., 655 Ave. of the Americas, New York, NY 10010. TEL 212-989-5800.
FAX 212-633-3990. TELEX 420643 AEP UI. (Subscr. to: Box 882, Madison Sq. Sta., New York, NY 10159-0882) Ed. Antonio Maria Costa. (also avail. in microform from UMI; reprint service avail.; reprint service avail. from SWZ) **Indexed:** ABI Inform., ASSIA, BPIA, Bus.Ind., C.R.E.J., Curr.Cont., Deep Sea Res.& Oceanogr.Abstr., Fut.Surv., Int.Polit.Sci.Abstr., J. of Econ.Lit., Polit.Sci.Abstr., Sociol.Abstr., SSCI, Tr.& Indus.Ind., World Agri.Econ.& Rural Sociol.Abstr. **Document type:** academic/scholarly publication.
—BLDSC (5040.843000); Faxon; Genuine Article; SWETS; UMI; UnCover. **CCC.**
Description: Focuses upon the economic, social and political interdependencies between national and regional systems.
Refereed Serial

JOURNAL OF POLITICAL AND MILITARY SOCIOLOGY. see SOCIOLOGY

JOURNAL OF POLITICAL ECONOMY. see BUSINESS AND ECONOMICS

320 UK ISSN 1356-9317
▼**JOURNAL OF POLITICAL IDEOLOGIES.** Announced for publication in 1996. 3/yr. £24 to individuals; institutions £78 (effective 1996). Carfax Publishing Co., P.O. Box 25, Abingdon, Oxon. OX14 3UE, England. TEL 44-1235-555335.
FAX 44-1235-553559. (N. American subscr. to: Carfax Publishing Co., 875-81 Massachusetts Ave., Cambridge, MA 02139) **Document type:** academic/scholarly publication.

320 UK ISSN 0963-8016
JA1.A1
JOURNAL OF POLITICAL PHILOSOPHY. 1993. q. £120($154) (foreign £120) (effective 1996). Basil Blackwell Ltd., 108 Cowley Rd., Oxford OX4 1JF, England. TEL 44-1865-791100.
FAX 44-1865-791347. Eds. Robert Goodin, Chandran Kukathas. adv.; illus. circ. 550. (also avail. in microform from UMI) **Document type:** academic/scholarly publication.
—BLDSC (5040.886000); UMI. **CCC.**
Description: Devoted to the study of theoretical issues arising out of the moral, legal, and political life.
Refereed Serial

954.9 320 PK
JOURNAL OF POLITICAL SCIENCE. (Text in English) 1971. a. Rs.80($4) Government College, Department of Political Science, Lahore, Pakistan. (Subscr. to: No. C-40, G O R III, Shadman, Lahore, Pakistan. TEL 412592) Eds. Hameed A.K. Rai, Ahmed Husain. adv.; bk.rev.; bibl.; charts; stat. circ. 200. **Indexed:** A.B.C.Pol.Sci., Amer.Hist.& Life, Hist.Abstr. **Document type:** academic/scholarly publication.
Formerly: Journal of History and Political Science.

320 US ISSN 0098-4612
JA1
JOURNAL OF POLITICAL SCIENCE (CLEMSON). 1973. s-a. $11.95. (South Carolina Political Science Association) Clemson University, Department of Political Science, Clemson, SC 29631.
TEL 803-656-3233. FAX 803-656-0258. Ed. Martin Slann. adv.; bk.rev. circ. 300. **Indexed:** A.B.C.Pol.Sci., Amer.Hist.& Life, Hist.Abstr. **Document type:** academic/scholarly publication.

320 II ISSN 0047-2700
JQ201
JOURNAL OF POLITICAL STUDIES. (Text in English) 1968. s-a. Rs.30($5) D.A.V. College, Post-Graduate Department of Political Science, Jullundur, Punjab, India. Ed. K.C. Mahendru. adv.; bk.rev.; bibl. circ. 500. (also avail. in microfilm) **Indexed:** Int.Polit.Sci.Abstr.

320 US ISSN 0022-3816
JA1
JOURNAL OF POLITICS. 1939. q. $25 to individuals (foreign $35); institutions $50 (foreign $60); students $10 (foreign $20). (Southern Political Science Association) University of Texas Press, Box 7819, Austin, TX 78713. TEL 512-471-7233. FAX 512-320-0668. TELEX 776453 UTEXPRES AUS. E-mail: leah@utpress.ppb.utexas.edu. Eds. Jon Bond, Edward Portis. adv. contact: Leah Dixon. bk.rev.; bibl.; charts; index. circ. 4,000. (also avail. in microform from UMI) **Indexed:** A.B.C.Pol.Sci., Acad.Ind., Amer.Bibl.Slavic & E.Eur.Stud., Amer.Hist.& Life, Bk.Rev.Ind. (1965-), Child.Bk.Rev.Ind. (1965-), Commun.Abstr., Curr.Cont., Hist.Abstr., Int.Polit.Sci.Abstr., Int.Polit.Sci.Abstr., Lang.& Lang.Behav.Abstr., P.A.I.S., Pers.Lit., Polit.Sci.Abstr., Res.High.Educ.Abstr., Soc.Sci.Ind., SSCI. **Document type:** academic/scholarly publication.
—BLDSC (5040.900000); Faxon; Genuine Article; SWETS; UMI; UnCover. **CCC.**
Description: Covers American, comparative, and international political science. Includes various methodological approaches.

JOURNAL OF PROGRESSIVE HUMAN SERVICES. see SOCIAL SERVICES AND WELFARE

300 150 301 II ISSN 0970-3357
JOURNAL OF RURAL DEVELOPMENT. (Text in English) 1967. q. Rs.150($50) Ministry of Rural Development, National Institute of Rural Development, Rajendranagar, Hyderabad 500 030, India. TEL 245001. FAX 245277. TELEX 0425-6510 NIRD IN. Ed. T.C.A. Srinivasaramanujan. bk.rev.; charts; illus. circ. 1,000. **Indexed:** Apic.Abstr., ASSIA, Curr.Cont., Dairy Sci.Abstr., Energy Ind., Energy Info.Abstr., Forest.Abstr., Geo.Abstr., IDA, Int.Polit.Sci.Abstr., Lang.& Lang.Behav.Abstr., Rural Ext.Educ.& Tr.Abstr., Sociol.Abstr., World Agri.Econ.& Rural Sociol.Abstr. **Document type:** academic/scholarly publication.
—BLDSC (5052.127400); Genuine Article.
Formed by the 1982 merger of: Rural Development Digest; Behavioural Sciences and Rural Development (ISSN 0379-797X); Which was formerly (until 1977): Behavioural Sciences and Community Development (ISSN 0005-7843)
Description: Studies research in rural development with emphasis on social science aspects.

JOURNAL OF SEXUAL LIBERTY. see LAW — Civil Law

320 US ISSN 0278-839X
H1
JOURNAL OF SOCIAL, POLITICAL AND ECONOMIC STUDIES. 1976. q. $40 to individuals; libraries and institutions $80. Council for Social and Economic Studies, Box 34070, N.W., Washington, DC 20043. TEL 202-371-2700. FAX 202-371-1523. Ed. Roger Pearson. bk.rev.; index. circ. 925. **Indexed:** A.B.C.Pol.Sci., Amer.Bibl.Slavic & E.Eur.Stud, Amer.Hist.& Life, Arts & Hum.Cit.Ind., ASSIA, Chic.Per.Ind., Curr.Cont., Energy Ind., Energy Info.Abstr., Hist.Abstr., Int.Polit.Sci.Abstr., Lang.& Lang.Behav.Abstr., Mag.Ind., Mid.East: Abstr.& Ind., P.A.I.S., Polit.Sci.Abstr., Sociol.Abstr., SSCI. **Document type:** academic/scholarly publication.
●Also available online. Vendor(s): University Microfilms International.
—BLDSC (5064.790000); Faxon; Genuine Article; SWETS; UMI; UnCover.
Former titles: Journal of Social and Political Studies (ISSN 0193-5941); Journal of Social and Political Affairs (ISSN 0362-580X)
Description: An academic level publication providing in-depth data relating to contemporary events and issues of international interest and significance.

320 US ISSN 0895-724X
JOURNAL OF SOCIAL, POLITICAL AND ECONOMIC STUDIES MONOGRAPH SERIES. 1975. irreg., latest vol.24. Council for Social and Economic Studies, Box 34070, Washington, DC 20043.
TEL 202-371-2700. FAX 202-372-1523. **Document type:** monographic series.
Description: Deals with contemporary issues of national and world interest in historical perspectives. Emphasis is on data rather than theory.

JOURNAL OF SOUTHEAST ASIAN STUDIES. see HISTORY — History Of Asia

POLITICAL SCIENCE

320 350.6   II
JOURNAL OF STATE AND ADMINISTRATION. (Text in English) 1978. s-a. Rs.35($10) Sambalpur University, Department of Political Science and Public Administration, Jyoti Vihar, Burla, Sambalpur, Orissa 768017, India. Eds. Drs. A.P. Padhi & Kvrao. adv.; bk.rev. circ. 600.

320   **UK**   **ISSN 0951-6298**
JA1.A1   **CODEN: JTPOEF**
JOURNAL OF THEORETICAL POLITICS. q. £34 to individuals; institutions £115 (effective 1996). Sage Publications Ltd., 6 Bonhill St., London EC2A 4PU, England. TEL 0171-374-0645. FAX 0171-374-8741. E-mail: market@sageltd.co.uk. Ed.Bd. adv.; B&W page £180; trim 180 x 114; adv. contact: Bernie Folan. bk.rev.; charts. **Indexed**: ASCA, Curr.Cont., IBZ, Int.Polit.Sci.Abstr., Intl.Bibl.S.S.Pol.Sci., Polit.Sci.Abstr., Sage Pub.Admin.Abstr., Sociol.Abstr., SSCI. **Document type**: academic/scholarly publication. —BLDSC (5069.075600); Faxon; Genuine Article; SWETS; UnCover.
    Description: An international journal fostering the development of theory in the study of political processes.
    Refereed Serial

956.940   **SZ**
JUEDISCHE RUNDSCHAU MACCABI; la gazette Juive. (Text in French, German) 1941. w. 70 SFr. Juedische Rundschau Maccabi GmbH, Postfach 298, CH-4009 Basel, Switzerland. TEL 061-272589. FAX 061-272804. Ed. Peter Bollag. adv.; bk.rev. circ. 5,000. **Document type**: newspaper.
    Description: Newspaper of interest to Jews in Switzerland and abroad. Covers religion, politics, economics, news about Israel, culture, etc.

320 053.1   **GW**
JUNG UND LIBERAL. q. DM.5. Verlag Junge Liberale, Niebuhrstr. 53, 53113 Bonn, Germany. TEL 0228-215023. FAX 0228-261326. Ed. Maria-Christina Nimmerfroh. adv. contact: Maria-Christina Nimmerfroh. circ. 10,000.

320   **GW**
JUNGE LIBERALE BAYERN. FORUM. 1983. q. Junge Liberale Bayern e.V., Agnesstr. 47, 80798 Munich, Germany. TEL 089-12600960. FAX 089-1294149. adv. circ. 1,000. **Document type**: bulletin.

JUNGES FORUM. see HISTORY — History Of Europe

954   II
JUNIOR STATESMAN. (Text in English) 1969. w. Rs.35. Statesman House, 4 Chowringhee Sq., Calcutta 700001, India.
    Description: Discusses current affairs.

JURIDICAL REVIEW; law journal of Scottish universities. see LAW

320   **MQ**
JUSTICE.* w. Parti Progressiste Martiniquais, Rue de Tailis Clariere, Fort-de-France, Martinique. Ed. G. Thimotee. circ. 8,000.

KAILASH; an interdisciplinary journal of Himalayan studies. see HISTORY — History Of Asia

KANSAI UNIVERSITY REVIEW OF LAW AND POLITICS. see LAW

328   **US**   **ISSN 0270-4331**
KFK20
KANSAS. LEGISLATIVE RESEARCH DEPARTMENT. REPORT ON KANSAS LEGISLATIVE INTERIM STUDIES. 1971. a. free. Legislative Research Department, Topeka, KS 66612. TEL 913-296-3181. circ. controlled.

320   **US**
THE KANSAS INTELLIGENCER. m. $12. Rt. 1, Box 7A, Morganville, KS 67468. Ed. R.W. Clack.
    Description: Discusses controversial issues such as Congress scandals, military actions and funding for obscene art.

320 947   **RU**   **ISSN 0869-1924**
JN6598.K4
KENTAVR. (Former name of issuing body: Institut Marksizma-Leninizma pri TS.K. K.P.S.S.) (Text in Russian) 1957. bi-m. $116 (effective 1996). Izdatel'stvo Feniks, Ul. Vil'gel'ma Pika 4, kor. 2, 129256 Moscow, Russia. TEL 7-95-1811450. FAX 7-95-1811579. (Dist. by: Mezhdunarodnaya Kniga, Bolshaya Yakimanka, 39, 117049 Moscow, Russia) Ed. Vahan G. Emin. bk.rev.; film rev.; software rev.; bibl.; index. circ. 6,000. **Indexed**: Amer.Hist.& Life, Curr.Dig.Sov.Press, Hist.Abstr., Int.Bibl.Soc.Sci. **Document type**: academic/scholarly publication.
    Formerly (until Sep. 1991): Voprosy Istorii K.P.S.S. (ISSN 0320-8907)
    Description: Publishes articles on political history of Russia; political processes in modern Russia and abroad; social and political philosophy; Christian approaches to history, law, polical science.

KENTUCKY JOURNAL. see PUBLIC ADMINISTRATION

320   **KE**   **ISSN 0376-8465**
JX1873.K42
KENYA. MINISTRY OF FOREIGN AFFAIRS. DIRECTORY OF DIPLOMATIC CORPS & INTERNATIONAL ORGANIZATIONS. Key Title: Directory of Diplomatic Corps and International Organizations. a. KShs.200. Ministry of Foreign Affairs., Protocol Department, Nairobi, Kenya. (Subscr. to: Government Press, Haile Selaissie Ave., P.O. Box 30128, Nairobi, Kenya. TEL 254-2-334075) **Document type**: directory, government publication.
    Formerly: Kenya. Ministry of Foreign Affairs. Diplomatic Directory.

967.62   **KE**   **ISSN 0023-0472**
KENYA WEEKLY NEWS.* no.2256, 1968. w. 60s. D. A. Hawkins Ltd., P.O. Box 2768, Nairobi, Kenya. Ed. Jack Ensoll. adv.; bk.rev.; charts; film rev.; illus.; play rev. circ. 7,000. **Document type**: newspaper.

320   II
KERALASABDAM; independent political Malayalam weekly. (Text in Malayalam) 1972. w. newsstand price: Rs.4. R. Krishnaswamy Memorial Building, Lekshminada, Kollam 691 013, Kerala, India. TEL 0474-72403. FAX 0474-70710. TELEX 0886-296 RKY. Ed. B.A. Rajakrishnan. adv.; B&W page Rs.6000; 250 x 180; adv. contact: N. Krishnan.

320 052   **UK**   **ISSN 0140-7562**
KEVREN. (Text in Cornish and English) 1970. s-a. £3. Cowethas Flamank, 101 Haytor Ave., Seacrest, Paignton, Devon TQ4 7TB, England. TEL 0803-529944. Ed. A.M. Casey. bk.rev. circ. 100. (processed)
    Description: Discusses the political, cultural and environmental state of Cornwall.

320   **UK**   **ISSN 0338-0181**
DS63.5
KHAMSIN; journal of revolutionary socialists of the Middle East. no.6, 1978. q. £3.50 to individuals; £12 to institutions. Zed Books, 57 Caledonian Rd., London N1, England. Ed.Bd. adv.; bk.rev.; bibl. circ. 2,000. **Indexed**: Left Ind. (1983-1990).
—CCC.

322   **US**   **ISSN 0892-7588**
DS559.912
KHANG CHIEN. (Text in Vietnamese) m. $22. Khang Chien News Co., 123 Stockton Ave., San Jose, CA 95126. TEL 408-363-1078. FAX 408-363-1178. (Subscr. to: Box 7826, San Jose, CA 95150-7826) Ed. Nguyen Thuc.

320 614.7   **CN**   **ISSN 0823-6526**
KICK IT OVER. 1981. q. $9. Kick it Over Collective, P.O. Box 5811, Sta. A, Toronto, ON M5W 1P2, Canada. adv.; bk.rev.; film rev.; rec.rev. circ. 1,300. (back issues avail.) **Indexed**: Alt.Press Ind. **Document type**: consumer publication.
    Description: Explores political, social and personal issues from an anarchist, feminist and ecological perspective.

320.5   **SW**   **ISSN 0345-6188**
KLASSKAMPEN. 1970. irreg. (4-5/yr.). SEK 240 membership (effective 1991). K P M L, P.O. Box 31187, S-400 32 Goeteborg, Sweden.

KOBLENZER GEOGRAPHISCHES KOLLOQUIUM. see GEOGRAPHY

320   **DK**   **ISSN 0906-0928**
KOEBENHAVNS UNIVERSITET. INSTITUT FOR STATSKUNDSKAB. FORSKNINGSRAPPORT. 1974. irreg. DKK 20 per issue. University of Copenhagen, Institute of Political Studies, Rosenborggade 15, DK-1130 Koebenhavn K, Denmark. TEL 45-35-32-33-66. FAX 45-35-32-33-99. illus.
    Formerly (until 1990): Koebenhavns Universitet. Institut for Samfundsfag og Forvaltning. Forskningsrapport (ISSN 0900-274X)

349 320   **JA**   **ISSN 0454-1723**
KOKUGAKUIN UNIVERSITY. FACULTY OF LAW AND POLITICS. JOURNAL/KOKUGAKUIN HOGAKU. 1963. 3000 Yen. Kokugakuin University, Faculty of Law and Politics, 4-10-28 Higashi, Shibuya-ku, Tokyo 150, Japan. TEL 03-5466-0304. FAX 03-5466-0757. **Document type**: academic/scholarly publication.
—BLDSC (5101.776000).

320.532   **GW**   **ISSN 0723-7669**
KOMMUNE; Forum fuer Politik - Oekonomie - Kultur. 1973. m. DM.87. Kuehl Verwaltung GmbH & Co. Verlags KG, Mainzer Landstr. 147, 60327 Frankfurt, Germany. FAX 069-732605. Ed.Bd. adv.; bk.rev. circ. 4,000.
—BLDSC (5105.440000).
    Formerly: Kommunismus und Klassenkampf.

320.532   **BW**   **ISSN 0023-3102**
HX8
KOMMUNIST BELORUSSII. (Editions in Byelorussian, Russian) 1959. m. 6 Rub. (Kommunisticheskaya Partiya Belorussii, Tsentral'nyi Komitet) Izdatel'stvo Zvyazda, Leninskii prospekt, 77, Minsk, Belarus. (Dist. by: Mezhdunarodnaya Kniga, Dimitrova ul. 39, Moscow, G-200, Russia) Ed. Ya.I. Kachan. bk.rev.; bibl.

320.532   **KR**   **ISSN 0023-3110**
HX8
KOMMUNIST UKRAINY. (Editions in Russian and Ukrainian) 1925. m. 7.20 Rub. Vul. Ordzkonikidze 8, 254025 Kiev, Ukraine. TEL 044-291-5752. Ed. Ya E. Pashko. bk.rev.; bibl. circ. 21,700 (Rus.ed.); 11,200 (Ukr.ed.). (also avail. in microfilm from KTO)

320.5   **SW**   **ISSN 1100-973X**
KOMMUNISTEN. 1979. bi-m. SEK 60 (effective 1990). Kommunistiska Partiet i Sverige (KPS), P.O. Box 17104, S-104 62 Stockholm.

320.532   **RU**
KOMMUNISTICHESKAYA PARTIYA SOVETSKOGO SOYUZA. VYSSHAYA PARTIINAYA SHKOLA. UCHENYE ZAPISKI. 1973. irreg. 1.14 Rub. Izdatel'stvo Mysl', Leninskii Prospekt 15, 117071 Moscow B-71, Russia.

320.532   **YU**   **ISSN 0023-320X**
KOMUNIST. (Editions in Albanian, Macedonian, Serbo-Croatian, Slovenian; shortened editions in Bulgarian, Hungarian, Italian, Romanian, Ruthenian, Slovakian) 1925. w. $25. (Savez Komunista Jugoslavije) Komunist, Trg Marksa i Engelsa 11, 11000 Belgrade, Yugoslavia. Ed. Vlajko Krivokapic.

320   **KO**
KONGRES HA-TSIYONI. HAHLATOT/WORLD ZIONIST ORGANIZATION. ZIONIST CONGRESS.* (Text in Hebrew) irreg. World Zionist Organization - Kongres ha-Tsiyoni, P.O. Box 92, Jerusalem 91920, Israel. TEL 02-527156. FAX 02-533542.

320   **KO**
KOREA FOCUS ON CURRENT TOPICS. (Text in English) 1993. bi-m. 3500 Won($5) per no. Korea Foundation, 526 Namdaemunno 5-ga, Chung-gu, Seoul, S. Korea. TEL 02-752-6171. FAX 02-757-2049. (Subscr. to: C.P.O. Box 2147, Seoul, S. Korea) Ed. Son Chu-Whan.

320 330   **KO**
KOREA POLICY SERIES.* no.16, 1973. irreg. Korean Overseas Information Service, Seoul, S. Korea.

320.531   **KN**   **ISSN 0454-4072**
DS930
KOREA TODAY. (Editions in Arabic, Chinese, English, French, Russian, Spanish) m. $39. Foreign Languages Publishing House, Pyongyang, N. Korea. TELEX 37018 EPB KP. (Dist. by: Korean Publications Exchange Association, Export Section, P.O. Box 222, Pyongyang, N. Korea. FAX 8502-814632) Ed. Nam-Suk Hahn. charts; illus. **Indexed**: GeoRef.

POLITICAL SCIENCE

KOREAN AFFAIRS REPORT. see *BUSINESS AND ECONOMICS — Economic Situation And Conditions*

327 KO ISSN 0377-0451
JX1
KOREAN JOURNAL OF INTERNATIONAL STUDIES. (Text in English) 1970. q. $35 to individuals; $40 to institutions. Korean Institute of International Studies, K.P.O. Box 426, Seoul 110-604, S. Korea. TEL 02-752-7727. FAX 02-752-7710. TELEX K-26439. Ed. Chong-Ki Choi. adv.; bk.rev.; bibl. circ. 1,200. (back issues avail.) **Indexed:** Abstr.Mil.Bibl., Asian-Pac.Econ.Lit., Geo.Abstr., Int.Polit.Sci.Abstr., Met.Abstr.
—BLDSC (5113.562000); UnCover.
Description: Aims to act as a forum for discussion on peace research and international relations, with emphasis on the East Asian region.

320 US
KOREAN RESEARCH BULLETIN. vol.6, 1976. s-a. free. Korean Research Council, 1565 Miramar Ave., Seaside, CA 93955. Ed. Sae Woon Chang.

320 301.412 KN
HQ1765.6
KOREAN WOMEN.* (Editions in English, French) q. Korean Democratic Women's Union, Central Committee, Pyongyang, N. Korea. illus.

KRIEGSOPFER- UND BEHINDERTEN. RUNDSCHAU; Zeitschrift fuer Kriegsopfer und Behindertenfragen, Sozialpolitik Versorgungsbrecht und Gesellschaftspolitik. see *SOCIOLOGY*

320.531 GW ISSN 0178-7691
KRISIS; beitraege zur kritik der warengesellschaft. 1986. irregr., no.12, 1993. DM.16 per no. (Verein fuer Kritische Gesellschaftswissenschaft e.V.) Horlemann Verlag, Postfach 1307, 53572 Bad Honnef, Germany. TEL 02224-5589. FAX 02224-5429. Ed. Norbert Trenkle. adv. contact: Robert Kurz. circ. 900 (paid). (back issues avail.) **Document type:** academic/scholarly publication.

329.9 SW ISSN 0284-9941
KRISTDEMOKRATEN. 1965. w. SEK 345. Samhaellsgemenskaps Foerlags AB, P.O. Box 19098, S-104 32 Stockholm, Sweden. TEL 46-8-15-05-45. FAX 46-8-612-79-53. Ed. Stefan Attefall. adv.: B&W page SEK 15000, color page SEK 19400; trim 255 x 375. bk.rev.; illus.; circ. 9,700 (controlled). (tabloid format)
Formerly (until vol.9, 1988): Samhaellsgemenskap (ISSN 0036-3782)

320 328 KO ISSN 0027-8580
KUKHOEBO/NATIONAL ASSEMBLY REVIEW. (Text in Korean) 1949. m. free. National Assembly, c/o Secretary-General, 1-1 Yeoidodong, Yeongdungpo-ku, Seoul, S. Korea. TEL 788-2058. FAX 788-3348. Ed. Man Seop. charts; illus.; stat.; circ. 5,500 (controlled).
Description: Provides current information on the National Assembly.

322.4 GW ISSN 0723-8088
KULTURREVOLUTION. 2/yr. DM.27; newsstand price: DM.15. Klartext Verlag, Dickmannstr. 2-4, 45143 Essen, Germany. TEL 0201-8620631. FAX 0201-8620622. **Document type:** bulletin.

KURIER (LIESBORN); der christlichen Mitte. see *RELIGIONS AND THEOLOGY*

960 BS ISSN 0023-5733
DT790
KUTLWANO/MUTUAL UNDERSTANDING. (Text in English and Setswana) 1962. m. P.100. Information & Broadcasting, Private Bag 0060, Botswana Rd., City Centre-Main Mall, Gaborone, Botswana. TEL 267-32541. FAX 267-352971. Ed. Russ Molosiwa. adv.: B&W page P.650. charts; illus.; circ. 24,000 (controlled). **Document type:** directory, government publication.
Description: Features development issues in the country.

320 AT
LABOR REVIEW. 1959-1984; N.S. 1987. q. Aus.$10 (foreign Aus.$20). Victorian Labor College, P.O. Box 39, Trades Hall, Carlton South, Vic. 3053, Australia. TEL 03-499-2386. Ed. Chris Gaffney. adv.; bk.rev. circ. 1,300.
Formerly (until no.18): Labor College Review (ISSN 0159-1908)
Description: Includes articles on politics, economics and history from a Marxist viewpoint.

329 AT ISSN 0819-9825
LABOR TIMES. 1966. m. $50. Australian Labor Party, New South Wales Branch, c/o J. Della Bosca, 377 Sussex St., Sydney, N.S.W. 2000, Australia. TEL 02-264-2732. FAX 02-264-2574. Ed. Jarka Sipka. adv.; bk.rev. circ. 16,000.
Formerly (until 1987): Australian Labor Party. A.L.P. (ISSN 0045-0669)

329.9 AT ISSN 0159-3544
LABOR VOICE. 1959. bi-m. Aus.$12. Australian Labor Party, Western Australia Branch, 2nd Fl., Labor Centre, 82 Beaufort St., Perth, W.A. 6000, Australia. FAX 09-2279585. Ed. John A. Cowdell. adv.; bk.rev.; illus.; circ. 10,000 (controlled). (tabloid format)
Formerly (until 1979): Western Sun (ISSN 0043-423X)

LABOUR & TRADE UNION REVIEW. see *LABOR UNIONS*

320.532 IE ISSN 0790-1712
LABOUR COMMENT (CORK). 1968. fortn. I£10. Labour Comment (Cork) Ireland, 26 Church Ave., Roman St., Cork, Ireland. FAX 021-506360. (Co-sponsor: Brotherhood of Irish Compositors) Ed. Patrick Noel Maloney. adv.; bk.rev. circ. 1,000. **Document type:** newsletter.
Former titles (until 1984): Comment (Dublin); Communist Comment.

320 UK ISSN 0260-3810
LABOUR PARTY. CAMPAIGN BRIEFING. 1980. m. £7. Labour Party, Policy Directorate, 150 Walworth Rd., London SE17 1JT, England. FAX 01-701-6363. Ed. Nick Sigler. s-a. index. circ. 3,000. (back issues avail.)
Description: Review of main items of political interest to Labour Party members and supporters.

329.9 UK ISSN 0309-3689
LABOUR STUDENT. 1980. 3/yr. £3. Labour Students, 150 Walnorth Rd., London SE17 1JT, England. adv.; bk.rev.; illus. circ. 12,000.
Formerly: Socialist Youth (ISSN 0260-7336)

320 US
LAISSEZ FAIRE BOOKS FREE MARKET CATALOG. 1973. m. free. Laissez Faire Books, 938 Howard St., San Francisco, CA 94103. TEL 415-541-9780. FAX 415-541-0597. Ed. Jim Powell. adv.; bk.rev.; tr.lit. circ. 50,000. **Document type:** catalog.
Former titles: Laissez Faire Free Market Catalog; Laissez Faire Libertarian Catalog.

943 GW ISSN 0340-7837
LAND AKTUELL. 1949. s-m. DM.32. Katholische Landvolkbewegung, Drachenfelsstr. 23, 53604 Rhoendorf, Germany. TEL 02224-71031. FAX 02224-78971. Ed. Hans-Peter Ollig. bk.rev. circ. 7,000. **Document type:** newspaper.
Formerly: Dorf Aktuell (ISSN 0012-5547)

320 410 US
LANGUAGE AND IDEOLOGY. 1991. irreg. price varies. Praeger Publishers (Subsidiary of: Greenwood Publishing Group Inc.), 88 Post Rd. W., Box 5007, Westport, CT 06881-5007. TEL 203-226-3571. FAX 203-222-1502. **Document type:** monographic series.

320 II
LATIN AMERICA LETTER. (Text in English) 1981. m. Rs.500($100) K.K. Roy (Private) Ltd., 55 Gariahat Rd., P.O. Box 10210, Calcutta 700 019, India. Ed. K.K. Roy.

LATIN AMERICA REPORT. see *BUSINESS AND ECONOMICS — Economic Situation And Conditions*

LATIN AMERICAN PERSPECTIVES; a journal on capitalism and socialism. see *SOCIAL SCIENCES: COMPREHENSIVE WORKS*

LATIN AMERICAN REGIONAL REPORTS - ANDEAN GROUP. see *BUSINESS AND ECONOMICS — Economic Situation And Conditions*

LATIN AMERICAN WEEKLY REPORT. see *BUSINESS AND ECONOMICS — Economic Situation And Conditions*

LAVORO E SOCIETA; economia-cultura-politica-sociologia. see *BUSINESS AND ECONOMICS*

LAW & POLICY. see *LAW*

LAW AND POLITICAL REVIEW. see *LAW*

LAW AND STATE; a biannual collection of recent German contributions to these fields. see *LAW — International Law*

055.1 IT ISSN 0023-9526
LAZIO.* q. Via dei Frentani 4, Rome, Italy. (tabloid format)

LEADER IN ACTION. see *EDUCATION*

LEADERSHIP QUARTERLY; an international journal of political, social and behavioral science. see *BUSINESS AND ECONOMICS — Management*

LEAGUE OF WOMEN VOTERS OF GEORGIA. LEGISLATIVE NEWSLETTER. see *LAW*

320 LE
LEBANESE JOURNAL OF POLITICAL SCIENCE.* (Text in Arabic, English, French) s-a. P.O. Box 3865, Beirut, Lebanon. Ed. Bechir Aridi. bibl.

320 IS
LEBNS FRAGN. (Text in Yiddish) 1951. q. $20. Brith Haavoda - Arbeter Ring, 48 Kalisher St., Tel Aviv 65165, Israel. TEL 972-3-5714010. FAX 972-3-5714010. Ed. Yitzhak Luden. bk.rev. circ. 2,500.

944 FR ISSN 0024-0133
LECTURES FRANCAISES; revue de la politique francaise. 1957. m. 250 F. (foreign 290 F.) Diffusion de la Pensee Francaise, Chire-en-Montreuil, 86190 Vouille, France. TEL 49-51-83-04. FAX 49-51-63-50. Ed. Jean Auguy. adv.; bk.rev.; bibl. circ. 7,500.

320 IE
LEFT. 1980. 6/yr. donations. Irish Democratic Youth Movement, 30 Gardiner Place, Dublin 1, Ireland. TEL 01-740716. FAX 01-787921. TELEX WP-EI-31490. Ed.Bd. illus. circ. 25,000.
Former titles: Socialist Youth; Challenge (Dublin).

320.531 US
LEFT COURT.* 1983. irreg. $10 (foreign $20). Socialist Party of Illinois, 6452 N. Bosworth Ave., No.1, Chicago, IL 60626. TEL 312-764-1851. adv.; bk.rev. circ. 600. (also avail. in microform; back issues avail.)

322.4 US
K1
THE LEGAL REFORMER. Short title: A L R. 1979. q. $15 membership. (Organization of Americans for Legal Reform) HALT, Inc., 1319 F St., N.W., Ste. 300, Washington, DC 20004. TEL 202-247-9600. FAX 202-347-9606. Ed. Theresa Meehan Rudy. bk.rev. circ. 70,000. **Document type:** newsletter.
Formerly (until vol.8, no.4, 1988): Americans for Legal Reform (ISSN 0739-6813)

320.531 CU
LEGALIDAD SOCIALISTA. q. $15 in N. and S. America; Europe $16; elsewhere $18. (Fiscalia General de la Republica) Ediciones Cubanas, Obispo No. 527, Apdo. 605, Havana, Cuba. (Alt. addr.: San Rafael No. 3, Havana, 2, Cuba)

POLITICAL SCIENCE

350 US ISSN 0362-9805
JF501
LEGISLATIVE STUDIES QUARTERLY. 1976. q. $35 to individuals (foreign $45); institutions $70 (foreign $80). University of Iowa, Comparative Legislative Research Center, 349 Schaeffer Hall, Iowa City, IA 52242. TEL 319-335-2361. FAX 319-335-3211. Ed.Bd. adv.; bk.rev.; bibl.; charts; index. circ. 1,000. (also avail. in microform from UMI; reprint service avail. from UMI,WSH) **Indexed:** A.B.C.Pol.Sci., Amer.Bibl.Slavic & E.Eur.Stud, Curr.Cont., Int.Polit.Sci.Abstr., Polit.Sci.Abstr., SSCI. **Document type:** academic/scholarly publication.
—BLDSC (5181.461000); Faxon; Genuine Article; SWETS; UMI; UnCover. **CCC.**

320 US
LEGISLATIVE UPDATE (DALLAS); opinion ballot, national poll & voting records. 1958. m. $125 membership. National "Write Your Congressman" Inc., 9696 Skillman, Ste. 170, Dallas, TX 75243. FAX 214-324-5245. Ed. Charles Huston. circ. 75,000 (paid). **Document type:** newsletter.
Description: Contains excerpts from congressmen's speeches, opinion polls and letters to the editor on major national issues including SDI, abortion, gun control, taxation and government spending. Includes a ballot on state issues to be sent to representatives in congress & governors.

328 II ISSN 0024-0508
LEGISLATOR. (Text in English) 1969. m. Rs.12. D-32 Kirti Nagar, New Delhi 15, India. Ed. Raj Sauldie. adv.; illus.; stat.

320.9 GH ISSN 0024-0540
DT510.A1
LEGON OBSERVER.* 1966. fortn. $27.30. Legon Society on National Affairs, POB 11, Legon, Ghana. Ed. Ebow Daniel. bk.rev.; charts. **Indexed:** Curr.Cont.Africa.

329.9 GW
LEHEL AKTUELL. 1973. q. DM.13.80. (Sozialdemokratische Partei Deutschland) S P D - Ortsverein Lehel, c/o Dr. Thomas Lange, Knobelstr. 30, 80538 Munich, Germany. TEL 089-222918. adv. circ. 7,200. (back issues avail.) **Document type:** bulletin.

320 FR
LETTRE DE L'O F C E. 1982. 10/yr. 122 F. to individuals (foreign 153 F.); institutions 225 F. (foreign 255 F.). (Observatoire Francais des Conjonctures Economiques) Presses de la Fondation Nationale des Sciences Politiques, 44 rue du Four, 75006 Paris, France. TEL 44-39-39-60. FAX 1-45-48-04-41. TELEX 201 002 F. **Indexed:** ELLIS, P.A.I.S.For.Lang.Ind.

329 FR
LETTRE DE LA NATION. d. 210 F. Rassemblement pour la Republique, 123 rue de Lille, 75340 Paris Cedex 07, France. TEL 49-55-63-96. (Subscr. to: Etape Communication, 282 bd Saint-Germain, 75341 Paris Cedex 07, France)
Description: A daily look at French and international politics.

329 FR ISSN 1143-1210
LETTRE DE LA NATION MAGAZINE. w. 220 F. Rassemblement pour la Republique, 123 rue de Lille, 75340 Paris Cedex 07, France. TEL 49-55-63-97. (Subscr. to: Etape Communication, 282 bd Saint-Germain, 75341 Paris Cedex 07, France. TEL 49-55-64-59) Eds. Patrick Rizzi, Alain Parchowski. illus.

320.51 DK ISSN 0047-4460
DL101
LIBERAL. 1970. 4/yr. DKK 120. Venstres Landsorganisation, Soelleroedvej 30, 2840 Holte, Denmark. Ed. Claus Hjort Frederiksen. circ. 3,500.

329.3 RU
LIBERAL. 1990. irreg. 100 Rub. per issue. Liberal'no-demokraticheskaya Partiya Sovetskogo Soyuza, c/o A.Kh. Khalitov, Ed., Sovkhoz im. Lenina, d.13, kv.126, Leninskii r-on, Moskovskaya obl., Russia. TEL 548-6993. adv. circ. 150,000. **Document type:** newspaper.

320.51 UK ISSN 0954-5735
LIBERAL DEMOCRAT NEWS. 1946. w. £26. Liberal Democrats, 4 Cowley St., Westminster, London SW1P 3NB, England. TEL 0171-222-4422. FAX 0171-222-7904. Ed. David Boyle. adv. contact: Ian Walton. bk.rev.; illus. circ. 11,000. (back issues avail.) **Document type:** newspaper.
—UMI.
Former titles: Social and Liberal Democrats News; (until 1988): Social Democrat (ISSN 0024-1849); Liberal News Commentary.
Description: Reports on current affairs, social issues, and internal Party news.

332.4 329.3 CE
LIBERAL REVIEW. 1986. q. Rs.150($20) Liberal Party, 88-1 Rosmead Place, Colombo 7, Sri Lanka. TEL 582779. FAX 588875. TELEX 22658-GLAXY-CE. Eds. Chanaka Amaratunga, Rajiva Wijesinha. adv.; bk.rev.; circ. 1,000 (controlled).
Description: Covers Sri Lankan political events from a liberal perspective.

329.3 JA ISSN 0286-3553
DS889
LIBERAL STAR. (Text in English) 1972. m. $12. Liberal Democratic Party of Japan, 1-11-23 Nagata-Cho, Chiyoda-ku, Tokyo 100, Japan. TEL 03-3581-6211. Ed. Koichi Yamaguchi. circ. 500,000.

320.51 SW ISSN 0024-1857
LIBERAL UNGDOM. 1934. q. SEK 100 (effective 1990). Folkpartiets Ungdomsfoerbund - Youth Organization of the Swedish Liberal Party, P.O. Box 6508, 113 83 Stockholm, Sweden. FAX 8-349591. Ed. David Nystrom. adv.; bk.rev.; illus. circ. 15,000.
Formerly (until 1961): Frisinnad Ungdom.

DE LIBERALE VROUW. see *WOMEN'S INTERESTS*

320.532 IJ ISSN 0024-1881
LIBERATION; a third dimension of Marxism in India. 1968-19??; resumed 1991. q. c/o Arup Pal, 8A, Picnic Garden First Ln., Calcutta 700 039, India. Ed. Arindam Sen.

320.531 US ISSN 1051-7871
HX1
LIBERATION AND MARXISM. 1989. q. $10 to individuals; institutions $15. W W Publishers Inc., 55 W. 17th St., 5th Fl., New York, NY 10011. TEL 212-627-2994. FAX 212-675-7869. Ed. David Perez. bk.rev. circ. 2,000. (back issues avail.) **Indexed:** Alt.Press Ind.
—UMI.
Formerly: Liberation! (ISSN 1047-594X)

320.532 IT
LIBERAZIONE. 1991. w. L.50000. Partito della Rifondazione Comunista, Via Marianna Dionigi 57, 00193 Rome, Italy. TEL 06-3222599. FAX 06-3222598. Ed. Sergio Garavini. circ. 106,000. **Document type:** newspaper.

320.5 LB ISSN 0024-1962
LIBERIAN AGE.* 1946. d. $9. True Whig Party, Carey St., Monrovia, Liberia. Ed. Stanton B. Peabody. adv.; illus. circ. 4,000. (tabloid format; also avail. in microform) **Document type:** newspaper.

320 UK ISSN 0953-7791
LIBERTARIAN ALLIANCE. ATHEIST NOTES. irreg. £15($30) Libertarian Alliance, 25 Chapter Chambers, Esterbrooke St., London SW1P 4NN, England. TEL 0171-821-5502. FAX 0171-834-2031. E-mail: liberty@capital.demon.co.uk. **Document type:** monographic series.

322.4 UK ISSN 0267-7121
LIBERTARIAN ALLIANCE. BACKGROUND BRIEFINGS. 1985. irreg. £10($20) Libertarian Alliance, 25 Chapter Chambers, Esterbrooke St., London SW1P 4NN, England. TEL 0171-821-5502. FAX 0171-834-2031. E-mail: liberty@capital.demon.co.uk. Ed.Bd. adv.; bk.rev.; film rev.; bibl. circ. 1,000. (back issues avail.) **Document type:** monographic series.

323.4 UK ISSN 0267-677X
LIBERTARIAN ALLIANCE. CULTURAL NOTES. 1983. irreg. £15($30) Libertarian Alliance, 25 Chapter Chambers, Esterbrooke St., London SW1P 4NN, England. TEL 0171-821-5502. FAX 0171-834-2031. E-mail: liberty@capital.demon.co.uk. Ed.Bd. adv.; bk.rev.; film rev.; bibl. circ. 1,000. (back issues avail.) **Document type:** monographic series.

332.4 UK ISSN 0267-6761
LIBERTARIAN ALLIANCE. FOREIGN POLICY PERSPECTIVES. 1983. irreg. £15($30) Libertarian Alliance, 25 Chapter Chambers, Esterbrooke St., London SW1P 4NN, England. TEL 0171-821-5502. FAX 0171-834-2031. E-mail: liberty@capital.demon.co.uk. Ed.Bd. adv.; bk.rev.; film rev.; bibl. circ. 1,000. (back issues avail.) **Document type:** monographic series.

320 UK ISSN 0953-7783
LIBERTARIAN ALLIANCE. PAMPHLETS. 1980. irreg. £15($30) Libertarian Alliance, 25 Chapter Chambers, Esterbrooke St., London SW1P 4NN, England. TEL 0171-821-5502. FAX 0171-834-2031. E-mail: liberty@capital.demon.co.uk. **Document type:** monographic series.

332.4 UK ISSN 0267-7156
LIBERTARIAN ALLIANCE. PERSONAL PERSPECTIVES. 1984. irreg. £15($30) Libertarian Alliance, 25 Chapter Chambers, Esterbrooke St., London SW1P 4NN, England. TEL 0171-821-5502. FAX 0171-834-2031. E-mail: liberty@capital.demon.co.uk. Ed.Bd. adv.; bk.rev.; film rev.; bibl. circ. 1,000. (back issues avail.) **Document type:** monographic series.

322.4 UK ISSN 0267-7059
LIBERTARIAN ALLIANCE. POLITICAL NOTES. 1979. irreg. £15($30) Libertarian Alliance, 25 Chapter Chambers, Esterbrooke St., London SW1P 4NN, England. TEL 0171-821-5502. FAX 0171-834-2031. E-mail: liberty@capital.demon.co.uk. Ed.Bd. adv.; bk.rev.; film rev.; bibl. circ. 1,000. (back issues avail.) **Document type:** monographic series.

300 320 UK ISSN 0267-7067
LIBERTARIAN ALLIANCE. SCIENTIFIC NOTES. 1985. irreg. £15($30) Libertarian Alliance, 25 Chapter Chambers, Esterbrooke St., London SW1P 4NN, England. TEL 0171-821-5502. FAX 0171-834-2031. E-mail: liberty@capital.demon.co.uk. Ed.Bd. adv.; bk.rev.; film rev.; bibl. circ. 1,000. (back issues avail.) **Document type:** monographic series.

320 UK ISSN 0267-7180
LIBERTARIAN ALLIANCE. STUDY GUIDES. 1985. irreg. £15($30) Libertarian Alliance, 25 Chapter Chambers, Esterbrooke St., London SW1P 4NN, England. TEL 0171-821-5502. FAX 0171-834-2031. E-mail: liberty@capital.demon.co.uk. **Document type:** monographic series.

322.4 UK ISSN 0268-2923
LIBERTARIAN ALLIANCE. TACTICAL NOTES. 1985. irreg. £15($30) Libertarian Alliance, 25 Chapter Chambers, Esterbrooke St., London SW1P 4NN, England. TEL 0171-821-5502. FAX 0171-834-2031. E-mail: liberty@capital.demon.co.uk. Ed.Bd. adv.; bk.rev.; film rev.; bibl. circ. 1,000. (back issues avail.) **Document type:** monographic series.

322.4 UK
LIBERTARIAN ALLIANCE. WORLD REPORTS. 1985. irreg. £15($30) Libertarian Alliance, 25 Chapter Chambers, Esterbrooke St., London SW1P 4NN, England. TEL 0171-821-5502. FAX 0171-843-2031. E-mail: liberty@capital.demon.co.uk. Ed.Bd. adv.; bk.rev.; film rev.; bibl. circ. 1,000. (back issues avail.) **Document type:** monographic series.
Formerly (until 1985): Liberation Alliance. International Reports.

POLITICAL SCIENCE

320.5 US ISSN 0047-4517
LIBERTARIAN FORUM.* 1969. m. $15. 215 W. 88th St., Apt. 2E, New York, NY 10024-2328. Ed. Murray N. Rothbard. adv.; bk.rev.; bibl.; cum.index every 2 yrs. circ. 750. (looseleaf format; also avail. in microform from UMI; reprint service avail. from UMI)
Formerly: Libertarian.

320 UK ISSN 0959-566X
LIBERTARIAN HERITAGE. 1990. irreg. Libertarian Alliance, 25 Chapter Chambers, Esterbrooke St., London SW1P 4NN, England. TEL 0171-821-5502. FAX 0171-834-2031. E-mail: liberty@capital.demon.co.uk. **Document type:** monographic series.

320 UK ISSN 0959-5678
LIBERTARIAN HERITAGE REPRINTS. irreg. Libertarian Alliance, 25 Chapter Chambers, Esterbrooke St., London SW1P 4NN, England. TEL 0171-821-5502. FAX 0171-834-2031. E-mail: liberty@capital.demon.co.uk. **Document type:** monographic series.

322.4 UK ISSN 0267-6788
LIBERTARIAN NEWS. 1982. irreg. £15($30) Libertarian Alliance, 25 Chapter Chambers, Esterbrooke St., London SW1P 4NN, England. TEL 0171-821-5502. FAX 0171-834-2031. E-mail: liberty@capital.demon.co.uk. Ed.Bd. adv.; bk.rev.; film rev.; bibl. circ. 1,000. (back issues avail.) **Document type:** monographic series.

322.4 US ISSN 8755-139X
LIBERTARIAN PARTY NEWS. 1972. m. $25. (Libertarian National Committee) Solstice, Inc., Box 3391, Gainesville, GA 30503. TEL 404-536-5243. E-mail: 71610,3614@compuserve.com. Ed. Burton R. Langhenry. adv.; bk.rev. circ. 18,000. **Document type:** newspaper.

322.4 UK ISSN 0267-6796
LIBERTARIAN REPRINTS. 1979. irreg. £15($30) Libertarian Alliance, 25 Chapter Chambers, Esterbrooke St., London SW1P 4NN, England. TEL 0171-821-5502. FAX 0171-834-2031. E-mail: liberty@capital.demon.co.uk. Ed.Bd. adv.; bk.rev.; film rev.; bibl. circ. 1,000. (back issues avail.) **Document type:** monographic series.

320 UK ISSN 0267-7199
LIBERTARIAN STUDENT. 1985. irreg. £15($30) Libertarian Alliance, 25 Chapter Chambers, Esterbrooke St., London SW1P 4NN, England. TEL 0171-821-5502. FAX 0171-834-2031. E-mail: liberty@capital.demon.co.uk. **Document type:** monographic series.

LIBERTAS. see *COLLEGE AND ALUMNI*

LIBERTY (PORT TOWNSEND). see *LITERARY AND POLITICAL REVIEWS*

322.7 US ISSN 0145-7667
DS141
LIBERTY BELL. 1973. m. $45. Liberty Bell Publications, Box 211, Reedy, WV 25270. TEL 304-927-4486. Ed. George P. Dietz. adv.; bk.rev. circ. 9,500. (back issues avail.)

320 LH ISSN 0259-4137
DB153
LIECHTENSTEIN POLITISCHE SCHRIFTEN. 1972. irreg., no.21. 88 SFr. Verlag der Liechtensteinischen Akademischen Gesellschaft, Am Schraegen Weg 2, Postfach 44, FL-9490 Vaduz, Liechtenstein. TEL 075-2322424. FAX 075-2322837. circ. 1,000. **Document type:** monographic series.

320 US
LIGHT & LIBERTY.* m. $1 per no. 3525 Main St., Stone Ridge, NY 12484-5612. Ed. Lawrence E. Christopher.
Description: Discusses topics relating to civil rights and individual liberty.

322.4 US
LIMIT. 1974. m. $5. Libertarian Republican Alliance, 1149 E. 32nd St., Brooklyn, NY 11210. Ed. Elliott Capon. adv.; bk.rev. circ. 500.

320.531 IT
LINEAMENTI; quale marxismo oggi. 1985. q. L.1100. Edizioni GB, Via Curzola 9, 35135 Padova, Italy. TEL 604102. circ. 2,000.

320 II
LINK. (Text in English) 1958. w. newsstand price: Rs.4. United India Periodicals Pvt. Ltd., Link House, Bahadur Shah Zafar Marg, New Delhi 110002, India. TEL 3312439. Ed. Sitanshu Das; Pub. N.S. Raghave. adv.: B&W page Rs.2500, color page Rs.4000; bleed 210 x 275. circ. 8,675.

320.531 GW ISSN 0024-404X
HX6
LINKS; Sozialistische Zeitung. 1969. m. DM.75. (Sozialistisches Buero) Verlag 2000 GmbH, Bleichstr. 5-7, 63065 Offenbach, Germany. TEL 069-885006. Ed.Bd. adv.; bk.rev.; illus. (tabloid format) **Indexed:** Rehabil.Lit. **Document type:** bulletin.

LITIGATION UNDER THE FEDERAL OPEN GOVERNMENT LAWS. see *LAW*

320.5 UK ISSN 0047-4827
LIVERPOOL NEWSLETTER. 1960. m. £4($10) (effective 1995). (Gild of St. George) Third Way Publications Ltd., P.O. Box 1243, London SW7 3PB, Englandd. TEL 0171-373-3432. Ed. Kevin Aspen. adv. contact: Richard Chance. bk.rev. circ. 200. **Document type:** newsletter.

320 UK ISSN 0955-2448
HX3
LIVING MARXISM. 1988. m. £19.50 (foreign £23). (Revolutionary Communist Party) Junius Publications Ltd., BCM JPLTD, London WC1N 3XX, England. TEL 0171-278-7699. FAX 0171-278-9844. E-mail: junius@junius.co.uk. Ed. Mick Hume. adv.: B&W page £1050, color page £1250; adv. contact: Phil Johnson. bk.rev.; film rev.; play rev. circ. 25,000. (also avail. in microfilm) **Document type:** bulletin.
—BLDSC (5282.860000).
Description: Provides news and current-affairs commentary and analysis, along with regular features on social issues, science, arts, and culture.

329 AT
LOBBY. 1973. q. Aus.$10 to non-members. Australian Labor Party, Australian Capital Territory Branch, Labor Club, Chandler St., Belconnen, A.C.T. 2617, Australia. Ed. Lembit Suur. adv.; bk.rev. circ. 1,500.
Former titles: Australian Labor Party. A.C.T. Branch. Magazine; Australian Labor Party. A.C.T. Branch. Newsletter.

320 UK ISSN 0964-0436
LOBSTER. 1983. 2/yr. £5 (Europe £7; elsewhere £8). 214 Westbourne Ave., Hull HU5 3JB, England. TEL 01482-447558. Ed. Robin Ramsay. adv.; bk.rev.; illus. circ. 1,000. **Document type:** newsletter.

322.4 GW
LOKALES; Stadtzeitung fuer Babenhausen. 1981. 4/yr. free. Buendnis 90 - Die Gruenen, Neugasse 1, 64832 Babenhausen, Germany. TEL 06073-62452. FAX 06073-4634. circ. 7,000. **Document type:** newsletter.

328 II ISSN 0024-595X
LOKTANTRA SAMIKSHA. (Text in Hindi) 1969. q. Rs.30($10) Institute of Constitutional and Parliamentary Studies, 18-21 Vithalbhai Patel House, Rafi Marg, New Delhi 110001, India. Ed. O.P. Khadasia.

LOOK JAPAN. see *BUSINESS AND ECONOMICS — International Development And Assistance*

059.95 HK
LOOK MAGAZINE. (Text in Chinese) 1958. m. $20. Chih Luen Press, B1, Carnarvon Mansion, 10th Fl., 12, Carnarvon Rd., Kowloon, Hong Kong. Ed. Smarlo Ma. bk.rev. **Indexed:** Mag.Ind.
Formerly: Look Fortnightly (ISSN 0024-6387)

353 US
JK1759
LOOKING AHEAD (OKLAHOMA CITY). 1942. m. $10. National Education Program, Box 11000, Oklahoma City, OK 73136-1100. TEL 405-425-5035. FAX 405-425-5108. Ed. Pendleton Woods. bk.rev. circ. 20,000. (also avail. in microform from UMI; reprint service avail. from UMI) **Document type:** newsletter.
—UMI.
Former titles (until 1995): National Program Letter (ISSN 0027-9943); Harding College Letter.
Description: Presents editorials generally representing conservative viewpoints.

320 US ISSN 1070-2938
▼**THE LOS ANGELES LETTER;** Los Angeles from the ground up. 1995. s-m. $50. Alex Hartley, Ed. & Pub., 1138 S. Hayworth Ave., Los Angeles, CA 90035-2604. TEL 213-937-8718. FAX 213-937-9044. E-mail: Alexhart@Alexhart.com. **Document type:** newsletter.

335 US ISSN 1065-2000
LOVE AND RAGE. 1990. 6/yr. $9 free to qualified personnel. Box 853, New York, NY 10009-0853. TEL 718-834-9077. E-mail: ny@nyxter.blythe.org. bk.rev. circ. 4,000. **Document type:** newspaper.
Refereed Serial

320 US
LOYOLA LECTURE SERIES IN POLITICAL ANALYSIS. 1977. irreg. price varies. University of Notre Dame Press, Notre Dame, IN 46556. TEL 219-631-6346. FAX 219-631-8148. (Orders to: 11030 S. Langley Ave., Chicago, IL 60628. TEL 800-621-2736. FAX 800-621-8476; Overseas orders to: Eurospan University Press Group, Order Dept., 3 Henrietta St., London WC2E 8LU, England) Ed. T.S. Engeman. **Document type:** academic/scholarly publication.

320 301 BL ISSN 0102-6445
LUA NOVA; cultura e politica. 1984. 3/yr. $60 to individuals; institutions $90. CEDEC, Rua Airosa Galvao, 64, 05002-070 Sao Paulo, SP, Brazil. TEL 55-11-871-2966. FAX 55-11-871-2123. Ed. Gabriel Cohn. circ. 2,000. **Document type:** academic/scholarly publication.
Description: Provides theoretical studies, research, and contemporary debates in political science and sociology.

320 SG
LUTTE. 1977. q. Parti Africain de l'Independance, B.P. 820, Dakar, Senegal. Ed. Bara Goudiaby. circ. 1,000.

320 FR ISSN 0458-5143
LUTTE DE CLASSE; pour la reconstruction de la quatrieme internationale. 1956. m. (10/yr.). 100 F. (foreign 140 F.). Lutte Ouvriere, B.P. 233, 75865 Paris Cedex 18, France. Ed. Michel Rodinson. **Document type:** newsletter.

320 FR ISSN 0024-7650
LUTTE OUVRIERE. 1968. w. 300 F. (foreign 450 F.). Lutte Ouvriere, B.P. 233, 75865 Paris Cedex 18, France. Ed. Michel Rodinson. circ. 17,000. **Document type:** newspaper.

322.4 FR ISSN 0150-4428
LYS ROUGE; revue trimestrielle d'etudes royalistes. 1976. q. 90 F. Societe Nationale Presse Francaise, 17 rue des Petits Champs, 75001 Paris, France. TEL 42-97-42-57. Ed. Yvam Aumont. circ. 1,000.

320 MR ISSN 0851-0229
M A P ACTUALITE; daily national and international political news bulletin. 1976. d. DH.1401.56($173.89) Maghreb Arab Press, 122 Av. Allal Ben Abdellah, B.P. 1049, Rabat, Morocco. TEL 76-40-83. FAX 670-97. TELEX 310-44. Ed. Abdeljalil Fenjiro.

M I R S LEGISLATIVE REPORT. (Michigan Information and Research Service, Inc.) see *PUBLIC ADMINISTRATION*

320 US ISSN 0076-1729
M L SEIDMAN MEMORIAL TOWN HALL LECTURE SERIES. 1967. a. $5. Rhodes College, 2000 N. Pkwy., Memphis, TN 38112. TEL 901-726-3818. Ed. Daniel L. Cullen. circ. 600 (controlled). **Document type:** monographic series.

320 US ISSN 0464-1973
M O P S A NEWSLETTER. 1957. a. $10. Missouri Political Science Association, c/o George Connor, Sect.-Treas., Dept. of Political Science, Southwest Missouri State University, Springfield, MO 65804. TEL 417-836-6956. bibl.; circ. 80 (controlled). **Document type:** newsletter.

POLITICAL SCIENCE

320   FR   ISSN 0243-6450
JA11
M O T S. (Mots, Ordinateurs, Textes, Societes); les langages du politique. (Text in French, summaries in English, French, Spanish) 1980. q. 260 F. to individuals (foreign 305 F.); institutions 350 F. (foreign 420 F.). Presses de la Fondation Nationale des Sciences Politiques, 44 rue du Four, 75006 Paris, France. TEL 44-39-39-60. FAX 1-45-48-04-41. Ed. Maurice Tournier. adv.; bk.rev.; abstr.; bibl. circ. 800.
—BLDSC (5978.718300). **CCC.**
    Formerly: Travaux de Lexicometrie et Lexicologie Politique (ISSN 0294-796X)

956.940 296   US   ISSN 0017-6850
HA-MAAPIL. 1962. m. membership. Habonim Dror Labor Zionist Youth, 27 W. 20th St., 9th Fl., New York, NY 10011. TEL 212-255-1796. Ed. Charles Boxbaum. circ. 1,650. (processed)
    Description: University students' progressive Zionist journal.

MCCARVILLE - HILL REPORT. see PUBLIC ADMINISTRATION

MACEDONIAN TRIBUNE. see CLUBS

320   US   ISSN 1049-9776
PQ4627.M2
MACHIAVELLI STUDIES. 1987. a. $15 to individuals; institutions $25. University of New Orleans, Foreign Language Department, New Orleans, LA 70148. TEL 504-286-6657. Eds. Edmund Jacobitti, Victor A. Santi. bk.rev.; bibl. **Document type:** academic/scholarly publication.

320   US   ISSN 1083-3684
▼**MADISON REVIEW (TALLAHASSEE)**. 1995. q. $20 to individuals (foreign $32); libraries $35 (foreign $47). James Madison Institute for Public Policy, P.O. Box 13894, Tallahassee, FL 32317-3894. TEL 904-386-3131. FAX 904-386-1807. Ed. Thomas R. Dye; Pub. J. Stanley Marshall. **Document type:** academic/scholarly publication.
    Description: Encourages the study and application of Madisonian principles of limited government and individual freedom. Reports on the need for federalism and both the successes and failures from America's laboratories of democracy.

306.874 320   AG   ISSN 0327-1129
MADRES DE PLAZA DE MAYO. 1984. m. $60. Asociacion Madres de Plaza de Mayo, Hipolito Yrigoyen 1442, 1089 Buenos Aires, Argentina. TEL 54-1-3836430. FAX 54-1-9540381. circ. 5,000 (paid).
    Description: Covers all activities of the association of mothers: cultural events, speeches, and educational topics.

320.531   GW   ISSN 0024-967X
MAERKISCHE ZEITUNG. 1957. m. DM.60. Landsmannschaft Berlin-Mark Brandenburg, Landesverband Berlin, Stresemannstr. 90, 10117 Berlin, Germany. TEL 2611046. Ed. Herbert Willmann. adv.; bk.rev.; abstr.; illus.; circ. 8,500 (controlled). **Document type:** newspaper.

THE MAGHREB REVIEW; a quarterly journal on all aspects of North African and Islamic studies from AD 600 to the present day. see HISTORY — History Of Africa

614.7 323.4   US
MAINE PROGRESSIVE. 1986. m. $12. Invert, Box 776, Monroe, ME 04951. TEL 207-525-7776. (Subscr. to: Box 1084, Damariscotta, ME 04543) Ed. Larry Dansinger. adv.; bk.rev. circ. 3,000. (tabloid format; back issues avail.)
    Description: Contains information on political and social change activities in Maine.

320   US   ISSN 1059-3535
MAJOR CONCEPTS IN POLITICS AND POLITICAL THEORY. irreg., vol.4, 1994. price varies. Peter Lang Publishing, Inc., 62 W. 45th St., 4th Fl., New York, NY 10036. TEL 212-302-6740. Ed. Garrett Ward Sheldon. (back issues avail.) **Document type:** academic/scholarly publication, monographic series.
—BLDSC (5353.604315).
    Description: Focuses on major concepts in politics and political theory in prominent traditions, periods, and thinkers.

320   UG
MAKERERE POLITICAL REVIEW.* 1971. irreg. Makerere Political Society, Political Science Department, Makerere University, Kampala, Uganda. Ed. Amos Danson Twino. bibl.

320.531   CE
MAKSVADAYA. (Text in Singhalese) 1970. irreg. Nava Sama Samaja Party, 17 Barracks Lane, Colombo 2, Sri Lanka. Ed. Vickamabahu Karanarathne. adv.; bk.rev. circ. 500.

320   MW   ISSN 0076-3225
MALAWI. MINISTRY OF LOCAL GOVERNMENT. ANNUAL REPORT. a. K.0.50. Government Printer, Box 37, Zomba, Malawi.

959.5   MY   ISSN 0047-5629
DS591
MALAYSIAN DIGEST. 1969. m. free. Ministry of Foreign Affairs, External Information Division - Kementerian Luar Negeri, Wisma Putra, 50602 Kuala Lumpur, Malaysia. TEL 03-2488088. Ed. Sulochana K. Indran. charts; illus. circ. 25,000. (tabloid format)
    Description: Discusses current political, economic, social and cultural affairs.

320 914   UK   ISSN 0542-4550
DG987
MALTA YEARBOOK. a. $10. New Product Newsletter Co. Ltd., 1A Chesterfield St., London W.1., England.

320   MP
MANAY INDER/OUR PLATFORM. (Text in Mongolian) 1990. m. Mongolian People's Revolutionary Party, Ulan Bator, Mongolia.
    Formerly: Namyn Am'dral.

322.4   US
MANTOOTH REPORT. 1979. m. $20. RR 1, Box 387, Salem, IN 47167. TEL 812-883-2435. FAX 812-883-2435. Ed. Don Mantooth. adv.; bk.rev. circ. 2,000. (tabloid format; back issues avail.) **Document type:** newspaper.
    Description: Contains political and economic news of the real world and the new world order.

956.940   IS
MAPAM; direct line from Israel. 1982. m. Department of International Affairs, P.O. Box 1777, Tel Aviv 61016, Israel. circ. 1,000.

329.3 350   US
MARK SIEGEL AND ASSOCIATES WASHINGTON INSIDER. 1987. fortn. $125. Mark Siegel & Associates, 1030 15th St., N.W., Ste.408, Washington, DC 20005. TEL 202-371-5600. Eds. Mark Siegel, Brian Sailer. **Document type:** newsletter.
    Description: Report on national politics and government from Democratic Party's perspective.

320   GW
MARKTGEFLUESTER. 1986. irreg. (1-2/yr.). Sozialdemokratische Partei Deutschland, Ortsvereine im Markt Maroldsweisach, Meininger Str. 4, 96126 Maroldsweisach, Germany. TEL 09532-325.

322.4   FR   ISSN 0298-9204
MAROC REPRESSION. 1978. bi-m. 25 Fr. per no. Association de Soutien aux Comites de Lutte Contre la Repression au Maroc, 14 rue de Nanteuil, 75015 Paris, France. TEL 45-32-01-89. Ed. Francois Della Sudda. adv.; bk.rev. **Document type:** bulletin.
    Formerly (until 1985): Comite de Lutte Contre la Repression au Maroc. Bulletin (ISSN 0997-0711)

320.531   IT
MARX CENTOUNO; rivista internazionale di dibattio teorico e politico. N.S. 1990. 3/yr. L.35000. Edizioni Associate s.r.l., Festa del Perdono 6, 20122 Milan, Italy. TEL 02-58303958.

MARX MEMORIAL LIBRARY BULLETIN. see LIBRARY AND INFORMATION SCIENCES

MARXISM AND THE MASS MEDIA; towards a basic bibliography. see COMMUNICATIONS

320   FR   ISSN 1157-7762
MARXISME AUJOURD'HUI. 1990. q. 30 F. per no. Federation des Cercles le Marxisme Aujourd'hui, 7 chemin du Charmeyran, 38700 La Tronche, France. Ed. Pierre Broue.

320.531   IT
MARXISMO OGGI. 1987. bi-m. L.4000 per no. Marxismo Oggi, Via Alberto da Giussano 15, 20145 Milan, Italy. TEL 02-434224. Ed. Gian Mario Cazzaniga. adv.

320.531   II   ISSN 0025-4134
MARXIST VEEKSHANAM; theoretical discussion forum. (Text in Malayalam; summaries in English) 1970. m. Rs.20. Kerala Institute of Marxist Studies, 6-589 P.T.P. Nagar, Trivandrum, India. Ed. K.V. Surendranath. adv.; bk.rev.; bibl. circ. 2,000. (tabloid format; also avail. in cards)

320   GW   ISSN 0542-7770
HX6
MARXISTISCHE BLAETTER;* fuer Probleme der Gesellschaft, Wirtschaft und Politik. 1963-1992. bi-m. DM.39. Neue Impulse Verlag, Hoffnungstr. 18, 45127 Essen, Germany. Ed. Kurt Steinhaus. adv.; bk.rev.; index. circ. 8,000. (back issues avail.) **Indexed:** INIS Atomind., P.A.I.S.For.Lang.Ind.
—CCC.

MARXISTISCHE STUDIEN. see SOCIAL SCIENCES: COMPREHENSIVE WORKS

320.531   SW   ISSN 0047-6072
HX9.S9
MARXISTISKT FORUM.* vol.6, 1970. bi-m. Kommunistiska Foerbundet, Kvrkkullen Vaksala, c/o Frycklund, 755 90 Uppsala, Sweden. Ed. Bo Gustafsson. illus.

MARYLAND REPORT. see PUBLIC ADMINISTRATION

320   UK
AL-MASSAR. 1983. w. £50. At-Tayar Press Ltd., P.O. Box 36, Great Missenden, Bucks HP16 0HS, England. TEL 02406-6288. Ed. Sami Farag Ali. circ. 10,000.

320.5   US
THE MATCH; an anarchist journal. 1969. q. $10. Fred Woodworth, Ed. & Pub., Box 3488, Tucson, AZ 85722. bk.rev. circ. 1,750.

320   UY
MATE AMARGO. 1986. 2/yr. Movimiento de Liberacion Nacional, Bartolome Mitre 1431-Of. 203, Montevideo, Uruguay. TEL 91 56 08. Dir. Emundo Canalda. circ. 22,500.

MATERIAUX POUR L'HISTOIRE DE NOTRE TEMPS. see HISTORY — History Of Europe

320   UK   ISSN 0265-444X
DT469.M4
MAURITIAN INTERNATIONAL. 1964. q. £12 (Europe £18; rest of world £22) for 3 yrs.; newsstand price: £0.50. Nautilus Publishing Co., P.O. Box 4100, London SW20 0XN, England. TEL 0181-947-1912. Ed. Jacques K. Lee. adv.; bk.rev.; illus. circ. 27,000. **Document type:** newspaper.
    Formerly: Voice of Mauritians.
    Description: News items and editorials pertaining to Mauritius, the southern Indian Ocean region, and Mauritians living overseas.

329.9   CE
MAVBIMA. (Text in Singhalese) w. Rs.0.35 per no. Ceylon Communist Party, 91 Cotta Rd., Colombo 8, Sri Lanka.

320   US   ISSN 1055-8489
MAXINE'S PAGES. 1987. q. $1 per no. Crystal Rain Research Agency, Box 866, Manchester, GA 31816. TEL 706-846-9332. Ed. Elaine Long. bk.rev.; circ. 137 (controlled). (looseleaf format) **Document type:** directory, newsletter.
    Description: Network publication for police and political activists.

058.7   SW   ISSN 0025-665X
MEDBORGAREN. 1915. 6/yr. SEK 100. Moderata Samlingspartiets Riksorganisation - Swedish Moderate Party, P.O. Box 1243, 111 82 Stockholm, Sweden. FAX 46-8-216123. Ed. Folke Schoett. adv.; bk.rev.; abstr.; charts; illus. circ. 100,000. (also avail. in audio cassette)
    Formerly (until vol.2, 1920): Allmaenna Valmansfoerbundets Maanadsblad.

MEDIA MONITOR (WASHINGTON). see COMMUNICATIONS

POLITICAL SCIENCE

MEDIAWATCH. see *JOURNALISM*

320   AT   ISSN 0085-3224
MELBOURNE JOURNAL OF POLITICS. 1968. a. Aus.$10. University of Melbourne, Political Science Department, Parkville, Vic. 3052, Australia. TEL 03-344-6571. TELEX AA35185 UNIMEL. Ed.Bd. adv.; bk.rev. circ. 1,000. (back issues avail.) **Indexed:** Aus.P.A.I.S. **Document type:** academic/scholarly publication.
—UnCover.
Refereed Serial

320   AT
MELBOURNE POLITICS MONOGRAPHS. 1973. a. Aus.$8.95. University of Melbourne, Department of Political Science, Parkville, Vic. 3052, Australia. FAX 344-7894. Ed.Bd. adv.; bk.rev.; bibl. circ. 1,000. **Document type:** monographic series.

949.3   BE   ISSN 0025-908X
DH403
MEMO FROM BELGIUM. (Editions in Dutch, English, French, German, Italian, Spanish) 1960. irreg. free. Ministere des Affaires Etrangeres, 2 rue Quatre Bras, 1000 Brussels, Belgium. (For English edition inquire: Consulat General de Belgique, Information Officer, 50 Rockefeller Plaza, Ste. 1104, New York, NY 10020, U.S.A.) charts; illus. circ. 3,000. **Indexed:** P.A.I.S.

320   US
MENSAJE; un periodico veraz y combativo. (Text in Spanish) 1980. w. $25. Latin American News and Book Inc., 614 Franklin St., Elizabeth, NJ 07206. TEL 908-355-8835. FAX 908-527-9160. Ed. Jesus M. Tenreiro. adv.; B&W page $800; 10 x 15. circ. 52,000. (tabloid format)
Description: Focuses on international, national, state and local political issues and news.

MERCURE; hebdomadaire financier, economique et politique. see *GENERAL INTEREST PERIODICALS — Belgium*

320   US   ISSN 1068-2538
UA23.A1
MERSHON MEMO. 1975. q. free. Mershon Center, 1501 Neil Ave., Columbus, OH 43201-2602. TEL 614-292-1681. FAX 614-292-2407. TELEX MERSCHCTR. bibl.; circ. 3,000 (controlled). **Document type:** newsletter.
Former titles (until vol.13, no.3, 1988): Mershon Center Communique; *(until vol.13, no.2, 1988):* Mershon Center Report Quarterly.
Description: Activities and works-in-progress related to national and international security studies by faculty associates of the center.

MESOAMERICA. see *HISTORY — History Of North And South America*

MEXICO & N A F T A REPORT. see *BUSINESS AND ECONOMICS — Economic Situation And Conditions*

327   XR   ISSN 0543-7962
D839
MEZINARODNI POLITIKA. 1956. m. 10 Kc. per no. Ustav Mezinarodnich Vztahu, Nerudova 3, 118 50 Prague 1, Czech Republic. TEL 42-2-539-455. Ed. Dobroslav Matejka. bk.rev.; charts; illus.; index. circ. 15,000.

320   US
MICHIGAN: AROUND AND ABOUT. 1985. m. $10. George Wahr Publishing Company, 304 1-2 S. State St., Ann Arbor, MI 48104. TEL 313-668-6097; 800-805-2497. Ed. Elizabeth Davenport; Pub. George Wahr. circ. 1,200. **Document type:** newsletter.
Description: Contains ommentary and analysis on domestic and international events and issues.

320   US   ISSN 0733-4486
JA1
MICHIGAN JOURNAL OF POLITICAL SCIENCE. 1980. 2/yr. $12 (effective 1996). University of Michigan, Michigan Journal of Political Science, 5620 Haven Hall, Ann Arbor, MI 48109-1045. TEL 313-764-6386. E-mail: ethan@umich.edu.; Site addr.: gopher.itd.umich.edu. Ed. Peter Harbage. adv.; bk.rev.; circ. 1,000 (controlled). **Indexed:** Amer.Hist.& Life, Hist.Abstr., Int.Polit.Sci.Abstr., Polit.Sci.Abstr. **Document type:** academic/scholarly publication.
●Also available online.
Description: Covers all aspects of political science including, but not limited to, political theory, methodology, world politics, comparative politics, American government, public policy, economics, sociology and political economy. All papers written by graduate and undergraduate students.

320   330.9   UK   ISSN 0076-8502
MIDDLE EAST AND NORTH AFRICA (YEAR); survey and directory of lands of Middle East and North Africa. 1948. a. $325. Europa Publications, 18 Bedford Sq., London WC1B 3JN, England. TEL 0171-580-8236. FAX 0171-636-1664. TELEX 21540 EUROPA G. **Document type:** academic/scholarly publication, directory.
—BLDSC (5761.350000).
Description: Covers economic, social, cultural, and political affairs.

320   CN   ISSN 0705-8594
DS63.1
MIDDLE EAST FOCUS; Canada's magazine on the contemporary Middle East. 1978. q. Can.$15. Canadian Academic Foundation for Peace in the Middle East, P.O. Box 81509, 1057 Steeles Ave. W., North York, ON M2R 3X1, Canada. TEL 416-963-9477. Ed. Irving Abella. bk.rev. circ. 4,000. **Indexed:** Curr.Cont.M.E., Geo.Abstr., Mid.East: Abstr.& Ind., Polit.Sci.Abstr.

327
MIDDLE EAST INSTITUTE NEWSLETTER. bi-m. $50 membership. Middle East Institute, 1761 N St. N.W., Washington, DC 20036. TEL 202-785-0191. FAX 202-331-8861. Eds. Marcia Annis, Sarah Bright. bibl. circ. 1,750. **Document type:** newsletter.
Description: Covers events and activities at the Middle East Institute.

956   US   ISSN 0047-7249
MIDDLE EAST INTERNATIONAL. 1971. fortn. $65 to individuals; libraries $79; institutions $132. Middle East International (Publishers) Ltd., 1700 17th St., NW, Washington, DC 20009. FAX 202-232-8376. Ed. Michael Wall. bk.rev. circ. 10,000. (also avail. in microform from UMI; reprint service avail. from UMI) **Indexed:** Curr.Cont.M.E., Mid.East: Abstr.& Ind., Per.Islam., Polit.Sci.Abstr.
—BLDSC (5761.378000); Faxon; SWETS; UMI; UnCover.
Description: Political and social developments in the Middle East and Arab world.

320   915.602   US   ISSN 0276-5632
DS63.2.U5
MIDDLE EAST POLICY SURVEY. 1980. m. $150. Middle East Policy Group, 3405 Rodman St. N. W., Washington, DC 20008. TEL 202-363-3495. FAX 202-352-4513. Ed. Richard Straus. circ. 500. (back issues avail.) **Document type:** newsletter.
Description: Insider's guide to Middle East events, issues, and personalities.

956   US   ISSN 1073-9467
CODEN: MEQUFZ
▼**MIDDLE EAST QUARTERLY.** 1994. q. $35 in the U.S.; foreign $55; students $25. Middle East Forum, 1920 Chestnut St., Ste. 600, Philadelphia, PA 19103-4624. TEL 215-569-9225. FAX 215-569-9229. (Subscr. to: Box 3000, Denville, NJ 07834-9943. TEL 800-562-1973) Ed. Daniel Pipes; Pub. Albert J. Wood. adv. contact: Army Shargel. bk.rev.; charts. circ. 1,900. **Indexed:** Ind.Islam, Ind.Jew.Per., Int.Polit.Sci.Abstr. **Document type:** academic/scholarly publication.
—BLDSC (5761.400700). CCC.
Description: Educates readers about Middle East trends and current events and seeks to construct a framework for a U.S. policy in the region.

MIDDLE EAST STUDIES ASSOCIATION BULLETIN. see *SOCIAL SCIENCES: COMPREHENSIVE WORKS*

MIDEAST MONITOR. see *HISTORY — History Of The Near East*

MIDSTREAM; a monthly Jewish review. see *LITERARY AND POLITICAL REVIEWS*

320   US
MIDWEST POLITICAL CONSULTANT. 1987. m. $50. Christian Schock and Associates, 1079 Paradise Acres, Galesburg, IL 61401. TEL 809-343-3006. Ed. Christian Schock. bk.rev. **Document type:** newsletter, trade publication.
Description: Focuses on politics and political campaigning.

325   IT   ISSN 0391-5492
MIGRANTI-PRESS. (Supplement to: Servizio Migranti) 1979. w. L.45000. Fondazione Migrantes, Via Aurelia 481, 00165 Rome, Italy.
FAX 06-662-0530. TELEX 623328 UCEI I.

320   628   UK   ISSN 0887-378X
RA418.3.U6   CODEN: MIQUES
THE MILBANK QUARTERLY. 1923. q. $33 to individuals; institutions $66. (Milbank Memorial Fund) Basil Blackwell Ltd., 108 Cowley Rd., Oxford OX4 1JF, England. TEL 44-1865-791100. FAX 44-1865-791347. Ed. P. Cleary. charts; illus.; stat. circ. 3,000. (also avail. in microform from UMI; microfiche; reprint service avail. from UMI) **Indexed:** Abstr.Health Care Manage.Stud., Abstr.Hyg., Abstr.Soc.Geront., Acad.Ind., Arts & Hum.Cit.Ind., B.P.I., Biol.Abstr., BPIA, Chem.Abstr., Curr.Cont., Curr.Lit.Fam.Plan., Fut.Surv., Hlth.Ind., Hosp.Lit.Ind., Ind.Med., Med. Care Rev., Mid.East: Abstr.& Ind., Nutr.Abstr., P.A.I.S., Psychol.Abstr. (1988-), Risk Abstr., Sage Fam.Stud.Abstr., Sage Pub.Admin.Abstr., Soc.Work Res.& Abstr., Sociol.Abstr., SSCI, Tr.& Indus.Ind. **Document type:** academic/scholarly publication.
—BLDSC (5766.040000); Faxon; Genuine Article; SWETS; UMI; UnCover. **CCC.**
Former titles: Health and Society (ISSN 0160-1997); Milbank Memorial Fund Quarterly (ISSN 0026-3745)
Description: Contains scholarly articles on research and policy analysis in health care focusing on economic, social, demographic, ethical and philosophical aspects.

320   AG
MILITANCIA (BUENOS AIRES, 1973);* Peronista para la liberacion. 1973. s-m. Arg.$3 per no. c/o Arturo Apicella e Hijo, 319 Esmera Ida, Buenos Aires, Argentina. Ed. Carlos Maria Duhalde. illus.

320   AG
MILITANCIA (BUENOS AIRES, 1986). 1986. m. Nestor Vicente, Parana 761 1 A, Buenos Aires, Argentina.

320   MX
MILITANCIA: TEMAS DEL SOCIALISMO.* 1974. bi-m. Mex.$15 per copy. Milan 28-104, Mexico 6, D.F., Mexico. Ed. Rodolfo F. Pena. bk.rev.; film rev.

320.531   US   ISSN 0026-3885
MILITANT; a socialist newsweekly published in the interests of the working people. (Supplement avail.: International Socialist Review) 1928. w. $45 to individuals; institutions $80. 408 Printing and Publishing Co., 410 West St., New York, NY 10014. TEL 212-243-6392. FAX 212-924-6040. Ed. George Fyson. adv.; bk.rev. circ. 6,000. (tabloid format; also avail. in microform from UMI; back issues avail.; reprint service avail. from UMI)
—UMI.
Description: Covers developments in the labor movement, women's rights issues and racial issues. Coverage is international.

320.532   CU   ISSN 0864-2362
MILITANTE COMUNISTA. 1967. m. $3. Partido Comunista, Calle 11, No. 160, Vedado, Havana, Cuba. TEL 7-32-7581. Dir. Manuel Menendez. circ. 200,000.

320   PK
MILLAT. (Text in Urdu) 1978. w. Rs.4. Islamabad Publications, 9 Hamid Chambers, Aab Parah, Islamabad, Pakistan.

POLITICAL SCIENCE

320 309.173 353   US   ISSN 1080-1200
▼MILLER CENTER JOURNAL. 1994. q. $6.95 per no. 2201 Old Ivy Rd., Box 5106, Charlottesville, VA 22905. TEL 804-924-7236. FAX 804-982-2739. E-mail: kurt8b@University of Virginia.EDU. Ed. Kenneth W. Thompson. bk.rev. Indexed: Amer.Hist.& Life (1994-), Hist.Abstr. (1994-). **Document type:** academic/scholarly publication.

320.9   US   ISSN 0026-4474
MINDSZENTY REPORT. 1958. m. $16 (foreign $20). Cardinal Mindszenty Foundation, Inc., Box 11321, St. Louis, MO 63105. TEL 314-727-6279. FAX 314-727-5849. Ed. John Boland; Pub. Eleanor Schlafly. circ. 12,000. (also avail. in microform from UMI)
—UMI.
 Formerly: Release (St. Louis).

MINNESOTA'S JOURNAL OF LAW & POLITICS. see *LAW*

320.5   FR   ISSN 0996-9640
MINUTE. 1962. w. 430 F. S E C, 16-18 place de Chapelle, 75018 Paris, France. TEL 1-42-85-54-54. FAX 1-48-74-23-64. Ed. Jean Claude Goudeau. adv.; bk.rev.; film rev.; play rev.; bibl.; illus. circ. 220,000. (tabloid format)
 Formerly (until 1989): Minute, le Chardon (ISSN 0987-903X); Which was formed by the 1987 merger of: Minute (ISSN 0026-573X) & Chardon (ISSN 0982-7757)

320   CC   ISSN 1003-1936
MINZHU/DEMOCRACY. (Text in Chinese) 1989. m. Y14.40. Minjin Zhongyang Weiyuanhui, No. 98, Gulou Xin'anli, Beijing 100009, People's Republic of China. TEL 4035673. Ed. Mao Qibin. adv.; bk.rev.
 Description: Covers politics, education, science and cultural issues.

320 340   CC   ISSN 1003-1723
MINZHU YU FAZHI/DEMOCRACY & LEGAL SYSTEMS. (Text in Chinese) m. $41.30. (Zhongguo Faxuehui - China Jurisprudence Society) Minzhu yu Fazhi Bianjibu, No.100, Dongsi 10 Tiao, Beijing 100007, People's Republic of China. TEL 4016660-115. (Dist. in US by: China Books & Periodicals, Inc., 2929 24th St., San Francisco, CA 94110. TEL 415-282-2994) Wang Shuren.

320   CC   ISSN 1003-0026
MINZHU YU KEXUE/DEMOCRACY AND SCIENCE. (Text in Chinese) bi-m. Jiusan Xueshe Zhongyang Weiyuanhui, No. 4, Banshang Hutong, Xisi, Beijing 100034, People's Republic of China. TEL 6011627. Ed. Li Fengming.

320   US
MISSOURI ANNUAL CAMPAIGN FINANCE REPORT. 1979. a. free. Missouri Ethics Commission, Box 1254, Jefferson City, MO 65102. TEL 314-751-3077. FAX 314-526-3242. Ed. Marion Sinnett. circ. 1,000. **Document type:** government publication.

320.5   SW   ISSN 0026-7449
MODERAT DEBATT. 1934. bi-m. SEK 100($5) Moderata Ungdomsfoerbundet - Young Conservatives, P.O. Box 1243, 111 82 Stockholm, Sweden. FAX 8-203449. Ed. Carolyn Nyman. adv.; bk.rev. circ. 30,000.
 Former titles (until 1969): Ung Hoeger; (until 1947): Ungsvensk Loesen.

MODERN ASIAN STUDIES. see *ORIENTAL STUDIES*

MODERN JUDAISM. see *ETHNIC INTERESTS*

320   SG
MOMSAREEW. 1958. m. Parti Africain de l'Independance, B.P. 820, Dakar, Senegal. Ed. Malamine Badji. circ. 2,000.

321.6   UK
MONARCHY. 1948. q. £20($40) Monarchist League, International Headquarters, BM Monarchist, London WC1N 3XX, England. TEL 01892-835899. E-mail: nicklaw@cix.compulink.co.uk. Ed. Nicholas Law. adv.: B&W page £90. bk.rev.; bibl.; illus. circ. 1,200. **Document type:** newsletter.
 Former titles (until 1993): Monarchist League Newsletter; Monarchist Newsletter; Monarchist (ISSN 0047-7834)

321   CN   ISSN 0319-4019
MONARCHY CANADA. 1970. q. Can.$15 to individuals; institutions Can.$20. (Monarchist League of Canada) Loyalty Publications, 3050 Yonge St., Ste. 206, Toronto, ON M4N 2K4, Canada. TEL 416-482-4157. FAX 416-482-4157. (Subscr. addr.: P.O. Box 1057, Oakville, ON L6J 5E9, Canada) Ed. Arthur Bousfield. adv.; bk.rev.; charts; illus. circ. 8,000.
 Formerly: Canadian Monarchist.
 Description: Looks at monarchy from a Canadian perspective and at Canada from a monarchist one. Offers current and historical articles on constitutional, social and political affairs, as well as personality profiles and reviews of books and the arts.

MONASH UNIVERSITY. CENTRE OF SOUTHEAST ASIAN STUDIES. MONASH PAPERS ON SOUTHEAST ASIA. see *HISTORY — History Of Asia*

960   FR   ISSN 1241-5294
MONDE ARABE MAGHREB, MACHREK. Key Title: Monde Arabe. 1964. q. 260 F. (Europe 315 F., elsewhere 400 F.). (Fondation Nationale des Politiques et Direction de la Documentation) Documentation Francaise, 29-31 Quai Voltaire, 75340 Paris Cedex 07, France. TEL 1-40-15-70-00. FAX 40-15-72-30. (Subscr. to: 124 rue Henri Barbusse, 93308 Aubervilliers Cedex, France. TEL 48-39-56-00. FAX 48-39-56-01) bk.rev.; bibl.; cum.index. circ. 2,000. (also avail. in microfiche from DFR) **Indexed:** Curr.Cont.Africa, Curr.Cont.M.E., Documentatieblad, Rural Recreat.Tour.Abstr., World Agri.Econ.& Rural Sociol.Abstr. **Document type:** government publication.
 —BLDSC (5906.882500).
 Former titles (until 1992): Maghreb, Machrek, Monde Arabe (ISSN 0336-6324); (until 1973): Maghreb (ISSN 0024-9890)

335.83   FR   ISSN 0026-9433
MONDE LIBERTAIRE. 1954. w. 290 F. (foreign 400 F.) (effective 1995-1996). Federation Anarchiste, 145 rue Amelot, 75011 Paris, France. TEL 48-05-34-08. FAX 49-29-98-59. Ed. Jean-Jaques Legois. adv. contact: Andre Devriendt. bk.rev.; film rev.; tele.rev.; bibl. circ. 17,500. **Document type:** newspaper. Refereed Serial

320   IT   ISSN 0391-6855
AP37
MONDO; settimanale di economia, politica e cultura. 1949. w. L.158000. Rizzoli Editore-Corriere della Sera, Via A. Rizzoli 2, 20132 Milan, Italy. TEL 39-2-2588. Ed. Redento Mori. adv.: page L.21810000; adv. contact: Flavio Biondi. circ. 51,888. **Indexed:** P.A.I.S.For.Lang.Ind.

320.5   IT
MONDO NUOVO. 11/yr. L.60000. Editoriale Il Mondo Nuovo S.p.A., Corso Cristoforo Colombo 10, 20144 Milan, Italy. TEL 39-2-89410001. FAX 39-2-58101726. Ed. Gian Luigi Falabrino.

329.9   IT   ISSN 0392-1115
MONDO OPERAIO. Variant title: Mondoperaio. 1948. m. L.50000. (Partito Socialista Italiano) Mondo Operaio Edizioni Avanti S.p.A., Via Tomacelli 146, 00186 Rome, Italy. Ed. Luciano Vasconi. adv.; bk.rev.; film rev.; play rev. circ. 15,000. **Indexed:** ELLIS.

MONDO PADANO. see *BUSINESS AND ECONOMICS — Chamber Of Commerce Publications*

MONETARY DIGEST. see *BUSINESS AND ECONOMICS — Investments*

MONGOLIA REPORT. see *BUSINESS AND ECONOMICS — Economic Situation And Conditions*

MONITOR (RANCHO PALOS VERDE); we the people and our two cents worth. see *PUBLIC ADMINISTRATION*

320.531   US   ISSN 0027-0520
HX1
MONTHLY REVIEW; an independent socialist magazine. 1949. m. (bi-m. Jul.-Aug.). $25 to individuals (foreign $29); institutions $45 (foreign $48). Monthly Review Press, 122 W. 27th St., 10th fl., New York, NY 10001. TEL 212-691-2555. FAX 212-727-3676. E-mail: mreview@igc.apc.org. Eds. Paul M. Sweezy, Harry Magdoff. adv.; bk.rev.; index; circ. 6,000 (paid). (also avail. in microform from UMI; reprint service avail. from UMI) **Indexed:** Acad.Ind., Alt.Press Ind., Amer.Bibl.Slavic & E.Eur.Stud., Amer.Hist.& Life, Bus.Ind., Hist.Abstr., Lang.& Lang.Behav.Abstr., Left Ind. (1982-), Mag.Ind., Mid.East: Abstr.& Ind., P.A.I.S., PROMT, R.G., Rural Recreat.Tour.Abstr., Soc.Sci.Ind., SSCI, Tr.& Indus.Ind., World Agri.Econ.& Rural Sociol.Abstr. ●Also available online. Vendor(s): University Microfilms International.
 —BLDSC (5947.800000); Faxon; Genuine Article; SWETS; UMI; UnCover.
 Description: Uses Marxist thought to critique contempory conditions.

MOSCA NEWS. see *BUSINESS AND ECONOMICS*

335   RU   ISSN 0320-8087
MOSKOVSKII UNIVERSITET. VESTNIK. SERIYA 13: TEORIYA NAUCHNOGO KOMMUNIZMA. (Text in Russian; contents page in English) bi-m. 12.90 Rub. Moskovskii Universitet, Ul. Gertsena 5-7, 103009 Moscow, Russia. bk.rev.; bibl.; index. **Document type:** academic/scholarly publication.

320   GP   ISSN 0981-7034
MOUN/PEOPLE; a cultural review from Guadeloupe. 1985. bi-m. 180 F. Media Press Gwadloup, B.P. 128, 97184 Pointe-a-Pitre, Guadeloupe. Ed. Danik A. Zandwonis. adv. circ. 3,500.

320   RM
MUNCA DE PARTID.* m. 30 lei($25) Partidul Comunist Roman, Comitetul Central, c/o Rompresfilatelia, Calea Grivitei 64-66, P.O. Box 12-201, Bucharest, Rumania. Ed.Bd. illus.

320   AG
MUNDO ARABE.* 1981. m. Camara de Comercio, 25 de Mayo, 67, 1002 Buenos Aires, Argentina.

MUNDO ISRAELITA; actualidad de la semana en Israel y en el mundo judio. see *GENERAL INTEREST PERIODICALS — Israel*

320 200   PK   ISSN 0464-0756
MUSLIM WORLD; weekly review of the Motamar. (Includes: World Muslim Conference Proceedings) (Text in English) 1963. w. Rs.60($30) World Muslim Congress - Motamar Al-Alam al-Islami, Box 5030, Karachi 74000, Pakistan. FAX 92-21-466878. Ed. Inamullah Khan. adv.; charts. **Indexed:** Abstr.Musl.Rel., Amer.Hist.& Life, Arts & Hum.Cit.Ind., Curr.Cont., Hist.Abstr., Rel.& Theol.Abstr.

329   GW   ISSN 0027-5093
MUT. 1965. m. DM.246. Mut-Verlag, Bahnhofstr. 1, 27330 Asendorf, Germany. TEL 04253-566. Ed. Bernhard C. Wintzek. bk.rev.; illus. **Document type:** bulletin.
 Description: Non-political publication promoting unity, justice, freedom and world peace.

MUZEUM JIHOVYCHODNI MORAVY. ACTA MUSEALIA. see *HISTORY — History Of Europe*

POLITICAL SCIENCE 5335

341.2 BE ISSN 0255-3813
UA646.3
N A T O REVIEW. French edition: Revue de l'O T A N. Norwegian edition: N A T O Nytt. Danish edition: N A T O Nyt. Dutch edition: N A V O Kroniek. German edition: N A T O Brief. Greek edition: Deltio N A T O. Italian edition: Notizie N A T O. Portuguese edition: Noticias da O T A N. Spanish edition: Revista de la O T A N. Turkish edition: N A T O Dergisi (ISSN 0255-3902) (Text in English) 1953. bi-m. (Norwegian, Greek, Portuguese, Turkish eds. q.; Icelandic ed., a.). free. North Atlantic Treaty Organization, Office of Information and Press, B-1110 Brussels, Belgium. TEL 32-2-7284111. FAX 32-2-7284579. Ed. Peter Jenner. bk.rev.; bibl. circ. 260,000. (also avail. in microform from UMI; reprint service avail. from UMI) Indexed: A.B.C.Pol.Sci., Abstr.Mil.Bibl., DM & T, Ind.Free Per., Key to Econ.Sci., Mid.East: Abstr.& Ind., PMR, Pt.de Rep.
—BLDSC (6033.690000); Faxon; UMI; UnCover.
Formerly: N A T O Letter (ISSN 0027-6057)
Description: International information on political and defense subjects, as well as some economic and scientific topics relevant to NATO. Contributions from leading experts, politicians, academics, and NATO officials.

N C B A REPORTS. (National Commodity & Barter Association) see BUSINESS AND ECONOMICS — Public Finance, Taxation

320 AU
N F Z - NEUE FREIE ZEITUNG. 1973. w. S.9 per no. Die Freiheitlichen, Kaerntnerstr. 28, A-1010 Vienna, Austria. TEL 01-5123535. FAX 01-5123277. Ed. Walter Howadt. adv.; bk.rev.; illus. **Document type:** newspaper.
Supersedes: Neue Front: Zeitung der Freiheitlichen.

N G O NETWORKER. (Non-Governmental Organization) see ENVIRONMENTAL STUDIES

NAALSOEGAT. see RELIGIONS AND THEOLOGY

956.940 320.55
296.7 305.4 US ISSN 0888-191X
DS150.L3
NA'AMAT WOMAN. 1926. 5/yr. $10 to non-members (effective 1995). Na'Amat U S A, The Women's Labor Zionist Organization of America, Inc., 200 Madison Ave., New York, NY 10016. TEL 212-725-8010. Ed. Judith A. Sokoloff. adv.; bk.rev.; illus. circ. 30,000. (also avail. in microform from AJP) Indexed: Ind.Jew.Per.
Formerly: Pioneer Woman (ISSN 0032-0021)

972 MX ISSN 0027-7509
AP63
NACION; organo de accion nacional. 1941. fortn. Mex.$60000($45) Estudios y Publicaciones Economicas y Sociales, S.A., Cerrada de Eugenia, 25, Col. del Valle, Delegacion Benito Juarez, Apartado Postal 32-470, CP 03100 Mexico DF, Mexico. TEL 536-18-31. FAX 525-687-2922. adv.; charts; illus. circ. 15,000 (controlled).

NANZAN UNIVERSITY. CENTER FOR LATIN AMERICAN STUDIES. WORKING PAPER. see HISTORY — History Of North And South America

320 PK
NAQIB-I MILLAT. (Text in Urdu) vol.2, 1978. w. Rs.3. Maulvi Hidayatullah, Kucha Chen Teliyan, Bazar Wachchuwali, Shah Alam Market, Lahore, Pakistan.

947 RU ISSN 0236-0918
NARODNYI DEPUTAT. 1957. 24/yr. $156 (effective 1996). (Russia) Narodnyi Deputat, Ul. Chekhova 3-10, 103800 Moscow, GSP K-6, Russia. TEL 095-299-4055. (Dist. in U.S. by: Victor Kamkin Inc., 4956 Boiling Brook Pkwy, Rockville, MD 20852. TEL 301-881-5973) Ed. M.I. Piskotin. bibl.; illus. circ. 58,180.
Former titles (until 1990): Sovety Narodnykh Deputatov (ISSN 0201-5250); (until 1977): Sovety Deputatov Trudyashchikhsya (ISSN 0132-1374)

320 II
NATION AND THE WORLD. (Text in English) 1991. fortn. Rs.175($35) (effective Jan. 1994). Indian Publications Ltd., A-13 Nizamuddin W., 1st F., Nizamuddin West, New Delhi 110 013, India. TEL 91-11-4620808. FAX 91-11-4622614. Ed. Saiyid Hamid; Pub. Arif Mohammad Khan. adv.: B&W page Rs.6000, color page Rs.12000; 164 x 240. bk.rev. circ. 10,000.
Description: Covers the trends in politics, economy, business, science, medicine, environment and art.

323.4 US ISSN 0888-1391
NATIONAL ALLIANCE (NEW YORK). 1977. w. $15. National Alliance, Inc., 500 Greenwich St., Ste. 210, New York, NY 10013. TEL 212-941-5800. Ed. Jacqueline Salit. adv.; bk.rev. circ. 100,000.
Formerly: New York Alliance; Supersedes (in 1979): Don't Mourn, Organize.
Description: Political and cultural newsweekly aimed at a black, gay, women's and progressive readership.

808.8 UK
NATIONAL AWAMI PARTY OF BANGLADESH (IN GREAT BRITAIN). BULLETIN.* irreg., no.5, 1973. National Awami Party of Bangla Desh, 86 Oakleigh Road, London N.11, England. Ed. Fazlul Huq.

NATIONAL DIRECTORY OF CORPORATE PUBLIC AFFAIRS. see BUSINESS AND ECONOMICS — Trade And Industrial Directories

320 UK
NATIONAL FRONT HISTORICAL SOCIETY, 1967-1990. JOURNAL. 1990. 2/yr. £120. National Front Historical Society, P.O. Box 228, London E12, England. Ed. Derek Kirkwood. **Document type:** academic/scholarly publication.
Description: Studies the history of the National Front and related topics.

320 II
NATIONAL GUARD. (Text in English) m. Rs.20($12) Ashok Walia, 103-a, Kamla Nagar, Delhi 110007, India. Ed. R.P. Ahluwalia. adv.; illus. **Indexed:** Air Un.Lib.Ind.

320 US ISSN 0360-4217
JK1
NATIONAL JOURNAL;* the weekly on politics and government. (Includes s-a supplement: Capital Source) 1969. w. $939. National Journal, Inc. (Subsidiary of: Times Mirror Company), 1501 M St., N.W., Ste. 300, Washington, DC 20005. TEL 202-739-8400. FAX 202-833-8069. Ed. Richard S. Frank. adv.: B&W page $6800, color page $9000; trim 8 1/2 x 11. bk.rev.; charts; illus.; s-a. index. circ. 6,200. (also avail. in microfilm from UMI) Indexed: Bank.Lit.Ind., CAD CAM Abstr., Energy Ind., Energy Info.Abstr., Environ.Abstr., Med.Care Rev., P.A.I.S., Pers.Lit., Polit.Sci.Abstr., Sel.Water Res.Abstr., Tel.Abstr., Telegen.
●Also available online. Vendor(s): University Microfilms International.
—BLDSC (6026.150000); Faxon; SWETS; UMI; UnCover. CCC.
Incorporates: National Issues Outlook (ISSN 0092-9778); **Former titles:** National Journal Reports (ISSN 0091-3685); National Journal (ISSN 0027-9560)
Description: Provides policymakers with nonpartisan analysis of major national policy issues.

320 AT ISSN 0811-3300
NATIONAL LEADER. 1948. q. Aus.$8. National Party of Australia - N.S.W., 5th Fl., 30 Carrington St., Sydney, N.S.W. 2000, Australia. TEL 02-299-5811. FAX 02-299-5636. Ed. Liam Bathgate. adv.
—UnCover.
Description: Discusses matters affecting rural and metropolitan electorates.

322.4 AT ISSN 0310-0154
NATIONAL MESSAGE. vol.2, 1975. q. Aus.$0.20 per no. Australian Citizens for Freedom, P.O. Box 1881, Brisbane, Qld. 4001, Australia. Ed. Harold J. Wright. circ. 1,000.

320 US ISSN 1057-1655
E184.A1
NATIONAL MINORITY POLITICS. 1988. m. $29. Richberg Communications, Inc., 13555 Bammel N. Houston, STe. 227, Houston, TX 77066. TEL 713-444-4265. FAX 713-583-9534. Ed. Gwenevere Daye Richardson. bk.rev. circ. 10,000.
●Also available online. Vendor(s): NewsNet (PO05).
Description: News and opinion magazine featuring black and Hispanic conservatives; provides latest information on political trends and elections involving minority groups.

329 US ISSN 0077-5282
NATIONAL PARTY PLATFORMS. SUPPLEMENT. (Sixth edition covers 1840-1976; supplement in 1982 covers 1980) 1961. irreg. latest 1982. price varies. University of Illinois Press, 1325 S. Oak St., Champaign, IL 61820. TEL 217-333-0950. FAX 217-244-8082. Ed. Donald B. Johnson. **Document type:** academic/scholarly publication.

320 US
NATIONAL POLICY WATCH. 1985. bi-m. $15. National Center for Public Policy Research, 300 Eye St., N.E., Ste. 3, Washington, DC 20002. TEL 202-543-1286. FAX 202-543-4779. circ. 7,000.
●Also available online.
Description: Covers taxation, U.S. domestic policy and international relations from a conservative viewpoint.

320 US ISSN 0896-629X
JK1 CODEN: NPSREL
NATIONAL POLITICAL SCIENCE REVIEW. a. $21.95. (National Conference of Black Political Scientists) Transaction Publishers, Transaction Periodicals Consortium, Department 3901, Rutgers University, New Brunswick, NJ 08903. TEL 908-445-2280. FAX 908-445-3138. Ed. Mathew Holden. Indexed: Int.Polit.Sci.Abstr. **Document type:** academic/scholarly publication.
Description: Examines the theoretical and empirical aspects of politics and policies that advantage or disadvantage groups by reasons of race, ethnicity, sex, and other factors.

320.52 US ISSN 0028-0038
AP2
NATIONAL REVIEW; a journal of fact and opinion. 1955. fortn. $57. National Review, Inc., 150 E. 35th St., New York, NY 10016. TEL 212-679-7330. FAX 212-696-0309. Ed. John O'Sullivan; Pub. Edward A. Capano. adv.: B&W page $6693, color page $9990; 8 1/4 x 10 7/8; adv. contact: Donald Burkett. bk.rev.; illus.; index. circ. 260,000. (also avail. in microform from UMI; reprint service avail. from UMI) Indexed: Acad.Ind., Amer.Bibl.Slavic & E.Eur.Stud., Bk.Rev.Dig., Bk.Rev.Ind. (1965-), Child.Bk.Rev.Ind. (1965-), Curr.Lit.Fam.Plan., Film Lit.Ind. (1973-), Fut.Surv., Mag.Ind., Media Rev.Dig., Mid.East: Abstr.& Ind., Pers.Lit., PMR, Polit.Sci.Abstr., PSI, R.G., TOM. **Document type:** consumer publication.
●Also available online. Vendor(s): Knight-Ridder, Inc. Also available on CD-ROM. Producer(s): University Microfilms International.
—BLDSC (6031.050000); Faxon; Genuine Article; UMI; UnCover. CCC.
Description: Discusses national and international issues from a conservative viewpoint; includes books, arts, and manners.

320 355 PH ISSN 0115-5113
NATIONAL SECURITY REVIEW. 1973. q. free. National Defense College of the Philippines, Fort Bonifacio, Rizal, Philippines. Ed.Bd. bibl.; charts. circ. 2,000. Indexed: Artbibl, Ind.Phil.Per.

320 US
NATIONAL VANGUARD; toward a new consciousness, a new order, a new people. 1978. bi-m. $12. National Alliance, Box 90, Hillsboro, WV 24946. TEL 304-653-4600. Ed. William L. Pierce. (back issues avail.)

POLITICAL SCIENCE

324.24   US   ISSN 0028-0372
E740
NATIONAL VOTER. 1951. 4/yr. $15 to non-members. League of Women Voters of the U S, 1730 M St., N.W., 10th, Washington, DC 20036. TEL 202-429-1965. FAX 202-429-0854. Eds. William H. Woodwell, Ellen Weir; Pub. Monica Sullivan. adv.; B&W page $3300; trim 8 1/4 x 11. bk.rev.; index. circ. 110,000. (also avail. in microfilm from UMI) **Document type:** consumer publication.
—UMI.
   Description: Nonpartisan articles on public policy and campaign issues of interest to the American electorate.

320.1   UK   ISSN 1354-5078
▼**NATIONS AND NATIONALISM.** 1995. 3/yr. £59($89) (effective 1996). (Association for the Study of Ethnicity and Nationalism) Cambridge University Press, Edinburgh Bldg., Shaftesbury Rd., Cambridge CB2 2RU, England. TEL 01223-312393. FAX 01223-315052. TELEX 851817256. (N. American addr.: Cambridge University Press, Journals Dept., 40 W. 20th St., New York, NY 10011. TEL 212-924-3900. FAX 212-691-3239) Ed.Bd. adv.; bk.rev. **Document type:** academic/scholarly publication.
—BLDSC (6033.595000). **CCC.**
   Description: Responds to the growing interest in the study of nationalism and nationalist movements throughout the world.
   Refereed Serial

NATURE, SOCIETY, AND THOUGHT; a journal of dialectical and historical materialism. see *SOCIAL SCIENCES: COMPREHENSIVE WORKS*

329   PL   ISSN 0137-141X
NAUKI POLITYCZNE. Issue titles vary. 1974. irreg., 13, 1993. price varies. Adam Mickiewicz University Press, Nowowiejskiego 55, 61-734 Poznan, Poland. TEL 527-380. FAX 61-526425. TELEX 413260 UAMPL. Ed.Bd. **Document type:** academic/scholarly publication.
—BLDSC (9120.471000).
   Description: Contains current research results on one author in the field of political science including Ph.D. works and other monographs.

322.4   CE
NAVA SAMA SAMAJA BULLETINE. (Text in English) 1985. irreg. Nava Sama Samaja Party, 17 Barracks Lane, Colombo 2, Sri Lanka. Ed. Vickamabahu Karanarathne. adv.; bk.rev.

NAVE PARVA. see *TRAVEL AND TOURISM*

320   UK   ISSN 0307-0832
NAVIN WEEKLY. 1975. w. £32. 59-61 Broughton Rd., Fulham, London SW6 2LA, England. Ed. Ramesh Kumar. adv.; bk.rev.; film rev.; tr.lit. circ. 55,000. **Document type:** newspaper.

NEAR EAST - SOUTH ASIA REPORT. see *BUSINESS AND ECONOMICS — Economic Situation And Conditions*

NEPAL - ANTIQUARY; journal of social-historical research and digest. see *ORIENTAL STUDIES*

320   NP
NEPALESE JOURNAL OF POLITICAL SCIENCE. 1979. s-a. Tribhuvan University, Political Science Instruction Committee, Kirtipur Multiple Campus, Kathmandu, Nepal.

320.531   GW
NEUE ARBEITERPRESSE. 1976. w. DM.65 (Europe DM.85; elsewhere DM.125). Bund Sozialistischer Arbeiter, Postfach 100105, 45001 Essen, Germany. TEL 0201-870130. FAX 0201-8701333. Ed. Bettina Rippert. bk.rev. **Document type:** newspaper.

320.531   SZ   ISSN 0028-3134
DER NEUE BUND.* 1935. q. Escherbund, Malojaweg 36, CH-8048 Zurich, Switzerland. Ed. Eva Lezzi. bk.rev.; charts; tr.lit.; index; cum.index every 20 yrs. circ. 200.

320.5   GW   ISSN 0177-6738
H5
DIE NEUE GESELLSCHAFT - FRANKFURTER HEFTE. 1954. m. DM.99. Verlag J.H.W. Dietz Nachf. GmbH, In der Raste 2, 53129 Bonn, Germany. TEL 0228-238083. FAX 0228-234104. Ed. Peter Glotz. adv.; bk.rev.; index. circ. 6,500. **Indexed:** CERDIC, P.A.I.S.For.Lang.Ind. **Document type:** academic/scholarly publication.
—Faxon; SWETS. **CCC.**
   Formerly (until 1985): Neue Gesellschaft (ISSN 0028-3177); Incorporates (since 1984): Frankfurter Hefte (ISSN 0015-9999)

320.9   GW   ISSN 0028-3258
NEUE KOMMENTARE. 1958. m. DM.60. Georg Herde, Mauerweg 20, 60316 Frankfurt, Germany. index. (looseleaf format)

320   GW   ISSN 0934-9200
HV6022.G3
NEUE KRIMINALPOLITIK. 1989. q. DM.60. Nomos Verlagsgesellschaft mbH und Co. KG, Waldseestr. 3-5, 76530 Baden-Baden, Germany. TEL 07221-2104-0. FAX 07221-210427. TELEX 781201. (Subscr. to: Postfach 610, 76484 Baden-Baden, Germany) **Document type:** bulletin.

320.5   AU   ISSN 0028-3274
DER NEUE MAHNRUF; Zeitschrift fuer Freiheit, Recht und Demokratie. 1948. m. S.70. Bundesverband Oesterreichischer Widerstandskaempfer und Opfer des Faschismus, Lassallestr. 40, A-1020 Vienna, Austria. TEL 01-265389. Ed. Oskar Wiesflecker. adv. contact: Oskar Wiesflecker. bk.rev.; charts; illus. circ. 4,500. **Document type:** bulletin.

320.9   GW   ISSN 0028-3320
H5
NEUE POLITISCHE LITERATUR; Berichte ueber das internationale Schrifttum. (Supplement avail.: Neue Politische Literatur. Beihefte. (ISSN 0176-604X)) 1956. 3/yr. DM.98. Peter Lang GmbH Europaeischer Verlag der Wissenschaften, Eschborner Landstr. 42-50, 60489 Frankfurt a.M., Germany. TEL 069-7807050. FAX 069-785893. Ed.Bd. adv.; B&W page DM.800; trim 120 x 190; adv. contact: Rita Bebenroth. bk.rev.; bibl.; index, cum.index: 1966-1975 (vols.11-20). circ. 880. (back issues avail.; reprint service avail. from SCH) **Indexed:** Amer.Hist.& Life, Hist.Abstr., P.A.I.S.For.Lang.Ind. **Document type:** academic/scholarly publication.
—SWETS. **CCC.**

320   AU
DAS NEUE WORT. 1972. m. S.150. Volkssozialistische Bewegung Oesterreichs, Apfelgasse 1-7, 1040 Vienna, Austria. Ed. Alfred Warton. bk.rev. circ. 5,000.
   Description: Newsletter of Socialist analysis and opinion.

320   GW
NEUIGKEIDNBLAEDDLE. 1982. q. free. Sozialdemokratische Partei Deutschlands (SPD), Ortsverein Gartenstadt-Theuerbruennlein-Eselhohe, Kornmarkt 17, 97421 Schweinfurt, Germany. TEL 049-9721-21429. (Subscr. to: c/o Traudl Steinmueller, Wilhelm-Zinn-Str. 20, D-8720 Schweinfurt, Germany) circ. 2,200. (back issues avail.)

350   US   ISSN 0196-7355
JK8501
NEVADA PUBLIC AFFAIRS REVIEW. 1960. irreg. $10 for 2 nos. University of Nevada, Reno, Senator Alan Bible Center for Applied Research, Reno, NV 89557. TEL 702-784-6718. Ed. J.M. Winter. circ. 2,000.
   Former titles (until 1979): Nevada Public Affairs Report (ISSN 0364-3921); Governmental Research Newsletter (ISSN 0017-2677)
   Description: Each issue features in-depth report and analysis of a current policy issue relevant to Nevada.

320 363.35   US
NEW ABOLITIONIST. 1982. q. $15. Nuclear Free America, 325 E. 25th St., Baltimore, MD 21218. TEL 410-235-3575. FAX 410-462-1039. Ed. Chuck Johnson. bk.rev. circ. 6,000. (tabloid format; back issues avail.)
   Description: Covers the international Nuclear Free Zone movement, with information about campaigns and related topics.

320 330   UK   ISSN 0140-1378
DT1
NEW AFRICAN YEARBOOK. a. £38($80) (overseas £40) (effective 1995-1996). I.C. Publications Ltd., 7 Coldbath Sq., London EC1R 4LQ, England. TEL 0171-713-7711. FAX 0171-713-7898. TELEX 8811757 ARABY G. Ed. Alan Rake. adv. circ. 6,000. **Document type:** directory.
—BLDSC (6081.752500).
   Formed by the merger of: New African Yearbook: West and Central; New African Yearbook: East and South.
   Description: Provides information on Africa including the major facts and figures on 53 countries.

320.532   II   ISSN 0047-9500
NEW AGE. 1953; N.S. 1964. w. $55. Communist Party of India, 15 Kotla Rd., New Delhi 110002, India. TELEX 3165982 CNS IN. Ed. Pauly V. Parakal. adv.; bk.rev.; film rev.; play rev.; charts; illus. circ. 15,000. (tabloid format) **Indexed:** Child.Bk.Rev.Ind.

THE NEW ALIYON. see *ETHNIC INTERESTS*

320 051   US
NEW AMERICAN (APPLETON). 1965; N.S. 1985. bi-w. $39. American Opinion Publishing Inc., Box 8040, Appleton, WI 54913. TEL 414-749-3784. FAX 414-749-3785. Ed. Gary Benoit. adv.; bk.rev. circ. 50,000. (also avail. in microform from UMI; reprint service avail. from UMI) **Indexed:** G.Soc.Sci.& Rel.Per.Lit.
—UMI.
   Formed by the 1985 merger of: American Opinion (ISSN 0003-0236); Review of the News (ISSN 0034-6802)
   Description: For constitutional conservatives and economic libertarians. Focuses on political science, social opinion and economic theory, while rejecting an accidental view of history and exposing the behind-the-scences forces shaping American politics and culture.

NEW ARABIAN STUDIES. see *HISTORY — History Of The Near East*

320.532   II
NEW DEMOCRACY.* 1972. m. Rs.12. Committee of Communist Revolutionaries, 129-A Circular Garden Reach Rd., Calcutta 23, India. Ed. Ranajit Samaddar. bibl.

320   CN   ISSN 0827-6153
NEW DIRECTIONS (VANCOUVER, 1985). 1985. bi-m. $20 to individuals; institutions $25. Pacific New Directions Publishing Society, Box 34279, Sta. D, Vancouver, BC V6J 4P2, Canada. TEL 604-266-6830. FAX 604-438-3149. Ed. Bob Smith. adv.: B&W page $350. circ. 1,600.

NEW DIRECTIONS IN PUBLIC ADMINISTRATION RESEARCH. see *PUBLIC ADMINISTRATION*

320.531 331   UK   ISSN 0266-7835
NEW GROUND. 1983. q. £10 (foreign £18). Socialist Environment and Resources Association, 11 Goodwin St., London N4 3HQ, England. TEL 0171-263-7424. FAX 0171-272-3044. Ed. Chris Hewett. adv.; bk.rev.; charts; illus.; stat. circ. 2,500. **Document type:** newsletter.
   Formerly: S E R A News.
   Description: Covers environmental issues from a socialist point of view and provides theoretical articles on Green Socialism.

320   NR   ISSN 0794-439X
NEW HORIZON; Nigeria's Marxist monthly. 1975. m. £N48($24) I F & W O G Enterprises, P.O. Box 2165, Mushin, Lagos, Nigeria. Ed. Ikpe Etokudo. circ. 25,000.

320.531   US   ISSN 0737-3724
HX1
NEW INTERNATIONAL; a magazine of Marxist politics and theory. French edition: Nouvelle Internationale (ISSN 0827-0929); Spanish edition: Nueva Internacional (ISSN 1056-8921) 1983. irreg. price varies. 408 Printing & Publishing Co., 410 West St., New York, NY 10014. TEL 212-243-6392. FAX 212-924-6040. Ed.Bd. adv.; bk.rev. circ. 2,500. (back issues avail.) **Indexed:** Alt.Press Ind.

NEW LEFT REVIEW. see *LITERARY AND POLITICAL REVIEWS*

POLITICAL SCIENCE

320   US
NEW LIBERTARIAN; the magazine of record of the libertarian movement. 1971. bi-m. $25. New Libertarian Company of Free Traders, 17220 Newhope, Ste. 201, Fountain Valley, CA 92708. FAX 310-839-0975. Ed. Samuel Edward Konkin, III. adv.: B&W page $300, color page $1000; trim 8 1/4 x 10 3/4. bk.rev. circ. 2,000. (also avail. in microfiche)
Former titles: New Libertarian Weekly; New Libertarian Notes.
Description: Covers news of the movement and analysis of the world.

956.94   IS   ISSN 0028-6427
DS41
NEW OUTLOOK; Middle East magazine. (Text in English) 1957. 6/yr. $48 to institutions; students $31 (effective 1993). (Israel Peace Research Society) Hashkafah Hadashah, 9 Gordon St., Tel Aviv 63458, Israel. TEL 972-3-5236496. FAX 972-3-5232252. (U.S. subscr. to: Friends of New Outlook, 159 E. 65th St., New York, NY 10021) Ed. Chaim Shur. adv.; bk.rev.; film rev.; play rev.; charts; illus.; stat.; index. circ. 7,000. (also avail. in microform from MIM,UMI; reprint service avail. from UMI) Indexed: Alt.Press Ind., HR Rep. (1988-), P.A.I.S.
—Faxon; UMI; UnCover.

322.4   TZ
NEW OUTLOOK TANZANIA. Variant title: New Outlook. 1976. m. EAs.90($30) P.O. Box 165, Dar es Salaam, Tanzania. Ed. Joe Kamuzora.

321.8   US   ISSN 0893-7850
E839.5
NEW PERSPECTIVES QUARTERLY. Short title: N P Q. 1967. q. $75 (Canada and Mexico $80; elsewhere $90). Center for the Study of Democratic Institutions, 10951 W. Pico Blvd., Ste. 300, Los Angeles, CA 90064. TEL 310-474-0011. FAX 310-474-8061. Ed. Nathan Gardels; Pub. Stanley Sheinbaum. adv. contact: Beth Seeley. bk.rev.; illus. circ. 15,000. (also avail. in microform from UMI; back issues avail., reprint service avail. from UMI) Indexed: Acad.Ind., P.A.I.S., Per.Islam., PSI, Soc.Sci.Ind. Document type: academic/scholarly publication.
●Also available online. Vendor(s): University Microfilms International.
Available only on CD-ROM.
—BLDSC (6084.924200); Faxon; UMI; UnCover.
Formerly (until 1988): Center for the Study of Democratic Institutions. Center Magazine (ISSN 0008-9125)
Description: Examines social and political thought on economics, environment, politics, culture, and the critical issues of our common future.

320   US   ISSN 0739-3148
JA1
NEW POLITICAL SCIENCE. 1979. q. $30 to individuals (foreign $35); institutions $65 (foreign $70). Caucus for a New Political Science, c/o John C. Berg, Treas., Department of Government, Suffolk University, Boston, MA 02108-2770. TEL 617-573-8126. FAX 617-367-4623. E-mail: j.berg@acad.suffolk.edu. Ed. Harry Vanden; Pub. Dennis Moran. adv. contact: John C. Berg. bk.rev.; circ. 250 (paid). Indexed: Alt.Press Ind., Left Ind. (1982-), Polit.Sci.Abstr. Document type: academic/scholarly publication.
—BLDSC (6085.750000); Faxon; UMI; UnCover.
Description: Discusses political science scholarship from a radical perspective.
Refereed Serial

320.531   US   ISSN 0028-6494
HX1   CODEN: NEPOEM
NEW POLITICS; a journal of socialist thought. 1961-1978; resumed, N.S. 1986. s-a. $20 to individuals (foreign $24); institutions $30 (foreign $34) (effective 1993). New Politics Associates, Inc., 328 Clinton St., Brooklyn, NY 11231. TEL 718-237-2048. (Subscr. to: Box 310098, Brooklyn, NY 11231-0098) Eds. Julius Jacobson, Phyllis Jacobson. adv.; bk.rev.; bibl.; index. circ. 3,000. (microform; also avail. in microform from UMI; reprint service avail. from UMI) Indexed: Alt.Press Ind., Int.Polit.Sci.Abstr., Left Ind., P.A.I.S., Polit.Sci.Abstr. Document type: consumer publication.
—BLDSC (6085.800000); Faxon; UMI; UnCover.

329.821 052   UK
NEW TIMES; journal of Democratic Left. 1990. fortn. £22 (Europe £32; elsewhere £37). Democratic Left, 6 Cynthia St., London N1 9JF, England. TEL 0171-278-4451. FAX 0171-278-4425. Ed. Anne Coddington. adv.; bk.rev. circ. 5,000. (tabloid format; also avail. in microform from WMP; back issues avail.) Document type: bulletin.
Former titles (until 1991): Changes (London, 1990) (ISSN 0960-748X); (until 1990): 7 Days.

320   US   ISSN 1070-7727
NEW UNIONIST. 1973. m. $5. New Union Party, 621 W. Lake St., Ste. 210, Minneapolis, MN 55408. TEL 612-823-2593. Ed. Jeff Miller. bk.rev. circ. 9,000. Document type: newspaper.
Description: Analyzes contemporary political-economic developments from a revolutionary viewpoint; promotes a program for socially-owned, democratic economy and workplace government.

320   DK   ISSN 0108-1829
NEW UNITED NATIONS PUBLICATIONS. 1982. irreg. (5-6/yr.). free. F N S Informationskontor for de Nordiske Lande - United Nations Information Centre for the Nordic Countries, H.C. Andersens Boulevard 37, 1553 Copenhagen V, Denmark. Indexed: Soils & Fert.
Formerly: United Nations Publications.

320 330   US   ISSN 0895-8505
NEW WEST NOTES. 1987. m. $150. Box 221364, Sacramento, CA 95822. TEL 916-395-0709. Ed. Bill Bradley.
Formerly: Larkspur Report.
Description: Reports on national political and economic issues from a California perspective.

988.1   GY   ISSN 0028-7008
NEW WORLD. 1963. fortn. New World Associates, 215 King St., Georgetown, Guyana. Ed. David De Caires. adv.; bk.rev.; illus. circ. 800. (processed)

320   US
NEW YORK PEARL. q. Committee for Public Education and Religious Liberty, 165 E. 56 St., New York, NY 10022. TEL 212-223-8012. Dir. Vivian Lindermayer. Document type: newsletter.
Formerly: Pearl Newsletter.

NEW ZEALAND SLAVONIC JOURNAL. see HUMANITIES: COMPREHENSIVE WORKS

320.531   NZ
NEW ZEALAND TRIBUNE. 1966. m. NZ.$21.60 (foreign NZ.$48). (Socialist Unity Party of New Zealand) Socialist Publishing & Distributing Co., P.O. Box 11478, Manners St., Wellington, New Zealand. TEL 64-4-2368857. FAX 64-4-2368862. adv.; illus. (tabloid format)
Description: Includes discussion on political, economic and social development.

320.9   US   ISSN 0028-8969
HX1
NEWS & LETTERS. 1955. 10/yr. $2.50. News & Letters Committees, 59 E. Van Buren St., Ste. 707, Chicago, IL 60605-1212. TEL 312-663-0839. FAX 312-663-9069. Eds. Lou Turner, Felix Martin. bk.rev.; film rev.; illus. circ. 6,000. (tabloid format; also avail. in microform from UMI; back issues avail.; reprint service avail. from UMI) Indexed: Alt.Press Ind. Document type: newspaper.
—UMI.
Description: Journal of labor, civil rights, women's liberation, and anti-war struggles nationally and internationally with an emphasis on Marxist-Humanist theory.

329.6   US
NEWS CUBA. 1983. m. free. Cuba Independiente y Democratica, 10021 S.W. 37th Terr., Miami, FL 33165. TEL 305-551-8484. FAX 305-559-9365. Ed. Huber Matos, Jr. circ. 15,000. (back issues avail.) Document type: newsletter.
Description: To inform politicians, academicians, newsmen, and university students about Cuba.

320.9   AT   ISSN 0159-7345
NEWS DIGEST - INTERNATIONAL. 1963. q. Aus.$6($7) International Information Centre, Box 535, Parramatta, N.S.W. 2150, Australia. TEL 02-630-2309. Ed. J.P. Kedys. adv.; bk.rev.; bibl.; charts; illus.; stat.; index, cum.index. circ. 7,000. (back issues avail.)
Description: Covers international politics, communism, history, defense and economy.

327   US
NEWS FROM GREECE. 1974? 22/yr. free. Embassy of Greece, Press and Information Office, 2211 Massachusetts Ave., N.W., Washington, DC 20008. TEL 202-332-2727. FAX 202-265-4931. illus. circ. 3,000. Document type: government publication.
Formerly: Greece.

NEWS FROM THE WHITE HOUSE. see RELIGIONS AND THEOLOGY — Other Denominations And Sects

322.4   US   ISSN 1064-1556
NEWS NOTES (WASHINGTON); a bi-monthly newsletter of information on international justice and peace issues. 1975. bi-m. $10 (effective Apr. 1991). Maryknoll Fathers and Brothers, Justice and Peace Office, Box 29132, Washington, DC 20017-0132. TEL 202-832-1780. FAX 202-832-5195. E-mail: mknolldc@igc.apc.org. Ed. Terence Miller. adv.; bk.rev. circ. 1,300. Indexed: HR Rep. Document type: newsletter.
Description: Covers international justice and peace issues.

NEWSCOPE - ELEMENTARY EDITION; weekly news summary and teaching quiz. see EDUCATION — Teaching Methods And Curriculum

NEWSCOPE - HIGH SCHOOL - COLLEGE EDITION; a weekly news summary and teaching quiz. see EDUCATION — Teaching Methods And Curriculum

NEWSCOPE - MIDDLE - INTERMEDIATE - JUNIOR HIGH SCHOOL EDITION; a weekly news summary and teaching quiz. see EDUCATION — Teaching Methods And Curriculum

NEWSNAMES - CURRENT EVENTS. see EDUCATION — Teaching Methods And Curriculum

NEWSPUZZLER: CURRENT EVENTS. see EDUCATION — Teaching Methods And Curriculum

NEWSQUESTIONNAIRE: CURRENT EVENTS. see EDUCATION — Teaching Methods And Curriculum

320.531   VN
NGUOI DAI BIEU NHAN DAN/PEOPLE'S DEPUTY. 1988. bi-m. 35 Ngo Quyen, Hanoi, Socialist Republic of Vietnam. TEL 52861. Ed. Nguyen Ngoc Tho.
Description: Disseminates resolutions of the National Assembly and Council of State.

322.4   UK
NICARAGUA UPDATE. 3/yr. £1 per no. Nicaragua Solidarity Campaign, 129 Seven Sisters Rd., London N7 7QG, England. TEL 0171-272-9619. FAX 0171-272-5476. bk.rev.; circ. 1,750. Document type: newsletter.
Formerly: Nicaragua Today (ISSN 0269-4832)

320   US   ISSN 0885-5706
F1521
NICARAGUAN PERSPECTIVES.* 1981. q. $18 to institutions. (Nicaragua Information Center) Berkeley - Leon Sister City Association, Box 1004, Berkeley, CA 94701-1004. adv.; bk.rev. circ. 3,000. (back issues avail.) Indexed: Alt.Press Ind., HR Rep., Left Ind. (1983-), Polit.Sci.Abstr.

NIEUW GELUID. see RELIGIONS AND THEOLOGY — Judaic

320   NG   ISSN 0545-9532
NIGER: FRATERNITE - TRAVAIL - PROGRES. w. Ministere de l'Information, B.P. 368, Niamey, Niger. Ed. Sahidou Alou. illus.

320.5 333.7   SW   ISSN 1100-763X
NISSE HULT. Variant title: N H. 1987. bi-m. SEK 75 (effective 1991). Miljoepartiet De Groenas Ungdomsfoerbund, P.O. Box 1244, S-221 05 Lund, Sweden.
Former titles: Ung Groen; New Zine.

324.998   GL   ISSN 0904-1567
NIVIARSIAQ. (Text in Danish, Greenlandic) 1975. m. (Siumut) Atuagassiivik - Eskimo Press, P.O. Box 357, 3900 Nuuk, Greenland. FAX 22319.
Former titles (until 1987): Siumut (ISSN 0105-5968); (until 1977): Sujumut (ISSN 0105-5372)

320   AG   ISSN 0327-5248
NO HAY DERECHO. 1990. bi-m. Libertador 2640, 1636 Olivos (BA), Argentina. Eds. Alejandro Rua, Martin Clemente.

POLITICAL SCIENCE

320 US ISSN 0078-0979
NOMOS. 1958. a. price varies. (American Society for Political and Legal Philosophy) New York University Press, 70 Washington Sq. S., New York, NY 10012. TEL 212-998-2575; 800-996-3833. FAX 212-995-3833. TELEX 235128 NYU UR. Eds. Alan Wertheimer, John W. Chapman. **Indexed:** A.I.C.P., Int.Polit.Sci.Abstr. **Document type:** academic/scholarly publication.

301 320 US ISSN 1052-0384
NONVIOLENT SANCTIONS; news from the Albert Einstein Institution. 1989. q. Albert Einstein Institution, 50 Church St., 3rd Fl., Cambridge, MA 02138-3726. TEL 617-876-0311. FAX 617-876-0837. circ. 800. (back issues avail.) **Document type:** newsletter.
  Description: Covers news and information about the strategic use of nonviolent action in conflicts around the world.

945 IT ISSN 0029-1188
DG401
NORD E SUD. 1954. q. L.77000 to individuals; institutions L.110000; foreign L.132000 (effective 1993). Edizioni Scientifiche Italiane S.p.A., Via Chiatamone 7, 80121 Naples, Italy. TEL 081-7645768. FAX 081-7646477. Ed. Antonio Aurigemma. adv.; bk.rev.; charts; illus.; index. circ. 1,100. **Indexed:** Int.Polit.Sci.Abstr. —Faxon.

320 GW ISSN 0940-5585
NORDEUROPA FORUM. q. DM.88. Nomos Verlagsgesellschaft mbH und Co. KG, Waldseestr. 3-5, 76530 Baden-Baden, Germany. TEL 07221-2104-0. FAX 07221-210427. TELEX 781201. (Subscr. to: Postfach 610, 76484 Baden-Baden, Germany) **Document type:** bulletin.

320.5 SW ISSN 0345-8628
NORRBOTTNINGEN. Abbreviated title: N B. Variant titles: Veckotidningen Norrbottningen. Nya Norrbottningen. 1956. w. SEK 180 (effective 1990). Norrbottningen, P.O. Box 255, S-951 23 Luleaa, Sweden.

NORSK OEKONOMISK TIDSSKRIFT. see *BUSINESS AND ECONOMICS*

320 NO ISSN 0801-1745
NORSK STATSVITENSKAPELIG TIDSSKRIFT/NORWEGIAN POLITICAL SCIENCE JOURNAL. (Text in Norwegian; summaries in English) 1975. q. NOK 425 in Nordic countries; elsewhere $76 (effective 1996). (Norwegian Association for Political Science) Scandinavian University Press, P.O. Box 2959-Toeyen, N-0608 Oslo, Norway. TEL 47-22-57-54-00. FAX 47-22-57-53-53. E-mail: journals@scup.no. (U.S. addr.: Scandinavian University Press North America, 875-84 Massachusetts Ave., Cambridge, MA 02139, U.S.A.. TEL 516-352-7300) Eds. Dag Ingvar Jacobsen, Idar Magne Holme. adv. contact: Kirsten Solheim. bk.rev.; index. circ. 600. (back issues avail.) **Document type:** academic/scholarly publication.
  Formerly (until 1985): Statsviteren (ISSN 0800-6245)
  Description: Publishes articles on and analyses of politics, public administration, political behavior and international politics.

NORTH AMERICAN FARMER. see *AGRICULTURE*

320 US
NORTH CAROLINA INSIGHT. 1978. q. $36 to individuals; libraries $50. North Carolina Center for Public Policy Research, Inc., Box 430, Raleigh, NC 27602. TEL 919-832-2839. FAX 919-832-2847. Ed. Mike McLaughlin. adv. circ. 2,000. **Document type:** academic/scholarly publication, consumer publication.
  Description: Focuses on public policy issues and problems affecting North Carolina state and local government.

320 KO ISSN 1012-4470
NORTH KOREA NEWS. (Text in English) w. Naewoe Press, 42-2 Chuja-dong, P.O. Box 9708, Chung-gu, Seoul 100-240, S. Korea. Ed. One Hoe Kim.

320 GW ISSN 0340-014X
DS930
NORTH KOREA QUARTERLY. (Text in English) 1974. q. DM.80 (foreign DM.86). Institut fuer Asienkunde - Institute of Asian Affairs, Rothenbaumchaussee 32, 20148 Hamburg, Germany. TEL 040-443001. FAX 040-4107945. illus. **Document type:** academic/scholarly publication.
  —UnCover.

320 910.03 US
NORTH STAR.* q. $10. 731 21st Ave., San Francisco, CA 94121-3809. Ed. Steve Hiatt. **Indexed:** Alt.Press Ind.

320 301.2 II ISSN 0970-7913
NORTH-EAST INDIA COUNCIL FOR SOCIAL SCIENCE RESEARCH. JOURNAL. (Text in English) 1977. s-a. Rs.70($18) North-East India Council for Social Science Research, B.T. Hostel, Laitumkhrah, Shillong 793 003, Meghalaya, India. TEL 224501. Ed.Bd; Pub. B. Datta Ray. adv.; bk.rev. circ. 500. **Document type:** academic/scholarly publication.

320 II ISSN 0301-6404
DS401
NORTH-EASTERN AFFAIRS. (Text in English) 1972. q. Rs.10.($14) c/o S. Sarin, Ed., Jowai Rd., Shillong 3, India. adv.; bk.rev.; charts; illus.

320 341 US ISSN 1040-8614
NORTHERN IRELAND NEWS SERVICE; NINS NewsBreak. 1985. w. $44. Box 57, Albany, NY 12211-0057. TEL 518-329-3003. Ed. Rev. Francis G. McCloskey. circ. 266. (back issues avail.) **Document type:** bulletin.
  ●Also available online. Vendor(s): NewsNet (IT74).
  Description: Irish republican, nationalist and loyalist news sources and spokespersons, also British and Irish governments' Northern Ireland Office. Covers Anglo-Irish relations, public demonstrations, street and border disputes, business openings and closings, application of MacBride Principles, employment and unemployment, and the churches.

320 US ISSN 0890-9776
NORTHWESTLETTER. 1981. fortn. $167. Box 2361, Washington, DC 20013. TEL 202-546-2547. FAX 202-546-2734. Ed. Larry Swisher. **Document type:** newsletter.
  Description: Focuses on politics and issues of Pacific Northwest--Idaho, Oregon and Washington--in the nation's capitol.

320 CU
NOSOTROS. bi-m. $24 in S. America; N. America $26; elsewhere $30. Union de Jovenes Comunistas, Obispo No. 527, Apdo. 605, Havana, Cuba.

320.351 NE ISSN 0298-7902
NOTEBOOKS FOR STUDY AND RESEARCH. French edition: Cahiers d'Etude et de Recherche (ISSN 0298-7899) (Text in English) 1986. 4/yr. £40 (outside Europe £12 or $20). International Institute for Research and Education - Institut International de Recherche et de Formation, Postbus 53290, 1007 RG Amsterdam, Netherlands. TEL 31-20-6717263. FAX 31-20-6732106. Ed. Peter Drucker; Pub. Pierre Rousset. adv. circ. 1,000. **Document type:** academic/scholarly publication.
  Description: Educational tool for students, trade unionists and social activists, covering Europe, both East and West, the Americas, Africa and the major issues of socialist theory.

960 SG ISSN 0029-3954
DT1
NOTES AFRICAINES. 1939. q. 60 F. Institut Fondamental d'Afrique Noire - Cheikh Anta Diop, B.P. 206, Dakar, Senegal. Ed. Abdoulaye Bara Diop. charts; illus.; maps; cum.index: 1939-1948, 1949-1963, 1964-1976. circ. 1,500. **Indexed:** A.I.C.P., Documentatieblad.

329.6
NOTI CUBA. (Text in Spanish) 1983. w. free. Cuba Independiente y Democratica, 10021 S.W. 37th Terr., Miami, FL 33165. TEL 305-551-8484. FAX 305-559-9365. Ed. Huber Matos, Jr. circ. 3,500. (back issues avail.) **Document type:** newsletter.
  Description: To inform politicians, academicians, and newsmen about Cuba in Spanish-language areas.

322.4 US ISSN 1060-4189
F1401
NOTISUR; South American & Caribbean political affairs. w. $125 to individuals; institutions $225. University of New Mexico, Latin American Institute, Latin America Data Base, 801 Yale N.E., Albuquerque, NM 87131-1016. TEL 505-277-6839. FAX 505-277-5989. Ed. Kent Norsworthy. **Document type:** academic/scholarly publication.
  ●Also available online. Vendor(s): Knight-Ridder, Inc., Lexis-Nexis, NewsNet.
  Also available on CD-ROM. Producer(s): NISC (Latin American Studies - Vol.2).
  Formerly (until Apr. 1993): Central America Update (ISSN 1054-8882)
  Description: Covers political develoments in the Caribbean, Central and South America from an alternative perspective, with an emphasis on human rights issues and regional peace initiatives.

320 296 FR
NOTRE VOIX.* (Text in Yiddish) vol.37, 1974. bi-m. 50 F. B. Goutmann, Ed. & Pub., 52 rue Rene Boulanger, 75010 Paris, France.

320 MF
NOUVEAU MILITANT. (Text in French) w. Mouvement Militant Mauricien, 21, rue Poudriere, Port Louis, Mauritius.
  Former titles: Peuple; Militant.

NOUVEAUX CAHIERS DE L'EST. see *LITERATURE*

320 330.9 FR ISSN 1141-9946
DT1
NOUVEL AFRIQUE ASIE. 1969. m. 220 F.($75) Societe d'Editions Afriasial, 3 rue de Metz, 75010 Paris, France. TEL 40-22-06-72. FAX 45-23-28-02. Ed. Simon Malley. adv. contact: Barbara Malley. bk.rev. circ. 100,000. **Indexed:** Curr.Cont.Africa.
  Former titles (until 1987): Afrique-Asie (ISSN 0302-6485); (until 1972): Africasia (ISSN 1141-9954).
  Description: Covers the politics, culture and economy of Africa and the Middle East.

322.4 IV ISSN 1018-7480
NOUVEL HORIZON. 1990. Front Populaire Ivoirien, Abidjan, Ivory Coast. circ. 15,000.

320.5 FR ISSN 0244-7878
LE NOUVEL HUMANISME. 1970. q. 12 F. (foreign 15 F.). Georges Krassovsky, Ed. & Pub., B.P. 164, 75664 Paris Cedex 14, France. illus. (tabloid format)
  Formerly (until 1981): Combat pour l'Homme (ISSN 0045-7469)
  Description: Dedicated to ecology, disarmament and human rights.

NOUVELLES UNIVERSITAIRES EUROPEENES/EUROPEAN UNIVERSITY NEWS. see *EDUCATION*

320 UK ISSN 0143-3563
DB361
NOVA HRVATSKA.* (Text in Croatian) 1958. s-m. $85. Nova Hrvatska Ltd., 30 Fleet St., London EC4Y 1AJ, England. Ed. J. Kusan. adv.; bk.rev. circ. 15,000.

320.5 SW ISSN 0281-4285
NU; det liberala nyhetsmagasinet. 1983. w. SEK 250 (effective 1991). Nu, P.O. Box 6508, S-113 83 Stockholm, Sweden.

322.4 900 US ISSN 0883-9875
NUCLEAR RESISTER; a chronicle of hope. 1980. every 6 weeks. $20 for 10 issues (Canada $23; elsewhere $30) (effective 1995). National No-Nukes Prison Support Collective, Box 43383, Tucson, AZ 85733. TEL 602-323-8697. E-mail: nukeresister@igc.apc.org. Eds. Jack Cohen-Joppa, Felice Cohen-Joppa. stat. circ. 800. (tabloid format; also avail. in microfiche from UMI; back issues avail.) **Document type:** newsletter.
  Formerly (until 1982): National No-Nukes Prison Support Collective. Newsletter.
  Description: Dedicated to jailed and imprisoned anti-nuclear activists in the United States and Canada. Provides comprehensive reporting on arrests and jailings of the civilly disobedient, while encouraging support for those behind bars.

320 613.194 US
NUDITARIAN. bi-m. $1 per no. 1118 Magnolia, Ste. 230, Burbank, CA 91506. Ed. Fred Heiser. **Document type:** consumer publication.

320 AG
NUESTRA PALABRA.* 1973. w. $2 per no. Partido Comunista, Entre Rios 1031, Buenos Aires, Argentina. Ed. Fernando Nadra. bk.rev. (tabloid format)

320 EC
NUEVA. 1974. m. Apdo. 3224, Quito, Ecuador. Dir. Magdalena Jaramillo de Adoum. adv.; illus.

320 VE ISSN 0251-3552
F1401
NUEVA SOCIEDAD; revista latinoamericana bimestral. 1972. bi-m. Bs.1900 (Latin America $50; elsewhere $80) (effective 1995). Editorial Nueva Sociedad Ltda., Apdo. 61712, Chacao, Caracas 1060-A, Venezuela. TEL 58-2-2651849. FAX 58-2-2673397. Ed. Sergio Chejfec; Pub. Heidulf Schmidt. adv.; bk.rev.; index. circ. 7,500. **Indexed:** Hisp.Amer.Per.Ind. (1972-).
—SWETS.
Description: Covers political, economic and cultural reviews of Latin America. Includes topics such as international relations, trade unions and various social movements.

320.1 IT ISSN 0391-4356
NUOVI STUDI POLITICI. 1971. q. L.38000. Bulzoni Editore, Via dei Liburni 14, 00185 Rome, Italy. TEL 06-4455207. FAX 06-4450355. Ed. Salvatore Valitutti.

320.9 IT ISSN 0029-6384
NUOVO OSSERVATORE.* 1961. m. (11/yr.) L.50000 (foreign L.80000). Nuovo Osservatore S.R.L., Piazza di Pietra 31, 00186 Rome, Italy. TEL 6787583. FAX 6785813. (Dist. by: Parrini & Co., Piazza Colonna 361, 00187 Rome, Italy) Dir. Vincenzo Scotti. adv.; bk.rev. circ. 20,000.
Description: Examines principal political and social problems.

320.5 SW ISSN 0347-8750
NY FRAMTID. 1977-1984; resumed 1989. q. SEK 60 (effective 1990). Kristdemokratiska Ungdomsfoerbundet (KDU), P.O. Box 5039, S-101 26 Stockholm, Sweden.

320.531 NO ISSN 0803-3498
NY TID; sosialistisk ukeavis. 1975. w. NOK 410. A S Ny Tid, Schweigaardsgt. 34, Oslo 1, Norway. FAX 02-172260. Ed. Bernt Eggen. adv.; bk.rev.; illus. circ. 10,000. (tabloid format)
Incorporates: Orientering (ISSN 0030-5480)

320.5 SW ISSN 1100-6447
NYLIBERALEN; Frihetsfrontens tidning. Variant title: Tidskriften Nyliberalen. 1989. q. SEK 100 (effective 1991). Nyliberalen, P.O. Box 2039, S-183 02 Taeby, Sweden.

320 NO ISSN 0800-336X
JA26
NYTT NORSK TIDSSKRIFT; a Norwegian journal of politics, research and culture. 1984. q. NOK 495 in Nordic countries; elsewhere $92 (effective 1996). Scandinavian University Press, P.O. Box 2959 Toeyen, N-0608 Oslo, Norway. TEL 47-22-57-54-00. FAX 47-22-57-53-53. (U.S. addr.: Scandinavian University Press, 200 Meacham Ave., Elmont, NY 11003. TEL 516-352-7300) Eds. Rune Slagstad, Francis Sejersted, Hans Skjerveheim. adv.; bk.rev.; index. circ. 2,600. **Indexed:** Amer.Hist.& Life (until 1991), Hist.Abstr. (until 1991).
Description: Focuses on politics, scientific research, and culture.

O I O C NEWSLETTER. (Oriental and India Office Collections) see *ORIENTAL STUDIES*

323.4 AU ISSN 0029-7534
OBEROESTERREICHISCHE F P O - NACHRICHTEN FUER FREIHEIT UND RECHT. 1956. m. S.180($10.50) Freiheitliche Partei Oesterreichs, Landesgruppe Oberoesterreich, Bluetenstr. 21-1, Postfach 3, A-4041 Linz, Austria. Ed. Hannes Lackner. adv.; bk.rev.; tr.lit.; index. circ. 15,000.

322.4 US ISSN 0279-103X
UB343
OBJECTOR; journal of draft and military counseling. 1979. every 8 wks. $17 to individuals and high school libraries; institutions and foreign $22. Central Committee for Conscientious Objectors, Western Region, 655 Sutter, No. 514, San Francisco, CA 94102. FAX 415-474-2311. Ed. Sam Diener. adv.; bk.rev.; index. circ. 1,000. (back issues avail.)
Description: News articles and information on the military and the draft, focusing on community-organizational, legislative, and legal issues pertaining to conscientious objection, discrimination and harassment in the military, the need for combat and other military services counseling.

320 AU
OBSERVER; Zeitschrift fuer Politik und Wirtschaft. fortn. S.500. H. Schnurr Zeitungen- und Nachrichtengesellschaft mbH, Postfach 39, A-5023 Salzburg, Austria. TEL 066232-4071. FAX 06323-4073. adv.; bk.rev.
Formerly (until 1984): Zyklus.

OBSERVER OF BUSINESS & POLITICS. see *BUSINESS AND ECONOMICS*

320.531 HK
OCTOBER REVIEW/SHIH YUEH P'ING LUN. (Text mainly in Chinese; table of contents and some articles in English) bi-m. HK.$12. G.P.O. Box 10144, Hong Kong. TEL 3-862780. illus.
Description: Covers world news, events, and politics from a socialist perspective.

ODONIST PRISON PROJECT AND SECOND MOUNTAIN KINDRED. JOINT PUBLICATION. see *RELIGIONS AND THEOLOGY — Other Denominations And Sects*

DIE OEFFENTLICHE VERWALTUNG; Zeitschrift fuer oeffentliches Recht und Verwaltungswissenschaft. see *PUBLIC ADMINISTRATION*

OEKOLOGIEPOLITIK. see *CONSERVATION*

329.9 AU ISSN 0029-9308
DB99.1
OESTERREICHISCHE MONATSHEFTE; Zeitschrift fuer Politik. 1945. m. S.200. Oesterreichische Volkspartei, Bundespartei, Lichtenfelsgasse 7, A-1010 Vienna, Austria. TEL 0222-40126531. FAX 0222-4066272. Ed. Gerhard Wiflinger. adv.; bk.rev.; charts; illus.; stat.; index. circ. 3,000. **Indexed:** P.A.I.S.For.Lang.Ind. **Document type:** bulletin.
—BLDSC (6307.967000).
Description: Publication of the Bundespartei covering Austrian and foreign politics, economics, and ecology. Includes list of events.

943.6 AU ISSN 0029-9375
DR1
OESTERREICHISCHE OSTHEFTE. (Text in German; occasionally in English) 1959. q. S.784. Oesterreichisches Ost- und Suedosteuropa Institut, Josefsplatz 6, A-1010 Vienna, Austria. Ed. Walter Lukan. adv.; bk.rev.; charts; stat.; index. circ. 800. **Indexed:** Amer.Hist.& Life, Hist.Abstr. **Document type:** bulletin.
—BLDSC (6308.200000); Faxon.

320 AU ISSN 0378-5149
OESTERREICHISCHE ZEITSCHRIFT FUER POLITIKWISSENSCHAFT. 1972. q. S.400. (Oesterreichische Gesellschaft fuer Politikwissenschaft) Institut fuer Staats- und Politikwissenschaft, Hohenstaufengasse 9-7, A-1010 Vienna, Austria. TEL 0222-40103. FAX 0222-5334403. Ed.Bd. adv. contact: W. Manoschek. circ. 2,500. **Indexed:** P.A.I.S.For.Lang.Ind. **Document type:** academic/scholarly publication.
Description: Studies political science with special emphasis on Austrian politics.

320 AU ISSN 0170-0847
JN2012.3
OESTERREICHISCHES JAHRBUCH FUER POLITIK. a. price varies. Verlag fuer Geschichte und Politik, Neulinggasse 26, A-1030 Vienna, Austria. TEL 0222-7126258-0. FAX 0222-712625819. Ed.Bd. **Indexed:** A.B.C.Pol.Sci. **Document type:** academic/scholarly publication.

956.94 IS ISSN 0017-8926
OFAKIM. (Text in Hebrew) 1970. 8/yr. $90. Am Oved Ltd. Publishers, P.O. Box 470, Tel Aviv 61003, Israel. TEL 972-3-291526. FAX 972-2-298911. circ. 3,000.

320.5 SW ISSN 0348-5447
OFFENSIV; marxistiska tidningen foer arbetarroerelsen. 1973. bi-m. SEK 100. Offensiv, P.O. Box 374, S-123 03 Farsta, Sweden.

335 FR ISSN 0078-3803
OFFICE UNIVERSITAIRE DE RECHERCHE SOCIALISTE. CAHIERS. 1969. m. 340 F. (foreign 450 F.). Office Universitaire de Recherche Socialiste (OURS), 86 rue de Lille, Paris 7e, France. TEL 45-55-08-60. FAX 45-55-66-33. Ed. Denis Lefebvre. adv.; bk.rev. circ. 1,500. **Document type:** bulletin.

OGGI E DOMANI. see *PUBLIC ADMINISTRATION*

363 US ISSN 1072-8724
K15
OHIO POLITICAL REVIEW. 1993. m. 5124 Mayfield Rd., No. 294, Lyndhurst, OH 44124.

353 US ISSN 0030-1795
OKLAHOMA OBSERVER. 1969. s-m. $25. Troy Enterprises, Co., 500 N.E. 39 Terr., Box 53371, Oklahoma City, OK 73152. TEL 405-525-5582. Ed. Frosty Troy; Pub. Helen B. Troy. adv.: B&W page $419; 10 1/2 x 14; adv. contact: Helen B. Troy. bk.rev.; film rev.; circ. 8,000 (paid). (tabloid format; also avail. in microform from UMI; reprint service avail. from UMI) **Indexed:** Access (1975-). **Document type:** newspaper.
—UMI.
Description: Offers commentary on politics, government, education, and social issues.

320 330.9 US
ON PRINCIPLE.* 1982. fortn. $43. Apriori Publishing, 278 Gorwin Dr., Holliston, MA 01746-1533. Ed. Donald A. Feder. bk.rev.; illus.; index. circ. 1,700.
Formerly: First Principle.

320.531 UK ISSN 0308-1230
ON TARGET. 1970. 4/yr. £1.20($3.50) Middle East Research and Action Group, 5 Caledonian Rd., London N.1., England. Eds. Stephen Vines, Edward Rosen. adv.; bk.rev.; illus. (also avail. in microfilm from UMI)
Incorporates: Flashpoint (ISSN 0046-4058)

ON THE LINE (NEW YORK). see *BUSINESS AND ECONOMICS — Labor And Industrial Relations*

329.9 NE ISSN 0167-028X
ONS BURGERSCHAP; nationaal-gereformeerd staatkundig tijdschrift. 1948. m. fl.30. Gereformeerd Politiek Verbond - Reformed Political Association, P.O. Box 439, 3800 AK Amersfoort, Netherlands. TEL 31-33-613546. FAX 31-33-610132. (Co-sponsor: Groen van Prinsterer Stichting) Ed.Bd. adv.; bk.rev.; index. circ. 13,600.
Formerly: Ons Politeuma (ISSN 0030-2740)

329.3 CN ISSN 0028-4564
ONTARIO NEW DEMOCRAT. 1961. 8/yr. Can.$5. New Democratic Party of Ontario, 184 Main St., Toronto, Ont. M4E 2W1, Canada. TEL 416-699-6637. Ed. Mike Foster. adv.; bk.rev. circ. 30,000.

OPEN MAGAZINE PAMPHLET SERIES. see *POLITICAL SCIENCE — International Relations*

OPEN SECRETS; all the truth that's fit to release. see *HISTORY — History Of North And South America*

322.48 CR
OPINION POPULAR. 1982? m. $5 or exchange basis. Movimiento Nacional Revolucionario de El Salvador, Apdo. 230 (2050), San Pedro de Montes de Oca, Costa Rica. **Indexed:** HR Rep.

322.4 IT
L'OPINIONE (WEEKLY). w. L.120000. Societa Editoriale Attivita Culturali, Via Leccosa 58, 00186 Rome, Italy. TEL 39-6-6861172. FAX 39-6-6547612. adv.: page L.7500000. bk.rev.

320 JA
OPINIONS/SEIRON.* (Text in Japanese) 1973. m. 4800 Yen. Sankei Publishing Ltd., Sankei-Honsha Bldg., 1-7-2 Otemachi, Chiyoda-ku, Tokyo, 100, Japan. Ed. Masashi Onoda.

POLITICAL SCIENCE

059.91　　　　　YU　ISSN 0030-3895
OPSTINA; casopis za teoriju i praksu razvoja opstine. (Text in Serbo-Croatian) 1948. m. 800 din. Zavod za Javnu Upravu, Belgrade, Nemanjina 22, Belgrade, Yugoslavia. Ed. Miodrag Visnjic. adv.; bk.rev.; bibl. circ. 1,200.

327.172　　　　　US
OREGON PEACEWORKER. 1989. 10/yr. $15. Oregon PeaceWorks, 333 State St., Salem, OR 97301. TEL 503-371-8002. FAX 503-585-2767. Ed. Peter Bergel. circ. 11,000. **Document type:** newspaper.

ORGANIZING. see SOCIAL SERVICES AND WELFARE

320.532 330　　　　　IT
ORIENTAMENTI NUOVI PER LA PICCOLA E MEDIA INDUSTRIA. 1978. m. L.12000. Partito Comunista Italiano, Via delle Botteghe Oscure 4, 00186 Rome, Italy. Ed. Federico Brini. adv. circ. 10,000.

OSSERVATORE POLITICO LETTERARIO. see LITERARY AND POLITICAL REVIEWS

940 947　　　GW　ISSN 0030-6428
DR1
OSTEUROPA; Zeitschrift fuer Gegenwartsfragen des Ostens. 1950. m. DM.114 (students DM.76.80). (Deutsche Gesellschaft fuer Osteuropakunde) Deutsche Verlags-Anstalt GmbH, Postfach 106012, 70094 Stuttgart, Germany. TEL 0711-2631-0. FAX 0711-2631-292. Ed. A. Steininger. adv.; bk.rev.; bibl.; charts; index. circ. 2,450. (reprint service avail. from SCH) **Indexed:** A.B.C.Pol.Sci., Amer.Hist.& Life (until 1993), CERDIC, Geo.Abstr., Hist.Abstr. (until 1993), Int.Polit.Sci.Abstr., Key to Econ.sci., Lang.& Lang.Behav.Abstr., P.A.I.S.For.Lang.Ind., RILM, SCIMP (1991-), SSCI. **Document type:** academic/scholarly publication.
—BLDSC (6312.190000); Faxon; Genuine Article; SWETS. **CCC.**

320　　　　　IS　ISSN 0792-4615
THE OTHER ISRAEL. (Text in English) 1983. irreg. (4-5/yr.). $30 to individuals; institutions $50; students & pensioners $15. Israeli Council for Israeli - Palestinian Peace, P.O. Box 2542, Holon 58125, Israel. TEL 972-3-5565804. (U.S. address: America - Israel Council for Israeli - Palestinian Peace, 4186 Cornell Ave., Downers Grove, IL 60515) Ed. Adam Keller. circ. 4,000. (also avail. in microfiche; back issues avail.) **Document type:** newsletter.
Description: Covers the Israeli peace movement; comments on events in Israel and the Middle East.

OTTAWA WEEKLY UPDATE. see PUBLIC ADMINISTRATION

OUR GENERATION. see SOCIOLOGY

320　　　　　AQ
OUTLET. 1975. w. (Antigua Caribbean Liberation Movement) Outlet Publishers, P.O. Box 493, McKinnons, Antigua, W.I. TEL 809-462-4425. Ed. Tim Hector. circ. 5,500.

OVERVIEW. see BUSINESS AND ECONOMICS — Economic Situation And Conditions

P A G E JOURNAL. (Peace and Global Education) see EDUCATION — Teaching Methods And Curriculum

320.9　　　　　US　ISSN 0030-7807
P A R ANALYSIS. 1951. irreg. Public Affairs Research Council of Louisiana, Inc., Box 14776, Baton Rouge, LA 70898-4776. TEL 504-926-8414. FAX 504-926-8417. Ed. Mark Drennen. charts; stat. circ. 7,000. **Indexed:** ERIC, P.A.I.S. **Document type:** newsletter.
Formerly: P.A.R. News Analysis.

320　　　　　GW
P & A (Preiswert & Attraktiv) 1977. q. DM.5. P & A, Schuelerzeitung am Gymnasium Pegnitz, Wilhelm-von-Humboldt Str. 7, 91257 Pegnitz, Germany. circ. 600.

P & M. (Politics & Money) see BUSINESS AND ECONOMICS — Banking And Finance

320.52　　　　　CN
P.C. TALK. irreg. (4-5/yr.). membership. Progressive Conservative Association of Alberta, 9919 106th St., Edmonton, Alta. T5K 1E2, Canada. adv. circ. 80,000.
Former titles: P.C. Action (Year); Progressive Conservative Association of Alberta. Progress Bulletin.

320　　　　　UK　ISSN 0955-6281
P S A NEWS. 1975. 4/yr. £28. Political Studies Association of the United Kingdom, Department of Public Administration, University of Ulster, Derry BT48 7JL, N. Ireland. TEL 0504-265261. FAX 0504-267261. Ed. Neil Collins. adv.; bk.rev. circ. 2,000. **Document type:** newsletter.
Formerly (until 1988): Political Studies Association of the United Kingdom. Newsletter (ISSN 0144-7440)
Description: Contains articles, news, listings on contemporary political studies.

320 338　　　　　UK
P S I: REPORT SERIES. 1933. irreg. £130 (includes Discussion Papers; Studies in European Politics; Policy Studies. Policy Studies Institute, 100 Park Village East, London NW1 3SR, England. TEL 071-387-2171. FAX 071-388-0914.
Formerly: P E P (ISSN 0030-7947)

320　　　　　US　ISSN 1049-0965
JA28
P S: POLITICAL SCIENCE & POLITICS. Variant title: Political Science & Politics. 1968. q. membership. American Political Science Association, 1527 New Hampshire Ave., N.W., Washington, DC 20036. TEL 202-483-2512. FAX 202-483-2657. Ed. Robert J.P. Hauck. adv.: page $545. circ. 16,000. (also avail. in microform from UMI; reprint service avail. from UMI; back issues avail.) **Indexed:** A.B.C.Pol.Sci., Chic.Per.Ind., Curr.Cont., Int.Polit.Sci.Abstr., Pers.Lit., Polit.Sci.Abstr., Soc.Sci.Ind. **Document type:** trade publication.
—Faxon; SWETS; UMI; UnCover. **CCC.**
Incorporates (1974-1990): Political Science Teacher (ISSN 0896-0828)
Description: For the political science audience; includes articles of contemporary political analysis, and to feature news of the profession and its members.
Refereed Serial

320　　　　　CU
PABLO.* 16/yr. Union de Periodistas y Escritores de Cuba, Calle 28, No. 452, Vedado, Apdo. 6646, Havana, Cuba. TEL 7-22-5892. circ. 53,000.

990　　　　　CN　ISSN 0030-851X
DU1
PACIFIC AFFAIRS; an international review of Asia and the Pacific. 1927. q. $55 to individuals; institutions $40. Pacific Affairs, University of British Columbia, 2029 West Mall, Vancouver, BC V6T 1Z2, Canada. TEL 604-822-6508. FAX 604-822-9452. Ed. Ian Slater. adv.; bk.rev.; index; circ. 3,000 (paid). (also avail. in microform from UMI; microfiche; back issues avail.; reprint service avail. from UMI) **Indexed:** A.B.C.Pol.Sci., Abstr.Anthropol., Abstr.Mil.Bibl., Acad.Ind., Amer.Bibl.Slavic & E.Eur.Stud., Amer.Hist.& Life, Asian-Pac.Econ.Lit., Bk.Rev.Dig., Bk.Rev.Ind. (1965-), Can.B.P.I., Child.Bk.Rev.Ind. (1965-), CMI, Curr.Cont., E.I., Geo.Abstr., Hist.Abstr., Hum.Ind., IDA, Int.Lab.Doc., Int.Polit.Sci.Abstr., Key to Econ.Sci., Mid.East: Abstr.& Ind., P.A.I.S., Rural Devel.Abstr., Rural Recreat.Tour.Abstr., So.Pac.Per.Ind., Soc.Sci.Ind., SSCI, World Agri.Econ.& Rural Sociol.Abstr.
●Also available online. Vendor(s): University Microfilms International.
—BLDSC (6328.700000); Faxon; Genuine Article; SWETS; UMI; UnCover. **CCC.**
Description: Scholarly journal dealing with Asia and the Pacific.

PACIFIC ISLANDS MONTHLY. see BUSINESS AND ECONOMICS — Economic Situation And Conditions

PAKISTAN. NATIONAL ASSEMBLY. DEBATES. OFFICIAL REPORT. see PUBLIC ADMINISTRATION

PAMIETNIKARSTWO POLSKIE. see HISTORY — History Of Europe

335.83　　　　　IT
PANTAGRUEL;* rivista anarchica di analisi sociale, economica, filosofica e metodologica. (Supplement to: Anarchismo) 1981. 3/yr. Edizioni Anarchismo, Casella Postale 61, 95100 Catania, Italy.

PARAMETERS (CARLISLE BARRACKS); United States Army War College. see MILITARY

328　　　　　GW　ISSN 0031-2258
DAS PARLAMENT; die Woche im Bundeshaus. (Supplement avail.: Aus Politik und Zeitgeschichte (ISSN: 0479-611X)) 1950. w. DM.52.80. Bundeszentrale fuer Politische Bildung, Berliner Freiheit 7, 53111 Bonn, Germany. TEL 0228-515229. FAX 0228-515113. bk.rev.; index. circ. 125,000. (also avail. in microform from NRP) **Document type:** government publication, newspaper.

328　　　　　UK　ISSN 0031-2282
PARLIAMENTARIAN. 1920. q. £25 to non-members (overseas £32) (effective 1994). Commonwealth Parliamentary Association, Headquarters, 7 Old Palace Yard, Westminster, London SW1P 3JY, England. TEL 0171-799-1460. FAX 0171-222-6073. TELEX 911569 CPA HQG. Ed. Andrew Imlach. adv.; bk.rev.; illus.; index, cum.index: 1966-1980, 1981-1985, 1986-1990. circ. 10,200. (also avail. in microfilm from UMI; reprint service avail. from UMI) **Indexed:** A.B.C.Pol.Sci., Br.Hum.Ind., Curr.Cont., Int.Polit.Sci.Abstr., Mid.East: Abstr.& Ind., P.A.I.S., Polit.Sci.Abstr., So.Pac.Per.Ind., SSCI. **Document type:** academic/scholarly publication.
—BLDSC (6406.830000); Faxon; SWETS; UMI; UnCover.
Formerly: Journal of the Parliaments of the Commonwealth.

328　　　　　UK　ISSN 0031-2290
JN101
PARLIAMENTARY AFFAIRS; devoted to all aspects of parliamentary democracy. 1947. q. £64($115) (effective 1996). (Hansard Society for Parliamentary Government) Oxford University Press, Oxford Journals, Walton St., Oxford OX2 6DP, England. TEL 01865-267907. FAX 01865-267773. TELEX 837330-OXPRES-G. E-mail: jnlorders@oup.co.uk. (U.S. subscr. to: Oxford University Press Inc., 2001 Evans Rd., Cary, NC 27513. TEL 919-677-0977. FAX 919-677-1714) Ed. F.F. Ridley. adv. contact: Jane Parker. bk.rev.; charts; illus.; index, cum.index. circ. 1,650. (also avail. in microform from UMI) **Indexed:** A.B.C.Pol.Sci., Abstr.Crim.& Pen., Amer.Hist.& Life (until 1993), Br.Hum.Ind., Curr.Cont., ELLIS, Euro.LJI, Hist.Abstr. (until 1993), Int.Polit.Sci.Abstr., Lang.& Lang.Behav.Abstr., LJI, Mid.East: Abstr.& Ind., P.A.I.S., Polit.Sci.Abstr., Soc.Sci.Ind., SSCI. **Document type:** academic/scholarly publication.
—BLDSC (6406.840000); Faxon; Genuine Article; SWETS; UMI; UnCover. **CCC.**
Description: Covers all aspects of government and politics directly or indirectly connected with Parliament and parliamentary systems in Britain and throughout the world.

322　　　　　AT　ISSN 0813-541X
PARLIAMENTARY HANDBOOK OF THE COMMONWEALTH OF AUSTRALIA. 1915. irreg. (approx every 3 yrs.). price varies. Australian Government Publishing Service, G.P.O. Box 84, Canberra, A.C.T. 2601, Australia. TEL 61-6-295-4411. FAX 61-6-295-4455. TELEX AA62013. illus. circ. 2,000. **Document type:** government publication, directory.
—**CCC.**
Former titles: Australian Parliamentary Handbook; Parliamentary Handbook of the Commonwealth of Australia.

328　　　　　US　ISSN 0048-2994
JF515
PARLIAMENTARY JOURNAL. 1960. q. $20 (Canada $22.50; elsewhere $25) (effective 1996). American Institute of Parliamentarians, 10535 Metropolitan Ave., Kensington, MD 20895-2627. TEL 301-946-9220. FAX 301-949-5255. Ed. Martha J. Haun. bk.rev. circ. 1,400. (also avail. in microform from UMI; back issues avail.; reprint service avail. from UMI) **Indexed:** Mid.East: Abstr.& Ind. **Document type:** academic/scholarly publication.
—UMI.
Description: Articles on parliamentary procedure in organizations, including informal articles on homeowners associations and condos.

POLITICAL SCIENCE 5341

320.531   IT   ISSN 1122-5300
HX7
PAROLECHIAVE. 1958. 3/yr. L.58500 (foreign L.75000). Donzelli Editore, Via Mentana 2, 0185 Rome, Italy. TEL 39-6-4440600. FAX 39-6-4440607. Ed. Franco Zannino. adv.; bk.rev.; bibl.; index. circ. 2,500. (back issues avail.) **Indexed:** Int.Polit.Sci.Abstr.
    Formerly (until 1993): Problemi del Socialismo (ISSN 0552-1807)

320   IE   ISSN 0709-6941
PARTICIPATION. (Text in English and French) 1977. 3/yr. (plus annual supplement). $40 non-members. International Political Science Association, c/o University College Dublin, Department of Politics, Belfield, Dublin 4, Ireland. TEL 01-7068182. FAX 01-7061171. E-mail: ipsa@ollamh.ucd.ie. circ. controlled.
    —BLDSC (6407.230000).
    Formerly: International Political Science Association. Circular (ISSN 0074-7459)

329.11   FR   ISSN 1150-5567
PARTICIPER. m. (10/yr.). 100 F. (Acteurs Economiques et Sociaux) Etape Communication, 123 rue de Lille, 75341 Paris Cedex 07, France. TEL 49-55-63-88. (Subscr. to: 282 bd Saint-Germain, 75341 Paris Cedex 07, France. TEL 49-55-64-59) (Affiliate: Rassemblement pour la Republique) Ed. Raymond Bault. illus.

329.9   SP
PARTIDO SOCIALISTA POPULAR. CONGRESO. (ACTAS).* no.3, 1976. irreg. Tucar Ediciones S.A., Eduardo Dato 21, Madrid 10, Spain.

320   PE
PARTIDO SOCIALISTA REVOLUCIONARIO. INFORMES.* 1977. irreg. Partido Socialista Revolucionario, Avda. Parque de la Reserva 865, Apdo. 11-0586, Lima 11, Peru. Ed. Francisco Moncloa.

329.9   II   ISSN 0377-2667
HX3
PARTY LIFE; journal of the Communist Party of India. (Text in English) 1964. m. Rs.24($15.25) (Communist Party of India) People's Publishing House Private Ltd., 5E Rani Jhansi Road, New Delhi 110055, India. Ed. M. Farooqi. circ. 2,500.

320   UK   ISSN 1354-0688
JF2011
▼**PARTY POLITICS;** international journal for the study of political parties and political organizations. 1995. q. £32 to individuals; institutions £99 (effective 1996). Sage Publications Ltd., 6 Bonhill St., London EC2A 4PU, England. TEL 0171-374-0645. FAX 0171-374-8741. E-mail: market@sageltd.co.uk. Ed.Bd. adv.; B&W page £180; trim 195 x 114; adv. contact: Bernie Folan. **Indexed:** Polit.Sci.Abstr. **Document type:** academic/scholarly publication.
    Description: Provides a forum for discussion of the character and organization of political parties, and their role within their various national political systems.

320   CU
PATRIA. m. Antiguos Alumnos del Seminario Martiano, Fragua Martiana, Principe y Hospital, Havana, Cuba.

320   AG
PATRIA Y PUEBLO. 1986. m. Arg.$20. Juan Bautista Alberdi 1878 Dpto. 2, C.P. 1406, Buenos Aires, Argentina. Ed. Carlos A. D'Aprile.

320.5 305.8   US
THE PATRIOT REVIEW. irreg., approx. bi-m. $24 for 12 issues. Christian Patriot Association, Box 905, Sandy, OR 97055. TEL 503-668-4941. adv. **Document type:** newspaper.
    Description: Discusses tax resistance, extremist political theories and conspiracies.

320.9   SW   ISSN 0048-3087
PAX; tidning foer fred. 1972. 6/yr. SEK 120 to individuals; institutions SEK 200 (effective 1995). Svenska Freds- och Skiljedomsfoereningen, Brannkyrkagatan 76, P.O. Box 17515, 118 91 Stockholm, Sweden. TEL 46-0-8-658-21-80. FAX 46-0-8-668-18-70. E-mail: pax@nm.apc.ong. Ed. Lars Truedson. adv. contact: Olov Agne. bk.rev.; bibl.; illus. circ. 10,000.
    ●Also available online.
    Description: Extensive peace magazine.

322.4   US
PEACE & JUSTICE NEWS. 6/yr. Peace & Justice Center, 1935 Lewiston Dr., Louisville, KY 40216. TEL 502-448-8581.

320   US
PEACE CHRONICLE. 1975. bi-m. $45 (subscr. includes Peace & Change). Consortium on Peace Research, Education and Development, c/o Institute for Conflict Analysis & Resolution, George Mason University, 4103 Cahin Bridge Rd., Ste. 315, Fairfax, VA 22030-4444. TEL 805-273-1302. Ed. Barbara J. Wien. adv.: page $150. circ. 1,000. **Document type:** newsletter.

322.4   US
PEACE CURRENTS.* bi-m. $10. Sacramento Peace Center, 414 T St., Sacramento, CA 95814-6914. TEL 916-446-0787. adv.; illus. circ. 1,000.

PEACE DEVELOPMENTS. see HUMANITIES: COMPREHENSIVE WORKS

322.4   US
PEACE EDUCATION CENTER MONTHLY OF PEACE AND JUSTICE ACTION. 1981. 11/yr. $5. Peace Education Center, 1118 S. Harrison, East Lansing, MI 48823. TEL 517-351-4648. Ed. Mary Catharine Knightwright. bk.rev. circ. 800.
    Formerly: Peace Education Center Newsletter.

322.4 327 374   US
PEACE GAZETTE. 1969. 11/yr. $15. Mount Diablo Peace Center, 65 Eckley Ln., Walnut Creek, CA 94596. Eds. Denise Dashiell, Jerry Podell. bk.rev.; illus.; circ. 2,500 (controlled). (reprint service avail.)
    Description: Features articles on current peace and justice issues and highlights urgent political actions and activities.

341.1   UK   ISSN 0031-3548
JX1901
PEACE NEWS; for nonviolent revolution. 1936. m. £7.50 (foreign £12). Peace News Ltd., 5 Caledonian Rd., London N1 9DX, England. TEL 0171-278-3344. FAX 0171-278-0444. Ed. Ken Simons. adv. contact: Dominique Saillard. bk.rev.; film rev.; play rev.; illus. circ. 2,500. (tabloid format; also avail. in microform from UMI,HPL; back issues avail.; reprint service avail. from UMI) **Indexed:** Alt.Press Ind. **Document type:** newspaper.
    ●Also available online.
    Incorporates: W R I Newsletter (ISSN 0085-7882)

322.4   US   ISSN 0735-4134
PEACE NEWSLETTER; central New York's voice for peace and social justice. 1936. m. $12 to individuals; institutions $15. Syracuse Peace Council, 924 Burnet Ave., Syracuse, NY 13203. TEL 315-472-5478. E-mail: Site addr.: listserv@mizzou1.missouri.edu. Ed.Bd. adv.: page $700. bk.rev. circ. 4,500. (also avail. in microform from UMI; back issues avail.) **Indexed:** HR Rep. **Document type:** newsletter.
    ●Also available online.
    —UMI.
    Description: Provides a forum for articles that discuss issues of concern to the peace movement and aims to facilitate community interaction.

320   CN   ISSN 0553-4283
JX1901
PEACE RESEARCH REVIEWS. 1967. irreg. (approx. 3/yr.). $72 for 6 nos. Peace Research Institute-Dundas, 25 Dundana Ave., Dundas, ON L9H 4E5, Canada. TEL 905-628-2356. FAX 905-628-1830. Ed. Hanna Newcombe. circ. 400. **Indexed:** A.B.C.Pol.Sci., Abstr.Mil.Bibl., Amer.Hist.& Life (until 1993), Hist.Abstr. (until 1993), Mid.East.: Abstr.& Ind. **Document type:** academic/scholarly publication.
    —Faxon; SWETS; UnCover.
    Description: Monograph series usually with several hundred references.

320   UK   ISSN 1040-2659
JX1901   CODEN: PEAREC
PEACE REVIEW; the international quarterly of world peace. 1989. q. £28 to individuals; institutions £94 (effective 1996). (University of San Francisco) Carfax Publishing Co., P.O. Box 25, Abingdon, Oxon. OX14 3UE. TEL 44-1235-555335. FAX 44-1235-553559. (N. American subscr. to: Carfax Publishing Co., 875-81 Massachusetts Ave., Cambridge, MA 02139) Ed. Robert Elias. adv.; bk.rev. circ. 500. **Indexed:** Int.Polit.Sci.Abstr. **Document type:** academic/scholarly publication.
    —UnCover.
    Description: Multidisciplinary, international journal of research and analysis, focussing on current issues and controversies that underlie the promotion of a more peaceful world.

341.1 200   NZ
PEACEMAKER. 1936. q. NZ$5 (foreign NZ$10). New Zealand Christian Pacifist Society, 3 Muir Ave., Christchurch 3, Aotearoa, New Zealand. Ed. Richard Thompson. bk.rev. circ. 450. (tabloid format) **Indexed:** CERDIC. **Document type:** newsletter.
    Former titles: C.P.S. Bulletin; Peace Bulletin; New Zealand Christian Pacifist (ISSN 0028-7997)

320   US   ISSN 0748-0725
PEACEWORK; peace and social justice newsletter. 1972. m. $10. American Friends Service Committee, Inc., New England Regional Office, 2161 Massachusetts Ave., Cambridge, MA 02140. TEL 617-661-6130. FAX 617-354-2832. Ed. Pat Farren. bk.rev. circ. 2,500. (also avail. in microform) **Indexed:** Alt.Press Ind. **Document type:** newsletter.
    Description: Promotes global thought and local action for nonviolent social change.

320   AG
PENSAMIENTO Y NACION;* revista de doctrina politica y de cultura. 1981. bi-m. Pensamiento y Nacion Editora S.R.L., c/o Leopoldo Frenkel, Ed., Juncal 2101, Buenos Aires, Argentina.

320.531   FR
PENSEE (PARIS). (Text in French; summaries in English) 1939. q. 400 F. (foreign 700 F.). Institut des Recherches Marxistes, 64 bd. Auguste Blanqui, 75013 Paris, France. Ed. Antoine Casanova. adv.; bk.rev.; cum.index. circ. 5,000. **Indexed:** Amer.Hist.& Life, CERDIC, Hist.Abstr., Int.Polit.Sci.Abstr.

320.5   IT   ISSN 0031-4846
JA18
PENSIERO POLITICO; rivista di storia delle idee politiche e sociali. 1968. 3/yr. L.78000 (foreign L.98000) (effective 1995) US $67.50 (effective 1996). Casa Editrice Leo S. Olschki, Casella Postale 66, 50100 Florence, Italy. TEL 39-55-6530684. FAX 39-55-6530214. Ed. S. Mastellone. adv.; bk.rev.; bibl. circ. 1,000. **Indexed:** Amer.Hist.& Life, Hist.Abstr., Int.Polit.Sci.Abstr., M.L.A. **Document type:** academic/scholarly publication.
    —BLDSC (6422.640000).

320.5   IT   ISSN 1122-0767
PENSIERO POLITICO. BIBLIOTECA. 1969. irreg., no.21, 1994. price varies. Casa Editrice Leo S. Olschki, Casella Postale 66, 50100 Florence, Italy. TEL 39-55-6530684. FAX 39-55-6530214. **Document type:** monographic series.

969   SE   ISSN 0031-4994
THE PEOPLE. (Text in Creole, English, & French) m. $5. Seychelles People's United Party (SPPF), Victoria St., Box 154, Victoria, Mahe, Seychelles. Ed. Jacques Hodoul. circ. 1,000.

320.531   US   ISSN 0199-350X
HX1
THE PEOPLE (PALO ALTO). 1891. s-m. (22/yr.). $4. Socialist Labor Party of America, 111 W. Evelyn Ave., Ste. 209, Sunnyvale, CA 94086. TEL 408-245-2047. FAX 408-245-2049. (Subscr. to: 914 Industrial Ave., Palo Alto, CA 94303) bk.rev.; illus. circ. 9,300. (tabloid format; also avail. in microform from UMI,BHP; microfilm from KTO; reprint service avail. from UMI) **Indexed:** Alt.Press Ind. **Document type:** newspaper.
    —UMI.
    Formerly (until 1979): Weekly People (ISSN 0043-1885)
    Description: Marxists analysis and commentary about major socioeconomic developments affecting working people. Resource for labor, politics, economics, and history.

POLITICAL SCIENCE

951.9   JA   ISSN 0031-5036
PEOPLE'S KOREA. (Text in English, French, Spanish) 1961. w. (Sat.) 12000 Yen($100) Choson Shinbo Co., Inc., 2-4 Tsukudo -Hachiman-cho, Shinjuku-ku, Tokyo 162, Japan. FAX 03-3268-5881. Ed. Song Jae Ryong. adv.; bk.rev.; illus. circ. 30,000. **Document type:** newspaper.

320   II   ISSN 0971-1619
PEOPLE'S MANIFESTO. (Text in English) 1990. bi-m. Rs.60($20) (effective 1993). AVM Surenji Goyal, Ed. & Pub., 69 Poorvi Marg, Vasant Vihar, New Delhi 110057, India. TEL 672327. FAX 6845622. (Subscr. to: Central News Agency Private Ltd., P-23 Connaught Circus, New Delhi 110 001, India. TEL 344448) adv.: page Rs.2000; trim 18 x 23. bk.rev. circ. 5,000. **Document type:** consumer publication.
Description: Covers social, economic and political issues. Aims to promote heritage values, good governance, and consciousness of health and harmony.

954   II   ISSN 0377-2713
HX3
PEOPLE'S POWER. (Text in English) 1972. m. per no. Unity Compound, Juhu, Bombay 54, India. Ed.Bd. bibl.

320   US   ISSN 1081-4787
PEOPLE'S TRIBUNE. Bilingual edition: Tribuno del Pueblo (ISSN 1081-5112) 1974. m. $20 to individuals; institutions $30. People's Tribune, Box 3524, Chicago, IL 60654. TEL 312-486-3551. E-mail: pt@noc.org. Ed. Laura Garcia. bk.rev.; illus. circ. 15,000. **Document type:** newspaper.
Description: Provides revolutionary commentary on the issues of the day.

322.4   SJ
PEOPLE'S VOICE. (Text in English) irreg., vol.2, no.7, 1980. Tigray People's Liberation Front, Foreign Relations Bureau, Box 8177, Khartoum, Sudan.

320   UK   ISSN 0268-2419
PEP TALK. 1984. 3/yr. £10. Peace Pledge Union, 6 Endsleigh St., London WC1H 0DX, England. TEL 44-171-387-5501.
Description: Covers peace education, world studies, conflict resolution, curriculum development, teaching methods, co-operative play.

PERIPHERIE; Zeitschrift fuer Politik und Oekonomie in der dritten Welt. see BUSINESS AND ECONOMICS — International Development And Assistance

300   FR   ISSN 0031-5478
PERMANENCES; organe de formation civique. 1963. 10/yr. 350 F. price varies. (Office International Oeuvres Formation Civique) Montalza, 49 rue des Renaudes, 75017 Paris, France. bk.rev. circ. 5,000.

320   AG
PERONISTA; para la liberacion nacional. m. Ayolas 2251, 2000 Rosario, Argentina. Dir. Hugo A. Bagli. adv.; bk.rev. (tabloid format)
Formerly: Reflexion.

PERSONNEL SERVICE NEWSLETTER. see OCCUPATIONS AND CAREERS

320   US   ISSN 0164-3169
AP62
PERSPECTIVA MUNDIAL; una revista socialista destinada a defender los intereses del pueblo trabajador. (Text and summaries in Spanish) 1977. m. (except Aug.). $17. 408 Printing & Publishing Co., 410 West St., New York, NY 10014. TEL 212-243-6392. FAX 212-924-6040. Ed. Martin Koppel. adv.; bk.rev.; charts; illus.; stat. circ. 3,100. (also avail. in microform from UMI; back issues avail.) **Indexed:** Alt.Press Ind.

320   II
PERSPECTIVE ON CURRENT AFFAIRS. 1976. s-a. Rs.120($40) Natraj Publishers, 17 Rajpur Rd., Dehra Dun, Uttar Pradesh, India. TEL 91-135-23382. Ed. Sohan Lall. adv.; bk.rev. circ. 9,000.
Description: Deals with current Indian and international political, economic and military affairs.

028.1   US   ISSN 1045-7097
JA1
PERSPECTIVES ON POLITICAL SCIENCE. 1972. q. $45 to individuals; institutions $90. (Helen Dwight Reid Educational Foundation) Heldref Publications, 1319 18th St, N.W., Washington, DC 20036-1802. TEL 202-296-6267. FAX 202-296-5149. Ed. Lisa Culp Neikirk. adv. contact: Raymond Rallo. bk.rev. circ. 700. (also avail. in microform; reprint service avail.) **Indexed:** A.B.C.Pol.Sci., Amer.Hist.& Life, Bk.Rev.Ind. (1981-), Child.Bk.Rev.Ind. (1981-), Hist.Abstr., Int.Polit.Sci.Abstr., Polit.Sci.Abstr. **Document type:** academic/scholarly publication.
● Also available on CD-ROM. Producer(s): University Microfilms International.
—BLDSC (6428.149950); Faxon; SWETS; UMI; UnCover. **CCC.**
Formerly (until 1990): Perspective (Washington) (ISSN 0048-3494); 2Incorporates (1973-1990): Teaching Political Science (ISSN 0092-2013)
Refereed Serial

001.45 960   US
PERSPECTIVES ON SOUTHERN AFRICA. 1971. irreg., no.50, 1993. price varies. University of California Press, 2120 Berkeley Way, Berkeley, CA 94720. TEL 510-642-4247. FAX 510-643-7127. (Orders to: California-Princeton Fulfillment Services, 1445 Lower Ferry Rd., Ewing, NJ 08618. TEL 800-777-4726. FAX 800-999-1958) **Document type:** monographic series.
Description: Examines various aspects of the history, politics, culture, and sociology of South Africa.
Refereed Serial

320.531 301 327   GW
PERSPEKTIVEN D S (Demokratischen Sozialismus) 1984. q. DM.34 (foreign DM.42) (effective 1996). (Hochschulinitiative Demokratischer Sozialismus) Schueren Presseverlag GmbH, Deutschhausstr. 31, 35037 Marburg, Germany. TEL 06421-63084. FAX 06421-681190. Ed.Bd. adv.; bk.rev. circ. 1,200. **Document type:** academic/scholarly publication.
Formerly: P D S (ISSN 0176-0750)

320.532   RU   ISSN 0131-2278
HQ799.R9
PERSPEKTIVY. 1918. m. $73. Izdatel'stvo Molodaya Gvardiya, Novodmitrovskaya ul. 5A, 125015 Moscow, Russia. TEL 972-0546. FAX 972-0582. TELEX 411261 FAKEL. (Dist. by: Mezhdunarodnaya Kniga, Ul. Dimitrova D.39, 113095 Moscow, Russia; Dist. in U.S. by: Victor Kamkin Inc., 4956 Boiling Brook Pkwy, Rockville, MD 20852. TEL 301-881-5973) Ed. Z.G. Apresian. adv.; bk.rev.; bibl.; illus.; tr.lit.; index. circ. 125,000. **Indexed:** Curr.Dig.Sov.Press.
Formerly (until 1991): Molodoi Kommunist (ISSN 0026-9077)

PHILIPPINES YEARBOOK OF THE FOOKIEN TIMES. see BUSINESS AND ECONOMICS — Banking And Finance

320 100   FR   ISSN 1162-325X
PHILOSOPHIE POLITIQUE; revue internationale de philosophie politique. 1992. s-a. 320 F. (foreign 380 F.) (effective 1996). Presses Universitaires de France, Departement des Revues, 14 av. du Bois-de-l'Epine, 91300 Evry Cedex, France. TEL 60-77-82-05. FAX 60-79-20-45. TELEX PUF 600 474 F. Ed. Blandine Kriegel. **Indexed:** Int.Polit.Sci.Abstr. **Document type:** academic/scholarly publication.
Description: Clarifies current problems of the contemporary world and provides an interdisciplinary forum to discuss them.

320   US   ISSN 0048-3915
H1
PHILOSOPHY AND PUBLIC AFFAIRS. 1971. q. $28 to individuals; institutions $48; students $14. Princeton University Press, 41 William St., Princeton, NJ 08540. TEL 609-258-4900. FAX 609-258-6305. E-mail: jhardy@pupress.princeton.edu. (Dist. by: Johns Hopkins University Press, Journals Publishing Division, 701 W. 40th St., Ste. 275, Baltimore, MD 21211. TEL 410-516-6980) Ed. Marshall Cohen. index. circ. 2,790. (also avail. in microform from UMI; back issues avail.; reprint service avail. from UMI,WSH) **Indexed:** A.B.C.Pol.Sci., Abstr.Crim.& Pen., Arts & Hum.Cit.Ind., Crim.Just.Abstr., Curr.Cont., Fut.Surv., Hum.Ind., Int.Polit.Sci.Abstr., Lang.& Lang.Behav.Abstr., Leg.Cont., Mid.East: Abstr.& Ind., Phil.Ind., Polit.Sci.Abstr., SSCI. **Document type:** academic/scholarly publication.
● Also available online. Vendor(s): University Microfilms International.
—BLDSC (6464.650000); Faxon; Genuine Article; SWETS; UMI; UnCover.

954.9   PK   ISSN 0031-9651
PICTORIAL NEWS REVIEW. (Text in English) 1970. m. Rs.300($30) Pictorial News Review Publications, 1 Victoria Chambers, Hajji Abdullah Haroon Rd., Karachi 74400, Pakistan. TEL 5682694. FAX 21-735276. TELEX 23035 PCOKR PK 284. Ed. Mahmudul Aziz; Pub. Mahmudul Aziz. adv.; bk.rev.; charts; illus. circ. 5,000. (also avail. in microfilm)
Description: Highlights political developments in Pakistan and abroad. Includes activities of the diplomatic and consular corps and features on other countries. For executives, parliamentarians, Pakistanis abroad, and foreigners in Pakistan.

320   US
PITTSBURGH SERIES IN POLICY & INSTITUTIONAL STUDIES. 1983. irreg. price varies. University of Pittsburgh Press, 127 N. Bellefield Ave., Pittsburgh, PA 15260. TEL 800-666-2211. FAX 412-624-7380. Ed. Bert A. Rockman. **Document type:** monographic series.

320   CN   ISSN 0703-1866
PLOUGHSHARES MONITOR. 1977. q. Can.$25($25) (Canadian Council of Churches) Project Ploughshares, Waterloo, ON N2L 3G6, Canada. TEL 519-888-6541. FAX 519-885-0014. E-mail: Plough@watservl.uwaterloo.ca. Ed.Bd. bk.rev. circ. 7,000. **Indexed:** HR Rep.
Description: Provides information on disarmament, militarism, global security, Canadian military production and exports, regional conflicts and alternatives to Canadian security policies.

322.4   US
PLOWSHARE NEWS. 1979. 10/yr. donation. Plowshare Peace Center, Box 1623, Roanoke, VA 24008. TEL 703-985-0808. Eds. Polly Branch, Pat Pratali. bk.rev.; illus. circ. 900.

329   FR
LE POING ET LA ROSE. 1970. irreg. Parti Socialiste, 10 rue de Solferino, 75333 Paris Cedex 07, France. Ed. Lionel Jospin.
Formerly: Bulletin Socialiste (ISSN 0068-4155)

320   CR   ISSN 1018-0664
POLEMICA. 1981. 3/yr. Instituto Centroamericano de Documentacion e Investigaciones Sociales, Paseo de los Estudiantes, Apdo. 1006, San Jose, Costa Rica. TEL 33-3964. FAX 506-24-4407. (Subscr. to: Secy. Gen. de FLASCO, Apdo. Postal 5429, 1000 San Jose, Costa Rica) Ed. Gabriel Aguilera Peralta. **Indexed:** HR Rep.

320   US   ISSN 0160-2675
H62.5.U5
POLICY GRANTS DIRECTORY. 1977. irreg. $5 to individuals; institutions $12. Policy Studies Organization, University of Illinois, 361 Lincoln Hall, Urbana, IL 61801. TEL 217-359-8541. Eds. Stuart Nagel, Marian Neef. bibl.; charts; stat.; index. circ. 2,400. (reprint service avail. from UMI) **Document type:** directory.
Description: Covers governmental and private funding sources for policy studies research. Also contains suggestions for applicants and for funding sources.

POLICY OPTIONS/OPTIONS POLITIQUES. see PUBLIC ADMINISTRATION

POLITICAL SCIENCE 5343

320 070.5   US   ISSN 0272-0671
H61
POLICY PUBLISHERS AND ASSOCIATIONS DIRECTORY. 1980. irreg. $5 to individuals; institutions $12. Policy Studies Organization, University of Illinois at Urbana-Champaign, 361 Lincoln Hall, Urbana, IL 61801. TEL 217-359-8541. Eds. Stuart Nagel, Kathleen Burkholder. (reprint service avail. from UMI) **Document type:** directory.
Description: Covers activities, procedures, and other information for policy-relevant journals, book publishers, scholarly associations, and interest groups.

320   US   ISSN 0270-1200
H62.5.U5
POLICY RESEARCH CENTERS DIRECTORY. 1978. irreg. to individuals; institutions $12. Policy Studies Organization, University of Illinois, 361 Lincoln Hall, Urbana, IL 61801. TEL 217-359-8541. Eds. Stuart Nagel, Marian Neef. bibl.; charts; stat.; index. circ. 2,400. (reprint service avail. from UMI) **Document type:** directory.
Description: Covers university and non-university centers, institutes, and organizations that conduct policy studies research. Also contains generalizations for understanding and improving such centers.

320   US   ISSN 0146-5945
H1
POLICY REVIEW. 1977. q. $22. Heritage Foundation, 214 Massachusetts Ave., N.E., Washington, DC 20002. TEL 202-546-4400. FAX 202-546-8328. Ed. Adam Meyerson. adv.: B&W page $600; trim 8 1/2 x 11. bk.rev.; bibl.; charts; index. circ. 13,500. (back issues avail.; reprint service avail. from WSH) **Indexed:** A.B.C.Pol.Sci., Bk.Rev.Ind. (1980-), Child.Bk.Rev.Ind. (1980-), Curr.Cont., Environ.Abstr., Fut.Surv., HR Rep., Human Resour.Abstr., Int.Polit.Sci.Abstr., Int.Polit.Sci.Abstr., Key to Econ.Sci., Mag.Ind., Mid.East: Abstr.& Ind., P.A.I.S., Polit.Sci.Abstr., PROMT, Sage Pub.Admin.Abstr., Sage Urb.Stud.Abstr., Soc.Sci.Ind (until 1994), Sociol.Abstr., SSCI, Urb.Aff.Abstr. **Document type:** academic/scholarly publication.
●Also available online. Vendor(s): Lexis-Nexis.
—BLDSC (6543.327850); CIS; Faxon; Genuine Article; SWETS; UMI; UnCover.

320   NE   ISSN 0032-2687
H1   CODEN: PLSCBZ
POLICY SCIENCES; an international journal devoted to the improvement of policy making. 1970. q. fl.393 to institutions; $252 to institutions in U.S. (effective 1996). Kluwer Academic Publishers, Postbus 17, 3300 AA Dordrecht, Netherlands. TEL 31-78-392392. FAX 31-78-392254. TELEX 29245 KAPG NL. E-mail: SERVICES@WKAP.NL. (Dist. by: Kluwer Academic Publishing Group, P.O. Box 322, 3300 AH Dordrecht, Netherlands. TEL 31-78-392392. FAX 31-78-546474; N. America dist. addr.: Box 358, Accord Sta., Hingham, MA 02018-0358. TEL 617-871-6600. FAX 617-871-6528) Ed. Douglas Torgerson. adv.; bk.rev.; illus. (also avail. in microform from UMI; reprint service avail. from SWZ) **Indexed:** A.B.C.Pol.Sci., ASCA, ASSIA, Commun.Abstr., Cont.Pg.Manage., Curr.Cont., E.I., Educ.Admin.Abstr., Energy Ind., Energy Info.Abstr., Fut.Surv., Human Resour.Abstr., Inform.Sci.Abstr., Int.Polit.Sci.Abstr., Int.Polit.Sci.Abstr., J.of Econ.Lit., Lang.& Lang.Behav.Abstr., Med.Care Rev., Mid.East: Abstr.& Ind., Mult.Ed.Abstr., P.A.I.S., Polit.Sci.Abstr., Risk Abstr., Sage Pub.Admin.Abstr., Sage Urb.Stud.Abstr., SCIMP, Sociol.Abstr., SSCI, Urb.Aff.Abstr. **Document type:** academic/scholarly publication.
—BLDSC (6543.328000); Faxon; Genuine Article; SWETS; UMI; UnCover. **CCC.**
Refereed Serial

320 338   UK   ISSN 0144-2872
H96
POLICY STUDIES. 1976. q. £118 to individuals; institutions £118 (effective 1996). (Policy Studies Institute) Carfax Publishing Co., P.O. Box 25, Abingdon, Oxon. OX14 3UE, England. TEL 01235-555335. FAX 01235-553559. (Subsc. in N. America to: Carfax Publishing Co., 875-81 Massachusetts Ave., Cambridge, MA 02139) **Indexed:** Cont.Pg.Manage., Int.Lab.Doc., Key to Econ.Sci., Mid.East: Abstr.& Ind., P.A.I.S. **Document type:** academic/scholarly publication.
—BLDSC (6543.328900); Faxon; UnCover. **CCC.**

309.2   US   ISSN 0362-6016
H62.5.U5
POLICY STUDIES DIRECTORY. 1972. irreg. $5 to individuals; institutions $12. Policy Studies Organization, University of Illinois at Urbana-Champaign, 361 Lincoln Hall, Urbana, IL 61801. TEL 217-359-8541. Eds. Stuart Nagel, Marian Neef. bibl.; charts; stat.; index. circ. 2,400. (reprint service avail. from UMI) **Document type:** directory.
Description: Covers policy studies activities in American political science departments and interdisciplinary policy studies programs at the Ph.D., M.A., and B.A. levels.

320   US   ISSN 0190-292X
H1
POLICY STUDIES JOURNAL. 1972. q. $24 to individuals; institutions $108 (includes Policy Studies Review) (effective 1995). Policy Studies Organization, University of Illinois, 361 Lincoln Hall, Urbana, IL 61801. TEL 217-359-8541. Ed. Stuart S. Nagel. adv.; bk.rev. circ. 2,400. (also avail. in microform; reprint service avail. from UMI) **Indexed:** A.B.C.Pol.Sci., Abstr.Crim.& Pen., Amer.Bibl.Slavic & E.Eur.Stud., Amer.Hist.& Life, ASSIA, Curr.Cont., E.I., Educ.Admin.Abstr., Environ.Abstr., Fut.Surv., Geo.Abstr., Hist.Abstr., Human Resour.Abstr., IDA, Inform.Sci.Abstr., Int.Polit.Sci.Abstr., Lang.& Lang.Behav.Abstr., Mid.East: Abstr.& Ind., P.A.I.S., Pers.Lit., Polit.Sci.Abstr., Risk Abstr., Sage Pub.Admin.Abstr., Sage Urb.Stud.Abstr., Sociol.Abstr., SSCI, Tel.Abstr. **Document type:** academic/scholarly publication.
●Also available online. Vendor(s): University Microfilms International.
—BLDSC (6543.329100); CIS; Faxon; Genuine Article; SWETS; UMI; UnCover. **CCC.**
Description: Covers the application of political science and social science to important public policy problems.

309.2   US   ISSN 0275-4002
H62.5.U5
POLICY STUDIES PERSONNEL DIRECTORY. 1979. irreg. to individuals; institutions $12. Policy Studies Organization, 361 Lincoln Hall, University of Illinois, Urbana, IL 61801. TEL 217-359-8541. Eds. Stuart Nagel, Nancy Munshaw. bibl.; charts; stat.; index. circ. 2,400. (reprint service avail. from UMI) **Document type:** directory.
Description: Contains descriptions of individuals interested in policy studies with regard to their interests, affiliations, backgrounds, publications, and research activities.

320   US   ISSN 0278-4416
H97
POLICY STUDIES REVIEW. 1981. q. $24 to individuals; students $18; institutions $108 (includes Public Policy Journal) (effective 1995). Policy Studies Organization, University of Illinois, 361 Lincoln Hall, 702 S. Wright, Urbana, IL 61801. TEL 217-359-8541. Ed.Bd. (also avail. in microfilm from UMI; microfiche from UMI,KTO; reprint service avail. from UMI) **Indexed:** A.B.C.Pol.Sci., Amer.Hist.& Life, ASSIA, Curr.Cont., E.I., Educ.Admin.Abstr., Energy Info.Abstr., Environ.Abstr., Fut.Surv., Geo.Abstr., Hist.Abstr., Human Resour.Abstr., IDA, Inform.Sci.Abstr., Int.Polit.Sci.Abstr., Lang.& Lang.Behav.Abstr., P.A.I.S., Pers.Lit., Polit.Sci.Abstr., Sage Pub.Admin.Abstr., Sage Urb.Stud.Abstr., Soc.Sci.Ind. (1994-), Sociol.Abstr., SSCI. **Document type:** academic/scholarly publication.
—BLDSC (6543.329400); CIS; Faxon; SWETS; UMI; UnCover. **CCC.**
Description: Covers the application of political and social science to important public policy problems.

320 301   IT   ISSN 1120-9488
POLIS; ricerche e studi su societa e politica in Italia. 1987. 3/yr. L.120000. Societa Editrice Il Mulino, Strada Maggiore, 37, 40125 Bologna, Italy. TEL 39-51-256011. FAX 39-51-256034. Ed. Marzio Barbagli. adv. circ. 1,300. (back issues avail.) **Indexed:** Int.Polit.Sci.Abstr.
—BLDSC (6543.503000).

320   PL   ISSN 0208-7375
HM7
POLISH POLITICAL SCIENCE. (Text in English) 1967. a. price varies. Polskie Towarzystwo Nauk Politycznych, Palac Kultury i Nauki, pok. 1704, 00-901 Warsaw, Poland. TEL 48-22-209539. Ed. Longin Pastusiak. circ. 700. **Indexed:** Int.Polit.Sci.Abstr. **Document type:** academic/scholarly publication.
—BLDSC (6543.722000).
Formerly (until 1981): Polish Round Table (ISSN 0079-3000)
Description: Basic problems of political theory, political organization and functioning of society.

POLIT; a journal of literature and politics. see *LITERATURE*

320   VE   ISSN 0303-9757
POLITEIA. 1972. irreg., no.13, 1990. price varies. Universidad Central de Venezuela, Instituto de Estudios Politicos, Facultad de Ciencias Juridicas y Politicas, Caracas, Venezuela. FAX 6621913. (Subscr. to: Servicio de Distribucion y Venta, Biblioteca Central, Universidad Central, Caracas, Venezuela) bk.rev. circ. 2,000. **Indexed:** Int.Polit.Sci.Abstr.

320   SI   ISSN 0217-7587
POLITEIA. (Text in English) 1971. a. S.$2.50. National University of Singapore, Political Science Society, c/o Department of Political Science, Kent Ridge, Singapore 0511, Singapore. Ed. Leong Sook Mei. adv.; bk.rev. circ. 2,000.
Formerly: University of Singapore Political Science Society. Journal.

320   SA   ISSN 0256-8845
POLITEIA. 1982. s-a. R.16.50 (overseas $5.46) (effective 1996). University of South Africa, P.O. Box 392, Pretoria 0001, South Africa. FAX 27-12-429-3221. TELEX 350068. (reprint service avail. from UMI) **Document type:** academic/scholarly publication.
Description: Articles on political science, public administration, municipal government and administration, international politics and strategic studies.

320   BL
POLITICA. 1976. q. Cr.$50. Fundacao Milton Campos para Pesquisas e Estudos Politicos, Camara dos Deputados, Edificio do Congresso Nacional, 70160 Brasilia, D.F., Brazil. Dir. Walter Costa Porto. bk.rev. circ. 5,000.

320   UY   ISSN 0079-3027
POLITICA.* irreg. Editorial Arca, Colonia 1263, Montevideo, Uruguay.

320   CL   ISSN 0716-1077
POLITICA. 1982. s-a. Esc.300($11) Universidad de Chile, Instituto de Ciencia Politica, Calle Belgrado No. 10, Santiago, Chile. Ed. Bernardino Bravo Lira. bk.rev. circ. 500. **Indexed:** P.A.I.S.For.Lang.Ind.

320   IT
POLITICA E SOCIETA.* 1976. m. L.10000. Partito Comunista Italiano, Comitato Regionale Toscano, Via Antognoli 8, 50127 Florence, Italy. Dir. Renzo Cassigoli.

320 330   IT   ISSN 1120-9496
POLITICA ECONOMICA. 1985. 3/yr. L.120000. Societa Editrice Il Mulino, Strada Maggiore, 37, 40125 Bologna, Italy. TEL 39-51-256011. FAX 39-51-256034. Ed. Paolo Bosi. adv.; index. circ. 1,000. (back issues avail.) **Indexed:** J.of Econ.Lit.

320 330   IT   ISSN 0391-2264
POLITICA ED ECONOMIA/POLITICS AND ECONOMICS. 1970. bi-m. L.70000 (foreign L.110000). Donzelli Editori, Via Mentana 2, 00185 Rome, Italy. TEL 39-6-4440600. FAX 39-6-4440607. Ed. Guglielmo Ragozzino. circ. 15,000. **Indexed:** Rural Recreat.Tour.Abstr., World Agri.Econ.& Rural Sociol.Abstr.
—SWETS.

POLITICAL SCIENCE

320   SP   ISSN 0213-6856
DP85.8
POLITICA EXTERIOR. 1987. bi-m. (plus supplements). 6500 ptas. (Europe 9000 ptas.; elsewhere 11000 ptas.). Estudios de Politica Exterior, S.A., Padilla 6, 28006 Madrid, Spain. TEL 5777251. FAX 5777252. Ed. Dario Valcarcel. adv.; bk.rev.; charts; illus. circ. 10,000. **Indexed**: Int.Polit.Sci.Abstr. **Document type**: consumer publication.
—SWETS.
   Description: Covers international political affairs.

320   FR   ISSN 1143-4562
POLITICA HERMETICA. 1987. a. 120 F. L'Age d'Homme, 5, rue Ferou, 75006 Paris, France. TEL 46-34-18-51. FAX 40-51-71-02. bk.rev.

320   IT   ISSN 1120-950X
POLITICA IN ITALIA; i fatti dell'anno e le interpretazioni. 1986. a. (Istituto Carlo Cattaneo) Societa Editrice Il Mulino, Strada Maggiore 37, 40125 Bologna, Italy. TEL 39-51-256011. FAX 39-51-256034. circ. 1,500. (back issues avail.)

322.4   VE   ISSN 0798-1147
POLITICA INTERNATIONAL; revista Venezolana de asuntos mundiales y politica exterior. 1986. q. Bs.160($25) Politica Internacional, Apdo. 6475, Caracas 1010, Venezuela. bk.rev.

320   AG
POLITICA OBRERA. bi-m. $4. Partido Obrero, Ayacucho 444, 1026 Buenos Aires, Argentina. TEL 54-1-953-3824. FAX 54-1-953-7164. bk.rev. circ. 5,000.

320   SP
POLITICA SOCIAL. q. 2200 ptas.($24) Centro de Estudios Constitucionales, Plaza de la Marina Espanola, 9, Apdo. 50.877, Madrid 13, Spain.

330 320   AG
POLITICA Y ECONOMIA.* m. Arg.$120. 25 de Mayo 486, Buenos Aires, Argentina. illus.; stat.

320.532   US   ISSN 0032-3128
HX1
POLITICAL AFFAIRS; journal of Marxist thought. 1922. m. $18 to individuals; institutions $27. (Communist Party, U.S.A.) Political Affairs Publishers, Inc., 235 W. 23rd St., New York, NY 10011. TEL 212-989-4994. Ed. Joe Sims. adv.; bk.rev.; index. circ. 5,000. (also avail. in microfilm from UMI; reprint service avail. from KTO,UMI) **Indexed**: Alt.Press Ind., Amer.Bibl.Slavic & E.Eur.Stud., Chic.Per.Ind., Mid.East: Abstr.& Ind., P.A.I.S., Polit.Sci.Abstr. **Document type**: academic/scholarly publication.
—Faxon; SWETS; UMI; UnCover.
   Supersedes (1928-1944): Communist.

320   US   ISSN 1047-1987
JA73
POLITICAL ANALYSIS. 1989. a. University of Michigan Press, Order Department, Box 1104, Ann Arbor, MI 48106-1104. TEL 313-764-4392. FAX 313-936-0456. TELEX 4320815. Ed. Malcolm Litchfield. **Document type**: academic/scholarly publication.
—UnCover.

POLITICAL AND LEGAL ANTHROPOLOGY. see *SOCIOLOGY*

320   US   ISSN 1070-1753
E839.5
THE POLITICAL ANIMAL. 1973. bi-w. $150 (effective 1994). The Political Animal Co., 1000 W. Sunset Blvd., 2nd Fl., Los Angeles, CA 90012-2197. TEL 213-276-9223. FAX 213-276-9224. Ed. Bill Homer; Pub. Bill Homer. (back issues avail.) **Document type**: newsletter.
   Former titles (until 1993): Joe Scott's The Political Animal (ISSN 0747-5659); Political Animal (ISSN 0195-9670)
   Description: Covers news and issues in national politics and government.

320   US   ISSN 0190-9320
JA74.5
POLITICAL BEHAVIOR. 1979. q. $180 (foreign $210) (effective 1996). Plenum Publishing Corp., 233 Spring St., New York, NY 10013-1578. TEL 212-620-8000. FAX 212-463-0742. TELEX 23-421139. Ed. R.A. Brody. adv.; index. (also avail. in microform from UMI; microfilm from JSC; back issues avail; reprint service avail. from UMI) **Indexed**: A.B.C.Pol.Sci., Int.Polit.Sci.Abstr., Mid.East: Abstr.& Ind., Polit.Sci.Abstr., Psychol.Abstr. (1981-), Sociol.Abstr. **Document type**: academic/scholarly publication.
—BLDSC (6543.873000); Faxon; UMI; UnCover. CCC.
   Description: Publishes interdisciplinary studies, both theoretical and empirical, of groups and individuals as they interact with the political process. *Refereed Serial*

320   US   ISSN 1058-4609
JF1525.P8   CODEN: PLCMEM
POLITICAL COMMUNICATION; an international journal. 1980. q. £106($175) (effective 1996). Taylor & Francis Inc., 1900 Frost Rd., Ste. 101, Bristol, PA 19007. TEL 215-785-5800; 800-821-8312. FAX 215-785-5515. (Subscr. in Europe to: Taylor & Francis Ltd., Rankine Rd., Basingstoke, Hants. RG24 8PR, England. TEL 44-1256-840366. FAX 44-1256-479438) Ed. Doris Graber. adv.; bk.rev.; abstr. **Indexed**: A.B.C.Pol.Sci., Commun.Abstr., Int.Polit.Sci.Abstr., Lang.& Lang.Behav.Abstr., P.A.I.S., Polit.Sci.Abstr., Soc.Sci.Ind. (1994-), Sociol.Abstr. **Document type**: academic/scholarly publication.
—BLDSC (6543.879500); Faxon; SWETS; UnCover. CCC.
   Formerly (until 1992): Political Communication and Persuasion (ISSN 0195-7473)
   Description: Examines the roles of governmental, intergovernmental, and nongovernmental organizations as political communicators. *Refereed Serial*

320   AT
HM1   CODEN: CSRDD9
POLITICAL CROSSROADS; an international socio-political journal. 1978. s-a. $60 to individuals; institutions $240. James Nicholas Publishers, P.O. Box 244, Albert Park, Vic. 3206, Australia. TEL 03-696-5545. FAX 613-699-2040. Ed. Joseph Zajda. adv.; bk.rev. (also avail. in microform from UMI; back issues avail.) **Indexed**: Int.Polit.Sci.Abstr., Sociol.Abstr. **Document type**: academic/scholarly publication.
   Formerly: Crossroads.
   Description: Examines international and comparative aspects of political theory, international relations and socio-economic and cultural factors as reflected in political, economic and administrative organizations, patterns of power, leadership, ideology and culture, with special focus on the USA, Russia and Europe. *Refereed Serial*

320   US
POLITICAL FINANCE & LOBBY REPORTER. 1980. s-m. $287. Amward Publications, Inc., 2030 Clarendon Blvd., Ste. 401, Arlington, VA 22201. TEL 703-525-7227. FAX 703-525-3536. Ed. Edward P. Zuckerman. bk.rev. (also avail. in looseleaf format; back issues avail.) **Document type**: newsletter.
●Also available online. Vendor(s): Lexis-Nexis, NewsNet (PO02).
   Former titles (until 1993): P A Cs and Lobbies (ISSN 0886-6457); Political Finance - Lobby Reporter (ISSN 0270-353X)
   Description: Covers campaign finance and lobbying developments.

320.9   UK   ISSN 0962-6298
JC319
POLITICAL GEOGRAPHY. 8/yr. £248($395) (effective 1996). Butterworth - Heinemann, Part of the Reed Elsevier group, Linacre House, Jordan Hill, Oxford OX2 8DP, England. TEL 01865-310366. FAX 01865-310898. TELEX 83111 BHPOXF G. (Subscr. to: Elsevier Science Ltd., P.O. Box 800, Kidlington, Oxford OX5 1DX, England. TEL 44-1865-843000. FAX 44-1865-843010; Subscr. in U.S. and Canada to: Elsevier Science, 660 White Plains Rd., Tarrytown, NY 10591-5153. TEL 914-524-9200. FAX 914-333-2444) Ed. P.J. Taylor. bk.rev.; index. (also avail. in microform from UMI; back issues avail.) **Indexed**: A.B.C.Pol.Sci., E.I., Environ.Per.Bibl., Geo.Abstr., IDA, Int.Polit.Sci.Abstr., P.A.I.S., Polit.Sci.Abstr., SSCI. **Document type**: academic/scholarly publication.
—BLDSC (6543.885950); Faxon; Genuine Article; SWETS; UMI; UnCover. CCC.
   Formerly (until 1992): Political Geography Quarterly (ISSN 0260-9827)
   Description: For students of political studies with an interest in the geographical or spatial aspects of their subject. Provides a central focus for developments in this subdiscipline. *Refereed Serial*

320 309   US   ISSN 0193-175X
JF37
POLITICAL HANDBOOK OF THE WORLD. 1928. a. $49.95. (State University of New York at Binghamton, Center for Social Analysis) McGraw-Hill, Inc., 1221 Ave. of the Americas, New York, NY 10020. TEL 212-512-2000. Ed. Arthur S. Banks. circ. 7,000. (reprint service avail. from KTO)
—BLDSC (6543.886000).
   Formerly: Political Handbook and Atlas of the World (ISSN 0079-3035)

320   UK
POLITICAL PARTIES OF THE WORLD. 1980. triennial. £85. Longman Group UK Ltd., Westgate House, The High, Harlow, Essex CM20 1YR, England. TEL 0279-442601. Ed. Alan J. Day.

320 301   US   ISSN 0198-8719
JA1
POLITICAL POWER AND SOCIAL THEORY; a research annual. 1980. a. $63.50 to institutions. J A I Press Inc., 55 Old Post Rd., No. 2, Box 1678, Greenwich, CT 06836-1678. TEL 203-661-7602. Ed. Maurice Zeitlin. **Indexed**: Amer.Bibl.Slavic & E.Eur.Stud., Int.Polit.Sci.Abstr., Lang.& Lang.Behav.Abstr., Sociol.Abstr. (1980-).
—BLDSC (6543.888000). CCC.

320   UK   ISSN 0032-3179
JA8
POLITICAL QUARTERLY. 1930. q. £68($130) (foreign £81) (effective 1996). Basil Blackwell Ltd., 108 Cowley Rd., Oxford OX4 1JF, England. TEL 01865-791100. FAX 01865-791347. TELEX 937022 OXBOOK G. Eds. Colin Cranch, David Marquand. adv.; bk.rev.; index. (also avail. in microfilm from RPI,PMC) **Indexed**: A.B.C.Pol.Sci., ASSIA, Br.Hum.Ind., Commun.Abstr., Curr.Cont., Hum.Ind., Int.Polit.Sci.Abstr., Mid.East: Abstr.& Ind., P.A.I.S., Polit.Sci.Abstr., Soc.Sci.Ind., SSCI, World Agri.Econ.& Rural Sociol.Abstr. **Document type**: academic/scholarly publication.
—BLDSC (6543.890000); Faxon; Genuine Article; SWETS; UMI; UnCover. CCC.

320   US   ISSN 1051-4287
POLITICAL REPORT. 1978. fortn. $197. 717 Second St., N.E., Washington, DC 20002. Ed. Stuart Rothenberg.
   Description: Reports on congressional campaigns and elections and provides analysis on national political trends and developments.

320   US   ISSN 0898-4271
JK2283
POLITICAL RESOURCE DIRECTORY. 1987. a. $95. (American Association of Political Consultants) Political Resources, Inc., Box 3177, Burlington, VT 05401. TEL 802-660-2869. FAX 802-864-9502. Ed. Carol Hess. adv. **Document type**: directory.
   Description: Comprehensive information on political professional organizations.

POLITICAL RISK LETTER. see *BUSINESS AND ECONOMICS — International Commerce*

POLITICAL SCIENCE

POLITICAL RISK SERVICES. COUNTRY REPORTS: WORLD SERVICE. see *BUSINESS AND ECONOMICS — Economic Situation And Conditions*

POLITICAL RISK SERVICES. COUNTRY REPORTS: ALGERIA. see *BUSINESS AND ECONOMICS — Economic Situation And Conditions*

POLITICAL RISK SERVICES. COUNTRY REPORTS: ARGENTINA. see *BUSINESS AND ECONOMICS — Economic Situation And Conditions*

POLITICAL RISK SERVICES. COUNTRY REPORTS: BOLIVIA. see *BUSINESS AND ECONOMICS — Economic Situation And Conditions*

POLITICAL RISK SERVICES. COUNTRY REPORTS: BRAZIL. see *BUSINESS AND ECONOMICS — Economic Situation And Conditions*

POLITICAL RISK SERVICES. COUNTRY REPORTS: BULGARIA. see *BUSINESS AND ECONOMICS — Economic Situation And Conditions*

POLITICAL RISK SERVICES. COUNTRY REPORTS: CAMEROON. see *BUSINESS AND ECONOMICS — Economic Situation And Conditions*

POLITICAL RISK SERVICES. COUNTRY REPORTS: CHILE. see *BUSINESS AND ECONOMICS — Economic Situation And Conditions*

POLITICAL RISK SERVICES. COUNTRY REPORTS: CHINA. see *BUSINESS AND ECONOMICS — Economic Situation And Conditions*

POLITICAL RISK SERVICES. COUNTRY REPORTS: COLOMBIA. see *BUSINESS AND ECONOMICS — Economic Situation And Conditions*

POLITICAL RISK SERVICES. COUNTRY REPORTS: COSTA RICA. see *BUSINESS AND ECONOMICS — Economic Situation And Conditions*

POLITICAL RISK SERVICES. COUNTRY REPORTS: COTE D'IVOIRE. see *BUSINESS AND ECONOMICS — Economic Situation And Conditions*

POLITICAL RISK SERVICES. COUNTRY REPORTS: CZECH REPUBLIC. see *BUSINESS AND ECONOMICS — Economic Situation And Conditions*

POLITICAL RISK SERVICES. COUNTRY REPORTS: DOMINICAN REPUBLIC. see *BUSINESS AND ECONOMICS — Economic Situation And Conditions*

POLITICAL RISK SERVICES. COUNTRY REPORTS: ECUADOR. see *BUSINESS AND ECONOMICS — Economic Situation And Conditions*

POLITICAL RISK SERVICES. COUNTRY REPORTS: EGYPT. see *BUSINESS AND ECONOMICS — Economic Situation And Conditions*

POLITICAL RISK SERVICES. COUNTRY REPORTS: EL SALVADOR. see *BUSINESS AND ECONOMICS — Economic Situation And Conditions*

POLITICAL RISK SERVICES. COUNTRY REPORTS: GABON. see *BUSINESS AND ECONOMICS — Economic Situation And Conditions*

POLITICAL RISK SERVICES. COUNTRY REPORTS: GUATEMALA. see *BUSINESS AND ECONOMICS — Economic Situation And Conditions*

POLITICAL RISK SERVICES. COUNTRY REPORTS: GUINEA. see *BUSINESS AND ECONOMICS — Economic Situation And Conditions*

POLITICAL RISK SERVICES. COUNTRY REPORTS: HAITI. see *BUSINESS AND ECONOMICS — Economic Situation And Conditions*

POLITICAL RISK SERVICES. COUNTRY REPORTS: HONDURAS. see *BUSINESS AND ECONOMICS — Economic Situation And Conditions*

POLITICAL RISK SERVICES. COUNTRY REPORTS: HONG KONG. see *BUSINESS AND ECONOMICS — Economic Situation And Conditions*

POLITICAL RISK SERVICES. COUNTRY REPORTS: HUNGARY. see *BUSINESS AND ECONOMICS — Economic Situation And Conditions*

POLITICAL RISK SERVICES. COUNTRY REPORTS: INDIA. see *BUSINESS AND ECONOMICS — Economic Situation And Conditions*

POLITICAL RISK SERVICES. COUNTRY REPORTS: INDONESIA. see *BUSINESS AND ECONOMICS — Economic Situation And Conditions*

POLITICAL RISK SERVICES. COUNTRY REPORTS: IRAN. see *BUSINESS AND ECONOMICS — Economic Situation And Conditions*

POLITICAL RISK SERVICES. COUNTRY REPORTS: IRAQ. see *BUSINESS AND ECONOMICS — Economic Situation And Conditions*

POLITICAL RISK SERVICES. COUNTRY REPORTS: ISRAEL. see *BUSINESS AND ECONOMICS — Economic Situation And Conditions*

POLITICAL RISK SERVICES. COUNTRY REPORTS: JAMAICA. see *BUSINESS AND ECONOMICS — Economic Situation And Conditions*

POLITICAL RISK SERVICES. COUNTRY REPORTS: KENYA. see *BUSINESS AND ECONOMICS — Economic Situation And Conditions*

POLITICAL RISK SERVICES. COUNTRY REPORTS: KUWAIT. see *BUSINESS AND ECONOMICS — Economic Situation And Conditions*

POLITICAL RISK SERVICES. COUNTRY REPORTS: LIBYA. see *BUSINESS AND ECONOMICS — Economic Situation And Conditions*

POLITICAL RISK SERVICES. COUNTRY REPORTS: MALAYSIA. see *BUSINESS AND ECONOMICS — Economic Situation And Conditions*

POLITICAL RISK SERVICES. COUNTRY REPORTS: MEXICO. see *BUSINESS AND ECONOMICS — Economic Situation And Conditions*

POLITICAL RISK SERVICES. COUNTRY REPORTS: MOROCCO. see *BUSINESS AND ECONOMICS — Economic Situation And Conditions*

POLITICAL RISK SERVICES. COUNTRY REPORTS: NICARAGUA. see *BUSINESS AND ECONOMICS — Economic Situation And Conditions*

POLITICAL RISK SERVICES. COUNTRY REPORTS: NIGERIA. see *BUSINESS AND ECONOMICS — Economic Situation And Conditions*

POLITICAL RISK SERVICES. COUNTRY REPORTS: OMAN. see *BUSINESS AND ECONOMICS — Economic Situation And Conditions*

POLITICAL RISK SERVICES. COUNTRY REPORTS: PAKISTAN. see *BUSINESS AND ECONOMICS — Economic Situation And Conditions*

POLITICAL RISK SERVICES. COUNTRY REPORTS: PANAMA. see *BUSINESS AND ECONOMICS — Economic Situation And Conditions*

POLITICAL RISK SERVICES. COUNTRY REPORTS: PERU. see *BUSINESS AND ECONOMICS — Economic Situation And Conditions*

POLITICAL RISK SERVICES. COUNTRY REPORTS: PHILIPPINES. see *BUSINESS AND ECONOMICS — Economic Situation And Conditions*

POLITICAL RISK SERVICES. COUNTRY REPORTS: POLAND. see *BUSINESS AND ECONOMICS — Economic Situation And Conditions*

POLITICAL RISK SERVICES. COUNTRY REPORTS: ROMANIA. see *BUSINESS AND ECONOMICS — Economic Situation And Conditions*

POLITICAL RISK SERVICES. COUNTRY REPORTS: RUSSIA. see *BUSINESS AND ECONOMICS — Economic Situation And Conditions*

POLITICAL RISK SERVICES. COUNTRY REPORTS: SAUDI ARABIA. see *BUSINESS AND ECONOMICS — Economic Situation And Conditions*

POLITICAL RISK SERVICES. COUNTRY REPORTS: SINGAPORE. see *BUSINESS AND ECONOMICS — Economic Situation And Conditions*

POLITICAL RISK SERVICES. COUNTRY REPORTS: SOUTH AFRICA. see *BUSINESS AND ECONOMICS — Economic Situation And Conditions*

POLITICAL RISK SERVICES. COUNTRY REPORTS: SOUTH KOREA. see *BUSINESS AND ECONOMICS — Economic Situation And Conditions*

POLITICAL RISK SERVICES. COUNTRY REPORTS. SRI LANKA. see *BUSINESS AND ECONOMICS — Economic Situation And Conditions*

POLITICAL RISK SERVICES. COUNTRY REPORTS: SUDAN. see *BUSINESS AND ECONOMICS — Economic Situation And Conditions*

POLITICAL RISK SERVICES. COUNTRY REPORTS: SYRIA. see *BUSINESS AND ECONOMICS — Economic Situation And Conditions*

POLITICAL RISK SERVICES. COUNTRY REPORTS: TAIWAN. see *BUSINESS AND ECONOMICS — Economic Situation And Conditions*

POLITICAL RISK SERVICES. COUNTRY REPORTS: TUNISIA. see *BUSINESS AND ECONOMICS — Economic Situation And Conditions*

POLITICAL RISK SERVICES. COUNTRY REPORTS: TURKEY. see *BUSINESS AND ECONOMICS — Economic Situation And Conditions*

POLITICAL RISK SERVICES. COUNTRY REPORTS: UKRAINE. see *BUSINESS AND ECONOMICS — Economic Situation And Conditions*

POLITICAL RISK SERVICES. COUNTRY REPORTS: UNITED ARAB EMIRATES. see *BUSINESS AND ECONOMICS — Economic Situation And Conditions*

POLITICAL RISK SERVICES. COUNTRY REPORTS: URUGUAY. see *BUSINESS AND ECONOMICS — Economic Situation And Conditions*

POLITICAL RISK SERVICES. COUNTRY REPORTS: VENEZUELA. see *BUSINESS AND ECONOMICS — Economic Situation And Conditions*

POLITICAL RISK SERVICES. COUNTRY REPORTS: VIETNAM. see *BUSINESS AND ECONOMICS — Economic Situation And Conditions*

POLITICAL RISK SERVICES. COUNTRY REPORTS: ZAIRE. see *BUSINESS AND ECONOMICS — Economic Situation And Conditions*

POLITICAL RISK SERVICES. COUNTRY REPORTS: ZAMBIA. see *BUSINESS AND ECONOMICS — Economic Situation And Conditions*

POLITICAL RISK SERVICES. COUNTRY REPORTS: ZIMBABWE. see *BUSINESS AND ECONOMICS — Economic Situation And Conditions*

POLITICAL RISK SERVICES. EXECUTIVE REPORTS: ANGOLA. see *BUSINESS AND ECONOMICS — Economic Situation And Conditions*

POLITICAL RISK SERVICES. EXECUTIVE REPORTS: AUSTRALIA. see *BUSINESS AND ECONOMICS — Economic Situation And Conditions*

POLITICAL RISK SERVICES. EXECUTIVE REPORTS: AUSTRIA. see *BUSINESS AND ECONOMICS — Economic Situation And Conditions*

POLITICAL RISK SERVICES. EXECUTIVE REPORTS: BANGLADESH. see *BUSINESS AND ECONOMICS — Economic Situation And Conditions*

POLITICAL RISK SERVICES. EXECUTIVE REPORTS: BELGIUM. see *BUSINESS AND ECONOMICS — Economic Situation And Conditions*

POLITICAL RISK SERVICES. EXECUTIVE REPORTS: BOTSWANA. see *BUSINESS AND ECONOMICS — Economic Situation And Conditions*

POLITICAL RISK SERVICES. EXECUTIVE REPORTS: BURMA. see *BUSINESS AND ECONOMICS — Economic Situation And Conditions*

POLITICAL RISK SERVICES. EXECUTIVE REPORTS: CANADA. see *BUSINESS AND ECONOMICS — Economic Situation And Conditions*

POLITICAL SCIENCE

POLITICAL RISK SERVICES. EXECUTIVE REPORTS: CONGO. see *BUSINESS AND ECONOMICS — Economic Situation And Conditions*

POLITICAL RISK SERVICES. EXECUTIVE REPORTS: CUBA. see *BUSINESS AND ECONOMICS — Economic Situation And Conditions*

POLITICAL RISK SERVICES. EXECUTIVE REPORTS: DENMARK. see *BUSINESS AND ECONOMICS — Economic Situation And Conditions*

POLITICAL RISK SERVICES. EXECUTIVE REPORTS: FINLAND. see *BUSINESS AND ECONOMICS — Economic Situation And Conditions*

POLITICAL RISK SERVICES. EXECUTIVE REPORTS: FRANCE. see *BUSINESS AND ECONOMICS — Economic Situation And Conditions*

POLITICAL RISK SERVICES. EXECUTIVE REPORTS: GERMANY. see *BUSINESS AND ECONOMICS — Economic Situation And Conditions*

POLITICAL RISK SERVICES. EXECUTIVE REPORTS: GHANA. see *BUSINESS AND ECONOMICS — Economic Situation And Conditions*

POLITICAL RISK SERVICES. EXECUTIVE REPORTS: GREECE. see *BUSINESS AND ECONOMICS — Economic Situation And Conditions*

POLITICAL RISK SERVICES. EXECUTIVE REPORTS: GUYANA. see *BUSINESS AND ECONOMICS — Economic Situation And Conditions*

POLITICAL RISK SERVICES. EXECUTIVE REPORTS: IRELAND. see *BUSINESS AND ECONOMICS — Economic Situation And Conditions*

POLITICAL RISK SERVICES. EXECUTIVE REPORTS: ITALY. see *BUSINESS AND ECONOMICS — Economic Situation And Conditions*

POLITICAL RISK SERVICES. EXECUTIVE REPORTS: JAPAN. see *BUSINESS AND ECONOMICS — Economic Situation And Conditions*

POLITICAL RISK SERVICES. EXECUTIVE REPORTS: NETHERLANDS. see *BUSINESS AND ECONOMICS — Economic Situation And Conditions*

POLITICAL RISK SERVICES. EXECUTIVE REPORTS: NEW ZEALAND. see *BUSINESS AND ECONOMICS — Economic Situation And Conditions*

POLITICAL RISK SERVICES. EXECUTIVE REPORTS: NORWAY. see *BUSINESS AND ECONOMICS — Economic Situation And Conditions*

POLITICAL RISK SERVICES. EXECUTIVE REPORTS: PAPUA NEW GUINEA. see *BUSINESS AND ECONOMICS — Economic Situation And Conditions*

POLITICAL RISK SERVICES. EXECUTIVE REPORTS: PARAGUAY. see *BUSINESS AND ECONOMICS — Economic Situation And Conditions*

POLITICAL RISK SERVICES. EXECUTIVE REPORTS: PORTUGAL. see *BUSINESS AND ECONOMICS — Economic Situation And Conditions*

POLITICAL RISK SERVICES. EXECUTIVE REPORTS: PUERTO RICO. see *BUSINESS AND ECONOMICS — Economic Situation And Conditions*

POLITICAL RISK SERVICES. EXECUTIVE REPORTS: QATAR. see *BUSINESS AND ECONOMICS — Economic Situation And Conditions*

POLITICAL RISK SERVICES. EXECUTIVE REPORTS: SPAIN. see *BUSINESS AND ECONOMICS — Economic Situation And Conditions*

POLITICAL RISK SERVICES. EXECUTIVE REPORTS: SURINAME. see *BUSINESS AND ECONOMICS — Economic Situation And Conditions*

POLITICAL RISK SERVICES. EXECUTIVE REPORTS: SWEDEN. see *BUSINESS AND ECONOMICS — Economic Situation And Conditions*

POLITICAL RISK SERVICES. EXECUTIVE REPORTS: SWITZERLAND. see *BUSINESS AND ECONOMICS — Economic Situation And Conditions*

POLITICAL RISK SERVICES. EXECUTIVE REPORTS: THAILAND. see *BUSINESS AND ECONOMICS — Economic Situation And Conditions*

POLITICAL RISK SERVICES. EXECUTIVE REPORTS: TRINIDAD & TOBAGO. see *BUSINESS AND ECONOMICS — Economic Situation And Conditions*

POLITICAL RISK SERVICES. EXECUTIVE REPORTS: UNITED KINGDOM. see *BUSINESS AND ECONOMICS — Economic Situation And Conditions*

POLITICAL RISK SERVICES. EXECUTIVE REPORTS: UNITED STATES. see *BUSINESS AND ECONOMICS — Economic Situation And Conditions*

POLITICAL RISK SERVICES. EXECUTIVE REPORTS: YEMEN. see *BUSINESS AND ECONOMICS — Economic Situation And Conditions*

320   NZ   ISSN 0032-3187
JA1
POLITICAL SCIENCE. 1948. s-a. NZ.$40 to individuals; institutions NZ.$44 (effective 1995 & 1996). (Victoria University of Wellington, School of Political Science & Public Administration) Victoria University Press, P.O. Box 600, Wellington, New Zealand. E-mail: politics@vuw.ac.nz. Eds. G. Debnan, R. Vasil. adv.; bk.rev.; bibl, charts, illus.; cum.index every 2 yrs. circ. 600. (back issues avail.; reprint service avail. from KTO,SCH) **Indexed:** A.B.C.Pol.Sci., Amer.Hist.& Life, Br.Hum.Ind., Curr.Cont., E.I., Hist.Abstr., Int.Polit.Sci.Abstr., Mid:East: Abstr.& Ind., Polit.Sci.Abstr., SSCI. **Document type:** academic/scholarly publication.
—BLDSC (6543.908000); Genuine Article; UnCover. **CCC.**

320   US   ISSN 0032-3195
H1
POLITICAL SCIENCE QUARTERLY; the journal of public and international affairs. 1886. q. $39 to individuals; institutions $146 (effective 1996). Academy of Political Science, 475 Riverside Dr., Ste. 1274, New York, NY 10115-1274. TEL 212-870-2500. FAX 212-870-2202. E-mail: aps321@ad.com. Ed. Demetrios Caraley. adv.: page $300; adv. contact: Michael Cirillo. bk.rev.; circ. 8,000 (paid). (also avail. in microform from UMI,PMC; reprint service avail. from KTO,UMI) **Indexed:** A.B.C.Pol.Sci., Abstr.Bk.Rev.Curr.Leg.Per., Acad.Ind., Amer.Bibl.Slavic & E.Eur.Stud., Amer.Hist.& Life, Bk.Rev.Dig., Bk.Rev.Ind. (1965-), CERDIC, Chic.Per.Ind., Child.Bk.Rev.Ind. (1965-), Curr.Cont., Curr.Cont.M.E., E.I., Fut.Surv., Hist.Abstr., Int.Polit.Sci.Abstr., Mid:East: Abstr.& Ind., P.A.I.S., Polit.Sci.Abstr., Refug.Abstr., Rural Recreat.Tour.Abstr., Sage Urb.Stud.Abstr., Soc.Sci.Ind., Soc.Work Res.& Abstr., SSCI, World Agri.Econ. & Rural Sociol.Abstr. **Document type:** academic/scholarly publication.
●Also available online. Vendor(s): University Microfilms International.
—BLDSC (6543.914000); Faxon; Genuine Article; SWETS; UMI; UnCover.
Description: Publishes in-depth articles on domestic and international affairs.
Refereed Serial

320   II   ISSN 0554-5196
JA26
POLITICAL SCIENCE REVIEW. 1961. q. Rs.70($50) (typically set in Dec.). University of Rajasthan, Department of Political Science, Bapunagar, Jaipur 302 004, India. TEL 511071-267. Ed. Dr. S.L. Verma. adv.; bk.rev.; bibl.; index. circ. 500. (also avail. in microfilm from UMI; back issues avail; reprint service avail. from UMI) **Indexed:** A.B.C.Pol.Sci., Amer.Hist.& Life, Hist.Abstr., Int.Polit.Sci.Abstr.

320   US   ISSN 0091-3715
JA1
POLITICAL SCIENCE REVIEWER; an annual review of books. 1971. a. $10. Intercollegiate Studies Institute, 14 S. Bryn Mawr Ave., Ste. 100, Bryn Mawr, PA 19010. TEL 215-525-7501. Ed. George W. Carey. adv.; bk.rev. circ. 2,000. (also avail. in microform from UMI; back issues avail.) **Indexed:** Bk.Rev.Ind. (1980-), Child.Bk.Rev.Ind. (1980-), Int.Polit.Sci.Abstr.
—SWETS; UMI.
Description: Features articles on classic and contemporary studies in law and politics.

320   II   ISSN 0032-3209
POLITICAL SCIENTIST. (Text in English) 1964. s-a. Rs.10.($3.) Ranchi University, Department of Political Science, Ranchi 834008, Bihar, India. Ed. Ram Naresh Trivedi. adv.; bk.rev.; charts. circ. 500. **Indexed:** Int.Polit.Sci.Abstr.

320   UK   ISSN 0306-6061
H1
POLITICAL SOCIAL ECONOMIC REVIEW. no.5, 1976. bi-m. £50 (foreign £60). N O P Market Research Ltd., Tower House, Southampton St., London WC2E 7HN, England. TEL 071-612-0100. FAX 071-612-0547. Ed. Elaine Winter. charts; illus.; stat. circ. 175. **Document type:** bulletin.
Supersedes: N O P Political Bulletin.
Description: Studies by NOP Market Research on political, social and economic topics.

320   UK   ISSN 0032-3217
JA1
POLITICAL STUDIES. 1953. 5/yr. £85($171) (foreign £99) (effective 1996). (Political Studies Association of the United Kingdom) Basil Blackwell Ltd., 108 Cowley Rd., Oxford OX4 1JF, England. TEL 01865-791100. FAX 01865-791347. TELEX 837022 OXBOOK G. Ed. Jack Hayward. adv.; bk.rev.; index, cum.index every 10 yrs. (also avail. in microfilm from UMI; back issues avail.) **Indexed:** A.B.C.Pol.Sci., Amer.Hist.& Life, ASSIA, Br.Hum.Ind., Curr.Cont., Hist.Abstr., Int.Polit.Sci.Abstr., Lang.& Lang.Behav.Abstr., Mid:East: Abstr.& Ind., P.A.I.S., Polit.Sci.Abstr., Soc.Sci.Ind., Sociol.Abstr., SSCI, Tech.Educ.Abstr. **Document type:** academic/scholarly publication.
—BLDSC (6543.924000); Faxon; Genuine Article; SWETS; UMI; UnCover. **CCC.**

320   US   ISSN 0090-5917
JA1.A1
POLITICAL THEORY; an international journal of political philosophy. 1973. q. $59 to individuals; institutions $198 (effective Sep. 1995). Sage Publications, Inc., 2455 Teller Rd., Thousand Oaks, CA 91320. TEL 805-499-0721. FAX 805-499-0871. E-mail: libraries@sagepub.com. (Overseas subscr. to: Sage Publications Ltd., 6 Bonhill Rd., London EC2A 4PU, England; Sage Publications India Pvt. Ltd., P.O. Box 4215, New Delhi 110 048, India) Ed. Tracy B. Strong. adv.; bk.rev.; bibl.; index. circ. 2,200. (also avail. in microfilm from UMI; back issues avail.; reprint service avail. from UMI) **Indexed:** A.B.C.Pol.Sci., Amer.Bibl.Slavic & E.Eur.Stud., Amer.Hist.& Life, ASSIA, CERDIC, Curr.Cont., Hist.Abstr., Int.Polit.Sci.Abstr., Mid:East: Abstr.& Ind., P.A.I.S., Phil.Ind., Polit.Sci.Abstr., Sage Urb.Stud.Abstr., SSCI. **Document type:** academic/scholarly publication.
—BLDSC (6543.926000); Faxon; Genuine Article; SWETS; UMI; UnCover. **CCC.**
Description: Provides a forum for the diverse orientations in the study of political ideas, including the history of political thought, modern theory, conceptual analysis, and polemic argumentation.

320   AT   ISSN 1032-9641
POLITICAL THEORY NEWSLETTER. 1989. s-a. free. Australian National University, Research School of Social Sciences, Political Science Program, Canberra, A.C.T. 0200, Australia. FAX 61-6-2493051. E-mail: b.hindess@coombs.anu.edu.au.
Refereed Serial

320 305.4   US
POLITICAL WOMAN HOTLINE; charting our progress towards equality. 1992. w. $10. Political Woman, Inc., 276 Chatterton Pkwy., White Plains, NY 10606. TEL 914-285-9761. E-mail: polwoman@aol.com. Eds. Robert Fertik, Antonia Stolper. circ. 2,200. **Document type:** newsletter.
●Available only online.
Supersedes: Political Woman (White Plains) (ISSN 1069-6652)
Description: For feminist office holders, policy leaders, activists and others interested in the women's political movement.

POLITICHE DEL LAVORO. see *BUSINESS AND ECONOMICS — Labor And Industrial Relations*

POLITICAL SCIENCE

320   BU   ISSN 0861-4830
H8
POLITICHESKI IZSLEDVANIIA. (Text in Bulgarian) q. 80 lv. Bulgarska Assoziaziia po Politiceski Izsledvaniia, 7 Noemvri St., 1, 1040 Sofia, Bulgaria. Ed. Dobrin Kanev. **Document type:** academic/scholarly publication.
—BLDSC (0130.115800).
    Formerly (until 1990): Suvremenni Sotsialni Teorii (ISSN 0204-6709)

320   UK   ISSN 0962-0206
D860
THE POLITICIAN; international socio-political magazine. 1990. fortn. Politician International Research and Publishing, P.O. Box 657, London NW3 4EQ, England. TEL 071-794-8047. FAX 071-794-7440. Ed. Moustafa Ahmed.

320   CI   ISSN 0032-3241
JA26
POLITICKA MISAO/POLITICAL THOUGHT; casopis za politicke nauke. (Text in Croatian; summaries in English) 1964. q. $15. Sveuciliste u Zagrebu, Fakultet Politickih Nauka, Lepusiceva 6, 41000 Zagreb, Croatia. FAX 412-283. Ed. Davor Rodin. bk.rev.; abstr.; bibl. circ. 1,200. (tabloid format) **Indexed:** Amer.Hist.& Life, Hist.Abstr., Int.Polit.Sci.Abstr.

320   IT   ISSN 0032-325X
POLITICO; rivista italiana di scienze politiche. (Text and summaries in English, French, and Italian) 1950. q. L.70000 (foreign L.105000). (Universita degli Studi di Pavia, Istituto di Scienze Politiche) Casa Editrice Dott. A. Giuffre, Via Busto Arsizio 40, 20151 Milan, Italy. TEL 39-2-38000905. FAX 39-2-3809582. Ed. Pasquale Scaramozzino. adv.; B&W page L.500000. bk.rev.; bibl.; index. circ. 1,100. **Indexed:** A.B.C.Pol.Sci., Amer.Hist.& Life, ELLIS, Hist.Abstr., Int.Polit.Sci.Abstr., Lang.& Lang.Behav.Abstr., Mid.East: Abstr.& Ind., P.A.I.S.For.Lang.Ind.
—SWETS; UnCover.

322.4   US   ISSN 0032-3276
POLITICS. Running title: B I P A C Politics. 1964. q. $30. Business-Industry Political Action Committee, Political Education Council, 1747 Pennsylvania Ave., N.W., Washington, DC 20006. TEL 202-833-1880. FAX 202-833-2338. Ed. Don R. Kendall. bk.rev. circ. 23,000. **Indexed:** A.B.C.Pol.Sci. (until 1989).
—BLDSC (6543.938000).
    Description: Digest of political trends and developments of interest to the business community.

320   UK   ISSN 0263-3957
POLITICS. 1981. 3/yr. £41($78) (foreign £58) (effective 1996). (Political Studies Association of the United Kingdom) Basil Blackwell Ltd., 108 Cowley Rd., Oxford OX4 1JF, England. TEL 0865-791100. FAX 0865-791347. TELEX 837022-OXBOOK-G. Ed. Andrew Taylor. adv.; bk.rev. circ. 1,200. (also avail. in microform from UMI; back issues avail.) **Indexed:** ASSIA, Int.Polit.Sci.Abstr. **Document type:** bulletin.
—BLDSC (6543.937500); UMI. **CCC**.

320   US   ISSN 0032-3292
H1   CODEN: PSOCEX
POLITICS AND SOCIETY. 1970. q. $54 to individuals; institutions $161 (effective Sep. 1995). Sage Publications, Inc., 2455 Teller Rd., Thousand Oaks, CA 91320. TEL 805-499-0721. FAX 805-499-0871. E-mail: libraries@sagepub.com. (Overseas subscr. to: Sage Publications Ltd., 6 Bonhill St., London EC2A 4PU, England; Sage Publications India Pvt. Ltd., P.O. Box 4215, New Delhi 110 048, India) Ed.Bd. adv.; bk.rev. circ. 1,400. (also avail. in microform from UMI; back issues avail.; reprint service avil. from SCH) **Indexed:** A.B.C.Pol.Sci., Amer.Bibl.Slavic & E.Eur.Stud., Amer.Hist.& Life, ASSIA, Curr.Cont., E.I., Hist.Abstr., Int.Polit.Sci.Abstr., Left Ind. (1982-), Mid.East: Abstr.& Ind., Polit.Sci.Abstr., Soc.Sci.Ind., SSCI. **Document type:** academic/scholarly publication.
—BLDSC (6543.944000); Faxon; Genuine Article; SWETS; UMI; UnCover.
    Description: Analyzes politics, its social roots, and consequences.
    Refereed Serial

320 301   UK   ISSN 0954-6030
D1050
POLITICS AND SOCIETY IN GERMANY, AUSTRIA AND SWITZERLAND. 3/yr. Institute of German, Austrian and Swiss Affairs, University Park, Nottingham NG7 2RD, England. TEL 0602-484848. Ed. David Childs. **Indexed:** Int.Polit.Sci.Abstr. **Document type:** academic/scholarly publication.

320   GW   ISSN 0939-6071
JA76   CODEN: POIDEC
POLITICS AND THE INDIVIDUAL; international journal of political socialization and political psychology. 1991. 2/yr. DM.74 to individuals; institutions DM.86. Verlag Dr. K. Kraemer, Postfach 130584, 20105 Hamburg, Germany. TEL 040-4101429. FAX 040-455770. Ed.Bd. adv.; bk.rev. **Indexed:** Psychol.Abstr. (1991-). **Document type:** academic/scholarly publication.
—BLDSC (6543.941600).
    Description: Investigates the relationship between individuals and politics.

320   US   ISSN 1064-6809
JK1012
POLITICS IN AMERICA. 1981. biennial. $79.95 hardcover; softcover $49.95. Congressional Quarterly Inc., 1414 22nd St., N.W., Washington, DC 20037. TEL 202-887-8500. FAX 202-887-6706. Ed. Phil Duncan.
●Also available online.
    Description: Profiles of every member of Congress, both in Washington and at home. Describes their backgrounds, districts, key votes, committee seats, and campaign funds. Covers election races.

320   US
POLITICS IN LATIN AMERICA. 1982. irreg. price varies. Praeger Publishers (Subsidiary of: Greenwood Publishing Group Inc.), 88 Post Rd. W., Box 5007, Westport, CT 06881-5007. TEL 203-226-3571. FAX 203-222-1502. **Document type:** monographic series.

320   US
POLITICS IN MINNESOTA. 1983. 22/yr. $48. Political Communications, Inc., 525 Park St., Ste. 211, St. Paul, MN 55103. TEL 612-293-3911. Eds. Wy Spano, D.J. Leary. **Document type:** newsletter.
    Description: Reports on Minnesota politics.

320   UK   ISSN 0959-8480
JA8
POLITICS REVIEW. 1991. q. £17.50 (rest of Europe £23; elsewhere £28.50) (effective 1996). Philip Allan Publishers Ltd., Market Pl., Deddington, Oxon. OX15 0SE, England. TEL 01869-338652. FAX 01869-338803. adv. contact: Ceri Jenkins.
—BLDSC (6543.949650).

320.52   UK   ISSN 0307-7039
POLITICS TODAY. 1946. fortn. £21. Conservative and Unionist Central Office, 32 Smith Sq., London SW1P 3HH, England. Ed.Bd. index. (reprint service avail. from SCH) **Indexed:** Mag.Ind., Mid.East: Abstr.& Ind.
—BLDSC (6543.950000).
    Supersedes: Notes on Current Politics (ISSN 0029-4055) & Overseas Review (ISSN 0030-7491)

320   BE   ISSN 0048-475X
POLITIEKE DOKUMENTATIE. 1969. q. 500 Fr. to individuals; institutions 750 Fr. Instituut voor Europese Vorming V.Z.M., P-A Lenoirstraat 13, B-1090 Brussels, Belgium. Ed. J.D. Peeters. adv.; bk.rev.; bibl.; index every 3 yrs. circ. 350. (reprint service avail. from UMI)

320   FI   ISSN 0032-3365
JN6701.A1
POLITIIKKA. (Text in Finnish or Swedish; summaries in English) 1959. q. FIM 160 (outside Scandinavia FIM 180). Finnish Political Science Association, Department of Political Science, Aabo Akademi University, FIN-20500 Turku, Finland. TEL 358-0-1912527. FAX 358-0-1912068. Ed. Teija Tiilikainen. adv. contact: Dag Ancilar. bk.rev.; charts; illus.; index. circ. 1,400. **Indexed:** A.B.C.Pol.Sci., Amer.Hist.& Life, Hist.Abstr., Int.Polit.Sci.Abstr., Sociol.Abstr.
—BLDSC (6543.958000).

320   GW   ISSN 0342-5746
POLITIK - AKTUELL FUER DEN UNTERRICHT. 1975. w. DM.80. Madog Verlag GmbH, Broicher Dorfstr. 28, 41564 Kaarst, Germany. TEL 02131-64053. Ed. E. Bizer. bk.rev. circ. 2,500.

320 330   TU
POLITIK EKONOMIK BULTEN GAZETESI. 1986. w. Buyukdere Cad. 81-16, 80300 Mecidiyekoy - Istanbul, Turkey. TEL 90-212-2885250. FAX 90-212-2727457.

320   GW
POLITIK UND GESELLSCHAFT. WUERZBURGER UNIVERSITAETSSCHRIFTEN. 1991. irreg., vol.4, 1994. Ergon-Verlag, Grombuehlstr. 7, 97080 Wuerzburg, Germany. TEL 0931-280084. FAX 0931-282872. Ed.Bd. **Document type:** monographic series.
    Refereed Serial

320 330   LI
POLITIKA. (Text in Lithuanian) m. Politika Inc. Ltd., Maironio 1, 2600 Vilnius, Lithuania. Ed. Mr. Algimantas.
    Formerly (until 1988): Komunistas (ISSN 0134-3114)

320   GR   ISSN 1105-9745
POLITIKA THEMATA. 1973. w. J. Chorn, Ed. & Pub., Ipsilantou 25, 106 75 Athens, Greece. TEL 30-1-721-8421. FAX 30-1-722-4353. adv. circ. 5,544. **Document type:** consumer publication.

320   SA   ISSN 0258-9346
JA26
POLITIKON; South African journal of political science. (Text and summaries in Afrikaans, English) 1974. s-a. $50 (effective 1996). Staatkundige Vereniging van Suid Afrika - Political Science Association of South Africa, P.O. Box 1041, Florida 1710, South Africa. FAX 27-11-7825500. E-mail: ajv@rau3.rau.ac.za. Ed. P.v.d.P. Du Toit. adv.; bk.rev. circ. 1,300. (also avail. in microfilm from UMI; reprint service avail. from UMI) **Indexed:** A.B.C.Pol.Sci., Documentatieblad, Ind.S.A.Per, Int.Polit.Sci.Abstr. **Document type:** academic/scholarly publication.
—BLDSC (6544.040000); Faxon; UMI; UnCover.
    Description: Advances the study of political science, international politics and related topics through scholarly discourse and dissemination of research results.
    Refereed Serial

320   BW   ISSN 0130-8254
POLITINFORMATOR I AGITATOR. 1932. s-m. 0.06 Rub. Kommunisticheskaya Partiya Belorussii, Tsentral'nyi Komitet, Leninskii Prospekt, 77, 220041, Minsk, Belarus. illus.

320   FR   ISSN 0244-7827
JQ1872
POLITIQUE AFRICAINE. 1981. q. 320 F. (Europe 395 F.; elsewhere 490 F.) (effective 1996). (Association des Chercheurs de Politique Africaine) Karthala Editions, 22-24 Bd. Arago, 75013 Paris, France. TEL 43-31-15-59. FAX 45-35-27-05. TELEX 250303 PUBLICXPARIS. Ed.Bd. adv.; bk.rev.; bibl. circ. 3,500. **Indexed:** Bibl.Ling., Documentatieblad, Int.Polit.Sci.Abstr., Rural Devel.Abstr., World Agri.Econ.& Rural Sociol.Abstr.
—BLDSC (6544.093000).
    Description: Provides analysis and political news of contemporary Africa.

320 327   FR
POLITIQUE ETRANGERE. q. (Institut Francais des Relations Internationales) Armand Colin (Subsidiary of: Masson), 103 bd. St-Michel, 75005 Paris, France. TEL 1-46-34-19-12. FAX 1-43-26-96-38. TELEX 201 269 F. Ed. Dominique Moisi. circ. 4,500. **Indexed:** ELLIS, Int.Polit.Sci.Abstr.

327   FR   ISSN 0180-9563
POLITIQUE ETRANGERE DE LA FRANCE. 1935. 6/yr. 435 F. (Europe 565 F., elsewhere 755 F.). (Ministere des Relations Exterieures) Documentation Francaise, 29-31 Quai Voltaire, 75340 Paris Cedex 07, France. TEL 1-40-15-70-00. FAX 40-15-72-30. TELEX 215 666 DOCFRAN. (Subscr. to: 124 rue Henry Barbusse, 93308 Aubervilliers Cedex, France. TEL 48-39-56-00. FAX 48-39-56-01) (Co-sponsor: Institut Francais de Relations Internationales) bk.rev.; bibl.; index. circ. 1,500. (also avail. in microfiche from DFR) **Indexed:** A.B.C.Pol.Sci., Abstr.Mil.Bibl., Amer.Hist.& Life, E.I., Hist.Abstr., Key to Econ.Sci., P.A.I.S.For.Lang.Ind., Pt.de Rep. (1979-), Rural Recreat.Tour.Abstr., World Agri.Econ.& Rural Sociol.Abstr. **Document type:** government publication.
—BLDSC (6544.110000); Faxon; SWETS.
    Formerly (until 1969): Politique Etrangere (ISSN 0032-342X)

POLITICAL SCIENCE

320　　　　　　　FR　　ISSN 0221-2781
D839
POLITIQUE INTERNATIONALE. (Text in French; summaries in English and Spanish) 1978. q. 225.25 F. to individuals (foreign 374 F.); institutions 267.74 F. (foreign 416.50 F.). 11 rue du Bois de Boulogne, 75116 Paris, France. TEL 45-00-15-26. FAX 45-00-38-79. Ed. Patrick Wajsman. adv.; bk.rev. **Indexed:** A.B.C.Pol.Sci. (1994-), ELLIS, Int.Polit.Sci.Abstr.
—BLDSC (6544.112000); SWETS.

LES POLITIQUES SOCIALES. see *SOCIAL SERVICES AND WELFARE*

320　　　　　　　GW　　ISSN 0554-5455
POLITISCHE BILDUNG. 1967. q. DM.27. Saarbach GmbH, Postfach 101610, 50456 Cologne, Germany. TEL 0221-234631. adv.; bk.rev. circ. 5,000.
—BLDSC (6544.114100).

320　　　　　　　GW　　ISSN 0032-3446
H5
DIE POLITISCHE MEINUNG; Monatsschrift zu Fragen der Zeit. 1956. m. DM.98. Verlag A. Fromm, Postfach 1948, 49009 Osnabrueck, Germany. TEL 0541-310334. FAX 0541-310440. Ed. Peter Hopen. adv.; bk.rev.; charts. circ. 7,000. **Indexed:** P.A.I.S.For.Lang.Ind. **Document type:** bulletin.
—BLDSC (6544.115000).

320　　　　　　　SZ　　ISSN 0251-351X
POLITISCHE RUNDSCHAU/REVUE POLITIQUE; Zeitschrift fuer Kultur, Politik und Wirtschaft. (Text in German, French) 1921. q. 20 SFr. Freisinnig-Demokratische Partei der Schweiz, Postfach 6136, Bahnhofplatz 10, CH-3001 Bern, Switzerland. TEL 031-3113438. Ed. Anna-Marie Kappeler. bk.rev.; bibl.; stat. (tabloid format) **Document type:** bulletin.

320　　　　　　　GW　　ISSN 0032-3462
H35
POLITISCHE STUDIEN. 1950. bi-m. DM.53.40. (Hanns-Seidel-Stiftung e.V.) Atwerb Verlag KG, Forsthausstr. 5A, 82031 Munich, Germany. TEL 089-6492829. FAX 089-6492822. adv.; bk.rev.; charts; index. circ. 4,000. (also avail. in microform from MIM,UMI; reprint service avail. from UMI) **Indexed:** CERDIC, Geo.Abstr., Int.Polit.Sci.Abstr., P.A.I.S.For.Lang.Ind., SSCI. **Document type:** academic/scholarly publication.
—BLDSC (6544.125000); UMI. **CCC.**

320　　　　　　　GW　　ISSN 0032-3470
JA14
POLITISCHE VIERTELJAHRESSCHRIFT. 1960. q. DM.132 (students DM.99) (effective 1996). (Deutsche Vereinigung fuer Politische Wissenschaft) Westdeutscher Verlag GmbH, Postfach 1546, 65005 Wiesbaden, Germany. TEL 0611-534389. FAX 0611-534430. Ed.Bd. adv.; bk.rev. circ. 1,900. **Indexed:** A.B.C.Pol.Sci., Amer.Hist.& Life, Hist.Abstr., Int.Polit.Sci.Abstr., P.A.I.S.For.Lang.Ind., Peace Res.Abstr. **Document type:** academic/scholarly publication.
—Faxon; Genuine Article; SWETS.

320　　　　　　　FR　　ISSN 0295-2319
POLITIX; travaux de science politique. (Text in French; summaries in English, French) 1988. q. 265 F. to individuals (foreign 315 F.); institutions 395 F. (foreign 460 F.). Presses de la Fondation Nationale des Sciences Politiques, 44 rue du Four, 75006 Paris, France. TEL 44-39-39-60.
FAX 1-45-48-04-41. Ed.Bd. abstr. **Indexed:** Int.Polit.Sci.Abstr.
Description: Forum for political scientists, sociologists, historians, geographers, economists, and anthropologists.

320　　　　　　　US　　ISSN 0032-3497
JA3
POLITY. 1968. q. $25 to individuals; institutions $45. Northeastern Political Science Association, Thompson Hall, University of Massachusetts, Amherst, MA 01003. TEL 413-545-1354. FAX 413-545-4902. Ed. M.J. Peterson. adv.; bk.rev.; index, cum.index every 3 vols.; circ. 1,300 (paid). (also avail. in microform from UMI; back issues avail., reprint service avail. from UMI) **Indexed:** A.B.C.Pol.Sci., Amer.Bibl.Slavic & E.Eur.Stud., Amer.Hist.& Life, Curr.Cont., E.I., Fut.Surv., Hist.Abstr., Human Resour.Abstr., Int.Polit.Sci.Abstr., Mid.East: Abstr.& Ind., Polit.Sci.Abstr., Sage Pub.Admin.Abstr., Sage Urb.Stud.Abstr., Soc.Sci.Ind (1994-), SSCI. **Document type:** academic/scholarly publication.
—BLDSC (6544.155000); Faxon; SWETS; UMI; UnCover.
Description: Covers American politics, comparative politics, political theory and international relations.

POLSKA MYSL POLITYCZNA XIX I XX WIEKU. see *HISTORY — History Of Europe*

945　　　　　　　IT　　ISSN 0032-437X
POPOLO DEL FRIULI-VENEZIA GIULIA. 1963. 10/yr. L.100 per no. Comitato Regionale della Democrazia Cristiana, Piazza S. Giovanni 5, 34122 Trieste, Italy. Ed.Bd. circ. 10,500.

320　　　　　　　IT
POPOLO E LIBERTA. 1976. w. L.15000. Partito Popolare Italiano, Piazzetta Matilde Serao 7, 80132 Naples, Italy. Ed. Morani Volturno. adv.; bk.rev.

950　　　　　　　US　　ISSN 0032-4515
JK4101
POPULAR GOVERNMENT. 1931. q. $12. University of North Carolina at Chapel Hill, Institute of Government, Campus Box 3330, Knapp Bldg., Chapel Hill, NC 27599-3330. TEL 919-966-4119. FAX 919-962-2707. Ed. Robert P. Joyce. adv. contact: Katrina W. Hunt. bk.rev.; charts; illus.; index, cum.index every 3 yrs. circ. 5,050. (also avail. in microform from UMI; reprint service avail. from UMI) **Indexed:** HRIS, P.A.I.S. **Document type:** academic/scholarly publication.
—Faxon; UMI; UnCover.
Description: Includes articles on North Carolina state and local government.

320 910 900　　　GW　　ISSN 0932-2272
PORTUGAL - MAGAZIN. 1979. q. DM.48. Deutsch-Portugiesische Gesellschaft e.V., Weyerstr. 48-52, 50676 Cologne, Germany. TEL 0221-2070312. FAX 0221-236464. TELEX 8881828-PNEUD. Ed. Peter Neufert. adv.; bk.rev.; charts; illus. circ. 950. (looseleaf format)
Formerly: Portugal - Nachrichten (ISSN 0722-6713)

329.9　　　　　　PO
PORTUGAL SOCIALISTA. 1967. q. Socialist Party, Rua da Emenda 46, 1200 Lisbon, Portugal. TEL 01-3464375. Dir. Antonio Reis. circ. 5,000.

PORTUGUESE TIMES. see *ETHNIC INTERESTS*

329.9　　　　　　DR
POSICION SOCIALISTA. 3/yr. Editora Nuevo Rumbo, Apdo. Postal 2298, Santo Domingo, Dominican Republic.

322.4 600　　　　US　　ISSN 1065-0075
HC79.D4
POSITIVE ALTERNATIVES. 1975. 4/yr. $35 to individuals; low income individuals $15. Center for Economic Conversion, 222C View St., Ste. C, Mountain View, CA 94041. TEL 415-968-8798. FAX 415-968-1126. Ed. Bruce Allen. bk.rev. circ. 7,500. **Document type:** newsletter.
Formerly (until vol.15, no.3, 1990): Plowshare Press.
Description: International newsletter on economic conversion, which promotes the orderly redirection of resources from the military economy to more socially useful and environmentally sustainable economic activity.

322.4　　　　　　NR　　ISSN 0331-9911
POSITIVE REVIEW. 1978. q. $18. University of Ife, Department of African Languages & Literatures, Ile-Ife, Nigeria. (Subscr. outside of Africa to: Hans Zell, Box 56, Oxford OX1 3EI, England) Ed.Bd. bk.rev.

320　　　　　　　GW　　ISSN 0032-5201
AP50
POSSEV; obchshestvenno-politicheskii zhurnal. (Text in Russian) 1945. 6/yr. DM.70. Possev-Verlag, Flurscheideweg 15, 65936 Frankfurt a.M., Germany. TEL 069-341265. FAX 069-343841. Ed. M. Gorbanevsky. adv.; bk.rev.; bibl.; illus.; index. circ. 3,000. (also avail. in microform) **Document type:** academic/scholarly publication.
—**CCC.**

329.9　　　　　　US
POST-AMERIKAN. 1972. 6/yr. $5. Box 3452, Bloomington, IL 61701. TEL 309-828-7232. adv.; bk.rev.; film rev.; play rev.; charts; illus. circ. 3,500. (tabloid format; also avail. in microfiche; back issues avail.) **Indexed:** Alt.Press Ind. **Document type:** newspaper.

320　　　　　　　US
POSTCONTEMPORARY INTERVENTIONS. 1989. irreg. Duke University Press, Box 90660, Durham, NC 27708-0660. TEL 919-687-3600. FAX 919-688-4574. Eds. Stanley Fish, Fredric Jameson.

320　　　　　　　FR　　ISSN 0152-0768
POUVOIRS. 1977. q. 325 F. (foreign 415 F.). Editions du Seuil, 27 rue Jacob, 75006 Paris, France. Dirs. Philippe Ardant, Olivier Duhamel. bk.rev.; bibl. (reprint service avail. from KTO,SCH) **Indexed:** A.B.C.Pol.Sci., ELLIS, Int.Polit.Sci.Abstr.
—BLDSC (6571.420000); SWETS. **CCC.**
Description: Covers the political aspects of the economy, social life and culture.

329.3　　　　　　PO　　ISSN 0870-2144
POVO LIVRE. 1974. w. Esc.5000. Social Democratic Party, Rua S. Caetano 9, 1200 Lisbon, Portugal. TEL 01-9352140. FAX 3976967. Dir. Pacheco Pereira. **Document type:** newspaper.

320　　　　　　　CN
POWER (TORONTO). 1975. m. $40 donation. Samisdat Publishers Ltd., 206 Carlton St., Toronto, ON M5A 2L1, Canada. TEL 416-922-9850. FAX 416-922-8614. (Addr. in the U.S.: Samisdat Publishers, Box 971, Niagara Falls, NY 14302) Ed. Ernst Zuendel. bk.rev. circ. 50,000. **Document type:** newsletter.
Description: Presents an alternative viewpoint that current interpretations of the Holocaust and its extent are incorrect.

320.532　　　　　RU
POZITSIYA. 1991. w. 0.15 Rub. per issue. Ul. Krasnoznamenskaya 21-33, 180007 Pskov, Russia. TEL 3-83-50. Ed. A.Ya. Kirsanov. circ. 3,000.

320　　　　　　　PL　　ISSN 0032-6186
PRACA I ZABEZPIECZENIA SPOLECZNE. (Text in Polish; summaries in English) 1959. m. Panstwowe Wydawnictwo Ekonomiczne, Niecala 4a, Warsaw, Poland. TEL 48-22-278001. Ed. Wieslaw Krencik. bk.rev.; bibl.; charts; index. circ. 6,000.

320 301.16　　　　US　　ISSN 1062-5623
PRAEGER SERIES IN POLITICAL COMMUNICATIONS. 1990. irreg. price varies. Praeger Publishers (Subsidiary of: Greenwood Publishing Group Inc.), 88 Post Rd. W., Box 5007, Westport, CT 06881-5007. TEL 203-226-3571. FAX 203-222-1502. **Document type:** monographic series.

320 330　　　　　US　　ISSN 1072-2882
PRAEGER SERIES IN POLITICAL ECONOMY. 1988. irreg. price varies. Praeger Publishers (Subsidiary of: Greenwood Publishing Group Inc.), 88 Post Rd. W., Box 5007, Westport, CT 06881-5007. TEL 203-226-3571. FAX 203-222-1502. **Document type:** monographic series.

320　　　　　　　US　　ISSN 1062-0931
PRAEGER SERIES IN PRESIDENTIAL STUDIES. 1992. irreg. price varies. Praeger Publishers (Subsidiary of: Greenwood Publishing Group Inc.), 88 Post Rd. W., Box 5007, Westport, CT 06881-5007. TEL 203-226-3571. FAX 203-222-1502. **Document type:** monographic series.

POLITICAL SCIENCE

320   US   ISSN 1061-5261
PRAEGER SERIES IN TRANSFORMATIONAL POLITICS AND POLITICAL SCIENCE. 1992. irreg. price varies. Praeger Publishers (Subsidiary of: Greenwood Publishing Group Inc.), 88 Post Rd. W., Box 5007, Westport, CT 06881-5007. TEL 203-226-3571. FAX 203-222-1502. **Document type:** monographic series.

320   PH   ISSN 0116-709X
DS686.614
PRAXIS; journal of political science. (Text in English) 1987. a. P.30($3.20) (De La Salle University, Political Science Department) De La Salle University Press, 2401 Taft Ave., Manila, Philippines. TEL 2-59-48-32. FAX 632-521-9094. adv.; bk.rev. circ. 300. **Document type:** academic/scholarly publication.
   Description: Publishes scholarly articles reflecting significant quantitative or qualitative research. Includes speeches, research reports, and "state of the art" papers.

320   AG
PRENSA OBRERA. 1982. w. $100. (Partido Obrero) Editorial Rumbos, S.R.L., Ayacucho 444, Buenos Aires, Argentina. TEL 953-7164. Ed. Eduardo Salas. bk.rev. circ. 16,000.

321.804   US   ISSN 0360-4918
JK501
PRESIDENTIAL STUDIES QUARTERLY. 1972. q. $40. Center for the Study of the Presidency, 208 E. 75th St., New York, NY 10021. TEL 212-249-1200. FAX 212-628-9503. Ed. R. Gordon Hoxie. adv.; bk.rev.; bibl. circ. 13,500. (also avail. in microform from UMI; reprint service avail. from UMI) **Indexed:** A.B.C.Pol.Sci., Amer.Hist.& Life, Bk.Rev.Ind. (1989-), Child.Bk.Rev.Ind. (1989-), Commun.Abstr., Hist.Abstr., Human Resour.Abstr., Int.Polit.Sci.Abstr., Mid.East: Abstr.& Ind., P.A.I.S., Pers.Lit., Polit.Sci.Abstr., Sage Fam.Stud.Abstr., Sage Pub.Admin.Abstr., Sage Urb.Stud.Abstr. **Document type:** academic/scholarly publication.
●Also available online. Vendor(s): University Microfilms International.
—BLDSC (6609.880000); Faxon; SWETS; UMI; UnCover.
   Formerly: Center for the Study of the Presidency. Center House Bulletin (ISSN 0098-809X)
   Refereed Serial

320   GW
PRESSEDIENST P D S. w. DM.26 for 3 mos. Partei des Demokratischen Sozialismus, Parteivorstand, Kleine Alexanderstr. 28, 10178 Berlin, Germany. TEL 030-28409657. FAX 030-28409400. Ed. Hanno Harnisch. **Document type:** newsletter.

320   PE   ISSN 1021-6480
PRETEXTOS. 1990. s-a. $20 per no. Centro de Estudios y Promocion del Desarrollo (DESCO), Leon de la Fuente 110, Lima 17, Peru. TEL 14-627193. FAX 14-617309. adv. circ. 1,000. (back issues avail.) **Document type:** academic/scholarly publication.

320 301   IT   ISSN 0390-3338
PRIMO MAGGIO;* saggi e documenti per una storia di classe. 1974. 3/yr. Colletivo Editoriale Calusca, Via Isonzo 44, 52100 Arezzo, Italy.

325   CN
PRINCE EDWARD ISLAND. CIVIL SERVICE COMMISSION. ANNUAL REPORT. 1963. a. free. Civil Service Commission, P.O. Box 2000, Charlottetown, PEI C1A 7N8, Canada. TEL 902-368-4185. FAX 902-368-5544. circ. 125.

320 900   US
PRINCETON STUDIES IN INTERNATIONAL HISTORY AND POLITICS. 1991. irreg. price varies. Princeton University Press, 41 William St., Princeton, NJ 08540. TEL 609-258-4900. FAX 609-258-6305. E-mail: jhardy@pupress.princeton.edu. **Document type:** monographic series.

968.063   SA
PRISMA. (Text in Afrikaans and English) 1963. m. free. House of Representatives, Administration - Raad van Verteenwoordigers, Administrasie, Private Bag 9008, Cape Town 8000, South Africa. Ed. C.W. Jonker. bk.rev.; abstr.; illus.; stat.; index. circ. 22,000. **Indexed:** Ind.S.A.Per. **Document type:** government publication.
   Formerly (until 1986): Alpha (ISSN 0002-6379)

320 352   US
PRIVATIZATION WATCH. 1976. m. $135 to individuals & businesses; non-profits $75 (effective 1995). Reason Foundation, 3415 S. Sepulveda Blvd., Ste. 400, Los Angeles, CA 90034-6060. TEL 310-391-2245. FAX 310-391-4395. Ed. John O'Leary. adv. contact: Raymond Ng. circ. 1,000. (back issues avail.) **Document type:** newsletter.
   Formerly (until 1988): Fiscal Watchdog.
   Description: Covers news in the area of the privatization of government services.

320   SZ
PRO UND KONTRA. 1982. irreg. 8 Fr. Schweizerische Arbeitsgemeinschaft fuer Demokratie, Feldeggstr. 65, Postfach 387, 8034 Zurich, Switzerland. circ. 3,000. (back issues avail.)

329.9   UK
PROBLEMS OF COMMUNISM AND CAPITALISM. 1974. 4/yr. £17. Problems of Communism Committee, 10 Athol St., Belfast BT12 4GX, N. Ireland. Ed. Jack Lane. circ. 750. **Indexed:** A.B.C.Pol.Sci. (until 1992), Acad.Ind., Curr.Cont., Ind.U.S.Gov.Per., Mid.East: Abstr.& Ind., P.A.I.S., Soc.Sci.Ind., SSCI, World Agri.Econ.& Rural Sociol.Abstr. **Document type:** academic/scholarly publication.
   Formerly: Problems of Communism.
   Description: Review of events and ideas relevant to social organization.

335   II
PROBLEMS OF NATIONAL LIBERATION. (Text in English) 1974. irreg. Rs.3. Ranadhir Dasgupta, 10 Bondel Rd., Calcutta 700019, India. Eds. Satyendra Narayan Mazumdar, Narahari Kaviraj. adv.; bk.rev. circ. 1,000.

320.532   US   ISSN 1075-8216
HX1
PROBLEMS OF POST-COMMUNISM. 1952-1992 (June); resumed 1994. bi-m. $120 to institutions (foreign $150) (effective Jul. 1995). M.E. Sharpe, Inc., 80 Business Park Dr., Armonk, NY 10504. TEL 914-273-1800; 800-541-6563. FAX 914-273-2106. Ed. Constantine C. Menges. bk.rev.; illus.; index. circ. 34,000. (also avail. in microform from UMI; reprint service avail. from UMI,ISI) **Indexed:** A.B.C.Pol.Sci. (until 1992), Amer.Bibl.Slavic & E.Eur.Stud., CERDIC, Curr.Cont., Econ.Abstr., Hist.Abstr. (until 1992), HR Rep., Ind.U.S.Gov.Per., P.A.I.S., Peace Res.Abstr., Polit.Sci.Abstr., Rural Devel.Abstr., Soc.Sci.Ind., SSCI. **Document type:** academic/scholarly publication.
—Faxon; Genuine Article; UMI; UnCover. **CCC.**
   Formerly: Problems of Communism (ISSN 0032-941X)
   Refereed Serial

PROBLEMY DAL'NEGO VOSTOKA. see *HISTORY — History Of Europe*

332.4   ES   ISSN 0259-9864
PROCESO; informativo semanal. 1980. w. Col.60($35) Universidad Centroamericana, Center for Information, Documentation and Research Support, Apdo. 01-16B, San Salvador, El Salvador. TEL 503-240011. FAX 503-240288. (Subscr. to: Apdo. 01-575, San Salvador, El Salvador) index. circ. 1,200. (looseleaf format)
   Description: Analyzes the current political, economic, military, labor and human rights situation of El Salvador.

PROFANE EXISTENCE. see *MUSIC*

PROFESIONALES Y CUADROS. see *BUSINESS AND ECONOMICS*

320   US
PROFILES (ARLINGTON);* a non-partisan view of politics, people and issues. Variant title: Political Profiles. 1985. bi-m. $30. Political Profiles Inc., 5871 Colfax Ave., Alexandria, VA 22311-1013.

320 972   US
PROFMEX SPECIAL PAPERS SERIES. 1993. irreg., latest no.4, Jul. 1994. $5 per no. University of Texas at El Paso, Center for Inter-American and Border Studies, Publications Program, c/o Gloria Macias, Man. Ed., El Paso, TX 79968-0002. TEL 915-747-5271. FAX 915-747-5574. E-mail: AVVM%UTEP@UTEPVM.UTEP.edu. **Document type:** monographic series.

320   MQ   ISSN 0478-5118
PROGRESSISTE. w. Parti Progressiste Martiniquais, Rue de Tallis Clariere, Fort-de-France, Martinique. Ed. Paul Gabourg. circ. 13,000.

320.5   US   ISSN 0033-0736
AP2
PROGRESSIVE (MADISON). 1909. m. $30 to individuals; institutions $50. Progressive, Inc., 409 E. Main St., Madison, WI 53703. TEL 608-257-4626. FAX 608-257-3373. (Subscr. to: Cable Publishers, Box 421, Mt. Morris, IL 61054) Ed. Erwin Knoll; Pub. Matthew Rothschild. adv. contact: Matthew Rothschild. bk.rev.; film rev.; index. circ. 30,000. (also avail. in microform from UMI; back issues avail.; reprint service avail. from UMI) **Indexed:** Acad.Ind., Alt.Press Ind., Amer.Bibl.Slavic & E.Eur.Stud., Bk.Rev.Ind. (1979-), Chic.Per.Ind., Child.Bk.Rev.Ind. (1979-), Environ.Per.Bibl., Fut.Surv., Mag.Ind., Media Rev.Dig., Mid.East: Abstr.& Ind., P.A.I.S., Peace Res.Abstr., PMR, R.G., Sage Pub.Admin.Abstr.
●Also available online. Vendor(s): University Microfilms International.
—BLDSC (6924.640000); Faxon; Genuine Article; UMI; UnCover. **CCC.**
   Description: Investigative reporting, analysis, and commentary on political, economic and social issues, culture, and the arts.

320   US
PROJECT; ruling class conspiracy analysis for investors & political activists. 1974. m. $30. (A-albionic Society) A-albionic Research, Box 20273, Ferndale, MI 48220. Ed. Lloyd Miller. adv.; bk.rev. circ. 1,000. (looseleaf format; back issues avail.)
   Formerly (until 1984): Conspiracy Digest.
   Description: Tests theory that Vatican and Neo-British Empire are in covert battle for world hegemony.

320.5   SW   ISSN 0345-9578
PROLETAEREN. 1970. w. SEK 375 (effective 1990). K P M L, P.O. Box 31187, S-400 32 Goeteborg, Sweden.

320   II   ISSN 0377-3086
PROLETARIAN PATH. (Text in English) bi-m. Rs.12. 25-1 Jyotish Roy Rd., Calcutta 53, India. Eds. D.V. Rao, Muni Guha. bibl.; charts.

320   IT   ISSN 0393-8026
PROMETHEUS (MILAN); rivista internazionale di politica della scienza. 4/yr. L.96000 (foreign L.120000) (effective 1993). Franco Angeli Editore, Viale Monza, 106, Casella Postale 17175, 20100 Milan, Italy. TEL 02-2895762.

320   US   ISSN 1047-0239
HM263   CODEN: PORVE9
PROPAGANDA REVIEW. 1987. q. $20 to individuals; institutions $40. Media Alliance, Bldg. D, Fort Mason, San Francisco, CA 94123. Ed. Johan Carlisle. **Indexed:** Alt.Press Ind.

PROPHETIC OBSERVER. see *RELIGIONS AND THEOLOGY — Other Denominations And Sects*

320   CN
PROSPECTUS.* (Text in French and English) 1968. q. free. Progressive Conservative Youth Federation, c/o Progressive Conservative Party of Canada, 275 Slater St., Ottawa, ON K1P 5H9, Canada. Ed. Debbie Collinson. circ. 15,000. (tabloid format)

320   IT   ISSN 0391-271X
PROSPETTIVE NEL MONDO. 1976. m. Editoriale e Finanziaria Le Monnier, S.p.A., Via A. Meucci 2, Casella Postale 202, 50100 Florence, Italy.

320 330   IT
PROVINCIA IBLEA. s-m. L.3000. c/o Giovanni Gurrieri, Viale N. Colaianni 41, 97100 Ragusa, Italy. adv. circ. 1,500.

320   IT
PROVO RADICALE.* 1971. q. L.3000. Via Baccina 90, 00184 Rome, Italy. Ed. Massimo Teodori. bk.rev.

PUBLIC ADMINISTRATION AND DEVELOPMENT; an international journal of training, research and practice. see *BUSINESS AND ECONOMICS — International Development And Assistance*

PUBLIC ADMINISTRATION SURVEY. see *PUBLIC ADMINISTRATION*

POLITICAL SCIENCE

320   US   ISSN 0555-5914
JK6501
PUBLIC AFFAIRS. 1960. irreg. (approx. 3/yr.). free. University of South Dakota, Governmental Research Bureau, 414 E. Clark St., Vermillion, SD 57069. TEL 605-677-5702. Ed. Steve Feimer. charts; illus. circ. 1,800. **Indexed:** P.A.I.S. **Document type:** monographic series.
     Description: Each issue focuses on a different public policy issue.

PUBLIC AFFAIRS COMMENT. see *SOCIAL SCIENCES: COMPREHENSIVE WORKS*

320.9 350   US   ISSN 0033-3417
JK8701
PUBLIC AFFAIRS REPORT. 1960. bi-m. free. University of California at Berkeley, Institute of Governmental Studies, 109 Moses Hall, Berkeley, CA 94720. TEL 510-642-6723. FAX 510-642-3020. Ed. Gerald Lubenow. charts; stat. circ. 5,000. (reprint service avail. from UMI) **Indexed:** Environ.Abstr., Med.Care Rev., P.A.I.S., Sage Fam.Stud.Abstr. **Document type:** newsletter.

320   US   ISSN 1053-7724
HE8700.76.U6
PUBLIC AFFAIRS VIDEO ARCHIVES. CATALOG. 1988. s-a. Purdue University, Public Affairs Video Archives, Stewart Ctr. G-39, W. Lafayette, IN 47907. **Document type:** catalog.

PUBLIC CHOICE. see *BUSINESS AND ECONOMICS*

320   US   ISSN 0275-9322
THE PUBLIC EYE (CAMBRIDGE). 1977-1988; resumed Dec. 1992. 4/yr. $29 to individuals & non-profit organizations; other institutions $39. Political Research Associates, 678 Massachusetts Ave., Ste. 702, Cambridge, MA 02139-3355. TEL 617-661-9313. Eds. Judith Glaubman, Jean Hardisty. bk.rev.; bibl. (also avail. in microfilm) **Indexed:** Alt.Press Ind., HR Rep. **Document type:** newsletter.
     Description: Monitors the political activities and publications of the American right-wing, and provides in-depth analysis of right-wing political activism and emerging trends.

PUBLIC INTEREST. see *SOCIAL SCIENCES: COMPREHENSIVE WORKS*

PUBLIC JUSTICE REPORT. see *LAW*

320.9   US   ISSN 0033-362X
HM261.A1   CODEN: POPQAE
PUBLIC OPINION QUARTERLY. 1937. q. $22 to individuals; institutions $45; students $19. (American Association for Public Opinion Research) University of Chicago Press, Journals Division, 5720 S. Woodlawn Ave., Chicago, IL 60637. TEL 312-753-3347. FAX 312-753-0811. TELEX 25-4603. (Subscr. to: Box 37005, Chicago, IL 60637) Ed. Stanley Presser. adv.; bk.rev.; charts; index, cum.index: vols.1-46. (also avail. in microfilm from UMI,CIS; reprint service avail. from UMI,SCH) **Indexed:** A.B.C.Pol.Sci., ABI Inform, Abstr.Crim.& Pen., Acad.Ind., Account.Ind. (1974-), Amer.Bibl.Slavic & E.Eur.Stud., Amer.Hist.& Life, ASSIA, Bk.Rev.Ind. (1980-), Bus.Ind., Child.Bk.Rev.Ind. (1980-), Commun.Abstr., Cont.Pg.Manage., Crim.Just.Abstr., Curr.Cont., Hist.Abstr., Int.Polit.Sci.Abstr., Lang.& Lang.Behav.Abstr., Mag.Ind., Mark.Res.Abstr. (1963-), Mid.East: Abstr.& Ind., P.A.I.S., Polit.Sci.Abstr., Psychol.Abstr. (1936-), Res.High.Educ.Abstr., Soc.Sci.Ind., Sociol.Abstr. (1952-), SRI, SSCI. **Document type:** academic/scholarly publication.
—BLDSC (6967.850000); Faxon; Genuine Article; SWETS; UMI; UnCover. **CCC.**
     Refereed Serial

320 070   US
PUBLIC OPINION REPORT. 1988. q. free. Brown University, A. Alfred Taubman Center for Public Policy and American Institutions, Public Opinion Laboratory, Box 1977, Providence, RI 02912. TEL 401-863-2201. Ed. Darrell West. circ. 800. **Document type:** newsletter.
     Description: Reports of public opinion surveys in Rhode Island.

320   US   ISSN 1050-5067
HM261
PUBLIC PERSPECTIVE; a review of public opinion and polling. 1989. bi-m. $38.50 to individuals; institutions $105. Roper Center for Public Opinion Research, Box 440, Storrs, CT 06269. TEL 203-486-4440. FAX 203-486-6308. Ed. Everett C. Ladd. adv. contact: David M. Wilber. circ. 3,000 (controlled). **Document type:** academic/scholarly publication.
● Also available online. Vendor(s): Lexis-Nexis (PUBPER).
—UnCover.
     Description: Provides comprehensive data and analysis for current topics in public opinion, for political, media, government, academic and business analysts.

321.02   US   ISSN 0048-5950
JK1
PUBLIUS; the journal of federalism. 1971. q. $25 to individuals (foreign $35); institutions $35 (foreign $45). Meyner Center for the Study of State and Local Government, Kirby Hall of Civil Rights, Lafayette College, Easton, PA 18042-1785. TEL 610-250-5598. FAX 610-559-4048. E-mail: tja@lafibm.lafayette.edu. Eds. Daniel J. Elazar, John Kincaid. adv. contact: June A. Thompson. bk.rev.; bibl.; charts; stat.; index. circ. 1,000. (also avail. in microform from UMI; reprint service avail. from UMI) **Indexed:** A.B.C.Pol.Sci., Amer.Hist.& Life, Curr.Cont., Hist.Abstr., Int.Polit.Sci.Abstr., Lang.& Lang.Behav.Abstr., Mid.East: Abstr.& Ind., P.A.I.S., Polit.Sci.Abstr., Sage Pub.Admin.Abstr., Sage Urb.Stud.Abstr., Soc.Sci.Ind. (1994-), Sociol.Abstr., SSCI. **Document type:** academic/scholarly publication.
—BLDSC (7156.095000); Faxon; SWETS; UMI; UnCover.

329.6   US
PUEBLO UNIDO. (Text in Spanish) 1986. bi-m. free. Cuba Independiente y Democratica, 10021 S.W. 37th Terr., Miami, FL 33165. TEL 305-551-8484. FAX 305-559-9365. Ed. Huber Matos, Jr. circ. 10,000. (looseleaf format; back issues avail.) **Document type:** newsletter.
     Description: Sent to Cuba via underground ways to inform Cubans about democracy.

320   MX   ISSN 0188-1094
PUNTO FINAL INTERNACIONAL. m. Mex.$80($60) Centro Latinoamericano de Comunicaciones, San Lorenzo 173, Interior 101, Colonia del Valle, Mexico.

320   UY
PURIFICACION. 1977. irreg. Instituto Nacional de Investigaciones Historicas y Geopoliticas, Avda. 18 de Julio 2226, Montevideo, Uruguay. Ed. J.J. Scapusio.

320   KN
THE PYONGYANG TIMES. (Editions in English, French, Spanish) w. $10.40. Sochon-dong, Sosong District, Pyongyang, N. Korea. TEL 5-1951. TELEX 37018 EPB KP. (Dist. by: Korean Publications Exchange Association, Export Section, P.O. Box 222, Pyongyang, N. Korea. FAX 850-2-814632) **Document type:** newspaper.

320 301 330 100   US   ISSN 0738-9752
B823.3
Q J I. (Quarterly Journal of Ideology) 1976. q. $20 to individuals; institutions $35. Louisiana State University, Shreveport, 1 University Pl., Shreveport, LA 71115-2399. TEL 318-797-5235. FAX 318-797-5358. Eds. Norman A. Dolch, Laurie Morrow. adv.; bk.rev. circ. 500. **Indexed:** Lang.& Lang.Behav.Abstr., Sociol.Abstr. **Document type:** academic/scholarly publication.
—UnCover.
     Description: Publishes qualitative, philosphical and theoretical papers analyzing ideological issues in sociology, economics, history, political science and other fields, with a multidisciplinary perspective.
     Refereed Serial

320   US
QATAR NEWS. 1974. bi-m. free. Embassy of the State of Qatar, 600 New Hampshire Ave., Washington, DC 20037. TEL 202-338-0111. FAX 202-337-2686. circ. 6,000.

329.9   CC   ISSN 1001-8239
QIU ZHI/SEEK KNOWLEDGE. (Text in Chinese) 1984. m. Y1.60 per no. (Zhongguo Gongchandang, Tianjin Shi-Wei Dangxiao - Chinese Communist Party, Tianjin City Committee Party School) Qiu Zhi Bianjibu, 4, Yuliang Dao, Nankai Qu, Tianjin 300191, People's Republic of China. TEL 362087. (Dist. by: China Publications Foreign Trade Corp., Tianjin Branch, 27 Hubei Lu, Tianjin, P.R.C.) Ed. Gao Xiaokun. adv. contact: Yang Gongying. circ. 30,000. **Document type:** government publication.

329.9   IT   ISSN 0033-4901
HD8473
QUADERNI DI AZIONE SOCIALE. 1970. bi-m. L.45000. Via G. Marocora, 18-20, Rome, Italy. FAX 5840462. Ed. D. Rosati. adv.; bk.rev. circ. 2,500.

320   IT
▼**QUADERNI DI SCIENZA POLITICA.** 1994. 3/yr. L.60000 (foreign L.90000) (effective 1994). Casa Editrice Dott. A. Giuffre, Via Busto Arsizio, 40, 20151 Milan, Italy. TEL 39-2-38089200.

QUADERNI FIORENTINI PER LA STORIA DEL PENSIERO GIURIDICO MODERNO. see *LAW*

QUE FAIRE DE L'ECONOMIE. see *PHILOSOPHY*

320 917.106   CN   ISSN 0824-2348
QUEBECER. French edition (ISSN 0824-1783) (Text in English) 1982. q. Can.$10. Alliance Quebec, 630 Rene Levesque Blvd., Ste. 930, Montreal, PQ H3B 1S6, Canada. TEL 514-875-2771. FAX 514-875-7507. Ed. David Ferrabee. bk.rev. circ. 15,000.

320   PE   ISSN 0250-9806
QUEHACER; realidad nacional-problemas y alternativas. 1979. bi-m. $45 in America; Europe $60. Centro de Estudios y Promocion del Desarrollo (DESCO), Leon de la Fuente 110, Magdalena del Mar, Lima 17, Peru. TEL 14-627193. FAX 14-617309. adv. circ. 15,000. (back issues avail.) **Indexed:** P.A.I.S.For.Lang.Ind.

322 327   IT   ISSN 1121-3353
QUESTE ISTITUZIONI; cronache del sistema politico. 1973. q. L.75000 (effective 1996). (Gruppo di Studio Societa e Istituzioni) Ques.I.Re s.r.l., Via E.Q. Visconti 8, 00198 Rome, Italy. TEL 39-6-3215319. FAX 39-6-3215283. Ed. Sergio Ristuccia. adv. contact: Giorgio Pagano. bk.rev.; illus. circ. 2,000. (tabloid format) **Document type:** monographic series.
     Description: Covers problems related to the public policy of the central government and the local administration in Italy, European integration, the relationship between Church and State, territorial management, non-profit sector, and institutions and new computer technologies.

320.531   YU   ISSN 0033-6351
HX365.5
QUESTIONS ACTUELLES DU SOCIALISME. English edition: Socialist Thought and Practice (ISSN 0583-7200); German edition: Sozialistische Theorie und Praxis (ISSN 0350-476X); Italian edition: Questioni Attuali del Socialismo (ISSN 0351-0107); Russian edition: Sotsialisticheskaya Mysl' i Praktika (ISSN 0350-4751); Serbo-Croatian edition: Aktuelna Pitanja Socijalizma. (Spanish edition: Cuestiones Actuales del Socialismo (ISSN 0350-8846); Arabic edition (ISSN 0350-5413)) (Text in French) 1951. m. $30. Komunist, Trg Marksa i Engelsa 11, 11000 Belgrade, Yugoslavia. Ed. Branko Prnjat.

945   IT   ISSN 0033-6378
QUESTITALIA. vol.13, 1970. m. S. Croce 598, Venice, Italy. Ed. Wladimiro Dorigo. bk.rev.; bibl.

QUINNIPIAC LAW REVIEW. see *LAW*

320   US   ISSN 0033-6629
QUIXOTE; the anti-capitalist renegade post- and future Marxist wordslingers collective. 1965. m. $20. (Post- and Future Marxist Renegade Collective) Quixote Press, Inc., 2407 Watts St., Houston, TX 77030-1829. TEL 713-667-6639. Eds. Morris Edelson, Melissa Bondy. adv.; bk.rev.; film rev.; play rev. circ. 200. (processed)
     Formerly: Quickoats.

320   SA
QUO VADIS? (PRETORIA). (Text in Afrikaans, English) 1993. irreg. Afrikaner-Volksfront, Posbus 7934, Pretoria 0001, South Africa. illus. (tabloid format) **Document type:** newspaper.

POLITICAL SCIENCE

320 320 US ISSN 0882-3456
QUORUM REPORT. 1982. s-m. $140. Texas Analyst, Inc., Box 8, Austin, TX 78767. TEL 713-728-5921. FAX 713-728-9400. Ed. Harvey Kronberg; Pub. Cathy Mincberg. bk.rev. **Document type:** newsletter.
Description: Reports on Texas government and politics.

320 330 II
R.B.R.R. KALE MEMORIAL LECTURES. 1937. a.; none published 1947 or 1970. price varies. Gokhale Institute of Politics and Economics, Pune 411004, India. TEL (0212)54287. (Dist. by: Orient Longman, Ltd., Nicol Rd., Ballard Estate, Bombay 400 038, India)

R N I B CONTENTION. (Royal National Institute for the Blind) see HANDICAPPED — Visually Impaired

R S A REVIEW/R S A OORSIG. see BUSINESS AND ECONOMICS — Economic Situation And Conditions

320 US ISSN 0033-7617
HD4802
RADICAL AMERICA. 1967. q. $22 to individuals; institutions $38.70. Alternative Education Project, Inc., One Summer St., Somerville, MA 02143. TEL 617-628-6585. Ed.Bd. adv.; bk.rev.; index. circ. 5,000. (also avail. in microform from UMI; back issues avail.; reprint service avail. from UMI) **Indexed:** Alt.Press Ind., Amer.Bibl.Slavic & E.Eur.Stud., Amer.Hist.& Life, Film Lit.Ind. (1990-), Hist.Abstr., Lang.& Lang.Behav.Abstr., Left Ind. (1982-), Mid.East: Abstr.& Ind., Polit.Sci.Abstr., Sociol.Abstr., Wom.Stud.Abstr. **Document type:** academic/scholarly publication.
—BLDSC (7228.090000); Faxon; SWETS; UMI; UnCover.
Description: Independent journal exerting much influence on the Democratic left with its articles, left and feminist balanced between historical perspective and topical strategy.

324.248 DK ISSN 0107-279X
RADIKAL POLITIK. 1972. fortn. DKK 75. Radikale Venstre - Danish Social-Liberal Party, Christiansborg, 1240 Copenhagen K, Denmark. TEL 45-33-37-47-47. FAX 45-33-13-72-51. adv.; bk.rev. circ. 6,000.
Formerly (until, 1981): Fremsyn (ISSN 0107-2803)

320 327 US ISSN 0079-9491
RADNER LECTURES. irreg., no.7, 1976. Columbia University Press, 562 W. 113th St., New York, NY 10025. TEL 212-666-1000. **Document type:** monographic series.

RAIN. see ENVIRONMENTAL STUDIES

322.44 US
RAINBOW NETWORK NEWSLETTER. 1983. a. $2. Slough Press, Box 1385, Austin, TX 78767. Ed. Chuck Taylor. adv.; bk.rev. circ. 500. (looseleaf format) **Document type:** newsletter, catalog.
Formerly: Nonviolent Anarchist Newsletter.

320.532 DK ISSN 0109-1700
RAMBUKKEN. 1983. s-a. free. (Danmarks Kommunistiske Parti-Marxister-Leninister i Aarhus Amt) Arbejderens Bogbutik, Munkegade 2, 8000 Aarhus C, Denmark. illus.

320 053.1 GW ISSN 0004-7899
RAN; ein politisches Jugendmagazin. 1948. m. DM.40. (Deutscher Gewerkschaftsbund) Bund-Verlag GmbH, Postfach 900840, 51118 Cologne, Germany. Ed. Klaus-Juergen Eichhorst. adv.; bk.rev.; illus. circ. 50,000. **Document type:** bulletin.
—CCC.
Formerly: Aufwaerts.

320 US ISSN 0740-9281
RAND RESEARCH REVIEW. 1977. 3/yr. free. Rand Corporation, Publications Department, 1700 Main St., Box 2138, Santa Monica, CA 90407-2138. TEL 310-393-0411. FAX 310-393-4818. TELEX 9103436878. Ed. Ann M. Shoben. charts; illus. circ. 12,000.
—BLDSC (7254.410800); Faxon.
Description: Reports on Rand Corporation's research programs of matters affecting the nation's security and domestic welfare.

320 UK ISSN 0951-4066
RAVEN. 1987. q. £11 to individuals (foreign £12); institutions £16 (foreign £20). Freedom Press, 84b Whitechapel High St., London E1 7QX, England. TEL 071-247-9249. circ. 2,000. **Document type:** academic/scholarly publication.

320 301 US
READINGS IN SOCIAL AND POLITICAL THEORY. 1984. irreg. price varies. New York University Press, 70 Washington Square S., New York, NY 10012. TEL 212-998-2575; 800-996-3833. FAX 212-995-3833. TELEX 235128 NYU UR. **Document type:** monographic series.

320 GO ISSN 0486-106X
REALITES GABONAISES. (Text in French) 1960. irreg. (3-4/yr.). 1000 Fr.CFA($44.12) Institut Pedagogique National, B.P. 813, Libreville, Gabon. Ed. M.A. Bouanga. illus. **Indexed:** Curr.Cont.Africa.

REASON; free minds and free markets. see LITERARY AND POLITICAL REVIEWS

RECHTS- UND STAATSWISSENSCHAFTEN. see LAW

RECHTSWISSENSCHAFT UND SOZIALPOLITIK. see LAW

320 AT
RED AND BLACK. 1964. irreg. (1-2/yr.). Aus.$6. P.O. Box 12, Quaama, N.S.W. 2550, Australia. Ed. Jack Grancharoff. bk.rev. circ. 200. (back issues avail.)
Description: Features anarchism, libertarianism and feminism.

RED MENACE; a libertarian socialist newsletter. see LITERARY AND POLITICAL REVIEWS

321 AT ISSN 1320-6435
RED POLITICS; a journal for the discussion of revolutionary ideas. 1993. irreg. Aus.$12 to individuals (Aus$.18 in Europe & N. America); institutions Aus.$35. R P Publishing, 2-77 Holden St. N., Fitzroy, Vic. 3068, Australia. E-mail: davidm@union3.su.swin.edu.au.
●Available only online.

320.9 GW ISSN 0034-2092
REDAKTIONS-ARCHIV; Zahlenbilder aus Gesellschaft, Wirtschaft, Politik und Recht. 1955. m. DM.168. Erich Schmidt Verlag GmbH & Co. (Berlin), Genthiner Str. 30G, 10785 Berlin, Germany. TEL 030-2500850. FAX 030-25008521. Ed. G. Huck. charts; illus.; stat.; index. circ. 1,200. (looseleaf format) **Document type:** academic/scholarly publication.

320 CN
REFORM PARTY OF CANADA. NATIONAL BULLETIN. w. Reform Party of Canada, Reform Fund Canada, 833 4th Ave. S.W., Ste. 600, Calgary, Alta. T2P 0K5, Canada. TEL 403-269-1990. FAX 403-269-4077.

320 CN ISSN 0842-3148
REFORMER. 4/yr. Reform Party of Canada, 833 4th Ave. S.W., Ste. 600, Calgary, Alta. T2P 0K5, Canada. TEL 403-269-1990. FAX 403-269-4077. Ed. Laurie Watson. circ. 290,000.

056.940 CN ISSN 0384-9120
REGARDS SUR ISRAEL. (Text in French) 1973. m. free. Canada Israel Committee, 1310 Avenue Green, Suite 710, Montreal, Que. H3Z 2B2, Canada. TEL 514-934-0771. Ed. Michel M. Solomon. adv.; bk.rev.; illus. circ. 4,000.

320 UK
THE REGIONALIST. 1982. irreg. £1.50 to individuals; institutions £7.50. c/o David Robins, Ed., 16 Adolphus St. West, Seaham Harbour, Durham, England. bk.rev. circ. 500. (processed) **Document type:** bulletin.
Formerly: Regionalist Seminar (ISSN 0264-522X)

320 US ISSN 0147-0590
K18 CODEN: REGUD4
REGULATION (WASHINGTON, 1977); the Cato review of business & government. 1977. 3/yr. $18 to individuals (foreign $23); institutions $28 (foreign $33). Cato Institute, 1000 Massachusetts Ave., N.W., Washington, DC 20001-5403. TEL 202-842-0200. FAX 202-842-3490. Ed. William A. Niskanen. (reprint service avail. from WSH) **Indexed:** ABI Inform., Bank.Lit.Ind., BPIA, Bus.Ind., Med.Care Rev., P.A.I.S., Tr.& Indus.Ind.
—BLDSC (7345.670000); Faxon; SWETS; UMI; UnCover.
Description: Features items on economics, law, politics of government regulation and reviews recent scholarship.

967.571 RW ISSN 1013-6371
RELEVE. 1976. m. $27. Office Rwandais d'Information, B.P. 83, Kigali, Rwanda. TEL 75-665. TELEX 557. Ed. Christophe Mfizi. adv.; bk.rev.; illus. circ. 1,000. **Document type:** newspaper.
Incorporates: Rwanda-Carrefour d'Afrique (ISSN 0036-0481)
Description: Covers politics, economics and culture.

320 UK ISSN 0968-252X
RENEWAL (LONDON); politics - movements - ideas. 1993. q. £20. Labour Co-Ordinating Committee Publishing Ltd., Freepost, London SE18 3BR, England. adv. contact: Alan MacDougall. **Document type:** academic/scholarly publication.
—BLDSC (7364.193200).
Description: Publishes material on economic policy, public services, the democratic agenda, cultural strategy, and other issues that are geared towards renewing the Labour Party.

320 MX ISSN 0188-5650
RENGLON. 1986. q. Mex.$2500. Editorial Terra Firme, Priv. de la Providencia 38, Sn. Jeronimo Lidice, Mexico 20, D.F., Mexico. Ed. Ulises Canchola Gutierrez. bk.rev. circ. 2,000.

RENMIN ZHENGXIE BAO/C P P C C GAZETTE. see PUBLIC ADMINISTRATION

972.93 DR ISSN 0034-446X
RENOVACION. 1936. fortn. RD.$6. Puerta del Sol, Calle Jose Reyes esq. El Conde, Santo Domingo, Dominican Republic. Ed. Olga Quisqueya Viuda Martinez. adv.; charts; illus. circ. 15,000. (back issues avail.)

329.3 SG
RENOVATEUR. m. Parti Democratique Senegalais - Renovation, B.P. 12172, Dakar, Senegal.

REPORT FROM THE CAPITAL. see RELIGIONS AND THEOLOGY — Protestant

REPORT FROM THE HILL. see LAW

320.9 UK ISSN 0034-4737
D410
REPORT ON WORLD AFFAIRS. 1919. q. £5($14) Fitzken Publishers, 3 Alma Sq., London NW8 6QD, England. (also avail. in microform from MIM,UMI; microfilm from WMP; reprint service avail. from UMI)
Formerly: Report on Foreign Affairs.

324.21 UK ISSN 0034-4893
REPRESENTATION: JOURNAL OF ELECTORAL RECORD AND COMMENT. N.S. 1960. q. £25 to individuals; institutions £30. The Arthur McDougall Fund, 6 Chancel St., London SE1 0UU, England. TEL 44-171-620-1080. FAX 44-171-928-4366. Ed. Paul Wilder. adv.; bk.rev. circ. 2,000. **Indexed:** Amer.Hum.Ind. **Document type:** academic/scholarly publication.
—BLDSC (7690.700000).

320 IE
REPSOL PAMPHLETS. irreg. no.7, 1971. Republican Educational Department, 30 Gardiner Place, Dublin 1, Ireland. Ed.Bd. charts.

329 US ISSN 0363-9290
JK1967
REPUBLICAN ALMANAC. biennial. $60. Republican National Committee, Computer Services Division, 310 First St., S.E., Washington, DC 20003. TEL 202-863-8670. FAX 202-863-8851. Ed. Clark H. Bensen. illus.
Description: Provides statistical data and information on federal, state, county elections on a state by state basis.

POLITICAL SCIENCE

320 UK ISSN 0144-7548
REPUBLICAN ENGLISHMAN. 1979. irreg. Republican Party of England, 44 Water St., Accrington, Lancs. BB5 6QZ, England. Ed. Thomas Smith. bk.rev. circ. 50.

329.6 US
REPUBLICAN WOMAN. 1972. q. $15. National Federation of Republican Women, 310 First St. S.E., Washington, DC 20003. TEL 202-547-9341. FAX 202-547-8485. Ed. Karen Johnson. bk.rev.; illus. circ. 130,000.
 Former titles (until Oct.-Nov. 1987): New Challenge (Washington); Challenge (Washington) (ISSN 0045-6233)

320 GW
DER REPUBLIKANER; offizielles Organ der Bundespartei. 1984. m. (Bundespartei Der Republikaner) K S Druck, Postfach 1148, 26359 Wilhelmshaven, Germany. **Document type:** newsletter.

320 BE ISSN 0486-4700
JA1.A1
RES PUBLICA. (Text in Dutch, English, French, summaries in English) 1959. 4/yr. 2000 BEF. Politologisch Instituut, Van Evenstraat 2B, B-3000 Leuven, Belgium. TEL 32-16-283250. FAX 32-16-283253. Ed. Wilfried Dewachter. adv.: B&W page 12000 BEF. circ. 1,000. (reprint service avail. from WSH) **Indexed:** A.B.C.Pol.Sci., Int.Bibl.Soc.Sci., Int.Polit.Sci.Abstr., Lang.& Lang.Behav.Abstr., M.L.A., Sociol.Abstr., SSCI. **Document type:** academic/scholarly publication.
 —SWETS.
 Description: Belgian journal of political science.

RESEARCH IN POLITICAL ECONOMY; an annual compilation of research. see *BUSINESS AND ECONOMICS — Economic Systems And Theories, Economic History*

RESEARCH IN SOCIAL PROBLEMS AND PUBLIC POLICY; a research annual. see *SOCIOLOGY*

RESEAUX; revue interdisciplinaire de philosophie morale et politique. see *PHILOSOPHY*

322.4 US
RESOURCE CENTER FOR NON VIOLENCE. NEWSLETTER. 1979. 2/yr. donations. Resource Center for Non Violence, 515 Broadway, Santa Cruz, CA 95060-4621. TEL 408-423-1626. Ed. Jim Wake. circ. 4,000. (tabloid format) **Document type:** newsletter.

RESPONSIVE COMMUNITY; rights and responsibilities. see *SOCIOLOGY*

320 PE ISSN 0250-9792
RESUMEN SEMANAL. Running title: D E S C O Resumen Semanal. 1978. w. (50/yr.). $150. Centro de Estudios y Promocion del Desarrollo (DESCO), Leon de la Fuente 110, Lima 17, Peru. TEL 14-627193. FAX 14-617309. adv. circ. 3,000.

320.5 100 UK ISSN 0034-5970
JX1901
RESURGENCE; journal of the ecological and spiritual culture. 1966. bi-m. £16($45) Resurgence Limited, Salem Cottage, Trelill, Bodmin, Cornwall PL30 3HZ, England. TEL 01237-441293. FAX 01237-441203. Ed. Satish Kumar. adv. contact: Stephanie Neil. bk.rev.; index. circ. 10,000. **Indexed:** Environ.Per.Bibl. (1990-), Fut.Surv. **Document type:** bulletin.
 —BLDSC (7785.410000).
 Incorporates: Undercurrents (ISSN 0306-2392)

RETHINKING MARXISM. see *BUSINESS AND ECONOMICS — Economic Systems And Theories, Economic History*

320 IT
RETI - PRATICHE E SAPERI DI DONNE. 1970? bi-m. L.41000 (foreign L.61000). Editori Riuniti, Via Serchio 9-11, 00198 Rome, Italy. TEL 06-866383. FAX 06-8416096. TELEX EDIRIU I 625292. Ed. Maria Luisa Boccia. bk.rev.; bibl.; illus. circ. 12,000. (back issues avail.)
 Supersedes (in 1987): Donne e Politica - Women and Politics (ISSN 0393-6775)

320 AT ISSN 0310-9143
RETRIEVAL. (Text in English and French) 1971. m. Aus.$4. P.O. Box 51, Fitzroy, Vic. 3065, Australia.

320.531 FR ISSN 0034-6292
REVEIL SOCIALISTE DE LANNEMEZAN.* 1966. m. 10 F.($2) Federation des Hautes Pyrenees du Parti Socialiste Unifie, 6 rue du 4 Septembre, Lannemezan, France. Ed. Leopold Dasque. bk.rev. circ. 2,500.

REVIEW OF CENTRAL AND EAST EUROPEAN LAW. see *LAW*

320 330.9 UK ISSN 0953-8259
HB1 CODEN: RPECEI
REVIEW OF POLITICAL ECONOMY. 1989. q. £42 to individuals; institutions £144 (effective 1996). Carfax Publishing Co., P.O. Box 25, Abingdon, Oxon. OX14 3UE, England. TEL 44-1235-555335. FAX 44-1235-553559. (N. American subscr. to: Carfax Publishing Co., 875-81 Massachusetts Ave., Cambridge, MA 02139) Ed. John Pheby. **Document type:** academic/scholarly publication.
 —BLDSC (7794.119000); Faxon; SWETS; UnCover.

920 US ISSN 0034-6705
JA1
REVIEW OF POLITICS. 1939. q. $25 to individuals (foreign $29); institutions $30 (foreign $34). University of Notre Dame, Review of Politics, Box B, Notre Dame, IN 46556. TEL 219-631-6623. Ed. Walter Nicgorskis. adv. contact: Dennis W. Moran. bk.rev.; index. circ. 1,700. (also avail. in microform from UMI,PMC; reprint service avail. from KTO,UMI) **Indexed:** A.B.C.Pol.Sci., Acad.Ind., Amer.Bibl.Slavic & E.Eur.Stud., Amer.Hist.& Life, Bk.Rev.Ind. (1980-), Cath.Ind., Child.Bk.Rev.Ind. (1980-), Curr.Cont., Hist.Abstr., Int.Polit.Sci.Abstr., Mid.East: Abstr.& Ind., P.A.I.S., Polit.Sci.Abstr., Sage Pub.Admin.Abstr., Soc.Sci.Ind., SSCI. **Document type:** academic/scholarly publication.
 —BLDSC (7794.120000); Faxon; SWETS; UMI; UnCover.

325 TZ
REVIEW OF REFUGEE ISSUES. 1989. irreg. University of Dar es Salaam, African Refugee Study Centre, P.O. Box 35046, Dar es Salaam, Tanzania. **Indexed:** P.L.E.S.A.

320 AG ISSN 0034-7019
REVISTA ARGENTINA DE CIENCIA POLITICA.* vol.2, 1961. irreg. Asociacion Argentina de Ciencia Politica, Solis 443, Buenos Aires, Argentina. bk.rev.

320 AG
REVISTA ARGENTINA DE ESTUDIOS POLITICOS. 1945. 3/yr. Instituto Argentino de Estudios Politicos, Mansilla 2698, Buenos Aires, Argentina. bk.rev.; bibl.

320 DR
REVISTA ATENEO DOMINICANO. 1976. m. RD.$10. Calle Felix Mariano Lluberes 18, Apdo. Postal 263-2, Santo Domingo, Dominican Republic. Ed. Julio J. Julia. bk.rev.; bibl.

320 BL ISSN 0034-7191
JA5
REVISTA BRASILEIRA DE ESTUDOS POLITICOS. (Text in Portuguese) 1956. s-a. $40. Universidade Federal de Minas Gerais, Av. A. Cabral 211 s. 1206, 30170-000 Belo Horizonte (MG), Brazil. Eds. Orlando M. Carvalho, Raul Machado Horta. adv.; bk.rev.; bibl.; charts; cum.index. circ. 3,400. **Indexed:** A.B.C.Pol.Sci., Amer.Hist.& Life, Hisp.Amer.Per.Ind. (1970-), Hist.Abstr., Int.Polit.Sci.Abstr., P.A.I.S.For.Lang.Ind. **Document type:** academic/scholarly publication.
 —BLDSC (7844.700000).

320 UY
REVISTA COMPANERO. 1991. bi-m. 2000 N$ per no. Impresa Editorial Espacio s.r.l., Daniel Fernandez Crespo 2242, Montevideo, Uruguay. TEL 94-2518. Ed. Hugo Cores.

REVISTA DE DERECHO Y CIENCIAS POLITICAS. see *LAW*

320 330.9 BL ISSN 0101-3157
HC186
REVISTA DE ECONOMIA POLITICA. q. $40. Centro de Economia Politica, Avda. Jorge Joao Saad 104, 05618-000 Sao Paulo, SP, Brazil. TEL 011-02801222. **Indexed:** Hisp.Amer.Per.Ind. (1986-).

320 CU
REVISTA DE ESTUDIOS EUROPEOS. 1987. 4/yr. $22 in S. America; N. America $24; elsewhere $28. (Centro de Estudios Europeos) Ediciones Cubanas, Obispo No. 527, Apdo. 605, Havana, Cuba. (U.S. Dist.: Publications Exchanges Inc., 8306 Mills Dr., Ste. 241, Miami, FL 33183. TEL 800-375-2822) Ed. Jose Eloy Valdes. adv.

320 SP ISSN 0048-7694
H8
REVISTA DE ESTUDIOS POLITICOS. (Text in Spanish; summaries in English and French) 1940. q. 4800 ptas.($61) (Centro de Estudios Constitucionales) Libreria Europa, Valverde 32, 1o, 28004 Madrid, Spain. TEL 91-5325069. Ed. Pedro de Vega. bk.rev.; bibl. circ. 1,500. **Indexed:** A.B.C.Pol.Sci., Amer.Hist.& Life, CERDIC, Hist.Abstr., Int.Polit.Sci.Abstr.
 —BLDSC (7854.510000); SWETS.

320 BL
JL2400
REVISTA DEMOCRACIA. 1985. m. $80 to individuals; institutions $85. Instituto Brasileiro de Analises Sociais e Economicas, Rua Vicente de Sousa 29, 22251-070 Botafogo, RJ, Brazil. TEL 55-21-286-6161. FAX 286-0541. Ed. Nilo Sergio Gomes. charts; illus.; stat.; index. circ. 3,500.
 Formerly: Politicas Governamentais (ISSN 0104-1436)

320 BL
REVISTA DO MERCOSUL/REVISTA DEL MERCOSUR; revista mensal bilingue de integracao latino-americana. (Text in Portuguese, Spanish) 1992. m. Cr.$96000 (Arg.$48; 72 g.; Urg.$76800; US$48). Editora Terceiro Mundo, Rua da Gloria 122 - 105-106, 20241 Rio de Janeiro, RJ, Brazil. TEL 021-242-0763. FAX 5521-252-8455. **Document type:** consumer publication.

320 DR ISSN 0259-1049
REVISTA ESTUDIOS DOMINICANOS. 1984. 3/yr. $8. (Instituto de Estudios Dominicanos) Liberia America, Apdo. Postal 20693, Calle Ciriaco Ramirez No. 49, 3 Piso, Santo Domingo, Dominican Republic. circ. 300.

320 SP ISSN 0210-7716
D1
REVISTA HISTORIA, INSTITUCIONES, DOCUMENTOS. (Text in Greek, Latin, Spanish) 1974. a. price varies. Universidad de Sevilla, Departamentos de Historia Medieval, Historia del Derecho, Paleografia y Diplomatica, Servicio de Publicaciones, Valparaiso 5, 41013 Seville, Spain. TEL 954-231958. FAX 954-232245.

320 MX ISSN 0185-1918
JA5
REVISTA MEXICANA DE CIENCIAS POLITICAS Y SOCIALES. 1955. q. Mex.$90($90) (effective 1995). Universidad Nacional Autonoma de Mexico, Facultad de Ciencias Politicas y Sociales, Division de Estudios de Postgrado, Ciudad Universitaria, 04510 Mexico D.F., Mexico. Ed. Alfredo Romero Castilla. adv.; bk.rev.; bibl.; charts; index. **Indexed:** A.B.C.Pol.Sci., Amer.Hist.& Life, Hisp.Amer.Per.Ind. (1970-), Hist.Abstr., Int.Polit.Sci.Abstr., Lang.& Lang.Behav.Abstr.
 —SWETS.
 Former titles: Revista Mexicana de Ciencia Politica (ISSN 0034-9976); Ciencias Politicas y Sociales.

320 342 SP ISSN 0211-5581
JA26
REVISTA POLITICA COMPARADA. 1980. q. 1500 ptas. Universidad Internacional Menendez Pelayo, Palacio de la Magdalena, Santander, Spain. (Dist. by: Distribuciones Oficiales Reunidas, S.A., C. Plaza 15, 2o piso, 28043 Madrid, Spain. TEL 759-70-49) circ. 2,500.

320.531 US ISSN 0193-3612
REVOLUTION. Spanish edition: Revolucion (ISSN 0193-3493) 1973. irreg., approx. 2/yr. $14 to individuals; libraries $20. (Revolutionary Communist Party, Central Committee) R C P Publications, Inc., Box 3486, Merchandise Mart, Chicago, IL 60654. TEL 312-663-5920. bk.rev.; index. circ. 5,000. (also avail. in microfilm from UMI; reprint service avail. from UMI) **Indexed:** Alt.Press Ind.

960 322.4   AE   ISSN 0035-0621
REVOLUTION AFRICAINE.* (Text in French) 1963. w. $126. Front de Liberation Nationale, Blvd. Zirout Yousuf, Algiers, Algeria. (Dist. in US by: African Imprint Library Service, Box 350, West Falmouth, MA 02574. TEL 508-540-5378) Ed. Zoubir Zemzoum. adv.; bk.rev.; film rev.; play rev.; charts; illus. circ. 5,000.

331.88   AE   ISSN 0484-8365
REVOLUTION ET TRAVAIL. (Editions in Arabic, French) m. Union General des Travailleurs Algeriens, 1 rue Abdelkader Benbarek, Pl. du 1er Mai, Algiers, Algeria. TEL 2-66-73-53. TELEX 65051. (Dist. in US by: African Imprint Library Service, Box 350, West Falmouth, MA 02574. TEL 508-540-5378) Ed. Lakhdari Mohamed Lakhdar.

329.82   US   ISSN 0193-3485
REVOLUTIONARY WORKER. Spanish edition: Obrero Revolucionario. 1979. w. $40 to individuals; institutions $52. (Revolutionary Communist Party) R C P Publications, Inc., Box 3486, Merchandise Mart, Chicago, IL 60654. TEL 312-663-5920. bk.rev.; charts; illus.; stat.; tr.lit.; index. circ. 50,000. (tabloid format; back issues avail.)

REVUE ALGERIENNE DES SCIENCES JURIDIQUES. see *LAW*

341 327   SZ   ISSN 0035-1091
JX3
REVUE DE DROIT INTERNATIONAL DE SCIENCES DIPLOMATIQUES ET POLITIQUES. (Text in English, French, German, Italian) 1923. q. 180 SFr. to Europe, U.S. and Canada; elsewhere 190 SFr. Case Postale 5055, CH-1211 Geneva 11, Switzerland. TEL 022-8198282. FAX 022-8198222. Ed. C.L. Heinbach. index. (also avail. in microfiche from IDC; reprint service avail. from SWZ) **Indexed:** Int.Polit.Sci.Abstr. **Document type:** academic/scholarly publication.
—BLDSC (7898.520000); SWETS.

320   FR   ISSN 0751-6614
HC271
REVUE DE L'O F C E. Cover title: Observations et Diagnostiques Economiques. (Text in French, summaries in English) 1982. 4/yr. 305 F. to individuals (foreign 365 F.); institutions 460 F. (foreign 520 F.). (Observatoire Francais des Conjonctures Economiques) Presses de la Fondation Nationale des Sciences Politiques, 44 rue du Four, 75006 Paris, France. TEL 44-39-39-60. FAX 1-45-48-04-41. TELEX 201 002 F. **Indexed:** ELLIS.
—CCC.

956 960   SY   ISSN 0035-1245
REVUE DE LA PRESSE ARABE. (Text in French) 1948. s-w. £S5000($725) Office Arabe de Presse et de Documentation, P.O. Box 3550, 67 Place Chahbandar, Damascus, Syria. Ed. A. Khani.
Formerly: Bulletin de la Presse Arabe.

REVUE DU DROIT PUBLIC ET DE LA SCIENCE POLITIQUE EN FRANCE ET A L'ETRANGER. see *LAW*

960   SG   ISSN 0035-3027
DT1
REVUE FRANCAISE D'ETUDES POLITIQUES AFRICAINES. 1966. m. 12000 Fr.CFA. Societe Africaine d'Edition, B.P. 1877, Dakar, Senegal. (And 32 rue de l'Echiquier, Paris, France) adv.; bk.rev.; bibl.; charts; index. circ. 4,000. **Indexed:** Curr.Cont.Africa, Int.Lab.Doc., Rural Recreat.Tour.Abstr., World Agri.Econ.& Rural Sociol.Abstr.

320   SG   ISSN 0338-2060
DE100
REVUE FRANCAISE D'ETUDES POLITIQUES MEDITERRANEENNES. 1975. m. (10/yr.). 10000 Fr.CFA. Societe Africaine d'Edition, B.P. 1877, Dakar, Senegal. (And 32 rue de l'Echiquier, Paris, France) Ed. Paulette Decraene. **Indexed:** Rural Recreat.Tour.Abstr., World Agri.Econ.& Rural Sociol.Abstr.

320 944   FR
▼**REVUE FRANCAISE D'HISTOIRE DES IDEES POLITIQUES.** 1995. s-a. 250 F. to individuals; libraries 350 F. (effective 1995). Editions A. de J. Picard, 82 rue Bonaparte, 75006 Paris, France. FAX 43-26-42-64. Ed. Guillaume Bacot. bibl. **Document type:** academic/scholarly publication.

320   FR   ISSN 0035-2950
JA11
REVUE FRANCAISE DE SCIENCE POLITIQUE. (Text in French, summaries in English, French) 1951. bi-m. 380 F. to individuals (foreign 425 F.); institutions 660 F. (foreign 710 F.). (Fondation Nationale des Sciences Politiques) Presses de la Fondation Nationale des Sciences Politiques, 44 rue du Four, 75006 Paris, France. TEL 44-39-39-60. FAX 1-45-48-04-41. (Co-sponsor: Association Francaise de Science Politique) Ed. Jean-Luc Parodi. bk.rev.; abstr.; bibl.; index. circ. 3,500. (reprint service avail. from SCH) **Indexed:** A.B.C.Pol.Sci., Amer.Hist.& Life, E.I., Hist.Abstr., Int.Lab.Doc., Int.Polit.Sci.Abstr., P.A.I.S.For.Lang.Ind., Pt.de Rep. (1979-), SSCI.
—BLDSC (7904.420000); Faxon; SWETS; UnCover. CCC.
Description: Scientific presentation of research, ideas and methodological criticism of politics.

320 328   FR   ISSN 0035-385X
REVUE POLITIQUE ET PARLEMENTAIRE; economie, finance, urbanisme. 1894. bi-m. 610 F. (effective 1991). 110 rue de Rivoli, 75001 Paris, France. adv.; bk.rev.; charts; illus.; stat.; index. circ. 10,000. (also avail. in microform; reprint service avail. from SCH) **Indexed:** ELLIS, Int.Polit.Sci.Abstr., P.A.I.S.For.Lang.Ind.
—BLDSC (7942.550000); SWETS.

320.531   FR   ISSN 0035-4139
REVUE SOCIALISTE; revue de culture politique et sociale. 1885. m. 77 F.($15.50) Parti Socialiste et Cercle d'Etudes Socialistes Jean Jaures, 16 rue Vigee Le Brun, 75015 Paris, France. Ed. R. Pagosse. adv.; bk.rev.; index.

THE RIGHT GUIDE; a guide to conservative and right-of-center organizations. see *BUSINESS AND ECONOMICS — Trade And Industrial Directories*

RIGHT TO KNOW AND THE FREEDOM TO ACT. see *POLITICAL SCIENCE — Civil Rights*

320   SW   ISSN 0346-5470
RIKSDAGENS AARSBOK; uppslagsbok foer dig som vill veta vad Riksdagen beslutat under aaret. 1906. a. SEK 125 (effective 1990). Riksdagen, S-100 12 Stockholm, Sweden.
Former titles (until 1974): Riksdag (ISSN 0346-5527); (until 1949): Lagtima Riksdagen.

320.9   IT   ISSN 0035-5380
RINASCITA; rassegna politica di attualita, economia, e cultura. (Supplement to: Contemporaneo) 1944. w. L.16000. Unita S.p.A., Via d' Aracoeli 13, 00186 Rome, Italy. TEL 06-4951251. Ed. Luciano Barca. adv.; bk.rev.; abstr.; bibl.; charts; illus.; index. circ. 80,000.

320.5   US   ISSN 0035-5526
JK2351
RIPON FORUM. 1965-1980; resumed 1981. bi-m. $20 to individuals; students $10. Ripon Society, 227 Massachusetts Ave., N.E., Ste. 201, Washington, DC 20002. TEL 202-546-1292. Ed. David Beiler. adv.; bk.rev.; cum.index. circ. 3,500. (also avail. in microfilm from UMI; reprint service avail. from UMI) **Indexed:** Polit.Sci.Abstr.
—Faxon; UMI; UnCover.
Formerly: Ripon Society Newsletter.

322   PO   ISSN 0870-9912
RISCO.* 1985. 4/yr. $15. Editorial Fragmentos, Travessa Estevao Pinto, 6-A, 1000 Lisbon, Portugal. Dir. Joao Carlos Espada. adv.; bk.rev. circ. 2,000.

320   II
RISING SUN. (Text in English) 1971. w. Rs.15. 52-A Kodam Bakkam, High Road, Madras 600034, India. Ed. Murasoli Maran. adv.; bk.rev.; illus.

324.2734   US   ISSN 1072-5687
RISING TIDE. 1993. bi-m. $12. Republican National Committee, 310 First St., S.E., Washington, DC 20003. TEL 202-863-8885. Ed. Chuck Greener.
Description: Serves as a forum for the Republican Party's principles and agenda.

320   GW
RISSENER JAHRBUCH. 1956. a. DM.25. Rissener Landstr. 193, 22559 Hamburg, Germany. TEL 040-81-80-21. Ed. Hans Rissen. index. circ. 2,000. (back issues avail.)

320   GW   ISSN 0722-8767
RISSENER RUNDBRIEF. 1956. m. DM.40. Rissener Landstr. 193, 2000 Hamburg 56, Germany. TEL 040-818021. Ed. Hans Rissen. circ. 2,500. (back issues avail.)
Formerly (until 1974): Rissener Auslese (ISSN 0722-8708)

RIVISTA AMMINISTRATIVA DELLA REPUBBLICA ITALIANA. see *LAW*

320   IT
RIVISTA D'EUROPA. 1978. a. L.35000. Bibliotheca di Gabriele Chiusano, Largo Olgiata 15-106, 00123 Rome, Italy. Ed. Lido Chiusano.

320   IT   ISSN 0048-8402
JA18
RIVISTA ITALIANA DI SCIENZA POLITICA. (Text in Italian; summaries in English) 1971. 3/yr. L.65000 (foreign L.120000). Societa Editrice Il Mulino, Strada Maggiore, 37, 40125 Bologna, Italy. TEL 39-51-256011. FAX 39-51-256034. Eds. Giovanni Sartori, M. Cotta. adv.; B&W page L.2750000. bk.rev.; bibl.; index. circ. 1,700. (tabloid format; back issues avail.) **Indexed:** A.B.C.Pol.Sci., Amer.Hist.& Life, Hist.Abstr., Int.Polit.Sci.Abstr., Lang.& Lang.Behav.Abstr., SSCI.
—SWETS.

320.532   CN   ISSN 0047-6110
ROAD OF THE PARTY. 1970. irreg. Can.$20. Communist Party of Canada (Marxist - Leninist), Central Committee, Box 666, Station C, Montreal, Que., Canada. TEL 416-252-3658. (Dist. by: National Publications Centre, Box 727, Adelaide Station, Toronto, Ont. M5C 2J8, Canada) Ed. Hardial S. Bains. charts; illus.
Formerly (until 1980): Mass Line.

335   UK   ISSN 0483-2027
ROBOTNIK. (Text in Polish; summaries in English) vol.81, 1975. q. Polish Socialist Party in Exile, 84 Fordhook Ave., London W. 5, England. Ed. Leszek Talko. bk.rev. circ. 2,000.

329.9   MY   ISSN 0048-8461
ROCKET. vol.6, 1971. bi-m. M.$3.20. Democratic Action Party of Malaysia, 77 Jalan, 20-9 Paramount Garden, Petaling Jaya, Selangor, Malaysia. FAX 04-361909. Ed.Bd. bk.rev.; charts; illus. circ. 35,000. (tabloid format)

320.5   SW   ISSN 0280-6010
ROED PRESS. 1972. 8/yr. SEK 70 (effective 1990). Kommunistisk Ungdom (KU), Laangg. 20, S-413 28 Goeteborg, Sweden.
Former titles (until 1982): Stormklockan; (until 1977, vol.10): K U - Stormklockan.

320.531   DK   ISSN 0906-6047
DEN ROEDE TRAAD. 1962. w. DKK 150 to individuals; institutions DKK 250. Socialistisk Arbejderparti, Studiestraede 24, 3. sal, P.O. Box 1029, DK-1007 Copenhagen K, Denmark. TEL 31-373217. Ed. Soeren Soendergaard. adv.; bk.rev.; bibl.; illus. circ. 2,500.
Formed by the merger of (1971-1991): Klassekampen (ISSN 0023-2025); Formerly (1962-1971): Debat (ISSN 0415-1232); (1976-1991): Arbejderavisen (ISSN 0105-1733); (1969-1991): Solidaritet (ISSN 0901-8255)

320 350   II
ROLE OF STATE LEGISLATURES IN THE FREEDOM STRUGGLE. 1976. irreg. Rs.30. Indian Council of Historical Research, 35 Ferozeshah Rd., New Delhi 110011, India. (Dist. by: People's Publishing House Ltd., Rani Jhansi Rd., New Delhi 110 005, India)

328 071   US   ISSN 0035-788X
JK1
ROLL CALL; the newspaper of Capitol Hill. 1955. s-w. (Mon. & Thu.). $210. Roll Call, Inc. (Subsidiary of: Economist Newspaper Group, Inc.), 900 Second St., N.E., Ste. 107, Washington, DC 20002. TEL 202-289-4900. FAX 202-289-2205. Ed. Stacy Mason; Pub. Laurie Battaglia. adv.: B&W page $6200, color page $7200; adv. contact: Karen Whitman. bk.rev.; illus.; stat.; circ. 4,500 (paid); 12,000 (controlled). (tabloid format) **Document type:** newspaper.
●**Also available online. Vendor(s):** Lexis-Nexis.
Description: Provides an insider perspective on happenings in Congress.

POLITICAL SCIENCE

320.532 GW ISSN 0936-1421
ROTE FAHNE; Wochenzeitung der M L P D. 1970. w. DM.70. (Marxistisch-Leninistische Partei Deutschland) Neuer Weg Verlag & Druck GmbH, Kaninenberghoehe 2, 45136 Essen, Germany. TEL 0201-25914. FAX 0201-268577. bk.rev.; illus. **Document type:** newspaper.

320.532 GW ISSN 0939-2947
ROTER MORGEN. 1967. fortn. DM.36. (Kommunistischen Partei Deutschlands) Zeitungsverlag Roter Morgen, Postfach 401051, 70410 Stuttgart, Germany. TEL 0711-8702209. FAX 0711-8702445. (Subscr. to: Postfach 1942, 61289 Bad Homburg, Germany) Pub. Diethard Moeller. circ. 900. (looseleaf format; back issues avail.) **Document type:** newspaper.

320 FR
ROUGE. 1969. w. 400 F. (foreign 500 F.). La Breche, 2 rue Richard Lenoir, 93100 Montreuil, France. TEL 48-59-00-80. circ. 10,000.

322.4 FR ISSN 0151-5772
ROYALISTE; bi-mensuel de l'action Royaliste. 1971. bi-m. 270 F. Societe Nationale Presse Francaise, 17 rue des Petits Champs, 75001 Paris, France. TEL 42-97-42-57. Ed. Bertrand Renouvin. bk.rev.; film rev. circ. 15,000. (back issues avail.)
  Formerly: N.A.F.

320 US ISSN 0300-6093
ROYALTON REVIEW. 1966. q. $10. Royalton College Press, Box 218, South Royalton, VT 05068. TEL 802-763-7766. Ed. Ming Ming Du. **Indexed:** P.A.I.S.

320 AA
RRUGA E PARTISE. m. $9.24. Parti du Travail d'Albanie, Tirana, Albania.

320.532 IS
RUSSIA & C I S OVERVIEW. (Commonwealth of Independent States) (Text in English) 1985. m. $20 (foreign $40). International Research Center on Contemporary Society, P.O. Box 687, Jerusalem 91006, Israel. TEL 972-2-636126. FAX 972-2-664069. Ed. Ilya Zemtsov. **Document type:** newsletter.
  Formerly: U S S R Overview.
  Description: Reports and analyses of domestic developments, foreign policy and military activities in Russia and the Commonwealth of Independent States.

320.531 US
DK285.5
RUSSIA & EURASIA DOCUMENTS ANNUAL. 1987. a. $75. Academic International Press, Box 1111, Gulf Breeze, FL 32562-1111. Ed. J.L. Black.
  Former titles (until 1992): U S S R Documents Annual (ISSN 1051-3507); (until 1988): U S S R Documents (ISSN 1048-1125)

RUSSIA AND THE SUCCESSOR STATES BRIEFING SERVICE. see *BUSINESS AND ECONOMICS*

320.9 947 UK ISSN 1351-9263
RUSSIA BRIEFING. 1993. m. £245 (rest of Europe $500; elsewhere $510); with Eastern Europe Newsletter £410 (rest of Europe $810; elsewhere $830). E E N Ltd., 70 Bassein Park Rd., London W12 9RZ, England. TEL 0181-743-2829. FAX 0181-743-8637. Ed. Charles Meynell. index. (back issues avail.) **Document type:** bulletin.
  ●Also available online.
  Description: Reviews and analyzes political developments in Russia.

RUSSIAN POLITICS AND LAW; a journal of translations. see *LAW*

947 US ISSN 1061-1428
AS261
RUSSIAN SOCIAL SCIENCE REVIEW; a journal of translations. 1960. bi-m. $138 to institutions (foreign $190) (effective Jul. 1995). M.E. Sharpe, Inc., 80 Business Park Dr., Armonk, NY 10504. TEL 914-273-1800; 800-541-6563. FAX 914-273-2106. Ed. Patricia A. Kolb. adv.; index. (also avail. in microform from UMI; back issues avail.) **Indexed:** Mid.East: Abstr.& Ind., P.A.I.S., Soc.Sci.Ind. **Document type:** academic/scholarly publication.
  ●Also available online. Vendor(s): University Microfilms International.
  —BLDSC (8052.920000); Faxon; SWETS; UMI; UnCover. **CCC**.
  Formerly (until 1992): Soviet Review (ISSN 0038-5794)
  Refereed Serial

S A I P A; journal of public administration - tydskrif vir publieke administrasie. (South African Institute of Public Administration) see *PUBLIC ADMINISTRATION*

320 US ISSN 0899-7225
K6
S C A FREE SPEECH YEARBOOK. Variant title: Free Speech Yearbook. 1960. a. price varies. (Speech Communication Association) Southern Illinois University Press, Box 3697, Carbondale, IL 62901. TEL 618-453-6618. FAX 618-453-1221. Ed. Dale Herbeck. bk.rev. circ. 700. **Document type:** proceedings.
  —UnCover.
  Former titles (until 1970): Speech Association of America. Committee on Freedom of Speech. Yearbook (ISSN 0584-8679); Freedom of Speech Yearbook (ISSN 0071-9366)

324.248 DK ISSN 0902-1612
S F STATUS. (Socialistisk Folkeparti) 1975. a. DKK 75. Socialistiske Perspektiver Forlag, Silkeborgvej 13, DK-8000 Aarhus C, Denmark. TEL 45 86 20 28 22. Ed. Arly Eskildsen. adv.; bk.rev. circ. 800.
  Former titles: Socialistisk Folkeparti. Status (ISSN 0108-7908); S F Status.

320 301 GW ISSN 0170-4613
HX6
S P W. (Sozialistische Politik und Wirtschaft) 1978. bi-m. DM.58 (foreign DM.61). S P W Verlag GmbH, Fresienstr. 26, 44289 Dortmund, Germany. TEL 0231-402410. FAX 0231-402416. E-mail: spw-verlag@link-do.donut.ruhr.com. Ed.Bd. adv. contact: Hans-Peter Schulz. bk.rev. circ. 3,000. (back issues avail.) **Document type:** bulletin.

322.4 US
S T R A I G H T. m? Society to Reform All Immoral Godless Homosexual Trash, Box 5251, Denver, CO 80217-5251. bk.rev. **Document type:** newsletter.
  Description: Encourages people to apply Biblical teachings to their everyday lives, argues against government interference, and presents the ideology that homosexuality is a sin.

320 AU ISSN 0036-1585
S Z.* (Sozialwirtschaftliche Korrespondenz) (Text in German) vol.22, 1973. m. S.220. Ed. Magdalena Troestler, Christian-Coulin Str. 13, Postfach 324, A-4021 Linz, Austria. adv.; bk.rev.; bibl.

320 340 US ISSN 0486-8161
SACRAMENTO NEWSLETTER. 1947. w. $60. Information for Public Affairs, Inc., 2101 K St., Sacramento, CA 95816. TEL 916-444-2840. FAX 916-444-2339. Ed. Thomas Hoeber. circ. 500. (back issues avail.) **Document type:** newsletter.
  Description: Overview of state legislation, government and politics.

ST. VINCENT GOVERNMENT INFORMATION SERVICE NEWS BULLETIN. see *PUBLIC ADMINISTRATION*

320.531 DK ISSN 0907-0974
SALT. 1933. 12/yr. DKK 300. S P Forlag, Silkeborgvej 13, DK-8000 Aarhus C, Denmark. Ed. Lars Christensen. bk.rev. circ. 1,000.
  Formed by the merger of (1936-1992): Tiden (ISSN 0108-8246); (1980-1992): Praksis (ISSN 0107-2129)
  Description: Journal of politics and Marxist theory.

SAMISDAT; Stimmen aus den "anderen Russland". see *HISTORY — History Of Europe*

320 US
SAN DIEGO LIBERTARIAN. 1973. m. $12. San Diego Libertarian Party, Box 16449, San Diego, CA 92176. TEL 619-273-1776. FAX 619-274-1776. Ed. Betsy Mill. adv.; bk.rev. circ. 900. (back issues avail.) **Document type:** newsletter.
  Description: Newsletter with events and articles of interest to people with a distaste for big government at every level.

320 SZ
ST. GALLER STUDIEN ZUR POLITIKWISSENSCHAFT. 1975. irreg., no.14, 1992. price varies. Paul Haupt AG, Falkenplatz 14, CH-3001 Bern, Switzerland. TEL 031-3012345. FAX 031-3014669. **Document type:** monographic series.

320 294.5 II
SANT SIPAHI. (Text in Punjabi) vol.27, 1972. m. Rs.10. Lal Haveli, Gate Mahan Singh, Amritsar 24, India. adv.
  Description: Covers Sikh politics and religion.

954.9 BG
SAPTAHIKA THIKANA. Variant title: Thikana. (Text in Bengali) 1976. w. Tk.0.50 per no. Abul Hossain Mir, Ed. & Pub., Press Club Bhavan, Mujib Sarak, Jessore, Bangladesh.
  Description: Covers political news and views.

954 IN
SATYACHAR. (Text in Gujarati) 1947. fortn. Rs.5. Shukla Hariprasad, Ed. & Pub., Halvad 363330, Gujarat, India. adv. circ. 500.
  Former titles: Red Light; Sahakar (ISSN 0036-2603)

945 IT ISSN 0036-5157
SAVOIA. 1962. bi-m. membership. Gruppo Savoia, Casella Postale 1233, 20101 Milan, Italy. TEL 39-2-2822619. Ed.Bd. bk.rev.; illus. circ. 1,600.

320 US ISSN 1061-7167
HV7240
SBORNIK/DOCUMENTS. (Text in English, Russian) 1990. q. $5. American Society of Former Soviet Political Prisoners, Inc., Box 8637, New York, NY 10116-4655. TEL 718-859-7387. Ed. Mikhail Malinin. adv.; bk.rev. (back issues avail.) **Document type:** bulletin.

320 NO ISSN 0080-6757
JN7001
SCANDINAVIAN POLITICAL STUDIES. (Text in English) 1965; N.S. 1978. q. NOK 545 in Nordic countries; elsewhere $108 (effective 1996). (Nordic Political Science Association) Scandinavian University Press, P.O. Box 2959 Toeyen, N-0608 Oslo, Norway. TEL 47-22-57-54-00. FAX 47-22-57-53-53. (U.S. addr.: Scandinavian University Press, 200 Meacham Ave., Elmont, NY 11003. TEL 516-352-7300) Eds. Knut Heidar, Lawrence Rose. adv.; bk.rev.; bibl.; index. circ. 600. (also avail. in microform from UMI; back issues avail.: reprint service avail. from ISI) **Indexed:** A.B.C.Pol.Sci., Amer.Hist.& Life, Hist.Abstr., Int.Polit.Sci.Abstr., Polit.Sci.Abstr., Stud.Wom.Abstr. **Document type:** academic/scholarly publication.
  —BLDSC (8087.572000); Faxon; Genuine Article; SWETS; UMI; UnCover. **CCC**.
  Supersedes (1968-1977): Scandinavian Political Studies Yearbook.
  Description: Presents political studies on Scandinavia to an international forum of political scientists and sociologists.

943 GW ISSN 0036-6250
SCHOEFFE; Zeitschrift fuer Schoeffen und Schiedskommissionen. 1954. m. DM.24. (Ministerium fuer Justiz) Staatsverlag der DDR, Otto-Grotewohl-Str. 17, 10117 Berlin, Germany. adv.; bk.rev.; charts; index. circ. 52,000. **Document type:** government publication.

320 US ISSN 0891-1614
SCHOOL OF INTERNATIONAL STUDIES. PUBLICATIONS ON RUSSIA AND EASTERN EUROPE. Key Title: Publications on Russia and Eastern Europe of the School of International Studies, University of Washington. 1969. irreg., no.12, 1983. price varies. (University of Washington, School of International Studies) University of Washington Press, Box 50096, Seattle, WA 98105. TEL 206-543-4050. **Document type:** monographic series.
  Formerly: Publications on Russia and Eastern Europe (ISSN 0079-7790)
  Refereed Serial

POLITICAL SCIENCE

320   UK
SCHOOLS OF THOUGHT IN POLITICS. 1991. irreg. (1-3/yr.) price varies. Edward Elgar Publishing Ltd., 8 Lansdown Pl., Cheltenham, Glos. GL50 2HU, England. TEL 01242-226934. FAX 0242-262111. (Dist. in the U.S. by: Ashgate Publishing Co., Old Post Rd., Brookfield, VT 05036. TEL 800-535-9544) Ed. Brian Barry. (back issues avail.) **Document type:** monographic series.
    Description: Reproduces selections from the most significant articles in major areas of teaching and research in political science.

SCHULER LECTURES IN HISTORY AND POLITICAL SCIENCE. see *HISTORY*

322.4 801 792   GW   ISSN 0722-8988
SCHWARZER FADEN; Vierteljahresschrift fuer Lust und Freiheit. 1980. q. DM.25. Trotzdem Verlag, Postfach 1159, 71117 Grafenau, Germany. TEL 07033-45273. FAX 07033-44264. Ed. Wolfgang Haug. adv.; bk.rev.; bibl.; illus.; film rev.; play rev.; cum.index. circ. 3,000. **Document type:** bulletin.

320 358 290   US   ISSN 0048-9581
Q127.U6   CODEN: SGVRAO
SCIENCE AND GOVERNMENT REPORT. 1971. s-m. $455 (effective 1995). Science and Government Reports, Inc., Box 6226A, Northwest Sta., Washington, DC 20015. TEL 800-822-1970. FAX 202-362-2790. Ed. Daniel S. Greenberg; Pub. Daniel S. Greenberg. bk.rev.; circ. 1,500 (paid). (also avail. in microfilm from UMI; reprint service avail. from UMI) **Document type:** newsletter.
—CASDDS; Genuine Article; UMI. **CCC.**
    Description: Provides news and analysis of policy and political developments that affect research and development.

300 500   US   ISSN 0036-8237
H1
SCIENCE & SOCIETY; an independent journal of Marxism. 1936. q. $23 to individuals (foreign $38); institutions $75 (foreign $90) (effective 1995). Guilford Publications, Inc., 72 Spring St., 4th Fl., New York, NY 10012. TEL 212-431-9800. FAX 212-966-6708. Ed. David Laibman; Pub. Robert Matloff. adv. contact: Marian Robinson. bk.rev.; index, cum.index every 25 yrs. circ. 1,900. (also avail. in microform from MIM,UMI,KTO; reprint service avail. from UMI,ISI,SCH) Indexed: A.B.C.Pol.Sci., Acad.Ind., Alt.Press Ind., Amer.Bibl.Slavic & E.Eur.Stud., Amer.Hist.& Life, ASCA, ASSIA, Bk.Rev.Ind. (1965-), Child.Bk.Rev.Ind. (1965-), Curr.Cont., Energy Ind., Energy Info.Abstr., Hist.Abstr., Int.Lab.Doc., Int.Polit.Sci.Abstr., J.of Econ.Lit., Left Ind. (1982-), Mid.East: Abstr.& Ind., P.A.I.S., Polit.Sci.Abstr., So.Pac.Per.Ind., Soc.Sci.Ind., SSCI, 01447750xxx.Behav.Abstr. **Document type:** academic/scholarly publication.
●Also available online. Vendor(s): University Microfilms International.
—BLDSC (8134.190000); Faxon; Genuine Article; SWETS; UMI; UnCover. **CCC.**
    Description: Examines new ideas in economic and social thought.
Refereed Serial

SCIENCE AS CULTURE. see *SCIENCES: COMPREHENSIVE WORKS*

072.941   UK   ISSN 0036-9071
SCOTS INDEPENDENT. 1926. m. £8.75 (foreign £12.50). Scots Independent (Newspapers) Ltd., 51 Cowane St., Stirling FK8 1JW, Scotland. TEL 0786-473523. Ed. Kenneth Fee. adv.; bk.rev.; play rev.; stat. circ. 9,000. (tabloid format) **Document type:** newspaper.

320   UK   ISSN 0966-0356
JN1187
SCOTTISH AFFAIRS. 1976. q. £25 to individuals; institutions £40. Unit for the Study of Government in Scotland, 31 Buccleuch Pl., Edinburgh EH8 9JT, Scotland. TEL 0131-650-4197. FAX 0131-668-3263. Ed. Lindsay Paterson. adv.: B&W page £320. bk.rev.; bibl.; stat. circ. 900. (back issues avail.) **Document type:** academic/scholarly publication.
—BLDSC (8205.989600).
    Formerly (until 1992): Scottish Government Yearbook.
Refereed Serial

320   UK   ISSN 0262-4591
SEARCHLIGHT (LONDON). 1974. m. £18 to individuals; institutions £26. Searchlight Magazine Ltd., 37B New Cavendish St., London W1M 8JR, England. TEL 0171-284-4040. FAX 0171-284-4040. Ed. Gerry Gable. adv.; bk.rev.; illus.; index. circ. 8,000. (back issues avail.) **Document type:** bulletin.
    Description: Coverage of contemporary fascism and neo-nazi organizations in Britain, Europe, the U.S. and occasionally elsewhere.

320   GT
SECRETARIA PERMANENTE DEL TRATADO GENERAL DE INTEGRACION ECONOMICA CENTROAMERICANA. BOLETIN ESTADISTICO. no.31, Mar. 1976. q. $10 (foreign $15) (effective 1993). Secretaria Permanente del Tratado General de Integracion Economica Centroamericana - Permanent Secretary of the General Treaty of Central American Economic Integration, Apdo. 1237, 4 Avenida No. 10-25, Zona 14, 01901 Guatemala City, Guatemala. TEL 682151. FAX 502-681071. TELEX 6203 SIECA GU. Ed. Eduardo Bolanos. charts; stat.
    Formerly (until 1993): Integracion en Cifras (ISSN 0252-8746)

341.1   UK   ISSN 0967-0106
JX1901   CODEN: SDIAER
SECURITY DIALOGUE. 1970. q. £30 to individuals; institutions £96 (effective 1996). (International Peace Research Institute, Oslo, NO) Sage Publications Ltd., 6 Bonhill St., London EC2A 4PU, England. TEL 0171-374-0645. FAX 0171-374-8741. E-mail: market@sageltd.co.uk. Ed. Magne Barth. adv.: B&W page £200; trim 190 x 115; adv. contact: Bernie Folan. abstr.; bibl. (also avail. in microform from UMI) Indexed: Abstr.Mil.Bibl., Amer.Hist.& Life, Curr.Cont., Curr.Mil.& Polit.Lit., Hist.Abstr., HR Rep., IBZ, INIS Atomind., Int.Polit.Sci.Abstr., Intl.Bibl.S.S.Pol.Sci., P.A.I.S., Peace Res.Abstr., Per.Islam. (1991-), Polit.Sci.Abstr., Refug.Abstr., Risk Abstr., Sage Pub.Admin.Abstr., Sociol.Abstr., SSCI. **Document type:** bulletin.
—BLDSC (8217.178000); Faxon; Genuine Article; SWETS; UMI; UnCover.
    Formerly (until 1992): Bulletin of Peace Proposals (ISSN 0007-5035)
    Description: Discusses contemporary international and intergroup affairs, searching for solutions to conflict situations in the light of general peace research theory.
Refereed Serial

320 355   US   ISSN 1063-4150
HV6432
SECURITY INTELLIGENCE. 1986. bi-w. $390. Interests, Ltd., 8512 Cedar St., Silver Spring, MD 20910-4322. TEL 301-588-7916. FAX 301-588-2085. Ed. Frank G. McGuire. adv.; bk.rev.
●Also available online. Vendor(s): NewsNet (IT64).
—**CCC.**
    Former titles (until 1992): Security Intelligence Report (ISSN 1055-8144); (until 1991): Counter-Terrorism and Security Intelligence (ISSN 1053-1939); Counter-Terrorism (ISSN 0887-6398)
    Description: Focuses on security intelligence, aviation security and ideological violence.

909   JA   ISSN 0582-4532
AP95.J2
SEKAI/WORLD. (Text in Japanese) 1946. m. 8100 Yen. Iwanami Shoten Publishers, 2-5-5 Hitotsubashi, Chiyoda-ku, Tokyo 101-02, Japan. FAX 03-3239-9618. (Dist. overseas by: Japan Publications Trading Co., Ltd., Box 5030, Tokyo International, Tokyo 100-31, Japan; Or: 1255 Howard St., San Francisco, CA 94103) circ. 100,000.

320   US
SELF-GOVERNANCE. (Editions in English, French, Spanish) 1990. q. free. (International Center for Self-Governance) I C S Press, 720 Market St., 5th Fl., San Francisco, CA 94102-2500. TEL 415-981-5353. FAX 415-986-4878. Ed. Elise Paylan Schoux. adv. contact: Kevin Heverin. bk.rev.; abstr.; bibl.; charts; illus.; stat.; tr.lit.; index. circ. 20,000. (back issues avail.) **Document type:** newsletter.
    Description: Explores the theory and practice of self-government world-wide, through past and present experimentation and evolving literature.

320   US   ISSN 0745-7170
HF1019
SELF-RELIANT. 1982. 10/yr. $12. F J L Publishing Co., 817 Stark Circle, Yardley, PA 19067-4313. Ed. Frank Lyons.
    Formerly (until 1983): Traders' Journal (ISSN 0744-7558)

329.9   CU
SEMANARIO INFANTIL PIONERO. w. $50 in N. America; S. America $72; Europe $82; elsewhere $85. (Union de Jovenes Comunistas (UJC), Organizacion de Pioneros "Jose Marti") Ediciones Cubanas, Obispo No. 527, Apdo. 605, Havana, Cuba. TEL 32-5556-60. Dir. Pedro Gonzalez. illus. circ. 210,000.

320   CR
SEMANARIO LIBERTAD. 1962. w. Partido del Pueblo Costarricense, Apdo. 10138, Calle 4, Avda. 8 y 10, 1000 San Jose, Costa Rica. TEL 23-7651. Ed. Jose A. Zuniga. circ. 10,000.

SEMINARIA PA'LANTE. see *LITERARY AND POLITICAL REVIEWS*

SENNACHIE. see *HISTORY*

320   FR   ISSN 0080-8938
SERIE AFRIQUE NOIRE. 1970. irreg. price varies. (Institut d'Etudes Politiques de Bordeaux) Editions A. Pedone, 13 rue Soufflot, 75005 Paris, France.
—**CCC.**

320   FR   ISSN 0586-9889
SERIE VIE LOCALE. 1969. irreg. price varies. (Institut d'Etudes Politiques de Bordeaux, Centre d'Etude et de Recherche sur la Vie Locale) Editions A. Pedone, 13 rue Soufflot, 75005 Paris, France.
—**CCC.**

325   IT   ISSN 0037-2803
SERVIZIO MIGRANTI. 1965. bi-m. L.45000. Fondazione Migrantes, Via Aurelia, 481, 00165 Rome, Italy. FAX 06-662-0530. TELEX 623328 UCEI I. adv.; bk.rev.; stat.; index. circ. 2,700.
    Formerly: Ufficio Centrale per l'Emigrazione Italiana, Bollettino.

320   US
THE SHADOW. 1988. m. $10; newsstand price: $0.50. Shadow Press, Box 20298, New York, NY 10009. TEL 212-921-4317. Eds. Chris Flash, A. Kronstadt. adv.: half page $100. illus. cols./p.: 4; pp./issue: 24. (back issues avail.) **Document type:** newspaper.
    Description: Covers housing, homelessness, police brutality, political lying and other issues.

329.9   JA
SHAKAI SHINPO. s-w. 800 Yen per mo. Social Democratic Party of Japan - Nihon Shakaito, 1-8-1 Nagato-cho, Chiyoda-ku, Tokyo, Japan. FAX 81-03-3580-0691. **Document type:** newspaper.

320   UK   ISSN 0262-9860
SHAKTI. 1978. m. £12. (National Association for Asian Youth) Catbird Productions Ltd., 46 High St., Southall, Middx. UB1 3DB, England. Ed. Ravi Jain. adv.; bk.rev.; film rev. circ. 8,500. (back issues avail.)
    Formerly: N A A Y Information Bulletin.

HA-SHAVUA. see *BUSINESS AND ECONOMICS — Cooperatives*

SHIMANE LAW REVIEW. see *LAW*

320   MP
SHINE UYE/NEW GENERATION. (Text in English, Mongolian) w. 120 tugrik($1) Mongolian Newspaper Company, Erkhuu Street - 5, Ulan Bator, Mongolia. TEL 55208. Ed. S. Amarsanaa. circ. 15,000. (tabloid format)

SHVUT; Jewish problems in the USSR and Eastern Europe. see *ETHNIC INTERESTS*

320 954.9   PK
SIND JOURNAL OF POLITICAL SCIENCE AND MODERN HISTORY; an international publication. (Text in English) 1975. s-a. Rs.25($10) University of Sind, Department of Political Science & Modern History, Jamshoro, Sind, Pakistan. (Subscr. in U.S., Canada, and other Western countries to: Edinboro State College, Office of International Education, Box 318, Edinboro, PA 16412) (Co-sponsor: Edinboro State College, Department of History) Ed.Bd. adv.

POLITICAL SCIENCE

SINTESE. see *PHILOSOPHY*

SIR GEORGE EARLE MEMORIAL LECTURE ON INDUSTRY AND GOVERNMENT. see *BUSINESS AND ECONOMICS*

320.532   CC   ISSN 1002-9907
SIXIANG ZHENGZHI GONGZUO YANJIU/STUDY IN IDEOLOGY AND POLITICS. (Text in Chinese) m. Zhongguo Zhigong Sixiang Zhengzhi Gongzuo Yanjiuhui, Dong Yuan, 9 Xihuangchenggen Nanjie, Dong Cheng Qu, Beijing 100032, People's Republic of China. TEL 66-6982. Ed. Yang Wenshang. Document type: academic/scholarly publication.

320   LE
SIYASSA WA STRATEGIA/POLITICS AND STRATEGY/POLITIQUE ET STRATEGIE. (Text in Arabic) 1981. 36/yr. $1500. Dar Naaman lith-Thaqafah, P.O. Box 567, Jounieh, Lebanon. TEL 961-9-935096. Ed. Naji Naaman. index.
    Description: Covers regional political, economic, and strategic issues affecting the Arab world.

320.5   SW   ISSN 1101-9522
SKAANEKURIREN. 1989. q. SEK 50 membership (effective 1990). Skaanepartiet, Malmgatan 16, S-211 32 Malmoe, Sweden.

SKUPNOST; glasilo slovenske skupnosti. see *ETHNIC INTERESTS*

SLEZSKE ZEMSKE MUZEUM. CASOPIS. SERIE B. VEDY HISTORICKE. see *HISTORY — History Of Europe*

SLICK TIMES. see *LITERARY AND POLITICAL REVIEWS*

SLOVAK PRESS DIGEST. see *ETHNIC INTERESTS*

SLOVANSKE STUDIE. see *HISTORY — History Of Europe*

943.7 947   XR   ISSN 0037-6922
AP52
SLOVANSKY PREHLED/SLAVONIC REVIEW. (Text in Czech; summaries in English, German, Russian) 1898. bi-m. DM.141. Ceska Akademie Ved, Historicky Ustav, Vysehradska 49, 128 26 Prague 2, Czech Republic. TEL 53-15-45. (Dist. in Western countries by: Kubon & Sagner, P.O. Box 34 01 08, 8000 Munich 34, Germany) Ed. Antonin Dolejsi. bk.rev.; abstr.; illus.; index, cum.index. circ. 1,750. **Indexed:** Amer.Hist.& Life, Bibl.Ling., Hist.Abstr.
    Description: Scholarly articles on the history and culture of the central, southeast and east European nations, their mutual relations and their relations to the West.

SLOVENSKA AKADEMIJA ZNANOSTI IN UMETNOSTI. FILOZOFSKI VESTNIK/ACTA PHILOSOPHICA. see *PHILOSOPHY*

SLOVENSKA ARCHIVISTIKA. see *HISTORY — History Of Europe*

320   IS   ISSN 0334-7621
SMOL. 1979. m. IS.40($20) Israeli Socialist Left, P.O. Box 33076, Tel Aviv 61 330, Israel. TEL 03-663154. FAX 03-450917. Ed. Nimrod Oved. adv.; bk.rev. circ. 3,700.
    Description: Provides news on the Israeli-Palestinian struggle for peace. Covers Marxist views on workers' struggle, Israel, the Middle East and the Third World.

SOCIAL ALTERNATIVES. see *SOCIOLOGY*

320.9   UK   ISSN 0037-7694
THE SOCIAL CREDITER;* for political and economic realism. 1933. bi-m. £10. 002 R from Tidal Publications, Box 2318 V, G.P.O., Melbourne, Australia, P.O. Box 13855, 170 Portobello High St., Edinburgh EH15 1YD, Scotland. TEL 0131-657-4740. Ed. Donald Neale; Pub. Iain McGregor. bk.rev.; index 1960-1995; circ. 800 (paid). Document type: academic/scholarly publication.

320.531   US
SOCIAL DEMOCRAT.* 1972. irreg. $2. Young Social Democrats, 815 Fifteenth St., N.W., No. 511, Washington, DC 20005-2201. TEL 202-638-1515. FAX 202-347-5585. adv.; bk.rev. circ. 1,500.

SOCIAL, ECONOMIC AND POLITICAL STUDIES OF THE MIDDLE EAST. see *HISTORY — History Of The Near East*

SOCIAL RESEARCH; an international journal of political and social science. see *SOCIAL SCIENCES: COMPREHENSIVE WORKS*

320   II
SOCIAL SCIENCE PROBINGS. (Text in English) 1984. q. Rs.80($25) People's Publishing House Private Ltd., 5-E Rani Jhansi Road, New Delhi 110 055, India. Ed. R.S. Sharma. circ. 1,000.

320   US   ISSN 0885-4300
HX1
SOCIALISM AND DEMOCRACY. 1985. 3/yr. $15 to individuals; libraries $24. City University of New York, Graduate School, Research Group on Socialism and Democracy, Box 375, Graduate Center, 33 W. 42nd St., New York, NY 10036-8099. TEL 212-642-2445. Ed.Bd. adv.; bk.rev. circ. 1,000. (also avail. in microform from UMI) **Indexed:** Alt.Press Ind., Amer.Hist.& Life, Hist.Abstr., IBR, IBZ, Int.Polit.Sci.Abstr., Left Ind. (1985-), P.A.I.S., Polit.Sci.Abstr., Sociol.Abstr. (1987-).
   —BLDSC (8318.243730); Faxon; UMI; UnCover.

335.43   RU   ISSN 0132-148X
SOCIALISM: THEORY AND PRACTICE. (Editions in English, French, German, Spanish) 1978. m. $5. Novosti Press Agency, 4 Zubovsky Boulevard, Moscow, Russia. (Subscr. to: Eastern News Distributors, Inc. 55 W. 15th St., New York, NY 10011) illus.

320.531   BE   ISSN 0037-8127
HX5
SOCIALISME. 1954. bi-m. 800 BEF. Institut Emile Vandervelde, 13 Bd. de l'Empereur, 1000 Brussels, Belgium. TEL 32-2-5132019. Ed. Andre Flahaut. adv.; bk.rev.; film rev.; abstr. circ. 2,000. **Indexed:** ASCA, Int.Polit.Sci.Abstr., P.A.I.S.For.Lang.Ind., SSCI.
   —BLDSC (8318.244500).

320   PO
SOCIALISMO & POLITICA. 3/yr. c/o F. Marcelo Curto, Av. da Republica, 36, Lado A 3rd Fl. Esq., 1000 Lisbon, Portugal. Ed. Herdeiros de Jose Trigo de Morais.

320.531   SP   ISSN 1130-1295
HX236
SOCIALISMO DEL FUTURO. (Editions in English, French, German, Greek, Italian, Polish, Portuguese, Russian, Spanish) 1990. s-a. 2400 ptas. for 4 nos. Fundacion Sistema, Fuencarral, 127 1o, 28010 Madrid, Spain. FAX 91-448-73-19. FAX 91-448-73-39. circ. 15,000.
    Description: Covers international political debate, representing the different trends of the European left.

320.531   PE   ISSN 0252-8827
SOCIALISMO Y PARTICIPACION. 1977. q. $55 (foreign $60) (effective 1995). (Centro de Estudios para el Desarrollo y la Participacion (CEDEP)) Ediciones Socialismo y Participacion, Av. Jose Faustino Sanchez Carrion 790-798, Magdalena del Mar, Lima 17, Peru. TEL 54-14-4629833. FAX 51-14-4616446. E-mail: postmaster@cedep.org.pe. (And: Apdo. 110201, 11 Lima, Peru) Ed. Jorge Diaz Herrera. adv. contact: Hector Bejar Rivera. bk.rev.; charts; stat.; cum.index; 1977-1979. circ. 1,500. **Indexed:** Int.Polit.Sci.Abstr. Document type: academic/scholarly publication.
    Description: Dedicated to the study and analysis of the economic, social, political and cultural reality of Peru. Also looks at the rest of Latin America and the Third World.

329.81   US   ISSN 0884-6154
HX1
SOCIALIST. 1972. m. $8. Socialist Party, U.S.A., 5502 W. Adams Blvd., Los Angeles, CA 90016. TEL 213-939-8287. Ed. Charles Curtiss. adv.; bk.rev.; film rev. circ. 2,000.
    Formerly: Socialist Tribune.
    Description: Provides news and editorials of interest to democratic socialists.

320.531   UK   ISSN 0049-0946
SOCIALIST AFFAIRS. 1951. q. £12($25) (Socialist International) Longman Group UK Ltd., Fourth Ave., Harlow, Essex CM19 5AA, England. TEL 0279-442601. (Subscr. to: 8 Flowers Mews, Archway Close, London N19 3TB England) Ed. Harry Drost. adv.; bk.rev.; bibl. circ. 10,000. **Indexed:** Alt.Press Ind.
   —BLDSC (8318.245500); UMI. **CCC.**
    Formerly: S I I - Socialist International Information (ISSN 0036-1534)

320.531   US   ISSN 0037-8194
SOCIALIST FORUM.* 1969. irreg., no.19, 1992. $10. Institute for Democratic Socialism, 180 Varick St., 12th Fl., New York, NY 10014-4606. TEL 212-962-0390. Ed. Michael Lighty. bk.rev.; bibl.; illus. circ. 1,000. (also avail. in microform from UMI)
    Description: Informs readers of the activities, political direction and strategy and debates of the Democratic Socialists of America.

320.531   II   ISSN 0037-8208
SOCIALIST INDIA. (Text in English) 1970. w. Rs.25. All India Congress Committee, Publications Department, 5 Dr. Rajendra Prasad Rd., New Delhi 110001, India. Ed. P.V. Narasimha Rao. adv.; bk.rev.; illus. circ. 5,000.

335.4   CE
SOCIALIST NATION. (Text in English) w. Rs.3.75 per no. Lanka Sama Samaja Party, 42 Jayakantha Lane, Colombo 5, Sri Lanka.
    Description: Focuses on Trotskyism.

320.351   II   ISSN 0970-8863
SOCIALIST PERSPECTIVE; a quarterly journal of social sciences. (Text in English) 1973. q. Rs.40($10) (typically set in July). Council for Political Studies, 140-20E, South Sinthee Rd., 1st Fl., Calcutta 700 050, India. TEL 557-5351. Ed. A.K. Mukhopadhyay. adv.; bk.rev.; index; circ. 1,000 (controlled).
   —UnCover.

335   UK   ISSN 0081-0606
HX15
SOCIALIST REGISTER; a survey of movements and ideas. 1964. a. price varies. Merlin Press Ltd., 10 Malden Rd., London NW5 3HR, England. FAX 071-284-3092. Ed.Bd. bk.rev. circ. 4,000. Document type: bulletin.
   —BLDSC (8318.248500). **CCC.**

320.531   US   ISSN 0161-1801
HX1
SOCIALIST REVIEW. 1970. q. $28 to individuals (foreign $40); institutions $65 (foreign $77) (effective 1996). (Center for Social Research and Education) Duke University Press, Box 90660, Durham, NC 27708-0660. TEL 919-687-3600. FAX 919-688-4574. Ed. David Trend. adv.; bk.rev. circ. 5,500. (also avail. in microform from UMI; back issues avail.; reprint service avail. from SCH,UMI) **Indexed:** Acad.Ind., Alt.Press Ind., Int.Polit.Sci.Abstr., Int.Polit.Sci.Abstr., Lang.& Lang.Behav.Abstr., Left Ind. (1982-), Mid.East: Abstr.& Ind., Polit.Sci.Abstr., Sociol.Abstr., SSCI. Document type: academic/scholarly publication.
   —BLDSC (8318.248800); Faxon; Genuine Article; SWETS; UMI; UnCover.
    Former titles: Socialist Revolution (ISSN 0037-8240); (1959-1967): Studies on the Left (ISSN 0585-7449)
    Description: Operates within the broad consensus that there is no contradiction between democracy and socialism. Post-Fordism, queer identity, technoscience, and the politics of memory are special issues.

320.531   UK   ISSN 0037-8259
HX3
SOCIALIST STANDARD. 1904. m. £10 (foreign £20). Socialist Party of Great Britain, 52 Clapham High St., London SW4 7UN, England. TEL 0171-622-3811. FAX 0171-720-3665. Ed.Bd. bk.rev.; illus.; index. circ. 4,000. (also avail. in microfilm from RPI; back issues avail.) Document type: bulletin.
    Description: Presents the case for a world society based on common ownership and democratic control of productive resources.

320.531　　　　CN　　ISSN 0712-1970
SOCIALIST STUDIES/ETUDES SOCIALISTES. 1979. a. Societe des Etudes Socialistes, University College, No. 471, University of Manitoba, Winnipeg, MB R3T 2M8, Canada.
—BLDSC (8318.248980).

320.531　　　　　　　UK
SOCIALIST STUDIES; analysis of capitalist system from a Marxist viewpoint. 1991. a. free. Socialist Party of Great Britain, Head Office, 71 Ashbourne Ct., Woodside Park Rd., London N12 8SB, England. Pub. Cyril May.
Description: Analyzes the capitalist system and democracy from a Marxist viewpoint.

320.531　　　　CN　　ISSN 0836-7094
SOCIALIST WORKER. 1975. 11/yr. Can.$10($16) (elsewhere Can.$20). International Socialist, P.O. Box 339, Sta. E, Toronto, Ont. M6H 4E3, Canada. FAX 416-469-5930. bk.rev. circ. 2,000. **Indexed:** Alt.Press Ind.
Description: Marxist analysis of Canadian, American and international social and political issues. Anti-Stalinist and non-dogmatic.

320.531　　　　　　　NQ
EL SOCIALISTA. fortn. Partido Revolucionario de los Trabajadores, Apdo. SV-68, Managua, Nicaragua. Ed. Bonifacio Miranda Bengoechea.

320.531　　　　SW　　ISSN 0346-1491
SOCIALISTISK DEBATT. 1967-1969; resumed 1971. bi-m. SEK 175 (effective 1991). Vaenstertpartiet, Kungsg. 84, S-112 27 Stockholm, Sweden.

320.532　　　　DK　　ISSN 0108-1861
SOCIALISTISK INFORMATION. 1980. m. DKK 100 to individuals; (foreign DKK 150); institutions DKK 200. Socialistisk Arbejderparti, Noerre Alle 11 A, P.O. Box 547, DK-2200 Copenhagen N, Denmark. TEL 45-35-37-32-17. FAX 45-35-37-32-17. Ed. Mads Bruun Pedersen. adv.: B&W page DKK 1000. bk.rev.; illus. circ. 600.

320.5　　　　　SW　　ISSN 0346-1505
SOCIALISTISKT FORUM; socialdemokratisk debattidskrift. 1971. bi-m. SEK 90 (effective 1995). Socialistiskt Forum, P.O. Box 60, S-101 21 Stockholm, Sweden. Ed. Stina Ljungkvist.

320.5　　　　　SW　　ISSN 0281-7489
SOCIALISTISKT PERSPEKTIV. 1980. 10/yr. Socialistiskt Perspektiv, P.O. Box 4110, S-163 Spaanga, Sweden.

320 360 301　　　XR　　ISSN 0049-0962
SOCIALNI POLITIKA.* (Editions in English and Slovak) 1950. m. 36 Kc.($9) Ministersto Prace a Socialnich Veci, Na Poricnim Pravu 1, 120 07 Prague 2, Czech Republic. (Dist. by: Artia, Ve Smeckach 30, 111 27 Prague 1, Czech Republic) Ed. Lubomir Cermak. bk.rev.; charts; illus.; stat. circ. 6,000.
Formerly: Socialni Zabezpeceni.

SOCIETE FRANCAISE. see *SOCIOLOGY*

SOCIETE SAINT-JEAN-BAPTISTE DE MONTREAL. INFORMATION NATIONALE. see *SOCIOLOGY*

SOCIETY & NATURE/KOINONIA KAI PHYSI; the international journal of political ecology. see *ENVIRONMENTAL STUDIES*

320　　　　　YU　　ISSN 0489-5967
SOCIJALIZAM; casopis Saveza komunista Jugoslavije. 1958. m. 2160 din.($26) (Savez Komunista Jugoslavije) Komunist, Trg Marksa i Engelsa 11, 11000 Belgrade, Yugoslavia. Ed. Stipe Suvar. bk.rev. **Indexed:** Int.Polit.Sci.Abstr.

SOCIOLOGIA Y POLITICA. see *SOCIOLOGY*

SOCIOLOGIE ET SOCIETES. see *SOCIOLOGY*

320 914.7　　　　　BU
SOFIA NEWS; weekly for politics, economics, culture, tourism and sport. (Editions in English, French, German and Russian) 1969. w. $20. Sofia Press, 113 Lenin Blvd., Sofia, Bulgaria. (Dist. by: Hemus, 6, Rouski Blvd., 1000 Sofia, Bulgaria) charts; illus. circ. 30,000. (looseleaf format)

320.531　　　　BU　　ISSN 0204-9619
HX361
SOFIISKI UNIVERSITET. KATEDRA PO NAUCHEN KOMUNIZM. GODISHNIK. (Text in Bulgarian) irreg., vol.72, 1979. 2.36 lv. Sofiiski Universitet, Katedra po Nauchen Komunizm., Sofia, Bulgaria. Ed. S. Petrov. circ. 550.
Formerly: Sofiiski Universitet. Ideologicheski Katedri. Godishnik.

972　　　　　MX　　ISSN 0038-0857
SOL DE URUAPAN.* w. Mex.$30. Asociacion Periodistica Uruapense, Av. Cupatitzio 175, Uruapan, Michoacan, Mexico. Ed. Prof. Sabas Tolentino. adv.; illus. (tabloid format)

320.5　　　　　FR　　ISSN 0038-1012
SOLEIL;* journal de la droite nationale et populaire. (Supplement avail.) 1966. w. 50 F.($10.) 4 Bis rue Caillaux, 75013 Paris, France. Eds. Andre Cantelaube, Pierre Sedos. bk.rev.; charts. circ. 20,000.

320　　　　　IT
SOLIDARIETA LOMBARDIA. bi-m.? L.20000. Piazza S. Ambrogio 15, 20123 Milan, Italy. TEL 80-98-31.

320.531　　　　　UK
SOLIDARITY; a libertarian socialist journal. 1960. q. £6. London Solidarity, 123 Lathom Rd., London E6, England. TEL 01-552-3985. Ed.Bd. circ. 2,000.

320　　　　　CH　　ISSN 1019-8636
SOOCHOW JOURNAL OF POLITICAL SCIENCE/DONGWU ZHENGZHI XUEBAO. 1977. a. $20 per no. Soochow University, Wai Shuang Hsi, Shih Lin, Taipei, Taiwan, Republic of China. FAX 886-02-8812317. (reprint service avail.) **Document type:** academic/scholarly publication.
Supersedes in part (in 1992): Soochow Journal of Political Science and Sociology (ISSN 0259-3785); Which was formerly: Soochow Journal of Social and Political Sciences.

329.3　　　　　SG
SOPI.* 1988. w. Parti Democratique Senegalais, 5 bd Dial Diop, Dakar, Senegal. Ed. Cheikh Koureyssi Ba.

320.531　　　　FI　　ISSN 0038-1616
HX9
SOSIALISTINEN AIKAKAUSLEHTI. 1905. 4/yr. Fmk.55. Osoite Saariniemenkatu 6, 00530 Helsinki 53, Finland. Ed. Matti Linnanahde. adv.; bk.rev.; illus. circ. 6,000. **Indexed:** World Bibl.Soc.Sec.

SOSIALOEKONOMEN. see *BUSINESS AND ECONOMICS*

329.9　　　　　AA
SOT. (Text in Albanian; summaries in English) 1991. m? Partia Socialiste e Shqiperise - Socialist Party of Albania, Bulevardi Deshmoret e Kombit, Tirana, Albania. TEL 355-42-27409. FAX 355-42-27417.

SOUTH AFRICA FOUNDATION REVIEW. see *BUSINESS AND ECONOMICS — Economic Situation And Conditions*

320　　　　　SA　　ISSN 1019-620X
SOUTH AFRICA IN THE NINETIES: PROSPECTS FOR SOLUTIONS. Variant title: Prospects. 1992. q. R.28. Human Sciences Research Council, Group: Social Dynamics, Private Bag X41, Pretoria 0001, South Africa. circ. 4,000. **Document type:** newsletter.
Description: Publishes in-depth critical and analytical contributions on change in South Africa, especially progress towards a free and democratic society.

968　　　　　SA　　ISSN 0038-2515
SOUTH AFRICAN OBSERVER; a journal for realists. 1955. m. R.20($18) S.E.D. Brown, Ed. & Pub., Box 2401, Pretoria, South Africa. TEL 012-322-2950. FAX 012-322-0215. bk.rev. circ. 6,000. **Indexed:** Documentatieblad.

320 330.9　　　UK　　ISSN 0268-0661
F1401
SOUTH AMERICA, CENTRAL AMERICA AND THE CARIBBEAN (YEAR). 1985. biennial. $295. Europa Publications, 18 Bedford Sq., London WC1B 3JN, England. TEL 0171-580-8236. FAX 0171-636-1664. TELEX 21540 EUROPA G. bibl.; stat. **Document type:** academic/scholarly publication, directory.
—CCC.
Description: Contains essays on important aspects of economic and political life in Latin America and a general essay on the Caribbean. Provides up-to-date statistical survey on each of the major countries and a directory of essential names and addresses.

SOUTH ASIAN STUDIES. see *HISTORY — History Of Asia*

SOUTHEAST ASIA REPORT. see *BUSINESS AND ECONOMICS — Economic Situation And Conditions*

320　　　　　UK　　ISSN 0967-828X
DS520
SOUTH EAST ASIA RESEARCH. 1993. s-a. £20($32) to individuals; institutions £51 ($82) (effective 1996). (University of London, School of Oriental and African Studies) In Print Publishing Ltd., 9 Beaufort Terrace, Brighton BN2 2SU, England. TEL 01273-682836. FAX 01273-620958. (Subscr. to: Turpin Distribution Services Ltd., Blackhorse Rd., Letchworth, Herts. SG6 1HN, England. TEL 01462-672555. FAX 01462-480947) Ed. Ian Brown. bk.rev. **Indexed:** Amer.Hist.& Life (1993-), Hist.Abstr. (1993-). **Document type:** academic/scholarly publication.
—BLDSC (8351.453000).
Description: Contains original research papers on Southeast Asia studies, focusing on political, social, cultural, and legal issues.
Refereed Serial

320　　　　　SI　　ISSN 0377-5437
DS502
SOUTHEAST ASIAN AFFAIRS. (Text in English) 1974. a. S.$25($18.50) for soft cover; hard cover S$48 ($35). Institute of Southeast Asian Studies, Heng Mui Keng Terrace, Pasir Panjang Rd., Singapore 0511, Singapore. TEL 7780955. FAX 7781735. TELEX RS 37068 ISEAS. E-mail: pubsunit@merlion.iseas.ac.sg. (Subscr. in U.S. to: Ashgate, Old Post Rd., Brookfield, VT 05036. TEL 802-276-3162) (reprint service avail. from SCH) **Indexed:** Int.Polit.Sci.Abstr. **Document type:** academic/scholarly publication.
—Faxon.
Formerly: Institute of Southeast Asian Studies. Annual Review.
Description: Reviews major political, economic and social issues of each country in Southeast Asia.

320.05　　　　US　　ISSN 0730-2177
JA1
SOUTHEASTERN POLITICAL REVIEW. 1973. q. $18 to individuals; institutions $35 (effective Jan. 1993). (Georgia Political Science Association) Georgia Southern University, Department of Political Science, Landrum Box 8101, Statesboro, GA 30460-8101. TEL 912-681-5698. FAX 912-764-6466. Ed. Roger N. Pajari. adv. contact: G. Lane VanTassell. bk.rev.; stat. circ. 425. **Indexed:** Amer.Bibl.Slavic & E.Eur.Stud., Int.Polit.Sci.Abstr. **Document type:** academic/scholarly publication.
—BLDSC (8352.470000); Faxon.
Formerly: G P S A Journal (ISSN 0092-9395)
Description: Publishes manuscripts from all subjects of political science, including articles of general interest, articles on Southern politics, and research notes.
Refereed Serial

THE SOUTHERN AFRICA EXCLUSIVE; bulletin covering financial and political trends for southern Africa. see *BUSINESS AND ECONOMICS — Economic Situation And Conditions*

916　　　　　UK　　ISSN 0966-8802
SOUTHERN AFRICA MONTHLY REGIONAL BULLETIN. 1992. m. £120($180) in U.K. and Europe; rest of world $220. SouthScan Ltd., P.O. Box 724, London N16 5RZ, England. TEL 0171-923-1467. FAX 0171-923-2545. **Document type:** bulletin.
Description: Economic and political analysis of southern African countries based on network of local correspondents.

POLITICAL SCIENCE

SOUTHERN CONE REPORT. see *BUSINESS AND ECONOMICS — Economic Situation And Conditions*

322.4 US
SOUTHERN LIBERTARIAN MESSENGER. 1972. m. $6. Quality Education, Inc., 511 Wellington Ave., Reading, PA 19609-2313. Ed. John T. Harllee. adv.; bk.rev.; charts; illus.; stat. circ. 800. (also avail. in microform from UMI; back issues avail.) **Indexed:** Alt.Press Ind.

320 US ISSN 0739-3938
SOUTHERN POLITICAL REPORT. 1978. fortn. $157. Southern Political Report, Box 15507, Washington, DC 20003-5507. TEL 202-547-8098. Ed. Hastings Wyman, Jr. circ. 650 (paid). (back issues avail.)
Description: Focuses on the politics and politicians of the 12 Southern states.

916 UK ISSN 0952-7524
DT1001
SOUTHSCAN; a bulletin of southern African affairs. 1986. w. £190($285) in U.K. and Europe; rest of world £210($310). SouthScan Ltd., P.O. Box 724, London N16 5RZ, England. TEL 0171-923-1467. FAX 0171-923-2545. E-mail: southscan@gn.apc.org.uk. bk.rev. **Document type:** bulletin.
●Also available online.
Description: News and analysis of current situation in South Africa and region.

320 UK ISSN 0049-1713
DK274
SOVIET ANALYST. 1972. 10/yr. £150($325) World Reports Ltd., 108 Horseferry Rd., Westminster, London SW1P 2EF, England. TEL 071-222-3836. FAX 071-233-0185. Ed. Christopher Story. (back issues avail.) **Document type:** newsletter.
Description: Analyzes political and economic developments in the USSR, with special emphasis on strategic deception intelligence.

947 II ISSN 0038-5522
SOVIET LAND. (Text in English) vol.23, 1970. s-m. Rs.7. U.S.S.R. Embassy in India, Information Department, 25 Barakhamba Rd., New Delhi 110001, India. Ed. G.L. Kolokolov.

SOVIET STUDIES. see *SOCIOLOGY*

329.9 GW ISSN 0038-6030
DER SOZIALDEMOKRAT. 1955. m. DM.1955. (Sozialdemokratische Partei Deutschlands) Presse und Bildung GmbH, Fischerfeldstr. 7-11, 60311 Frankfurt a.M., Germany. TEL 069-299888-0. FAX 069-293757. adv.; charts; illus. (tabloid format) **Document type:** bulletin.

320.531 GW ISSN 0722-7353
SOZIALIST; Zeitschrift Marxistische Sozialdemokratenlinnen. 1975. bi-m. DM.28. Verein fuer Soziale Verstaendigung und Internationale Cooperation, Im Koerbchen 10, 37079 Goettingen, Germany. TEL 0551-631216. Ed. Andreas Fisahn. adv.; bk.rev.; film rev. circ. 2,000. (back issues avail.) **Document type:** bulletin.

SOZIALISTISCHE ERZIEHUNG; Zeitschrift fuer Erziehung, Bildung, Kultur. see *EDUCATION*

320 GW ISSN 0341-1117
SOZIALPOLITISCHE INFORMATIONEN. 1967. irreg. Bundesminister fuer Arbeit und Sozialordung, Postfach 14 02 80, 5300 Bonn 1, Germany. TEL 0228-527-1. Ed. Ludger Reuber.

320.531 US
SPARK (DETROIT). 1971. bi-w. $8. Box 1047, Detroit, MI 48231.

320.531 US ISSN 0038-6596
SPARTACIST. (Supplement to: Workers Vanguard) 1964. irreg. $1.50 per no. (free with subscr. to Workers Vanguard). (Spartacist League) Spartacist Publishing Co., Box 1377, New York, NY 10116. TEL 212-732-7861. Ed.Bd. **Indexed:** Alt.Press Ind. **Document type:** newspaper.

329.82 331 IT
SPARTACO. 1980. q. L.6000. (Lega Trotskista d'Italia) Luigi Candreva Ed. & Pub., c/o Fidacaro, C.P. 1591, 20101 Milan, Italy. circ. 2,000. **Document type:** newspaper.

320 CN ISSN 0383-9370
SPEAK UP! 1973. q. Can.$16. (Christians Concerned for Racial Equality) Bible Holiness Movement, Box 223, Sta. A, Vancouver, BC V6C 2M3, Canada. TEL 604-498-3895. Ed. Giliaras Urbonas. adv.; bk.rev.; illus. circ. 3,000. (tabloid format; back issues avail.) **Document type:** newsletter.

SPECTRUM (LEXINGTON); journal of state government. see *PUBLIC ADMINISTRATION*

320 GR
SPOTLIGHT. m. (Institute of Political Studies) George Nicolopoulos, Ed. & Pub., 13, Kerkyras St., GR - 16342 Athens, Greece.

323.4 US ISSN 0191-6270
SPOTLIGHT (WASHINGTON). 1975. w. $38. Cordite Fidelity Inc., 300 Independence Ave. S.E., Washington, DC 20003. TEL 202-544-1794. Ed. Paul J. Croke. adv. contact: James Wolfington. bk.rev.; circ. 112,000 (paid). (also avail. in microform from UMI) **Document type:** newspaper.
—UMI.
Supersedes: Liberty Lowdown; Former titles: National Spotlight; Liberty Letter (ISSN 0024-2098)

320 US ISSN 0584-9365
DT1
SPOTLIGHT ON AFRICA. 1966. bi-m. $10. American-African Affairs Association, 1001 Connecticut Ave., N.W., Ste. 1135, Washington, DC 20036. TEL 202-223-5110. Ed. J.A. Parker. bk.rev. circ. 1,500. **Document type:** newsletter.

320 GW ISSN 0038-884X
DER STAAT; Zeitschrift fuer Staatslehre, Oeffentliches Recht und Verfassungsgeschichte. (Suppplements avail.) 1962. q. DM.148. Duncker und Humblot GmbH, Postfach 410329, 12113 Berlin, Germany. TEL 030-7900060. FAX 030-79000631. Ed.Bd. adv.; bk.rev.; index. **Indexed:** CERDIC, Int.Polit.Sci.Abstr., P.A.I.S.For.Lang.Ind. **Document type:** academic/scholarly publication.
—BLDSC (8425.530000); Faxon; SWETS. CCC.

320 GW ISSN 0038-8858
K23
STAAT UND RECHT. 1952. m. DM.96. (Akademie fuer Staats- und Rechtswissenschaft der DDR) Staatsverlag der DDR, Otto Grotewohl Str. 17, 10117 Berlin, Germany. **Indexed:** Rural Recreat.Tour.Abstr., World Agri.Econ.& Rural Sociol.Abstr.

320 SZ ISSN 0038-8874
STAATSBUERGER; Magazin fuer Wirtschaft und Politik. vol.57, 1973. 6/yr. 60 SFr. (Schweizer Staatsbuergerliche Gesellschaft) Leipziger und Partner, Dorfplatz 4, CH-8126 Zumikon, Switzerland. TEL 01-9181844. FAX 01-9181884. Ed. E. Schreyger. adv.; bk.rev.; bibl. circ. 4,000. **Document type:** bulletin.

320 GW
STAFFEL AKTUELL; Buergerinformation der SPD. 1984. q. Sozialdemokratische Partei Deutschlands (SPD), Ortsbezirk Staffel, c/o Frank Schmidt, Ed., Koblenzer 23a, 65556 Limburg, Germany. TEL 06431-26545. **Document type:** newspaper.

STANFORD LAWYER. see *LAW*

322.4 US
STANISLAUS CONNECTIONS. 1970. m. $15 donation. Modesto Peace - Life Center - Stanislaus Safe Energy Committee, Box 134, Modesto, CA 95353. TEL 209-529-5750. adv.; bk.rev. circ. 5,000. (back issues avail.) **Document type:** newspaper.
Formerly: Modesto Peace - Life Center - Stanislaus Safe Energy Committee. Newsletter.

320 CE
STATE; a Marxist quarterly. (Text in English) 1975. q. Lanka Sama Samaja Party, Colombo, Sri Lanka.

STATE CAPITOLS REPORT; the weekly briefing on news from the 50 states. see *PUBLIC ADMINISTRATION*

STATE GOVERNMENT (WASHINGTON); guide to current issues and activities. see *PUBLIC ADMINISTRATION*

352 US ISSN 0039-0119
JK2403
STATE GOVERNMENT NEWS; the monthly magazine covering all facets of state government. 1958. m. $39 (foreign $45). The Council of State Governments, 3560 Iron Works Pike, Box 11910, Lexington, KY 40578-1910. TEL 606-244-8000. FAX 606-244-8001. Ed. Elaine Stuart. adv.; index. circ. 17,000. (also avail. in microfiche from WSH) **Indexed:** Acid Pre.Dig., Energy Ind., Energy Info.Abstr., Manage.Cont., P.A.I.S., Polit.Sci.Abstr., Sage Urb.Stud.Abstr.
—Faxon; UMI; UnCover.
Description: Covers events and developments in the administrative, legislative and judicial branches of state government.

STATE GOVERNMENT RESEARCH CHECKLIST. see *PUBLIC ADMINISTRATION*

353 US ISSN 0147-6041
JK2403
STATE LEGISLATURES. 1975. m. $49 (Canada $51.50). National Conference of State Legislatures, 1560 Broadway, Ste. 700, Denver, CO 80202-5140. TEL 303-830-2200. FAX 303-863-8003. Ed. Karen Hansen. adv.; index. circ. 14,957. **Indexed:** Acad.Ind., P.A.I.S., Polit.Sci.Abstr., Sage Urb.Stud.Abstr.
—Faxon; UMI. CCC.
Description: Presents articles on state tax reform, education, child welfare, criminal justice, health care and other public policy issues.

320 NR
STATESMAN. 1973. a. £N1($3.40) Political Science Student Association, Political Science Students Association, University of Ibadan, Department of Political Science, Ibadan, Nigeria. Ed. Doji Ajayi. adv.; bk.rev.; bibl. circ. 500.

954 II ISSN 0039-0321
STATESMAN WEEKLY; news and comments from "The Statesman" of New Delhi and Calcutta. 1924. w. Statesman Ltd., Statesman House, 4 Chowringhee Sq., Calcutta 700 001, India. Ed. Sunanda Kumar Datta-Ray. adv.; bk.rev.; illus.; mkt. circ. 1,000.

320 US ISSN 0081-4601
JA51
THE STATESMAN'S YEAR - BOOK (YEAR); statistical and historical annual of the states of the world. 1864. a., 130th ed., 1993-94. $85. St. Martin's Press, 175 Fifth Ave., New York, NY 10010. TEL 800-221-7945. TELEX TWX 710-581-6459. Ed. John Paxton. index. circ. 35,000.
Description: Listing of political, social, and economic institutions and structures by country worldwide.

320 IT ISSN 0392-9701
HF19
STATO E MERCATO. 1981. 3/yr. L.68000 (foreign L.120000). Societa Editrice Il Mulino, Strada Maggiore, 37, 40125 Bologna, Italy. TEL 39-51-256011. FAX 39-51-256034. Eds. Gian Primo Cella, Carlo Trigilia. adv.: B&W page L.2000000. index. circ. 1,500. (back issues avail.) **Indexed:** Int.Polit.Sci.Abstr., P.A.I.S.For.Lang.Ind. —BLDSC (8457.800000); SWETS.

948.5 SW ISSN 0039-0747
H8
STATSVETENSKAPLIG TIDSKRIFT. 1897. 4/yr. SEK 150 (effective 1991). Fahlbeckska Stiftelsen, P.O. Box 52, S-221 00 Lund, Sweden. Ed. Lennart Lundquist. adv.; bk.rev.; charts; index. circ. 900. **Indexed:** A.B.C.Pol.Sci., Amer.Hist.& Life, Hist.Abstr., Int.Polit.Sci.Abstr.
Formerly (until 1964): Statsvetenskaplig Tidskrift foer Politik, Statistik, Ekonomi.

320 AU
STEIRISCHE NACHRICHTEN; freiheitliche Zeitung fuer die Steiermark. 1962. m. S.9. Freiheitliche Partei Landesgruppe Steiermark, Griesplatz 10-2, A-8020 Graz, Austria. TEL 0316-9072210. FAX 0316-9072219. bibl.; software rev.; tr.lit. (looseleaf format; also avail. in diskette format; back issues avail.) **Document type:** newsletter.

POLITICAL SCIENCE

320   SW   ISSN 0346-6620
STOCKHOLM STUDIES IN POLITICS. (Text in Swedish or English; summaries in English) 1971. irreg. price varies. University of Stockholm, Department of Political Science - Stockholms Universitet. Statsvetenskapliga Institutionen, S-106 91, Stockholm, Sweden. FAX 46-8-15-25-29. TELEX 8105199 UNIVERS. **Document type:** academic/scholarly publication, monographic series.
  Description: Contains dissertations in politics.

STOKVIS STUDIES IN HISTORICAL CHRONOLOGY & THOUGHT. see *HISTORY*

320 355   AT
STRATEGIC AND DEFENCE STUDIES CENTRE NEWSLETTER. 1981. q. free to qualified personnel. Strategic and Defence Studies Centre, Australian National University, Canberra, A.C.T. 0200, Australia. TEL 61-6-2438537. FAX 61-6-2480816. TELEX AA62694 SOPAC. E-mail: helen.hookey@anu.edu.au. Ed. Helen Wilson. bk.rev. circ. 1,250. **Document type:** newsletter.

STRATEGIQUE. see *MILITARY*

STRUGGLE; a magazine of proletarian revolutionary literature. see *LITERARY AND POLITICAL REVIEWS*

STUDI CRITICI; rivista di etica, filosofia e politica. see *PHILOSOPHY*

STUDI PARLAMENTARI E DI POLITICA COSTITUZIONALE. see *LAW*

320   PL   ISSN 1230-3135
JA26
STUDIA POLITYCZNE. 1968-1990; resumed 1992. q. $42. Polska Akademia Nauk, Instytut Studiow Politycznych, Palac Kultury i Nauki, Pietro XVII, pok.17-10, 00-901 Warsaw. (Dist. by: Ars Polona, Krakowskie Przedmiescie 7, 00-068 Warsaw, Poland) Ed. A. Bodnar. bk.rev. circ. 1,260. **Indexed:** Amer.Hist.& Life, Hist.Abstr.
  Formerly (until 1990): Studia Nauk Politycznych.

STUDIA UNIVERSITATIS "BABES-BOLYAI". SOCIOLOGIA - POLITOLOGIA. see *SOCIOLOGY*

STUDIEN ZU POLITIK UND VERWALTUNG. see *LAW*

320   UK   ISSN 0898-588X
E183
STUDIES IN AMERICAN POLITICAL DEVELOPMENT. 1986. s-a. £38($66) (effective 1996). Cambridge University Press, Edinburgh Bldg., Shaftesbury Rd., Cambridge DB2 2RU, England. TEL 01223-312393. FAX 01223-315052. TELEX 851817256. (N. American addr.: Cambridge University Press, Journals Dept., 40 W. 20th St., New York, NY 10011. TEL 212-924-3900. FAX 212-691-3239) Eds. Karen Orren, Stephen Skowronek. adv.; bk.rev. (back issues avail.) **Indexed:** Int.Polit.Sci.Abstr. **Document type:** academic/scholarly publication.
  —BLDSC (8489.086500); Faxon; UMI; UnCover.
  Description: Covers American political change and institutional development from a historical perspective.

STUDIES IN CHURCH AND STATE. see *RELIGIONS AND THEOLOGY*

STUDIES IN DEFENSE POLICY. see *MILITARY*

947   NE   ISSN 0925-9392
B809.8   CODEN: SEETE3
STUDIES IN EAST EUROPEAN THOUGHT. (Text in English, French and German) 1961. q. fl.373 to institutions; $239 to institutions in U.S. (effective 1996). Kluwer Academic Publishers, Postbus 17, 3300 AA Dordrecht, Netherlands. TEL 31-78-392392. FAX 019287766254. TELEX 29245 KAPG NL. E-mail: SERVICES@WKAP.NL. (Dist. by: Kluwer Academic Publishers Group, P.O. Box 322, 3300 AH Dordrecht, Netherlands. TEL 31-78-392392. FAX 31-78-546474; N. America dist. addr.: Box 358, Accord Sta., Hingham, MA 02018-0358. TEL 617-871-6600. FAX 617-871-6528) (Co-sponsors: Fribourg University, Institute of East European Studies; Munich University, Seminar for Political Theory) Ed. Edward M. Swiderski. adv.; bk.rev.; bibl.; index. (also avail. in microform from UMI; reprint service avail. from SWZ) **Indexed:** A.B.C.Pol.Sci., Amer.Hist.& Life, Arts & Hum.Cit.Ind., ASCA, Bull.Signal., Curr.Cont., Hist.Abstr., IBR, IBZ, Int.Polit.Sci.Abstr., Phil.Ind., Polit.Sci.Abstr., SSCI. **Document type:** academic/scholarly publication.
  —BLDSC (8490.413600); Faxon; Genuine Article; SWETS; UMI; UnCover. **CCC.**
  Formerly (until 1992): Studies in Soviet Thought (ISSN 0039-3797)
  Description: Provides a forum for writings on philosophy, philosophers and schools of philosophy connected with East and central Europe, including Russia, the Ukraine and the Baltic nations.
  Refereed Serial

320   II
STUDIES IN ELECTORAL POLITICS IN THE INDIAN STATES. (Text in English) irreg. Manohar Book Service, 2 Daryaganj, Ansari Rd., Panna Bhawan, Delhi 110006, India. Eds. Myron Weiner, John Osgood Field. charts, stat.

320 338   UK
STUDIES IN EUROPEAN POLITICS. 1979. irreg. £55 includes P S I Report Series; Discussion Papers; Policy Studies. Policy Studies Institute, 100 Park Village East, London NW1 3SR, England. TEL 071-387-2171. FAX 071-388-0914.

320   US   ISSN 0273-1231
STUDIES IN FREEDOM. 1981. irreg. price varies. (Freedom House) Greenwood Press, Inc. (Subsidiary of: Greenwood Publishing Group Inc.), 88 Post Rd. W., Box 5007, Westport, CT 06881-5007. TEL 203-226-3571. FAX 203-222-1502.

320   US   ISSN 0081-7996
STUDIES IN HISTORICAL AND POLITICAL SCIENCE. EXTRA VOLUMES. irreg., vol.15, 1968. (Johns Hopkins University) Bergman Publishers, Inc., 224 W. 20th St., New York, NY 10011. TEL 212-685-9074.

320   US   ISSN 0081-802X
STUDIES IN INTERNATIONAL AFFAIRS (BALTIMORE). 1967. irreg, no.26, 1975. price varies. (Washington Center of Foreign Policy Research) Johns Hopkins University Press, 710 W. 40th St., Ste. 275, Baltimore, MD 21211. TEL 410-516-6900. FAX 410-516-6998. (reprint service avail. from UMI)

320   US
STUDIES IN INTERNATIONAL POLITICAL ECONOMY. 1978. irreg., latest vol.25, 1993. University of California Press, 2120 Berkeley Way, Berkeley, CA 94720. TEL 510-642-4247. FAX 510-643-7127. (Subscr. to: California-Princeton Fulfillment Services, 1445 Lower Ferry Rd., Ewing, NJ 08618. TEL 800-777-4726. FAX 800-999-1958) Ed.Bd. **Document type:** monographic series.
  Incorporates: Science, Technology, and the Changing World Order Series.
  Description: Discusses how political policy affects economic conditions.

320.531   US
STUDIES IN MARXISM. 1977. irreg. (Marxist Educational Press) M E P Publications, University of Minnesota, 116 Church St., S.E., Minneapolis, MN 55455-0112. TEL 612-647-9748. Ed. Harold Schwartz. adv. circ. 1,500. **Document type:** academic/scholarly publication.
  Description: Devoted to application of Marxist methods of analysis to various fields of study.

320 330.1   CN   ISSN 0707-8552
STUDIES IN POLITICAL ECONOMY; socialist review. 1979. 3/yr. $24 to individuals; institutions $48; students $15. (Social Sciences and Humanities Research Council of Canada) Politecon, Box 4729, Station E, Ottawa, ON K1S 5H9, Canada. TEL 613-788-2600. bk.rev. circ. 1,000. (back issues avail.) **Indexed:** Alt.Press Ind., Can.B.P.I., Can.Per.Ind., Int.Polit.Sci.Abstr., Lang.& Lang.Behav.Abstr., Left Ind. (1984-), P.A.I.S., Polit.Sci.Abstr.
  —BLDSC (8491.223720); UnCover. **CCC.**
  Description: Scholarly journal providing detailed analyses of current issues and informed commentary on topics in Canadian and international political economy.
  Refereed Serial

320   US   ISSN 1073-2349
LA229
STUDY WAR NO MORE. 1991. q. $25 to individuals; institutions $35; students $20 (effective 1995 & 1996). (University Conversion Project) Public Search, Inc., Box 748, Cambridge, MA 02142. TEL 713-522-9299. FAX 713-524-6525. E-mail: UCP@IGE.APC.ORG. (Subscr. to: UCP, Box 748, Cambridge, MA 02138. TEL 617-354-9363) Eds. Rich Cowan, Dalya Massachi. adv.; B&W page $190; adv. contact: Rich Cowan. bk.rev.; bibl.; charts; stat. circ. 1,500. (back issues avail.) **Document type:** academic/scholarly publication, bulletin.
  Formerly (until 1994): War Research Info Service (ISSN 1058-823X)
  Description: Directed to campus peace researchers and activists who educate about the military domination of society and its influence on academia. Provides detailed biographies, statistics, and lists of organizations working to end war and convert military research to peaceful ends.

SUB-SAHARAN AFRICA REPORT. see *BUSINESS AND ECONOMICS — Economic Situation And Conditions*

940   GW   ISSN 0722-480X
H5
SUEDOST-EUROPA. ZEITSCHRIFT FUER GEGENWARTSFORSCHUNG; Quellen und Berichte ueber Staat, Verwaltung, Recht, Bevoelkerung, Wirtschaft, Wissenschaft und Veroeffentlichungen in Suedosteuropa. 1952. bi-m. DM.94. (Suedost-Institut) R. Oldenbourg Verlag GmbH, Rosenheimerstr. 45, 81671 Munich, Germany. TEL 089-45051-0. FAX 089-45051266. (Subscr. to: Postfach 801360, 81613 Munich, Germany) Ed.Bd. bibl.; charts; stat.; index. **Indexed:** Int.Polit.Sci.Abstr. **Document type:** academic/scholarly publication.
  —BLDSC (8509.285000). **CCC.**
  Formerly: Wissenschaftlicher Dienst Suedosteuropa (ISSN 0043-695X)

320   GW   ISSN 0722-8821
SUEDOSTASIEN AKTUELL. bi-m. DM.121 (foreign DM.130; students DM.60). Institut fuer Asienkunde - Institute of Asian Affairs, Rothenbaumchaussee 32, 20148 Hamburg, Germany. TEL 040-443001. FAX 040-4107945. **Document type:** academic/scholarly publication.

320   US   ISSN 0146-2156
SUMMARY OF CONGRESS. 1976. biennial. included in subscription to Taylor's Encyclopedia of Government Officials. Political Research, Inc., Tegoland at Bent Tree, 16850 Dallas Pkwy., Dallas, TX 75248. TEL 214-931-8827. FAX 214-248-7159.
  Description: Chronological list of all bills passed by both sessions of Congress with section on major legislation.

SURMACH. see *MILITARY*

320   IS   ISSN 0792-4747
SURVEY OF ARAB AFFAIRS. (Text in English) 1985. q. $18 to individuals; institutions $25. Jerusalem Center for Public Affairs, 13 Tel Hai St., Jerusalem 92107, Israel. TEL 972-2-619281. FAX 972-2-619112. (U.S. subscr. to: Center for Jewish Commmunity Studies, 1616 Walnut St., No. 513, Philadelphia, PA 19103. TEL 215-204-1459. FAX 215-204-7784)
  Description: Analysis of the political attitudes of Israeli and Palestinian Arabs.

POLITICAL SCIENCE

320.9   UK   ISSN 0039-6214
DA20
SURVEY OF CURRENT AFFAIRS. 1955. m. £32. H.M.S.O., P.O. Box 276, London SW8 5DT, England. abstr.; charts; stat.; index. (also avail. in microform from UMI; reprint service avail. from UMI) **Indexed:** ELLIS, Key to Econ.Sci., Polit.Sci.Abstr., So.Pac.Per.Ind. **Document type:** government publication.
—UMI.
Formerly: Survey of British and Commonwealth Affairs.

320.5   SW   ISSN 1101-7597
SVEAMAAL; frispraakig nationell tidning foer debatt och information. 1991. 10/yr. SEK 150 (effective 1991). Sveamaal, P.O. Box 20085, S-104 60 Stockholm, Sweden.

320.5   SW   ISSN 0346-2161
SVENSK LINJE. 1942. bi-m. SEK 75 (effective 1991). Fria Moderata Studentfoerbundet, P.O. Box 2294, S-103 17 Stockholm, Sweden.

320.5   SW   ISSN 0346-2366
SVENSKA NYHETER. 1970-1984; resumed 1988. q. Frisinnada Unions-Partiet, Presstjaenst, Bua 6186, S-440 80 Elloes, Sweden.

320.5   SW   ISSN 1102-271X
SVERIGES FRAMTID. 1990. q. SEK 100 (effective 1991). Foereningen Sveriges Framtid (FSF), Pl. 498, S-114 79 Stockholm, Sweden.

320.531   XO   ISSN 0139-6803
SVET SOCIALISMU. vol.27, 1965. w. $94. (Svaz Ceskoslovensko-Sovetskeho Pratelstvi - Union of the Czechoslovak-Soviet Friendship) Obzor, Spitalska ul. 35, 815 85 Bratislava, Slovakia. (Subscr. to: Artia, Ve Smeckach 30, 111 27 Prague 1, Slovakia) Ed. Josef Masin. illus. circ. 105,000.
Formerly: Svet Sovetu (ISSN 0039-7024)

320.532   RU   ISSN 0869-4435
SVOBODNAYA MYSL; teoreticheskii i politicheskii zhurnal. (Former name of issuing body: Kommunisticheskaya Partiya Sovetskogo Soyuza, Tsentral'nyi Komitet) 1924. m. $92 (effective 1996). Svobodnaya Mysl, Ul. Marksa i Engelsa 5, Moscow 1119875, Russia. (Dist. by: Mezhdunarodnaya Kniga, B. Yakimanka 39, 117049 Moscow, Russia; Dist. in U.S. by: Victor Kamkin Inc., 4956 Boiling Brook Pkwy, Rockville, MD 20852. TEL 301-881-5973) Ed. N.B. Bikkenin. bk.rev.; index. circ. 995,000. (also avail. in microfilm from KTO) **Indexed:** Curr.Dig.Sov.Press, Lang.& Lang.Behav.Abstr.
Former titles (until 1991): Kommunist (ISSN 0131-1212); (until 1952): Bol'shevik.

328   SW   ISSN 0280-0365
JN7934
SWEDEN. RIKSDAGEN; ledamoeter och riksdagsorgan. a. SEK 25 (effective 1990). Riksdagen Foervaltningskontor, Informationsenheten, S-100 12 Stockholm, Sweden. FAX 08-218878. (Dist. by: Riksdagens Tryckeriexpedition, 100 12 Stockholm, Sweden) circ. 10,000.
Formerly: Sweden. Riksdagen. Foerteckning oever Riksdagens Ledamoeter.

320.948 339.948   SW   ISSN 1104-9197
▼**SWEDISH EXAMPLE;** international newsletter. 1994. q. free. Nordic News Network, P.O. Box 1181, S-181 23 Lidingoe, Sweden. TEL 46-8-731-92-00. FAX 46-8-731-92-00. Ed. Al Burke. **Document type:** newsletter.
●Available only online.

320   UK   ISSN 0049-271X
SWINTON JOURNAL.* vol.16, 1971. q. 10s. Swinton Conservative College, Mealhouse Lane, Bolton, Lancs. BL1 1DE, England. Ed. Stephen Eyres. adv.; bk.rev.; bibl.

320.5   UK   ISSN 0965-1411
T P S BULLETIN. 1964. s-a. £5 (foreign $16). Thomas Paine Society, 43 Wellington Gardens, Selsey, W. Sussex PO20 ORF, England. TEL 01243-605730. Ed. R.W. Morrell. adv.; bk.rev.; bibl.; illus. circ. 670. **Indexed:** Abstr.Engl.Stud. **Document type:** bulletin.
Former titles (until 1985): Journal of Radical History; T P S Bulletin (ISSN 0049-3813)

967   TZ   ISSN 0049-2817
JQ2945.A1
TAAMULI; a political science forum. (Text in English) 1970. s-a. Sh.25. University of Dar es Salaam, Department of Political Science, P.O. Box 35042, Dar es Salaam, Tanzania. TEL 255-51-43130. FAX 255-51-43395. Ed. Samuel Mushi. adv.; bk.rev. circ. 1,000. (also avail. in microform from UMI) **Indexed:** Amer.Hist.& Life, Curr.Cont.Africa, Documentatieblad, Hist.Abstr. **Document type:** academic/scholarly publication.
—BLDSC (8595.896300).

TAIWAN YANJIU/TAIWAN STUDY. see *SOCIAL SCIENCES: COMPREHENSIVE WORKS*

320   US
TAKING SIDES: CLASHING VIEWS ON CONTROVERSIAL POLITICAL ISSUES. irreg., 7th ed., 1990. $13.95. Dushkin Publishing Group, Sluice Dock, Guilford, CT 06437-9989. TEL 203-453-4351. FAX 203-453-6000. Eds. Stanley Feingold, George McKenna; Pub. Mimi Egan. illus. **Document type:** academic/scholarly publication.

320   UK   ISSN 0955-8780
TALKING POLITICS. 1988. 3/yr. £20 (Europe £23) to individuals; institutions £27 (Europe £27). Politics Association, 64 W. Hill Dr., Dartford, Kent DA1 3EA, England. TEL 01322-75145. **Indexed:** A.B.C.Pol.Sci. (1988-). **Document type:** academic/scholarly publication.
—BLDSC (8601.407250).
Incorporates (1972-1988): Teaching Politics (ISSN 0305-7771)

320   CH   ISSN 1015-9436
TAMKANG JOURNAL: AREA STUDIES. (Text in Chinese and English) NT.$120($4) Tamkang University, Area Studies Publication Association, Chin-hua St. Lane 199, No. 5, Taipei, Taiwan 10610, Republic of China. Ed. Stephan Hsu.

320   AU
TANGENTE. bi-m. S.45. Ring Freiheitlicher Jugend, Schaeffergasse 18, A-1010 Vienna, Austria. TEL 01-5811489. Ed. Eolda Christ. adv. circ. 6,000. **Document type:** corporate report.

320   TZ
TANZANIA PUBLISHING HOUSE. INAUGURAL LECTURE SERIES. irreg. Tanzania Publishing House, 47 Samora Machel Ave., P.O. Box 2138, Dar es Salaam, Tanzania. TEL 051-32164. (Dist. outside Africa by: African Books Collective Ltd., The Jam Factory, 27 Park End St., Oxford OX1 1HU, England. TEL 0865-726686. FAX 0865-793298) **Document type:** monographic series.

320.532   VN
TAP CHI CONG SAN/COMMUNIST REVIEW. 1955. m. 1 Nguyen Thuong Hien, Hanoi, Socialist Republic of Vietnam. TEL 52061. Ed. Ha Xuan Truong. circ. 55,000.
Formerly: Hoc Tap.

320 336   US
TAX WATCH. vol.5, no.2, 1992. q. membership. South Carolina Association of Taxpayers, Box 50799, Columbia, SC 29250. TEL 803-782-6913. **Document type:** newsletter.
Description: Covers issues relating to tax reform and citizen initiatives.

320 350   US   ISSN 0082-2183
JK6
TAYLOR'S ENCYCLOPEDIA OF GOVERNMENT OFFICIALS, FEDERAL AND STATE. 1967. biennial (plus q. supplements). $585 (includes q. Cumulative Supplement; World of Politics; Summary of Congress; State Leadership Chart; 50 State Legislative Review; Supplement Organizer). Political Research, Inc., Tegoland at Bent Tree, 16850 Dallas Pkwy., Dallas, TX 75248. TEL 214-931-8827. FAX 214-248-7159. Ed. John Clements. index. **Document type:** directory.
Description: Directory of current federal and state American government officials.

100 600   FR   ISSN 1251-0777
TEKHNEMA; journal of philosophy and technology. (Text in English) 1993. a. 40 F.($10) to individuals; institutions 80 F. ($20). American University of Paris, 31 av. Bosquet, 75007 Paris, France. FAX 45-55-17-89. E-mail: ASUMITS@LUCY.WELLESLEY.EDU. Ed.Bd. illus. circ. 800.
Description: Elicits thoughtful experimentation and experimental thinking concerning a post-Cold War world whose rhythms, impasses and hopes are articulated within an ever-accelerating process of technological advance.

320   MX
TEMAS NACIONALES. 1975. irreg. Mex.$25($2.50) Instituto de Estudios Politicos Economicos y Sociales, Insurgentes Norte, 59, Mexico, D.F., Mexico. charts. **Document type:** monographic series.

TEME. see *SOCIOLOGY*

320   IT   ISSN 1121-3566
TEMPI SUPPLEMENTARI. 1991. m. Primo Carnera s.r.l., Via Daniello Cartoli 11, 00152 Rome, Italy. TEL 39-6-5803205. Ed. Vincenzo Sparagna. adv.: B&W page L.24000000. **Document type:** newspaper.

320   IE
TEOIRIC. 1971. q. 40p. (Sinn Fein the Workers' Party) Repsol Publications, 30 Gardiner Pl., Dublin 1, Ireland. Ed.Bd. bk.rev. circ. 1,500.

320   IT   ISSN 0394-1248
JA18
TEORIA POLITICA. 1983. 3/yr. L.72000 (foreign L.90000) (effective 1993). Franco Angeli Editore, Viale Monza, 106, Casella Postale 17175, 20100 Milan, Italy. TEL 02-2895762. Ed. Luigi Bonanate. **Indexed:** Int.Polit.Sci.Abstr.

320   XV   ISSN 0040-3598
TEORIJA IN PRAKSA; revija za druzbena vprasanja. (Text in Slovenian) 1964. m. 1000 din. Univerza Edvarda Kardelja v Ljubljani, Fakulteta za Sociologijo, Politicne Vede in Novinarstvo, Kardeljeva ploscad 5, 61000 Ljubljana, Slovenia. TEL 341-461. (Co-sponsor: Kulturna Skupnost Slovenije) Ed. Andrej Kirn. bk.rev.; index. circ. 4,500. (back issues avail.) **Indexed:** Int.Polit.Sci.Abstr.

630   FR   ISSN 0040-3814
TERRE; hebdomadaire paysan du parti communiste francais. 1933. w. 83 F. 29 rue des Recollets, 75481 Paris Cedex 10, France. TEL 42-05-23-80. FAX 42-09-64-62. Ed. Maurice Duplessis. adv.; bk.rev.; film rev.; play rev.; illus.; stat. circ. 197,000. **Document type:** newspaper.

960   CX   ISSN 0049-3473
TERRE AFRICAINE.* vol.4, 1966. w. 1000 Fr.CFA. B.P. 373, Bangui, Central African Republic. adv.; charts; illus.

TESINSKO. see *HISTORY — History Of Europe*

320   VE
TESTIMONIOS VIOLENTOS. irreg., no.6, 1982. Universidad Central de Venezuela, Facultad de Ciencias Economicas y Sociales, Division de Publicaciones, Caracas, Venezuela.

TEXAS AGENDA. see *PUBLIC ADMINISTRATION*

350 320   US   ISSN 0164-9221
TEXAS GOVERNMENT NEWSLETTER. 1973. 36/yr. $30. Box 13274, Austin, TX 78711. TEL 512-323-5051. Ed. Thomas L. Whatley; Pub. Thomas L. Whatley. bk.rev. circ. 1,400. **Document type:** newsletter.
Description: Contains information about Texas state government and politics; includes reviews of news and in-depth analysis of single topics.

POLITICAL SCIENCE

320   US   ISSN 0191-0930
JK4801
TEXAS JOURNAL OF POLITICAL STUDIES. 1978. s-a. $7.95 individual; institutions $10. Sam Houston State University, Department of Political Science, Huntsville, TX 77341. TEL 409-294-1462. FAX 409-294-3622. E-mail: Pol.ESD@SHJU.edu. Ed. Jim Carter; Pub. Edwin S. Davis. adv. contact: Edwin S. Davis. bk.rev.; circ. 150 (paid). **Document type:** academic/scholarly publication.
   Description: Publishes the spectrum of social science research that relates to international, national, state and local political systems.
   Refereed Serial

320.5   US   ISSN 0040-4519
TEXAS OBSERVER; a journal of free voices. 1954. fortn. $32. Texas Observer Publishing Co., 307 W. Seventh St., Austin, TX 78701-2917. TEL 512-477-0746. Ed. Louis Dubose; Pub. Ronnie Dugger. adv. contact: Cliff Olofson. bk.rev.; film rev.; play rev.; charts; illus.; index, cum.index: 1954-1981; circ. 8,300 (paid). (also avail. in microfilm from UMI; back issues avail). **Indexed:** Access (1975-).
   —UMI; UnCover.
   Description: Analyzes political, economic, and social issues.

320.52   US   ISSN 0897-2710
TEXAS TRIBUNE. s-a. Box 15405, Austin, TX 78761. TEL 512-836-1316.

320 350   US   ISSN 0890-5924
TEXAS WEEKLY. 1984. w. (50/yr.). $175 (via fax or modem $230). P P S, Inc., Box 5306, Austin, TX 78763. TEL 512-322-9332. FAX 512-453-0027. Ed. Sam Kinch, Jr. **Document type:** newsletter.
   Description: Nonpartisan reports on Texas government and politics.

320 940 330   GW   ISSN 0944-1557
THAT WAS YUGOSLAVIA. Croatian edition: Hrvatska Domovina (ISSN 0179-3055) (Text in English) 1982. m. DM.24($20) Ost-Dienst, Hudtwalckerstr. 26, 22299 Hamburg, Germany. TEL 040-462702. FAX 040-462769. Ed. Hans Peter Rullmann. adv.; bk.rev. circ. 3,000. **Indexed:** HR Rep. **Document type:** bulletin.
   Formerly (until 1992): That's Yugoslavia (ISSN 0179-3063)

THESIS ELEVEN; a journal of critical social theory. see *SOCIOLOGY — Abstracting, Bibliographies, Statistics*

320   US   ISSN 1067-3237
E184.A1
THIRD FORCE. bi-m. $22 to individuals; institutions $55. Center for Third World Organizing, 1218 E. 21st St., Oakland, CA 94606. TEL 510-533-7583. FAX 510-533-0923. E-mail: ctwo@igc.apc.org. Ed. John Anner. adv.; film rev.; play rev.; illus. circ. 3,000. **Indexed:** Alt.Press Ind.
   Formerly (until 1993): Minority Trendsletter.
   Description: Examines the issues affecting and the conditions of minority communities, including local activism, labor organizing, and environmental racism.

322.4   UK   ISSN 0959-5031
THIRD WAY (LONDON); voice of the radical centre. 1980. q. £5 (Europe £6; rest of world £7). Third Way Publications Ltd., P.O. Box 1243, London SW7 3PB, England. TEL 0171-373-3432. E-mail: 100071.746@compuserve. Ed. Patrick Harrington. adv.; bk.rev.; illus. circ. 3,000. **Document type:** consumer publication.
   Former titles: Third Way - Beyond Capitalism and Communism; (until 1990): Third Way (London, 1980); Nationalism Today (ISSN 0260-2407)
   Description: A voice of opposition to all forms of authoritarianism, promoting popular democracy and preservation of the European cultural identity.

051 322.4   US   ISSN 0317-0659
THIRD WORLD FORUM. 1974. q. $30. Association on Third World Affairs, Inc., 1629 K St., N.W., Ste. 802, Washington, DC 20006. TEL 202-331-8455. FAX 202-785-3605. Ed. LuAnne Feik. bk.rev.; illus. circ. 2,500. (back issues avail.) **Indexed:** HR Rep. **Document type:** newsletter.
   Description: Covers political changes, building democracy, development and trade. Includes interviews with Third World VIPs.

320   CN   ISSN 0381-3746
L11
THIS MAGAZINE. 1966. 8/yr. Can.$23.99 to individuals (foreign Can.$34); institutions Can.$35.31 (foreign Can.$35). Red Maple Foundation, 16 Skey La., Toronto, ON M6J 3S4, Canada. TEL 416-588-6580. FAX 416-588-6638. E-mail: this__magazine@intacc.web.net. (Subscr. to: 35 Riviera Dr., Markham, ON L3R 8N4, Canada. TEL 905-946-0406) Ed. Naomi Klein. adv.; B&W page $935; 8 1/2 x 11 3/4; adv. contact: Alex Lukashevsky. bk.rev. circ. 8,000. (also avail. in microfilm from UMI,MML; reprint service avail. from UMI, MML) **Indexed:** Abstr.Pop.Cult., Alt.Press Ind., Can.B.P.I., Can.Educ.Ind., Can.Per.Ind., Mid.East: Abstr.& Ind., New Per.Ind.
   —UMI; UnCover.
   Former titles: This Magazine: Education, Culture, Politics; This Magazine Is About Schools (ISSN 0040-6228)
   Description: Presents critical, intelligent writing about culture, politics and the arts.

329.9   GY   ISSN 0040-6635
JL689.A8
THUNDER. (Text in English) 1950. q. G.$300. People's Progressive Party, Freedom House, 41 Robb St., Georgetown, Guyana. Ed. Ralph Ramkarran. bk.rev. circ. 7,000. (tabloid format)

951   II   ISSN 0040-6708
DS785.A1
TIBETAN REVIEW. (Text in English) 1968. m. Rs.60 (foreign Rs.400). c/o Tibetan SOS Youth Hostel, Sector 14 Ext. Rohini, Delhi 110 085, India. TEL 7269702. E-mail: edotpr@tibrev.uni.ernet.in. (Subscr. in U.S. to: Potala Publications, 241 E. 32nd St., New York, NY 10016. TEL 212-213-5010) Ed. Tsering Wangyal. adv.; bk.rev.; index. circ. 2,500. **Indexed:** HR Rep. (1985-).
   Formerly: Voice of Tibet.
   Description: Covers news from Tibet, Tibetans in exile, interviews, social, cultural and political commentary, and aspects of Tibetan religion, history, medicine and arts and crafts.

948.5   SW   ISSN 0040-6988
TIDSKRIFTEN HEIMDAL. 1962. 3-4/yr. SEK 100 (effective 1991). Foereningen Heimdal, P.O. Box 2043, S-750 02 Uppsala, Sweden. FAX 018-113099. adv.; bk.rev.; illus. circ. 800.
   Former titles (until vol.5, 1965): Heimdals Hornstoetar; (until vol.7, 1964): Hornstoetar.

TIEN PHONG/VANGUARD. see *CHILDREN AND YOUTH — For*

335   NE   ISSN 0303-9935
HX9.D8
TIJDSCHRIFT VOOR SOCIALE GESCHIEDENIS. 1975. q. fl.70 to individuals; institutions fl.90 (effective July 1995). (Stichting tot Beoefening van de Sociale Geschiedenis - Dutch Association for Social History) Uitgeverij Verloren, Larenseweg 123, 1221 CL Hilversum, Netherlands. TEL 31-35-6859856. FAX 31-35-6836557. Ed.Bd. adv.; bk.rev. circ. 1,450. **Document type:** academic/scholarly publication.
   —SWETS.

329.3   RU
TIKHVIISKAYA PLOSHCHAD'. 1990. 6/yr. 2 Rub. per issue. Irkutskaya Organizatsiya "Demokraticheskii Soyuz", Mikroraion Pervomaiskii, d.42, kv.80, 664058 Irkutsk, Russia. Ed. Irina Shishkina. circ. 3,000.

320 920   UK   ISSN 0082-4399
TIMES GUIDE TO THE HOUSE OF COMMONS; complete survey of Parliament after a General Election. 1880. irreg., latest Apr. 1992. £25. Times Books Ltd., 77-85 Fulham Palace Rd., Hammersmith, London W6 8JB, England. TEL 081-741-7070. FAX 081-307-4440. Ed. Alan Wood. index. circ. 7,500. **Document type:** directory.

TOUCHSTONE (CHICAGO); the touchstone of the pilgrim Church's self-understanding is dialogue. see *RELIGIONS AND THEOLOGY — Roman Catholic*

320.531   RU
TOVARISHCH. 1991. w. Novokuznetskaya Gorodskaya Organizatsiya K.P.S.S., Ul. Sverdlova 20, 654083 Novokuznetsk, Kemerovkskaya Oblast', Russia. TEL 46-27-22. Ed. N.N. Tkachenko. circ. 5,000. **Document type:** newspaper.

320   CU
TRABAJO POLITICO. s.m. Ministerio de las Fuerzas Armadas Revolucionarias, Plaza de la Revolucion, Apdo. Postal 7034, Havana, Cuba.

320 327 360 600   IT
TRANSIZIONE. 1985. bi-m. L.40000. (Istituto Gramsci Emilia-Romagna) Nuova Casa Editrice Cappelli, Via Marsili 9, I-40121 Bologna, Italy. circ. 1,500. (back issues avail.)
   Formerly: Problemi della Transizione.

329.9   MF
TRAVAILLEUR. (Text in English and French) 1968. fortn. Rs.26($6) Mauritius People's Progressive Party, Box 545, Port Louis, Mauritius. Ed. Teekaran Sibsurun. adv.; bk.rev.; bibl.; illus. circ. 15,000.

320.531   FR   ISSN 0754-281X
TRAVAILLEURS. 1982. m. 200 F. (Parti pour une Alternative Communiste) Presse d'Aujourd'hui, B.P. 90, 75962 Paris Cedex 20, France. Ed. M. Cuisinier.
   Supersedes in part: Humanite Rouge (ISSN 0018-750X)

329.9   CK
TRIBUNA ROJA. 1971. q. Pro-Maoist Communist Party (MOIR), Apdo. Aereo 19042, Bogota, Colombia. TEL 243-0371. Dir. Carlos Naranjo. circ. 300,000.

TRIBUNE. see *LABOR UNIONS*

320.531   TR
TRIBUNE; a journal of socialist thought. m. Commonwealth Publishers International Ltd., Box 1016, Port-of-Spain, Trinidad & Tobago, W.I.

320.5   FR   ISSN 0397-7242
TRIBUNE GAULLISTE. 1976. bi-m. 40 F. (Union des Jeunes pour le Progres) T G Presse, 91 rue du Faubourg Saint Denis, 75010 Paris, France. Ed. Gilbert Trompas. adv.; charts; illus. (tabloid format)
   Supersedes: Renaissance Deux-Mille (ISSN 0034-4311)

320.531   FR
TRIBUNE INTERNATIONALE. 1970. 12/yr. 150 F.($14) 87 rue du Faubourg Saint Denis, 75010 Paris, France. Ed. Luis Favre. bibl.
   Formerly (until 1980): Nouvelles Etudes Marxistes (ISSN 0029-4918)

320   US   ISSN 1081-5112
TRIBUNO DEL PUEBLO. English edition: People's Tribune (ISSN 1081-4787) (Text in English, Spanish) 1975. m. $10 to individuals; institutions $15. Tribuno del Peublo, Box 3524, Chicago, IL 60654. TEL 312-486-3551. Ed. Richard Monje. **Document type:** newspaper.
   Description: Provides revolutionary commentary on the issues of the day.

059.91   YU   ISSN 0041-302X
TRINAESTI MAJ; casopis saveznog sekretarijata za unutresnje poslove. 1948. bi-m. 40 din. Savezni Sekretarijat za Unutresnje Poslove, Kneza Milosa 92, Box 870, Belgrade, Yugoslavia. Ed. Radoman Zarkovic.

320.531   AU   ISSN 0041-3356
TROTZDEM; das sozialistische Jugendmagazin. 1948. m. S.15. Sozialistische Jugend Oesterreichs - Socialist Youth of Austria, Neustiftgasse 3, A-1070 Vienna, Austria. FAX 931243-85. TELEX 75312469-SJOE-A. Ed. M. Winkler. adv.; bk.rev.; film rev.; illus. circ. 40,000.

320 327   GW
TUDUV-STUDIE. REIHE POLITIKWISSENSCHAFTEN. 1983. irrege. price varies. Tuduv Verlagsgesellschaft mbH, Gabelsbergerstr. 15, 80333 Munich, Germany.

320   US   ISSN 0082-6774
TULANE STUDIES IN POLITICAL SCIENCE. 1954. irreg., vol.19, 1992. price varies. Tulane University, Department of Political Science, New Orleans, LA 70118. TEL 504-865-5166. FAX 504-862-8745. circ. 500. **Document type:** academic/scholarly publication, monographic series.
   —BLDSC (9070.397500).

POLITICAL SCIENCE

320 US ISSN 0831-2931
TURNING THE TIDE; journal of anti-racist activisim, research and education. 1988. 4/yr. $15 to individuals; institutions $25. People Against Racist Terror, Box 1990, Burbank, CA 91507.
TEL 310-288-5003. E-mail: mnovick@igc.apc.org. Ed. Michael Novick. **Document type:** newspaper.
Description: Fights against racism, sexism, colonialism.

320 GW ISSN 0564-9021
H5
TUTZINGER STUDIEN; Texte und Dokumente zur politischen Bildung. 1971-1981; N.S. 1985. s-a. DM.8.40. Evangelische Akademie Tutzing, Postfach 1227, 82327 Tutzing, Germany.
TEL 08158-251-112. FAX 08158-251133. Ed. Axel Schwanebeck. bk.rev.; bibl. **Document type:** academic/scholarly publication.

324.2 SW ISSN 0281-2657
TVAERDRAG. 1983. bi-m. SEK 40 (effective 1990). Sveriges Socialdemokratiska Ungdomsfoerbund (SSU), P.O. Box 11544, S-100 61 Stockholm, Sweden.
Supersedes: P Information.

TYGODNIK GDANSKI. see *LABOR UNIONS*

THE TYNDALL REPORT. see *COMMUNICATIONS — Television And Cable*

U R P E NEWSLETTER. (Union for Radical Political Economics) see *BUSINESS AND ECONOMICS*

320 330.9 UK ISSN 0956-0904
HC101
THE U S A AND CANADA (YEAR). 1989. triennial. $375. Europa Publications, 18 Bedford Sq., London WC1B 3JN, England. TEL 0171-631-3361. FAX 0171-636-1664. TELEX 21540 EUROPA G. **Document type:** academic/scholarly publication, directory.
—BLDSC (9124.785000).
Description: Provides a detailed analytical survey of these neighboring North American nations and of their constituent states, provinces, and territories.

U S NEWS & WORLD REPORT. see *GENERAL INTEREST PERIODICALS — United States*

320.531 US
U S S R TODAY. (Supplements avail.) 1981. irreg., 8th ed., 1991. $18 (foreign $22). Current Digest of the Soviet Press, 3857 N. High St., Columbus, OH 43214-3747. TEL 614-292-4234.
FAX 614-267-6310. Eds. Robert Ehlers, Fred Schulze. **Document type:** monographic series.

320 US
UGANDA NEWSLETTER. 1968. m. free. Embassy of the Republic of Uganda, 5909 16th St., N.W., Washington, DC 20011. TEL 202-726-7100. circ. 3,000.

320 HU ISSN 1215-1386
UJ MAGYARORSZAG; national edition. Budapest edition (ISSN 1215-0185) 1991. d. 3480 Ft. Publica Rt., Blaha Lujza ter 3, P.O. Box 1410, 1085 Budapest, Hungary. TEL 266-5009. FAX 266-2288. Ed. Laszlo Fabian. adv.; bk.rev. circ. 60,000. **Document type:** newspaper.
Description: Includes articles on politics, culture and science.

947 US ISSN 0041-6010
DK508.A2
THE UKRAINIAN QUARTERLY; a journal of Ukranian and international affairs. (Text in English) 1944. q. $25. Ukrainian Congress Committee of America, Inc., 203 Second Ave., New York, NY 10003.
TEL 212-228-6840. FAX 212-254-4721. adv.; bk.rev.; cum.index. circ. 5,000. (also avail. in microform from UMI) Indexed: Amer.Bibl.Slavic & E.Eur.Stud., Amer.Hist.& Life, Hist.Abstr., M.L.A., P.A.I.S. **Document type:** academic/scholarly publication.
—Faxon; UMI.

320 330 KR ISSN 0964-4326
UKRAINIAN REPORTER. (Text in English) 1991. s.a. £55($120) to individuals; institutions £110($230). Ukrainian Press Agency, Vul. Sonyachna 14, Kiev 252190, Ukraine. TEL 449-0426. (UK addr.: 78b Kensington Park Rd., London W11 2PL, England. TEL 071-221-0533) Ed. Taras Kuzio.
Description: Devoted to politics, parliamentary reports, economic reforms, new legislation, evolution of civil society and foreign policy.

UKRAINIAN REVIEW. see *ETHNIC INTERESTS*

320 UK
ULSTER NATION. 1988. q. £5 (Europe £6; rest of world £7). Third Way Publications Ltd., P.O. Box 1243, London SW7 3PB, England. TEL 0171-373-3432. E-mail: 100071.746@compuserve. Ed. David Kerr. adv.; bk.rev.; illus. circ. 200. **Document type:** bulletin.
Description: Promotes the identity and culture of the Ulster nation and advocates political independence for Northern Ireland.

UMEAA STUDIES IN POLITICS AND PUBLIC ADMINISTRATION. see *PUBLIC ADMINISTRATION*

322.4 AU ISSN 1015-8529
UMFELD. 1983. m. S.100 (foreign S.250). Schulgasse 46-9, A-1180 Vienna, Austria. TEL 0222-4248623. Ed. Guenter Ofner. adv.; bk.rev. circ. 4,000.
Document type: bulletin.
Formerly: Gruene Demokraten.

320 SA ISSN 0814-0693
UMSEBENZI. 1985. 6/yr. newsstand price: R.0.50 per issue. (South African Communist Party) Inkululeko Publications, P.O. Box 1027, Johannesburg 2000, South Africa. TEL 27-11-3393644.
FAX 27-11-3396680. Ed.Bd. circ. 30,000.
Description: News journal of the South African Communist Party.

320 US
UNDERGROUND BEAT. q. $5 per no. Beat Club Productions, 1718 M St. N.W., No. 154, Washington, DC 20036.
Description: Advocates free expression on political and social issues.

320.5 SW ISSN 0346-3508
UNG CENTER. 1927. 8/yr. SEK 90 (effective 1990). Centerns Ungdomsfoerbund, P.O. Box 22087, S-104 22 Stockholm, Sweden. (also avail. in audio cassette)
Formerly (until 1964): S L U - Bladet.

320.5 SW ISSN 1100-0848
UNGA GARDET. 1977. 5/yr. SEK 60 (effective 1991). Foerbundscentralen, Kommunistisk Ungdom, Kungsg. 84, S-112 27 Stockholm, Sweden.

332.4 PN
UNIDAD. fortn. Partido del Pueblo de Panama, Calle 1a, Perejil, Panama City, Panama. Dir. Carlos F. Changmarin.

320 GW
UNION. 1948. q. DM.29.50. (Christlich-Demokratische Union (CDU)) Union GmbH und Co. KG, Schanzenstr. 82, 40479 Duesseldorf, Germany. TEL 0211-5502-0. FAX 0211-574116. adv.; bk.rev. circ. 600,000. **Document type:** bulletin.

320 MQ
UNION. w. Union Departmentaliste Martiniquaise, Fort-de-France, Martinique. Ed. Jean Maran.

UNION DEMOCRACY REVIEW. see *LABOR UNIONS*

329.9 IT ISSN 0391-7002
UNITA. 1924. d. L.46500. (Partito Comunista Italiano) Unita S.p.A., Via d'Aracoeli 13, 20162 Milan, Italy. Eds. Luca Pavolini, Claudio Petruccioli. adv.; bk.rev.; film rev.; play rev.; bibl.; charts; illus.; tr.lit.; circ. 400,000 (controlled). (also avail. in microfilm)
Document type: newspaper.

320.532 IT ISSN 0390-038X
UNITA PROLETARIA. 1975. m. L.6000. Via Tomacelli 146, 00186 Rome, Italy.

329.9 SG ISSN 0850-8445
UNITE AFRICAINE. 1974. m. Parti Socialiste Senegalais, B.P. 22010, Dakar, Senegal.

320 MY
UNITED MALAYS NATIONAL ORGANISATION. ANNUAL REPORT. 1949. a. free to party delegates. United Malays National Organisation, Tingkat 38, Menara Dato Oun, Jalan Tun Ismail, 50480 Kuala Lumpur, Malaysia. TEL 03-2939511. circ. 3,000.
Formerly: United Malays National Organisation. Penvata.

UNITED NATIONS. GENERAL ASSEMBLY. ANNEXES. see *BUSINESS AND ECONOMICS*

UNITED NATIONS. GENERAL ASSEMBLY. OFFICIAL RECORDS. see *BUSINESS AND ECONOMICS*

UNITED NATIONS. GENERAL ASSEMBLY. PROVISIONAL RECORDS. see *BUSINESS AND ECONOMICS*

UNITED NATIONS ASSOCIATION OF THE REPUBLIC OF CHINA NEWS LETTER. see *POLITICAL SCIENCE — International Relations*

UNITED NATIONS DISARMAMENT YEARBOOK. see *MILITARY*

UNITED NATIONS ECONOMIC AND SOCIAL COUNCIL. DISARMAMENT STUDY SERIES. see *MILITARY*

320 US ISSN 0160-9890
JK1011 CODEN: CODIDS
U.S. CONGRESS. CONGRESSIONAL DIRECTORY. (Avail. in 3 eds.: paperbound; clothbound; thumb-indexed) a. Office of the Congressional Directory, Rm. SH-808, Hart Office Bldg., Washington, DC 20510-6650. TEL 202-224-6810. (Dist. by: Bernan, 4611-F Assembly Dr., Lanham, MD 20706. TEL 301-459-7666. FAX 301-459-0056; Also avail. from: Superintendent of Documents, U.S. Government Printing Office, Mail Stop SSOP, Washington, DC 20402-9328; Alt. editorial addr.: Joint Committee on Printing, Rm. SH-818, Hart Senate Office Bldg., Washington, DC 20510-6650. TEL 202-224-5241. FAX 202-224-1176) Eds. Leslie Mason, Duane Nystrom. circ. 100,000. (also avail. in microform from UMI) **Document type:** directory, government publication.

328 US ISSN 0363-7239
KF35. CODEN: CGLRB3
U.S. CONGRESS. CONGRESSIONAL RECORD; proceedings and debates of the Congress. 1873. d. (when Congress is in session). $225 (foreign $281.25). U.S. Congress, Washington, DC 20515.
TEL 202-275-2051. FAX 202-275-0019. TELEX 710-822-8413 USGPO WSH. (Subscr. to: Superintendent of Documents, U.S. Government Printing Office, Box 371954, Pittsburgh, PA 15250-7954. TEL 202-512-1800. FAX 202-512-2250; Or: Bernan, 4611 Assembly Dr., Lanham, MD 20706-4391. TEL 800-274-4447. FAX 301-459-0056) (also avail. in microform from UMI,PMC; magnetic tape; microfiche; back issues avail.) **Document type:** government publication, proceedings.
●Also available online.
Also available on CD-ROM.
—BLDSC (3415.963000); CASDDS.
Description: Contains verbatim reports of congressional debates and other proceedings, including daily summaries.

320 US ISSN 0145-7284
KF4886
U.S. FEDERAL ELECTION COMMISSION. ANNUAL REPORT. 1975. a. free. U.S. Federal Election Commission, Washington, DC 20463.
TEL 202-219-3420; 800-424-9530. (Also avail. from: Bernan, 4611-F Assembly Dr., Lanham, MD 20706. TEL 800-274-4447. FAX 301-459-7666) charts; illus.; stat. circ. 1,800. (also avail. in microfilm; back issues avail.) **Document type:** government publication.
Description: Summarizes legal issues and describes F.E.C. programs, internal operations and efforts to administer federal election law.

POLITICAL SCIENCE

320 980 US
U.S. FOREIGN BROADCAST INFORMATION SERVICE. DAILY REPORTS: LATIN AMERICA. (Vol. VI) 1979. d. (microfiche w.) $525 in N. America; microfiche $230 (foreign $1050). U.S. National Technical Information Service, 5285 Port Royal Rd., Springfield, VA 22161. TEL 703-487-4600. FAX 703-321-8547. TELEX 64617. (also avail. in microfiche)
 Description: Features news accounts, commentaries, and government statements from Latin American broadcasts, press agency transmissions, newspapers and periodicals published in the previous 48 to 72 hours.

320 956 US
U.S. FOREIGN BROADCAST INFORMATION SERVICE. DAILY REPORTS: NEAR EAST & SOUTH ASIA. (Vol. V; includes the Arabian Peninsula & Iraq, and South Asia)) d. $525 in N. America; microfiche $230 (foreign $1050). U.S. National Technical Information Service, 5285 Port Royal Rd., Springfield, VA 22161. TEL 703-487-4600. (also avail. in microfiche) Indexed: Mid.East: Abstr.& Ind.
 Formed by the merger of: U.S. Foreign Broadcast Information Service. Daily Reports -South Asia & U.S. Foreign Broadcast Information Service. Daily Reports - Middle East and Africa; Which was formerly: U.S. Foreign Broadcast Information Service. Daily Reports: Middle East and North Africa (ISSN 0270-9384)

320 951 US
U.S. FOREIGN BROADCAST INFORMATION SERVICE. DAILY REPORTS: PEOPLE'S REPUBLIC OF CHINA. (Vol. I) d. (microfiche w.) $525 in N. America; microfiche $230 (foreign $1050). U.S. National Technical Information Service, 5285 Port Royal Rd., Springfield, VA 22161. TEL 703-487-4600. FAX 703-321-8547. TELEX 64617. (also avail. in microfiche)

320 960 US
U.S. FOREIGN BROADCAST INFORMATION SERVICE. DAILY REPORTS: SUB-SAHARAN AFRICA. (Vol. VIII) d. (microfiche w.) $525 in N. America; microfiche $230 (foreign $1050). U.S. National Technical Information Service, 5285 Port Royal Rd., Springfield, VA 22161. TEL 703-487-4600. FAX 702-321-8547. TELEX 64617. (also avail. in microfiche)

320 950 US
U.S. FOREIGN BROADCAST INFORMATION SERVICE. DAILY REPORTS (F B I S). (In 8 Vols.: Vol.I: People's Republic of China; Vol.II: Eastern Europe; Vol.III: Central Eurasia; Vol.IV: East Asia; Vol.V: Near East & South Asia; Vol.VI: Latin America; Vol.VII: Western Europe; Vol.V: III Sub-Saharan Africa) 1978. d. $525 in N. America; microfiche $230 (elsewhere $1050). U.S. National Technical Information Service, 5285 Port Royal Rd., Springfield, VA 22161. TEL 703-487-4600. FAX 703-321-8547. TELEX 64617. (also avail. in microfiche)
 Description: Features news accounts, commentaries, and government statements from foreign broadcasts, press agency transmissions, newspapers, and periodicals published in the previous 48 to 72 hours.

320 940 US ISSN 0271-0269
D1065.U5
U.S. FOREIGN BROADCAST INFORMATION SERVICE. DAILY REPORTS: WESTERN EUROPE. (Vol. VII) d. (microfiche w.) $525 in N. America; microfiche $230 (foreign $1050). U.S. National Technical Information Service, 5285 Port Royal Rd., Springfield, VA 22161. TEL 703-487-4600. FAX 703-321-8547. TELEX 64617. (also avail. in microfiche)

U.S. OFFICE OF THE FEDERAL REGISTER. WEEKLY COMPILATION OF PRESIDENTIAL DOCUMENTS. see *PUBLIC ADMINISTRATION*

327.73 US ISSN 0270-370X
E840
UNITED STATES FOREIGN POLICY; a report of the Secretary of State. 1969. a. U.S. Department of State, 2201 C St., N.W., Washington, DC 20520. TEL 202-634-3600.

UNITED STATES GOVERNMENT MANUAL. see *PUBLIC ADMINISTRATION*

UNIVERSIDAD DE LOS ANDES. FACULTAD DE CIENCIAS JURIDICAS Y POLITICAS. ANUARIO. see *LAW*

320 IT
UNIVERSITA DEGLI STUDI DI TRIESTE. FACOLTA DI SCIENZE POLITICHE. PUBBLICAZIONI. 1975. irreg., no.20, 1981. price varies. Casa Editrece Dott. A. Giuffre, Via Busto Arsizio 40, 20151 Milan, Italy. TEL 02-38000905. FAX 02-38009582. bibl. Document type: monographic series.

UNIVERSITA KARLOVA. ACTA UNIVERSITATIS CAROLINAE. PHILOSOPHICA ET HISTORICA. see *HISTORY — History Of Europe*

327 301 US ISSN 0068-6093
UNIVERSITY OF CALIFORNIA AT BERKELEY. INTERNATIONAL AND AREA STUDIES. RESEARCH SERIES. (Former name of issuing body: Institute of International Studies) 1961. irreg. (2-3/yr.). price varies. University of California at Berkeley, International and Area Studies, 2223 Fulton St., 3rd Fl., Berkeley, CA 94720. TEL 415-642-7189. FAX 415-643-7062. E-mail: bojana@uclink2.berkeley.edu. Ed. Bojana Ristich. (back issues avail.) Indexed: GeoRef. Document type: monographic series.
—BLDSC (7769.970000).
 Description: Publishes scholarly research in comparative and international studies in social sciences.

UNIVERSITY OF DENVER JOURNAL. see *COLLEGE AND ALUMNI*

320 US ISSN 0196-0369
UNIVERSITY OF TEXAS, AUSTIN. LYNDON B. JOHNSON SCHOOL OF PUBLIC AFFAIRS. POLICY RESEARCH PROJECT REPORT SERIES. 1971. irreg., no.90, 1989. University of Texas at Austin, Lyndon B. Johnson School of Public Affairs, Drawer Y, Austin, TX 78713-7450. TEL 512-471-4962. charts; stat. Document type: academic/scholarly publication, government publication.
—BLDSC (6543.327700).
 Former titles: University of Texas at Austin. Lyndon B. Johnson School of Public Affairs. Policy Research Project Report; University of Texas at Austin. Lyndon B. Johnson School of Public Affairs. Seminar Research Report.

320 UK
▼**UNIVERSITY OF YORK. DEPARTMENT OF POLITICS. WORKING PAPER.** 1994. irreg. University of York, Department of Politics, York YO1 5DD, England. TEL 01904-433546. FAX 01904-433563. Ed. John Crump. Document type: monographic series.

320 PL ISSN 1230-6177
UNIWERSYTET GDANSKI. ZESZYTY NAUKOWE. NAUKI POLITYCZNE. (Text in Polish; summaries in English and Russian) 1972. irreg., latest no.10. price varies. Uniwersytet Gdanski, Wydzial Humanistyczny, c/o Biblioteka Glowna, Ul. Armii Krajowej 110, 81-824 Sopot, Poland. TEL 51-0061. TELEX 051 2247 BMOR PL. (Dist. by: Ars Polona-Ruch, Krakowskie Przedmiescie 7, 00-680 Warsaw, Poland) Ed. Romuald Stanczyk. Document type: academic/scholarly publication.
—BLDSC (9512.434200).
 Formerly (until 1990): Uniwersytet Gdanski. Wydzial Humanistyczny. Zeszyty Naukowe. Nauki Polityczne (ISSN 0208-4732)
 Description: Covers political sciences and theory of politics, political organization of society, social policy, educational policy, and problems of economics of education.

320 PL ISSN 0137-2378
JA49
UNIWERSYTET JAGIELLONSKI. ZESZYTY NAUKOWE. PRACE Z NAUK POLITYCZNYCH. (Text in Polish; summaries English or Russian) 1971. irreg., vol.21, 1984. price varies. Uniwersytet Jagiellonski, Ul. Golegia 24, 31-007 Krakow, Poland. (Dist. by: Ars Polona, Krakowskie Przedmiescie 7, 00-068 Warsaw, Poland) Ed. P. Sarnecki. circ. 420.

UNIWERSYTET SLASKI W KATOWICACH. PRACE NAUKOWE. Z PROBLEMATYKI PRAWA PRACY I POLITYKI SOCJALNEJ. see *LAW*

320 PL ISSN 0137-5822
JA26
UNIWERSYTET WARSZAWSKI. INSTYTUT NAUK POLITYCZNYCH. ZESZYTY NAUKOWE. 1974. irreg., vol.17, 1992. price varies. Wydawnictwa Uniwersytetu Warszawskiego, Ul. Nowy Swiat 4, 00-497 Warsaw, Poland. TEL 48-22-625-3044. (Dist. by: Ars Polona, Krakowskie Przedmiescie 7, 00-068 Warsaw, Poland) circ. 300.

320 GW
UNSER DORFBLAETTCHEN. 1984. 7/yr. S P D Ortsverein Erkeln, Gelle Breite 2, 33034 Brakel, Germany. TEL 05272-8290. Ed. Ekkehard Korte. circ. 300. Document type: newsletter.

320 GW
UNSERE STADT. 1975. 3/yr. S P D Stadtverband Landau, Karl-Sauer-Str. 8, 76829 Landau, Germany. TEL 06341-86230. Ed. Elisabeth Morawietz. adv. Document type: bulletin.

320.5 SW ISSN 0346-3788
UTSIKT. 1935. irreg. 4-5/yr. SEK 100 (effective 1990). Folkpartiet - Swedish Liberal Party, P.O. Box 6508, 113 83 Stockholm, Sweden. FAX 08-349591. Ed. Anette Britalk. adv.; bk.rev.; illus. circ. 65,000.
 Former titles (until 1956): Folkpartiet; (until 1937): Folkpartiet i Riksdagen och Riket.

320 UK ISSN 0958-0336
VACHER'S EUROPEAN COMPANION. 1972. q. £38. Vacher's Publications, 113 High St., Berkhamsted, Herts. HP4 2DJ, England. TEL 01442-876135. FAX 01442-870148. Ed. Elizabeth Gunn. adv. contact: A.S. Kerswill. circ. 2,000. (also avail. in microform from UMI) Indexed: Br.Ceram.Abstr. Document type: directory.
—BLDSC (9138.696000); UMI.
 Description: A diplomatic, political and commercial reference book for Western Europe.

320.5 SW ISSN 1101-9182
VAENSTERPRESS. 1972. 10/yr. SEK 75 (effective 1991). Vaensterpartiet, Kungsg. 84, S-112 27 Stockholm, Sweden.
 Former titles (until 1991): Nytt fraan Vensterpartiet; (until 1990, vol.5): V P K - Information.

327 SW ISSN 0042-2134
VAERLDSHORISONT. 1947. bi-m. SEK 100. Svenska FN-Foerbundet - United Nations Association of Sweden, Box 15115, S-104 65 Stockholm 15, Sweden. TEL 46-8-6449835. FAX 08-6418876. Ed. Lott Jansson. adv.; bk.rev.; illus.; index. circ. 9,000.
 Description: Directed to inform and be a forum for debate about the UN and UN-related questions.

320 IV
VAILLANTE AFRIQUE.* (Text in French) 1973. bi-m. Centre National CV-AV, B.P. 1287, Abidjan, Ivory Coast. Ed.Bd. adv.; bk.rev.

320 LS
VALASAN PATHET LAO. (Text in Lao) q. 80 rue Sethathirath, BP 989, Vientiane, Laos. TEL 2405. illus. circ. 2,000.

320 UK ISSN 0950-5229
VANGUARD. 1987. q. £12 for 8 nos. (National Front) Vanguard Publications, P.O. Box 2269, London E6 3RF, England. TEL 0181-471-6872. FAX 0181-592-3009. Ed. Stephen Ebbs. adv. contact: Ian Anderson. bk.rev. circ. 8,000. (back issues avail.) Document type: bulletin.

320 BL
VANGUARDA. 1993. bi-m. Cr.$2400. Editora Vanguarda, Rua Rocha Miranda 99-201, 20530-000 Usina Rio de Janeiro RJ, Brazil. Ed. Hector Duarte Filho.

320.532 330.9 KO ISSN 0251-2971
VANTAGE POINT; developments in North Korea. (Text in English) 1978. m. free. Naewoe Press, 42-2 Chuja-dong, Box 9708, Chung-gu, Seoul 100-240, S. Korea. Ed. Li Ik-Sang. index. circ. 3,000. Indexed: Bk.Rev.Ind., Int.Polit.Sci.Abstr.

320 NP
VASHUDHA. (Text in English) m. T.L. Shrestha, Ed. & Pub., Makhan, Kathmandu, Nepal.
 Description: Covers social, political and economic affairs.

POLITICAL SCIENCE

329.9 IS
DER VEG. (Text in Yiddish) 1965. w. $17. Communist Party of Israel, P.O. Box 26205, Tel-Aviv, Israel. Ed. Meir Vilner.

329.9 FR ISSN 0995-0583
VENDREDI; l'hebdomadaire des Socialistes. (Supplement avail.: Paris Vendredi (ISSN 1146-0296)) 1989. w. (42/yr.). 280 F. to individuals; institutions 500 F. (Parti Socialiste) Nouvelles Editions de l'An 2000, 10 rue de Solferino, 75333 Paris Cedex 07, France. TEL 45-56-77-00. FAX 45-51-47-03. TELEX 200 174 F. Ed. Lyne Cohen-Solal. adv.; bk.rev.; illus. circ. 190,000.

VENTO DEL SUD; periodico di lotta meridionale. see *ETHNIC INTERESTS*

320 NO ISSN 0333-1393
VERDEN OG VI. 1965. bi-m. NOK 150. Communist Party of Norway, Postboks 3715, Gamlebyen, 0135 Oslo 1, Norway. FAX 2-671796. Ed. Hans Petter Hansen. adv.; bk.rev.; bibl. circ. 1,200.

320 GW ISSN 0944-4513
VEREIN DEUTSCHER ARCHIVARE. FACHGRUPPE 6. MITTEILUNGEN. 1977. a. Archiv fuer Christlich-Demokratische Politik der Konrad-Adenauer-Stiftung e.V., Rathausallee 12, 53757 Sankt Augustin, Germany. TEL 02241-246210. FAX 02241-246669. Ed. Guenter Buchstab. **Document type:** academic/scholarly publication.
  Formerly (until 1991): Parlaments- und Parteistiftungsarchivare Berichten (ISSN 0933-6958)

320 340 GW ISSN 0083-5676
VERFASSUNG UND VERFASSUNGSWIRKLICHKEIT. 1966. irreg., vol.12, 1978. price varies. Duncker und Humblot GmbH, Postfach 410329, 12113 Berlin, Germany. TEL 030-7900060. FAX 030-79000631. Eds. Ferdinand A. Hermens, Werner Kaltefleiter. adv.; bk.rev. **Document type:** monographic series.

LA VETTA D'ITALIA; mensile di politica e di cultura dell'Alto Adige. see *BIOGRAPHY*

320 CH ISSN 0582-9860
AP95.C4
VICTORIOUS. Key Title: Shengli zhi Guang. (Text mainly in Chinese; occasionally in English) 1953. m. NT.$600 039505788; Hong Kong $67; Asia-Pacific region $75; elsewhere $83. New China Publication Service - Hsin Chung-kuo Ch'u Pan She, 7F, 3 Hsinyi Rd. Sec. 1, Taipei, Taiwan, Republic of China. TEL 02-396-9856. Ed. Kao Chuan-hsi. adv.; bk.rev.; illus. circ. 30,000.
  Formerly (until 1984): Torch of Victory.

320.531 GW ISSN 0259-5818
VIERTE INTERNATIONALE; Zeitschrift fuer internationalen Marxismus. 1986. s-a. DM.45. Arbeiterpresse Verlag, Postfach 100105, 45001 Essen, Germany. TEL 0201-8701340. FAX 0201-8701333. Ed. David North. (back issues avail.) **Document type:** bulletin.

320.9 UK ISSN 0042-5834
VIEWPOINT (LONDON, 1965). 1965. q. Delane Press, 157 Vicarage Rd., London E10 5DU, England. TEL 0181-539-3876. Ed. Ronald King; Pub. Ronald King. bk.rev.; illus.; circ. controlled.
  Description: Political review with particular emphasis on corporatism, freemasonry, and subversion of the social order.

973 US ISSN 0042-739X
AP2
VITAL ISSUES; the journal of African American speeches. 1950-1984; N.S. 1991. q. $39. (Center for Information on America) Bethune - Dubois Publications, 600 New Hampshire Ave., N.W., Ste. 1125, Washington, DC 20037. Ed. Teta V. Banks; Pub. C. DeLores Tuck. adv. contact: Robert Simpson. bibl.; charts; index. circ. 5,000. (also avail. in microform from UMI; reprint service avail. from UMI) **Indexed:** P.A.I.S., Vert.File Ind. **Document type:** academic/scholarly publication.
  —UMI.

VLASTIVEDNE MUZEUM V OLOMOUCI. ZPRAVY. see *HISTORY — History Of Europe*

VLASTIVEDNY CASOPIS PAMIATKY A MUZEA. see *HISTORY — History Of Europe*

VOCE DELL'EMIGRANTE. see *ETHNIC INTERESTS*

320 IT ISSN 0390-4628
VOCE DELLA CAMPANIA. m. L.20000. Cinqueprint S.r.l., Via Catullo 64, 80122 Naples, Italy. TEL 081-669339. Ed. Andrea Cinquegrani.
  Description: Covers politics for political leaders.

VOICE OF THE UNIONS. see *BUSINESS AND ECONOMICS — Labor And Industrial Relations*

320 US
VOICES (BURNSVILLE). 1981. bi-m. $15. (Fellowship for Reconciliation) Rural Southern Voice for Peace, 1898 Hannah Branch Rd., Burnsville, NC 28714. TEL 704-675-5933. FAX 704-675-9335. Ed. Pat Riviere. bk.rev. circ. 2,500. (also avail. in microform from UMI; back issues avail.)
  Formerly (until no.66, 1993): Rural Southern Voice for Peace (ISSN 1055-3908)
  Description: Promotes grassroots organizing to build a network of nonviolent activism to foster peace, ecological awareness, and political, spiritual and social alternatives in the rural communities and small cities of the southeastern US.

320 IT
VOLKSBOTE. (Text in German) 1946. w. L.54000 (U.S. L.150700) (effective 1994). Athesia-Druck G.m.b.H., Weinbergweg 7, 39100 Bolzano (Bozen), Italy. TEL 0471-925111. FAX 0471-925440. adv. contact: Ilse Egger. circ. 425,000.
  Description: Contains information on political and local current events.

320 IT ISSN 0392-5013
HX821
VOLONTA; laboratorio di ricerche anarchiche. 1946. q. L.40000. Editrice A Coop. a.r.l., Via Rovetta 27, 20127 Milan, Italy. TEL 2846923. Ed. Luciano Lanza. index. circ. 1,500. (back issues avail.)
  Description: Theories and ideas concerning anarchist and libertarian movements.

320 US
VOLUNTARYIST. 1982. bi-m. $18 (overseas $23). Voluntaryists, Box 1275, Gramling, SC 29348. TEL 803-472-2750. Ed. Carl Watner. adv.; bk.rev. circ. 300. (back issues avail.)
  Description: Advocates a nonstate, pro free-market, anti-electoral and nonviolent position on social change.

320 GW ISSN 0507-4150
AP30
VORGAENGE; Zeitschrift fuer Buergerrechte und Gesellschaftspolitik. 1962. q. DM.64 (students DM.46.40) (foreign DM.70). Verlag Leske und Budrich GmbH, Postfach 300551, 51334 Leverkusen, Germany. TEL 02171-2079. FAX 02171-41209. Ed. Dieter Hoffmann. adv.; bk.rev.; bibl. circ. 4,500. **Indexed:** CERDIC. **Document type:** academic/scholarly publication.

943 GW ISSN 0042-8949
VORWAERTS. 1876. m. DM.27. Vorwaerts Verlag GmbH, Suedstr. 133, 53175 Bonn, Germany. TEL 0228-95113-0. FAX 0228-9511316. Ed. Frank Suplie. adv.; bk.rev.; illus. **Document type:** newsletter.

320 360 US
VOTE AND SURVEY; magazine of political, social and economic issues. 1986. m. $26. Gibbs Publishing Company, Box 600927, N. Miami Beach, FL 33160. Ed. James Calvin Gibbs. adv.; bk.rev. circ. 15,000.

VRIJE UNIVERSITEIT AMSTERDAM. CENTER FOR THE STUDY OF RELIGION AND POLITICS. STUDIES. see *RELIGIONS AND THEOLOGY*

320 301.412 US
W C P S QUARTERLY. 1982. q. $25 to individuals; institutions $30 (membership). Women's Caucus for Political Science, c/o American Political Science Association, Department of Political Science, Wayne State University, Detroit, MI 48202. TEL 313-577-6342. FAX 313-577-1274. Ed. Cynthia Duquette. adv.; bk.rev.; circ. 1,075 (paid). **Document type:** newsletter.
  Description: Information on WCPS events, networking, job openings, communications.

W Z B - MITTEILUNGEN. (Wissenschaftszentrum Berlin fuer Sozialforschung) see *SOCIAL SCIENCES: COMPREHENSIVE WORKS*

WAGNER LATIN AMERICAN NEWSLETTER. see *HISTORY — History Of North And South America*

320.531 AU ISSN 0042-9996
DIE WAHRHEIT; Betriebszeitung der Voest-Alpine. 1950. m. S.2 per no. Sozialistische Partei Oesterreichs, Bezirksorganisation Linz-Stadt, Landstr. 36, A-4020 Linz, Austria. (Betriebsektion Voest Alpine) adv.; bk.rev.; play rev.; charts; illus.; stat. circ. 16,000. **Document type:** newspaper.

967.3 322.4 TZ ISSN 0043-020X
WAR COMMUNIQUES.* no.15, 1969. free. Departamento de Informacao e Propaganda do Commite Central, MPLA - Partido do Trabalho, Luanda, Tanzania. (processed)

320 JA ISSN 0511-196X
WASEDA POLITICAL STUDIES. (Text in English) 1957. a. free. Waseda University, Graduate School of Political Science, 1-6-1 Nishi-Waseda, Shinjuku-ku, Tokyo 169, Japan. TEL 03-3203-4141. **Indexed:** Int.Polit.Sci.Abstr.

320 330 JA ISSN 0287-7007
JA26
WASEDA SEIJI KEIZAIGAKU ZASSHI/WASEDA JOURNAL OF POLITICAL SCIENCE AND ECONOMICS. (Text in Japanese) 1925. bi-m. Waseda Daigaku, Seiji Keizai Gakkai - Waseda University, Society of Political Science and Economics, 6-1 Nishi-Waseda 1-chome, Shinjuku-ku, Tokyo 160, Japan. Ed. Seiichi Iwakura. bk.rev. circ. 3,000.
  —BLDSC (9263.080000); UnCover.

320 US ISSN 0887-8064
F192.3
WASHINGTON INFORMATION DIRECTORY (YEAR). 1976. a. $99.95. Congressional Quarterly Inc., 1414 22nd St., N.W., Washington, DC 20037. TEL 202-887-8500. FAX 202-887-6706. **Document type:** directory.
  —BLDSC (9263.155000).
  Description: Organizes thousands of names, addresses, and phone numbers for the federal government and the many private groups in its orbit. Includes name and subject indexes; organized by area of activity.

320 US ISSN 0749-1050
WASHINGTON INQUIRER. 1981. w. $33. Council for the Defense of Freedom, 4455 Connecticut Ave., N.W., Washington, DC 20008. TEL 202-364-4401. FAX 202-364-4098. Ed. Arthur D. Randall. adv.; bk.rev. circ. 6,000.
  Description: Publishes international news about human freedoms from government tyranny, US strategic and military matters.

320.9 956 US ISSN 1053-3230
WASHINGTON INSTITUTE FOR NEAR EAST POLICY. POLICY FORUM. PROCEEDINGS. Key Title: Proceedings of the Washington Institute Policy Forum. 1985. a. Washington Institute for Near East Policy, 1828 L St., N.W., Ste. 1050, Washington, DC 20036. **Document type:** proceedings.

320.9 956 US
WASHINGTON INSTITUTE FOR NEAR EAST POLICY. POLICY PAPERS. irreg., no.37, 1994. price varies. Washington Institute for Near East Policy, 1828 L St., N.W., Ste. 1050, Washington, DC 20036. **Document type:** monographic series.

POLITICAL SCIENCE 5365

973 328   US   ISSN 0043-0633
E838
THE WASHINGTON MONTHLY. 1969. 10/yr. $26 to individuals; institutions US$39.50 (foreign $46.50). Washington Monthly Co., 1611 Connecticut Ave., N.W., Washington, DC 20009. TEL 202-462-0128. FAX 202-332-8413. Ed. Charles Peters; Pub. Hilary Ross. adv.: B&W page $2500; color page $4000; 7 1/4 x 9 3/4; adv. contact: Hilary Ross. bk.rev.; illus. circ. 33,000. (also avail. in microform from UMI; back issues avail.) **Indexed:** Acad.Ind., Amer.Hist.& Life, Bk.Rev.Ind. (1978-), Child.Bk.Rev.Ind. (1978-), Fut.Surv., Hist.Abstr., Int.Polit.Sci.Abstr., Mag.Ind., Mid.East: Abstr.& Ind., P.A.I.S., Pers.Lit., Polit.Sci.Abstr., R.G., Rehabil.Lit., Soc.Sci.Ind. **Document type:** consumer publication.
●Also available online. Vendor(s): Knight-Ridder, Inc., University Microfilms International.
—BLDSC (9263.170000); Faxon; SWETS; UMI; UnCover.
   Description: Covers politics and government for journalists, government workers, business people, and educators with articles about the White House, Congress and federal government, and current affairs.

320 051   US   ISSN 0748-6359
DU30
THE WASHINGTON PACIFIC REPORT; the insider's newsletter highlighting the latest developments of interest involving the insular Pacific. 1982. s-m. $164 (foreign $189) (effective 1996). Washington Pacific Publications, Inc., Box 26142, Alexandria, VA 22313-6142. TEL 703-519-7757. FAX 703-548-0633. E-mail: WMRB25a@prodigy.com. Ed. Fred Radewagen; Pub. Fred Radewagen. (back issues avail.) **Document type:** newsletter.
   Description: Covers current events in the Pacific islands and offers analysis on political topics, especially U.S. government actions that affect these nations.

322.4   US   ISSN 1050-2823
WASHINGTON PEACE LETTER. 1963. m. (11/yr.) $25. Washington Peace Center, 2111 Florida Ave., N.W., Washington, DC 20008. TEL 202-234-2000. FAX 202-265-5233. Ed. Vicki Linton. adv.; bk.rev. circ. 5,000. (tabloid format; back issues avail.) **Document type:** newsletter.
   Formerly: Washington Peace Center. Newsletter.
   Description: Covers nonviolent peace and social justice activities at the international, national and local levels, especially in the Washington, DC, area with and antiracist analysis.

322.4   US
WASHINGTON REPORT (ST. PETERSBURG); dedicated to exposing the Washington standards of greed, corruption, self-indulgence and the Great American Dream of profit at all cost! 1979. m. $25. Editors Release Service, Box 10309, St. Petersburg, FL 33733-0309. TEL 813-866-1598. FAX 813-866-1598. Ed. William A. Leavell. circ. 17,000. **Indexed:** Rehabil.Lit. **Document type:** newsletter.
   Formerly: Washington C.R.A.P. Report.
   Description: Reports of the Washington political scene not generally covered by the media.

320 330.9   US   ISSN 0733-8104
HC800.A1
WASHINGTON REPORT ON AFRICA. 1982. s-m. $367.20 to academic institutions (Canada and Mexico $377.20; elsewhere $397.20); others $459 (Canada and Mexico $469; elsewhere $499) (effective 1996). Welt Publishing, LLC, 1413 K St., N.W., Ste. 1400, Washington, DC 20005. TEL 202-371-0555; 800-898-INTL. FAX 202-408-9369. Ed. John Justin Ford; Pub. Leo G.B. Welt. bk.rev.; bibl.; charts; stat. circ. 1,650. (looseleaf format; back issues avail.) **Document type:** newsletter.
   Formerly: African Business and Trade.
   Description: Provides news and analysis on business and economic developments throughout Africa.

320   US   ISSN 0887-428X
E839.5
WASHINGTON SPECTATOR. 1975. s-m. $10. Public Concern Foundation, Box 20065, London Terrace Sta., NY 10011. TEL 212-741-2365. FAX 212-366-6585. Ed. Ben A. Franklin; Pub. Phillip Frazer. bk.rev.; circ. 60,000 (paid). (also avail. in microform from UMI; back issues avail.; reprint service avail. from UMI) **Document type:** newsletter.
—UMI.
   Formerly: Washington Spectator - Between the Lines (ISSN 0145-160X); Formed by the 1976 merger of: Washington Spectator (ISSN 0162-3133); Between the Lines (ISSN 0006-0305)
   Description: Provides information on major news developments, including political, social and economic issues.

320   US   ISSN 0197-8403
WEEKLY CONGRESSIONAL MONITOR; weekly listing of all scheduled Congressional committee hearings, with witnesses. 1969. w. $498. Congressional Quarterly Inc., 1414 22nd St., N.W., Washington, DC 20037. TEL 800-432-2250; 800-432-2250. FAX 202-728-1863. Ed. Brian Nutting. (looseleaf format)
●Also available online.
   Formerly: Monday Monitor.
   Description: Provides schedule of congressional action, including the agenda for committee and subcommittee hearings and witness lists.

320 301   NR   ISSN 0795-896X
WEEKLY PROBES. 1988. w. £N52($40) Crier Communications Ltd., P.O. Box 681, Surulere, Lagos, Nigeria. TEL 01-921198. Ed. Bosun Adewunmi. circ. 50,000.

WEEKLY REVIEW. see *PUBLIC ADMINISTRATION*

320   US
▼**THE WEEKLY STANDARD.** 1995. w. $79.96. 1150 17th St., N.W., 5th Fl., Washington, DC 20036. TEL 202-293-4900; 800-677-8600. FAX 202-293-4901. (Subscr. to: Box 96133, Washington, DC 20090-6133) Ed. Fred Barnes; Pub. William Kristol. adv. **Document type:** consumer publication.
   Description: Forum for conservative perspectives on political issues.

320.532   GW
WEG DER PARTEI; Theoretisches Organ der K P D. 1985. irreg. DM.42 per 6 issues. (Kommunistische Partei Deutschlands) Zeitungsverlag Roter Morgen, Postfach 401051, 70410 Stuttgart, Germany. TEL 0711-8702209. FAX 0711-8702445. (Subscr. to: Postfach 1942, 61289 Bad Homburg, Germany) Pub. Diethard Moeller. circ. 500. (back issues avail.) **Document type:** proceedings.

320.531   AU   ISSN 0043-2024
WEG UND ZIEL;* Monatsschrift fuer Theorie und Praxis des Marxismus-Leninismus. (Supplement avail.) 1936. m. S.200. Schoenngasse 15-17, A-1020 Vienna, Austria. Ed. Erwin Scharf. adv.; bk.rev.; charts; illus.; index. circ. 5,000.

320   AU
DIE WEISSE ROSE; analytische Schriften. 1988. q. S.200 (foreign S.300). Postfach 192, A-1060 Vienna, Austria. TEL 0222-5645255. Ed. Albert Pethoe. adv.; bk.rev. **Document type:** monographic series.

942   UK   ISSN 0043-2458
WELSH NATION. 1932. m. £10. (Plaid Cymru - Welsh Nationalist Party) Welsh Nation Office, 51 Cathedral Dr., Cardiff CF1 9HD, Wales. TEL 0222-231944. FAX 0222-222506. Ed. Ashley Drake. adv.; bk.rev.; illus. circ. 10,000. (tabloid format; also avail. in microfilm from WMP) **Document type:** bulletin.

320   GW
WENTORFER COURIER. 1974. q. Sozialdemokratische Partei Deutschlands, Ortsverein Wentorf bei Hamburg, Sandweg 22, 2057 Wentorf, Germany. TEL 040-7201143. circ. 3,500. (looseleaf format; back issues avail.)

966   UK   ISSN 0043-2962
DT491
WEST AFRICA. 1917. w. $170. West Africa Publishing Co. Ltd., 43-45 Coldharbour Ln., Camberwell, London SE5 9NR, England. TEL 0171-737-2946. FAX 0171-978-8334. TELEX 892420-WESTAF-G. Ed. Kaye Whiteman. adv. contact: Danny Idollor. bk.rev.; illus.; index. circ. 30,000. (also avail. in microform) **Indexed:** Child.Lit.Abstr., Curr.Cont.Africa, HR Rep. (1984-), Key to Econ.Sci., M.L.A., Polit.Sci.Abstr., PROMT, Rural Ext.Educ.& Tr.Abstr., Rural Recreat.Tour.Abstr., World Agri.Econ.& Rural Sociol.Abstr. **Document type:** newspaper.
—BLDSC (9298.674000); Faxon; UnCover.

WEST AFRICAN JOURNAL OF SOCIOLOGY AND POLITICAL SCIENCE. see *SOCIOLOGY*

WEST BENGAL. see *PUBLIC ADMINISTRATION*

WEST COAST LIBERTARIAN. see *LITERARY AND POLITICAL REVIEWS*

WEST EUROPE REPORT. see *BUSINESS AND ECONOMICS — Economic Situation And Conditions*

320 330.9   UK   ISSN 0953-6906
HC240.A1
WESTERN EUROPE (YEAR); a political and economic survey. 1988. triennial. $335. Europa Publications, 18 Bedford Sq., London WC1B 3JN, England. TEL 0171-580-8236. FAX 0171-636-1664. TELEX 21540 EUROPA G. bibl.; charts; stat. **Document type:** academic/scholarly publication, directory.
—BLDSC (9300.717800).
   Description: Covers recent history and politics, economy, geography, social affairs, media and communications, transport, and tourism.

320 341.37   NP
WESTERN POLICIES. (Text in English) 1985. a. $100. Siveast Consultants, Inc., USA, c/o P.O. Box 8510, Kathmandu, Nepal. (UK subscr. to: Dr. Ramasastry, c/o Overseas Customer Service, Midland Bank Blc., Poultry and Princes St., London EC2, England) Ed. C.V. Ramasastry. adv.; bk.rev.; circ. 10 (controlled). (looseleaf format) **Document type:** academic/scholarly publication.
   Formerly: N A T O - Warsaw and Strategies (ISSN 0749-0674)
   Description: Provides a forum for objective analysis of various issues that confront the Western nations due to their policies.

320   UK   ISSN 1355-9753
WESTMINSTER CONFIDENTIAL. 1955. 40/yr. £45. Parliamentary Profile Services Ltd., 2 Queen Anne's Gate Bldgs., Dartmouth St., London SW1H 9BP, England. TEL 0171-222-5884. FAX 0171-222-5889. Ed. Andrew Roth. circ. 150. **Document type:** newsletter.

320   GW
WEYHER WECKER. 1985. s-a. Sozialdemokratische Partei Deutschlands, c/o R. von Larcher, Boettcherei 210, 28844 Weyhe, Germany. circ. 7,000. **Document type:** bulletin.

051   US   ISSN 0512-5804
D410
WHAT THEY SAID; the yearbook of world opinion. 1969. a. $42.90. Monitor Book Co., Box 9078, Palm Springs, CA 92263. TEL 619-323-2270. Eds. Alan F. Pater, Jason R. Pater. **Document type:** monographic series.
   Description: Standard source for contemporary quotations derived from speeches, news conferences, interviews, TV and radio broadcast, forums, symposia, lectures, and congressional hearings.

320   CH   ISSN 0512-5278
WHAT'S HAPPENING ON THE CHINESE MAINLAND. 1974. fortn. free. Chung Hwa Information Service, PO Box 337, Taipei, Taiwan, Republic of China. (U.S. subscr. to: Chinese Information Service, 159 Lexington Ave., New York, NY 10016) Ed.Bd. circ. 3,200.

WHITE HOUSE WEEKLY. see *PUBLIC ADMINISTRATION*

WHO'S WHO IN AMERICAN POLITICS. see *BIOGRAPHY*

WHO'S WHO IN ASIAN AND AUSTRALASIAN POLITICS. see *BIOGRAPHY*

POLITICAL SCIENCE

WHO'S WHO IN CONGRESS. see *BIOGRAPHY*

WHO'S WHO IN EUROPEAN POLITICS. see *BIOGRAPHY*

320   GW
WINDESHEIMER RUNDSCHAU. 1982. s-a. free. Sozialdemokratische Partei Deutschlands (SPD), Ortsverein Windesheim, Waldstr. 13, 6531 Windesheim, Germany. TEL 06707-564. circ. 750. (tabloid format)

320   GW   ISSN 0175-9485
WIR SELBST; Zeitschrift fuer nationale Identitaet. 1979. bi-m. DM.33. Verlag Siegfried Bublies, Postfach 168, 56001 Koblenz, Germany. TEL 0261-32337. Ed. Siegfried Bublies.

320.531   GW   ISSN 0937-6240
HC244.A1
DIE WIRTSCHAFTLICHE ENTWICKLUNG IN DEN SOZIALISTISCHEN LAENDERN OSTEUROPAS ZUR JAHRESWENDE. (Subseries of: H W W A Report (ISSN 0179-2253)) 1974. a. (H W W A - Institut fuer Wirtschaftforschung, Hamburg) Verlag Weltarchiv GmbH, Neuer Jungfernstieg 21, 20347 Hamburg, Germany. TEL 040-3562354. FAX 040-351900.
    Former titles (until 1985): Wirtschaftliche Entwicklung in Ausgewaehlten Sozialistischen Laendern Osteuropas zur Jahreswende (ISSN 0722-4729); (until 1982): Wirtschaftliche Entwicklung in den Sozialistischen Laendern (ISSN 0721-5568); (until 1979): Wirtschaftliche Entwicklung in Osteuropa (ISSN 0171-9467)

320 330   US
WOLFE'S VERSION; a socio-political-economic analysis. 1975. m. $24. James F. Wolfe, Ed. & Pub., Box 99, Blue Springs, MO 64015. TEL 314-635-3154. bk.rev. (back issues avail.) **Document type:** newsletter.
    Description: Discusses economics and how they affect Missouri and national politics.

320 305.4   US   ISSN 0195-7732
HQ1236
WOMEN & POLITICS (BINGHAMTON). 1980. q. $200 (foreign $280) (effective 1996). Haworth Press, Inc., 10 Alice St., Binghamton, NY 13904. TEL 607-722-5857; 800-342-9678. FAX 607-722-1424. TELEX 4932599. Ed. Janet M. Clark. adv.; bk.rev.; charts; illus. circ. 534. (also avail. in microfiche from UMI; back issues avail.; reprint service avail. from HAW) **Indexed:** A.B.C.Pol.Sci., Alt.Press Ind., Amer.Bibl.Slavic & E.Eur.Stud., Amer.Hist.& Life, Chic.Per.Ind., Excerp.Med., Hist.Abstr., Int.Polit.Sci.Abstr., Lang.& Lang.Behav.Abstr., Mult.Ed.Abstr., P.A.I.S., Polit.Sci.Abstr., Soc.Sci.Ind. (1994-), Sociol.Abstr., Stud.Wom.Abstr., Urb.Aff.Abstr., Wom.Stud.Abstr. (1980-).
    —BLDSC (9343.275000); Faxon; Genuine Article; Haworth; UnCover.
    Description: Dedicated to uniting the field of women's studies with political science, sociology, and psychology.
    Refereed Serial

320 305.4   US
WOMEN AND POLITICS (WESTPORT). 1985. irreg. price varies. Praeger Publishers (Subsidiary of: Greenwood Publishing Group Inc.), 88 Post Rd. W., Box 5007, Westport, CT 06881-5007. TEL 203-226-3571. FAX 203-222-1502. **Document type:** monographic series.

WOMEN IN WORLD POLITICS; biographies of women currently in government legislatures worldwide. see *BIOGRAPHY*

322.4   US
WOMEN'S INTERNATIONAL LEAGUE FOR PEACE AND FREEDOM. PROGRAM AND LEGISLATIVE ACTION. q. $12. Women's International League for Peace and Freedom, 1213 Race St., Philadelphia, PA 19107-1691. TEL 215-563-7110. FAX 215-563-5527. E-mail: wilpfnat@igc.apc.org. Ed. Wendy Rosenfield. circ. 700. (also avail. in microfilm; back issues avail.) **Document type:** newsletter.
    Formed by the merger of: Legislative Reports (Philadelphia); Women's International League for Peace and Freedom. Program and Action Bulletin.
    Description: Provides up-to-the-minute information about national legislation and movement actions within the organization's goals. Covers civil rights, environmental, militarism, labor, and women's issues.

320 301.412   US   ISSN 0195-1688
HQ1236.5.U6
WOMEN'S POLITICAL TIMES. 1971. 4/yr. $20. National Women's Political Caucus, 1211 Connectiicut Ave., N.W., Ste. 425, Washington, DC 20036. TEL 202-898-1100. Ed. Pat Reilly. adv.; bk.rev. circ. 30,000. (tabloid format)

956.940 296   SA
WOMEN'S ZIONIST ORGANIZATION OF SOUTH AFRICA. NEWS AND VIEWS. 1949. a. membership. Women's Zionist Organization of South Africa, P.O. Box 29203, Sandringham 2131, South Africa. TEL 27-11-4851020. FAX 27-11-6401325. Ed. Sonia Benjamin. adv.; bk.rev.; play rev.; charts; illus. circ. 12,500.
    Formerly: Women's Zionist Council of South Africa. News and Views (ISSN 0043-7603)

320   US   ISSN 1077-5846
THE WOODLANDS FORUM. 1984. 2/yr. free. Center for Global Studies, 2001 Timberloch Pl., Box 4000, The Woodlands, TX 77380. FAX 713-377-5802. Ed. Jeff Awalt. bk.rev. circ. 10,000.

320.531   US   ISSN 0276-363X
WORKERS' ADVOCATE. 1969. m. $11. (Marxist-Leninist Party of the U.S.A.) Marxist-Leninist Publications, Box 8706, Emeryville, CA 94662. (tabloid format)

320   US   ISSN 0882-6366
WORKERS' ADVOCATE SUPPLEMENT. 1985. m. $12. (Marxist-Leninist Party of the U.S.A) Marxist-Leninist Publications, Box 8706, Emeryville, CA 94662.

329.9 331.8   US
WORKER'S DEMOCRACY. 1981. q. $6 to individuals; institutions $12. Worker's Democracy Press, Box 24115, St. Louis, MO 63130. Ed. Don Fitz. adv.; illus. circ. 400.

320   US   ISSN 0276-0746
WORKERS VANGUARD. 1971. fortn. $10 (includes subscr. to Spartacist, Women and Revolution, and several other titles). (Spartacist League) Spartacist Publishing Co., Box 1377, New York, NY 10116. TEL 212-732-7861. Ed. Jan Norden. bibl.; illus. (tabloid format) **Indexed:** Alt.Press Ind. **Document type:** newspaper.
    Formerly: Workers Action.

320.531   US   ISSN 0043-809X
WORKERS WORLD. 1959. w. $20. (Workers World Party) W W Publishers Inc., 55 W. 17th St., 5th Fl., New York, NY 10011. TEL 212-627-2994. FAX 212-675-7869. TELEX 6503925801. Ed. Deirdre Griswold. bk.rev. circ. 12,500. (tabloid format; also avail. in microform from UMI) **Indexed:** Alt.Press Ind. **Document type:** newspaper.

322.4   US
WORKING CLASS OPPOSITION/OPOSICION OBRERA. (Text in English, Spanish) 1981. m. $20. (Internationalist Workers Party (Fourth International)) October Publications, 3309 1-2 Mission St., Ste. 135, San Francisco, CA 94110. TEL 415-695-0340. (Co-sponsor: International Workers League) Eds. Ted Baker, Claudia Mejia. bk.rev.; illus. circ. 3,500.
    Description: Covers political events throughout the world from a socialist and communist perspective.

327   NZ   ISSN 0043-8189
WORLD AFFAIRS. 1945. 3/yr. NZ.$5.50. United Nations Association of New Zealand, P.O. Box 11-750, Wellington, New Zealand. Ed. Joan Morrell. bk.rev.; illus.; maps. circ. 700. (also avail. in microform from UMI; reprint service avail. from UMI) **Indexed:** Polit.Sci.Abstr., SSCI. **Document type:** academic/scholarly publication.
    —UMI. CCC.

320 051   US   ISSN 1043-1535
JK6
THE WORLD ALMANAC OF U.S. POLITICS. 1990. a. $16.95 (hardcover $29.95). World Almanac Books (Subsidiary of: Funk & Wagnalls), 1 International Blvd., Mahwah, NJ 07495. (also avail. in microform from UMI) **Document type:** directory.
    Description: Provides complete information on all three branches of the federal, state, and local governments.

WORLD BANK COUNTRY STUDY. see *BUSINESS AND ECONOMICS — International Development And Assistance*

WORLD BANK REGIONAL AND SECTORAL STUDIES. see *BUSINESS AND ECONOMICS — International Development And Assistance*

WORLD BUSINESS REVIEW. see *BUSINESS AND ECONOMICS — International Commerce*

320   SZ   ISSN 1013-0365
WORLD DIRECTORY OF PARLIAMENTS. (Text in English, French) a. free. Inter-Parliamentary Union, Place du Petit-Saconnex, CH-1211 Geneva 19, Switzerland. TEL 022-7344150. FAX 022-7333141. **Document type:** directory.

320.9   II
WORLD FOCUS. (Text in English) 1980. m. Rs.40($12) H. S. Chhabra, F-15 Bhagat Singh Market, New Delhi-110001, India.

320   SU
WORLD NEWS DIGEST. 1979. 2/yr. $34 s.R.120. Muslim World League, P.O. Box 538, Mecca, Saudi Arabia. Ed. Dr. Hasan Zaman. adv. circ. 1,500. (back issues avail.)

320   US   ISSN 0094-2316
JK1
WORLD OF POLITICS. 1971. m. included in subscription to Taylor's Encyclopedia of Government Officials, Federal and State. Political Research, Inc., Tegoland at Bent Tree, 16850 Dallas Parkway, Dallas, TX 75248. TEL 214-931-8827. FAX 214-248-7159. Ed. John Clements. charts; illus.; s-a. index.
    Description: Covers current events and developments in the U.S. government.

322.4   US   ISSN 0893-0228
WORLD PEACEMAKERS QUARTERLY.* 1979. q. $5. World Peacemakers Inc., 11427 Scottsbury Terr., Germantown, MD 20876-6010. TEL 202-265-7582. Ed. William J. Price. circ. 1,000. **Document type:** newsletter.
    Description: Presents alternatives for U.S. foreign policy and action based on religious faith.

WORLD POLITICS (BALTIMORE); a quarterly journal of international relations. see *POLITICAL SCIENCE — International Relations*

320.531   UK   ISSN 0269-9141
A WORLD TO WIN. (Editions in English, Farsi, Spanish, Turkish) 1985. q. £12($20) A World to Win, 27 Old Gloucester St., London WC1N 3XX, England. FAX 0171-831-9489. TELEX 262433 W6787. (Dist. in the U.S. by: Revolution Books, 13 E. 16th St., New York, NY 10003) Ed. Don Horne; Pub. K. Muralidharan. adv. contact: Don Horne. bk.rev. circ. 5,000. **Document type:** academic/scholarly publication.
    Description: Takes a Maoist internationalist look at the main events and issues throughout the political arena.

320   US
WORLD WAR THREE. irreg. Box 20271, New York, NY 10009.
    Description: Includes graphic arts, poetry.

956.940 296   IS   ISSN 0084-2516
WORLD ZIONIST ORGANIZATION. GENERAL COUNCIL. ADDRESSES, DEBATES, RESOLUTIONS.* (Text in English) a. World Zionist Organization, P.O. Box 92, Jerusalem 91920, Israel. TEL 02-527156. FAX 02-533542.

296 059   IS
WORLD ZIONIST PRESS SERVICE. (Text mainly in English and Russian; occasionally in various languages) m. World Zionist Organization, Department of Information, P.O. Box 92, Jerusalem 91920, Israel. TEL 972-2-527156. FAX 972-2-513542. (U.S. office: 110 E. 59th St., New York, NY 10022. TEL 212-339-6020) Ed. June Spitzer.
    Formerly: World Zionist Organization Press Service.

320   NP
WORLDWIDE ANTI-CORRUPTION AUTHORITY. 1980. a. $350. Siveast Consultants, Inc., USA, P.O. Box 5810, Kathmandu, Nepal.
    Description: Lists distinguished civil service personnel for their anti-corruption efforts.

WORLDWIDE DIRECTORY OF DEFENSE AUTHORITIES. see *MILITARY*

WORLDWIDE GOVERNMENT REPORT. see *PUBLIC ADMINISTRATION*

POLITICAL SCIENCE

WUQUF; beitraege zur entwicklung von staat und gesellschaft in nordafrika. see *HISTORY — History Of Africa*

320 SG
XARELI. fortn. And Jef - Mouvement Revolutionnaire Pour la Democratie Nouvelle, B.P. 12136, Dakar, Senegal. TEL 22-54-63. circ. 7,000.

320 CC ISSN 1000-4513
HM141
XIANDAI LINGDAO/MODERN LEADER. (Text in Chinese) 1986. bi-m. Y6.60. (Shanghai Kexue Yanjiusuo - Shanghai Scientific Research Institute) Xiandai Lingdao Bianjibu, 52 Yongfu Road, Shanghai 200031, People's Republic of China. TEL 4332558. Ed. Feng Zhijun. adv.: B&W page Y5000; adv. contact: Hengxin Chen. bk.rev. circ. 40,000.
Description: Explores the science and the art of leadership in China.

320 CC
XUANCHUAN SHOUCE/PROPAGANDA HANDBOOK. s-m. Beijing Ribao She - Beijing Daily, 34, Xibaobei Hutong, Dongdan, Beijing 100734, People's Republic of China. Ed. Wang Minying.

329.9 CC
XUEXI YU YANJIU. (Text in Chinese) m. Y1 per no. (Zhongguo Beijing Shiwei) Xuexi yu Janjiu Zazhishe, No. 6, Chegongzhuang Dajie, Beijing 100044, People's Republic of China. TEL 896061. (Dist. outside China by: China International Book Trading Corp., P.O. Box 399, Beijing, P.R.C.) Ed. Tao Yifan.

320 UK
Y DDRAIG GOCH. (Text in Welsh) 1925. bi-m. £4.80. Plaid Cymru (Welsh Nationalist Party), 51 Cathedral Rd., Caerdydd, De Morgannwg, Cymru CF1 9HD, Wales. TEL 0222-231944. FAX 0222-222506. adv.; bk.rev. circ. 5,000. (also avail. in microfilm from WMP) **Document type:** bulletin.

320 IS ISSN 0792-2337
DS150.L3
YA'AD. (Text in Hebrew) 1971. 3/yr. Documentation & Research Center of Hashomer Hatzair, Givat Haviva, M.P. Menashe 37 850, Israel. TEL 063-78944. Ed. David Zait.
Formerly (until **1988**): Ma'asef (ISSN 0334-3952)
Description: Studies in the history of the Israeli labor movement and socialism.

320 IS ISSN 0334-1003
HX9.H4
YALKUT LEMACHSHAVA SOTZIALISTIT. (Text in Hebrew) 1984. q. IS.15. Yad Tabenkin, Efal 52960, Israel. TEL 972-3-5343311. FAX 972-3-5346376. Ed. Dan Karmon. bk.rev. circ. 650. **Document type:** academic/scholarly publication.

320 CC
YAN - ZHAO XIANGYIN. (Text in Chinese) bi-m. Hebei Sheng Zhengzhi Xieshang Weiyuanhui, 34, Weiming Jie, Shijiazhuang, Hebei 050051, People's Republic of China. TEL 23477. Ed. Wang Xin.

320 350 US
YEARBOOK OF MARYLAND LEGISLATORS. quadrennial. $175. Bancroft Information Group, Inc., Box 65360, Baltimore, MD 21209. TEL 410-358-0658. FAX 410-764-1967. Ed. Bruce Bortz.

YELLOW SHEET REPORT. see *PUBLIC ADMINISTRATION*

320 KO
YONSEI UNIVERSITY. INSTITUTE OF EAST AND WEST STUDIES. ANNUAL REPORT. a. Yonsei University, Institute of East and West Studies, 134 Shinchon-Dong, Seodaemoon-gu, Seoul 120-749, S. Korea. TEL 02-361-3506. FAX 02-393-9027. TELEX K29127.

YOUNG AGE; social and cultural fortnightly. see *SOCIOLOGY*

369.4 UK ISSN 0513-5982
YOUNG FABIAN PAMPHLET. 1961. irreg., no.52, 1992. £3.50($5.50) per vol. Fabian Society, 11 Dartmouth St., London SW1H 9BN, England. TEL 0171-222-8877. FAX 0171-976-7153. Ed.Bd. charts, stat. circ. 5,500. (reprint service avail. from KTO)

320.55 296.7 US ISSN 0044-0809
BM1
YOUNG ISRAEL VIEWPOINT. 1937. m. (except July & Aug.). $5 to non-members. National Council of Young Israel, 3 W. 16th St, New York, NY 10011. TEL 212-929-1525. FAX 212-727-9526. Ed. Tovah Holzer. adv.; bk.rev.; circ. 40,000 (controlled). (tabloid format; also avail. in microfilm from AJP)

YOUNG JUDAEAN. see *ETHNIC INTERESTS*

956.940 296 US ISSN 0044-1171
YOUTH AND NATION;* magazine for radical Jewish youth. 1934. q. $2.50. Hashomer Hatzair Zionist Youth Movement, 224 W. 35th St., New York, NY 10001. TEL 212-868-0388. Ed. Allan Lutzker. bk.rev.; film rev.; play rev. circ. 1,500.
Incorporates: Neged Hazerem.

YOUTH & SOCIETY. see *CHILDREN AND YOUTH — About*

320.532 YU ISSN 0350-9508
YUGOSLAV INFORMATION BULLETIN; of the League of Communists of Yugoslavia & the Socialist Alliance of Working People of Yugoslavia. French edition: Bulletin d'Information Yougoslave (ISSN 0407-825X); Spanish edition: Boletin de Informacion Yugoslavo (ISSN 0350-7777) (Text in English) 1974. m. free. Komunist, Trg Marksa i Engelsa 11, 11000 Belgrade, Yugoslavia. Ed. Jovan Lakicevic. bk.rev.

320 CN
YUKON NEW DEOMOCRAT. 1973. a. Yukon New Democratic Party, Box 4659, Whitehorse, Yukon Y1A 3V7, Canada.

322.4 323.4 US ISSN 1056-5507
HN51
Z MAGAZINE. 1988. m. $26 to individuals; institutions $35 (foreign $50). (Institute for Social and Cultural Communications) Z Magazine, 18 Millfield St., Woods Hole, MA 02543. TEL 508-548-9063. FAX 508-457-0626. E-mail: zsysop@zbbs.com. Eds. Michael Albert, Lydia Sargent. bk.rev.; film rev.; illus. circ. 26,000. (back issues avail.) **Indexed:** Alt.Press Ind.
—Faxon; UnCover.
Formerly: Zeta Magazine (ISSN 0896-1328)
Description: Covers U.S. politics, feminism, ecology, foreign news, racism, economics and political activism.

960 ZR ISSN 0251-298X
DT1
ZAIRE-AFRIQUE; economie, culture, vie sociale. 1961. m. 5000 Fr.CFA($60) Centre d'Etudes pour l'Action Sociale, 9, ave Pere Boka, B.P. 3375, Kinshasa-Gombe, Zaire. TEL 30066. Eds. Rene Beeckmans, Kikassa Mwanalessa. adv.; bk.rev.; bibl.; index. circ. 4,500. (tabloid format) **Indexed:** Bibl.Ling., CERDIC, Curr.Cont.Africa, Documentatieblad, Rural Recreat.Tour.Abstr., World Agri.Econ.& Rural Sociol.Abstr.
Formerly (until 1971): Congo-Afrique (ISSN 0010-5767)

057.8 XN ISSN 0044-1872
ZASTITA. (Text in Macedonian) vol.6, 1966. m. $2.60. Sojuzot na Trudovite Invalidi na Makedonija, Marsala Tita, Box 437, Skopje, Macedonia.

ZEITBUEHNE. see *BUSINESS AND ECONOMICS — Economic Situation And Conditions*

ZEITSCHRIFT FUER LATEINAMERIKA WIEN. see *HISTORY — History Of North And South America*

320 350 GW ISSN 0340-1758
JN3971.A7
ZEITSCHRIFT FUER PARLAMENTSFRAGEN. 1970. q. DM.48 (students DM.34) (effective 1996). (Deutsche Vereinigung fuer Parlamentsfragen) Westdeutscher Verlag GmbH, Postfach 1546, 65005 Wiesbaden, Germany. TEL 0611-534389. FAX 0611-534430. bk.rev.; bibl. circ. 2,400. (reprint service avail. from SCH) **Indexed:** Int.Polit.Sci.Abstr. **Document type:** academic/scholarly publication.
—BLDSC (9476.500000); Faxon; SWETS. **CCC.**

320 GW ISSN 0044-3360
JA14
ZEITSCHRIFT FUER POLITIK. 1907; N.S. 1954. q. DM.98. (Hochschule fuer Politik) Carl Heymanns Verlag KG, Luxemburgerstr. 449, 50939 Cologne, Germany. TEL 0221-94373-0. FAX 0221-94373901. Ed.Bd. adv.; bk.rev.; bibl.; index. circ. 1,350. **Indexed:** A.B.C.Pol.Sci, Int.Polit.Sci.Abstr., P.A.I.S.For.Lang.Ind., P.A.I.S., SSCI. **Document type:** bulletin.
—BLDSC (9484.300000); SWETS.

320 GW ISSN 0514-2776
ZEITSCHRIFT FUER SOZIALREFORM. 1954. m. DM.816. Verlag Chmielorz GmbH und Co., Marktplatz 13, 65183 Wiesbaden, Germany. TEL 0611-36098-0. FAX 0611-301303. Ed.Bd. (back issues avail.) **Document type:** academic/scholarly publication.
—CCC.

329.3 630 KR
ZEMLIA I VOLIA/LAND AND FREEDOM. 1990. m. Ukrainian Democratic Peasants Party, Vul. 700-richya Lvova 63, kv.213, Lvov 58, Ukraine. TEL 599-671. circ. 20,000.

320.531 SW ISSN 0044-3980
ZENIT; nordisk socialistisk tidskrift. 1956. q. SEK 150($9) Tidskriftsfoereningen Zenit, P.O. Box 11596, S-221 05 Lund, Sweden. TEL 46-13-37-66. Ed.Bd. adv.; bk.rev.; abstr. circ. 2,000.

320.531 GW ISSN 0044-4278
ZENTRALBLATT FUER SOZIALVERSICHERUNG, SOZIALHILFE UND VERSORGUNG; Zeitschrift fuer das Recht der Sozialen Sicherheit. (Text in German; summaries in English and French) 1947. m. DM.177.60. Asgard-Verlag Dr. Werner Hippe KG, Einsteinstr. 10, 56587 St. Augustin, Germany. TEL 02241-3164-0. Ed. Horst Straesser. adv.; bk.rev.; bibl. ratio. circ. 1,000. **Indexed:** World Bibl.Soc.Sec.

320 UY
ZETA. 1985; N.S. 1989. w. Partido por el Gobierno del Pueblo Lista 99, Cuareim 1473, Montevideo, Uruguay. TEL 90-68-17. Dir. Omar Prego.

ZHENGFA LUNTAN/POLITICAL SCIENCE & LAW TRIBUNE; zhongguo zhengfa daxue xuebao. see *LAW*

ZHENGZHI JIAOYU/POLITICAL EDUCATION. see *EDUCATION*

ZHENGZHI YU FALU/POLITICS AND LAW. see *LAW*

324 CC ISSN 1000-3355
JA26
ZHENGZHIXUE YANJIU/POLITICAL SCIENCE RESEARCH. (Text in Chinese) 1985. bi-m. $25.20. (Zhongguo Shehui Kexueyuan, Zhengzhixue Yanjiusuo - Chinese Academy of Social Sciences, Institute of Political Science) Zhongguo Shehui Kexueyuan Chubanshe, Gulou Xidajie A 158, Beijing, People's Republic of China. (Dist. in US by: China Books & Periodicals, Inc., 2929 24th St., San Francisco, CA 94110. TEL 415-282-2994)

329.9 951 CC
ZHONG GONG DANGSHI YANJIU/JOURNAL OF CHINESE COMMUNIST PARTY HISTORY. (Text in Chinese) bi-m. $36. Zhonggong Zhongyang Dangshi Yanjiushi - Central Committee of Chinese Communist Party, Party History Research Center, P.O. Box 1924, Beijing 100091, People's Republic of China. TEL 2581534. (Dist. in US by: China Books & Periodicals, Inc., 2929 24th St., San Francisco, CA 94110. TEL 415-282-2994) Ed. Li Chuanhua.

320 951 CC
ZHONGGONG DANGSHI/HISTORY OF THE CHINESE COMMUNIST PARTY. (Text in Chinese) s-m. Zhongguo Zhonggong Dangshi Xuehui, Zhongyang Dangxiao, Nanyuan Nei, P.O. Box 1924, Beijing 100091, People's Republic of China. TEL 2581534. Ed. Wang Zhixin.

320 CC
ZHONGGUO MINZHENG. (Text in Chinese) m. Shehui Baozhang Baoshe, No. A-12, Shifangyuan, Beijing 100036, People's Republic of China. TEL 8652657. Ed. Zhou Juncheng.

POLITICAL SCIENCE — ABSTRACTING, BIBLIOGRAPHIES, STATISTICS

320   CC
ZHONGGUO QINGYUN/CHINESE YOUTH MOVEMENT. (Text in Chinese) bi-m. Gongqingtuan Zhongyang, Qingyunshi Yanjiushi, 25, Xisanhuan Beilu, Beijing 100081, People's Republic of China. TEL 8021144. Ed. Zhang Xiuxue.

322.4   PL
ZIELONY SZTANDAR. 1931. w. Polskie Stronnictwo Ludowe (PSL) - Polish Peasant Party, Ul. Grzybowska 4, 00-950 Warsaw, Poland. TEL 48-22-207554. Ed. Pawel Popiak. circ. 195.800.

320   GW
DIE ZIGARRE. 1970. s-a. Sozialdemokratische Partei Deutschlands (SPD), Ortsverein Hatzenbuehl, c/o Dieter Boehm, Schuberstr. 7, 76770 Hatzenbuehl, Germany. TEL 07275-4803.

329   IS
ZO HA-DEREKH. (Text in Hebrew) 1965. w. $21. Communist Party of Israel, P.O. Box 26205, Tel Aviv, Israel. Ed. Tamar Gozansky.

ZSHURNALIST. see *JOURNALISM*

327   NE   ISSN 0044-5428
ZUID - AFRIKA; onafhankelijk maandblad, uitgegeven door Z A S M in Amsterdam. Short title: Z - A. 1924. 10/yr. fl.27.50. Zuid - Afrikaansche Stichting Moederland, Keizersgracht 141, 1015 CK Amsterdam, Netherlands. TEL 31-20-6249318. FAX 31-20-6382596. Ed.Bd. adv.; bk.rev.; abstr.; bibl.; illus.; index. circ. 1,250.
Description: Covers political developments in South Africa, with commentary from a Dutch point of view.

057.8   II   ISSN 0044-5479
ZULQARNAIN. (Text in Urdu) 1903. w. Rs.30. Nizami Press, Badaun, Uttar Pradesh, India. Ed. Moonis Nizami. adv.; bk.rev.; abstr.; bibl.; tr.lit. circ. 20,000. (also avail. in microfilm)

322.4   GW   ISSN 0044-5487
ZUM NACHDENKEN. 1963. irreg., vol.35, 1992. free. Hessische Landeszentrale fuer Politische Bildung, Rheinbahnstr. 2, 65185 Wiebaden, Germany. FAX 0611-3682653. Ed. Herbert Lilge. adv. circ. 7,000.

ZUR POLITIK UND ZEITGESCHICHTE. see *HISTORY*

320   CR
15 DIAS EN COSTA RICA.* 1971. m. Casa Presidencial, San Jose, Costa Rica. illus.

320 350   US   ISSN 0164-0356
50 STATE LEGISLATIVE REVIEW. 1977. biennial. included in subscription to Taylor's Encyclopedia of Government Officials, Federal and State. Political Research, Inc., Tegoland at Bent Tree, 16850 Dallas Pkwy., Dallas, TX 75248. TEL 214-931-8827. FAX 214-248-7159.
Description: Summary of laws dealing with topics of national concern passed in each state.

320   AG
84;* semanario politico independiente. 1982. w. Montevideo 373, Buenos Aires, Argentina. Ed. Carlos Garramuno.

320   IT
1989 RIVISTA DI SCIENZE POLITICHE. 1991. s-a. L.35000 (Europe L.60000; elsewhere L.70000). (Societa Campana di Scienze Politiche e Sociali 1989) Giannini Editore, Via Mezzocannone 8, 80134 Naples, Italy. TEL 081-5526068. Ed. Ernesto Mazzetti.

POLITICAL SCIENCE — Abstracting, Bibliographies, Statistics

320 016   US   ISSN 0001-0456
Z7161   CODEN: ABPSC
A B C POL SCI; a bibliography of contents: political science and government. 1969. 6/yr. (including index). price varies. A B C-Clio, 130 Cremona, Box 1911, Santa Barbara, CA 93116-1911. TEL 805-968-1911. FAX 805-685-9685. Ed. Helene Wright; Pub. Heather Cameron. adv. contact: Laura Wilson. cum.index. **Document type:** abstracting/indexing.
●Also available on CD-ROM.
Description: Lists and indexes the table of contents of over 300 essential international political science journals.

AFRICAN STUDIES ABSTRACTS. see *SOCIAL SCIENCES: COMPREHENSIVE WORKS — Abstracting, Bibliographies, Statistics*

ALTERNATIVE PRESS INDEX; an index to alternative and radical publications. see *LITERARY AND POLITICAL REVIEWS — Abstracting, Bibliographies, Statistics*

324.94912   IC   ISSN 1017-6667
ALTHINGISKOSNINGAR/ELECTIONS TO THE ALTHING. (Text in Icelandic; table headings in English) 1882. irreg. Hagstofa Islands - Statistics Iceland, Skuggasund 3, IS-150 Reykjavik, Iceland. TEL 354-560-9800. FAX 354-562-8865. E-mail: hagstofa@hag.stjr.is. Dir. Hallgrimur Snorrason. (back issues avail.) **Document type:** government publication.

327.73   US   ISSN 1070-1583
Z6465.U5
AMERICAN FOREIGN POLICY INDEX; a guide to foreign policy and foreign relations publications of the U.S. government. 1993. q. Congressional Information Service, Part of the Reed Elsevier group, 4520 East-West Hwy., Bethesda, MD 20814. TEL 605-654-1550; 800-638-8380. FAX 301-654-4033. TELEX 292386 CIS UR. Ed. Polly Todd. **Document type:** abstracting/indexing.

950 015   SI   ISSN 0004-4520
DS1
ASIAN ALMANAC; weekly abstracts of Asian affairs. (Text in English) 1963. w. S.$300($150) P.O. Box 2737, Singapore 9047, Singapore. Ed. Vedagiri T. Sambandan. index. circ. 600. (looseleaf format; back issues avail.)

BIBLIOGRAFIA DE POLITICA INDUSTRIAL. see *BUSINESS AND ECONOMICS — Abstracting, Bibliographies, Statistics*

BIBLIOGRAPHIES AND INDEXES IN LAW AND POLITICAL SCIENCE. see *LAW — Abstracting, Bibliographies, Statistics*

320.531   US   ISSN 1056-5515
BIBLIOGRAPHIES OF BRITISH STATESMEN. 1988. irreg. price varies. Greenwood Press, Inc. (Subsidiary of: Greenwood Publishing Group Inc.), 88 Post Rd. W., Box 5007, Westport, CT 06881-5007. TEL 203-226-3571. FAX 203-222-1502. **Document type:** monographic series.

320 973   US   ISSN 1061-6500
BIBLIOGRAPHIES OF THE PRESIDENTS OF THE UNITED STATES. 1988. irreg. price varies. Greenwood Press, Inc. (Subsidiary of: Greenwood Publishing Group Inc.), 88 Post Rd. W., Box 5007, Westport, CT 06881-5007. TEL 203-226-3571. FAX 203-222-1502. **Document type:** monographic series.

320 900   US   ISSN 1056-5523
BIBLIOGRAPHIES OF WORLD LEADERS. 1989. irreg. price varies. Greenwood Press, Inc. (Subsidiary of: Greenwood Publishing Group Inc.), 88 Post Rd. W., Box 5007, Westport, CT 06881-5007. TEL 203-226-3571. FAX 203-222-1502. **Document type:** monographic series.

320 016   GW   ISSN 0067-8015
BIBLIOTHECA IBERO-AMERICANA. 1959. irreg. price varies. (Ibero-Amerikanisches Institut, Berlin) Colloquium Verlag, Luetzowstr. 105, 10785 Berlin, Germany. Ed. Dietrich Briesemeister. circ. 1,000.

320   GW   ISSN 0939-463X
BOCHUM. AMT FUER STATISTIK, STADTFORSCHUNG UND WAHLEN. REIHE "WAHLEN IN BOCHUM". 1946. irreg. DM.20. Amt fuer Statistik, Stadtforschung und Wahlen, 44777 Bochum, Germany. TEL 0234-9108510. FAX 0234-9108512. charts; stat. **Document type:** government publication.
Description: Report and survey of general elections.

320   US
CENSUS OF POPULATION AND HOUSING: POPULATION AND HOUSING CHARACTERISTICS FOR CONGRESSIONAL DISTRICTS. (Series CPH4; individual reports avail. for each state, Puerto Rico, and Virgin Islands) 1961. decennial. price varies. U.S. Bureau of the Census, Data User Services Division, Washington, DC 20233. TEL 301-457-4100. (Orders to: Superintendent of Documents, U.S. Government Printing Office, Box 371954, Pittsburgh, PA 15250-7954. TEL 202-512-1800. FAX 202-512-2250; Or: Bernan, 4611-F Assembly Dr., Lanham, MD 20706. TEL 301-459-7666. FAX 301-459-0056) (also avail. in microfiche)

320   US
CONGRESSIONAL RECORD SCANNER. 180/yr. $395. Congressional Quarterly Inc., 1414 22nd St., N.W., Washington, DC 20037. TEL 800-432-2250. FAX 202-728-1863. Ed. Evelyn Russell. (looseleaf format) **Document type:** abstracting/indexing.
●Also available online.
Description: Abstracts to each day's Congressional Record.

CONNEXIONS DIGEST; a social change sourcebook. see *POLITICAL SCIENCE*

320   EI
COUNCIL OF EUROPE. DOCUMENTATION SECTION. BIBLIO BULLETIN. SERIES: CRISES. 1992. q. free. Council of Europe, Documentation Section, BP 431 R6, 67006 Strasbourg, France. TEL 88-41-20-00. FAX 88-36-70-57. TELEX EUR870 943 F. circ. 300. **Document type:** bibliography.
Description: Bibliographic references to periodical articles and books available in library and documentation centers on subjects relevant to the Council of Europe in the field of international relations. Includes a topical section giving extracts, facts and figures or news on a particular country or event.

327   EI
COUNCIL OF EUROPE. DOCUMENTATION SECTION. BIBLIO BULLETIN. SERIES: EAST - WEST RELATIONS. 1990. 6/yr. free. Council of Europe, Documentation Section, BP 431 R6, 67006 Strasbourg, France. TEL 88-41-20-00. FAX 88-36-70-57. TELEX EUR 870 943F. (Dist. in U.S. by: Manhattan Publishing Co., 225 Lafayette St., New York, NY 10012) circ. 300. **Document type:** bibliography.
Description: Bibliographic references to periodical articles and books available in the Library and Documentation Centers on subjects relevant to the Council of Europe in the field of East-West relations. Includes a topical section giving extracts, facts and figures, or news on a particular country or event.

320 016 330   EI
COUNCIL OF EUROPE. DOCUMENTATION SECTION. BIBLIO BULLETIN. SERIES: POLITICAL, ECONOMIC AND SOCIAL AFFAIRS. 1972. m. free. Council of Europe, Documentation Section, BP 431 R6, 67006 Strasbourg, France. TEL 88-44-20-00. FAX 88-36-70-57. TELEX EUR 870 943F. (Dist. in U.S. by: Manhattan Publishing Co., 225 Lafayette St., New York, NY 10012) circ. 300. **Document type:** bibliography.
Former titles: Council of Europe. Central Library. Biblio Bulletin. Series: Political and Social Affairs; Council of Europe. Documentation Section and Library. Bibliographical Bulletin. Series: Political, Economic and Social Affairs; Council of Europe. Documentation Section and Library. Bibliographical Bulletin. Series: Political and Economic Affairs.
Description: Index of periodical articles on international relations, politics, economic and social affairs.

POLITICAL SCIENCE — ABSTRACTING, BIBLIOGRAPHIES, STATISTICS

960 016   US   ISSN 0011-3255
Z3501
CURRENT BIBLIOGRAPHY ON AFRICAN AFFAIRS. 1968. q. $137 (effective 1996). Baywood Publishing Co., Inc., 26 Austin Ave., Box 337, Amityville, NY 11701. TEL 516-691-1270. FAX 516-691-1770. Ed. Paula Boesch. bk.rev.; bibl.; author index. (back issues avail.) **Indexed:** Bibl.Ling., CERDIC, Curr.Cont.Africa, Documentatieblad, M.L.A. **Document type:** bibliography.
   Description: Features commentary and bibliographic section.

077 015   US   ISSN 1067-7542
D839
CURRENT DIGEST OF THE POST-SOVIET PRESS. 1949. w. $880 to institutions (foreign $920) (effective 1995). Current Digest of the Soviet Press, 3857 N. High St., Columbus, OH 43214-3747. TEL 614-292-4234. FAX 614-267-6310. Ed. Fred C. Schulze. abstr.; charts; illus.; q. index, a. cum.index. circ. 1,000. (also avail. in microfiche; microfilm; back issues avail.) **Indexed:** Int.Polit.Sci.Abstr., Mid.East: Abstr.& Ind., P.A.I.S. **Document type:** academic/scholarly publication.
●Also available online. Vendor(s): Lexis-Nexis. —BLDSC (3496.345000); Faxon; SWETS; UnCover. CCC.
   Formerly (until 1992): Current Digest of the Soviet Press (ISSN 0011-3425); **Incorporates:** Current Abstracts of the Soviet Press (ISSN 0011-3166)
   Description: Translations or abstracts of materials selected from major Russian-language periodicals from Russia and other countries in the former Soviet Union.

320.531   US
CURRENT DIGEST OF THE POST-SOVIET PRESS. ANNUAL INDEX. 1976. a. $42.50 (foreign $50). Current Digest of the Soviet Press, 3857 N. High St., Columbus, OH 43214-3747. TEL 614-292-4234. FAX 614-267-6310. Ed. Fred C. Schulze. (also avail. in microfiche) **Document type:** academic/scholarly publication, abstracting/indexing.
   Formerly (until 1992): Current Digest of the Soviet Press. Annual Index (ISSN 1049-4197)

320   US   ISSN 1074-0007
CURRENT DIGEST OF THE POST-SOVIET PRESS. QUARTERLY INDEX. 1949. q. $45 (foreign $55). Current Digest of the Soviet Press, 3857 N. High St., Columbus, OH 43214-3747. TEL 614-292-4234. FAX 614-267-6310. Ed. Fred C. Schulze. **Document type:** academic/scholarly publication, abstracting/indexing.
   Formerly (until 1992): Current Digest of the Soviet Press. Quarterly Index.

CURRENT MILITARY AND POLITICAL LITERATURE. see MILITARY — Abstracting, Bibliographies, Statistics

011   US   ISSN 1046-4239
Z1223.Z9
DECLASSIFIED DOCUMENTS CATALOG. 1975. 6/yr. $1110. Primary Source Media, 12 Lunar Dr., Drawer AB, Woodbridge, CT 06525. TEL 203-397-2600; 800-444-0799. FAX 203-397-3893. (also avail. in microfiche from RPI; back issues avail.) **Document type:** catalog, abstracting/indexing.
   Formerly: Declassified Documents Quarterly Catalog (ISSN 0099-0957)
   Description: Includes information regarding United States' post-World War II international relations from the Cold War through the Vietnam era. Provides a comprehensive compilation of documents microfilmed, abstracted, and indexed as they are released by government agencies or obtained from the National Archives and Presidential Libraries.

DEUTSCHE BUECHER. see LITERATURE — Abstracting, Bibliographies, Statistics

320 350   US   ISSN 1071-796X
Z7165.U5
DIRECTORY OF POLITICAL NEWSLETTERS. 1990. a. $45. Government Research Service, 701 Jackson, Ste. 304, Topeka, KS 66603. TEL 913-232-7720. FAX 913-232-1615. Ed. Lynn Hellebust. **Document type:** bibliography, directory.
   Former titles: Directory of Political Periodicals (ISSN 1057-0578); (until 1990): Directory of Political Newsletters (ISSN 1052-9896)
   Description: Lists periodicals which focus primarily on domestic politics and government.

327 015   GW   ISSN 0342-040X
Z3509
DOKUMENTATIONSDIENST AFRIKA. AUSGEWAEHLTE NEUERE LITERATUR. (Text in English, French and German) 1973. 4/yr. DM.80. Deutsches Uebersee-Institut, Uebersee-Dokumentation, Neuer Jungfernstieg 21, 20354 Hamburg, Germany. TEL 040-3562598. FAX 040-3562512. circ. 120. **Document type:** bibliography.

327   GW   ISSN 0720-2032
DOKUMENTATIONSDIENST AFRIKA. KURZBIBLIOGRAPHIE. (Text in English, French and German) 1980. irreg. Deutsches Uebersee-Institut, Uebersee-Dokumentation, Neuer Jungfernstieg 21, 20354 Hamburg, Germany. TEL 040-3562598. FAX 040-3562512. **Document type:** bibliography.

327   GW   ISSN 0342-0442
DOKUMENTATIONSDIENST AFRIKA. REIHE A. (Text in English, French and German) 1973. irreg. Deutsches Uebersee-Institut, Uebersee-Dokumentation, Neuer Jungfernstieg 21, 20354 Hamburg, Germany. TEL 040-3562598. FAX 040-3562512. circ. 150. **Document type:** bibliography.

327   GW   ISSN 0936-9171
DOKUMENTATIONSDIENST ASIEN UND SUEDPAZIFIK. AUSGEWAEHLTE NEUERE LITERATUR. (Text in English and German) 1975. 4/yr. DM.80. Deutsches Uebersee-Institut, Uebersee-Dokumentation, Neuer Jungfernstieg 21, 20354 Hamburg, Germany. TEL 040-3562598. FAX 040-3562512. circ. 110. **Document type:** bibliography.

327   GW   ISSN 0938-3638
DOKUMENTATIONSDIENST ASIEN UND SUEDPAZIFIK. KURZBIBLIOGRAPHIE. (Text in English and German) 1978. irreg. Deutsches Uebersee-Institut, Uebersee-Dokumentation, Neuer Jungfernstieg 21, 20354 Hamburg, Germany. TEL 040-3562598. FAX 040-3562512. **Document type:** bibliography.

327   GW   ISSN 0937-5929
DOKUMENTATIONSDIENST ASIEN UND SUEDPAZIFIK. REIHE A. (Text in English and German) 1974. irreg. Deutsches Uebersee-Institut, Uebersee-Dokumentation, Neuer Jungfernstieg 21, 20354 Hamburg, Germany. TEL 040-3562598. FAX 040-3562512. circ. 150. **Document type:** bibliography.

327   GW   ISSN 0342-037X
Z7165.L3
DOKUMENTATIONSDIENST LATEINAMERIKA. AUSGEWAEHLTE NEUERE LITERATUR/DOCUMENTACION LATINOAMERICANA. BOLETIN BIBLIOGRAFICO. (Text in English, German, Spanish) 1971. 3/yr. DM.20 per no. Deutsches Uebersee-Institut, Uebersee-Dokumentation, Neuer Jungfernstieg 21, 20354 Hamburg, Germany. TEL 040-3562598. FAX 040-3562512. circ. 420. **Document type:** bibliography.
   Description: Annotated bibliography of articles in periodicals on Latin American development.

327   GW   ISSN 0937-5937
Z3013.5
DOKUMENTATIONSDIENST VORDERER ORIENT. AUSGEWAEHLTE NEUERE LITERATUR. (Text in English, French and German) 1970. 4/yr. DM.80. Deutsches Uebersee-Institut, Uebersee-Dokumentation, Neuer Jungfernstieg 21, 20354 Hamburg, Germany. TEL 040-3562598. FAX 040-3562512. circ. 150. **Document type:** bibliography.

327   GW   ISSN 0938-2666
DOKUMENTATIONSDIENST VORDERER ORIENT. KURZBIBLIOGRAPHIE. (Text in English, French and German) 1978. irreg. Deutsches Uebersee-Institut, Uebersee-Dokumentation, Neuer Jungfernstieg 21, 20354 Hamburg, Germany. TEL 040-3562598. FAX 040-3562512. **Document type:** bibliography.

327   GW   ISSN 0937-5945
DOKUMENTATIONSDIENST VORDERER ORIENT. REIHE A. (Text in English, French and German) 1973. irreg. Deutsches Uebersee-Institut, Uebersee-Dokumentation, Neuer Jungfernstieg 21, 20354 Hamburg, Germany. TEL 040-3562598. FAX 040-3562512. circ. 150. **Document type:** bibliography.

EDITORIALS ON FILE; newspaper editorial reference service with index. see JOURNALISM — Abstracting, Bibliographies, Statistics

328   PN   ISSN 0250-4316
ESTADISTICA PANAMENA. SITUACION POLITICA, ADMINISTRATIVA Y JUSTICIA. SECCION 611. REPRESENTACION POLITICA. ESTADISTICA ELECTORAL. 1960. irreg. Bl.1.50. Direccion de Estadistica y Censo, Contraloria General, Apdo. 5213, Panama 5, Panama. FAX 507-69-7294. circ. 1,000. **Document type:** government publication, bulletin.
   Formerly (until 1978): Estadistica Panamena. Estadistica Electoral (ISSN 0078-897X)

314 320   FI
FINLAND. TILASTOKESKUS. VALTIOLLISET VAALIT. KANSANEDUSTAJAIN VAALIT/FINLAND. STATISTIKCENTRALEN. STATLIGA VAL. RIKSDAGSMANNAVALEN/FINLAND. CENTRAL STATISTICAL OFFICE. NATIONAL ELECTIONS. PARLIAMENTARY ELECTIONS. (Section XXIX A of Official Statistics of Finland) (Text in Finnish, Swedish and English) 1909. irreg. FIM 32. Tilastokeskus, Annankatu 44, SF-00100 Helsinki 10, Finland.
   Formerly: Finland. Tilastokeskus. Kansanedustajain Vaalit (ISSN 0355-2209)

320 011   FI   ISSN 0355-2195
FINLAND. TILASTOKESKUS. VALTIOLLISET VAALIT. TASAVALLAN PRESIDENTIN VAALIT VALISIJAMIESTEN. (Text in English, Finnish, Swedish) 1926. every 6 yrs. FIM 35. Tilastokeskus - Central Statistical Office of Finland, Annankatu 44, SF-00101 Helsinki 10, Finland.

324.94912   IC   ISSN 1017-6675
FORSETAKJOER/PRESIDENTIAL ELECTIONS. (Text in Icelandic; table headings in English) 1952. irreg. Hagstofa Islands - Statistics Iceland, Skuggasund 3, IS-150 Reykjavik, Iceland. TEL 354-560-9800. FAX 354-562-8865. E-mail: hagstofa@hag.stjr.is. Dir. Hallgrimur Snorrason. (back issues avail.) **Document type:** government publication.

HISTORICAL ABSTRACTS. PART A: MODERN HISTORY ABSTRACTS, 1450-1914. see HISTORY — Abstracting, Bibliographies, Statistics

HISTORICAL ABSTRACTS. PART B: TWENTIETH CENTURY ABSTRACTS, 1914 TO THE PRESENT. see HISTORY — Abstracting, Bibliographies, Statistics

HISTORICAL ABSTRACTS. PART B: TWENTIETH CENTURY ABSTRACTS, 1914 TO THE PRESENT. ANNUAL INDEX. see HISTORY — Abstracting, Bibliographies, Statistics

HUMAN RIGHTS ORGANIZATIONS & PERIODICALS DIRECTORY. see POLITICAL SCIENCE — Civil Rights

320   II   ISSN 0250-9660
JA26
I C S S R JOURNAL OF ABSTRACTS AND REVIEWS: POLITICAL SCIENCE. (Text in English) 1973. s-a. Rs.30 to individuals; institutions Rs.50. Indian Council of Social Science Research, 35 Ferozshah Rd., New Delhi 110 001, India. TEL 91-11-388342. FAX 91-11-388037. TELEX 31-61083-ISSR-IN. Ed. S.K. Chaubey. adv.; bk.rev.; bibl.; index. circ. 550. (back issues avail.) **Document type:** abstracting/indexing.
   Description: Abstracts of articles in political science published in Indian journals.

320 011   US   ISSN 0191-1058
Z1223.5.I3
ILLINOIS. STATE LIBRARY, SPRINGFIELD. PUBLICATIONS OF THE STATE OF ILLINOIS.. a. free. State Library, 300 S. Second St., Springfield, IL 62701. TEL 217-782-4887. FAX 217-782-6437. (also avail. in microform) **Document type:** government publication, bibliography.

POLITICAL SCIENCE — ABSTRACTING, BIBLIOGRAPHIES, STATISTICS

327 011 US
INDEX: FOREIGN BROADCAST INFORMATION SERVICE DAILY REPORTS: AFRICA SUB-SAHARA. 1980. m. (plus annual cumulation). $225. NewsBank, Inc., 58 Pine St., New Canaan, CT 06840-5426. TEL 203-966-1100. FAX 203-966-6254. Ed. Jean Austin. (also avail. in microfiche; back issues avail.)
●Also available on CD-ROM.
 Former titles: Index: Foreign Broadcast Information Service Daily Reports: South Asia (ISSN 0731-3233); Index: Foreign Broadcast Information Service Daily Reports: Sub-Saharan Africa.

327 011 US ISSN 0271-1761
DS701
INDEX: FOREIGN BROADCAST INFORMATION SERVICE DAILY REPORTS: CHINA. 1975. m. (plus annual cumulation). $225. NewsBank, Inc., 58 Pine St., New Canaan, CT 06840-5426. TEL 203-966-1100. FAX 203-966-6254. Ed. Jean Austin. (also avail. in microfiche; back issues avail.)
●Also available on CD-ROM.
 Formerly: Index: Foreign Broadcast Information Service Daily Reports: People's Republic of China.

327 011 US
INDEX: FOREIGN BROADCAST INFORMATION SERVICE DAILY REPORTS: EAST ASIA. 1978. m. (plus annual cumulation). $225. NewsBank, Inc., 58 Pine St., New Canaan, CT 06840-5426. TEL 203-966-1100. FAX 203-966-6254. Ed. Jean Austin. (also avail. in microfiche; back issues avail.)
●Also available on CD-ROM.
 Formerly: Index: Foreign Broadcast Information Service Daily Reports: Asia and Pacific (ISSN 0272-3875)

327 011 US ISSN 0731-4116
DJK1.D34 Suppl
INDEX: FOREIGN BROADCAST INFORMATION SERVICE DAILY REPORTS: EASTERN EUROPE. 1978. m. (plus annual cumulation). $225. NewsBank, Inc., 58 Pine St., New Canaan, CT 06840-5426. TEL 203-966-1100. FAX 203-966-6254. Ed. Jean Austin. (also avail. in microfiche; back issues avail.)
●Also available on CD-ROM.

327 011 US ISSN 0278-1360
F1401
INDEX: FOREIGN BROADCAST INFORMATION SERVICE DAILY REPORTS: LATIN AMERICA. 1978. m. (plus annual cumulation). $225. NewsBank, Inc., 58 Pine St., New Canaan, CT 06840-5426. TEL 203-966-1100. FAX 203-966-6254. Ed. Jean Austin. (also avail. in microfiche; back issues avail.)
●Also available on CD-ROM.

327 011 US
INDEX: FOREIGN BROADCAST INFORMATION SERVICE DAILY REPORTS: NEAR EAST AND SOUTH ASIA. 1980. m. (plus annual cumulation). $225. NewsBank, Inc., 58 Pine St., New Canaan, CT 06840-5426. TEL 203-966-1100. FAX 203-966-6254. Ed. Jean Austin. (also avail. in microfiche; back issues avail.)
●Also available on CD-ROM.
 Former titles: Index: Foreign Broadcast Information Service Daily Reports: Middle East and Africa; Index: Foreign Broadcast Information Service Daily Reports: Middle East and North Africa (ISSN 0736-3427)

327 011 US
INDEX: FOREIGN BROADCAST INFORMATION SERVICE DAILY REPORTS: WESTERN EUROPE. 1978. m. (plus annual cumulation). $225. NewsBank, Inc., 58 Pine St., New Canaan, CT 06840-5426. TEL 203-966-1100. FAX 203-966-6254. Ed. Jean Austin. (also avail. in microfiche; back issues avail.)
●Also available on CD-ROM.

327 011 US
DK1
INDEX: FOREIGN BROADCAST INFORMATION SERVICE REPORTS: CENTRAL EURASIA. 1977. m. (plus annual cumulation). $225. NewsBank, Inc., 58 Pine St., New Canaan, CT 06840-5426. TEL 203-966-1100. FAX 203-966-6254. (back issues avail.)
●Available only on CD-ROM.
 Former titles (until 1993): Index: Foreign Broadcast Information Service Daily Reports: Central Eurasia (ISSN 1062-9939); (until 1992): Index: Foreign Broadcast Information Service Daily Reports: Soviet Union (ISSN 0731-3276)

INDEX OF AFRICAN SOCIAL SCIENCE PERIODICAL ARTICLES. see *SOCIAL SCIENCES: COMPREHENSIVE WORKS — Abstracting, Bibliographies, Statistics*

INDIA AND WORLD AFFAIRS: AN ANNUAL BIBLIOGRAPHY. see *HISTORY — Abstracting, Bibliographies, Statistics*

INDICE ESPANOL DE CIENCIAS SOCIALES. SERIES B: ECONOMICS, SOCIOLOGY AND POLITICAL SCIENCE. see *BUSINESS AND ECONOMICS — Abstracting, Bibliographies, Statistics*

327 016 YU
INSTITUT ZA MEDUNARODNU POLITIKU I PRIVREDU. BILTEN DOKUMENTACIJE. 1972. s-a. Institut za Medjunarodnu Politiku i Privredu - Institute of International Politics and Economics, Makedonska 25, Box 750, Belgrade, Yugoslavia. Ed. Vera Sekulic. bibl.

320 016.32 UK ISSN 0085-2058
Z7163
INTERNATIONAL BIBLIOGRAPHY OF THE SOCIAL SCIENCES. POLITICAL SCIENCE. Title page also reads: International Bibliography of Political Science. (Text in English, French) 1953. a. £125($230) in U.K. & Europe. (British Library of Political and Economic Science) Routledge, 11 New Fetter Ln., London EC4P 4EE, England. TEL 071-583-9855. FAX 071-583-0701. TELEX 263398-ROUT-G. adv. (reprint service avail. from KTO) **Document type:** academic/scholarly publication, abstracting/indexing, bibliography.
 Description: Indexes monographs and the contents of over 2500 journals in the social sciences from a selective bibliography by subject, geographical terms, and author.

320 IE ISSN 0020-8345
JA36
INTERNATIONAL POLITICAL SCIENCE ABSTRACTS/DOCUMENTATION POLITIQUE INTERNATIONALE. (Summaries in English, French) 1951. bi-m. $290. International Political Science Association, c/o University College Dublin, Department of Politics, Belfied, Dublin 4, Ireland. TEL 01-7068182. FAX 01-7061171. E-mail: ipsa@ollamh.ucd.ie. Ed. Serge Hurtig. adv.; index, cum.index. circ. 1,500. (back issues avail.) **Indexed:** E.I. **Document type:** abstracting/indexing.
 —BLDSC (4544.960000).
 Description: Abstracts of political science articles in periodicals and yearbooks worldwide.

320 352 310 US
IOWA OFFICIAL REGISTER. 1892. biennial. free. Secretary of State of Iowa, Statehouse, Des Moines, IA 50319. TEL 515-281-8993. FAX 515-242-6235. (Subscr. to: Secretary of State Office, Statehouse, Des Moines, IA 50319) illus. circ. 13,000. **Document type:** directory, government publication.

JOINT ACQUISITIONS LIST OF AFRICANA. see *ANTHROPOLOGY — Abstracting, Bibliographies, Statistics*

JOURNALS OF DISSENT AND SOCIAL CHANGE; a bibliography of titles in the California State University, Sacramento, library. see *SOCIOLOGY — Abstracting, Bibliographies, Statistics*

327 011 UK ISSN 0950-6128
D410
KEESING'S RECORD OF WORLD EVENTS. 1931. 12/yr. £137 (Europe £141; elsewhere £164). Longman Group UK Ltd., Westgate House, 6th Fl., The High, Harlow, Essex CM20 1YR, England. TEL 0279-442601. FAX 0279-444501. (Dist. in U.S. and Canada by: Keesing's Contemporary Archives, Box 1584, Birmingham, AL 35201) Ed. Roger East. charts; q. index. circ. 5,000. (also avail. in microfiche from RPI) **Indexed:** Refug.Abstr. **Document type:** directory.
●Also available online.
 —BLDSC (5088.350500); SWETS; UMI. **CCC.**
 Formerly: Keesing's Contemporary Archives (ISSN 0022-9679)

KUKHOE HOEUIROK SAEGIN/INDEX TO THE NATIONAL ASSEMBLY DEBATES. see *PUBLIC ADMINISTRATION — Abstracting, Bibliographies, Statistics*

980 US ISSN 0090-9416
F1401
LATIN AMERICAN INDEX. 1972. s-m. $367.20 to academic institutions (Canada and Mexico $377.20; elsewhere $397.20); others $459 (Canada and Mexico $469; elsewhere $499) (effective 1995). Welt Publishing, LLC, 1413 K St., N.W., Ste. 1400, Washington, DC 20005. TEL 202-371-0555; 800-898-INTL. FAX 202-408-9369. Ed. John Justin Ford; Pub. Leo G.B. Welt. bk.rev.; bibl.; charts; stat.; tr.lit. circ. 3,500. (looseleaf format; back issues avail.; reprint service avail. from KTO) **Document type:** abstracting/indexing, newsletter.
 Description: Provides news and analysis on business and economic developments throughout Latin America and the Caribbean.

320 016 US ISSN 0733-2998
Z7164.S67
LEFT INDEX; a quarterly index to periodicals of the left. 1982. q. $30 to individuals; institutions $70. Reference and Research Services, 511 Lincoln St., Santa Cruz, CA 95060. TEL 408-426-4479. Ed. Joan Nordquist. (back issues avail.) **Document type:** abstracting/indexing.
 —BLDSC (5181.307850).
 Description: Provides a subject author index to the contents of periodicals with a leftist perspective.

N T I S TITLE INDEX. (U.S. National Technical Information Service) see *TECHNOLOGY: COMPREHENSIVE WORKS — Abstracting, Bibliographies, Statistics*

920 US ISSN 0737-397X
NAMES IN THE NEWS. 1978. m. (q. and a. cumulations). price varies. NewsBank, Inc., 58 Pine St., New Canaan, CT 06840-5426. TEL 203-966-1100. FAX 203-966-6254. (paper index; articles on microfiche; CD ROM index)

324 NE ISSN 0168-4884
NETHERLANDS. CENTRAAL BUREAU VOOR DE STATISTIEK. STATISTIEK DER VERKIEZINGEN. GEMEENTERADEN/NETHERLANDS. CENTRAL BUREAU OF STATISTICS. ELECTION STATISTICS. MUNICIPAL COUNCILS. (Text in Dutch and English) 1946. irreg. Centraal Bureau voor de Statistiek, Prinses Beatrixlaan 428, Voorburg, Netherlands. (Subscr. to: SDU - Publishers, Christoffel Plantijnstraat 2, Postbus 20014, 2500 EA The Hague, Netherlands) **Document type:** government publication.

324 NE ISSN 0168-5686
NETHERLANDS. CENTRAAL BUREAU VOOR DE STATISTIEK. STATISTIEK DER VERKIEZINGEN. TWEEDE KAMER DER STATEN-GENERAAL/NETHERLANDS. CENTRAL BUREAU OF STATISTICS. ELECTION STATISTICS. SECOND CHAMBER OF THE STATES-GENERAL. (Text in Dutch and English) 1946. irreg. Centraal Bureau voor de Statistiek, Prinses Beatrixlaan 428, Voorburg, Netherlands. (Subscr. to: SDU - Uitgeverij, Christoffel Plantijnstraat 2, Postbus 20014, 2500 EA The Hague, Netherlands) **Document type:** government publication.

THE NEW YORK TIMES INDEX HIGHLIGHTS. see *JOURNALISM — Abstracting, Bibliographies, Statistics*

320 RU
NOVAYA LITERATURA PO SOTSIAL'NYM I GUMANITARNYM NAUKAM. NAUKOVEDENIE; bibliograficheskii ukazatel' 1992. m. $95. Rossiiskaya Akademiya Nauk, Institut Nauchnoi Informatsii po Obshchestvennym Naukam, Ul. Krasikova 28-21, 117418 Moscow V-418, Russia. Ed. N.I. Makeshin. **Document type:** bibliography.
 Formed by the merger of (1947-1992): Novaya Inostrannaya Literatura po Obshchestvennym Naukam. Naukovedenie (ISSN 0134-2800); (1947-1992): Novaya Sovetskaya Literatura po Obshchestvennym Naukam. Naukovedenie (ISSN 0134-2754)

POLITICAL SCIENCE — ABSTRACTING, BIBLIOGRAPHIES, STATISTICS

341.1 016   US   ISSN 0031-3599
JX1901
PEACE RESEARCH ABSTRACTS JOURNAL. 1964. bi-m. $98 to individuals; institutions $350 (effective Sep. 1995). Sage Publications, Inc., 2455 Teller Rd., Thousand Oaks, CA 91320. TEL 805-499-0721. FAX 805-499-0871. E-mail: libraries@sagepub.com. (Overseas subscr. to: Sage Publications Ltd., 6 Bonhill St., London EC2A 4PU, England; Sage Publications India Pvt. Ltd., P.O. Box 4125, New Delhi 110 048, India) Ed. Dr. Hanna Newcombe. abstr.; index. circ. 400. (back issues avail.; reprint service avail.) Indexed: Abstr.Mil.Bibl. **Document type:** abstracting/indexing.
—CCC.
Description: Abstracts papers, articles, and books dealing with questions of war and peace.

320 920   UK
PEOPLE IN POWER. 1987. bi-m. £142($222) Longman Group UK Ltd., Westgate House, The Highl, Harlow, Essex CM20 1YR, England. TEL 0279 442601. Ed. Ian Gorvin. (looseleaf format)

475   US
POLITICAL SCIENCE ABSTRACTS. 1967. a. price varies. I F I - Plenum (Subsidiary of: Plenum Publishing Corp.), 233 Spring St., New York, NY 10013. TEL 212-620-8000. FAX 212-463-0742. TELEX 23-421139. **Document type:** abstracting/indexing.
Formerly: Universal Reference System: Political Science, Government, and Public Policy Series. Annual Supplement.
Description: Covers all aspects of political science and related fields.

907   US   ISSN 0887-171X
POLLING REPORT.* 1985. fortn. (w. in fall of even numbered yrs.). $195 (students & teachers $78). Polling Report, Inc., P.O. Box 42580, Washington, DC 20015-0580. TEL 202-544-5455. FAX 202-544-1695. Ed. Thomas H. Silver. bk.rev. circ. 1,000. **Document type:** newsletter.
Description: Reports results of public opinion surveys on political, public affairs and business issues. Provides analytical articles by pollsters, academics and other opinion experts.

321.07   US
PRACTICAL ANARCHY.* 1991. q. $7. Spunk Press, P.O. Box 721, Madison, WI 53701-0721. TEL 608-251-4307. E-mail: CTMUNSON@MACC.WISC.EDU. Ed. Chuck Munson. adv.; bk.rev.; bibl. circ. 350. (looseleaf format; back issues avail.) **Document type:** newsletter.
●Also available online.
Description: Provides a forum for readers interested in exploring the practical aspects of anarchy. Also covers cooperative housing, communal agriculture, Native American struggles, and women's interests.

320   EI
RECENT PUBLICATIONS ON THE EUROPEAN UNION RECEIVED BY THE LIBRARY/PUBLICACIONES RECIENTES SOBRE LA UNION EUROPEA RECIBIDAS POR LA BIBLIOTECA/NYE PUBLIKATIONER OM DEN EUROPAEISKE UNION MODTAGET AF BIBLIOTEKET/NEUERSCHEINUNGEN UEBER DIE EUROPAEISCHE UNION EINGEGANGEN IN DER BIBLIOTHEK/PUBLICATIONS RECENTES SUR L'UNION EUROPEENNE RECUES PAR LA BIBLIOTHEQUE/PUBBLICAZIONI RECENTI SULL'UNIONE EUROPEA RECEVUTE DALLA BIBLIOTECA. bi-m. 168 ECU. (European Commission) Office for Official Publications of the European Community, 2985 Luxembourg, Luxembourg.
Formerly: Recent Publications on the European Communities Received by the Library (ISSN 0257-1080)

327 016   EI   ISSN 0774-112X
HC241
RECHERCHES UNIVERSITAIRES SUR L'INTEGRATION EUROPEENNE/UNIVERSITY RESEARCH ON EUROPEAN INTEGRATION. (Text in English and French) 1963. irreg. price varies. (European Community Institute for University Studies) Commission of the European Communities, 200, rue de la Loi, B-1049 Brussels, Belgium. Ed. Anne-Marie Nantermoz. adv. contact: Rebecca Zahn. circ. 4,000. **Document type:** abstracting/indexing.
●Also available online.
Former titles (until 1981): Etudes Universitaires sur l'Integration Europeenne (ISSN 0071-2213); (until 1967): Recherches et Etudes Universitaires sur l'Integration Europeenne (ISSN 0776-5568)

320 310   US   ISSN 1074-1658
HA1446
RUSSIA & EURASIA FACTS & FIGURES ANNUAL. 1977. a. $75. Academic International Press, Box 1111, Gulf Breeze, FL 32562-1111. (back issues avail.)
—BLDSC (8052.664200).
Formerly (until 1993): U S S R Facts and Figures Annual (ISSN 0148-7760)

S C A D BULLETIN. (Systeme Communautaire d'Acces a la Documentation) see *LAW — Abstracting, Bibliographies, Statistics*

320 011   UK   ISSN 0307-9201
HT1501
SAGE RACE RELATIONS ABSTRACTS. 1976. q. £50 to individuals; institutions £160 (effective 1996). (Institute of Race Relations) Sage Publications Ltd., 6 Bonhill St., London EC2A 4PU, England. TEL 0171-374-0645. FAX 0171-374-8741. E-mail: market@sageltd.co.uk. Ed. Louis Kushnick. adv.: B&W page £180; trim 170 x 105; adv. contact: Bernie Folan. bibl.; index. (back issues avail.) **Document type:** academic/scholarly publication.
Description: Discusses discrimination, education, employment, health, politics, law and legislation.

327 011   SA
SOUTH AFRICAN INSTITUTE OF INTERNATIONAL AFFAIRS. BIBLIOGRAPHICAL SERIES/SUID-AFRIKAANSE INSTITUUT VAN INTERNASIONALE AANGELEENTHEDE. BIBLIOGRAFIESE REEKS. 1976. a. price varies. South African Institute of International Affairs, P.O. Box 31596, Braamfontein 2017, South Africa. TEL 27-11-339-2021. FAX 27-11-339-2154. TELEX 4-27291 SA. **Document type:** bibliography.

STATISTICAL ABSTRACT OF LATIN AMERICA. see *HISTORY — Abstracting, Bibliographies, Statistics*

STUDIES IN PSEPHOLOGY. see *POPULATION STUDIES — Abstracting, Bibliographies, Statistics*

324.94912   IC   ISSN 1021-5646
SVEITARSTJORNARKOSNINGAR/LOCAL GOVERNMENT ELECTIONS. (Text in Icelandic; table headings in English) 1934. irreg. Hagstofa Islands - Statistics Iceland, Skuggasund 3, IS-150 Reykjavik, Iceland. TEL 354-560-9800. FAX 354-562-8865. E-mail: hagstofa@hag.stjr.is. Dir. Hallgrimur Snorrason. (back issues avail) **Document type:** government publication.

315.61   TU
TURKEY. DEVLET ISTATISTIK ENSTITUSU. MAHALLI IDARELER SECIMI SONUCLARI/TURKEY. STATE INSTITUTE OF STATISTICS. RESULTS OF ELECTIONS OF LOCAL ADMINISTRATIONS. (Text in English, Turkish) 1965. irreg., latest 1989. Devlet Istatistik Enstitusu - State Institute of Statistics, Necatibey Caddesi No. 114, 06100 Ankara, Turkey. TEL 90-312-4185027. FAX 90-312-4170432. (also avail. in diskette format) **Document type:** government publication.

315.61   TU
TURKEY. DEVLET ISTATISTIK ENSTITUSU. MILLETVEKILI GENEL SECIMI SONUCLARI/TURKEY STATE INSTITUTE OF STATISTICS. RESULTS OF GENERAL ELECTION OF REPRESENTATIVES. (Text in English, Turkish) 1962. irreg., latest 1991. $88.05. Devlet Istatistik Enstitusu - State Institute of Statistics, Necatibey Caddesi No. 114, 06100 Ankara, Turkey. TEL 90-312-4185027. FAX 90-312-4170432. (also avail. in diskette format) **Document type:** government publication.

315.61   TU
TURKEY. STATE INSTITUTE OF STATISTICS. RESULTS OF GENERAL ELECTION OF REPRESENTATIVES. B: PROVINCE. (Text in English, Turkish) 1962. irreg., latest 1991. $14.65. Devlet Istatistik Enstitusu - State Institute of Statistics, Necatibey Caddesi No. 114, 06100 Ankara, Turkey. TEL 90-4-4176440. FAX 90-4-4253387. **Document type:** government publication.

327 016   UN   ISSN 0250-5584
Z6481
U N D O C: CURRENT INDEX. (United Nations Documents) (Text in English) 1950. q. (plus annual cummulation on microfiche). $150 for complete series. United Nations Publications, Room DC2-853, New York, NY 10017. TEL 212-963-8302; 800-253-9646. FAX 212-963-3489. (Or: Distribution and Sales Section, Palais des Nations, CH-1211 Geneva 10, Switzerland) (also avail. in microfiche; reprint service avail. from KTO) **Document type:** bibliography, abstracting/indexing.
—BLDSC (9090.038000).
Formerly (until 1979): U N D E X (ISSN 0041-7351)
Description: Gives a comprehensive coverage of UN documentation including full bibliographic description, subject, author, and title indexes, and a check-list of UN documents received at Headquarters.

341.13   UN   ISSN 0082-8084
Z7161
UNITED NATIONS. ECONOMIC AND SOCIAL COUNCIL. INDEX TO PROCEEDINGS. Chinese edition (ISSN 0252-547X) 1946. a. price varies. United Nations Publications, Rm. DC2-853, New York, NY 10017. TEL 212-963-8302; 800-253-9646. FAX 212-963-3489. (Or: Distribution and Sales Section, Palais des Nations, CH-1211 Geneva 10, Switzerland) (also avail. in microfiche; reprint service avail. from KTO) **Document type:** abstracting/indexing.
—BLDSC (1973.980000).

341.13   UN   ISSN 0082-8157
UNITED NATIONS. GENERAL ASSEMBLY. INDEX TO PROCEEDINGS. Arabic edition (ISSN 0251-7655); Chinese edition (ISSN 0251-7647); French edition: Nations Unies. Assemblee Generale. Index des Actes (ISSN 0258-3682) (Issued as subseries of Official Records. Supplements) 1946. a. price varies. United Nations Publications, Rm. DC2-853, New York, NY 10017. TEL 212-963-8302; 800-253-9646. FAX 212-963-3489. (Or: Distribution and Sales Section, Palais des Nations, CH-1211 Geneva 10, Switzerland) (reprint service avail. from KTO) **Document type:** abstracting/indexing.
Formerly: Resolutions of the General Assembly of the United Nations (ISSN 0082-8211)

341.13   UN   ISSN 0082-8408
JX1977
UNITED NATIONS. SECURITY COUNCIL. INDEX TO PROCEEDINGS. Chinese edition (ISSN 0251-3994) 1946. a. price varies. United Nations Publications, Rm. DC2-853, New York, NY 10017. TEL 212-963-8302; 800-253-9646. FAX 212-963-3489. (Or: Distribution and Sales Section, Palais des Nations, CH-1211 Geneva 10, Switzerland) (also avail. in microfiche; reprint service avail. from KTO) **Document type:** abstracting/indexing.

341.13   UN   ISSN 0082-8491
UNITED NATIONS. TRUSTEESHIP COUNCIL. INDEX TO PROCEEDINGS. 1953. a. $4. United Nations Publications, Room DC2-853, New York, NY 10017. TEL 212-963-8302; 800-253-9646. FAX 212-963-3489. (Or: Distribution and Sales Section, Palais des Nations, CH-1211 Geneva 10, Switzerland) (also avail. in microfiche; reprint service avail. from KTO) **Document type:** abstracting/indexing.

POLITICAL SCIENCE — CIVIL RIGHTS

327 016   UN   ISSN 0251-6616
Z949
UNITED NATIONS LIBRARY. MONTHLY BIBLIOGRAPHY. PART 1: BOOKS, OFFICIAL DOCUMENTS, SERIALS.
(Text in English and French) 1971. bi-m. $60. United Nations Publications, Rm. DC2-853, New York, NY 10017. TEL 212-963-8302; 800-253-9646. FAX 212-963-3489. (Or: Distribution and Sales Section, Palais des Nations, CH-1211 Geneva 10, Switzerland) **Indexed:** Popul.Ind. **Document type:** bibliography.
Formerly (until 1977): United Nations Library. Monthly List of Books Catalogued in the Library of the United Nations. (ISSN 0041-7394)
Description: A subject compilation of newly acquired books, official documents and periodicals received in the UN Library in Geneva.

327 016   UN   ISSN 0251-6624
UNITED NATIONS LIBRARY. MONTHLY BIBLIOGRAPHY. PART 2: SELECTED ARTICLES. (Text in English and French) 1971. m. $60. United Nations Publications, Rm. DC2-853, New York, NY 10017. TEL 212-963-8302; 800-253-9646. FAX 212-963-3489. (Or: Distribution and Sales Section, Palais des Nations, CH-1211 Geneva 10, Switzerland) circ. 1,610. **Document type:** abstracting/indexing.
Formerly (until 1977): United Nations Library. Monthly List of Selected Articles (ISSN 0041-7408)
Description: A worldwide list of selected journal articles on political, legal, economic, financial and other topics of current United Nations interest.

U.S. DEPARTMENT OF STATE. LIBRARY. COMMERCIAL LIBRARY PROGRAM. PUBLICATIONS LIST. see *LIBRARY AND INFORMATION SCIENCES — Abstracting, Bibliographies, Statistics*

320   US   ISSN 0148-6063
Z7163
UNITED STATES POLITICAL SCIENCE DOCUMENTS. 1975. a. $407 (foreign $413). University of Pittsburgh, Mid-Atlantic Technology Applications Center (MTAC), 823 William Pitt Union, Pittsburgh, PA 15260. TEL 412-648-7000. FAX 412-648-7003. Ed. Maxine Heller. circ. 300. **Document type:** academic/scholarly publication, abstracting/indexing.
● Also available online. Vendor(s): Knight-Ridder, Inc. (File no.93).
Description: Directed to scholars and educators conducting research in the political, social, and policy sciences. Contains in-depth abstracts of all articles found in approximately 150 major journals published in the U.S. within a given year. Subject areas covered are domestic and foreign policy, international politics, behavioral sciences, public administration, economics and all areas of political science.

WASHINGTON SUMMARY. see *LAW — Abstracting, Bibliographies, Statistics*

ZIONIST LITERATURE. see *PUBLISHING AND BOOK TRADE — Abstracting, Bibliographies, Statistics*

POLITICAL SCIENCE — Civil Rights

323.9   US   ISSN 0896-8217
A A A A NEWS.* q. $15. American Association for Affirmative Action, 8835 Allison Point, Idianapolis, IN 46250. TEL 312-329-2512. FAX 312-329-9131. Ed. Patricia O'Keefe. adv.; bk.rev. circ. 1,500.

323.4   UK
A A M BRIEFINGS SERIES. 1990. irreg. £3. Anti-Apartheid Movement, 13 Mandela St., London NW1 0DW, England. TEL 071-387-7966. FAX 071-388-0173.

323.4   US
A C L U NEWS. 1936. 6/yr. $20 includes membership. American Civil Liberties Union of Northern California, 1663 Mission, San Francisco, CA 94103. TEL 415-621-2488. FAX 415-255-1478. Ed. Elaine Elinson; Pub. Dorothy Ehrlich. bk.rev. circ. 30,000. (tabloid format) **Document type:** newsletter.

323.4   AT   ISSN 1032-2205
A C S J C OCCASIONAL PAPERS. 1988. q. Aus.$4.95. Australian Catholic Social Justice Council, Leo XIII House, 19 Mackenzie St., N. Sydney, N.S.W. 2060, Australia. TEL 61-2-9565811. FAX 61-2-9565782.

325   US   ISSN 0749-2642
A D C TIMES. vol.12, 1991. 10/yr. American-Arab Anti-Discrimination Committee, 4201 Connecticut Ave., N.W., Washington, DC 20008. **Indexed:** Per.Islam. (1991-).

323.4   US   ISSN 1061-5202
DS146.U6
A D L ON THE FRONTLINE. 1943. 7/yr. $12. Anti-Defamation League, 823 United Nations Plaza, New York, NY 10017. TEL 212-490-2525. Ed. Jane R. Ornauer. illus. circ. 110,000. (also avail. in microform from UMI; reprint service avail. from UMI) **Indexed:** HR Rep., Ind.Jew.Per. **Document type:** newsletter.
—UMI.
Formerly (until 1991): A D L Bulletin (ISSN 0001-0936)

323.4   SA
A F R A NEWS. (Text in English) N.S. 1988. bi-m. Association for Rural Advancement, P.O. Box 2517, Pietermaritzburg 3200, South Africa. TEL 0331-57607. FAX 0331-455106. circ. 900. (tabloid format; back issues avail.) **Document type:** newsletter.
Former titles (until no.20, 1993): A F R A Newsletter; (until 1988): A F R A Report.
Description: Aims to publicize rural removals and farm worker conditions, and encourage rural African development in Natal, South Africa.

323.4   SA
A F R A SPECIAL REPORTS. 1980. irreg. Association for Rural Advancement, P.O. Box 2517, Pietermaritzburg 3200, South Africa. TEL 0331-57607. FAX 0331-455106. Ed. Marie Dyer. circ. 1,400. (looseleaf format; back issues avail.)

A U T WOMAN. see *EDUCATION — Higher Education*

ABYA YALA NEWS; linking Indian people of the Americas. see *ETHNIC INTERESTS*

323.4   US
ACCESS REPORTS - FREEDOM OF INFORMATION. 1975. bi-w. $325. Access Reports, Inc., 1624 Dogwood Lane, Lynchburg, VA 24503. TEL 804-384-5334. FAX 804-384-8272. Ed. Harry A. Hammitt. abstr.; charts; stat.; q. index. (looseleaf format; back issues avail.) **Document type:** newsletter.
● Also available online. Vendor(s): NewsNet (GT10).
Formerly: Access Reports (ISSN 0364-7625)

323.4 327   PL   ISSN 0524-4544
ACTA UNIVERSITATIS WRATISLAVIENSIS. PRAWO. (Text in Polish; summaries in English, French, German) 1956. irreg. price varies. (Uniwersytet Wroclawski) Wydawnictwo Uniwersytetu Wroclawskiego, Pl. Uniwersytecki 9-13, 50-137 Wroclaw, Poland. TEL 44-10-06. (Dist. by: Ksiegarnia Uniwersytetu Wroclawskiego, Pl. Uniwersytecki 9-13, 50-137 Wroclaw, Poland) Ed. Stanislaw Kazmierczyk. circ. 300. **Document type:** academic/scholarly publication.

ACTA UNIVERSITATIS WRATISLAVIENSIS. PRZEGLAD PRAWA I ADMINISTRACJI. see *PUBLIC ADMINISTRATION*

ACTING OUT. see *SOCIAL SERVICES AND WELFARE*

323.4 340   US
THE ADVOCATE (INDIANAPOLIS).* 1983. q. $10. Indiana Civil Liberties Union, 1031 E. Washington St., Indianapolis, IN 46202-3952. TEL 317-635-4059. FAX 317-635-4105. Ed. Susan Miller. bk.rev.; illus. circ. 7,000. **Indexed:** C.L.I.

AFFIRMATIVE ACTION REGISTER; the E E O recruitment publication. see *OCCUPATIONS AND CAREERS*

AFRICAN-AMERICAN GRADUATES OF KENTUCKY DIRECTORY. see *EDUCATION — Higher Education*

AFRICAN COMMUNIST. see *POLITICAL SCIENCE*

323.4 301.45   US
AGE DISCRIMINATION. (2nd edition, 1986; subseries of: Individual Rights Series) 1981. 3 base vols. (plus a. supplement). $300. Shepard's - McGraw-Hill, Inc., Box 35300, Colorado Springs, CO 80935-3530. TEL 800-525-2474. Ed. Howard Eglit. (looseleaf format) **Document type:** trade publication.
Description: Annotates more than 3,200 cases and hundreds of statutory and regulatory provisions.

AIM MAGAZINE (CHICAGO). see *ETHNIC INTERESTS*

323.4   CN   ISSN 1188-875X
JC599.L3
ALERTA. 1977. 6/yr. Can.$20 to individuals; institutions Can.$35. Inter-Church Committee on Human Rights in Latin America, 129 St. Clair Ave. W., Toronto, ON M4V 1N5, Canada. TEL 416-921-0801. FAX 416-921-3843. E-mail: ICCHRLA@web.apc.org. Ed. Kathy Price. circ. 1,200. **Document type:** newsletter.
Formerly: Inter-Church Committee on Human Rights in Latin America. Newsletter (ISSN 0226-661X)
Description: Issues and information regarding human rights in Latin America.

323.4   GW
ALL-EUROPEAN HUMAN RIGHTS YEARBOOK. 1991. a. N.P. Engel Verlag, Gutenbergstr. 29, 77694 Kehl, Germany. TEL 07851-2463. FAX 07851-4234. (US subscr. to: N.P. Engel, 3608 S. 12th St., Arlington, VA 22204. TEL 703-920-3126. FAX 703-920-3127) **Document type:** bulletin.

301.4   US
AMERICAN FEMINIST. 1973. q. $35. Feminists for Life of America, Inc., 733 15th St. NE, Ste. 1100, Washington, DC 20005. TEL 202-737-3352. FAX 202-737-0414. Ed. Frederica Mathewes-Green. adv.; bk.rev. circ. 6,000. **Document type:** newsletter, bulletin.
Formerly (until 1994): Sisterlife Journal.
Description: Devoted to the philosophy of "pro-life feminism", which holds that abortion is detrimental to women and undermines the moral foundation of feminism. Reports current legislative issues.

AMERICANS WITH DISABILITIES ACT TECHNICAL ASSISTANCE MANUAL: TITLE I. see *SOCIAL SERVICES AND WELFARE*

AMERICANS WITH DISABILITIES ACT TECHNICAL ASSISTANCE MANUAL: TITLE II. see *SOCIAL SERVICES AND WELFARE*

AMERICANS WITH DISABILITIES ACT TECHNICAL ASSISTANCE MANUAL: TITLE III. see *SOCIAL SERVICES AND WELFARE*

355.224   US   ISSN 0003-1933
AMNESTY ACTION. 1967. bi-m. $25 includes membership to individuals; students and senior citizens $15. Amnesty International U S A, 322 Eighth Ave., New York, NY 10001. TEL 212-807-8400. Ed. Ron LaJoie. bk.rev.; illus. circ. 300,000. **Indexed:** Alt.Press Ind., HR Rep.

323.4   CN   ISSN 0831-9227
AMNESTY INTERNATIONAL. CANADIAN SECTION (ENGLISH SPEAKING). BULLETIN. 1974. 6/yr. Can.$15 to individuals; institutions Can.$25. Amnesty International, Canadian Section (English Speaking), 214 Montreal Rd., Ste. 401, Vanier, ON K1L 1A4, Canada. TEL 613-744-7667. FAX 613-746-2411. Ed. Patricia Acheson. bk.rev.; tr.lit. circ. 10,000. (back issues avail.) **Document type:** newsletter.
Description: News, feature and action-oriented material setting out Amnesty International's concerns regarding human rights violations around the world.

370 323.4   AT   ISSN 0256-0771
AMNESTY INTERNATIONAL AUSTRALIAN NEWSLETTER. 1983. m. Aus.$40. Amnesty International Australia, Private Bag 23, Broadway, N.S.W. 2007, Australia. FAX 211-3608. TELEX AA123206. Ed. June McGowan. bk.rev. circ. 14,000. **Document type:** newsletter.

355.224   UK   ISSN 0308-6887
AMNESTY INTERNATIONAL NEWSLETTER. (Editions in Arabic, English, French and Spanish) 1963. m. £7($12) for Newsletter; with Amnesty International Report £22($41). Amnesty International, 1 Easton St., London WC1X 8DJ, England. TEL 44-71-413-5500. FAX 44-71-956-1157. TELEX 28502. bk.rev. circ. 35,000. (also avail. in microfiche from IDC) **Indexed:** HR Rep. (1968-1990). **Document type:** newsletter.
Former titles: Amnesty International Monthly (ISSN 0003-1941); Amnesty International Review.

AMNESTY INTERNATIONAL REPORT. see *POLITICAL SCIENCE — International Relations*

POLITICAL SCIENCE — CIVIL RIGHTS

ANGLES; the magazine of Vancouver's lesbian, gay and bisexual communities. see *HOMOSEXUALITY*

323.4 UK ISSN 0003-5580
DT763
ANTI-APARTHEID NEWS. 1965. 6/yr. £10($30) (foreign £15) to individuals; institutions £13.50 (foreign £17). Anti-Apartheid Movement, 13 Mandela St., London NW1 0DW, England. TEL 071-387-7966. FAX 071-388-0173. Ed.Bd. adv.; bk.rev.; charts; illus. circ. 20,000. **Document type:** newspaper.
 Description: News and analysis on events in South Africa and campaigning information on the Anti-apartheid struggle.

ANTI-CENSORSHIP NEWSLETTER. see *SOCIOLOGY*

323.4 UK
ANTI-SLAVERY REPORTER. 1840. q. £15 membership. Anti-Slavery International, The Stableyard, Broomgrove Rd., London SW9 9TL, England. TEL 0171-984-9555. FAX 0171-783-4110. Ed. Mark Robertson. adv. contact: Adam Robertson. bk.rev. circ. 2,500. **Document type:** newsletter.

323.4 296.7 UK ISSN 1350-0996
DS145
ANTISEMITISM WORLD REPORT (YEAR). 1992. a. £11.50($23) throughout Europe; elsewhere £13.50. Institute of Jewish Affairs, 79 Wimpole St., London W1M 7DD, England. FAX 0171-935-3252. E-mail: ija@ort.org. **Document type:** academic/scholarly publication.
 Description: Monitors anti-Semitism throughout the world and identifies trouble spots. Assesses each country's history of anti-Semitism; anti-Semitic parties and organizations; anti-Semitism in mainstream political, cultural, and religious life; denial of the Holocaust; opinion polls; anti-Semitism in the media; legal matters; and efforts to combat anti-Semitism.

323.4 SP ISSN 0210-301X
ANUARIO DE DERECHO CIVIL. a. (plus q. updates). 6400 ptas. (foreign 7300 ptas.). Ministerio de Justicia, Centro de Publicaciones, Secretaria General Tecnica, Gran Via, 76-8, 28013 Madrid, Spain. TEL 547-54-22. FAX 559-29-48. **Document type:** government publication.

323.4 US ISSN 0044-8931
ARMED CITIZEN NEWS. no.52, 1975. bi-m. $10. National Association to Keep and Bear Arms, Box 78336, Seattle, WA 98178. TEL 206-226-0467. Ed. Bill Pike. adv.; bk.rev.; illus. circ. 20,000.

323.4 UK ISSN 1011-3983
THE ARTICLE 19 BULLETIN. Variant title: Article XIX: The Article 19 Newsletter. 1987. 3/yr. £15($30) membership. International Centre Against Censorship, Lancaster House, 33 Islington High St., London N1 9LH, England. TEL 0171-278-9292. FAX 0171-713-1356. E-mail: article19@gn.apc.org. (Dist. by: Central Books, 99 Wallis Rd., London E9 5LN, England. TEL 0181-986-4854. FAX 0181-533-5821) Ed. Malcolm Smart; Pub. Frances D'Souza. circ. 11,000. (back issues avail.) **Document type:** bulletin, newsletter.
 Description: Examines the fundamental right to freedom of expression issues related to Article 19 of the Universal Declaration of Human Rights.

ASIAN AMERICAN POLICY REVIEW. see *ETHNIC INTERESTS*

ASYNJUR. see *PHILOSOPHY*

323.4 AT ISSN 1035-0519
AUSTCARE NEWS. 1976. 3/yr. Aus.$5. Australians Care for Refugees, 69-71 Parramatta Rd., Camperdown, Sydney, N.S.W. 2050, Australia. TEL 02-565-9111. Ed. John Sawkins. bk.rev. circ. 11,000.
 Description: Covers refugee issues and policy.

323.4 US ISSN 1043-6898
JK2446
BALLOT ACCESS NEWS. 1985. 13/yr. $7. Coalition for Free and Open Elections, Box 470296, San Francisco, CA 94147. TEL 415-922-9779. Ed. Richard Winger. bk.rev. circ. 980. **Document type:** newsletter.
 Description: Focuses on the rights of voters to support minor political parties and describes the progress being made against restrictive ballot access laws. Covers First Amendment rights of all parties (major and minor).

BATTERED WOMEN'S DIRECTORY. see *WOMEN'S INTERESTS*

323.4 US ISSN 0006-2499
K2
BILL OF RIGHTS JOURNAL. 1952. a. $15. National Emergency Civil Liberties Committee, 175 Fifth Ave., Rm. 814, New York, NY 10010. TEL 212-673-2040. FAX 212-460-8359. Ed. Jeff Kisseloff. (also avail. in microform from UMI; reprint service avail. from UMI,WSH) **Indexed:** Alt.Press Ind., C.L.I., L.R.I., Leg.Per.
—UMI.

323.4 300 US ISSN 0895-5786
BLUEPRINT FOR SOCIAL JUSTICE. 1948. 10/yr. $10. Twomey Center for Peace through Justice, Loyola University, Box 12, New Orleans, LA 70118. TEL 504-861-5830. FAX 504-861-5833. Ed. Richard McCarthy; Pub. Ted Quant. circ. 3,500. (back issues avail.) **Document type:** academic/scholarly publication.

THE BODY POLITIC; monthly pro-choice news report. see *BIRTH CONTROL*

BORDER LINES. see *POLITICAL SCIENCE — International Relations*

323.4 IE
BOTTOM DOG. 1976. m. £2($5) 109 O'Malley Park, Limerick, Ireland. Ed. Joe Harrington. bk.rev.; film rev. circ. 1,000. (back issues avail.)

BRAILLE MONITOR (INKPRINT EDITION). see *HANDICAPPED — Visually Impaired*

323.4 CN ISSN 0830-0437
KEB458.A72
BRITISH COLUMBIA. COUNCIL OF HUMAN RIGHTS. ANNUAL REPORT. a. free. B.C. Council of Human Rights, Parliament Bldgs., Victoria, BC V8V 1X4, Canada. TEL 604-387-3710. FAX 604-387-3643. **Document type:** government publication.

054.1 FR ISSN 0007-2672
BRULOT. 1936. m. 30 F. (foreign 35 F.). Gustave Arthur Dassonville, Ed. & Pub., 30b rue Moliere, 93170 Bagnolet, France. bk.rev.; abstr.; bibl. circ. 3,500.

BUERGERRECHTE & POLIZEI. see *CRIMINOLOGY AND LAW ENFORCEMENT*

323.4 CN ISSN 0847-9798
BULLETIN AGIR. 1979. q. Can.$30. Amnistie Internationale, Section Canadienne Francophone, 6250 bd. Monk, Montreal, PQ H4E 3H7, Canada. TEL 514-766-9766. FAX 514-766-2088. Ed. Michel Frenette; Pub. Michel Frenette. circ. 35,000. **Document type:** bulletin.
 Description: Updates the human rights situation around the world and highlights the activities of the branch.

C A A NEWSLETTER (SAN FRANCISCO). (Chinese for Affirmative Action) see *ETHNIC INTERESTS*

C A A T NEWSLETTER. (Campaign Against Arms Trade) see *POLITICAL SCIENCE*

C A B NEWS. (National Association of Citizens Advice Bureaux) see *LAW*

C C C O ACTION ALERT. (Central Committee for Conscientious Objectors) see *MILITARY*

355.224 US ISSN 0008-5952
UB342.U5
C C C O NEWS NOTES;* covering war, peace and conscience. 1949. 4/yr. $6 to libraries; free to others. Central Committee for Conscientious Objectors, 1515 Cherry St., Philadelphia, PA 19102-1403. TEL 215-545-4626. Ed. Robert A. Seeley. adv.; bk.rev.; bibl. circ. 40,000. (tabloid format; also avail. in microform from UMI; reprint service avail. from UMI) **Indexed:** Alt.Press Ind. **Document type:** newsletter.
—UMI.
 Description: News items on contemporary issues pertaining to peace activism and conscientious objection.

323.4 AT
C C H R NEWSLETTER. 1972. irreg., latest Nov. 1985. Aus.$12($15) Citizens Committee on Human Rights, 24 Waymouth St., Adelaide, S.A. 5000, Australia. Ed. Colin Harris. circ. 350. (back issues avail.)

323.4 362.4 US
C D R REPORTS. 1983. m. $10. Council for Disability Rights, 176 W. Adams St., Chicago, IL 60603. TEL 312-444-9484. FAX 312-444-1977. Ed. Josephine E. Holzer. circ. 3,500. (also avail. in magnetic tape; large print edition in 14 pt.) **Document type:** newsletter.

323 CL ISSN 0717-1773
C H I P NEWS. (Text in English) 1990. d. $120 to individuals; institutions $360. Chile Information Project, P.O. Box 53331, Santiago, Chile. TEL 56-2-7775376. FAX 56-2-735-2267. E-mail: anderson@chip.mic.cl. Ed. Maxine Lowy; Pub. Steve Anderson. **Document type:** newsletter.
 Description: Summarizes Chilean news, with special emphasis on trade, environment and mining issues.

C L G R O NEWSLETTER. (Coalition for Lesbian and Gay Rights in Ontario) see *HOMOSEXUALITY*

323.4 910.03 US ISSN 0300-743X
E185.5
C O R E MAGAZINE. vol.3, 1973. q. $10. (Congress of Racial Equality) C O R E Publications, 30 Cooper Sq., No. 9, New York, NY 10003-7151. TEL 212-598-4000. FAX 212-982-0184. Ed. George Holmes. adv. contact: Kwazi Akyeampong. bk.rev.; film rev.; charts; illus. circ. 50,000.

CAHIERS DE FEMINISME. see *WOMEN'S STUDIES*

CAHIERS DE L'AVENIR DE LA BRETAGNE. see *HISTORY*

CAMPUS WATCH. see *EDUCATION — Higher Education*

CANADA. INFORMATION COMMISSIONER. ANNUAL REPORT. see *LAW — International Law*

CAPITAL PUNISHMENT (YEAR). see *CRIMINOLOGY AND LAW ENFORCEMENT*

CAREERS GUIDE FOR SCHOOLS. see *OCCUPATIONS AND CAREERS*

CATACOMBES; messager supraconfessionel de l'Eglise du silence. see *RELIGIONS AND THEOLOGY*

323.4 309 CN ISSN 0824-2062
CATALYST (TORONTO). 1978. 10/yr. Can.$15 to non-members. Citizens for Public Justice, 229 College St., Ste. 311, Toronto, ON M5T 1R4, Canada. TEL 416-979-2443. Ed. Andrew Brouwer. adv.; bk.rev.; illus. circ. 4,000. **Indexed:** Lang.& Lang.Behav.Abstr., Telegen.
 Former titles: Committee for Justice and Liberty. Newsletter (ISSN 0705-2103); C J L Foundation. Newsletter.
 Description: Provides a catalyst for Christian political action and reviews CPJ activities.

CATHOLIC NEAR EAST MAGAZINE. see *RELIGIONS AND THEOLOGY — Roman Catholic*

CENSORSHIP NEWS. see *JOURNALISM*

CENSORSHIP NEWS. see *JOURNALISM*

POLITICAL SCIENCE — CIVIL RIGHTS

323.4 US ISSN 1068-4166
JC599.C6
CHINA RIGHTS FORUM; the journal of human rights in China. (Text in English, Chinese) 1990. q. $25 to individuals (foreign $30); institutions $30 (foreign $35). Human Rights in China, 485 Fifth Ave., 3rd Fl., New York, NY 10017. TEL 212-661-2909. FAX 212-972-0905. Ed. Sophia Woodman. bk.rev. circ. 3,500. (back issues avail.) **Indexed:** HR Rep. (1992-). **Document type:** newsletter.
—UnCover.
Formerly: Human Rights Tribune (ISSN 1057-0748)
Description: Includes news, opinions, theoretical discussions, reports and interviews with dissidents.

327 US ISSN 0735-8237
DS779.20
CHINA SPRING. Key Title: Zhongguo zhi Chun. (Text in Chinese) 1982. m. $28 to individuals; institutions $60. China Spring Research Inc., 74-14 Woodside Ave., Elmhurst, NY 11373. TEL 718-429-6777. FAX 718-476-1602. (Subscr. to: Box 701400, Trainsmeadow Sta., Flushing, NY 11370-9998) adv.; bk.rev. circ. 6,000. (back issues avail.)
Description: Covers human rights, economics, and the politics of China.

CHRISTIANS IN CRISIS. see *RELIGIONS AND THEOLOGY*

323.4 US ISSN 0009-790X
JC599.U5
CIVIL LIBERTIES (NEW YORK). 1931. irreg. $20 membership. American Civil Liberties Union, 132 W. 43rd St., New York, NY 10036. TEL 212-944-9800. FAX 212-869-9065. Ed. Jean Carey Bond. bk.rev.; illus. circ. 275,000. **Indexed:** Alt.Press Ind., HR Rep. **Document type:** newsletter.

CIVIL LIBERTIES ALERT. see *MEETINGS AND CONGRESSES*

323.4 US
CIVIL LIBERTIES OF WASHINGTON. 1969. irreg. (5-6/yr.) $25. American Civil Liberties Union of Washington, 705 Second Ave., Ste. 300, Seattle, WA 98104. TEL 206-624-8124. Ed. Doug Honig. adv.; bk.rev.; illus. circ. 9,500. (tabloid format) **Document type:** newsletter.
Formerly: Civil Liberties (Seattle) (ISSN 0045-7051)
Description: Reports the activities and concerns of ACLU of Washington.

CIVIL LIBERTIES REPORTER. see *LAW — Civil Law*

320 AT
CIVIL LIBERTY. 1968. q. Aus.$25. New South Wales Council for Civil Liberties, P.O. Box 201, Glebe, N.S.W. 2037, Australia. TEL 02-660-7582. FAX 02-566-4162. Ed. Ken Buckley. adv.; bk.rev.; illus. circ. 1,000. **Document type:** newsletter.

323.4 UK
JC571
CIVIL LIBERTY AGENDA. 1976. q. £7 (foreign £8.50). National Council for Civil Liberties, 21 Tabard St., London SE1 4LA, England. TEL 0171-403-3888. FAX 0171-407-5354. E-mail: liberty@gn.apc.org. Ed. Kate Wilkinson. adv.; bk.rev. circ. 8,000. **Indexed:** HR Rep. (1991-). **Document type:** newsletter.
Former titles (until 1991): Civil Liberty (ISSN 0267-5153); (until 1985): Rights (ISSN 0308-8227)
Description: Examines human rights and rights abuses in the U.K.

CIVIL RIGHTS AND CIVIL LIBERTIES LITIGATION: A LAW OF SECTION 1983. see *LAW — Civil Law*

CIVIL RIGHTS MONITOR. see *LAW — Civil Law*

323.4 SA ISSN 0045-706X
CIVIL RIGHTS NEWSLETTER. 1954. irreg. R.15($30) Civil Rights League, P.O. Box 394, Claremont 7735, South Africa. Ed.Bd. adv.; bk.rev. circ. 500. **Document type:** newsletter.

COALITION FOR PRISONERS' RIGHTS NEWSLETTER. see *CRIMINOLOGY AND LAW ENFORCEMENT*

323.4 PY
COMITE DE IGLESIAS PARA AYUDAS DE EMERGENCIA. CUADERNOS. 1987. irreg. no.11, 1991. Comite de Iglesias para Ayudas de Emergencia, Gral Diaz 429, Asuncion, Paraguay.

323.4 PY
COMITE DE IGLESIAS PARA AYUDAS DE EMERGENCIA. ESTUDIOS. irreg., no.17, 1990. Comite de Iglesias para Ayudas de Emergencia, Gral Diaz 429, Asuncion, Paraguay.

323.4 PY
COMITE DE IGLESIAS PARA AYUDAS DE EMERGENCIA. NOTAS TRIMESTRALES. no.20, 1991. q. 40000 g. to individuals (America $25; Europe $30); institutions 50000 g. (America $30; Europe $35). Comite de Iglesias para Ayudas de Emergencia, Gral Diaz 429, Asuncion, Paraguay. TEL 595-21-445161. **Indexed:** HR Rep. (1989-).

323.4 054.1 FR
COMITE SOLIDARITE PHILIPPINES. BULLETIN. q. Comite Solidarite Philippines, 68 rue de Babylone, 75007 Paris, France.

323.4 US
COMMUNICATOR (DES MOINES). 1975. s-a. Iowa Civil Rights Commission, 211 E. Maple St., 2nd Fl., Des Moines, IA 50309-1858. TEL 515-281-4121. FAX 515-242-5840. Ed. Carol Anne Leach. illus. circ. 2,000. **Document type:** newsletter.
Formerly (until 1980): Challenger.
Description: News of agency's work, civil rights events in Iowa, and articles on civil rights issues.

323.4 333.7 CN ISSN 0823-8669
CONSCIENCE CANADA NEWSLETTER. 1979. 4/yr. Can.$15. Conscience Canada Inc., Box 8601, Vic. Cent. PO, Victoria, BC V8W 3S2, Canada. TEL 604-384-5532. FAX 604-383-9155. Ed. Jane-Orion Smith. bk.rev.; illus. circ. 2,500. (back issues avail.) **Document type:** newsletter.
Description: Supports the exercise of freedom of conscience and religion, especially the direction of taxes to peace instead of the military, and educating the public on this right.

261 SZ ISSN 0259-0360
CONSCIENCE ET LIBERTE. English edition: Conscience and Liberty. German edition: Gewissen und Freiheit. 1948; N.S. 1971. 2/yr. 30 SFr. International Association for the Defense of Religious Liberty - Association Internationale pour la Defense de la Liberte Religieuse, Schosshaldenstr. 17, CH-3006 Bern, Switzerland. TEL 031-446262. FAX 031-446266. Ed. Gianfranco Rossi. bk.rev.; bibl. circ. 10,750. **Indexed:** CERDIC. **Document type:** bulletin.

323.4 US ISSN 0742-7115
K3
CONSTITUTIONAL COMMENTARY. 1984. 3/yr. $18. (University of Minnesota, Law School) Constitutional Commentary Inc., 229 19th Ave. S., Minneapolis, MN 55455. TEL 612-625-4819. FAX 612-625-2011. Eds. Daniel Farber. adv.; bk.rev. circ. 600. (also avail. in microfiche from WSH; back issues avail.; reprint service avail. from WSH) **Indexed:** Abstr.Bk.Rev.Curr.Leg.Per., C.L.I., Leg.Per. **Document type:** academic/scholarly publication.
●Also available online. Vendor(s): West Services, Inc.
—Faxon; UnCover.
Description: Topical, inter-disciplinary journal on constitutional law.

341.48 EI
COUNCIL OF EUROPE. STANDING COMMITTEE ON THE EUROPEAN CONVENTION ON ESTABLISHMENT (INDIVIDUALS). PERIODICAL REPORT. 1971. irreg. Council of Europe, Publishing and Documentation Service, 67075 Strasbourg Cedex, France. (Dist. in U.S. by: Manhattan Publishing Co., One Croton Point Ave., Box 650, Croton-on-Hudson, NY 10520)

323.4 US ISSN 0010-9991
COUNCILOR.* 1959. s-m. $8. Councilor of LA, Inc., c/o June A. Touchstone, 7616 England Dr., Plano, TX 75025-3115. Ed. Ned Touchstone. adv.; bk.rev.; illus. circ. 21,850. (tabloid format)

323.4 US ISSN 1042-3060
JC599.S58
THE CRIMEAN REVIEW; voice of the Crimean Tatar human rights movement. 1986. 2/yr. Crimean Foundation, Box 307, Essex St. Sta., Boston, MA 02112. **Indexed:** Per.Islam. (1991-).
Description: Covers human rights issues pertaining to the Crimean Tatars, including the history of mass deportations, and current struggles.

THE CRISIS (BALTIMORE); a record of the darker races. see *ETHNIC INTERESTS*

323.4 US ISSN 1045-4098
JC599.C85
CUBA: POLITICAL EXECUTIONS AND HUMAN RIGHTS. a. Cuban Committee for Human Rights, Box 1260, Hoya Sta., Washington, DC 20054.

323.4 US
CUBA SURVEY. 10/yr. $150. Cuban American National Foundation, 1000 Thomas Jefferson St., N.W., Ste. 505, Washington, DC 20007. TEL 202-265-2822.

323.4 US
CUBAN AMERICAN NATIONAL FOUNDATION. PUBLICATION. irreg. no.28, 1988. Cuban American National Foundation, 1000 Thomas Jefferson St., N.W., Ste. 505, Washington, DC 20007. TEL 202-265-2822. **Document type:** academic/scholarly publication, monographic series.

DEATH ROW U.S.A. REPORTER. see *CRIMINOLOGY AND LAW ENFORCEMENT*

DENDRON NEWS. see *MEDICAL SCIENCES — Psychiatry And Neurology*

323.4 SP ISSN 1133-3812
DERECHOS HUMANOS. q. 1500 ptas.($30) (foreign 3000 ptas.). Asociacion Pro-Derechos Humanos de Espana, Jose Ortega y Gasset 77, 2o, 28006 Madrid, Spain. TEL 91-402-23-12. FAX 91-402-84-99. Dir. Jose Antonio Perez. circ. 5,000. **Indexed:** HR Rep. (1986-).
Description: Centers on the defense of human rights and freedoms worldwide.

323.4 CR
DESAPARECIDOS EN CENTROAMERICA. a. Asociacion Centroamericana de Familiares de Detenidos - Desaparecidos, Apdo. Postal 8188, 1000 San Jose, Costa Rica. TEL 506-337850. FAX 506-552160.

323.4 US
DIRECTORY OF PERSECUTED SCIENTISTS, ENGINEERS AND HEALTH PROFESSIONALS. irreg. $15 per no. American Association for the Advancement of Science, Science and Human Rights Program, 1333 H St., N.W., Washington, DC 20005. TEL 202-326-6790. **Document type:** directory.

DISABILITY RAG & RESOURCE. see *HANDICAPPED*

DOCUMENTACO E DIREITO COMPARADO. see *POLITICAL SCIENCE*

DOOR OF HOPE INTERNATIONAL. see *RELIGIONS AND THEOLOGY — Protestant*

DREAD TIMES; news for the Nazarite. see *RELIGIONS AND THEOLOGY*

DULWICH CENTRE NEWSLETTER. see *PSYCHOLOGY*

323.4 US
DYKES, DISABILITY & STUFF. q. $20 to individuals; institutions $50. Box 8773, Madison, WI 53714. adv.: page $200; trim 8 1/2 x 11. (also avail. in audio cassette; Braille)
Description: Discusses racism, especially in the disability civil rights movement and in the lesbian community.

DZIENNIK POLSKI I DZIENNIK ZOLNIERZA/POLISH DAILY AND THE SOLDIERS DAILY. see *ETHNIC INTERESTS*

323.4 296.7 UK ISSN 1350-1674
DS135.R92
EAST EUROPEAN JEWISH AFFAIRS; a journal on Jewish problems in Eastern Europe. 1971. s-a. £35($60) Institute of Jewish Affairs, 79 Wimpole St., London W1M 7DD, England. TEL 0171-935-8266. FAX 0171-935-3252. E-mail: ija@ort.org. (Co-sponsor: American Jewish Committee) Ed. H. Spier. adv.; bk.rev.; bibl.; index. circ. 1,500. (also avail. in microform from UMI; reprint service avail. from UMI) **Indexed:** Amer.Hist.& Life, Hist.Abstr., HR Rep. (1985-), Ind.Jew.Per., Mid.East: Abstr.& Ind. **Document type:** academic/scholarly publication.
—BLDSC (3646.306000); SWETS; UMI; UnCover.
Formerly (until 1991): Soviet Jewish Affairs (ISSN 0038-545X)
Description: Publishes studies relevant to the understanding of the position and prospects of Jews in former Communist-governed countries.

POLITICAL SCIENCE — CIVIL RIGHTS

323.4   FR   ISSN 0012-9224
ECHO DE LA LIBERTE DE L'OUEST; organe mensuel independant de Defense des Libertes Scolaires et Familiales. no.212, 1969. m. 35 F. Defense des Libertes Scolaires et Familiales, 10 rue Jules-Dauban, Angers, France. Ed. J. Bouyer. bk.rev.

331   US
EMPLOYMENT IN THE MAINSTREAM. 1975. bi-m. $25. Mainstream, Inc., 3 Bethesda Metro Center, Ste. 830, Bethesda, MD 20814. TEL 301-654-2400. FAX 301-654-2403. Ed. Fritz Rumpel. bk.rev. circ. 1,300. (magnetic tape; back issues avail.) **Document type:** newsletter.
    Formerly (until 1995): In the Mainstream (ISSN 0888-9724)
    Description: Reports on the practical and legal issues of bringing persons with disabilities into the workplace.

EQUAL OPPORTUNITIES INTERNATIONAL. see *WOMEN'S STUDIES*

EQUAL RIGHTS. see *WOMEN'S INTERESTS*

EQUALITY N O W!. (National Organization for Women) see *WOMEN'S INTERESTS*

EQUALITY NEWS. see *ETHNIC INTERESTS*

ETHIOPIAN JEWRY REPORT. see *RELIGIONS AND THEOLOGY — Judaic*

ETHNIES; droits de l'homme et peuples autochtones. see *ETHNIC INTERESTS*

323.4   EI   ISSN 0379-8461
EUROPEAN COMMISSION OF HUMAN RIGHTS. DECISIONS AND REPORTS. (Text in English, French) 1975. q. $12. Council of Europe, Publishing and Documentation Service, 67075 Strasbourg Cedex, France. (Dist. in U.S. by: Manhattan Publishing Co., One Croton Point Ave., Box 650, Croton, NY 10520)

323.4   NE   ISSN 0071-2701
EUROPEAN CONVENTION ON HUMAN RIGHTS. YEARBOOK. (Not issued in 1964) 1959. a., vol.33, 1994 (for year 1990). price varies. (Council of Europe, EI) Martinus Nijhoff Publishers, Human Rights and International Law (Subsidiary of: Kluwer Academic Publishers Group), Postbus 163, 3300 AD Dordrecht, Netherlands. TEL 31-78-334911. FAX 31-78-334254. TELEX 29245 KAPG NL. (Dist. by: Kluwer Academic Publishers Group, P.O. Box 322, 3300 AH Dordrecht, Netherlands. TEL 31-78-524400. FAX 31-78-524474; N. America dist. addr.: Box 358, Accord Sta., Hingham, MA 02018-0358. TEL 617-871-6600. FAX 617-871-6528) **Indexed:** Int.Polit.Sci.Abstr., Refug.Abstr. **Document type:** monographic series.
    Refereed Serial

323.4   GW   ISSN 0073-3903
EUROPEAN COURT OF HUMAN RIGHTS. PUBLICATIONS. SERIES A: JUDGMENTS AND DECISIONS/COUR EUROPEENNE DES DROITS DE L'HOMME. PUBLICATIONS. SERIE A: ARRETS ET DECISIONS. (Text in English and French) 1961. irreg., vol.292, 1995. Carl Heymanns Verlag KG, Luxemburgerstr. 449, 50939 Cologne, Germany. TEL 0221-94373-0. FAX 0221-94373901. **Document type:** monographic series.

323   GW   ISSN 0073-3911
EUROPEAN COURT OF HUMAN RIGHTS. PUBLICATIONS. SERIES B: PLEADINGS, ORAL ARGUMENTS AND DOCUMENTS/COUR EUROPEENNE DES DROITS DE L'HOMME. PUBLICATIONS. SERIE B: MEMOIRES, PLAIDOIRIES ET DOCUMENTS. (Text in English and French) 1961. irreg., vol.100, 1994. price varies. Carl Heymanns Verlag KG, Luxemburgerstr. 449, 50939 Cologne, Germany. TEL 0221-94373-0. FAX 0221-94373901. **Document type:** monographic series.

323.4 340   SW   ISSN 0281-5206
EUROPEAN HUMAN RIGHTS. (Text in Arabic, Danish, English, French, German, Japanese, Norwegian, Polish, Russian, Swedish and Spanish; summaries in English) 1983. irreg. voluntary donations. European Human Rights, Marknadsvaegen 289, S-183 34 Taby, Sweden. TEL 47-08-768-13-98210. Ed. Ditlieb Felderer. bk.rev. circ. 360,000. (back issues avail.) **Document type:** bulletin.

EUROPEAN HUMAN RIGHTS REPORTS. see *LAW*

EVERYONE'S BACKYARD. see *ENVIRONMENTAL STUDIES — Waste Management*

323.4   UK   ISSN 0958-3971
EXILE. m. free. British Refugee Council, 3 Bondway, London SW8 1SJ, England. TEL 0171-582-6922. FAX 0171-582-9929. Ed. Toby Buxton. circ. 2,250. (back issues avail.) **Document type:** newsletter.
    Description: Provides a public awareness forum for the plight of refugees in the U.K. and elsewhere on issues related to asylum.

EXILFORSCHUNG; ein internationales Jahrbuch. see *SOCIOLOGY*

EXPONENT II; a quarterly newspaper concerning Mormon women, published by Mormon women, and of interest to Mormon women and others. see *WOMEN'S INTERESTS*

F E W'S NEWS AND VIEWS. (Federally Employed Women Inc.) see *WOMEN'S INTERESTS*

F O I A UPDATE. (Freedom of Information Act) see *JOURNALISM*

FAIR HOUSING: DISCRIMINATION IN REAL ESTATE, COMMUNITY DEVELOPMENT AND REVITALIZATION. see *HOUSING AND URBAN PLANNING*

FATHERS' JOURNAL. see *MEN'S STUDIES*

344.73 347.304   US   ISSN 1043-7274
KF3464
FEDERAL EQUAL OPPORTUNITY REPORTER. 1982. bi-w. $875. L R P Publications (Subsidiary of: Axon Group), 747 Dresher Rd., Box 980, Horsham, PA 19044-0980. TEL 215-784-0941. FAX 215-784-9639. Ed. Allison Vehling. index. (looseleaf format; back issues avail.)
    —CCC.

FEDERAL STAFFING DIGEST. see *PUBLIC ADMINISTRATION*

FEMMES D'ICI. see *WOMEN'S INTERESTS*

FINANCIAL PRIVACY REPORT. see *BUSINESS AND ECONOMICS — Banking And Finance*

323.4   US   ISSN 0363-0447
KF4742
FIRST PRINCIPLES. 1975. 4/yr. $15. (Center for National Security Studies, Washington Legislative Office) American Civil Liberties Union (Washington, DC), 122 Maryland Ave., N.E., Washington, DC 20002. TEL 202-544-1681. FAX 202-546-0738. (National Headquarters addr.: 132 W. 43rd St., New York, NY 10036) Ed. Gary Stern. bk.rev. circ. 3,500. **Indexed:** HR Rep. **Document type:** newsletter.
    Description: Articles and commentaries by experts on the relationship between national security and civil liberties.

323.4   US   ISSN 0740-0195
E185.5
FOCUS (WASHINGTON, 1970). 1986. m. $15. Joint Center for Political Studies, Inc., 1090 Vermont Ave., NW, Ste. 1100, Washington, DC 20005-4905. Ed. Sherille Ismail. charts; stat.; cum.index: 1972-1985. circ. 12,000. (back issues avail.) **Indexed:** Ind.Jew.Per., P.A.I.S., SRI.

323.4   SA   ISSN 0960-572X
DT737
FOCUS ON POLITICAL REPRESSION IN SOUTH AFRICA. 1975-1991 (no.93). bi-m. £10($20) (International Defence and Aid Fund for Southern Africa (IDAFSA), I D A F Research, Information and Publications Department) University of the Western Cape, Private Bag X17, Bellville 7535, South Africa. TEL 071-359 9181. FAX 071-359-9690. TELEX 28110. (U.S. subscr. addr.: International Defence and Aid Fund for Southern Africa, U.S. Committee, Box 17, Cambridge, MA 02138) Ed.Bd. circ. 3,500. (back issues avail.) **Indexed:** HR Rep. (1987-).
    Former titles (until 1990): Focus on Political Repression in South Africa and Namibia (ISSN 0959-4078); (until 1989): Focus on Political Repression in Southern Africa (ISSN 0308-3586)
    Description: Focuses on repression by the apartheid regime and its illegal occupation of Namibia, and on resistance to its rule.

323.4   IS
FOCUS SOVIET JEWRY. (Text in English) 1986. m. free. Israel Public Council for Soviet Jewry, Rehov Bak 1, Tel Aviv 67019, Israel. TEL 03-338267. FAX 3-334950. (Co-sponsor: World Zionist Organization) Ed. Deborah Lipson. circ. 6,000.
    Description: Reports on the situation of Jews in the Soviet Union.

FORWARD. see *SOCIAL SCIENCES: COMPREHENSIVE WORKS*

320 360   US   ISSN 0882-3723
FOURTH WORLD JOURNAL. 1972. bi-m. $10. Fourth World Movement, 7600 Willow Hill Dr., Landover, MD 20785-4658. TEL 301-336-9489. FAX 301-336-0092. Ed. Susan M. Devins. adv. contact: Susan Devins. circ. 9,500. **Indexed:** HR Rep. (1989-). **Document type:** newsletter.
    Description: News and views from the Fourth World Movement, USA, for people concerned by poverty.

323.6   UK   ISSN 0965-2051
FREE CHOICE. 1980. bi-m. £10($20) Freedom Organisation for the Right to Enjoy Smoking Tobacco (F O R E S T), 2 Grosvenor Gardens, London SW1W 0DH, England. TEL 0171-823-6550. FAX 0171-823-4534. Ed. Marjorie Nicholson. bk.rev. circ. 5,000. **Document type:** newsletter.
    ●Also available online.
    Description: Advocates for the right for people to smoke in public places and speaks out against legislation restricting smoking in the U.K. and worldwide.

323.4 956   AT   ISSN 0157-3845
FREE PALESTINE. 1979. bi-m. Aus.$10($20) P L O Office, c/o A. Kazak, Pub., P.O. Box 4646, Kingston, A.C.T. 2604, Australia. TEL 61-62-733711. FAX 61-62-733903. Ed.Bd. bk.rev. circ. 4,500. **Document type:** academic/scholarly publication, bulletin.
    Description: Covers developments in the Israel-Palestinian conflict.

323.4   US
FREE SPEECH NEWSLETTER. 1966. 3/yr. free. Speech Communication Association, 5105 Backlick Rd., Bldg. E., Annandale, VA 22003. TEL 703-750-0533. FAX 703-914-9471. Ed. Paul A. Barefield. circ. 225. **Document type:** newsletter.
    Formerly: Free Speech.

FREEDOM OF EXPRESSION IN HONG KONG: ANNUAL REPORT. see *JOURNALISM*

323.4   US   ISSN 1054-3090
JC571   CODEN: FREVEP
FREEDOM REVIEW; documenting the universal struggle for freedom with emphasis on strengthening democratic institutions. 1970. bi-m. $20. Freedom House, 120 Wall St., 26th Fl., New York, NY 10005-3904. TEL 212-514-8040. FAX 212-514-8050. Ed. Roger Kaplan. adv. contact: Pei Koay. bk.rev.; index. circ. 2,000. (also avail. in microfilm from UMI; back issues avail.; reprint service avail. from UMI) **Indexed:** Amer.Bibl.Slavic & E.Eur.Stud., Amer.Hist.& Life, Hist.Abstr., HR Rep. (1982-), P.A.I.S., Polit.Sci.Abstr. **Document type:** consumer publication.
    —BLDSC (4033.360400); Faxon; UMI; UnCover. CCC.
    Formerly: Freedom at Issue (ISSN 0016-0520); **Which incorporated:** Freedom Appeals (ISSN 0196-0695)

323.4   UK   ISSN 0957-3070
FREEDOM TODAY. 1976. bi-m. £8. (Freedom Association Ltd.) Far and Wide Publishers Ltd., 35 Westminster Bridge Rd., London SE1 7JB, England. TEL 01-928-9925. FAX 01-928-9524. Ed. Philip Vander Elst. adv.; bk.rev. circ. 10,000.
    Formerly (until 1988): Free Nation (ISSN 0309-3980)

POLITICAL SCIENCE — CIVIL RIGHTS

323.4   US   ISSN 1059-6372
FREEDOM WRITER; a hard look at the hard right. 1984. 12/yr. $25. Institute for First Amendment Studies, Inc., Box 589, Great Barrington, MA 01230. TEL 413-528-3800. FAX 413-528-4466. E-mail: ifas@crocker.com. Ed. Skipp Porteous. bk.rev.; cum.index; circ. 8,000 (controlled). (looseleaf format; also avail. in microfiche; back issues avail.) **Document type:** newsletter.
Description: Promotes human rights and the preservation of traditional American freedoms as guaranteed by the Constitution's Bill of Rights, with emphasis on separation of church and state issues.

323.4   GW   ISSN 0016-0911
DIE FREIHEITSGLOCKE/BELL OF FREEDOM. 1950. 11/yr. DM.30($20) Gemeinschaft Ehemaliger Politischer Haeftlinge (VOS), Borsigallee 6, 53125 Bonn, Germany. TEL 0228-257496. Ed. E. Reese. bk.rev.; index. circ. 4,800.

323.4   US   ISSN 0741-353X
FROM THE STATE CAPITALS. CIVIL RIGHTS. Variant title: Civil Rights - From the State Capitals. 1946. w. $235 (effective 1994). Wakeman-Walworth, Inc., 300 N. Washington St., Alexandria, VA 22314. TEL 703-549-8606. FAX 703-549-1372. Ed. Keyes Walworth. (processed; back issues avail.) **Document type:** newsletter.
●Also available online. Vendor(s): West Services, Inc.
—CCC.
Former titles: From the State Capitals. Racial Relations and Civil Rights (ISSN 0734-0893); From the State Capitals. Racial Relations (ISSN 0016-1896)
Description: Analyzes state and local governmental action in the U.S. on ethnic, race and sex discrimination, desegregation, affirmative action, discrimination compensation, gay rights, the civil rights of persons with disablities.

323.4 341.481   NE   ISSN 0927-3840
FRONTAAL. 1993. m. fl.17.50 membership. Amnesty International, Dutch Section, Keizersgracht 620, 1017 ER Amsterdam, Netherlands. TEL 31-20-6264436. FAX 31-20-6240889. Ed. Danielle Pinedo. circ. 3,000 (paid). **Document type:** bulletin, newsletter.
Description: Provides background on current concerns and developments in the field of human rights and within the organization, for a youth audience.

FULL DISCLOSURE; for truth, justice, and the American way. see *CRIMINOLOGY AND LAW ENFORCEMENT — Security*

G L A A D BULLETIN. (Gay and Lesbian Alliance against Defamation) see *HOMOSEXUALITY*

G L B AMES NEWSLETTER. (Gays, Lesbians and Bisexuals of Ames) see *HOMOSEXUALITY*

GAY SCOTLAND; for lesbians, gays & bisexuals. see *HOMOSEXUALITY*

323.4   US
GEORGIA CIVIL RIGHTS REPORT. q. $15. Center for Democratic Renewal and Education, Inc., Box 50469, Atlanta, GA 30302. TEL 404-221-0025. FAX 404-221-0045. **Document type:** newsletter.

323.4 914   GW
▼**GESELLSCHAFT FUER BEDROHTE VOELKER. TASCHENKALENDER**. 1994. a. DM.12. Lamuv Verlag GmbH, Nikolaikirchhof 7, 37073 Goettingen, Germany. TEL 0551-44024. FAX 0551-41392. **Document type:** bulletin.

GLAUBE IN DER 2. WELT; Zeitschrift fuer Religionsfreiheit und Menschenrechte. see *RELIGIONS AND THEOLOGY*

323.4 341.481   NE   ISSN 0927-3824
GLOBAAL. 1992. q. fl.52.50 membership. Amnesty International, Dutch Section, Keizersgracht 620, 1017 ER Amsterdam, Netherlands. TEL 31-20-6264436. FAX 31-20-6240889. Ed. Willem Offenberg. circ. 130,000 (paid). **Document type:** bulletin.
Description: Provides an overview of current concerns, action suggestions, and developments in the field of human rights.

323 051   US   ISSN 1060-0884
JC571
GLOBAL JUSTICE. 1990. 3/yr. $10. Center on Rights Development, GSIS, 2201 South Gaylord St., Denver, CO 80208. TEL 303-871-2523. Eds. Nikhil Aziz Hemmady, Joy Sobrpena. circ. 300.

DIE GLOCKE VOM ETTERSBERG. see *HISTORY — History Of Europe*

GRACE AND TRUTH. see *RELIGIONS AND THEOLOGY — Roman Catholic*

GRAUER PANTHER. see *GERONTOLOGY AND GERIATRICS*

THE GUIDE: GAY TRAVEL, ENTERTAINMENT, POLITICS, AND SEX. see *HOMOSEXUALITY*

GUIDE MAGAZINE (SEATTLE). see *HOMOSEXUALITY*

GUIDE TO AMERICAN STATE AND LOCAL LAWS ON SOUTH AFRICA. see *LAW — International Law*

323.4   US
HAITI INFO; news from the people and organizations of Haiti's grassroots democratic movement. 1992. fortn. $30 to individuals; institutions $80. Haitian Information Bureau, c/o Lynk Air, Box 407139, Fort Lauderdale, FL 33340-7139. E-mail: hib@igc.org.apc. Ed.Bd; Pub. Robert Duval. bk.rev. **Document type:** newsletter.

323.4 200   US   ISSN 0896-243X
HARMONY (SAN FRANCISCO); voices for a just future. 1987. bi-m. $12 (U.K. £10; elsewhere $16). Sea Fog Press, Inc., Box 210056, San Francisco, CA 94121-0056. TEL 415-221-8527. Ed. Rose Evans; Pub. Rose Evans. adv.; bk.rev. circ. 1,170. **Document type:** consumer publication.
Description: Covers ethics and the reverence for life. Opposes the death penalty, war, abortion, euthanasia, racism, and economic injustice.

HARVARD BLACKLETTER JOURNAL. see *LAW*

HARVARD CIVIL RIGHTS - CIVIL LIBERTIES LAW REVIEW. see *LAW — Civil Law*

323.4   US   ISSN 1057-5057
K8
HARVARD HUMAN RIGHTS JOURNAL. 1988. a. $15 (Canada $18). Harvard University, Law School, Publications Center, Hastings Hall, Cambridge, MA 02138. TEL 617-495-3694. circ. 500. (also avail. in microfiche from WSH; reprint service avail. from WSH) **Indexed:** HR Rep. (1988-). **Document type:** academic/scholarly publication.
—BLDSC (4267.183000); UnCover.
Formerly (until 1989): Harvard Human Rights Yearbook (ISSN 1047-0174)
Description: Explores issues in human rights studies.

HEALTH AND HUMAN RIGHTS. see *PUBLIC HEALTH AND SAFETY*

HERTHA. see *WOMEN'S INTERESTS*

HOLOCAUST EDUCATION. see *HISTORY — History Of Europe*

HOLOCAUST STUDIES ANNUAL. see *HISTORY — History Of Europe*

323.4   FR   ISSN 0180-8524
HOMMES ET LIBERTES. 1961. 4/yr. 100 F. (outside the E.U. 150 F.). Ligue des Droits de l'Homme, 27 rue Jean Dolent, 75014 Paris, France. TEL 47-05-14-01.
Formerly (until 1977): Ligue des Droits de l'Homme. Bulletin National (ISSN 0180-8516)
Description: Covers issues in civil liberties worldwide.

HOMOSEXUAL INFORMATION CENTER. NEWSLETTER. see *HOMOSEXUALITY*

323.4   AT   ISSN 0818-0954
HRVATSKA SLOBODA. * (Text in Croatian and English) 1985. bi-m. Aus.$40($30) Croatian Cultural & Welfare Association, Croatian Information Office, 642A Barkly St., Footseray West, Vic. 3012, Australia. Ed. Anton Babic. circ. 3,000. (tabloid format)
Description: Promotes the establishment of a free and democratic state of Croatia.

HUMAN RESOURCES MANAGEMENT - EQUAL EMPLOYMENT OPPORTUNITY. see *BUSINESS AND ECONOMICS — Personnel Management*

323.4   US   ISSN 0046-8185
K8
HUMAN RIGHTS. 1970. 4/yr. $17 to non-members. American Bar Association, Individual Rights and Responsibilities Section, 750 N. Lake Shore Dr., Chicago, IL 60611. TEL 312-988-5990. FAX 312-988-6281. E-mail: quadev@attmail.com. Ed. Vicki Quade. adv.; bk.rev.; bibl. circ. 7,000. (also avail. in microfilm from RRI; microfiche from WSH; reprint service avail. from RRI,WSH) **Indexed:** C.L.I., HR Rep., L.R.I., Leg.Per., Soc.Sci.Ind. (until 1994), SSCI. **Document type:** trade publication.
●Also available online. Vendor(s): West Services, Inc. (HUMRT).
—BLDSC (4336.437000); Faxon; UMI; UnCover.
Description: News articles, features, and commentary on human rights and individual rights and responsibilities.

323.4   US   ISSN 0273-2521
JC571
HUMAN RIGHTS (BOCA RATON). (Subseries of: S I R S Social Issues (ISSN 0740-3127)) 1978. a. price varies; a. supplement $17. Social Issues Resources Series, Box 2348, Boca Raton, FL 33427-2348. TEL 407-994-0079; 800-232-7477. FAX 407-994-4704. (looseleaf format; also avail. in microfiche; back issues avail.)
Description: Reprints articles that probe worldwide human rights violations.

323.4   CN
HUMAN RIGHTS ACT OF BRITISH COLUMBIA. 1976. a. free. B.C. Council of Human Rights, Parliament Bldgs., Victoria, BC V8V 1X4, Canada. TEL 604-387-3710. FAX 604-387-3643. **Document type:** government publication.
Supersedes: British Columbia. Human Rights Commission. Annual Report (ISSN 0706-5426)

323.4   UN   ISSN 0251-7019
HUMAN RIGHTS BULLETIN. French edition: Bulletin des Droits de l'Homme (ISSN 0251-6993) (Text in English) 1969-1982; resumed 1986. q. free. United Nations, Centre for Human Rights, Palais des Nations, 8-14 avenue de la Paix, 1211 Geneva 10, Switzerland. circ. 3,500.
Description: Examines the Declaration's impact on international law.

323.4   US
HUMAN RIGHTS BULLETIN (NEW YORK). 1945. s-a. $35 (foreign $40) (subscr. includes International League for Human Rights. Annual Report). International League for Human Rights, 432 Park Ave. S., Ste. 1103, New York, NY 10016-8013. TEL 212-684-1221. FAX 212-684-1696. Ed. Charles H. Norchi. circ. 3,600. **Indexed:** HR Rep. **Document type:** bulletin.
Formerly: Rights of Man.

323.4   UK   ISSN 0965-934X
HUMAN RIGHTS CASE DIGEST. 1990. bi-m. £24 to members; non-members £32. (British Institute of Human Rights) Sweet & Maxwell, Kings College, Strand, London WC2R 2LS, England. (Subscr. to: Sweet & Maxwell Ltd., Cheriton House, North Way, Andover, Hants. SP10 5BE, England. TEL 0264-342899. FAX 0264-342899)
Description: Contains summaries of all decisions of the European Court of Human Rights, full texts of all resolutions of the Committee of Ministers, and synopses of other important legal documents.

323.4   CN
HUMAN RIGHTS COUNCIL DECISIONS. irreg (36-40/yr.). Can.$150. B.C. Council of Human Rights, Victoria, BC V8V 1X4, Canada. TEL 604-387-3710. FAX 604-387-3643. (Subscr. to: Crown Publications, 546 Yates St., Victoria, BC V8W 1K8, Canada. TEL 604-386-4636) **Document type:** government publication.

POLITICAL SCIENCE — CIVIL RIGHTS

323.4 UN ISSN 1014-5567
K3240.4
HUMAN RIGHTS FACT SHEET. irreg., latest no.21. United Nations, Centre for Human Rights, 8-14, avenue de la Paix, CH-1211 Geneva 10, Switzerland. TEL 022-7346011. FAX 022-7339879. TELEX 289696. **Document type:** bulletin.
  Description: Intends to assist in better understanding basic human rights, what the United Nations is doing to promote and protect them and the international machinery available to help realize those rights.

341 NE ISSN 1381-0537
HUMAN RIGHTS IN DEVELOPING COUNTRIES YEARBOOK. (Text in English) a. (Norwegian Institute of Human Rights) Kluwer Law International (Subsidiary of: Wolters Kluwer N.V.), Postbus 85889, 2508 CN The Hague, Netherlands. TEL 31-70-3081500. FAX 31-70-3081515. (Dist. by: Libresso Distribution Centre, P.O. Box 23, 7400 GA Deventer, Netherlands. TEL 31-5700-33155. FAX 31-5700-33834; Dist. in N. America by: Kluwer Law International, 675 Massachusetts Ave., Cambridge, MA 02139. TEL 617-354-8595. FAX 617-354-8595) (Co-publisher: Nordic Human Rights Publications) Ed.Bd. **Document type:** academic/scholarly publication.
  —BLDSC (4336.439210).
  Formerly (until 1994): Human Rights in Developing Countries.
  Refereed Serial

323.4 CN ISSN 0275-049X
JC571
HUMAN RIGHTS INTERNET REPORTER. 1976. 2/yr. $60 to individuals; institutions $80. Human Rights Internet, c/o Human Rights Centre, University of Ottawa, 57 Louis Pasteur, Ottawa, ON K1N 6N5, Canada. TEL 613-564-3492. FAX 613-564-4054. Ed. Laurie S. Wiseberg. adv.; bk.rev.; bibl.; index. circ. 2,000. (also avail. in microform; back issues avail.) Indexed: Alt.Press Ind., Amer.Bibl.Slavic & E.Eur.Stud. **Document type:** bibliography.
  —Faxon; SWETS.
  Formerly: Human Rights Internet Newsletter (ISSN 0163-9048)

HUMAN RIGHTS LAW JOURNAL. see *LAW — Constitutional Law*

323.4 UN ISSN 1014-4986
HUMAN RIGHTS NEWSLETTER. French edition: Courrier des Droits de l'Homme (ISSN 1014-4978) 4/yr. United Nations, Centre for Human Rights, Palais des Nations, 8-14 avenue de la Paix, CH-1211 Geneva 10, Switzerland. TEL 4122-7346011. FAX 4122-7339879. TELEX 289696. **Document type:** newsletter.

338.025 323.4 US ISSN 0098-0579
KF4741
HUMAN RIGHTS ORGANIZATIONS & PERIODICALS DIRECTORY. 1973. biennial. $39.95 to individuals; institutions $44.95. Meiklejohn Civil Liberties Institute, Box 673, Berkeley, CA 94701-0673. TEL 510-848-0599. FAX 510-848-6008. Ed.Bd. bibl. circ. 2,000. **Document type:** directory, bibliography.
  Description: Descriptions of over 1000 U.S. local and national organizations that focus on human rights.

323.4 US
HUMAN RIGHTS RESOURCES. 1985. bi-m. $20. Human Rights Resource Center, 615 B St., San Rafael, CA 94901-3805. Ed. Patrisha Tulloch. circ, 1,500.
  Description: Provides brief news reports and information for community groups, law enforcement agencies, and schools to deal with tensions resulting from intolerance and discrimination.

323.05 CN ISSN 1188-6226
JC571
HUMAN RIGHTS TRIBUNE/TRIBUNE DES DROITS HUMAINS. (Text in English, French) 1992. q. Can.$4.95($3.95) per no. Human Rights Internet, c/o Human Rights Centre, University of Ottawa, 57 Louis Pasteur, Ottawa, ON K1N 6N5, Canada. TEL 613-564-3492. FAX 613-564-4054. Ed. Laurie S. Wiseberg.

323.4 US ISSN 1079-2325
JC599.A36
HUMAN RIGHTS WATCH AFRICA. 1989. irreg. $40. Human Rights Watch, 485 Fifth Ave., New York, NY 10017-6104. TEL 212-972-8400. FAX 212-972-0905. E-mail: hrwatchnyc@igc.apc.org.
  Formerly (until 1994): Africa Watch (ISSN 1062-2217)
  Description: Monitors and promotes observance of internationally recognized human rights in Africa.

323.4 US ISSN 1077-6710
HUMAN RIGHTS WATCH AMERICAS. irreg. $40. Human Rights Watch, Americas, 485 Fifth Ave., New York, NY 10017-6104. TEL 212-972-8400. FAX 212-972-0905. E-mail: hrwnyc@hrw.org.
  Formerly (until 1994): Americas Watch (ISSN 1068-8919)
  Description: Monitors and promotes observance of internationally recognized human rights in the Americas.

323.4 US ISSN 1079-1876
HUMAN RIGHTS WATCH HELSINKI. irreg. $40. Human Rights Watch, Helsinki, 485 Fifth Ave., New York, NY 10017-6104. TEL 212-972-8400. FAX 212-972-0905. E-mail: hrwnyc@hrw.org. Indexed: HR Rep. (1987-).
  Formerly (until 1994): Helsinki Watch.
  Description: Monitors and promotes observance of internationally recognized human rights in Croatia.

323.4 US ISSN 1080-6199
HUMAN RIGHTS WATCH MIDDLE EAST. irreg. $40. Human Rights Watch, Middle East, 485 Fifth Ave., New York, NY 10017-6104. TEL 212-972-8400. FAX 212-972-0905. E-mail: hrwnyc@hrw.org.
  Former titles (until 1994): Middle East Watch (ISSN 1068-8900); (until 1991): News from Middle East Watch (ISSN 1061-6241)
  Description: Monitors and promotes observance of internationally recognized human rights in the Middle East.

323.3 305.4 US
HUMAN RIGHTS WATCH WOMEN'S RIGHTS PROJECT. irreg. $40. Human Rights Watch, Women's Rights Project, 485 Fifth Ave., New York, NY 10017-6104. TEL 212-972-8400. FAX 212-972-0905. E-mail: hrwnyc@hrw.org.

323.4 US ISSN 1054-948X
JC571
HUMAN RIGHTS WATCH WORLD REPORT. 1990. a. $30. Human Rights Watch, 485 Fifth Ave., New York, NY 10017-6104. TEL 212-972-8400. Ed. Kenneth Roth.
  Description: Monitors and promotes human rights throughout the world.

323.4 CK
HUMAN RIGHTS WORKING PAPER. (Editions in English, Spanish) 1991. irreg. (approx. 4./yr.). $10. Instituto Latinoamericano de Servicios Legales Alternativos - Inter-American Legal Services Association, P.O. Box 077844, Bogota, Colombia. TEL 571-2455995. FAX 571-2884854. E-mail: ilsa@colnodo.wpc.org. Ed. Leslie Wirpsa.

323.4 GW ISSN 1015-5945
HUMAN RIGHTS WORLDWIDE. (Text in English) 1990. bi-m. $10. Internationale Gesellschaft fuer Menschenrechte, Kaiserstr. 72, 60329 Frankfurt a.M., Germany. TEL 069-236971. FAX 069-234100. Ed. Robert Chambers. circ. 5,000. **Document type:** bulletin.

HUMAN SERVE CAMPAIGN NEWSLETTER. see *SOCIAL SERVICES AND WELFARE*

323.4 100 AT
HUMANIST VIEWPOINTS. vol.7, 1969. m. Aus.$20 (effective Jul. 1993). Humanist Society of New South Wales Inc., 10 Shepherd St., Chippendale, N.S.W. 2008, Australia. Ed. J. Tendys. adv.; bk.rev. circ. 200. **Document type:** newsletter.
  Formerly (until 1979): Viewpoints (ISSN 0042-5877)

323.4 MP
HUNIY ERH/HUMAN RIGHTS. (Text in Mongolian) m. tG.250. Voluntary Committee for Defence of Human Rights, P.O. Box 107, Ulan Bator 24, Mongolia. Ed. N. Tsevegmid. circ. 3,000. **Document type:** newsletter.

HYPERBOREAN. see *PHILOSOPHY*

323.4 SZ
I A F INFORMATION. (Text in English and French) q. 60 SFr. International Abolitionist Federation, 11 rue des Savoires, CH-1205 Geneva, Switzerland. TEL 022-7813060. FAX 022-7813133. Ed. Helene Sackstein. **Document type:** bulletin.
  Formerly (until 1993): Revue Abolitionniste.

I J A REPORTS. (Institute of Jewish Affairs) see *ETHNIC INTERESTS*

I L G A BULLETIN. (International Lesbian and Gay Association) see *HOMOSEXUALITY*

I S T A ADVOCATE. (Indiana State Teachers Association) see *EDUCATION*

I W G I A DOCUMENTS; documentation of oppression of ethnic groups in various countries. (International Work Group for Indigenous Affairs) see *ANTHROPOLOGY*

I W G I A YEARBOOK. (International Work Group for Indigenous Affairs) see *ANTHROPOLOGY*

IMAGE (FORT WORTH). see *BUILDING AND CONSTRUCTION*

IMPARTIAL CITIZEN. see *ETHNIC INTERESTS*

323.1 US ISSN 0046-8967
INDIAN AFFAIRS. 1949. 3/yr. $10. Association on American Indian Affairs, Inc., 245 Fifth Ave., Ste. 1801, New York, NY 10016. FAX 212-685-4692. Ed. Merrill O'Connor. bk.rev. circ. 40,000. (also avail. in microform from UMI; reprint service avail. from UMI) Indexed: Anthropol.Lit. **Document type:** newsletter.
  —UMI.

INDIGENOUS AFFAIRS. (International Work Group for Indigenous Affairs) see *ANTHROPOLOGY*

323.4 UK
INDONESIA HUMAN RIGHTS CAMPAIGN. OCCASIONAL REPORTS. (Text in English and Indonesian) irreg. Indonesia Human Rights Campaign, 111 Northwood Rd., Thornton Heath, Surrey CR7 8HW, England. TEL 0181-771-2904. FAX 0181-653-0322. E-mail: gn:tapol. **Document type:** monographic series.
  Description: Covers diverse topics related to human rights in Indonesia. Includes source documents in the original and translations into English.
  Refereed Serial

INFOCUS NEWS MAGAZINE. see *ETHNIC INTERESTS*

INFORMATIVO LEGAL RODRIGO. see *LAW*

323.4 US ISSN 1041-4940
KF8700.A16
INSTITUTE FOR CIVIL JUSTICE. ANNUAL REPORT. 1988. a. Rand Corporation, Publications Department, 1700 Main St., Box 2138, Santa Monica, CA 90406-2138.

323.4 CR
INSTITUTO INTERAMERICANO DE DERECHOS HUMANOS. BOLETIN. English edition: Interamerican Institute of Human Rights. Newsletter. no.28, 1992. q. Instituto Interamericano de Derechos Humanos - Interamerican Institute of Human Rights, Apdo. Postal 10081, 1000 San Jose, Costa Rica. TEL 506-234-04-04. FAX 506-234-09-55. Ed. Natalia Dobles Trejos. circ. 1,000. **Document type:** newsletter.
  Description: Contains information on the main activities of the Institute's programs and projects and on the activities of the Interamerican Court of Human Rights.

323.4 CR
INSTITUTO INTERAMERICANO DE DERECHOS HUMANOS. BOLETIN DOCUMENTAL. irreg., no.6, 1992. $4. Instituto Interamericano de Derechos Humanos, Apdo. Postal 10081, 1000 San Jose, Costa Rica. TEL 506-234-04-04. FAX 506-234-09-55. **Document type:** monographic series.

POLITICAL SCIENCE — CIVIL RIGHTS

323.4   CR   ISSN 1015-5074
INSTITUTO INTERAMERICANO DE DERECHOS HUMANOS. REVISTA. (Text in English, Spanish) 1985. s-a. $30 (effective Jan. 1995). Instituto Interamericano de Derechos Humanos - Interamerican Institute of Human Rights, Apdo. Postal 10081, 1000 San Jose, Costa Rica. TEL 506-234-04-04. FAX 506-234-09-55. Ed. Daniel Zovatto. circ. 1,300. (back issues avail.) **Document type:** academic/scholarly publication.
    Description: Covers the main achievements and events concerning human rights in the inter-american system.

323   US   ISSN 0074-0764
INTER-AMERICAN COMMISSION OF WOMEN. SPECIAL ASSEMBLY. FINAL ACT/COMISION INTERAMERICANA DE MUJERES. ASAMBLEA EXTRARODINARIA. ACTA FINAL. 3rd, 1963. biennial. price varies. Organization of American States, 1889 F St., N.W., Washington, DC 20006. TEL 703-941-1617. circ. 3,000.

INTERHEMISPHERIC RESOURCE CENTER. BULLETIN. see POLITICAL SCIENCE — International Relations

323.4   SZ   ISSN 0259-3696
INTERNATIONAL CHILDREN'S RIGHTS MONITOR. French edition: Tribune Internationale des Droits de l'Enfant. Spanish edition: Tribuna Internacional de los Derechos del Nino. (Text in English) 1983. q. 30 SFr. to individuals; institutions 50 SFr. Defence for Children International, P.O. Box 88, CH-1211 Geneva 20, Switzerland. TEL 022-7340558. FAX 022-7401145. TELEX 414128-DCI-CH. bk.rev. circ. 6,500. (also avail. in microfiche) **Indexed:** HR Rep. (1984-), Refug.Abstr. **Document type:** bulletin.
    Description: Attempts to foster awareness about, and efforts in favor of, children and their rights throughout the world, by informing its readers about the needs and initiatives in this area.

323.4   SZ
INTERNATIONAL DOCUMENTATION ON MACEDONIA. (Text in English and French) 1979. irreg., vol.13, 1982. 120 Fr.($60) Case Postale 37, 1292 Chambesy, Geneva, Switzerland. Ed. Theodore D. Dimitrov. bibl.; charts; illus.; index. (back issues avail.)

323.4 341   UK   ISSN 1351-542X
K3239.23
▼**INTERNATIONAL HUMAN RIGHTS REPORTS.** 1994. 3/yr. $95. University of Nottingham, Department of Law, Burton St., Nottingham NG1 4BU, England. TEL 0602-418418. FAX 0602-486489. (Dist. by: Wm. W. Gaunt & Sons, Inc., Gaunt Bldg., 3011 Gulf Dr., Holmes Beach, FL 34217-2199. TEL 813-778-5211. FAX 813-778-5252) (reprint service avail. from WSH) **Document type:** bulletin.
    Description: Aims to provide access to a range of international documents relating to human rights required by academics, students, practitioners and others.

362.7   NE   ISSN 0927-5568
K9
THE INTERNATIONAL JOURNAL OF CHILDREN'S RIGHTS. (Text in English) 1993. q. fl.350 to institutions; $224 to institutions in U.S. (effective 1996). Kluwer Law International (Subsidiary of: Wolters Kluwer N.V.), Postbus 85889, 2508 CN The Hague, Netherlands. TEL 31-70-3081500. FAX 31-70-3081515. E-mail: SERVICES@WKAP.NL. (Dist. by: Kluwer Academic Publishers Group, P.O. Box 322, 3300 AH Dordrecht, Netherlands. TEL 31-78-546392. FAX 31-78-546477; N. America dist. addr.: Box 358, Accord Sta., Hingham, MA 02018-0358. TEL 617-871-6600. FAX 617-871-6528) Eds. Michael Freeman, Geraldine van Bueren. (reprint service avail. from SWZ,WSH) **Indexed:** Viol.& Abuse Abstr. **Document type:** academic/scholarly publication.
—BLDSC (4542.165500). **CCC.**
    Description: Covers critical scholarship and practical policy development in all fields relating to children's rights, including law, sociology, social work, health, education and psychiatry.
    Refereed Serial

INTERNATIONAL JOURNAL OF REFUGEE LAW. see POLITICAL SCIENCE — International Relations

323.4 341   NE   ISSN 0927-5908
JF1061
INTERNATIONAL JOURNAL ON GROUP RIGHTS. (Text in English) 1993. q. fl.375 to institutions; $240 to institutions in U.S. (effective 1996). Kluwer Law International (Subsidiary of: Wolters Kluwer N.V.), Postbus 85889, 2508 CN The Hague, Netherlands. TEL 31-70-3081500. FAX 31-70-3081515. E-mail: SERVICES@WKAP.NL. (Dist. by: Kluwer Academic Publishers Group, P.O. Box 322, 3300 AH Dordrecht, Netherlands. TEL 31-78-546392. FAX 31-78-546477; N. America dist. addr.: Box 358, Accord Sta., Hingham, MA 02018-0358. TEL 617-871-6600. FAX 617-871-6528) Ed. Yonah Alexander. (reprint service avail. from SWZ,WSH) **Indexed:** IDA. **Document type:** academic/scholarly publication.
—BLDSC (4542.270500); UnCover. **CCC.**
    Description: Discusses legal, political and social issues arising from the presence of identifiable groups within society, examining groups distinguishable because of racial, ethnic, linguistic, cultural or religious factors.
    Refereed Serial

323.4   US
INTERNATIONAL P.E.N. WRITERS-IN-EXILE CENTER'S NEWSLETTER. 1965. q. free to qualified personnel. International P.E.N., Writers in Exile Center, 42 Derby Ave., Orange, CT 06477. TEL 203-397-1479. FAX 203-737-4233. Ed. Clara Gyorgyey. bk.rev. circ. 150. (looseleaf format; back issues avail.) **Document type:** newsletter.
    Description: Provides an update about international prisoners and a list of their publications, also includes international news.

INTERNATIONAL STUDIES. NORDIC SEMINAR ON HUMAN RIGHTS. PROCEEDINGS. see LAW

323.4   NE   ISSN 0924-4751
INTERNATIONAL STUDIES IN HUMAN RIGHTS. (Text in English) irreg., vol.30, 1993. price varies. Kluwer Academic Publishers, P.O. Box 17, 3300 AA Dordrecht, Netherlands. TEL 31-78-392392. FAX 31-78-392254. TELEX 29245 KAPG NL. (Dist. by: Kluwer Academic Publishers Group, P.O. Box 322, 3300 AH Dordrecht, Netherlands. TEL 31-78-392392. FAX 31-78-546474; N. America dist. addr.: Box 358, Accord Sta., Hingham, MA 02018-0358. TEL 617-871-6600. FAX 617-871-6528) **Document type:** monographic series.
—BLDSC (4549.787500).
    Refereed Serial

323.4 341   US   ISSN 0894-394X
INTO THE NIGHT; a newsletter for freedom for political prisoners held in the U.S. 1987. irreg. $15. Into the Night News, 1980 65th St., Brooklyn, NY 11204. Ed. D. Stokes. bk.rev.; bibl.; tr.lit. circ. 1,000. **Document type:** newsletter.

320   US
IOWA CIVIL RIGHTS COMMISSION. ANNUAL REPORT. no.8, 1975. a. Iowa Civil Rights Commission, 211 E. Maple St., 2nd Fl., Des Moines, IA 50309-1858. TEL 515-281-4121. FAX 515-242-5840. circ. 1,000. **Document type:** government publication.

323.4   US
IOWA CIVIL RIGHTS COMMISSION. CASE REPORTS. 1977. a. free. Iowa Civil Rights Commission, 211 E. Maple St., 2nd Fl., Des Moines, IA 50309-1858. TEL 515-281-4121. FAX 515-242-5840. circ. 1,000. **Document type:** government publication.
    Description: Decisions from the Hearings, Iowa District Court of Appeals and Iowa Supreme Court on Commission cases.

ISRAEL UPDATE. see HOMOSEXUALITY

323 341   NE   ISSN 0333-5925
ISRAEL YEARBOOK ON HUMAN RIGHTS. (Text in English) 1971. a., vol.22, 1993 (for year 1992). fl.190 (effective 1993). (Tel Aviv University, Faculty of Law, IS) Martinus Nijhoff Publishers, Human Rights and International Law (Subsidiary of: Kluwer Academic Publishers Group), P.O. Box 163, 3300 AD Dordrecht, Netherlands. TEL 31-78-334911. FAX 31-78-334254. TELEX 29245 KAPG NL. (Dist. by: Kluwer Academic Publishers Group, P.O. Box 322, 3300 AH Dordrecht, Netherlands. TEL 31-78-524400. FAX 31-78-524474; N. America dist. addr.: Box 358, Accord Sta., Hingham, MA 02018-0358. TEL 617-871-6600. FAX 617-871-6528) Ed. Yoram Dinstein. bk.rev.; cum.index: vols.1-20 in vol.21. circ. 1,500. (back issues avail.; reprint service avail. from WSH) **Indexed:** A.B.C.Pol.Sci., HR Rep. (1989-), Int.Polit.Sci.Abstr. **Document type:** academic/scholarly publication.
—BLDSC (4583.960000); UnCover.
    Description: Publishes studies by distinguished scholars on issues pertaining to human rights in peace and war, with particular emphasis on problems relevant to Israel and the Jewish people.

ISSUES & VIEWS; an open forum on issues affecting the black community. see ETHNIC INTERESTS

323.4   VE   ISSN 1023-6813
▼**IUDICUM ET VITA;** jurisprudencia nacional de America Latina en Derechos Humanos. 1994. q. Instituto Interamericano de Derechos Humanos, Apdo. Postal 10081, 1000 San Jose, Costa Rica. Ed. Jaime Ordonez. **Document type:** academic/scholarly publication.

323.4 340   JM
J.C.H.R. NEWS LETTER. 1974. q. $20. Jamaica Council of Human Rights, 131 Tower St., Kingston, Jamaica, W.I. TEL 809-92-25012. Ed. Florizelle A. O'Connor. bk.rev. circ. 2,000. (also avail. in microfiche) **Indexed:** HR Rep.

JACKSONVILLE FREE PRESS. see ETHNIC INTERESTS

323.4 342   US
JERICHO NEWSLETTER. 1993. m. $10. St. Catherine's Universal Life Church, Box 1983, Cincinnati, OH 45201-1983. Ed. Heidi Teblos-Stephens. (back issues avail.) **Document type:** newsletter.
    Description: Covers legislation and litigation concerning prisoners' rights. Includes personal stories and exposes on conditions and abuses in the U.S. criminal justice system to enlighten and move to reform.

JEWS AND THE JEWISH PEOPLE - PETITIONS, LETTERS AND APPEALS FROM SOVIET JEWS/EVREI I EVREISKI NAROD - PETICII PIS'MA I OBRASENI EVREEV S S S R. see ETHNIC INTERESTS

323.4   IS
DS101
JEWS IN EASTERN EUROPE. (Text in English) 1985; N.S. 1993. 3/yr. $30. Hebrew University, Center for Research and Documentation of East European Jewry, Givat Ram, 91904 Jerusalem, Israel. TEL 972-2-584271. FAX 972-2-666804. bk.rev. circ. 500. **Document type:** academic/scholarly publication.
    Former titles (until 1993): Jews and Jewish Topics in the Soviet Union and Eastern Europe (ISSN 0334-6641); (until 1989): Jews and Jewish Topics in Soviet and East European Publications (ISSN 0334-6242)
    Description: Includes articles, reviews, documents and testimony concerning Jews and Jewish topics in the former Soviet Union and Eastern Europe.

JEWS OF THE SOVIET UNION; immigration and struggle in the 1980's. see RELIGIONS AND THEOLOGY — Judaic

323. 918.103   BL
JORNAL DA FUNAI. 1986. m. free. Fundacao Nacional do Indio, Assessoria de Comunicacao Social, Quadra 702 Sul, Projecao "A" Ed. Lex, Sala 301, Brasilia, D.F., Brazil. illus.

POLITICAL SCIENCE — CIVIL RIGHTS

323 301 US ISSN 0047-2492
HN51
JOURNAL OF INTERGROUP RELATIONS.* 1958-1968; N.S. 1971. q. $14. National Association of Human Rights Workers, c/o Broward Cy. Human Relations, 115 S. Andrews Ave., Rm. 116, Fort Lauderdale, FL 33301. Ed. Gloria Battle. adv.; bk.rev. circ. 800. (tabloid format; also avail. in microfilm from UMI; reprint service avail. from UMI) **Indexed:** Amer.Hist.& Life (until 1991), C.I.J.E., Commun.Abstr., Hist.Abstr. (until 1991).
—BLDSC (5007.548500); Faxon; UMI; UnCover.

338.91 UK ISSN 0951-6328
HV640 CODEN: JRESEQ
JOURNAL OF REFUGEE STUDIES. 1988. q. £64($118) (effective 1996). (Refugee Studies Programme) Oxford University Press, Oxford Journals, Walton St., Oxford OX2 6DP, England. TEL 01865-267907. FAX 01865-267773. TELEX 837330-OXPRES-G. E-mail: jnlorders@oup.co.uk. (U.S. subscr. to: Oxford University Press Inc., 2001 Evans Rd., Cary, NC 27513. TEL 919-677-0977. FAX 919-677-1714) Ed. Roger Zetter. adv. contact: Jane Parker. bk.rev. circ. 700. (reprint service avail. from WSH) **Indexed:** Geo.Abstr., HR Rep. (1988-), IDA, Refug.Abstr. **Document type:** academic/scholarly publication.
—BLDSC (5048.550000); SWETS; UMI; UnCover. **CCC.**
Description: Academic exploration of the complex problems of forced migration and national and international responses. Includes anthropology, economics, health and education, international relations, law, politics, psychology and sociology.

323.4 296 SW ISSN 1104-4950
JUDARNA I F.D. SOVJET. 1973. irreg., (4-6/yr.). free. Svenska Kommitten foer Judarna i f.d. Sovjet - Swedish Committee for Jews in the Former U S S R, P.O. Box 5053, S-102 42 Stockholm, Sweden. TEL 46-8-664-53-38. FAX 46-8-664-05-91. Ed. Robin Lapidus. charts. circ. 2,600. **Indexed:** Inform.Sci.Abstr. **Document type:** newsletter.
Formerly (until vol.5, 1991): Judarna i Sovjet.

JULI-MAGAZIN. see *MEETINGS AND CONGRESSES*

JURISPRUDENTIE VOOR GEMEENTEN. see *LAW*

323.4 AT ISSN 0157-6011
JUSTICE TRENDS. 1977. q. free. Australian Catholic Social Justice Council, Leo XIII House, 19 Mackenzie St., N. Sydney, N.S.W. 2060, Australia. TEL 02-956-5811. FAX 02-956-5782. circ. 6,000. **Indexed:** HR Rep.

KENTUCKY DIRECTORY OF BLACK ELECTED OFFICIALS. see *PUBLIC ADMINISTRATION*

323.4 JA ISSN 0910-0156
H8.J3
KOKUSAI KENKYU/INTERNATIONAL STUDIES. (Text in Japanese and various languages) 1984. irreg. (approx. 1/yr.). exchange basis. Chubu University, Institute for International Studies - Chubu Daigaku, Kokusai Chiiki Kenkyujo, Matsumoto-machi 1200, Kasugai-shi, Aichi-ken 487, Japan. TEL 0568-51-1111.

KOLA. see *LITERATURE*

323.4 327 951.9 US
KOREA UPDATE. 1981. q. $20. Korea Church Coalition for Peace, Justice & Reunification, 475 Riverside Dr., Rm. 634, New York, NY 10115. TEL 212-870-2123. FAX 212-870-2881. Ed. Paul Kim. bk.rev.; bibl.; stat. circ. 1,700. (back issues avail.) **Indexed:** HR Rep. (1985-). **Document type:** newsletter.
Description: Analysis of the human rights situation and U.S. policy relating to peace, reunification and justice in the Korean Penninsula.

323.4 GW ISSN 0023-4834
K11
KRITISCHE JUSTIZ. 1968. q. DM.42. Nomos Verlagsgesellschaft mbH und Co. KG, Waldseestr. 3-5, 76530 Baden-Baden, Germany. TEL 07221-21040. FAX 07221-210427. (Subscr. to: Postfach 610, 76484 Baden-Baden, Germany) Ed.Bd. adv.; index. circ. 5,000. (reprint service avail. from SCH) **Indexed:** Abstr.Crim.& Pen., INIS Atomind., Int.Polit.Sci.Abstr. **Document type:** academic/scholarly publication.
—SWETS. **CCC.**

KURDISTAN. see *POLITICAL SCIENCE — International Relations*

323.4 AT
LABOR NATIONAL HERALD. 1894. bi-m. Aus.$15. (Australian Labor Party, South Australian Branch) Workers Weekly Herald Pty. Ltd., A.L.P. Office, Trades Hall, 11 South Terrace, Adelaide, S.A. 5000, Australia. TEL 61-8-2118744. FAX 61-8-2314095. Ed. Gary Orr. adv.; bk.rev. circ. 35,000. (tabloid format; back issues avail.) **Document type:** newspaper.
Formerly: Herald (ISSN 0815-9904)
Description: Political publication serving the Australian Labor Party.

LAMBDA UPDATE. see *HOMOSEXUALITY*

323.4 350 AT ISSN 0313-6353
LAND RIGHTS NEWS; a newspaper for Aboriginals people and their supporters. no.6, 1976. 4/yr. Northern Territory Land Councils, P.O. Box 39843, Winnellie, N.T. 0821, Australia. TEL 089-817011. FAX 089-816899. TELEX AA85042. bk.rev. circ. 4,000. **Document type:** newspaper.

LAW & INEQUALITY; a journal of theory and practice. see *LAW*

323.4 301.415 US ISSN 1062-0680
K12
LAW & SEXUALITY; a review of lesbian and gay legal issues. a. Tulane University, School of Law, 6329 Freret St., New Orleans, LA 70118. TEL 504-865-5969. FAX 504-865-6748. (also avail. in microfiche from WSH; reprint service avail. from WSH) **Document type:** academic/scholarly publication.
Description: Examines legal issues affecting gays and lesbians, including sexual discrimination and sexual harassment.

323.4 US
LAW GROUP DOCKET. 1981. s-a. $15. International Human Rights Law Group, 1601 Connecticut Ave., N.W., Ste. 700, Washington, DC 20009. bk.rev. circ. 4,000. **Indexed:** HR Rep. **Document type:** bulletin.
Description: Monitors human rights violations and promotes international human rights law.

323.4 340.5 US
LAWYERS' COMMITTEE FOR CIVIL RIGHTS UNDER LAW. COMMITTEE REPORT. 1970. s-a. $20 to non-members. Lawyers' Committee for Civil Rights under Law, 1450 G St., N.W., Ste. 400, Washington, DC 20005. TEL 202-662-8600. Ed. David A. Balcom. circ. 4,000. **Document type:** newsletter.

LEFT. see *POLITICAL SCIENCE*

323.4 326.7 US
LEGAL RIGHTS OF CHILDREN. (2nd edition, 1994) 1984. 3 base vols. (plus a supplement). $255. Shepard's - McGraw-Hill, Inc., Box 35300, Colorado Springs, CO 80935-3530. TEL 800-525-2474. Ed. Donald T. Kramer. **Document type:** trade publication.
Description: Covers every issue concerning children's rights, including economic interests, children as litigants, public benefit programs, custody disputes, rights of adolescents, and protection of children from exploitation.

LESBIAN CONNECTION. see *HOMOSEXUALITY*

323.4 UK ISSN 0024-1873
D839
LIBERATION. 1958. bi-m. £10 (overseas £15). 490 Kingsland Rd., London E8 4AE, England. TEL 0171-254-6223. adv. contact: Maggie Bowden. bk.rev.; bibl. circ. 1,000. **Document type:** bulletin.
Formerly: Colonial Freedom News.

LIBERTARIAN ALLIANCE. CULTURAL NOTES. see *POLITICAL SCIENCE*

323.4 US ISSN 0894-3036
LINKS: HEALTH AND DEVELOPMENT REPORT.* 1983. q. $15 to individuals; institutions $25 (foreign $25) (effective 1993). National Central American Health Rights Network, 775 E. 19th St., Brooklyn, NY 11230-1807. TEL 212-732-4790. Ed. Tom Frieden. adv.; bk.rev.
Formerly: Links.
Description: Promotes health in the Third World and works to keep the American public informed of health and human rights issues in the area.

LOK RAJYA. see *EDUCATION*

M A L D E F NEWSLETTER. (Mexican American Legal Defense and Educational Fund) see *ETHNIC INTERESTS*

MCDONALD QUARTERLY; the topical report on diversity issues. see *BUSINESS AND ECONOMICS — Personnel Management*

MAGICKAL PAGAN NEWS. see *PARAPSYCHOLOGY AND OCCULTISM*

323.4 GW ISSN 0025-0511
DIE MAHNUNG. 1953. m. DM.24. Bund der Verfolgten des Naziregimes Berlin e.V., Mommsenstr. 27, 10629 Berlin, Germany. TEL 030-3242632. Ed.Bd. adv.; bk.rev. **Document type:** bulletin.

323.4 CN ISSN 0383-5588
JC599.C2
MANITOBA. HUMAN RIGHTS COMMISSION. ANNUAL REPORT. 1974. a. free. Human Rights Commission, 301-259 Portage Ave., Winnipeg, MB R3B 2A9, Canada. TEL 204-945-3007. illus. circ. 3,500.

323.4 US
MARTIN LUTHER KING, JR. CENTER FOR NON-VIOLENT SOCIAL CHANGE NEWSLETTER. 1973. irreg. donations. Martin Luther King, Jr. Center for Non-Violent Social Change, 449 Auburn Ave., N.E., Atlanta, GA 30312. TEL 404-524-1956. Ed. Hilda R. Tompkins. illus. circ. 30,000. **Document type:** newsletter.
Formerly: Martin Luther King, Jr. Center for Social Change Newsletter.

MARTYRDOM AND RESISTANCE. see *ETHNIC INTERESTS*

323.4 SA ISSN 0025-6188
MAYIBUYE. N.S. 1975. 11/yr. African National Congress, P.O. Box 61884, Marshalltown 2107, South Africa. TEL 330-7143. FAX 330-7144. circ. 8,000.
Description: Discusses political and social change in South Africa.

323.4 US
MEDIA NETWORK'S GUIDE TO FILMS ON APARTHEID AND THE SOUTHERN AFRICAN REGION. 1985. a. $3. Media Network, 39 W. 14th St., Ste. 403, New York, NY 10011. TEL 212-929-2663. Ed. Martha Wallner.

323.4 NO ISSN 0800-0735
JC585
MENNESKER OG RETTIGHETER; Nordic journal on human rights. 1983. q. NOK 330 in Nordic countries; elsewhere $63 (effective 1996). (Norwegian Institute for Human Rights) Scandinavian University Press, P.O. Box 2959 Toeyen, N-0608 Oslo, Norway. TEL 47-22-57-54-00. FAX 47-22-57-53-53. Ed.Bd.

323.4 AU ISSN 0025-9616
DAS MENSCHENRECHT. 1946. q. S.300($6) Oesterreichische Liga fuer Menschenrechte, Hermanngasse 9-14, A-1070 Vienna, Austria. Ed. F.J. Bister. adv.; bk.rev.; charts; illus.; cum.index. circ. 3,000. **Document type:** bulletin.
—BLDSC (5678.495500).

323.4 GW ISSN 0171-5976
MENSCHENRECHTE; Dokumente - Schicksale - Informationen. 1976. 5/yr. DM.26. Internationale Gesellschaft fuer Menschenrechte, Kaiserstr. 72, 60329 Frankfurt a.M., Germany. TEL 069-236971. FAX 069-234100. TELEX 4185181-IGFM-D. bk.rev. circ. 6,000. (back issues avail.) **Document type:** bulletin.

323.4 US
MICHIGAN. CIVIL RIGHTS COMMISSION. ANNUAL REPORT. 1964. a. free. Department of Civil Rights, 303 W. Kalamazoo, 4th Fl., Lansing, MI 48913. TEL 517-373-1189. Ed. James H. Horn II. circ. 1,000.
Former titles (until 1972): Civil Rights in Michigan; (until 1970): Michigan. Civil Rights Commission. Report (ISSN 0076-7875)
Description: Activities and accomplishments of the Michigan Civil Rights Commission. Describes the Commission's and Department's on-going efforts to obtain access and protection for individuals who have been denied equal opportunity in areas of jurisdiction.

POLITICAL SCIENCE — CIVIL RIGHTS

323.4　　　　　　　US　ISSN 0047-7087
MICHIGAN CIVIL RIGHTS COMMISSION NEWSLETTER.
1971. q. free. Department of Civil Rights, 303 W. Kalamazoo, 4th Fl., Lansing, MI 48913. TEL 517-373-1189. Ed.Bd. charts; illus.; stat. circ. 7,000. **Document type:** newsletter.
　Description: Activities and accomplishments of the Michigan Civil Rights Commission.

323　　　　　　　　US　ISSN 0076-9118
JC599.U52
MINNESOTA. DEPARTMENT OF HUMAN RIGHTS. BIENNIAL REPORT. 1967. biennial. free. Department of Human Rights, 500 Bremer Tower, 7th & Minnesota, St. Paul, MN 55101. TEL 612-296-5663. circ. 1,000.

301.45 910.03　　　　UK　ISSN 0305-6252
MINORITY RIGHTS GROUP. REPORT. 1970. 6/yr. £37 to individuals; institutions £55. Minority Rights Group, 379 Brixton Rd., London SW9 7DE, England. TEL 0171-978-9498. FAX 0171-738-6265. bibl.; illus.; stat. circ. 1,500. **Indexed:** HR Rep., IDA, Int.Lab.Doc., Refug.Abstr. **Document type:** monographic series.
—BLDSC (7551.382000). **CCC.**
　Description: Investigates the plights of minority and majority groups suffering discrimination and prejudice - and works to educate and alert public opinion.

323.4 350 347　　　　US
MONITOR (ATLANTA). 3/yr. $35 individual membership; institutional $75; libraries $40; foreign $45. Center for Democratic Renewal and Education, Inc., Box 50469, Atlanta, GA 30302. TEL 404-221-0025. FAX 404-221-0045. **Document type:** newsletter.
　Description: Opposes hate group violence and recruiting.

323.4 296.7　　　　　US
MONITOR (WASHINGTON). bi-w. $60. Union of Councils for Soviet Jews, 1819 H St., N.W., Ste. 230, Washington, DC 20006-3603. TEL 202-775-9770. FAX 202-775-9776. Ed. David Waksberg.
　Formerly (until 1990): Refusnik Update.
　Description: Contains news on the transformation to a democratic society in the former Soviet Union and on issues of concern to human rights activists.

323.4　　　　　　　FI
MY LIFE DEPENDS ON YOU. 1981. a. free. Martti Koski, Ed. & Pub., Kanervakummuntie 5, 21290 Rusko, Finland. TEL 921-788482. bk.rev. circ. 5,000. **Document type:** bulletin.
　Description: Examines electrical brain manipulation and the issue of human experimentation.

N A A F A NEWSLETTER. (National Association to Advance Fat Acceptance, Inc.) see *NUTRITION AND DIETETICS*

323.4 305.4　　　　US
N C O M D R NEWS. 1983. a. $5 per no. National Clearinghouse on Marital & Date Rape, 2325 Oak St., Berkeley, CA 94708. TEL 510-529-1582. bk.rev. circ. 500. **Document type:** newsletter.

N O W NEWS (BOSTON). (National Organization for Women) see *WOMEN'S INTERESTS*

323.4　　　　　　　US　ISSN 0746-0201
N.Y. CIVIL LIBERTIES. 1953. q. membership. New York Civil Liberties Union, 132 W. 43rd St., New York, NY 10036-6503. Ed. Norman Siegel. bk.rev. circ. 25,000. (tabloid format; also avail. in microform from UMI; reprint service avail. from UMI) **Indexed:** Alt.Press Ind.
　Formerly: Civil Liberties in New York (ISSN 0009-7926)

323.4　　　　　　　XV　ISSN 0353-5347
NASA SLOVENIJA. (Includes supplements: Manuals about Employment, Health and Insurance Security) (Text in Slovenian) 1978. m. 2750 din.($13) T.O.Z.D. Delavska Enotnost, N.sol.o. Celovska 43, N.sub.o. CGP Delo, Box 313-VI, 61001 Ljubljana, Slovenia. Ed. Matjaz Vizjak.
　Formerly (until 1989): Nas Delavec (ISSN 1318-1351)

323.4　　　　　　　AT　ISSN 0047-8792
NATIONAL COUNCIL OF WOMEN OF AUSTRALIA. QUARTERLY BULLETIN. 1969. q. Aus.$3. National Council of Women of Australia, P.O. Box 693, Turramurra, N.S.W. 2074, Australia. TEL 489-2252. Ed.Bd. illus. circ. 760. **Document type:** bulletin.

NATIONAL GAY AND LESBIAN TASK FORCE. TASK FORCE REPORTS. see *HOMOSEXUALITY*

NATIONAL PRISON PROJECT JOURNAL. see *CRIMINOLOGY AND LAW ENFORCEMENT*

NATIONAL PRISON PROJECT STATUS REPORT. see *CRIMINOLOGY AND LAW ENFORCEMENT*

323.1　　　　　　　US　ISSN 0047-9314
NEIGHBORS - INTERRACIAL LIVING.* 1971. bi-m. $25. National Neighbors, 3130 Mayfield Rd., Cleveland Heights, OH 44118. Ed. Lisa Gitlin. bk.rev.; illus. circ. 3,000.

NETHERLANDS QUARTERLY OF HUMAN RIGHTS. see *LAW — International Law*

NETWORK CONNECTION; national Catholic social justice lobby. see *RELIGIONS AND THEOLOGY — Roman Catholic*

NETWORK NEWS (CLEVELAND). see *PSYCHOLOGY*

323.4　　　　　　　US
NETWORKER (WASHINGTON). 8/yr. $30 membership. Interfaith Impact for Justice and Peace, 110 Maryland Ave., NE, Washington, DC 20002. TEL 202-543-2800.
　Description: Covers environment, human needs, international peace, justice for women, human rights, health care.

323.4　　　　　　　UK　ISSN 0047-9586
HN381　　　　　　　　　CODEN: NEWCEL
NEW COMMUNITY. q. £30 to individuals; institutions £118 (effective 1996). (Community Relations Commission) Carfax Publishing Co., P.O. Box 25, Abingdon, Oxon. OX14 3UE, England. TEL 01235-555335. FAX 01235-553559. (Subscr. in N. America to: 875-81 Massachusetts Ave., Cambridge, MA 02139) Ed. Malcolm Cross. **Indexed:** RILM, Sociol.Educ.Abstr. **Document type:** academic/scholarly publication.
—BLDSC (6082.880000); SWETS. **CCC.**
　Formerly (until 1971): Community (ISSN 0010-3764)
　Description: Studies human migration and ethnic relations in Europe and throughout the world.

323.4　　　　　　　US
NEW PARTY. 1978. a. Sophia Circle, 8319 Fulham Ct., Richmond, VA 23227. TEL 804-266-7400. Ed. Jerome Gorman.
　Description: Advocates the nationalization of health insurance and the abolishment of the death penalty and military conscription.

323.4　　　　　　　US
NEW YORK (STATE). DIVISION OF HUMAN RIGHTS. ANNUAL REPORT. 1946. a. free. Division of Human Rights, 55 W. 125th St., New York, NY 10027. TEL 212-870-8400. FAX 212-870-8552. circ. 3,000.
　Former titles: State of Human Rights in New York; New York (State). Division of Human Rights. Annual Report.

323.4　　　　　　　US　ISSN 8756-8926
K14
NEW YORK LAW SCHOOL JOURNAL OF HUMAN RIGHTS. 1982. s-a. $22 (foreign $27). New York Law School, 57 Worth St., New York, NY 10013-2960. TEL 212-431-2112. circ. 1,000. (reprint service avail. from WSH) **Indexed:** C.L.I., HR Rep. (1988-), Leg.Per.
—BLDSC (6089.340800).

NEW ZEALAND BILL OF RIGHTS REPORTS. see *LAW — Constitutional Law*

NEW ZEALAND TRIBUNE. see *POLITICAL SCIENCE*

NEWS NETWORK INTERNATIONAL. see *RELIGIONS AND THEOLOGY*

322 301.45　　　　　US
NEWSWATCH. no.69, 1975. m. $36. National Conference on Soviet Jewry, Soviet Jewry Research Bureau, 730 Broadway, 2nd Fl., New York, NY 10003-9511. TEL 212-780-9500. FAX 212-780-0888. Ed. Deborah Hart Strober. circ. 1,500. **Indexed:** HR Rep. **Document type:** newsletter.
　Former titles: Newsbreak (New York); National Conference on Soviet Jewry. Press Service; National Conference on Soviet Jewry. News Bulletin.

NICARAGUA MONITOR. see *BUSINESS AND ECONOMICS — International Development And Assistance*

323.4　　　　　　　AT
NON-SMOKERS' UPDATE. 1978. q. Aus.$40. Non-Smokers' Movement of Australia Inc., Box 6 Trades Hall, 4 Goulburn St., Sydney, N.S.W. 2000, Australia. TEL 61-2-264-6243. FAX 61-2-267-4393. Ed. Arthur Chesterfield-Evans. adv.; bk.rev. circ. 2,500. (back issues avail.) **Document type:** newsletter.
　Formerly (until 1994): Clean Air Clarion (ISSN 0155-2899)
　Description: Covers politics and health effects of tobacco, concentrating on Australia.

323.4　　　　　　　NP
NORTH AMERICAN AND EUROPEAN SENTINEL. 1980. a. $100. Siveast Consultants, Inc., USA, P.O. Box 8510, Kathmandu, Nepal. (Alt. addr.: 9-11-1 Goutami Nagar, Kovvur 534350, West Godavari District, Andhra, India) Ed. C.V. Ramasastry.
　Description: Examines human rights issues.

341.1　　　　　　　UN　ISSN 0029-7593
HT1521
OBJECTIVE: JUSTICE. French edition: Objectif: Justice (ISSN 0378-9934) 1971. s-a. $12. United Nations Publications, Room DC2-853, New York, NY 10017. TEL 212-963-8302; 800-253-9646. FAX 212-963-3489. (And: Distribution and Sales Section, Palais des Nations, CH-1211 Geneva, Switzerland) Ed. Hosni Khalifa. bibl.; charts; illus. (also avail. in microform from UMI; reprint service avail. from UMI) **Indexed:** ELLIS, P.A.I.S., So.Pac.Per.Ind.
—Faxon; UMI.
　Description: Dedicated to the promotion of justice through the self-determination of peoples, the elimination of apartheid and racial discrimination, and the advancement of human rights.

ON GUARD. see *MILITARY*

ONE COUNTRY; the earth is but one country, and mankind its citizens. see *ENVIRONMENTAL STUDIES*

323.4　　　　　　　CN　ISSN 0702-0538
JC599.C2
ONTARIO. HUMAN RIGHTS COMMISSION. ANNUAL REPORT. Title varies slightly. (Text in English and French) 1962. a. free. Human Rights Commission, 400 University Ave., Toronto, ON M7A 2R9, Canada. TEL 416-314-4528. FAX 416-314-4533. circ. 10,000.

OPEN FORUM. see *LAW*

THE OTHER SIDE (PHILADELPHIA); justice rooted in discipleship. see *RELIGIONS AND THEOLOGY*

323.4　　　　　　　US
OUR STRUGGLE/NUESTRA LUCHA. (Text in English,Spanish) 1981. irreg. (4-5/yr.). $15. 2827 Cantania Way, Sacramento, CA 95826. TEL 916-361-9072. E-mail: duane-campbell@QMbridge.CCS.CSUS.edu. Ed. Duane Campbell. bk.rev. circ. 250.
　Description: Conveys common concerns of the Latino rights movement and democratic socialism. Demands economic democracy, equality and self-determination in Latin America and in the barrios of the US.

OUTLINES; the voice of the gay and lesbian community. see *HOMOSEXUALITY*

323.4　　　　　　　UK　ISSN 0260-6402
OUTSIDER. 1978. 4/yr. £0.50 per no. Minority Rights Group, 379 Brixton Rd., London SW9 7DE, England. TEL 0171-978-9498. FAX 0171-738-6265. **Document type:** newsletter.
　Formerly: Minority Rights Group. Newsletter.

POLITICAL SCIENCE — CIVIL RIGHTS

323.4   SZ
P C R INFORMATION; reports and background papers. 1979. 2/yr. free. World Council of Churches, Programme to Combat Racism, 150 Rte. de Ferney, Box 2100, CH-1211 Geneva 2, Switzerland. TEL 022-7916111. FAX 022-791-0361. TELEX 415730-OIK-CH. Ed. Bob Scott. bk.rev. circ. 5,000.

323.4   US
P.S. 1979. bi-m. $5. Prolifers for Survival, 1213 E. Dunklin, Jefferson City, MO 65101. TEL 919-942-7615. Ed. Patricia Narciso. circ. 3,400.

323.4   IT
PACE DIRITTI DELL'UOMO DIRITTI DEI POPOLI. 1987. 3/yr. L.65000 (foreign L.85000) (effective 1995). (Universita di Padova, Centro Studi e Formazione sui Diritti dell'Uomo e dei Popoli) Casa Editrice Dott. Antonio Milani, Via Jappelli 5-6, 35121 Padua, Italy. TEL 39-49-656677. FAX 39-49-8752900. index. circ. 2,700. (back issues avail.)

323.4   US   ISSN 0737-5549
PALESTINE HUMAN RIGHTS CAMPAIGN NEWSLETTER.* 1981. bi-m. $25. Palestine Human Rights Information Center, 4201 Connecticut Ave. N.W., Ste. 500, Washington, DC 20008-1158. circ. 5,500. (back issues avail.)

PALESTINE YEARBOOK OF INTERNATIONAL LAW. see *LAW — International Law*

320   PY
PARAGUAY NOTICIAS. 1982. m. $48. Espana 596, Asuncion, Paraguay. TEL 24-845. Ed. Rafaela Guanes.
Description: Covers politics, human rights, indian matters, and trade unions in Paraguay.

322.4   IT   ISSN 0031-3130
PATRIA INDIPENDENTE; quindicinale della Resistenza e degli ex-combattenti. 1951. fortn. L.30000 (foreign L.50000) (effective 1995). Associazione Nazionale Partigiani d'Italia, Comitato Nazionale, Via degli Scipioni 271, 00192 Rome, Italy. TEL 39-6-3211309. FAX 39-6-3218495. Dir. A. Bartolini. adv.; bk.rev.; film rev.; bibl.; illus. circ. 20,000.

200 301.6   NE   ISSN 1382-3574
PATTERNS IN RECONCILIATION. (Text in English) 2/yr. fl.25($13) (£8). International Fellowship of Reconciliation, Spoorstraat 38, 1815 BK Alkmaar, Netherlands. TEL 31-72-123014. FAX 31-72-151102. E-mail: ifor@gn.apc.org. Ed. Shelley Anderson. circ. 1,000. (back issues avail.) Document type: monographic series.
Formerly (until 1994): International Fellowship of Reconciliation. Occasional Paper Series.
Description: Covers topics relating to peace, justice, nonviolence and conflict resolution.

323.4 296.7   UK   ISSN 0031-322X
DS145
PATTERNS OF PREJUDICE. 1967. q. £34 to individuals; institutions £90 (effective 1996). (Institute of Jewish Affairs) Sage Publications Ltd., 6 Bonhill St., London EC2A 4PU, England. TEL 0171-374-0645. FAX 0171-374-8741. E-mail: market@sageltd.co.uk. (Co-sponsor: World Jewish Congress) Ed.Bd. adv.: B&W page £200; trim 190 x 114; adv. contact: Bernie Folan. bk.rev.; bibl.; index. circ. 1,750. (also avail. in microform from UMI; reprint service avail. from UMI) Indexed: A.I.C.P., Amer.Hist.& Life, Bull.Signal., CERDIC, Hist.Abstr., HR Rep. (1987-), IBR, IBZ, Ind.Artic.Jew.Stud., Ind.Jew.Per., Intl.Bibl.S.S.Soc.Cult.Anthro., Per.Islam., Rel.Ind.One, Sage Race Rel.Abstr., Viol.& Abuse Abstr. Document type: academic/scholarly publication.
—BLDSC (6412.985000); UMI.
Description: Studies national and international conditions, causes and manifestations of racial, religious and ethnic discrimination and prejudice, with particular reference to anti-Semitism.
Refereed Serial

323.4   AG
PAZ Y JUSTICIA. 1973. q. $25 (effective 1995). Paz y Justicia SRL, Piedras 730, 1070 Buenos Aires, Argentina. TEL 541-361-5745. E-mail: serpaj@wamani.apc.org. adv. contact: Adolfo Perez Esquivel. bk.rev.; bibl. circ. 1,500. (tabloid format) Indexed: HR Rep. (1986-). Document type: bulletin.

323.4 327   US
JX1901
PEACE & DEMOCRACY. 1984. s-a. $7 to individuals; institutions $15. Campaign for Peace and Democracy, Box 1640, Cathedral Sta., New York, NY 10025. TEL 212-666-5924. FAX 212-662-5892. E-mail: camppeacedem@igc.apc.org. Eds. Joanne Landy, Jennifer Scarlott. adv. contact: Joanne Landry. bk.rev. circ. 9,000. (back issues avail.) Indexed: Alt.Press Ind., HR Rep. (1992-), Left Ind. (1985-), Polit.Sci.Abstr.
Formerly: Peace and Democracy News (ISSN 0749-5900)
Description: Promotes international dialogue and common action from below by linking members of the peace movement, environmentalists, trade unionists, feminists, and gay and minority rights activists with democratic movements throughout the world.

341.1   UK
JX1974.7
PEACE REGISTER. 1967. a. £20($35) (Bertrand Russell Peace Foundation) Spokesman, Bertrand Russell House, 45 Gamble St., Nottingham NG7 4ET, England. TEL 01602-708318. FAX 01602-420433. Ed. Ken Coates. adv.; bk.rev. circ. 2,000. (back issues avail.) Indexed: HR Rep. Document type: bulletin.
—BLDSC (3739.200000).
Formerly (until 1993): End Papers (ISSN 0262-7922); Which incorporated: Spokesman (ISSN 0024-5992); London Bulletin.
Description: Forum for the discussion of international affairs with a particular focus on nuclear disarmament issues.

323.4 336   US   ISSN 1065-254X
PEACE TAX FUND NEWSLETTER. 1970. q. $25 to non-members. National Campaign for a Peace Tax Fund, 2121 Decatur Pl., N.W., Washington, DC 20008. TEL 202-483-3751. FAX 202-986-0667. circ. 5,000. (back issues avail.) Document type: newsletter.
Description: Covers the status of legislation establishing conscientious objection to military taxes.

323.4 200   US
PHILIPPINE WITNESS. 1985. q. $10 donation. Church Coalition for Human Rights in the Philippines, 110 Maryland Ave., N.E., Box 70, Washington, DC 20002. TEL 202-543-1094. FAX 202-546-0090. Ed. Katheryn Johnson. bk.rev.; bibl.; charts; illus. circ. 2,000. (looseleaf format) Document type: newsletter.
Description: Ecumenical coalition of churches and church-related organizations addressing the issue of human rights.

323.4   US
PIPELINE (WASHINGTON). s-a. $20. Alliance for Justice, 1601 Connecticut Ave., N.W., Ste. 600, Washington, DC 20009. TEL 202-532-3224. FAX 202-265-2150. Ed. Carol Seifert. circ. 2,000. Document type: newsletter.
Description: Educates the public-interest community about Alliance for Justice and member activities.

PLAEDOYER; das Magazin fuer Recht und Politik. see *LAW*

323.4 914   GW   ISSN 0720-5058
POGROM. 1970. bi-m. DM.48. Gesellschaft fuer Bedrohte Voelker, Gemeinnuetziger Verein e.V. - Society for Threatened Peoples, Postfach 2024, 37010 Goettingen, Germany. TEL 0551-49906-0. FAX 0551-58028. Ed. Tilman Zuelch. adv. contact: Guenther Schierloh. bk.rev.; bibl.; illus. circ. 6,000. Indexed: HR Rep. (1985-). Document type: academic/scholarly publication.

320   US
POINT BLANK. 1971. m. $15 includes membership. Citizens Committee for the Right to Keep and Bear Arms, 12500 N.E. 10th Pl., Bellevue, WA 98005. TEL 206-454-4911. FAX 206-451-3959. Ed. John M. Snyder. adv. contact: Joseph P. Tartaro. bk.rev. circ. 150,000. Document type: newsletter.
Description: Information on federal and state firearms rights and related legislation.

320.5   US   ISSN 0032-2318
POINT OF VIEW. 1968. fortn. $35 to individuals; institutions $50. Box 99530, Cleveland, OH 44199. TEL 216-321-2527. Ed. Roldo S. Bartimole. bk.rev.; illus. circ. 720. (also avail. in microform from UMI; reprint service avail. from UMI) Indexed: CINAHL. —UMI.

323.4 296   US
POST-SOVIET JEWRY REPORT. 1975. q. $36. Action for Post-Soviet Jewry, Inc., 24 Crescent St., Ste. 306, Waltham, MA 02154. TEL 617-893-2331. FAX 617-647-9474. Ed. Judy Patkin. (looseleaf format; back issues avail.) Document type: bulletin.
Formerly: Soviet Jewry Report.
Description: Updates readers on situation of Jews in former Soviet Union and on organization's effort to help.

PRISONERS AND THE LAW. see *CRIMINOLOGY AND LAW ENFORCEMENT*

PRISONERS' ASSISTANCE DIRECTORY. see *CRIMINOLOGY AND LAW ENFORCEMENT*

323.4   US   ISSN 0272-9989
JC596.2.U5
PRIVACY. (Subseries of: S I R S Social Issues (ISSN 0740-3127)) 1973. a. price varies; a. supplement $17. Social Issues Resources Series, Box 2348, Boca Raton, FL 33427-2348. TEL 407-994-0079; 800-232-7477. FAX 407-994-4704. (looseleaf format; also avail. in microfiche; back issues avail.)
Description: Reprints articles that discuss legal issues concerning an individual's right to privacy.

323.4   US   ISSN 0145-7659
KF1262.A15
PRIVACY JOURNAL; an independent monthly on privacy in a computer age. 1974. m. $109. Robert Ellis Smith, Ed. & Pub., Box 28577, Providence, RI 02908. TEL 401-274-7861. bk.rev.; tr.lit.; index, cum.index. circ. 2,100. (looseleaf format; also avail. in microform from UMI; back issues avail.; reprint service avail. from UMI) Indexed: Bank.Lit.Ind., Comput.Lit.Ind. Document type: academic/scholarly publication.
●Also available online. Vendor(s): NewsNet.
Description: Reports on legislation, legal trends, new technology, and public attitudes affecting the confidentiality of information and the individual's right to privacy.

323.4 340   US   ISSN 1063-7222
PRIVACY TIMES. 1981. fortn. $275 in U.S. & Canada; elsewhere $300 (effective 1994). Privacy Times Inc., Box 21501, Washington, DC 20009. TEL 202-829-3660. FAX 202-829-3653. Ed. Evan Hendricks.

322.4   US
PRO-LIFE REPORTER. 1973. q. $10. United States Coalition for Life, Box 315, Export, PA 15632. Pub. Randy Engel. bk.rev.; bibl.; illus. circ. 2,750.

323.4   US   ISSN 0392-9177
PROBE (SANTA BARBARA). 1968. irreg. donations. Box 13390 UCSB, Santa Barbara, CA 93107. Ed. Perry Adams. adv.; bk.rev.; illus. circ. 15,000. (tabloid format)
Formerly: Argo.

323.4 364.6   UN   ISSN 1020-1688
PROFESSIONAL TRAINING SERIES. 1993. irreg., no.3, 1994. United Nations, Centre for Human Rights, Crime Prevention and Criminal Justice Branch, Palais des Nations, 8-14 ave. de la Paix, 1211 Geneva 10, Switzerland. TEL 4122-346011. FAX 4122-7339879. TELEX 289696.

PROLIFE NEWS. see *PUBLIC HEALTH AND SAFETY*

323.4   IT
QUADERNI DELLA SOCIETA CIVILE. (Supplement to: Notizie ARCI) 3/yr. A R C I Confederazione Regionale della Sicilia, Via Trapani 3, 90141 Palermo, Italy. TEL 091-324917. FAX 091-323794. Ed. Carmen Bertolazzi.

323.4 289.6   CN   ISSN 0229-1916
QUAKER CONCERN. 1977. q. donations. Canadian Friends Service Committee, 60 Lowther Ave., Toronto, ON M5R 1C7, Canada. TEL 416-920-5213. Ed. Peter Chapman. bk.rev.; illus. circ. 3,500. (tabloid format; back issues avail.) Document type: newsletter.

POLITICAL SCIENCE — CIVIL RIGHTS

QUAKER SERVICE BULLETIN. see *RELIGIONS AND THEOLOGY — Protestant*

255   NE
R I. (Text in English) 1977. 6/yr. fl.45($25) (£15). International Fellowship of Reconciliation, Spoorstraat 38, 1815 BK Alkmaar, Netherlands. TEL 31-72-123014. FAX 31-72-151102. E-mail: ifor@gn.apc.org. Ed. Shelley Anderson. adv.; bk.rev. circ. 1,000. (also avail. in microfiche; back issues avail.) Indexed: Alt.Press Ind. Document type: newsletter.
    Former titles (until 1994): Reconciliation International; (until 1985): I F O R Report (ISSN 0167-174X)
    Description: Covers peace and justice issues, religious response to social issues, nonviolence training and education, and the relevance of nonviolent methods of social change and conflict resolution.

301.45   SA   ISSN 0033-734X
DT763
RACE RELATIONS NEWS. 1938. q. R.1 per no. South African Institute of Race Relations, P.O. Box 97, Johannesburg 2000, South Africa. Ed. T. Coggin. adv.; bk.rev.; index. circ. 3,000. **Indexed:** A.I.C.P., HR Rep. Document type: newspaper.

301.45   SA   ISSN 0258-7246
DT763
RACE RELATIONS SURVEY. 1948. a. South African Institute of Race Relations, P.O. Box 97, Johannesburg 2000, South Africa. circ. 6,000. **Indexed:** HR Rep.
    —BLDSC (7225.953500).
    Former titles: Survey of Race Relations in South Africa (ISSN 0081-9778); Race Relations Survey.

323.4   NQ
REFLEXION. 1992. q.? Asociacion Nicaraguense Pro-Derechos Humanos, Bo. Bolonia, Emb. Alemana, 2c. Abajo, 1c. al Lago, Apdo. Postal 669, Managua, Nicaragua. TEL 505-2-668062. FAX 505-2-661352. E-mail: anpdh@nicarao.apc.org.

323.4   SZ
REFUGEE REPORTS. (Text mainly in English; occasionally in French and Spanish) irreg. free. World Council of Churches, Refugee and Migration Service, 150 route de Ferney, P.O. Box 2100, CH-1211 Geneva 2, Switzerland. TEL 022-791-6111. FAX 022-791-0361. TELEX 415730-OIK-CH. circ. 2,000. (back issues avail.) **Indexed:** Refug.Abstr. Document type: bulletin.
    Formerly: Refugees.

323.4 200   US
RELIGIOUS FREEDOM ALERT.* m. $1 per no. Coalition for Religious Freedom, 5817 Dawes Ave., Alexandria, VA 22311-1114. **Document type:** newsletter.
    Description: Advocates religious freedom.

REPORT ON SCIENCE AND HUMAN RIGHTS. see *SCIENCES: COMPREHENSIVE WORKS*

327   US
REPORT ON THE SITUATION ON HUMAN RIGHTS IN THE REPUBLIC OF GUATEMALA. 1962. irreg., latest 1983. $6. Inter-American Commission on Human Rights, 1889 F. St. N.W., Ste. 820E, Washington, DC 20006. TEL 202-789-6000. (Subscr. to: General Secretatiat, Organization of American States, Office of Publications, Washington, DC 20006)

REPORTERS SANS FRONTIERES. ANNUAL REPORT. see *JOURNALISM*

323.4   US
REPRODUCTIVE RIGHTS UPDATE. q. American Civil Liberties Union, Reproductive Freedom Project, 132 W. 43rd St., New York, NY 10036. TEL 212-944-9800. E-mail: gopher://aclu.org:6601. Ed. Shrrill Cohen.
    Description: Analyzes current national or state policies, legislation, and regulations related to reproductive freedom. Offers an in-depth examination of selected issues.

305   US   ISSN 1048-1222
HC54
RESEARCH IN INEQUALITY AND SOCIAL CONFLICTS. 1989. a. J A I Press, Inc., 55 Old Post Rd., Greenwich, CT 06836.

RESEARCH ON ECONOMIC INEQUALITY. see *BUSINESS AND ECONOMICS — Economic Situation And Conditions*

323.4 327   US   ISSN 0897-2613
RESIST NEWSLETTER. 1967. m. (10/yr.). $15. 1 Summer St., Sommerville, MA 02143. TEL 617-623-5110. Ed. Stephaie Poggi. bk.rev. circ. 5,000. (back issues avail.) **Document type:** newsletter.
    Description: Articles on topics of interest to all those concerned with peace and social justice. Covers AIDS, reproductive rights, homelessness, environmental movements, lesbian and gay organizing, Middle East and Third World organizing efforts.

RESPONSE (LOS ANGELES). see *ETHNIC INTERESTS*

323.4   BE   ISSN 0777-3579
REVUE TRIMESTRIELLE DES DROITS DE L'HOMME. 1968. q. 3200 BEF. Etablissements Emile Bruylant, 67 rue de la Regence, 1000 Brussels, Belgium. TEL 32-2-5129845. FAX 32-2-5117202. adv.; bk.rev.; bibl.; index. circ. 1,000. **Indexed:** HR Rep. (1968-1976), Int.Polit.Sci.Abstr. Document type: academic/scholarly publication.
    —CCC.
    Former titles (until 1990): Revue des Droits de l'Homme (ISSN 0035-1989); (until 1969): Droits de l'Homme (ISSN 0991-885X)

LA REVUE UNIVERSELLE DES DROITS DE L'HOMME. see *LAW — Constitutional Law*

323.4   US
RIGHT TO KNOW AND THE FREEDOM TO ACT. 1987. irreg. (2-3/yr.). $15. National Committee Against Repressive Legislation, 3321 12th St., N.E., Washington, DC 20017. TEL 202-529-4225. FAX 202-526-4611. Ed. Kit Gage. bk.rev.; charts; illus. circ. 4,000. (looseleaf format; back issues avail.)
    Incorporates (in 1992): F B I News; **Former titles:** N C A R L - D C Memo; Abolition News (ISSN 0001-3234)
    Description: Monitors developments related to protection of First Amendment rights, with particular focus on the activities of the FBI and CIA.

323.4   US   ISSN 0035-5283
JC599.U5
RIGHTS. 1952. q. $20. National Emergency Civil Liberties Committee, 175 Fifth Ave., Rm. 814, New York, NY 10010. TEL 212-673-2040. FAX 212-460-8359. Ed. Jeff Kisseloff. adv.; bk.rev.; illus. circ. 10,000. **Indexed:** Alt.Press Ind., HR Rep., PMR. Document type: newsletter.
    —Faxon.

323.4   CN
RIGHTS AND FREEDOMS.* q. Canadian Human Rights Reporter, Inc., 1253 McGill College., Ste. 470, Montreal, PQ H3B 2Y5, Canada. TEL 819-449-6072. Ed. Charles Walden.

323.4   CN   ISSN 1187-3272
RIGHTS AND LIBERTIES. 1978. q. membership. Manitoba Association for Rights and Liberties, 500-283 Bannatyne Ave., Winnipeg, MB R3B 3B2, Canada. TEL 204-947-0213. FAX 204-956-1137. E-mail: telnet://winnie.freenet.mb.ca. Ed. L.K. Harris. bk.rev. circ. 300. (back issues avail.) **Document type:** newsletter.
    Formerly: M A R L Newsletter.

RIVISTA INTERNAZIONALE DEI DIRITTI DELL'UOMO. see *LAW*

323.4   NE   ISSN 0927-7889
DE ROZELINKS. Key Title: Roze Links. q. fl.19.50 (effective 1994). RozeLinks - Groenlinks Platform voor Seksuele Diversiteit, Postbus 700, 1000 AS Amsterdam, Netherlands. TEL 31-20-6202212. bk.rev. circ. 150. **Document type:** newsletter.
    Formerly (until Dec. 1991): Roze 3 (ISSN 0923-6457); Which was formed by the 1989 merger of: Homobevrijding & Vlindertje (ISSN 0925-6156)

301.45   UK
RUNNYMEDE BULLETIN. 1969. 10/yr. £13 to individuals; voluntary organizations £16; institutions £20. Runnymede Trust, 11 Princelet St., London E1 6QH, England. TEL 0171-375-1496. Eds. Kaushika Amin, Paul Coleman. adv.; bk.rev.; bibl. circ. 3,000. (looseleaf format) **Document type:** bulletin.
    Former titles: Race and Immigration: Runnymede Trust Bulletin (ISSN 0262-9925); Runnymede Trust Bulletin (ISSN 0142-971X); Race Relations Bulletin (ISSN 0033-7323)

S O C M SENTINEL. (Save Our Cumberland Mountains) see *ENVIRONMENTAL STUDIES*

323.4   US   ISSN 0891-608X
S P S C LETTER. 1979. q. $5 donation. Saharan Peoples Support Committee, 217 E. Lehr, Ada, OH 45810. TEL 419-634-3666. Ed. Anne Lippert. bk.rev.; charts. circ. 750. **Indexed:** HR Rep.

SAGE: A SCHOLARLY JOURNAL ON BLACK WOMEN. see *WOMEN'S STUDIES*

323.4   US
SAHARAN PEOPLE'S SUPPORT COMMITTEE. MONOGRAPH SERIES. irreg. Saharan People's Support Committee, 217 E. Lehr, Ada, OH 45810. TEL 419-634-3666. **Document type:** monographic series.

320.5   SA   ISSN 0036-4843
DT751
SASH. (Text in English) 1956. q. R.20 (overseas R.60). Black Sash, 5 Long St., Mowbray 7700, South Africa. TEL 021-685-3513. FAX 021-685-7510. Ed.Bd. bk.rev.; charts; illus. circ. 2,000. **Indexed:** HR Rep. (1985-). **Document type:** academic/scholarly publication.
    Formerly: Black Sash.

323.4   IT
SAVONA A C L I. 1985. m. L.5000($10) Associazioni Cristiane Lavoratori Italy, P.zza Marconi 2, 17100 Savona, Italy. TEL 019 21075.

SCENE OUT. see *HOMOSEXUALITY*

SCHIEDSAMTSZEITUNG. see *LAW*

SETTLEMENTS INFORMATION NETWORK AFRICA NEWSLETTER. see *HOUSING AND URBAN PLANNING*

341.1   US   ISSN 0080-9160
SHALOM; Jewish peace letter. 1941. q. $5. Jewish Peace Fellowship, Box 271, Nyack, NY 10960. TEL 914-358-4601. FAX 914-358-4924. Ed. Murray Polner. bk.rev.; circ. 3,000 (controlled). (back issues avail.) **Document type:** newsletter.
    Formerly: Jewish Peace Fellowship Newsletter (ISSN 0021-664X)
    Description: Addresses the question of peace.

SHEPARD'S - MCGRAW-HILL. INDIVIDUAL RIGHTS SERIES. see *LAW — Constitutional Law*

323.4   AG
SIN ANESTESIA. m.? Asociacion Sin Anestesia, Oyentes por la Libre Expresion, Campana 889, Of. 1, 1712 Castelar, Buenos Aires, Argentina. Ed. Luis Alperin.

SKOTAVILLE HISTORY SERIES. see *LITERATURE*

SKUPNOST; glasilo slovenske skupnosti. see *ETHNIC INTERESTS*

SLAVERY & ABOLITION; a journal of slave and post-slave studies. see *SOCIOLOGY*

SOCIAL IDENTITIES. see *SOCIOLOGY*

323.4   SA
SOUTH AFRICA. HUMAN RIGHTS COMMISSION. MONTHLY REPORT. Short title: H R C Monthly Report. (Text in English) 1988. m. free. Human Rights Commission, P.O. Box 32723, Braamfontein 2017, South Africa. **Document type:** newsletter.
    Formerly (until Feb. 1994): Monthly Repression Report (ISSN 1021-4119); Formed by the 1993 merger of (1990-1992): Area Repression Report (ISSN 1017-6144) & Human Rights Update (ISSN 1017-6160)

SOUTH AFRICAN HUMAN RIGHTS YEARBOOK. see *LAW*

POLITICAL SCIENCE — CIVIL RIGHTS

323.4   SA
SOUTH AFRICAN INSTITUTE OF RACE RELATIONS. SPECIAL REPORTS. irreg. (approx. 6/yr.). South African Institute of Race Relations, P.O. Box 31044, Braamfontein 2017, South Africa. TEL 403-3600. FAX 011-403-3671.

323.4 340   SA   ISSN 0258-7203
K23
SOUTH AFRICAN JOURNAL ON HUMAN RIGHTS. (Text in English) 1985. 3/yr. R.90($48) (University of the Witwatersrand, Centre for Applied Legal Studies) Juta & Co. Ltd., P.O. Box 14373, Kenwyn 7790, South Africa. TEL 021-797-5101.
FAX 021-761-5010. (Dist. in N. America by: Wm. W. Gaunt & Sons, Inc., Gaunt Bldg., 3011 Gulf Dr., Holmes Beach, FL 34217-2199) Ed.Bd. adv.; bk.rev.; index. circ. 1,000. (back issues avail.) **Indexed:** Documentatieblad, Foreign Leg.Per., HR Rep (1984-), Int.Polit.Sci.Abstr., Polit.Sci.Abstr. **Document type:** academic/scholarly publication.
—BLDSC (8338.869000); UnCover.
   Description: Covers human rights issues from a legal perspective.

305.895   PK
SOUTH ASIAN MINORITY AFFAIRS. (Text in English) 1992. irreg., approx. s-a. Rs.60($30) Centre for South Asian Studies, University of the Punjab, Quaid-i-Azam Campus, Lahore 54590, Pakistan. TEL 92-42-8564014. FAX 92-42-5867206. Ed. Rafique Ahmad. (back issues avail.) **Document type:** academic/scholarly publication.
   Description: Promotes respect for human rights and freedom, particularly those guaranteed to minorities under international law and the treaties of the UN.

SOUTHEAST ASIAN REFUGEE STUDIES NEWSLETTER. see ETHNIC INTERESTS

SOUTHEAST ASIAN REFUGEE STUDIES PROJECT. OCCASIONAL PAPERS. see ETHNIC INTERESTS

323.4 910.03   CN   ISSN 0820-5582
DT751
SOUTHERN AFRICA REPORT. 1985. 5/yr. Can.$16 to individuals; institutions Can.$40. Toronto Committee for the Liberation of Southern Africa, 603 1/2 Parliament St., Toronto, ON M4X 1P9, Canada. TEL 416-967-5562. FAX 416-978-8189. adv.; bk.rev.; film rev.; illus. circ. 800. (reprint service avail.)
   Description: Serves the anti-apartheid movement by providing in-depth articles analyzing political events and trends in Southern Africa, Canada and the United States.

323.4   US   ISSN 0193-2446
JC599.U5
SOUTHERN CHANGES. 1978. q. $30 to individuals; institutions $75. Southern Regional Council, Inc., 134 Peachtree St., N.W., Ste. 1900, Atlanta, GA 30303-1825. TEL 404-522-8764.
FAX 404-522-8791. Ed. Allen Tullos; Pub. Steve Suitts. adv. contact: Ellen Spears. bk.rev.; index. circ. 6,000. (also avail. in microform from UMI) back issues avail.; reprint service avail. from UMI) **Indexed:** Amer.Hist.& Life, Hist.Abstr. **Document type:** academic/scholarly publication.
—UMI.
   Former titles: New South; South Today; Southern Voices.
   Description: Reports on regional politics, civil, worker's and women's rights, literature and the arts. Provides a forum for opinion about issues affecting the South.

SOUTHERN COMMUNITIES. see HOUSING AND URBAN PLANNING

SOUTHERN WOMEN: THE INTERSECTION OF RACE, CLASS AND GENDER. see WOMEN'S STUDIES

SPARTACIST CANADA. see POLITICAL SCIENCE — International Relations

SPARTACUS INTERNATIONAL GAY GUIDE. see HOMOSEXUALITY

323.4   US   ISSN 0012-4427
THE SPECTRUM (TOPEKA). 1969. s-a. free. Kansas Human Rights Commission, 900 S.W. Jackson St., Ste. 851 S., Topeka, KS 66612-1258.
TEL 913-296-3206. FAX 913-296-6729. Ed. Steven J. Ramirez. bk.rev.; charts; illus. circ. 6,700. **Document type:** government publication, newsletter.
   Formerly (until 1983): Docket.

323.4   UK   ISSN 0955-5943
SRI LANKA MONITOR. 1988. m. £50 to individuals; institutions £100. British Refugee Council, 3 Bondway, London SW8 1SJ, England.
TEL 0171-582-6922. FAX 0171-582-6922. Ed. Malcolm Rodgers. **Indexed:** HR Rep. **Document type:** newsletter.
   Description: Informs nongovernment organizations, refugees, politicians, and journalists about the civil rights situation in Sri Lanka and on Sri Lankan refugees worldwide.

STANFORD GAY AND LESBIAN AWARENESS WEEK PROGRAM. see HOMOSEXUALITY

323   US   ISSN 0148-6985
E185.5
STATE OF BLACK AMERICA. 1975. a. $18. (National Urban League) Transaction Publishers, Transaction Periodicals Consortium, Department 3092, Rutgers University, New Brunswick, NJ 08903.
TEL 908-445-2280. FAX 908-445-3138. Ed. Janet Dewart. (also avail. in microfiche from CIS) **Indexed:** SRI. **Document type:** academic/scholarly publication.
—Faxon; UnCover.
   Description: Record of trends and events in black America. Educators, public officials, and community leaders analyze recent developments in economics, education, housing, legislation, politics, and race relations as they affect and are affected by Afro-Americans.

323.4   US
STATISTICAL PROOF OF DISCRIMINATION. (2nd edition, 1994; subseries of: Trial Practice Publications) 1980. base vol. (plus a. supplement). $125. Shepard's - McGraw-Hill, Inc., Box 35300, Colorado Springs, CO 80935-3530. TEL 800-525-2474. Eds. Ramona L. Paetzold, Steven L. Wilborn. **Document type:** trade publication.
   Description: Introduces many substantive requirements of proof under disparate treatment and disparate impact theories of discrimination.

323.4   GW   ISSN 0175-4467
STREIT; feministische Rechtszeitschrift. 1983. q. DM.68 (effective 1996). Verein Frauen Streiten fuer Ihr Recht, c/o Sabine Heinke, Wyckstr. 8, 28213 Bremen, Germany. TEL 0421-2239719. bk.rev.; index. circ. 1,600. (back issues avail.) **Document type:** bulletin.
   Description: Discusses legal issues from a feminist perspective

STUDIES IN HUMAN RIGHTS. see POLITICAL SCIENCE — International Relations

323.4 572   UK   ISSN 1353-0488
SURVIVAL (LONDON, 1993). 1983. biennial. £15. Survival International, 11-15 Emerald St., London WC1N 3QL, England. TEL 0171-242-1441.
FAX 0171-242-1771. bk.rev.; film rev. circ. 15,000. (also avail. in microfiche) **Indexed:** A.I.C.P., Anthropol.Lit. **Document type:** newsletter.
   Formerly: Survival International News (ISSN 0265-1327)
   Description: Reports on tribal peoples and their right to decide their own future.

323.4 572   UK   ISSN 0308-2857
SURVIVAL INTERNATIONAL ANNUAL REVIEW. 1988. irreg. Survival International, 11-15 Emerald St., London WC1N 3QL, England. TEL 0171-242-1441. FAX 0171-242-1771. **Document type:** corporate report.
   Description: Covers the field projects and violations cases handled by the organization in the past year.

SURVIVAL INTERNATIONAL REVIEW. see ANTHROPOLOGY

323.4 950   US
TAIWAN COMMUNIQUE. 1980. 6/yr. $25. International Committee for Human Rights in Taiwan, Box 15182, Chevy Chase, MD 20825. TEL 202-244-9871. FAX 301-468-5932. Ed. Gerrit von der Wees. adv. contact: Mei-chin Chen. circ. 3,300. **Indexed:** HR Rep. (1985-). **Document type:** newsletter.
   Description: Supports the establishment of a free and democratic political system in Taiwan.

323.4   US
▼**TAKING SIDES: CLASHING VIEWS ON CONTROVERSIAL ISSUES IN RACE AND ETHNICITY.** 1994. irreg. $13.95. Dushkin Publishing Group, Sluice Dock, Guilford, CT 06437-9989. TEL 203-453-4351. FAX 203-453-6000. Ed. Richard C. Monk; Pub. Mimi Egan. illus. **Document type:** academic/scholarly publication.

323.4   UK   ISSN 1356-1154
TAPOL. 1973. bi-m. £16 to individuals; institutions £22; students £8. Indonesia Human Rights Campaign, 111 Northwood Rd., Thornton Heath, Surrey CR7 8HW, England. TEL 0181-771-2904. FAX 0181-653-0322. E-mail: tapol@gn.apc.org. Eds. C. Budiardjo, S.L. Liem. bk.rev. circ. 1,165. (also avail. in microform) **Indexed:** HR Rep. (1985-). **Document type:** bulletin.
   Refereed Serial

TENANTS' BULLETIN. see REAL ESTATE

323.4   US
TEXAS BILL OF RIGHTS; a commentary and litigation manual. 1987. base vol. (plus a. supplement). $90. Butterworth Legal Publishers (Salem) (Subsidiary of: Reed Elsevier plc), 8 Industrial Way, Bldg. C, Salem, NH 03079. TEL 800-548-4001.
FAX 603-898-9858. Ed. James C. Harrington.
   Description: Analysis of Texas courts' protection of individual freedom in such areas as equal protection, due process, free speech and assembly, privacy and criminal procedure.

THIS WEEK IN TEXAS. see HOMOSEXUALITY

323.44 341   SW   ISSN 0348-5803
TIDSKRIFT FOER FOLKETS RAETTIGHETER. (Text in Swedish; summaries in English) 1977-1988; resumed 1990. q. SEK 200. FiB - Juristerna, c/o E. Goethe, Skeppstav 17, S-124 30 Bandhagen, Sweden. TEL 46-8-24-60-04. FAX 46-8-411-25-90. Ed. Erik Goethe. bk.rev. circ. 1,025.
   Supersedes: FiB - Juristbladet.
   Description: Focuses on issues of law, particularly freedom of the press and international law for the layman.

TRANSITIONS (MANHASSET). see MEN'S STUDIES

TRENDS IN HOUSING. see HOUSING AND URBAN PLANNING

331.8   MV
TRUDOVOI TIRASPOL. (Text in Russian, Ukrainian) 1989. w. newsstand price: 30 Rub. United Council of Labour Collective of Tiraspol, 25 October, Tiraspol, Moldova. TEL 3-04-12. illus. cols./p.: 6; pp./issue: 4. (back issues avail.) **Document type:** newspaper.
   Formerly: Bastuyuchy Tiraspol.
   Description: Covers politics and labor movement.

323.4   US
JK2391.N35
THE TRUTH AT LAST. 1963. m. $15. (American Segregation Party) Truth at Last, Inc., Box 1211, Marietta, GA 30061. TEL 404-422-1180. Ed. Edward R. Fields. bk.rev. circ. 30,000. (tabloid format; also avail. in microfilm from UMI)
—UMI.
   Formerly: Thunderbolt (ISSN 0040-6643)

323.4   UK   ISSN 0960-3069
TURKEY BRIEFING. 1987. q. £20 (outside Europe $45). Turkey Briefing Group, 87 Glebe St., London W4 2BB, England. TEL 0181-994-4632. (Subscr. to: 3 Bluecoat Bldgs., Claypath, Durham DH1 1RF, England. FAX 0191-384-3767) bk.rev. circ. 500. (looseleaf format) **Document type:** newsletter.

TYGODNIK SOLIDARNOSC/SOLIDARITY WEEKLY. see BUSINESS AND ECONOMICS — Economic Situation And Conditions

POLITICAL SCIENCE — CIVIL RIGHTS

323.4 US ISSN 0897-9669
DJK50
UNCAPTIVE MINDS; a journal of information and opinion on Eastern Europe. 1988. q. $30 (Canada & Mexico $35, elsewhere $40). Institute for Democracy in Eastern Europe, 2000 P St., N.W., Ste. 400, Washington, DC 20036-5915. TEL 202-466-7105. FAX 202-466-7140. E-mail: idee@dgs.dgsys.com. Eds. Eric Chenoweth, Irena Lasota. adv. contact: Eugene Kublanow. circ. 4,500. (back issues avail.) **Indexed:** HR Rep. (1988-).
—Faxon.
Description: Covers Eastern Europe, and former Soviet Union, political and social developments, human rights and democratic movements.

323.4 NP
U.N. SENTINEL. 1980. a. $100. Siveast Consultants, Inc., USA, P.O. Box 8510, Kathmandu, Nepal. (Alt. addr.: 9-11-1 Goutami Nagar, Kovvur 534350, West Godavari District, Andhra, India) Ed. C.V. Ramasastry.
Description: Examines U.N. policies and human rights issues.

THE UNITED NATIONS BLUE BOOKS SERIES. see POLITICAL SCIENCE — International Relations

323.4 US ISSN 0082-9641
U.S. COMMISSION ON CIVIL RIGHTS. CLEARINGHOUSE PUBLICATIONS. 1965. irreg., no.97, 1992. U.S. Commission on Civil Rights, 624 Ninth St., N.W., Rm. 600, Washington, DC 20425.
TEL 202-376-8128. FAX 202-376-1163. (back issues avail.) **Document type:** monographic series, government publication.
—BLDSC (3278.538500).
Description: Explores and discusses matters that may come under the jurisdiction of the Civil Rights Act of 1964.

340.5 US
U.S. COMMISSION ON CIVIL RIGHTS. CONSULTATIONS AND CONFERENCES. irreg., latest 1991. free. U.S. Commission on Civil Rights, Clearinghouse Division, 624 Ninth St., N.W., Rm. 600, Washington, DC 20425. TEL 202-376-8128. FAX 202-376-1163. (back issues avail.) **Document type:** monographic series, government publication.
Description: Presents the results from commission conferences and roundtable discussions.

340.5 US
U.S. COMMISSION ON CIVIL RIGHTS. HEARINGS. 1974? irreg., latest 1988. free. U.S. Commission on Civil Rights, Clearinghouse Division, 624 Ninth St., N.W., Rm. 600, Washington, DC 20425.
TEL 202-376-8128. FAX 202-376-1163. (back issues avail.) **Document type:** government publication, monographic series.
Description: Presents results of hearings held before the commission.

340.5 US
U.S. COMMISSION ON CIVIL RIGHTS. STAFF REPORTS. 1974? irreg., latest 1993. free. U.S. Commission on Civil Rights, Clearinghouse Division, 624 Ninth St., N.W., Rm. 600, Washington, DC 20425.
TEL 202-376-8128. FAX 202-376-1163. (back issues avail.) **Document type:** monographic series, government publication.
Description: Discusses important civil rights issues in the U.S.

340.5 US
U.S. COMMISSION ON CIVIL RIGHTS. STATE ADVISORY COMMITTEE REPORTS. ALABAMA. irreg., latest 1992. free. U.S. Commission on Civil Rights, Clearinghouse Division, 624 Ninth St., N.W., Rm. 600, Washington, DC 20425. TEL 202-376-8128.
FAX 202-376-1163. (back issues avail.) **Document type:** government publication, monographic series.

340.5 US
U.S. COMMISSION ON CIVIL RIGHTS. STATE ADVISORY COMMITTEE REPORTS. ALASKA. irreg., latest 1989. free. U.S. Commission on Civil Rights, Clearinghouse Division, 624 Ninth St., N.W., Rm. 600, Washington, DC 20425. TEL 202-376-8128.
FAX 202-376-1163. (back issues avail.) **Document type:** monographic series, government publication.

340.5 US
U.S. COMMISSION ON CIVIL RIGHTS. STATE ADVISORY COMMITTEE REPORTS. ARIZONA. irreg., latest 1992. free. U.S. Commission on Civil Rights, Clearinghouse Division, 624 Ninth St., N.W., Rm. 600, Washington, DC 20425. TEL 202-376-8128.
FAX 202-376-1163. (back issues avail.) **Document type:** monographic series, government publication.

340.5 US
U.S. COMMISSION ON CIVIL RIGHTS. STATE ADVISORY COMMITTEE REPORTS. ARKANSAS. irreg., latest 1992. free. U.S. Commission on Civil Rights, Clearinghouse Division, 624 Ninth St., N.W., Rm. 600, Washington, DC 20425. TEL 202-376-8128. FAX 202-376-1163. (back issues avail.) **Document type:** monographic series, government publication.

340.5 US
U.S. COMMISSION ON CIVIL RIGHTS. STATE ADVISORY COMMITTEE REPORTS. CALIFORNIA. irreg., latest 1991. free. U.S. Commission on Civil Rights, Clearinghouse Division, 624 Ninth St., N.W., Rm. 600, Washington, DC 20425. TEL 202-376-8128. FAX 202-376-1163. (back issues avail.) **Document type:** monographic series, government publication.

340.5 US
U.S. COMMISSION ON CIVIL RIGHTS. STATE ADVISORY COMMITTEE REPORTS. COLORADO. irreg., latest 1989. free. U.S. Commission on Civil Rights, Clearinghouse Division, 624 Ninth St., N.W., Rm. 600, Washington, DC 20425. TEL 202-376-8128. FAX 202-376-1163. (back issues avail.) **Document type:** monographic series, government publication.

340.5 US
U.S. COMMISSION ON CIVIL RIGHTS. STATE ADVISORY COMMITTEE REPORTS. CONNECTICUT. irreg., latest 1990. free. U.S. Commission on Civil Rights, Clearinghouse Division, 624 Ninth St., N.W., Rm. 600, Washington, DC 20425. TEL 202-376-8128. FAX 202-376-1163. (back issues avail.) **Document type:** monographic series, government publication.

340.5 US
U.S. COMMISSION ON CIVIL RIGHTS. STATE ADVISORY COMMITTEE REPORTS. DELAWARE. irreg., latest 1989. free. U.S. Commission on Civil Rights, Clearinghouse Division, 624 Ninth St., N.W., Rm. 600, Washington, DC 20425. TEL 202-376-8128. FAX 202-376-1163. (back issues avail.) **Document type:** monographic series, government publication.

340.5 US
U.S. COMMISSION ON CIVIL RIGHTS. STATE ADVISORY COMMITTEE REPORTS. DISTRICT OF COLUMBIA. irreg., latest 1989. free. U.S. Commission on Civil Rights, Clearinghouse Division, 624 Ninth St., N.W., Rm. 600, Washington, DC 20425. TEL 202-376-8128. FAX 202-376-1163. (back issues avail.) **Document type:** monographic series, government publication.

340.5 US
U.S. COMMISSION ON CIVIL RIGHTS. STATE ADVISORY COMMITTEE REPORTS. FLORIDA. irreg., latest 1991. free. U.S. Commission on Civil Rights, Clearinghouse Division, 624 Ninth St., N.W., Rm. 600, Washington, DC 20425. TEL 202-376-8128. FAX 202-376-1163. (back issues avail.) **Document type:** monographic series, government publication.

340.5 US
U.S. COMMISSION ON CIVIL RIGHTS. STATE ADVISORY COMMITTEE REPORTS. GEORGIA. irreg., latest 1989. free. U.S. Commission on Civil Rights, Clearinghouse Division, 624 Ninth St., N.W., Rm. 600, Washington, DC 20425. TEL 202-376-8128. FAX 202-376-1163. (back issues avail.) **Document type:** monographic series, government publication.

340.5 US
U.S. COMMISSION ON CIVIL RIGHTS. STATE ADVISORY COMMITTEE REPORTS. HAWAII. irreg., latest 1989. free. U.S. Commission on Civil Rights, Clearinghouse Division, 624 Ninth St., N.W., Rm. 600, Washington, DC 20425. TEL 202-376-8128. FAX 202-376-1163. **Document type:** government publication.

340.5 US
U.S. COMMISSION ON CIVIL RIGHTS. STATE ADVISORY COMMITTEE REPORTS. ILLINOIS. irreg., latest 1993. free. U.S. Commission on Civil Rights, Clearinghouse Division, 624 Ninth St., N.W., Rm. 600, Washington, DC 20425. TEL 202-376-8128. FAX 20-376-1163. (back issues avail.) **Document type:** monographic series, government publication.

340.5 US
U.S. COMMISSION ON CIVIL RIGHTS. STATE ADVISORY COMMITTEE REPORTS. INDIANA. irreg., latest 1992. free. U.S. Commission on Civil Rights, Clearinghouse Division, 624 Ninth St., N.W., Rm. 600, Washington, DC 20425. TEL 202-376-8128. FAX 202-376-1163. (back issues avail.) **Document type:** monographic series, government publication.

340.5 US
U.S. COMMISSION ON CIVIL RIGHTS. STATE ADVISORY COMMITTEE REPORTS. IOWA. irreg., latest 1993. free. U.S. Commission on Civil Rights, Clearinghouse Division, 624 Ninth St., N.W., Rm. 600, Washington, DC 20425. TEL 202-376-8128. FAX 202-376-1163. (back issues avail.) **Document type:** monographic series, government publication.

342.73 323 US
U.S. COMMISSION ON CIVIL RIGHTS. STATE ADVISORY COMMITTEE REPORTS. IDAHO. irreg. free. U.S. Commission on Civil Rights, Clearinghouse Division, 624 Ninth St., N.W., Rm. 600, Washington, DC 20425. TEL 202-376-8128. FAX 202-376-1163. (back issues avail.) **Document type:** monographic series, government publication.

340.5 US
U.S. COMMISSION ON CIVIL RIGHTS. STATE ADVISORY COMMITTEE REPORTS. JOINT REPORTS. 1980? irreg., latest 1991. free. U.S. Commission on Civil Rights, Clearinghouse Division, 624 Ninth St., N.W., Rm. 600, Washington, DC 20425. TEL 202-376-8128. FAX 202-376-1163. (back issues avail.) **Document type:** monographic series, government publication.

340.5 US
U.S. COMMISSION ON CIVIL RIGHTS. STATE ADVISORY COMMITTEE REPORTS. KANSAS. irreg., 1992. free. U.S. Commission on Civil Rights, Clearinghouse Division, 624 Ninth St., N.W., Rm. 600, Washington, DC 20425. TEL 202-376-8128. FAX 202-376-1163. (back issues avail.) **Document type:** monographic series, government publication.

340.5 US
U.S. COMMISSION ON CIVIL RIGHTS. STATE ADVISORY COMMITTEE REPORTS. KENTUCKY. irreg., lastest 1989. free. U.S. Commission on Civil Rights, Clearinghouse Division, 624 Ninth St., N.W., Rm. 600, Washington, DC 20425. TEL 202-376-8128. FAX 202-376-1163. **Document type:** monographic series, government publication.

340.5 US
U.S. COMMISSION ON CIVIL RIGHTS. STATE ADVISORY COMMITTEE REPORTS. LOUISIANA. irreg., 1993. free. U.S. Commission on Civil Rights, Clearinghouse Division, 624 Ninth St., N.W., Rm. 600, Washington, DC 20425. TEL 202-376-8128. FAX 202-376-1163. (back issues avail.) **Document type:** monographic series, government publication.

340.5 US
U.S. COMMISSION ON CIVIL RIGHTS. STATE ADVISORY COMMITTEE REPORTS. MAINE. irreg., latest 1989. free. U.S. Commission on Civil Rights, Clearinghouse Division, 624 Ninth St., N.W., Rm. 600, Washington, DC 20425. TEL 202-376-8128. FAX 202-376-1163. **Document type:** government publication.

340.5 US
U.S. COMMISSION ON CIVIL RIGHTS. STATE ADVISORY COMMITTEE REPORTS. MASSACHUSETTS. irreg., latest 1992. free. U.S. Commission on Civil Rights, Clearinghouse Division, 624 Ninth St., N.W., Rm. 600, Washington, DC 20425. TEL 202-376-8128. FAX 202-376-1163. (back issues avail.) **Document type:** monographic series, government publication.

POLITICAL SCIENCE — CIVIL RIGHTS

340.5 US
U.S. COMMISSION ON CIVIL RIGHTS. STATE ADVISORY COMMITTEE REPORTS. MICHIGAN. irreg., latest 1990. free. U.S. Commission on Civil Rights, Clearinghouse Division, 624 Ninth St., N.W., Rm. 600, Washington, DC 20425. TEL 202-376-8128. FAX 202-376-1163. (back issues avail.) **Document type:** monographic series, government publication.

340.5 US
U.S. COMMISSION ON CIVIL RIGHTS. STATE ADVISORY COMMITTEE REPORTS. MINNESOTA. irreg., latest 1993. free. U.S. Commission on Civil Rights, Clearinghouse Division, 624 Ninth St., N.W., Rm. 600, Washington, DC 20425. TEL 202-376-8128. FAX 202-376-1163. (back issues avail.) **Document type:** monographic series, government publication.

340.5 US
U.S. COMMISSION ON CIVIL RIGHTS. STATE ADVISORY COMMITTEE REPORTS. MISSOURI. irreg., latest 1990. free. U.S. Commission on Civil Rights, Clearinghouse Division, 624 Ninth St., N.W., Rm. 600, Washington, DC 20425. TEL 202-376-8128. FAX 202-376-1163. (back issues avail.) **Document type:** monographic series, government publication.

340.5 US
U.S. COMMISSION ON CIVIL RIGHTS. STATE ADVISORY COMMITTEE REPORTS. MONTANA. irreg., latest 1981. free. U.S. Commission on Civil Rights, Clearinghouse Division, 624 Ninth St., N.W., Rm. 600, Washington, DC 20425. TEL 202-376-8128. FAX 202-376-1163. **Document type:** government publication.

340.5 US
U.S. COMMISSION ON CIVIL RIGHTS. STATE ADVISORY COMMITTEE REPORTS. NEBRASKA. irreg., latest 1990. free. U.S. Commission on Civil Rights, Clearinghouse Division, 624 Ninth St., N.W., Rm. 600, Washington, DC 20425. TEL 202-376-8128. FAX 202-376-1163. (back issues avail.) **Document type:** monographic series, government publication.

340.5 US
U.S. COMMISSION ON CIVIL RIGHTS. STATE ADVISORY COMMITTEE REPORTS. NEVADA. irreg., latest 1992. free. U.S. Commission on Civil Rights, Clearinghouse Division, 624 Ninth St., N.W., Rm. 600, Washington, DC 20425. TEL 202-376-8128. FAX 202-376-1163. (back issues avail.) **Document type:** monographic series, government publication.

340.5 US
U.S. COMMISSION ON CIVIL RIGHTS. STATE ADVISORY COMMITTEE REPORTS. NORTH CAROLINA. irreg., 1991. free. U.S. Commission on Civil Rights, Clearinghouse Division, 624 Ninth St., N.W., Rm. 600, Washington, DC 20425. TEL 202-376-8128. FAX 202-376-1163. (back issues avail.) **Document type:** monographic series, government publication.

340.5 US
U.S. COMMISSION ON CIVIL RIGHTS. STATE ADVISORY COMMITTEE REPORTS. NORTH DAKOTA. irreg., latest 1993. free. U.S. Commission on Civil Rights, Clearinghouse Division, 624 Ninth St., N.W., Rm. 600, Washington, DC 20425. TEL 202-376-8128. FAX 202-376-1163. (back issues avail.) **Document type:** monographic series, government publication.

340.5 US
U.S. COMMISSION ON CIVIL RIGHTS. STATE ADVISORY COMMITTEE REPORTS. NEW HAMPSHIRE. irreg., latest 1982. U.S. Commission on Civil Rights, Clearinghouse Division, 624 Ninth St., N.W., Rm. 600, Washington, DC 20425. TEL 202-376-8128. FAX 202-376-1163. (back issues avail.) **Document type:** monographic series, government publication.

340.5 US
U.S. COMMISSION ON CIVIL RIGHTS. STATE ADVISORY COMMITTEE REPORTS. NEW JERSEY. irreg., latest 1990. free. U.S. Commission on Civil Rights, Clearinghouse Division, 624 Ninth St., N.W., Rm. 600, Washington, DC 20425. TEL 202-376-8128. FAX 202-376-1163. (back issues avail.) **Document type:** monographic series, government publication.

340.5 US
U.S. COMMISSION ON CIVIL RIGHTS. STATE ADVISORY COMMITTEE REPORTS. NEW MEXICO. irreg., latest 1989. free. U.S. Commission on Civil Rights, Clearinghouse Division, 624 Ninth St., N.W., Rm. 600, Washington, DC 20425. TEL 202-376-8128. FAX 202-376-1163. **Document type:** government publication.

340.5 US
U.S. COMMISSION ON CIVIL RIGHTS. STATE ADVISORY COMMITTEE REPORTS. NEW YORK. irreg., latest 1992. free. U.S. Commission on Civil Rights, Clearinghouse Division, 624 Ninth St., N.W., Rm. 600, Washington, DC 20425. TEL 202-376-8128. FAX 202-376-1163. (back issues avail.) **Document type:** monographic series, government publication.

340.5 US
U.S. COMMISSION ON CIVIL RIGHTS. STATE ADVISORY COMMITTEE REPORTS. OHIO. irreg., latest 1989. free. U.S. Commission on Civil Rights, Clearinghouse Division, 624 Ninth St., N.W., Rm. 600, Washington, DC 20425. TEL 202-376-8128. FAX 202-376-1163. (back issues avail.) **Document type:** monographic series, government publication.

340.5 US
U.S. COMMISSION ON CIVIL RIGHTS. STATE ADVISORY COMMITTEE REPORTS. OKLAHOMA. irreg., latest 1989. U.S. Commission on Civil Rights, Clearinghouse Division, 624 Ninth St., N.W., Rm. 600, Washington, DC 20425. TEL 202-376-8128. FAX 202-376-1163. **Document type:** government publication.

340.5 US
U.S. COMMISSION ON CIVIL RIGHTS. STATE ADVISORY COMMITTEE REPORTS. PENNSYLVANIA. irreg., latest 1990. free. U.S. Commission on Civil Rights, Clearinghouse Division, 624 Ninth St., N.W., Rm. 600, Washington, DC 20425. TEL 202-376-8128. FAX 202-376-1163. (back issues avail.) **Document type:** monographic series, government publication.

340.5 US
U.S. COMMISSION ON CIVIL RIGHTS. STATE ADVISORY COMMITTEE REPORTS. RHODE ISLAND. irreg., latest 1990. free. U.S. Commission on Civil Rights, Clearinghouse Division, 624 Ninth St., N.W., Rm. 600, Washington, DC 20425. TEL 202-376-8128. FAX 202-376-1163. (back issues avail.) **Document type:** monographic series, government publication.

340.5 US
U.S. COMMISSION ON CIVIL RIGHTS. STATE ADVISORY COMMITTEE REPORTS. SOUTH CAROLINA. irreg., latest 1991. free. U.S. Commission on Civil Rights, Clearinghouse Division, 624 Ninth St., N.W., Rm. 600, Washington, DC 20425. TEL 202-376-8128. FAX 202-376-1163. **Document type:** government publication.

340.5 US
U.S. COMMISSION ON CIVIL RIGHTS. STATE ADVISORY COMMITTEE REPORTS. SOUTH DAKOTA. irreg., latest 1993. free. U.S. Commission on Civil Rights, Clearinghouse Division, 624 Ninth St., N.W., Rm. 600, Washington, DC 20425. TEL 202-376-8128. FAX 202-376-1163. **Document type:** government publication.

340.5 US
U.S. COMMISSION ON CIVIL RIGHTS. STATE ADVISORY COMMITTEE REPORTS. TENNESSEE. irreg., latest 1989. free. U.S. Commission on Civil Rights, Clearinghouse Division, 624 Ninth St., N.W., Rm. 600, Washington, DC 20425. TEL 202-376-8128. FAX 202-376-1163. (back issues avail.) **Document type:** monographic series, government publication.

340.5 US
U.S. COMMISSION ON CIVIL RIGHTS. STATE ADVISORY COMMITTEE REPORTS. TEXAS. irreg., latest 1990. free. U.S. Commission on Civil Rights, Clearinghouse Division, 624 Ninth St., N.W., Rm. 600, Washington, DC 20425. TEL 202-367-8128. FAX 202-376-1163. **Document type:** monographic series, government publication.

340.5 US
U.S. COMMISSION ON CIVIL RIGHTS. STATE ADVISORY COMMITTEE REPORTS. UTAH. irreg., latest 1990. free. U.S. Commission on Civil Rights, Clearinghouse Division, 624 Ninth St., N.W., Rm. 600, Washington, DC 20425. TEL 202-376-8128. FAX 202-376-1163. **Document type:** government publication.

340.5 US
U.S. COMMISSION ON CIVIL RIGHTS. STATE ADVISORY COMMITTEE REPORTS. VERMONT. irreg., latest 1991. free. U.S. Commission on Civil Rights, Clearinghouse Division, 624 Ninth St., N.W., Rm. 600, Washington, DC 20425. TEL 202-376-8128. FAX 202-376-1163. (back issues avail.) **Document type:** monographic series, government publication.

342.73 323
U.S. COMMISSION ON CIVIL RIGHTS. STATE ADVISORY COMMITTEE REPORTS. VIRGINIA. irreg. free. U.S. Commission on Civil Rights, Clearinghouse Division, 624 Ninth St., N.W., Rm. 600, Washington, DC 20425. TEL 202-376-8128. FAX 202-376-1163. (back issues avail.) **Document type:** monographic series, government publication.

340.5 US
U.S. COMMISSION ON CIVIL RIGHTS. STATE ADVISORY COMMITTEE REPORTS. WASHINGTON. irreg., 1980. free. U.S. Commission on Civil Rights, Clearinghouse Division, 624 Ninth St., N.W., Rm. 600, Washington, DC 20425. TEL 202-376-8128. FAX 202-376-1163. **Document type:** government publication.

340.5 US
U.S. COMMISSION ON CIVIL RIGHTS. STATE ADVISORY COMMITTEE REPORTS. WISCONSIN. irreg., latest 1992. free. U.S. Commission on Civil Rights, Clearinghouse Division, 624 Ninth St., N.W., Rm. 600, Washington, DC 20425. TEL 202-376-8128. FAX 202-376-1163. (back issues avail.) **Document type:** monographic series, government publication.

340.5 US
U.S. COMMISSION ON CIVIL RIGHTS. STATE ADVISORY COMMITTEE REPORTS. WYOMING. irreg., latest 1988. free. U.S. Commission on Civil Rights, Clearinghouse Division, 624 Ninth St., N.W., Rm. 600, Washington, DC 20425. TEL 202-376-8128. FAX 202-376-1163. (back issues avail.) **Document type:** monographic series, government publication.

340.5 US
U.S. COMMISSION ON CIVIL RIGHTS. STATE ADVISORY COMMITTEE REPORTS. WEST VIRGINIA. irreg., latest 1993. free. U.S. Commission on Civil Rights, Clearinghouse Division, 624 Ninth St., N.W., Rm. 600, Washington, DC 20425. TEL 202-376-8128. FAX 202-376-1163. (back issues avail.) **Document type:** monographic series, government publication.

340.5 US
U.S. COMMISSION ON CIVIL RIGHTS. STATUTORY AND INTERIM REPORTS. 1975? irreg. (1-2/yr.). free. U.S. Commission on Civil Rights, Clearinghouse Division, 624 Ninth St., N.W., Rm. 600, Washington, DC 20425. TEL 202-376-8128. FAX 202-376-1163. (back issues avail.) **Document type:** monographic series, government publication.
Description: Presents the results of studies and surveys, investigations of civil rights complaints, and appraisals of federal laws and policies undertaken by the commission. Deals with issues of long-term interest.

U.S. DEPARTMENT OF THE INTERIOR. I B I A CITATOR - DESCRIPTIVE WORD INDEX. see *PUBLIC ADMINISTRATION*

U.S. DEPARTMENT OF THE INTERIOR. INTERIOR BOARD OF INDIAN APPEALS. see *PUBLIC ADMINISTRATION*

U.S. EQUAL EMPLOYMENT OPPORTUNITY COMMISSION. ANNUAL REPORT. see *BUSINESS AND ECONOMICS — Labor And Industrial Relations*

323.4 US ISSN 1054-3481
UNITED STATES ANTI-APARTHEID NEWSLETTER. 1988. q. $10. American Friends Service Committee, Inc., Peace Education Division, 1501 Cherry St., Philadelphia, PA 19102. TEL 215-241-7501. FAX 215-864-0104. **Document type:** newsletter.
Description: Promotes communication among organizations that educate, campaign, and organize against apartheid in South Africa.

POLITICAL SCIENCE — CIVIL RIGHTS

UNIVERSITY OF MEMPHIS. CENTER FOR RESEARCH ON WOMEN. RESEARCH PAPERS. see *WOMEN'S STUDIES*

URBAN LEAGUE REVIEW. see *ETHNIC INTERESTS*

323.4 572   UK
URGENT ACTION BULLETIN. (Editions in English, French, Hindi, Italian, Portuguese and Spanish) 1982. irreg. (10/yr.) Survival International, 11-15 Emerald St., London WC1N 3QL, England. TEL 0171-242-1441. FAX 0171-242-1771. **Indexed:** HR Rep. (1985-1987). **Document type:** bulletin.
   Description: Covers events affecting the rights and treatment of indigenous groups.

323.4   GW
V I A MAGAZIN; Fachzeitschrift fuer Praktiker. 1986. bi-m. DM.2.50. Verband der Initiativgruppen in der Auslaenderarbeit e.V., Theaterstr. 10, 53111 Bonn, Germany. TEL 0228-655553. circ. 800.

323.4   GT
▼**VERDAD Y VIDA.** 1994. q. Q.32 (foreign $12). Oficina de Derechos Humanos del Arzobispado de Guatemala, 7a Avda. 7-21, zona 1, Apdo. Postal 723; 01001 Guatemala City, Guatemala. (In US: Box 02-5289, Miami, FL 33102-5289)

323.4   AT
VICTORIA, AUSTRALIA. EQUAL OPPORTUNITY COMMISSION. ANNUAL REPORT. 1979. a. free. Equal Opportunity Commission, 4th Fl., 356 Collins St., Melbourne, Vic, 3000, Australia. TEL 03-602-3338. FAX 03-670-2922. circ. 500. **Document type:** government publication.
   Former titles: Victoria, Australia. Office of the Commissioner for Equal Opportunity. Annual Report (ISSN 1036-9538); Victoria, Australia. Office of the Commissioner for Equal Opportunity and the Victorian Equal Opportunity Board. Annual Report; Victoria, Australia. Equal Opportunity Board. Annual Report.

VIOLENCE AGAINST WOMEN. see *SOCIOLOGY*

323.4   US   ISSN 1075-7651
▼**THE VOICE AND THE VISION;** your guide to understanding issues of race, class and color. 1994. q. $12. Content Communications, Box 4763, Topeka, KS 66604. TEL 913-233-9066. Ed. Jacalyn Mindell. adv.; bk.rev. circ. 10,000. (back issues avail.) **Document type:** consumer publication.

VOICE OF CHOICE. see *RELIGIONS AND THEOLOGY — Other Denominations And Sects*

323.4 200   US
VOICE OF REASON. 1981. q. $10. Americans for Religious Liberty, Box 6656, Silver Spring, MD 20916. TEL 301-598-2447. FAX 310-598-1685. Ed. Edd Doerr. bk.rev. circ. 900. (back issues avail.) **Document type:** newsletter.
   Description: Covers church - state relations and civil liberties issues.

VOICE OF THE BLACK COMMUNITY. see *ETHNIC INTERESTS*

323.4   ES
VOZ/VOICE; information and analysis bulletin. (Text in English) 1992. m. Comision de Derechos Humanos No Gubernamental - Non-governmental Human Rights Commission of El Salvador, Urb. La Esperanza, Pasaje 1, No. 119, San Salvador, El Salvador.
   Description: Provides reports and analysis on occurrences in El Salvador.

323.4 365.64   RU   ISSN 0868-9520
VYZOV. 1990. 6/yr. 3.20 Rub. per no. Permskii Gorispolkom, Upravlenie Vnutrennikh Del, Ul. Druzhby 34, 614600 Perm, Russia. TEL 48-39-24. FAX 32-52-19. Ed. D.E. Krasik. circ. 50,000 (controlled).

W D L NEWS. (Workers Defense League, Inc.) see *BUSINESS AND ECONOMICS — Labor And Industrial Relations*

323.4   US   ISSN 1077-145X
W I D BULLETIN. 3/yr. $12 or exchange basis. Michigan State University, Women and International Development Program, 202 International Center, E. Lansing, MI 48824-1035. TEL 517-353-5040. FAX 517-353-7254. Ed. Rita S. Gallin. circ. 2,000. **Document type:** bulletin.
   Formerly: W I D Newsletter.
   Description: Resource guide, contains information on scholarship, conferences, employment opportunities and other news of interest to WID researchers, practitioners and policy makers.

338.91   US   ISSN 0888-7772
W I D FORUM. 1984. irreg., no.22, 1990. Michigan State University, Women and International Development Program, 202 International Center, E. Lansing, MI 48824-1035. TEL 517-353-5040. FAX 517-353-7254. Ed. Rita S. Gallin. circ. 250. **Document type:** monographic series, academic/scholarly publication.
   Description: Features short reports that describe research projects and development programs and review current policy issues.

W I N NEWS; all the news that is fit to print by, for, about women. (Women's International Network) see *WOMEN'S STUDIES*

323.4   US   ISSN 0892-3116
W R E E - VIEW OF WOMEN. (Text mainly in English; occasionally in Spanish) 1976. q. $6. Women for Racial and Economic Equality, 198 Broadway, Rm. 606, New York, NY 10038. TEL 212-385-1103. Ed. Jan C. Jamshidi. adv.; bk.rev. circ. 15,000.
   Former titles: W R E E - View; (until 1983): W R E E - View of Women.
   Description: Covers racism, affirmative action, women's economic security and equality.

323.4 284   GW   ISSN 0936-6520
WAS UNS BETRIFFT; Zeitschrift fuer Kriegsdienstverweigerer und Zivildienstleistende. Short title: W U B. 1970. q. DM.12. Evangelische Arbeitsgemeinschaft zur Betreuung der Kriegsdienstverweigerer (EAK), Carl-Schurz-Str. 17, 28209 Bremen, Germany. FAX 0421-3491961. (Subscr. to: Buero Pfarrer Schlueter, Postfach 260230, 50515 Cologne, Germany) circ. 55,000. (back issues avail.) **Document type:** bulletin.

WASHINGTON (STATE). EMPLOYMENT SECURITY DEPARTMENT. AFFIRMATIVE ACTION INFORMATION. see *BUSINESS AND ECONOMICS — Labor And Industrial Relations*

WASHINGTON EQUAL TIMES. see *WOMEN'S INTERESTS*

323.4   US   ISSN 0512-610X
DT1
WASHINGTON NOTES ON AFRICA. 1972. 3/yr. $30 individual membership; libraries $20. Washington Office on Africa, 110 Maryland Ave., N.E., Washington, DC 20002. TEL 202-546-7961. FAX 202-546-1545. (also avail. in microfiche; back issues avail.) **Document type:** academic/scholarly publication.
   Description: Deals with the civil rights issues and international relations of southern Africa, especially regarding issues and legislation.

323.4   US   ISSN 0083-8594
JC599.U52
WEST VIRGINIA. HUMAN RIGHTS COMMISSION. REPORT.* 1961. a. free. Human Rights Commission, 1321 Plaza E., Ste. 104, Charleston, WV 25301-1405. TEL 304-348-2616. circ. 1,000.

323.4 326.7   CN
▼**WILSON ON CHILDREN AND THE LAW.** 1994. q. Can.$225. Butterworths Canada Ltd., Part of the Reed Elsevier group, 75 Clegg Rd., Markham, ON L6G 1A1, Canada. TEL 905-479-2665. FAX 905-479-2826. Ed. Jeffery Wilson. **Document type:** trade publication.
   Description: For practitioners, accountants, and child care professionals, including social workers. Examines in detail statutory provisions and common-law principles governing the rights of children.

WITCHCRAFT DIGEST. see *PARAPSYCHOLOGY AND OCCULTISM*

323.1 301.412   US   ISSN 0049-7770
WOMAN ACTIVIST; an action bulletin for women's rights from the courthouse to the White House. 1971. m. (10/yr.). $17. Woman Activist, Inc., 2310 Barbour Rd., Falls Church, VA 22043. Ed. Flora Crater. adv.; bk.rev.; charts; stat.; circ. 600 (controlled). (processed; also avail. in microform) **Document type:** newsletter.
   Description: Covers social and legal issues important to equal opportunities for women.

323.4   US
WOMEN STRIKE FOR PEACE. LEGISLATIVE ALERT. 1979. 10/yr. $15 (effective 1995-1996). Women Strike for Peace (Washington), 110 Maryland Ave., N.E., Ste.302, Washington, DC 20002. TEL 202-543-2660. FAX 202-546-0090. Ed. Edith Villastrigo. bk.rev. circ. 3,300. (looseleaf format; back issues avail.) **Document type:** newsletter.
   Description: Contains legislative updates on peace and human rights issues.

323.4   US
WOMEN'S WATCH; reporting on law and policy change in accordance with the principles of the Convention on the Elimination of All Forms of Discrimination Against Women. m. $20. International Women's Rights Action Watch, Women, Public Policy and Development Program, Humphrey Institute of Public Affairs, University of Minnesota, 301 - 19th Ave. S., Minneapolis, MN 55455. Ed.Bd.

323.4 341.481   NE   ISSN 0165-4241
WORDT VERVOLGD. 1968. m. fl.52.50 membership. Amnesty International, Dutch Section, Keizersgracht 620, 1017 ER Amsterdam, Netherlands. TEL 31-20-6264436. FAX 31-20-6240889. Ed. Willem Offenberg. adv. contact: Maria de Groot. circ. 30,000 (paid). **Document type:** bulletin, newsletter.
   Description: Provides background to current concerns and developments in the human rights field and within the organization.

323.4 572   CN
WORLD COUNCIL OF INDIGENOUS PEOPLES. NEWSLETTER. 1987. irreg. (4-6/yr.). World Council of Indigenous Peoples, 555 King Edward Ave., 2nd Fl., Ottawa, ON K1N 6N5, Canada. TEL 613-230-9030. Ed. Donald Rojoas Marota. **Document type:** newsletter.
   Description: Contains news and events of the organization, whose purpose is to advance the self-sufficiency and autonomy of indigenous peoples.

WORLD DIRECTORY OF HUMAN RIGHTS RESEARCH AND TRAINING INSTITUTIONS. see *BUSINESS AND ECONOMICS — Trade And Industrial Directories*

WORLD NEWS DIGEST. see *POLITICAL SCIENCE*

323.4   CH
WORLD OUTLOOK/SHIJIE ZHANWANG. (Text in English) 1992. bi-m. NT.$500 (Asia $25; elsewhere $30). World League for Freedom and Democracy, Taipei, 3Fl., 333 Tun Hua South Rd., Sec. 2, Taipei, Taiwan 106, Republic of China. TEL 886-2-7387944. FAX 886-2-736-3349. TELEX 26364 WLFD ROC. Ed. Pao-chi Lung.

WORLD UNIVERSITY SERVICE. ACADEMIC FREEDOM. see *EDUCATION*

323.4   UN   ISSN 0084-4098
YEARBOOK ON HUMAN RIGHTS. (Editions in English and French) 1946. irreg., latest 1985. price varies. United Nations Publications, Rm. DC2-853, New York, NY 10017. TEL 212-963-8302; 800-253-9646. FAX 212-963-3489. (Or: Distribution and Sales Section, CH-1211 Geneva 10, Switzerland) (also avail. in microfiche; reprint service avail. from KTO) **Indexed:** Refug.Abstr. —BLDSC (9413.300000).

ZEICHEN. see *RELIGIONS AND THEOLOGY — Protestant*

323.4   GW   ISSN 0342-5851
ZEITLUPE. 1975. 2/yr. free. Bundeszentrale fuer Politische Bildung, Referat IV-2, Berliner Freiheit 7, 53111 Bonn, Germany. TEL 0228-515224. FAX 0228-515113. Eds. Hannegret Wurzel, Ulf Marwege. circ. 500,000. (back issues avail.) **Document type:** bulletin.

323.4　　　GW　　ISSN 0721-5746
ZEITSCHRIFT FUER AUSLAENDERRECHT UND AUSLAENDERPOLITIK. Short title: Z A R. q. DM.89. Nomos Verlagsgesellschaft mbH und Co. KG, Waldseestr. 3-5, 76530 Baden-Baden, Germany. TEL 07221-21040. FAX 07221-210427. (Subscr. to: Postfach 610, 76484 Baden-Baden, Germany) circ. 2,000. **Indexed:** ELLIS, Refug.Abstr. **Document type:** newsletter.
—BLDSC (9426.775000). **CCC.**

323.4　　　GW　　ISSN 0170-0413
ZEITSCHRIFT FUER DEUTSCHES UND INTERNATIONALES BAURECHT. 1978. bi-m. DM.240 (foreign DM.268). (Deutsche Gesellschaft fuer Baurecht e.V., Institut fuer Deutsches und Internationales Baurecht) Bauverlag GmbH, Postfach 1460, 65004 Wiesbaden, Germany. TEL 06123-700-0. FAX 06123-700122. Eds. H.G. Watzke, W. Soefker. adv. contact: H.J. Kopp. circ. 2,000. **Document type:** academic/scholarly publication.

323.4　　　GW
4-3 FACHZEITSCHRIFT ZU KRIEGSDIENSTVERWEIGERUNG, WEHRDIENST UND ZIVILDIENST. 1982. q. DM.26. D F G - V K, Schwanenstr. 16, 42551 Velbert, Germany. TEL 02051-4217. FAX 02051-4210. circ. 1,000.
Description: Provides information about conscientious objection to military service and alternative civilian service.

10 THINGS JESUS WANTS YOU TO KNOW. see RELIGIONS AND THEOLOGY — Roman Catholic

POLITICAL SCIENCE — International Relations

see also Law–International Law

327　　　US　　ISSN 0743-8834
A C O A ACTION NEWS.* s-a. \$15 to individuals; institutions \$25. American Committee on Africa, 17 John St., Fl. 12, New York, NY 10038-4010. TEL 212-962-1210. FAX 212-964-8570. Ed. Richard Knight. bibl.; tr.lit.

327 341　　　UK
▼**A C R O N Y M BOOKLET SERIES.** 1994. irreg., no.6, Apr. 1995. £5 per no. A C R O N Y M Consortium, c/o Verification Technology Information Centre (VERTIC), Carrara House, 20 Embankment Pl., London WC2N 6NN. TEL 0171-925-0867. FAX 0171-925-0861. E-mail: vertic@gn.apc.org. (back issues avail.) **Document type:** monographic series.
Description: Provides a summary and analysis of negotiations on a comprehensive nuclear test ban treaty and the Non-proliferation Treaty Review and Extension Conference.

320　　　FR
A D U K. (Adresar Ukraintsiv u Vilnomu Sviti) 1973. irreg. Premiere Imprimerie Ukrainienne en France, 3, rue du Sabot, 75006 Paris, France. illus.

A.I.D. HIGHLIGHTS. (U.S. Agency for International Development) see BUSINESS AND ECONOMICS — International Development And Assistance

325.21　　　US　　ISSN 1066-3584
A N E R A NEWSLETTER. 1969. q. free. American Near East Refugee Aid, Inc., 1522 K St., N.W., No. 202, Washington, DC 20005. TEL 202-347-2558. FAX 202-682-1637. E-mail: gubser@access.digex.net. Ed. Traci Little. bk.rev.; illus. circ. 34,000. **Indexed:** HR Rep. **Document type:** newsletter.
Description: Information about ANERA activities: economic development and relief in the West Bank, Gaza Strip and Lebanon.

327　　　NR
A P R I JOURNAL. 1986. bi-m. £N48(\$40) African Peace Research Institute, P.O. Box 51757, Falomo, Ikoyi, Lagos, Nigeria. TEL 633437. Ed. Temitope Oguntayo. bk.rev.; stat.; cum.index. circ. 250. (back issues avail.)
Formerly: A P R I Newsletter.
Description: Carries and analyzes information on current peace research issues, i.e. environment, violence conflict, disarmament, and foreign debt.

A P S NEWS SERVICE. (Arab Press Service) see ENERGY

A S A E INTERNATIONAL NEWS. (American Society of Association Executives) see BUSINESS AND ECONOMICS — Management

325　　　AU　　ISSN 0001-2947
HV640
A W R BULLETIN; quarterly on refugee problems. (Text in English, French, German, Italian) 1963. q. S.440 (effective 1996). (Association for the Study of the World Refugee Problems) Wilhelm Braumueller, Universitaets-Verlagsbuchhandlung GmbH, Servitengasse 5, A-1092 Vienna, Austria. TEL 01-3191159. FAX 01-3102805. Eds. Michael Wollenschlaeger, Eugen Antalovsky. adv. contact: Susanne Mondl. bk.rev.; index. circ. 1,000. **Indexed:** HR Rep., Refug.Abstr. **Document type:** bulletin.
—BLDSC (1840.700000).

327　　　BO
ACADEMIA DIPLOMATICA BOLIVIANA. REVISTA ANUAL. 1991. a. Ministerio de Relaciones Exteriores y Culto, Academia Diplomatica Boliviana, Plaza Murillo esq. Junin, La Paz, Bolivia. TEL 366269. **Document type:** academic/scholarly publication.

327　　　US　　ISSN 1056-5752
JX1901
ACCESS RESOURCE BRIEF. 12/yr. \$49. ACCESS: A Security Information Service, 1511 K St., N.W., Ste. 643, Washington, DC 20005. TEL 202-783-6050. FAX 202-783-4767. Ed. Bruce Seymore II. bibl.; charts. circ. 2,500. (back issues avail.) **Document type:** newsletter.
Description: Provides an overview of timely issues relating to international affairs, peace and security; lists sources of information from diverse viewpoints and suggested readings representing the full political spectrum.
Refereed Serial

327　　　US　　ISSN 1045-4829
ACCESS SECURITY SPECTRUM. 2/yr. ACCESS: A Security Information Service, 1511 K St., N.W., Ste. 643, Washington, DC 20005. TEL 202-783-6050. FAX 202-783-4767. **Document type:** monographic series.

327　　　IT
ACQUE E TERRE; bimestrale di politica internazionale e cooperazione allo sviluppo. 1991. bi-m. L.50000 (foreign L.100000). Acque e Terre s.r.l., Via Andrea Costa 20, 30172 Venice Mestre, Italy. TEL 39-41-983058. FAX 39-41-981679. Eds. Vettor Maria Corsetti, Nereo Laroni. adv. circ. 10,000. **Document type:** newspaper.

327　　　US　　ISSN 0890-118X
ACROSS FRONTIERS. 1983. q. \$10 to individuals; institutions \$25. Box 2382, Berkeley, CA 94702. Ed. A. Winton Jackson. bk.rev.; illus. circ. 2,000. (back issues avail.) **Indexed:** Alt.Press Ind., Left Ind.

327　　　UK　　ISSN 0567-932X
U162
THE ADELPHI PAPERS. 1964. 10/yr. £94(\$155) (effective 1996). (International Institute for Strategic Studies) Oxford University Press, Oxford Journals, Walton St., Oxford OX2 6DP, England. TEL 44-1865-267907. FAX 44-1865-267773. E-mail: jnlorders@oup.co.uk. (Subscr. in U.S. to: Oxford University Press Inc., 2001 Evans Rd., Cary, NC 27513. TEL 919-677-0977. FAX 919-677-1714) bibl.; charts; stat. circ. 7,000. (also avail. in microform from UMI; back issues avail.; reprint service avail. from UMI) **Indexed:** Abstr.Mil.Bibl., PROMT. **Document type:** academic/scholarly publication.
—BLDSC (0680.400000); Faxon; SWETS; UMI; UnCover. **CCC.**
Description: Contains monographs analyzing current and future problems of international security concerns.

AFFARI SOCIALI INTERNAZIONALI. see SOCIOLOGY

AFGHANISTAN STUDIES JOURNAL. see HISTORY — History Of Asia

AFRICA; rivista trimestrale di studi e documentazione. see HISTORY — History Of Africa

AFRICA. see HISTORY — History Of Africa

327　　　US　　ISSN 0748-4356
DT38
AFRICA INSIDER; a twice monthly report on US-African affairs from Washington, DC. 1984. fortn. \$37.50 to individuals (foreign \$67.50); institutions \$75 (foreign \$175). Matthews Associates, Box 53398, Temple Heights Sta., Washington, DC 20009. TEL 301-309-6632. Ed. Dan Matthews. **Document type:** newsletter.
Description: Covers political and foreign affairs analysis in relations between Africa and the United States.

327　　　US　　ISSN 0001-9836
DT1
AFRICA REPORT. 1957. bi-m. \$36 to individuals; institutions \$48. African-American Institute, 833 United Nations Plaza, New York, NY 10017. TEL 212-949-5666. FAX 212-682-6174. TELEX 666565 AFRAM. (Subscr. to: Box 3000, Denville, NJ 07834) Ed. Margaret A. Novicki. adv.; bk.rev.; charts; illus.; index. circ. 14,000. (also avail. in microform from UMI; back issues avail.; reprint service avail. from SWZ,UMI) **Indexed:** A.B.C.Pol.Sci., Abstr.Mil.Bibl., Acad.Ind., Amer.Hist.& Life, Bibl.Ind., Curr.Cont.Africa, Curr.Cont.M.E., Documentatieblad, Geo.Abstr., Hist.Abstr., HR Rep. (1969-), Hum.Ind., IDA, M.L.A., Mid.East: Abstr.& Ind., P.A.I.S., Per.Islam. (1991-), Polit.Sci.Abstr., Refug.Abstr., Rural Recreat.Tour.Abstr., Soc.Sci.Ind., World Agri.Econ.& Rural Sociol.Abstr.
●Also available online. Vendor(s): University Microfilms International.
—BLDSC (0732.180000); Faxon; SWETS; UMI; UnCover.
Description: Covers African political and economic developments.

327　　　NR
AFRICAN JOURNAL OF INTERNATIONAL AFFAIRS & DEVELOPMENT. s-a. \$35.95 to individuals (£25.95); institutions \$65.95 (£46.95). Obafemi Awolowo University, Department of International Relations, University P.O. Box 1044, Ile-Ife, Osun State, Nigeria. (Subscr. to: College Press Ltd., 27 Are Ave., New Bodija, Secretariat, P.O. Box 30678, Ibadan, Oyo State, Nigeria. TEL 234-36-231780. FAX 234-36-241000) Eds. Jide Owoeye, Adebayo Olukoshi. bk.rev. **Document type:** academic/scholarly publication.
Description: Publishes articles on the legal, political, diplomatic, economic, environmental, sociocultural, and military issues at the core of Africa's foreign relations and world affairs.

327　　　GW　　ISSN 0340-5796
AFRIKA. (Editions in English and French) 1960. bi-m. Afrika-Verlag, Raiffeisenstr. 24, 85276 Pfaffenhofen, Germany. TEL 08441-8690. FAX 08441-76582. Eds. Inga Krugmann-Randolf, Ursula Bell. adv. contact: R. Metzner. bk.rev.; charts; illus. circ. 30,000. **Indexed:** Curr.Cont.Africa. **Document type:** bulletin.

AFRIKA SUED. see BUSINESS AND ECONOMICS — International Development And Assistance

960　　　FR　　ISSN 0002-0478
DT348
AFRIQUE CONTEMPORAINE; documents d'Afrique noire et de Madagascar. 1962. q. 260 F. (Europe 315 F., elsewhere 400 F.). Documentation Francaise, 29-31 Quai Voltaire, 75344 Paris Cedex 07, France. TEL 1-4015-7000. Ed. Michel Gavd. bk.rev.; bibl.; charts; stat. circ. 2,000. (also avail. in microfiche from DFR) **Indexed:** Bibl.Ling., Curr.Cont.Africa, Documentatieblad, IDA, Int.Polit.Sci.Abstr.
—BLDSC (0735.320000); SWETS.
Description: Looks at important political, economic, social and cultural events in sub-Saharan Africa, Madagascar and Indian Ocean islands.

940　　　BE　　ISSN 0002-080X
AGENOR. (Text in English) 1967. q. 1800 Fr. Agenor Societe Cooperative, 22 rue Toulouse, B-1040 Brussels, Belgium. FAX 2-230-5957. Ed. John Lambert. adv.; illus. circ. 1,000. (also avail. in microfilm from RPI; back issues avail.) **Indexed:** Mid.East: Abstr.& Ind.

AHFAD JOURNAL; women and change. see WOMEN'S STUDIES

AKTUELLER INFORMATIONSDIENST MODERNER ORIENT/ORIGINAL NEWS AND COMMENTS FROM MIDDLE EASTERN NEWSPAPERS. see ORIENTAL STUDIES

POLITICAL SCIENCE — INTERNATIONAL RELATIONS

327 331   UK   ISSN 0950-8473
AL DIA. (Text in Spanish) 1987. m. £137($178) Latin American Newsletters, 61 Old St., London EC1V 9HX, England. TEL 0171-251-0012. FAX 0171-253-8193. Ed. Miguel Angel Diez. (back issues avail.) **Document type:** newsletter.

949.65   AA   ISSN 0002-4643
ALBANIA OGGI. vol.3, 1970. bi-m. Associazione Nazionale Italia Albania, c/o Ndermarrja e Librit, Tirana, Albania. Ed. Giorgio Puglisi. adv.; charts; illus.

327 954 942   II   ISSN 0002-5585
ALL-INDIA ANGLO-INDIAN ASSOCIATION. REVIEW. vol.39, 1968. m. All India Anglo-Indian Association, Bombay Life Bldg., Connaught Circus, New Delhi 110001, India. Ed. Frank Anthony. bk.rev.; charts; illus.

ALTERNATIVE TRADING NEWS. see *BUSINESS AND ECONOMICS — International Development And Assistance*

327   US   ISSN 0304-3754
HC59.7
ALTERNATIVES (BOULDER); social transformation and humane governance. 1974. q. $35 to individuals; institutions $75. (World Order Models Project, Centre for the Study of Developing Societies, International Peace Research Institute Meigaku) Lynne Rienner Publishers, 1800 30th St., Ste. 314, Boulder, CO 80301-1032. TEL 303-444-6684. FAX 303-444-0824. Ed.Bd. adv.; index. circ. 1,000. (also avail. in microfilm from UMI,WSH; microfiche from UMI; reprint service avail. from UMI,WSH) **Indexed:** A.B.C.Pol.Sci., ALt.Press Ind., Amer.Hist.& Life, Art Ind., Biog.Ind., C.L.I., Environ.Abstr., Fut.Surv., Hist.Abstr., Leg.Per., Mag.Ind., P.A.I.S., R.G., Refug.Abstr. **Document type:** academic/scholarly publication.
—BLDSC (0803.670000); Genuine Article; SWETS; UMI; UnCover. **CCC**.
Description: Analyzes the structure of current world problems, presenting alternative scenarios and policies, to promote discussion of ways to achieve a more equitable future.

AMERICAN ASSEMBLY. REPORT. see *POLITICAL SCIENCE*

AMERICAN FOREIGN POLICY INDEX; a guide to foreign policy and foreign relations publications of the U.S. government. see *POLITICAL SCIENCE — Abstracting, Bibliographies, Statistics*

327   US   ISSN 1080-3920
E840
AMERICAN FOREIGN POLICY INTERESTS. 1977. bi-m. $130 to institutions (foreign $170) (effective Jul. 1995). (National Committee on American Foreign Policy) M.E. Sharpe, Inc., 80 Business Park Dr., Armonk, NY 10504. TEL 914-273-1800; 800-541-6563. FAX 914-273-2106. bibl. circ. 1,500. (back issues avail.) **Document type:** academic/scholarly publication.
Former titles: American Foreign Policy Newsletter (ISSN 0738-3169); (until 1982): National Committee on American Foreign Policy. Newsletter.

327 973   US
AMERICAN FOREIGN POLICY LIBRARY. irreg. price varies. Harvard University Press, 79 Garden St., Cambridge, MA 02138. TEL 617-495-2600.
FAX 617-495-5898. **Document type:** monographic series.
Refereed Serial

327   GW
AMERICAN-GERMAN STUDIES/DEUTSCH-AMERIKANISCHE STUDIEN. (Text and summaries in English, German) 1985. irreg. price varies. Verlag Hans-Dieter Heinz, Steiermaerkerstr. 132, 70469 Stuttgart, Germany. Ed.Bd. bk.rev. circ. 400. (back issues avail.) **Indexed:** M.L.A.

327 296   US   ISSN 0275-5661
DS101
AMERICAN JEWISH ALTERNATIVES TO ZIONISM. REPORT. 1969. irreg. (2-3/yr.). contribution. American Jewish Alternatives to Zionism, Inc., 347 Fifth Ave., Ste. 605A, New York, NY 10016-5010. TEL 212-213-9125. FAX 212-213-9142. bk.rev. circ. 1,500.

AMERICAN O R T FEDERATION. YEARBOOK. see *ETHNIC INTERESTS*

327   US   ISSN 0272-2011
F1008
AMERICAN REVIEW OF CANADIAN STUDIES. 1971. q. $60 to individuals; institutions $105. Association for Canadian Studies in the U S, One Dupont Circle, Ste. 620, Washington, DC 20036. TEL 202-887-6375. FAX 202-296-8379. Ed. Robert Thacker. adv.; bk.rev.; bibl. circ. 1,200. (also avail. in microform from MML,UMI; reprint service avail. from UMI) **Indexed:** Amer.Bibl.Slavic & E.Eur.Stud, Amer.Hist.& Life, Bibl.Engl.Lang.& Lit., Can.B.P.I., Can.Lit.Ind., Can.Per.Ind., Can.Wom.Per.Ind., CMI, Hist.Abstr., Polit.Sci.Abstr. **Document type:** academic/scholarly publication.
—Faxon; UMI; UnCover.
Formerly: A C S U S Newsletter (ISSN 0193-6093)

327 370.196 500   US
AMERICANS FOR THE UNIVERSALITY OF UNESCO NEWSLETTER. 1985. q. (with occasional supplement issues). $25. Americans for the Universality of Unesco, Box 18418, Asheville, NC 28814. TEL 704-253-5383. FAX 704-252-9728. Ed. John E. Fobes. bk.rev. circ. 3,000. (back issues avail.) **Document type:** newsletter.
Description: Contains news and commentary on Unesco, including multilateral cooperation in education, science, culture, and communication, as well as the U.S. role in these matters.

AMERICAS. see *HUMANITIES: COMPREHENSIVE WORKS*

327 338.91   CN
AMERICAS UPDATE. 1979. bi-m. Can.$25 to individuals; institutions Can.$40. Latin American Working Group, 603 1-2 Parliament St., Toronto, ON M4X 1P9, Canada. TEL 416-966-4773. FAX 416-921-0071. (Co-sponsor: Jesuit Centre for Social Faith and Justice) Ed. Kathy Price. circ. 2,000. (looseleaf format; back issues avail.) **Indexed:** HR Rep. **Document type:** bulletin.
●Also available online. Vendor(s): Knight-Ridder, Inc., NewsNet.
Formerly: Central America Update (ISSN 0823-7689)
Description: Provides analysis of events in Latin America and the Caribbean; highlights Canada's relations to the region.

AMITIES. see *RELIGIONS AND THEOLOGY — Roman Catholic*

327 947 954   II
AMITY. (Text in English) 1972. m. Indo-Soviet Cultural Society, Barakhamba Rd., Connaught Circus, New Delhi 110001, India. adv.; bk.rev.; illus. circ. 5,000.
Formerly: I S C U S Bulletin (ISSN 0019-0616)

323   UK   ISSN 0309-068X
AMNESTY INTERNATIONAL REPORT. (Editions in English, French, Arabic and Spanish) 1962. a. £22($41) (subscr. includes Amnesty International Newsletter). Amnesty International, 1 Easton St., London WC1X 8DJ, England. TEL 44-71-413-5500.
FAX 44-71-956-1157. TELEX 28502. (also avail. in microfiche from IDC) **Indexed:** HR Rep., Refug.Abstr. **Document type:** corporate report.
—BLDSC (0859.395000).
Formerly: Amnesty International Annual Report (ISSN 0569-9495)

980   BO   ISSN 0003-2948
ANDES;* revista interamericana. 1967. $1.50 per no. Casilla 4171, La Paz, Bolivia.
Description: Explores politics and government in Latin America.

327 942 943   UK   ISSN 0003-3340
ANGLO-GERMAN REVIEW. 1954. q. £1 per no. to non-members. Anglo-German Association, 158 Buckingham Palace Rd., London SW1W 9TR, England. TEL 44-171-259-9922. Ed. John Thum. adv. contact: P. Johnston. bk.rev. circ. 1,000. **Document type:** academic/scholarly publication, newsletter.
Description: Discusses relations between Britain and Germany, activities of the Association.

327 942 946   UK   ISSN 0003-3383
ANGLO-SPANISH QUARTERLY REVIEW. 1951. q. £8 (foreign £17). Anglo-Spanish Society, 61 Pont St., London SW1X 0GB, England. TEL 0279-724024. Ed. A.T. Wright. adv.; bk.rev.; illus.; index every 5 yrs. circ. 950.
Description: Publishes articles on matters of Anglo-Spanish interest, Spanish culture, civilization and history.

327   FR   ISSN 0066-295X
ANNUAIRE DIPLOMATIQUE ET CONSULAIRE DE LA REPUBLIQUE FRANCAISE. 1858. a. membership. Ministere des Affaires Etrangeres, Direction du Personnel et de l'Administration Generale, 23 rue La Perouse, 75016 Paris, France. (Subscr. to: L'Imprimerie Nationale, B.P. 514, 59505 Douai Cedex, France. TEL 27-93-70-70) Ed. Sarah Ausseil. adv. circ. 3,000.

327 320   US
ANNUAL EDITIONS: WORLD POLITICS. 1977. a. $12.95. Dushkin Publishing Group, Sluice Dock, Guilford, CT 06437-9989. TEL 203-453-4351; 800-243-6532. FAX 203-453-6000. Ed. Helen Purkitt; Pub. Ian Nielsen. illus. **Document type:** academic/scholarly publication.
Refereed Serial

327   UK   ISSN 0962-3868
ANNUAL REVIEW OF EUROPEAN COMMUNITY AFFAIRS (YEAR). (Text in English) 1990. a. 2400 BEF. (Centre for European Policy Studies, BE) Brassey's (UK) Ltd., 33 John St., London WC1N 2AT, England. TEL 0171-753-7777. FAX 0171-753-7794. (Subscr. to: Turpin Distribution Services, Distribution Centre, Blackhorse Rd., Letchworth, Herts. SG6 1HN, England. TEL 01462-672555. FAX 01462-480947)
—BLDSC (1522.506000).
Description: Provides E.C. specialists, students, and general readers with a comprehensive and authoritative account of E.C. developments.

ANNUAL REVIEW OF PROJECT PERFORMANCE AUDIT RESULTS. see *BUSINESS AND ECONOMICS — International Development And Assistance*

341.13 327   US   ISSN 0066-4340
JX1977.A1
ANNUAL REVIEW OF UNITED NATIONS AFFAIRS. 1949. a. price varies. Oceana Publications, Inc., Dobbs Ferry, NY 10522. TEL 914-693-8100.
FAX 914-693-0402. circ. 500. (back issues avail.)
—BLDSC (1529.500000).
Description: Reviews activities of the United Nations.

327   IT
ANNUARIO DIPLOMATICO DELLA REPUBBLICA ITALIANA. 1963. a. Ministero degli Affari Esteri, Rome, Italy. circ. 1,500.
Formerly: Annuario Diplomatico del Regno d'Italia.
Description: Covers areas of diplomatic and administrative personnel.

956 960   UK   ISSN 0003-7389
ARAB.* 1967. m. League of Arab States, 52 Green St., London W1Y 3RH, England. bk.rev.; charts; illus.; stat.

956   KE
ARAB WORLD. (Text in English and Kiswahili) 1972. bi-m. League of Arab States, Uchumi House, 10th Fl., Box 30770, Nairobi, Kenya. illus.
Formerly: Voice of Egypt.

327   IT
ARCOBALENO DI PACE; materiali e strumenti per una cultura di pace nella solidarieta. 1991. bi-m. Caritas Italiana, Viale F. Baldelli 41, 00146 Rome, Italy. TEL 06-541921. FAX 06-5410300. Ed. Giuseppe Benvegnu Pasini.
Description: Covers peace and solidarity.

327   SY
ARD. 1973. fortn. Al-Ard Institute of Palestine Studies - Muassasat al-Ard Lil-Dirasat al-Filastiniyah, Box 3392, Damascus, Syria. illus.

ARENA; informativni drustveno politicki ilustrirani tjednik. see *POLITICAL SCIENCE*

POLITICAL SCIENCE — INTERNATIONAL RELATIONS

355   AG   ISSN 0325-0792
ARGENTINA. ESCUELA DE DEFENSA NACIONAL. REVISTA. 1973. s-a. exchange basis. Escuela de Defensa Nacional, Maipu 262, 1084 Buenos Aires, Argentina. TEL 54-1-326-1318. FAX 54-1-325-3510. Ed. Col. Hugo G. Sarno. adv.; charts; illus.; index. circ. 1,600. **Indexed:** Abstr.Mil.Bibl. **Document type:** academic/scholarly publication, government publication.
  Formerly (until 1974): Argentina. Escuela Nacional de Guerra. Revista (ISSN 0325-0784)
  Description: Articles cover politics, foreign affairs, national defense and geopolitics.

327   AG
ARGENTINA. MINISTERIO DE RELACIONES EXTERIORES Y CULTO. REVISTA. 1974. q. free. Ministerio de Relaciones Exteriores y Culto, Buenos Aires, Argentina.

947   AI   ISSN 0004-2293
ARMENYA SEGODNIA. English edition: Armenia Today. 1966. bi-m. free. Armenian Society for Friendship and Cultural Relations with Foreign Countries, Ul. Abovian, 3, Erevan, Armenia. TEL 56-45-14. Ed. Arsen Kakossian. charts; illus. circ. 60,000. **Indexed:** Numis.Lit.

341.37   US   ISSN 0886-3490
ARMS CONTROL REPORTER. 1982. m. (11/yr.). $175 to students (foreign $185); institutions $375 (foreign $385); businesses and government $625 (foreign $635). Institute for Defense and Disarmament Studies, 675 Massachusetts Ave., 8th Fl., Cambridge, MA 02139-3309. TEL 617-354-4337. FAX 617-354-1450. TELEX 403618 IDDS USA UD. E-mail: idds@world.std.com. Ed. Jessie Saacke; Pub. Randall Forsberg. abstr.; charts; stat. circ. 330. (looseleaf format; also avail. in diskette format; back issues avail.) **Document type:** academic/scholarly publication.
  Description: Comprehensive compilation of all public information on all international arms control negotiations and relevant weapons. Non-partisan chronologies, texts, and analysis.

ARMS CONTROL TODAY. see *POLITICAL SCIENCE*

ASIA - AFRICA FORUM. see *ETHNIC INTERESTS*

327   US
ASIA - PACIFIC OBSERVER. 1991. q. free. East-West Center Public Education, Public Affairs Office, 1777 East-West Road, Honolulu, HI 96848. TEL 808-944-7194. Ed. Grady Timmons. **Document type:** newsletter.
  Formerly: East-West Center. Views (ISSN 1055-9795)
  Description: Reports on analysis of contemporary issues in the region conducted by East-West Center researchers and their colleagues worldwide.

327   US
ASIA SERIAL REPORTS: KOREA: KULLOJA. irreg. $360 in US, Canada, Mexico; elsewhere $720. (Joint Publications Research Service) U.S. National Technical Information Service, 5825 Port Royal Rd., Springfield, VA 22161. TEL 703-487-4630.

327   US
ASIA SERIAL REPORTS: VIET NAM: TOP CHI CHONG SAN. irreg. $300 in U.S., Canada, Mexico; elsewhere $600. (Joint Publications Research Service) U.S. National Technical Information Service, 5825 Port Royal Rd., Springfield, VA 22161. TEL 703-487-4630.

327   US   ISSN 0092-7678
DS33.4.U6
ASIAN AFFAIRS: AN AMERICAN REVIEW. Key Title: Asian Affairs (New York). 1973. q. $36 to individuals; institutions $71. (American-Asian Educational Exchange, Inc.) Heldref Publications, 1319 18th St., N.W., Washington, DC 20036-1802. TEL 202-296-6267. FAX 202-296-5149. (Co-sponsor: Helen Dwight Reid Educational Foundation) Ed. John Neikirk. adv. contact: Raymond Rallo. circ. 390. (also avail. in microform; reprint service avail.) **Indexed:** A.B.C.Pol.Sci., Amer.Bibl.Slavic & E.Eur.Stud, Amer.Hist.& Life, ASSIA, Hist.Abstr., Int.Polit.Sci.Abstr., Mid.East: Abstr.& Ind., P.A.I.S., Per.Islam. (1991-), Polit.Sci.Abstr. **Document type:** academic/scholarly publication.
  ●Also available on CD-ROM. Producer(s): University Microfilms International.
  —BLDSC (1742.270500); Faxon; UMI; UnCover. **CCC.**
  Formerly: Southeast Asian Perspectives.
  Description: Focuses on U.S. policy in Asia, as well as on the domestic politics, economics, and international relations of the Asian countries.
Refereed Serial

320.9   JA
ASIAN PARLIAMENTARIANS' UNION. CENTRAL SECRETARIAT. REPORT ON MEETING OF APU SECRETARIES-GENERAL IN TOKYO.* 1972. a. Asian Parliamentarians' Union, TBR Bldg., Room 807, 2-10-2 Nagata-cho, Chiyoda-ku, Tokyo, Japan.

ASIAN PERSPECTIVE; biannual journal of regional & international affairs. see *POLITICAL SCIENCE*

327   JA   ISSN 0911-3843
ASIAN SECURITY. (Text in English) 1984. a. $40. Research Institute for Peace and Security, Roppongi Denki Bldg., 6-1-20 Roppongi, Minato-ku, Tokyo 106, Japan. FAX 81-3-3478-3105. Ed. Masataka Kosaka. circ. 3,000. (back issues avail.) **Indexed:** Int.Polit.Sci.Abstr. **Document type:** academic/scholarly publication.
  —BLDSC (1742.745300).

327   US   ISSN 0749-0062
ASIAN STUDIES CENTER BACKGROUNDER. 1983. irreg., no.134, 1994. Heritage Foundation, 214 Massachusetts Ave., N.E., Washington, DC 20002. TEL 202-546-4400. FAX 202-546-8328. Ed. Richard Odermatt. (looseleaf format)
  ●Also available online. Vendor(s): Lexis-Nexis.

327 382   FR   ISSN 0153-3657
ASSOCIATION POUR L'ETUDE DES PROBLEMES D'OUTRE MER. DOCUMENTATION-DEVELOPPEMENT. 1947. 8/yr. 1200 F. Association pour l'Etude des Problemes d'Outre Mer, 190 Bd. Haussmann, 75008 Paris, France. TEL 44-95-99-82. Ed. J. Alibert. charts; stat. **Document type:** bulletin.
  Description: Specializes in the south Sahara African region.

327   NE   ISSN 0167-1847
ATLANTISCH PERSPEKTIEF. 1963. 8/yr. fl.25 (effective 1994). Stichting Atlantische Commissie, Laan van Meerdervoort 96, 2517 AR The Hague, Netherlands. TEL 31-70-3639495. FAX 31-70-3646309. E-mail: atlantis@gds.nl. Ed. Mrs. L.F.M. Sprangers; Pub. A.P. Venema. adv. contact: N.T.J. Hoekstra. bk.rev. circ. 2,000. **Indexed:** Key to Econ.Sci.
  Formerly: Atlantische Tijdingen (ISSN 0067-0235)
  Description: Covers issues related to international security.

327   GW
AUSBLICK (LUEBECK); Zeitschrift fuer deutsch-skandinavische Beziehungen. 1949. s-a. DM.20. Deutsche Auslandsgesellschaft, Holstenstr. 17, 23552 Luebeck, Germany. TEL 0451-76320. FAX 0451-74873. Ed. Karsten Jessen. adv.; bk.rev. circ. 1,500. **Document type:** academic/scholarly publication.

327   GW   ISSN 0004-8194
D839
AUSSENPOLITIK; Zeitschrift fuer internationale Fragen. (Editions in English and German) 1950. q. DM.56 (English ed. DM.50). Interpress Verlag GmbH, Hartwicusstr. 3-4, 22087 Hamburg, Germany. TEL 040-228070. FAX 040-22807260. TELEX 214733. adv. contact: Karin Reinecke. bk.rev.; index. circ. 6,100 (English ed.); 2,500 (German ed.). (also avail. in microfiche; reprint service avail. from KTO) **Indexed:** A.B.C.Pol.Sci., Amer.Hist.& Life, Curr.Cont., ELLIS, Hist.Abstr., Int.Polit.Sci.Abstr., P.A.I.S.For.Lang.Ind., Peace Res.Abstr., Per.Islam. (1991-), Polit.Sci.Abstr., Rural Recreat.Tour.Abstr., SCIMP (1991-), So.Pac.Per.Ind., SSCI, World Agri.Econ.& Rural Sociol.Abstr. **Document type:** academic/scholarly publication.

327   AT
AUSTRALIA. DEPARTMENT OF FOREIGN AFFAIRS AND TRADE. SELECT DOCUMENTS ON INTERNATIONAL AFFAIRS; international treaties and conventions. a. price varies. Department of Foreign Affairs and Trade, Treaties Support Unit, Administrative Bldg., Parkes, A.C.T. 2600, Australia. TEL 61-6-261-3509. FAX 61-6-261-2144. (Subscr. to Australian Government Publishing Service, Kingston, A.C.T. 2604, Australia) circ. 200. **Document type:** government publication.
  Formerly: Australia. Department of Foreign Affairs. Select Documents on International Affairs (ISSN 0519-5950); Incorporates: Australia. Department of Foreign Affairs. International Treaties and Conventions (ISSN 0084-7135)
  Description: Contains the texts of new multilateral treaties of importance to Australia.

327   AT
AUSTRALIAN-AMERICAN NEWS N.S.W. ANNUAL EDITION. irreg. Aus.$50 per no. Australian-American Association, N.S.W. Division, 39-41 Lower Fort St., Sydney, N.S.W. 2000, Australia. Ed. T. Padley. adv.; illus.

994 327   UK   ISSN 1035-7718
DU80
AUSTRALIAN JOURNAL OF INTERNATIONAL AFFAIRS. 1947. 3/yr. £34($48) to individuals; institutions £62($104) (effective 1996). (Australian Institute of International Affairs) Carfax Publishing Co., P.O. Box 25, Abingdon, Oxon. OX14 3UE, England. TEL 44-1235-555335. FAX 44-1235-553559. (N. American subscr. to: Carfax Publishing Co., 871-885 Massachusetts Ave., Cambridge, MA 02139) Ed. S. Lawson. adv.; bk.rev.; charts. circ. 2,600. (also avail. in microfilm; reprint service avail. from UMI) **Indexed:** A.B.C.Pol.Sci., Abstr.Mil.Bibl., Amer.Hist.& Life, Asian-Pac.Econ.Lit., Aus.P.A.I.S., Br.Hum.Ind, Curr.Cont., E.I., GdIns., Hist.Abstr., Int.Polit.Sci.Abstr., Mid.East: Abstr.& Ind., P.A.I.S., Per.Islam. (1991-), PROMT, So.Pac.Per.Ind. **Document type:** academic/scholarly publication.
  —BLDSC (1809.110000); Faxon; Genuine Article; SWETS; UMI; UnCover. **CCC.**
  Formerly: Australian Outlook (ISSN 0004-9913)

327   AT
AUSTRALIA'S OVERSEAS AID PROGRAM. 1973. a. price varies. (Department of the Treasury) Australian Government Publishing Service, G.P.O. Box 84, Canberra, A.C.T. 2601, Australia. TEL 61-6-295-4411. FAX 61-6-295-4455. **Document type:** government publication.
  Former titles: Australia's Overseas Development Assistance Program. Budget Paper (ISSN 0726-1063) & Australia's Overseas Development Assistance (ISSN 0312-9217); Australia's External Aid (ISSN 0310-6152)

943.6   US   ISSN 0005-0520
DB1
AUSTRIAN INFORMATION. 1947? m. free. Austrian Press and Information Service, 3524 International Ct., N.W., Washington, DC 20008-3035. TEL 202-895-6775. FAX 202-895-6772. TELEX 440010. Ed. Martin Eichtinger. bk.rev.; illus. circ. 18,000. (also avail. in microform from UMI) **Document type:** newsletter.
  ●Also available online.
  —UMI.

AYIN L'TZION. see *ETHNIC INTERESTS*

POLITICAL SCIENCE — INTERNATIONAL RELATIONS

327   TU
AYNA; uluslararasi iliskiler, iletisim, egitim'de. (Text in Turkish, summaries in English) 1993. 4/yr. TL.280000 (Europe & Middle East $40; Far East & USA $50). Sita Politik Tinitim Danismanlik Hizmetleri A.S., Abide-i Hurriyet Cad. No: 78-15, Sisli - Istanbul 80260, Turkey. TEL 90-212-2472157. FAX 90-212-2255623. Ed. O. Suat Ozcelebi. adv. contact: N. Seler Cebecioglu. bk.rev.; illus.
    Description: Publishes articles on topics in international relations, communications and education affecting Turkey, the Middle East and the Turkish speaking nations of Central Asia.

B.C. VOICE. see *WOMEN'S INTERESTS*

327 355   GW   ISSN 0302-9468
AP30
B G S. (Bundesgrenzschutz) 1974. m. DM.48. (Bundesministerium des Innern) A. Bernecker Verlag, Unter dem Schoeneberg 1, 34212 Melsungen, Germany. Ed. Otto Wiegand. bk.rev. circ. 16,200.
—CCC.

320   LE
BACKGROUND REPORTS. (Text in Arabic) 3/mo. Dar Assayad S.A.L., P.O. Box 1038, Hazmieh, Beirut, Lebanon. FAX 961-1-456373. TELEX 44224 SAYAD LE. (U.K. Addr.: c/o Contact PR & Mgt. (UK) Ltd., 3 Park Place, 12 Lawn Ln., London SW8, England. TEL 44-71-582-2220) Ed. Hassan el Khoury. adv. contact: Salim Zreik.

327   US   ISSN 0382-8352
BACKGROUNDER. 1977. irreg., no.1019, 1994. $125 (subscr. includes Issue Bulletins & Backgrounder Update). Heritage Foundation, 214 Massachusetts Ave., N.E., Washington, DC 20002. TEL 202-546-4400. FAX 202-546-8328. Ed. Richard Odermatt. **Indexed:** INIS Atomind.
●Also available online. Vendor(s): Lexis-Nexis.

327 341   UK   ISSN 0969-6040
BAILRIGG MEMORANDA. 1992. irreg., no.12. £10. University of Lancaster, Centre for Defence & International Security Studies, Cartmel College, Lancaster LA1 4YL, England. TEL 01524-594254. FAX 01524-594258. Ed. Humphry Crum Ewing. adv. contact: Martin Edmonds. **Document type:** academic/scholarly publication.

327 341   UK   ISSN 0969-6032
BAILRIGG PAPERS ON INTERNATIONAL SECURITY. 1980. irreg., no.22. £10. University of Lancaster, Centre for Defence & International Security Studies, Cartmel College, Lancaster LA1 4YR, England. TEL 01524-594254. FAX 01524-594258. Ed. Humphry Crum Ewing. adv. contact: Martin Edmonds. **Document type:** monographic series.
—BLDSC (1856.759000).

327   US
BALTIC CHRONOLOGY. 1986. m. $40 (effective 1995-1996). United Baltic Appeal (U B A - B A T U N), 115 W. 183rd St., Bronx, NY 10453. TEL 718-367-8802. FAX 718-562-7434. Eds. Janis Riekstins, Raimonds Kerno. circ. 1,000 (paid). (back issues avail.) **Document type:** newsletter.
    Description: Summarizes important events in the Lithuania, Latvia, and Estonia from various government, scholarly, and news sources.

341.13   UN   ISSN 0067-4419
JX1977.A37
BASIC FACTS ABOUT THE UNITED NATIONS. irreg. $5. United Nations Publications, Room DC2-853, New York, NY 10017. TEL 212-963-8302; 800-253-9646. FAX 212-963-3489. (Or: Distribution and Sales Section, Palais des Nations, CH-1211 Geneva 10, Switzerland)

327   GW
BEGEGNUNG UND AUSTAUSCH MIT FRANZOSEN. 1973. a. free. Deutsch-Franzoesisches Jugendwerk, Rhoenderferstr. 23, 53604 Bad Honnef, Germany. TEL 02224-1808-63. FAX 02224-1808-52. circ. 60,000. **Document type:** bulletin.

971 327   CN   ISSN 0005-7983
F1034
BEHIND THE HEADLINES. 1940. 4/yr. Can.$13($11) Canadian Institute of International Affairs, 15 King's College Circle, Toronto, ON M5S 2V9, Canada. TEL 416-979-1851. FAX 416-979-8575. Ed. Gayle Fraser. circ. 1,800. (also avail. in microfilm from UMI; reprint service avail. from UMI) **Indexed:** Amer.Hist.& Life, Can.B.P.I., Can.Per.Ind., CMI, Hist.Abstr., Vert.File Ind. **Document type:** monographic series.
—SWETS; UMI.
    Description: A series of pamphlets for the general reader on current international affairs.

327 956   LE   ISSN 1019-0732
DS87.5
BEIRUT REVIEW. 1991. s-a. $24 to individuals; institutions $48. Lebanese Center for Policy Studies, Tayyar Bldg., Mkalles, Sin al-Fil, Beirut, Lebanon. TEL 961-1-490561. FAX 961-1-601787. (Subscr. outside Lebanon to: LCPS, Box 1377, Highland Park, NJ 08904, USA. TEL 908-220-0885. FAX 908-937-6697) Eds. Paul E. Salem, Michael Bacos Young. bk.rev.; bibl. **Indexed:** Per.Islam. (1992-).
    Description: Contains articles on political and economic affairs in Lebanon and the Middle East, and a chronology of events.

327   SW   ISSN 0281-7993
BISTAANDSANTROPOLOGEN. 1983. s-a. Stockholms Universitet, Socialantropologiska Institutionen, Sektionen foer Utvecklingsstudier, S-106 91 Stockholm, Sweden.

327   GR
BLUELINE; Greek and Mediterranean report. (Supplement avail.: Blueline Documents) (Text in English) m. (Institute of Political Studies) Dimitris Dimopolous, 28 Pericleous St., GR 143 43 Nea Halkidona, Athens, Greece.

327 323.4   US   ISSN 1065-1411
F787
BORDER LINES. 1993. 11/yr. $20. Interhemispheric Resource Center, Box 4506, Albuquerque, NM 87196. TEL 505-842-8288. FAX 505-246-1601. Ed. Harry Browne. circ. 1,000. (tabloid format; back issues avail.) **Document type:** newsletter.
    Description: Covers U.S.-Mexico border issues.

BRAZIL WATCH. see *BUSINESS AND ECONOMICS — Economic Situation And Conditions*

327   US
BREAKING THE SIEGE. 1989. bi-m. $20 (foreign $30). Middle East Justice Network, Box 495, Boston, MA 02112. TEL 617-542-5056. FAX 617-861-3783. **Document type:** newsletter.

237   UK
BRITAIN AND EUROPE DURING (YEAR). 1973. a. $20. Research Publications International Ltd., P.O. Box 45, Reading RG1 8HF, England. TEL 0734-583247. FAX 0734-591325. (Dist. in U.S. by: Research Publications Inc., 12 Lunar Dr., Drawer AB, Woodbridge, CT 06525) (back issues avail.) **Document type:** abstracting/indexing.
    Description: Guide to microfilm collection.

BRITISH COUNCIL ANNUAL REPORT AND ACCOUNTS (YEAR). see *EDUCATION — Higher Education*

915.554 059.915   FR
BULITAN-I KHABAR-I KURDISTAN. (Text in Persian) no.245, 1990. irreg. (Hizb-i Dimukrat-i Kurdistan-i Iran - Democratic Party of the Iranian Kurdistan) Association Franco-Kurde, B.P. 102, 75623 Paris cedex 13, France.

950 322.4   US   ISSN 0007-4810
DS1
BULLETIN OF CONCERNED ASIAN SCHOLARS. 1968. q. $22 to individuals (foreign $23); institutions $55 (foreign $56). Bulletin of Concerned Asian Scholars, Inc., 3239 9th St., Boulder, CO 80304-2112. TEL 303-449-7439. Ed. Nancy Doub; Pub. Bill Doub. adv. contact: Cathy Wrenn. bk.rev.; bibl.; charts; illus. circ. 1,600. (also avail. in microform from UMI; reprint service avail. from UMI,ISI; back issues avail.) **Indexed:** Alt.Press Ind., Amer.Hist.& Life, Curr.Cont., E.I., Geo.Abstr., Hist.Abstr., HR Rep. (1988-), IDA, Int.Lab.Doc., Left Ind. (1982-), Mid.East: Abstr.& Ind., Polit.Sci.Abstr., SSCI. **Document type:** academic/scholarly publication.
—BLDSC (2458.145000); Faxon; Genuine Article; SWETS; UMI; UnCover.
    Formerly: C C A S Newsletter.
Refereed Serial

327   US   ISSN 0096-3402
TK9145   CODEN: BASIAP
BULLETIN OF THE ATOMIC SCIENTISTS; magazine of science and world affairs. 1945. 6/yr. $30 in U.S.; Canada & Mexico $34.50; elsewhere $37.50. Educational Foundation for Nuclear Science, 6042 S. Kimbark Ave., Chicago, IL 60637. TEL 312-702-2555. FAX 312-702-0725. Ed. Mike Moore. adv.: B&W page $1200; adv. contact: Cherec Dillon. bk.rev.; illus.; index. circ. 15,000. (also avail. in microform from UMI,MIM; reprint service avail. from UMI) **Indexed:** A.B.C.Pol.Sci., Acad.Ind., Amer.Bibl.Slavic & E.Eur.Stud., Amer.Hist.& Life (until 1992), Biog.Ind., Biol.Abstr., Biol.Dig., Bk.Rev.Dig., Bk.Rev.Ind. (1965-), C.I.J.E., Chem.Abstr., Child.Bk.Rev.Ind. (1965-), Curr.Adv.Ecol.Sci., Curr.Cont., Energy Info.Abstr., Energy Rev., Environ.Abstr., Environ.Per.Bibl. (1989-), Excerp.Med., Fut.Surv., Gen.Sci.Ind., GeoRef, Hist.Abstr. (until 1992), Ind.Sci.Rev., INIS Atomind., Mag.Ind., Media Rev.Dig., Met.Abstr., Mid.East: Abstr.& Ind., Nucl.Sci.Abstr., PMR, Polit.Sci.Abstr., Pollut.Abstr., R.G., Risk Abstr., Sci.Cit.Ind., So.Pac.Per.Ind., Sociol.Abstr., SSCI, Telegen, World Alum.Abstr. **Document type:** academic/scholarly publication.
●Also available online. Vendor(s): University Microfilms International.
Also available on CD-ROM. Producer(s): University Microfilms International.
—BLDSC (2408.000000); CIS; Ei; Faxon; Genuine Article; SWETS; UMI; UnCover. **CCC.**
    Formerly: Science and Public Affairs Bulletin of the Atomic Scientists (ISSN 0007-5094)
    Description: Helps redefine international security in terms that embrace economic, environmental, cultural, and military issues.

327   GW   ISSN 0435-7183
D839
BUNDESINSTITUT FUER OSTWISSENSCHAFTLICHE UND INTERNATIONALE STUDIEN. BERICHTE. 1967. irreg. DM.250. Bundesinstitut fuer Ostwissenschaftliche und Internationale Studien, Lindenbornstr. 22, 50823 Cologne, Germany. TEL 0221-5747-0. FAX 0221-5747110. bibl. circ. 1,100. **Document type:** government publication.
—BLDSC (1913.516000).

327 338.91   US
BUSINESS COUNCIL FOR THE U N BRIEFING. Variant title: B C U N Briefing. 1987. q. Business Council for the U N, 60 E. 42nd St., Rm. 2925, New York, NY 10165. TEL 212-661-1772. Ed. Andrea Neidorf. circ. 4,500. (tabloid format; back issues avail.)
    Formerly (until 1984): F Y I to C E O's.

327   JA   ISSN 0917-7566
HF3828.U5
BY THE WAY; bridging the US - Japan perception gap. (Text in Japanese, English) 1991. bi-m. $33 (foreign $45). Raifu-sha Co. Ltd., 2-1-8 Sarugaku-cho, Chiyoda-ku, Tokyo 101, Japan. TEL 03-3294-0579. FAX 03-3294-0530. (Subscr. in US to: By the Way, USA, Inc., Box 10671, Seattle, WA 98110-9910) Eds. Masashi Yoneta, D.H. Hina.
—UnCover.
    Description: Provides an insight into Japan and the issues it now faces, with a special focus on its relationship with the United States.

POLITICAL SCIENCE — INTERNATIONAL RELATIONS

327 US ISSN 0739-9189
C A L C REPORT. 1975. q. $30 (effective 1995 & 1996). National Clergy and Laity Concerned, 340 Mead Rd., Decatur, GA 30030. TEL 404-377-1983. FAX 404-377-5367. Ed. Leslie Withers. adv.; bk.rev.; illus. circ. 10,000. (back issues avail.) **Indexed:** HR Rep. **Document type:** newsletter.
 Incorporates: T W C Bulletin (Third World Caucus); Formerly: American Report.

C C I A BACKGROUND INFORMATION. (World Council of Churches, Commission of the Churches on International Affairs) see *RELIGIONS AND THEOLOGY*

327 BE ISSN 0962-3876
C E P S PAPERS. (Text in English) 1983. irreg. 600 BEF. Centre for European Policy Studies, BE, Place du Congres, 1, 1000 Brussels, Belgium. TEL 32-2-2182247. FAX 32-2-2194151. (back issues avail.) **Indexed:** ELLIS. **Document type:** monographic series.
 —BLDSC (3113.696000); SWETS.
 Description: Provides in-depth analysis of timely topics relating to E.U. policies.
 Refereed Serial

327 330.1 BE
C E P S WORKING DOCUMENTS. (Text in English) 1983. irreg. 300 BEF per no. Centre for European Policy Studies, Place du Congres 1, 1000 Brussels, Belgium. TEL 32-2-2182247. FAX 32-2-2194151. (back issues avail.) **Document type:** monographic series.
 Formed by the merger of: C E P S Working Documents (Economic) & C E P S Working Documents (Political).
 Refereed Serial

327 SW ISSN 1100-4177
C E S I C STUDIES IN INTERNATIONAL CONFLICT. (Text in English, Swedish) 1989. irreg. price varies. Lund University Press, P. O. Box 141, S-221 00 Lund, Sweden. TEL 46-46-31-20-00. FAX 46-46-30-53-38. E-mail: Order@Studli.se. Eds. G. Rystad, S. Taegil. **Document type:** academic/scholarly publication.

C F B CALGARY. see *MILITARY*

327 EI
C O M DOCUMENTS. (Text in Danish, Dutch, English, French, German, Greek, Italian, Portuguese, Spanish) 1983. s-m. $2410. Office for Official Publications of the European Communities, L-2985 Luxembourg, Luxembourg. (Dist. in the U.S. by: Unipub, 4611-F Assembly Dr., Lanham, MD 20706-4391. TEL 800-274-4888. FAX 301-459-0056) (also avail. in microfiche) **Indexed:** Intl.Polym.Sci.& Tech., RAPRA.

C S I CONGRESSIONAL RECORD ABSTRACTS: FOREIGN AFFAIRS EDITION. see *PUBLIC ADMINISTRATION — Abstracting, Bibliographies, Statistics*

CAHIERS DE LA SECURITE INTERIEURE. see *CRIMINOLOGY AND LAW ENFORCEMENT — Security*

CALL TO PEACEMAKING. see *RELIGIONS AND THEOLOGY — Other Denominations And Sects*

327 UK ISSN 0959-6844
CAMBRIDGE STUDIES IN INTERNATIONAL RELATIONS. 1988. irreg. Cambridge University Press, Edinburgh Bldg., Shaftesbury Rd., Cambridge CB2 2RU, England. TEL 01223-312393. FAX 01223-315052. TELEX 817256. (N. American addr.: Cambridge University Press, 40 W. 20th St., New York, NY 10011. TEL 212-924-3900. FAX 212-691-3239) **Document type:** monographic series.
 —BLDSC (3015.993700).

327 CN ISSN 0701-8576
CANADA. DEPARTMENT OF EXTERNAL AFFAIRS. REFERENCE PAPERS. irreg. Department of External Affairs, External Information Programs Division, 125 Sussex Dr., Ottawa, Ont. K1A 0G2, Canada. TEL 613-996-9134.

327 CN ISSN 0832-0683
F1034.2
CANADA AMONG NATIONS. a. (Carleton University, Norman Paterson School of International Affairs) Carleton University Press, Colonel By Drive, Ottawa, ON K1S 5B6, Camada. TEL 613-788-3740. FAX 613-788-2893.
 Description: Provides a review of world events and Canadian foreign policy.

327 US ISSN 1047-1073
CANADIAN - AMERICA PUBLIC POLICY. 1990. q. $21 (foreign $26; typically set in Jan.) (University of Maine, Canadian - American Center) Canadian - American Center, 154 College Ave., Orono, ME 04473-1591. TEL 207-581-4220. FAX 207-581-4223. Ed. Robert H. Babcock. adv. circ. 200. **Indexed:** Int.Polit.Sci.Abstr. **Document type:** monographic series.
 —Faxon.
 Description: Focuses on contemporary issues in United States-Canada relations.

327 CN ISSN 0317-5693
AS4.U825
CANADIAN COMMISSION FOR UNESCO. ANNUAL REPORT. (Text in English, French) 1958. a. free. Canadian Commission for Unesco, Box 1047, Ottawa, ON K1P 5V8, Canada. TEL 613-566-4325. circ. 4,000.

CANADIAN COMMISSION FOR UNESCO. BULLETIN/COMMISSION CANADIENNE POUR L'UNESCO. BULLETIN. see *EDUCATION*

327 CN ISSN 0315-9795
JX1515.A2
CANADIAN FOREIGN RELATIONS.* Cover title: Annual Review. (Text in English and French) a. Department of External Affairs, Domestic Information Division, 125 Sussex Dr., Ottawa, ON K1A 0G2, Canada. TEL 613-996-9134. illus.
 ●Also available online. Vendor(s): QL Systems Ltd.

CANADIAN JEWISH HERALD. see *ETHNIC INTERESTS*

CANADIAN WORLD FEDERALIST/FEDERALISTE MONDIAL DU CANADA. see *LAW — International Law*

CANADO-AMERICAIN. see *ETHNIC INTERESTS*

327 330.9 US ISSN 0894-0223
CARIBBEAN NEWSLETTER. 1980. q. $15 to individuals; institutions $17; foreign $18 (effective Jan. 1994). Friends for Jamaica Collective, Box 20392, Park West Sta., New York, NY 10025. Ed.Bd. bk.rev.; film rev.; illus.; tr.lit. circ. 500. (also avail. in microfiche; back issues avail.) **Indexed:** HR Rep. **Document type:** newsletter.
 Formerly: Friends for Jamaica Newsletter.

327 382 US ISSN 0271-6577
CARIBBEAN STUDIES NEWSLETTER. 1974. q. $30. (Caribbean Studies Association) City College of New York, Department of Political Science, Convent Ave. & 138th St., New York, NY 10031. TEL 212-690-5470. Ed. J.A. Braveboy-Wagner. adv. circ. 1,000. (back issues avail.) **Document type:** newsletter.
 Description: News of academic and general interest on Caribbean politics and government, teaching and research.

327 CN ISSN 0383-2848
CARLETON UNIVERSITY, OTTAWA. NORMAN PATERSON SCHOOL OF INTERNATIONAL AFFAIRS. BIBLIOGRAPHY SERIES. 1975. irreg. (1-2/yr). Can.$6 per no. (Carleton University, Norman Paterson School of International Affairs) Carleton University Press, Ottawa, ON K1S 5B6, Canada. TEL 613-788-2600. FAX 613-788-2889. Ed. Vivian Cummins. circ. 600. **Document type:** bibliography.

942 UK ISSN 0257-7860
CARN. 1973. q. $26. Celtic League, c/o Bernard Maffat, 11 Hilltop View, Farmhill, Braddan, Isle of Man, England. TEL 01624-627128. Ed. Patricia Bridson. adv.; bk.rev. circ. 2,000.
 Formed by the merger of: Breton News (ISSN 0006-9671); Celtic League Annual; Celtic News (ISSN 0008-8773)

327 100 US
CARNEGIE COUNCIL NEWSLETTER. 1984. q. Carnegie Council on Ethics and International Affairs, c/o Matthew Mattern, Mng. Ed., Merrill House, 170 E. 64th St., New York, NY 10021-7478. TEL 212-838-4120. FAX 212-752-2432. **Document type:** newsletter.
 Description: Contains information regarding Carnegie Council activities.

CATHOLIC NEAR EAST MAGAZINE. see *RELIGIONS AND THEOLOGY — Roman Catholic*

327 SZ
CAUX INFORMATION; Informationsdienst Moralische Aufruestung. 1949. m. 32 SFr. (foreign 37 SFr.). Caux Information, Postfach 4419, CH-6002 Luzern, Switzerland. TEL 041-422213. FAX 041-422214. Ed. Marianne Spreng. bk.rev.; charts; illus. circ. 1,900. **Document type:** newsletter.
 Description: Offers ideas about resolution of conflicts through personal, social and economic change.

327 AG
HF1509
CEINAR. 1975. 3/yr. Arg.$1200($16) Centro de Estudios Internacionales Argentinos, Defensa 251, 1B, 1065 Buenos Aires, Argentina. Ed. Luis Dallanegra Pedraza. adv.; bk.rev. circ. 1,500. **Indexed:** Abstr.Mil.Bibl.
 Formerly: Revista Argentina de Relaciones Internacionales (ISSN 0325-1888)

327 US ISSN 0732-0078
CENTER FOR PEACE AND CONFLICT STUDIES. OCCASIONAL PAPERS. 1981. irreg. price varies. Wayne State University, Center for Peace and Conflict Studies, 2319 Faculty Administration Bldg., Detroit, MI 48202. TEL 313-577-3453.
 Description: Articles on the peacemaking process.

341.1 US
CENTER FOR PEACE AND CONFLICT STUDIES - DETROIT COUNCIL FOR WORLD AFFAIRS. NEWSLETTER. 1965. 4/yr. membership. Wayne State University, Center for Peace and Conflict Studies, 2319 Faculty Administration Bldg., Detroit, MI 48202. TEL 313-577-3453. (Co-sponsor: Detroit Council for World Affairs) bibl. circ. 1,000. (processed) **Document type:** newsletter.
 Formerly: Center for Teaching About Peace and War. Newsletter (ISSN 0008-9133)
 Description: News and articles on the peacemaking process.

CENTERVIEWS. see *BUSINESS AND ECONOMICS — International Commerce*

CENTRAL AND INNER ASIAN STUDIES. see *HISTORY — History Of Asia*

327 629.1 US
CENTRAL EURASIA SERIAL REPORTS: AVIATION AND COSMONAUTICS. irreg. $240 in U.S., Canada, Mexico; elsewhere $480. (Joint Publications Research Service) U.S. National Technical Information Service, 5825 Port Royal Rd., Springfield, VA 22161. TEL 703-487-4630.
 Formerly: U S S R Serial Reports: Aviation and Cosmonautics.

327 355 US
CENTRAL EURASIA SERIAL REPORTS: FOREIGN MILITARY REVIEW. irreg. $480 in U.S., Canada, Mexico; elsewhere $960. (Joint Publications Research Service) U.S. National Technical Information Service, 5825 Port Royal Rd., Springfield, VA 22161. TEL 703-487-4630.
 Formerly: U S S R Serial Reports: Foreign Military Review.

327 BE
CENTRE FOR EUROPEAN POLICY STUDIES. NEWSLETTER. q. free. Centre for European Policy Studies, Place du Congres 1, 1000 Brussels, Belgium. TEL 32-2-2182247. FAX 32-2-2194151. (back issues avail.) **Document type:** newsletter.

POLITICAL SCIENCE — INTERNATIONAL RELATIONS

327   IS   ISSN 0792-4143
DS119.7
CHALLENGE; a magazine of Israeli-Palestinian coexistence. (Text in English) 1990. bi-m. $35 to individuals; institutions $60 (effective 1995). Challenge for Peace and Progress, P.O. Box 32107, Jerusalem 91320, Israel. TEL 972-2-255382. FAX 972-2-251614. E-mail: chall@baraka.gn.apc.org. Ed. Roni Ben Efrat; Pub. Shimon Tzabar. adv. contact: John M. Tyler. bk.rev.; illus.; maps; stat.; cum.index: 1990-1994; circ. 1,500 (paid). (back issues avail.) **Indexed:** Alt.Press Ind. (1993-). **Document type:** academic/scholarly publication.
Description: Covers news and events in Israel, the Occupied Territories and the so-called Palestinian autonomous regions, with emphasis on human rights and efforts to secure a just peace. Advocates a two-state settlement to the conflict between Israel and the Palestinians.

CHALLENGE (LONDON, 1961). see *RELIGIONS AND THEOLOGY — Protestant*

341.1   SZ   ISSN 1017-2874
CHANGER. 1964. bi-m. 33 SFr. (foreign 35 SFr.). Caux Edition S.A., Rue du Panorama, CH-1824 Caux, Switzerland. FAX 021-9629355. Ed. Jean-Jacques Odier. adv.; bk.rev. circ. 2,500. **Document type:** bulletin.
Former titles: Changer - Tribune de Caux; (until 1979): Tribune de Caux; Which incorporates: Courrier d'Information-Rearmement Moral (ISSN 0011-0523)

327   365.64   US   ISSN 0162-2951
JF37
CHIEFS OF STATE AND CABINET MEMBERS OF FOREIGN GOVERNMENTS. m. $130 in U.S., Canada, Mexico; elsewhere $260. (Central Intelligence Agency) U.S. National Technical Information Service, 5825 Port Royal Rd., Springfield, VA 22161. TEL 703-487-4630. (also avail. in microfiche from CIS; reprint service avail. from CIS) **Indexed:** Amer.Stat.Ind. (1980-).
Description: Lists approximately 155 governments.

CHILDREN AND WAR NEWSLETTER; a newsletter for adults. see *CHILDREN AND YOUTH — About*

327   UK
CHILEAN NEWS. 1942. 2/yr. £13. Anglo Chilean Society, 12 Devonshire St., London W1N 2DS, England. TEL 01-580-1271. Ed. M.C. Cannon. bk.rev.; bibl.; illus.; circ. 600 (controlled).

327   CC
CHINA AND AFRICA/ZHONGGUO YU FEIZHOU. (Editions in English, French) m. Ministry of Culture, Foreign Language Bureau, 24 Baiwanzhuang Lu, Fuwai, Beijing 100037, People's Republic of China. TEL 8315599. Ed. Zhang Lifang.

327   US   ISSN 1044-890X
CHINA AND PACIFIC RIM LETTER. 1977. bi-m. $50 to non-members. U.S. Global Strategy Council, 1800 K St., N.W., Ste. 1102, Washington, DC 20006. TEL 202-466-6029. FAX 202-331-0109. (Co-sponsor: Committee for a Free China) bk.rev. circ. 1,000. (back issues avail.)
Formerly (until 1988): China Letter.
Description: Assesses elements of Asia societies that shape their relationship with the rest of the world in political, economic, cultural, ethical and security exchange.

327   CC
CHINA & THE WORLD; Beijing Review foreign affairs series. (Text in English) 1982. m.? Beijing Review, 24 Baiwanzhuang Rd., Beijing, People's Republic of China. (Dist. by: China Publications Center (Guoji Shudian), P.O. Box 399, Beijing, P.R.C.) Ed. Zhou Guo.

327   PH   ISSN 0117-1186
CHINA CURRENTS. (Text in English) q. P.200($10) Philippine - China Development Resource Center, 23 Madison St., New Manila, Quezon City 1112, Philippines. TEL 632-721-4651. Ed.Bd.
Description: Covers contemporary developments in China, overseas Chinese, and Philippine-Chinese relations.

327   JA
CHINA DIRECTORY (YEAR)/ZHONGGUO ZUZHIBIE RENMINGBU/CHUGOKU SOSHIKIBETSU JINMEIBO. (Text in Chinese and English) 1971. a. 16000 Yen($110) Radiopress, Inc., R-Bldg. Shinjuku 5F, 33-8, Wakamatsu-cho, Shinjuku-ku, Tokyo 162, Japan. TEL 03-5273-2171. FAX 03-5273-2180. bk.rev.; index. circ. 2,500. (back issues avail.) **Document type:** directory.
Description: Organization-based directory of 7,000 Chinese leaders and 2,000 organizations. Covers state council structural reforms, new cabinet members and other changes of past year; names listed in Chinese and Pinyin romanization.

951   II   ISSN 0009-4455
DS777.55
CHINA REPORT; a journal of East Asian studies. 1964. q. $45 to individuals; institutions $90 (effective Sep. 1995). (Centre for the Study of Developing Societies) Sage Publications India Pvt. Ltd., P.O. Box 4215, New Delhi 110 048. TEL 91-11-644-4958. FAX 91-11-647-2446. (Overseas subscr.to: Sage Publications Ltd., 6 Bonhill St., London EC2A 4PU, England. TEL 44-071-374-0645. FAX 44-071-374-8741; Subscr. in N. America to: Sage Publications, Inc., Box 5084, Thousand Oaks, CA 91359. TEL 805-499-0721. FAX 805-499-0871) Ed. Mandranjan Mohanty; Pub. Tejeshwar Singh. adv.: page Rs.1000; adv. contact: Sunanda Ghosh. bk.rev.; stat.; index. circ. 700. (also avail. in microfilm from UMI; back issues avail.) **Indexed:** Amer.Hist.& Life, Geo.Abstr., Hist.Abstr., IDA, Key to Econ.Sci., Polit.Sci.Abstr., Rural Devel.Abstr., World Agri.Econ.& Rural Sociol.Abstr. **Document type:** academic/scholarly publication.
—BLDSC (3180.233000); SWETS; UMI.
Description: Encourages the increased understanding of contemporary China and its East Asian neighbors, their cultures and ways of development, and their impact on India and other South Asian countries.
Refereed Serial

CHINA SPRING. see *POLITICAL SCIENCE — Civil Rights*

327   FR   ISSN 0529-8016
CITES UNIES. 1957. q. 100 F. World Federation of United Towns, 22, rue d'Alsace, 92300 Levallois, France. TEL 47-39-36-86. FAX 47-39-36-85. adv.; bk.rev. circ. 7,000.

327   355   900   US
CIVILIAN-BASED DEFENSE. 1982. 4/yr. $15. Civilian-Based Defense Association, Box 92, Omaha, NE 68101-0092. TEL 402-558-2085. E-mail: CBDA@igc.apc.org. Ed. Peter Bergel. bk.rev. circ. 500. (looseleaf format; back issues avail.)
Formerly (until 1992): Civilian - Based Defense: News and Opinion (ISSN 0886-6015)
Description: Explores civilian-based defense, a strategy in which well prepared but unarmed civilians resist invasions and coups d'etat through noncooperation, strikes, demonstrations, sanctions.

CIVIS MUNDI. see *POLITICAL SCIENCE*

327   US   ISSN 0145-9686
JF37
CLEMENTS' ENCYCLOPEDIA OF WORLD GOVERNMENTS. 1974. biennial (with q. supplements). $485 (includes Clements' International Report, cumulative quarterly Supplements and Supplement Organizer). Political Research, Inc., Tegoland at Bent Tree, 16850 Dallas Pkwy., Dallas, TX 75248. TEL 214-931-8827. FAX 214-248-7159. Ed. John Clements.
Description: Directory of current information on the economy, people, climate, government, officials and foreign affairs of each independent nation.

327   US   ISSN 0145-9678
CLEMENTS' INTERNATIONAL REPORT. 1976. m. included in subscription to Clements' Encyclopedia of World Governments. Political Research, Inc., Tegoland at Bent Tree, 16850 Dallas Pkwy., Dallas, TX 75248. TEL 214-931-8827. FAX 214-248-7159. Ed. John Clements.
Description: Covers current events and developments throughout the world.

COLD WAR INTERNATIONAL HISTORY PROJECT BULLETIN. see *HISTORY*

327   NR
COLLEGE PRESS. ANNUAL LECTURE SERIES. a. $5. College Press, University P.O. Box 1014, Ife-Ife, Oshun State, Nigeria. TEL 234-36-231780. FAX 234-036-231-780.

327   UK   ISSN 0141-8513
COMMONWEALTH CURRENTS. 1978. q. free. Commonwealth Secretariat, Information and Public Affairs Division, Marlborough House, Pall Mall, London SW1Y 5HX, England. TEL 0171-747-6386. FAX 0171-839-9081. bk.rev. circ. 31,000. **Indexed:** Apic.Abstr., So.Pac.Per.Ind. **Document type:** newsletter, government publication.
—BLDSC (3339.647000).
Supersedes: Commonwealth Diary of Coming Events (ISSN 0309-0388); Commonwealth Record of Recent Events.

COMMONWEALTH INSTITUTE, LONDON. ANNUAL REPORT. see *GEOGRAPHY*

327   IS
DS63.2.S65
COMMONWEALTH OF INDEPENDENT STATES AND THE MIDDLE EAST. (Text in English) 1976. m. $40 (effective 1993). Hebrew University, Marjorie Mayrock Center for Soviet and East European Research, c/o Faculty of Social Sciences, Mount Scopus, Jerusalem 91905, Israel. TEL 972-2-883180. FAX 972-2-322545. TELEX 26458. Ed. Stefani Hoffman. circ. 300. **Indexed:** HR Rep. **Document type:** academic/scholarly publication.
Formerly: Soviet Union and the Middle East (ISSN 0334-4142)

COMPARE NOTES SERIES. see *ETHNIC INTERESTS*

327   IT   ISSN 0010-5066
JX1903
COMUNITA INTERNAZIONALE. (Text in English, French and Italian) 1946. q. L.100000 (foreign L.200000) (effective 1993). (Societa Italiana per l'Organizzazione Internazionale) Editoriale Scientifica s.r.l., Via Gen. V. Giordano Orsini 42, 80132 Naples, Italy. TEL 081-7646084. Ed. Luigi Ferrari Bravo. adv.; bk.rev.; index. circ. 3,000. **Indexed:** A.B.C.Pol.Sci., Amer.Hist.& Life, ELLIS, Hist.Abstr., P.A.I.S.For.Lang.Ind.
—BLDSC (3399.200000); SWETS.

327   341   UK
CONFIDENCE BUILDING MATTERS. 1992. irreg., no.5, Mar. 1995. £10 per no. Verification Technology Information Centre (VERTIC), Carrara House, 20 Embankment Pl., London WC2N 6NN, England. TEL 0171-925-0867. FAX 0171-925-0861. E-mail: vertic@gn.apc.org. (back issues avail.) **Document type:** monographic series.

CONFIDENTIAL A-I-R LETTER. see *CRIMINOLOGY AND LAW ENFORCEMENT*

327   UK   ISSN 0266-0377
JX4471
CONFLICT BULLETIN. (Supplement to: Conflict Studies (ISSN 0069-8792)) 1970. 3/yr. Research Institute for the Study of Conflict and Terrorism, 136 Baker St., London W1M 1FH, England. TEL 0171-224-2659. FAX 0171-486-3064. Ed. Joan Bates. adv.; bk.rev. circ. 1,000. **Document type:** bulletin.

327   UK   ISSN 0069-8792
D839
CONFLICT STUDIES. (Supplement avail.: Conflict Studies (ISSN 0069-8792)) 1969. 10/yr. £85($165) Research Institute for the Study of Conflict and Terrorism, 136 Baker St., London W1M 1FH, England. TEL 0171-224-2659. FAX 0171-486-3064. (Dist. addr.: 133 Downhall Rd., Rayleigh, Essex S56 9PB, England. TEL 01268-784725) Ed. Joan Bates. adv.: page DM.300; trim 9 7/10 x 6 4/5; adv. contact: Joan Bates. bk.rev. circ. 1,250. (back issues avail.) **Indexed:** Abstr.Crim.& Pen., Abstr.Mil.Bibl., Int.Polit.Sci.Abstr., Mid.East: Abstr.& Ind. **Document type:** bulletin.
—BLDSC (3410.660000); Faxon, SWETS; UMI.

POLITICAL SCIENCE — INTERNATIONAL RELATIONS

944 001.3   **FR**   ISSN 1148-2664
DE100
CONFLUENCES, MEDITERRANEE. 1991. q. 280 F. (foreign 320 F.). Editions l' Harmattan, 77 rue Blomet, 75015 Paris, France. TEL 48-42-47-44. Ed. Jean-Paul Chagnollaud.
Description: Studies political and cultural questions of concern to the peoples and societies of the Mediterranean basin.

327   **CC**   ISSN 1003-3408
CONTEMPORARY INTERNATIONAL RELATIONS. Chinese edition: Xiandai Guoji Guanxi (ISSN 1000-6192) (Text in English) 1991. m. $60. Xiandai Guoji Guanxi Yanjiusuo - China Institute of Contemporary International Relations, No. A-2, Wanshousi, Haidian, Beijing 100081, People's Republic of China. TEL 86-1-841-8640. FAX 86-1-841-8641. Ed. Chen Qida. circ. 500. **Document type:** academic/scholarly publication.
Description: Contains analyses by prominent Chinese scholars on various issues of contemporary international relations.

327   **UK**   ISSN 1352-3260
JX1974   CODEN: CNSPEG
CONTEMPORARY SECURITY POLICY. 1980. 3/yr. £38($58) to individuals; institutions £110 ($185) (effective 1996). Frank Cass, Newbury House, 890-900 Eastern Ave., Newbury Park, Ilford, Essex 1G2 7HH, England. TEL 44-181-599-8866. FAX 44-181-599-0984. E-mail: 1000067,1576@compuserve.com. Eds. Stuart Croft, Terry Terriff. adv.: B&W page £195 ($275); adv. contact: Anne Kidson. bk.rev.; index. (also avail. in microfilm from UMI; back issues avail.) **Indexed:** Abstr.Mil.Bibl., Amer.Hist.& Life (until 1993), Hist.Abstr. (until 1993), Int.Polit.Sci.Abstr., P.A.I.S., Polit.Sci.Abstr. **Document type:** academic/scholarly publication.
—BLDSC (3425.302600); SWETS; UMI; UnCover. CCC.
Formerly (until 1993): Arms Control (ISSN 0144-0381)
Description: Covers the gamut of security agreements and security in the post-Cold War world, including issues of arms control and disarmament.
Refereed Serial

327 948   **UK**   ISSN 0010-8367
JX1   CODEN: COCFEF
COOPERATION AND CONFLICT; Nordic journal of international studies. 1965. q. £31 to individuals; institutions £85 (effective 1996). (Nordic International Studies Association, NO) Sage Publications Ltd., 6 Bonhill St., London EC2A 4PU, England. TEL 0171-374-0645. FAX 0171-374-8741. E-mail: market@sageltd.co.uk. Ed. Bengt Sundelius. adv.: B&W page £180; trim 165 x 110; adv. contact: Bernie Folan. bk.rev.; charts; index. circ. 600. (also avail. in microform from UMI; back issues avail.; reprint service also avail. from ISI) **Indexed:** A.B.C.Pol.Sci., Abstr.Mil.Bibl., Amer.Hist.& Life (until 1993), Hist.Abstr. (until 1993), Human Resour.Abstr., Int.Polit.Sci.Abstr., Mid.East: Abstr.& Ind., P.A.I.S., Polit.Sci.Abstr., Sage Pub.Admin.Abstr., Sociol.Abstr. **Document type:** academic/scholarly publication.
—BLDSC (3464.120000); Faxon; SWETS; UMI; UnCover. CCC.
Description: Reflects the vitality and diversity of contemporary Scandinavian international relations research and addresses critical issues in the scholarly search for a better grasp on the complexities of world affairs.
Refereed Serial

327   **CL**
COSAS. 1976. fortn. Almirante Pastene 329, Providencia, Santiago, Chile. TEL 2-225-8630. FAX 2-225-7799. TELEX 340905. Ed. Monica Comandari Kaiser. circ. 25,000.

341.1   **US**   ISSN 0010-955X
COSMOPOLITAN CONTACT. (Text in various languages) 1962. irreg. $4. (Planetary Legion for Peace - PLP) Pantheon Press - General Enterprises, Box 89300, Honolulu, HI 96830-9300. Ed. Romulus Rexner. adv.; bk.rev.; illus. circ. 1,500. (processed; back issues avail.)

COUNCIL OF EUROPE. COMMITTEE OF INDEPENDENT EXPERTS ON THE EUROPEAN SOCIAL CHARTER. CONCLUSIONS. see *SOCIAL SERVICES AND WELFARE*

327.73   **US**   ISSN 0192-236X
JX27.C6
COUNCIL ON FOREIGN RELATIONS. ANNUAL REPORT. a. Council on Foreign Relations, Inc., 58 E. 68th St., New York, NY 10021. TEL 212-734-0400. (also avail. in microfilm from PMC) **Document type:** corporate report.
Formerly: Council on Foreign Relations. President's Report (ISSN 0093-4615)

COUNCIL ON HEMISPHERIC AFFAIRS NEWS AND ANALYSIS. see *BUSINESS AND ECONOMICS — International Development And Assistance*

327 330.9   **US**
COUNTRIES IN CRISIS. 1989. irreg. $25. Gale Research Inc., St. James Press, 835 Penobscot Bldg., Detroit, MI 48226-4232. TEL 800-877-4253.
Description: Focuses on nations facing a period of turmoil in their domestic affairs, international affairs or both. Includes background information and detailed analyses.

500   **UN**
COURIER (PARIS). (Supplement avail. in Braille) (Editions in Arabic, Basque, Bulgarian, Catalan, Chinese, Dutch, English, Finnish, French, German, Greek, Hausa, Hindi, Italian, Korean, Macedonian, Malaysian, Pushto, Persian, Portuguese, Russian, Serbo-Croatian, Sinhala, Slovene, Spanish, Swahili, Swedish, Tamil, Thai, Turkish, Urdu and Vietnamese; Braille supplements in English, French, Korean, Spanish) 1948. m. $55. Unesco, 7-9 Place de Fontenoy, 75700 Paris, France. TEL 45-77-16-10. (Dist. in U.S. by: Unipub, 4611-F Assembly Dr., Lanham, MD 20706-4391. TEL 800-274-4888) Ed. Adel Rifaat. bibl.; illus. circ. 37,300 (English ed. only). (also avail. in microform from UMI) **Indexed:** Acad.Ind., Arts & Hum.Cit.Ind., Curr.Cont., Excerp.Med., Gdlns, Mag.Ind., Peace Res.Abstr. R.G., So.Pac.Per.Ind.
●Also available online. Vendor(s): Knight-Ridder, Inc.
—BLDSC (9090.173000); SWETS; UnCover.
Formerly: Unesco Courier (ISSN 0041-5278)

COVERT INTELLIGENCE LETTER. see *MILITARY*

THE CRIMEAN REVIEW; voice of the Crimean Tatar human rights movement. see *POLITICAL SCIENCE — Civil Rights*

CRITIQUE OF TRADE UNION RIGHTS IN COUNTRIES AFFILIATED WITH THE LEAGUE OF ARAB STATES. see *LABOR UNIONS*

327   **FR**   ISSN 1150-7454
HC59.7
CROISSANCE; le monde en developpement. 1961. m. (11/yr.). 330 F. (foreign 360 F.). Malesherbes Publications, 163 bd. Malesherbes, 75017 Paris, France. TEL 48-88-46-00. FAX 48-88-46-01. TELEX 649 333 F. Ed. Jean-Claude Petit. adv.; bk.rev.; bibl.; charts; illus. circ. 30,000. **Indexed:** Int.Lab.Doc., Pt.de Rep. (1990-).
—BLDSC (3487.704000).
Formerly (until 1991): Croissance des Jeunes Nations (ISSN 0011-1686)
Description: Information on developing nations.

341.1   **US**   ISSN 0011-2054
CROSSROADS (PITTSBURGH).* 1970. m. $1.50. Youth Institute for Peace in the Middle East, Box 81865, Pittsburgh, PA 15217. Ed. Kristeen Bruun. illus.; tr.lit. circ. 10,000. (also avail. in microfilm from UMI; reprint service avail. from UMI)

327   **US**   ISSN 0011-2062
CROSSROADS COMMUNIQUE.* 1962. q. Operation Crossroads Africa, Inc., 475 Riverside Dr. No.916, New York, NY 10027. TEL 212-242-8550. Ed. Michael John Weber. adv.; bk.rev. circ. 8,000.

327   **UK**
CROWN AGENTS REVIEW. 1976. 3/yr. free. Crown Agents for Oversea Governments and Administrations, St. Nicholas House, Sutton, Surrey SM1 1EL, England. TEL 0181-643-3311. FAX 0181-643-8232. TELEX 916205 CALOND G. Ed. S. Adamson. illus. circ. 7,000. (also avail. in microfiche) **Indexed:** P.A.I.S.
Formerly: Crown Agents Quarterly Review.
Description: Development-related topics for developing nations and practitioners.

327   **US**   ISSN 0196-0830
F1751
CUBA UPDATE. 1977. bi-m. $25 to non-members. Center for Cuban Studies, Inc., 124 W. 23rd St., New York, NY 10011. TEL 212-242-0559. Ed. Sandra Levinson. adv.; bk.rev.; illus. circ. 2,000. **Indexed:** Alt.Press Ind. (1992-), HR Rep. (1985-1988). **Document type:** academic/scholarly publication.
—UnCover.
Description: Progress of the advancement of Cuban society and relations between Cuba and other nations are featured. Perspectives of Cuban barrios, workplaces and culture find space here.

327 320   **EI**   ISSN 0252-0869
CULTURAL POLICY. French edition: Politiques Culturelles. (Editions in English, French) 1977. q. free. Council of Europe, Publishing and Documentation Service B.P. 431R6, 67075 Strasbourg Cedex, France. Ed. Sezen Germen. bk.rev.; bibl.; stat. (back issues avail.)

327   **FR**   ISSN 1157-996X
U240   CODEN: CCONEF
CULTURES ET CONFLITS. 1991. q. 250 F. (foreign 300 F.). (Centre d'Etude des Conflits) Editions l' Harmattan, 7 rue de l'Ecole-Polytechnique, 75005 Paris, France. TEL 43-54-79-10. FAX 43-25-82-03. Ed. Didier Bigo. **Indexed:** Int.Polit.Sci.Abstr.

CURRENT BIBLIOGRAPHY ON AFRICAN AFFAIRS. see *POLITICAL SCIENCE — Abstracting, Bibliographies, Statistics*

327   **US**   ISSN 0161-6641
JK1
CURRENT ISSUES (ALEXANDRIA); critical issues confronting the nation and the world. 1977. a. $12.95. Close Up Foundation, 44 Canal Center Plaza, Ste. 6501, Alexandria, VA 22314-1592. TEL 800-765-3131. FAX 703-706-0002. Ed. Chuck Sass; Pub. Cindy Graff Hobson. adv. contact: Jill Sander. charts; illus.; stat.; index. circ. 63,000. **Document type:** academic/scholarly publication.
Description: Covers ten foreign and ten domestic policy issues. Contains an introduction to the issue, key questions, background and history, current issues (what's happening now), and outlook (what to expect in the future).

327   **US**   ISSN 1061-9186
DK510.763
CURRENT POLITICS AND ECONOMICS OF RUSSIA. 1990. q. $265 (effective 1996). Nova Science Publishers, Inc., 6080 Jericho Tpke., Ste. 207, Commack, NY 11725-2808. TEL 516-499-3103. FAX 516-499-3146. E-mail: novasci1@aol.com. **Document type:** academic/scholarly publication.
—BLDSC (3501.284710); UnCover.
Formerly (until 1991): Current Politics of the Soviet Union (ISSN 1048-7387); Incorporates (in 1991): Political and Economic Spectrum of the Soviet Union (ISSN 1057-2295)
Description: Presents current information concerning the changing political situation in Russia.

CURRENT WORLD LEADERS; almanac & international issues. see *POLITICAL SCIENCE*

327   **CY**   ISSN 1015-2873
CYPRUS DIPLOMATIST. 1989. bi-m. 16-18 Halkokondyli St., P.O. Box 660, Nicosia, Cyprus. TEL 357-2-366866. Ed. George Lantis. circ. 2,000.

CZECHOSLOVAK HISTORY NEWSLETTER. see *ETHNIC INTERESTS*

327 364.4   **US**
D I S A M JOURNAL. 1982. q. $12. Defense Institute of Security Assistance Management, c/o Mr. John Lindbloom, DISAM-DRP Bldg. 125, 2335 Seventh St., Wright-Patterson Air Forace Base, OH 45433-7803. TEL 513-255-2994. FAX 513-255-4319. Ed. Lou Samelson. circ. 2,800. **Indexed:** Air Un.Lib.Ind.

POLITICAL SCIENCE — INTERNATIONAL RELATIONS

327   **CC**
DANGDAI SHIJIE YU SHEHUIZHUYI/CONTEMPORARY WORLD AND SOCIALISM. (Text in Chinese) 1989. q. Y3.75 per no. Zhongyang Malie Zuzuo Bianyi-ju, Shujie Shehui Zhuyi Yanjiusuo - Institute for World Socialism Studies, 36, Xixie Jie, Xidan, Beijing 100032, People's Republic of China. TEL 6037038. FAX 6024817. Ed. Hu Wenjian. adv. contact: Chen Lin. bk.rev. circ. 2,500. **Document type:** academic/scholarly publication.
  Formerly (until vol.4, 1993): Guoji Gongyunshi Yanjiu - Studies of History of International Communist Movement (ISSN 1003-3858)
  Description: Studies the history, theories and practices of world socialism, as well as the present conditions and developments of international politics and economics.

327   **DK**   **ISSN 0107-0487**
DANSK UDENRIGSPOLITISK AARBOG. 1979. a. DKK 99.95. (Dansk Udenrigspolitisk Institut) Samfundsvidenskabeligt Forlag, D.J.O.F., Gothersgade 133, DK-1123 Copenhagen K, Denmark.

327   **GW**   **ISSN 0340-6296**
DARMSTAEDTER BLAETTER FUER KULTURELLE EVOLUTION. 1956. m. DM.40. Darmstaedter Blaetter Verlag, Haubachweg 5, 64285 Darmstadt, Germany. TEL 06151-48196. Ed. Gunther Schwarz. circ. 3,000. **Document type:** academic/scholarly publication.

327   **UK**   **ISSN 1353-9884**
DAVID DAVIES MEMORIAL INSTITUTE OF INTERNATIONAL STUDIES. OCCASIONAL PAPER. 1993. irreg. (2-3/yr.). (included with subscr. to International Relations (ISSN 0047-1178)). David Davies Memorial Institute of International Studies, 2 Chadwick St., London SW1P 2EP, England. TEL 0171-222-4063. FAX 0171-233-2863. Ed. Mary Unwin. circ. 1,000 (controlled). **Document type:** monographic series.
  Description: Seeks to advance and promote the development of international relations in all its aspects and to carry out and instigate research and study in this field.

327   **DK**   **ISSN 0108-8580**
DAYANISMA/SOLIDARITET. (Text in Danish and Turkish) 1983. bi-m. DKK 30. Tyrkisk-Dansk Forening, Klostergade 37, 8000 Aarhus C, Denmark. illus.

DEADLINE. see *JOURNALISM*

DECLASSIFIED DOCUMENTS CATALOG. see *POLITICAL SCIENCE — Abstracting, Bibliographies, Statistics*

DEFENSE ANALYSIS. see *MILITARY*

DEFENSE FOREIGN AFFAIRS HANDBOOK; political, economic & defense data on every country in the world. see *MILITARY*

320   **UK**   **ISSN 1351-0347**
JC421
▼**DEMOCRATIZATION.** 1994. 3/yr. £38($45) to individuals; institutions £90 ($135) (effective 1996). Frank Cass, Newbury House, 890-900 Eastern Ave., Newbury Park, Ilford, Essex IG2 7HH, England. TEL 44-181-599-8866. FAX 44-181-599-0984. E-mail: 100067,1576@compuserve.com. Eds. Peter Burnell, Ian Campbell. adv.: B&W page £195 ($275); adv. contact: Anne Kidson. bk.rev.; index. Indexed: Amer.Hist.& Life (1994-), Hist.Abstr. (1994-). **Document type:** academic/scholarly publication.
—BLDSC (3550.572500).
  Description: Seeks to promote a better understanding of the process of democratization, particularly in developing nations and in post-Communist societies.
  Refereed Serial

DESTINY; the new Black American mainstream. see *ETHNIC INTERESTS*

DEVELOPMENT (OXFORD). see *BUSINESS AND ECONOMICS — International Development And Assistance*

DEVELOPMENT AND CHANGE. see *SOCIAL SCIENCES: COMPREHENSIVE WORKS*

DEVELOPMENT BUSINESS. see *BUSINESS AND ECONOMICS — International Development And Assistance*

327   **US**
DEVELOPMENT CONNECTIONS.* 1957. bi-m. $30. Society for International Development, 1875 Connecticut Ave, N.W, Ste. 900, Washington, DC 20009-5728. TEL 202-347-1800. FAX 202-638-1374. Ed. Lawrence R. Goldman. adv.; bk.rev.; index. circ. 1,500. (back issues avail.)
  Former titles (until 1987): Society for International Development. Newsletter; International Society for Community Development. Newsletter.

327   **338.9**   **SW**   **ISSN 0345-2328**
HD82
DEVELOPMENT DIALOGUE; a journal of international development cooperation. 1972. 1-2/yr. free. Dag Hammarskjold Foundation, Dag Hammarskjoeld Centre, Oevre Slottsgatan 2, S-753 10 Uppsala, Sweden. TEL 018-127272. FAX 018-122072. TELEX 76234 DHCENT. Ed. Olle Nordberg. bk.rev. circ. 12,000. Indexed: Asian-Pac.Econ.Lit., Commun.Abstr., Documentatieblad, E.I., HR Rep., IDA, Mid.East: Abstr.& Ind., Rural Devel.Abstr., Rural Recreat.Tour.Abstr., World Agri.Econ.& Rural Sociol.Abstr.
—BLDSC (3579.019700); Faxon.

327   **CN**
DEVELOPMENT STUDIES WORKING PAPERS. 1990. irreg. Can.$6. (Carleton University, Norman Paterson School of International Affairs) Carleton University Press, Ottawa, ON K1S 5B6, Canada. TEL 613-788-2600. FAX 613-788-2889. **Document type:** monographic series.

327   **AU**
DIALOGO; Austria-America Latina. (Text in Portuguese, Spanish) 1982. a. free. Oesterreichisches Lateinamerika Institut, Schmerlingplatz 8, A-1010 Vienna, Austria. TEL 0222-5233315. Ed.Bd. adv. circ. 3,000. (back issues avail.) **Document type:** bulletin.

327   **US**   **ISSN 0012-2262**
DIALOGUE (WASHINGTON)/FACETAS. Czech translation: Spektrum (Prague). (Distribution by U.S. embassies; not distributed within continental U.S.) (Text in various languages) 1968. q. U.S. Information Agency, 301 4th St., S.W., Washington, DC 20547. TEL 202-619-4196. FAX 202-619-4173. Ed. Peter J. Laine. bk.rev. circ. 140,000. **Document type:** government publication.
  Description: Magazine of ideas, trends and developments in American society and culture, edited for a foreign audience of the leadership and intellectual elites.

327   **TS**
AL-DIBLOMASI/DIPLOMAT. (Text in Arabic) 1980. q. exchange basis. Ministry of Foreign Affairs, Department of Legal Affairs and Studies - Wizarat al-Kharijiyyah, Idarat al-Shu'un al-Qanuniyyah wal-Dirasat, P.O. Box 1, Abu Dhabi, United Arab Emirates. TEL 652200. FAX 668015. TELEX 22217 KHARJIYA EM. circ. 500 (controlled).
  Description: Publishes studies and research in diplomatic affairs and international relations, as well as news of conferences, official reports and documents pertaining to international matters.

DICKINSON JOURNAL OF INTERNATIONAL LAW. see *LAW — International Law*

DIGEST OF WORLD EVENTS. see *HISTORY*

327   **UY**
DIPLOMACIA EN ACCION; revista de la politica exterior uruguaya. 1991. q. $18 in S. America; elsewhere $25. 18 de Julio 2103, Apto. 1002, Montevideo, Uruguay. Ed. Sergio Jellinek. **Document type:** consumer publication.

DIPLOMACY & STATECRAFT. see *HISTORY — History Of Europe*

327   **UK**   **ISSN 0951-032X**
DIPLOMAT; the review of the diplomatic and consular world. 1947. bi-m. £40($120) Diplomatist Associates Ltd., 58 Theobalds Rd., London, England. TEL 0171-405-4878. FAX 0171-831-0667. Ed. Shaen Catherwood. adv.; bk.rev.; illus.; stat.; circ. 3,000 (controlled). **Document type:** trade publication.
  Formerly: Diplomatist (ISSN 0012-3110)
  Description: Contains articles of interest to businesspersons and those in government service who need to maintain contact with the foreign diplomatic community in London.

327   **PK**
DIPLOMAT. (Text in English) 1972. m. Rs.75. 442-2 Jauharabad, Karachi 38, Pakistan. Ed. Mohammed Ali Jilani. adv.; charts; illus.

327   **GW**
DIPLOMATEN SPIEGEL. 1992. a. DM.5. ProPress Verlag GmbH, Am Buschhof 8, 53227 Bonn, Germany. TEL 0228-970970. FAX 0228-444296. circ. 30,000. **Document type:** trade publication.

327   **UK**
DIPLOMATIC & CONSULAR YEAR BOOK. 1978. a. £14.95($25) Blakes (Corporate) Ltd., 12-14 High Rd., London N2 9JP, England. Ed. Gina Senko. adv.; bk.rev. circ. 5,000.

327   **CN**   **ISSN 0486-4514**
JX1729.A2
DIPLOMATIC CORPS AND CONSULAR AND OTHER REPRESENTATIVES IN CANADA/CORPS DIPLOMATIQUE ET REPRESENTANTS CONSULAIRES ET AUTRES AU CANADA. (Text in English and French) 1969. irreg. Can.$2.75. Department of External Affairs, Ottawa, Ont. K1A 0G2, Canada. TEL 613-996-9134.

DIPLOMATIC HISTORY. see *HISTORY*

327   **NP**
DIPLOMATIC LIST AND LIST OF REPRESENTATIVES OF UNITED NATIONS AND ITS SPECIALIZED AGENCIES AND OTHER MISSIONS. (Text in English) a. Protocol Division, Ministry of Foreign Affairs, Kathmandu, Nepal.

327.2   **NZ**
DIPLOMATIC LIST - DIPLOMATIC AND CONSULAR REPRESENTATIVES IN NEW ZEALAND. 1943. s-a. NZ.$31.60. Ministry of Foreign Affairs and Trade, Private Bag 18-901, Wellington 1, New Zealand. TEL 64-4-4728-877. circ. 2,100. **Document type:** directory.
—CCC.
  Former titles: New Zealand Diplomatic Corps and Consular and Other Representatives (ISSN 0111-6142) & Overseas Representatives in New Zealand and New Zealand Representatives Overseas.
  Description: Provides a comprehensive list of contact details and staff of foreign diplomatic missions in New Zealand.

341.7 327   **GW**   **ISSN 0172-3227**
DIPLOMATIC OBSERVER/OBSERVATEUR DIPLOMATIQUE/INTERNATIONALES DIPLOMATISCHES MAGAZIN. (Text in English, French, German) 1972. m. DM.55($16.50) Institute for International Sociological Research, Wiener Weg 6, 50858 Cologne, Germany. TEL 0221-486019. (Co-sponsor: Akademie fuer Diplomatie und Internationale Beziehungen) Ed. Edward Ellenberg. adv.; bk.rev. circ. 11,000. **Document type:** academic/scholarly publication.

327   **US**   **ISSN 1052-0309**
JX1625
DIPLOMATIC RECORD. 1990. a. Westview Press, 5500 Central Ave., Boulder, CO 80301. TEL 303-444-3541. FAX 303-449-3356. **Document type:** academic/scholarly publication.
—BLDSC (3589.359200).

327   **UK**   **ISSN 0419-1714**
JX1783
DIPLOMATIC SERVICE LIST. a. price varies. H.M.S.O., P.O. Box 276, London SW8 5DT, England. circ. 3,000. **Document type:** government publication.
—BLDSC (3589.380000).

POLITICAL SCIENCE — INTERNATIONAL RELATIONS

327   US   ISSN 0363-8200
JX1977.A1
DIPLOMATIC WORLD BULLETIN AND DELEGATES WORLD BULLETIN;* dedicated to serving the United Nations and the international community. vol.12, 1982. fortn. $45. Diplomatic World Bulletin Publications, Inc., 763 UN Plaza, New York, NY 10017. TEL 212-747-9500. Ed. Richard A. Holman. adv.; illus.; tr.lit. (tabloid format)
    Formerly: Delegates World Bulletin.

DIPLOMATISCHE AKADEMIE. JAHRBUCH. see EDUCATION — Teaching Methods And Curriculum

327   AU
DIPLOMATISCHER PRESSEDIENST/DIPLOMATIC PRESS SERVICE. (Text in English, German) 1990. bi-m. S.400($66) Diplomatischer Pressedienst, Neustiftgasse 104, A-1070 Vienna, Austria. TEL 01-5268080. FAX 01-5261810. Ed. Eduard Knapp. adv.: page S.15000; adv. contact: A. Wurzer. bk.rev.; circ. 5,000. (back issues avail.) **Document type:** bulletin.

327   US
DIRECTORY OF PEACE STUDIES PROGRAMS. a? Consortium on Peace Research, Education and Development, George Mason University, 4400 University Dr., Fairfax, VA 22030. TEL 703-993-3639. FAX 703-993-1302. **Document type:** directory.

DOCUMENTS D'ACTUALITE INTERNATIONALE. see LAW — International Law

DOKUMENTE; Zeitschrift fuer den deutsch-franzoesischen Dialog. see GENERAL INTEREST PERIODICALS — Germany

327   338.91   GW
DRITTE-WELT-KALENDER. 1982. a. DM.12. Lamuv Verlag GmbH, Nikolaikirchhof 7, 37073 Goettingen, Germany. TEL 0551-44024. FAX 0551-41392. Ed. Karl-Klaus Rabe. **Document type:** bulletin.

DRITTE WELT MATERIALIEN. see HISTORY

323.4   FR   ISSN 0012-6373
DROIT DE VIVRE. vol.34, 1967. m. 80 F. 40 Rue de Paradis, 75010 Paris, France. Ed. Bernard Lecache. adv.; film rev.; illus.; play rev.

327   US
DUKE UNIVERSITY. CENTER FOR INTERNATIONAL STUDIES. PUBLICATIONS. 1956. irreg. price varies. Duke University Press, Center for International Studies, 6697 College Sta., Durham, NC 27708. TEL 919-684-2173. FAX 919-684-8644. TELEX 802829.
    Formerly (until 1983): Duke University. Commonwealth-Studies Center. Publications (ISSN 0070-7473)

327   GW   ISSN 0721-2178
E & Z - ENTWICKLUNG UND ZUSAMMENARBEIT. 1960. m. DM.33. Deutsche Stiftung fuer Internationale Entwicklung, Postfach 303210, 10729 Berlin, Germany. TEL 030-2606-0. FAX 030-2606375. (Subscr. to: Frankfurter Societaets Druckerei, Postfach 100801, 60008 Frankfurt a.M., Germany. TEL 069-75014366. FAX 069-75014855) Eds. Reinhold Thiel, Christiane Kahrmann. adv.; bk.rev. circ. 10,000. **Document type:** consumer publication. —CCC.
    Description: Discussion of theories and strategies involving international development.

327   EI   ISSN 0960-5398
D2009
E L F. (European Labour Forum) 1990. 4/yr. £10 (foreign £12). (European Parliament, Socialist Group) Spokesman, Bertrand Russell House, 45 Gamble St., Nottingham NG7 4ET, England. TEL 01602-708318. FAX 01602-420433. Ed. Ken Coates. adv.; bk.rev. circ. 5,000. **Document type:** newsletter.
    —BLDSC (3829.747900).
    Description: Covers and analyzes developments in Europe and beyond from the perspective of members of the Socialist Group of the European Parliament.

327   UK
E L T S A NEWSLETTER. 1974. irreg. (3-4/yr.). £2.50. End Loans to South Africa, c/o Methodist Church, 56 Camberwell Rd., London SE5 OEN, England. TEL 071-708-4702. FAX 071-708-5751. bk.rev. circ. 1,000. (looseleaf format) **Indexed:** HR Rep. **Document type:** newsletter.

327   GW
E U INFORMATIONEN. (Europaeischen Union) 1989. m. Europaeische Kommission, Vertretung in der Bundesrepublik Deutschland, Zitelmannstr. 22, 53113 Bonn, Germany. TEL 0228-53009-0. FAX 0228-5300950. Ed. Armin Czysz. circ. 80,000. **Document type:** bulletin.
    Formerly (until 1993): E G Informationen.

EAST ASIA; international review of economic, political and social development. see BUSINESS AND ECONOMICS — Economic Situation And Conditions

EAST EUROPEAN REPORTER. see BUSINESS AND ECONOMICS — Economic Situation And Conditions

327   940 950   UK   ISSN 0012-8627
D839
EAST-WEST DIGEST. 1965. fortn. £10($24) Foreign Affairs Publishing Co., 139 Petersham, Nr. Richmond, Surrey, England. Ed. D.G. Stewart-Smith. adv.; bk.rev.; index. circ. 5,000. (also avail. in microfilm from UMI; reprint service avail. from UMI)

327   NE   ISSN 0924-543X
EAST-WEST PERSPECTIVES. (Text in English) 1976. irreg. price varies. (East-West Foundation) Kluwer Academic Publishers, Postbus 17, 3300 AA Dordrecht, Netherlands. TEL 31-78-392392. FAX 31-78-392254. TELEX 29245 KAPG NL. (Dist. by: Kluwer Academic Publishers Group, P.O. Box 322, 3300 AH Dordrecht, Netherlands. TEL 31-78-392392. FAX 31-78-546474; N. America dist. addr.: Box 358, Accord Sta., Hingham, MA 02018-0358. TEL 617-871-6600. FAX 617-871-6528) Ed.Bd. charts; stat. **Indexed:** Mid.East: Abstr.& Ind. **Document type:** monographic series.
    Refereed Serial

327   330.9   US
ECONOMIC AND ENERGY INDICATORS. s-m. $155 per no. in N. America; elsewhere $290. (U.S. Central Intelligence Agency) U.S. National Technical Information Service, 5825 Port Royal Rd., Springfield, VA 22161. TEL 703-487-4630. (also avail. in microfiche from CIS; reprint service avail. from CIS) **Indexed:** Amer.Stat.Ind. (1976-).
    Formerly (until 1985): Economic Indicators.
    Description: Provides information on changes in domestic and external economic activities of major non-communist developed countries. Updated from press ticker and Embassy reporting.

327   330   CN   ISSN 0849-3391
ECONOMIC JUSTICE REPORT; global issues of economic justice. 1973. 4/yr. Can.$25 to individuals (foreign Can.$30); institutions Can.$40. Ecumenical Coalition for Economic Justice, 11 Madison Ave., Toronto, ON M5R 2S2, Canada. TEL 416-921-4615. FAX 416-942-5356. E-mail: gattfly@web.apc.org. bk.rev.; illus. circ. 1,000. **Document type:** newsletter.
    Former titles: GATT-Fly Report (ISSN 0228-359X); GATT-Fly.

325   SZ
ECUMENICAL REFUGEE AND MIGRATION NEWS. (Text in English) m. World Council of Churches, 150 route de Ferney, P.O. Box 2100, CH-1211 Geneva 2, Switzerland. TEL 022-7916111. FAX 022-7981346. TELEX 415730-OIK-CH. **Document type:** newsletter.

327   II
EGYPT NEWS. (Text in English) 1954. w. free. Embassy of the Arab Republic of Egypt, Press Bureau, 1-50M, Niti Marge, Chanakyapuri, New Delhi 110021, India. TEL 6876653. FAX 677209. TELEX 72245EGND IN. Ed. Fawzy Algammal. bk.rev. circ. 2,000. **Document type:** newsletter.
    Formerly: Cairo Bulletin; Cairo Information Bulletin.

ELDERS; een kroniek van zaken buiten de grenzen. see POPULATION STUDIES

327   301   GW
AS2.5
ENCYCLOPEDIA OF WORLD PROBLEMS AND HUMAN POTENTIAL. (In 2 vols.) 1976. irreg., 4th ed., 1994. DM.898($575) (Union of International Associations, BE) K.G. Saur Verlag KG, A part of Reed Reference Publishing, Ortlerstr. 8, 81373 Munich, Germany. TEL 089-76902-0. FAX 089-76902150. (Subscr. to: Postfach 701620, 81316 Munich, Germany; US addr.: K.G. Saur, 121 Chanlon Rd., New Providence, NJ 07974. TEL 908-665-3576) bibl. **Document type:** directory.
    Formerly: Yearbook of World Problems and Human Potential (ISSN 0304-0089)
    Description: Focuses on more than 13,000 issues of global concern. The entries in the main section describes the nature of each problem, its origins and incidence, and possible political and social responses.

ENERGY POLICY STUDIES. see ENERGY

ENFANTS DU MONDE. see SOCIAL SERVICES AND WELFARE

327   US
ENGLISH SPEAKING UNION TODAY. 1953. 3/yr. membership. English-Speaking Union of the United States, 16 E. 69th St., New York, NY 10021. TEL 212-879-6800. FAX 212-772-2886. Dir. David Olyphant. adv. circ. 18,000. **Document type:** newsletter.
    Former titles: English Speaking: The E-S U News; English-Speaking Union News (ISSN 0013-8371)

327   US   ISSN 1059-6402
JC599.L3
ENLACE; politica y derechos humanos en las Americas. (Text in Spanish) 1975. q. $20 to individuals; institutions $25. Washington Office on Latin America, 4 C St., N.E., Washington, DC 20002. TEL 202-544-8045. FAX 202-546-5288. Ed. Rachel Neild. charts; index, cum.index. circ. 2,000. (looseleaf format; back issues avail.) **Document type:** newsletter.
    Supersedes (in 1991): Latin America Update (ISSN 0738-601X)

ENVIRONMENT WATCH: LATIN AMERICA; news and analysis for business and policy professionals. see ENVIRONMENTAL STUDIES

ENVIRONMENT WATCH: WEST EUROPE. see ENVIRONMENTAL STUDIES

327   UK   ISSN 0964-4016
GE170
ENVIRONMENTAL POLITICS. 1992. q. £42($55) to individuals; institutions £115 ($155) (effective 1996). Frank Cass, Newbury House, 890-900 Eastern Ave., Newbury Park, Ilford, Essex 1G2 7HH, England. TEL 44-181-599-8866. FAX 44-181-599-0984. E-mail: 100067,1576@compuserve.com. Eds. Michael Waller, Stephen Young. adv.; B&W page £195 ($275); adv. contact: Anne Kidson. bk.rev.; index. **Indexed:** Geo.Abstr., IDA, Int.Polit.Sci.Abstr., Soc.Sci.Ind. (1994-). **Document type:** academic/scholarly publication.
    —BLDSC (3791.538000); UnCover. CCC.
    Description: Presents academic study of environmental politics with a focus on the industrialized countries.
    Refereed Serial

327   GW   ISSN 0939-7507
ERZIEHERBRIEF. 1952. 5/yr. DM.36($27) Arbeitsgemeinschaft Sudetendeutscher Lehrer und Erzieher e.V., Hochstr. 8, 81669 Munich, Germany. TEL 089-480003-28. (Co-sponsor: Haus des Deutschen Ostens) Ed. Ernst Korn. circ. 1,400 (paid). **Document type:** academic/scholarly publication, newsletter.
    Formerly: Sudetendeutscher Erzieherbrief.

ESPERANTO. see LINGUISTICS

ESPERANTO-DOKUMENTOJ. NOVA SERIO. see LINGUISTICS

EST - OVEST. see BUSINESS AND ECONOMICS — Economic Situation And Conditions

POLITICAL SCIENCE — INTERNATIONAL RELATIONS

327　　　　　　　MX　ISSN 0185-0350
HC106.7
ESTADOS UNIDOS: PERSPECTIVA LATINOAMERICANA. CUADERNOS SEMESTRALES. 1976. s-a. Centro de Investigacion y Docencia Economicas, Difusion de Publicaciones, Apdo. Postal 116-114, 01130 Mexico, D.F., Mexico. adv. circ. 4,000.

THE ESTIMATE; political and security intelligence analysis of North Africa, the Middle East, South Asia, East Asia, & the Pacific. see MILITARY

327　　　　　　　US
THE ESTIMATES.* 1989. fortn. $295 (foreign $330). International Estimates, 3030 S. Abingdon St., Arlington, DC 22206-1605. TEL 202-332-0849.

327　　　　　　　CL　ISSN 0716-0240
F1414.2
ESTUDIOS INTERNACIONALES. 1967. q. Esc.6500 (foreign $49) to individuals; institutions ESC.8000 (foreign $58) (effective 1996). Universidad de Chile, Instituto de Estudios Internacionales, Condell 249, Casilla 14187, Suc. 21, Santiago 9, Chile. TEL 56-2-2745377. FAX 56-2-2740155. E-mail: inesint@abello.dic.uchile.cl. Ed. Pilar Alamos Varas. adv.; bk.rev.; index. circ. 550. **Indexed:** Amer.Hist.& Life (until 1993), Hisp.Amer.Per.Ind. (1970-), Hist.Abstr. (until 1993). **Document type:** academic/scholarly publication.
—Faxon; SWETS.
Refereed Serial

327　　　　　　　SP　ISSN 0211-5727
ESTUDIOS INTERNACIONALES. q. 2200 ptas.($24) Centro de Estudios Constitucionales, Plaza de la Marina Espanola, 9, Apartado 50.877, Madrid 13, Spain. **Indexed:** A.B.C.Pol.Sci.

327　　　　　　　US
ETHICS & INTERNATIONAL AFFAIRS (JOURNAL). 1987. a. $10. Carnegie Council on Ethics and International Affairs, c/o Matthew Mattern, Mng. Ed., Merrill House, 170 E. 64th St., New York, NY 10021-7478. TEL 212-838-4120. FAX 212-752-2432. Ed. Joel Rosenthal. **Indexed:** Geo.Abstr., Int.Polit.Sci.Abstr., Per.Islam. (1991-).
Description: Presents applications of ethics to international affairs from a variety of perspectives.
Refereed Serial

327 170　　　　　　US　ISSN 0892-6794
JX1255
ETHICS AND INTERNATIONAL AFFAIRS (NEWSLETTER); a college-level curriculum development program. 1987. s-a. Carnegie Council on Ethics and International Affairs, c/o Matthew Mattern, Mng. Ed., Merrill House, 170 E. 64th St., New York, NY 10021-7478. TEL 212-838-4120. FAX 212-752-2432. Ed. Joel Rosenthal. **Indexed:** IDA. **Document type:** newsletter.
—BLDSC (3814.656700); Faxon; UnCover.
Description: College level curriculum development program for teaching ethics and international affairs.

327　　　　　　　CN　ISSN 0014-2123
D849
ETUDES INTERNATIONALES. (Text in French) 1970. q. Can.$45 to individuals (foreign Can.$50); institutions Can.$55 (foreign Can.$60); students Can.$35. Institut Quebecois des Hautes Etudes Internationales, Pavillon de Koninck, Universite Laval, Quebec, PQ G1K 7P4, Canada. TEL 418-656-2462. Ed. Gerard Hervouet. adv.; bk.rev.; index, cum.index. circ. 1,500. **Indexed:** A.B.C.Pol.Sci., Amer.Hist.& Life (until 1991), Can.B.P.I., Can.Per.Ind., Curr.Cont., Documentatieblad, Hist.Abstr. (until 1991), Int.Polit.Sci.Abstr., Int.Polit.Sci.Abstr., P.A.I.S.For.Lang.Ind., Peace Res.Abstr., Periodex, Polit.Sci.Abstr., Pt.de Rep. (1979-), SSCI. **Document type:** academic/scholarly publication.
—BLDSC (3820.720000); Faxon; SWETS.
Description: Publishes articles and reviews that cover important international political affairs.

327　　　　　　　NE　ISSN 0928-8635
EUR NIEUWS. 1989. s-m. Samsom H.D. Tjeenk Willink B.V. (Subsidiary of: Wolters Kluwer N.V.), Postbus 316, 2400 AH Alphen aan den Rijn, Netherlands. TEL 31-1720-66822. FAX 31-1720-66639.

327　　　　　　　EI　ISSN 1021-1675
EUR-OP NEWS. French edition (ISSN 1021-1683); German edition (ISSN 1021-1667) (Text in English) 1992. 4/yr. free. (Commission of the European Communities) Office for Official Publications of the European Communities, 2 rue Mercier, L-2985 Luxembourg, Luxembourg. TEL 352-49-92-81. FAX 352-48-85-73. (Dist. in US by: Unipub, 4611-F Assembly Dr., Lanham, MD 20706-4391) Ed. Alexander von Witzleben. circ. 295,000. **Document type:** newspaper.
—BLDSC (3828.050000).

327　　　　　　　BE　ISSN 1021-4208
EURO-EAST. French edition: Euro-Est (ISSN 1021-4216) (Text in English) 1992. m. 21950 BEF (effective 1995). Europe Information Service, Rue de Geneve, 6, 1140 Brussels, Belgium. TEL 32-2-242-6020. FAX 32-2-242-9410. Ed. Eric van Puyvelde. **Document type:** newsletter.
●Also available online. Vendor(s): Lexis-Nexis. Also available on CD-ROM.
Description: Covers EU relations with Central and Eastern Europe.

327　　　　　　　NE　ISSN 0924-5413
EURO-LATIN AMERICAN RELATIONS. (Text in English) 1987. irreg. price varies. Kluwer Academic Publishers, Postbus 17, 3300 AA Dordrecht, Netherlands. TEL 31-78-392392. FAX 31-78-392254. TELEX 29245 KAPG NL. (Dist. by: Kluwer Academic Publishers Group, P.O. Box 322, 3300 AH Dordrecht, Netherlands. TEL 31-78-392392. FAX 31-78-546474; N. America dist. addr.: Box 358, Accord Sta., Hingham, MA 02018-0358. TEL 617-871-6600. FAX 617-871-6528) **Document type:** monographic series.
Refereed Serial

940 327　　　　　　GW　ISSN 0014-2476
D839
EUROPA-ARCHIV; Zeitschrift fuer internationale Politik. 1946. s-m. DM.190. (Deutsche Gesellschaft fuer Auswaertige Politik e.V.) Verlag fuer Internationale Politik GmbH, Postfach 1529, 53005 Bonn, Germany. TEL 0228-7290010. FAX 0228-695734. Ed. Wolfgang Wagner. adv.; bk.rev.; bibl.; charts; index. cum.index: 1946-1965, 1966-1970, 1971-1975, 1976-1980, 1981-1985. circ. 5,000. (reprint service avail. from ISI) **Indexed:** A.B.C.Pol.Sci., Abstr.Mil.Bibl., Amer.Hist.& Life, Curr.Cont., Geo.Abstr., Hist.Abstr., Int.Polit.Sci.Abstr., Key to Econ.Sci., P.A.I.S.For.Lang.Ind., Peace Res.Abstr, SSCI. **Document type:** bulletin.
—Faxon; Genuine Article. **CCC.**

320 330　　　　　　AU　ISSN 0304-2782
JN12
EUROPAEISCHE RUNDSCHAU. 1973. q. S.320. Herold Druck und Verlag GmbH, Faradaygasse 6, A-1032 Vienna, Austria. TEL 01-4083400. FAX 01-521615386. Ed. Paul Lendvai. adv. contact: Leopold Kurz. bk.rev.; bibl. circ. 2,750. **Indexed:** ELLIS, P.A.I.S.For.Lang.Ind. **Document type:** bulletin.
—BLDSC (3829.361000).

327 341　　　　　　GW　ISSN 0071-2329
EUROPAEISCHE SCHRIFTEN. 1963. irreg. (Institut fuer Europaeische Politik, Bonn) Europa Union Verlag GmbH, Bachstr. 32, Postfach 1529, 53115 Bonn, Germany. TEL 0228-7290010. FAX 0228-695734. TELEX 8-86822. Ed. Wolfgang Wessels.

940 327　　　　　　GW
EUROPAEISCHE ZEITUNG. 1949. m. DM.49.80 (foreign DM.60.80). (Europa-Union Deutschland e.V.) Europa Union Verlag GmbH, Bachstr. 32, Postfach 1529, 53115 Bonn, Germany. TEL 0228-7290010. FAX 0228-695734. TELEX 8-86822. Eds. Gerhard Eickhorn, Claus Schoendube. adv.; bk.rev.; illus. circ. 40,000. **Indexed:** ELLIS.
Former titles: Europaeische Zeitung Europa-Union (ISSN 0343-6659); Europa-Union (ISSN 0014-2611)

940 943　　　　　　GW　ISSN 0721-3018
EUROPAEISCHES FORUM. (Supplement to: Europaeische Zeitung) 1949. m. Europa Union Verlag GmbH, Bachstr. 32, 53115 Bonn, Germany. TEL 0228-7290010. FAX 0228-695734. TELEX 8-86822. bk.rev. circ. 40,000.
Formerly: Informationsdienst des Deutschen Rates der Europaeischen Bewegung (ISSN 0020-0549)

320.5　　　　　　AU　ISSN 0014-2727
EUROPASTIMME.* 1960. bi-m. Europaeische Foederalistische Bewegung, Jahnweg 5, A-8330 Feldbach, Austria. Ed. Wolfgang Wratschgo. bk.rev.; illus.; stat. circ. 10,000.

EUROPE. see BUSINESS AND ECONOMICS — Economic Situation And Conditions

327　　　　　　　UK　ISSN 0306-0772
EUROPEAN CAMPAIGNER. 1973. q. £15. European Movement, 158 Buckingham Palace Rd., London SW1W 9TR, England. TEL 071-824-8388. FAX 071-824-8124. adv.; bk.rev.; charts; illus. circ. 6,000. **Indexed:** Met.Abstr. **Document type:** newsletter.
Formerly: Facts.
Description: Covers developments in the field of European integration and argues for increased European unity.

EUROPEAN COMMUNITIES. ECONOMIC AND SOCIAL CONSULTATIVE ASSEMBLY. ANNUAL REPORT. see BUSINESS AND ECONOMICS

327　　　　　　　IE
EUROPEAN DOCUMENT SERIES. q. I£30 to non-members; members £20. Institute of European Affairs, 8 North Great George's St., Dublin 1, Ireland. Ed. Tony Brown. **Document type:** academic/scholarly publication.
Description: Designed to highlight the texts of important speeches, papers and reports on European issues and themes.

327　　　　　　　BE　ISSN 1021-4283
EUROPEAN INSIGHT. French edition: Lettre Europeenne (ISSN 1021-4291) (Text in English) 1982. w. 16200 BEF (effective 1995). Europe Information Service, Rue de Geneve, 6, 1140 Brussels, Belgium. TEL 32-2-242-6020. FAX 32-2-242-9410.
●Also available online. Vendor(s): Lexis-Nexis.
Description: Covers events in the EU in the preceding week.

327 382　　　　　　IT　ISSN 0394-6444
D1050
EUROPEAN JOURNAL OF INTERNATIONAL AFFAIRS. (Text in English) q. L.70000 to individuals (foreign $54); institutions L.100000 (foreign $77). Erasmus Press, Via dei Giubbonari, 30, 00186 Rome, Italy. TEL 687-31-96. FAX 687-25-49. Ed. Giuseppe Sacco. bk.rev.; illus. **Indexed:** Int.Polit.Sci.Abstr.
—UnCover.

327　　　　　　　UK　ISSN 1354-0661
JX1
▼**EUROPEAN JOURNAL OF INTERNATIONAL RELATIONS.** 1995. q. £32 to individuals; institutions £99 (effective 1996). (European Consortium for Political Research, Standing Group on International Relations) Sage Publications Ltd., 6 Bonhill St., London EC2A 4PU, England. TEL 0171-374-0645. FAX 0171-374-8741. E-mail: market@sageltd.co.uk. Ed. Walter Carlsnaes. adv.: B&W page £180; trim 190 x 113; adv. contact: Bernie Folan. **Indexed:** Int.Polit.Sci.Abstr., Polit.Sci.Abstr. **Document type:** academic/scholarly publication.
—BLDSC (3829.730300).
Description: Aims to stimulate and disseminate the latest research in international relations. Addresses methodological and epistemological questions as well as conceptual and empirical developments within the major sub-areas of the field.

328.3　　　　　　EI　ISSN 0423-7846
JN32
EUROPEAN PARLIAMENT. BULLETIN. (Supplements with title Annex accompany some issues) w. European Parliament, Secretariat, L-2929 Luxembourg, Luxembourg. FAX 43-70-09. **Document type:** bulletin.

327　　　　　　　UK
EUROPEAN POLICY FOCUS. irreg. £6. MacLennan Ward Research Ltd., 40 Pendle Rd., London SW16 6RU, England. TEL 0181-769-6789. FAX 0181-677-7112. E-mail: mac.ward@geo2.poptel.org.uk. **Document type:** monographic series.
—BLDSC (3829.788100).

POLITICAL SCIENCE — INTERNATIONAL RELATIONS

327 UK ISSN 0966-2839
UA646
EUROPEAN SECURITY. 1992. q. £38($48) to individuals; institutions £98 ($145) (effective 1996). Frank Cass, Newbury House, 890-900 Eastern Ave., Newbury Park, Ilford, Essex 1G2 7HH, England. TEL 44-181-599-8866. FAX 44-181-599-0984. E-mail: 100067,1576@compuserve.com. Eds. Christopher Donnelly, Jacob Kipp. adv.: B&W page £195 ($275); adv. contact: Anne Kidson. bk.rev.; index. (back issues avail.) **Indexed:** Int.Polit.Sci.Abstr. **Document type:** academic/scholarly publication.
—BLDSC (3829.970343).
Description: Publishes articles, essays, and reviews on the new architecture, concepts, institutions, problems, and prospects for European security in the wake of the end of the Cold War.
Refereed Serial

327 BE ISSN 1021-4143
EUROPEAN SOCIAL POLICY. French edition: Lettre Sociale Europeenne (ISSN 1021-4151) (Text in English) 1991. m. 22600 BEF (effective 1995). Europe Information Service, Rue de Geneve, 6, 1140 Brussels, Belgium. TEL 32-2-242-6020. FAX 32-2-242-9410. **Document type:** bulletin.
●Also available online. Vendor(s): Lexis-Nexis. Also available on CD-ROM.

THE EUROPEAN UNION ENCYCLOPEDIA AND DIRECTORY (YEAR). see *ENCYCLOPEDIAS AND GENERAL ALMANACS*

EUROSCOPE; providing access to information necessary to do business in the European Union. see *LAW — International Law*

940 IT ISSN 0014-3235
EUROSUD. 1966. w. L.155000($150) Centro Studi Comunita Europee, c/o Eurocampus, Strata Prov. Bitonto, Km. 2.200, S. Spirito, 70032 Bitonto, Italy. index; circ. 1,800 (controlled). (looseleaf format)

327 338.91 US ISSN 1063-6323
HF1532.92
EUROWATCH. 1989. bi-w. $797 (foreign $819). L R P Publications, Dresher Rd., Box 980, Horsham, PA 19044-0980. TEL 800-341-7874. FAX 215-784-9639. Ed. Michael C. Petrovsky. index. (back issues avail.) **Document type:** newsletter.
—CCC.
Formerly (until 1991): 1992: The External Impact of European Unification (ISSN 1043-4380)
Description: News and analysis from European capitals and Washington, DC, on how US and other business interests are affected by the Europeans Community's program to remove national barriers and create a "single market" for the trade and movement of goods, service, capital, and labor.

341.13 UN ISSN 0251-690X
JX1977.A37
EVERYONE'S UNITED NATIONS. French edition: Ce Qu'il Faut Savoir des Nations Unies (ISSN 0251-6896); Spanish edition: Naciones Unidas. Origenes, Organizacon, Actividades (ISSN 0251-6918) 1948. irreg., latest no.10. $14.95 per no. United Nations Publications, Room DC2-853, New York, NY 10017. TEL 212-963-8302; 800-253-9646. FAX 212-963-3489. (Or: Distribution and Sales Section, Palais des Nations, CH-1211 Geneva 10, Switzerland)
Formerly (until 1979): Everyman's United Nations (ISSN 0071-3244)

327 EI
EVROPA. (Text in Russian) 1992. bi-m. Commission of European Communities (Moscow), Astakhovsky per. 2-10, 109027 Moscow, Russia. TEL 7-095-9567583. FAX 7-095-9563615. (Dist. by: Independent Press, ul. Pravdy 24, Moscow, Russia. TEL 7-095-2574723. FAX 7-095-2574546) circ. 100,000.
Description: Aims to make the population of the CIS and the Baltic States more aware of what the European Community is, how it is developing and what it is trying to do in Russia and other CIS states.

327 US ISSN 8755-433X
EXECUTIVE MEMORANDUM. 1982. irreg., no.404, 1994. newsstand price: $2. Heritage Foundation, 214 Massachusetts Ave., N.E., Washington, DC 20002. TEL 202-546-4400. FAX 202-546-8328. (looseleaf format; back issues avail.)
●Also available online. Vendor(s): Lexis-Nexis.

EXIL. see *SOCIAL SERVICES AND WELFARE*

327 DK ISSN 1395-2781
F N BLADET. 1950. 6/yr. DKK 225($8) (effective 1996). Danish United Nations Association - F N -Forbundet, Skindergade 26, 1, DK-1159 Copenhagen K, Denmark. TEL 45-33-12-39-39. FAX 45-33-12-10-58. (Co-sponsor: Ministry of Foreign Affairs) Ed. Lasse Budtz. adv.; bk.rev.; illus. circ. 1,500.
Supersedes: Verden og Vi; (1950-1969): Verden og Vi (ISSN 0505-2521); Formed by the merger of (1964-1969): F N - Bladet (ISSN 0906-3196)

327 US ISSN 1066-3479
AL-FAJR JERUSALEM PALESTINIAN WEEKLY. (English edition of daily Al-Fajr (East Jerusalem)) 1980. w. $50 to individuals and libraries (foreign $75); students $40. Omar International, Inc., 16 Crowell St., Hempstead, NY 11550. TEL 516-485-5905. FAX 516-564-8850. TELEX 967701 OMAR HEM. Ed. Hanna Siniora. bk.rev. circ. 5,000. (also avail. in microfilm from IDC) **Indexed:** Per.Islam (1991-). **Document type:** newspaper.
Formerly: Jerusalem Al-Fajr.
Description: Provides news coverage of Palestinians under Israeli occupation.

THE FATE OF THE ARABIAN PENINSULA. see *ENERGY*

320.5 LU ISSN 0014-9268
FEDERALISTE EUROPEEN. vol.16, 1968. s-a. $2.50. Conseil Luxembourgeois du Mouvement Europeen, 20 B, rue Louvigny, B.P. 105, Luxembourg, Luxembourg. bk.rev.; bibl.

FILMOTECA ULTRAMARINA PORTUGUESA. BOLETIM. see *HISTORY*

327 FI ISSN 0071-528X
FINLAND. ULKOASIAINMINISTERIO. ULKAPOLIITTISIA LAUSUNTOJA JA ASIAKIRJOJA. (Text in Finnish; occasionally in English, French, German and Swedish) 1959. s-a. Ulkoasiainministerio - Ministry for Foreign Affairs, PL 176, 00160 Helsinki, Finland. TEL 90-134151. circ. 2,000. **Document type:** government publication.

327 US ISSN 1046-1868
D839
FLETCHER FORUM OF WORLD AFFAIRS. 1977. s-a. $16 to individuals (foreign $30); institutions $25 (foreign $39). Fletcher School of Law and Diplomacy, Tufts University, Medford, MA 02155. TEL 617-623-3610. FAX 617-627-3979. Ed. Linda Maguire. adv. contact: Maria Farnon. bk.rev.; charts; illus. circ. 1,000. (also avail. in microfiche from WSH; reprint service avail. from WSH) **Indexed:** A.B.C.Pol.Sci., Amer.Bibl.Slavic & E.Eur.Stud., Amer.Hist.& Life (until 1993), C.C.L.P., C.L.I., Hist.Abstr. (until 1993), Int.Polit.Sci.Abstr., L.R.I., Leg.Cont., P.A.I.S., Polit.Sci.Abstr. **Document type:** academic/scholarly publication.
●Also available online. Vendor(s): West Services, Inc.
—BLDSC (3950.532000); Faxon; UnCover.
Formerly (until vol.12, no.2, 1988): Fletcher Forum (ISSN 0147-0981)
Description: Analyzes outstanding problems of international law, politics, economics, business, and diplomacy. Provides articles, commentaries and book reviews written by noted professionals and graduate students in international relations.

FLYGTNINGE NYT. see *SOCIAL SERVICES AND WELFARE*

320.96 UK ISSN 0959-9576
FOCUS ON AFRICA. 1990. q. (British Broadcasting Corporation) B B C African Service, Bush House, P.O. Box 76, Strand, London WC2 4PH, England. TEL 44-171-2403456. FAX 44-171-3790519. Ed. Robin White. adv.; illus.; circ. 32,000 (paid). **Document type:** consumer publication.
—Faxon.
Description: Covers political developments and news of Africa, and provides information on B.B.C. African Service programming.

FOOD FIRST NEWS & VIEWS. see *POLITICAL SCIENCE*

327 US ISSN 0015-7120
D410 CODEN: FRNAA3
FOREIGN AFFAIRS. 1922. bi-m. $44. Council on Foreign Relations, Inc., 58 E. 68th St., New York, NY 10021. TEL 212-734-0400. Ed. James F. Hoge, Jr. adv.: B&W page $7300, color page $10250. bk.rev.; index. circ. 110,000. (also avail. in microform from UMI,MIM,WSH,PMC; reprint service avail. from KTO,WSh) **Indexed:** A.B.C.Pol.Sci., ABI Inform, Abstr.Mil.Bibl., Acad.Ind., Amer.Hist.& Life, Asian-Pac.Econ.Lit., Bk.Rev.Ind. (1984-), BPIA, C.R.E.J., Chic.Per.Ind., Child.Bk.Rev.Ind. (1984-), Curr.Cont.M.E., Deep Sea Res.& Oceanogr.Abstr., E.I., Econ.& Market.Abstr., Fut.Surv., Hist.Abstr., HR Rep. (1969-), INIS Atomind., Int.Lab.Doc., Int.Polit.Sci.Abstr., J.of Econ.Lit., Key to Econ.Sci., Mag.Ind., Mid.East: Abstr.& Ind., P.A.I.S., Peace Res.Abstr., Polit.Sci.Abstr., PROMT, R.G., Soc.Sci.Ind., SSCI, Tr.& Indus.Ind., World Bank.Abstr. **Document type:** academic/scholarly publication.
●Also available online. Vendor(s): Lexis-Nexis, University Microfilms International.
Also available on CD-ROM. Producer(s): University Microfilms International.
—BLDSC (3986.800000); Faxon; Genuine Article; SWETS; UMI; UnCover.
Description: Magazine on international politics and economic thought.

327 NP
FOREIGN AFFAIRS JOURNAL. (Text in English) 1976. 3/yr. Rs.25. Bhola Bikrum Rana, Ed. & Pub., 5-287 Lagon, Kathmandu, Nepal.

959.5 327 MY ISSN 0126-690X
FOREIGN AFFAIRS MALAYSIA. 1966. q. free. Ministry of Foreign Affairs - Kementerian Luar Negeri, Jalan Wisma Putra, Kuala Lumpur, Malaysia. illus. circ. 6,000. **Indexed:** Abstr.Mil.Bibl.
—BLDSC (3986.810000).

327 II
FOREIGN AFFAIRS RECORD. 1955. m. Ministry of External Affairs, External Publicity Division, New Delhi, India. (U.S. address: Consulate General of India, 3 E. 64th St., New York, NY 10021) index. circ. 1,600.

327 II ISSN 0015-7155
FOREIGN AFFAIRS REPORTS. (Text in English) 1952. m. $45. Indian Council of World Affairs, Sapru House, Barakhamba Rd., New Delhi 110001, India. Ed. S.C. Parasher. index. circ. 800. **Indexed:** Abstr.Mil.Bibl., Int.Polit.Sci.Abstr.

327 US ISSN 0071-7320
JX1705
FOREIGN CONSULAR OFFICES IN THE UNITED STATES. (Subseries of: U.S. Department of State. Department and Foreign Service Series) 1932. a. U.S. Department of State, 2201 C St. N.W., Washington, DC 20520. TEL 202-655-4000. (Dist. by: Supt. of Documents, Washington, DC 20402)

FOREIGN GOVERNMENT OFFICES IN CALIFORNIA; a directory. see *PUBLIC ADMINISTRATION*

327 US ISSN 0015-7228
E744
FOREIGN POLICY (WASHINGTON). 1970. q. $33. Carnegie Endowment for International Peace, 2400 N St., N.W., Ste. 700, Washington, DC 20037. TEL 202-862-7940. (Subscr. to: Foreign Policy, Box 56616, Boulder, CO 80322-6616. TEL 800-678-0916) Ed. Charles William Maynes. adv. contact: Krista Mueller. bk.rev.; a.v. index. circ. 25,000. (also avail. in microform from UMI; reprint service avail. from UMI,WSH) **Indexed:** A.B.C.Pol.Sci., Abstr.Mil.Bibl., Acad.Ind., Access, Amer.Bibl.Slavic & E.Eur.Stud., Amer.Hist.& Life, C.L.I., Curr.Cont., Curr.Cont.M.E., Deep Sea Res.& Oceanogr.Abstr., Fut.Surv., Hist.Abstr., HR Rep. (1985-), INIS Atomind., Leg.Per., Mag.Ind., Mar.Aff.Bibl., P.A.I.S., Per.Islam. (1991-), PMR, Polit.Sci.Abstr., PROMT, R.G., Rural Recreat.Tour.Abstr., Soc.Sci.Ind., SSCI, World Agri.Econ.& Rural Sociol.Abstr. **Document type:** academic/scholarly publication.
●Also available online. Vendor(s): University Microfilms International.
Also available on CD-ROM.
—BLDSC (3987.105000); Faxon; Genuine Article; SWETS; UMI; UnCover. **CCC.**
Description: Journal of political science and international relations.

POLITICAL SCIENCE — INTERNATIONAL RELATIONS

327   US   ISSN 0017-8780
E744
FOREIGN POLICY ASSOCIATION. HEADLINE SERIES. 1935. 4/yr. $20 (effective 1994). Foreign Policy Association, 470 Park Ave. S., New York, NY 10016-6819. TEL 212-481-8100. FAX 212-481-9275. Ed. Nancy Hoepli-Phalon. bibl.; charts; illus.; maps. circ. 8,000. (also avail. in microfilm from UMI; back issues avail.; reprint service avail. from UMI,KTO) **Indexed:** Hum.Ind., P.A.I.S., Soc.Sci.Ind. **Document type:** academic/scholarly publication.
—BLDSC (4274.655000); UMI; UnCover.

327 341   US   ISSN 1052-7036
E840
FOREIGN POLICY BULLETIN; the documentary record of United States foreign policy. 1990. bi-m. $54 (foreign $69.60). Mediacom, Inc. (Washington), 4812 Butterworth Pl., N.W., Washington, DC 20016. TEL 202-686-5230. Ed. Paul E. Auerswald; Pub. Paul E. Auerswald. bk.rev.; index. (back issues avail.) **Indexed:** P.A.I.S. **Document type:** academic/scholarly publication, bulletin.
●Also available online. Vendor(s): Ovid Technologies, Data-Star, Knight-Ridder, Inc.
—UnCover.
Description: Documents all major events in contemporary U.S. foreign relations as they happen, including texts from Congress as well as the Executive Branch and from other governments and international organizations. Lists Treaty Actions and new releases in the State Department's Foreign Relations of the United States series.

327   US   ISSN 0071-7355
JX233
FOREIGN RELATIONS OF THE UNITED STATES. 1861. irreg. price varies. U.S. Department of State, Bureau of Public Affairs, Office of the Historian, 2201 C St., N.W., Washington, DC 20520. TEL 202-655-4000. (Orders to: Superintendent of Documents, U.S. Government Printing Office, Box 371954, Pittsburgh, PA 15250. TEL 202-512-1800. FAX 202-512-2250; Or: Bernan, 4611-F Assembly Dr., Lanham, MD 20706. TEL 800-274-4447. FAX 301-459-0056) **Document type:** government publication.

327   UK   ISSN 0951-0338
FOREIGN SERVICE. 1986. s-a. £15($30) Diplomatist Associates Ltd., 58 Theobalds Rd., London WC1X 8SF, England. TEL 0171-405-4874. FAX 0171-831-0667. Ed. Sophie Cameron. adv.; bk.rev.; index. circ. 3,000 (controlled). (back issues avail.) **Document type:** trade publication.
Description: Covers British diplomatic and export activities worldwide. Includes profiles of foreign offices and updates on recent events affecting U.K. diplomats.

327   US   ISSN 0015-7279
FOREIGN SERVICE JOURNAL. 1924. 11/yr. $40 (foreign $50). American Foreign Service Association, 2101 E St., N.W., Washington, DC 20037. TEL 202-338-4045. FAX 202-338-6820. Ed. Karen Krebsbach. adv.; bk.rev.; illus.; index. circ. 15,000. (also avail. in microform from UMI; reprint service avail. from UMI) **Indexed:** Amer.Bibl.Slavic & E.Eur.Stud., Amer.Hist.& Life, Hist.Abstr., Mid.East: Abstr.& Ind., P.A.I.S., Pers.Lit.
—UnCover.
Former titles (until 1951): American Foreign Service Journal (ISSN 0360-8425); American Consular Bulletin.

327   MX   ISSN 0185-013X
D839
FORO INTERNACIONAL. 1960. 4/yr. Mex.$76($32) to individuals (foreign $42); institutions $50 (foreign $60) (effective 1995). Colegio de Mexico, A.C., Departamento de Publicaciones, Camino al Ajusco 20, Col. Pedregal de Santa Teresa, 10740 Mexico, D.F., Mexico. TEL 525-6455955. FAX 525-6450464. TELEX 1777585 COLME. Ed. Francisco Fil Villegas. adv.; bk.rev.; bibl.; charts; index. cum.index. circ. 2,000. (back issues avail.) **Indexed:** A.B.C.Pol.Sci., Amer.Hist.& Life, Hisp.Amer.Per.Ind. (1970-), Hist.Abstr., Int.Polit.Sci.Abstr., P.A.I.S.For.Lang.Ind.
—BLDSC (4008.950000); Faxon; SWETS.

327   GW
FORSCHUNGEN ZU OSTEUROPA. 1986. irreg. Edition Temmen, Hohenlohestr. 21, 28209 Bremen, Germany. TEL 0421-344280. FAX 0421-348094. Ed.Bd. **Document type:** academic/scholarly publication.

338.91   NO   ISSN 0803-9410
D880
FORUM FOR DEVELOPMENT STUDIES. 2/yr. NOK 150 in Nordic countries; elsewhere NOK 200. Norsk Utenrikspolitisk Institutt - Norwegian Institute of International Affairs, P.O. Box 8159 Dep., N-0033 Oslo, Norway. TEL 47-22-17-70-50. FAX 47-22-17-70-15. E-mail: PUB@NUPI.NO. Ed. Olav Stokke. **Indexed:** Geo.Abstr., IDA, Int.Polit.Sci.Abstr. **Document type:** academic/scholarly publication.
—BLDSC (4024.085190). CCC.
Formerly (until 1992): Forum for Utviklingsstudier (ISSN 0332-8244)

354   FR   ISSN 0182-7502
FRANCE. MEDIATEUR. RAPPORT ANNUEL DU MEDIATEUR. 1973. a. Imprimerie Nationale, B.P. 637, 59506 Douai Cedex, France.

327   FR   ISSN 0247-4468
FRANCE. MINISTERE DE LA COOPERATION. SERVICE DE L'INFORMATION ET DE LA COMMUNICATION. ETUDES ET DOCUMENTS. Key Title: Etudes et Documents - Ministere de la Cooperation. irreg. Ministere de la Cooperation, Service de l'Information et de la Communication, 20 rue Monsieur, 75700 Paris, France. circ. 500. **Document type:** monographic series.
Former titles: France. Ministere des Relations Exterieures. Sous-Directions des Etudes et Developpement. Etudes et Documents; France. Ministere de la Cooperation. Sous-Direction des Etudes de Developpement. Etudes et Documents; France. Ministere de la Cooperation. Services des Etudes et Questions Internationales. Etudes et Documents.

327   FR   ISSN 0071-8181
FRANCE - ALLEMAGNE. 1967. irreg. (approx. 3/yr.). free. Internationale Union of Mayors, Mairie de Paris, 75196 Paris, France.

944   FR   ISSN 0015-959X
DC1
FRANCE INFORMATIONS.* (Text in English, French and Spanish) 1967. m. free. Secretariat d'Etat aux Affaires Etrangeres Charge de la Cooperation, Direction de l'Aide au Developpement, 37 Quai d'Orsay, 75007 Paris, France. Ed. Janine Landau.

FRANCE - PAYS ARABES. see HISTORY — History Of The Near East

327 944 970   FR   ISSN 0015-9751
FRANCE - U.S.A; journal des relations Franco-Americaines. 1945. q. 20 F. Association France Etats Unis, 6 bd. de Grenelle, 75015 Paris, France. TEL 45-77-48-92. adv.; bk.rev.; illus. circ. 5,000. (tabloid format)

341.1   SW   ISSN 0016-0288
FRED OCH FRIHET. (Text in Swedish; occasional articles in Danish or Norwegian) 1927. q. SEK 50 (effective 1991). Women's International League for Peace and Freedom, Swedish Section - Internationella Kvinnofoerbundet foer Fred och Frihet, Svenska Sektionen, Tjaerhovsg. 9, 116 21 Stockholm, Sweden. TEL 46-08-702-98-10. FAX 46-08-702-19-73. Ed. Ingrid Segerstedt Wiberg. bk.rev.; illus.; cum.index every 5 years. circ. 1,750.
Formerly (until vol.4, 1938): Internationella Kvinnofoerbundets foer Fred och Frihet Medlemsblad.

DIE FRIEDENS - WARTE; Blaetter fuer internationale Verstaendigung und zwischenstaatliche Organisation. see LAW — International Law

327   US   ISSN 0077-0582
G S I S MONOGRAPH SERIES IN WORLD AFFAIRS. 1963. irreg., latest 1990. price varies. (University of Denver, Graduate School of International Studies) Lynne Rienner Publishers, 1800 30th St., Ste. 314, Boulder, CO 80301. TEL 303-444-6684. FAX 303-444-0824. Ed. Karen A. Feste. adv. circ. 1,000. **Indexed:** Int.Polit.Sci.Abstr., SSCI. **Document type:** monographic series.

327   II
GANDHI PEACE FOUNDATION LECTURES. 1976. irreg. Gandhi Peace Foundation, 221-223 Deen Dayal Upadhyaya Marg, New Delhi 110002, India.

327   GW   ISSN 0930-8571
GEHEIM. English edition: Top Secret (ISSN 0935-3909) 1985. 4/yr. DM.45($45) Geheim Verlag, Postfach 270324, 50509 Cologne, Germany. TEL 0221-175755. Ed. Michael Opperskalski. adv. contact: Fred Zimmerman. bk.rev. circ. 3,500. (back issues avail.) **Document type:** bulletin.

320.3 918.903   UY   ISSN 0250-7609
GEOSUR. (Includes monographic supplements) 1979. 6/yr. $90 (effective 1996). Asociacion Sudamericana de Estudios Geopoliticos e Internacionales, Casilla de Correos 5006, 11200 Montevideo, Uruguay. TEL 598-2-692953. FAX 598-2-961923. Ed. Bernardo Quagliotti de Bellis. adv. contact: Richard Gonzalez. bk.rev.; circ. 1,500 (controlled). **Indexed:** Abstr.Mil.Bibl. **Document type:** newspaper.

327   UK   ISSN 0964-4008
JN3201
GERMAN POLITICS. 1992. 3/yr. £35($50) to individuals; institutions £85 ($98) (effective 1996). Frank Cass, Newbury House, 890-900 Eastern Ave., Newbury Park, Ilford, Essex, England. TEL 44-181-599-8866. FAX 44-181-599-0984. E-mail: 100067,1576@compuserve.com. Ed.Bd. adv.: B&W page £195 ($275); adv. contact: Anne Kidson. index. (back issues avail.) **Indexed:** Int.Polit.Sci.Abstr. **Document type:** academic/scholarly publication.
—BLDSC (4162.150600). CCC.
Description: Presents the academic study of domestic German politics, together with treatment of international European Community and security issues from a German perspective.
Refereed Serial

GERMANY. DEUTSCHER BUNDESTAG. WISSENSCHAFTLICHE DIENSTE. MATERIALIEN. see BIBLIOGRAPHIES

327   GW   ISSN 0016-9390
GEWALTFREIE AKTION; Vierteljahreshefte fuer Frieden und Gerechtigkeit. 1969. q. DM.12. Versoehnungsbund e.V., Kuehlenstr. 5a-7, 25436 Uetersen, Germany. TEL 030-7423818. FAX 04122-1023. Ed. Gernot Jochheim. adv.; bk.rev.; bibl. circ. 6,000. **Document type:** bulletin.

327   US   ISSN 0886-6198
D839
GLOBAL AFFAIRS.* 1986. q. $24 (foreign $45). International Security Council, 2000 L St., N.W., Ste. 506, Washington, DC 20036-4907. TEL 212-828-0802. FAX 202-429-2563. Ed. Charles M. Lichenstein. adv.; bk.rev. circ. 8,700. **Indexed:** A.B.C.Pol.Sci., Int.Polit.Sci.Abstr., Polit.Sci.Abstr.
—Faxon; UnCover.
Description: Provides a forum for responsible and expert views on international security affairs.

327   US   ISSN 1075-2846
   CODEN: GLGOFI
▼**GLOBAL GOVERNANCE;** a review of multilateralism and international organizations. 1995. 3/yr. $32 to individuals; institutions $65. Lynne Rienner Publishers, 1800 30th St., Ste. 314, Boulder, CO 80301. TEL 303-444-6684. FAX 303-444-0824. (Co-sponsors: Academic Council on the United Nations; United Nations University) Eds. Roger Coate, Craig Murphy. bibl.; charts. (back issues avail.) **Document type:** academic/scholarly publication.
—BLDSC (4195.415000). CCC.
Description: Discusses issues relating to the entire range of global problems, including economic development, peace and security, human rights and the protection of the environment, as well as the multilateral processes designed to solve them.
Refereed Serial

GLOBAL LINKS. see BUSINESS AND ECONOMICS — International Development And Assistance

POLITICAL SCIENCE — INTERNATIONAL RELATIONS

327 US ISSN 0730-9112
GLOBAL REPORT; progress toward a world of peace with justice. 1977. irreg. (approx. 4/yr.). $20. Center for War - Peace Studies, 218 E. 18th St., New York, NY 10003. TEL 212-475-1077. FAX 212-260-6384. Ed. Richard Hudson. circ. 5,000. **Document type:** newsletter.
Description: Chronicles events at the United Nations, with a perspective of improving the effectiveness of the organization.

GLOBAL RISK ASSESSMENTS; issues, concepts and applications. see BUSINESS AND ECONOMICS — International Commerce

327 US
GLOBAL STUDIES: AFRICA. irreg., 4th ed., 1991. $13.95. Dushkin Publishing Group, Sluice Dock, Guilford, CT 06437-9989. TEL 203-453-4351. FAX 203-453-6000. Ed. Jeff Ramsey; Pub. Ian Nielsen. illus.

327 951 US ISSN 1050-2025
GLOBAL STUDIES: CHINA. 1984. irreg., 4th ed., 1991. $13.95. Dushkin Publishing Group, Sluice Dock, Guilford, CT 06437-9989. TEL 203-453-4351. FAX 203-453-6000. Ed. Suzanne Ogden; Pub. Ian Nielsen. illus. **Document type:** academic/scholarly publication.

327 US ISSN 1061-2823
DK1.5
GLOBAL STUDIES: COMMONWEALTH OF INDEPENDENT STATES AND CENTRAL - EASTERN EUROPE. 1986. irreg. $13.95. Dushkin Publishing Group, Sluice Dock, Guilford, CT 06437-9989. TEL 203-453-4351. FAX 203-453-6000. Ed. Minton F. Goldman; Pub. Ian Nielsen. illus. **Document type:** academic/scholarly publication.
Formerly (until 1992): Global Studies: Soviet Union and Eastern Europe (ISSN 1052-7796)

327 US ISSN 1059-5988
DS801
GLOBAL STUDIES: JAPAN AND THE PACIFIC RIM. 1991. irreg. $13.95. Dushkin Publishing Group, Sluice Dock, Guilford, CT 06437-9989. TEL 203-453-4351. FAX 203-453-6000. Ed. Dean Collinwood; Pub. Ian Nielsen. illus. **Document type:** academic/scholarly publication.

327 US ISSN 1061-2831
F1401
GLOBAL STUDIES: LATIN AMERICA. irreg., 4th ed., 1990. $13.95. Dushkin Publishing Group, Sluice Dock, Guilford, CT 06437-9989. TEL 203-453-4351. FAX 203-453-6000. Ed. Paul Goodwin; Pub. Ian Nielsen. illus. **Document type:** academic/scholarly publication.

327 US ISSN 1056-6848
DS41
GLOBAL STUDIES: MIDDLE EAST. irreg., 3rd ed., 1990. $13.95. Dushkin Publishing Group, Sluice Dock, Guilford, CT 06437-9989. TEL 203-453-4351. FAX 203-453-6000. Ed. William Spencer; Pub. Ian Nielsen. illus. **Document type:** academic/scholarly publication.

327 US ISSN 1059-2334
D1050
GLOBAL STUDIES: WESTERN EUROPE. 1989. irreg., 2nd ed., 1991. $13.95. Dushkin Publishing Group, Sluice Dock, Guilford, CT 06437-9989. TEL 203-453-4351. FAX 203-453-6000. Ed. Henri J. Warmenhoven; Pub. Ian Nielsen. illus. **Document type:** academic/scholarly publication.

GLOBE UNION. see PHILATELY

327 UK ISSN 0072-6397
GREAT BRITAIN. FOREIGN AND COMMONWEALTH OFFICE. TREATY SERIES. 1892. irreg. H.M.S.O., P.O. Box 276, London SW8 5DT, England. (reprint service avail. from UMI) **Document type:** government publication.
—CCC.

327.73 US ISSN 0072-727X
E744
GREAT DECISIONS. (Supplements avail.) 1955. a. $11 (effective Jan. 1994). Foreign Policy Association, 470 Park Ave. S., New York, NY 10016-6819. TEL 212-481-8100. FAX 212-481-9275. Ed. Nancy Hoepli-Phalon. charts; illus.; maps. circ. 70,000. (reprint service avail. from UMI) **Indexed:** Abstr.Mil.Bibl., SRI. **Document type:** academic/scholarly publication.
Description: Focuses on key foreign policy issues with background, current data and alternative options for the US.

327 SP
GRUPO ESPANOL DE LA UNION INTERPARLAMENTARIA. BOLETIN DE INFORMACION. 1968. q. free. Cortes Espanolas, Grupo Espanol de la Union Interparlamentaria, Madrid, Spain.

327 KN
GUKJESAENGHWAL/INTERNATIONAL LIFE. (Text in English and Korean) 1986. m. Pyongyang, N. Korea.
Description: Covers North Korea's foreign policy and international events.

327 330 UK ISSN 0953-5411
GULF STATES NEWSLETTER. 1975. fortn. $520 (effective Jan. 1993). Middle East Newsletters, P.O. Box 124, Crawley, Sussex RH10 3YT, England. TEL 01342-712929. FAX 01342-712829. Ed. Andrew Rathmell; Pub. J.L. Christie. bk.rev. **Indexed:** Per.Islam. (1991-). **Document type:** newsletter.
Description: Covers political, economic and defense issues in the Gulf Region.

327 382 CC ISSN 0452-8832
GUOJI WENTI YANJIU/INTERNATIONAL STUDIES. (Text in Chinese; summaries and table of contents in English) q. $12.95. (Zhongguo Guoji Wenti Yanjiusuo - China Institute of International Studies) Shijie Zhishi Chubanshe - World Affairs Press, 31-A, Waijiaobu Jie, Beijing 100005, People's Republic of China. (Dist. outside China by: China International Book Trading Corp., P.O. Box 2820, Beijing, P.R.C.; Dist. in US by: China Books & Periodicals, Inc., 2929 24th St., San Francisco, CA 94110. TEL 415-282-2994) Ed. Ma Yaohui.
—UnCover.
Formerly: Journal of International Studies.

327 CC ISSN 0452-8778
GUOJI ZHANWANG/INTERNATIONAL PROSPECT. (Text in Chinese) s-m. Shanghai Guoji Wenti Yanjiusuo - Shanghai Research Institute of International Issues, No.1, Alley 845, Julu Lu, Shanghai 200040, People's Republic of China. TEL 4334263.

327 658 CY ISSN 0256-5935
H C J COMMUNICATIONS REPORT. 1984. m. $395. H C J Communications Ltd., P.O. Box 5704, Nicosia, Cyprus. Ed. Christian Doumit. adv.; bk.rev. (back issues avail.)
Description: Covers educational trends in the Middle East.

HAITI NEWS. see BUSINESS AND ECONOMICS — International Development And Assistance

327 UK
HALIFAX NUCLEAR DISARMAMENT GROUP NEWSLETTER. 1980. 6/yr. £1($15) c/o Julian Harber, Ed., 17 Bankhouse Lane, Salterhebble, Halifax, England. circ. 400. (back issues avail.) **Document type:** newsletter.
Formerly: Halifax Nuclear Disarmament Group. Bulletin.
Description: Covers events and current issues of the Halifax Disarmament Group.

327 GW ISSN 0936-0018
HAMBURGER BEITRAEGE ZUR FRIEDENSFORSCHUNG UND SICHERHEITSPOLITIK. (Text in English, German) 1986. irreg. (8-12/yr.). Institut fuer Friedensforschung und Sicherheitspolitik, An der Universitaet Hamburg, Falkenstein 1, 22587 Hamburg, Germany. TEL 040-869054. FAX 040-8663615. adv. circ. 500. **Document type:** monographic series.
Description: Covers research in peace and national security. Each volume devoted to a single topic.

327 US ISSN 0194-3790
G122
HANDBOOK OF THE NATIONS. 1979. irreg., 10th ed., 1990. $95. Gale Research Inc., 835 Penobscot Bldg., Detroit, MI 48226. TEL 313-961-2242. FAX 313-961-6083. TELEX 810-221-7086.
Description: Reprint of the CIA's World Factbook.

HARRIMAN REVIEW. see LITERARY AND POLITICAL REVIEWS

327 382 US ISSN 0739-1854
D839
HARVARD INTERNATIONAL REVIEW. 1979. q. $16 to individuals (foreign $26); institutions $26 (foreign $36). Harvard International Relations Council, Inc., Box 401, Cambridge, MA 02238. TEL 617-495-9607. FAX 617-596-4472. (Subscr. to: P.O. Box 3000, Denville, NJ 07834-9452) Ed. Ramin Toloui; Pub. Edwin U. adv. contact: Jonathan Steinberg. bk.rev. circ. 15,000. (also avail. in microform from UMI; back issues avail.) **Indexed:** Curr.Cont., P.A.I.S., Per.Islam. (1991-). **Document type:** consumer publication.
—BLDSC (4267.210000); Faxon; Genuine Article; SWETS; UMI; UnCover. CCC.
Description: Covers international affairs. Contains penetrating analyses by today's most influential and insightful world leaders, scholars and professionals.

327 US ISSN 1068-1485
D839
THE HARVARD JOURNAL OF WORLD AFFAIRS. 1992. 2/yr. $20 to individuals; institutions $40 (effective 1994). Harvard University, John F. Kennedy School of Government, 273 Taubman Bldg., 79 John F. Kennedy St., Cambridge, MA 02138. TEL 617-496-0517. FAX 617-496-9027. bk.rev.; cum.index every 5 yrs. circ. 1,000. (also avail. in microform; back issues avail.) **Document type:** academic/scholarly publication.
—BLDSC (4267.460000).
Description: Policymakers and scholars of international policy provide analysis of issues of emerging concern in policy fields including security, trade, health, environment.
Refereed Serial

341 327 US ISSN 0073-0734
JX1295.H45
HARVARD UNIVERSITY. CENTER FOR INTERNATIONAL AFFAIRS. ANNUAL REPORT. 1961. a. free. Harvard University, Center for International Affairs, 1737 Cambridge St., Cambridge, MA 02138. TEL 617-495-4420. FAX 617-495-8292. Ed. Jennifer Duffy. circ. 3,000.

HELLENIC JOURNAL. see ETHNIC INTERESTS

327 US ISSN 0898-3038
F1401
HEMISPHERE; a magazine of Latin American and Caribbean affairs. 1988. 3/yr. $20 (foreign $27). Latin American and Caribbean Center, Florida International University, University Park, Miami, FL 33199. TEL 305-348-2894. FAX 305-348-3593. Ed. Edvardo A. Gamarra. adv.; bk.rev. circ. 2,000. **Indexed:** Hisp.Amer.Per.Ind. (1988-), Polit.Sci.Abstr. **Document type:** academic/scholarly publication.
—UnCover.
Description: Dedicated to provoking debate on the problems, initiatives and achievements of Latin America and the Caribbean.

327 GW
HESSISCHE STIFTUNG FRIEDENS- UND KONFLIKTFORSCHUNG. MITTEILUNGEN; Bericht ueber Organisation und laufende Forschung. 1971. a. DM.5. Hessische Stiftung Friedens- und Konfliktforschung, Leimenrode 29, 60322 Frankfurt a.M., Germany. TEL 069-9591040. FAX 069-558481. Ed. Eva von Hase-Mihalik. circ. 180. **Document type:** academic/scholarly publication.
Description: Review of progress of the Institute's research programs.

POLITICAL SCIENCE — INTERNATIONAL RELATIONS

HISTORIC PALESTINE SERIES. see *ETHNIC INTERESTS*

327 382   HK   ISSN 0257-3636
HONG KONG COUNTDOWN: PERSPECTIVES ON CHANGE. (Text in English) 1984. 18/yr. HK.$1150($147) N & N International (Hong Kong) Ltd., GPO Box 8926, Hong Kong. FAX 852-856-5648. Ed. R.B. Cunningham. **Document type:** newsletter.
Description: Newsletter that focuses on news and analyses leading up to the return of Hong Kong from the British to Chinese rule in 1997.

327   GW   ISSN 0724-0279
HORIZONT (COLOGNE); Magazin fuer internationale Beziehungen. 1979. bi-m. DM.30. Horizont Verlag GmbH, Eifelstr. 8, 50677 Cologne, Germany. Ed. Ferenc Pal Balazs. adv.

327   CC
HUAN QIU/GLOBE. (Text in Chinese) m. $33.20. (Xinhua News Agency) Huan Qiu Zazhishe, 57 Xuanwumen Xidajie, Beijing 100800, People's Republic of China. TEL 3073511. (Dist. in US by: China Books & Periodicals, Inc., 2929 24th St., San Francisco, CA 94110. TEL 415-282-2994) Ed. Ye Jin.

327   US   ISSN 1056-9391
AS30
HUDSON INSTITUTE BRIEFING PAPER. m. Hudson Institute, Herman Kahn Center, 5395 Emerson Way, Box 26-919, Indianapolis, IN 46226-0919. TEL 317-545-1000. FAX 317-545-9639. TELEX 855477. Ed. Sam Karnick. circ. 4,000.

327   US
Q180.U5
HUDSON INSTITUTE REPORT. 1962. q. free. Hudson Institute, Herman Kahn Center, 5395 Emerson Way, Box 26-919, Indianapolis, IN 46226. TEL 317-545-1000. FAX 317-545-9639. TELEX 855477. circ. 9,200.
Formerly: Hudson Institute. Report to the Members (ISSN 0073-3776)

327   US   ISSN 1079-2309
HUMAN RIGHTS WATCH ASIA. 1985. irreg. $40. Human Rights Watch, Asia, 485 Fifth Ave., New York, NY 10017-6104. TEL 212-972-8400. FAX 212-972-0905. E-mail: hrwnyc@hrw.org.
Formerly (until 1994): Asia Watch (ISSN 1062-2225)
Description: Covers Asian human rights issues.

327   UK
I C A B A. 1984. 3/yr. free. End Loans to South Africa, c/o Methodist Church, 56 Camberwell Rd., London SE5 0FN, England. TEL 071-708-4702. FAX 071-708-5751. Ed. Hugo Burdick.

341.1   SZ
I C A NEWS. (Text in English) 6/yr. membership. International Co-Operative Alliance, 15, rte. des Morillons, CH-1218 Grand-Saconnex, Switzerland. TEL 022-7984121. FAX 022-7984122. TELEX 415620-ICA-CH. Ed. Mary Treacy. **Document type:** newsletter.

327 301   NR
I F R A DOCUMENTS IN SOCIAL SCIENCES AND HUMANITIES. (Former name of issuing bodey: Centre de Recherches d'Echanges et de Documentation Universitaire) 1992. irreg. price varies. Institute Francais de Recherche en Afrique - French Institute for Research in Africa, Institute of African Studies, University of Ibadan, U.I. P.O. Box 21540, Ibadan, Oyo State, Nigeria. **Document type:** monographic series.
Formerly: C R E D U Documents in Social Sciences and Humanities.
Description: Contains scholarly articles on various political and sociological issues affecting Nigeria and other African nations.

327 301   NR
I F R A OCCASIONAL PUBLICATIONS. (Former name of issuing body: Centre de Recherches d'Echanges et de Documentation Universitaire) 1992. irreg. price varies. Institut Francais de Recherche en Afrique - French Institute for Research in Africa, Institute of African Studies, University of Ibadan, U.I. P.O. Box 21540, Ibadan, Oyo State, Nigeria. **Document type:** monographic series.
Formerly: C R E D U Occasional Publications.
Description: Discusses democracy and other political and sociological topics pertaining to African nations.

327   US
I G C C NEWSLETTER. 1989. 2/yr. free. Institute on Global Conflict and Cooperation, University of California, San Diego, 9500 Gilman Dr., Dept. 0518, La Jolla, CA 92093-0518. TEL 619-534-1979. FAX 619-534-7655. E-mail: jpournel@ucsd.edu. Ed. Jennifer Pournelle. circ. 8,000. **Document type:** newsletter.
●Also available online.
Description: News, information, and articles on foreign affairs and international relations conferences and programs sponsored by IGCC.

327   JA   ISSN 0285-2608
I H J BULLETIN. (Text in English) 1981. q. 1000 Yen($10) International House of Japan, Inc., 11-16 Roppongi 5-chome, Minato-ku, Tokyo 106, Japan. TEL 03-3470-3211. FAX 03-3470-3170. Ed. Tatsuya Tanami. bk.rev. circ. 7,500. (back issues avail.) **Document type:** bulletin.

327   AU
I I P OCCASIONAL PAPER. (Text in English) 1989. irreg. S.60. International Institute for Peace, Moellwaldplatz 5, A-1040 Vienna, Austria. TEL 0431-5046437. FAX 0431-5053236. Ed. Peter Stania. circ. 200. **Document type:** monographic series.

327   IT
I S P I FAX LETTER. 1992. bi-w. price varies. Istituto per gli Studi di Politica Internazionale, Via Clerici 5, 20121 Milan, Italy. **Document type:** academic/scholarly publication.

IDEAS AND INFORMATION ABOUT DEVELOPMENT EDUCATION. see *EDUCATION* — *International Education Programs*

IHR PROGRAMM. see *HISTORY* — *History Of Europe*

IMPARTIAL CITIZEN. see *ETHNIC INTERESTS*

327 641   UK
IMPLEMENTATION MATTERS. 1992. irreg., no.4, 1995. £10 per no. Verification Technology Information Centre (VERTIC), Carrara House, 20 Embankment Pl., London WC2N 6NN, England. TEL 0171-925-0867. FAX 0171-925-0861. E-mail: vertic@gn.apc.org. (back issues avail.) **Document type:** monographic series.

327   IE
IMPLICATIONS FOR IRELAND. 1991. irreg. I£5. Institute of European Affairs, 8 North Great George's St., Dublin 1, Ireland. **Document type:** monographic series.

320   US   ISSN 1055-9809
D860
IN DEPTH (WASHINGTON). 1991. 3/yr. $12. Washington Institute for Values in Public Policy, 1015 18th St., N.W., Ste. 300, Washington, DC 20036-5204. TEL 202-293-7440. FAX 202-293-9393. Ed. Richard L. Rubenstein. adv. **Document type:** academic/scholarly publication.
—Faxon.
Description: Covers a wide range of foreign and public policy issues confronting the American policy.

341.1   IT   ISSN 0019-3496
L'INCONTRO; pacifist periodical independent. 1949. m. L.15000($15) Via Consolata N. 11, 10122 Torino, Italy. TEL 521-20-00. Ed. Dr. Bruno Segre. adv.; bk.rev.; illus. circ. 8,000. **Document type:** newspaper.

327 382   US   ISSN 1064-4431
INDEPENDENT NEWSPAPER FROM RUSSIA. Selected English translation of: Nezavisimaya Gazeta. (Selected semi-monthly Russian language version also avail.: Nezavisimaya Gazeta (ISSN 1064-444X)) 1991. s-m. $38. Cynthia Neu, Ed. & Pub., 7338 Dartford Dr., Ste. 9, McLean, VA 22102. TEL 703-827-0414. FAX 703-827-8923. circ. 1,000 (paid); 7,000 (controlled). **Document type:** newspaper.
Description: Provides political and business communications between the U.S. and Russia.

327 016   US   ISSN 0193-905X
HM261
INDEX TO INTERNATIONAL PUBLIC OPINION. 1980. a. price varies. (Survey Research Consultants International, Inc.) Greenwood Press, Inc. (Subsidiary of: Greenwood Publishing Group Inc.), 88 Post Rd. W., Box 5007, Westport, CT 06881-5007. TEL 203-226-3511. FAX 203-222-1502. Eds. Elizabeth Hann Hastings, Philip K. Hastings.

327   II   ISSN 0376-9771
DS401
INDIA INTERNATIONAL CENTRE QUARTERLY. (Text in English) 1974. q. Rs.60($16.50) India International Centre, 40 Lodi Estate, New Delhi 110003, India. Ed.Bd. adv.; bk.rev.; bibl. circ. 2,400. **Indexed:** Ind.India, Int.Polit.Sci.Abstr.

954   II   ISSN 0251-3048
D410
INDIA QUARTERLY. (Text in English) 1945. q. $40. Indian Council of World Affairs, Sapru House, Barakhamba Rd., New Delhi 110001, India. Ed. S.C. Parashar. adv.; bk.rev.; bibl.; index. circ. 2,000. **Indexed:** A.B.C.Pol.Sci., Abstr.Mil.Bibl., Amer.Hist.& Life, Hist.Abstr., Int.Polit.Sci.Abstr., Mid.East: Abstr.& Ind., P.A.I.S.
—Faxon; SWETS; UnCover.

327   II   ISSN 0970-6402
INDIAN JOURNAL OF ASIAN AFFAIRS. (Text in English) 1988. s-a. $25. Indian Journal of Asian Affairs, 4-87 Jawahar Nagar, Jaipur-302 004, India. TEL 0141-562227. Ed. B.M. Jain. adv.: Gaj Raj/Bhandari; adv. contact: Gaj Raj Bhandari. bk.rev. circ. 250. **Document type:** academic/scholarly publication.
—UnCover.
Description: Analyzes contemporary and current Asian political, economic, social and military affairs.

327 330.9   FR   ISSN 0294-6475
DT365
INDIAN OCEAN NEWSLETTER. French edition: Lettre de l'Ocean Indien (ISSN 0294-6467) (Editions in English, French) 1981. w. 3850 F.($710) Indigo Publications, 10, rue de Sentier, 75002 Paris, France. TEL 44-88-26-10. FAX 44-88-26-15. Ed. Maurice Botbol. bk.rev.; index. circ. 1,500. (looseleaf format; back issues avail.) **Indexed:** HR Rep. **Document type:** newsletter.
Description: Covers newsworthy, diplomatic, political and economic events in African countries of the Indian Ocean region.

327 954   II   ISSN 0537-2704
JX21
INDIAN YEARBOOK OF INTERNATIONAL AFFAIRS. 1952-1968; N.S. 1973. a. (Indian Study Group of International Affairs) University of Madras, c/o Director, Publications Division, Madras 600 005, India. TEL 91-44-568778. FAX 91-44-566693. bk.rev.; index.
Description: Looks at law and international relations.

327 330.9   GW
INDIEN WIRTSCHAFTSNACHRICHTEN. 1972. m. free. Indische Botschaft, Adenauerallee 262-264, 53113 Bonn, Germany. TEL 0228-5405146. FAX 0228-5405153. Eds. Debnath Shaw, Tanmaya Lal. bk.rev.; charts; illus.; stat. circ. 5,500. **Document type:** newsletter.
Formerly: Indien (ISSN 0046-9149)

INDO-BRITISH REVIEW; a journal of history. see *HISTORY* — *History Of Asia*

INDO-IRANICA. see *LITERATURE*

327   II
INDO-ISRAEL. (Text in English) vol.16, 1973. bi-m. Rs.1 per no. Bombay Zionist Association, 41 Hamam St., Bombay 400 023, India. Ed. E.M. Jacob. illus.

327   II
INDO-KOREAN FRIENDSHIP. 1970. m. R.0.60 per no. All India Indo-Korean Friendship Association, F60 Bhagat Singh Market, New Delhi 1, India. Ed. Amar Nath Vidyalankar. adv.; bk.rev. circ. 2,000.

POLITICAL SCIENCE — INTERNATIONAL RELATIONS

327 US
INDOCHINA DIGEST. 1987. w. $35 to individuals (foreign $45); corporations $350 (foreign $450). Indochina Project, 2001 S St., N.W., Ste. 740, Washington, DC 20009. TEL 202-483-9222. FAX 202-483-9214. TELEX 6503397753 MCI UW. circ. 1,500. **Document type:** newsletter.
Description: Tracks developments in or related to Indochina, with emphasis on business, economics, and politics.

327 US
INDOCHINA NEWSLETTER. 1980. 5/yr. $15. Asia Resource Center, 2161 Massachusetts Ave., Cambridge, MA 02140. TEL 617-497-5273. FAX 617-354-2832. adv. contact: Paul Shannoo. bk.rev.; cum.index: 1980-94; circ. 1,000 (controlled). (back issues avail.) **Document type:** newsletter.
Incorporates: Asia Insights.
Description: Examines the legacy of the Vietnam war in an attempt to counter attempts by those who support U.S. intervention to rewrite the history and lessons of the Vietnam experience. Focuses on developments inside Indochina and U.S. policy toward the region.

INDONESIAN QUARTERLY. see POLITICAL SCIENCE

327 IO ISSN 0046-9173
DS638
INDONESIAN REVIEW OF INTERNATIONAL AFFAIRS. 1970. q. $1.50 per no. Indonesian Institute of International Affairs, 82 Jalan Tjikini Raya, Jakarta 4, Indonesia. Eds. A. Subardjo Djovoadisuryo, S. Suryodpuro. adv. circ. 2,000.

INFORMATION PROCHE-ORIENT. see LITERARY AND POLITICAL REVIEWS

327 GW
INFORMATIONEN. 1978. q. Ohne Rustung Leben, Furtbachstr. 10, 70178 Stuttgart, Germany. TEL 0711-6409620. FAX 0711-6407980. Ed. Gerhard Voss. circ. 6,000.

327 CH ISSN 0250-961X
INSIDE CHINA MAINLAND. (Text in English) 1979. m. $17 in Asia; elsewhere $20. Institute of Current China Studies, P.O. Box 14-19, Taipei, Taiwan, Republic of China. Ed. Jerry R. Hung. index. circ. 7,000. (back issues avail.) **Document type:** academic/scholarly publication.
—BLDSC (4518.151800); Faxon; UnCover.
Description: Presents translations of reprinted and original articles concerning issues of policy and politics in mainland China.

327 338.91 AT ISSN 0814-1185
INSIDE INDONESIA. 1983. q. $28 to individuals; institutions $40. Indonesia Resources & Information Programme, P.O. Box 190, Northcote, Vic. 3070, Australia. TEL 61-3-94811581. Ed.Bd. adv.; bk.rev. circ. 2,000. (back issues avail.)
Description: Reports on Indonesian culture, politics, economy and human rights.

327 IS ISSN 0792-9749
INSIDE ISRAEL; Israel's investigative news source. (Text in English) 1993. m. $98 (effective 1994). P.O. Box 489, Beit Shemesh, Israel. FAX 972-2-911685. (U.S. subscr. to: Inside Israel, 1456 Second Ave., Ste. 142, New York, NY 10021. TEL 212-642-8289) Eds. Barry Chamish, Joel Bainerman. **Indexed:** Ind.Jew.Per. **Document type:** newsletter.
Description: Covers Israeli affairs, including domestic policy issues, diplomacy and foreign affairs, economic concerns, intelligence matters, and the Palestinian question.

327 AT ISSN 1038-6726
JX1162
INSIGHT (CANBERRA). 1992. fortn. Department of Foreign Affairs and Trade, Overseas Information Branch, P.O. Box 12, Canberra. A.C.T. 2601, Australia. TEL 06-261-3983. FAX 06-261-3900. Ed. Sam Leone. circ. 6,800.
—UnCover.
Description: Disseminates information about Australia's foreign affairs and trade issues.

320 US
INSIGHTS IN INTERNATIONAL AFFAIRS. irreg., no.5. price varies. University of California at Berkeley, International and Area Studies, 2223 Fulton St., 3rd Fl., Berkeley, CA 94720. TEL 415-642-7189. FAX 415-643-7062. E-mail: bojana@uclink2.berkeley.edu. Ed. Bojana Ristich. (back issues avail.) **Document type:** monographic series, academic/scholarly publication.

320 FR ISSN 0294-3069
INSTITUT DES RECHERCHES MARXISTES. RECHERCHES INTERNATIONALES. 1957. q. 250 F. (foreign 500 F.). Institut des Recherches Marxistes, 64 bd. Auguste Blanqui, 75013 Paris, France. adv.; bk.rev.; cum.index. circ. 2,500.
—BLDSC (7309.090000).
Formerly (until 1981): Recherches Internationales a la Lumiere du Marxisme (ISSN 0486-1345); **Supersedes:** Recherches Sovietiques.

INSTITUT ZUR ERFORSCHUNG DER EUROPAEISCHEN ARBEITERBEWEGUNG. MITTEILUNGSBLATT. see LABOR UNIONS

355 327 II ISSN 0970-0161
UA11
INSTITUTE FOR DEFENCE STUDIES AND ANALYSES. STRATEGIC ANALYSIS. (Text in English) 1977. m. Rs.72. Institute for Defence Studies and Analyses, Sapru House, Barakhamba Rd., New Delhi 110001, India. Ed. Jasjit Singh. circ. 2,000.

327 US
INSTITUTE FOR EAST WEST STUDIES. ANNUAL REPORT. 1981. a. free. Institute for East West Studies, 360 Lexington Ave., New York, NY 10017. TEL 212-557-2570. FAX 212-949-8043. TELEX 760-8127 EWS. Ed. Judith Train. bk.rev. **Document type:** bulletin.
Formerly: Institute for East - West Security Studies. Annual Report.

327 IE
INSTITUTE OF EUROPEAN AFFAIRS. OCCASIONAL PAPERS. irreg., no.2. I£5. Institute of European Affairs, 8 North Great George's St., Dublin 1, Ireland. Ed. Paul Tansey. **Document type:** monographic series.

327 JA ISSN 0915-5082
INSTITUTE OF INTERNATIONAL RELATIONS. RESEARCH PAPERS. SERIES A; for advanced studies on peace and development in Asia. (Text in English) 1970. irreg., no.64, 1995. 825 Yen per no. Sophia University, Institute of International Relations, 7-1 Kioi-cho, Chiyoda-ku, Tokyo 102, Japan. TEL 03-3238-3561. FAX 03-3238-3592. E-mail: kokusai@hoffman.cc.sophia.ac.jp. circ. 300. (also avail. in microfiche; microfilm; back issues avail.) **Document type:** academic/scholarly publication.
—BLDSC (7754.080000).

327 JA ISSN 0915-5090
INSTITUTE OF INTERNATIONAL RELATIONS. RESEARCH PAPERS. SERIES B. (Text in English) irreg., no.10, 1994. 825 Yen per no. Sophia University, Institute of International Relations, 7-1 Kioi-cho, Chiyoda-ku, Tokyo 102, Japan. TEL 03-3238-3561. FAX 03-3238-3592. (back issues avail.) **Document type:** academic/scholarly publication.
Description: Contains essays and addresses by members of the IIR or guest lecturers.

327 BL
INSTITUTO CULTURAL ITALO-BRASILEIRO. CADERNO. no.8, 1972. irreg. Instituto Cultural Italo-Brasileiro, Rua Frei Caneca 1071, Sao Paulo, Brazil. **Document type:** monographic series.

327 GW ISSN 0720-5120
INTEGRATION. 1978. q. DM.36. (Institut fuer Europaeische Politik, Bonn) Europa Union Verlag GmbH, Bachstr. 32, 53115 Bonn, Germany. TEL 0228-7290020. FAX 0228-698437. circ. 3,500. **Indexed:** ELLIS. **Document type:** bulletin.
—BLDSC (4531.816290). CCC.
Incorporates (in 1992): Europaeische Integration. Mitteilungen.
Description: European integration in science and research.

327 UK ISSN 0268-4527
INTELLIGENCE AND NATIONAL SECURITY. 1986. q. £38($48) to individuals; institutions £125 ($195) (effective 1996). Frank Cass, Newbury House, 890-900 Eastern Ave., Newbury Park, Ilford, Essex 1G2 7HH, England. TEL 44-181-599-8866. FAX 44-181-599-0984. E-mail: 100067,1576@compuserve.com. Eds. Christopher Andrew, Michael Handel. adv.: B&W page £195 ($275); adv. contact: Anne Kidson. bk.rev.; index. (also avail. in microfilm from UMI; back issues avail.) **Indexed:** Int.Pol.Sci.Abstr., Polit.Sci.Abstr. **Document type:** academic/scholarly publication.
—BLDSC (4531.827000); UMI. **CCC.**
Description: Covers the history of intelligence and counterintelligence by the major powers.
Refereed Serial

341.1 US ISSN 0094-5072
D839
INTERDEPENDENT. 1974. q. $10 membership. United Nations Association of the USA, 485 Fifth Ave., 2nd Fl., New York, NY 10017-6104. TEL 212-697-3232. FAX 212-682-9185. Ed. John Tessitore. adv. contact: Susan Woolfson. bk.rev.; illus.; circ. 23,000 (paid). **Document type:** newspaper.
Formerly: Vista (ISSN 0042-711X)
Description: Covers world affairs and features news and analysis of global issues shaping international politics not found in the mainstream media.

327 323.4 US ISSN 0891-2688
INTERHEMISPHERIC RESOURCE CENTER. BULLETIN. (Text in English) 1985. q. $5. Interhemispheric Resource Center, Box 4506, Albuquerque, NM 87196. TEL 505-842-8288. FAX 505-246-1601. Ed. Tom Barry. circ. 3,500. (tabloid format; back issues avail.) **Document type:** newsletter.
Description: Covers research and analysis of current international issues including US policy in third world countries.

327 NO ISSN 0020-577X
D839
INTERNASJONAL POLITIKK. (Text in Norwegian; summaries in English) 1937. 4/yr. NOK 280 in Scandinavia; elsewhere NOK 350. Norsk Utenrikspolitisk Institutt - Norwegian Institute of International Affairs, Postboks 8159, Dep., N-0033 Oslo, Norway. TEL 47-22-17-70-50. FAX 47-22-17-70-15. E-mail: PUB@NUPI.NO. Ed. Iver B. Neumann. adv.; bk.rev.; charts; stat.; cum.index. circ. 2,250. (also avail. in microform from UMI; reprint service avail. from UMI) **Indexed:** A.B.C.Pol.Sci., Abstr.Mil.Bibl., Amer.Hist.& Life, Hist.Abstr., INIS Atomind., Int.Polit.Sci.Abstr., SSCI. —BLDSC (4534.925000); Genuine Article; UMI. **CCC.**

INTERNATIONAL ADMINISTRATION; law and management practices in international organizations. see LAW — International Law

327 UK ISSN 0020-5850
JX1
INTERNATIONAL AFFAIRS. 1922. q. £56($89) (effective 1996). (Royal Institute of International Affairs) Cambridge University Press, Edinburgh Bldg., Shaftesbury Rd., Cambridge CB2 2RU, England. TEL 01223-312393. FAX 01223-315052. TELEX 851817256. (N. American addr.: Cambridge University Press, Journals Dept., 40 W. 20th St., New York, NY 10011. TEL 212-924-3900. FAX 212-691-3239) Ed. J.E. Spence. adv.; bk.rev.; index, cum.index. (also avail. in microform from PMC; back issues avail.; reprint service avail.) **Indexed:** A.B.C.Pol.Sci., Abstr.Mil.Bibl., Acad.Ind., Amer.Hist.& Life, Br.Hum.Ind., C.R.E.J., Curr.Cont., Curr.Cont.M.E., E.I., ELLIS, Geo.Abstr., Hist.Abstr., IDA, Int.Polit.Sci.Abstr., Key to Econ.Sci., Lang.& Lang.Behav.Abstr., Mid.East: Abstr.& Ind., P.A.I.S., Polit.Sci.Abstr., Risk Abstr., Rural Recreat.Tour.Abstr., Soc.Sci.Ind., SSCI, World Agri.Econ.& Rural Sociol.Abstr. **Document type:** academic/scholarly publication.
—BLDSC (4535.630000); Faxon; Genuine Article; SWETS; UMI. **CCC.**
Description: Promotes the flow of information and ideas on international political, economic, legal and related questions.

POLITICAL SCIENCE — INTERNATIONAL RELATIONS

327   RU   ISSN 0130-9641
D839
INTERNATIONAL AFFAIRS; a monthly journal of world politics, diplomacy and international relations. Russian edition: Mezhdunarodnaya Zhizn' (ISSN 0130-9625); French edition: Vie Internationale (ISSN 0130-9633) (Text in English) 1955 (Eng.ed.); 1954 (Russ.ed.) m. $7. (Ministry of Foreign Affairs) International Affairs Ltd., 14 Gorokhovskii Pereulok, Moscow K-16, Russia. Ed. Boris D. Piadyshev. bk.rev.; charts; maps; index. (also avail. in microform) **Indexed:** A.B.C.Pol.Sci., Amer.Hist.& Life, Hist.Abstr., Mar.Aff.Bibl., Mid.East: Abstr.& Ind., P.A.I.S., Polit.Sci.Abstr.
—BLDSC (4535.633000); Faxon; UnCover.
Description: Features articles on the Russia's stand at various international forums. Presents an analysis of the world economic situation and diplomacy. Covers some aspects of international law.

INTERNATIONAL COUNTERTERRORISM & SECURITY. see CRIMINOLOGY AND LAW ENFORCEMENT — Security

327   US
INTERNATIONAL CRISIS BEHAVIOR. vol.2, 1983. irreg., vol.6, 1989. price varies. University of California Press, 2120 Berkeley Way, Berkeley, CA 94720. TEL 510-642-4247. FAX 510-643-7127. (Orders to: California-Princeton Fulfillment Services, 1445 Lower Ferry Rd., Ewing, NJ 08618. TEL 800-777-4726. FAX 800-999-1958) (back issues avail.) **Document type:** monographic series.
Description: Examines periods of international crisis during the 20th century.
Refereed Serial

327   TZ
INTERNATIONAL DIPLOMATIC REVIEW. 1987. 2/yr. Centre for Foreign Relations, P.O. Box 2824, Dar es Salaam, Tanzania. **Indexed:** P.L.E.S.A.

327   US
INTERNATIONAL ESTIMATE SERIES.* 1988. irreg. price varies. International Estimates, 3030 S. Abingdon St., Arlington, VA 22206-1605. TEL 202-332-0849.

INTERNATIONAL FRIENDSHIP AND GOOD WILL BULLETIN. see SOCIAL SERVICES AND WELFARE

327   SZ   ISSN 0926-9045
INTERNATIONAL GENEVA YEARBOOK. 1985. a. 52 SFr. Verlag Peter Lang AG, Jupiterstr. 15, CH-3000 Bern 15, Switzerland. TEL 031-9411122. FAX 031-9411131. TELEX 912651-PELA-CH. **Document type:** academic/scholarly publication.

341.1   US   ISSN 0305-0629
JX1   CODEN: INIAAH
INTERNATIONAL INTERACTIONS; empirical research in industrial relations. 1974. 4/yr. (in 1 vol., 4 nos./vol.). 106 ECU to individuals (effective 1996). Gordon and Breach Science Publishers, c/o International Publishers Distributor, 820 Town Center Dr., Langhorne, PA 19047. TEL 215-750-2642. FAX 215-750-6343. (Subscr. to: International Publishers Distributor, P.O. Box 90, Reading, Berkshire RG1 8JL, England. TEL 44-173-456-8316) Ed. Harvey Starr. adv.; bk.rev.; abstr.; bibl.; charts; illus.; index. cum.index. (also avail. in microform) **Indexed:** Mid.East: Abstr.& Ind., P.A.I.S., Peace Res.Abstr., Soc.Sci.Ind.
—BLDSC (4541.431000); Faxon; UnCover. **CCC.**
Formerly: War - Peace Report (ISSN 0043-0277); Incorporating: New Priorities (ISSN 0047-9837)
Refereed Serial

327   CN   ISSN 0020-7020
D839
INTERNATIONAL JOURNAL. (Text in English, French) 1946. q. Can.$32.10($29.25) to individuals; institutions Can.$39 ($34). Canadian Institute of International Affairs, 15 King's College Circle, Toronto, ON M5S 2V9, Canada. TEL 416-979-1851. FAX 416-979-8575. Ed. Kim Richard Nossal. adv.; bk.rev.; index. circ. 1,700. (also avail. in microfilm from UMI; back issues avail.; reprint service avail. from KTO,UMI) **Indexed:** A.B.C.Pol.Sci., Abstr.Mil.Bibl., Amer.Bibl.Slavic & E.Eur.Stud., Amer.Hist.& Life (until 1992), Bus.Ind., Can.B.P.I., Can.Per.Ind., CMI, Hist.Abstr. (until 1992), Int.Lab.Doc., Int.Polit.Sci.Abstr., Int.Polit.Sci.Abstr., Mar.Aff.Bibl., Mid.East: Abstr.& Ind., P.A.I.S., Polit.Sci.Abstr., SSCI, World.Agri.Econ.& Rural Sociol.Abstr. **Document type:** academic/scholarly publication.
—BLDSC (4541.450000); Faxon; Genuine Article; SWETS; UMI; UnCover. **CCC.**
Description: Devoted to scholarly articles on post-1945 international affairs; often publishes several articles on a single theme.
Refereed Serial

INTERNATIONAL JOURNAL OF DRUG POLICY. see DRUG ABUSE AND ALCOHOLISM

327   US   ISSN 0891-4486
JA76   CODEN: ICSOE2
INTERNATIONAL JOURNAL OF POLITICS, CULTURE, AND SOCIETY. 1987. q. $235 (foreign $275) (effective 1996). (Florida Atlantic University) Human Sciences Press, Inc. (Subsidiary of: Plenum Publishing Corp.), 233 Spring St., New York, NY 10013. TEL 212-620-8000. FAX 212-463-0742. TELEX 23-421139. Ed.Bd. adv.; bk.rev. circ. 500. (also avail. in microfilm from UMI) **Indexed:** Curr.Cont., IMFL, Int.Polit.Sci.Abstr., Lang.& Lang.Behav.Abstr., Polit.Sci.Abstr., Soc.Sci.Ind., Soc.Work Res.& Abstr., Sociol.Abstr., Sociol.Educ.Abstr. **Document type:** academic/scholarly publication.
—BLDSC (4542.473000); Faxon; SWETS; UMI; UnCover. **CCC.**
Formerly: International Journal of Politics, Culture, and State.
Description: Provides a forum for discussion, dialogue and debate on points of tension between state and civil society, between nations and global institutions.
Refereed Serial

325.21 340.5   UK   ISSN 0953-8186
K9
INTERNATIONAL JOURNAL OF REFUGEE LAW. 1989. q. £72($135) (effective 1996). Oxford University Press, Oxford Journals, Walton St., Oxford OX2 6DP, England. TEL 01865-267907. FAX 01865-267773. TELEX 837330-OXPRES-G. E-mail: jnlorders@oup.co.uk. (U.S. subscr. to: Oxford University Press Inc., 2001 Evans Rd., Cary, NC 27513. TEL 919-677-0977. FAX 919-677-1714) Ed. Guy S. Goodwin-Gill. adv. contact: Jane Parker. bk.rev.; index. circ. 950. (reprint service avail. from WSH) **Indexed:** Euro.LJI, HR Rep. (1989-), LJI, Refug.Abstr. **Document type:** academic/scholarly publication.
—BLDSC (4542.525600); SWETS; UMI; UnCover. **CCC.**
Description: Aims to stimulate research and thinking on refugee law and its development.

327   US   ISSN 0742-3640
INTERNATIONAL JOURNAL ON WORLD PEACE. 1984. q. $20 to individuals; institutions $30; students $10. Professors World Peace Academy, University of Toledo, Toledo, OH 43606. (Subscr. to: IJWP, 2700 W. University Ave., Ste. 47, St. Paul, MN 55114) Ed. Panos B. Bardis. adv.; bk.rev.; index. circ. 10,000. (also avail. in microform from UMI; back issues avail.) **Indexed:** Curr.Cont., Geo.Abstr., Int.Polit.Sci.Abstr., Key to Econ.Sci., Lang.& Lang.Behav.Abstr., P.A.I.S., Peace Res.Abstr., Psychol.Abstr., S.S.C.I., Soc.Work Res.& Abstr., Soc.Work Res.& Abstr., Sociol.Abstr., Sociol.Educ.Abstr., SOPODA. **Document type:** academic/scholarly publication.
—BLDSC (4542.701900); Faxon; Genuine Article; UMI; UnCover.
Description: All aspects of peace are discussed; theory and practice, qualitative and quantitive, past, present and future. International debate is emphasized.

INTERNATIONAL LAW NEWS. see LAW — International Law

INTERNATIONAL LAW REPORTS. see LAW — International Law

INTERNATIONAL LEADS. see LIBRARY AND INFORMATION SCIENCES

INTERNATIONAL MONEY & POLITICS. see BUSINESS AND ECONOMICS — Investments

341.1   US   ISSN 0020-8183
JX1901   CODEN: IOCMFZ
INTERNATIONAL ORGANIZATION. 1947. q. $36 to individuals (foreign $52); institutions $92 (foreign $108); students $25 (foreign $41). (I O Foundation) M I T Press, 55 Hayward St., Cambridge, MA 02142. TEL 617-253-2889. FAX 617-258-6779. E-mail: journals-orders@mit.edu. (Editorial addr.: Center for International Studies, University of Southern California, Los Angeles, CA 90089-0035) Ed. John S. Odell. adv.; bk.rev.; bibl.; charts; index. circ. 2,760. (also avail. in microform from MIM,UMI; back issues avail.; reprint service avail. from KTO,UMI) **Indexed:** A.B.C.Pol.Sci., Amer.Hist.& Life, ASSIA, C.L.I., Commun.Abstr., Curr.Cont., Deep Sea Res.& Oceanogr.Abstr., Fut.Surv., Hist.Abstr., HR Rep. (1969-), INIS Atomind., Int.Bibl.Soc.Sci., Int.Lab.Doc., Int.Polit.Sci.Abstr, J.of Econ.Lit., Key to Econ.Sci., L.R.I., Mid.East: Abstr.& Ind., P.A.I.S., Polit.Sci.Abstr., Rural Recreat.Tour.Abstr., SCIMP (1982-), Soc.Sci.Ind., SSCI, World Agri.Econ.& Rural Sociol.Abstr.
—BLDSC (4544.850000); Faxon; Genuine Article; SWETS; UMI; UnCover. **CCC.**
Description: Covers political and economic affairs affecting foreign policy and history.
Refereed Serial

INTERNATIONAL ORGANIZATION AND THE EVOLUTION OF WORLD SOCIETY. see LAW — International Law

341.1   GW
INTERNATIONAL PEACE RESEARCH NEWSLETTER. 1963. q. $30 to non-members. International Peace Research Association, Beethovenallee 4, 53173 Bonn, Germany. TEL 0228-356032. FAX 0228-356050. Ed. Mahendra Kumar. adv. contact: Paul Smoker. bk.rev.; abstr.; bibl. circ. 1,600. (also avail. in microform from UMI; reprint service avail. from SCH,UMI) **Indexed:** HR Rep., Mid.East: Abstr.& Ind., Refug.Abstr. **Document type:** newsletter.
—UMI.
Former titles: I P R A Newsletter; International Peace Research Newsletter (ISSN 0020-8213)

327   UK   ISSN 1353-3312
JX1981.P7
▼**INTERNATIONAL PEACEKEEPING.** 1994. q. £35($45) to individuals; institutions £98 ($155) (effective 1996). Frank Cass, Newbury House, 890-900 Eastern Ave., Newbury Park, Ilford, Essex IG2 7HH, England. TEL 44-181-599-8866. FAX 44-181-599-0984. E-mail: 100067,1576@compuserve.com. Ed.Bd. adv.; B&W page £195 ($275); adv. contact: Anne Kidson. bk.rev.; index. **Indexed:** Amer.Hist.& Life (1994-), Hist.Abstr. (1994-). **Document type:** academic/scholarly publication.
—BLDSC (4544.892000).
Refereed Serial

327 355   NE   ISSN 1380-748X
                             CODEN: IPEAEF
▼**INTERNATIONAL PEACEKEEPING.** (Text in English) 1994. bi-m. fl.189 to institutions; $121 to institutions in U.S. (effective 1996). Kluwer Law International (Subsidiary of: Wolters Kluwer N.V.), Postbus 85889, 2508 CN The Hague, Netherlands. TEL 31-70-3081500. FAX 31-70-3081515. E-mail: SERVICES@WKAP.NL. (Dist. by: Kluwer Academic Publishers Group, P.O. Box 322, 3300 AH Dordrecht, Netherlands. TEL 31-78-546392. FAX 31-78-546477; In N. America: Kluwer Law International, 675 Massachusetts Ave., Cambridge, MA 02139. TEL 617-354-0140. FAX 617-354-8595) Ed. Michael Bothe. (back issues avail.) **Document type:** newsletter.
—BLDSC (4544.891500). **CCC.**
Description: Reports and analyzes developments in international peacekeeping, with emphasis on legal and policy issues.
Refereed Serial

POLITICAL SCIENCE — INTERNATIONAL RELATIONS

327　　　　　US　　ISSN 0738-6508
INTERNATIONAL POLICY REPORT. 1975. 6/yr. $9.50. Center for International Policy, 1755 Massachusetts Ave., N.W., Ste. 324, Washington, DC 20036. TEL 202-232-3317. FAX 202-232-3440. Ed. Jim Morrell. circ. 1,500. (looseleaf format) **Indexed:** HR Rep.
Description: Reports on US policy towards the Third World and its impact on human rights and human needs.

327　　　　　UK　　ISSN 0192-5121
JA1.A1
INTERNATIONAL POLITICAL SCIENCE REVIEW/REVUE INTERNATIONALE DE SCIENCE POLITIQUE. Abbreviated title: I P S R - R I S P. (Text in English, French) 1980. q. £45 to individuals; institutions £98. (International Political Science Association) Sage Publications Ltd., 6 Bonhill St., London EC2A 4PU, England. TEL 0171-374-0645. FAX 0171-374-8741. E-mail: market@sageltd.co.uk. Eds. Nazli Choucri, Jean Laponce. adv.: B&W page £180; trim 200 x 120; adv. contact: Bernie Folan. abstr.; index. (also avail. in microfilm from WSH,PMC; microform from UMI; back issues avail.) **Indexed:** A.B.C.Pol.Sci., Int.Polit.Sci.Abstr., Mid.East: Abstr.& Ind., Peace Res.Abstr., Polit.Sci.Abstr., Soc.Sci.Ind. (1994-). **Document type:** academic/scholarly publication.
—BLDSC (4544.965200); Faxon; Genuine Article; SWETS; UMI; UnCover. **CCC.**
Description: Creates and disseminates rigorous political enquiry free of any subdisciplinary or other orthodoxy.
Refereed Serial

327　　　　　IS　　ISSN 0020-840X
INTERNATIONAL PROBLEMS; society and politics. (Text in English, French, Hebrew) 1963. s-a. IS.35($30) Israel Institute of International Affairs, Israel Graduates Social Sciences & Humanities, 21 Hess St., Tel Aviv 63324, Israel. TEL 972-3-296482. (Editorial addr.: P.O. Box 17027, Tel Aviv 61170, Israel) Ed. Marian Mushkat. adv. contact: Ami Tamir. bk.rev.; bibl.; index, cum.index. circ. 5,000. (tabloid format; also avail. in microfilm from UMI; reprint service avail. from UMI) **Indexed:** Abstr.Mil.Bibl., Amer.Hist.& Life, Hist.Abstr., Ind.Heb.Per., Int.Polit.Sci.Abstr., Mid.East: Abstr.& Ind., P.A.I.S., Peace Res.Abstr. **Document type:** academic/scholarly publication, newspaper.
—SWETS; UMI; UnCover.

INTERNATIONAL PUBLIC RELATIONS REVIEW. see *ADVERTISING AND PUBLIC RELATIONS*

327　　　　　UK　　ISSN 0047-1178
JX1
INTERNATIONAL RELATIONS. 1954. 3/yr. £25($50) membership (includes Occasional Papers). David Davies Memorial Institute of International Studies, 2 Chadwick St., London SW1P 2EP, England. TEL 0171-222-4063. FAX 0171-233-2863. Ed. Mary Unwin. adv.; bk.rev.; circ. 1,000 (controlled). **Indexed:** A.B.C.Pol.Sci., Amer.Hist.& Life, Euro.LJI, Hist.Abstr., Int.Polit.Sci.Abstr., LJI, Mar.Aff.Bibl., Rural Recreat.Tour.Abstr., World Agri.Econ.& Rural Sociol.Abstr. **Document type:** academic/scholarly publication.
—BLDSC (4545.820000); Faxon; UnCover.
Description: Seeks to advance and promote the development of international relations in all its aspects and to carry out and instigate research and study in this field.

327　　　　　NE　　ISSN 0924-5162
INTERNATIONAL RELATIONS OF SOCIALIST COUNTRIES. (Text in English) 1985. irreg. price varies. Kluwer Academic Publishers, Postbus 17, 3300 AA Dordrecht, Netherlands. TEL 31-78-392392. FAX 31-78-392254. TELEX 29245 KAPG NL. (Dist. by: Kluwer Academic Publishers Group, P.O. Box 322, 3300 AH Dordrecht, Netherlands. TEL 31-78-392392. FAX 31-78-546474; N. America dist. addr.: Box 358, Accord Sta., Hingham, MA 02018-0358. TEL 617-871-6600. FAX 617-871-6528) **Document type:** monographic series.

327　　　　　UK
▼**INTERNATIONAL RELATIONS RESEARCH DIRECTORY.** 1995. irreg. $160. Europa Publications Ltd., 18 Bedford Sq., London WC1G 3JN, England. TEL 0171-580-8236. FAX 0171-636-1664. (Orders to: Sales and Publicity, 43 Gower St., London WC1E 6HH, England. TEL 0171-631-3361. FAX 0171-637-0922) **Document type:** directory.
Description: Lists major research institutes worldwide concerned with international relations. Enumerates journals and periodicals in the field.

327　　　　　US　　ISSN 0740-669X
D839
INTERNATIONAL REPORT (IRVINE). 1983. 3/yr. $6 to individuals; libraries $15; institutions $50. Box 4882, Irvine, CA 92716. FAX 714-725-2346. Ed. Raul Fernandez. adv. circ. 500. **Indexed:** HR Rep. **Document type:** newsletter.
Formerly: Colombia Report.
Description: Analyzes world news.

327　　　　　US　　ISSN 0162-2889
JX1901
INTERNATIONAL SECURITY. 1976. q. $34 to individuals (foreign $50); institutions $92 (foreign $108); students $20 (foreign $36). (Harvard University, Center for Science and International Affairs) M I T Press, 55 Hayward St., Cambridge, MA 02142. TEL 617-253-2889. FAX 617-258-6779. E-mail: journals-orders@mit.edu. Ed. Steven E. Miller. adv. circ. 5,530. (also avail. in microform from UMI; back issues avail.; reprint service avail. from UMI,SCH) **Indexed:** A.B.C.Pol.Sci., Abstr.Mil.Bibl., Air Un.Lib.Ind., Amer.Bibl.Slavic & E.Eur.Stud., Amer.Hist.& Life, DM& T, Fut.Surv., Hist.Abstr., INIS Atomind., Int.Polit.Sci.Abstr., Mid.East: Abstr.& Ind., P.A.I.S., Polit.Sci.Abstr., PROMT, Risk Abstr., SSCI.
—BLDSC (4548.895500); Faxon; Genuine Article; SWETS; UMI; UnCover. **CCC.**
Description: Essays on all aspects of the control and use of force from all political viewpoints. Articles cover contemporary policy issues, probing the historical and theoretical and questions behind them.
Refereed Serial

INTERNATIONAL SKYLINE. see *COMMUNICATIONS*

INTERNATIONAL SPECTATOR. see *POLITICAL SCIENCE*

327 900　　　　　NE　　ISSN 0924-4867
INTERNATIONAL STRAITS OF THE WORLD. 1978. irreg., vol.11, 1989. price varies. Kluwer Academic Publishers, Postbus 17, 3300 AA Dordrecht, Netherlands. TEL 31-78-392392. FAX 31-78-392254. TELEX 29245 KAPG NL. (Dist. by: Kluwer Academic Publishers Group, P.O. Box 322, 3300 AH Dordrecht, Netherlands. TEL 31-78-392392. FAX 31-78-546474; N. America dist. addr.: Box 358, Accord Sta., Hingham, MA 02018-0358. TEL 617-871-6600. FAX 617-871-6528) **Document type:** monographic series.
—BLDSC (4549.720000).
Refereed Serial

327　　　　　II　　ISSN 0020-8817
JX18
INTERNATIONAL STUDIES. 1961. q. $48 to individuals; institutions $105 (effective Sep. 1995). (Jawaharlal Nehru University, School of International Studies) Sage Publications India Pvt. Ltd., P.O. Box 4215, New Delhi 110 048, India. TEL 91-11-644-4958. FAX 91-11-647-2426. (Subscr. overseas to: Sage Publications Ltd., 6 Bonhill St., London EC2A 4PU, England. TEL 44-071-374-0645. FAX 44-071-374-8741; Subscr. in N. America to: Sage Publications, Inc., 2455 Teller Rd., Thousand Oaks, CA 91320. TEL 805-499-0721. FAX 805-499-0871) Ed. K.R. Singh; Pub. Tejeshwar Singh. adv.: page Rs.1000; adv. contact: Sunanda Ghosh. bibl.; index. circ. 900. (also avail. in microform from UMI; back issues avail.; reprint service avail.) **Indexed:** Abstr.Mil.Bibl., Amer.Hist.& Life, Asian-Pac.Econ.Lit., E.I., Hist.Abstr., Int.Polit.Sci.Abstr., Mid.East: Abstr.& Ind., Rural Recreat.Tour.Abstr., World Agri.Econ.& Rural Sociol.Abstr. **Document type:** academic/scholarly publication.
—BLDSC (4549.750000); Faxon; SWETS; UMI; UnCover.
Formerly: International Studies Newsletter (ISSN 0097-8965)
Description: Presents an Asian perspective on international affairs and area studies through original research articles that concentrate on issues and problems of contemporary relevance.
Refereed Serial

327　　　　　US　　ISSN 0094-7768
JX1291
INTERNATIONAL STUDIES NOTES. 1974. 3/yr. $20. American Graduate School of International Management (Thunderbird), 15249 N. 59th Ave., Glendale, AZ 85306-6000. TEL 602-978-7182. FAX 602-439-9622. Ed. Llewellyn D. Howell. adv. circ. 3,500. (also avail. in microform from UMI) **Indexed:** A.B.C.Pol.Sci., Amer.Hist.& Life (until 1993), Hist.Abstr. (until 1993).
—BLDSC (4549.794000); UnCover.
Description: Provides a challenging multidisciplinary forum for exchange of research, curricular and program reports on international affairs.

327 355　　　　　NE　　ISSN 0924-4794
INTERNATIONAL STUDIES ON TERRORISM. (Text in English) 1986. irreg. price varies. Kluwer Academic Publishers, Postbus 17, 3300 AA Dordrecht, Netherlands. TEL 31-78-392392.
FAX 31-78-392254. TELEX 29245 KAPG NL. (Dist. by: Kluwer Academic Publishers Group, P.O. Box 322, 3300 AH Dordrecht, Netherlands. TEL 31-78-392392. FAX 31-78-546474; N. America dist. addr.: Box 358, Accord Sta., Hingham, MA 02018-0358. TEL 617-871-6600. FAX 617-871-6528) **Document type:** monographic series.
Refereed Serial

327　　　　　US　　ISSN 0020-8833
D839　　　　　CODEN: ISTQEN
INTERNATIONAL STUDIES QUARTERLY. (Supplement avail.: Mershon International Studies Review) 1957. 4/yr. $197 to institutions in N. America (elsewhere $205). (International Studies Association) Blackwell Publishers, 238 Main St., Cambridge, MA 02142. TEL 617-547-7110. FAX 617-547-0789. Ed.Bd. adv.: page $400; trim 5 x 8 1/2. charts; index. circ. 4,400. (also avail. in microform from UMI; back issues avail.; reprint service avail.) **Indexed:** A.B.C.Pol.Sci., Amer.Bibl.Slavic & E.Eur.Stud., Amer.Hist.& Life, Curr.Cont., Deep Sea Res.& Oceanogr.Abstr., Hist.Abstr., Human Resour.Abstr., Int.Polit.Sci.Abstr., Int.Polit.Sci.Abstr., Mid.East: Abstr.& Ind., P.A.I.S., Peace Res.Abstr., Polit.Sci.Abstr., PROMT, Risk Abstr., Sage Urb.Stud.Abstr., Soc.Sci.Ind., SSCI, Stud.Wom.Abstr. **Document type:** academic/scholarly publication.
—BLDSC (4549.800000); Faxon; Genuine Article; SWETS; UMI; UnCover. **CCC.**
Formerly: Background.
Description: Presents theoretical and practical papers addressing the various political, economic, social, or cultural forces affecting more than one society and supporting diverse outlooks and practices.
Refereed Serial

327 011　　　　　US　　ISSN 1041-3944
D880
INTERNATIONAL THIRD WORLD STUDIES - JOURNAL AND REVIEW. 1989. s-a. $30 to individuals; institutions $55. Oasis Publishing Co., Box 30242, Lincoln, NE 68502-0242. TEL 402-466-9665. Ed. Peter Suzuki. circ. 300. (back issues avail.)
Description: Explores Third World issues within the disciplines of literature, linguistics, education, and political science.

330　　　　　II
INTERNATIONAL UNDERSTANDING. vol.2, 1966. m. Rs.60($26) Indian Institute of International Understanding, G-36, Connaught Circus, P.O. Box 618, New Delhi 110001, India. (Subscr. to: Central New Agency, 23-90 Connaught Circus, New Delhi, 110 001) Ed. S.S. Bhatia. adv.; bk.rev.; charts; illus. circ. 25,000.
Supersedes: Economic Review and Report (ISSN 0013-0311)

INTERNATIONAL WOMEN'S NEWS. see *WOMEN'S INTERESTS*

POLITICAL SCIENCE — INTERNATIONAL RELATIONS

327 338.9 GW ISSN 0945-2419
CODEN: IPGEE3
INTERNATIONALE POLITIK UND GESELLSCHAFT. (Text in German; summaries in English, French) 1960. q. DM.68. (Friedrich-Ebert-Stiftung, Forschung Institut) Verlag H.J.W. Dietz Nachf. GmbH, In der Raste 2, 53129 Bonn, Germany. TEL 0228-238083. FAX 0228-234104. Ed. Alfred Pfaller. adv. contact: Margret Reichert. bk.rev.; abstr.; bibl.; index. circ. 3,500. **Indexed:** Documentatieblad, Int.Polit.Sci.Abstr., P.A.I.S.For.Lang.Ind., Rural Recreat.Tour.Abstr., World Agri.Econ. & Rural Sociol.Abstr. **Document type:** academic/scholarly publication.
—BLDSC (4554.520500).
 Former titles (until 1993): Vierteljahresberichte - Probleme der Internationalen Zusammenarbeit (ISSN 0936-451X); (until 1983): Vierteljahresberichte - Probleme der Entwicklungslaender (ISSN 0015-7910)

327 GW
INTERNATIONALE POLITIK UND WIRTSCHAFT. irreg., vol.58, 1990. price varies. (Deutsche Gesellschaft fuer Auswaertige Politik) R. Oldenbourg Verlag GmbH, Rosenheimerstr. 145, 81671 Munich, Germany. TEL 089-45051-0. FAX 089-45051207. (Subscr. to: Postfach 801360, 81613 Munich, Germany) **Document type:** monographic series.

960 327 GW ISSN 0020-9430
DT1
INTERNATIONALES AFRIKAFORUM. 1965. q. DM.118. (Europaeisches Institut fuer Politische, Wirtschaftliche und Soziale Fragen e.V.) Weltforum Verlag, Marienburgerstr. 22, 50968 Cologne, Germany. Eds. Hans-Gert Braun, Alois Graf von Waldburg-Zeil. adv.; bk.rev. **Indexed:** Curr.Cont.Africa, Documentatieblad, Key to Econ.Sci., P.A.I.S.For.Lang.Ind., World Agri.Econ.& Rural Sociol.Abstr. **Document type:** academic/scholarly publication.
—BLDSC (4556.760000).

960 327 GW ISSN 0020-9449
INTERNATIONALES ASIENFORUM. 1970. q. DM.110. (Europaeisches Institut fuer Politische, Wirtschaftliche und Soziale Fragen e.V.) Weltforum Verlag, Marienburgerstr. 22, 50968 Cologne, Germany. Eds. Detlef Kantowsky, Alois Graf von Waldburg-Zeil. adv.; bk.rev. **Indexed:** Amer.Hist.& Life, E.I., Hist.Abstr., Int.Lab.Doc., Int.Polit.Sci.Abstr., Key to Econ.Sci., Mid.East: Abstr.& Ind., P.A.I.S.For.Lang.Ind., SSCI. **Document type:** academic/scholarly publication.
—BLDSC (4557.003000); UnCover.

327 GW ISSN 0934-9685
INTERNATIONALES HANDBUCH - LAENDER AKTUELL. 1936. w. DM.96 per quarter. Munzinger-Archiv GmbH, Albersfelderstr. 34, 88213 Ravensburg, Germany. TEL 0751-76931-0. FAX 0751-652424. Ed. Dr. Ludwig Munzinger. circ. 1,500. **Document type:** newsletter.
 Formerly: Internationales Handbuch (ISSN 0020-949X)

327 SW ISSN 0020-952X
INTERNATIONELLA STUDIER. 1968. q. SEK 197 in the Nordic countries; elsewhere SEK297. Utrikespolitiska Institutet - Swedish Institute of International Affairs, P.O. Box 1253, 111 82 Stockholm, Sweden. FAX 8-201049. Ed. Erland Jansson. adv.; bk.rev.; charts. circ. 2,500. **Document type:** academic/scholarly publication.

327 US
INTERNEWSLETTER AFRIQUE; la seule revue de presse Americaine en Francais sur l'Afrique. (Text in French) 1977. s-m. $599 to individuals; libraries $499. Internews Media Services Inc., 1199 National Press Bldg., Washington, DC 20045-0001. TEL 202-347-4575. FAX 703-734-6956. Ed. Marie-Benoite Allizon. adv. (looseleaf format; back issues avail.)

328 SZ ISSN 0020-5079
JX1930
INTER-PARLIAMENTARY BULLETIN. (Editions in English, French) 1921. q. 19 SFr. Inter-Parliamentary Union, Place du Petit-Saconnex, CH-1211 Geneva 19, Switzerland. TEL 022-7344150. FAX 022-7333141. TELEX 414217-IPU-CH. adv.; bk.rev. circ. 1,600 (French ed.); 1,600 (English ed.). **Indexed:** Mid.East: Abstr.& Ind., P.A.I.S. **Document type:** bulletin.

320 SZ
INTER-PARLIAMENTARY UNION. SUMMARY RECORDS OF THE INTER-PARLIAMENTARY CONFERENCES. (Text in English and French) 1897. s-a. 30 SFr. Inter-Parliamentary Union, Place du Petit-Saconnex, CH-1211 Geneva 19, Switzerland. TEL 022-7344150. FAX 022-7333141. TELEX 414217-IPU-CH. circ. 800. **Document type:** bulletin.
 Formerly: Inter-Parliamentary Union. Conference Proceedings (ISSN 0074-1051)

INTRIGUE. see CRIMINOLOGY AND LAW ENFORCEMENT — Security

327 IR ISSN 1016-6130
D1
IRANIAN JOURNAL OF INTERNATIONAL AFFAIRS. (Text in English) 1989. q. $30. Institute of Political and International Studies, P.O. Box 19395-1793, Tehran, Iran. TEL 98-21-2571010. FAX 98-21-270964. Ed. Abbas Maleki. bk.rev. **Document type:** academic/scholarly publication.
—BLDSC (4567.528850).

327 IR ISSN 0378-990X
JX18
IRANIAN REVIEW OF INTERNATIONAL RELATIONS/REVUE IRANIENNE DES RELATIONS INTERNATIONALES. (Text in French and English) 1974. q. Rs.250($18) University of Teheran, Center for International Studies, Englehab Ave., Teheran 14174, Iran. Dir. Prof. Habibi. bk.rev.; abstr.; bibl. circ. 2,000. **Document type:** academic/scholarly publication.
 Formerly (until 1975): Relations Internationales (ISSN 1016-1589)

327 338.91 IE ISSN 0332-1460
DA964.A2
IRISH STUDIES IN INTERNATIONAL AFFAIRS. 1979. a. I£6 to individuals; institutions I£10. Royal Irish Academy, 19 Dawson St., Dublin 2, Ireland. TEL 01-762570. FAX 01-762346. Ed. J. Bradley. (back issues avail.) **Document type:** academic/scholarly publication.
—BLDSC (4574.830000).

327 UK ISSN 1353-7121
▼**ISRAEL AFFAIRS.** 1994. q. £35($45) to individuals; institutions £85 ($115) (effective 1996). Frank Cass, 890-900 Eastern Ave., Newbury Park, Ilford, Essex IG2 7HH, England. TEL 44-181-599-8866. FAX 44-181-599-0984. E-mail: 100067,1576@compuserve.com. Ed. Efraim Karsh. adv.: B&W page £195 ($275); adv. contact: Anne Kidson. bk.rev.; index. **Document type:** academic/scholarly publication.
 Description: Covers Israeli history, politics, literature, art, strategic affairs, economics, the Arab-Israeli conflict, and Israel-diaspora relations. *Refereed Serial*

ISRAEL HORIZONS; the socialist Zionist journal. see POLITICAL SCIENCE

327 DK
ISRAEL INFORMATION. 1980. irreg. free. Israelske Ambassade, Lundevangsvej 4, SK-2900 Hellerup, Denmark. TEL 31-62-62-88. FAX 31-62-19-38. circ. 1,500. **Document type:** newsletter.
 Formerly: Israelske Ambassade. Information (ISSN 0108-3783)

ISRAEL UND PALAESTINA; Zeitschrift fuer Dialog. see POLITICAL SCIENCE

327 956.94 US ISSN 0883-9832
ISRAELI FOREIGN AFFAIRS; an independent research report on Israel's diplomatic and military activities around the world. 1984. 11/yr. $27 to individuals; institutions $42. Israeli Foreign Affairs, Box 19850, Sacramento, CA 95819. FAX 916-736-0274. TELEX MCIUW 295-2402. Ed. Jane Hunter. circ. 850. (back issues avail.)
 Description: Provides annotated coverage of Israel's activities in developing world, Israeli nuclear weapons, US-Israeli relations, intelligence issues, covert activities.

327 US ISSN 1055-3754
DS119.7
ISRAELI - PALESTINIAN DIGEST.* q. Washington Area Jews for an Israeli-Palestinian Peace, 1851 Columbia Rd., N.W., Apt. 405, Washington, DC 20009. Ed. Seth Grimes.

327 CH ISSN 1013-2511
ISSUES & STUDIES. (Text in English) 1964. m. $44 to individuals, institutions $64. Institute of International Relations, 64 Wan Shou Rd., Mucha, Taiwan, Republic of China. Ed.Bd; Pub. Yu-ming Shaw. adv.; stat.; index. (also avail. in microform from UMI; reprint service avail. from ISI, UMI). **Indexed:** A.B.C.Pol.Sci., Amer.Hist.& Life, Asian-Pac.Econ.Lit., Curr.Cont., Geo.Abstr., Hist.Abstr., Int.Polit.Sci.Abstr., Polit.Sci.Abstr., Risk Abstr., Rural Devel.Abstr., SSCI, World Agri.Econ.& Rural Sociol.Abstr. **Document type:** newsletter.
—BLDSC (4584.120000); Faxon; Genuine Article; SWETS; UMI.
 Description: Highlights world affairs and communist problems.

327 SI
ISSUES IN SOUTHEAST ASIAN SECURITY. 1984. irreg., no.16, 1993. price varies. Institute of Southeast Asian Studies, Heng Mui Keng Terrace, Pasir Panjang, Singapore 0511, Singapore. TEL 7780955. FAX 7781735. TELEX RS 37068 ISEAS. E-mail: pubsunit@merlion.iseas.ac.sg. (Subscr. in U.S. to: Ashgate, Old Post Rd., Brookfield, VT 05036. TEL 802-276-3162) **Document type:** academic/scholarly publication.
 Description: International relations and strategic studies pertaining to the Asia-Pacific region.

327 US ISSN 0075-2142
JACOB BLAUSTEIN LECTURES IN INTERNATIONAL AFFAIRS. 1967. irreg., no.2, 1971. Columbia University Press, 562 W. 113th St., New York, NY 10025. TEL 212-666-1000. **Document type:** monographic series.

327 GW ISSN 0936-9872
JX1904
JAHRBUCH FRIEDEN (YEAR); konflikte - abruestung - friedensarbeit. 1989. a. (Arbeitsgemeinschaft fuer Friedens- und Konfliktforschung) C.H. Beck'sche Verlagsbuchhandlung, Wilhelmstr. 9, 80801 Munich, Germany. TEL 089-38189338. FAX 089-38189398. Ed.Bd. (back issues avail.) **Document type:** bulletin.

327 SA ISSN 1021-7495
JAN SMUTS HOUSE NEWS. 1993. q. South African Institute of International Affairs, P.O. Box 31596, Braamfontein 2017, South Africa. TEL 27-11-339-2021. FAX 27-11-339-2154. **Document type:** newsletter.

JAPAN DEFENSE & SECURITY REPORT. see MILITARY

327 UK ISSN 0955-5803
DS801
JAPAN FORUM. 1989. 2/yr. £60($112) (effective 1995). (British Association for Japanese Studies) Oxford University Press, Oxford Journals, Walton St., Oxford OX2 6DP, England. TEL 01865-267907. FAX 01865-267773. TELEX 837330-OXPRES-G. E-mail: jnlorders@oup.co.uk. (U.S. subscr. to: Oxford University Press Inc., 2001 Evans Rd., Cary, NC 27513. TEL 919-677-0977. FAX 919-677-1714) Eds. John Chapman, Ian Neary. adv. contact: Jane Parker. bk.rev. circ. 900. **Indexed:** Asian-Pac.Econ.Lit., Int.Polit.Sci.Abstr. **Document type:** academic/scholarly publication.
—BLDSC (4648.271000); SWETS; UMI; UnCover. CCC.
 Description: Provides scholarly articles on Japanese culture, both historical and contemporary.

327 JA ISSN 0913-8773
D839
JAPAN REVIEW OF INTERNATIONAL AFFAIRS. q. Japan Institute of International Affairs, Toranomon Bitui Bldg., 3-8-1 Kasumigaseki, Chiyoda-ku, Tokyo 100, Japan. TEL 03-3503-7261. FAX 03-3503-7292. TELEX 02223469 JIIA J. Ed. Nobuo Matsunaga. **Indexed:** Asian-Pac.Econ.Lit. **Document type:** monographic series.
—BLDSC (4648.776000); Faxon; UnCover.

POLITICAL SCIENCE — INTERNATIONAL RELATIONS

960 FR ISSN 0021-6089
AP27
JEUNE AFRIQUE; le devoir d'informer - la liberte d'ecrire. (Supplement avail: Jeune Afrique Plus (ISSN 0757-116X)) 1960. w. 16 F. per no. J A Press, 57 bis rue d'Auteuil, 75016 Paris, France. TEL 44-30-19-60. FAX 45-20-09-69. Ed. Bechir Ben Yahmed. adv.; bk.rev.; charts; illus. circ. 100,000. (also avail. in microfilm; reprint service avail.) **Indexed:** Curr.Cont.Africa, Curr.Cont.M.E., Key to Econ.Sci., Pt.de Rep. (1991-).
—BLDSC (4668.220000).
Formerly: J A.
Description: Features articles about events taking place in Africa and important figures of African descent.

327 US ISSN 0449-0754
E740.J6
JOHN BIRCH SOCIETY. BULLETIN. 1959. m. $20. John Birch Society, Box 8040, Appleton, WI 54913. FAX 414-749-3785. Ed. Gary Benoit. adv.; bk.rev. circ. 30,000. (back issues avail.) **Document type:** bulletin.

327 968 SA ISSN 0258-2422
JOURNAL FOR CONTEMPORARY HISTORY/JOERNAAL VIR EIETYDSE GESKIEDENIS. 1976. 2/yr. $22 (effective 1996). University of the Orange Free State, Institute for Contemporary History - Universiteit van die Oranje-Vrystaat, Instituut vir Eietydse Geskiedenis, P.O. Box 2320, Bloemfontein 9300, South Africa. TEL 27-51-4012250. FAX 27-51-473416. E-mail: incb@rs.uovs.ac.za. Ed. P.W. Coetzer. adv.: B&W page $65. abstr.; illus. **Indexed:** Ind.S.A.Per. **Document type:** academic/scholarly publication.
—BLDSC (4965.229000).
Formerly: Journal for Contemporary History and International Relations.
Description: Publishes articles on contemporary South African and international political, constitutional and social history.
Refereed Serial

327 US ISSN 0275-3588
DS36
JOURNAL OF ARAB AFFAIRS. 1981. s-a. $25 (effective 1993). M E R G Analytica, Box 26385, Fresno, CA 93729-6385. FAX 209-323-4758. (Subscr. to: 7872 Fairview Rd., Boulder, CO 80303) Ed. Tawfic E. Farah. adv.; bk.rev. circ. 1,300. (also avail. in microform from UMI; reprint service avail. from SCH) **Indexed:** A.B.C.Pol.Sci., Curr.Cont., Int.Polit.Sci.Abstr., P.A.I.S., SSCI.
—Genuine Article; UMI; UnCover.

320 330 US ISSN 0886-5655
F787
JOURNAL OF BORDERLAND STUDIES. 1986. 2/yr. $25 membership; libraries $20. Association for Borderlands Scholars, Department of Economics, Box 30001, New Mexico State University, Las Cruces, NM 88003. TEL 505-646-3113. FAX 505-646-1915. (Co-sponsor: New Mexico State University) Eds. Jim Peach, Anthony Popp. adv.; bk.rev.; cum.index: 1986-1990. circ. 425. (back issues avail.) **Indexed:** Hisp.Amer.Per.Ind. (1986-). **Document type:** academic/scholarly publication.
—UnCover.
Description: Multidisciplinary journal focusing on international borders.

942 UK ISSN 0306-3631
JN248
THE JOURNAL OF COMMONWEALTH & COMPARATIVE POLITICS. 1961. 3/yr. £38($55) to individuals; institutions £98 ($145) (effective 1996). Frank Cass, Newbury House, 890-900 Eastern Ave., Newbury Park, Ilford, Essex IG2 7HH, England. TEL 44-181-599-8866. FAX 44-181-599-0984. E-mail: 1000067,1576@compuserve.com. Eds. Arnold Hughes, David Potter. adv.: B&W page £195 ($275); adv. contact: Ann Kidson. bk.rev.; index. (also avail. in microfilm from UMI; back issues avail.) **Indexed:** A.B.C.Pol.Sci., Amer.Hist.& Life, Asian-Pac.Econ.Lit., Curr.Cont., Documentatieblad, Hist.Abstr., IDA, Int.Polit.Sci.Abstr., Lang.& Lang.Behav.Abstr., Mid.East: Abstr.& Ind., P.A.I.S., Polit.Sci.Abstr., Rural Devel.Abstr., Rural Recreat.Tour.Abstr., So.Pac.Per.Ind., SSCI, World Agri.Econ.& Rural Sociol.Abstr. **Document type:** academic/scholarly publication.
—BLDSC (4961.250000); Faxon; Genuine Article; SWETS; UMI; UnCover. **CCC.**
Formerly: Journal of Commonwealth Political Studies (ISSN 0021-9908)
Description: Features articles on the comparative politics of Commonwealth countries.
Refereed Serial

327 UK ISSN 1352-3279
HX3
JOURNAL OF COMMUNIST STUDIES AND TRANSITION POLITICS. 1985. q. £36($48) to individuals; institutions £115 ($170) (effective 1996). Frank Cass, Newbury House, 890-900 Eastern Ave., Newbury Park, Ilford, Essex IG2 7HH, England. TEL 44-181-599-8866. FAX 44-181-599-0984. E-mail: 1000067,1576@compuserve.com. Ed.Bd. adv.: B&W page £195 ($275); adv. contact: Anne Kidson. bk.rev.; index. (also avail. in microform from UMI; back issues avail.) **Indexed:** A.B.C.Pol.Sci., Geo.Abstr., IDA, Int.Polit.Sci.Abstr., Polit.Sci.Abstr. **Document type:** academic/scholarly publication.
—BLDSC (4961.665100); UMI; UnCover. **CCC.**
Formerly (until 1994): Journal of Communist Studies (ISSN 0268-4535)
Description: Covers the study of communism and its current transformation, following the effects of this upheaval or communist parties worldwide.
Refereed Serial

327 UK ISSN 0965-8130
JOURNAL OF CONFLICT PROCESSES. 1993. 4/yr. Lentz Foundation, Liverpool John Moores University, 98 Mount Pleasant, Liverpool L3 5UZ, England. TEL 051-231-3871. FAX 051-707-0423. **Document type:** academic/scholarly publication.
—BLDSC (4965.129000).

JOURNAL OF CONFLICT RESOLUTION; research on war and peace between and within nations. see *SOCIAL SCIENCES: COMPREHENSIVE WORKS*

327 KO ISSN 1010-1608
DS501
JOURNAL OF EAST ASIAN AFFAIRS. 1980-1983; resumed. s-a. $10 (foreign $14). Research Institute for International Affairs, C.P.O. Box 6856, Seoul 100-668, S. Korea. TEL 82-2-565-3557. FAX 82-2-565-3558. Ed. Kwang-mo Koo. circ. 2,000. **Indexed:** A.B.C.Pol.Sci. (1993-), Asian-Pac.Econ.Lit., Sage Fam.Stud.Abstr., Sage Urb.Stud.Abstr.
—**CCC.**

327 UK ISSN 0958-9287
JOURNAL OF EUROPEAN SOCIAL POLICY. 1991. q. £43 (Europe £45; rest of world £47($80)) to individuals; institutions £85(Europe £87; rest of world £94($160)). Longman Group UK Ltd., Longman House, Burnt Mill, Harlow, Essex CM20 2JE, England. TEL 01279-426721. FAX 01279-431059. E-mail: longhe@cityscape.co.uk. Ed.Bd. adv.; bk.rev. circ. 400. **Document type:** academic/scholarly publication.
—BLDSC (4979.609000); SWETS. **CCC.**
Description: Comprehensive, up-to-date coverage of key European social policy issues.
Refereed Serial

327 US ISSN 0022-1937
F1401
JOURNAL OF INTERAMERICAN STUDIES AND WORLD AFFAIRS. 1959. q. $42 to individuals (foreign $50); institutions $96 (foreign $104); students $20 (foreign $28) (effective 1996). University of Miami, North - South Center Publications, Box 248205, Coral Gables, FL 33124-3027. TEL 305-284-8914. FAX 305-284-5083. (Subscr. to: Lynne Rienner Publishers, 1800 30th St., No. 314, Boulder, CO 80301. TEL 303-444-6684. FAX 303-444-0824) Ed. Jaime Suchlicki. bk.rev.; charts; index. circ. 6,370. (also avail. in microfilm from UMI; back issues avail.; reprint service avail. from UMI) **Indexed:** A.B.C.Pol.Sci., Abstr.Mil.Bibl., Amer.Bibl.Slavic & E.Eur.Stud, Amer.Hist.& Life, CERDIC, Curr.Cont., Hisp.Amer.Per.Ind. (1970-), Hist.Abstr., Hum.Ind., Int.Polit.Sci.Abstr., Mid.East: Abstr.& Ind., P.A.I.S., Polit.Sci.Abstr., Soc.Sci.Ind., SSCI. **Document type:** academic/scholarly publication.
●Also available online. Vendor(s): University Microfilms International.
—BLDSC (5007.541000); Faxon; Genuine Article; SWETS; UMI; UnCover. **CCC.**
Description: Explores contemporary issues and problems facing nations in the Western Hemisphere.
Refereed Serial

327 US ISSN 0022-197X
JX1
JOURNAL OF INTERNATIONAL AFFAIRS. 1947. s-a. $14 to individuals (foreign $18); institutions $28 (foreign $32). Columbia University, Journal of International Affairs, Box 4, International Affairs Bldg., New York, NY 10027. TEL 212-854-4775. FAX 212-864-4847. Ed. Matthew Tiedemann. adv.; bk.rev.; cum.index every 5 yrs. circ. 4,000. (also avail. in microform from UMI; reprint service avail. from UMI) **Indexed:** A.B.C.Pol.Sci., Amer.Bibl.Slavic & E.Eur.Stud, Amer.Hist.& Life, Asian-Pac.Econ.Lit., C.L.I., Hist.Abstr., Hum.Ind., Int.Polit.Sci.Abstr., L.R.I., Mid.East: Abstr.& Ind., P.A.I.S., Soc.Sci.Ind.
●Also available online. Vendor(s): University Microfilms International.
—BLDSC (5007.550000); Faxon; Genuine Article; SWETS; UMI; UnCover. **CCC.**
Formerly (until 1952): Columbia Journal of International Affairs (ISSN 1045-3466)
Description: Scholarly analysis of international affairs issues.

300 KO
JOURNAL OF INTERNATIONAL AFFAIRS.* (Text in Korean) 1970. m. 6000 Won($12) Kukje Publishing House, 187-39 Daejo-Dong, Eunpyeong-gu, Seoul 122-030, S. Korea. Ed. Ho Jik Hwang. adv.; bk.rev.; index. **Indexed:** A.B.C.Pol.Sci., Abstr.Mil.Bibl., L.R.I., Mar.Aff.Bibl., Soc.Sci.Ind, SSCI.

327 JA ISSN 0910-5476
JOURNAL OF INTERNATIONAL STUDIES. (Text in English or Japanese; abstracts in English and Japanese) 1978. 2/yr. 1456 Yen per no. Sophia University, Institute of International Relations, 7-1 Kioi-cho, Chiyoda-ku, Tokyo 102, Japan. TEL 03-3238-3561. FAX 03-3238-3592. Ed. Kawaguchi Kazuko. bk.rev. circ. 500. (also avail. in microfiche) **Indexed:** Geo.Abstr., Int.Polit.Sci.Abstr. **Document type:** academic/scholarly publication.
—BLDSC (5007.686650).
Description: Offers a unique perspective on world-wide subjects to specialists in international relations and international comparative studies from a Japanese perspective.
Refereed Serial

JOURNAL OF LATIN AMERICAN AFFAIRS. see *HISTORY — History Of North And South America*

327 340 UK ISSN 1357-2334
▼**THE JOURNAL OF LEGISLATIVE STUDIES**. 1995. a. £38($50) to individuals; institutions £100 ($165) (effective 1996). Frank Cass, 890-900 Eastern Ave., Newbury Park, Ilford, Essex IG2 7HH, England. TEL 44-181-599-8866. FAX 44-181-599-0984. E-mail: 100067,1576@compuserve.com. Ed. Philip Norton. adv.: B&W page £195 ($275); adv. contact: Anne Kidson. bk.rev.; index. **Document type:** academic/scholarly publication.
—BLDSC (5010.276500).
Description: Covers all aspects of legislative research and development for scholars and researchers of legislative studies.
Refereed Serial

POLITICAL SCIENCE — INTERNATIONAL RELATIONS

341.1   UK   ISSN 0022-3433
AS9
JOURNAL OF PEACE RESEARCH; an interdisciplinary and international quarterly of scholarly work in peace research. 1964. q. £30 to individuals; institutions £102 (effective 1996). (International Peace Research Institute, Oslo, NO) Sage Publications Ltd., 6 Bonhill St., London EC2A 4PU, England. TEL 0171-374-0645. FAX 0171-374-8741. E-mail: market@sageltd.co.uk. Eds. Nils Petter Gleditsch, Malvern Lumsden. adv.: B&W page £200; trim 200 x 125; adv. contact: Bernie Folan. bk.rev.; charts; illus.; stat.; index. (also avail. in microform from UMI) Indexed: A.B.C.Pol.Sci., Abstr.Mil.Bibl., Amer.Hist.& Life, Bk.Rev.Ind., Br.Hum.Ind., Curr.Cont., Curr.Mil.& Polit.Lit., Fut.Surv., Hist.Abstr., HR Rep. (1987-), Human Resour.Abstr., IBZ, Int.Lab.Doc., Int.Polit.Sci.Abstr., Intl.Bibl.S.S.Pol.Sci., Lang.& Lang.Behav.Abstr., Mid.East: Abstr.& Ind., P.A.I.S., Peace Res.Abstr, Per.Islam., Polit.Sci.Abstr., Risk Abstr., Sage Pub.Admin.Abstr., Sage Urb.Stud.Abstr., Soc.Sci.Ind., Soc.Work Res.& Abstr., Sociol.Abstr., SSCI. **Document type:** academic/scholarly publication.
—BLDSC (5030.100000); Faxon; SWETS; UMI; UnCover.
    Description: Provides a global focus on conflict and peacemaking. Encourages a wide conception of peace but focuses on the causes of violence and conflict resolution.
    Refereed Serial

327   UK   ISSN 1357-7379
THE JOURNAL OF REGIONAL AND FEDERAL STUDIES; an international journal. 1991. 3/yr. £38($50) to individuals; institutions £95 ($135) (effective 1996). Frank Cass, Newbury House, 890-900 Eastern Ave., Newbury Park, Ilford, Essex IG2 7HH, England. TEL 44-181-599-8866. FAX 44-181-599-0984. E-mail: 100067,1576@compuserve.com. Ed. John Loughlin. adv.: B&W page £195 ($275); adv. contact: Anne Kidson. bk.rev.; index. (back issues avail.) Indexed: A.B.C.Pol.Sci. (1994-), Geo.Abstr., Int.Polit.Sci.Abstr., Polit.Sci.Abstr. **Document type:** academic/scholarly publication.
—BLDSC (7336.705900).
    Formerly (until Spring 1995): Regional Politics and Policy (ISSN 0959-230X)
    Description: Covers scholarly research into the region as a political and administrative entity, as well as a social science concept.
    Refereed Serial

327   UK   ISSN 0140-2390
U162
THE JOURNAL OF STRATEGIC STUDIES. 1978. q. £38($55) to individuals; institutions £130 ($195) (effective 1996). Frank Cass, Newbury House, 890-900 Eastern Ave., Newbury Park, Ilford, Essex IG2 7HH, England. TEL 44-181-599-8866. FAX 44-181-599-0984. E-mail: 100067,1576@compuserve.com. Eds. Amos Perlmutter, John Gooch. adv.: B&W page £195 ($275); adv. contact: Anne Kidson. bk.rev.; index. (also avail. in microfilm from UMI; back issues avail.) Indexed: Abstr.Mil.Bibl., Amer.Hist.& Life, Curr.Cont., Hist.Abstr., Int.Polit.Sci.Abstr., Polit.Sci.Abstr., Psychol.Abstr., SSCI. **Document type:** academic/scholarly publication.
—BLDSC (5066.873000); Ei; Genuine Article; SWETS; UMI; UnCover. CCC.
    Description: Covers both contemporary and historical issues in the field of strategic studies.
    Refereed Serial

JOURNAL OF THE THIRD WORLD SPECTRUM. see *ORIENTAL STUDIES*

JOURNAL OF THIRD WORLD STUDIES. see *HISTORY*

237   JA   ISSN 0453-0950
JOURNAL OF WORLD AFFAIRS/KAIGAI JIJO. (Text in English, Japanese) m. 3600 Yen. Takushohu University, Institute of World Studies, 4-14, Kohinata 3-chome, Bunkyo-ku, Tokyo 112, Japan. Ed. Muneyoshi Date.
—BLDSC (5072.639000).

JUS GENTIUM; diritto delle relazioni internazionali. see *LAW — International Law*

JUSTPEACE. see *RELIGIONS AND THEOLOGY*

327   AT   ISSN 0311-0419
KABAR. 1969. 10/yr. Aus.$12. Australia Indonesia Association of New South Wales, G.P.O. Box 802, Sydney, N.S.W. 2001, Australia. Ed. Megan Lavender. adv.; bk.rev. circ. 150.
    Formerly: Australia Indonesia Association of New South Wales. Bulletin.

338   US
KALEIDOSCOPE: CURRENT WORLD DATA. 1956. w. A B C-Clio, 130 Cremona, Box 1911, Santa Barbara, CA 93116-1911. TEL 805-968-1911. FAX 805-685-9685. Ed. Timothy O'Donnell; Pub. Heather Cameron. adv. contact: Laura Wilson. stat.; index. (cards) **Document type:** directory.
● Also available online. Vendor(s): Lexis-Nexis.
    Former titles: Deadline Data on World Affairs (ISSN 0011-5061); D M S I Market Intelligence Reports.
    Description: Provides statistical data and current events information on countries of the world; states and provinces of the US and Canada; international organizations; and other selected topics.

327 614.7 301   NE   ISSN 0925-5893
KAN ANDERS. vol. 4, 1981. 5/yr. fl.22.50 (effective 1994). Kan Anders, Werkgemeenschap voor Pacifisme, Ekologie en Socialisme, Vlamingstraat 82, 2611 LA Delft, Netherlands. TEL 31-15-2121694. Ed.Bd. adv.; bk.rev.; illus.; circ. 1,100 (controlled).

327 956.94   LE
KATIB AL-FILASTINI. (Text in Arabic) 1978. irreg. £L150. Ittihad al-Amm lil-Kuttab wa-al-Sahafiyin al-Filastiniyin, Box 3075, Beirut, Lebanon.

KERK EN VREDE. see *RELIGIONS AND THEOLOGY*

327   JA   ISSN 0285-7928
KOKUSAI KYORYOKU/INTERNATIONAL COOPERATION. (Text in Japanese) 1953. m. 500 Yen per no. Japan International Cooperation Agency, Box 216, Mitsui Bldg., Shinjuku-ku, Tokyo 163, Japan. TEL 81-3-3346-5026. FAX 81-3-3346-5032. E-mail: matuyama@ific.or.jp. Ed. Kenzo Osima. bk.rev. circ. 17,000.
    Formerly: Kaigai Gijutsu Kyoryoku.

KOLEINU. see *RELIGIONS AND THEOLOGY — Judaic*

320.9   SW   ISSN 0023-3013
KOMMENTAR; oberoende socialistisk tidskrift. 1966. 4/yr. SEK 175 (effective 1994). Kommentar, Box 4253, S-102 63 Stockholm, Sweden. TEL 46-8-643-95-95. Ed. Lars Thunegard. bk.rev.; bibl.; charts; illus.; index. cum.index every 5 yrs. circ. 2,500. (processed)
    Formerly (until 1968): Foer Vietnam.

KONTAKT (COPENHAGEN, 1948). see *SOCIAL SCIENCES: COMPREHENSIVE WORKS*

327 382   HK   ISSN 1016-2658
THE KOREA LETTER. (Text in English) 1991. m. $495. N & N International (Hong Kong) Ltd., P.O. Box 54332, North Point Post Office, Hong Kong. FAX 852-856-5648. Ed. R.B. Cunningham.
    Description: Covers political and economic developments in North & South Korea.

327 332.6   HK   ISSN 1016-6106
KOREA LETTER (NIHONBAN). (Text in Japanese) 1990. m. N & N International (Hong Kong) Ltd., G.P.O. Box 8926, Hong Kong. FAX 852-856-5648.

KOREA UPDATE. see *POLITICAL SCIENCE — Civil Rights*

327   KO
KOREAN JOURNAL OF INTERNATIONAL RELATIONS. 1963. irreg. Korean Association of International Relations, c/o Graduate School of Public Administration, Seoul National University, 119 Tongsung-Dong, Chongno-Ku, Seoul, S. Korea.

327   US   ISSN 0163-0229
DS922
KOREAN REVIEW. 1978. bi-m. $10 to individuals; institutions $15. Korean Review, Box 32, Knickerbocker Sta., New York, NY 10002. Ed. S.J. Noumoff. Indexed: Asian-Pac.Econ.Lit.

951.9   SW   ISSN 0023-4079
KOREANSK JOURNAL. (Text in Swedish; summaries in English) 1950. irreg. (4-6/yr.) SEK 25($5) Swedish-Korean Society, Box 3259, S-103 65 Stockholm 3, Sweden. TEL 46-8-759-59-75. Eds. Aake J. Ek. adv.; bk.rev.; film rev.; play rev.; abstr.; illus.; stat.; tr.lit. circ. 4,500. **Document type:** bulletin, newspaper.

327   HU   ISSN 0133-0616
KULPOLITIKA/FOREIGN AFFAIRS. (Text in Hungarian; summaries in English and Russian) 1974. q. $23.50. (Magyar Kulugyi Intezet) Lapkiado Vallalat, Lenin korut 9-11, 1073 Budapest 7, Hungary. TEL 222-408. (Subscr. to: Kultura, Box 149, H-1389 Budapest, Hungary) Ed. Gyula Bognar. bk.rev.; bibl.

KULTUUR JA ELU/CULTURE AND LIFE. see *ETHNIC INTERESTS*

915.554 059.915   FR
KURDISTAN. (Text in Persian) no.159, 1990. m. (Hizb-i Dimukrat-i Kurdistan-i Iran - Democratic Party of the Iranian Kurdistan) Association Franco-Kurde, B.P. 102, 75623 Paris cedex 13, France.

327 338.91   CN   ISSN 0316-3393
L A W G LETTER. 1967. irreg. Can.$6 per no. Latin American Working Group, 603 1-2 Parliament St., Toronto, ON M4X 1P9, Canada. TEL 416-966-4773. FAX 416-921-0071. Ed.Bd. bk.rev.; illus. circ. 7,000. Indexed: HR Rep.
    Description: Focuses on Canada's trade, aid and investment links to South and Central America.

327   GH   ISSN 0855-076X
L E C I A BULLETIN. 1991. a. (University of Ghana, Legon Centre for International Affairs) Ghana University Press, Legon, Nr. Accra, Ghana.

327   GW
LAGEBERICHT AUS AUSTRALIEN. 1976. m. free. Australian Embassy, Public Affairs Section, Godesberger Allee 107, 53175 Bonn, Germany. TEL 0228-8130170. FAX 0228-8103144. Eds. Sandi Logan, Guenter Schlothauer. circ. 3,000. **Document type:** newsletter.
    Description: News about Australia and its affairs in German.

327   GW   ISSN 0176-2818
LATEINAMERIKA (HAMBURG); Analysen - Daten - Dokumentation. (Text in German; summaries in English, Portuguese or Spanish) 1984. 3/yr. DM.60 (students DM.45). Institut fuer Iberoamerika-Kunde, Alsterglacis 8, 20354 Hamburg, Germany. TEL 040-414782-01. FAX 040-41478241. **Document type:** academic/scholarly publication.

327   AU
LATEINAMERIKA ANDERS PANORAMA. 1976. s-m. S.300. Informationsgruppe Lateinamerika, Muenzwardeingasse 2, A-1061 Vienna, Austria. TEL 02-2186412. FAX 01-3173095. E-mail: apia-lans@telebox.ada.at. Eds. Werner Hoertner, Hermann Klosius. adv.; bk.rev. circ. 1,000. (back issues avail.) **Document type:** newsletter.
    Formerly (until 1993): Lateinamerika Anders Report.
    Description: News and background information on Latin America.

LATEINAMERIKA NACHRICHTEN. see *BUSINESS AND ECONOMICS — International Development And Assistance*

327   US   ISSN 0736-4148
LATIN AMERICA AND CARIBBEAN CONTEMPORARY RECORD. 1981. a. $380. Holmes & Meier Publishers, Inc., 160 Broadway E. Wing, New York, NY 10038. TEL 212-374-0100. FAX 212-374-1313. (U.K. addr.: Book Representation & Distribution, Ltd., 244 A London Rd., Hadleigh, Essex SS7 2DE, England. TEL 702-552912. FAX 702-556095) Eds. James Malloy, Eduardo Gamarra. adv.; bk.rev.; bibl.; charts; illus.; stat.; index. (back issues avail.)
    Description: Comprehensive analysis of events and trends by scholars, journalists and area experts.

LATIN AMERICAN TIMES. see *BUSINESS AND ECONOMICS — International Commerce*

327   US   ISSN 1066-1344
E184.S75   CODEN: LSTJEZ
LATINO STUDIES JOURNAL. 1990. 3/yr. $30 to individuals; institutions $40. Latino, Latin American & Caribbean Studies, Northeastern University, Dept. of Sociology & Anthropology, 521 Holmes Hall, Boston, MA 02115. Ed. Felix Padilla. adv.; bk.rev.
Refereed Serial

LAW OF THE SEA INSTITUTE. OCCASIONAL PAPER. see *LAW — Maritime Law*

LAW OF THE SEA INSTITUTE. PROCEEDINGS OF THE ANNUAL CONFERENCE. see *LAW — Maritime Law*

LAWYERS' COMMITTEE ON NUCLEAR POLICY NEWSLETTER. see *LAW*

LEADERS. see *BUSINESS AND ECONOMICS — International Commerce*

327   UK
LEAGUE SENTINEL. 1989. bi-m. £4 (foreign £5). (League of St. George) League Enterprises, 27 Old Gloucester St., London WC1N 3XX, England. Ed. E. Shepherd. circ. 500. (looseleaf format; back issues avail.) **Document type:** newsletter.
Description: British and European nationalist political newsletter combining fascist and national socialist ideas.

327   US   ISSN 1043-5913
DS80.A2
LEBANON NEWS (ARABIC EDITION). 1981. w. $50. Lebanese Information and Research Center, 1730 M St., N.W., Ste. 807, Washington, DC 20036. TEL 202-785-6666. FAX 202-785-6628. TELEX 64427-LEBANON WSH. Ed. Robert Farah. bk.rev. circ. 6,000. **Document type:** newspaper.
Description: Political publication reporting events and their impact on Lebanese political and daily life.

327   US   ISSN 0742-9665
LEBANON NEWS (ENGLISH EDITION). 1978. m. $30. Lebanese Information and Research Center, 1730 M St., N.W., Ste. 807, Washington, DC 20036. TEL 202-785-6666. FAX 202-785-6628. TELEX 64427-LEBANON WSH. Ed. Joseph G. Bou-Saada. circ. 10,000. **Document type:** newsletter.
Description: Political articles, editorials and a daily progress report about events and their effect on Lebanese daily life.

327 956   LE   ISSN 1019-0740
DS80.95
LEBANON REPORT. 1990. m. $37.50 to individuals; institutions $75. Lebanese Center for Policy Studies, Tayyar Bldg., Mkalles, Sin al-Fil, Beirut, Lebanon. TEL 961-1-490561. FAX 961-1-601787. (Subscr. outside Lebanon to: LCPS, Box 1377, Highland Park, NJ 08904, USA. TEL 908-220-0885. FAX 908-937-6697) Ed. Michael Bacos Young. (back issues avail.) **Document type:** newsletter.
Description: Analyzes political, diplomatic, military and economic trends in Lebanon, and developments in the Middle East affecting the Lebanese situation.

LEONARD HORWIN COLLECTION. see *ETHNIC INTERESTS*

327   LO   ISSN 0460-2099
LESOTHO. MINISTRY OF FOREIGN AFFAIRS. DIPLOMATIC AND CONSULAR LIST. 1976. a. $1. Ministry of Foreign Affairs, Maseru, Lesotho. circ. 500.

320   FR
LETTRE DU CONTINENT. 1985. 23/yr. 3250 F.($620) Indigo Publications, 10, rue du Sentier, 75002 Paris, France. TEL 44-88-26-10. FAX 44-88-26-15. Ed. Maurice Botbol. **Document type:** newsletter.
Description: Carries decisive information on French-speaking Africa.

327   FR   ISSN 1157-9676
LETTRE FRANCE - U.R.S.S.. 1945. m. (10/yr.) 180 F. Association France - U.R.S.S., 61 rue Boissiere, 75116 Paris, France. TEL 45-01-59-00. FAX 45-53-28-76. TELEX FRANURS 612950F. adv.; bk.rev. circ. 54,000.
Formerly (until 1991): France U.R.S.S. Magazine (ISSN 0399-9505)

327   FR
PN3
LETTRE INTERNATIONAL. (Supplement to: Politique Aujourd'hui (Paris)) 1984. q. 14-16 rue des Petits-Hotels, 75010 Paris, France.

327 956 945   IT   ISSN 0024-1504
DS63.2.I8
LEVANTE. (Text in Arabic and Italian) 1953. q. L.35000 (foreign L.55000). Centro per le Relazioni Italo-Arabe, Via Caroncini 19, 00197 Rome, Italy. TEL 06-8077291. FAX 06-8078029. Ed. Ilda Ricasoli. adv.; bk.rev.; bibl.; charts; illus.; stat.; cum.index: 1953-1968.
Description: Includes articles written on Italian-Arab relations, with emphasis on Arab culture.

327   CC   ISSN 1003-2282
LIANHEGUO JISHI/UNITED NATIONS CHRONICLE. (Text in Chinese) 1984. q. Zhongguo Duiwai Fanyi Chuban Gongsi, No. 4, Taipingqiao Dajie, Beijing 100810, People's Republic of China. TEL 662134. Ed. Zheng Yuzhi.

LIBERATION. see *POLITICAL SCIENCE — Civil Rights*

327.666   LB   ISSN 0300-2241
JX1122
LIBERIA. DEPARTMENT OF STATE. NEWSLETTER.* 1974. w. free. Department of State, Monrovia, Liberia. circ. 500.

354   LB
LIBERIA. MINISTRY OF FOREIGN AFFAIRS. ANNUAL REPORT.* a. Ministry of Foreign Affairs, Monrovia, Liberia.

327   GW   ISSN 0341-9762
LIBERTAS; European review. (Text in English and German) 1976. q. DM.60. Libertas Verlag, Hintere Gasse 35-1, 71063 Sindelfingen, Germany. TEL 07031-811855. FAX 07031-813693. TELEX 7265320-HJZD. Ed. Hans-Juergen Zahorka. adv.; bk.rev. circ. 1,400. **Indexed:** CERDIC, ELLIS, Int.Polit.Sci.Abstr., Sociol.Abstr. **Document type:** bulletin.
Description: Quarterly on European and international politics, economics, philosophy, social science and legal issues in favor of European integration and Atlantic alliance.

LIBERTY AT BAY; issues impacting on freedom in our time. see *BUSINESS AND ECONOMICS — Economic Situation And Conditions*

956   US   ISSN 0024-4007
DS119.7
LINK (NEW YORK). 1967. bi-m. $35. Americans for Middle East Understanding, Inc., 475 Riverside Dr., Rm. 570, New York, NY 10115. TEL 212-870-2336. FAX 212-870-2050. Ed. J. Mahoney. bk.rev.; abstr.; bibl.; illus. circ. 50,000. **Indexed:** High.Educ.Curr.Aware.Bull., HR Rep. —Faxon; UnCover.

327 350   NE   ISSN 0927-202X
LOKAAL & MONDIAAL - VAKMATIG. 1992. 4/yr. fl.39.50 (effective 1994). V N G Uitgeverij, P.O. Box 30435, 2500 GK The Hague, Netherlands. TEL 31-70-3738888. FAX 31-70-3462901. Eds. P. Knip, E.J. Hertogs. adv.; bk.rev. circ. 1,000. (back issues avail.) **Document type:** trade publication.
Description: For specialists in the field of international cooperation and development assistance.

327 355 341   UK   ISSN 0966-2847
JF195.C5
LOW INTENSITY CONFLICT & LAW ENFORCEMENT. 1992. 3/yr. £40($50) to individuals; institutions £95 ($135) (effective 1996). Frank Cass, Newbury House, 890-900 Eastern Ave., Newbury Park, Ilford, Essex IG2 7HH, England. TEL 44-181-599-8866. FAX 44-181-599-0984. E-mail: 100067,1576@compuserve.com. Ed. Graham H. Turbiville, Jr. adv.; B&W page £195 ($275); adv. contact: Anne Kidson. bk.rev.; index. (back issues avail.) **Indexed:** Int.Polit.Sci.Abstr. **Document type:** academic/scholarly publication. —BLDSC (5296.459200). CCC.
Description: Addresses a range of military, security, and law-enforcement issues associated with conflict short of general war.
Refereed Serial

327   RM   ISSN 1220-4366
LUMEA. (Text in English, French, German, Rumanian, Russian, Spanish) 1963. w. 104 lei($18) (Uniunea Ziaristilor din Romania) Rompres, the National Press Agency, Piata Presei Libere 1, 71341 Bucharest, Rumania. TEL 185081. (Subscr. to: ILEXIM, P.O. Box 136-137, 13 Decembrie St., No. 3, 11226 Bucharest, Rumania) Ed. Darie Novaceanu. circ. 110,000.
Former titles (until 1991): Lumea Azi (ISSN 1220-4358); (until 1990): Lumea (ISSN 0459-9896)

327 294.392   SZ   ISSN 1018-9904
LUNGTA. (Editions in English, French) 2/yr. 25 SFr. to Switzerland and Europe; rest of world 30 SFr. Amnye Machen Institute, P.O. Box 188, CH-1401 Yverdon-les-Bains, Switzerland. TEL 024-219019. (Co-sponsor: Comite Suisse de Soutien au Peuple Tibetain) Ed. Jamyang Norbu. adv. contact: Sean Jones. **Document type:** academic/scholarly publication.
Description: Publishes articles on the arts, literature, culture and history of Tibet.

327   PH
M F A REVIEW.* 1974. m. (Ministry of Foreign Affairs) Office of Press and Public Affairs, Dept. of Foreign Affairs, PICC Bldg., Agrifina Circle, Manila, Philippines.

016.3   DK   ISSN 0900-5099
M S BIBLIOTEKSNYT. 1968. 12/yr. DKK 230 to individuals; institutions DKK 450. Mellemfolkeligt Samvirke - Danish Association for International Co-operation, Borgergade 14, DK-1300 Copenhagen K, Denmark. TEL 45-33-32-62-44. FAX 45-33-15-62-43. bk.rev. circ. 600.
Description: Registers and annotates 1,800 books and 3,000 articles on Third World affairs.

327   CN
MCNAUGHTON PAPERS; the Canadian journal of strategic studies. 2/yr. Can.$15. Canadian Institute of Strategic Studies, 76 St. Clair Ave., W., Ste. 502, Toronto, ON M4V 1N2, Canada. TEL 416-964-6632. FAX 416-964-5833. E-mail: ciss@inforomp.net. Ed. Alex Morrison. adv. contact: Mark Larsen. **Document type:** academic/scholarly publication.

327   FR   ISSN 1150-4447
MAGHREB CONFIDENTIEL. 1990. w. (46/yr.). 2750 F.($500) Indigo Publications, 10 rue du Sentier, 75002 Paris, France. TEL 33-1-44-88-26-10. FAX 33-1-44-88-26-15. Ed. Maurice Botbol. circ. 1,000. (back issues avail.)
Description: Insight into the politics and economy of North African countries.

327   HU   ISSN 0541-9220
DB956
MAGYAR KULPOLITIKAI EVKONYV. 1968. a. $7.20. Magyar Kulugyminiszterium, Doumentacios Foosztaly, Hungary. (Dist. by: Kultura, I. Fo utca 32, 1011 Budapest, Hungary)

327 300   GW   ISSN 0542-6758
MARE BALTICUM. 1965. a. DM.15. Ostsee-Akademie Travemuende, Europaweg 3, 23570 Luebeck, Germany. TEL 04502-803203. FAX 04502-803200. Ed. Joerg Hackmann. adv.; bk.rev.; bibl.; charts; illus.; index. circ. 3,000. (back issues avail.) **Document type:** academic/scholarly publication.

327   IS
MARJORIE MAYROCK CENTER FOR SOVIET AND EAST EUROPEAN RESEARCH. OCCASIONAL PAPERS. (Text in English) irreg. price varies. Hebrew University, Marjorie Mayrock Center for Soviet and East European Research, c/o Faculty of Social Sciences, Mount Scopus, Jerusalem 91905, Israel. TEL 972-2-883180. FAX 972-2-322545. TELEX 26458. **Document type:** academic/scholarly publication.

327   GW
MATERIALIEN ZUM INTERNATIONALEN KULTURAUSTAUSCH/STUDIES IN INTERNATIONAL CULTURAL RELATIONS. 1972. irreg. Institut fuer Auslandsbeziehungen, Charlottenplatz 17, 70173 Stuttgart, Germany. TEL 0711-2225112. FAX 0711-2264346. Ed. Susanne Sporrer. (back issues avail.) **Document type:** monographic series.

POLITICAL SCIENCE — INTERNATIONAL RELATIONS

---

327 **MF** ISSN 0085-3194
MAURITIUS DIRECTORY OF THE DIPLOMATIC CORPS. 1969. a. Rs.30. (Ministry of External Affairs, Tourism and Immigration) Government Printing Office, Port Louis, Mauritius. (Subscr. to: La Tour Koenig, Pointe aux Sables, Port Louis, Mauritius. TEL 2345294. FAX 2084011) circ. 400. **Document type:** government publication, directory.

MEDIA CRITIC; a critical review of the news media's recent coverage of the world political economy. see *BUSINESS AND ECONOMICS — Economic Situation And Conditions*

MEDICINE AND WAR. see *MEDICAL SCIENCES*

327 **US** ISSN 1047-4552
D839
MEDITERRANEAN QUARTERLY; a journal of global issues. 1989. q. $24 to individuals (foreign $36); institutions $44 (foreign $56); students $12 (foreign $24) (effective 1996). Duke University Press, Box 90660, Durham, NC 27708-0660. TEL 919-687-3600. FAX 919-688-4574. Ed. Nikolaos A. Stavrou. **Indexed:** Int.Polit.Sci.Abstr., Polit.Sci.Abstr. **Document type:** academic/scholarly publication.
—BLDSC (5534.743000); Faxon; UnCover.
Refereed Serial

327 **YU** ISSN 0025-8555
D839
MEDJUNARODNI PROBLEMI. English edition (ISSN 0352-5554) (Text in Serbo-Croatian; summaries in English and Russian) 1959. q. 520 din. Institut za Medjunarodnu Politiku i Privredu - Institute of International Politics and Economics, Makedonska 25, P.O. Box 750, Belgrade, Yugoslavia. Ed. Brana Markovic. **Indexed:** A.B.C.Pol.Sci., Amer.Hist.& Life, Hist.Abstr., Int.Polit.Sci.Abstr.

327 **DK** ISSN 0904-9789
MELLEMOEST INFORMATION. 1984. m. DKK 1000. Odense Universitet, Mellemoest Information, Campusvej 55, 5230 Odense M, Denmark. FAX 09-158928. TELEX 59918. Ed. Charlotte Wien. **Document type:** newsletter.
Former titles (until 1989): Arabiske Verden. (ISSN 0901-1374); (until 1985): Odense Universitet. Arabisk Informationscenter. Nyhedsbrev (ISSN 0109-582X)

MEZINARODNI POLITIKA. see *POLITICAL SCIENCE*

MIDDLE EAST: ABSTRACTS AND INDEX. see *ABSTRACTING AND INDEXING SERVICES*

MIDDLE EAST CONTEMPORARY SURVEY. see *HISTORY — History Of The Near East*

327 **US** ISSN 0731-9371
D839
MIDDLE EAST INSIGHT. 1980. bi-m. $27 to individuals; institutions and corporations $50. International Insight, Inc., 1200 18th St., N.W., Washington, DC 20036-2506. TEL 202-466-2146. FAX 202-466-2147. TELEX 201962 NEIN UR. E-mail: mideast@dgs.dgsys.com. Ed. George A. Nader. adv.; bk.rev. circ. 5,000. (back issues avail.) **Indexed:** P.A.I.S., Polit.Sci.Abstr.
—BLDSC (5761.376800).
Description: Covers contemporary Middle East developments for businessmen, diplomats and observers.

---

327 **US** ISSN 0026-3141
DS1
MIDDLE EAST JOURNAL. 1947. q. $30 to individuals; institutions $40. Middle East Institute, 1761 N St., N.W., Washington, DC 20036. TEL 202-785-0191. Ed. Mary-Jane Deeb. adv.; bk.rev.; bibl.; charts; index, cum.index: 1947-1966, 1967-1977. circ. 4,500. (also avail. in microform from UMI; reprint service avail. from SCH,UMI) **Indexed:** A.B.C.Pol.Sci., A.I.C.P., Acad.Ind., Amer.Bibl.Slavic & E.Eur.Stud., Amer.Hist.& Life, Bibl.Ling., Bk.Rev.Ind. (1965-), Child.Bk.Rev.Ind. (1965-), Curr.Cont., Curr.Cont.M.E., Documentatieblad, G.Soc.Sci.& Rel.Per.Lit., Geo.Abstr., Hist.Abstr., Hum.Ind., IDA, Int.Lab.Doc., Int.Polit.Sci.Abstr., Key to Econ.Sci., Mid.East: Abstr.& Ind., P.A.I.S., Popul.Ind., Ref.Sour., Rural Recreat.Tour.Abstr., Soc.Sci.Ind., SSCI, World Agri.Econ.& Rural Sociol.Abstr. **Document type:** academic/scholarly publication.
●Also available online. Vendor(s): University Microfilms International.
—BLDSC (5761.380000); Faxon; Genuine Article; SWETS; UMI; UnCover.

327 **US** ISSN 0026-315X
MIDDLE EAST MONITOR. 1971. m. $98. Middle East Monitor, Box 236, Ridgewood, NJ 07451-0236. FAX 808-545-1058. Ed. Amir N. Ghazaii. (also avail. in microfiche; back issues avail.) **Document type:** newsletter.
—BLDSC (5761.390080); UMI.

MIDDLE EAST OBSERVER. see *BUSINESS AND ECONOMICS*

382 327 **US** ISSN 1061-1924
DS41
MIDDLE EAST POLICY. 1982. q. $35 in U.S. and Canada; elsewhere $55; newsstand price: $7.95. Middle East Policy Council, 1730 M St., N.W., Ste. 512, Washington, DC 20036. TEL 202-296-6767. FAX 202-296-5791. TELEX 440506-AMARA-UI. Ed. Anne Joyce. adv. contact: Anne Joyce. bk.rev.; cum.index: 1982-1993 in vol.46; circ. 7,500 (controlled). (also avail. in microform from UMI; reprint service avail. from WSH) **Indexed:** A.B.C.Pol.Sci., Bk.Rev.Ind. (1983-), Child.Bk.Rev.Ind. (1983-), Curr.Cont.M.E., HR Rep. (1989-1991) Ind.Islam., Int.Polit.Sci.Abstr., Mid.East: Abstr.& Ind., P.A.I.S., Per.Islam. (1991-), Polit.Sci.Abstr. **Document type:** academic/scholarly publication.
—BLDSC (5761.400200); Faxon; UMI; UnCover.
Formerly (until 1992): American Arab Affairs (ISSN 0731-6763)
Description: Provides viewpoints on recent developments that affect U.S. - Middle East policy.

956 **US** ISSN 0026-3230
MIDEAST REPORT.* 1967. s-m. $385 (foreign $410). MidEast Report, Inc., 3 Coppel Dr., Ste. 602, Tenafly, NJ 07670-2903. TEL 212-714-3530. FAX 212-714-3510. TELEX 236328 MIDE UR. Ed. Jocelyne Mizrahi. (processed)

MIGRANTENSTUDIES. see *ETHNIC INTERESTS*

320.9 **UK** ISSN 0026-3737
MILAP WEEKLY. 1965. w. £65. 59-61 Broughton Rd., Fulham, London SW6 2LA, England. Ed. Ramesh Kumar Soni. adv.; bk.rev.; film rev.; tr.lit. circ. 70,000. (avail. on records) **Document type:** newspaper.

320.5 **FR** ISSN 0026-3877
MILITANT; revue nationaliste pour la defense de l'identite francaise et europeenne. 1967. s-m. 300 F. (foreign 475 F.) (effective 1995). B.P. 154, 75463 Paris Cedex 10, France. TEL 42-39-14-49. Ed. M. Vernhettes. adv.; bk.rev.; illus. circ. 2,000. **Document type:** newspaper.
Description: Covers world news of a political or nationalistic nature.

327 355 **SZ**
MILIZ; das Magazin fuer Sicherheits- und Friedenspolitik. 4/yr. 53 SFr. Miliz Verlags AG, Postfach, CH-8040 Zurich, Switzerland. TEL 01-4510700. FAX 01-4512313. Ed. Toni Wagner. adv. contact: Rainer Kupper. **Document type:** consumer publication.

---

327 **UK** ISSN 0305-8298
JX1 CODEN: MILLFB
MILLENNIUM; journal of international studies. 1971. 3/yr. £20($33) to individuals; institutions £45($75); students £12($20). (London School of Economics & Political Science) Millennium Publishing Group, Houghton St., London WC2A 2AE, England. TEL 0171-955-7438. FAX 0171-955-7446. Eds. Eivind Hovden, Ed Keene. adv. contact: Milena Dragicevii. bk.rev.; index. circ. 900. (also avail. in microfilm from UMI) **Indexed:** A.B.C.Pol.Sci., A.I.C.P., Abstr.Mil.Bibl., Amer.Hist.& Life, Br.Hum.Ind., Hist.Abstr., Int.Polit.Sci.Abstr., Intl.Ind.TV, P.A.I.S., Polit.Sci.Abstr. **Document type:** academic/scholarly publication.
—BLDSC (5773.945000); Faxon; Genuine Article; SWETS; UMI; UnCover.

MIROVAYA EKONOMIKA I MEZHDUNARODNYE OTNOSHENIYA. see *BUSINESS AND ECONOMICS*

327 **NE** ISSN 0165-6546
DS611
MOESSON; onafhankelijk Indisch tijdschrift. 1958. s-m. fl.95. Tjalie Robinson B.V., Bergstraat 27, 3811 NE Amersfoort, Netherlands. TEL 31-33-611611. Ed. Vivian Boon. adv.; bk.rev.; bibl.; charts; illus. circ. 7,500.
Formerly: Tong-Tong (ISSN 0040-9189)

327 **FR** ISSN 0026-9395
JX3
LE MONDE DIPLOMATIQUE. 1954. m. 210 F. (foreign 270 F.). Monde, 5 rue Antoine Bourdelle, 75015 Paris, France. TEL 1-40-65-25-25. FAX 1-45-48-23-96. TELEX 650 572. (Subscr. to: Immeuble Sirius, 1 place Hubert-Beuve-Mery, 94852 Ivry-sur-Seine Cedex, France. TEL 49-60-32-90) Ed. Micheline Paunet. illus.; index. circ. 165,000. (also avail. in microfilm from RPI) **Indexed:** ELLIS, HR Rep. (1990-), Int.Lab.Doc., Pt.de Rep. (1979-), Refug.Abstr.
—SWETS.

327 614 **US** ISSN 1042-3249
MONTHLY PLANET.* 1985. m. $15. Nuclear Weapons Freeze of Santa Cruz County, 320 Cedar St., Ste. G., Santa Cruz, CA 95060-4362. TEL 408-429-8755. Ed. John Govsky. adv.; bk.rev.; illus.; index. circ. 15,000. (tabloid format; back issues avail.)
●Also available online.
Description: Covers the peace movement and disarmament worldwide, with a focus on local grassroots activism.

327 **BE** ISSN 1021-4224
MONTHLY REPORT ON EUROPE. French edition: Rapport Mensuel sur l'Europe (ISSN 0259-7527) (Text in English) m. 20300 BEF (effective 1995). Europe Information Service, Rue de Geneve, 6, 1140 Brussels, Belgium. TEL 32-2-242-6020. FAX 32-2-242-9410. **Indexed:** ELLIS.
Description: Reviews of noteworthy institutional, legislative, monetary, business and political events and developments in the EU.

327 **IS**
MOSHE DAYAN CENTER FOR MIDDLE EASTERN AND AFRICAN STUDIES. BULLETIN. (Text in English) s-a. free. Tel Aviv University, Moshe Dayan Center for Middle Eastern and African Studies, P.O. Box 39012, Tel Aviv 69978, Israel. TEL 972-3-6409646. FAX 972-3-6415802. **Document type:** bulletin.

POLITICAL SCIENCE — INTERNATIONAL RELATIONS

980 US ISSN 1071-4839
F1401
N A C L A REPORT ON THE AMERICAS. 1967. bi-m. $27 to individuals; institutions $50. North American Congress on Latin America, Inc., 475 Riverside Dr., Rm. 454, New York, NY 10115. TEL 212-870-3146. FAX 212-870-3305. Ed. Fred Rosen. adv. contact: Deborah Elman. bk.rev.; abstr.; charts. circ. 11,000. (also avail. in microfilm from UMI; back issues avail.; reprint service avail. from UMI) **Indexed:** Alt.Press Ind., Hisp.Amer.Per.Ind. (1972-), HR Rep., Left Ind. (1982-), P.A.I.S., Peace Res.Abstr., Polit.Sci.Abstr., Soc.Sci.Ind. (1994-). **Document type:** consumer publication.
—BLDSC (6011.315600); Faxon; SWETS; UMI; UnCover.
Former titles: Report on the Americas (ISSN 1058-5397); N A C L A Report on the Americas (ISSN 0149-1598); N A C L A's Latin America and Empire Report (ISSN 0095-5930); N A C L A News (ISSN 0048-0630)
Description: Provides coverage of political, social and economic conditions in Latin America, including opposition movements, the impact of U.S. foreign policy, multinational investments, human rights developments, and historical and cultural issues.

N A F S A GOVERNMENT AFFAIRS BULLETIN. (National Association for Foreign Student Affairs) see *EDUCATION — International Education Programs*

N A F S A NEWSLETTER. (National Association for Foreign Student Affairs) see *EDUCATION*

355 BE
N A T O BASIC DOCUMENTS/O T A N DOCUMENTS FONDAMENTAUX. 1975. irreg. North Atlantic Treaty Organization, Office of Information and Press, B-1110 Brussels, Belgium. TEL 32-2-7284567.

N A T O DATA. see *MILITARY*

355 BE
N A T O FINAL COMMUNIQUES/O T A N COMMUNIQUES FINALS. 1970. a. North Atlantic Treaty Organization, Office of Information and Press, 1110 Brussels, Belgium. TEL 32-2-7284567.

355 BE ISSN 0549-7175
JX1393
N A T O HANDBOOK. French ed.: Manuel de l' O T A N. (Editions in various languages) 1952. irreg. free. North Atlantic Treaty Organization, Office of Information and Press, B-1110 Brussels, Belgium. TEL 32-2-7284111. FAX 32-2-7284579. TELEX 23-867.

327 355 GW ISSN 0169-1821
UA646
N A T O'S SIXTEEN NATIONS. (North Atlantic Treaty Organization) 1955. 6/yr. DM.105($76) Moench Verlagsgesellschaft mbH, Postfach 140261, 53057 Bonn, Germany. TEL 0228-6483-0. FAX 0228-6483109. TELEX 8869429-MVB-D. Ed. Frederick Bonnart. adv.: B&W page $4600, color page $8500; trim 10 5/8 x 7 5/16; adv. contact: Ute Steuer. circ. 22,921. **Indexed:** Abstr.Mil.Bibl., Air Un.Lib.Ind., DM & T, Mid.East: Abstr.& Ind. **Document type:** trade publication.
—BLDSC (6033.701000); UnCover.
Formerly: N A T O's Nations.

327 NO ISSN 0800-0018
D839
N U P I NOTAT. Variant title: N U P I Working Paper. (Text in English, Norwegian) 1970. irreg. no.522, 1995. NOK 40. Norsk Utenrikspolitisk Institutt - Norwegian Institute of International Affairs, Postboks 8159, Dep., N-0033 Oslo, Norway. TEL 47-22-17-70-50. FAX 47-22-17-70-15. E-mail: PUB@NUPI.NO. **Indexed:** Abstr.Mil.Bibl.
—BLDSC (6187.026200).

327 NO ISSN 0804-7235
N U P I RAPPORT. (Text in English, Norwegian) irreg., no.188, 1995. NOK 150. Norsk Utenrikspolitisk Institutt - Norwegian Institute of International Affairs, Postboks 8159, Dep., 0033 Oslo 1, Norway. TEL 47-22-17-70-50. FAX 47-22-17-70-15. E-mail: PUB@NUPI.NO.
Former titles (until 1994): N U P I Forskningsrapport (ISSN 0803-8503); (until 1992): N U P I Rapport (ISSN 0800-000X)

NAJDA NEWSLETTER. see *WOMEN'S INTERESTS*

327 US
NATIONAL COMMITTEE ON U.S.-CHINA RELATIONS. NOTES FROM THE NATIONAL COMMITTEE. 1969. 3/yr. $5. National Committee on U.S.-China Relations, Inc., 777 U.N. Plaza, New York, NY 10017. TEL 212-922-1385. FAX 212-557-8258. Ed.Bd. bk.rev.; charts. circ. 3,000.
Formerly: National Committee on U.S. China Relations. Highlights of Notes.
Description: Reports on committee activities and current trends in China.

327 US ISSN 0884-9382
E840
NATIONAL INTEREST. 1985. q. $26 (effective 1994). National Affairs, Inc., 1112 16th St., N.W., Ste. 540., Washington, Washington, DC 20036. TEL 202-467-4884. FAX 202-467-0006. (Subscr. to: Box 3000, Dept. NI, Denville, NJ 07834) Ed.Bd. adv.; bk.rev. circ. 6,000. (also avail. in microform from UMI; back issues avail.) **Indexed:** Amer.Hist.& Life, Hist.Abstr., Int.Polit.Sci.Abstr., P.A.I.S., Polit.Sci.Abstr., Polit.Sci.Abstr., Soc.Sci.Ind. (1994-). **Document type:** academic/scholarly publication.
—BLDSC (6025.934000); Faxon; SWETS; UMI; UnCover.
Description: Presents analyses of American foreign policy and of issues that confront the U.S.

NATIONAL POLICY WATCH. see *POLITICAL SCIENCE*

327 UK ISSN 1353-7113
▼**NATIONALISM & ETHNIC POLITICS.** 1995. q. £35($45) to individuals; institutions £95 ($125) (effective 1996). Frank Cass, 890-900 Eastern Ave., Newbury Park, Ilford, Essex IG2 7HH, England. TEL 44-181-599-8866. FAX 44-181-599-0984. E-mail: 100067,1576@compuserve.com. Ed. William Safran. adv.: B&W page £195 ($275); adv. contact: Anne Kidson. bk.rev.; index. **Document type:** academic/scholarly publication.
—BLDSC (6033.445900).
Description: Explores the varied political aspects of nationalism and ethnicity, comparing and contrasting state and community claims and dealing with such factors as citizenship, race, religion, economic development, immigration, language, and the international environment.
Refereed Serial

NEAR EAST FOUNDATION. ANNUAL REPORT. see *BUSINESS AND ECONOMICS — International Development And Assistance*

956 296.7 US ISSN 0028-176X
DS41
NEAR EAST REPORT; a Washington newsletter on American policy in the Middle East. 1957. bi-w. $50. Near East Research, Inc., 440 First St., N.W., Ste. 607, Washington, DC 20001. TEL 202-639-5200. FAX 202-347-4916. Ed. Raphael Danziger. adv. contact: Diana Ball. bk.rev.; index. circ. 55,000. (also avail. in microfilm from UMI; reprint service avail. from UMI) **Indexed:** HR Rep., Ind.Jew.Per. **Document type:** newspaper.
—UMI.

327 US ISSN 0748-4526
HD42 CODEN: NEJOEQ
NEGOTIATION JOURNAL; on the process of dispute settlement. 1985. q. $225 (foreign $265) (effective 1996). (Program on Negotiation) Plenum Publishing Corp., 233 Spring St., New York, NY 10013-1578. TEL 212-620-8000. FAX 212-463-0742. TELEX 23-421139. Ed. Jeffrey Z. Rubin. adv.; bibl. (also avail. in microfilm from JSC; back issues avail.; reprint service avail. from WSH) **Indexed:** Crim.Just.Abstr., Curr.Cont., Int.Polit.Sci.Abstr., Polit.Sci.Abstr., Psychol.Abstr. (1991-). **Document type:** academic/scholarly publication.
—BLDSC (6075.154000); Faxon; Genuine Article; SWETS; UMI; UnCover. **CCC**
Refereed Serial

327 GW ISSN 0548-2801
NEUE HEIMAT. 1973. bi-m. (Vereinigung fuer Verbindungen mit Buergern deutscher Herkunft in Ausland) Verlag Zeit im Bild, Julian Grimau-Allee 10, 8010 Dresden, Germany. Ed. Heinz Vierich. charts; illus. circ. 12,000.

NEW CENTURY. see *BUSINESS AND ECONOMICS*

NEW HAVEN STUDIES IN INTERNATIONAL LAW AND WORLD PUBLIC ORDER. see *LAW — International Law*

327 UK ISSN 0305-9529
D839
NEW INTERNATIONALIST. 1970. m. £22.70($35.58) to individuals; institutions £45($60). New Internationalist Publications Ltd., 55 Rectory Rd., Oxford OX4 1BW, England. TEL 01865-728181. FAX 01865-793152. E-mail: greennet@newint. (Canadian addr.: 35 Riviera Dr., Unit 17, Markham, Ont. L3R 8N4. TEL 416-946-0406. FAX 416-946-0410; U.S. addr.: Box 1143, Lewiston, NY 14092. TEL 905-946-0407. FAX 905-946-0410) Ed.Bd. adv. contact: Alison Ware. bk.rev.; film rev.; charts; illus.; stat.; index. circ. 65,000. (back issues avail.) **Indexed:** Alt.Press Ind., Gdlns., Geo.Abstr., Int.Lab.Doc., Mid.East: Abstr.& Ind., Peace Res.Abstr., Rural Recreat.Tour.Abstr., World Agri.Econ.& Rural Sociol.Abstr. **Document type:** consumer publication.
—BLDSC (6084.255000); Faxon; UnCover.
Formerly: Internationalist.
Description: World issues and the relationships between the world's rich and poor nations.

NEW MUSES. see *LITERATURE — Poetry*

341.1 UK ISSN 0028-6990
NEW WORLD. 1958. q. £4. United Nations Association of Great Britain & Northern Ireland, 3 Whitehall Court, London SW1A 2EL, England. TEL 0171-930-2931. FAX 0171-930-5893. TELEX 837883-SPEND-G. Ed. Malcolm Harper. adv. contact: Harold Stern. bk.rev.; illus. circ. 6,000. **Document type:** newsletter.

327 NZ ISSN 0114-4693
NEW ZEALAND. MINISTRY OF EXTERNAL RELATIONS AND TRADE. MOORE REPORT. 1989. m. Ministry of External Relations and Trade, Private Bag 18-901, Wellington, New Zealand. TEL 64-4-472-8877. FAX 64-4-473-7412.

327.931 NZ
NEW ZEALAND. MINISTRY OF FOREIGN AFFAIRS AND TRADE. ANNUAL REPORT. (Subseries of: New Zealand. Ministry of Foreign Affairs) a. NZ.$12.80. Ministry of Foreign Affairs and Trade, Private Bag 18-901, Wellington 1, New Zealand. TEL 64-4-4728-877. **Document type:** government publication.
Former titles: New Zealand. Ministry of External Relations and Trade. Annual Report; New Zealand. Ministry of Foreign Affairs. Report.

327 NZ
NEW ZEALAND. MINISTRY OF FOREIGN AFFAIRS AND TRADE. INFORMATION BULLETIN. 1982. irreg. free. Ministry of Foreign Affairs and Trade, Publications, Private Bag 18-901, Wellington, New Zealand. TEL 64-4-472-8877. **Document type:** government publication, bulletin.
Former titles (until no.44, 1994): New Zealand. Ministry of External Relations and Trade. Information Bulletin (ISSN 0114-6203); (until 1989): New Zealand. Ministry of Foreign Affairs. Information Bulletin (ISSN 0111-8315)

354.931 NZ
NEW ZEALAND. MINISTRY OF FOREIGN AFFAIRS AND TRADE. OVERSEAS POSTS; a list of New Zealand representative abroad. s-a. NZ.$26.50. Ministry of Foreign Affairs and Trade, Private Bag 18-901, Wellington, New Zealand. TEL 64-4-472-8877. circ. 1,900. **Document type:** government publication.
Former titles: New Zealand. Ministry of External Relations and Trade. Overseas Posts (ISSN 0114-6971); (until 1989): New Zealand Representatives Overseas (ISSN 0110-201X); Which supersedes in part (in 1975): Overseas Representatives in New Zealand and New Zealand Representatives Overseas.
Description: Lists New Zealand's representatives around the world, including names and contact details.

341 NZ
NEW ZEALAND. MINISTRY OF FOREIGN AFFAIRS AND TRADE. TREATY SERIES. irreg. price varies. Ministry of Foreign Affairs and Trade, Private Bag 18-901, Wellington, New Zealand. TEL 64-4-472-8877. FAX 64-4-473-7412. **Document type:** government publication.
Formerly: New Zealand. Ministry of External Relations and Trade. Treaty Series.

POLITICAL SCIENCE — INTERNATIONAL RELATIONS

327 332.6   NZ
NEW ZEALAND FOREIGN AFFAIRS AND TRADE RECORD. 1992. 11/yr. NZ.$140.80. Ministry of Foreign Affairs and Trade, Private Bag 18-901, Wellington, New Zealand. TEL 64-4-472-8877. circ. 500. **Document type:** government publication.
Formerly: New Zealand External Relations and Trade Record (ISSN 1171-7092)
Description: Contains speeches on foreign policy and trade issues by New Zealand government cabinet ministers and senior officials, plus a diary of events.

327   NZ   ISSN 0113-1044
NEW ZEALAND INSTITUTE OF INTERNATIONAL AFFAIRS. OCCASIONAL PAPER (NO.). 1986. irreg. New Zealand Institute of International Affairs, P.O. Box 600, Wellington, New Zealand. TEL 64-4-4727430. FAX 64-4-4731261.
—BLDSC (6219.114600).

327   NZ   ISSN 0110-0262
D839
NEW ZEALAND INTERNATIONAL REVIEW. 1976. bi-m. NZ.$38 (foreign NZ.$43) (effective until July, 1995). New Zealand Institute of International Affairs, Box 600, Wellington 2, New Zealand. TEL 64-4-4727-430. FAX 644--4731-261. Ed. Ian McGibbon. adv. contact: Ian McGibbon. bk.rev.; circ. 1,500 (controlled). **Indexed:** Abstr.Mil.Bibl., Int.Polit.Sci.Abstr., So.Pac.Per.Ind. **Document type:** bulletin.
—UnCover. CCC.

327   II   ISSN 0971-1341
NEWS REVIEW ON AFRICA. (Text in English) 1986. m. Rs.110. Institute for Defence Studies and Analyses, Sapru House, Barakhamba Rd., New Delhi 110001, India. Ed. Jasjit Singh. circ. 40.

327   II
NEWS REVIEW ON AMERICAS. (Text in English) 1986. m. Rs.110. Institute for Defence Studies and Analyses, Sapru House, Barkhamba Rd., New Delhi 110001, India. Ed. Jasjit Singh. circ. 55.

355   II
NEWS REVIEW ON EAST ASIA. (Text in English) 1968. m. Rs.110. Institute for Defence Studies & Analyses, Sapru House, Barakhamba Rd., New Delhi 110001, India. Ed. Jasjit Singh. circ. 280.
Former titles: News Review on China, Mongolia and the Koreas; News Review on China.

327   II
NEWS REVIEW ON EUROPE & EURASIA. (Text in English) 1972. m. Rs.110. Institute for Defence Studies and Analyses, Sapru House, Barakhamba Rd., New Delhi 110001, India. Ed. Jasjit Singh. circ. 45.
Former titles: News Review on U.S.S.R. and Europe; News Review on North America and Europe; Supersedes in part: News Review on East Asia, Australasia and West Asia.

327   II
NEWS REVIEW ON SOUTH ASIA AND INDIAN OCEAN. (Text in English) 1967. m. Rs.150. Institute for Defence Studies and Analyses, Sapru House, Barakhamba Rd., New Delhi 110001, India. Ed. Jasjit Singh. circ. 150.
Former titles (1972-1977): News Review on South Asia; (1968-1971): News Review on Pakistan.

355.03   II   ISSN 0971-1333
NEWS REVIEW ON SOUTH EAST ASIA, AUSTRALASIA AND INDO-CHINA. (Text in English) 1972. m. Rs.110. Institute for Defence Studies and Analyses, Sapru House, Barakhamba Rd., New Delhi 110001, India. Ed. Jasjit Singh. circ. 80.
Former titles: News Review on South East Asia, and Australasia; News Review on Japan, South East Asia, and Australia; (1969-1972): New Review on Countries Bordering India.

327   II
NEWS REVIEW ON WEST ASIA. (Text in English) 1971. m. Rs.110. Institute for Defence Studies and Analyses, Sapru House, Barakhamba Rd., New Delhi 110001, India. Ed. Jasjit Singh. circ. 80.
Supersedes in part (1970-1972): News Review on East Asia, Australasia and West Asia.

NEWS TIBET. see *ETHNIC INTERESTS*

327   NE   ISSN 0028-9876
NIEUW WERELD NIEUWS. 1968. m. fl.30 (students fl.15). (Nieuwsdienst Morele Herbewapening - Moral Rearmament News Service) Nederlandse Stichting voor Morele Herbewapening, Amaliastr. 10, 2514 JC The Hague, Netherlands. TEL 31-70-3643591. FAX 31-70-3617209. Eds. A.R. Burger, P. Hintzen. adv.; bk.rev.; illus. circ. 1,750. **Document type:** newsletter.
Description: News and reports of events concerning moral rearmament.

327   NR   ISSN 0331-2151
DT515.62
NIGERIA BULLETIN ON FOREIGN AFFAIRS. 1971. s-a. £N90($30) (Nigerian Institute of International Affairs, Library Department) N I I A Press, Kofo Abayomi Rd., G.P.O. Box 1727, Lagos, Nigeria. Ed. D. Nworah. bk.rev.; bibl. (back issues avail.) **Indexed:** Mid.East: Abstr.& Ind. **Document type:** bulletin.
Description: Contains a collection of documents, papers and commentaries about Nigerian foreign policy, edited by the Library Department of the Nigerian Institute of International Affairs.

327 338.91   NR   ISSN 0189-0816
DT30.5
NIGERIA FORUM. 1981. q. £N90($30) (Nigerian Institute of International Affairs, Library Department) N I I A Press, Kofo Aboyomi Rd., G.P.O. Box 1727, Lagos, Nigeria. (Dist. in the U.S. by: First Western Corp., 6323 Beachway Dr., Falls Church, VA 22044) adv.; bk.rev.; bibl.; charts; stat.; index. circ. 3,000. (back issues avail.)
Description: Provides factual and authoritative information about current world issues by scholars, statesmen, soldiers, and university students.

916.69   NR   ISSN 0078-0685
DT515
NIGERIA YEAR BOOK. (Text in English) 1952. a. price varies. Daily Time of Nigeria, P.O. Box 139, Lagos, Nigeria. TEL 900850-9. Ed. Gbenga Odusunya. adv.

327 080   NR   ISSN 0331-6262
JX1
NIGERIAN INSTITUTE OF INTERNATIONAL AFFAIRS. LECTURE SERIES. (Text in English) 1969. irreg., latest no.72. £N15($6) (Library Department) N I I A Press, Kofo Abayomi Rd., G.P.O. Box 1727, Lagos, Nigeria. (Dist. outside Africa by: African Books Collective Ltd., The Jam Factory, 27 Park End St., Oxford OX1 1HU, England. TEL 0865-726686. FAX 0865-793298) **Indexed:** Abstr.Rural Dev.Trop. **Document type:** monographic series.
—BLDSC (5180.568000).

327   NR   ISSN 0331-6254
NIGERIAN INSTITUTE OF INTERNATIONAL AFFAIRS. MONOGRAPH SERIES. (Text in English) 1979. irreg., latest no.14. price varies. N I I A Press, G.P.O. Box 1727, Kofo Aboyomi Rd., Victoria Island, Lagos, Nigeria. (Dist. outside Africa by: African Books Collective Ltd., The Jam Factory, 27 Park End St., Oxford OX1 1HU, England. TEL 0865-726686. FAX 0865-793298; Dist. in the U.S. by: First Western Corp., 6323 Beachway Dr., Falls Church, VA 22044) charts; stat. (back issues avail.) **Document type:** monographic series.

327.05   NR   ISSN 0331-3646
JX18
NIGERIAN JOURNAL OF INTERNATIONAL AFFAIRS. Abbreviated title: N J I A. 1975. s-a. £N90($30) (Nigerian Institute of International Affairs, Library Department) N I I A Press, Kofo Aboyomi Rd., G.P.O. Box 1727, Lagos, Nigeria. (Dist. by: College Press Publishers and Bookshops, 27 Are Ave., New Bodija, P.O. Box 30678, Ibadan, Oyo State, Nigeria. TEL 234-36-231780; Dist. in the U.S. by: First Western Corp., 6323 Beachway Dr., Falls Church, VA 22044) bk.rev.; bibl.; charts; stat.; index. (back issues avail.) **Indexed:** Documentatieblad, Int.Polit.Sci.Abstr. **Document type:** academic/scholarly publication.
Description: Publishes scholarly articles on topics in international affairs, with special sections on official documents.

327   NR   ISSN 0189-5001
JX18
NIGERIAN JOURNAL OF INTERNATIONAL STUDIES. Abbreviated title: N J I S. 1975. s-a. $40. (Nigerian Society of International Affairs) N I I A Press, G.P.O. Box 1727, Lagos, Nigeria. (Dist. by: College Press Publishers and Bookshops, 27 Are Ave., New Bodija, P.O. Box 30678, Ibadan, Oyo State, Nigeria. TEL 234-36-231780; Dist. in U.S. by: First Western Corp., 6323 Beachway Dr., Falls Church, VA 22044) Ed. A. Bolaji Akinyemi. adv.; bk.rev. circ. 1,000. **Document type:** academic/scholarly publication.

327   NR   ISSN 0331-8524
NIGERIAN JOURNAL OF POLITICAL SCIENCE. (Text in English) 1979. s-a. £N7.50($12) Ahmadu Bello University, Department of Political Science, Zaire, Nigeria. Ed. Ibrahim Gambari. circ. 3,000. (back issues avail.)

320   US
NIMITZ LECTURES. irreg. price varies. University of California at Berkeley, International and Area Studies, 2223 Fulton St., 3rd Fl., Berkeley, CA 94720. TEL 415-642-7189. FAX 415-643-7062. E-mail: bojana@uclink2.berkeley.edu. Ed. Bojana Ristich. (back issues avail.) **Document type:** academic/scholarly publication, monographic series.

327 355   US   ISSN 1073-6700
JX1974.73
THE NONPROLIFERATION REVIEW. 1993. q. $40 to individuals; institutions $75. Monterey Institute of International Studies, Center for Nonproliferation Studies, 425 Van Buren St., Monterey, CA 93940. TEL 408-647-4193. FAX 408-647-4199. E-mail: cns@miis.edu. Ed. James Clay Moltz. adv. contact: Sarah J. Diehl. circ. 1,200. **Document type:** academic/scholarly publication.
—BLDSC (6117.340350).
Formed by the merger of (1991-1993): Missile Monitor (ISSN 1060-8273); (1990-1993): Eye on Supply (ISSN 1061-1592)
Description: Features articles by leading academicians and government officials, interviews with nonproliferation experts, and chronologies of weapons development and arms control regimes.
Refereed Serial

322.4   US   ISSN 8755-7428
JX1901
NONVIOLENT ACTIVIST. 1945. bi-m. $15 to individuals (overseas $30); institutions $25 (overseas $40). War Resisters League, 339 Lafayette St., New York, NY 10012-2782. TEL 212-228-0450. FAX 212-228-6193. Ed. Judith Pasternak. adv.: B&W page $300; 8 1/2 x 11. bk.rev.; film rev.; illus.; cum.index. circ. 13,000. (also avail. in microform from UMI; back issues avail.) **Indexed:** Alt.Press Ind., HR Rep.
—UMI.
Formerly (until 1984): W R L News (ISSN 0042-9791)
Description: Provides political analysis from a pacifist perspective.

327   BE   ISSN 0779-6641
NOORD - ZUID CAHIER; tijdschrift voor ontwikkelingssamenwerking. (Text in Flemish) 1974. q. 800 BEF. V.Z.W. Wereldwijd, Arthur Goemaerelei 69, B-2018 Antwerp, Belgium. Ed. Bob Hendrickx. circ. 1,500. **Document type:** bulletin.
Formerly: Tijdschrift voor Ontwikkelingssamenwerking.
Description: Covers all aspects of North-South relations, including population, structural adjustment, food security, democracy.

327   GW   ISSN 0933-1743
NORD - SUED AKTUELL. 1987. q. DM.88. Deutsches Uebersee-Institut, Uebersee-Dokumentation, Neuer Jungfernstieg 21, 20354 Hamburg, Germany. TEL 040-3562593. FAX 040-3562512. Ed. Joachim Betz. **Document type:** academic/scholarly publication.
—BLDSC (6117.730000).

301.29   NO
NORGE-AMERIKA FORENINGEN. YEARBOOK. 1945. a. free. Norway-America Association, Drammensvn. 20C, 0255 Oslo 2, Norway. Ed. Bjorn Heimar. adv.; bk.rev.; illus. circ. 2,000.
Supersedes: Norge-Amerika Foreningen. Report.

NORTE; revista hispanoamericana. see *LITERATURE*

POLITICAL SCIENCE — INTERNATIONAL RELATIONS

355   BE
NORTH ATLANTIC TREATY ORGANIZATION. FACTS AND FIGURES/ALLIANCE ATLANTIQUE. STRUCTURE, FAITS ET CHIFFRES. (Editions i nDutch, English, french, German, Italian, Spanish) 1957. irreg., latest 1989. North Atlantic Treaty Organization, Office of Information and Press, B-1110 Brussels, Belgium. TEL 32-2-7284111.

327   JA
NORTH KOREA DIRECTORY (YEAR); comprehensive guide to North Korean organizations and leadership. (Text in English, Chinese) 1988. a. 6000 Yen($60) (effective Sep. 1993). Radiopress, Inc., 5th Fl., R-Bldg. Shinjuku, 33-8 Wakamatsu-cho, Shinjuku-ku, Tokyo 162, Japan. TEL 03-5273-2171. FAX 03-5273-2180. **Document type:** directory.
   Description: Lists personnel and structural changes in North Korea's government, state organs, political parties, and mass organizations. Lists names in Chinese characters, Roman letters, and Japanese hiragana.

362.87 241.4   NO   ISSN 0804-8754
NORWEGIAN REFUGEE COUNCIL. REPORTS. (Text in English) 1992. 2-6/yr. free. Flyktningeraadet - Norwegian Refugee Council, Pilestredet 15 B, P.O. Box 6758, St. Olavs Plass, N-0130 Oslo, Norway. TEL 47-22-11-65-00. FAX 47-22-11-65-01. Ed. Ove Narvesen. **Document type:** corporate report, proceedings.
   Description: Publishes reports on research, workshops and conferences concerned with refugees worldwide.

327   FR   ISSN 0754-3786
NOUVELLES DU VIETNAM. N.S. 1976. q. Ambassade de la Republique Socialiste du Vietnam en France, 62 rue Boileau, 75016 Paris, France. Dir. M. Aquettaz. illus. circ. 500.
   Formerly: Bulletin du Vietnam.

947 D410   RU   ISSN 0137-0723
NOVOE VREMYA. English edition: New Times (ISSN 0206-1473) (Editions in Czech, English, French, German, Greek, Italian, Polish, Portuguese, Russian, Spanish) 1943. w. $128. Izdatel'sty Dom Novoe Vremya, Pl. Pushkina, Moscow 103782 GSP, Russia. TEL 229-88-72. FAX 095-200-4223. TELEX 411164A NEWT SU. Eds. Aleksandr Pumpyanskii (Rus.ed.), Sergei Goliakov (Eng.ed.). adv.; bk.rev.; bibl.; charts; illus.; index. circ. 100,000. (also avail. in microform from UMI,MIM,BHP) **Indexed:** P.A.I.S.

320.531   IT   ISSN 0029-621X
NUOVA RIVISTA INTERNAZIONALE/NEW INTERNATIONAL REVIEW; problemi della pace e del socialismo. m. L.65000 (L.89000 foreign). (Partito Comunista Italiano) Editori Riuniti, Via Serchio 9-11, 00198 Rome, Italy. TEL 06-866383. FAX 06-8416096. TELEX EDIRIU I 625292. Ed. Bernardino Bernardini. bk.rev. circ. 5,000.

327 960   ET
O A U ECHO. (Text in Arabic, English or French) 1980. m. free. Organization of African Unity, General Secretariat, Press and Information Division, Box 2343, Addis Ababa, Ethiopia. TELEX 21046 OAU. Ed. I. Dagash. circ. 7,500.

327   MM   ISSN 1024-6282
▼**OCCASIONAL PAPERS ON ISLANDS AND SMALL STATES.** 1994. irreg. Foundation for International Studies, Islands and Small States Institute, St. Paul's St., Valletta VLT 07, Malta. **Document type:** monographic series.

327   US
ODYSSEY (BRATTLEBORO). 1972. s-a. free. World Learning, Kipling Rd., Box 676, Brattleboro, VT 05302-0676. TEL 802-257-7751. FAX 802-258-3163. illus. circ. 60,000. **Document type:** newsletter.
   Former titles: Odyssey International (ISSN 0197-1972); Odyssey (ISSN 0473-7881)

OESTERREICH - POLEN, AUSTRIA - POLSKA. see *ETHNIC INTERESTS*

327 DB47   AU   ISSN 1015-616X
OESTERREICHISCHES JAHRBUCH FUER INTERNATIONALE POLITIK. 1960. a. (Oesterreichischen Institut fuer Internationale Politik) Boehlau Verlag GmbH & Co. KG, Sachsenplatz 4-6, Postfach 87, A-1201 Vienna, Austria. TEL 0222-3302427-0. FAX 0222-3302432. TELEX 114506-SPRIW-A. bk.rev.; index. **Indexed:** P.A.I.S.For.Lang.Ind. **Document type:** bulletin.
   Formerly (until 1984): Oesterreichische Zeitschrift fuer Aussenpolitik (ISSN 0029-960X)

327 JN15   EI   ISSN 0378-6986
OFFICIAL JOURNAL OF THE EUROPEAN COMMUNITIES. C SERIES: INFORMATION AND NOTICES; notifications of open competitions. Spanish edition: Diario Oficial de las Comunidades Europeas. C. Comunicaciones e Informaciones (ISSN 0257-7763); Portuguese edition: Jornal Oficial das Comunidades Europeias. C. Comunicaoes e Informacoes (ISSN 0257-7771); German edition: Amtsblatt der Europaeischen Gemeinschaften. C. Mitteilungen und Bekanntmachungen (ISSN 0376-9461); Danish edition: Europiske Faellesskabers Tidende. C. Meddelelser og Oplynsninger (ISSN 0378-7001); Italian edition: Gazzetta Ufficiale delle Comunita Europee. C. Comunicazioni ed Informazioni (ISSN 0378-701X) French edition: Journal Officiel des Communaute Europeenes. C. Communications et Informations (EI ISSN 0378-7052) Dutch edition: Publikatieblad van de Europese Gemeenschappen. C. Mededelingen en Bekendmakingen (EI ISSN 0378-7079) Greek edition: Episeme Efemerida ton Europaikon Koinoteton. C. Anakoinoseies Kai Plerofories (EI ISSN 0250-815X) (Editions in Danish, Dutch, English, French, German, Italian) d. $45. (Commission of the European Communities) Office for Official Publications of the European Communities, L-2985 Luxembourg, Luxembourg. (Dist. in the U.S. by: Unipub, 4611-F Assembly Dr., Lanham, MD 20706-4391. TEL 800-274-4888. FAX 301-459-0056) **Indexed:** Dairy Sci.Abstr., EC Ind., ELLIS, Fuel & Energy Abstr., Intl.Polym.Sci.& Tech., RAPRA, World Surf.Coat., World Text.Abstr. —BLDSC (6239.825000).

327   EI
OFFICIAL JOURNAL OF THE EUROPEAN COMMUNITIES. L & C: LEGISLATION AND COMPETITION. (Editions in Danish, Dutch, English, French, German, Italian) d. $750. Office for Official Publications of the European Communities, L-2985 Luxembourg, Luxembourg. (Dist. in the U.S. by: Unipub, 4611-F, Assembly Dr., Lanham, MD 20706-4391. TEL 800-274-4888. FAX 301-459-0056) (also avail. in microfiche) **Indexed:** Cadscan, EC Ind., ELLIS, Intl.Polym.Sci.& Tech., Lead Abstr., RAPRA, Rural Recreat.Tour.Abstr., World Agri.Econ.& Rural Sociol.Abstr., Zincscan. **Document type:** academic/scholarly publication.
●Also available on CD-ROM.
—BLDSC (6239.830000).
   Formerly: Official Journal of the European Communities. L Series: Legislation (ISSN 0378-6978)

341.1 338   NE   ISSN 0030-3232
ONZE WERELD. 1957. m. fl.79.25. Nederlandse Organisatie voor Internationale Ontwikkelingssamenwerking - Netherlands Organization for International Development Cooperation, Editorial Room, Kloveniersburgwal 23, 1011 JV Amsterdam, Netherlands. FAX 31-20-6251288. Ed. Stan Termeer. adv.; bk.rev.; bibl.; charts; illus.; stat.; index; circ. 41,000 (paid). **Document type:** newspaper.

327   US
OPEN MAGAZINE PAMPHLET SERIES. 1991. every 6 weeks. $35 for 10 nos. to individuals; institutions $40; students $30. Open Media, Box 2726, Westfield, NJ 07091. TEL 908-789-9608. FAX 908-654-3829. Eds. Greg Ruggiero, Stuart Sahulka. circ. 10,000. (back issues avail.) **Document type:** academic/scholarly publication.
   Description: Publishes lecture transcripts, interviews and articles critical of U.S. foreign and domestic policy, presenting scholarly analyses and radical perspectives on the media, the Middle East and struggles against corporate power.

327 333.79   CY
OPERATIONS IN OIL DIPLOMACY. 1972. m. $800 (includes subscr. to A P S News Service, Strategic Balance in the Middle East, Fate of the Arabian Peninsula, Re-Drawing the Islamic Map) (effective 1994-1996). Arab Press Service, P.O. Box 3896, Nicosia, Cyprus. FAX 357-2-350265. s-a. index. **Document type:** bulletin.
   Description: Provides unique surveys of ruling families involved in oil, trade relations, and factors influencing decisions.

327 D839   US   ISSN 0030-4387
ORBIS (GREENWICH); a journal of world affairs. 1957. q. $50 to individuals (foreign $70); institutions $175 (foreign $195) (effective 1996). (Foreign Policy Research Institute) J A I Press Inc., 55 Old Post Rd., No. 2, Box 1678, Greenwich, CT 06836-1678. TEL 203-661-7602. FAX 203-661-0792. (Addr. in Europe: J A I Press Ltd., The Courtyard, 28 High St., Hampton Hill, Mddx. TW12 1PD, England. TEL 44-181-943-9296. FAX 44-181-943-9317) Ed. Patrick L. Clawson. adv.; bk.rev.; charts; illus.; index. circ. 3,500. (also avail. in microform from KTO,UMI; back issues avail.; reprint service avail. from KTO) **Indexed:** A.B.C.Pol.Sci., Abstr.Mil.Bibl., Acad.Ind., Amer.Hist.& Life, ASSIA, Curr.Cont., Fut.Surv., Hist.Abstr., HR Rep., Int.Polit.Sci.Abstr., Key to Econ.Sci., Mid.East: Abstr.& Ind., P.A.I.S., Peace Res.Abstr, Polit.Sci.Abstr., Risk Abstr., Soc.Sci.Ind. **Document type:** academic/scholarly publication.
—BLDSC (6277.850000); Faxon; Genuine Article; SWETS; UMI; UnCover. **CCC.**
   Description: Contains articles on contemporary international affairs.

ORGANIZATION OF AMERICAN STATES. DIRECTORY. see *BUSINESS AND ECONOMICS — Trade And Industrial Directories*

341.18   US
ORGANIZATION OF AMERICAN STATES. GENERAL ASSEMBLY. ACTAS Y DOCUMENTOS. irreg. price varies. Organization of American States, Department of Publications, 1889 F St., N.W., Washington, DC 20006. TEL 703-941-1617. circ. 2,000.

327   US
OUTPOST. 1972. m. membership. Americans for a Safe Israel, 147 E. 76th St., No. 5, New York, NY 10021-2824. TEL 212-628-9400. Ed. Ruth King. bk.rev.; illus. circ. 10,000. (back issues avail.) **Indexed:** So.Pac.Per.Ind. **Document type:** newsletter.

610 327 JC571   US   ISSN 1054-1675
P H R RECORD. 1986. q. $40 (physicians $50; students $15). Physicians for Human Rights, 100 Boylston St., Ste. 702, Boston, MA 02116-4610. TEL 617-695-0041. FAX 617-695-0307. E-mail: phrusa@igc.apc.org. Eds. Susannah Sirkin, Barbara Ayotte. bk.rev. circ. 5,000. (also avail. in microform) **Document type:** newsletter.

P S R MONITOR. (Physicians for Social Responsibility) see *PUBLIC HEALTH AND SAFETY*

P S R REPORTS. (Physicians for Social Responsibility) see *PUBLIC HEALTH AND SAFETY*

362.87 341.4   NO   ISSN 0803-5016
PAA FLUKT - NYHETER. 1991. m. free. Flyktningeraadet - Norwegian Refugee Council, Pilestredet 15 B, P.O. Box 6758, St. Olavs Plass, N-0130 Oslo, Norway. TEL 47-22-11-65-00. FAX 47-22-11-65-01. Eds. Eva Grinde, Ove Narvesen. illus. circ. 6,500. **Document type:** newsletter.
   Description: Publishes news on political refugee situations worldwide.

362.87 341.4   NO   ISSN 0804-6166
▼**PAA FLUKT - TEMA.** 1994. 6/yr. inne. Flyktningeraadet - Norwegian Refugee Council, Pilestredet 15 B, P.O. Box 6758, St. Olavs Plass, Norway. TEL 47-22-11-65-00. FAX 47-22-11-65-01. Eds. Ove Narvesen, Eva Grinde. illus. circ. 7,000. **Document type:** newsletter.
   Description: Each issue is devoted to a single theme on refugees in a specific geographical area.

POLITICAL SCIENCE — INTERNATIONAL RELATIONS

327   FI   ISSN 0355-1849
PAASIKIVI - SERUAN. MONISTESARJA. (Text in Finnish) 1973. irreg., no.107, 1992. Ulkopoliittinen Instituutti, Mannerheim intre 15 A, FIN-00260 Helsinki, Finland. TEL 358-0-490-100. FAX 358-0-490-989. (processed)
  Description: Consists of speeches at the Paasikivi Society.

327 355   AT   ISSN 1031-9379
PACIFIC RESEARCH. 1986. q. Aus.$25 (effective 1996). Peace Research Centre, Research School of Pacific Studies, Australian National University, Canberra, A.C.T. 0200, Australia. TEL 061-6-249-3098. FAX 061-6-249-0174. TELEX A62694. E-mail: peace@commbs.anu.edu.au. Ed. Romesh Thakur. adv.; bk.rev. circ. 2,200. **Indexed:** Aus.P.A.I.S., Int.Polit.Sci.Abstr. **Document type:** academic/scholarly publication.
  Formerly (until May 1988): Peace Research Centre Newsletter (ISSN 0818-2469)
  Description: Critical analysis of defense and foreign policy of all goverments in Asia-Pacific region. Includes arms control, disarmament, and peacekeeping.

057 327   UK   ISSN 0951-2748
DU29
PACIFIC REVIEW. 1988. q. £35 (U.S. and Canada $60; rest of world £37) to individuals; institutions £84 (U.S. and Canada $115; rest of world £88). Routledge, 11 New Fetter Ln., London EC4P 4EE, England. TEL 0171-583-9855. FAX 0171-842-2298. TELEX 263398-ROUT-G. E-mail: sample.journals@routledge.com. (Subscr. to: ITPS Ltd., Cheriton House, Andover, Hants. SP10 5BE, England. TEL 01264-342919. FAX 01264-342807) Ed. Richard Higgott. adv.: page £175; trim 115 x 190. bk.rev. **Indexed:** Asian-Pac.Econ.Lit., Geo.Abstr., IDA, Int.Polit.Sci.Abstr., Polit.Sci.Abstr. **Document type:** academic/scholarly publication.
  —BLDSC (6330.877000); Faxon; SWETS; UMI; UnCover. **CCC.**
  Description: Provides an interdisciplinary forum for the exchange of ideas and trends in Pacific politics, history, military strategy, economics and culture.

327   SI   ISSN 0218-1924
PACIFIC STRATEGIC PAPERS. (Text in English) 1990. irreg., no.8, 1994. price varies. Institute of Southeast Asian Studies, Heng Mui Keng Terrace, Off Pasir Panjang Rd., Singapore 0511, Singapore. TEL 778-0955. FAX 778-1735. TELEX RS 37068 ISEAS. E-mail: pubsunit@merlion.iseas.ac.sg. (Subscr. in U.S. to: Ashgate, Old Post Rd., Brookfield, VT 05036. TEL 802-276-3162) **Document type:** monographic series, academic/scholarly publication.
  —BLDSC (6331.510000).
  Description: Monograph series on regional issues of current interest in the Asian-Pacific region.

327   UK   ISSN 0048-265X
JX1901
PACIFIST. 1961. 6/yr. £6. Peace Pledge Union, 6 Endsleigh St., London, W.C.1, England. Ed. Jan Melichar. bk.rev.; illus. circ. 1,600. (microfilm)
  Incorporating: Peace Pledge Union Newsletter.
  Description: Theory, practice and history of pacifism and non-violence.

327   PK   ISSN 0030-980X
DS376
PAKISTAN HORIZON. (Text in English) 1948. q. Rs.160($32) Pakistan Institute of International Affairs, P.O. Box 1447, Aiwan-i-Sadar Rd., Karachi 74200, Pakistan. Ed. Hafeez R. Khan. adv.; bk.rev.; index. circ. 1,000. (also avail. in microform from UMI; reprint service avail. from UMI) **Indexed:** A.B.C.Pol.Sci., Abstr.Mil.Bibl., Amer.Hist.& Life (until 1993), Hist.Abstr. (until 1993), Int.Lab.Doc., Int.Polit.Sci.Abstr., Mid.East: Abstr.& Ind.
  —UMI.
  Description: Facilitates understanding of international affairs and promotes the scientific study of international issues.

954.91   PK   ISSN 1019-729X
PAKISTAN JOURNAL OF SOCIAL SCIENCE. (Text in English) 1974. s-a. Rs.15($8) Quaid-i-Azam University, Faculty of Science, c/o Bookshop, Bookbank and Publication Cell, Islamabad, Pakistan. **Document type:** academic/scholarly publication.
  Formerly (until 1983): Scrutiny.
  Description: International and Pakistan studies.

PALESTINE REFUGEES TODAY. see SOCIAL SERVICES AND WELFARE

338.025 327   UK   ISSN 0265-458X
PAN-EUROPEAN ASSOCIATIONS; a directory of multi-national organisations in Europe. 1983. irreg., no. 3, 1995. £94($188) C.B.D. Research Ltd., 15 Wickham Rd., Beckenham, Kent BR3 2JS, England. TEL 0181-650-7745. FAX 0181-650-0768. Ed. C.A.P. Henderson. circ. 2,000. **Document type:** directory.
  —BLDSC (6357.371200).

330.9   GW   ISSN 0932-7592
PANEUROPA DEUTSCHLAND. 1977. q. DM.20. (Paneuropa Union und Paneuropa-Jugend) Paneuropa-Verlag, Karlstr. 57, 80333 Munich, Germany. TEL 089-554683. FAX 089-594768. Eds. W. Stock, D. Phil. adv.; bk.rev. circ. 50,000. (back issues avail.)
  Formerly: Paneuropa-Jugend in Paneuropa Deutschland.

341.1   US   ISSN 0031-2568
PARTNERS (WASHINGTON). (Text in English and Spanish) 1967. bi-m. free. Partners of the Americas, 1424 K St., N.W., Washington, DC 20005. TEL 202-628-3300. Ed. Cynthia Kenny. charts; illus. circ. 15,000.

327   GW
PARTNERSCHAFT MIT DER ARABISCHEN WELT; Berichte und Meinungen ueber die Deutsch-Arabische Zusammenarbeit. Arabic edition: Al-Ta'awun Ma'a al Alam al Arabi. (Editions in Arabic and German) 1957. m. free. Inter Nationes e.V., Kennedyallee 91-103, 53175 Bonn, Germany. TEL 0228-880-0. FAX 0228-880457. TELEX 17228308. Ed. Hassan Suliak. circ. 200 (German ed.); 1,000 (Arabic ed.). **Document type:** newsletter.
  Description: Covers German-Arabic political and economic relations.

327 330.9   GW
PATRIKA. (Text in English) 1993. q. free. Indische Botschaft, Adenauerallee 262-264, 53113 Bonn, Germany. TEL 0228-5405146. FAX 0228-5405153. Eds. Debnath Shaw, Suresh Chowdhary. circ. 2,000. **Document type:** newsletter.

341.1   SZ   ISSN 0031-3327
JX1901
PAX ET LIBERTAS. (Text in English) 1925. q. 20 SFr. Women's International League for Peace and Freedom, 1 rue Varembe, CH-1211 Geneva 20, Switzerland. FAX 022-7401063. TELEX 427993-WILDE-CH. Ed. Janet Bruin. adv.; bk.rev. circ. 2,000. (processed) **Document type:** academic/scholarly publication.
  Description: Analyzes economic, social, political and military developments and trends with a focus on women.

327   CU   ISSN 0864-2052
PAZ Y SOBERANIA. 1961. q. free. Cuban Movement for Peace and Sovereignty of Peoples, Linea No. 556, Vedado, Havana, Cuba. TEL 809 32-0506. Ed. Miguel Sosa Herrera.
  Description: Promotes materials on the struggle for peace and freedom and the sovereignty of all cultures.

341.1   US   ISSN 0813-7307
JX1974.7
PEACE ACTION. (Former name of issuing body: SANE - Freeze, Inc.) 1961. 4/yr. $25 to libraries (effective Oct. 1991). Peace Action, 1819 H St., N.W., Ste. 640, Washington, DC 20006-3603. TEL 202-862-9740. FAX 202-862-9762. Ed. Monica Green. bk.rev.; charts; illus. circ. 77,000. (looseleaf format; also avail. in microfilm from UMI; reprint service avail. from UMI) **Document type:** newsletter.
  —UMI.
  Former titles (until 1993): SANE - Freeze News; (until 1990): SANE World - Freeze Focus (ISSN 0036-4304)

327   US   ISSN 0149-0508
JX1901   CODEN: PCHAEG
PEACE & CHANGE; a journal of peace research. 1972. q. $55 to individuals; institutions $145 (effective Sep. 1995). (Consortium on Peace Research, Education and Development) Sage Publications, Inc., 2455 Teller Rd., Thousand Oaks, CA 91320. TEL 216-672-3143. E-mail: libraries@sagepub.com. (Overseas subscr. to: Sage Publications Ltd., 6 Bonhill St., London EC2A 4PU, England; Sage Publications India Pvt. Ltd., P.O. Box 4215, New Delhi 110 048, India) (Co-sponsor: Peace History Society) Eds. Scott L. Bills, Sudarshan Kapoor. adv.; bk.rev. circ. 1,300. (back issues avail.; reprint service avail.) **Indexed:** Abstr.Mil.Bibl., Amer.Hist.& Life, Hist.Abstr., HR Rep., Int.Polit.Sci.Abstr., Mid East: Abstr.& Ind., P.A.I.S., Peace Res.Abstr., Polit.Sci.Abstr., Sage Pub.Admin.Abstr., Sage Urb.Stud.Abstr. **Document type:** academic/scholarly publication.
  —BLDSC (6413.757000); Faxon; UMI; UnCover. **CCC.**
  Description: Publishes scholarly and interpretive articles related to the achieving of a peaceful, just, and humane society. Articles relate to peace and war, social change, conflict resolution, and appropriate justice.

PEACE & DEMOCRACY. see POLITICAL SCIENCE — Civil Rights

341.1   US   ISSN 0015-9093
JX1965
PEACE AND FREEDOM. 1941. q. $12. Women's International League for Peace and Freedom, 1213 Race St., Philadelphia, PA 19107-1691. TEL 215-563-7110. FAX 215-563-5527. E-mail: wilpfnatt@igc.apc.org. (Affiliate: Jane Addams Peace Association) Ed. Wendy Rosenfield. adv.; bk.rev.; charts. circ. 10,000. (also avail. in microform from UMI; reprint service avail. from UMI) **Indexed:** Alt.Press Ind. **Document type:** newsletter.
  —UMI; UnCover.
  Formerly: Four Lights.
  Description: Devoted to the women's peace movement in the U.S. and other countries. Covers the empowerment of women, racism, the redirection of U.S. budget priorities, women's history, feminism and peace.

341.1   UK   ISSN 0031-3491
PEACE AND FREEDOM. N.S. 1952. s-a. £15. Women's International League for Peace and Freedom, 7a Hepburn Rd., Bristol BS2 8UD, England. TEL 0117-942-7878. Ed.Bd. bk.rev. circ. 500. **Document type:** newsletter.

341.1   AU   ISSN 0031-3513
PEACE AND THE SCIENCES. (Text in English) 1970. q. S.380. International Institute for Peace, Moellwaldplatz 5, A-1040 Vienna, Austria. TEL 0431-5046437. FAX 0431-5053236. Ed. Lev Voronkov. bk.rev. circ. 500. (processed) **Indexed:** Int.Polit.Sci.Abstr., Polit.Sci.Abstr. **Document type:** academic/scholarly publication.
  Supersedes: Nuclear Energy.

(YEAR) PEACE CALENDAR; nothing but the truth: activists speak in court. see LITERATURE — Poetry

327   US
PEACE CONVERSION TIMES. 1981. q. $25 to members; low income students $15. Alliance for Survival, 200 N. Main St., Ste. M-2, Santa Ana, CA 92701-4851. FAX 714-547-6322. Ed. Kim Madison. adv.; bk.rev. circ. 8,000. (also avail. in microform)
  Description: Devoted to peace, social justice and safe energy. Features action alerts, children's items and a southern California events calendar.

PEACE CORPS TIMES. see BUSINESS AND ECONOMICS — International Development And Assistance

POLITICAL SCIENCE — INTERNATIONAL RELATIONS

341.1 FI ISSN 0031-594X
PEACE COURIER. (Editions in English, Arabic) 1966. m. $12 to individuals; institutions $30. World Peace Council, Peace Courier ry., WPC Liaisons Office's Information Centre, P.O. Box 114, FIN-00180 Helsinki, Finland. TEL 358-0-6931044. FAX 358-0-6933703. E-mail: Cserve:100144,1501. Ed. Sadhan Mukherjee. adv.; bk.rev.; bibl.; illus.; cum.index. circ. 2,500.
   Description: Reports news of activities fostering peace throughout the world, and discusses problem areas where human rights violations occur. Also provides extensive coverage on worldwide ecological issues and nuclear weapons testing.

PEACE GAZETTE. see *POLITICAL SCIENCE*

327 355 CN ISSN 0826-9521
PEACE MAGAZINE. 1985. 6/yr. Can.$17.50($20) Canadian Disarmament Information Service (CANDIS), 736 Bathurst St., Toronto, ON M5S 2R4, Canada. TEL 416-533-7581. FAX 416-531-6214. E-mail: mspencer@web.apc.org. Ed. Metta Spencer. adv. contact: Brian Burch. bk.rev. circ. 4,000. **Indexed:** Alt.Press Ind., Can.B.P.I.
   Description: Contains articles on military, peace keeping, disarmament.

341.1 AT ISSN 0816-9004
PEACE PLANS. (Text in English, French, German) 1964. irreg. Aus.$1 per microfiche. Libertarian Microfiche Publishing, 35 Oxley St, Berrima, N.S.W. 2577, Australia. TEL 048-771-436. Ed. John M. Zube. adv.; bk.rev.; bibl.; index, cum.index. (microfiche)
   Description: Emphasis on individual rights: individual secessionism, monetary freedom and minority an tuonomy.

PEACE REGISTER. see *POLITICAL SCIENCE — Civil Rights*

327 US ISSN 1049-0779
JX1901
PEACE REPORTER. 1986. q. $35 membership. National Peace Foundation, 1835 K St. N.W., Ste. 610, Washington, DC 20006-1203. TEL 202-223-1770. FAX 202-223-1718. Ed. Kathleen J. Lansing. circ. 15,000. (looseleaf format; back issues avail.) **Document type:** newsletter.
   Formerly (until 1990): Peace Institute Reporter (ISSN 0890-8702)
   Description: Provides information on peace education and developments of other peace programs. Informs members of growth and development of the Foundation and of the US Institute of Peace.

327 CN ISSN 0008-4697
JX1904.5
PEACE RESEARCH. 1969. 4/yr. Can.$24($27) to individuals; institutions Can.$36($39). M.V. Naidu, Ed. & Pub., Brandon University, Brandon, Man. R7A 6A9, Canada. TEL 204-729-9010. FAX 204-726-4573. TELEX 07-502721. adv.; bk.rev.; index. circ. 1,000. (also avail. in microfiche from UMI; reprint service avail.) **Indexed:** Can.B.P.I.
—Faxon; UnCover.
   Description: Scientific and scholarly work on world peace, focusing on the problems of violence, war, armaments, peace movements, human rights, developmental issues, environmental security, nonviolence and peace education.

327 AT
PEACE RESEARCH CENTRE WORKING PAPERS. 1986. irreg. Aus.$4 per no. (Australian National University) Peace Research Centre, Research School of Pacific Studies, Australian National University, Canberra, A.C.T. 0200, Australia. TEL 6-249-3098. FAX 6-249-0174. (back issues avail.) **Document type:** monographic series.

327 CN ISSN 1187-3485
JX1
PEACEKEEPING & INTERNATIONAL RELATIONS. 1972. bi-m. Can.$25($25) Canadian Institute of Strategic Studies, 76 St. Clair Ave. W., Ste. 502, Toronto, ON M4V 1N2, Canada. TEL 416-964-6632. FAX 416-964-5833. E-mail: ciss@inforamp.net. Ed. Alex Morrison. adv. contact: Mark Larsen. bk.rev.; bibl.; illus.; circ. 1,500 (paid). (also avail. in microform from UMI) **Indexed:** Abstr.Mil.Bibl., Amer.Bibl.Slavic & E.Eur.Stud., Amer.Hist.& Life, Can.Per.Ind., CMI, Curr.Cont., Hist.Abstr., Mid.East: Abstr.& Ind., P.A.I.S., Pt.de Rep. **Document type:** academic/scholarly publication.
   ●Also available online. Vendor(s): University Microfilms International.
   —BLDSC (6413.795708); UMI. **CCC.**
   Incorporates: International Perspectives (ISSN 0381-4874); Which incorporates: International Canada (ISSN 0027-0512); Supersedes: External Affairs (ISSN 0014-5432)

341.1 US ISSN 0031-3602
JX1901
PEACEMAKER. 1948. m. $10. Peacemaker Movement, Box 627, Garberville, CA 95440. Eds. Kathy Epling, Paul Encimer. bk.rev. circ. 1,200. (tabloid format; also avail. in microfilm from UMI; reprint service avail. from UMI) **Indexed:** Alt.Press Ind.
—UMI.
   Description: Advocates non-violent resistance to the government.

PEOPLE (KANSAS CITY). see *EDUCATION — International Education Programs*

327 UN ISSN 0252-0079
JX1977.2.A1
PERMANENT MISSIONS TO THE UNITED NATIONS. French edition: Missions Permanentes aupres de l'Organisation des Nations Unies (ISSN 0252-0060) (Subseries of: United Nations. Document) (Text in English) 1966. s-a. $25. United Nations, Protocol Section, Geneva Office - Section du Protocole des Nations Unies a Geneve, Bureau 143, Palais des Nations, CH-1211 Geneva 10, Switzerland. (And: United Nations Sales and Publications, Rm. DC2-853, New York, NY 10017. TEL 212-963-8302) circ. 3,000.

PERSPEKTIVEN D S. (Demokratischen Sozialismus) see *POLITICAL SCIENCE*

327 BO
PERU.* 1972. m. Embajada del Peru en Bolivia, Avda. 6 de Agosto 2190, La Paz, Bolivia. charts; illus.

327 PE
PERU. MINISTERIO DE RELACIONES EXTERIORES. BOLETIN TRIMESTRAL. q. Ministerio de Relaciones Exteriores, Lima, Peru.

PHILIPPINES CHINESE HISTORICAL ASSOCIATION. ANNALS. see *HISTORY — History Of Asia*

327 950 US
THE PHILIPPINES: NEWS AND VIEWS. 1990. s-m. free. Philippine Embassy, 1617 Massachusetts Ave., N.W., Washington, DC 20036. TEL 202-483-1414. Ed. MacArthur F. Corsino. circ. 1,000 (controlled). (tabloid format; back issues avail.)
   Description: Covers Philippine conditions and developments, US-Philippine relations, and Philippine embassy activities.

PITT LATIN AMERICAN SERIES. see *SOCIAL SCIENCES: COMPREHENSIVE WORKS*

PLAIN TRUTH; proclaiming the Gospel of Jesus Christ. see *RELIGIONS AND THEOLOGY — Other Denominations And Sects*

POLEMICAL DOCUMENTS SERIES. see *ETHNIC INTERESTS*

327 GW ISSN 0930-4584
POLEN UND WIR; Zeitschrift fuer Deutsch-Polnische Verstaendigung. 1984. q. DM.20. Deutsche-Polnische Gesellschaft der Bundesrepublik Deutschland e.V., Platanenstr. 21, 40233 Duesseldorf, Germany. TEL 0211-6803073. FAX 0211-6912989. Ed. Christa Huebner. adv. contact: Martin Nene Nooy. bk.rev.; bibl.; illus.; film rev. circ. 2,600.

POLISH-ANGLOSAXON STUDIES. see *HISTORY*

327 PL ISSN 1230-4999
JX18
THE POLISH QUARTERLY OF INTERNATIONAL AFFAIRS. Polish edition: Sprawy Miedzynarodowe (ISSN 0038-853X) (Text in English) 1973. q. $30 to individuals; institutions $50. Polski Instytut Spraw Miedzynarodowych, Warecka 1a, 00-950 Warsaw, Poland. TEL 48-22-278888. FAX 48-22-263026. Ed. Henryk Szlajfer. bk.rev.; bibl. circ. 500. **Indexed:** Int.Polit.Sci.Abstr.
   Former titles (until 1992): International Affairs Studies (ISSN 0867-4493); (until 1991): International Relations (ISSN 0239-2283); (until 1984): Studies on International Relations (ISSN 0324-8283)

320 355 BL ISSN 0102-2636
POLITICA E ESTRATEGIA. 1983. q. $30. Sociedade Brasileira de Cultura, Centro de Estudos Estrategicos, Alameda Eduardo Prado, 705, C.P. 30004, 01218-010 Sao Paulo SP, Brazil. Ed. Antonio Carlos Pereira. adv. circ. 6,000. **Indexed:** Hisp.Amer.Per.Ind. (1989-).

327 BL
POLITICA EXTERNA. 1992. q.? Rua do Triunfo 177, Sta. Ifigenia, 01212 Sao Paulo SP, Brazil. TEL 011-223-6522. FAX 011-233-6290. **Document type:** academic/scholarly publication.
   Description: Forum for debate on important international matters and on Brazil's foreign politics.

327 IT ISSN 0032-3101
POLITICA INTERNAZIONALE. 1969. bi-m. L.100000 (foreign L.120000) (effective 1995). Institute for Relations with Africa, Latin America and the Middle East (IPALMO), Via del Tritone 62-B, 00187 Rome, Italy. TEL 39-6-6792734. FAX 39-6-6797849. (Subscr. to: Licosa, Via Duca di Calabria, 1-1, 50125 Florence, Italy) Ed. Marcello Villari. adv.; bk.rev.; index. circ. 5,000. (back issues avail.) **Indexed:** Abstr.Mil.Bibl., Int.Polit.Sci.Abstr. **Document type:** academic/scholarly publication.
—SWETS.
   Description: Covers relations with developing countries in Africa, Latin America and Middle East.

POLITICAL CROSSROADS; an international socio-political journal. see *POLITICAL SCIENCE*

POLITICAL DIGEST SERIES. see *ETHNIC INTERESTS*

327 947 US
POLITICAL HISTORY OF RUSSIA. 1990. q. $270 (effective 1996). Nova Science Publishers, Inc., 6080 Jericho Tpke., Ste. 207, Commack, NY 11725-2808. TEL 516-499-3103. FAX 516-499-3146. E-mail: novasci1@aol.com. **Document type:** academic/scholarly publication.
—UnCover.
   Former titles: Political Archives of Russia; Political Archives of the Soviet Union (ISSN 1049-7714)

327 US ISSN 1075-6183
POLITICAL RISK SERVICES ON C D - R O M. 12/yr. $8995 (effective 1995). Political Risk Services, Box 248, E. Syracuse, NY 13057-0248. TEL 315-431-0511. FAX 315-431-0200.
   ●Available only on CD-ROM.

POLITICAL SCIENTIST. see *POLITICAL SCIENCE*

POLITICS AND THE LIFE SCIENCES. see *MEDICAL SCIENCES*

POLITIQUE ETRANGERE. see *POLITICAL SCIENCE*

327 PL ISSN 0044-1929
POLSKI INSTYTUT SPRAW MIEDZYNARODOWYCH. ZBIOR DOKUMENTOW/INSTITUT POLONAIS DES AFFAIRES INTERNATIONALES. RECUEIL DE DOCUMENTS. (Text in original language of documents with Polish translation) 1936. q. $30 to individuals; institutions $50. Polski Instytut Spraw Miedzynarodowych, Warecka 1a, 00-950 Warsaw, Poland. TEL 48-22-278888. FAX 48-22-263026. Ed. Jerzy Menkes. cum.index: 1945-1954, 1955-1964. circ. 500.

POLITICAL SCIENCE — INTERNATIONAL RELATIONS

341 327 US ISSN 1068-8862
PRINCETON UNIVERSITY. CENTER OF INTERNATIONAL STUDIES. MONOGRAPH SERIES. 1990. irreg., no.5, 1992. price varies. Princeton University, Center of International Studies, Bendheim Hall, Princeton University, Princeton, NJ 08544. TEL 609-258-4851. FAX 609-258-3988. (back issues avail.; reprint service avail. from UMI) **Document type:** monographic series.

341 327 US ISSN 1068-8870
PRINCETON UNIVERSITY. CENTER OF INTERNATIONAL STUDIES. PROGRAM ON U S - JAPAN RELATIONS. MONOGRAPH SERIES. 1991. irreg., no.3, 1993. price varies. Princeton University, Center of International Studies, Bendheim Hall, Princeton University, Princeton, NJ 08544. TEL 609-258-4851. FAX 609-258-3988. (back issues avail.; reprint service avail. from UMI) **Document type:** monographic series.

327 US ISSN 1068-8854
PRINCETON UNIVERSITY. CENTER OF INTERNATIONAL STUDIES. WORLD ORDER STUDIES PROGRAM: OCCASIONAL PAPERS. 1975. irreg., no.23, 1992. price varies. Princeton University, Center of International Studies, Bendheim Hall, Princeton University, Princeton, NJ 08544. TEL 609-258-4851. FAX 609-258-3988. (reprint service avail. from UMI) **Document type:** monographic series.
—BLDSC (9356.957000).

320 300 FR ISSN 0015-9743
H3 CODEN: PPOSEQ
PROBLEMES POLITIQUES ET SOCIAUX; articles et documents d'actualite mondiale. 1970. 18/yr. 490 F. (Europe 610 F., elsewhere 810 F.). Documentation Francaise, 29-31 Quai Voltaire, 75344 Paris Cedex 07, France. TEL 1-40-15-70-00. FAX 40-15-72-30. (Subscr. to: 124 rue Henri Barbusse, 93308 Aubervilliers Cedex, France. TEL 48-39-56-00. FAX 48-39-56-01) index. circ. 4,000. (also avail. in microfiche from DFR) **Indexed:** Geo.Abstr., Int.Lab.Doc., Pt.de Rep. (1989-). **Document type:** government publication.
—BLDSC (6617.871900); SWETS.
Formerly: France. Direction de la Documentation Articles et Documents.

PROFILE OF JEWISH DISSIDENTS SERIES. see *ETHNIC INTERESTS*

327 NZ ISSN 1171-2031
PROGRAMME PROFILES - NEW ZEALAND OFFICIAL DEVELOPMENT ASSISTANCE. 1980. a. free. Ministry of Foreign Affairs and Trade, Development Cooperation Division, Private Bag 18-901, Wellington 1, New Zealand. TEL 64-4-472-8877. FAX 64-4-472-8571. **Document type:** government publication.
Former titles (until 1991): Programme Profiles - New Zealand Bilateral Assistance Programme (ISSN 0114-6254); (until 1986): New Zealand. Ministry of Foreign Affairs. External Aid Division. Project Profiles (ISSN 0111-5251)

900 327 PL ISSN 0033-2437
DK4010
PRZEGLAD ZACHODNI. (Text in Polish, German; summaries in English) 1945. q. $40. Instytut Zachodni, Stary Rynek 78-79, 61-772 Poznan, Poland. Ed. Hanka Dmochowska. bk.rev.; bibl.; charts; stat.; index. circ. 600. **Indexed:** Amer.Hist.& Life, Hist.Abstr.
—BLDSC (6944.930000).

PSYCHOLOGISTS FOR SOCIAL RESPONSIBILITY. NEWSLETTER. see *PSYCHOLOGY*

327 960 BS ISSN 0256-2316
DT1
PULA; Botswana journal of African studies. (Text in English) 1978. s-a. $20 per no. National Institute of Development Research and Documentation, University of Botswana, Private Bag 0022, Gaborone, Botswana. TEL 267-356364. FAX 267-357573. E-mail: nir@wn.apc.org. Ed. T.T. Fako. bk.rev. (back issues avail.) **Indexed:** P.I.E.S.A. (1988-). **Document type:** academic/scholarly publication.
Description: Publishes articles devoted primarily to African studies, with emphasis on southern Africa. *Refereed Serial*

QUAKER SERVICE BULLETIN. see *RELIGIONS AND THEOLOGY* — *Protestant*

QUESTE ISTITUZIONI; cronache del sistema politico. see *POLITICAL SCIENCE*

327 FR
QUINZAINE AFRICAINE. fortn. 4000 F. Agence Transcontinentale de Presse, 28 rue de Navarin, 75009 Paris, France. TEL 45-26-02-75. FAX 40-16-09-51. TELEX 281 342.

R C D A. (Religion in Communist Dominated Areas) see *RELIGIONS AND THEOLOGY*

327 UK ISSN 0951-4171
R I I A DISCUSSION PAPERS. 1987. irreg., no.50, 1994. £6 per no. Royal Institute of International Affairs, Chatham House, 10 St. James's Sq., London SW1Y 4LE, England. TEL 0171-957-5700. FAX 0171-957-5710. E-mail: riiapublicat@gn.apc.org. Ed. Margaret May. adv. contact: Thomas Lee. **Document type:** academic/scholarly publication.
Description: Provides an independent forum for discussion and debate on current international issues.

991 959 AT
R I M A: REVIEW OF INDONESIAN AND MALAYSIAN AFFAIRS; a semi-annual survey of political, economic, social and cultural aspects of Indonesia and Malaysia. 1967. s-a. Aus.$33 (foreign Aus.$85). University of Sydney, School of Asian Studies, Dept. of Southeast Asian Studies, Sydney, N.S.W. 2006, Australia. TEL 61-2-692-3173. Ed.Bd. adv.; bk.rev. circ. 400. **Indexed:** Amer.Hist.& Life (1993-), Asian-Pac.Econ.Lit., Aus.P.A.I.S., E.I., Hist.Abstr. (1993-), M.L.A. **Document type:** academic/scholarly publication.
—UnCover.
Former titles: Review of Indonesian and Malayan Affairs (ISSN 0034-6594); R I M A: Review of Indonesian and Malayan Affairs.

R U S I NEWSBRIEF. (Royal United Services Institute for Defence Studies) see *MILITARY*

RACE AND CLASS; a journal for Black and Third World liberation. see *SOCIOLOGY*

RADNER LECTURES. see *POLITICAL SCIENCE*

327 US ISSN 0882-312X
RANGEL'S REPORTS. 1977. q. $10. (Second Republic Research Center (SRRC)) Bravado Feature Service, Box 2498, Rockefeller Ctr. Sta., New York, NY 10185. Ed. Marc Rangel. illus. circ. 2,000.
Formerly (until 1984): Second Republic Newsletter (ISSN 0146-2547); **Supersedes:** Bravado.

327 IT
RASSEGNA DEL MONDO ARABO. N.S. vol.16, 1976. m. Lega degli Stati Arabi a Roma, Piazzale delle Belle Arti 6, Rome, Italy. Ed. Kris Mancuso. charts; illus.

RAZVOJ/DEVELOPMENT; casopis za probleme drustveno-ekonomskog razvoja, zemalja u razvoju i medunarodnih odnosa. see *BUSINESS AND ECONOMICS — International Development And Assistance*

327 CY
RE-DRAWING THE ISLAMIC MAP. 1972. m. $800 (includes subscr. to A P S News Service, Strategic Balance in the Middle East, Fate of the Arabian Peninsula, Operations in Oil Diplomacy) (effective 1994-1996). Arab Press Service, P.O. Box 3896, Nicosia, Cyprus. FAX 357-2-350265. s-a. index. **Document type:** bulletin.
Description: Surveys Islamic states and political activities.

RECHERCHES UNIVERSITAIRES SUR L'INTEGRATION EUROPEENNE/UNIVERSITY RESEARCH ON EUROPEAN INTEGRATION. see *POLITICAL SCIENCE — Abstracting, Bibliographies, Statistics*

327 325.1 US
REFUGEE AND IMMIGRANT RESOURCE DIRECTORY (YEAR). 1987. biennial. $47.50. Denali Press, Box 021535, Juneau, AK 99802-1535. TEL 907-586-6014. FAX 907-463-6780. **Document type:** directory.
Description: Includes information on over 2,250 local, regional and national organizations, associations, agencies, academic programs, research centers, museums and other groups in the United States that offer services to provide information and policy analysis about refugees and immigrants.

REFUGEE REPORTS. see *POLITICAL SCIENCE — Civil Rights*

323.1 UN ISSN 1014-1235
REFUGEES MAGAZINE. (Supplement to: Refugees (ISSN 0252-791X)) (Editions in English, French, German, Italian, Japanese, Russian, Spanish) 1968. q. United Nations High Commissioner for Refugees, P.O. Box 2500, 1211 Geneva 2, Switzerland. TEL 22-739-81-11. FAX 22-739-8449. TELEX 412972 PIHC CH. Ed. Ron Redmond. circ. 205,000. **Indexed:** Refug.Abstr. **Document type:** newsletter.
Formerly (until 1982): U N H C R Report (ISSN 0041-5308)
Description: Publishes articles, interviews and dossiers describing the problems and plight of refugees around the world, as well as human rights, development, environment, political and social matters related to population movements.

REGIONAL OUTLOOK: SOUTHEAST ASIA. see *BUSINESS AND ECONOMICS — Economic Situation And Conditions*

327 GW ISSN 0936-8965
REIHE DER VILLA VIGONI. 1989. irreg. (Verein der Villa Vigoni e.V.) Max Niemeyer Verlag, Postfach 2140, 72011 Tuebingen, Germany. TEL 07071-98940. FAX 07071-989450. **Document type:** monographic series.
Description: Reports on political, historical and cultural relations between Germany and Italy.

327 MX ISSN 0185-0814
JX9
RELACIONES INTERNACIONALES. (Text in Spanish; abstracts in English, French, Spanish) 1973. q. Mex.$80($90) (effective 1994). Universidad Nacional Autonoma de Mexico, Facultad de Ciencias Politicas y Sociales, Coordinacion de Relaciones Internacionales, Ciudad Universitaria, 04510 Mexico D.F., Mexico. Ed. Jose Ignacio Martinez. bk.rev.; bibl. circ. 1,000. **Indexed:** Hisp.Amer.Per.Ind. (1973-), Int.Polit.Sci.Abstr.
Formerly: Revista de Relaciones Internacionales.

327 FR ISSN 0335-2013
D410
RELATIONS INTERNATIONALES. 1974. q. 330 F.($65) (Institut Universitaire de Hautes Etudes Internationales, Geneva, SZ) Societe d'Etudes Historiques des Relations Internationales Contemporaines (S.E.H.R.I.C.), 11 Cite Veron, 75018 Paris, France. Eds. Pierre Guillen, Marlis Steinert. bk.rev.; bibl.; cum.index: 1974-1994. **Indexed:** Int.Polit.Sci.Abstr. **Document type:** academic/scholarly publication.
—BLDSC (7352.077000); SWETS.

327 FR ISSN 1157-5417
RELATIONS INTERNATIONALES ET STRATEGIQUES. 1991. q. 280 F. (foreign 350 F.) (effective 1996). Instituts de Relations Internationales et Strategiques, Universite Paris-Nord, Av. J.B. Clement, 93430 Villetaneuse, France. TEL 49-40-33-36. FAX 49-40-36-06. Ed. Pascal Boniface.
—BLDSC (7352.077500).

327 IT ISSN 0034-3846
D410
RELAZIONI INTERNAZIONALI. (Text in English and Italian) 1936. q. L.60000($85) (Istituto per gli Studi di Politica Internazionale) Elemond Periodici s.r.l., Via D. Trentacoste 7, 20134 Milan, Italy. TEL 02-215631. FAX 02-26410847. Ed. Dr. Gerolamo Fiori. adv.; bk.rev.; charts; illus.; index. circ. 5,000.
—UnCover.

POLITICAL SCIENCE — INTERNATIONAL RELATIONS

327 US ISSN 0748-0571
JX1932
REPORT OF A VANTAGE CONFERENCE. 1973. irreg., no.15, 1989. free. Stanley Foundation, 216 Sycamore St., Ste. 500, Muscatine, IA 52761. TEL 319-264-1500. FAX 319-264-0864. circ. 10,000.
Formerly: Vantage Conference Report (ISSN 0145-8833)
Description: Discusses the evolving world situation and addresses timely, emerging issues.

327 330.9 US ISSN 1043-3856
REPORT ON GUATEMALA. 1978. q. $12 to individuals; institutions and foreign $18 (effective 1995 & 1996). Guatemala News and Information Bureau, Box 28594, Oakland, CA 94604. TEL 510-835-0810. E-mail: gnib@igc.apc.org. Ed. David Loeb. adv.; bk.rev.; bibl.; charts; illus.; stat. circ. 1,200. (also avail. in microfiche; back issues avail.) **Indexed:** HR Rep. **Document type:** newsletter.
Formerly (until 1987): Guatemala!
Description: Articles, news briefs, interviews, and resource listings on the politics and domestic and foreign policy of this Central American country.

REPORT ON SCIENCE AND HUMAN RIGHTS. see SCIENCES: COMPREHENSIVE WORKS

RESIST NEWSLETTER. see POLITICAL SCIENCE — Civil Rights

327 UK ISSN 0305-6244
HC501
REVIEW OF AFRICAN POLITICAL ECONOMY. 1973. q. £28 to individuals; institutions £118 (effective 1996). Carfax Publishing Co., P.O. Box 25, Abingdon, Oxon. OX14 3UE, England. TEL 01235-521154. FAX 01235-553559. (Subscr. in N. America to: Carfax Publishing Co., 875-81 Massachusetts Ave., Cambridge, MA 02139) Eds. Jan Burgess, David Seddon. adv.; bk.rev.; index. circ. 1,500. (also avail. in microfiche) **Indexed:** Alt.Press Ind., Curr.Cont.Africa, Documentatieblad, IDA, Mult.Ed.Abstr., P.A.I.S., Rice Abstr., Rural Devel.Abstr., Stud.Wom.Abstr., World Agri.Econ.& Rural Sociol.Abstr. **Document type:** academic/scholarly publication.
—BLDSC (7786.769000); Faxon; SWETS; UMI. **CCC.**
Refereed Serial

327 YU ISSN 0486-6096
D839
REVIEW OF INTERNATIONAL AFFAIRS; politics, economics, law, science, culture. French edition: Revue de Politique Internationale (ISSN 0035-1695); German edition: International Politik (ISSN 0535-4129); Russian edition: Mezhdunarodnaya Politika (ISSN 0350-2511); Serbian edition: Medunarodna Politika (ISSN 0543-3657); Spanish edition: Politica International (ISSN 0352-1958) (Text in English) 1950. fortn. $34. (Assembly of the SFRY) Medjunarodna Politika, Nemanjina 34, 11000 Belgrade, Yugoslavia. TEL 641-546. Dir. Ranko Petkovic. bk.rev.; index. circ. 18,000. (reprint service avail. from JRC) **Indexed:** HR Rep. (1986-), P.A.I.S., Rural Recreat.Tour.Abstr., World Agri.Econ.& Rural Sociol.Abstr.
—Faxon; SWETS; UnCover.
Description: Focuses on foreign policy, military treaties and strategies, economic developments and disarmament.

341.1 SZ ISSN 0034-6608
REVIEW OF INTERNATIONAL COOPERATION. (Text in English) 1908. q. 60 SFr. International Co-operative Alliance, 15, rte. des Morillons, CH-1218 Grand Saconnex, Switzerland. TEL 022-798-4121. FAX 022-798-4122. TELEX 415620-ICA-CH. adv.; bk.rev.; illus.; stat.; index. circ. 4,500. (also avail. in microform from UMI; reprint service avail. from UMI) **Indexed:** P.A.I.S., Rural Recreat.Tour.Abstr., World Agri.Econ.& Rural Sociol.Abstr. **Document type:** academic/scholarly publication.
—BLDSC (7790.900000); UMI.

REVIEW OF INTERNATIONAL POLITICAL ECONOMY. see BUSINESS AND ECONOMICS — Economic Situation And Conditions

327 UK ISSN 0260-2105
JX1
REVIEW OF INTERNATIONAL STUDIES. 1974. q. £56($89) (effective 1996). (British International Studies Association) Cambridge University Press, Edinburgh Bldg., Shaftesbury Rd., Cambridge CB2 2RU, England. TEL 01223-312393. FAX 01223-315052. TELEX 851817256. (N. American addr.: Cambridge University Press, Journals Dept., 40 W. 20th St., New York, NY 10011. TEL 212-924-3900. FAX 212-691-3239) Ed. Paul Taylor. adv.; bk.rev.; index. (back issues avail.) **Indexed:** A.B.C.Pol.Sci., Abstr.Mil.Bibl., Amer.Hist.& Life, Hist.Abstr., Int.Polit.Sci.Abstr., P.A.I.S., Polit.Sci.Abstr. **Document type:** academic/scholarly publication.
—BLDSC (7790.940000); Faxon; SWETS; UMI; UnCover. **CCC.**
Description: Reviews politics, law, history and other areas of social science in the international arena.

327 CK ISSN 0121-2710
REVISTA CANCILLERIA DE SAN CARLOS. 1989. s-a. free. Ministerio de Relaciones Exteriores, Carrera 5, 9-03 Santafe de Bogota, Colombia. TEL 2838665. FAX 3416777. Ed. Juan Gustavo Cobo Borba; Pub. Isadora de Norden.

REVISTA DE DERECHO INTERNACIONAL Y CIENCIAS DIPLOMATICAS. see LAW — International Law

327 BO ISSN 0034-9194
REVISTA DIPLOMATICA E INTERNACIONAL. 1966. m. $1.50. Casilla 1598, La Paz, Bolivia. Ed. Cesar La Faye. adv.; bk.rev.; illus.

327 MX
REVISTA MEXICANA DE POLITICA EXTERIOR. 1983. q. Mex.$60 (U.S. and Canada $25) (effective 1994). Instituto Matias Romero de Estudios Diplomaticos, Reforma Norte 707, Esq. Av. Peralvillo, Col. Morales, 06200 Mexico, D.F., Mexico. TEL 529-95-14. FAX 327-30-31. Ed. Dulce Maria Mendez. **Document type:** government publication.

327 CU ISSN 0049-4682
REVISTA TRICONTINENTAL. French edition: Revue Tricontinental (ISSN 0864-1587); English edition: Tricontinental Magazine (ISSN 0864-1595) 1967. bi-m. $10. Organization of Solidarity of the Peoples of Asia, Africa, and Latin America, Apdo. Postal 4224 y 6130, Calle C No. 668 e-27 y 29 Vedado, Havana, Cuba. TEL 809-30-5510. TELEX 512259. (Dist. by: Ediciones Cubanas, Obispo No. 527, Aptdo. 605, Havana, Cuba) Ed. Jose M. Ortiz. bk.rev.; charts; illus. circ. 12,000 (other eds. 10,000 ea.). (back issues avail.) **Indexed:** HR Rep.

943 FR
REVUE D'ALLEMAGNE ET DES PAYS DE LANGUE ALLEMANDE. 1969. q. 260 F. (foreign 300 F.) (effective 1995 & 1996). (Centre d'Etudes Germaniques) Societe d'Etudes Allemandes, 8 rue des Ecrivains, 67081 Strasbourg Cedex, France. TEL 88-36-45-14. FAX 88-52-92-28. Ed. Christiane Falbisaner; Pub. Jean-Paul Bled. adv.; bk.rev.; bibl.; charts. **Indexed:** Amer.Hist.& Life, Hist.Abstr., Int.Polit.Sci.Abstr. **Document type:** academic/scholarly publication.
Formerly: Revue d'Allemagne (ISSN 0035-0974)

327 CN ISSN 0703-6337
REVUE D'INTEGRATION EUROPEENNE/JOURNAL OF EUROPEAN INTEGRATION. 1977. q. Can.$40. Canadian Council for European Affairs - Conseil Canadien des Affaires Europeennes, c/o Department of Political Studies, University of Saskatchewan, Saskatoon, SK S7N 0W0, Canada. TEL 306-966-5231. FAX 306-966-5250. (Subscr. to: Periodica, C.P. 444, Outremont, PQ H2V 4R6, Canada. TEL 514-274-5468. FAX 514-274-0201) Eds. H.J. Michelmann, Panayotis Soldatos. adv.; bk.rev. circ. 400. **Indexed:** ELLIS, Int.Polit.Sci.Abstr., Pt.de Rep. (1983-). **Document type:** academic/scholarly publication.
—BLDSC (4979.660000); SWETS.
Formerly (until 1980): Centre d'Etudes et de Documentation Europeennes. Bulletin d'Information Documentaire.
Description: Focuses on political, economic, legal and social integration in Western Europe and worldwide.

327 MG
REVUE DIPLOMATIQUE DE L'OCEAN INDIEN. (Text in French) 1982. q. $29. Communication et Media Ocean Indien, Rue H. Rabesahala, B.P. 46, Antsakaviro, 101 Antananarivo, Madagascar. TEL 22536. FAX 34534. TELEX 22225. Ed. Georges Ranaivasoa. adv.; bk.rev. circ. 3,000.

REVUE DU MARCHE UNIQUE EUROPEEN. see BUSINESS AND ECONOMICS — International Commerce

327 FR
REVUE FRANCO-UKRAINIENNE ECHANGES. 1972. bi-m. 100 F. Association Franco Ukrainienne, 26 villa Auguste Blanqui, 75013 Paris, France. Ed. M. Musianowycz. adv.; bibl.; illus. circ. 1,200.

327 BE ISSN 1370-0731
▼**REVUE INTERNATIONALE DE POLITIQUE COMPAREE.** (Text in French) 1994. 3/yr. 1750 BEF to individuals (Europe 2100 BEF; elsewhere 2150 BEF); institutions 2700 BEF (Europe 3050 BEF; elsewhere 3100 BEF). De Boeck Universite, Fonds Jean-Paques 4, 1348 Louvain-la-Neuve, Belgium. TEL 32-10-482500. FAX 32-10-482519. Ed. S. Duchesne. abstr. **Document type:** academic/scholarly publication.
Description: Publishes original articles contributing to the comparative analysis of political phenomena.

327.4 RM ISSN 0048-8178
DR201
REVUE ROUMAINE D'ETUDES INTERNATIONALES. Rumanian edition: Revista Romana de Studii Internationale. (Text in English, French, Russian) 1967. 6/yr. 180 lei($56) (Asociatia de Drept International si Relatii Internationale "N. Titulescu" - Romanian Association for International Law and International Relations) Editura Academiei Romane, Calea Victoriei 125, 79717 Bucharest, Rumania. (Dist. by: Rompresfilatelia, Calea Grivitei 64-66, P.O. Box 12-201, 78104 Bucharest, Rumania) Ed. A. Pop. bk.rev.; bibl. circ. 1,500. (tabloid format) **Indexed:** Abstr.Mil.Bibl, Amer.Hist.& Life, Hist.Abstr., Int.Polit.Sci.Abstr.

327 US ISSN 1067-0149
F787
RIO BRAVO. 1991. s-a. University of Texas - Pan American, Center for International Studies, LA 102, Edinburg, TX 78539. TEL 210-381-2541. FAX 210-381-2268.

RISK MANAGEMENT REVIEW. see BUSINESS AND ECONOMICS — International Commerce

327 UK
RIVISTA; the journal of the British-Italian Society. 1941. bi-m. £4.50 to non-members (foreign £9); free to members. British-Italian Society, 39 Grosvenor St., London W1X 9FE, England. TEL 071-495-5536. adv.; bk.rev. circ. 600.

327 IT ISSN 0035-6611
JX7
RIVISTA DI STUDI POLITICI INTERNAZIONALI. 1934. q. L.60000. Giuseppe Vedovato, Ed. & Pub., Lungarno del Tempio 40, 50121 Florence, Italy. adv.; bk.rev.; bibl.; index, cum.index: 1934-1983. circ. 1,200. **Indexed:** A.B.C.Pol.Sci., Amer.Hist.& Life (until 1993), Hist.Abstr. (until 1993), Int.Polit.Sci.Abstr. **Document type:** academic/scholarly publication.
—SWETS.

327 UK ISSN 0035-8533
AP4
THE ROUND TABLE; the commonwealth journal of international affairs. 1910. q. £39 to individuals; institutions £148 (effective 1996). Carfax Publishing Co., P.O. Box 25, Abingdon, Oxon. OX14 3UE, England. TEL 01235-555335. FAX 01235-553559. (Subscr. in N. America to: Carfax Publishing Co., 875-81 Massachusetts Ave., Cambridge, MA 02139) Ed. P. Lyon. adv.; bk.rev.; index. (also avail. in microform from UMI; microfiche; back issues avail.) **Indexed:** A.B.C.Pol.Sci., Amer.Hist.& Life, Geo.Abstr., Hist.Abstr., IDA, Int.Polit.Sci.Abstr., Mid.East: Abstr.& Ind., P.A.I.S., Polit.Sci.Abstr., Rural Recreat.Tour.Abstr., So.Pac.Per.Ind., Soc.Sci.Ind., SSCI, World Agri.Econ.& Rural Sociol.Abstr. **Document type:** academic/scholarly publication.
—BLDSC (8025.800000); Faxon; SWETS; UMI; UnCover. **CCC.**
Refereed Serial

POLITICAL SCIENCE — INTERNATIONAL RELATIONS

ROYAL UNITED SERVICES INSTITUTE OF AUSTRALIA. JOURNAL. see *MILITARY*

327 332.6   HK
RUSSIAN FAR EAST LETTER. (Text in English) 1993. m. $495. N & N International (Hong Kong) Ltd., G.P.O. Box 8926, Hong Kong. FAX 852-856-5648. Ed. Edward Neilan.
    Description: Contains analysis and commentary on the development of Russian Far East, focusing on the development around Vladivostok, Khabarovsk and Nakhodka.

327   US
RUSSIAN FOREIGN POLICY TODAY; the Soviet legacy and post-Soviet beginnings. 1983. irreg., 5th ed., 1992. $15 (foreign $19) (effective 1995). Current Digest of the Soviet Press, 3857 N. High St., Columbus, OH 43214-3747. TEL 614-292-4234. FAX 614-267-6310. Ed. Gordon Livermore.
    Document type: monographic series.
    Formerly (until 1992): Soviet Foreign Policy Today Series.

327 301   AT
RUSSIAN POLITICS AND SOCIETY; international review of Russian studies. 1990. s-a. $48 to individuals; institutions $95. James Nicholas Publishers, P.O. Box 244, Albert Park, Vic. 3206, Australia. TEL 61-3-696-5545. FAX 613-699-2040. Ed. Joseph Zajda. adv.; bk.rev.; index. **Document type:** academic/scholarly publication.
    Former titles (until 1995): Russian Society & Soviet Society (ISSN 1034-7437); Soviet Review (ISSN 1033-6257)
    Description: Concerned with all aspects of contemporary Russian society, including the economy, labor and management, Russian foreign policy, political culture and leadership, minorities in Russia, religion, women studies, youth organizations, vocational training, schools and higher education.
    Refereed Serial

327   JA   ISSN 0911-8152
DK1
RUSSIAN STUDIES. s-a. Japan Institute of International Affairs, Toranomon Mitui Bldg., 3-8-1 Kasumigaseki, Chiyoda-ku, Tokyo 100, Japan. TEL 03-3503-7261. FAX 03-3503-7292. TELEX 02223469 JIIA J. Ed. Nobuo Matsunaga. **Document type:** monographic series.

940   GW   ISSN 0036-0414
RUSSLAND UND WIR; ein Forum. 1961. q. DM.16. (Deutsch-Russlaendische Gesellschaft e.V.) Russland und Wir - Verlag und Handlung, Sindlinger Weg 1, 61350 Bad Homburg, Germany. TEL 06172-35191. Ed. Siegfried Keiling. adv.; bk.rev. circ. 2,000.
    Description: Covers political, social and economic news and developments affecting relations between Germany and Russia.

327   US   ISSN 0036-0775
D839
S A I S REVIEW; a journal of international affairs. 1956-1975; resumed 1981. s-a. $14 to individuals; institutions $28; students $12. Johns Hopkins Foreign Policy Institute, Paul H. Nitze School of Advanced International Studies, 1740 Massachusetts Ave., N.W., Washington, DC 20036. TEL 202-663-5766. FAX 202-663-5782. (Subscr. to: 1619 Massachusetts Ave., N.W., Washington, DC 20036) Ed. Thomas Conroy. adv. contact: Sheila Ward. bk.rev.; index. circ. 2,000. **Indexed:** A.B.C.Pol.Sci., Abstr.Mil.Bibl., Amer.Bibl.Slavic & E.Eur.Stud., Amer.Hist.& Life, Hist.Abstr., P.A.I.S., Polit.Sci.Abstr., Soc.Sci.Ind. (1994-), SSCI. **Document type:** academic/scholarly publication.
    —BLDSC (8070.270000); Faxon; SWETS; UnCover.
    Description: Analyses contemporary international issues and recent publications on foreign affairs.

327   RH
S A P E S SEMINAR AND OCCASIONAL PAPER SERIES. 1989. irreg. (8-10/yr.). price varies. (Southern Africa Political Economy Series) S A P E S Trust, 4 Deary Ave., Belgravia, P.O. Box MP111, Mt. Pleasant, Harare, Zimbabwe. TEL 263-4-727875. FAX 263-4-732735. TELEX 26464 AAPS ZW.
    Document type: monographic series.
    Description: Short monographs and research papers on issues pertaining to the economy, politics and development of Southern African countries.

327   SW   ISSN 0348-2626
S A R E C REPORT. (Text in English) 1976. irreg. (2-5/yr.). Swedish Agency for Research Cooperation with Developing Countries - Styrelsen foer U-Landsforskning, P.O. Box 16140, S-103 23 Stockholm, Sweden. bibl.; illus. circ. 4,000.
    —BLDSC (8076.033800).
    Formerly: S I D A Development Studies.

327   UK
S I N. (Studies in Nonviolence) 3/yr. £3. Peace Pledge Union, Dick Sheppard House, 6 Endsleigh Street, London WC1H 0DX, England. TEL 01-387-5501.
    Description: Explores theoretical and practical aspects of nonviolence.

327 341.37   UK   ISSN 0267-2537
S I P R I CHEMICAL & BIOLOGICAL WARFARE STUDIES. irreg. price varies. (Stockholm International Peace Research Institute, SW) Oxford University Press, Oxford Journals, Walton St., Oxford OX2 6DP, England. TEL 01865-267907. FAX 01865-267773. TELEX 837330-OXPRES-G. E-mail: jnlorders@oup.co.uk. (U.S. subscr. to: Oxford University Press Inc., 2001 Evans Rd., Cary, NC 27513. TEL 919-677-0977. FAX 919-677-1714) **Document type:** academic/scholarly publication.
    —BLDSC (8286.040000).

327   UK
S I P R I YEARBOOK; world armaments and disarmament. 1969. a. price varies. (Stockholm International Peace Research Institute, SW) Oxford University Press, Oxford Journals, Walton St., Oxford OX2 6DP, England. TEL 01865-267907. FAX 01865-267773. TELEX 837330-OXPRES-G. E-mail: jnlorders@oup.co.uk. (U.S. subscr. to: Oxford University Press Inc., 2001 Evans Rd., Cary, NC 27513. TEL 919-677-0977. FAX 919-677-1714) Ed. Tim Barton.
    —CCC.
    Formerly: World Armaments and Disarmament: S I P R I Yearbook (ISSN 0347-2205)
    Description: Detailed information on arms and arms control developments in nuclear weapons and world military expenditure.

SAMANTHA SMITH FOUNDATION NEWSLETTER. see *CHILDREN AND YOUTH — For*

SAN MARINO (REPUBBLICA). DIPARTIMENTO AFFARI ESTERI. NOTIZIA. see *PUBLIC ADMINISTRATION*

SARVODAYA. see *SOCIAL SERVICES AND WELFARE*

327   SZ
SCHWEIZERISCHE GESELLSCHAFT FUER AUSSENPOLITIK. SCHRIFTENREIHE. 1972. irreg., no.11, 1992. price varies. Paul Haupt AG, Falkenplatz 14, CH-3001 Bern, Switzerland. TEL 031-3012345. FAX 031-3014669. **Document type:** monographic series.

327 500   US   ISSN 1048-7042
SCIENCE AND GLOBAL SECURITY MONOGRAPH SERIES. irreg., latest vol.2. price varies. Gordon and Breach Science Publishers, c/o International Publishers Distributor, 820 Town Center Dr., Langhorne, PA 19047. TEL 215-750-2642. FAX 215-750-6343. (Subscr. to: International Publishers Distributor, P.O. Box 90, Reading, Berkshire RG1 8JL, England. TEL 44-173-456-8316) Ed. H.A. Feiveson. **Document type:** monographic series.
    Refereed Serial

SEA POWER. see *MILITARY*

327.1   US   ISSN 0889-4876
SECURITY AFFAIRS. 1978. m. Jewish Institute for National Security Affairs, 1717 K St., N.W., Ste. 300, Washington, DC 20006. TEL 202-833-0020. FAX 202-296-6452. Ed. Jim Colbert. **Document type:** newsletter.

327 355   UK   ISSN 0963-6412
UA10.5
SECURITY STUDIES. 1991. q. £36($48) to individuals; institutions £125 ($170) (effective 1996). Frank Cass, Newbury House, 890-900 Eastern Ave., Newbury Park, Ilford, Essex IG2 7HH, England. TEL 44-181-599-8866. FAX 44-181-599-0984. E-mail: 100067,1576@compuserve.com. Eds. Amos Perlmutter, Benjamin Frankel. adv.: B&W page £195 ($275); adv. contact: Anne Kidson. bk.rev.; index. (back issues avail.) **Indexed:** Int.Polit.Sci.Abstr.
    Document type: academic/scholarly publication.
    —BLDSC (8217.219900). **CCC.**
    Description: Covers international security and the role of force in international politics.
    Refereed Serial

327 956   UK   ISSN 0308-8421
SEMINAR FOR ARABIAN STUDIES. PROCEEDINGS. 1971. a. price varies. Seminar for Arabian Studies, 15 Crathie Rd., London SE12 8BT, England. bk.rev. circ. 200. **Indexed:** Anthropol.Lit., Bibl.Ling. **Document type:** proceedings.
    —BLDSC (6849.117500).

351   SG
SENEGAL. LISTE DU CORPS DIPLOMATIQUE. irreg. Imprimerie Nationale, Rufisque, Senegal.
    Supersedes: Senegal. Service du Protocole. Liste Diplomatique et Consulaire.

327   FR   ISSN 0080-8903
SENNACIECA REVUO. (Text in Esperanto) 1952. a. $8. Sennacieca Asocio Tutmonda, 67 av. Gambetta, 75020 Paris, France. TEL 47-97-87-05. bk.rev.

327   FR   ISSN 1163-0442
SENNACIULO. (Text in Esperanto) 1988. m. $50. Sennacieca Asocio Tutmonda, 67 av. Gambetta, 75020 Paris, France. TEL 47-97-87-05.

327   BL
SERIE CAPISTRANO DE ABREU. 1982. a. Colegio Pedro II, Secretaria de Ensino, Campo da Sao Cristovao, 177 CEP 20291, Rio de Janeiro, Brazil.

SHALOM. see *ETHNIC INTERESTS*

327 332.6   HK
SHANGHAI LETTER. (Text in English) 1993. m. $495. N & N International (Hong Kong) Ltd., G.P.O. Box 8926, Hong Kong. FAX 852-856-5648. Ed. Edward Neilan.
    Description: Contains analysis and commentary on political risk, business development, and economics in Shanghai. Aimed at business executives, diplomats, government officials, and intelligence analysts.

327   CC   ISSN 0583-0176
SHIJIE ZHISHI/WORLD AFFAIRS. (Text in Chinese) 1934. s-m. $48.70. Shijie Zhishi Chubanshe - World Affairs Press, 31-A Waijiaobu Jie, Dongcheng Qu, Beijing 100005, People's Republic of China. TEL 5125544. (Dist. in US by: China Books & Periodicals, Inc., 2929 24th St., San Francisco, CA 94110. TEL 415-282-2994) Ed. Yao Dongqiao.

327   UA   ISSN 0583-4597
D839
AL-SIASSA AL-DAWLYA. (Text in English) 1965. q. $45 in N. America (effective 1994). Mu'assasat al-Ahram, Sharia al-Galaa, Cairo, Egypt. TEL 02-758333. FAX 02-745888. TELEX 92001. (In N. America: Al-Ahram International, 405 Lexington Ave., New York, NY 10174. TEL 212-972-6440. FAX 212-686-0285) Ed. Butrus Ghali. **Indexed:** Curr.Cont.M.E.

327   GW   ISSN 0175-274X
JX1903
SICHERHEIT UND FRIEDEN. Short title: S und F. q. DM.49. Nomos Verlagsgesellschaft mbH und Co. KG, Waldseestr. 3-5, 76530 Baden-Baden, Germany. TEL 07221-21040. FAX 07221-210427. (Subscr. to: Postfach 610, 76484 Baden-Baden, Germany) circ. 5,000.
    Document type: bulletin.
    —BLDSC (8053.653600). **CCC.**

POLITICAL SCIENCE — INTERNATIONAL RELATIONS

324   LE
AS-SIHAFA WAL-I'LAM/PRESS AND INFORMATION/PRESSE ET INFORMATION. (Text in Arabic, English, French) 1987. m. $3000. Dar Naaman lith-Thaqafah, P.O. Box 567, Jounieh, Lebanon. TEL 961-9-935096. Ed. Naji Naaman. index.
Description: Analysis of Arab world affairs as reported in Arab and international media.

327 915.3   TS
AL-SIJIL AL-SHAHRI LI-AHDATH AL-ALAM/MONTHLY RECORD OF WORLD EVENTS. (Text in Arabic) 1981. m. Ministry of Information and Culture, Information Department, P.O. Box 17, Abu Dhabi, United Arab Emirates. TEL 453000. circ. 1,000 (controlled).
Description: Reviews international events and their impact on the U.A.E.

940   IT   ISSN 0393-0416
SINISTRA EUROPEA. 1959. bi-m. L.20000 (foreign L.30000). Piazza Augusto Imperatore 32, 00186 Rome, Italy. TEL 06-68-78-689. Ed. Luciano Fraschetti. adv.; bk.rev.; illus. (back issues avail.)
Formerly (until 1975): Iniziativa Europea (ISSN 0020-1340)
Description: Political forum that covers socialism and other left wing movements throughout Europe as well as the United States.

327   CH   ISSN 0377-5321
SINO-AMERICAN RELATIONS. 1975. q. $30. Chinese Culture University Press, Chinese Culture University, Hwa Kang, Taiwan 11114, Republic of China. FAX 02-861-5487. Ed. Yu-Tang Daniel Lew. adv.; bk.rev. circ. 1,500. **Indexed:** C.L.I., Leg.Per. **Document type:** academic/scholarly publication.

327 355   UK   ISSN 0959-2318
U240
SMALL WARS AND INSURGENCIES. 1990. 3/yr. £33($48) to individuals; institutions £98 ($145) (effective 1996). Frank Cass, Newbury House, 890-900 Eastern Ave., Newbury Park, Ilford, Essex 1G2 7HH, England. TEL 44-181-599-8866. FAX 44-181-599-0984. E-mail: 100067,1576@compuserve.com. Eds. Ian Beckett, Thomas Durell-Young. adv.: B&W page £195 ($275); adv. contact: Anne Kidson. bk.rev.; index. (back issues avail.) **Indexed:** Amer.Hist.& Life (1993-), Hist.Abstr. (1993-), Int.Polit.Sci.Abstr., Polit.Sci.Abstr. **Document type:** academic/scholarly publication.
—BLDSC (8310.169100); UnCover.
Description: Provides a forum to discuss the historical, political, social, economic, and psychological aspects of conflict.
Refereed Serial

327   US   ISSN 1043-1578
HV6001
SOCIAL JUSTICE; a journal of crime, conflict and world order. 1974. q. $35 to individuals; institutions $80 (foreign $85) (effective 1995). Global Options, Box 40601, San Francisco, CA 94140. TEL 415-550-1703. Ed. Gregory Shank. adv. contact: Kim Maddox. bk.rev.; charts; stat.; circ. 3,500 (paid). (also avail. in microform from UMI; back issues avail.; reprint service avail. from UMI) **Indexed:** Abstr.Crim.& Pen., Alt.Press Ind., HR Rep., Left Ind. (1982-), Mid.East: Abstr.& Ind., P.A.I.S., Sociol.Abstr. **Document type:** academic/scholarly publication.
—BLDSC (8318.121300); Faxon; Genuine Article; SWETS; UMI; UnCover.
Former titles: Crime and Social Justice (ISSN 0094-7571); (until 1988): Contemporary Marxism (ISSN 0193-8703); Supersedes: Synthesis (San Francisco) (ISSN 0193-869X); Incorporates: Issues in Criminology (ISSN 0021-2385)
Description: Combines analyses of global issues (peaceful resolution of conflicts, state terrorism, and human rights) with domestic policy concerns such as reducing crime as well as race and gender discrimination.
Refereed Serial

327   US   ISSN 0740-6169
E183.7
SOCIETY FOR HISTORIANS OF AMERICAN FOREIGN RELATIONS. NEWSLETTER. 1970. q. $15. Society for Historians of American Foreign Relations (S.H.A.F.R.), c/o Tennessee Technological University, Department of History, Cookeville, TN 38505. TEL 615-372-3332. FAX 615-372-6142. Ed. William Brinker. adv.: page $100. abstr.; bibl. circ. 1,500. **Indexed:** Amer.Hist.& Life, Hist.Abstr. **Document type:** newsletter.
Description: Publishes scholarly articles and contains general material of interest to society members.

327 301   US
SOCIOLOGICAL STUDIES. irreg. $150 in U.S., Canada, Mexico; elsewhere $300. (Joint Publications Research Service) U.S. National Technical Information Service, 5825 Port Royal Rd., Springfield, VA 22161. TEL 703-487-4630.
Formerly: U S S R Serial Reports: Sociological Studies.

968   SW   ISSN 1104-5965
SOEDRA AFRIKA. 1964. 11/yr. SEK 150. Afrikagrupperna i Sverige - Africa Groups of Sweden, Barnaengsgat 23, S-116 41 Stockholm, Sweden. FAX 46-8-640-36-60. Ed. Kerstin Bjurman. adv.; bk.rev.; illus.; cum.index: 1968-1980 (vols.1-55). circ. 4,500. **Document type:** bulletin, newsletter.
Former titles (until 1994): Afrikabulletinen (ISSN 0346-9158); (until 1975): Soedra Afrika (ISSN 0038-0490)

327   FR   ISSN 0296-4333
SOLIDARITE ATLANTIQUE. 1984. bi-m. 150 F.($30) Union Nationale Inter-Universitaire (UNI), 8, rue de Musset, 75016 Paris, France. TEL 45-25-34-65. FAX 45-25-51-33. Ed. Dominique Ansery. adv.; bk.rev. circ. 20,000.

327   US
SOUNDINGS FROM AROUND THE WORLD; an idea exchange in rural development communication. 1970. s-a. $5 to industrialized nations; developing nations free. World Neighbors, Inc., 4127 N.W. 122nd St., Oklahoma City, OK 73120-8869. TEL 405-752-9700. FAX 405-752-9393. E-mail: 6358930@mcimail.com. Ed. Debra A. Johnson. bk.rev.; film rev.; charts; illus.; circ. 1,700 (controlled).

327   UN   ISSN 1014-8388
SOURCE (NEW YORK, 1989). 1989. q. United Nations Development Programme, Division of Information, One UN Plaza, New York, NY 10017. Ed. Lloyd Garrison.

327   SA
DT770
SOUTH AFRICAN INSTITUTE OF INTERNATIONAL AFFAIRS. BIENNIAL REPORT OF THE NATIONAL CHAIRMAN. 1978. biennial. R.10. South African Institute of International Affairs, P.O. Box 31596, Braamfontein 2017, South Africa. TEL 27-11-339-2021. FAX 27-11-339-2154. TELEX 4-27291 SA. **Document type:** corporate report.
Former titles (until 1984): South African Institute of International Affairs. Report of the National Chairman; South African Institute of International Affairs. Biennial Council Report; Supersedes (1966-1977): South African Institute of International Affairs. Annual Report (ISSN 0081-2439)

327   SA
SOUTH AFRICAN INSTITUTE OF INTERNATIONAL AFFAIRS. OCCASIONAL PAPERS. irreg. price varies. South African Institute of International Affairs, P.O. Box 31596, Braamfontein 2017, South Africa. TEL 27-11-339-2021. FAX 27-11-339-2154. TELEX 4-27291 SA. **Document type:** monographic series.

327   SA
SOUTH AFRICAN INSTITUTE OF INTERNATIONAL AFFAIRS. SPECIAL STUDIES. 1977. irreg. price varies. South African Institute of International Affairs, P.O. Box 31596, Braamfontein 2017, South Africa. TEL 27-11-339-2021. FAX 27-11-339-2154. TELEX 4-27291 SA. **Document type:** monographic series.

327   SA   ISSN 1022-0461
THE SOUTH AFRICAN JOURNAL OF INTERNATIONAL AFFAIRS. Running title: S A J I A. (Text in English) 1993. 2/yr. R.30($30) to individuals; institutions R.40($40) (effective 1996). South African Institute of International Affairs, P.O. Box 31596, Braamfontein 2017, South Africa. TEL 27-11-339-2021. FAX 27-11-339-2154. Ed. Alan Begg. bk.rev. **Document type:** academic/scholarly publication.
—BLDSC (8338.880000).
Description: Publishes original essays and review articles on topics in international relations.

320.9   KO
SOUTH-NORTH DIALOGUE IN KOREA. 1973. q. free. (Office of the South-North Dialogue, National Unification Board) Korea Foundation, 526, 5-ga, Namdaemunno, Chung-gu, C.P.O. Box 2147, Seoul, S. Korea. TEL 735-8766. circ. 30,000.

327   NL
SOUTH PACIFIC COMMISSION. ANNUAL REPORT. (Text in English and French) 1948. a. free. South Pacific Commission, B.P. D5, 98848 Noumea Cedex, New Caledonia. **Indexed:** Field Crop Abstr., Herb.Abstr.
Formerly: South Pacific Commission. South Pacific Report (ISSN 0081-2854)

327   NL   ISSN 1017-9283
SOUTH PACIFIC CONFERENCE. REPORT. French edition: Conference de Pacifique Sud. Rapport (ISSN 1017-9291) (Text in English) 1950. a. South Pacific Commission, B.P. D5, Noumea, Cedex, New Caledonia. TEL 687-262000. FAX 687-263818. TELEX 3139 NM SOPACOM.

052   RH
SOUTHERN AFRICA POLITICAL AND ECONOMIC MONTHLY. Short title: S A P E M. (Text in English, Portuguese) 1987. m. Z.$50 to individuals ($50 in Africa; Europe $60; elsewhere $70); institutions Z.$70 ($70 in Africa; Europe $90; elsewhere $100). (Southern Africa Political Economy Series) S A P E S Trust, 4 Deary Ave., Belgravia, P.O. Box MP111, Mt. Pleasant, Harare, Zimbabwe. TEL 263-4-727875. FAX 263-4-732735. TELEX 26464 AAPS ZW.
Description: Covers politics and current events, social science research, gender issues, and the arts.

SPACE NEWS (SPRINGFIELD). see *AERONAUTICS AND SPACE FLIGHT*

320 331   CN   ISSN 0229-5415
SPARTACIST CANADA. 1975. bi-m. Can.$3 (foreign Can.$8). (Trotskyist League of Canada) Spartacist Canada Publishing Association, Box 6867, Sta. A, Toronto, ON M5W 1X6, Canada. TEL 416-593-4138. FAX 416-593-1529. Ed. John Masters. (back issues avail.) **Document type:** newspaper.

327   XR
SPEKTRUM. Czech translation of: Dialogue (Washington) (US ISSN 0012-2262) 1972. q. free. Americke Velvyslanectvi - American Embassy (Prague), Trziste 15, 125 48 Prague 1, Czech Republic. FAX 011-431-408-8288. adv.; bk.rev.; illus. circ. 1,200. **Document type:** government publication.
Formed by the merger of: Americka Kultura; Americka Veda.

327 330.9   GW   ISSN 0176-425X
F1414.2
SPIEGEL DER LATEINAMERIKANISCHEN PRESSE/BOLETIN DE PRENSA LATINOAMERICANA. (Text in English, Portuguese, Spanish) 1976. m. DM.125. Institut fuer Iberoamerika-Kunde, Alsterglacis 8, 20354 Hamburg, Germany. TEL 040-414782-01. FAX 040-41478241. Eds. Guilherme de Almeida, Wolfgang Grenz. circ. 350. **Document type:** bulletin.
Formerly (until 1984): Aktueller Informationsdienst Lateinamerika (ISSN 0342-0388)

POLITICAL SCIENCE — INTERNATIONAL RELATIONS

327   PL   ISSN 0038-853X
SPRAWY MIEDZYNARODOWE. English edition: Polish Quarterly of International Affairs (ISSN 1230-4999) (Text in Polish) 1948. q. $30 to individuals; institutions $50. Polski Instytut Spraw Miedzynarodowych, Ul. Warecka 1a, 00-950 Warsaw, Poland. TEL 48-22-278888. FAX 48-22-263026. Ed. Henryk Szlajfer. bk.rev.; bibl. circ. 1,500. (also avail. in microform from UMI; reprint service avail. from UMI) **Indexed:** Int.Polit.Sci.Abstr.
—UMI.

327   US   ISSN 0278-1859
JX1
STATE (WASHINGTON). 1961. m. (except Aug.). $22. U.S. Department of State, Washington, DC 20520. TEL 202-655-4000. (Orders to: Supt. of Documents, Washington, DC 20402) illus. (also avail. in microform from MIM,UMI; reprint service avail. from UMI) **Indexed:** Amer.Bibl.Slavic & E.Eur.Stud, Ind.U.S.Gov.Per., P.A.I.S., Pers.Lit.
—Faxon; UMI; UnCover.
Formerly: U.S. Department of State. Newsletter (ISSN 0041-7629)

327 301   IS   ISSN 0334-2514
JQ1825.P3
STATE, GOVERNMENT AND INTERNATIONAL RELATIONS. 1971. s-a. IS.20. Hebrew University of Jerusalem, Leonard Davis Institute for International Relations, Jerusalem 91905, Israel. FAX 972-2-883111. (Co-publisher: Bialik Institute) Ed. Gabriel Sheffer. adv.; bk.rev.; cum.index. circ. 1,000. (back issues avail.) **Document type:** academic/scholarly publication.

STEIRISCHE KRIEGSOPFER ZEITUNG. see *MILITARY*

327   PL   ISSN 0209-0961
D839
STOSUNKI MIEDZYNARODOWE. 1982. irreg., vol.16, 1992. (Uniwersytet Warszawski, Instytut Stosunkow Miedzynarodowych) Wydawnictwa Uniwersytetu Warszawskiego, Ul. Nowy Swiat 4, 00-497 Warsaw, Poland. TEL 48-22-6253044. (Dist. by: Ars Polona, Krakowskie Przedmiescie 7, 00-068 Warsaw, Poland) Ed. Jozef Kukulka. circ. 400.

327 333.79   CY
STRATEGIC BALANCE IN THE MIDDLE EAST. 1972. m. $800 (includes APS News Service, Fate of the Arabian Peninsula, Operations in Oil Diplomacy, Re-Drawing the Islamic Map) (effective 1994-1996). Arab Press Service, P.O. Box 3896, Nicosia, Cyprus. FAX 357-2-350265. s-a. index. **Document type:** bulletin.
Description: Provides military surveys of the Arab nations, the Palestinian movement, Israel, and Iran.

STRATEGIC BRIEFING. see *BUSINESS AND ECONOMICS — Economic Situation And Conditions*

STRATEGIC REVIEW. see *MILITARY*

327   SA   ISSN 1013-1108
UA10.5
STRATEGIC REVIEW FOR SOUTHERN AFRICA. (Text in English) 1979. 2/yr. R.42.50($45) includes I S S U P Bulletin (effective 1995). University of Pretoria, Institute for Strategic Studies, Pretoria 0002, South Africa. TEL 27-12-420-2407. FAX 27-12-43-2185. TELEX 3-22723. E-mail: PULLES@libarts.up.ac.za. Ed. M. Hough. bk.rev. circ. 1,500. (back issues avail.) **Indexed:** INIS Atomind.
Formerly (until 1988): I S S U P Strategic Review (ISSN 0250-1961)
Description: Contains articles on current strategic matters.

327   UK   ISSN 0459-7230
U162
STRATEGIC SURVEY. 1967. 1/yr. £20($32) (effective 1996). (International Institute for Strategic Studies) Oxford University Press, Oxford Journals, Walton St., Oxford OX2 6DP, England. TEL 44-1865-267907. FAX 44-1865-267773. E-mail: jnlorders@oup.co.uk. (Subscr. in U.S. to: Oxford University Press Inc., 2001 Evans Rd., Cary, NC 27513. TEL 919-677-0977. FAX 919-677-1714) Ed. Sidney Bearman. charts. circ. 13,000. **Indexed:** Int.Polit.Sci.Abstr. **Document type:** academic/scholarly publication.
—BLDSC (8474.032000); Faxon; SWETS; UMI. **CCC.**
Description: Examines the year's significant events and their importance for international security.

327 001.3   US   ISSN 1040-2136
JA1
STRATEGIES (LOS ANGELES); a journal of theory, culture and politics. 1988. s-a. $12 to individuals; institutions $20 (foreign $16). University of California at Los Angeles, Strategies Collective, 4289 Bunche Hall, Los Angeles, CA 90024. TEL 310-599-5006. Ed.Bd. adv. circ. 250. **Indexed:** Film Lit.Ind. (1989-). **Document type:** academic/scholarly publication.
—Faxon.
Description: Tames an interdisciplinary examination of theory, culture and politics.

327   US   ISSN 0748-9641
JX1932
STRATEGY FOR PEACE U.S. FOREIGN POLICY CONFERENCE. REPORT. 1960. a. free. Stanley Foundation, 216 Sycamore St., Ste. 500, Muscatine, IA 52761. TEL 319-264-1500. FAX 319-264-0864. circ. 22,000.
—BLDSC (8474.041000); UnCover.
Formerly: Strategy for Peace Conference. Report (ISSN 0081-5942)
Description: Recommendations as developed through conference discussions among policy shapers in the U.S. government, academia and private sector.

327   BE   ISSN 0770-2965
D839
STUDIA DIPLOMATICA. (Text occasionally in English) 1948. bi-m. 3500 BEF in Europe; elsewhere 4200 BEF. Institut Royal des Relations Internationales, Rue Belliard 65, 1040 Brussels, Belgium. TEL 32-2-2302230. FAX 32-2-2305230. Ed. E. Yakemtchouk. adv.; bk.rev.; index, cum.index. circ. 2,500. **Indexed:** A.B.C.Pol.Sci., Abstr.Mil.Bibl, ELLIS, Int.Polit.Sci.Abstr., P.A.I.S. **Document type:** academic/scholarly publication.
—BLDSC (8482.385000); SWETS; UnCover.
Formerly: Chronique de Politique Etrangere (ISSN 0009-6059)

327   US   ISSN 1057-610X
HM136   CODEN: SCTREO
STUDIES IN CONFLICT AND TERRORISM. 1978. q. £91($150) (effective 1996). Taylor & Francis Inc., 1900 Frost Rd., Ste. 101, Bristol, PA 19007. TEL 215-785-5800; 800-821-8312. FAX 215-785-5515. (Subscr. in Europe to: Taylor & Francis Ltd., Rankine Rd., Basingstoke, Hants. RG24 8PR, England. TEL 44-1256-840366. FAX 44-1256-479438) Eds. George K. Tanham, Bruce Hoffman. adv.; bk.rev.; index. **Indexed:** A.B.C.Pol.Sci., Abstr.Crim.& Pen., Abstr.Mil.Bibl., Air Un.Lib.Ind., Amer.Hist.& Life (until 1991), Curr.Cont., Hist.Abstr. (until 1991), Int.Polit.Sci.Abstr., Mid.East: Abstr.& Ind., Polit.Sci.Abstr., Psychol.Abstr. (1985-), Pub.Admin.Abstr., Soc.Sci.Ind. (1994-), SSCI. **Document type:** academic/scholarly publication.
—BLDSC (8490.284000); Faxon; Genuine Article; SWETS; UnCover. **CCC.**
Formed by the merger of (1978-1992): Conflict (ISSN 0149-5941); (1977-1992): Terrorism (Bristol) (ISSN 0149-0389)
Description: Focuses on conflicts short of formal war, such as guerilla warfare, revolution, unconventional warfare, and terrorism, and on nonphysical conflicts of an economic, social, or political nature.
Refereed Serial

327   IE
STUDIES IN EUROPEAN UNION. 1991. irreg. Institute of European Affairs, 8 North Great George's St., Dublin 1, Ireland. **Document type:** academic/scholarly publication, monographic series.

323.4   US   ISSN 0146-3586
STUDIES IN HUMAN RIGHTS. 1975. irreg., latest 1992. price varies. Greenwood Press, Inc. (Subsidiary of: Greenwood Publishing Group Inc.), 88 Post Rd. W., Box 5007, Westport, CT 06881-5007. TEL 203-226-3571. FAX 203-222-1502. Ed. George W. Shepherd.
—BLDSC (8490.688000).

327 900   UK
STUDIES IN INTELLIGENCE. 1989. irreg. Frank Cass, Newbury House, 890-900 Eastern Ave., Newbury Park, Ilford, Essex IG2 7HH. TEL 44-181-599-8866. FAX 44-181-599-0984. E-mail: 100067,1576@compuserve.com. (Dist in the U.S. by: I.S.B.S., 5804 N.E. Hassalo St., Portland, OR 97213-3644) Eds. Christopher Andrew, Michael Handel. **Document type:** monographic series.

327   BE
STUDIES IN INTERNATIONAL RELATIONS. 1973. irreg., no.5, 1986. Leuven University Press, Krakenstraat 3, B-3000 Leuven, Belgium. TEL 32-16-324175. FAX 016-323782.

327   FI   ISSN 0782-8454
SUOMI - U S A. 1946. bi-m. FIM 70. Suomi-Amerikka Yhdistysten Liitto - League of Finnish-American Societies, Mechelininkatu 10A, FIN-00100 Helsinki, Finland. FAX 358-0-408974. Ed. Aarne I. Valikangas. adv.; bk.rev.; circ. 40,000 (controlled).
Formerly (until 1985): Suomi - Finland - U S A (ISSN 0781-447X)

327 355 364   US   ISSN 1051-0923
SURVEILLANT; acquisitions and commentary for intelligence and security professionals. 1990. bi-m. $96 (Canada $104; elsewhere $114). (National Intelligence Book Center) Surveillant - N I B C Press, 2020 Pennsylvania Ave., N.W., Ste. 165, Washington, DC 20006-1846. TEL 202-797-1234. FAX 202-331-7456. E-mail: ebancrof@interserv.com or 70346,1166@compuserve.com. Ed. Elizabeth Bancroft; Pub. Bagley Fordyce. adv. contact: Cameron LaClair. bk.rev.; bibl.; software rev.; video rev.; circ. 8,000 (paid). **Document type:** newsletter.
—CCC.
Description: Covers the newest nonfiction espionage and intelligence publications worldwide, on a wide variety of current and historical topics in all media for librarians, academics, politicians, researchers, government and corporate security professionals, and diplomats.

327   US   ISSN 0308-6798
SURVEY OF INTERNATIONAL AFFAIRS. irreg. price varies. (Royal Institute of International Affairs, UK) Oxford University Press, 200 Madison Ave., New York, NY 10016. TEL 212-679-7300.

341.1   UK   ISSN 0039-6338
U162
SURVIVAL (OXFORD). 1959. q. £39($62) (effective 1996). (International Institute for Strategic Studies) Oxford University Press, Oxford Journals, Walton St., Oxford OX2 6DP, England. TEL 44-1865-267907. FAX 44-1865-267773. E-mail: jnlorders@oup.co.uk. (U.S. subscr. to: Oxford University Press Inc., 2001 Evans Rd., Cary, NC 27513. TEL 919-677-0977. FAX 919-677-1714) adv. contact: Jane Parker. bk.rev.; index. circ. 6,500. (also avail. in microform from UMI; reprint service avail. from SWZ,UMI) **Indexed:** Abstr.Mil.Bibl, Air Un.Lib.Ind., Amer.Hist.& Life, Curr.Cont.M.E., Hist.Abstr., Int.Polit.Sci.Abstr., Soc.Sci.Ind. (1994-). **Document type:** academic/scholarly publication.
—BLDSC (8553.050000); Faxon; SWETS; UMI; UnCover. **CCC.**
Description: Contains original documents, articles and book reviews providing a forum for both policy debate and academic discussion.

327   US   ISSN 0895-6286
E183.8.R9
SURVIVING TOGETHER; a quarterly on grassroots cooperation in Eurasia. 1983. 4/yr. $25 to individuals; institutions $35; students $20. I S A R, 1601 Connecticut Ave. N.W., Ste. 301, Washington, DC 20009. TEL 202-387-3034. FAX 202-667-3291. E-mail: isar@igc.apc.org. Eds. Eliza Klose, Leanne Grossman. adv. contact: Tertia Speiser. bk.rev. circ. 4,500. (back issues avail.)
Description: Chronicles the multi-faceted relationship between Americans and the peoples of the former Soviet Union. Covers sustainable economics and agriculture, technical assistance and aid, and the development of civil society and cultural pride.

SWISS - AMERICAN HISTORICAL SOCIETY. REVIEW. see *HISTORY*

327   DK   ISSN 0109-579X
SYDSLESVIG I DAG.* 1946. q. membership. Syslesvigsk Udvalg af Maj 1945, Store Kongensgade 69, 1264 Copenhagen K, Denmark. illus.
Formerly (until 1977): Braendende Spoergsmaal (ISSN 0109-5803)

POLITICAL SCIENCE — INTERNATIONAL RELATIONS

956.91   SY   ISSN 0039-7962
HC497.S8
SYRIE ET MONDE ARABE; etude mensuelle economique, politique et statistique. (Text in French) 1951. m. £S2500($275) Office Arabe de Presse et de Documentation, P.O. Box 3550, 67 Place Chahbandar, Damascus, Syria. Eds. A. Khani, Raghda Bittar. charts; stat. **Indexed:** Curr.Cont.M.E., Key to Econ.Sci., P.A.I.S.For.Lang.Ind.
—BLDSC (8589.070000).

327   US
TAKING SIDES: CLASHING VIEWS ON CONTROVERSIAL ISSUES IN WORLD POLITICS. irreg., 3rd ed., 1991. $13.95. Dushkin Publishing Group, Sluice Dock, Guilford, CT 06437-9989. TEL 203-453-4351. FAX 203-453-6000. Ed. John Rourke; Pub. Mimi Egan. **Document type:** academic/scholarly publication.

327   US
TALKING POINTS. irreg. newsstand price: $3.50. Heritage Foundation, 214 Massachusetts Ave., N.E., Washington, DC 20002. TEL 202-546-4400. FAX 202-546-8328.
•Also available online. Vendor(s): Lexis-Nexis.
Description: Presents checklists, questions and answers, plus facts and analyses about complex national issues.

327   IS
TEL AVIV UNIVERSITY. DAVID HOROWITZ INSTITUTE FOR THE RESEARCH OF DEVELOPING COUNTRIES. ANNUAL REPORT. (Text in English) a. Tel Aviv University, David Horowitz Institute for the Research of Developing Countries, Tel Aviv, Israel.

327   IS
TEL AVIV UNIVERSITY. DAVID HOROWITZ INSTITUTE FOR THE RESEARCH OF DEVELOPING COUNTRIES. RESEARCH REPORTS AND PAPERS. (Text in English, Hebrew) 1972. irreg. Tel Aviv University, David Horowitz Institute for the Research of Developing Countries, Tel Aviv, Israel. circ. 250. (looseleaf format)

327 355   UK   ISSN 0954-6553
HV6431
TERRORISM AND POLITICAL VIOLENCE. 1989. q. £42($48) to individuals; institutions £135 ($195) (effective 1996). (Research Institute for the Study of Conflict and Terrorism) Frank Cass, Newbury House, 890-900 Eastern Ave., Newbury Park, Ilford, Essex IG2 7HH, England. TEL 44-181-599-8866. FAX 44-181-599-0984. E-mail: 100067,1576@compuserve.com. Eds. David C. Rapoport, Paul Wilkinson. adv.: B&W page £195 ($275); adv. contact: Anne Kidson. bk.rev. **Indexed:** Br.Hum.Ind., Int.Polit.Sci.Abstr., Polit.Sci.Abstr. **Document type:** academic/scholarly publication.
—BLDSC (8796.127000); SWETS; UnCover. **CCC.**
Description: Offers academic study of all aspects of terrorism and political violence.
Refereed Serial

TERRORISM: DOCUMENTS OF INTERNATIONAL AND LOCAL CONTROL. see *LAW — International Law*

TERRORISM: DOCUMENTS OF INTERNATIONAL AND LOCAL CONTROL. SECOND SERIES. see *LAW — International Law*

TERRORISME & VIOLENCE POLITIQUE. see *CRIMINOLOGY AND LAW ENFORCEMENT*

327 641   UK
TEST BAN VERIFICATION MATTERS. 1990. irreg., no.8, Jan. 1995. £2 per no. Verification Technology Information Centre, Carrara House, 20 Embankment Pl., London WC2N 6NN, England. TEL 0171-925-0867. FAX 0171-925-0861. E-mail: vertic@gn.apc.org. (back issues avail.) **Document type:** monographic series.
Supersedes in part (in 1994): Verification Matters.

327   TH   ISSN 0125-6459
DS586
THAILAND. MINISTRY OF FOREIGN AFFAIRS. FOREIGN AFFAIRS NEWSLETTER. no.9, 1977. m. free. Ministry of Foreign Affairs, Department of Information, Bangkok, Thailand. TEL 2226875. FAX 222-1941. circ. 8,000. **Document type:** newsletter.
Formerly: Thailand. Ministry of Foreign Affairs. News Bulletin.

327 341   US   ISSN 1046-2066
HF1413
THIRD WORLD WITHOUT SUPERPOWERS: COLLECTED DOCUMENTS OF THE GROUP OF 77. 1981. irreg., vol.20, 1993. price varies. Oceana Publications, Inc., 75 Main St., Dobbs Ferry, NY 10522. TEL 914-693-8100. FAX 914-693-0402. Ed. Karl P. Sauvant. circ. 400. (back issues avail.)
Description: Compilation of documents and reports issued by ad hoc committees as well as declarations adopted by ministerial-level meetings and conferences.

327   KO
THIS MONTH IN KOREA. (Text in English) m. Korea International Relations Institute, 37-2, 2-ka, Namsan-dong, Chung-ku, Seoul, S. Korea. TEL 752-6310. Ed. Suh Myung-Suk.

327   CC
TIBET STUDIES. (Text in English) s-a. Tibetan Academy of Social Sciences, Lhasa, Tibet, People's Republic of China. (Dist. by: China International Book Trading Corporation, 21 Chegongzhuang Xilu, Beijing 100044, People's Republic of China) Ed. Trin-ley Top Gyal.

DER TIROLER; Zeitung fuer ein einiges und freies Tirol. see *HISTORY — History Of Europe*

327 628   US   ISSN 1063-4134
D839
TOWARD FREEDOM; a progressive perspective on world events. 1952-19??; resumed 1990. 8/yr. $25; newsstand price: $2.95. Toward Freedom, Inc., 209 College St., Burlington, VT 05401. TEL 802-658-2523. FAX 802-658-3738. Ed. Greg Guma; Robin/Lloyd. adv. contact: Mike Riley. bk.rev.; maps; index. circ. 4,500. (tabloid format) **Document type:** newsletter.
Description: Offers a progressive perspective on international events, issues, and culture.

327   US   ISSN 0041-0063
JX1
TOWSON STATE JOURNAL OF INTERNATIONAL AFFAIRS. 1967. s-a. $3. Towson State University, Department of Political Science, Towson, MD 21204. TEL 410-830-3526. Ed. T. Nicholas Moroney. adv. contact: Amira Ali. bk.rev; adv. rate: 750. **Indexed:** Amer.Bibl.Slavic & E.Eur.Stud, Amer.Hist.& Life, Hist.Abstr., Mid.East: Abstr.& Ind. **Document type:** academic/scholarly publication.
Description: Gives all students an opportunity to publish their ideas and findings in the the field of International Affairs and related subjects.

949.2   NE   ISSN 0023-3412
TRACTATENBLAD VAN HET KONINKRIJK DER NEDERLANDEN. (Text mainly in Dutch; occasionally in English, French) 1951. 200/yr. (Ministerie van Buitenlandse Zaken) Staatsuitgeverij, Chr. Plantijnstraat 2, 2515 TZ The Hague, Netherlands. index. circ. 500. **Indexed:** Key to Econ.Sci.

327   US   ISSN 0192-477X
HC101
TRANSATLANTIC PERSPECTIVES. 1979. 3/yr. free. German Marshall Fund of the United States, 11 Dupont Circle, N.W., Washington, DC 20036. TEL 202-745-3950. FAX 202-265-1662. Ed. E. Jane Beckwith. bk.rev.; circ. 9,000 (controlled). **Indexed:** Ind.Free Per., Sage Pub.Admin.Abstr., Sage Urb.Stud.Abstr. **Document type:** newsletter.
—BLDSC (9020.567700).
Description: Contains articles on U.S.-European relations and projects supported by the Fund, and grants lists and financials.

947   BE   ISSN 0779-3812
TRANSITIONS; ex-revue des pays de l'est. 1960. 2/yr. 1000 BEF to individuals (foreign 1250 BEF); institutions 1500 BEF (foreign 1750 BEF). Universite Libre de Bruxelles, Institut de Sociologie, Centre de Recherches Interdisciplinaires sur la Transition vers l'Economie de Marche des Pays de l'Est, Ave. Jeanne 44, 1050 Brussels, Belgium. TEL 32-2-650-33-60. FAX 32-2-650-35-21. **Document type:** academic/scholarly publication.
—BLDSC (9020.867000).
Former titles (until 1993): Revue des Pays de l'Est (ISSN 0303-9617); (until 1972): Universite Libre de Bruxelles. Centre d'Etude des Pays de l'Est. Revue du Centre d'Etude des Pays de l'Est et du Centre National pour l'Etude des Etats de l'Est (ISSN 0008-9699)

TRANSIZIONE. see *POLITICAL SCIENCE*

327   GW   ISSN 0344-9823
TRANSNATIONAL. irreg. price varies. Europa Union Verlag GmbH, Bachstr. 32, 53115 Bonn, Germany. TEL 0228-7290010. FAX 0228-695734. TELEX 8-86822.

060 327   BE   ISSN 0250-4928
AS1   CODEN: WZSUDS
TRANSNATIONAL ASSOCIATIONS/ASSOCIATIONS TRANSNATIONALES. (Text in English and French) 1949. bi-m. 1750 BEF($56) Union of International Associations - Union des Associations Internationales, 40 rue Washington, 1050 Brussels, Belgium. TEL 32-2-6401808. FAX 32-2-6460525. Ed. J. Raeymaeckers. adv.; bk.rev.; bibl.; charts; illus.; stat.; index. **Indexed:** P.A.I.S., Rural Devel.Abstr. **Document type:** academic/scholarly publication.
—CASDDS; SWETS; UnCover. **CCC.**
Formerly (until vol.29, 1977): International Associations (ISSN 0020-6059)
Description: Covers topics and trends relating to international and transnational organizations, including NGOs, regional associations, legal, social and language issues.

327 364   UK   ISSN 1357-7387
▼**TRANSNATIONAL ORGANIZED CRIME.** 1995. q. £38($50) to individuals; institutions £90 ($145) (effective 1996). Frank Cass, 890-900 Eastern Ave., Newbury Park, Ilford, Essex IG2 7HH, England. TEL 44-181-599-8866. FAX 44-181-599-0984. E-mail: 100067,1576@compuserve.com. Ed. Phil Williams. adv.: B&W page £195 ($145); adv. contact: Anne Kidson. bk.rev.; index. **Document type:** trade publication.
Description: Takes a multidisciplinary look at cross-border criminal activities, the transnational criminal organizations that engage in them, and the threat they pose at both the national and international levels.
Refereed Serial

320.5   SZ   ISSN 0252-9505
TRANSNATIONAL PERSPECTIVES; an independent journal of world politics and social policy. 1974. 3/yr. $20. Case Postale 161, CH-1211 Geneva 16, Switzerland. TEL 033-50047406. FAX 033-50047452. Ed. Rene Wadlow; Pub. Rene Wadlow. adv.; bk.rev.; illus. circ. 6,000. (also avail. in microfiche) **Indexed:** HR Rep. (1985-), P.A.I.S., Refug.Abstr. **Document type:** academic/scholarly publication.
Formerly: World Federalist (ISSN 0043-843X)

327   SI   ISSN 0082-6316
TRENDS IN SOUTHEAST ASIA. (Text in English) 1971. irreg., no.9, 1986. price varies. Institute of Southeast Asian Studies, Heng Mui Keng Terrace, Pasir Panjang, Singapore 0511, Singapore. TEL 7780955. FAX TEL 7780955. TELEX RS 37068 ISEAS. E-mail: pubsunit@merlion.iseas.ac.sg. (Subscr. in U.S. to: Ashgate, Old Post Rd., Brookfield, VT 05036. TEL 802-276-3162) **Document type:** academic/scholarly publication.
Description: Political trends in Southeast Asia.

327   US   ISSN 0275-5351
D839
TRIALOGUE; report of the annual plenary meeting. 1973. a. $20 includes Task Force Reports, Triangle Papers. Trilateral Commission, 345 E. 46 St., New York, NY 10017. TEL 212-661-1180. FAX 212-949-7268. Ed. Cjarles B. Heck; Pub. Charles B. Heck. circ. 5,500. **Indexed:** P.A.I.S. **Document type:** academic/scholarly publication.

327   US
TRIANGLE PAPERS. 1973. irreg. (approx. 1-2/yr.). $20 (includes Trialogue). Trilateral Commission, 345 E. 46th St., New York, NY 10017. TEL 212-661-1180. FAX 212-949-7268. TELEX 235128 NYU UR. Ed. Charles B. Heck; Pub. Charles B. Heck. circ. 3,000. (back issues avail.) **Document type:** academic/scholarly publication.

THE TRIBUNE. see *WOMEN'S INTERESTS*

327   FR   ISSN 0988-9914
TRIMESTRE DU MONDE. 1988. q. 210 F. to individuals; institutions 280 F. Observatoire des Relations Internationales, 10 av. Pierre Larousse, 92241 Malakoff, France. TEL 42-53-27-65. FAX 46-56-08-59. Ed. Fereydoun A. Khavand. **Indexed:** Int.Polit.Sci.Abstr.

POLITICAL SCIENCE — INTERNATIONAL RELATIONS

327 341 UK ISSN 0966-9221
TRUST AND VERIFY. 1989. 10/yr. £15 to individuals; institutions £25. Verification Technology Information Centre (VERTIC), Carrara House, 20 Embankment Pl., London WC2N 6NN, England. TEL 0171-925-0867. FAX 0171-925-0861. E-mail: vertic@gn.apc.org. **Document type:** bulletin.
Description: Updates readers on events on the fast-moving field of verification technology.

TUDUV-STUDIE. REIHE POLITIKWISSENSCHAFTEN. see POLITICAL SCIENCE

TURKEY BRIEFING. see POLITICAL SCIENCE — Civil Rights

THE TURKISH TIMES. see ETHNIC INTERESTS

327 RU ISSN 0320-7986
TWENTIETH CENTURY AND PEACE; bulletin of the Soviet Peace Committee. Russian edition: Vek 20 i Mir. French edition: Vingtieme Siecle et la Paix. German edition: 20 Jahrhundert und der Frieden. Spanish edition: Siglo 20 y la Paz. (Editions in English, French, German, Russian, Spanish) 1958. m. 1.20 Rub. Sovetskii Komitet Zashchity Mira - Soviet Peace Committee, 16-2 Gorky St., 103009 Moscow, Russia. TEL 200-38-07. Ed. Anatoly Belyaev. adv.; bk.rev. **Indexed:** Curr.Dig.Sov.Press. **Document type:** bulletin.
Description: Includes controversial topical themes like Chernobyl, perestroika and glasnost. Retrospective material on the Stalin years, Russian involvement in World War II and the 1917 Revolution add historical perspective to current events.

366 US
TWENTIETH CENTURY FUND. NEWSLETTER. 1949. irreg. (approx. 3/yr.). free. Twentieth Century Fund, 41 E. 70th St., New York, NY 10021. TEL 212-535-4441. FAX 212-535-7534. Ed. Beverly Goldberg. circ. 10,000. (reprint service avail. from KTO) **Indexed:** Vert.File Ind. **Document type:** newsletter.
Former titles: Twentieth Century Fund. Bulletin; Twentieth Century Fund. Newsletter (ISSN 0041-4611)

TWENTY-FIRST CENTURY POLICY REVIEW; an American, Caribbean and African forum. see BUSINESS AND ECONOMICS — International Development And Assistance

U N C H S (HABITAT) SHELTER BULLETIN. (United Nations Centre for Human Settlements (Habitat)) see HOUSING AND URBAN PLANNING

U N C H S HABITAT NEWS. (United Nations Centre for Human Settlements (Habitat)) see HOUSING AND URBAN PLANNING

341.1 UN ISSN 0251-7329
JX1977.A1
U N CHRONICLE. (Editions in English, French and Spanish) 1964. 11/yr. $20. United Nations Publications, Room DC2-853, New York, NY 10017. TEL 212-963-8302; 800-253-9646. FAX 212-963-3489. (Or: Distribution and Sales Section, Palais des Nations, CH-1211 Geneva 10, Switzerland) bk.rev.; bibl.; charts; illus.; index. circ. 7,000. (also avail. in microfiche from UMI) **Indexed:** Acad.Ind., C.L.I., Deep Sea Res.& Oceanogr.Abstr., Hlth.Ind., HR Rep. (1986-1987), Leg.Per., Mag.Ind., PMR, R.G., Soc.Sci.Ind.
●Also available online. Vendor(s): University Microfilms International.
—BLDSC (9083.570000); Faxon; SWETS; UMI; UnCover.
Formerly: U N Monthly Chronicle (ISSN 0041-5367); Which superseded: United Nations Review.
Description: Contains reports on the wide-ranging activities of the entire UN system as it deals with problems ranging from food and health to nuclear disarmament and the world economy.

327 355 UN ISSN 1012-4934
JX1974
U N I D I R NEWSLETTER/LETTRE DE L'U N I D I R. (Text in English and French) 1988. q. $25. United Nations Institute for Disarmament Research, Palais des Nations, CH-1211 Geneva 10, Switzerland. TEL 04122-9174254. FAX 04122-9170176. Ed. Chantal de Jonge Oudraat. bk.rev.; bibl. circ. 4,700. **Document type:** newsletter, academic/scholarly publication.
Description: Each issue focuses on a specific subject in the field of disarmament and international security. Also includes conference announcements and news from institutes.

327 US
U N REFORM CAMPAIGNER; dedicated to building a more effective United Nations systems. 1976. s-a. $10. Campaign for U N Reform, Box 15270, Washington, DC 20003-0270. TEL 202-546-3956. Ed. Eric Cox. circ. 2,000.
Description: Bipartisan national political organization doing lobbying, electioneering and educational work promoting a more effective United Nations system.

327 UN
U N STUDIES. 1982. irreg. Heritage Foundation, 214 Massachusetts Ave., N.E., Washington, DC 20002. TEL 202-546-4400. (looseleaf format; also avail. in microfiche; back issues avail.)

327 333.7 US
U S ASSOCIATION FOR THE CLUB OF ROME NEWSLETTER. 1977. irreg. (6-8/yr.). $35. U S Association for the Club of Rome, 4 Linden Sq., Wellesley, MA 02181. TEL 617-235-5320. FAX 617-237-2842. Ed. David Dodson Gray. bk.rev. circ. 350. (tabloid format) **Document type:** newsletter.

327 US ISSN 0164-3886
DS701
U S - CHINA REVIEW. 1975. q. $16 to individuals; institutions $20 (foreign $22). U S - China Peoples Friendship Association, 122 W. 27th St., 10th Fl., New York, NY 10001-6227. TEL 212-736-7355. Ed. Hugh Deane. adv.; bk.rev.; circ. 17,000 (controlled). **Indexed:** Mid.East: Abstr.& Ind., New Per.Ind. **Document type:** academic/scholarly publication.
—UnCover.
Incorporates: New China (ISSN 0161-0643)
Description: Features articles on Chinese politics, economics, social trends and culture, as well as on U.S.-China relations.

327 US ISSN 1070-4973
E183.8.I55
U S - IRAN REVIEW. 1993. m. Forum on American - Iranian Relations (FAIR Foundation), 2000 L St., N.W., Ste. 200, Washington, DC 20036. TEL 202-416-1635. Ed. Joseph Schecla.

U S - THIRD WORLD POLICY PERSPECTIVES. see HISTORY

327 DK ISSN 0903-7845
UDENRIGS; det udenrigspolitiske magasin. 1945. q. DKK 250 (typically set in Mar.). Udenrigspolitiske Selskab - Foreign Policy Society, Amaliegade 40 A, DK-1256 Copenhagen K, Denmark. TEL 33-14-88-86. FAX 33-14-85-20. Eds. Torben Krogh, Brita V. Andersen. adv.; bk.rev.; charts; illus.; stat.; index. circ. 2,000. (back issues avail.)
Formerly: Fremtiden (ISSN 0016-1020)

327 DK ISSN 0041-5693
UDENRIGSPOLITISKE SKRIFTER. 1953. q. DKK 119. Udenrigspolitiske Selskab - Foreign Policy Society, Amaliegade 40 A, 1256 Copenhagen K, Denmark. Ed.Bd. circ. 2,000.

327 330.904 DK ISSN 0106-0570
UDVIKLING/DEVELOPMENT. 10/yr. DKK 85. Danida, Ministry of Foreign Affairs - Danish International Development Assistance, Asiatisk Plads 2, DK-1448 Copenhagen K, Denmark. TEL 33-92-08-48. FAX 33-92-07-10. TELEX 31292-ETR-DK. Ed. Jesper Soe. illus. **Document type:** government publication.

327 GW ISSN 0343-0553
UEBERBLICK; Zeitschrift fuer oekumenische Begegnung und internationale Zusammenarbeit. 1965. q. DM.25. Verlag Dienste in Uebersee, Esplanade 14, 20354 Hamburg, Germany. TEL 040-341444. FAX 040-353800. Ed.Bd. bk.rev.; film rev.; charts; illus. circ. 16,000. (back issues avail.) **Document type:** bulletin.

327 FI ISSN 0501-0659
ULKOPOLITIIKKA/FINNISH JOURNAL OF FOREIGN AFFAIRS/UTRIKESPOLITIK. 1972. q. FIM 140. Ulkopoliittinen Instituutti - Finnish Institute of International Affairs, Mannerheimintre 15 A, FIN-00260 Helsinki, Finland. TEL 358-0-490-100. FAX 358-0-490-989. Ed. Jyrki Iivonen. circ. 3,000.
Description: Specializes in foreign policy questions.

ULTIMATE ISSUES. see RELIGIONS AND THEOLOGY — Judaic

327 UN ISSN 0082-7509
UNESCO. RECORDS OF THE GENERAL CONFERENCE. PROCEEDINGS. (Text in English, French, Russian and Spanish) irreg., 26th session, 1991. price varies. Unesco, 7-9 Place de Fontenoy, 75700 Paris, France. **Document type:** proceedings.

327 UN ISSN 0082-7517
UNESCO. RECORDS OF THE GENERAL CONFERENCE. RESOLUTIONS. (Text in Arabic, English, French, Spanish and Russian) irreg., 26th session, 1991. price varies. Unesco, 7-9 Place de Fontenoy, 75700 Paris, France. TEL 45-77-16-10. **Document type:** proceedings.

327 UN ISSN 0082-7525
UNESCO. REPORT OF THE DIRECTOR-GENERAL ON THE ACTIVITIES OF THE ORGANIZATION. (Text in Arabic, English, French, Russian and Spanish) 1959. biennial. price varies. Unesco, 7-9 Place de Fontenoy, 75700 Paris, France. (also avail. in microfiche from CIS) **Indexed:** IIS.
—BLDSC (7448.080000).

327 UN
UNESCO ASSOCIATION - U S A NEWSLETTER. 1974. bi-m. $20. Unesco Association - U S A, Inc., 5815 Lawton Ave., Oakland, CA 94618-1510. TEL 510-654-4638. FAX 510-658-3469. Ed. Dorothy Hackbarth. **Document type:** newsletter.
Description: Conveys the global impact and the importance of understanding America's place in the world by creating an understanding of international issues.

327 US ISSN 0250-779X
JX1904.5
UNESCO YEARBOOK ON PEACE AND CONFLICT STUDIES. 1981. a. price varies. (United Nations Educational, Scientific and Cultural Organization) Greenwood Press, Inc. (Subsidiary of: Greenwood Publishing Group Inc.), 88 Post Rd. W., Box 5007, Westport, CT 06881-5007. TEL 203-226-3571. FAX 203-222-1502. Ed. Hylke Tromp. **Indexed:** GeoRef.

327 US ISSN 0193-4783
UNITED KINGDOM - COMMONWEALTH OF NATIONS - DIRECTORY OF GOVERNMENTS. (Supplement avail.: Across the Seas (ISSN 0733-0081)) 1979. irreg., latest 1987. $50. Political Research, Inc., Tegoland at Bent Tree, 16850 Dallas Pkwy., Dallas, TX 75248. TEL 214-931-8827. FAX 214-248-7159. Ed. John Clements. **Document type:** directory.
Description: Covers geography, history, government, officials, economy and trade of the United Kingdom and the Commonwealth of Nations.

341.13 UN
UNITED NATIONS. CONFERENCE ON TRADE AND DEVELOPMENT. TRADE AND DEVELOPMENT BOARD. OFFICIAL RECORDS. SUPPLEMENTS. 1965. irreg. price varies. United Nations Publications, Rm. DC2-853, New York, NY 10017. TEL 212-963-8302; 800-253-9646. FAX 212-963-3489. TELEX 28-96-96. (Or: Palais des Nations, 1211 Geneva 10, Switzerland) circ. 3,500. (also avail. in microfiche)
Formerly: United Nations. Trade and Development Board. Official Records. Supplements (ISSN 0082-8483)
Description: Includes numbered supplements which contain the resolutions and decisions of the Trade and Development Board; reports and resolutions and decisions of its main subsidiary bodies.

POLITICAL SCIENCE — INTERNATIONAL RELATIONS

341.13 UN ISSN 0082-8092
UNITED NATIONS. ECONOMIC AND SOCIAL COUNCIL. OFFICIAL RECORDS. irreg. price varies. United Nations Publications, Rm. DC2-853, New York, NY 10017. TEL 212-963-8302; 800-253-9646. FAX 212-963-3489. (Or: Distribution and Sales Section, Palais des Nations, CH-1211 Geneva 10, Switzerland) (also avail. in microfiche)

341.13 UN ISSN 0082-8416
UNITED NATIONS. SECURITY COUNCIL. OFFICIAL RECORDS. (Supplement avail.) irreg. price varies. United Nations Publications, Rm. DC2-853, New York, NY 10017. TEL 212-963-8302; 800-253-9646. FAX 212-963-3489. (Or: Distribution and Sales Section, Palais des Nations, CH-1211 Geneva 10, Switzerland) (also avail. in microfiche)
—BLDSC (6242.487000).

341.13 UN ISSN 0257-067X
UNITED NATIONS. SECURITY COUNCIL. OFFICIAL RECORDS. SUPPLEMENT. French edition: Nations Unies. Conseil de Securite. Documents Officials. Supplement (ISSN 0257-0769); Russian edition: Organizatsiya Ob'edinennykh Natsii. Sovet Bezopasnosti. Ofitsial'nye Otchety. Dopolnenie (ISSN 0257-1250); Spanish edition: Naciones Unidas. Consejo de Seguridad. Documentos Oficiales. Suplemento (ISSN 0257-0971) 1950. a. United Nations Publications, Room DC2-853, New York, NY 10017. TEL 212-963-8302; 800-253-9646. FAX 212-963-3489. (Or: Distribution and Sales Section, Palais des Nations, CH-1211 Geneva 10, Switzerland)

341.13 UN ISSN 0082-8505
UNITED NATIONS. TRUSTEESHIP COUNCIL. OFFICIAL RECORDS. irreg., 39th session, 1972. price varies. United Nations Publications, Rm. DC2-853, New York, NY 10017. TEL 212-963-8302; 800-253-9646. FAX 212-963-3489. (Or: Distribution and Sales Section, Palais des Nations, CH-1211 Geneva 10, Switzerland) (also avail. in microfiche)
—BLDSC (6242.493000).

327 330 UN
UNITED NATIONS. TRUSTEESHIP COUNCIL. OFFICIAL RECORDS. ANNEXES - SESSIONAL FASCICLE. 1946. a. United Nations Publications, Rm. DC-0853, New York, NY 10017. TEL 212-963-8302; 800-253-9646. FAX 212-963-3489. Text in English, French.

327 330 UN
UNITED NATIONS. TRUSTEESHIP COUNCIL. OFFICIAL RECORDS. RESOLUTIONS. (Text in English, French) 1946? a. United Nations Publications, Rm. DC2-0853, New York, NY 10017. TEL 212-963-8302; 800-253-9646. FAX 212-963-3489.

341.13 UN ISSN 0082-8513
UNITED NATIONS. TRUSTEESHIP COUNCIL. OFFICIAL RECORDS. SUPPLEMENTS. irreg. price varies. United Nations Publications, Rm. DC2-853, New York, NY 10017. TEL 212-963-8302; 800-253-9646. FAX 212-963-3489. (Or: Distribution and Sales Section, Palais des Nations, CH-1211 Geneva 10, Switzerland) (also avail. in microfiche)

327 330 UN
UNITED NATIONS. TRUSTEESHIP COUNCIL. OFFICIAL RECORDS. VERBATIM RECORDS OF PLENARY MEETINGS. (Text in English, French) 1946? a. United Nations Publications, Rm. DC-0853, New York, NY 10017. TEL 212-963-8302; 800-253-9646. FAX 212-963-3489.

341.13 UN ISSN 0082-8521
JX1977.A37
UNITED NATIONS. YEARBOOK. Key Title: Yearbook of the United Nations. 1946. a. price varies. (United Nations, Department of Public Information) United Nations Publications, Rm. DC2-853, New York, NY 10017. TEL 212-963-8902; 800-253-9646. FAX 212-963-3489. (Or: Distribution and Sales Section, Palais des Nations, CH-1200 Geneva 10, Switzerland) index. (also avail. in microfiche; reprint service avail. from KTO) **Indexed:** Refug.Abstr.
—CCC.

327 370.196 CN
UNITED NATIONS ASSOCIATION IN CANADA. QUARTERLY BULLETIN. (Text in English, French) 1975. q. Can.$20. United Nations Association in Canada, 808-63 Sparks St., Ottawa, ON K1P 5A6, Canada. TEL 613-232-5751. FAX 613-563-2455. Ed. Francois Coutu. bk.rev. circ. 3,500. **Document type:** bulletin.

327 UN ISSN 0457-8074
UNITED NATIONS ASSOCIATION OF THE REPUBLIC OF CHINA NEWS LETTER. (Text in English) 1950. m. free. United Nations Association of the Republic of China, 101 Ning Po West St., Taipei, Taiwan, Republic of China. TEL 02-301-2654. Ed. Lei Pao-chung. circ. 1,400. **Document type:** newsletter.
Description: Discusses political reform, trade policy, economics, foreign relations, and news about mainland China and Taiwan.

327 323.4 UN
▼**THE UNITED NATIONS BLUE BOOKS SERIES.** 1995. irreg. $29.95 per vol. United Nations Publications, Rm. DC2-853, Dept. 060D, New York, NY 10017. TEL 212-963-8302; 800-253-9646. FAX 212-963-3489. **Document type:** monographic series.
Description: Details U.N. efforts at international peace-keeping, human rights monitoring, international development, nonproliferation, and conflict resolutions.

327 AT ISSN 0814-1967
UNITED NATIONS GENERAL ASSEMBLY: REPORT OF THE AUSTRALIAN DELEGATION. 1946. a. price varies. Australian Government Publishing Service, G.P.O. Box 84, Canberra, A.C.T. 2601, Australia. TEL 61-6-295-4612. FAX 61-6-295-4500.
—CCC.
Formerly: Australian Mission to the United Nations. United Nations General Assembly. Australian Delegation. Report.

341.23 NZ ISSN 0110-1951
DU400
UNITED NATIONS HANDBOOK (YEAR). a. $16. Ministry of Foreign Affairs and Trade, Private Bag 18-901, Wellington 1, New Zealand. **Document type:** government publication.
Supersedes: United Nations and Related Agencies Handbook.
Description: Contains a current list of all the organizations in the U.N. with membership roster. Explains their aims, committee structure, and the legal basis for their existence.

341.13 US ISSN 0743-9180
UNITED NATIONS ISSUES CONFERENCE. REPORT. 1970. a. free. Stanley Foundation, 216 Sycamore St., Ste. 500, Muscatine, IA 52761. TEL 319-264-1500. FAX 319-264-0864. circ. 12,000.
—BLDSC (7673.780000).
Former titles: Conference on United Nations Procedures. Report (ISSN 0069-8601); Conference on Organization and Procedures of the United Nations Report.
Description: Reports discussion of current concern or organizational procedure by groups of officials and academic specialists.

341.13 US ISSN 0748-433X
UNITED NATIONS OF THE NEXT DECADE CONFERENCE. REPORT. 1965. a. free. Stanley Foundation, 216 Sycamore St., Ste. 500, Muscatine, IA 52761. TEL 319-264-1500. FAX 319-264-0864. circ. 15,000.
—BLDSC (7673.787000).
Description: Discussion of a major issue and its future implications by groups of officials and international experts.

327 341 UN ISSN 0817-9751
UNITED NATIONS REVIEW. 1971. bi-m. free. United Nations Information Centre, G.P.O. Box 4045, Sydney, N.S.W. 2001, Australia. TEL 02-283-1144. FAX 02-283-1319. circ. 1,800. (reprint service avail. from WSH) **Indexed:** Mag.Ind. **Document type:** newsletter.
Formerly (until 1986): United Nations in Action (ISSN 0310-1975)
Description: Covers United Nation matters of general interest.

327 382 338.91 US ISSN 0746-6455
UNITED NATIONS WEEKLY REPORT. 1982. w. $93. Renate B. McCarter, Ed. & Pub., 823 Park Ave., New York, NY 10021. TEL 212-288-8505. circ. 1,400. (back issues avail.)

354.47 US ISSN 0145-0700
JN6521
U.S. CENTRAL INTELLIGENCE AGENCY. APPEARANCES OF SOVIET LEADERS. s-a. U.S. Central Intelligence Agency, Washington, DC 20505. (Dist. to non-U.S. Government users by: Document Expediting (DOCEX) Project, Library of Congress, Washington, DC 20540)

327 US ISSN 0012-3099
JX1705
U.S. DEPARTMENT OF STATE. DIPLOMATIC LIST. q. $8.50 (foreign $10.65). U.S. Department of State, Office of Information Services, Washington, DC 20520. TEL 202-655-4000. (Subscr. to: Superintendent of Documents, Box 371954, Pittsburgh, PA 15250-7954. TEL 202-512-1800. FAX 202-512-2250) (also avail. in microform from PMC; back issues avail.) **Document type:** directory, government publication.
Description: Lists foreign diplomats in and around Washington, DC.

327 US ISSN 0023-0790
JX1705
U.S. DEPARTMENT OF STATE. KEY OFFICERS OF FOREIGN SERVICE POSTS; guide for business representatives. s-a. $5 (foreign $6.25). U.S. Department of State, Office of Information Services, Washington, DC 20520. TEL 202-655-4000. (Subscr. to: Superintendent of Documents, Box 371954, Pittsburgh, PA 15250-7954. TEL 202-512-1800. FAX 202-512-2250) (back issues avail.) **Document type:** directory, government publication.
●Also available online. Vendor(s): Knight-Ridder, Inc.
Description: Lists key officers at Foreign Service posts, as well as embassies, legations, and consulates general.

327.73 US ISSN 1051-7693
JX232
U.S. DEPARTMENT OF STATE DISPATCH. 1939. w. $91 (foreign $113.75). U.S. Department of State, Bureau of Public Affairs, Office of Public Communication, 2201 C St., N.W., Washington, DC 20502. TEL 202-647-6265. (Subscr. to: Superintendent of Documents, U.S. Government Printing Office, Box 371954, Pittsburgh, PA 15250-7954. TEL 202-512-1800. FAX 202-512-2250) Ed. Colleen Elliott. bibl.; charts; illus.; index. circ. 10,000. (also avail. in microform from UMI,MCA,BHP,PMC; microfiche from BHP; reprint service avail. from UMI; back issues avail.) **Indexed:** Acad.Ind., Amer.Bibl.Slavic & E.Eur.Stud, C.L.I., Deep Sea Res.& Oceanogr.Abstr., Ind.U.S.Gov.Per., Key to Econ.Sci., Leg.Per., Mag.Ind., Mid.East: Abstr.& Ind., P.A.I.S., Pers.Lit., PMR, PROMT, R.G. **Document type:** government publication.
●Also available online. Vendor(s): Knight-Ridder, Inc.
—BLDSC (3501.284600); SWETS; UMI; UnCover.
Incorporates (in 1991): U.S. Department of State. Bureau of Public Affairs. Current Policy (ISSN 0196-8939) & Gist (Washington) (ISSN 0364-2623); **Formerly (until 1990):** U.S. Department of State. Bulletin (ISSN 0041-7610)
Description: Compiles major speeches, congressional testimony, policy statements, fact sheets, and other foreign-policy information from the U.S. Department of State.

327 US
U.S. FOREIGN BROADCAST INFORMATION SERVICE. TRENDS. w. $240 in N. America (foreign $480). U.S. National Technical Information Service, 5285 Port Royal Rd., Springfield, VA 22161. TEL 703-487-4600. FAX 703-321-8547. TELEX 64617. (also avail. in microfiche)
Formerly: Trends in Communist Media.
Description: Offers expert analysis of international political events.

327 US ISSN 0083-3088
U.S. PEACE CORPS. ANNUAL REPORT. 1962. irreg. free. U.S. Peace Corps, 1990 K St., N.W., Washington, DC 20526. TEL 202-254-5010. Ed. James C. Flanigan.

POLITICAL SCIENCE — INTERNATIONAL RELATIONS

327 US
UNITED STATES IN THE WORLD: FOREIGN PERSPECTIVES. 1975. irreg., no.4, 1985. price varies. University of Chicago Press, 5801 S. Ellis Ave., Chicago, IL 60637. TEL 312-702-7899. Ed. Akira Iriye. adv.; bk.rev. (reprint service avail. from UMI,ISI)
Refereed Serial

327 US ISSN 0083-0208
UNITED STATES PARTICIPATION IN THE UNITED NATIONS; report by the President to Congress. (Subseries of: International Organization and Conference Series) 1947. a. U.S. Department of State, Bureau of International Organization Affairs, 2201 C St., N.W., Washington, DC 20520. (Subscr. to: Superintendent of Documents, U.S. Government Printing Office, Box 371954, Pittsburgh, PA 15250-7954. TEL 202-783-3238. FAX 202-512-2233) **Document type:** government publication.

327.2 CL
UNIVERSIDAD DE GUAYAQUIL. ESCUELA DE DIPLOMACIA. REVISTA. 1973. irreg. Universidad de Guayaquil, Escuela de Diplomacia, Calle Chile 900, Apdo. 471, Guayaquil, Chile.

UNIVERSIDAD DE PANAMA. FACULTAD DE DERECHO Y CIENCIAS POLITICAS. CUADERNOS. see *LAW*

327 GW ISSN 0341-3233
UNIVERSITAET HAMBURG. INSTITUT FUER INTERNATIONALE ANGELEGENHEITEN. VEROEFFENTLICHUNGEN. 1975. irreg., vol. 11, 1983. price varies. Nomos Verlagsgesellschaft mbH und Co. KG, Waldseestr. 3-5, 76530 Baden-Baden, Germany. TEL 07221-21040. FAX 07221-210427. (Subscr. to: Postfach 610, 76484 Baden-Baden, Germany) **Indexed:** Rural Recreat.Tour.Abstr., World Agri.Econ.& Rural Sociol.Abstr. **Document type:** proceedings.

UNIVERSITAET HAMBURG. INSTITUT FUER INTERNATIONALE ANGELEGENHEITEN. WERKHEFTE. see *LAW — International Law*

327 BE
UNIVERSITE DE PAIX. 1976. 4/yr. 200 BEF (effective 1995-1996). Universite de Paix - University of Peace, Bd. du Nord 4, 5000 Namur, Belgium. TEL 32-81-226102. FAX 32-81-231882. Ed. Francois Bazier. bk.rev. circ. 4,000. **Document type:** academic/scholarly publication, newsletter.
Formerly (until 1989): U P Informations (ISSN 0777-8171)
Description: Reports news and information on non-violent conflict resolution methods, including mediation and negotiation, peace education, and peace problems in general.

320 US
UNIVERSITY OF CALIFORNIA AT BERKELEY. INTERNATIONAL AND AREA STUDIES. EXPLORATORY ESSAYS. irreg., no.2. price varies. University of California at Berkeley, International and Area Studies, 2223 Fulton St., 3rd Fl., Berkeley, CA 94720. TEL 415-642-7189. FAX 415-643-7062. E-mail: bojana@uclink2.berkeley.edu. Ed. Bojana Ristich. **Document type:** monographic series, academic/scholarly publication.

320 US ISSN 0731-6321
UNIVERSITY OF CALIFORNIA AT BERKELEY. INTERNATIONAL AREA STUDIES. POLICY PAPERS IN INTERNATIONAL AFFAIRS. (Former name of issuing body: Institute of International Studies) 1977. irreg. (2-3/yr.). price varies. University of California at Berkeley, International and Area Studies, 2223 Fulton St., 3rd Fl., Berkeley, CA 94720. TEL 415-642-7189. FAX 415-643-7062. E-mail: bojana@uclink2.berkeley.edu. Ed. Bojana Ristich. (back issues avail.) **Document type:** academic/scholarly publication, monographic series.
—BLDSC (6543.327200).
Description: Publishes essays on important current policy issues related to international affairs.

UNIVERSITY OF CAMBRIDGE. FACULTY OF ECONOMICS AND POLITICS. RESEARCH PAPER. see *BUSINESS AND ECONOMICS*

327 UK
UNIVERSITY OF EDINBURGH. DEPARTMENT OF POLITICS. WORKING PAPER SERIES. irreg., no.13, 1993. University of Edinburgh, Department of Politics, 31 Buccleuch Pl., Edinburgh EH8 9JT, Scotland. **Document type:** academic/scholarly publication, monographic series.
—BLDSC (9350.107100).

327 SA ISSN 0257-1447
UNIVERSITY OF PRETORIA. INSTITUTE FOR STRATEGIC STUDIES. BULLETIN. Key Title: I S S U P Bulletin. 1979. 4/yr. R.42.50($45) (includes Strategic Review for Southern Africa) (effective 1995). University of Pretoria, Institute for Strategic Studies, Pretoria 0002, South Africa. TEL 27-12-420-2407. FAX 27-12-43-2185. TELEX 3-22723 SA. E-mail: PULLES@libarts.up.ac.za. **Document type:** bulletin.

327 US
UPDATE CENTRAL AMERICA. 1981. 10/yr. $15. Inter-Religious Task Force on Central America, 475 Riverside Dr., Rm. 563, New York, NY 10115. TEL 212-870-3383. circ. 2,000. (tabloid format; back issues avail.)
Description: Mobilize U.S. religious and solidarity activities toward a more just U.S. policy towards Central America.

327.481 NO
UTENRIKSPOLITISKE SKRIFTER/NORWEGIAN FOREIGN POLICY STUDIES. (Text in English, Norwegian) irreg. Norsk Utenrikspolitisk Instiutt - Norwegian Institute of International Affairs, Postboks 8159, Dep., 0033 Oslo 1, Norway. TEL 47-22-17-70-50. FAX 47-22-17-70-15. E-mail: PUB@NUPI.NO.

327 341 UK
V E R T I C MATTERS. Variant title: V E R T I C Annual Report. 1987. a. Verification Technology Information Centre (VERTIC), Carrara House, 20 Embankment Pl., London WC2N 6NN, England. TEL 0171-925-0867. FAX 0171-925-0861. E-mail: vertic@gn.apc.org. (back issues avail.) **Document type:** corporate report.

VAART FOERSVAR. see *MILITARY*

327 SW ISSN 0042-2754
VAERLDSPOLITIKENS DAGSFRAGOR. 1940. 12/yr. SEK 208 in the Nordic countries; elsewhere SEK 308. Utrikespolitiska Institutet - Swedish Institute of International Affairs, Box 1253, 111 82 Stockholm, Sweden. Ed. Ulla Nordloef. charts. circ. 7,500. **Document type:** academic/scholarly publication, consumer publication.

VENTO DEL SUD; periodico di lotta meridionale. see *ETHNIC INTERESTS*

327 GW ISSN 0042-384X
VEREINTE NATIONEN. 1962. bi-m. DM.45($28) (Deutsche Gesellschaft fuer die Vereinten Nationen) Nomos Verlagsgesellschaft mbH und Co. KG, Waldseestr. 3-5, 76530 Baden-Baden, Germany. TEL 07221-21040. FAX 07221-210427. Ed. Volker Weyel. adv.; bk.rev.; charts; stat.; illus. circ. 3,600. **Indexed:** P.A.I.S.For.Lang.Ind. **Document type:** bulletin.
—SWETS.
Description: Presents articles, reports and documentation concerning the procedures and actions of the UN

327 341 UK ISSN 1355-5847
VERIFICATION (YEAR). 1991. a. price varies. Verification Technology Information Centre (VERTIC), Carrara House, 20 Embankment Pl., London WC2N 6NN, England. TEL 0171-925-0867. FAX 0171-925-0861. E-mail: vertic@gn.apc.org. Eds. J.B. Poole, R. Guthrie. **Document type:** bulletin.
Formerly (until 1993): Verification Report (Year) (ISSN 0963-1607)

327 341 UK
VERIFICATION MATTERS BRIEFING PAPER. 1990. irreg., no.2, Mar. 1995. £2 per no. Verification Technology Information Centre (VERTIC), Carrara House, 20 Embankment Pl., London WC2N 6NN, England. TEL 0171-925-0867. FAX 0171-925-0861. E-mail: vertic@gn.apc.org. (back issues avail.) **Document type:** monographic series.
Supersedes in part (in 1994): Verification Matters.

327 GW
VEROEFFENTLICHUNGEN ZUR KULTUR UND GESELLSCHAFT IM OESTLICHEN EUROPA. 1992. irreg. DM.29.80. (Universitaet Bremen, Forschungsstelle Osteuropa) Edition Temmen, Hohenlohestr. 21, 28209 Bremen, Germany. TEL 0421-344280. FAX 0421-348094. Ed. Horst Temmen. **Document type:** academic/scholarly publication.

327 AU
VERZEICHNIS DER KONSULARISCHEN VERTRETUNGEN IN OESTERREICH. 1973. bi-m. Bundesministerium fuer Auswaertige Angelegenheiten, Ballhausplatz 2, A-1014 Vienna, Austria. circ. controlled. **Document type:** directory, government publication.

327 355.115 US ISSN 1063-9381
VETERANS FOR PEACE JOURNAL. 1986. q. $15. Veterans for Peace, Inc., Box 3881, Portland, ME 04104. TEL 207-773-1431. FAX 207-773-0804. Ed. Jerry Gensio. bk.rev. circ. 2,500. (back issues avail.) **Document type:** newsletter.
Description: Addresses the issues of foreign policy, the cost of war, disarmament, peaceful conflict, and United Nations reform.

327 380 HK
VIET NAM NGAU NAY. s-m. $525. Beca Investments Ltd., Bank of America Bldg., No. 606, Harcourt Rd., Central, Hong Kong. TEL 8122614. FAX 8126046. **Document type:** newsletter.
Description: Monitors Vietnamese and international press and information.

327 IT
VIEWS; rivista socialista di politica internazionale. 1991. q. L.50000 (effective 1992). Istituto per la Cooperazione Internazionale Politica, Economica e Culturale, Via Uffici del Vicario 49, 00186 Rome, Italy. TEL 06-6797585. Ed.Bd.

VIGIL/HA-MISHMAR. see *ETHNIC INTERESTS*

327 GW ISSN 0938-863X
VILLA VIGONI. JAHRBUCH. 1990. a. (Verein der Villa Vigoni e.V.) Max Niemeyer Verlag, Postfach 2140, 72011 Tuebingen, Germany. TEL 07071-98940. FAX 07071-989450. circ. 2,000. **Document type:** academic/scholarly publication.

327 FR ISSN 1149-8315
VINGTIEME SIECLE FEDERALISTE. no.396, 1968. q. 160 F. La Federation, 244 rue de Rivoli, 75001 Paris, France. Ed. Jacques Bassot. bk.rev.; bibl.

266 276 BE ISSN 0042-7527
G1
VIVANT UNIVERS; revue de la promotion humaine et chretienne en Afrique et dans le monde. 1934. bi-m. 1168 BEF($30) ASBL "Grands Lacs", 115 Chaussee de Dinant, 5000 Namur, Belgium. Ed. R.P. Boom. adv.; bk.rev.; abstr.; bibl.; charts; illus.; stat. circ. 20,000. **Indexed:** World Agri.Econ.& Rural Sociol.Abstr.
Formerly: Vivante Afrique.

327 943 947 GW ISSN 0042-8337
VOLK AUF DEM WEG. 1951. m. DM.48. Landsmannschaft der Deutschen aus Russland e.V., Raitelsbergstr. 49, 70188 Stuttgart, Germany. TEL 0711-16659-0. FAX 0711-2864413. Ed. Herr Kampen. bk.rev.; illus. circ. 4,000. **Document type:** bulletin.

327 NE ISSN 0923-0815
VREDE; maandblad voor vredesvraagstukken. 1964. m. fl.37.50. Stichting Vredesopbouw, Oosterkade 13, 3582 AT Utrecht, Netherlands. Ed.Bd. bk.rev. circ. 1,500.
Former titles: Vredesopbouw (ISSN 0042-9120); Stichting Vredesopbouw. Maandschrift.

W H Y; challenging hunger and poverty. (World Hunger Year) see *SOCIAL SERVICES AND WELFARE*

327 952 970 US
WASHINGTON - JAPAN JOURNAL. 1957. q. $10 to non-members; members $8 (foreign $20). Japan-America Society of Washington Inc., 1020 19th St., N.W., LL, Washington, DC 20036-6101. TEL 202-289-8290. FAX 202-789-8265. Ed. Patricia R. Kearns. adv.; bk.rev.; illus. circ. 3,000.
Formerly: Japan-America Society of Washington. Bulletin (ISSN 0021-4299)

POLITICAL SCIENCE — INTERNATIONAL RELATIONS

332.6 US ISSN 0278-937X
WASHINGTON PAPERS. 1972. irreg. (Center for Strategic and International Studies) Praeger Publishers (Subsidiary of: Greenwood Publishing Group Inc.), 88 Post Rd., W., Box 5007, Westport, CT 06881. TEL 203-226-3571. FAX 203-222-1502. Ed. Walter Laqueur. (back issues avail.)
—BLDSC (9263.240000).

327 US ISSN 0163-660X
D839
WASHINGTON QUARTERLY. 1978. q. $32 to individuals (foreign $48); institutions $82 (foreign $98); students $20 (foreign $36). (Center for Strategic and International Studies) M I T Press, 55 Hayward St., Cambridge, MA 02142. TEL 617-253-2889. FAX 617-258-6779. E-mail: journals-orders@mit.edu. (Editorial addr.: Center for Strategic and International Studies, 1800 K St. N.W., Ste. 400, Washington, DC 20006) Ed. Brad Roberts. adv.; index. circ. 3,000. (also avail. in microform from UMI; back issues avail.; reprint service avail. from SCH,UMI) **Indexed:** A.B.C.Pol.Sci., Abstr.Mil.Bibl., Amer.Bibl.Slavic & E.Eur.Stud., Amer.Hist.& Life (until 1993), Curr.Cont., Hist.Abstr. (until 1993), Int.Polit.Sci.Abstr., Mid.East: Abstr.& Ind., P.A.I.S., Polit.Sci.Abstr., Risk Abstr., Soc.Sci.Ind. (1994-), SSCI.
●Also available online. Vendor(s): Lexis-Nexis.
—BLDSC (9263.243000); Faxon; Genuine Article; SWETS; UMI; UnCover. **CCC.**
Formerly: Washington Review of Strategic and International Studies (ISSN 0147-1465)
Description: Essays on foreign and defense policy, international economics, as well as emerging international issues.

327 US ISSN 8755-4917
DS63.1
WASHINGTON REPORT ON MIDDLE EAST AFFAIRS; a survey of United States relations with Middle East countries. 1982. 9/yr. $19 to individuals; institutions $50. American Educational Trust (A E T), Box 53062, Washington, DC 20009. TEL 202-939-6050; 800-368-5788. FAX 202-265-4574. Ed. Richard H. Curtiss; Pub. Andrew Killgore. adv. contact: Greg Noakes. bk.rev.; illus. circ. 33,000. **Indexed:** Polit.Sci.Abstr. **Document type:** academic/scholarly publication.
—Faxon; UnCover.
Description: Provides nonpartisan coverage of all aspects of Middle Eastern affairs, including political, social, religious, cultural and economic issues, analysis of U.N. debate and policy, and relevant events in other regions affecting the Middle East and the Islamic world, emphasizing viewpoints not readily available in the mainstream U.S. media.

327 330.9 US ISSN 0275-5599
WASHINGTON REPORT ON THE HEMISPHERE. 1980. fortn. $175 to individuals; institutions $298.50. Council on Hemispheric Affairs, 724 9th St., N.W., Ste. 401, Washington, DC 20001. TEL 202-393-3322. FAX 202-393-3423. Ed. Laurence R. Birns. bk.rev.; index. circ. 1,500. **Indexed:** HR Rep.
Description: Organization that monitors US, Canadian and Latin-American relations as well as political, free trade, diplomatic, financial, environmental, economic and social issues in the western hemisphere.

940 327 GW ISSN 0049-7134
WELTGESCHEHEN. 1964. q. DM.50. Siegler & Co. Verlag fuer Zeitarchive GmbH, Einsteinstr. 10, 53757 Sankt Augustin, Germany. TEL 02241-3164-0. FAX 02241-316436. adv.; abstr.; stat.; index, cum.index. circ. 800. **Indexed:** E.I. **Document type:** academic/scholarly publication.
Formerly: Internationales Europaforum (ISSN 0020-9465)
Description: Articles on contemporary history, documentary style, information on foreign countries, their politics and economy.

WERELDBRIEF. see RELIGIONS AND THEOLOGY

WERELDWIJD; tijdschrift over evangelizatie en ontwikkeling. see RELIGIONS AND THEOLOGY

327 GW
WERKSTATT 3 - PROGRAMM. 1979. m. free. Verein Werkstatt 3, Nernstweg 32-34, 22765 Hamburg, Germany. TEL 040-392191. FAX 040-3909866. circ. 10,000.
Description: Information about the problems of the relations between industrialized countries and developing countries.

327 950 970 CH ISSN 0043-3047
DS895.F7
WEST & EAST/CHUNG-MEI YUEH-K'AN; an independent monthly. (Text in Chinese, English) 1956. m. NT.$300($10) (Sino-American Cultural and Economic Association) Chang Chao Wen-yi, No. 23 Hungchow S. Rd., Sec. 1, 11th Fl., Taipei, Taiwan, Republic of China. TEL 02-3914200. Ed. Yih-hsien Yu. adv.; charts; stat. circ. 2,400.
Description: Sino-American exchange of cultural and economic news.

327 UK ISSN 0140-2382
JN94.A1
WEST EUROPEAN POLITICS. 1978. q. £40($65) to individuals; institutions £134 ($195) (effective 1996). Frank Cass, Newbury House, 890-900 Eastern Ave., Newbury Park, Ilford, Essex 1G2 7HH. TEL 44-181-599-8866. FAX 44-181-599-0954. E-mail: 100067,1576@compuserve.com. Eds. Vincent Wright, Gordon Smith. adv.: B&W page £195 ($275); adv. contact: Anne Kidson. bk.rev.; index. (also avail. in microform from UMI; back issues avail.) **Indexed:** A.B.C.Pol.Sci, Amer.Hist.& Life, Geo.Abstr., Hist.Abstr., Int.Polit.Sci.Abstr., Lang.& Lang.Behav.Abstr., P.A.I.S., Polit.Sci.Abstr., Soc.Sci.Ind. (1994-), Stud.Wom.Abstr. **Document type:** academic/scholarly publication.
●Also available online. Vendor(s): Information Access Co.
Also available on CD-ROM.
—BLDSC (9298.917000); Faxon; SWETS; UMI; UnCover. **CCC.**
Description: Covers all major political and social developments in all Western European countries.
Refereed Serial

WESTERN POLICIES. see POLITICAL SCIENCE

327 GW
WHO'S WHO IN EUROPEAN INTEGRATION STUDIES. (Text in English) irreg. Nomos Verlagsgesellschaft mbH und Co. KG, Waldseestr. 3-5, 76530 Baden-Baden, Germany. TEL 07221-21040. FAX 07221-210427. **Document type:** directory.

WHO'S WHO IN INTERNATIONAL AFFAIRS. see BIOGRAPHY

327 AU ISSN 1010-1721
WIENER BLAETTER ZUR FRIEDENSFORSCHUNG. 1974. 4/yr. S.280. Universitaetszentrum fuer Friedenforschung, Schottenring 21, A-1010 Vienna, Austria. TEL 01-313381247. FAX 01-3109589. Eds. Rudolf Weiler, Sigrid Poellinger. adv.; bk.rev. circ. 500. **Document type:** academic/scholarly publication.

320.9 US ISSN 0274-5852
WILLIAM WINTER COMMENTS; a twice monthly personal newsletter on current world affairs. 1961. s.m. $33.50. William Winter, Ed. & Pub., 6025 El Escorpion Rd., Woodland Hills, CA 91367-1199. TEL 818-347-7417. FAX 818-347-7417. TELEX 299374 WINT UR. maps. circ. 10,000. (also avail. in microfilm from UMI; reprint service avail. from UMI) **Document type:** newsletter.
—UMI.
Formerly: Comments on Current World Affairs (ISSN 0043-5619)

WOMEN STRIKE FOR PEACE. LEGISLATIVE ALERT. see POLITICAL SCIENCE — Civil Rights

327 BE
WORKING - PARTY REPORTS. (Text in English) 1989. irreg. 3000 BEF per no. Centre for European Policy Studies, Place du Congres 1, 1000 Brussels, Belgium. TEL 32-2-2182247. FAX 32-2-2194151. (back issues avail.)
Refereed Serial

327 US ISSN 1058-1766
WORLD AFFAIRS (BOCA RATON). (Subseries of: S I R S Global Perspectives (ISSN 1058-1731)) 1991. a. $80. Social Issues Resources Series, Box 2348, Boca Raton, FL 33427-2348. TEL 407-994-0079; 800-232-7477. FAX 407-994-4704. (looseleaf format; also avail. in microfiche; back issues avail.) **Indexed:** Int.Polit.Sci.Abstr.
Description: Reprints 70 articles documenting important current international affairs worldwide.

341.1 US ISSN 0043-8200
JX1901
WORLD AFFAIRS (WASHINGTON). 1837. q. $38 to individuals; institutions $58. (American Peace Society) Heldref Publications, 1319 Eighteenth St., N.W., Washington, DC 20036-1802. TEL 202-296-6267. FAX 202-296-5149. (Co-sponsor: Helen Dwight Reid Educational Foundation) Eds. Joyce Horn, Evron M. Kirkpatrick. adv. contact: Raymond Rallo. bk.rev. circ. 700. (also avail. in microform from UMI; reprint service avail.) **Indexed:** A.B.C.Pol.Sci., Amer.Bibl.Slavic & E.Eur.Stud., Amer.Hist.& Life (until 1991), Arts & Hum.Cit.Ind., Bk.Rev.Ind., Curr.Cont., Hist.Abstr. (until 1991), Mid.East: Abstr.& Ind., P.A.I.S., Soc.Sci.Ind., SSCI. **Document type:** academic/scholarly publication.
●Also available online. Vendor(s): University Microfilms International.
—BLDSC (9352.430000); Faxon; Genuine Article; SWETS; UMI.
Refereed Serial

327 US ISSN 0090-7103
D839
WORLD AFFAIRS REPORT. (Print ed. ceased vol.20, 1991) 1970. irreg. California Institute of International Studies, Hoover Institution, Stanford, CA 94305-6010. TEL 415-322-2026. FAX 415-723-1687. Ed. Ronald Hilton. adv.; bk.rev.; bibl. (also avail. in microfilm from UMI; reprint service avail. from UMI) **Indexed:** A.B.C.Pol.Sci., Abstr.Mil.Bibl, Amer.Hist.& Life, Hist.Abstr., Mid.East: Abstr.& Ind. **Document type:** academic/scholarly publication.
●Available only online.
—UMI; UnCover. **CCC.**
Formerly: California Institute of International Studies. Report (ISSN 0068-564X)
Description: Contains general information on international relations.

WORLD CITIZEN NEWS. see LAW — International Law

327 UK ISSN 0965-3783
JX1625
WORLD DIRECTORY OF DIPLOMATIC REPRESENTATION. 1992. irreg. $375. Europa Publications, 18 Bedford Sq., London WC1B 3JN, England. TEL 0171-580-8236. FAX 0171-636-1664. TELEX 21540 EUROPA G. **Document type:** directory.
Description: Lists diplomats by individual and country worldwide.

327 US ISSN 0196-2574
WORLD FEDERALIST NEWSLETTER. 1976. q. $5. World Federalist Association, 418 7th St., S.E., Washington, DC 20003. TEL 202-546-3950. FAX 202-546-3749. E-mail: wfa@igc.apc.org. Ed. Aaron Knight. bk.rev.; illus. circ. 10,000. (also avail. in microform from UMI) **Document type:** newsletter.
Description: Discusses options for world peace, economic progress and a liveable environment. Also proposes a restructured U.N.

341.1 II ISSN 0043-8448
WORLD FEDERATION. (Text in English) 1929. m. Rs.120. Shiva Kumar, Ed. & Pub., P.M.V. Keshighat, Vrindaban, Uttar Pradesh, India. bk.rev. **Document type:** newspaper.

327 US ISSN 0161-2360
WORLD GOODWILL COMMENTARY; a bulletin on current trends in world affairs. 1968. irreg. donations. (Lucis Trust) Lucis Publishing Co., 113 University Place, 11th Fl., Box 722, Cooper Sta., New York, NY 10276. TEL 212-982-8770. (Or: 1 rue de Varembe (3e), C.P. 31, 1211 Geneva 20, Switzerland; Or: 3 Whitehall Ct., Suite 54, London SW1A 2EF, England) Ed.Bd. bibl. circ. 12,000.

327 UK
WORLD IN CONFLICT. 1987. irreg. $40. Brassey's (UK) Ltd., 33 John St., London WC1N 2AT, England. TEL 0171-753-7777. FAX 0171-753-7794. Ed. John Laffin. **Document type:** bulletin.

POLITICAL SCIENCE — INTERNATIONAL RELATIONS

327   II   ISSN 0043-857X
WORLD INFORMO; current events of national and international importance and matters connected with the United Nations and its specialized agencies. (Text in English) 1953. m. Rs.5. United Schools Organisation of India, U S O House, 6 Special Institutional Area, New Delhi 110 067, India. FAX 09111-6862042. Ed. J.L. Jain. adv. circ. 6,500.

WORLD LINK. see *BUSINESS AND ECONOMICS — Macroeconomics*

327   US
WORLD NEIGHBORS IN ACTION; a newsletter for overseas project personnel. French edition: Voisins Mondiaux en Action. Spanish edition: Vecinos Mundiales en Accion. 1965. s-a. $10 to industrialized countries; developing countries free. World Neighbors, Inc., 4127 N.W. 122nd St., Oklahoma City, OK 73120-8869. TEL 405-752-9700. FAX 405-752-9393. E-mail: 6358930@mcimail.com. Ed. Debra Johnson. bibl.; charts; illus.; cum.index. circ. 2,166. (back issues avail.) **Document type:** newsletter.

WORLD NEWSMAP OF THE WEEK - HEADLINE FOCUS; world news and world geography. see *GEOGRAPHY*

327   US   ISSN 0193-3329
D839
WORLD OPINION UPDATE. 1977. m. $65 to individuals (overseas $70); educational institutions $50 (Canada $55; overseas $65) (effective 1995). (Survey Research Consultants International, Inc.) Hastings Publications, 156 Bulkley St., Box 25, Williamstown, MA 01267. TEL 413-458-4414. FAX 413-458-4414. TELEX 951-443. Eds. Elizabeth Hann Hastings, Philip K. Hastings. index. circ. 1,000. **Document type:** newsletter.

327   US   ISSN 0895-7452
D839
WORLD OUTLOOK; a journal of international affairs. 1985. s-a. $10. Dartmouth College, Trustees, Hinman Box 6025, Hanover, NH 03755. TEL 603-646-1345. FAX 603-640-2168. Ed. Neel Doshi. bk.rev. circ. 1,000. **Indexed:** P.A.I.S. **Document type:** academic/scholarly publication.
—BLDSC (9356.959800). CCC.
 Description: Provides a non-partisan forum for original thinking on international affairs.

327   US   ISSN 0740-2775
D839
WORLD POLICY JOURNAL. 1983. q. $17.95 to individuals; institutions $33. World Policy Institute, 65 Fifth Ave., Ste. 413, New York, NY 10003-3003. TEL 212-229-5808. FAX 212-229-5579. Ed. James Chace. adv. contact: Peter Schmul. bk.rev.; charts. circ. 5,000. (also avail. in microform from UMI; back issues avail.) **Indexed:** A.B.C.Pol.Sci., Alt.Press Ind., Amer.Hist.& Life, Curr.Cont., Fut.Surv., Hist.Abstr., HR Rep. (1988-), Int.Polit.Sci.Abstr., Lang.& Lang.Behav.Abstr., Left Ind. (1983-), P.A.I.S., Polit.Sci.Abstr., Soc.Sci.Ind. (1994-), Sociol.Abstr., SSCI. **Document type:** academic/scholarly publication.
●Also available online. Vendor(s): University Microfilms International.
—BLDSC (9358.073000); Faxon; Genuine Article; SWETS; UMI; UnCover.
 Description: Covers progressive international affairs including global security issues, trade and economic policy, environmental concerns and developments in Europe, Latin America, Asia, and Africa. Also contains book reviews, profiles, and reportage.

327 320.3 909.82   US   ISSN 0043-8871
D839
WORLD POLITICS (BALTIMORE); a quarterly journal of international relations. 1948. q. $24 to individuals; institutions $51. (Princeton University, Center of International Studies) Johns Hopkins University Press, Journals Publishing Division, 2715 N. Charles St., Baltimore, MD 21218-4319. TEL 410-516-6987. FAX 410-516-6968. Ed. John Waterbury. adv.: page $290; adv. contact: Tara Dorai-Berry. bk.rev.; index. circ. 3,940. (also avail. in microform from UMI; back issues avail.; reprint service avail. from SCH,UMI) **Indexed:** A.B.C.Pol.Sci., Abstr.Mil.Bibl., Acad.Ind., Amer.Bibl.Slavic & E.Eur.Stud., Amer.Hist.& Life, Bk.Rev.Dig., Bk.Rev.Ind. (1965-), Child.Bk.Rev.Ind. (1965-), Curr.Cont., E.I., Fut.Surv., Geo.Abstr., Hist.Abstr., IDA, Int.Polit.Sci.Abstr., Mag.Ind., Mid.East: Abstr.& Ind., P.A.I.S., Polit.Sci.Abstr., Rural Recreat.Tour.Abstr., Sage Pub.Admin.Abstr., Soc.Sci.Ind., SSCI, World Agri.Econ. & Rural Sociol.Abstr. **Document type:** academic/scholarly publication.
—BLDSC (9358.080000); Faxon; Genuine Article; SWETS; UMI; UnCover. CCC.
 Description: Publishes scholarly manuscripts on topics in international relations, comparative politics, political theory, foreign policy and modernization. *Refereed Serial*

327   AT   ISSN 0043-8960
WORLD REVIEW; a journal of contemporary relevance. 1962. 4/yr. Aus.$22 (foreign Aus.$25). Australian Institute of International Affairs, Queensland Branch, P.O. Box 279, Indooroopilly, Brisbane, Qld. 4068, Australia. TEL 074-24-1575. Ed.Bd. adv.; bk.rev. circ. 1,000. **Indexed:** Aus.P.A.I.S., Curr.Cont., Gdlns. **Document type:** academic/scholarly publication.
—Faxon; UnCover.

327   UK   ISSN 0043-9134
D410
WORLD TODAY. 1945. m. $60 to individuals; institutions $80; students $40. Royal Institute of International Affairs, Chatham House, 10 St. James's Sq., London SW1Y 4LE, England. TEL 0171-957-5700. FAX 0171-957-5710. E-mail: riiapublicat@gn.apc.org. Ed. C. Cviic. adv. contact: Lieselotte Duvivier. bk.rev.; index. circ. 4,000. (also avail. in microform from UMI) **Indexed:** A.B.C.Pol.Sci., Abstr.Mil.Bibl., ASSIA, Curr.Cont., Documentatieblad, ELLIS, Int.Lab.Doc., Int.Polit.Sci.Abstr., Key to Econ.Sci., Mar.Aff.Bibl., Mid.East: Abstr.& Ind., P.A.I.S., Polit.Sci.Abstr., Rural Recreat.Tour.Abstr., Soc.Sci.Ind., SSCI, World Agri.Econ.& Rural Sociol.Abstr. **Document type:** academic/scholarly publication.
—BLDSC (9360.150000); Faxon; Genuine Article; SWETS; UMI; UnCover. CCC.

341.37   US
WORLD TREATY INDEX. 1975. irreg., 2nd, 1984. A B C-Clio, 130 Cremona, Box 1911, Santa Barbara, CA 93116-1911. TEL 805-968-1911. FAX 805-685-9685. Ed. Peter H. Rohn. **Document type:** directory.

327   II   ISSN 0043-9185
WORLD UNION. (Text in English) 1961. o.a. Rs.20($8) World Union International Centre, Pondicherry 605002, India. Ed. M.P. Pandit. adv.; bk.rev.; charts; illus. circ. 1,200.

WORLD VISION. see *RELIGIONS AND THEOLOGY — Protestant*

327   US   ISSN 1065-0997
AP2
THE WORLDPAPER; international news and views. (Text primarily in English; occasionally in Bulgarian, Chinese, Japanese, Polish, Russian, Spanish) 1978. m. $18 (foreign $28). World Times, Inc., 210 World Trade Center, Boston, MA 02210. TEL 617-439-5400. FAX 617-439-5415. TELEX 6817273 WORLDP. E-mail: 74372,2136@compuserve.com. Ed. Daniel Passent; Pub. Wilford H. Welch. adv.: page $35000; adv. contact: Wilford H. Welch. bk.rev.; index. circ. 1,500,000. (tabloid format; back issues avail.) **Indexed:** Per.Islam. **Document type:** newspaper.
●Also available online. Vendor(s): Lexis-Nexis.
 Description: Contains international news and views on political, social and economic issues of global importance, featuring writers indigenous to the regions they write about.

WORLDVIEW MAGAZINE. see *BUSINESS AND ECONOMICS — International Development And Assistance*

327 355   US
WORLDWIDE REPORT: ARMS CONTROL. irreg. (approx. 100/yr.) $7 per no. (foreign $14 per no.) U.S. Joint Publications Research Service, Box 12507, Arlington, VA 22209. TEL 703-487-4630. (Orders to: NTIS, Springfield, VA 22161)

327   CC   ISSN 1000-6192
XIANDAI GUOJI GUANXI. English edition: Contemporary International Relations (ISSN 1003-3408) (Text in Chinese; summaries in English) 1981. m. $48. Xiandai Guoji Guanxi Yanjiusuo - China Institute of Contemporary International Relations, No. A-2, Wanshousi, Haidian, Beijing 100081, People's Republic of China. TEL 86-1-8418640. FAX 86-1-8418641. Ed. Liu Seqing. adv. contact: Ding Shunzhen. bk.rev. circ. 10,000. **Document type:** academic/scholarly publication.
 Description: Contains comprehensive analyses by prominent Chinese and foreign scholars on various issues on contemporary international relations. *Refereed Serial*

YADERNYI KONTROL'. see *MILITARY*

327   NE   ISSN 0920-4792
D901
YEARBOOK OF EUROPEAN STUDIES/ANNUAIRE D'ETUDES EUROPEENNES. (Text mainly in English; occasionally in French) 1988. a. price varies. (University of Amsterdam, Department of European Studies) Editions Rodopi B.V., Keizersgracht 302-304, 1016 EX Amsterdam, Netherlands. TEL 31-20-6227507. FAX 31-20-6380948. E-mail: F.van.der.Zee@Rodopi.nl. (In N. America: 233 Peachtree St., N.E., Ste. 404, Atlanta GA 30303-1504. TEL 800-225-3998. FAX 404-522-7116) Ed. J.Th. Leerssen. **Document type:** academic/scholarly publication.
 Description: Interdisciplinary studies involving literature, history, law, and economics to assess topics within the field of European relations.

327.471   FI   ISSN 0355-0079
DK451.7
YEARBOOK OF FINNISH FOREIGN POLICY. (Text in English) 1973. a. FIM 80. Ulkopoliittinen Instituutti - Finnish Institute of International Affairs, Mannerheimintre 15 A, FIN-00260 Helsinki, Finland. TEL 358-0-490-100. FAX 358-0-490-989. Ed. Jyrki Iivonen. **Indexed:** A.B.C.Pol.Sci., Int.Polit.Sci.Abstr.
 Description: Deals with domestic and international questions impinged relating to Finland's foreign policy.

327   GW   ISSN 0084-3814
JX1904   CODEN: YIORD4
YEARBOOK OF INTERNATIONAL ORGANIZATIONS/ANNUAIRE DES ORGANISATIONS INTERNATIONALES. (In 3 vols.: Vol. 1: Organization Descriptions and Index; Vol. 2: International Organization Participation: Country Directory of Secretariats and Membership (Geographic Volume); Vol. 3: Global Action Networks: Classified Directory by Subject and Region (Subject Volume)) (Text in English; index in English and French) 1910. a. DM.1298($875) (Union of International Associations, BE) K.G. Saur Verlag KG, A part of Reed Reference Publishing, Ortlerstr. 8, 81373 Munich, Germany. TEL 089-76902-0. FAX 089-76902150. (Subscr. to: Postfach 701620, 81316 Munich, Germany; N. America subscr. to: K.G. Saur, 121 Chanlon Rd., New Providence, NJ 07974-9903, USA. TEL 908-464-6800) **Document type:** directory.
●Also available on CD-ROM. Producer(s): K.G. Saur Verlag.
—BLDSC (9414.010000); CASDDS.
 Description: Provides detailed information for organizations in every field of human endeavor. Lists organizations, administrators, embassies and government agencies concerned with international affairs.

YEARBOOK OF THE EUROPEAN COMMUNITIES AND OF THE OTHER EUROPEAN ORGANIZATIONS/ANNUAIRE DES COMMUNAUTES EUROPEENNES ET DES AUTRES ORGANISATIONS EUROPEENNES/JAHRBUCH DER EUROPAEISCHEN GEMEINSCHAFTEN UND DER ANDEREN EUROPAEISCHEN ORGANISATIONEN. see *PUBLIC ADMINISTRATION*

POPULATION STUDIES

327 FI ISSN 0781-2442
YHDISTYNEIDEN KANSAKUNTIEN YLEISKOKOUS (YEAR). (Text in Finnish; occasionally in English) 1957. a. Ulkoasiainministerio - Ministry for Foreign Affairs, PL 176, SF-00161 Helsinki, Finland. TEL 90-134151. FAX 629840. TELEX 1000306. circ. 650. **Document type:** government publication.
Formerly: Suomen Osallistuminen Yhdistyneiden Kansakuntien Toimintaan (ISSN 0081-9441)

327 CC
YOU SHENG. English edition: Friendly Voice. (Text in Chinese) bi-m. Zhongguo Renmin Duiwai Youhao Xiehui, No. 1, Taijichang, Beijing 100740, People's Republic of China. TEL 5122782. Ed. Gu Zixin.

327 UK ISSN 0958-4234
YOUNG INDIA. 1989. q. £8($16) N R I Forum (UK), P.O. Box 42, Wellingborough NN8 3HL, England. Ed. Bharat Ratna Kurukshetra; Pub. Bharat Ratna Kurukshetra. adv.; bk.rev. **Document type:** academic/scholarly publication.
Description: Devoted to politics and ideology in India and to the re-unification of India in its borders as in 1947.

YOUR UNITED NATIONS; official guidebook. see *HISTORY*

227 YU
YUGOSLAVIA. FEDERAL SECRETARIAT FOR FOREIGN AFFAIRS. DIPLOMATIC LIST. (Text in French) 1946. a. free. Savezni Sekretarijat za Inostrane Poslove - Federal Secretariat for Foreign Affairs, Belgrade, Yugoslavia. circ. 1,000. **Document type:** government publication, directory.
Formerly (until Mar. 1991): Liste des Membres du Corps Diplomatique a Beograd.

ZA RUBEZHOM; obozrenie inostrannoi pressy. see *LITERARY AND POLITICAL REVIEWS*

327 GW ISSN 0044-2976
DD68
ZEITSCHRIFT FUER KULTURAUSTAUSCH. 1962. q. DM.40($18) Institut fuer Auslandsbeziehungen, Charlottenplatz 17, 70173 Stuttgart, Germany. TEL 0711-2225112. FAX 0711-2264346. Ed. Susanne Sporrer. adv. contact: Evelyn Thrieue. bk.rev.; bibl.; illus.; rec.rev.; index. circ. 6,000. **Indexed:** Documentatieblad, P.A.I.S.For.Lang.Ind. **Document type:** academic/scholarly publication.
—Faxon.
Formerly: Institut fuer Auslandsbeziehungen. Mitteilungen.

327 CC
ZHONGGUO ZHI YOU/FRIENDS OF CHINA. (Text in Chinese) bi-m. Zhongguo zhi You Zazhishe, No. A-3, Fucheng Lu, Beijing 100037, People's Republic of China. TEL 894831. Ed. Shen Deyi.

341.1 GW
ZIVILCOURAGE; antimilitaristische Zeitschrift. 1964; N.S. 1975. q. DM.12. Deutsche Friedensgesellschaft-Vereinigte Kriegsdienstgegner (DFG-VK), Schwanenstr. 16, 42551 Velbert, Germany. FAX 0228-665843. adv.; bk.rev.; film rev.; illus. circ. 12,000.
Formerly: Courage.

1066; tidsskrift for historisk forskning. see *HISTORY — History Of Europe*

POLLUTION

see *Environmental Studies–Pollution*

POPULATION STUDIES

see also *Birth Control*

325.1 US
A C I M NEWSLETTER. 1952. 4/yr. free. American Committee on Italian Migration, 352 W. 44th St., New York, NY 10036. TEL 212-247-7373. Ed. Rev. Walter Tonelotto. circ. 10,000. **Document type:** newsletter.
Formerly: A C I M Dispatch.

A F R A NEWS. (Association for Rural Advancement) see *POLITICAL SCIENCE — Civil Rights*

312 331 GW ISSN 0177-1566
A I D - AUSLAENDER IN DEUTSCHLAND. 1984. q. Isoplan Institut, Martin-Luther-Str. 20, 66111 Saarbruecken, Germany. TEL 0681-936460. FAX 0681-9364611. (Co-sponsor: Bundesministerium fuer Arbeit und Sozialordnung) circ. 30,000. (back issues avail.) **Document type:** bulletin.
Description: Provides information for people working toward the integration of foreigners in Germany.

A P D U NEWSLETTER. (Association of Public Data Users) see *STATISTICS*

A P L I C COMMUNICATOR. (Association for Population - Family Planning Library & Information Center International) see *LIBRARY AND INFORMATION SCIENCES*

312 GW ISSN 0937-907X
HB848
ACTA DEMOGRAPHICA. 1990. a. DM.85. (Deutsche Gesellschaft fuer Bevoelkerungswissenschaft) Physica-Verlag GmbH und Co., Postfach 105280, 69042 Heidelberg, Germany. TEL 06221-487492. FAX 06221-413982. TELEX 461723-SPHDB-D. (Subscr. to: Springer-Verlag, Auftragsbearbeitung, Postfach 311340, 10643 Berlin, Germany; In N. America: Springer Verlag New York Inc., Box 2485, Secaucus, NJ 07096-2491. TEL 201-348-4033) Ed.Bd. **Document type:** monographic series.
Description: Covers empirical and theoretical topics in population research.

ADVANCES IN POPULATION; psychosocial perspectives. see *PSYCHOLOGY*

312 UN ISSN 0258-980X
AFRICAN POPULATION NEWSLETTER (BILINGUAL EDITION). (Text in English and French) 1970. s-a. free. United Nations Economic Commission for Africa, Population Division, P.O. Box 3001, Addis Ababa, Ethiopia. TELEX 21029. Ed.Bd. bk.rev. circ. 1,500. **Document type:** newsletter.
Formed by the 1980 merger of: Informations sur la Population en Afrique (ISSN 0252-4805); African Population Newsletter (ISSN 0084-599X)

312 US ISSN 1063-3707
AKCENS. q. free. Department of Labor, Research & Analysis Section, Data Center, Box 25501, Juneau, AK 99802-5501. TEL 907-465-6026. FAX 907-465-2101. **Document type:** government publication.
Description: Provides current information on available United States Census Bureau and Alaska Department of Labor publications, machine readable data and other products. Includes articles on demographic trends and information on upcoming Census Bureau and Alaska demographic activities.

312 US
ALABAMA STATE DATA CENTER NEWSLETTER. 1985. q. free. University of Alabama, Center for Business and Economic Research (CBER), Alabama State Data Center, Box 870221, Tuscaloosa, AL 35487. TEL 205-348-6191. FAX 205-348-2951. Ed. Annette Watters. illus. (back issues avail.) **Document type:** newsletter.

312 US ISSN 1063-3790
HA235
ALASKA POPULATION OVERVIEW; (year) census & estimates. a. free. Department of Labor, Research & Analysis Section, Box 25501, Juneau, AK 99802-5501. TEL 907-465-6029. FAX 907-465-2101. **Indexed:** SRI. **Document type:** government publication.
Description: Population estimates for Alaska and its boroughs and census areas by age and sex. Includes information on historical trends in births, deaths, and migration.

312 CN
ALBERTA - EDMONTON SERIES REPORT. 1977. irreg. free. Population Research Laboratory, Department of Sociology, University of Alberta, Edmonton, Alta. T6G 2H4, Canada. TEL 403-492-4659. (reprint service avail. from MML)
Formerly: Edmonton Area Series Report (ISSN 0703-8763)
Description: Data gathered from the annual All Alberta Study.

ALLEES ALL AROUND; includes Alley, Ally, Allie, Alyea. see *GENEALOGY AND HERALDRY*

325 US
AMERICAN COUNCIL FOR NATIONALITIES SERVICE. ISSUE PAPER SERIES. 1985. irreg. (3-5/yr.). $4 per no. American Council for Nationalities Service, 1717 Massachusetts Ave., N.W., Ste. 701, Washington, DC 20036. TEL 202-347-3507.
Description: Reports on critical refugee issues and policy matters.

312 US ISSN 0163-4089
HB3505 CODEN: AMDEEF
AMERICAN DEMOGRAPHICS; consumer trends for business leaders. 1979. m. $69. American Demographics, Inc., Box 68, Ithaca, NY 14851-0068. TEL 607-273-6343; 800-828-1133. FAX 607-273-3196. (Subscr. to: Box 58184, Boulder, CO 80322-8184) Ed. Brad Edmondson. adv. contact: Michelle De Chant. bk.rev.; charts; illus.; stat.; index, cum.index: 1981-1993. circ. 35,000. (also avail. in microform from UMI; back issues avail.; reprint service avail. from UMI) **Indexed:** ABI Inform., B.P.I., BPIA, Bus.Ind., Chic.Per.Ind., CLOA, Curr.Lit.Fam.Plan., Environ.Abstr., Fut.Surv., Hlth.Ind., Manage.Cont., P.A.I.S., Popul.Ind., PROMT, Tr.& Indus.Ind.
●Also available online. Vendor(s): Dow Jones News Retrieval, Lexis-Nexis, University Microfilms International.
—BLDSC (0812.737000); CIS; Faxon; SWETS; UMI; UnCover. CCC.
Description: Covers consumer trends for marketers, planners and other business leaders.

312 US
AMERICAN MARKETPLACE; including U.S. Census Report. 1980. bi-w. $228 (effective Sep. 1992). Business Publishers, Inc., 951 Pershing Dr., Silver Spring, MD 20910-4464. TEL 301-587-6300. FAX 301-585-9075. Ed. David Speights. bk.rev.; charts; stat. (looseleaf format) **Document type:** newsletter.
●Also available online. Vendor(s): NewsNet (AD13).
—CCC.
Formerly: U S Census Report (ISSN 0276-2900)
Description: Prepared for marketing professionals and business planners. Includes news on consumer trends, population shifts, employment gains and losses.

304 US ISSN 0741-2150
AMERICAN UNIVERSITY STUDIES. SERIES 16. ECONOMICS. 1984. irreg. Peter Lang Publishing, Inc., 62 W. 45th St., 4th Fl., New York, NY 10036. TEL 212-302-6740. Ed. Christopher Myers. **Document type:** academic/scholarly publication, monographic series.

316 AO
ANGOLA. MINISTERIO DA SAUDE. DEPARTAMENTO DE ESTATISTICA. RELATORIO ESTATISCO. a. Ministerio da Saude, Departamento de Estatistica, Rua Diogo Cao, Luanda, Angola.

312 FR ISSN 0066-2062
HB848
ANNALES DE DEMOGRAPHIE HISTORIQUE. (Text in English, French) 1970. a. price varies. (Societe de Demographie Historique) Editions de l' Ecole des Hautes Etudes en Sciences Sociales, 131 bd. St-Michel, 75005 Paris, France. TEL 46-33-57-46. FAX 44-07-08-89. (Dist. by: Centre Interinstitutionnel pour la Diffusion de Publications en Sciences Humaines, 131 bd. St-Michel, 75005 Paris, France. TEL 43-54-47-15. FAX 43-54-80-73) (reprint service avail. from SWZ) **Indexed:** Amer.Hist.& Life, Hist.Abstr., Popul.Ind.
—BLDSC (0971.450000).

312 FR ISSN 0152-9757
ANNUAIRE DES CENTRES DE RECHERCHE DEMOGRAPHIQUE/DIRECTORY OF DEMOGRAPHIC RESEARCH CENTERS. 1974. irreg., 2nd, 1980. free. Committee for International Cooperation in National Research in Demography, 27 rue du Commandeur, 75675 Paris Cedex 14, France. **Document type:** directory.

325 US ISSN 0891-6683
HB3633.A3
ASIA - PACIFIC POPULATION & POLICY. 1987. q. free. (Program on Population) Center for Cultural and Technical Interchange Between East and West, Inc., 1777 East-West Rd., Honolulu, HI 96848. TEL 808-944-7480. FAX 808-944-7490. TELEX 989171 EWC UD. Ed. Sidney B. Westley. circ. 3,600. **Indexed:** Geo.Abstr., IDA.

POPULATION STUDIES

301.426   UN   ISSN 0259-238X
HA4551
ASIA - PACIFIC POPULATION JOURNAL. 1986. q. United Nations Economic and Social Commission for Asia and the Pacific (ESCAP), Population Division, United Nations Bldg., Rajdamnern Ave., Bangkok 10200, Thailand. Ed. Nibhon Debavalya. bk.rev.; abstr.; bibl.; charts; illus. circ. 2,000. (also avail. in microfiche from CIS; back issues avail.) **Indexed:** IIS.
—BLDSC (1742.261300); UnCover.

325   PH   ISSN 0117-1968
JV8490
ASIAN AND PACIFIC MIGRATION JOURNAL; a quarterly on human mobility. (Text in English) 1992. q. P.600 (foreign $45) (effective 1996). Scalabrini Migration Center, P.O. Box 10541, Broadway Centrum, Aurora Blvd., 1113 Quezon City, Philippines. TEL 02-787-071. FAX 02-721-4296. E-mail: graziano@irf.pfi.net. Ed. Graziano Battistella. bk.rev. (back issues avail.) **Indexed:** Asian-Pac.Econ.Lit. **Document type:** academic/scholarly publication.
—BLDSC (1742.354500).
Description: Stimulates research and analysis on migration and refugee movements from and within Asia and the Pacific.
Refereed Serial

325   PH   ISSN 1013-8064
ASIAN MIGRANT. (Text in English) 1987. q. $22 (effective 1996). Scalabrini Migration Center, P.O. Box 10541, Broadway Centrum, Aurora Blvd., 1113 Quezon City, Philippines. TEL 02-787-071. FAX 02-721-4296. E-mail: graziano@irf.pfi.net. Ed. Graziano Battistella. bk.rev. **Indexed:** Ind.Phil.Per. **Document type:** academic/scholarly publication.
—UnCover.
Description: Designed for field operators and practitioners.

312   CR
ASOCIACION DEMOGRAFICA COSTARRICENSE. MEMORIA. a. Asociacion Demografica Costarricense, Apdo. Postal 10203, 1000 San Jose, Costa Rica. TEL 506-31-4425. FAX 506-31-4430.

312   AT
AUSTRALIAN INSTITUTE OF FAMILY STUDIES. ANNUAL REPORT. 1981. a. free. Australian Institute of Family Studies, 300 Queen St., Melbourne, Vic. 3000, Australia. TEL 61-3-2147888. TELEX 61-3-2147839. circ. 1,000.

312   GW   ISSN 0722-1509
HB848
B I B MITTEILUNGEN. 1980. 4/yr. Bundesinstitut fuer Bevoelkerungsforschung, Gustav-Stresemann-Ring 6, 65180 Wiesbaden, Germany. TEL 0611-752235. FAX 0611-39544. TELEX 4186511-STB-D. Ed. Charlotte Hoehn. bk.rev. circ. 1,000. **Document type:** government publication.
Description: Contains national and international population information and demographic news relevant to policy makers, social scientists, the press and other researchers.

300   US
BALANCE REPORT.* 1973. q. membership. Population-Environment Balance, Inc., 2000P St., N.W., Ste. 210, Washington, DC 20036-5915. TEL 202-879-3000. FAX 202-879-3019. Ed. M. Nowak. circ. 10,000.
Former titles: Balance; (until May 1986): Other Side (Washington).
Description: Covers a variety of U.S. population issues including family planning, immigration, and environmental carrying capacity.

BANGLADESH DEVELOPMENT STUDIES. see *BUSINESS AND ECONOMICS — Economic Situation And Conditions*

312   II
BARODA REPORTER. (Text in English) 1960. a. free. Population Research Centre, Maharajah Sayajirao University of Baroda, Faculty of Science, Baroda 390 002, India. TEL 328898. Ed. M.M. Gandotra. adv.; bk.rev.; abstr.; bibl.; charts; illus.; stat. circ. 500. (record) **Document type:** newsletter.
Description: Newsletter of the center, describing research projects and findings.

312   BE
BELGIUM. CENTRUM VOOR BEVOLKINGS- EN GEZINSSTUDIEN. PROGRESS REPORT. 1975. a. Centrum voor Bevolkings- en Gezinsstudien - Centre d'Etude de la Population et de la Famille, Markiesstraat 1, 1000 Brussels, Belgium. TEL 32-2-5073569. FAX 32-2-5073419. **Document type:** government publication.
Formerly: Belgium. Centre d'Etude de la Population et de la Famille. Annual Report.

312   SZ   ISSN 0258-784X
BEVOELKERUNGSBEWEGUNG IN DER SCHWEIZ/MOUVEMENT DE LA POPULATION EN SUISSE. (Text in French and German) 1867. a. 12 SFr. Bundesamt fuer Statistik, Schwarztorstr. 96, CH-3003 Bern, Switzerland. TEL 031-3236011. FAX 031-3236061. **Document type:** government publication.

312   GW   ISSN 0072-1867
HA1235
BEVOELKERUNGSSTRUKTUR UND WIRTSCHAFTSKRAFT DER BUNDESLAENDER. a. DM.25.20. Statistisches Bundesamt, 65180 Wiesbaden, Germany. TEL 0611-75-1. FAX 0611-724000. TELEX 61186-STBA-D. **Document type:** government publication.

312   BE   ISSN 0772-764X
HB3603
BEVOLKING EN GEZIN. (Text in Dutch; summaries in English) 1962. 3/yr. 440 BEF. (Nederlands Interuniversitair Demografisch Instituut, NE) Uitgeverij Pelckmans, Kapelsestraat 222, B-2950 Kapellen, Belgium. TEL 32-3-664-5320. FAX 32-3-665-0263. (Co-sponsor: Ministere de la Sante Publique et de la Famille, Centrum voor Bevolkings- en Gezinsstudien) bk.rev. circ. 1,200. **Indexed:** Lang.& Lang.Behav.Abstr., Popul.Ind.
—SWETS.

325.1   US
BORDER WATCH. 1983. m. $15. American Immigration Control Foundation, Box 525, Monterey, VA 24465. TEL 703-468-2022. Ed.Bd. bk.rev. circ. 200,000. **Document type:** newsletter, monographic series.
Formerly: A I C F Report.
Description: Covers immigration to the United States from a restrictionist point of view.

325.2   SW   ISSN 0345-1798
BRIDGE. Swedish edition: Bryggan (ISSN 0345-178X) (Text in English) 1972. q. SEK 50($15) Samfundet Emigrantforskningens Fraemjande - Society for the Promotion of Emigration Research, P.O. Box 331, S-651 08 Karlstad, Sweden. Ed. Erik Gustavson. adv.; bk.rev.; illus.; index. circ. 1,500.

312 333.33   CN   ISSN 0828-2919
HA747.B7
BRITISH COLUMBIA POPULATION FORECAST. a. Can.$20. Ministry of Government Services, B C Stats, 553 Superior St., Victoria, BC V8V 1X4, Canada. TEL 604-387-1502. FAX 604-387-0329. charts; stat. **Document type:** government publication.
Description: Provides details on British Columbia population growth by age and gender.

BRITISH GENEALOGICAL BIBLIOGRAPHIES. see *GENEALOGY AND HERALDRY — Abstracting, Bibliographies, Statistics*

325.2 948   SW   ISSN 0345-178X
BRYGGAN. English edition: Bridge (ISSN 0345-1798) 1972. q. SEK 50($15) Samfundet Emigrantforskningens Fraemjande, Postbox 331, 651 08 Karlstad, Sweden. Ed. Erik Gustavson. adv.; bk.rev. circ. 1,500.
Former titles (until vol.4, 1972): Bryggan; (until vol.2, 1972): Emigranten.

BULLETIN ON AGEING. see *GERONTOLOGY AND GERIATRICS*

301.426   UA
C D C NEWSLETTER. (Text in English) 1969. 2/yr. free. Cairo Demographic Centre, No. 78, St. No. 4, Hadhaba el-Olya, Mokattam 11571, Cairo, Egypt. TEL 5060950. Ed. Dr. Hisham Makhlouf. adv.; bk.rev. circ. 2,000. **Indexed:** Popul.Ind. **Document type:** newsletter.

C E D P A NETWORK. (Centre for Development and Population Activities) see *WOMEN'S INTERESTS*

C M J S CENTERPIECES. (Cohen Center for Modern Jewish Studies) see *ETHNIC INTERESTS*

CAHIERS DE L'EMIGRATION RUSSE. see *LITERATURE*

362   FR   ISSN 0007-9995
RA18
CAHIERS DE SOCIOLOGIE ET DE DEMOGRAPHIE MEDICALES. 1961. q. 380 F.($60) (foreign 400 F.) (effective 1996). Centre de Sociologie et Demographie Medicales, 60 bd. de Latour-Maubourg, 75007 Paris, France. TEL 45-55-73-77. FAX 45-55-87-94. Ed.Bd. bk.rev.; charts; stat.; index. **Indexed:** Abstr.Hyg., Biol.Abstr., Excerp.Med., Ind.Med., Trop.Dis.Bull.
—BLDSC (2952.240000).

301.32   CN   ISSN 0380-1721
CAHIERS QUEBECOIS DE DEMOGRAPHIE. 1975. 2/yr. Can.$25 (foreign Can.$35). Association des Demographes du Quebec, C.P. 403, succ. Cote-des-Neiges, Montreal, PQ H3S 2S7, Canada. TEL 514-848-2138. FAX 514-848-4539. E-mail: dgauv@vax2.concordia.ca. Ed. Danielle Gauvreau. bk.rev. **Indexed:** P.A.I.S.For.Lang.Ind., Popul.Ind., Pt.de Rep. (1982-). **Document type:** academic/scholarly publication.

CAMBRIDGE STUDIES IN POPULATION, ECONOMY AND SOCIETY IN PAST TIME. see *HISTORY*

CANADA'S IMMIGRATION AND CITIZENSHIP BULLETIN. see *LAW — Civil Law*

312   CN   ISSN 0380-1489
HB848   CODEN: CSTPEM
CANADIAN STUDIES IN POPULATION. (Text in English, French) 1974. s-a. price varies. University of Alberta, Department of Sociology, Population Research Laboratory, Edmonton, AB T6G 2H4, Canada. TEL 403-492-4659. FAX 403-492-2589. Ed. Herb Northcott. bk.rev.; index: 1974-1983. circ. 350. (back issues avail.) **Indexed:** Popul.Ind.
—UnCover.
Description: Articles on population studies, both methodological and substantive.

CELEBRATE LIFE (STAFFORD). see *BIRTH CONTROL*

312   US
CENSUS HIGHLIGHTS.* (Supplement to: University of Virginia. Center for Public Service. Reports) 1991. m. $12. University of Virginia, Center for Public Service, 918 Emmet St., N., Ste. 300, Charlottesville, VA 22903-4832. TEL 804-924-3396. FAX 804-924-4538.
Description: Identifies trends emerging from the 1990 Census.

312   US
CENTER FOR MIGRATION STUDIES. BIBLIOGRAPHIES AND DOCUMENTATION SERIES. 1970. irreg., latest 1992. price varies. Center for Migration Studies, 209 Flagg Pl., Staten Island, NY 10304-1199. TEL 718-351-8800. FAX 718-667-4598. (back issues avail.) **Document type:** monographic series, bibliography.

312   US
CENTER FOR MIGRATION STUDIES. GIOVANNI SCHIAVO COLLECTION. 1976. irreg., latest 1993. price varies. Center for Migration Studies, 209 Flagg Pl., Staten Island, NY 10304-1199. TEL 718-351-8800. FAX 718-667-4598. (back issues avail.) **Document type:** monographic series.

312   US
CENTER FOR MIGRATION STUDIES. OCCASIONAL PAPERS AND DOCUMENTATION SERIES. 1976. irreg., latest 1994. price varies. Center for Migration Studies, 209 Flagg Pl., Staten Island, NY 10304-1199. TEL 718-351-8800. FAX 718-667-4598. **Document type:** monographic series.

312   US
CENTER FOR MIGRATION STUDIES. PASTORAL SERIES. 1961. irreg., latest Fall 1994. price varies. Center for Migration Studies, 209 Flagg Pl., Staten Island, NY 10304-1199. TEL 718-351-8800. FAX 718-667-4598. (back issues avail.) **Document type:** monographic series.

325.1 US ISSN 8756-4467
CENTER FOR MIGRATION STUDIES NEWSLETTER. 1974. s-a. free. Center for Migration Studies, 209 Flagg Pl., Staten Island, NY 10304-1199. TEL 718-351-8800. FAX 718-667-4598. Ed. Lydio F. Tomasi. adv. contact: Carolyn Durante. bk.rev. circ. 1,000. (tabloid format; back issues avail.; reprint service avail. from UMI) **Indexed:** Refug.Abstr. **Document type:** newsletter.
 Description: Reports on research publications, conferences and documentation activities of the Center for Migration Studies.

CENTRE DE GEOGRAPHIE HUMAINE ET SOCIALE. TRAVAUX. see *GEOGRAPHY*

CENTRE FOR URBAN AND COMMUNITY STUDIES. MAJOR REPORT SERIES. see *HOUSING AND URBAN PLANNING*

CENTRE FOR URBAN AND COMMUNITY STUDIES. RESEARCH PAPERS. see *HOUSING AND URBAN PLANNING*

312 PY ISSN 1017-6047
CENTRO DE DOCUMENTACION Y ESTUDIOS. INFORMATIVO CAMPESINO. 1988. m. $60. Centro de Documentacion y Estudios, Pai Perez 737, Asuncion, Paraguay. (Dist. by: D.I.P.P., Box 2507, Asuncion, Paraguay) Ed. Quintin Riquelme. circ. 1,000.

312 UN ISSN 0378-5386
HB3530.5.A3
CENTRO LATINOAMERICANO DE DEMOGRAFIA. BOLETIN DEMOGRAFICO. (Text in English and Spanish) 1968. s-a. $10. United Nations, Centro Latinoamericano de Demografia - United Nations, Latin American and Demographic Center, Casilla 91, Santiago, Chile. TEL 2102000. bibl.; charts; stat. circ. 1,000. (also avail. in microfiche from CIS; back issues avail.) **Indexed:** IIS, P.A.I.S.For.Lang.Ind., Popul.Ind.
 Description: Contains population projections and estimates, birth and death rates for the Latin American and Caribbean countries.

312 UN ISSN 0303-1829
HB3530.5.A3
CENTRO LATINOAMERICANO DE DEMOGRAFIA. NOTAS DE POBLACION; revista latinoamericana de demografia. (Text in Spanish; summaries in English) 1973. s-a. $20. United Nations, Centro Latinoamericano de Demografia - United Nations, Latin American Demographic Center, Casilla 91, Santiago, Chile. TEL 2102000. bk.rev.; index. circ. 1,000. (also avail. in microfiche from CIS; back issues avail.) **Indexed:** IIS, P.A.I.S.For.Lang.Ind.
—Faxon.
 Description: Recent studies on population dynamics in Latin America and the Caribbean, information on work in the field of demographics.

312 UN ISSN 0503-3934
HA755
CENTRO LATINOAMERICANO DE DEMOGRAFIA. SERIE A/LATIN AMERICAN DEMOGRAPHIC CENTRE. SERIE A. (1989 Catalog avail.) 1962. irreg. $6 per no. United Nations, Centro Latinoamericano de Demografia - United Nations, Latin American Demographic Centre, Casilla 91, Santiago, Chile. TEL 2102000. stat. circ. 400.

312 UN ISSN 0503-3942
CENTRO LATINOAMERICANO DE DEMOGRAFIA. SERIE C/LATIN AMERICAN DEMOGRAPHIC CENTRE. SERIE C. (1987 Catalog available) 1963. irreg. $6 per no. United Nations, Centro Latinoamericano de Demografia, Casilla 91, Santiago, Chile. stat. circ. 400.

312 UN ISSN 0503-3950
CENTRO LATINOAMERICANO DE DEMOGRAFIA. SERIE D/LATIN AMERICAN DEMOGRAPHIC CENTRE. SERIE D. (1989 Catalog available) 1962. irreg. $6 per no. United Nations, Centro Latinoamericano de Demografia, Casilla 91, Santiago, Chile. circ. 400.

312 UN
CENTRO LATINOAMERICANO DE DEMOGRAFIA. SERIE E/LATIN AMERICAN DEMOGRAPHIC CENTRE. SERIE E. (1989 Catalog avail.) 1967. irreg. price varies. United Nations, Centro Latinoamericano de Demografia, Casilla 91, Santiago, Chile. stat.

312 UN
CENTRO LATINOAMERICANO DE DEMOGRAFIA. SERIE OI: PUBLICACIONES CONJUNTAS CON INSTITUCIONES NACIONALES DE PAISES DE AMERICA LATINA. 1967. irreg. $6 per no. United Nations, Centro Latinoamericano de Demografia - United Nations, Latin American Demographic Centre, Casilla 91, Santiago, Chile. stat.

312 US ISSN 1044-8403
HB3654.A3
CHINESE JOURNAL OF POPULATION SCIENCE. English translation of: Zhongguo Renkou Kexue (CC ISSN 1000-7881) (Text in English) 1989. q. $305 (effective 1996). (Zhongguo Shehui Kexueyuan, Renkou Yanjiusuo, CC - Chinese Academy of Social Sciences, Institute of Population Research) Allerton Press, Inc., 150 Fifth Ave., New York, NY 10011. TEL 212-924-3950. FAX 212-463-9684. Ed. Tian Xueyuan. (back issues avail.) **Indexed:** Asian-Pac.Econ.Lit. **Document type:** academic/scholarly publication.
—BLDSC (3180.559500); Faxon. **CCC.**
 Description: Covers population research in China, including population theories, and population age and sex structures.

COLOMBIA. DEPARTAMENTO ADMINISTRATIVO NACIONAL DE ESTADISTICA. ANUARIO DEMOGRAFICO. see *POPULATION STUDIES* — Abstracting, Bibliographies, Statistics

312 FR
COMITE INTERNATIONAL DE COOPERATION DANS LES RECHERCHES NATIONALES EN DEMOGRAPHIE. ACTES DES SEMINAIRES. 1973. irreg. Committee for International Cooperation in National Research in Demography, 27 rue du Commandeur, 75675 Paris Cedex 14, France.

383 914.2 301 UK ISSN 0268-4160
HM104
CONTINUITY AND CHANGE; a journal of social structure, law and demography in past societies. 1986. 3/yr. £63($99) (effective 1996). Cambridge University Press, Edinburgh Building, Shaftesbury Rd., Cambridge CB2 2RU, England. TEL 01223-312393. FAX 01223-315052. TELEX 851817256. (N. American addr.: Cambridge University Press, Journals Dept., 40 W. 20th St., New York, NY 10011. TEL 212-924-3900. FAX 212-691-3239) Eds. Lloyd Bonfield, Richard Wall. adv.; bk.rev. (also avail. in microform from UMI; back issues avail.; reprint service avail. from SWZ,WSH) **Indexed:** Geo.Abstr., PSI. **Document type:** academic/scholarly publication.
—BLDSC (3425.688700); SWETS; UMI; UnCover. **CCC.**
 Description: Covers historical sociology concerned with long-term continuities and discontinuity in the structures of past societies, with emphasis on methodological studies. Combines elements from history, sociology, law, demography, economics, and anthropology.

COUNTY GENEALOGICAL BIBLIOGRAPHIES. see *GENEALOGY AND HERALDRY* — Abstracting, Bibliographies, Statistics

312 MX ISSN 0187-6171
HA761
CUADERNOS DE POBLACION. 1987. a. Instituto Nacional de Estadistica, Geografia e Informatica, Secretaria de Programacion y Presupuesto, Prol. Heroe de Nacozari 2301 Sur, Puerta 11, Acceso, 20270 Aguascalientes, Ags., Mexico. TEL 49-18-19-48. FAX 491-807-39.

312 301.2 HU ISSN 0011-8249
HB3592.H8
DEMOGRAFIA; review of population sciences. (Text in Hungarian; summaries and contents page in English and Russian) 1958. q. 264 Ft.($28) (Magyar Tudomanyos Akademia, Demografiai Bizottsag) Statisztikai Kiado Vallalat, Kaszasdulo u. 2, P.O. Box 99, 1300 Budapest 3, Hungary. TEL 803-311. TELEX 22-6699. (Subscr. to: Kultura, Box 149, 1389 Budapest, Hungary) (Co-sponsor: Kozponti Statisztikai Hivatal) Ed. Andras Klinger. bk.rev.; bibl.; charts; stat.; index. circ. 1,000. **Indexed:** Amer.Hist.& Life, Curr.Cont., Hist.Abstr., Lang.& Lang.Behav.Abstr., Popul.Ind.

312 KR ISSN 0207-0383
HB3608.U5
DEMOGRAFICHESKIE ISSLEDOVANIYA; respublikanskii mezhvedomstvennyi sbornik nauchnykh trudov. (Text in Russian) 1970. a. (Akademiya Nauk Ukrainy, Institut Ekonomiki) Vidavnitstvo Naukova Dumka, Vul. Tereshchenkivska 3, 252601 Kiev, Ukraine. TEL 044-224-4068. FAX 044-224-7060. (Dist. by: Mezhdunarodnaya Kniga, B. Yakimanka 39, 117049 Moscow, Russia) Ed. V.S. Steshenko.
—BLDSC (0052.675000).

312 US
DEMOGRAPHIC GUIDE TO ARIZONA (YEAR). 1967. a. free. Department of Economic Security, Population Statistics Unit, Box 6123, SC-45Z, Phoenix, AZ 85005. TEL 602-542-5984. circ. 2,000.
 Formerly: Population Estimates of Arizona (ISSN 0079-3906)

312 UN ISSN 0566-5302
DEMOGRAPHIC HANDBOOK FOR AFRICA/GUIDE DEMOGRAPHIE DE L'AFRIQUE. (Text in English and French) irreg., latest 1978. United Nations Economic Commission for Africa, P.O. Box 3001, Addis Ababa, Ethiopia.

910 US ISSN 0275-9594
DEMOGRAPHIC MONOGRAPHS. 1968. irreg., vol.9, 1970. price varies. Gordon & Breach Science Publishers, c/o International Publishers Distributor, 820 Town Center Dr., Langhorne, PA 19047. TEL 215-750-2642. FAX 215-750-6343. (Subscr. to: International Publishers Distributor, P.O. Box 90, Reading, Berkshire RG1 8JL, England. TEL 44-173-456-8316) Ed.Bd. **Document type:** monographic series.
 Refereed Serial

312 UN ISSN 0082-8041
HA17
DEMOGRAPHIC YEARBOOK. (Text in English and French) 1949. a. price varies. (United Nations, Department of Economic and Social Affairs) United Nations Publications, Room DC2-853, New York, NY 10017. TEL 212-963-8302; 800-253-9646. FAX 212-963-3489. (Dist. by: United Nations Sales Section, Room DC2-0853, New York, NY; or Palais des Nations, CH-1211 Geneva 10, Switzerland) (also avail. in microfiche from CIS) **Indexed:** IIS.
—BLDSC (3550.605000).

312 CM ISSN 0151-1408
DEMOGRAPHIE AFRICAINE: BULLETIN DE LIAISON. (Supplement avail.: Groupe de Demographie Africaine. Etudes et Documents) 1979. 3/yr. free. Institut de Formation et de Recherche Demographiques (I F O R D), B.P. 1556, Yaounde, Cameroon. TEL 22-24-71. adv. circ. 1,000. **Indexed:** Popul.Ind.
 Formerly: Demographie en Afrique d'Expression Francaise: Bulletin de Liaison.

312 FR ISSN 0070-3362
DEMOGRAPHIE ET SOCIETES. 1960. irreg. price varies. (Ecole Pratique des Hautes Etudes, Centre de Recherches Historiques) Librairie Touzot, 38 rue Saint Sulpice, 75278 Paris Cedex 06, France.

312 US ISSN 0070-3370
HB881.A1
DEMOGRAPHY. 1964. q. $85. Population Association of America, 1722 N St., N.W., Washington, DC 20036-2983. TEL 202-429-0891. FAX 202-785-0146. circ. 4,000. **Indexed:** ABI Inform., Abstr.Hyg., Asian-Pac.Econ.Lit., ASSIA, Biostat., Chic.Per.Ind., Curr.Lit.Fam.Plan., Environ.Abstr., Geo.Abstr., IDA, IMFL, Ind.Med., Int.Lab.Doc., J.of Econ.Lit., Mid.East: Abstr.& Ind., P.A.I.S., Popul.Ind., Soc.Sci.Ind., SSCI, Trop.Dis.Bull. **Document type:** academic/scholarly publication.
—BLDSC (3550.610000); CIS; Faxon; SWETS; UMI; UnCover.

312 II ISSN 0970-454X
HB848
DEMOGRAPHY INDIA; population - society - economy - environment - interactions. (Text in English) 1972. s-a. $40. (Indian Association for the Study of Population) Hindustan Publishing Corp., 4805-24 Bharat Ram Rd., Flat Nos. 1&2, 1st Fl., Daryaganj, New Delhi 110 002, India. TEL 9-11-3254401. FAX 9-11-6863511. Ed. M.E. Khan. bk.rev.; charts; stat. circ. 950. (back issues avail.) **Indexed:** IDA, Popul.Ind., Trop.Dis.Bull. **Document type:** academic/scholarly publication.
—BLDSC (3550.612000); UnCover.

POPULATION STUDIES

312   NE   ISSN 0169-1473
HB848
DEMOS. 1972. 10/yr. free. Nederlands Interdisciplinair Demografisch Instituut - Netherlands Interdisciplinary Demographic Institute, Lange Houtstraat 19, 2511 CV The Hague, Netherlands. TEL 31-70-3565200. FAX 31-70-3647187. TELEX 31138 NIDI NL. circ. 5,000. Indexed: Popul.Ind.
    Formerly (until 1985): Demografie (ISSN 0166-574X)

DENMARK. DANMARKS STATISTIK. BEFOLKNINGENS BEVAEGELSER. see *POPULATION STUDIES — Abstracting, Bibliographies, Statistics*

948.95 325.9   DK   ISSN 0107-8720
DEUTSCHER VOLKSKALENDER NORDSCHLESWIG. (Text in German) 1924. a. DKK 35. Deutscher Schul- und Sprachverein fuer Nordschleswig, Ramsherred 49A, P.O. Box 242, DK-6200 Aabenraa, Denmark. TEL 45-74-62-41-03. FAX 45-74-62-73-61. Ed. Franz Christiansen. bk.rev.; illus. circ. 2,500.
    Description: Directed to the German minority in Denmark. Focuses on cultural subjects

DIALOGO. see *SOCIOLOGY*

DIASPORA: A JOURNAL OF TRANSNATIONAL STUDIES. see *SOCIAL SCIENCES: COMPREHENSIVE WORKS*

325.1   US   ISSN 0277-724X
HV89
DIRECTORY OF NONPROFIT IMMIGRATION COUNSELING AGENCIES. a. U.S. Immigration and Naturalization Service, 425 I St., N.W., Washington, DC 20536. TEL 202-724-7796.

325   IT   ISSN 0391-3457
DOSSIER EUROPA - EMIGRAZIONE. 1964. m. L.30000 (foreign L.35000). Centro Studi Emigrazione, Via Dandolo 58, 00153 Rome, Italy. TEL 58-09-764. adv.; bk.rev.; charts; stat.; index. circ. 1,000. (processed; back issues avail.)
    Formerly: C.S.E.R. Selezione (ISSN 0007-9081)
    Description: Discusses the sociological and pastoral aspects of migration, with an emphasis on Europe.

312   BE
DOSSIERS DE DEMOGRAPHIE DE LA BELGIQUE. 1975. irreg. 325 Fr. (Societe Belge de Demographie) Editions Derouaux, 10, Place St.-Jacques, Liege, Belgium. (looseleaf format)

301.426   II
DYNAMICS OF POPULATION AND FAMILY WELFARE. (Text in English) 1979. biennial (in 8 vols.). (International Institute for Population Sciences) Himalaya Publishing House, 12-13, Dr. Bhalerao Marg, Bombay 400004, India. Ed. K.B. Pathak.
    Description: Presents findings of the research work by the Institute faculty and consultants.

301.32   UN   ISSN 0258-1914
E S C W A POPULATION BULLETIN. (Text in Arabic, English) 1970. s-a. price varies. (Economic and Social Commission for Western Asia, Social Development and Population Division) United Nations Publications, Rm. DC2-853, New York, NY 10017. TEL 212-963-8302; 800-253-9646. FAX 212-963-3489. Ed. Walid Halil. bk.rev. circ. 1,800. (back issues avail.) **Indexed:** Trop.Dis.Bull. —BLDSC (6552.203000).
    Former titles: E C W A Population Bulletin; U N Economic and Social Office. Population Bulletin.
    Description: Presents articles on population and related issues relevant to Arab countries and theoretical and methodological subjects of relevance to population training in the Arab world.
    Refereed Serial

325   US
▼**EAST - WEST CENTER PROGRAM ON POPULATION. ASIA - PACIFIC POPULATION RESEARCH REPORTS.** 1995. irreg., no.4, 1995. free. Center for Cultural and Technical Interchange Between East and West, Inc., 1777 East-West Rd., Honolulu, HI 96848. TEL 808-944-7401. FAX 808-944-7490. E-mail: WARDS@EWC.bitnet. Ed. Sandra E. Ward. circ. 1,000.

312   EC   ISSN 0070-8909
ECUADOR. INSTITUTO NACIONAL DE ESTADISTICA Y CENSOS. ANUARIO DE ESTADISTICAS VITALES. Former name of issuing body--Division de Estadistica y Censos. (In 2 vols.): Nacimientos y Difuntos; Matrimonios y Divorcios) 1954. a. Esc.47000($58) for both vols. Instituto Nacional de Estadistica y Censos, 10 de Agosto no. 229, Quito, Ecuador. TEL 593-2-581900. FAX 593-2-580041. circ. 500.

325   NE   ISSN 0013-4082
ELDERS; een kroniek van zaken buiten de grenzen. 1964. m. free. Netherlands Emigration Service, Muzenstraat 30, 2511 VW The Hague, Netherlands. TEL 070-624611. Ed. J.W. van Eyk. bk.rev.; illus.; stat. circ. 3,500.

312   BL
ENCONTRO NACIONAL DE ESTUDOS POPULACIONAIS. vol.8, 1992. a. Associacao Brasileira de Estudos Populacionais, Rua General Jardim, 770 cj. 3-D, 01223-010 Sao Paulo SP, Brazil.

325   US   ISSN 0899-8167
ESCOGE LA VIDA!. (Text in Spanish) 1984. bi-m. $10 donation. Vida Humana Internacional, 4345 S.W. 72nd Ave., Ste. E, Miami, FL 33155. TEL 305-662-1497. FAX 305-662-1499. Ed. Magaly Llaguno. bk.rev. circ. 6,000. **Document type:** newsletter.
    Description: Features news stories from the United States and other parts of the world, as well as articles on current affairs and family health.

312 910   FR   ISSN 0755-7809
HB848
ESPACES - POPULATIONS - SOCIETES. (Text and summaries in English, French) 1983. 3/yr. 360 F. (effective 1996). Universite des Sciences et Technologies de Lille, UFR de Geographie, 59655 Villeneuve d'Ascq Cedex, France. TEL 20-43-65-52. FAX 20-43-44-41. Ed. Pierre-Jean Thumerelle. adv. contact: Jean Pierre Bondue. bk.rev.; index. (back issues avail.) **Indexed:** Geo.Abstr. **Document type:** academic/scholarly publication.
    —BLDSC (3811.327000).
    Description: Explores the links between space, population and societies.

312   CK
ESTUDIOS DE POBLACION. 1976. m. Asociacion Colombiana para el Estudio de la Poblacion, Departamento de Publicaciones, Carrera 23 no. 39-82, Bogota, D.E. 1, Colombia. (Co-sponsor: Consejo de Poblacion) Ed. Rafael Salazar Santos.

312   MX   ISSN 0186-7210
HB3531
ESTUDIOS DEMOGRAFICOS Y URBANOS. (Text in Spanish; summaries in English, Spanish) 1986. 3/yr. Mex.$57($35) to individuals (foreign $44); institutions $55 (foreign $62) (effective 1995). (Colegio de Mexico, A.C., Centro de Estudios Demograficos y de Desarrollo Urbano) Colegio de Mexico, A.C., Departamento de Publicaciones, Camino al Ajusco 20, 01000 Mexico, D.F., Mexico. TEL 525-645-5955. FAX 525-645-0464. TELEX 1777585 COLME. Ed. Beatriz Figueroa. adv.; bk.rev.; abstr. circ. 1,000. **Indexed:** Hisp.Amer.Per.Ind. (1991-).

325   AG   ISSN 0326-7458
JV7398
ESTUDIOS MIGRATORIOS LATINOAMERICANOS. 1985. 3/yr. Arg.$330($33) in America; elsewhere $36. Centro de Estudios Migratorios Latinoamericanos (CEMLA), Independencia 20, 1099 Buenos Aires C.F., Argentina. FAX 331-0832. Dir. Luigi Favero. adv.; bk.rev. circ. 800. **Indexed:** Amer.Hist.& Life, Hist.Abstr., Sociol.Abstr.
    —BLDSC (3812.775800).

EUGENICS SPECIAL INTEREST GROUP BULLETIN. see *BIOLOGY — Genetics*

312   NE   ISSN 1381-3579
▼**EUROPEAN STUDIES OF POPULATION.** (Text in English) 1995. irrege. price varies. Kluwer Academic Publishers, Postbus 17, 3300 AA Dordrecht, Netherlands. TEL 31-78-392392. FAX 31-78-392254. (Dist. by: Kluwer Academic Publishers Group, P.O. Box 322, 3300 AH Dordrecht, Netherlands. TEL 31-78-392392. FAX 31-78-546474; N. America dist. addr.: Box 358, Accord Sta., Hingham, MA 02018-0358. TEL 617-871-6600. FAX 617-871-6528) **Document type:** monographic series.
    Description: Publishes interdisciplinary demographic research with special emphasis on Europe.

312   IS   ISSN 0333-9041
FAMILIES IN ISRAEL. (Text in English and Hebrew) a. $12. Central Bureau of Statistics, P.O. Box 13015, Jerusalem 91 130, Israel. TEL 02-553400.

FAMILY HISTORY NEWS & DIGEST. see *GENEALOGY AND HERALDRY*

FEDERAL IMMIGRATION LAWS AND REGULATIONS. see *LAW*

312   US
HB3525.F6
FLORIDA POPULATION STUDIES. 1955. 3/yr. $30. University of Florida, College of Business Administration, Bureau of Economic and Business Research, Box 117140, 221 Matherly Hall, Gainesville, FL 32611-7140. TEL 904-392-0171. FAX 904-392-4739. Ed. Ann Pierce. circ. 1,250. **Indexed:** SRI. **Document type:** bulletin.
    Formerly (until 1994): University of Florida. Bureau of Economic and Business Research. Population Studies (ISSN 0071-6030)
    Description: Contains projections of the Florida population by county through the year 2020, as well as data on the number of Florida households, average household size, and estimates and projections by age, race, and sex.

325.2   GW
FLUECHTLINGS FORUM. 1985. s-a. German Red Cross, General Secretariat, Friedrich-Ebert-Allee 71, 53113 Bonn, Germany. TEL 02281541-298. circ. 3,000.

FORECAST (NEW YORK); the magazine of demographics and business statistics. see *BUSINESS AND ECONOMICS — Abstracting, Bibliographies, Statistics*

310   FR   ISSN 0071-8823
FRANCE. INSTITUT NATIONAL D'ETUDES DEMOGRAPHIQUES. CAHIERS DE TRAVAUX ET DOCUMENTS. 1946. irreg., no.134, 1994. price varies. Institut National d'Etudes Demographiques, 27 rue du Commandeur, 75675 Paris Cedex 14, France. TEL 42-18-20-00. FAX 42-18-21-99. Ed. H. Leridon.

GAZETTEER; alphabetical list of localities with statistics on population, number of houses and main source of water supply. see *BUSINESS AND ECONOMICS — Abstracting, Bibliographies, Statistics*

301.32   IT   ISSN 0016-6987
HB881   CODEN: GNUSA7
GENUS. (Text in Italian; summaries in English and French) 1934. s-a. L.80000 (foreign 100 S.Fr.). (Universita di Roma, Dipartimento di Scienze Demografiche) E S I A Books and Journals, Via Palestro, 30, 00185 Rome, Italy. TEL 39-6-4441221. FAX 39-6-4477743. Ed. Antonio Golini. adv.; bk.rev.; bibl. circ. 3,000. **Indexed:** A.I.C.P., Abstr.Hyg., Amer.Hist.& Life, Anthropol.Lit., Biol.Abstr., Curr.Adv.Ecol.Sci., Curr.Cont., Hist.Abstr., Popul.Ind. **Document type:** academic/scholarly publication.
    —BLDSC (4116.700000); SWETS.
    Description: International journal devoted to various aspects of demography: demographical analysis, historical demography, economic demography, social demography, theory of population policy.

GEOGRAPHICAL VIEW POINT. see *GEOGRAPHY*

GEORGETOWN IMMIGRATION LAW JOURNAL. see *LAW*

GERONTOLOSKO DRUSTVO S R SRBIJE. see *GERONTOLOGY AND GERIATRICS*

POPULATION STUDIES

GHANA LIVING STANDARDS SURVEY. ROUND REPORT. see BUSINESS AND ECONOMICS — Abstracting, Bibliographies, Statistics

GHANA LIVING STANDARDS SURVEY. RURAL COMMUNITIES IN GHANA. see BUSINESS AND ECONOMICS — Abstracting, Bibliographies, Statistics

312   GH   ISSN 0855-1308
GHANA POPULATION STUDIES. Key Title: University of Ghana Population Studies. 1969. irreg., no.10. price varies. University of Ghana, Institute of Statistical, Social and Economic Research, P.O. Box 74, Legon, Ghana. **Document type:** academic/scholarly publication.

312   UN
GLOBAL POPULATION POLICY DATABASE (YEAR). a. United Nations, Department of Economic and Social Development, Development Information, Rm. DC1-1090, New York, NY 10017. TEL 212-963-4296.

301.426   SW
GOETEBORGS UNIVERSITET. DEMOGRAPHIC RESEARCH INSTITUTE. REPORTS. no.14, 1974. irreg. Goteborgs Universitet, Demographic Research Institute, Viktoriagatan 13, S-411 25 Goteborg, Sweden. (Dist. by: Almqvist & Wiksell International, 26 Gamla Brogatan, S-111 20 Stockholm, Sweden)

GREAT BRITAIN. CENTRAL STATISTICAL OFFICE. REGIONAL TRENDS. see STATISTICS

312 610   UK   ISSN 0072-6400
GREAT BRITAIN. GENERAL REGISTER OFFICE. STUDIES ON MEDICAL AND POPULATION SUBJECTS. 1948. irreg. price varies. H.M.S.O., P.O. Box 276, London SW8 5DT, England. (reprint service avail. from UMI) **Document type:** government publication.
—BLDSC (8491.101000).

312   UK   ISSN 0950-7574
HA1123
GREAT BRITAIN. OFFICE OF POPULATION CENSUSES AND SURVEYS. POPULATION ESTIMATES: ENGLAND AND WALES. 1957. a. price varies. H.M.S.O., P.O. Box 276, London SW8 5DT, England. **Document type:** government publication.
Formerly (until 1974): Great Britain. Registrar General. Annual Estimates of the Population of England and Wales and of Local Authority Areas (ISSN 0301-7141)

314   DK   ISSN 0105-0885
HB1946.A3
GROENLANDS BEFOLKNING/KALATDLIT NUNANE INUIT. (Text in Danish and Greenlandic) 1976. a. free. Statsministeriet, Groenlandsdepartmentet, Hausergade 3, 1128 Copenhagen K, Denmark. circ. 600.

312   UN
GUIDE TO SOURCES OF INTERNATIONAL POPULATION ASSISTANCE. (Text in English, French, Spanish) 1976. triennial. $20 per issue. United Nations Population Fund, 220 E. 42nd St., Rm. 2306, New York, NY 10017. circ. 3,000. (also avail. in microfilm)
Description: Contains information on the types of assistance international and other agencies and organizations provide in the population field.

325   CN   ISSN 0842-3989
H L I CANADIAN REPORT. Key Title: Canadian Special Report - Human Life International Canada. (Text in French) m. Can.$35($20) Human Life International in Canada Inc., P.O. Box 7400, Sta. V, Vanier, ON K1L 8E4, Canada. TEL 613-745-9405. FAX 613-745-9868.
Formerly: H L I Sister Lucille's Special Canadian Report.

325   US   ISSN 0899-2673
H L I REPORTS. 1983. m. $30 donation. Human Life International, 7845-E Airpark Rd., Gaithersburg, MD 20879. TEL 301-670-7884. FAX 301-869-7363. Ed. William Marshner. adv. contact: Vernon Kirby. charts; illus.; stat.; tr.lit. circ. 25,000. (looseleaf format; back issues avail.) **Document type:** newsletter.
Former titles (until 1984): H L I Report; Loveline.
Description: Provides international reservoir of pro-life and pro-family information and perspectives.

325   CN
H L I REPORTS. m. $35. Human Life International in Canada Inc., P.O. Box 7400, Sta. V, Vanier, ON K1L 8E4, Canada. TEL 613-745-9405. FAX 613-745-9868.
Formerly: H L I Reports - Canada.

312   TU
HACETTEPE UNIVERSITY. INSTITUTE OF POPULATION STUDIES. TURKISH POPULATION AND HEALTH SURVEY. 1968. quinquennial. Hacettepe University, Institute of Population Studies - Hacettepe Universitesi, Nufus Etutleri Enstitusu, Ankara, Turkey. FAX 90-312-3118141. TELEX 42237 HTK TR. Ed. Dr. Ergul Tuncbilek. **Document type:** academic/scholarly publication.

300   US
HAVE YOU HEARD?.* 1986. q. membership. Population - Environment Balance, Inc., 2000 P St., N.W., Ste. 210, Washington, DC 20036-5915. TEL 202-879-3000. FAX 202-879-3019. Ed. M. Nowak.
Description: Provides updates and information on U.S. population issues.

HISTORICKA DEMOGRAFIE. see HISTORY — History Of Europe

312   HU   ISSN 0134-0050
HB849
HISTORISCH-DEMOGRAPHISCHE MITTEILUNGEN/COMMUNICATIONS DE DEMOGRAPHIE HISTORIQUE/REVIEW OF HISTORICAL DEMOGRAPHY. (Text in French and German) 1971. irreg. DM.6($4) Eotvos Lorand Tudomanyegyetem, Allam es Jogtudomanyi Kar, Statisztikai Tanszek - University Eotvus Lorand, Faculty of Law, Department of Statistics, Egyetem ter 1-3, H-1364 Budapest, Hungary. FAX 1-1174-114. TELEX 225467. Ed. Jozsef Kovacsics. bk.rev.; stat. **Indexed:** Popul.Ind.

HOMMES ET MIGRATIONS. see SOCIOLOGY

HUMAN GEOGRAPHY/JIMBUN-CHIRI. see GEOGRAPHY

325   US   ISSN 0899-420X
HUMAN LIFE INTERNATIONAL. SPECIAL REPORT. 1981. m. $30 donation. Human Life International, 7845-E Airpark Rd., Gaithersburg, MD 20879. TEL 301-670-7884. FAX 301-869-7363. Ed. Rev. Paul Marx. stat.; cum.index: 1981-1988. circ. 25,000. (looseleaf format; back issues avail.) **Document type:** newsletter.
Formerly: Human Life International. Letter Dr. Report.
Description: Accounts of Rev. Marx's pro-life missionary travels.

312   US
HUMAN SURVIVAL. 1973. $30 membership (effective 1996). Negative Population Growth, Inc., 210 The Plaza, Box 1206, Teaneck, NJ 07666. TEL 201-837-3555. FAX 201-837-0288. Ed. Donald Mann. bk.rev.; circ. 19,000 (paid). **Document type:** newsletter.

HUNGARY. KOZPONTI STATISZTIKAI HIVATAL. DEMOGRAFIAI EVKONYV. see POPULATION STUDIES — Abstracting, Bibliographies, Statistics

325   US   ISSN 0018-8514
KF4819.A15
I AND N REPORTER. (Immigration and Naturalization) Variant title: I N S Reporter. 1943. q. $9. U.S. Immigration and Naturalization Service, 425 I St., N.W., Washington, DC 20536. TEL 202-724-7796. Ed.Bd. charts; illus.; stat.; index. circ. 3,200. **Indexed:** Amer.Hist.& Life, Hist.Abstr.

301.426   II
I I P S NEWSLETTER. (Text in English) 1960. q. free. International Institute for Population Sciences, Govandi Station Rd., Deonar, Bombay 400 088, India. TEL 22-5563254. Eds. Parveen Nangia, B.M. Ramesh. bibl.; charts; illus. circ. 1,300. **Document type:** newsletter.
Formerly: International Institute for Population Studies. Newsletter (ISSN 0047-0716)
Description: Contains organization news as well as summaries of new dissertations.

I M C H NEWSLETTER. (Institute of Maternal and Child Health) see CHILDREN AND YOUTH — About

325   SZ
I O M NEWS. (Editions in English, French, Spanish) 1979. m. free. International Organization for Migration, 17 route des Morillons, P.O. Box 71, CH-1211 Geneva 19, Switzerland. TEL 022-7179242. Ed. Regina Boucault. circ. controlled. (also avail. in microfiche from CIS) **Indexed:** IIS, Refug.Abstr. **Document type:** bulletin.
Former titles (until 1993): I O M Monthly Dispatch; I C M Monthly Dispatch; Intergovernmental Committee for European Migration. Monthly Dispatch.
Description: Covers current activities of the organization on refugee and migration movements and programs.

325 613.9   UK
I P P F ANNUAL REPORT. (Text in English, French, Spanish) 1974. a. free. International Planned Parenthood Federation, Regent's College, Inner Circle, Regent's Park, London NW1 4NS, England. TEL 0171-486-0741. FAX 0171-487-7950. TELEX 919573 IPEPEE G. Ed. Jeremy Hammand. illus. **Document type:** corporate report.
Former titles: I P P F in Action; International Planned Parenthood Federation. Annual Report (ISSN 0307-6857)

325 613.9   UK   ISSN 0019-0357
CODEN: IPPMAY
I P P F MEDICAL BULLETIN. French edition: Bulletin Medicale de l'I P P F (ISSN 0306-7815); Spanish edition: Boletin Medico de I P P F (ISSN 0306-7823) 1966. bi-m. free to qualified personnel. International Planned Parenthood Federation, Regent's College, Inner Circle, Regent's Park, London NW1 4NS, England. TEL 0171-486-0741. FAX 0171-487-7950. TELEX 919573 IPEPEE G. Ed. Carmel McHenry. circ. 30,000 (controlled). **Indexed:** Abstr.Hyg., Excerp.Med., Trop.Dis.Bull. **Document type:** academic/scholarly publication.
—BLDSC (4567.450000).
Description: Provides up-to-date information on clinical aspects and developments in the field of family planning practice.

325 613.9   UK   ISSN 0261-6998
I P P F OPEN FILE. m. free. International Planned Parenthood Federation, Regent's College, Inner Circle, Regent's Park, London NW1 4NS, England. TEL 071-486-0741. FAX 071-487-7950. TELEX 919573 IPEPEE G. Ed. Rupert Walker. circ. 2,000 (controlled). **Document type:** newsletter.

325 613.9   UK   ISSN 1350-5106
I P P F PLANNED PARENTHOOD CHALLENGES. Variant title: Planned Parenthood Challenges. 1993. s-a. (free to family planning organizations). International Planned Parenthood Federation, Regent's College, Inner Circle, Regent's Park, London SW1 4NS, England. TEL 0171-486-0741. FAX 0171-487-7950. TELEX 919573 IPEPEE G. Ed. Jeremy Hamand. circ. (controlled). **Document type:** newsletter.

312   BE   ISSN 0771-2022
HB848
I U S S P NEWSLETTER/U I E S P BULLETIN DE LIAISON. (Text in English, French) 3/yr. $10 per no. International Union for the Scientific Study of Population, 34 rue des Augustins, B-4000 Liege, Belgium. FAX 041-223847. TELEX 42648 POPUN. charts; stat. circ. 2,000. (back issues avail.)

312   BE   ISSN 0253-4010
I U S S P PAPERS/U I E S P DOCUMENTS DE L'UNION. 1974. irreg. price varies. International Union for the Scientific Study of Population, 34 rue des Augustins, B-4000 Liege, Belgium. FAX 041-223847. TELEX 42648 POPUN. bibl.; charts; illus.; stat. (back issues avail.)

325.1   US   ISSN 0749-5951
IMMIGRANT COMMUNITIES & ETHNIC MINORITIES IN THE UNITED STATES & CANADA. 1984. irreg., no.82, 1993. price varies. A M S Press, Inc., 56 E. 13th St., New York, NY 10003. TEL 212-777-4700. FAX 212-995-5413. (back issues avail.)
—BLDSC (4369.637150).
Description: Monographs on ethnic enclaves and communities within the United States and Canada.

POPULATION STUDIES

325.1 942.006   UK   ISSN 0261-9288
JV1.A2
IMMIGRANTS AND MINORITIES. 1982. 3/yr. £38($55) to individuals; institutions £98 ($145) (effective 1996). Frank Cass, Newbury House, 890-900 Eastern Ave., Newbury Park, Ilford, Essex IG2 7HH, England. TEL 44-181-599-8866. FAX 44-181-599-0984. E-mail: 100067,1576@compuserve.com. Eds. Colin Holmes, Kenneth Lunn. adv.: B&W page £195 ($275); adv. contact: Anne Kidson. bk.rev.; bibl.; index. (also avail. in microform from UMI; back issues avail.) **Indexed:** Amer.Hist.& Life, ASSIA, E.I., Geo.Abstr., Hist.Abstr., IDA, Int.Polit.Sci.Abstr., Mult.Ed.Abstr. **Document type:** academic/scholarly publication.
—BLDSC (4369.637500); Faxon; UMI; UnCover.
   Description: Covers research into the history of immigration and related studies. Seeks to deal with complex themes involved with a broad sweep of ethnic and minority relations within a historical context.
Refereed Serial

325.1   US   ISSN 0899-5400
E184.A1
IMMIGRATION DIGEST. 1987. irreg. (2-3/yr.). $10 per no. Family History World, Box 22045, Salt Lake City, UT 84122. TEL 801-250-6717. Ed. Arlene H. Eakle. bk.rev. circ. 400.
   Description: Provides current information on new resources to link your immigrant ancestors with their origins: naming patterns and changed name forms, exit documents and where to find them, passenger lists and naturalizations, administrative boundary maps.

325.1   US   ISSN 0579-4374
E184.A1
IMMIGRATION HISTORY NEWSLETTER. 1969. s-a. $17 to individuals; institutions $32 (includes journal). Immigration History Society, University of Pittsburgh, 405 Bellefield Hall, Pittsburgh, PA 15260. TEL 215-925-8090. Ed. Joe Makarewicz. bk.rev.; bibl. circ. 750. **Indexed:** Amer.Hist.& Life (until 1990), Hist.Abstr. (until 1990).

IMMIGRATION LAW ADVISORY. see *LAW*

IMMIGRATION LAW & PRACTICE. see *LAW*

325.1   CN   ISSN 0835-3808
KE4454.A45
IMMIGRATION LAW REPORTER. SECOND SERIES. N.S. 1988. 12/yr. (in 3 vols.). Can.$130. Carswell, One Corporate Plaza, 2075 Kennedy Rd., Scarborough, ON M1T 3V4, Canada. TEL 416-609-8000. FAX 416-298-5094. Ed. Cecil L. Rotenberg. adv. contact: M. Lalani. (reprint service avail. from WSH)
   Description: Features timely reporting of decisions of the Immigration Appeal Board and of the Courts in immigration matters. Provides annotations and articles of particular interest to the practitioner, highlighting practice issues and immigration policy.

325.1   US   ISSN 0892-547X
KF4802
IMMIGRATION POLICY & LAW. 1987. bi-w. $497 (foreign $517). L R P Publications, 747 Dresher Rd., Box 980, Horsham, PA 19044-0980. TEL 215-784-0860; 800-341-7874. FAX 215-784-9639. TELEX 285656 BNAI WSH. Ed. Laurel Kalser, Esq. (back issues avail.) **Document type:** newsletter.
—CCC.
   Description: Covers the Immigration Reform and Control Act of 1986. Reports on requirements and procedures, litigation, enforcement action, activities of the Immigration and Naturalization Service and the Congress.

IMMIGRATION PROCEDURES HANDBOOK. see *LAW*

312   US   ISSN 1073-1997
IMMIGRATION REVIEW. 1989. q. $16 (effective 1995). Center for Immigration Studies, 1815 H St., N.W., Ste. 1010, Washington, DC 20006. TEL 202-466-8185. FAX 202-466-8076. Ed. Rosemary Jenks. bk.rev.; charts; illus.; stat.; tr.lit.; cum.index: 1989-1993. circ. 2,600. **Document type:** academic/scholarly publication.
   Formerly: Scope.
   Description: Covers all immigration issues, from population and environment to economics, social services and immigration law.

304.8 325   US
IMMIGRATION THEORY AND POLICY SERIES. 1975. irreg., latest 1994. $14.50 per no. Center for Migration Studies, 209 Flagg Pl., Staten Island, NY 10304-1199. TEL 718-351-8800. FAX 718-667-4598. (back issues avail.) **Document type:** academic/scholarly publication.
   Description: Publishes essays dealing with immigration policy and theory.

325.1   US
IMMIGRATION WATCH. m. 717 Second St. N.E., Ste. 307, Washington, DC 20002.

325   US   ISSN 0275-634X
IN DEFENSE OF THE ALIEN; proceedings of the Annual National Legal Conference on Immigration & Refugee Policy. 1978. a. $14.95. Center for Migration Studies of New York, Inc., 209 Flagg Pl., Staten Island, NY 10304-1199. TEL 718-351-8800. FAX 718-667-4598. E-mail: lftoc@csiunx.it.cuny.edu. Ed.Bd. circ. 850. (back issues avail.) **Indexed:** Refug.Abstr. **Document type:** proceedings.
   Description: Legal, legislative and socio-economic developments in migration and refugee policy. For students, lawyers and social workers interested in the current legal and policy issues on migration and refugees.

INDIAN HEALTH TRENDS AND SERVICES. see *PUBLIC HEALTH AND SAFETY*

INDIANA FACTBOOK. see *ENCYCLOPEDIAS AND GENERAL ALMANACS*

INDUCED ABORTION: A WORLD REVIEW. see *BIRTH CONTROL*

312   BL   ISSN 0100-7173
INFORME DEMOGRAFICO. 1980. irreg. $41.50. Fundacao Sistema Estadual de Analise de Dados, Av. Casper Libero, 464, 01033 Sao Paulo, Brazil. circ. 500.
   Description: Devoted to specific topics such as: mortality rates, migration and the fertility rate in the state of Sao Paulo.

301.32   US   ISSN 0277-2302
AP2
INSTAURATION. 1975. m. $35. Howard Allen Enterprises, Inc., Box 76, Cape Canaveral, FL 32920. Ed. Wilmot Robertson. adv.; bk.rev.; film rev. **Document type:** academic/scholarly publication.
   Description: Explores the effects of population group dynamics on contemporary political, economic and social issues.

312   CM
INSTITUT DE FORMATION ET DE RECHERCHE DEMOGRAPHIQUES. ANNALES. 1975. 2/yr. free. Institut de Formation et de Recherche Demographiques (I F O R D), B.P. 1556, Yaounde, Cameroon. TEL 22-24-71. circ. 500.

312   II   ISSN 0070-3311
INSTITUTE OF ECONOMIC GROWTH. CENSUS STUDIES. (Text in English) 1969. irreg. Rs.30. Institute of Economic Growth, Univeristy of Enclave, New Delhi 110007, India.

312   II
INSTITUTE OF ECONOMIC RESEARCH. PUBLICATIONS ON DEMOGRAPHY. (Text in English) irreg. price varies. Institute of Economic Research, Director, Vidyagiri, Dharwar 580004, Karnataka, India. FAX 836-41001.

INSTITUTO NACIONAL DE ESTADISTICA Y CENSOS. SERIE ESTADISTICA. see *POPULATION STUDIES — Abstracting, Bibliographies, Statistics*

312   IS   ISSN 0333-9874
INTEGRATED RURAL DEVELOPMENT. PUBLICATIONS. (Text in English) irreg., latest 1991. price varies. Development Study Center, P.O. Box 2355, Rehovot 76122, Israel. TEL 972-8-474111. FAX 972-8-475884.

301.32   II
INTERNATIONAL INSTITUTE FOR POPULATION SCIENCES. DIRECTOR'S REPORT. (Text in English) 1956. a. free. International Institute for Population Sciences, Govandi Station Rd., Deonar, Bombay 400 088, India. TEL 22-5563254. Dir. K.B. Pathak. circ. 800.
   Former titles: International Institute for Population Studies. Annual Report; Demographic Training and Research Centre. Annual Report; International Institute for Population Studies. Director's Report.

312 910   UK
▼**INTERNATIONAL JOURNAL OF POPULATION GEOGRAPHY.** 1995. q. $195 to institutions worldwide. John Wiley & Sons Ltd., Journals, Baffins Ln., Chichester, W. Sussex PO19 1UD, England. TEL 01243-779777. FAX 01243-776128. (Subscr. in the Americas to: John Wiley & Sons, Inc., 605 Third Ave., New York, NY 10158. TEL 212-850-6645. FAX 212-850-6021) Ed.Bd. (also avail. in microform from UMI; back issues avail.) **Document type:** academic/scholarly publication.
Refereed Serial

312 910   UK   ISSN 1077-3495
▼**INTERNATIONAL JOURNAL OF POPULATION GEOGRAPHY.** 1995. q. $195 (effective 1996). John Wiley & Sons Ltd., Journals, Baffins Ln., Chichester, Sussex PO19 1UD, England. TEL 44-1243-779777. FAX 44-1243-776128. E-mail: subinfo@jwiley.com. (Subscr. in the Americas to: John Wiley & Sons, Inc., 605 Third Ave., New York, NY 10158-0012. TEL 212-850-6645. FAX 212-850-6021) Eds. H. Jones, R.I. Woods. (back issues avail.) **Document type:** academic/scholarly publication.
Refereed Serial

312   SZ   ISSN 0020-7985
JV6001.A1
INTERNATIONAL MIGRATION. (Text mainly in English; occasionally French or Spanish) 1961. q. $30 to individuals; institutions $40. International Organization for Migration, 17 route des Morillons, P.O. Box 71, CH-1211 Geneva 19, Switzerland. TEL 022-7179242. Ed. R.T. Appleyard. bk.rev.; bibl.; charts; stat.; index. circ. 3,800. (also avail. in microfiche from CIS; reprint service avail. from WSH) **Indexed:** Amer.Hist.& Life, Asian-Pac.Econ.Lit., Chic.Per.Ind., Geo.Abstr., Hist.Abstr., IDA, IIS, Int.Lab.Doc., Key to Econ.Sci., Lang.& Lang.Behav.Abstr., Popul.Ind., Refug.Abstr., SSCI. **Document type:** bulletin.
—BLDSC (4544.230000); Faxon; Genuine Article; SWETS; UnCover.
   Formed by the merger of: Migration; R E M P Bulletin.
   Description: Covers current migration issues as analyzed by demographers, economists and sociologists all over the world. Includes reports and announcements of events and new publications.

325 300   US   ISSN 0197-9183
JV6001
INTERNATIONAL MIGRATION REVIEW; a quarterly studying sociological, demographic, economic, historical, and legislative aspects of human migration movements and ethnic group relations. 1964. q. $27.50 to individuals; institutions $44. Center for Migration Studies, 209 Flagg Pl., Staten Island, NY 10304-1199. TEL 718-351-8800. FAX 718-667-4598. Ed. Silvano M. Tomasi. adv. contact: Carolyn Durante. bk.rev.; abstr.; bibl.; charts; stat.; index, cum.index. circ. 2,500. (also avail. in microform from UMI; back issues avail.; reprint service avail. from UMI) **Indexed:** A.I.C.P., Abstr.Anthropol., Amer.Bibl.Slavic & E.Eur.Stud., Amer.Hist.& Life, Asian-Pac.Econ.Lit., ASSIA, C.I.J.E., Chic.Per.Ind., Curr.Cont., E.I., Geo.Abstr., Hisp.Amer.Per.Ind. (1977-), Hist.Abstr., HR Rep. (1981-), IDA, IMFL, Lang.& Lang.Behav.Abstr., Mid.East: Abstr.& Ind., Mult.Ed.Abstr., P.A.I.S., Polit.Sci.Abstr., Popul.Ind., Refug.Abstr., Rural Recreat.Tour.Abstr., Sage Fam.Stud.Abstr., So.Pac.Per.Ind., Soc.Sci.Ind., Soc.Work Res.& Abstr., Sociol.Abstr., SSCI, Stud.Wom.Abstr., World Agri.Econ.& Rural Sociol.Abstr. **Document type:** academic/scholarly publication.
●Also available online. Vendor(s): University Microfilms International.
—BLDSC (4544.245000); Faxon; Genuine Article; SWETS; UnCover.
   Formerly: International Migration Digest (ISSN 0020-7993)
   Description: Contains articles and research notes on migration and refugee issues.
Refereed Serial

325   CN   ISSN 0383-2767
INTERNATIONAL NEWSLETTER ON MIGRATION. 1971. irreg. University of Waterloo, Waterloo, ON N2L 3GI, Canada. TEL 519-885-1211. **Document type:** newsletter.
     Formerly: International Migration Newsletter (ISSN 0383-2759)

325   SZ
INTERNATIONAL ORGANIZATION FOR MIGRATION. ANNUAL REPORT. (Editions in English, French and Spanish) 1969. a. free. International Organization for Migration, 17 route des Morillons, P.O. Box 71, CH-1211 Geneva 19, Switzerland. TEL 022-7179242. circ. 5,000. (also avail. in microfiche from CIS; reprint service avail. from WSH) **Indexed:** IIS. **Document type:** corporate report.
     Former titles: International Organization for Migration. Annual Review; Intergovernmental Committee for Migration. Annual Review; Intergovernmental Committee for Migration. Review of Achievements; Intergovernmental Committee for European Migration. Review of Achievements.
     Description: Report of the organization covering migration activities, migration for development programs, migration planning, cooperation and research, administration, management, finance, information and publications.

312   BE   ISSN 0074-9338
INTERNATIONAL POPULATION CONFERENCE. PROCEEDINGS. French edition: Congres International de la Population. Proceedings (ISSN 0254-5217) quadrennial. price varies. International Union for the Scientific Study of Population, 34 rue des Augustins, B-4000 Liege, Belgium. FAX 041-223847. TELEX 42648 POPUN. **Indexed:** Popul.Ind. **Document type:** proceedings.

INTERNATIONAL RESCUE COMMITTEE. FIELD REPORTS. see SOCIAL SERVICES AND WELFARE

304.8 305.4   SW   ISSN 0348-6435
INVANDRARKVINNAN. 1974. q. SEK 110. Riksfoerbundet Internationella Foereningen foer Invandrarkvinnor - R I F F I, Nortullsgatan 45, S-113 45 Stockholm, Sweden. TEL 46-8-30-21-89. Ed. Karin Svanebro.

325.1 948   SW   ISSN 0345-5505
INVANDRARRAPPORT; invandrarnas debatt- och kulturtidskrift. 1973. q. SEK 200. Immigrant Institutet, Katrinedalsgatan 43, S-502 54 Boras, Sweden. TEL 46-33-13-60-70. FAX 46-33-13-60-75. Ed. Miguel Benito. adv.; bk.rev.; bibl.
     Description: Covers all aspects of immigration in Sweden: refugees, bilingual education, immigrant authors and organizations, and immigration law and legislation.

301.32   UN   ISSN 0363-5155
HQ763
INVENTORY OF POPULATION PROJECTS IN DEVELOPING COUNTRIES AROUND THE WORLD. (Text in English, French) 1975. a. $20. United Nations Population Fund, 220 E. 42nd St., Rm. 2306, New York, NY 10017. circ. 3,000. (also avail. in microfiche from CIS) **Indexed:** C.I.S.Abstr., IIS.
     Description: Contains information on population projects, listed by country and geographic region, and supported by both national and international agencies and organizations.

ITALIA NOSTRA. SEZIONE DI TRENTO. BOLLETTINO. see ENVIRONMENTAL STUDIES

ITALY. ISTITUTO NAZIONALE DI STATISTICA. POPOLAZIONE E MOVIMENTO ANAGRAFICO DEI COMUNI. see POPULATION STUDIES — Abstracting, Bibliographies, Statistics

J C W I BULLETIN. (Joint Council for the Welfare of Immigrants) see LAW

JAHRBUCH FUER FRAENKISCHE LANDESFORSCHUNG. see HISTORY — History Of Europe

312   JA
JAPAN. INSTITUTE OF POPULATION PROBLEMS. ANNUAL REPORT. 1977. a. free. Ministry of Health and Welfare, Institute of Population Problems - Jinko Mondai Kenkyusho, 2-2, 1-chome, Kasumigaseki, Chiyoda-ku, Tokyo 100, Japan.

312   IS
JEWISH POPULATION SERIES. irreg. Magnes Press, Hebrew University, Jerusalem, P.O. Box 7695, Jerusalem 91076, Israel. TEL 972-2-660341. FAX 972-2-633370. **Document type:** monographic series.

312   JA   ISSN 0387-2793
JINKO MONDAI KENKYU/JOURNAL OF POPULATION PROBLEMS. (Text in Japanese; summaries in English) 1940. q. free. Ministry of Health and Welfare, Institute of Population Problems - Kosei-sho Jinko Mondai Kenkyujo, 1-2-2 Kasumigaseki, Chiyoda-ku, Tokyo 100, Japan. bk.rev.; stat. **Indexed:** Popul.Ind.
     —BLDSC (5041.145000).

325 613.9   US   ISSN 0887-0241
JOHNS HOPKINS UNIVERSITY. POPULATION INFORMATION PROGRAM. POPULATION REPORTS. ENGLISH EDITION.* 1973. 4/yr. free to qualified personnel. Johns Hopkins University, Population Information Program, 111 Market Pl., Baltimore, MD 21202-4012. TEL 410-659-6300. TELEX 240430. Ed. Ward Rinehart. bibl.; charts; illus.; stat. circ. 81,000. (looseleaf format; back issues avail.) **Indexed:** Popul.Ind. **Document type:** monographic series.
     Formerly: George Washington University. Population Information Program. Population Reports.

325 613.9   US   ISSN 0887-025X
JOHNS HOPKINS UNIVERSITY. POPULATION INFORMATION PROGRAM. POPULATION REPORTS. FRENCH EDITION.* 1973. 4/yr. free to qualified personnel. Johns Hopkins University, Population Information Program, 111 Market Pl., Baltimore, MD 21202-4012. TEL 410-659-6300. TELEX 240430. Ed. Ward Rinehart. bibl.; charts; illus.; stat. circ. 11,600. (looseleaf format; back issues avail.) **Indexed:** Popul.Ind. **Document type:** monographic series.
     Formerly: George Washington University. Population Information Program. Population Reports.

325 613.9   US   ISSN 0887-0276
JOHNS HOPKINS UNIVERSITY. POPULATION INFORMATION PROGRAM. POPULATION REPORTS. PORTUGUESE EDITION.* 1973. 4/yr. free to qualified personnel. Johns Hopkins University, Population Information Program, 111 Market Pl., Baltimore, MD 21202-4012. TEL 410-659-6300. TELEX 240430. Ed. Ward Rinehart. bibl.; charts; illus.; stat. circ. 14,000. (looseleaf format; back issues avail.) **Indexed:** Popul.Ind. **Document type:** monographic series.
     Formerly: George Washington University. Population Information Program. Population Reports.

325 613.9   US   ISSN 0887-0268
JOHNS HOPKINS UNIVERSITY. POPULATION INFORMATION PROGRAM. POPULATION REPORTS. SPANISH EDITION.* 1973. 4/yr. free to qualified personnel. Johns Hopkins University, Population Information Program, 111 Market Pl., Baltimore, MD 21202-4012. TEL 410-659-6300. TELEX 240430. Ed. Ward Rinehart. bibl.; charts; illus.; stat. circ. 40,000. (looseleaf format; back issues avail.) **Indexed:** Popul.Ind. **Document type:** monographic series.
     Formerly: George Washington University. Population Information Program. Population Reports.

JOURNAL OF BIOSOCIAL SCIENCE. see BIOLOGY — Genetics

312   TH   ISSN 0857-2143
HB848
JOURNAL OF DEMOGRAPHY/WARASARN PRACHAKORNSATR. 1985. s-a. $10. Chulalongkorn University, Institute of Population Studies, Phyathai Rd., Bangkok, Thailand. TEL 2511133. circ. 500. **Document type:** academic/scholarly publication.

312   IO   ISSN 0126-0251
HA1815
JOURNAL OF INDONESIAN DEMOGRAPHY/MAJALAH DEMOGRAFI INDONESIA. (Text in English or Indonesian) 1974. s-a. Rps.15000($35) (effective 1995). Universitas Indonesia, Lembaga Demografi, Jalan Salemba 4, Jakarta 10430, Indonesia. TEL 336539. FAX 62-21-380-0187. Eds. Prijono Tjiptoherijanto, Rozy Munir. adv.; bk.rev. circ. 1,000. **Indexed:** E.I., Popul.Ind. **Document type:** academic/scholarly publication.
     —UnCover.

JOURNAL OF ONE-NAME STUDIES. see GENEALOGY AND HERALDRY

330   GW   ISSN 0933-1433
HB849.41   CODEN: JPECEW
JOURNAL OF POPULATION ECONOMICS. (Text in English) 1988. q. DM.380($276) (effective 1996). (European Society for Population Economics) Springer-Verlag, Heidelberger Platz 3, 14197 Berlin, Germany. TEL 030-8207-0. FAX 030-8214091. E-mail: orders@springer.de. (Subscr. in N. America to: Springer-Verlag New York, Inc., 44 Hartz Way, Secaucus, NJ 07096-2491. TEL 201-348-4033. FAX 201-348-4505) **Ed.Bd. Indexed:** Asian-Pac.Econ.Lit., Curr.Cont. **Document type:** academic/scholarly publication.
     —BLDSC (5041.144000); Faxon; Genuine Article; SWETS; UMI; UnCover. **CCC.**
     Description: Focuses on the relation between economics and demographics, and addresses diverse topics in this area.

JOURNAL OF POPULATION, HEALTH AND SOCIAL WELFARE. see SOCIAL SERVICES AND WELFARE

JOURNAL OF REFUGEE STUDIES. see POLITICAL SCIENCE — Civil Rights

312
KANSAS. DEPARTMENT OF HEALTH AND ENVIRONMENT. ANNUAL SUMMARY OF VITAL STATISTICS. 1940. a. (additional copies $5 each). Department of Health and Environment, Center for Health and Environmental Statistics, 900 S.W. Jackson, Topeka, KS 66612-1290. TEL 913-296-5640. FAX 913-296-7025. charts; stat.; circ. 1,000 (controlled). (also avail. in microfiche from CIS) **Indexed:** SRI. **Document type:** government publication.
     Description: Summarizes the births, deaths, abortions, marriages and marriage dissolutions that occur in the state. Includes graphs of items of interest and statistical analyses of the vital events.

KIBBUTZ STUDIES. see BUSINESS AND ECONOMICS — Cooperatives

312 325   KO   ISSN 1225-3804
HN730.5   CODEN: KJPDEP
KOREA JOURNAL OF DEVELOPMENT. (Text in English) 1972. s-a. 8000 Won($15) Seoul National University, Population and Development Studies Center, 56-1 Shillim-dong, Kwanak-ku, Seoul 151-742, S. Korea. TEL 82-2-880-6313. FAX 82-2-873-6764. TELEX SNUROK K29664. Ed. Il Chul Kim. bk.rev.; bibl. circ. 500. **Indexed:** Rural Devel.Abstr.
     Formerly: Seoul National University. Population and Development Studies Center. Bulletin.
     Description: Provides a forum for studies in population and social development related to Korea and other Asian countries.

574   JA   ISSN 0386-4561
QH352
KOTAIGUN SEITAI GAKKAI KAIHO/SOCIETY OF POPULATION ECOLOGY. REPORT. (Text in Japanese) 1962. irreg., no.51, 1994. 9000 Yen. Kotaigun Seitai Gakkai, Ogawa Higashi Iru, Shimodachuri Dori, Kamigamo-ku, Kyoto 602, Japan. **Document type:** newsletter.

LIBYA. CENSUS AND STATISTICS DEPARTMENT. GENERAL POPULATION CENSUS. see POPULATION STUDIES — Abstracting, Bibliographies, Statistics

301.412 312   US   ISSN 1073-7057
LINKX. (Former name of issuing body: Center for Population Options) vol.7, no.2, 1991. q. $15. Advocates for Youth, 1025 Vermont Ave., N.W., Ste. 200, Washington, DC 20005. TEL 202-347-5700. FAX 202-347-2263. Ed. Charles Seagle. bk.rev. (looseleaf format; back issues avail.; reprint service avail.) **Document type:** newsletter.
     Formerly: Clinic News.
     Description: Discusses adolescent reproductive health as it relates to school-based, and school-linked health centers.

POPULATION STUDIES

312   UK   ISSN 0143-2974
HB3583
LOCAL POPULATION STUDIES. (Occasional supplements) 1968. s-a. £6 (foreign £7). 27 Trumpington St., Cambridge CB2 1QA, England. TEL 01223-333185. Ed. Kevin Schuerer. adv. contact: R. Bridgen. bk.rev.; bibl.; charts; stat. circ. 1,500. (also avail. in microform from UMI; back issues avail.; reprint service avail. from UMI) **Indexed:** Amer.Hist.& Life, Br.Hum.Ind., Geo.Abstr., Hist.Abstr., Popul.Ind. **Document type:** academic/scholarly publication.
—BLDSC (5290.044700); Faxon; UMI; UnCover.

LOCATION GUIDES FOR FAMILY AND LOCAL HISTORIANS. see *GENEALOGY AND HERALDRY*

312   US
MAINE. DEPARTMENT OF HUMAN SERVICES. POPULATION ESTIMATES FOR MINOR CIVIL DIVISIONS BY COUNTY. 1981. a. $4.40. Department of Human Services, Office of Data, Research, and Vital Statistics, State House Sta. No.11, Augusta, ME 04333. TEL 207-624-5445. Ed. Ellen M. Naor. circ. 500. **Document type:** government publication.
Description: Population estimates of MCD's by age group.

301.32   MY   ISSN 0126-8104
MALAYSIA. NATIONAL POPULATION AND FAMILY DEVELOPMENT BOARD. BULETIN KELUARGA. 1969. q. free. National Population and Family Development Board, Box 10416, Jalan Raja Laut, 50712 Kuala Lumpur, Malaysia. TEL 2937555. TELEX POPMAL MA 31911. Ed. Raj Abdul Karim. abstr.; stat.
Document type: government publication.
Description: Discusses family development, population and family planning.

301.32   MY   ISSN 0128-1232
MALAYSIAN JOURNAL OF FAMILY STUDIES. (Text in English) 1989. a. $10. National Population and Family Development Board, P.O. Box 10416, Jalan Raja Laut, 50712 Kuala Lumpur, Malaysia. TEL 2937555. FAX 03-2921357. Ed. Ang Eng Suan. circ. 500.
Description: Provides various results of research in the area of family development in Malaysia.

MALTA. CENTRAL OFFICE OF STATISTICS. DEMOGRAPHIC REVIEW. see *POPULATION STUDIES — Abstracting, Bibliographies, Statistics*

MARYLAND TOMORROW. see *HOUSING AND URBAN PLANNING*

312   US   ISSN 0889-8480
HB849.51   CODEN: MPSTEG
MATHEMATICAL POPULATION STUDIES; an international journal of mathematical demography. 1988. 4/yr. 147 ECU (effective 1996). Gordon & Breach Science Publishers, c/o International Publishers Distributor, 820 Town Center Dr., Langhorne, PA 19047. TEL 215-750-2642. FAX 215-750-6343. (Subscr. to: International Publsihers Distributor, P.O. Box 90, Reading, Berkshire RG1 8JL, England. TEL 44-173-456-8316) Ed. Marc Artzrouni. (also avail. in microform) **Indexed:** Geo.Abstr. **Document type:** academic/scholarly publication.
—BLDSC (5402.576570); Faxon. **CCC.**
Refereed Serial

304.8   SW
MIGRANTER. 1971. 6/yr. SEK 100 (effective 1991). Statens Invandrarverk - Swedish Immigration Board, P.O. Box 6113, 600 06 Norrkoeping, Sweden. TEL 11-15-60-00. FAX 10-18-29-71. Eds. Lillemor Sahlberg, Mark Olson. bk.rev. circ. 11,000. **Document type:** government publication.
Formerly: Ny is Sverige (ISSN 0345-8660)

325   FR   ISSN 0335-0894
MIGRANTS FORMATION. 1973. q. 100 F. (foreign 130 F.). Centre National de Documentation Pedagogique, 29 rue de l'Ulm, 75230 Paris Cedex 05, France. (Subscr. to: CNDP - Abonnements, B.P. 21, Square St. Charles, 75012 Paris, France) Ed. Jean-Paul Tauvel. bk.rev.; bibl. **Indexed:** Abstr.Musl.Rel., Refug.Abstr.
—BLDSC (5761.528000).
Description: Offers information and discussion on education, immigration and educational development of children, young adults and adults.

325   FR   ISSN 0397-944X
Z7164.I3
MIGRANTS NOUVELLES. 1974. 10/yr. 60 F. (foreign 85 F.). Centre National de Documentation Pedagogique, 29 rue de l'Ulm, 75230 Paris Cedex 05, France. (Subscr. to: CNDP - Abonnements, B.P. 21, Square St. Charles, 75012 Paris, France) Ed. Jean-Paul Tauvel. charts; stat. **Indexed:** Refug.Abstr.
Description: Provides information briefs on all aspects of immigration.

312   US
MIGRATION AND ETHNICITY SERIES. 1972. irreg. price varies. Center for Migration Studies, 209 Flagg Pl., Staten Island, NY 10304-1199. TEL 718-351-8800. FAX 718-667-4598. (back issues avail.) **Document type:** academic/scholarly publication.

325   SZ   ISSN 0026-3583
MIGRATION NEWS; an international biannual on migration and refugees. French edition: Migrations. Spanish edition: Migraciones. (Text in English) 1952-1988; resumed 1991. s-a. $10. International Catholic Migration Commission, 37-39 rue de Vermont, CH-1211 Geneva 20 CIC, Switzerland. TEL 334150. FAX 347929. TELEX 28100-ICMC-CH. adv.; bk.rev.; charts; index, cum.index. circ. 1,800. **Indexed:** HR Rep., P.A.I.S, Refug.Abstr.
Description: Devoted to the application of Christian principles in migration, population, land settlement, and refugee service.

301.3   SZ   ISSN 0544-1188
JV6001.A1
MIGRATION TODAY. (Editions in English, French and Spanish) 1963. 2/yr. free. World Council of Churches, Refugee and Migration Service, 150 route de Ferney, P.O. Box 2100, CH-1211 Geneva 2, Switzerland. TEL 022-7916111. FAX 022-7910361. TELEX 415730 OIK CH. Ed. Patrick Taran. bk.rev. circ. 5,000. **Indexed:** Abstr.Musl.Rel., C.I.J.E., CERDIC, HR Rep. (1981-1985), P.A.I.S., Stud.Wom.Abstr. **Document type:** newsletter.
—BLDSC (5761.535000).

301.32 300   US   ISSN 1058-5095
JV6001
MIGRATION WORLD; a bi-monthly magazine focusing on the newest immigrant and refugee groups; policy and legislation; resources. 1973. 5/yr. $19 to individuals (foreign $24); institutions $25 (foreign $30). Center for Migration Studies, 209 Flagg Place, Staten Island, NY 10304-1199. TEL 718-351-8800. FAX 718-667-4598. Ed. Lydio Tomasi. adv. contact: Lydio Tomasi. bk.rev.; abstr.; illus. circ. 1,800. (tabloid format; also avail. in microfilm; back issues avail.) **Indexed:** Amer.Hist.& Life, C.I.J.E., Chic.Per.Ind., Geo.Abstr., Hist.Abstr., HR Rep. (1989-), IDA, Mid.East: Abstr.& Ind., P.A.I.S., Polit.Sci.Abstr., Refug.Abstr., Sociol.Abstr. **Document type:** academic/scholarly publication.
●Also available online. Vendor(s): University Microfilms International.
—BLDSC (5761.537300); Faxon; UnCover.
Formerly: Migration Today (ISSN 0197-9175)
Description: Contains articles, legal analyses, dateline updates on recent immigrants and refugees.

312   US   ISSN 0734-032X
MISSOURI POPULATION ESTIMATES; by county, by age, by sex. a. $15. Department of Health, Center for Health Statistics, Box 570, Jefferson City, MO 65102. TEL 314-751-6272. Ed. Garland Land. **Document type:** government publication.

312   US   ISSN 0077-0930
                               CODEN: MPOBA6
MONOGRAPHS IN POPULATION BIOLOGY. 1967. irreg., no.27, 1989. price varies. Princeton University Press, 41 William St., Princeton, NJ 08540. TEL 609-258-4900. FAX 609-258-6305. E-mail: jhardy@pupress.princeton.edu. (reprint service avail. from UMI) **Indexed:** Biol.Abstr., Ind.Med. **Document type:** monographic series.
—BLDSC (5915.960000).

312   US
MONTHLY PRODUCT ANNOUNCEMENT. 1980. m. free. U.S. Bureau of the Census, Data User Services Division, Washington, DC 20233. TEL 301-457-4100. FAX 301-457-4714. Ed. Mary Kilbride. circ. 9,000. (also avail. in microfiche from CIS; reprint service avail. from CIS) **Indexed:** Amer.Stat.Ind. (1981-), MEDOC. **Document type:** government publication.
●Also available online. Vendor(s): CompuServe, Inc., Knight-Ridder, Inc.
Description: Lists all media products as they are currently released by the Census Bureau.

MOSELLA. see *GEOGRAPHY*

MOUVEMENT NATUREL DE LA POPULATION DE LA GRECE. see *POPULATION STUDIES — Abstracting, Bibliographies, Statistics*

MOVIMIENTO NATURAL DE LA POBLACION DE ESPANA. see *POPULATION STUDIES — Abstracting, Bibliographies, Statistics*

N A T O ADVANCED SCIENCE INSTITUTES SERIES D: BEHAVIOURAL AND SOCIAL SCIENCES. (North Atlantic Treaty Organization) see *SOCIAL SCIENCES: COMPREHENSIVE WORKS*

312   BU   ISSN 0205-0617
HB3627
NASELENIE. 1983. q. 1.62 lv. per issue. (Bulgarska Akademiia na Naukite) Publishing House of the Bulgarian Academy of Sciences, Acad. G. Bonchev. St., Bldg. 6, 1113 Sofia, Bulgaria. (Dist. by: Hemus, 6 Rouski Blvd., 1000 Sofia, Bulgaria) circ. 800. (reprint service avail. from IRC) **Indexed:** Bibl.Ind., BSL Econ.
—BLDSC (0119.255000).

312   NE   ISSN 0923-3512
NEDERLANDS INTERDISCIPLINAIR DEMOGRAFISCH INSTITUUT. PUBLICATION. (Text in English) 1976. irreg., vol.29, 1993. price varies. Swets & Zeitlinger bv, Heereweg 347, 2161 CA Lisse, Netherlands. TEL 31-2521-35111. FAX 31-2521-15888. TELEX 41325 SZLIS NL. (Dist. in N. America by: Swets & Zeitlinger, 440 Creamery Way, Ste. A, Exton, PA 19341. TEL 800-447-9387. FAX 610-524-5366) (Co-sponsor: Population and Family Study Centre) **Document type:** monographic series.
—BLDSC (7098.528000).
Supersedes (in 1988): Publications of the Netherlands Interuniversity Demographic Institute and the Population and Family Study Centre (ISSN 0166-6312)
Refereed Serial

312   NE   ISSN 0922-7210
NEDERLANDS INTERDISCIPLINAIR DEMOGRAFISCH INSTITUUT. RAPPORT - REPORT - BERICHT - RAPPORTO. Key Title: NiDi Rapport. 1988. irreg. price varies. Nederlands Interdisciplinair Demografisch Instituut - Netherlands Interdisciplinary Demographic Institute, Lange Houtstraat 19, 2511 CV The Hague, Netherlands. TEL 31-70-3565200. FAX 31-70-3647187. TELEX 31138 NIDI NL. Ed.Bd. circ. 125. (back issues avail.)
Supersedes (1973-1988): Nederlands Interuniversitair Demografisch Instituut. Working Papers (ISSN 0920-9719); (1974-1988): Nederlands Interdisciplinair Demografisch Instituut. Intern Rapport (ISSN 0925-6954)

312   NQ
NICARAGUA. INSTITUTO NACIONAL DE ESTADISTICAS Y CENSOS. BOLETIN DEMOGRAFICO. no.2, 1978. irreg. C.$15($4) per no. Instituto Nacional de Estadisticos y Census, Apdo. Postal 4031, Managua, Nicaragua. stat. **Document type:** government publication.
Formerly: Nicaragua. Oficina Ejecutiva de Encuestos y Censos. Boletin Demografico.

312   CN   ISSN 0714-0541
HT127
NORTHERN ONTARIO DIRECTORY; information guide to unincorporated communities & Indian reserves. 1979. irreg. Ministry of Northern Development and Mines, Communications Services, 159 Cedar St., 6th Fl., Sudbury, ON P3E 6A5, Canada. TEL 705-670-7107. FAX 705-670-7108. circ. 1,000. **Document type:** government publication, directory.

NUEVA LEY DE INMIGRACION. see *LAW*

312 US ISSN 0732-1597
NUMBERS NEWS. 1983. m. $149. American Demographics, Inc., Box 68, Ithaca, NY 14851-0068. TEL 607-273-6343. FAX 607-273-3196. Ed. Diane Crispell. stat. circ. 1,300. (reprint service avail. from UMI) **Document type:** newsletter.
—CCC.

325.2 IT
NUOVA PUGLIA EMIGRAZIONE. 1985. q. (Associazioni Regionali di Rappresentanza e Tutela degli emigranti e Loro Famiglie) Grafichena, Viale Stazione, 177, 72015 Fasano (BR), Italy. TEL 080-714681. Ed. Angelo Di Summa.
   Formerly (until 1991): Puglia Emigrazione (ISSN 1120-3412)

325 US
NUOVA VIA. 1968. 4/yr. free. American Committee on Italian Migration, 352 W. 44th St., New York, NY 10026-5419. TEL 212-247-7373. circ. 5,000. **Document type:** newsletter.

301.32 MG
NY MPONIN'I MADAGASIKARA. (Text in French or Malagasy) 1975. irreg. Direction de la Recherche Scientifique et Technique, Section de Demographie, B.P. 4096, Antananarivo, Madagascar.

312 614 US
OKLAHOMA. DEPARTMENT OF HEALTH. MONTHLY VITAL STATISTICS REPORT. 1974. m. Department of Health, N.E. Tenth and Stonewall, Box 53551, Oklahoma City, OK 73105. TEL 405-271-5600. circ. 400. **Document type:** government publication.

OVERSEAS VISITOR SURVEY (YEAR). see *TRAVEL AND TOURISM*

312 US ISSN 0300-6816
HB848
P A A AFFAIRS. 1968. q. $5. Population Association of America, 1722 N St., N.W., Washington, DC 20036-2983. TEL 202-429-0891. FAX 202-785-0146. circ. 2,600. **Indexed:** Curr.Lit.Fam.Plan. **Document type:** newsletter.
   Description: General items of interest to members.

325
P R I REVIEW. 1991. bi-m. $25 donation. (Population Research Institute) Human Life International, 7845-E Airpark Rd., Gaithersburg, MD 20879. TEL 301-670-1864. FAX 301-869-7363. Ed. Jean Guilfoyle. adv. contact: Vernon Kirby. (also avail. in looseleaf format; back issues avail.) **Document type:** newsletter.
   Description: Examines the consequences of world population growth and reports findings.

PACIFIC VIEWPOINT; specialises in the study of development, change and underdevelopment. see *BUSINESS AND ECONOMICS — International Development And Assistance*

PASSAGES. see *CHILDREN AND YOUTH — About*

PATEL'S IMMIGRATION LAW DIGEST. see *LAW*

PENNSYLVANIA VITAL STATISTICS. see *POPULATION STUDIES — Abstracting, Bibliographies, Statistics*

325 613.9 UK ISSN 0968-1655
GF1
PEOPLE AND THE PLANET. 1992. q. £10($20) International Planned Parenthood Federation, Regent's College, Inner Circle, Regent's Park, London NW1 4NS, England. TEL 0171-486-0741. FAX 0171-487-7950. TELEX 919573 IPEPEE G. (Co-sponsors: U.N. Population Fund; World Conservation Union, I.P.P.F., World Wide Fund for Nature International) Ed. John Rowley. circ. 20,000 (controlled). **Document type:** academic/scholarly publication.
—BLDSC (6422.875100).
   Description: Explores the interrelationships between population, environment and development.

325 613.9 UK ISSN 0309-0736
PLANNED PARENTHOOD IN EUROPE. 1972. 3/yr. free. International Planned Parenthood Federation, Europe Region, Regent's College, Inner Circle, Regent's Park, London NW1 4NS, England. TEL 0171-486-0741. FAX 0171-487-7950. TELEX 919573 IPEPEE G. Ed. Evert Ketting. bk.rev.; cum.index: 1972-1976, 1977-1990. circ. 3,500. **Indexed:** Curr.Lit.Fam.Plan. **Document type:** academic/scholarly publication.
—BLDSC (6508.700000).

301.32 MY ISSN 0127-9068
POFAM. (Text in English) 1986. s-a. free. National Population and Family Development Board, P.O. Box 10416, Jalan Raja Laut, 50712 Kuala Lumpur, Malaysia. TEL 2937555. FAX 03-2921357. TELEX POP MAL MA 31911. Ed. Annuar Maaruf. circ. 3,000.
   Description: Discusses various aspects of family development and population issues in Malaysia.

312 US
POPLINE. 1979. 6/yr. $25. Population Institute, 107 Second St., N.E., Washington, DC 20002. TEL 202-544-3300. FAX 202-544-0068. Ed. Harold N. Burdett. circ. 61,200. (tabloid format)
   Description: News and feature service provided to more than 2,100 daily newspapers worldwide. Explores, analyzes, and evaluates facts and public policies relating to the problems of world over-population.

312 UN ISSN 0251-8996
HB848
POPULATION. (Editions in Arabic, English, French, Spanish) 1975. m. free. United Nations Population Fund, 220 E. 42nd St., Rm.2307, New York, NY 10017. Ed. Alex Marshall. bk.rev.; illus. (reprint service avail. from SCH) **Indexed:** Curr.Lit.Fam.Plan., Trop.Dis.Bull.
   Formerly: Population Newsletter (ISSN 0048-4849)
   Description: Focuses on the organization's programs, policies and strategies as they relate to population activities worldwide.

312 FR ISSN 0032-4663
HB881 CODEN: POPUAQ
POPULATION. 1946. bi-m. 500 F. (foreign 570 F.) (includes 1 no. in English) (effective 1995). Institut National d'Etudes Démographiques, 27 rue du Commandeur, 75675 Paris Cedex 14, France. TEL 42-18-20-00. FAX 42-18-21-99. Ed. P. Festy. circ. 4,500. (reprint service avail. from SCH) **Indexed:** Geo.Abstr.
—BLDSC (6552.000000); Faxon; SWETS. **CCC**.
   Incorporates: Demographie et Sciences Humaines (ISSN 0070-3354)

325 628 US ISSN 0273-2548
HB848
POPULATION (BOCA RATON). (Subseries of: S I R S Social Issues (ISSN 0740-3127)) 1974. a. price varies; a. supplement $17. Social Issues Resources Series, Box 2348, Boca Raton, FL 33427-2348. TEL 407-994-0079; 800-232-7477. FAX 407-994-4704. (looseleaf format; also avail. in microfiche; back issues avail.; reprint service avail. from SCH)
   Description: Reprints articles that explore the social and environmental implications of rapid population growth.

312 US ISSN 0197-2235
POPULATION (WASHINGTON); briefing papers on issues of national and international importance in the population field. 1976. irreg. price varies. Population Crisis Committee, 1120 Nineteenth St., N.W., Ste. 550, Washington, DC 20036. TEL 202-659-1833. FAX 202-293-1795. TELEX 440450. charts; stat. circ. 55,000. **Indexed:** Curr.Lit.Fam.Plan.

312 ET
POPULATION AND DEVELOPMENT BULLETIN. (Not published 1991-1993) (Text in English) 1990. 2/yr. Ministry of Planning & Economic Development, Population and Development Planning Unit, P.O. Box 1037, Addis Ababa, Ethiopia. TEL 251-1-552800. FAX 251-1-553844. TELEX 21531. index. **Indexed:** P.L.E.S.A. (1990-). **Document type:** government publication, bulletin.
   Description: Covers demographic issues relating to development projects and public health initiatives.

312 301.32 US ISSN 0098-7921
HB848
POPULATION AND DEVELOPMENT REVIEW. (Supplements avail.) (Text in English; summaries in English, French, Spanish) 1975. q. $32. Population Council, 1 Dag Hammarskjold Plaza, New York, NY 10017. TEL 212-339-0500. FAX 212-755-6052. Ed. Paul Demeny. bk.rev.; abstr.; charts; index, cum.index: vols. 1-10 in 1985, vols.11-15 in 1990. circ. 5,000. (also avail. in microfilm from UMI; reprint service avail from UMI) **Indexed:** A.B.C.Pol.Sci., Abstr.Hyg., Amer.Bibl.Slavic & E.Eur.Stud., Amer.Hist.& Life, Anthropol.Lit., Asian-Pac.Econ.Lit., ASSIA, Curr.Cont., Curr.Lit.Fam.Plan., E.I., Environ.Abstr., Geo.Abstr., Hist.Abstr., IDA, IMFL, Int.Lab.Doc., J.of Econ.Lit., Lang.& Lang.Behav.Abstr., Mid.East: Abstr.& Ind., P.A.I.S., Popul.Ind., Ref.Sour., Rural Recreat.Tour.Abstr., Sage Fam.Stud.Abstr., Sage Urb.Stud.Abstr., Soc.Sci.Ind. (1994-), Sociol.Abstr., SSCI, Trop.Dis.Bull., Urb.Aff.Abstr., World Agri.Econ. & Rural Sociol.Abstr. **Document type:** academic/scholarly publication.
—BLDSC (6552.010000); CIS; Faxon; Genuine Article; SWETS; UMI; UnCover.

POPULATION AND ENVIRONMENT; a journal of interdisciplinary studies. see *PSYCHOLOGY*

312 NE ISSN 0169-1422
POPULATION AND FAMILY IN THE LOW COUNTRIES. (Text in English) 1976. irreg. price varies. (Nederlands Interdisciplinair Demografisch Instituut - Netherlands Interdisciplinary Demographic Institute) Swets & Zeitlinger bv, Heereweg 347, 2161 CA Lisse, Netherlands. TEL 31-2521-35111. FAX 31-2521-15888. TELEX 41325. (Dist. in N. America by: Swets & Zeitlinger, 440 Creamery Way, Ste. A, Exton, PA 19341. TEL 800-447-9387. FAX 610-524-5366) (Co-sponsor: Centrum voor Bevolkings- en Gezinsstudien - Population and Family Study Centre) Ed.Bd. **Document type:** monographic series.

312 US ISSN 0032-468X
HB881.A1 CODEN: POPBA3
POPULATION BULLETIN. 1945. 4/yr. $7 per no. Population Reference Bureau, Inc., 1875 Connecticut Ave., N.W., Ste. 520, Washington, DC 20009. TEL 202-483-1100. Ed. Mary Kent. charts; stat. circ. 6,000. (also avail. in microform from UMI; microfiche from CIS) **Indexed:** Acad.Ind., ASSIA, Biol.Abstr., Curr.Cont., Curr.Lit.Fam.Plan., E.I., Environ.Abstr., Fut.Surv., Geo.Abstr., IDA, Mid.East: Abstr.& Ind., P.A.I.S., Popul.Ind., PROMT, Sci.Cit.Ind., Soc.Sci.Ind., SRI, SSCI. **Document type:** trade publication.
—BLDSC (6552.200000); CIS; Faxon; Genuine Article; SWETS; UMI; UnCover.
   Description: Focuses on national and world issues in the field by recognized authorities.

325 UN ISSN 0251-7604
HB848
POPULATION BULLETIN OF THE UNITED NATIONS. French edition: Bulletin Demographique des Nations Unies (ISSN 0251-7612); Spanish edition: Boletin de Poblacion de las Naciones Unidas (ISSN 0251-7590) (Text in English, French, Spanish) 1948. irreg. price varies. (United Nations, Department of Economic and Social Development) United Nations Publications, Sales Section, Rm. DC2-0853, New York, NY 10017. TEL 212-963-8302; 800-253-9646. FAX 212-963-3489. (also avail. in microfiche from CIS) **Indexed:** Abstr.Rural Dev.Trop., IIS.
—BLDSC (6552.206900).

312 BH
POPULATION CENSUS MAJOR FINDINGS. every 10 yrs., latest 1991. $10. Ministry of Finance, Central Statistical Office, Belmopan, Belize. TEL 08-22207. FAX 08-23206. **Document type:** government publication.
   Description: Presents a compendium of statistical tables which represents some of the major results from the census. Some descriptive commentaries and in depth demographic and socio-economic analyses are included.

POPULATION STUDIES

312   PP   ISSN 0079-3868
POPULATION CENSUS OF PAPUA NEW GUINEA. POPULATION CHARACTERISTICS BULLETIN SERIES. 1966. irreg., latest 1980. K.5. National Statistical Office, P.O. Wards Strip, Papua New Guinea. FAX 675-255057. TELEX FINANCE NE 22312. Ed. Nick Suvulo. circ. 842. **Document type:** government publication.

312   US   ISSN 0361-7858
HB848   CODEN: POPCA6
POPULATION COUNCIL ANNUAL REPORT. 1952. a. free. Population Council, 1 Dag Hammarskjold Plaza, New York, NY 10017. TEL 212-339-0500. FAX 212-755-6052. Ed. Robert Heidel. **Indexed:** Biol.Abstr. **Document type:** corporate report.

312 370   UN   ISSN 1014-6660
POPULATION EDUCATION IN ASIA AND THE PACIFIC NEWSLETTER AND FORUM. 1974. s-a. free or on exchange basis. Unesco, Principal Regional Office for Asia and the Pacific, Regional Clearing House on Population Education and Communication, P.O. Box 1425, Bangkok 10500, Thailand. TEL 391-0703. FAX 391-0866. TELEX 20591 604. Ed. C.L. Villanueva. bk.rev.; charts; illus. circ. 3,000. **Indexed:** ERIC.
—BLDSC (6552.237100).
Former titles: Population Education in Asia and the Pacific Newsletter (ISSN 0251-4621); Population Education in Asia Newsletter; Which superseded: Unesco. Regional Office for Education in Asia. Regional Conference Reports (ISSN 0503-4469)
Description: Examines regional and international news as well as innovation in population education.

312 300   FR   ISSN 0184-7783
HB848
POPULATION ET SOCIETES. 1968. m. 65 F. (foreign 100 F.) (effective 1995). Institut National d'Etudes Demographiques, 27 rue du Commandeur, 75675 Paris Cedex 14, France. TEL 42-18-20-00. FAX 42-18-21-99. Ed. M. Levy. charts; stat.; cum.index: 1968-1975, 1976-1981. circ. 40,000. **Indexed:** Popul.Ind.

301.32   UN   ISSN 0252-3639
POPULATION HEADLINERS. (Text in English) 1971. m. free upon request. United Nations Economic and Social Commission for Asia and the Pacific (ESCAP), Population Division, United Nations Bldg., Rajadamnern Ave, Bangkok 10200, Thailand. charts; illus. circ. 5,500. **Indexed:** So.Pac.Per.Ind., Trop.Dis.Bull.
Formerly: Asian Population Programme News (ISSN 0084-6821)

301.32   TH   ISSN 0125-6440
POPULATION NEWSLETTER. 1969. irreg. (3-4/yr.). free. Chulalongkorn University, Institute of Population Studies, Phyathai Rd., Bangkok 10330, Thailand. TEL 2511133-34. bk.rev. circ. 3,500. (tabloid format) **Indexed:** Abstr.Hyg. **Document type:** newsletter.

POPULATION OF THE MUNICIPALITIES OF THE NETHERLANDS. see *POPULATION STUDIES — Abstracting, Bibliographies, Statistics*

312 330.9   NE   ISSN 0167-5923
HB848   CODEN: PRPRE8
POPULATION RESEARCH AND POLICY REVIEW. (Text in English) 1980. bi-m. fl.537 to institutions; $345 to institutions in U.S. (effective 1996). Kluwer Academic Publishers, Postbus 17, 3300 AA Dordrecht, Netherlands. TEL 31-78-392392. FAX 31-78-392254. TELEX 29245 KAPG NL. E-mail: SERVICES@WKAP.NL. (Dist. by: Kluwer Academic Publishers Group, P.O. Box 322, 3300 AH Dordrecht, Netherlands. TEL 31-78-392392. FAX 31-78-546474; N. America dist. addr.: Box 358, Accord Sta., Hingham, MA 02018-0358. TEL 617-871-6600. FAX 617-871-6528) Ed. Larry Barnett. (also avail. in microform from UMI; back issues avail.; reprint service avail. from SWZ) **Indexed:** ASCA, Asian-Pac.Econ.Lit., Curr.Cont., Geo.Abstr., IDA, IMFL, Ind.Per.Art.Relat.Law, Int.Polit.Sci.Abstr., J.of Econ.Lit., P.A.I.S., Polit.Sci.Abstr., Popul.Ind., Sage Pub.Admin.Abstr., Sage Urb.Stud.Abstr., Soc.Work Res.& Abstr., Sociol.Abstr., SSCI. **Document type:** academic/scholarly publication.
—BLDSC (6552.482000); Faxon; Genuine Article; SWETS; UMI; UnCover. **CCC**.
Description: Promotes the use of empirical research in the analysis and formulation of public policy relevant to demographic issues.
Refereed Serial

312   US
POPULATION RESEARCH CENTER NEWSLETTER. vol.3, no.1, 1991. irreg. University of Texas at Austin, Population Research Center, Main Bldg. 1800, Austin, TX 78712-1088. TEL 512-471-5514. FAX 512-471-4886. **Document type:** newsletter.
Description: Contains research and administrative news of the center's activities.

312 917.602   US   ISSN 0191-913X
POPULATION RESEARCH CENTER PAPERS. 1979. irreg., vol.10, no.12. $4 per no. University of Texas at Austin, Population Research Center, Main Bldg. 1800, Austin, TX 78712-1088. TEL 512-471-5514. FAX 512-471-4886. **Document type:** monographic series.

312   CN
POPULATION RESEARCH LABORATORY. RESEARCH DISCUSSION PAPER SERIES. 1973. irreg. free. Population Research Laboratory, Department of Sociology, University of Alberta, Edmonton, Alta. T6G 2H4, Canada. TEL 403-492-4659. (reprint service avail. from MML)
Formerly: Population Research Laboratory. Discussion Paper Series (ISSN 0317-2473)
Description: Research papers in the field of population studies, survey research and methodology.

301.3   UK   ISSN 0032-4728
HB848   CODEN: POSTA4
POPULATION STUDIES. 1947. 3/yr. £48($110) Population Investigation Committee, London School of Economics, Houghton St., London WC2A 2AE, England. TEL 0171-955-7666. FAX 0171-955-6833. TELEX 24655-BLPES-G. Ed.Bd. adv. contact: Doreen Castle. bk.rev.; index; circ. 3,000 (paid). (also avail. in microform from UMI; reprint service avail. from UMI) **Indexed:** A.I.C.P., Abstr.Hyg., Abstr.Rural Dev.Trop., Amer.Hist.& Life, ASSIA, Biol.Abstr., Br.Hum.Ind., Curr.Cont., Curr.Lit.Fam.Plan., E.I., Environ.Per.Bibl (1985-), Excerp.Med., Geo.Abstr., Hist.Abstr., IDA, Key to Econ.Sci., Lang.& Lang.Behav.Abstr., Mid.East: Abstr.& Ind., P.A.I.S., Popul.Ind., Rural Recreat.Tour.Abstr., Sociol.Abstr. (1952-), SSCI, Trop.Dis.Bull., World Agri.Econ.& Rural Sociol.Abstr. **Document type:** academic/scholarly publication.
—BLDSC (6553.000000); Faxon; Genuine Article; SWETS; UMI; UnCover. **CCC**.
Description: Covers the field of demography: population movements, the effectiveness of birth control programs, fertility and economic and social implications of demographic trends.

312   UN   ISSN 0082-805X
JX1977
POPULATION STUDIES. (Editions in English, French, Spanish) 1948. irreg., no.110, 1988. price varies. (United Nations, Department of Economic and Social Affairs) United Nations Publications, Room DC2-853, New York, NY 10017. TEL 212-963-8302; 800-253-9646. FAX 212-963-3489. **Indexed:** Geo.Abstr., IDA, J.of Econ.Lit., Nutr.Abstr., World Bank.Abstr.
—BLDSC (6553.105000).

312   CN   ISSN 0712-5828
POPULATION STUDIES CENTRE. HIGHLIGHTS. 1982. s-a. free. Population Studies Centre, Rm. 3227 SSC, University of Western Ontario, London, ON N6A 5C2, Canada. TEL 519-661-3819. FAX 519-661-3200. Ed. Suzanne Shiel. circ. 300. (looseleaf format) **Document type:** newsletter.
Description: Presents current projects and publications of the Centre and its associates.

301.426   US   ISSN 0749-2448
POPULATION TODAY. 1973. 11/yr. membership. Population Reference Bureau, Inc., 1875 Connecticut Ave., N.W., Ste. 520, Washington, DC 20009. TEL 202-483-1100. Ed. Susan Kalish. charts; illus.; stat. circ. 6,000. (also avail. in microfilm; microfiche from CIS; microform from UMI; reprint service avail. from UMI) **Indexed:** Curr.Lit.Fam.Plan., Environ.Abstr., Popul.Ind., Sage Fam.Stud.Abstr., Sage Urb.Stud.Abstr., SRI. **Document type:** newsletter.
—BLDSC (6553.230000); CIS; Faxon; SWETS; UMI; UnCover.
Formerly (until 1984): Intercom (Washington) (ISSN 0092-444X)

312   UK   ISSN 0307-4463
HB3583
POPULATION TRENDS. 1975. q. £31.60 (effective 1993). (Office of Population Services and Surveys) H.M.S.O., 51 Nine Elms Ln., London SW8 5DR, England. TEL 071-873-0011. FAX 071-873-8463. (Subscr. to: H.M.S.O., Publications Centre, P.O. Box 276, London SW8 5DT, England. TEL 071-873-9090. FAX 071-873-8200) charts; illus.; stat. circ. 1,700. **Indexed:** Abstr.Hyg., ASSIA, Curr.Adv.Ecol.Sci., Lang.& Lang.Behav.Abstr., Nutr.Abstr., Popul.Ind., Trop.Dis.Bull. **Document type:** government publication.
—BLDSC (6553.250000).

312   US   ISSN 0736-7716
POPULATION TRENDS AND PUBLIC POLICY. 1980. irreg. $5. Population Reference Bureau, Inc., 1875 Connecticut Ave., N.W., Ste. 520, Washington, DC 20009. TEL 202-483-1100. circ. 6,000. (also avail. in microfiche from CIS) **Indexed:** Popul.Ind., SRI. **Document type:** monographic series.
Description: Discusses policy implications of current demographic trends.

301.32   UN   ISSN 0251-6861
HB848
POPULI. French edition (ISSN 0251-687X) (Test in English, French, Spanish) 1974. q. $14. United Nations Population Fund - Fonds des Nations Unies pour la Population, 220 E. 42nd St., New York, NY 10017. TEL 212-297-5031. FAX 212-557-6416. (Subscr. to: U.N.F.P.A., Information and External Relations Division, 220 E. 42nd St., New York, NY 10017. TEL 212-297-5026) Ed. Abid Aslam. bk.rev.; illus. (also avail. in microfiche from CIS) **Indexed:** Curr.Lit.Fam.Plan., Environ.Abstr., Geo.Abstr., IIS, P.A.I.S., Popul.Ind. **Document type:** academic/scholarly publication.
—BLDSC (6553.380000); Faxon; UnCover.
Description: Covers a broad range of topics such as development, media and population, and individual decision-making on childbearing and child spacing.

301.3   FR   ISSN 0032-583X
POUR LA VIE. revue d'etudes familiales. 1945. q. 15 F. 28 Place Saint-Georges, Paris (9e), France. Ed. E. Videcoq. index. cum.index: 1945-1968.

301.4   PL   ISSN 0552-2234
PROBLEMY RODZINY. (Text in Polish; summaries in English) 1961. bi-m. $60. Towarzystwo Rozwoju Rodziny, Ul. Schillera 4-35, 00-248 Warsaw, Poland. TEL 48-2-319310. Ed. Zofia Dabrowska-Caban. bk.rev.; abstr.; bibl.; stat.; circ. 1,000 (controlled).
—BLDSC (6617.957500).
Description: Presents papers on demography, legislation, sociology and sexology.

POPULATION STUDIES

325   US
PROGRAM ON POPULATION. OCCASIONAL PAPERS. 1970. irreg., no.122, 1994. $7 per no. (free to qualified personnel). (Program on Population) Center for Cultural and Technical Interchange Between East and West, Inc., 1777 East-West Rd., Honolulu, HI 96848. TEL 808-944-7401. FAX 808-944-7490. TELEX 989171 EWC UD. E-mail: wards@ewc.bitnet. Ed. Sandra E. Ward. circ. 700. (also avail. in microfiche from CIS) **Indexed:** Geo.Abstr., IDA, SRI. **Document type:** academic/scholarly publication.
    Former titles (until 1992): East-West Population Institute. Papers; East-West Center. Papers; East-West Population Institute. Working Papers (ISSN 0732-0531)

325   US
PROGRAM ON POPULATION. WORKING PAPERS. irreg., no.75, 1994. $3 per no. (Program on Population) Center for Cultural and Technical Interchange Between East and West, Inc., 1777 East-West Rd., Honolulu, HI 96848. TEL 808-944-7469. FAX 808-944-7490. TELEX 989171 EWC UD. E-mail: kawamoto@EWC.bitnet. Ed. Connie Kawamoto. **Indexed:** IDA.
    Formerly (until 1992): East-West Population Institute. Working Papers.

312   301.32   PL   ISSN 0079-7189
HB3608.7
PRZESZLOSC DEMOGRAFICZNA POLSKI; materialy i studia. (Text in Polish; summaries in English) 1967. irreg., no.19, 1994. price varies. (Polska Akademia Nauk, Komitet Nauk Demograficznych) Wydawnictwo Naukowe P W N, Ul. Miodowa 10, 00-251 Warsaw, Poland. Ed. Irena Gieysztor. bibl. circ. 300. **Indexed:** Popul.Ind.

312   FR
RAPPORT SUR LA SITUATION DEMOGRAPHIQUE DE LA FRANCE. 1970. a. 30 F. Institut National d'Etudes Demographiques, 27 rue du Commandeur, 75675 Paris Cedex 14, France. TEL 42-18-20-00. FAX 42-18-21-99. Ed. P. Festy. bk.rev.; stat. circ. 2,000.

304.6   EI
RECENT DEMOGRAPHIC DEVELOPMENTS IN EUROPE AND NORTH AMERICA. French edition: Evolution Demographique Recente en Europe et en Amerique du Nord. a. Council of Europe, Publishing and Documentation Service, 67075 Strasbourg Cedex, France. TEL 88-41-20-00. FAX 88-41-27-80. TELEX 870 943 EUR F.
    Formerly (until 1992): Recent Demographic Developments in Europe.
    Description: Provides an analysis of the structure and evolution of the major components of population: population growth, marriage and divorce, fertility, mortality and migration.

325   CN   ISSN 0229-5113
REFUGE; Canada's periodical on refugees. French edition (ISSN 0229-5121) 1981. 10/yr. Can.$50 (foreign $60). (York University, Centre for Refugee Studies) York Lanes Press, 351 York Lanes, 4700 Keele St., North York, ON M3J 1P3, Canada. TEL 416-736-5843. FAX 416-736-5837. E-mail: REFUGE@YORKVM1. Ed. Howard Adelman. circ. 1,200. **Indexed:** HR Rep. (1985-), Refug.Abstr.
—BLDSC (7336.295000).
    Description: Dedicated to the encouragement of assistance to refugees by providing a forum for sharing information and opinion on Canadian and international issues pertaining to refugees.

REFUGEE AND IMMIGRANT RESOURCE DIRECTORY (YEAR). see *POLITICAL SCIENCE — International Relations*

325   US   ISSN 0884-3554
HV640.4.U54
REFUGEE REPORTS. 1979. m. $40. American Council for Nationalities Service, 1717 Massachusetts Ave., N.W., Ste. 701, Washington, DC 20036. TEL 202-347-3507. Eds. Virginia Hamilton, Bill Frelick. bk.rev. circ. 2,000. (also avail. in microfiche from CIS) **Indexed:** HR Rep. (1985-1988), Refug.Abstr., SRI. **Document type:** newsletter.

312   CC
RENKOU DONGTAI. (Text in Chinese) bi-m. Y7.20. Zhongguo Renkou Qingbao Yanjiu Zhongxin - China Population Research Center, P.O. Box 2444, Beijing 100081, People's Republic of China.
    Description: Contains papers on China's population problem, applications of population theory, and the interrelationship between population and development.

304.6   CC   ISSN 1000-6087
HB3654.A3
RENKOU YANJIU/POPULATION STUDIES. (Text in Chinese; table of contents in English) 1977. bi-m. Y9($24.30) Zhongguo Renmin Daxue, Renkou Lilun Yanjiusuo - People's University, Institute of Population Theory, 39 Haidian Lu, Haidian Qu, Beijing 100872, People's Republic of China. TEL 285431-2895. (Dist. outside China by: China International Book Trading Corp., P.O. Box 399, Beijing, P.R.C.; Dist. in US by: China Books & Periodicals, Inc., 2929 24th St., San Francisco, CA 94110. TEL 415-282-2994) Ed. Liu Zheng.
—UnCover.
    Description: Contains papers on population studies and demographics, as well as news of meetings and academic activities.

301.32   312   CC   ISSN 1003-8426
RENKOU YU FAZHAN/POPULATION AND DEVELOPMENT. (Text in Chinese) 1987. q. Y5.60($2.40) Sichuan University, Renkou Yanjiusuo - Population Studies Institute, Jiugenqiao, Sichuan Daxue Xiaonei, Chengdu, Sichuan 610064, People's Republic of China. TEL 583875. Ed. Cheng Xianmin. circ. 1,000. **Document type:** academic/scholarly publication.
—BLDSC (6552.008000).

304.6   339   CC   ISSN 1000-4149
HB3654.A3
RENKOU YU JINGJI/POPULATION & ECONOMICS. (Text in Chinese; table of contents in English) 1980. bi-m. Y22.80($33) Shoudu Jingji Maoyi Daixue, Renkou Jingji Yanjiusuo - Capital University of Economics and Business, Hongmiao, Chaoyang District, Beijing 100026, People's Republic of China. TEL 5061188-472. (Dist. outside China by: China International Book Trading Corp., P.O. Box 399, Beijing, P.R.C.; Or: China Publications Export Corp., P.O. Box 782, Beijing, P.R.C.; Dist. in US by: China Books & Periodicals, Inc., 2929 24th St., San Francisco, CA 94110. TEL 415-282-2994) Ed. Feng Litian.
—UnCover.
    Description: Publishes papers interrelating population studies and economics. Also includes publication news and software reviews.

312   CC   ISSN 1005-4820
RENKOU YU YOUSHENG/POPULATION AND BETTER BIRTH. (Text in Chinese) 1985. q. Y12. Zhejiang Yike Daxue, Renkou Yanjiusuo - Zhejiang Medical University, Population Research Institute, 157 Yan'an Lu, Hangzhou, Zhejiang 310006, People's Republic of China. TEL 86-571-7022700. FAX 86-571-771571. Ed. Ding Deyun. adv. contact: Wang Ruizi. bk.rev.; circ. 45,000. circ. 45,000 (paid). **Document type:** academic/scholarly publication.
    Description: Covers population studies, information on domestic and foreign populations, pregnancy care, birth control, and contraceptives.

301.32   CC
RENKOU ZHANXIAN/POPULATION FRONT. (Text in Chinese) q. Hebei Sheng Jihua Shengyu Weiyuanhui, Renkou Xuehui - Hebei Provincial Family Planning Committee, Population Association, 1 Yuhua Lu, Shijiazhuang, Hebei 050016, People's Republic of China. TEL 49941. Ed. Wang Mingyuan.

312   CN   ISSN 0715-9293
HB3529
REPORT ON THE DEMOGRAPHIC SITUATION IN CANADA. (Catalogue 91-209) (Text in English, French) 1983. a. Can.$26($36) Statistics Canada, Publications Division, Ottawa, ON K1A 0T6, Canada. TEL 800-267-6677. FAX 613-951-1582. **Document type:** government publication.
    Description: Examines population growth at national and provincial levels, marriage and divorce rates, fertility and mortality, international and domestic migration patterns.

REPRODUCTIONS. see *BIOLOGY*

325   NE   ISSN 0080-1623
RESEARCH GROUP FOR EUROPEAN MIGRATION PROBLEMS. PUBLICATIONS. 1951. irreg. price varies. Kluwer Academic Publishers, Postbus 17, 3300 AA Dordrecht, Netherlands. TEL 31-78-392392. FAX 31-78-392254. TELEX 29245 KAPG NL. (Dist. by: Kluwer Academic Publishers Group, Postbus 322, 3300 AH Dordrecht, Netherlands. TEL 31-78-392392. FAX 31-78-546474; N. America dist. addr.: Box 358, Accord Sta., Hingham, MA 02018-0358. TEL 617-871-6600) Ed. G. Beyer. **Document type:** monographic series.
Refereed Serial

301.32   330   US   ISSN 0163-7878
HB848
RESEARCH IN POPULATION ECONOMICS; an annual compilation of research. 1978. a. $63.50 to institutions. J A I Press Inc., 55 Old Post Rd., No. 2, Box 1678, Greenwich, CT 06836-1678. TEL 203-661-7602. Ed. Paul Schultz. **Indexed:** Curr.Cont., Popul.Ind.
—BLDSC (7755.077600); Faxon. **CCC.**

301.426   US   ISSN 0957-2856
RESEARCH MONOGRAPHS ON HUMAN POPULATION BIOLOGY. 1978. irreg. price varies. Oxford University Press, 200 Madison Ave., New York, NY 10016. TEL 212-679-7300. Ed. G. Ainsworth Harrison. **Document type:** monographic series.
—BLDSC (7743.356000).

595.7   JA   ISSN 0034-5466
CODEN: KOGSBN
RESEARCHES ON POPULATION ECOLOGY/KOTAIGUN SEITAIGAKU NO KENKYU. (Text in English) 1962. s-a. 18000 Yen. Society of Population Ecology - Kotaigun Seitai Gakkai, Ogawa Higashi Iru, Shimodachuri Dori, Kamigyo-ku, Kyoto 602, Japan. Ed. Kenji Fujisaki. circ. 1,000. **Indexed:** Bio-Contr.News & Info., Biol.Abstr., Curr.Adv.Ecol.Sci., Curr.Cont., Deep Sea Res.& Oceanogr.Abstr., Ecol.Abstr., Environ.Per.Bibl. (1976-), Environ.Per.Bibl., Forest.Abstr., Geo.Abstr., Helminthol.Abstr., Maize Abstr., Rev.Appl.Entomol., Rice Abstr., Soils & Fert., Sport Fish.Abstr., Triticale Abstr., Wild.Rev., Zoo.Rec. **Document type:** academic/scholarly publication.
—BLDSC (7777.050000); Faxon; Genuine Article; UnCover. **CCC.**

325.2   UK   ISSN 0143-9316
RESIDENT ABROAD; the magazine for expatriates. 1979. m. £42 (rest of Europe £49; North Africa and the Middle East £64; elsewhere £78). Financial Times Business Information, Magazines (Subsidiary of: Financial Times Group), 2 Greystoke Pl., Fetter Ln., London EC4A 1ND, England. TEL 0171-240-9391. FAX 0171-240-7946. TELEX 296926 BUSINF G. (Subscr. to: 126 Jermyn St., London SW1Y 4UJ, England) Ed. David Phillips. adv.; bk.rev. circ. 19,500. (also avail. in microform from UMI) **Document type:** trade publication.
—UMI.
    Description: Reports on all tax and financial issues residents abroad are likely to encounter.

325   301.4   DR
RESUMENES SOBRE POBLACION DOMINICANA. 1984. s-a. $9. Asociacion Dominicana Pro-Bienestar de la Familia, Socorro Sanchez, No. 64, Zona 1, Apdo. Postal 1053, Santo Domingo, D.N., Dominican Republic. (Co-sponsor: Federacion Internacional de Planificacion de la Familia) (Affiliate: International Planned Parenthood Federation)

312   FR   ISSN 0377-8967
HB848
REVIEW OF POPULATION REVIEWS. French edition: Revue des Revues Demographiques (ISSN 0377-8959) 1976. q. free. Committee for International Cooperation in National Research in Demography, 27 rue du Commandeur, 75675 Paris Cedex 14, France. Ed. Leon Tabah. bk.rev. (back issues avail.) **Indexed:** Popul.Ind.

REVISTA DE ADMINISTRACAO MUNICIPAL. see *PUBLIC ADMINISTRATION — Municipal Government*

POPULATION STUDIES

312 BL ISSN 0101-7217
REVISTA DOCPOP; resumos sobre populacao no Brasil. 1982. 2/yr. $52.10. Fundacao Sistema Estadual de Analise de Dados, Av. Casper Libero, 464, 01033 Sao Paulo, CP 8223, Brazil. TEL 011-2292433. bibl. circ. 500. (back issues avail.) **Indexed:** P.A.I.S.For.Lang.Ind.
Description: Discusses general population, mortality, fertility, migration, spatial distribution, nuptiality and family, characteristics and needs of the population.

325 PE
REVISTA PERUANA DE POBLACION. 1992. s-a. Asociacion Multidisciplinaria de Investigacion y Docencia en Poblacion, Av. Salaverry 2461, Lima 27, Peru. TEL 705145. FAX 222950. bk.rev.

312 BG ISSN 1010-3783
HB850.5.B3
RURAL DEMOGRAPHY. (Text in English) 1974. s-a. $6. University of Dhaka, Institute of Statistical Research and Training, Ramna, Dhaka 1000, Bangladesh. Ed.Bd. charts; stat. **Indexed:** Popul.Ind.
—BLDSC (8052.422000).

312 RW
RWANDA. OFFICE NATIONAL DE LA POPULATION. FAMILLE, SANTE, DEVELOPPEMENT/IMBONEZAMULYANGO. (Text in French, Kinyarwanda) 1984. a. 550 Fr. Office National de la Population, Service de l'Information, B.P. 914, Kigali, Rwanda. **Indexed:** P.L.E.S.A.
Document type: government publication.

312 US
S D S U CENSUS DATA CENTER. NEWSLETTER. irreg. South Dakota State University, Data Center, Box 504, Brookings, SD 57006. Ed. James Satterlee.

301.32 NL
S P C - I L O REPORTS ON MIGRATION, EMPLOYMENT AND DEVELOPMENT IN THE SOUTH PACIFIC. 1983. irreg., no.24b, 1992. South Pacific Commission, B.P. D5, Noumea, Cedex, New Caledonia. TEL 687-262000. FAX 687-263818. TELEX 3139 NM SOPACOM. **Document type:** monographic series.

305.8 DK ISSN 0109-0429
SAMSPIL; tidskrift om invandrere. 1983. 8/yr. DKK 200. Ministry of Interior, Invandrerbladet, Samspil, P.O. Box 1098, 1009 Copenhagen K, Denmark. FAX 45-33-15-03-43. Ed. Arly Christensen. bk.rev.; illus. circ. 2,500.

325 PH
SCALABRINI MIGRATION CENTER. OCCASIONAL PAPERS. (Text in English) irreg. Scalabrini Migration Center, P.O. Box 10541, Broadway Centrum, 1112 Quezon City, Philippines. TEL 02-787-071. FAX 02-721-4296. E-mail: graziano@irf.pfi.net. Ed. Graziano Battistella.
Description: Contains papers on the study of socio-demographic, economic, political, psychological, historical, legislative and religious aspects of human migration and refugee movements from and within Asia.

325.1
SERIE INMIGRACION AL CONO SUR DE AMERICA. (Text in Spanish) 1985. irreg., vol.5, 1989. price varies. Organization of American States, Instituto Panamericano de Geografia e Historia - Organizacion de los Estados Americanos, 1889 F St., N.W., Washington, DC 20006-4499. TEL 202-458-3527. FAX 202-458-3534. (Distr. by: Center for Promotion and Distribution of Publications, Box 66398, Washington, DC 20035)

SERVICE DE CENTRALISATION DES ETUDES GENEALOGIQUES ET DEMOGRAPHIQUES DE BELGIQUE. NOUVELLES BREVES. see *GENEALOGY AND HERALDRY*

312 IT ISSN 0394-8323
SERVIZI DEMOGRAFICI; rivista mensile dei servizi di anagrafe, stato civile, elettorale, statistica, e leva dei comuni. 1982. m. (11/yr.) L.190000 (effective 1994). Maggioli Editore, Viale Vespucci 12-n, Casella Postale 290, 47037 Rimini, Italy. TEL 0541-626777. FAX 0541-622020. Ed.Bd. adv.: B&W page L.1350000, color page L.2100000; trim 115 x 195.

325 FI ISSN 0355-3779
SIIRTOLAISUUS/MIGRATION. 1974. q. FIM 40($12) Siirtolaisuusinstituutti - Institute of Migration, Piispankatu 3, SF-20500 Turku, Finland. TEL 358-21-317-536. FAX 358-21-2333-460. Ed. Olavi Koivukangas. adv.; bk.rev.; circ. 1,400 (controlled). **Document type:** academic/scholarly publication.
Description: Covers historical as well as recent trends in population movements, including ethnical issues as a related field.

325 FI ISSN 0356-9659
SIIRTOLAISUUSTUTKIMUKSIA. A. Swedish edition: Migrationsstudier. B (ISSN 0358-0083); English edition: Migration Studies. C (ISSN 0356-780X) 1975. irreg. price varies. Siirtolaisuusinstituutti - Institute of Migration, Piispankatu 3, 20500 Turku, Finland. TEL 358-9-21-317-536. FAX 358-9-21-333-460. Dir. Olavi Koivukangas. bk.rev.; charts; stat. circ. 1,000. **Document type:** academic/scholarly publication.
Description: Covers historical as well as recent trends in population movements.

SOCIAL BIOLOGY. see *BIOLOGY — Genetics*

312 FR
SOCIO-ECONOMIC DIFFERENTIAL MORTALITY IN INDUSTRIALIZED SOCIETIES. 1980. a. free. Committee for International Cooperation in National Research in Demography (CICRED), 27 rue du Commander, 75675 Paris Cedex 14, France. circ. 500.

312 AT
SOUTH AUSTRALIA. DEPARTMENT OF HOUSING AND URBAN DEVELOPMENT. POPULATION PROJECTION FOR SOUTH AUSTRALIA AND STATISTICAL DIVISIONS. irreg. Aus.$15 per no. Department of Housing and Urban Development, G.P.O. Box 667, Adelaide, S.A. 5001, Australia. TEL 618-207-2000. FAX 618-207-2050. **Document type:** government publication.
Formerly: South Australia. Department of Environment and Planning. Population Projection for South Australia.

312 AT
SOUTH AUSTRALIA. DEPARTMENT OF HOUSING AND URBAN DEVELOPMENT. STATE AND REGIONAL PROJECTIONS. BULLETIN. 1989. irreg. Aus.$2 per no. Department of Housing and Urban Development, G.P.O. Box 667, Adelaide, S.A. 5001, Australia. TEL 618-207-2000. FAX 618-207-2050. **Document type:** government publication.
Formerly: South Australia. Department of Environment and Planning. State Regional Projections. Bulletin (ISSN 1032-8793)

312 US
SOUTH CAROLINA. STATE DATA CENTER. NEWSLETTER. q. Budget and Control Board, Division of Research & Statistical Services, Rembert C. Dennis Bldg., 1000 Assembly St., Rm. 442, Columbia, SC 29201. TEL 803-734-3788. FAX 803-734-3619. **Document type:** government publication.

312 US
SOUTHERN DEMOGRAPHIC NEWS.* 1971. q. $10. Southern Demographic Association, c/o John Marcum, 2801 S. University Ave., Little Rock, AR 72204-1000. TEL 502-569-5161. FAX 502-569-5018. circ. 300. (tabloid format) **Document type:** newsletter.
Former titles: S D A Newsletter; S R D G Newsletter.
Description: Provides news and short articles about population studies and association members and activities.

325 US ISSN 0739-2559
SPECTRUM (ST. PAUL). 1975. irreg., latest 1988. $2 per no. University of Minnesota, Immigration History Research Center, 826 Berry St., St. Paul, MN 55114. TEL 612-627-4208. FAX 612-627-4190. Ed. Joel Wurl. bk.rev.; illus. circ. 500. (back issues avail.)

301.3 YU ISSN 0038-982X
HB848
STANOVNISTVO. (Text in Serbian; summaries and contents page in English, French and Russian) 1963. q. $14.20. Institut Drustvenih Nauka u Beogradu, Centar za Demografska Istrazivanja, Narodnog Fronta 45, Belgrade, Yugoslavia. Ed. Miladin Kovacevic. adv.; bk.rev.; charts; illus.; stat.; index. circ. 800. **Indexed:** Popul.Ind.

312 UN
STATE OF WORLD POPULATION. a. United Nations Population Fund, 220 E. 42nd St., New York, NY 10017. Ed. Alex Marshall.

325 IT ISSN 0039-2936
STUDI EMIGRAZIONE/ETUDES MIGRATIONS. (Text and summaries in English, French, Italian, Spanish) 1964. 4/yr. L.48000 (foreign L.55000). Centro Studi Emigrazione, Via Dandolo 58, 00153 Rome, Italy. TEL 58 09 764. Ed.Bd. adv.; bk.rev.; abstr.; bibl.; charts; stat.; index. circ. 1,500. (back issues avail.) **Indexed:** IDA, Lang.& Lang.Behav.Abstr., P.A.I.S.For.Lang.Ind., Popul.Ind., Refug.Abstr.
—BLDSC (8481.820000).
Description: Explores the phenomenon of massive population displacement.

312 PL ISSN 0039-3134
HB881.A1
STUDIA DEMOGRAFICZNE. (Text in English, Polish; summaries in English) 1963. q. 200000 Zl.($10) (Polska Akademia Nauk, Komitet Nauk Demograficznych) D T P Akapit, Spolka z o.o., Ul. Skolimowska 4 m. 11, 00-795 Warsaw, Poland. TEL 48-22-200211. (Dist. by: Rush S.A. Oddzial Warszawa, ul. Towarowa 28, 00-958 Warsaw, Poland) Ed. Marek Okolski. bk.rev.; abstr.; charts; stat. circ. 520. **Indexed:** Popul.Ind. **Document type:** academic/scholarly publication.

301.3 PL ISSN 0137-5210
STUDIA POLONIJNE. (Text in Polish; summaries in English) 1976. irreg. price varies. Katolicki Uniwersytet Lubelski, Towarzystwo Naukowe, Ul. Gliniana 21, 20-616 Lublin, Poland. index. circ. 3,125.

312 330 GW ISSN 0721-0086
STUDIEN ZUR BEVOELKERUNGSOEKONOMIE. 1981. irreg. price varies. I F O Institut fuer Wirtschaftsforschung, Poschingerstr. 5, 8000 Munich 86, Germany. TEL 089-9224-0. circ. 400.
Description: Publication on population topics.

312 US ISSN 1048-163X
STUDIES IN DEMOGRAPHY. 1987. irreg., vol.6, 1991. price varies. University of California Press, 2120 Berkeley Way, Berkeley, CA 94720. TEL 510-643-7127. FAX 510-643-7127. (Orders to: California-Princeton Fulfillment Services, 1445 Lower Ferry Rd., Ewing, NJ 08618. TEL 800-777-4726. FAX 800-999-1958) Ed.Bd. (back issues avail.) **Document type:** monographic series.
—BLDSC (8490.338000).
Description: Discusses family planning, migration, and other phenomena that affect population size. *Refereed Serial*

301.426 US ISSN 0039-3665
HQ763 CODEN: SFPLA3
STUDIES IN FAMILY PLANNING. 1963. bi-m. $24. Population Council, 1 Dag Hammarskjold Plaza, New York, NY 10017. TEL 212-339-0500. FAX 212-755-6052. Ed. Julie Reich. charts; abstr.; index. circ. 6,000. (also avail. in microform from KTO,UMI; reprint service avail. from UMI) **Indexed:** Abstr.Hyg., Adol.Ment.Hlth.Abstr., ASCA, ASSIA, Biol.Abstr., CINAHL, Curr.Cont., Curr.Lit.Fam.Plan., Environ.Abstr., Environ.Ind., Excerp.Med., Geo.Abstr., I.P.A., IDA, IMFL, Ind.Med., Mid.East: Abstr.& Ind., Mult.Ed.Abstr., Nutr.Abstr., P.A.I.S., Popul.Ind., Rural Ext.Educ.& Tr.Abstr., Rural Recreat.Tour.Abstr., So.Pac.Per.Ind., Sp.Ed.Needs Abstr., SSCI, Stud.Wom.Abstr., Trop.Dis.Bull., World Agri.Econ.& Rural Sociol.Abstr. **Document type:** academic/scholarly publication.
—BLDSC (8490.545000); Faxon; Genuine Article; SWETS; UMI; UnCover.
Incorporates: Current Publications in Family Planning (ISSN 0011-3867)

POPULATION STUDIES

312   GW
STUDIES IN MIGRATION AND MINORITIES. 1992. irreg. DM.48.80. Lit Verlag, Dieckstr. 56, 48145 Muenster, Germany. TEL 0251-231972. Ed. Dietrich Thraenhardt. **Document type:** monographic series.

312   301.32   US
STUDIES IN POPULATION. 1974. irreg., latest 1990. Academic Press, Inc., 525 B St., Ste. 1900, San Diego, CA 92101-4495. TEL 619-231-0926. FAX 619-699-6715. (Subscr. to: Order Dept., 6277 Sea Harbor Dr., 4th Fl., Orlando, FL 32887. TEL 800-321-5068) Ed. H.H. Winsborough. (reprint service avail. from ISI) **Indexed:** Math.R. **Document type:** monographic series.

312   US   ISSN 0147-1104
STUDIES IN POPULATION AND URBAN DEMOGRAPHY. 1975. irreg. price varies. Greenwood Press, Inc. (Subsidiary of: Greenwood Publishing Group Inc.), 88 Post Rd. W., Box 5007, Westport, CT 06881-5007. TEL 203-226-3571. FAX 203-222-1502. Ed. Kingsley Davis. **Document type:** monographic series.

325   US   ISSN 1078-4179
TEACHER'S PET TERM PAPER. 1985. q. $3. Zero Population Growth, 1400 16th St., N.W., Ste. 320, Washington, DC 20036. TEL 202-332-2200. FAX 202-332-2302. Ed. Pamela Wasserman. bk.rev.; charts; illus. circ. 4,000. (back issues avail.) **Document type:** newsletter.

614   312   PY
TEMAS DE POBLACION. 1968. bi-m. free or exchange basis. Centro Paraguayo de Estudios de Poblacion, Edif. El Dorado, piso 8, Manduvira y O'Leary, Asuncion, Paraguay. TEL 447334. Ed. Helio Vera. bk.rev. circ. 3,500.
Formerly: Temas Medicos.

312   US
TEXAS POPULATION PERSPECTIVE. s-a.? University of Texas at Austin, Population Research Center, Main 1800, Austin, TX 78712-1127. Ed. Jennifer Scalora. bk.rev. **Document type:** newsletter.
Description: Reports on center, students, faculty, and grant funding news.

THEORETICAL POPULATION BIOLOGY; an international journal. see BIOLOGY

312   FR   ISSN 0988-8233
TOUT EN CARTES. 1988. q. 310 F. Prodige, 51 rue de Prony, 75017 Paris, France. (Subscr. to: 36 rue de Picpus, 75012 Paris, France) Dir. Catherine Villeneuve.

312   US   ISSN 0897-0556
TOWARD THE 21ST CENTURY. 1988. q. $25. Population Institute, 107 Second St., N.E., Washington, DC 20002. TEL 202-544-3300. FAX 202-544-0068. Ed. Harold N. Burdett. circ. 3,000.

312   TU   ISSN 0259-6334
HB3633.4.A3
TURKISH JOURNAL OF POPULATION STUDIES/NUFUSBILIM DERGISI. 1979. a. TL.10000($7) Hacettepe University, Institute of Population Studies - Hacettepe Universitesi, Nufus Etutleri Enstitusu, Ankara, Turkey. FAX 90-312-3118141. TELEX 42237 HTK TR. Ed. Dr. Ergul Tuncbilek. circ. 1,000. **Document type:** academic/scholarly publication.
Description: Features applied and theoretical articles in the field of population studies.

THE U K WEALTH DIRECTORY. see BUSINESS AND ECONOMICS — Trade And Industrial Directories

THE U S A WEALTH DIRECTORY. see BUSINESS AND ECONOMICS — Trade And Industrial Directories

301.3   UN   ISSN 0066-8451
JX1977
UNITED NATIONS. ECONOMIC AND SOCIAL COMMISSION FOR ASIA AND THE PACIFIC. ASIAN POPULATION STUDIES SERIES. (Text in English) 1967. irreg. free. United Nations Economic and Social Commission for Asia and the Pacific (ESCAP), Population Division, United Nations Bldg., Rajadamnern Ave., Bangkok 10200, Thailand. (Dist. by: United Nations Publications, Room LX-2300, New York, NY 10017; Or: Distribution and Sales Section, Palais des Nations, CH-1211 Geneva 10, Switzerland) **Indexed:** Popul.Ind.
—BLDSC (1742.725000).

312   340   UN   ISSN 0364-3417
K2000.A53
UNITED NATIONS POPULATION FUND. ANNUAL REVIEW OF POPULATION LAW. a. $45. United Nations Population Fund, 220 E. 42nd St., Rm. 2306, New York, NY 10017. (Co-sponsor: Harvard Law School) Ed. Reed Boland. bibl.
Description: Compendium of national, regional and international legal developments in population and related fields.

312   UN
UNITED NATIONS POPULATION FUND. (YEAR) REPORT. Cover title: U N F P A (Year) Report. a. United Nations Population Fund, 220 E. 42nd St., Rm. 2307, New York, NY 10017. (also avail. in microfiche from CIS) **Indexed:** IIS.

U.S. CENTERS FOR DISEASE CONTROL. MORBIDITY AND MORTALITY WEEKLY REPORT. see PUBLIC HEALTH AND SAFETY

U.S. CENTERS FOR DISEASE CONTROL. MORBIDITY AND MORTALITY WEEKLY REPORT. RECOMMENDATIONS AND REPORT. see PUBLIC HEALTH AND SAFETY

325   US   ISSN 0083-1220
U.S. IMMIGRATION AND NATURALIZATION SERVICE. ADMINISTRATIVE DECISIONS UNDER IMMIGRATION AND NATIONALITY LAWS. 1940. irreg. price varies. U.S. Immigration and Naturalization Service, Board of Immigration Appeals, Washington, DC 20530. TEL 202-724-7796.

325   US   ISSN 0083-1247
JV6414
U.S. IMMIGRATION AND NATURALIZATION SERVICE. ANNUAL REPORT. 1892. a. price varies. U.S. Immigration and Naturalization Service, 425 I St., N.W., Washington, DC 20536. TEL 202-724-7796. **Document type:** government publication.

312   US   ISSN 0896-4416
UNITED STATES POPULATION DATA SHEET. 1981. a. $3 to non-members. Population Reference Bureau, Inc., 1875 Connecticut Ave., N.W., Ste. 520, Washington, DC 20009. TEL 202-483-1100. Ed. Carl Haub. charts; stat. circ. 15,000. (also avail. in diskette format; wall chart format) **Indexed:** SRI.
—BLDSC (9100.172700).
Description: Provides population, demographic and social indicators by state.

UNIVERSITY OF DAR ES SALAAM. BUREAU OF RESOURCE ASSESSMENT AND LAND USE PLANNING. ANNUAL REPORT. see ENVIRONMENTAL STUDIES

UNIVERSITY OF DAR ES SALAAM. BUREAU OF RESOURCE ASSESSMENT AND LAND USE PLANNING. RESEARCH PAPER. see ENVIRONMENTAL STUDIES

UNIVERSITY OF DAR ES SALAAM. BUREAU OF RESOURCE ASSESSMENT AND LAND USE PLANNING. RESEARCH REPORT. see ENVIRONMENTAL STUDIES

312   301.2   NR
UNIVERSITY OF LAGOS. HUMAN RESOURCES RESEARCH UNIT. MONOGRAPH. 1974. irreg. (University of Lagos, Human Resources Research Unit) Lagos University Press, Publishing Division, P.O. Box 12003, Lagos, Nigeria. **Document type:** monographic series.

301.32   US
UNIVERSITY OF MICHIGAN. POPULATION STUDIES CENTER. REPORT. 1961. irreg., latest 1991-1994. free. University of Michigan, Population Studies Center, Ann Arbor, MI 48104. TEL 313-998-7275. FAX 313-998-7415. Ed. Cindy Glovinsky. circ. 600. **Document type:** academic/scholarly publication.
Formerly: University of Michigan. Population Studies Center. Annual Report (ISSN 0360-3660)

312   US
UNIVERSITY OF VIRGINIA. CENTER FOR PUBLIC SERVICE. REPORTS.* (Supplement avail.: Census Highlights) 1991. a. University of Virginia, Center for Public Service, 918 Emmet St., N., Ste. 300, Charlottesville, VA 22903-4832. TEL 804-924-3396. FAX 804-924-4538.
Description: Analyzes specific areas of census data. Discusses how emerging demographic trends are shaping the Commonwealth's character and its public policy choice at the state, regional, and local levels.

312   US
UNIVERSITY OF WISCONSIN AT MADISON. APPLIED POPULATION LABORATORY. ECONOMIC SERIES. 1993. irreg., nos.90-2, 1993. University of Wisconsin at Madison, Applied Population Laboratory, Department of Rural Sociology, 308 Agricultural Hall, Madison, WI 53706. TEL 608-262-1515. **Document type:** monographic series.

301.3   US   ISSN 0084-0734
UNIVERSITY OF WISCONSIN, MADISON. APPLIED POPULATION LABORATORY. POPULATION NOTES. 1961. irreg., no.21, Feb. 1991. free. University of Wisconsin at Madison, Applied Population Laboratory, Department of Rural Sociology, 308 Agricultural Hall, Madison, WI 53706. TEL 608-262-1515. circ. 800. **Document type:** academic/scholarly publication.
Description: Overview of specific topics concerning Wisconsin's population.

301.3   US   ISSN 0084-0742
UNIVERSITY OF WISCONSIN, MADISON. APPLIED POPULATION LABORATORY. POPULATION SERIES. 1961. irreg., nos.90-5, 1993. price varies. University of Wisconsin at Madison, Applied Population Laboratory, Department of Rural Sociology, 308 Agricultural Hall, Madison, WI 53706. TEL 608-262-1515. circ. 500. **Document type:** monographic series.

V I A MAGAZIN; Fachzeitschrift fuer Praktiker. (Verband der Initiativgruppen in der Auslaenderarbeit e.V.) see POLITICAL SCIENCE — Civil Rights

325.1   282   CN   ISSN 0823-2687
VIVRE ENSEMBLE; bulletin de liaison en pastorale interculturelle. 4/yr. Can.$10. Centre Justice et Foi, Secteur des Communautes Culturelles, 25 rue Jarry Ouest, Montreal, PQ H2P 1S6, Canada. adv. contact: Therese Benguerel.
Description: Aims to welcome immigrants entering Quebec to the church.

VOCE DI FIUME. see HISTORY

312   IO   ISSN 0125-9679
HB848
WARTA DEMOGRAFI. (Text in Indonesian) 1971. 6/yr. Rps.21000($30) (effective 1994). University of Indonesia, Faculty of Economics, Demographic Institute, Jalan Salemba Raya 4, Jakarta 10430, Indonesia. TEL 06221-336434. FAX 06221-3102457. TELEX 69158 UI JKT IA. Ed. Aris Ananta. bk.rev. circ. 600. **Indexed:** E.I. **Document type:** academic/scholarly publication.
●Also available on CD-ROM.
Description: Covers current issues on demographic topics in Indonesia.

WASHINGTON (STATE). EMPLOYMENT SECURITY DEPARTMENT. ANNUAL DEMOGRAPHIC INFORMATION. see OCCUPATIONS AND CAREERS

312   US   ISSN 0091-5254
HA711
WISCONSIN POPULATION PROJECTIONS. 1969. irreg., 3rd ed., 1975. $5. Department of Administration, Bureau of Program Management, Madison, WI 53702. TEL 608-266-1694. (Subscr. to: Document Sales Unit, 202 S. Thornton Ave., Madison, WI 53702) stat. **Document type:** government publication.

WORLD BANK LIVING STANDARDS MEASUREMENT STUDY. see BUSINESS AND ECONOMICS — International Development And Assistance

POPULATION STUDIES — Abstracting, Bibliographies, Statistics

312   US   ISSN 0085-8315
WORLD POPULATION DATA SHEET. 1962. a. $3. Population Reference Bureau, Inc., 1875 Connecticut Ave., N.W., Ste. 520, Washington, DC 20009. TEL 202-483-1100. FAX 202-328-3937. Eds. Carl Haub, Machiko Yanagishita. stat. circ. 130,000. (also avail. in microfiche from CIS; diskette format; wall chart format) **Indexed:** Energy Ind., Energy Info.Abstr., SRI.

312   US   ISSN 0895-3341
HA154
WORLD POPULATION PROFILE. (Part of WP Series) 1985. biennial. price varies. U.S. Bureau of the Census, Data User Services Division, Washington, DC 20233. TEL 310-457-4100. FAX 301-457-4714. (Orders to: Superintendent of Documents, U.S. Government Printing Office, Box 371954, PA 15250-7954. TEL 202-512-1800. FAX 202-512-2250; Or: Bernan, 4611-F Assembly Dr., Lanham, MD 20706. TEL 301-459-7666. FAX 301-459-0056) **Document type:** government publication.

312   FI   ISSN 0506-3590
HB848
YEARBOOK OF POPULATION RESEARCH IN FINLAND/VAESTOENTUTKIMUKSEN VUOSIKIRJA. (Text in English) 1946. a. FIM 110. Vaestoliitto - Population Research Institute, Kalevankatu 16 A, P.O. Box 849, FIN-00101 Helsinki, Finland. TEL 358-0-640235. FAX 358-0-6121211. E-mail: VL__UMM@cc.helsinki.fi. Ed. Jarl Lindgren. adv.; bk.rev.; bibl. circ. 700. **Indexed:** Popul.Ind. **Document type:** monographic series, academic/scholarly publication.
—BLDSC (9415.570000).
   Description: Includes articles on questions of current interest in demography in Finland. Also population data compiled at the institute, and a bibliography of the Finnish population research every other year.

312   IS
YIDIOT HAMERCAZ LEDEMOGRAFIA. 1979. s-a. Ministry of Employment and Welfare, Demography Center, P.O. Box 915, Jerusalem 91 008, Israel. Ed. Simon Yair. circ. 1,500. **Document type:** government publication.

304.8 914.3 929   US
YORKER PALATINE NEWSLETTER. 1982. q. $19. Palatines to America, New York State Chapter, 9666 Elpis Rd., Camden, NY 13316. TEL 315-245-0990. Ed. Eila Schiffer. (looseleaf format; back issues avail.) **Document type:** newsletter.
   Description: Promotes German immigration to North America. Covers the Hudson and Mohawk valleys of New York.

YUGOSLAVIA. SAVAZNI ZAVOD ZA STATISTIKU. DEMOGRAFSKA STATISTIKA. see *POPULATION STUDIES — Abstracting, Bibliographies, Statistics*

312   US   ISSN 0199-0071
Z P G REPORTER. 1969. 6/yr. $20 to libraries. Zero Population Growth, Inc., 1400 16th St., N.W., Ste. 320, Washington, DC 20036. TEL 202-332-2200. FAX 202-332-2302. E-mail: zpg@igc.apc.org. Ed. Laura Dillon. adv.; bk.rev.; charts; stat. circ. 65,000. (tabloid format) **Indexed:** Curr.Lit.Fam.Plan., Environ.Abstr. **Document type:** newspaper.
—CIS.
   Formerly: Z P G National Reporter (ISSN 0049-8718)

325   ZA   ISSN 0084-4802
ZAMBIA. IMMIGRATION DEPARTMENT. REPORT. 1964. a. K.100. Zambia Government Printing Department, P.O. Box 30136, Lusaka, Zambia. **Document type:** government publication.
   Description: Reports on immigration control and the issuance of employment permits in Zambia.

ZEITLUPE. see *POLITICAL SCIENCE — Civil Rights*

312   GW   ISSN 0340-2398
HB848
ZEITSCHRIFT FUER BEVOELKERUNGSWISSENSCHAFT: DEMOGRAPHIE. (Text in German; summaries in English, French and German) 1975. q. DM.96. (Bundesinstitut fuer Bevoelkerungsforschung) Harald Boldt Verlag GmbH, Postfach 1110, 56135 Boppard a.R., Germany. TEL 06742-2511. FAX 06742-3013. **Document type:** academic/scholarly publication.
—CCC.

POPULATION STUDIES — Abstracting, Bibliographies, Statistics

AGE AND SEX PROFILE OF OVERSEAS VISITORS TO THE U K (YEAR). see *TRAVEL AND TOURISM — Abstracting, Bibliographies, Statistics*

312   US   ISSN 0066-0752
HA1
AMERICAN STATISTICAL ASSOCIATION. SOCIAL STATISTICS SECTION. PROCEEDINGS. 1958. a. $49 to non-members; members $34. American Statistical Association, 1429 Duke St., Alexandria, VA 22314-3402. TEL 703-684-1221. FAX 703-684-2037. (also avail. in microform from UMI) **Indexed:** Curr.Ind.Stat. **Document type:** proceedings.
—BLDSC (6636.205000); UMI.

312   PE
ANUARIO DE NACIMIENTOS. a. Instituto Nacional de Estadistica, Av. 28 de Julio No. 1056, Lima, Peru. circ. 300.

318   AG   ISSN 0326-2936
HA954
ARGENTINA. INSTITUTO NACIONAL DE ESTADISTICA Y CENSOS. ANUARIO ESTADISTICO. (Editions in English, Spanish) 1948. a. Arg.$30($45) (effective 1994). Instituto Nacional de Estadística y Censos, Avda. Julio A. Roca, 609 P.B., 1067 Buenos Aires, Argentina. TEL 54-1-3499662. FAX 54-1-3499621. (also avail. in diskette format) **Document type:** government publication.

312.097   US   ISSN 0364-0728
HA251
ARKANSAS VITAL STATISTICS. 1970. a. free. Department of Health, Center for Health Statistics, Slot 19, 4815 W. Markham St., Little Rock, AR 72205-3867. TEL 501-661-2368. illus.; stat. (also avail. in microfiche from CIS) **Indexed:** SRI. **Document type:** government publication.
   Formerly: Arkansas. Bureau of Vital Statistics. Annual Report of Births, Deaths, Marriages and Divorces as Reported to the Bureau of Vital Statistics (ISSN 0094-3576)

312   AT   ISSN 1031-055X
AUSTRALIA. BUREAU OF STATISTICS. AUSTRALIAN DEMOGRAPHIC STATISTICS. 1979. q. Aus.$18.50 per no. Australian Bureau of Statistics, P.O. Box 10, Belconnen, A.C.T. 2616, Australia. stat. circ. 1,072. **Document type:** government publication.
   Description: Summarizes the rates of birth, deaths, infant deaths, marriages, divorces, interstate and overseas movements and latest population estimates for Australia.

312 319.4   AT   ISSN 1031-0150
AUSTRALIA. BUREAU OF STATISTICS. BIRTHS, AUSTRALIA. 1968. a. Aus.$15. Australian Bureau of Statistics, P.O. Box 10, Belconnen, A.C.T. 2616, Australia. TEL 062-527911. FAX 062-516009. circ. 422. **Document type:** government publication.
   Description: Provides detailed statistics on confinements and live births presented in 26 tables.

312   AT   ISSN 1031-2005
RA407.5.A8
AUSTRALIA. BUREAU OF STATISTICS. CAUSES OF DEATH, AUSTRALIA. 1962. a. Aus.$19. Australian Bureau of Statistics, P.O. Box 10, Belconnen, A.C.T. 2616, Australia. TEL 062-527911. FAX 062-516009. circ. 476. **Document type:** government publication.
   Formerly (until 1978): Causes of Death (Canberra) (ISSN 0067-0766)
   Description: Contains number of deaths by sex and selected age groups classified according to the World Health Organization's International Classification of Diseases.

350 312.2   AT   ISSN 1031-0223
AUSTRALIA. BUREAU OF STATISTICS. DEATHS, AUSTRALIA. a. Aus.$18.50. Australian Bureau of Statistics, P.O. Box 10, Belconnen, A.C.T. 2616, Australia. TEL 062-527911. FAX 062-516009. illus. circ. 427. **Document type:** government publication.
   Description: Contains the numbers of deaths classified by age, sex, birthplace, marital status; occupation, month of death, cause of death and usual residence of deceased by state or territory.

312   AT   ISSN 1036-2673
AUSTRALIA. BUREAU OF STATISTICS. DEMOGRAPHY, AUSTRALIAN CAPITAL TERRITORY. 1990. a. Aus.$18. Australian Bureau of Statistics, P.O. Box 10, Belconnen, A.C.T. 2616, Australia. **Document type:** government publication.
   Description: Contains statistics on births, deaths, marriages and divorces.

312   AT   ISSN 1031-2234
AUSTRALIA. BUREAU OF STATISTICS. ESTIMATED RESIDENT POPULATION BY AGE AND SEX IN STATISTICAL LOCAL AREAS, AUSTRALIAN CAPITAL TERRITORY. 1986. a. Aus.$25. Australian Bureau of Statistics, P.O. Box 10, Belconnen, A.C.T. 2616, Australia. **Document type:** government publication.
   Description: Contains estimates of resident population by sex and 5-year age groups for the statistical local areas (mostly Canberra suburbs) of the Australian Capital Territory.

312 319.4   AT   ISSN 0810-0039
HA3001
AUSTRALIA. BUREAU OF STATISTICS. ESTIMATED RESIDENT POPULATION BY SEX AND AGE: STATES AND TERRITORIES OF AUSTRALIA. 1968. a. Aus.$27. Australian Bureau of Statistics, P.O. Box 10, Belconnen, A.C.T. 2616, Australia. TEL 062-527911. FAX 062-516009. circ. 838. **Document type:** government publication.
   Description: Estimates population for each state and territory classified by sex and age.

312   AT   ISSN 1031-7643
AUSTRALIA. BUREAU OF STATISTICS. ESTIMATED RESIDENT POPULATION IN STATISTICAL LOCAL AREAS, AUSTRALIAN CAPITAL TERRITORY. 1978. a. Aus.$20. Australian Bureau of Statistics, P.O. Box 10, Belconnen, A.C.T. 2616, Australia. **Document type:** government publication.
   Formerly: Estimated Resident Population, Suburbs of Canberra Statistical District.
   Description: Contains estimates of resident population of the statistical local areas (mostly Canberra suburbs) of the Australian Capital Territory.

312.5 319.4   AT   ISSN 1322-8692
AUSTRALIA. BUREAU OF STATISTICS. MARRIAGES AND DIVORCES, AUSTRALIA. 1960. a. Aus.$12. Australian Bureau of Statistics, P.O. Box 10, Belconnen, A.C.T. 2616, Australia. TEL 062-527911. FAX 062-516009. **Document type:** government publication.
   Formed by the merger of (1967-1993): Marriages, Australia (ISSN 1031-0452); (1960-1993): Divorces, Australia (ISSN 1031-2188); Which was formerly (until 1976): Divorces (Canberra) (ISSN 0587-5757)
   Description: Contains registrations of marriages classified according to State or Territory of registration, age, previous marital status and coutry of birth of bridegrooms and brides, and type of celebrant. Registered marriages dissovled are classified by age and previous marital status of parties at time of marriage, duration of the marriage at final separation, country of birth, and numbers of children.

312 310   AT   ISSN 1322-8765
▼**AUSTRALIA. BUREAU OF STATISTICS. MIGRATION, AUSTRALIA.** 1994. a. Aus.$29. Australian Bureau of Statistics, P.O. Box 10, Belconnen, A.C.T. 2616, Australia. **Document type:** government publication.
   Description: Contains information on international and internal migration and the estimated resident population by birthplace.

312   AT   ISSN 1036-2614
AUSTRALIA. BUREAU OF STATISTICS. NEW SOUTH WALES OFFICE. DEMOGRAPHY, NEW SOUTH WALES. 1990. a. Aus.$29. Australian Bureau of Statistics, New South Wales Office, St. Andrews House, Sydney Square, George St., Sydney, N.S.W. 2000, Australia. **Document type:** government publication.
   Formed by the merger of (1945-1989): Divorces, New South Wales (ISSN 1031-2196); (1976-1989): Marriages, New South Wales (ISSN 0728-2230); (1976-1989): Births, New South Wales (ISSN 0728-2222)
   Description: Contains detailed statistics on births, marriages, divorces and deaths.

POPULATION STUDIES — ABSTRACTING, BIBLIOGRAPHIES, STATISTICS

312   AT   ISSN 1037-6569
AUSTRALIA. BUREAU OF STATISTICS. NEW SOUTH WALES OFFICE. ESTIMATED RESIDENT POPULATION BY AGE AND SEX IN STATISTICAL LOCAL AREAS, NEW SOUTH WALES. 1987. a. Aus.$30. Australian Bureau of Statistics, New South Wales Office, St. Andrews House, Sydney Square, George St., Sydney, N.S.W. 2000, Australia. **Document type:** government publication.
Formerly: Age and Sex Distribution of the Estimated Resident Population of Statistical Local Areas, New South Wales.

312   AT   ISSN 1030-9187
AUSTRALIA. BUREAU OF STATISTICS. NEW SOUTH WALES OFFICE. ESTIMATED RESIDENT POPULATION OF STATISTICAL LOCAL AREAS, NEW SOUTH WALES, PRELIMINARY. 1983. a. Aus.$25. Australian Bureau of Statistics, New South Wales Office, St. Andrews House, Sydney Square, George St., Sydney, N.S.W. 2000, Australia. **Document type:** government publication.
Formerly: Estimated Resident Population of Local Government Areas, New South Wales, Preliminary.
Description: Contains preliminary estimated resident population of municipalities and shires grouped in statistical areas.

312 332   AT
AUSTRALIA. BUREAU OF STATISTICS. NEW SOUTH WALES OFFICE. MONTHLY SUMMARY OF STATISTICS, NEW SOUTH WALES. 1931. m. Aus.$14 per no. Australian Bureau of Statistics, New South Wales Office, St. Andrews House, Sydney Square, George St., Sydney, N.S.W. 2000, Australia. stat. **Document type:** government publication.
Description: Covers population and vital statistics, employment and unemployment, wages and prices, production, building, finance, trade and transport.

312   AT   ISSN 1035-820X
AUSTRALIA. BUREAU OF STATISTICS. NORTHERN TERRITORY OFFICE. DEMOGRAPHY, NORTHERN TERRITORY. 1976. a. Aus.$18. Australian Bureau of Statistics, Northern Territory Office, MLC Bldg., 6th Fl., 81 Smith St., Darwin, N.T. 0800, Australia. **Document type:** government publication.
Supersedes in part (in 1990): Estimated Resident Population of Selected Areas, Northern Territory, Preliminary (ISSN 1035-8218)
Description: Provides statistics on births, deaths, marriages and divorces.

312   AT   ISSN 1320-6974
AUSTRALIA. BUREAU OF STATISTICS. NORTHERN TERRITORY OFFICE. RESIDENT POPULATION ESTIMATES FOR STATISTICAL LOCAL AREAS, NORTHERN TERRITORY, PRELIMINARY. 1976. a. Aus.$10.50. Australian Bureau of Statistics, Northern Territory Office, MLC Bldg., 6th Fl., 81 Smith St., Darwin, N.T. 0800, Australia. **Document type:** government publication.
Formerly: Estimated Resident Population of Selected Local Government Areas, Northern Territory.
Description: Contains estimates of population and annual growth rates in statistical local areas of Northern Territory.

312   AT   ISSN 1031-0495
AUSTRALIA. BUREAU OF STATISTICS. OVERSEAS ARRIVALS AND DEPARTURES, AUSTRALIA (MONTHLY). 1965. m. Aus.$10 per no. Australian Bureau of Statistics, P.O. Box 10, Belconnen, A.C.T. 2616, Australia. **Document type:** government publication.
Description: Features short summary of visitors arriving and residents departing short-term.

312   AT   ISSN 0814-3951
AUSTRALIA. BUREAU OF STATISTICS. POPULATION ESTIMATES, AUSTRALIA. 1983. irreg., latest 1986. free. Australian Bureau of Statistics, P.O. Box 10, Belconnen, A.C.T. 2616, Australia. TEL 062-527911. FAX 062-516009. circ. 539. **Document type:** government publication.
Description: Shows quarterly estimates of resident population and components of population growth for states, territories and Australia.

312 310   AT   ISSN 1320-6494
AUSTRALIA. BUREAU OF STATISTICS. POPULATION SURVEY MONITOR. 1993. q. Aus.$10. Australian Bureau of Statistics, P.O. Box 10, Belconnen, A.C.T. 2616, Australia. **Document type:** government publication.
Description: Presents statistics collected from an omnibus household survey which collects data on a wide and varied range of topics each quarter.

312   AT   ISSN 0816-3391
HB3675
AUSTRALIA. BUREAU OF STATISTICS. PROJECTIONS OF THE POPULATIONS OF AUSTRALIA, STATES AND TERRITORIES. 1955. irreg., latest 1989. Aus.$35. Australian Bureau of Statistics, P.O. Box 10, Belconnen, A.C.T. 2616, Australia.
TEL 062-527911. FAX 062-516009. circ. 429.
Document type: government publication.
Formerly (until 1984): Projections of the Population.
Description: Contains number and percentage of population at selected ages, sex, sex ratios, mean and median ages.

312   AT   ISSN 1037-3594
AUSTRALIA. BUREAU OF STATISTICS. QUEENSLAND OFFICE. AGE AND SEX DISTRIBUTION OF THE ESTIMATED RESIDENT POPULATION, QUEENSLAND. 1981. a. Aus.$31 (on disk Aus.$80). Australian Bureau of Statistics, Queensland Office, 313 Adelaide St., Brisbane, Qld. 4000, Australia. TEL 07-222-6022. FAX 07-229-6171. TELEX AA 40271. (also avail. in diskette format (ISSN 1032-7274)) **Document type:** government publication.
Formerly (until 1986): Age and Sex Distribution of the Estimated Resident Population in Local Authority Areas.
Description: Contains estimated resident population by sex and five-year age groups for each statistical local area, statistical division, statistical subdivision, statistical district and local government area.

312   AT   ISSN 1036-2649
AUSTRALIA. BUREAU OF STATISTICS. QUEENSLAND OFFICE. DEMOGRAPHY, QUEENSLAND. 1983. a. Aus.$29. Australian Bureau of Statistics, Queensland Office, 313 Adelaide St., Brisbane, Qld. 4000, Australia. TEL 07-222-6022. FAX 07-229-6171. TELEX AA 40271. **Document type:** government publication.
Formed by the 1990 merger of: Demographic Summary, Queensland (ISSN 0816-3537); Demography: Small Area Summary, Queensland (ISSN 1031-217X); Births, Queensland (ISSN 0815-8681); Divorces, Queensland (ISSN 0816-0783); Marriages, Queensland (ISSN 1030-2638)
Description: Provides detailed statistics on births, deaths, infant deaths, marriages and divorces.

312   AT   ISSN 1030-911X
AUSTRALIA. BUREAU OF STATISTICS. QUEENSLAND OFFICE. ESTIMATED RESIDENT POPULATION AND AREA, QUEENSLAND, PRELIMINARY. 1972. a. Aus.$25. Australian Bureau of Statistics, Queensland Office, 313 Adelaide St., Brisbane, Qld. 4000, Australia. stat. circ. 1,100. (processed) **Document type:** government publication.
Incorporates (in 1994): Estimated Resident Population and Area, Queensland (ISSN 1031-8100); (until 1987): Estimated Resident Population and Area for Local Authority Areas, Queensland (ISSN 1032-903X); Population Estimates and Areas for Local Authority Areas.
Description: Covers population and area for statistical local areas, statistical divisions and statistical districts.

312   AT   ISSN 1031-6264
AUSTRALIA. BUREAU OF STATISTICS. QUEENSLAND OFFICE. ESTIMATED RESIDENT POPULATION: COMPONENTS OF CHANGE, QUEENSLAND. 1966. irreg., latest 1986. Aus.$3. Australian Bureau of Statistics, Queensland Office, 313 Adelaide St., Brisbane, Qld. 4000, Australia. TEL 07-222-6022. FAX 07-222-6022. TELEX AA 40271. **Document type:** government publication.
Formerly: Population Growth and Growth Rates in the Intercensal Period in Statistical Divisions and Local Authority Areas.
Description: Contains post-censal revisions of annual statistical local area population estimates and components of change for the latest intercensal period.

312   AT
AUSTRALIA. BUREAU OF STATISTICS. QUEENSLAND OFFICE. ESTIMATED RESIDENT POPULATION, QUEENSLAND. 1976. irreg. Aus.$25. Australian Bureau of Statistics, Queensland Office, 313 Adelaide St., Brisbane, Qld. 4000, Australia. TEL 07-222-6022. FAX 07-229-6171. TELEX AA 40271.
Formerly: Estimated Resident Population in Local Authority Areas.
Description: Estimated resident population of each local goverment area, statistical division and statistical district at Census dates with revised intercensal estimates.

312   AT
AUSTRALIA. BUREAU OF STATISTICS. QUEENSLAND OFFICE. FERTILITY TRENDS IN QUEENSLAND. 1984. irreg. Aus.$1.80. Australian Bureau of Statistics, Queensland Office, 313 Adelaide St., Brisbane, Qld. 4000, Australia. TEL 07-222-6022. FAX 07-229-6171. TELEX AA 40271.

312 310   AT   ISSN 1321-179X
AUSTRALIA. BUREAU OF STATISTICS. REGIONAL POPULATION GROWTH, AUSTRALIA. 1993. a. Aus.$19. Australian Bureau of Statistics, P.O. Box 10, Belconnen, A.C.T. 2616, Australia. **Document type:** government publication.
Description: Population growth in States and Territories, Statistical Divisions, Subdivisions, major population centres, and high growth Statistical Local Areas.

312   AT   ISSN 1036-2657
HB1095
AUSTRALIA. BUREAU OF STATISTICS. SOUTH AUSTRALIAN OFFICE. DEMOGRAPHY, SOUTH AUSTRALIA. 1969. a. Aus.$30. Australian Bureau of Statistics, South Australian Office, G.P.O. Box 2272, Adelaide, S.A. 5001, Australia. FAX 08-237-7566. **Document type:** government publication.
Formed by the 1990 merger of: Divorces, South Australia (ISSN 1031-2218); Marriages, South Australia (ISSN 1031-2706); Births, South Australia (ISSN 0067-088X); Part of (1969-1990): Deaths, South Australia (ISSN 0067-0898)
Description: Details statistics on births, deaths, infant deaths, marriages and divorces.

312   AT   ISSN 1032-5670
AUSTRALIA. BUREAU OF STATISTICS. SOUTH AUSTRALIAN OFFICE. ESTIMATED RESIDENT POPULATION BY AGE AND SEX IN STATISTICAL LOCAL AREAS, SOUTH AUSTRALIA. 1981. a. Aus.$25. Australian Bureau of Statistics, South Australian Office, G.P.O. Box 2272, Adelaide, S.A. 5001, Australia. **Document type:** government publication.
Description: Estimates resident population in statistical divisions, subdivisions and statistical local areas by age and sex.

301   AT   ISSN 1035-8404
AUSTRALIA. BUREAU OF STATISTICS. TASMANIAN OFFICE. DEMOGRAPHY, TASMANIA. 1990. a. Aus.$27. Australian Bureau of Statistics, Tasmanian Office, G.P.O. Box 66A, Hobart, Tas. 7001, Australia. **Document type:** government publication.
Formed by the merger of (1979-1990): Divorce, Tasmania (ISSN 0727-1875); (1983-1990): Births, Tasmania (ISSN 0814-8147); (1983-1990): Deaths, Tasmania (ISSN 0814-8155); (1983-1990): Marriages, Tasmania (ISSN 0814-8163)
Description: Contains statistics on births, deaths, infant deaths, marriages and divorces.

312   AT   ISSN 0815-1873
AUSTRALIA. BUREAU OF STATISTICS. TASMANIAN OFFICE. POPULATION STATISTICS, TASMANIA. 1984. a. Aus.$25. Australian Bureau of Statistics, Tasmanian Office, G.P.O. Box 66A, Hobart, Tas. 7001, Australia. **Document type:** government publication.
Description: Contains estimated resident population by age and sex, time series analysis of state population growth and components of change.

5440 POPULATION STUDIES — ABSTRACTING, BIBLIOGRAPHIES, STATISTICS

312 AT ISSN 1036-2622
AUSTRALIA. BUREAU OF STATISTICS. VICTORIAN OFFICE. DEMOGRAPHY, VICTORIA. 1990. a. Aus.$29 per no. Australian Bureau of Statistics, Victorian Office, G.P.O. Box 2796Y, Melbourne, Vic. 3001, Australia. **Document type:** government publication.
Formed by the merger of (1981-1989): Births, Victoria (ISSN 1031-1963); (1981-1989): Deaths, Victoria (ISSN 1031-2161); (1981-1989): Marriages, Victoria (ISSN 0812-9029); (1981-1989): Divorces, Victoria (ISSN 1031-220X)
Description: Provides detailed statistics on births, deaths, infant deaths, marriages and divorces.

312 310 AT ISSN 0819-6575
AUSTRALIA. BUREAU OF STATISTICS. VICTORIAN OFFICE. ESTIMATED RESIDENT POPULATION IN STATISTICAL LOCAL AREAS, VICTORIA, PRELIMINARY. 1955. a. Aus.$25. Australian Bureau of Statistics, Victorian Office, G.P.O. Box 2796Y, Melbourne, Vic. 3001, Australia. circ. 3,000. **Document type:** government publication.
Former titles (until 1983): Estimated Resident Population in Local Government Areas, Victoria; Estimated Population in Local Government Areas, Victoria (ISSN 0705-6257); Estimated Population and Dwellings by Local Government Areas.
Description: Preliminary estimated resident population for statistical local areas, statistical districts, and statistical divisions.

312 AT ISSN 1036-2665
AUSTRALIA. BUREAU OF STATISTICS. WESTERN AUSTRALIAN OFFICE. DEMOGRAPHY, WESTERN AUSTRALIA. 1990. a. Aus.$28. Australian Bureau of Statistics, Western Australian Office, 30 Terrace Rd., E. Perth, W.A. 6004, Australia. **Document type:** government publication.
Description: Contains statistics on births, deaths, marriages and divorces.

312 AT ISSN 1031-8577
AUSTRALIA. BUREAU OF STATISTICS. WESTERN AUSTRALIAN OFFICE. ESTIMATED RESIDENT POPULATION BY AGE AND SEX IN STATISTICAL LOCAL AREAS, WESTERN AUSTRALIA. 1979. a. Aus.$26. Australian Bureau of Statistics, Western Australian Office, 30 Terrace Rd., E. Perth, W.A. 6004, Australia. **Document type:** government publication.
Estimated Resident Population in Local Government Areas, Western Australia.
Description: Contains estimates of resident population by age and sex and percentage increases in total population from the previous year.

312 AT ISSN 1031-606X
AUSTRALIA. BUREAU OF STATISTICS. WESTERN AUSTRALIAN OFFICE. ESTIMATED RESIDENT POPULATION IN STATISTICAL LOCAL AREAS, WESTERN AUSTRALIA, PRELIMINARY. 1984. a. Aus.$20. Australian Bureau of Statistics, Western Australian Office, 30 Terrace Rd., E. Perth, W.A. 6004, Australia. **Document type:** government publication.
Formerly: Estimated Resident Population in Local Government Areas, Western Australia, Preliminary.
Description: Contains preliminary estimated resident population of statistical local areas in Western Australia and percentage increase from the previous year.

312 AT
AUSTRALIA. BUREAU OF STATISTICS. WESTERN AUSTRALIAN OFFICE. WESTERN AUSTRALIA'S SENIORS. 1986. irreg., latest 1991. Aus.$25. Australian Bureau of Statistics, Western Australian Office, 30 Terrace Rd., E. Perth, W.A. 6004, Australia. **Document type:** government publication.
Description: Presents a wide range of statistics on the aged in Western Australia.

AUSTRALIAN FAMILY AND SOCIETY ABSTRACTS. see SOCIOLOGY — Abstracting, Bibliographies, Statistics

312 AU ISSN 0258-8676
AUSTRIA. STATISTISCHES ZENTRALAMT. DEMOGRAPHISCHES JAHRBUCH OESTERREICHES. (Subseries of: Beitraege zur Oesterreichischen Statistik) 1951. a. S.360. Oesterreichisches Statistisches Zentralamt, Hintere Zollamtsstr. 2b, A-1033 Vienna, Austria. TEL 0222-71128-7414. FAX 0222-7156828. circ. 480. **Document type:** government publication.
Formerly: Austria. Statistisches Zentralamt. Die Natuerliche Bevoelkerungsbewegung (ISSN 0067-2335)
Description: Demographic yearbook for Austria.

BARBADOS. REGISTRATION OFFICE. REPORT ON VITAL STATISTICS & REGISTRATIONS. see PUBLIC ADMINISTRATION — Abstracting, Bibliographies, Statistics

312.09489 DK ISSN 0108-8076
HA1471
BEFOLKNINGEN I KOMMUNERNE/POPULATIONS OF MUNICIPALITIES. 1971. a. DKK 156.80 (diskette DKK 1216). Danmarks Statistik, Sejroegade 11, DK-2100 Copenhagen OE, Denmark. TEL 45-39-17-39-17. FAX 45-31-18-48-01. TELEX 16236. stat. (also avail. in diskette format; back issues avail.) **Document type:** government publication.
Formerly: Denmark. Danmarks Statistik. Befolkningen i de Enkelte Kommuner.

309 BE ISSN 0304-8888
HA1391
BELGIUM. INSTITUT NATIONAL DE STATISTIQUE. BEVOLKINGSSTATISTIEKEN. Key Title: Bevolkingsstatistieken - Nationaal Instituut voor de Statistiek. French edition: Statistiques Demographiques - Institut National de Statistique (ISSN 0067-5490) 1973. 4/yr. 1000 BEF (foreign 1250 BEF). Institut National de Statistique - Nationaal Instituut voor de Statistiek, Leuvenseweg 44, B-1000 Brussels, Belgium. TEL 32-2-5486211. FAX 32-2-5486367. **Document type:** government publication.

312 BE ISSN 0067-5490
HB1433
BELGIUM. INSTITUT NATIONAL DE STATISTIQUE. STATISTIQUES DEMOGRAPHIQUES. Key Title: Statistiques Demographiques - Institut National de Statistique. Dutch edition: Bevolkingsstatistiek - Nationaal Instituut voor de Statistiek. 1969. irreg. (3-4/yr.). 1000 BEF (foreign 1250 BEF). Institut National de Statistique, 44 rue de Louvain, B-1000 Brussels, Belgium. TEL 32-2-5486211. FAX 32-2-5486367. Indexed: P.A.I.S.For.Lang.Ind. **Document type:** government publication.
Incorporates (1954-1969): Belgium. Institut National de Statistique. Mouvement de la Population des Communes.

312.2 BE
BELGIUM. INSTITUT NATIONAL DE STATISTIQUE. STATISTIQUES DES CAUSES DE DECES. irreg., latest 1987. 340 BEF (foreign 425 BEF). Institut National de Statistique, 44 rue de Louvain, B-1000 Brussels, Belgium. TEL 32-2-5486211. FAX 32-2-5486367. **Document type:** government publication.

BOCHUM. AMT FUER STATISTIK, STADTFORSCHUNG UND WAHLEN. STATISTICAL YEARBOOK. see HOUSING AND URBAN PLANNING — Abstracting, Bibliographies, Statistics

312 BL ISSN 0101-2207
HA973
BRAZIL. FUNDACAO INSTITUTO BRASILEIRO DE GEOGRAFIA E ESTADISTICA. ESTATISTICAS DO REGISTRO CIVIL. 1974. a. $70. Fundacao Instituto Brasileiro de Geografia e Estatistica, Centro de Documentacao e Disseminacao de Informacoes, Rua General Canabarro 666, 2o andar, Maracana 20271-201 Rio de Janeiro RJ, Brazil. TEL 55-21-2645424. FAX 55-21-2289575. **Document type:** government publication.
Formerly (until 1978): Registro Civil do Brasil (ISSN 0100-1493); Supersedes (1959-1964): Brazil. Servico de Estatistica Demografica, Moral y Politica. Registro Civil (ISSN 0524-3610)

BRITISH COLUMBIA REGIONAL INDEX. see BUSINESS AND ECONOMICS — Abstracting, Bibliographies, Statistics

312 UA
C D C MONOGRAPHS. STUDIES IN AFRICAN AND ASIAN DEMOGRAPHY. 1970. a. $20. Cairo Demographic Centre - Al-Markaz al-Dimugrafi bil-Qahirah, No. 78, St. No. 4, Hadhaba el-Olya, Mokattam 11571, Cairo, Egypt. TEL 5060950. FAX 5062797. TELEX 92034 DP UN. Ed. Dr. Hisham Makhlouf. circ. 200. (back issues avail.) **Document type:** monographic series.
Description: Studies in demography and related fields.

312 UA
C D C OCCASIONAL PAPERS. 1972. irreg., no.6, 1991. $5 per no. Cairo Demographic Centre, No. 78, St. No. 4, Hadhaba el-Olya, Mokattam 11571, Cairo, Egypt. TEL 5060950. FAX 5062797. TELEX 92034 DP UN. Ed. Dr. Hisham Makhlouf. circ. 200. (back issues avail.) **Document type:** academic/scholarly publication.
Description: Studies in demography and related fields.

312 UA
▼**C D C SERIES ON POPULATION AND DEVELOPMENT**. 1994. irreg., no.10, 1994. $5 per no. Cairo Demographic Center, No. 78, St. No. 4, Hadhaba El-Olya, Mokattam 11571, Cairo, Egypt. Ed. Dr. Hisham Makhlouf. **Document type:** academic/scholarly publication.

312 UA
C D C WORKING PAPERS. 1981. irreg., no.36, 1994. $5 per no. Cairo Demographic Centre, No. 78, St. No. 4, Hadhaba el-Olya, Mokattam 11571, Cairo, Egypt. TEL 5060950. FAX 5062797. TELEX 92034 DP UN. Ed. Dr. Hisham Makhlouf. circ. 200. (back issues avail.) **Document type:** academic/scholarly publication.
Description: Studies in demography and related fields.

310 US ISSN 1050-3021
HC107.C23
CALIFORNIA POPULATION CHARACTERISTICS (YEAR); regional market update and projections. 1988. a. $195. Center for Continuing Study of the California Economy, 610 University Ave., Palo Alto, CA 94301. TEL 415-321-8550. Ed. Stephen Levy.
Description: Detailed analyses of age, sex, ethnic group, household status and income of California's present and future residents. Contains mid-decade estimates and projections to 2005. Includes labor force and occupational data, and analysis and discussion of trends in California.

CANADA. STATISTICS CANADA. FAMILY INCOMES, CENSUS FAMILIES. see BUSINESS AND ECONOMICS — Abstracting, Bibliographies, Statistics

312 IT ISSN 1121-0958
RA407.5.I8
CAUSE DI MORTE. 1989. a. L.29000 (effective 1991). Istituto Nazionale di Statistica, Via Cesare Balbo 16, 00100 Rome, Italy. FAX 06-46735198. **Document type:** government publication.
Description: Presents data relevant to the causes of death and infant mortality.

317 CU
CENSO DE POBLACION Y VIVIENDAS. (Issued from 1972 as a number of Anuario Estadistico de Cuba) a. free. Comite Estatal de Estadisticas, Centro de Informacion Cientifico-Tecnica, Direccion de Informacon y Relaciones Internacionales, Almendares No. 156, esq. a Desague, Gaveta Postal 6016, Havana, Cuba. charts; stat. **Document type:** government publication.

312 BL ISSN 0104-3145
CENSO DEMOGRAFICO. 1940. decennial. Fundacao Instituto Brasileiro de Geografia e Estatistica, Centro de Documentacao e Disseminacao de Informacoes, Rua General Canabarro 666, 2o andar, Maracana 20271-201 Rio de Janeiro, Brazil. TEL 55-21-2645424. FAX 555-21-2289575. **Document type:** government publication.

312 016 US
CENSUS CATALOG AND GUIDE. 1946. a. $17.50. U.S. Bureau of the Census, Data User Services Division, Washington, DC 20233. TEL 301-457-4100. FAX 301-457-4714. (Orders to: Superintendent of Documents, U.S. Government Printing Office, Box 371954, Pittsburgh, PA 15250-7954. TEL 202-512-1800. FAX 202-512-2250; Or: Bernan, 4611-F Assembly Dr., Lanham, MD 20706. TEL 301-459-7666. FAX 301-459-0056) Ed. Gary M.Young. circ. 7,500. (also avail. in microfiche) **Document type:** government publication.
Formerly: Bureau of the Census Catalog (ISSN 0007-618X)

POPULATION STUDIES — ABSTRACTING, BIBLIOGRAPHIES, STATISTICS

312   CK
COLOMBIA. DEPARTAMENTO ADMINISTRATIVO NACIONAL DE ESTADISTICA. ANUARIO DEMOGRAFICO.
a. Departamento Administrativo Nacional de Estadistica, Banco Nacional de Datos, Apdo Nacional 80043, Bogota D.E., Colombia. **Document type:** government publication.

314   IT   ISSN 0010-4965
COMUNE DI ROMA. UFFICIO DI STATISTICA E CENSIMENTO. NOTIZIARIO STATISTICO MENSILE.
1948. m. L.3750 per no. Comune di Roma, Ufficio di Statistica - Censimento e Toponomastica, Via della Greca 5, 00186 Rome, Italy. circ. 650. **Document type:** government publication.

COUNTY AND CITY EXTRA; annual metro, city and county data book. see *STATISTICS*

312   BL   ISSN 0103-4448
CRIANCAS E ADOLESCENTES; indicadores sociais. 1987. a. $80. Fundacao Instituto Brasileiro de Geografia e Estatistica, Centro de Documentacao e Disseminacao de Informacoes, Rua General Canabarro 666, 2o andar, Maracana 20271-201 Rio de Janeiro, Brazil. TEL 55-21-2645424. FAX 55-21-2289575. **Document type:** government publication.

312 339   US
CURRENT POPULATION REPORTS: CONSUMER INCOME. MONEY INCOME OF HOUSEHOLDS, FAMILIES AND PERSONS IN THE UNITED STATES (YEAR). (Subseries of Series P-60 (ISSN 0730-4803)) a. $16. U.S. Bureau of the Census, Data User Services Division, Washington, DC 20233. TEL 301-457-4100. FAX 301-457-4714. (Subscr. to: Superintendent of Documents, U.S. Government Printing Office, Box 371954, Pittsburgh, PA 15250-7954. TEL 202-512-1800. FAX 202-512-2250; Or: Bernan, 4611-F Assembly Dr., Lanham, MD 20706. TEL 301-459-7666. FAX 301-459-0056) **Document type:** government publication.
●Also available online. Vendor(s): CompuServe, Inc., Knight-Ridder, Inc.
Former titles: Current Population Reports: Consumer Income. Money Income in (Year) of Families and Persons in the United States; Money Income in (Year) of Families, Unrelated Individuals and Persons in the United States (ISSN 0073-5698)
Description: Provides information on the proportions of families and persons at various income levels.

312   US
CURRENT POPULATION REPORTS: POPULATION CHARACTERISTICS. GEOGRAPHICAL MOBILITY. (Subseries of Series P-20) 1948. a. U.S. Bureau of the Census, Data User Services Division, Washington, DC 20233. TEL 301-457-4100. FAX 301-457-4714. (Subscr. to: Superintendent of Documents, U.S. Goverment Printing Office, Box 371954, Pittsburgh, PA 15250-7954. TEL 202-512-1800. FAX 202-512-2250) **Document type:** government publication.
●Also available online. Vendor(s): CompuServe, Inc., Knight-Ridder, Inc.
Formerly: Current Population Reports: Population Characteristics. Mobility of the Population of the United States (ISSN 0076-986X)

312   US
CURRENT POPULATION REPORTS: POPULATION CHARACTERISTICS. HOUSEHOLD AND FAMILY CHARACTERISTICS. (Subseries of Series P-20) a. $11. U.S. Bureau of the Census, Data User Services Division, Washington, DC 20233. TEL 301-457-4100. FAX 301-457-4714. (Subscr. to: Superintendent of Documents, U.S. Government Printing Office, Box 371954, Pittsburgh, PA 15250-7954. TEL 202-512-1800. FAX 202-512-2250; Or: Bernan, 4611-F Assembly Dr., Lanham, MD 20706. TEL 301-459-7666. FAX 301-459-0056) **Document type:** government publication.

312   US
CURRENT POPULATION REPORTS: POPULATION CHARACTERISTICS. MARITAL STATUS AND LIVING ARRANGEMENTS. (Subseries of Series P-20) a. $16. U.S. Bureau of the Census, Data User Services Division, Washington, DC 20233. TEL 301-457-4100. FAX 301-457-4714. (Subscr. to: Superintendent of Documents, U.S. Government Printing Office, Box 371954, Pittsburgh, PA 15250-7954. TEL 202-512-1800. FAX 202-512-2250; Or: Bernan, 4611-F Assembly Dr., Lanham, MD 20706) (also avail. in microfiche from CIS; reprint service avail. from CIS) **Document type:** government publication.
●Also available online. Vendor(s): CompuServe, Inc., Knight-Ridder, Inc.
Formerly: Current Population Reports: Population Characteristics. Marital Status and Family Status (ISSN 0082-9501)

312   US
CURRENT POPULATION REPORTS: POPULATION CHARACTERISTICS. RESIDENTS OF FARMS AND RURAL AREAS. (Subseries of Series P-20) 1947. a. $5. U.S. Bureau of the Census, Data User Services Division, Washington, DC 20233. TEL 301-457-4100. FAX 301-457-4714. (Subscr. to: Superintendent of Documents, U.S. Government Printing Office, Box 371954, Pittsburgh, PA 15250-7954. TEL 202-512-1800. FAX 202-512-2250; Or: Bernan, 4611-F Assembly Dr., Lanham, MD 20706. TEL 301-459-7666. FAX 301-459-0056) **Document type:** government publication.
Formerly: Current Population Reports: Population Characteristics. Rural and Rural Farm Population; Incorporates (in 1987): Current Population Reports: Rural and Rural Farm Population; Which was formerly (until 1986): Current Population Reports: Farm Population.

312   US
CURRENT POPULATION REPORTS: POPULATION CHARACTERISTICS. SCHOOL ENROLLMENT: SOCIAL AND ECONOMIC CHARACTERISTICS OF STUDENTS. (Subseries of Series P-20) a. $9. U.S. Bureau of the Census, Data User Services Division, Washington, DC 20233. TEL 301-457-4100. FAX 301-457-4714. (Subscr. to: Superintendent of Documents, U.S. Government Printing Office, Box 371954, Pittsburgh, PA 15250-7954. TEL 202-512-1800. FAX 202-512-2250; Or: Bernan, 4611-F Assembly Dr., Lanham, MD 20706. TEL 301-459-7666. FAX 301-459-0056) **Document type:** government publication.
●Also available online. Vendor(s): CompuServe, Inc., Knight-Ridder, Inc.
Formerly: U.S. Bureau of the Census. Current Population Reports: School Enrollment: October (Year) (ISSN 0082-9528)

312   US
CURRENT POPULATION REPORTS: POPULATION ESTIMATES AND PROJECTIONS. UNITED STATES POPULATION ESTIMATES BY AGE, SEX, RACE AND HISPANIC ORIGIN. (Subseries of Series P-25) a. U.S. Bureau of the Census, Data User Services Division, Washington, DC 20233. TEL 301-457-4100. FAX 301-457-4714. (Subscr. to: Superintendent of Documents, U.S. Government Printing Office, Box 371954, Pittsburgh, PA 15250-7954. TEL 202-512-1800. FAX 202-512-2250) **Indexed:** Rehabil.Lit. **Document type:** government publication.
●Also available online. Vendor(s): CompuServe, Inc., Knight-Ridder, Inc.
Former titles: Current Population Reports: Population Estimates and Projections. United States Population Estimates by Age, Sex and Race; Current Population Reports: Population Estimates and Projections. Estimates of the Population of the United States by Age, Race and Sex; Current Population Reports, P-25: Population Estimates and Projections. Estimates of the Population of the United States by Age, Color and Sex (ISSN 0071-1624); Also incorporates: Current Population Reports: Population Estimates and Projections. United States Population Estimates and Components of Change.

312   US   ISSN 0363-6836
HA195
CURRENT POPULATION REPORTS: SERIES P-20. POPULATION CHARACTERISTICS. 1947. irreg. $101 (foreign $126.25) (includes Series P-23 and Series P-60). U.S. Bureau of the Census, Data User Services Division, Washington, DC 20233. TEL 301-457-4100. FAX 301-457-4714. (Subscr. to: Superintendent of Documents, U.S. Government Printing Office, Box 371954, Pittsburgh, PA 15250-7954. TEL 202-512-1800. FAX 202-512-2250; Or: Bernan, 4611-F Assembly Dr., Lanham, MD 20706. TEL 301-459-7666. FAX 301-459-0056) (also avail. in microfiche from CIS; back issues avail.; reprint service avail. from CIS and the Census Bureau) **Indexed:** Amer.Stat.Ind., Curr.Lit.Fam.Plan. **Document type:** government publication.
Incorporates (in 1987): Current Population Report: Farm Population (Series P-27) (ISSN 1048-6283)
Description: Compiles current national and, occasionally, local regional data on geographic residence and mobility, fertility, education, school enrollment, marital status and numbers and characteristics of households and families.

312   US   ISSN 0498-8485
HA203
CURRENT POPULATION REPORTS: SERIES P-23. SPECIAL STUDIES. 1949. irreg. $101 (foreign $126.25) (includes Series P-20 and Series P-60). U.S. Bureau of the Census, Data User Services Division, Washington, DC 20233. TEL 301-457-4100. FAX 301-457-4714. (Subscr. to: Superintendent of Documents, U.S. Government Printing Office, Box 371954, Pittsburgh, PA 15250-7954. TEL 202-512-1800. FAX 202-512-2250) **Document type:** government publication.

312   US   ISSN 0738-453X
HA195
CURRENT POPULATION REPORTS: SERIES P-25. POPULATION ESTIMATES AND PROJECTIONS. 1947. m. (plus a. supplement). $30 (foreign $37.50). U.S. Bureau of the Census, Data User Services Division, Washington, DC 20233. TEL 301-457-4100. FAX 301-457-4714. (Subscr. to: Superintendent of Documents, U.S. Government Printing Office, Box 371954, Pittsburgh, PA 15250-7954. TEL 202-512-1800. FAX 202-512-2250) (also avail. in microfiche from CIS; reprint service avail. from CIS and the Census Bureau) **Indexed:** Amer.Stat.Ind. (1976-). **Document type:** government publication.
●Also available online. Vendor(s): CompuServe, Inc., Knight-Ridder, Inc.
Incorporates in 1993: Current Population Reports: Series P-26. Population Estimates and Projections (Irreg.).
Description: Estimates the total population of the U.S. and provides half-year figures broken down by age, color, and sex.

312   US   ISSN 0270-6660
CURRENT POPULATION REPORTS: SERIES P-28. SPECIAL CENSUSES. 1937. irreg. U.S. Bureau of the Census, Data User Services Division, Washington, DC 20233. TEL 301-457-4100. FAX 301-457-4714. (Subscr. to: Superintendent of Documents, U.S. Government Printing Office, Box 371954, Pittsburgh, PA 15250-7954. TEL 202-783-3238. FAX 202-512-2233) **Document type:** government publication.

312 339   US   ISSN 0730-4803
HC110.I5
CURRENT POPULATION REPORTS: SERIES P-60. CONSUMER INCOME. 1947. irreg. $101 (foreign $126.25) (subscr. includes Series P-20 and Series P-23). U.S. Bureau of the Census, Data User Services Division, Washington, DC 20233. TEL 301-457-4100. FAX 301-457-4714. (Subscr. to: Superintendent of Documents, U.S. Government Printing Office, Box 371954, Pittsburgh, PA 15250-7954. TEL 202-512-1800. FAX 202-512-2250) **Document type:** government publication.

POPULATION STUDIES — ABSTRACTING, BIBLIOGRAPHIES, STATISTICS

301 US ISSN 0886-5698
HA203
CURRENT POPULATION REPORTS: SERIES P-70. HOUSEHOLD ECONOMIC INDICATORS. 1983. bi-m. $31 (foreign $38.75). U.S. Bureau of the Census, Data User Services Division, Washington, DC 20402. TEL 301-457-4100. FAX 301-457-4714. (Subscr. to: Superintendent of Documents, U.S. Government Printing Office, Box 371954, Pittsburgh, PA 15250-7954. TEL 202-512-1800. FAX 202-512-2250) (also avail. in microfiche from CIS; reprint service avail. from CIS and the Census Bureau) **Document type:** government publication.
●Also available online. Vendor(s): CompuServe, Inc., Knight-Ridder, Inc.

312.8 CY ISSN 0590-4846
CYPRUS. DEPARTMENT OF STATISTICS AND RESEARCH. DEMOGRAPHIC REPORT. (Text in English, Greek) 1963. a. £C4. Ministry of Finance, Department of Statistics and Research, 13 Lord Byron Ave., Nicosia, Cyprus. TEL 357-2-302349. FAX 357-2-456712. **Document type:** government publication.
Description: Provides population estimates by month: births and fertility statistics, death, and mortality statistics.

310 CY
CYPRUS. DEPARTMENT OF STATISTICS AND RESEARCH. DEMOGRAPHIC SURVEY. (YEAR). (Text in English) 1980. irreg. £C5. Ministry of Finance, Department of Statistics and Research, 13 Lord Byron Ave., Nicosia, Cyprus. TEL 357-2-302349. FAX 357-2-456712. **Document type:** government publication.
Formerly: Cyprus. Department of Statistics and Research. Multi-Round Demographic Survey. Main Report.
Description: Presents data on the socioeconomic structure of the population, fertility and internal migration.

310 CY
CYPRUS. DEPARTMENT OF STATISTICS AND RESEARCH. MULTI-ROUND DEMOGRAPHIC SURVEY. MIGRATION IN CYPRUS. (Text in English) 1983. irreg. £C1.50. Ministry of Finance, Department of Statistics and Research, 13 Lord Byron Ave., Nicosia, Cyprus. TEL 357-2-302349. FAX 357-2-456712. **Document type:** government publication.
Description: Analyzes recent and lifetime migration in Cyprus with an examination of variables, such as sex, age, present and previous place of residence, place of birth, type of movement, and reason for moving.

CYPRUS. DEPARTMENT OF STATISTICS AND RESEARCH. TOURISM, MIGRATION AND TRAVEL STATISTICS. see TRAVEL AND TOURISM — Abstracting, Bibliographies, Statistics

312 012 UN ISSN 0378-5378
HB3530.5
D O C P A L RESUMENES SOBRE POBLACION EN AMERICA LATINA/D O C P A L LATIN AMERICAN POPULATION ABSTRACTS. (Text in English and Spanish) 1977. a. $20. United Nations, Centro Latinoamericano de Demografia - United Nations, Latin American Demographic Centre, Casilla 91, Santiago, Chile. TEL 2102000. circ. 1,000. (back issues avail.) **Indexed:** P.A.I.S.For.Lang.Ind., Popul.Ind.
Description: Abstracts of published and non-published literature on population written in or about Latin America and the Caribbean.

312 CL
DEMOGRAFIA. 1909. a. Esc.2400 (US $16.60; elsewhere $21.10) (effective 1994). Instituto Nacional de Estadisticas, Casilla 498, 3 Santiago, Chile.

312 XR ISSN 0011-8265
DEMOGRAFIE. (Text in Czech; summaries in English and Russian) 1959. q. $44.70. Cesky Statisticky Urad, Sokolovska 142, 186 04 Prague 8, Czech Republic. TEL 42-2-6604-2451. FAX 42-2-6631-0429. Ed. Jerina Ruzkova. bk.rev.; stat.; index. circ. 1,800. **Indexed:** Popul.Ind.
Supersedes in part: Statistika a Demografie.
Description: Reviews the research of the population trends.

330.9 312 GH
DEMOGRAPHIC AND HEALTH SURVEY (YEAR). irreg., latest 1993. $10. Statistical Service, Information Section, P.O. Box 1098, Accra, Ghana. TEL 233-21-663758. FAX 233-21-667069. TELEX 2205 MIFAEP GH. **Document type:** government publication.

312.09489 DK ISSN 0070-3478
HA1473
DENMARK. DANMARKS STATISTIK. BEFOLKNINGENS BEVAEGELSER. (Text in Danish; notes in English) 1931. a. DKK 140. Danmarks Statistik, Sejroegade 11, DK-2100 Copenhagen OE, Denmark. TEL 45-31-29-82-22. FAX 45-31-18-48-01. TELEX 16236. **Document type:** government publication.

614 363.12509489 DK ISSN 0070-3516
DENMARK. DANMARKS STATISTIK. FAERDSELSUHELD. (Text in Danish, notes in English) 1930. a. DKK 46.72. Danmarks Statistik, Sejroegade 11, DK-2100 Copenhagen OE, Denmark. TEL 45-31-29-82-22. FAX 45-31-18-48-01. TELEX 16236. **Document type:** government publication.

312 DK ISSN 0108-5646
DOEDSAARSAGERNE/CAUSES OF DEATH IN DENMARK. (Included in the series: Vitalstatistik) (Text in Danish and English) 1980. a. DKK 75. Sundhedsstyrelsen, Amaliegade 13, 1012 Copenhagen K, Denmark. (Orders to: Statens Information, P.O. Box 1103, 1009 Copenhagen K, Denmark) **Document type:** government publication.
Formerly: Doedsaarsagerne i Kongeriget Danmark.

325 US
▼**EAST - WEST CENTER PROGRAM ON POPULATION. ASIA - PACIFIC POPULATION RESEARCH ABSTRACTS.** 1995. irreg., no.4, 1995. free. Center for Cultural and Technical Interchange Between East and West, Inc., 1777 East-West Rd., Honolulu, HI 96848. TEL 808-944-7401. FAX 808-944-7490. TELEX 989171 EWC UD. E-mail: WARDS@EWC.bitnet. Ed. Sandra E. Ward. circ. 7,000. **Document type:** abstracting/indexing.

325 EC
ECUADOR. INSTITUTO NACIONAL DE ESTADISTICA Y CENSOS. ENCUESTA ANUAL DE MIGRACION INTERNACIONAL. a. Esc.25000($23) (effective 1993). Instituto Nacional de Estadistica y Censos, Av. 10 de Agosto 229, Quito, Ecuador. TEL 593-2-581900. FAX 593-2-580041. **Document type:** government publication.

312 310 PN ISSN 0379-4237
ESTADISTICA PANAMENA. SITUACION DEMOGRAFICA. SECCION 221. ESTADISTICAS VITALES. (In 3 vols.; vol.1: Matrimonios y Divorcios; vol.2: Nacimientos Vivos y Defunciones Fetales; vol.3: Defunciones) 1957. a. Bl.1.75 (foreign Bl.4) (effective 1995). Direccion de Estadistica y Censo, Contraloria General, Apdo. 521430, Panama 5, Panama. FAX 507-69-7294. circ. 950. **Document type:** government publication, bulletin.
Description: Presents data on marriages and divorces, live births and stillbirths, and deaths, arranged by province and by other factors.

325.7287 PN ISSN 1022-6605
JV7429
ESTADISTICA PANAMENA. SITUACION DEMOGRAFICA. SECCION 231. MOVIMIENTO INTERNACIONAL DE PASAJEROS. 1957. a. Bl.0.50 (foreign Bl.1.50) (effective 1995). Direccion de Estadistica y Censo, Contraloria General, Apdo. Postal 5213, Panama 5, Panama. FAX 507-69-7294. circ. 750. **Document type:** government publication, bulletin.
Formerly: Estadistica Panamena. Situacion Demografica. Seccion 231. Migracion Internacional (ISSN 0378-4975)
Description: Offers information on the entrance and exiting of passengers at airports, seaports and other land destinations.

312 310 AT ISSN 1321-1625
ESTIMATED RESIDENT POPULATION BY AGE AND SEX IN STATISTICAL LOCAL AREAS, VICTORIA. 1988. a. Aus.$30. Australian Bureau of Statistics, Victorian Office, G.P.O. Box 2796Y, Melbourne, Vic. 3001, Australia. **Document type:** government publication.
Description: Gives extensive data on Victoria's estimated resident population.

312 015 NE ISSN 0168-6577
Z7164.D3
EUROPEAN JOURNAL OF POPULATION/REVUE EUROPEENNE DE DEMOGRAPHIE. (Text and summaries in English, French) 1970-1983; resumed 1985. q. fl.413 to institutions; $264 to institutions in U.S. (effective 1996). (European Association for Population Studies) Kluwer Academic Publishers, Postbus 17, 3300 AA Dordrecht, Netherlands. TEL 31-78-392392. FAX 31-78-392254. TELEX 29245 KAPG NL. E-mail: SERVICES@WKAP.NL. (Dist. by: Kluwer Academic Publishers Group, P.O. Box 322, 3300 AA Dordrecht, Netherlands. TEL 31-78-392392. FAX 31-78-546474; N. American dist. addr.: Box 258 Accord Sta., Hingham, MA 02018-0358. TEL 617-871-6600. FAX 617-871-6528) Eds. Daniel Courgeau, John Simons. adv.; bk.rev.; index. circ. 400. (tabloid format; back issues avail.; reprint service avail. from SWZ) **Indexed:** ASCA, Curr.Cont., Geo.Abstr., IDA, P.A.I.S., Popul.Ind., Sage Fam.Stud.Abstr., Sociol.Abstr., SSCI. **Document type:** academic/scholarly publication.
—BLDSC (3829.737500); Faxon; Genuine Article; SWETS; UnCover. **CCC.**
Formerly (until 1983): European Demographic Information Bulletin (ISSN 0046-2756)
Description: Reports and analyzes demographic experiences, including theoretical explanations, research strategies and policy implications.
Refereed Serial

312 BL ISSN 0103-4731
FAMILIA; indicadores sociais. 1981. a. $60. Fundacao Instituto Brasileiro de Geografia e Estatistica, Centro de Documentacao e Disseminacao de Informacoes, Rua General Canabarro 666, 20 andar, Maracana 20271-201 Rio de Janeiro, Brazil. TEL 55-21-2645424. FAX 55-21-2289575. **Document type:** government publication.

312 FJ
FIJI. BUREAU OF STATISTICS. FIJI FERTILITY SURVEY. 1974. irreg. $2.50 (effective through 1996). Bureau of Statistics, P.O. Box 2221, Suva, Fiji. **Document type:** government publication.

312 FJ
FIJI. BUREAU OF STATISTICS. POPULATION OF FIJI; monograph for the U N World population. 1974. irreg. free. Bureau of Statistics, P.O. Box 2221, Suva, Fiji. **Document type:** monographic series, government publication.

FIJI. BUREAU OF STATISTICS. TOURISM AND MIGRATION STATISTICS. see TRAVEL AND TOURISM — Abstracting, Bibliographies, Statistics

312 FI
FINLAND. TILASTOKESKUS. KUOLLEISUUS. KUOLLEISUUS- JA ELOONJAAMISTAULUJA/FINLAND. STATISTIKCENTRALEN. DOEDLIGHET. DOEDLIGHETS- OCH LIVSLAENGDSTABELLER/FINLAND. CENTRAL STATISTICAL OFFICE. MORTALITY. LIFE TABLES. (Text in English, Finnish and Swedish) 1924. irreg. Tilastokeskus, Annankatu 44, SF-00100 Helsinki 10, Finland. **Document type:** government publication.
Formerly: Finland. Tilastokeskus. Kuolleisuus- Ja Eloonjaamistauluja (ISSN 0355-2128)

312 FI ISSN 0784-8447
FINLAND. TILASTOKESKUS. VAESTOE/FINLAND. STATISTIKCENTRALEN. BEFOLKNING/FINLAND. CENTRAL STATISTICAL OFFICE. POPULATION. (Section VIA of Official Statistics of Finland) (Text in English, Finnish and Swedish) 1871. a. FIM 145. Tilastokeskus, Annankatu 44, SF-00100 Helsinki 10, Finland. (Subscr. to: Government Printing Centre, Box 516, SF-00100 Helsinki 10, Finland) **Document type:** government publication.
Formerly: Finland. Tilastokeskus. Vaestonmuutokset (ISSN 0430-5612)

312 FI
FINLAND. TILASTOKESKUS. VAESTOE- JA ASUNTOLASKENTA/FINLAND. STATISTIKCENTRALEN. FOLK- OCH BOSTADSRAEKNINGEN/FINLAND. CENTRAL STATISTICAL OFFICE. POPULATION AND HOUSING CENSUS. (Section VI C of Official Statistics of Finland) (Text in English, Finnish and Swedish) 1950. irreg. (approx. every 5 years), latest 1985. price varies. Tilastokeskus, Annankatu 44, SF-00100 Helsinki 10, Finland. **Document type:** government publication.
Formerly: Finland. Tilastokeskus. Vaestolaskenta (ISSN 0355-2136)

POPULATION STUDIES — ABSTRACTING, BIBLIOGRAPHIES, STATISTICS

312   US
FLORIDA. DEPARTMENT OF HEALTH AND REHABILITATIVE SERVICES. VITAL NEWS AND QUARTERLY VITAL STATISTICS REPORT. Cover title: Vital News. q. free. Department of Health and Rehabilitative Services, Public Health Statistics Section, Office of Vital Statistics, Box 210, Jacksonville, FL 32231. TEL 904-359-6960. FAX 904-359-6697. charts; stat. circ. 1,500. **Document type:** government publication, newsletter.
  Formerly: Florida. Department of Health and Rehabilitative Services. Quarterly Vital Statistics Report.

310   US
FLORIDA VITAL STATISTICS. 1935. a. first copy free. Department of Health & Rehabilitative Services, Public Health Statistics Section, Office of Vital Statistics, Box 210, Jacksonville, FL 32231-0042. TEL 904-359-6960. FAX 904-359-6993. E-mail: health@gold.acns.fsu.edu. charts. circ. 2,000.
Indexed: SRI. **Document type:** government publication.
  Description: Contains data compiled from original records of live births, deaths, fetal deaths, marriages, and dissolutions of marriage. Includes current population figures, extensive analyses of causes of death and historical trends.

325   FR   ISSN 0769-0398
FRANCE. OFFICE DES MIGRATIONS INTERNATIONALES. OMISTATS. 1967. a. 100 F. Office des Migrations Internationales, Service de la Communication, 44 rue Bargue, 75732 Paris Cedex 15, France. TEL 45-66-27-22. FAX 47-34-88-57. TELEX 250 677 OFMIDEX. circ. 500. **Document type:** directory.
  Formerly: France. Office National d'Immigration. Statistiques de l'Immigration (ISSN 0071-903X)

312   US   ISSN 0741-0182
HA321
GEORGIA DESCRIPTIONS IN DATA. 1982. biennial. $10 hardcopy; computer diskettes $10. Operational Support and Development, Office of Planning and Budget, 254 Washington St., S.W., Rm. 640, Atlanta, GA 30334-8501. TEL 404-656-0911. FAX 404-656-3828. Ed. Marty Sik. circ. 1,000 (controlled). **Indexed:** SRI.
  Supersedes: Georgia. State Data Center. City Population Estimates (ISSN 0362-3904)

312   US
GEORGIA VITAL STATISTICS REPORT. 1947. a. price varies. Department of Human Resources, Division of Public Health, 2 Peachtree St., S.W., Ste. 3-522, Atlanta, GA 30303-3186. TEL 404-657-6321. circ. 500 (controlled). **Indexed:** SRI. **Document type:** government publication.
  Former titles (until 1983): Georgia Vital Statistics Data Book; Georgia Vital and Health Statistics (ISSN 0362-0662); Georgia Vital Morbidity Statistics (ISSN 0072-1379)
  Description: Disseminates selected information by race and age on births, deaths, marriages, divorces, abortions and projected populations for the calendar year.

312   GW
GERMANY. STATISTISCHES BUNDESAMT. BEVOELKERUNG UND ERWERBSTAETIGKEIT. REIHE 1: GEBIET UND BEVOELKERUNG. 1960. a. DM.9. Statistisches Bundesamt, 65180 Wiesbaden, Germany. TEL 0611-75-1. FAX 0611-724000. TELEX 61186-STBA-D. **Document type:** government publication.
  Formerly: Germany (Federal Republic, 1949-). Statistisches Bundesamt. Bevoelkerung und Kultur. Reihe 1: Bevoelkerungsstand und Entwicklung (ISSN 0072-1786)

312   GW   ISSN 0072-1794
GERMANY. STATISTISCHES BUNDESAMT. FACHSERIE 1, BEVOELKERUNG UND ERWERBSTAETIGKEIT, REIHE 1: GEBIET UND BEVOELKERUNG. 1959. a. DM.29.50. Statistisches Bundesamt, 65180 Wiesbaden, Germany. TEL 0611-75-1. FAX 0611-724000. TELEX 61186-STBA-D. **Document type:** government publication.

312   GW
GERMANY. STATISTISCHES BUNDESAMT. FACHSERIE 1, BEVOELKERUNG UND ERWERBSTAETIGKEIT, REIHE 3: HAUSHAELTE UND FAMILIEN. 1969. irreg. DM.28.90. Statistisches Bundesamt, 65180 Wiesbaden, Germany. TEL 0611-75-1. FAX 0611-724000. TELEX 61186-STBA-D. **Document type:** government publication.

016   BE
GEZINSWETENSCHAPPELIJKE DOCUMENTATIE; Jaarboek. 1976. a. 2200 BEF (effective 1994). Leuven University Press, Krakenstraat 3, B-3000 Leuven, Belgium. TEL 32-16-324175. FAX 32-16-323782. Ed.Bd. circ. 800. **Document type:** academic/scholarly publication.
  Formerly (until 1983): Gezinssociologische Documentatie.

330.9 312   GH
GHANA. STATISTICAL SERVICE. POPULATION CENSUS - DEMOGRAPHIC AND ECONOMIC CHARACTERISTICS. irreg., latest 1984. $90. Statistical Service, Information Section, P.O. Box 1098, Accra, Ghana. TEL 233-21-663758. FAX 233-21-667069. TELEX 2205 MIFAEP GH. **Document type:** government publication.

330.9 312   GH
GHANA. STATISTICAL SERVICE. POPULATION CENSUS - SPECIAL REPORT ON LOCALITIES. (Comprises 10 regional vols.) irreg., latest 1984. $75 for set of 10 vols. Statistical Service, Information Section, P.O. Box 1098, Accra, Ghana. TEL 233-021-663758. FAX 233-021-667069. TELEX 2205 MIFAEP GH. **Document type:** government publication.

325   US
H I A S STATISTICAL ABSTRACT. vol.14, 1973. a. free. H I A S Inc., 333 Seventh Ave., New York, NY 10001-5004. charts. circ. 1,000. (processed) **Indexed:** Refug.Abstr.

312   US   ISSN 0093-3481
HB3525.H3
HAWAII. DEPARTMENT OF HEALTH. RESEARCH AND STATISTICS OFFICE. R & S REPORT. Key Title: R & S Report (Honolulu). 1973. irreg. free. Department of Health, Research and Statistics Office, Box 3378, Honolulu, HI 96801. TEL 808-548-6454. stat. **Document type:** government publication.

325 352.7   MF
HOUSING AND POPULATION CENSUS OF MAURITIUS. RESULTS. (Issued in 7 vols.) irreg., latest 1990. price varies. Central Statistical Office, Toorawa Centre, Cr. S.S. R & J. Mosque Sts., Port Louis, Mauritius. TEL 230-234-5294. FAX 230-208-4011. (Subscr. to: Government Printing Office, Ramtoolah Bldg., Sir S. Ramgoolam St., Port Louis, Mauritius) (back issues avail.) **Document type:** government publication.

312   HU   ISSN 0073-4020
HA1201
HUNGARY. KOZPONTI STATISZTIKAI HIVATAL. DEMOGRAFIAI EVKONYV. 1965. a. 495 Ft. Statisztikai Kiado Vallalat, Kaszasdulo u. 2, P.O.B.99, 1300 Budapest 3, Hungary. TEL 688-635. TELEX 22-6699. circ. 1,200. **Document type:** government publication.

312   BE
I P D WORKING PAPERS. (Text in English) 1975. irreg. price varies. Vrije Universiteit Brussel, Interuniversity Programme in Demography, Pleinlaan 2, B-1050 Brussels, Belgium. TEL 32-2-6292040. FAX 32-2-6292282. E-mail: esrbalck@vub.ac.be. Ed. R. Lesthaeghe. bibl.; charts; stat. circ. 200. **Indexed:** Popul.Ind. **Document type:** monographic series.
  Formerly (until 1983): Demografie.
  Description: Presents research results in pre-publication form. Covers demographic issues relating to Western Europe and Africa, including fertility, family, economic and historical demography, demographic theory, and other topics.

325.1   CN
IMMIGRATION HIGHLIGHTS. 4/yr. Can.$30. Ministry of Government Services, B C Stats, 553 Superior St., Victoria, BC V8V 1X4, Canada. TEL 604-387-1502. FAX 604-387-0329. **Document type:** government publication.
  Description: Features immigrant landings to British Columbia and Canada by place of origin, destination and immigration status: independent or dependent, entrepreneur and investor.

312   II
INDIA. MINISTRY OF HOME AFFAIRS. VITAL STATISTICS DIVISION. SAMPLE REGISTRATION BULLETIN. (Text in English) 1964. biennial. Ministry of Home Affairs, Vital Statistics Division, Registrar General, West Block No. 1, R. K. Puram, New Delhi 110066, India. charts; stat. (processed) **Document type:** bulletin.
  Incorporates: India. Office of the Registrar General. Newsletter (ISSN 0537-0035)

312.2   II
INDIA. MINISTRY OF HOME AFFAIRS. VITAL STATISTICS DIVISION. SURVEY OF CAUSES OF DEATH (RURAL). (Text in English) a. Ministry of Home Affairs, Vital Statistics Division, Registrar General, West Block No. 1, R. K. Puram, New Delhi 110066, India. stat.
  Formerly: India. Ministry of Home Affairs. Vital Statistics Division. Causes of Death: a Survey.

312   EC
INSTITUTO NACIONAL DE ESTADISTICA Y CENSOS. SERIE ESTADISTICA. 1970. quinquennial. Esc.24000($45) Instituto Nacional de Estadistica y Censos, Quito, Ecuador.

312   BE   ISSN 0255-0849
Z7164.D3
INTERNATIONAL BIBLIOGRAPHY OF HISTORICAL DEMOGRAPHY/BIBLIOGRAPHIE INTERNATIONALE DE LA DEMOGRAPHIE HISTORIQUE. (Text in English, French) 1978. a. $10. International Union for the Scientific Study of Population, 34 rue des Augustins, B-4000 Liege, Belgium. FAX 041-223847. TELEX 42648 POPUN. Ed.Bd. bibl.; index. circ. 4,000. (back issues avail.) **Indexed:** Popul.Ind. **Document type:** bibliography.

312   US
INTERNATIONAL POPULATION DATA. irreg. U.S. Bureau of the Census, Data User Services Division, Washington, DC 20233. TEL 301-457-4100. FAX 301-457-4714. **Document type:** government publication.
  ●Also available online. Vendor(s): CompuServe, Inc., Knight-Ridder, Inc.
  Former titles: Current Population Reports: International Population Data; Current Population Reports: International Population Reports (ISSN 0082-9498)

312   IE   ISSN 0790-7710
IRELAND. CENTRAL STATISTICS OFFICE. QUARTERLY REPORT ON VITAL STATISTICS.. q. I£15. Government Publications Office, Trade and Postal Sales, 4-5 Harcourt Rd., Dublin 2, Ireland. TEL 01-6613111. FAX 01-4780645. **Document type:** government publication.
  Formerly: Ireland. Central Statistics Office. Quarterly Report on Births, Deaths and Marriages and on Certain Infectious Diseases (ISSN 0790-6811)
  Description: Reports on births, deaths and marriages in each county.

312   IS   ISSN 0075-0999
ISRAEL. CENTRAL BUREAU OF STATISTICS. CAUSES OF DEATH. (Subseries of its Special Series) (Text in Hebrew and English) 1950. irreg. price varies. Central Bureau of Statistics, Box 13015, Jerusalem 91 130, Israel. TEL 02-21 12 11. **Document type:** government publication.

325.1   IS   ISSN 0302-816X
HA1931
ISRAEL. CENTRAL BUREAU OF STATISTICS. IMMIGRATION TO ISRAEL. (Text in English and Hebrew) a. Central Bureau of Statistics, P.O. Box 13015, Jerusalem 91 130, Israel. TEL 02-211211.

325.1   IS   ISSN 0334-9721
ISRAEL. CENTRAL BUREAU OF STATISTICS. PROJECTIONS OF POPULATION IN JUDEA, SAMARIA AND GAZA AREA UP TO 2002. (Text in English and Hebrew) irreg. $6. Central Bureau of Statistics, P.O. Box 13015, Jerusalem 91 130, Israel. TEL 02-553400. **Document type:** government publication.

312   IS   ISSN 0333-8169
ISRAEL. CENTRAL BUREAU OF STATISTICS. SUICIDES AND ATTEMPTED SUICIDES. Key Title: Suicides and Attempted Suicides in Israel. (Text in Hebrew and English) 1968? irreg., latest 1976. price varies. Central Bureau of Statistics, Box 13015, Jerusalem 91 130, Israel. TEL 02-21 12 11. **Document type:** government publication.

5444 POPULATION STUDIES — ABSTRACTING, BIBLIOGRAPHIES, STATISTICS

310   IS   ISSN 0075-1111
ISRAEL. CENTRAL BUREAU OF STATISTICS. VITAL STATISTICS. (Subseries of its Special Series) (Text in English and Hebrew) 1960. irreg., no.745, 1981. price varies. Central Bureau of Statistics, Box 13015, Jerusalem 91 130, Israel. TEL 02-21 12 11. **Document type:** government publication.

301.32   IT
ITALY. ISTITUTO NAZIONALE DI STATISTICA. MOVIMENTO MIGRATORIO DELLA POPOLAZIONE RESIDENTE; iscrizioni e cancellazioni anagrafiche. 1988. a. Istituto Nazionale di Statistica, Via Cesare Balbo 16, 00100 Rome, Italy.
Supersedes in part: Statistiche Demografiche. Tomo 1. Parte Seconda.

312   IT
ITALY. ISTITUTO NAZIONALE DI STATISTICA. NASCITE E DECESSI. 1988. a. Istituto Nazionale di Statistica, Via Cesare Balbo 16, 00100 Rome, Italy. FAX 06-46735198.
Supersedes in part: Statistiche Demografiche. Tomo 2. Parte Prima.

314   IT   ISSN 0075-1863
HA1363
ITALY. ISTITUTO NAZIONALE DI STATISTICA. POPOLAZIONE E MOVIMENTO ANAGRAFICO DEI COMUNI. 1964. a. L.23000 (effective 1992). Istituto Nazionale di Statistica, Via Cesare Balbo 16, 00100 Rome, Italy. FAX 06-46735198. circ. 11,000. **Document type:** government publication.
Formerly: Italy. Istituto Centrale di Statistica. Popolazione e Circoscrizioni Amministrative dei Comuni; Supersedes in part: Statistiche Demografiche. Tomo 2. Parte Seconda.

312   IT
HA1363
ITALY. ISTITUTO NAZIONALE DI STATISTICA. STATISTICHE DEMOGRAFICHE. (In 2 vols.) 1951. a. L.18900 per vol. Istituto Nazionale di Statistica, Via Cesare Balbo 16, 00100 Rome, Italy. FAX 06-46735198. circ. 1,200. **Document type:** government publication.
Former titles: Italy. Istituto Centrale di Statistica. Statistiche Demografiche; Italy. Istituto Centrale di Statistica. Annuario di Statistiche Demografiche (ISSN 0075-1685)

325   JA   ISSN 0448-7117
JAPAN. MANAGEMENT AND COORDINATION AGENCY. STATISTICS BUREAU. POPULATION ESTIMATES SERIES. (Text in English) quinquennial. no.64, 1992. Management and Coordination Agency, Statistics Bureau - Somu-cho, Tokei-Kyoku, 19-1 Wakamatsu-cho, Shinjuku-ku, Tokyo 162, Japan. **Document type:** government publication.
Description: Contains population estimates by prefecture for a period of four years.

330 325   JA   ISSN 0448-3960
JAPAN. MINISTRY OF HEALTH AND WELFARE. STATISTICS AND INFORMATION DEPARTMENT. REPORT ON SURVEY OF SOCIO-ECONOMIC ASPECTS ON VITAL EVENTS. Key Title: Jinko Dotai Shakai Keizaimen Chosa Hokoku. (Text in Japanese) 1962. a. price varies. Ministry of Health and Welfare, Statistics and Information Department - Koseisho Daijin Kanbo Tokei Johobu, 7-3 Ichigaya-Honmura-cho, Shinjuku-ku, Tokyo 162, Japan. TEL 03-3260-3181. FAX 03-3269-8824. (Subscr. to: Health & Welfare Statistics Association, 5-13-14 Roppongi, Minato-ku, Tokyo, Japan. TEL 03-3586-3361. FAX 03-3584-4710) **Document type:** government publication.

312 015 310   JA   ISSN 0449-5314
HA37
JAPAN. STATISTICS BUREAU. NEWS BULLETIN.* (Text in English) 1967. q. free. Somucho, Tokeikyoku - Management and Coordination Agency, Statistics Bureau, 19-1 Wakamatsu-cho, Shinjuku-ku, Tokyo 162, Japan. bibl.

312   JA   ISSN 0286-1410
HB2111
JAPAN STATISTICAL ASSOCIATION. ANNUAL REPORT ON THE INTERNAL MIGRATION IN JAPAN DERIVED FROM THE BASIC RESIDENT REGISTERS. (Text in English, Japanese) a. 3000 Yen. Nihon Tokei Kyokai - Japan Statistical Association, Crest 21, 6-21, Yocho-machi, Shinjuku-ku, Tokyo 162, Japan. TEL 03-5269-3051. FAX 03-5269-3058. (Subscr. to: Government Publications Service Center, 2-1 Kasumigaseki 1-chome, Chiyoda-ku, Tokyo 100, Japan)

312 310   JA
JAPAN STATISTICAL ASSOCIATION. POPULATION CENSUS OF JAPAN. (Text in Japanese) quinquennial. Nihon Tokei Kyokai, Crest 21, 6-21, Yocho-machi, Shinjuku-ku, Tokyo 162, Japan. TEL 03-5269-3051. FAX 03-5269-3058.

312   KE
KENYA. CENTRAL BUREAU OF STATISTICS. POPULATION CENSUS. irreg. KShs.1000 for 1994 ed. Ministry of Finance and Planning, Central Bureau of Statistics, P.O. Box 30266, Nairobi, Kenya. (Subscr. to: Government Press, Haile Selassie Ave., P.O. Box 30128, Nairobi, Kenya. TEL 254-2-334075) stat. **Document type:** government publication.

312   KO
KOREA (REPUBLIC). NATIONAL STATISTICAL OFFICE. ANNUAL REPORT ON THE INTERNAL MIGRATION STATISTICS. (Text in English and Korean) 1970. a. 6500 Won. National Statistical Office, Hanta Bldg., 647-15, Yoksam-dong, Kangnam-gu, Seoul 135-080, S. Korea. TEL 02-222-1971. (Subscr. to: Korean Statistical Association, Room 302, Chungok Building, 561-30, Sinsa-dong, Gangnam-gu, Seoul 135-120, S. Korea. TEL 02-517-0382. FAX 02-725-4347) circ. 300. **Document type:** government publication.
Formerly: Korea (Republic). Economic Planning Board. Yearbook of Migration Statistics.

315 312   KO
KOREA (REPUBLIC). NATIONAL STATISTICAL OFFICE. POPULATION & HOUSING CENSUS REPORT. (Text in English and Korean) 1925. quinquennial. 68850 Won($375) National Statistical Office, Hanta Bldg., 647-15, Yoksam-dong, Kangnam-gu, Seoul 135-120, S. Korea. TEL 02-222-1971. (Subscr. to: Korean Statistical Association, Room 302, Chungok Building, 516-30, Sinsa-dong, Gangnam-gu, Seoul 135-120, S. Korea. TEL 02-517-0382. FAX 02-725-4347) circ. 1,600. **Document type:** government publication.
Formerly: Korea (Republic). National Bureau of Statistics. Population and Housing Census Report.

312   KU
KUWAIT. CENTRAL STATISTICAL OFFICE. GENERAL POPULATION CENSUS/KUWAIT. AL-IDARAH AL-MARKAZIYYAH LIL-IHSA'. AL-TA'DAD AL-AAM LIL-SUKKAN. (In 3 vols.) (Text in Arabic) 1957. irreg., 7th, 1985. Central Statistical Office - Al-Idarah al-Markaziyyah lil-Ihsa', P.O. Box 26188, Safat 13122, Kuwait. TEL 965-2428200. FAX 965-2430464. TELEX 22468 TAKHTET KT. **Document type:** government publication.

312   KU
KUWAIT. CENTRAL STATISTICAL OFFICE. VITAL STATISTICS - A SUMMARISED ANALYSIS BULLETIN/KUWAIT. AL-IDARAH AL-MARKAZIYYAH LIL-IHSA'. TAHLIL AL-IHSA'AT AL-HAYAWIYYAH. Variant title: Annual Bulletin for Vital Statistics Analysis. (Text in Arabic) 1976. irreg., latest 1986. Central Statistical Office - Al-Idarah al-Markaziyyah lil-Ihsa', P.O. Box 26188, Safat 13122, Kuwait. TEL 965-2428200. FAX 965-2430464. TELEX 22468 TAKHTET KT. **Document type:** government publication.
Description: Provides statistical information on demographic changes, including birth and death rates, fertility, infant mortality, and marriage and divorce rates.

312   KU
KUWAIT. CENTRAL STATISTICAL OFFICE. VITAL STATISTICS - BIRTHS AND DEATHS/KUWAIT. AL-IDARAH AL-MARKAZIYYAH LIL-IHSA'. AL-IHSA'AT AL-HAYAWIYYAH - AL-MAWALID WAL-WAFAYAT. (Text in Arabic, English) 1965. a., latest 1986. Central Statistical Office - Al-Idarah al-Markaziyyah lil-Ihsa', P.O. Box 26188, Safat 13122, Kuwait. TEL 965-2428200. FAX 965-2430464. TELEX 22468 TAKHTET KT. **Document type:** government publication.

KUWAIT. CENTRAL STATISTICAL OFFICE. VITAL STATISTICS - MARRIAGE AND DIVORCE/KUWAIT. AL-IDARAH AL-MARKAZIYYAH LIL-IHSA'. AL-IHSA'AT AL-HAYAWIYYAH - AL-ZAWAJ WAL-TALAQ. see MATRIMONY — Abstracting, Bibliographies, Statistics

301.32 310   CY
LABOUR FORCE AND MIGRATION SURVEY. irreg. £C6 per no. Ministry of Finance, Department of Statistics and Research, 13 Lord Byron Ave., Nicosia, Cyprus. TEL 357-2-302349. FAX 357-2-456712. **Document type:** government publication.
Description: Provides a complete set of tables on the demographic characteristics of the population in its various dissections, potential labor force and migration.

312   LY   ISSN 0075-9236
LIBYA. CENSUS AND STATISTICS DEPARTMENT. GENERAL POPULATION CENSUS. (Text in Arabic and English) 1954. decennial. free. Secretariat of Planning, Census and Statistics Department, P.O. Box 600, Tripoli, Libya. **Document type:** government publication.

016.312   NE   ISSN 0921-1160
LITERATUUR- EN DOKUMENTATIEOVERZICHT N I D I - BIBLOTHEEK. 1978. q. free. Nederlands Interdisciplinair Demografisch Instituut - Netherlands Interdisciplinary Demographic Institute, Lange Houtstraat 19, 2511 CV The Hague, Netherlands. TEL 31-70-3647187. TELEX 31138 NISI NL. Ed. T.J. Augenbroe-Siebenga. circ. 225. **Indexed:** Popul.Ind. **Document type:** bibliography.

325   CN
LOCAL HEALTH AREA POPULATION ESTIMATES AND PROJECTIONS. a. Can.$150. Ministry of Government Services, B C Stats, 553 Superior St., Victoria, BC V8V 1X4, Canada. TEL 604-387-1502. FAX 604-387-0329. **Document type:** government publication.
Description: Provides detailed historical and forecast population statistics by age and gender, including components of change to the year 2021 for 80 sub-provincial areas.

312   LU
LUXEMBOURG. SERVICE CENTRAL DE LA STATISTIQUE ET DES ETUDES ECONOMIQUES. COLLECTION RP: RECENSEMENT DE LA POPULATION ET MOUVEMENT DE LA POPULATION. 1962. irreg. 250 Fr. per no. Service Central de la Statistique et des Etudes Economiques, 6 bd. Royal, B.P. 304, 2013 Luxembourg, Luxembourg. TEL 478-4268. FAX 46-42-89. **Document type:** government publication.
Formerly: Luxembourg. Service Central de la Statistique et des Etudes Economiques. Collection RP: Recensement de la Population (ISSN 0076-1613)

312   LU   ISSN 1012-6643
LUXEMBOURG. SERVICE CENTRAL DE LA STATISTIQUE ET DES ETUDES ECONOMIQUES. INDICATEURS RAPIDES. SERIE E: NAISSANCCES, MARIAGES, DIVORCES, DECES. q. Service Central de la Statistique et des Etudes Economiques, 6 bd. Royal, B.P. 304, 2013 Luxembourg, Luxembourg. TEL 478-4268. FAX 46-42-89. (looseleaf format) **Document type:** government publication.

312 614.86   LU   ISSN 1012-6651
LUXEMBOURG. SERVICE CENTRAL DE LA STATISTIQUE ET DES ETUDES ECONOMIQUES. INDICATEURS RAPIDES. SERIE F: ACCIDENTS CORPORELS DE LA CIRCULATION ROUTIERE. m. Service Central de la Statistique et des Etudes Economiques, 6 bd. Royal, B.P. 304, 2013 Luxembourg, Luxembourg. TEL 478-4268. FAX 46-42-89. (looseleaf format) **Document type:** government publication.

POPULATION STUDIES — ABSTRACTING, BIBLIOGRAPHIES, STATISTICS

312   **LU**
LUXEMBOURG. SERVICE CENTRAL DE LA STATISTIQUE ET DES ETUDES ECONOMIQUES. INDICATEURS RAPIDES. SERIE J: RESULTATS DE L'ENQUETE DE CONJONCTURE. m. Service Central de la Statistique et des Etudes Economiques, 6 bd. Royal, B.P. 304, 2013 Luxembourg, Luxembourg. TEL 478-4268. FAX 46-42-89. (looseleaf format) **Document type:** government publication.

312   **LU**   ISSN 1019-6471
LUXEMBOURG EN CHIFFRES (YEAR); Le Luxembourg en Chiffres (Year). English edition: Luxembourg in Figures (ISSN 1019-648X); German edition: Luxemburg in Zahlen (ISSN 1019-6501); Dutch edition: Luxemburg in Cijfers (ISSN 1019-6498) a. free. Service Central de la Statistique et des Etudes Economiques, 6 bd. Royal, B.P. 304, 2013 Luxembourg, Luxembourg. TEL 478-4268. FAX 46-42-89. circ. 100,000. **Document type:** government publication.
Description: Presents figures for territory, climate, population, economic and social situation, and the environment.

312   **MH**
MACAO. DIRECCAO DOS SERVICOS DE ESTATISTICA E CENSOS. CENSOS DA POPULACAO/MACAO. CENSUS AND STATISTICS DEPARTMENT. POPULATION CENSUS. (Text in Chinese, Portuguese) 1950. every 10 yrs. free. Direccao dos Servicos de Estatistica e Censos, Rua Inacio Baptista, No. 4-6, P.O. Box 3022, Macao. TEL 853-3995311. FAX 853-307825. **Document type:** government publication.

312   **MH**   ISSN 0872-4482
MACAO. DIRECCAO DOS SERVICOS DE ESTATISTICA E CENSOS. ESTATISTICAS DEMOGRAFICAS/MACAO. CENSUS AND STATISTICS DEPARTMENT. DEMOGRAPHIC STATISTICS. (Text in Chinese, Portuguese) 1984. q. plus a. review. free. Direccao dos Servicos de Estatistica e Censos, Rua Inacio Baptista, No.4-6, P.O. Box 3022, Macao. TEL 853-3995311. FAX 853-307825. **Document type:** government publication.
Description: Presents the latest figures for movement of population, births, deaths, marriages, divorces and immigration.

312   **MH**
MACAO. DIRECCAO DOS SERVICOS DE ESTATISTICA E CENSOS. ESTIMATIVAS DA POPULACAO RESIDENTE EM MACAU/MACAO. CENSUS AND STATISTICS DEPARTMENT. ESTIMATION OF RESIDENT POPULATION IN MACAO. (Text in Chinese, Portuguese) 1991. a. free. Direccao dos Servicos de Estatistica e Censos, Rua Inacio Baptista, No. 4-6, P.O. Box 3022, Macao. TEL 853-3995311. FAX 853-307825. **Document type:** government publication.

312   **MH**
MACAO. DIRECCAO DOS SERVICOS DE ESTATISTICA E CENSOS. RECENSEAMENTO DOS ALOJAMENTOS INFORMAIS/MACAO. CENSUS AND STATISTICS DEPARTMENT. CENSUS OF INFORMAL ACCOMODATION. (Text in Chinese, Portuguese) 1988. irreg. free. Direccao dos Servicos de Estatistica e Censos, P.O. Box 3022, Macao. TEL 853-3995311. FAX 853-307825. **Document type:** government publication.

312   **US**
MAINE. DEPARTMENT OF HUMAN SERVICES. VITAL STATISTICS. 1892. a. $10.50. Department of Human Services, Office of Data, Research, and Vital Statistics, State House Sta. No. 11, Augusta, ME 04333. TEL 207-624-5445. Ed. Ellen M. Naor. circ. 500. (also avail. in microfiche from CIS) **Indexed:** SRI. **Document type:** government publication.
Former titles: Maine. Department of Human Services. Bureau of Health Planning and Development. Vital Statistics; Maine. Division of Research and Vital Records. Annual Statistical Report.

312   **MW**   ISSN 0076-3306
MALAWI. NATIONAL STATISTICAL OFFICE. POPULATION CENSUS FINAL REPORT. 1966. irreg. (approx. every 10 yrs.). K.9. National Statistical Office, Commissioner for Census and Statistics, P.O. Box 333, Zomba, Malawi. TEL 265-50-522-377. FAX 265-50-523-130. TELEX 44015 CENSUS MI. **Document type:** government publication.

310   **MW**
MALAWI. NATIONAL STATISTICAL OFFICE. URBAN HOUSEHOLD EXPENDITURE SURVEY. 1968. irreg. K.13. National Statistical Office, Commissioner for Census and Statistics, P.O. Box 333, Zomba, Malawi. TEL 265-50-522-377. FAX 265-50-523-130. TELEX 44015 CENSUS MI. **Document type:** government publication.
Formerly: Malawi. National Statistical Office. Household Income and Expenditure Survey (ISSN 0076-3276)

312   **MY**   ISSN 0127-8312
HA4600.6
MALAYSIA. DEPARTMENT OF STATISTICS. QUARTERLY REVIEW OF MALAYSIAN POPULATION STATISTICS. (Text in English) 1986. q. M.$11 per no. Department of Statistics, Wisma Statistik, Jalan Cenderasari, 50514 Kuala Lumpur, Malaysia. TEL 03-2922133. FAX 03-2937018. **Document type:** government publication.

312   **MY**
MALAYSIA. DEPARTMENT OF STATISTICS. VITAL STATISTICS MALAYSIA (YEAR). (Text in English, Malay) 1963. a. M.$35. Department of Statistics - Jabatan Perangkaan, Wisma Statistik, Jalan Cenderasari, 50514 Kuala Lumpur, Malaysia. TEL 03-2922133. FAX 03-2937018. circ. 800. **Document type:** government publication.
Formerly: Malaysia. Department of Statistics. Vital Statistics, Peninsular Malaysia (ISSN 0127-466X)

312   **MY**   ISSN 0126-9267
MALAYSIA. DEPARTMENT OF STATISTICS. VITAL STATISTICS SARAWAK. (Text in English) 1966. a. M.$5. Department of Statistics, Wisma Statistik, Jalan Cenderasari, 50514 Kuala Lumpur, Malaysia. TEL 60-3-2937471. FAX 60-3-2937018. (Dist. by: Department of Statistics, Malaysia (Sarawak Branch), 5th Fl., Bangunan Tun Datuk, Patinggi Tuanku Hj. Bujang, 93514 Kuching, Sarawak, Malaysia) **Document type:** government publication.

312   **MM**   ISSN 0076-3470
MALTA. CENTRAL OFFICE OF STATISTICS. DEMOGRAPHIC REVIEW. 1960. a. L.1. Central Office of Statistics, Auberge d'Italie, Merchants' St., Valletta, Malta. FAX 356-248483. (Subscr. to: Publications Bookshop, Auberge de Castille, Valletta, Malta) **Document type:** government publication.

312   **MF**
MAURITIUS. CENTRAL STATISTICAL OFFICE. DIGEST OF DEMOGRAPHIC STATISTICS. 1985. a. Rs.100 (effective Jun. 1995). Central Statistical Office, Toorawa Centre, Cr. S.S. R & J. Mosque Sts., Port Louis, Mauritius. (Subscr. to: Government Printing Office, Ramtoolah Bldg., Sir S. Ramgoolam St., Port Louis, Mauritius. TEL 230-234-5294. FAX 230-208-4011) **Document type:** government publication.

312   **MF**
MAURITIUS. CENTRAL STATISTICAL OFFICE. HOUSING AND POPULATION CENSUS. ANALYSIS REPORTS. (Issued in 8 vol.) irreg., latest 1990. Rs.150 per vol. Central Statistical Office, Toorawa Centre, Cr. S.S. R & J Mosque Sts., Port Louis, Mauritius. TEL 230-234-5294. FAX 230-208-4011. (Subscr. to: Government Printing Office, Ramtoolah Bldg., Sir S. Ramgoolam St., Port Louis, Mauritius) (back issues avail.) **Document type:** government publication.
Formerly (until 1990): Mauritius. Central Statistical Office. Housing and Population Census. Analytical Reports.

325.2   **CN**
MIGRATION HIGHLIGHTS. 4/yr. Can.$30. Ministry of Government Services, B C Stats, 553 Superior St., Victoria, BC V8V 1X4, Canada. TEL 604-387-1502. FAX 604-387-0329. **Document type:** government publication.
Description: Provides detailed current information on the flow of people between B.C. and other provinces and territories. Contains components of population change.

312   **US**
MISSOURI MONTHLY VITAL STATISTICS. 1967. m. free. Department of Health, Center for Health Statistics, Box 570, Jefferson City, MO 65102. TEL 314-751-6272. Ed. Garland Land. charts; stat. circ. 800. **Document type:** government publication.
Description: Contains vital statistics data and short analytical article concerning public health issues.

312   **MR**   ISSN 0851-6804
MOROCCO. DIRECTION DE LA STATISTIQUE. POPULATION ACTIVE URBAINE, PREMIERS RESULTATS. (Editions in Arabic, French) a. DH.33. Direction de la Statistique, B.P. 178, Rabat, Morocco. TEL 212-7-77-36-06. FAX 212-7-77-32-17. TELEX 36714. **Document type:** government publication.

312   **MR**   ISSN 0851-6804
MOROCCO. DIRECTION DE LA STATISTIQUE. POPULATION ACTIVE URBAINE, RESULTATS DETAILLES. (Text in French) a. DH.99. Direction de la Statistique, B.P. 178, Rabat, Morocco. TEL 212-7-77-36-06. FAX 212-7-77-32-17. TELEX 36714. **Document type:** government publication.

312   **GR**   ISSN 0077-6114
MOUVEMENT NATUREL DE LA POPULATION DE LA GRECE. (Text in French, Greek) 1956. irreg., latest 1987. $12. National Statistical Service of Greece, Statistical Information and Publications Division - Ethniki Statistiki Yperesia tes Ellados, 14-16 Lykourgou, 10 166 Athens, Greece. TEL 30-1-3244-748. FAX 30-1-3222-205. TELEX 216734 ESYE GR. (back issues avail.) **Document type:** government publication.

325   **SP**   ISSN 0077-1767
MOVIMIENTO NATURAL DE LA POBLACION DE ESPANA. 1958. a. Instituto Nacional de Estadistica, P. de la Castellana, 183, 28071 Madrid, Spain.

312 614   **NE**   ISSN 0168-4000
HA1381
NETHERLANDS. CENTRAAL BUREAU VOOR DE STATISTIEK. JAARSTATISTIEK VAN DE BEVOLKING/NETHERLANDS. CENTRAL BUREAU OF STATISTICS. ANNUAL POPULATION STATISTICS. (Supplement to: Maandstatistiek van Bevolking en Volksgezondheid) 1971. a. Centraal Bureau voor de Statistiek, Prinses Beatrixlaan 428, Voorburg, Netherlands. (Orders to: SDU - Publishers, Christoffel Plantijnstraat 2, Postbus 20014, 2500 EA The Hague, Netherlands) circ. 1,000. **Document type:** government publication.
Formerly: Netherlands. Centraal Bureau voor de Statistiek. Jaaroverzicht Bevolking en Bevolking en Volksgezondheid.

312   **NE**   ISSN 0024-8711
HA1381
NETHERLANDS. CENTRAAL BUREAU VOOR DE STATISTIEK. MAANDSTATISTIEK VAN DE BEVOLKING. 1953. m. fl.82. Centraal Bureau voor de Statistiek, Prinses Beatrixlaan 428, Voorburg, Netherlands. (Dist. by: SDU - Publishers, Christoffel Plantijnstraat, The Hague, Netherlands) stat.; index. circ. 785. **Document type:** government publication.

312   **US**   ISSN 0095-5523
HA511
NEW HAMPSHIRE VITAL STATISTICS. 1880. a. Bureau of Vital Records and Health Statistics, Division of Public Health Services, Concord, NH 03301. TEL 603-271-4651. circ. 350. **Indexed:** SRI. **Document type:** government publication.

312   **NZ**   ISSN 0113-3667
HA3171
NEW ZEALAND. DEPARTMENT OF STATISTICS. DEMOGRAPHIC TRENDS. a. NZ.$49.95. Department of Statistics, P.O. Box 2922, Wellington, New Zealand. TEL 04-495-4600. FAX 04-472-9135. **Document type:** government publication.
Former titles: New Zealand. Department of Statistics. Demographic Trends Bulletin (ISSN 0112-9155); New Zealand. Department of Statistics. Population and Migration. Part A: Population (ISSN 0110-375X); Supersedes in part: New Zealand. Department of Statistics. Population and Migration; New Zealand. Department of Statistics. Statistical Report of Population, Migration and Building. (ISSN 0077-9903)

312   **NZ**
NEW ZEALAND. DEPARTMENT OF STATISTICS. POPULATION CENSUS: AGES, MARITAL STATUS AND FERTILITY. quinquennial, latest 1986, issued 1988. NZ.$29.95. Department of Statistics, P.O. Box 2922, Wellington, New Zealand. **Document type:** government publication.
Formerly: New Zealand. Department of Statistics. Population Census: Ages and Marital Status (ISSN 0077-9687)

POPULATION STUDIES — ABSTRACTING, BIBLIOGRAPHIES, STATISTICS

312   NZ
NEW ZEALAND. DEPARTMENT OF STATISTICS. POPULATION CENSUS: BIRTHPLACES AND ETHNIC ORIGIN. quinquennial, latest 1986, issued 1988. NZ.$25.50. Department of Statistics, P.O. Box 2922, Wellington, New Zealand. **Document type:** government publication.
    Formerly: New Zealand. Department of Statistics. Population Census: Race (ISSN 0077-9776)

312   NZ   ISSN 0077-9695
NEW ZEALAND. DEPARTMENT OF STATISTICS. POPULATION CENSUS: DWELLINGS. quinquennial, latest 1986, issued 1987. NZ.$19.95. Department of Statistics, P.O. Box 2922, Wellington, New Zealand. **Document type:** government publication.

312   NZ
NEW ZEALAND. DEPARTMENT OF STATISTICS. POPULATION CENSUS: EDUCATION AND TRAINING. quinquennial, latest 1986 issued 1988. NZ.$20.50. Department of Statistics, P.O. Box 2922, Wellington, New Zealand. **Document type:** government publication.
    Formerly: New Zealand. Department of Statistics. Population Census: Education (ISSN 0077-9709)

312   NZ
NEW ZEALAND. DEPARTMENT OF STATISTICS. POPULATION CENSUS: FAMILIES. quinquennial, latest 1986, issued 1988. NZ.$20.50. Department of Statistics, P.O. Box 2922, Wellington, New Zealand. **Document type:** government publication.
    Former titles: New Zealand. Department of Statistics. Population Census: Households and Families; New Zealand. Department of Statistics. Population Census: Households (ISSN 0077-9725)

312   NZ   ISSN 0110-8700
NEW ZEALAND. DEPARTMENT OF STATISTICS. POPULATION CENSUS: GENERAL INFORMATION. quinquennial, latest 1986, issued 1988. NZ.$30.65. Department of Statistics, P.O. Box 2922, Wellington, New Zealand. **Document type:** government publication.
    Formerly: New Zealand. Department of Statistics. Population Census: General Report (ISSN 0077-9717)

312   NZ
NEW ZEALAND. DEPARTMENT OF STATISTICS. POPULATION CENSUS: INCOMES AND WELFARE PAYMENTS. quinquennial, latest 1986, issued 1988. NZ.$20.50. Department of Statistics, P.O. Box 2922, Wellington, New Zealand. **Document type:** government publication.
    Former titles: New Zealand. Department of Statistics. Population Census: Incomes and Social Security Benefits; New Zealand. Department of Statistics. Population Census: Incomes (ISSN 0077-9733)

310 312   NZ
NEW ZEALAND. DEPARTMENT OF STATISTICS. POPULATION CENSUS: INTERNAL MIGRATION. 1971. quinquennial, latest 1986, issued 1988. NZ.$25.50. Department of Statistics, P.O. Box 2922, Wellington, New Zealand. **Document type:** government publication.

312   NZ
NEW ZEALAND. DEPARTMENT OF STATISTICS. POPULATION CENSUS: LABOUR FORCE. quinquennial, latest 1986, issued 1988. NZ.$30.65. Department of Statistics, P.O. Box 2922, Wellington, New Zealand. (Subscr. to: Government Printing Office, Publications, Private Bag, Wellington, New Zealand) **Document type:** government publication.
    Formerly: New Zealand. Department of Statistics. Population Census: Industries and Occupations (ISSN 0077-9741)

312   NZ
NEW ZEALAND. DEPARTMENT OF STATISTICS. POPULATION CENSUS: MAORI POPULATION AND DWELLINGS. quinquennial, latest 1986, issued 1988. NZ.$30.65. Department of Statistics, P.O. Box 2922, Wellington, New Zealand. **Document type:** government publication.

312   NZ   ISSN 0077-9784
NEW ZEALAND. DEPARTMENT OF STATISTICS. POPULATION CENSUS: RELIGIOUS PROFESSIONS. quinquennial, latest 1986, issued 1988. NZ.$20.50. Department of Statistics, P.O. Box 2922, Wellington, New Zealand. **Document type:** government publication.

312   NZ
NEW ZEALAND. DEPARTMENT OF STATISTICS. POPULATION CENSUS: TOTAL POPULATION STATISTICS. quinquennial, latest 1986. NZ.$20.50. Department of Statistics, P.O. Box 2922, Wellington, New Zealand. **Document type:** government publication.
    Formerly: New Zealand. Department of Statistics. Population Census. Location and Increase of Population. Part A: Population Size and Distribution; Which supersedes in part: New Zealand. Department of Statistics. Population Census. Increase and Location of Population (ISSN 0077-9792)

319.4   NZ   ISSN 0111-8617
NEW ZEALAND HEALTH INFORMATION SERVICE. FETAL AND INFANT DEATHS. Key Title: Fetal and Infant Deaths. 1964. a. NZ.$30. New Zealand Health Information Service, Ministry of Health, 133 Molesworth St., P.O. Box 5013, Wellington, New Zealand. TEL 04-496-2188. FAX 04-496-2340. circ. controlled.
    Former titles: New Zealand. Health Statistical Services. Fetal and Infant Deaths; New Zealand. National Health Statistics Centre. Fetal and Infant Deaths.

NEW ZEALAND HEALTH INFORMATION SERVICE. HOSPITAL AND SELECTED MORBIDITY DATA. see HOSPITALS — Abstracting, Bibliographies, Statistics

312.2   NZ   ISSN 0548-9911
RA407.5.N4
NEW ZEALAND HEALTH INFORMATION SERVICE. MORTALITY AND DEMOGRAPHIC DATA. a. NZ.$30. New Zealand Health Information Service, Ministry of Health, 133 Molesworth St., P.O. Box 5013, Wellington, New Zealand. TEL 04-469-2188. FAX 04-496-2340. circ. controlled. **Document type:** government publication.
    Formerly: New Zealand. Health Statistical Services. Mortality and Demographic Data.

312   NQ
NICARAGUA. INSTITUTO NACIONAL DE ESTADISTICAS Y CENSOS. ESTADISTICAS VITALES. q. Instituto Nacional de Estadisticas y Censos, Apdo. Postal 4031, Managua, Nicaragua. **Document type:** government publication.

312   US   ISSN 0078-1371
NORTH CAROLINA VITAL STATISTICS. 1916. a. free. Department of Environment, Health and Natural Resources, State Center for Health and Environmental Statistics, Box 29538, Raleigh, NC 27626-0538. TEL 919-733-4728. **Indexed:** SRI. **Document type:** government publication.

304.6021   NO   ISSN 0801-6690
HA1501
NORWAY. STATISTISK SENTRALBYRAA. BEFOLKNINGSSTATISTIKK HEFTE 2/NORWAY. CENTRAL BUREAU OF STATISTICS. POPULATION STATISTICS VOL.2. (Subseries of its Norges Offisielle Statistikk) (Text in English and Norwegian) a. NOK 80. Statistisk Sentralbyraa, Box 8131 Dep., N-0033 Oslo, Norway. TEL 47-22-864500. FAX 47-22-864976. circ. 1,500. **Document type:** government publication.
    Formerly: Norway. Statistisk Sentralbyraa. Folkmengde Etter Alder og Ekteskapelig Status - Norway. Central Bureau of Statistics. Population by Age and Marital Status (ISSN 0550-7170)

312   US
OKLAHOMA POPULATION ESTIMATES. 1967. a. free. Employment Security Commission, Office of Economic Analysis, 213 Will Rogers Bldg., Oklahoma City, OK 73105. Ed. Roger Jacks. charts; stat. circ. 850. **Document type:** government publication.

312   US
OMAHA - COUNCIL BLUFFS METROPOLITAN AREA PLANNING AGENCY. POPULATION, HOUSEHOLD AND HOUSING UNIT ESTIMATES. irreg. $20. Omaha - Council Bluffs Metropolitan Area Planning Agency, 2222 Cuming St., Omaha, NE 68102-4328. TEL 402-444-6866. FAX 402-342-0949. circ. 500.
    Formerly: Omaha - Council Bluffs Metropolitan Area Planning Agency. Population and Housing Unit Estimates.
    Description: Intercensal estimates by census tract of population and housing units in Douglas and Sarpy counties in Nebraska and Pottawattamie county in Iowa.

312 325   PP   ISSN 1017-6551
PAPUA NEW GUINEA INTERNATIONAL ARRIVALS AND DEPARTURES. 1957. q. K.7 (foreign K.8). National Statistical Office, P.O. Wards Strip, Papua New Guinea. FAX 675-255057. TELEX FINANCE NE 22312. Ed. Nick Suvulo. circ. 200. **Document type:** government publication.
    Former titles: Papua New Guinea International Migration; Papua New Guinea Overseas Migration (ISSN 0031-1510); Papua New Guinea Territory. Quarterly Migration Bulletin.
    Description: Contains statistics compiled from passenger arrival and departure cards; provides a breakdown of persons arriving in Papua New Guinea, by purpose of journey, age, nationality and occupation, overseas address and length of stay in Papua.

312   US
PENNSYLVANIA VITAL STATISTICS. 1951. a. free. Department of Health, State Center for Health Statistics & Research, Box 90, Harrisburg, PA 17108. TEL 717-783-2548. circ. 1,000. (also avail. in microfiche from CIS) **Indexed:** SRI. **Document type:** government publication.
    Formerly: Pennsylvania Natality and Mortality Statistics.

315 312   PH   ISSN 0116-1520
PHILIPPINE YEARBOOK. (Text in English) 1940. biennial, lastest 1992. $90. National Statistics Office, Ramon Magsaysay Blvd., Box 779, Manila, Philippines. FAX 610794. circ. 1,200. **Document type:** government publication.

315   PH   ISSN 0116-2675
HA1821
PHILIPPINES. NATIONAL STATISTICS OFFICE. VITAL STATISTICS REPORT. a., latest 1989. $30. National Statistics Office, Ramon Magsaysay Blvd., Box 779, Manila, Philippines. FAX 610794. circ. 250. **Document type:** government publication.
    Formerly: Philippines. National Census and Statistics Office. Vital Statistical Report.

PLACES, TOWNS AND TOWNSHIPS. see STATISTICS

301.426   II
POPULATION ABSTRACTS. (Text in English) 1990. a. Rs.30. International Institute for Population Sciences, Govandi Station Rd., Deonar, Bombay 400088, India. Eds. R.T. Randeria, K.V.R. Rao. circ. 500. **Document type:** abstracting/indexing.
    Description: Abstracts of articles in journals and publications acquired by the Institute's library.

312   GR
POPULATION DE LA GRECE AU RECENSEMENT. (Text in Greek; summaries in French) 1940. decennial. price varies. National Statistical Service of Greece, Statistical Information and Publications Division - Ethniki Statistiki Yperesia tes Ellados, 14-16 Lykourgou, 101 66 Athens, Greece. TEL 30-1-3244-748. FAX 30-1-3222-205. TELEX 216734 ESYE GR. (back issues avail.) **Document type:** government publication.

301.42   US   ISSN 0032-4701
Z7164.D3
POPULATION INDEX. 1935. q. $95. Princeton University, Office of Population Research, 21 Prospect Ave., Princeton, NJ 08544-2091. TEL 609-258-4949. FAX 609-258-1039. Ed. Richard Hankinson. adv.; abstr.; bibl.; charts; index, cum.index. circ. 1,265. (also avail. in microfilm from UMI; reprint service avail. from UMI) **Indexed:** Curr.Cont., Curr.Lit.Fam.Plan., E.I., P.A.I.S., SSCI. **Document type:** bibliography, abstracting/indexing.
    ●Also available online. Vendor(s): National Library of Medicine.
Also available on CD-ROM. Producer(s): SilverPlatter Information, Inc.
—UMI.
    Description: Annotated bibliographies of current works on population topics.

312   NE   ISSN 0168-3853
POPULATION OF THE MUNICIPALITIES OF THE NETHERLANDS. (Text in Dutch and English) 1944. a. Centraal Bureau voor de Statistiek, Prinses Beatrixlaan 428, Voorburg, Netherlands. (Orders to: SDU - Publishers, Christoffel Plantijnstraat, The Hague, Netherlands) **Document type:** government publication.

312 UK
POPULATION PROJECTIONS FOR THE COUNTIES AND DISTRICT HEALTH AUTHORITIES OF WALES. irreg. Welsh Office, Statistical Directorate, New Crown Bldg., Cathays Park, Cardiff CF1 3NQ, Wales. TEL 01222-825054. FAX 01222-825350. **Document type:** government publication.

312 PO ISSN 0379-7007
PORTUGAL. INSTITUTO NACIONAL DE ESTATISTICA. CENTRO DE ESTUDOS DEMOGRAFICOS. CADERNO. 1976. irreg., no.9, 1988. Instituto Nacional de Estatistica, 1078 Lisbon Codex, Portugal. (Orders to: Imprensa Nacional, Casa da Moeda, Direccao Comercial, rua D. Francisco Manuel de Melo 5, 1000 Lisbon, Portugal) charts. **Document type:** monographic series.

312 PO
PORTUGAL. INSTITUTO NACIONAL DE ESTATISTICA. ESTATISTICAS DEMOGRAFICAS. CONTINENTE, ACORES E MADEIRA. 1887. a. Esc.5000. Instituto Nacional de Estatistica, Av. Antonio Jose de Almeida, 1078 Lisbon Codex, Portugal. (Orders to: Imprensa Nacional, Casa da Moeda, Direccao Comercial, rua D. Francisco Manuel de Melo 5, 1000 Lisbon, Portugal)
Former titles: Portugal. Instituto Nacional de Estatistica. Estatisticas Demograficas. Continente e Ilhas Adjacentes (ISSN 0377-2284); Portugal. Instituto Nacional de Estatistica. Estatisticas Demograficas; Portugal. Instituto Nacional de Estatistica. Anuario Demografico. (ISSN 0079-4104)

312 PO ISSN 0871-875X
HB3621
PORTUGAL. INSTITUTO NACIONAL DE ESTATISTICA. GABINETE DE ESTUDOS DEMOGRAFICOS. ESTUDOS DEMOGRAFICOS. 1945. irreg. Instituto Nacional de Estatistica, 1078 Lisbon Codex, Portugal. (Orders to: Imprensa Nacional, Casa da Moeda, Direccao Comercial, rua D. Francisco Manuel de Melo 5, 1000 Lisbon, Portugal) **Indexed:** Popul.Ind.
Formerly: Portugal. Instituto Nacional de Estatistica. Centro de Estudos Demograficos. Revista (ISSN 0079-4082)

312 PR
PUERTO RICO. DEPARTMENT OF HEALTH. OFFICE OF HEALTH STATISTICS. DIVISION OF STATISTICS AND REPORTS. ANNUAL VITAL STATISTICS REPORT/INFORME ANUAL DE ESTADISTICAS VITALES. (Text in English and Spanish) 1970. a. Department of Health, Auxiliary Secretariat of Planning, Evaluation and Statistics, Division of Statistics, P.O. Box 70184, San Juan, PR 00936. TEL 809-274-7875. FAX 809-274-7877. circ. 1,100. **Document type:** government publication.
Former titles: Puerto Rico. Department of Health. Office of Planning, Evaluation and Reports. Division of Statistics and Reports. Annual Vital Statistics Reports; Puerto Rico. Division of Demographic Registry and Vital Statistics. Annual Vital Statistics Report (ISSN 0555-6511)
Description: Information on population, deaths, births, marriages and divorces by municipality and regions.

325.2 UN
HV640
REFUGEE SURVEY QUARTERLY. (Text in English, French, Spanish) 1982. q. $40 to individuals and organizations; libraries $60. United Nations High Commissioner for Refugees, Centre for Documentation on Refugees (CDR), Case Postale 2500, CH-1211 Geneva 2, Switzerland. TEL 022-739-8458. FAX 022-739-8682. TELEX 415740 HCR CH. E-mail: UNHCR.CDR@oln.comlink.apc.org. Ed. Sharon Rusu. bk.rev. circ. 1,150. (back issues avail.) **Indexed:** HR Rep. **Document type:** abstracting/indexing. —SWETS.
Formerly (until 1994): Refugee Abstracts (ISSN 0253-1445)
Description: Collection of abstracted literature concerning refugees, references to bibliographies, reviews of recent books, basic texts and announcements of new publications, meetings and conferences. Includes a selection of country reports and an expanded section on refugee or human rights related legal documentation.

312 CN
REGIONAL POPULATION ESTIMATES AND PROJECTIONS. a. Can.$80. Ministry of Government Services, B C Stats, 553 Superior St., Victoria, BC V8V 1X4, Canada. TEL 604-387-1502. FAX 604-387-0329. **Document type:** government publication.
Description: Provides historical and forecast population by age and sex, including components of change for regional districts.

312 CF
REPUBLIQUE DE CONGO EN QUELQUES CHIFFRES. 1980. a. 3500 Fr.CFA. Centre National de la Statistique et des Etudes Economiques, B.P. 2031, Brazzaville, Congo. TEL 83-36-94. **Document type:** government publication.

312 GR
RESULTATS DU RECENSEMENT DE LA POPULATION ET DES HABITATIONS. (In 5 Vols.: Vol.1: Population; Vol.2: Caracteristiques Demographiques et Sociales; Vol.3: Caracteristiques Economiques; Vol.4: Habitations, Conditions de Logement des Menages; Vol.5: Caracteristiques Demographiques, Sociales et Economiques de la Population des Departements d'Attique, Salonique, Le Reste de Grece Central et Euubee, Peloponese et Iles Ioniennes.) (Text in French and Greek) 1951. decennial. price varies. National Statistical Service of Greece, Statistical Information and Publications Division - Ethniki Statistiki Yperesia tes Ellados, 14-16 Lykourgou, 101 66 Athens, Greece. TEL 30-1-3244-748. FAX 30-1-3222-205. TELEX 216734 ESYE GR. **Document type:** government publication.

312 US ISSN 0091-3073
HA611
RHODE ISLAND. DEPARTMENT OF HEALTH. VITAL STATISTICS. a. free. Department of Health, 3 Capitol Hill, Rm. 101, Providence, RI 02908-5097. TEL 401-277-2812. **Indexed:** SRI. **Document type:** government publication.
Formerly: Report of Vital Statistics for Rhode Island (ISSN 0095-0467)

312 330 IT ISSN 0035-6832
HB3599
RIVISTA ITALIANA DI ECONOMIA DEMOGRAFIA E STATISTICA. 1947. 4/yr. L.30000. Societa Italiana di Economia Demografia e Statistica, Casella Postale 12003, 00136 Rome-Belsito, Italy. Dir. Giovanni Somogyi. bk.rev.; bibl. circ. 1,000.

325.2 910.09 XK
ST. LUCIA. STATISTICAL DEPARTMENT. ANNUAL MIGRATION AND TOURISM STATISTICS. 1980. a. EC$6. Statistical Department, New Government Bldg., Block C, 2nd Fl., Conway, Castries, St. Lucia, W.I. TEL 809-45-22697. FAX 809-45-31648. TELEX 6394 FORAFF. Ed. Bryan Boxill. **Document type:** government publication.

325.2 XK
ST. LUCIA. STATISTICAL DEPARTMENT. QUARTERLY MIGRATION & TOURISM STATISTICS. 1980. q. EC$6 per no. Statistical Department, New Government Bldg., Block C, 2nd Fl., Conway, Castries, St. Lucia, W.I. TEL 809-45-22697. FAX 809-92-31648. TELEX 6394 FORAFF. Ed. Bryan Boxill. **Document type:** government publication.

312 XK
ST. LUCIA. STATISTICAL DEPARTMENT. VITAL STATISTICS REPORT. 1984. a. EC$15. Statistical Department, New Government Bldg., Block C, 2nd Fl., Conway, Castries, St. Lucia, W.I. TEL 809-45-22697. FAX 809-45-31648. TELEX 6394 FORAFF. Ed. Bryan Boxill. **Document type:** government publication.

312 UK ISSN 0080-7869
SCOTLAND. REGISTRAR GENERAL. ANNUAL REPORT. 1855. a. price varies. H.M.S.O., P.O. Box 276, London SW8 5DT, England. (reprint service avail. from UMI) **Document type:** government publication.

016.312 NE ISSN 0167-4757
Z7164.D3
SELECTED ANNOTATED BIBLIOGRAPHY OF POPULATION STUDIES IN THE NETHERLANDS. (Text in English) 1975. a. Nederlands Interdisciplinair Demografisch Instituut - Netherlands Interdisciplinary Demographic Institute, Lange Houtstraat 19, 2511 CV The Hague, Netherlands. TEL 31-70-3565200. FAX 31-70-3647187. TELEX 31138 NIDI NL. (Co-sponsor: Netherlands Demographic Society) Ed. T.J. Augenbroe-Siebenga. circ. 750. **Indexed:** Popul.Ind. **Document type:** bibliography.
Supersedes (1970-1973): Bibliografie van in Nederland Verschenen Demografische Studies.

310 CN ISSN 1188-3642
HA39.C23
SELECTED VITAL STATISTICS AND HEALTH STATISTICS INDICATORS. ANNUAL REPORT. 1944. a. Can.$16.95. Ministry of Health, Division of Vital Statistics, 818 Fort St., Victoria, BC V8W 1H8, Canada. TEL 604-952-2558. FAX 604-952-2587. (Dist. by: Crown Publications Inc., 521 Fort St., Victoria, BC V8W 1E7, Canada. TEL 604-386-4636. FAX 604-386-0221) Ed. R.J. Danderfer. circ. 700. **Document type:** government publication.
Formerly (until 1990): Vital Statistics of the Province of British Columbia (ISSN 0702-9446)
Description: Presents comprehensive information pertaining to the births, deaths and marriages of British Columbians.

319 SE
SEYCHELLES. PRESIDENT'S OFFICE. STATISTICS DIVISION. CENSUS. irreg., latest 1977. Rs.80. President's Office, Department of Finance, Statistics Division, Box 206, Mahe, Seychelles. **Document type:** government publication.

312 310 SE
SEYCHELLES. PRESIDENT'S OFFICE. STATISTICS DIVISION. POPULATION AND VITAL STATISTICS. 1982. s-a. Rs.5. President's Office, Department of Finance, Statistics Division, Box 206, Mahe, Seychelles. **Document type:** government publication.

312 SA
SOUTH AFRICA. CENTRAL STATISTICAL SERVICE. BIRTHS. (Report No. 03-05-01) a., latest 1991. R.6 (foreign R.6.60). Central Statistical Service - Sentrale Statistiekdiens, Private Bag X44, Pretoria 0001, South Africa. TEL 27-12-310-8911. FAX 27-12-310-8500. (Orders to: Government Printing Works, Private Bag X85, Pretoria 0001, South Africa) **Document type:** government publication.
Former titles: South Africa. Central Statistical Service. Births - Whites, Coloureds and Asians (ISSN 0258-7807); South Africa. Central Statistical Service. Report on Births: White, Coloured and Asian; South Africa. Department of Statistics. Report on Births: Whites, Coloureds, Asians; South Africa. Department of Statistics. Report on Births.

316.8 SA
SOUTH AFRICA. CENTRAL STATISTICAL SERVICE. CURRENT POPULATION SURVEY - COLOUREDS AND ASIANS. (Report No. 03-44-01) a., latest 1991. R.8 (foreign R.10). Central Statistical Service - Sentrale Statistiekdiens, Private Bag X44, Pretoria 0001, South Africa. TEL 27-12-310-8911. FAX 27-12-310-8500. (Orders to: Government Printing Works, Private Bag X85, Pretoria 0001, South Africa) **Document type:** government publication.
Formerly (until 1991): South Africa. Central Statistical Service. Current Population Survey - Coloureds, Asians and Blacks.

316.8 SA
SOUTH AFRICA. CENTRAL STATISTICAL SERVICE. DEMOGRAPHIC STATISTICS. a., latest 1993. free. Central Statistical Service - Sentrale Statistiekdiens, Private Bag X44, Pretoria 0001, South Africa. TEL 27-12-310-8911. FAX 27-12-310-8500. (also avail. in poster format) **Document type:** government publication.
Description: Presents current demographic information on South Africa.

POPULATION STUDIES — ABSTRACTING, BIBLIOGRAPHIES, STATISTICS

316.8 SA
SOUTH AFRICA. CENTRAL STATISTICAL SERVICE. POPULATION CENSUS. ADJUSTMENT FOR UNDERCOUNT. (Report No. 03-01-26) irreg., latest 1991. R.6 (foreign R.7.50). Central Statistical Service - Sentrale Statistiekdiens, Private X44, Pretoria 0001, South Africa. TEL 27-12-310-8911. FAX 27-12-310-8500. (Orders to: Government Printing Works, Private Bag X85, Pretoria 0001, South Africa) **Document type:** government publication.

316.8 SA
SOUTH AFRICA. CENTRAL STATISTICAL SERVICE. POPULATION CENSUS. AGE BY DEVELOPMENT REGION, STATISTICAL REGION AND DISTRICT (URBAN AND NON-URBAN). (Report No. 03-01-03) irreg., latest 1991. R.14 (foreign R.17.50). Central Statistical Service - Sentrale Statistiekdiens, Private Bag X44, Pretoria 0001, South Africa. TEL 27-12-310-8911. FAX 27-12-310-8500. (Orders to: Government Printing Works, Private Bag X85, Pretoria 0001, South Africa) **Document type:** government publication.

316.8 SA
SOUTH AFRICA. CENTRAL STATISTICAL SERVICE. POPULATION CENSUS. DURATION OF STAY BY DEVELOPMENT REGION, STATISTICAL REGION AND DISTRICT. (Report No. 03-01-04) 1991. irreg. R.14 (foreign R.17.50). Central Statistical Service - Sentrale Statistiekdiens, Private Bag X44, Pretoria 0001, South Africa. TEL 27-12-310-8911. FAX 27-12-310-8500. (Orders to: Government Printing Works, Private Bag X85, Pretoria 0001, South Africa) **Document type:** government publication.

316.8 SA
SOUTH AFRICA. CENTRAL STATISTICAL SERVICE. POPULATION CENSUS. DWELLINGS. (Report No. 03-01-24) 1991. irreg. R.14 (foreign R.17.50). Central Statistical Service - Sentrale Statistiekdiens, Private Bag X44, Pretoria 0001, South Africa. TEL 27-12-310-8911. FAX 27-12-310-8500. (Orders to: Government Printing Works, Private Bag X85, Pretoria 0001, South Africa) **Document type:** government publication.

316.8 SA
SOUTH AFRICA. CENTRAL STATISTICAL SERVICE. POPULATION CENSUS. ECONOMIC CHARACTERISTICS OF THE POPULATION. (Report No. 03-01-23) irreg., latest 1991. R.14 (foreign R.17.50). Central Statistical Service - Sentrale Statistiekdiens, Private Bag X44, Pretoria 0001, South Africa. TEL 27-12-310-8911. FAX 27-12-310-8500. (Orders to: Government Printing Works, Private Bag X85, Pretoria 0001, South Africa) **Document type:** government publication.
Formerly (until 1991): South Africa. Central Statistical Service. Population Census. Economic Characteristics.

316.8 SA
SOUTH AFRICA. CENTRAL STATISTICAL SERVICE. POPULATION CENSUS. ECONOMIC SECTOR BY DEVELOPMENT REGION, STATISTICAL REGION AND DISTRICT. (Report No. 03-01-09) irreg., latest 1991. R.14 (foreign R.17.50). Central Statistical Service - Sentrale Statistiekdiens, Private Bag X44, Pretoria 0001, South Africa. TEL 27-12-310-8911. FAX 27-12-310-8500. (Orders to: Government Printing Works, Private Bag X85, Pretoria 0001, South Africa) **Document type:** government publication.
Formerly (until 1991): South Africa. Central Statistical Service. Population Census. Industry by Development Region, Statistical Region and District (Urban and Non-urban).

316.8 SA
SOUTH AFRICA. CENTRAL STATISTICAL SERVICE. POPULATION CENSUS. GEOGRAPHICAL DISTRIBUTION OF THE POPULATION. (Report No. 03-01-02) irreg., latest 1991. R.14 (foreign R.17.50). Central Statistical Service - Sentrale Statistiekdiens, Private Bag X44, Pretoria 0001, South Africa. TEL 27-12-310-8911. FAX 27-12-310-8500. (Orders to: Government Printing Works, Private Bag X85, Pretoria 0001, South Africa) **Document type:** government publication.
Description: Includes information on population group and sex, with comparative historical data for the years 1970-1991.

316.8 SA
SOUTH AFRICA. CENTRAL STATISTICAL SERVICE. POPULATION CENSUS. HOME LANGUAGE BY DEVELOPMENT REGION, STATISTICAL REGION AND DISTRICT. (Report No. 03-01-06) 1991. irreg. R.14 (foreign R.17.50). Central Statistical Service - Sentrale Statistiekdiens, Private Bag X44, Pretoria 0001, South Africa. TEL 27-12-310-8911. FAX 27-12-310-8500. (Orders to: Government Printing Works, Private Bag X85, Pretoria 0001, South Africa) **Document type:** government publication.

316.8 SA
SOUTH AFRICA. CENTRAL STATISTICAL SERVICE. POPULATION CENSUS. HOUSEHOLDS. (Report No. 03-01-25) 1991. irreg. R.14 (foreign R.17.50). Central Statistical Service - Sentrale Statistiekdiens, Private Bag X44, Pretoria 0001, South Africa. TEL 27-12-310-8911. FAX 27-12-310-8500. (Orders to: Government Printing Works, Private Bag X85, Pretoria 0001, South Africa) **Document type:** government publication.

316.8 SA
SOUTH AFRICA. CENTRAL STATISTICAL SERVICE. POPULATION CENSUS. INCOME BY DEVELOPMENT REGION, STATISTICAL REGION AND DISTRICT. (Report No. 03-01-10) 1991. irreg. R.14 (foreign R.17.50). Central Statistical Service - Sentrale Statistiekdiens, Private Bag X44, Pretoria 0001, South Africa. TEL 27-12-310-8911. FAX 27-12-310-8500. (Orders to: Government Printing Works, Private Bag X85, Pretoria 0001, South Africa) **Document type:** government publication.

316.8 SA
SOUTH AFRICA. CENTRAL STATISTICAL SERVICE. POPULATION CENSUS. LEVEL OF EDUCATION BY DEVELOPMENT REGION, STATISTICAL REGION AND DISTRICT (URBAN AND NON-URBAN). (Report No. 03-01-07) irreg., latest 1991. R.14 (foreign R.17.50). Central Statistical Service - Sentrale Statistiekdiens, Private Bag X44, Pretoria 0001, South Africa. TEL 27-12-310-8911. FAX 27-12-310-8500. (Orders to: Government Printing Works, Private Bag X85, Pretoria 0001, South Africa) **Document type:** government publication.

316.8 SA
SOUTH AFRICA. CENTRAL STATISTICAL SERVICE. POPULATION CENSUS. OCCUPATION BY DEVELOPMENT REGION, STATISTICAL REGION AND DISTRICT. (Report No. 03-01-08) irreg., latest 1991. R.14 (foreign R.17.50). Central Statistical Service - Sentrale Statistiekdiens, Private Bag X44, Pretoria 0001, South Africa. TEL 27-12-310-8911. FAX 27-12-310-8500. (Orders to: Government Printing Works, Private Bag X85, Pretoria 0001, South Africa) **Document type:** government publication.

SOUTH AFRICA. CENTRAL STATISTICAL SERVICE. POPULATION CENSUS. RELIGION BY DEVELOPMENT REGION, STATISTICAL REGION AND DISTRICT. see RELIGIONS AND THEOLOGY — Abstracting, Bibliographies, Statistics

316.8 SA
SOUTH AFRICA. CENTRAL STATISTICAL SERVICE. POPULATION CENSUS. SELECTED STATISTICAL REGIONS. (Reports avail. for nine statistical regions: Cape Peninsula, No. 03-01-11 (Social Characteristics) & No. 03-01-12 (Economic Characteristics); Port Elizabeth - Uitenhage, No. 03-01-13; Durban - Pinetown - Inanda - Chatsworth, No. 03-01-14; East Rand, No. 03-01-15; Johannesburg - Randburg, No. 03-01-16 (Social Characteristics) & No. 03-01-17 (Economic Characteristics); West Rand, No. 03-01-18; Pretoria - Wonderboom - Soshanguve, No. 03-01-19; Vereeniging - Vanderbijlpark - Sasolburg, No. 03-01-20; Bloemfontein, No. 03-01-21) irreg., latest 1991. R.14 per report (foreign R.17.50). Central Statistical Service - Sentrale Statistiekdiens, Private Bag X44, Pretoria 0001, South Africa. TEL 27-12-310-8911. FAX 27-12-310-8500. (Orders to: Government Printing Works, Private Bag X85, Pretoria 0001, South Africa) **Document type:** government publication.
Description: Provides statistical data on age, home language, religion and denomination, level of occupation and income by suburb, as well as information on population group and sex, type of dwelling and household size by income group.

316.8 SA
SOUTH AFRICA. CENTRAL STATISTICAL SERVICE. POPULATION CENSUS. SOCIAL CHARACTERISTICS OF THE POPULATION. (Report No. 03-01-22) irreg., latest 1991. R.14 (foreign R.17.50). Central Statistical Service - Sentrale Statistiekdiens, Private Bag X44, Pretoria 0001, South Africa. TEL 27-12-310-8911. FAX 27-12-310-8500. (Orders to: Government Printing Works, Private Bag X85, Pretoria 0001, South Africa) **Document type:** government publication.
Formerly (until 1991): South Africa. Central Statistical Service. Population Census. Social Characteristics.
Description: Provides statistical information on the age, home language, marital status, country of birth and citizenship, religion and denomination, level of education, occupation, literacy and income by population group and sex.

316.8 SA
SOUTH AFRICA. CENTRAL STATISTICAL SERVICE. POPULATION CENSUS. SUMMARISED RESULTS AFTER ADJUSTMENT FOR UNDERCOUNT. (Report No. 03-01-01) 1991. irreg. R.14 (foreign R.17.50). Central Statistical Service - Sentrale Statistiekdiens, Private Bag X44, Pretoria 0001, South Africa. TEL 27-12-310-8911. FAX 27-12-310-8500. (Orders to: Government Printing Works, Private Bag X85, Pretoria 0001, South Africa) **Document type:** government publication.

316.8 SA
SOUTH AFRICA. CENTRAL STATISTICAL SERVICE. POPULATION CENSUS (YEAR). (Report No. 03-01-00) irreg., latest 1991. R.12 (foreign R.15). Central Statistical Service - Sentrale Statistiekdiens, Private Bag X44, Pretoria 0001, South Africa. TEL 27-12-310-8911. FAX 27-12-310-8500. (Orders to: Government Printing Works, Private Bag X85, Pretoria 0001, South Africa) **Document type:** government publication.
Description: Presents summarized results before adjustment for undercounting.

316.8 SA
SOUTH AFRICA. CENTRAL STATISTICAL SERVICE. PROJECTIONS. (Report No. 03-04-01) irreg., latest 1988. R.4.40 (foreign R.5.50). Central Statistical Service - Sentrale Statistiekdiens, Private Bag X44, Pretoria 0001, South Africa. TEL 27-12-310-8911. FAX 27-12-310-8500. (Orders to: Government Printing Works, Private Bag X85, Pretoria 0001, South Africa) **Document type:** government publication.
Description: Projections of the population to 2010 by age, sex, population group and compound annual growth rates, and other demographic indicators.

306.5 316.8 SA
SOUTH AFRICA. CENTRAL STATISTICAL SERVICE. REPORT ON MARRIAGES AND DIVORCES - WHITES, COLOUREDS AND ASIANS - SOUTH AFRICA. (Report No. 03-07-01) 1972. a., latest 1992. R.10 (foreign R.11). Central Statistical Service - Sentrale Statistiekdiens, Private Bag X44, Pretoria 0001, South Africa. TEL 27-12-310-8911. FAX 27-12-310-8500. (Orders to: Government Printing Works, Private Bag X85, Pretoria 0001, South Africa) **Document type:** government publication.
Former titles: South Africa. Central Statistical Service. Report on Marriages and Divorces: South Africa; South Africa. Department of Statistics. Report on Marriages and Divorces: South Africa.

316.8 SA ISSN 1013-7319
SOUTH AFRICA. CENTRAL STATISTICAL SERVICE. SOUTH AFRICAN LIFE TABLES. (Report No. 02-06-04) irreg., latest for years 1984-1986. R.2.31 (foreign R.2.89). Central Statistical Service - Sentrale Statistiekdiens, Private Bag X44, Pretoria 0001, South Africa. TEL 27-12-310-8911. FAX 27-12-310-8500. (Orders to: Government Printing Works, Private Bag X85, Pretoria 0001, South Africa) **Document type:** government publication.
Description: Lists life expectancy according to age, sex and population group.

POPULATION STUDIES — ABSTRACTING, BIBLIOGRAPHIES, STATISTICS

316.8   SA
SOUTH AFRICA. CENTRAL STATISTICAL SERVICE. STATISTICAL RELEASE. MARRIAGES AND DIVORCES. (No. P0307) a., latest 1992. free. Central Statistical Service - Sentrale Statistiekdiens, Private Bag X44, Pretoria 0001, South Africa. TEL 27-12-3108911. FAX 27-12-3108500. **Document type:** government publication.
  Supersedes: South Africa. Central Statistical Service. Statistical News Release. Marriages and Divorces - Whites, Coloureds and Asians.
  Description: Provides statistics on marriage and divorce rates in the South African population.

316.8   SA
SOUTH AFRICA. CENTRAL STATISTICAL SERVICE. STATISTICAL RELEASE. MID-YEAR ESTIMATES (POPULATION). (No. P0302) a. free. Central Statistical Service - Sentrale Statistiekdiens, Private Bag X44, Pretoria 0001, South Africa. TEL 27-12-310-8911. FAX 27-12-310-8500. **Document type:** government publication.

316.8   SA
SOUTH AFRICA. CENTRAL STATISTICAL SERVICE. STATISTICAL RELEASE. POPULATION CHARACTERISTICS (YEAR); Boipatong, Bophelong, Evaton, Orange Farm, Sebokeng and Sharpeville. (No. P0301.3) a., latest 1990. free. Central Statistical Service - Sentrale Statistiekdiens, Private Bag X44, Pretoria 0001, South Africa. TEL 27-12-310-8911. FAX 27-12-310-8500. (back issues avail.) **Document type:** government publication.
  Description: Sample survey for a specific area to determine population growth since the previous census.

316.8   SA
SOUTH AFRICA. CENTRAL STATISTICAL SERVICE. STATISTICAL RELEASE. PRELIMINARY RESULTS POPULATION CENSUS (YEAR). (No. P0301) irreg., latest 1991. free. Central Statistical Service - Sentrale Statistiekdiens, Private Bag X44, Pretoria 0001, South Africa. TEL 27-12-310-8911. FAX 27-12-310-8500. **Document type:** government publication.
  Description: Results listed by enumerator area and population group.

316.8   SA
SOUTH AFRICA. CENTRAL STATISTICAL SERVICE. STATISTICAL RELEASE. RECORDED BIRTHS. (No. P0305) a., latest 1992. free. Central Statistical Service - Sentrale Statistiekdiens, Private Bag X44, Pretoria 0001, South Africa. TEL 27-12-310-8911. FAX 27-12-310-8500. **Document type:** government publication.
  Formerly (until 1992): South Africa. Central Statistical Service. Statistical News Release. Births - Whites, Coloureds and Asians.

316.8   SA
SOUTH AFRICA. CENTRAL STATISTICAL SERVICE. STATISTICAL RELEASE. RECORDED DEATHS. (No. P0309) a., latest 1991. free. Central Statistical Service - Sentrale Statistiekdiens, Private Bag X44, Pretoria 0001, South Africa. TEL 27-12-310-8911. FAX 27-12-310-8500. **Document type:** government publication.
  Supersedes (in 1991): South Africa. Central Statistical Service. Statistical News Release. Deaths - Whites, Coloureds and Asians; South Africa. Central Statistical Service. Statistical News Release. Deaths - Blacks.

316.8   SA
SOUTH AFRICA. CENTRAL STATISTICAL SERVICE. STATISTICAL RELEASE. REGIONAL MID-YEAR ESTIMATES - REPUBLIC OF SOUTH AFRICA. (No. P0302.1) irreg. free. Central Statistical Service, Private Bag X44, Pretoria 0001, South Africa. TEL 27-12-310-8911. FAX 27-12-310-8500. **Document type:** government publication.

316.8   SA
SOUTH AFRICA. CENTRAL STATISTICAL SERVICE. STATISTICAL RELEASE. TOURISM AND IMMIGRATION. (No. P0351) m. free. Central Statistical Service - Sentrale Statistiekdiens, Private Bag X44, Pretoria 0001, South Africa. TEL 27-12-310-8911. FAX 27-12-310-8500. **Document type:** government publication.
  Formerly: South Africa. Central Statistical Service. Statistical News Release. Tourism and Immigration.

301.32 916.804   SA
SOUTH AFRICA. CENTRAL STATISTICAL SERVICE. TOURISM AND MIGRATION. (Report No. 03-51-01) a., latest 1991. R.8 (foreign R.10). Central Statistical Service - Sentrale Statistiekdiens, Private Bag X44, Pretoria 0001, South Africa. TEL 27-12-310-8911. FAX 27-12-310-8500. (Orders to: Government Printing Works, Private Bag X85, Pretoria 0001, South Africa) **Document type:** government publication.
  Formerly: South Africa. Department of Statistics. Tourism and Migration.

312   US   ISSN 0094-6338
HA621
SOUTH CAROLINA VITAL AND MORBIDITY STATISTICS. 1972. a. Department of Health and Environmental Control, Office of Vital Records and Public Health Statistics, 2600 Bull St., Columbia, SC 29201. TEL 803-734-4860. FAX 803-734-5131. circ. 900. (also avail. in microfiche from CIS) **Indexed:** SRI. **Document type:** government publication.

STADT DUISBURG. DATEN UND INFORMATION. see *PUBLIC ADMINISTRATION — Abstracting, Bibliographies, Statistics*

STATECO. see *BUSINESS AND ECONOMICS — Abstracting, Bibliographies, Statistics*

317 312   JM
STATISTICAL INSTITUTE OF JAMAICA. DEMOGRAPHIC STATISTICS. 1971. a. $21. Statistical Institute of Jamaica, 9 Swallowfield Rd., Kingston 5, Jamaica, W.I. FAX 809-92-64859. stat. circ. 126. (back issues avail.)
  Formerly: Jamaica. Department of Statistics. Demographic Statistics.

312 630   IO   ISSN 0126-2912
HA1811
STATISTICAL YEAR BOOK OF INDONESIA. (Text in English, Indonesian) 1976. a. Rps.25000($15.50) Central Bureau of Statistics - Biro Pusat Statistik, Jalan Dr. Sutomo No. 8, Box 3, Jakarta Pusat, Indonesia. TEL 21-372808. circ. 1,500. **Document type:** government publication.

312   GW
STATISTISCHER JAHRESBERICHT DER STADT MUENSTER. 1948. a. DM.25. Statistisches Amt, Postfach 5909, 48127 Muenster, Germany. TEL 02534-971112. FAX 02534-971199. **Document type:** government publication.

324.6   II
STUDIES IN PSEPHOLOGY. 1990. 3/yr. Rs.550($200) K.K. Roy (Private) Ltd., 55 Gariahat Rd., P.O. Box 10210, Calcutta 700 019, India. Ed. K.K. Roy. adv.; abstr.; bibl.; index. circ. 2,100.
  Description: Provides an international forum for all psephologists to discuss and analyze elections and patterns of voting behavior in their respective areas of interest.

312   TH
SURVEY OF MIGRATION INTO KHON KAEN PROVINCE. (Text in English, Thai) irreg., latest 1989. National Statistical Office, Statistical Information Division, Larn Luang Rd., Bangkok 10100, Thailand. TEL 662-281-0333. FAX 662-281-3814. **Document type:** government publication.

312   TH
SURVEY OF MIGRATION INTO SURAT THANI PROVINCE. (Text in English, Thai) irreg., latest 1989. National Statistical Office, Statistical Information Division, Larn Luang Rd., Bangkok 10100, Thailand. TEL 662-281-0333. FAX 662-281-3814. **Document type:** government publication.

315 312   TH   ISSN 0858-0391
SURVEY OF MIGRATION INTO THE BANGKOK METROPOLIS. (Text in English and Thai) 1974. irreg., latest 1988. National Statistical Office, Statistical Data Bank and Information Dissemination Division, Larn Luang Rd., Bangkok 10100, Thailand. TEL 662-281-0333. FAX 662-2813814. charts; stat. **Document type:** government publication.
  Description: Reports on a survey concerning migration to the Bangkok Metropolis.

312   SW   ISSN 0082-0156
SWEDEN. STATISTISKA CENTRALBYRAAN. BEFOLKNINGSFOERAENDRINGAR. (In 3 parts: Part 1 (ISSN 0347-6707); Part 2 (ISSN 0347-6715); Part 3 (ISSN 0347-6723)) (Text in Swedish; summaries in English) 1911. a. SEK 620 for 3 vols. Publishing Unit, S-701 89 Oerebro, Sweden. circ. 1,600. **Document type:** government publication.

312   SW
SWEDEN. STATISTISKA CENTRALBYRAAN. FOLKMAENGD. (In 3 parts: Part 1-2 (ISSN 0347-6677); Part 3 (ISSN 0347-6693)) (Text in English; summaries in English) 1910. a. SEK 330 for 2 vols. Statistiska Centralbyraan, Publishing Unit, S-701 89 Oerebro, Sweden. circ. 2,700. **Document type:** government publication.

312   SW   ISSN 0082-0245
HB2077
SWEDEN. STATISTISKA CENTRALBYRAAN. STATISTISKA MEDDELANDEN. SERIE BE, BEFOLKNING OCH LEVNADSFOERHAALANDEN. Variant title: Sweden. Statistiska Centralbyraan. Statistiska Meddelanden. Serie B, Befolkning. Variant title: Sweden. Statistiska Centralbyraan. Serie B, Befolkning och Val. (Text in Swedish; table heads and summaries in English) 1963. irreg. SEK 500. Statistiska Centralbyraan, Publishing Unit, S-701 89 Oerebro, Sweden. circ. 1,700. **Indexed:** Popul.Ind. **Document type:** government publication.
  Formerly (until vol.9, 1965): Sweden. Statistiska Centralbyraan. B.

312.5   SZ
SWITZERLAND. BUNDESAMT FUER STATISTIK. BILANZ DER WOHNBEVOLKERUNG IN DEN GEMEINDEN DER SCHWEIZ - BILAN DEMOGRAPHIQUE DES COMMUNES SUISSES. 1971. a. 25 SFr. Bundesamt fuer Statistik, Schwarztorstr. 96, CH-3003 Bern, Switzerland. TEL 031-3236011. FAX 031-3236061. stat. circ. 750. **Document type:** government publication.
  Formerly: Switzerland. Bundesamt fuer Statistik. Heiraten, Lebendgeborene und Gestorbene in den Gemeinden - Marriages, Naissances et Deces dans les Communes.

312 315   CH   ISSN 1019-603X
TAIWAN DEMOGRAPHY QUARTERLY. (Text in Chinese, English) 1965. q. NT.$120. Ministry of the Interior, Department of Population, Statistics and Census Division, Taipei, Taiwan, Republic of China. TEL 886-02-382-1394. Ed.Bd. charts; stat. **Document type:** government publication.
  Formerly (until Jan. 1975): Taiwan Demography Monthly.
  Description: Contains data of vital statistics produced from centralized tabulation program and monthly data of birth, death and marriage as well as the quarterly data of international migration.

301.32   TZ
TANZANIA. BUREAU OF STATISTICS. MIGRATION STATISTICS. 1968-1971; resumed 1979. irreg., latest 1985 (for the year 1981). Bureau of Statistics, Box 796, Dar es Salaam, Tanzania. (Dist. by: Government Publications Agency, Box 1801, Dar es Salaam, Tanzania) **Document type:** government publication.

312   US   ISSN 0495-257X
HA651
TEXAS VITAL STATISTICS. 1973. a. free. Department of Health, Bureau of Vital Statistics, 1100 W. 49th St., Austin, TX 78756. TEL 512-458-7111. circ. 3,000. (also avail. in microfiche from CIS) **Indexed:** SRI. **Document type:** government publication.

312   CL
TRANSICION DE LA FECUNDIDAD EN CHILE. 1989. a. Esc.1750 (US $12.10; elsewhere $14.20) (effective 1994). Instituto Nacional de Estadisticas, Av. Bulnes 418, Casilla 498, Correo 3 Santiago, Chile. **Document type:** government publication.

312 317.29   TR   ISSN 0564-2612
HA867
TRINIDAD AND TOBAGO. CENTRAL STATISTICAL OFFICE. CONTINUOUS SAMPLE SURVEY OF POPULATION. 1964. a. T.T.$20. Central Statistical Office, 35-41 Queen St., P.O. Box 98, Port-of-Spain, Trinidad & Tobago, W.I. TEL 809-625-3705. (Dist. by: Government Printing Office, 2-4 Victoria Ave., Port-of-Spain, Trinidad & Tobago, W.I.) **Document type:** government publication.

POPULATION STUDIES — ABSTRACTING, BIBLIOGRAPHIES, STATISTICS

301.32   TR   ISSN 0303-4410
HA867
TRINIDAD AND TOBAGO. CENTRAL STATISTICAL OFFICE. ESTIMATED INTERNAL MIGRATION. BULLETIN.. 1974. irreg. Central Statistical Office, 35-41 Queen St., P.O. Box 98, Port-of-Spain, Trinidad & Tobago, W.I. TEL 809-625-3705. (Dist. by: Government Printing Office, 2-4 Victoria Ave., Port-of-Spain, Trinidad & Tobago, W.I.) **Document type:** government publication, bulletin.

312   TR   ISSN 0082-6553
HA867
TRINIDAD AND TOBAGO. CENTRAL STATISTICAL OFFICE. POPULATION AND VITAL STATISTICS; REPORT. 1953. a. T.T.$10. Central Statistical Office, 35-41 Queen St., P.O. Box 98, Port-of-Spain, Trinidad & Tobago, W.I. TEL 809-625-3705. (Dist. by: Government Printer, 2-4 Victoria Ave., Port-of-Spain, Trinidad & Tobago, W.I.) **Document type:** government publication.

TURKEY. DEVLET ISTATISTIK ENSTITUSU. BOSANMA ISTATISTIKLERI/TURKEY. STATE INSTITUTE OF STATISTICS. DIVORCE STATISTICS. see *MATRIMONY — Abstracting, Bibliographies, Statistics*

TURKEY. DEVLET ISTATISTIK ENSTITUSU. EVLENME ISTATISTIKLERI/TURKEY. STATE INSTITUTE OF STATISTICS. MARRIAGE STATISTICS. see *MATRIMONY — Abstracting, Bibliographies, Statistics*

315.61   TU
TURKEY. DEVLET ISTATISTIK ENSTITUSU. GENEL NUFUS SAYIMI. GECICI SONUCLAR/TURKEY. STATE INSTITUTE OF STATISTICS. CENSUS OF POPULATION. PRELIMINARY RESULTS. (Text in English, Turkish) 1961. irreg., latest 1990. Devlet Istatistik Enstitusu - State Institute of Statistics, Necatibey Caddesi No. 114, 06100 Ankara, Turkey. TEL 90-4-4176440. FAX 90-4-4253387. circ. 1,025. **Document type:** government publication.

315.61   TU
TURKEY. DEVLET ISTATISTIK ENSTITUSU. GENEL NUFUS SAYIMI. IDARI BOLUNUS/TURKEY. STATE INSTITUTE OF STATISTICS. CENSUS OF POPULATION. ADMINISTRATIVE DIVISION. (Text in English, Turkish) 1928. irreg., latest 1990. Devlet Istatistik Enstitusu - State Institute of Statistics, Necatibey Caddesi No. 114, 06100 Ankara, Turkey. TEL 90-312-4185027. FAX 90-312-4170432. (also avail. in diskette format) **Document type:** government publication.

315.61   TU
TURKEY. DEVLET ISTATISTIK ENSTITUSU. GENEL NUFUS SAYIMI. NUFUSAN SOSYAL VE EKONOMIK NITELIKLERI/TURKEY. STATE INSTITUTE OF STATISTICS. CENSUS OF POPULATION. SOCIAL AND ECONOMIC CHARACTERISTICS OF POPULATION. (Text in English, Turkish) 1969. irreg., latest 1985. $100. Devlet Istatistik Enstitusu - State Institute of Statistics, Necatibey Caddesi No. 114, 06100 Ankara, Turkey. TEL 90-312-4185027. FAX 90-312-4170432. circ. 1,600. (also avail. in diskette format) **Document type:** government publication.

362.28021   TU   ISSN 1300-1159
TURKEY. DEVLET ISTATISTIK ENSTITUSU. INTIHAR ISTATISTIKLERI/TURKEY. STATE INSTITUTE OF STATISTICS. SUICIDE STATISTICS. Key Title: Intihar Istatistikleri. (Text in English, Turkish) 1977. a., latest 1991. $25. Devlet Istatistik Enstitusu - State Institute of Statistics, Necatibey Caddesi No. 114, 06100 Ankara, Turkey. TEL 90-312-4185027. FAX 90-312-4170432. circ. 800. **Document type:** government publication.

306.9021   TU   ISSN 1300-1191
TURKEY. DEVLET ISTATISTIK ENSTITUSU. OLUM ISTATISTIKLERI (IL VE ILCE MERKEZLERINDE)/TURKEY. STATE INSTITUTE OF STATISTICS. DEATH STATISTICS (IN PROVINCIAL AND DISTRICT CENTERS). Key Title: Olum Istatistikleri. (Text in English, Turkish) 1959. a., latest 1990. $25. Devlet Istatistik Enstitusu - State Institute of Statistics, Necatibey Caddesi No. 114, 06100 Ankara, Turkey. TEL 90-312-4185027. FAX 90-312-4170432. circ. 910. **Document type:** government publication.

315.61   TU
TURKEY. DEVLET ISTATISTIK ENSTITUSU. TURKIYE NUFUS ARASTIRMASI/TURKEY. STATE INSTITUTE OF STATISTICS. TURKISH DEMOGRAPHIC SURVEY. (Text in English, Turkish) a., latest 1989. $40. Devlet Istatistik Enstitusu - State Institute of Statistics, Necatibey Caddesi No. 114, 06100 Ankara, Turkey. TEL 90-312-4185027. FAX 90-312-4170432. (also avail. in diskette format) **Document type:** government publication.

315.61   TU
TURKEY. STATE INSTITUTE OF STATISTICS. CENSUS OF POPULATION. INTERNAL MIGRATION BY PERMANENT RESIDENCE. (Text in English, Turkish) 1941. irreg., latest 1990. $110. Devlet Istatistik Enstitusu - State Institute of Statistics, Necatibey Caddesi No. 114, 06100 Ankara, Turkey. TEL 90-312-4185027. FAX 90-312-4170432. circ. 1,220. (also avail. in diskette format) **Document type:** government publication.

314   UN   ISSN 0041-7416
UNITED NATIONS. POPULATION AND VITAL STATISTICS REPORT. 1949. q. $30. (United Nations, Department of International Economic and Social Affairs) United Nations Publications, Room DC2-0853, New York, NY 10017. TEL 212-963-9302; 800-253-9646. FAX 212-963-3489. (also avail. in microfiche from CIS) **Indexed:** IIS.
Description: Provides latest census data, plus worldwide demographic statistics on birth and mortality.

312   US   ISSN 0082-9390
U.S. BUREAU OF THE CENSUS. CENSUS OF POPULATION. (Issued in several series) 1790. decennial. price varies. U.S. Bureau of the Census, Data User Services Division, Washington, DC 20233. TEL 301-763-4100. (Subscr to: Superintendent of Documents, U.S. Government Printing Office, Box 371954, Pittsburgh, PA 15205-7954. TEL 202-783-3238. FAX 202-512-2233) **Document type:** government publication.

312   US
U.S. BUREAU OF THE CENSUS. 1990 CENSUS OF POPULATION AND HOUSING. POPULATION AND HOUSING CHARACTERISTICS FOR CENSUS TRACTS AND BLOCK NUMBERING AREAS. ALABAMA. irreg. U.S. Department of Commerce, Bureau of the Census, Economics and Statistics Administration, 14th St. between Constitution & E Sts., N.W., Washington, DC 20230. (Avail. from: Superintendent of Documents, U.S. Government Printing Office, Box 317954, Pittsburgh, PA 15250-7954. TEL 202-783-3238. FAX 202-512-2233) stat.

U.S. NATIONAL CENTER FOR HEALTH STATISTICS. CATALOG OF PUBLICATIONS. see *PUBLIC HEALTH AND SAFETY — Abstracting, Bibliographies, Statistics*

312   US   ISSN 0364-0396
HA203
U.S. NATIONAL CENTER FOR HEALTH STATISTICS. MONTHLY VITAL STATISTICS REPORT. Key Title: Monthly Vital Statistics Report. (Supplements accompany some numbers) 1952. m., no. 13 of each vol. is annual summary. free. U.S. National Center for Health Statistics, Data Dissemination Branch, 6525 Belcrest Rd., Hyattsville, MD 20782. TEL 301-436-8500. E-mail: nchsquery@nch10a.em.cdc.gov. (also avail. in microfiche from CIS; reprint service avail. from CIS) **Indexed:** Abstr.Health Care Manage.Stud., Abstr.Hyg., Amer.Stat.Ind. (1973-), Curr.Lit.Fam.Plan., MEDOC, Nutr.Abstr., Popul.Ind., PROMT, Rehabil.Lit., Trop.Dis.Bull. **Document type:** government publication. *Refereed Serial*

U.S. NATIONAL CENTER FOR HEALTH STATISTICS. VITAL AND HEALTH STATISTICS. SERIES 1. PROGRAMS AND COLLECTION PROCEDURES. see *PUBLIC HEALTH AND SAFETY — Abstracting, Bibliographies, Statistics*

U.S. NATIONAL CENTER FOR HEALTH STATISTICS. VITAL AND HEALTH STATISTICS. SERIES 2. DATA EVALUATION AND METHODS RESEARCH. see *PUBLIC HEALTH AND SAFETY — Abstracting, Bibliographies, Statistics*

U.S. NATIONAL CENTER FOR HEALTH STATISTICS. VITAL AND HEALTH STATISTICS. SERIES 3. ANALYTICAL STUDIES. see *PUBLIC HEALTH AND SAFETY — Abstracting, Bibliographies, Statistics*

U.S. NATIONAL CENTER FOR HEALTH STATISTICS. VITAL AND HEALTH STATISTICS. SERIES 4. DOCUMENTS AND COMMITTEE REPORT. see *PUBLIC HEALTH AND SAFETY — Abstracting, Bibliographies, Statistics*

U.S. NATIONAL CENTER FOR HEALTH STATISTICS. VITAL AND HEALTH STATISTICS. SERIES 5. COMPARATIVE INTERNATIONAL VITAL AND HEALTH STATISTICS REPORTS. see *PUBLIC HEALTH AND SAFETY — Abstracting, Bibliographies, Statistics*

U.S. NATIONAL CENTER FOR HEALTH STATISTICS. VITAL AND HEALTH STATISTICS. SERIES 6. COGNITION AND SURVEY MEASUREMENT. see *PUBLIC HEALTH AND SAFETY — Abstracting, Bibliographies, Statistics*

U.S. NATIONAL CENTER FOR HEALTH STATISTICS. VITAL AND HEALTH STATISTICS. SERIES 10. DATA FROM THE HEALTH INTERVIEW SURVEY. see *PUBLIC HEALTH AND SAFETY — Abstracting, Bibliographies, Statistics*

U.S. NATIONAL CENTER FOR HEALTH STATISTICS. VITAL AND HEALTH STATISTICS. SERIES 11. DATA FROM THE HEALTH AND NUTRITION EXAMINATION SURVEY. see *PUBLIC HEALTH AND SAFETY — Abstracting, Bibliographies, Statistics*

U.S. NATIONAL CENTER FOR HEALTH STATISTICS. VITAL AND HEALTH STATISTICS. SERIES 14. DATA ON HEALTH RESOURCES. see *PUBLIC HEALTH AND SAFETY — Abstracting, Bibliographies, Statistics*

U.S. NATIONAL CENTER FOR HEALTH STATISTICS. VITAL AND HEALTH STATISTICS. SERIES 20. DATA ON MORTALITY. see *PUBLIC HEALTH AND SAFETY — Abstracting, Bibliographies, Statistics*

U.S. NATIONAL CENTER FOR HEALTH STATISTICS. VITAL AND HEALTH STATISTICS. SERIES 21. DATA ON NATALITY, MARRIAGE, AND DIVORCE. see *PUBLIC HEALTH AND SAFETY — Abstracting, Bibliographies, Statistics*

U.S. NATIONAL CENTER FOR HEALTH STATISTICS. VITAL AND HEALTH STATISTICS. SERIES 23. DATA FROM THE NATIONAL SURVEY OF FAMILY GROWTH. see *PUBLIC HEALTH AND SAFETY — Abstracting, Bibliographies, Statistics*

U.S. NATIONAL CENTER FOR HEALTH STATISTICS. VITAL AND HEALTH STATISTICS. SERIES 24. COMPILATIONS OF DATA ON NATALITY, MORTALITY, DIVORCE, AND INDUCED TERMINATIONS OF PREGNANCY. see *PUBLIC HEALTH AND SAFETY — Abstracting, Bibliographies, Statistics*

314 312   IT
UNIVERSITA DEGLI STUDI DI PADOVA. FACOLTA DI SCIENZE STATISTICHE, DEMOGRAFICHE ED ATTUARIALI. SERIE ESTRATTI. 1969. irreg., no.204, 1980. (Universita degli Studi di Padova, Facolta di Scienze Statistiche, Demografiche ed Attuariali) C L E U P, Via G. Prati, 19, 35100 Padua, Italy. bibl.

314 312   IT
UNIVERSITA DEGLI STUDI DI PADOVA. FACOLTA DI SCIENZE STATISTICHE, DEMOGRAFICHE ED ATTUARIALI. SERIE PUBBLICAZIONI. 1971. irreg., no.16, 1981. (Universita degli Studi di Padova, Facolta di Scienze Statistiche, Demografiche ed Attuariali) C L E U P, Via G. Prati, 19, 35100 Padua, Italy.

312   UY
URUGUAY. DIRECCION GENERAL DE ESTADISTICA Y CENSOS. ESTADISTICAS VITALES. (Vol. from 1978 contains 1975 statistics) 1961-1974; N.S. 1978. irreg. Direccion General de Estadistica y Censos, Montevideo, Uruguay. **Document type:** government publication.

312.5   US   ISSN 0148-8694
HB1145.U8
UTAH MARRIAGE AND DIVORCE ANNUAL REPORT. a. $10. Department of Health, Bureau of Vital Records, Box 142855, Salt Lake City, UT 84114-2855. TEL 801-538-6186. (also avail. in microfiche from CIS) **Indexed:** SRI. **Document type:** government publication.
Formerly: Marriage and Divorce in Utah (ISSN 0093-9641)

614 US ISSN 0500-7720
HA664
UTAH VITAL STATISTICS ANNUAL REPORT. a. $10. Department of Health, Bureau of Vital Records, Box 142855, Salt Lake City, UT 84114-2855. TEL 801-538-6186. **Document type:** government publication.

312 NN
VANUATU. STATISTICS OFFICE. CENSUS OF POPULATION (YEAR). BASIC TABLES. (Text in English and French) 1972. irreg. $25. Statistics Office, Private Mail Bag 19, Port-Vila, Vanuatu. TEL 678-22110. FAX 678-24583. stat. circ. 300. **Document type:** government publication.
  Former titles: Vanuatu. National Planning and Statistics Office. Census of Population (Year). Base Tables; (until 1983): Vanuatu. Condominium Bureau of Statistics. Census of Population and Housing, Vila and Santo, Preliminary Results.

312 NN
VANUATU. STATISTICS OFFICE. OVERSEAS MIGRATION. (Text in English, French) 1972. a. 500 vatu($5) Statistics Office, Private Mail Bag 19, Port-Vila, Vanuatu. TEL 678-22110. FAX 678-24583. charts; stat. circ. 300. (processed) **Document type:** government publication.
  Former titles: Vanuatu. National Planning and Statistics Office. Overseas Migration; Vanuatu. Bureau of Statistics. Overseas Migration (ISSN 0259-7543)
  Description: Presents movements of residents, and arrivals of visitors, people on holidays and people staying in hotels cross-classified by age, sex, nationality, intended length of stay and purpose of visit.

312 US ISSN 0161-8695
HA375
VITAL STATISTICS OF IOWA. 1975. a. $5. Department of Public Health, Bureau of Vital Statistics, Des Moines, IA 50319. TEL 515-281-4945. FAX 515-281-4958. Ed. Michael Dare. stat. circ. 400. (also avail. in microfiche) **Indexed:** SRI. **Document type:** government publication.
  Formed by the merger of: Iowa Summary of Vital Statistics (ISSN 0090-5143); Iowa Detailed Report of Vital Statistics (ISSN 0362-9473)

VITAL STATISTICS OF THE UNITED STATES. see *PUBLIC HEALTH AND SAFETY — Abstracting, Bibliographies, Statistics*

312 UK ISSN 0956-0793
WELSH INTER CENSAL SURVEY. irreg. Welsh Office, Statistical Directorate, New Crown Bldg., Cathays Park, Cardiff CF1 3NQ, Wales. TEL 01222-825054. FAX 01222-825350. **Document type:** government publication.

312 UN ISSN 0257-4403
WORLD POPULATION PROJECTIONS; estimates and projections with related demographic statistics. a. $34.95. World Bank, 1818 H St., N.W., Washington, DC 20433. TEL 202-473-2939. (U.S. orders to: The World Bank, Box 7247-8619, Philadelphia, PA 19170-8619. TEL 202-473-1155. FAX 202-676-0581)
  —BLDSC (9358.084000).
  Description: Compiles demographic statistics on the world's population, with projections to the year 2150 for 206 nations.

312 YU ISSN 0084-4357
HA1631
YUGOSLAVIA. SAVAZNI ZAVOD ZA STATISTIKU. DEMOGRAFSKA STATISTIKA. 1956. a. 100 din.($1.11) Savezni Zavod za Statistiku, Kneza Milosa 20, Belgrade, Yugoslavia. TEL 38-11-681999. circ. 600. **Document type:** government publication.
  Formerly: Yugoslavia. Savezni Zavod za Statistiku. Vitalna Statistika.

316 325 ZA ISSN 0084-4543
JV8975.Z3
ZAMBIA. CENTRAL STATISTICAL OFFICE. MIGRATION STATISTICS. Title varies: Zambia. Central Statistical Office. Migration Statistics: Immigrants and Visitors. 1965. a. $4. Central Statistical Office, P.O. Box 31908, Lusaka, Zambia. TEL 260-1-211231. **Document type:** government publication.

316 312 ZA ISSN 0084-456X
HA1977.R48
ZAMBIA. CENTRAL STATISTICAL OFFICE. VITAL STATISTICS. Variant title: Zambia. Central Statistical Office. Registered Births, Marriages and Deaths (Vital Statistics). 1965. a. $1. Central Statistical Office, P.O. Box 31908, Lusaka, Zambia. TEL 260-1-211231. **Document type:** government publication.

ZIMBABWE. CENTRAL STATISTICAL OFFICE. MONTHLY MIGRATION AND TOURIST STATISTICS. see *TRAVEL AND TOURISM — Abstracting, Bibliographies, Statistics*

POSTAL AFFAIRS

see *Communications–Postal Affairs*

POULTRY AND LIVESTOCK

see *Agriculture–Poultry and Livestock*

PRINTING

760 US ISSN 0275-9470
NC998.5.A1
A I G A GRAPHIC DESIGN U S A. 1980. a. $65. (American Institute of Graphic Arts) Watson - Guptill Publications, 1515 Broadway, New York, NY 10036. (Subscr. to: 1695 Oak St., Lakewood, NJ 09701. TEL 800-451-1741. FAX 908-363-0338) **Document type:** trade publication.
  Supersedes: A I G A Best Books Show; Communication Graphics; Covers; Insides.

760 US ISSN 0736-5322
NC997.A1
A I G A JOURNAL OF GRAPHIC DESIGN. 1947; suspended 1953-1965. q. $21.50. American Institute of Graphic Arts, 164 5th Ave., New York, NY 10010-5900. TEL 212-807-1990. FAX 212-807-1799. E-mail: aiganatl@aol.com. Ed. Steven Heller; Pub. Richard Grefe. adv. contact: Michelle Kalvert. bk.rev.; bibl.; illus. circ. 9,000. **Indexed:** DAAI. **Document type:** trade publication.
  —BLDSC (0773.122500).
  Former titles (1965-1982): American Institute of Graphic Arts. Journal (ISSN 0065-8820); (1947-1953): A I G A Journal (ISSN 0197-6907)
  Description: Focuses on criticism, professional practice, review, debate and the history of graphic design.

686.2 US ISSN 0898-1078
A P H A LETTER. Variant title: A P H A Newsletter. 1974. q. membership. American Printing History Association, Box 4922, Grand Central Sta., New York, NY 10163. Ed. Edward Colker. circ. 1,000. **Document type:** newsletter.

686.2
A T F NEWSLETTER. 1978. irreg. $2 (foreign $4). American Typecasting Fellowship, Box 263, Terra Alta, WV 26764. TEL 304-789-2455. Ed. Richard L. Hopkins. adv.; bk.rev. circ. 300. **Document type:** newsletter.
  Description: Articles on the preservation and promotion of hot-metal typecasting equipment and technology.

655 370 UK ISSN 0308-6795
A T P A S PRINTING EDUCATION & TRAINING JOURNAL. 1952. 3/yr. £1. Association of Teachers of Printing and Allied Subjects, c/o Frank Chapple, Ed., 15 Sandy Lane, Westerham, Kent, England. adv.; bk.rev.; illus. circ. 1,000.
  Formerly: A T P A S Bulletin (ISSN 0001-2769)

AARETS BOGARBEJDE. see *PUBLISHING AND BOOK TRADE*

760 US
ABRACADABRA. 1988. a. $25 includes membership. Alliance for Contemporary Book Arts, Box 24415, Los Angeles, CA 90024. TEL 213-258-2959. Ed. Gerald Lange. bk.rev. circ. 500. **Indexed:** Child.Lit.Abstr. **Document type:** academic/scholarly publication.
  Description: Provides a medium for studying and promoting the arts of the book, including printing, typography, papermaking, calligraphy, bookbinding, and illustration.

686.2 SA ISSN 1071-3263
AFRICAN PRINTER. 1993. q. R.50.16 (overseas R.150) (free to qualified personnel). Graphix Publications (Pty) Ltd., P.O. Box 751119, Gardenview 2047, South Africa. TEL 27-11-6224800. FAX 27-11-6222480. (In U.S.: c/o K.J. Moran, V.P. Sales & Mktg., Coast Publishing, Inc., 1680 S.W. Bayshore Blvd., Port St. Lucie, FL 34984. TEL 407-879-6666. FAX 407-879-7388) Ed. Mel Kruis. adv.: B&W Page $1450, color page $2600; trim 8.28 x 11.71. circ. 5,733. **Document type:** trade publication.

760 DK ISSN 0900-3193
AKTUEL GRAFISK INFORMATION. Swedish edition: Aktuell Grafisk Information (ISSN 0347-9846); Norwegian edition: Aktuell Grafisk Informasjon. 1970. m. DKK 395 (Swedish ed. SEK 395). Forlaget Aktuel Viden A-S, Strandgade 4C, DK-1401 Copenhagen, Denmark. TEL 45-53-90-70-55. FAX 45-53-90-64-77. Eds. Elisabeth Bitsch Christensen (Danish ed.); Peter Ollen (Swedish ed.); Ingvild Kristoffesen (Norwegian ed.). adv.: B&W page DKK 6100, color page DKK 8700; trim 242 x 360. circ. 20,162 (10,662 Danish ed.; 9,500 Swedish ed.). **Document type:** trade publication.

686.2 SP
ALABRENT. 12/yr. 5000 ptas. in Europe; America 6500 ptas. (effective 1995). Alabrent Ediciones, Valencia 501 entlo 1a, 08013 Barcelona, Spain. TEL 34-3-2653211. FAX 34-3-2651320. Ed. Ramon Arnella Paris. circ. 5,000.

686.2 US ISSN 0002-8916
TP949 CODEN: AMIKAK
AMERICAN INKMAKER; * for manufacturers of printing inks and related graphic arts specialty colors. 1923. m. $18. MacNair Publications, 445 Broadhollow RD., Melville, NY 11747-3601. Ed. Francine Del Vescoro. adv.; bk.rev.; charts; illus.; pat.; tr.lit.; tr.mk.; index. circ. 4,000. **Indexed:** Abstr.Bull.Inst.Pap.Chem., Chem.Abstr., Graph.Arts Lit.Abstr., Key to Econ.Sci., PROMT, World Surf.Coat. —BLDSC (0820.500000); CASDDS; Ei; Faxon; SWETS; UMI.

655 US ISSN 0744-6616
Z119
AMERICAN PRINTER (CHICAGO, 1982). 1883. m. $50. Intertec Publishing Corp., 29 N. Wacker Dr., Chicago, IL 60606. TEL 312-726-2802. FAX 312-726-3091. Ed. Jill Roth. adv.: B&W page $7500, color page $9700. bk.rev.; illus.; tr.lit.; circ. 93,780 (controlled). (also avail. in microfilm from UMI) **Indexed:** A.S.& T.Ind., ABI Inform., B.P.I., Bus.Ind., Chem.Abstr., Graph.Arts Lit.Abstr., Photo.Abstr., Print.Abstr., PROMT, PSI, Tr.& Indus.Ind.
  ●Also available online. Vendor(s): University Microfilms International.
  —BLDSC (0853.228100); Faxon; SWETS; UMI; UnCover. CCC.
  Former titles (until 1982): American Printer and Lithographer (ISSN 0192-9933); (until 1979): Inland Printer - American Lithographer (ISSN 0020-1502)
  Description: Covers the printing and lithographic industry including its allied manufacturing and service segments.

760 AG ISSN 0004-105X
ARGENTINA GRAFICA. 1935. 4/yr. $7 per no. to non-members. Camara de Industriales Graficos de la Argentina, Ramon L. Falcon 1657-59, 1405 Buenos Aires C.F., Argentina. TEL 631-5120. Ed. Lorenzo F. Heavey. adv.; charts; illus.; tr.lit. circ. 2,500.

PRINTING

686.2 331   US
AROUND THE BARGAINING LOOP. m. $250 to non-members; members $125. Graphic Arts Employers of America, 100 Daingerfield Rd., Alexandria, VA 22314. TEL 703-519-8150. FAX 703-548-4165. Ed. William Solomon. circ. 325.
   Description: Contract language from negotiated collective bargaining agreements.

760   MX   ISSN 0004-3508
ARTES GRAFICAS EN MEXICO.* 1949. bi-m. Mex.$40($8) Sociedad de Industriales de las Artes Graficas, Dr Arce 88, Mexico City, Mexico. Dir. Pablo Martinez Malpica. adv.

ARTIKEL 5; das Wirtschaftsmagazin der Printmedien. see *PUBLISHING AND BOOK TRADE*

760   FR   ISSN 0984-9602
ARTS GRAPHIQUES MAGAZINE. 1987. 4/yr. C N F S, 15 rue Massena, 94700 Maisons-Alfort, France. TEL 48-99-44-71. FAX 48-98-59-21. Ed. Frederique Contencin. circ. 25,000.

686.2   US
ASCENDERS. q. Autologic Incorporated, 1050 Rancho Conejo Blvd., Newbury Park, CA 91320. TEL 805-498-9611. Ed. Peter Jedrzejek.

686.2   SI
ASIAN PRINTER MAGAZINE. 1988. 6/yr. Aus.$60 (Asia $30; Europe & US $50). Callaghan Publishing Pte. Ltd., 39 Rowell Rd., Singapore 0820, Singapore. TEL 65-299-2485. FAX 65-299-2485. Ed. Peter Loh. adv.; bk.rev.; illus.; index. circ. 10,556. (back issues avail.) **Indexed:** Print.Abstr. **Document type:** trade publication.
   Formerly: South East Asian Printer Magazine (ISSN 0129-1262)
   Description: Technical journal for graphic industry management and production, for managers of print shops, trade shops, typesetters, art studios, publishers and packaging companies.

686.2   HK   ISSN 1012-8662
ASIAN PRINTING; the magazine for the graphic arts industry. (Text in Chinese and English) 1989. m. HK.$260($69) Travel & Trade Publishing (Asia) Ltd., 16-F, Capitol Centre, 5-19 Jardine's Bazaar, Causeway Bay, Hong Kong. TEL 890-3067. FAX 895-2378. TELEX 76591-TPAL-HX. Ed. Chris Hunter. circ. 5,358.
   Description: For those who buy and sell printing in Asia and between Asia and the rest of the world.

686.2 380.1   HK   ISSN 0258-218X
ASIAN PRINTING DIRECTORY. a. $25. Travel & Trade Publishing (Asia) Ltd., 16-F, Capitol Centre, 5-19 Jardine's Bazaar, Causeway Bay, Hong Kong. TEL 890-3067. FAX 895-2375. TELEX 76591-TPAL-HX. Ed. Chris Hunter. **Document type:** directory.
   Description: Gives expanded detail on major suppliers of export quality print products in 10 Asian countries.

760   GW
ASSOCIATION EUROPEENNE DES GRAVEURS ET DES FLEXOGRAPHES. BULLETIN PROFESSIONNEL. 3/yr. Association Europeene des Graveurs et des Flexographes, Postfach 1869, 65008 Wiesbaden, Germany. TEL 0611-803115. FAX 0611-803113. **Document type:** trade publication.

763   AT   ISSN 0159-2319
AUSTRALIAN LITHOGRAPHER, PRINTER, AND PACKAGER. 1964. bi-m. Aus.$35. (Australian Institute of Packaging) Prestige Publishing Pty. Ltd., G.P.O. Box 5158, Sydney, N.S.W. 2001, Australia. Ed. F. Stern. adv.; bk.rev.; index. circ. 8,936. (reprint service avail.) **Indexed:** Graph.Arts Abstr., Graph.Arts Lit.Abstr., Print.Abstr.
   Formerly: Australian Lithographer (ISSN 0004-9700); Incorporates: Printer and Packager.

686.2   AT   ISSN 1033-1522
AUSTRALIAN PRINTER MAGAZINE. 1950. m. Aus.$50 (foreign Aus.$80) (effective 1996). Calmor & Associates Pty. Ltd., P.O. Box 1316, North Sydney, N.S.W. 2059, Australia. TEL 02-922-6133. FAX 02-922-4734. Ed. Patrick Howard. adv. contact: Derek Brown. bk.rev.; illus.; index. circ. 9,881. **Indexed:** C.I.S. Abstr., Graph.Arts Lit.Abstr., Print.Abstr. **Document type:** trade publication.
—BLDSC (1818.315000).
   Formerly: Australasian Printer Magazine (ISSN 0004-8453)
   Description: Journal of graphic industry management and production. For printers, trade shops, typesetters, art studios, publishers and packaging companies.

686.2   UK
B P I F LIST OF MEMBERS. Former titles (until 1995): B P I F Services List of Members. 1982. a. £90. British Printing Industries Federation, 11 Bedford Row, London, WC1R 4DX, England. TEL 0171-242-6904. FAX 0171-405-7784. adv.; index. circ. 3,700. **Document type:** directory.
   (until 1992): Printers Yearbook; Printing Industries Annual (ISSN 0308-1443); British Federation of Master Printers. Master Printers Annual (ISSN 0068-1989)
   Description: Buyer's guide to the U.K. printing industry concerning B.P.I.F. committees and services.

BEIKOKU TOKKYO SHOROKU. SOKUTEI, SEIMITSU KIKI, INSATSU, ONKYO, KYOIKU HEN/U.S. PATENT ABSTRACTS. MEASURING, PRECISION INSTRUMENT, PRINTING, SOUND RECORDING, EDUCATION. see *PATENTS, TRADEMARKS AND COPYRIGHTS — Abstracting, Bibliographies, Statistics*

BIBLIOGRAPHY NEWSLETTER. see *LIBRARY AND INFORMATION SCIENCES*

BIBLIOPHILIA. see *HISTORY — History Of Europe*

BIBLIOTHECA HUNGARICA ANTIQUA. see *PUBLISHING AND BOOK TRADE*

BOARD REPORT FOR GRAPHIC ARTISTS. see *ADVERTISING AND PUBLIC RELATIONS*

686.2   DK   ISSN 0106-0619
BOGTRYKKERNE - DISTRIKTSBLADENE. 1922. m. Dansk Bogtrykker- og Presseforening, City Vest, P.O. Box 1559, DK-8220 Brabrand, Denmark. adv. circ. 1,600.
   Formerly (until 1977): Vort Medlemsblad (ISSN 0902-6347)

BOGVENNEN. see *PUBLISHING AND BOOK TRADE*

686.2 070.172   AT
BORDER WATCH. 1861. 4/w. Aus.$75. Border Watch Pty. Ltd., P.O. Box 309, Mount Gambler, S.A. 5290, Australia. TEL (087) 25 73 33. Ed. Gary Trotter. adv. circ. 9,101.

686.2   AT   ISSN 0811-3971
BRANDYWINE DOCUMENTS ON THE HISTORY OF BOOKS & PRINTING. (Text in Dutch, English, French and Russian) 1980. irreg. (1-2/yr.). price varies. Brandywine Press & Archive, 20 Murray Rd., Beecroft, N.S.W. 2119, Australia. TEL (02)863627. Ed. J.P. Wegner. (back issues avail.)
   Formerly: Brandywine Documents on Printing and Printing History.

686.2   AT   ISSN 0157-5619
BRANDYWINE KEEPSAKE. (Text in English, German and Russian) 1979. a. price varies. Brandywine Press & Archive, 20 Murray Rd., Beecroft, N.S.W. 2119, Australia. TEL (02)86-3627. (back issues avail.)

BRITAIN'S TOP 300 PRINTERS. see *BUSINESS AND ECONOMICS — Trade And Industrial Directories*

760   SZ
BRITISH DESIGN & ART DIRECTION ANNUAL. 1962. a. (Designers & Art Directors Association) Polygon Editions S.A.R.L., In den Ziegelhoefen 151, CH-4054 Basel, Switzerland. TEL 01-2514276. FAX 01-2524380. (U.S. subscr. to: Rizzoli International Publications Inc., 300 Park Ave. S., New York, NY 10010) Ed. Edward Booth-Clibborn. **Indexed:** Mgmt.& Market.Abstr.
   Formerly: Design and Art Direction Annual.

686.2   UK   ISSN 0007-1684
Z119
BRITISH PRINTER; leading technical journal of the printing industry. 1888. m. £55. Maclean Hunter Ltd., Maclean Hunter House, Chalk Lane, Cockfosters Rd., Barnet, Herts EN4 0BU, England. TEL 081-242-3000. FAX 081-242-3185. TELEX 299072-MACHUN-G. Ed. Andy Thomas. adv.; bk.rev.; illus.; index. circ. 14,014. **Indexed:** Abstr.Bull.Inst.Pap.Chem., Br.Tech.Ind., Graph.Arts Lit.Abstr., Print.Abstr. **Document type:** trade publication.
—BLDSC (2340.000000); SWETS.

686.2   SZ   ISSN 0007-5736
BULLETIN TECHNIQUE; industrie graphique et technique de communication. 1966. 5/yr. 40 Fr. (Schweizerische Lithografenbund) Conzett & Huber AG, Baslerstr. 30, Postfach, 8048 Zurich, Switzerland. (Co-sponsor: Verband der Schweizer Druckindustrie) Ed.Bd. adv.; bk.rev.; charts; illus.; index. **Indexed:** Chem.Abstr.

686.2   FR   ISSN 0572-7529
BUREAU INTERNATIONAL DES SOCIETES GERANT LES DROITS D'ENREGISTREMENT ET DE REPRODUCTION MECANIQUE. BULLETIN. 1959. irreg. Bureau International des Societtes Gerant les Droits d'Enregistrement et de Reproduction Mecanique - International Bureau of the Societies Administering the Rights of Mechanical Recording and Reproduction, 56, Av. Kleber, 75116 Paris, France. TEL 47-04-57-04. FAX 47-55-11-53.

655   US
BUSINESS DOCUMENTS. 10/yr. $145. North American Publishing Co., 401 N. Broad St., Philadelphia, PA 19108. TEL 215-238-5300. FAX 215-238-5457. Ed. William Drennan. adv. circ. 6,500. **Document type:** trade publication.
   Former titles: Forms and Label Purchasing; Forms and Systems Professional; Incorporates: Forms Professional.
   Description: Serves the needs and interests of business document managers, buyers and users. Covers forms and systems design, electronic applications and management.

655   US   ISSN 1044-758X
HF5371   CODEN: BFLSEP
BUSINESS FORMS, LABELS AND SYSTEMS. 1963. s-m. $49 (foreign $74). North American Publishing Co., 401 N. Broad St., Philadelphia, PA 19108. TEL 215-238-5300. FAX 215-238-5457. Ed. William Drennan. adv.; tr.lit. (also avail. in microform from UMI; reprint service avail. from UMI) **Indexed:** Graph.Arts Lit.Abstr., INSPEC (1989-), Print.Abstr. **Document type:** trade publication.
—BLDSC (2933.663500); UMI. **CCC.**
   Former titles: Business Forms and Systems (ISSN 0745-3914); Business Forms Reporter (ISSN 0007-6767)
   Description: Reports on trends, product developments, design techniques and new information on marketing and manufacturing of business forms and related products.

BUSINESS RATIO REPORT: PAINT & PRINTING INK MANUFACTURERS; an industry sector analysis. see *PAINTS AND PROTECTIVE COATINGS*

686.2 658.788
658.8   UK   ISSN 0951-2519
BUSINESS RATIO REPORT: PRINT AND PACKAGING MACHINERY; an industry sector analysis. 1987. a. I C C Business Ratios Ltd., Freepost, Field House, Hampton, Mddx. TW12 1BR, England. TEL 081-783-0977. FAX 081-783-1940. charts; stat. **Document type:** trade publication.
—BLDSC (6612.998300).

686.2 658.8   UK   ISSN 0261-9423
BUSINESS RATIO REPORT: PRINTERS - INTERMEDIATE; an industry sector analysis. 1978. a. I C C Business Ratio Reports, Freepost, Field House, Hampton, Mddx. TW12 1BR, England. TEL 081-783-0977. FAX 081-783-1940. charts; stat. **Document type:** trade publication.
—BLDSC (6613.510000).

PRINTING

686.2 658.8   UK   ISSN 0261-9431
BUSINESS RATIO REPORT: PRINTERS - MAJOR; an industry sector analysis. 1978. a. I C C Business Ratios Ltd., Freepost, Field House, Hampton, Mddx. TW12 1BR, England. TEL 081-783-0977. FAX 081-783-1940. charts; stat. **Document type:** trade publication.
—BLDSC (6613.525000).

686.2   CN   ISSN 0849-0767
CANADIAN PRINTER. (Directory number avail.) 1892. m. Can.$45 (foreign Can.$90) includes Printing Product Guide. Maclean-Hunter Ltd., Business Publication Division, Maclean-Hunter Bldg., 777 Bay St., Toronto, ON M5W 1A7, Canada. TEL 416-596-5884. FAX 416-596-5965. Ed. Nick Hancock. adv.: B&W page $3055, color page $4170; 8 1/8 x 10 7/8. bk.rev.; abstr.; charts; illus.; stat.; tr.lit.; index. circ. 11,277. (also avail. in microform from UMI) **Indexed:** Abstr.Bull.Inst.Pap.Chem., Can.B.P.I., Graph.Arts Lit.Abstr., Print.Abstr.
—BLDSC (3044.059000). **CCC.**
Formerly (until 1989): Canadian Printer and Publisher (ISSN 0008-4816)
Description: Deals with shifting markets and economic conditions, changing technology and evolving management techniques.

686.2   FR   ISSN 0247-039X
Z119
CARACTERE; magazine des professionnels de l'imprime. 1949. 24/yr. 530 F. (foreign 734 F.) (effective Jan. 1994). Groupe Information et Professions, 1 cite Bergere, 75009 Paris, France. TEL 44-69-55-50. FAX 40-22-02-70. TELEX 285 485. Eds. Caroline Aubry, Yvon Guemard. adv.; bk.rev.; abstr.; bibl.; charts; illus.; index. circ. 8,000. **Indexed:** Photo.Abstr., Print.Abstr.
—BLDSC (3050.900000). **CCC.**

CATALOGO DELLA GRAFICA ITALIANA. see *ART*

760   US
CLIP BITS. m. Dynamic Graphics, Inc., 6000 N. Forest Park Dr., Peoria, IL 61614. TEL 309-688-8800. FAX 309-688-3075. Ed. Dan Witte.

686.2   SZ   ISSN 0590-8450
TA418.76   CODEN: COTGAV
COATING. 1968. m. Bankgasse 8, CH-9001 St. Gallen, Switzerland. TEL 071-223239. FAX 071-228761. TELEX 719220. Ed. H. Wilthauer. circ. 4,200.
—BLDSC (3292.540000); CASDDS; Ei; Faxon; SWETS.

COLOR PUBLISHING. see *PUBLISHING AND BOOK TRADE*

COLOUR. see *PUBLISHING AND BOOK TRADE*

686.2   SA
COMMERCIAL PRINTING. fortn. Lord Doddinghurst Publications, 170 Hendrick Verwoerd Dr., Randburg, Box 70352, Bryanston, Johannesburg, South Africa. adv.

COMMUNICATION ARTS. see *ADVERTISING AND PUBLIC RELATIONS*

686 760   FR   ISSN 0763-1278
COMMUNICATION IMPRIMEE. 1983. 6/yr. 250 F. Editions Technorama, 31 place Saint-Ferdinand, 75017 Paris, France. TEL 45-74-67-43. FAX 45-72-63-21. Ed. Remy Baschet. adv. circ. 4,350.
Description: Deals with the promotion and development of communication by printed matter.

686.2   BE   ISSN 0778-6271
COMPRES - GRAFIEK; vaktijdschrift voor de grafische en aanverwante sectoren. French edition: Compres - Graphique (ISSN 0778-6263) (Text in Dutch) 1936. every 3 wks. 1500 BEF. Uitgeverij Compres, Mevr. Courtmansstraat 41, 2600 Antwerpen-Berchem, Belgium. FAX 32-3-2811008. Ed. Andre van Huffel; Pub. Koen Goderis. adv.; bk.rev.; illus. circ. 5,500. **Document type:** trade publication.
—BLDSC (3366.394100).
Formerly (until 1991): Grafiek (ISSN 0017-2944)

CONNOISSEURS GUIDE TO CALIFORNIA WINE. see *BEVERAGES*

CONTEMPORARY GRAPHIC ARTISTS; a biographical, bibliographical, and critical guide to current illustrators, animators, cartoonists, designers, and other graphic artists. see *BIOGRAPHY*

686.2 760   US   ISSN 1046-9087
CONTEMPORARY PRINT PORTFOLIO; a guide to prices, new editions & sources. 1990. s-a. $59.95 (foreign $80). Bon a Tirer Publishing, Box 3480, Shawnee Mission, KS 66203. TEL 913-236-4828. Ed. Joseph E. Zanatta.

686.2   US
COPY IMAGING AND REPRODUCTION. (Supplement to: Quick Printing) 1981. bi-m. $25. P T N Publishing Corp., 445 Broad Hollow Rd., Ste. 21, Melville, NY 11747-4722. TEL 800-308-NEWS. FAX 516-249-5774. (Co-publisher: Quion Communications, Inc.) Ed. Dan Witte. adv.: B&W page $1000, color page $1500. circ. 35,234.
●Also available online.
Formerly: Copy Magazine (ISSN 0897-9405)
Description: Covers digital and electronic imaging and reproduction technologies, products and processes used to create, reproduce and finish documents.

CRIBB REPORT; a broker's report on the free newspaper, shopper, and specialty paper industry. see *BUSINESS AND ECONOMICS — Investments*

686.2   SP
DE PRE-IMPRESION. 1989. m. (except July-Aug. combined). 4000 ptas.($31) Alabrent Ediciones, Valencia 501 entlo. 1a, 08013 Barcelona, Spain. TEL 34-3-265-32-11. FAX 34-3-265-13-20. Ed. Ramon Arnella Paris. circ. 4,000. **Document type:** trade publication.
Description: Covers pre-press.

686.2   US   ISSN 0889-423X
DEALER COMMUNICATOR; a nationwide link between dealers and their suppliers in the printing and imaging industry. 1980. m. $30. Fichera Publications, 777 S. State Rd. 7, Margate, FL 33068. TEL 305-971-4360; 800-327-8999. FAX 305-971-4362. adv.: B&W page $6465, color page $7460. bk.rev. circ. 9,110. (tabloid format) **Document type:** trade publication.
Description: Presents news about products and graphic arts dealers.

760   NE   ISSN 0923-9790
N6941.D45
DELINEAVIT ET SCULPSIT. 1989. irreg. (2-3/yr.). $50 for 5 nos. Stichting 'Vrienden van het Prentenkabinet der Rijksuniversiteit te Leiden', c/o Print Room of the University, Rapenburg 65, NL 2311 GJ Leiden, Netherlands. TEL 31-71-272790. Ed. J. Bolten. **Document type:** academic/scholarly publication.
Description: Deals with the graphic arts of the Netherlands before 1850.

DIE DEUTSCHE SCHRIFT; Zeitschrift zur Foerderung von Gotisch, Schwabacher und Fraktur. see *ART*

DEUTSCHER DRUCKER. see *PAPER AND PULP*

686.2   US   ISSN 1053-3699
DISCOUNT & WHOLESALE PRINTING NEWSLETTER. 1990. biennial. $4.50. Wellthe Publishing, c/o Prosperity & Profits Unlimited, Box 416, Denver, CO 80201-0416. TEL 303-575-5676. Ed. A. Doyle. circ. 3,000. (looseleaf format) **Document type:** newsletter.
Description: Lists sources for discount and wholesale printing.

686.2   GW
DRUCK - A B C. bi-m. Zentral-Fachausschuss fuer die Druckindustrie, Kurfuerstenanlage 69, 69115 Heidelberg, Germany.

686.2   SZ
DRUCK BULLETIN. q. Postfach 1116, CH-8048 Zurich, Switzerland. TEL 01-9285631. FAX 01-9285630. Ed. Tony Holenstein. circ. 2,700.

686.2   GW
DRUCK INTERN. m. Verband der Druckindustrie Westen-Lippe e.V., Schwanenwall 23, 44135 Dortmund, Germany. TEL 0231-579765. TELEX 22264.

686.2   GW   ISSN 0012-6462
Z119
DRUCK-PRINT. (Text in English and German) 1863. m. DM.148.20 (foreign DM.214.20). P. Keppler Verlag GmbH und Co. KG, Industriestr. 2, 63150 Heusenstamm, Germany. TEL 06104-6060. FAX 06104-606145. Ed. H. Schloesser. adv.; bk.rev.; abstr.; charts; illus.; stat. circ. 9,250. **Indexed:** Excerpt.Med., Graph.Arts Lit.Abstr. **Document type:** trade publication.
—CCC.

686.2   GW
DRUCK-SACHEN; Informationsdienst der deutschen Druckindustrie. a. Bundesverband Druck E.V., Biebricher Allee 79, 65187 Wiesbaden, Germany. FAX 0611-803113. Ed. Peter Klemm.

686.2 676   GW   ISSN 0946-5235
DRUCK UND PAPIER. m. DM.30. Industriegewerkschaft Medien, Postfach 102451, 70020 Stuttgart, Germany. TEL 0711-2018-0. FAX 0711-2018262. circ. 110,000. **Document type:** trade publication.

686.2   SZ   ISSN 0046-0737
DRUCKINDUSTRIE. 1970. 22/yr. 85 SFr. (foreign 105 SFr.). Zollikofer AG, Fuerstenlandstr. 122, CH-9001 St. Gallen, Switzerland. TEL 071-297777. FAX 071-297487. Ed. Franz Wick. adv.: B&W page 1810 SFr., color page 2300 SFr.; trim 187 x 270; adv. contact: Franz Wick. charts; illus. circ. 13,000. **Indexed:** Print.Abstr. **Document type:** trade publication.
—BLDSC (3627.670000).
Description: Articles by Swiss members of the Euro Graphic Press Association.

686.2   GW   ISSN 0012-6500
Z119
DER DRUCKSPIEGEL; Zeitschrift fuer Deutsche und internationale Drucktechnik. 1946. m. DM.103.20. Druckspiegel Verlagsgesellschaft mbH & Co., Borsigstr. 1-3, 63150 Heusenstamm, Germany. TEL 06104-606370. FAX 06104-606444. TELEX 410131. Ed.Bd. adv.: B&W page DM.4880; color page DM.8930; trim 185 x 270. bk.rev.; charts; illus.; index. circ. 12,906. **Indexed:** Graph.Arts Lit.Abstr., Print.Abstr. **Document type:** trade publication.
—SWETS. **CCC.**
Description: Provides information on technical developments in the fields of typesetting, data systems technology, computer publishing, typography, printing technology and print converting.

686.2   GW   ISSN 0012-6519
Z119
DRUCKWELT; Journal der Unternehmer und Fuehrungskraefte. 1951. m. DM.126 (foreign DM.158). Schluetersche Verlagsanstalt GmbH und Co., Hans-Boeckler-Allee 7, 30173 Hannover, Germany. TEL 0511-8550-0. FAX 0511-8550-100. (Subscr. to: Postfach 5440, 30054 Hannover, Germany) Ed.Bd. adv.; bk.rev.; bibl.; charts; illus.; index. circ. 8,022. **Indexed:** Print.Abstr., PROMT. **Document type:** trade publication.
—BLDSC (3627.850000). **CCC.**
Formerly: Graphische Woche.

686.2   CN   ISSN 0828-9638
E & B GUIDE. (Estimators & Buyers') Key Title: Graphic Monthly Estimators' & Buyers Guide. 1984. a. Can.$25. North Island Sound Ltd., 1606 Sedlescomb Dr., Unit 8, Mississauga, ON L4X 1M6, Canada. TEL 905-625-7070. FAX 905-625-4856. Pub. Alexander Donald. adv. contact: Andrew Luke. circ. 8,000. **Document type:** trade publication, directory.
Description: Directory for the graphic arts industry with over 800 listings in 115 categories.

686.2 331   US
EMPLOYER RESOURCES NEWSLETTER. bi-m. $350 to non-members; members $175. Graphic Arts Employers of America, 100 Daingerfield Rd., Alexandria, VA 22314. TEL 703-519-8150. FAX 703-548-4165. Ed. William Solomon. circ. 325.
Description: Discusses current events in industrial relations.

764.8   SP
EN SERIGRAFIA. 1986. 6/yr. 4500 ptas. in Europe; America 6000 ptas. Alabrent Ediciones, Valencia 501 entlo. 1a, 08013 Barcelona, Spain. TEL 3-265-32-11. FAX 3-265-13-20. Ed. Ramon Arnella Paris. circ. 3,000.

PRINTING

686 FR
ENSEIGNES MAGAZINE. 6/yr. Info-Pub, 92 rue Jean-Pierre-Timbaud, 75011 Paris, France. TEL 43-38-48-00. Ed. Maria Dominique Guerin. circ. 9,000.

686.2 US
ENVIRONMENTAL ADVISOR. q. $60 to non-members; members $30. National Association of Printers and Lithographers, 780 Palisade Ave., Teaneck, NJ 07666-3129. TEL 201-342-0700. FAX 201-692-0286. Ed. Monica McCabe. circ. 4,000. (also avail. in looseleaf format) **Document type:** newsletter.
Formerly: Political Advisor.
Description: Covers state and federal legislation, issues and trends concerning safety, health and the environment, for the commercial printing industry.

760 SZ
EUREPRO. CONGRESS SUMMARIES. a. Eurepro, Schosshaldenstr. 20, CH-3000 Bern 32, Switzerland. TEL 031-431511.
Formerly: Union Internationale des Industries Graphiques de Reproduction. Congress Summaries.

760 UK
EUROFORMS. bi-m. The White House, 60 High St., Potters Bar, Herts EN4 5AB, England. TEL 0707-56828. FAX 0707-45322. TELEX 892623-LABELEX-G. Ed. B. Hunt.
Description: Provides information about all aspects of materials, technology, markets and applications for the forms and continuous stationery industry and its suppliers in Europe.

686.2 UK
THE EUROPEAN SCREEN PRINTER MAGAZINE. 1989. s-a. £15. Federation of European Screen Printers Association, 7A West St., Reigate, Surrey RH2 9BL, England. TEL 01737-240788. FAX 01737-240770. Ed. Derek Down. adv.: page £1200; trim 210 x 297; adv. contact: Nigel Steffens. circ. 4,000. (back issues avail.) **Document type:** trade publication.
Description: Offers an in-depth profile on member countries. Covers environmental concerns, E.E.C. legislation, new technology, and developments in Eastern Europe.

686.2 GW ISSN 0938-1236
EUROPRINTER. 4/yr. DM.58($36) Deutscher Drucker Verlag GmbH, Postfach 4124, 73744 Ostfildern, Germany. TEL 0711-444005. FAX 0711-442099. Ed. Theodor Anton. adv. contact: H.-J. Kunstleben. **Document type:** trade publication.

760 BE
F E B E L G R A TIJDSCHRIFT. fortn. Federatie van de Belgische Industrie, Dambruggestraat 60, Postbus 1, D-2008 Antwerpen, Belgium. TEL 2317118.

686.2 NE ISSN 0169-4391
F N V MAGAZINE (AMSTERDAM). 1955. fortn. fl.225. Box 9354, 1006 AJ Amsterdam, Netherlands. TEL 31-20-6143105. FAX 31-20-6151091. Ed. R.U. Tilborg. adv.; bk.rev.; film rev.; charts; illus.; circ. 48,500 (controlled).
Former titles (until 1985): Drukwerk (ISSN 0168-1303); Grafia; Druk en Papier (ISSN 0017-2871)

686.2 GW ISSN 0015-5322
F O G R A LITERATURDIENST. 1955. m. DM.495 to non-members; members DM.371. Forschungsgesellschaft Druck e.V., Postfach 800469, 81604 Munich, Germany. TEL 089-431820. FAX 089-4316896. bk.rev. circ. 550. Indexed: Graph.Arts Lit.Abstr., Print.Abstr. **Document type:** abstracting/indexing.

686.2 GW
F O G R A LITERATURPROFILE. 1975. bi-m. DM.495 to non-members; members DM.371. Forschungsgesellschaft Druck e.V., Postfach 800469, 81604 Munich, Germany. TEL 089-431820. FAX 089-4316896. **Document type:** abstracting/indexing.

686.2 GW ISSN 0015-5330
F O G R A MITTEILUNGEN. 1953. 2/yr. membership. Forschungsgesellschaft Druck e.V., Postfach 800469, 81604 Munich, Germany. TEL 089-431820. FAX 089-4316896. bk.rev. circ. 2,500. Indexed: Graph.Arts Lit.Abstr., Print.Abstr. **Document type:** bulletin.
—BLDSC (3964.350000).

686.2 608.7 GW
F O G R A PATENTSCHAU. 1952. m. DM.700 to non-members; members DM.525. Forschungsgesellschaft Druck e.V., Postfach 800469, 81604 Munich, Germany. TEL 089-431820. FAX 089-4316896. pat.; stat. **Document type:** abstracting/indexing.
Formerly: Fogra-Patentkurzberichte.

686 FR ISSN 1156-5209
FAB. 10/yr. Societe Tarif Media S.A., 5 rue la Boetie, 75008 Paris, France. TEL 44-56-31-56. FAX 42-66-49-05. Ed. Daniel Dussausaye. circ. 10,000.

686.2 SZ
FACHHEFTE BULLETIN TECHNIQUE; grafische Industrie und Kommunikationstechnik. French edition: Bulletin Technique (ISSN 0007-5736) (Editions in French and German) 1954. 5/yr. 44 Fr. (Schweizerischer Lithographenbund) Conzett & Huber AG, Baslerstr. 30, Postfach, 8048 Zurich, Switzerland. TEL 01-522500. FAX 01-4912922. (Co-sponsor: Verband der Schweizer Druckindustrie) Ed.Bd. adv.; bk.rev.; bibl.; charts; illus., index. Indexed: Abstr.Bull.Inst.Pap.Chem., Chem.Abstr., Print.Abstr.
Formerly: Fachhefte fuer Chemigraphie, Lithographie und Tiefdruck (ISSN 0014-6374)

FACTOTUM. see LIBRARY AND INFORMATION SCIENCES

686.2 US
FINISH LINE. 1992. q. free. Foil Stamping & Embossing Association, Box 56652, Washington, DC 20040. TEL 202-882-7949. FAX 202-882-7969. Ed. Mary P. Fuller. circ. 5,000. **Document type:** trade publication.
Formerly: F S E A Flash Bulletin.
Description: Contains association, industry and goverment-related news.

686.2 US ISSN 1051-7324
FLEXO. 1976. m. $46 (foreign $63) (effective 1995). Foundation of Flexographic Technical Association, 900 Marconi Ave., Ronkonkoma, NY 11779-7212. TEL 516-737-6023. FAX 516-737-6813. Ed. Linda M. Casatelli; Pub. David A. Silverman. adv.: B&W page $2220, color page $3045; adv. contact: Diane Seddio. circ. 10,000. Indexed: Curr.Pack.Abstr., Graph.Arts Lit.Abstr., Print.Abstr. **Document type:** trade publication.
—BLDSC (3950.678000).
Formerly (until 1984): Flexographic Technical Journal (ISSN 0734-6980)

686.2 US ISSN 1051-6352
FLEXO ESPANOL. (Text in Spanish) 1986. q. $20 (effective 1994). Foundation of Flexographic Technical Association, 900 Marconi Ave., Ronkonkoma, NY 11779-7212. TEL 516-737-6023. FAX 516-737-6813. Ed. Graciela Gilbride; Pub. David A. Silverman. adv.: B&W page $1226, color page $2011; adv. contact: Diane Seddio. index. circ. 7,000. (back issues avail.)

686.2 GW
FLEXOPRINT. bi-m. DM.109.20 (foreign DM.153). P. Keppler Verlag GmbH und Co. KG, Industriestr. 2, 63150 Heusenstamm, Germany. TEL 06104-6060. FAX 06104-606145. **Document type:** trade publication.

686.2 US ISSN 0532-1700
FORM. 1963. m. $44 to non-members; members $24 (effective 1994 & 1995). National Business Forms Association, 433 E. Monroe Ave., Alexandria, VA 22301. TEL 703-836-6232. FAX 703-836-2241. Ed. Brad Holt. adv.: B&W page $1555, color page $2530; 8 1/8 x 10 7/8. bk.rev.; illus.; index. circ. 11,932. Indexed: Graph.Arts Lit.Abstr. **Document type:** trade publication.

FORMAT; Zeitschrift fuer verbale und visuelle Kommunikation. see ART

686.2 US ISSN 1042-3028
FORMSMFG. 1987. 9/yr. $73. I B F Itional Business Forms Industries, Inc., 2111 Wilson Blvd., Ste. 350, Arlington, VA 22201-3042. TEL 703-841-9191. FAX 703-522-5750. Ed. Judith Polas. adv. circ. 3,297.
Description: For manufacturers of business forms, labels, direct mail and information systems.

070 US
FOSSIL; historians of amateur journalism. 1904. q. $16. Fossils, Inc., 112 E. Burnett St., Stayton, OR 97383. FAX 503-769-4520. bk.rev. circ. 200.

686.2 Z252.5.F6
FOUNDATION OF FLEXOGRAPHIC TECHNICAL ASSOCIATION. REPORT OF THE PROCEEDINGS: ANNUAL MEETING AND TECHNICAL FORUM. Key Title: Report of the Proceedings. Annual Meeting and Technical Forum. 1959. a. $26 to members. Foundation of Flexographic Technical Association, 900 Marconi Ave., Ronkonkoma, NY 11779-7212. TEL 516-737-6023. FAX 516-737-6813. illus. circ. 1,500.
Formerly: Flexographic Technical Association. Report of the Proceedings: Annual Meeting and Technical Forum (ISSN 0428-5670)

FOUR P NEWS; India's leading journal on pulp, paper, printing and packaging. see PAPER AND PULP

686.2 FR
FRANCE BUREAUTIQUE. 1951. bi-m. 9 rue d'Hanoi, 69626 Villeurbanne Cedex, France. TEL 78-93-03-41. FAX 72-44-23-49. Ed. H. Clique. adv. circ. 2,000.
Formerly (until 1985): France Mecanographique (ISSN 0758-5586)

760 FR ISSN 0015-9565
FRANCE GRAPHIQUE. 1947. m. 600 F.($85) Edipresse, 16 rue Guillaume Tell, 75017 Paris, France. TEL 47-66-00-05. FAX 47-66-46-94. Ed. Gerard Schmitt. adv.; bk.rev.; charts; illus.; index. circ. 5,000.

686.2 US ISSN 1048-0293
Z119
G A T F WORLD. 1989. bi-m. $90 to non-members. Graphic Arts Technical Foundation, 4615 Forbes Ave., Pittsburgh, PA 15213-3796. TEL 412-621-6941. FAX 412-621-3049. TELEX 9103509221. Dir. Frank S. Benevento; Pub. Frances Wieloch. **Document type:** academic/scholarly publication.
—BLDSC (4089.228600); UMI.
Incorporates (1971-1989): E C B Newsletter (ISSN 0895-6928); (1947-1989): Graphic Arts Abstracts (ISSN 0017-3282); (1970-1989): G A T F Environmental Control Report (ISSN 0046-2241); (1970-1989): G A T F (Year).
Description: Dedicated to the advancement of the graphic communications industries worldwide.

686.2 SA
G D R. m. R.57 in Africa; elsewhere R.115 (free to qualified personnel). Graphix Publications (Pty) Ltd., P.O. Box 751119, Gardenview 2047, South Africa. TEL 27-11-6224800. FAX 27-11-6222480. adv. **Document type:** trade publication.

686.2 AU ISSN 0016-3562
G L V MITTEILUNGEN. (Graphische Lehr- und Versuchsanstalt) 1959. irreg. (1-2/yr.). free. Hoehere Graphische Bundes Lehr und Versuchsanstalt, Leyserstr. 6, A-1140 Vienna, Austria. Ed. Dr. Wilhelm Mutschlechner. bk.rev.; charts; illus.; index. circ. 500.

686.2 UK
G P M U JOURNAL. 10/yr. Graphic Paper & Media Union, Ossory House, 5 Brereton Rd., Bedford MK40 1HU, England. TEL 01234-219676. FAX 01234-218640. Ed. T. Dubbins.

686.2 331.88 SP
G R E M I. 1978. m. (11/yr.). 1400 ptas. Gremio de Industrias Graficas de Barcelona y Provincia, Gran Via les Corts Catalanes 645, planta 6o, 08010 Barcelona, Spain. TEL 3-317-10-08. FAX 3-317-62-29. circ. 2,000.

686.2 SW ISSN 0017-288X
GRAFIA. 1895-1910; resumed 1911. 16/yr. SEK 180. Grafiska Fackfoerbundet - Graphic Workers Union, P.O. Box 1101, S-111 81 Stockholm, Sweden. Ed. Sven-Aake Aulin. adv.; bk.rev.; illus.; index. circ. 46,592. (also avail. in audio cassette)
Incorporates: Grafisk Revy (ISSN 0017-2987)

PRINTING 5455

686.2   SP   ISSN 0017-2901
Z119
GRAFICAS. 11/yr. Blasco de Garay 76, 1o, 28015 Madrid, Spain. TEL 1-445-25-64. Ed. F. de Pablo Cereceda. circ. 2,500.

686.2   GW   ISSN 0937-8421
GRAFICAS MUNDIALES. (Text in Spanish) 1908. 4/yr. DM.58($36) Deutscher Drucker Verlag GmbH, Postfach 4124, 73744 Ostfildern, Germany. TEL 0711-444005. FAX 0711-415299. Ed. Theodor J. Anton. adv.: page $2320; trim 210 x 297; adv. contact: Wolfgang Blum. charts; illus.; stat.; tr.lit. circ. 10,000. **Document type:** trade publication.
  Formerly: Arte Tipografico (ISSN 0004-346X)

686.2   NE   ISSN 0017-2936
GRAFICUS: onafhankelijk weekblad voor de grafische en communicatie-industrie. 1917. w. fl.187.50 includes Graficus Magazine (foreign fl.425) (effective 1995). Wegener Tijl Tijdschriften Groep B.V., Postbus 9943, 1006 AP Amsterdam, Netherlands. TEL 31-20-5182828. FAX 31-20-5182850. Ed. Leon van Velzen. adv.: bk.rev.; abstr.; charts; illus.; pat.; stat. circ. 8,124. **Indexed:** Key to Econ.Sci. **Document type:** trade publication.
  —SWETS.

686.2   NE
GRAFICUS MAGAZINE. 1987. q. fl.187.50 includes Graficus (foreign fl.425) (effective 1995). Wegener Tijl Tijdschriften Groep B.V., Postbus 9943, 1006 AP Amsterdam, Netherlands. TEL 31-20-5182828. FAX 31-20-5182850. Ed. Leon van Velzen. Pub. Mrs. A. Staal. adv.: bk.rev. circ. 5,638. **Document type:** trade publication.
  Description: Covers development in the graphics industry.

760   SW   ISSN 0346-9727
GRAFIKNYTT. 1958. bi-m. SEK 125. Grafiksaellskapet, Roedbodtorget 2, S-111 52 Stockholm, Sweden. TEL 46-8-21-68-46. FAX 46-8-21-93-84.

686.2   NE   ISSN 0922-1328
GRAFISCH NEDERLAND; informatie voor en over grafisch management. 1970. bi-w. fl.120. Koninklijk Verbond van Grafische Ondernemingen, Postbus 220, 1180 AE Amstelveen, Netherlands. TEL 31-20-5475678. FAX 31-20-5475475. Ed. Alwin van Steijn; Pub. R.W. Spee. adv.: bk.rev.; charts; illus.; index. circ. 6,000. **Indexed:** Abstr.Bull.Inst.Pap.Chem., Excerpt.Med., Key to Econ.Sci.
  Former titles: Repro en Druk; Drukkerswereld (ISSN 0012-6713)

686.2   SZ
GRAFISCHES GEWERBE. 11/yr. Bahnhofstr. 5, CH-9463 Oberriet, Switzerland. TEL 071-782010. FAX 071-782453. Ed. Heinz Buchal. circ. 3,500.

686.2   SW   ISSN 0017-2979
GRAFISK FAKTORSTIDNING. 1914. 8/yr. SEK 225 (effective 1995). Grafiska Faktors- och Tjaenstemannafoerbundet - Graphical Managers and Overseers Association, Sankt Eriksgatan 26 III, P.O. Box 12069, S-102 22 Stockholm, Sweden. TEL 46-8-6935597. Ed. Kerstin Orsen. adv.; bk.rev.; circ. 3,500 (controlled). **Document type:** trade publication.

686.2   NO   ISSN 0802-2593
GRAFISK INSIDE. 1973. m. NOK 345. Grafisk Inside AS, P.O. Box 9076 Groenland, N-0133 Oslo, Norway. TEL 47-22-20-80-90. FAX 47-22-20-89-68. Ed. Henning Jakobsen. adv.: B&W page NOK 6050, color page NOK 9050; trim 184 x 270; adv. contact: Svein Arnesen. circ. 3,100. **Document type:** trade publication.
  Formerly (until 1988): Grafisk (ISSN 0801-3934)
  Description: Through specialist articles, interviews and stories, reflects the changing situation and developments in the world of graphics - both nationally and internationally.

686.029   DK   ISSN 0905-7986
GRAFISK LEVERANDOERHAANDBOG; produktion udstyr til den grafiske branche. 1978. a. Forlaget De Grafiske Haandboeger, Finsensvej 80, 2000 Frekeriksberg, Denmark. TEL 45-38-88-32-22. FAX 45-38-88-30-38. adv. circ. 4,188.
  Formerly: Leverandoerhaandbogen (ISSN 0904-5945)

686.2   DK   ISSN 0017-2995
DE GRAFISKE FAG. 1921. 10/yr. DKK 400. Grafisk Arbejdsgiverforening, Helgavej 26, DK-5230 Odense M, Denmark. TEL 45-66-13-06-01. FAX 45-66-13-61-15. Ed. Eivind S. Johansen. adv.: B&W page DKK 10600, color page DKK 14500; trim 263 x 186. bk.rev.; illus. circ. 83,000.
  Formerly (until 1991): Bogtrykkerbladet (ISSN 0006-5730)

686.2   DK   ISSN 0109-0879
GRAFISKE FUNKTIONAERER. 1981-1990. irreg. membership. Grafiske Funktionaerers Landsforening, Christian IX's Gade 7, 1111 Copenhagen K, Denmark. illus.
  Former titles: Grafiske Funktionaerers Landsforening. Orientering (ISSN 0109-0860); Grafiske Funktionaerers Landesforening. Medlemsblad (ISSN 0105-9041)

760   SW   ISSN 0017-3002
GRAFISKT FORUM. 1895. m. SEK 450. Grafiska Foeretagen, P.O. Box 16383, Blasieholmsgatan 4 A, S-103 27 Stockholm, Sweden. TEL 468-762-6800. FAX 468-611-6102. E-mail: grafiskt_forum@notis.postnet.se. Ed. Gunnar Svensson. adv.: B&W page SEK 9650, color page SEK 14500; trim 192 x 272; adv. contact: Gunilla Loefberg. bk.rev.; abstr.; charts; illus.; index; circ. 4,200 (controlled).
  Formerly (until 1982): Grafisit Forum: Med Nordisk Boktryckarekonst; Formed by the 1962 merger of: Nordisk Boktryckarekonst; Grafiskt Forum: Svenska Boktryckarfoereningens Meddelanden; Which was formerly (until 1935): Svenska Boktryckarefoereningens Meddelanden.

686.2   IT
GRAPH. 6/yr. L.59000 (foreign L.113000). Gruppo Editoriale J C E, Via Ferri 6, 20092 Cinisello Balsamo (MI), Italy. TEL 39-2-660251. FAX 39-2-6727620. TELEX 352376 JCEMIL I. Ed. Jacopo Castelfranchi. adv.: B&W page L.1800000, color page L.2950000; trim 210 x 280. circ. 6,621.

686   FR
GRAPH ECHOS. 21/yr. Editions du Gaillard, 29 rue de la Fontaine-au-Roi, 75011 Paris, France. TEL 43-38-99-77. FAX 43-38-50-13. Ed. Karine Schamme. circ. 7,000.

760   US
GRAPHIC ARTS. a. Northeastern University, 271 Huntington Ave., Boston, MA 02115-4546. TEL 617-437-2000.

655   US   ISSN 1044-7970
Z244.6.U5
GRAPHIC ARTS BLUE BOOK. DELAWARE VALLEY - OHIO EDITION; directory of graphic arts operating firms and suppliers in Ohio, Pennsylvania, Delaware, Maryland, District of Columbia, and its Virginia suburbs. 1910. biennial. $85. A.F. Lewis Co., Inc., 245 5th Ave., New York, NY 10016. TEL 212-679-0770. FAX 212-545-7963. adv.; index. circ. 7,500. **Document type:** directory.
  Formerly: Printing Trades Blue Book. Delaware Valley - Ohio Edition (ISSN 0193-3949)

655   US   ISSN 1044-8527
Z475
GRAPHIC ARTS BLUE BOOK. METRO NEW YORK - NEW JERSEY EDITION; directory of graphic arts operating firms and suppliers in metropolitan New York and New Jersey. 1910. a. $85. A.F. Lewis Co., Inc., 245 5th Ave., New York, NY 10016. TEL 212-679-0770. FAX 212-545-7963. adv.; index. circ. 6,000. **Document type:** directory.
  Formerly: Printing Trades Blue Book. New York Edition (ISSN 0079-5348)

655   US   ISSN 1044-8535
Z475
GRAPHIC ARTS BLUE BOOK. MIDWESTERN EDITION; directory of graphic arts operating firms and suppliers in Illinois, Indiana, Michigan, Wisconsin, Missouri, Iowa, Minnesota and North and South Dakota. 1970. a. $85. A.F. Lewis Co., Inc., 245 5th Ave., New York, NY 10016. TEL 212-679-0770. FAX 212-545-7963. (And: 15 Spinning Wheel Rd., Hinsdale, IL 60521. TEL 708-323-9777) Eds. Bill Curran, Linda Kubista Curran. adv.; index. circ. 12,000. **Document type:** directory.
  Former titles: Graphic Arts Green Book (ISSN 0147-1651); Graphic Arts Trade Directory and Register (ISSN 0072-5498)

655   US   ISSN 1044-646X
Z475
GRAPHIC ARTS BLUE BOOK. NORTHEASTERN EDITION; directory of graphic arts operating firms and suppliers in New England and upstate New York. 1910. biennial. $85. A.F. Lewis Co., Inc., 245 5th Ave., New York, NY 10016. TEL 212-679-0770. FAX 212-545-7963. adv.; index. circ. 6,000. **Document type:** directory.
  Formerly: Printing Trades Blue Book. Northeastern Edition (ISSN 0079-5356)

655   US   ISSN 1044-7989
Z475
GRAPHIC ARTS BLUE BOOK. SOUTHEASTERN EDITION; directory of graphic arts operating firms and suppliers in Virginia (except D.C. suburbs), W. Virginia, North Carolina, South Carolina, Georgia, Florida, Kentucky, Tennessee, Alabama, Mississippi. 1910. biennial. $85. A.F. Lewis Co., Inc., 245 5th Ave., New York, NY 10016. TEL 212-679-0770. FAX 212-545-7963. adv.; index. circ. 8,000. **Document type:** directory.
  Formerly: Printing Trades Blue Book. Southeastern Edition (ISSN 0079-5364)

686.2025   US
▼**GRAPHIC ARTS BLUE BOOK. TEXAS CENTRAL;** directory of graphic arts operating firms and suppliers in Texas, New Mexico, Colorado, Kansas, Nebraska, Oklahoma, Louisiana and Arkansas. 1995. biennial. $85. A.F. Lewis & Co., Inc., 245 5th Ave., New York, NY 10016. TEL 212-679-0770. FAX 212-545-7963. circ. 8,000. **Document type:** directory.

381.2025   US
GRAPHIC ARTS BLUE BOOK. WESTERN; directory of graphic arts operating firms and suppliers in California, Oregon, Washington, Nevada, Arizona, Idaho, Montana, Wyoming, Hawaii, Utah and Alaska. biennial. $85. A.F. Lewis Co., Inc., 245 5th Ave., New York, NY 10016. TEL 212-679-0770. FAX 212-545-7963. circ. 12,000. **Document type:** directory.
  Formerly: Graphic Arts Blue Book. West Coast Edition (ISSN 1046-8005)

686.2   US   ISSN 1047-9325
CODEN: GAMOE4
GRAPHIC ARTS MONTHLY. 1929. m. $85 (Canada $165; Mexico $154; elsewhere $170). Cahners Publishing Company (New York), Division of Reed Elsevier Inc., 249 W. 17th St., New York, NY 10011. TEL 212-463-6834. FAX 212-463-6530. (Subscr. to: 44 Cook St., Denver, CO 80206-5800. TEL 800-662-7776) Ed. Rodger Ynostroza; Pub. Ronald C. Andriani. adv.; illus.; tr.lit.; index; circ. 89,000 (controlled). (also avail. in microfiche from CIS; back issues avail.) **Indexed:** Abstr.Bull.Inst.Pap.Chem., B.P.I, Bus.Ind., Chem.Abstr., Graph.Arts Lit.Abstr., Photo.Abstr., Print.Abstr., Resour.Ctr.Ind., SRI, Tr.& Indus.Ind. **Document type:** trade publication.
  ●Also available online. Vendor(s): Knight-Ridder, Inc., Lexis-Nexis.
  —BLDSC (4211.950000); CASDDS; Faxon; SWETS; UMI; UnCover. CCC.
  Formerly: Graphic Arts Monthly and the Printing Industry (ISSN 0017-3312)
  Description: For corporate management, production management, production operations in the printing industries. Highlights cost and time saving methods of combining ink, paper and type into a quality finished product.

686.2 070.5   US   ISSN 0884-6901
GRAPHIC COMMUNICATIONS WORLD; the Monday morning briefing for senior management. 1968. fortn. $297 to individuals; educational institutions $172; foreign $322. Green Sheet Communications, Inc., Box 727, Hartsdale, NY 10530-0727. TEL 914-472-3051. FAX 914-472-3880. Ed. John R. Werner. bk.rev.; circ. 4,000 (paid). (back issues avail.) **Indexed:** Abstr.Bull.Inst.Pap.Chem., Graph.Arts Lit.Abstr. **Document type:** trade publication.
  Description: Covers new technology and management trends for senior management in the printing and publishing industry.

760   JA
GRAPHIC DESIGN IN JAPAN. (Text in English) a. $248. Intercontinental Marketing Corp., I.P.O. Box 5056, Tokyo 100-30, Japan. TEL 81-3-3661-7458. FAX 81-3-3667-9646.

ULRICH'S INTERNATIONAL PERIODICALS DIRECTORY 1996

PRINTING

760 659.1 US ISSN 0274-7499
GRAPHIC DESIGN: U S A. 1965. m. $60. Kaye Publishing Corporation, 1556 3rd Ave. Ste. 405, New York, NY 10128-3106. TEL 212-534-5003. FAX 212-534-4415. Ed. Gordon D. Kaya. adv.: B&W page $3590. bk.rev.; illus.; tr.lit.; circ. 30,186 (controlled). **Indexed:** Graph.Arts Lit.Abstr. **Document type:** trade publication.
Formerly: Graphics: U S A (ISSN 0017-3428); Incorporates: Graphics: New York.
Description: Covers production, advertising, communication, graphic design and art.

686.2 760 CN ISSN 0227-2806
GRAPHIC MONTHLY. 1980. 6/yr. Can.$28. North Island Publishing, 1606 Sedlescomb Dr., Unit 8, Mississauga, ON L4X 1M6, Canada. TEL 905-625-7070. FAX 905-625-4856. Ed. Nancy Clark; Pub. Alexander Donald. adv. contact: Andrew Luke. circ. 10,086. (also avail. in microfilm) **Document type:** trade publication.
Description: Serves as a reference tool for owners and managers by providing how-to advice and product and service information. Covers news and issues affecting printers today.

686.2 US
GRAPHIC NETWORK. 1984. m. $45 (effective 1993). 729 Washington Rd., Pittsburgh, PA 15228. TEL 412-341-3744; 800-899-1817. FAX 412-341-6344. Pub. J.E. Scherer. adv.: B&W page $2980, color page $4180; 8 1/2 x 11. bk.rev. circ. 30,000. (back issues avail.) **Document type:** trade publication.
Description: For graphic consumers and producers in Mid-Atlantic area.

686.2 070.5 US
GRAPHIC NEWS. 1986. m. membership. Printing Industry of Minnesota, Inc., 450 North Syndicate, Ste. 200, St. Paul, MN 55104. TEL 612-646-4826. FAX 612-646-8673. Ed. Kathleen Conroy. circ. 5,000 (controlled). **Document type:** newsletter.

686.2 UK ISSN 0952-4118
GRAPHIC REPRO. 1986. m. 99 Maybury Rd., Woking, Surrey GU21 5HX, England. TEL 0483-740271. FAX 0483-740397. Ed. N. Walker. bk.rev. circ. 10,000. **Document type:** trade publication.
Description: Reviews technical developments and trade news in the pre-press field, including graphic design, typesetting, color reproduction, proofing, and platemaking.

GRAPHICOMMUNICATOR. see LABOR UNIONS

686.2 US
GRAPHICS.* 1945. bi-m. $59. Graphic U.S., Inc., 1556 Third Ave., Ste. 405, New York, NY 10128-3106. TEL 212-889-9611. Ed. Lyle Metzdorf. adv. circ. 29,000.

686.2 US
GRAPHICS UPDATE. 1985. m. $15 to non-members. Printing Association of Florida, Inc., Box 170010, Hialeah, FL 33017-0010. TEL 305-558-4855. FAX 305-823-8965. Ed. Gene Strul. adv.: B&W page $1053, color page $1210.950435444881/2 x 11. bk.rev.; circ. 10,520 (controlled).

686.2 IT ISSN 0017-3436
GRAPHICUS. 1911. 10/yr. L.150000. Associazione Culturale Progresso Grafico, Via Morgari 36/B, 10125 Turin, Italy. TEL 39-11-6690577. FAX 39-11-6689200. Ed. Luciano Lovera. adv.: B&W page L.1750000, color page L.2450000; adv. contact: Mario Mercalli. bk.rev.; bibl.; charts; illus.; index; circ. 6,250 (controlled). **Indexed:** Chem.Abstr., Graph.Arts Lit.Abstr., Print.Abstr. **Document type:** trade publication.
—BLDSC (4212.520000).

GRAPHIS; international journal of visual communication. see ART

GRAPHIS ANNUAL REPORTS. see ART

GRAPHIS DESIGN; international annual of design and illustration. see ART

GRAPHIS LETTERHEAD. see ART

GRAPHIS LOGO. see ART

686.2 AU ISSN 0017-3479
GRAPHISCHE REVUE OESTERREICHS; Fachzeitschrift fuer das gesamte graphische Gewerbe. 1899. bi-m. S.500. Gewerkschaft Druck und Papier, Seidengasse 15, A-1070 Vienna, Austria. Ed. Josef Keller. adv.; bk.rev.; charts; illus.; tr.lit.; index. circ. 4,800. **Indexed:** Print.Abstr. **Document type:** trade publication.

763 AU ISSN 0075-2266
Z119
GRAPHISCHE UNTERNEHMUNGEN OESTERREICHS. JAHRBUCH. 1930. a. S.450. Hauptverband der Graphischen Unternehmungen Oesterreichs, Gruenangergasse 4, A-1010 Vienna, Austria. TEL 01-5126609. FAX 01-513282619. Ed. Hans Inmann. adv.: page S.6500; trim 170 x 240; adv. contact: Elisabeth Kraus. circ. 980. **Document type:** directory.

686.2 SA
GRAPHIX; the monthly journal for the graphic communications industry. 1973. m. R.142.50 includes GDR (in Africa R.210; elsewhere R.350) (effective 1995). Graphix Publications (Pty) Ltd., P.O. Box 751119, Gardenview 2047, South Africa. TEL 27-11-622-4800. FAX 27-11-6222480. Ed. Marita Nortje. adv.; bk.rev. circ. 4,000. **Indexed:** Ind.S.A.Per. **Document type:** trade publication.
Description: South African journal for the printing and graphic arts industries.

686.2 AT
GRAPHIX. 1948. m. $50. Peter Isaacson Publications Pty. Ltd., 45-50 Porter St., Prahran, Vic. 3181, Australia. TEL 03-245-7777. FAX 03-245-7606. Ed. Peter Kohn. adv. circ. 6,957. (also avail. in microform from UMI; reprint service avail. from UMI) **Document type:** trade publication.
—CCC.
Former titles (until 1975): Graphic Arts (ISSN 0310-5792); (until 1971): Graphic Arts Bulletin (ISSN 0017-3290)

686.2 GW ISSN 0015-7775
GRAVEUR FLEXOGRAF; Fachzeitung fuer Formenbauer, Formgestalter und Fertigungstechniker, Graveure, Gurtler. (Supplements avail.) 1875. m. DM.133.92. Ruehle-Diebener Verlag GmbH und Co. KG, Postfach 700450, 70574 Stuttgart, Germany. TEL 0711-97667-0. FAX 0711-9766749. adv. contact: Werner Class. abstr.; charts; illus. circ. 4,910. **Document type:** trade publication.

686.2 US ISSN 0894-4946
Z258
GRAVURE. 1950. q. $42 (effective 1995). Gravure Association of America, Inc., 1200A Scottsville Rd., Rochester, NY 14624-5703. TEL 716-436-2150. FAX 716-436-7689. Ed. John Sippel. adv.: B&W page $1878, color page $2973; 8 1/2 x 11; adv. contact: Holli Vogt. bk.rev.; charts; illus. circ. 1,800. **Indexed:** Graph.Arts Lit.Abstr., Print.Abstr. **Document type:** trade publication.
Former titles (until 1986): Gravure Bulletin (ISSN 0160-8789); Gravure Technical Association Bulletin (ISSN 0017-3576)
Description: For customers, suppliers and printers of gravure printing process.

686.2 US ISSN 0271-1699
TD195.P7
GRAVURE ENVIRONMENTAL NEWSLETTER. 1972. s-a. membership. Gravure Association of America, Inc., Gravure Environmental Council, 1200A Scottsville Rd., Rochester, NY 14624-5703. TEL 716-436-2150. FAX 716-436-7689. Ed. Gregory Tyszka. circ. 1,400 (controlled). (back issues avail.) **Indexed:** Graph.Arts Lit.Abstr. **Document type:** newsletter.
Formerly: Gravure Environmental and O S H A Newsletter (ISSN 0091-5203)

760 SP
GREM. 12/yr. Graphic Arts Trade Association of Madrid, Villalar 6 1o Izqda., 28001 Madrid, Spain. TEL 1-577-63-44. FAX 1-577-43-78.

GUIDE TO THE PRODUCERS OF POLYURETHANE ADHESIVES AND SEALANTS IN EUROPE. see PAINTS AND PROTECTIVE COATINGS

686.2 338 UK
GUIDEBOOK TO THE EUROPEAN PRINTING INKS INDUSTRY. 1993. irreg. £300. I A L Consultants, 314-316 Harbour Yard, Chelsea Harbour, London SW10 0XD, England. TEL 071-376-3676. FAX 071-376-8281. **Document type:** trade publication.

GUILD OF BOOK WORKERS JOURNAL. see PUBLISHING AND BOOK TRADE

LE GUTENBERG; relieur et cartonnier. see LABOR UNIONS

686.209 GW ISSN 0933-6230
GUTENBERG-GESELLSCHAFT. KLEINE DRUCKE. 1926. irreg. membership. Gutenberg-Gesellschaft e.V., Liebfrauenplatz 5, 55116 Mainz, Germany. TEL 06131-226420. FAX 06131-123488. Eds. 2,000. (back issues avail.) **Document type:** monographic series.
Description: Results of research on the history of printing; activities of the Gutenberg-Gesellschaft.

686.209 GW ISSN 0072-9094
Z1008
GUTENBERG - JAHRBUCH. 1926. a. DM.130. Gutenberg-Gesellschaft e.V., Liebfrauenplatz 5, 55116 Mainz, Germany. TEL 06131-226420. FAX 06131-123488. Ed. Stephan Fuessel. adv.; bk.rev.; index (1926-1975); (1976-1986). circ. 2,200. **Indexed:** M.L.A. **Document type:** academic/scholarly publication.
Description: Research results in the history of printing worldwide.

686.2 GW ISSN 0073-0173
HANDBUCH FUER DIE DRUCKINDUSTRIE BERLIN. 1946. a. DM.10. Kupijai und Prochnow, Verlag und Druckerei, Bluecherstr. 22, 1000 Berlin 61, Germany.

686.2 SZ
HELVETISCHE TYPOGRAPHIA. 6/yr. Monbijoustr. 61, Postfach 64, CH-3000 Bern 23, Switzerland. TEL 0131-3715566. FAX 031-3710837. Ed. Ewald Ackermann. circ. 4,200. **Document type:** trade publication.

686.2 GW ISSN 0177-2945
HIGH QUALITY; Zeitschrift ueber das Gestalten, das Drucken und das Gedruckte. Short title: H Q. (Text in German; summaries in English) 1985. 3/yr. DM.75 (foreign DM.125). (Heidelberger Druckmaschinen Aktiengesellschaft) High Quality GmbH, Zaehringerstr. 2, 69115 Heidelberg, Germany. TEL 06221-184020. FAX 06221-165024. Eds. Guenter Braus, Rolf Mueller. circ. 14,000. **Indexed:** DAAI. **Document type:** trade publication.
Description: Magazine about graphic design and printing.

686.2 US ISSN 0737-1020
Z119
HIGH VOLUME PRINTING. bi-m. $45. Innes Publishing Company, Box 368, Northbrook, IL 60065. TEL 708-564-5940. Ed. Catherine Stanulis; Pub. Steve Austin. adv. contact: Steve Austin. circ. 42,000. (also avail. microform from UMI) **Indexed:** Graph.Arts Lit.Abstr., INSPEC, Print.Abstr., PROMT. **Document type:** trade publication.
—Faxon; UMI.

686.2 US
HOT OFF THE PRESS. 1988. 3/yr. Graham Communications, 40 Oval Rd., Quincy, MA 02170. TEL 617-328-0069. FAX 617-471-1504. Ed. Mary-Beth Sorgi; Pub. John R. Graham. circ. 3,000. **Document type:** trade publication, newsletter.

729 US ISSN 0886-0483
NC1000 CODEN: HOWWEH
HOW; the magazine of ideas and techniques in graphic design. 1985. bi-m. $49 (includes How's Business Annual). F & W Publications, Inc., 1507 Dana Ave., Cincinnati, OH 45207. TEL 513-531-2222. Ed. Kathleen Reinmann. adv.: B&W page $2075, color page $2870. circ. 36,202. **Indexed:** Ind.How To Do It (1990-).
—UMI; UnCover.
Description: Describes how graphic design professionals create their work.

760 659.1   US
HOW'S BUSINESS ANNUAL. (Special Nov.-Dec. issue of How magazine) 1987. a. $12. F & W Publications, Inc., 1507 Dana Ave., Cincinnati, OH 45207. TEL 513-531-2222. FAX 513-531-4744.
Description: Describes how graphic design professionals create their work.

686.2   BE   ISSN 0018-9782
I G F - JOURNAL; journal of the printing, bookbinding and paper workers in all countries. (Editions in English, French, German, Spanish and Swedish) 1950. s.a. free. International Graphical Federation, Rue des Fripiers 17, Bloc 2, Galerie du Centre, 1000 Brussels, Belgium. TEL 32-2-223-18-14. FAX 32-2-223-02-20. circ. 2,500. **Indexed:** Print.Abstr.
Incorporates (in 1973): International Graphical Federation. Conference. Proceedings (ISSN 0074-6169)

I G MEDIEN FORUM. (Industriegewerkschaft) see PUBLISHING AND BOOK TRADE

I T U REVIEW. (International Typographical Union) see LABOR UNIONS

IMAGE WORLD; careers in graphic communications. see OCCUPATIONS AND CAREERS

070 686.2   MX
IMPRESOR; al servicio de las artes graficas. (Text in English, Spanish) 1977. m. Mex.$150($175) (effective Nov. 1994). Imprentas Menra, S.A., Sta. Ma. la Rivera 9-103, 06400 Mexico D.F., Mexico. TEL 525-546-8725. FAX 525-566-1038. Ed. Joaquin Menendez Rangel. adv. contact: Teresa Menendez Martin. bk.rev.; illus.; stat.; tr.lit. circ. 10,000. (tabloid format) **Document type:** trade publication.
Formerly: Impresor Internacional.
Description: Covers the graphic arts industry. Includes industry news, new techniques and machinery, politics and cultural notes.

760   FR
IMPRESSIONS. 1976. q. Imprimerie Nationale, B.P. 514, 59505 Douai Cedex, France. TEL 27-93-70-90. FAX 27-93-70-96. TELEX 120 389 F. Ed. Gabin Caillard.

760   VE
IMPRIMASE. 1958. 6/yr. free. Asociacion de Industrialse de Artes Graficas de Venezuela, Edificio Camara de Industriales, Piso 2, Esq. Puente Anauco, Apdo. 14.405, Caracas 1011A, Venezuela. adv.; bk.rev. circ. 2,000.

686.209   GW
IMPRIMATUR. NEUE FOLGE; ein Jahrbuch fuer Buecherfreunde. triennial, vol.15, 1993. price varies. Harrassowitz Verlag, Taunusstr. 14, 65183 Wiesbaden, Germany. TEL 0611-530-0. FAX 0611-530570. TELEX 4186135. (Subscr. to: Postfach 2929, 65019 Wiesbaden, Germany) Ed. Eva Hanebutt-Benz. **Indexed:** M.L.A. **Document type:** monographic series.
Formerly: Imprimatur. Jahrbuch fuer Buecherfreunde. Neue Folge (ISSN 0073-5620)

686.2   FR
IMPRIMERIE FRANCAISE.* m. Federation Francaise des Travailleurs du Livre, 263 rue de Paris, 93100 Montrenil, France. adv.

IMPRINT. see LABOR UNIONS

686.2   US   ISSN 0883-6973
                            CODEN: INHGEY
IN HOUSE GRAPHICS. 1984. m. $117. United Communications Group, 11300 Rockville Pike, Ste. 1100, Rockville, MD 20852-3030. TEL 301-816-8950. FAX 301-816-8945. Ed. Ronnie Lipton. bk.rev.; charts; illus.; index. (back issues avail.)
—CCC.
Description: Gives news and how-to design tips for copy and editing, photography, printing and production to help communicators produce high-quality ads, brochures and publications.

686.2   US   ISSN 0891-8996
Z119
IN-PLANT PRINTER INCLUDING CORPORATE IMAGING; the in-plant management magazine. 1961. bi-m. $45 (foreign $65). Innes Publishing Company, Box 368, Northbrook, IL 60065. TEL 708-564-5940. Ed. Steve Klebba; Pub. Mary Ellen Innes. adv.; bk.rev.; abstr.; charts; illus.; tr.lit.; index. circ. 42,000. (also avail. in microform from UMI; reprint service avail. from UMI) **Indexed:** Graph.Arts Lit.Abstr., Print.Abstr., Resour.Ctr.Ind.
—UMI.
Former titles: In-Plant Printer and Electronic Publisher; In-Plant Printer (ISSN 0019-3232); In-Plant Offset Printer.

655   US   ISSN 1043-1942
Z252.5.05
IN-PLANT REPRODUCTIONS. 1951. m. $65 (free to qualified personnel) (foreign $87). North American Publishing Co., 401 N. Broad St., Philadelphia, PA 19108. TEL 215-238-5300. FAX 215-238-5457. Ed. Bob Neubauer. adv.; bk.rev.; charts; illus.; stat. circ. 41,000. (also avail. in microform from UMI; reprint service avail. from UMI) **Indexed:** Abstr.Bull.Inst.Pap.Chem., Graph.Arts Lit.Abstr., Print.Abstr., Resour.Ctr.Ind. **Document type:** trade publication.
—SWETS; UMI; UnCover. **CCC.**
Former titles (until 1988): In-Plant Reproductions and Electronic Publishing (ISSN 0886-3121); (until 1985): In-Plant Productions (ISSN 0198-9065); (until 1979): Reproductions Review and Methods (ISSN 0164-4327); Graphic Arts Supplier News (ISSN 0017-3355); Reproductions Methods; Reproductions Review (ISSN 0034-4974).
Description: Written for management and technical personnel connected with basic printing and production processes and techniques in non-commercial printing environments. Examines in-plant and electronic publishing concerns for business, industry and government.

686.2 658.2   SA   ISSN 1022-355X
IN PRINT. 1992. q. Southern African Printing College, P.O. Box 1084, Honeydew 2040, South Africa. illus. **Document type:** newsletter.

686.2 658.2   US
IN-REGISTER NEWSLETTER.* 1982. bi-m. $36. In-Register, Inc., Box 480313, San Francisco, CA 94146-0313. TEL 415-467-8760. FAX 415-467-8762. Ed. Richard Michaels. bk.rev.; charts; stat.; tr.lit. circ. 500. (back issues avail.)
Description: Information for wide range of print buyers or suppliers, industry trends, libraries and research.

INDIAN NEWSPAPER SOCIETY PRESS HANDBOOK (YEAR). see JOURNALISM

655   II   ISSN 0019-6185
INDIAN PRINT & PAPER;* a journal for printers, papermakers and the allied industries. 1934. q. Rs.8($2) Commercial Products Ltd., 95 Park Street, Calcutta 700 016, India. Ed. Bimal Bose. adv.; bk.rev.; abstr.; bibl.; charts; illus.; stat.; index. **Indexed:** Chem.Abstr.

686.2 676.3   US   ISSN 1054-2434
Z244.6.L29
INDUSTRIA GRAFICA Y ARTES GRAFICAS. (Text in Spanish) 1967. 12/yr. $100 (foreign $120). C C International Publishing, Inc., 1680 S.W. Bayshore Blvd., Port St. Lucie, FL 34984. TEL 407-879-6666. FAX 407-879-7388. Ed. Miguel Garzon. adv.: B&W page $3980. bk.rev. circ. 23,000. **Indexed:** Graph.Arts Lit.Abstr., Packag.Sci.Tech. **Document type:** trade publication.
Formed by the merger of: Industria Grafica (ISSN 0120-7601) & Artes Graficas U S A (ISSN 0164-1905); **Incorporates:** Export Graficas U S A (ISSN 0741-7160); **Formerly:** Artes Graficas (ISSN 0004-3494)
Description: International trade publication with technical articles covering the printing, newspaper and graphic arts industries.

INDUSTRIEGEWERKSCHAFT MEDIEN. SCHRIFTENREIHE FUER BETRIEBSRATE. see PUBLISHING AND BOOK TRADE

764.8   FR   ISSN 0980-9112
INFO - SERI. 11/yr. 14 av. Henry Dunant, B.P. 38, 93250 Villemomble, France. TEL 48-55-05-49. FAX 48-55-11-88. Ed. Claude Douat. circ. 4,200.

686.2   UK   ISSN 0956-9456
INK & PRINT INTERNATIONAL. 1958. q. £15.30 (overseas £22). (Society of British Printing Ink Manufacturers) Batiste Publications Ltd., Pembroke House, Campsbourne Rd., Hornsey, London N8 7PE, England. TEL 0181-340-3291. FAX 0181-341-4840. TELEX 267727 BATGRP G. Ed. Dr. R.H. Leach. adv.; illus.; tr.lit. circ. 2,500. **Indexed:** Abstr.Bull.Inst.Pap.Chem., Br.Tech.Ind., Chem.Abstr., Graph.Arts Lit.Abstr., Key to Econ.Sci., Print.Abstr., PROMT, World Surf.Coat. **Document type:** trade publication.
—BLDSC (4514.451000); CASDDS; Ei.
Former titles (until 1988): Ink and Print (ISSN 0263-497X); (until 1982): British Ink Maker (ISSN 0007-0831)

686.2   US   ISSN 1079-9281
Z119
INK ON PAPER; new imaging technologies and business strategies. 1981. m. $175. W. Caslon & Co., 100 Parkwood Ave., Rochester, NY 14620-3402. TEL 716-461-4294. FAX 716-271-4442. (Subscr. to: 3100 Bronson Hill Rd., Livonia, NY 14487-9716. TEL 716-346-2776. FAX 716-346-2276) Eds. Miles & Donna Southworth. bk.rev.; bibl.; charts; illus.; index; circ. 350 (paid). (looseleaf format; back issues avail.)
—BLDSC (4514.458000).
Formerly (until 1995): Quality Control Scanner (ISSN 0739-6732)
Description: Focuses on the revolution taking place in imaging technologies and the associated workflow changes needed to make money in the printing-publishing business today.

686.2   UK   ISSN 0143-9871
INKLINGS. 1948. 3/yr. Coates Lorilleux, Cray Avenue, St. Mary Cray, Orpington, Kent BR5 3PP, England. TEL 0689-27080. Ed. C. Armstrong. circ. 10,000. **Indexed:** Print.Abstr.

686.2   US
INKLINGS (EDISON). vol.2, no.4, 1993. bi-m. J.H. Huber Corporation, Printing Ink Division, 333 Thornall St., Edison, NJ 08818. Ed. Joe Witek.

686.2   JA   ISSN 0020-1766
INSATSUKAI/PRINTING WORLD. (Text in Japanese) 1950. m. 20400 Yen (foreign $170); newsstand price: 2000 Yen. Nippon Insatsu Shinbunsha - Japan Printing News Co., Ltd., 16-8, 1-chome, Shintomi, Chuo-ku, Tokyo 104, Japan. TEL 03-3553-5681. FAX 03-3553-5684. Ed. Akiko Ito. adv.: page 130000 Yen; 260 x 180. illus. circ. 8,500. **Indexed:** Chem.Abstr. **Document type:** trade publication.

686.2   US   ISSN 1044-3746
Z252.5.I49
INSTANT & SMALL COMMERCIAL PRINTER. 1982. 10/yr. $45. Innes Publishing Company, Box 368, Northbrook, IL 60065. TEL 708-564-5940. Ed. Jeanette Clinkunbroomer. circ. 53,000. (also avail. in microform from UMI) **Indexed:** Graph.Arts Lit.Abstr. **Document type:** trade publication.
—UMI.
Formerly: Instant Printer (ISSN 0744-3854)

686   FR   ISSN 0397-1392
INTEGREE. 1976. 6/yr. 13 rue Rougemont, 75009 Paris, France. TEL 47-70-40-38. Ed. B. Girard. circ. 5,000.

INTERNATIONAL DIRECTORY OF PRIVATE PRESSES. see BUSINESS AND ECONOMICS — Trade And Industrial Directories

686.2   GW
INTERPRINT. (Text in Russian) 2/yr. Deutscher Drucker Verlag GmbH, Postfach 4124, 73744 Ostfildern, Germany. TEL 0711-444005. FAX 0711-415299. Ed. W. Pincus Jespert. adv.: page DM.5190; trim 210 x 297; adv. contact: Wolfgang Blum. circ. 20,000. **Document type:** trade publication.

686.2   IE   ISSN 0790-2026
IRISH PRINTER. 1969. m. £20. Jemma Publications Ltd., 22 Brookfield Ave., Blackrock, Dublin, Ireland. TEL 886946. FAX 881098. (Subscr. to: P.O. Box 1973, Rathmines, Dublin 6, Ireland) Ed. Frank Corr. adv.; bk.rev.; illus. circ. 1,850. **Indexed:** Print.Abstr.
Formerly: Modern Irish Printer.

ISRAEL BOOK TRADE DIRECTORY; a guide to publishers, printers, booksellers and the book trade in Israel. see PUBLISHING AND BOOK TRADE

PRINTING

686.2   IT   ISSN 0021-2784
Z119
L'ITALIA GRAFICA. 1946. 6/yr. L.42000 (foreign L.84000). (Associazione Nazionale Italiana delle Industrie Grafiche - National Association of the Italian Graphics Industry) Promotec Editoriale, Palazzo Taurus 2, 20041 Agrate Brianza (MI), Italy. TEL 39-6091807. FAX 39-6091806. Ed. Silvano Boroli. adv.: color page L.2548000; trim 210 x 297; adv. contact: Roberta Reineke. bk.rev. circ. 12,000. **Indexed:** Graph.Arts Lit.Abstr., Print.Abstr.

686.2   JA   ISSN 0072-548X
JAPAN GRAPHIC ARTS. (Text in English) 1959. a. 4,500 Yen (foreign $45). (Japan Federation of Printing Industries) Nippon Insatsu Shinbunsha - Japan Printing News Co., Ltd., 16-8, 1-chome, Shintomi, Chuo-ku, Tokyo 104, Japan. TEL 03-3553-5681. FAX 03-3553-5684. Ed. Akiko Ito. adv.: page 150000 Yen; 255 x 180. bk.rev.; charts; stat. circ. 5,000. **Indexed:** Graph.Arts Lit.Abstr. **Document type:** trade publication.
Description: Covers the trends and development in Japanese printing and related industries for printers, traders and managers.

686.221   JA
JAPAN TYPOGRAPHY ANNUAL/NIHON TAIPOGURAFI NENKAN. (Text in Japanese; title and captions for plates in English) 1974. a. $195. (Japan Typography Association - Nihon Taipogurafi Kyokai) Intercontinental Marketing Corp., I.P.O. Box 5056, Tokyo 100-30, Japan. illus.
Formerly: Nihon Retaringu Nenkan.

760   JA
CODEN: NIGRAA
JAPANESE SOCIETY OF PRINTING SCIENCE AND TECHNOLOGY. BULLETIN. (Text in Japanese; summaries in English) vol.15, 1975. q. Japanese Society of Printing Science and Technology - Insatsu Gakkai Shuppanbu, 1-16-8 Shinlomi, Chuo-ku, Tokyo 104, Japan. adv.; bk.rev.; abstr.; charts; illus. **Indexed:** Graph.Arts Lit.Abstr., JTA. —CASDDS.
Formerly: Technical Association of Graphic Arts of Japan. Bulletin (ISSN 0040-0874)

760   JA
JAPANESE SOCIETY OF PRINTING SCIENCE AND TECHNOLOGY. BULLETIN (OVERSEAS EDITION). (Text in English) 1969. q. $20. Japanese Society of Printing Science and Technology - Insatsu Gakkai Shuppanbu, 1-16-8 Shinlomi, Chuo-ku, Tokyo 104, Japan. Ed. Masakazu Kawamata. **Indexed:** Graph.Arts Lit.Abstr., Print.Abstr.
Formerly: Technical Association of Graphic Arts of Japan. Bulletin (Overseas Edition).

655.1   GW   ISSN 0932-4372
Z119
JOURNAL FUER DRUCKGESCHICHTE/JOURNAL D'HISTOIRE DE L'IMPRIMERIE/JOURNAL OF PRINTING HISTORY. 1988. 2/yr. Typostudio Schumacher-Gebler, Goethestr. 21, 80336 Munich, Germany.

686.2   UK   ISSN 1352-7126
KEY NOTE REPORT: PRINTING. Variant title: Printing. 1993. irreg. £185. Key Note Publications Ltd., Field House, 72 Oldfield Rd., Hampton, Middlesex TW12 2HQ, England. TEL 0181-783-0755. FAX 0181-783-1720. **Document type:** trade publication.
● Also available online.
Also available on CD-ROM.

686.2   UK   ISSN 0954-4518
KEY NOTE REPORT: PRINTING INKS. Variant title: Printing Inks. irreg. £185. Key Note Publications Ltd., Field House, 72 Oldfield Rd., Hampton, Middlesex TW12 2HQ, England. TEL 0181-783-0755. FAX 0181-783-1720. **Document type:** trade publication.
● Also available online.
Also available on CD-ROM.
—BLDSC (6614.265000).

KOMPASS SELECT EXPORT. PAPER INDUSTRY, GRAPHIC ARTS. see *PAPER AND PULP*

686.2   GW
L & D - LIEFERANTEN UND DIENSTLEISTER FUER VERLAGE UND AGENTUREN. 1989. a. DM.60. Presse Fachverlag, Eidelstedterweg 22, 20255 Hamburg, Germany. TEL 040-565031. FAX 040-5602920. Ed. Hans van Treeck. adv.: page DM.2320; adv. contact: Manuela Busche. circ. 3,800. (back issues avail.) **Document type:** directory.

LETOPIS' PECHATNYKH PROIZVEDENII IZOBRAZITEL'NOGO ISKUSSTVA. see *ART*

686.2   US   ISSN 0738-9302
Z250
LIGATURE. vol.2, 1983. 2/yr. $1.50. World Typeface Center, Inc., 303 Park Ave. S., 2nd Fl., New York, NY 10010-3601. Tom Carnase, Pres. adv. circ. 40,000. **Indexed:** Graph.Arts Lit.Abstr., Print.Abstr.

686.2   IT   ISSN 0024-3744
LINEAGRAFICA; international review of graphic design and visual communications. 1983. bi-m. L.200000($135) (effective 1996). Progetto Editrice s.r.l., Corso Garibaldi 64, 20121 Milan, Italy. TEL 39-2-6575351. Ed. Giusi Brivio. adv.; bk.rev. circ. 21,000. (back issues avail.) **Indexed:** DAAI.
Formerly: Nuova Linea Grafica.
Description: Covers the world of graphics and visual communication. Includes articles on calligraphy, computer images and technology.

686.2   UK   ISSN 0264-732X
LITHO WEEK. 1979. w. £136. Haymarket Magazines Ltd., 38-42 Hampton Rd., Teddington, Middx. TW11 0JE, England. TEL 081-943-5000. TELEX 895-2440-HAYMRT-G. Ed. Simon Kanter. adv.; bk.rev.; illus.; circ. 12,832 (controlled). **Indexed:** Br.Tech.Ind., Chem.Abstr., Fluidex, Graph.Arts Lit.Abstr., Print.Abstr.
Formerly: Lithoprinter Week (ISSN 0024-4929)

760   HU   ISSN 0479-480X
Z119
MAGYAR GRAFIKA/HUNGARIAN GRAPHIC ARTS. (Text in Hungarian; summaries in German and Russian) 1957. bi-m. $60 (effective 1995 & 1996). Papires Nyomdaipari Mueszaki Egyesuelet, Fo utca 68, Pf. 433, 1371 Budapest 2, Hungary. (Subscr. to: Kultura, Box 149, 1389 Budapest, Hungary) Ed. Miklos Gara. adv. contact: Anne Wertheim. bk.rev.; abstr.; bibl.; charts; illus.; index. circ. 3,000. **Indexed:** Chem.Abstr., Graph.Arts Lit.Abstr. **Document type:** academic/scholarly publication, trade publication.

686.2   CN   ISSN 0025-0996
LE MAITRE IMPRIMEUR. (Text in French) 1937. m. Can.$25. Association des Arts Graphiques du Quebec, Inc., 65, rue de Castelnau Ouest, Bureau 101, Montreal, PQ H2R 2W3, Canada. TEL 514-274-7446. FAX 514-274-7482. Ed. Charles-Henri Dube. adv.: B&W page $1125, color page $1960; adv. contact: Jules Cote. charts; illus. circ. 4,294. **Indexed:** Pt.de Rep.

760   MX
MERCADO DE LAS ARTES GRAFICAS. 1974. 6/yr. Publi-Representaciones, Tlacotalpan No. 109-204, Mexico 7, DF, Mexico. Ed. Armando Ramirez. adv. circ. 4,000.

686   US   ISSN 0895-5719
MESSAGES (CAMBRIDGE). 1987. q. $25 ($40 international). Society for Environmental Graphic Design, One Story St., Cambridge, MA 02138-4924. TEL 617-868-3381. FAX 617-868-3591. Ed. Sarah Speare. adv.; bk.rev.; circ. 1,500 (controlled). (back issues avail.) **Indexed:** DAAI. **Document type:** newsletter.
Description: Reports on the society's news and events. Regular columns include A.D.A. Update, S.E.G.D. Regional News, Member News, Allied Organization News, and Resources.

686.2   CH
MODERN PRINTING.* (Text in Chinese) 1973. bi-m. Jeng-yih Lin, 12, Lane 28, Tunghwa St., Taipei, Taiwan, Republic of China. adv.; illus.

686.2   US   ISSN 1068-9257
MODERN REPROGRAPHICS. 1993. m. $30. Avis, 3737 N. Magnolia Ave., 1st Fl., Chicago, IL 60613-3601. TEL 312-686-1238. FAX 312-868-1052. E-mail: EdBA8767@AOL.com. Ed. Ed Avis. adv.; illus.; circ. 6,000 (controlled). **Document type:** trade publication.
Description: Covers the world of large - format reproduction, from engineering document reproduction to poster making.

NATIONAL AMATEUR. see *JOURNALISM*

763   US   ISSN 0893-4975
NATIONAL ASSOCIATION OF PRINTERS AND LITHOGRAPHERS. SPECIAL REPORTS. bi-w. $25.50 to non-members; members $15.50. National Association of Printers and Lithographers, 780 Palisade Ave., Teaneck, NJ 07666. TEL 201-342-0700. FAX 201-692-0286.

NEW COLLAGE MAGAZINE. see *LITERATURE*

655   US   ISSN 0162-8771
Z119
NEW ENGLAND PRINTER AND PUBLISHER. 1938. m. $11. New England Printer & Publisher Inc., 12 Carleton Dr., Box 810, Newburyport, MA 01950. TEL 508-462-9461. FAX 508-462-9160. Ed. Jean Hansen; Pub. Norman G. Hansen. adv.: B&W page $600, color page $1245; trim 8 1/2 x 11. bk.rev.; illus.; tr.lit.; circ. 3,360 (paid); 680 (controlled). **Indexed:** Graph.Arts.Abstr., Graph.Arts Lit.Abstr. **Document type:** trade publication.
Formerly: New England Printer and Lithographer (ISSN 0028-484X)
Description: Information on regional and national industry and trade association news. Calendar of regional and national events, supplier product-services, and new literature.

NEW YORK TYPOGRAPHICAL UNION NUMBER SIX. BULLETIN. see *LABOR UNIONS*

686.2   AT   ISSN 1171-0829
NEW ZEALAND PRINTER. 6/yr. Aus.$40 (foreign Aus.$50). Calmor & Associates Pty. Ltd., P.O. Box 1316, North Sydney, N.S.W. 2059, Australia. TEL 02-922-6133. FAX 02-922-4734. Ed. Patrick Howard. adv. contact: Paul Callhan. circ. 3,970. **Document type:** trade publication.
Description: Technical journal circulates to managers of print shops, trade shops, typesetters, art studios, publishers and packaging companies.

NEWS & VIEWS (PORTLAND). see *BUSINESS AND ECONOMICS — Marketing And Purchasing*

760   GR
NEWS OF GRAPHIC ARTS. 1982. m. Dr.1500($30) Fakinov, 157 Nokratous St., 176 73 Kallithea, Athens, Greece. Ed. D. Fakinov. circ. 5,200. (back issues avail.)

686.2   GW
NEWSPAPER TECHNIQUES. French edition: Techniques de Presse. German edition: Zeitungstechnik. (Text in English) 1962. m. DM.220 to non-members (members DM.110) (effective 1996). I N C A - F I E J Research Association (IFRA), Washingtonplatz 1, 64287 Darmstadt, Germany. TEL 06151-7005-0. FAX 06151-700572. Ed. G.B. Smith. adv.; bk.rev. circ. 5,200. **Indexed:** Print.Abstr. **Document type:** trade publication.
Formerly: Monthly Newspaper Techniques (ISSN 0019-333X)
Description: Contents focus exclusively on problems relating to newspaper production.

646.2   NR   ISSN 0189-0506
NIGERIAN PRINTER. 1980. q. $30. Nigerian Printer Publications, P.O. Box 632, Yaba, Nigeria. TEL 082-221782. Ed. Austin Odiadi. circ. 3,000.
Description: Technological articles and current technology and applications.

655   JA   ISSN 0546-0719
NIHON INSATSU NENKAN/JAPAN PRINTING ART ANNUAL. (Text in Japanese) 1957. a. 9000 Yen (foreign $75). Nippon Insatsu Shinbunsha - Japan Printing News Co., Ltd., 16-8, 1-chome, Shintomi, Chuo-ku, Tokyo 104, Japan. TEL 03-3553-5681. FAX 03-3553-5684. Ed. Akiko Ito. adv.: page 180000 Yen; 255 x 180. circ. 4,500. **Document type:** trade publication.

PRINTING

686.2   JA
NIPPON INSATSU SHINBUN/JAPAN PRINTING NEWS. (Text in Japanese) 1943. s-w. 21600 Yen (foreign $180). Nippon Insatsu Shinbunsha - Japan Printing News Co., Ltd., 16-8, 1-chome, Shintomi, Chuo-ku, Tokyo 104, Japan. TEL 03-3553-5681. FAX 03-3553-5684. Ed. Toshio Murata. adv.: B&W page 350000 Yen, color page 800000; 530 x 383. circ. 15,000. **Document type:** newspaper, trade publication.

686   NO   ISSN 0029-1978
NORSK GRAFISK TIDSSKRIFT. 1892. m. NOK 300. Grafiske Bedrifter, Landsforeningen - Norwegian Federation of Graphic Enterprises, c/o Beate Lystad, N-150 Oslo, Norway. Ed. Tom Prent. adv.: B&W page NOK 6500, color page NOK 9500; trim 215 x 305. bk.rev.; stat.; tr.lit. circ. 2,400.

NOUVELLES DE L'ESTAMPE. see *ART*

686.2   BE   ISSN 0029-4926
NOUVELLES GRAPHIQUES/GRAFISCH NIEUWS. (Editions in Dutch and French) 1950. s-m. 1500 BEF. Keesing Uitgevers N.V., 2-20 Keesinglaan, B-2100 Deurne, Belgium. TEL 32-3-3605300. FAX 32-3-3243898. TELEX 32507 KEESNG B. Ed. Alain Vermeire; Pub. Steven van de Rijt. adv.; bk.rev.; charts; illus.; tr.lit. circ. 7,300 (4,200 Dutch ed.; 3,100 French ed.). (back issues avail.) **Indexed:** Print.Abstr. **Document type:** trade publication.
—BLDSC (6176.782800).

NOVUM GEBRAUCHSGRAPHIK/INTERNATIONAL JOURNAL FOR COMMUNICATION DESIGN. see *ADVERTISING AND PUBLIC RELATIONS*

NYT FOR BOGVENNER. see *PUBLISHING AND BOOK TRADE*

686   AU   ISSN 0029-9170
DAS OESTERREICHISCHE GRAPHISCHE GEWERBE. 1949. m. S.650. Landesinnung Druck, Gruenangergasse 4, A-1010 Vienna, Austria. Ed. Hans Inmann. adv. contact: Vera Lindenberg. bk.rev.; charts; illus.; tr.lit.; index. circ. 1,900. **Document type:** trade publication.

686.2   UK   ISSN 0263-4384
OFFSET PRINTING & REPRODUCTION. 1969. m. £50. Maclean Hunter Ltd., Maclean Hunter House, Chalk Lane, Cockfosters Rd., Barnet, Herts EN4 0BU, England. TEL 081-242-3000. FAX 081-242-3185. TELEX 299072-MACHUN-G. illus.; stat. circ. 14,167. **Indexed:** Br.Tech.Ind., Build.Manage.Abstr., Graph.Arts Lit.Abstr., INSPEC (1991-). **Document type:** trade publication.
Incorporates: Reproduction (ISSN 0034-4958); **Former titles:** Offset Printer; Offset Printing; Small Offset Printing (ISSN 0037-7201)

OFFSETPRAXIS; Europaeische Fachzeitschrift fuer Offset-, Kleinoffset-Druck, Reprofotografie und Fotosatz. see *PHOTOGRAPHY*

686.2 676.2   AT   ISSN 0158-6319
P A T E F A NEWS BULLETIN. 1979. m. membership. Printing & Allied Trades Employers Federation of Australia, 77 Lithgow Street, St. Leonards, N.S.W. 2065, Australia. TEL 61-2-3721222. FAX 61-2-3721288. adv.; bk.rev. circ. 2,650. **Document type:** newsletter, trade publication. **Description:** Informs members about industry events, technology, government action, marketing trends.

P I R A ANNUAL REVIEW OF RESEARCH & SERVICES. (Paper, Printing & Packaging Industries Research Association) see *PAPER AND PULP*

686.2   US   ISSN 0895-1608
TS196.7
PACKAGE PRINTING & CONVERTING; diemaking and diecutting, flexography, gravure and offset. 1974. m. $49 (free to qualified personnel) (foreign $73). North American Publishing Co., 401 N. Broad St., Philadelphia, PA 19108. TEL 215-238-5300. FAX 215-238-5457. Ed. David Luttenberger. adv.; bk.rev.; charts; illus.; stat.; index. circ. 24,100. (also avail. in microform from UMI; reprint service avail. from UMI) **Indexed:** Abstr.Bull.Inst.Pap.Chem., Curr.Pack.Abstr., Graph.Arts Lit.Abstr., Int.Packag.Abstr., Packag.Sci.Tech. **Document type:** trade publication.
—BLDSC (6331.979000); Faxon; UMI. **CCC.**
Former titles: Package Printing (ISSN 0163-9234); (until Mar. 1978): Package Printing and Diecutting (ISSN 0012-2556); Which was formed by the merger of: Diemaking, Diecutting and Converting (ISSN 0012-2556); Gravure (ISSN 0017-3568); Flexography Printing and Converting. **Description:** Focuses on new machinery and new methods in the specialized field of printing and converting packages, boxes, cartons, bags and cellophane.

686   FI   ISSN 1235-905X
PAINOMAAILMA. 1906. 8/yr. FIM 450 (effective 1996). Painomaailma Oy, Loennrotinkatu 11 A, FIN-00120 Helsinki, Finland. TEL 358-0-2287-7242. FAX 358-0-603-914. Eds. Seppo Vuorio, Mirja Mantynen. adv.: B&W page FIM 6900, color page FIM 12700; trim 183 x 270. bk.rev.; circ. 3,200 (controlled). **Document type:** trade publication.
Former titles: Kirjapainotaito Graafikko; Graafikko (ISSN 0017-2731)

PAINT AND INK INTERNATIONAL. see *PAINTS AND PROTECTIVE COATINGS*

PERSPECTIVES (LIBERTY). see *BUSINESS AND ECONOMICS — Management*

686.2   IT   ISSN 0032-2709
POLIGRAFICO ITALIANO. 1960. m. L.85000($125) Zeta's s.r.l., Via Kolbe 8, 20137 Milan, Italy. TEL 39-2-76110075. FAX 39-2-7387371. Ed. Zuliani Ruggero. adv.: B&W page L.1980000, color page L.2940000. bk.rev.; adv.; charts; illus.; pat.; tr.lit.; index. circ. 10,000. **Description:** Concerns the polygraphic field: publishers, trade printers, phototypesetters, bindery plants, and paper industry.

686.2   PL   ISSN 0373-9864
CODEN: POLGDZ
POLIGRAFIKA. 1947. m. $171. (Stowarzyszenie Inzynierow i Technikow Mechanikow Polskich, Sekcja Poligrafow) Oficyna Wydawnicza SIMP Press, Ltd., Ul. Zurawia 22, 00-515 Warsaw, Poland. (Dist. by: Ars Polona-Ruch, Krakowskie Przedmiescie 7, Warsaw, Poland) Ed. Apolinary Brodecki. circ. 2,400. **Indexed:** Chem.Abstr.
—CASDDS.

665   RU   ISSN 0032-2717
CODEN: PLGFAH
POLIGRAFIYA. 1924. bi-m. $97 (effective 1996). (Komitet po Pechati Soveta Ministrov) Izdatel'stvo Kniga, 50, Gorky St., 125047 Moscow, Russia. Ed. A.I. Ovsyannikav. bk.rev.; bibl.; charts; illus.; index. circ. 27,000. (tabloid format) **Indexed:** Abstr.Bull.Inst.Pap.Chem., Chem.Abstr., Graph.Arts Lit.Abstr.
—BLDSC (0130.050000); CASDDS.

686.2   XR   ISSN 1210-5368
POLYGRAF - TYPOGRAFIA.* 1888. m. Typograficka Beseda, Nam. W. Churchilla 2, 113 59 Prague 3, Czech Republic. (Dist. by: Artia, Ve Smeckach 30, 111 00 Prague 1, Czech Republic)
Formerly (until 1992): Typografia (ISSN 0322-9068)

686.2   GW   ISSN 0032-3845
Z119
POLYGRAPH; trade magazine for the printing industry and communications technology. 1947. s-m. DM.186. Polygraph Verlag GmbH, Schaumainkai 85, 60596 Frankfurt a.M., Germany. TEL 069-630086-0. FAX 069-63008650. Ed. Walter Mikolasch; Pub. Ulrike Schulz. adv.; bk.rev.; charts; illus.; mkt.; pat.; tr.lit.; index. circ. 13,000. **Indexed:** Bibl.Cart., C.I.S. Abstr., Excerp.Med., Graph.Arts Lit.Abstr. **Document type:** trade publication.
—SWETS. **CCC.**
Description: Trade news of the graphic arts industry.

686   GW   ISSN 0943-0083
POLYGRAPH INTERNATIONAL; magazine for the printing industry and communication technology. (Text in English; summaries in French, Spanish) 1952. 6/yr. DM.102. Polygraph Verlag GmbH, Schaumainkai 85, 60596 Frankfurt a.M., Germany. TEL 069-630086-0. FAX 069-63008650. Ed. Walter Mikolasch; Pub. Ulrike Schulz. adv.; charts; illus.; mkt.; tr.lit. circ. 9,000. **Indexed:** Graph.Arts Lit.Abstr., Print.Abstr. **Document type:** trade publication.
Former titles: Export Polygraph International (ISSN 0937-9924); E P I - Export Polygraph International (ISSN 0343-5199)

760   SP
PRENSA DE LA INDUSTRIA GRAFICA. 1989. 10/yr. 6000 ptas. Trebol Comunicacion S.A., Dr. Esquerdo 105, 28007 Madrid, Spain. TEL 91-5737400. FAX 91-4096452. Ed. Enrique Nieto de las Cuevas. adv. contact: Jesus Garcia Huertas. bk.rev. circ. 4,700. **Document type:** trade publication.

686.2   US   ISSN 8750-2224
PREPRESS BULLETIN. 1911. bi-m. $15 (foreign $17). International Prepress Association, 552 W. 167 St., South Holland, IL 60473. TEL 708-596-5110. FAX 708-596-5112. Ed. Bessie Halfacre. adv.: B&W page $385, color page $1135; adv. contact: Harry Yocherer. bk.rev.; charts; illus.; stat. circ. 2,000. **Indexed:** Graph.Arts Lit.Abstr., Photo.Abstr. **Document type:** trade publication.
Former titles (until 1984): Photoplatemakers Bulletin (ISSN 0031-8841); (until 1968): Photoengravers Bulletin (ISSN 0097-5877)
Description: Provides management and technical information on the graphic arts prepress industry.

686   US
PREPRESS MARKET WATCH. 1992. q. $40 to non-members; members $30. National Association of Printers and Lithographers, 780 Palisade Ave., Teaneck, NY 07666. TEL 201-342-0700. FAX 201-692-0286. Ed. Andrew Paparozzi.

760   SP
PRESS-GRAPH. 12/yr. Mallorca 219 5o 2a, 08008 Barcelona, Spain. TEL 3-323-75-54. FAX 3-323-74-63. Ed. Francisco J. Romero. circ. 5,000.

686.2 760   CN
PRESSPECTIVE. q. free. L G M Graphics Inc., 737 Moray St., Winnipeg, MB R3J 9Z9, Canada. TEL 204-889-9050; 800-665-3316. FAX 204-889-9897. **Document type:** newsletter.

PRESSTIME. see *JOURNALISM*

686.2   UK   ISSN 0032-8529
PRINT. 1968. 10/yr. £10. National Graphical Association (N G A), Graphic House, 63-67 Bromham Rd., Bedford MK40 2AG, England. FAX 0234-218640. Ed. A.D. Dubbins. adv.; bk.rev.; illus.; index. (tabloid format)
—UMI.
Former titles: Graphical Journal; Incorporates: S L A D E Journal; Which was formerly: Process Journal (ISSN 0032-9614)

PRINT; America's graphic design magazine. see *COMPUTERS — Computer Graphics*

PRINT. see *PUBLISHING AND BOOK TRADE*

686.2   AU
PRINT. 9/yr. Austria GmbH, Loquaiplatz 12, A-1061 Vienna, Austria. TEL 01-59960-0. FAX 01-5996022. Ed. Friedrich Hubeni. circ. 12,500.

PRINTING

686.2   CN   ISSN 0380-2752
PRINT ACTION. 1962. 12/yr. Can.$29($39.95) Youngblood Publishing Co. Ltd., 2240 Midland Ave., Ste. 201, Scarborough, ON M1P 4R8, Canada. TEL 416-299-6007. FAX 416-299-6674. Ed. Julian Mills. adv.: B&W page Can.$3650, color page Can.$4625. bk.rev.; stat.; tr.lit. circ. 15,000.
Document type: trade publication.
Description: Covers the graphic arts and printing industries in Canada.

686.2   UK
PRINT & CONVERTING MATTERS. 1984. q. £4 (Europe £6; elsewhere £7) (effective 1996). A.E. Morgan Publications Ltd., Stanley House, 9 West St., Epson, Surrey KT18 7RL, England. TEL 01285-760434. FAX 01285-760594. Ed. Sophie Matthews; Pub. Terence Morgan. adv. contact: Peter Halstead. circ. 12,500. (back issues avail.; reprint service avail.)
Document type: trade publication.
Former titles: Print & Converting Monthly (ISSN 0964-959X); Print Monthly; (until 1988): Print Advertiser.
Description: Covers all printing industry and allied trades with exception of screen printers.

686   US   ISSN 0273-9550
PRINT & GRAPHICS. 1980. m. $39 (free to qualified personnel). East-West Communications, 911 N. Fillmore St., Arlington, VA 22201-2127. TEL 703-525-4800. FAX 703-525-4805. Ed. Charles Kerwin. adv.: B&W page $995, color page $1590. bk.rev.; software rev.; circ. 20,000 (controlled). (also avail. in diskette format)
Description: Trade publication for the Mid-Atlantic graphic arts industry. Features include technology and industry segment focus, product news, business briefs, installations, and people.

686   UK   ISSN 0267-7644
PRINT & PAPER SERIES. 1981. m. £45. Sherwood House, Nottingham Rd., Loughborough, Leics LA11 1EU, England. TEL 0509-610808. FAX 0509-217609. Ed. D. Cook-Howe. circ. 15,000. **Document type:** trade publication.
Description: Directed to senior staff of printing, packaging, publishing, paper, advertising, and in-plant printing companies.

686.2   UK
PRINT AND PRODUCTION MANUAL. 1986. biennial. £95. Blueprint (Subsidiary of: Chapman & Hall), 2-6 Boundary Row, London SE1 8HN, England. TEL 0171-865-0066. FAX 0171-522-9623. TELEX 290164 CHAPMA G. E-mail: journal@chall.mhs.compuserve.com. (Dist. by: International Thomson Publishing Services Ltd., Cheriton House, North Way, Andover, Hants. SP10 5BE, England. TEL 01264-342713. FAX 01264-342807; N. American orders to: Chapman & Hall, One Penn Plaza, 41st Fl., New York, NY 10019. TEL 212-564-1060. FAX 212-564-1505) Ed.Bd. **Document type:** trade publication.

686.2   US
PRINT BUSINESS REGISTER.* 1986. fortn. $247. Quoin Research, Inc., 20 E. Jackson Blvd., Chicago, IL 60604-2203. TEL 312-226-5600. FAX 312-226-4640. Ed. Rod Piechowski. circ. 650.
Formerly: Print Mergers and Acquisitions.
Description: Follows activities in the commercial printing industry, including mergers and acquisitions, major contracts, installations, bankruptcies, trends, and legal proceedings of note.

686.2   UK   ISSN 0959-3896
PRINT BUYERS DIRECTORY. 1989. a. £70. British Printing Industries Federation, 11 Bedford Row, London WC1R 4DX, England. TEL 0171-242-6904. FAX 0171-405-7784. Ed. Christine Hutton.
Document type: directory.
—BLDSC (2265.614410).

686.2   US   ISSN 1061-0510
PRINT BUYERS REVIEW.* 1989. bi-m. $9.95. Successful Media, 256 Cedar St., Ashland, MA 01721-1936. TEL 617-340-2066. FAX 617-426-1456. Ed. Robert F. Dixon. adv.: B&W page $1275, color page $1825. circ. 15,000.
Description: Covers the process of buying materials for printing and book publishing.

655   US   ISSN 0048-5314
PRINT-EQUIP NEWS. 1965. m. $24. P - E N Publications Inc., 215 Allen Ave., Box 5540, Glendale, CA 91201-5540. TEL 818-954-9495. FAX 818-954-0452. Ed. Paul B. Kissel; Pub. Richard E. Jutras. adv.: B&W page $1275, color page $1825; adv. contact: Jeff Jutras. illus. circ. 25,800. (tabloid format) **Indexed:** Graph.Arts Lit.Abstr.
Document type: trade publication, newspaper.

686.2 330.9   US
PRINT MARKET OUTLOOK. m. $159 (foreign $179). Cahners Publishing Company (New York), Division of Reed Elsevier Inc., 249 W. 17th St., New York, NY 10011. TEL 212-463-6834. FAX 212-463-6530. (Subscr. to: 44 Cook St., Denver, CO 80206)
Description: Includes economic analyses, statistics, industry and buying market forecasts, and other market data for companies in and supplying the graphic arts industry.

686.2   GW   ISSN 0944-7482
PRINT UND PRODUKTION; das Magazine. 1988. bi-m. DM.60. Media Daten Verlag GmbH, Am Klingenweg 4, 67714 Walluf, Germany. TEL 06123-700-0. FAX 06123-700122. Ed. Wolfgang Dorn. adv.: color page DM.7500; trim 240 x 335. circ. 2,100.
Document type: trade publication.
Formerly (until 1993): Print (ISSN 0935-5944)
Description: For printers and print buyers.

686.2   US   ISSN 0192-6314
PRINTERS HOT LINE. w. $119. United Advertising Publications, Inc., 15400 Knoll Tr., Ste. 500, Dallas, TX 75248. TEL 214-233-5131. FAX 214-233-5514. adv.: B&W page $735, color page $900. circ. 15,000. **Document type:** trade publication.
Description: Designed to stimulate business between buyers and sellers of new and used equipment, and providers and users of related services and supplies.

686.2   US
PRINTERS HOT LINE INTERNATIONAL. 1991. bi-m. United Advertising Publications, Inc., 15400 Knoll Trail, Ste. 500, Dallas, TX 75248. TEL 214-233-5131. FAX 214-239-3173. adv.: B&W page $770; trim 7 7/8 x 10 3/4. circ. 10,000. **Document type:** trade publication.

686.2   US
PRINTER'S INK. 1984. q. free. Thomson-Shore, Inc., 7300 W. Joy Rd., Box 305, Dexter, MI 48130-0305. TEL 313-426-3939. FAX 313-426-6219. Ed. Ned Thomson. circ. 21,000. **Document type:** academic/scholarly publication, newsletter.
Description: Comments on the printing and binding of soft and hard bound books. Provides ideas to help the publisher hold down costs and speed up production time.

686.2   NZ   ISSN 0048-5330
Z119
PRINTERS NEWS. 1942. m. NZ.$37.50. Printing Industries Federation of New Zealand (Inc.), Box 1422, Wellington, New Zealand. TEL 04-723 497. FAX 04-723-534. Ed. W.R. Johnson. adv.; bk.rev. circ. 1,100.
—BLDSC (6613.530000).

686.2   US
PRINTER'S NORTHWEST TRADER. 1970. m. $10. Eagle Newspapers, Inc., Box 450, Woodburn, OR 97071. TEL 800-426-2416. FAX 503-981-1253. Ed. Sandra Hubbard. adv. contact: Rod Strollery. bk.rev. circ. 5,850. **Document type:** trade publication.
Description: Serves the print and graphic arts industry in Oregon, Washington, Idaho, Montana, Alaska and Northern California.

686.2   UK
PRINTERS WORKSHOP. 1989. bi-m. free. Aydee Marketing Ltd., 159 Cambridge St., Aylesbury, Bucks. HP20 1BQ, England. TEL 01296-4343811. FAX 0296-436936. Ed. Jenny Henderson. adv. contact: Neil Hampson. circ. 9,000. (back issues avail.) **Document type:** trade publication.
Description: Contains product information for managers of print shops.

686.2   UK
PRINTING AND BOOKBINDING TRADE REVIEW; equipment - materials - production. 1958. m. £3. George L. Howe Press Service Ltd., 85 Elmhurst Dr., Hornchurch, Essex RM11 1PB, England. Ed. George L. Howe. adv.; bk.rev.; charts; illus.; tr.lit.

PRINTING & PACKAGING; with Arabian food and packaging. see PACKAGING

PRINTING & PUBLISHING: LATIN AMERICAN INDUSTRIAL REPORT. see PUBLISHING AND BOOK TRADE

PRINTING AND PUBLISHING NEWSLETTER. see OCCUPATIONAL HEALTH AND SAFETY

686.2 338   US
PRINTING BUSINESS REPORT. 1979. q. $150 to non-members; members $50. National Association of Printers and Lithographers, 780 Palisade Ave., Teaneck, NJ 07666. TEL 201-342-0707. FAX 201-692-0286. Ed. Andrew D. Paparozzi. circ. 4,000. (looseleaf format; back issues avail.)
Incorporates (1989-1992): Printing Sales Index; **Former titles (until 1992):** Business Indicator Report; Quarterly Printing Industry Business Indicator Report.

686.209   UK   ISSN 0144-7505
PRINTING HISTORICAL SOCIETY BULLETIN. 1980. 2/yr. £20($35) membership. Printing Historical Society, St. Bride Institute, Bride Ln., Fleet St., London EC4Y 8EE, England. Ed. Andrew Boag. bibl. **Document type:** bulletin.
—BLDSC (2685.040000).
Supersedes: Printing Historical Society Newsletter (ISSN 0556-1515)

686.209   UK   ISSN 0079-5321
Z119
PRINTING HISTORICAL SOCIETY JOURNAL. 1965. a. £20($35) membership. Printing Historical Society, St. Bride Institute, Bride Ln., Fleet St., London EC4Y 8EE, England. Ed. Margaret Smith. circ. 650. **Indexed:** Artbibl.Mod., Br.Hum.Ind. **Document type:** academic/scholarly publication.
—BLDSC (4843.250000).

686.209   US   ISSN 0192-9275
Z124.A2
PRINTING HISTORY. s-a. $30 to individuals (foreign $35); institutions $35 (foreign $40). American Printing History Association, Box 4922, Grand Central Sta., New York, NY 10163. TEL 212-930-0802. Ed. David Pankow. **Indexed:** Lib.Lit. **Document type:** academic/scholarly publication.
—BLDSC (6614.050000); UnCover.

686.2   US   ISSN 0032-860X
PRINTING IMPRESSIONS. 1958. m. $75 (free to qualified personnel) (foreign $159). North American Publishing Co., 401 N. Broad St., Philadelphia, PA 19108. TEL 215-238-5300. FAX 215-238-5457. Ed. Mark Michelson. adv.; bk.rev. circ. 94,046. (also avail. in microform from UMI; reprint service avail. from UMI) **Indexed:** Abstr.Bull.Inst.Pap.Chem., Curr.Pack.Abstr., Graph.Arts Lit.Abstr. **Document type:** trade publication.
—BLDSC (6614.100000); Faxon; SWETS; UMI. CCC.
Incorporates: Printing Management (ISSN 0032-8650)
Description: Features marketing studies, equipment reviews and coverage of international exhibits and conferences for the commercial printing market.

686.2   UK   ISSN 0307-7195
Z120
PRINTING INDUSTRIES. 1901. m. £50 to non-members. British Printing Industries Federation, 11 Bedford Row, London WC1R 4DX, England. TEL 0171-242-6904. FAX 0171-405-7784. adv.; bk.rev.; illus.; index. circ. 7,000. **Indexed:** Graph.Arts Lit.Abstr. **Document type:** trade publication.
—BLDSC (6614.130000).
Formerly: British Federation of Master Printers. Members Circular (ISSN 0007-0696)
Description: Geared toward printing industry managers.

PRINTING

686.2 US ISSN 0191-8273
PRINTING JOURNAL. 1974. m. free to qualified personnel. East-West Communications, 911 N. Fillmore St., Arlington, VA 22201-2127. TEL 703-525-4800. FAX 703-525-4805. Ed. Geoff Lindsay. adv.: B&W page $1559, color page $2084. bk.rev.; illus.; circ. 18,000 (controlled). (tabloid format) Indexed: Graph.Arts Abstr., Graph.Arts Lit.Abstr.
  Description: Covers marketplace trends, issues and technology affecting the graphics arts industry in the Pacific and Mountain States, including Alaska and Hawaii.

686.2 658 US
PRINTING MANAGER. 1979. q. $30 to non-members; members $20. National Association of Printers and Lithographers, 780 Palisade Ave., Teaneck, NJ 07666. TEL 201-342-0700. FAX 201-692-0286. Ed. Dawn LosPaluto. bk.rev. circ. 5,000. (back issues avail.)

686.2 US ISSN 1046-8595
Z119
PRINTING NEWS - EAST. 1928. 51/yr. $24.95 (Canada $30.95; elsewhere $39.95). P T N Publishing Corp., 445 Broad Hollow Rd., Melville, NY 11474-4722. TEL 516-845-2700. FAX 516-845-7109. Ed. Joann Strashun. adv.: B&W page $985, color page $1735. bk.rev.; illus.; tr.lit. circ. 9,000. (tabloid format) Indexed: Abstr.Bull.Inst.Pap.Chem., Graph.Arts Lit.Abstr.
Document type: trade publication.
  —CCC.
  Formerly (until Oct. 1989): Printing News (ISSN 0032-8626)
  Description: Devoted primarily to the Greater New York and Philadelphia Metropolitan Areas. Contains news, economic forecasts, upcoming trade shows, services to the trade, technical updates and industry leader profiles.

655 UK ISSN 0032-8642
PRINTING PRODUCT INFORMATION CARDS. 1969. 3/yr. free. Maclean Hunter Ltd., Maclean Hunter House, Chalk Lane, Cockfosters Rd., Barnet, Herts EN4 0BU, England. TEL 081-242-3000. FAX 081-242-3185. TELEX 299072-MACHUN-G. adv.; tr.lit. circ. 12,299. **Document type:** bulletin.

686.2 UK ISSN 1355-6193
PRINTING PRODUCT NEWS. 1990. q. £8.50($20) Manor Publishing Ltd., Unit 7, Edison Rd., Highfield Industrial Estate, Hampden Park, Eastbourne, E. Sussex BN23 6PT, England. TEL 01323-507474. FAX 01323-509306. Ed. Tony Clark; Pub. Gary Stolton. adv.: page £925; trim 297 x 210; adv. contact: Helen Roberts. circ. 6,000. **Document type:** trade publication.
  Formerly (until 1994): Professional Print Supplier (ISSN 0964-0495)

686.2 II ISSN 0401-3956
PRINTING TIMES. (Text in English) 1955. bi-m. Rs.210($3.37) All India Federation of Master Printers, E-14, 3rd Fl., South Extn. Market Part II, New Delhi 110 049, India. TEL 11-6449855. FAX 11-6419510. Ed. V.N. Chhabra. adv.; bk.rev.; illus. circ. 2,000. (back issues avail.)

686.2 UK ISSN 0079-5372
PRINTING TRADES DIRECTORY. 1960. a. £93 (foreign £118). Miller Freeman Information Services (Subsidiary of: United News & Media), Riverbank House, Angel Ln., Tonbridge, Kent TN9 1SE, England. TEL 01732-362666. FAX 01732-767301. TELEX 957829. Ed. Gwen Young. adv. contact: Elaine Soni. circ. 3,000. **Document type:** directory.
  —BLDSC (6615.091000).
  Description: Lists printers, suppliers of equipment, material, and services.

686.2 UK ISSN 0032-8715
Z119
PRINTING WORLD. 1878. w. £78 (foreign £112). Miller Freeman Publishers Ltd. (Subsidiary of: Morgan-Grampian plc.), Benn House, Sovereign Way, Tonbridge, Kent TN9 1RW, England. TEL 01732-364422. FAX 01732-361534. TELEX 95132 BENTON G. Ed. Gareth Ward; Pub. David Barrett. adv. contact: Andy Jordan. bk.rev.; illus.; pat.; index. circ. 13,300. (also avail. in microform from UMI; reprint service avail. from UMI) Indexed: Br.Tech.Ind., Graph.Arts Lit.Abstr., Key to Econ.Sci. **Document type:** trade publication.
  —BLDSC (6615.105000); UMI. **CCC.**
  Incorporates: Printing Today; Which was formerly: Printing Equipment and Materials (ISSN 0032-8596)

686.2 UK
PRINTLINK INTERNATIONAL. (Text in Arabic) m. £48. International Printing Communications Ltd., P.O. Box 923, Crownhill Industry, Milton Keynes MK8 0AY. TEL 0908-561444. FAX 0908-569564. TELEX 826373-PRINT-G. Ed. M. Yousry. adv.: B&W page £1365, color page £1595; trim 272 x 186. **Document type:** trade publication.
  Description: Provides technology guides, in-depth features and analysis for the graphic, printing, converting, finishing and allied industries in the Arab world.

PRINTMAKING TODAY. see ART

686.2 681.65 UK
PRINTSHOP. no.6, May 1981. q. £6.50. Franchise Publications, James House, 37 Nottingham Rd., London SW17 7EA, England. Ed. Robert Riding. adv.; illus.

686.2 UK ISSN 0967-2486
PRINTWEAR & PROMOTION. 1952. m. £29.75 (overseas £42). Batiste Publications Ltd., Pembroke House, Campsbourne Rd., Hornsey, London N8 7PE, England. TEL 0181-340-3291. FAX 0181-341-4840. TELEX 267727 BATGRP G. Ed. Geoff Ellis. adv.; illus.; tr.lit. Indexed: Graph.Arts Lit.Abstr., Int.Packag.Abstr. **Document type:** trade publication.
  —BLDSC (8211.785000).
  Former titles (until 1992): Screenprint Wear (ISSN 0967-2494); (until 1991): Screen Process (ISSN 0953-3338); (until 1987): Screenprinting (ISSN 0952-2719); Point of Sale and Screenprinting (ISSN 0261-1309); (until 1981): Point of Sale News (ISSN 0036-9586); (until 1970): Screen Printing and Point of Sale News.

686.2 CN ISSN 1192-473X
PRODUCTION IMPRIMEE. 1992. bi-m. Can.$19($40) Editions Info Presse, 4316 St-Laurent Blvd., Ste. 400, Montreal, PQ H2W 1Z3, Canada. TEL 514-842-5873. FAX 514-842-2422. Ed. Bruno Gautier. adv.: B&W or color page Can.$1800; trim 8 1/2 x 11.

686.2 UK ISSN 0032-9878
PRODUCTION JOURNAL. 1958. 10/yr. £25 (overseas £35). Newspaper Society, Bloomsbury House, 74-77 Great Russell St., London WC1B 3DA, England. TEL 0171-636-7014. FAX 0171-631-5119. Ed. Gary Cullum. adv. contact: Terry Gunter. charts; illus.; stat.; index; circ. 3,000 (controlled). (tabloid format) Indexed: Abstr.Bull.Inst.Pap.Chem., Graph.Arts Lit.Abstr., INSPEC (1984-1986). **Document type:** trade publication.
  —BLDSC (6853.150000).

686.2 659.1 DK ISSN 0105-7758
PRODUKTIONSHAANDBOGEN; virksomheder med grafisk produktion - reklamevirksomhed. a. Forlaget de Grafiske Haandboeger, Finsensvj 80, 2000 Frederiksberg, Denmark. TEL 45-38-88-32-22. FAX 45-38-88-30-38. adv. circ. 4,958. **Document type:** directory.
  Description: Directory of prepress, printing, and printfinishing companies in Denmark.

686.2 UK ISSN 0308-4205
Z120
PROFESSIONAL PRINTER. 1957. bi-m £15 (foreign £21) (effective 1996). Institute of Printing, 8 Lonsdale Gardens, Tunbridge Wells, Kent TN1 1NU, England. TEL 01892-538118. FAX 01892-518028. Ed. F.J. Trowman. adv.; bk.rev.; illus.; index. circ. 2,500. (also avail. in microform from UMI; reprint service avail. from UMI) Indexed: Abstr.Bull.Inst.Pap.Chem., Br.Tech.Ind., Graph.Arts Lit.Abstr., P.I.R.A. **Document type:** trade publication.
  —BLDSC (6864.206000); UMI.
  Incorporates: Printing Technology (ISSN 0032-8685)

PUBLISHING & PRODUCTION EXECUTIVE. see *PUBLISHING AND BOOK TRADE*

760 UK
Q P. (Quick Printer) bi-m. P.O. Box 40, Crowborough, E. Sussex TN6 3PT, England. TEL 081-348-3433. FAX 081-348-4827. Ed. Catherine Arthur. circ. 7,200.

QUAERENDO; a quarterly journal from the Low Countries devoted to manuscripts and printed books. see *PUBLISHING AND BOOK TRADE*

686 US
▼**QUALITY IMPROVEMENT QUARTERLY.** 1994. q. $40. (Rochester Institute of Technology, Technical and Education Center of the Graphic Arts) National Association of Printers and Lithographers, 780 Palisade Ave., Teaneck, NJ 07666-3129. TEL 201-342-0700. FAX 201-692-0286. Ed. Patrick Henry. **Document type:** trade publication.
  Formerly: Quality Action Planner.

686.2 US
QUICK PRINTERS HOT LINE. 1991. bi-m. United Advertising Publications, Inc., 15400 Knoll Tr., Ste. 500, Dallas, TX 75248. TEL 214-233-5131. FAX 214-239-3173. adv.: B&W page $735; trim 7 7/8 x 10 3/4. circ. 15,000. **Document type:** trade publication.

686.2 US ISSN 0191-4588
QUICK PRINTING; the information source for commercial copyshops and printshops. 1977. m. $25. P T N Publishing Corp., 445 Broad Hollow Rd., Ste. 21, Melville, NY 11747-4722. TEL 800-308-NEWS. FAX 516-249-5774. Ed. Bob Hall. adv.: B&W page $3775, color page $4850; trim 8 1/8 x 10 7/8. charts; illus.; stat. circ. 66,263. (back issues avail.) Indexed: Graph.Arts Lit.Abstr.
  —BLDSC (7216.410000).

R S V P: THE DIRECTORY OF ILLUSTRATION AND DESIGN. see *BUSINESS AND ECONOMICS — Trade And Industrial Directories*

686 IT ISSN 0033-9687
RASSEGNA GRAFICA. 1950. fortn. L.50000 (foreign L.200000). Editrice Arti Poligrafiche Europee, Via Casella, 16, 20156 Milan, Italy. TEL 39-2-330221. FAX 39-2-39214341. Ed. Antonio Ghiorzo. adv.: B&W page L.4200000, color page L.5200000; trim 266 x 392. charts; illus.; circ. 13,000 (controlled). **Document type:** trade publication.

686.2 SZ
REPRO BULLETIN. q. Verband Schweizerischer Reprografie-Betriebe - Association Suisses des Ateliers Reprographie, Postfach 319, CH-8034 Zurich, Switzerland. TEL 01-2624477. Ed. Viktor Schmid. adv. contact: Rene Collioud. **Document type:** trade publication.

676.2 686.2 US ISSN 0736-1238
REPRODUCTION BULLETIN. 1954. q. free. Andrews Paper & Chemical Co., Inc., 1 Channel Dr., Box 509, Port Washington, NY 11050. TEL 516-767-2800. FAX 516-767-1632. Ed. Peter Muller. bk.rev.; pat.; cum.index: nos.1-84 (1954-1974). circ. 2,500. Indexed: Abstr.Bull.Inst.Pap.Chem., Chem.Abstr. **Document type:** bulletin, trade publication.
  Formerly: Reproduction Paper News Bulletin (ISSN 0034-4966)
  Description: Contains items of interest on Diazotpe reproduction processes.

RESEARCH COMMITTEE FOR GRAPHIC SIMULATION AND VISUALIZATION OF MULTIPHASE FLOW. PROCEEDINGS. see *PHYSICS — Optics*

PRINTING

686.2 GW
S I P - SIEBDRUCK INFOPOST; Fachzeitschrift fuer grafischen/industriellen Siebdruck, SignMaking und Werbetechnik. 1984. 10/yr. DM.48. S I P - Siebdruck Infopost, Postfach 246, 55562 Sobernheim, Germany. TEL 06751-6150. FAX 06751-4014. Eds. Karl Kahlstatt, Eberhard Lendle. adv.: B&W page DM.1600, color page DM.2600; trim 270 x 190. circ. 4,500. **Document type**: trade publication.

686.2 FR
S N I L INFOS. 6/yr. S N I L - C G C, 25 rue de Koufra, 59155 Faches-Thumesnil, France. TEL 20-53-83-02. Ed. Serge Deltour. circ. 10,000.

686.2 UK
S P A NEWS. q. membership. Screen Printing Association (UK) Ltd., Association House, 7A West St., Reigate, Surrey RH2 9BL, England. TEL 0737-240792. FAX 0737-240770. circ. 250. **Document type**: newsletter.
Formerly: Display Producers and Screen Printers Association. Monthly.

686.2 SZ
S Z V BULLETIN. 6/yr. Baumackerstr. 42, CH-8050 Zurich, Switzerland. TEL 01-3125015. FAX 01-3113132. circ. 1,000.

686.2 SZ
S Z V FLASH. 26/yr. Baumackerstr. 42, CH-8050 Zurich, Switzerland. TEL 01-3125015. FAX 01-3113132. Ed. Thomas Kaehr. circ. 1,000.

686.2 UK
SCOTTISH DECORATORS' YEAR BOOK AND REVIEW. a. £10. Scottish Decorators Federation, 1 Grindlay St. Ct., Edinburgh EH3 9AR, Scotland. TEL 0131-221-1527. FAX 0131-221-1528. Ed. C.W. Aitken. adv. circ. 500. **Document type**: trade publication.
Formerly: Scottish Decorators' Review.

686.2 UK ISSN 0966-4238
SCOTTISH PRINT. 1991. q. 3 Park St. South, Glasgow G3 6BG, England. TEL 041-332-3255. FAX 041-332-2012. Ed. G. Young. circ. 7,200.
Description: Details developments in the printing industry.

686.231 SW ISSN 1400-3724
▼**SCREEN**; facktidning foer anvaendare och producenter av screentryck. 1995. q. SEK 250 (effective 1996); newsstand price: SEK 65. Kellerman & Oeqvist, P.O. Box 515, Oestra Kyrkogatan 24, S-611 10 Nykoeping, Sweden. TEL 46-155-21-98-15. FAX 46-155-21-98-59. Ed. Roland Oeqvist.

686.2 UK ISSN 0960-3778
SCREEN & DISPLAY. m. £30 (foreign £36) (effective 1996). A.E. Morgan Publications Ltd., Stanley House, 9 West St., Epsom, Surrey KT18 7RL, England. TEL 01372-741411. FAX 01372-744493. circ. 5,000. **Document type**: trade publication.

686.2 US ISSN 0036-9594
TT273
SCREEN PRINTING. Spanish edition: Screen Printing en Espanol (ISSN 1070-7239) 1953. m., plus a Buyers' Guide. $39. S T Publications Inc., 407 Gilbert Ave., Cincinnati, OH 45202. TEL 513-421-2050. FAX 513-421-5144. Ed. Steve Duccilli. adv.: B&W page $1915, color page $2815. bk.rev.; stat.; tr.lit. circ. 15,000. (back issues avail.) **Indexed**: Abstr.Bull.Inst.Pap.Chem., Art & Archaeol.Tech.Abstr., Graph.Arts Lit.Abstr., Photo.Abstr. **Document type**: trade publication.
—BLDSC (8211.759700); SWETS. **CCC**.
Description: Aimed at all types of screen printers. Features tips, new products, technology updates, and industry news.

686.2 US ISSN 1070-7239
SCREEN PRINTING EN ESPANOL. English edition: Screen Printing (ISSN 0036-9594) (Text in Spanish) 1993. bi-m., plus a Buyers' Guide. $30. S T Publications Inc., 407 Gilbert Ave., Cincinnati, OH 45202. TEL 513-421-2050. FAX 513-421-5144. Ed. Steve Duccilli. adv.: B&W page $1750; color page $2650. circ. 15,000 (paid). **Document type**: trade publication.
—Ei.
Description: Offers practical advice on various screen printing techniques and technology for Spanish-speaking screen printers of all skill levels, product specialties, and nationalities.

686.2 US ISSN 1053-6221
SCREEN PRINTING NETWORK. 1989. 13/yr. Virgo Publishing Inc., 4141 N. Scottsdale Rd., No.316, Scottsdale, AZ 85251. TEL 602-483-0014. FAX 602-483-1247. Ed. Marcia Flint.

686.2 US ISSN 1063-5521
SCREEN PRINTING TODAY. 1992. bi-w. Virgo Publishing, Inc., 4141 N. Scottsdale Rd., No. 316, Scottsdale, AZ 85251. TEL 602-990-1101. FAX 602-990-0819. Ed. Glenn Bischoff. adv.: B&W page $1390, color page $1690; trim 8 1/8 x 10 7/8. circ. 20,000.

686.2 US ISSN 1051-1032
SCREENPLAY. 1979. m. $36. S T Publications Inc., 407 Gilbert Ave., Cincinnati, OH 45202. TEL 513-421-2050. FAX 513-421-5144. Ed. Mark Goodridge. adv.: B&W page $1995; color page $2895. circ. 23,300. **Document type**: trade publication.
Description: Offers advice in various aspects of garment graphics production.

686.2 US ISSN 0279-053X
SCREENPRINTING & GRAPHIC IMAGING ASSOCIATION INTERNATIONAL. TABLOID. (Former name of issuing body: Screen Printing Association International) m. membership only. Screenprinting & Graphic Imaging Association International, 10015 Main St., Fairfax, VA 22031. TEL 703-385-1335. Pub. John M. Crawford. **Document type**: trade publication.

686.2 CN ISSN 0834-9304
SECOND IMPRESSIONS. 1985. bi-m. Can.$24 (foreign Can.$40). 344401 Alberta Inc., 12644-126 St., Edmonton, AB T5L 0X7, Canada. TEL 403-455-1718. FAX 403-451-4786. E-mail: 71023,2150@compuserve.com. Pub. Micheal Staley. adv.: B&W page Can.$950. circ. 10,000.

686.2 SZ
SENEFELDER. 1899. 12/yr. Postfach, CH-3000 Bern 25, Switzerland. TEL 031-3367211. FAX 031-3312301. Ed. Nicklaus Lenenberger. circ. 7,500. **Document type**: trade publication.

760 FR ISSN 0999-7903
SERI MAGAZINE. bi-m. Ediscreen, 14 av. Henry Dunant, B.P. 38, 93250 Villemomble, France. TEL 48-66-97-26. FAX 48-55-11-88. Ed. Claude Douat. circ. 3,000.

686.2 IT ISSN 0394-5901
SERIGRAFIA. 1956. bi-m. $67. Zeta's s.r.l., Via P.M. Kolbe 8, 20137 Milan, Italy. TEL 39-2-716332. FAX 39-2-7387371. Ed. Zuliani Ruggero. adv.: B&W page L.1800000, color page L.2580000. circ. 2,800.
Description: Concerns the screen printing field.

686 US
SHEETFED OPERATIONS QUARTERLY. q. $40. (Graphic Arts Technical Foundation) National Association of Printers and Lithographers, 780 Palisade Ave., Teaneck, NJ 07666-3129. TEL 201-342-0700. FAX 201-692-0286. **Document type**: trade publication.

686.2 GW ISSN 0178-2835
SIEBDRUCK; die Europaeische Fachzeitschrift fuer graphischen und industriellen Siebdruck. 1952. m. DM.97. Draeger Druck GmbH, Schwertfegerstr. 7, 23556 Luebeck, Germany. TEL 0451-87999-0. FAX 0451-87999-66. Ed. Michael Ringelsiep. circ. 4,500. (back issues avail.) **Document type**: trade publication.
—BLDSC (8271.930000); SWETS.

SIGN BUSINESS. see ADVERTISING AND PUBLIC RELATIONS

686.2 NE ISSN 0037-5268
SILK SCREEN; Nederlands vaktijdschrift voor zeefdruk. 1952. m. fl.150. Eisma B.V. Publishers, Celsiusweg 37, B012062299, 8901 BC Leeuwarden, Netherlands. TEL 058-152545. FAX 058-154000. adv.; illus. circ. 1,400. **Indexed**: Excerp.Med. **Document type**: trade publication.
—SWETS.

760 UK
SOCIETY OF GRAPHIC ARTISTS. PUBLICATION. a. Society of Graphic Artists, 17 Carlton House Terrace, London SW1Y 5BD, England.

686.4 004.7 US ISSN 1077-1271
THE SOLUTION. 1990. 6/yr. $45 (Canada $60; elsewhere $85) includes World Business Solution. Solution Magazines, Box 10765, Phoenix, AZ 85064-0765. TEL 602-234-0363. Ed. Mary Hancock. adv.; illus. **Document type**: trade publication.
Description: Covers technical issues relating to remanufacturing, refilling and recharging laser printer and photocopy toner cartridges.

686.4 004.7 US ISSN 1077-1298
SOLUTION INTERNATIONALE. 1990. 6/yr. $85 includes World Business Solution. Solution Magazines, Box 10765, Phoenix, AZ 85064-0765. TEL 602-234-0363. Ed. Mary Hancock. adv.; illus. **Document type**: trade publication.
Description: Covers technical issues relating to the remanufacturing, refilling and recharging of laser printer and photocopy machine toner cartridges. Covers the industry worldwide.

SOUTH AFRICAN TYPOGRAPHICAL JOURNAL/SUID-AFRIKAANSE TIPOGRAFIESE JOERNAAL. see LABOR UNIONS

686.2 760 US ISSN 0274-774X
SOUTHERN GRAPHICS; covering the graphic arts in the South. 1924. m. $15. P T N Publishing Corp., 445 Broad Hollow Rd., Ste. 21, Melville, NY 11747-4722. TEL 800-308-NEWS. FAX 516-249-5774. Ed. Kenneth Moran. adv.: B&W page $2115, color page $3015; trim 8 1/8 x 10 7/8. bk.rev.; illus. circ. 21,959. **Indexed**: Graph.Arts Lit.Abstr.
Formed by the merger of: Southern Printer and Lithographer; Graphics (Kissimmee) (ISSN 0192-7256); Graphic Communications.
Description: Covers entire graphic arts industry in 14 Southern states.

686 US
SPOTTING THE NEWS; a publication designed to promote interest and co-operation among prepress plants & suppliers. 1936. bi-m. $20. Southeastern Prepress Association, 109 Dogwood Pt., Eatonton, GA 31024. TEL 706-485-8146. FAX 706-485-5271. Ed. Dana D. Kastory. adv. contact: Dana Kastory. bk.rev. (back issues avail.) **Document type**: trade publication.
Description: Offers technical and personal articles of interest to the graphic arts profession.

686 US ISSN 0886-7682
CODEN: SSGRE3
STEP-BY-STEP GRAPHICS; the how-to reference magazine for traditional and electronic graphic designers. 1985. bi-m. $42. 6000 N. Forest Park Dr., Peoria, IL 61614-3592. TEL 309-688-2300. FAX 309-698-0831. Ed. Gregory Sharpless; Pub. Nancy Aldrich-Ruenzel. adv.: B&W page $1485, color page $2235. bk.rev.; illus.; tr.lit.; cum.index. circ. 46,000. (back issues avail.) **Indexed**: DAAI. **Document type**: newsletter.
—BLDSC (8464.213500); CASDDS; SWETS; UnCover.

686.2 US
T A G A NEWSLETTER. q. $85. Technical Association of the Graphic Arts, 68 Lomb Memorial Dr., Rochester, NY 14623-5604. TEL 716-475-7470. FAX 716-475-2250. Ed. Karen Lawrence. **Document type**: trade publication, newsletter.

PRINTING — ABSTRACTING, BIBLIOGRAPHIES, STATISTICS

686.2 US ISSN 0082-2299
Z244 CODEN: TAPRAV
T A G A PROCEEDINGS; technical papers presented at annual meeting. 1949. a. $95 (foreign $120). Technical Association of the Graphic Arts, 68 Lomb Memorial Dr., Rochester, NY 14623-5604. TEL 716-475-7470. FAX 716-475-2250. Ed. Richard S. Fisch. index, cum.index: 1949-1985. circ. 1,000. (back issues avail.) **Indexed:** Abstr.Bull.Inst.Pap.Chem., Graph.Arts Lit.Abstr. **Document type:** proceedings, trade publication.
—BLDSC (8598.230000); CASDDS; UMI.

686.2 US ISSN 0895-6529
T & E NEWS. 1973. 9/yr. free. Rochester Institute of Technology, Technical and Education Center of the Graphic Arts, 66 Lomb Memorial Dr., Rocherster, NY 14623. TEL 716-475-2549. FAX 716-475-7052. Ed. Sandy Richolson. bk.rev.; charts; illus. circ. 26,000. **Indexed:** Abstr.Bull.Inst.Pap.Chem. **Document type:** newsletter.
Former titles: T and E Center Newsletter (ISSN 0276-9611); Graphic Arts Research Center. G A R C Newsletter (ISSN 0271-9479)
Description: Provides information on training, seminars and research for the graphic arts industry.

686.2 GW
TAG FUER TAG. 1939. bi-m. free. Berufsgenossenschaft Druck und Papierverarbeitung, Rheinstr. 6-8, 65185 Wiesbaden, Germany. TEL 0611-131-0. FAX 0611-131222. Ed. Peter Trefz. circ. 120,000. **Document type:** consumer publication.

760 FR
TAMIS. 11/yr. Info-Pub, 92 rue Jean-Pierre Timbaud, 75011 Paris, France. TEL 43-38-48-00. FAX 43-38-02-06. Ed. Isabelle Coqueux. circ. 10,000.

TECHNICAL COMMUNICATION. see *COMMUNICATIONS*

686.2 US
TECHNICAL GUIDE BOOK OF SCREEN PRINTING. (Former name of issuing body: Screen Printing Association International) a. (plus s-a. supplements). membership only. Screenprinting & Graphic Imaging Association International, 10015 Main St., Fairfax, VA 22031. TEL 703-385-1335. Pub. John M. Crawford. **Document type:** trade publication.

686.2 CU
TECNICA GRAFICA. q. $22 in N. America; S. America $24; Europe $28. (Ministerio de Cultura, Departamento de Informacion Cientifico-Tecnica, CEDE Poligrafico) Ediciones Cubanas, Obispo No. 527, Apdo. 605, Havana, Cuba.

686.2 CU
TECNICA GRAFICA. SUPLEMENTO. 3/yr. (Ministerio de Cultura, Departamento de Informacion Cientifico-Tecnica, CEDE Poligrafico) Ediciones Cubanas, Obispo No. 527, Apdo. 605, Havana, Cuba.

686.2 SP
TECNO ALABRENT. 1991. m. (except Aug. & Dec.). 12000 ptas.($92) in Europe; America 16000 ptas. Alabrent Ediciones, Valencia 501 entlo. 1a, 08013 Barcelona, Spain. TEL 34-3-265-32-11. FAX 34-3-263-13-20. circ. 3,000. **Document type:** trade publication.

686.2 US ISSN 1043-2302
TEXAS PRINTER. 1988. q. Printing Industries Association of Texas, 910 W. Mockingbird Ln., Dallas, TX 75247-5174. TEL 817-332-8236. FAX 817-877-1862. Ed. Nolan Moore. circ. 4,000. **Document type:** trade publication.

686.2 GR ISSN 0257-4292
TIPOGRAFIA; a fortnightly review of graphic arts and paper. Key Title: E Tipografia. (Quarterly edition also avail.) (Text in Greek) 1958. fortn. Dr.8000. Athens Typographic Organization Ltd., 16 Alkamenous St., 104 39 Athens, Greece. TEL 30-1-8813-673. FAX 30-1-8814-853. Ed. Fotis Landas; Pubs. G. Ventouris, K. Raftopoulou. adv.: B&W page $500 (DM.980); 380 x 260; adv. contact: Fotis Landas. bk.rev. circ. 3,000. (tabloid format) **Document type:** newspaper.
Description: Informs about innovations, industry developments, and new products.

TOKYO ART DIRECTORS ANNUAL/A D C NENKAN. see *ADVERTISING AND PUBLIC RELATIONS*

686.2 US
TYPESETTERS OF CHARLESTON.* w. 54 John Street, Charleston, SC 29403.

686.2 SZ ISSN 0041-4840
TYPOGRAFISCHE MONATSBLAETTER; Schweizer Graphische Mitteilungen-revue suisse de l'imprimerie. (Text in English, French and German) 1882. bi-m. 110 SFr. (foreign 135 SFr.). (Gewerkschaft Druck und Papier) Zollikofer AG, Fuerstenlandstr. 122, CH-9001 St. Gallen, Switzerland. TEL 071-297777. FAX 071-297384. adv.; bk.rev.; bibl.; charts; illus.; mkt. circ. 3,000. **Indexed:** DAAI. **Document type:** trade publication.
—SWETS.

686.2 US ISSN 0275-6870
Z243.A2
TYPOGRAPHY. 1980. a. $45. (Type Directors Club of New York) Watson - Guptill Publications, 1515 Broadway, New York, NY 10036. (Subscr. to: 1695 Oak St., Lakewood, NJ 08701. TEL 800-451-1741. FAX 908-363-0338) circ. 20,000. **Document type:** trade publication.

686 US ISSN 0362-6245
Z119 CODEN: ULCCDC
U & L C. (Upper and Lower Case); the international journal of type and graphic design. 1974. q. $30 for 3 yrs.(free to qualified personnel). International Typeface Corp., 866 Second Ave., New York, NY 10017. TEL 212-371-0699. FAX 212-752-4752. Ed. Margaret Richardson. adv.: B&W page $4625, color page $7000. bk.rev.; illus. circ. 180,000. (tabloid format; also avail. in microfiche from UMI; back issues avail.) **Indexed:** Artbibl.Mod., DAAI, Graph.Arts Lit.Abstr.
—CASDDS; Faxon; SWETS; UMI.

686.2 SZ ISSN 1019-4754
U G R A MITTEILUNGEN. (Text in French, German) 1963. 3/yr. 20 SFr. Verein zur Foerderung Wissenschaftlicher Untersuchungen in der Graphischen Industrie, c/o E M P A, Postfach 977, CH-9001 St. Gallen, Switzerland. TEL 071-300431. FAX 071-300199. TELEX 881349-EMPA-CH. Ed. Walter Steiger. bk.rev.; bibl.; charts; illus. circ. 3,800. **Indexed:** Abstr.Bull.Inst.Pap.Chem. **Document type:** bulletin.
Description: Provides professional information for and of the graphics industry.

686.2 SZ
V S D - MITTEILUNGEN. fortn. 67 Fr. (foreign 85 Fr.). Verband der Schweizer Druckindustrie, Schosshaldenstr. 20, CH-3000 Bern 32, Switzerland. TEL 031-431511. FAX 031-443738. adv.; bk.rev.

686.2 SZ
V S F - BULLETIN. irreg. Vereinigung Schweizerischer Formularhersteller, Schosshaldenstr. 20, CH-3000 Bern 32, Switzerland. TEL 031-3511511. **Document type:** bulletin.

686.2 US
WASHINGTON INDUSTRY AND ASSOCIATION NEWS. 1960. q. free. Acropolis Books Ltd., 425 Wood Duck Dr., Sarasota, FL 34236-1823. Ed. A.J. Hackl. adv.; bk.rev.; circ. 3,500 (controlled).

686.209 GW ISSN 0724-9586
WOLFENBUETTELER SCHRIFTEN ZUR GESCHICHTE DES BUCHWESENS. 1977. irreg., vol.22, 1994. price varies. Harrassowitz Verlag, Taunusstr. 14, 65183 Wiesbaden, Germany. TEL 0611-530-0. FAX 0611-530570. TELEX 4186135. (Subscr. to: Postfach 2929, 65019 Wiesbaden, Germany) Ed. Paul Raabe. **Document type:** monographic series.

686.4 004.7 US ISSN 1077-128X
WORLD BUSINESS SOLUTION. 1990. 6/yr. free to qualified personnel. Solution Magazines, Box 10765, Phoenix, AZ 85064-0765. TEL 602-234-0363. Ed. Mary Hancock. adv.; illus. **Document type:** trade publication.
Formerly (until 1991): Business Solution.
Description: Covers business issues relating to the worldwide toner cartridge remanufacturing and recharging industry.

686.2 GW ISSN 0147-4804
Z119
WORLD WIDE PRINTER. 1977. bi-m. DM.72($45) Deutscher Drucker Verlag GmbH, Postfach 4124, 73744 Ostfildern, Germany. TEL 0711-444005. FAX 0711-415299. Ed. W. Pincus Jaspert. adv.: page $4780; trim 210 x 297; adv. contact: Wolfgang Blum. charts; illus.; stat. circ. 22,600. (also avail. in microform from UMI) **Indexed:** Graph.Arts Lit.Abstr. **Document type:** trade publication.
—UMI; UnCover. **CCC.**

686.2 GW
▼**WORLD-WIDE PRINTER CHINA SPECIAL.** (Text in Chinese) 1994. 2/yr. Deutscher Drucker Verlag GmbH, Postfach 4124, 73744 Ostfildern, Germany. TEL 0711-444005. FAX 0711-415299. Ed. W. Pincus Jaspert. **Document type:** trade publication.

686.2 CC ISSN 1004-6267
YINSHUA ZAZHI/PRINTING FIELD. (Text in Chinese) 1972. bi-m. Y3 (foreign $5) (effective 1995). Shanghai Yinshua Jishu Yanjiusuo - Shanghai Printing Technology Institute, No. 60, Lane 1209, Xinzha Lu, Shanghai 200041, People's Republic of China. TEL 021-258-0014. FAX 021-255-3562. (Dist. by: China International Book Trading Corporation, No. 35, Che Gong Zhuang Rd. W., Beijing, China. TEL 0861-841-2026. FAX 0861-841-2048) Ed. Huang Junhao; Pub. Yu Zhihui. adv.: B&W page $1000, color page $2000; trim 187 x 260; adv. contact: Ding Shihua. bk.rev. circ. 22,000. **Document type:** trade publication.
Description: For directors, managers, engineers and technicians of research institutes and printing houses.

ZUGAKU KENKYU/JOURNAL OF GRAPHIC SCIENCE OF JAPAN. see *ART*

PRINTING — Abstracting, Bibliographies, Statistics

686.2 US
AMERICAN STATISTICAL ASSOCIATION. STATISTICAL GRAPHICS SECTION. PROCEEDINGS. a., 7th ed. $27 to non-members; members $18. American Statistical Association, 1429 Duke St., Alexandria, VA 22314-3402. TEL 703-684-1221. FAX 703-684-2037. **Indexed:** Curr.Ind.Stat. **Document type:** proceedings.

016 686.2 NE ISSN 0303-5964
Z117
ANNUAL BIBLIOGRAPHY OF THE HISTORY OF THE PRINTED BOOK AND LIBRARY. Key Title: A B H B. (Text in English) 1973. a., vol.22, 1993 (for the year 1991). fl.265 (effective 1993). (International Federation of Library Associations and Institutions, Committee on Rare Books and Manuscripts) Kluwer Academic Publishers, Postbus 17, 3300 AA Dordrecht, Netherlands. TEL 31-78-392392. FAX 31-78-392254. TELEX 29245 KAPG NL. (Dist. by: Kluwer Academic Publishers Group, P.O. Box 322, 3300 AH Dordrecht, Netherlands. TEL 31-78-392392. FAX 31-78-546474; N. America dist. addr.: Box 358, Accord Sta., Hingham, MA 02018-0358. TEL 617-871-6600. FAX 617-871-6528) Ed. H.D.L. Vervliet. **Document type:** bibliography.
Refereed Serial

760 US ISSN 1073-6611
NE65
ART PRICE INDEX INTERNATIONAL. (In 2 vols.) 1992. a. $175. Sound View Press, 10 Boston Post Rd., Madison, CT 06443. TEL 203-245-2246. FAX 203-245-3589. Ed. Peter Hastings Falk; Pub. Peter Hastings Falk. adv.; circ. 3,000 (paid). **Document type:** directory.
Formerly (until 1993): Print Price Index (ISSN 1058-2339)
Description: Documents all fine art, including paintings, drawings, prints, photographs, and watercolors sold at auction. Contains international coverage with about 150,000 entries.

686.2 AT ISSN 0811-3963
BRANDYWINE BIBLIOGRAPHY. 1981. irreg. price varies. Brandywine Press & Archive, 20 Murray Rd., Beecroft, N.S.W. 2119, Australia. TEL (02)863627. Ed. J.P. Wegner. (back issues avail.)

PRINTING — COMPUTER APPLICATIONS

686.2 070   CN   ISSN 0575-9412
Z487
CANADA. STATISTICS CANADA. PRINTING, PUBLISHING AND ALLIED INDUSTRIES. (Catalogue 36-251) (Text in English and French) 1920. a. Can.$35($42) (foreign $49). Statistics Canada, Publications Sales and Services, Ottawa, Ont. K1A 0T6, Canada. TEL 613-951-7277. FAX 613-951-1584. **Document type:** government publication.
   Description: Annual census of manufactures.

DESIGN AND APPLIED ARTS INDEX. see ART — Abstracting, Bibliographies, Statistics

686.2   AT   ISSN 0729-6568
DIRECTORY OF COMPANY HISTORIES OF THE BOOK INDUSTRIES/VERZEICHNIS VON JUBILAEUMSSCHRIFTEN DER GRAPHISCHEN INDUSTRIE. (Text in English and German) 1981. irreg., approx. a. Aus.$10($7.15) Brandywine Press and Archive, 20 Murray Road, Beecroft, N.S.W. 2119, Australia. TEL (02)863627. Ed. Juergen P. Wegner. circ. 100. (back issues avail.)

GRAPHIC DESIGNERS' INDEX. see ART — Abstracting, Bibliographies, Statistics

760   US   ISSN 1064-9638
Z119
INSTITUTE OF PAPER SCIENCE AND TECHNOLOGY. GRAPHIC ARTS BULLETIN. 1954. m. $450 per vol. in N. America; elsewhere $500. Institute of Paper Science and Technology, 500 10th St. N.W., Atlanta, GA 30318. TEL 404-853-9500. FAX 404-853-9510. Ed. Rosanna M. Bechtel. bk.rev. circ. 350. **Indexed:** Abstr.Bull.Inst.Pap.Chem., Print.Abstr. **Document type:** abstracting/indexing.
   Former titles: Graphic Arts Literature Abstracts (ISSN 0090-8207); Graphic Arts Progress (ISSN 0017-3347); Which incorporates (1951-1953): Graphic Arts Index; Which supersedes: P I A Management Reports.
   Description: Abstracts trade, technical and patent literature on the graphic arts.

686 016   RU
NOVOSTI TEKHNICHESKOI LITERATURY. POLIGRAFICHESKAYA PROMYSHLENNOST'. 1969. m. $4. (Komitet po Pechati Soveta Ministrov) Izdatel'stvo Kniga, 50, Gorky St., 125047 Moscow, Russia.

665 016   UK   ISSN 0031-109X
Z118.A3
PRINTING ABSTRACTS. 1946. m. $1105.20. Pira International, Randalls Rd., Leatherhead, Surrey KT22 7RU, England. TEL 0372-376161. FAX 0372-360104. Ed. Julie Kent; Pub. Marie Rushton. bk.rev.; abstr.; index. **Indexed:** Curr.Cont., Graph.Arts Lit.Abstr., World Surf.Coat., World Text.Abstr. **Document type:** abstracting/indexing.
●Also available online. Vendor(s): Data-Star, Knight-Ridder, Inc., Orbit Search Service (PIRA), STN International.
—BLDSC (6613.620000). **CCC.**

686.2 016   RU   ISSN 0235-2222
Z119
REFERATIVNYI ZHURNAL. IZDATEL'SKOE DELO I POLIGRAFIYA. 1975. m. $184 (effective 1996). Vsesoyuznyi Institut Nauchno-Tekhnicheskoi Informatsii (VINITI), Baltiiskaya ul. 14, Moscow A-219, Russia. (Subscr. to: Mezhdunarodnaya Kniga, Dimitrova ul. 39, 113095 Moscow, Russia) **Document type:** abstracting/indexing.
   Formerly: Referativnyi Zhurnal. Ekonimika, Organizatsiya, Tekhnologiya i Oborudovanie Poligraficheskogo Proizvodstva (ISSN 0320-5223)

PRINTING — Computer Applications

see also Computers–Computer Graphics

686.2   US
DESKTOP FOR PROFIT. m. $123.50 to non-members; members $95. National Association of Printers and Lithographers, 780 Palisade Ave., Teaneck, NJ 07666-3129. TEL 201-342-0700. FAX 201-692-0286. Ed. Patrick Henry. **Document type:** trade publication.

DUNN REPORT; electronic publishing & prepress systems news & views. see PUBLISHING AND BOOK TRADE

ELECTRONIC PUBLISHING & TYPEWORLD; the first newspaper for digital publishing professionals. see PUBLISHING AND BOOK TRADE — Computer Applications

686.2 659.1 070.3   US
G C A REVIEW. 1988. m. membership. Graphic Communications Association, 100 Daingerfield Rd., Alexandria, VA 22314. TEL 703-519-8160. FAX 703-548-2867. Ed. Vivian Sanchez. circ. 800. **Document type:** newsletter.
   Formerly (until 1991): Perspectives (Alexandria).

GOVERNMENT PUBLISHER. see PUBLISHING AND BOOK TRADE — Computer Applications

686.2   US
IMAGING SUPPLIES ANNUAL; product overview and supplies market directory. a. $125 (foreign $140). BIS Strategic Decisions, One Longwater Cir., Norwell, MA 02061-1620. TEL 617-982-9500. FAX 617-982-1724. Ed. Robert Leahey. **Document type:** directory.
   Formerly: Datek Imaging Supplies Annual (ISSN 1057-4875); Incorporates: Annual Guide to Ribbons and Toner.
   Description: Editorial, product directories and supplies market articles of ribbons, toner, ink-jet ink, technology specific media, and printwheel industries.

686.2   US   ISSN 1050-6993
IMAGING SUPPLIES MONTHLY. 1987. m. $350 (foreign $400). BIS Strategic Decisions, One Longwater Cir., Norwell, MA 02061-1620. TEL 617-982-9500. FAX 617-982-1724. Ed. Marla Boswarth.
—CCC.
   Formerly: Datek Imaging Supplies Monthly.
   Description: The only newsletter covering the imaging supplies industries. Coverage includes consumables for electronic printers, copiers, and other imaging equipment for the office, industry and home.

686.2 070   US   ISSN 1042-0304
Z286.E43
PRE-. 1989. 9/yr. $30. Cowles Business Media, 21800 Oxnard St., Ste. 250, Woodland Hills, CA 91367-3633. TEL 818-593-6100. FAX 818-593-6153. Ed. Howard Fenton. adv.: B&W page $3760, color page $4380; 8 x 10 3/4. bk.rev. circ. 33,000. **Document type:** trade publication.
   Description: Aimed at users, buyers, and specifiers of electronic design and pre-press products and services. Covers news, trends, and products in the field.

PREPRESS COMPUTING MAGAZINE. see PUBLISHING AND BOOK TRADE — Computer Applications

686.2   US
PRINT MEDIA GAZETTE; a communication for imaging professionals from Kodak's Printing & Publishing Imaging Print Media Group. 1992. bi-m. Eastman Kodak Co., Professional, Printing and Publishing Imaging, 343 State St., Rochester, NY 14650-0405. TEL 716-724-4000. FAX 716-724-9624.

686.2 640.73   US   ISSN 0890-7234
TK7887.7
PRINTERS BUYER'S GUIDE AND HANDBOOK. 1985. 2/yr. Bedford Communications, Inc., 150 Fifth Ave., New York, NY 10011. TEL 212-807-8220. FAX 212-807-8737.

686.21   US   ISSN 0887-7556
PRINTOUT. 1977. m. $392 (foreign $442). BIS Strategic Decisions, One Longwater Cir., Norwell, MA 02061-1620. TEL 617-982-9500. FAX 617-982-1724. Ed. Adina Levin. index. **Document type:** newsletter.
—CCC.
   Incorporates (1981-1987): Printout Magazine (ISSN 0738-6613)
   Description: Covers company, product and market developments in the computer printer and printer-related industries.

R & R NEWS. (Recharging & Recycling) see COMPUTERS — Hardware

PRODUCTION OF GOODS AND SERVICES

see Business and Economics–Production of Goods and Services

PROTESTANTISM

see Religions and Theology–Protestant

PSYCHIATRY AND NEUROLOGY

see Medical Sciences–Psychiatry and Neurology

PSYCHOLOGY

see also Medical Sciences–Psychiatry and Neurology

301.1   US   ISSN 1064-4210
A A - B A NEWSLETTER. 1978. q. $50 includes membership. American Anorexia - Bulimia Association, Inc., 293 Central Park W., Ste. 1R, New York, NY 10024. TEL 212-501-8351. FAX 212-501-0342. bk.rev.; bibl. circ. 7,000. **Document type:** newsletter.
   Description: For professionals and lay persons; includes ongoing updates on clinical and research information on eating disorders; recognition and inspirational support for sufferers, the recovered, families and caregivers; and information and outreach on prevention.

155.4   US
A A C R C NEWSLETTER. 1986. bi-m. $50. American Association of Children's Residential Centers, 1021 Prince St., Alexandria, VA 22314-2971. TEL 703-838-7522. FAX 703-684-5968. Ed. Claudia C. Waller. circ. 350. **Document type:** newsletter.

155   US
A B A NEWSLETTER (KALAMAZOO). 1977. q. $40 to non-members. Association for Behavior Analysis, Western Michigan University, Kalamazoo, MI 49008-5052. TEL 616-387-4494. FAX 616-387-4457. Ed. P.A. Lamal. adv.; bk.rev. circ. 2,300. **Document type:** newsletter.
   Description: Covers association activities, news and conference announcements.

A B S A M E NEWSLETTER. (Association for the Behavioral Sciences and Medical Education) see MEDICAL SCIENCES — Psychiatry And Neurology

157   US
A D A A REPORTER. 1990. q. $25. Anxiety Disorders Association of America, 6000 Executive Blvd., Ste. 513, Rockville, MD 20852. TEL 301-231-9350. Ed. Joel Klaverkamp. adv. circ. 6,000. (tabloid format)
   Description: Includes scientific articles, self-help information, and association news items.

A D A M H A NEWS. (Alcohol, Drug Abuse, and Mental Health Administration) see DRUG ABUSE AND ALCOHOLISM

150   US   ISSN 1065-8025
A D H D REPORT. (Attention Deficit Hyperactivity Disorder) 1993. bi-m. $65 (foreign $70) to individuals; institutions $80 (foreign $85). Guilford Publications, Inc., 72 Spring St., New York, NY 10012. TEL 212-431-9800. FAX 212-966-6708. Ed. Russell A. Barkley; Pub. Robert Matloff. adv. contact: Marian Robinson. bk.rev.; abstr.; bibl.; index. circ. 3,500. **Document type:** newsletter.
—CCC.
   Description: Offers relevant information from research, workshops, and clinical work on ADHD, as well as from recent scientific publications and conferences from around the world.

A E C A RESOURCE BOOK SERIES. see CHILDREN AND YOUTH — About

A E P APPOINTMENTS BROADSHEET. (Association of Educational Psychologists) see OCCUPATIONS AND CAREERS

PSYCHOLOGY

A H A F JOURNAL. (American Handwriting Analysis Foundation) see *EDUCATION*

158 US
A H P PERSPECTIVE.* 1962. m. $59 to individuals; students $39. Association for Humanistic Psychology, 45 Franklin St., Ste. 315, San Francisco, CA 94102-6017. TEL 415-346-7929. FAX 415-346-7993. Ed. Mary King. adv. contact: Greg Kervin. bk.rev. circ. 6,000. (back issues avail.) **Document type:** newsletter.
  Formerly: A H P Newsletter.

A M S STUDIES IN MODERN SOCIETY. see *PUBLIC HEALTH AND SAFETY*

301.1 610 155.4 US
A N A D: WORKING TOGETHER. 1979. q. $25 membership. National Association of Anorexia Nervosa and Associated Disorders, Box 7, Highland Park, IL 60035. TEL 708-831-3438. FAX 708-433-4632. Ed.Bd. bk.rev. circ. 15,000. **Document type:** newsletter.
  Description: Discusses issues and challenges facing persons suffering from eating disorders and related afflictions.

301.19 167 US
A N R E D ALERT. 1979. 10/yr. $15. Anorexia Nervosa & Related Eating Disorders, Inc., Box 5102, Eugene, OR 97405. TEL 503-344-1144. Ed. Dr. J. Bradley Rubel. bk.rev. circ. 15,000. (back issues avail.) **Document type:** newsletter.
  Description: Causes, consequences, symptoms and treatment of anorexia nervosa and bulimia nervosa.
  Refereed Serial

150 US ISSN 0001-2114
BF1
A P A MONITOR. 1970. 12/yr. $27.50 to non-members (foreign $39.50); institutions $32.50 (foreign $56.50). American Psychological Association, 750 First St., N.E., Washington, DC 20002-4242. TEL 202-336-5560. FAX 202-336-5568. Ed. Laurie Denton. adv. contact: Jodi Ashcraft. charts; illus.; tr.lit. circ. 100,000. (also avail. in microform from UMI) **Document type:** newspaper.
  —Faxon; UMI.
  Incorporates: American Psychological Association. Employment Bulletin.
  Description: Reports on the science, practice, and social responsibility activities of psychology, including latest legislative developments affecting mental health, education, and research support.

152 II
A P R C JOURNAL OF EXPERIMENTAL PSYCHOLOGY. (Text in English) 1978. 2/yr. Rs.50($22.75) Agra Psychological Research Cell, Tiwari Kothi, Belanganj, Agra 282004, India. Ed. Govind Tiwari. (reprint service avail. from ISI)

150 US ISSN 1050-4672
A P S OBSERVER. 1988. bi-m. $35 to individuals (foreign $50); institutions $50 (foreign $65) (effective 1995). American Psychological Society, 1010 Vermont Ave., N.W., Ste. 1100, Washington, DC 20005-4907. TEL 202-783-2077. FAX 202-783-2083. E-mail: LHerring@Bitnic.Educom.Edu. Ed. K. Lee Herring; Pub. Alan G. Kraut. adv.: B&W page $1450; trim 8 1/2 x 11; adv. contact: Martha Tralka. circ. 15,030. **Document type:** newsletter.
  Description: Covers the Society activities and news on political and research issues of importance to scienctific psychologists.

155 US ISSN 0001-2300
A R G R JOURNAL. 1959. s-a. $1. Association for Research in Growth Relationships, c/o Thomas P. Nally, University of Rhode Island, Dept. of Education, Kingston, RI 02881. TEL 401-792-2564. Eds. Richard Clark, Gerald Wohlfred. bk.rev.; charts; stat. circ. 200. (processed)

152 US
A S D NEWSLETTER. 1984. q. membership. Association for the Study of Dreams, Box 1600, Vienna, VA 22183. TEL 703-242-8888. FAX 510-527-7929. Ed. Alan Siegel. bk.rev.; abstr.; bibl.; charts; illus. circ. 750. (back issues avail.) **Document type:** newsletter.
  Description: International, multidisciplinary, basic and applied dream research.

301.1 150 VE ISSN 1011-6281
A V E P S O FASCICULO. 1983. a. Bs.45($6) Asociacion Venezolana de Psicologia Social, Apdo. 47101, Los Chaguaramos, Caracas 1041-A, Venezuela. TEL 6624751; 619811-30, Ext. 2643, 3043. Ed. Beatriz Rodriguez. circ. 500. (back issues avail.) **Indexed:** Psychol.Abstr.

150 DK ISSN 0900-8527
AARHUS UNIVERSITET. PSYKOLOGISK SKRIFTSERIE AARHUS. (Text in Danish; summaries in English) irreg. Aarhus Universitet, Psykologisk Institut, DK-8000 Aarhus C, Denmark. **Indexed:** Psychol.Abstr.
  Formerly (until 1979): Psychological Reports Aarhus (ISSN 0105-2861)

ABHIGYAN; the journal of foundation for organization research and education. see *SOCIAL SCIENCES: COMPREHENSIVE WORKS*

150 US
ACADEMIC PRESS SERIES IN COGNITION AND PERCEPTION. 1973. irreg., latest 1988. Academic Press, Inc., 525 B St., Ste. 1900, San Diego, CA 92101-4495. TEL 619-231-0926. FAX 619-699-6715. (Subscr. to: Order Dept., 6277 Sea Harbor Dr., 4th Fl., Orlando, FL 32887. TEL 800-321-5068) Eds. Edward C. Carterette, Morton P. Friedman. (reprint service avail. from ISI) **Document type:** monographic series.
  Refereed Serial

150 US ISSN 0192-1088
RC500
ACADEMY FORUM. 1956. q. $20. American Academy of Psychoanalysis, 47 E. 19th St., 6th Fl., New York, NY 10003-1323. TEL 212-475-7980. FAX 212-425-8101. Ed. Jane Simon. adv. contact: Miriam Paluba. bk.rev. circ. 4,000. **Document type:** academic/scholarly publication.
  Formerly (until 1977): Academy (ISSN 0197-5781)

ACTA PAEDOLOGICA; an international journal of child development. see *CHILDREN AND YOUTH — About*

150 NE ISSN 0001-6918
BF1 CODEN: APSOAZ
ACTA PSYCHOLOGICA; international journal of psychonomics. (Text in English) 1941. 9/yr. fl.957($584) (effective 1996). North-Holland (Subsidiary of: Elsevier Science B.V.), P.O. Box 211, 1000 AE Amsterdam, Netherlands. TEL 31-20-4853911. FAX 31-20-4853598. TELEX 18582 ESPA NL. (Subscr. in U.S. and Canada to: Elsevier Science Inc., Box 882, Madison Sq. Sta., New York, NY 10159. TEL 212-989-5800. FAX 212-633-3990) Ed. J.G.W. Raaijmakers. adv.; bibl.; illus.; index. (also avail. in microform from UMI; back issues avail.; reprint service avail. SWZ) **Indexed:** ASCA, ASSIA, Bibl.Ind., Biol.Abstr., Commun.Abstr., Curr.Cont., Ind.Med., Lang.& Lang.Behav.Abstr., Mid.East: Abstr.& Ind., Psychol.Abstr. (1950-), Res.High.Educ.Abstr., Sociol.Abstr., SSCI. **Document type:** academic/scholarly publication.
  —BLDSC (0661.490000); Faxon; Genuine Article; SWETS; UnCover. **CCC.**
  Description: Publishes original papers reporting on experimental studies, as well as theoretical and review articles, in human experimental psychology.
  Refereed Serial

152 FI ISSN 0515-3115
ACTA PSYCHOLOGICA FENNICA. (Text in Finnish) 1951. irreg. (1-2/yr.). FIM 60. Finnish Psychological Society, Mariankatu 7 C, 00170 Helsinki, Finland. TEL 90-608586. Ed. Jari Wurmi. circ. 700.

370.15 150 PL ISSN 0208-6093
L51
ACTA UNIVERSITATIS LODZIENSIS: FOLIA PAEDAGOGICA ET PSYCHOLOGICA. (Text in German and Polish; summaries in English and German) 1955-1974; N.S. 1980. irreg. (Uniwersytet Lodzki, Wydzial Pedagogiki i Psychologii) Wydawnictwo Uniwersytetu Lodzkiego, Ul. Jaracza 34, Lodz, Poland. TEL 331671. charts. **Document type:** academic/scholarly publication.
  —BLDSC (0585.208000).
  Supersedes in part: Uniwersytet Lodzki. Zeszyty Naukowe. Seria 1: Nauki Humanistyczno-Spoleczne (ISSN 0076-0358)
  Description: Contains articles from the fields of history, theory of social education, didactics, social pedagogics and psychology, as well as reports and proceedings of scientific conferences organized by Department of Pedagogics and Psychology in the University of Lodz.

370.15 150 HU ISSN 0324-7260
LA682
ACTA UNIVERSITATIS SZEGEDIENSIS DE ATTILA JOZSEF NOMINATAE. SECTIO PAEDAGOGICA ET PSYCHOLOGICA. (Text in English or Hungarian) 1956. a. exchange basis. Attila Jozsef University, c/o E. Szabo, Exchange Librarian, Dugonics ter 13, P.O.B. 393, Szeged H-6701, Hungary. (Subscr. to: Kultura, Box 149, H-1389 Budapest, Hungary) Ed. Gyorgy Agoston. circ. 300. Indexed: M.L.A. **Document type:** academic/scholarly publication.
  Description: Journal of Hungarian education with the use of psychology as an auxiliary science for education.

150 PL ISSN 0137-110X
ACTA UNIVERSITATIS WRATISLAVIENSIS. PRACE PSYCHOLOGICZNE. 1972. irreg. price varies. (Uniwersytet Wroclawski) Wydawnictwo Uniwersytetu Wroclawskiego, Pl. Uniwersyteck 9-13, 50-137 Wroclaw, Poland. TEL 44-10-06. (Dist. by: Ksiegarnia Uniwersytetu Wroclawskiego, Pl. Uniwersytecki 9-13, 50-137 Wroclaw, Poland) Ed. Marian Kulczycki. circ. 300. **Document type:** academic/scholarly publication.

ADOLESCENCE; an international quarterly devoted to the physiological, psychological, psychiatric, sociological, and educational aspects of the second decade of human life. see *CHILDREN AND YOUTH — About*

150 JA ISSN 0918-1490
ADORERIAN/ADLERIAN. (Text in Japanese) 1984. 3/yr. 5000 Yen. Nihon Adora Shinri Gakkai - Japanese Society of Adlerian Psychology, 5-12-15-301 Nishinakajima, Yodogawa-ku, Osaka 532, Japan. TEL 06-306-4699. FAX 06-306-0160. Ed. Samuel M. Kamata. adv. contact: Shunsaku Noda. **Document type:** academic/scholarly publication.
  Refereed Serial

150 UK
ADVANCES IN ADOLESCENT MENTAL HEALTH. 1986. irreg., vol.4, 1990. $88. Jessica Kingsley Publishers, 116 Pentonville Rd., London N1 9JB, England. TEL 071-833-2307. FAX 071-837-2917. (U.S. subscr. to: Taylor & Francis, 1900 Frost Rd., Ste. 101, Bristol, PA 19007-1598. TEL 800-821-8312. FAX 215-785-5515) Eds. Arlene Stiffman, Ronald Feldman. **Document type:** monographic series.

150 301.1 US ISSN 0883-3656
HM251
ADVANCES IN APPLIED SOCIAL PSYCHOLOGY. 1980. irreg., vol.3, 1986. $49.95 cloth. Lawrence Erlbaum Associates, Inc., 10 Industrial Dr., Mahwah, NJ 07430-2262. TEL 201-236-9500. FAX 201-236-0072. Eds. M.J. Saks, L. Saxe. (back issues avail.) Indexed: Curr.Cont., Psychol.Abstr. **Document type:** monographic series.
  Refereed Serial

150 UK
ADVANCES IN BEHAVIORAL ASSESSMENT OF CHILDREN AND FAMILIES. 1984. irreg., vol.5, 1991. $85. Jessica Kingsley Publishers, 116 Pentonville Rd., London N1 9JB, England. TEL 071-833-2307. FAX 071-837-2917. (U.S. subscr. to: Taylor & Francis, 1900 Frost Rd., Ste. 101, Bristol, PA 19007-1598. TEL 800-821-8312. FAX 215-785-5515) Ed. Ronald Prinz. **Document type:** monographic series.
  Formerly (until 1986): Advances in the Behavioral Measurement of Children.

PSYCHOLOGY

155 591   US   ISSN 0099-6246
CODEN: ADBBBW
ADVANCES IN BEHAVIORAL BIOLOGY. 1971. irreg., vol.42, 1994. price varies. Plenum Publishing Corp., 233 Spring St., New York, NY 10013-1578. TEL 212-620-8000. FAX 212-463-0742. TELEX 23-421139. (back issues avail.) **Document type:** monographic series.
—BLDSC (0699.910000); CASDDS; Faxon; UnCover. **CCC.**
Refereed Serial

152.8 330.9   US   ISSN 0890-0159
HB1
ADVANCES IN BEHAVIORAL ECONOMICS. 1987. irreg., vol.2, 1990. price varies. Ablex Publishing Corporation, 355 Chestnut St., Norwood, NJ 07648. TEL 201-767-8450. FAX 201-767-6717. TELEX 135-393. Eds. Leonard Green, John Kagel. **Document type:** academic/scholarly publication.

150   UK   ISSN 0146-6402
RC489.B4   CODEN: ABRTDI
ADVANCES IN BEHAVIOUR RESEARCH AND THERAPY; an international journal for reviews and reports of original research. 1978. 4/yr. £225($336) (effective 1995). Elsevier Science Ltd., Pergamon, P.O. Box 800, Kidlington, Oxford OX5 1DX, England. TEL 44-1865-843000. FAX 44-1865-843010. E-mail: nlinfo-f@elsevier.nl; usinfo-f@elsevier.com; forinfo-kyf04035@niftyserve.or.jp; Site addr.: http://www.elsevier.nl/. (Subscr. in U.S. and Canada to: Elsevier Science, 660 White Plains Rd., Tarrytown, NY 10591-5153. TEL 914-524-9200. FAX 914-333-2444) Eds. S. Rachman, T. Wilson. (also avail. in microform from UMI) **Indexed:** Abstr.Crim.& Pen., Adol.Ment.Hlth.Abstr., ASSIA, Biol.Abstr., Excerpt.Med., Ind.Sci.Rev., Psychol.Abstr. (1977-), SSCI. **Document type:** academic/scholarly publication.
—BLDSC (0699.916000); Faxon; Genuine Article; SWETS; UMI; UnCover. **CCC.**
Description: Publishes extended reports and reviews of research in the theory and practice of behavior therapy.
Refereed Serial

155 618.92   US   ISSN 0065-2407
BF721   CODEN: ADCDA8
ADVANCES IN CHILD DEVELOPMENT AND BEHAVIOR. 1963. irreg., vol.24, 1993. Academic Press, Inc., 525 B St., Ste. 1900, San Diego, CA 92101-4495. TEL 619-231-0926. FAX 619-699-6715. (Subscr. to: Order Dept., 6277 Sea Harbor Dr., 4th Fl., Orlando, FL 32887. TEL 800-321-5068) Eds. L.P. Lipsitt, Charles C. Spiegel. index. (reprint service avail. from ISI) **Indexed:** Biol.Abstr., Ind.Med., SSCI. **Document type:** monographic series.
—BLDSC (0703.800000); SWETS; UnCover. **CCC.**
Refereed Serial

150 616.8   US   ISSN 0940-8606
ADVANCES IN CHILD NEUROPSYCHOLOGY. irreg., vol.3, 1995. Springer-Verlag, 175 Fifth Ave., New York, NY 10010. TEL 212-460-1500. FAX 212-473-6272. Eds. Michael Tramontana, Stephen Hooper. **Document type:** academic/scholarly publication, monographic series.
—BLDSC (0703.810000).

155.4   US   ISSN 0149-4732
RJ503.3   CODEN: ACCPE7
ADVANCES IN CLINICAL CHILD PSYCHOLOGY. 1977. irreg., vol.17, 1994. price varies. Plenum Publishing Corp., 233 Spring St., New York, NY 10013-1578. TEL 212-620-8000. FAX 212-463-0742. TELEX 23-421139. Eds. Benjamin Lahey, Alan Kazdin. **Indexed:** Psychol.Abstr. (1993-), SSCI. **Document type:** monographic series.
—BLDSC (0703.910000); Faxon; Genuine Article; UnCover. **CCC.**
Refereed Serial

ADVANCES IN COGNITION AND EDUCATIONAL PRACTICE. see *EDUCATION — Teaching Methods And Curriculum*

150   US
ADVANCES IN COMPARATIVE PSYCHOLOGY. 1991. irreg. price varies. Praeger Publishers (Subsidiary of: Greenwood Publishing Group Inc.), 88 Post Rd. W., Box 5007, Westport, CT 06881-5007. TEL 203-226-3571. FAX 203-222-1502. **Document type:** monographic series.

152   NE
▼**ADVANCES IN CONSCIOUSNESS RESEARCH.** (Text in English) 1995. irreg. price varies. John Benjamins Publishing Co., Amsteldijk 44, P.O. Box 75577, 1070 AN Amsterdam, Netherlands. TEL 31-20-6738156. FAX 31-20-6792956. (In N. America: Box 27519, Philadelphia, PA 19118-0519. TEL 215-836-1200. FAX 215-836-1204) Eds. Maxim I. Stamenov, Gordon G. Globus. **Document type:** monographic series.
Description: Provides a forum for scholars from various scientific disciplines and fields of knowledge relating to all aspects of consciousness, including cognitive psychology, linguistics, brain science, and philosophy.

155   UK   ISSN 0276-9913
BF1
ADVANCES IN DESCRIPTIVE PSYCHOLOGY. 1981. irreg., vol.4, 1985. $88. (Society for Descriptive Psychology) Jessica Kingsley Publishers, 116 Pentonville Rd., London N1 9JN, England. TEL 071-278-0433. FAX 071-837-2917. (U.S. subscr. to: Taylor & Francis, 1900 Frost Rd., Ste. 101, Bristol, PA 19007-1598. TEL 800-821-8312. FAX 215-785-5515) Eds. Keith E. Davis, Thomas O. Mitchell. **Indexed:** Psychol.Abstr. **Document type:** monographic series.
—**CCC.**
Refereed Serial

150   UK
ADVANCES IN DEVELOPMENTAL DISORDERS. 1987. irreg., vol.2, 1994. $85. Jessica Kingsley Publishers, 116 Pentonville Rd., London N1 9JB, England. TEL 071-833-2307. FAX 071-837-2917. (U.S. subscr. to: Taylor & Francis, 1900 Frost Rd., Ste. 101, Bristol, PA 19007-1598. TEL 800-821-8312. FAX 215-785-5515) Eds. Rowland Barrett, Johnny Matson. **Document type:** monographic series.

155   US   ISSN 0275-3049
BF712
ADVANCES IN DEVELOPMENTAL PSYCHOLOGY. 1981. irreg., vol.4, 1986. $49.95. Lawrence Erlbaum Associates, Inc., 10 Industrial Dr., Mahwah, NJ 07430-2262. TEL 201-236-9500. FAX 201-236-0072. Ed. Michael E. Lamb. bibl.; charts; illus. (back issues avail.) **Indexed:** Curr.Cont., Psychol.Abstr. **Document type:** monographic series.
Refereed Serial

150 614.7   US   ISSN 0891-7531
ADVANCES IN ENVIRONMENTAL PSYCHOLOGY. 1978. irreg., vol.6, 1986. $29.95. Lawrence Erlbaum Associates, Inc., 10 Industrial Dr., Mahwah, NJ 07430-2262. TEL 201-236-9500. FAX 201-236-0072. Ed. A.H. Lebovits. (back issues avail.) **Indexed:** Curr.Cont., Psychol.Abstr. **Document type:** academic/scholarly publication.
Refereed Serial

ADVANCES IN EXPERIMENTAL SOCIAL PSYCHOLOGY. see *SOCIOLOGY*

301.1   UK   ISSN 0270-9228
RC488.5   CODEN: AFITE2
ADVANCES IN FAMILY INTERVENTION, ASSESSMENT AND THEORY. 1980. irreg., vol.6, 1993. $99. Jessica Kingsley Publishers, 116 Pentonville Rd., London N1 9JB, England. TEL 071-833-2307. FAX 071-837-2917. (Dist. in U.S. by: Taylor & Francis, 1900 Frost Rd., Ste. 101, Bristol PA 19007-1598. TEL 215-785-5800. FAX 215-785-5515) Ed. John P. Vincent. **Indexed:** Psychol.Abstr. **Document type:** academic/scholarly publication.
—BLDSC (0706.470000).
Description: Provides an arena for clinical family researchers to share their work and grapple with the complicated issues involved in conceptualizing, assessing, and intervening with problem families.

ADVANCES IN HEALTH EDUCATION: CURRENT RESEARCH. see *EDUCATION — Teaching Methods And Curriculum*

332.1   NE   ISSN 0921-2647
TA166
ADVANCES IN HUMAN FACTORS - ERGONOMICS. 1984. irreg., vol.19A&B, 1993. price varies. Elsevier Science B.V., Books Division, P.O. Box 211, 1000 AE Amsterdam, Netherlands. TEL 31-20-4853911. FAX 31-20-4853705. TELEX 18582 ESPA NL. E-mail: nlinfo-f@elsevier.nl; usinfo-f@elsevier.com; forinfo-kyf04035@niftyserve.or.jp; Site addr.: http://www.elsevier.nl/. (Subscr. in U.S. and Canada to: Elsevier Science Inc., Box 882, Madison Sq. Sta., New York, NY 10159. TEL 212-989-5800) **Document type:** monographic series, proceedings.
—BLDSC (0709.067000); Ei; Faxon. **CCC.**
Refereed Serial

ADVANCES IN INFANCY RESEARCH. see *MEDICAL SCIENCES — Pediatrics*

150   US   ISSN 0163-5379
LB1051
ADVANCES IN INSTRUCTIONAL PSYCHOLOGY. 1978. irreg., vol.3, 1989. $59.95 cloth. Lawrence Erlbaum Associates, Inc., 10 Industrial Dr., Mahwah, NJ 07430-2262. TEL 201-236-9500. FAX 201-236-0072. Ed. Robert Glaser. illus. (back issues avail.) **Indexed:** Curr.Cont., Psychol.Abstr. **Document type:** academic/scholarly publication.
Refereed Serial

ADVANCES IN LEARNING AND BEHAVIORAL DISABILITIES. see *EDUCATION — Special Education And Rehabilitation*

614.58   US   ISSN 0749-7423
BF501
ADVANCES IN MOTIVATION AND ACHIEVEMENT. 1984. a. $63.50 to institutions. J A I Press Inc., 55 Old Post Rd., No. 2, Box 1678, Greenwich, CT 06836-1678. TEL 203-661-7602. FAX 203-661-0792. (Addr. in the U.K. and Europe: J A I Press Ltd., The Courtyard, 28 High St., Hampton Hill, Mddx. TW12 1PD, England. TEL 44-81-943-9296. FAX 44-81-943-9317) Ed. Martin L. Maehr.
—BLDSC (0709.453000); Faxon; UnCover.

155   US   ISSN 8755-0032
QP363.5
ADVANCES IN NEURAL AND BEHAVIORAL DEVELOPMENT. 1985. irreg., vol.4, 1992. price varies. Ablex Publishing Corporation, 355 Chestnut St., Norwood, NJ 07648. TEL 201-767-8450. FAX 201-767-6717. TELEX 135-393. Ed. Paul Shinkman. **Document type:** academic/scholarly publication.
—BLDSC (0709.475000).
Refereed Serial

155   US   ISSN 1051-5534
ADVANCES IN PERSONAL CONSTRUCT PSYCHOLOGY. 1990. biennial. J A I Press Inc., 55 Old Post Rd., No. 2, Box 1678, Greenwich, CT 06830. TEL 203-661-7602. Eds. Robert A. Neimeyer, Greg J. Neimeyer.
—BLDSC (0709.598600).

150 616.8   US   ISSN 0278-2367
BF698.4
ADVANCES IN PERSONALITY ASSESSMENT. 1982. irreg., vol.8, 1990. $49.95 cloth. Lawrence Erlbaum Associates, Inc., 10 Industrial Dr., Mahwah, NJ 07430-2262. TEL 201-236-9500. FAX 201-236-0072. Eds. James N. Butcher, Charles D. Spielberger. (back issues avail.) **Indexed:** Curr.Cont., Psychol.Abstr. **Document type:** monographic series.
—BLDSC (0709.599000); UnCover.
Refereed Serial

150 325   UK
ADVANCES IN POPULATION; psychosocial perspectives. 1992. irreg., vol.2, 1994. $99. Jessica Kingsley Publishers, 116 Pentonville Rd., London N1 9JB, England. TEL 071-833-2307. FAX 071-837-2917. (U.S. subscr. to: Taylor & Francis, 1900 Frost Rd., Ste. 101, Bristol, PA 19007-1598. TEL 800-821-8312. FAX 215-785-5515) Ed. Lawrence Severy. **Document type:** monographic series.

PSYCHOLOGY

150 NE ISSN 0166-4115
CODEN: ADPSEK
ADVANCES IN PSYCHOLOGY. 1980. irreg., vol.107, 1994. price varies. Elsevier Science B.V., Books Division, P.O. Box 211, 1000 AE Amsterdam, Netherlands. TEL 31-20-4853911. FAX 31-20-4853705. TELEX 18582 ESPA NL. E-mail: nlinfo-f@elsevier.nl; usinfo-f@elsevier.com; forinfo-kyf04035@niftyserve.or.jp; Site addr.: http://www.elsevier.nl/. (Subscr. in U.S. and Canada to: Elsevier Science Inc., Box 882, Madison Sq. Sta., New York, NY 10159. TEL 212-989-5800) **Document type:** monographic series.
—BLDSC (0711.065000); Faxon.
Refereed Serial

150 UK
ADVANCES IN PSYCHOPHYSIOLOGY. 1985. irreg., vol.5, 1993. $99. Jessica Kingsley Publishers, 116 Pentonville Rd., London N1 9JB, England. TEL 071-833-2307. FAX 071-837-2917. (Dist. by: Kogan Page Ltd., 120 Pentonville Rd., London N1 9JN, England. TEL 071-278-0433. FAX 071-837-6348; Subscr. in U.S. to: Taylor & Francis, 1900 Frost Rd., Ste.101, Bristol, PA 19007-1598. TEL 800-821-8312. FAX 215-785-5515) Ed.Bd. **Document type:** monographic series.

370.15 US ISSN 0270-3920
LB1027.55
ADVANCES IN SCHOOL PSYCHOLOGY. 1981. irreg., vol.7, 1990. $39.95 cloth. Lawrence Erlbaum Associates, Inc., 10 Industrial Dr., Mahwah, NJ 07430-2262. TEL 201-236-9500. FAX 201-236-0072. Ed. Thomas R. Kratochwill. (back issues avail.) **Indexed:** Curr.Cont., Psychol.Abstr. **Document type:** monographic series.
Refereed Serial

157 NE ISSN 0923-019X
BF575.A6 CODEN: ATRSE6
ADVANCES IN TEST ANXIETY RESEARCH. 1982. irreg., vol. 7, 1992. fl.89.50($44.75) Swets & Zeitlinger bv, Heereweg 347, 2161 CA Lisse, Netherlands. TEL 31-2521-35111. FAX 31-2521-15888. TELEX 41325. (Dist. in N. America by: Swets & Zeitlinger, 440 Creamery Way, Ste. A. Exton, PA 19341. TEL 800-447-9387. FAX 610-524-5366) Ed.Bd. (back issues avail.) **Document type:** monographic series.
—BLDSC (0711.598500).

155.937 US ISSN 0196-1934
BD444
ADVANCES IN THANATOLOGY.* q. $66.50. Foundation of Thanatology, Foundation Book & Periodical Division, 630 W. 168th St., New York, NY 10032. TEL 212-928-2066. Ed. David Peretz. adv. (also avail. in microform from UMI; back issues avail.)
—BLDSC (0711.605000); UMI; UnCover.
Formerly: Journal of Thanatology (ISSN 0047-2832).
Description: Articles cover life threatening disease, dying, death, bereavement, hospice care, and widowhood.

152.8 371.3 US ISSN 0278-2359
BF431
ADVANCES IN THE PSYCHOLOGY OF HUMAN INTELLIGENCE. 1982. irreg., vol.5, 1989. $49.95 cloth. Lawrence Erlbaum Associates, Inc., 10 Industrial Dr., Mahwah, NJ 07430-2262. TEL 201-236-9500. FAX 201-236-0072. Ed. Robert J. Sternberg. (back issues avail.) **Indexed:** Curr.Cont., Psychol.Abstr. **Document type:** monographic series.
Refereed Serial

150 US ISSN 0748-6103
BF575.A3
ADVANCES IN THE STUDY OF AGGRESSION. 1984. irreg., vol.2, 1986. Academic Press, Inc., 525 B St., Ste. 1900, San Diego, CA 92101-4495. TEL 619-231-6616. FAX 619-699-6715. (Subscr. to: Order Dept., 6277 Sea Harbor Dr., 4th Fl., Orlando, FL 32887. TEL 800-321-5068) Eds. J. Robert, Caroline Blanchard. (back issues avail.) **Indexed:** Viol.& Abuse Abstr.
Refereed Serial

150 US ISSN 0065-3454
QL750 CODEN: ADSBBF
ADVANCES IN THE STUDY OF BEHAVIOR. 1965. irreg., vol.22, 1993. Academic Press, Inc., 525 B St., Ste. 1900, San Diego, CA 92101-4495. TEL 619-231-0926. FAX 619-699-6715. (Subscr. to: Order Dept., 6277 Sea Harbor Dr., 4th Fl., Orlando, FL 32887. TEL 800-321-5068) Ed.Bd. index. (reprint service avail. from ISI) **Indexed:** Biol.Abstr., Curr.Adv.Ecol.Sci., Dairy Sci.Abstr., Ind.Sci.Rev., Sci.Cit.Ind.
—BLDSC (0711.590000); Faxon; SWETS. **CCC.**
Refereed Serial

152 301.16 US ISSN 0190-9703
ADVANCES IN THE STUDY OF COMMUNICATION AND AFFECT. 1974. irreg., vol.11, 1986. price varies. Plenum Publishing Corp., 233 Spring St., New York, NY 10013-1578. TEL 212-620-8000. FAX 212-463-0742. TELEX 23-421139. **Document type:** monographic series.
Refereed Serial

616.89 US
THE ADVOCATE (ALEXANDRIA). 1976. 10/yr. $25. American Mental Health Counselor Association, 5999 Stevenson Ave., Alexandria, VA 22304. TEL 800-326-2642; 800-326-2642. FAX 703-751-1696. Ed. Carol L. Hocker. adv.; bk.rev. circ. 10,500. (tabloid format) **Document type:** newsletter.
Description: Covers professional issues, legal issues, licensure and certification, third party payment, consumer concerns.

ADVOCATE (BETHESDA). see *EDUCATION — Special Education And Rehabilitation*

AFTERLOSS; the monthly newsletter to comfort and care for those who mourn. see *MEDICAL SCIENCES — Psychiatry And Neurology*

616.89 UK ISSN 1359-1789
▼**AGGRESSION AND VIOLENT BEHAVIOR.** Announced for publication in 1996. q. £128($204) (effective 1996). Elsevier Science Ltd., Pergamon, P.O. Box 800, Kidlington, Oxford OX5 1DX, England. TEL 44-1865-843000. FAX 44-1865-843010. (Subscr. in U.S. and Canada to: Elsevier Science, 660 White Plains Rd., Tarrytown, NY 10591-5153. TEL 914-524-9200. FAX 914-333-2444) adv. **Document type:** academic/scholarly publication.
Refereed Serial

350 US ISSN 0096-140X
BF575.A3 CODEN: AGBEDU
AGGRESSIVE BEHAVIOR; a multidisciplinary journal devoted to the experimental and observational analysis of conflict in humans and animals. 1975. bi-m. $660 (foreign $753) (effective 1996). (International Society for Research on Aggression) John Wiley & Sons, Inc., Journals, 605 Third Ave., New York, NY 10158. TEL 212-850-6645. FAX 212-850-6021. TELEX 12-7063. E-mail: SUBINFO@JWILEY.COM. (Subscr. outside the Americas to: John Wiley & Sons Ltd., Baffins Ln., Chichester, W. Sussex PO19 1UD, England. TEL 44-1234-779777. FAX 44-1234-776128) Ed. Ronald Baenninger. adv.; bk.rev.; bibl.; charts; illus.; index. (also avail. in microform from UMI; back issues avail.; reprint service avail. from ISI) **Indexed:** Adol.Ment.Hlth.Abstr., Biol.Abstr., Chem.Abstr., Commun.Abstr., Curr.Adv.Ecol.Sci., Curr.Cont., Excerp.Med., Ind.Sci.Rev., Ind.Vet., Mid East: Abstr.& Ind., Peace Res.Abstr., Pig News & Info., Psychol.Abstr. (1974-), Sci.Cit.Ind., Sport Fish.Abstr., SSCI, Vet.Bull., Wild.Rev., Zoo.Rec. **Document type:** academic/scholarly publication.
●Also available online.
—BLDSC (0736.285000); CASDDS; EMDOCS; Faxon; Genuine Article; SWETS; UnCover. **CCC.**
Description: Devoted to the empirical and theoretical analysis of conflict and the scientific understanding of agression in human and animals.
Refereed Serial

618.97 NE ISSN 0928-9917
CODEN: AGCOEW
▼**AGING AND COGNITION;** a journal of normal and dysfunctional development. (Section B of Neuropsychology, Development and Cognition) (Text in English) 1994. q. fl.314($173) (effective 1994). Swets & Zeitlinger bv, P.O. Box 825, 2160 SZ Lisse, Netherlands. TEL 31-2521-35111. FAX 31-2521-15888. TELEX 41325. E-mail: orders@swets.nl. (Dist. in N. America by: Swets & Zeitlinger, 440 Creamery Way, Ste. A, Exton, PA 19341. TEL 800-447-9387. FAX 610-524-5366) Ed.Bd. **Indexed:** Excerp.Med. (1995-). **Document type:** academic/scholarly publication.
—BLDSC (0736.330000); Genuine Article.
Description: Publishes research in normal and dysfunctional aspects of cognitive development in adulthood and aging, integrating theory, method and research findings in the fields of cognitive gerontology and neuropsychology.
Refereed Serial

AIDS PREVENTION AND MENTAL HEALTH. see *MEDICAL SCIENCES — Communicable Diseases*

371.42 JA
AIIKU TSUSHIN/LETTERS OF HUMAN GROWTH. (Text in Japanese) q. Shin Aiiku Shinri Kenkyukai - Japanese Study Group of Humanistic Education, c/o Mr. Shigeo sato, 941, Hayashi, Atsugi-shi, Kanagawa-ken 243, Japan.

157 US
AMERICAN ACADEMY OF BEHAVIORAL MEDICINE. NEWSLETTER. 1980. q. $60. American Academy of Behavioral Medicine, 13140 Coit Rd., Ste. 307, LB 132, Dallas, TX 75240-5758. TEL 214-458-8334. FAX 214-490-5228. Ed. George Mount. **Document type:** newsletter.
Description: Provides clinical applications for mental health professionals.

AMERICAN ACADEMY OF PSYCHIATRY AND THE LAW. NEWSLETTER. see *LAW*

150.19 US ISSN 0090-3604
RC500 CODEN: JAAPCC
AMERICAN ACADEMY OF PSYCHOANALYSIS. JOURNAL. 1973. 4/yr. $45 (foreign $65) to individuals; institutions $130 (foreign $150). (American Academy of Psychoanalysis) Guilford Publications, Inc., 72 Spring St., 4th Fl., New York, NY 10012. TEL 212-431-9800. FAX 212-966-6708. Ed. Jules Bemporad; Pub. Robert Matloff. adv. contact: Marian Robinson. bk.rev.; index. circ. 1,500. (also avail. in microform; back issues avail.; reprint service avail. from ISI,UMI) **Indexed:** Adol.Ment.Hlth.Abstr., Biol.Abstr., Curr.Cont., Excerp.Med., Ind.Med., PSI, Psychoanal.Abstr., Psychol.Abstr. (1973-), Psychol.R.G., Soc.Work Res.& Abstr., SSCI.
—BLDSC (4683.735000); EMDOCS; Faxon; Genuine Article; SWETS; UMI; UnCover. **CCC.**
Refereed Serial

157 US
AMERICAN ASSOCIATION OF SUICIDOLOGY. PROCEEDINGS OF THE ANNUAL MEETING. 8th., 1975. a. price varies. American Association of Suicidology, 4201 Connecticut Ave., Ste. 310, Washington, DC 20008-1158. TEL 303-692-0985. Ed. Dr. David Lester. circ. 1,000. (looseleaf format; back issues avail.) **Document type:** proceedings.

614.58 614.58 US ISSN 0895-8009
CODEN: MAMREB
AMERICAN ASSOCIATION ON MENTAL RETARDATION. MONOGRAPHS. 1973. irreg. price varies. American Association on Mental Retardation, 444 N. Capitol St., Washington, DC 20001-1512. TEL 202-387-1968. FAX 202-387-2193. Ed. Gary Siperstein. **Document type:** monographic series.
—BLDSC (5914.216600).
Formerly (until 1987): American Association on Mental Deficiency. Monographs (ISSN 0730-7128)

AMERICAN BEHAVIORAL SCIENTIST. see *SOCIAL SCIENCES: COMPREHENSIVE WORKS*

155.3 301 US
AMERICAN CROSSDRESSER. 1990. q. $10 (effective 1995). Chevalier Publications, Box 194, Tulare, CA 93275. Ed. Carol Beecroft. circ. 1,500. (back issues avail.)
Description: Covers heterosexual crossdressing.

PSYCHOLOGY

301.4 US
AMERICAN FAMILY THERAPY ACADEMY NEWSLETTER. 1980. q. $24. American Family Therapy Association, Inc., 2020 Pennsylvania Ave., N.W., Ste. 273, Washington, DC 20006. adv.; bk.rev. circ. 1,000. (back issues avail.) **Document type:** newsletter.
Formerly: American Famly Therapy Association Newsletter.

616.89 US ISSN 0742-3187
AMERICAN GROUP PSYCHOTHERAPY MONOGRAPH SERIES. 1984. irreg., no.7. price varies. International Universities Press, Inc., 59 Boston Post Rd., Box 1524, Madison, CT 06443-1524. TEL 203-245-4000. Ed. Dr. Howard Kibel. **Document type:** monographic series.
Refereed Serial

AMERICAN IMAGO; a psychoanalytic journal for culture, science and the arts. see *MEDICAL SCIENCES — Psychiatry And Neurology*

AMERICAN INDIAN AND ALASKA NATIVE MENTAL HEALTH RESEARCH. see *ETHNIC INTERESTS*

AMERICAN JOURNAL OF ART THERAPY; art in psychotherapy, education, and rehabilitation. see *EDUCATION — Special Education And Rehabilitation*

AMERICAN JOURNAL OF COMMUNITY PSYCHOLOGY. see *SOCIOLOGY*

AMERICAN JOURNAL OF DANCE THERAPY. see *DANCE*

150 301 US ISSN 0192-6187
RC488.5 CODEN: IJFPDM
AMERICAN JOURNAL OF FAMILY THERAPY. 1973. q. $38 to individuals (foreign $46); institutions $75 (foreign $83). Brunner-Mazel Publishing Co., 19 Union Sq. W., New York, NY 10003. TEL 212-924-3344. FAX 212-242-6339. Ed. S. Richard Sauber. bk.rev.; index. circ. 2,000. (also avail. in microform from UMI; reprint service avail. from UMI) **Indexed:** Adol.Ment.Hlth.Abstr., C.I.J.E., Curr.Cont., IMFL, Lang.& Lang.Behav.Abstr., Mid.East: Abstr.& Ind., Mult.Ed.Abstr., Psychol.Abstr. (1973-), Sage Fam.Stud.Abstr., Soc.Work Res.& Abstr., Sp.Ed.Needs Abstr., SSCI. **Document type:** academic/scholarly publication.
—BLDSC (0824.620000); Faxon; Genuine Article; SWETS; UMI; UnCover.
Former titles (until 1979): International Journal of Family Counseling (ISSN 0147-1775); (until 1976): Journal of Family Counseling (ISSN 0093-3171)
Description: Provides an interdisciplinary forum for innovation, theory, research and clinical practice in family therapy.

301.1 340 US ISSN 0733-1290
K1
AMERICAN JOURNAL OF FORENSIC PSYCHOLOGY;* interfacing issues of psychology and law. (Supplement avail.: Dementia) 1983. q. $65 to individuals (foreign $80). (American College of Forensic Psychology) Edward Miller, Ed. & Pub., Box 560, Shaftsbury, VT 05262-0560. TEL 714-831-0236. Ed. Debra Miller. bk.rev. circ. 500. (also avail. in microfilm from PMC; microform from WSH; back issues avail.; reprint service avail. from WSH) **Indexed:** Psychol.Abstr.
—BLDSC (0824.645000).
Description: For psychologists used as expert witnesses in civil and criminal court cases.
Refereed Serial

616.89 US ISSN 0002-9432
RA790.A1 CODEN: AJORAG
AMERICAN JOURNAL OF ORTHOPSYCHIATRY. 1930. q. $45 to individuals; institutions $65. American Orthopsychiatric Association, Inc., 330 Seventh Ave., 18th Fl., New York, NY 10001. TEL 212-564-5930. FAX 212-564-6180. (Subscr. to: 49 Sheridan Ave., Albany, NY 12201-1413) Ed. Ellen Bassuk. adv. contact: Jean Arbeiter. bibl.; charts; illus.; index, cum.index. circ. 13,000. (also avail. in microform from UMI; reprint service avail. from UMI) **Indexed:** Abstr.Crim.& Pen., Acad.Ind., Adol.Ment.Hlth.Abstr., ASSIA, Bibl.Dev.Med.& Child Neur., Bibl.Ind., Biol.Abstr., Chem.Abstr., Child.Devel.Abstr., CINAHL, Crim.Just.Abstr., Curr.Adv.Ecol.Sci., Curr.Cont., Curr.Lit.Fam.Plan., Educ.Ind., Except.Child.Educ.Abstr., Excerp.Med., Hosp.Lit.Ind., IMFL, Ind.Med., Ind.Sci.Rev., Int.Nurs.Ind., Lang.& Lang.Behav.Abstr., Ment.Retard.Abstr., Mult.Ed.Abstr., Nutr.Abstr., Psychol.Abstr. (1930-), Psychol.Abstr., Psycscan C.P., Psycscan D.P., Risk Abstr., Sage Fam.Stud.Abstr., Sci.Cit.Ind., Soc.Sci.Ind., Soc.Work Res.& Abstr., Sp.Ed.Needs Abstr., SSCI, Stud.Wom.Abstr. **Document type:** academic/scholarly publication.
—BLDSC (0829.250000); Faxon; Genuine Article; SWETS; UMI; UnCover. **CCC.**
Refereed Serial

616.891 US ISSN 0002-9548
RC321 CODEN: AJPYA8
AMERICAN JOURNAL OF PSYCHOANALYSIS. 1941. q. $175 (foreign $205) (effective 1996). (Association for the Advancement of Psychoanalysis) Human Sciences Press, Inc. (Subsidiary of: Plenum Publishing Corp.), 233 Spring St., New York, NY 10013. TEL 212-620-8000. FAX 212-463-0742. TELEX 23-421139. Ed. Douglas H. Ingram. adv.; bk.rev.; bibl.; index, cum.index: 1941-1965. (also avail. in microform from UMI; reprint service avail. from UMI) **Indexed:** Abstr.Soc.Work., Biol.Abstr., Chem.Abstr., Chicago Psychoanal.Lit.Ind., Curr.Cont., Educ.Ind., Excerp.Med., IMFL, Ind.Med., Ind.Med., Mid.East: Abstr.& Ind., Psychoanal.Abstr., Psychol.Abstr. (1928-), Soc.Work Res.& Abstr., SSCI. **Document type:** academic/scholarly publication.
—BLDSC (0835.300000); Faxon; SWETS; UMI; UnCover. **CCC.**
Description: Intended to communicate modern concepts of psychoanalytic theory and practice, plus related investigations in allied fields.
Refereed Serial

150 US ISSN 0002-9556
BF1 CODEN: AJPCAA
AMERICAN JOURNAL OF PSYCHOLOGY. 1887. q. $35 to individuals (foreign $42); institutions $80 (foreign $87). (University of Illinois at Urbana-Champaign) University of Illinois Press, 1325 S. Oak St., Champaign, IL 61820. TEL 217-333-0950. FAX 217-244-8082. Ed. Don Dulany. adv.: B&W page $125; adv. contact: Ann Lowry. bk.rev.; bibl.; charts; stat.; index, cum.index every 25 vols. circ. 2,500. (also avail. in microform from MIM,UMI,PMC; reprint service avail. from KTO,UMI) **Indexed:** Acad.Ind., Adol.Ment.Hlth.Abstr., ASSIA, Biol.Abstr., Bk.Rev.Ind. (1980-), C.I.S. Abstr., Chem.Abstr., Child.Bk.Rev.Ind. (1980-), Commun.Abstr., Curr.Cont., Ergon.Abstr., Ind.Med., Lang.& Lang.Behav.Abstr., Mid.East: Abstr.& Ind., Mult.Ed.Abstr., Pers.Lit., Psychol.Abstr. (1925-), Soc.Sci.Ind., SSCI. **Document type:** academic/scholarly publication.
—BLDSC (0835.500000); Faxon; Genuine Article; SWETS; UMI; UnCover. **CCC.**
Refereed Serial

AMERICAN POLYGRAPH ASSOCIATION NEWSLETTER. see *CRIMINOLOGY AND LAW ENFORCEMENT*

370.15 US ISSN 1052-7958
RC500
AMERICAN PSYCHOANALYST. 1967. q. $27.50 to individuals (foreign $47.50); institutions $50 (foreign $70) (effective 1993). (American Psychoanalytic Association) Analytic Press, Inc., 365 Broadway, Hillsdale, NJ 07642. TEL 201-358-9477. FAX 201-358-0621. Ed. Dr. William Jeffrey. circ. 4,000. (back issues avail.) **Document type:** newsletter.
Formerly: American Psychoanalytic Association. Newsletter.
Description: Features information of the association, essays on the history of psychoanalysis in America, and interviews with leading analysts.

616.891 US ISSN 0003-0651
BF173.A2 CODEN: JAPOAE
AMERICAN PSYCHOANALYTIC ASSOCIATION. JOURNAL. (Supplements avail.) 1953. q. $92.50 to individuals (foreign $126.50); institutions $112.50 (foreign $149). International Universities Press, Inc., 59 Boston Post Rd., Box 1524, Madison, CT 06443-1524. TEL 203-245-4000. FAX 203-245-0775. Ed. Dr. Arnold D. Richards. adv.; bk.rev.; abstr.; bibl.; charts; index, cum.index: vols.1-22, vols.23-33. circ. 6,500. (back issues avail.) **Indexed:** Adol.Ment.Hlth.Abstr., ASSIA, Biol.Abstr., Curr.Cont., Excerp.Med., Ind.Med., Mid.East: Abstr.& Ind., Psychoanal.Abstr., Psychol.Abstr. (1953-), SSCI. **Document type:** academic/scholarly publication.
—BLDSC (4692.070000); Faxon; Genuine Article; SWETS; UnCover.
Description: Covers articles in clinical and theoretical applied psychoanalytic studies.
Refereed Serial

150 US ISSN 0065-9843
AMERICAN PSYCHOANALYTIC ASSOCIATION. JOURNAL. MONOGRAPH. 1953. irreg., no.4, 1971. International Universities Press, Inc., 59 Boston Post Rd., Box 1524, Madison, CT 06443-1524. TEL 203-245-4000. **Indexed:** Biol.Abstr., SSCI. **Document type:** monographic series.
Refereed Serial

150.19 US
AMERICAN PSYCHOANALYTIC ASSOCIATION. WORKSHOP SERIES. 1985. irreg., no.8. price varies. International Universities Press, Inc., 59 Boston Post Rd., Box 1524, Madison, CT 06443-1524. TEL 203-245-4000. Ed. Scott Dowling.
Refereed Serial

AMERICAN PSYCHOLOGICAL ASSOCIATION. DIRECTORY. see *BIOGRAPHY*

150 US ISSN 0003-066X
BF1 CODEN: AMPSAB
AMERICAN PSYCHOLOGIST. 1946. m. $150 to non-members (foreign $190); institutions $286 (foreign $370). American Psychological Association, 750 First St., N.E., Washington, DC 20002-4242. TEL 202-336-5600. FAX 202-336-5568. Ed. Raymond D. Fowler. adv. contact: Jodi Ashcraft. illus.; index. circ. 102,300. (also avail. in microform from UMI,PMC; back issues avail.; reprint service avail. from KTO) **Indexed:** Acad.Ind., Adol.Ment.Hlth.Abstr., Amer.Bibl.Slavic & E.Eur.Stud., ASSIA, Biol.Abstr., C.I.J.E., CERDIC, Chem.Abstr., Child Devel.Abstr., Commun.Abstr., Crim.Just.Abstr., Curr.Adv.Ecol.Sci., Curr.Cont., Fut.Surv., Ind.Med., Int.Nurs.Ind., Lang.& Lang.Behav.Abstr., M.L.A., Mid.East: Abstr.& Ind., Mult.Ed.Abstr., Pers.Lit., PSI, Psychol.Abstr. (1946-), Res.High.Educ.Abstr., Risk Abstr., Sage Fam.Stud.Abstr., Sage Pub.Admin.Abstr., Soc.Sci.Ind., Soc.Work Res.& Abstr., SSCI, Stud.Wom.Abstr., Tech.Educ.Abstr. **Document type:** academic/scholarly publication.
—BLDSC (0853.400000); Faxon; Genuine Article; SWETS; UMI; UnCover. **CCC.**
Description: Publishes empirical, theoretical and practical articles.
Refereed Serial

362.29 US ISSN 0740-0454
AMERICAN UNIVERSITY STUDIES. SERIES 8. PSYCHOLOGY. 1983. irreg. Peter Lang Publishing, Inc., 62 W. 45th St., 4th Fl., New York, NY 10036. TEL 212-302-6740. Ed. Christopher Myers. **Document type:** academic/scholarly publication, monographic series.
Refereed Serial

AMSTERDAM STUDIES IN THE THEORY AND HISTORY OF LINGUISTIC SCIENCE. SERIES 2: CLASSICS IN PSYCHOLINGUISTICS. see *LINGUISTICS*

158 PO ISSN 0870-8231
RC500
ANALISE PSICOLOGICA. 1977. q. $77 in Europe; elsewhere $87. Instituto Superior de Psicologia Aplicada, Rua Jardim do Tabaco, 44, 1100 Lisbon, Portugal. TEL 351-1-8863184. FAX 351-1-8860954. E-mail: dir@dir.ispa.email400.marconi.sva.pt. Ed. Frederico Pereira. adv. contact: Jorge Senos. bk.rev. **Indexed:** Psychol.Abstr. (1992-). **Document type:** academic/scholarly publication.

PSYCHOLOGY

150.19 808.8 US
ANALYTICAL PSYCHOLOGY CLUB OF NEW YORK. BULLETIN. 1938. 8/yr. membership. Analytical Psychology Club of New York, 28 E. 39th St., New York, NY 10016. TEL 212-697-7877. Ed.Bd. bk.rev.; film rev. circ. 300.
    Description: Covers club business, programs and brief accounts of talks.

150 SZ ISSN 0301-3006
RC500 CODEN: ANAPC4
ANALYTISCHE PSYCHOLOGIE. (Text in German; summaries in English and German) 1970. q. 120 SFr.($92) to individuals; institutions 120 SFr.($92) (effective 1996). S. Karger AG, Allschwilerstr. 10, P.O. Box, CH-4009 Basel, Switzerland. TEL 061-3061111. FAX 061-3061234. E-mail: Karger@Karger.ch. Eds. G. Bovensiepar, C.A. Meier. adv.; bk.rev.; bibl. circ. 1,700. (also avail. in microform from UMI) **Indexed:** Biol.Abstr., Curr.Cont., Psychoanal.Abstr., Psychol.Abstr. (1974-), SSCI. **Document type:** academic/scholarly publication.
    —Genuine Article; SWETS. **CCC**.
    Supersedes: Zeitschrift fuer Analytische Psychologie und ihre Grenzgebiete (ISSN 0049-8580)
    Refereed Serial

150 410 US ISSN 0895-366X
ANCHOR POINT MAGAZINE; the international magazine for effective neuro-linguistic communication. 1987. m. $39 (Canada $49; elsewhere $59). Anchor Point Associates, Inc., 346 S. 500 E. No. 200, Salt Lake City, UT 84102. FAX 303-841-8705. Ed. David Moerby. adv.; bk.rev.; charts; illus.; circ. 4,500 (paid). (back issues avail.) **Document type:** trade publication.

301.1 150 IO ISSN 0126-1215
ANDA; majalah psikologi populer. irreg. Yayasan Bina Psikologi, c/o Mulyono & Associates, Gedung Pant Trisula, Jalan Menteng Raya 35, Box 3216, Jakarta, Indonesia.

150
ANDROS DIGEST.* 1982. 17/yr. $39. PeopleScience, Inc., 20 Pine Valley Ln., Jamesburg, NJ 08831-2705. Ed. Fred Streit.

150 001.3 IT
ANIMA. 1988. a. L.40000 (foreign L.60000) for 2 yrs. S.U.FI., Casella Postale 18.265, Florence, Italy. TEL 698185. Ed. Francesco Donfrancesco. circ. 450. **Indexed:** Bull.Signal.
    Description: Multidisciplinary forum featuring readings on archetypical psychology, religion, art and humanities.

ANIMAL BEHAVIOUR. see *BIOLOGY — Zoology*

591.5 US ISSN 0090-4996
QL785 CODEN: ALBVAB
ANIMAL LEARNING & BEHAVIOR. 1973. q. $92 (foreign $99) (effective 1996). Psychonomic Society, Inc., 1710 Fortview Rd., Austin, TX 78704. TEL 512-462-2442. Ed. Robert Rescorla. adv.; illus. circ. 1,250. (also avail. in microform from KTO,UMI; back issues avail.; reprint service avail. from UMI) **Indexed:** Biol.Abstr., Curr.Adv.Ecol.Sci., Excerp.Med., Gen.Sci.Ind., Ind.Sci.Rev., Nutr.Abstr., Psychol.Abstr. (1973-), Risk Abstr., Sci.Cit.Ind., Sport Fish.Abstr., SSCI, Wild.Rev., Zoo.Rec. **Document type:** academic/scholarly publication.
    —BLDSC (0905.002000); EMDOCS; Faxon; Genuine Article; SWETS; UMI; UnCover. **CCC**.
    Description: Includes articles on animal learning, motivation, emotion and comparative behavior.
    Refereed Serial

157 FR ISSN 0992-5481
ANNALES DE CLINIQUES PSYCHOLOGIQUES. 1988. a. (Laboratoire de Cliniques Psychologiques) Presses Universitaires de Rennes, 2 rue du Doyen D. Leroy, 35044 Rennes Cedex, France. TEL 99-54-66-35. FAX 99-33-07-95.
    Description: Studies practical observations, clinical interventions.

616.8 FR ISSN 0003-4487
CODEN: AMPYAT
ANNALES MEDICO-PSYCHOLOGIQUES. 1843. 10/yr. 1218 F. (foreign 1487 F.) (effective 1996). (Societe Medico-Psychologique) Masson - Periodiques, Villa Laromiguiere, 75005 Paris, France. TEL 1-40-46-62-00. FAX 1-40-46-62-01. Ed. L. Vidart. bk.rev.; abstr.; illus.; index. circ. 2,000. (reprint service avail. from ISI) **Indexed:** Biol.Abstr., Biotech.Abstr., C.I.S. Abstr., Curr.Cont., Excerp.Med., Ind.Med., Psychol.Abstr. (1927-). **Document type:** academic/scholarly publication.
    —BLDSC (0984.150000); Faxon; Genuine Article; SWETS; UMI. **CCC**.
    Description: Deals with topical matters such as the training of psychologists, the relation between psychiatry and neurology, the development of psychotherapy.

ANNALES UNIVERSITATIS MARIAE CURIE-SKLODOWSKA. SECTIO J. PAEDAGOGIA - PSYCHOLOGIA. see *EDUCATION*

ANNALS OF BEHAVIORAL SCIENCES AND MEDICAL EDUCATION. see *MEDICAL SCIENCES — Psychiatry And Neurology*

155.4 UK ISSN 0747-7902
BF712 CODEN: ACDEED
ANNALS OF CHILD DEVELOPMENT. 1984. irreg., vol.9, 1994. $75. Jessica Kingsley Publishers, 116 Pentonville Rd., London N1 9JB, England. TEL 071-833-2307. FAX 071-837-2917. (Dist in U.S. by: Taylor & Francis, 1900 Frost Rd., Ste. 101, Bristol PA 19007-1598. TEL 215-785-5800. FAX 215-785-5515) Ed. Ross Vasta. **Document type:** academic/scholarly publication.
    —BLDSC (1040.225000); UnCover. **CCC**.
    Description: Presents an array of topics by scholars in their respective specialties.
    Refereed Serial

152.8 US ISSN 0747-5241
BF38
ANNALS OF THEORETICAL PSYCHOLOGY. 1984. irreg., vol.10, 1995. Plenum Publishing Corp., 233 Spring St., New York, NY 10013-1578. TEL 212-670-8000. FAX 212-463-0742. TELEX 23-421139. Ed. L.P. Mos. **Document type:** monographic series.
    —BLDSC (1044.690000); UnCover.
    Refereed Serial

150 FR ISSN 0003-5033
BF2
ANNEE PSYCHOLOGIQUE. (Text in French; summaries in English, French) 1884. q. 520 F. (foreign 630 F.) (effective 1996). Presses Universitaires de France, Departement des Revues, 14 Avenue du Bois-de-l'Epine, B.P.90, 91003 Evry Cedex, France. TEL 1-60-77-82-05. FAX 1-60-79-20-45. TELEX PUF 600 474 F. Ed. Maire-France Ehrlich. bk.rev.; charts; index. circ. 1,500. (also avail. in microform; reprint service avail. from KTO) **Indexed:** Curr.Cont., Ind.Med., Lang.& Lang.Behav.Abstr., Psychol.Abstr. (1925-), SSCI.
    —BLDSC (1049.250000); Faxon; Genuine Article; SWETS. **CCC**.
    Description: Presents original research, critical reviews, bibliographic analyses.

155 US ISSN 1042-2463
BF712
ANNUAL ADVANCES IN APPLIED DEVELOPMENTAL PSYCHOLOGY. 1985. a. price varies. Ablex Publishing Corporation, 355 Chestnut St., Norwood, NJ 07648. TEL 201-767-8450. FAX 201-767-6717. TELEX 135-393. Ed. Irving Sigel. **Indexed:** Psychol.Abstr. **Document type:** academic/scholarly publication.
    —BLDSC (1075.035000).
    Formerly (until 1987): Advances in Applied Developmental Psychology (ISSN 0748-8572)

150 US
ANNUAL EDITIONS: DYING, DEATH, AND BEREAVEMENT. 1993. a. $12.95. Dushkin Publishing Group, Sluice Dock, Guilford, CT 06437-9989. TEL 203-453-4351. FAX 203-453-6000. Ed.Bd; Pub. Ian Nielsen. illus. **Document type:** academic/scholarly publication.

370.15 US ISSN 0731-1141
LB1051
ANNUAL EDITIONS: EDUCATIONAL PSYCHOLOGY. 1981. a. $12.95. Dushkin Publishing Group, Sluice Dock, Guilford, CT 06437-9989. TEL 203-453-4351. FAX 203-453-6000. Ed.Bd; Pub. Ian Nielsen. illus. **Document type:** academic/scholarly publication.
    Refereed Serial

ANNUAL EDITIONS: HUMAN DEVELOPMENT. see *BIOLOGY — Physiology*

ANNUAL EDITIONS: HUMAN SEXUALITY. see *BIOLOGY*

158.105 US ISSN 0198-912X
BF698.A1
ANNUAL EDITIONS: PERSONAL GROWTH AND BEHAVIOR. 1975. a. $12.95. Dushkin Publishing Group, Sluice Dock, Guilford, CT 06437-9989. TEL 203-453-4351. FAX 203-453-6000. Ed. Karen G. Duffy; Pub. Ian Nielsen. illus.; index. (back issues avail.) **Document type:** academic/scholarly publication.
    Formerly: Annual Editions: Readings in Personality and Adjustment (ISSN 0361-3836)
    Refereed Serial

150 US ISSN 0272-3794
BF149
ANNUAL EDITIONS: PSYCHOLOGY. 1971. a. $12.95. Dushkin Publishing Group, Sluice Dock, Guilford, CT 06437-9989. TEL 203-453-4351. FAX 203-453-6000. Ed. Karen Duffy; Pub. Ian Nielsen. illus. **Document type:** academic/scholarly publication.
    Formerly: Annual Editions: Readings in Psychology (ISSN 0197-0542)
    Refereed Serial

150 US ISSN 0092-5055
RC500 CODEN: APSACT
ANNUAL OF PSYCHOANALYSIS. (Until vol.16, 1989, published by International Universities Press) 1973. a., vol.21, 1993. price varies. (Chicago Institute for Psychoanalysis) Analytic Press, Inc., 365 Broadway, Hillsdale, NJ 07642. TEL 201-358-9477. FAX 201-358-0621. Ed. Jerome Winer. **Indexed:** Biol.Abstr., Psychoanal.Abstr., Psychol.Abstr. (1973-).
    —BLDSC (1092.900000); UnCover. **CCC**.

150 US ISSN 0066-4308
BF30 CODEN: ARPSAC
ANNUAL REVIEW OF PSYCHOLOGY. 1950. a. $46 (foreign $51) (effective Jan. 1995). Annual Reviews Inc., 4139 El Camino Way, Box 10139, Palo Alto, CA 94303-0139. TEL 415-493-4400; 800-523-8635. FAX 415-855-9815. E-mail: annrevu@class.org. Ed. Janet T. Spence. bibl.; index, cum.index. (also avail. in microform from UMI; back issues avail.; reprint service avail.) **Indexed:** Adol.Ment.Hlth.Abstr., Biol.Abstr., Chem.Abstr., Child Devel.Abstr., Curr.Adv.Ecol.Sci., Curr.Cont., DSH Abstr., Excerp.Med., Ind.Med., Ind.Sci.Rev., Lang.& Lang.Behav.Abstr., M.M.R.I., Psychol.Abstr. (1950-), Psycscan D.P., Sci.Cit.Ind., Soc.Sci.Ind., SSCI. **Document type:** academic/scholarly publication.
    ●Also available online. Vendor(s): University Microfilms International.
    —BLDSC (1528.400000); Faxon; Genuine Article; SWETS; UMI; UnCover. **CCC**.
    Description: Original critica reviews of the significant primary literature and current developments in psychology.

155.3 US ISSN 1053-2528
HQ60 CODEN: ARXREJ
ANNUAL REVIEW OF SEX RESEARCH. 1990. a. $35 to individuals; institutions $55 (effective 1993). Society for the Scientific Study of Sex, Box 208, Mt. Vernon, IA 52314. TEL 319-895-8407. FAX 319-895-6203. Ed. John Bancroft. **Indexed:** IMFL, Psychol.Abstr. (1990-). **Document type:** academic/scholarly publication.
    —BLDSC (1528.830000).
    Description: Publishes 7-10 chapters that integrate multidisciplinary research and provide up-to-date summaries of knowledge on selected human sexological issues.

ANTHROZOOS; a multidisciplinary journal on the interactions of people, animals, and nature. see *ANTHROPOLOGY*

PSYCHOLOGY

150 SP ISSN 0066-5126
ANUARIO DE PSICOLOGIA. (Text in Spanish; summaries in English and French) 1969. q. $50. Universidad de Barcelona, Facultad de Psicologia, Avenida de Chile, S-N, 08028 Barcelona, Spain. TEL 334-61-00. (Dist. by: Editorial Fontalba, S.A., Valencia 359, 6o 1a, 08009 Barcelona, Spain. TEL 93-458-5508. FAX 93-458-6602) Ed. Miguel Siguan. bk.rev. circ. 1,000. **Indexed:** Psychol.Abstr. (1962-).
—BLDSC (1565.132000).

152.4 616.8 US ISSN 1070-9797
RC531 CODEN: ANXIEW
▼**ANXIETY.** 1994. bi-m. $180 (foreign $262.50) (effective 1996). John Wiley & Sons, Inc., Journals, 605 Third Ave., New York, NY 10158. TEL 212-850-6645. FAX 212-850-6021. TELEX 12-7063. E-mail: SUBINFO@JWILEY.COM. (Subscr. outside the Americas to: John Wiley & Sons Ltd., Baffins Ln., Chichester, W. Sussex PO19 1UD, England. TEL 44-1243-779777. FAX 44-1243-446218) (also avail. in microform from UMI; back issues avail.) **Document type:** academic/scholarly publication.
—BLDSC (1566.608000).
Refereed Serial

157 US ISSN 1061-5806
BF575.A6 CODEN: AXSCEP
ANXIETY, STRESS AND COPING. 1988. 4/yr. (in 1 vol., 4 nos./vol.) 111 ECU (effective 1996). Harwood Academic Publishers, c/o International Publishers Distributor, 820 Town Center Dr., Langhorne, PA 19047. TEL 215-750-2642. FAX 215-750-6343. (Subscr. to: International Publishers Distributor, P.O. Box 90, Reading, Berkshire, RG1 8JL England. TEL 44-173-456-8316) Ed. J.B. Davies. (also avail. in microform) **Indexed:** Mult.Ed.Abstr., Psychol.Abstr. (1988-). **Document type:** academic/scholarly publication.
—BLDSC (1566.612000); Faxon; SWETS; UnCover. **CCC.**
Formerly: Anxiety Research (ISSN 0891-7779)
Description: Emphasizes research reports, theoretical papers, and interpretive reviews or meta-analysis of the literature.
Refereed Serial

150.19 UK ISSN 0962-1849
RC467
APPLIED AND PREVENTIVE PSYCHOLOGY. 1992. q. £61($105) (effective 1996). (American Association of Applied and Preventive Psychology) Cambridge University Press, Edinburgh Bldg., Shaftesbury Rd., Cambridge CB2 2RU, England. TEL 01223-312393. FAX 01223-315052. TELEX 851917256. (N. American addr.: Cambridge University Press, Journals Dept., 40 W. 20th St., New York, NY 10011. TEL 212-924-3900. FAX 212-691-3239) Ed. Samuel Osipow. adv. (back issues avail.) **Indexed:** IMFL, Psychol.Abstr. (1974-). **Document type:** academic/scholarly publication.
—BLDSC (1571.442000); UMI; UnCover. **CCC.**
Description: Focuses on the scientific, epidemiological, or public health approach to psychological problems.

APPLIED ANIMAL BEHAVIOUR SCIENCE; an international scientific journal reporting on the application of ethology to animals used by man. see *BIOLOGY — Zoology*

150 US ISSN 1068-8595
CODEN: ABSREI
APPLIED BEHAVIORAL SCIENCE REVIEW. 1993. s-a. $70 to individuals (foreign $85); institutions $140 (foreign $155) (effective 1996). J A I Press Inc., 55 Old Post Rd., No. 2, Box 1678, Greenwich, CT 06836-1678. TEL 203-661-7602. FAX 203-661-0792. (Addr. in Europe: J A I Press Ltd., The Courtyard, 28 High St., Hampton Hill, Mddx. TW12 1PD, England. TEL 44-81-943-9296. FAX 44-81-943-9317) Ed.Bd. (also avail. in microform from UMI; back issues avail.) **Document type:** academic/scholarly publication.
—BLDSC (1571.830000).

370.15 150 UK ISSN 0888-4080
BF311 CODEN: ACPSED
APPLIED COGNITIVE PSYCHOLOGY. 1987. 7/yr. $415 (foreign $415) (effective 1996). John Wiley & Sons Ltd., Journals, Baffins Ln., Chichester, W. Sussex PO19 1UD, England. TEL 01243-779777. FAX 01243-776128. TELEX 86290 WIBOOK G. (Subscr. in the Americas to: John Wiley & Sons, Inc., 605 Third Ave., New York, NY 10158. TEL 212-850-6645. FAX 212-850-6021) Eds. G. Davies, M. Pressley. adv.; bk.rev.; charts; illus.; index. circ. 644. (also avail. in microform from UMI; reprint service avail. from SWZ,UMI) **Indexed:** Abstr.Hum.Comp.Inter., ASSIA, Cont.Pg.Educ., Curr.Cont., Psychol.Abstr. (1983-), SSCI. **Document type:** academic/scholarly publication.
—BLDSC (1571.936500); Faxon; Genuine Article; SWETS; UMI; UnCover. **CCC.**
Formerly (until 1987): Human Learning (ISSN 0277-6707)
Description: Reviews and reports papers dealing with psychological analyses of problems of memory, learning, thinking, language, and consciousness as they are reflected in the real world.
Refereed Serial

APPLIED ERGONOMICS; human factors in technology and society. see *ENGINEERING*

150 658.3 US ISSN 1055-9094
APPLIED H.R.M. RESEARCH. (Human Resources Management) 1990. s-a. $40 to individuals; institutions $60 (effective 1995). Society of I-O Graduates, Department of Psychology, Radford University, Radford, VA 24142. TEL 703-831-5513. Ed. Michael A. Surrette. (back issues avail.) **Document type:** academic/scholarly publication.
Description: Publishes scientific articles of interest to professionals in human resource management and industrial organization, as well as personnel specialists and industrial psychologists.
Refereed Serial

APPLIED NEUROPSYCHOLOGY. see *MEDICAL SCIENCES — Psychiatry And Neurology*

APPLIED PSYCHOLINGUISTICS; psychological studies of language processes. see *LINGUISTICS*

APPLIED PSYCHOLINGUISTICS AND COMMUNICATION DISORDERS. see *LINGUISTICS*

150 US ISSN 0146-6216
BF39
APPLIED PSYCHOLOGICAL MEASUREMENT. 1976. q. $75 to institutions (foreign $86) (effective 1995). Applied Psychological Measurement, Inc., N657 Elliott Hall, University of Minnesota, 75 E. River Rd., Minneapolis, MN 55455. TEL 612-625-0342. FAX 612-626-2079. E-mail: djweiss@maroon.tc.umn.edu. Ed. David J. Weiss. adv.; bk.rev.; circ. 975 (paid). (also avail. in microfiche from UMI; back issues avail.) **Indexed:** Biol.Abstr., Child Devel.Abstr., Psychol.Abstr. (1977-), Psycscan, SSCI. **Document type:** academic/scholarly publication.
—BLDSC (1576.550000); Faxon; Genuine Article; SWETS; UMI; UnCover. **CCC.**
Description: Presents empirical research on the application of techniques of psychological measurement to substantive problems in all areas of psychology and related disciplines.
Refereed Serial

158 UK ISSN 0269-994X
BF636.A1 CODEN: ADPYE4
APPLIED PSYCHOLOGY; an international review. (Text in English; abstracts in French) 1951. q. £50($85) to individuals (outside the E.U. £55); institutions £120 (outside the E.U. £125 ($220)) (effective 1996). (International Association of Applied Psychology) Lawrence Erlbaum Associates Ltd., 27 Palmeira Mansions, Church Rd., Hove, E. Sussex BN3 2FA, England. TEL 01273-207411. FAX 01273-205612. (Subscr. to: Turpin Distribution Services Ltd., Blackhorse Rd., Letchworth, Herts. SG6 1HN, England. TEL 01462-672555. FAX 01462-480947) Ed. Michael Frese. adv.: page £235; 100 x 180. circ. 2,000. **Indexed:** Adol.Ment.Hlth.Abstr., Cont.Pg.Manage., Curr.Cont., Ergon.Abstr., Psychol.Abstr. (1968-), Psycscan, SSCI. **Document type:** academic/scholarly publication.
—BLDSC (1576.555000); Faxon; SWETS; UnCover.
Formerly: International Review of Applied Psychology.
Description: Serves as a forum for the scholarly exchange of research findings and professional standards and promotes awareness of important professional issues.
Refereed Serial

301.1 150 GW
ARBEITEN ZUR SOZIALWISSENSCHAFTLICHEN PSYCHOLOGIE. 1972. irreg. price varies. Aschendorffsche Verlagsbuchhandlung, Soesterstr. 13, 48155 Muenster, Germany. TEL 0251-690-0. FAX 0251-690143. **Document type:** monographic series.

150.19 GW ISSN 0721-9628
ARBEITSHEFTE KINDERPSYCHOANALYSE. 1982. a. DM.36. Gesamthochschule Kassel, Wissenschaftliches Zentrum II, Gottschalkstr. 26, 34127 Kassel, Germany. TEL 0561-8042807. FAX 0561-8042330. Ed. Hilde Kipp. bk.rev. circ. 700. (back issues avail.) **Document type:** academic/scholarly publication.

301.1 150 UK ISSN 0260-4523
ARCHITECTURAL PSYCHOLOGY NEWSLETTER. 1969. 4/yr. £8. Architectural Psychology Research Unit, Kingston Polytechnic, Knights Park, Kingston-upon-Thames, Surrey KT1 2QJ, England. TEL 01-549-6151. **Document type:** newsletter.
Description: Research concerned with the interrelationship between people and their physical surroundings.

ARCHITECTURE & BEHAVIOUR/ARCHITECTURE ET COMPORTEMENT. see *ARCHITECTURE*

150 GW ISSN 0066-6475
BF3 CODEN: APSYCX
ARCHIV FUER PSYCHOLOGIE. (Text in English and German) 1903. q. DM.124. Bouvier Verlag Herbert Grundmann, Am Hof 28, 53113 Bonn, Germany. Ed. W.D. Froehlich. adv.; illus. circ. 600. (also avail. in microfilm from PMC; back issues avail.) **Indexed:** Abstr.Crim.& Pen., Ger.J.Psych., Ind.Med., Psychol.Abstr., SSCI.
—UnCover. **CCC.**
Supersedes: Archiv fuer die Gesamate Psychologie.

ARCHIV FUER RELIGIONSPSYCHOLOGIE. see *RELIGIONS AND THEOLOGY*

150 SZ ISSN 0003-9640
BF2
ARCHIVES DE PSYCHOLOGIE. (Text in English and French) 1901. q. 78 SFr. to individuals; institutions 138 SFr. (Universite de Geneve, Faculte de Psychologie et des Sciences de l'Education, Section de Psychologie) Editions Medecine et Hygiene, Case Postale 456, CH-1211 Geneva 4, Switzerland. TEL 022-3469355. FAX 022-3475610. Ed.Bd. charts; cum.index irreg. circ. 600. **Indexed:** Psychol.Abstr. (1959-). **Document type:** academic/scholarly publication.
—BLDSC (1640.450000); SWETS; UMI; UnCover. **CCC.**

ARCHIVES OF CLINICAL NEUROPSYCHOLOGY. see *MEDICAL SCIENCES — Psychiatry And Neurology*

157.744   NE   ISSN 1381-1118
▼ARCHIVES OF SUICIDE RESEARCH. (Text in English) 1995. q. fl.258 to institutions; $165 to institutions in U.S. (effective 1996). (International Academy of Suicide Research) Kluwer Academic Publishers, Postbus 17, 3300 AA Dordrecht, Netherlands. TEL 31-78-392392. FAX 31-78-392254. E-mail: SERVICES@WKAP.NL. (Dist. by: Kluwer Academic Publishers Group, P.O. Box 322, 3300 AH Dordrecht, Netherlands. TEL 31-78-392392. FAX 31-78-546474; N. America dist. addr.: Box 358, Accord Sta., Hingham, MA 02018-0358. TEL 617-871-6600. FAX 617-871-6528) Ed. A.A. Leenaars. **Document type:** academic/scholarly publication.
—BLDSC (1643.175000). **CCC.**
  Description: Publishes original contributions on the study of suicide and suicide prevention, including pertinent aspects of pharmacotherapy, psychiatry, psychology and sociology.
  Refereed Serial

ARCHIVIO DI PSICOLOGIA, NEUROLOGIA E PSICHIATRIA. see MEDICAL SCIENCES — Psychiatry And Neurology

ARQUIVOS DE SAUDE MENTAL DO ESTADO DE SAO PAULO. see MEDICAL SCIENCES — Psychiatry And Neurology

ART THERAPY. see EDUCATION — Special Education And Rehabilitation

616.89   UK   ISSN 0197-4556
RC489.A7   CODEN: APCYAJ
THE ARTS IN PSYCHOTHERAPY; an international journal. 1973. 5/yr. £205($326) (effective 1996). Elsevier Science Ltd., Pergamon, P.O. Box 800, Kidlington, Oxford OX5 1DX, England. TEL 44-1865-843000. FAX 44-1865-843010. E-mail: nlinfo-f@elsevier.nl; usinfo-f@elsevier.com; forinfo-kyf04035@niftyserve.or.jp; Site addr.: http://www.elsevier.nl/. (Subscr. in U.S. and Canada to: Elsevier Science, 660 White Plains Rd., Tarrytown, NY 10591-5153. TEL 914-524-9200. FAX 914-333-2444) Ed. Robert J. Landy. adv.; bk.rev. (also avail. in microfilm from UMI; reprint service avail. from ISI,UMI) **Indexed:** Artbibl.Mod., Biol.Abstr., Curr.Cont., Except.Child.Educ.Abstr., Excerp.Med., Psychol.Abstr. (1973-), SSCI. **Document type:** academic/scholarly publication.
—BLDSC (1736.825000); Faxon; Genuine Article; SWETS; UMI; UnCover. **CCC.**
  Formerly: Art Psychotherapy (ISSN 0090-9092)
  Description: Innovative research in artistic inquiry and expression and its use in the treatment of mental disorders.
  Refereed Serial

370   II   ISSN 0971-2909
ASIAN JOURNAL OF PSYCHOLOGY AND EDUCATION. (Text in English) 1976. 6/yr. Rs.140($39.50) Agra Psychological Research Cell, Tiwari Kothi, Belanganj, Agra 282004, India. Eds. B.V. Patel, N.S. Chauhan. adv.; bk.rev. (reprint service avail. from ISI) **Indexed:** Psychol.Abstr.

301.1 150   VE
ASOCIACION VENEZOLANA DE PSICOLOGIA SOCIAL. REVISTA. 1978. q. $25 to individuals; institutions $30. Asociacion Venezolana de Psicologia Social (AVEPSO), Apdo. 47101, Los Chaguaramos, Caracas 1041-A, Venezuela. TEL 619811-30 Ext. 2643. Ed. Leoncio Barrios. adv.; bk.rev. circ. 500. (back issues avail.) **Document type:** academic/scholarly publication.
  Formerly (until 1994): Asociacion Venezolana de Psicologia Social. Boletin (ISSN 1011-6273)
  Description: Features theoretical and methodological papers and information about social psychology in Latin America.

150 362   US   ISSN 1072-4702
▼ASSESSMENT IN REHABILITATION AND EXCEPTIONALITY. 1994. q. $40 to individuals (foreign $48); institutions $120 (foreign $140). Psychological Assessment Resources, Inc., 16204 N. Florida Ave., Lutz, FL 33549. TEL 813-968-3003. FAX 813-968-2598. (Subscr. to: Box 998, Odessa, FL 33556. TEL 800-331-8378) Eds. H. Thompson Prout, Douglas C. Strohmer. adv.; abstr.; index; circ. 250 (paid). (back issues avail.) **Document type:** academic/scholarly publication.
—BLDSC (1746.639300).
  Description: Publishes contributions on the assessment of exceptional and/or disabled individuals, including discussion of implications in rehabilitation and education.
  Refereed Serial

150 610   US
BF319.5.B5
ASSOCIATION FOR APPLIED PSYCHOPHYSIOLOGY AND BIOFEEDBACK. PROCEEDINGS OF THE ANNUAL MEETING. 1972. a. $30 to non-members; members $15. Association for Applied Psychophysiology and Biofeedback, 10200 W. 44th Ave., Ste. 304, Wheat Ridge, CO 80033. TEL 303-422-8436. FAX 303-422-8894. Ed. Francine Butler. adv. circ. 2,000. **Document type:** proceedings.
  Formerly: Biofeedback Society of America. Proceedings of the Annual Meeting (ISSN 0094-0895)

ASSOCIATION FOR CHILD PSYCHOANALYSIS. NEWSLETTER. see CHILDREN AND YOUTH — About

155.937   US
ASSOCIATION FOR DEATH EDUCATION & COUNSELING. FORUM NEWSLETTER. 6/yr. $80 individual membership; institutional $160. Association for Death Education & Counseling, 638 Prospect Ave., Hartford, CT 06105-4298. TEL 203-586-7503. FAX 203-586-7550. Ed. Lois Chapman Dick. adv.; bk.rev. circ. 1,600. **Document type:** newsletter.

370.15   US   ISSN 1054-0792
ASSOCIATION FOR PAST-LIFE RESEARCH AND THERAPIES. NEWSLETTER. Running title: A P R T Newsletter. 1980. a. $10. Association for Past-Life Research and Therapies, Inc., Box 20151-0151, Riverside, CA 92516. TEL 909-784-1570. Ed. Terry Nash. adv.; bk.rev. circ. 800. **Document type:** newsletter.
  Description: Articles by past-life regression therapists and researchers, includes case histories and techniques, alternative therapies.

616.891   US   ISSN 0004-542X
RC500
ASSOCIATION FOR PSYCHOANALYTIC MEDICINE. BULLETIN. 1961. s-a. $10. Association for Psychoanalytic Medicine, 4560 Delafield Ave., Bronx, NY 10471. TEL 212-874-0070. Ed. Dr. Richard Zimmer. bk.rev.; cum.index: 1961-1967; circ. 1,500 (controlled).

155.4 572 790.1   US
ASSOCIATION FOR THE STUDY OF PLAY NEWSLETTER. 1974. 3/yr. $15. Association for the Study of Play, Box 6375, Georgetown, TX 78626. (Subscr. to: c/o E.P. Jonnsen, Dept. of Educational Psychology, University of Kansas, Lawrence, KS 66945-2338) Ed. Dan Hilliard. circ. 200. (back issues avail.) **Document type:** newsletter.
  Description: Covers social science and humanistic study of play behavior.

158.2   US
ASSOCIATION FOR TRANSPERSONAL PSYCHOLOGY. NEWSLETTER. q. $75 with membership only. Transpersonal Institute, 345 California Ave., Palo Alto, CA 94306. TEL 415-327-2066. Ed.Bd. adv.; illus. (also avail. in microfilm) **Document type:** newsletter.
  Formerly: Association for Transpersonal Development. Newsletter.
  Description: Publishes news and information for and about members of the association, and original articles on transpersonal psychology.

152   US   ISSN 1047-0387
BF321
ATTENTION AND PERFORMANCE. irreg. Lawrence Erlbaum Associates, Inc., 10 Industrial Dr., Mahwah, NJ 07430-2262. TEL 201-236-9500. FAX 201-236-0072.
—BLDSC (1772.810000); Genuine Article.

ATTI DELLO PSICODRAMMA. see THEATER

AUSTRALIAN AND NEW ZEALAND JOURNAL OF FAMILY THERAPY. see SOCIOLOGY

616.89   AT   ISSN 0728-6155
AUSTRALIAN JOURNAL OF PSYCHOTHERAPY. 1982. s-a. Aus.$40 to individuals; libraries and institutions Aus.$50. Psychotherapy Association of Australia, c/o Secretary, 25 Marchall Ave., St. Leonards, N.S.W. 2065, Australia. TEL 02 436-3031. Ed. L. Rumiz. adv.; bk.rev. circ. 400. (back issues avail.)

AUSTRALIAN PARAPSYCHOLOGICAL REVIEW. see PARAPSYCHOLOGY AND OCCULTISM

150   AT   ISSN 0005-0067
        CODEN: AUPCBK
AUSTRALIAN PSYCHOLOGIST. 1966. 3/yr. Aus.$55 to individuals; institutions Aus.$65 (foreign Aus.$85). Australian Psychological Society, c/o Prof. Graham Davidson, Ed., Department of Social Sciences, University of Central Queensland, Rockhampton M.C., Qld. 4702, Australia. FAX 079-309501. (Subscr. to: Australian Psychological Society, Clunies Ross House, 191 Royal Parade, Parkville, Vic. 3052, Australia) adv.; bk.rev.; abstr.; charts; illus.; index. circ. 9,500. **Indexed:** ASSIA, Aus.Educ.Ind., Aus.P.A.I.S., Biol.Abstr., Child Devel.Abstr., Curr.Cont., Psychol.Abstr. (1966-), Res.High.Educ.Abstr., SSCI. **Document type:** academic/scholarly publication.
—BLDSC (1818.350000); Faxon; UnCover.
  Description: Publishes articles of relevance to professional and applied psychologists, and generally to Australian psychologists.
  Refereed Serial

AUTISM RESEARCH REVIEW INTERNATIONAL. see MEDICAL SCIENCES — Psychiatry And Neurology

152   CK   ISSN 0120-3797
AVANCES EN PSICOLOGIA CLINICA LATINOAMERICANA. 1982. a. $7 to individuals; institutions $14. Foundation for the Advancement of Psychology, Apdo. 92621, Bogota, Colombia. Ed. Ruben Ardila. adv.; bk.rev.; bibl.; illus.; stat. circ. 2,500. **Indexed:** Biol.Abstr., Curr.Cont., Psychol.Abstr. (1982-). **Document type:** academic/scholarly publication.
—BLDSC (1837.110500). **CCC.**
  Description: Articles on all areas of clinical psychology: diagnosis, psychotherapy, research and prevention programs.

128.5 133   US
THE AZRAEL PROJECT NEWSLETTER. 1988. s-a. $10. Westgate Press Ltd., 5219 Magazine St., New Orleans, LA 70115. TEL 405-899-3077. Ed. Lorraine Chandler. adv.: page $80, trim 8 1/2 x 11; adv. contact: Daniel Kemp. bk.rev. (back issues avail.) **Document type:** newsletter.
  Description: Puts forth the word of the Angel of Death to conquer fear through understanding. Helps people understand the nature of death and to gain a macrocosmic understanding of it and of life.

150   JA   ISSN 0386-1856
BAIOFIDOBAKKU KENKYU/JAPANESE JOURNAL OF BIOFEEDBACK RESEARCH. (Text in English, Japanese) 1973. 2/yr. 1000 Yen. Nihon Baiofidobakku Gakkai - Society of Japanese Biofeedback Research, Jochi Daigaku Bungakubu Shinrigaku Kenkyushitsu, 7, Kioicho, Chiyoda-ku, Tokyo 102, Japan. **Indexed:** Psychol.Abstr. (1990-).

150   BG   ISSN 1022-7466
BANGLADESH JOURNAL OF PSYCHOLOGY. (Text in English) 1968. a. $10. Bangladesh Psychological Association, Dept. of Psychology, University of Dhaka, Dhaka 1000, Bangladesh. TEL 88-2-864553. circ. 400. (reprint service avail.) **Document type:** academic/scholarly publication.
  Description: Contains research and review articles on all branches of psychology.

PSYCHOLOGY

301.1 150 US ISSN 0197-3533
HM251 CODEN: BASPEG
BASIC AND APPLIED SOCIAL PSYCHOLOGY. 1980. 8/yr. $95 to individuals (foreign $140); institutions $395 (foreign $440). Lawrence Erlbaum Associates, Inc., 10 Industrial Dr., Mahwah, NJ 07430-2262. TEL 201-236-9500. FAX 201-236-0072. Eds. Martin M. Chemers, Frederick T. Rhodewalt. adv.: page $275; 5 x 8. bk.rev.; abstr.; bibl.; charts; illus.; stat. circ. 1,000. **Indexed:** Curr.Cont., Psychol.Abstr. (1980-), Psycscan, SSCI.
—BLDSC (1863.913300); Faxon; SWETS; UMI; UnCover.
Description: Presents material relevant to basic and applied research in all areas of social psychology in order to bring relevant social psychological studies from other specialties and disciplines to the attention of social psychologists.
Refereed Serial

150 US ISSN 0738-6729
BF199
THE BEHAVIOR ANALYST. 1978. s-a. $35 to individuals (foreign $50); institutions $85 (foreign $95); students $15 (foreign $30). Society for the Advancement of Behavior Analysis, 260 Wood Hall, Western Michigan University, Kalamazoo, MI 49008-5052. TEL 616-387-4495. FAX 616-387-4457. Ed. Margaret Vaughan. adv.; bk.rev.; cum.index. circ. 2,300. (also avail. in audio cassette; back issues avail.) **Indexed:** Behav.Abstr., Curr.Cont., Psychol.Abstr. (1982-), SSCI. **Document type:** academic/scholarly publication.
—BLDSC (1876.652500); Faxon; Genuine Article; SWETS; UnCover.
Description: Devoted to trend issues, policies, and developments in behavior analysis.
Refereed Serial

150 US ISSN 1053-8348
BF199 CODEN: BEPHE5
BEHAVIOR AND PHILOSOPHY. 1972. 3/yr. $35 to individuals; institutions $60; students $13. Cambridge Center for Behavioral Studies, 675 Massachusetts Ave., Cambridge, MA 02139-3309. TEL 617-491-9020. FAX 617-491-1072. (Subscr. to: Boyd Printing, 49 Sheridan Ave., Albany, NY 12210) Ed. Max Hocutt. adv.; bk.rev.; illus. circ. 600. **Indexed:** Adol.Ment.Hlth.Abstr., Biol.Abstr., Curr.Cont., Excerp.Med., Mid.East: Abstr.& Ind., Phil.Ind., Psychol.Abstr. (1972-), SSCI. **Document type:** academic/scholarly publication.
—BLDSC (1876.670000); Faxon; Genuine Article; SWETS; UMI; UnCover.
Formerly (until vol.12, no.2, 1982): Behaviorism (ISSN 0090-4155)
Description: Publishes the philosophical reflections of psychologists and the psychological ruminations of philosophers in papers that are both scientifically sound and philosophically significant.
Refereed Serial

301 US ISSN 1064-9506
BF199
BEHAVIOR AND SOCIAL ISSUES. 1978. 3/yr. $35 to individuals; institutions $60; students $13. Cambridge Center for Behavioral Studies, 675 Massachusetts Ave., Cambridge, MA 02139-3309. TEL 617-491-9020. FAX 617-491-1072. (Subscr. to: Boyd Printing, 49 Sheridan Ave., Albany, NY 12210) Ed. Janet E. Ellis. adv.; bk.rev.; illus. circ. 400. **Indexed:** Psychol.Abstr. (1991-). **Document type:** academic/scholarly publication.
—BLDSC (1876.677000).
Former titles (until 1990): Behavior Analysis and Social Action (ISSN 1065-1047); (until 1986): Behaviorists for Social Action Journal (ISSN 0739-5051)
Description: Publishes scholarly articles that advance the analysis of human social behavior, particularly with application to understanding existing social problems.
Refereed Serial

150 658 US ISSN 0193-6271
BEHAVIOR IMPROVEMENT NEWS; the behavior modification newsletter. 1977. m. $36. Behavior Improvement Associates, Box 296, New Paltz, NY 12561. (Subscr. to: Research Press, 2612 N. Mattis, Champaign, IL 61820) Ed. Marlene Casley. bk.rev.; bibl.; index. (looseleaf format; back issues avail.)

150 US ISSN 0145-4455
BF637.B4
BEHAVIOR MODIFICATION. 1977. q. $61 to individuals; institutions $194 (effective Sep. 1995). Sage Publications, Inc., 2455 Teller Rd., Thousand Oaks, CA 91320. TEL 805-499-0721. FAX 805-499-0871. E-mail: libraries@sagepub.com. (Overseas subscr. to: Sage Publications Ltd., 6 Bonhill St., London EC2A 4PU, England; Sage Publications India Pvt. Ltd., P.O. Box 4215, New Delhi 110 048, India) Eds. Michel Hersen, Alan S. Bellack. adv.; bk.rev.; index. circ. 1,500. (back issues avail.; reprint service avail.) **Indexed:** Adol.Ment.Hlth.Abstr., Curr.Cont., Excerp.Med., Human Resour.Abstr., Ind.Med., Mid.East: Abstr.& Ind., Psychol.Abstr. (1977-), Psychol.R.G., Sage Fam.Stud.Abstr., Sage Urb.Stud.Abstr., Soc.Sci.Ind., SSCI, Viol.& Abuse Abstr. **Document type:** academic/scholarly publication.
—BLDSC (1876.720000); Faxon; Genuine Article; SWETS; UMI; UnCover. **CCC.**
Description: Describes assessment and modification techniques for problems in psychiatric, clinical, educational, and rehabilitational settings.

572 US ISSN 0743-3808
BF180 CODEN: BRMCEW
BEHAVIOR RESEARCH METHODS, INSTRUMENTS, AND COMPUTERS. 1968. q. $118 (foreign $126) (effective 1996). Psychonomic Society, Inc., 1710 Fortview Rd., Austin, TX 78704. TEL 512-462-2442. Ed. Robert W. Proctor. adv. circ. 1,150. (also avail. in microform from KTO,UMI; back issues avail.; reprint service avail. from UMI) **Indexed:** Biol.Abstr., Curr.Adv.Ecol.Sci., Curr.Cont., Ergon.Abstr., Geo.Abstr., INSPEC (1987-), Lang.& Lang.Behav.Abstr., Mid.East: Abstr.& Ind., Psychol.Abstr. (1968-), Sport Fish.Abstr., SSCI, Wild.Rev., Zoo.Rec. **Document type:** academic/scholarly publication.
—BLDSC (1876.832000); Faxon; Genuine Article; SWETS; UMI; UnCover. **CCC.**
Formerly (until 1984): Behavior Research Methods and Instrumentation (ISSN 0005-7878)
Description: Contains articles in the areas of methods, techniques and instrumentation of research in experimental psychology.
Refereed Serial

301.1 US ISSN 0278-8403
BEHAVIOR THERAPIST. 1978. 10/yr. $38. Association for Advancement of Behavior Therapy, 305 Seventh Ave., Ste. 16A, New York, NY 10001-6008. TEL 212-647-1890. FAX 212-647-1865. Ed. Jacqueline Persons. adv.: B&W page $360. bk.rev. circ. 4,500. **Indexed:** Psychol.Abstr., Yrbk.Assoc.Educ.& Rehab.Blind. **Document type:** academic/scholarly publication.
—BLDSC (1876.900000); Faxon; SWETS; UnCover.
Formerly: Association for Advancement of Behavior Therapy. Newsletter.

150 US ISSN 0005-7894
RC489.B4 CODEN: BHVTAK
BEHAVIOR THERAPY. 1970. 4/yr. $130 (foreign $148) (effective 1996). Association for Advancement of Behavior Therapy, 305 Seventh Ave., Ste. 16A, New York, NY 10001. Ed. Lizette Peterson. adv.: B&W page $275. circ. 3,500. **Indexed:** Adol.Ment.Hlth.Abstr., Behav.Med.Abstr., Biol.Abstr., Curr.Cont., Except.Child.Educ.Abstr., Excerp.Med., Mid.East: Abstr.& Ind., Mult.Ed.Abstr., Psychol.Abstr., Psycscan C.P., Soc.Sci.Ind. (1994-), Sp.Ed.Needs Abstr., SSCI, Stud.Wom.Abstr. **Document type:** academic/scholarly publication.
—BLDSC (1876.930000); Faxon; Genuine Article; SWETS; UnCover. **CCC.**
Description: Interdisciplinary journal which presents treatment research covering theory, methodology, clinical and ethical issues.
Refereed Serial

150 574 616.8 UK ISSN 0140-525X
QP360 CODEN: BBSCDH
BEHAVIORAL AND BRAIN SCIENCES; an international journal of current research and theory with open peer commentary. 1978. q. £156($230) (effective 1996). (American Psychological Association) Cambridge University Press, Edinburgh Bldg., Shaftesbury Rd., Cambridge CB2 2RU, England. TEL 01223-312393. FAX 01223-315052. TELEX 851817256. (N. America addr.: Cambridge University Press, Journals Dept., 40 W. 20th St., New York, NY 10011. TEL 212-924-3900. FAX 212-691-3239) (Co-sponsors: American Psychological Society, American Sociological Association) Ed. Stevan Harnad. adv.; bk.rev.; charts; illus.; index. (also avail. in microform from UMI; back issues avail.; reprint service avail. from SWZ) **Indexed:** Art.Int.Abstr., Biol.Abstr., Curr.Adv.Ecol.Sci., Curr.Cont, Excerp.Med., Ind.Sci.Rev., INSPEC (1987-), Lang.& Lang.Behav.Abstr., Psychol.Abstr. (1978-), Sociol.Abstr., SSCI, Telegen. **Document type:** academic/scholarly publication.
—BLDSC (1877.293000); Faxon; Genuine Article; SWETS; UMI; UnCover. **CCC.**
Description: Covers psychology, neuroscience, behavioral biology, and cognitive science.

BEHAVIORAL ECOLOGY AND SOCIOBIOLOGY. see *ENVIRONMENTAL STUDIES*

BEHAVIORAL EDUCATOR. see *EDUCATION — Teaching Methods And Curriculum*

616.8 US ISSN 0896-4289
RB152 CODEN: BEMEEF
BEHAVIORAL MEDICINE; investigations of environmental influences on health and behavior. 1975. q. $48 to individuals; institutions $90; foreign $102. (Helen Dwight Reid Educational Foundation) Heldref Publications, 1319 Eighteenth St., N.W., Washington, DC 20036-1802. TEL 202-396-6267. FAX 202-296-5149. Ed. Martha Wedeman. adv. contact: Raymond Rallo. bk.rev.; charts; stat.; index. circ. 1,000. (also avail. in microfilm; back issues avail.; reprint service avail.) **Indexed:** Abstr.Anthropol., Adol.Ment.Hlth.Abstr., ASSIA, Behav.Med.Abstr., Biol.Abstr., Curr.Cont., Excerp.Med., Ind.Med., Mid.East: Abstr.& Ind., Psychol.Abstr. (1975-), Psycscan, SSCI. **Document type:** academic/scholarly publication.
●Also available on CD-ROM. Producer(s): University Microfilms International.
—BLDSC (1877.560000); Faxon; Genuine Article; SWETS; UMI; UnCover. **CCC.**
Formerly: Journal of Human Stress (ISSN 0097-840X)
Description: Interdisciplinary journal for physicians, psychologists, nurses, educators, and all who are concerned with behavioral and social influences on mental and physical health.
Refereed Serial

156 616.8 US ISSN 0735-7044
BF1 CODEN: BENEDJ
BEHAVIORAL NEUROSCIENCE. 1983. bi-m. $146 to non-members (foreign $166); members $73; institutions $292 (foreign $335). American Psychological Association, 750 First St., N.E., Washington, DC 20002-4242. TEL 202-336-5600. FAX 202-336-5568. Ed. Larry R. Squire. adv. contact: Jodi Ashcraft. charts; illus.; index. circ. 2,100. (also avail. in microform from UMI,PMC) **Indexed:** Abstr.Anthropol., Anim.Breed.Abstr., Biol.Abstr., Biol.& Agr.Ind., Chem.Abstr., Curr.Adv.Ecol.Sci., Dairy Sci.Abstr., Dent.Ind., Excerp.Med., Ind.Med., Ind.Sci.Rev., INIS Atomind., NRN, Nutr.Abstr., Poult.Abstr., Psychol.Abstr. (1983-), Sci.Cit.Ind., Soc.Sci.Ind., Sport Fish.Abstr., Wild.Rev., Zoo.Rec. **Document type:** academic/scholarly publication.
—BLDSC (1877.610000); CASDDS; Faxon; Genuine Article; SWETS; UMI; UnCover. **CCC.**
Supersedes in part (1947-1982): Journal of Comparative and Physiological Psychology (ISSN 0021-9940)
Description: Covers research in the broad field of the biological bases of behavior; includes occasional review and theoretical articles that make original contributions to the field.
Refereed Serial

BEHAVIORAL RESEARCH IN ACCOUNTING. see *BUSINESS AND ECONOMICS — Accounting*

150 340 UK ISSN 0735-3936
K2 CODEN: BSLADR
BEHAVIORAL SCIENCES AND THE LAW. 1983. q. $295 (foreign $295) (effective 1996). John Wiley & Sons Ltd., Journals, Baffins Ln., Chichester, W. Sussex PO19 1UD, England. TEL 01243-779777. FAX 01243-776128. TELEX 86290 WIBOOK G. (Subscr. in the Americas to: John Wiley & Sons, Inc., 605 Third Ave., New York, NY 10158. TEL 212-850-6645. FAX 212-850-6021) Ed. R. Wettstein. circ. 788. (also avail. in microform from UMI; reprint service avail. from SWZ,WSH) **Indexed:** C.L.I., Excerp.Med., Psychol.Abstr. (1983-). **Document type:** academic/scholarly publication.
—BLDSC (1877.905000); Genuine Article; UMI; UnCover. **CCC.**
Description: Explores the dynamics between mental health and the law.

BEHAVIOUR; an international journal of behavioural biology. see BIOLOGY — Zoology

301.1 150 UK ISSN 0144-929X
QA75.5 CODEN: BEITD5
BEHAVIOUR AND INFORMATION TECHNOLOGY. 1982. bi-m. £188($310) (effective 1996). Taylor & Francis Ltd., Rankine Rd., Basingstoke, Hants. RG24 8PR, England. TEL 44-1256-840366. FAX 44-1256-479438. TELEX 858540. E-mail: info@tandf.co.uk. (Subscr. in N. America to: Taylor & Francis Inc., 1900 Frost Rd., Ste. 101, Bristol, PA 19007-1598. TEL 800-821-5800. FAX 215-785-5515) Ed. T.F.M. Stewart. adv.; bk.rev. **Indexed:** Abstr.Hum.Comp.Inter., ASSIA, Commun.Abstr., Compumath, Comput.Abstr., Ergon.Abstr., INSPEC (1983-), Psychol.Abstr. (1982-), Robomat. **Document type:** academic/scholarly publication.
—BLDSC (1876.660000); CASDDS; Ei; Faxon; Genuine Article; SWETS. **CCC.**
Description: Covers all aspects of human-computer interaction.
Refereed Serial

150 AT ISSN 0813-4839
RC489.B4 CODEN: BHCAE8
BEHAVIOUR CHANGE. 1984. 4/yr. Aus.$33($145) to individuals (foreign Aus.$60); institutions Aus.$63 (foreign Aus.$83) (effective through June 1996). (Australian Behaviour Modification Association) Australian Academic Press Pty. Ltd., 32 Jeays St., Bowen Hills, Qld. 4006, Australia. Ed. Matthew R. Sanders. **Indexed:** Excerp.Med., Psychol.Abstr. (1984-), Sp.Ed.Needs Abstr.
—BLDSC (1876.679000); UMI; UnCover. **CCC.**
Description: Publishes research involving the application of behavioural and cognitive-behavioural principles and techniques to the assessment and treatment of health, social, organizational, community and educational problems.

150 UK ISSN 0005-7967
RC321 CODEN: BRTHAA
BEHAVIOUR RESEARCH AND THERAPY; an international multi-disciplinary journal. 1963. m. £445($708) (effective 1996). Elsevier Science Ltd., Pergamon, P.O. Box 800, Kidlington, Oxford OX5 1DX, England. TEL 44-1865-843000. FAX 44-1865-843010. E-mail: nlinfo-f@elsevier.nl; usinfo-f@elsevier.com; forinfo-kyf04035@niftyserve.or.jp; Site addr.: http://www.elsevier.nl/. (Subscr. in U.S. and Canada to: Elsevier Science, 660 White Plains Rd., Tarrytown, NY 10591-5153. TEL 914-524-9200. FAX 914-333-2444) Ed. S. Rachman. adv.: B&W page $550, color page $1350. bk.rev.; charts; illus.; index. circ. 4,300. (also avail. in microfiche from MIM; microfilm from UMI; back issues avail.) **Indexed:** Abstr.Crim.& Pen., Adol.Ment.Hlth.Abstr., Behav.Med.Abstr., Bibl.Dev.Med.& Child Neur., Biol.Abstr., Child Devel.Abstr., CINAHL, Curr.Adv.Ecol.Sci., Curr.Cont., Dent.Ind., Excerp.Med., Ind.Med., M.L.A., Psychol.Abstr. (1963-), Psycscan C.P., SSCI. **Document type:** academic/scholarly publication.
—BLDSC (1876.810000); Faxon; Genuine Article; SWETS; UMI; UnCover. **CCC.**
Incorporates (1979-1992): Behavioral Assessment (ISSN 0191-5401)
Description: Focuses on the application of existing modern learning theory to psychiatric and social problems, relating learning to maladaptive behavior.
Refereed Serial

150 UK ISSN 1352-4658
RC489.B4
BEHAVIOURAL AND COGNITIVE PSYCHOTHERAPY. 1972. q. £38($65) (British Association for Behavioural and Cognitive Psychotherapies) Wisepress Ltd., 89a Quicks Rd., Wimbledon, London SW19 1EX, England. TEL 0181-715-1812. FAX 0181-715-1727. Ed. Paul Salkovskis; Pub. Penelope Head. adv. contact: Penelope Head. bk.rev. circ. 2,000. **Indexed:** ASSIA, Psychol.Abstr. (1981-), Sp.Ed.Needs Abstr., SSCI. **Document type:** academic/scholarly publication.
—BLDSC (1877.293500); Faxon; Genuine Article; SWETS. **CCC.**
Formerly (until 1993): Behavioural Psychotherapy (ISSN 0141-3473)
Description: Multidisciplinary original research, of an experimental or clinical nature, that contributes to the theory, practice, and evaluation of behavior therapy.

BEHAVIOURAL PHARMACOLOGY; an international forum in which behaviour and pharmacology receive equal attention. see PHARMACY AND PHARMACOLOGY

150 UK ISSN 0953-7074
BEHAVIOURAL PSYCHOTHERAPIST. 1981. 3/yr. £15 to non-members. British Association for Behavioural Psychotherapy, Well at Work Research Unit, Blackford Pavillion, Astley Ainslie Hospital, Edinburgh EH9 2HL, Scotland. TEL 081-715-1725. FAX 081-715-1727. (Subscr. to: Howard Lomas, 23 Partridge Dr., Baxenden, Accrington, Lancs. RB5 2RL, England) Ed. Dr. Pamela J. Baldwin. adv.; bk.rev. circ. 1,700. **Document type:** newsletter.
Formerly: British Association for Behavioural Psychotherapy. Newsletter (ISSN 0262-3110)
Description: Gives news of the association's events and allows for the exchange of information among members.

157 GW ISSN 0722-8902
BEITRAEGE ZUR INDIVIDUALPSYCHOLOGIE. 1978. irreg., no.21, 1995. price varies. Ernst Reinhardt Verlag, Kemnatenstr. 46, 80639 Munich, Germany. TEL 089-1783005. FAX 089-1781827. **Document type:** monographic series.

155.4 GW ISSN 0340-0123
BEITRAEGE ZUR PSYCHODIAGNOSTIK DES KINDES. 1972. irreg., no.7, 1984. price varies. Ernst Reinhardt Verlag, Kemnatenstr. 46, 80639 Munich, Germany. TEL 089-1783005. FAX 089-1781827. Eds. G. Biermann, M. Kos. **Document type:** monographic series.

614.58 GW ISSN 0173-0967
BEITRAEGE ZUR PSYCHOLOGIE UND SOZIOLOGIE DES KRANKEN MENSCHEN. 1974. irreg., no.6, 1986. price varies. Ernst Reinhardt Verlag, Kemnatenstr. 46, 80639 Munich, Germany. TEL 089-1783005. FAX 089-1781827. Eds. G. Biermann, J. von Troschke. **Document type:** monographic series.

155.2 GW ISSN 0067-5210
 CODEN: BSXFAV
BEITRAEGE ZUR SEXUALFORSCHUNG. 1952. irreg., vol.66, 1990. price varies. (Deutsche Gesellschaft fuer Sexualforschung) Ferdinand Enke Verlag, Postfach 300366, 70443 Stuttgart, Germany. TEL 0711-135798-0. FAX 0711-135798-30. TELEX 07252275-GTV-D. Ed.Bd. (reprint service avail. from IRC) **Indexed:** Biol.Abstr., Excerp.Med., Ind.Med. **Document type:** monographic series.

BEREAVEMENT CARE; an international journal for those who help bereaved people. see SOCIAL SERVICES AND WELFARE

BETHLEM AND MAUDSLEY GAZETTE. see MEDICAL SCIENCES — Psychiatry And Neurology

BIBLIOGRAPHY OF ANXIETY DISORDERS. see PSYCHOLOGY — Abstracting, Bibliographies, Statistics

150 610 US ISSN 1081-5937
BIOFEEDBACK (WHEAT RIDGE). a. Association for Applied Psychophysiology and Biofeedback, 10200 W. 44th Ave., Ste. 304, Wheat Ridge, CO 80033. TEL 303-422-8436. FAX 303-422-8894. **Document type:** bulletin.

613 US ISSN 0363-3586
BF319.5.B5 CODEN: BSELDP
BIOFEEDBACK & SELF REGULATION. 1975. q. $265 (foreign $310) (effective 1996). Plenum Publishing Corp., 233 Spring St., New York, NY 10013-1578. TEL 212-620-8000. FAX 212-463-0742. TELEX 23-421139. Eds. Robert R. Freedman, Mary R. Cook. adv. (also avail. in microfilm from JSC; back issues avail.) **Indexed:** Adol.Ment.Hlth.Abstr., Biol.Abstr., Curr.Adv.Ecol.Sci., Curr.Cont., Dent.Ind., Excerp.Med., Ind.Med., INSPEC (1979-), Psychol.Abstr. (1977-). **Document type:** academic/scholarly publication.
—BLDSC (2072.140000); Faxon; Genuine Article; SWETS; UMI; UnCover. **CCC.**
Refereed Serial

574 150 NE ISSN 0301-0511
  CODEN: BLPYAX
BIOLOGICAL PSYCHOLOGY. 1973. bi-m. fl.912($556) (effective 1996). North-Holland (Subsidiary of: Elsevier Science B.V.), P.O. Box 211, 1000 AE Amsterdam, Netherlands. TEL 31-20-4853911. FAX 31-20-4853598. TELEX 18582 ESPA NL. (Subscr. in U.S. and Canada to: Elsevier Science Inc., Box 882, Madison Sq. Sta., New York, NY 10159. TEL 212-989-5800. FAX 212-633-3990) Ed. R.E. Jennings. adv.; bk.rev.; charts; index. circ. 375. (also avail. in microform from UMI; back issues avail.; reprint service avail. from ISI) **Indexed:** Behav.Med.Abstr., Chem.Abstr., Commun.Abstr., Curr.Adv.Ecol.Sci., Curr.Cont., Dent.Ind., Excerp.Med., Ind.Med., Psychol.Abstr. (1973-), SSCI. **Document type:** academic/scholarly publication.
—BLDSC (2077.560000); CASDDS; Faxon; Genuine Article; SWETS; UnCover. **CCC.**
Description: Publishes original scientific papers on the biological aspects of psychological states and processes.
Refereed Serial

150 370 610 IT ISSN 0392-2529
BIOPSYCHE; rivista di scienze antropologiche. 1970. q. L.15000. Ispasa Societa Cooperativa, Corso Italia, 104, 95129 Catania, Italy. TEL 095-532181. bk.rev. (back issues avail.)

BIRD BEHAVIOR; an international and interdisciplinary multimedia journal. see BIOLOGY — Ornithology

150 618 US ISSN 0734-3124
RG658
BIRTH PSYCHOLOGY BULLETIN. 1979. s-a. $9. Association for Birth Psychology, 444 E. 82nd St., New York, NY 10028. TEL 212-988-6617. Ed. Leslie Feher. bk.rev. circ. 500. (back issues avail.) **Indexed:** ERIC, Psychol.Abstr.
Description: Clinical, theoretical, and empirical articles on the psychological impact of pregnancy, birth, and the neonatal period.

155.3 IC ISSN 1021-7150
BLEIKT OG BLATT. bi-m. ISK 3294($50) Frodi Ltd., Seljavegur 2, IS-101 Reykjavik, Iceland. TEL 354-515-5500. FAX 354-515-5599. Ed. Thorarinn J. Magnusson. adv.: B&W page ISK 46900, color page ISK 81800; trim 190 x 270. circ. 14,000.
Description: Focuses on issues and events related to sex and the relationship between the sexes. Contributors are chiefly physicians, psychologists, sex therapists, nurses and other members of the medical and health professions.

BODYWORK SERIES. see NEW AGE PUBLICATIONS

270.15 CU ISSN 0253-5742
BOLETIN DE PSICOLOGIA. 1971. irreg. free. Ministerio de Salud Publica, Hospital Psiquiatrico de la Habana, Avenida de Independencia No. 26520, Mazorra, Havana, Cuba. TEL 5683-2465. Dr. Noemi Perez. adv. circ. 6,000. **Indexed:** Psychol.Abstr.

158 IT ISSN 0006-6761
BOLLETTINO DI PSICOLOGIA APPLICATA. 1954. q. L.50000 to individuals (foreign L.90000); institutions L.90000 (foreign L.120000). Organizzazioni Speciali, Via Scipione Ammirato 37, 50136 Florence, Italy. TEL 39-55-660997. FAX 39-55-669446. Ed. Saulo Sirigatti; Pub. Jacopo Tarantino. bk.rev.; bibl.; charts. circ. 1,000. (also avail. in microform from UMI; reprint service avail. from UMI) **Indexed:** Biol.Abstr., Lang.& Lang.Behav.Abstr., Psychol.Abstr. (1956-), SSCI. **Document type:** bulletin.
—BLDSC (2240.700000).
Refereed Serial

PSYCHOLOGY

150   US   ISSN 0278-2626
QP376
BRAIN AND COGNITION. 1982. 9/yr. $293 (foreign $347.50) (effective 1996). Academic Press, Inc., Journal Division, 525 B St., Ste. 1900, San Diego, CA 92101-4495. TEL 619-230-1840. FAX 619-699-6800. (Subscr. to: Box 620000, Orlando, FL 32891-8340. TEL 800-543-9534) Ed. Harry A. Whitaker. adv. (back issues avail.) **Indexed:** Child Devel.Abstr., Curr.Adv.Ecol.Sci., Ind.Sci.Rev., Psychol.Abstr. (1982-), Sci.Cit.Ind., SSCI. **Document type:** academic/scholarly publication.
—BLDSC (2268.032000); Faxon; Genuine Article; SWETS; UnCover. **CCC.**
    Description: Presents clinical case histories, original research papers, reviews, notes, and commentaries on neuropsychology.
    Refereed Serial

150 410   US   ISSN 0093-934X
RC423.A1   CODEN: BRLGA
BRAIN AND LANGUAGE. 1974. m. $486 (foreign $594) (effective 1996). Academic Press, Inc., Journal Division, 525 B St., Ste. 1900, San Diego, CA 92101-4495. TEL 619-230-1840. FAX 619-699-6800. (Subscr. to: Box 620000, Orlando, FL 32891-8340. TEL 800-543-9534) Ed. Harry A. Whitaker. (back issues avail.) **Indexed:** Abstr.Anthropol., Bibl.Dev.Med.& Child Neur., Bibl.Ling., Curr.Adv.Ecol.Sci., Curr.Cont., Dent.Ind., Excerp.Med., Ind.Med., Ind.Sci.Rev., INIS Atomind., Lang.& Lang.Behav.Abstr. (1974-), Ling.Abstr., M.L.A., Psychol.Abstr. (1974-), Sci.Cit.Ind., SSCI. **Document type:** academic/scholarly publication.
—BLDSC (2268.040000); EMDOCS; Faxon; Genuine Article; SWETS; UnCover. **CCC.**
    Description: Original theoretical, clinical, and experimental papers on human language and communication: speech, hearing, reading, writing, and higher language functions, as they relate to brain structure and function.
    Refereed Serial

BRAIN – MIND; bulletin of breakthroughs. see *MEDICAL SCIENCES — Psychiatry And Neurology*

BREATH SERIES; a progression of pranayama practices. see *NEW AGE PUBLICATIONS*

616.89   UK   ISSN 0954-0350
BRITISH ASSOCIATION OF PSYCHOTHERAPISTS. JOURNAL. 1968. s-a. £8 per no. (effective 1995). British Association of Psychotherapists, c/o Mary Stumpfl, 21 Cantelowes Rd., London NW1 9XR, England. TEL 0181-452-9823. FAX 0181-452-5182. adv.; bk.rev. circ. 700. **Document type:** academic/scholarly publication.
—BLDSC (4712.930000).
    Formerly: British Association of Psychotherapists. Bulletin (ISSN 0268-6643)
    Description: Covers topics related to Freudian or Jungian psycho-dynamic psychotherapy.

301.1 150   UK   ISSN 0144-6657
BF1   CODEN: BJCPDW
BRITISH JOURNAL OF CLINICAL PSYCHOLOGY. 1962. q. £140($266) includes British Journal of Health Psychology (effective 1996). British Psychological Society, St. Andrews House, 48 Princess Rd. E., Leicester LE1 7DR, England. TEL 0116-254-9568. FAX 0116-247-0787. (Subscr. to: Turpin Distribution Services Ltd., Blackhorse Rd., Letchworth, Herts. SG6 1HN, England. TEL 01462-672555. FAX 01462-480947) Ed. Chris Brewin. adv. contact: H. Daeuker. bk.rev.; charts; illus.; index. circ. 3,350. (also avail. in microform from UMI,SWZ; reprint service avail. from ISI/SWZ) **Indexed:** Abstr.Crim.& Pen., Adol.Ment.Hlth.Abstr., ASSIA, Behav.Med.Abstr., Bibl.Dev.Med.& Child Neur., Biol.Abstr., CINAHL, Curr.Adv.Ecol.Sci., Curr.Cont., Dent.Ind., Excerp.Med., IMFL, Ind.Med., Lang.& Lang.Behav.Abstr., Psychol.Abstr. (1981-), Psycscan C.P., Sociol.Educ.Abstr., SSCI. **Document type:** academic/scholarly publication.
—BLDSC (2307.230000); Faxon; Genuine Article; SWETS; UMI; UnCover. **CCC.**
    Supersedes in part (in 1981): British Journal of Social and Clinical Psychology (ISSN 0007-1293)
    Description: Presents new findings, theoretical, methodological and review papers on all aspects of clinical and health psychology.
    Refereed Serial

THE BRITISH JOURNAL OF CRIMINOLOGY; delinquency and deviant social behaviour. see *CRIMINOLOGY AND LAW ENFORCEMENT*

BRITISH JOURNAL OF DEVELOPMENTAL DISABILITIES. see *EDUCATION — Special Education And Rehabilitation*

155   UK   ISSN 0261-510X
BF712
BRITISH JOURNAL OF DEVELOPMENTAL PSYCHOLOGY. 1983. q. £105($198) (effective 1996). British Psychological Society, St. Andrew House, 48 Princess Rd. E., Leicester LE1 7DR, England. TEL 0116-254-9568. FAX 0116-247-0787. (Subscr. to: Turpin Distribution Services Ltd., Blackhorse Rd., Letchworth, Herts. SG6 1HN, England. TEL 01462-672555. FAX 01462-480947) Ed. Paul Harris. adv. contact: H. Daeuker. bk.rev.; charts; illus.; index. circ. 1,300. (also avail. in microform from SWZ; microform from UMI; reprint service avail. from ISI,SWZ) **Indexed:** ASSIA, Bibl.Dev.Med.& Child Neur., IMFL, Lang.& Lang.Behav.Abstr., Psychol.Abstr. (1983-), Psycscan D.P., Yrbk.Assoc.Educ.& Rehab.Blind. **Document type:** academic/scholarly publication.
—BLDSC (2307.480000); Faxon; Genuine Article; SWETS; UMI; UnCover. **CCC.**
    Description: Publishes empirical, conceptual, and review articles on all aspects of development.
    Refereed Serial

370.15 150   UK   ISSN 0007-0998
LB1051.A2   CODEN: BJESAE
BRITISH JOURNAL OF EDUCATIONAL PSYCHOLOGY. 1931. q. £65($124) (effective 1996). British Psychological Society, St. Andrews House, 48 Princess Rd. E., Leicester LE1 7DR, England. TEL 0116-254-9568. FAX 0116-247-0787. (Subscr. to: Turpin Distribution Services Ltd., Blackhorse Rd., Letchworth, Herts. SG6 1HN, England. TEL 01462-672555. FAX 01462-480947) Ed. M. Youngman. adv. contact: H. Daeuker. bk.rev.; bibl.; charts; illus.; index. circ. 2,500. (also avail. in microform from SWZ; reprint service avail. from SWZ) **Indexed:** Adol.Ment.Hlth.Abstr., ASSIA, Bibl.Dev.Med.& Child Neur., Biol.Abstr., Br.Educ.Ind., C.I.J.E., Child Devel.Abstr., Curr.Cont., Educ.Ind., Educ.Tech.Abstr., High.Educ.Curr.Aware.Bull., Ind.Med., Lang.& Lang.Behav.Abstr., Lang.Teach.& Ling.Abstr., Psychol.Abstr. (1931-), Res.High.Educ.Abstr., SOMA, SSCI, Stud.Wom.Abstr. **Document type:** academic/scholarly publication.
—BLDSC (2307.650000); Faxon; Genuine Article; SWETS; UnCover. **CCC.**
    Description: Reports on the spectrum of educational research.
    Refereed Serial

616.8   UK   ISSN 1359-107X
▼**BRITISH JOURNAL OF HEALTH PSYCHOLOGY.** Announced for publication in 1996. q. free with subscription to British Journal of Clinical Psychology. British Psychological Society, St. Andrews House, 48 Princess Rd. E., Leicester LE1 7DR, England. TEL 0116-254-9568. FAX 0116-247-0787. (Subscr. to: Turpin Distribution Services Ltd., Blackhorse Rd., Letchworth, Herts. SG6 1HN, England. TEL 01462-672555. FAX 01462-480947) **Document type:** academic/scholarly publication.

152.8   UK   ISSN 0007-1102
BF1
BRITISH JOURNAL OF MATHEMATICAL AND STATISTICAL PSYCHOLOGY. 1948. s-a. £102($194) (effective 1996). British Psychological Society, St. Andrews House, 48 Princess Rd. E., Leicester LE1 7DR, England. TEL 0116-254-9568. FAX 0116-247-0787. (Subscr. to: Turpin Distribution Services Ltd., Blackhorse Rd., Letchworth, Herts. SG6 1HN, England. TEL 01462-672555. FAX 01462-480947) Ed. Philip T. Smith. adv. contact: H. Daeuker. bk.rev.; charts; illus.; index. circ. 700. (also avail. in microform from SWZ; microform from UMI; reprint service avail. from ISI) **Indexed:** Compumath, Comput.Abstr., Curr.Cont., Curr.Ind.Stat., Ind.Med., J.Cont.Quant.Meth., Mark.Res.Abstr. (1965-1991), Math.R., Psychol.Abstr. (1953-), Psycscan, SSCI, Trop.Dis.Bull. **Document type:** academic/scholarly publication.
—BLDSC (2311.300000); Faxon; Genuine Article; SWETS; UMI; UnCover. **CCC.**
    Description: Reports on psychological issues from the perspective of a mathematical, statistical, or other formal aspect.
    Refereed Serial

616.89 150   UK   ISSN 0007-1129
RC321   CODEN: BJMPAB
BRITISH JOURNAL OF MEDICAL PSYCHOLOGY. 1920. q. £113($214) (effective 1996). British Psychological Society, St. Andrews House, 48 Princess Rd. E., Leicester LE1 7DR, England. TEL 0116-254-9568. FAX 0116-247-0787. (Subscr. to: Turpin Distribution Services Ltd., BlackhorsenRd., Letchworth, Herts. SG6 1HN, England. TEL 01462-672555. FAX 01462-480947) Ed. Dr. J. Birtchnell. adv. contact: H. Daeuker. bk.rev.; charts; illus.; index. circ. 2,750. (also avail. in microform from SWZ,UMI; reprint service avail. from ISI,SWZ) **Indexed:** Adol.Ment.Hlth.Abstr., Behav.Med.Abstr., Bibl.Dev.Med.& Child Neur., Biol.Abstr., Chem.Abstr., CINAHL, Curr.Adv.Ecol.Sci., Curr.Cont., Dent.Ind., Excerp.Med., IMFL, Ind.Med., Ind.Sci.Rev., Lang.& Lang.Behav.Abstr., Mid.East: Abstr.& Ind., Nutr.Abstr., Psychol.Abstr. (1926-), Sci.Cit.Ind., SSCI. **Document type:** academic/scholarly publication.
—BLDSC (2311.850000); Faxon; Genuine Article; SWETS; UMI; UnCover. **CCC.**
    Description: Contains original theory and research from psychodynamic and interpersonal psychology.
    Refereed Serial

616.89   UK   ISSN 0309-7757
    CODEN: BJPSD4
BRITISH JOURNAL OF PROJECTIVE PSYCHOLOGY. 1955. a. £20 (effective Jan. 1993). British Society for Projective Psychology, Department of Psychology, Parkhead Hospital, 81 Salamanca St., Glasgow G31 5BA, Scotland. TEL 041-554-7951. FAX 041-551-8318. Ed. Zahid Mahmood. adv.; bk.rev. circ. 200. (back issues avail.) **Indexed:** Psychol.Abstr. (1968-). **Document type:** academic/scholarly publication.
—UnCover. **CCC.**
    Formerly: British Journal of Projective Psychology and Personality Study.
    Description: Devoted to projective approaches and research in psychology.

150   UK   ISSN 0007-1269
BF1   CODEN: BJSGAE
BRITISH JOURNAL OF PSYCHOLOGY. 1904. q. £151($288) (effective 1995). British Psychological Society, St. Andrews House, 48 Princess Rd. E., Leicester LE1 7DR, England. TEL 0166-254-9568. FAX 0166-247-0787. (Subscr. to: Turpin Distribution Services Ltd., Blackhorse Rd., Letchworth, Herts. SG6 1HN, England. TEL 01462-672555. FAX 01462-480947) Ed. A.J. Chapman. adv. contact: H. Daeuker. bk.rev.; bibl.; charts; illus. circ. 2,900. (also avail. in microform from UMI; reprint service avail. from ISI,SWZ) **Indexed:** Abstr.Crim.& Pen., Adol.Ment.Hlth.Abstr., ASSIA, Bibl.Dev.Med.& Child Neur., Biol.Abstr., Br.Educ.Ind., Br.Hum.Ind., C.I.J.E., Commun.Abstr., Curr.Adv.Ecol.Sci., Curr.Cont., Ergon.Abstr., IMFL, Ind.Med., INSPEC, Lang.& Lang.Behav.Abstr., M.L.A., Mark.Res.Abstr. (1963-), Mid East: Abstr.& Ind., Psychol.Abstr. (1926-), Res.High.Educ.Abstr., Risk Abstr., So.Pac.Per.Ind., Soc.Sci.Ind., SSCI, Tech.Educ.Abstr. **Document type:** academic/scholarly publication.
●Also available online. Vendor(s): University Microfilms International.
—BLDSC (2321.000000); Faxon; Genuine Article; SWETS; UMI; UnCover. **CCC.**
    Description: Publishes empirical studies, critical reviews of the literature and theoretical contributions on psychology.
    Refereed Serial

PSYCHOLOGY

301.1 150   UK   ISSN 0144-6665
BF1   CODEN: BJSPDA
BRITISH JOURNAL OF SOCIAL PSYCHOLOGY. 1962. q. £105($194) (effective 1996). British Psychological Society, St. Andrews House, 48 Princess Rd. E., Leicester LE1 7DR, England. TEL 0116-2549568. FAX 0116-2470787. (Subscr. to: Turpin Distribution Services Ltd., Blackhorse Rd., Letchworth, Herts. SG6 1HN, England. TEL 01462-672555. FAX 01462-480947) Ed. Dr. Russell Spears. adv. contact: H. Daeuker. bk.rev.; charts; illus.; index. circ. 2,000. (also avail. in microform from UMI; reprint service avail. from ISI) **Indexed:** Abstr.Crim.& Pen., Adol.Ment.Hlth.Abstr., ASSIA, Bibl.Dev.Med.& Child Neur., Biol.Abstr., Br.Hum.Ind., Commun.Abstr., Curr.Adv.Ecol.Sci., Curr.Cont., Excerp.Med., High.Educ.Curr.Aware.Bull., IMFL, Ind.Med., Lang.& Lang.Behav.Abstr., Mark.Res.Abstr. (1981-), Mid.East: Abstr.& Ind., Psychol.Abstr. (1981-), Res.High.Educ.Abstr., Sociol.Educ.Abstr., SSCI, Stud.Wom.Abstr. **Document type:** academic/scholarly publication.
—BLDSC (2324.784000); Faxon; Genuine Article; SWETS; UMI; UnCover. **CCC.**
   Supersedes in part (in 1981): British Journal of Social and Clinical Psychology (ISSN 0007-1293)
   Description: Describes applications of social psychology. Includes research and review papers. *Refereed Serial*

150   UK   ISSN 0309-7773
BF11
BRITISH PSYCHOLOGICAL SOCIETY. ANNUAL REPORT. a. free. British Psychological Society, St. Andrews House, 48 Princess Rd. E., Leicester LE1 7DR, England. TEL 0116-254-9568. FAX 0116-247-0787. circ. 23,000. **Document type:** corporate report.
—BLDSC (1127.250000).

BRITISH PSYCHOLOGICAL SOCIETY. EDUCATION SECTION. REVIEW. see *EDUCATION*

BRITISH SOCIETY FOR MUSIC THERAPY. BULLETIN. see *MUSIC*

BROWN UNIVERSITY CHILD AND ADOLESCENT BEHAVIOR LETTER; monthly reports on the problems of children and adolescents growing up. see *CHILDREN AND YOUTH — About*

150   JA   ISSN 0288-3538
BUKKYO DAIGAKU SHINRIGAKU KENKYUJO KIYO/JOURNAL OF PSYCHOLOGY. (Text in Japanese) 1983. a. Bukkyo Daigaku, Shinrigaku Kenkyujo - Bukkyo University, Research Institute for Psychology, Kitahananobocho, Murasakino, Kita-ku, Kyoto 603, Japan.
●Also available online. Vendor(s): University Microfilms International.

150   FR   ISSN 0007-4403
BULLETIN DE PSYCHOLOGIE. 1947. q. 530 F. to individuals; institutions 705 F. Universite de Paris, Groupe d'Etudes de Psychologie, 17 rue de la Sorbonne, 75005 Paris, France. Ed. Dir. D. Voutsinas. bk.rev.; abstr.; bibl.; charts. **Indexed:** Psychol.Abstr. (1962-). **Document type:** academic/scholarly publication.
—BLDSC (2884.450000); SWETS.
   Formerly (until 1951): Universite de Paris. Groupe d'Etudes de Psychologie. Bulletin (ISSN 0242-5452)

616.89   CN   ISSN 0832-7475
BULLETIN I R P. 1986. irreg. price varies. Institute of Psychological Research, Inc., 34 Fleury St. W., Montreal, PQ H3L 1S9, Canada. TEL 514-382-3000. FAX 514-382-3007. Eds. Jean-Marc Chevrier, Malko von Osten. **Document type:** bulletin.

375 371.3   US
BUROS - NEBRASKA SERIES ON MEASUREMENT AND TESTING. 1982. irreg. Buros Institute of Mental Measurements, 135 Bancroft Hall, University of Nebraska-Lincoln, Lincoln, NE 68588-0348. TEL 402-472-6203. FAX 402-472-6207. Ed. Linda L. Murphy.
   Description: Each publication in the series focuses on an individual issue within the assessment field.

370.15 150   US   ISSN 1052-3101
C A C D JOURNAL. vol.9, 1989. a. $8. California Association for Counseling and Development, 2555 E. Chapman Ave., Ste. 201, Fullerton, CA 92631-3617. TEL 714-871-6460. FAX 714-871-5132. Ed. Dr. Patricia Wickwire. adv.; charts; stat. circ. 3,000.
   Description: Presents articles in the field of counseling and guidance for professionals.

C A P S REPORT NEWSLETTER; fellowship, personal news, membership, convention. (Christian Association for Psychological Studies, Inc.) see *RELIGIONS AND THEOLOGY*

150   BL
CADERNOS DE PSICOLOGIA APLICADA.* s-a. Centro de Orientacao e Selecao Psicotencia, Rua Jacinto Gomes 540, Porto Algre (R.S.), Brazil. bibl. **Indexed:** Psychol.Abstr.

616.89 301.4   FR   ISSN 0241-5453
CAHIERS CRITIQUES DE THERAPIE FAMILIALE ET DE PRATIQUES DE RESEAUX. 2/yr. 290 F. Institut de la Famille, 46 rue de Metz, 31000 Toulouse, France. (Subscr. to: Dunod, Centrale des Revues (CDR), 11 rue Gossin, 92543 Montrouge Cedex, France. TEL 1-46-56-52-66)
   Description: Proposes a systematic analysis of social change on both a small and large scale.

616.89   BE
▼**CAHIERS DE PSYCHOLOGIE CLINIQUE.** (Text in French) 1994. 2/yr. 1750 BEF (foreign 2070 BEF) (effective 1995). De Boeck Universite, Fond Jean-Paques 4, B-1348 Louvain-la-Neuve, Belgium. TEL 32-10-482509. FAX 32-10-482519. Ed. Liliane Dirkx. **Document type:** academic/scholarly publication.

150   FR   ISSN 0249-9185
CAHIERS DE PSYCHOLOGIE COGNITIVE/CURRENT PSYCHOLOGY OF COGNITION. Abbreviated title: C P C. 1962. bi-m. 756 F.($130) (effective 1996). Association pour la Diffusion des Recherches en Sciences Cognitives de Langue Francaise, I B H O P, Traverse Charles Susini, 13388 Marseille Cedex 13, France. TEL 91-66-00-69. FAX 91-61-14-20. Ed. Jean-Paul Caverni; Pub. Francoise Joubaud. **Indexed:** Psychol.Abstr. (1981-).
—Genuine Article.
   Formerly (until 1980): Cahiers de Psychologie (ISSN 0373-8965)
   Description: Features short papers emphasizing experimental work, and target articles focusing on significant and controversial contributions. Also includes theoretical, review, advance and integrative empirical articles.

301.1 150   BE   ISSN 0777-0707
CAHIERS INTERNATIONAUX DE PSYCHOLOGIE SOCIALE. (Text in French, summaries in English, French, Spanish) 1989. q. 3000 BEF (Europe 3250 BEF; elsewhere 3300 BEF) (effective 1995). De Boeck Universite, Fond Jean-Paques 4, B-1348 Louvain-la-Neuve, Belgium. TEL 32-10-482509. FAX 32-10-482519. Ed. P. de Visscher. **Indexed:** Psychol.Abstr. (1989-). **Document type:** academic/scholarly publication.
   Description: Discusses various aspects of social psychology.

614.58   US   ISSN 1062-8193
RC488.5
CALIFORNIA THERAPIST. 1989. bi-m. $24. California Association of Marriage and Family Therapists, 7901 Raytheon Rd., San Diego, CA 92111-1606. TEL 619-292-2633. FAX 619-292-2666. Ed. Mary Riemersma. adv.; bk.rev.; charts; illus.; stat.; tr.lit. circ. 26,000. **Document type:** trade publication.
   Description: For and about CA licensed marriage, family and child counselors.

CANADA'S MENTAL HEALTH. see *MEDICAL SCIENCES*

150   CN   ISSN 0008-400X
    CODEN: CJBSAA
CANADIAN JOURNAL OF BEHAVIOURAL SCIENCE/REVUE CANADIENNE DES SCIENCES DU COMPORTEMENT. (Text in English, French) 1969. q. Can.$71.50($73.70) Canadian Psychological Association, Vincent Rd., Old Chelsea, PQ J0X 2N0, Canada. Ed. Richard Ckement. adv.; bk.rev.; charts; tr.lit.; index. circ. 2,800. (also avail. in microform from UMI; back issues avail.) **Indexed:** Adol.Ment.Hlth.Abstr., Biol.Abstr., Can.B.P.I., Can.Wom.Per.Ind., Curr.Adv.Ecol.Sci., Curr.Cont., Excerp.Med., Ind.Sci.Rev., Lang.& Lang.Behav.Abstr., Mid.East: Abstr.& Ind., Mult.Ed.Abstr., Psychol.Abstr. (1969-), Sci.Cit.Ind., Sp.Ed.Needs Abstr., SSCI, Stud.Wom.Abstr.
—BLDSC (3028.700000); Faxon; Genuine Article; SWETS; UnCover. **CCC.**
   Description: Covers abnormal, behavioral and psychotherapeutic intervention strategies, child and developmental, clinical, community, education, environmental, organizational behavior and development, personality, psychometrics.

150 301.1   CN   ISSN 0713-3936
CANADIAN JOURNAL OF COMMUNITY MENTAL HEALTH/REVUE CANADIENNE DE SANTE MENTALE COMMUNAUTAIRE. 2/yr. Can.$40 (US $36; elsewhere $40). (Canadian Periodical for Community Studies Inc.) Wilfrid Laurier University Press, Waterloo, ON N2L 3C5, Canada. TEL 519-884-1970. FAX 519-725-1399. Ed. Geoffrey Nelson. index. **Indexed:** Psychol.Abstr. (1983-), Soc.Work Res.& Abstr. **Document type:** academic/scholarly publication.
—BLDSC (3031.046000).
   Description: Devoted to the sharing of information and valid knowledge about phenomena pertinent to the mental well-being of Canadians and their communities.

150   CN   ISSN 1196-1961
BF1   CODEN: CJEPEK
CANADIAN JOURNAL OF EXPERIMENTAL PSYCHOLOGY/REVUE CANADIENNE DE PSYCHOLOGIE EXPERIMENTALE. (Text in English and French) 1947. q. Can.$71.50($73.70) Canadian Psychological Association, Vincent Rd., Old Chelsea, PQ J0X 2N0, Canada. TEL 819-827-3927. FAX 819-827-4639. E-mail: PSYCAN@ACADVM1.UOTTAWA.CA. Ed. Colin MacLeod. adv.; bibl.; charts; illus.; index, cum.index: 1947-1961. circ. 2,600. (also avail. in microform from JAI,UMI; reprint service avail. from UMI) **Indexed:** Adol.Ment.Hlth.Abstr., ASCA, ASSIA, Biol.Abstr., Can.B.P.I., Child Devel.Abstr., Curr.Adv.Ecol.Sci., Curr.Cont., Ergon.Abstr., Ind.Med., Lang.& Lang.Behav.Abstr., Mult.Ed.Abstr., Psychol.Abstr. (1947-), RADAR, Soc.Sci.Ind., Sp.Ed.Needs Abstr., SSCI, Yrbk.Assoc.Educ.& Rehab.Blind. **Document type:** academic/scholarly publication.
—BLDSC (3031.410000); Faxon; Genuine Article; SWETS; UMI; UnCover. **CCC.**
   Former titles (until 1993): Canadian Journal of Psychology (ISSN 0008-4255); (until 1947): Canadian Psychology Association. Bulletin (ISSN 0382-8654)
   Description: Publishes reports of empirical research in general experimental psychology, focusing on studies of learning, perception, motivation and cognition in animals and humans.

155.3   CN   ISSN 1188-4517
    CODEN: CJHSEA
CANADIAN JOURNAL OF HUMAN SEXUALITY. 1986. q. Can.$35 to individuals; institutions Can.$50; students Can.$20. Sex Information and Education Council of Canada, 850 Coxwell Ave., East York, ON M4C 5R1, Canada. TEL 416-466-5304. FAX 416-778-0785. Ed. F. Michael Barrett. bk.rev. circ. 1,000. **Indexed:** Can.B.P.I.
—BLDSC (3031.710000).
   Formerly (until 1992): S I E C C A N Journal (ISSN 0844-3718)
   Description: Includes scholarly articles, research papers, reviews, conference announcements and special theme issue.

PSYCHOLOGY

370.15 150   CN   ISSN 0829-5735
CANADIAN JOURNAL OF SCHOOL PSYCHOLOGY. 1985. 2/yr. Can.$42($32) Canadian Association of School Psychologists, Faculty of Education Clinic, University of Alberta, Edmonton, AB T6G 2G5, Canada. TEL 403-492-5718. FAX 403-492-1318. Ed. Henry L. Janzen. adv.; bk.rev. circ. 500. (back issues avail.) **Indexed:** Psychol.Abstr. (1993-). **Document type:** academic/scholarly publication.
—BLDSC (3035.518000).
Description: For psychologists, counsellors, teachers and administrators involved in any type of work in schools or other educational institutions.

150   CN   ISSN 0068-9211
CANADIAN MENTAL HEALTH ASSOCIATION. ANNUAL REPORT/ASSOCIATION CANADIENNE POUR LA SANTE MENTALE. RAPPORT ANNUEL. 1926. a. free. Canadian Mental Health Association, 2160 Yonge St., Toronto, ON M4S 2Z3, Canada. TEL 416-484-7750. **Indexed:** Curr.Cont. **Document type:** corporate report.

150   CN   ISSN 0708-5591
BF1   CODEN: CPSGD2
CANADIAN PSYCHOLOGY. (Text in English, French) 1959. q. Can.$71.50($73.70) Canadian Psychological Association, Vincent Rd., Old Chelsea, PQ J0X 2N0, Canada. TEL 819-827-3927. FAX 819-827-4639. Ed. Patrick O'Neill. adv.; bk.rev. circ. 4,600. (also avail. in microform; back issues avail.) **Indexed:** ASSIA, Biol.Abstr., Can.B.P.I., Can.Per.Ind., Can.Wom.Per.Ind., CMI, Curr.Cont., Lang.& Lang.Behav.Abstr., Mid.East: Abstr.& Ind., Psychol.Abstr. (1960-), SSCI. **Document type:** academic/scholarly publication.
—BLDSC (3044.105000); Faxon; Genuine Article; UMI; UnCover. **CCC.**
Former titles: Canadian Psychological Review (ISSN 0318-2096); Canadian Psychologist.
Description: Publishes theoretical, integrative and applied articles of interest to a broad cross-section of psychologists.

150   US
CARE NETWORK. 1987. bi-m. $24. Publishing House, Inc., 7380 Lowell Blvd., Box 215, Westminster, CO 80030. TEL 303-428-9829. FAX 303-430-1676. Ed. Joe Reid. adv.: B&W page $1200. circ. 5,000.

CAREER DEVELOPMENT QUARTERLY. see OCCUPATIONS AND CAREERS

CAREER PLANNING & ADULT DEVELOPMENT JOURNAL. see EDUCATION — Adult Education

CAREER PLANNING AND ADULT DEVELOPMENT NETWORK NEWSLETTER; a newsletter for career counselors, educators, and human resource specialists. see EDUCATION — Adult Education

150.19 155.4   US
CARNEGIE-MELLON SYMPOSIA ON COGNITION SERIES. Variant title: Carnegie Symposium on Cognition. 1974. irreg., vol.23, 1992. Lawrence Erlbaum Associates, Inc., 10 Industrial Dr., Mahwah, NJ 07430-2262. TEL 201-236-9500. FAX 201-236-0072. Ed. David Klahr. **Indexed:** Curr.Cont., Psychol.Abstr. **Document type:** monographic series.

616.89   AT   ISSN 1321-9324
CASE STUDIES; in brief and family therapy. 1986. s-a. Aus.$25 to individuals; institutions Aus.$36. (Eastwood Family Therapy Centre) Michael Durrant & Assoc. Pty. Ltd., P.O. Box 630, Epping, N.S.W. 2121, Australia. TEL 61-2-8682799. FAX 61-2-8768943. Ed. Michael Durrant.
—BLDSC (3058.145680).
Formerly (until vol.8, 1994): Family Therapy Case Studies (ISSN 0818-3538)
Description: Designed to provide practical examples and information for working therapists.

150   US
CENTENNIAL PSYCHOLOGY SERIES. 1982. irreg. price varies. Praeger Publishers (Subsidiary of: Greenwood Publishing Group Inc.), 88 Post Rd. W., Box 5007, Westport, CT 06881-5007. TEL 203-226-3571. FAX 203-222-1502. **Document type:** monographic series.

616.89   IT   ISSN 0392-3398
CENTRO RICERCHE BIOPSICHICHE. (Text in Italian; summaries in English) 1957. irreg. free. Centro Ricerche Biopsichiche, Via Dante 60, 35139 Padua, Italy. TEL 39-49-657996. Ed. Giorgio Foresti. bk.rev. circ. 600. **Indexed:** Psychol.Abstr. **Document type:** academic/scholarly publication, bulletin.

150   XR   ISSN 0009-062X
BF8.C9   CODEN: CEPSBC
CESKOSLOVENSKA PSYCHOLOGIE/CZECHOSLOVAK PSYCHOLOGY. (Text mainly in Czech or Slovak; occasionally in English, German, Russian; summaries in English and Russian) 1957. bi-m. DM.141. Ceska Akademie Ved, Psychologicky Ustav, Prukynova 2, 110 00 Prague 1, Czech Republic. (Dist. in Western countries by: Kubon & Sagner, P.O. Box 34 01 08, 8000 Munich 34, Germany) Ed. J. Linhart. adv.; bk.rev.; charts; illus.; stat.; index. circ. 2,800. **Indexed:** Bibl.Ling., Biol.Abstr., C.I.S. Abstr., Child Devel.Abstr., Curr.Cont., Ergon.Abstr., Psychol.Abstr. (1957-), SSCI.
—BLDSC (3122.500000).
Description: Covers all fields of psychology, theoretical and applied. Includes basic research into general and social psychology, survey studies which have been given preference and reports on important conferences and institutes.

CHALLENGE ADVOCATE. see SOCIAL SERVICES AND WELFARE

CHANGES; an international journal of psychology and psychotherapy. see SOCIAL SERVICES AND WELFARE

150   US   ISSN 0892-1504
HV5132
CHANGES (DEERFIELD BEACH). 1986. bi-m. $18. U S Journal Inc., Enterprise Center, 3201 S.W. 15th St., Deerfield Beach, FL 33442-8190. TEL 305-360-0909. adv.: B&W page $1966; color page $2430. tr.lit.; circ. 85,300. circ. 10,000 (controlled). **Document type:** consumer publication.
Formerly: Changes - the Magazine for Personal Growth.
Description: Aimed at people creating positive changes in their lives.

CHEIRON NEWSLETTER. see SOCIAL SCIENCES: COMPREHENSIVE WORKS

CHILD ABUSE REVIEW. see SOCIAL SERVICES AND WELFARE

CHILD AND ADOLESCENT SOCIAL WORK JOURNAL. see SOCIOLOGY

155.4 157   US   ISSN 0731-7107
RJ504
CHILD & FAMILY BEHAVIOR THERAPY. 1978. q. $285 (foreign $399) (effective 1996). Haworth Press, Inc., 10 Alice St., Binghamton, NY 13904. TEL 607-722-5857; 800-342-9678. FAX 607-722-1424. Ed. Cyril M. Franks. adv.; bk.rev.; film rev.; bibl.; charts; stat. circ. 532. (also avail. in microfiche from HAW; back issues avail.; reprint service avail. from HAW) **Indexed:** Abstr.Crim.& Pen., Adol.Ment.Hlth.Abstr., Behav.Abstr., Bull.Signal., C.I.J.E., Child Devel.Abstr., Curr.Cont., Educ.Ind., Except.Child Educ.Abstr., IMFL, Lang.& Lang.Behav.Abstr., Mult.Ed.Abstr., Psychol.Abstr. (1979-), Rehabil.Lit., Sage Fam.Stud.Abstr., Soc.Work Res.& Abstr., Sociol.Abstr., Sociol.Educ.Abstr., Sp.Ed.Needs Abstr., SSCI.
—BLDSC (3172.915100); Faxon; Genuine Article; Haworth; SWETS; UnCover.
Formerly (until 1982): Child Behavior Therapy (ISSN 0162-1416)
Description: Scholarly and interdisciplinary journal devoted to research and clinical applications in behavior therapy with children and adolescents, as well as the enhancement of parenting.
Refereed Serial

CHILD AND YOUTH CARE FORUM; an independent journal of day and residential child and youth care practice. see CHILDREN AND YOUTH — About

CHILD ASSESSMENT NEWS. see CHILDREN AND YOUTH — About

CHILD BEHAVIOR AND DEVELOPMENT. see MEDICAL SCIENCES — Pediatrics

CHILD DEVELOPMENT. see CHILDREN AND YOUTH — About

CHILD MALTREATMENT. see CHILDREN AND YOUTH — About

616.8 155.4   NE   ISSN 0929-7049
▼**CHILD NEUROPSYCHOLOGY**; a journal on normal and abnormal development in childhood and adolescence. (Section C of Neuropsychology, Development and Cognition) (Text and summaries in English) 1995. 3/yr. fl.145($79.50) to individuals; institutions fl.264($145). Swets & Zeitlinger bv, P.O. Box 825, 2160 SZ Lisse, Netherlands. TEL 31-2521-35111. FAX 31-2521-15888. TELEX 41325 SZLIS NL. E-mail: orders@swets.nl. (N. American dist. addr.: Swets & Zeitlinger, 440 Creamery Way, Ste. A, Exton, PA 19341. TEL 610-524-5355) Ed.Bd. adv.; bk.rev.; abstr.; index; circ. 500 (paid). (also avail. in microfilm from SWZ; back issues avail.) **Document type:** academic/scholarly publication.
—BLDSC (3172.944795).
Description: Publishes research on the neuropsychological dimension of development in childhood and adolescence, and promotes the integration of theories, methods and research findings in child and developmental neuropsychology.
Refereed Serial

CHILD STUDY JOURNAL. see EDUCATION

155.4 362.7   UK
CHILDREN'S ENVIRONMENTS; theory, research, policy and applications. 1984. q. £35($99) to individuals; institutions in the E.U. £99 (N. America $169; elsewhere £109) (effective 1995). (Center for Human Environments, US) Chapman & Hall, Journals Department (Subsidiary of: International Thomson Publishing Group), 2-6 Boundary Row, London SE1 8HN, England. TEL 0171-865-0066. FAX 0171-522-9623. TELEX 290164 CHAPMA G. E-mail: journal.chall.mhs.compuserve.com. (Dist. by: International Thompson Publishing Services Ltd., Cheriton House, North Way, Andover, Hants. SP10 5BE, England. TEL 01264-342713. FAX 01264-642807; N. American subscr. to: Champan & Hall, Journals Promotion Dept., One Penn Plaza, 41st Fl., New York, NY 10119. TEL 212-564-1060. FAX 212-564-1505) Ed. Roger A. Hart. adv.; bk.rev.; bibl. circ. 500. (reprint service avail.) **Indexed:** Child Devel.Abstr., Psychol.Abstr. (1986-). **Document type:** academic/scholarly publication.
—BLDSC (3172.991370); UnCover. **CCC.**
Former titles (until vol.9, 1992): Children's Environments Quarterly (ISSN 0886-0505); (until 1984): Childhood City Quarterly (ISSN 0738-1484); Childhood City Newsletter.
Description: Serves as both a forum among child environment research scholars and a bridge to practice and policy in environmental design, planning, and education for children.
Refereed Serial

150 130   CH   ISSN 1013-9656
CHINESE JOURNAL OF PSYCHOLOGY. (Text in Chinese or English; abstracts in Chinese, English) 1958. s-a. $25 to individuals; institutions $40 (effective 1996). Chinese Psychological Association, c/o Department of Psychology, National Taiwan University, Taipei 10764, Taiwan, Republic of China. FAX 886-2-3629909. Ed. Chia-Hung Hsu. adv. circ. 500. (back issues avail.) **Indexed:** ASCA, Biol.Abstr., Curr.Cont., Psychol.Abstr. (1990-), SSCI. **Document type:** academic/scholarly publication.
Formerly: Acta Psychologica Taiwanica (ISSN 0065-1613)
Refereed Serial

CLASS: CLASSIFICATION LITERATURE AUTOMATED SEARCH SERVICE. see MATHEMATICS

150.19   SP   ISSN 0210-0657
RC475
CLINICA Y ANALISIS GRUPAL; revista de psicoterapia, psicoanalisis y grupo. (Text in Spanish; summaries in English, French) 1976. 3/yr. 6000 ptas. (Europe $80, elsewhere $90) (effective 1995) 6300 ptas. (effective 1996). Grupo Quipu de Psicoterapia Sociedad Cooperativa Ltda., Principe de Vergara 35, 28001 Madrid, Spain. TEL 577-60-39. FAX 34-1-5779734. Ed. Isabel Sanfeliu. adv. contact: Nicolas Caparros. bk.rev.; index. circ. 1,500. (back issues avail.) **Indexed:** Psychol.Abstr. (1984-).

CLINICAL CHILD PSYCHOLOGY & PSYCHIATRY. see
CHILDREN AND YOUTH — About

616.8   NE   ISSN 0920-1637
CODEN: CLNEEC
THE CLINICAL NEUROPSYCHOLOGIST. (Section D of: Neuropsychology, Development and Cognition) (Text in English) 1987. 4/yr. $107 for individuals; institutions $180. Swets & Zeitlinger bv, P.O. Box 825, 2160 SZ Lisse, Netherlands. TEL 31-2521-35111. FAX 31-2521-15888. TELEX 41325. E-mail: orders@swets.nl. (Dist in N. America by: Swets & Zeitlinger, 440 Creamery Way, Ste. A, Exton, PA 19341. TEL 800-447-9387. FAX 610-524-5366) Eds. Byron P. Rourke, Kenneth M. Adams. circ. 3,000. (reprint service avail. from SWZ) **Indexed:** Excerp.Med., Psychol.Abstr. (1987-). **Document type:** academic/scholarly publication.
—BLDSC (3286.310680); Faxon; Genuine Article; UnCover. **CCC.**

157   US   ISSN 0009-9244
BF1
THE CLINICAL PSYCHOLOGIST. 1946. 4/yr. membership. American Psychological Association, Division 12 Central Office, Box 22727, Oklahoma City, OK 73123-1727. TEL 405-721-2792. (Editorial addr.: Ferkauf Graduate School of Psychology, Yeshiva University, 1300 Morris Park Ave., Bronx, NY 10461. TEL 718-430-4201) Ed. Lawrence Siegel. circ. 6,000. **Indexed:** Psychol.Abstr., Psyscan C.P., Rehabil.Lit. **Document type:** academic/scholarly publication, newsletter.
—UMI. **CCC.**
Refereed Serial

616.89   UK   ISSN 1063-3995
CODEN: CPPSEO
CLINICAL PSYCHOLOGY & PSYCHOTHERAPY. 1993. q. $175 (foreign $175) (effective 1996). John Wiley & Sons Ltd., Journals, Baffins Ln., Chichester, W. Sussex PO19 1UD, England. TEL 01273-779777. FAX 01273-776128. TELEX 86290 WIBOOK G. (Subscr. in the Americas to: John Wiley & Sons, Inc., 605 Third Ave., New York, NY 10158. TEL 212-850-6645. FAX 212-850-6021) Eds. Paul Emmelkamp, Mick Power. circ. 178. (also avail. in microform from UMI; back issues avail.) **Document type:** academic/scholarly publication.
—BLDSC (3286.343500); Genuine Article.
Description: Presents papers on various presetations within clinical psychology and psychotherapy, with special emphasis on theoretical papers outlining innovations within existing approaches.
Refereed Serial

157   UK   ISSN 0269-0144
CLINICAL PSYCHOLOGY FORUM. m. £30($160) to individuals (foreign £80); institutions £60. British Psychological Society, St. Andrews House, 48 Princess Rd., E., Leicester LE1 7DR, England. TEL 0116-254-9568. FAX 0116-247-0787. Ed. Craig Wewyes. (reprint service avail. from ISI)
—BLDSC (3286.344000).
Refereed Serial

157.9   UK   ISSN 0272-7358
RC467   CODEN: CPSRDZ
CLINICAL PSYCHOLOGY REVIEW. 1981. 8/yr. £342($544) (effective 1996). Elsevier Science Ltd., Pergamon, P.O. Box 800, Kidlington, Oxford OX5 1DX, England. TEL 44-1865-843000. FAX 44-1865-843010. E-mail: nlinfo-f@elsevier.nl; usinfo-f@elsevier.com; forinfo-kyf04035@niftyserve.or.jp; Site addr.: http://www.elsevier.nl/. (Subscr. in U.S. and Canada to: Elsevier Science, 660 White Plains Rd., Tarrytown, NY 10591-5153. TEL 914-524-9200. FAX 914-333-2444) Eds. Alan S. Bellack, Michel Hersen. adv.; B&W page $550, color page $1350. (also avail. in microfilm from UMI) **Indexed:** Abstr.Crim.& Pen., Curr.Cont., Dok.Arbeitsmed., Excerp.Med., Psychol.Abstr. (1981-), Psyscan C.P., SSCI. **Document type:** academic/scholarly publication.
—BLDSC (3286.345500); Faxon; Genuine Article; SWETS; UMI; UnCover. **CCC.**
Description: Publishes original research and reviews on topics germane to clinical psychology, including psychopathology, psychotherapy, community mental health, behavioral medicine and child development.
Refereed Serial

616.89   US   ISSN 0969-5893
▼**CLINICAL PSYCHOLOGY: SCIENCE AND PRACTICE.** 1994. q. £105($155) (effective 1996). (American Psychological Association, Division 12 - Clinical Psychology Division) Oxford University Press, Journals, 2001 Evans Rd., Cary, NC 27513. TEL 919-677-0977; 800-852-7323. FAX 919-677-1714. E-mail: jnlorders@oup-usa.org. (Subscr. outside N. America to: Oxford University Press, Journals, Walton St., Oxford OX2 6DP, England. TEL 44-1865-56767. FAX 44-1865-267773) Ed. Alan E. Kazdin. circ. 6,370. **Document type:** academic/scholarly publication.
—BLDSC (3286.343400); UMI.
Description: Publishes topical reviews of research, theory and application, including assessment, intervention, service delivery, and professional issues.

152   US   ISSN 8756-3207
CLINICIAN'S RESEARCH DIGEST. 1983. m. $73 to non-members (foreign $113); members $40 (foreign $56); institutions $97 (foreign $181). American Psychological Association, 750 First St., N.E., Washington, DC 20002-4242. TEL 202-336-5600. FAX 202-336-5568. Ed. Douglas Snyder. **Document type:** newsletter.
Description: Highlights current information on clinical research and professional practice in a concise manner.

153.4   NE   ISSN 0010-0277
BF311   CODEN: CGTNAU
COGNITION; international journal of cognitive psychology. (Text in English; summaries in French) 1972. m. fl.1500($915) (effective 1996). Elsevier Science B.V., P.O. Box 211, 1000 AE Amsterdam, Netherlands. TEL 31-20-4853911. FAX 31-20-4853598. TELEX 18582 ESPA NL. E-mail: nlinfo-f@elsevier.nl; usinfo-f@elsevier.com; forinfo-kyf04035@niftyserve.or.jp; Site addr.: http://www.elsevier.nl/. (Subscr. in U.S. and Canada to: Elsevier Science Inc., Box 882, Madison Sq. Sta., New York, NY 10159-0882. TEL 212-989-5800. FAX 212-633-3990) Ed. Jacques Mehler. adv.; bibl.; charts; illus.; index. (also avail. in microform from UMI; back issues avail.; reprint service avail. from SWZ) **Indexed:** A.I.Abstr., Adol.Ment.Hlth.Abstr., Bibl.Ling., Biol.Abstr., CAD CAM Abstr., Child Devel.Abstr., Curr.Cont., Lang.& Lang.Behav.Abstr., Lang.Teach.& Ling.Abstr., M.L.A., Phil.Ind., Psychol.Abstr. (1972-), Sci.Cit.Ind., SSCI. **Document type:** academic/scholarly publication.
—BLDSC (3292.870000); Faxon; Genuine Article; SWETS; UnCover. **CCC.**
Description: Publishes theoretical and experimental papers covering all aspects of the study of the mind. Includes research papers in the fields of psychology, linguistics, neuroscience, ethology, philosophy and epistemology.
Refereed Serial

153.4   US
COGNITION AND COMPUTING. 1987. irreg., vol.3, 1991. price varies. Ablex Publishing Corporation, 355 Chestnut St., Norwood, NJ 07648. TEL 201-767-8450. FAX 201-767-6717. TELEX 135-393. Eds. John Black, Elliot Soloway. **Document type:** academic/scholarly publication.

301.1 150   UK   ISSN 0269-9931
BF309   CODEN: COEMEC
COGNITION AND EMOTION. 1987. bi-m. £60($105) to individuals (outside the E.U. £65); institutions £154 (outside the E.U. £160 ($270)) (effective 1996). Lawrence Erlbaum Associates Ltd., 27 Palmeira Mansions, Church Rd., Hove, E. Sussex BN3 2FA, England. TEL 01273-207411. FAX 01273-205612. (Subscr. to: Turpin Distribution Services Ltd., Blackhorse Rd., Letchworth, Herts. SG6 1HN, England. TEL 01462-672555. FAX 01462-480947) Ed. Fraser N. Watts. adv.: page £175; 115 x 190. bk.rev. circ. 1,000. **Indexed:** Psychol.Abstr. (1987-), Sociol.Abstr. **Document type:** academic/scholarly publication.
—BLDSC (3292.871500); Faxon; SWETS; UnCover.
Description: Explores the interrelationship of cognition and emotion.
Refereed Serial

370.15   US   ISSN 0737-0008
LB1060
COGNITION AND INSTRUCTION. 1984. q. $39 to individuals (foreign $64); institutions $170 (foreign $200). Lawrence Erlbaum Associates, Inc., 10 Industrial Dr., Mahwah, NJ 07430-2262. TEL 201-236-9500. FAX 201-236-0072. Eds. Isabel Beck, Leona Schauble. adv.: page $425; 5 x 8. **Indexed:** Abstr.Hum.Comp.Inter., Psychol.Abstr. (1985-), Tech.Educ.Abstr. **Document type:** academic/scholarly publication.
—BLDSC (3292.872000); SWETS; UnCover.
Description: Interdisciplinary journal devoted to cognitive investigations of instruction and learning.
Refereed Serial

COGNITION AND LANGUAGE; a series in psycholinguistics. see *LINGUISTICS*

COGNITION AND LITERACY. see *EDUCATION*

150   SP   ISSN 0214-3550
COGNITIVA. (Text in English, Spanish) 1988. s-a. Aprendizaje, S.L., Ctra. de Canillas 138, 16C, 28043 Madrid, Spain. TEL 388-38-74. FAX 300-35-27. Ed. Manuel de Vega. adv. circ. 1,100. **Indexed:** Psychol.Abstr. (1988-). **Document type:** academic/scholarly publication.
—SWETS.
Description: Publishes original empirical and theoretical contributions concerning human cognitive processes.
Refereed Serial

370.15 150   US   ISSN 0885-2014
BF1
COGNITIVE DEVELOPMENT. 1986. q. $45 to individuals; institutions $115. Ablex Publishing Corporation, 355 Chestnut St., Norwood, NJ 07648. TEL 201-767-8450. FAX 201-767-6717. TELEX 135-393. Ed. Katherine Nelson. index. circ. 500. (back issues avail.; reprint service avail. from ISI) **Indexed:** Psychol.Abstr. (1983-). **Document type:** academic/scholarly publication.
—BLDSC (3292.876600); Faxon; Genuine Article; SWETS; UnCover. **CCC.**

616.89   UK   ISSN 1354-6805
▼**COGNITIVE NEUROPSYCHIATRY.** Announced for publication in 1996. q. £30($59.50) to individuals (outside the E.U. £35); institutions £60 (outside the E.U. £65 ($110)) (effective 1996). Lawrence Erlbaum Associates Ltd., 27 Palmeira Mansions, Church Rd., Hove, E. Sussex BN3 2 FA, England. TEL 01273-207411. FAX 01273-205612. (Subscr. to: Turpin Distribution Services Ltd., Blackhorse Rd., Letchworth, Herts. SG6 1HN, England. TEL 01462-672555. FAX 01462-480947) Eds. Anthony S. David, Peter Halligan. **Document type:** academic/scholarly publication.
Description: Promotes the study of cognitive processes underlying psychological and behavioral abnormalities, including psychotics symptoms, with and without organic brain disease.

157 616.89   UK   ISSN 0264-3294
CODEN: COGNEP
COGNITIVE NEUROPSYCHOLOGY. 1984. bi-m. £80($139) to individuals (outside the E.U. £85); institutions £245 (outside the E.U. £250 ($425)) (effective 1996). Lawrence Erlbaum Associates Ltd., 27 Palmeira Mansions, Church Rd., Hove, E. Sussex BN3 2FA, England. TEL 01273-207411. FAX 01273-205612. (Subscr. to: Turpin Distribution Services Ltd., Blackhorse Rd., Letchworth, Herts. SG6 1HN, England. TEL 01462-672555. FAX 01462-480947) Ed. Max Coltheart. adv.: page £180; 115 x 190. bk.rev. circ. 1,000. **Indexed:** Bibl.Dev.Med.& Child Neur., Excerp.Med., Psychol.Abstr. (1984-). **Document type:** academic/scholarly publication.
—BLDSC (3292.879000); Faxon; SWETS; UnCover.
Description: Studies cognitive processes from a neuropsychological perspective.
Refereed Serial

PSYCHOLOGY

153.4 US ISSN 0010-0285
BF309 CODEN: CGPSBQ
COGNITIVE PSYCHOLOGY. 1970. bi-m. $246 (foreign $294) (effective 1996). Academic Press, Inc., Journal Division, 525 B St., Ste. 1900, San Diego, CA 92101-4495. TEL 619-230-1840. FAX 619-699-6800. (Subscr. to: Box 620000, Orlando, FL 32891-8340. TEL 800-543-9534) Ed. Douglas L. Medin. adv.; abstr.; bibl.; charts; stat. (back issues avail.) Indexed: Adol.Ment.Hlth.Abstr., C.I.J.E., Child Devel.Abstr., Commun.Abstr., Curr.Cont., INSPEC (1971-1986), Lang.& Lang.Behav.Abstr., M.L.A., Mid.East: Abstr.& Ind., Psychol.Abstr. (1970-), Psycscan D.P., Soc.Sci.Ind., SSCI. **Document type:** academic/scholarly publication.
—BLDSC (3292.880000); Faxon; Genuine Article; SWETS; UnCover. **CCC.**
  Description: Concerned with advances in the study of memory, language processing, perception, problem solving, and thinking. Presents original empirical, theoretical, and tutorial papers, methodological articles, and critical reviews.
  Refereed Serial

020 410 US ISSN 0364-0213
BF311 CODEN: COGSD5
COGNITIVE SCIENCE; a multidisciplinary journal of artificial intelligence, psychology, and language. 1977. q. $60 to individuals (foreign $70); institutions $155 (foreign $150). (Cognitive Science Society, Inc.) Ablex Publishing Corporation, 355 Chestnut St., Norwood, NJ 07648. TEL 201-767-8450. FAX 201-767-6717. TELEX 135-393. Ed. Martin Ringle. index. circ. 2,400. (back issues avail.; reprint service avail. from ISI) Indexed: A.I.Abstr., Abstr.Hum.Comp.Inter., Art.Int.Abstr., C.I.J.E., CAD CAM Abstr., Curr.Cont., Energy Info.Abstr., Excerp.Med., INSPEC (1987-), Lang.& Lang.Behav.Abstr., M.L.A., Psychol.Abstr. (1977-), Sociol.Abstr., SSCI. **Document type:** academic/scholarly publication.
—BLDSC (3292.885000); Faxon; Genuine Article; SWETS; UnCover. **CCC.**
  Description: Publishes articles on such topics as knowledge representation, inference, memory process, learning, problem solving, planning, perception, natural language understanding, connectionism, brain theory, motor control, intentional systems, and other areas of multidisciplinary concern.

301.1 US ISSN 0732-1295
COGNITIVE SCIENCE SERIES (CAMBRIDGE). irreg., vol.9, 1989. Harvard University Press, 79 Garden St., Cambridge, MA 02138. TEL 617-495-2600. FAX 617-495-5898. **Document type:** monographic series.
  Refereed Serial

150 US
COGNITIVE SCIENCE SERIES: TECHNICAL MONOGRAPHS AND EDITED COLLECTIONS. 1981. irreg., vol.13, 1991. $99.95. Lawrence Erlbaum Associates, Inc., 10 Industrial Dr., Mahwah, NJ 07430-2262. TEL 201-236-9500. FAX 201-236-0072. Ed. Andrew Ortony. bibl.; charts; illus. Indexed: Curr.Cont., Psychol.Abstr. **Document type:** monographic series.
  Refereed Serial

153 US
BF311
COGNITIVE SCIENCE SOCIETY. ANNUAL CONFERENCE. PROCEEDINGS. 1986. a. Lawrence Erlbaum Associates, Inc., 10 Industrial Dr., Mahwah, NJ 07430-2262. TEL 201-236-9500. FAX 201-236-0072. adv. contact: Sharon Levy. **Document type:** proceedings.
  Formerly: Cognitive Science Society. Annual Conference. Program (ISSN 1047-1316)

152 NE ISSN 0256-663X
COGNITIVE SYSTEMS. 1985. irreg., (4 nos/vol.). fl.120 per vol. European Society for the Study of Cognitive Systems, c/o Dept. for Psychology, University of Groningen, P.O. Box 72, 9700 AB Groningen, Netherlands. FAX 31-50-636304. Ed. G.J. Dalenoort. bk.rev. circ. 60. (back issues avail.) Indexed: Psychol.Abstr. **Document type:** academic/scholarly publication.
—BLDSC (3292.892500).

150 US ISSN 0147-5916
BF311 CODEN: CTHRD8
COGNITIVE THERAPY AND RESEARCH. 1977. bi-m. $295 (foreign $345) (effective 1996). Plenum Publishing Corp., 233 Spring St., New York, NY 10013-1578. TEL 212-620-8000. FAX 212-463-0742. TELEX 23-421139. Ed. Philip C. Kendall. adv. (also avail. in microfilm from JSC; back issues avail.) Indexed: Adol.Ment.Hlth.Abstr., Behav.Abstr., Biol.Abstr., Curr.Cont., Excerp.Med., IMFL, Mult.Ed.Abstr., Psychol.Abstr. (1977-), Psycscan C.P., Ref.Zh., SSCI. **Document type:** academic/scholarly publication.
—BLDSC (3292.895000); Faxon; Genuine Article; SWETS; UMI; UnCover. **CCC.**
  Refereed Serial

155.4 370 FR ISSN 0246-4950
COLLECTION ORIENTATIONS. irreg. price varies. Editions Scientifiques et Psychologiques, 6 bis, rue Andre Chenier, 92130 Issy-les-Moulineaux, France. TEL 46-45-38-12. FAX 40-95-73-32. TELEX 270 105 F. Ed. G. Pihouee.

156 FR ISSN 0993-7536
COLLECTION PSYCHOLOGIE. irreg. price varies. Editions Scientifiques et Psychologiques, 6 bis, rue Andre Chenier, 92130 Issy-les-Moulineaux, France. TEL 46-45-38-12. FAX 40-95-73-32. TELEX 270 105 F. Ed. T. Ego.

COLLECTION PSYCHOLOGIE ET PEDAGOGIE DE LA MUSIQUE. see *MUSIC*

152 790.1 FR
COLLECTION PSYCHOLOGIE ET PEDAGOGIE DU SPORT. irreg. price varies. Editions Scientifiques et Psychologiques, 6 bis, rue Andre Chenier, 92130 Issy-les-Moulineaux, France. TEL 46-45-38-12. FAX 40-95-73-32. TELEX 270 105 F. Ed. A. Vom Hofe.

158.7 FR ISSN 0981-7727
COLLECTION PSYCHOLOGIE ET PEDAGOGIE DU TRAVAIL. 1986. irreg. price varies. Editions Scientifiques et Psychologiques, 6 bis, rue Andre Chenier, 92130 Issy-les-Moulineaux, France. TEL 46-45-38-12. FAX 40-95-73-32. TELEX 270 105 F. Ed. B. Gillet.

156 FR ISSN 1242-5028
COLLECTION TESTS PSYCHOLOGIQUES. 1992. irreg. price varies. Editions Scientifiques et Psychologiques, 6 bis, rue Andre Chenier, 92130 Issy-les-Moulineaux, France. TEL 46-45-38-12. FAX 40-95-73-32. TELEX 270 104 F. Ed. R. Simonnet.

150 CN
COLLEGE OF PSYCHOLOGISTS OF ONTARIO. BULLETIN. 1973. q. Can.$10. College of Psychologists of Ontario, 1246 Yonge St., Ste. 201, Toronto, ON M4T 1W5, Canada. TEL 416-961-8817. FAX 416-961-2635. index; circ. 2,400 (controlled). **Document type:** bulletin.
  Formerly: Ontario Board of Examiners in Psychology. Bulletin.
  Description: Covers professional affairs, discipline, licensing, training and public policy.

156 109 US ISSN 0267-9469
COMMENTS & CRITICISMS. 1983. irreg. Prytaneum Press, 1015 Bryan, Amarillo, TX 79102. TEL 806-372-7888. Ed. Don D. Davis. bk.rev. circ. 500.

150 658 US ISSN 0884-934X
COMMITMENT - PLUS NEWSLETTER; if you get dedication and teamwork from your people, you'll get high performance from your organization. 1972. m. $97. (Quality & Productivity Management Association) Pride Publications, 300 Martingale Rd., Ste.230, Schaumburg, IL 60173. TEL 708-619-2909. Ed. Clem Russo. bk.rev.; index. circ. 3,500. **Document type:** newsletter.
—**CCC.**
  Incorporates (in 1992): Behavioral Sciences Newsletter (ISSN 0361-4646)

616.89 200 US ISSN 0885-8500
COMMON BOUNDARY; exploring spirituality, psychotherapy and creativity. 1980. bi-m. $22. Common Boundary, Inc., 5272 River Rd., Ste. 650, Bethesda, MD 20816. TEL 301-652-9495. FAX 301-652-0579. Ed. Anne A. Simpkinson; Pub. Charles Simpkinson. adv.: B&W page $1240; adv. contact: Grace Ogden. bk.rev. circ. 30,000. (also avail. in microform from UMI; back issues avail.) **Document type:** consumer publication.
  Description: Articles, news and research for people interested in the interface between spirituality, psychology and the creative arts.

COMMON GROUND (SAN ANSELMO); resources for personal transformation. see *NEW AGE PUBLICATIONS*

301.1 US
COMMON GROUND HAWAII. * 4/yr. $4. 750 Amana St., Ste. 301, Honolulu, HI 96814-5002. TEL 808-239-7190. adv.

370 US ISSN 0164-775X
COMMUNIQUE (SILVER SPRING). * 8/yr. $30. National Association of School Psychologists, 4340 East West Hwy., Ste. 402, Bethesda, MD 20814-4411. TEL 301-608-0500. FAX 301-608-2514. Ed. Peg Dawson. adv.; bk.rev. circ. 175,000. (tabloid format) **Document type:** newsletter.
  Description: Publishes practical professional articles to help school psychologists. Also includes research, job listings, convention information, organizational news, and legislative updates.

COMMUNITY MENTAL HEALTH JOURNAL. see *SOCIAL SERVICES AND WELFARE*

COMMUNITY PSYCHIATRY JOURNAL. see *MEDICAL SCIENCES — Psychiatry And Neurology*

370.15 150 IS
COMMUNITY STRESS PREVENTION. (Text in English and Hebrew) 1985. q. free. Community Stress Prevention Centre, Merkaz Habriut, Kiryat Shmona 10200, Israel. TEL 972-6-958827. FAX 972-6-950740. Eds. Mooli Lahad, Alan Cohen. bk.rev. circ. 100. **Document type:** bulletin.
  Formerly: School Psychology Emergency Centre. Newsletter.
  Description: Covers the work and activities of the Centre.

616.89 US
COMPASSIONATE FRIENDS NATIONAL NEWSLETTER. q. $15 (Canada $18; elsewhere $20). Compassionate Friends, Inc., 900 Jorie Blvd., Box 3696, Oak Brook, IL 60522-3696. TEL 708-990-0010. FAX 708-990-0246. Eds. Pat & Wayne Loder. **Document type:** newsletter.
  Formerly: Compassionate Friends Newsletter.
  Description: Written by and for bereaved parents.

616.89 US
COMPASSIONATE FRIENDS SIBLING NEWSLETTER; written by and for bereaved siblings. vol.4, no.2, 1993. q. $7.50 (Canada $10; elsewhere $15). Compassionate Friends, Inc., 900 Jorie Blvd., Box 3696, Oak Brook, IL 60522-3696. TEL 708-990-0010. FAX 708-990-0246. **Document type:** newsletter.

COMPREHENSIVE PSYCHIATRY. see *MEDICAL SCIENCES — Psychiatry And Neurology*

616.89 US ISSN 0275-7222
RC475
COMPREHENSIVE PSYCHOTHERAPY. 1980. irreg., vol.4, 1984. Gordon & Breach Science Publishers, c/o International Publishers Distributor, 820 Town Center Dr., Langhorne, PA 19047. TEL 215-750-2642. FAX 215-750-6343. (Subscr. to: International Publishers Distributor, P.O. Box 90, Reading, Berkshire RG1 8JL, England. TEL 44-173-456-8316) Ed. P. Olsen. (also avail. in microfilm; microfiche) **Document type:** monographic series.
  Refereed Serial

COMPUTERS IN HUMAN BEHAVIOR. see *SOCIOLOGY — Computer Applications*

PSYCHOLOGY

301.1 150   IT   ISSN 0392-7504
BF1
COMUNICAZIONI SCIENTIFICHE DI PSICOLOGIA GENERALE. 1976. s-a. L.62000 to individuals; institutions L.72000; foreign L.88000 (effective 1993). Edizioni Scientifiche Italiane S.p.A., Via Chiatamone, 7, 80121 Naples, Italy. TEL 081-7645768. FAX 081-7646477. Ed. Marta Olivetti Belardinelli.
Formerly (until 1981): Communicazioni Scientifiche della Cattedra di Psicologia Generale IV (ISSN 0392-7555)

150.9   FR   ISSN 0245-8829
CONFLUENTS PSYCHANALYTIQUES. 1980. irreg. Societe d'Edition les Belles Lettres, 95 bd. Raspail, 75006 Paris, France. TEL 1-45485826. FAX 1-45485860.

CONNECTICUT HOSPICE NEWSLETTER; making today count. see *PHYSICAL FITNESS AND HYGIENE*

153.4   US   ISSN 1053-8100
BF309
CONSCIOUSNESS AND COGNITION; an international journal. 1992. q. $202 (foreign $233) (effective 1996). Academic Press, Inc., Journal Division, 525 B St., Ste. 1900, San Diego, CA 92101-4495. TEL 619-230-1840. FAX 619-699-6800. (Subscr. to: Box 620000, Orlando, FL 32891-8340. TEL 800-543-9534) Eds. Bernard Baars, William Banks. bk.rev. (back issues avail.) **Indexed:** Chem.Abstr., Psychol.Abstr. (1992-). **Document type:** academic/scholarly publication.
—BLDSC (3417.864800); Faxon; Genuine Article; UnCover. **CCC.**
Description: Provides a forum for a natural-science approach to the issues of consciousness, voluntary control, and self. Features two types of articles: empirical research (in the form of regular articles and short reports) and theoretical articles.
Refereed Serial

152   US   ISSN 0146-5457
QP411
CONSCIOUSNESS AND SELF-REGULATION: ADVANCES IN RESEARCH AND THEORY. 1976. irreg, vol.4, 1986. price varies. Plenum Publishing Corp., 233 Spring St., New York, NY 10013-1578. TEL 212-620-8000. FAX 212-463-0742. TELEX 23-421139. Eds. Gary Schwartz, David Shapiro. **Document type:** monographic series.
—BLDSC (3417.865000).
Formerly: Consciousness and Self-Regulation: Advances in Research.
Refereed Serial

800 700   US   ISSN 1052-8164
NX165
CONSTRUCTIVE CRITICISM; a journal of construct psychology and the arts. 1991. s-a. $25 (foreign $30). Constructive Publishing, Inc., Box 162, Gambier, OH 43022. TEL 614-393-2834. Ed. Cintra Whitehead. film rev.; play rev.; bibl. (back issues avail.)
Description: Covers the application of construct psychology to the arts.

150.19   US   ISSN 1061-4087
BF637.C56
CONSULTING PSYCHOLOGY JOURNAL: PRACTICE AND RESEARCH.* 4/yr. $52 to non-members; members $26; institutions $73. American Psychological Association, Division of Consulting Psychology, 750 1st St., N.E., Washington, DC 20002-4242. TEL 202-336-5600. FAX 202-336-5568. Ed. H. Skipton Leonard. adv.: B&W page $175; trim 6 7/8 x 9 1/4; adv. contact: Jodi Ashcraft. circ. 1,050. **Indexed:** Psychol.Abstr. (1992-).
—BLDSC (3424.011000).
Description: Provides a source of knowledge and ideas in the field of consultation.

CONTEMPORARY EDUCATIONAL PSYCHOLOGY. see *EDUCATION*

301.4   US   ISSN 0892-2764
CONTEMPORARY FAMILY THERAPY; an international journal. 1979. q. $285 (foreign $335) (effective 1996). Human Sciences Press, Inc. (Subsidiary of: Plenum Publishing Corp.), 233 Spring St., New York, NY 10013-1578. TEL 212-620-8000. FAX 212-463-0742. Ed. William C. Nichols. adv.; bk.rev. (reprint service avail. from ISI,UMI) **Indexed:** Adol.Ment.Hlth.Abstr., ASSIA, Biol.Abstr., C.I.J.E., Curr.Cont., IMFL, Mult.Ed.Abstr., Past.Care & Couns.Abstr., Psychol.Abstr. (1979-), Soc.Work Res.& Abstr., Sp.Ed.Needs Abstr., SSCI, Stud.Wom.Abstr. **Document type:** academic/scholarly publication.
—BLDSC (3425.181810); Faxon; Genuine Article; UMI; UnCover. **CCC.**
Formerly (until 1986): International Journal of Family Therapy (ISSN 0148-8384)
Description: Presents latest theory, research, and practice with an emphasis on examination of the family within the socioeconomic matrix of which it is an integral part.
Refereed Serial

CONTEMPORARY HYPNOSIS. see *MEDICAL SCIENCES — Hypnosis*

616.89   US   ISSN 0010-7530
RC500   CODEN: CPPSBL
CONTEMPORARY PSYCHOANALYSIS. 1964. q. $55 to individuals (foreign $67); institutions $79.50 (foreign $91.50). William Alanson White Psychoanalytic Institute, 20 W. 74th St., New York, NY 10023. TEL 212-873-0725.
FAX 212-362-6967. Ed. Jay Greenberg. bk.rev.; index. circ. 1,650. (back issues avail.) **Indexed:** Biol.Abstr., Curr.Cont., Mid.East: Abstr.& Ind., Psychoanal.Abstr., Psychol.Abstr. (1968-), Soc.Work Res.& Abstr., Sociol.Abstr., SSCI. **Document type:** academic/scholarly publication.
—BLDSC (3425.230000); Faxon; Genuine Article; SWETS; UMI; UnCover. **CCC.**
Description: Presents a scholarly approach to the contemporary psychoanalytic scene. Covers a wide range of subjects, from schizophrenia and the neuroses, to group processes and community psychiatry, from a clinical perspective.
Refereed Serial

155   US   ISSN 0010-7549
BF1
CONTEMPORARY PSYCHOLOGY; a journal of reviews. 1956. m. $128 to non-members (foreign $168); members $64 (foreign $80); institutions $255 (foreign $339). American Psychological Association, 750 First St., N.E., Washington, DC 20002-4242. TEL 202-336-5600. FAX 202-336-5568. Ed. John H. Harvey. adv.; bk.rev.; film rev.; illus.; index. circ. 4,500. (also avail. in microform) **Indexed:** Adol.Ment.Hlth.Abstr., Biol.Abstr., Bk.Rev.Ind. (1975-), Chic.Per.Ind., Child.Bk.Rev.Ind. (1975-), Curr.Cont., Mult.Ed.Abstr., Risk Abstr., SSCI. **Document type:** academic/scholarly publication.
—BLDSC (3425.250000); Faxon; Genuine Article; SWETS; UMI; UnCover. **CCC.**
Description: Publishes articles dealing with new concepts, trends and issues in every arena of psychology.
Refereed Serial

150   UK
CONTEMPORARY PSYCHOLOGY SERIES. irreg., vol.10, 1994. Taylor & Francis Ltd., Rankine Rd., Basingstoke, Hants RG24 8PR, England. TEL 01256-840366. FAX 01256-479438. Ed. Mary McMurran. **Document type:** monographic series.

616.89   UK   ISSN 0969-1936
CONTEXT (CANTERBURY); a news magazine of family therapy. 1989. q. £9.50. A F T Publishing, 47 St. Augustine Rd., Canterbury, Kent CT1 14R, England. TEL 44-227-452155. (Subscr. to: Association for Family Therapy, 18 Winnipeg Dr., Lakeside, Cardiff CF2 6ET, Wales. TEL 44-222-753162) Ed. John Hills. adv. contact: Kate Hills. bk.rev.; film rev.; play rev.; index. circ. 1,600. (back issues avail.) **Document type:** bulletin.
Description: Covers the study and psychotherapeutic treatment of families.

616.89   BL
CONTRIBUICOES EM PSICOLOGIA, PSIQUIATRIA E PSICANALISE. irreg. Editora Campus Ltda. (Subsidiary of: Elsevier Science B.V.), Rua Sete de Setembro 111-16 andar, 20159-900 Centro, Rio de Janeiro RJ, Brazil. TEL 021-222-5340. FAX 021-252-2904. **Document type:** monographic series.

150   US   ISSN 0736-2714
CONTRIBUTIONS IN PSYCHOLOGY. 1983. irreg. price varies. Greenwood Press, Inc. (Subsidiary of: Greenwood Publishing Group Inc.), 88 Post Rd. W., Box 5007, Westport, CT 06881-5007. TEL 203-226-3571. FAX 203-222-1502. bibl.; index.
—BLDSC (3461.153000).

155.4   US
CONTRIBUTIONS TO RESIDENTIAL TREATMENT. 1957. a. $20. American Association of Children's Residential Centers, 1021 Prince St., Alexandria, VA 22314-2971. TEL 703-838-7522. FAX 703-684-5968. Ed. Claudia C. Waller. circ. 200. (back issues avail.) **Document type:** proceedings.

616.8   US   ISSN 0093-1551
RC321
CORRECTIVE AND SOCIAL PSYCHIATRY AND JOURNAL OF BEHAVIORAL TECHNOLOGY METHODS AND THERAPY. 1954. q. $60 (foreign $65). Martin Psychiatric Research Foundation, Box 3365, Fairfield, CA 94533-0587. FAX 7078640910. Ed. Dr. Clyde V. Martin. adv.; bk.rev.; film rev.; charts; illus. circ. 1,200. (also avail. in microform from UMI; back issues avail.; reprint service avail. from KTO) **Indexed:** Adol.Ment.Hlth.Abstr., Chic.Per.Ind., Crim.Just.Abstr., Curr.Cont., Excerp.Med., Mid.East: Abstr.& Ind., Psychol.Abstr., SSCI.
—BLDSC (3472.172000); Faxon; UMI; UnCover.
Formerly: Corrective and Social Psychiatry and Journal of Applied Behavior Therapy (ISSN 0091-2611); **Supersedes:** Corrective Psychiatry and Journal of Social Therapy (ISSN 0010-9053)
Refereed Serial

COUNSELING AND VALUES. see *RELIGIONS AND THEOLOGY — Roman Catholic*

157.9   US   ISSN 0011-0000
BF637.C6   CODEN: CPSYB
THE COUNSELING PSYCHOLOGIST. 1973. q. $55 to individuals; institutions $184 (effective Sep. 1995). (American Psychological Association, Division 17) Sage Publications, Inc., 2455 Teller Rd., Thousand Oaks, CA 91320. TEL 805-499-0721. FAX 805-499-0871. E-mail: libraries@sagepub.com. (Overseas subscr. to: Sage Publications Ltd., 6 Bonhill St., London EC2A 4PU, England; Sage Publications India Pvt. Ltd., P.O. Box 4215, New Delhi 110 048, India) Ed. Gerald L. Stone. adv. circ. 5,400. (also avail. in microform from UMI; back issues avail.; reprint service avail. from UMI) **Indexed:** Adol.Ment.Hlth.Abstr., C.I.J.E., Curr.Cont., Educ.Ind., IMFL, Mid.East: Abstr.& Ind., Psychol.Abstr. (1969-), Soc.Sci.Ind., SSCI, Viol.& Abuse Abstr. **Document type:** academic/scholarly publication.
—BLDSC (3481.330000); Faxon; SWETS; UMI; UnCover. **CCC.**
Description: Presents timely coverage, especially in new or developing areas of practice and research, of topics of immediate interest to counseling psychologists.

371.42   US   ISSN 1078-8719
COUNSELING TODAY. 1958. m. $37 to individuals; institutions $49 (effective 1996). American Counseling Association, 5999 Stevenson Ave., Alexandria, VA 22304-3300. TEL 703-823-9800. FAX 703-823-0252. (Subscr. to: Box 2513, Birmingham, AL 35201-2513. TEL 205-995-1567. FAX 205-995-1588) Ed. Jennifer L. Sacks. adv.; B&W page $1872, color page $2572. bk.rev.; film rev. circ. 60,000. (tabloid format; reprint service avail. from UMI)
—UnCover. **CCC.**
Formerly: Guidepost (ISSN 0017-5323)

PSYCHOLOGY

616.89   UK   ISSN 0264-9977
CODEN: CPQUEZ
COUNSELLING. q. £26 (N. America £33). British Association for Counselling, 1 Regent Pl., Rugby, Warks. CV21 2PJ, England. TEL 01788-550899. FAX 01788-562189. Ed. Stephen Palmer. adv. contact: Sally Cook. bk.rev.; index. circ. 12,000. (also avail. in magnetic tape; back issues avail.) **Document type:** academic/scholarly publication, newsletter.
—BLDSC (3481.337000).
    Description: Directed to those interested in working in counselling and psychotherapy and to members of related professions, including nursing and teaching.
Refereed Serial

150 616.8   UK   ISSN 0951-5070
CODEN: CPQUEZ
COUNSELLING PSYCHOLOGY QUARTERLY. 1988. q. £54 to individuals; institutions £196 (effective 1996). Carfax Publishing Co., P.O. Box 25, Abingdon, Oxon. OX14 3UE, England. TEL 01235-555335. FAX 01235-553559. (Subscr. in N. America to: Carfax Publishing Co., 875-81 Massachusetts Ave., Cambridge, MA 02139) Ed. W.J. Alladin. adv.; bk.rev. (also avail. in microfiche) **Indexed:** Mult.Ed.Abstr., Psychol.Abstr. (1988-), Sp.Ed.Needs Abstr. **Document type:** academic/scholarly publication.
—BLDSC (3481.338300); UMI; UnCover. **CCC**.
Refereed Serial

371.4   US   ISSN 0011-0035
CODEN: CESUDZ
COUNSELOR EDUCATION AND SUPERVISION. 1961. 4/yr. $18 to individuals; institutions $36 (effective 1996). (Association for Counselor Education and Supervision) American Counseling Association, 5999 Stevenson Ave., Alexandria, VA 22304-3300. TEL 703-823-9800. FAX 703-823-0252. (Subscr. to: Box 2513, Birmingham, AL 35201-2513. TEL 205-995-1567. FAX 205-995-1588) Ed. Margaret L. Fong. adv.; index. circ. 4,200. (also avail. in microform from UMI; reprint service avail. from UMI) **Indexed:** A.D.&D., C.I.J.E., Cont.Pg.Educ., Curr.Cont., Educ.Ind., Mult.Ed.Abstr., Psychol.Abstr. (1966-), Sp.Ed.Needs Abstr., SSCI.
—BLDSC (3481.350000); Faxon; SWETS; UMI; UnCover. **CCC**.
    Description: Covers theory, practice and research on pre-service and in-service preparation and supervision.

CREATIVE CHILD AND ADULT QUARTERLY. see *CHILDREN AND YOUTH — About*

301.1 150   US   ISSN 1040-0419
CREATIVITY RESEARCH JOURNAL. 1988. q. $45 to individuals (foreign $70); institutions $110 (foriegn $135). Lawrence Erlbaum Associates, Inc., 10 Industrial Dr., Mahwah, NJ 07430-2262. TEL 201-236-9500. FAX 201-236-0072. Ed. Mark Runco. adv.: page $425; 7 x 10. abstr.; bibl. circ. 400. (back issues avail.; reprint service avail.) **Indexed:** Psychol.Abstr. (1988-). **Document type:** academic/scholarly publication.
—BLDSC (3487.252000); Genuine Article; UnCover.
    Description: Publishes scholarly research capturing the full range of approaches to the study of creativity: aesthetic, behavioral, clinical, cognitive, cross-cultural, developmental, educational, genetic, organizational, psychoanalytic, and psychometric.

CRIMINAL JUSTICE & BEHAVIOR; an international journal. see *CRIMINOLOGY AND LAW ENFORCEMENT*

157.744   US   ISSN 0227-5910
CRISIS; the journal of crisis intervention and suicide prevention. 1980. q. $49. (International Association for Suicide Prevention) Hogrefe & Huber Publishers, Box 2487, Kirkland, WA 98083. TEL 206-820-1500. FAX 206-823-8324. Eds. D.C. Clark, A.J.F.M. Kerkhof. adv. **Indexed:** Ind.Med., Psychol.Abstr. (1980-), Soc.Sci.Ind. **Document type:** academic/scholarly publication.
—BLDSC (3487.382350); Faxon.
    Description: Articles on the research and clinical aspects of how to prevent suicides, and how to intervene in severe emotional crises.

150   US   ISSN 1064-5136
CODEN: CITTEW
▼**CRISIS INTERVENTION AND TIME-LIMITED TREATMENT**. 1994. 3/yr. 48 ECU (effective 1996). Harwood Academic Publishers, c/o International Publishers Distributor, 820 Town Center Dr., Langhorne, PA 19047. TEL 215-750-2642. FAX 215-750-6343. (Subsc. to: International Publishers Distributor, PO Box 90, Reading, Berkshire, RG1 8JL, England. TEL 44-173-456-8316) (also avail. in microform)
—**CCC**.
    Description: Focuses on the latest clinical innovations and research of those working in crisis intervention settings.

618.92   US
CRITICAL ISSUES IN DEVELOPMENTAL & BEHAVIORAL PEDIATRICS. 1987. irreg., latest 1993. price varies. Plenum Publishing Corp., 233 Spring St., New York, NY 10013-1578. TEL 212-620-8000. FAX 212-463-0742. TELEX 23-421139. Ed. Martin Gottlieb. (back issues avail.) **Document type:** monographic series.
    Formerly: Developmental and Behavioral Pediatrics: Selected Topics.
Refereed Serial

150   NE   ISSN 0926-5430
CROSS CULTURAL PSYCHOLOGY MONOGRAPHS. (Text in English) 1991. irreg., no.4, 1994. Tilburg University Press, Postbus 90153, 5000 LE Tilburg, Netherlands. TEL 31-13-662909. FAX 31-13-662996. (back issues avail.) **Document type:** monographic series.

CROSS-CULTURAL RESEARCH; the journal of comparative social science. see *SOCIAL SCIENCES: COMPREHENSIVE WORKS*

150 301.2   US
CROSS-CULTURAL RESEARCH METHODS. 1977. irreg. price varies. Sage Publications, Inc., 2455 Teller Rd., Thousand Oaks, CA 91320. TEL 805-499-0721. FAX 805-499-0871. E-mail: libraries@sagepub.com. (Overseas subscr. to: Sage Publications Ltd., 6 Bonhill St., London EC2A 4PU, England; Sage Publications India Pvt. Ltd., P.O. Box 4125, New Delhi 110 048, India) Eds. Walter J. Lonner, John W. Berry. (back issues avail.) **Document type:** monographic series.
    Former titles: Sage Series in Cross-Cultural Research and Methodology; Cross-Cultural Reseearch and Methodology Series.

150   CK   ISSN 0120-4653
CUADERNOS DE PSICOLOGIA. 1976. 2/yr. $10. Universidad del Valle, Departmento de Psicologia, Apdo. Aereo 25360, Cali, Colombia. FAX 23-392311. Dir. Sonia Meluk. adv.; bk.rev. circ. 1,000. **Indexed:** Psychol.Abstr. **Document type:** academic/scholarly publication.

157   US
CULT AWARENESS NETWORK NEWS; alerting the world to the dangers of destructive cults. 1980. m. $35 (foreign $45). Cult Awareness Network, 2421 W. Pratt Blvd., Ste. 1173, Chicago, IL 60645. TEL 312-267-7777. Ed. Cynthia S. Kisser. bk.rev. circ. 2,000. (tabloid format; back issues avail.) **Document type:** newsletter.
    Description: News briefs and feature articles on destructive cults, indoctrination and conversion techniques, and legal and social issues concerning cult activity.

155.4   US
CULTURAL CONTEXT OF INFANCY. 1989. irreg., vol.2, 1991. price varies. Ablex Publishing Corporation, 355 Chestnut St., Norwood, NJ 07648. TEL 201-767-8450. FAX 201-767-6717. TELEX 135-393. Ed. J. Kevin Nugent. **Document type:** academic/scholarly publication.

CULTURAL DIVERSITY AND MENTAL HEALTH. see *SOCIOLOGY*

150 301   UK   ISSN 1354-067X
CODEN: CUPSFQ
▼**CULTURE & PSYCHOLOGY**. 1995. q. £32 to individuals; institutions £99 (effective 1996). Sage Publications Ltd., 6 Bonhill St., London EC2A 4PU, England. TEL 0171-374-0645. FAX 0171-374-8741. E-mail: market@sageltd.co.uk. Ed. Jaan Valsiner. adv.: B&W page £180; trim 176 x 109; adv. contact: Bernie Folan. **Indexed:** ASSIA, Sociol.Abstr. **Document type:** academic/scholarly publication.
—BLDSC (3491.668740).
    Description: Interdisciplinary journal that develops a critical and socially embedded understanding of the self by drawing on diverse literatures and theoretical perspectives.

150.19   UK   ISSN 0963-7214
BF1   CODEN: CDPSE8
CURRENT DIRECTIONS IN PSYCHOLOGICAL SCIENCE. 1992. bi-m. £80($132) (effective 1996). (American Psychological Society) Cambridge University Press, Edinburgh Bldg., Shaftsbury Rd., Cambridge CB2 2RU, England. TEL 01223-312393. FAX 01223-315052. TELEX 851817256. (N. American addr.: Cambridge University Press, Journals Dept., 40 W. 20th St., New York, NY 10011. TEL 212-924-3900. FAX 212-691-3239) Eds. Sandra W. Scarr, Charles R. Gallistel. adv.; bk.rev. (back issues avail.) **Indexed:** Psychol.Abstr. (1992-). **Document type:** academic/scholarly publication.
—BLDSC (3496.357000); Genuine Article; UMI; UnCover. **CCC**.
    Description: Contains concise reviews of important trends and controversies in psychology.

616.89   US
CODEN: CIPPEY
CURRENT ISSUES IN PSYCHOANALYTIC PRACTICE. MONOGRAPHS. 1984. irreg. price varies. Brunner-Mazel Publishing Co., 19 Union Sq. W., New York, NY 10003. TEL 212-924-3344. FAX 212-242-6339. Ed. Herbert S. Strean. (back issues avail.) **Indexed:** Excerp.Med., Psychol.Abstr. **Document type:** academic/scholarly publication, monographic series.
—BLDSC (3499.075500).
    Formerly: Current Issues in Psychoanalytic Practice. Journal (ISSN 0737-7851)

150   US
CURRENT PSYCHOLOGY (HENDERSONVILLE). 1979. m. $25. Psychological Press, Box 309, Hendersonville, TN 37075. (also avail. in microform from UMI) **Indexed:** Psychol.Abstr.

150   US   ISSN 1046-1310
BF1
CURRENT PSYCHOLOGY (NEW BRUNSWICK); developmental - learning - personality - social. 1981. q. $68 to individuals (foreign $100); institutions $136 (foreign $168) (effective Aug. 1995). Transaction Publishers, Transaction Periodicals Consortium, Department 3092, Rutgers University, New Brunswick, NJ 08903. TEL 908-445-2280. FAX 908-445-3138. (Subscr. in Europe and Israel to: Swets & Zeitlinger bv, Heereweg 347, 2161 CA Lisse, Netherlands. TEL 31-2521-35111. FAX 31-2521-15888) Eds. Noel P. Sheehy, Nathaniel Pallone. circ. 400. **Indexed:** Curr.Cont., HRIS, IMFL, Psychol.Abstr. (1981-), Sage Fam.Stud.Abstr., Soc.Sci.Ind. **Document type:** academic/scholarly publication.
—BLDSC (3501.601000); Faxon; Genuine Article; SWETS; UMI; UnCover. **CCC**.
    Former titles: Current Psychological Research and Reviews (ISSN 0737-8262); Current Psychological Research; Current Psychological Reviews.
    Description: Provides an international forum for the rapid dissemination of psychological information.
Refereed Serial

150   US   ISSN 8755-0040
BF431
CURRENT TOPICS IN HUMAN INTELLIGENCE. 1985. irreg., vol.2, 1991. price varies. Ablex Publishing Corporation, 355 Chestnut St., Norwood, NJ 07648. TEL 201-767-8450. FAX 201-767-6717. TELEX 135-393. Ed. Douglas Detterman. **Indexed:** Psychol.Abstr. **Document type:** academic/scholarly publication.
—BLDSC (3504.883950).

PSYCHOLOGY

370.15 150   **US**
CURRENT TOPICS IN LEARNING DISABILITIES. 1984. irreg. price varies. Ablex Publishing Corporation, 355 Chestnut St., Norwood, NJ 07648. TEL 201-767-8450. FAX 201-767-6717. TELEX 135-393. Eds. James McKinney, Lynne Feagans. **Document type:** academic/scholarly publication.

150 301   **PL**   **ISSN 0239-3271**
CZŁOWIEK I SPOŁECZEŃSTWO. (Text in Polish, occasionally in English) 1984. a., vol.10, 1993. (Adam Mickiewicz University, Institute of Sociology) Adam Mickiewicz University Press, Nowowiejskiego 55, 61-734 Poznan, Poland. TEL 527-380. TELEX 413260 UAM PL. Ed.Bd. bk.rev. circ. 300. (back issues avail.) **Document type:** academic/scholarly publication.
—BLDSC (3508.529000).
   Description: Covers psychology, sociology and education.

616.89   **GW**   **ISSN 0935-2066**
D G I P - INTERN. 1982. q. membership. Deutsche Gesellschaft fuer Individualpsychologie e.V., Marktstr. 12, 99867 Gotha, Germany. TEL 03621-29691. Ed. Horst Groener. adv.; bk.rev. circ. 1,800. **Document type:** newsletter.

DANMARKS LAERERHOEJSKOLE. INSTITUT FOR PAEDAGOGIK OG PSYKOLOGI. TESTSAMLING. see *EDUCATION*

DARSHANA INTERNATIONAL; an international quarterly of philosophy, psychology, sociology, psychical research, religion and mysticism. see *PHILOSOPHY*

DAY CARE AND EARLY EDUCATION. see *SOCIAL SERVICES AND WELFARE*

150   **CC**
DAZHONG XINLIXUE/POPULAR PSYCHOLOGY.* (Text in Chinese) bi-m. Huadong Shifan Daxue, Jiaoyu Kexue Xueyuan - East China Normal University, School of Education, c/o Zeng Xingchu, Ed., 3663 Zhongshan Beilu, Shanghai 200062, People's Republic of China. TEL 2518532. (Co-sponsor: Shanghai Society of Psychology)

613   **US**   **ISSN 0161-4835**
DEATH. 1978. m. $9.95. Bad Seed, Inc., 116 W. 14th St., New York, NY 10011. TEL 212-898-8001. Ed. Mara Mills. adv. circ. 250,000. (tabloid format)

155.937   **US**   **ISSN 0273-2483**
HQ1073.5.U6
DEATH AND DYING. (Subseries of: S I R S Social Issues (ISSN 0740-3127)) 1979. a. price varies; a. supplement $17. Social Issues Resources Series, Box 2348, Boca Raton, FL 33427-2348. TEL 407-994-0079; 800-232-7477. FAX 407-994-4704. (looseleaf format; also avail. in microfiche; back issues avail.)
   Description: Reprints important articles that examine social, philosophical, and ethical aspects of death.

150   **US**   **ISSN 0748-1187**
BF789.D4   **CODEN: DESTEA**
DEATH STUDIES; education - counseling - care - law - ethics. 1977. bi-m. £106($175) (effective 1996). Taylor & Francis Inc., 1900 Frost Rd., Ste. 101, Bristol, PA 19007-1598. TEL 215-785-5800; 800-821-8312. FAX 215-785-5515. (Subscr. in Europe to: Taylor & Francis Ltd., Rankine Rd., Basingstoke, Hants. RG24 8PR, England. TEL 44-1256-840366. FAX 44-1256-479438) Ed. Robert A. Neimeyer. adv.; bk.rev.; abstr.; bibl.; charts; illus.; index. circ. 800. (also avail. in microform from UMI; back issues avail.; reprint service avail. from UMI) **Indexed:** Abstr.Soc.Geront., C.I.J.E., CERDIC, CINAHL, Cont.Pg.Educ., Curr.Cont., Excerp.Med., Mult.Ed.Abstr., Past.Care & Couns.Abstr., Per.Islam. (1991-), Psychol.Abstr. (1977-), Res.High.Educ.Abstr., Risk Abstr., Sage Fam.Stud.Abstr., Soc.Work Res.& Abstr., Sociol.Abstr., Sp.Ed.Needs Abstr., SSCI. **Document type:** academic/scholarly publication.
—BLDSC (3535.960460); Faxon; Genuine Article; SWETS; UnCover. **CCC.**
   Formerly (until 1985): Death Education (ISSN 0145-7624)
   Description: Provides an international and interdisciplinary forum in the field of death studies. Refereed papers cover education, counseling, bioethics, and psychosocial research.
Refereed Serial

150.19   **FR**
DECOUVERTE FREUDIENNE. 3/yr. 230 F. (effective 1992). (Universite de Toulouse II (le Mirail)) Presses Universitaires du Mirail, 56 rue du Taur, 31000 Toulouse, France. TEL 61-22-58-31. FAX 61-21-84-20. (back issues avail.)

616.89   **US**   **ISSN 1062-6417**
   CODEN: DRESES
DEPRESSION. 1993. bi-m. $168 (foreign $261) (effective 1996). John Wiley & Sons, Inc., Journals, 605 Third Ave., New York, NY 10158. TEL 212-850-6645. FAX 212-850-6021. TELEX 12-7063. E-mail: SUBINFO@JWILEY.COM. (Subscr. outside the Americas to: John Wiley & Sons Ltd., Baffins Ln., Chichester, W. Sussex PO19 1UD, England. TEL 44-1243-779777. FAX 44-1243-776128) Ed. Charles B. Nemeroff. (also avail. in microform from UMI; back issues avail.) **Indexed:** Excerp.Med. (1994-), Psychol.Abstr. (1993-). **Document type:** academic/scholarly publication.
—BLDSC (3554.590030).
Refereed Serial

616.89   **US**
▼**DEPRESSION AND STRESS.** 1995. s-a. $45 (foreign $84) to individuals; institutions $65 (foreign $104). International Universities Press, Inc., 59 Boston Post Rd., Box 1524, Madison, CT 06443-1524. TEL 203-245-4000. FAX 203-245-0775. Eds. George Pollock, Harold Visotsky. **Document type:** academic/scholarly publication.
   Description: Makes various views and contributions available on the entire topic of depression and stress.
Refereed Serial

150   **UK**   **ISSN 0954-5794**
RC454.4
DEVELOPMENT AND PSYCHOPATHOLOGY. 1989. q. £75($130) (effective 1996). Cambridge University Press, Edinburgh Building, Shaftesbury Rd., Cambridge CB2 2RU, England. TEL 01223-312393. FAX 01223-315052. TELEX 851817256. (N. American addr.: Cambridge University Press, Journals Dept., 40 W. 20th St., New York, NY 10011. TEL 212-924-3900. FAX 212-691-3239) Eds. Dante Cicchetti, Barry Nurcombe. adv. (back issues avail.) **Indexed:** IMFL, Psychol.Abstr. (1989-). **Document type:** academic/scholarly publication.
—BLDSC (3578.855000); Faxon; Genuine Article; SWETS; UMI; UnCover. **CCC.**
   Description: Devoted to the publication of original empirical, theoretical and review papers that address the interrelationship of normal and pathological development in adults and children.
Refereed Serial

155 613.62   **US**   **ISSN 0279-4098**
DEVELOPMENTAL DISABILITIES SPECIAL INTEREST SECTION NEWSLETTER. (Consists of 11 sections: Administration and Management; Developmental Disabilities; Education; Gerontology; Home & Community Health; Mental Health; Physical Disabilities; School Systems; Sensory Integration; Technology; Work Programs) vol.12, no.2, 1989. q. $15. American Occupational Therapy Association, Inc., Box 31220, Bethesda, MD 20824-1220. TEL 301-652-2682. FAX 301-652-7711. **Document type:** newsletter.
   Formerly: American Occupational Therapy Association. Developmental Disabilities Specialty Section. Newsletter (ISSN 0194-6390)

370.15   **US**   **ISSN 8756-5641**
   CODEN: DENEE8
DEVELOPMENTAL NEUROPSYCHOLOGY; an international journal of life-span issues in neuropsychology. 1985. q. $47.50 to individuals (foreign $72.50); institutions $195 (foreign $220). Lawrence Erlbaum Associates, Inc., 10 Industrial Dr., Mahwah, NJ 07430-2262. TEL 201-236-9500. FAX 201-236-0072. Ed. Dennis L. Molfese, Francis J. Pirozzolo. adv.: page $375; 5 x 8. circ. 750. (back volumes avail.) **Indexed:** Psychol.Abstr. (1985-). **Document type:** academic/scholarly publication.
—BLDSC (3579.057300); Faxon; SWETS; UMI; UnCover.
   Description: Covers issues concerning the structure and function of both the developing and the aging brain.
Refereed Serial

DEVELOPMENTAL PSYCHOBIOLOGY. see *BIOLOGY*

155   **US**   **ISSN 0012-1649**
BF699   **CODEN: DEVPA9**
DEVELOPMENTAL PSYCHOLOGY. 1969. bi-m. $122 to non-members (foreign $142); members $61 (foreign $71); institutions $243 (foreign $286). American Psychological Association, 750 First St., N.E., Washington, DC 20002-4242. TEL 202-336-5600. FAX 202-336-5568. Ed. Carolyn Zahn-Waxler. adv. contact: Jodi Ashcraft. bibl.; charts; stat. circ. 5,500. (also avail. in microform from UMI; reprint service avail. from UMI; back issues avail.) **Indexed:** Abstr.Crim.& Pen., Adol.Ment.Hlth.Abstr., ASSIA, Bibl.Dev.Med.& Child Neur., Bibl.Ling., Biol.Abstr., C.I.J.E., Child Devel.Abstr., Commun.Abstr., Crim.Just.Abstr., Curr.Adv.Ecol.Sci., Curr.Cont., Energy Ind., Energy Info.Abstr., M.L.A., Mid.East: Abstr.& Ind., Mult.Ed.Abstr., Psychol.Abstr. (1969-), Psycscan D.P., Soc.Sci.Ind., Soc.Work Res.& Abstr., Sp.Ed.Needs Abstr., SSCI, Stud.Wom.Abstr. **Document type:** academic/scholarly publication.
—BLDSC (3579.059000); Faxon; Genuine Article; SWETS; UMI; UnCover. **CCC.**
   Description: Empirical contributions that advance knowledge and theory about human psychological growth and development from infancy to old age.
Refereed Serial

150   **US**   **ISSN 0273-2297**
BF721
DEVELOPMENTAL REVIEW; perspectives in behavior and cognition. 1981. q. $142 (foreign $172) (effective 1996). Academic Press, Inc., Journal Division, 525 B St., Ste. 1900, San Diego, CA 92101-4495. TEL 619-230-1840. FAX 619-699-6800. (Subscr. to: Box 620000, Orlando, FL 32891-8340. TEL 800-543-9534) Ed. Grover J. Whitehurst. adv.; index. (back issues avail.) **Indexed:** Child Devel.Abstr., Psychol.Abstr. (1981-), Psycscan D.P., SSCI. **Document type:** academic/scholarly publication.
—BLDSC (3579.059780); Faxon; Genuine Article; SWETS; UnCover. **CCC.**
   Description: Provides child and developmental, child clinical, and educational psychologists with articles that reflect current thinking and covers scientific developments.
Refereed Serial

157   **US**
DEVELOPMENTS IN CLINICAL PSYCHOLOGY. 1984. irreg. price varies. Ablex Publishing Corporation, 355 Chestnut St., Norwood, NJ 07648. TEL 201-767-8450. FAX 201-767-6717. TELEX 135-393. Ed. Glenn R. Caddy. **Document type:** academic/scholarly publication.

DEVIANCE ET SOCIETE. see *SOCIOLOGY*

DEVIANT BEHAVIOR; an interdisciplinary journal. see *SOCIOLOGY*

DI CYAN BULLETIN. see *MEDICAL SCIENCES — Psychiatry And Neurology*

150   **US**
DIAGNOSIS AND TREATMENT OF MENTAL DISORDERS. irreg. (approx. 1/yr.) Guilford Publications, Inc., 72 Spring St., New York, NY 10012. TEL 212-431-9800; 800-365-7006. FAX 212-966-6708. Ed. Allen Frances; Pub. Robert Matloff. **Document type:** monographic series.
   Description: Dedicated to diagnosing and treating specific mental disorders or groups of disorders, especially borderline personality disorder.

155.28   **GW**   **ISSN 0012-1924**
   CODEN: DGNSAQ
DIAGNOSTICA; Zeitschrift fuer psychologische Diagnostik, zugleich Informationsorgan ueber psychologische Tests und Untersuchungsmethoden. (Text in German; summaries in English) 1955. q. DM.94. Hogrefe Verlag fuer Psychologie, Rohnsweg 25, 37085 Goettingen, Germany. TEL 0551-496090. FAX 0551-4960988. Ed. H. Westmeyer. adv.; bk.rev.; bibl.; charts. circ. 1,200. (also avail. in microfiche from UMI) **Indexed:** Biol.Abstr., Ger.J.Psych., Psychol.Abstr. (1964-). **Document type:** academic/scholarly publication.
—BLDSC (3579.670000); SWETS.

PSYCHOLOGY

150 US
DIALOGUES IN CONTEMPORARY PSYCHOLOGY SERIES. 1981. irreg. price varies. Praeger Publishers (Subsidiary of: Greenwood Publishing Group Inc.), 88 Post Rd. W., Box 5007, Westport, CT 06881-5007. TEL 203-226-3571. FAX 203-222-1502. **Document type:** monographic series.

DIDAKOMETRY AND SOCIOMETRY. see *EDUCATION*

DIMENSIONS (RIMROCK). see *PARAPSYCHOLOGY AND OCCULTISM*

301.1 US
DIPLOMATE. 1981. s-a. membership. American Board of Professional Psychology, 2100 E. Broadway, Ste. 313, Columbia, MO 65201-6082. TEL 314-875-1267. FAX 314-443-1199. Ed. Robert W. Goldberg. circ. 2,500 (controlled). (looseleaf format; back issues avail.) **Document type:** newsletter.

616.89 US ISSN 1062-0788
DIRECTIONS IN MENTAL HEALTH COUNSELING. 1991. m. $145. Hatherleigh Company Ltd., 420 E. 51st St., New York, NY 10022. TEL 212-355-0882; 800-367-2550. FAX 212-308-7930. Eds. Barbara Herlimy, Gerald Corey. index. (looseleaf format; back issues avail.; reprint service avail.) **Document type:** academic/scholarly publication.
  Description: Presents developments in mental health counseling. Approved by various boards for continuing education credits.

DIRECTORY FOR EXCEPTIONAL CHILDREN; a listing of educational and training facilities. see *EDUCATION — Special Education And Rehabilitation*

DIRECTORY OF GRADUATE TRAINING IN BEHAVIOR THERAPY. see *EDUCATION — Guides To Schools And Colleges*

DIRECTORY OF PSYCHOLOGY INTERNSHIPS: PROGRAMS OFFERING BEHAVIORAL TRAINING. see *EDUCATION — Guides To Schools And Colleges*

157.744 US
DIRECTORY OF SUICIDE PREVENTION AND CRISIS INTERVENTION CENTERS. a. $15. American Association of Suicidology, 4201 Connecticut Ave., N.S. Ste, 310, Washington, DC 20008-1158. TEL 303-692-0985. **Document type:** directory.

156 FR ISSN 0766-5350
DIRES. 2/yr. 70 F. Universite de Montpellier (Universite Paul Valery), Centre d'Etudes Freudiennes de Montpellier, B.P. 5043, 34032 Montpellier Cedex 1, France. TEL 67-14-20-00. bk.rev.
  Description: Presents poetical and analytical research.

150 301 UK ISSN 0957-9265
P302 CODEN: DISOEN
DISCOURSE & SOCIETY. 1990. q. £32 to individuals; institutions £95 (effective 1996). Sage Publications Ltd., 6 Bonhill St., London EC2A 4PU, England. TEL 0171-374-0645. FAX 0171-374-8741. E-mail: market@sageltd.co.uk. Ed. Teun A. van Dijk. adv.: B&W page £180; trim 190 x 114; adv. contact: Bernie Folan. **Indexed:** Bibl.Ling., Commun.Abstr., Curr.Cont., Film Lit.Ind., IBZ, Int.Bibl.Soc.Sci., Int.Polit.Sci.Abstr., Lang.& Lang.Behav.Abstr., Ling.Abstr., M.L.A., Sociol.Abstr., SSCI. **Document type:** academic/scholarly publication.
—BLDSC (3595.810000); SWETS; UnCover.
  Description: Explores the relevance of discourse analysis to the social sciences, with a particular focus on the political implications of discourse and communication.
  Refereed Serial

616.89 US ISSN 0896-2863
DISSOCIATION; progress in the dissociative disorders. 1988. q. $48 to individuals; institutions $60; members $36. International Society for the Study of Multiple Personality and Dissociation, 5700 Old Orchard Rd., 1st Fl., Skokie, IL 60077. **Indexed:** Psychol.Abstr. (1988-). **Document type:** academic/scholarly publication.
—BLDSC (3602.503500); UnCover.
  Refereed Serial

DOBUTSU SHINRIGAKU KENKYU/JAPANESE JOURNAL OF ANIMAL PSYCHOLOGY. see *BIOLOGY — Zoology*

616.891 FR ISSN 0012-477X
DOCUMENTS ET DEBATS. 1970. irreg. (4-5/yr.). membership. Association Psychoanalytique de France, 24 Place Dauphine, 75006 Paris, France. Ed. Dr. G. Rosolato. bk.rev.; abstr.; bibl. circ. 200. (processed) **Document type:** bulletin.
  Description: Explores psychoanalytic techniques.

155.3 236 367 US
DOMINANT NEWSLETTER. 1975. 10/yr. $20. Skye Publishing, Box 324, Riverside, IL 60546. Ed. Jonathan Lee. adv.; bk.rev. circ. 300. (looseleaf format; back issues avail.)

150 JA ISSN 0389-312X
DOSHISHA SHINRI/DOSHISHA PSYCHOLOGICAL REVIEW. (Text in Japanese) a. Doshisha Daigaku, Bungakubu, Shinrigaku Kenkyushitsu - Doshisha University, Faculty of Letters, Department of Psychology, 601, Genbucho, Karasuma Higashi Iru, Imadegawa Dori, Kamigyo-ku, Kyoto 602, Japan.

616.891 792 US
DRAMASCOPE. s-a. $10 (effective 1994). National Association for Drama Therapy, 2022 Cutter Dr., League City, TX 77573. TEL 713-538-1689. Ed. Nina Strongylov. adv. contact: Kathryn Templeton-Chalfont. bk.rev. (looseleaf format) **Document type:** newsletter.
  Description: Publishes news, information and resources of interest to drama and creative arts therapists.

DREAM NETWORK; a quarterly journal exploring dreams and myth. see *NEW AGE PUBLICATIONS*

DREAM SWITCHBOARD. see *EDUCATION*

DREAMING. see *BIOLOGY — Physiology*

616.89 AT ISSN 1030-2883
DULWICH CENTRE NEWSLETTER. 1987. q. Aus.$40 (overseas $28). Dulwich Centre Publications, Hutt St., P.O. Box 7192, Adelaide, S.A. 5000, Australia. TEL 61-8-2233966. FAX 61-8-2324441. (N. American subscr. to: Yaletown Family Therapy, Box 34185, Sta. D, Vancouver, BC V6J 4N1, Canada) Ed. Cheryl White. **Document type:** newsletter.
—BLDSC (3631.036625); UnCover.
  Description: Explores the question how workers form different cultural and gender positions can protect against gender and cultural bias in their work on a day-to-day basis.

155.4 UK ISSN 1057-3593
HQ771 CODEN: EDPAEA
EARLY DEVELOPMENT AND PARENTING; an international journal of research and practice. 1992. q. $165 (foreign $165) (effective 1996). John Wiley & Sons Ltd., Journals, Baffins Ln., Chichester, W. Sussex PO19 1UD, England. TEL 01243-779777. FAX 01243-776128. TELEX 86290 WIBOOK G. (Subscr. in the Americas to: John Wiley & Sons, Inc., 605 Third Ave., New York, NY 10158. TEL 212-850-6645. FAX 212-850-6021) Ed.Bd. circ. 162. (also avail. in microform from UMI; back issues avail.) **Document type:** academic/scholarly publication.
—BLDSC (3642.960900); Genuine Article; UMI. CCC.
  Description: Contains theoretical, empirical and methodological papers covering all aspects related to psychological development during infancy and early childhood.
  Refereed Serial

EARLY EDUCATION AND DEVELOPMENT. see *EDUCATION*

616.89 US ISSN 1064-0266
EATING DISORDERS; the journal of treatment and prevention. 1992. q. $38 to individuals (foreign $46); institutions $80 (foreign $88). Brunner-Mazel Publishing Co., 19 Union Sq. W., New York, NY 10003. TEL 212-924-3344. FAX 212-242-6339. Ed. Leigh Cohn. **Document type:** academic/scholarly publication.
—BLDSC (3646.939100).
  Description: Provides a wide range of practical and informative viewpoints for professionals involved in the treatment of and education in eating disorders.

EATING DISORDERS REVIEW; current clinical information for the professional treating eating disorders. see *NUTRITION AND DIETETICS*

370.1 US ISSN 1040-7413
BF353 CODEN: ECPSEN
ECOLOGICAL PSYCHOLOGY. 1989. q. $36 to individuals (foreign $61); institutions $180 (foreign $205). (International Society for Ecological Psychology) Lawrence Erlbaum Associates, Inc., 10 Industrial Dr., Mahwah, NJ 07430-2262. TEL 201-236-9500. FAX 201-236-0072. Ed. William Mace. adv.: page $275; 5 x 8. **Indexed:** Psychol.Abstr. (1989-). **Document type:** academic/scholarly publication.
—BLDSC (3649.050000); SWETS; UnCover.
  Description: Presents empirical, theoretical, and methodological papers in the form of research reports, target articles and commentary.
  Refereed Serial

EDUCATION AND PSYCHOLOGY REVIEW. see *EDUCATION*

370.15 150 155.4 UK
EDUCATIONAL & CHILD PSYCHOLOGY. 1984. q. £28 (overseas £33) (effective 1995). British Psychological Society, Division of Educational and Child Psychology, St. Andrews House, 48 Princess Rd. E., Leicester LE1 7DR, England. Ed. Peter Graves. circ. 1,000. (back issues avail.) **Indexed:** Psychol.Abstr. (1985-). **Document type:** academic/scholarly publication.
—BLDSC (3661.363300).
  Formerly: British Psychology Society. Division of Educational and Child Psychology. Papers (ISSN 0267-1611)
  Description: Deals with the research and professional practice of educational and child psychology.
  Refereed Serial

370 150 SW ISSN 0070-9263
LB1051 CODEN: EPINDT
EDUCATIONAL AND PSYCHOLOGICAL INTERACTIONS. (Text in English) 1964. irreg. Malmoe School of Education, Inst. foer Pedagogik och Specialmetodik, Box 23501, S-200 45 Malmoe, Sweden. FAX 46-40-325-210. Ed. Aake Bjerstedt. (back issues avail.) **Indexed:** Child Devel.Abstr., Cont.Pg.Educ., Educ.Tech.Abstr., Mult.Ed.Abstr., Psychol.Abstr., Sociol.Abstr., Sp.Ed.Needs Abstr.
—BLDSC (3661.365000).

155.28 370.15 US ISSN 0013-1644
BF1 CODEN: EPMEAJ
EDUCATIONAL AND PSYCHOLOGICAL MEASUREMENT; devoted to the development and application of measures of individual differences. 1941. q. $75 to individuals; institutions $152 (effective Sep. 1995). 2455 Teller Rd., Thousand Oaks, CA 91320. TEL 805-499-0721. FAX 805-499-0871. E-mail: libraries@sagepub.com. (Subscr. to: Sage Publications, Inc., Box 5084, Thousand Oaks, CA 91359; Overseas subscr. to: Sage Publications Ltd., 6 Bonhill St., London EC2A 4PU, England; Sage Publications India Pvt. Ltd., P.O. Box 4215, New Delhi 110 048, India) Ed. Bruce Thompson. bk.rev.; bibl.; charts; index. circ. 2,700. (also avail. in microform from UMI; back issues avail.; reprint service avail. from UMI) **Indexed:** Acad.Ind., Adol.Ment.Hlth.Abstr., C.I.J.E., Chem.Abstr., CINAHL, Compumath, Cont.Pg.Educ., Educ.Ind., Except.Child.Educ.Abstr., High.Educ.Curr.Aware.Bull., Mark.Res.Abstr. (1963-), Mid.East: Abstr.& Ind., Pers.Lit., Psychol.Abstr. (1941-), Psycscan, Res.High.Educ.Abstr., Soc.Sci.Ind. (1994-), Sp.Ed.Needs Abstr., SSCI. **Document type:** academic/scholarly publication.
—BLDSC (3661.366000); Faxon; SWETS; UnCover. CCC.
  Description: Discusses problems in the field of measuring individual differences and reports research on the development and use of tests and measurements in education.

PSYCHOLOGY 5483

370.15 US ISSN 0046-1520
LB1051 CODEN: EDPSDT
EDUCATIONAL PSYCHOLOGIST. 1963. q. $39.50 to individuals (foreign $64.50); institutions $190 (foreign $215). (American Psychological Association, Division of Educational Psychology) Lawrence Erlbaum Associates, Inc., 10 Industrial Dr., Mahwah, NJ 07430-2262. TEL 201-236-9500. FAX 201-236-0072. Ed. Gavriel Salomon. adv.: page $425; 7 x 10. index. circ. 3,700. (also avail. in microform from UMI; reprint service avail. from UMI) **Indexed:** Educ.Ind., Mult.Ed.Abstr., Psychol.Abstr. (1973-), Tech.Educ.Abstr. **Document type:** academic/scholarly publication.
—BLDSC (3661.530000); Faxon; SWETS; UMI; UnCover.
  Description: Provides detailed explorations of new educational concepts and accepted educational practices.
  Refereed Serial

370.15 180 UK ISSN 0144-3410
LB1051 CODEN: EDPSFV
EDUCATIONAL PSYCHOLOGY; an international journal of experimental educational psychology. 1981. q. £57 to individuals; institutions £198 (effective 1996). Carfax Publishing Co., P.O. Box 25, Abingdon, Oxon. OX14 3UE, England. TEL 01235-555335. FAX 01235-553559. (Subscr. in N. America to: Carfax Publishing Co., 875-81 Massachusetts Ave., Cambridge, MA 02139) Eds. Kevin Wheldall, Richard Riding. adv.; bk.rev.; stat.; index. circ. 1,000. (also avail. in microfiche) **Indexed:** Child Devel.Abstr., Child.Lit.Abstr., Cont.Pg.Educ., Mult.Ed.Abstr., Psychol.Abstr (1981-), Sociol.Educ.Abstr., SOMA, Sp.Ed.Needs Abstr., Stud.Wom.Abstr., Tech.Educ.Abstr. **Document type:** academic/scholarly publication.
—BLDSC (3661.535000); Faxon; SWETS; UMI; UnCover. CCC.
  Refereed Serial

370.15 150 UK ISSN 0266-7363
EDUCATIONAL PSYCHOLOGY IN PRACTICE. 4/yr. £99 (Europe £101; elsewhere £110). (Association of Educational Psychologists) Pitman Publishing, 128 Long Acre, London WC2E 9AN, England. TEL 0171-379-7383. FAX 0171-240-5771. (Subscr. to: Journals Dept., Fourth Ave., Harlow, Essex CM19 5AA, England. TEL 01279-623924) Ed. Phil Stringer. adv.; bk.rev.; bibl.; illus.; index. circ. 2,800. (also avail. in microfilm; back issues avail.; reprint service avail. from UMI) **Indexed:** Cont.Pg.Educ., Psychol.Abstr. (1974-), Tech.Educ.Abstr. **Document type:** academic/scholarly publication.
—BLDSC (3661.540000); UMI; UnCover.
  Formerly: A E P Journal (ISSN 0309-3573)
  Description: Features new ideas and the latest developments, plus informational articles about the practical aspects of educational psychology.
  Refereed Serial

EDUCATIONAL PSYCHOLOGY REVIEW. see *EDUCATION*

158 RU ISSN 0321-2173
EKSPERIMENTAL'NAYA I PRIKLADNAYA PSIKHOLOGIYA. 1968. irreg. 0.80 Rub. per issue. Sankt-Peterburgskii Universitet, Universitetskaya Nab. 7-9, St. Petersburg V-164, Russia. circ. 5,150.

150 RU
EKSPERIMENTAL'NOE ISSLEDOVANIE LICHNOSTI I TEMPERAMENTA. (Subseries of: Permskii Gosudarstvennyi Pedagogicheskii Institut. Uchenye Zapiski) irreg. 0.50 Rub. Permskii Gosudarstvennyi Pedagogicheskii Institut, Perm, Russia. Ed. Bronislaw Aleksandrovich Vyatkin. illus.

371.4 US ISSN 0013-5976
LB1027.5 CODEN: ESGCD7
ELEMENTARY SCHOOL GUIDANCE & COUNSELING. 1965. 4/yr. $45 to individuals; institutions $49 (effective 1996). (American School Counselor Association) American Counseling Association, 5999 Stevenson Ave., Alexandria, VA 22304-3300. TEL 703-823-9800. FAX 703-823-0252. (Subscr. to: Box 2513, Birmingham, AL 35201-2513. TEL 205-995-1567. FAX 205-995-1588) Ed. Edwin Gerler, Jr. adv.; bk.rev.; charts; stat.; index. circ. 18,000. (also avail. in microform from UMI; reprint service avail. from UMI) **Indexed:** C.I.J.E., Cont.Pg.Educ., Educ.Ind., Mult.Ed.Abstr., Psychol.Abstr. (1968-), Sp.Ed.Needs Abstr.
—BLDSC (3727.150000); Faxon; SWETS; UMI; UnCover. CCC.
  Description: Focuses on issues of interest to elementary, middle school and junior high school counselors, principals and teachers, and mental health professionals who counsel children and families.

150 US
EMOTION; theory, research and experience. 1980. irreg., vol.5, 1990. Academic Press, Inc., 525 B St., Ste. 1900, San Diego, CA 92101-4495. TEL 619-231-0926. FAX 619-699-6715. (Subscr. to: Order Dept., 6277 Sea Harbor Dr., 4th Fl., Orlando, Fl 32887. TEL 800-321-5068) (reprint service avail. from ISI)
  Refereed Serial

155.3 530.01 GW ISSN 0720-0579
EMOTION; Wilhelm-Reich-Zeitschrift ueber Triebenergie, Charakterstruktur, Krankheit, Natur und Gesellschaft. 1980. s-a. DM.20. (Wilhelm-Reich-Initiative Berlin) Nexus-Verlag, Fichardstr. 38, 60322 Frankfurt a.M., Germany. Ed.Bd. adv.; bk.rev.; cum.index. circ. 3,000. (back issues avail.)

EMPLOYEE TESTING & THE LAW; reporting legal, technical, and business developments in employee testing. see *BUSINESS AND ECONOMICS — Personnel Management*

EMPORIA STATE RESEARCH STUDIES. see *HISTORY — History Of North And South America*

616.89 US
ENCOUNTERER. 1971. irreg. $5 for 20 nos. Golden Gate Foundation for Group Treatment, Box 1141, Vallejo, CA 94590. Ed. Dr. F.H. Ernst.

370.15 US
ENCYCLOPEDIC DICTIONARY OF PSYCHOLOGY. irreg., 3rd ed., 1985. $14.95. Dushkin Publishing Group, Sluice Dock, Guilford, CT 06437-9989. TEL 203-453-4351. FAX 203-453-6000. Ed. Terry F. Pettijohn; Pub. Rick Connelly. illus.

150 GW ISSN 0938-3522
ENERGIE UND CHARAKTER. 1990. 2/yr. DM.30. Gottschedstr. 2, 13357 Berlin, Germany. TEL 030-4653882. FAX 030-6223140. Eds. David Boadella, Bernhard Maul. adv.: page DM.500; adv. contact: Bernhard Maul. index; circ. 1,000. (back issues avail.) **Document type:** academic/scholarly publication.

150 US ISSN 1050-5326
RC489.B5
ENERGY & CONSCIOUSNESS. 1991. s-a. $25. Institute of Core Energetics, 115 E. 23rd St., New York, NY 10010. TEL 212-982-9637. Ed. Jacqueline Carleton. adv. contact: Joan Groom. bk.rev. **Document type:** academic/scholarly publication.

ENFANCE; psychologie, pedagogie, neuro-psychiatrie, sociologie. see *CHILDREN AND YOUTH — About*

ENGRAMI. see *MEDICAL SCIENCES — Psychiatry And Neurology*

158 MX ISSN 0185-1594
ENSENANZA E INVESTIGACION EN PSICOLOGIA. 1975. a. Mex.$290($25) Consejo Nacional para la Ensenanza e Investigacion en Psicologia, c/o Universidad Iberoamericana, Prol. Paseo de la Reforma 880, Lomas de Santa Fe, 01210 Mexico D.F., Mexico. Ed. Dr. Juan Lafarga. adv.; bk.rev.; abstr.; bibl.; index. circ. 1,000. (also avail. in microfilm from UMI; reprint service avail. from UMI) **Indexed:** Biol.Abstr., Psychol.Abstr. **Document type:** academic/scholarly publication.

150 AG
ENTREDICHOS. 1983. m. La Rioja 718, Buenos Aires, Argentina.

ENVIRONMENT AND BEHAVIOR. see *SOCIOLOGY*

EOS; revista Argentina de arte y psicoanalisis. see *ART*

EQUINE BEHAVIOUR. see *SPORTS AND GAMES — Horses And Horsemanship*

ERGONOMIA; prodotti, lavoro, ricerca. see *ENGINEERING*

ERGONOMICS; an international journal of research and practice in human factors and ergonomics. see *ENGINEERING*

ERGONOMICS IN DESIGN; the magazine of human factors applications. see *ENGINEERING*

THE ERGONOMIST. see *ENGINEERING*

150 US
ESALEN CATALOG. 1961. 3/yr. $15. Esalen Institute, Big Sur, CA 93920. TEL 408-667-3000. FAX 408-667-2724. Ed. Margaret Livingston. circ. 25,000. **Document type:** catalog.

ESSENTIALS OF ADOLESCENCE.* 1975. m. (11/yr.). $25. PeopleScience, Inc., 20 Pine Valley Ln., Jamesburg, NJ 08831-2705. Ed. Fred Streit. circ. 2,200. (back issues avail.)
  Formerly: Essence of Adolescence.

150 SP ISSN 0210-9395
BF5
ESTUDIOS DE PSICOLOGIA. 1980. s-a. Aprendizaje, S.L., Ctr. de Canillas 138, 2o 16C, 28043 Madrid, Spain. TEL 388-38-74. FAX 300-35-27. Ed. Angel Riviere. adv. circ. 1,100.
—SWETS.
  Description: Publishes empirical research, theoretical essays and bibliographic reviews in the field of current general psychology.
  Refereed Serial

301.1 150 IT ISSN 0392-0658
RJ131
ETA EVOLUTIVA; rivista di scienze dello sviluppo. (Text in Italian; summaries in English) 1978. 3/yr. L.70000 (foreign L.80000). Giunti Gruppo Editoriale S.p.A., Via Bolognese 165, 50139 Florence, Italy. TEL 055-66791. FAX 055-6679298. Ed. Dr. Massimo Casini. adv. contact: Alessandro Mantegazzini. circ. 2,000. (back issues avail.) **Indexed:** Psychol.Abstr. (1979-). **Document type:** academic/scholarly publication.
—BLDSC (3814.194000).
  Description: Contains theoretical work and experimental research on the evolutive age, covering several areas of interest: psychology, sociology, pedagogy, genetics, and psychoanalysis.

370.15 150 US ISSN 1050-8422
BJ1725
ETHICS & BEHAVIOR. 1991. q. $27.50 to individuals (foreign $52.50); institutions $170 (foreign $195). Lawrence Erlbaum Associates, Inc., 10 Industrial Dr., Mahwah, NJ 07430-2262. TEL 201-236-9500. FAX 201-236-0072. Ed. Gerald P. Koocher. adv.: page $375; 5 x 8. bk.rev. **Indexed:** Psychol.Abstr. (1991-). **Document type:** academic/scholarly publication.
—BLDSC (3814.655500); UnCover.
  Description: Publishes articles on an array of topics pertaining to various moral issues and conduct.
  Refereed Serial

150 GW ISSN 0940-9882
ETHNOPSYCHOLOGISCHE MITTEILUNGEN. (Text in German; summaries in English, German) 1992. s-a. DM.40. Universitaet Koblenz-Landau, Fachbereich Psychologie, Im Fort 7, 76829 Landau, Germany. TEL 06341-280249. FAX 06341-280101. Ed. Renaud van Quekelberghe. bk.rev. circ. 140. **Document type:** academic/scholarly publication.

ETHOLOGY. see *BIOLOGY — Zoology*

ETOLOGIA. see *BIOLOGY — Zoology*

PSYCHOLOGY

150   GW   ISSN 0942-7600
EUROPAEISCHE COLLEGIUM FUER BEWUSSTSEINSTUDIEN. JAHRBUCH. 1991. a. DM.36. V W B - Verlag fuer Wissenschaft und Bildung, Markgrafenstr. 67, 10969 Berlin, Germany. TEL 030-2510415. FAX 030-2510412. Eds. Hanscarl Leuner, Michael Schlichting. (back issues avail.) **Document type:** academic/scholarly publication.
— **Description:** Researches altered states of consciousness caused by psychological procedures or psycho-active substances.

157 301.1   UK   ISSN 1072-4133
RC552.E18   CODEN: EEDRE8
EUROPEAN EATING DISORDERS REVIEW. 1986. q. $115 (efective 1996). (Eating Disorders Association) John Wiley & Sons Ltd., Journals, Baffins Ln., Chichester, W. Sussex PO19 1UD, England. TEL 01243-779777. FAX 01243-776218. TELEX 86290 WIBOOK G. (Subscr. in the Americas to: John Wiley & Sons, Inc., 605 Third Ave., New York, NY 10158. TEL 212-850-6645. FAX 212-850-6021) Ed. Alan Cockett. adv.; bk.rev. circ. 419. (also avail. in microform from UMI; back issues avail.) **Indexed:** Excerp.Med., Psychol.Abstr. **Document type:** academic/scholarly publication.
—BLDSC (3829.693600); Genuine Article.
Former titles (until 1994): Eating Disorders Review (ISSN 1067-1633); (until 1993): British Review of Bulimia and Anorexia Nervosa (ISSN 0950-3005)
Description: Covers all aspects of bulimia and anorexia nervosa for the complete range of professionals who deal with patients suffering from these eating disorders.
Refereed Serial

EUROPEAN JOURNAL FOR HIGH ABILITY. see *CHILDREN AND YOUTH — About*

155   UK   ISSN 0954-1446
BF309   CODEN: EJCPEW
EUROPEAN JOURNAL OF COGNITIVE PSYCHOLOGY. 1989. q. £55($98) to individuals (outside the E.U. 60); institutions £115 (outside the E.U. £120 ($205)) (effective 1996). (European Society for Cognitive Psychology) Lawrence Erlbaum Associates Ltd., 27 Palmeira Mansions, Church Rd., Hove, E. Sussex BN3 2FA, England. TEL 01273-207411. FAX 01273-205612. (Subscr. to: Turpin Distribution Services Ltd., Blackhorse Rd., Letchworth, Herts. SG6 1HN, England. TEL 01462-672555. FAX 01462-480947) Ed. Lars-Goran Nilsson. adv.: page £175; 100 x 180. **Indexed:** Bibl.Ling., Psychol.Abstr. (1989-), Sociol.Abstr. **Document type:** academic/scholarly publication.
—BLDSC (3829.728150); SWETS; UnCover.
Formerly: European Cognitive Psychology.
Description: Focuses on articles of either a theoretical or a review nature to provide an integrated rather than empirical approach.
Refereed Serial

156   UK   ISSN 0890-2070
BF698.A1
EUROPEAN JOURNAL OF PERSONALITY. (Text in English; summaries in English, French and German) 1987. 5/yr. $425 (foreign $425) (effective 1996). (European Association of Personality Psychology) John Wiley & Sons Ltd., Journals, Baffins Ln., Chichester, W. Sussex PO19 1UD, England. TEL 02143-779777. FAX 01243-776128. TELEX 86290 WIBOOK G. (Subscr. in the Americas to: John Wiley & Sons, Inc., 605 Third Ave., New York, NY 10158. TEL 212-850-6645. FAX 212-850-6021) Ed. G. Van Heck. bk.rev. circ. 291. (also avail. in microform from UMI; back issues avail.; reprint service avail. from SWZ) **Indexed:** Curr.Cont., Mult.Ed.Abstr., Psychol.Abstr. (1987-). **Document type:** academic/scholarly publication.
—BLDSC (3829.733800); Genuine Article; SWETS; UMI; UnCover. **CCC.**
Description: Reflects all areas of current research in personality psychology with emphasis on human individuality.

152   US   ISSN 1015-5759
EUROPEAN JOURNAL OF PSYCHOLOGICAL ASSESSMENT. 3/yr. $54 to individuals; institutions $78. (European Association of Psychological Assessment) Hogrefe & Huber Publishers, Box 2487, Kirkland, WA 98083. TEL 206-820-1500; 800-228-3749. FAX 206-823-8324. Eds. R. Fernandez-Ballesteros, F. Silva. **Indexed:** Psychol.Abstr. (1985-). **Document type:** academic/scholarly publication.
—BLDSC (3829.737800).
Description: Presents articles which provide seminal information on both theoretical and applied developments in the field of psychological testing.

EUROPEAN JOURNAL OF PSYCHOLOGY OF EDUCATION. see *EDUCATION*

301.1   UK   ISSN 0046-2772
HM251   CODEN: EJSPA6
EUROPEAN JOURNAL OF SOCIAL PSYCHOLOGY. 1971. 9/yr. $595 (foreign $595) (effective 1996). John Wiley & Sons Ltd., Journals, Baffins Ln., Chichester, W. Sussex PO19 1UD, England. TEL 01243-779777. FAX 01243-776128. TELEX 86290 WIBOOK G. (Subscr. in the Americas to: John Wiley & Sons, Inc., 605 Third Ave., New York, NY 10158. TEL 212-850-6645. FAX 212-850-6021) Ed. Nick Emler. adv.; bk.rev.; charts. circ. 1,355. (also avail. in microform from UMI; back issues avail.; reprint service avail. from ISI,SWZ,UMI) **Indexed:** Adol.Ment.Hlth.Abstr., ASSIA, Commun.Abstr., Curr.Cont., Excerp.Med., Lang.& Lang.Behav.Abstr., Mid.East: Abstr.& Ind., Mult.Ed.Abstr., Psychol.Abstr. (1971-), Sp.Ed.Needs Abstr., SSCI, Stud.Wom.Abstr. **Document type:** academic/scholarly publication.
—BLDSC (3829.739000); Faxon; Genuine Article; SWETS; UMI; UnCover. **CCC.**
Description: Promotes communication among social psychology researchers in Europe and provides a bridge between European and other research traditions.
Refereed Serial

158.7   UK   ISSN 1359-432X
                                CODEN: EWOPED
EUROPEAN JOURNAL OF WORK AND ORGANIZATIONAL PSYCHOLOGY. 1991. q. £40 to individuals (outside the E.U. £45($72)); institutions £80 (outside the E.U. £85($144)) (effective 1996). (International Association of Applied Psychology) Lawrence Erlbaum Associates Ltd., 27 Palmeira Mansions, Church Rd., Hove, E. Sussex BN3 2FA, England. TEL 01273-207411. FAX 01273-205612. (Subscr. to: Turpin Distribution Services Ltd., Blackhorse Rd., Letchworth, Herts. SG6 1HN, England. TEL 01462-672555. FAX 01462-480947) Ed. Charles De Wolff. adv.: page £175; 115 x 190. bk.rev. **Document type:** academic/scholarly publication.
—BLDSC (3830.370850).
Formerly: European Work and Organizational Psychologist (ISSN 0960-2003)
Description: Provides a bridge between academies who enlarge the knowledge base of work psychology and practitioners who apply this knowledge to clients and organizations.

301.15   US   ISSN 0892-7286
EUROPEAN MONOGRAPHS IN SOCIAL PSYCHOLOGY. 1971. irreg., no.35, 1985. (European Association of Experimental Social Psychology) Academic Press, Inc., 525 B St., Ste. 1900, San Diego, CA 92101-4495. TEL 619-231-0926. FAX 619-699-6715. (Subscr. to: Order Dept., 6277 Sea Harbor Dr., 4th Fl., Orlando, FL 32887. TEL 800-321-5068) Ed. H. Tajfel. (reprint service avail. from ISI) **Indexed:** Psychol.Abstr. **Document type:** monographic series.

150   NE
EUROPEAN RESEARCH IN BEHAVIOUR THERAPY. (Text in English) irreg., vol.10, 1992. Swets & Zetlinger bv, Heereweg 347, 2161 CA Lisse, Netherlands. TEL 31-2521-35111. FAX 31-2521-15888. (Dist. in N. America by: Swets & Zeitlinger, 440 Creamery Way, Ste. A, Exton, PA 19341. TEL 800-447-9387. FAX 610-524-5366) **Document type:** proceedings.

301.1 150   UK   ISSN 1046-3283
HM251   CODEN: ERSPEW
EUROPEAN REVIEW OF SOCIAL PSYCHOLOGY. 1990. 1/yr. $9 (foreign $9) (effective 1996). John Wiley & Sons Ltd., Journals, Baffins Ln., Chichester, W. Sussex PO19 1UD, England. TEL 01243-779777. FAX 01243-776218. TELEX 86290 WIBOOK G. (Subscr. in the Americas to: John Wiley & Sons, Inc., 605 Third Ave., New York, NY 10158. TEL 212-850-6645. FAX 212-850-6021) Eds. W. Stroebe, M. Hewstone. circ. 68. (also avail. in microform from UMI; back issues avail.) **Document type:** academic/scholarly publication.
—BLDSC (3829.953300); UMI. **CCC.**
Description: Reflects the dynamism of social psychology in Europe and the attention now paid to European ideas and research.
Refereed Serial

155   AU   ISSN 0938-2623
EVOLUTION AND COGNITION. 1991. 4/yr. DM.260. Springer-Verlag, Sachsenplatz 4-6, Postfach 89, A-1201 Vienna, Austria. TEL 0222-3302415. FAX 0222-3302426. (U.S. subscr. to: Springer-Verlag New York, Inc., Box 2485, Secaucus, NJ 07096-2491. TEL 201-348-4033) Ed. F.M. Wuketits. (also avail. in microfilm from UMI; back issues avail.) **Document type:** academic/scholarly publication.
—**CCC.**
Description: Interdisciplinary forum devoted to all aspects of cognition, at both the animal and human level.

EVOLVING WOMAN. see *WOMEN'S INTERESTS*

EXCEPTIONAL CHILDREN. see *CHILDREN AND YOUTH — About*

EXISTENZANALYSE. see *MEDICAL SCIENCES — Psychiatry And Neurology*

612.67   US   ISSN 0361-073X
QP86   CODEN: EAGRDS
EXPERIMENTAL AGING RESEARCH. 1975. q. £100($165) (effective 1996). Taylor & Francis, 1900 Frost Rd., Ste. 101, Bristol, PA 19007-1598. TEL 215-785-5800; 800-821-8312. FAX 215-785-5515. (Subscr. in the U.K. to: Taylor & Francis Ltd., Rankine Rd., Basingstoke, Hants. RG24 0PR, England. TEL 44-1256-840366. FAX 44-1256-479438) Ed. Jeffrey W. Elias. adv. contact: Louis Fancher. bk.rev.; illus.; index. circ. 1,500. (also avail. in microform from UMI; back issues avail.; reprint service avail. from UMI) **Indexed:** Abstr.Soc.Geront., Behav.Med.Abstr., Biol.Abstr., Chem.Abstr., CINAHL, CLOA, Curr.Cont., Excerp.Med., Helminthol.Abstr., Ind.Med., Ind.Sci.Rev., INIS Atomind., NRN, Psychol.Abstr. (1975-), Sci.Cit.Ind. **Document type:** academic/scholarly publication.
—BLDSC (3838.570000); CASDDS; Faxon; Genuine Article; SWETS; UMI; UnCover.
Description: Takes a multidisciplinary, scientific approach in dealing with all areas of scientific inquiry, human and animal, involving aging and the elderly.

150 615   US   ISSN 1064-1297
RM315   CODEN: ECLPES
EXPERIMENTAL AND CLINICAL PSYCHOPHARMACOLOGY. 1993. q. $60 to non-members (foreign $75); members $30 (foreign $75); institutions $120 (foreign $150). American Psychological Association, 750 First St., N.E., Washington, DC 20002-4242. TEL 202-336-5600. FAX 202-336-5568. Ed. Charles Schuster. circ. 1,900. **Indexed:** Excerp.Med. (1995-), Psychol.Abstr. (1993-). **Document type:** academic/scholarly publication.
—BLDSC (3838.654000).
Description: Advances research and development of theory in psychopharmacology.

EXPERT EVIDENCE; international digest of human behaviour science and law. see *LAW*

FALLING LEAF. see *MILITARY*

PSYCHOLOGY

392 301　　　　　GW　　ISSN 0342-2747
FAMILIENDYNAMIK; interdisziplinaere Zeitschrift fuer systemorientierte Praxis und Forschung. 1976. q. DM.115. Verlag Klett-Cotta, Rotebuehlstr. 77, 70178 Stuttgart, Germany. TEL 0711-6672-0. FAX 0711-6159702. Eds. Helm Stierlin, Josef Duss-von Werdt. adv.: B&W page DM.925; trim 180 x 113; adv. contact: Winifred Kretschmar. circ. 3,800. **Document type:** academic/scholarly publication.
—BLDSC (3865.553900). **CCC.**

FAMILIENMAGAZIN. see *CHILDREN AND YOUTH — About*

150 306.8　　　　　US　　ISSN 1066-4807
RC488.5
THE FAMILY JOURNAL; counseling and therapy for couples and families. 1993. q. $38 (effective 1996). (International Association of Marriage and Family Counselors) American Counseling Association, 5999 Stevenson Ave., Alexandria, VA 22304-3300. TEL 703-823-9800. FAX 703-823-0252. (Subscr. to: Box 2513, Birmingham, AL 35201-2513. TEL 205-995-1567. FAX 205-995-1588) Ed. Jon Carlson. circ. 7,000.
—BLDSC (3865.564279); UMI. **CCC.**
Description: Emphasizes practical information based on the most up-to-date research and therapies on marriage and family counseling.

150 370　　　　　US　　ISSN 0732-9962
HQ10
FAMILY LIFE EDUCATOR. 1982. 4/yr. $35 to individuals; institutions $55. E T R Associates, Box 1830, Santa Cruz, CA 95061-1830. TEL 408-438-4060. FAX 408-438-4284. Ed. Kay Clark; Pub. Mary Nelson. bk.rev.; abstr.; bibl. circ. 3,500. **Document type:** academic/scholarly publication.
—UnCover.
Description: For educators in the field of family life education at the middle school and high school levels, including relevant articles, news, and teaching tools.

FAMILY PERSPECTIVE. see *SOCIOLOGY*

158　　　　　US　　ISSN 0014-7370
RC488.5.A1　　　　　CODEN: FAPRA
FAMILY PROCESS.* 1962. q. $27 to individuals; institutions $44. Family Process, Inc., 70 W. Allendale Ave., Ste. D, Allendale, NJ 07401-1798. TEL 201-612-9868. FAX 201-612-9892. (Subscr. to: Box 6889, Syracuse, NY 13217) Ed. Peter Steinglass. adv.; bk.rev.; abstr.; bibl.; charts; index. circ. 12,000. (also avail. in microform from UMI; back issues avail.; reprint service avail. from SWZ,UMI) **Indexed:** Adol.Ment.Hlth.Abstr., ASSIA, CINAHL, Commun.Abstr., Curr.Cont., Excerp.Med., IMFL, Ind.Med., Lang.& Lang.Behav.Abstr., Mid.East: Abstr.& Ind., Mult.Ed.Abstr., Past.Care & Couns.Abstr., Psychol.Abstr. (1962-), Sage Fam.Stud.Abstr., Soc.Work Res.& Abstr., SSCI, Stud.Wom.Abstr.
—BLDSC (3865.576000); Faxon; Genuine Article; SWETS; UMI; UnCover. **CCC.**
Description: Covers family mental health and psychotherapy.

157.61　　　　　US　　ISSN 0739-0882
RC488.5
FAMILY THERAPY NETWORKER. 1982. bi-m. $20. Family Therapy Network, Inc., 7705 13th St., N.W., Washington, DC 20012. TEL 202-829-2452. FAX 202-726-7983. (Subscr. to: 8528 Bradford Rd., Silver Spring, MD 20901. TEL 301-589-6536) Ed. Richard Simon. adv.: B&W page $850, color page $1350. bk.rev. circ. 60,000. (back issues avail.) **Indexed:** Soc.Work Res.& Abstr.
—BLDSC (3865.576390); Faxon; UnCover.
Description: Professional journal for social workers, psychologists, therapists and educators.

301.4　　　　　US　　ISSN 0277-6464
FAMILY THERAPY NEWS. 1969. bi-m. $20 to individuals; institutions $35. American Association for Marriage and Family Therapy, 1100 17th St. N.W., 10th Fl., Washington, DC 20036. Ed. Joan Goldberg. adv.: B&W page $1400. circ. 21,000. (reprint service avail. from UMI) **Document type:** newsletter.
Formerly: American Association for Marriage and Family Therapy Newsletter.

150 305.4　　　　　UK　　ISSN 0959-3535
HQ1206　　　　　CODEN: FEPSFF
FEMINISM & PSYCHOLOGY. 1991. q. £32 to individuals; institutions £96 (effective 1996). Sage Publications Ltd., 6 Bonhill St., London EC2A 4PU, England. TEL 0171-374-0645. FAX 0171-374-8741. E-mail: market@sageltd.co.uk. Ed. Sue Wilkinson. adv.: B&W page £200; trim 185 x 114; adv. contact: Bernie Folan. bk.rev. **Indexed:** ASCA, Curr.Cont., IBZ, Mult.Ed.Abstr., Psychol.Abstr. (1991-), Psychol.Abstr., Sage Fam.Stud.Abstr., SSCI, Stud.Wom.Abstr., Wom.Stud.Abstr. **Document type:** academic/scholarly publication.
—BLDSC (3905.195980); Faxon.
Description: Fosters the development of feminist theory and practice in psychology and represents the concerns of women in a wide range of contexts across the academic-applied 'divide'.
Refereed Serial

157.7　　　　　US
FEMME MIRROR. 1976. q. $35. Tri Ess, Box 194, Tulane, CA 93275. TEL 209-688-9246. Ed. Carol Beecroft. circ. 1,200. **Document type:** consumer publication.
Description: For heterosexual transvestites and cross-dressers

FILOZOFSKI FAKULTET - ZADAR. RAZDIO FILOZOFIJE, PSIHOLOGIJE, SOCIOLOGIJE I PEDAGOGIJE. RADOVI. see *PHILOSOPHY*

150　　　　　US
FLORIDA PSYCHOLOGIST. 1950. bi-m. $60 to non-members. Florida Psychological Association, 408 Office Plaza, Tallahassee, FL 32301-2757. TEL 904-656-2222. FAX 904-942-4586. E-mail: flapsya@freenet.scri.fsu.edu. Ed. Michelle Morris. adv.: page $275; 7 1/2 x 10. bk.rev; bibl. circ. 1,700. **Document type:** newsletter.
Formerly: F P (ISSN 0046-4171)

614.58
FOCUS (ALEXANDRIA). 1980. q. $15. National Mental Health Association, 1021 Prince St., Alexandria, VA 22314-2971. TEL 703-684-7722. FAX 703-684-5968. Ed. Anne T. Salassi. bk.rev. circ. 10,000. (tabloid format; back issues avail.) **Document type:** newsletter.
Description: Provides information on issues of relevance to state and local Mental Health Associations, consumers of mental health services, advocates, policy-makers, researchers, mental health professionals and other service providers.

301.1 150　　　　　IT　　ISSN 0393-5418
FOGLI DI INFORMAZIONE. (Text in Italian; summaries in English) 1972. m. L.100000($30) Cooperativa Centro di Documentazione, Via Orafi 29, Casella Postale 347, 51100 Pistoia, Italy. TEL 0573-367144.

616.89　　　　　GW　　ISSN 0945-2540
▼**FORENSISCHE PSYCHIATRIE UND PSYCHOTHERAPIE.** (Text in English, German; summaries in English, French, German) 1994. 2/yr. DM.40($30) Pabst Science Publishers, Am Eichengrund 28, 49525 Lengerich, Germany. TEL 05484-308. FAX 05484-550. Ed. Heinfried Duncker. adv.; bk.rev. **Document type:** academic/scholarly publication.

138　　　　　SZ　　ISSN 0015-7694
FORM UND GEIST; illustrierte Blaetter fuer angewandte Menschenkenntnis und Sozialreform. 1941. bi-m. 27 SFr.($10.50) Helioda-Verlag, Hardturmstr. 284, CH-8005 Zurich, Switzerland. Ed. W. Alispach. bk.rev.; illus. circ. 4,000. **Document type:** bulletin.

150　　　　　UK　　ISSN 0015-833X
FORUM (LONDON, 1967); the journal of human relations and psycho-sexual studies. 1967. m. £39. (Forum International) Northern & Shell Publications, Northern & Shell Bldg., P.O. Box 381, Millharbour, London E14 9TW, England. TEL 44-171-987-5090. FAX 44-171-987-2160. (U.S. addr.: Penthouse Forum, 1965 Broadway, New York, NY 10023-5965. TEL 212-496-6100) Ed. Elizabeth Coldwell. adv.: color page £1300; adv. contact: Sonia Francis. bk.rev.; illus.; index. circ. 90,000. **Indexed:** Res.High.Educ.Abstr. **Document type:** academic/scholarly publication.

150.19　　　　　GW　　ISSN 0178-7667
FORUM DER PSYCHOANALYSE; Zeitschrift fuer klinische Theorie und Praxis. 1985. 4/yr. DM.168($122) (effective 1996). Springer-Verlag, Heidelberger Platz 3, 14197 Berlin, Germany. TEL 030-8207-0. FAX 030-8214091. E-mail: orders@springer.de. (Subscr. in N. America to: Springer-Verlag New York, Inc., 44 Hartz Way, Secaucus, NJ 07096-2941. TEL 201-348-4033. FAX 201-348-4505) Ed. Friedrich Beese. (also avail. in microform from UMI; back issues avail.; reprint service avail. from ISI) **Indexed:** Excerp.Med., Psychol.Abstr. (1993-). **Document type:** academic/scholarly publication.
—BLDSC (4024.098000); Genuine Article; UMI. **CCC.**

156　　　　　GW　　ISSN 0720-0447
BF3
FORUM KRITISCHE PSYCHOLOGIE. 1978. s-a. DM.34 (students DM.28). Argument-Verlag GmbH, Rentzelstr. 1, 20146 Hamburg, Germany. TEL 040-456018. FAX 040-445189. Ed. Klaus Holzkamp. (back issues avail.) **Document type:** academic/scholarly publication.

155.937　　　　　US　　ISSN 0160-7081
FOUNDATION OF THANATOLOGY. ARCHIVES.* q. $66.50. Foundation of Thanatology, Foundation Book & Periodical Division, 630 W. 168th St., New York, NY 10032. TEL 212-928-2066. Ed. Austin H. Kutscher. (also avail. in microform from UMI; back issues avail.)
Description: Contains abstracts of conference proceedings on aging, dying, death, bereavement, and grief.

616.89 300　　　　　UK　　ISSN 0267-0887
BF175.4.C84
FREE ASSOCIATIONS; psychoanalysis, groups, politics, culture. 1984. q. £25 to individuals; institutions £50. Free Associations Books, 26 Freegrove Rd., London N7 9RQ, England. TEL 01 609-5646. (And: Guilford Publications, Inc., 72 Spring St., 4th Fl., New York, NY 10012. TEL 212-431-9800) (Co-publisher: Guilford Publications, Inc.) Ed. Robert M. Young. adv.; bk.rev.; abstr.; bibl.; index. circ. 2,000. (also avail. in microform from UMI; back issues avail.; reprint service avail. from ISI) **Indexed:** Alt.Press Ind., ASSIA, Chicago Psychoanal.Lit.Ind., Left Ind. (1985-), Psychol.Abstr. (1993-), Sociol.Abstr.
—BLDSC (4033.310000); UMI. **CCC.**
Description: Covers from clinical to cultural studies on psychodynamic approaches to human nature, culture and society.

155.937 393　　　　　CN　　ISSN 1180-3479
FRONTIERES; les vivants et les morts. 1988. 3/yr. Can.$20 to individuals; institutions Can.$31. Universite de Quebec a Montreal, Service des Publications, Centre d'Etudes sur la Mort, Box 8888, Succ. A, Montreal, PQ H3C 3P8, Canada. TEL 514-987-8537. FAX 514-987-7856. Ed. Eric Volant. adv.; bk.rev.; film rev.; bibl.; illus.; stat.; circ. 1,500 (controlled). (back issues avail.)
Description: Discusses death and grieving for professionals and volunteers in the health services.

370.15 150　　　　　US
FRONTIERS IN PSYCHOTHERAPY. 1990. irreg. price varies. Ablex Publishing Corporation, 355 Chestnut St., Norwood, NJ 07648. TEL 201-767-8450. FAX 201-767-6717. TELEX 135-393. Ed. Edward Tick. **Document type:** academic/scholarly publication.

150　　　　　JA　　ISSN 0917-8163
FUKUSHIMA SHINRIGAKU ZASSHI/FUKUSHIMA JOURNAL OF PSYCHOLOGY. (Text in Japanese) 1990. a. Fukushima Shinri Gakkai - Fukushima Psychological Association, c/o Fukushima Daigaku Kyoikugakubu, Kyoiku Shinrigaku Kyoshitsu, 2 Sugumichi, Asakawa, Matsukawamachi, Fukushima-shi, Fukushima-ken 960-12, Japan. TEL 81-245-48-5151. FAX 81-245-48-3181. E-mail: kfukuda@post.ipc.fukushima-v.ac.jp.

155.937　　　　　US
G E I NEWSLETTER.* 1979. q. $5. Grief Education Institute, 4596 E. Iliff Ave., Denver, CO 80222-6021. Ed. Carole Rawland. bk.rev. circ. 2,000. **Document type:** newsletter.

PSYCHOLOGY

301.1 150 510   US   ISSN 0899-8256
QA269   CODEN: GEBEEF
GAMES AND ECONOMIC BEHAVIOR. 1989. m. $306 (foreign $366) (effective 1996). Academic Press, Inc., Journal Division, 525 B St., Ste. 1900, San Diego, CA 92101-4495. TEL 619-230-1840. FAX 619-699-6800. (Subscr. to: Box 620000, Orlando, FL 32891-8340. TEL 800-543-9534) Ed. Ehud Kalai. (back issues avail.) **Indexed:** J.of Econ.Lit. **Document type:** academic/scholarly publication.
—BLDSC (4069.168000); Faxon; Genuine Article; SWETS; UnCover. **CCC.**
     Description: Deals with game-theoretic modeling in the social, biological and mathematical sciences. Addresses the beliefs in the importance of interchange of game-theoretic ideas leading to a mathematical science of games and economic behavior.

150   NE   ISSN 0921-5360
BF8.D8   CODEN: GEGEE6
GEDRAG & GEZONDHEID; tijdschrift voor psychologie - journal of psychology. (Text in Dutch, English) 1952. 6/yr. fl.83.50. Uitgeverij De Tijdstroom b.v., P.O. Box 19135, 3501 DC Utrecht, Netherlands. TEL 31-30-586900. FAX 31-30-586950. Ed. G.J.J. Calis. adv.; bk.rev.; bibl.; charts; illus.; index. circ. 1,000. **Indexed:** Biol.Abstr., Curr.Cont., Psychol.Abstr. (1973-), Risk Abstr., SSCI.
—BLDSC (4095.760900); SWETS.
     Former titles (until 1986): Gedrag (ISSN 0377-7308); Which was formed by the 1973 merger of: Hypothese (ISSN 0018-8352); Nijmeegs Tijdschrift voor Psychologie (ISSN 0029-0475); Which was formerly titled (until 1969): Gawein (ISSN 0016-5271)

GEISTIGE BEHINDERUNG; Fachzeitschrift der Lebenshilfe fuer geistig Behinderte. see *EDUCATION — Special Education And Rehabilitation*

GENESIS OF BEHAVIOR. see *MEDICAL SCIENCES — Psychiatry And Neurology*

155   US   ISSN 0740-9583
BF712
GENETIC EPISTEMOLOGIST. 1971. q. $65 to members; students $25. Jean Piaget Society, Department of Psychology, Pennsylvania State University, University Park, PA 16802. TEL 302-451-2311. (Subscr. to: Wm. M. Gray, Treas., Jean Piaget Society, Dept. of Education in Psychology, University of Toledo, Toledo, OH 43606-3390. TEL 419-537-2481) Ed. David S. Palermo. adv.; bk.rev.; circ. 550 (paid). **Document type:** newsletter.
—BLDSC (4111.849000).
     Description: Interdisciplinary study of human knowledge and its development.
     Refereed Serial

156 155   US   ISSN 8756-7547
LB1101   CODEN: GSGMEQ
GENETIC, SOCIAL, AND GENERAL PSYCHOLOGY MONOGRAPHS. 1926. q. $98. (Helen Dwight Reid Educational Foundation) Heldref Publications, 1319 Eighteenth St., N.W., Washington, DC 20036-1802. TEL 202-296-6267. FAX 202-296-5149. Ed. Doris Chalfin. bibl.; charts; s-a. index. circ. 880. (back issues avail.; reprint service avail. from SWZ,UMI) **Indexed:** Abstr.Soc.Work, Biol.Abstr., Child Devel.Abstr., Child.Devel.Abstr., Curr.Adv.Ecol.Sci., Curr.Cont., DSH Abstr., Except.Child.Educ.Abstr., Excerp.Med., Ind.Med., Lang.& Lang.Behav.Abstr., Mult.Ed.Abstr., Psychol.Abstr. (1926-), Psycscan D.P., Risk Abstr., Soc.Work Res.& Abstr., SSCI, Stud.Wom.Abstr. **Document type:** academic/scholarly publication.
    ● Also available on CD-ROM. Producer(s): University Microfilms International.
—BLDSC (4111.916000); Faxon; Genuine Article; SWETS; UMI; UnCover. **CCC.**
     Formerly: Genetic Psychology Monographs (ISSN 0016-6677)
     Refereed Serial

GESELLSCHAFT FUER LOGOTHERAPIE UND EXISTENZANALYSE. TAGUNGSBERICHTE. see *MEDICAL SCIENCES — Psychiatry And Neurology*

150 616.89   US   ISSN 0190-0412
GESTALT JOURNAL. 1978. s-a. $30 to individuals; institutions $45. Center for Gestalt Development, Inc., Box 990, Highland, NY 12528-0990. TEL 914-691-7192. Ed. Joe Wysong. adv.; bk.rev. circ. 2,000. (back issues avail.) **Indexed:** Psychol.Abstr. (1978-).
—BLDSC (4163.350000); UnCover.
     Description: Articles and reviews relating to the theory and practice of Gestalt therapy.

150.19   GW   ISSN 0170-057X
BF203
GESTALT THEORY; an international multidisciplinary journal. (Text in English, German) 1979. q. DM.166 (students DM.96) (effective 1996). (Society for Gestalt Theory and Its Applications (GTA)) Westdeutscher Verlag GmbH, Postfach 1546, 65005 Wiesbaden, Germany. TEL 0611-534389. FAX 0611-534430. Ed.Bd. adv.; bk.rev. circ. 550. **Indexed:** Ger.J.Psych., Psychol.Abstr. (1979-). **Document type:** academic/scholarly publication.
—BLDSC (4163.400000). **CCC.**

GIFTED CHILD QUARTERLY. see *CHILDREN AND YOUTH — About*

GIFU SHISHUNKI KENKYU/GIFU SOCIETY OF ADOLESCENTOLOGY. JOURNAL. see *CHILDREN AND YOUTH — About*

GIORNALE DI NEUROPSICHIATRIA DELL'ETA EVOLUTIVA. see *MEDICAL SCIENCES — Psychiatry And Neurology*

150.5   IT   ISSN 0390-5349
BF1
GIORNALE ITALIANO DI PSICOLOGIA/ITALIAN JOURNAL OF PSYCHOLOGY. 1974. 5/yr. L.140000. Societa Editrice Il Mulino, Strada Maggiore, 37, 40125 Bologna, Italy. TEL 39-51-256011. FAX 39-51-256034. Ed. C.A. Umilta. adv.; index. circ. 1,300. (back issues avail.) **Indexed:** Child Devel.Abstr., Psychol.Abstr. (1981-).
—BLDSC (4178.243000).

150   IT   ISSN 0391-2515
BF84
GIORNALE STORICO DI PSICOLOGIA DINAMICA. 1977. s-a. L.30000 per no. Liguori Editore s.r.l., Via Mezzocannone 19, 80134 Naples, Italy. TEL 081-5527139. Ed. Aldo Carotenuto. **Indexed:** Psychoanal.Abstr., Psychol.Abstr. (1981-). **Document type:** monographic series.

GNOSIS; a journal of the Western inner traditions. see *NEW AGE PUBLICATIONS*

150 016   SW   ISSN 0301-0996
                        CODEN: GPSRDB
GOETEBORG PSYCHOLOGICAL REPORTS. (Text in English) 1971. irreg. (5-8/yr.). SEK 25($7.50) per no. Goeteborgs Universitet, Department of Psychology, Haraldsgatan 1, S-413 14 Goeteborg, Sweden. TEL 46-31-773-1656. FAX 46-31-773-4628. E-mail: Lillemor.Ostberg@psy.gu.se. Ed. Dr. Carl Martin Allwood. circ. 400. **Indexed:** Psychol.Abstr.
—BLDSC (4201.950000).

150   SZ   ISSN 0172-3421
GORGO. 1979. 2/yr. 47 SFr. Schweizer Spiegel Verlag AG, Mittelstr. 21, CH-8008 Zurich, Switzerland. TEL 01-3836959. (Subscr. to: Buch Service Basel, Postfach, CH-4002 Basel, Switzerland. TEL 061-2729470) Ed. Adolf Guggenbuehl-Craig. adv.; page 400 SFr.; adv. contact: Allan Guggenbuehl. bk.rev.; illus. **Document type:** academic/scholarly publication.

150 591   US
GORILLA. 1976. s-a. $30. Gorilla Foundation, Box 620-530, Woodside, CA 94062. TEL 415-851-8505. Ed. Dr. Francine Patterson. bk.rev. circ. 30,000. (tabloid format; back issues avail.) **Document type:** academic/scholarly publication.
     Description: Reports of the results and progress of ongoing study of gorilla behavior and interspecies communication, with other topics relating to the preservation and captive maintenance of gorillas.

150 378   US
BF77
GRADUATE STUDY IN PSYCHOLOGY. 1971. a. $19.95 to non-members; members $17.95. American Psychological Association, 750 First St., N.E., Washington, DC 20002. TEL 202-336-1003. FAX 202-336-5502. Ed. Cynthia G. Baum. circ. 15,000. **Indexed:** Psychol.Abstr. **Document type:** directory.
     Former titles (until 1991): Graduate Study in Psychology and Associated Fields (ISSN 0742-7220); (until 1983): Graduate Study in Psychology (ISSN 0072-5277)

616.89   US   ISSN 0362-4021
RC488.A1   CODEN: GROUDE
GROUP (NEW YORK). 1977. q. $95 (foreign $110) (effective 1996). (Eastern Group Psychotherapy Society) Human Sciences Press, Inc. (Subsidiary of: Plenum Publishing Corp.), 233 Spring St., New York, NY 10013-1578. TEL 212-620-8000. FAX 212-463-0742. TELEX 23-421139. Ed. Peter J. Schlachet. bk.rev.; index. circ. 1,200. (also avail. in microform from UMI; reprint service avail. from ISI,UMI) **Indexed:** Biol.Abstr., Curr.Cont., Excerp.Med., IMFL, Psychol.Abstr. (1982-). **Document type:** academic/scholarly publication.
—BLDSC (4220.165000); Genuine Article; UMI; UnCover.
     Description: Advances, theoretical and clinical contributions, and research in dynamic group psychotherapy.

616.8   UK
GROUP ANALYSIS; journal of group-analytic psychotherapy. 1967. q. £38 to individuals; institutions £106 (effective 1996). Sage Publications Ltd., 6 Bonhill St., London EC2A 4PU, England. TEL 0171-374-0645. FAX 0171-374-8741. E-mail: market@sageltd.co.uk. Ed. Malcolm Pines. adv.: B&W page £200; trim 170 x 100; adv. contact: Bernie Folan. bk.rev. **Indexed:** ASSIA, Excerp.Med., IBZ, Psychol.Abstr. (1990-), Sociol.Abstr., Stud.Wom.Abstr. **Document type:** academic/scholarly publication.
—BLDSC (4220.170000); SWETS; UnCover.
     Formerly: Group Analysis: International Panel and Correspondence (ISSN 0533-3164)
     Description: Concerned with all approaches to the theory, practice and experience of analytic group psychotherapy.

GROUP & ORGANIZATION MANAGEMENT; an international journal. see *BUSINESS AND ECONOMICS — Personnel Management*

616.89   US
GROUP CIRCLE. q. American Group Psychotherapy Association, 25 E. 21st St., 6th Fl., New York, NY 10010. TEL 212-477-2677. FAX 212-979-6627. Ed. Harold S. Bernard. circ. 4,000 (controlled). **Document type:** newsletter.
     Formerly: A G P A Newsletter.

GROUPWORK. see *SOCIAL SERVICES AND WELFARE*

616.89   GW   ISSN 0939-4273
GRUPPENANALYSE; Zeitschrift fuer gruppenanalytische Psychotherapie, Beratung und Supervision. (Text in German; summaries in English, German) 1991. DM.42.40. (Institut fuer Gruppenanalyse Heidelberg e.V.) Mattes Verlag GmbH, Postfach 103866, 69028 Heidelberg, Germany. TEL 06221-459321. FAX 06221-459322. Ed.Bd. adv.: B&W page DM.300; trim 160 x 240. bk.rev. (back issues avail.) **Document type:** academic/scholarly publication.

155 301   GW   ISSN 0046-6514
                        CODEN: GRUPDT
GRUPPENDYNAMIK; Zeitschrift fuer angewandte Sozialpsychologie. 1970. q. DM.81 (foreign DM.87) (students DM.56). Verlag Leske und Budrich GmbH, Postfach 300551, 51334 Leverkusen, Germany. TEL 02171-2079. FAX 02171-41209. Ed.Bd. bk.rev. circ. 1,800. (back issues avail.) **Indexed:** Ger.J.Psych., Psychol.Abstr. (1970-). **Document type:** academic/scholarly publication.
—BLDSC (4223.458000); Genuine Article. **CCC.**

PSYCHOLOGY

150   GW   ISSN 0085-1302
GRUPPENPSYCHOTHERAPIE UND GRUPPENDYNAMIK. BEIHEFTE. 1972. irreg. price varies. Vandenhoeck und Ruprecht, Robert-Bosch-Breite 6, 37079 Goettingen, Germany. TEL 0551-6959-0. FAX 0551-695917. (Subscr. to: 37070 Goettingen, Germany) Ed. A. Heigl-Evers. circ. 1,900. **Indexed:** Excerp.Med. **Document type:** monographic series.

158 301.4   US
GUILFORD FAMILY THERAPY SERIES. irreg. (approx. biennial). Guilford Publications, Inc., 72 Spring St., New York, NY 10012. TEL 212-431-9800; 800-365-7006. FAX 212-966-6708. **Document type:** monographic series.
   Description: Equips therapists and social workers with theoretical and clinical texts on family development and family therapy. The influences of ethnicity, therapist behavior, life transitions, social changes, personal authority, intervention and resistance on families are examined.

GUILFORD LAW AND BEHAVIOR SERIES. see *LAW*

616.89   US
GUILFORD PSYCHOANALYSIS SERIES. irreg. (approx. biennial). Guilford Publications, Inc., 72 Spring St., New York, NY 10012. TEL 212-431-9800; 800-365-7006. FAX 212-966-6708. **Document type:** monographic series.

158 301.1   US
GUILFORD SERIES ON PERSONAL RELATIONSHIPS. irreg. (approx. 2/yr.). Guilford Publications, Inc., 72 Spring St., New York, NY 10012. TEL 212-431-9800; 800-365-7006. FAX 212-966-6708. Ed. Steve Duck. **Document type:** monographic series.
   Description: Develops theory and methods. Critically reviews content areas, while exploring the interactions and conflicts that exist in relationships and friendships.

157   US   ISSN 0884-5808
HAKOMI FORUM. 1984. a. $10. Hakomi Institute, Box 1873, Boulder, CO 80306. TEL 303-443-6209. FAX 303-443-8613. Ed. Gregory J. Johanson. bk.rev.; cum.index. circ. 1,000. (back issues avail.) **Indexed:** Psychol.Abstr. **Document type:** academic/scholarly publication.
   Description: Journal for therapists with an emphasis on transpersonal, body-centered, cognitive aspects of therapy. Aims to foster the principles of unity, organicity, mind-body holism, mindfulness, and non-violence.

159.94   NE   ISSN 0924-817X
HANDBOOK OF ANXIETY. (Text in English) 1987. irreg., vol.5, 1992. price varies. Elsevier Science B.V., Books Division, P.O. Box 211, 1000 AE Amsterdam, Netherlands. TEL 31-20-4853911. FAX 31-20-4853705. TELEX 18582 ESPA NL. E-mail: nlinfo-f@elsevier.nl; usinfo-f@elsevier.com; forinfo-kyf04035@niftyserve.or.jp; Site addr.: http://www.elsevier.nl/. (Subscr. in U.S. and Canada to: Elsevier Science Inc., Box 882, Madison Sq. Sta., New York, NY 10159. TEL 212-989-5800) Ed.Bd. (back issues avail.) **Document type:** monographic series.
   Description: Covers the identification and treatment of anxiety and related disorders, including biological, cultural and clinical aspects.
Refereed Serial

155.4 613.7   US   ISSN 0899-3122
          CODEN: HPHEAR
HANDBOOK OF PSYCHOLOGY AND HEALTH SERIES. 1982. irreg., vol.5, 1987. $49.95. Lawrence Erlbaum Associates, Inc., 10 Industrial Dr., Mahwah, NJ 07430-2262. TEL 201-236-9500. FAX 201-236-0072. Eds. Andrew Baum, Jerome E. Singer. (back issues avail.) **Indexed:** Curr.Cont., Psychol.Abstr. **Document type:** monographic series.
Refereed Serial

155.2   US
HANDWRITING ANALYSIS REGISTRY.* a. GraphoMedia Publishing, 4724 Lincoln Blvd., 302, Marina Del Rey, CA 90292-6902. Ed. Marjorie Clayton.
   Formerly: Directory of Handwriting Analysts (ISSN 0731-3888)

150   UK   ISSN 0266-4771
BF173
HARVEST. 1954. a. £13.50($25) Analytical Psychology Club, 37 York Street Chambers, York St., London W1H 1DE, England. TEL 071-724-5661. Ed. Renos Papadopoulos. adv.; bk.rev. circ. 600. **Document type:** academic/scholarly publication.
   Description: Concerned with the depth psychology of C.G. Jung.

155   JA   ISSN 0915-731X
HATTATSU NO SHINRIGAKU TO IGAKU/JAPANESE JOURNAL OF DEVELOPMENTAL PSYCHOLOGY AND MEDICINE. (Text in Japanese) 1990. q. 2060 Yen. Igaku Shinkosha, 29-12-1403, Hongo 5-chome, Bunkyo-ku, Tokyo 113, Japan.

155   JA   ISSN 0915-9029
HATTATSU SHINRIGAKU KENKYU/JAPANESE JOURNAL OF DEVELOPMENTAL PSYCHOLOGY. (Text in Japanese; summaries in English) 1990. s-a. Nihon Hattatsu Shinri Gakkai - Japan Society of Developmental Psychology, Shirayuri Joshi Daigaku Jido Bunka Gakka, 1-25, Midorigaoka, Chofu-shi, Tokyo 182, Japan. FAX 03-3326-9417. **Indexed:** Psychol.Abstr. (1990-).
—BLDSC (4651.650000).

616.89   US   ISSN 1065-8289
THE HEALING WOMAN. 1992. m. $30 (Canada $36) (effective 1995 & 1996). Margot Silk Forrest, Ed. & Pub., Box 3038, Moss Beach, CA 94038. TEL 415-728-0339. FAX 415-728-1324. adv. contact: Anita Montero. bk.rev.; illus.; circ. 5,000 (paid). **Indexed:** Viol.& Abuse Abstr. **Document type:** newsletter.
   Description: Written by and for women survivors of child sexual abuse, their friends and supportive family members, and the professionals who help them heal.

150   US   ISSN 0278-6133
R726.5
HEALTH PSYCHOLOGY. 1982. bi-m. $180 (foreign $223) (effective 1996). American Psychological Association, Division of Health Psychology, 750 First St., N.E., Washington, DC 20002-4242. TEL 202-336-5600. FAX 202-336-5568. Ed. David S. Krantz. adv.; bk.rev.; abstr.; bibl.; charts; illus.; stat. circ. 9,000. **Indexed:** ASCA, Behav.Med.Abstr., Curr.Cont., NRN, Psychol.Abstr. (1982-), Risk Abstr. **Document type:** academic/scholarly publication.
—BLDSC (4275.105200); Faxon; Genuine Article; SWETS; UMI; UnCover. **CCC**.
   Description: Addresses the relationship between behavior and health.
Refereed Serial

HELEN DOWLING INSTITUTE FOR BIOPSYCHOSOCIAL MEDICINE. PUBLICATION. see *MEDICAL SCIENCES*

150   CN   ISSN 0085-1493
HERE AND NOW; a brief of news from the IPR. (Text and summaries in French) 1969. irreg. free. Institute of Psychological Research, Inc., 34 Fleury St. W., Montreal, PQ H3L 1S9, Canada. TEL 514-382-3000. FAX 514-382-3007. Ed. Jean-Marc Chevrier. adv.; bk.rev.; circ. 2,000 (controlled).

155   JA
HERUSU SAIKOROJISUTO/HEALTH PSYCHOLOGIST. (Text in Japanese) q. Nihon Kenko Shinri Gakkai - Japanese Association of Health Psychology, Waseda Daigaku Bungakubu Oda Kenkyushitsu, 24-1, Toyama 1-chome, Shinjuku-ku, Tokyo 162, Japan.

155   JA   ISSN 0386-3158
BF1
HIROSHIMA FORUM FOR PSYCHOLOGY. (Text in English) 1974. biennial. Hiroshima University, Faculty of Education, Department of Psychology - Hiroshima Daigaku Kyoikugakubu Shinrigaku Kenkyushitsu, 1-2, Kagamiyama 1-chome, Higashihiroshima-shi, Hiroshima-ken 724, Japan. **Indexed:** Psychol.Abstr. (1975-).
—BLDSC (4315.596900).

155 610   JA   ISSN 0917-6934
HIROSHIMA SHUDO DAIGAKU RINSHO SHINRIGAKU KENKYU/HIROSHIMA SHUDO UNIVERSITY. BULLETIN OF CLINICAL PSYCHOLOGY. (Text in Japanese; summaries in English) 1991. a. 2500 Yen. Hiroshima Shudo Daigaku, Shinrigaku Kyoshitsu - Hiroshima Shudo University, Department of Psychology, 1717, Otsuka, Numatacho, Asaminami-ku, Hiroshima-shi 731-31, Japan. TEL 81-82-830-1139. FAX 81-82-848-6633. adv. contact: Mamoru Asada. bk.rev. **Document type:** bulletin.
Refereed Serial

150 301.1   US   ISSN 0739-9863
RC451.5.H57   CODEN: HJBSEZ
HISPANIC JOURNAL OF BEHAVIORAL SCIENCES. (Text in English, Spanish) 1979. q. $54 to individuals; institutions $142 (effective Sep. 1995). (University of California at Los Angeles) Sage Publications, Inc., 2455 Teller Rd., Thousand Oaks, CA 91320. TEL 805-499-0721. FAX 805-499-0871. E-mail: libaries@sagepub.com. (Overseas subscr. to: Sage Publications Ltd., 6 Bonhill St., London EC2A 4PU, England; Sage Publications India Pvt. Ltd., P.O. Box 4215, New Delhi 110 048, India) Ed. Dr. Amado M. Padilla. adv.; bk.rev.; film rev.; index. circ. 1,200. (also avail. in microfilm from UMI; back issues avail.; reprint service avail. from UMI) **Indexed:** C.I.J.E., Chic.Per.Ind., Curr.Cont., High.Educ.Abstr., Hisp.Amer.Per.Ind. (1989-), IMFL, Mult.Ed.Abstr., Psychol.Abstr. (1979-), Soc.Sci.Ind. (1994-), Sp.Ed.Needs Abstr., SSCI. **Document type:** academic/scholarly publication.
—BLDSC (4315.772700); Faxon; Genuine Article; UMI; UnCover. **CCC**.
   Description: Contains empirical articles, case study reports, and scholarly notes of theoretical or methodological interest pertaining to Hispanics. Focuses on the fields of anthropology, linguistics, psychology, public health, and sociology.

150   FR   ISSN 0018-4314
HOMME LIBRE; fils de la terre. 1960. q. 50 F. (foreign 64 F.). Cercle d'Etudes Psychologiques, B.P. 205, 42005 St. Etienne Cedex 1, France. Ed. Marcel Renoulet. bk.rev.; bibl.

301   FR   ISSN 0563-9743
HM3
HOMO; psychologie, education, culture, societe. (Text in French; summaries in English) 1953. a. 65 F. (effective 1994). (Universite de Toulouse II (le Mirail)) Presses Universitaires du Mirail, 56 rue du Taur, 31000 Toulouse, France. TEL 61-22-58-31. FAX 61-21-84-20. Ed. J.P. Martineau. (back issues avail.) **Indexed:** Biol.Abstr., SSCI. **Document type:** academic/scholarly publication.
—BLDSC (4326.330000).
   Description: Presents fundamental or applied research, methodolgical confrontation, clinical studies and essays in the fields of psychology, education, culture and society.

616.89   HK   ISSN 0379-4490
HONG KONG PSYCHOLOGICAL SOCIETY. BULLETIN. (Text in English; abstracts in Chinese) 1978. s-a. HK.$125. Hong Kong Psychological Society Ltd., c/o Department of Education Studies, Hong Kong Baptist University, Kowllon Tong, Hong Kong. FAX 852-2339-7894. TELEX 50301 CUHK HX. Ed. Hing Keung Ma. bk.rev. circ. 300. (back issues avail.) **Indexed:** Human Resour.Abstr., Psychol.Abstr. (1979-), Sage Fam.Stud.Abstr., Sage Urb.Stud.Abstr. **Document type:** academic/scholarly publication.
—BLDSC (2555.320300). **CCC**.

155   US   ISSN 0148-8686
GF7
HUMAN BEHAVIOR AND ENVIRONMENT. 1976. irreg., vol.13, 1994. price varies. Plenum Publishing Corp., 233 Spring St., New York, NY 10013-1578. TEL 212-620-8000. FAX 212-463-0742. TELEX 23-421139. Eds. Irwin Altman, J.F. Wohlwill. (back issues avail.) **Indexed:** Psychol.Abstr. **Document type:** monographic series.
—BLDSC (4335.985000). **CCC**.
Refereed Serial

HUMAN - COMPUTER INTERACTION (HILLSDALE); a journal of theoretical, empirical, and methodological issues of user psychology and of system design. see *COMPUTERS*

PSYCHOLOGY

574.1   SZ   ISSN 0018-716X
CODEN: HUDEA8
HUMAN DEVELOPMENT. (Text in English) 1958. bi-m. 77.25 SFr.($59.50) to individuals; institutions 309 SFr.($238) (effective 1996). S. Karger AG, Allschwilerstr. 10, P.O. Box, CH-4009 Basel, Switzerland. TEL 061-3061111. FAX 061-3061234. E-mail: Karger@Karger.ch. Ed. D. Kuhn. adv.; bk.rev.; bibl.; charts; illus.; index. circ. 2,200. (also avail. in microform; reprint service avail. from SWZ) **Indexed:** Adol.Ment.Hlth.Abstr., Biol.Abstr., CLOA, Curr.Adv.Ecol.Sci., Curr.Cont., Educ.Ind., Excerp.Med., Ind.Med., M.L.A., Mid.East: Abstr.& Ind., Psychol.Abstr. (1958-), Psycscan D.P., Rehabil.Lit., SSCI. **Document type:** academic/scholarly publication.
—BLDSC (4336.050000); Faxon; Genuine Article; SWETS; UnCover. **CCC.**
  Formerly: Vita Humana.
  Description: Scholarly articles on psychological development over an entire lifespan, from infancy through aging.
  Refereed Serial

253.5   US   ISSN 0197-3096
BV4012
HUMAN DEVELOPMENT (HARTFORD). 1980. q. $24 (foreign $31); newsstand price: $8 (foreign $10). Jesuit Educational Center for Human Development, 127 Lake St.on St., Brighton, MA 02135-3898. TEL 617-562-0766. FAX 617-562-0668. Ed. Dr. James J. Gill. bk.rev. circ. 13,000. (back issues avail.) **Indexed:** C.I.J.E., Cath.Ind., Educ.Ind., Lang.& Lang.Behav.Abstr.
—BLDSC (4336.052000); SWETS.
  Description: Directed to people involved in religious leadership, education, spiritual direction, pastoral care and religious information.

155   US
HUMAN DEVELOPMENT (NORWOOD). 1986. irreg., vol.4, 1991. price varies. Ablex Publishing Corporation, 355 Chestnut St., Norwood, NJ 07648. TEL 201-767-8450. FAX 201-767-6717. TELEX 135-393. Ed. Sidney Strauss. **Document type:** academic/scholarly publication.
  Refereed Serial

HUMAN EVOLUTION, BEHAVIOR, AND INTELLIGENCE. see *BIOLOGY — Genetics*

HUMAN FACTORS. see *ENGINEERING*

HUMAN FACTORS AND ERGONOMICS SOCIETY ANNUAL MEETING. PROCEEDINGS. see *ENGINEERING*

HUMAN FACTORS AND ERGONOMICS SOCIETY BULLETIN. see *ENGINEERING*

HUMAN FACTORS IN INFORMATION TECHNOLOGY. see *COMPUTERS — Information Science And Information Theory*

HUMAN MOVEMENT SCIENCE; journal devoted to pure and applied research on human movement. see *MEDICAL SCIENCES*

HUMAN NATURE; an interdisciplinary biosocial perspective. see *SOCIAL SCIENCES: COMPREHENSIVE WORKS*

152   US   ISSN 0895-9285
HUMAN PERFORMANCE. 1988. q. $49.50 to individuals (foreign $74.50); institutions $210 (foreign $235). Lawrence Erlbaum Associates, Inc., 10 Industrial Dr., Mahwah, NJ 07430-2262. TEL 201-236-9500. FAX 201-236-0072. Eds. Frank J. Landy, Sheldon Zedeck. adv.; bk.rev.: page $275; 5 x 8. **Indexed:** Psychol.Abstr. (1988-). **Document type:** academic/scholarly publication.
—BLDSC (4336.265000); Faxon; SWETS; UnCover.
  Description: For behavioral scientists interested in the factors that motivate and influence excellence in human behavior, publishes research and theory that investigates the nature of goal-directed human activity.
  Refereed Serial

370.15 150   UK   ISSN 0955-4815
HUMAN POTENTIAL MAGAZINE. 1977. q. £10 (includes Resource Directory). Human Potential, 5 Barb Mews, Brook Green, London W6 7PA, England. TEL 0171-371-2432. Ed. Jill Frankham. adv.; bk.rev. circ. 3,000. **Document type:** consumer publication.
—BLDSC (4336.358000).
  Formerly (until 1988): Human Potential Resources (ISSN 0263-5100)
  Description: Covers psychology, human consciousness and personal development.

370.15 155.5 301   US   ISSN 0885-1174
BF575.S75
HUMAN STRESS: CURRENT SELECTED RESEARCH. 1986. a. $37.50. A M S Press, Inc., 56 E. 13th St., New York, NY 10003. TEL 212-777-4700. FAX 212-995-5413. Ed. James H. Humphrey. bk.rev.; index. (back issues avail.)
—BLDSC (4336.466800).
  Formerly: Human Stress Current Advances in Research.
  Description: Articles on biological and behavioral problems related to stress.

150   UK   ISSN 0960-9830
HUMAN SYSTEMS; the journal of systemic consultation and management. 1990. q. £30 (Europe £37.70; elsewhere £40) to individuals; institutions £40 (Europe £48; elsewhere £54). University of Leeds, Department of Psychology, Leeds Family Therapy & Research Centre, Leeds LS2 9JT, England. TEL 0113-2335728. FAX 0113-2335700. (Subscr. to: K C C International, 2 Wyvil Ct., Trenchold St., London SW8 2TG, England. TEL 0171-720-7301. FAX 0171-720-7302) (Co-sponsor: Kensington Consultation Centre) Eds. Peter Stratton, Philippa Selignman. adv. contact: Peter Lang. bk.rev.; software rev.; video rev.; circ. 750 (paid) **Document type:** academic/scholarly publication.
—BLDSC (4336.467500).
  Refereed Serial

150   US   ISSN 0887-3267
THE HUMANISTIC PSYCHOLOGIST. 1973. 3/yr. $20 to individuals (foreign $24); institutions $40 (foreign $44). American Psychological Association, Division of Humanistic Psychology, Psychology Dept., W. Georgia College, Carrollton, GA 30118. TEL 404-836-6510. FAX 404-836-6791. E-mail: aanstoos@sun.cc.westga.edu. Ed. Christopher M. Anastoos, Ed. adv.; bk.rev.; circ. 1,200 (paid). (back issues avail.) **Indexed:** Psychol.Abstr. (1986-). **Document type:** academic/scholarly publication.
—BLDSC (4336.530800).
  Description: Publishes contributions that advance the field of humanistic psychology, broadly defined.
  Refereed Serial

HUMOR; international journal of humor research. see *SOCIAL SCIENCES: COMPREHENSIVE WORKS*

HYMAN BLUMBERG SYMPOSIUM SERIES. see *EDUCATION*

HYPNOTHERAPY TODAY. see *MEDICAL SCIENCES — Hypnosis*

616.89   US
I A B M C P NEWSLETTER. 1980. q. $45. International Academy of Behavioral Medicine, Counseling and Psychotherapy, 6750 Hillcrest Plaza Dr., Ste. 304, Dallas, TX 75230. TEL 214-458-8334. FAX 214-490-5228. Ed. George Mount. adv.; bk.rev. circ. 1,000. (back issues avail.) **Document type:** newsletter.
  Refereed Serial

301.1   FR   ISSN 0046-9688
I F E P P INFORMATIONS. 1970. q. 20 F. Institut de Formation et d'Etudes Psycho-Sociologiques et Pedagogiques, 140 bis rue de Rennes, Paris 6, France. Ed. B. Honore. bk.rev.

150   BE   ISSN 0772-9367
I L S M H NEWS. (Text in English, French, German, Spanish) a. free. International League of Societies for Persons with Mental Handicap, 248 Av. Louise, Bte. 17, B-1050 Brussels, Belgium. TEL 32-2-647-61-80. FAX 32-2-647-29-69. Ed. P.J. Renoir. bk.rev. circ. 15,000 (7,000 English ed.; 4,000 French ed.; 2,000 German ed.; 2,000 Spanish ed.). **Document type:** newsletter.
  Former titles: International League of Societies for Persons with Mental Handicap. News; International League of Societies for the Mentally Handicapped. World Congress Proceedings. (ISSN 0074-6754)
  Description: Publishes various pamphlets, position papers, reports of seminars, conferences and more.

156   US
I P A BULLETIN. a. (included in subscr. to Journal of Psychohistory). International Psychohistorical Association, Box 314, New York, NY 10024. Ed. J. Lee Shneidman.

I P O ANNUAL PROGRESS REPORT. (Instituut voor Perceptie Onderzoek) see *LINGUISTICS*

I S P T JOURNAL OF RESEARCH IN EDUCATIONAL & PSYCHOLOGICAL TESTING & MEASUREMENT. (Institute for Studies in Psychological Testing) see *EDUCATION*

152.8   II
I S P T QUARTERLY BULLETIN. q. Rs.50($50) Institute for Studies in Psychological Testing, 101 Doon Vihar, Jakhan, Dehradun 248001, India.
  Description: Provides information regarding Institute members, news, awards, honors and its publication. Occasionally, an article is also published on psychological testing.

616.89   US   ISSN 1075-7783
I S S M P & D NEWS. 1983. bi-m. $125 membership; institutions $80. International Society for the Study of Multiple Personality & Dissociation, 5700 Old Orchard Rd., 1st Fl., Skokie, IL 60077-1057. TEL 708-966-4322. FAX 708-966-9418. **Document type:** newsletter.
  Description: Focus is on recent news from other organizations of interest to members, news for US and international affiliates, and current issues concerning the field of multiple personality and dissociative states.

614.58   IT   ISSN 0019-1647
IGIENE MENTALE. 1957. q. L.10000. Lega Italiana di Igiene e Profilassi Mentale, Ospedale Psichiatrico Provinciale di Trapani, Trapani, Italy. Ed.Bd. adv.; bk.rev.; abstr.; charts; illus.; stat.; index, cum.index. circ. 250. **Indexed:** Excerp.Med.

370.15 150   US   ISSN 1041-8377
IMAGERY TODAY. 1983. s-a. $10 (effective 1995 & 1996). (International Imagery Association) Brandon House, Inc., Box 240, Bronx, NY 10471. circ. 13,014.

133 152   US   ISSN 0276-2366
BF311
IMAGINATION, COGNITION AND PERSONALITY. 1981. q. $127 (effective 196). Baywood Publishing Co., Inc., 26 Austin Ave., Box 337, Amityville, NY 11701. TEL 516-691-1270. FAX 516-691-1770. Eds. Dr. Kenneth S. Pope, Dr. Jerome L. Singer. bk.rev. (back issues avail.) **Indexed:** Biol.Abstr., Excerp.Med., Psychol.Abstr. (1981-). **Document type:** academic/scholarly publication.
—BLDSC (4368.996200); Faxon; UnCover.
  Supersedes (1973-1980): Journal of Altered States of Consciousness (ISSN 0094-5498);
  Formerly: International Journal of Altered States of Consciousness.
  Description: Authoritative articles examine the diverse uses of imagery, fantasy, consciousness in psychotherapy, behavior modification, and related areas of study.
  Refereed Serial

IMAGO; revista de psicoanalisis, psiquiatria y psicologia. see *MEDICAL SCIENCES — Psychiatry And Neurology*

IMPACT (AUSTIN). see *MEDICAL SCIENCES — Psychiatry And Neurology*

616.89   US   ISSN 1077-2413
▼IN SESSION: PSYCHOTHERAPY IN PRACTICE. 1995. q. $95 to institutions (Canada and Mexico $135; elsewhere $150). John Wiley & Sons, Inc., Journals, 605 Third Ave., New York, NY 10158. TEL 212-850-6645. FAX 212-850-6021. TELEX 12-7063. E-mail: SUBINFO@JWILEY.COM. (Subscr. outside the Americas to: John Wiley & Sons Ltd., Baffins Ln., Chichester, W. Sussex PO19 1UD, England. TEL 44-1243-779777. FAX 44-1243-776128) Ed.Bd. (also avail. in microform from UMI; back issues avail.) **Document type:** academic/scholarly publication.
Refereed Serial

150   IT   ISSN 0391-3198
INCONSCIO E CULTURA. 1978. irreg., no.19, 1992 (numbers not published consecutively). price varies. Liguori Editore s.r.l., Via Mezzocannone 19, 80134 Naples, Italy. TEL 081-5527139. Ed. Aldo Carotenuto. **Document type:** monographic series.

153.4 370.15   US   ISSN 1075-7333
▼**INDEPENDENT THINKING REVIEW.** 1994. q. $18 (students $9) (effective 1994). Resources for Independent Thinking, 4067 Hardwick, No. 129, Lakewood, CA 90712-2324. TEL 310-630-3678. FAX 310-630-7389. Ed. Sharon Presley. bk.rev.; film rev.; video rev.; bibl. (back issues avail.) **Document type:** newsletter.
Formerly (until vol.1, no.2, 1994): Resources for Independent Thinking Review.
Description: Publishes articles, reviews and listings of resources that promote independent thinking, critical thinking and personal self-empowerment for a general audience.

158   II   ISSN 0019-4247
INDIAN ACADEMY OF APPLIED PSYCHOLOGY. JOURNAL. (Text in English) vol.17, 1974. 2/yr. Rs.50($10) to individuals; institutions Rs.150($25). Indian Academy of Applied Psychology, University of Madras, Department of Psychology, Madras 5, India. Ed. Habib Ahmed. adv. contact: V. Natarajan. charts; stat.; index. **Indexed:** Psychol.Abstr. (1964-).
Document type: academic/scholarly publication.
—BLDSC (4761.900000).

158   II   ISSN 0019-5073
BF636.A1   CODEN: IJAPBI
INDIAN JOURNAL OF APPLIED PSYCHOLOGY. (Text in English) 1964. s-a. $50. University of Madras, Department of Psychology, c/o Director, Publications Division, Madras 600 005, India. TEL 91-44-568778. FAX 91-44-566693. TELEX 416376 ONOMIN. Ed. P. Anantha Krishnan. adv.; bk.rev.; charts; index. circ. 200. (also avail. in microfilm from UMI; reprint service avail. from UMI) **Indexed:** Biol.Abstr., Psychol.Abstr., Sp.Ed.Needs Abstr.
—BLDSC (4410.300000); UMI; UnCover.

301.1 150   II   ISSN 0970-0897
BF1
INDIAN JOURNAL OF BEHAVIOUR. (Text in English) 1976. bi-m. $50 to individuals; institutions Rs.100($100). Institute of Psychological Research, 52, 10th Cross, West of Chord Rd., II Stage, Bangalore 560 086, India. Ed. Dr. T.R. Rao. adv.; bk.rev. circ. 500. (reprint service avail.) **Indexed:** Biol.Abstr., Indian Psychol.Abstr., Psychol.Abstr. (1976-). **Document type:** academic/scholarly publication.
—BLDSC (4410.368000); UnCover.

152   II   ISSN 0303-2582
RC467
INDIAN JOURNAL OF CLINICAL PSYCHOLOGY. (Text in English) 1974. s-a. Rs.150($50) Indian Association of Clinical Psychologists, c/o Institute of Mental Health, Madras 600 010, India. Ed. S.K. Rangaswami. adv.; bk.rev.; abstr.; bibl.; index. circ. 700. **Indexed:** Indian Psychol.Abstr., Lang.& Lang.Behav.Abstr., Psychol.Abstr. (1974-), Psychol.R.G., Sociol.Abstr. **Document type:** academic/scholarly publication.
—BLDSC (4410.750000).

150   II   ISSN 0970-3748
INDIAN JOURNAL OF CURRENT PSYCHOLOGICAL RESEARCH. (Text in English) 1986. s-a. Rs.100($32) to individuals; institutions Rs.125 ($40). National Psychological Corporation, Bhargava Bhavan, 4 - 230 Kacheri Ghat, Agra - 282004, U.P., India. TEL 65780. Ed. S.N. Rai. adv.; bk.rev. **Indexed:** Psychol.Abstr. (1986-).
—BLDSC (4410.970000).
Description: Publishes empirical and critical review articles in the field of psychology.

370.15 150   II   ISSN 0046-9009
INDIAN JOURNAL OF PSYCHOMETRY AND EDUCATION. (Text in English) 1970. s-a. Rs.100($10) Indian Psychometric and Educational Research Association, University of Patna, Dept. of Education, Patna 800 004, India. (Dist. by: Nandini Enterprises, 23-451 Wazirpura, Agra-282 003, India) Ed. R.P. Singh. adv.; bk.rev.; bibl.; charts. circ. 500. **Indexed:** Lang.& Lang.Behav.Abstr., Psychol.Abstr. (1970-).

156   II   ISSN 0019-6215
BF1
INDIAN PSYCHOLOGICAL REVIEW. (Text in English) 1954. 6/yr. Rs.165($51.50) Agra Psychological Research Cell, Tiwari Kothi, Belanganj, Agra 282004, India. Eds. S. Jalota, M.C. Joshi. adv.; bk.rev. (reprint service avail. from ISI) **Indexed:** Psychol.Abstr.
—BLDSC (4428.200000); UnCover.

150   US   ISSN 0277-7010
BF1
INDIVIDUAL PSYCHOLOGY; the journal of Adlerian research, theory & practice. 1940. q. $30 to individuals; institutions $59. (North American Society of Adlerian Psychology) University of Texas Press, Box 7819, Austin, TX 78713. TEL 512-471-4531. FAX 512-320-0668. TELEX 776453 UTEXPRES AUS. E-mail: leah@utpress.ppb.utexas.edu. Ed. Guy J. Manaster. adv. contact: Leah Dixon. bk.rev.; bibl.; charts; stat.; index. circ. 1,900. (reprint service avail. from UMI,KTO) **Indexed:** Adol.Ment.Hlth.Abstr., Biol.Abstr., Curr.Cont., Curr.Lit.Fam.Plan., IMFL, Ind.Med., Lang.& Lang.Behav.Abstr., Mid.East: Abstr.& Ind., Psychoanal.Abstr., Psychol.Abstr. (1982-), Res.High.Educ.Abstr., Soc.Work Res.& Abstr., SSCI. **Document type:** academic/scholarly publication.
—BLDSC (4437.505000); Faxon; Genuine Article; SWETS; UMI; UnCover. **CCC.**
Former titles (until 1981): Journal of Individual Psychology (ISSN 0022-1805); Individual Psychologist; American Journal of Individual Psychology; Individual Psychology Bulletin; Individual Psychology News.
Description: Presents current scholarly and professional research dealing with all aspects of the theories founded by Alfred Adler.

618.92   US   ISSN 0163-6383
BF719   CODEN: IBDEDP
INFANT BEHAVIOR AND DEVELOPMENT; an international & interdisciplinary journal. 1978. q. $50 to individuals; institutions $115. Ablex Publishing Corporation, 355 Chestnut St., Norwood, NJ 07648. TEL 201-767-8450. FAX 201-767-6717. TELEX 135-393. Ed. Carolyn Rovee-Collier. bk.rev.; index. circ. 1,200. (back issues avail.; reprint service avail. from ISI) **Indexed:** Bibl.Dev.Med.& Child Neur., Biol.Abstr., Chicago Psychoanal.Lit.Ind., Child Devel.Abstr., Curr.Cont., Excerp.Med., Lang.& Lang.Behav.Abstr., M.L.A., Psychol.Abstr. (1979-), Psycscan D.P., Sociol.Abstr., Sp.Ed.Needs Abstr., SSCI. **Document type:** academic/scholarly publication.
—BLDSC (4478.270000); Faxon; Genuine Article; SWETS; UnCover. **CCC.**
Refereed Serial

INFANT MENTAL HEALTH JOURNAL. see *MEDICAL SCIENCES — Pediatrics*

INFANZIA. see *CHILDREN AND YOUTH — About*

155.4 157   IT
INFANZIA PSICOANALISI E ISTITUZIONI. 1981. irreg., no.8, 1992. price varies. Liguori Editore s.r.l., Via Mezzocannone, 19, 80134 Naples, Italy. TEL 081-5527139. Ed. Bianca Iaccarino. **Document type:** monographic series.

155 370   SP   ISSN 0210-3702
LB1051
INFANZIA Y APRENDIZAJE. 1978. q. Aprendizaje, S.L., Crta. de Canillas, 138, 28043 Madrid, Spain. TEL 388-38-74. FAX 300-35-27. Eds. Pablo del Rio, Amelia Alvarez. adv. circ. 3,000. **Indexed:** Psychol.Abstr. (1982-).
—SWETS.
Description: Concerned with the psychology of development-education processes. Publishes original articles on empirical research and literary reviews and theoretical essays.
Refereed Serial

INFORMATION AND BEHAVIOR. see *COMMUNICATIONS*

INFORMATIONSBULLETINEN; tidskrift foer sjaelvfoersoerjning, miljoe, energi, odling, kultur, politik, solidaritet och fred. see *SOCIAL SCIENCES: COMPREHENSIVE WORKS*

INKLINKS (MNDELIN). see *EDUCATION — Special Education And Rehabilitation*

150   SA   ISSN 1022-0798
INNOVANT. (Text in Afrikaans, English) 1993. q. R.12. Sentrum vir Mensilike Ontwikkeling in Psigososiele Konteks - CEMCO - Centre for Human Advancement in Psychosocial Context, Department of Psychology, University of Pretoria, Lynnwood Rd., Brooklyn 0181, South Africa. TEL 27-12-4203430. FAX 27-12-4202404. E-mail: fieddijk@libarts.up.ac.za. Ed. Carina Fiedeldey-Van Dijk. **Document type:** academic/scholarly publication.
Refereed Serial

INSIDER'S GUIDE TO GRADUATE PROGRAMS IN CLINICAL PSYCHOLOGY. see *EDUCATION — Guides To Schools And Colleges*

INSTITUTE FOR POSITIVE WEIGHT MANAGEMENT NEWSLETTER. see *NUTRITION AND DIETETICS*

150   UK   ISSN 0073-9561
INSTITUTE OF PSYCHOPHYSICAL RESEARCH. PROCEEDINGS. 1968. irreg. £30 per vol. Institute of Psychophysical Research, 118 Banbury Rd., Oxford OX2 6JU, England. TEL 01865-58787. FAX 01865-58064. (Dist. in the U.S. by: State Mutual Book & Periodical Service Ltd., 521 Fifth Ave., New York, NY 10017) Ed.Bd. circ. 2,500. (back issues avail.) **Document type:** proceedings, monographic series.

370 150   RM
INSTITUTUL DE SUBINGINERI ORADEA. LUCRARI STIINTIFICE: SERIA PEDAGOGIE, PSIHOLOGIE, METODICA. (Text in Rumanian, occasionally in English or French; summaries in English, French, German or Rumanian) 1967. irreg. Institutul de Subingineri Oradea, Calea Armatei Rosii Nr. 5, 3700 Oradea, Rumania.
Formerly: Institutul Pedagogic Oradea. Lucrari Stiintifice: Seria Pedagogie, Psihologie, Metodica; which continues in part (in 1973): Institutul Pedagogica Oradea. Lucrari Stiintifice: Seria Istorie, Stiinte Sociale, Pedagogie; which superseded in part (in 1971): Institutul Pedagogica Oradea. Lucrari Stiintifice: Seria A and Seria B; which was formerly (until 1969): Institutul Pedagogic Oradea. Lucrari Stiintifice.

INSTRUCTIONAL SCIENCE; an international journal of learning and cognition. see *EDUCATION*

INTEGRAL PSYKOANALYS; psykoterapi, sociologi, filosofi. see *MEDICAL SCIENCES — Psychiatry And Neurology*

150   RU
INTEGRAL'NOE ISSLEDOVANIE INDIVIDUAL'NOSTI. 1977. irreg. 1 Rub. Permskii Gosudarstvennyi Pedagogicheskii Institut, Perm, Russia. TEL 32-85-90. Ed. Bronislav Aleksandrovich Vyatkin. circ. 700.

PSYCHOLOGY

152 US ISSN 1053-881X
BF1 CODEN: IPBSEK
INTEGRATIVE PHYSIOLOGICAL AND BEHAVIORAL SCIENCE. 1965. q. $106 to individuals (foreign $130); institutions $196 (foreign $220) (effective Aug. 1995). (Pavlovian Society) Transaction Publishers, Transaction Periodicals Consortium, Department 3092, Rutgers University, New Brunswick, NJ 08903. TEL 908-445-2280. FAX 908-445-3138. Ed. Stewart G. Wolf. index. circ. 550. (also avail. in microform from UMI) **Indexed:** Biol.Abstr., Chem.Abstr., Curr.Adv.Ecol.Sci., Curr.Cont., Curr.Ref.Fish Res., Dent.Ind., Excerp.Med., Hosp.Lit.Ind., Ind.Med., Psychol.Abstr. (1966-), Sci.Cit.Ind., SSCI. **Document type:** academic/scholarly publication.
—BLDSC (4531.816580); CASDDS; Faxon; Genuine Article; SWETS; UMI; UnCover. **CCC.**
Former titles: Pavlovian Journal of Biological Science (ISSN 0093-2213); Conditional Reflex (ISSN 0010-5392)
Description: Contains articles pertaining to empirical, theoretical, review, apparatus, and historical topics.

155.4 GW ISSN 0342-6831
INTEGRATIVE THERAPIE; Zeitschrift fuer vergleichende Psychotherapie und Methodenintegration. (Text in German; summaries in English) 1975. q. DM.64 (students DM.50). (Fritz Perls Institut) Junfermann Verlag, Imadstr. 40, 33102 Paderborn, Germany. TEL 05251-34034. FAX 05251-36371. Ed. Hilarion Petzold. adv.; bk.rev.; index. circ. 2,500. **Document type:** academic/scholarly publication.

370.15 150 US ISSN 0160-2896
BF431 CODEN: NTLLDT
INTELLIGENCE (NORWOOD); a multidisciplinary journal. 1977. q. $55 to individuals; institutions $135. Ablex Publishing Corporation, 355 Chestnut St., Norwood, NJ 07648. TEL 201-767-8450. FAX 201-767-6717. TELEX 135-393. Ed. Douglas Detterman. bk.rev.; index. circ. 650. (back issues avail.; reprint service avail. from ISI) **Indexed:** A.I.Abstr., ASSIA, Biol.Abstr., C.I.J.E., Child Devel.Abstr., Curr.Cont., Lang.& Lang.Behav.Abstr., Psychol.Abstr. (1977-), Sociol.Abstr. **Document type:** academic/scholarly publication.
—BLDSC (4531.826500); Faxon; Genuine Article; SWETS; UnCover. **CCC.**
Refereed Serial

150.19 IT
INTERAZIONI; clinica e ricerca psicoanalitica su individuo-coppia-famiglia. s-a. L.50000 (foreign L.85000) (effective 1993). (Istituto di Psicoterapia Psicoanalitica della Famiglia) Franco Angeli Editore, Viale Monza 106, 20127 Milan, Italy. Ed. Anna M. Nicolo.

370.15 150 100 US ISSN 8755-612X
INTERBEHAVIORIST; a quarterly newsletter of interbehavior psychology. 1970. q. $13 to individuals (foreign $15); institutions $20; students $10. c/o Linda Hayes, Ed., Dept. of Psychology, University of Nevada, Reno, NV 89557. TEL 913-864-4840. E-mail: dwf@pogonip.scs.unr.edu. adv.; bk.rev. circ. 125. (back issues avail.)
Description: Includes news, information, discussions, comments and brief articles pertaining to interbehavioral psychology. Provides a contextualistic, integrated-field approach to the natural science of behavior.

150 300 AG ISSN 0325-8203
BF5
INTERDISCIPLINARIA; revista de psicologia y ciencias afines/journal of psychology and related sciences. (Text in English and Spanish) 1980. s-a. $30 (foreign $42) to individuals; institutions $40 (foreign $47). (National Research Council of Argentina) Centro Interamericano de Investigaciones Psicologicas y Ciencias Afines, Tte. Gral. Juan D. Peron 2158, 1040 Buenos Aires, Argentina. TEL 953-1477. FAX 953-3541. E-mail: postmaster@ciipme.edu.ar. Eds. Dr. Horacio J.A. Rimoldi, Dr. Maria Cristina Richaud de Minzi. bk.rev. circ. 600. **Indexed:** Psychol.Abstr. (1983-). **Document type:** academic/scholarly publication, monographic series.
—BLDSC (4533.356240).

155 AG ISSN 0326-1913
INTERDISCIPLINARIA MONOGRAPHS. 1982. irreg. price varies. (National Research Council of Argentina) Centro Interamericano de Investigaciones Psicologicas y Ciencias Afines, Tte. Gral. Juan D. Peron 2158, 1040 Buenos Aires, Argentina. TEL 953-1477. FAX 953-3541. E-mail: postmaster@ciipme.edu.ar. Eds. Horacio J.A. Rimoldi, Dr. Maria Cristina Richaud de Minzi. circ. 500. **Document type:** academic/scholarly publication, monographic series.
Description: Covers a study of some perceptual and personality correlations of problem solving solutions.

INTERFACES: LINGUISTICS, PSYCHOLOGY AND HEALTH THERAPEUTICS; an international journal of research, notes and commentary. *see* LINGUISTICS

150 NE
INTERNATIONAL ASSOCIATION FOR CROSS-CULTURAL PSYCHOLOGY. INTERNATIONAL CONFERENCE. SELECTED PAPERS. irreg., 9th, 1990, Newcastle, Australia. fl.90($68) Swets & Zeitlinger bv, Heereweg 347, 2161 CA Lisse, Netherlands. TEL 31-2521-35111. FAX 31-2521-15888. TELEX 41325. (Dist. in N. America by: Swets & Zeitlinger, 440 Creamery Way, Ste. A, Exton, PA 19341. TEL 800-477-9387. FAX 610-524-5366) **Document type:** proceedings.

572 II ISSN 0020-613X
H1
INTERNATIONAL BEHAVIOURAL SCIENTIST. (Text in English) 1969. q. Rs.25($6.50) Sadhna Prakashan, Rastogi St., Subhash Bazar, Meerut 2, India. Ed. D.P. Rastogi. adv.; bk.rev.; abstr.; bibl.; charts; illus. circ. 500. (also avail. in microfilm from UMI; reprint service avail. from UMI) **Indexed:** Curr.Cont., Int.Polit.Sci.Abstr., Lang.& Lang.Behav.Abstr., Ref.Zh., Sociol.Abstr.
—UMI.

157 615.7 UK ISSN 0268-1315
CODEN: ICLPE4
INTERNATIONAL CLINICAL PSYCHOPHARMACOLOGY. 1986. q. £195($330) to institutions (effective 1995). Rapid Communications of Oxford Ltd., The Old Malthouse, Paradise St., Oxford OX1 1LD, England. TEL 01865-790447. FAX 01865-244012. E-mail: rapidcom@vax.oxford.ac.uk. Eds. Trevor Silverstone, Stuart Montgomery. adv. contact: Julie Gribben. **Indexed:** Excerp.Med. (1993-), Ind.Med., Psychol.Abstr. (1986-), Sci.Cit.Ind. **Document type:** academic/scholarly publication.
●Also available on CD-ROM.
—BLDSC (4538.674500); ADONIS; Faxon; Genuine Article; SWETS; UnCover. **CCC.**
Description: Bridges the gap between research and clinical practice in psychopharmacology.

150 SZ ISSN 0074-3364
INTERNATIONAL CONGRESS FOR ANALYTICAL PSYCHOLOGY. PROCEEDINGS. irreg., 12th, Chicago, 1992. International Association for Analytical Psychology, c/o Yvonne Trueb-Teucher, Sec.-Gen., Postfach 115, CH-8042 Zurich, Switzerland. **Document type:** proceedings.

150 GW ISSN 0085-2112
INTERNATIONAL CONGRESS OF PSYCHOLOGY. PROCEEDINGS.* (Published by host national organization: Great Britain, 1969; Japan, 1972; France, 1976; German Democratic Republic, 1980; Mexico, 1984) quadrennial; 1988, 24th, Australia. International Union of Psychological Science, c/o Prof. Kurt Pawlik, Universitaet Hamburg, Psychologisches Institut, Von Melle Park 11, D-2000 Hamburg 13, Germany. **Document type:** proceedings.

616.89 NO ISSN 0803-706X
CODEN: IFOPE6
INTERNATIONAL FORUM OF PSYCHOANALYSIS. (Text in English) 1992. q. NOK 770 in Nordic countries; elsewhere $124 (effective 1996). (International Federation of Psychoanalytic Societies (IFPS)) Scandinavian University Press, P.O. Box 2959 Toeyen, N-0608 Oslo, Norway. TEL 47-22-57-54-00. FAX 47-22-57-53-53. Ed. Jan Stensson. **Indexed:** Excerp.Med. (1994-), Psychol.Abstr. (1981-).
—BLDSC (4540.345505).
Description: Promotes articles demonstrating clinical experience and interest in revising or expanding psychoanalytic theory.

INTERNATIONAL JOURNAL FOR THE PSYCHOLOGY OF RELIGION. *see* RELIGIONS AND THEOLOGY

INTERNATIONAL JOURNAL OF ADOLESCENCE AND YOUTH. *see* CHILDREN AND YOUTH — About

INTERNATIONAL JOURNAL OF AVIATION PSYCHOLOGY. *see* AERONAUTICS AND SPACE FLIGHT

155 UK ISSN 0165-0254
BF712 CODEN: IJBDDY
INTERNATIONAL JOURNAL OF BEHAVIORAL DEVELOPMENT. 1978. q. £62($110) to individuals (outside the E.U. £67); institutions £180 (outside the E.U. £186 ($315)) (effective 1996). (International Society for the Study of Behavioral Development) Lawrence Erlbaum Associates Ltd., 27 Palmeira Mansions, Church Rd., Hove, E. Sussex BN3 2FA, England. TEL 01273-207411. FAX 01273-205612. (Subscr. to: Turpin Distribution Services Ltd., Blackhorse Rd., Letchworth, Herts. SG6 1HN, England. TEL 01462-672555. FAX 01462-480947) Ed. Linda Seigel. adv.: page £210; 115 x 190. bk.rev. (also avail. in microform from UMI) **Indexed:** ASSIA, Biol.Abstr., C.I.J.E., Child Devel.Abstr., CINAHL, Curr.Cont., IMFL, Mult.Ed.Abstr., PSI, Psychol.Abstr. (1978-), Psyscan D.P., Sociol.Abstr., SSCI, Stud.Wom.Abstr. **Document type:** academic/scholarly publication.
—BLDSC (4542.128000); Faxon; SWETS; UMI; UnCover. **CCC.**
Description: Promotes the discovery and application of knowledge about developmental processes at all stages of the lifespan, from infancy through old age.
Refereed Serial

150 301 US ISSN 1070-5503
R726.5
▼**INTERNATIONAL JOURNAL OF BEHAVIORAL MEDICINE.** 1994. q. $40 to individuals (foreign $65); institutions $115 (foreign $140). (International Society of Behavioral Medicine) Lawrence Erlbaum Associates, Inc., 10 Industrial Dr., Mahwah, NJ 07430-2262. TEL 201-236-9500. FAX 201-236-0072. Ed. Neil Schneiderman. adv.: page $350; 5 x 8. **Document type:** academic/scholarly publication.
—BLDSC (4542.128700).
Description: Devoted to furthering an understanding of scientific relations between sociocultural, psychosocial, and behavioral principles on the one hand and biological processes, physical health, and illness on the other.

INTERNATIONAL JOURNAL OF BIOSOCIAL AND MEDICAL RESEARCH; bridging the gap between the natural and social sciences to better understand human behavior. *see* NUTRITION AND DIETETICS

INTERNATIONAL JOURNAL OF CONFLICT MANAGEMENT. *see* BUSINESS AND ECONOMICS — Management

INTERNATIONAL JOURNAL OF EATING DISORDERS. *see* NUTRITION AND DIETETICS

616.8 US ISSN 0020-7284
RC488 CODEN: IJGPAO
INTERNATIONAL JOURNAL OF GROUP PSYCHOTHERAPY. 1951. q. $60 to individuals (foreign $80); institutions $135 (foreign $155) (effective 1995). (American Group Psychotherapy Association) Guilford Publications, Inc., 72 Spring St., 4th Fl., New York, NY 10012. TEL 212-431-9800. FAX 212-966-6708. Ed. Dr. William Piper; Pub. Robert Matloff. adv. contact: Marian Robinson. bk.rev.; abstr.; bibl.; charts; stat.; index. circ. 5,400. (back issues avail.; reprint service avail. from ISI,UMI) **Indexed:** Adol.Ment.Hlth.Abstr., ASSIA, Biol.Abstr., Curr.Cont., Excerp.Med., Ind.Med., Int.Nurs.Ind., Lang.& Lang.Behav.Abstr., Mid.East: Abstr.& Ind., Psychol.Abstr. (1951-), Soc.Work Res.& Abstr., SSCI. **Document type:** academic/scholarly publication.
—BLDSC (4542.270000); EMDOCS; Faxon; Genuine Article; SWETS; UMI; UnCover. **CCC.**
Description: Devoted to reporting and interpreting the research and practice of group psychotherapy.
Refereed Serial

PSYCHOLOGY

301.1 320   US   ISSN 0047-0732
HN1   CODEN: IJGTB3
INTERNATIONAL JOURNAL OF GROUP TENSIONS. 1971. q. $225 (foreign $265) (effective 1996). (International Organization for the Study of Group Tensions) Human Sciences Press, Inc. (Subsidiary of: Plenum Publishing Corp.), 233 Spring St., New York, NY 10013-1578. TEL 212-620-8000. FAX 212-463-0742. TELEX 23-4211339. Eds. Benjamin B. Wolman, Herbert H. Krauss. adv.; bk.rev.; bibl.; index. (also avail. in microform from UMI; reprint service avail. from UMI) **Indexed:** Int.Polit.Sci.Abstr., Mid.East: Abstr.& Ind., Polit.Sci.Abstr., Psychol.Abstr., SSCI. **Document type:** academic/scholarly publication.
—BLDSC (4542.272000); Faxon; UMI; UnCover.
Description: Publishes research findings and theoretical analyses pertaining to bias, prejudice, discrimination, hostility, and violence - and methods of resolving these conflicts.
Refereed Serial

INTERNATIONAL JOURNAL OF HUMAN FACTORS IN MANUFACTURING. see *COMPUTERS — Automation*

614.58   US   ISSN 0020-7411
RA790.A1   CODEN: IJMHBV
INTERNATIONAL JOURNAL OF MENTAL HEALTH. 1972. q. $442 to institutions (foreign $498) (effective Jul. 1995). M.E. Sharpe, Inc., 80 Business Park Dr., Armonk, NY 10504. TEL 914-273-1800; 800-541-6563. FAX 913-273-2106. Ed. Dr. Martin Gittelman. adv.; bk.rev. (back issues avail.) **Indexed:** Adol.Ment.Hlth.Abstr., ASSIA, Biol.Abstr., Child Devel.Abstr., Curr.Cont., Excerp.Med., IMFL, Mid.East: Abstr.& Ind., Psychol.Abstr. (1972-), Soc.Sci.Ind., SSCI, Stud.Wom.Abstr. **Document type:** academic/scholarly publication.
—BLDSC (4542.352000); EMDOCS; Faxon; Genuine Article; SWETS; UMI; UnCover. **CCC.**
Refereed Serial

INTERNATIONAL JOURNAL OF PSYCHIATRY IN MEDICINE; an international journal of medical psychology and psychiatry in the general hospital. see *MEDICAL SCIENCES — Psychiatry And Neurology*

150.19   UK   ISSN 0020-7578
BF173.A2   CODEN: IJPSAA
INTERNATIONAL JOURNAL OF PSYCHO-ANALYSIS. (Text in English; summaries in French, German, Spanish) 1920. bi-m. £140($280) (outside the E.U. £175) (effective 1996). Institute of Psychoanalysis, 63 New Cavendish St., London W1M 7RD, England. TEL 0171-323-5312. FAX 0171-580-4952. Ed. David Tucket. adv. contact: Evelyn Cantor. bk.rev.; index. circ. 7,200. (back issues avail.) **Indexed:** Biol.Abstr., Curr.Cont., Excerp.Med., Ind.Med., Mid.East: Abstr.& Ind., Mult.Ed.Abstr., Psychoanal.Abstr., Psychol.Abstr. (1929-), SSCI. **Document type:** academic/scholarly publication.
—BLDSC (4542.498000); EMDOCS; Faxon; Genuine Article; SWETS; UMI; UnCover. **CCC.**
Incorporates (in 1992): International Psycho-Analytical Association. Bulletin (ISSN 0306-2643)
Refereed Serial

INTERNATIONAL JOURNAL OF PSYCHOLINGUISTICS. see *LINGUISTICS*

150   UK   ISSN 0020-7594
BF1   CODEN: IJPSBB
INTERNATIONAL JOURNAL OF PSYCHOLOGY/JOURNAL INTERNATIONAL DE PSYCHOLOGIE. (Text in English, French) 1966. bi-m. £35($68) to individuals (outside the E.U. £39); institutions £125 (outside the E.U. £130 ($238)) (effective 1996). (International Union of Psychological Science) Lawrence Erlbaum Associates Ltd., 27 Palmeira Mansions, Church Rd., Hove, E. Sussex BN3 2FA, England. TEL 01273-207411. FAX 01273-205612. (Subscr. to: Turpin Distribution Services Ltd., Blackhorse Rd., Letchworth, Herts. SG6 1HN, England. TEL 01462-672555. FAX 01462-480947) Ed. Francois Dore. adv.: page £175; 110 x 190. bk.rev.; abstr.; charts; illus.; stat. circ. 1,500. (also avail. in microform; reprint service avail. from ISI,SWZ) **Indexed:** Adol.Ment.Hlth.Abstr., ASSIA, Biol.Abstr., Curr.Cont., Mid.East: Abstr.& Ind., Psychol.Abstr. (1966-), SSCI, Stud.Wom.Abstr., Tech.Educ.Abstr. **Document type:** academic/scholarly publication.
—BLDSC (4542.506000); Faxon; SWETS; UnCover. **CCC.**

150   NE   ISSN 0167-8760
                        CODEN: IJPSEE
INTERNATIONAL JOURNAL OF PSYCHOPHYSIOLOGY. (Text in English) 1983. 9/yr. fl.1839($1121) (effective 1996). (International Organization of Psychophysiology) Elsevier Science B.V., P.O. Box 211, 1000 AE Amsterdam, Netherlands. TEL 31-20-4853911. FAX 31-20-4853598. TELEX 18582 ESPA NL. E-mail: nlinfo-f@elsevier.nl; usinfo-f@elsevier.com; forinfo-kyf04035@niftyserve.or.jp; Site addr.: http://www.elsevier.nl/. (Subscr. in U.S. and Canada to: Elsevier Science Inc., Box 882, Madison Sq. Sta., New York, NY 10159. TEL 212-989-5800. FAX 212-633-3990) Ed.Bd. adv.; bk.rev. circ. 750. (also avail. in microform from UMI; back issues avail.) **Indexed:** Curr.Cont., Excerp.Med., Ind.Med., Psychol.Abstr. (1983-). **Document type:** academic/scholarly publication.
—BLDSC (4542.506500); Faxon; Genuine Article; SWETS; UnCover. **CCC.**
Description: Covers all aspects of psychophysiology.
Refereed Serial

INTERNATIONAL JOURNAL OF PSYCHOSOMATICS. see *MEDICAL SCIENCES*

INTERNATIONAL JOURNAL OF REHABILITATION AND HEALTH. see *HANDICAPPED*

616.89   UK   ISSN 0884-724X
RC480.55   CODEN: IJTPEP
INTERNATIONAL JOURNAL OF SHORT TERM PSYCHOTHERAPY. 1986. q. $285 (foreign $285) (effective 1996). (Institute for Short Term Psychotherapy) John Wiley & Sons Ltd., Journals, Baffins Ln., Chichester, W. Sussex PO19 1UD, England. TEL 01243-779777. FAX 01243-776128. TELEX 86290 WIBOOK G. (Subscr. in the Americas to: John Wiley & Sons, Inc., 605 Third Ave., New York, NY 10158. TEL 212-850-6645. FAX 212-850-6021) Ed. Paul Fink. circ. 296. (back issues avail.; reprint service avail. from SWZ) **Indexed:** Psychol.Abstr. (1990-). **Document type:** academic/scholarly publication.
—BLDSC (4542.548000); Faxon; UMI.
Description: Offers the researcher and the practitioner access to ongoing systematic research and developments in the spectrum of short-term psychotherapies.

INTERNATIONAL JOURNAL OF SPORT PSYCHOLOGY. see *MEDICAL SCIENCES — Sports Medicine*

155.4   UK   ISSN 0965-2531
GV1201
INTERNATIONAL PLAY JOURNAL. (Text in English; summaries in French and Spanish) 1993. 3/yr. £79 to institutions in the E.U. (N. America $135; elsewhere £85) (effective 1995). Chapman & Hall, Journals Department (Subsidiary of: International Thomson Publishing Group), 2-6 Boundary Row, London SE1 8HN, England. TEL 0171-865-0066. FAX 0171-522-9623. TELEX 290164 CHAPMA G. E-mail: journal@chall.mhs.compuserve.com. (Dist. by: International Thomson Publishing Services Ltd., Cheriton House, North Way, Andover, Hants. SP10 5BE, England. TEL 01264-342713. FAX 01264-342807; N. American subscr. to: Chapman & Hall, Journals Promotion Department, One Penn Plaza, 41st Fl., New York, NY 10119. TEL 212-564-1060. FAX 212-564-1505) Ed. Bob Hughes. adv. (reprint service avail.) **Document type:** academic/scholarly publication.
—BLDSC (4544.953150). **CCC.**
Description: Publishes research papers and practice-based articles on all aspects of play.
Refereed Serial

150   US   ISSN 0047-116X
BF1
INTERNATIONAL PSYCHOLOGIST. 1959. q. $24 to non-members. International Council of Psychologists, Inc., c/o John M. Davis, Sec'y-Gen., Dept. of Psychology, Southwest Texas State Univ., San Marcos, TX 78666-4616. (Subscr. to: Box 62, Hopkinton, RI 02833-0062. TEL 401-377-3092. FAX 401-377-6013) Ed. Carleton Shay. adv.; bk.rev.; abstr. circ. 1,700. (looseleaf format; back issues avail.) **Document type:** newsletter.
—BLDSC (4545.350000).

INTERNATIONAL REGISTRY OF ORGANIZATION DEVELOPMENT PROFESSIONALS AND ORGANIZATION DEVELOPMENT HANDBOOK. see *BUSINESS AND ECONOMICS — Personnel Management*

150   UK
INTERNATIONAL REVIEW OF HEALTH PSYCHOLOGY. 1992. irreg. John Wiley & Sons Ltd., Journals, Baffins Ln., Chichester, W. Sussex PO19 1UD, England. TEL 01243-779777. FAX 01243-776128. TELEX 86290 WIBOOK G. (Subscr. in the Americas to: John Wiley & Sons, Inc., 605 Third Ave., New York, NY 10158. TEL 212-850-6645. FAX 212-850-6021) Ed.Bd. **Document type:** academic/scholarly publication.

158.7   UK   ISSN 0886-1528
HF5548.7
INTERNATIONAL REVIEW OF INDUSTRIAL AND ORGANIZATIONAL PSYCHOLOGY. 1986. 1/yr. $9 (foreign $9) (effective 1996). John Wiley & Sons Ltd., Journals, Baffins Ln., Chichester, W. Sussex PO19 1UD, England. TEL 01243-779777. FAX 01243-776128. TELEX 86290 WIBOOK G. (Subscr. in the Americas to: John Wiley & Sons, Inc., 605 Third Ave., New York, NY 10158. TEL 212-850-6645. FAX 212-850-6021) Eds. Cary Cooper, Ivan Robertson. circ. 139. (also avail. in microform from UMI; back issues avail.) **Document type:** academic/scholarly publication.
—BLDSC (4547.325000); SWETS; UMI. **CCC.**
Description: Provides reviews in the field of industrial and organizational psychology.
Refereed Serial

156   UK   ISSN 1058-4994
BF531
INTERNATIONAL REVIEW OF STUDIES ON EMOTION. 1991. biennial. John Wiley & Sons Ltd., Journals, Baffins Lane, Chichester, Sussex PO19 1UD, England. TEL 01243-779777. FAX 01243-776128. TELEX 96290 WIBOOK G. **Document type:** academic/scholarly publication.
—BLDSC (4547.749000).

INTERNATIONAL SERIES IN THE PSYCHOLOGY OF RELIGIONS. see *RELIGIONS AND THEOLOGY*

INTERNATIONALES SYMPOSIUM GEGEN DROGEN IN DER SCHWEIZ. see *DRUG ABUSE AND ALCOHOLISM*

INTERVENTION IN SCHOOL AND CLINIC; an interdisciplinary journal directed to an international audience of teachers and specialists working with capable but underachieving children and youth. see *EDUCATION — Special Education And Rehabilitation*

IRISH JOURNAL OF PSYCHOLOGICAL MEDICINE. see *MEDICAL SCIENCES — Psychiatry And Neurology*

150   UK   ISSN 0303-3910
                        CODEN: IRJPAR
IRISH JOURNAL OF PSYCHOLOGY. 1971. q. I£48($80) Psychological Society of Ireland, c/o Queen's University, School of Psychology, Belfast BT7 1NN, N. Ireland. TEL 01232-245133. FAX 01232-664144. Eds. Kenneth Brown, Carol McGuinness. adv.; bk.rev.; bibl.; charts. circ. 950. **Indexed:** Biol.Abstr., Br.Educ.Ind., Curr.Cont., IMFL, Psychol.Abstr. (1971-), Ref.Zh., SSCI. **Document type:** academic/scholarly publication.
—BLDSC (4572.200000); Genuine Article; UnCover.

616.89 156   IS   ISSN 0334-6080
BF8.H4
ISRAEL QUARTERLY OF PSYCHOLOGY. (Text in Hebrew) irreg. (1-2/yr.). membership. Histadrut Hapsikologim B'yisrael - Israel Psychological Association, Frishman 74, Tel Aviv 65456, Israel. FAX 972-3-5230763. adv.; bk.rev. circ. 3,000. **Document type:** academic/scholarly publication.

364 345   UK   ISSN 0266-6863
ISSUES IN CRIMINOLOGICAL AND LEGAL PSYCHOLOGY. 1981. irreg., no.22, 1995. £7 per no. British Psychological Society, Division of Criminological and Legal Psychology, St. Andrew's House, 48 Princess Rd. E., Leicester LE1 7DR, England. TEL 0116-254-9568. FAX 0116-247-0787. E-mail: bps1@uk.ac.le. Eds. Geoffrey Stephenson, Noel Clark. circ. 250. (back issues avail.) **Indexed:** Psychol.Abstr. (1981-). **Document type:** monographic series.
—BLDSC (4584.190000).
Description: Conveys recent research and debate in the fields of criminology and legal psychology to an academic readership
Refereed Serial

ISSUES IN MENTAL HEALTH NURSING. see *MEDICAL SCIENCES — Nurses And Nursing*

PSYCHOLOGY

616.89 US ISSN 1075-0754
RC475
ISSUES IN PSYCHOANALYTIC PSYCHOLOGY. 1978. 3/yr. $15. Washington Square Institute, 41 E. 11th St., New York, NY 10003. TEL 212-477-2600. Ed. Dr. Elliot Kronish. bk.rev. circ. 50. (back issues avail.) **Indexed:** Psychol.Abstr. (1975-). **Document type:** academic/scholarly publication.
 Formerly (until 1993): Issues in Ego Psychology (ISSN 0097-6555)
 Description: Publishes papers on psychoanalytic theory, technique, and psychotherapy.

613.7 155.3 CN ISSN 1192-1358
IT'S OKAY!. 1992. q. Can.$23.95. Phoenix Counsel Inc., 1 Springbank Dr., St. Catharines, ON L2S 2K1, Canada. Ed. Linda Crabtree; Pub. Linda Crabtree. adv.; bk.rev.; illus. circ. 3,500. **Document type:** consumer publication.
 Description: Offers sympathetic advice on sexuality, sex, self-esteem and disability with first-person articles, peotry, reviews. Provides frank talk on how bowel and bladder conditions, impotence, and other physical disabilities affect sexuality and how to overcome these obstacles.

J A S C T NEWSLETTER. (Japanese Association of Sex Counselors and Therapists) see MEDICAL SCIENCES

150 GW ISSN 0075-2363
JAHRBUCH DER PSYCHOANALYSE; Beitraege zur Theorie und Praxis. 1964. irreg., vol.32, 1994. price varies. Friedrich Frommann Verlag Guenther Holzboog, Koenig-Karl-Str. 27, 70372 Stuttgart, Germany. TEL 0711-9559690. FAX 0711-9559691. Ed.Bd. adv. contact: Ingrid Bachleitner. circ. 1,000. (reprint service avail. from KTO,SCH) **Indexed:** Psychoanal.Abstr., Psychol.Abstr. (1981-). **Document type:** academic/scholarly publication.
 —BLDSC (4632.050000).

150 GW ISSN 0942-1408
GR880
JAHRBUCH FUER ETHNOMEDIZIN UND BEWUSSTSEINSFORSCHUNG/YEARBOOK FOR ETHNOMEDICINE AND THE STUDY OF CONSCIOUSNESS. (Text in English, German) 1992. a. DM.48. V W B - Verlag fuer Wissenschaft und Bildung, Markgrafenstr. 67, 10969 Berlin, Germany. TEL 030-2510415. FAX 030-2510412. Ed. Dr. Christian Raetsch. **Document type:** academic/scholarly publication.
 Description: Presents information on aspects of ethnomedical systems related to human consciousness and its various states.

150 GW ISSN 0939-5806
GR880
JAHRBUCH FUER TRANSKULTURELLE MEDIZIN UND PSYCHOTHERAPIE/YEARBOOK OF CROSS-CULTURAL MEDICINE AND PSYCHOTHERAPY. (Text in English, German) 1990. a. DM.58. (Internationales Institut fuer Kulturvergleichende Therapieforschung) V W B - Verlag fuer Wissenschaft und Bildung, Markgrafenstr. 67, 10969 Berlin, Germany. TEL 030-2510415. FAX 030-2510412. Ed. Walter Andritzky. (back issues avail.) **Document type:** academic/scholarly publication.
 Description: Contains research on all aspects of ethnic and alternative healing methods.

JAPANESE BULLETIN OF ARTS THERAPY. see ART

157 JA ISSN 0017-7547
JAPANESE JOURNAL OF CRIMINAL PSYCHOLOGY/HANZAI SHINRIGAKU KENKYU. (Text in Japanese; summaries in English) 1963. 3/yr. 2400 Yen($30) Japanese Association of Criminal Psychology, 2-11-7 Hikawadai, Nerima-ku, Tokyo, Japan. TEL 03-3559-5084. Ed. Tatsuo Kasai. circ. 1,200. **Indexed:** Psychol.Abstr. (1969-). **Document type:** academic/scholarly publication.

370.15 150 JA ISSN 0021-5015
 CODEN: JJEPAP
JAPANESE JOURNAL OF EDUCATIONAL PSYCHOLOGY. (Text in Japanese; contents page in English) 1953. q. 16000 Yen. Japanese Association of Educational Psychology - Nihon Kyoiku Shinri Gakkai, c/o Faculty of Education, University of Tokyo, 7-3-1 Hongo, Bunkyo-ku, Tokyo 113, Japan. Ed.Bd. adv.; bk.rev.; charts; circ. controlled. **Indexed:** Psychol.Abstr. (1956-), SSCI. **Document type:** academic/scholarly publication.
 —BLDSC (4651.750000).

618.89 JA ISSN 0389-3723
JAPANESE JOURNAL OF PSYCHOPATHOLOGY/RINSHO SEISHIN BYORI. (Text in Japanese) 1980. s-a. Seiwa Shoten Co. Ltd., 2-5, Kamitakaido 1-chome, Suginami-ku, Tokyo 168, Japan. TEL 03-304-3822. Ed.Bd.

150 JA ISSN 0021-5368
BF76.5 CODEN: JPREAV
JAPANESE PSYCHOLOGICAL RESEARCH. (Text in English, French, German) 1954. q. $120. Japanese Psychological Association, 40-14-902 Hongo 2-chome, Bunkyo-ku, Tokyo 113, Japan. TEL 03-3814-3953. FAX 03-3814-3954. (Dist. by: Business Center for Academic Societies Japan, 5-16-9 Honkomagome, Bunkyo-ku, Tokyo 113, Japan. TEL 03-5814-5811) abstr.; charts; illus.; index. circ. 6,000. **Indexed:** Biol.Abstr., Curr.Cont., Ergon.Abstr., Psychol.Abstr. (1954-), SSCI.
 —BLDSC (4661.100000); Faxon; Genuine Article; SWETS; UnCover.

JEDNOTNA SKOLA; journal for pedagogical theory and praxis and psychology. see EDUCATION

155 PO ISSN 0870-4783
JORNAL DE PSICOLOGIA. (Text in Portuguese; summaries in English) 1982. q. Esc.1500 to individuals (foreign $30); institutions Esc.3000 (foreign $40) (effective 1993). Grupo de Estudos e Reflexao em Psicologia, R. das Taipas, 76, 4000 Porto, Portugal. TEL 02-310230. Ed. Rui Abrunhosa Goncalves. adv.; bk.rev.; bibl.; charts; stat. circ. 1,000. (back issues avail.) **Indexed:** Psychol.Abstr. (1984-). **Document type:** academic/scholarly publication.
 Description: Presents discussions and research in the field of psychology and other related sciences. Includes theoretical and research articles, brief reports and interviews.

158 US ISSN 0193-3922
BF637.C6
JOURNAL FOR SPECIALISTS IN GROUP WORK. 1978. 4/yr. $18 to individuals; institutions $24 (effective 1996). (Association for Specialists in Group Work) American Counseling Association, 5999 Stevenson Ave., Alexandria, VA 22304-3300. TEL 703-823-9800. FAX 703-823-0252. (Subscr. to: Box 2513, Birmingham, AL 35201-2513. TEL 205-995-1567. FAX 205-995-1588) Ed Arthur M. Horne. circ. 6,000. (also avail. in microfiche; reprint service avail. from UMI) **Indexed:** C.I.J.E., Lang.& Lang.Behav.Abstr., Psychol.Abstr. (1979-), Soc.Work Res.& Abstr., Sp.Ed.Needs Abstr.
 —BLDSC (5066.138000); UMI; UnCover. **CCC.**
 Formerly: Together (Washington, 1975) (ISSN 0161-0333)
 Description: Includes empirical research, history of group work, work with groups, theoretical discussions and current group literature reviews.

155 300 UK ISSN 0021-8308
HM132
JOURNAL FOR THE THEORY OF SOCIAL BEHAVIOUR. 1971. q. £229($406) (foreign £252) (effective 1996). Basil Blackwell Ltd., 108 Cowley Rd, Oxford OX4 1JF, England. TEL 0865-791100. FAX 0865-791347. TELEX 837022-OXBOOK-G. Ed. Charles W. Smith. adv. circ. 800. (reprint service avail. from SWZ,UMI) **Indexed:** Adol.Ment.Hlth.Abstr., ASSIA, Int.Polit.Sci.Abstr., Mid.East: Abstr.& Ind., Mult.Ed.Abstr., Phil.Ind., Psychol.Abstr. (1971-), Res.High.Educ.Abstr., SSCI.
 —BLDSC (5069.076000); Faxon; Genuine Article; SWETS; UMI; UnCover. **CCC.**

155.4 US ISSN 0091-0627
RJ499.A1 CODEN: JABCAA
JOURNAL OF ABNORMAL CHILD PSYCHOLOGY. 1973. bi-m. $375 (foreign $440) (effective 1996). Plenum Publishing Corp., 233 Spring St., New York, NY 10013-1578. TEL 212-620-8000. FAX 212-463-0742. TELEX 23-421139. Ed. Donald K. Routh. adv.; bibl.; charts. (also avail. in microfilm from JSC; back issues avail.) **Indexed:** Abstr.Crim.& Pen., Adol.Ment.Hlth.Abstr., ASSIA, Behav.Med.Abstr., Bibl.Dev.Med.& Child Neur., Biol.Abstr., C.I.J.E., Child Devel.Abstr., Curr.Cont., Except.Child.Educ.Abstr., Excerp.Med., IMFL, Ind.Med., Mid.East: Abstr.& Ind., Mult.Ed.Abstr., Psychol.Abstr. (1977-), Psycscan D.P., Ref.Zh, Sp.Ed.Needs Abstr., SSCI. **Document type:** academic/scholarly publication.
 —BLDSC (4918.820000); EMDOCS; Faxon; Genuine Article; SWETS; UMI; UnCover. **CCC.**
 Refereed Serial

157 US ISSN 0021-843X
RC321 CODEN: JAPCAC
JOURNAL OF ABNORMAL PSYCHOLOGY. 1906. q. $79 to non-members (foreign $94); members $39 (foreign $47); institutions $158 (foreign $188). American Psychological Association, 750 First St., N.E., Washington, DC 20002-4242. TEL 202-336-5600. FAX 202-336-5568. Ed. Milton E. Strauss. adv.; charts; index. circ. 8,400. (also avail. in microform from UMI,PMC; back issues avail.; reprint service avail. from KTO,UMI) **Indexed:** Abstr.Crim.& Pen., Abstr.Health Care Manage.Stud., Acad.Ind., ASSIA, Behav.Med.Abstr., Biol.Abstr., Biol.Dig., Crim.Just.Abstr., Curr.Cont., Dok.Arbeitsmed., Except.Child.Educ.Abstr., Excerp.Med., Hlth.Ind., Ind.Med., M.L.A., Mid.East: Abstr.& Ind., Mult.Ed.Abstr., Psychol.Abstr. (1925-), Psycscan C.P., Sage Fam.Stud.Abstr., Soc.Sci.Ind., Sp.Ed.Needs Abstr., SSCI, Stud.Wom.Abstr. **Document type:** academic/scholarly publication.
 —BLDSC (4918.840000); EMDOCS; Faxon; Genuine Article; SWETS; UMI; UnCover. **CCC.**
 Description: Provides articles on basic research and theory in the broad field of abnormal behavior.
 Refereed Serial

364 US ISSN 1055-3835
HV9275
JOURNAL OF ADDICTIONS & OFFENDER COUNSELING. 1980. 2/yr. $9 to individuals; institutions $15 (effective 1996). (International Association of Addictions and Offender Counselors) American Counseling Association, 5999 Stevenson Ave., Alexandria, VA 22304-3300. TEL 703-823-9800. FAX 703-823-0252. (Subscr. to: Box 2513, Birmingham, AL 35201-2513. TEL 205-995-1567. FAX 205-995-1588) Ed. Bob Shearer. adv. contact: Stephen Brooks. circ. 1,500. (also avail. in microform from UMI; reprint service avail. from UMI) **Indexed:** Crim.Just.Abstr., Psychol.Abstr. (1990-), Soc.Work Res.& Abstr.
 —UMI; UnCover. **CCC.**
 Formerly: Journal of Offender Counseling (ISSN 0275-8598)
 Description: Covers sexual crime, drug and alcohol abuse and prison overcrowding.

JOURNAL OF ADOLESCENCE. see CHILDREN AND YOUTH — About

JOURNAL OF ADOLESCENT RESEARCH. see CHILDREN AND YOUTH — About

155.6 US ISSN 1068-0667
HQ799.95 CODEN: JADEEU
▼**JOURNAL OF ADULT DEVELOPMENT.** 1994. q. $115 (foreign $135) (effective 1996). Plenum Publishing Corp., 233 Spring St., New York, NY 10013-1578. TEL 212-620-8468. FAX 212-463-0742. TELEX 23421139. Ed. Jack Demick. (also avail. in microfilm from JSC) **Document type:** academic/scholarly publication.
 —BLDSC (4918.943600); Faxon; Genuine Article. **CCC.**
 Description: Publishes broad studies of the positive aspects of adult development, pure cognition or reasoning from an interdisciplinary approach, and appreciations of a range of developmental theories and methodologies for understanding adults across the life span.
 Refereed Serial

JOURNAL OF AGING & IDENTITY. see GERONTOLOGY AND GERIATRICS

JOURNAL OF ANALYTIC SOCIAL WORK. see SOCIAL SERVICES AND WELFARE

616.89 UK ISSN 0021-8774
BF173.A2 CODEN: JANPA7
JOURNAL OF ANALYTICAL PSYCHOLOGY. 1955. 4/yr. £46 (U.S. and Canada $75; rest of world £48) to individuals; institutions £75 (U.S. and Canada $110; rest of world £80). Routledge, 11 New Fetter Ln., London EC4P 4EE, England. TEL 0171-583-9855. FAX 0171-842-2298. TELEX 263398-ROUT-G. E-mail: sample.journals@routledge.com. (Subscr. to: ITPS Ltd., Cheriton House, Andover, Hants SP10 5BE, England. TEL 01264-342919. FAX 01264-342807) Ed.Bd. adv.: page £200; trim 115 x 190. bk.rev.; bibl.; index. circ. 1,800. (also avail. in microfilm) **Indexed:** ASSIA, Biol.Abstr., Curr.Cont., Excerp.Med., Ind.Med., Mid.East: Abstr.& Ind., Psychoanal.Abstr., Psychol.Abstr. (1955-), SSCI, Yrbk.Assoc.Educ.& Rehab.Blind. **Document type:** academic/scholarly publication.
—BLDSC (4928.500000); EMDOCS; Faxon; Genuine Article; SWETS; UnCover. **CCC**.

157 616.8 UK ISSN 0887-6185
RC531 CODEN: JADIE8
JOURNAL OF ANXIETY DISORDERS. 1987. bi-m. £185($295) (effective 1996). Elsevier Science Ltd., Pergamon, P.O. Box 800, Kidlington, Oxford OX5 1DX, England. TEL 44-1865-843000. FAX 44-1865-843010. E-mail: nlinfo-f@elsevier.nl; usinfo-f@elsevier.com; forinfo-kyf04035@niftyserve.or.jp; Site addr.: http://www.elsevier.nl/. (Subscr. in U.S. and Canada to: Elsevier Science, 660 White Plains Rd., Tarrytown, NY 10591-5153. TEL 914-524-9200. FAX 914-333-2444) Eds. Cynthia G. Last, Michel Hersen. index. circ. 1,500. (also avail. in microfilm from UMI; back issues avail.) **Indexed:** Excerp.Med., Psychol.Abstr. (1987-). **Document type:** academic/scholarly publication.
—BLDSC (4939.300000); Faxon; Genuine Article; SWETS; UMI; UnCover. **CCC**.
Description: Publishes interdisciplinary research dealing with all aspects of anxiety disorders for all age groups (child, adolescent, adult and geriatric), including assessment, diagnosis, psychosocial and pharmacological treatment, epidemiology and prevention.
Refereed Serial

JOURNAL OF APPLIED ANIMAL WELFARE SCIENCE. see *ANIMAL WELFARE*

155 US ISSN 0021-8855
BF636.A1 CODEN: JOABAW
JOURNAL OF APPLIED BEHAVIOR ANALYSIS. 1968. q. $64. Society for the Experimental Analysis of Behavior, Inc. (Lawrence), c/o Department of Human Development, University of Kansas, Lawrence, KS 66045. TEL 913-843-0008. Ed. David Wacker. adv.; bk.rev.; charts; illus.; index; circ. 5,500 (paid). (also avail. in microfilm; back issues avail.) **Indexed:** Adol.Ment.Hlth.Abstr., ASSIA, Biol.Abstr., C.I.J.E., Child Devel.Abstr., Commun.Abstr., Cont.Pg.Manage., Curr.Cont., Except.Child.Educ.Abstr., Ind.Med., INIS Atomind., Mid.East: Abstr.& Ind., Psychol.Abstr. (1968-), Psycscan, Soc.Sci.Ind., SSCI, Yrbk.Assoc.Educ.& Rehab.Blind.
—BLDSC (4940.450000); Faxon; Genuine Article; SWETS.
Refereed Serial

150 US ISSN 1071-2089
R726.7
JOURNAL OF APPLIED BEHAVIORAL RESEARCH. 1993. 4/yr. $149 (foreign $164). Bellwether Publishing, Ltd., 8640 Guilford Rd., Ste. 200, Columbia, MD 21046. TEL 410-290-3870. FAX 410-290-8726. Ed. Andrew Baum. abstr.; bibl.; charts; index. **Document type:** academic/scholarly publication.
—BLDSC (4940.570000).
Refereed Serial

158 US ISSN 0021-8863
H1 CODEN: JABHAP
JOURNAL OF APPLIED BEHAVIORAL SCIENCE. 1965. q. $61 to individuals; institutions $160 (effective Sep. 1995). Sage Publications, Inc., 2455 Teller Rd., Thousand Oaks, CA 91320. TEL 805-499-0721. FAX 805-499-0871. E-mail: libraries@sagepub.com. (Overseas subscr. to: Sage Publications Ltd., 6 Bonhill St., London EC2A 4PU, England; Sage Publications India Pvt. Ltd., P.O. Box 4215, New Delhi 110 048, India) Ed. Clayton Alderfer. adv.; bk.rev.; abstr.; charts; index. circ. 2,800. (back issues avail.; reprint service avail.) **Indexed:** A.B.C.Pol.Sci., ABI Inform., ASSIA, BPIA, Cont.Pg.Manage., Curr.Cont., Educ.Admin.Abstr., Educ.Ind., Int.Polit.Sci.Abstr., Lang.& Lang.Behav.Abstr., Manage.Cont., Mult.Ed.Abstr., Pers.Lit., Psychol.Abstr. (1965-), Psycscan, Sage Fam.Stud.Abstr., Sage Pub.Admin.Abstr., SCIMP, Soc.Sci.Ind., SSCI, Stud.Wom.Abstr., Tech.Educ.Abstr. **Document type:** academic/scholarly publication.
—BLDSC (4940.500000); Faxon; SWETS; UMI; UnCover. **CCC**.
Description: Reports the latest interdisciplinary research on behavioral science and its applications to social policy, organization development, and community activity.

155 US ISSN 0193-3973
BF636.A1
JOURNAL OF APPLIED DEVELOPMENTAL PSYCHOLOGY. 1980. 2/yr. $60 to individuals; institutions $165. Ablex Publishing Corporation, 355 Chestnut St., Norwood, NJ 07648. TEL 201-767-8450. FAX 201-767-6717. TELEX 135-393. Ed. Irving E. Sigel. circ. 450. (back issues avail.; reprint service avail. from ISI) **Indexed:** Biol.Abstr., Child Devel.Abstr., Psychol.Abstr. (1980-), Psycscan D.P., Sociol.Abstr.
—BLDSC (4942.450000); Faxon; Genuine Article; SWETS; UnCover. **CCC**.
Refereed Serial

158 US ISSN 0021-9010
BF1 CODEN: JAPGBP
JOURNAL OF APPLIED PSYCHOLOGY. 1917. bi-m. $122 to non-members (foreign $142); members $61 (foreign $71); institutions $243 (foreign $286). American Psychological Association, 750 First St., N.E., Washington, DC 20002-4242. TEL 202-336-5600. FAX 202-336-5568. Ed. Philip Bobko. adv.; bibl.; charts; index. circ. 6,200. (also avail. in microfilm from UMI,PMC; reprint service avail. from KTO,UMI) **Indexed:** Abstr.Crim.& Pen., Acad.Ind., Adol.Ment.Hlth.Abstr., ASSIA, Biol.Abstr., BPIA, CINAHL, Commun.Abstr., Comput.Abstr., Cont.Pg.Manage., Crim.Just.Abstr., Curr.Cont., Dok.Arbeitsmed., Educ.Admin.Abstr., Educ.Ind., Ergon.Abstr., Excerp.Med., Hlth.Ind., Ind.Med., Int.Aerosp.Abstr., Int.Lab.Doc., Int.Nurs.Ind., Mid.East: Abstr.& Ind., Mult.Ed.Abstr., Pers.Lit., Psychol.Abstr. (1926-), Psycscan, Res.High.Educ.Abstr., Risk Abstr., SCIMP, Soc.Sci.Ind., SOMA, Sp.Ed.Needs Abstr., SSCI, Stud.Wom.Abstr. **Document type:** academic/scholarly publication.
—BLDSC (4947.000000); Faxon; Genuine Article; SWETS; UMI; UnCover. **CCC**.
Description: Research on applications of psychology in work settings such as industry, correction systems, government, and educational institutions.
Refereed Serial

158 US ISSN 0021-9029
HM251 CODEN: JASPBX
JOURNAL OF APPLIED SOCIAL PSYCHOLOGY. 1971. 24/yr. $559 (foreign $619) (effective 1996). V.H. Winston & Son, Inc., c/o Bellwether Publishing, Ltd., 8640 Guilford Rd., Ste. 200, Columbia, MD 21046. TEL 410-290-3870. FAX 410-290-8726. Ed. Andrew Baum. abstr.; charts; illus.; stat.; index. circ. 1,100. (back issues avail.) **Indexed:** Abstr.Crim.& Pen., ASSIA, Crim.Just.Abstr., Curr.Cont., Curr.Lit.Fam.Plan., Excerp.Med., Mid.East: Abstr.& Ind., Mult.Ed.Abstr., Psychol.Abstr. (1971-), Psycscan, Soc.Sci.Ind., Sociol.Educ.Abstr., Sportsearch, SSCI, Stud.Wom.Abstr. **Document type:** academic/scholarly publication.
—BLDSC (4947.080000); Faxon; Genuine Article; SWETS; UnCover. **CCC**.
Refereed Serial

JOURNAL OF APPLIED SPORT PSYCHOLOGY. see *MEDICAL SCIENCES — Sports Medicine*

JOURNAL OF AUTISM AND DEVELOPMENTAL DISORDERS. see *MEDICAL SCIENCES — Psychiatry And Neurology*

JOURNAL OF BEHAVIOR THERAPY AND EXPERIMENTAL PSYCHIATRY; an interdisciplinary journal. see *MEDICAL SCIENCES — Psychiatry And Neurology*

150.194 US ISSN 1053-0819
LB1060.2 CODEN: JBEDE5
JOURNAL OF BEHAVIORAL EDUCATION. 1991. q. $155 (foreign $180) (effective 1996). Human Sciences Press, Inc. (Subsidiary of: Plenum Publishing Corp.), 233 Spring St., New York, NY 10013. TEL 212-620-8000. FAX 212-463-0742. TELEX 23-421139. Ed. Nirbhay N. Singh. adv. **Indexed:** Psychol.Abstr. (1991-). **Document type:** academic/scholarly publication.
—BLDSC (4951.260000); Faxon; UnCover. **CCC**.
Description: Intended as a forum for research on the application of behavioral principles and technology to education.
Refereed Serial

JOURNAL OF BEHAVIORAL MEDICINE. see *MEDICAL SCIENCES — Psychiatry And Neurology*

JOURNAL OF BIBLICAL COUNSELING. see *RELIGIONS AND THEOLOGY*

155.84 US ISSN 0095-7984
E185.625 CODEN: JBPSE3
JOURNAL OF BLACK PSYCHOLOGY. 1974. q. $53 to individuals; institutions $149 (effective Sep. 1995). (Association of Black Psychologists) Sage Publications, Inc., 2455 Teller Rd., Thousand Oaks, CA 91320. TEL 805-499-0721. FAX 805-499-0871. E-mail: libraries@sagepub.com. (Overseas subscr. to: Sage Publications Ltd., 6 Bonhill St., London EC2A 4PU, England) Ed. Dr. Ann Kathleen Burlew. adv.; bk.rev. circ. 2,600. (also avail. in microform from UMI; back issues avail.; reprint service avail. from UMI) **Indexed:** Adol.Ment.Hlth.Abstr., IMFL, Psychol.Abstr. (1974-), Soc.Sci.Ind. (1994-). **Document type:** academic/scholarly publication.
—BLDSC (4954.180000); Faxon; UMI; UnCover. **CCC**.
Description: Publishes scholarly contributions within the field of psychology on the experience of Black and other minority populations from an Afrocentrist perspective in such issues as cognition, personality, social behavior, child development, education, and clinical application.

JOURNAL OF BRITISH MUSIC THERAPY. see *EDUCATION — Special Education And Rehabilitation*

158.7 330 US ISSN 0889-3268
JOURNAL OF BUSINESS & PSYCHOLOGY. 1986. q. $245 (foreign $285) (effective 1996). (Business Psychology Research Institute) Human Sciences Press, Inc. (Subsidiary of: Plenum Publishing Corp.), 233 Spring St., New York, NY 10013-1578. TEL 212-620-8000. FAX 212-463-0742. TELEX 23-421139. Ed. John W. Jones. adv. (reprint service avail. from UMI) **Indexed:** B.P.I., Psychol.Abstr. (1986-), Tech.Educ.Abstr. **Document type:** academic/scholarly publication.
—BLDSC (4954.661070); Faxon; UMI; UnCover. **CCC**.
Description: Highlights empirical research, case studies, and literature reviews dealing with psychological programs implemented in business settings.
Refereed Serial

150 658.3 US ISSN 1069-0727
HF5381.A1 CODEN: JOAAEX
JOURNAL OF CAREER ASSESSMENT. 1993. q. $40 to individuals; institutions $120. Psychological Assessment Resources, Inc., 16204 N. Florida Ave., Lutz, FL 33549. TEL 813-968-3003. FAX 813-968-2598. (Subscr. to: Box 998, Odessa, FL 33556. TEL 800-331-8378) Ed. W. Bruce Walsh. adv.; index. (back issues avail) **Document type:** academic/scholarly publication.
Description: Focusses on the process and techniques by which counselors and others gain understanding of the individual faced with the necessity of making informed career decisions.
Refereed Serial

PSYCHOLOGY

150 US ISSN 1062-1024
RJ499.A1 CODEN: JCFSES
JOURNAL OF CHILD AND FAMILY STUDIES. 1992. q. $135 (foreign $160) (effective 1996). Human Sciences Press, Inc. (Subsidiary of: Plenum Publishing Corp.), 233 Spring St., New York, NY 10013-1578. TEL 212-620-8000. FAX 212-463-0742. TELEX 12-421139. Ed. Nirbhay N. Singh. adv. contact: Daniel S. Lipner. **Indexed:** Psychol.Abstr. (1992-), Soc.Sci.Ind. (1994-). **Document type:** academic/scholarly publication.
—BLDSC (4957.426000); Faxon; UMI; UnCover. **CCC.**
Description: Devoted to publishing original papers on basic and applied research, program evaluation, service delivery and policy issues. Studies dealing with the early identification, prevention, diagnosis, treatment and rehabilitation of emotional disorders in children and adolescents are a primary focus, as well as family studies with a central mental health perspective.
Refereed Serial

JOURNAL OF CHILD LANGUAGE. see *CHILDREN AND YOUTH — About*

155.4 UK ISSN 0021-9630
RJ499.A1 CODEN: JPPDAI
JOURNAL OF CHILD PSYCHOLOGY & PSYCHIATRY & ALLIED DISCIPLINES. 1960. 8/yr. £232($369) (effective 1996). (Association of Child Psychology and Psychiatry) Elsevier Science Ltd., Pergamon, P.O. Box 800, Kidlington, Oxford OX5 1DX, England. TEL 44-1865-843000. FAX 44-1865-843010. E-mail: nlinfo-f@elsevier.nl; usinfo-f@elsevier.com; forinfo-kyf04035@niftyserve.or.jp; Site addr.: http://www.elsevier.nl/. (Subscr. in U.S. and Canada to: Elsevier Science, 660 White Plains Rd., Tarrytown, NY 10591-5153. TEL 914-524-9200. FAX 914-333-2444) Eds. Eric Taylor, Dorothy Bishop. adv.: B&W page $550, color page $1350. bk.rev.; charts; illus.; index. circ. 4,700. (also avail. in microfiche from MIM; microfilm from UMI; back issues avail.; reprint service avail. from UMI) **Indexed:** Abstr.Crim.& Pen., Adol.Ment.Hlth.Abstr., ASSIA, Bibl.Dev.Med.& Child Neur., Biol.Abstr., C.I.J.E., Child Devel.Abstr., CINAHL, Curr.Cont., Educ.Ind., Except.Child.Educ.Abstr., Excerp.Med., Ind.Med., Mid.East: Abstr.& Ind., Mult.Ed.Abstr., Nutr.Abstr., Psychol.Abstr. (1960-), Psycscan D.P., Risk Abstr., Soc.Sci.Ind. (1994-), Sp.Ed.Needs Abstr., SSCI. **Document type:** academic/scholarly publication.
—BLDSC (4957.800000); EMDOCS; Faxon; Genuine Article; SWETS; UMI; UnCover. **CCC.**
Description: Primarily concerned with child and adolescent psychology and psychiatry, including experimental and developmental studies and especially developmental psychopathology.
Refereed Serial

155.4 616.89 UK ISSN 0075-417X
JOURNAL OF CHILD PSYCHOTHERAPY. 1963. 3/yr. £32 (U.S. and Canada $52; rest of world £36) to individuals; institutions £70 (U.S. and Canada $105; rest of world £75). (Association of Child Psychotherapists) Routledge, 11 New Fetter Ln., London EC4P 4EE, England. TEL 0171-583-9855. FAX 0171-842-2298. E-mail: sample.journals@routledge.com. (Subscr. to: ITPS Ltd., Cheriton House, North Way, Andover, Hants SP10 5BE, England. TEL 01264-342919. FAX 01264-342807) Eds. Marianne Parsons, Ann Horne. adv.: page £150; trim 115 x 190. bk.rev. circ. 2,000. (reprint service avail.) **Indexed:** Abstr.Soc.Work, Child Devel.Abstr., Mid.East: Abstr.& Ind., Psychol.Abstr. (1977-). **Document type:** academic/scholarly publication.
—BLDSC (4957.900000); UnCover.
Description: Contains articles on theory, technique, and the practice of psychoanalytic psychotherapy with children, young people, and their families.

JOURNAL OF CHILD SEXUAL ABUSE; research, treatment & program innovations for victims, survivors & offenders. see *SOCIAL SERVICES AND WELFARE*

JOURNAL OF CLASSIFICATION. see *MATHEMATICS*

155.4 US ISSN 0047-228X
BF721 CODEN: JCCPD3
JOURNAL OF CLINICAL CHILD PSYCHOLOGY. 1972. q. $47.50 to individuals (foreign $72.50); institutions $215 (foreign $240). (American Psychological Association, Clinical Child Psychology) Lawrence Erlbaum Associates, Inc., 10 Industrial Dr., Mahwah, NJ 07430-2262. TEL 201-236-9500. FAX 201-236-0072. Ed. Jan L. Culbertson. adv.: page $425; 5 x 8. bk.rev.; illus. circ. 1,700. (also avail. in microform; reprint service avail. from UMI) **Indexed:** Abstr.Crim.& Pen., ASSIA, Bibl.Dev.Med.& Child Neur., Child Devel.Abstr., Curr.Cont., Except.Child.Educ.Abstr., IMFL, Mid.East: Abstr.& Ind., Psychol.Abstr. (1972-), Psycscan C.P., Psycscan D.P., SSCI. **Document type:** academic/scholarly publication.
—BLDSC (4958.384000); Faxon; SWETS; UMI; UnCover.
Description: Features the research and viewpoints of child advocates in all disciplines.
Refereed Serial

JOURNAL OF CLINICAL GEROPSYCHOLOGY. see *GERONTOLOGY AND GERIATRICS*

616.891 US ISSN 1076-044X
CODEN: JCIPEY
JOURNAL OF CLINICAL PSYCHOANALYSIS. 1992. q. $51.50 to individuals (foreign $93.50); institutions $77.50 (foreign $116.75). International Universities Press, Inc., 59 Boston Post Rd., Box 1524, Madison, CT 06443-1524. TEL 203-245-4000. FAX 203-245-0775. TELEX 282986 IUP BK. Eds. Dr. Herbert Wyman, Dr. Stephen Rittenberg. bk.rev. **Indexed:** Excerp.Med. (1994-), Psychol.Abstr. (1992-). **Document type:** academic/scholarly publication.
—BLDSC (4958.689000).
Description: Explains, in jargon-free language, what actually happens in an analysis.
Refereed Serial

157 US ISSN 0021-9762
RC321 CODEN: JCPYAO
JOURNAL OF CLINICAL PSYCHOLOGY. 1945. bi-m. $45 to individuals; libraries $140. Clinical Psychology Publishing Co., Inc., 4 Conant Sq., Brandon, VT 05733. TEL 802-247-6871. FAX 802-247-6853. Ed. Dr. Vladimir Pishkin. adv.; charts; index. circ. 2,529. (also avail. in microform from UMI; back issues avail.) **Indexed:** Abstr.Crim.& Pen., Abstr.Health Care Manage.Stud., Adol.Ment.Hlth.Abstr., ASSIA, Biol.Abstr., C.I.J.E., Chem.Abstr., Chic.Per.Ind., CINAHL, Commun.Abstr., Crim.Just.Abstr., Curr.Cont., Dent.Ind., Excerp.Med., Hosp.Lit.Ind., IMFL, Ind.Med., Ind.Sci.Rev., Int.Nurs.Ind., Lang.& Lang.Behav.Abstr., Mid.East: Abstr.& Ind., Nutr.Abstr., Psychol.Abstr. (1945-), Psycscan C.P., Sage Fam.Stud.Abstr., Sci.Cit.Ind., Soc.Sci.Ind., Soc.Work Res.& Abstr., SSCI. **Document type:** academic/scholarly publication.
●Also available online. Vendor(s): University Microfilms International.
—BLDSC (4958.690000); EMDOCS; Faxon; Genuine Article; SWETS; UMI; UnCover.
Refereed Serial

616.89 US ISSN 1068-9583
CODEN: JLPSE5
▼**JOURNAL OF CLINICAL PSYCHOLOGY IN MEDICAL SETTINGS.** 1994. q. $115 (foreign $135) (effective 1996). Plenum Publishing Corp., 233 Spring St., New York, NY 10013-1578. TEL 212-620-8000. FAX 212-463-0742. TELEX 23-421139. Ed. Ronald H. Rozensky. adv. (also avail. in microfilm from JSC; back issues avail.) **Document type:** academic/scholarly publication.
—BLDSC (4958.690550); Genuine Article.
Description: Explores theoretical and applied research in clinical science, clinical practice and service delivery, education and professional issues.
Refereed Serial

JOURNAL OF COGNITIVE NEUROSCIENCE. see *MEDICAL SCIENCES — Psychiatry And Neurology*

616.89 US ISSN 0889-8391
JOURNAL OF COGNITIVE PSYCHOTHERAPY. 1987. q. $39 to individuals (foreign $44); institutions $74 (foreign $85) (effective 1996). (International Association of Cognitive Psychotherapy) Springer Publishing Company, 536 Broadway, New York, NY 10012-3955. TEL 212-431-4370. FAX 212-941-7842. Ed. Thomas Dowd. adv.; bk.rev.; abstr. **Indexed:** Excerp.Med., Psychol.Abstr. (1987-). **Document type:** academic/scholarly publication, trade publication.
—BLDSC (4958.799200); Faxon; UnCover. **CCC.**
Description: Devoted to the advancement of the clinical practice of cognitive psychotherapy in its broadest sense. Merges theory, research and practice to provide an international forum investigating clinical implications of theoretical developments and research findings.
Refereed Serial

378 US ISSN 0897-5264
LB2343
JOURNAL OF COLLEGE STUDENT DEVELOPMENT. 1959. 6/yr. $45. American College Personnel Association, One Dupont Circle, Ste. 300, Washington, DC 20036-1110. TEL 202-835-2272. FAX 202-296-3286. Ed. Gregory Blimling. adv.; abstr.; index; circ. 8,000 (paid). (also avail. in microform from UMI; reprint service avail. from UMI) **Indexed:** C.I.J.E., Chic.Per.Ind., Coll.Stud.Pers.Abstr., Cont.Pg.Educ., Educ.Admin.Abstr., Educ.Ind., Mult.Ed.Abstr., PSI, Psychol.Abstr. (1965-), Soc.Work Res.& Abstr., SSCI. **Document type:** academic/scholarly publication.
—BLDSC (4958.816000); Faxon; SWETS; UMI; UnCover.
Formerly (until 1987): Journal of College Student Personnel (ISSN 0021-9789)
Description: In-depth coverage of topics such as student development, alcohol and drug use, needs of special populations and career planning.
Refereed Serial

616.89 US ISSN 8756-8225
JOURNAL OF COLLEGE STUDENT PSYCHOTHERAPY. 1986. q. $175 (foreign $245) (effective Mar. 1995). Haworth Press, Inc., 10 Alice St., Binghamton, NY 13904. TEL 607-722-5857; 800-342-9678. FAX 607-722-1424. Ed. Leighton C. Whitaker. adv.; bk.rev. circ. 406. (also avail. in microfiche from UMI; back issues avail.; reprint service avail. from HAW) **Indexed:** C.I.J.E., High.Educ.Abstr., IMFL, Psychol.Abstr. (1986-), Sage Fam.Stud.Abstr., Sage Pub.Admin.Abstr., Soc.Work Res.& Abstr., Sociol.Abstr., Sociol.Educ.Abstr., Sp.Ed.Needs Abstr., Stud.Wom.Abstr., Tech.Educ.Abstr. **Document type:** academic/scholarly publication.
—BLDSC (4958.830000); Haworth; UnCover.
Description: Enhances the lives of college and university students by stimulating high-quality practice theory, and research in mental and personal development.
Refereed Serial

JOURNAL OF COMMUNICATION. see *COMMUNICATIONS*

617.8 US ISSN 0021-9924
RC423.A1 CODEN: JCDIAI
JOURNAL OF COMMUNICATION DISORDERS. 1968. bi-m. $399 to institutions (effective 1996). Elsevier Science Inc., 655 Ave. of the Americas, New York, NY 10010. TEL 212-989-5800. FAX 212-633-3990. TELEX 420643 AEP UI. (Subscr. to: Box 882, Madison Sq. Sta., New York, NY 10159-0882) Ed. R.W. Rieber. adv.; bk.rev.; charts; illus. (also avail. in microform from UMI; reprint service avail. from SWZ) **Indexed:** ASSIA, Bibl.Dev.Med.& Child Neur., Biol.Abstr., C.I.J.E., Curr.Cont., Dent.Ind., DSH Abstr., Except.Child.Educ.Abstr., Excerp.Med., Ind.Med., Lang.& Lang.Behav.Abstr. (1977-), Mid.East: Abstr.& Ind., Psychol.Abstr. (1967-), Rehabil.Lit., Sociol.Abstr., SSCI, Yrbk.Assoc.Educ.& Rehab.Blind. **Document type:** academic/scholarly publication.
—BLDSC (4961.600000); EMDOCS; Faxon; Genuine Article; SWETS; UMI; UnCover. **CCC.**
Incorporates (1991-1994): Clinics in Communication Disorders (ISSN 1054-8505)
Description: Provides up-to-date information on clinical and research advances in a wide range of hearing and speech disorders.
Refereed Serial

301.1 150 UK ISSN 1052-9284
HM251 CODEN: JLCPEX
JOURNAL OF COMMUNITY AND APPLIED SOCIAL PSYCHOLOGY. 1986. 5/yr. $245 (foreign $245) (effective 1996). John Wiley & Sons Ltd., Journals, Baffins Ln., Chichester, Sussex PO19 1UD, England. TEL 01243-779777. FAX 01243-776128. TELEX 86290 WIBOOK G. (Subscr. in the Americas to: John Wiley & Sons, Inc., 605 Third Ave., New York, NY 10158. TEL 212-850-6645. FAX 212-850-6021) Eds. Geoffrey M. Stephenson, Jim Orford. circ. 194. (also avail. in microform from UMI; back issues avail.) **Indexed:** ASSIA, Curr.Cont., Mult.Ed.Abstr., Psychol.Abstr. (1987-). **Document type:** academic/scholarly publication.
—BLDSC (4961.693000); Genuine Article; SWETS; UMI; UnCover. **CCC.**
Formerly (until 1990): Social Behaviour (ISSN 0885-6249)
Description: Fosters international communication among those concerned with the social psychological analysis and critical understanding of community issues and problems and to develop this understanding in the context of proposals for intervention and social policy.
Refereed Serial

132 301.15 US ISSN 0090-4392
RC467 CODEN: JCPSD9
JOURNAL OF COMMUNITY PSYCHOLOGY. 1973. q. $45 to individuals; libraries $140. Clinical Psychology Publishing Co., Inc., 4 Conant Sq., Brandon, VT 05733. TEL 802-247-6871. FAX 802-247-6853. Ed. Dr. Raymond P. Lorion. adv.; index. circ. 820. (also avail. in microform from UMI; back issues avail.) **Indexed:** Adol.Ment.Hlth.Abstr., Commun.Abstr., Curr.Cont., IMFL, Lang.& Lang.Behav.Abstr., Mid.East: Abstr.& Ind., PSI, Psychol.Abstr. (1973-), Sage Pub.Admin.Abstr., SSCI. **Document type:** academic/scholarly publication.
—BLDSC (4961.750000); Faxon; Genuine Article; SWETS; UMI; UnCover.
Refereed Serial

156 US ISSN 0735-7036
BF1 CODEN: JCOPDT
JOURNAL OF COMPARATIVE PSYCHOLOGY. 1983. q. $50 to non-members (foreign $65); members $25 (foreign $33); institutions $100 (foreign $130). American Psychological Association, 750 First St., N.E., Washington, DC 20002-4242. TEL 202-336-5600. FAX 202-336-5568. Ed. Charles T. Snowdon. adv.; charts; illus.; index. circ. 1,600. (also avail. in microform from UMI; reprint service avail. from UMI) **Indexed:** Adol.Ment.Hlth.Abstr., Anim.Breed.Abstr., Biol.Abstr., Biol.& Agr.Ind., Chem.Abstr., Ecol.Abstr., Ind.Med., Ind.Sci.Rev., INIS Atomind., Psychol.Abstr. (1926-), Sci.Cit.Ind., Soc.Sci.Ind. **Document type:** academic/scholarly publication.
—BLDSC (4963.300000); CASDDS; Faxon; Genuine Article; SWETS; UMI; UnCover. **CCC.**
Supersedes in part (1947-1982): Journal of Comparative and Physiological Psychology (ISSN 0021-9940)
Description: Laboratory and field studies of the behavioral patterns of various species as they relate to evolution, development, ecology, control and functional significance.
Refereed Serial

153 500 UK ISSN 1355-8250
BF309
▼ **JOURNAL OF CONSCIOUSNESS STUDIES;** controversies in science & the humanities. (Includes section: Consciousness Research Abstracts) 1994. bi-m. £25($40) to individuals; institutions £48 ($77) (effective 1996). Imprint Academic, P.O. Box 1, Thorverston, Exeter, Devon EX5 5YX, England. TEL 01392-841600. E-mail: keith@imprint.co.uk. (Subscr. in the U.S. to: c/o Prof. Jonathan Shear, Department of Philosophy, Virginia Commonwealth Univ., Richmond, VA 23284-2025. TEL 804-282-2119. FAX 804-282-2119) Ed.Bd; Pub. Keith Sutherland. adv.; page £250 ($400); adv. contact: Sandra Good. bk.rev./ circ. 3,000 (paid). (back issues avail.) **Document type:** academic/scholarly publication.
—BLDSC (4965.160000).
Description: Publishes original scholarship and reviews in the new field of consciousness research, integrating developments in the sciences and humanities.
Refereed Serial

155 US ISSN 1072-0537
BF698.9.P47 CODEN: JCPYES
JOURNAL OF CONSTRUCTIVIST PSYCHOLOGY. 1988. q. £103($170) (effective 1996). Taylor & Francis Inc., 1900 Frost Rd., Ste. 101, Bristol, PA 19007-1598. TEL 215-785-5800; 800-821-8312. FAX 215-785-5515. (Subscr. in Europe to: Taylor & Francis Ltd., Rankine Rd., Basingstoke, Hants. RG24 8PR, England. TEL 44-1256-840366. FAX 44-1256-479438) Eds. Robert A. Neimeyer, Greg J. Neimeyer. (also avail. in microform from UMI; reprint service avail. from UMI) **Indexed:** Psychol.Abstr. (1988-). **Document type:** academic/scholarly publication.
—BLDSC (4965.194000). **CCC.**
Formerly (until 1994): International Journal of Personal Construct Psychology (ISSN 0893-603X)
Description: Presents empirical research, conceptual analyses, critical reviews, case studies on personal construct theory and related approaches to psychology.
Refereed Serial

157 616.8 US ISSN 0022-006X
BF1 CODEN: JCLPBC
JOURNAL OF CONSULTING AND CLINICAL PSYCHOLOGY. 1968. bi-m. $130 to non-members (foreign $150); members $65; institutions $273 (foreign $316). American Psychological Association, 750 First St., N.E., Washington, DC 20002-4242. TEL 202-336-5600. FAX 202-336-5568. Ed. Larry E. Beutler. adv.; bibl.; charts; illus.; index. circ. 12,000. (also avail. in microform from UMI,PMC; reprint service avail. from KTO,UMI) **Indexed:** Abstr.Crim.& Pen., Acad.Ind., Adol.Ment.Hlth.Abstr., ASSIA, Behav.Med.Abstr., Biol.Abstr., C.I.J.E., Commun.Abstr., Crim.Just.Abstr., Curr.Cont., Dok.Arbeitsmed., Except.Child.Educ.Abstr., Excerp.Med., Hlth.Ind., Ind.Med., Mid.East: Abstr.& Ind., Mult.Ed.Abstr., Psychol.Abstr. (1937-), Psyscan C.P., Risk Abstr., Sage Fam.Stud.Abstr., Soc.Sci.Ind., Soc.Work Res.& Abstr., Sp.Ed.Needs Abstr., SSCI. **Document type:** academic/scholarly publication.
—BLDSC (4965.195000); EMDOCS; Faxon; Genuine Article; SWETS; UMI; UnCover. **CCC.**
Formerly: Journal of Consulting Psychology (ISSN 0095-8891)
Description: Research on techniques of diagnosis and treatment in disordered behavior as well as studies of populations of clinical interest.
Refereed Serial

150 US ISSN 0894-8577
RC489.E93
JOURNAL OF CONTEMPLATIVE PSYCHOTHERAPY. 1980. 2/yr. $15 per no. to individuals; institutions $25. Naropa Institute, 2130 Arapahoe Ave., Boulder, CO 80302. TEL 303-444-0202. Ed. Dr. Karen Kissel Wegela. bk.rev. circ. 3,000. (back issues avail.) **Indexed:** Psychol.Abstr. **Document type:** academic/scholarly publication.
Formerly: Naropa Institute Journal of Psychology (ISSN 0271-7557)
Description: Publishes articles exploring the clinical application of contemplative disciplines in the practice of psychotherapy.

616.89 US ISSN 0022-0116
RC475 CODEN: JCPTBA
JOURNAL OF CONTEMPORARY PSYCHOTHERAPY. 1970. q. $235 (foreign $275) (effective 1996). Human Sciences Press, Inc. (Subsidiary of: Plenum Publishing Corp.), 233 Spring St., New York, NY 10013-1578. TEL 212-620-8000. FAX 212-463-0742. TELEX 23-421139. Ed. Erwin Parson. adv.; bk.rev; bibl.; charts. (also avail. in microfilm from UMI; reprint service avail. from ISI,UMI) **Indexed:** Abstr.Soc.Work., Excerp.Med., IMFL, Mid.East: Abstr.& Ind., Psychol.Abstr. (1968-), Rehabil.Lit., Soc.Work Res.& Abstr., SSCI. **Document type:** academic/scholarly publication.
—BLDSC (4965.240000); Faxon; SWETS; UMI; UnCover. **CCC.**
Description: Presents progressive research and clinical papers covering advances in psychotherapeutic concepts and methodology. Offers an eclectic approach to the promotion of emotional health and maturity.
Refereed Serial

371.4 US ISSN 0748-9633
HF5381.A1
JOURNAL OF COUNSELING & DEVELOPMENT. 1922. bi-m. $60 to individuals; institutions $97 (effective 1996). American Counseling Association, 5999 Stevenson Ave., Alexandria, VA 22304-3300. TEL 703-823-9800. FAX 703-823-0252. (Subscr. to: Box 2513, Birmingham, AL 35201-2513. TEL 205-995-1567. FAX 205-995-1588) Ed. Edwin L. Herr. adv.; index. circ. 58,000. (also avail. in microform from UMI; reprint service avail. from UMI,SCH) **Indexed:** Acad.Ind., ASSIA, Bk.Rev.Ind. (1965-1984, 1986-1987), C.I.J.E., Child.Bk.Rev.Ind. (1965-1984, 1986-1987), Coll.Stud.Pers.Abstr., Curr.Cont., Educ.Admin.Abstr., Educ.Ind., Except.Child.Educ.Abstr., Hlth.Ind., Human Resour.Abstr., Mag.Ind., Mult.Ed.Abstr., Past.Care & Couns.Abstr., Psychol.Abstr. (1952-), Psyscscan, Rehabil.Lit., Risk Abstr., Sage Fam.Stud.Abstr., Sage Pub.Admin.Abstr., Soc.Work Res.& Abstr., SOMA, Sp.Ed.Needs Abstr., SSCI, Work Rel.Abstr.
● Also available online. Vendor(s): University Microfilms International.
—BLDSC (4965.445000); Faxon; Genuine Article; SWETS; UMI; UnCover. **CCC.**
Formerly (until 1984): Personnel and Guidance Journal (ISSN 0031-5737)
Description: Publishes archival materials and contains authoritative in-depth articles on professional and scientific issues, research of interest to practitioners, and new techniques or practices.

150 371.4 US ISSN 0022-0167
BF637.C6
JOURNAL OF COUNSELING PSYCHOLOGY. 1954. q. $65 to non-members (foreign $80); members $39; institutions $130 (foreign $160). American Psychological Association, 750 First St., N.E., Washington, DC 20002-4242. TEL 202-336-5600. FAX 202-336-5568. Ed. Clara Hill. adv.; bibl.; charts; index. circ. 8,700. (also avail. in microform from UMI; reprint service avail. from UMI) **Indexed:** Abstr.Crim.& Pen., Adol.Ment.Hlth.Abstr., ASSIA, Bk.Rev.Ind. (1965-1979), C.I.J.E., Child.Bk.Rev.Ind. (1965-1979), Child Devel.Abstr., Curr.Cont., Educ.Ind., Mid.East: Abstr.& Ind., Mult.Ed.Abstr., Psychol.Abstr. (1954-), Psyscan C.P., Rehabil.Lit., Res.High.Educ.Abstr., Sage Fam.Stud.Abstr., Soc.Sci.Ind., Soc.Work Res.& Abstr., Sp.Ed.Needs Abstr., SSCI, Stud.Wom.Abstr., Tech.Educ.Abstr. **Document type:** academic/scholarly publication.
—BLDSC (4965.450000); Faxon; Genuine Article; SWETS; UMI; UnCover. **CCC.**
Description: Empirical studies about counseling processes and interventions, theoretical articles about counseling, and studies dealing with evaluation of counseling applications and programs.
Refereed Serial

616.89 US ISSN 0897-4446
RC488.5 CODEN: JCTHEV
JOURNAL OF COUPLES THERAPY; studies in the enhancement of intimacy and bonding for the clinical practitioner. 1989. q. $95 (foreign $133) (effective 1996). Haworth Press, Inc., 10 Alice St., Binghamton, NY 13904. TEL 607-722-5857; 800-342-9678. FAX 607-722-1424. Ed. Barbara Jo Brothers. adv.; bk.rev. (also avail. in microfiche from UMI; reprint service avail. from HAW) **Indexed:** IMFL, Soc.Work Res.& Abstr. **Document type:** academic/scholarly publication.
—Haworth.
Description: Devoted entirely to the study of human bonding and intimacy. For couples therapists, marriage, family and clinical practitioners who deal with couples and intimacy and bonding issues as a focus in their practice.
Refereed Serial

JOURNAL OF CREATIVE BEHAVIOR. see *EDUCATION*

PSYCHOLOGY

155
BF728
US   ISSN 0022-0221
CODEN: JCPGB5
JOURNAL OF CROSS-CULTURAL PSYCHOLOGY. 1970. bi-m. $62 to individuals; institutions $219 (effective Sep. 1995). (International Association for Cross-Cultural Psychology) Sage Publications, Inc., 2455 Teller Rd., Thousand Oaks, CA 91320. TEL 805-499-0721. FAX 805-499-0871. E-mail: libraries@sagepub.com. (Overseas subscr. to: Sage Publications Ltd., 6 Bonhill St., London EC2A 4PU, England; Sage Publications India Pvt. Ltd., P.O. Box 4215, New Delhi 110 048, India) (Co-sponsor: Western Washington University, Center for Cross-Cultural Research) Eds. Walter Lonner, John E. Williams. adv.; bk.rev.; charts; illus.; cum.index. circ. 2,000. (also avail. in microfilm from UMI; back issues avail.; reprint service avail. from UMI) **Indexed:** Abstr.Anthropol., Abstr.Crim.& Pen., Adol.Ment.Hlth.Abstr., ASSIA, C.I.J.E., Chic.Per.Ind., Child Devel.Abstr., Commun.Abstr., Curr.Cont., Lang.& Lang.Behav.Abstr., Mid.East: Abstr.& Ind., Mult.Ed.Abstr., PHRA, Psychol.Abstr. (1970-), Psychol.R.G., Sage Fam.Stud.Abstr., Soc.Sci.Ind., SSCI, Stud.Wom.Abstr., Viol.& Abuse Abstr. **Document type:** academic/scholarly publication.
—BLDSC (4965.670000); Faxon; Genuine Article; SWETS; UMI. **CCC.**
   Description: Presents behavioral and social research concentrating on psychological phenomena as differentially conditioned by culture, focusing on individual members of cultural groups.

616.89
UK   ISSN 1351-8372
JOURNAL OF DEMENTIA CARE. 1993. bi-m. £36 (rest of Europe £48; elsewhere £72). Hawker Publications, 140 Battersea Park Rd., London SW11 4NB, England. TEL 0171-720-2108. FAX 0171-498-3023. Ed. Sue Benson. adv. circ. 3,000. **Document type:** academic/scholarly publication.
—BLDSC (4968.230000).
   Description: Provides practical information, research, and networking for individuals working with people with dementia.
Refereed Serial

JOURNAL OF DEVELOPMENTAL AND BEHAVIORAL PEDIATRICS. see *MEDICAL SCIENCES — Pediatrics*

JOURNAL OF EARLY ADOLESCENCE. see *CHILDREN AND YOUTH — About*

JOURNAL OF ECONOMIC PSYCHOLOGY. see *BUSINESS AND ECONOMICS — Marketing And Purchasing*

JOURNAL OF EDUCATION AND PSYCHOLOGY. see *EDUCATION*

JOURNAL OF EDUCATIONAL AND PSYCHOLOGICAL CONSULTATION. see *EDUCATION*

370.15 150
LB1051.A2
US   ISSN 0022-0663
JOURNAL OF EDUCATIONAL PSYCHOLOGY. 1910. q. $85 to non-members (foreign $100); members $42 (foreign $50); institutions $170 (foreign $200). American Psychological Association, 750 First St., N.E., Washington, DC 20002-4242. TEL 202-336-5600. FAX 202-336-5568. Ed. Joel R. Levin. adv.; bibl.; charts; index. circ. 5,500. (also avail. in microform from UMI,PMC; reprint service avail. from UMI) **Indexed:** Acad.Ind., Adol.Ment.Hlth.Abstr., Bibl.Dev.Med.& Child Neur., Biol.Abstr., C.I.J.E., Child Devel.Abstr., Commun.Abstr., Cont.Pg.Educ., Educ.Admin.Abstr., Educ.Ind., Educ.Tech.Abstr., Except.Child.Educ.Abstr., High.Educ.Curr.Aware.Bull., Ind.Med., Lang.Teach.& Ling.Abstr., Mid.East: Abstr.& Ind., Mult.Ed.Abstr., Psychol.Abstr. (1926-), Psycscan D.P., Res.High.Educ.Abstr., Sage Fam.Stud.Abstr., SOMA, Sp.Ed.Needs Abstr., SSCI, Stud.Wom.Abstr., Tech.Educ.Abstr. **Document type:** academic/scholarly publication.
—BLDSC (4973.200000); Faxon; Genuine Article; SWETS; UMI; UnCover. **CCC.**
   Description: Deals with learning and cognition, psychological development, relationships, and adjustment of the individual, especially as related to the problems of instruction. Articles pertain to all levels of education and to all age groups.
Refereed Serial

371.42
HF5382.5.U5
US   ISSN 0022-0787
CODEN: JECODE
JOURNAL OF EMPLOYMENT COUNSELING. 1965. 4/yr. $30 (effective 1996). (National Employment Counselors Association) American Counseling Association, 5999 Stevenson Ave., Alexandria, VA 22304-3300. TEL 703-823-9800. FAX 703-823-0252. (Subscr. to: Box 2513, Birmingham, AL 35201-2513. TEL 205-995-1567. FAX 205-995-1588) Ed. Robert Drummond. adv.; bk.rev.; index. circ. 2,700. (also avail. in microform from UMI; reprint service avail. from UMI) **Indexed:** ASSIA, BPIA, C.I.J.E., Curr.Cont., Int.Lab.Doc., Psychol.Abstr. (1969-), Sage Fam.Stud.Abstr., Soc.Work Res.& Abstr., SSCI.
—BLDSC (4977.700000); Faxon; Genuine Article; UMI; UnCover. **CCC.**
   Description: Focuses on developing trends in organizational behavior and state-of-the-art personnel practices.

150
BF353
UK   ISSN 0272-4944
CODEN: JEPSEO
JOURNAL OF ENVIRONMENTAL PSYCHOLOGY. 1980. q. £102 (effective 1996). Academic Press Ltd. (Subsidiary of: Harcourt Brace & Company Ltd.), 24-28 Oval Rd., London NW1 7DX, England. TEL 44-171-267-4466. FAX 44-171-482-2293. TELEX 25775 ACPRES G. (Subscr. to: Harcourt Brace & Company, Foots Cray High St., Sidcup, Kent DA14 5HP, England. TEL 44-181-300-3322. FAX 44-181-309-0807) Ed. David V. Canter. (reprint service avail. from SWZ) **Indexed:** ASSIA, Br.Tech.Ind., Ergon.Abstr., Psychol.Abstr. (1981-), Psyscan, Sage Fam.Stud.Abstr., Sage Urb.Stud.Abstr. **Document type:** academic/scholarly publication.
—BLDSC (4979.389000); Faxon; Genuine Article; SWETS; UnCover. **CCC.**
   Description: Publishes international research contributions in a broad range of disciplines relating to the study of the transactions and interrelationships between people and their sociophysical surroundings (including man-made and natural environments) as well as relevant applications to the social and biological sciences and the environmental professions.

150
PN56.P93
US   ISSN 0737-4828
JOURNAL OF EVOLUTIONARY PSYCHOLOGY. 1979. 2/yr. $25 membership. Institute for Evolutionary Psychology, 5117 Forbes Ave., Pittsburgh, PA 15213. TEL 412-621-7057. Ed. Paul Neumarkt. bk.rev.; film rev.; play rev. circ. 300. **Indexed:** M.L.A. **Document type:** academic/scholarly publication.
●Also available on CD-ROM.
—BLDSC (4979.643000).
   Description: Presents psychological interpretation of literature, art, film and poetry.

155.4 152
BF721
US   ISSN 0022-0965
CODEN: JECPAE
JOURNAL OF EXPERIMENTAL CHILD PSYCHOLOGY. 1964. 9/yr. $468 (foreign $557) (effective 1996). Academic Press, Inc., Journal Division, 525 B St., Ste. 1900, San Diego, CA 92101-4495. TEL 619-230-1840. FAX 619-699-6800. (Subscr. to: Box 620000, Orlando, FL 32891-8340. TEL 800-543-9534) Ed. Hayne Reese. adv.; charts; index. (back issues avail.) **Indexed:** Adol.Ment.Hlth.Abstr., ASSIA, Bibl.Dev.Med.& Child Neur., Biol.Abstr., C.I.J.E., Child Devel.Abstr., Curr.Cont., Educ.Ind., Ind.Med., Mid.East: Abstr.& Ind., Psychol.Abstr. (1964-), Psycscan D.P., Sci.Cit.Ind., Soc.Sci.Ind., SSCI. **Document type:** academic/scholarly publication.
—BLDSC (4981.300000); Faxon; Genuine Article; SWETS; UnCover. **CCC.**
   Description: Covers all aspects of the behavior of children.
Refereed Serial

152
QL750
US   ISSN 0097-7403
CODEN: JPAPDG
JOURNAL OF EXPERIMENTAL PSYCHOLOGY: ANIMAL BEHAVIOR PROCESSES. Short title: J E P: A B P. 1975. q. $56 to non-members (foreign $71); members $28 (foreign $36); institutions $112 (foreign $142). American Psychological Association, 750 First St., N.E., Washington, DC 20002-4242. TEL 202-336-5600. FAX 202-336-5568. Ed. Stewart H. Hulse. circ. 2,000. (also avail. in microform from UMI; reprint service avail. from UMI) **Indexed:** Biol.Abstr., Child Devel.Abstr., Curr.Cont., Ind.Med., Ind.Sci.Rev., Psychol.Abstr. (1975-), Sci.Cit.Ind., Soc.Sci.Ind., Sport Fish.Abstr., Wild.Rev., Zoo.Rec. **Document type:** academic/scholarly publication.
—BLDSC (4982.501000); Faxon; Genuine Article; SWETS; UMI; UnCover. **CCC.**
   Supersedes in part: Journal of Experimental Psychology (ISSN 0022-1015)
   Description: Experimental studies on the basic mechanisms of perception, learning, motivation and performance, especially in nonhuman animals.
Refereed Serial

152
US   ISSN 1076-898X
▼**JOURNAL OF EXPERIMENTAL PSYCHOLOGY: APPLIED.** 1995. q. $100 (foreign $130) (effective 1996). American Psychological Association, 750 First St., N.E., Washington, DC 20002-4242. TEL 202-336-6123. FAX 202-336-5568. **Document type:** academic/scholarly publication.
   Description: Publishes empirical investigations in experimental psychology that bridge practically oriented problems and psychological theory, focusing on the testing of models of cognitive processing or behavior in applied settings.
Refereed Serial

152
BF180
US   ISSN 0096-3445
CODEN: JPGEDD
JOURNAL OF EXPERIMENTAL PSYCHOLOGY: GENERAL. Short title: J E P: GEN. 1975. q. $50 to non-members (foreign $65); members $25 (foreign $33); institutions $100 (foreign $130). American Psychological Association, 750 First St., N.E., Washington, DC 20002-4242. TEL 202-336-5500. FAX 202-336-5568. Ed. Earl Hunt. adv.; charts; illus.; stat.; index. circ. 3,100. (also avail. in microform from UMI; back issues avail.; reprint service avail. from UMI,KTO) **Indexed:** Biol.Abstr., Child Devel.Abstr., Curr.Cont., Ergon.Abstr., Ind.Med., Mid.East: Abstr.& Ind., Psychol.Abstr. (1926-), Risk Abstr., Soc.Sci.Ind., SSCI, Yrbk.Assoc.Educ.& Rehab.Blind. **Document type:** academic/scholarly publication.
—BLDSC (4982.503000); Faxon; Genuine Article; SWETS; UMI; UnCover. **CCC.**
   Supersedes in part: Journal of Experimental Psychology (ISSN 0022-1015)
   Description: Presents reports of interest to all experimental psychologists.
Refereed Serial

152.05
BF311
US   ISSN 0096-1523
CODEN: JPHPDH
JOURNAL OF EXPERIMENTAL PSYCHOLOGY: HUMAN PERCEPTION AND PERFORMANCE. Short title: J E P: H P P. 1975. bi-m. $140 to non-members (foreign $160); members $70 (foreign $80); institutions $280 (foreign $323). American Psychological Association, 750 First St., N.E., Washington, DC 20002-4242. TEL 202-336-5600. FAX 202-336-5568. Ed. Thomas Carr. circ. 2,800. (also avail. in microform from UMI; reprint service avail. from UMI) **Indexed:** ASSIA, Biol.Abstr., C.I.J.E., Child Devel.Abstr., Commun.Abstr., Curr.Cont., Dent.Ind., Ergon.Abstr., Ind.Med., Psychol.Abstr. (1975-), Soc.Sci.Ind., SSCI. **Document type:** academic/scholarly publication.
—BLDSC (4982.507000); Faxon; Genuine Article; SWETS; UMI; UnCover. **CCC.**
   Supersedes in part: Journal of Experimental Psychology (ISSN 0022-1015)
Refereed Serial

PSYCHOLOGY

152 US ISSN 0278-7393
LB1051 CODEN: JEPCEA
JOURNAL OF EXPERIMENTAL PSYCHOLOGY: LEARNING, MEMORY, AND COGNITION. Short title: J E P: L M C. 1975. bi-m. $150 to non-members (foreign $170); members $75 (foreign $85); institutions $300 (foreign $343). American Psychological Association, 750 First St., N.E., Washington, DC 20002-4242. TEL 202-336-5600. FAX 202-336-5568. Ed. Keith Rayner. circ. 3,600. (also avail. in microform from UMI; reprint service avail. from UMI) **Indexed:** Biol.Abstr., C.I.J.E., Child Devel.Abstr., Curr.Cont., Ergon.Abstr., Ind.Med., Psychol.Abstr. (1975-), Soc.Sci.Ind., SSCI. **Document type:** academic/scholarly publication.
—BLDSC (4982.509000); Faxon; Genuine Article; SWETS; UMI; UnCover. **CCC.**
Formerly (until Jan. 1982): Journal of Experimental Psychology: Human Learning and Memory (ISSN 0096-1515); Which supersedes in part: Journal of Experimental Psychology (ISSN 0022-1015)
Description: Experimental studies on fundamental encoding, transfer, memory, and cognitive processes in human behavior.
Refereed Serial

152 301.1 US ISSN 0022-1031
HM251 CODEN: JESPAQ
JOURNAL OF EXPERIMENTAL SOCIAL PSYCHOLOGY. 1965. bi-m. $248 (foreign $304) (effective 1996). Academic Press, Inc., Journal Division, 525 B St., Ste. 1900, San Diego, CA 92101-4495. TEL 619-230-1840. FAX 619-699-6800. (Subscr. to: Box 620000, Orlando, FL 32891-8340. TEL 800-543-9534) Ed. Charles Judd. (back issues avail.) **Indexed:** Abstr.Crim.& Pen., ASSIA, Biol.Abstr., Commun.Abstr., Crim.Just.Abstr., Curr.Cont., Mid.East: Abstr.& Ind., Psychol.Abstr. (1965-), Soc.Sci.Ind., SSCI. **Document type:** academic/scholarly publication.
—BLDSC (4982.700000); Faxon; Genuine Article; SWETS; UnCover. **CCC.**
Description: Publishes original research and theory on human social behavior and related phenomena.
Refereed Serial

150 US ISSN 1058-0476
HQ1 CODEN: JFEIEE
JOURNAL OF FAMILY AND ECONOMIC ISSUES. 1978. q. $225 (foreign $265) (effective 1996). Human Sciences Press, Inc. (Subsidiary of: Plenum Publishing Corp.), 233 Spring St., New York, NY 10013-1578. TEL 212-620-8000. FAX 212-463-0742. TELEX 23-421139. Eds. Ramona Kay, Zachary Heck. adv.; bk.rev.; film rev.; bibl.; charts; stat.; index. (back issues avail.); reprint service avail. from UMI) **Indexed:** Abstr.Soc.Work., Community Ment.Health Rev., Curr.Cont., Educ.Ind., Except.Child Educ.Abstr., IMFL, Mid.East: Abstr.& Ind., Psychol.Abstr. (1980-), Sage Fam.Stud.Abstr., SSCI. **Document type:** academic/scholarly publication.
—BLDSC (4983.645000); Faxon; UMI; UnCover. **CCC.**
Former titles (until 1991): Lifestyles: Family and Economic Issues (ISSN 0882-3391); Alternative Lifestyles (ISSN 0161-570X)
Description: Covers family consumer behavior, household division of labor and productivity, the relationship between economic and noneconomic decisions, and interrelationships between work and family life.
Refereed Serial

155 US ISSN 0893-3200
JOURNAL OF FAMILY PSYCHOLOGY. 1987. q. $50 to non-members (foreign $65); members $30 (foreign $38); institutions $87 (foreign $117). American Psychological Association, Division of Family Psychology, 750 First St., N.E., Washington, DC 20002-4242. TEL 202-336-5600. FAX 202-336-5568. Ed. Ronald Levant. circ. 7,800. **Indexed:** IMFL, Psychol.Abstr. (1987-), Soc.Sci.Ind (1994-). **Document type:** academic/scholarly publication.
—BLDSC (4983.733000); Faxon; SWETS; UMI; UnCover. **CCC.**
Description: Delivers a variety of perspectives on the study of family systems, emphasizing empirical research on a wide range of family-related topics.

616.89 US ISSN 0897-5353
CODEN: JFAPEF
JOURNAL OF FAMILY PSYCHOTHERAPY; the quarterly journal of case studies, treatment reports, and strategies in clinical practice. 1985. q. $125 (foreign $175) (effective 1996). Haworth Press, Inc., 10 Alice St., Binghamton, NY 13904. TEL 607-722-5857; 800-342-9678. FAX 607-722-1424. TELEX 4932599 HAWORTH. Ed. Terry Trepper. adv.: page $300. bk.rev. circ. 354. (also avail. in microfiche from UMI; back issues avail.; reprint service avail. from HAW) **Indexed:** Biol.Dig., DNP, Excerp.Med., IMFL, Ind.Med., Ind.Per.Art.Relat.Law, Past.Care & Couns.Abstr., Psychol.Abstr. (1985-), Ref.Zh., Sage Fam.Stud.Abstr., Soc.Work Res.& Abstr., Sociol.Abstr., Sp.Ed.Needs Abstr., Stud.Wom.Abstr. **Document type:** academic/scholarly publication.
—BLDSC (4983.735000); Haworth; SWETS; UnCover.
Formerly (until 1988): Journal of Psychotherapy and the Family (ISSN 0742-9703)
Description: Provides an exchange for clinicians across the disciplines to share solutions to difficult family problems. Offers detailed clinical case studies, descriptions of successful treatment programs, innovative strategies in clinical practice.
Refereed Serial

JOURNAL OF FAMILY STUDIES. see *MATRIMONY*

JOURNAL OF FAMILY THERAPY. see *MEDICAL SCIENCES — Psychiatry And Neurology*

JOURNAL OF FEMINIST FAMILY THERAPY. see *WOMEN'S STUDIES*

150 301 US ISSN 0094-730X
RC423.A1 CODEN: JFDID8
JOURNAL OF FLUENCY DISORDERS. 1974. q. $304 to institutions (effective 1996). Elsevier Science Inc., 655 Ave. of the Americas, New York, NY 10010. TEL 212-989-5800. FAX 212-633-3990. TELEX 420643 AEP UI. (Subscr. to: Box 882, Madison Sq. Sta., New York, NY 10159-0882) Ed. Gene J. Brutten. adv.; bk.rev. (also avail. in microform from UMI) **Indexed:** Biol.Abstr., Curr.Cont., DSH Abstr., Excerp.Med., Lang.& Lang.Behav.Abstr. (1978-), Psychol.Abstr. (1981-), Rehabil.Lit., Sociol.Abstr., Sp.Ed.Needs Abstr., SSCI. **Document type:** academic/scholarly publication.
—BLDSC (4984.450000); EMDOCS; Faxon; Genuine Article; SWETS; UnCover. **CCC.**
Description: Provides comprehensive coverage of clinical, experimental, and theoretical aspects of stuttering, including the latest remediation techniques.
Refereed Serial

JOURNAL OF GAY & LESBIAN PSYCHOTHERAPY. see *HOMOSEXUALITY*

JOURNAL OF GAY, LESBIAN & BISEXUAL IDENTITY. see *HOMOSEXUALITY*

150 US ISSN 0022-1309
BF1 CODEN: JGPSAY
THE JOURNAL OF GENERAL PSYCHOLOGY; experimental, physiological, and comparative psychology. 1927. q. $93. (Helen Dwight Reid Educational Foundation) Heldref Publications, 1319 Eighteenth St., N.W., Washington, DC 20036. TEL 202-296-6267. FAX 202-296-5149. Ed. Mara Dale; Pub. Walter E. Beach. bibl.; charts; index. circ. 1,550. (also avail. in microform; back issues avail.; reprint service avail. from SWZ) **Indexed:** Abstr.Crim.& Pen., Abstr.Soc.Work., ASSIA, Biol.Abstr., Biol.& Agr.Ind., C.I.J.E., Chem.Abstr., Child Devel.Abstr., Commun.Abstr., Curr.Adv.Ecol.Sci., Curr.Cont., Curr.Ref.Fish Res., Dent.Ind., Ergon.Abstr., Except.Child Educ.Abstr., Excerp.Med., Ind.Med., Indian Psychol.Abstr., Lang.&Lang.Behav.Abstr., Psychol.Abstr. (1928-), Soc.Sci.Ind., Soc.Work Res.& Abstr., SSCI. **Document type:** academic/scholarly publication.
●Also available online. Vendor(s): University Microfilms International.
Also available on CD-ROM. Producer(s): University Microfilms International.
—BLDSC (4989.200000); Faxon; Genuine Article; SWETS; UMI; UnCover. **CCC.**
Refereed Serial

150 US ISSN 1059-7700
RB155.7 CODEN: JGCOET
JOURNAL OF GENETIC COUNSELING. 1992. q. $145 (foreign $170) (effective 1996). (National Society of Genetic Counselors, Inc.) Human Sciences Press, Inc. (Subsidiary of: Plenum Publishing Corp.), 233 Spring St., New York, NY 10013-1578. TEL 212-620-8432. FAX 212-463-0742. TELEX 23-421139. Ed. Deborah L. Eunpu. adv. **Indexed:** IMFL, Psychol.Abstr. (1992-). **Document type:** academic/scholarly publication.
—BLDSC (4989.700000); Faxon; UMI. **CCC.**
Description: Covers psychosocial issues, educational and counseling techniques, legislation and regulations affecting genetic counseling, and other issues related to the provision of counseling services.
Refereed Serial

155 156 US ISSN 0022-1325
L11 CODEN: JGPYAI
THE JOURNAL OF GENETIC PSYCHOLOGY; developmental and clinical psychology. 1891. q. $95. (Helen Dwight Reid Educational Foundation) Heldref Publications, 1319 Eighteenth St., N.W., Washington, DC 20036-1802. TEL 202-296-6267. FAX 202-296-5149. Ed. Elizabeth Bruce. bibl.; charts; index. circ. 1,450. (also avail. in microfilm from PMC; reprint service avail. from SWZ) **Indexed:** Abstr.Soc.Work., Adol.Ment.Hlth.Abstr., Bibl.Dev.Med.& Child Neur., Biol.Abstr., C.I.J.E., Child Devel.Abstr., Curr.Adv.Ecol.Sci., Curr.Cont., DSH Abstr., Except.Child Educ.Abstr., Excerp.Med., Ind.Med., Indian Psychol.Abstr., Lang.& Lang.Behav.Abstr., Mid.East: Abstr.& Ind., Mult.Ed.Abstr., Psychol.Abstr. (1932-), Psycscan D.P., Soc.Sci.Ind., Soc.Work Res.& Abstr., SSCI, Stud.Wom.Abstr. **Document type:** academic/scholarly publication.
●Also available online. Vendor(s): University Microfilms International.
Also available on CD-ROM. Producer(s): University Microfilms International.
—BLDSC (4989.900000); Faxon; Genuine Article; SWETS; UMI; UnCover. **CCC.**
Refereed Serial

130 US ISSN 0022-1449
JOURNAL OF GRAPHOANALYSIS. 1929. m. International Graphoanalysis Society, 111 N. Canal St., Chicago, IL 60606. TEL 312-930-9440. Ed. William Harms; Pub. S.A. Ferrara. bk.rev.; abstr.; bibl.; charts; illus.; tr.lit. circ. 35,000. **Document type:** academic/scholarly publication.

150.19 US ISSN 0731-1273
RC488.A1
JOURNAL OF GROUP PSYCHOTHERAPY, PSYCHODRAMA & SOCIOMETRY. 1947. q. $43 to individuals (foreign $54); institutions $69 (foreign $80). (American Society of Group Psychotherapy and Psychodrama) Heldref Publications, 1319 Eighteenth St., N.W., Washington, DC 20036-1802. TEL 202-296-6267. FAX 202-296-5149. (Co-sponsor: Helen Dwight Reid Educational Foundation) Eds. Helen Kress, Martha Wedeman. adv. contact: Raymond Rallo. bk.rev. circ. 1,000. (also avail. in microform; reprint service avail.) **Indexed:** ASSIA, Curr.Cont., Psychol.Abstr. (1950-), Sociol.Abstr., SSCI. **Document type:** academic/scholarly publication.
●Also available on CD-ROM. Producer(s): University Microfilms International.
—BLDSC (4996.522000); Faxon; UMI; UnCover. **CCC.**
Former titles (until 1982): Group Psychotherapy, Psychodrama and Sociometry (ISSN 0146-6178); Handbook of International Sociometry (ISSN 0160-4635); (until 1975): Group Psychotherapy and Psychodrama (ISSN 0096-0586); Group Psychotherapy (ISSN 0017-4734); Sociometry, a Journal of Interpersonal Relations.
Description: Articles on the application of action methods to psychotherapy, consulting, and education.
Refereed Serial

PSYCHOLOGY

616.8   UK   ISSN 1359-1053
▼**JOURNAL OF HEALTH PSYCHOLOGY**; an interdisciplinary, international journal. Announced for publication in 1996. q. £30($48) to individuals; institutions £90($144) (effective 1996). Sage Publications Ltd., 6 Bonhill St., London EC2 4PU, England. TEL 44-171-3740645. FAX 44-171-3748741. E-mail: folan@sageltd.co.uk. Ed. David Marks. **Document type:** academic/scholarly publication.
    Description: Publishes research in health psychology from around the world.

152.4 610   UK   ISSN 0306-7297
QP303   CODEN: JHMSDT
JOURNAL OF HUMAN MOVEMENT STUDIES. 1975. m. £355 (foreign £475). Teviot Scientific Publications Ltd., 82 Great King St., Edinburgh EH3 6QU, Scotland. TEL 031-332-8764. FAX 031-343-2633. Ed. W.J. Irvine. bk.rev.; cum.index. **Indexed:** Biol.Abstr., Curr.Cont., Ergon.Abstr., Excerp.Med., Lang.& Lang.Behav.Abstr., Phys.Ed.Ind., Sportsearch (1975-), SSCI. **Document type:** academic/scholarly publication.
   —BLDSC (5003.418000); Faxon; Genuine Article; SWETS; UnCover. **CCC.**

371.42   US   ISSN 0735-6846
LB1715
JOURNAL OF HUMANISTIC EDUCATION AND DEVELOPMENT. 1962. q. $18 to individuals; institutions $24 (effective 1996). (Association for Humanistic Education and Development) American Counseling Association, 5999 Stevenson Ave., Alexandria, VA 22304-3300. TEL 703-823-9800. FAX 703-823-0252. (Subscr. to: Box 2513, Birmingham, AL 35201-2513. TEL 205-995-1567. FAX 205-995-1588) Ed. Richard J. Hazler. adv.; abstr.; bibl. circ. 3,500. (also avail. in microform from UMI; reprint service avail. from UMI) **Indexed:** C.I.J.E., Cont.Pg.Educ., Educ.Ind., Mult.Ed.Abstr., Psychol.Abstr., Soc.Work Res.& Abstr., Sociol.Educ.Abstr., Sp.Ed.Needs Abstr. **Document type:** academic/scholarly publication.
   —BLDSC (5003.445000); Faxon; SWETS; UMI; UnCover. **CCC.**
    Former titles (until 1982): Humanistic Educator (ISSN 0362-9783); (until 1975): Student Personnel Association for Teacher Education. Journal (ISSN 0036-1836)
    Description: Addresses issues and concerns affecting counselors and educators committed to developing humanistic education practices in schools.

150 170   US   ISSN 0022-1678
BF1
JOURNAL OF HUMANISTIC PSYCHOLOGY. 1961. q. $52 to individuals; institutions $172 (effective Sep. 1995). (Association for Humanistic Psychology) Sage Publications, Inc., 2455 Teller Rd., Thousand Oaks, CA 91320. TEL 805-499-0721. FAX 805-499-0871. E-mail: libraries@sagepub.com. (Overseas subscr. to: Sage Publications Ltd., 6 Bonhill St., London EC2A 4PU, England; Sage Publications India Pvt. Ltd., P.O. Box 4215, New Delhi 110 048, India) Ed. Thomas C. Greening. adv.; bk.rev.; stat.; index, cum.index: 1961-1979. circ. 3,000. (also avail. in microform from UMI; back issues avail.; reprint service avail. from UMI) **Indexed:** ASSIA, C.I.J.E., Commun.Abstr., Curr.Cont., Lang.& Lang.Behav.Abstr., Mid.East: Abstr.& Ind., Mult.Ed.Abstr., Psychol.Abstr. (1961-), Soc.Sci.Ind. (1994-), SSCI. **Document type:** academic/scholarly publication.
   —BLDSC (5003.450000); Faxon; Genuine Article; SWETS; UMI; UnCover. **CCC.**
    Description: Provides an interdisciplinary forum for contributions and controversies in humanistic psychology as applied to personal growth, interpersonal encounters, social problems, and philosophical issues.

301.1 150   II   ISSN 0379-3885
BF1
JOURNAL OF INDIAN PSYCHOLOGY. 1977. s-a. $6 to individuals; institutions $9. (Andhra University, Department of Psychology & Parapsychology) Andhra University Press and Publications, Waltair, Visakhapatnam 530 003, Andhra Pradesh, India. **Indexed:** Psychol.Abstr. (1978-).
   —BLDSC (5005.330000).
    Formerly: Indian Psychology.

JOURNAL OF INSTRUCTIONAL PSYCHOLOGY. see
EDUCATION

616.89   MX
JOURNAL OF INTEGRATIVE AND ECLECTIC PSYCHOTHERAPY. 1982. 4/yr. $34 to individuals (foreign $39); institutions $65 (foreign $70). International Academy of Eclectic Psychotherapists, c/o Emmanuel O. Olukotun, Apdo. 51042, 45080 Guadalajara, Jalisco, Mexico. FAX 36-21-00-61. adv.; bk.rev. circ. 500. **Indexed:** Psychol.Abstr.
   —BLDSC (5007.538420). **CCC.**
    Formerly (until 1986): International Journal of Eclectic Psychotherapy (ISSN 0729-8579)
    Description: Forum for the exploration and advancement of integrative psycho-social treatments and the synthesis of therapy methods, theories and formats.

JOURNAL OF INTERPERSONAL VIOLENCE; concerned with the study and treatment of victims and perpetrators of physical and sexual violence. see CRIMINOLOGY AND LAW ENFORCEMENT

JOURNAL OF INVITATIONAL THEORY AND PRACTICE. see EDUCATION

301.1 150   US   ISSN 0261-927X
P40
JOURNAL OF LANGUAGE AND SOCIAL PSYCHOLOGY. 1982. q. $64 to individuals; institutions $185 (effective Sep. 1995). (Multilingual Matters Ltd., UK) Sage Publications, Inc., 2455 Teller Rd., Thousand Oaks, CA 91320. TEL 805-499-0721. FAX 805-499-0871. E-mail: libraries@sagepub.com. (Overseas subscr. to: Sage Publications Ltd., 6 Bonhill St., London EC2A 4PU, England; Sage Publications India Pvt. Ltd., P.O. Box 4125, New Delhi 110 048, India) Eds. James Bradac, Kathy Kellermann. adv.; bk.rev.; index. circ. 500. (back issues avail.; reprint service avail.) **Indexed:** Bibl.Ling., Lang.& Lang.Behav.Abstr. (1985-), Lang.Teach.& Ling.Abstr., Ling.Abstr., Psychol.Abstr. (1983-). **Document type:** academic/scholarly publication.
   —BLDSC (5010.096000); SWETS; UnCover. **CCC.**
    Description: Explores the social dimensions of language and the linguistic implications of social life.

JOURNAL OF LEARNING DISABILITIES. see EDUCATION — Special Education And Rehabilitation

JOURNAL OF MANAGERIAL PSYCHOLOGY. see BUSINESS AND ECONOMICS — Management

301.4   US   ISSN 0194-472X
HQ1   CODEN: JMFTA
JOURNAL OF MARITAL AND FAMILY THERAPY. 1975. q. $45 to individuals; institutions $75. American Association for Marriage and Family Therapy, 1100 17th St., N.W., 10th Fl., Washington, DC 20036. Ed. Douglas Sprenkle. adv.; bk.rev. circ. 20,000. (also avail. in microform from UMI,KTO) **Indexed:** Abstr.Soc.Work., Adol.Ment.Hlth.Abstr., Biol.Abstr., C.I.J.E., CERDIC, Curr.Cont., Excerp.Med., IMFL, Lang.& Lang.Behav.Abstr., Past.Care & Couns.Abstr., Psychol.Abstr. (1975-), Sage Fam.Stud.Abstr., Soc.Work Res.& Abstr., Sociol.Abstr., SSCI, Stud.Wom.Abstr. **Document type:** bulletin.
●Also available online. Vendor(s): University Microfilms International.
   —BLDSC (5012.060000); Faxon; Genuine Article; SWETS; UMI; UnCover.
    Formerly (until 1979): Journal of Marriage and Family Counseling (ISSN 0094-5102)

JOURNAL OF MASS MEDIA ETHICS. see COMMUNICATIONS

150   US   ISSN 0022-2496
BF1   CODEN: JMTPAJ
JOURNAL OF MATHEMATICAL PSYCHOLOGY. 1964. q. $306 (foreign $370) (effective 1996). Academic Press, Inc., Journal Division, 525 B St., Ste. 1900, San Diego, CA 92101-4495. TEL 619-230-1840. FAX 619-699-6800. (Subscr. to: Box 620000, Orlando, FL 32891-8340. TEL 800-543-9534) Ed. Thomas S. Wallsten. adv.; bibl.; charts. (back issues avail.) **Indexed:** Biol.Abstr., Child Devel.Abstr., Compumath, Curr.Cont., INSPEC (1992-), J.Cont.Quant.Meth., Math.R., Psychol.Abstr. (1964-), SSCI. **Document type:** academic/scholarly publication.
   —BLDSC (5012.420000); Faxon; Genuine Article; SWETS; UnCover. **CCC.**
    Description: Presents theoretical and empirical research in all areas of mathematical psychology. *Refereed Serial*

JOURNAL OF MEMORY AND LANGUAGE. see LINGUISTICS

JOURNAL OF MENTAL HEALTH ADMINISTRATION. see PUBLIC HEALTH AND SAFETY

JOURNAL OF MENTAL HEALTH AND AGING. see GERONTOLOGY AND GERIATRICS

362.2   US   ISSN 1040-2861
BF637.C6
JOURNAL OF MENTAL HEALTH COUNSELING. 1979. q. $61 to individuals; institutions $119 (effective 1996). American Counseling Association, 5999 Stevenson Ave., Alexandria, VA 22304-3300. TEL 703-823-9800; 800-326-2642. FAX 703-823-0252. (Subscr. to: Box 2513, Birmingham, AL 35201-2513. TEL 205-995-1567. FAX 205-995-1588; Alt. addr.: P.O. Drawer 22370, Alexandria, VA 22304) Ed. Earl J. Ginter. circ. 13,500. **Indexed:** C.I.J.E., Psychol.Abstr. (1983-), Soc.Work Res.& Abstr. **Document type:** academic/scholarly publication.
   —BLDSC (5017.687000); Faxon; SWETS; UMI; UnCover. **CCC.**
    Formerly: A M H C A Journal (ISSN 0193-1830)
    Description: Disseminates pertinent theory, therapeutic applications, and research related to mental health counseling.

150   US   ISSN 0364-5541
BF367
JOURNAL OF MENTAL IMAGERY. 1977. 4/yr. $40 to individuals; institutions $80 (effective 1995 & 1996). (International Imagery Association) Brandon House, Inc., Box 240, Bronx, NY 10471. Ed. Dr. Akhter Ahsen. adv.; bk.rev.; charts. (back issues avail.) **Indexed:** Curr.Cont., Psychol.Abstr. (1977-), Soc.Sci.Ind.
   —BLDSC (5017.690000); Faxon; SWETS; UnCover.

150 121   US   ISSN 0271-0137
BF1
JOURNAL OF MIND AND BEHAVIOR. 1980. q. $42 to individuals; institutions $73. Institute of Mind & Behavior, Box 522, Village Sta., New York, NY 10014. TEL 212-595-4853. Ed. Dr. Raymond Russ. adv.; bk.rev.; abstr.; charts; illus.; stat.; index; circ. 1,190 (controlled). **Indexed:** Curr.Cont., INSPEC (1991-), Lang.& Lang.Behav.Abstr., Phil.Ind., Phil.Ind., Psychol.Abstr. (1981-), Soc.Work Res.& Abstr., Sociol.Abstr., SSCI. **Document type:** academic/scholarly publication.
   —BLDSC (5020.140000); Faxon; Genuine Article; SWETS; UMI; UnCover.
    Description: Publishes articles pertaining to mind and body epistemology in the social sciences, theory of consciousness and ideation, and historical investigations of science and issues pertaining to the ethical study of cognition, self-awareness and higher functions of consciousness in animals. *Refereed Serial*

152.3   US   ISSN 0022-2895
QP303   CODEN: JMTBAB
JOURNAL OF MOTOR BEHAVIOR. Short title: J M B. 1969. q. $55 to individuals; institutions $110. (Helen Dwight Reid Educational Foundation) Heldref Publications, 1319 Eighteenth St., N.W., Washington, DC 20036-1802. TEL 202-296-6267. FAX 202-296-5149. Ed. Betty Adelman. abstr.; bibl.; charts; illus. circ. 1,300. (also avail. in microform; reprint service avail.) **Indexed:** Biol.Abstr., Child Devel.Abstr., Curr.Cont., Ergon.Abstr., Excerp.Med., Lang.& Lang.Behav.Abstr., Phys.Ed.Ind., Psychol.Abstr. (1970-), Sp.Ed.Needs Abstr., Sportsearch (1974-), SSCI. **Document type:** academic/scholarly publication.
●Also available on CD-ROM. Producer(s): University Microfilms International.
   —BLDSC (5021.050000); Faxon; Genuine Article; SWETS; UMI; UnCover. **CCC.**
Refereed Serial

371.9 US ISSN 0883-8534
LC3701
JOURNAL OF MULTICULTURAL COUNSELING AND DEVELOPMENT. 1972. 4/yr. $15 to individuals; institutions $19 (effective 1996). (Association for Multicultural Counseling and Development) American Counseling Association, 5999 Stevenson Ave., Alexandria, VA 22304-3300. TEL 703-823-9800. FAX 703-823-0252. (Subscr. to: Box 2513, Birmingham, AL 35201-2513. TEL 205-995-1567. FAX 205-995-1588) Ed. Frederick Harper. adv. circ. 4,000. (also avail. in microform from UMI; reprint service avail. from UMI) **Indexed:** C.I.J.E., Educ.Ind., Psychol.Abstr. (1973-), Soc.Work Res.& Abstr.
—BLDSC (5021.058000); Faxon; Genuine Article; UMI; UnCover. **CCC.**
Formerly: Journal of Non-White Concerns in Personnel and Guidance (ISSN 0090-5461)
Description: Issues include state-of-the-art multicultural counseling research and reports on applications of the latest theoretical ideas and concepts.

155.937 US ISSN 0891-4494
BF789.D4 CODEN: JNDAE7
JOURNAL OF NEAR-DEATH STUDIES. 1981. q. $195 (foreign $230) (effective 1996). (International Association for Near-Death Studies) Human Sciences Press, Inc. (Subsidiary of: Plenum Publishing Corp.), 233 Spring St., New York, NY 10013-1578. TEL 212-620-8000. FAX 212-463-0742. TELEX 23-421139. Ed. Dr. Bruce Greyson. adv.; bk.rev. (reprint service avail. from UMI) **Indexed:** IMFL, Psychol.Abstr. (1981-), Soc.Work Res.& Abstr. **Document type:** academic/scholarly publication.
—BLDSC (5021.392000); UMI; UnCover. **CCC.**
Formerly (until 1986): Anabiosis: The Journal for Near-Death Studies (ISSN 0743-6238)
Description: Publishes articles on the empirical effects and theoretical implications of near-death experiences.
Refereed Serial

301.3 150 US ISSN 0191-5886
BF353 CODEN: JNVBDV
JOURNAL OF NONVERBAL BEHAVIOR. 1976. q. $245 (foreign $285) (effective 1996). Human Sciences Press, Inc. (Subsidiary of: Plenum Publishing Corp.), 233 Spring St., New York, NY 10013-1578. TEL 212-620-8000. FAX 212-463-0742. TELEX 23-421139. Ed. Judith A. Hall. adv. (also avail. in microform from UMI; reprint service avail. from ISI,UMI) **Indexed:** Biol.Abstr., C.I.J.E., Child Devel.Abstr., Commun.Abstr., Curr.Adv.Ecol.Sci., Curr.Cont., Human Resour.Abstr., IMFL, M.L.A., Mult.Ed.Abstr., Psychol.Abstr. (1976-), Psychol.R.G., Saf.Sci.Abstr., Sage Fam.Stud.Abstr., Soc.Work Res.& Abstr., Sp.Ed.Needs Abstr., SSCI. **Document type:** academic/scholarly publication.
—BLDSC (5022.843000); Faxon; Genuine Article; SWETS; UMI; UnCover. **CCC.**
Formerly (until 1979): Environmental Psychology and Nonverbal Behavior (ISSN 0361-3496)
Description: Presents theoretical and empirical research on nonverbal communications, including paralanguage, proxemics, facial expressions, eye contact, face-to-face interaction, and nonverbal emotive expression.
Refereed Serial

158 UK ISSN 0963-1798
HF5548.8 CODEN: JOCCEF
JOURNAL OF OCCUPATIONAL AND ORGANIZATIONAL PSYCHOLOGY. 1922. q. £102($194) (effective 1996). British Psychological Society, St. Andrews House, 48 Princess Rd. E., Leicester LE1 7DR, England. TEL 0116-254-9568. FAX 0116-247-0787. (Subscr. to: Turpin Distribution Services Ltd., Blackhorse Rd., Letchworth, Herts. SG6 1HN, England. TEL 01462-672555. FAX 01462-480947) Ed. Anthony Keenan. adv. contact: H. Dauker. bk.rev.; charts; illus.; index. circ. 2,660. (also avail. in microform from SWZ; microform from UMI; reprint service avail. from ISI,SWZ) **Indexed:** ABI Inform., Account.& Data Proc.Abstr., Anbar., ASSIA, Biol.Abstr., BMT, BPIA, Br.Educ.Ind., Br.Hum.Ind., Bus.Ind., C.I.S. Abstr., Cont.Pg.Manage., Curr.Cont., Ergon.Abstr., Hlth.Ind., Ind.Med., INSPEC, Int.Lab.Doc., Lang.& Lang.Behav.Abstr., Manage.Cont., Mult.Ed.Abstr., Noise Pollut.Publ.Abstr., Pers.Lit., Psychol.Abstr. (1975-), Psyscan, Res.High.Educ.Abstr., SCIMP, Sp.Ed.Needs Abstr., SSCI, Stud.Wom.Abstr., Tech.Educ.Abstr., Tr.& Indus.Ind. **Document type:** academic/scholarly publication.
—BLDSC (5026.082000); Faxon; Genuine Article; SWETS; UMI; UnCover. **CCC.**
Former titles: Journal of Occupational Psychology (ISSN 0305-8107); Occupational Psychology (ISSN 0029-7976)
Description: Examines industrial and organizational psychology, describes and interprets new research about people at work.
Refereed Serial

JOURNAL OF OFFENDER REHABILITATION; a multidisciplinary journal of innovation in research, services, and programs in corrections and criminal justice. see *CRIMINOLOGY AND LAW ENFORCEMENT*

150 US ISSN 0160-8061
HD58.7
JOURNAL OF ORGANIZATIONAL BEHAVIOR MANAGEMENT. 1977. s-a. $200 (foreign $280) (effectvie 1996). Haworth Press, Inc., 10 Alice St., Binghamton, NY 13904. TEL 607-722-5857; 800-342-9678. FAX 607-722-1424. TELEX 4932599. Ed. Thomas C. Mawhinney. adv.; bk.rev. circ. 590. (also avail. in microfiche from HAW; reprint service avail. from HAW) **Indexed:** ABI Inform., Abstr.Health Care Manage.Stud., Behav.Abstr., BPIA, Bull.Signal., Bus.Ind., Human Resour.Abstr., Manage.Cont., Oper.Res.Manage.Sci., Pers.Lit., Pers.Manage.Abstr., Psychol.Abstr. (1978-), Psyscan, Qual.Contr.Appl.Stat., Sage Pub.Admin.Abstr., Tr.& Dev.Alert, Tr.& Indus.Ind. **Document type:** academic/scholarly publication.
—BLDSC (5027.068000); Faxon; Haworth; SWETS; UnCover.
Description: Devoted to behavior management in organizations; provides systematic and effective approaches to behavior management.
Refereed Serial

301.1 150 UK ISSN 0894-3796
HD6951 CODEN: JORBEJ
JOURNAL OF ORGANIZATIONAL BEHAVIOUR. 1979. 8/yr. $545 (foreign $545) (effective 1996). John Wiley & Sons Ltd., Journals, Baffins Ln., Chichester, W. Sussex PO19 1UD, England. TEL 01243-779777. FAX 01243-776128. TELEX 86290 WIBOOK G. (Subscr. in the Americas to: John Wiley & Sons, Inc., 605 Third Ave., New York, NY 10158-0012. TEL 212-850-6645. FAX 212-850-6021) Ed. Cary L. Cooper. (also avail. in microform from UMI; back issues avail.; reprint service avail. from ISI,SWZ,UMI) **Indexed:** ABI Inform., ASSIA, BPIA, Bus.Ind., Cont.Pg.Manage., Curr.Cont., Ergon.Abstr., Int.Lab.Doc., Lang.& Lang.Behav.Abstr., Mult.Ed.Abstr., Noise Pollut.Publ.Abstr., Psychol.Abstr. (1982-), Psyscan, Sage Fam.Stud.Abstr., SCIMP (1982-), SSCI, Tr.& Indus.Ind. **Document type:** academic/scholarly publication.
—BLDSC (5027.066000); Faxon; Genuine Article; SWETS; UMI; UnCover. **CCC.**
Formerly (until 1988): Journal of Occupational Behaviour (ISSN 0142-2774)
Description: Aims to report and review the growing research in the industry-organizational behavior fields, and in all topics associated with occupational-organizational behavior.
Refereed Serial

JOURNAL OF PARAPSYCHOLOGY; a scientific quarterly dealing with extrasensory perception, the psychokinetic effect and related topics. see *PARAPSYCHOLOGY AND OCCULTISM*

THE JOURNAL OF PASTORAL CARE. see *RELIGIONS AND THEOLOGY*

155.4 US ISSN 0146-8693
RJ503.3 CODEN: JPPSDW
JOURNAL OF PEDIATRIC PSYCHOLOGY. 1976. bi-m. $365 (foreign $425) (effective 1996). (Society of Pediatric Psychology) Plenum Publishing Corp., 233 Spring St., New York, NY 10013-1578. TEL 212-620-8000. FAX 212-463-0742. TELEX 23-421139. Ed. Annette M. LaGreca. adv. (also avail. in microfilm from JSC; back issues avail.) **Indexed:** Behav.Med.Abstr., Bibl.Dev.Med.& Child Neur., Biol.Abstr., Child Devel.Abstr., CINAHL, Curr.Cont., Excerp.Med., IMFL, Ind.Med., Psychol.Abstr. (1975-), Psyscan D.P., Risk Abstr., Soc.Work Res.& Abstr., Sociol.Abstr., Sp.Ed.Needs Abstr. **Document type:** academic/scholarly publication.
—BLDSC (5030.260000); Faxon; Genuine Article; SWETS; UMI; UnCover. **CCC.**
Formerly: Pediatric Psychology.
Refereed Serial

155.2 US ISSN 0022-3506
BF1 CODEN: JOPEAE
JOURNAL OF PERSONALITY. 1932. q. $48 to individuals (foreign $60); institutions $105 (foreign $117) (effective 1996). Duke University Press, Box 90660, Durham, NC 27708-0660. TEL 919-687-3600. FAX 919-688-4574. Ed. Howard Tennen. adv.; bibl.; charts; illus.; index. circ. 2,000. (also avail. in microform from MIM,UMI; reprint service avail. from ISI,UMI) **Indexed:** Acad.Ind., Adol.Ment.Hlth.Abstr., ASSIA, Biol.Abstr., Commun.Abstr., Curr.Cont., Educ.Ind., Ind.Med., Lang.& Lang.Behav.Abstr., Mid.East: Abstr.& Ind., Past.Care & Couns.Abstr., Psychol.Abstr. (1945-), Risk Abstr., Soc.Sci.Ind., SSCI.
—BLDSC (5030.900000); Faxon; Genuine Article; SWETS; UMI; UnCover. **CCC.**
Refereed Serial

152 158.3 II ISSN 0970-1206
JOURNAL OF PERSONALITY AND CLINICAL STUDIES. (Text in English) bi-m. (Association of Clinical Psychologists) Habib Ahmad, c/o Samar Offset Printers, 1788 Kalan Mahal Daryaganj, New Dehli 110 002, India. Ed.Bd. **Indexed:** Psychol.Abstr. (1985-).
—BLDSC (5030.900500).

155.2 US ISSN 0022-3514
HM251 CODEN: JPSPB2
JOURNAL OF PERSONALITY AND SOCIAL PSYCHOLOGY. (Contains material formerly covered by the Journal of Abnormal and Social Psychology) 1965. m. $265 to non-members (foreign $305); members $110 (foreign $126); institutions $525 (foreign $609). American Psychological Association, 750 First St., N.E., Washington, DC 20002-4242. TEL 202-336-5600. FAX 202-336-5568. Ed.Bd. adv.; charts; stat.; index. circ. 5,700. (also avail. in microform from UMI; reprint service avail. from UMI) **Indexed:** Acad.Ind., Adol.Ment.Hlth.Abstr., ASSIA, Biol.Abstr., C.I.J.E., Chic.Per.Ind., Child Devel.Abstr., Commun.Abstr., Crim.Just.Abstr., Curr.Cont., Educ.Admin.Abstr., Ind.Med., INIS Atomind., Int.Polit.Sci.Abstr., M.L.A., Mark.Res.Abstr. (1965-), Mid.East: Abstr.& Ind., PSI, Psychol.Abstr. (1965-), Psyscan D.P., Sage Fam.Stud.Abstr., Sage Urb.Stud.Abstr., Soc.Sci.Ind., Soc.Work Res.& Abstr., Sp.Ed.Needs Abstr., Sportsearch, SSCI, Stud.Wom.Abstr. **Document type:** academic/scholarly publication.
—BLDSC (5030.901000); Faxon; Genuine Article; SWETS; UMI; UnCover. **CCC.**
Description: Covers research in three major areas: attitudes and social cognition; interpersonal relations and group processes; and personality processes and individual differences.
Refereed Serial

PSYCHOLOGY

155.2 US ISSN 0022-3891
BF698.4
JOURNAL OF PERSONALITY ASSESSMENT. vol.34, 1970. 6/yr., in 2 vols. $65 to individuals (foreign $110); institutions $230 (foreign $275). (Society for Personality Assessment) Lawrence Erlbaum Associates, Inc., 10 Industrial Dr., Mahwah, NJ 07430-2262. TEL 201-236-9500. FAX 201-236-0072. Ed. Bill N. Kinder. adv.: page $525; 5 x 8. bk.rev.; abstr.; bibl.; charts; illus.; index. circ. 2,700. (also avail. in microform from UMI; reprint service avail. from UMI,SCH) **Indexed:** Adol.Ment.Hlth.Abstr., ASSIA, Biol.Abstr., C.I.S.Abstr., Child Devel.Abstr., Curr.Cont., Except.Child.Educ.Abstr., Excerp.Med., Ind.Med., Lang.& Lang.Behav.Abstr., Mid.East: Abstr.& Ind., Psychol.Abstr. (1971-), Psycscan C.P., SSCI. **Document type:** academic/scholarly publication. —BLDSC (5030.950000); Faxon; SWETS; UMI; UnCover.
Formerly: Journal of Projective Techniques and Personality Assessment.
Description: Presents commentaries, case reports, and research studies dealing with the application of methods of personality assessment.
Refereed Serial

370.15 US ISSN 0885-579X
RC554
JOURNAL OF PERSONALITY DISORDERS. 1986. 4/yr. $37.50 to individuals (foreign $57.50); institutions $115 (foreign $135) (effective 1995). (International Society for the Study of Personality Disorders) Guilford Publications, Inc., 72 Spring St., 4th Fl., New York, NY 10012. TEL 212-431-9800. FAX 212-966-6708. Eds. Theodore Millon, Allen J. Frances; Pub. Robert Matloff. adv. contact: Marian Robinson. bk.rev.; index. circ. 1,300. (reprint service avail. from ISI,UMI) **Indexed:** Biol.Abstr., Excerp.Med., Psychol.Abstr. (1987-), Soc.Work Res.& Abstr. —BLDSC (5030.955000); Genuine Article; SWETS; UMI; UnCover. **CCC.**
Description: Presents new research, and clinical techniques for assessing, diagnosing and treating personality disorders.
Refereed Serial

150 US ISSN 0047-2662
BF204.5 CODEN: JPHPAE
JOURNAL OF PHENOMENOLOGICAL PSYCHOLOGY; studies in the science of human experience and behavior. (Text in English, French and German; summaries in English) 1970. 2/yr. $40 to individuals; libraries $50. Humanities Press, 165 First Ave., Atlantic Highlands, NJ 07716-1289. TEL 908-872-1441. FAX 908-872-0717. Ed. Frederick J. Wertz. adv.; bk.rev.; index. (also avail. in microform from UMI; reprint service avail. from UMI) **Indexed:** Curr.Cont., Psychol.Abstr. (1970-), SSCI. **Document type:** academic/scholarly publication. —BLDSC (5034.100000); Faxon; Genuine Article; SWETS; UMI; UnCover.
Description: For the application of phenomenological research to the problems of psychology.

JOURNAL OF POETRY THERAPY; the interdisciplinary journal of practice, theory, research, and education. see LITERATURE — Poetry

150 616.8 US ISSN 0737-1195
JOURNAL OF POLYMORPHOUS PERVERSITY. 1984. s-a. $14 to individuals; institutions $20; foreign $21.75. Wry-Bred Press, Inc., Box 1454 Madison Sq. Sta., New York, NY 10159-1454. TEL 212-689-5473. FAX 212-689-6859. Ed. Glenn C. Ellenbogen. bk.rev. circ. 4,125. (back issues avail.) **Document type:** consumer publication.
Description: Humorous and satirical look at the fields of psychology, psychiatry, medicine and education.

613 US ISSN 0278-095X
RA790.A1 CODEN: JPPRDT
JOURNAL OF PRIMARY PREVENTION. 1980. q. $245 (foreign $290) (effective 1996). (Vermont Conference on Primary Prevention of Psychopathology) Human Sciences Press, Inc. (Subsidiary of: Plenum Publishing Corp.), 233 Spring St., New York, NY 10013-1578. TEL 212-620-8000. FAX 212-463-0742. TELEX 23-421139. Ed. Thomas P. Gullotta. adv. (reprint service avail. from ISI,UMI) **Indexed:** Adol.Ment.Hlth.Abstr., Biol.Abstr., Excerp.Med., IMFL, Psychol.Abstr. (1980-), Sociol.Abstr. **Document type:** academic/scholarly publication. —BLDSC (5042.370000); Faxon; UMI; UnCover. **CCC.**
Formerly (until vol.2): Journal of Prevention (ISSN 0163-514X)
Description: Presents theoretical, empirical, and methodological research on preventative intervention in human services and discusses innovative programs and concepts.
Refereed Serial

JOURNAL OF PSYCHOACTIVE DRUGS; a multidisciplinary forum. see DRUG ABUSE AND ALCOHOLISM

370.15 150 US ISSN 0734-2829
LB1131 CODEN: JPSAES
JOURNAL OF PSYCHOEDUCATIONAL ASSESSMENT. 1982. q. $45 to individuals; institutions $120. Clinical Psychology Publishing Co., Inc., 4 Conant Sq., Brandon, VT 05733. TEL 802-247-6871. FAX 802-247-6853. Ed. Dr. Bruce Bracken. adv.; bk.rev.; bibl.; charts; illus.; index. circ. 700. (back issues avail.) **Indexed:** Psychol.Abstr. (1983-). **Document type:** academic/scholarly publication. —BLDSC (5043.275000); Faxon; UnCover.
Refereed Serial

900 150 US ISSN 0145-3378
HQ768 CODEN: JOPSDP
JOURNAL OF PSYCHOHISTORY. 1973. q. $48 to individuals; institutions $129. Association for Psychohistory, Inc., 140 Riverside Dr., New York, NY 10024-2605. TEL 212-799-2294. Ed. Lloyd deMause. adv.; bk.rev.; illus.; circ. 6,000 (paid). (also avail. in microform from UMI; reprint service avail. from UMI) **Indexed:** Amer.Hist.& Life, Anthropol.Lit., Child Devel.Abstr., Child.Lit.Abstr., Curr.Lit.Fam.Plan., Hist.Abstr., IMFL, Lang.& Lang.Behav.Abstr., Mid.East: Abstr.& Ind., Polit.Sci.Abstr., Psychol.Abstr. (1973-), Sociol.Abstr. **Document type:** academic/scholarly publication. —BLDSC (5043.280000); Faxon; SWETS; UMI; UnCover. **CCC.**
Incorporates (1978-1988): Journal of Psychoanalytic Anthropology (ISSN 0278-2944); **Formerly** (until 1976): History of Childhood Quarterly (ISSN 0091-4266)
Description: Contains research in the psychological study of history.
Refereed Serial

JOURNAL OF PSYCHOLINGUISTIC RESEARCH. see LINGUISTICS

150 II ISSN 0022-3972
BF1 CODEN: JPSRB8
JOURNAL OF PSYCHOLOGICAL RESEARCHES. (Text in English) 1957. 3/yr. $75. Madras Psychology Society, University of Madras, Department of Psychology, Madras 5, India. TEL 91-44-568778. FAX 91-44-566693. TELEX 416376 ONOMIN. Ed. K.V. Kaliappan. adv.; bk.rev.; charts; index. circ. 400. (also avail. in microform from UMI; reprint service avail. from UMI) **Indexed:** Biol.Abstr., Psychol.Abstr. **Document type:** academic/scholarly publication. —BLDSC (5043.310000); Faxon; SWETS; UMI; UnCover.

150 US ISSN 0895-8750
JOURNAL OF PSYCHOLOGICAL TYPE. 1984. 4/yr. $88 (foreign $99). Association for Psychological Type, c/o Department of Psychology, Mississippi State Univ., Box 6161, Mississippi State, MS 39762. TEL 601-325-7655. Ed. Thomas G. Carskadoon. (back issues avail.) **Indexed:** Psychol.Abstr. (1991-). **Document type:** academic/scholarly publication. —BLDSC (5043.321000); UnCover.
Formerly (until vol.7): Research in Psychological Type.
Description: Publishes research, theoretical discussions and applications of psychological type and the Myers-Briggs Type Indicator.
Refereed Serial

150 US ISSN 0733-4273
BR110
JOURNAL OF PSYCHOLOGY AND CHRISTIANITY. 1982. q. $80 to individuals; libraries $50 (effective 1996). Christian Association for Psychological Studies, Inc., c/o Robert R. King, Jr., Box 310400, New Braunfels, TX 78131-0400. TEL 210-629-2277. FAX 210-629-2342. Ed. Peter C. Hill. adv. contact: Robert R. King, Jr. bk.rev.; circ. 2,400 (paid). (also avail. in microfilm from UMI; back issues avail.; reprint service avail. from UMI) **Indexed:** A.S.& T.Ind., Educ.Ind., PSI, Psychol.Abstr. (1982-), R.G., Rel.& Theol.Abstr. (1986-), Rel.Ind.One, Soc.Sci.Ind. **Document type:** academic/scholarly publication. —BLDSC (5043.405000); Faxon; UMI.
Supersedes (1974-1981): Christian Association for Psychological Studies. Bulletin; **Incorporates:** Christian Association for Psychological Studies. Proceedings (ISSN 0092-072X)
Description: Investigation of theoretical and applied issues in the relationship of Christianity and the psychological and pastoral professions.
Refereed Serial

155.3 US ISSN 0890-7064
BF692 CODEN: JPSXET
JOURNAL OF PSYCHOLOGY & HUMAN SEXUALITY. 1988. q. $185 (foreign $259) (effective 1996). Haworth Press, Inc., 10 Alice St., Binghamton, NY 13904. TEL 607-722-5857; 800-372-9678. FAX 607-722-1424. TELEX 4932599. Ed. Eli Coleman. adv.; bk.rev. circ. 436. (also avail. in microform from HAW; reprint service avail. from HAW) **Indexed:** IMFL, Psychol.Abstr. (1988-), Soc.Work Res.& Abstr. **Document type:** academic/scholarly publication. —BLDSC (5043.408000); Faxon; Haworth; UnCover.
Description: Publishes original articles and reviews about human sexuality.
Refereed Serial

156 296 US ISSN 0700-9801
BF51 CODEN: JPJUD8
JOURNAL OF PSYCHOLOGY AND JUDAISM. 1976. q. $225 (foreign $265) (effective 1996). Human Sciences Press, Inc. (Subsidiary of: Plenum Publishing Corp.), 233 Spring St., New York, NY 10013-1578. TEL 212-620-8000. FAX 212-463-0742. TELEX 12-421139. Ed. Dr. Reuben P. Bulka. adv.; bk.rev. circ. 1,000. (also avail. in microform from UMI; reprint service avail. from ISI,UMI) **Indexed:** Curr.Cont., Excerp.Med., G.Soc.Sci.& Rel.Per.Lit., Ind.Jew.Per., Mid.East: Abstr.& Ind., MLA, Past.Care & Couns.Abstr., Psychol.Abstr., Rel.& Theol.Abstr. (1979-), Rel.Ind.One, SSCI. **Document type:** academic/scholarly publication. —BLDSC (5043.410000); Faxon; UMI; UnCover. **CCC.**
Incorporates (1986-1991): Journal of Aging and Judaism (ISSN 0884-8688)
Description: Explores the relationship between modern psychology and Judaism on philosophical and clinical levels.
Refereed Serial

150 200 US ISSN 0091-6471
BF1 CODEN: JPSTDG
JOURNAL OF PSYCHOLOGY AND THEOLOGY; an evangelical forum for the integration of psychology and theology. 1973. q. $38 (foreign $40) (effective 1995). Biola University, Rosemead School of Psychology, 13800 Biola Ave., La Mirada, CA 90639-0001. TEL 310-903-4727. FAX 310-903-4786. E-mail: JPT_Weil@peter.biola.edu. Ed. Patricia L. Pike. adv. contact: Beverley Schlapper. bk.rev. circ. 1,700. (also avail. in microfilm from UMI; back issues avail.; reprint service avail. from UMI) **Indexed:** Arts & Hum.Cit.Ind., CERDIC, Chr.Per.Ind., Curr.Cont., G.Soc.Sci.& Rel.Per.Lit., IMFL, Old Test.Abstr., Psychol.Abstr. (1973-), Psychol.R.G., Rel.& Theol.Abstr. (1973-), Rel.Ind.One, SSCI. **Document type:** academic/scholarly publication.
●Also available online. Vendor(s): Knight-Ridder, Inc., Ovid Technologies.
—BLDSC (5043.420000); Faxon; Genuine Article; SWETS; UMI.
Description: Communicates recent scholarly thinking on the interrelationships of psychological and theological concepts and considers the application of these concepts to a variety of professional settings.

PSYCHOLOGY 5501

150   US
BF1
JOURNAL OF PSYCHOLOGY: INTERDISCIPLINARY & APPLIED; the general field of psychology. 1936. bi-m. $110. (Helen Dwight Reid Educational Foundation) Heldref Publications, 1319 Eighteenth St., N.W., Washington, DC 20036-1802. TEL 202-296-6267. FAX 202-296-5149. Ed. Doris Chalfin. bibl.; index. circ. 1,420. (reprint service avail. from SWZ) **Indexed:** Abstr.Soc.Work., Acad.Ind., Biol.Abstr., C.I.J.E., CERDIC, Chem.Abstr., Chic.Per.Ind., Child Devel.Abstr., Commun.Abstr., Crim.Just.Abstr., DSH Abstr., Ergon.Abstr., Except.Child.Educ.Abstr., Excerp.Med., Ind.Med., Indian Psychol.Abstr., Int.Polit.Sci.Abstr., Lang.& Lang.Behav.Abstr., Mid.East: Abstr.& Ind., Mult.Ed.Abstr., Psychol.Abstr. (1935-), SSCI, Stud.Wom.Abstr. **Document type:** academic/scholarly publication.
—BLDSC (5043.400000); Genuine Article; SWETS; UMI; UnCover. **CCC.**
Formerly: Journal of Psychology (ISSN 0022-3980)
Refereed Serial

150   US   ISSN 0882-2689
BF698.4   CODEN: JPBAEB
JOURNAL OF PSYCHOPATHOLOGY AND BEHAVIORAL ASSESSMENT. 1979. q. $275 (foreign $325) (effective 1996). Plenum Publishing Corp., 233 Spring St., New York, NY 10013-1578. TEL 212-620-8000. FAX 212-463-0742. TELEX 23-421139. Ed. Henry E. Adams. adv.; bk.rev. (also avail. in microfilm from JSC; back issues avail.) **Indexed:** Adol.Ment.Hlth.Abstr., Biol.Abstr., Curr.Cont., Excerp.Med., IMFL, Psychol.Abstr. (1979-), Ref.Zh., Soc.Work Res.& Abstr., SSCI. **Document type:** academic/scholarly publication.
—BLDSC (5043.430000); Faxon; Genuine Article; SWETS; UMI; UnCover. **CCC.**
Formerly (until 1986): Journal of Behavioral Assessment (ISSN 0164-0305)
Refereed Serial

JOURNAL OF PSYCHOPHARMACOLOGY. see *PHARMACY AND PHARMACOLOGY*

616.8   US   ISSN 0269-8803
JOURNAL OF PSYCHOPHYSIOLOGY. 1987. q. $149. Hogrefe & Huber Publishers, Box 2487, Kirkland, WA 98083. TEL 206-820-1500. FAX 206-823-8324. Ed. G. Barrett. adv.; bk.rev. **Indexed:** Excerp.Med., Psychol.Abstr. (1987-). **Document type:** academic/scholarly publication.
—BLDSC (5043.465000); Genuine Article; SWETS; UMI; UnCover. **CCC.**
Description: Outlet for original research in all areas employing psychophysiological techniques.

158   US   ISSN 0894-9085
RC489.R3
JOURNAL OF RATIONAL-EMOTIVE AND COGNITIVE-BEHAVIOR THERAPY. 1983. q. $245 (foreign $285) (effective 1996). (Institute for Rational-Emotive Therapy) Human Sciences Press, Inc. (Subsidiary of: Plenum Publishing Corp.), 233 Spring St., New York, NY 10013-1578. TEL 212-620-8000. FAX 212-463-0742. TELEX 23-421139. Eds. Russel Grieger, Paul J. Woods. adv.; bk.rev.; illus. (also avail. in microfilm from UMI; reprint service avail. from UMI) **Indexed:** Adol.Ment.Hlth.Abstr., Lang.& Lang.Behav.Abstr., Psychol.Abstr. (1966-). **Document type:** academic/scholarly publication.
—BLDSC (5046.800000); UMI; UnCover. **CCC.**
Formerly (until 1987): Journal of Rational-Emotive Therapy (ISSN 0748-1985); Supersedes (1966-1983): Rational Living (ISSN 0034-0049)
Description: Provides a forum for the stimulation and maintenance of rational-emotive therapy and other forms of cognitive-behavior therapy.
Refereed Serial

370.1   US   ISSN 1054-0830
RC489.R43
JOURNAL OF REGRESSION THERAPY. 1986. a. $15 (effective 1995)libraries $15. Association for Past-Life Research and Therapies, Inc., Box 20151, Riverside, CA 92516-0151. TEL 909-784-1570. FAX 909-789-8440. Ed. Russell Davis. bk.rev. circ. 1,200. **Document type:** academic/scholarly publication.
Description: Compilation of articles submitted by professionals in the field of Regression Therapy. Includes case histories, therapeutic principles and techniques, and research.
Refereed Serial

155.3 155.4   UK   ISSN 0264-6838
    CODEN: JRIPE3
JOURNAL OF REPRODUCTIVE AND INFANT PSYCHOLOGY. Abbreviated title: J R I P. 1983. q. £36 to individuals; institutions £108 (effective 1996). (Society for Reproductive and Infant Psychology) Carfax Publishing Co., P.O. Box 25, Abingdon, Oxon. OX14 3UE, England. TEL 44-1235-555335. FAX 44-1235-553559. (N. American subscr. to: Carfax Publishing Co., 875-81 Massachusetts Ave., Cambridge, MA 02139) Eds. A. Walker, D. Messer. bk.rev. **Indexed:** Curr.Cont., Mult.Ed.Abstr., Psychol.Abstr. (1983-). **Document type:** academic/scholarly publication.
—BLDSC (5049.620000); UMI. **CCC.**
Description: Reports and reviews research on the psychological, behavioural, medical and social aspects of reproduction, birth and infancy.
Refereed Serial

152   US   ISSN 0092-6566
BF1   CODEN: JRPRA6
JOURNAL OF RESEARCH IN PERSONALITY. 1965. q. $238 (foreign $287) (effective 1996). Academic Press, Inc., Journal Division, 525 B St., Ste. 1900, San Diego, CA 92101-4495. TEL 619-230-1840. FAX 619-699-6800. (Subscr. to: Box 620000, Orlando, FL 32891-8340. TEL 800-543-9534) Ed. David Funder. adv.; charts. (back issues avail.) **Indexed:** Adol.Ment.Hlth.Abstr., ASSIA, Biol.Abstr., Commun.Abstr., Crim.Just.Abstr., Curr.Adv.Ecol.Sci., Curr.Cont., Excerp.Med., Mid.East: Abstr.& Ind., Psychol.Abstr. (1971-), Soc.Work Res.& Abstr., SSCI. **Document type:** academic/scholarly publication.
—BLDSC (5052.025000); Faxon; Genuine Article; SWETS; UnCover. **CCC.**
Formerly: Journal of Experimental Research in Personality (ISSN 0022-1023)
Description: Examines issues in the field of personality and in related fields basic to the understanding of personality.
Refereed Serial

JOURNAL OF RESEARCH ON ADOLESCENCE. see *CHILDREN AND YOUTH — About*

153.83 519.542   US   ISSN 0895-5646
HB615   CODEN: JRUNEN
JOURNAL OF RISK AND UNCERTAINTY. 1988. bi-m. fl.677 to institutions; $435 to institutions in U.S. (effective 1996). Kluwer Academic Publishers Boston, Box 358, Accord Sta., Hingham, MA 02018-0358. TEL 617-871-6600. FAX 617-871-6528. TELEX 200190. (Dist. outside N. America by: Kluwer Academic Publishers Group, P.O. Box 322, 3300 AH Dordrecht, Netherlands. TEL 31-78-392392. FAX 31-78-546474) Ed. W. Kip Viscusi. adv. (also avail. in microform from UMI; reprint service avail. from SWZ,UMI) **Indexed:** ASCA, Curr.Cont., Geo.Abstr., J.of Econ.Lit., Oper.Res.Manage.Sci., Qual.Contr.Appl.Stat., SSCI, Zent.Math. **Document type:** academic/scholarly publication.
—BLDSC (5052.101000); Faxon; Genuine Article; SWETS; UMI; UnCover. **CCC.**
Description: Publishes original theoretical and empirical contributions dealing with the analysis of risk-bearing behavior and decision making under uncertainty.
Refereed Serial

150   US   ISSN 1061-0405
BF1
JOURNAL OF RUSSIAN AND EAST EUROPEAN PSYCHOLOGY; a journal of translations. 1968. bi-m. $557 to institutions (foreign $630) (effective Jul. 1995). M.E. Sharpe, Inc., 80 Business Park Dr., Armonk, NY 10504. TEL 914-273-1800; 800-541-6563. FAX 914-273-2106. Ed. Michael Cole. adv.; charts; index. (back issues avail.) **Indexed:** Adol.Ment.Hlth.Abstr., Biol.Abstr., Psychol.Abstr. (1979-). **Document type:** academic/scholarly publication.
—BLDSC (5052.128950); Faxon; SWETS; UMI; UnCover. **CCC.**
Formerly: Soviet Psychology (ISSN 0038-5751)
Refereed Serial

370.15   UK   ISSN 0022-4405
LB3013.6   CODEN: JSCPAA
JOURNAL OF SCHOOL PSYCHOLOGY. 1963. q. £103($163) (effective 1996). Elsevier Science Ltd., Pergamon, P.O. Box 800, England. TEL 44-1865-843000. FAX 44-1865-843010. E-mail: nlinfo@elsevier.nl; usinfo-f@elsevier.com; forinfo-kyf04035@niftyserve.or.jp; Site addr.: http://www.elsevier.nl/. (Subscr. in U.S. and Canada to: Elsevier Science, 660 White Plains Rd., Tarrytown, NY 10591-5153. TEL 914-524-9200. FAX 914-333-2444) Ed. Joel Meyers. adv.; bk.rev.; abstr.; bibl.; index. circ. 2,000. (also avail. in microfilm from UMI; reprint service avail. from ISI,UMI) **Indexed:** Adol.Ment.Hlth.Abstr., ASCA, C.I.J.E., Cont.Pg.Educ., Curr.Cont., Educ.Ind., Except.Child Educ.Abstr., Lang.& Lang.Behav.Abstr., Mult.Ed.Abstr., Psychol.Abstr. (1963-), Sp.Ed.Needs Abstr., SSCI. **Document type:** academic/scholarly publication.
—BLDSC (5052.670000); Faxon; Genuine Article; SWETS; UMI; UnCover. **CCC.**
Description: Publishes original articles on research and practice relevant to the development of school psychology as both a scientific and an applied specialty.
Refereed Serial

155.3   US   ISSN 0092-623X
RC556   CODEN: JSMTB
JOURNAL OF SEX & MARITAL THERAPY. 1974. q. $38 to individuals (foreign $46); institutions $75 (foreign $83). Brunner-Mazel Publishing Co., 19 Union Sq. W., New York, NY 10003. TEL 212-924-3344. FAX 212-242-6339. Ed.Bd. adv.; bk.rev.; index. circ. 2,000. (also avail. in microform from UMI; reprint service avail. from ISI,UMI) **Indexed:** Adol.Ment.Hlth.Abstr., Behav.Med.Abstr., Biol.Abstr., Curr.Cont., Excerp.Med., Ind.Med., Lang.& Lang.Behav.Abstr., Mid.East: Abstr.& Ind., Mult.Ed.Abstr., Psychol.Abstr. (1974-), Sage Fam.Stud.Abstr., SSCI, Stud.Wom.Abstr. **Document type:** academic/scholarly publication.
—BLDSC (5064.017000); EMDOCS; Faxon; Genuine Article; SWETS; UMI; UnCover.
Description: Provides a contemporary forum on new clinical techniques and conceptualizations and research in sex and marital therapy.

JOURNAL OF SEX EDUCATION AND THERAPY. see *EDUCATION*

155.3   US   ISSN 0022-4499
HQ5   CODEN: JSXRAJ
JOURNAL OF SEX RESEARCH. 1965. q. $53 to individuals (members $40); institutions $85 (effective 1994). Society for the Scientific Study of Sex, Box 208, Mount Vernon, IA 52314. TEL 319-895-8407. FAX 319-895-6203. Ed. Elizabeth Rice Allgeier. adv.; bk.rev.; charts; illus.; stat. circ. 1,600. (also avail. in microfilm from UMI; back issues avail.; reprint service avail. from SWZ,UMI) **Indexed:** Abstr.Anthropol., Adol.Ment.Hlth.Abstr., ASSIA, Behav.Med.Abstr., Commun.Abstr., Curr.Cont., Curr.Lit.Fam.Plan., Excerp.Med., IMFL, Lang.& Lang.Behav.Abstr., Mid.East: Abstr.& Ind., Mult.Ed.Abstr., Psychol.Abstr. (1967-), Sociol.Abstr., SSCI, Stud.Wom.Abstr. **Document type:** academic/scholarly publication.
●Also available online. Vendor(s): University Microfilms International.
—BLDSC (5064.020000); EMDOCS; Faxon; SWETS; UMI; UnCover.
Description: Publishes selected research on issues in human sexuality.
Refereed Serial

150   UK   ISSN 1355-2600
▼**JOURNAL OF SEXUAL AGGRESSION**. 1994. s-a. £37.50 (N. America $65; rest of world £45) (effective 1996). (National Association for the Development of Work with Sex Offenders) Whiting & Birch Ltd., P.O. Box 872, Forest Hill, London SE23 8HL, England. TEL 0181-244-2421. FAX 0181-244-2448. Ed. Marilyn Cardozo. bk.rev. **Document type:** academic/scholarly publication.
—BLDSC (5064.040000).

JOURNAL OF SLEEP RESEARCH. see *MEDICAL SCIENCES*

JOURNAL OF SLEEP RESEARCH. SUPPLEMENT. see *MEDICAL SCIENCES*

PSYCHOLOGY

301.1
RC467
US ISSN 0736-7236
JOURNAL OF SOCIAL AND CLINICAL PSYCHOLOGY. 1983. q. $37.50 to individuals (foreign $55.50); institutions $115 (foreign $132.50) (effective 1995). Guilford Publications, Inc., 72 Spring St., 4th Fl., New York, NY 10012. TEL 212-431-9800. FAX 212-966-6708. Ed. C.R. Snyder; Pub. Robert Matloff. adv. contact: Marian Robinson. bk.rev.; index. circ. 700. (back issues avail.; reprint service avail. from ISI,UMI). **Indexed:** Curr.Cont., Mult.Ed.Abstr., Psychol.Abstr. (1983-), Soc.Work Res.& Abstr., Sp.Ed.Needs Abstr., Stud.Wom.Abstr., Viol.& Abuse Abstr. **Document type:** academic/scholarly publication.
—BLDSC (5064.718000); Faxon; Genuine Article; SWETS; UMI; UnCover. **CCC.**
Description: Covers theory, research and practice in the growing interface of social and clinical psychology.
Refereed Serial

150 574
GN365.9
US ISSN 1061-7361
CODEN: JSESEX
JOURNAL OF SOCIAL AND EVOLUTIONARY SYSTEMS. 1978. q. $100 to individuals (foreign $120); institutions $240 (foreign $250) (effecive 1996). J A I Press Inc., 55 Old Post Rd., No. 2, Greenwich, CT 06836-1678. TEL 203-661-7602. FAX 203-661-7602. (Addr. in Europe: J A I Press Ltd., The Courtyard, 28 High St., Hampton Hill, Mddx. TW12 1PD, England. TEL 44-81-943-9296. FAX 44-81-943-9317) Ed.Bd. adv.; bk.rev.; bibl. (also avail. in microform from UMI; back issues avail.) **Indexed:** Bibl.Ling., Psychol.Abstr., SSCI. **Document type:** academic/scholarly publication.
—BLDSC (5064.735000); Faxon; Genuine Article; UnCover. **CCC.**
Supersedes (in 1991): Journal of Social and Biological Structures (ISSN 0140-1750)

150
UK ISSN 0265-4075
CODEN: JSRLE9
JOURNAL OF SOCIAL AND PERSONAL RELATIONSHIPS. 1984. q. £39 to individuals; institutions £120 (effective 1996). Sage Publications Ltd., 6 Bonhill St., London EC2A 4PU, England. TEL 0171-374-0645. FAX 0171-374-8741. E-mail: market@sageltd.co.uk. Ed. Steve Duck. adv.; B&W page £180; trim 185 x 114; adv. contact: Bernie Folan. bk.rev. **Indexed:** ASSIA, Commun.Abstr., Curr.Cont., IBZ, Psychol.Abstr. (1988-), Sage Fam.Stud.Abstr., Sociol.Abstr., Sociol.Educ.Abstr., SSCI, Stud.Wom.Abstr. **Document type:** academic/scholarly publication.
—BLDSC (5064.740000); Faxon; SWETS; UnCover.
Description: Multidisciplinary examination of personal relationships, drawing on materials from the fields of social, clinical and developmental psychology, communications, and sociology.
Refereed Serial

155.205 302
BF698.A1
US ISSN 0886-1641
CODEN: JSBPE9
JOURNAL OF SOCIAL BEHAVIOR AND PERSONALITY. 1986. q. $30 to individuals; libraries $65 (foreign $73). Select Press, Box 37, Corte Madera, CA 94976-0037. TEL 415-924-1612. FAX 415-924-7179. (back issues avail.) **Indexed:** Psychol.Abstr. (1986-). **Document type:** academic/scholarly publication.
—BLDSC (5064.751500); Faxon; Genuine Article; UnCover.
Description: Studies psychology, sociology, speech, management and other social sciences from an academic approach.
Refereed Serial

JOURNAL OF SOCIAL DISTRESS AND THE HOMELESS. see *SOCIAL SERVICES AND WELFARE*

301.1 150
HN51
US ISSN 0022-4537
CODEN: JSISAF
JOURNAL OF SOCIAL ISSUES. 1944. q. $245 (foreign $290) (effective 1996). (Society for the Psychological Study of Social Issues) Plenum Publishing Corp., 233 Spring St., New York, NY 10013-1578. TEL 212-620-8000. FAX 212-463-0742. TELEX 23-421139. Ed. Daniel Perlman. adv.; abstr.; bibl.; charts; index, cum.index. (also avail. in microfilm from UMI,PMC; reprint service avail. from KTO,UMI) **Indexed:** A.B.C.Pol.Sci., Abstr.Anthropol., Abstr.Crim.& Pen., Acad.Ind., Amer.Hist.& Life, ASSIA, Bus.Ind., C.I.J.E., Commun.Abstr., Crim.Just.Abstr., Curr.Cont., Curr.Lit.Fam.Plan., Educ.Admin.Abstr., Geo.Abstr., Hist.Abstr., IMFL, Int.Polit.Sci.Abstr., Lang.& Lang.Behav.Abstr., Mark.Res.Abstr. (1963-), Mid.East: Abstr.& Ind., P.A.I.S., Peace Res.Abstr., Polit.Sci.Abstr., Psychol.Abstr. (1945-), Psycscan, Sage Fam.Stud.Abstr., Sage Urb.Stud.Abstr., Soc.Sci.Ind., Soc.Work Res.& Abstr., Sp.Ed.Needs Abstr., SSCI, Stud.Wom.Abstr. **Document type:** academic/scholarly publication.
●Also available online. Vendor(s): University Microfilms International.
—BLDSC (5064.755000); Faxon; Genuine Article; SWETS; UMI; UnCover. **CCC.**
Refereed Serial

301.1 150
HM251.A1
US ISSN 0022-4545
CODEN: JSPSAG
THE JOURNAL OF SOCIAL PSYCHOLOGY. 1929. bi-m. $110. (Helen Dwight Reid Educational Foundation) Heldref Publications, 1319 Eighteenth St., N.W., Washington, DC 20036-1802. TEL 202-296-6267. FAX 202-296-5149. Ed. Mary Kanakis. bibl.; charts; index. circ. 2,350. (also avail. in microfilm from UMI; reprint service avail. from SWZ) **Indexed:** Abstr.Crim.& Pen., Abstr.Soc.Work, Adol.Ment.Hlth.Abstr., ASSIA, Biol.Abstr., Child Devel.Abstr., Commun.Abstr., Crim.Just.Abstr., Curr.Cont., DSH Abstr., Except.Child Educ.Abstr., Excerp.Med., Ind.Med., Indian Psychol.Abstr., Int.Polit.Sci.Abstr., Lang.& Lang Behav.Abstr., Mid.East: Abstr.& Ind., Mult.Ed.Abstr., Pers.Lit., PSI, Psychol.Abstr. (1929-), Res.High.Educ.Abstr., Soc.Sci.Ind., Soc.Work Res.& Abstr., SOMA, SSCI, Stud.Wom.Abstr., Tech.Educ.Abstr. **Document type:** academic/scholarly publication.
●Also available online. Vendor(s): University Microfilms International.
—BLDSC (5064.800000); Faxon; Genuine Article; SWETS; UMI; UnCover. **CCC.**
Refereed Serial

150
GV706.4
US ISSN 0895-2779
JOURNAL OF SPORT AND EXERCISE PSYCHOLOGY. Short title: J S E P. 1979. q. $36 to individuals (foreign $40); institutions $88 (foreign $92); students $24 (foreign $28). Human Kinetics Publishers, Inc., Box 5076, Champaign, IL 61825-5076. TEL 217-351-5076. FAX 217-351-2674. Ed. Thelma S. Horn. adv. contact: Pamela Anderson. bk.rev.; bibl.; charts; illus.; stat.; index. circ. 1,700. (back issues avail.) **Indexed:** Biol.Abstr., Child Devel.Abstr., Curr.Cont., Educ.Ind., Ergon.Abstr., Phys.Ed.Ind., Psychol.Abstr. (1979-), Sportsearch (1988-), SSCI. **Document type:** academic/scholarly publication.
—BLDSC (5066.183500); Faxon; Genuine Article; SWETS; UnCover. **CCC.**
Formerly: Journal of Sport Psychology (ISSN 0163-433X)
Description: Multidisciplinary journal designed to stimulate and communicate research and theory. Examines the influence of psychological variables on sport performance and the influence of sport participation on psychological phenomena.
Refereed Serial

JOURNAL OF SPORT BEHAVIOR. see *SPORTS AND GAMES*

370.15 150
L11
US ISSN 0022-4774
CODEN: JSTLAF
JOURNAL OF STRUCTURAL LEARNING. 4/yr. 111 ECU (effective 1996). (International Study Group for Mathematics Learning) Gordon & Breach Science Publishers, c/o International Publishers Distributor, 820 Town Center Dr., Langhorne, PA 19047. TEL 215-750-2642. FAX 215-750-6343. (Subscr. to: International Publishers Distributor, P.O. Box 90, Reading, Berkshire RG1 8JL, England. TEL 44-173-456-8316) (Co-sponsor: Structural Learning Society) Ed. Joseph M. Scandura. adv.; index. (also avail. in microform) **Indexed:** Curr.Cont., Educ.Tech.Abstr., Psychol.Abstr. (1971-), SSCI, Stud.Wom.Abstr., Tech.Educ.Abstr. **Document type:** academic/scholarly publication.
—Faxon; UnCover. **CCC.**
Description: Presents study and teaching methods.
Refereed Serial

616.89
US
JOURNAL OF SYSTEMIC THERAPIES. 1981. q. $36 to individuals (foreign $41); institutions $65 (foreign $70) (effective 1995). Guilford Publications, Inc., 72 Spring St., New York, NY 10012. TEL 212-431-9800. FAX 212-966-6708. Ed. Don Efron; Pub. Robert Matloff. adv. contact: Marian Robinson. bk.rev. circ. 1,200. (back issues avail.) **Indexed:** Psychol.Abstr. (1983-). **Document type:** academic/scholarly publication.
—UnCover. **CCC.**
Formerly: Journal of Strategic and Systematic Therapies (ISSN 0711-5075)
Description: Presents provocative ideas and methods that work with families, individuals and groups. Explores brief therapies, solution-focused models, narrative therapies, constructionism and therapeutic conversations.

152
BF1
US ISSN 0022-5002
CODEN: JEABAU
JOURNAL OF THE EXPERIMENTAL ANALYSIS OF BEHAVIOR. Abbreviated title: J A E B. 1958. bi-m. $110 (effective 1996). Society for the Experimental Analysis of Behavior, Inc., c/o Psychology Department, Indiana University, Bloomington, IN 47405. TEL 812-339-4718. Ed. Richard L. Shull. adv. contact: Devonia Stein. bk.rev.; bibl.; charts; index, cum.index: vols.1-20; 21-40; 41-60. circ. 2,500. (also avail. in microform from PMC; back vols. avail.) **Indexed:** ASSIA, Biol.Abstr., Chem.Abstr., Curr.Cont., Excerp.Med., Ind.Med., INIS Atomind., Mid.East: Abstr.& Ind., Psychol.Abstr. (1958-), Psychol.R.G., Soc.Sci.Ind., SSCI. **Document type:** academic/scholarly publication.
—BLDSC (4979.700000); CASDDS; Faxon; Genuine Article; SWETS; UnCover.
Description: Presents original experiments relevant to the behavior of individual organisms.

150
BF1
US ISSN 0022-5061
CODEN: JHBSA5
JOURNAL OF THE HISTORY OF THE BEHAVIORAL SCIENCES. 1965. q. $45 to individuals; libraries $115. Clinical Psychology Publishing Co., Inc., 4 Conant Sq., Brandon, VT 05733. TEL 802-247-6871. FAX 802-247-6853. Ed. Dr. Barbara Ross. adv.; bk.rev.; index. circ. 800. (also avail. in microform from UMI; back issues avail.; reprint service avail. from UMI) **Indexed:** Abstr.Anthropol., Amer.Bibl.Slavic & E.Eur.Stud., Amer.Hist.& Life, ASCA, ASSIA, Curr.Cont., Hist.Abstr., Ind.Med., Lang.& Lang.Behav.Abstr., Mid.East: Abstr.& Ind., Psychol.Abstr. (1965-), Psychol.R.G., Sociol.Abstr., SSCI. **Document type:** academic/scholarly publication.
—BLDSC (5000.600000); Faxon; Genuine Article; SWETS; UMI; UnCover.
Refereed Serial

JOURNAL OF THE LEARNING SCIENCES; a journal of ideas and their applications. see *EDUCATION*

JOURNAL OF THE PSYCHOLOGY OF RELIGION. see *RELIGIONS AND THEOLOGY*

PSYCHOLOGY

158   US   ISSN 0022-524X
BF1   CODEN: JTPSAN
JOURNAL OF TRANSPERSONAL PSYCHOLOGY. 1969. s-a. $24 to individuals; institutions $32. Transpersonal Institute, 345 California Ave., Palo Alto, CA 94306. TEL 415-327-2066. Ed. Miles A. Vich. bk.rev. circ. 3,800. (also avail. in microform from UMI) **Indexed:** Curr.Cont., Psychol.Abstr. (1969-), Psychol.R.G., Soc.Sci.Ind., SSCI. **Document type:** academic/scholarly publication.
—BLDSC (5069.870000); Faxon; Genuine Article; SWETS; UMI; UnCover.
Description: Focus on psychological and spiritual states, experiences, practices and concepts.

370.15 150   US   ISSN 0894-9867
RC552.P67   CODEN: JTSTEB
JOURNAL OF TRAUMATIC STRESS. 1988. q. $215 (foreign $250) (effective 1996). Plenum Publishing Corp., 233 Spring St., New York, NY 10013-1578. TEL 212-620-8000. FAX 212-463-0742. TELEX 23-421139. Ed. Bonnie L. Green. adv. (also avail. in microfilm from JSC; back issues avail.) **Indexed:** Excerp.Med. (1995-), IMFL, Ind.Med. (1994-), Psychol.Abstr. (1988-). **Document type:** academic/scholarly publication.
—BLDSC (5070.520000); Faxon; Genuine Article; SWETS; UMI; UnCover. **CCC.**
Refereed Serial

158   US   ISSN 0001-8791
HF5381.A1   CODEN: JVBHA2
JOURNAL OF VOCATIONAL BEHAVIOR. 1971. bi-m. $342 (foreign $408) (effective 1996). Academic Press, Inc., Journal Division, 525 B St., Ste. 1900, San Diego, CA 92101-4495. TEL 619-230-1840. FAX 619-699-6800. (Subscr. to: Box 620000, Orlando, FL 32891-8340. TEL 800-543-9534) Ed. Howard E.A. Tinsley. index. (back issues avail.) **Indexed:** ASSIA, C.I.J.E., Chic.Per.Ind., CINAHL, Curr.Cont., Lang.& Lang.Behav.Abstr., Mid.East: Abstr.& Ind., Pers.Lit., Psychol.Abstr. (1971-), Psycscan, SSCI, Stud.Wom.Abstr. **Document type:** academic/scholarly publication.
—BLDSC (5072.510000); Faxon; Genuine Article; SWETS; UnCover. **CCC.**
Description: Publishes empirical and theoretical articles that expand knowledge of vocational behavior and career development across the life span.

JOURNAL OF YOUTH AND ADOLESCENCE; a multidisciplinary research publication. see *CHILDREN AND YOUTH — About*

JOURNALS OF GERONTOLOGY. SERIES B: PSYCHOLOGICAL SCIENCES & SOCIAL SCIENCES. see *GERONTOLOGY AND GERIATRICS*

150.19   CN
JUNG AT HEART; studies in Jungian psychology by Jungian analysts. 1989. irreg. free. Inner City Books, Box 1271, Sta. Q, Toronto, ON M4T 2P4, Canada. TEL 416-927-0355. FAX 416-924-1814. Ed. Daryl Sharp. circ. 3,000. **Document type:** newsletter.
Description: Promotes the understanding and practical application of the work of C.G. Jung.

150   US
JUNGIAN PSYCHOLOGY; a comprehensive guide. 1982. a. $1. Yes Bookshop, 1035 31st St., N.W., Washington, DC 20007. TEL 202-338-2727. Ed. Cris Popenoe.

155 301.1   MY   ISSN 0127-8029
BF8.M35
JURNAL PSIKOLOGI MALAYSIA. (Text in English and Malay) 1972. a. $15. Penerbit Universiti Kebangsaan Malaysia, 43600 UKM Bangi, Selangor, Malaysia.
—UnCover.
Description: Discusses various fields of psychology such as social, developmental, physiological, industrial, counseling, and others particularly relevant to Malaysia.

JYVASKYLA STUDIES IN EDUCATION, PSYCHOLOGY AND SOCIAL RESEARCH. see *EDUCATION*

616.89   JA   ISSN 0917-0383
KANAGAWA RINSHO SHINRIGAKU KENKYU/KANAGAWA CLINICAL PSYCHOLOGY. (Text in Japanese) 1990. a. Kanagawa Rinsho Shinrigaku Kenkyu Kyokai - Kanagawa Research Association for Clinical Psychology, c/o Ken Shogaisha Kosei Sodanjo, 4-2, Sawatari, Kanagawa-ku, Yokohama-shi, Kanagawa-ken 221, Japan.

616.8 615.7   JA   ISSN 0918-0354
KANAGAWA SEISHIN YAKURI/KANAGAWA JOURNAL OF PSYCHOPHARMACOLOGY.* (Text in Japanese) 1988. a. Kanagawa Seishin Yakuri Konwakai - Kanagawa Society of Psychopharmacology, c/o Japanese Pharmacological Society, Yayoi 2-4-16, Bunkyo-ku, Tokyo 113, Japan.

KAYA TAO. see *SOCIOLOGY*

153.4   US   ISSN 0952-1194
KEELE COGNITION SEMINARS. 1987. biennial. price varies. Oxford University Press, 200 Madison Ave., New York, NY 10016. TEL 212-679-7300.
Document type: proceedings.
—BLDSC (5088.330200).

DAS KIND. see *CHILDREN AND YOUTH — About*

616.89   GW   ISSN 0942-6051
KINDERANALYSE. 1992. q. DM.120. Verlag Klett-Cotta, Rotebuehlstr. 77, 70178 Stuttgart, Germany. TEL 0711-6672-0. FAX 0711-6159702. Ed. Jochen Stork. adv. contact: Winifred Kretschmar. **Document type:** academic/scholarly publication.

616.89   GW   ISSN 0343-9429
KLINISCHE PSYCHOLOGIE UND PSYCHOPATHOLOGIE. 1978. irreg., no.57, 1993. price varies. Ferdinand Enke Verlag, Postfach 300366, 70443 Stuttgart, Germany. TEL 0711-135798-0. FAX 0711-135798-30. TELEX 07252275-GTV-D. Ed. H. Remschmidt. (reprint service avail. from IRC) **Document type:** monographic series.

310   JA   ISSN 0385-5481
KODO KEIRYOGAKU/JAPANESE JOURNAL OF BEHAVIORMETRICS. (Text in Japanese; summaries in English) 1974. a. Nihon Kodo Keiryo Gakkai - Behaviormetric Society of Japan, 6-7, Minami-Azabu 4-chome, Minato-ku, Tokyo 106, Japan. **Indexed:** Psychol.Abstr. (1983-). **Document type:** academic/scholarly publication.
—BLDSC (4651.013000).

616.89   JA   ISSN 0910-6529
KODO RYOHO KENKYU/JAPANESE JOURNAL OF BEHAVIOR THERAPY. (Text in English or Japanese; summaries in English) 1974. s-a. 5000 Yen. Nihon Kodo Ryoho Gakkai - Japanese Association of Behavior Therapy, c/o Masahiko Sogiyama, Sec.-Gen., Institute of Special Education, University of Tsukuba, 1-1-1 Tennoudai Tsukuba, Ibaraki 305, Japan. TEL 0298-53-6719. FAX 0298-53-6719. (Subscr. to: Iwasaki Gakujutsu Shuppansha Inc., 1-4-8 Kohinata, Bunkyo-ku, Tokyo 112, Japan) Ed. Yuji Sakano. adv.; bk.rev.; index. circ. 1,200. (back issues avail.) **Indexed:** Psychol.Abstr. (1984-). **Document type:** academic/scholarly publication.
—BLDSC (4651.010000).
Description: Covers experimental and clinical research in behavior therapy.
Refereed Serial

156   GW   ISSN 0938-7986
BF309   CODEN: KOGNEB
KOGNITIONSWISSENSCHAFT. 1990. 4/yr. DM.248($180) (effective 1996). Springer-Verlag, Heidelberger Platz 3, 14197 Berlin, Germany. TEL 030-8207-0. FAX 030-8214091. E-mail: orders@springer.de. (Subscr. in N. America to: Springer-Verlag New York, Inc., 44 Hartz Way, Secaucus, NJ 07096-2491. TEL 201-348-4033. FAX 201-348-4505) Ed.Bd. (also avail. in microform from UMI) **Document type:** academic/scholarly publication.
—UMI. **CCC.**

616.8   JA   ISSN 0023-2807
KOKORO TO SHAKAI/MIND AND SOCIETY. (Text in Japanese) 1969. q. 1500 Yen($5) Nihon Seishin Eiseikai - Japan Mental Health Society, 91 Benten-cho, Shinjuku-ku, Tokyo 162, Japan. Ed. Dr. Haruo Akimoto.

157   GW   ISSN 0937-289X
KRANKENHAUSPSYCHIATRIE. 1990. q. DM.128. Ferdinand Enke Verlag, Postfach 300366, 70443 Stuttgart, Germany. TEL 0711-135798-0. FAX 0711-135798-30. TELEX 07252275-GTV-D. Eds. F. Reimer, V. Faust. (reprint service avail. from IRC) **Document type:** academic/scholarly publication.
—BLDSC (5118.146300).

616.89   NE   ISSN 0167-238X
KWARTAALSCHRIFT VOOR DIRECTIEVE THERAPIE EN HYPNOSE. 4/yr. fl.115 to individuals; institutions fl.165; students fl.85 (effective 1995). Bohn Stafleu van Loghum B.V. (Subsidiary of: Wolters Kluwer N.V.), P.O. Box 246, 3990 GA Houten, Netherlands. TEL 31-3403-95711. FAX 31-3403-50903. adv.; bk.rev. circ. 2,000.

370   JA   ISSN 0452-9650
KYOIKU SHINRIGAKU NENPO/ANNUAL REPORT OF EDUCATIONAL PSYCHOLOGY IN JAPAN. 1961. a. 4000 Yen. Japanese Association of Educational Psychology - Nihon Kyoiku Shinri Gakkai, c/o Faculty of Education, University of Tokyo, 7-3-1 Hongo, Bunkyo-ku, Tokyo 113, Japan. Ed. Noboru Sakano. adv. contact: Seijun Takano. **Document type:** academic/scholarly publication.

616.89   JA   ISSN 0285-4562
KYUSHU DAIGAKU SHINRI RINSHO KENKYU/KYUSHU UNIVERSITY. PSYCHOLOGICAL CLINIC. ARCHIVES. (Text in Japanese) 1982. a. Kyushu Daigaku, Kyoikugakubu, Shinri Kyoiku Sodanshitsu, 19-1, Hakozaki 6-chome, Higashi-ku, Fukuoka-shi, Fukuoka-ken 812, Japan.

LANGUAGE ACQUISITION; a journal of developmental linguistics. see *LINGUISTICS*

LANGUAGE AND COGNITIVE PROCESSES. see *LINGUISTICS*

LANGUAGE SCIENCES; a world journal of the sciences of language. see *LINGUISTICS*

LATERALITY. see *MEDICAL SCIENCES — Psychiatry And Neurology*

808.87   US   ISSN 0731-1788
LAUGHING MATTERS. 1981. q. $15. Saratoga Institute, Humor Project, 110 Spring St., Saratoga Springs, NY 12866. TEL 518-587-8770. Ed. Dr. Joel Goodman. bk.rev.; illus.; cum.index. circ. 10,000. (back issues avail.)

LAW AND HUMAN BEHAVIOR. see *LAW*

LAW AND PSYCHOLOGY REVIEW. see *LAW*

LEADERSHIP QUARTERLY; an international journal of political, social and behavioral science. see *BUSINESS AND ECONOMICS — Management*

370.15 150   US   ISSN 1041-6080
LB1051   CODEN: LIDIEI
LEARNING AND INDIVIDUAL DIFFERENCES; a multidisciplinary journal in education. 1989. q. $70 to individuals (foreign $90); institutions $165 (foreign $185) (effective 1996). J A I Press Inc., 55 Old Post Rd., No. 2, Box 1678, Greenwich, CT 06836-1678. TEL 203-661-7602. FAX 203-661-0792. (Addr. in Europe: J A I Press Ltd., The Courtyard, 28 High St., Hampton Hill, Mddx. TW12 1PD, England. TEL 44-81-943-9296. FAX 44-81-943-9317) Ed. H. Lee Swanson. (also avail. in microform from UMI; back issues avail.) **Indexed:** Psychol.Abstr. (1989-). **Document type:** academic/scholarly publication.
—BLDSC (5179.325880); Faxon; Genuine Article; UnCover. **CCC.**

LEARNING AND MOTIVATION. see *EDUCATION*

616.89   GW   ISSN 0343-4591
LEBENDIGE SEELSORGE; Zeitschrift fuer alle Fragen der Seelsorge. 1949. s-m. DM.63. Seelsorge Verlag Echter, Juliuspromenade 64, 97070 Wuerzburg, Germany. Ed. Lothar Roos. adv. contact: Thomas Haeussner. **Document type:** academic/scholarly publication.
—BLDSC (5179.622900).

158 364 614.19   UK   ISSN 1355-3259
▼**LEGAL AND CRIMINOLOGICAL PSYCHOLOGY.** Announced for publication in 1996. s-a. £50($97) (effective 1996). British Psychological Society, St. Andrews House, 48 Princess Rd. E., Leicester LE1 7DR, England. TEL 0116-254-9568. FAX 0116-2470787. (Subscr. to: Turpin Distribution Services Ltd., Blackhorse Rd., Letchworth, Herts. SG6 1HN, England. TEL 01462-672555. FAX 01462-480947) **Document type:** academic/scholarly publication.

LEISURE STUDIES. see *LEISURE AND RECREATION*

PSYCHOLOGY

LESBIAN AND GAY COUNSELLING NEWS. see *HOMOSEXUALITY*

301.1 150   UK   ISSN 0267-7172
LIBERTARIAN ALLIANCE. PSYCHOLOGICAL NOTES. 1985. irreg. £15($30) Libertarian Alliance, 25 Chapter Chambers, Esterbrooke St., London SW1 4NN, England. TEL 0171-821-5502. FAX 0171-834-2031. E-mail: liberty@capital.demon.co.uk. **Document type:** monographic series.

150 301   US   ISSN 0161-9454
BF712
LIFE-SPAN DEVELOPMENT AND BEHAVIOR. 1978. a. Lawrence Erlbaum Associates, Inc., 10 Industrial Dr., Mahwah, NJ 07430-2262. TEL 201-236-9500. FAX 201-236-0072.
—BLDSC (5208.962400); Faxon; UnCover.

LITERATURE AND PSYCHOLOGY; a quarterly journal of literary criticism as informed by depth psychology. see *LITERATURE*

LIVING HEALTHY; learning to live with digestive disease. see *MEDICAL SCIENCES — Gastroenterology*

152   UK   ISSN 0966-8349
CODEN: LOSCEF
LOCATION SCIENCE. 1993. q. £164($261) (effective 1996). Elsevier Science Ltd., Pergamon, P.O. Box 800, Kidlington, Oxford OX5 1DX, England. TEL 44-1865-843000. FAX 44-1865-843010. E-mail: nlinfo-f@elsevier.nl; usinfo-f@elsevier.com; forinfo-kyf04035@niftyserve.or.jp; Site addr.: http://www.elsevier.nl/. (Subscr. in U.S. and Canada to: Elsevier Science, 660 White Plains Rd., Tarrytown, NY 10591-5153. TEL 914-524-9200. FAX 914-333-2444) Ed.Bd. (also avail. in microfilm from UMI; back issues avail.) **Indexed:** INSPEC (1993-). **Document type:** academic/scholarly publication.
—BLDSC (5290.060000); SWETS; UMI. **CCC.**
Description: Publishes interdisciplinary papers on the theory and modelling of location problems, including the underlying processes related to locational decisions, as well as issues of implementation and specific applications of location modelling.
Refereed Serial

LONGITUDINAL RESEARCH IN THE SOCIAL AND BEHAVIORAL SCIENCES; an interdisciplinary series. see *SOCIAL SCIENCES: COMPREHENSIVE WORKS*

370.15 150   US   ISSN 8756-4610
R726.5
LOSS, GRIEF & CARE; a journal of professional practice. 1986. q. $150 (foreign $210) (effective 1996). Haworth Press, Inc., 10 Alice St., Binghamton, NY 13904. TEL 607-722-5857; 800-342-9678. FAX 607-722-1424. TELEX 4932599. Ed. Austin H. Kutscher. adv.; bk.rev. circ. 307. (also avail. in microfiche from UMI; reprint service avail. from HAW) **Indexed:** ASSIA, IMFL, Int.Polit.Sci.Abstr., LISA, Past.Care & Couns.Abstr., Psychol.Abstr., Ref.Zh., Soc.Work Res.& Abstr., Sociol.Abstr. **Document type:** academic/scholarly publication.
—BLDSC (5294.735000); Haworth; UnCover.
Description: Explores the critical issues of psychosocial care for chronically, critically, and terminally ill patients and their family members.
Refereed Serial

158   US   ISSN 1056-3954
LOTUS; the journal for personal transformation. 1991. 5/yr. $19.50; newsstand price: 4.95. Lotus Publishing, Inc, 4032 S. Lamar Blvd., Ste. 500-137, Austin, TX 78704-7900. TEL 918-683-4560. FAX 918-683-2466. Ed. Mary Nurrie Stearns. adv. contact: Mary Ann Vavalette. illus.; circ. 32,500 (paid). **Document type:** consumer publication.
Description: Covers a variety of personal growth issues and strategies.

LOVING BROTHERHOOD NEWSLETTER; a journal for personal and planetary transformation. see *HOMOSEXUALITY*

LUND STUDIES IN PSYCHOLOGY OF RELIGION. see *RELIGIONS AND THEOLOGY*

150   GW   ISSN 0933-3347
BF173.A2
LUZIFER-AMOR; Zeitschrift zur Geschichte der Psychoanalyse. 1988. s-a. DM.48. Edition Diskord, Schwarzlocher Str. 104-b, 72070 Tuebingen, Germany. TEL 07071-40102. FAX 07071-44710. Eds. Gerd Kimmerle, Hanna Gekle. adv.; bk.rev. circ. 1,000. (back issues avail.) **Document type:** academic/scholarly publication.

M I D S NEWSLETTER. (Miscarriage, Infant Death, and Stillbirth) see *WOMEN'S STUDIES*

150   HU   ISSN 0025-0279
BF8.H8
MAGYAR PSZICHOLOGIAI SZEMLE/HUNGARIAN PSYCHOLOGICAL REVIEW. (Text in Hungarian; summaries in English, Russian) 1928. q. 720 Ft. (Magyar Tudomanyos Akademia) Akademiai Kiado, Publishing House of the Hungarian Academy of Sciences, P.O. Box 245, H-1519 Budapest, Hungary. TEL 181-2134. FAX 166-6466. TELEX 22-6228 AKNYO H. (Co-sponsor: Magyar Pszichologiai Tarsasag) Ed. P. Popper. adv.; bk.rev.; index. **Indexed:** C.I.S. Abstr., Curr.Cont., Lang.& Lang.Behav.Abstr., Psychol.Abstr. (1934-). **Document type:** academic/scholarly publication.

150 301 574   II   ISSN 0025-1615
MANAB MON; a journal depicting the modern trends in psychology, biology, and sociology. (Text in English) 1972. q. Rs.8($1) Pavlov Institute, 132-1A Bidhan Sarani, Calcutta 4, India. Ed. Dr. D.N. Ganguly. adv.; bk.rev. circ. 1,000.

150   II   ISSN 0025-1984
MANAS; a journal of scientific psychology. (Text in English) 1954. s-a. Rs.25($6) (Behavioural Sciences Centre) Manasayan, 32 Netaji Subhash Marg, New Delhi 110002, India. Ed.Bd. adv.; bk.rev. circ. 300. (back issues avail.) **Indexed:** Psychol.Abstr.
—UnCover.

MANKIND QUARTERLY; an international quarterly journal dealing with both physical and cultural anthropology including related subjects such as psychology, demography, genetics, linguistics and mythology. see *ANTHROPOLOGY*

MANTEIA; a magazine for the mantic arts. see *PARAPSYCHOLOGY AND OCCULTISM*

370.15   XR
MASARYKOVA UNIVERSITA. FILOZOFICKA FAKULTA. SBORNIK PRACI. I: RADA PEDAGOGICKO - PSYCHOLOGICKA. 1966. irreg. (approx. a). price varies. Masarykova Universita, Filozoficka Fakulta, A. Novaka 1, 660 88 Brno, Czech Republic. FAX 41-211241. bk.rev. **Indexed:** Psychol.Abstr. **Document type:** proceedings.
Formerly: Universita J.E. Purkyne. Filozoficka Fakulta. Sbornik Praci. I: Rada Pedagogicko - Psychologicka (ISSN 0068-2705)
Description: Covers all aspects of pedagogics and psychology.

152 510   UK   ISSN 1354-6791
▼**MATHEMATICAL COGNITION.** 1995. s-a. £15($30) to individuals (outside the E.U. £17.50); institutions £30 (outside the E.U. £32.50 ($55)) (effective 1996). Lawrence Erlbaum Associates Ltd., 27 Palmeira Mansions, Church Rd., Hove, E. Sussex BN3 2FA, England. TEL 01273-207411. FAX 01273-205612. (Subscr. to: Turpin Distribution Services Ltd., Blackhorse Rd., Letchworth, Herts. SG6 1HN, England. TEL 01462-672555. FAX 01462-480947) (back issues avail.) **Document type:** academic/scholarly publication.

MATHEMATICS EDUCATION LIBRARY. see *EDUCATION*

MEASUREMENT AND EVALUATION IN COUNSELING AND DEVELOPMENT. see *EDUCATION*

301.1 150 340   US   ISSN 0739-4098
KF9084.A15
MEDIATION QUARTERLY. 1983. q. $49 to individuals; institutions $82. (Academy of Family Mediators) Jossey-Bass Inc., Publishers, 350 Sansome St., 5th Fl., San Francisco, CA 94104. TEL 415-433-1767. FAX 415-433-0499. Ed. Peter R. Maida. bk.rev. circ. 1,400. (back issues avail.) **Indexed:** IMFL, Psychol.Abstr. (1983-), Sage Fam.Stud.Abstr., Sage Urb.Stud.Abstr., Sociol.Abstr. **Document type:** academic/scholarly publication.
—BLDSC (5525.380000); Faxon; UMI; UnCover.
Description: Covers the latest developments in the theory and practice of mediation, an alternative to traditional means of resolving conflicts such as those involving family members, labor and management, landlords and tenants, neighbors, and others.
Refereed Serial

MEDICAL HYPNOANALYSIS JOURNAL. see *MEDICAL SCIENCES — Hypnosis*

MEDICINA E PSICHE/MEDICINE AND MIND; semestrale di psicologia medica e di filosofia della medicina - semi-annual journal of philosophy of medicine and medical psychology. see *MEDICAL SCIENCES — Psychiatry And Neurology*

301.1 150   GW   ISSN 0936-7780
P96.P75
MEDIENPSYCHOLOGIE; Zeitschrift fuer Individual- und Massenkommunikation. (Text in German and English) 1989. q. DM.94 (students DM.70.50) (effective 1996). Westdeutscher Verlag GmbH, Postfach 1546, 65005 Wiesbaden, Germany. TEL 0611-534389. FAX 0611-534430. Ed.Bd. adv.; bk.rev.; index. circ. 500. (back issues avail.) **Indexed:** Psychol.Abstr. (1992-). **Document type:** academic/scholarly publication.

MEGAMOT; behavioural sciences quarterly. see *SOCIOLOGY*

152   UK   ISSN 0965-8211
BF371   CODEN: MEMOFV
MEMORY. 1993. q. £45($85) to individuals (outside the E.U. £49); institutions £95 (outside the E.U. £99 ($180)) (effective 1996). Lawrence Erlbaum Associates Ltd., 27 Palmeira Mansions, Church Rd., Hove, E. Sussex BN3 2FA, England. TEL 01273-207411. FAX 01273-205612. (Subscr. to: Turpin Distribution Services Ltd., Blackhorse Rd., Letchworth, Herts. SG6 1HN, England. TEL 01462-672555. FAX 01462-480947) Eds. Susan E. Gathercole, Martin A. Conway. adv.: page £175; 110 x 190. circ. 250. **Document type:** academic/scholarly publication.
—BLDSC (5678.000000); SWETS.
Description: Covers high-quality research in all areas of memory, including experimental studies and developmental, educational, neuropsychological, clinical, and social research on memory.

152   US   ISSN 0090-502X
BF371   CODEN: MYCGAO
MEMORY AND COGNITION. 1973. bi-m. $128 (foreign $140) (effective 1996). Psychonomic Society, Inc., 1710 Fortview Rd., Austin, TX 78704. TEL 512-462-2442. Ed. Geoffrey Loftus. adv.; bibl.; illus. circ. 2,400. (also avail. in microform from KTO,UMI; back issues avail.; reprint service avail. from UMI) **Indexed:** Biol.Abstr., Child Devel.Abstr., Commun.Abstr., Curr.Adv.Ecol.Sci., Curr.Cont., Ergon.Abstr., Excerp.Med., Lang.& Lang.Behav.Abstr., M.L.A., Mid.East: Abstr.& Ind., Psychol.Abstr. (1973-), SSCI. **Document type:** academic/scholarly publication.
—BLDSC (5678.300000); EMDOCS; Faxon; Genuine Article; SWETS; UMI; UnCover. **CCC.**
Description: Covers human memory, learning, conceptual processes, psycholinguistics, and problem solving, along with reports of work in computer simulation and experimental social psychology.
Refereed Serial

MENNINGER CLINIC. BULLETIN; a journal for the mental health professions. see *MEDICAL SCIENCES — Psychiatry And Neurology*

PSYCHOLOGY

362.2 616.8   US   ISSN 1066-937X
THE MENNINGER LETTER; your national resource for mental health. 1993. m. $24. Menninger Clinic, Box 829, Topeka, KS 66601-0829.
TEL 913-273-7500; 800-289-9311.
FAX 913-273-8625. Ed. Dr. Glen O. Gabbard. circ. 78,000. **Document type**: consumer publication, newsletter.
  Description: Contains popularly written information for lay persons designed to promote emotional well-being and to enhance public understanding of mental health concerns.

MENNINGER PERSPECTIVE. see *MEDICAL SCIENCES — Psychiatry And Neurology*

MENSA RESEARCH JOURNAL. see *EDUCATION*

MENTAL CAPACITY: MEDICAL AND LEGAL ASPECTS OF THE AGING. see *GERONTOLOGY AND GERIATRICS*

614.58 790.1   US
THE MENTAL EDGE. 4/yr. $15. 18607 Ventura Blvd., Ste. 310, Tarzana, CA 91356. TEL 818-344-4464. E-mail: Compuserve 76473,546. Ed. J.P. Erickson. **Document type**: newsletter.
  Description: Covers specific procedures to enhance sports performance and discusses how top athletes use mental training to boost their athletic skills.

150   US   ISSN 0272-9962
RA790.A1
MENTAL HEALTH. (Subseries of: S I R S Social Issues (ISSN 0740-3127)) 1979. a. price varies; a. supplement $17. Social Issues Resources Series, Box 2348, Boca Raton, FL 33427-2348.
TEL 407-994-0079; 800-232-7477.
FAX 407-994-4704. (looseleaf format; also avail. in microfiche; back issues avail.)
  Description: Reprints articles that explore the causes of mental illnesses and their effects on society.

150   US
MENTAL HEALTH AND PSYCHOPATHOLOGY: A MACARTHUR FOUNDATION RESEARCH NETWORK SERIES. irreg. (approx. 1/yr.). Guilford Publications, Inc., 72 Spring St., New York, NY 10012.
TEL 212-431-9800; 800-365-7006.
FAX 212-966-6708. Ed. David J. Kupfer. **Document type**: monographic series.

155.4 362.7 616.8   US
MENTAL HEALTH IN CHILDREN. 1975. irreg. $69.95. P J D Publications Ltd., Box 966, Westbury, NY 11590. TEL 516-626-0650. FAX 516-626-5546. Ed. Dr. D.V. Siva Sankar; Pub. Barbara Sankar. (back issues avail.) **Document type**: academic/scholarly publication.
  Description: Articles for professionals in the area of child mental health.

MENTAL HEALTH LAW NEWS. see *LAW — Civil Law*

MENTAL HEALTH LAW REPORTER. see *LAW — Civil Law*

150   US
MENTAL HEALTH LIBRARY SERIES. irreg., no.3, 1994. International Universities Press, Inc., 59 Boston Post Rd., Box 1524, Madison, CT 06443-1524.
TEL 203-245-4000. FAX 203-245-0775. Ed. Dr. George H. Pollock. **Document type**: academic/scholarly publication, monographic series.

616.89   UK   ISSN 0963-0201
MENTAL HEALTH MATTERS. 1962. q. membership. Northern Ireland Association for Mental Health, 80 University St., Belfast BT7 1HE, N. Ireland.
FAX 0232-234940. Ed. Margery Magee. bk.rev.; circ. 1,700 (controlled). **Document type**: newsletter.
  Former titles (until 1991): Beacon House Bulletin (ISSN 0144-2368); Northern Ireland Association for Mental Health. Newsletter; Beacon House News.

614.58   UK   ISSN 1353-2650
▼**MENTAL HEALTH RESEARCH REVIEW**. 1994. m. free. P S S R U, University of Kent at Canterbury, Canterbury, Kent CT2 7NF, England.
TEL 01227-764000. FAX 01227-764327. E-mail: a.stewart@ukc.ac.uk. Eds. Alan Stewart, Daniel Chisholm. **Document type**: academic/scholarly publication.
  —BLDSC (5678.584700).

370.15 613.62   US   ISSN 0279-4136
MENTAL HEALTH SPECIAL INTEREST SECTION NEWSLETTER. (Consists of 11 sections: Administration and Management; Developmental Disabilities; Education; Gerontology; Home & Community Health; Mental Health; Physical Disabilities; School System; Sensory Integration; Technology; Work Programs) vol.12; no.4, 1989. q. $15. American Occupational Therapy Association, Inc., Box 31220, Bethesda, MD 20824-1220. TEL 301-652-2682. FAX 301-652-7711. **Document type**: newsletter.
  Formerly: American Occupational Therapy Association. Mental Health Specialty Section. Newsletter (ISSN 0194-6382)

362.2 301.1   US   ISSN 1058-1103
MENTAL HEALTH WEEKLY; news for policy and program decision-makers. w. $469 to individuals (Canada $489; elsewhere $509); institutions $499 (Canada $519; elsewhere $539) (effective Jul. 1995). Manisses Communications Group, Inc., Box 9758, Providence, RI 02906-9758. TEL 401-861-6020; 800-333-7771. FAX 401-861-6370. Ed. Gary A. Enos. **Indexed**: Except.Child.Educ.Abstr., Pers.Lit. **Document type**: newsletter.
  ●Also available online.
  —UMI. CCC.
  Incorporates (in 1991): Addiction Program Management (ISSN 0897-4934); (1970-1991): Behavior Today (ISSN 0005-7924); Which incorporates: Sexuality Today (ISSN 0148-883X); Marriage and Divorce Today (ISSN 0148-8821)
  Description: Public policy and economic issues for mental health professionals and policy makers in the public, private and nonprofit sectors.

151.22 371.26   US   ISSN 0076-6461
Z5814.P8
MENTAL MEASUREMENTS YEARBOOK. 1938. biennial. price varies. Buros Institute of Mental Measurements, 135 Bancroft, University of Nebraska-Lincoln, Lincoln, NE 68588-0348. TEL 402-472-6203. FAX 402-472-6207. (Dist. by: University of Nebraska Press, 312 N. 14th St., Lincoln, NE 68588-0484. TEL 402-472-3584. FAX 402-472-6214) Eds. Jane Close Conoley, James C. Impara. **Document type**: directory.
  ●Also available on CD-ROM.
  Description: Contains descriptions and candidly critical reviews of commercially available test instruments. Reviews done by professionals in the assessment, measurement or subject area.
  Refereed Serial

MENTALITIES/MENTALITES. see *HISTORY*

301.1 150   IT
MENTE E SOCIETA. 1985. irreg., no.7, 1992. price varies. Liguori Editore s.r.l., Via Mezzocannone, 19, 80134 Naples, Italy. TEL 081-5527139. Ed. Guglielmo Bellelli. **Document type**: monographic series.

MERIDIAN; Zeitschrift fuer Kosmobiologie, Astrologie und angewandte Psychologie. see *NEW AGE PUBLICATIONS*

150 301   US   ISSN 0272-9679
HQ1   CODEN: MPQUA5
MERRILL - PALMER QUARTERLY. 1954. q. $40 to individuals; institutions $75; students $24 (effective 1995). (Merrill - Palmer Institute) Wayne State University Press, Leonard N. Simons Bldg., 4809 Woodward Ave., Detroit, MI 48201-1309.
TEL 313-577-6120. FAX 313-577-6131. Ed. Kathryn Wildfong; Arthur Evans, Dir. adv. contact: Ann Schwartz. bk.rev.; charts; illus.; index. circ. 1,290. (also avail. in microform from UMI) **Indexed**: Abstr.Soc.Work., Adol.Ment.Hlth.Abstr., Bibl.Dev.Med.& Child Neur., Biol.Abstr., C.I.J.E., Child.Devel.Abstr., Curr.Cont., DSH Abstr., Educ.Ind., Except.Child.Educ.Abstr., IMFL, Lang.& Lang.Behav.Abstr., Mid.East: Abstr.& Ind., Mult.Ed.Abstr., PSI, Psychol.Abstr. (1954-), Psycscan D.P., Sage Fam.Stud.Abstr., Soc.Work Res.& Abstr., Sociol.Abstr., Sociol.Educ.Abstr., Sp.Ed.Needs Abstr., SSCI. **Document type**: academic/scholarly publication.
  Formerly (until 1960): Merrill - Palmer Quarterly of Behavior and Development (ISSN 0026-0150)
  Description: Publishes theoretical and empirical papers in the areas of human development and family-child relationships.
  Refereed Serial

METAPHOR AND SYMBOLIC ACTIVITY. see *LINGUISTICS*

METHODOLOGIA; pensiero linguaggio modelli - thought language models. see *LINGUISTICS*

301.1 355   US   ISSN 0899-5605
U22.3
MILITARY PSYCHOLOGY. 1989. q. $40 to individuals (foreign $65); institutions $195 (foreign $220). (American Psychological Association, Division 19) Lawrence Erlbaum Associates, Inc., 10 Industrial Dr., Mahwah, NJ 07430-2262. TEL 201-236-9500. FAX 201-236-0072. Ed. Martin F. Wiskoff. adv.: page $325; 5 x 8. **Indexed**: Psychol.Abstr. (1989-). **Document type**: academic/scholarly publication.
  —BLDSC (5768.167000); Ei; UnCover.
  Description: Presents behavioral science research papers having military applications in clinical and health psychology, cognition and training, human factors, manpower and personnel, social and organizational systems, and testing and measurement.
  Refereed Serial

MIND - BODY MEDICINE. see *MEDICAL SCIENCES — Psychiatry And Neurology*

330 614.7   US
MIND MATTERS REVIEW. 1988. q. 20 F.($15) Carrie L Drake, Ed. & Pub., 2040 Polk St., Box 234, San Francisco, CA 94109. adv.; bk.rev. circ. 1,000. (back issues avail.)
  Description: Forum for discussion on the politics of mind, encompassing politics of religion, psychiatry, science, ideology.

155.4   US   ISSN 0076-9266
BF721   CODEN: MSCRBG
MINNESOTA SYMPOSIA ON CHILD PSYCHOLOGY SERIES. 1966. irreg., vol.24, 1991. $49.95. (University of Minnesota, Institute of Child Development) Lawrence Erlbaum Associates, Inc., 10 Industrial Dr., Mahwah, NJ 07430-2262. TEL 201-236-9500. FAX 201-236-0072. (back issues avail.) **Indexed**: Biol.Abstr., Curr.Cont., Psychol.Abstr., SSCI.
  —BLDSC (5810.490000).

MISCELANEA COMILLAS; revista de teologia y ciencias humanas. see *RELIGIONS AND THEOLOGY*

616.89   GW   ISSN 0342-3174
MITEINANDER LEBEN LERNEN; Zeitschrift fuer Tiefenpsychologie, Persoenlichkeitsbildung und Kulturforschung. bi-m. DM.28. Institut fuer Tiefenpsychologie, Eichenallee 6, 14050 Berlin, Germany. TEL 030-3023034. Ed. Josef Rattner. **Document type**: academic/scholarly publication.
  Formerly (until 1976): Leben Lernen (ISSN 0341-8286)

150   US   ISSN 0361-5227
RC500
MODERN PSYCHOANALYSIS. 1976. s-a. $15 to individuals (Canada $20; elsewhere $30); institutions $30 (Canada $35; elsewhere $40) (effective 1995). Center for Modern Psychoanalytic Studies, 16 W. 10th St., New York, NY 10011. TEL 212-260-7050. FAX 212-260-7052. Ed. Phyllis W. Meadow; Pub. Cyril Z. Meadow. bk.rev.; index. **Indexed**: Chicago Psychoanal.Lit.Ind., CINAHL, Mid.East: Abstr.& Ind., Psychoanal.Abstr., Psychol.Abstr. (1976-). **Document type**: academic/scholarly publication.
  —BLDSC (5894.420000); Faxon; UMI; UnCover.
  Description: Dedicated to extending the theory and practice of psychoanalysis to the full range of emotional disorders.
  Refereed Serial

150   PL   ISSN 0077-0515
MONOGRAFIE PSYCHOLOGICZNE. (Text in Polish; summaries in English and Russian) 1968. irreg., vol.59, 1991. price varies. Polska Akademia Nauk, Komitet Nauk Psychologicznych, Ul. Stawki 5-7, pok. 316, 00-183 Warsaw, Poland. (Dist. by: Ars Polona-Ruch, Krakowskie Przedmiescie 7, Warsaw, Poland) Ed. Tadeusz Tomaszewski. **Indexed**: Math.R. **Document type**: academic/scholarly publication.

PSYCHOLOGY

155   US   ISSN 0749-1190
CODEN: MPSYEV
MONOGRAPHS IN PSYCHOBIOLOGY. 1985. irreg., vol.6, 1989. price varies. Gordon & Breach Science Publishers, c/o International Publishers Distributor, 820 Town Center Dr., Langhorne, PA 19047. TEL 215-750-2642. FAX 215-750-6343. (Subscr. to: International Publishers Distributor, P.O. Box 90, Reading, Berkshire RG1 8JL, England. TEL 44-173-456-8316) Ed. S.A. Corson. **Document type:** monographic series.
—BLDSC (5915.972000).
Refereed Serial

MONOGRAPHS ON INFANCY. see *MEDICAL SCIENCES — Pediatrics*

150   US   ISSN 0146-7239
BF683   CODEN: MOEMDJ
MOTIVATION AND EMOTION. 1977. q. $255 (foreign $295) (effective 1996). Plenum Publishing Corp., 233 Spring St., New York, NY 10013-1578. TEL 212-620-8000. FAX 212-463-0742. TELEX 23-421139. Ed. Alice M. Isen. adv. (also avail. in microfilm from JSC; back issues avail.) **Indexed:** Biol.Abstr., Child Devel.Abstr., Curr.Cont., Psychol.Abstr. (1977-), SSCI. **Document type:** academic/scholarly publication.
—BLDSC (5969.060000); Faxon; Genuine Article; SWETS; UMI; UnCover. **CCC.**
Refereed Serial

152   US   ISSN 0027-3171
BF39   CODEN: MVBRAV
MULTIVARIATE BEHAVIORAL RESEARCH. 1966. q. $39 to individuals (foreign $64); institutions $195 (foreign $220). Lawrence Erlbaum Associates, Inc., 10 Industrial Dr., Mahwah, NJ 07430-2262. TEL 201-236-9500. FAX 201-236-0072. Ed. Stanley A. Mulaik. adv.: page $325; 5 x 8. index. circ. 905. (also avail. in microform from UMI; back issues avail.) **Indexed:** Biol.Abstr., Biostat., C.I.J.E., Commun.Abstr., Compumath, Curr.Cont., J.Cont.Quant.Meth., Lang.& Lang.Behav.Abstr., Mid.East: Abstr.& Ind., Psychol.Abstr. (1966-), Psycscan, Sci.Cit.Ind., SSCI. **Document type:** academic/scholarly publication.
—BLDSC (5983.300000); Faxon; SWETS; UMI; UnCover.
Description: Reports results of behavioral research employing multivariate methods.
Refereed Serial

157   US   ISSN 0147-3964
BF698.A1   CODEN: MCREDA
MULTIVARIATE EXPERIMENTAL CLINICAL RESEARCH; a journal for basic behavioral research into personality dynamics and clinical psychology. 1973. q. $29 to individuals (foreign $35); institutions $50 (foreign $56). Psychology Press, c/o Dr. Charles Burdsal, Ed., Department of Psychology, No.34, Wichita State University, Wichita, KS 67208. TEL 316-689-3170. adv.; bk.rev. circ. 200. (processed) **Indexed:** Biol.Abstr., Curr.Cont., Excerpt.Med., IMFL, Psychol.Abstr., Sci.Cit.Ind., SSCI. **Document type:** academic/scholarly publication.
—BLDSC (5983.350000); Faxon; Genuine Article; UnCover.
Formerly: Journal of Multivariate Experimental Personality and Clinical Psychology (ISSN 0149-9688)
Description: Outlet for clinical and personality researches using sophisticated, multivariate experimental methods. Both manipulative and non-manipulative research is accepted.

MUSIC THERAPY PERSPECTIVES. see *MUSIC*

MUSIKPSYCHOLOGIE. see *MUSIC*

616.89   GW   ISSN 0172-5505
ML3920
MUSIKTHERAPEUTISCHE UMSCHAU. (Text in German; summaries in English) 4/yr. DM.106 (foreign DM.110). Vandenhoeck und Ruprecht, Robert-Bosch-Breite 6, 37079 Goettingen, Germany. TEL 0551-695926. FAX 0551-695917. Ed. V. Bernius. **Indexed:** Dok.Arbeitsmed., Excerpt.Med., Psychol.Abstr., RILM. **Document type:** academic/scholarly publication.
—UMI. **CCC.**
Description: Publication containing studies in music oriented therapy, and its application in medicine, psychotherapy, and psychology.

658.3   SA   ISSN 0259-1839
N I P R NEWS. (Text in Afrikaans, English) 1974. 3/yr. free. National Institute for Personnel Research, Box 32410, Braamfontein 2017, South Africa. FAX 011-403-2353. Eds. J. Duckitt, C. Marais. circ. 7,000.

150 410   SZ   ISSN 1022-2456
▼ **N L P WORLD.** (Neuro-Linguistic Programming) 1994. 3/yr. 70 SFr. to individuals; institutions 105 SFr. Les 3 Chausseurs, CH-1413 Orzens, Switzerland. TEL 021-8877721. FAX 021-8877976. E-mail: 100031,3620@compuserve. Ed. G. Peter Winnington. adv.; bk.rev. **Document type:** academic/scholarly publication.
—BLDSC (6113.857900).
Description: Studies the modeling of subjective experience and applies the models to communications, including education, the caring professions, sales and intra-company communication.
Refereed Serial

NAGOYA DAIGAKU KYOYOBU KIYO B. SHIZEN KAGAKU, SHINRIGAKU/NAGOYA UNIVERSITY. COLLEGE OF GENERAL EDUCATION. RESEARCH BULLETIN B. NATURAL SCIENCE AND PSYCHOLOGY. see *SCIENCES: COMPREHENSIVE WORKS*

370.15 150   US   ISSN 1067-1161
NATIONAL CHARACTER LABORATORY NEWSLETTER. 1971. q. $5. National Character Laboratory, 4635 Leeds Ave., El Paso, TX 79903. TEL 915-562-5046. Ed. A.J. Stuart, Jr. bk.rev.; abstr.; bibl.; stat. circ. 150. **Document type:** newsletter.
Description: Reports research results on character, and encourages and coordinates further research.

150.19   US   ISSN 0077-5339
NATIONAL PSYCHOLOGICAL ASSOCIATION FOR PSYCHOANALYSIS. BULLETIN. 1950. biennial. National Psychological Association for Psychoanalysis, Inc., 150 W. 13th St., New York, NY 10011. TEL 212-924-7440. FAX 212-989-7543. circ. 7,000. **Document type:** bulletin.

150.19   US
NATIONAL PSYCHOLOGICAL ASSOCIATION FOR PSYCHOANALYSIS. NEWS AND REVIEWS. 1970. 3/yr. $10. National Psychological Association for Psychoanalysis, Inc., 150 W. 13th St., New York, NY 10011. TEL 212-924-7440. FAX 212-989-7543. Ed. Harvey A. Kaplan. circ. 1,000. **Document type:** newsletter.

NATIONAL REGISTER OF PROFESSIONAL HYPNOTHERAPISTS. see *MEDICAL SCIENCES — Hypnosis*

159   US   ISSN 0146-7875
BF683   CODEN: NSMPB3
NEBRASKA SYMPOSIUM ON MOTIVATION (PUBLICATION). (Subseries of: Research in Motivation Series) 1953. a. price varies. (University of Nebraska, Department of Psychology) University of Nebraska Press, 312 N. 14th St., Box 880484, Lincoln, NE 68588-0484. TEL 402-472-3581. FAX 402-472-6214. index, cum.index. (back issues avail.) **Indexed:** Ind.Med., Psychol.Abstr., SSCI. **Document type:** academic/scholarly publication.
—BLDSC (6068.380000); Genuine Article; UnCover.
Formerly: Current Theory and Research in Motivation (ISSN 0070-2099)
Description: Includes timely paper topics for the Nebraska Symposium which deal with all aspects of motivation.

155 658   CN   ISSN 1188-2921
NEIL MUSCOTT'S SUCCESS NEWSLETTER; strategies and stories for successful people. 1991. bi-m. free. Neil Muscott Seminars, 529 Manning Ave., Toronto, Ont. M6G 2V8, Canada. TEL 416-532-1433. FAX 416-537-7361. Ed. Neil Muscott. adv.; bk.rev. circ. 2,000. (looseleaf format)

370.15 374   US
NETWORK NEWS (CLEVELAND). 1966. s-a. $10. Center for Nonviolent Communication, 3229 Bordeaux, Sherman, TX 75090. TEL 216-371-1123. FAX 216-371-1703. Ed. Gloria Huges. circ. 5,000. (back issues avail.) **Document type:** newsletter.
Formerly: Newsletter for Soulmates.

NEUROBIOLOGY OF LEARNING AND MEMORY. see *MEDICAL SCIENCES — Psychiatry And Neurology*

NEUROPSYCHOLOGICAL REHABILITATION; an international journal. see *MEDICAL SCIENCES — Psychiatry And Neurology*

NEUROPSYCHOLOGY. see *MEDICAL SCIENCES — Psychiatry And Neurology*

NEUROPSYCHOLOGY AND COGNITION. see *MEDICAL SCIENCES — Psychiatry And Neurology*

616.8   NE   ISSN 1380-3395
CODEN: JCENE
NEUROPSYCHOLOGY, DEVELOPMENT AND COGNITION. SECTION A: JOURNAL OF CLINICAL AND EXPERIMENTAL NEUROPSYCHOLOGY. 1979. bi-m. fl.1675 for Sections A,B,C,D (effective 1995). Swets & Zeitlinger bv, P.O. Box 825, 2160 SZ Lisse, Netherlands. TEL 31-2521-35111. FAX 31-2521-15888. TELEX 41325. E-mail: orders@swets.nl. (Dist. in N. America by: Swets & Zeitlinger, 440 Creamery Way, Ste. A, Exton, PA 19341. TEL 800-447-9387. FAX 610-524-5366) Eds. L. Costa, B.P. Rourke. abstr. (reprint service avail. from SWZ) **Indexed:** Behav.Med.Abstr., Biol.Abstr., Child Devel.Abstr., Excerpt.Med., Ind.Med., Psychol.Abstr. (1979-), Psyscscan C.P. **Document type:** academic/scholarly publication.
—BLDSC (4958.375000); ADONIS; Faxon; Genuine Article; SWETS; UnCover. **CCC.**
Supersedes (in 1994): Journal of Clinical and Experimental Neuropsychology (ISSN 0168-8634); **Formerly:** Journal of Clinical Neuropsychology (ISSN 0165-0475)
Refereed Serial

NEUROPSYCHOLOGY REVIEW. see *MEDICAL SCIENCES — Psychiatry And Neurology*

155.4   US   ISSN 0195-2269
BF721   CODEN: NDCDDI
NEW DIRECTIONS FOR CHILD DEVELOPMENT. 1978. q. $54 to individuals; institutions $75. Jossey-Bass Inc., Publishers, 350 Sansome St., 5th Fl., San Francisco, CA 94104. TEL 415-433-1767. FAX 415-433-0499. Ed. William Damon. bibl. circ. 550. (back issues avail.; reprint service avail. from UMI) **Indexed:** Biol.Abstr., Child Devel.Abstr., Educ.Ind., IM, Psychol.Abstr. **Document type:** monographic series.
—BLDSC (6083.326000); SWETS; UMI; UnCover.
Description: Covers the latest findings in developmental psychology; addresses children's cognitive, social, moral, and emotional growth.

NEW DIRECTIONS FOR MENTAL HEALTH SERVICES. see *MEDICAL SCIENCES — Psychiatry And Neurology*

150   UK   ISSN 0732-118X
BF1
NEW IDEAS IN PSYCHOLOGY; international journal of innovative theory in psychology. 1983. 3/yr. £177($282) (effective 1996). Elsevier Science Ltd., Pergamon, P.O. Box 800, Kidlington, Oxford OX5 1DX, England. TEL 44-1865-843000. FAX 44-1865-843010. E-mail: nlinfo-f@elsevier.nl; usinfo-f@elsevier.com; forinfo-kyf04053@niftyserve.or.jp; Site addr.: http://www.elsevier.nl/. (Subscr. in U.S. and Canada to: Elsevier Science, 660 White Plains Rd., Tarrytown, N Y10591-5153. TEL 914-524-9200. FAX 914-333-2444) Ed. Richard Kitchener. adv.: B&W page $550, color page $1350. (also avail. in microfilm from UMI) **Indexed:** ASCA, Curr.Adv.Ecol.Sci., Psychol.Abstr. (1983-). **Document type:** academic/scholarly publication.
—BLDSC (6084.249500); Faxon; Genuine Article; SWETS; UMI; UnCover. **CCC.**
Refereed Serial

370.15 150   US   ISSN 0896-3126
NEW JERSEY JOURNAL OF SCHOOL PSYCHOLOGY. 1982. irreg. $7 to non-members; libraries $10. New Jersey Association of School Psychologists, c/o Valerie Hill, 25 Round Top Rd., Warren, NJ 07059-5521. bk.rev. circ. 700. **Indexed:** Psychol.Abstr.

150   US   ISSN 0077-9008
BF173.A2
NEW YORK PSYCHOANALYTIC INSTITUTE. KRIS STUDY GROUP. MONOGRAPHS. 1965. irreg., no.7, 1984. price varies. International Universities Press, Inc., 59 Boston Post Rd., Box 1524, Madison, CT 06443-1524. TEL 203-245-4000. Ed. Dr. Edward Joseph. **Indexed:** Biol.Abstr. **Document type:** monographic series.
Refereed Serial

150   US   ISSN 0028-7687
NEW YORK STATE PSYCHOLOGIST.* 1948. m. $20. Foundation of New York State Psychological Association, Inc., Executive Park E., Albany, NY 12203. TEL 212-787-6487. FAX 914-683-5223. Ed. Laurence S. Baker. adv.; bk.rev.; charts; illus.; stat.; tr.lit. circ. 4,000. (back issues avail.) Indexed: Psychol.Abstr.

150   NZ   ISSN 0112-109X
CODEN: NZJPF7
NEW ZEALAND JOURNAL OF PSYCHOLOGY. 1972. s-a. NZ.$25 (effective 1995 & 1996). New Zealand Psychological Society, c/o Business Manager, P.O. Box 4092, Wellington, New Zealand. TEL 64-4-8015414. FAX 64-4-8015366. E-mail: m.corballis@auckland.ac.nz. Ed. Prof. Michael Corballis. adv.; bk.rev.; circ. 900 (controlled). (back issues avail.) Indexed: Curr.Cont., Psychol.Abstr. (1972-), Risk Abstr., SSCI. Document type: academic/scholarly publication.
—BLDSC (6094.655000); Genuine Article. CCC.
Formerly (until 1983): New Zealand Psychologist.

370.15   US   ISSN 0894-1750
NEWSLETTER OF THE FREUDIAN FIELD. 1987. s-a. $10 to individuals; institutions $20. Foundation Freudian Field, c/o Ellie Ragland-Sullivan, Ed., Department of English, 107 Tate Hall, University of Missouri, Columbia, MO 65211. bk.rev. circ. 900. Document type: newsletter.
—BLDSC (6108.648500); Faxon.
Description: Dedicated to discussion of Jacques Lacan's teachings in psychoanalysis, as well as in literary, film and art theory.

157.744   US
NEWSLINK (DENVER). q. membership. American Association of Suicidology, 4201 Connecticut Ave., N.W., Ste. 310, Washington, DC 20008-1156. TEL 303-692-0985. circ. 1,500.
Description: Provides suicide prevention information.

616.89   JA
NIHON KODO RYOHO GAKKAI NYUZU RETA/JAPANESE ASSOCIATION OF BEHAVIOR THERAPY. NEWSLETTER. (Text in Japanese) s-a. Nihon Kodo Ryoho Gakkai, Tsukuba Daigaku Shinshinshougai Gakuenki, 1-1-1, Tennoudai, Tsukuba-shi, Ibaraki-ken 305, Japan. Document type: newsletter.

NINTH STREET CENTER JOURNAL. see HOMOSEXUALITY

616.89 617   JA   ISSN 0917-950X
NO SHINKEI GEKA JANARU/JAPANESE JOURNAL OF NEUROSURGERY. (Text in Japanese, summaries in English, Japanese) 1992. q. Nihon No Shinkei Geka Konguresu - Japanese Congress of Neurological Surgeons, 2-1-1 Hongo, Bunkyo-ku, Tokyo 113, Japan. Indexed: Excerp.Med. (1994-). Document type: academic/scholarly publication.

150   DK   ISSN 0029-1463
BF8.D3   CODEN: NOPSAW
NORDISK PSYKOLOGI. (Text mainly in Danish, Norwegian, Swedish; occasionally in English; summaries in English) 1949. 6/yr. DKK 460 (effective 1996). Hans Reitzels Forlag, Koebmagergade 62, 4. sal, P.O. Box 1073, DK-1008 Copenhagen K, Denmark. TEL 45-33-14-04-51. FAX 45-33-15-51-55. (Dist. by: Munksgaard International Publishers, Koebmagergade 62, 4. sal, P.O. Box 2148, DK-1016 Copenhagen K, Denmark) Ed. Per Schultz Joergensen. adv.; bk.rev.; bibl.; charts; illus.; stat.; index. circ. 1,500. Indexed: Biol.Abstr., Chem.Abstr., Psychol.Abstr. (1949-), SSCI. Document type: academic/scholarly publication.
—Genuine Article. CCC.

370.15 150   DK   ISSN 0900-8772
NORDISK PSYKOLOGISK LITTERATUR. (Supplement to: Nordisk Psykologi) a. DKK 257. Munksgaard International Publishers, 35 Noerre Soegade, P.O. Box 2148, DK-1016 Copenhagen K, Denmark.

NORDISK TIDSSKRIFT FOR SPESIALPEDAGOGIKK/POHJOISMAINEN ERTYISKASVATUKSEN AIKAKAUSLEHTI. see EDUCATION — Special Education And Rehabilitation

159   US   ISSN 0889-9428
NORTH AMERICAN SOCIETY OF ADLERIAN PSYCHOLOGY. NEWSLETTER. 1967. m. $10. North American Society of Adlerian Psychology, 65 E. Wacker Pl., Ste. 400, Chicago, IL 60601-3703. TEL 312-201-5917. FAX 312-629-8801. circ. 1,000. Document type: newsletter.
Description: Information on news and activities of the Society. Covers recent conventions in the field.

616.89   FR   ISSN 0223-565X
NOUVELLE REVUE DE PSYCHANALYSE. 1970. 2/yr. 375 F. for two yrs. Editions Gallimard, 5 rue Sebastien-Bottin, 75007 Paris, France. TEL 33-1-46-59-89-00. Ed. J.B. Pontalis. Indexed: Psychoanal.Abstr., Psychol.Abstr. Document type: academic/scholarly publication.
—BLDSC (6176.838000).

NUTRITION HEALTH REVIEW. see NUTRITION AND DIETETICS

ODENSE UNIVERSITY STUDIES IN PSYCHIATRY AND MEDICAL PSYCHOLOGY. see MEDICAL SCIENCES — Psychiatry And Neurology

ODGOJ I SAMOUPRAVLJANJE. see EDUCATION

614.58   US
OKLAHOMA. DEPARTMENT OF MENTAL HEALTH AND SUBSTANCE ABUSE SERVICES. ANNUAL REPORT. a. free. Department of Mental Health and Substance Abuse Services, Box 53277, Oklahoma City, OK 73152. TEL 405-522-3908. FAX 405-522-3650. Ed. Rosemary Brown. circ. 1,000. Document type: government publication.
Former titles: Oklahoma. Department of Mental Health. Annual Report; Mental Health Care in Oklahoma. Annual Report.

150 616   US   ISSN 0030-2228
BF789.D4   CODEN: OMGABX
OMEGA: JOURNAL OF DEATH AND DYING. 1969. 8/yr. (in 2 vols., 4 nos./vol.). $174 (effective 1996). Baywood Publishing Co., Inc., 26 Austin Ave., Box 337, Amityville, NY 11701. TEL 516-691-1270. FAX 516-691-1770. Ed. Dr. Robert J. Kastenbaum. bk.rev.; abstr.; bibl.; charts. (back issues avail.) Indexed: ASSIA, Biol.Abstr., C.I.J.E., CINAHL, Compumath, Excerp.Med., Lang.& Lang.Behav.Abstr., Psychol.Abstr. (1970-), Soc.Sci.Ind. Document type: academic/scholarly publication.
—BLDSC (6256.425000); Faxon; SWETS; UnCover.
Description: Guide for clinicians, social workers, and health professionals dealing with problems in crisis management, such as terminal illness, fatal accidents, catastrophes, suicide and bereavement.
Refereed Serial

ON COURSE; weekly inspiration for the inner journey. see NEW AGE PUBLICATIONS

150   CN   ISSN 0030-3054
RC467
ONTARIO PSYCHOLOGIST. 1969. bi-m. Can.$60. Ontario Psychological Association, 730 Yonge St., Ste. 221, Toronto, ON M4Y 2B7, Canada. TEL 416-961-5552. FAX 416-961-5516. Ed. Dr. D. Rudzinski. adv.: B&W page $750. bk.rev.; bibl.; charts; illus.; stat. circ. 1,400. (also avail. in microform from UMI; reprint service avail. from MML,UMI) Indexed: Psychol.Abstr. Document type: newsletter.
—UMI.

301.1 309   US
ONTARIO SYMPOSIA ON PERSONALITY AND SOCIAL COGNITION SERIES. 1981. irreg., vol.6, 1990. $49.95. Lawrence Erlbaum Associates, Inc., 10 Industrial Dr., Mahwah, NJ 07430-2262. TEL 201-236-9500. FAX 201-236-0072. Ed.Bd. index. Indexed: Curr.Cont., Psychol.Abstr.

150   US
OREGON PSYCHOLOGY.* 1959. 3/yr. $15 to non-members. Oregon Psychological Association, 147 S.E. 102nd Ave., Portland, OR 97216-2703. Ed. Richard S. Colman. adv.; bk.rev.; circ. 700 (controlled). (tabloid format)
Formerly: Oregon Psychological Association. Newsletter (ISSN 0471-9336)

ORGANISATIONSBERATUNG, SUPERVISION, CLINICAL MANAGEMENT. see BUSINESS AND ECONOMICS — Personnel Management

150   US
ORGANIZATIONAL AND OCCUPATIONAL PSYCHOLOGY. 1979. irreg., vol.18, 1987. Academic Press, Inc., 525 B St., Ste. 1900, San Diego, CA 92101-4495. TEL 619-231-0926. FAX 619-699-6715. (Subscr. to: Order Dept., 6277 Sea Harbor Dr., 4th Fl., Orlando, FL 32887. TEL 800-321-5068) Ed. P. Warr. (reprint service avail. from ISI) Document type: monographic series.

ORGANIZATIONAL BEHAVIOR AND HUMAN DECISION PROCESSES; a journal of fundamental research and theory in applied psychology. see BUSINESS AND ECONOMICS — Management

150 158.7   FR   ISSN 0249-6739
ORIENTATION SCOLAIRE ET PROFESSIONNELLE. 1972. q. 250 F. (foreign 310 F.). Institut National d'Etude du Travail et d'Orientation Professionnelle, 41 rue Gay Lussac, 75005 Paris, France. TEL 44-10-78-33. Ed. M. Huteau. adv.; bk.rev.; abstr.; bibl.; charts; stat.; index. circ. 2,000. (back issues avail.) Indexed: Bull.Signal., Psychol.Abstr. (1972-).
—BLDSC (6291.213000); SWETS.
Formerly: B I N O P Bulletin (ISSN 0005-3147)

150   II
OSMANIA UNIVERSITY. DEPARTMENT OF PSYCHOLOGY. RESEARCH BULLETIN. (Text in English) 1965. irreg. Osmania University, Department of Psychology, Hyderabad 500007, Andhra Pradesh, India. Ed. Shalini Bhogle. bk.rev.; bibl.; charts; stat.; circ. controlled. Indexed: Psychol.Abstr.

OTTAR; om sexualitet, samlevnad, samhaelle. see SOCIOLOGY

OUR GIFTED CHILDREN. see CHILDREN AND YOUTH — About

150   US
P S C P TIMES.* 1971. irreg. (6-8/yr.). $5. Philadelphia Society of Clinical Psychologists, Cedarbrook Hill Apts, E. Mall Bld. 1, Wyncote, PA 19095-2601. Eds. Lita L. Schwartz, Frank A. Melone. circ. 200.

155.3   NE   ISSN 0167-4749
PAEDO ALERT NEWS MAGAZINE. Short title: P A N Magazine. 1979. 5/yr. fl.40($20) Spartacus International Ltd., Box 3496, 1001 AG Amsterdam, Netherlands. Ed. Roger Hunt. adv.; bk.rev.; illus. circ. 4,000.

PAIDIKA; the journal of paedophilia. see HOMOSEXUALITY

150   PK   ISSN 1019-438X
PAKISTAN JOURNAL OF CLINICAL PSYCHOLOGY. (Text in English) 1992. 2/yr. R.100($32) (effective 1994). University of Karachi, Institute of Clinical Psychology, 118, Block 20, Abul Asar Hafeez Jalindhri Rd., Gulistan-e-Jauhar, Karachi 75290, Pakistan. TEL 92-21-8113584. Ed. Farrukh Z. Ahmad. circ. 500. (back issues avail.) Indexed: ExtraMED. Document type: academic/scholarly publication.
●Also available on CD-ROM.
Description: Publishes experimental, clinical and theoretical articles, social surveys, comments and special reviews of clinical issues in psychology.

150   PK   ISSN 0030-9869
BF1
PAKISTAN JOURNAL OF PSYCHOLOGY. (Text in English) 1965-1976 (Dec.); resumed 1979. 2/yr. R.100($32) (effective 1994). University of Karachi, Institute of Clinical Psychology, 118, Block 20, Abul Asar Hafeez Jalindhri Rd., Gulistan-e-Jauhar, Karachi 75290, Pakistan. TEL 92-21-8113584. Ed. Farrukh Z. Ahmad. adv.; bk.rev.; charts. circ. 500. (back issues avail.) Indexed: ExtraMED, Psychol.Abstr. Document type: academic/scholarly publication.
●Also available on CD-ROM.
—BLDSC (6341.800000).
Description: Publishes theoretical and research articles covering a wide range of issues in psychology.

PALLIATIVE CARE INDEX. see MEDICAL SCIENCES — Abstracting, Bibliographies, Statistics

PSYCHOLOGY

158 615.89   US
▼**THE PANIC RELIEF NEWS.** 1994. irreg. (approx. 4/yr.). free. Panic Relief, Inc., 981 Shephard Ave., North Brunswick, NJ 08902-2252. TEL 908-937-4832. Ed. Judy Slepian; Pub. Don Slepian. adv.; illus. **Document type:** newsletter.
Description: Informs persons suffering from panic disorders and offers support from a holistic health perspective, often from personal experience. Seeks to inspire people to take control of their lives and regain or improve self-esteem.

301.1 301.4   US   ISSN 0737-5123
PARENTING STUDIES.* 1984. q. Eterna International, Inc., Box 6558, Flushing, NY 11365-6558. Ed. Sedahlia Jasper Crase. abstr.; charts; illus.; index. **Indexed:** Psychol.Abstr.

150.19   FR   ISSN 0769-4679
PAS TANT; revue de la Decouverte Freudienne. 3/yr. 220 F. to individuals; students 180 F. (effective 1993). (Universite de Toulouse II (le Mirail)) Presses Universitaires du Mirail, 56 rue du Taur, 31000 Toulouse, France. TEL 61-22-58-31. FAX 61-21-84-20. Dir. Michel Lapeyre. (back issues avail.) **Document type:** academic/scholarly publication.

150 200   US   ISSN 0031-2789
BV4012
PASTORAL PSYCHOLOGY. 1952. bi-m. $285 (foreign $335) (effective 1996). Human Sciences Press, Inc. (Subsidiary of: Plenum Publishing Corp.), 233 Spring St., New York, NY 10013-1578. TEL 212-620-8000. FAX 212-463-0742. TELEX 23-421139. Ed. Lewis R. Rambo. adv.; bk.rev. (also avail. in microfilm from UMI; reprint service avail. from ISI,UMI) **Indexed:** Psychol.Abstr. (1982-), Rel.& Theol.Abstr. (1969-). **Document type:** academic/scholarly publication.
—BLDSC (6409.300000); Faxon; SWETS; UMI; UnCover. **CCC.**
Description: Examines pastoral counseling, and brings psychological and behavioral science into relation and dialogue with the work of the ministry.
Refereed Serial

PATHWAYS (NEW YORK). see *MEDICAL SCIENCES — Psychiatry And Neurology*

301.1   US
PATHWAYS (TAKOMA PARK);* DC resources. 1978. 4/yr. $10. Riverdell Communications, Inc., Box 30863, Bethesda, MD 20824-0863. TEL 202-829-3289. FAX 202-882-2551. Ed. Lou de Sabla. adv.; bk.rev. circ. 40,000.

150   US   ISSN 1078-1919
▼**PEACE AND CONFLICT: JOURNAL OF PEACE PSYCHOLOGY.** 1995. q. $30 to individuals (foreign $55); institutions $75 (foreign $100). (American Psychological Association, Division of Peace Psychology) Lawrence Erlbaum Associates, Inc., 10 Industrial Dr., Mahwah, NJ 07430-2262. TEL 201-236-9500. FAX 201-236-0072. Ed. Milton Schwebel. adv.: page $375; 5 x 8. **Document type:** academic/scholarly publication.
—BLDSC (6413.759000).
Description: Reflects the essential reality of human consciousness and social and societal relations.

370.5 155.4   SW   ISSN 0346-5004
PEDAGOGISK-PSYKOLOGISKA PROBLEM. 1964. irreg. Malmoe School of Education, Inst. foer Pedagogik och Specialmetodik, Box 23501, S-20045 Malmoe, Sweden. FAX 46-40-325-210. Ed. Aake Bjerstedt. (back issues avail.) **Indexed:** Psychol.Abstr.

155.4 618.92   US   ISSN 0278-4998
PEDIATRIC MENTAL HEALTH. 1982. bi-m. $36 (foreign $40). Pediatric Projects, Inc., Box 571555, Tarzana, CA 91357-1555. TEL 818-705-3660; 800-947-0947. E-mail: medpubl@kaiwan.com. Ed. Pat Azarnoff. bk.rev.; bibl.; tr.list; index. circ. 2,200. **Document type:** newsletter.
Description: Covers research and practice about supported parenting, therapeutic play and psychological preparation of ill, disabled or hospitalized children.

PEER COUNSELLOR JOURNAL. see *SOCIAL SERVICES AND WELFARE*

150 613.7   US   ISSN 1070-6674
PELIZZA'S POSITIVE PRINCIPLES FOR BETTER LIVING. 1993. bi-m. $12. Pelizza & Associates, Box 225, North Chatham, NY 12132. TEL 518-766-4849. Ed. Phillip Niles; Pub. John Pelizza. adv. contact: Bonnie Pelizza. bk.rev. circ. 1,000. (looseleaf format) **Document type:** newsletter.

PEPSY. PEDAGOGISK LITTERATUR I NORDEN/PEPSY. DATABASE OF EDUCATIONAL LITERATURE IN THE NORDIC COUNTRIES. see *EDUCATION*

150 617.7   UK   ISSN 0301-0066
BF311   CODEN: PCTNBA
PERCEPTION. (Text in English, French and German) 1972. m. $530 (effective 1996). Pion Ltd., 207 Brondesbury Park, London NW2 5JN, England. TEL 0181-459-0066. FAX 0181-451-6454. E-mail: sales@pion.demon.co.uk. Ed. R.L. Gregory. adv.: page $280; trim 230 x 132; adv. contact: Diana Mallett. bk.rev.; index. **Indexed:** Abstr.Hum.Comp.Inter., ASSIA, Commun.Abstr., Dent.Ind., Excerp.Med., Ind.Med., Mid.East: Abstr.& Ind., Psychol.Abstr. (1972-). **Document type:** academic/scholarly publication.
—BLDSC (6423.150000); Faxon; SWETS; UnCover.
Description: Reports experimental results and theoretical ideas in the fields of animal, human and machine perception.
Refereed Serial

152   US   ISSN 0031-5117
BF233   CODEN: PEPSBJ
PERCEPTION & PSYCHOPHYSICS. 1966. 8/yr. $172 (foreign $185) (effective 1996). Psychonomic Society, Inc., 1710 Fortview Rd., Austin, TX 78704. TEL 512-462-2442. Ed. Myron Braunstein. adv.; charts; illus.; index. circ. 1,800. (also avail. in microform from KTO,UMI; back issues avail.; reprint service avail. from UMI) **Indexed:** Biol.Abstr., Commun.Abstr., Curr.Adv.Ecol.Sci., Curr.Cont., Dent.Ind., Ergon.Abstr., Excerp.Med., Int.Aerosp.Abstr., Lang.& Lang.Behav.Abstr., M.L.A., Mult.Ed.Abstr., Psychol.Abstr. (1966-), RILM, Sp.Ed.Needs Abstr., SSCI. **Document type:** academic/scholarly publication.
—BLDSC (6423.200000); Faxon; Genuine Article; SWETS; UMI; UnCover. **CCC.**
Description: Contains articles that deal with sensory processes, perception and psychophysics. Some theoretical and evaluative reviews are published.
Refereed Serial

152   US   ISSN 0031-5125
BF311   CODEN: PMOSAZ
PERCEPTUAL AND MOTOR SKILLS. 1949. bi-m. (2 vols./yr.). $250 (effective 1996). Dr. C.H. Ammons & Dr. R.B. Ammons, Eds. & Pubs., Box 9229, Missoula, MT 59807. bk.rev.; bibl.; charts; illus.; index. circ. 2,000. (also avail. in microform from PMC) **Indexed:** Abstr.Anthropol., Bibl.Dev.Med.& Child Neur., Biol.Abstr., C.I.J.E., Child Devel.Abstr., CINAHL, Commun.Abstr., Curr.Cont., Dent.Ind., DSH Abstr., Ergon.Abstr., Except.Child.Educ.Abstr., Excerp.Med., HRIS, Ind.Med., Lang.& Lang.Behav.Abstr., M.L.A., Mid.East: Abstr.& Ind., Mult.Ed.Abstr., Nutr.Abstr., Phys.Ed.Ind., Psychol.Abstr. (1952-), RILM, Risk Abstr., Sci.Cit.Ind., Soc.Sci.Ind., Sp.Ed.Needs Abstr., Sportsearch (1974-), SSCI, Stud.Wom.Abstr. **Document type:** academic/scholarly publication.
—BLDSC (6423.300000); Faxon; SWETS; UnCover.
Description: Encourages scientific originality and creativity. Includes experimental or theoretical articles dealing with perception or motor skills, especially as affected by experience.
Refereed Serial

157   US
▼**PERSONALITY AND CLINICAL PSYCHOLOGY.** 1994. irreg. Lawrence Erlbaum Associates, Inc., 10 Industrial Dr., Mahwah, NJ 07430-2262. TEL 201-236-9500. FAX 201-236-0072. Ed. Irving B. Weiner. **Document type:** academic/scholarly publication.
Description: Book series addressing a broad range of issues related to the work of clinicians and researchers, including theory, methodology, empirical findings and practical applications.

150   UK   ISSN 0191-8869
BF698.A1   CODEN: PEIDD9
PERSONALITY AND INDIVIDUAL DIFFERENCES; an international journal of research into the structure and development of personality and the causation of individual differences. 1980. m. £583($927) (effective 1996). (International Society for the Study of Individual Differences) Elsevier Science Ltd., Pergamon, P.O. Box 800, Kidlington, Oxford OX5 1DX, England. TEL 44-1865-843000. FAX 44-1865-843010. (Subscr. in U.S. and Canada to: Elsevier Science, 660 White Plains Rd., Tarrytown, NY 10591-5153. TEL 914-524-9200. FAX 914-333-2444) Ed. H.J. Eysenck. adv.: B&W page $550, color page $1350. circ. 1,500. (also avail. in microform from UMI,PMC) **Indexed:** ASSIA, Biol.Abstr., Curr.Cont., PSI, Psychol.Abstr., SSCI. **Document type:** academic/scholarly publication.
—BLDSC (6428.010500); Faxon; Genuine Article; SWETS; UMI; UnCover. **CCC.**
Description: Publishes experimental, theoretical and review articles which aim to integrate the major factors of personality with empirical paradigms from experimental, physiological, animal, clinical, educational, criminological or industrial psychology.
Refereed Serial

150   US   ISSN 0146-1672
BF698.A1
PERSONALITY AND SOCIAL PSYCHOLOGY BULLETIN. 1975. m. $94 to individuals; institutions $485 (effective Sep. 1995). (Society for Personality and Social Psychology) Sage Publications, Inc., 2455 Teller Rd., Thousand Oaks, CA 91320. TEL 805-499-0721. FAX 805-499-0871. E-mail: libraries@sagepub.com. (Overseas subscr. to: Sage Publications Ltd., 6 Bonhill St., London EC2A 4PU, England; Sage Publications India Pvt. Ltd., P.O. Box 4215, New Delhi 110 048, India) Ed. John Davidio. adv. circ. 4,200. (also avail. in microform from UMI; back issues avail.; reprint service avail. from UMI) **Indexed:** Adol.Ment.Hlth.Abstr., ASSIA, Commun.Abstr., Curr.Cont., IMFL, PSI, Psychol.Abstr. (1974-), Sage Fam.Stud.Abstr., Sage Urb.Stud.Abstr., Soc.Sci.Ind., SSCI, Stud.Wom.Abstr., Viol.& Abuse Abstr. **Document type:** bulletin.
—BLDSC (6428.011500); Faxon; Genuine Article; SWETS; UMI; UnCover. **CCC.**
Formerly: American Psychological Association. Division of Personality and Social Psychology. Proceedings.
Description: Publishes theoretical articles and empirical reports of research in all areas of personality and social psychology.

150   NE
PERSONALITY PSYCHOLOGY IN EUROPE. irreg., vol.4, 1993. Tilburg University Press, Postbus 90153, 5000 LE Tilburg, Netherlands. TEL 31-13-662909. FAX 31-13-662996. Ed.Bd. **Document type:** monographic series.
—BLDSC (6428.011600).

150   US   ISSN 0079-0931
  CODEN: PEPSDL
PERSONALITY, PSYCHOPATHOLOGY AND PSYCHOTHERAPY; a series of texts, monographs and treatises. 1967. irreg., vol.39, 1989. Academic Press, Inc., 525 B St., Ste. 1900, San Diego, CA 92101-4495. TEL 619-231-0926. FAX 619-699-6715. (Subscr. to: Order Dept., 6277 Sea Harbor Dr., 4th Fl., Orlando, FL 32887. TEL 800-321-5068) Eds. David T. Lykken, Philip C. Kendall. (reprint service avail. from ISI) **Indexed:** Chem.Abstr. **Document type:** monographic series.
—CASDDS.
Formerly: Personality and Psychopathology.
Refereed Serial

156   II   ISSN 0970-8111
PERSONALITY STUDY AND GROUP BEHAVIOUR. (Text in English) 1981. s-a. Rs.30 to individuals; institutions Rs.40 (foreign $30). Guru Nanak Dev University, Publication Office, Amritsar 143 005, India. TEL 0183-258837. FAX 0183-258820. TELEX 384 274 GNDU IN. Ed. Satvir Singh; Pub. Jagjit Singh Walia. circ. 500. **Indexed:** Psychol.Abstr. **Document type:** academic/scholarly publication.
—BLDSC (6428.011700).
Description: Examines research reports and other related scholarly endeavors which have a theoretical, empirical orientation.

158　　　　　　　US　　ISSN 0031-5826
HF5549.A2　　　　　CODEN: PPSYAQ
PERSONNEL PSYCHOLOGY. 1948. q. $55 (foreign $61) (effective 1993). Personnel Psychology, Inc., 745 Haskins Rd., Ste. A, Bowling Green, OH 43402-1600. TEL 419-352-1562. FAX 419-352-2645. Ed. Michael A. Campion. adv.; bk.rev.; charts; index. circ. 3,300. (also avail. in microform from UMI) **Indexed:** ABI Inform., B.P.I., Bk.Rev.Ind. (1980-), BPIA, Bus.Ind., C.I.J.E., Child.Bk.Rev.Ind. (1980-), Commun.Abstr., Cont.Pg.Manage., Curr.Cont., Educ.Admin.Abstr., Manage.Cont., Pers.Lit., Pers.Manage.Abstr., Psychol.Abstr. (1949-), Psyscan, SCIMP, SSCI, Tr.& Dev.Alert, Work Rel.Abstr. **Document type:** academic/scholarly publication.
●Also available online. Vendor(s): Information Access Co., University Microfilms International.
—BLDSC (6428.095000); Faxon; Genuine Article; SWETS; UMI; UnCover. **CCC.**
Description: Research articles on industrial psychology, employees and the workplace.
Refereed Serial

301.1 150　　　CK　　ISSN 0120-3878
BF5
PERSPECTIVAS EN PSICOLOGIA. (Editions in English and Spanish) 1982. a. Col.$400($6) Fundacion Universidad de Manizales, Facultad de Psicologia, Apdo. Aereo 868, Manizales, Colombia. Ed.Bd. bk.rev. circ. 1,000. **Indexed:** Psychol.Abstr.

150　　　　　　　US
PERSPECTIVES (SAN FRANCISCO).* 1980. 3/yr. $5. Saybrook Institute, 450 Pacific Ave., San Francisco, CA 94133-4640. TEL 415-441-5034. Ed. Linda Conti. bk.rev. circ. 300.

PERSPECTIVES IN LAW AND PSYCHOLOGY. see *LAW*

150　　　　　　　UK　　ISSN 1057-8994
BF698.A1
PERSPECTIVES IN PERSONALITY. 1985. irreg., vol.3, 1991. $175. Jessica Kingsley Publishers, 116 Pentonville Rd., London N1 9JB, England. TEL 0171-833-2307. FAX 0171-837-2917. (U.S. subscr. to: Taylor & Francis, 1900 Frost Rd., Ste. 101, Bristol, PA 19007-1598. TEL 800-821-8312. FAX 215-785-5515) Eds. Robert Hogan, Warren Jones. **Document type:** academic/scholarly publication.
—BLDSC (6428.149000); Faxon.

370.15 150　　　II　　ISSN 0971-1562
PERSPECTIVES IN PSYCHOLOGICAL RESEARCHES. (Text in English and Hindi) 1978. s-a. free. 410 Opposite Gupta Medical, Asifgani, Purani Kotwali, Azamgarh 276 001, India. TEL 0546-222006. Ed. Dr. Ramji Srivastava. adv.; bk.rev.; stat. circ. 1,000.
—BLDSC (6428.161200).

616.89　　　　　　US　　ISSN 0735-4037
PERSPECTIVES IN PSYCHOTHERAPY. 1983. irreg., latest vol.2. Gordon & Breach Science Publishers, c/o International Publishers Distributor, 820 Town Center Dr., Langhorne, PA 19047. TEL 215-750-2642. FAX 215-750-6343. (Subscr. to: International Publishers Distributor, P.O. Box 90, Reading, Berkshire RG1 8JL, England. TEL 44-173-456-8316) Ed. P. Olsen. **Document type:** monographic series.
Refereed Serial

PHARMACOLOGY, BIOCHEMISTRY AND BEHAVIOR. see *BIOLOGY — Biological Chemistry*

616.89　　　　　　PH
PHILIPPINE JOURNAL OF COUNSELING PSYCHOLOGY. (Text in English) 1987. a. P.30($3.20) (De La Salle University, Department of Psychology, Guidance and Counseling) De La Salle University Press, 2401 Taft Ave., Manila, Philippines. TEL 2-59-48-32. FAX 632-521-9094. (Co-sponsor: Philippine Association for Counselor Education, Research & Supervision (PACERS)) adv.; bk.rev. circ. 300. **Document type:** academic/scholarly publication.
Description: Publishes original contributions on counseling in different populations. Emphasizes empirical studies on counseling techniques and intervention strategies; the development and validation of assessment instruments; group treatment programs; and counselor education and supervision. Also accepts reviews, concept papers, and research notes.

150　　　　　　　PH
PHILIPPINE JOURNAL OF PSYCHOLOGY. 1968. s-a. P.40($5) Psychological Association of the Philippines, Philippine Social Science Council (PSSC) Bldg., Commonwealth Ave., Diliman, Quezon City, Philippines. Ed. Allen L. Tan. adv.; charts; illus. circ. 175. (tabloid format) **Indexed:** Ind.Phil.Per., Psychol.Abstr.

156　　　　　　　UK　　ISSN 0951-5089
PHILOSOPHICAL PSYCHOLOGY. 1988. q. £64 to individuals; institutions £174 (effective 1996). Carfax Publishing Co., P.O. Box 25, Abingdon, Oxon. OX14 3UE, England. TEL 01235-555335. FAX 01235-553559. (Subscr. in N. America to: Carfax Publishing Co., 875-81 Massachusetts Ave., Cambridge, MA 02139) Eds. John Rust, Bill Bechtel. **Indexed:** Psychol.Abstr. (1988-). **Document type:** academic/scholarly publication.
—BLDSC (6462.260000); Genuine Article; SWETS; UMI; UnCover. **CCC.**
Description: Deals with the application of philosophical psychology to the cognitive and brain sciences, and to areas of applied psychology. Of interest to advanced students in philosophy, psychology, computer science, linguistics and the neurosciences.
Refereed Serial

150　　　　　　　PL　　ISSN 0079-2993
BF1　　　　　　　　　CODEN: PPBUDY
POLISH PSYCHOLOGICAL BULLETIN. (Text in English) 1970. q. $40. Polska Akademia Nauk, Komitet Nauk Psychologicznych - Polish Academy of Sciences, Committee of Psychological Sciences, Ul. Stawki 5-7, 00-183 Warsaw, Poland. (Dist. by: Ars Polona, Krakowskie Przedmiescie 7, 00-068 Warsaw, Poland) Ed. Dariusz Dolinski. bibl. circ. 500. **Indexed:** Bibl.Ling., Curr.Cont., Psychol.Abstr. (1970-), Sage Fam.Stud.Abstr., Sp.Ed.Needs Abstr., SSCI.
—BLDSC (6543.723000); UnCover.

POLYGRAPH (SEVERNA PARK). see *CRIMINOLOGY AND LAW ENFORCEMENT*

158　　　　　　　US　　ISSN 0199-0039
HB848　　　　　　　　CODEN: PENVDK
POPULATION AND ENVIRONMENT; a journal of interdisciplinary studies. 1978. bi-m. $285 (foreign $335) (effective 1996). (American Psychological Association, Division of Population and Environmental Psychology) Human Sciences Press, Inc. (Subsidiary of: Plenum Publishing Corp.), 233 Spring St., New York, NY 10013-1578. TEL 212-620-8000. FAX 212-463-0742. TELEX 23-421139. Ed. Virginia Abernethy. adv.; bk.rev.; charts; index. (also avail. in microfilm from UMI; reprint service avail. from ISI,UMI) **Indexed:** Abstr.Hyg., Biol.Abstr., C.I.J.E., Coll.Stud.Pers.Abstr., Curr.Adv.Ecol.Sci., Curr.Cont., Curr.Lit.Fam.Plan., Environ.Abstr., Environ.Per.Bibl. (1989-), Excerp.Med., G.Soc.Sci.& Rel.Per.Lit., Lang.& Lang.Behav.Abstr., P.A.I.S., Popul.Ind., Psychol.Abstr. (1978-), Psyscan, Saf.Sci.Abstr., Soc.Work Res.& Abstr., Sociol.Abstr., SSCI. **Document type:** academic/scholarly publication.
—BLDSC (6552.022000); Faxon; Genuine Article; SWETS; UMI; UnCover. **CCC.**
Former titles (until vol.4, 1981): Journal of Population (ISSN 0146-1052); Population (New York).
Description: Explores relationships between population and societal, cultural, and physical environments. Covers demographic variables linked to lifestyle, law, health, business, economics, and international relations.
Refereed Serial

150 330　　　　US　　ISSN 0742-9940
HX1
PRACTICE (NEW YORK); the magazine of psychology and political economy. 1983. 2/yr. $10 to individuals, institutions $15. Eastside Institute for Short-Term Psychotherapy, 500 Greenwich St., Ste. 201, New York, NY 10013. TEL 212-941-8906. FAX 212-941-8340. Ed. Lois Holzman. adv.; bk.rev.; film rev. circ. 2,000. (back issues avail.) **Indexed:** Alt.Press Ind., Sociol.Abstr. **Document type:** academic/scholarly publication.
—BLDSC (6597.119600); UnCover.
Formerly: Struggle (ISSN 0146-8006)
Description: An international forum for dialogue on psychology, ideology, education and politics.

150　　　　　　　US
PRACTICING PROFESSIONAL SERIES. irreg. (approx. 2/yr.). Guilford Publications, Inc., 72 Spring St., New York, NY 10012. TEL 212-431-9800; 800-365-7006. FAX 212-966-6708. Ed. Michael J. Mahoney. **Document type:** monographic series.
Description: Devoted to communicating practical information about counseling and psychotherapy. Serves as an accessible and understandable source for practical knowledge about specific issues.

PRAGMATICS AND DISCOURSE ANALYSIS. see *LINGUISTICS*

150　　　　　　　IT　　ISSN 1120-9380
PRATICA ANALITICA; saggi di psicologia junghiana. 1990. s-a. L.35000($30) Moretti e Vitali Editori, Via Betty Ambiveri 15, 24126 Bergamo, Italy. TEL 39-35-321588. FAX 39-35-321647. Ed. Salvatore Zingale.

PRAXIS DER KINDERPSYCHOLOGIE UND KINDERPSYCHIATRIE. see *MEDICAL SCIENCES — Psychiatry And Neurology*

150 616.89　　　GW　　ISSN 0085-5073
PRAXIS DER KINDERPSYCHOLOGIE UND KINDERPSYCHIATRIE. BEIHEFTE. 1958. irreg. price varies. Vandenhoeck und Ruprecht, Robert-Bosch-Breite 6, 37079 Goettingen, Germany. TEL 0551-6959-0. FAX 0551-695917. (Subscr. to: 37070 Goettingen, Germany) Ed. Annemarie Duehrssen. **Indexed:** Ind.Med., Lang.& Lang.Behav.Abstr., Psychol.Abstr., SSCI. **Document type:** monographic series.

PRAXIS SPIEL UND GRUPPE. see *EDUCATION*

PRE- AND PERI-NATAL PSYCHOLOGY JOURNAL. see *MEDICAL SCIENCES — Obstetrics And Gynecology*

157 370　　　　US　　ISSN 0886-6694
PREVENTING SEXUAL ABUSE. 1986. 4/yr. $32. S A F E Institute, c/o Molly Davis, Ed., 1225 N.W. Murray Rd., Ste. 214, Portland, OR 97229. TEL 503-644-6600. FAX 503-643-3798. bk.rev. circ. 2,800.

150　　　　　　　US　　ISSN 0164-5056
PRIMAL INSTITUTE NEWSLETTER. 1978. q. $11 (foreign $15). Primal Institute, 10379 W. Pico Blvd., Los Angeles, CA 90064-2608. TEL 310-785-9456. FAX 310-785-9481. Ed. Vivian Janov. bk.rev.; index. circ. 1,600. (back issues avail.) **Document type:** newsletter.
Supersedes (1973-1978): Journal of Primal Therapy (ISSN 0091-9772)
Description: Contains personal narratives and experiences of patients and therapists involved with primal therapy. Also discusses scientific, medical and psychological discoveries relating to primal therapy.

PRIMATES; journal of primatology. see *BIOLOGY — Zoology*

370.15 150　　　US　　ISSN 0731-2326
PROBLEM BEHAVIOR MANAGEMENT; educator's resource service. 1982. base vol. (plus s-a. updates), 2nd ed., 1992. $139 (foreign $167). Aspen Publishers, Inc., 200 Orchard Ridge Dr., Gaithersburg, MD 20878. TEL 301-417-7500. FAX 301-417-7550.

158.7　　　　　　US　　ISSN 0277-4178
PROBLEMS OF INDUSTRIAL PSYCHIATRIC MEDICINE SERIES. irreg., vol.11, 1985. prices varies. Human Sciences Press, Inc. (Subsidiary of: Plenum Publishing Corp.), 233 Spring St., New York, NY 10013-1578. TEL 212-620-8000. FAX 212-463-0742. TELEX 23-421139. Ed. Sherman N. Keiffer. (reprint service avail. from UMI) **Document type:** monographic series.
Refereed Serial

150 371.4　　　　US
PROFESSIONAL CHRISTIAN COUNSELOR. 1983. q. $25 to non-members. United Association of Christian Counselors International, 170 Kenwood Ave., Harrisburg, PA 17109-3731. TEL 717-652-7688. Ed. Arthur L. Sprunger. adv.; bk.rev.; film rev. circ. 1,000. (tabloid format) **Document type:** newsletter.
Former titles: Paraclete Counselor; Christian Communique.
Description: Covers all areas of professional counseling and counselor education that are based on a Christian worldview.

PSYCHOLOGY

158.7 — US
PROFESSIONAL PRACTICE SERIES. irreg. (approx. biennial). (Society for Industrial and Organizational Psychology) Guilford Publications, Inc., 72 Spring St., New York, NY 10012. TEL 212-431-9800; 800-365-7006. FAX 212-966-6708. Ed. Douglas W. Bray. **Document type:** monographic series.
Description: Generates better understanding of contemporary issues in human resources management. Case studies, longitudinal and empirical research and theoretical frameworks illustrate how organizations can respond to diversity, manage change, and use communication to function effectively.

150 — US ISSN 0735-7028
RC467
PROFESSIONAL PSYCHOLOGY: RESEARCH AND PRACTICE. 1969. bi-m. $73 to non-members (foreign $93); members $36 (foreign $146); institutions $146 (foreign $189). American Psychological Association, 750 First St., N.E., Washington, DC 20002-4242. TEL 202-336-5600. FAX 202-336-5568. Ed. Patrick Deleon. adv.; index. circ. 6,800. (also avail. in microform from UMI; back issues avail.; reprint service avail. from UMI) **Indexed:** Abstr.Health Care Manage.Stud., Adol.Ment.Hlth.Abstr., Crim.Just.Abstr., Curr.Cont., Mid.East. Abstr.& Ind., Psychol.Abstr. (1969-), Psycscan C.P., Sage Fam.Stud.Abstr., Soc.Sci.Ind. (1994-), SSCI. **Document type:** academic/scholarly publication.
—BLDSC (6864.211000); Faxon; Genuine Article; SWETS; UMI; UnCover. **CCC.**
Formerly (until 1982): Professional Psychology (ISSN 0033-0175)
Description: Articles on techniques and practices used in the application of psychology, including applications of research, standards of practice, interprofessional relations, delivery of services, and training.
Refereed Serial

616.8 — US ISSN 0099-037X
BF637.B4 CODEN: PBMOE8
PROGRESS IN BEHAVIOR MODIFICATION. 1975. irreg., vol.20, 1986. Academic Press, Inc., 525 B St., Ste. 1900, San Diego, CA 92101-4495. TEL 619-231-0926. FAX 619-699-6715. (Subscr. to: Order Dept., 6277 Sea Harbor Dr., 4th Fl., Orlando, FL 32887. TEL 800-321-5068) Ed. M. Hersen. (reprint service avail. from ISI) **Indexed:** Adol.Ment.Hlth.Abstr., Ind.Med., SSCI. **Document type:** monographic series.
—**CCC.**

152 — US ISSN 1056-7151
BF698 CODEN: PEPRBG
PROGRESS IN EXPERIMENTAL PERSONALITY AND PSYCHOPATHOLOGY RESEARCH. Variant title: Experimental Personality and Psychopathology Research. 1964-1986 (vol.14); N.S. 1992. irreg. Springer Publishing Company, 536 Broadway, New York, NY 10012-3955. TEL 212-431-4370. FAX 212-941-7842. Ed.Bd. (reprint service avail. from ISI) **Indexed:** Biol.Abstr., Ind.Med. **Document type:** monographic series.
—BLDSC (6868.368000).
Formerly (1964-1986): Progress in Experimental Personality Research (ISSN 0079-6255)
Description: Explores research into the causes and treatment of personality disorders.

131 — US ISSN 0363-0951
QP351 CODEN: PPPPDL
PROGRESS IN PSYCHOBIOLOGY AND PHYSIOLOGICAL PSYCHOLOGY. 1967. irreg., vol.15, 1992. Academic Press, Inc., 525 B St., Ste. 1900, San Diego, CA 92101-4495. TEL 619-231-0926. FAX 619-699-6715. (Subscr. to: Order Dept., 6277 Sea Harbor Dr., 4th Fl., Orlando, FL 32887. TEL 800-321-5068) Ed. Alan N. Epstein. (reprint service avail. from ISI) **Indexed:** Curr.Adv.Ecol.Sci. **Document type:** monographic series.
—BLDSC (6873.662000); Faxon; UnCover. **CCC.**
Former titles: Progress in Psychobiology and Physiological Psychology; (until vol.6): Progress in Physiological Psychology (ISSN 0079-6670)
Refereed Serial

155.4 — US
PROGRESS NOTES. 1976. 3/yr. membership. Society of Pediatric Psychology, Ferkauf Graduate School of Psychology, Yeshiva University, Mazer Hall, 1300 Morris Park Ave., Bronx, NY 10461. TEL 212-430-4201. FAX 212-430-3252. (Subscr. to: Debra Bendelt Estroff, 887 Praderia Circle, Fremont, CA 94539) Ed Lawrence J. Siegel. adv. circ. 1,000.
Formerly: Society of Pediatric Psychology. Newsletter.

150 — MX ISSN 1405-0951
PROMETEO (MEXICO CITY); fuego para el propio conocimiento. 1992. 3/yr. $25 (effective 1995). Universidad Iberoamericana, Departamento de Desarollo Humano, Prol. Paseo de la Reforma 880, Col. Lomas de Santa Fe, 01210 Mexico DF, Mexico. TEL 5-292-18-91. FAX 5-726-90-48. Ed. Juan Lafarga. bk.rev.; bibl.; illus. circ. 3,000. **Document type:** academic/scholarly publication.
Description: Forum for dialogue on the diverse technical and methodological trends in psychology.

150 — PL ISSN 0048-5675
BF26 CODEN: PRZPBF
PRZEGLAD PSYCHOLOGICZNY/PSYCHOLOGICAL REVIEW. (Text in Polish; summaries in English and Russian) 1952. q. $54. Polskie Towarzystwo Psychologiczne, Ul. Stawki 5-7, 00-183 Warsaw, Poland. (Dist. by: Ars Polona-Ruch, Krakowskie Przedmiescie 7, Warsaw, Poland) Ed. R. Stachowski. bk.rev.; index. circ. 2,200. (also avail. in microform from UMI; reprint service avail. from UMI) **Indexed:** Acad.Ind., C.I.J.E., Curr.Adv.Ecol.Sci., Lang.& Lang.Behav.Abstr., Psychol.Abstr. (1952-).

150 — US ISSN 0033-2569
LJ121
PSI CHI NEWSLETTER. 1934. q. $6.25 (foreign $8.50). Psi Chi National Office, 407 E. Fifth St., No. B, Chattanooga, TN 37403-1823. TEL 615-756-2044. FAX 615-265-1529. Ed. Kay Wilson. circ. 20,000. **Document type:** newspaper.

PSICHIATRIA E PSICOTERAPIA ANALITICA/ANALYTIC PSYCHOTHERAPY AND PSYCHOPATHOLOGY. see *MEDICAL SCIENCES — Psychiatry And Neurology*

150 — SP ISSN 0377-8320
BF5
PSICODEIA; revista de psicologia. 1975. m. 1200 ptas. (Instituto de Aplicaciones Psicologicas y Parapsicologicas) Ediciones I N A P P, Habana 66, Madrid 16, Spain. Ed. Carlos Gil Munoz. adv.; bk.rev.; illus. circ. 15,000.

150 — PO
PSICOLOGIA. irreg., vol.9 no.3, 1994. price varies. (Associacao Portuguesa de Psicologia) Ediciões Afrontamento, Lda., Rua de Costa Cabral, 859, Apdo. 2009, 4201 Porto Codex, Portugal. TEL 351-2-529271. FAX 351-2-591777. **Indexed:** Psychol.Abstr. (1980-).

150 — IT ISSN 0390-346X
PSICOLOGIA CONTEMPORANEA. 1974. bi-m. L.28000 (foreign L.39000). Giunti Gruppo Editoriale S.p.A., Via Bolognese 165, 50139 Florence, Italy. TEL 39-55-66791. FAX 39-55-6679298. adv.: B&W page L.3750000, color page L.6000000.

158.7 — IT ISSN 0048-5691
PSICOLOGIA E LAVORO. 1968. 3/m. L.70000($27) Patron Editore, Via Badini, 12, 40050 Bologna, Italy. adv.; bk.rev.; bibl.; stat. circ. 1,000. **Indexed:** Psychol.Abstr.

150 — IT ISSN 0393-1064
PSICOLOGIA ITALIANA. 1979. 3/yr. L.52000 (foreign L.63000) to non-members. (Societa Italiana di Psicologia) Nuova Italia Scientifica, Via Sardegna 50, 00187 Roma, Italy. **Document type:** academic/scholarly publication.

PSICOLOGIA MEDICA; revista argentina de psicologia medica, psicoterapia y ciencias afines. see *MEDICAL SCIENCES — Psychiatry And Neurology*

150 616.99 — IT
PSICOLOGIA ONCOLOGICA/PSYCHO-ONCOLOGY. (Text in Italian; summaries in English, French) 1992. q. L.60000($90) (effective 1994). (Societa Italiana di Psicologia Oncologica) Liviana Medicina, Via A. De Gasperi 55, 80133 Naples, Italy. TEL 39-81-5524733. FAX 39-81-5518295. Ed. Francesco de Falco.

370.15 150 — BL ISSN 0102-3772
PSICOLOGIA: TEORIA E PESQUISA/PSYCHOLOGY: THEORY AND RESEARCH. (Text in Portuguese; summaries in English, Portuguese) 1985. q. $15. Universidade de Brasilia, Instituto de Psicologia, Campus Universitario, 70910-900 Brasilia DF, Brazil. TEL 61-274-6455. FAX 61-273-6378. E-mail: revptp@guarany.cpd.unb.br. Ed. M. Angela G. Feitosa. bk.rev. circ. 1,000. (back issues avail.) **Indexed:** Psychol.Abstr. (1985-). **Document type:** academic/scholarly publication.
Description: Publishes research reports, theoretical studies, reports of professional experience, critical reviews, and technical notes related to psychology.
Refereed Serial

616.89 — SP ISSN 0211-5549
CODEN: PSICE3
PSICOPATOLOGIA. q. 5900 ptas.($65) (effective 1995). Editorial Garsi, S.A., Juan Bravo 46, 28006 Madrid, Spain. TEL 34-1-4021212. FAX 34-1-4020954. Dir. Dr. Alonso Fernandez. circ. 700. **Indexed:** Psychol.Abstr.
—BLDSC (6945.864000).

150 — SP ISSN 0214-9915
PSICOTHEMA: REVISTA DE PSICOLOGIA. 1989. s-a. 6000 ptas.($45) to individuals; institutions 12000 ptas. ($100) (effective 1994). Universidad de Oviedo, Facultad de Psicologia, Departamento de Psicologia, C. San Francisco 3, 33003 Oviedo, Spain. TEL 34-85-104486. FAX 34-85-104488. Ed. Jose Muniz. **Indexed:** Psychol.Abstr. (1993-).
—BLDSC (6945.865500); Genuine Article.

PSIHIJATRIJA DANAS/PSYCHIATRY TODAY. see *MEDICAL SCIENCES — Psychiatry And Neurology*

150 — RM ISSN 1220-6555
PSIHOLOGIA. 1991. q. Piata Presei Libere 1, 79781 Bucharest, Rumania. Ed. Adina Chelcea. circ. 30,000.

158 — RU
PSIKHOLOGICHESKIE ISSLEDOVANIYA. no.6, 1976. irreg. Moskovskii Universitet, Ul. Gertsena 5-7, 103009 Moscow, Russia. circ. 5,500.

150 — BU ISSN 0204-644X
PSIKHOLOGIIA. 1973. q. 1.60 lv. Druzhestvo na Psikholozite, c/o Kathedre of Psychology, Sofia University, Blvd. Rusky 15, Sofia, Bulgaria. (Dist. by: Hemus, 6, Rouski Blvd., 1000 Sofia, Bulgaria) Ed. S. Ganovski. circ. 500. **Indexed:** Psychol.Abstr.
—BLDSC (0134.680000).

PSIQUIS; revista de psiquiatria, psicologia y psicosomatica. see *MEDICAL SCIENCES — Psychiatry And Neurology*

370.15 150 — US
PSYCH DISCOURSE. 1970. m. $110. Association of Black Psychologists, Box 55999, Washington, DC 20040-5999. TEL 202-722-0808. Ed. Dr. Halford Fairchild. adv.: page $650; 7 x 9. circ. 1,500. (back issues avail.) **Document type:** academic/scholarly publication.
Formerly: Association of Black Psychologists Newsletter.
Description: Covers news of member and chapter activities. Includes original articles, letters and essays.

150.19 — GW ISSN 0033-2623
BF173.A2 CODEN: PSYEDK
PSYCHE; Zeitschrift fuer Psychoanalyse und ihre Anwendungen. 1947. m. DM.180. Verlag Klett-Cotta, Rotebuehlstr. 77, 70178 Stuttgart, Germany. TEL 0711-6672-0. FAX 0711-6159702. Ed. Margarete Mitscherlich. adv.: B&W page DM.1320; trim 180 x 113; adv. contact: Winifred Kretschmar. bk.rev.; abstr.; bibl.; charts; index. circ. 7,000. (reprint service avail.) **Indexed:** Excerp.Med., Ger.J.Psych., Ind.Med., Psychol.Abstr. (1947-), SSCI. **Document type:** academic/scholarly publication.
—BLDSC (6946.115000); Faxon; Genuine Article. **CCC.**

150 — IT
PSYCHE; rassegna di psicoterapia umanistico-esistenziale, di psicoterapia autogena e psicoterapie brevi. 1981; N.S. 1993. 3/yr. L.70000. C I S S P A T, Piazza De Gasperi, 41, 35100 Padua, Italy. TEL 049-650861. Ed. Marilla Malugani.

153   AT   ISSN 1324-454X
PSYCHE; an interdisciplinary journal of research on consciousness. Online edition (ISSN 1039-723X) 1993. s-a. Aus.$45 to individuals; institutions Aus.$90. Monash University, Department of Computer Science, Clayton Vic. 3168, Australia. TEL 61-3-94271242. FAX 61-3-99055146. E-mail: patrickw@cs.monash.edu. (Subscr. to: M I T Press Journls, 55 Hayward St., Cambridge, MA 02142-1399, U.S.A.. TEL 617-253-2889. FAX 617-258-6779) Ed. Patrick Wilken. **Document type:** academic/scholarly publication.
●Also available online.
Description: Dedicated to supporting the interdisciplinary exploration of the nature of consciousness and it relation to the brain.
Refereed Serial

PSYCHIATRIC & PSYCHOLOGICAL EVIDENCE. see *LAW*

150 301   US
RC439.5
PSYCHIATRIC REHABILITATION JOURNAL. 1976. 4/yr. $45 to individuals; institutions $80 (effective 1995). Boston University, Sargent College of Allied Health Professions, Department of Rehabilitation Counseling, 930 Commonwealth Ave., Boston, MA 02215. TEL 617-353-3549. FAX 617-353-9209. (Co-sponsor: International Association of Psychosocial Rehabilitation Services) Eds. William Anthony, Irvin Rutman; Pub. Dr. LeRoy Spaniol. adv.; bk.rev. circ. 1,300. (also avail. in microfilm; reprint service avail. from UMI) **Indexed:** Adol.Ment.Hlth.Abstr., C.I.N.L., Community Ment.Health Rev., Ind.Med., Nurs.Abstr., Psychol.Abstr. (1977-), Rehabil.Lit. **Document type:** academic/scholarly publication.
—BLDSC (4515.486400); SWETS; UMI; UnCover. **CCC.**
Formed by the 1995 merger of: Psychosocial Rehabilitation Journal (ISSN 0147-5622) & Innovations and Research (ISSN 1062-7553)
Description: Provides information relevant to the rehabilitation of persons with severe psychiatric disability. Publishes papers from mental health and rehabilitation professionals, consumers and family members.
Refereed Serial

PSYCHIATRY PSYCHOLOGY AND LAW. see *MEDICAL SCIENCES — Psychiatry And Neurology*

PSYCHO-ANALYTIC PSYCHOTHERAPY IN SOUTH AFRICA. see *MEDICAL SCIENCES — Psychiatry And Neurology*

PSYCHO GERIATRIE. see *GERONTOLOGY AND GERIATRICS*

PSYCHO-LINGUA; a biannual research journal devoted to communicative behavior. see *LINGUISTICS*

PSYCHO-ONCOLOGY; journal of the psychological, social and behavioral dimensions of cancer. see *MEDICAL SCIENCES — Oncology*

150 616.89   NE   ISSN 0924-6290
PSYCHOANALYSE EN CULTUUR. English edition: Psychoanalysis and Culture. (Text in Dutch) 1990. irreg. price varies. Thesis Publishers, P.O. Box 14791, 1001 LG Amsterdam, Netherlands. TEL 31-20-6255429. FAX 31-20-6203395. E-mail: thesis@thesis.aps.nl. (back issues avail.) **Document type:** monographic series, academic/scholarly publication.

616.89   NE
PSYCHOANALYSIS AND CULTURE. Dutch edition: Psychoanalyse en Culture (ISSN 0924-6290) (Text in English) 1990. irreg., vol.5, 1994. price varies. Editions Rodopi B.V., Keizersgracht 302-304, 1016 EX Amsterdam, Netherlands. TEL 31-20-6227507. FAX 31-20-6380948. E-mail: F.van.der.Zee@Rodopi.nl. (In N. America: 233 Peachtree St., N.E., Ste. 404, Atlanta, GA 30303-1504. TEL 800-225-3998. FAX 404-522-7116) (back issues avail.) **Document type:** monographic series, academic/scholarly publication.

616.891   US   ISSN 1057-5723
PSYCHOANALYSIS AND PSYCHOTHERAPY. 1983. s-a. $38.50 to individuals (foreign $62.50); institutions $72 (foreign $96). (Postgraduate Center for Mental Health) International Universities Press, Inc., 59 Boston Post Rd., Box 1524, Madison, CT 06443-1524. TEL 203-245-4000. FAX 203-245-0775. Eds. Bernard F. Riess, Edith Gould. bk.rev.; index. circ. 1,000. **Indexed:** Psychoanal.Abstr., Psychol.Abstr. **Document type:** academic/scholarly publication.
—BLDSC (6946.265300).
Formerly (until 1989): Dynamic Psychotherapy (ISSN 0736-508X)
Description: Represents contemporary thinking, application and recent advances in the art and techniques of dynamic psychotherapy-psychoanalysis.

616.89   US   ISSN 1044-2103
BF173.A2
PSYCHOANALYTIC BOOKS; a quarterly journal of reviews. 1990. q. $50 to individuals (foreign $60); institutions $90 (foreign $100). Psychoanalytic Books, Inc., 211 E. 70th St., New York, NY 10021. TEL 212-628-8792. FAX 212-628-8453. E-mail: psabooks@datagram.com. Ed. Dr. Joseph Reppen. adv.: B&W page $250; adv. contact: Francesca Reppen. bk.rev.; index; circ. 1,000 (paid). (back issues avail.) **Document type:** academic/scholarly publication.
Description: Reviews of books in psychoanalysis including Freud studies, history of psychoanalysis, psychobiography, psychohistory, and psychoanalytic study of literature and the arts.

150.19 616.891   US
PSYCHOANALYTIC CROSSCURRENTS. 1985. irreg. price varies. New York University Press, 70 Washington Square S., New York, NY 10012. TEL 212-998-2575; 800-996-3833. FAX 212-995-3833. TELEX 235128 NYU UR. Ed. Leo Goldberger. **Document type:** monographic series.

616.89   US   ISSN 1048-1885
RC500
PSYCHOANALYTIC DIALOGUES; a journal of relational perspectives. 1991. q. $42.50 to individuals (foreign $67.50); institutions $95 (foreign $120) (effective 1995). Analytic Press, Inc., 365 Broadway, Hillsdale, NJ 07642. TEL 201-358-9477. FAX 201-358-0621. Ed. Stephen A. Mitchell. circ. 2,300. (back issues avail.) **Indexed:** Psychol.Abstr. (1991-). **Document type:** academic/scholarly publication.
—BLDSC (6946.267000). **CCC.**
Description: Psychoanalytic contributions on interpersonal psychoanalysis, object relations theory, self psychology, infant research and child development.

150   US   ISSN 0735-1690
RC500
PSYCHOANALYTIC INQUIRY; a topical journal for mental health professionals. 1980. q. $55 to individuals (foreign $80); institutions $130 (foreign $155) (effective 1995). Analytic Press, Inc., 365 Broadway, Hillsdale, NJ 07642. TEL 201-358-9477. FAX 201-358-0621. Ed. Dr. Joseph D. Lichtenberg. circ. 1,300. (back issues avail.) **Indexed:** Psychoanal.Abstr., Psychol.Abstr. (1983-). **Document type:** academic/scholarly publication.
—BLDSC (6946.269000); Genuine Article; UMI. **CCC.**
Description: Each issue dedicated to a specific topic in psychoanalysis, psychotherapy, infant research or child development.

150 616.8   US   ISSN 0736-9735
PSYCHOANALYTIC PSYCHOLOGY. 1984. q. $50 to individuals (foreign $75); institutions $195 (foreign $220). (American Psychological Association, Division of Psychoanalysis) Lawrence Erlbaum Associates, Inc., 10 Industrial Dr., Mahwah, NJ 07430-2262. TEL 201-236-9500. FAX 201-236-0072. Ed. Bertram J. Cohler. adv.: page $375; 5 x 8. bk.rev.; abstr.; bibl. **Indexed:** Psychoanal.Abstr., Psychol.Abstr. (1984-). **Document type:** academic/scholarly publication.
—BLDSC (6946.269600); UMI; UnCover.
Description: Forum for the study of psychoanalytic issues in psychology and psychological issues in psychoanalysis.
Refereed Serial

616.89   US   ISSN 0033-2828
BF173.A2   CODEN: PSQAAX
PSYCHOANALYTIC QUARTERLY. 1932. q. $80 (effective 1996). Psychoanalytic Quarterly, Inc, 175 Fifth Ave., Rm. 517, New York, NY 10010. TEL 212-982-9358. Ed. Dr. Owen Renik. bk.rev.; abstr.; bibl.; index, cum.index: vols.1-35, 36-45, 46-55. circ. 3,500. **Indexed:** Abstr.Soc.Work, Chicago Psychoanal.Lit.Ind., Curr.Cont., Ind.Med., Lang.& Lang.Behav.Abstr., Mid.East: Abstr.& Ind., Psychoanal.Abstr., Psychol.Abstr. (1932-), Soc.Work Res.& Abstr., SSCI. **Document type:** academic/scholarly publication.
—BLDSC (6946.270000); Faxon; Genuine Article; SWETS; UnCover.

150 616.89   US   ISSN 0033-2836
BF1   CODEN: PSREAG
PSYCHOANALYTIC REVIEW. 1913. bi-m. $42 (foreign $67) to individuals; institutions $175 (foreign $200) (effective 1995). (National Psychological Association for Psychoanalysis, Inc.) Guilford Publications, Inc., 72 Spring St., 4th Fl., New York, NY 10012. TEL 212-431-9800. FAX 212-966-6708. Ed. Martin Schulman; Pub. Robert Matloff. adv. contact: Marian Robinson. bk.rev.; film rev.; play rev.; bibl.; index. circ. 1,600. (also avail. in microform from UMI; back issues avail.; reprint service avail. from ISI,UMI) **Indexed:** Abstr.Anthropol., Abstr.Crim.& Pen., Abstr.Engl.Stud., Biol.Abstr., Curr.Cont., Excerp.Med., Film Lit.Ind. (1985-), IMFL, Ind.Med., Lang.& Lang.Behav.Abstr., Mid.East: Abstr.& Ind., Psychoanal.Abstr., Psychol.Abstr. (1926-), Sci.Cit.Ind., Soc.Work Res.& Abstr., Sociol.Abstr., SSCI, Yrbk.Assoc.Educ.& Rehab.Blind.
—BLDSC (6946.273000); Faxon; Genuine Article; SWETS; UMI; UnCover. **CCC.**
Incorporates (1952-19??): Psychoanalysis.
Description: Covers contemporary psychoanalytical theory and practice, and psychoanalytical themes in art, film and literature.
Refereed Serial

150   US   ISSN 0079-7294
H9
PSYCHOANALYTIC STUDY OF SOCIETY. a. price varies. Analytic Press, Inc., 365 Broadway, Hillsdale, NJ 07642. TEL 201-358-9447. FAX 201-358-0621. Eds. L. Bryce Boyer, Ruth M. Boyer. (back issues avail.) **Indexed:** Anthropol.Lit.
—UnCover. **CCC.**
Description: Devoted to the application of psychoanalysis to the social sciences, literature, and the arts.

155.4   US   ISSN 0079-7308
BF721   CODEN: PYACAZ
PSYCHOANALYTIC STUDY OF THE CHILD. 1945. a. price varies. Yale University Press, Box 209040, New Haven, CT 06520. TEL 203-432-0940. Ed. Dr. Albert J. Solnit. **Indexed:** Biol.Abstr., Educ.Ind., Excerp.Med., Ind.Med., Psychoanal.Abstr., Psychol.Abstr. (1945-), SSCI, Yrbk.Assoc.Educ.& Rehab.Blind.
—BLDSC (6946.275000); Faxon; SWETS; UnCover.

PSYCHOANALYTISCHE BLAETTER ZU KLINIK, FORSCHUNG, ZEITGESCHEHEN. see *MEDICAL SCIENCES — Psychiatry And Neurology*

152.05   US   ISSN 0889-6313
QP360   CODEN: PSYBEC
PSYCHOBIOLOGY. 1973. q. $87 (foreign $94) (effective 1996). Psychonomic Society, Inc, 1710 Fortview Rd., Austin, TX 78704. TEL 512-462-2442. Ed. Paul E. Gold. adv.; illus. circ. 1,100. (also avail. in microform from KTO,UMI; back issues avail.; reprint service avail. from UMI) **Indexed:** Biol.Abstr., Chem.Abstr., Curr.Adv.Ecol.Sci., Curr.Cont., Dairy Sci.Abstr., Ergon.Abstr., Excerp.Med., Nutr.Abstr., Psychol.Abstr. (1973-). **Document type:** academic/scholarly publication.
—BLDSC (6946.276530); CASDDS; Faxon; Genuine Article; SWETS; UMI. **CCC.**
Formerly: Physiological Psychology (ISSN 0090-5046)
Description: Includes articles on all of the allied fields of the neurosciences that are related directly to behavior and experience. Experimental, review and theoretical papers are published.
Refereed Serial

PSYCHOLOGY

616.89 US
PSYCHODRAMA NETWORK NEWS. q. membership. American Society of Group Psychotherapy and Psychodrama, 6728 Old McLean Village Dr., McLean, VA 22101. TEL 703-556-9222. FAX 703-556-8729. Ed. Kate Hudgins. adv. contact: Cheryl Kieday. bk.rev. circ. 800. **Document type:** newsletter.

150 US ISSN 0363-891X
D16.16 CODEN: PSRVD2
PSYCHOHISTORY REVIEW. vol.5, 1976. 3/yr. $22 to individuals; institutions $44. Sangamon State University, c/o Larry Shiner, Ed., Springfield, IL 62794-9243. adv.; bk.rev. circ. 600. (also avail. in microform from UMI; back issues avail.; reprint service avail. from UMI) **Indexed:** Amer.Hist.& Life, Hist.Abstr., Lang.& Lang.Behav.Abstr., Psychol.Abstr. (1978-), Soc.Work Res.& Abstr. **Document type:** academic/scholarly publication.
—BLDSC (6946.277400); Faxon; UMI; UnCover. **CCC.**
Formerly: Group for the Use of Psychology in History. Newsletter (ISSN 0162-9999)

150 JA ISSN 0033-2852
BF1 CODEN: PYLGAY
PSYCHOLOGIA/PUSHIKOROGIA; an international journal of psychology in the Orient. (Text in English) 1957. q. $40 to individuals; institutions $60. Psychologia Society - Pushikorogia-kai, Dept. of Educational Psychology, Faculty of Education, Kyoto University, Yoshida Honmachi, Sakyo-ku, Kyoto 606, Japan. FAX 81-75-753-3020. Ed. Noboru Sakano. adv.; bk.rev.; index. circ. 900. (back issues avail.) **Indexed:** Lang.& Lang.Behav.Abstr., Mid.East: Abstr.& Ind., Psychol.Abstr. (1957-), Sociol.Abstr., SSCI.
—BLDSC (6946.278000); Faxon; Genuine Article; UnCover.

370.15 150 XO ISSN 0555-5574
PSYCHOLOGIA A PATOPSYCHOLOGIA DIETATA. 1966. bi-m. Vyskumny Ustav Detskej Psychologie a Patopsychologie, Zahradnicka 93, 831 05 Bratislava, Slovakia. (Subscr. to: Slovart, Gottwaldovo nam. 6, 805-32 Bratislava, Slovakia) Ed. Karol Adamovic. circ. 3,500. **Indexed:** Psychol.Abstr. (1966-).
—BLDSC (6946.279000).

370.15 XO
PSYCHOLOGIA A SKOLA. 1972. irreg. (approx. 2/yr.). price varies. Slovenske Pedagogicke Nakladatelstvo, Sasinkova 5, 815 60 Bratislava, Slovakia.

150 370 PL
PSYCHOLOGIA-PEDAGOGIKA. 1961. irreg., no.103, 1994. price varies. Adam Mickiewicz University Press, Nowowiejskiego 55, 61-734 Poznan, Poland. TEL 527-380. FAX 61-526425. TELEX 413260 UAMPL. Ed.Be. bk.rev. **Indexed:** Psychol.Abstr. **Document type:** academic/scholarly publication.
—BLDSC (9120.480000).
Formerly: Uniwersytet im. Adama Mickiewicza w Poznaniu. Wydzial Historyczny. Prace. Seria Psychologia-Pedagogika (ISSN 0083-4254)
Description: Contains current research results of one author in the field of psychology, including monographs and Ph.D. works.

150 GW
PSYCHOLOGIA UNIVERSALIS FORSCHUNGSERGEBNISSE AUS DEM GESAMTGEBIET DER PSYCHOLOGIE. 1952. irreg., no.49, 1987. price varies. Verlag Anton Hain GmbH, Savignystr. 53, 60325 Frankfurt a.M., Germany. Ed.Bd. **Indexed:** Psychol.Abstr.

PSYCHOLOGIA WYCHOWAWCZA/EDUCATIONAL PSYCHOLOGY. see EDUCATION

150 BE ISSN 0033-2879
BF30 CODEN: PBELAN
PSYCHOLOGICA BELGICA. (Supplement avail.) (Text and summaries in English) 1954. q. 1200 BEF (effective 1995). Societe Belge de Psychologie - Belgische Vereniging voor Psychologie, Tienesstraat 102, B-3000 Leuven, Belgium. TEL 32-16-326013. FAX 32-16-286000. E-mail: betty.vandenbaviere@psy.kuleuven.ac.be. Eds. A. Vandierendonck, G. Lories. adv.; bk.rev.; abstr.; cum.index. circ. 450. (back issues avail.) **Indexed:** Biol.Abstr., C.I.S. Abstr., Curr.Cont., Psychol.Abstr. (1961-), SSCI. **Document type:** academic/scholarly publication.
—BLDSC (6946.287000); Genuine Article. *Refereed Serial*

152 US ISSN 1040-3590
CODEN: PYASEJ
PSYCHOLOGICAL ASSESSMENT. 1989. q. $73 to non-members (foreign $88); members $36 (foreign $44); institutions $146 (foreign $176). American Psychological Association, 750 First St., N.E., Washington, DC 20002-4242. TEL 202-336-5600. FAX 202-336-5568. Ed. James N. Butcher. circ. 6,700. **Indexed:** Excerpt.Med. (1995-), Psychol.Abstr. (1989-), Psycscan C.P., Soc.Sci.Ind. (1994-). **Document type:** academic/scholarly publication.
—BLDSC (6946.293500); Faxon; SWETS; UMI; UnCover. **CCC.**
Description: Original empirical articles concerning clinical assessment and evaluations. *Refereed Serial*

150 SA
PSYCHOLOGICAL ASSOCIATION OF SOUTH AFRICA. PROCEEDINGS. (Text in Afrikaans, English) 1962. a., 11th, 1992, Durban. free. Psychological Association of South Africa, P.O. Box 74119, Lynnwood Ridge 0040, South Africa. TEL 27-12-326-1981. **Document type:** proceedings.
Formerly: Psychological Institute of the Republic of South Africa. Proceedings.

150 US ISSN 0033-2909
BF1 CODEN: PSBUAI
PSYCHOLOGICAL BULLETIN. 1904. bi-m. $126 to non-members (foreign $146); members $61 (foreign $71); institutions $251 (foreign $294). American Psychological Association, 750 First St., N.E., Washington, DC 20002-4242. TEL 202-336-5568. FAX 202-336-5568. Ed. Robert J. Sternberg. adv.; charts; illus.; index. circ. 7,700. (also avail. in microform from UMI,PMC; reprint service avail. from UMI,KTO) **Indexed:** Abstr.Crim.& Pen., Acad.Ind., Adol.Ment.Hlth.Abstr., ASSIA, Biol.Abstr., C.I.J.E., Child Devel.Abstr., Crim.Just.Abstr., Curr.Adv.Ecol.Sci., Curr.Cont., Educ.Admin.Abstr., Ergon.Abstr., Ind.Med., M.L.A., Mark.Res.Abstr. (1963-), Mid.East: Abstr.& Ind., Nutr.Abstr., Psychol.Abstr. (1926-), Psycscan C.P., Psycscan D.P., Psycscan, Soc.Sci.Ind., Soc.Work Res.& Abstr., SOMA, Sp.Ed.Needs Abstr., SSCI, Stud.Wom.Abstr. **Document type:** academic/scholarly publication.
—BLDSC (6946.300000); Faxon; Genuine Article; SWETS; UMI; UnCover. **CCC.**
Description: Comprehensive and integrative reviews and interpretations of critical substantive and methodological issues and practical problems from all the areas of psychology. *Refereed Serial*

370.15 150 US ISSN 1047-840X
BF1 CODEN: PINQEY
PSYCHOLOGICAL INQUIRY; an international journal of peer commentary and review. 1990. q. $40 to individuals (foreign $65); institutions $220 (foreign $245). Lawrence Erlbaum Associates, Inc., 10 Industrial Dr., Mahwah, NJ 07430-2262. TEL 201-236-9500. FAX 201-236-0072. Ed. Lawrence A. Pervin. adv.; page $375; 7 x 10. bk.rev. **Indexed:** Psychol.Abstr. (1990-). **Document type:** academic/scholarly publication.
—BLDSC (6946.380000); Faxon; UnCover.
Description: Publishes theoretical and issue-oriented articles in the areas of personality, social, developmental, health, and clinical psychology. *Refereed Serial*

616.89 US ISSN 0048-5748
CODEN: PSYIA
PSYCHOLOGICAL ISSUES. 1959. irreg., no.63, 1995. price varies. International Universities Press, Inc., 59 Boston Post Rd., Box 1524, Madison, CT 06443-1524. TEL 203-245-4000. Ed. Herbert Schlesinger. illus. **Indexed:** Biol.Abstr., Ind.Med., Mid.East: Abstr.& Ind., Psychol.Abstr., SSCI. **Document type:** monographic series.
—BLDSC (6946.400000).
Formerly: Psychological Issues. Monograph (ISSN 0079-7359) *Refereed Serial*

150 US ISSN 0033-2925
BF173.A2
PSYCHOLOGICAL PERSPECTIVES; a Jungian review. 1970. s-a. $22 (foreign $26). C.G. Jung Institute of Los Angeles, 10349 W. Pico Blvd., Los Angeles, CA 90064-2694. TEL 310-556-1193. FAX 310-556-2290. Ed. Ernest L. Rossi. adv.; bk.rev.; film rev.; index. circ. 18,000. (also avail. in microform from UMI; reprint service avail. from UMI) **Indexed:** Psychol.Abstr. **Document type:** academic/scholarly publication.
—BLDSC (6946.510000); UMI; UnCover. **CCC.**
Description: Journal of Jungian thought featuring articles, interviews, poetry, and fiction. Explores themes and issues of personal, cultural, and global interest from a unique perspective which integrates archetypal and leading edge thinking in the arts and sciences.

150 152 US ISSN 0033-2933
BF1 CODEN: PYRCAI
PSYCHOLOGICAL RECORD; a quarterly journal in theoretical and experimental psychology. 1937. q. $30 to individuals; students $20; institutions $65 (effective 1995). Kenyon College, Gambier, OH 43022-9623. TEL 614-427-5377. FAX 614-427-4950. Ed. Charles E. Rice. adv.; bk.rev.; index. circ. 1,500. (also avail. in microform from UMI; back issues avail.; reprint service avail. from UMI,ISI) **Indexed:** Abstr.Crim.& Pen., Adol.Ment.Hlth.Abstr., ASSIA, Biol.Abstr., Child Devel.Abstr., Crim.Just.Abstr., Curr.Adv.Ecol.Sci., Curr.Cont., Ind.Med., Lang.& Lang.Behav.Abstr., Mid.East: Abstr.& Ind., Nutr.Abstr., Psychol.Abstr. (1937-), Sci.Cit.Ind., Soc.Sci.Ind., SSCI. **Document type:** academic/scholarly publication.
●Also available online. Vendor(s): University Microfilms International.
—BLDSC (6946.520000); Faxon; Genuine Article; SWETS; UMI; UnCover. **CCC.** *Refereed Serial*

150 US ISSN 0033-2941
BF21 CODEN: PYRTAZ
PSYCHOLOGICAL REPORTS. 1955. bi-m. (2 vols./yr.). $250 (effective 1996). Dr. C.H. Ammons & Dr. R.B. Ammons, Eds. & Pubs., Box 9229, Missoula, MT 59807. bk.rev.; charts; illus.; stat.; index. circ. 1,800. (also avail. in microform) **Indexed:** Abstr.Crim.& Pen., Adol.Ment.Hlth.Abstr., Biol.Abstr., CERDIC, Chic.Per.Ind., CINAHL, Commun.Abstr., Crim.Just.Abstr., Curr.Cont., Curr.Lit.Fam.Plan., Dent.Ind., Ergon.Abstr., Excerp.Med., IMFL, Ind.Med., Lang.& Lang.Behav.Abstr., Mid.East: Abstr.& Ind., Mult.Ed.Abstr., PSI, Psychol.Abstr. (1955-), Res.High.Educ.Abstr., Risk Abstr., Sage Fam.Stud.Abstr., Sci.Cit.Ind., Soc.Sci.Ind., SSCI, Stud.Wom.Abstr. **Document type:** academic/scholarly publication.
—BLDSC (6946.525000); Faxon; SWETS; UnCover.
Description: Carries experimental, theoretical, and speculative articles in the field of general psychology. *Refereed Serial*

150 GW ISSN 0340-0727
BF3 CODEN: PSREDJ
PSYCHOLOGICAL RESEARCH; an international journal of perception, cognition and action. (Text in English) 1921. 4/yr. DM.579($420) (effective 1996). Springer-Verlag, Heidelberger Platz 3, 14197 Berlin, Germany. TEL 030-8207-0. FAX 030-8214091. E-mail: orders@springer.de. (Subscr. in N. America to: Springer-Verlag New York, Inc., 44 Hartz Way, Secaucus, NJ 07096-2491. TEL 201-348-4033. FAX 201-348-4505) Ed.Bd. cum.index: vols.1-36. (also avail. in microform from UMI; reprint service avail. from ISI) **Indexed:** Biol.Abstr., Curr.Cont., Ind.Med., Mid.East: Abstr.& Ind., Psychol.Abstr. (1973-), SSCI. **Document type:** academic/scholarly publication.
—BLDSC (6946.527000); Faxon; Genuine Article; SWETS; UMI; UnCover. **CCC.**
Superseded: Psychologische Forschung.
Description: Emphasizes the theoretical implications of the research reported.

PSYCHOLOGY

150   SW   ISSN 0555-5620
BF21.A1
PSYCHOLOGICAL RESEARCH BULLETIN. (Text in English) 1961. irreg. (approx. 6/yr.). free. Lunds Universitet, Department of Psychology, Paradisgatan 5 P, 223 50 Lund, Sweden. TEL 046-10 87 69. FAX 46-46-10-42-09. Ed.Bd. bibl.; charts; cum.index. circ. 450. **Indexed:** Psychol.Abstr. **Document type:** academic/scholarly publication.
—BLDSC (6946.528000); UnCover.
    Description: Empirical psychological studies, frequently concerned with personality.

150   II   ISSN 0970-6097
BF76.5
PSYCHOLOGICAL RESEARCH JOURNAL. 1977. s-a. Rs.50($20) (effective 1991). Psychological Research Academy, Suite 9, 37 Syed Amir Ali Ave., Calcutta 700019, India. Ed.Bd. adv.; bk.rev.; index. **Indexed:** G.Indian Per.Lit., Indian Psychol.Abstr., Psychol.Abstr.

150   US   ISSN 0033-295X
BF1   CODEN: PSRVAX
PSYCHOLOGICAL REVIEW. 1894. q. $73 to non-members (foreign $88); members $44; institutions $146 (foreign $176). American Psychological Association, 750 First St., N.E., Washington, DC 20002-4242. TEL 202-336-5600. FAX 202-336-5568. Ed. Robert A. Bjork. adv.; bibl.; charts; index. circ. 7,000. (also avail. in microform from UMI;PMC; reprint service avail. from KTO) **Indexed:** Acad.Ind., ASSIA, Biol.Abstr., C.I.J.E., Child Devel.Abstr., Cont.Pg.Manage., Curr.Adv.Ecol.Sci., Curr.Cont., Curr.Lit.Fam.Plan, Ergon.Abstr., Ind.Med., Lang.& Lang.Behav.Abstr., M.L.A., Mark.Res.Abstr. (1963-), Mid.East: Abstr.& Ind., Psychol.Abstr. (1924-), Psycscan D.P., Soc.Sci.Ind., Soc.Work Res.& Abstr., Sp.Ed.Needs Abstr., SSCI, Yrbk.Assoc.Educ.& Rehab.Blind. **Document type:** academic/scholarly publication.
—BLDSC (6946.530000); Faxon; Genuine Article; SWETS; UMI; UnCover. **CCC.**
    Description: Includes articles that make theoretical contributions to all areas of scientific psychology.
Refereed Serial

150.19   UK   ISSN 0956-7976
BF1   CODEN: PSYSET
PSYCHOLOGICAL SCIENCE. 1990. £90($136) (effective 1996). (American Psychological Society) Cambridge University Press, Edinburgh Bldg., Shaftesbury Rd., Cambridge CB2 2UR, England. TEL 01223-312393. FAX 01223-315052. TELEX 851817256. (N. American addr.: Cambridge University Press, Journals Dept., 40 W. 20th St., New York, NY 10011. TEL 212-924-3900. FAX 212-691-3239) Ed. John Kihlstrom. adv.; bk.rev. (back issues avail.) **Indexed:** Psychol.Abstr. (1990-), Soc.Sci.Ind. (1994-). **Document type:** academic/scholarly publication.
—BLDSC (6946.530300); Faxon; Genuine Article; UMI; UnCover. **CCC.**
    Description: Provides a forum for research, theory and application in psychology and the closely related behavioral, cognitive, neural and social sciences.

150   US   ISSN 1040-404X
PSYCHOLOGICAL SCIENCE AGENDA. 1988. bi-m. free. American Psychological Association, Science Directorate, 750 First Ave., N.E., Washington, DC 20002-4242. TEL 202-336-6000. FAX 202-336-5953. Ed. Deborah Segal. circ. 25,000. **Document type:** newsletter.
    Description: Discusses what is going on in the field of psychological science (research), and what is happening at the American Psychological Association's Science Directorate.

150   II   ISSN 0033-2968
BF1
PSYCHOLOGICAL STUDIES. (Text in English) 1956. 3/yr. Rs.200($30) Department of Psychology, University of Calicut, Calicut 673 635, Kerala, India. Ed. M.A. Faroqi. adv.; bk.rev.; charts; illus.; stat.; index. circ. 500. (reprint service avail. from ISI) **Indexed:** Psychol.Abstr. (1956-), Sci.Cit.Ind., SSCI. **Document type:** academic/scholarly publication.
—BLDSC (6946.531100); SWETS.

150   DK   ISSN 1395-0878
▼**PSYCHOLOGICAL YEARBOOK (YEAR).** (Text in English) 1994. a. 141. Museum Tusculanum Press, University of Copenhagen, Njalsgade 92, DK-2300 Copenhagen S, Denmark. TEL 45-35-32-91-09. FAX 45-35-32-91-13. Ed. Axel Mortensen. **Document type:** academic/scholarly publication.
    Description: Contains presentations of research built upon an innovative tradition. Many psychological schools and scientific traditions are represented.

150   NE   ISSN 0167-6598
PSYCHOLOGIE. 1982. 11/yr. fl.82.50 (effective 1994). Swets & Zeitlinger bv, Heereweg 347, 2161 CA Lisse, Netherlands. TEL 31-2521-35111. FAX 31-2521-15888. TELEX 41325 SZLIS NL. (Dist. in N. America by: Swets & Zeitlinger, 440 Creamery Way, Ste. A, Exton, PA 19341. TEL 800-447-9387. FAX 610-524-5366) Ed. Rita Kohnstamm. (back issues avail.) **Document type:** academic/scholarly publication, consumer publication.
—SWETS.
    Description: Covers current psychological knowledge for an educated lay readership.

PSYCHOLOGIE ET EDUCATION. see *EDUCATION*

152.8   FR   ISSN 0296-8770
PSYCHOLOGIE ET PSYCHOMETRIE. s-a. 110 F. Editions Scientifiques et Psychologiques, 6 bis, rue Andre Chenier, 92130 Issy-les-Moulineaux, France. TEL 46-45-38-12. FAX 40-95-73-32. TELEX 270 105 F. Eds. Pierre Favreau, Francis Van Dam.
—BLDSC (6946.532080).

150   FR   ISSN 0033-2984
BF2   CODEN: PSFRAT
PSYCHOLOGIE FRANCAISE. 1956. 4/yr. 510 F. (Societe Francaise de Psychologie) Dunod, 15 rue Gossin, 92543 Montrouge Cedex, France. TEL 33-1-40-92-65-00. FAX 33-1-40-92-65-97. TELEX 634 916 F. (Subscr. to: Centrale des Revues, 11 rue Gossin, 92543 Montrouge Cedex, France. TEL 33-1-46-56-52-66) Ed. C. Bonnet. bibl.; charts; illus.; index. circ. 2,800. (reprint service avail. from SWZ) **Indexed:** Biol.Abstr., Lang.& Lang.Behav.Abstr., Psychol.Abstr. (1956-), SSCI.
—BLDSC (6946.532200); Faxon. **CCC.**
    Description: Publishes reviews of original investigations, articles covering theoretical reflection regarding the practice of psychology.

150   GW   ISSN 0340-1677
PSYCHOLOGIE HEUTE. 1974. m. DM.94. Verlag Julius Beltz GmbH, Am Hauptbahnhof 10, 69469 Weinheim, Germany. TEL 06201-60070. FAX 06201-600782. TELEX 465500-BELTZD. Ed. Heiko Ernst. adv.; bk.rev.; bibl.; charts; illus.; stat.; index. circ. 80,000. **Indexed:** Excerp.Med. **Document type:** academic/scholarly publication.
—BLDSC (6946.532240); SWETS. **CCC.**
    Description: Covers the behavioral sciences.

301.1 150   CN   ISSN 0714-3494
PSYCHOLOGIE PREVENTIVE. 1982. s-a. Can.$9.50 to individuals (foreign Can.$20); institutions Can.$12 (foreign Can.$25). Societe de Recherche en Orientation Humaine Inc., 2120, est rue Sherbrooke, Bur. 212, Montreal, PQ H2K 1C3, Canada. TEL 514-523-5677. FAX 514-523-9999. Ed. Ghislaine Picard-Mayer. adv.; bk.rev.; index. circ. 1,200. (back issues avail.) **Indexed:** Pt.de Rep. (1987-). **Document type:** academic/scholarly publication.
    Description: Covers problems of family, youth, education and health.

301.1 900   GW   ISSN 0935-0179
PSYCHOLOGIE UND GESCHICHTE. 1989. q. DM.90 (foreign DM.97). Verlag Leske und Budrich GmbH, Postfach 300551, 51334 Leverkusen, Germany. TEL 02171-2079. FAX 02171-41209. Ed.Bd. circ. 150. **Document type:** academic/scholarly publication.

301.1 150   GW   ISSN 0170-0537
PSYCHOLOGIE UND GESELLSCHAFTSKRITIK. 1977. 4/yr. DM.52. (Initiative Kritischer Psychologinnen und Psychologen e.V.) Mabuse Verlag GmbH, Kasselerstr. 1A, 60486 Frankfurt a.M., Germany. TEL 069-705053. FAX 069-704152. Ed. Siegfried Grubitzsch. adv.; bk.rev.; index. circ. 2,500. (back issues avail.) **Document type:** academic/scholarly publication.
    Description: Critique of mainstream psychology in theory and practice; social foundation of psychology.

150   GW   ISSN 0079-7405
PSYCHOLOGIE UND PERSON. 1961. irreg., no.26, 1990. price varies. Ernst Reinhardt Verlag, Kemnatenstr. 46, 80639 Munich, Germany. TEL 089-1783005. FAX 089-1781827. **Document type:** monographic series.

150 790.1   GW   ISSN 0945-6031
PSYCHOLOGIE UND SPORT. q. DM.50 (students DM.40). (Arbeitsgemeinschaft fuer Sportpsychologie) Verlag Karl Hofmann, Postfach 1360, 73603 Schorndorf, Germany. TEL 07181-402-0. FAX 07181-402111. **Document type:** academic/scholarly publication.

158   XR   ISSN 0033-300X
HF5548.8   CODEN: PSVPB2
PSYCHOLOGIE V EKONOMICKE PRAXI/APPLIED INDUSTRIAL PSYCHOLOGY; casopis pro pomoc hospodarske praxi. (Text in Czech or Slovak; summaries in English, French, German, Russian) 1966. q. 35 Kc.($13.20) (Universita Karlova, Filosoficka Fakulta) Vydavatelstvi Karolinum, Ovocny trh 5, 116 36 Prague 1, Czech Republic. FAX 42-2-24212041. E-mail: uhlar@dec59.ruk.cuni.cz. (Subscr. to: Artia, Ve Smeckach 30, 111 27 Prague 1, Czech Republic) Eds. Jiri Hoskovec, Jiri Stikar. bk.rev.; abstr.; bibl.; charts; illus.; stat.; index. circ. 700. (tabloid format; also avail. in microform) **Indexed:** C.I.S. Abstr., Ergon.Abstr., Psychol.Abstr. **Document type:** academic/scholarly publication.

150   GW   ISSN 0941-3049
PSYCHOLOGIE VERSTEHEN. 1992. s-a. DM.14. Papillon Verlag, Buehne 330, 34434 Borgentreich, Germany. TEL 05643-8344. FAX 05643-8344. Ed. Dr. Kurt Guss. adv.; bk.rev. **Document type:** academic/scholarly publication.

054.1   FR
PSYCHOLOGIES.* 1970. m. 9 F. per no. Loft International, 1 rue Lord Byron, 75008 Paris, France. Ed. Jacques Mousseau. adv.; bk.rev.; illus.; index. circ. 80,000. **Indexed:** Curr.Cont., Pt.de Rep. (1979-), SSCI.
—BLDSC (6946.532800).
    Formerly (until 1983): Psychologie (ISSN 0032-1583)

150   GW   ISSN 0033-3018
BF3
PSYCHOLOGISCHE BEITRAEGE; Vierteljahresschrift fuer alle Gebiete der Psychologie. (Text in English, German; summaries in English, French, German) 1953. 4/yr. DM.121. (Deutsche Gesellschaft fuer Psychologie) Pabst Science Publishers, Eichengrund 28, 49525 Lengerich, Germany. TEL 05484-308. FAX 05484-550. Ed.Bd. adv.; bk.rev.; abstr.; bibl.; charts; index, cum.index every 10 yrs. **Indexed:** Biol.Abstr., Curr.Cont., Ergon.Abstr., Ger.J.Psych., Psychol.Abstr. (1953-), SSCI. **Document type:** academic/scholarly publication.
—BLDSC (6946.533500); SWETS.

150   GW   ISSN 0033-3042
BF3
PSYCHOLOGISCHE RUNDSCHAU. (Text in German; summaries in English) 1949. q. DM.63. (Deutsche Gesellschaft fuer Psychologie) Hogrefe Verlag fuer Psychologie, Rohnsweg 25, 37085 Goettingen, Germany. TEL 0551-496090. FAX 0551-4960988. (Co-Sponsor: Berufsverband Deutscher Psychologen) Ed. W. Tock. adv.; bk.rev.; abstr.; charts; index. circ. 6,200. **Indexed:** Child Devel.Abstr., Psychol.Abstr. (1929-), SSCI. **Document type:** academic/scholarly publication.
—Faxon; Genuine Article; SWETS.

150   UK   ISSN 0952-8229
THE PSYCHOLOGIST. vol.34, 1981. m. £48. British Psychological Society, St. Andrews House, 48 Princess Rd., E., Leicester LE1 7DR, England. TEL 0166-254-9568. FAX 0166-247-0787. Eds. Mary Boyle, E. Mapstone. adv.; bk.rev.; abstr. circ. 22,500. (also avail. in microform from UMI; reprint service avail. from ISI;SWZ,UMI) **Indexed:** Br.Hum.Ind., Curr.Adv.Ecol.Sci., Curr.Cont., Ergon.Abstr., Psychol.Abstr., SSCI.
—BLDSC (6946.534680); UMI; UnCover. **CCC.**
    Formerly (until 1988): British Psychological Society. Bulletin (ISSN 0007-1692)
Refereed Serial

PSYCHOLOGY

150 327 US
PSYCHOLOGISTS FOR SOCIAL RESPONSIBILITY. NEWSLETTER. 1982. q. $40 membership. Psychologists for Social Responsibility, 2607 Connecticut Ave., N.W., Washington, DC 20008. TEL 202-745-7084. Ed. Anne Anderson. **Document type:** newsletter.
Description: Networking newsletter for professional psychologists, students of psychology, and others interested in conflict resolution and prevention of war.

150 US ISSN 0033-3077
BF1 CODEN: PYCHBR
PSYCHOLOGY; a journal of human behavior. 1964. q. $19 (foreign $21.50). Institute for Leadership and Organization Effectiveness, 1195 Stroud Ct., Westerville, OH 43081-1134. FAX 614-292-7999. Ed. Dr. Joseph Cangemi. adv.; bk.rev. circ. 3,000. (also avail. in microform from UMI; reprint service avail. from UMI) **Indexed:** Biol.Abstr., C.I.J.E., Commun.Abstr., Curr.Cont., Int.Polit.Sci.Abstr., Lang.& Lang.Behav.Abstr., Psychol.Abstr. (1965-). **Document type:** academic/scholarly publication.
—BLDSC (6946.535200); Faxon; Genuine Article; SWETS; UMI; UnCover.
Description: Devoted to the basic research, theory, and techniques in the general field of psychology.
Refereed Serial

PSYCHOLOGY AND AGING. see *GERONTOLOGY AND GERIATRICS*

150 II
PSYCHOLOGY AND DEVELOPING SOCIETIES. 1989. s-a. $37 to individuals; institutions $78 (effective Sep. 1995). (University of Allahabad, Center for Advanced Study in Psychology) Sage Publications India Pvt. Ltd., P.O. Box 4215, New Delhi 110 048, India. TEL 91-11-744-4958. FAX 91-11-647-2426. (Overseas subscr. to: Sage Publications Ltd., 6 Bonhill St., London EC2A 4PU, England. TEL 44-071-374-0645. FAX 44-071-374-8741; Subscr. in N. America to: Sage Publications, Inc. 2455 Teller Rd., Thousand Oaks, CA 91320. TEL 805-499-0721. FAX 805-499-0871) Ed. R.C. Tripathi; Pub. Tejeshwar Singh. adv.: page Rs.1000; adv. contact: Sunanda Ghosh. abstr. circ. 500. (back issues avail.; reprint service avail.) **Indexed:** IMFL, Psychol.Abstr. (1989-). **Document type:** academic/scholarly publication.
Description: Provides an international forum for psychologists concerned with problems of developing societies. Publishes theoretical, empirical, and review papers that help further our understanding of the problems of these societies.
Refereed Serial

155 US ISSN 0887-0446
R726.7 CODEN: PSHEE4
PSYCHOLOGY & HEALTH; an international journal. 1987. 4/yr. 99 ECU (effective 1996). Harwood Academic Publishers, c/o International Publishers Distributor, 820 Town Center Dr., Langhorne, PA 19047. TEL 215-750-2642. FAX 215-750-6343. (Subscr. to: International Publishers Distributor, P.O. Box 90, Reading, Berkshire RG1 8JL, England. TEL 44-173-456-8316) Ed. Dr. John Weinman. (also avail. in microform) **Indexed:** Behav.Med.Abstr., CINAHL, Mult.Ed.Abstr., Psychol.Abstr. (1987-). **Document type:** academic/scholarly publication.
—BLDSC (6946.535325); Faxon; SWETS; UnCover. CCC.
Description: Health psychology forum dealing with the psychological and social factors in the etiology and outcome of physical illnesses. Promotes physical well-being through health education, prevention and behavior change.
Refereed Serial

616.89 UK
PSYCHOLOGY AND HEALTH SERIES. a. price varies. Chapman & Hall, 2-6 Boundary Row, London SE1 8HN, England. TEL 0171-865-0066. FAX 0171-522-9623. TELEX 290164 CHAPMA G. E-mail: journal@chall.mhs.compuserve.com. (Dist. by: International Thompson Publishing Services Ltd., Cheriton House, North Way, Andover, Hants. SP10 5BE, England. TEL 01264-342713. FAX 01264-342807; Orders in N. America to: Chapman & Hall, One Penn Plaza, 41st Fl., New York, NY 10019. TEL 212-564-1060. FAX 212-564-1505) Ed. Donald Marcer. index. (back issues avail.) **Document type:** monographic series.

301.1 150 US ISSN 0742-6046
PSYCHOLOGY & MARKETING. 1984. 8/yr. $432 (foreign $556) (effective 1996). John Wiley & Sons, Inc., Journals, 605 Third Ave., New York, NY 10158. TEL 212-850-6645. FAX 212-850-6021. TELEX 12-7063. E-mail: SUBINFO@JWILEY.COM. (Subscr. outside the Americas to: John Wiley & Sons, Ltd., Baffins Ln., Chichester, W. Sussex PO19 1UD, England. TEL 44-1243-779777. FAX 44-1243-776128) Ed. Dr. Ronald J. Cohen. adv. contact: Roberta Frederick. circ. 700. (also avail. in microform from UMI; back issues avail.) **Indexed:** Psychol.Abstr. (1988-). **Document type:** academic/scholarly publication.
—BLDSC (6946.535340); Faxon; SWETS; UMI; UnCover. CCC.
Description: Promotes an understanding of the nature and operation of psychological principles, as applied to strategies in the marketing industry.
Refereed Serial

370.15 301 613.7 US ISSN 0885-7423
GV706
PSYCHOLOGY AND SOCIOLOGY OF SPORT: CURRENT SELECTED RESEARCH. 1986. a. $37.50. A M S Press, Inc., 56 E. 13th St., New York, NY 10003. TEL 212-777-4700. FAX 212-995-5413. Eds. Lee Vander Velden, James H. Humphrey. index. (back issues avail.)
—BLDSC (6946.535430).
Description: Research on contemporary problems of interest to behavioral scientists in the area of sport.

616.89 SA
PSYCHOLOGY BULLETIN. (Text in English) 1990. s-a. (University of the Western Cape, Department of Psychology) Psychology Resource Centre, Private Bag X17, Bellville 7535, South Africa. TEL 27-21-959-2283. FAX 27-21-959-3515. Eds. Norman Duncan, Ashley van Niekerk. circ. 1,000 (controlled). **Document type:** academic/scholarly publication.
Formerly (until vol.3, no.1, 1993): Psychology Quarterly.
Refereed Serial

345 US ISSN 1068-316X
  CODEN: PCLAE2
▼**PSYCHOLOGY, CRIME AND LAW.** 1994. 4/yr. 61 ECU (effective 1996). Harwood Academic Publishers, c/o International Publishers Distributor, 820 Town Center Dr., Langhorne, PA 19047. TEL 215-750-2642; 800-545-8398. FAX 215-750-6343. (Subscr. to: International Publishers Distributor, P.O. Box 90, Reading, Berkshire RG1 8JL, England. TEL 44-173-456-8316) (back issues avail.) **Document type:** academic/scholarly publication.

PSYCHOLOGY FOR LIVING. see *RELIGIONS AND THEOLOGY*

616.89 US ISSN 1354-8506
▼**PSYCHOLOGY, HEALTH & MEDICINE.** Announced for publication in 1996. 3/yr. £38 to individuals; institutions £88 (effective 1996). Carfax Publishing Co., P.O. Box 25, Abingdon, Oxon. OX14 3UE, England. TEL 44-1235-555335. FAX 44-1235-553559. (N. American subscr. to: Carfax Publishing Co., 875-81 Massachusetts Ave., Cambridge, MA 02139) **Document type:** academic/scholarly publication.

150 II ISSN 0971-4472
PSYCHOLOGY IN PROGRESS. (Text in English) 1993. q. $50 to individuals; institutions Rs.$100($100). Institute of Psychological Research, 52, 10th Cross, West of Chord Rd., II Stage, Bangalore 560 086, India. Ed. T.R. Rao. adv. **Document type:** academic/scholarly publication.
Formerly (until 1994): Indian Journal of Psychological Development.

370.15 150 US ISSN 0033-3085
LB1101
PSYCHOLOGY IN THE SCHOOLS. 1964. q. $35 to individuals; libraries $100. Clinical Psychology Publishing Co., Inc., 4 Conant Sq., Brandon, VT 05733. TEL 802-247-6871. FAX 802-247-6853. Ed. Dr. Gerald B. Fuller. adv.; bk.rev.; bibl.; index. circ. 1,700. (also avail. in microform from MIM,UMI; back issues avail.) **Indexed:** Adol.Ment.Hlth.Abstr., C.I.J.E., Cont.Pg.Educ., Educ.Ind., Except.Child.Educ.Abstr., IMFL, Lang.& Lang.Behav.Abstr., Mult.Ed.Abstr., Psychol.Abstr. (1965-), SOMA, Sp.Ed.Needs Abstr., SSCI, Tech.Educ.Abstr. **Document type:** academic/scholarly publication.
—BLDSC (6946.536400); Faxon; Genuine Article; SWETS; UMI; UnCover.
Refereed Serial

PSYCHOLOGY OF ADDICTIVE BEHAVIORS. see *DRUG ABUSE AND ALCOHOLISM*

152.5 US ISSN 0079-7421
BF683 CODEN: PYLMAI
PSYCHOLOGY OF LEARNING AND MOTIVATION: ADVANCES IN RESEARCH AND THEORY. 1967. irreg., vol.29, 1993. Academic Press, Inc., 525 B St., Ste. 1900, San Diego, CA 92101-4495. TEL 619-231-0926. FAX 619-699-6715. (Subscr. to: Order Dept., 6277 Sea Harbor Dr., 4th Fl., Orlando, FL 32887. TEL 800-321-5068) Ed. K.W. Spence. (reprint service avail. from ISI) **Indexed:** Educ.Ind., SSCI. **Document type:** monographic series.
—BLDSC (6946.535700); UnCover. CCC.

PSYCHOLOGY OF MUSIC. see *MUSIC*

155 305.4 UK ISSN 0361-6843
HQ1206 CODEN: PWOQDY
PSYCHOLOGY OF WOMEN QUARTERLY. 1976. 3/yr. £80($118) (effective 1996). (American Psychological Association, Division 35) Cambridge University Press, Edinburgh Bldg., Shaftesbury Rd., Cambridge CB2 2RU, England. TEL 01223-312393. FAX 01223-315052. TELEX 851817256. (N. American addr.: Cambridge University Press, Journals Dept., 40 W. 20th St., New York, NY 10011. TEL 212-924-3900. FAX 212-691-3239) Ed. Nancy Russoi. adv. (also avail. in microform from UMI; back issues avail.; reprint service avail. from SWZ) **Indexed:** Abstr.Anthropol., Adol.Ment.Hlth.Abstr., ASSIA, C.I.J.E., Child Devel.Abstr., Curr.Cont., Curr.Lit.Fam.Plan., Human Resour.Abstr., IMFL, Mult.Ed.Abstr., Psychol.Abstr. (1976-), Res.High.Educ.Abstr., Sage Pub.Admin.Abstr., Sage Urb.Stud.Abstr., Soc.Sci.Ind., Soc.Work Res.& Abstr., Sociol.Abstr., Sp.Ed.Needs Abstr., SSCI, Stud.Wom.Abstr., Wom.Stud.Abstr. (1976-). **Document type:** academic/scholarly publication.
—BLDSC (6946.538000); Faxon; Genuine Article; SWETS; UMI; UnCover. CCC.
Description: Publishes current and important findings in the field of psychology of women and gender.
Refereed Serial

150 350 US ISSN 1076-8971
▼**PSYCHOLOGY, PUBLIC POLICY, AND LAW.** 1995. q. $100 (foreign $130) (effective 1996). American Psychological Association, 750 First St., N.E., Washington, DC 20002-4242. TEL 202-336-5600. FAX 202-336-5568. **Document type:** academic/scholarly publication.
Description: Links psychological science with policy and law. Evaluates the contributions of psychology to policy and law issues, assesses policy alternatives, and articulates research needs in psychology that address policy and legal issues.
Refereed Serial

150 PK ISSN 0033-3093
PSYCHOLOGY QUARTERLY. (Text in English) 1964. q. Rs.30($15) Government College, Psychology Department, Lahore, Pakistan. Ed. Syed Azhar Ali Rizvi. bk.rev.; charts; stat. circ. 300. **Indexed:** CINAHL, Psychol.Abstr.
Formerly: Journal of Psychology.

150   UK   ISSN 0960-2925
PSYCHOLOGY RESEARCH. q. £5. Salomons Centre, Broomhill Rd., Southborough, Tunbridge Wells, Kent TN3 0TG, England. TEL 01892-515152. FAX 01892-539102. Ed.Bd. adv. contact: Jenny Miah. bk.rev. **Document type:** academic/scholarly publication.
—BLDSC (6946.536230).
Formerly (until 1990): Psychology Research on Placement.

150   UK   ISSN 1354-1129
▼**PSYCHOLOGY REVIEW.** 1994. q. £15.95 (rest of Europe £23; elsewhere £28.50) (effective 1996). Philip Allan Publishers Ltd., Market Pl., Deddington, Oxon. OX15 0SE, England. TEL 01869-338652. FAX 01869-338803. Ed. Patrick Fox. **Document type:** academic/scholarly publication.
—BLDSC (6946.536350).

150   US   ISSN 0033-3107
BF1   CODEN: PSTOAM
PSYCHOLOGY TODAY. 1967-1989 (Dec.); resumed 1991. bi-m. $18. Sussex Publishers Inc., 49 E. 21st St., 11th Fl., New York, NY 10010. TEL 212-260-7210. FAX 212-260-7445. (Individual subscr. to: Box 55046, Boulder, CO 80322. TEL 800-234-8361) Ed. Owen Lipstein. adv.; bk.rev.; bibl.; charts; illus.; stat.; index. circ. 341,472. (also avail. in microform) **Indexed:** Acad.Ind., ASSIA, Biol.Dig., Bk.Rev.Ind. (1973-), Can.B.P.I., CCR, Child.Bk.Rev.Ind. (1973-), CMI, Crim.Just.Abstr., Curr.Cont., Curr.Lit.Fam.Plan., Except.Child.Educ.Abstr., Excerp.Med., Film Lit.Ind. (1983-), Fut.Surv., G.Soc.Sci.& Rel.Per.Lit., High.Educ.Curr.Aware.Bull., Hlth.Ind., Mag.Ind., Mid.East: Abstr.& Ind., Peace Res.Abstr., Pers.Lit., PMR, R.G., Soc.Sci.Ind., Sportsearch, SSCI, TOM. **Document type:** consumer publication.
●Also available online. Vendor(s): Knight-Ridder, Inc., University Microfilms International. Also available on CD-ROM. Producer(s): University Microfilms International.
—BLDSC (6946.537000); Faxon; SWETS; UMI; UnCover.
Refereed Serial

150   NE   ISSN 0033-3115
DE PSYCHOLOOG. 1966. m. fl.100 to individuals; institutions fl.185. (Nederlands Instituut van Psychologen - Netherlands Psychological Association) Van Gorcum en Co. B.V., P.O. Box 43, 9400 AA Assen, Netherlands. TEL 31-5920-46864. FAX 31-5920-72064. Ed.Bd. adv.; bk.rev.; abstr.; bibl.; index, cum.index. circ. 7,000. **Indexed:** Psychol.Abstr. (1972-). **Document type:** academic/scholarly publication.
—BLDSC (6946.539300); SWETS.

616.89   GW
PSYCHMED. q. DM.98 (foreign DM.108). M M V Medizin Verlag, Sektion Quintessenz, Schillerstr. 7, 80336 Munich, Germany. TEL 089-555808. FAX 089-5501772. **Document type:** academic/scholarly publication.

150   CN   ISSN 0033-3123
BF1
PSYCHOMETRIKA; a journal devoted to the development of psychology as a quantitative rational science. 1936. q. $100. Psychometric Society, c/o Ontario Institute for Studies in Education, 252 Bloor St., W., Toronto, ON M5S 1V6, Canada. (Subscr. to: Dr. Ralph DeAyala, University of Maryland, Dept. of Measurement, Statistics and Evaluation, 1230 Benjamin Bldg., College Park, MD 20742-1115) Ed. William Heiser. adv. contact: Cynthia Null. bk.rev.; abstr.; bibl.; charts; index. circ. 2,200. (also avail. in microform from UMI; reprint service avail. from UMI) **Indexed:** Biol.Abstr., C.I.J.E., Child Devel.Abstr., Commun.Abstr., Compumath, Curr.Cont., Curr.Ind.Stat., Ergon.Abstr., J.Cont.Quant.Meth., Math.R., Mid.East: Abstr.& Ind., Psycscan, SSCI, Stat.Theor.Meth.Abstr. (1936-). **Document type:** academic/scholarly publication.
—BLDSC (6946.540000); Faxon; Genuine Article; SWETS; UMI; UnCover. CCC.

PSYCHOMUSICOLOGY; a journal of research in music cognition. see *MUSIC*

150   US   ISSN 1069-9384
BF1   CODEN: PBUREN
PSYCHONOMIC BULLETIN & REVIEW. 1973; N.S. 1994. q. $100 (foreign $107) (effective 1996). Psychonomic Society, Inc., 1710 Fortview Rd., Austin, TX 78704. TEL 512-462-2442. FAX 512-462-1101. Ed. Henry L. Roediger, III. adv. circ. 2,200. (also avail. in microform from KTO,UMI; back issues avail.; reprint service avail. from UMI) **Indexed:** Biol.Abstr., Curr.Adv.Ecol.Sci., Curr.Cont., Ergon.Abstr., IMFL, M.L.A., Mid.East: Abstr.& Ind., Psychol.Abstr., SSCI. **Document type:** academic/scholarly publication, bulletin.
—BLDSC (6946.540550); CASDDS; Faxon; Genuine Article; SWETS; UMI; UnCover. CCC.
Formerly (until 1994): Psychonomic Society. Bulletin (ISSN 0090-5054)
Description: Publishes theoretical and review articles on topics in all areas of experimental psychology.
Refereed Serial

PSYCHOPHYSIOLOGY; an international journal. see *MEDICAL SCIENCES*

301.1 150   SZ   ISSN 1013-5987
PSYCHOSCOPE. (Text in French and German) 1980. 10/yr. 72 SFr. (students 40 SFr.). Foederation der Schweizer Psychologen (FSP), Administration Psychoscope, Choisystr. 11, CH-3000 Bern 14, Switzerland. TEL 031-3820856. FAX 031-3820857. Ed. Beatrice Thelen. adv.; bk.rev. circ. 4,300.
Formerly: Schweizer Psychologen. Bulletin.

PSYCHOSOCIAL NEWS. see *MEDICAL SCIENCES* — Hematology

301.1 150   GW   ISSN 0171-3434
PSYCHOSOZIAL; Zeitschrift fuer Analyse, Praevention und Therapie psychosozialer Konflikte und Krankheiten. 1978. q. DM.32. Psychosozial Verlag, Friedrichstr. 35, 35392 Giessen, Germany. TEL 0641-77819. FAX 0641-390716. Ed.Bd. adv.; bk.rev. circ. 4,500. **Document type:** academic/scholarly publication.
—SWETS.

DER PSYCHOTHERAPEUT. see *MEDICAL SCIENCES* — Psychiatry And Neurology

616.89   GW   ISSN 0946-3453
▼**DIE PSYCHOTHERAPEUTIN.** 1994. s-a. DM.45. Psychiatrie Verlag GmbH, Thomas-Mann-Str. 49a, 53111 Bonn, Germany. TEL 0228-695540. FAX 0228-695595. Ed. Dr. Ulrike Hoffmann-Richter. **Document type:** academic/scholarly publication.

616.89   AU   ISSN 0943-1950
PSYCHOTHERAPIE FORUM. 1993. q. DM.82($59) (effective 1996). Springer-Verlag, Sachsenplatz 4-6, Postfach 89, A-1201 Vienna, Austria. TEL 0222-3302415. FAX 0222-3302426. (Subscr. in N. America to: Springer-Verlag New York, Inc., 44 Hartz Way, Secaucus, NJ 07096-2491. TEL 201-348-4033. FAX 201-348-4505) **Document type:** academic/scholarly publication.
—BLDSC (6946.558240); UMI.

616.89   SZ   ISSN 0251-737X
                        CODEN: PSYTEW
PSYCHOTHERAPIES. (Text in French) 1981. q. 95 SFr. to individuals; institutions 135 SFr.). Editions Medecine et Hygiene, Case Postale 456, CH-1211 Geneva 4, Switzerland. FAX 022-3469355. FAX 022-3475610. Ed.Bd. adv.; bk.rev. circ. 900. (reprint service avail. from UMI) **Document type:** academic/scholarly publication.
—BLDSC (6946.558400). CCC.

616.89   US   ISSN 0164-078X
PSYCHOTHERAPY DIGEST. 1976. bi-m. $15. Box 1167, Del Mar, CA 92014. Ed. Victor Kops. bk.rev. circ. 1,000. (looseleaf format; back issues avail.)

150   US   ISSN 0163-1543
PSYCHOTHERAPY FINANCES. 1974. m. $48. Ridgewood Financial Institute, Inc., Box 509, Ridgewood, NJ 07451. TEL 201-447-3366. FAX 201-427-3644. Ed. Herbert Klein. bk.rev. circ. 7,000.
Formerly (until 1977): Psychotherapy Economics (ISSN 0092-184X)

616.89   US   ISSN 0731-7158
RC455.2.P73
PSYCHOTHERAPY IN PRIVATE PRACTICE; innovations in clinical methods and management, consultation and practice management. 1983. q. $175 (foreign $245) (effective 1996). Haworth Press, Inc., 10 Alice St., Binghamton, NY 13904. TEL 607-722-5857; 800-342-9678. FAX 607-722-1424. TELEX 4932599. Ed. Frank De Piano. adv.; bk.rev. circ. 453. (also avail. in microfiche from UMI; back issues avail.; reprint service avail. from HAW) **Indexed:** Behav.Abstr., Bull.Signal., Chicago Psychoanal.Lit.Ind., IMFL, P.A.I.S., Psychol.Abstr. (1983-), Soc.Work Res.& Abstr.
—BLDSC (6946.559400); Haworth; UnCover.
Description: Covers issues and methods in the development of private practice for psychotherapists.
Refereed Serial

616.89   US   ISSN 1062-9475
PSYCHOTHERAPY LETTER; resource exchange for psychotherapy professionals. 1989. m. $99 to individuals (Canada $109; elsewhere $119); institutions $139 (Canada $149; elsewhere $159) (effective Jul. 1995). Manisses Communications Group, Inc., Box 9758, Providence, RI 02940-9758. TEL 401-861-6020; 800-333-7771. FAX 401-861-6370. Eds. Linda Watts Jackim, Melissa DeMeo. **Document type:** newsletter.
—CCC.
Formed by the merger of (1989-1992): Brown University Family Therapy Letter (ISSN 1045-5051); Which was formerly (1986-1989): Family Therapy Today (ISSN 0887-9109); (1989-1992): Psychotherapy Today (ISSN 1047-9848)
Description: Resource exchange for psychotherapy professionals.

616.89   US   ISSN 0738-6176
                        CODEN: PSPAEW
THE PSYCHOTHERAPY PATIENT; a quarterly journal of attribute-focused practice. 1984. q. $135 (foreign $189) (effctive Mar. 1995). Haworth Press, Inc., 10 Alice St., Binghamton, NY 13904. TEL 607-722-5857; 800-342-9678. FAX 607-722-1424. TELEX 4932599. Ed. Mark Stern. adv.; bk.rev. circ. 277. (also avail. in microfiche from UMI; back issues avail.; reprint service avail. from HAW) **Indexed:** IMFL, Psychol.Abstr., Soc.Work Res.& Abstr. **Document type:** academic/scholarly publication.
—BLDSC (6946.559300); Haworth.
Description: Devotes each issue to diagnostic, behavioral, and phenomenological groupings.
Refereed Serial

370.15 616.8   US
PSYCHOTHERAPY, RECOVERY AND PERSONAL GROWTH UPDATE. 1987. m. $67. Cromwell - Sloan Publishing Company, 63 Vine Rd., Stamford, CT 06905-2012. TEL 203-323-6839. Ed. Paul Sloan. bk.rev.; abstr.; charts; illus. circ. 6,400. (back issues avail.)
Formerly: Understanding People.

616.89   US   ISSN 1050-3307
RC475
PSYCHOTHERAPY RESEARCH. 1991. q. $33 to individuals (foreign $48); institutions $70 (foreign $85) (effective 1995). (Society for Psychotherapy Research) Guilford Publications, Inc., 72 Spring St., 4th Fl., New York, NY 10012. TEL 212-431-9800. FAX 212-966-6708. Ed.Bd; Pub. Robert Matloff. adv. contact: Marian Robinson. circ. 1,260. **Indexed:** Psychol.Abstr. (1991-).
—BLDSC (6946.559430); UMI. CCC.
Description: International communication on empirical findings in research on psychotherapeutic process and outcome.
Refereed Serial

150   DK   ISSN 0107-1211
PSYKE & LOGOS. (Text in Danish; abstracts in English) 1980. 2/yr. DKK 245 (students DKK 180; foreign DKK 196). Dansk Psykologisk Forlag, Hans Knudsens Plads 1A, 2100 Copenhagen O, Denmark. TEL 45-31-18-27-57. FAX 45-31-18-57-58. Ed.Bd. bk.rev. circ. 600. (back issues avail.) **Indexed:** Psychol.Abstr. (1981-).
—BLDSC (6946.559790).

PSYCHOLOGY

614.58 150   SW   ISSN 0033-3212
PSYKISK HAELSA/MENTAL HEALTH. 1960. q. SEK 250 (students SEK 150) (effective 1996). Svenska Foereningen foer Psykisk Haelsovaard - Swedish Association for Mental Health, Saltmaetargatan 5, 2, P.O. Box 45124, S-104 30 Stockholm, Sweden. TEL 46-8-34-70-65. FAX 46-8-32-88-75. Ed. Eggert Nielsen. bk.rev. circ. 6,000. **Indexed:** Psychol.Abstr. **Document type:** academic/scholarly publication.

150   DK   ISSN 0901-7089
PSYKOLOG NYT. 1947. s-m. DKK 1000. Dansk Psykolog Forening - Danish Psychologists Association, Bjerregaards Sidevej 4, DK-2500 Valby, Denmark. TEL 45-31-16-33-55. FAX 45-36-44-08-55. Ed. Dorthe Thorning Mejlmede. adv.; bk.rev.; tr.lit. circ. 4,100. **Indexed:** Psychol.Abstr. **Document type:** bulletin, academic/scholarly publication.
    Formerly (until 1986): Dansk Psykolog Nyt (ISSN 0011-6432)

150   DK   ISSN 0900-5625
PSYKOLOGISK FORSKNINGSRAPPORT. (Text in Danish; summaries in English) 1983. irreg. free. University of Copenhagen, Department of Psychology, Njalsgade 94, 2300 Copenhagen S, Denmark. Ed. Benny Karpauschof. circ. 200.
    Formerly (until 1984): Psykologisk Laboratorium. Forskningsrapport (ISSN 0107-3060)

370.15 150   DK   ISSN 0906-219X
PSYKOLOGISK PAEDAGOGISK RAADGIVNING/JOURNAL OF SCHOOL PSYCHOLOGY; tidsskrift for paedagogisk psykologi og raadgivning. 1964. 6/yr. plus monographs. DKK 280 (students DKK 200; foreign DKK 224). Dansk Psykologisk Forlag, Hans Knudsen Plads 1A, 2100 Copenhagen OE, Denmark. TEL 45-31-18-27-57. FAX 45-31-18-57-58. Ed. Bjoern Glaesel. adv.; bk.rev.; abstr.; bibl.; index. circ. 1,400. (back issues avail.) **Indexed:** C.I.J.E., Psychol.Abstr. (1968-), Soc.Work Res.& Abstr., SSCI.
    Formerly: Skolepsykologi (ISSN 0037-6493)

150   DK   ISSN 0906-2483
PSYKOLOGISK SET. 1982. 4/yr. DKK 140 (foreign DKK 112). Dansk Psykologisk Forlag, Hans Knudsens Plads 1A, 2100 Copenhagen O, Denmark. TEL 45-31-18-27-57. FAX 45-31-18-57-58. Ed. Jan Enggaard. **Indexed:** Psychol.Abstr.
    Formerly (until 1990): Psykologi (ISSN 0107-8755)

150   HU   ISSN 0079-7456
BF636.A1
PSZICHOLOGIA A GYAKORLATBAN. 1963. irreg., vol.58, 1992. price varies. (Magyar Tudomanyos Akademia) Akademiai Kiado, Publishing House of the Hungarian Academy of Sciences, P.O. Box 245, H-1519 Budapest, Hungary. TEL 181-2134. FAX 166-6466. TELEX 22-6228 AKNYO H.

150   HU   ISSN 0079-7464
PSZICHOLOGIAI TANULMANYOK. (Text in Hungarian; summaries in English and German) 1958. irreg., vol.16, 1986. price varies. (Magyar Tudomanyos Akademia) Akademiai Kiado, Publishing House of the Hungarian Academy of Sciences, P.O. Box 245, H-1519 Budapest, Hungary. TEL 181-2134. FAX 166-6466. TELEX 22-6228 AKNYO H. **Indexed:** Psychol.Abstr.

150   US
PUBLICATIONS FOR THE ADVANCEMENT OF THEORY AND HISTORY IN PSYCHOLOGY. 1980. irreg. price varies. Ablex Publishing Corporation, 355 Chestnut St., Norwood, NJ 07648. TEL 201-767-8450. FAX 201-767-6717. TELEX 135-393. Ed. David Bakan. **Document type:** academic/scholarly publication.

PUDDING MAGAZINE; international journal of applied poetry. see *LITERATURE — Poetry*

PULSE OF THE PLANET. see *ENVIRONMENTAL STUDIES*

616.89   IT   ISSN 0390-0320
QUADRANGOLO. 1974. q. L.45000. (Centro Studi Psicologici "Lo Spazio") Bulzoni Editore, Via dei Liburni 14, 00185 Rome, Italy. (Co-sponsor: Societa Italiana di Psicoterapia di Gruppo) Ed. Emiliana Mazzonis.

150   US   ISSN 0033-5010
BF173.A2
QUADRANT; the journal of contemporary Jungian thought. 1967. s-a. $32 to individuals; institutions $55 (effective 1996). (C.G. Jung Foundation for Analytical Psychology, Inc.) Ablex, 28 E. 39th St., New York, NY 10016. TEL 212-697-6430. FAX 201-953-3989. TELEX 135-393. Ed. Stefanie Woodbridge. adv. contact: Arnold Devera. bk.rev.; charts; illus.; circ. 2,000 (controlled). (reprint service avail.) **Indexed:** M.L.A., Psychoanal.Abstr., Psychol.Abstr. (1985-). **Document type:** academic/scholarly publication.

QUALITY OF LIFE NEWS LETTER. see *MEDICAL SCIENCES*

152   UK   ISSN 0272-4987
QP351   CODEN: QJEADQ
QUARTERLY JOURNAL OF EXPERIMENTAL PSYCHOLOGY. SECTION A: HUMAN EXPERIMENTAL PSYCHOLOGY. 1948. q. £35($66) to individuals (outside the E.U. £38); institutions £146 (outside the E.U. £152 ($279)) (effective 1996). (Experimental Psychology Society) Lawrence Erlbaum Associates, Ltd., 27 Palmeira Mansions, Church Rd., Hove, E. Sussex BN3 2FA, England. TEL 01273-207411. FAX 01273-205612. (Subscr. to: Turpin Distribution Services Ltd., Blackhorse Rd., Letchworth, Herts. SG6 1HN, England. TEL 01462-672555. FAX 01462-480947) Ed. Stephen Marsell. adv.: page £220; 110 x 190. bk.rev.; bibl.; charts; index. circ. 1,600. **Indexed:** ASSIA, Biol.Abstr., Br.Educ.Ind., Curr.Adv.Cell & Devel.Biol., Curr.Cont., Dent.Ind., Ind.Med., Mid.East: Abstr.& Ind., Psychol.Abstr. (1981-), SSCI. **Document type:** academic/scholarly publication.
—BLDSC (7190.100000); Faxon; SWETS; UnCover.
    Supersedes in part (in 1981): Quarterly Journal of Experimental Psychology (ISSN 0033-555X)
    Description: Presents original papers in all branches of human experimental psychology without limitation.
Refereed Serial

152   UK   ISSN 0272-4995
QP351   CODEN: QJEBDT
QUARTERLY JOURNAL OF EXPERIMENTAL PSYCHOLOGY. SECTION B: COMPARATIVE AND PHYSIOLOGICAL PSYCHOLOGY. (Text in English; abstracts in French, Spanish) 1981. q. £22($46) to individuals (outside the E.U. £25); institutions £76 (outside the E.U. £81 ($149)) (effective 1996). (Experimental Psychology Society) Lawrence Erlbaum Associates, Ltd., 27 Palmeira Mansions, Church Rd., Hove, E. Sussex BN3 2FA, England. TEL 01273-207411. FAX 01273-205612. (Subscr. to: Turpin Distribution Srevices Ltd., Blackhorse Rd., Letchworth, Herts., SG6 1HN, England. TEL 01462-672555. FAX 01462-480947) Ed. Geoffrey Hall. bk.rev.; index. **Indexed:** ASSIA, Biol.Abstr., Curr.Adv.Cell & Devel.Biol., Dent.Ind., Ind.Med., Psychol.Abstr (1981-), SSCI. **Document type:** academic/scholarly publication.
—BLDSC (7190.200000); Faxon; SWETS.
    Supersedes in part (in 1981): Quarterly Journal of Experimental Psychology (ISSN 0033-555X)
    Description: Features articles on any topic within the field of animal psychology, not only on such traditional topics as conditioning, learning and motivation, but also on any aspect of animal behavior, comparative psychology, and ethology.
Refereed Serial

QUARTERLY REVIEW OF FILM AND VIDEO. see *MOTION PICTURES*

301.1 150   IT
RASSEGNA DI PSICOLOGIA. 1984, N.S. 3/yr. L.45000 (foreign L.70000) (effective 1993). (Universita di Roma La Sapienza, Dipartimenti di Psicologia e Psicologia dei Processi di Sviluppo e Socializzazione) Franco Angeli Editore, Via Monza 106, 20127 Milan, Italy. TEL 02-2827651. Eds. C. Pontecorvo Pipermo, P. Bonaiuto.

READING AND WRITING; an interdisciplinary journal. see *LINGUISTICS*

READING PSYCHOLOGY; an international quarterly. see *EDUCATION — Teaching Methods And Curriculum*

READINGS; a journal of reviews and commentary in mental health. see *MEDICAL SCIENCES — Psychiatry And Neurology*

REALITY CHANGE; a global Seth journal. see *NEW AGE PUBLICATIONS*

614.58 616.8 340   GW   ISSN 0724-2247
RECHT & PSYCHIATRIE. 1983. q. DM.60 (foreign DM.73). Psychiatrie Verlag GmbH, Thomas-Mann-Str. 49a, 53111 Bonn, Germany. TEL 0228-695540. FAX 0228-695595. Ed. Ingeborg Rakete. circ. 900. (back issues avail.) **Indexed:** Psychol.Abstr. (1987-). **Document type:** academic/scholarly publication.
    Description: Examines law and psychiatry.

155.4   US
HV741
RECLAIMING CHILDREN AND YOUTH; the journal of emotional and behavioral problems. 1992. q. $70. National Educational Service, 1610 W. 3rd St., P.O. Box 8, Bloomington, IN 47402. TEL 812-336-7700. FAX 812-336-7790. Ed. Nicholas Long. adv. contact: Nancy R. Shin. circ. 3,500 (paid). **Document type:** academic/scholarly publication.
    Formerly (until 1995): Journal of Emotional and Behavioral Problems (ISSN 1064-7023)
    Description: Interdisciplinary journal networking practitioners and policy leaders from diverse backgrounds who serve children and youth in conflict with self, family, school and community. Articles blend research with practical wisdom and a holistic perspective.
Refereed Serial

RECOVERY TODAY; the newsmagazine for today's recovering community. see *DRUG ABUSE AND ALCOHOLISM*

REFLECTIONS: NARATIVES OF PROFESSIONAL HELPING. see *SOCIAL SERVICES AND WELFARE*

616.89 371.9   US   ISSN 0090-5550
RM930.A1
REHABILITATION PSYCHOLOGY. 1954. q. $39 to individuals (foreign $44); institutions $74 (foreign $85) (effective 1996). (American Psychological Association, Division of Rehabilitation Psychology) Springer Publishing Company, 536 Broadway, New York, NY 10012-3955. TEL 212-431-4370. FAX 212-941-7842. Ed. Myron Eisenberg. adv.; bk.rev.; film rev.; charts. circ. 1,500. (back issues avail.) **Indexed:** Behav.Med.Abstr., Curr.Cont., Excerp.Med., IMFL, Multi.Scler.Abstr., Psychol.Abstr. (1972-), Rehabil.Lit., SSCI, Yrbk.Assoc.Educ.& Rehab.Blind. **Document type:** academic/scholarly publication.
—BLDSC (7350.290000); EMDOCS; Faxon; Genuine Article; UnCover.
    Description: Takes an interdisciplinary approach in addressing psychosocial and behavioral aspects of rehabilitation; covers topics that relate to the experience of chronic illness and disability throughout the lifespan.
Refereed Serial

150 301   UY   ISSN 0797-9754
BF5
RELACIONES. 1984. m. $38. Editorial Periodica S.R.L., Avda. Luis A. de Herrera, 1042, Ap. 708, 11300 Montevideo, Uruguay. TEL 02-62-11-08. FAX 47-34-19. Ed. Saul Paciuk. adv.; bk.rev. circ. 4,000. **Document type:** academic/scholarly publication.

616.89   GW   ISSN 0344-9602
REPORT PSYCHOLOGIE. 1974. 10/yr. DM.105 (foreign DM.120). Deutscher Psychologen Verlag GmbH, Heilsbachstr. 22, 53123 Bonn, Germany. TEL 0228-98731-0. FAX 0228-9873170. Ed. Petra Walkenbach. adv. contact: Petra Walkenbach. bk.rev. circ. 22,000. **Document type:** academic/scholarly publication.

155.3   US
REPRESENTATIONS BOOKS SERIES. 1987. irreg., no.6, 1992. price varies. University of California Press, 2120 Berkeley Way, Berkeley, CA 94720. TEL 510-642-7127. FAX 510-643-7127. (Orders to: California-Princeton Fulfillment Services, 1445 Lower Ferry Rd., Ewing, NJ 08618. TEL 800-777-4726. FAX 800-999-1958) (back issues avail.) **Document type:** monographic series.
    Description: Examines sexuality throughout Western history.

PSYCHOLOGY

301.1 150   US   ISSN 0034-4907
HM251   CODEN: RRSPD4
REPRESENTATIVE RESEARCH IN SOCIAL PSYCHOLOGY.
1970. a. $7 to individuals; institutions $20.
University of North Carolina at Chapel Hill,
Department of Psychology, Social Psychology
Graduate Students, Davie Hall, Campus Box 3270,
Chapel Hill, NC 27599-3270. TEL 919-962-7636.
FAX 919-962-2537. Ed. Anna A. Romero. adv.
contact: Anna A. Romero. bk.rev. circ. 300. (also
avail. in microform from PMC) **Indexed:**
Adol.Ment.Hlth.Abstr., Curr.Cont., Psychol.Abstr.,
SSCI. **Document type:** academic/scholarly publication.
—BLDSC (7692.000000); SWETS; UnCover.

**RESEARCH AND TEACHING IN DEVELOPMENTAL
EDUCATION.** see *EDUCATION*

150 616.8 362.7   US   ISSN 0362-2428
BF1   CODEN: RCPBD
**RESEARCH COMMUNICATIONS IN PSYCHOLOGY,
PSYCHIATRY AND BEHAVIOR.** 1976. q. $90 (foreign
$100). P J D Publications Ltd., Box 966, Westbury,
NY 11590. TEL 516-626-0650.
FAX 516-626-5546. Ed.Bd. adv.; bk.rev.; abstr.;
charts; illus.; index. (reprint service avail. from ISI)
Indexed: Biol.Abstr., Chem.Abstr., Curr.Adv.Ecol.Sci.,
Curr.Cont., Curr.Lit.Fam.Plan., Excerp.Med.,
Psychol.Abstr. (1976-).
—BLDSC (7736.550000); CASDDS; Faxon;
UnCover. **CCC.**
   Description: Information of value to experimental
psychologists, psychiatrists, behavioral scientists,
psychopharmacologists and basic and clinical
scientists.
   Refereed Serial

RESEARCH IN COMMUNITY AND MENTAL HEALTH; an
annual compilation of research. see *PUBLIC HEALTH
AND SAFETY*

301.18   US   ISSN 0191-3085
HD28
RESEARCH IN ORGANIZATIONAL BEHAVIOR; an annual
series of analytical essays and critical reviews.
1979. a. $63.50 to institutions. J A I Press Inc., 55
Old Post Rd., No. 2, Box 1678, Greenwich, CT
06836-1678. TEL 203-661-7602. Eds. Barry M.
Staw, L.L. Cummings. **Indexed:** ASCA, Int.Lab.Doc.,
Int.Polit.Sci.Abstr., Psychol.Abstr., SSCI.
—BLDSC (7750.600000); Faxon; SWETS; UnCover.
CCC.

RESEARCH ON SOCIAL WORK PRACTICE. see
SOCIOLOGY

**RESEARCH SYMPOSIUM ON THE PSYCHOLOGY AND
ACOUSTICS OF MUSIC. PROCEEDINGS.** see *MUSIC*

150.19 100   US   ISSN 1059-3551
THE RESHAPING OF PSYCHOANALYSIS; from Sigmund
Freud to Ernest Becker. irreg. Peter Lang Publishing,
Inc., 62 W. 45th St., 4th Fl., New York, NY 10036.
TEL 212-302-6740. FAX 212-302-7574. Ed. Barry
R. Arnold. **Document type:** academic/scholarly
publication, monographic series.
   Description: Elucidates the contributions of Ernest
Becker to the fields of psychoanalysis, religion, and
philosophy.

150.19   US   ISSN 0361-1531
RC321   CODEN: REXPB4
**REVIEW OF EXISTENTIAL PSYCHOLOGY AND
PSYCHIATRY.** 1961. 3/yr. $35 to individuals;
institutions $60. Humanities Press, 165 First Ave.,
Atlantic Highlands, NJ 07716-1289.
TEL 908-872-1441. FAX 908-872-0717. Ed. Keith
Hoeller. adv.; bk.rev. circ. 800. **Indexed:** Curr.Cont.,
Phil.Ind., Psychol.Abstr. **Document type:**
academic/scholarly publication.
—BLDSC (7790.550000); SWETS; UnCover.
   Formerly: Human Inquiries (ISSN 0034-656X)
   Description: Original essays and translations from
the fields of literature and philosophy as well as
psychology and psychiatry, presenting an existential
and phenomenological approach to the
understanding of human experience.
   Refereed Serial

150   CI   ISSN 0352-1605
BF8.S4   CODEN: RPSHDY
REVIJA ZA PSIHOLOGIJU. 1971. s-a. $15 (typically set
in Mar.). Drustvo Psihologa S R Hrvatske - Croatian
Psychological Association, Salajeva 3, Zagreb,
Croatia. TEL 041-613-155. FAX 041-513-834. Ed.
Vladimir Kolesaric. adv.; bk.rev. circ. 1,000. **Indexed:**
Psychol.Abstr.
   Description: Publishes original scientific papers,
theoretical contributions and critical surveys of
research in all fields of psychology and related
disciplines as well as relevant professional papers
and news.

370.15 150   AG
REVISTA ARGENTINA DE PSICOPEDAGOGIA. (Text in
Spanish; abstracts in English) 1981. q. $30.
Fundacion Suzuki, Charlone 1689, 1663 San Miguel
BA, Argentina. TEL 54-1-664-0771.
FAX 54-1-667-1476. Dir. Elizabeth J. Calvo de
Suzuki. adv.; bk.rev.; abstr.; bibl. circ. 500. **Document
type:** academic/scholarly publication.
   Supersedes (1975-1981): Revista de
Psicopedagogia.

150   CK   ISSN 0121-5469
BF5
REVISTA COLOMBIANA DE PSICOLOGIA. (Text in
Spanish; summaries in English, French, Spanish)
1956. irreg. exchange basis. Universidad Nacional
de Colombia, Departamento de Psicologia, Apdo.
Aereo 14490, Bogota D.C., Colombia.
TEL 571-269-6434. FAX 571-222-5285. Ed. Luis
Bernardo Lopez Caicedo. adv.; bk.rev.; abstr.; bibl.;
illus. circ. 1,000. **Document type:** academic/scholarly
publication.
   Formerly: Revista de Psicologia (ISSN
0120-2901)

301.1 150   CU   ISSN 0257-4322
REVISTA CUBANA DE PSICOLOGIA. (Text in Spanish;
summaries in English, Spanish) 3/yr. $17 in N.
America; S. America $18; Europe $22. Universidade
de La Habana, Calle I No. 302, Entre 15 y 17,
Havana 4, Cuba. TEL 32-5556-60. (Dist. by:
Ediciones Cubanas, Obispo No. 527, Apdo. 605,
Havana, Cuba)

616.89   BL   ISSN 0102-4205
REVISTA DE PSICANALISE INTEGRAL. 1978. a. $4.
(Sociedad Internacional de Trilogia Analitica -
International Society of Analytical Trilogy) Proton
Editora Ltda., Av. Reboucas 3115, C.E.P. 05401,
Sao Paolo, SP, Brazil. Ed. Marc Andre R. Keppe. adv.
circ. 1,500.
   Formerly: Analytical Trilogy.

616.89   AG   ISSN 0034-8740
RC321
REVISTA DE PSICOANALISIS. (Text in Spanish;
summaries in English and French) 1943. 6/yr. $80.
Asociacion Psicoanalitica Argentina, Rodriguez Pena
1674, Buenos Aires, Argentina. bk.rev.; abstr.; index.
circ. 2,000. (processed) **Indexed:** Excerp.Med.,
Psychoanal.Abstr., Psychol.Abstr. (1934-).
—BLDSC (7870.130000).

150   PE   ISSN 0254-9247
REVISTA DE PSICOLOGIA. 1983. s-a. $24. Pontificia
Universidad Catolica del Peru, Departamento de
Humanidades, Fondo Editorial, Apdo. 1761, Lima
100, Peru. Ed. Cecilia Thorne. adv. circ. 1,000.

157   BL   ISSN 0048-7740
REVISTA DE PSICOLOGIA NORMAL E PATOLOGICA.
1976-1979; N.S 1979. irreg. Pontificia
Universidade Catolica de Sao Paulo, Faculdade de
Psicologia, Rua Monte Alegre 984, Sao Paulo, Brazil.

150   SP   ISSN 0213-4748
REVISTA DE PSICOLOGIA SOCIAL. 1986. s-a.
Aprendizaje, S.L., Ctra. de Canillas 138, 16 C,
28043 Madrid, Spain. TEL 388-38-74.
FAX 300-35-27. Ed.Bd. adv. circ. 1,100. **Indexed:**
Psychol.Abstr. (1988-).
—SWETS.
   Description: Publishes articles on empirical and
theoretical research concerning ths study of behavior
from a theoretical perspective.
   Refereed Serial

150   RM   ISSN 0034-8759
BF8.R7
REVISTA DE PSIHOLOGIE. 1955. 4/yr. 100 lei($45)
(Academia Romana) Editura Academiei Romane,
Calea Victoriei 125, 79717 Bucharest, Rumania.
(Dist. by: Rompresfilatelia, Export-Import Presa,
Calea Grivitei 64-66, P.O. Box 12-201, 78104
Bucharest, Rumania) Ed. Constantin Voicu. bk.rev.;
index. circ. 1,400. **Indexed:** Biol.Abstr., C.I.S. Abstr.,
Child Devel.Abstr., Ergon.Abstr., Lang.&
Lang.Behav.Abstr., Nutr.Abstr., Psychol.Abstr.
(1961-).

150   CK   ISSN 0120-0534
BF5   CODEN: RLPSBM
REVISTA LATINOAMERICANA DE PSICOLOGIA. 1969.
3/yr. $25 to individuals; institutions $35.
Foundation for the Advancement of Psychology,
Apdo. 92621, Bogota, Colombia. Ed. Ruben Ardila.
adv.; bk.rev.; abstr.; bibl.; illus.; index. circ.
2,500. **Indexed:** Biol.Abstr., Curr.Cont.,
Psychol.Abstr. (1969-), SSCI. **Document type:**
academic/scholarly publication.
—SWETS. **CCC.**
   Description: International journal of all areas of
psychology.

150   MX   ISSN 0185-4534
**REVISTA MEXICANA DE ANALISIS DE LA
CONDUCTA/MEXICAN JOURNAL OF BEHAVIOR
ANALYSIS.** (Text in English and Spanish) 1975.
3/yr. $20 to individuals (Europe $25); institutions
$35 (Europe $40). (Mexican Society of Behavior
Analysis) Editorial Trillas, Apdo. Postal 21-182,
04000 Mexico, D.F., Mexico. TEL 5 547632. Ed.
Florente Lopez. adv. contact: Florente Lopez. bk.rev.;
bibl.; charts; illus.; stat.; index. circ. 1,000. (back
issues avail.) **Indexed:** Adol.Ment.Hlth.Abstr.,
Curr.Cont., Psychol.Abstr.
   Description: Presents original research in behavior
analysis and technical notes on diverse subjects of
interest to behavioral scientists.

150.19   PO
REVISTA PORTUGUESA DE PSICANALISE. 1985. irreg.,
no.13, 1994. Esc.2000 (Europe Esc.4500;
elsewhere Esc.5500). (Sociedade Portuguesa de
Psicanalise) Edicoes Afrontamento, Lda., Rua de
Costa Cabral, 859, Apdo. 2009, 4201 Porto Codex,
Portugal. TEL 351-2-529271. FAX 351-2-591777.
Eds. Carlos Amaral Dias, Jaime Milheiro.

150   UY   ISSN 0797-4876
REVISTA URUGUAYA DE PSICOLOGIA. 1978. s-a. $10
(or exchange basis). (Asociacion de Psicologos
Universitarios del Uruguay) Editorial Imago S.R.L.,
Gregorio Suarez 2719, Montevideo, Uruguay. Ed.
Ricardo Landeira. bk.rev. **Indexed:** Psychol.Abstr.
(1977-).

301.1   CN   ISSN 0080-2492
REVUE CANADIENNE DE PSYCHO-EDUCATION. (Text in
French; summaries in English and French) 1964.
biennial. Can.$25 to individuals; institutions
Can.$35. Universite de Montreal, Ecole de
Psycho-Education, 750 bd. Gouin est., Montreal, PQ
H2C 1A6, Canada. TEL 514-385-2510.
FAX 514-385-9825. Ed. Serge Larivee. bk.rev. circ.
600. **Indexed:** Canadiana, Psychol.Abstr. (1982-),
Pt.de Rep. (1983-), RADAR.
—BLDSC (7896.219000).

REVUE DE NEUROPSYCHOLOGIE. see *MEDICAL
SCIENCES — Psychiatry And Neurology*

158   FR   ISSN 1162-9088
BF636.A1
**REVUE EUROPEENE DE PSYCHOLOGIE
APPLIQUEE/EUROPEAN REVIEW OF APPLIED
PSYCHOLOGY.** 1951. q. 350 F. Editions du Centre
de Psychologie Appliquee, 48 av. Victor Hugo,
75783 Paris Cedex 16, France. TEL 45-01-83-26.
FAX 45-01-20-46. Eds. Robert Lepez, Claire Mays.
adv.; bk.rev.; bibl.; charts; illus.; index. circ. 1,000.
Indexed: Child Devel.Abstr., Excerp.Med., INSPEC,
Psychol.Abstr. (1950-), SSCI. **Document type:**
academic/scholarly publication.
—BLDSC (3829.942000); Faxon.
   Formerly (until 1991): Revue de Psychologie
Appliquee (ISSN 0035-1709)

PSYCHOLOGY

616.89   FR   ISSN 0035-2942
BF173.A2
REVUE FRANCAISE DE PSYCHANALYSE. (Includes special number: Congres des Psychanalyse des Langues Romanes. Rapports) 1927. q. 690 F. (foreign 830 F.) (effective 1996). (Societe Psychanalytique de Paris) Presses Universitaires de France, Departement des Revues, 14 av. du Bois-de-l'Epine, B.P. 90, 91003 Evry Cedex, France.
TEL 1-60-77-82-05. FAX 1-60-79-20-45. TELEX PUF 600 474 F. Ed.Bd. adv.; abstr.; bibl.; charts; index. (reprint service avail. from KTO) **Indexed:** Excerp.Med., Ind.Med., Psychoanal.Abstr., Psychol.Abstr. (1928-), SSCI.
—BLDSC (7904.280000); Faxon; Genuine Article; SWETS. **CCC.**
    Description: Covers all aspects of psychoanalysis.

301.1 150   FR   ISSN 0992-986X
                            CODEN: RIPSE4
REVUE INTERNATIONAL DE PSYCHOLOGIE SOCIALE/INTERNATIONAL REVIEW OF SOCIAL PSYCHOLOGY. (Text in English, French) s-a. 250 F. to individuals (foreign 300 F.); institutions 380 F. Presses Universitaires de Grenoble, B.P. 47, 38040 Grenoble, France. TEL 76-82-56-51. FAX 76-82-56-54. **Indexed:** Psychol.Abstr.
—BLDSC (7925.260000).

REVUE INTERNATIONALE DE PSYCHOPATHOLOGIE. see MEDICAL SCIENCES — Psychiatry And Neurology

REVUE INTERNATIONALE DE PSYCHOSOCIOLOGIE. see SOCIOLOGY

301.1 150   RM   ISSN 1220-5419
BF1
REVUE ROUMAINE DE PSYCHOLOGIE. (Text in English, French, German, Russian or Spanish) 1964. s-a. 80 lei to individuals; institutions 160 lei (effective 1992). (Academia Romana) Editura Academiei Romane, Calea Victoriei 125, 79717 Bucharest, Rumania. (Dist. by: Rompresfilatelia, Export-Import Presa, Calea Grivitei 64-66, P.O. Box 12-201, 78104 Bucharest, Rumania) bk.rev.; charts. circ. 750. **Indexed:** Child Devel.Abstr., Ergon.Abstr., Psychol.Abstr. (1964-).
    Formerly (until 1990): Revue Roumaine des Sciences Sociales. Serie de Psychologie (ISSN 0035-3892)

REVUE ZAIROISE DE PSYCHOLOGIE ET DE PEDAGOGIE. see EDUCATION

616.89   IT   ISSN 0391-996X
RICERCHE DI PSICOLOGIA. (Text in Italian; summaries in English and Italian) 1968. q. L.95000 (foreign L.130000) (effective 1993). (Universita degli Studi di Milano, Istituto di Psicologia) Franco Angeli Editore, Viale Monza 106, 20127 Milan, Italy. TEL 02-28-27-651. Ed. Marcello Cesa-Bianchi. adv.; bk.rev. **Indexed:** Anim.Behav.Abstr., Psychol.Abstr. (1979-).
    Formerly (until 1972): Annali di Psicologia.

158   IT
RISORSA UOMO. 1993. 3/yr. L.48000 (foreign L.70000) (effective 1993). Franco Angeli Editore, Viale Monza 106, 20127 Milan, Italy. TEL 02-28-27-651. Ed. V. Majer.

616.89   SZ   ISSN 1019-1976
RISS;* Zeitschrift fuer Psychoanalyse. 1986. 3/yr. 30 SFr. Minervastr. 13, CH-8032 Zurich, Switzerland. Ed.Bd. circ. 300.

616.89   IT   ISSN 0035-6492
RIVISTA DI PSICOANALISI/ITALIAN PSYCHOANALYTICAL SOCIETY. JOURNAL.* (Editions in English, Italian) 1955. q. L.70000($114) to individuals; institutions and libraries L.90000. Societa Psicoanalitica Italiana, Via Panama 48, 00198 Rome, Italy. Ed. Antonio Valdina. bk.rev.; bibl.; charts; index. circ. 1,500. (reprint service avail. from ISI) **Indexed:** Psychol.Abstr.
    Description: Covers research and study in the field of psychoanalysis.

150.19   IT   ISSN 0392-9787
RIVISTA DI PSICOLOGIA ANALITICA. 1970. s-a. L.50000. Casa Editirice Astrolabio, Via Gallonio 8, 00 161 Rome, Italy. TEL 4270177. FAX 06-429590. Ed. A. Carotenuto. bk.rev. circ. 1,500. **Document type:** academic/scholarly publication.
    Description: Covers research and study in the field of analytical psychology.

RIVISTA DI PSICOLOGIA DELL'ARTE. see ART

152   US   ISSN 1056-6511
ROCHESTER SYMPOSIUM ON DEVELOPMENTAL PSYCHOPATHOLOGY. 1989. a. University of Rochester Press, c/o Robert Easton, Man. Ed., Rochester, NY 14604. TEL 716-275-0419. FAX 716-271-8778. **Document type:** proceedings.
—BLDSC (8001.320000).

RON WARMOTH LETTER. see NEW AGE PUBLICATIONS

150   II   ISSN 0971-3492
S A M I K S A. (Text in English) 1947. a. $15. Indian Psychoanalytical Society, 14 Parsibagan Lane, Calcutta 700 009, India. TEL 35-8788. (Affiliate: International Psychoanalytical Association) Ed. S. Banerji. adv.; bk.rev. circ. 300. (back issues avail.) **Indexed:** Excerp.Med., Psychol.Abstr. **Document type:** academic/scholarly publication.
    Description: Presents scientific discussion of various aspects of psychoanalysis and related subjects.

616.89 362.1   US
S C I PSYCHOSOCIAL PROCESS. (Spinal Cord Injury) q. American Association of Spinal Cord Injury Psychologists and Social Workers, 75-20 Astoria Blvd., Jackson Heights, NY 11370-1177. Ed. Jason Mask. charts; illus.
    Description: For psychologists and social workers caring for spinal cord injured persons.

155.937 618   US
S H A R E NEWSLETTER. 1978. bi-m. $15 (donation) (effective May 1995). S H A R E Pregnancy & Infant Loss Support National Office, St. Joseph Health Center, 300 First Capital Dr., 63301, MO 63301. TEL 314-947-6164. Ed. Catherine A. Lammert. bk.rev.; film rev.; bibl. circ. 4,500. (looseleaf format) **Document type:** newsletter.
    Description: Provides guidance in bereavement following the death of a baby through miscarriage, stillbirth or newborn death. Includes writing from parents and information on support groups.

155.3   CN   ISSN 0834-0455
S I E C C A N NEWSLETTER. 1965. irreg. (2-3/yr.). Can.$35 to individuals; institutions Can.$50; students Can.$20. Sex Information and Education Council of Canada, 850 Coxwell Ave., East York, ON M4C 5R1, Canada. TEL 416-446-5304. FAX 416-778-0785. Ed. F. Michael Barrett. bk.rev.; film rev. circ. 1,000. **Document type:** newsletter.
    Formerly: S I E C C A N Newsletter Toronto (ISSN 0381-873X)
    Description: Features practical teaching and counselling ideas, articles, media reports and reviews.

SAGE FAMILY STUDIES ABSTRACTS. see SOCIOLOGY — Abstracting, Bibliographies, Statistics

155   US
SAGE SERIES ON INDIVIDUAL DIFFERENCES AND DEVELOPMENT. irreg., no.6, 1994. price varies. Sage Publications, Inc., 2455 Teller Rd., Thousand Oaks, CA 91320. TEL 805-499-0721. FAX 805-499-0871. E-mail: libraries@sagepub.com. (Overseas subscr. to: Sage Publications Ltd., 6 Bonhill St., London EC2A 4PU, England; Sage Publications India Pvt. Ltd., P.O. Box 4215, New Delhi 110 048, India) Ed. Robert Plomin. (back issues avail.) **Document type:** monographic series.
    Description: Provides a forum for a new wave of research that focuses on individual differences in behavioral development.

152   CN   ISSN 0833-0247
SANS FRONTIERES - LES FORCES PSYCHOLOGIQUES. (Text in French) 1986. s-a. Can.$9.10. Institut de Formation Humaine Integrale de Montreal, 55 Boulevard Gouin W., Montreal, PQ H3L 1H9, Canada. TEL 514-331-6861. FAX 514-331-7303. Ed. Julien Alain. circ. 1,000. (back issues avail.)
    Description: Psychological practices based on theoretical models, and clinical applications.

150   CN   ISSN 0383-6320
                          CODEN: SMQUEK
SANTE MENTALE AU QUEBEC. (Text in French; summaries in English and French) 1976. 2/yr. Can.$22 to individuals; institutions Can.$32; students Can.$19. Revue Sante Mentale au Quebec, C.P. 548, Succ. Place d'Armes, Montreal, PQ H2Y 3H3, Canada. TEL 514-844-5536. FAX 514-844-4194. Ed.Bd. circ. 1,200. **Indexed:** Pt.de Rep. (1982-), Soc.Work Res.& Abstr. **Document type:** academic/scholarly publication.
—BLDSC (8075.341000).
    Description: Publishes articles of experimental research and social innovation. Aims to fulfill the needs in development of scientific, academic and clinical knowledge.
    Refereed Serial

301.1 150   US   ISSN 0740-0853
BF204
SAYBROOK REVIEW. 1978. irreg. $10. Saybrook Institute, Graduate School and Research Center, 450 Pacific, 3rd. Fl., San Francisco, CA 94133. TEL 415-433-9200. FAX 433-433-9271. E-mail: rmelone@igc.apc.org. Ed. Rudy Melone. bk.rev. circ. 600. (back issues avail.) **Indexed:** Psychol.Abstr. **Document type:** academic/scholarly publication.
    Formerly: Humanistic Psychology Review.
    Description: Presents scholarly papers on a single topic in psychology or human science by invited scholars.
    Refereed Serial

150   SW   ISSN 0284-5717
                          CODEN: NTBEDQ
SCANDINAVIAN JOURNAL OF BEHAVIOUR THERAPY/NORDISK TIDSKRIFT FOER BETEENDETERAPI. (Supplement avail.) (Text in English and Scandinavian languages) 1971. q. SEK 150 in Europe; outside Europe $17. Swedish Association for Behaviour Therapy, Stockholm University, Department of Social Work, S-106 91 Stockholm, Sweden. FAX 46-8-16-57-96. Eds. Sten Roennberg, Gerhard Andersson. adv.; bk.rev.; charts; illus. circ. 1,000. (back issues avail.) **Indexed:** Behav.Med.Abstr., Psychol.Abstr. (1975-). **Document type:** academic/scholarly publication.
    Former titles (until vol.3, 1984): Nordisk Tidskrift foer Beteendeterapi; (until 1957): Beteendeterapi.
    Description: Articles on many different interpretations of what is behaviour therapy.

150   NO   ISSN 0036-5564
BF1   CODEN: SJPYA2
SCANDINAVIAN JOURNAL OF PSYCHOLOGY. (Text in English) 1960. q. NOK 825 in the Nordic countries; elsewhere NOK 875 (effective 1996). (Psychological Association of Denmark, Finland, Norway and Sweden) Scandinavian University Press, P.O. Box 2959 Toeyen, N-0608 Oslo, Norway. TEL 47-22-57-54-00. FAX 47-22-57-53-53. (U.S. addr.: Scandinavian University Press, 200 Meacham Ave., Elmont, NY 11003. TEL 516-352-7300) Ed. Kenneth Hugdahl. adv.; bibl.; charts; illus.; index, cum.index every 5 yrs. circ. 1,400. (tabloid format) **Indexed:** Adol.Ment.Hlth.Abstr., ASCA, ASSIA, Behav.Abstr., Biol.Abstr., Child Devel.Abstr., Curr.Cont., Dent.Ind., Ergon.Abstr., IMFL, Ind.Med., Lang.& Lang.Behav.Abstr., Mid.East: Abstr.& Ind., Psychol.Abstr. (1960-), Risk Abstr., Sociol.Abstr., SSCI.
—BLDSC (8087.520000); Faxon; Genuine Article; SWETS; UnCover. **CCC.**
    Description: Devoted to original scientific contributions from all fields of psychology.

SCHIEDSAMTSZEITUNG. see LAW

PSYCHOLOGY

371.42 US ISSN 0036-6536
LB1027.5 CODEN: SCCODV
SCHOOL COUNSELOR. 1953. 5/yr. $57 to individuals; institutions $65 (effective 1996). (American School Counselor Association) American Counseling Association, 5999 Stevenson Ave., Alexandria, VA 22304-3300. TEL 703-823-9800. FAX 703-823-0252. (Subscr. to: Box 2513, Birmingham, AL 35201-2513. TEL 205-995-1567. FAX 205-995-1588) Ed. Stanley Baker. adv.; bk.rev. circ. 17,000. (also avail. in microform from UMI) reprint service avail. from UMI) **Indexed:** C.I.J.E., Cont.Pg.Educ., Educ.Ind., Mult.Ed.Abstr., Psychol.Abstr. (1968-), Sage Fam.Stud.Abstr., Soc.Work Res.& Abstr., Sociol.Educ.Abstr., Sp.Ed.Needs Abstr.
—BLDSC (8092.720000); Faxon; SWETS; UMI; UnCover. **CCC.**
Formerly: Elementary Counselor (ISSN 0013-5941)
Description: Keeps the reader up-to-date with ideas and techniques on how to deal with current issues in elementary and secondary counseling.

370.15 150 US
SCHOOL PRACTITIONER SERIES. irreg. (approx. 3-4/yr.). Guilford Publications, Inc., 72 Spring St., 4th Fl., New York, NY 10012. TEL 212-431-9800; 800-365-7006. FAX 212-966-6708.
Description: Provides focused, readable, and prescriptive accounts of techniques for changing children's behavior.

SCHOOL PSYCHOLOGY INTERNATIONAL. see EDUCATION — Teaching Methods And Curriculum

370.15 US ISSN 1045-3830
LB1027.55 CODEN: SPSQE5
SCHOOL PSYCHOLOGY QUARTERLY. 1960. q. $35 to individuals (foreign $50); institutions $85 (foreign $100) (effective 1995). (American Psychological Association, Division of School Psychology) Guilford Publications, Inc., 72 Spring St., 4th Fl., New York, NY 10012. TEL 212-431-9800. FAX 212-966-6708. Ed. Joseph C. Witt. adv.; index. circ. 2,700. (reprint service avail. from UMI) **Indexed:** Psychol.Abstr. (1986-).
—BLDSC (8092.926500); Faxon; UMI; UnCover. **CCC.**
Formerly: Professional School Psychology (ISSN 0079-5933)
Description: Focuses on the scientific understanding of school psychology; covers new concepts in enhancing life experiences of children, families and schools.
Refereed Serial

370.15 US ISSN 0279-6015
LB1051
SCHOOL PSYCHOLOGY REVIEW.* 1972. 4/yr. $50 to individuals; institutions $80. National Association of School Psychologists, 4340 East West Hwy., Ste. 402, Bethesda, MD 20814-4411. TEL 301-608-0500. FAX 301-608-2514. Ed. Edward S. Shapiro. adv.; bk.rev.; abstr.; bibl.; charts; stat. circ. 18,000. (also avail. in microform from UMI; back issues avail.; reprint service avail. from UMI) **Indexed:** C.I.J.E., Cont.Pg.Educ., Educ.Ind., Psychol.Abstr. (1972-). **Document type:** academic/scholarly publication.
—BLDSC (8092.926600); Faxon; Genuine Article; SWETS; UMI; UnCover.
Formerly (until 1979): School Psychology Digest (ISSN 0160-5569)
Description: Covers research, training, and practice in school psychology.

150 SZ ISSN 0036-7869
SCHWEIZERISCHE ZEITSCHRIFT FUER PSYCHOLOGIE/REVUE SUISSE DE PSYCHOLOGIE/SWISS JOURNAL OF PSYCHOLOGY. (Text in French and German; abstracts in English, German) 1942. 4/yr. 75 SFr. (foreign 85 SFr.). (Societe Suisse de Psychologie) Verlag Hans Huber, Laengassstr. 76, CH-3000 Bern 9, Switzerland. TEL 031-3004500. FAX 031-3004590. Eds. Prof. Dr. Gabriel Mugny, Prof. Dr. R. Groner. bk.rev.; abstr.; bibl.; charts. circ. 1,000. **Indexed:** Biol.Abstr., Ger.J.Psych., Psychol.Abstr. (1973-), Risk Abstr., SSCI. **Document type:** academic/scholarly publication.
—BLDSC (8576.760500); Faxon; Genuine Article; SWETS. **CCC.**

150 CN ISSN 0841-7741
SCIENCE ET COMPORTEMENT; revue internationale et multidisciplinaire. (Text in French; summaries in English, French) 1970-1994; resumed. 3/yr. Can.$60 to individuals (US Can.$75); students Can.$35 (US Can.$45). Association Scientifique pour la Modification du Comportement, 7401 rue Hochelaga, Montreal, PQ H1N 3M5, Canada. TEL 514-253-8200. (Subscr. to: 309 rue Godin, Repentigny, PQ J6A 5Z8, Canada. TEL 514-585-2247) Ed. Michel Roberge. adv. contact: Gilles Trudel. bk.rev. circ. 300. (tabloid format) **Indexed:** Psychol.Abstr. (1979-), Pt.de Rep. (1983-).
—BLDSC (8142.917000).
Formerly: Revue de Modification du Comportement (ISSN 0383-056X)
Description: Covers psychology, special education and rehabilitation and psychiatry.
Refereed Serial

616.8 US ISSN 0164-7393
SCRIPT.* 9/yr. membership. International Transactional Analysis Association, 450 Pacific Ave., Ste. 250, San Francisco, CA 94137-4640. TEL 415-885-5992. FAX 415-885-5998. Ed. Laurie Hamilton. adv. contact: Elizabeth Ott. (tabloid format) **Document type:** newsletter.

SELECTION AND DEVELOPMENT REVIEW. see BUSINESS AND ECONOMICS — Management

301.1 150 UK ISSN 0306-0497
SELF & SOCIETY; European journal of humanistic psychology. 1973. bi-m. £10. (Association for Humanistic Psychology in Britain) Gale Centre Publications, Whitakers Way, Loughton, Essex IG10 1SJ, England. TEL 081-508-9344. FAX 081-508-1240. Ed. David Jones. adv.; bk.rev. circ. 1,200.
—BLDSC (8235.350000).
Description: Discusses human potential and research work in psychology and sociology; promotes a holistic view of life and the importance of the individual.

150 360 US
SELF HELP REPORTER NEWSLETTER. 1977. q. $10. National Self Help Clearinghouse, 25 W. 43rd St., Rm. 620, New York, NY 10036. TEL 212-642-2944. FAX 212-642-1956. Ed. Audrey Gartner. bk.rev. circ. 1,000. **Document type:** newsletter.
Description: Covers trends in the burgeoning self-help movement, describes mutual support group activities, and discusses the theoretical underpinnings of self-help mutual support.

SELF-HELP SOURCEBOOK; finding and forming mutual aid self-help groups. see SOCIAL SERVICES AND WELFARE

616.072 CN ISSN 1198-7340
▼**SEMINARS IN HEADACHE MANAGEMENT.** Announced for publication in 1996. q. $52 to individuals (outside U.S. and Canada $79); institutions $78 (outside U.S. and Canada $105) (effective 1996). Decker Periodicals, P.O. Box 620, LCD 1, Hamilton, ON L8N 3K7, Canada. TEL 908-522-7017; 800-568-7281. FAX 905-522-7839. E-mail: decker@io.org. (U.S. addr.: Box 785, Lewiston, NY 14092-0785) **Document type:** academic/scholarly publication.

150.18 US ISSN 0894-4520
QP431
SENSORY SYSTEMS. English translation of: Sensornye Sistemy (RU ISSN 0235-0092) 1987. q. $625 (foreign $730) (effective 1996). (Russian Academy of Sciences, RU) Plenum Publishing Corp., Consultants Bureau, 233 Spring St., New York, NY 10013-1578. TEL 212-620-8468. FAX 212-463-0742. TELEX 23-421139. Ed. M.A. Ostrovskii. bibl.; illus.; index. (also avail. in microfilm from JSC; back issues avail.) **Indexed:** Psychol.Abstr. (1987-). **Document type:** academic/scholarly publication.
—BLDSC (0420.807000); UMI. **CCC.**
Refereed Serial

155.937 US ISSN 0275-3510
SERIES IN DEATH EDUCATION, AGING, AND HEALTH CARE. Variant title: Death Education Series. 1979. irreg., unnumbered, latest 1991. price varies. Taylor & Francis Inc., 1900 Frost Rd., Ste. 101, Bristol, PA 19007-1598. TEL 215-785-5800; 800-821-8312. FAX 215-785-5515. Ed. Hannelore Wass. bibl.; charts; illus.; index. (back issues avail.; reprint service avail. from UMI) **Document type:** monographic series.
—CCC.
Refereed Serial

300 US ISSN 0740-3593
SEX OVER FORTY; a practical, authoritative newsletter directed to the sexual concerns of the mature adult. 1982. m. $36. D K T International, Inc., Box 1600, Chapel Hill, NC 27515. Eds. Drs. Douglas Whitehead, Shirley Zussman. bk.rev. circ. 55,000. **Document type:** newsletter.

155.3 301 US ISSN 0360-0025
HQ768 CODEN: SROLDH
SEX ROLES; a journal of research. 1975. 24/yr. $555 (foreign $650) (effective 1996). Plenum Publishing Corp., 233 Spring St., New York, NY 10013-1578. TEL 212-620-8000. FAX 212-463-0742. TELEX 23-421139. Ed. Sue Rosenberg Zalk. adv.; bk.rev.; bibl.; charts. (also avail. in microform from JSC; back issues avail.) **Indexed:** Adol.Ment.Hlth.Abstr., Anthropol.Lit., ASCA, ASSIA, C.I.J.E., Child Devel.Abstr., Commun.Abstr., Curr.Cont., Excerp.Med., IMFL, Lang.& Lang.Behav.Abstr., Mid.East: Abstr.& Ind., Mult.Ed.Abstr., Psychol.Abstr. (1978-), Res.High.Educ.Abstr., Risk Abstr., Sage Fam.Stud.Abstr., Soc.Sci.Ind., Soc.Work Res.& Abstr., Sociol.Abstr., Sociol.Educ.Abstr., SOMA, Sp.Ed.Needs Abstr., SSCI, Stud.Wom.Abstr., Wom.Stud.Abstr. (1975-). **Document type:** academic/scholarly publication.
—BLDSC (8254.457000); Faxon; Genuine Article; SWETS; UMI; UnCover. **CCC.**
Refereed Serial

306.705 US ISSN 1079-0632
CODEN: SAJTEY
SEXUAL ABUSE; a journal of research and treatment. 1988. q. $115 (foreign $135) (effective 1996). (Association for the Treatment of Sexual Abusers) Plenum Publishing Corp., 233 Spring St., New York, NY 10013-1578. TEL 212-620-8000. FAX 212-463-0742. TELEX 23-421139. Ed. Barry M. Maletzky. adv.; bk.rev. **Indexed:** Curr.Cont., Psychol.Abstr. (1988-). **Document type:** academic/scholarly publication.
—BLDSC (8254.482000). **CCC.**
Formerly (until vol.7, 1995): Annals of Sex Research (ISSN 0843-4611)
Description: Publishes clinical and theoretical material relating to the field of sexual abuse. Addresses causes, treatment and consequences for both perpetrators and victims.
Refereed Serial

155.3 610 UK ISSN 0267-4653
SEXUAL AND MARITAL THERAPY. 1986. q. £78 to individuals; institutions £198 (effective 1996). (Association of Sexual and Marital Therapists) Carfax Publishing Co., P.O. Box 25, Abingdon, Oxon. OX14 3UE, England. TEL 01235-555335. FAX 01235-553559. (Subscr. in N. America to: Carfax Publishing Co., 875-81 Massachusetts Ave., Cambridge, MA 02139) Eds. P. d'Ardenne, A.J. Riley. adv.; bk.rev.; illus.; stat.; index, cum.index. (also avail. in microfiche; back issues avail.) **Indexed:** ASSIA, Curr.Adv.Ecol.Sci., Mult.Ed.Abstr., Psychol.Abstr. (1986-), Stud.Wom.Abstr. **Document type:** academic/scholarly publication.
—BLDSC (8254.483000); UMI; UnCover. **CCC.**
Refereed Serial

150 US ISSN 0273-2564
HQ18.U5
SEXUALITY. (Subseries of: S I R S Social Issues (ISSN 0740-3127)) 1980. a. price varies; a. supplement $17. Social Issues Resources Series, Box 2348, Boca Raton, FL 33427-2348. TEL 407-994-4704; 800-232-7477. FAX 407-994-4704. (looseleaf format; also avail. in microfiche; back issues avail.)
Description: Reprints articles that deal with all aspects of sexuality.

PSYCHOLOGY

150   JA   ISSN 0386-1058
BF8.J3   CODEN: SHHYDJ
SHINRIGAKU HYORON/JAPANESE PSYCHOLOGICAL REVIEW. (Text in Japanese; some summaries in English or German) 1957. q. 5000 Yen to individuals; institutions 7000 Yen. Kyoto University, Faculty of Letters, Department of Psychology - Kyoto Daigaku Bungakubu Shinrigaku Kyushitsu, 54 Shogoin Kawara-cho, Sakyo-ku, Kyoto 606, Japan. Ed. Toshitsugu Hirano. illus. **Indexed:** Psychol.Abstr. (1969-).
—BLDSC (4661.150000).

150   JA   ISSN 0021-5236
CODEN: SHKEA5
SHINRIGAKU KENKYU/JAPANESE JOURNAL OF PSYCHOLOGY. (Text in Japanese; summaries in English) 1926. bi-m. $180. Japanese Psychological Association, 40-14-902 Hongo 2-chome, Bunkyo-ku, Tokyo 113, Japan. TEL 03-3814-3953. FAX 03-3814-3954. (Dist. by Business Center for Academic Societies Japan, 5-16-9 Honkomagome, Bunkyo-ku, Tokyo 113, Japan. TEL 03-5814-5811) adv.; abstr.; charts; illus.; index. circ. 7,000. **Indexed:** Biol.Abstr., Curr.Cont., Ind.Med., Psychol.Abstr. (1929-), SSCI. **Document type:** academic/scholarly publication.
—BLDSC (4658.300000); Genuine Article; UnCover.

150.19   AU   ISSN 1015-1184
BF173.A2
SIGMUND FREUD HOUSE BULLETIN. (Text in English) 1975. 2/yr. $55. Sigmund Freud Gesellschaft, Berggasse 19, A-1090 Vienna, Austria. TEL 01-3191596. FAX 01-3170279. Ed. Dr. Hans Lobner. bk.rev.; bibl. circ. 1,000. **Indexed:** Psychol.Abstr. **Document type:** bulletin.
Description: Contains papers on research in psychoanalysis, and the history of psychoanalysis including Freud's life and work.

616.89   IS   ISSN 0334-9330
RC321
SIHOT/DIALOGUE; Israel journal of psychotherapy. (Text in Hebrew; summaries in English and Hebrew) 1986. q. $35 (foreign $60). P.O. Box 767, Even Yehuda 40500, Israel. TEL 972-2-340868. FAX 972-9-699275. (Co-sponsor: Israel Psychological Association) Eds. A. Shalev, E. Chen. adv.; bk.rev. circ. 2,500. **Indexed:** Psychol.Abstr. (1991-). **Document type:** academic/scholarly publication.

SINISTRALIAN. see CLUBS

616.89   NO   ISSN 0049-0563
SINNETS HELSE. 1920. 8/yr. NOK 145. Mental Barnehjelp, Arbiens Gt. 1, Oslo 2, Norway. Ed. Kirsten Weidemann Ycharff. adv.; bk.rev.; bibl. circ. 12,000.
—CCC.

160 410   IT   ISSN 1120-9550
SISTEMI INTELLIGENTI; rivista quadrimestrale di scienze cognitive e intelligenza artificiale. 1989. 3/yr. L.120000. Societa Editrice Il Mulino, Strada Maggiore, 37, 40125 Bologna, Italy. TEL 39-51-256011. FAX 39-51-256034. Ed. Domenico Parisi. adv.; index. circ. 1,900. (back issues avail.) **Indexed:** Psychol.Abstr. (1989-).

156   US   ISSN 1046-4964
HM133   CODEN: SGREE3
SMALL GROUP RESEARCH; an international journal of theory, investigation and application. 1970. q. $61 to individuals; institutions $188 (effective Sep. 1995). Sage Publications, Inc., 2455 Teller Rd., Thousand Oaks, CA 91320. TEL 805-499-0721. FAX 805-499-0871. E-mail: libraries@sagepub.com. (Overseas subscr. to: Sage Publications Ltd., 6 Bonhill St., London EC2A 4PU, England; Sage Publications India Pvt. Ltd., P.O. Box 4125, New Delhi 110 048, India) Eds. Charles Garvin, Richard Brian Polley. adv.; bk.rev.; charts; index. circ. 1,300. (also avail. in microform from UMI; back issues avail.; reprint service avail. from UMI) **Indexed:** Abstr.Soc.Work., Adol.Ment.Hlth.Abstr., ASCA, ASSIA, C.I.J.E., Commun.Abstr., Curr.Cont., Educ.Admin.Abstr., Lang.& Lang.Behav.Abstr., Mid.East: Abstr.& Ind., Psychol.Abstr. (1970-), Sage Fam.Stud.Abstr., Sage Pub.Admin.Abstr., Sage Urb.Stud.Abstr., Soc.Work Res.& Abstr., SSCI. **Document type:** academic/scholarly publication.
—BLDSC (8309.995000); Faxon; Genuine Article; SWETS; UMI; UnCover. **CCC.**
Formerly: Small Group Behavior (ISSN 0090-5526); **Incorporates:** International Journal of Small Group Research (ISSN 8756-0275); Comparative Group Studies (ISSN 0010-4108)
Description: Presents research, theoretical advancements, and empirically supported applications with respect to all types of small groups.

340   US   ISSN 0272-765X
K23
SOCIAL ACTION AND THE LAW. 1973. 4/yr. $20 to individuals; institutions $30. c/o Robert Buckhout, Pub., Brooklyn College, Center for Responsive Psychology, Brooklyn, NY 11210. TEL 718-780-5960. Ed. Frank J. Sotolongo. adv.; bk.rev. circ. 1,000. (also avail. in microfiche) **Indexed:** C.L.I., ERIC, L.R.I., Lang.& Lang.Behav.Abstr., Psychol.Abstr., Sociol.Abstr.

301.1 130   NZ   ISSN 0301-2212
HM1   CODEN: SBHPAF
SOCIAL BEHAVIOR AND PERSONALITY; an international journal. 1973. q. $130. Society for Personality Research (Inc.), P.O. Box 1539, Palmerston North, New Zealand. TEL 64-6-355-5736. FAX 64-6-355-5736. E-mail: stewart@journal.manawatu.planet.co.nz. Ed. Robert A.C. Stewart. adv. circ. 1,600. (also avail. in microform from UMI; reprint service avail. from ISI; back issues avail.) **Indexed:** Abstr.Crim.& Pen., ASCA, ASSIA, Biol.Abstr., C.I.J.E., Child Devel.Abstr., Curr.Cont., High.Educ.Abstr., IMFL, Ind.Med., Lang.& Lang.Behav.Abstr., Psychol.Abstr. (1973-), Sociol.Abstr., Sportsearch, SSCI. **Document type:** academic/scholarly publication.
—BLDSC (8318.054500); Faxon; Genuine Article; SWETS; UMI; UnCover. **CCC.**
Incorporates (1984-1991): Psychology and Human Development (ISSN 1011-5021); (1978-1990): Third Force Psychology.
Description: Publishes research and theoretical papers on all aspects of social psychology, developmental psychology and personality.
Refereed Serial

155   US   ISSN 0278-016X
BF311
SOCIAL COGNITION; a journal of social, personality and developmental psychology. 1982. q. $37.50 to individuals (foreign $57.50); institutions $110 (foreign $130) (effective 1995). Guilford Publications, Inc., 72 Spring St., 4th Fl., New York, NY 10012. TEL 212-431-9800. FAX 212-966-6708. Ed. Donal Carlston; Pub. Robert Matloff. adv. contact: Marian Robinson. bk.rev.; index. circ. 760. (back issues avail.; reprint service avail. from UMI) **Indexed:** Biol.Abstr., Curr.Cont., IMFL, Mult.Ed.Abstr., Psychol.Abstr. (1982-), Sociol.Educ.Abstr., Sp.Ed.Needs Abstr. **Document type:** academic/scholarly publication.
—BLDSC (8318.073000); Faxon; Genuine Article; SWETS; UMI; UnCover. **CCC.**
Description: Examines the role of cognitive process in the study of personality, development and social behavior.
Refereed Serial

150 301.1   US
HM251
SOCIAL PSYCHOLOGICAL APPLICATIONS TO SOCIAL ISSUES. irreg., vol.3, 1994. (Society for the Psychological Study of Social Issues) Plenum Publishing Corp., 233 Spring St., New York, NY 10013-1578. TEL 212-620-8000. FAX 212-463-0742. **Indexed:** Psychol.Abstr. **Document type:** monographic series.
Formerly (until 1988): Applied Social Psychology Annual (ISSN 0196-4151)
Refereed Serial

SOCIAL PSYCHOLOGY OF EDUCATION. see EDUCATION

SOCIAL SERVICE JOBS. see OCCUPATIONS AND CAREERS

620   BE   ISSN 0081-0835
SOCIETE D'ERGONOMIE DE LANGUE FRANCAISE. ACTES DU CONGRES. 1963. irreg. (approx. a.). Societe d'Ergonomie de Langue Francaise, c/o D. Notte, Sec.-Gen., 64, rue d'Oprem, 1000 Brussels, Belgium. TEL 32-1-217-7363. FAX 32-2-218-1667. bk.rev. **Document type:** proceedings.

SOCIETY & ANIMALS; social scientific studies of the human experience of other animals. see ANIMAL WELFARE

SOCIETY FOR COMPANION ANIMAL STUDIES. JOURNAL. see ANIMAL WELFARE

616.89   UK
SOCIETY FOR EXISTENTIAL ANALYSIS. JOURNAL. 1989. s-a. £6.95. Society for Existential Analysis, c/o School of Psychotherapy and Counselling, Regent's College, Inner Circle, Regent's Park, London NW1 4NS, England. TEL 0171-487-7406. Eds. Hans W. Cohn, Simon Du Plock. adv.; bk.rev.; circ. 500 (paid). **Document type:** academic/scholarly publication.
Refereed Serial

155.3   US
THE SOCIETY NEWSLETTER. q. $20. Society for the Scientific Study of Sex, Box 208, Mt. Vernon, IA 52314. TEL 319-895-8407. FAX 319-895-6203. Ed. Peter Sandor Gardos. circ. 1,200. **Document type:** newsletter.
Description: Includes announcements and news of the society, as well as news and current information of interest to sex researchers, therapists, educators, and clinicians.

SOMATICS; magazine-journal of the mind body arts and sciences. see PHYSICAL FITNESS AND HYGIENE

SOMATOSENSORY AND MOTOR RESEARCH. see BIOLOGY — Physiology

SOUTH AFRICAN JOURNAL OF MUSIC THERAPY/SUID-AFRIKAANSE TYDSKRIF VIR MUSIEKTERAPIE. see MUSIC

150   SA   ISSN 0081-2463
BF1   CODEN: SAJPDL
SOUTH AFRICAN JOURNAL OF PSYCHOLOGY/SUID-AFRIKAANSE TYDSKRIF VIR SIELKUNDE. (Text and summaries in English) 1970. q. R.100. (Psychological Society of South Africa) Foundation for Education, Science & Technology, P.O. Box 1758, Pretoria 0001, South Africa. TEL 27-12-320-7803. Ed. L.M. Richter. adv. contact: L.M. Richter. bk.rev.; bibl.; charts; illus.; stat. circ. 2,400. **Indexed:** Arts & Hum.Cit.Ind., Biol.Abstr., CINAHL, Ergon.Abstr., Ind.S.A.Per., Mult.Ed.Abstr., Psychol.Abstr. (1970-), Sociol.Educ.Abstr., Sp.Ed.Needs Abstr., Stud.Wom.Abstr. **Document type:** academic/scholarly publication.
—BLDSC (8339.750000); Genuine Article. **CCC.**
Incorporates (in July 1983): Psychologia Africana (ISSN 0079-7332); (in Jan. 1979): South African Psychologist; Which was formerly: Journal of Behavioural Science (ISSN 0075-4145)
Description: Publishes empirical research, theoretical and methodological papers, review articles and short communications in the field of psychology.
Refereed Serial

301.1 616.8 360   GW   ISSN 0171-4538
SOZIALPSYCHIATRISCHE INFORMATIONEN. 1971. q. DM.48 (foreign DM.56). Psychiatrie Verlag GmbH, Thomas-Mann-Str. 49a, 53111 Bonn, Germany. TEL 0228-695540. FAX 0228-695595. Ed. Dr. Haselbeck. adv. circ. 2,000. (back issues avail.) **Document type:** academic/scholarly publication.
Description: A journal for people working in psychiatry: psychiatrists, doctors, social workers and nurses.

SPECIAL SERVICES IN THE SCHOOLS. see
EDUCATION — Special Education And Rehabilitation

150.19 790.1   US   ISSN 0888-4781
GV706.4   CODEN: SPPSEU
THE SPORT PSYCHOLOGIST. Short title: T S P. 1987. q. $36 to individuals (foreign $40); institutions $80 (foreign $84); students $24 (foreign $28). (International Society of Sport Psychology) Human Kinetics Publishers, Inc., Box 5076, Champaign, IL 61825-5076. TEL 217-351-5076. FAX 217-351-2674. Ed. Dr. Robin S. Vealey. adv. contact: Pamela Anderson. bibl.; charts. circ. 1,000. (back issues avail.) **Indexed:** Phys.Ed.Ind., Psychol.Abstr. (1987-), Sociol.Abstr., Sportsearch (1987-). **Document type:** academic/scholarly publication.
—BLDSC (8419.638000); Faxon; Genuine Article; SWETS; UnCover. **CCC.**
Description: Designed for educational and clinical sport psychologists. Focuses on applied research and practical application of results in providing psychological services to coaches and athletes.
Refereed Serial

150   SZ   ISSN 0253-4533
P37
SPRACHE & KOGNITION; Zeitschrift fuer Sprach- und Kognitionspsychologie und ihre Grenzgebiete. (Text in German; summaries in English and German) 1982. q. 102 SFr. to individuals; institutions 151 SFr. Verlag Hans Huber, Laenggassstr. 76, Postfach, CH-3000 Bern 9, Switzerland. TEL 031-3004500. FAX 031-3004590. Ed. Werner Deutsch. adv.; bk.rev.; index. circ. 800. **Indexed:** Ger.J.Psych., Psychol.Abstr. (1982-). **Document type:** academic/scholarly publication.
—BLDSC (8419.869250). **CCC.**

150   US   ISSN 0362-0522
BF173.A2   CODEN: SAATDM
SPRING JOURNAL; a journal of archetype and culture. 1941. s-a. $20. Box 583, Putnam, CT 06260. TEL 203-974-3428. FAX 203-974-3195. Eds. James Hillman, Charles Boer. adv. contact: Jay Livernois. bk.rev. circ. 3,000. (back issues avail.) **Indexed:** PMR, Psychol.Abstr. **Document type:** academic/scholarly publication.
—Faxon; UnCover.
Description: The oldest Jungian journal in the world, contains seminal articles on archetypal psychology that examine culture from an archetypal point of view. Includes research on Jung and critical examinations of his ideas in the light of post-Jungian development.
Refereed Serial

SPRINGER SERIES: FOCUS ON MEN. see *MEN'S HEALTH*

SPRINGER SERIES: FOCUS ON WOMEN. see *WOMEN'S HEALTH*

155   US
SPRINGER SERIES IN COGNITIVE DEVELOPMENT. 1982. irreg. price varies. Springer-Verlag, 175 Fifth Ave., New York, NY 10010. TEL 212-460-1500. FAX 212-473-6282. (Also: Berlin, Heidelberg, Tokyo and Vienna) **Document type:** monographic series.

301.1 150   US
SPRINGER SERIES IN SOCIAL PSYCHOLOGY. irreg. price varies. Springer-Verlag, 175 Fifth Ave., New York, NY 10010. TEL 212-460-1500. FAX 212-473-6272. (Also: Berlin, Heidelberg, Tokyo and Vienna) Ed. R.F. Kidd. **Document type:** monographic series.

158 616.8   US   ISSN 0278-6729
SPRINGER SERIES ON BEHAVIOR THERAPY AND BEHAVIORAL MEDICINE. 1976. irreg., latest 1994. price varies. Springer Publishing Company, 536 Broadway, New York, NY 10012-3955. TEL 212-431-4370. FAX 212-941-7842. Ed. Cyril M. Franks. **Document type:** monographic series.
—BLDSC (8424.751000).
Formerly (until 1980): Springer Series in Behavior Modification (ISSN 0272-9636)
Description: Focuses on the psychological and psychiatric treatment from a behaviorist perspective.

155.937   US   ISSN 0271-1192
SPRINGER SERIES ON DEATH AND SUICIDE. Variant title: Thanatos, the Springer Series on Death and Suicide. 1979. irreg., latest 1995. price varies. Springer Publishing Company, 536 Broadway, New York, NY 10012-3955. TEL 212-431-4370. Ed. Robert Kastenbaum. **Document type:** monographic series.
—BLDSC (8424.758000).
Description: Approaches topics on death and suicide from a psychological perspective.

STATE PLAN FOR DEVELOPMENTAL DISABILITIES. see
SOCIAL SERVICES AND WELFARE

150   SW   ISSN 0345-0139
CODEN: RPUSB7
STOCKHOLMS UNIVERSITET. PSYKOLOGISKA INSTITUTIONEN. REPORT SERIES. (Text in English) 1954. irreg. (approx. 20/yr.) $25. Stockholms Universitet, Psykologiska Institutionen, S-106 91 Stockholm, Sweden. FAX 468-159342. Ed.Bd. index. circ. 500. **Indexed:** Psychol.Abstr.

150   US   ISSN 1053-2161
BF575.S75
STRESS AND EMOTION. (Subseries of: Series in Clinical and Community Psychology) 1975. irreg., vol.14, 1993. price varies. Taylor & Francis, 1900 Frost Rd., Ste. 101, Bristol, PA 19007-1598. TEL 215-785-5800; 800-821-8312. FAX 215-785-5515. Eds. C.D. Spielberger, I.G. Sarason. bibl.; charts; illus.; index. (back issues avail.; reprint service avail. from UMI) **Indexed:** Psychol.Abstr. **Document type:** monographic series.
—BLDSC (8474.128650).
Formerly (until no.14, 1991): Stress and Anxiety (ISSN 0364-1112)
Refereed Serial

362.2   SW   ISSN 0280-2783
STRESSFORSKNINGSRAPPORTER. (Text in English, Swedish) 1967. irreg., vol.231, 1991. SEK 125. Karolinska Institutet, Institutionen foer Klinisk Neurovetenskap, Sektionen foer Stressforskning, P.O. Box 230, S-171 77 Stockholm, Sweden. TEL 46-08-7286400. FAX 46-08-344143. index. (back issues avail.) **Document type:** monographic series.
●Also available online.
—BLDSC (8474.141000).
Description: Interdisciplinary research in stress and work, health services, and psychosocial issues.

150 301   US   ISSN 1070-5511
QA278
▼**STRUCTURAL EQUATION MODELING;** a multidisciplinary journal. 1994. q. $35 to individuals (foreign $60); institutions $120 (foreign $145). Lawrence Erlbaum Associates, Inc., 10 Industrial Dr., Mahwah, NJ 07430-2262. TEL 201-236-9500. FAX 201-236-0072. Ed. Randall E. Schumacker. adv.: page $400; 5 x 8. bk.rev. **Document type:** academic/scholarly publication.
—BLDSC (8477.210000).
Description: Covers all academic disciplines with an interest in structural equation modeling, including psychology, sociology, educational research, political science, economics and management.

370.15 150   IT   ISSN 0393-6163
STUDI DI PSICOLOGIA DELL'EDUCAZIONE. 1982. q. L.45000. Casa Editrice Armando s.r.l., Viale Trastevere u. 236, 00153 Rome, Italy. TEL 06-5817245. FAX 06-5818564. Ed. Renzo Titone. bibl.; charts; illus.; stat. **Indexed:** Psychol.Abstr.

150   XO   ISSN 0039-3320
CODEN: STPSAK
STUDIA PSYCHOLOGICA; journal for basic research in psychological sciences. (Text and summaries in English, French, German, Russian and Slovak) 1958. 5/yr. $20. Slovak Academy of Sciences, Institute of Experimental Psychology, Dubravska cesta 9, 813 64 Bratislava, Slovakia. Ed. Dr. Damian Kovac. bk.rev.; charts; illus.; index. circ. 1,300. **Indexed:** ASCA, Biol.Abstr., Child Devel.Abstr., Curr.Cont., Psychol.Abstr. (1960-), SSCI. **Document type:** academic/scholarly publication.
—BLDSC (8483.202000); Genuine Article.
Description: Publishes original experimental and theoretical studies about results of investigations carried out in Czechoslovakia and abroad in the field of basic psychological research.

STUDIA PSYCHOLOGICA ET PAEDAGOGICA; series altera. see *EDUCATION*

150   PL   ISSN 0081-685X
CODEN: SPSLBL
STUDIA PSYCHOLOGICZNE. (Text in Polish; summaries in English and Russian) 1956. s-a. $24. Polska Akademia Nauk, Komitet Nauk Psychologicznych, Ul. Stawki 5-7, pok. 316, 00-183 Warsaw, Poland. Ed. Janusz Reykowski. **Indexed:** Lang.& Lang.Behav.Abstr., Psychol.Abstr. (1970-).
Description: Works concerning historical and experimental psychology, theoretical and methodological problems, social perception, personal communication.

150 370   RM
STUDIA UNIVERSITATIS "BABES-BOLYAI". PSYCHOLOGIA - PEDAGOGIA. 1990. s-a. exchange basis. Universitatea "Babes-Bolyai", Biblioteca Centrala Universitara, Str. Clinicilor Nr. 2, Cluj-Napoca 3400, Rumania. TEL 36-64-197092. FAX 36-64-179633. Ed. I. Haiduc. **Document type:** academic/scholarly publication.

155.4   GW   ISSN 0255-6715
STUDIEN ZUR KINDERPSYCHOANALYSE. JAHRBUCH. 1981. a. DM.35.10. Oesterreichische Studiengesellschaft fuer Kinderpsychoanalyse, AU, Robert-Bosch-Breite 6, 37079 Goettingen, Germany. TEL 0551-6959-0. FAX 0551-695917. circ. 450. **Document type:** academic/scholarly publication.
Description: Interested in pursuing questions and problems concerning theories and techniques within child psychoanalysis.
Refereed Serial

153.4 121   NE   ISSN 0924-0780
STUDIES IN COGNITIVE SYSTEMS. (Text in English) 1988. irreg., vol.15, 1993. price varies. Kluwer Academic Publishers, Postbus 17, 3300 AA Dordrecht, Netherlands. TEL 31-78-392392. FAX 31-78-392254. TELEX 29245 KAPG NL. (Dist. by: Kluwer Academic Publishers Group, P.O. Box 322, 3300 AH Dordrecht, Netherlands. TEL 31-78-392392. FAX 31-78-546474; N. America dist. addr.: Box 358, Accord Sta., Hingham, MA 02018-0358. TEL 617-871-6600. FAX 617-871-6528) **Document type:** monographic series.

STUDIES IN EDUCATION AND PSYCHOLOGY. see
EDUCATION

STUDIES IN EDUCATIONAL EVALUATION. see
EDUCATION

150 401   NE   ISSN 0924-4662
STUDIES IN LINGUISTICS AND PHILOSOPHY. 1978. irreg., vol.50, 1993. price varies. Kluwer Academic Publishers, 3300 AA Dordrecht, Netherlands. TEL 31-78-392392. FAX 31-78-392254. TELEX 29245 KAPG NL. (Dist. by: Kluwer Academic Publishers Group, P.O. Box 322, 3300 AH Dordrecht, Netherlands. TEL 31-78-392392. FAX 31-78-546474; N. America dist. addr.: Box 358, Accord Sta., Hingham, MA 02018-0358. TEL 617-871-6600. FAX 617-871-6528) Ed.Bd. **Indexed:** Bibl.Ling., Math.R. **Document type:** monographic series.
—BLDSC (8491.028000).
Formerly (until 1989): Synthese Language Library.
Refereed Serial

PSYCHOLOGY

158 616.89 US ISSN 1076-5514
STUDIES IN PSYCHOANALYTIC THEORY. 1991. s-a. $30. Texas Christian University, Box 32875, Ft. Worth, TX 76129. TEL 817-921-7221. FAX 817-921-7702. Ed. Christina Murphy. adv.: page $225; adv. contact: Christina Murphy. bk.rev.; circ. 500 (paid). (back issues avail.) Document type: academic/scholarly publication.
—BLDSC (8491.228800).
Description: Discusses the application of psychoanalytic theory to cultural studies in the arts, humanities, and social sciences.
Refereed Serial

STUDIES IN THE PSYCHOLOGY OF RELIGION. see *RELIGIONS AND THEOLOGY*

616.8 CN ISSN 0706-7992
SUBJECT TO CHANGE; a magazine of non-violent resistance. 1978. q. Alliance for Non-Violent Action, 253 College St., P.O. Box 235, Toronto, Ont. M5T 1R5, Canada. illus.
Description: Covers the war against women, native solidarity, and militarization of children. Promotes civil disobedience and covers international non-violent actions designed to end social injustice, as well as providing analysis on root causes of violence and oppression.

SUCCESS (NEW YORK); the magazine for today's entrepreneurial mind. see *OCCUPATIONS AND CAREERS*

150.19 US
SUGGESTION QUARTERLY. 1962. q. membership only. Association to Advance Ethical Hypnosis, c/o Nell R. Orndorf, M.A., 2675 Oakwood Dr., Cuyahoga Falls, OH 44221. bk.rev. circ. 1,200. Document type: academic/scholarly publication, bulletin.

157.744 US ISSN 0363-0234
RC569 CODEN: SLBEDP
SUICIDE AND LIFE-THREATENING BEHAVIOR. 1970. q. $40 to individuals (foreign $57.50); institutions $140 (foreign $157.50) (effective 1995). (American Association of Suicidology) Guilford Publications, Inc., 72 Spring St., 4th Fl., New York, NY 10012. TEL 212-431-9800. FAX 212-966-6708. Ed. Ronald W. Maris; Pub. Robert Matloff. adv. contact: Marian Robinson. bk.rev.; abstr.; bibl.; index. circ. 2,000. (also avail. in microform from UMI; back issues avail.; reprint service avail. from ISI,UMI) Indexed: Abstr.Crim.& Pen., Adol.Ment.Hlth.Abstr., ASCA, Biol.Abstr., C.I.J.E., CERDIC, Community Ment.Health Rev., Curr.Cont., Excerp.Med., Human Resour.Abstr., Ind.Med., Lang.& Lang.Behav.Abstr., Psychol.Abstr. (1971-), Sage Fam.Stud.Abstr., Sage Urb.Stud.Abstr., Sociol.Abstr., SSCI. Document type: academic/scholarly publication.
●Also available online. Vendor(s): University Microfilms International.
—BLDSC (8514.141000); Faxon; Genuine Article; SWETS; UMI; UnCover. CCC.
Former titles: Suicide (ISSN 0360-1390); Life Threatening Behavior (ISSN 0047-4592)
Description: Biological, statistical, psychological and sociological approaches to the full range of suicide issues.
Refereed Serial

150 US
SWISS MONOGRAPHS IN PSYCHOLOGY. irreg., vol.2, 1994. (Swiss Psychological Society) Hogrefe & Huber Publishers, Box 2487, Kirkland, WA 98083. TEL 206-820-1500. FAX 206-823-8324. Ed. Jean-Pierre Dauwalder. Document type: monographic series.

616.89 618 GW ISSN 0724-7923
BF173.A2
SYSTEM UBW; Zeitschrift fuer klassische Psychoanalyse. (Text in German; summaries in English, French) 1983. irreg. DM.52 for 4 nos. Ahriman Verlag GmbH, Stuebeweg 60, 79108 Freiburg, Germany. TEL 0761-502303. FAX 0761-502247. (Dist. by: Thanilo Verlag und Vertriebs GmbH, Postfach 710, 79007 Freiburg, Germany. TEL 0761-508001) Ed.Bd. (back issues avail.) Document type: academic/scholarly publication.
●Also available on CD-ROM.
—BLDSC (8589.164000).

150 US ISSN 0891-4451
SYSTEMS RESEARCH IN PHYSIOLOGY. 1982. irreg., vol.4, 1990. Gordon & Breach Science Publishers, c/o International Publishers Distributor, 820 Town Center Dr., Langhorne, PA 19047. TEL 215-750-2642. FAX 215-750-6343. (Subscr. to: International Publishers Distributor, P.O. Box 90, Reading, Berkshire RG1 8JL, England. TEL 44-173-456-8316) Ed. K.V. Sudakov. (also avail. in microform) Document type: monographic series.
—BLDSC (8589.425500).
Refereed Serial

155.3 301.4157 US ISSN 0884-9749
T V - T S TAPESTRY; the journal for persons interested in crossdressing & transsexualism. 1978. q. $40 (foreign $65). International Foundation for Gender Education, Inc., Box 367, Wayland, MA 01778. TEL 617-899-2212. FAX 617-899-5703. Ed. Vivian Allen. adv. contact: Y. Cook-Riley. bk.rev. circ. 10,000. (back issues avail.)

150 US
TAKING SIDES: CLASHING VIEWS ON CONTROVERSIAL ISSUES IN HUMAN SEXUALITY. irreg., 3rd ed., 1991. $13.95. Dushkin Publishing Group, Sluice Dock, Guilford, CT 06437-9989. TEL 203-453-4351. FAX 203-453-6000. Ed. Robert T. Francoeur; Pub. Mimi Egan. illus. Document type: academic/scholarly publication.

150 US
TAKING SIDES: CLASHING VIEWS ON CONTROVERSIAL MORAL ISSUES. irreg., 3rd ed., 1992. $13.95. Dushkin Publishing Group, Sluice Dock, Guilford, CT 06437-9989. TEL 203-453-4351. FAX 203-453-6000. Ed. Stephen Satris; Pub. Mimi Egan. illus. Document type: academic/scholarly publication.

150 US
TAKING SIDES: CLASHING VIEWS ON CONTROVERSIAL PSYCHOLOGICAL ISSUES. irreg., 6th ed., 1990. $13.95. Dushkin Publishing Group, Sluice Dock, Guilford, CT 06437-9989. TEL 203-453-4351. FAX 203-453-6000. Eds. Joseph Rubinstein, Brent Slife; Pub. Mimi Egan. illus. Document type: academic/scholarly publication.

TAROT NETWORK NEWS. see *NEW AGE PUBLICATIONS*

150 371.3 US ISSN 0098-6283
BF77
TEACHING OF PSYCHOLOGY. 1974. 4/yr. $25 to individuals (foreign $50); institutions $115 (foreign $140). (American Psychological Association, Division Two) Lawrence Erlbaum Associates, Inc., 10 Industrial Dr., Mahwah, NJ 07430-2262. TEL 201-236-9500. FAX 201-236-0072. Ed. Charles L. Brewer. adv.: page $425; 7 x 10. bk.rev.; film rev.; bibl.; charts; index. circ. 3,200. (also avail. in microform from UMI; back issues avail; reprint service avail. from UMI) Indexed: ASCA, C.I.J.E., Cont.Pg.Educ., Curr.Cont., Educ.Ind., ERIC, Psychol.Abstr. (1974-), Psychol.R.G., SSCI, Tech.Educ.Abstr. Document type: academic/scholarly publication.
—BLDSC (8614.330000); Faxon; SWETS; UMI; UnCover.
Description: Dedicated to improving the learning-teaching process at all educational levels: from secondary through college and graduate school, to continuing education.
Refereed Serial

150 US ISSN 0887-0217
TEACHING THINKING & PROBLEM SOLVING NEWSLETTER. 1979. bi-m. $29.50 to individuals (foreign $49.50); institutions $65 (foreign $85). (American Psychological Association, Clinical Psychology) Lawrence Erlbaum Associates, Inc., 10 Industrial Dr., Mahwah, NJ 07430-2262. TEL 201-236-9500. FAX 201-236-0072. (Co-publisher: Research for Better Schools) Ed. Francine S. Beyer. bk.rev. circ. 700. (tabloid format; back issues avail.) Document type: newsletter.
—SWETS.
Formerly (until 1985): Problem Solving.
Description: Covers current ideas and emerging programs in the area of education.
Refereed Serial

150 AG ISSN 0326-453X
TEMAS DE PSICOLOGIA SOCIAL. 1977. q.? Arg.$4 per no. (Primera Escuela Privada de Psicologia Social) Ediciones Cinco S.A., Florida 165, 2o piso, Ofc. 505, Buenos Aires, Argentina. TEL 343-8025. Ed. Ana P. de Quiroga.

616.89 610 370 IT ISSN 0391-2868
RC488.5
TERAPIA FAMILIARE. 1977. 3/yr. L.50000 (Europe L.60000; elsewhere L.70000) (effective 1994). Accademia di Psicoterapia della Famiglia, V.G.A. Guattani 15, 00161 Rome, Italy. TEL 06-44233030. Ed. Maurizio Andolfi. adv.; bk.rev.; cum.index: 1977-1986. circ. 3,000. (back issues avail.) Indexed: Psychol.Abstr. (1977-).
—BLDSC (8792.075000).

375 371.3 US ISSN 0361-025X
TESTS IN PRINT. 1961. quinquennial, no.4, 1994. price varies. Buros Institute of Mental Measurements, 135 Bancroft, University of Nebraska-Lincoln, Lincoln, NE 68588-0348. TEL 402-472-6203. FAX 402-472-6207. (Dist. by: University of Nebraska Press, 312 N. 14th St., Lincoln, NE 68588-0484. TEL 402-472-3584. FAX 402-472-6214) Ed. Linda L. Murphy. bibl.; cum.index. (back issues avail.) Document type: academic/scholarly publication.
Description: A reference listing over 4,000 test instruments that are commercially available in English. Includes description of tests, intended population, scores available, current pricing, and publisher name and address.

THANATOLOGY ABSTRACTS. see *PSYCHOLOGY — Abstracting, Bibliographies, Statistics*

155.937 US
THANATOLOGY LIBRARIAN; news of books on death, bereavement, loss & grief. 1979. s-a. $15. Center for Thanatology Research and Education Inc., 391 Atlantic Ave., Brooklyn, NY 11217-1701. TEL 718-858-3026. Ed. Roberta Halporn. bk.rev. circ. 4,000. (back issues avail.)

156 GW ISSN 0934-5272
HM291
THEMENZENTRIERTE INTERAKTION. (Text and summaries in English and German) 1987. s-a. DM.28 (effective 1996). Matthias Gruenewald Verlag GmbH, Max-Hufschmidt-Str. 4a, 55130 Mainz, Germany. TEL 06131-839055. FAX 06131-834322. Ed. Josef Wagner. adv. contact: Andrea Buchauer. bk.rev. (back issues avail.) Document type: academic/scholarly publication.

614.58 US
THEORETICAL ISSUES IN COGNITIVE SCIENCE. 1986. irreg. price varies. Ablex Publishing Corporation, 355 Chestnut St., Norwood, NJ 07648. TEL 201-767-8450. FAX 201-767-6717. TELEX 135-393. Ed. Zenon Pylyshyn. Document type: academic/scholarly publication.

THEORIA; a Swedish journal of philosophy. see *PHILOSOPHY*

370.15 150 UK ISSN 0959-3543
CODEN: THPSEJ
THEORY & PSYCHOLOGY. 1990. q. £30 to individuals; institutions £120 (effective 1996). Sage Publications Ltd., 6 Bonhill St., London EC2A 4PU, England. TEL 0171-374-0645. FAX 0171-374-8741. E-mail: market@sageltd.co.uk. Ed. Henderikus J. Stam. adv.: B&W page £180; trim 185 x 114; adv. contact: Bernie Folan. bk.rev. Indexed: Curr.Cont., Human Resour.Abstr., IBZ, Psychol.Abstr., Psychol.Abstr. (1991-), Sage Fam.Stud.Abstr., SSCI. Document type: academic/scholarly publication.
—BLDSC (8814.628600); Genuine Article; SWETS.
Description: Fosters theoretical dialogue and innovation within psychology, focusing on the emergent themes at the centre of contemporary psychological debate.
Refereed Serial

PSYCHOLOGY

155 618.92   US   ISSN 0735-6897
RJ131
THEORY AND RESEARCH IN BEHAVIORAL PEDIATRICS. 1982. irreg. vol.5, 1991. price varies. Plenum Publishing Corp., 233 Spring St., New York, NY 10013-1578. TEL 202-620-8000. FAX 212-463-0742. TELEX 23-421139. Ed.Bd. (back issues avail.) **Document type:** monographic series.
—BLDSC (8814.628800).
Refereed Serial

616.89   UK   ISSN 1350-4614
▼**THE THERAPIST.** 1994. q. European Therapy Studies Insititute, 1 Lovers Meadow, Chalvington, Hailsham, E. Sussex BN27 3TE, England. TEL 0323-811754. bk.rev. **Document type:** academic/scholarly publication.
—BLDSC (8814.763000).
Description: Discusses medical, social and economic topics affecting psychotherapists.

150   US   ISSN 1061-4362
THERAPISTS REPORT. 1989. q. $40 (effective 1993). American Association of Behavioral Therapists, Box 1737, Ormond Beach, FL 32175-1735. Ed. Dan J. Allen. adv. circ. 1,000. (back issues avail.) **Document type:** academic/scholarly publication.
Description: Disseminates information to behavioral therapists on what is new in the behavioral sciences.

150 100   UK   ISSN 1354-6783
▼**THINKING & REASONING.** 1995. q. £27.50($55) to individuals (outside the E.U. £32.50); institutions £55 (outside the E.U. £60 ($100)) (effective 1996). Lawrence Erlbaum Associates Ltd., 27 Palmeira Mansions, Church Rd., Hove, E. Sussex BN3 2FA, England. TEL 01273-207411. FAX 01273-205612. (Subscr. to: Turpin Distribution Services Ltd., Blackhorse Rd., Letchworth, Herts. SG6 1HN, England. TEL 01462-672555. FAX 01462-480947) Ed. Jonathan Evans. adv.: page £175; 110 x 190. **Document type:** academic/scholarly publication.
—BLDSC (8820.134600).
Description: Dedicated to the understanding of human thought processes, particularly reasoning. The primary focus is psychological studies of thinking.

TIROLER SCHULE. see *EDUCATION — Teaching Methods And Curriculum*

150   US
TODAY (BUFFALO).* m. Mental Health Association of Erie County, 999 Delaware Ave., Buffalo, NY 14209. TEL 716-886-1242. Ed. Frank Valvo. circ. 4,100.

150   JA   ISSN 0040-8743
BF1   CODEN: TPSFAD
TOHOKU PSYCHOLOGICA FOLIA. (Text in European languages) 1933. a. exchange basis. Tohoku Daigaku, Bungakubu Shinrigaku Kyoshitsu - Tohoku University, Faculty of Arts and Letters, Department of Psychology, Kawauchi, Sendai-shi, Miyagi-ken 980, Japan. Ed. Kinya Maruyama. charts; illus.; index. circ. 525. Indexed: Biol.Abstr., Child Devel.Abstr., Curr.Cont., Psychol.Abstr. (1933-). **Document type:** bulletin.
—BLDSC (8862.350000).

150 301   AG
TOPIA REVISTA; psicoanalisis, sociedad y cultura. 1991. 3/yr. Arg.$23 (foreign $25). Juan Maria Gutierrez 3809, 3o A, Buenos Aires, Argentina. TEL 54-1-802-5434. FAX 54-1-784-1967. E-mail: tp@topia.psico.net. Eds. Enrique Carpintero, Alejandro Vainer. adv.; bk.rev. **Document type:** newsletter.

TOPIQUE - REVUE FREUDIENNE. see *MEDICAL SCIENCES — Psychiatry And Neurology*

TOPOI; an international review of philosophy. see *PHILOSOPHY*

TOTAL HEALTH. see *NUTRITION AND DIETETICS*

616.8 370   US   ISSN 0362-1521
RC489.T7
TRANSACTIONAL ANALYSIS JOURNAL.* 1962. q. $40. International Transactional Analysis Association, 450 Pacific Ave., Ste. 250, San Francisco, CA 94133-4640. TEL 415-885-5992. FAX 415-885-5998. adv.; bk.rev.; abstr.; charts; index. circ. 5,000. (also avail. in microform from UMI; back issues avail.) Indexed: ASCA, Curr.Cont., Psychol.Abstr. (1974-), SSCI.
—BLDSC (9020.564000); UMI; UnCover.
Formerly: Transactional Analysis Bulletin (ISSN 0041-1051)

150   US
TRANSENDER.* 6/yr. free. Live and Learn, Box 6061, Sherman Oaks, CA 91413-6061. TEL 818-995-7121. Ed. Rich Monosson. adv.; illus.

150   FR   ISSN 0041-1868
T58.A2   CODEN: TRHUAH
TRAVAIL HUMAIN. (Text in French; occasionally in English) 1937. q. 410 F. (foreign 470 F.) (effective 1996). Presses Universitaires de France, Departement des Revues, 14 av. du Bois-de-l'Epine, B.P.90, 91003 Evry Cedex, France. TEL 1-60-77-82-05. FAX 1-60-79-20-45. TELEX PUF 600 474 F. Ed.Bd. bk.rev.; charts; illus.; index. circ. 1,500. (reprint service avail. from KTO) Indexed: ASCA, Biol.Abstr., C.I.S. Abstr., Chem.Abstr., Child Devel.Abstr., Curr.Cont., Ergon.Abstr., Excerp.Med., Int.Lab.Doc., P.A.I.S.For.Lang.Ind., Psychol.Abstr. (1933-), SSCI.
—BLDSC (9027.300000); EMDOCS; Faxon; Genuine Article; SWETS. **CCC.**
Description: Covers ergonomics, organization of work, personnel recruitment, and occupational health and safety.

155.3   US   ISSN 1052-3995
RC569.5.C55
TREATING ABUSE TODAY; an international magazine of abuse survivorship and therapy. 1991. bi-m. $39 to individuals; institutions $60. Clinical Training Publications, Inc., 2722 Eastlake Ave., E., Ste. 300, Seattle, WA 98102. TEL 206-329-9101; 800-847-3964. FAX 206-329-8462. E-mail: 76430.2614@Compuserve.com. Ed. David L. Calof. adv.: B&W page $290; 7 1/8 x 8 1/2; adv. contact: Anna Machan. bk.rev./ circ. 3,500 (paid). **Document type:** academic/scholarly publication.
—BLDSC (9046.830000).
Description: Contains timely information, contemporary issues and expert guidance regarding the treatment and recovery of survivors of sexual abuse.

150   US
TREATMENT MANUALS FOR PRACTITIONERS. irreg. (approx. 1/yr.) Guilford Publications, Inc., 72 Spring St., New York, NY 10012. TEL 212-431-9800; 800-365-7006. FAX 212-966-6708. Ed. David H. Barlow. **Document type:** monographic series.
Description: Presents results of successful treatment programs for specific psychological disorders. Each manual targets problems and illustrates step-by-step treatment protocols.

150   UK
▼**TRENDS IN ORGANIZATIONAL BEHAVIOR.** (Supplement to: Journal of Organizational Behavior) 1994. a. John Wiley & Sons Ltd., Baffins Ln., Chichester, W. Sussex PO19 1UD, England. TEL 01243-779777. FAX 01243-775878. Ed. Michael Coombs. **Document type:** monographic series.

157   GW
TRIERER PSYCHOLOGISCHE BERICHTE. (Text and summaries in English and German) 1974. irreg. free. Universitaet Trier, Fachgebiet Psychologie, 54286 Trier, Germany. TEL 0651-201-2970. FAX 0651-201-2961. E-mail: graeser@pcmail.uni-trier.de. Eds. Horst Graeser, Reinhold Scheller. cum.index: 1974-1988. **Document type:** academic/scholarly publication.

150   FI   ISSN 0356-8741
TURUN YLIOPISTO. PSYKOLOGIAN TUTKIMUKSIA. 1969. irreg. price varies. Turun Yliopisto, Psykologian Laitos - University of Turku, Dept. of Psychology, Arwidssonink 1, SF-20500 Turku 50, Finland. Ed. Kirsti Lagerspetz. circ. 500. **Document type:** academic/scholarly publication.
Supersedes in part: Turun Yliopisto. Psykologian Laitos. Reports (ISSN 0082-7037)

370.15 150   US
TUTORIAL MONOGRAPHS IN COGNITIVE SCIENCE. 1991. irreg. price varies. Ablex Publishing Corporation, 355 Chestnut St., Norwood, NJ 07648. TEL 201-767-8450. FAX 201-767-6717. TELEX 135-393. Ed. Nigel Shadbolt. **Document type:** academic/scholarly publication.

150.19   US   ISSN 8756-4963
                            CODEN: TYREE4
TYPE REPORTER; a monthly publication on psychological type. 1984. 8/yr. $16. Type Reporter, Inc., 11314 Chapel Rd., Fairfax, VA 22039-1523. TEL 703-823-3730. Ed. Susan Scanlon. bk.rev.; charts; illus. circ. 3,000. (back issues avail.)

301.1 150   SA   ISSN 0256-8896
U N I S A PSYCHOLOGIA. (Text in Afrikaans, English) 1974. s-a. R.8 (overseas $3.42 (effective 1996). University of South Africa, Department of Psychology, P.O. Box 392, Pretoria 0001, South Africa. FAX 27-12-429-3221. TELEX 350068. Ed. R.C. McKay. adv.; bk.rev. circ. 5,000. (back issues avail.) **Document type:** academic/scholarly publication.

155.9042 616.8   UK   ISSN 1353-2723
▼**UNDERSTANDING STRESS, ANXIETY AND DEPRESSION.** 1994. bi-m. N C N Publishing, 8 Bovingdon Rd., London SW6 2AP, England. TEL 0171-371-7674. FAX 0171-371-9790. Ed. Richard Hornsby. **Document type:** academic/scholarly publication.
—BLDSC (9090.005530).

370.15   SP   ISSN 0212-9728
UNIVERSIDAD DE MURCIA. ANALES DE PSICOLOGIA. (Text in English, Spanish) 1955. s-a. 3000 ptas. Universidad de Murcia, Secretariado de Publicaciones e Intercambio Cientifico, Santo Cristo, 1, 30001 Murcia, Spain. TEL 34-68-363014. FAX 34-68-363414. E-mail: agustinr@fcu.um.es. Ed. Agustin Romero Medina. **Document type:** academic/scholarly publication.
Supersedes in part (in 1984): Universidad de Murcia. Filosofia y Letras. Anales (ISSN 0463-9863)
Description: Publishes theoretical, empirical and methodological papers covering all aspects related to basic and applied scientific psychology.
Refereed Serial

150   FI   ISSN 0359-0216
UNIVERSITY OF TURKU. PSYCHOLOGICAL RESEARCH REPORTS. (Text in English) 1963. irreg. price varies. Turun Yliopisto, Psykologian Laitos - University of Turku, Department of Psychology, Arwidssonink 1, SF-20500 Turku 50, Finland. Ed. Kirsti Lagerspetz. circ. 500. **Document type:** academic/scholarly publication.
Supersedes in part: Turun Yliopisto. Psykologian Laitos. Reports (ISSN 0082-7037)

150   XO   ISSN 0083-419X
BF26   CODEN: PSYAD8
UNIVERZITA KOMENSKEHO. FILOZOFICKA FAKULTA. ZBORNIK: PSYCHOLOGICA. (Text in Slovak; summaries in English, German and Russian) 1961. irreg. exchange basis. Univerzita Komenskeho, Filozoficka Fakulta, c/o Ustredna Kniznica Filozofickej Fakulty, Gondova 2, 818 01 Bratislava, Slovakia. Ed. Julius Boros. circ. 400. Indexed: Psychol.Abstr. **Document type:** academic/scholarly publication.
Description: Covers all aspects of psychology.

370.14 150   PL   ISSN 1230-6096
UNIWERSYTET GDANSKI. ZESZYTY NAUKOWE. PSYCHOLOGIA. (Text in Polish; summaries in English, Russian) 1978. irreg., latest no.11. price varies. Uniwersytet Gdanski, Wydzial Humanistyczny, c/o Biblioteka Glowna, Ul. Armii Krajowej 110, 81-824 Sopot, Poland. TEL 51-0061. TELEX 051 2247 BMOR PL. (Dist. by: Ars Polona-Ruch, Krakowskie Przedmiescie 7, 00-680 Warsaw, Poland) circ. 250. **Document type:** academic/scholarly publication.
Formerly (until 1991): Uniwersytet Gdanski. Wydzial Humanistyczny. Zeszyty Naukowe. Psychologia (ISSN 0208-4562)
Description: Each volume covers a particular field of interest, such as creativity, attitudes toward religion, motivation of achievement, and family psychology.

PSYCHOLOGY

150 370   PL   ISSN 0083-4408
LB1051
UNIWERSYTET JAGIELLONSKI. ZESZYTY NAUKOWE. PRACE PSYCHOLOGICZNO-PEDAGOGICZNE. 1957. irreg., vol.34, 1983. price varies. Uniwersytet Jagiellonski, Ul. Gloegia 24, 31-007 Krakow, Poland. (Dist. by: Ars Polona, Krakowskie Przedmiescie 7, 00-068 Warsaw, Poland) Ed. Maria Susulowska. illus. **Document type:** academic/scholarly publication.

158.7   PL   ISSN 0208-5569
UNIWERSYTET SLASKI W KATOWICACH. PRACE NAUKOWE. PSYCHOLOGICZNE PROBLEMY FUNKCJONOWANIA CZLOWIEKA W SYTUACJI PRACY. (Text in Polish; summaries in English and Russian) 1980. irreg. price varies. Wydawnictwo Uniwersytetu Slaskiego, Ul. Bankowa 12B, 40-007 Katowice, Poland. TEL 48-32-596-915. FAX 48-32-599-605. TELEX 0315584 USKPL. (Dist. by: CHZ Ars Polona, P.O. Box 1001, 00-950 Warsaw, Poland) **Document type:** academic/scholarly publication.
    Description: Provides social psychological studies of human behaviour at work, especially on interpersonal relations, trust, injustice, leadership and attitudes to work, stress and resistance to change, employees appraisal.

153.4   US
VANCOUVER STUDIES IN COGNITIVE SCIENCE. irreg., vol.2, 1992. price varies. (Simon Fraser University) Oxford University Press, 200 Madison Ave., New York, NY 10016. TEL 212-679-7300. **Document type:** proceedings.

VEDANTA KESARI. see *RELIGIONS AND THEOLOGY — Hindu*

616.89   GW   ISSN 0721-7234
VERHALTENSTHERAPIE UND PSYCHOSOZIALE PRAXIS. 1968. q. DM.60. Deutsche Gesellschaft fuer Verhaltenstherapie, Neckarhalde 55, 72070 Tuebingen, Germany. TEL 07071-41211. FAX 07071-45021. adv.; bk.rev. circ. 7,000. (back issues avail.)

VIERTELJAHRESSCHRIFT FUER HEILPAEDAGOGIK UND IHRE NACHBARGEBIETE. see *EDUCATION — Special Education And Rehabilitation*

VIOLENCE AND VICTIMS. see *SOCIOLOGY*

150.19 069 910   US   ISSN 0892-4996
VISITOR BEHAVIOR. 1986. q. $20 to institutions; students $12. Center for Social Design, Box 3090, Jacksonville, AL 36245. TEL 205-782-5640. FAX 205-782-5640. Ed. Stephen Bitgood. adv.; bk.rev. circ. 500. (back issues avail.) **Document type:** newsletter.
    Description: Deals with all areas of visitor studies, covering research, evaluation, graphics and labels, orientation and circulation, and architectural design.

150   UK   ISSN 1350-6285
BF241   CODEN: VICOF6
▼**VISUAL COGNITION.** 1994. q. £27.50($55) to individuals (outside the E.U. £32.50); institutions £55 (outside the E.U. £60 ($100) (effective 1996). Lawrence Erlbaum Associates Ltd., 27 Palmeira Mansions, Church Rd., Hove, E. Sussex BN3 2 FA, England. TEL 01273-207411. FAX 01273-205612. (Subscr. to: Turpin Distribution Services Ltd., Blackhorse Rd., Letchworth, Herts. SG6 1HN, England. TEL 01462-672555. FAX 01462-480947) Ed. Glyn W. Humphreys. adv.: page £175; 110 x 190. **Document type:** academic/scholarly publication.
—BLDSC (9241.234000).
    Description: Publishes research papers on all aspects of visual cognition, including studies of visual object and face recognition, texture and surface perception, perceptual organization, visual attention, visual memory, and more.

VITA DELL'INFANZIA. see *EDUCATION*

616.89   US   ISSN 0042-8272
RC475
VOICES (DECATUR); the art and science of psychotherapy. 1965. q. $40 to individuals (foreign $55); institutions $80 (foreign $95) (effective 1996). American Academy of Psychotherapists, Box 607, Decatur, GA 30031. TEL 404-299-6336. FAX 404-299-0206. Ed. Monique Savlin. adv.; bk.rev.; illus.; cum.index. circ. 1,500. (also avail. in microform from UMI; audio cassette; reprint service avail. from UMI) **Indexed:** Psychol.R.G. **Document type:** academic/scholarly publication.
—BLDSC (9251.465000); Faxon; UMI; UnCover. *Refereed Serial*

150   RU   ISSN 0042-8841
BF8.R8   CODEN: VOPSAI
VOPROSY PSIKHOLOGII. (Text in Russian; summaries in English) 1955. bi-m. $117 (effective 1996). (Akademiya Pedagogicheskikh Nauk - Academy of Pedagogical Sciences) Izdatel'stvo Pedagogika, Smolensky per. 4, 100034 Moscow, Russia. (Dist. in U.S. by: Victor Kamkin Inc., 4956 Boiling Brook Pkwy, Rockville, MD 20852. TEL 301-881-5973) Ed. A.M. Matyushkin. index. **Indexed:** Biol.Abstr., Child Devel.Abstr., Curr.Cont., Int.Aerosp.Abstr., Psychol.Abstr. (1955-), SSCI.
—BLDSC (0044.130000); Genuine Article. **CCC**.

VYCHOVAVATEL. see *EDUCATION*

616.8   US   ISSN 0083-8977
W P S PROFESSIONAL HANDBOOK SERIES. 1965. irreg. price varies. Western Psychological Services, 12031 Wilshire Blvd., Los Angeles, CA 90025. TEL 310-478-2061; 800-478-7838. FAX 310-478-7838. Ed. Janet Hansen; Pub. Ira R. Manson. **Document type:** monographic series.

370.15 150   NR   ISSN 0331-0515
WEST AFRICAN JOURNAL OF EDUCATIONAL AND VOCATIONAL MEASUREMENT. 1973. s-a. £N5. West African Examinations Council, Test Development and Research Division, P.M.B. 1076, Yaba, Lagos State, Nigeria. TEL 234-1-861711. Ed. A.A. Awomolo. adv. circ. 250. **Indexed:** Psychol.Abstr. **Document type:** academic/scholarly publication.
Refereed Serial

WEST BENGAL. BUREAU OF EDUCATIONAL AND PSYCHOLOGICAL RESEARCH. see *EDUCATION*

616.58   US
WILLIAM ALANSON WHITE PSYCHOANALYTIC INSTITUTE. RECORD. 1966. 3/yr. membership. William Alanson White Psychoanalytic Institute, 20 W. 74th St., New York, NY 10023. TEL 212-873-0725. FAX 212-362-6967. Ed. James Garofallou. bk.rev.; illus. circ. 2,500. **Document type:** newsletter.
    Formerly (until 1994): W A W Newsletter (ISSN 0042-9511)

WINGSPAN: JOURNAL OF THE MALE SPIRIT. see *MEN'S STUDIES*

158 305.4   US   ISSN 0270-3149
RC451.4.W6   CODEN: WOTHDJ
WOMEN & THERAPY; a feminist quarterly of research and opinion. 1982. q. $190 (foreign $266) (effective 1996). Haworth Press, Inc., 10 Alice St., Binghamton, NY 13904. TEL 607-722-5857; 800-342-9678. FAX 607-722-1424. TELEX 4932599. Eds. Esther Rothblum, Ellen Cole. adv.; bk.rev. circ. 835. (also avail. in microfiche from UMI; back issues avail.; reprint service avail. from HAW) **Indexed:** Alt.Press Ind., Biol.Abstr., Bull.Signal., IMFL, Mult.Ed.Abstr., Psychol.Abstr. (1982-), Soc.Work Res.& Abstr., Stud.Wom.Abstr., Wom.Stud.Abstr. (1982-). **Document type:** academic/scholarly publication.
—BLDSC (9343.276000); Faxon; Haworth; SWETS; UnCover.
    Formerly: Women - Counseling Therapy and Mental Health Services.
    Description: Explores the multidimensional relationship between women and therapy, and feminist in orientation. Publishes descriptive, theoretical, clinical, and empirical perspectives on the topic and the therapeutic process.
Refereed Serial

WOMEN'S HEALTH: RESEARCH ON GENDER, BEHAVIOR, AND POLICY. see *WOMEN'S HEALTH*

158.7   UK   ISSN 0267-8373
HF5548.85
WORK AND STRESS. 1987. q. £109($180) (effective 1996). Taylor & Francis Ltd., Rankine Rd., Basingstoke, Hants. RG24 8PR, England. TEL 44-1256-840366. FAX 44-1256-479438. TELEX 858540. E-mail: info@tandf.co.uk. (Subscr. in N. America to: Taylor & Francis Inc., 1900 Frost Rd., Ste. 101, Bristol, PA 19007-1598. TEL 800-821-8312. FAX 215-785-5515) Ed. Dr. Tom Cox. (back issues avail.) **Indexed:** ASSIA, Behav.Med.Abstr., CINAHL, Cont.Pg.Manage., Psychol.Abstr. (1987-). **Document type:** academic/scholarly publication.
—BLDSC (9348.102000); Faxon; Genuine Article; SWETS; UnCover. **CCC**.
    Description: Features academic papers relating to stress, health and safety, and associated areas and scholarly articles of concern to the policy-makers, managers and trades unionists who have to deal with such issues.
Refereed Serial

WORLD COUNCIL FOR GIFTED AND TALENTED CHILDREN. YEARBOOK. see *EDUCATION — Special Education And Rehabilitation*

616.89 614.582   US
WORLD FEDERATION FOR MENTAL HEALTH. ANNUAL REPORT. a. $30 membership (developing nations $15). World Federation for Mental Health, Sheppard & Enoch Pratt Hospital, Box 6815, Baltimore, MD 21285-6815. TEL 410-938-3180. FAX 410-938-3183. Ed. Dr. Eugene B. Brody. circ. 4,000 (controlled). **Document type:** corporate report.
    Description: Reviews the organization's international activities of the past year.

616.89 614.582   US
WORLD FEDERATION FOR MENTAL HEALTH. NEWSLETTER. 1948. q. $30 for membership in developed countries; developing countries $15. World Federation for Mental Health, Sheppard & Enoch Pratt Hospital, Box 6815, Baltimore, MD 21285-6815. TEL 410-938-3180. FAX 410-938-4532. (Subscr. to: World Federation for Mental Health, 1021 Prince St., Alexandria, VA 22314-2971. TEL 703-838-7543) Ed. Dr. Eugene B. Brody. bibl. circ. 4,000. **Document type:** newsletter.
    Description: Provides members with information on the federation's activities at the United Nations, the World Health Organization, and around the world. Comments on mental health issues and contains a calendar of events.

150   US
WRITE-UP. 1972. 6/yr. $20 (foreign $30). National Society for Graphology, 250 W. 57th St., Ste. 2032, New York, NY 10107. TEL 212-265-1148. FAX 212-307-5671. Ed. Louise Erpelding. bk.rev. circ. 300. (back issues avail.) **Document type:** academic/scholarly publication, newsletter.
    Formerly: National Society for Graphology Newsletter.
    Description: Discusses topics of interest pertaining to the study of handwriting.

150.19   GW   ISSN 0344-8274
WUNDERBLOCK; Zeitschrift fuer Psychoanalyse. 1978. irreg. DM.70 for 4 nos. Verlag der Wunderblock, Konstanzer Str. 11, 10707 Berlin, Germany. TEL 030-8831122. Ed.Bd. adv.; bk.rev. (back issues avail.) **Document type:** academic/scholarly publication.

510   PL
WYZSZA SZKOLA PEDAGOGICZNA IM. KOMISJI EDUKACJI NARODOWEJ W KRAKOWIE. ROCZNIK NAUKOWO-DYDAKTYCZNY. PRACE PSYCHOLOGICZNE. 1963. irreg., no.2, 1988. price varies. Wydawnictwo Naukowe W S P, Ul. Karmelicka 41, 31-128 Krakow, Poland. TEL 33-78-20. (Co-sponsor: Ministerstwo Edukacji Narodowej)

150   PL   ISSN 0208-9564
WYZSZA SZKOLA PEDAGOGICZNA, OPOLE. ZESZYTY NAUKOWE. SERIA A. PSYCHOLOGIA. (Text in Polish; summaries in English) 1979. irreg., vol.9, 1992. price varies; also exchange basis. Wyzsza Szkola Pedagogiczna, Opole, Oleska 48, 45-951 Opole, Poland. TEL 48-77-383-87. (Dist. by: Ars Polona-Ruch, Krakowskie Przedmiescie 7, Warsaw, Poland) Ed. Wieslaw Lukaszewski. **Document type:** academic/scholarly publication.
—BLDSC (9512.478998).

150 CC ISSN 1000-6648
BF8.C5
XINLI KEXUE TONGXUN/INFORMATION ON PSYCHOLOGICAL SCIENCES. (Text in Chinese) 1965. bi-m. $41. Zhongguo Xinli Xuehui, 3663 Zhongshan Beilu, Shanghai 200062, People's Republic of China. TEL 2577577. (Dist. in US by: China Books & Periodicals, Inc., 2929 24th St., San Francisco, CA 94110. TEL 415-282-2994) Ed. Zhu Manshu. **Indexed:** Psychol.Abstr. (1984-).

155 CC ISSN 0439-755X
BF8.C5
XINLI XUEBAO/ACTA PSYCHOLOGICA SINICA. (Text in Chinese; summaries in English) 1956. q. $44.70. Science Press, Marketing and Sales Department, 16 Donghuangchenggen North St., Beijing 100717, People's Republic of China. TEL 4010642. FAX 4019810. adv. circ. 32,000. **Indexed:** Psychol.Abstr. **Document type:** academic/scholarly publication.
Description: Covers the basic theories of psychology, general, medical, physiological, child, and educational psychology. Also covers the history of psychology, and contains evaluations of academic studies and information on current academic activities.
Refereed Serial

YOGA INTERNATIONAL. see *NEW AGE PUBLICATIONS*

Z U M A - NACHRICHTEN. (Zentrum fuer Umfragen, Methoden und Analysen e.V.) see *SOCIOLOGY*

616.89 PK
ZEHAN. (Text in Urdu) 1978. q. Rs.12($1.50) Psychope, G.P.O. Box 1964, Lahore, Pakistan. Ed. Dr. Syed Azhar Ale Rizvi. adv.; bk.rev. circ. 500.

150 158 GW ISSN 0932-4089
ZEITSCHRIFT FUER ARBEITS- UND ORGANISATIONSPSYCHOLOGIE. Short title: A & O. 1956. q. DM.132. Hogrefe Verlag fuer Psychologie, Rohnsweg 25, 37085 Goettingen, Germany. TEL 0551-496090. FAX 0551-4960988. Ed. Heinz Schuler. adv.; bk.rev.; bibl.; charts. circ. 2,000. **Indexed:** C.I.S. Abstr., Dok.Arbeitsmed., Ger.J.Psych., Psychol.Abstr. (1959-). **Document type:** academic/scholarly publication.
—Faxon; Genuine Article; SWETS.
Former titles (until 1987): Psychologie und Praxis; Psychologie und Praxis Arbeits- und Organisationspsychologie; Psychologie und Praxis (ISSN 0033-2992)

152 SZ ISSN 0170-1789
ZEITSCHRIFT FUER DIFFERENTIELLE UND DIAGNOSTISCHE PSYCHOLOGIE. 1980. q. 118 SFr. (foreign 128 SFr.). Verlag Hans Huber, Laenggassstr. 76, CH-3000 Bern 9, Switzerland. TEL 031-3004500. FAX 031-3004590. Ed. Prof. Dr. H. Haecker. adv. circ. 800. **Indexed:** Psychol.Abstr. (1980-). **Document type:** academic/scholarly publication.
—BLDSC (9457.686000). **CCC.**

370.15 150 GW ISSN 0049-8637
L31 CODEN: ZEPPBI
ZEITSCHRIFT FUER ENTWICKLUNGSPSYCHOLOGIE UND PAEDAGOGISCHE PSYCHOLOGIE. (Text in German; summaries in English) 1969. q. DM.94. Hogrefe Verlag fuer Psychologie, Rohnsweg 25, 37085 Goettingen, Germany. TEL 0551-496090. FAX 0551-4960988. Ed. H. Mandl. adv.; bk.rev.; abstr.; bibl.; charts; illus. circ. 2,400. **Indexed:** Child Devel.Abstr., Curr.Cont., Ger.J.Psych., Psychol.Abstr. (1969-), SSCI. **Document type:** academic/scholarly publication.
—BLDSC (9458.600000); Genuine Article.

152 GW
BF3
ZEITSCHRIFT FUER EXPERIMENTELLE PSYCHOLOGIE. (Text in German; summaries in English and German) 1953. 4/yr. DM.178. Hogrefe Verlag fuer Psychologie, Rohnsweg 25, 37085 Goettingen, Germany. TEL 0551-496090. FAX 0551-4960988. Ed. Angela Friederici. adv.; bk.rev.; bibl.; charts; illus. circ. 800. **Indexed:** Curr.Cont., Excerp.Med., Ger.J.Psych., Ind.Med., Lang.& Lang.Behav.Abstr., Psychol.Abstr. (1953-), SSCI. **Document type:** academic/scholarly publication.
—Faxon; Genuine Article; SWETS.
Formerly: Zeitschrift fuer Experimentelle und Angewandte Psychologie (ISSN 0044-2712)

150 GW ISSN 0943-8149
ZEITSCHRIFT FUER GESUNDHEITSPSYCHOLOGIE. 1993. q. DM.94. Hogrefe Verlag fuer Psychologie, Rohnsweg 25, 37085 Goettingen, Germany. TEL 0551-496090. FAX 0551-4960988. Ed. P. Schwenkmezger. adv.; bk.rev.; abstr.; bibl.; illus. circ. 2,000. **Document type:** academic/scholarly publication.
—BLDSC (9463.225000).

150 GW ISSN 0342-393X
ZEITSCHRIFT FUER INDIVIDUALPSYCHOLOGIE. 1976. q. DM.76. Ernst Reinhardt Verlag, Kemnatenstr. 46, 80639 Munich, Germany. TEL 089-1783005. FAX 089-1781827. Ed.Bd. adv.; bk.rev. circ. 2,700. (reprint service avail. from ISI and UMI) **Indexed:** Psychoanal.Abstr., Psychol.Abstr. (1984-). **Document type:** academic/scholarly publication.
—CCC.

157 GW ISSN 0084-5345
ZEITSCHRIFT FUER KLINISCHE PSYCHOLOGIE - FORSCHUNG UND PRAXIS. (Text in German; summaries in English) 1972. q. DM.112. (Berufsverband Deutscher Psychologen) Hogrefe Verlag fuer Psychologie, Rohnsweg 25, 37085 Goettingen, Germany. TEL 0551-496090. FAX 0551-4960988. Ed. K. Hahlweg. adv.; bk.rev. circ. 3,200. **Indexed:** Excerp.Med., Ger.J.Psych., Psychol.Abstr. (1972-), SSCI. **Document type:** academic/scholarly publication.
—BLDSC (9467.775000); EMDOCS; Genuine Article; SWETS.

ZEITSCHRIFT FUER KLINISCHE PSYCHOLOGIE UND PSYCHOTHERAPIE. see *MEDICAL SCIENCES — Psychiatry And Neurology*

137.7 AU ISSN 0379-4458
ZEITSCHRIFT FUER MENSCHENKUNDE. ZENTRALBLATT FUER SCHRIFTPSYCHOLOGIE UND SCHRIFTVERGLEICHUNG. 1925. q. S.450 (effective 1996). Wilhelm Braumueller, Universitaets-Verlagsbuchhandlung GmbH, Servitengasse 5, A-1092 Vienna, Austria. TEL 01-3191159. FAX 01-3102805. Ed. Horst Kappen. adv. contact: Susanne Mondl. bk.rev.; charts; cum.index every 2 yrs. circ. 1,000. **Document type:** academic/scholarly publication.
—SWETS.
Former titles: Zeitschrift fuer Menschenkunde und Zentralblatt fuer Graphologie, Ausdruckswissenschaft und Charakterkunde (ISSN 0044-3085); Zeitschrift fuer Menschenkunde und Zentralblatt fuer Graphologie.

150 SZ ISSN 1016-264X
ZEITSCHRIFT FUER NEUROPSYCHOLOGIE. 1990. 2/yr. 86 SFr. (foreign 92 SFr.). Verlag Hans Huber, Laenggassstr. 76, CH-3000 Bern 9, Switzerland. TEL 031-3004500. FAX 031-3004590. Ed. Prof. Dr. W. Hartje. circ. 800. **Document type:** academic/scholarly publication.
—BLDSC (9475.455000).

370.15 SZ ISSN 1010-0652
LB1051 CODEN: ZPPSE5
ZEITSCHRIFT FUER PAEDAGOGISCHE PSYCHOLOGIE. (Text in English and German) 1987. q. 123 SFr. (foreign 133 SFr.) to individuals; institutions 196 SFr. (foreign 206 SFr.). Verlag Hans Huber, Laenggasstr. 76, CH-3000 Bern 9, Switzerland. TEL 031-3004500. FAX 031-3004590. Ed. Andreas Knapp. bk.rev. circ. 500. (back issues avail.) **Indexed:** Psychol.Abstr. (1987-), Sociol.Educ.Abstr., Sp.Ed.Needs Abstr., Tech.Educ.Abstr. **Document type:** academic/scholarly publication.
—BLDSC (9475.803000).

150 GW ISSN 0044-3409
QP351
ZEITSCHRIFT FUER PSYCHOLOGIE; mit Zeitschrift fuer angewandte Psychologie. 1890. 4/yr. DM.174 (foreign DM.180). Johann Ambrosius Barth, Postfach 102869, 69018 Heidelberg, Germany. TEL 06221-489281. FAX 06221-489205. Ed. F. Klix. adv.: B&W page DM.700; trim 167 x 240; adv. contact: Petra Schoene. bk.rev.; bibl.; charts; illus.; index. circ. 800. (reprint service avail. from SWZ) **Indexed:** Biol.Abstr., Ger.J.Psych., Ind.Med., Psychol.Abstr. (1929-), SSCI. **Document type:** academic/scholarly publication.
—BLDSC (9485.100000); Faxon; Genuine Article; SWETS. **CCC.**
Formed by the merger of: Zeitschrift fuer Angewandte Psychologie und Charakterkunde (ISSN 0323-8296); Zeitschrift fuer Psychologie (ISSN 0323-8342); Which was formerly (until 1940): Zeitschrift fuer Psychologie und Physiologie des Sinnesorgane. 1. Abteilung. Zeitschrift fuer Psychologie (ISSN 0233-2353)
Description: Publishes papers on experimental and theoretical psychology.

ZEITSCHRIFT FUER PSYCHOSOMATISCHE MEDIZIN UND PSYCHOANALYSE. BEIHEFTE. see *MEDICAL SCIENCES — Psychiatry And Neurology*

ZEITSCHRIFT FUER SEXUALFORSCHUNG. see *MEDICAL SCIENCES*

301.1 SZ ISSN 0049-867X
ZEITSCHRIFT FUER SOZIALPSYCHOLOGIE. (Text in German; summaries in English) 1970. q. 118 SFr. (foreign 128 SFr.). Verlag Hans Huber, Laenggassstr. 76, CH-3000 Bern 9, Switzerland. TEL 031-3004500. FAX 031-3004590. Ed. Hans-Werner Bierhoff. adv.; bk.rev.; abstr.; bibl. circ. 800. (reprint service avail. from SCH) **Indexed:** Can.Rev.Comp.Lit., Curr.Cont., Ger.J.Psych., Psychol.Abstr. (1970-), SSCI. **Document type:** academic/scholarly publication.
—BLDSC (9486.380000); SWETS. **CCC.**

616.89 GW ISSN 0723-9505
ZEITSCHRIFT FUER SYSTEMISCHE THERAPIE. q. DM.64 (foreign DM.72). Verlag Modernes Lernen - Dortmund, Borgmann KG, Hohe Str. 39, 44139 Dortmund, Germany. TEL 0231-128008. FAX 0231-125640. Ed. Juergen Hargens. **Document type:** academic/scholarly publication.
—BLDSC (9486.409000).

616.89 GW ISSN 0176-9855
ZEITSCHRIFT FUER TRANSAKTIONSANALYSE IN THEORIE UND PRAXIS. (Text in German; summaries in English) 1984. q. DM.60. (Deutsche Gesellschaft fuer Transaktions-Analyse e.V.) Junfermann Verlag, Imadstr. 40, 33102 Paderborn, Germany. TEL 05251-34034. FAX 05251-36371. index. (back issues avail.) **Document type:** academic/scholarly publication.

150 CC ISSN 1000-6729
ZHONGGUO XINLI WEISHENG ZAZHI/CHINESE MENTAL HEALTH JOURNAL. (Text in Chinese; abstracts in English) 1987. bi-m. $28 to individuals; institutions $50. Beijing Yike Daxue, Jingshen Weisheng Yanjiusuo - Beijing Medical University, Institute of Mental Health, Huayuan Beilu, Beijing 100083, People's Republic of China. TEL 861-2010890. FAX 861-2027314. (Co-sponsor: Chinese Mental Health Association) Ed. Peng Ruicong. adv. circ. 14,000 (paid). **Indexed:** Psychol.Abstr. (1992-). **Document type:** academic/scholarly publication.
●Also available online. Vendor(s): Knight-Ridder, Inc.
—BLDSC (3181.015100).
Description: Publishes postgraduate dissertations, research articles, and clinical practices in the fields of medicine, psychology, pedagogy and sociology, focusing on mental health issues
Refereed Serial

301.1 370 300 610 GW ISSN 0724-3766
ZWISCHENSCHRITTE; Beitraege zu einer morphologischen Psychologie. 1982. s-a. DM.20. Arbeitskreis Morphologische Psychologie e.V., Postfach 410273, 50862 Cologne, Germany. TEL 0221-449956. adv.; bk.rev.; bibl.; film rev.; play rev.; illus. circ. 1,500. (back issues avail.)

PSYCHOLOGY — Abstracting, Bibliographies, Statistics

310 150   JA   ISSN 0385-7417
BF76.5
BEHAVIORMETRIKA. (Text mainly in English) 1974. a. price varies. Nihon Kodo Keiryo Gakkai - Behaviormetric Society of Japan, 6-7, Minamiazabu 4-chome, Minato-ku, Tokyo 106, Japan. (U.S. addr.: 1255 Howard St., San Francisco, CA 94103) Ed. Haruo Yanai. **Indexed:** J.Cont.Quant.Meth., Lang.& Lang.Behav.Abstr., Psychol.Abstr. (1983-), Stat.Theor.Meth.Abstr. **Document type:** academic/scholarly publication.
—BLDSC (1878.070000); UnCover.

016 150   AG   ISSN 0523-1698
BIBLIOGRAFIA ARGENTINA DE PSICOLOGIA.* irreg., nos. 5-6, 1970. Ministerio de Cultura y Educacion, Direccion de Bibliotecos, 538 Calle 7, La Plata, Argentina.

150 011   US   ISSN 0360-277X
Z7203
BIBLIOGRAPHIC GUIDE TO PSYCHOLOGY. (Text in various languages) a. $205. G.K. Hall & Co., c/o MacMillan Publishing USA, 866 Third Ave., 18th Fl., New York, NY 10022. TEL 212-702-6789. (Subscr. to: Simon & Schuster, Library Reference Order Processing, 200 Old Tappan Rd., Old Tappan, NJ07675. TEL 800-223-2336) **Document type:** bibliography, abstracting/indexing.
Formerly: Psychology Book Guide.
Description: Lists all aspects of psychology catalogued during the past year by the Research Libraries of the N Y P L; includes additional entries from LC MARC tapes.

301.1 016   GW   ISSN 0303-5999
BIBLIOGRAPHIE DER DEUTSCHSPRACHIGEN PSYCHOLOGISCHEN LITERATUR. a. DM.376. (Zentralstelle fuer Psychologische Information und Dokumentation des Universitaet Trier) Vittorio Klostermann, Frauenlobstr. 22, 60487 Frankfurt a.M., Germany. TEL 069-774011. FAX 069-708038. (Subscr. to: Postfach 900601, 60446 Frankfurt a.M., Germany) **Document type:** bibliography.

150   US   ISSN 0742-681X
BIBLIOGRAPHIES AND INDEXES IN PSYCHOLOGY. 1984. irreg. price varies. Greenwood Press, Inc. (Subsidiary of: Greenwood Publishing Group Inc.), 88 Post Rd. W., Box 5007, Westport, CT 06881-5007. TEL 203-226-3571. FAX 203-222-1502.

157 011   US
BIBLIOGRAPHY OF ANXIETY DISORDERS. 1986. a. $5. Special Interest Group on Phobias and Related Anxiety Disorders, c/o Carol Linderman, 245 E. 87th St., New York, NY 10028. TEL 212-860-5560. FAX 212-744-5751. circ. 50. (looseleaf format) **Document type:** bibliography.

BIBLIOGRAPHY OF EDUCATION THESES IN AUSTRALIA. see *EDUCATION — Abstracting, Bibliographies, Statistics*

ERGONOMICS ABSTRACTS. see *ENGINEERING — Abstracting, Bibliographies, Statistics*

150 016   US
BF1
EUROPEAN PSYCHOLOGIST. 1977. q. $48 to individuals; institutions $75. (European Federation of Professional Psychology Associations) Hogrefe & Huber Publishers, Box 2487, Kirkland, WA 98083. TEL 206-820-1500. FAX 206-823-8324. Ed. K. Pawlik. adv.; bk.rev.; abstr.; tr.lit. **Indexed:** Psychol.Abstr. (1981-). **Document type:** academic/scholarly publication.
—BLDSC (4162.121000); UnCover.
Formerly (until 1995): German Journal of Psychology (ISSN 0705-5870)

150 016   II   ISSN 0971-524X
INDIAN PSYCHOLOGICAL ABSTRACTS AND REVIEWS. (Text in English) 1972. s-a. $49 to individuals; institutions $107 (effective Sep. 1995). (Indian Council of Social Science Research) Sage Publications India Pvt. Ltd., P.O. Box 4215, New Delhi 110 048, India. TEL 91-11-644-4958. FAX 91-11-647-2426. (Overseas subscr. to: Sage Publications Ltd., 6 Bonhill St., London EC2A 4PU, England. TEL 44-071-374-0645. FAX 44-071-374-8741; Subscr. in N. America to: Sage Publications, Inc., 2455 Teller Rd., Thousand Oaks, CA 91320. TEL 805-499-0721. FAX 805-499-0871) (Co-sponsor: Indian Psychological Association) Ed. B.N. Puhan; Pub. Tejeshwar Singh. adv.: page Rs.1000; adv. contact: Sunanda Ghosh. bk.rev.; abstr. circ. 500. (back issues avail.) **Document type:** academic/scholarly publication, abstracting/indexing.
Formerly (until 1994): Indian Psychological Abstracts (ISSN 0250-9679)
Description: Disseminates research-based information in the form of abstracts and review articles for researchers and professionals worldwide to keep abreast of research being conducted in India.
Refereed Serial

150 370   SP   ISSN 0213-019X
Z7161.A15
INDICE ESPANOL DE CIENCIAS SOCIALES. SERIES A: PSYCHOLOGY AND EDUCATIONAL SCIENCES. 1979. a. 8800 ptas. or exchange basis. Centro de Informacion y Documentacion Cientifica (Cindoc), Pinar, 25, 28006 Madrid, Spain. TEL 34-1-4112220. FAX 34-1-5645069. E-mail: bib_isoc@bib.csic.es. (also avail. in diskette format) **Document type:** abstracting/indexing.
●Also available online.
Also available on CD-ROM.
Supersedes in part (in 1982): Indice Espanol de Ciencias Sociales (ISSN 0211-1373)

156 016.05   US   ISSN 1062-7278
QL85
THE INTERACTIONS BIBLIOGRAPHY; the quarterly journal of research on human-animal relationships. 1990. 4/yr. $60 in N. America (diskette $50); elsewhere $75 (diskette $55) (effective 1995). Rockydell Resources, 8732 Rock Springs Rd., Penryn, CA 95663. TEL 916-663-3294. Ed. David C. Anderson. bk.rev.; circ. 100 (paid). (also avail. in diskette format; back issues avail.) **Document type:** abstracting/indexing, bibliography.
Formerly (until vol.3, 1992): Interactions of Man and Animals (ISSN 1056-991X)
Description: Cites journal articles, books and book reviews on the human-animal relationship, often quoting journal abstracts or conclusions. Also publishes short articles and news to promote bibliographic access to this multidisciplinary literature.

150   GW   ISSN 0075-2924
JAHRESKATALOG PSYCHOLOGIE. a. DM.36.80. Buchwerbung in Berlin GmbH, Luetzowstr. 105-106, 10785 Berlin, Germany. adv. **Document type:** bibliography.
Description: Bibliography of each year's new titles in psychology.

MENTAL HEALTH STATISTICAL NOTES. see *SOCIAL SERVICES AND WELFARE — Abstracting, Bibliographies, Statistics*

310 510   JA
NIHON KODO KEIRYO GAKKAI TAIKAI HAPPYO RONBUN SHOROKUSHU. (Text in Japanese) 1973. a. Nihon Kodo Keiryo Gakkai - Behaviormetric Society of Japan, 6-7, Minami-Azabu 4-chome, Minato-ku, Tokyo 106, Japan. abstr. **Document type:** academic/scholarly publication.
Description: Contains abstracts from the annual meeting of the society.

P A S C A L E 65: PSYCHOLOGIE, PSYCHOPATHOLOGIE, PSYCHIATRIE. see *MEDICAL SCIENCES — Abstracting, Bibliographies, Statistics*

370.15 150   SW   ISSN 0346-5039
Z5815.S8
PEDAGOGISK DOKUMENTATION. 1971. irreg. Malmoe School of Education, Inst. foer Pedagogik och Specialmetodik, Box 23501, S-20045 Malmoe, Sweden. FAX 46-40-325-210. Ed. Aake Bjerstedt. (back issues avail.)

150   UK   ISSN 1350-4126
HM132   CODEN: PRRLEY
▼**PERSONAL RELATIONSHIPS.** 1994. q. £79($126) (effective 1996). (International Society for the Study of Personal Relationships) Cambridge University Press, The Edinburgh Bldg., Shaftesbury Rd., Cambridge CB2 2RU, England. TEL 01223-312393. FAX 01223-315052. TELEX 851817256. (N. American addr.: Cambridge University Press, Journals Division, 40 W. 20th St., New York, NY 10011. TEL 212-924-3900. FAX 212-691-3239) Ed. Pat Noller. adv. (back issues avail.) **Indexed:** IMFL. **Document type:** academic/scholarly publication.
—BLDSC (6427.885200); Genuine Article; UMI. CCC.
Description: Promotes scholarship in personal relationships through a broad range of disciplines.
Refereed Serial

150 016 614   US   ISSN 0270-3114
RA421   CODEN: PHSEDF
PREVENTION IN HUMAN SERVICES; summaries, reviews & index to the world's literature in community mental health. 1976. s-a. $175 (foreign $245) (effective 1996). Haworth Press, Inc., 10 Alice St., Binghamton, NY 13904. TEL 607-722-5857; 800-342-9678. FAX 607-722-1424. TELEX 4932599. Ed. Robert Hess. adv.: B&W page $300. bk.rev.; abstr.; bibl.; illus.; cum.index. circ. 233. (also avail. in microfiche from UMI; back issues avail.; reprint service avail. from HAW) **Indexed:** Abstr.Health Care Manage.Stud, Adol.Ment.Hlth.Abstr., Biol.Abstr., Chicago Psychoanal.Lit.Ind., Child Devel.Abstr., Excerp.Med., Hosp.Lit.Ind., IMFL, Past.Care & Couns.Abstr., Psychol.Abstr. (1981-), Ref.Zh., Rehabil.Lit., Soc.Work Res.& Abstr., Sociol.Abstr. **Document type:** academic/scholarly publication, abstracting/indexing.
—BLDSC (6612.773000); Faxon; Haworth; SWETS; UnCover.
Formerly (until 1981): Community Mental Health Review (ISSN 0363-1605)
Description: Devoted to the application of the philosophy of prevention in mental health and other human services.
Refereed Serial

150.19 011   US   ISSN 1066-9884
PSYCHOANALYTIC ABSTRACTS. 1985. q. $49 to non-members (foreign $64); members $19.50 (foreign $27.50); institutions $99 (foreign $129). American Psychological Association, 750 First St., N.E., Washington, DC 20002-4242. TEL 202-336-5500. FAX 202-336-5568. circ. 5,200. **Document type:** abstracting/indexing.
Former titles: PsycSCAN: Psychoanalysis (ISSN 0889-5236); Psychoanalysis Abstracts.
Description: Produced in collaboration with APA Division 39 (Psychoanalysis). Full coverage of Psychological Abstracts is reviewed annually and journals are selected for PsycScan.

150 016   US   ISSN 0033-2887
BF1
PSYCHOLOGICAL ABSTRACTS. 1927. m. $1349 to institutions & non-members (foreign $1424); members $675 (foreign $750). American Psychological Association, 750 First St., N.E., Washington, DC 20002-4242. TEL 202-336-5500. FAX 202-336-5568. adv.; abstr.; cum.index. circ. 3,300. (also avail. in microform from UMI,PMC; reprint service avail. from UMI,KTO) **Indexed:** Ergon.Abstr., JAMA, Popul.Ind. **Document type:** abstracting/indexing.
●Also available online. Vendor(s): Ovid Technologies, DIMDI, Data-Star (PSYC), Knight-Ridder, Inc. (File no.11/PsycINFO), Orbit Search Service.
Also available on CD-ROM. Producer(s): American Psychological Assn., SilverPlatter Information, Inc. (PsycLIT).
—BLDSC (6946.290000); UMI.
Description: Nonevaluative summaries of the serial literature in psychology and related disciplines.

152 573   US   ISSN 0272-0582
PSYCHOLOGICAL CINEMA REGISTER; films and video in the behavioral sciences. Abbreviated title: P C R. 1944. a. Pennsylvania State University, Audio-Visual Services, University Park, PA 16802. TEL 800-826-0132. FAX 814-863-2574. circ. 9,000. **Document type:** catalog.

616.89 011   GW   ISSN 0722-1533
PSYCHOLOGISCHER INDEX; Referatedienst ueber die psychologische Literatur aus den deutschsprachigen Laendern. 1981. q. DM.192. (Universitaet Trier, Zentralstelle fuer Psychologische Information und Dokumentation) Hogrefe Verlag fuer Psychologie, Rohnsweg 25, 37085 Goettingen, Germany. TEL 0551-496090. FAX 0551-4960988. (back issues avail.) **Document type:** abstracting/indexing.

370.15 150   US
PSYCINFO NEWS. 1981. q. free. American Psychological Association, PsycINFO User Services, 750 First St., N.E., Washington, DC 20002-4242. TEL 202-336-5650; 800-374-2722. FAX 202-336-5633. Ed. William C. Hayward. circ. 8,000. **Document type:** newsletter.
Description: Contains search tips and news about forthcoming and existing PsycINFO products.

152 011   US   ISSN 0891-0685
PSYCSCAN: APPLIED EXPERIMENTAL AND ENGINEERING PSYCHOLOGY. 1989. q. $33 to non-members (foreign $48); members $19.50 (foreign $27.50); institutions $66 (foreign $96). American Psychological Association, 750 First St., N.E., Washington, DC 20002-4242. TEL 202-336-5500. FAX 202-336-5568. circ. 800. **Document type:** abstracting/indexing.
●Also available online.
Description: Abstracts derived from the PsycINFO Database. Topics include: human factors, ergonomics, computer applications, environment, safety and accidents, transportation and flight, and working conditions.

150   US   ISSN 0271-7506
BF636.A1
PSYCSCAN: APPLIED PSYCHOLOGY. 1981. q. $33 to non-members (foreign $48); members $19.50 (foreign $27.50); institutions $66 (foreign $96). American Psychological Association, 750 First St., N.E., Washington, DC 20002-4242. TEL 202-336-5500. FAX 202-336-5568. circ. 2,900. **Document type:** abstracting/indexing.
Description: Abstracts from a cluster of subscriber-selected journals in general area of applied psychology.

157   US   ISSN 0197-1484
RC467
PSYCSCAN: CLINICAL PSYCHOLOGY. 1980. q. $33 to non-members (foreign $48); members $19.50 (foreign $27.50); institutions $66 (foreign $96). American Psychological Association, 750 First St., N.E., Washington, DC 20002-4242. TEL 202-336-5500. FAX 202-336-5568. circ. 8,400. (back issues avail.) **Document type:** abstracting/indexing.
Description: Abstracts from subscriber-selected journals of interest to clinical psychologists.

150   US   ISSN 0197-1492
PSYCSCAN: DEVELOPMENTAL PSYCHOLOGY. 1980. q. $33 to non-members (foreign $48); members $19.50 (foreign $27.50); institutions $66 (foreign $96). American Psychological Association, 750 First St., N.E., Washington, DC 20002-4242. TEL 202-336-5500. FAX 202-336-5568. circ. 2,600. **Document type:** abstracting/indexing.
Description: Abstracts from subscriber-selected journals of interest to developmental psychologists.

155   US
PSYCSCAN: LEARNING DISORDERS AND MENTAL RETARDATION. 1982. q. $33 to non-members (foreign $48); members $19.50 (foreign $27.50); institutions $66 (foreign $96). American Psychological Association, 750 First St., N.E., Washington, DC 20002-4242. TEL 202-336-5500. FAX 202-336-5568. circ. 1,800. **Document type:** abstracting/indexing.
Former titles: PsycSCAN: Learning and Communication Disorders and Mental Retardation; PsycSCAN: Learning Disabilities - Mental Retardation (ISSN 0730-1928)
Description: Abstracts articles on learning disorders, communication disorders, and mental retardation, drawn from PsycINFO's annual coverage of more than 1,300 journals.

152.1   UK   ISSN 0143-7526
SENSORY PERCEPTION AND INFORMATION PROCESSING. 1980. m. £75 (effective 1995). S U B I S, Mansion House, 19 Kingfield Rd., Sheffield S11 9AS, England. TEL 0114-2554433. FAX 0114-2554626. E-mail: admin@sheffac.demon.co.uk. Ed. D. Chambers. **Document type:** abstracting/indexing.
—CCC.
Description: Current awareness service for researchers. Studies auditory, visual, touch, olfactory and taste perceptions.

155.937   US   ISSN 0196-0121
HQ1073
THANATOLOGY ABSTRACTS.* biennial. $20 per no. Foundation of Thanatology, Foundation Book & Periodical Division, 630 W. 168th St., New York, NY 10032. TEL 212-928-2066. Ed. Dr. Otto Margolis. adv. (back issues avail.) **Document type:** abstracting/indexing.
Formerly: Funeral Service Abstracts.
Description: Covers articles from 120 magazines.

U.S. NATIONAL CENTER FOR HEALTH STATISTICS. VITAL AND HEALTH STATISTICS. SERIES 6. COGNITION AND SURVEY MEASUREMENT. see PUBLIC HEALTH AND SAFETY — Abstracting, Bibliographies, Statistics

VYBER NOVINEK BRENSKYCH KNIHOVEN. SERIE F: PEDAGOGIKA, PSYCHOLOGIE. see EDUCATION — Abstracting, Bibliographies, Statistics

PUBLIC ADMINISTRATION

see also Public Administration–Computer Applications; Public Administration–Municipal Government; Housing and Urban Planning; Social Services and Welfare

350   IT   ISSN 0393-3938
A N C I RIVISTA. 1957. 12/yr. Associazione Nazionale dei Comuni Italiani, Via Dei Prefetti 46, 00186 Rome, Italy. TEL 39-6-680091. Ed. Giovanni Santo. adv.: color page L.6000000. circ. 50,000.

A P E L L NEWSLETTER. (Awareness and Preparedness for Emergencies at Local Level) see CIVIL DEFENSE

A P S A NEWSLETTER. (Australasian Political Studies Association) see POLITICAL SCIENCE

350   GW   ISSN 0341-0927
A V, DIE ANGESTELLTENVERSICHERUNG. 1954. m. DM.30. Bundesversicherungsanstalt fuer Angestellte, Dezernat fuer Presse- und Oeffentlichkeitsarbeit, 10704 Berlin, Germany. FAX 030-86527379. Ed. Joachim Kusch. bk.rev.; charts; stat. circ. 23,000. **Indexed:** World Bibl.Soc.Sec. **Document type:** government publication.
Formerly (until 1973): Angestelltenversicherung (ISSN 0003-312X)
Description: Covers social insurance laws and regulations, government reform, events. Includes announcements of events.

350   IT   ISSN 0391-3317
ABRUZZO NOTIZIE; notiziario sull'attivita legislativa del Consiglio Regionale. 1975. s-m. free. Servizio Informazione Stampa e Pubbliche Relazioni, Via Michele Jacobucci, 4, 67100 L'Aquila, Italy. circ. 8,500. (back issues avail.)

350   TS
ABU DHABI. AL-JARIDAH AL-RASMIYYAH/ABU DHABI. OFFICIAL GAZETTE. (Text in Arabic) 1968. m. Executive Council, General Secretary, P.O. Box 19, Abu Dhabi, United Arab Emirates. TEL 666444. circ. 1,200. **Document type:** government publication.
Description: Covers legislative and legal matters in the Emirate of Abu Dhabi.

ACCOUNTING FOR GOVERNMENT CONTRACTS: COST ACCOUNTING STANDARDS. see BUSINESS AND ECONOMICS — Accounting

ACCOUNTING FOR GOVERNMENT CONTRACTS: FEDERAL ACQUISITION REGULATION. see BUSINESS AND ECONOMICS — Accounting

ACCOUNTING FOR PUBLIC UTILITIES. see BUSINESS AND ECONOMICS — Accounting

350 323.4 330   PL   ISSN 0137-1134
ACTA UNIVERSITATIS WRATISLAVIENSIS. PRZEGLAD PRAWA I ADMINISTRACJI. (Text in English, German, Polish; summaries in English, French, German, Polish) 1972. irreg. price varies. (Uniwersytet Wroclawski) Wydawnictwo Uniwersytetu Wroclawskiego, Pl. Uniwersytecki 9-13, 50-137 Wroclaw, Poland. TEL 44-10-06. (Dist. by: Ksiegarnia Uniwersytetu Wroclawskiego, Pl. Uniwersytecki 9-13, 50-137 Wroclaw, Poland) Ed. Alfred Klein. circ. 250. **Document type:** academic/scholarly publication.

350   SP   ISSN 0210-007X
ADMINISTRACION PUBLICA. 3/yr. $44. (Centro de Estudios Constitucionales) Edisa, Lopez de Hoyos, 141, 28002 Madrid, Spain. TEL 415-97-12.

ADMINISTRACION Y DESARROLLO. see POLITICAL SCIENCE

350   IE   ISSN 0001-8325
JA26
ADMINISTRATION. 1953. q. I£38. Institute of Public Administration, 57-61 Lansdowne Rd., Dublin 4, Ireland. TEL 01-2697011. FAX 01-2698644. Ed. Tony McNamara. adv.; bk.rev.; charts; index. circ. 2,000. **Indexed:** A.B.C.Pol.Sci., Curr.Cont., Int.Polit.Sci.Abstr., Rural Recreat.Tour.Abstr., Sage Pub.Admin.Abstr., World Agri.Econ.& Rural Sociol.Abstr. **Document type:** trade publication.
—BLDSC (0681.950000); UnCover.

ADMINISTRATION AND POLICY JOURNAL. see POLITICAL SCIENCE

ADMINISTRATION AND POLITICAL SCIENCES REVIEW/MAJALLAT AL-ULUM AL-IDARIYYAH WAL-SIYASIYYAH. see POLITICAL SCIENCE

350   US   ISSN 0095-3997
JA3
ADMINISTRATION & SOCIETY. 1969. q. $63 to individuals; institutions $195 (effective Sep. 1995). Sage Publications, Inc., 2455 Teller Rd., Thousand Oaks, CA 91320. TEL 805-499-0721. FAX 805-499-0871. TELEX 516-1000799. E-mail: libraries@sagepub.com. (Overseas subscr. to: Sage Publications Ltd., 6 Bonhill St., London EC2A 4PU, England; Sage Publications India Pvt. Ltd., P.O. Box 4215, New Delhi 110 048, India) Ed. Gary L. Wamsley. adv.; abstr.; bibl.; charts; tr.lit.; index. circ. 1,250. (also avail. in microfilm from UMI; back issues avail.; reprint service avail.) **Indexed:** A.B.C.Pol.Sci., Amer.Hist.& Life, BPIA, Bus.Ind., C.I.J.E., Curr.Cont., E.I., Energy Ind., Energy Info.Abstr., Hist.Abstr., Int.Polit.Sci.Abstr., Manage.Cont., Mid.East: Abstr.& Ind., Mult.Ed.Abstr., P.A.I.S., Pers.Lit., Polit.Sci.Abstr., Sage Pub.Admin.Abstr., Sage Urb.Stud.Abstr., Sociol.Educ.Abstr., SOMA, SSCI, Tr.& Indus.Ind. **Document type:** academic/scholarly publication.
—BLDSC (0681.957000); Faxon; Genuine Article; SWETS; UMI; UnCover. **CCC.**
Formerly: Journal of Comparative Administration (ISSN 0021-9932)
Description: Deals with administration, bureaucracy, public organization, and public policy and how they affect politics and society.

350   BG
ADMINISTRATIVE AFFAIRS IN BANGLADESH. 1979. a. $5. University of Dhaka, Center for Administrative Studies, Ramna, Dhaka 1000, Bangladesh.

350   US
ADMINISTRATIVE ASSISTANTS ASSOCIATION OF THE U.S. HOUSE OF REPRESENTATIVES. NEWSLETTER. q. Administrative Assistants Association of the U.S. House of Representatives, 215 Cannon, Washington, DC 20515. TEL 202-225-3831. **Document type:** newsletter.

PUBLIC ADMINISTRATION

350 301.15   US   ISSN 0001-8392
HD28   CODEN: ASCQAG
ADMINISTRATIVE SCIENCE QUARTERLY. 1956. q. $50 to individuals (foreign $57); institutions $90 (foreign $97); students $28 (foreign $35) (effective 1995). Cornell University, Johnson Graduate School of Management, 20 Thornwood Dr., Ste. 100, Ithaca, NY 14850-1265. TEL 607-254-7143. FAX 607-254-7100. TELEX WUI 6713054. E-mail: karen@johnson.cornell.edu. Ed. Stephen R. Barley. adv. contact: Linda Pike. bk.rev.; charts; illus.; index, cum.index: 1956-1985. circ. 5,445. (also avail. in microform from UMI; back issues avail.) **Indexed**: A.B.C.Pol.Sci., ABI Inform., Account.Ind. (1974-), Amer.Hist.& Life, ASSIA, B.P.I., Bibl.Ind., BPIA, Bus.Ind., C.I.J.E., CINAHL, Commun.Abstr., Cont.Pg.Manage., Curr.Cont., Deep Sea Res.& Oceanogr.Abstr., E.I., Econ.Abstr., Educ.Admin.Abstr., Hist.Abstr., Int.Polit.Sci.Abstr., Int.Polit.Sci.Abstr., Key to Econ.Sci., Manage.Cont., Med.Care Rev., Mgmt.& Market.Abstr., Mid.East: Abstr.& Ind., Mult.Ed.Abstr., Oper.Res.Manage.Sci., P.A.I.S., Pers.Lit., Pers.Manage.Abstr., Psychol.Abstr. (1956-), Psycscan, Qual.Contr.Appl.Stat., Res.High.Educ.Abstr., Sage Pub.Admin.Abstr., SCIMP (1978-), Soc.Sci.Ind., Soc.Work Res.& Abstr., Sociol.Abstr., SOMA, SSCI. **Document type:** academic/scholarly publication.
●Also available online. Vendor(s): Dow Jones News Retrieval, Information Access Co., Knight-Ridder, Inc., Ovid Technologies, University Microfilms International.
—BLDSC (0696.517000); Faxon; Genuine Article; SWETS; UMI; UnCover. **CCC**.
Refereed Serial

350   II
THE ADMINISTRATOR. (Text in English) 1956. q. Rs.250($35) (effective 1992). (Lal Bahadur Shastri National Academy of Administration) New Age International Pvt. Ltd., Journals Division, 4835-24, Ansari Rd., Daryaganj, New Delhi 110 002, India. TEL 91-11-3267996. FAX 91-11-3267437. TELEX 031-66507 WEL IN. bk.rev.; bibl. circ. 1,200.
Document type: academic/scholarly publication.
Formerly: Lal Bahadur Shastri National Academy of Administration. Journal.

ADVANCE LOCATOR FOR CAPITOL HILL. see *POLITICAL SCIENCE*

ADVANCES IN MARKETING AND PUBLIC POLICY. see *BUSINESS AND ECONOMICS — Marketing And Purchasing*

ADVOCATE'S ADVOCATE. see *POLITICAL SCIENCE*

354.6   MR   ISSN 0007-9588
JQ1871.A1
AFRICAN ADMINISTRATIVE STUDIES. French edition: Cahiers Africains d'Administration Publique. (Editions in English, French) 1966. s-a. $40. Centre Africain de Formation et de Recherche Administratives pour le Developpement - African Training and Research Centre in Administration for Development, P.O. Box 310, Tangier, Morocco. TEL 936601. FAX 9-941415. TELEX 33664M. **Indexed**: Curr.Cont.Africa, Documentatieblad, Mid.East: Abstr.& Ind., Rural Recreat.Tour.Abstr., World Agri.Econ.& Rural Sociol.Abstr. **Document type:** academic/scholarly publication.

AFRICANUS; journal of development alternatives. see *POLITICAL SCIENCE*

350   TG
AGENCE TOGOLAISE DE PRESSE. BULLETIN D'INFORMATION. w. Agence Togolaise de Presse, 35 rue Binger, Lome, Togo.

350 370   US   ISSN 1058-1324
LB2825
AID FOR EDUCATION REPORT. 1991. s-m. $249. (Community Development Services, Inc.) C D Publications, 8204 Fenton St., Silver Spring, MD 20910. TEL 301-588-6380. FAX 301-588-6385.
Document type: newsletter.
Description: Public and private funding opportunities for all levels of education, plus updates on application deadlines, eligibility criteria for upcoming programs, funding levels and budget trends.

350   TS
AL-AIN. 1986. m. Municipal Government, P.O. Box 1003, Al-Ain, United Arab Emirates. TEL 635111. Ed. Musaad Ismail. circ. 1,000. **Document type:** government publication.
Formerly (until 1988): Majallat Baladiat al-Ain.
Description: Covers the activities of the municipality and local groups.

350   US   ISSN 0892-9084
HA221
ALABAMA COUNTY DATA BOOK. 1976. a. free. Department of Economic and Community Affairs, Box 5690, Montgomery, AL 36103-5690. TEL 205-242-5493. FAX 205-242-0776. Ed. Parker Collins. charts; stat. circ. 3,500. (also avail. in microfiche from CIS) **Indexed**: SRI. **Document type:** government publication.

350   US   ISSN 1072-7620
HA221
ALABAMA MUNICIPAL DATA BOOK. every 5 yrs. free. Department of Economic and Community Affairs, Box 5690, Montgomery, AL 36103-5690. TEL 205-242-5493. FAX 205-242-0776. Ed. Parker Collins. **Document type:** government publication.

353.9   US   ISSN 0095-3865
HJ11
ALASKA. LEGISLATURE. BUDGET AND AUDIT COMMITTEE. ANNUAL REPORT. Key Title: Annual Report - State of Alaska. Legislative Budget and Audit Committee. 1965. a. free. Legislative Budget and Audit Committee, Box W, Juneau, AK 99811. circ. 200. **Document type:** government publication.

350   US   ISSN 1072-8058
ALASKA LEGISLATIVE DIGEST. 1971. w. (Jan.-Jun.). $230. Information & Research Service, 3037 S. Circle, Anchorage, AK 99507. TEL 907-349-7711. FAX 907-522-1761. Ed. Tim Bradner.
Description: Provides analytical and interpretive coverage of Alaska legislative session, interim activity and administrative action.

353.9   US
JK9549.O4
ALASKA OMBUDSMAN REPORT. 1975. a. Office of Ombudsman, Box 113000, Juneau, AK 99811-3000. TEL 907-465-4970. FAX 907-465-3330. circ. 3,000. **Document type:** government publication.
Formerly: Alaska. Office of Ombudsman. Report of the Ombudsman (ISSN 0363-5376)

ALLAM ES IGAZGATAS. see *LAW*

ALLIANCE (OTTAWA). see *LABOR UNIONS*

350 352   GW   ISSN 0722-5474
ALTERNATIVE KOMMUNALPOLITIK; Fachzeitschrift fuer gruene und alternative Politik. 1982. bi-m. DM.48. Verein zur Foerderung der Kommunalpolitischen Arbeit, Herforder Str. 92, 33602 Bielefeld, Germany. TEL 0521-177517. FAX 0521-177568. adv.; bk.rev. circ. 4,000. (back issues avail.)

350   BH
AMANDALA. 1970. w. $50 (effective July 1991). Amandala Press, 3304 Partridge St., Belize City, Belize. TEL 02-77276. FAX 02-75934. (Subscr. to: Box 15, Belize City, Belize) Ed. Evan X. Hyde. circ. 9,500. **Document type:** newspaper.
Description: Community service publication.

353   US   ISSN 0275-0740
JK1
AMERICAN REVIEW OF PUBLIC ADMINISTRATION. 1967. q. $22 to individuals in US & Canada (elsewhere $25); institutions in US & Canada $50 (elsewhere $60). Georgia State University, School of Public Administration and Urban Studies, University Plaza, Atlanta, GA 30303-3083. TEL 404-651-4591. FAX 404-651-1378. E-mail: jzhou@cctr.umkc.edu. (Subscr. to: American Review of Public Administration, L.P. Cookingham Institute of Public Affairs, Henry W. Bloch School of Business and Public Administration, University of Missouri at Kansas City, Kansas City, MO 64110) (Co-sponsors: University of Missouri at Columbia; University of Missouri, St. Louis) Ed. John Clayton Thomas. adv. contact: Nicholas Peroff. bk.rev.; bibl. circ. 500. (also avail. in microform from UMI; back issues avail.) **Indexed**: A.B.C.Pol.Sci., ABI Inform, BPIA, Bus.Ind., Int.Polit.Sci.Abstr., Manage.Cont., P.A.I.S., Pers.Lit., Polit.Sci.Abstr., PSI, Sage Pub.Admin.Abstr., Tr.& Indus.Ind. **Document type:** academic/scholarly publication.
●Also available online. Vendor(s): Knight-Ridder, Inc., University Microfilms International.
—BLDSC (0853.800000); Faxon; SWETS; UMI; UnCover. **CCC**.
Formerly (until 1981): Midwest Review of Public Administration (ISSN 0026-346X)

350   US
AMERICAN SOCIETY FOR PUBLIC ADMINISTRATION. SECTION ON INTERNATIONAL AND COMPARATIVE ADMINISTRATION. OCCASIONAL PAPERS. 1974. irreg., latest 1992. $3 per no. American Society for Public Administration, Section on International and Comparative Administration, 1120 G St., N.W., Ste. 700, Washington, DC 20005. TEL 202-393-7878. Ed. Richard Ryan. circ. 550. (back issues avail.; reprint service avail. from KTO)

350   IT   ISSN 0044-8141
AMMINISTRARE. 1986. 3/yr. L.120000. (Istituto per la Scienza dell' Amministrazione Pubblica) Societa Editrice Il Mulino, Strada Maggiore, 37, 40125 Bologna, Italy. TEL 39-51-256011. FAX 39-51-256034. Ed. Ettore Rotelli. adv.; index. circ. 1,200. (back issues avail.) **Indexed**: Int.Polit.Sci.Abstr.

350   IT   ISSN 1122-0635
AMMINISTRAZIONE CIVILE. 1993. bi-m. L.220000. (Ministero dell'Interno) Maggioli Editore, Viale Vespucci 12-n, Casella Postale 290, 47037 Rimini, Italy. TEL 0541-626777. FAX 0541-622020.

350   IT   ISSN 0303-9722
AMMINISTRAZIONE ITALIANA. 1945. m. L.225000 (foreign L.320000). Societa Tipografica Barbieri, Noccioli & C., Casella Postale 567, 50053 Empoli, Italy. TEL 0571-920394. FAX 0571-920859. Eds. Antonio Romano, Giovanni la Torre. adv.; bk.rev.; index. circ. 3,800.
Description: Covers local and national Italian administration.

350   SZ   ISSN 0003-2115
AMTLICHER ANZEIGER. 1968. w. H. Akerets Erben AG, Postfach, 8600 Duebendorf, Switzerland. adv.; bk.rev. circ. 12,100.

350   GW
AMTSBLATT DER REGIERUNG VON UNTERFRANKEN. 1956. s-m. DM.41. Regierung von Unterfranken, 97064 Wuerzburg, Germany. TEL 0931-1380-1. FAX 0931-13877. bk.rev. circ. 1,100. **Document type:** government publication.

350   GW   ISSN 0934-8964
AMTSBLATT DER STADT MOENCHENGLADBACH. 1975. 2/m. DM.40. Presse- und Informationsamt, Rathaus Abtei, 41050 Moenchengladbach, Germany. TEL 02161-25-2592. FAX 02161-25-2609. TELEX 852788-STMG-D. circ. 1,400 (paid). (back issues avail.) **Document type:** government publication.

350   GW
AMTSBLATT DES LANDKREISES DILLINGEN AN DER DONAU. bi-m. Landkreis Dillingen an der Donau, Grosse Allee 24, 89407 Dillingen, Germany. TEL 09071-51-138.

PUBLIC ADMINISTRATION

350 GW
AMTSBLATT DES LANDKREISES HOF. 1972. s-m. DM.99.60. Landratsamt Hof, Schaumbergstr. 14, 95032 Hof, Germany. TEL 09281-57-0. FAX 09281-58340. Ed. I.A. Hoffmann. circ. 550. **Document type:** bulletin, government publication.

350 GW
AMTSBLATT GROSSE KREISSTADT LEINFELDEN-ECHTERDINGEN. 1976. w. Nussbaum Verlag, Postfach 1340, 71261 Weil, Germany. TEL 07033-525-0. circ. 18,000. **Document type:** bulletin.
Description: Official information of the municipality of Leinfelden-Echterdingen.

333.7 AG ISSN 0302-5705
QH113
ANALES DE PARQUES NACIONALES. 1945. irreg., no.15, 1982. 25000p. Administracion de Parques Nacionales, Santa Fe 690, 1059 Buenos Aires, Argentina. TEL 54-1-3110303. E-mail: 54-1-3158412. illus. circ. 4,000. **Document type:** government publication.
Supersedes (in 1955): Natura (ISSN 0470-3685) **Description:** Contains information on the national parks of the country.

658 II ISSN 0003-2964
ANDHRA PRADESH PRODUCTIVITY COUNCIL. TARGET. 1961. s-a. Rs.6. Andhra Pradesh Productivity Council, P.O. Box No. 21 (10-1-200, A.C. Guards), Hyderabad 500004, Andhra Pradesh, India. Ed. S. Rajagopala Reddi. adv.; bk.rev. circ. 1,000.
Formerly: Andhra Pradesh Productivity Council. Journal.

350 US ISSN 0278-4289
ANNALS OF PUBLIC ADMINISTRATION. 1982. irreg., vol.5, 1983. price varies. Marcel Dekker, Inc., 270 Madison Ave., New York, NY 10016. TEL 212-696-9000. FAX 212-685-4540. TELEX 421419. Ed. Jack Rabin.

350 BE ISSN 0066-2461
ANNUAIRE ADMINISTRATIF ET JUDICIAIRE DE BELGIQUE/ADMINISTRATIEF EN GERECHTELIJK JAARBOEK VOOR BELGIE. 1869. a. 6250 BEF. Etablissements Emile Bruylant, 67 rue de la Regence, 1000 Brussels, Belgium. TEL 32-2-5129845. FAX 32-2-5117202. circ. 3,000. **Document type:** directory.

916.7 GO
ANNUAIRE NATIONAL OFFICIEL DE LA REPUBLIQUE GABONAISE. 1973. a. 5000 Fr.CFA. Agence Havas Gabon, B.P. 213, Libreville, Gabon. adv.; illus.; stat. circ. 5,000. **Document type:** government publication.

350 US ISSN 1052-7532
JA1
ANNUAL EDITIONS: PUBLIC ADMINISTRATION. Key Title: Public Administration. 1990. a. $12.95. Dushkin Publishing Group, Sluice Dock, Guilford, CT 06437-9989. TEL 203-453-4351. FAX 203-453-6000. Ed. Howard R. Balanoff; Pub. Ian Nielsen. illus. **Document type:** academic/scholarly publication.
Refereed Serial

350 US
ANNUAL EDITIONS: STATE & LOCAL GOVERNMENT. 1978. a. $12.95. Dushkin Publishing Group, Sluice Dock, Guilford, CT 06437-9989. TEL 203-453-4351. FAX 203-453-6000. Ed. Bruce Stinebrickner; Pub. Ian Nielsen. **Document type:** academic/scholarly publication.
Refereed Serial

350 US ISSN 0731-339X
H50
ANNUAL GUIDE TO PUBLIC POLICY EXPERTS. a. $14.95. Heritage Foundation, 214 Massachusetts Ave., N.E., Washington, DC 20002. TEL 202-546-4400. FAX 202-546-8328. Ed. Thomas Atwood.
Description: Lists the names, addresses, phone and fax numbers of more than 1700 public policy experts under 89 categories ranging from national security to natural sciences.

350 320 US
ANNUAL REPORT ON PRIVATIZATION. a. $35 (effective 1995 & 1996). Reason Foundation, 3415 S. Sepulveda Blvd., Ste. 400, Los Angeles, CA 90034-6060. TEL 310-391-2245. FAX 310-391-4395. E-mail: reason@iia.org. Ed. John O'Leary. circ. 10,000. **Document type:** academic/scholarly publication.
Description: Covers contracting, infrastructure and public sector innovations in privitization and alternative service delivery.

350 IT ISSN 1122-8482
ANNUARIO AMMINISTRATIVO ITALIANO/ITALIAN ADMINISTRATIVE DIRECTORY. 1968. a. L.275000 (effective 1996). Guida Monaci S.p.A., Via Vitorchiano 107, 00189 Rome, Italy. TEL 39-6-3288805. FAX 39-6-3275693. TELEX 623324 MONACI. adv.: B&W page L.13300000.
Description: Directory of all Italian administrative activities.

350 340 LE ISSN 0570-8915
L'ARGUS DE LA LEGISLATION LIBANAISE. (Text mainly in French, occasionally in English) 1954. q. $280. Bureau of Lebanese and Arab Documentation, P.O. Box 165403, Beirut, Lebanon. (Subscr. to: Marcel Tawil, Bureau of Documentation, Postfach 2412, 79514 Loerrach, Germany. TEL 49-7621-2472. FAX 49-7621-2472.) circ. 1,000.
Description: Translations of the main legislative texts published in the Lebanese official gazette, and translation of Lebanese legislative documents, including all modifications.

350 320 US ISSN 0744-7477
ARIZONA CAPITOL TIMES. 1945. w. $42. Arizona News Service, 14 North 18th Ave., Phoenix, AZ 85007. TEL 602-258-7026. FAX 602-258-2504. Ed. Ned Creighton. adv. contact: Brenda Abranam. **Document type:** newspaper.
Formerly: Arizona Legislative Review.
Description: Covers Arizona political, legislative and state agency news.

350 342 320 US
ARKANSAS POLITICAL REPORT. 1983. s-m. $90. Arkansas Political Reports, 17410 Cantrell Rd., Ste. B-8, Little Rock, AR 72212. TEL 501-868-4400. FAX 501-868-4844. Ed. Mary Dillard. circ. 130. **Document type:** newsletter.
Formerly: Arkansas Report (ISSN 0273-2742) **Description:** Reports on political, legislative, and state government news in Arkansas.

350 US
ARKANSAS STATE DIRECTORY. 1973. biennial. $10. Prestige Press, 4200 Heritage Dr., North Little Rock, AR 72117. TEL 501-945-0866. FAX 501-945-5000. adv. circ. 4,000. **Document type:** directory.
Description: Directory of State of Arkansas government offices plus a section on federal government offices within Arkansas.

350 US
THE ART OF COMMUNICATION. q. National Association of County Information Officers, c/o National Association of Counties, 440 First St., N.W., 8th Fl., Washington, DC 20001. TEL 202-393-6226.
Description: Aimed at county government officials involved with disseminating public information.

ARTS & CULTURAL TIMES. see *ART*

350 HK ISSN 0259-8272
ASIAN JOURNAL OF PUBLIC ADMINISTRATION. (Text in English) 1979. 2/yr. HK.$120 (Southeast Asia $30; elsewhere $35). Hong Kong University, Department of Politics and Public Administration, Pokfulam Rd., Hong Kong. TEL 852-859-2393. FAX 852-858-3550. Ed.Bd. bk.rev. circ. 500. (back issues avail.) **Indexed:** Human.Resour.Abstr., Int.Polit.Sci.Abstr., Int.Polit.Sci.Abstr., Sage Pub.Admin.Abstr., Sage Urb.Stud.Abstr. **Document type:** academic/scholarly publication.
—BLDSC (1742.575000).

350 UK ISSN 0305-2044
ASSOCIATION OF COUNTY COUNCILS. YEARBOOK. a. £10. Association of County Councils, Eaton House, 66A Eaton Sq., London SW1W 9BH, England. TEL 0171-201-1571. FAX 0171-235-8458. Ed. Michael Baker. adv. circ. 6,750.

350 IT ISSN 0004-606X
ASTE GIUDIZIARIE. 1949. w. L.3360. Istituto Vendite Giudiziarie di Roma, Via della Cava Aurelia 98, Rome, Italy. Ed. R.F. Santagati. adv. circ. 20,000.

350 GW ISSN 0943-2426
AUSBILDUNG PRUEFUNG FORTBILDUNG; Zeitschrift fuer die staatliche und kommunale Verwaltung. 1975. m. DM.157.20. Richard Boorberg Verlag (Stuttgart), Scharrstr. 2, 70563 Stuttgart, Germany. TEL 0711-7385-0. Ed. Peter Neumann. adv.; bk.rev. circ. 2,500. (back issues avail.) **Document type:** bulletin.

AUSTIN REPORT. see *POLITICAL SCIENCE*

350 AT
AUSTRALIA. DEPARTMENT OF PLANNING AND DEVELOPMENT. ANNUAL REPORT. a. Department of Planning and Development, 477 Collins St., Ground Fl., Melbourne 3000, Australia. TEL 03-628-5059. FAX 03-628-5060. **Document type:** government publication.

354.9 AT ISSN 0313-6647
JA26
AUSTRALIAN JOURNAL OF PUBLIC ADMINISTRATION. 1938. q. Aus.$50 (foreign Aus.$70). Royal Institute of Public Administration Australia, G.P.O. Box 904, Sydney, N.S.W. 2001, Australia. TEL 51-2-228-4375. FAX 61-2-241-1920. (Subscr. to: G.P.O. Box 780, Sydney, N.S.W. 2001, Australia) Ed. Roger Wettenhall. adv.; bk.rev.; charts; stat.; cum.index: 1938-1976. circ. 5,700. **Indexed:** ASSIA, Aus.P.A.I.S., Curr.Cont., Int.Polit.Sci.Abstr., Polit.Sci.Abstr., Sage Pub.Admin.Abstr., SSCI. **Document type:** academic/scholarly publication.
—BLDSC (1811.500000); Faxon; Genuine Article; SWETS; UnCover.
Formerly: Public Administration (ISSN 0033-328X)

350 IT
AUTONOMIE E DIRITTO. 3/yr. Editrice Ila Palma, Via Isodoro La Lumia 5-7, 90139 Palermo, Italy. TEL 091-332051. Ed. Francesco Teresi.

B & P A. (Business & Public Affairs) see *BUSINESS AND ECONOMICS*

350 UK ISSN 0968-1531
JN500
B B C - VACHER'S BIOGRAPHICAL GUIDE. 1988. a. £55. (British Broadcasting Corporation) Vacher's Publications, 113 High St., Berkhamsted, Herts HP4 2DJ, England. TEL 01442-876135. FAX 01442-870148. Ed. Robbie Gibb. **Document type:** directory.
Description: Contains biographies of active members of the House of Lords and U.K. representatives of the European Parliament.

350 310 SZ
B F S AKTUELL. m. Bundesamt fuer Statistik, Schwarztorstr. 96, CH-3003 Bern, Switzerland. TEL 031-3236011. FAX 031-3236061. **Document type:** government publication.

350 US ISSN 0897-0726
BACKGROUNDER UPDATE. irreg., no.234, 1994. $2 per no. Heritage Foundation, 214 Massachusetts Ave., N.E., Washington, DC 20002. TEL 202-546-4400. FAX 202-546-8328. (looseleaf format; back issues avail.)
●Also available online. Vendor(s): Lexis-Nexis.

354.43 GW ISSN 0340-3505
BADEN - WUERTTEMBERGISCHE VERWALTUNGSPRAXIS. 1974. m. DM.198 (students DM.159). W. Kohlhammer GmbH, Hessbruehlstr. 69, 70565 Stuttgart, Germany. TEL 0711-7863-1. FAX 0711-7863263. Eds. Max Goegler, Kurt Gerhardt. adv.; bk.rev. circ. 2,000. **Indexed:** CERDIC. **Document type:** bulletin.
—CCC.
Formed by the merger of: Baden - Wuerttembergisches Verwaltungsblatt (ISSN 0005-3724); Verwaltungspraxis.

350 BA
BAHRAIN. MINISTRY OF INFORMATION. OFFICIAL GAZETTE/BAHRAIN. WIZARAT AL-ISTI'LAMAT. AL-JARIDAH AL-RASMIYAH. (Text in Arabic) 1957. w. Ministry of Information, P.O. Box 253, Isa Town, Bahrain. TEL 981555. FAX 682777. TELEX 8399. **Document type:** government publication.

PUBLIC ADMINISTRATION

348 US ISSN 0092-0959
KFO15
BALDWIN'S OHIO LEGISLATIVE SERVICE. 1971. m. $295. Banks - Baldwin Law Publishing Co., University Center, Box 1974, Cleveland, OH 44106. TEL 216-721-7373. FAX 216-721-8055.
Description: Contains the text of new legislation; case notes and other annotations; bill status and Index to Bills; selected analyses prepared by the Ohio Legislative Service Commission; and research aids.

351 BG
BANGLADESH. MINISTRY OF FOREIGN AFFAIRS. LIST OF THE DIPLOMATIC CORPS AND OTHER FOREIGN REPRESENTATIVES. (Text in English) irreg. Tk.5.75. Ministry of Foreign Affairs, Dhaka, Bangladesh. **Document type:** government publication.

350 BG
BANGLADESH JOURNAL OF PUBLIC ADMINISTRATION. 1987. s-a. Tk.40($10) (£7). Bangladesh Public Administration Training Centre, Attn: Asst. Publication Officer, Molla Mosharraf Hossain, Savar, Dhaka 1343, Bangladesh. TEL 831711-20-251. TELEX 632228-PATC-BJ. Ed. Mustafa Abdur Rahman. bk.rev.; abstr.; bibl.; charts. circ. 750.
● Also available online.
Incorporates: Administrative Science Review (ISSN 0001-8406)
Description: Contains articles, research, and comments.

350 BB ISSN 0377-144X
J137
BARBADOS. LEGISLATURE. HOUSE OF ASSEMBLY. MINUTES OF PROCEEDINGS. w. Legislature, House of Assembly, Bridgetown, Barbados, W.I. **Document type:** government publication.

350 BB ISSN 0377-1458
J137
BARBADOS. LEGISLATURE. SENATE. MINUTES OF PROCEEDINGS. w. Legislature, Senate, Bridgetown, Barbados, W.I. **Document type:** government publication.

320 350 GW ISSN 0723-7022
BAYERISCHE BUERGERMEISTER. 1917. m. DM.175. Verlagsgruppe Jehle - Rehm, Einsteinstr. 172, 81675 Munich, Germany. TEL 089-416006-0. FAX 089-4706998. Ed.Bd. circ. 2,500. (back issues avail.) **Document type:** bulletin.
—BLDSC (1871.188050).

BAYERISCHE VERWALTUNGSBLAETTER; Zeitschrift fuer oeffentliches Recht und oeffentliche Verwaltung. see *LAW*

354.43 GW ISSN 0934-6465
BAYERISCHES STAATSMINISTERIUM DES INNERN. ALLGEMEINES MINISTERIALBLATT. 1949. bi-w. DM.110. Staatsministerium des Innern, Odeonsplatz 3, 80539 Munich, Germany. TEL 089-2192-01. FAX 089-21921-2885. TELEX 524540-BYIM-D. Ed. Peter Abholzer. bk.rev. circ. 8,500. **Document type:** government publication.
Formerly (until 1988): Bayerisches Staatsministerium des Innern. Ministerialamtsblatt der Bayerischen Inneren Verwaltung (ISSN 0005-7185)

352 GW ISSN 0005-741X
DER BEAMTE IN RHEINLAND-PFALZ; Zeitschrift fuer Angehoerige des oeffentlichen Dienstes. 1949. m. membership. Deutscher Beamtenbund, Landesbund Rheinland-Pfalz, Adam-Karrilton-Str. 62, 55118 Mainz, Germany. Ed. Hans Eberhard Hielscher. adv. circ. 30,000.

351 NE ISSN 0921-8459
BEDRIJFSHULPVERLENING. 1984. 4/yr. fl.26 (effective 1994). (Nederlandse Vereniging Bedrijfshulpverlening) V N G Uitgeverij, P.O. Box 30435, 2500 GK The Hague, Netherlands. TEL 31-70-3738888. FAX 31-70-3469201. circ. 1,500. **Document type:** trade publication.

363.6 AU ISSN 0520-9048
BEGRIFFSBESTIMMUNGEN FUER DIE BUNDESSTATISTIKEN DER OESTERREICHISCHE ELEKTRIZITAETSWIRTSCHAFT. (Issued in cooperation with Osterreichische Elektrizitaetswirtschafts-A.G.) 1955. a. S.550. Bundesministerium fuer Wirtschaftliche Angelegenheiten, Bundeslastverteiler, Dienststelle Statistik, Am Hof 6a, A-1010 Vienna, Austria. Ed. Johann Precht. circ. 500. **Document type:** government publication.
Formerly: Brennstoffstatistik der Waermekraftwerke fuer die Oeffentliche Elektrizitaetsversorgung in Oesterreich.

350 NE ISSN 0166-9222
BELEIDSANALYSE. (Text in Dutch, English) 1972. q. fl.65. (Ministerie van Financien, Afdeling Beleidsevaluatie en Instrumentatie) S D U Uitgeverij, Chr. Plantijnstraat 2, 2515 TZ The Hague, Netherlands. TEL 31-70-3789111. FAX 31-70-3475778. (Editorial addr.: P.O. Box 20201, 2500 EE The Hague, Netherlands. TEL 31-70-3427372. FAX 31-70-3427934) Eds. H.O. Korte, J.C. Hellendoorn. bk.rev.; circ. 2,500. (paid). (back issues avail.) **Indexed:** Key to Econ.Sci. **Document type:** government publication, academic/scholarly publication.
—SWETS.

350 NE ISSN 0921-1934
BELEIDSWETENSCHAP; kwartaalschrift voor beleidsonderzoek en beleidspraktijk. 1987. q. Samsom H.D. Tjeenk Willink B.V. (Subsidiary of: Wolters Kluwer N.V.), Postbus 316, 2400 AH Alphen aan den Rijn, Netherlands. TEL 31-1720-66822. FAX 31-1720-66639. adv. **Indexed:** Int.Polit.Sci.Abstr.
—SWETS.

350 331 BE
BELGIUM. HOGE RAAD VOOR DE MIDDENSTAND. JAARVERSLAG VAN DE SECRETARIS GENERAAL. French edition: Belgium. Conseil Superieur des Classes Moyennes. Rapport Annuel du Secretaire General (ISSN 0067-5393) (Text in Dutch) 1951. a. free. Hoge Raad voor de Middenstand, Zaveltoren, J. Stevensstraat 7, B-1000 Brussels, Belgium. **Document type:** government publication.

BELGIUM. MINISTERE DE LA PREVOYANCE SOCIALE. RAPPORT GENERAL SUR LA SECURITE SOCIALE. see *SOCIAL SERVICES AND WELFARE*

354 NR
BENDEL STATE. MINISTRY OF INFORMATION, SOCIAL DEVELOPMENT AND SPORTS. ESTIMATE. a. £N5. Ministry of Information, Social Development and Sports, Printing and Stationery Division, P.M.B. 1099, Benin City, Nigeria. (Orders to: Bendel State Government Printer, Government Press, Benin City, Nigeria) **Document type:** government publication.
Formerly: Bendel State. Ministry of Home Affairs and Information. Mid-Western State Estimates.

350 BE ISSN 0005-8777
BENELUX PUBLIKATIEBLAD/BULLETIN BENELUX. (Belgium Netherlands Luxembourg) (Supplement to: Textes de Base Benelux - Basic Benelux Texts) (Text in Dutch, French) 1958. irreg. (approx. 3/yr.). 1.60 BEF per page. B E N E L U X Economic Union, Rue de la Regence 39, B-1000 Brussels, Belgium. (looseleaf format)
—BLDSC (2834.520000).

BERNAN GOVERNMENT PUBLICATIONS NEWS. see *LIBRARY AND INFORMATION SCIENCES*

350 NE ISSN 0927-3387
BESTUURSKUNDE. 1992. 8/yr. fl.97. (Vereniging voor Bestuurskunde) Vuga Uitgeverij B.V., Postbus 16400, 2500 BK The Hague, Netherlands. TEL 31-70-3614011. FAX 31-70-3632338. Ed. A.F.A. Korsten. adv.: B&W page fl.1050; color page fl.3010; trim 160 x 240. circ. 1,400. **Document type:** academic/scholarly publication.
—SWETS.
Description: Covers issues relating to public administration at the local and central levels. *Refereed Serial*

350 NE ISSN 0165-7194
BESTUURSWETENSCHAPPEN. 1947. 6/yr. fl.130 to individuals; institutions fl.155; students fl.80. V N G Uitgeverij, P.O. Box 30435, 2500 GK The Hague, Netherlands. TEL 31-70-3738888. FAX 31-70-3469201. adv.; index. circ. 1,000. **Indexed:** ELLIS, Excerp.Med., Key to Econ.Sci. **Document type:** trade publication.
—SWETS.

350 028.5 GW ISSN 0932-5492
BETREFF; Magazin fuer junge Leute im oeffentlichen Dienst. 1957. bi-m. Deutsche Beamtenbund Jugend, Erfurtstr. 32, 53125 Bonn, Germany. TEL 0228-773750. FAX 0228-774475. Ed. Ulrich Werth. adv.: B&W page DM.3198, color page DM.4060; trim 185 x 260. bk.rev. circ. 37,669. **Document type:** trade publication.

350 330 US ISSN 0894-9697
BILL SHIPP'S GEORGIA. 1987. w. $195. Word Merchants, Inc., Box 440755, Kennesaw, GA 30144-9513. TEL 404-422-2543. FAX 404-422-0227. Ed. Bill Shipp; Pub. Bill Shipp. **Document type:** newsletter.
Description: Covers Georgia government, politics and business.

350 NE ISSN 0167-1146
BINNENLANDS BESTUUR; wekelijks tijdschrift voor bestuurlijk Nederland. 1980. w. (44/yr.). fl.205. Samsom H.D. Tjeenk Willink B.V. (Subsidiary of: Wolters Kluwer N.V.), Postbus 316, 2400 AH Alphen aan den Rijn, Netherlands. TEL 31-1720-66822. FAX 31-1720-66639. (Editorial addr.: Postbus 1948, 1000 BX Amsterdam, Netherlands. TEL 31-20-6252424) adv. circ. 38,970. **Document type:** trade publication.
—SWETS.
Incorporates: Binnenlands Bestuur Management (ISSN 0922-3193).

353.002 US ISSN 0882-1593
E185.615
BLACK ELECTED OFFICIALS; a national roster. 1970. a. $32.50. Joint Center for Political Studies, Inc., 1090 Vermont Ave. N.W., Ste. 1100, Washington, DC 20005-4905. stat.; index. circ. 5,000. (also avail. in microfiche from CIS) **Indexed:** SRI.
Formerly: National Roster of Black Elected Officials (ISSN 0092-2935)

BLACKS IN GOVERNMENT - NEWS. see *ETHNIC INTERESTS*

350 UK
THE BLUE PAGES. w. £189 (Europe £220; rest of world £260) (effective 1996). Parliamentary Communications Ltd., 10 Little College St., Westminster, London SW1P 3SH, England. TEL 0171-233-1388. FAX 0171-976-0422. Ed. Patrick Cormack; Pub. Keith Young. **Document type:** bulletin.

350 US
BOARD OF IMMIGRATION APPEALS INTERIM DECISIONS. irreg. price varies. U.S. Immigration and Naturalization Services, Board of Immigration Appeals, 425 I St., Washington, DC 20536. TEL 202-514-1900. (Subscr. to: Superintendent of Documents, U.S. Government Printing Office, Box 371954, Pittsburgh, PA 15250-7954. TEL 202-512-1800. FAX 202-512-2250) **Document type:** government publication.
Description: Presents selected precedental decisions rendered by the Board of Immigration Appeals.

350 MH
BOLETIM OFICIAL. (Text in Portuguese) 1838. w. Rua da Imprensa Nacional, CP 33, Macao. TEL 853-573822. FAX 853-596802. Ed. Antonio de Vasconcelos Mendes Liz.

350 SP ISSN 1130-5894
BOLETIN OFICIAL DE NAVARRA. Basque edition from 1989: Nafarroako Aldizkari Ofiziala (ISSN 1130-586X) 1838. 3/wk. 8000 ptas. Gobierno de Navarra, Fondo de Publicaciones, Navas de Tolosa 21, 31002 Pamplona, Spain. TEL 34-48-107121. FAX 34-48-227673. **Document type:** government publication.
Former titles (until 1975): Boletin Oficial de la Provincia de Navarra (ISSN 1130-5878); (until 1846): Boletin Oficial de Pamplona (ISSN 1130-5886)

PUBLIC ADMINISTRATION

350 SP
BOLETIN OFICIAL DEL PARLAMENTO DE NAVARRA. 1980. irreg. 5000 ptas. includes Diario de Sesiones. (Parlamento Foral de Navarra) Gobierno de Navarra, Fondo de Publicaciones, Navas de Tolosa 21, 31002 Pamplona, Spain. TEL 34-48-107121. FAX 34-48-227673.

351 US ISSN 0068-0125
JK2403
BOOK OF THE STATES. (Supplements avail.) 1935. biennial. $79. The Council of State Governments, 3560 Iron Works Pike, Box 11910, Lexington, KY 40578-1910. TEL 606-244-8000. FAX 606-244-8001. Ed. Deborah A. Gona. index. circ. 11,000. (also avail. in microfiche from KTO,PMC,WSH) **Indexed:** SRI. **Document type:** directory.
   Description: Provides a comprehensive reference on all state government with information on reorganization, management, productivity, and efficiency efforts.

353.002 US ISSN 1041-6722
JK6
BRADDOCK'S FEDERAL-STATE-LOCAL GOVERNMENT DIRECTORY. 1975. irreg. (every 2-4 yrs.). $63.45. Braddock Communications, Inc., 909 N. Washington St., Alexandria, VA 22314-1555. TEL 703-549-6500. Eds. Paul A. Arnold, Thomas W. Jacobson. **Document type:** directory.
   Description: Provides list of middle and top level officials in the White House administation, photos and brief biographies of all members of Congress, the Supreme Court, and the executive officers of all the states.

631.6 BL ISSN 0101-5680
HD1741.B8
BRAZIL. DEPARTAMENTO NACIONAL DE OBRAS CONTRA AS SECAS. RELATORIO. Cover title: Relatorio D N O C S. 1945. a. free. Departamento Nacional de Obras Contra as Secas, Av. Duque de Caixias 1700, Fortaleza-Ceara 60000, Brazil. bk.rev.; charts; illus.; stat. (processed) **Indexed:** Biol.Abstr.

350 CN
BRITISH COLUMBIA. LEGISLATIVE ASSEMBLY. DEBATES (HANSARD DAILY). d. (during sessions). Can.$280. (Legislative Assembly) Crown Publications Inc., 521 Fort St., Victoria, BC V8W 1 7, Canada. TEL 604-386-4636. FAX 604-386-0221. **Document type:** government publication.

350 CN
BRITISH COLUMBIA. LEGISLATIVE ASSEMBLY. DEBATES (HANSARD PAPERBOUND). irreg. Can.$145. (Legislative Assembly) Crown Publications, 546 Yates St., Victoria, BC V8W 1K8, Canada. TEL 604-386-4636. FAX 604-386-0221. **Document type:** government publication.

350 CN
BRITISH COLUMBIA. LEGISLATIVE ASSEMBLY. JOURNALS. a. price varies. (Legislative Assembly) Crown Publications, 546 Yates St., Victoria, BC V8W 1K8, Canada. TEL 604-386-4636. FAX 604-386-0221. (back issues avail.) **Document type:** government publication.

350 CN ISSN 1185-3026
BRITISH COLUMBIA. LEGISLATIVE ASSEMBLY. THIRD READING BILLS. w. Can.$70. (Legislative Assembly) Crown Publications, 546 Yates St., Victoria, BC V8W 1K8, Canada. TEL 604-386-4636. FAX 604-386-0221. **Document type:** government publication.

350 CN ISSN 0712-0508
BRITISH COLUMBIA. OFFICE OF THE OMBUDSMAN. PUBLIC REPORT SERIES. Key Title: Public Report - Ombudsman of British Columbia. 1979. irreg., latest no.34. price varies. Office of the Ombudsman, 931 Fort St., Victoria, BC V8V 3K3, Canada. TEL 604-356-5725. FAX 604-660-1691. E-mail: cdaniels@dgvic2.ombd.gov.bc.ca. (Subscr. to: Crown Publications, 521 Fort St., Victoria, BC V8W 1E7, Canada. TEL 604-386-4636) (back issues avail.) **Document type:** government publication.

350 CN
BRITISH COLUMBIA LIST; of official personnel in Federal, Provincial and Municipal Governments in the Province of British Columbia. 1978. a. Can.$157.50. B and C List (1982) Ltd., 8278 Manitoba St., Vancouver, BC V5X 3A2, Canada. TEL 604-482-3100. FAX 604-482-3130. Ed. Bruce Hodding; Pub. S.R. Hyman. adv. contact: H.B. Hyman. circ. 1,500. **Document type:** directory.

051 US
THE BRONX REPORT; a message from Bronx Borough President. (Text in English, Spanish) q. free. Office of Borough President Fernando Ferrer, The Bronx County Bldg., 851 Grand Concourse, Bronx, NY 10451. Ed. Clint Roswell. **Document type:** government publication.

350 US ISSN 0896-3584
BUDGET AND THE REGION; a regional analysis of the President's budget request. 1976. a. price varies. Northeast - Midwest Institute, 218 D St., S.E., Washington, DC 20003. TEL 202-544-5200. FAX 202-544-0043. charts. (back issues avail.) **Indexed:** SRI.
   Description: Details the federal budget request for federal and state policy makers and staff.

354.666 LB
BUDGET OF THE GOVERNMENT OF LIBERIA.* 1960. a. Bureau of the Budget, Monrovia, Liberia.

BUILDING PERMIT ACTIVITY IN FLORIDA. see *BUILDING AND CONSTRUCTION*

350 GW
BULA; Beschaffungsdienst fur die Entscheider im Oeffentlichen Bereich. 1982. 9/yr. Rolf Soll Verlag GmbH, Postfach 650680, 22366 Hamburg, Germany. TEL 040-6066096. FAX 040-6012787. Ed. Erwin Bauer. adv.: B&W page DM.3352; trim 190 x 280; adv. contact: Rolf Soll. circ. 8,000. **Document type:** trade publication.

350 658 FR ISSN 0221-7090
BULLETIN DES ELUS LOCAUX. 1979. q. Association Nationale pour la Democratie Locale, 282 bd. Saint-Germain, 75341 Paris Cedex 07, France. TEL 49-55-63-13. (Affiliate: Rassemblement pour la Republique) Ed. Liliane Ricalens. adv. circ. 40,000.

354.43 GW ISSN 0007-5930
DIE BUNDESVERWALTUNG. 1951. m. DM.39. (Deutscher Beamtenbund, Verband der Beamten der Obersten Bundesbehoerden) Vereinigte Verlagsanstalt GmbH, Hoeherweg 278, 40231 Duesseldorf, Germany. TEL 0211-73570. FAX 0211-7357123. Ed. Reiner Hoffmann. adv. circ. 12,000. **Document type:** government publication.

350.814 US
C B A NEWSNOTES. irreg. Congressional Black Associates, 1504 Longworth, Washington, DC 20515. TEL 202-225-5865.

C B D WEEKLY RELEASE. (Commerce Business Daily) see *BUSINESS AND ECONOMICS*

350.6 CN
C C P A MONITOR. m. (10/yr.). Can.$100. Canadian Centre for Policy Alternatives, 251 Laurier Ave., W., Ste. 804, Ottawa, ON K1P 5J6, Canada. TEL 613-563-1341. FAX 613-233-1458.
   Formerly: C C P A Newsletter.
   Description: Devoted to the development of progressive alternatives to current social and economic policies.

C I S FEDERAL REGISTER INDEX. (Congressional Information Service) see *PUBLIC ADMINISTRATION — Abstracting, Bibliographies, Statistics*

C J WEEKLY. see *POLITICAL SCIENCE*

C P E R. (California Public Employee Relations) see *BUSINESS AND ECONOMICS — Labor And Industrial Relations*

363.6 UK
C R I DISCUSSION PAPERS. 1992. irreg. (approx. 1-2/yr.). £3.75 per vol. to non-members; members £3.25 (effective 1995). Chartered Institute of Public Finance and Accountancy, Centre for the Study of Regulated Industries, 3 Robert St., London WC2N 6BH, England. TEL 0171-895-8823. FAX 0171-895-8825. (back issues avail.) **Document type:** monographic series.
   Description: Reviews various aspects of the regulation of utilities, transportation industries, and mail services.

363.6 UK
C R I PROCEEDINGS SERIES. 1992. irreg. (approx. 2-3/yr.). £12.50 per vol. to non-members; members £10 (effective 1994). Chartered Institute of Public Finance and Accountancy, Centre for the Study of Regulated Industries, 3 Robert St., London WC2N 6BH, England. TEL 0171-895-8823. FAX 0171-895-8825. (back issues avail.) **Document type:** proceedings.
   Description: Provides a forum for persons interested in debating regulatory matters.

363.6 UK
C R I REGULATORY BRIEFS. no.2, 1992. irreg. (approx. 1-2/yr.). £12.50 per vol. to non-members; members £10 (effective 1994). Chartered Institute of Public Finance and Accountancy, Centre for the Study of Regulated Industries, 3 Robert St., London WC2N 6BH, England. TEL 0171-895-8823. FAX 0171-895-8825. (back issues avail.) **Document type:** monographic series.
   Description: Debates the principles and practice to lawyers and nonlawyers alike.

C S I CONGRESSIONAL RECORD REPORT. see *LAW*

C S I FEDERAL REGISTER. see *LAW*

363.3 US ISSN 0743-8494
C S P A STATESIDE. q. free to members. National Governors Association, Council of State Planning Agencies, 400 N. Capitol St., N.W., Ste. 295, Washington, DC 20001. TEL 202-624-5386. Ed. Jan Lipkin.

C T A P PUBLICATION. (Community Transportation Assistance Project) see *TRANSPORTATION*

350 MR
CAHIERS AFRICAINS D'ADMINISTRATION PUBLIQUE. English edition: African Administrative Studies (ISSN 0007-9588) (Editions in Arabic, English, French) 1966. s-a. $40. Centre Africain de Formation et de Recherche Administratives pour le Developpement, P.O. Box 310, Tangier, Morocco. TEL 936601. FAX 9-941415. TELEX 33664M. bk.rev.; bibl. circ. 2,000. **Indexed:** Documentatieblad, Int.Polit.Sci.Abstr. **Document type:** academic/scholarly publication.

350 II ISSN 0045-3838
CALCUTTA GAZETTE. (Published in 11 parts plus supplement) (Text in English) 1784. w. Rs.206.50. (Commerce & Industries Department) West Bengal Government Press, Publication Branch, 38 Gopal Nagar Rd., Alipore, Calcutta 27, India. (also avail. in microfiche from IDC) **Document type:** government publication.

CALCUTTA JOURNAL OF POLITICAL STUDIES. see *POLITICAL SCIENCE*

CALIFORNIA ARTS ADVOCATE. see *ART*

CALIFORNIA CORRIDORS. see *TRANSPORTATION*

312 US ISSN 0743-0868
CALIFORNIA COUNTY. 1985. bi-m. $22. (California State Association of Counties) G M W Communications, Inc., 9719 Lincoln Village Dr., Ste. 500, Sacramento, CA 95827. TEL 916-363-5000. FAX 916-363-5197. adv. circ. 7,500. **Document type:** government publication.
   Description: Covers public finance, social services, hospital operations, public works, state mandates, corrections and other county government and special district affairs.

5532 PUBLIC ADMINISTRATION

300 978 350   US   ISSN 0068-5615
HC107.C2
CALIFORNIA HANDBOOK; a comprehensive guide to sources of current information and action. 1969. irreg., 7th ed., 1994. $35. California Institute of Public Affairs, Box 189040, Sacramento, CA 95818. TEL 916-442-CIPA. FAX 916-442-2478. (Affiliate: The Claremont Graduate School) Ed. Thaddeus C. Trzyna. index. circ. 2,500. **Document type:** directory.
   Description: Directory of organizations and a bibliography of books, periodicals, and reports which provide information about the state and its problems, organized by subject and indexed by sources of information.

350   US   ISSN 0738-694X
CALIFORNIA IN PRINT. 1981. s-m. $75. Government Research, 815 N. La Brea, Ste. 197, Inglewood, CA 90302. TEL 213-678-3851. Ed. Jerry Jeffe. **Document type:** newsletter.
   Description: Lists publications released for public distribution by the California State Legislature, in addition to executive and judicial documents received by the State Legislature.

CALIFORNIA JOURNAL; the monthly analysis of state government and politics. see *POLITICAL SCIENCE*

350 333.33   US   ISSN 0891-382X
HT169.C2
CALIFORNIA PLANNING AND DEVELOPMENT REPORT. 1986. m. $199. Torf Fulton Associates, 1275 Sunnycrest Ave., Ventura, CA 93003-1212. TEL 805-642-7838. Ed. William Fulton; Pub. William Fulton. circ. 700. **Document type:** newsletter.
   ●Also available online. Vendor(s): Information Access Co., NewsNet (EV23).
   Description: Covers local government, real estate and urban planning issues, and environmental issues.

CALIFORNIA POLITICAL WEEK; calpeek. see *POLITICAL SCIENCE*

CALIFORNIA PRIDE. see *LABOR UNIONS*

CALIFORNIA PUBLIC AGENCY PRACTICE. see *LAW*

CALIFORNIA TAXATION. see *BUSINESS AND ECONOMICS* — *Public Finance, Taxation*

328 920   US   ISSN 0068-6530
CALIFORNIANS IN CONGRESS. 1955. biennial. free. (California Congressional Recognition Program) Claremont McKenna College, Department of Government, Claremont, CA 91711. TEL 714-621-8000. Eds. Alan Heslop, Florence Adams. circ. 2,500. (back issues avail.)

CAMERA DEI DEPUTATI. BOLLETTINO DI INFORMAZIONI COSTITUZIONALI E PARLAMENTARI. see *LAW — Constitutional Law*

350   US   ISSN 0890-3956
CAMPAIGN CALIFORNIA REPORT.* 1977. q. $20 includes membership. Campaign California, Box 4561, Chico, CA 95927-4561. FAX 916-447-8957. Ed. Karl Ory. circ. 35,000. (back issues avail.)
   Formerly: Economic Democrat (ISSN 0746-2603)

350   CN   ISSN 0382-1161
JL25
CANADA. COMMISSIONER OF OFFICIAL LANGUAGES. ANNUAL REPORT. (Text in English and French) 1971. a. free. Office of the Commissioner of Official Languages, Rm. 1414 110 O'Connor St., Ottawa, ON K1A 0T8, Canada. TEL 613-995-0730. Ed.Bd. **Document type:** government publication.
—BLDSC (1151.320000).

537   CN   ISSN 0825-0170
CANADA. NATIONAL ENERGY BOARD. INFORMATION BULLETINS. 1984. irreg. National Energy Board, 311-6th Ave., S.W., Calgary, AB T2P 3H2, Canada. TEL 403-292-4800. FAX 403-292-5503. **Document type:** government publication, monographic series.
   Formerly (until 1983): Canada. National Energy Board. Staff Papers.

350   CN   ISSN 0821-8641
CANADA. NATIONAL ENERGY BOARD. REGULATORY AGENDA. (Text in English and French) 1982. q. free. National Energy Board, 311 6th Ave., S.W., Calgary, AB T2P 3H2, Canada. TEL 403-292-4800. FAX 403-292-5503. circ. 1,500. **Document type:** government publication.
   Description: Provides information on recent hearing reports, forthcoming regulatory actions, and the status of ongoing proceedings.

350.722   CN
CANADA. TREASURY BOARD SECRETARIAT. ESTIMATES. PART I: GOVERNMENT EXPENDITURES PLAN/CANADA. CONSEIL DU TRESOR. BUDGET DES DEPENSES. PARTIE I: PLAN DE DEPENSES DU GOUVERNEMENT. (Text in English, French) 1977. a. free. Treasury Board, 140 O'Connor St., Ottawa, ON K1A 0R5, Canada. TEL 613-995-2855. charts; stat. **Document type:** government publication.
   Formerly: Canada. Treasury Board Secretariat. Federal Expenditure Plan (ISSN 0706-6007)

354   CN
CANADA. TREASURY BOARD SECRETARIAT. ESTIMATES. PART II: ESTIMATES/CANADA. CONSEIL DU TRESOR. PARTIE II: BUDGET DES DEPENSES PRINCIPAL. a. Can.$60. Canada Communications Group, Publishing Division, 140 O'Connor St., Ottawa, ON K1A 0S9, Canada. TEL 613-956-4800. stat. **Document type:** government publication.

CANADIAN FEDERAL GOVERNMENT HANDBOOK. see *BIOGRAPHY*

350   CN   ISSN 0045-4893
CANADIAN GOVERNMENT PROGRAMS AND SERVICES. bi-m. Can.$375. C C H Canadian Ltd., 6 Garamond Ct., North York, ON M3C 1Z5, Canada. TEL 416-441-2992; 800-268-4522. FAX 416-444-9011. index. **Document type:** trade publication.
   Description: Authoritative guide to federal government organizations, programs and services, government relations. Information on all departments: their structure, key personnel with addresses and phone numbers, jurisdictions, responsibilities, budgets, etc.

350   CN   ISSN 0834-1516
CODEN: CJPEE8
CANADIAN JOURNAL OF PROGRAM EVALUATION/REVUE CANADIENNE D'EVALUATION DE PROGRAMME. (Text and abstracts in English or French) 1986. s-a. Can.$75 to individuals (foreign $75); institutions Can.$45; students Can.$35. University of Calgary Press, 2500 University Dr. N.W., Calgary, AB T2N 1N4, Canada. TEL 403-220-7578. FAX 403-282-0085. E-mail: 75003@ucdasvm1.admin.ucalgary.ca. (Subscr. to: Canadian Evaluation Society, 309 James St., Ottawa, ON K1R 5M8. TEL 613-230-1007) Ed. Robert Segsworth. adv.: page Can.$300. bk.rev.; charts; stat. circ. 1,350. (back issues avail.) Indexed: Can.Wom.Per.Ind., Pub.Admin.Abstr., Sociol.Abstr. **Document type:** academic/scholarly publication.
   Description: Deals with all aspects of the theory and practic of evaluation.
   Refereed Serial

350.6   CN   ISSN 0229-2548
JL148
CANADIAN PARLIAMENTARY REVIEW. French edition (ISSN 0229-2556) (Editions in English, French) 1978. q. Can.$20. House of Commons, Parliamentary Associations Secretariat, Confederation Bldg., House of Parliament, P.O. Box 950, Ottawa, ON K1A 0A6, Canada. FAX 613-992-3674. (Co-sponsor: Commonwealth Parliamentary Association, Canadian Region) Ed. Gary Levy. adv.; bk.rev. circ. 3,500. Indexed: Can.B.P.I., Can.Per.Ind., CMI, P.A.I.S., Polit.Sci.Abstr. **Document type:** government publication.
—Faxon. **CCC**.

354.7   CN   ISSN 0008-4840
CANADIAN PUBLIC ADMINISTRATION/ADMINISTRATION PUBLIQUE DU CANADA. (Text in English, French) 1958. q. Can.$80 (foreign Can.$85). Institute of Public Administration of Canada - Institut d'Administration Publique du Canada, 150 Eglinton Ave. E., No. 305, Toronto, ON M4P 1E8, Canada. TEL 416-932-3666. FAX 416-932-3667. Ed. Paul G. Thomas. bk.rev.; bibl.; index. circ. 4,200. (also avail. in microfilm from MML) Indexed: A.B.C.Pol.Sci., Amer.Hist.& Life, ASSIA, BPIA, Bus.Ind., Can.B.P.I., Can.Per.Ind., CMI, Curr.Cont., Educ.Admin.Abstr., Hist.Abstr., Ind.Can.L.P.L., Int.Polit.Sci.Abstr., Manage.Cont., P.A.I.S., P.A.I.S.For.Lang.Ind., PHRA, Polit.Sci.Abstr., Pub.Admin.Abstr., Sage Pub.Admin.Abstr., SSCI. **Document type:** academic/scholarly publication.
—BLDSC (3044.150000); Faxon; Genuine Article; SWETS; UnCover.

CANADIAN UNION OF PUBLIC EMPLOYEES. THE PUBLIC EMPLOYEE. see *LABOR UNIONS*

359   US
CAPITOL GOVERNMENT REPORTS WEEKLY. 1980. w. $245 (effective 1994). Capitol Government Reports, Box 602, Santa Fe, NM 87504. TEL 505-988-9835. FAX 505-988-9835. Ed. Jack Flynn. **Document type:** newsletter.
   Description: Reports on New Mexico government and politics.

353 330   US   ISSN 0889-4841
CAPITOL UPDATE. 1981. fortn. $50 (effective 1995). Texas State Directory Press, Inc., Box 12186, Austin, TX 78711-2186. TEL 512-477-5698; 800-388-8075. FAX 512-473-2447. Ed. Julie F. Sayers; Pub. Scott Sayers. circ. 700. **Document type:** newsletter.
   Description: Reports on Texas government, politics and business.

350   US
CAPITOLINE. w. (Jan.-May). membership. Colorado Association of Commerce and Industry, 1776 Lincoln St., Ste. 1200, Denver, CO 80203. TEL 303-831-7411. FAX 303-860-1439. Ed. Marilyn Holmes. (fax deliv. avail.) **Document type:** newsletter.

350   IT   ISSN 0008-610X
U4
CARABINIERE. 1948. m. (11/yr.). L.25000 (foreign L.50000). Arma dei Carabinieri, Comando Generale, Pzza. Bligny 2, 00197 Rome, Italy. Ed. Pietro Zullino. adv.: B&W page L.7000000, color page L.10000000. bk.rev.; charts; illus.; stat. circ. 220,000.

350   US
CAROLINA REPORT. 1986. m. $64. Broach, Mijeski and Associates, Box 12074, Rock Hill, SC 29731. TEL 803-323-2200. Ed. Glen Broach. **Document type:** newsletter.
   Description: Covers South Carolina electoral politics, legislative affairs and public policy issues.

350   US
JK723.E9
CARROLL'S DIRECTORY (YEAR) LIBRARY EDITION. a. $137. Carroll Publishing, 1058 Thomas Jefferson St., N.W., Washington, DC 20007. TEL 202-333-8620. FAX 202-337-7020. **Document type:** directory.
   Formerly: Federal Executive Directory Annual (ISSN 1056-7275)
   Description: Covers both the executive and legislative branches of federal government plus their regional field offices.

350   US
JK6
CARROLL'S FEDERAL DIRECTORY; including Congress. bi-m. $197. Carroll Publishing Company, 1058 Thomas Jefferson St., N.W., Washington, DC 20007. TEL 202-333-8620. FAX 202-337-7020. (also avail. in diskette format) **Document type:** directory.
   Formerly: Federal Executive Directory (ISSN 0270-563X)
   Description: Directory of more than 35,000 key officials in executive and legislative branches of US federal government.

PUBLIC ADMINISTRATION 5533

350   US
JK723.E9
CARROLL'S FEDERAL REGIONAL DIRECTORY. s-a. $150. Carroll Publishing, 1058 Thomas Jefferson St., N.W., Washington, DC 20007. TEL 202-333-8620. FAX 202-337-7020. (also avail. in diskette format) **Document type:** directory.
●Also available on CD-ROM.
Formerly: Federal Regional Executive Directory (ISSN 0742-1729)
Description: Directory of over 20,000 key officials in regional field offices of US Cabinet departments, Congress, the courts, and federal administrative agencies.

350   US
▼**CARROLL'S LEGISLATIVE DIRECTORY.** 1995. s-a. $150. Carroll Publishing, 1058 Thomas Jefferson St., N.W., Washington, DC 20007. TEL 202-333-8620. FAX 202-337-7020. **Document type:** directory.
Description: Lists name, titles, office addresses, phone and fax numbers for over 30,000 Federal and state legislators and staff members.

CARROLL'S RUSSIAN GOVERNMENT DIRECTORY. see BUSINESS AND ECONOMICS — International Commerce

350   SP
CARTA LOCAL; boletin informativo. 1968. m. 5000 ptas. Federacion Espanola de Municipios y Provincias, C. Nuncio 8, 28005 Madrid, Spain. TEL 365-94-01. FAX 365-24-16. (Co-sponsor: Ministerio para las Administraciones Publicas) Ed. Jesus Diaz Lobo. adv.; bk.rev.; illus. circ. 14,500.
Supersedes (in 1990): Informacion Iberoamericana; Instituto de Estudios de Administracion Local. Oficina Tecnica de la O I C I. Boletin de Informacion; Instituto de Estudios de Administracion Local. Secretariado Iberoamericano de Municipios. Boletin de Informacion (ISSN 0210-0975)
Description: Contains administrative, economic, and judicial information. Includes interviews.

309.1   SG   ISSN 0376-771X
HC547.S4
CARTE D'IDENTITE DU SENEGAL. 1971. a. free. Ministere de l'Information et de Telecommunications, Direction de l'Information, 58 Bd. de la Republique, Dakar, Senegal. illus.; stat. **Document type:** government publication.

350   IT
CASALECCHIO NOTIZIE. 1973. 9/yr. free. Comune di Casalecchio di Reno (BO), Via Porrettana 266, Casalecchio di Reno (BO), Italy. TEL 051-598111. FAX 051-592671. circ. 14,000. (tabloid format; back issues avail.)

350   CJ
CAYMAN ISLANDS. GOVERNMENT INFORMATION SERVICES. ANNUAL REPORT. 1972. a. C.$10($12.20) Government Information Services, Tower Bldg., 3rd Fl., Georgetown, Grand Cayman, British W.I. FAX 809-949-8487. Ed. E. Patricia Ebanks. circ. 2,000. **Document type:** government publication.
Description: Official report on operations of Cayman Islands Government, giving a comprehensive picture of life in the islands.

328   CJ   ISSN 0300-4740
CAYMAN ISLANDS. LEGISLATIVE ASSEMBLY. MINUTES. 1966. irreg. price varies. Legislative Assembly, PO Box 890, Grand Cayman, Cayman Islands, British W.I. (processed) **Document type:** government publication.

350   IT
CE D R E S DOCUMENTI. 1981. q. free. Centro Documentazione e Ricerche Economico-Sociali, Via Galimberti 2-A, 15100 Alessandria, Italy. Ed. Carlo Beltrame. bk.rev. circ. 1,500.

CENTRE FOR ECONOMIC POLICY RESEARCH. BULLETIN. see BUSINESS AND ECONOMICS — Economic Systems And Theories, Economic History

CENTRE FOR ECONOMIC POLICY RESEARCH. DISCUSSION PAPERS. see BUSINESS AND ECONOMICS — Economic Systems And Theories, Economic History

350   FR   ISSN 0221-5918
CENTRE NATIONAL DE LA RECHERCHE SCIENTIFIQUE. ANNUAIRE EUROPEEN D'ADMINISTRATION PUBLIQUE. a. (Universite de Droite, d'Economie et des Sciences d'Aix-Marseille, Centre de Recherches Administratives) C N R S Editions, 20-22 rue St. Amand, 75015 Paris, France. TEL 45-33-16-00. FAX 45-33-92-13. TELEX 200 356 F. adv.; bk.rev.; index; circ. 1,500 (controlled). **Indexed:** Int.Polit.Sci.Abstr. **Document type:** directory.

350   CN
CHAPTER 290. 1982. q. Can.$95. (Municipal Officers' Association of British Columbia) Beaudell Publishing, 200-880 Douglas St., Victoria, BC V8W 2B7, Canada. TEL 604-383-7032. FAX 604-384-3000. Ed. R.A. Beauchamp. adv.; bk.rev. circ. 600. **Document type:** newsletter.

350   CC   ISSN 1001-599X
CHENGSHI GONGYONG SHIYE/PUBLIC UTILITIES. (Text in Chinese) 1987. bi-m. $18 (effective 1996). Shanghai Gongyong Shiye Yanjiusuo - Shanghai Municipal Research Institute of Public Utilities, 706 Hengshan Road, Shanghai 200030, People's Republic of China. TEL 0086-21-4314037. FAX 0086-21-3217616. Ed. Cai Chengmei. adv.: B&W page $350, color page $1000. **Document type:** academic/scholarly publication.
Description: Covers the developments and events in the field of public transit, taxi, ferry, and metro services, town gas and urban water supplies in China.

350   US   ISSN 0250-6114
F1402
CHIEFS OF STATE AND CABINET MINISTERS OF THE AMERICAN REPUBLICS. q. $4. Organization of American States, General Secretariat, Department of Publications, 1889 F St., N.W., Washington, DC 20006. TEL 703-941-1617.

CHINA DIRECTORY (YEAR)/ZHONGGUO ZUZHIBIE RENMINGBU/CHUGOKU SOSHIKIBETSU JINMEIBO. see POLITICAL SCIENCE — International Relations

350   US   ISSN 0009-7543
CITIZEN. 1941. m. $12. Colorado Association of Public Employees, 1390 Logan St., Rm. 402, Denver, CO 80203. TEL 303-832-1001; 800-245-2273. FAX 303-832-1004. Ed. Phillip Christie. adv. circ. 12,000. (tabloid format) **Document type:** newspaper.
Description: Provides commentary, editorials, news, articles, and announcements on the financial, policy, and membership issues that affect the Colorado Association of Public Employees and Colorado state employees.

350   IT
CITTA DI SARONNO. 1967. bi-m. free. Comune di Saronno, Via Roma, 19, Saronno (VA), Italy. circ. 15,000. (tabloid format; back issues avail.)

CITY & STATE TECHNOLOGY BUYER'S GUIDE. see BUSINESS AND ECONOMICS — Trade And Industrial Directories

CIVIL AIRCRAFT ACCIDENT REPORTS. see TRANSPORTATION — Air Transport

331.88   NR   ISSN 0331-085X
JQ3092.Z1
CIVIL SERVANT.* 1971. m. £N216. Nigeria Civil Service Union, 23 Tokunboh St., P.O. Box 862, Lagos, Nigeria. illus.

350   US
CIVIL SERVICE NEWS. irreg. free. U.S. Office of Personnel Management, Office of Public Policy, 1900 E St., Rm. 5F10, Washington, DC 20415. TEL 202-632-1212. (processed)
Formerly: Civil Service News Releases (ISSN 0009-8019)

CIVIL SERVICE NEWS. see LABOR UNIONS

350.6   PH   ISSN 0300-3620
JQ1412
CIVIL SERVICE REPORTER. (Text in English) 1956. q. free. Civil Service Commission, National Government Center, Constitution Hills, Diliman, Quezon City, Philippines. TEL 063-2-931-8119. FAX 063-2-931-7997. Ed. Theresa O. Castillo. bk.rev.; charts; illus.; stat. circ. 2,000. **Indexed:** Ind.Phil.Per. **Document type:** government publication.
Description: Serves as the official publication of the Civil Service Commission. Carries news, memorandum, announcements and more.

350   UK   ISSN 0302-329X
CIVIL SERVICE YEAR BOOK. a. £18.50. (Cabinet Office) H.M.S.O., P.O. Box 276, London SW8 5DT, England. TEL 01-873-9090. FAX 01-873-0011. **Document type:** government publication.
—BLDSC (3273.880000). **CCC.**
Formerly: British Imperial Calendar and Civil Service List.

350   US   ISSN 0893-0392
Z688.G6N46
COALITION ON GOVERNMENT INFORMATION NEWSLETTER. 1987. irreg. $10. Coalition on Government Information, c/o American Library Association, 110 Maryland Ave., N.E., Washington, DC 20002. TEL 202-547-4440. Ed. Anne Heanue. (back issues avail.) **Document type:** newsletter.

350 340   US
CODE OF MARYLAND REGULATIONS. Short title: C O M A R. 1976. a. $850. Division of State Documents, Box 2249, Annapolis, MD 21404-2249. TEL 410-974-2486. FAX 410-974-2546. Ed. Robert J. Colborn, Jr. **Document type:** government publication.
Description: Compilation of all Maryland agency regulations, governor's executive orders and Ethics Commission opinions.

350   CK
COLOMBIA. DEPARTAMENTO ADMINISTRATIVO NACIONAL DE ESTADISTICA. DIVISION POLITICO-ADMINISTRATIVA. 1953. irreg. Departamento Administrativo Nacional de Estadistica, Banco Nacional de Datos, Centro Administrativo Nacional, Apdo. Aereo 80043, Avenida Eldorado, Bogota, Colombia. illus.

350   US
COLORADO. DEPARTMENT OF ADMINISTRATION. DIVISION OF ACCOUNTS & CONTROL. COMPREHENSIVE ANNUAL FINANCIAL REPORT. 1876. a. free. Department of Administration, Division of Accounts & Control, 1525 Sherman St., Ste. 250, Denver, CO 80203-1717. TEL 303-866-3894. FAX 303-866-4233. circ. 500. **Indexed:** SRI. **Document type:** government publication.

350   US
COLORADO LEGISLATIVE DIGEST. 1974. d. when legislature is in session. $650. Shoemaker, Wham & Krisor, 1666 S. University Blvd., Denver, CO 80210. TEL 303-777-5501. FAX 303-698-0919. Ed. Jay Shoemaker. **Document type:** newsletter.

COLORADO STATESMAN. see POLITICAL SCIENCE

350 380   NE   ISSN 0925-4609
COMMA; magazine voor communicatie in de publieke sector. 1980. 10/yr. fl.125. (Vereniging voor Overheidscommunicatie) Vuga Uitgeverij B.V., P.O. Box 16400, 2500 BK The Hague, Netherlands. TEL 31-70-3614011. FAX 31-70-3625468. Ed. Ellen van der Loo. adv.: B&W page fl.1775, color page fl.3850; trim 215 x 297. illus. **Document type:** trade publication.
—SWETS.
Formerly (until 1989): Voorlichting (ISSN 0925-465X)
Description: Covers topics relating to communication and management in the health professions, scientific, educational and related fields.

350   RE
COMMENTAIRES DES PRINCIPALES DECISIONS DU TRIBUNAL ADMINISTRATIF DE LA REUNION. (Subseries of: Dossiers du Centre d'Etudes) 1974. a. 100 F. Centre Universitaire de la Reunion, Centre d'Etudes Administratives, 24, 26 av. de la Victoire, Saint-Denis, Reunion. circ. 150.

PUBLIC ADMINISTRATION

350   US
COMMENTS AND CORRECTIONS. 1981. m. $29. Box 65902, Salt Lake City, UT 84165. TEL 801-262-0677. FAX 801-262-6184. Ed. Robert W. Lee. bk.rev. **Document type:** newsletter.
Description: Comments on various local, national and international issues, including those affecting the Salt Lake City area.

354.94   AT   ISSN 1030-3170
COMMONWEALTH GOVERNMENT DIRECTORY. 1921. q. Aus.$160. Australian Government Publishing Service, G.P.O. Box 84, Canberra, A.C.T. 2601, Australia. TEL 61-6-295-4411. FAX 61-6-295-4455. TELEX AA62013. **Document type:** government publication, directory.
● Also available online.
Former titles (until 1987): Commonwealth Government Directory. Volume I, Offices and Personnel (ISSN 0810-3615); (until 1977): Commonwealth Government Directory (1977) (ISSN 0725-5403); (until 1976): A Guide to Commonwealth Government Departments and Authorities (ISSN 1035-7777); (until 1975): Australian Government Directory (ISSN 0311-2918); (until 1973): Directory to the Office of the Governor-General, the Parliament, the Executive Government, the Judiciary, Departments and Authorities (ISSN 1035-7742); (until 1961): Federal Guide (ISSN 1035-7734).

350   AT   ISSN 1032-2337
COMMONWEALTH OF AUSTRALIA GAZETTE: PERIODIC GAZETTE. irreg. price varies. Australian Government Publishing Service, G.P.O. Box 84, Canberra, A.C.T. 2601, Australia. TEL 61-6-295-4612. FAX 61-6-295-4500. **Document type:** government publication, newspaper.
Description: Contains lengthy government notices of non-urgent nature. Also covers business issues.

354.94   AT   ISSN 1032-2353
COMMONWEALTH OF AUSTRALIA GAZETTE: PUBLIC SERVICE GAZETTE. w. Aus.$395. (Australian Public Service) Australian Government Publishing Service, G.P.O. Box 84, Canberra, A.C.T. 2601, Australia. TEL 61-6-295-4411. FAX 61-6-295-4455. TELEX AA62013. stat. **Document type:** government publication, newspaper.
Formerly: Commonwealth of Australia Gazette.
Description: Contains notices concerning administrative matters, such as appointments, transfers and promotions.

350   MW
COMMONWEALTH PARLIAMENTARY ASSOCIATION. MALAWI BRANCH. CONFERENCE. REPORT OF PROCEEDINGS. irreg., 12th, 1980. Commonwealth Parliamentary Association, Malawi Branch, c/o Parliament of Malawi, PO Box 80, Zomba, Malawi.

350   MW
COMMONWEALTH PARLIAMENTARY ASSOCIATION. MALAWI BRANCH. EXECUTIVE COMMITTEE. ANNUAL REPORT. (Text in English) a. Commonwealth Parliamentary Association, Malawi Branch, c/o Parliament of Malawi, PO Box 80, Zomba, Malawi.

350   US
COMMONWEALTH REGISTER. 1982. 80/yr. $275. 51st Associates, 216 Briggs St., Harrisburg, PA 17102. TEL 717-238-1222. FAX 717-238-9512. Ed. Deborah Hildesheim. adv. contact: Rose M. Jeffries. circ. 300. **Document type:** newsletter.
Formerly: Legislative Reporter.
Description: Reports on the Pennsylvania General Assembly.

354   CN   ISSN 0707-9133
COMMUNICATOR (ST. JOHN'S). 1976. m. free. Newfoundland Association of Public Employees, P.O. Box 8100, St. John's, NF A1B 3M9, Canada. TEL 709-754-0700. FAX 709-754-0726. Ed. Trudi Brake. bk.rev.; illus. circ. 19,000.
Former titles: N A P E Journal (ISSN 0381-6826); N A P E News (ISSN 0318-1723)

350 352.7   US
COMMUNITY AFFAIRS. 1979. bi-m. free. Department of Community Affairs, 318 Forum Bldg., Harrisburg, PA 17120. TEL 717-787-2340. FAX 717-787-6074. Ed. Robert Sabbato, Jr. charts; illus. circ. 24,000. (tabloid format) **Document type:** government publication, newsletter.
Former titles (until 1987): D C A Reports.
Description: Reports on government issues and other relevant information for state and local government officials and agencies, as well as nonprofit organizations.

COMMUNITY CARE (EDINBURGH). see *SOCIAL SERVICES AND WELFARE*

COMMUNITY DEVELOPMENT JOURNAL. see *SOCIAL SERVICES AND WELFARE*

350   US   ISSN 1052-6552
COMMUNITY HEALTH FUNDING REPORT. 1990. s-m. $249. (Community Development Services, Inc.) C D Publications, 8204 Fenton St., Silver Spring, MD 20910. TEL 301-588-6380. FAX 301-588-6385. Ed. Aaron Leibel. (back issues avail.) **Document type:** newsletter.
Incorporates (1988-1993): Public Assistance Funding Report (ISSN 1056-7100); Which is formerly (until 1991): Public Assistance Success (ISSN 1050-3447); Which incorporates (1988-1991): Helping the Homeless (ISSN 1050-3439)
Description: Reviews of public and private health grant opportunities, including reports on eligibility requirements, funding levels and deadlines.

COMMUNITY RELATIONS REPORT. see *COMMUNICATIONS*

COMMUNITY SPIRIT MAGAZINE (CARMEL). see *ENVIRONMENTAL STUDIES*

350 340   US
COMPLETE LEGISLATIVE SERVICE. 1939. w. when in session. $275 for 2 yrs. Wisconsin Taxpayer Alliance, 335 W. Wilson St., Madison, WI 53703-3694. TEL 608-255-4581. Ed. Beulah Poulter. index. (looseleaf format) **Document type:** newsletter.

350   IT   ISSN 0394-8277
COMUNI D'ITALIA; rivista mensile di dottrina, giurisprudenza e tecnica amministrativa. 1964. m. (11/yr.). L.210000 (effective 1994). Maggioli Editore, Viale Vespucci 12-n, Casella Postale 290, 47037 Rimini, Italy. TEL 0541-626777. FAX 0541-622020. Ed. Francesco Savelli. adv.: B&W page L.1700000, color page L.2600000; trim 115 x 195. circ. 4,700.

350   MX   ISSN 0185-8114
COMUNIDAD INFORMATICA. 1988. q. free or exchange basis. Instituto Nacional de Estadistica, Geografia e Informatica, Secretaria de Programacion y Presupuesto, Prol. Heroe de Nacozri 2301 Sur, Puerta 11, Acceso, 20270 Aguascaliente, Ags., Mexico. TEL 49-18-19-48. FAX 491-807-39. circ. 500. **Document type:** government publication.

350 320   US
CONGRESS. 1978. s-a. free. Dirksen Congressional Center, 301 S. Fourth St., Ste. A, Pekin, IL 61554-4219. TEL 309-347-7113. FAX 309-347-6432. Ed. Linda Sams. bk.rev.; illus. circ. 10,000. **Document type:** newsletter.
Formerly: Dirksen Congressional Center. Report.
Description: Covers activities of the center relating to the study of Congress and its leaders.

CONGRESS AND THE NATION. see *POLITICAL SCIENCE*

CONGRESS AND THE PRESIDENCY. see *POLITICAL SCIENCE*

352   FR
CONGRESS OF LOCAL AND REGIONAL AUTHORITIES OF EUROPE. OFFICIAL REPORTS OF DEBATES. (Reports of 1st-3rd Sessions never published.) 1962. a. $17. Congress of Local and Regional Authorities of Europe, Publications Section, Strasbourg, France. (Dist. in U.S. by: Manhattan Publishing Co., Box 650 Croton-on-Hudson, NY 10520) (Affiliate: Council of Europe) bk.rev.
Former titles (until 1994): Standing Conference of Local and Regional Authorities of Europe. Official Reports of Debates; European Conference of Local and Regional Authorities. Official Reports of Debates; European Conference of Local Authorities. Official Reports of Debates (ISSN 0071-2620)

352   FR
CONGRESS OF LOCAL AND REGIONAL AUTHORITIES OF EUROPE. TEXTS ADOPTED. (For 1st and 2nd Sessions, Documents and Texts Adopted issued in one vol.) 1957. a. $7. Congress of Local and Regional Authorities of Europe, Publications Section, Strasbourg, France. (Dist. in U.S. by: Manhattan Publishing Co., Box 650, Croton-on-Hudson, NY 10520) bk.rev.
—BLDSC (8430.799000).
Former titles (until 1994): Standing Conference of Local and Regional Authorities of Europe. Texts Adopted; European Conference of Local and Regional Authorities. Texts Adopted; European Conference of Local Authorities. Texts Adopted (ISSN 0071-2639)

352   US   ISSN 0733-0200
CONGRESSIONAL ACTIVITIES. 1935. w. $1250. Oliphant Washington Service, Box 9808, Friendship Sta., Washington, DC 20016. TEL 202-298-7226. FAX 202-333-5006. Ed. John Oliphant. circ. 100. **Document type:** newspaper.
● Also available online. Vendor(s): NewsNet (GT20).

CONGRESSIONAL QUARTERLY SERVICE. WEEKLY REPORT. see *POLITICAL SCIENCE*

350 500   US   ISSN 0887-1914
CONGRESSIONAL REPORT: SCIENCE, ENERGY & ENVIRONMENT. 1985. s-m. $360. J. Anthony Malone, Ed. & Pub., 11300 Weddington St., North Hollywood, CA 91601. TEL 818-509-0384. **Document type:** newsletter.
Description: Briefings of Congressional events concerning science, energy and the environment.

350.6   US   ISSN 0193-8029
JK1
CONGRESSIONAL RESEARCH SERVICE REVIEW. 10/yr. U.S. Library of Congress, Congressional Research Service, Washington, DC 20540. TEL 202-707-5000. (Dist. by: Supt. of Documents, GPO, Washington, DC 20402) Ed. Karen Q. Wirt. **Indexed:** Ind.U.S.Gov.Per., P.A.I.S., Pers.Lit. —UnCover.

350   US
CONGRESSIONAL STAFF CLUB. BULLETIN. m. U.S. House of Representatives, Congressional Staff Club, 805 House Annex 1, Washington, DC 20515. TEL 202-224-3527. **Document type:** bulletin.

CONGRESSIONAL STAFF DIRECTORY. see *POLITICAL SCIENCE*

351 328.73   US   ISSN 0191-1422
JK1083   CODEN: CYBOD4
CONGRESSIONAL YELLOW BOOK; who's who in Congress, including committees and key staff. (Supplement avail.: Congressional Yellow Book Roster) 1975. q. $235 (foreign $285). Leadership Directories, Inc., 104 Fifth Ave., 2nd Fl., New York, NY 10011. TEL 212-627-4140. FAX 212-645-0931. Ed. Brian Combs. illus.; maps. circ. 13,000. **Document type:** directory.
● Also available on CD-ROM.
—CASDDS. CCC.
Formerly (until 1976): Directory of Key Congressional Aides.
Description: Lists all US Senators and Representatives, including photographs and biographical information; legislative responsibilities for key staff aides; committee and subcommittee assignments; maps with district boundaries and Congressional delegations; and top staff in Congressional support agencies.

353.9 US ISSN 0010-6119
CONNECTICUT GOVERNMENT. vol.23, 1970. s-a. free. University of Connecticut, Institute of Public Service, Storrs, CT 06269-4014. TEL 203-486-2828. charts; circ. controlled. **Indexed:** Sage Pub.Admin.Abstr.
  Description: Reprints of articles on questions of public policy which are of interest to Connecticut state and local government officials and employees.

350 US
CONNECTIONS (MONCKS CORNER). 1973. bi-m. South Carolina Public Service Authority, 1 Riverwood Dr., Moncks Corner, SC 29461-2912. TEL 803-761-4051. Ed. Dan Coleman. circ. 2,500.
  Formerly: Santee Cooper Digest.

CONSERVATION DIRECTORY; a listing of national and international organizations, agencies and officials concerned with natural resource use and management. see *CONSERVATION*

350.6 US
CONSOLIDATED FEDERAL FUNDS REPORT. 1981. a. price varies. U.S. Bureau of the Census, Data User Services Division, Washington, DC 20233. TEL 301-457-4100. FAX 301-457-4714. (Subscr. to: Superintendent of Documents, U.S. Government Printing Office, Box 317954, Pittsburgh, PA 15250-7954. TEL 202-512-1800. FAX 202-512-2250; Or: Bernan, 4611-F Assembly Dr., Lanham, MD 20706. TEL 301-459-7666. FAX 301-459-0056) (Co-sponsor: Office of Management and Budget) circ. 7,000. (also avail. in microfiche; magnetic tape) **Document type:** government publication.
  ●Also available online. Vendor(s): CompuServe, Inc., Knight-Ridder, Inc.
  Also available on CD-ROM.

350 US
CONTEMPORARY GOVERNMENT SERIES.* irreg. price varies. Houghton Mifflin Co., 222 Berkeley St., Boston, MA 02116-3764. TEL 617-725-5000. FAX 617-227-5409.

CONTEMPORARY WALES; an annual review of economic and social research. see *SOCIAL SCIENCES: COMPREHENSIVE WORKS*

CONTRACT MANAGEMENT. see *BUSINESS AND ECONOMICS — Marketing And Purchasing*

650 UK
CONTRAX WEEKLY. w. £396. Business Information Publications Ltd., 15 Woodlands Terrace, Glasgow G3 6DF, Scotland. TEL 0141-332-8247. FAX 0141-331-2652. Ed. L. Burges. **Document type:** directory.
  Description: Provides public-sector contract information.

333.79 US
HD9502.A2M348
CONTROVERSIAL ISSUES IN PUBLIC POLICY SERIES. irreg., vol. 6, 1992. price varies. Sage Publications, Inc., 2455 Teller Rd., Thousand Oaks, CA 91320. TEL 805-499-0721. FAX 805-499-0871. E-mail: libraries@sagepub.com. (Overseas subscr. to: Sage Publications Ltd., 6 Bonhill St., London EC2A 4PU, England; Sage Publications India Pvt. Ltd., P.O. Box 4125, New Delhi 110 048, India) Eds. Dennis Palumbo, Rita Mae Kelly. **Document type:** monographic series.

COOK POLITICAL REPORT. see *POLITICAL SCIENCE*

350 CN ISSN 0703-7384
CORPUS ADMINISTRATIVE INDEX. 1972. 4/yr. Can.$449 (foreign $440). Southam Information and Technology Group, 1450 Don Mills Rd., Don Mills, ON M3B 2X7, Canada. TEL 416-445-6641. FAX 416-442-2200. Ed. Mary Mancini.

363.6 658 US
CORRECTIONAL INDUSTRIES ASSOCIATION NEWSLETTER. 1973. q. membership. Correctional Industries Association, Inc., 5 Canoe Brook Dr., Princeton Juction, NJ 08550. FAX 609-275-1426. Ed. Wendy Webber. adv.: page $200; trim 7 1/2 x 10. circ. 1,500. **Document type:** newsletter.

COUNCIL OF JEWISH ORGANIZATIONS IN CIVIL SERVICE. COUNCIL NEWS. see *ETHNIC INTERESTS*

011 UK ISSN 0070-1211
COUNCILS, COMMITTEES AND BOARDS; a handbook of advisory, consultative, executive and similar bodies in British public life. 1970. biennial, no. 9, 1995. £120($240) C.B.D. Research Ltd., 15 Wickham Rd., Beckenham, Kent BR3 2JS, England. TEL 0181-650-7745. FAX 0181-650-0768. (Dist. in the U.S. by: Gale Research Co., Penobscot Bldg., Detroit, MI 48226) Ed. M.P. Glanville. index. circ. 2,000. **Document type:** directory.
  —BLDSC (3481.250000).
  Description: Lists 1,300 official and semi-official bodies in the U.K.

350 US
THE COUNTY ADMINISTRATOR. 1953. m. membership. National Association of County Administrators, P.O. Box 34435, Bethesda, MD 20827. TEL 301-469-7460. Ed. Alan Siegel. adv.; bk.rev. circ. 500. **Document type:** newsletter.
  Description: Covers issues affecting county governments.

COUNTY COMPASS. see *ETHNIC INTERESTS*

352 US ISSN 0011-0353
COUNTY PROGRESS; the business magazine for county officials. 1923. m. $17.50. (County Judges and Commissioners Association of Texas) Coursey Publishing Co., Box 519, Brownwood, TX 76804. TEL 915-643-2995. Ed. Robert Tindol; Pub. Mr. Pat Coursey. adv.: B&W page $400, color page $775. illus. circ. 1,800. **Document type:** trade publication.

350 FR ISSN 0045-8899
COURRIER DU PARLEMENT. 1960. bi-m. 290 F. Mereau, 175 bd. Anatole France, 93208 Saint-Denis, France. TEL 48-13-38-58. FAX 48-13-09-08. Ed. Sophie Schneider. circ. 23,000. (tabloid format)

350 US
CURRENT GOVERNMENTS REPORTS. a. U.S. Bureau of the Census, Governments Division, Washington, DC 20233. TEL 301-457-1523. (Subscr. to: Superintendent of Documents, U.S. Government Printing Office, Box 371954, Pittsburgh, PA 15250-7954. TEL 202-783-3238. FAX 202-512-2233) **Document type:** government publication.
  ●Available only online.

350 331 US ISSN 0193-5593
HD8011.A1
CURRENT GOVERNMENTS REPORTS: COUNTY GOVERNMENT EMPLOYMENT. (Series GE-4) a. price varies. U.S. Bureau of the Census, Governments Division, Washington, DC 20233. TEL 301-457-1523. (also avail. in microfiche) **Document type:** government publication.
  ●Available only online. Vendor(s): CompuServe, Inc., Knight-Ridder, Inc.

CURRENT GOVERNMENTS REPORTS: FINANCES OF EMPLOYEE RETIREMENT SYSTEMS OF STATE AND LOCAL GOVERNMENTS. see *BUSINESS AND ECONOMICS — Public Finance, Taxation*

350 US
CUSTOMS REGULATIONS OF THE UNITED STATES. base vol. (plus irreg. supplements). $68 (foreign $85) (effective 1995). U.S. Customs Service, 1301 Constitution Ave., N.W., Washington, DC 20229. (Subscr. to: Superintendent of Documents, U.S. Government Printing Office, Box 371954, Pittsburgh, PA 15250-7954. TEL 202-512-1800. FAX 202-512-2250) (looseleaf format) **Document type:** government publication.
  Description: Contains regulations made and published for the purpose of carrying out customs laws administered by the U.S. Customs Service.

350 CY
CYPRUS. MINISTRY OF FINANCE. ANNUAL REPORT. (Text in English) a. Ministry of Finance, Permanent Secretary, Nicosia, Cyprus. stat. **Document type:** government publication.
  Incorporates (in 1991): Cyprus. Department of Customs and Excise. Annual Report.

956.4 CY ISSN 0011-4456
CYPRUS BULLETIN. (Editions in Arabic, English, Greek) 1964. fortn. free. Press and Information Office, Nicosia, Cyprus. TEL 357-2-446981. FAX 357-2-453730. TELEX 2526 PIONIC. circ. 17,500. **Document type:** government publication, bulletin.

352 GW ISSN 0721-8206
D B B NACHRICHTEN FUER DEN OEFFENTLICHEN DIENST. 1952. q. membership. Deutscher Beamtenbund, Landesbund Bremen e.V., Dobbenweg 9, 28203 Bremen, Germany. Ed. Ingo A. Riemer. adv.; bk.rev.; stat. circ. 10,000.
  Formerly: Beamte im Lande Bremen (ISSN 0005-7401)

353.9 US
D E S ACTIVITIES REPORT. 1973. a. Department of Economic Security, Box 6123, Phoenix, AZ 85005. TEL 602-542-4791. illus.
  Formerly: Arizona. Department of Economic Security. Annual Report (ISSN 0094-0712)

D O T NEWS. (Department of Transport) see *TRANSPORTATION*

350 US
DAILY BULLETIN (CHAPEL HILL). 1935. irreg. University of North Carolina at Chapel Hill, Institute of Government, Campus Box 3330, Knapp Bldg., Chapel Hill, NC 27599-3330. TEL 919-966-4119. FAX 919-962-2707. Ed. Joseph S. Ferrell. circ. 2,000. **Document type:** bulletin.

350 US
KFl1212.D3
DAILY LEGISLATIVE REPORT (BATON ROUGE). 1974. d. (when in session). $300. Legiscon, Box 1643, Baton Rouge, LA 70821. TEL 504-343-9828. FAX 504-338-5243. Ed. Jim Lee. circ. 300. **Document type:** newsletter.

350 US
DAILY LEGISLATIVE REPORT (JACKSON). d. (when in session). $265 to non-members; members $150. Mississippi Economic Council, Box 232766, Jackson, MS 39225. TEL 601-969-0022. FAX 601-353-0247. Ed. Bob Pittman. **Document type:** newsletter.

350 US
DAILY LEGISLATIVE REPORTER. 1936. d. price varies. Oklahoma Business News Co., 605 N.W. 13 St., Ste. C, Oklahoma City, OK 73101. TEL 405-521-1405. FAX 405-521-0457. Ed. LeRoy A. Ritter. index. (back issues avail.)

DANISH GOVERNMENT SECURITIES. see *BUSINESS AND ECONOMICS — Banking And Finance*

DATA ON DANISH PUBLIC FOREIGN BORROWING. see *BUSINESS AND ECONOMICS — Banking And Finance*

353 US ISSN 0011-7323
HJ10
DECISIONS OF THE COMPTROLLER GENERAL OF THE UNITED STATES. m. $24. U.S. General Accounting Office, Office of Public Affairs, Box 6015, Gaithersburg, MD 20877. TEL 202-275-6241. (Subscr. to: Superintendent of Documents, U.S. Government Printing Office, Box 371954, Pittsburgh, PA 15250-7954. TEL 202-512-1800. FAX 202-512-2250) **Document type:** government publication.

DEFENSE ORGANIZATION SERVICE. see *MILITARY*

350 340 SJ
DEMOCRATIC REPUBLIC OF THE SUDAN GAZETTE/AL-JARIDAH AL-RASMIYAH LI-JUMHURIYAT AL-SUDAN AL-DIMUQRATIYAH. (Text in Arabic and English) m. Attorney General, Attorney General's Chambers, P.O. Box 302, Khartoum, Sudan. **Document type:** government publication.

350 340 SJ
DEMOCRATIC REPUBLIC OF THE SUDAN GAZETTE. LEGISLATIVE SUPPLEMENT. Variant title: Democratic Republic of the Sudan Gazette. Special Legislative Supplement. Arabic edition: Mulhaq al-Tashri lil-Jaridah al-Rasmiyah li-Jumhuriyat al-Sudan al-Dimuqratiyah. irreg. Attorney General, Attorney General's Chambers, PO Box 302, Khartoum, Sudan.

350 GW
DENKMALPFLEGE INFORMATIONEN; Bayerisches Landesamt fuer Denkmalpflege. 1974. irreg. Bayerisches Landesamt fuer Denkmalpflege, Hofgraben 4, 80539 Munich, Germany. TEL 089-2114-213. FAX 089-2114-300. Eds. Michael Petzet, Karlheinz Hemmeter. bk.rev.; circ. 3,000. (controlled). **Document type:** bulletin.

PUBLIC ADMINISTRATION

342.489 DK ISSN 0108-979X
JS6151
DENMARK. INDENRIGSMINISTERIET. INDENRIGSMINISTERIETS AFGOERELSER OG UDTALELSER OM KOMMUNALE FORHOLD. 1981. a. DKK 50. Indenrigsministeriet, Christiansborg Slotsplads 1, 1218 Copenhagen K, Denmark. TEL 33-923380. FAX 33-111239.

DEPARTMENT OF ENERGY ACQUISITION REGULATION. see BUSINESS AND ECONOMICS — Accounting

350 352.7 UK ISSN 0951-385X
DEPARTMENT OF TOWN AND COUNTRY PLANNING. WORKING PAPER SERIES. 1987. irreg. University of Newcastle-upon-Tyne, Department of Town and Country Planning, Newcastle-upon-Tyne NE1 7RU, England. TEL 091-232-8511. FAX 091-261-1182. Ed. Tim Shaw.

350 920 BL
DEPUTADOS BRASILEIROS: REPERTORIO BIOGRAFICO. 1963. every 4 yrs. Camara dos Deputados, c/o Biblioteca, Brasilia D.F., Brazil. TEL 061-318-6820. FAX 061-318-2116. circ. 2,000.
Formerly: Perfis Parlamentares.

350 GW ISSN 0340-8604
DEUTSCHE NOTAR-ZEITSCHRIFT. 1948. m. DM.130.80. (Bundesnotarkammer) C.H. Beck'sche Verlagsbuchhandlung, Wilhelmstr. 9, 80801 Munich, Germany. TEL 089-38189-338. FAX 089-38189-398. Ed.Bd. adv.: B&W page DM.2300, color page DM.4025; trim 194 x 120. circ. 9,800. (back issues avail.) Document type: bulletin.

DEUTSCHES VERWALTUNGSBLATT. see LAW

350 II ISSN 0251-317X
DEVELOPMENT POLICY AND ADMINISTRATIVE REVIEW. (Text in English) 1975. s-a. Rs.30($8) Harishchandra Mathur State Institute of Public Administration, Jaipur 302017, Rajasthan, India. Ed. M.L. Mehta. Indexed: Rural Recreat.Tour.Abstr., Sage Pub.Admin.Abstr., World Agri.Econ.& Rural Sociol.Abstr.

DIALOGUER. see SOCIOLOGY

350 US
DIALOGUES IN PUBLIC POLICY. Variant title: Brookings Dialogues in Public Policy. 1982. irreg. price varies. Brookings Institution, 1775 Massachusetts Ave., N.W., Washington, DC 20036-2188. TEL 202-797-6255. FAX 202-797-6195. (Subscr. to: Box 037, Washington, DC 20042-0037. TEL 202-797-6255) Document type: academic/scholarly publication.

350 GT
DIARIO DE CENTRO AMERICA. 1880. irreg. $54. 18 Calle No. 6-72, Zona 1, Guatemala. Ed. Luis Mendizabal R. adv.; bk.rev. circ. 10,000.
Formerly: Guatemalteco.

350 SP
DIARIO DE SESIONES DEL PARLAMENTO DE NAVARRA. 1980. irreg. 140 ptas. per no. (Parlamento Foral de Navarra) Gobierno de Navarra, Fondo de Publicaciones, Navas de Tolosa 21, 31002 Pamplona, Spain. TEL 34-48-107121. FAX 34-48-227673.

363.6 AT ISSN 0725-2455
DIARY OF SOCIAL LEGISLATION AND POLICY. 1980. a. Aus.$10. Australian Institute of Family Studies, 300 Queen St., Melbourne, Vic. 3000, Australia. TEL 61-3-2147888. FAX 61-3-2147839. (Co-sponsors: National Institute of Economic & Industry Research; Social Policy Research Centre) index. circ. 500. (back issues avail.)
Description: Summary of legislative and administrative changes by Australian state and federal governments.

034 350 FR
DICTIONNAIRE DES COMMUNES (LAVAUZELLE ET CIE). quadrennial. 295 F. per no. Editions Charles Lavauzelle, Le Prouet, B.P. 8, 87350 Panazol, France. FAX 55-58-45-25. TELEX 580 995 F.

350 FR
▼**DICTIONNAIRE PERMANENT: DROIT DES ETRANGERS.** 1995. base vol. (plus m. updates). 1260 F. for base vols. Editions Legislatives et Administratives, 80 ave. de la Marne, 92546 Montrouge Cedex, France. TEL 40-92-68-68. FAX 46-56-00-15. TELEX 632 855 F. Ed. Sylvia Laussinotte. (looseleaf format)
Description: Covers immigration law and national laws affecting non-natives.

350 GW
DIE DIENSTSTELLEN DES FREISTAATES BAYERN IN DEN KREISFREIEN STAEDTEN UND LANDKREISEN. 1980. a. DM.18. Bayerisches Landesamt fuer Statistik und Datenverarbeitung, Neuhauser Str. 8, 80331 Munich, Germany. Ed.Bd. Document type: government publication.

350 US ISSN 0733-0227
DIGEST OF ACTIVITIES OF CONGRESS. 1935. w. $300. Oliphant Washington Service, Box 9808, Friendship Sta., Washington, DC 20016. TEL 202-298-7226. FAX 202-333-5006. Ed. John Oliphant. circ. 200. Document type: newspaper.
●Also available online. Vendor(s): NewsNet.

323.4 CY
DIMOSIOS YPALLILOS/CIVIL SERVANT. fortn. Cyprus Civil Servants Association, 3 Dem. Severis Ave., Nicosia, Cyprus. TEL 02-442393. circ. 11,000.

350 GW ISSN 0937-3128
DIPLOMATISCHE MISSIONEN, KONSULARISCHE VERTRETUNGEN. m. DM.98. Deutscher Wirtschaftsdienst, Marienburgerstr. 22, 50968 Cologne, Germany. TEL 0221-93763-0. FAX 0221-9376399. (looseleaf format) Document type: directory.

DIRECTIONS IN GOVERNMENT. see BUSINESS AND ECONOMICS — Management

DIRECTORIO DEL GOBIERNO. see BUSINESS AND ECONOMICS — Trade And Industrial Directories

350 CC ISSN 1021-691X
DIRECTORY OF CHINESE GOVERNMENT ORGANS. (Text in English) biennial? $110. Xinhua News Agency, c/o Current Publications Ltd., 1503 Enterprise Bldg., 228 Queen's Rd. Central, G.P.O. Box 9848, Hong Kong. Document type: directory.
Description: Features comprehensive and authoritative coverage of the various institutions of the Chinese government.

350 US
DIRECTORY OF IDAHO GOVERNMENT OFFICIALS. a. Association of Idaho Cities, 3314 Grace St., Boise, ID 83703. TEL 208-344-8594. FAX 208-344-8677. Document type: directory.

350 US ISSN 1051-4988
JK2679
DIRECTORY OF LEGISLATIVE LEADERS (YEAR). a. $15 (effective 1992). National Conference of State Legislatures, 1560 Broadway, Ste. 700, Denver, CO 80202. TEL 303-830-2200. FAX 303-863-8003. Document type: directory.
Description: Directory of state presiding officers, majority and minority leaders and key staff members, listing capitol and district addresses, telephone and fax numbers, and home or business numbers.

362 US
DIRECTORY OF NEBRASKA SERVICES. 1983? a. free. Department of Public Institutions, Box 94728, Lincoln, NE 68509. TEL 402-471-4567. FAX 402-479-5145. Ed. Dale B. Johnson. circ. 1,500. Document type: government publication, directory.
Formerly: D P I Yellow Pages (ISSN 0360-4357)

352 US
DIRECTORY OF NEW MEXICO MUNICIPAL OFFICIALS. a. $25. New Mexico Municipal League, 1229 Paseo de Peralta, Box 846, Santa Fe, NM 87504-0846. TEL 505-982-5573. FAX 505-984-1392. Ed. William F. Fulginiti. adv. circ. 1,400. Document type: directory.
Formerly: Directory of Municipal Officials of New Mexico (ISSN 0070-5888)
Description: Names, addresses of all incorporated municipalities and elected and appointed officials in New Mexico.

352 US
DIRECTORY OF REGIONAL COUNCILS. 1969. a. $100 to non-members; members $30. National Association of Regional Councils, 1700 K St. N.W., Washington, DC 20006. TEL 202-457-0710. FAX 202-296-9352. Ed. Beverly Nykwest. adv.; maps. circ. 2,000. Document type: directory.
Former titles: National Association of Regional Councils. Directory (ISSN 0095-1455); Regional Council Directory (ISSN 0190-2334); Directory of Regional Councils (ISSN 0070-6205)
Description: Lists names, addresses, and phone numbers of regional councils throughout the US. Includes state maps with jurisdictional boundaries.

353.9 US ISSN 0440-4947
JK9330
DIRECTORY OF STATE, COUNTY, AND FEDERAL OFFICIALS. 1964. a. price varies. Legislative Reference Bureau, State Capitol, Honolulu, HI 96813. TEL 808-587-0690. FAX 808-587-0699. Document type: directory.

350 340 US ISSN 1042-4172
KF8700.A19
DIRECTORY OF STATE COURT CLERKS & COUNTY COURTHOUSES (YEAR). a. $65. Want Publishing Co., 1511 K St., N.W., Washington, DC 20005. TEL 202-783-1887. FAX 202-393-5106. E-mail: rwant@delphi.com (Internet). Document type: directory.
—CCC.

350 US
DIRECTORY OF TENNESSEE MUNICIPAL OFFICIALS. a. $60. University of Tennessee at Knoxville, Municipal Technical Advisory Service, 600 Henley, Ste. 120, Knoxville, TN 37996-4105. TEL 615-974-0411. Document type: directory.

350 336 US
DIRECTORY OF WISCONSIN LEGISLATIVE AND CONGRESSIONAL DISTRICTS. biennial. $1. Wisconsin Taxpayers Alliance, 335 W. Wilson St., Madison, WI 53703-3694. TEL 608-255-4581. maps.
Description: Contains maps of congressional, senate, and assembly districts, along with the names and addresses of persons representing each district.

350 SP ISSN 0214-4131
DISPOSICIONES GENERALES. fortn. (plus s-a. cum.). 25607 ptas. (foreign 28600 ptas.) (effective 1992). Boletin Oficial del Estado, Trafalgar, 29, 28071 Madrid, Spain. TEL 446-60-00. FAX 5933916. index.

350 US
DISTRICT COURT MONTHLY DIGEST. 1987. m. $72 to non-members; members $62. District of Columbia Bar, 1250 H St., N.W., Ste. 600, Washington, DC 20005-3908. TEL 202-331-4364. Ed. Alexander Pires. (looseleaf format; back issues avail.) Document type: newsletter.

350 SP ISSN 0012-4494
JA26
DOCUMENTACION ADMINISTRATIVA. 1958. q. 4420 ptas. (foreign 4700 ptas.). Instituto Nacional de Administracion Publica, C. Jose Maranon 12, 28010 Madrid, Spain. TEL 446-1700. (Co-sponsor: Ministerio para las Administraciones Publicas) adv.; bk.rev.; bibl.; charts; cum.index. circ. 2,500. Indexed: ELLIS, Int.Lab.Doc.

DOCUMENTS TO THE PEOPLE OF NEW YORK STATE. see LIBRARY AND INFORMATION SCIENCES

DOMESTIC MAIL MANUAL. see COMMUNICATIONS — Postal Affairs

354.729 DR
DOMINICAN REPUBLIC. OFICINA NACIONAL DE PRESUPUESTO. EJECUCION PRESUPUESTARIA. INFORME.* a. Oficina Nacional de Presupuesto, Santo Domingo, Dominican Republic. charts; stat.
Formerly: Dominican Republic. Oficina Nacional de Presupuesto. Ejecucion del Presupuesto.

PUBLIC ADMINISTRATION

354   DR
DOMINICAN REPUBLIC. SECRETARIA DE ESTADO DE OBRAS PUBLICAS Y COMUNICACIONES. OPC. 1972. irreg. free. Secretaria de Estado de Obras Publicas y Comunicaciones, c/o Director General de Programacion y Proyectos, Santo Domingo, Dominican Republic. adv.; index. circ. 1,000.
    Formerly: Dominican Republic. Secretaria de Obras Publicas y Comunicaciones. Estadistica (ISSN 0070-7066)

350   TS
DUBAI. HUKUMAT DUBAI. AL-JARIDAH AL-RASMIYYAH/DUBAI. GOVERNMENT OF DUBAI. OFFICIAL GAZETTE. (Text in Arabic, English) 1965. 6/yr. Hukumat Dubai - Government of Dubai, P.O. Box 446, Dubai, United Arab Emirates. TEL 531073. Ed. Ablah al-Rusan. circ. 500.
    Description: Publishes all local laws and local government decisions.

E E I WASHINGTON LETTER. see *ENGINEERING — Electrical Engineering*

350   628.53   US
E T R NEWS. (Employer Trip Reduction) q. free. Department of Transportation, CN 600, Trenton, NJ 08625. TEL 800-245-7665. **Document type:** government publication, newsletter.
    Description: Discusses New Jersey's efforts to comply with the 1990 Clean Air Act Amendments.

ECONOMIC DEVELOPMENT QUARTERLY; the journal of American revitalization. see *BUSINESS AND ECONOMICS — Economic Systems And Theories, Economic History*

350   US   ISSN 0278-8381
HA203
ECONOMIC INDICATORS (CHARLESTON). 1981. quinquennial. $25. West Virginia Research League, Inc., 405 Capitol St., Ste. 414, Charleston, WV 25301. TEL 304-346-9451. Ed. Sarah F. Roach. (looseleaf format) **Indexed:** Mag.Ind.
    Description: Presents quantitative data comparing important public policy functions in West Virginia and all states.

ECONOMIC OPPORTUNITY REPORT; the independent weekly source for news of all economic opportunity programs. see *SOCIAL SERVICES AND WELFARE*

350   ES
EL SALVADOR. MINISTERIO DEL INTERIOR. MEMORIA DE LABORES. a. Ministerio del Interior, Centro del Gobierno, San Salvador, El Salvador. **Document type:** government publication.

320   US   ISSN 0145-8124
KF4886.A45
ELECTION ADMINISTRATION REPORTS. 1971. 24/yr. $162. 5620 33rd St., N.W., Washington, DC 20015. TEL 202-244-5844. FAX 202-362-2304. Ed. Richard Smolka. bk.rev. (back issues avail.) **Document type:** newsletter.
    Formerly (until 1976): Electionews.
    Description: Covers all developments in election law and administration, voting machines and devices, and judicial decisions affecting elections.

ELECTRONIC PUBLIC INFORMATION NEWSLETTER. see *LIBRARY AND INFORMATION SCIENCES — Computer Applications*

ELETTRIFICAZIONE. see *ENERGY — Electrical Energy*

350   FR   ISSN 0422-9932
ELU LOCAL. 1960. m. membership. Mouvement National des Elus Locaux, 14 rue de Bretagne, 75003 Paris, France. TEL 42-74-34-90. FAX 42-74-60-60. Ed. Marc du Tartre. adv. circ. 19,000.

EMERGENCY PREPAREDNESS NEWS; contingency planning, crisis management, disaster relief. see *CIVIL DEFENSE*

EMPIRE STATE REPORT; the magazine of politics and public policy in New York State. see *POLITICAL SCIENCE*

EMPLOYMENT AND PAYROLLS IN WASHINGTON STATE BY COUNTY AND INDUSTRY; industries covered by the Employment Security Act and federal employment covered by Title 5, U.S.C. 85. see *BUSINESS AND ECONOMICS — Abstracting, Bibliographies, Statistics*

350   CK
ENCUENTRO NACIONAL DE INVESTIGADORES EN ADMINISTRACION. MEMORIAS. no.3, 1983. irreg. Universidad de Antioquia, Facultad de Ciencias Economicas, Apdo. Aereo 1226, Medellin, Colombia. (Co-sponsor: Facultad de Administracion de Empresas)

351   US   ISSN 0092-8380
JK468.C7
ENCYCLOPEDIA OF GOVERNMENTAL ADVISORY ORGANIZATIONS. 1973. biennial. $505 (effective July 1993). Gale Research Inc., 835 Penobscot Bldg., Detroit, MI 48226. TEL 313-961-2242; 800-877-4253. FAX 313-961-6083. TELEX 810-221-7086. Ed. Donna Batten. **Document type:** directory.
    —BLDSC (3738.592300).
    Description: Directory of contractors, consultants and other advisory businesses and organizations for the U.S. government.

ENCYCLOPEDIC DICTIONARY OF AMERICAN GOVERNMENT. see *POLITICAL SCIENCE*

350   336   UK   ISSN 0263-774X
H97
ENVIRONMENT AND PLANNING C: GOVERNMENT & POLICY. 1983. 4/yr. $195 (effective 1996). Pion Ltd., 207 Brondesbury Park, London NW2 5JN, England. TEL 0181-459-0066. FAX 0181-451-6454. E-mail: sales@pion.demon.co.uk. Eds. R.J. Bennett, H. Wolman. adv.; page $280; trim 230 x 132; adv. contact: Diana Mallett. bk.rev.; index. **Indexed:** Energy Rev., Geo.Abstr., IDA, Sage Pub.Admin.Abstr., Sage Urb.Stud.Abstr., SSCI. **Document type:** academic/scholarly publication.
    —BLDSC (3791.105600); Faxon; SWETS; UnCover.
    Description: Multidisciplinary, international approach to the study of theoretical economic, political, legal, fiscal and social issues related to government activities.
    Refereed Serial

350   614.7   US   ISSN 1061-155X
THE ENVIRONMENTAL CONTRACT OPPORTUNITY REPORT. Variant title: T E C O R. 1991. w. $274. United Communications Group, 11300 Rockville Pike, Ste. 1100, Rockville, MD 20852-3030. TEL 301-816-8950. FAX 301-816-8945. Ed. Nancy Becker.
    —CCC.
    Description: Presents environmental contract opportunities and awards from federal, state and local agencies.

350   HK
ENVIRONMENTAL HONG KONG (YEAR). (Text in English) a. HK.$17. Government Publication Centre, G.P.O. Bldg., Ground Fl., Connaught Place, Hong Kong, Hong Kong. TEL 5-8428801. (Subscr. to: Director of Information Services, Information Services Dept., 1 Battery Path, G-F, Central, Hong Kong) Ed.Bd.

EQUALITY STATE ALMANAC. see *BUSINESS AND ECONOMICS — Economic Situation And Conditions*

350   US
ERNIE MILLS' LEGISLATIVE REPORT. d. (during session); w. (during interim). $400 (30-day session); $550 (60-day session). Box 5141, Santa Fe, NM 87502. TEL 505-988-3991. Ed. Ernie Mills. **Document type:** newsletter.
    Description: Reports on New Mexico legislative activity and politics.

350   US   ISSN 1047-5257
ESSAYS IN PUBLIC WORKS HISTORY. 1976. irreg., no.17, 1991. $20. Public Works Historical Society, 106 W. 11th St., Ste. 1800, Kansas City, MO 64105-1806. TEL 816-472-6100. FAX 816-472-1610. Ed. Howard Rosen. **Document type:** monographic series.
    Description: Monographs detailing the planning and financing of public works.

ESTADISTICA PANAMENA. SITUACION ECONOMICA. SECCION 342. CUENTAS NACIONALES. see *BUSINESS AND ECONOMICS — Economic Situation And Conditions*

ESTUDIOS POLITICOS. see *POLITICAL SCIENCE*

350   EI
EUROPEAN COMMUNITIES. DIARIO OFICIAL. (Supplements avail.) 1986. d. (except Sun.). price varies. (European Communities) Boletin Oficial del Estado, Trafalgar, 29, 28071 Madrid, Spain. TEL 5382100. (also avail. in microfiche)

EUROPEAN ECONOMIC PERSPECTIVES. see *BUSINESS AND ECONOMICS — Economic Systems And Theories, Economic History*

F A R FASTSEARCH; Federal Acquisition regulations. see *BUSINESS AND ECONOMICS — Accounting*

F C C RECORD. see *COMMUNICATIONS*

F C N L WASHINGTON NEWSLETTER. (Friends Committee on National Legislation) see *POLITICAL SCIENCE*

F E W'S NEWS AND VIEWS. (Federally Employed Women Inc.) see *WOMEN'S INTERESTS*

F L R A REPORTS OF CASE DECISIONS, F S I P RELEASES AND ADMINISTRATIVE LAW JUDGE DECISIONS. (U.S. Federal Labor Relations Authority) see *BUSINESS AND ECONOMICS — Labor And Industrial Relations*

350   II   ISSN 0085-1795
F M U OCCASIONAL LECTURES. no.2, 1971. irreg. price varies. Indian Institute of Public Administration, Financial Management Unit, Indraprastha Estate, Ring Rd., New Delhi 110002, India.

F T C NEWSNOTES. (U.S. Federal Trade Commission) see *BUSINESS AND ECONOMICS — Production Of Goods And Services*

F T C WATCH. (Federal Trade Commission) see *BUSINESS AND ECONOMICS — International Commerce*

350   GW
FACHHOCHSCHULE DES BUNDES FUER OEFFENTLICHE VERWALTUNG. MITTEILUNGEN. 1979. 3/yr. free. Fachhochschule des Bundes fuer Oeffentliche Verwaltung, Willy-Brandt-Str. 1, 50321 Bruehl, Germany. TEL 02232-939-0. FAX 02232-9295100. Ed.Bd. adv.; bk.rev. circ. 900. (back issues avail.) **Document type:** bulletin.
    Description: Information and news of the German Federal Institute for Public Administration. Covers curriculum, activities, events.

FAULKNER AND GRAY'S MEDICINE AND HEALTH. see *MEDICAL SCIENCES*

FEDERAL ADMINISTRATIVE LAW. see *LAW*

350   US   ISSN 1074-2727
JK468.C7
FEDERAL ADVISORY DIRECTORY. 1993. s-a. $137. Carroll Publishing, 1058 Thomas Jefferson St., N.W., Washington, DC 20007. TEL 202-333-8620. FAX 202-337-7020. **Document type:** directory.
    Description: Complete contact information for the more than 15,000 members of over 800 federal advisory committees created by the President, Congress and federal agencies.

FEDERAL ARCHEOLOGICAL PROGRAMS AND ACTIVITIES: THE SECRETARY OF THE INTERIOR'S REPORT TO CONGRESS. see *ARCHAEOLOGY*

350   US   ISSN 1076-7274
FEDERAL ASSISTANCE DIRECTORY. 1993. s-a. $137. Carroll Publishing, 1058 Thomas Jefferson St., N.W., Washington, DC 20007. TEL 202-333-8620. FAX 202-337-7020. **Document type:** directory.
    Description: Comprehensive indexed descriptions of 1,300 federal assistance programs, including complete contact information.

350   US   ISSN 1050-3242
FEDERAL ASSISTANCE MONITOR. 1986. s.m. $249. (Community Development Services, Inc.) C D Publications, 8204 Fenton St., Silver Spring, MD 20910. TEL 301-588-6380. FAX 301-588-6385. Ed. Dave Kittross. index. (back issues avail.) **Document type:** newsletter.
    Description: Covers federal regulations, funding availability, legislative developments affecting funding of social and economic programs.

FEDERAL AUDIT POLICIES AND PROCEDURES GUIDE. see *BUSINESS AND ECONOMICS — Accounting*

PUBLIC ADMINISTRATION

350 US ISSN 0898-0071
FEDERAL BUDGET REPORT. 1981. fortn. $295. Price Waterhouse, 1251 Ave. of the Americas, New York, NY 10020. TEL 212-819-5000. Ed. Stan Collender.
—CCC.
Description: Analysis of congressional and presidential budget activities.

FEDERAL CONTRACTS REPORT. see *BUSINESS AND ECONOMICS — Production Of Goods And Services*

FEDERAL COURT CLERKS' NEWS. see *LAW — Judicial Systems*

353 US ISSN 0014-9071
HD8008.A1
FEDERAL EMPLOYEE. 1917. m. $15. National Federation of Federal Employees, 1016 16th St., N.W., Washington, DC 20036. TEL 202-862-4400. Ed. James M. Peirce, Jr. adv.; illus. circ. 80,000.
Indexed: Pers.Lit.
Description: Focuses on civil service work.

351 US ISSN 0071-4127
JK671
FEDERAL EMPLOYEES ALMANAC. 1954. a. $7.95. Federal Employees News Digest, Inc., 1850 Centennial Park Dr., Ste. 520, Reston, VA 22091-1996. TEL 703-648-9551; 800-989-3363. FAX 703-648-0265. Eds. Don Mace, Eric Yoder; Pub. Stephen Young. circ. 100. **Document type:** directory.
Description: Guide to the rules and policies that govern federal employees' rights, benefits and pay.

351 US ISSN 1065-0970
HD8008.A1
FEDERAL EMPLOYEES NEWS DIGEST. 1951. w. $56. Federal Employees News Digest, Inc., 1850 Centennial Park Dr., Ste. 520, Reston, VA 22091. TEL 703-648-9551; 800-989-3363. FAX 703-648-0265. Ed. Don Mace; Pub. Stephen Young. adv. contact: Kip Bright. s-a. index. circ. 35,000. (back issues avail.) **Indexed:** Pers.Lit. **Document type:** newsletter.
Formerly (until 1991): Weekly Federal Employees News Digest (ISSN 0430-1692); **Incorporates** (1983-1991): Federal Employee Weekly Up-date (ISSN 1043-1993); Which was formerly (until 1988): Federal Personnel Guide Weekly News Up-date (ISSN 0745-841X)
Description: Provides an overview of events that affect the career of federal employees.

363.5 US
FEDERAL FUNDS INFORMATION FOR STATES NEWSLETTER. 8/yr. $250. National Governors' Association, 444 N. Capitol St. N.W., Ste. 295, Washington, DC 20001. TEL 202-624-5849. (Co-sponsor: National Conference of State Legislatures) **Document type:** newsletter.

350 378 US ISSN 0194-2247
FEDERAL GRANTS & CONTRACTS WEEKLY; project opportunities in research, training and services. 1977. w. $369 (foreign $434). Capitol Publications Inc., 1101 King St., Ste. 444, Alexandria, VA 22314. TEL 703-683-4100. FAX 703-739-6501. Ed. Pam Moore; Pub. Cindy Carter. index. (looseleaf format) **Document type:** newsletter.
●Also available online. Vendor(s): NewsNet (GT37).
—CCC.
Incorporates (in 1991): S C I Grants News.
Description: Provides funding news, analysis, profiles of key agencies, updates on new legislation and regulations, budget development.

350.6 384 US ISSN 1068-7386
KF844.7
FEDERAL INFORMATION RESOURCES MANAGEMENT REGULATION. 1991. base vol. plus irreg. supplements. $58 (foreign $72.50). U.S. General Services Administration, G S A Bldg., 18th and F Sts., N.W., Washington, DC 20405. (Subscr. to: Superintendent of Documents, U.S. Government Printing Office, Box 371954, Pittsburgh, PA 15250-7954. TEL 202-512-1800. FAX 202-512-2250) (looseleaf format) **Document type:** government publication.
Description: Compiles government and contracting regulations for A.D.P. and telecommunications equipment and services to be used in conjunction with general procurement and contracting regulations in the F.A.R.

FEDERAL MOTOR VEHICLE FLEET REPORT. see *TRANSPORTATION — Automobiles*

350 US ISSN 0741-5109
JK404
FEDERAL ORGANIZATION SERVICE. base vol. (plus updates every 6 weeks). $635. Carroll Publishing, 1058 Thomas Jefferson St., N.W., Washington, DC 20007. TEL 202-333-8620. FAX 202-337-7020. (looseleaf format)
Formerly: Federal Organization Service - Civil.
Description: Organization charts identifying who's who in over 2,100 departments and offices of the civil branch of the federal government.

FEDERAL PERSONNEL GUIDE. see *BUSINESS AND ECONOMICS — Personnel Management*

FEDERAL PROCUREMENT UPDATE. see *BUSINESS AND ECONOMICS*

920 US ISSN 1061-3153
JK6
FEDERAL REGIONAL YELLOW BOOK; who's who in the federal government's departments, agencies, courts, military installations and service academies outside of Washington, DC. (Supplement to: Federal Yellow Book (ISSN 0145-6202) 1992. s-a. $180 (foreign $230). Leadership Directories, Inc., 104 Fifth Ave., 2nd Fl., New York, NY 10011. TEL 212-627-4140. FAX 212-645-0931. Ed. Claudia Finney. **Document type:** directory.
●Also available on CD-ROM.

FEDERAL REGULATORY DIRECTORY. see *POLITICAL SCIENCE*

FEDERAL RESEARCH IN PROGRESS DATABASE. see *ENGINEERING*

340 US ISSN 0164-4564
KF8830
FEDERAL RULES SERVICE. 1939. m. $826. Lawyers Cooperative Publishing (Subsidiary of: Thomson Professional Publishing), Aqueduct Bldg., Rochester, NY 14694. TEL 800-527-0430.
—CCC.

350 US ISSN 0735-3324
JK723.E9 CODEN: FSDIEM
FEDERAL STAFF DIRECTORY. 1982. s-a. $79. Staff Directories Ltd., Box 62, Mount Vernon, VA 22121. TEL 703-739-0900. FAX 703-739-0234. Ed. Wayne Walker; Pub. Ann L. Brownson. index. (also avail. in diskette format) **Document type:** directory.
●Also available on CD-ROM.
—CASDDS.
Description: Lists 32,000 federal, executive, and military personnel from the White House, Departments, and independent and quasi-agencies, including 2,600 biographies of key decision makers. Also includes descriptions of each agency responsibility with symbols to indicate which positions are presidential appointments.

353 US ISSN 1053-4652
FEDERAL STAFFING DIGEST. 1968. q. $8.50 (foreign $10.65) (effective 1995). U.S. Office of Personnel Management, Career Entry and Employee Development Group, 1900 E St., N.W., Washington, DC 20415-0001. TEL 202-606-0960. FAX 202-606-0390. (Subscr. to: Superintendant of Documents, U.S. Government Printing Office, Box 371954, Pittsburgh, PA 15250-7954. TEL 202-512-1800. FAX 202-512-2250) Ed. J. Michael Carmichael. bk.rev.; illus. circ. 30,000. (back issues avail.) **Indexed:** Ind.U.S.Gov.Per. **Document type:** bulletin, government publication.
Incorporates (as of 1989): Recruiting Highlights; Which was formerly (until 1989): Spotlight on Affirmative Employment Programs; E E O Spotlight; Equal Opportunity in Federal Employment; Equal Opportunity in Federal Government (ISSN 0013-9777)
Description: Covers full range of staffing issues, including labor markets, employment trends, recruiting and examining, personnel literature, and Federal employment policy and procedures.

353 US ISSN 0014-9233
FEDERAL TIMES. 1965. w. $52. Army Times Publishing Co., 6883 Commercial Dr., Springfield, VA 22159. TEL 800-368-5118. FAX 703-658-8314. Ed. Marianne Lester. adv.; bk.rev.; illus.; circ. 40,000 (paid). (tabloid format; also avail. in microform from UMI; reprint service avail. from UMI) **Indexed:** Pers.Lit. **Document type:** newspaper.
—UMI. CCC.
Description: Serving all federal government workers and US Postal employees.

350.6 US ISSN 0145-6202
JK6 CODEN: FYBOD3
FEDERAL YELLOW BOOK; who's who in the federal departments and agencies. 1976. q. $235 (foreign $285). Leadership Directories, Inc., 104 Fifth Ave., 2nd Fl., Ste. 1000, New York, NY 10011. TEL 212-627-4140. FAX 212-645-0931. Ed. Mary Forschler. adv. circ. 12,000. **Document type:** directory.
●Also available on CD-ROM.
—CASDDS. CCC.
Description: Lists administrators and top staff aides in the Executive Office of the President, Office of Management and Budget, the Cabinet, the National Security Council, 14 Cabinet-level departments, more than 70 federal agencies, and Federal Information Centers in 72 cities.

THE FEDERALIST. see *HISTORY — History Of North And South America*

FEDNEWS. see *LABOR UNIONS*

350 FJ
FIJI ROYAL GAZETTE. w. $105. Government Printing Department, P.O. Box 98, Suva, Fiji. (also avail. in microfilm from KTO) **Document type:** government publication.

350 FJ
FIJI TODAY. a. free. Ministry of Information, Broadcasting, Television and Telecommunications, Government Bldgs., Suva, Fiji. Dir. Eliki Bomani. **Document type:** government publication.
Formerly: Fiji Information.

FINANZA LOCALE; rivista mensile di contabilita e tributi degli enti locale e delle regioni. see *BUSINESS AND ECONOMICS — Public Finance, Taxation*

FISCAL LETTER. see *BUSINESS AND ECONOMICS — Public Finance, Taxation*

FLEXIBLE PACKAGING ASSOCIATION. LEGISLATIVE UPDATE. see *PACKAGING*

FLEXIBLE PACKAGING ASSOCIATION. REGULATORY REVIEW. see *PACKAGING*

FLORIDA ADMINISTRATIVE PRACTICE. see *LAW*

FLORIDA DIRECTORY. see *BUSINESS AND ECONOMICS — Trade And Industrial Directories*

350 US ISSN 1068-4433
FLORIDA INSIGHT. 1989. fortn. $95. Florida Communications Network, Inc., Box 2099, Gainesville, FL 32602. Ed. Jon Hotaling; Pub. Jon Mills. circ. 200. **Document type:** newsletter.
Description: Reports on all facets of government and politics in Florida, including the state legislature.

015 US ISSN 0430-7801
FLORIDA PUBLIC DOCUMENTS. 1968. m. with a. cum. free to qualified libraries. State Library, Documents Section, Tallahassee, FL 32399.
TEL 904-487-2651. bibl.; circ. controlled. **Document type:** government publication.
Formerly: Florida State Documents (ISSN 0071-6014)

FONCTION PUBLIQUE. see *LABOR UNIONS*

FOODLINES. see *SOCIAL SERVICES AND WELFARE*

350 US
FOREIGN GOVERNMENT OFFICES IN CALIFORNIA; a directory. 1978. irreg., 5th ed. 1992. $15. California Institute of Public Affairs, Box 189040, Sacramento, CA 95818. TEL 916-442-CIPA. FAX 916-442-2478. (Affiliate: The Claremont Graduate School) circ. 600. **Document type:** directory.
Description: Lists California consulates, trade missions, and tourist offices of the 90 countries officially represented in California, and nearest source of information for all countries not represented in California.

FORUM FOR APPLIED RESEARCH AND PUBLIC POLICY. see *ENVIRONMENTAL STUDIES*

FRANCE. ADMINISTRATION DES DIRECTIONS RÉGIONALES DE L'INDUSTRIE, DE LA RECHERCHE ET DE L'ENVIRONNEMENT. ANNUAIRE. see *ENERGY*

PUBLIC ADMINISTRATION

350 FR ISSN 0339-9338
FRANCE. CONSEIL NATIONAL DE LA COMPTABILITE. BULLETIN TRIMESTRIEL. 1970. q. 140 F. (foreign 150 F.). Conseil National de la Comptabilite, c/o Imprimerie Nationale, B.P. 514, 59505 Douai Cedex, France.

350 FR ISSN 0071-8513
FRANCE. CONSEIL NATIONAL DE LA COMPTABILITE. RAPPORT D'ACTIVITE. 1962. irreg., no.8, 1975. price varies. Conseil National de la Comptabilite, c/o Imprimerie Nationale, Etablissement de Douai. Route d'Auby, 59128 Flers-en-Escrebieux, France.

FRANCE. MINISTERE DE L'INTERIEUR. REPERTOIRE MENSUEL. see *CRIMINOLOGY AND LAW ENFORCEMENT*

350 614 FR
RA440.87.F8
FRANCE. MINISTERE DES AFFAIRES SOCIALES DE LA SANTE ET DE LA VILLE. BULLETIN OFFICIEL. w. 512 F. (foreign 669 F.). Ministere des Affaires Sociales de la Sante et de la Ville, 1 place de Fontenoy, 75350 Paris Cedex 07, France. FAX 40-56-60-00. (Subscr. to: Direction des Journaux Officiels, 26 rue Desaix, 75727 Paris Cedex 15, France) (also avail. in microfiche) **Document type:** bulletin.
  Former titles: France. Ministere des Affaires Sociales et de l'Integration. Bulletin Officiel; France. Ministere des Affaires Sociales et de la Solidarite Nationale. Secretariat d'Etat Charge de la Sante. Bulletin Officiel (ISSN 0758-1998)

350 331.11 FR ISSN 0759-0083
FRANCE. MINISTERE DES AFFAIRES SOCIALES ET DE LA SOLIDARITE NATIONALE. MINISTERE CHARGE DE L'EMPLOI. CONVENTIONS COLLECTIVES. w. Ministere des Affaires Sociales et de la Solidarite Nationale, Ministere Charge de l'Emploi, 1 place de Fontenoy, 75700 Paris, France. (Subscr. to: Direction des Journaux Officiels, 26 rue Desaix, 75727 Paris Cedex 15, France) charts.

328.44 FR ISSN 0755-2793
J341
FRANCE. PARLEMENT. ASSEMBLEE NATIONALE. BULLETIN. 1972. w. free. Parlement, Assemblee Nationale, Service de la Communication, Palais-Bourbon, 75355 Paris, France. FAX 40-63-69-65. circ. 6,700.

328.44 FR ISSN 1240-8409
FRANCE. PARLEMENT. ASSEMBLEE NATIONALE. BULLETIN DES COMMISSIONS. (Supplement avail.) irreg. 120 F. Parlement, Assemblee Nationale, Service de la Communication, Palais Bourbon, 75355 Paris, France.
  Description: Provides summaries of the works of the Commissions.

FRANCE FORUM. see *POLITICAL SCIENCE*

FROM THE STATE CAPITALS. CIVIL RIGHTS. see *POLITICAL SCIENCE — Civil Rights*

FROM THE STATE CAPITALS. ECONOMIC DEVELOPMENT. see *BUSINESS AND ECONOMICS — Production Of Goods And Services*

FROM THE STATE CAPITALS. EMPLOYEE POLICY FOR THE PRIVATE AND PUBLIC SECTORS. see *BUSINESS AND ECONOMICS — Personnel Management*

FROM THE STATE CAPITALS. ENVIRONMENTAL REGULATION. see *ENVIRONMENTAL STUDIES — Waste Management*

353 US ISSN 0734-1202
FROM THE STATE CAPITALS. FEDERAL ACTION AFFECTING THE STATES. Variant title: Federal Action Affecting the States from the State Capitals. 1946. w. $215 (foreign $235) (effective Dec. 1990). Wakeman-Walworth, Inc., 300 N. Washington St., Alexandria, VA 22314. TEL 703-549-8606. FAX 703-549-1372. (processed)
  —CCC.
  Description: Reports on key developments in Washington that impact on states, such as federal regulatory programs, court rulings and program funding.

FROM THE STATE CAPITALS. INSURANCE REGULATION. see *INSURANCE*

FROM THE STATE CAPITALS. MOTOR VEHICLE REGULATION. see *TRANSPORTATION — Automobiles*

FROM THE STATE CAPITALS. PUBLIC ASSISTANCE AND WELFARE TRENDS. see *SOCIAL SERVICES AND WELFARE*

363.6 353 US ISSN 0016-1888
FROM THE STATE CAPITALS. PUBLIC UTILITIES. Variant title: Public Utilities from the State Capitals. 1946. w. $215 (foreign $235) (effective Dec. 1990). Wakeman-Walworth, Inc., 300 N. Washington St., Alexandria, VA 22314. TEL 703-549-8606. FAX 703-549-1372.
  ●Also available online. Vendor(s): West Services, Inc.
  —CCC.
  Description: Reports on all forms of public utilities.

353.9 US ISSN 1061-9690
JK430
FROM THE STATE CAPITALS. THE OUTLOOK. Variant title: Outlook from the State Capitals. 1946. w. $215 (foreign $235) (effective Dec. 1990). Wakeman-Walworth, Inc., 300 N. Washington St., Alexandria, VA 22314. TEL 703-549-8606. FAX 703-549-1372. (processed)
  —CCC.
  Former titles (until 1991): From the State Capitals. General Trends (ISSN 0741-3475); From the State Capitals. General Fiscal Bulletin; (until 1984): From the State Capitals. General Bulletin (ISSN 0016-1691)
  Description: Reviews important areas of state legislation such as drug abuse, abortion, tax policies, environmental issues.

FUTURES; the journal of forecasting, planning and policy. see *BUSINESS AND ECONOMICS — Economic Situation And Conditions*

353 US ISSN 0016-3414
HJ9701
G A O REVIEW. 1967. q. $11. U.S. General Accounting Office, Office of Public Affairs, Box 6015, Gaithersburg, MD 20877. TEL 202-275-6241. (Subscr. to: Superintendent of Documents, U.S. Government Printing Office, Box 371954, Pittsburgh, PA 15250-7954. TEL 202-512-1800. FAX 202-512-2250) Ed. John D. Heller. bk.rev.; illus. circ. 7,000. (also avail. in microform from MIM,UMI; reprint service avail. from UMI) **Indexed:** BPIA, Bus.Ind., Ind.U.S.Gov.Per., P.A.I.S., Pers.Lit., Tr.& Indus.Ind. **Document type:** government publication.
  —UMI.

G M V. (Government and Military Video) see *COMMUNICATIONS — Video*

350 AT
G O: GOVERNMENT OFFICERS MAGAZINE OF ADMINISTRATION AND PURCHASING. 1983. m. $65. Peter Isaacson Publications Pty. Ltd., 45-50 Porter St., Prahran, Vic. 3181, Australia. TEL 03-245-7777. FAX 03-245-7606. Ed. Mike Sydell. adv.; bk.rev. circ. 3,524. (back issues avail.)
  Description: Comprehensive coverage of key issues, relevant news, management trends and administration programs for decision makers in government.

353 US ISSN 0016-3619
JS302
G R A REPORTER. 1949. q. $40 (effective Aug. 1993). Governmental Research Association, Inc., 315 Samford Hall, Samford University, Birmingham, AL 35229. TEL 205-870-2482. illus. circ. 300. **Document type:** newsletter.

350.6 US ISSN 0095-5620
TS199.U5
G S A SUPPLY CATALOG. a. plus irreg. updates. $33 (foreign $41.25). U.S. General Services Administration, Federal Supply Service, G S A Bldg., 18th and F Sts., N.W., Washington, DC 20405. (Subscr. to: Superintendent of Documents, U.S. Government Printing Office, Box 371954, Pittsburgh, PA 15250-7954. TEL 202-512-1800. FAX 202-512-2250) **Document type:** catalog, government publication.
  Description: Lists office products, tools, furniture used by the federal government that are available from G.S.A. supply and distribution facilities. Contains full ordering information, including prices.

350 MG ISSN 0255-9536
GAZETIM-PANJAKAN'NY REPOBLIKA DEMOKRATIKA MALAGASY/JOURNAL OFFICIEL DE LA REPUBLIQUE DEMOCRATIQUE DE MADAGASCAR. (Issued in 3 parts) (Text in French or Malagasy) w. FMG.123000 (foreign FMG.223800). Impr. National, B.P. 38, Antananarivo 101, Madagascar. TEL 236-75. Ed. Samuel Ramaroson.
  Formerly: Gazetim-panjakan'ny Repoblika Malagasy (ISSN 1017-2203)

350 NE ISSN 0165-7895
DE GEMEENTESTEM; tweewekelijks tijdschrift aan de belangen der gemeenten in Nederland gewijd. Key Title: Gemeente-stem. 1851. bi-w. fl.275. Samsom H.D. Tjeenk Willink B.V. (Subsidiary of: Wolters Kluwer N.V.), Postbus 316, 2400 AH Alphen aan den Rijn, Netherlands. TEL 31-1720-66822. adv. **Document type:** trade publication.
  —SWETS.

350 GW
DIE GEMEINDE (STUTTGART); Zeitschrift fuer die Staedte und Gemeinden, fuer Stadtraete, Gemeinderaete und Ortschaftsraete. 1877. s-m. DM.160. Gemeindetag Baden-Wuerttemberg, Panoramastr. 33, 70174 Stuttgart, Germany. TEL 0711-225720. FAX 0711-2257247. Ed. Christian Steger. adv.; bk.rev.; stat. circ. 5,000. (tabloid format) **Document type:** government publication.

350 US ISSN 1066-0119
GEORGIA COUNTY GOVERNMENT. 1947. m. $15 (effective 1994). Association County Commissioners of Georgia, 50 Hurt Pl., Ste. 1000, Atlanta, GA 30303. TEL 404-522-5022. FAX 404-525-2477. Ed. Kay R. Morgareidge. adv.; B&W page $400; adv. contact: Joe Cronic. cum.index: 1986-1993. circ. 4,700. **Document type:** government publication.
  Description: For local elected officials of Georgia counties. Covers legislative developments at state and local levels, local government administration, service delivery programs, strategies for efficient operations, and public works projects.

GERMAN BRIEF. see *BUSINESS AND ECONOMICS*

001.4 GW
GERMANY (FEDERAL REPUBLIC, 1949-). BUNDESMINISTERIUM FUER FORSCHUNG UND TECHNOLOGIE. BUNDESBERICHT FORSCHUNG.* 1979. irreg. free. Verlag Dr. Heger, Goethestr. 54, 53 Bonn-Bad Godesberg, Germany. **Indexed:** Nutr.Abstr.
  Formerly: Germany (Federal Republic, 1949-). Bundesministerium fuer Bildung und Wissenschaft. Forschungsbericht der Bundesregierung.

GILDEA REVIEW. see *ENVIRONMENTAL STUDIES*

GOETIKUSS. see *EDUCATION*

GOODS AND SERVICES BULLETIN. see *BUSINESS AND ECONOMICS — Production Of Goods And Services*

350 340 US ISSN 0739-6937
KFO431.A6
GOTHERMAN'S OHIO MUNICIPAL SERVICE. bi-m. $135. Banks - Baldwin Law Publishing Co., University Center, Box 1974, Cleveland, OH 44106. TEL 216-721-7373. FAX 216-721-8055. Ed. John E. Gotherman.
  Description: Commentary on municipal tort liability, municipal financing, environmental and property law affecting municipalities, and public employee collective bargaining; judicial and legislative developments tracked.

920 350 FR
GOUVERNEMENT ET LES CABINETS MINISTERIELS. (Pocket Edition) 6/yr. 135.68 F. Informations Rapides de l'Administration Francaise, 27, rue Jasmin, 75016 Paris, France. Dir. M. Saulgeot.

GOVERNMENT ACCOUNTING AND AUDITING DISCLOSURE MANUAL. see *BUILDING AND CONSTRUCTION — Carpentry And Woodwork*

GOVERNMENT ACCOUNTING AND FINANCIAL REPORTING MANUAL. see *BUSINESS AND ECONOMICS — Accounting*

PUBLIC ADMINISTRATION

350.029 US ISSN 1078-9812
JK1118
▼**GOVERNMENT AFFAIRS YELLOW BOOK**; who's who in government affairs. 1995. s-a. $180 (foreign $230). Leadership Directories, Inc., 104 Fifth Ave., 2nd Fl., New York, NY 10011. TEL 212-627-4140. FAX 212-645-6931. **Document type:** directory.
Description: Provides information on more than 18,000 government affairs experts.

350 UK ISSN 0967-3873
GOVERNMENT AND MUNICIPAL BUYERS GUIDE. 1935. a. £55. Miller Freeman Information Services (Subsidiary of: United News & Media), Riverbank House, Angel Ln., Tonbridge, Kent TN9 1SE, England. TEL 01732-362666. FAX 01732-767301. TELEX 957829. Ed. Maria Atkin. adv.; bk.rev. circ. 5,000. **Document type:** directory.
—BLDSC (4203.878000).
Former titles: Government and Municipal Contractors (ISSN 0140-5764); Sell's Government and Municipal Contractors Register (ISSN 0072-5129); Government and Municipal Contractors Register.
Description: Contains a list of specific buyers in local authorities, central government, and public service, in addition to information on manufacturers and suppliers to local governments.

353 US ISSN 0072-5153
GOVERNMENT CONTRACTS MONOGRAPHS. 1961. irreg., no.13, 1980. price varies. George Washington University, Government Contracts Program, 2100 Pennsylvania Ave., N.W., Ste. 250, Washington, DC 20052. TEL 202-223-2772. FAX 202-223-1387. **Document type:** monographic series.

GOVERNMENT CONTRACTS REPORTS. see *LAW*

350 US ISSN 1062-1466
JK6
GOVERNMENT DIRECTORY OF ADDRESSES AND TELEPHONE NUMBERS. 1992. a. $135. Omnigraphics, Inc., 2500 Penobscot Bldg., Detroit, MI 48226. TEL 313-961-1340; 800-234-1340. FAX 800-875-1340. Ed. Laurie Lanzen Harris. **Document type:** directory.
Description: Lists offices, titles, addresses and phone numbers for every key government entity in the U.S. at federal, state and local levels.

GOVERNMENT EMPLOYEE RELATIONS REPORT. see *BUSINESS AND ECONOMICS — Labor And Industrial Relations*

GOVERNMENT EQUIPMENT NEWS. see *BUSINESS AND ECONOMICS — Trade And Industrial Directories*

350 US ISSN 0017-2626
JK1 CODEN: GVEXAW
GOVERNMENT EXECUTIVE; * federal government's business magazine. 1969. 12/yr. $48. National Journal, Inc. (Subsidiary of: Times Mirror Company), 1501 M St., N.W., Ste. 300, Washington, DC 20005. TEL 202-739-8400. FAX 202-833-8069. Ed. Timothy B. Clark. adv.; bk.rev.; charts; illus.; index. circ. 60,000. (also avail. in microform from UMI; reprint service avail. from UMI) **Indexed:** Air Un.Lib.Ind., BPIA, Bus.Ind., Pers.Lit., Sage Pub.Admin.Abstr., Tr.& Indus.Ind.
●Also available online. Vendor(s): University Microfilms International.
—Faxon; SWETS; UMI; UnCover. **CCC.**

350 BS
GOVERNMENT GAZETTE. w? Private Bag 0081, Gaborone, Botswana. TEL 314441. TELEX 2414.

052 TZ
GOVERNMENT GAZETTE. 1964. w. POB 261, Zanzibar, Tanzania.
Description: Contains official announcements.

350 MF
GOVERNMENT GAZETTE OF MAURITIUS. (Text in English) irreg., no.34, 1981. Government Printing Office, Elizabeth II Ave., Port Louis, Mauritius. index.

350 MF
GOVERNMENT GAZETTE OF MAURITIUS. LEGAL SUPPLEMENT. ACT. (Text in English) irreg., no.2, 1981. Government Printing Office, Elizabeth II Ave., Port Louis, Mauritius.

350 MF
GOVERNMENT GAZETTE OF MAURITIUS. LEGAL SUPPLEMENT. GOVERNMENT NOTICE. (Text in English) irreg. Government Printing Office, Elizabeth II Ave., Port Louis, Mauritius.

350 MF
GOVERNMENT GAZETTE OF MAURITIUS. LEGAL SUPPLEMENT. PROCLAMATION. (Text in English) irreg., no.3, 1981. Government Printing Office, Elizabeth II Ave., Port Louis, Mauritius.

350 MF
GOVERNMENT GAZETTE OF MAURITIUS. SPECIAL LEGAL SUPPLEMENT. A BILL. (Text in English) irreg., no.7, 1981. Government Printing Office, Elizabeth II Ave., Port Louis, Mauritius.

350 US ISSN 0072-517X
HJ389.5
GOVERNMENT IN HAWAII; a handbook of financial statistics. 1954. a. $15. Tax Foundation of Hawaii, 1000 Bishop St., Ste. 904, Honolulu, HI 96813-4209. TEL 808-536-4587. FAX 808-536-4588. Ed. Lowell L. Kalapa. circ. 3,500. **Indexed:** Vert.File Ind.

GOVERNMENT INFORMATION QUARTERLY; an international journal of resources, services, policies, and practices. see *LIBRARY AND INFORMATION SCIENCES*

353 338.9 US ISSN 0017-2642
GOVERNMENT PRODUCT NEWS. 1962. m. $45 (free to qualified personnel). Penton Publishing (Subsidiary of: Pittway Company), 1100 Superior Ave., Cleveland, OH 44114-2543. TEL 216-696-7000. FAX 216-696-7658. (Subscr. to: Box 95759, Cleveland, OH 44101) Ed. Leslie Drahos. adv.; B&W page $6200, color page $7450. tr.lit.; circ. 85,000 (controlled). (tabloid format; also avail. in microform from UMI; reprint service avail. from UMI) **Indexed:** Tr.& Indus.Ind.
●Also available online. Vendor(s): Knight-Ridder, Inc. —UMI. **CCC.**
Former titles: Government Product News and Purchasing Digest; Government Purchasing Digest (ISSN 0017-2650)
Description: News, ideas, applications and literature of products and services utilized in government functions.

350 US ISSN 0896-0674
GOVERNMENT PRODUCTIVITY NEWS. 1987. 10/yr. $57 (foreign $65). c/o James Jarrett, Ed. & Pub., Box 27435, Austin, TX 78755-0435. TEL 512-343-1884. bk.rev. **Document type:** newsletter.

363.6 US ISSN 0737-5255
JK404
GOVERNMENT PROGRAMS AND PROJECTS DIRECTORY. irreg. $145. Gale Research Inc., 835 Penobscot Bldg., Detroit, MI 48226. TEL 800-877-4253. FAX 313-961-6083. TELEX 810-221-7086. Ed. Anthony T. Kruzas, Kay Gill. **Document type:** directory.
Description: Irregularly updated guide on American government programs and projects.

350.712 CN ISSN 0046-6220
GOVERNMENT PURCHASING GUIDE. 1969. m. Can.$35($50) Moorshead Publications Ltd., 797 Don Mills Rd., 10th Fl., North York, ON M3C 3S5, Canada. TEL 416-696-5488. FAX 416-696-7395. Ed. Ed. Zapletal. adv.: B&W page $3555, color page $4350; adv. contact: John Fergus. circ. 18,000 (controlled). (back issues avail.)
Description: For those who initiate, specify, review or purchase for all levels of government.

GOVERNMENT RELATIONS. see *BUSINESS AND ECONOMICS — Management*

GOVERNMENT STANDARD. see *LABOR UNIONS*

350 US ISSN 0148-4664
JK5401
GOVERNMENTAL AFFAIRS NEWSLETTER. 1966. 11/yr. $15. University of Missouri, Governmental Affairs Program, Professional Bldg., Rm. 206, Columbia, MO 65211. TEL 314-882-6401. Ed. Richard Dohm. **Document type:** newsletter.
Description: Covers Missouri government and politics.

350 US ISSN 0072-520X
JK3
GOVERNMENTAL RESEARCH ASSOCIATION DIRECTORY; directory of organizations and individuals professionally engaged in governmental research and related activities. 1938. a. $40 (effective Jan. 1993). Governmental Research Association, Inc., 315 Samford Hall, Samford University, Birmingham, AL 35229. TEL 205-870-2482. index. circ. 700. **Document type:** directory.

GOVERNMENTAL RISK MANAGEMENT MANUAL. see *INSURANCE*

GRADUATE PROGRAMS IN PUBLIC AFFAIRS AND PUBLIC ADMINISTRATION. see *EDUCATION — Guides To Schools And Colleges*

GRADUATE SCHOOL JOURNAL. see *EDUCATION — School Organization And Administration*

350 GW ISSN 0932-7894
GRAUE LITERATUR ZUR VERWALTUNGSWISSENSCHAFT. 1986. a. Fachhochschule des Bundes fuer Oeffentliche Verwaltung, Willy-Brandt-Str. 1, 50321 Bruehl, Germany. TEL 02232-929-0. FAX 02232-9295100. **Document type:** bibliography.

650 UK
GREAT BRITAIN. GOVERNMENT OPPORTUNITIES. m. £120. Business Information Publications Ltd., 15 Woodlands Terr., Glasgow G3 6DF, Scotland. TEL 0141-332-8247. FAX 0141-331-2652. **Document type:** directory, government publication.
Description: Provides information on government service contracts.

GREAT BRITAIN. HOUSE OF COMMONS. PARLIAMENTARY DEBATES. see *POLITICAL SCIENCE*

GREAT BRITAIN. HOUSE OF LORDS. PARLIAMENTARY DEBATES. see *POLITICAL SCIENCE*

650 UK ISSN 1352-447X
GREAT BRITAIN. MINISTRY OF DEFENCE. WORKS SERVICES OPPORTUNITIES. 1992. fortn. £95. (Ministry of Defence) Business Information Publications Ltd., 15 Woodlands Terr., Glasgow G3 6DF, Scotland. TEL 0141-332-8247. FAX 0141-331-2652. **Document type:** trade publication, government publication.
Description: Lists contacts for persons interested in participating in the Ministry of Defence building and public works program.

350 UK ISSN 0072-7032
GREAT BRITAIN. PUBLIC WORKS LOAN BOARD. REPORT. 1875. a. £5.35. Public Works Loan Board, 1 King Charles St., London SW1A 2AP, England. (Avail. from: H.M.S.O., P.O. Box 276, London SW8 5DT, England) circ. 500. **Document type:** government publication.
—**CCC.**

352 300 UK ISSN 0072-7350
GREATER LONDON PAPERS; problems of government of greater London. 1961. irreg., no.17, 1986. price varies. London School of Economics and Political Science, Houghton St., Aldwych, London WC2A 2AE, England. **Document type:** monographic series.

GUARDIAN (LEXINGTON). see *LAW*

GUIDA AGLI ACQUISTI PER GLI ENTI PUBBLICI. see *BUSINESS AND ECONOMICS — Trade And Industrial Directories*

350 IT
GUIDAZZURRA. (Annual directory avail.: Guidazzurra Amministrazione Centrale dello Stato) m. D'Anselmi Editore s.r.l., Via Sommacampagna 9, 00185 Rome, Italy. TEL 39-6-4463425. FAX 39-6-4463670.

GUIDE TO ARKANSAS FUNDING SOURCES. see *BUSINESS AND ECONOMICS — Management*

350 US
GUIDE TO GOVERNMENT CONTRACTING. 1991. base vol. (plus m. updates). $340. Commerce Clearing House, Inc., 4025 W. Peterson Ave., Chicago, IL 60646. TEL 312-583-8500.

PUBLIC ADMINISTRATION 5541

353.9 US ISSN 0072-8454
JQ6121
GUIDE TO GOVERNMENT IN HAWAII. 1961. irreg., 19th ed., 1993. price varies. Legislative Reference Bureau, State Capitol, Honolulu, HI 96813. TEL 808-587-0690. FAX 808-587-0699.

GUIDE TO HEALTH SERVICES OF THE WORLD. see *HOSPITALS*

353.9 US ISSN 0091-0716
JK6630
GUIDE TO NEBRASKA STATE AGENCIES. 1973. irreg. free. Nebraska Publications Clearinghouse, c/o Nebraska Library Commission, 1200 N St., No. 120, Lincoln, NE 68508-2023. Ed. Doris Garlow. circ. 300. (also avail. in microfiche)

354 II
H C M STATE INSTITUTE OF PUBLIC ADMINISTRATION. (Text in English) 1975. s-a. $8. Harishchandra Mathur State Institute of Public Administration, Jaipur 302004, India.

350 GW
HANDBUCH FUER DEN OEFFENTLICHEN DIENST IN DEUTSCHLAND. 1964. a. DM.24.80. Walhalla Fachverlag, Dolomitenstr. 1, 93057 Regensburg, Germany. TEL 0941-696710. FAX 0941-68568. Ed.Bd. **Document type:** government publication.
Formerly (until 1990): Deutscher Beamten Kalender.

350 NE ISSN 0017-7253
HANDELINGEN DER STATEN-GENERAAL. 1840. w. fl.1096. Staatsuitgeverij, Christoffel Plantijnstraat 2, Postbus 20014, 2500 JV The Hague, Netherlands. TEL 31-70-3789911. FAX 31-70-3475778. (also avail. in microfiche) **Document type:** government publication.

HARVARD JOURNAL OF LAW AND PUBLIC POLICY. see *LAW*

350 336 US
HAWAII. LEGISLATIVE AUDITOR. SPECIAL REPORTS. 1965. irreg. (3-5/yr.). free. Office of the Auditor, State Capitol, Honolulu, HI 96813. TEL 808-548-2450. charts; stat.

350 US ISSN 0073-1277
KFH20
HAWAII. LEGISLATIVE REFERENCE BUREAU. REPORT. 1951. irreg. free. Legislative Reference Bureau, State Capitol, Honolulu, HI 96813. TEL 808-587-0690. FAX 808-578-0699. **Document type:** government publication.

350 331 US ISSN 0194-2352
HEALTH GRANTS & CONTRACTS WEEKLY; selected federal project opportunities. 1978. w. $349 (foreign $414). Capitol Publications Inc., 1101 King St., Ste. 444, Alexandria, VA 22314. TEL 703-683-4100. FAX 703-739-6501. Pub. Cindy Carter. (looseleaf format) **Document type:** newsletter.
●Also available online. Vendor(s): NewsNet (HH10).
—CCC.
Description: Alerts health researchers, administrators and fundseekers to the latest funding announcements for federal health grants and contracts. Includes facts on scope of work, eligibility, amount of funds, application deadline and contact officers.

HEALTHCARE SYSTEM REFORM ALERT. see *INSURANCE*

350 US ISSN 0272-1155
JC573
HERITAGE LECTURES. 1980. irreg., no.515, 1995. price varies. Heritage Foundation, 214 Massachusetts Ave., N.E., Washington, DC 20002. TEL 202-546-4400. FAX 202-546-8328. index. (back issues avail.)
●Also available online. Vendor(s): Lexis-Nexis.

HOBSONS PUBLIC SECTOR CASEBOOK. see *OCCUPATIONS AND CAREERS*

HOME OFFICE LIST OF PUBLICATIONS. see *PUBLISHING AND BOOK TRADE*

350 HO
HONDURAS. CONGRESO NACIONAL. BOLETIN. irreg., no.18, 1982. Congreso Nacional, Oficina de Boletines y Publicaciones, Tegucigalpa, Honduras.

350 HK
HONG KONG. BUILDING DEVELOPMENT DEPARTMENT. BUILDING STATISTICS. (Text in English) m. HK.$20. (Buildings Ordinance Office) Government Publication Centre, G.P.O. Bldg., Ground Fl., Connaught Place, Hong Kong, Hong Kong. TEL 5-8428801. (Subscr. to: Director of Information Services, Information Services Dept., 1 Battery Path, G-F, Central, Hong Kong) Ed.Bd.

350 HK
HONG KONG. GOVERNMENT PUBLICATION CENTRE. INQUIRY REPORTS. (Editions in Chinese, English) irreg., latest 1984. price varies. Government Publication Centre, G.P.O. Bldg., Ground Fl., Connaught Place, Hong Kong, Hong Kong. TEL 842-8801. (Subscr. to: Director of Information Services, Information Services Dept., 1 Battery Path, G-F, Central, Hong Kong) Ed.Bd.

HONG KONG. LAW REFORM COMMISSION. REPORT. see *LAW — Judicial Systems*

350 HK
HONG KONG. LEGISLATIVE COUNCIL. FINANCE COMMITTEE. REPORT. (Text in English) a. HK.$160. (Finance Committee) Government Publication Centre, G.P.O. Bldg., Ground Fl., Connaught Place, Hong Kong, Hong Kong. TEL 842-8801. (Subscr. to: Director of Information Services, Information Services Dept., 1 Battery Path, G-F, Central, Hong Kong) Ed.Bd.

350 HK
HONG KONG. LEGISLATIVE COUNCIL. PROCEEDINGS. (Editions in Chinese, English) w. price varies. Government Publication Centre, G.P.O. Bldg., Ground Fl., Connaught Place, Hong Kong, Hong Kong. TEL 842-8801. (Subscr. to: Director of Information Services, Information Services Dept., 1 Battery Path, G-F, Central, Hong Kong) Ed.Bd. **Document type:** proceedings.

350 HK
HONG KONG. LEGISLATIVE COUNCIL. PUBLIC WORKS SUB-COMMITTEE. REPORT. (Text in English) a. HK.$200. (Public Works Sub-Committee) Government Publication Centre, G.P.O. Bldg., Ground Fl., Connaught Place, Hong Kong, Hong Kong. TEL 842-8801. (Subscr. to: Director of Information Services, Information Services Dept., 1 Battery Path, G-F, Central, Hong Kong) Ed.Bd.

350 HK
HONG KONG. PUBLIC SERVICE COMMISSION. CHAIRMAN'S REPORT. (Text in English) a. HK.$35. Government Publication Centre, G.P.O. Bldg., Ground Fl., Connaught Place, Hong Kong, Hong Kong. TEL 842-8801. FAX 845-9078. (Subscr. to: Director of Information Services, Information Services Dept., 1 Battery Path, G-F, Central, Hong Kong) Ed.Bd.

350.6 HK
HONG KONG. STANDING COMMISSION ON CIVIL SERVICE SALARIES AND CONDITIONS OF SERVICE. CIVIL SERVICE PAY. (Editions in Chinese and English) irreg., no.20, 1988. price varies. Government Publication Centre, G.P.O. Bldg., Ground Fl., Connaught Place, Hong Kong, Hong Kong. TEL 842-8801. (Subscr. to: Director of Information Services, Information Services Dept., 1 Battery Path, G-F, Central, Hong Kong) Ed.Bd.

350 HK
HONG KONG. TELEVISION ADVISORY BOARD. ANNUAL REPORT. (Editions in Chinese, English) a. HK.$45. Government Publication Centre, G.P.O. Bldg., Ground Fl., Connaught Place, Hong Kong, Hong Kong. (Subscr. to: Director of Information Services, Information Services Dept., 1 Battery Path, G-F, Central, Hong Kong) Ed.Bd.

350 HK
HONG KONG. URBAN COUNCIL. PROCEEDINGS. (Editions in Chinese, English) m. price varies. Government Publication Centre, G.P.O. Bldg., Ground Fl., Connaught Place, Hong Kong, Hong Kong. TEL 842-8801. FAX 845-9078. (Subscr. to: Director of Information Services, Information Services Dept., 1 Battery Path, G-F, Central Hong Kong) Ed.Bd. **Document type:** proceedings.

350 HK
HONG KONG GOVERNMENT GAZETTE. w. HK.$1820 (effective 1995). Government Information Services, Beaconsfield House, Queen's Rd., Central, Victoria, Hong Kong. TEL 2598-8194. (Subscr. to: Director of Information Services, Information Services Dept., 28F Siu On Centre, 188 Lockhart Rd., Wan Chai, Hong Kong) **Document type:** government publication.
Description: Latest Hong Kong legislation, notices, tenders and appointments.

350 US
HORIZONS (COLUMBUS); the newsletter of the Mid-Ohio Regional Planning Commission. 1969. q. free. Mid-Ohio Regional Planning Commission, 285 E. Main St., Columbus, OH 43215-5272. TEL 614-228-2663. FAX 614-621-2401. Ed. Jan Hiltner. illus.; tr.lit. circ. 5,300. **Indexed:** Chem.Abstr.
Former titles (until 1990): Mid-Ohio Review; Regional Review.

HOTLINE (FALLS CHURCH). see *POLITICAL SCIENCE*

350 UK ISSN 0309-0426
HOUSE MAGAZINE. 1976. w. £190 (Europe £220; rest of world £260) (effective 1996). Parliamentary Communications Ltd., 10 Little College St., Westminster, London SW1P 3SH, England. TEL 0171-233-1388. FAX 0171-976-0422. Ed. Patrick Cormack; Pub. Keith Young. adv.; bk.rev. circ. controlled. **Document type:** bulletin.

352.7 UK
HOUSING LEGISLATION MANUAL. base vol. (plus irreg. updates). £85 to members only (effective 1994-1995). Building Societies Association, 3 Savile Row, London W1X 1AF, England. TEL 0171-437-0655. FAX 0171-287-0109. (Co-sponsor: Council of Mortgage Lenders) (looseleaf format) **Document type:** trade publication.
Description: Covers U.K. legislation affecting housing in its broadest sense.

350 US
HUDSON OPINION. m. Hudson Institute, Herman Kahn Center, 5395 Emerson Way, Box 26-919, Indianapolis, IN 46226-0919. TEL 317-545-1000. FAX 317-545-9639. TELEX 855477. circ. 9,000.

350 US ISSN 0073-3873
HUMAN RESOURCES RESEARCH ORGANIZATION. PROFESSIONAL PAPERS.* 1966. irreg. free. Human Resources Research Organization, 66 Canal Center Plaza, Ste. 400, Alexandria, VA 22314. TEL 703-549-3611. (also avail. in microform from NTI) **Indexed:** Psychol.Abstr.

350 UK ISSN 1350-7516
HUME PAPERS ON PUBLIC POLICY. q. £36($63.50) to individuals within the E.U.; institutions £72 (outside the E.U. £79 ($127)) (effective 1996). (David Hume Institute) Edinburgh University Press, 22 George Sq., Edinburgh EH8 9LF, Scotland. TEL 44-131-650-6207. FAX 44-131-662-0053. TELEX 727442 UNIVED G. Ed. Hector MacQueen; Pub. Vivian C. Bone. adv. contact: Kathryn MacLean. **Document type:** academic/scholarly publication.
Description: Publishes research on issues of public policy with special reference to legal and economic aspects.
Refereed Serial

350 HK
I C A C COMMISSIONER'S ANNUAL REPORT. (Editions in Chinese, English) 1985. a. HK.$18. (Independent Commission Against Corruption) Government Publication Centre, G.P.O. Bldg., Ground Fl., Connaught Place, Hong Kong. TEL 842-8801. (Subscr. to: Director of Information Services, Information Services Dept., 1 Battery Path, G-F, Central, Hong Kong) Ed.Bd.

I C C REGISTER; a daily summary of motor carrier applications and of decisions issued. (U.S. Interstate Commerce Commission) see *BUSINESS AND ECONOMICS — Domestic Commerce*

350 II
I I P A NEWSLETTER. (Text in English) 1957. m. Rs.3($1) Indian Institute of Public Administration, Indraprastha Estate, Ring Rd., New Delhi 110002, India. Ed. T.N. Chaturvedi. **Document type:** newsletter.

PUBLIC ADMINISTRATION

350   IE
I M P A C T NEWS. 1951. 6/yr. Irish Municipal Public and Civil Trade Union, 8 Gardiner Pl., Dublin 1, Ireland. TEL 01-745588. FAX 01-742425. Ed. Sean Mackell. adv.; bk.rev. circ. 28,000. **Document type:** newsletter.
   Formerly: I P C S News.

350   UK   ISSN 0958-5222
I P M S BULLETIN. 1925. m. £19.50 (foreign £31). Institution of Professionals, Managers and Specialists, 75-79 York Rd., London SE1 7AQ, England. TEL 0171-928-9951. FAX 0171-928-5996. Ed. Charles Harvey. adv.; bk.rev.; illus.; index. circ. 88,641. **Document type:** trade publication.
   Former titles: I P C S Bulletin (ISSN 0265-0975); (until Jun. 1982): State Service (ISSN 0039-0151)

IDAHO GOVERNMENT DIGEST. see *LAW — Judicial Systems*

IDAHO LEGISLATIVE REPORT. see *LAW*

350   SU
AL-IDARAH AL-AAMAH. (Text in Arabic; summaries in English) a. SRI.20($8) Ma'had al-Idarah al-Aamah - Institute of Public Administration, P.O. Box 25, Riyadh 11141, Saudi Arabia. TEL 471160. abstr.
   Description: Publishes research on a variety of issues in public administration.

350   TS
AL-IDARAH WAL-TANMIYAH/ADMINISTRATION AND DEVELOPMENT. (Text in Arabic) 1986. 2/yr. Institute of Administration and Development, P.O. Box 779, Abu Dhabi, United Arab Emirates. TEL 654665. TELEX 23718. Ed. Said Khalifa al-Ghaith. circ. 2,000.
   Description: Presents research and analysis on administration and development in the U.A.E.

350   MK
AL-IDARI; dawriyyah mutakhassisah fi majal al-idarah al-aamah. q. 8 ORl. to individuals; institutions 20 ORl. Ministry of Civil Service, Institute of Public Administration, P.O. Box 4994, Ruwi, Muscat, Sultanate of Oman. TEL 602065. FAX 698763. TELEX 5105 ON. bibl.
   Description: Specialized research concerning issues in public administration.

IMMIGRATION THEORY AND POLICY SERIES. see *POPULATION STUDIES*

350   BL
IMPRENSA OFICIAL DO ESTADO DO RIO DE JANEIRO. 1975. d. Cr.$4800. (Secretaria Extraordinaria de Comunicacao Social) Imprensa Oficial, Rua Margues de Olinda, 15, Niteroi, Rio de Janeiro, Brazil. TEL 021-719-1122. adv. circ. 17,900. (tabloid format; also avail. in microfilm)

IMPRESA PUBBLICA; municipalizzazione. see *PUBLIC ADMINISTRATION — Municipal Government*

350   RW
IMVAHO. (Text in Kinyarwanda) 1960. w. Office Rwandais d'Information, B.P. 83, Kigali, Rwanda. TEL 75724. TELEX 557. circ. 51,000.

INDEPENDENT GASOLINE MARKETING. see *PETROLEUM AND GAS*

INDEX TO THE CODE OF FEDERAL REGULATIONS. see *PUBLIC ADMINISTRATION — Abstracting, Bibliographies, Statistics*

350   II   ISSN 0073-6171
INDIA. CENTRAL VIGILANCE COMMISSION. REPORT. (Text in English and Hindi) 1965. a. free. Central Vigilance Commission, No.3, Dr. Rajendra Prasad Road, New Delhi, India. circ. controlled.

354   II
INDIA. DEPARTMENT OF ECONOMIC AFFAIRS. BUDGET DIVISION. KEY TO THE BUDGET DOCUMENTS. (Text in English) a. Department of Economic Affairs, Budget Division, New Delhi, India.

INDIA. DEPARTMENT OF POWER. REPORT. see *ENERGY*

354   II   ISSN 0445-6831
INDIA. PARLIAMENT. PUBLIC ACCOUNTS COMMITTEE. REPORT ON THE ACCOUNTS. (Each report covers various agencies of the government.) (Text in English) 1947. a. Parliament, Public Accounts Committee, Lok Sabha Secretariat, New Delhi, India.

351.1   II   ISSN 0073-6236
INDIA. UNION PUBLIC SERVICE COMMISSION REPORT. (Report year ends Mar. 31) (Text in English) 1951. a. Union Public Service Commission, Minto Rd., New Delhi, India.

350   II   ISSN 0019-5561
JQ201
INDIAN JOURNAL OF PUBLIC ADMINISTRATION. (Text in English) 1955. q. Rs.60($25) Indian Institute of Public Administration, Indraprastha Estate, Ring Rd., New Delhi 110002, India. Ed. T.N. Chaturvedi. adv.; bk.rev.; abstr.; bibl.; index. (back issues avail.)
Indexed: A.B.C.Pol.Sci. (until 1993), ASSIA, E.I., Int.Lab.Doc., Rural Recreat.Tour.Abstr., World Agri.Econ.& Rural Sociol.Abstr.
   —BLDSC (4420.350000); Faxon; UnCover.

350   US
INDIANA ISSUES.* 1989. m. $95. David L. Lantz, Ed. & Pub., Thompson, Kerr and Associates, Inc., 11711 N. College Ave., Ste. 145, Carmel, IN 46032-5601. TEL 317-580-8161. FAX 317-580-8169.
   Description: Reports on public policy issues affecting Indiana.

350   US   ISSN 1076-8661
INDIANA LEGISLATIVE INSIGHT. 1989. 44/yr. $295. Box 383, Noblesville, IN 46060.
TEL 317-773-8715. FAX 317-773-9998. Ed. Edward D. Feigenbaum. circ. 300.
   Description: Reports on activities in the legislative and executive branches of Indiana state government and on state politics.

350   IO
INDONESIA. DEPARTEMEN PENERANGAN. SIARAN UMUM. irreg. Department of Information - Departemen Penerangan, Direktorat Publikasi, Jl. Merdeka Barat 7, Jakarta, Indonesia.

250   VE
INFORMACION AL DIA EN GESTION PUBLICA. 10/yr. Bs.3000 (Latin America and Caribbean $30; elsewhere $40) (effective 1995). Centro Latinoamericano de Administracion para el Desarrollo, Centro de Documentacion y Analisis de Informacion, C. Herrera Toro, Qta. CLAD, Sector Los Naranjos, Las Mercedes, Apdo. Postal 4181, Caracas 1010-A, Venezuela. TEL 922395. FAX 582-918427. E-mail: clad@dino.conicit.ve.

INFORMATION TECHNOLOGY FOR LOCAL GOVERNMENT. see *COMPUTERS — Data Communications And Data Transmission Systems*

INFORMATIONS RAPIDES DE L'ADMINISTRATION FRANCAISE. see *BIOGRAPHY*

INFOS FEDERALES. see *TRANSPORTATION*

INFRASTRUCTURE FINANCE; the magazine for global development. see *BUSINESS AND ECONOMICS — International Development And Assistance*

350 320   US   ISSN 0884-030X
INSIDE ALABAMA POLITICS.* 1984. 39/yr. $83. Inside Alabama Politics, Inc., 2465 Commercial Park Dr., Mobile, AL 36606-2031. Ed. Bessie Ford.

350 320   US   ISSN 1052-8857
INSIDE MICHIGAN POLITICS. 1987. bi-w. $160. 2029 S. Waverly Rd., Lansing, MI 48917-4263. TEL 517-487-6665. FAX 517-487-3830. Ed. William S. Ballenger. circ. 1,025. **Document type:** newsletter.
   Description: Covers Michigan government, politics and business.

350   US
INSIDE THE WHITE HOUSE. 1983. w. $595 (foreign $645). Inside Washington Publishers, Box 7167, Benjamin Franklin Sta., Washington, DC 20044. TEL 703-416-8500. FAX 703-416-8543. Ed. Peter Busowski. **Document type:** newsletter.
   Formerly: Inside the Administration.
   Description: Reports on national administration, economic, trade and regulatory policies.

350   FR   ISSN 1152-5096
INSTITUT INTERNATIONAL D'ADMINISTRATION PUBLIQUE. DOSSIERS ET DEBATS. 1979. a. 70 F. Institut International d'Administration Publique - International Institute of Public Administration, 2 av. de l'Observatoire, 75006 Paris, France. TEL 48-39-56-00. FAX 44-41-86-19. TELEX 204826 DOCFRAN. (Subscr. to: La Documentation Francaise, 29-31 quai Voltaire, 75340 Paris Cedex 07, France) Eds. Jacques Ziller, M.C. Meininger. circ. 1,200.
   Formerly: Institut International d'Administration Publique. Annee Administrative (ISSN 0984-8673)
   Description: Provides details on the organization and operation of public administration in France and other nations.

350   IE   ISSN 0073-9596
JN1400
INSTITUTE OF PUBLIC ADMINISTRATION, DUBLIN. ADMINISTRATION YEARBOOK AND DIARY. (Text mainly in English; some Irish) 1967. a. I£37. Institute of Public Administration, 59-61 Lansdowne Rd., Dublin 4, Ireland. TEL 01-2697011. FAX 01-2698644. Ed. James O'Donnell. adv. circ. 9,500. **Document type:** trade publication.
   —BLDSC (4567.800900).

350   IE   ISSN 0073-9588
INSTITUTE OF PUBLIC ADMINISTRATION, DUBLIN. ANNUAL REPORT. (Text mainly in English; some Irish) 1958. a. free. Institute of Public Administration, 57-61 Lansdowne Rd., Dublin 4, Ireland. TEL 01-2697011. FAX 01-2698644. Ed. Jim O'Donnell. adv. contact: Eileen Kelly. circ. 2,000. **Document type:** corporate report.

354   SJ   ISSN 0073-9618
INSTITUTE OF PUBLIC ADMINISTRATION, KHARTOUM. OCCASIONAL PAPERS. 1964. irreg. Institute of Public Administration, P.O. Box 1492, Khartoum, Sudan.

354   SJ   ISSN 0073-9626
INSTITUTE OF PUBLIC ADMINISTRATION, KHARTOUM. PROCEEDINGS OF THE ANNUAL ROUND TABLE CONFERENCE. (Text in Arabic or English) 1959. irreg. Institute of Public Administration, P.O. Box 1492, Khartoum, Sudan. **Document type:** proceedings.

350   AT   ISSN 0157-3594
INTERMEDIATOR.* 1979. m. Intermediator Productions, Boronia, Victoria, Australia. charts; illus.
   Incorporates (1970-1980): Commonwealth Professional (ISSN 0313-6299)

350   US
INTERNATIONAL ASSOCIATION OF CLERKS, RECORDERS, ELECTION OFFICIALS, AND TREASURERS. NEWS. q. membership. International Association of Clerks, Recorders, Election Officials, and Treasurers, Box 1012, Camden, NJ 08101-9998. TEL 609-963-0109. FAX 609-541-6198. circ. 1,400. **Document type:** newspaper.

350   UK   ISSN 0956-0998
THE INTERNATIONAL DIRECTORY OF GOVERNMENT. 1990. triennial. $345. Europa Publications, 18 Bedford Sq., London WC1B 3JN, England. TEL 0171-580-8236. FAX 0171-636-1664. TELEX 21540 EUROPA G. **Document type:** directory.
   Description: Provides detailed information on every government in the world.

350   BE   ISSN 0074-6479
INTERNATIONAL INSTITUTE OF ADMINISTRATIVE SCIENCES. REPORTS OF THE INTERNATIONAL CONGRESS. 1910. triennial since 1947; 22nd, 1992, Vienna. 500 BEF. International Institute of Administrative Sciences, 1 rue Defacqz, Bte.11, B-1050 Brussels, Belgium. TEL 32-2-5389165. FAX 32-2-5379702. **Document type:** proceedings.

350 US ISSN 0047-0724
HJ9701 CODEN: IJGADG
INTERNATIONAL JOURNAL OF GOVERNMENT AUDITING/REVUE INTERNATIONALE DE LA VERIFICATION DES COMPTES PUBLICS/REVISTA INTERNACIONAL DE ENTIDADES FISCALIZADORAS SUPERIORES. (Text in Arabic, English, French, German and Spanish) 1974. q. $5. International Organization of Supreme Audit Institutions, c/o U.S. General Accounting Office, 441 G St., N.W., Rm.7806, Washington, DC 20548. TEL 202-512-4707. FAX 202-512-4021. TELEX USGAOWSH 7108229273. Ed. Donald R. Drach. adv.; bk.rev.; illus.; index. circ. 6,500. (also avail. in microform from UMI; reprint service avail. from UMI) **Indexed:** ABI Inform, Account.& Data Proc.Abstr., Account.Ind. (1974-), BPIA, Bus.Ind., Manage.Cont., Mid.East: Abstr.& Ind., Tr.& Indus.Ind. **Document type:** academic/scholarly publication.
●Also available online. Vendor(s): University Microfilms International.
—BLDSC (4542.268000); Faxon; UMI. **CCC.**

350 US ISSN 0190-0692
JA1.A1 CODEN: IJPADR
INTERNATIONAL JOURNAL OF PUBLIC ADMINISTRATION. 1979. m. $462.50 to individuals; institutions $925. Marcel Dekker Journals, 270 Madison Ave., New York, NY 10016. TEL 212-696-9000. FAX 212-685-4540. TELEX 421419. (Subscr. to: Box 5017, Monticello, NY 12701) Eds. Jack Rabin, Thomas Vocino. (also avail. in microform from RPI) **Indexed:** ABI Inform., BPIA, Int.Polit.Sci.Abstr., Manage.Cont., Pers.Lit., Polit.Sci.Abstr., PSI, Sage Pub.Admin.Abstr., Sage Urb.Stud.Abstr., SSCI. **Document type:** academic/scholarly publication.
—BLDSC (4542.507000); Faxon; Genuine Article; SWETS; UMI; UnCover. **CCC.**

350 UK ISSN 1356-3475
▼**INTERNATIONAL PLANNING STUDIES.** Announced for publication in 1996. 3/yr. £24 to individuals; institutions £78 (effective 1996). Carfax Publishing Co., P.O. Box 25, Abingdon, Oxon. OX14 3UE, England. TEL 44-1235-555335. FAX 44-1235-553559. (N. American subscr. to: Carfax Publishing Co., 875-81 Massachusetts Ave., Cambridge, MA 02139) **Document type:** academic/scholarly publication.

350 US ISSN 1053-783X
INTERNATIONAL PUBLIC WORKS REVIEW.* 1990. q. $50. Maxco Publishing Co., Inc., 1275 Bloomfield Ave.,Ste. 3-54, Fairfield, NJ 07004-2708. TEL 201-785-0764. FAX 201-785-0447. adv.: B&W page $1475, color page $2140; trim 7 x 10. circ. 4,300.

350 658 UK ISSN 0020-8523
INTERNATIONAL REVIEW OF ADMINISTRATIVE SCIENCES. French edition: Revue Internationale des Sciences Administratives. (Editions in English, French, Spanish) q. £42 to individuals; institutions £140 (effective 1996). (International Institute of Administrative Sciences) Sage Publications Ltd., 6 Bonhill St., London EC2A 4PU, England. TEL 0171-374-0645. FAX 0171-374-8741. E-mail: market@sageltd.co.uk. Ed. Kenneth Kernaghan. adv.: B&W page £180; trim 185 x 114; adv. contact: Bernie Folan. bk.rev.; bibl.; index. cum.index every 5 yrs. circ. 11,000 (6,000 English ed.; 5,000 French ed.). (reprint service avail. from KTO) **Indexed:** A.B.C.Pol.Sci., ASCA, ASSIA, BPIA, Cont.Pg.Manage., Curr.Cont., E.I., IBZ, Int.Lab.Doc., Int.Polit.Sci.Abstr., Intl.Bibl.S.S.Pol.Sci., Key to Econ.Sci., Manage.Cont., Mid.East: Abstr.& Ind., P.A.I.S., P.A.I.S.For.Lang.Ind., Sage Pub.Admin.Abstr. **Document type:** academic/scholarly publication.
—BLDSC (4545.900000); Faxon; SWETS; UnCover.
Description: Presents comparative studies and national monographs on international administration, national civil services, controls on central government, administrative reform, public finance, regionalization and the history of administration.
Refereed Serial

350 US ISSN 1051-4694
H96
INTERNATIONAL REVIEW OF COMPARATIVE PUBLIC POLICY. 1989. a. J A I Press Inc., 55 Old Post Rd., Box 1678, Greenwich, CT 06836.
—**CCC.**

350 IT ISSN 0074-9435
INTERNATIONAL UNION OF LATIN NOTARIES. PROCEEDINGS OF CONGRESS. 1948. biennial, Amsterdam - 19 Congress, 1989. International Union of Latin Notaries., Notaio Federico Guasti, Via Localtelli n. 5, 20124 Milan, Italy. TEL 864151. adv.; bk.rev. **Document type:** proceedings.

350 US ISSN 0074-106X
INTER-UNIVERSITY CASE PROGRAM. CASE STUDY. (Title varies: I C P Case Series; at head of title: Cases in Public Administration and Policy Information) 1951. irreg. price varies. Inter-University Case Program, Inc., Box 229, Syracuse, NY 13210. Ed. E.A. Bock.

350 US ISSN 0738-9450
IOWA LEGISLATIVE NEWS SERVICE BULLETIN. 1979. d. (during session); w. (between sessions). $260. Iowa Legislative News Service, Box 8370, Des Moines, IA 50301. TEL 515-288-4676. Ed. Arthur A. Small, III. (reprint service avail.)
●Also available online.
Description: Reports on bill introductions, standing committee meetings and interim committee meetings, Attorney General's opinions, other governmental news.

350 IQ
IRAQ. MINISTRY OF INFORMATION. INFORMATION SERIES. irreg., no.72, 1977. Ministry of Information, Baghdad, Iraq.

350 IQ
IRAQ GOVERNMENT GAZETTE. (Editions in Arabic and English) 1922. w. (English ed.) irreg. (Arabic ed.). Ministry of Information, Baghdad, Iraq. circ. 4,450 (4,000 Arabic ed.; 450 English ed.).

350 IE
IRELAND. PUBLIC SERVICE ADVISORY COUNCIL. REPORT. 1975. a. (Public Service Advisory Council) Government Publications Sales Office, Sun Alliance House, Molesworth St., Dublin 2, Ireland. **Document type:** government publication.

350 IE
IRIS OIFIGIUIL. (Supplement avail.) (Text in English and Irish) 1922. 2/wk. I£400; newsstand price: I£3.75. Government Supplies Agency, 4-5 Harcourt Rd., Dublin 2, Ireland. TEL 01-6613111. FAX 01-4780645. Ed. C. Lucey. adv. contact: Marie Matthews. circ. 600. cols./p.: 2; pp./issue: 10. (back issues avail.) **Document type:** government publication, newspaper.

IRISH LAW REPORTS MONTHLY. see *LAW*

350 IS ISSN 0302-8976
ISRAEL. COMMISSIONER FOR COMPLAINTS FROM THE PUBLIC (OMBUDSMAN). ANNUAL REPORT. (Editions in Hebrew, occasionally in English) 1972. a. free. Commissioner for Complaints from the Public, Jerusalem, Israel. FAX 972-2-387768. circ. 2,000. **Document type:** government publication.

354 IV
IVORY COAST. DIRECTION DU BUDGET SPECIAL D'INVESTISSEMENT ET D'EQUIPMENT. RAPPORT DE PRESENTATION DU BUDGET SPECIAL D'INVESTISSEMENT ET D'EQUIPMENT.* a. Direction du Budget Special d'Investissement et d'Equipement, Imprimeriere Nationale, 7 av. Marchand, B.P. V 87, Abidjan, Ivory Coast. stat.

J C P S CONGRESSIONAL DISTRICT FACT BOOK. (Joint Center for Political Studies, Inc.) see *POLITICAL SCIENCE*

350 IS ISSN 0021-3705
DS101
J N F ILLUSTRATED; journal of land reclamation, afforestation and environmental improvement in Israel. (Editions in English, French, German, Portuguese and Spanish) 1927. a. free. Jewish National Fund, P.O. Box 283, Jerusalem, Israel. TEL 972-2-291333. FAX 972-2-291311. Ed. Lenny Labensohn. charts; illus. circ. 30,000. **Indexed:** Ind.Jew.Per. **Document type:** government publication.

350 TS
AL-JARIDAH AL-RASMIYYAH LI-DAWLAT AL-IMARAT AL-ARABIYYAH AL-MUTTAHIDAH/UNITED ARAB EMIRATES. OFFICIAL GAZETTE. (Text in Arabic) 1971. m. Wizarat al-Dawlah li-Shu'un Majlis al-Wuzara' - State Ministry of Cabinet Affairs, P.O. Box 899, Abu Dhabi, United Arab Emirates. TEL 651113. FAX 661172. Ed. Ahmad Muhammad Hamza. cum.index: 1971-1985. circ. 13,000.
Description: Publishes laws and governmental decisions from all U.A.E. Ministries.

JAVNA UPRAVA. see *LAW*

JINGJI GAIGE/ECONOMIC REFORM. see *BUSINESS AND ECONOMICS — Economic Systems And Theories, Economic History*

350 MC ISSN 1010-8742
JOURNAL DE MONACO. 1858. w. 310 F. (foreign 380 F.). Ministry of State, Monaco. TEL 93-15-80-00. FAX 93-15-82-17. Ed. Rainier Imperti. **Document type:** bulletin, government publication, trade publication.

JOURNAL OF COLLECTIVE NEGOTIATIONS IN THE PUBLIC SECTOR. see *BUSINESS AND ECONOMICS — Labor And Industrial Relations*

350 CE ISSN 0047-2360
JOURNAL OF DEVELOPMENT ADMINISTRATION. 1970. s-a. Rs.60($15) Sri Lanka Institute of Development Administration (SLIDA), c/o Additional Director (R.C. and P.), 28-10, Longdon Place, Colombo 07, Sri Lanka. Ed. K.P. Vimaladharma. bk.rev.; bibl.; charts. circ. 1,000. **Indexed:** Sri Lanka Sci.Ind.

350 UK ISSN 1350-1763
JN1
▼**JOURNAL OF EUROPEAN PUBLIC POLICY.** 1994. 4/yr. £34 (U.S. and Canada $50; rest of world £36) to individuals; institutions £80 (U.S. and Canada $120; rest of world £86). Routledge, 11 New Fetter Ln., London EC4P 4EE, England. TEL 0171-583-9855. FAX 0171-842-2298. E-mail: sample.journals@routledge.com. (Subscr. to: ITPS Ltd., Cheriton House, North Way, Andover, Hants SP10 5BE, England. TEL 01264-342919. FAX 01264-342807) Eds. Jeremy Richardson, Robert Lindley. adv.: page £150; trim 115 x 190. circ. 800. **Document type:** academic/scholarly publication.
—BLDSC (4979.608500).
Description: Provides a comprehensive source of analytical articles in the field of European public policy.

350 UK ISSN 1352-0237
Z7164.G7 CODEN: JGINEM
JOURNAL OF GOVERNMENT INFORMATION; an international review of policy, issues and resources. 1974. bi-m. £251($400) (effective 1996). Elsevier Science Ltd., Pergamon, P.O. Box 800, Kidlington, Oxford OX5 1DX, England. TEL 44-1865-843000. FAX 44-1865-843010.
E-mail: nlinfo-f@elsevier.nl; usinfo-f@elsevier.com; forinfo-kyf04035@niftyserve.or.jp; Site addr.: http://www.elsevier.nl/. (Subscr. in U.S. and Canada to: Elsevier Science, 660 White Plains Rd., Tarrytown, NY 10591-5153. TEL 914-524-9200. FAX 914-333-2444) Ed. Steven D. Zink. adv.; bk.rev.; charts. circ. 1,500. (also avail. in microfiche from MIM; microfilm from UMI; back issues avail.; reprint service avail. from UMI) **Indexed:** Amer.Hist.& Life, Bk.Rev.Ind. (1980-), Child.Bk.Rev.Ind. (1980-), Curr.Cont., Hist.Abstr., INSPEC (1994-), Int.Lab.Doc., Leg.Info.Manage.Ind., LHTN, Lib.Lit., Mid.East: Abstr.& Ind., P.A.I.S., SSCI. **Document type:** academic/scholarly publication.
—BLDSC (4996.423000); Faxon; Genuine Article; SWETS; UMI; UnCover. **CCC.**
Former titles (until vol.21, 1994): Government Publications Review (ISSN 0277-9390); Government Publications Review Including Acquisitions Guide; Which was formed by the 1982 merger of: Government Publications Review. Part A: Research Articles (ISSN 0196-335X); Government Publications Review. Part B: Acquisitions Guide to Significant Government Publications at All Levels (ISSN 0196-3368); Supersedes in part: Government Publications Review (ISSN 0093-061X)
Description: Covers production, distribution, library handling, bibliographic control, accessibility and use of government information in all formats and at all levels of government, including United Nations and international agencies.
Refereed Serial

PUBLIC ADMINISTRATION

350.0005   US   ISSN 1042-7309
JA1
JOURNAL OF MANAGEMENT SCIENCE & POLICY ANALYSIS. 1988. q. Marist College, Graduate Center for Public Policy and Administration, Poughkeepsie, NY 12601-1381. **Indexed:** A.B.C.Pol.Sci. (1992-), Int.Polit.Sci.Abstr.

350 320   US   ISSN 0276-8739
H97
JOURNAL OF POLICY ANALYSIS AND MANAGEMENT. 1981. q. $312 (foreign $374) (effective 1996). (Association for Public Policy Analysis and Management) John Wiley & Sons, Inc., Journals, 605 Third Ave., New York, NY 10158. TEL 212-850-6645. FAX 212-850-6021. E-mail: SUBINFO@JWILEY.COM. (Subscr. outside the Americas to: John Wiley & Sons Ltd., Baffins Ln. Chichester, W. Sussex PO19 1UD, England. TEL 44-1243-779777. FAX 44-1243-776128) Ed. Lee S. Friedman. adv.; bk.rev.; index. circ. 2,700. (also avail. in microform from UMI; back issues avail.; reprint service avail. from UMI) **Indexed:** A.B.C.Pol.Sci., Abstr.Health Care Manage.Stud., Amer.Bibl.Slavic & E.Eur.Stud., Amer.Hist.& Life, BPIA, Bus.Ind., Curr.Cont., Deep Sea Res.& Oceanogr.Abstr., Energy Ind., Energy Info.Abstr., Fut.Surv., Hist.Abstr., Human Resour.Abstr., INIS Atomind., Int.Polit.Sci.Abstr., J.of Econ.Lit., Med.Care Rev., Mid.East: Abstr.& Ind., P.A.I.S., Polit.Sci.Abstr., Sage Pub.Admin.Abstr., Sage Urb.Stud.Abstr., Soc.Sci.Ind., Soc.Work Res.& Abstr., SSCI, Tr.& Indus.Ind. **Document type:** academic/scholarly publication.
—BLDSC (5040.841400); Faxon; Genuine Article; SWETS; UMI; UnCover. **CCC.**
Supersedes (1929-1981): Public Policy (Cambridge) (ISSN 0033-3646); (1953-1980): Policy Analysis (ISSN 0098-2067)
Description: Encompasses issues and practices in policy analysis and public management for practitioners, researchers, economists, operations researchers, and consultants.
Refereed Serial

JOURNAL OF POLICY HISTORY. see *HISTORY*

350   US   ISSN 1053-1858
JA1   CODEN: JPRTEC
JOURNAL OF PUBLIC ADMINISTRATION RESEARCH AND THEORY. Variant title: J - P A R T. 1991. q. $40 to individuals; institutions $84. (University of Kansas, Department of Public Administration) Journal of Public Administration Research and Theory, Inc., Box 1897, Lawrence, KS 66044-8897. TEL 913-864-3527. FAX 913-864-5208. E-mail: GFRED@UKANVM.CC.UKANS.EDU. Ed. H. George Frederickson. adv. contact: Alicia Garbie. bk.rev.; index. circ. 500. (also avail. in microfilm from UMI) **Indexed:** Int.Polit.Sci.Abstr., Polit.Sci.Abstr., Soc.Sci.Ind. (1994-). **Document type:** academic/scholarly publication.
—BLDSC (5043.490500); UnCover. **CCC.**
Refereed Serial

350   PK   ISSN 0047-2751
HC440.5.A1
JOURNAL OF RURAL DEVELOPMENT AND ADMINISTRATION (PARD). (Text in English) vol.12, 1977. q. $15. Pakistan Academy for Rural Development, Academy Town, Peshawar, Pakistan. TEL 40296. Ed. Hasan Medhi Naqvi. bk.rev.; bibl.; charts; stat. circ. 1,000. **Indexed:** Abstr.Rural Dev.Trop., Irr.& Drain.Abstr., Poult.Abstr., Rural Devel.Abstr., Rural Ext.Educ.& Tr.Abstr., Soils & Fert., SSCI, World Agri.Econ.& Rural Sociol.Abstr.
—BLDSC (5052.127600).
Formerly: Academy Quarterly.

JOURNAL OF STATE AND ADMINISTRATION. see *POLITICAL SCIENCE*

350 320   GV   ISSN 0533-5701
JOURNAL OFFICIEL DE GUINEE. 1958. fortn. $16. Patrice Lumumba Printing Office, B.P. 156, Conakry, Guinea. adv.; illus.; stat. circ. 700.

350   IV
JOURNAL OFFICIEL DE LA COTE D'IVOIRE. w. Service Autonome des Journaux Officiels, B.P. V70, Abidjan, Ivory Coast. TEL 22-67-76. circ. 1,000. (also avail. in microfilm from KTO)

350   FT
JOURNAL OFFICIEL DE LA REPUBLIQUE DE DJIBOUTI. (Text in French) 1977. irreg. 5720 Fr.CFA. Secretaire General du Gouvernement, Djibouti, Djibouti. (Subscr. to: Impr. Administrative, B.P. 268, Djibouti, Djibouti) adv.

350   CM
JOURNAL OFFICIEL DE LA REPUBLIQUE DU CAMEROUN. (Text in French) fortn. B.P. 1603, Yaounde, Cameroon. TEL 23-12-77. TELEX 8403. circ. 4,000. (also avail. in microfilm from BHP)

350   NG
JOURNAL OFFICIEL DE LA REPUBLIQUE DU NIGER. 1960. fortn. B.P. 116, Naimey, Niger. TEL 72-39-30. Ed. Bonkoula Aminatou Mayaki. circ. 800.

350   SG
JOURNAL OFFICIEL DE LA REPUBLIQUE DU SENEGAL. 1856. w. Rufisque, Senegal.

350   GO
JOURNAL OFFICIEL DE LA REPUBLIQUE GABONAISE. 1959. fortn. B.P. 563, Libreville, Gabon. Ed. Emmanuel Obame.

350   DM
JOURNAL OFFICIEL DE LA REPUBLIQUE POPULAIRE DU BENIN. fortn. Porto-Novo, Benin.

350   RW
JOURNAL OFFICIEL DE LA REPUBLIQUE RWANDAISE. (Text in French) vol.18, 1979. s-m. Service des Affaires Juriques de la Presidence de la Republique, Kigali, Rwanda. (Subscr. to: Imprimerie Nationale du Rwanda, B.P. 351, Kigali, Rwanda)

350   MR
JOURNAL PARLEMENTAIRE.* 1977. m. Editions La Porte, 281 av. Mohammed V, Rabat, Morocco. adv.

JUDICIAL STAFF DIRECTORY. see *LAW — Judicial Systems*

JURISPRUDENTIE VOOR GEMEENTEN. see *LAW*

350   KE   ISSN 0075-5761
K I A OCCASIONAL PAPERS. 1968. irreg., latest no. 4. price varies. Kenya Institute of Administration, P.O. Lower Kabete, Nairobi, Kenya. Ed. H.K.M. Wacirah.

352   NR
KADUNA STATE. MINISTRY OF WORKS. REPORT.* 1960. a. price varies. Ministry of Works, Kaduna, Nigeria.
Formerly: North-Central State. Ministry of Works. Report (ISSN 0078-1762)

354.6   GH   ISSN 0022-7862
KAKYEVOLE. (Text in Nzema) 1956. m. NC.3.60. Information Services Department, P.O. Box 745, Accra, Ghana. TEL 228011. Ed. T.E. Kwesi. adv. circ. 10,000.

354.669   NR
KANO STATE OF NIGERIA GAZETTE. 1967. irreg. free. Government Printing Press, P.O. Box 469, Kano, Nigeria. circ. 3,500.
Continues: Northern Nigeria Gazette.

KARNATAKA. DEPARTMENT OF TOURISM. ANNUAL REPORT. see *TRAVEL AND TOURISM*

320   US
KENTUCKY DIRECTORY OF BLACK ELECTED OFFICIALS. 1970. quadrennial. free. Kentucky Commission on Human Rights, 332 W. Broadway, 7th Fl., Louisville, KY 40202. TEL 502-595-4024. FAX 502-595-4801. circ. 2,000. (reprint service avail.)

350   US
KENTUCKY HORIZONS. 1988. m. $10. Legislative Research Commission, State Capitol, Rm. 300, Frankfort, KY 40601. TEL 502-564-8100. Ed. Peggy Hyland.
Description: Covers emerging policy issues and innovative solutions to problems.

350 320   US   ISSN 1063-9357
KENTUCKY JOURNAL. 1989. 6/yr. $20. Kentucky Center for Public Issues, 167 West Main St., Ste. 310, Lexington, KY 40507. TEL 606-255-5361. FAX 606-233-0760. Ed. David G. Mudd. adv.; bk.rev. circ. 3,000. **Document type:** academic/scholarly publication, newspaper.
Description: Features ideas, research and current information on public policy in Kentucky.

350   KE
KENYA. CENTRAL BUREAU OF STATISTICS. DISTRICT DEVELOPMENT PLAN. (Consists of 1 vol. for each of 47 districts.) irreg. KShs.300 1994 ed. Ministry of Finance and Planning, Central Bureau of Statistics, P.O. Box 30266, Nairobi, Kenya. (Subscr. to: Government Press, Haile Selaissie Ave., P.O. Box 30128, Nairobi, Kenya. TEL 254-2-334075) **Document type:** government publication.

350 360   KE   ISSN 0378-8938
KENYA. MINISTRY OF COOPERATIVES AND SOCIAL SERVICES. SESSIONAL PAPERS. irreg, latest 1994. price varies. Ministry of Cooperatives and Social Services, Nairobi, Kenya. (Subscr. to: Government Press, Haile Selaissie Ave., P.O. Box 30128, Nairobi, Kenya. TEL 254-2-334075) (back issues avail.) **Document type:** monographic series, government publication.

338.9   KE
KENYA. MINISTRY OF FINANCE AND PLANNING. BUDGET SPEECH BY MINISTER FOR FINANCE AND PLANNING. (Text in English) a. Ministry of Finance and Planning, P.O. Box 30266, Nairobi, Kenya. (Subscr. to: Government Press, Haile Selaissie Ave., P.O. Box 30128, Nairobi, Kenya. TEL 254-2-334075) **Document type:** government publication.
Former titles: Kenya. Ministry of Finance and Economic Planning. Budget Speech; Kenya. Ministry of Finance. Speech Delivered to the National Assembly, Presenting the Budget.

350   KE
KENYA. MINISTRY OF FINANCE AND PLANNING. NATIONAL DEVELOPMENT PLAN. (Former name of issuing body: Ministry of Planning and National Development) irreg. KShs.550 for 1994-1996 ed. Ministry of Finance and Planning, P.O. Box 30266, Nairobi, Kenya. (Subscr. to: Government Press, Haile Selaissie Ave., P.O. Box 30128, Nairobi, Kenya. TEL 254-2-334075) **Document type:** government publication.

354   KE
KENYA. MINISTRY OF FINANCE AND PLANNING. PLAN IMPLEMENTATION REPORT. (Former name of issuing body: Kenya. Ministry of Planning and National Development) 1973. irreg. Ministry of Finance and Planning, P.O. Box 30266, Nairobi, Kenya. (Subscr. to: Government Press, Haile Selassie Ave., P.O. Box 30128, Nairobi, Kenya. TEL 254-2-334075) **Document type:** government publication.

350   KE
KENYA. OFFICE OF THE DISTRICT COMMISSIONER. ANNUAL REPORT. a. Office of the District Commissioner, S. Nyanza District, P.O. Box 1, Homa Bay, Kenya.

350   KE   ISSN 0075-5931
KENYA. PUBLIC ACCOUNTS COMMITTEE. ANNUAL REPORT. a. EAs.34. Government Printing and Stationery Department, P.O. Box 30128, Nairobi, Kenya.

KENYA GAZETTE. see *GENERAL INTEREST PERIODICALS — Kenya*

KNIGHT'S LOCAL GOVERNMENT REPORTS. see *LAW*

350   NE   ISSN 0168-9045
KORT BESTEK. 1970. bi-w. Samsom H.D. Tjeenk Willink B.V. (Subsidiary of: Wolters Kluwer N.V.), Postbus 316, 2400 AH Alphen aan den Rijn, Netherlands. TEL 31-1720-66822. FAX 31-1720-66639. **Document type:** trade publication.
Formerly (until 1985): Geknipt voor het Raadslid (ISSN 0165-1927)

350   GW   ISSN 0939-2041
KREIS WESEL. JAHRBUCH. a. (Oberkreisdirektor des Kreises Wesel) Boss-Verlag, Postfach 1150, 47511 Kleve, Germany. Ed. Meinhard Pohl. **Document type:** government publication.

PUBLIC ADMINISTRATION 5545

KUTLWANO/MUTUAL UNDERSTANDING. see *POLITICAL SCIENCE*

354.536   KU   ISSN 0023-575X
KUWAIT AL-YOUM. 1954. w. kD. 15. Ministry of Information, P.O. Box 193, Kuwait. FAX 2467770. TELEX 46151 MI KT. circ. 5,000.
Description: Arabic language review of Kuwaiti official decrees, laws, decisions, and tenders.

350   UK
L G I U DISCUSSION PAPERS. irreg., no.2, 1994. Local Government Information Unit, 1-5 Bath St., London EC1V 9QQ, England. TEL 0171-608-1051. FAX 0171-253-7406. **Document type:** monographic series.

350   UK
L G I U INFORMATION BRIEFING. m. Local Government Information Unit, 1-5 Bath St., London EC1V 9QQ, England. TEL 0171-608-1051. FAX 0171-253-7406. **Document type:** bulletin.

350   UK
L G I U SPECIAL BRIEFINGS. irreg. Local Government Information Unit, 1-5 Bath St., London EC1V 9QQ, England. TEL 0171-608-1051. FAX 0171-253-7406. **Document type:** bulletin.

LABOR (YEAR). see *BUSINESS AND ECONOMICS — Labor And Industrial Relations*

363.6   US
LAMPPOST. 1977. irreg. (every 2-3 mos.). Orange and Rockland Utilities, Inc., One Blue Hill Plaza, Pearl River, NY 10965. TEL 914-577-2546. Ed. Jonathan L. Yoder. circ. 4,000.
Description: Company and utility news for employees and utility professionals.

LAND RIGHTS NEWS; a newspaper for Aboriginals people and their supporters. see *POLITICAL SCIENCE — Civil Rights*

350   GW   ISSN 0939-0014
LANDES- UND KOMMUNALVERWALTUNG; Verwaltungsrecht-Zeitschrift fuer die Laender Berlin, Brandenburg, Mecklenburg-Vorpommern, Sachsen, Sachsen-Anhalt und Thueringen. Short title: L K V. 1991. m. DM.197.60 (students DM.155). C.H. Beck'sche Verlagsbuchhandlung, Wilhelmstr. 9, 80801 Munich, Germany. TEL 089-38189338. FAX 089-38189398. Ed.Bd. adv.: B&W page DM.2200, color page DM.3850; trim 260 x 186. circ. 2,500. (back issues avail.) **Document type:** bulletin.
●Also available on CD-ROM.

354.4   AU   ISSN 0023-7876
LANDESAMTSBLATT FUER DAS BURGENLAND. 1921. w. S.300. Amt der Burgenlaendischen Landesregierung, Freiheitsplatz 1, A-7001 Eisenstadt, Austria. adv.; bk.rev.; index. (looseleaf format) **Document type:** government publication.

LANDESGESETZE BRANDENBURG. see *LAW — Civil Law*

LANDESGESETZE FREISTAAT SACHSEN. see *LAW — Civil Law*

LANDESGESETZE FREISTAAT THUERINGEN. see *LAW — Civil Law*

LANDESGESETZE MECKLENBURG-VORPOMMERN. see *LAW — Civil Law*

LANDESGESETZE SACHSEN-ANHALT. see *LAW — Civil Law*

350   GW
LANDESHAUPTSTADT STUTTGART. AMTSBLATT. 1901. w. DM.36. Landeshauptstadt Stuttgart, Presse- und Informationsamt, Rathaus, Postfach 106034, 70049 Stuttgart, Germany. FAX 0711-2167705. bk.rev.; charts. circ. 57,000. (back issues avail.) **Document type:** government publication.
Formerly: Stuttgart. Amtsblatt.

DER LANDKREIS. see *HOUSING AND URBAN PLANNING*

LEADER (OTTAWA, 1986). see *LABOR UNIONS*

LEGAL ISSUES, GOVERNMENT PROGRAMS & THE ELDERLY (FLORIDA); a handbook for the advocates. see *LAW — Legal Aid*

350   US   ISSN 1068-2716
LEGISBRIEFS. 1993. 48/yr. $79. National Conference of State Legislatures, 1560 Broadway, Ste. 700, Denver, CO 80202. TEL 303-830-2200. FAX 303-863-8003. circ. 13,000. **Document type:** newsletter.
Description: Provides detailed coverage of specific issues facing state legislatures.

350   US
LEGISCON STATEHOUSE REPORT. 1975. w. $300. Legiscon, Box 1643, Baton Rouge, LA 70821. TEL 504-343-9828. FAX 504-338-5243. Ed. James A. Lee. **Document type:** newsletter.
Description: Covers Louisiana executive branch activity, interim legislative action and judicial decisions affecting state government.

350   US
LEGISLATIVE FINANCE PAPERS. 1985. irreg. (10-12/yr.), no.81, 1992. price varies. National Conference of State Legislatures, 1560 Broadway, Ste. 700, Denver, CO 80202-5140. TEL 303-830-2200. FAX 303-863-8003. **Document type:** newsletter.
Description: Comprehensive studies on state tax revenue and expenditure issues.

350   US   ISSN 1064-203X
LEGISLATIVE GAZETTE. 1978. w. (except July-Aug.). $99. Research Foundation of State University of New York, Box 7023, Albany, NY 12225. TEL 518-473-9732. FAX 518-486-6609. Ed. Glenn C. Doty. adv. circ. 18,000. **Document type:** newspaper.
Description: Covers New York legislative and related state government activity.

LEGISLATIVE STUDIES QUARTERLY. see *POLITICAL SCIENCE*

350 330.9   US
LEGISLATIVE WATCH (WASHINGTON). irreg. National Association of State Development Agencies, 750 First St., N.E., Ste. 710, Washington, DC 20002. TEL 202-898-1302.
Description: Aimed at state economic development directors and commissioners.

LEISURE MANAGER. see *LEISURE AND RECREATION*

350   LB
LIBERIA. INSTITUTE OF PUBLIC ADMINISTRATION. ANNUAL REPORT.* 1973. a. free. Institute of Public Administration, Monrovia, Liberia. circ. 200.

354   LB
LIBERIA. MINISTRY OF ACTION FOR DEVELOPMENT AND PROGRESS. ANNUAL REPORT.* a. Ministry of Action for Development and Progress, Monrovia, Liberia.

354   LB   ISSN 0304-7326
HD4366.L5
LIBERIA. MINISTRY OF PUBLIC WORKS. ANNUAL REPORT.* (Text in English) a. Ministry of Public Works, Monrovia, Liberia.

354   LB
LIBERIA. OFFICE OF NATIONAL PLANNING. ANNUAL REPORT TO THE PRESIDENT ON THE OPERATION AND ACTIVITIES.* 1961. a. Ministry of Planning and Economic Affairs, Randall St., P.O. Box 9016, Monrovia, Liberia.
Formerly: Liberia. Bureau of Economic Research and Statistics. Annual Report to the President on the Operation and Activities.

LIBRARY ADMINISTRATOR'S DIGEST. see *LIBRARY AND INFORMATION SCIENCES*

LIBRARY DEVELOPMENTS. see *LIBRARY AND INFORMATION SCIENCES*

LIBRI DELLE BIBLIOTECHE TRENTINE. see *ENVIRONMENTAL STUDIES*

LICENSEE CONTRACTOR AND VENDOR INSPECTION STATUS REPORT. see *ENERGY — Nuclear Energy*

LIST OF PROPRIETARY SUBSTANCES AND NONFOOD COMPOUNDS AUTHORIZED FOR USE UNDER U S D A INSPECTION AND GRADING PROGRAMS. see *CHEMISTRY*

331   US   ISSN 1057-5774
LISTS OF PARTIES EXCLUDED FROM FEDERAL PROCUREMENT OR NONPROCUREMENT PROGRAMS. 1988. m. $86 (foreign $107.50) (effective 1995). U.S. General Services Administration, Publications Office, 18th and F Sts., N.W., Washington, DC 20405. TEL 202-501-1794. FAX 202-501-4281. (Subscr. to: Superintendent of Documents, U.S. Government Printing Office, Box 371954, Pittsburgh, PA 15250-7954. TEL 202-512-1800. FAX 202-512-2250) **Document type:** government publication.
Description: Lists names and addresses of contractors excluded from doing business with the U.S. government because of fraud.

350   UK   ISSN 0964-4148
LOCAL EUROPE. 1990. m. £68 (overseas £83). London Research Centre, Research Library, 81 Black Prince Rd., London SE1 7SZ, England. TEL 0171-627-9661. FAX 0171-627-9664. Ed. Mark Cousins. adv. contact: Annabel Davies. **Document type:** abstracting/indexing.
Description: Covers all aspects of local government and urban affairs affected by the European Community.

350   AT
LOCAL GOVERNMENT PLANNING & ENVIRONMENT SERVICE N S W. (Volume A: Local Government Act & Index; Volume B: Legislation & Acts; Volume C: Commentary) 3 base vols. (vols. A & B updated 6/yr.; vol. C updated 4/yr.). $635. Butterworths, Division of Reed International Books Australia Pty. Ltd. (Subsidiary of: Reed Elsevier Australia Pty. Ltd.), 271-273 Lane Cove Rd., North Ryde, N.S.W. 2113, Australia. TEL 02-335-4444. FAX 02-335-4678. (looseleaf format)

350   AT
LOCAL GOVERNMENT SERVICE VICTORIA. 1991. irreg. (approx. 5/yr.). Aus.$395 with updates. Law Book Co. Ltd., 44-50 Waterloo Rd., North Ryde, N.S.W. 2113, Australia. TEL 02-936-6444. FAX 02-888-2229. TELEX ASHBOOK 27995. Ed.Bd. (looseleaf format)
Description: Includes the Local Government Act 1989 (Vic.), related legislation and extensive commentary on local government.

LOKAAL & MONDIAAL - VAKMATIG. see *POLITICAL SCIENCE — International Relations*

348.76301 350   US
LOUISIANA ADMINISTRATIVE CODE. irreg. $1080 includes supplement. Division of Administration, Office of the State Register, Box 94095, Baton Rouge, LA 70804-9095. TEL 504-342-5015. Ed. Laura Root. circ. 2,000. (back issues avail.)

348.76301 340   US   ISSN 0098-8545
KFL34.A2
LOUISIANA REGISTER. 1975. m. $110. Division of Administration, Office of the State Register, Box 94095, Baton Rouge, LA 70804-9095. TEL 504-342-5015. Eds. Suzanne McAndrew, Laura Root. index. circ. 957. (back issues avail.) **Document type:** government publication.

350   LU   ISSN 1021-058X
LUXEMBOURG. MINISTERE D'ETAT. BULLETIN D'INFORMATION ET DE DOCUMENTATION. q. Ministere d'Etat, 43 bd. Roosevelt, 2450 Luxembourg, Luxembourg.
Formerly (until 1991): Luxembourg. Ministere d'Etat. Bulletin de Documentation (ISSN 0251-4001)

350   US
M A P A ANNUAL REPORT. a. free. Omaha - Council Bluffs Metropolitan Area Planning Agency, 2222 Cuming St., Omaha, NE 68102-4328. TEL 402-444-6866. FAX 402-342-0949. circ. 1,000. **Document type:** government publication.

350   US
M A P A COMMUNITY ASSISTANCE REPORT. a. free. Omaha - Council Bluffs Metropolitan Area Planning Agency, 2222 Cuming St., Omaha, NE 68102-4328. TEL 402-444-6866. FAX 402-342-0949. circ. 1,000.

PUBLIC ADMINISTRATION

350 US
M A S S MEDIA. 1972. q. National Council of Social Security Management Associations, Box 1587, Lake Charles, LA 70605. TEL 318-478-0246. Ed. Bill Dixon. circ. 4,600. (back issues avail.) **Document type:** bulletin.

350 320 US
M I R S LEGISLATIVE REPORT. 1961. d. $1200. Michigan Information and Research Service, Inc., 421 West Ionia, Lansing, MI 48933. TEL 517-482-2125. FAX 517-482-1307. Ed. Todd W. Carter.
Description: Summarizes news regarding Michigan elections, politics, legislative and state government issues. Includes bill status information, committee and meeting schedules, and other related information and services.

350 US
M P S TODAY. ceased. w. free to qualified personnel. Missouri Public Service, COM 750-2A, 10700 East 350 Hwy., Kansas City, MO 64138. TEL 816-737-7549. Ed. Diane Walker.
Formerly (until 1991): M O P S C O News.

M S B A IN BRIEF. (Minnesota State Bar Association) see LAW

350 320 US ISSN 0732-0205
MCCARVILLE - HILL REPORT. 1980. 48/yr. $104. McCarville - Hill Publications, Box 30647, Midwest City, OK 73140. TEL 405-737-6021. FAX 405-737-0058. Eds. Mike McCarville, Neva Hill.
Former titles: McCarville - Gray Report & McCarville Report.
Description: Report on Oklahoma government and politics.

MAINE ADMINISTRATIVE PROCEDURE. see LAW — Judicial Systems

MAINE REGISTER: STATE YEARBOOK AND LEGISLATIVE MANUAL. see PUBLIC ADMINISTRATION — Municipal Government

350 IO ISSN 0125-9652
MAJALAH ADMINISTRASI NEGARA; Indonesian journal of public administration. 1959. q. Rps.6000. Lembaga Administrasi Negara, Jl. Veteran 10, Jakarta, Indonesia. adv.; bibl.; illus. circ. 1,000.

350 JO ISSN 1010-0709
AL-MAJALLAH AL-ARABIYYAH LIL-IDARAH/ARAB JOURNAL OF ADMINISTRATION. (Text in Arabic) 1977. q. $30 to individuals; institutions $50. Arab Administrative Development Organization - Al-Munathamah Al-Arabiyyah lil-Tanmiah Al-Idariyyah, P.O. Box 17159, Amman, Jordan. TEL 814118. FAX 816972. TELEX 21594 ARADO JO. Ed. Ahmed Sakr Ashour. adv.; bk.rev. circ. 2,000. (back issues avail.) **Document type:** academic/scholarly publication.
Description: Covers contemporary issues in administrative policy and practice, including case studies, responses to problems, development of administrative sciences in the Arab world, as well as a review of relevant experiences from international literature.
Refereed Serial

MAJOR LEGISLATION OF THE CONGRESS. see LAW — Constitutional Law

350 MW
MALAWI. ECONOMIC PLANNING DIVISION. MID-YEAR ECONOMIC REVIEW. (Text in English) 1971. a. Government Printer, P.O. Box 37, Zomba, Malawi.

350 MW
MALAWI. GOVERNMENT PRINTER. CATALOGUE OF PUBLICATIONS. (Text in English) 1974. q. Government Printer, P.O. Box 37, Zomba, Malawi.

350 MW
MALAWI GAZETTE SUPPLEMENT CONTAINING ACTS. (Text in English) irreg. Government Printer, P.O. Box 37, Zomba, Malawi.

350 MW
MALAWI GAZETTE SUPPLEMENT CONTAINING BILLS. (Text in English) irreg. Government Printer, P.O. Box 37, Zomba, Malawi.

350 MW
MALAWI GAZETTE SUPPLEMENT CONTAINING REGULATIONS, RULES, ETC.. (Text in English) irreg. Government Printer, P.O. Box 37, Zomba, Malawi.

350 MW
MALAWI GOVERNMENT DIRECTORY. (Text in English) a. Government Printer, P.O. Box 37, Zomba, Malawi. **Document type:** directory.

350 MW
MALAWI GOVERNMENT GAZETTE. (Text in English) 1894. w. K.12.60. Ministry of Finance, Government Printer, P.O. Box 37, Zomba, Malawi. TEL 523155. index.

350 658 II ISSN 0047-570X
MANAGEMENT IN GOVERNMENT. 1969. q. Rs.120($32) Department of Administrative Reforms and Public Grievances, Sardar Patel Bhawan, Parliament St., New Delhi 110 001, India. TEL 91-11-311691. FAX 91-11-3732133. Ed. Sushmita Dasgnpta. bk.rev.; abstr.; bibl.; charts; illus. circ. 1,000. (reprint service avail. from SCH) **Indexed:** CLOSS, Key to Econ.Sci. **Document type:** government publication.
Description: Covers public policy, personnel management, human resource development, administrative management, and other topics related to government management.

350 658 NE ISSN 1381-0928
▼**MANAGEMENTBLAD RIJKSDIENTS**. 1994. bi-m. (Ministerie van Binnenlandse Zaken) Samsom H.D. Tjeenk Willink B.V., Postbus 316, 2400 AH Alphen aan den Rijn, Netherlands. TEL 31-1720-66822. FAX 31-1720-66639. **Document type:** trade publication.

333
MANAGING THE NATION'S PUBLIC LANDS. 1980. a. U.S. Department of the Interior, Bureau of Land Management, Washington, DC 20240. circ. 2,500. **Document type:** government publication.
Description: Describes management of U.S. public lands. Includes Bureau's accomplishments, issues, goals for the preceding fiscal year.

350 US ISSN 1057-7025
MANDATE MONITOR. irreg. (10-12/yr.). $35 (Canada $38). National Conference of State Legislatures, 1560 Broadway, Ste. 700, Denver, CO 80202. TEL 303-830-2200. FAX 303-863-8003. **Document type:** newsletter.
Description: Complete guide to all congressional bills imposing mandates on state and local government, including bill or regulation number, title, and explanation indicating programs affected, and status of bill.

338.9 350 FR ISSN 0542-6685
MARCHES PUBLICS; la revue de l'achat public. 1953. 8/yr. 445 F. (Europe 515 F., elsewhere 635 F.). Ministere de l'Economie et des Finances, Commission Centrale des Marches, Tour de Lyon, 185 rue de Bercy, 75572 Paris Cedex 12, France. TEL 44-87-17-17. FAX 53-17-86-69. (Subscr. to: Documentation Francaise, 124 rue Henry Barbusse, 93308 Aubervilliers Cedex, France. TEL 48-39-56-00. FAX 48-39-56-01) Ed. Marie-Laurence Pitois-Pujade. bk.rev.; bibl.; stat.; index, cum.index. circ. 6,000. (also avail. in microfiche from DFR; back issues avail.)

MARK SIEGEL AND ASSOCIATES WASHINGTON INSIDER. see POLITICAL SCIENCE

MARYLAND. GENERAL ASSEMBLY. SUBJECT INDEX TO BILLS INTRODUCED IN THE SESSION. see LAW — Abstracting, Bibliographies, Statistics

MARYLAND. HOUSE OF DELEGATES. JOURNAL OF PROCEEDINGS. REGULAR SESSION. see LAW

MARYLAND. SENATE. JOURNAL OF PROCEEDINGS. REGULAR SESSION. see LAW

350 340 US
MARYLAND CONTRACT WEEKLY. 1974. w. $125. Division of State Documents, Box 2249, Annapolis, MD 21404-2249. TEL 410-974-2486. FAX 410-974-2546. Ed. Robert J. Colborn, Jr. circ. 2,600. **Document type:** government publication.
Former titles (until 1994): Maryland Register Contract Weekly (ISSN 1061-2696); (until 1992): Maryland Register Contract Supplement.
Description: State contract bid solicitation and award information, country and municipal contract information, and synopses of opinions rendered by State Board of Contract Appeals.

141 310 US ISSN 0094-4491
JK3831
MARYLAND MANUAL; a guide to Maryland state government. Title varies: Manual-State of Maryland. 1896. biennial. $20. State Archives, 350 Rowe Blvd., Annapolis, MD 21401. TEL 301-974-3916. FAX 301-974-3895. Ed. Diane P. Frese. charts; illus.; stat.; index. circ. 8,000. (back issues avail.)

348 US ISSN 0360-2834
KFM1234.A2
MARYLAND REGISTER. 1974. fortn. $100. Division of State Documents, Box 2249, Annapolis, MD 21404-2249. TEL 410-974-2486. FAX 410-974-2546. Ed. Robert J. Colborn, Jr. index. circ. 1,700. **Document type:** government publication.
Description: Official text of all proposed, adopted and emergency regulations, court rules, governor's executive orders, agency hearing and meeting notices.

350 320 US ISSN 1042-1564
MARYLAND REPORT. 1989. bi-w. $200. Bancroft Information Group, Inc., Box 65360, Baltimore, MD 21209. TEL 410-358-0658. FAX 410-764-1967. Ed. Bruce L. Bortz. (also avail. in microfiche from BHP) **Document type:** newsletter.
—CCC.
Description: News, analysis of Maryland government, politics and business.

MASSACHUSETTS CIVIL SERVICE REPORTER. see LAW

350 US ISSN 1057-4549
MASSACHUSETTS VOTER. 1972. 6/yr. $13. League of Women Voters of Massachusetts, 133 Portland St., Boston, MA 02114-1730. TEL 617-523-2999. FAX 617-248-0881. Ed. Gail O'Reilly. circ. 7,000. **Document type:** newsletter.
Former titles (until 1990): Voter (ISSN 0899-4935); State House Reporter.

MAURITIUS. MINISTRY OF WORKS AND INTERNAL COMMUNICATIONS. REPORT. see TRANSPORTATION

350 MF
MAURITIUS. OMBUDSMAN. REPORT. (Text in English) irreg., latest 1991. price varies. Government Printing Office, Elizabeth II Ave., Port Louis, Mauritius. (Subscr. to: La Tour Koenig, Pointe aux Sables, Port Louis, Mauritius. TEL 2345294. FAX 2084011)

350 MF
MAURITIUS. PUBLIC SERVICE COMMISSION. REPORT. (Text in English) triennial, latest 1978. Government Printing Office, Elizabeth II Ave., Port Louis, Mauritius. (Subscr. to: La Tour Koenig, Pointe aux Sables, Port Louis, Mauritius. TEL 2345294. FAX 2084011)

MAURITIUS DIRECTORY OF THE DIPLOMATIC CORPS. see POLITICAL SCIENCE — International Relations

MEAT AND POULTRY INSPECTION REGULATIONS; meat inspection, poultry inspection, rabbit inspection, voluntary inspection and certificate service of meat and poultry, humane slaughter of livestock. see AGRICULTURE — Poultry And Livestock

334 FR ISSN 0025-9179
MEMORIAL DES PERCEPTEURS ET RECEVEURS DES COMMUNES. 1826. m. 500 F. Publications Paul Dupont, 38 rue Croix des Petits Champs, 75001 Paris, France. TEL 42-36-06-87. FAX 40-39-01-23. index.

MICHIGAN. DEPARTMENT OF SOCIAL SERVICES. ASSISTANCE PAYMENTS STATISTICS. see SOCIAL SERVICES AND WELFARE

MICHIGAN STATE EMPLOYEES' RETIREMENT SYSTEM FINANCIAL AND STATISTICAL REPORT. see *BUSINESS AND ECONOMICS — Labor And Industrial Relations*

MILITSIYA. see *MILITARY*

350   DK   ISSN 0085-3461
MINISTERIALTIDENDE FOR KONGERIGET DANMARK. 1871. w. DKK 500. Justisministeriet, Sekretariatet for Retsinformation, Axeltorv 6, 5. sal, DK-1609 Copenhagen V, Denmark. TEL 45-33-32-52-22. FAX 45-33-91-28-01. adv. contact: Nina Koch. index; circ. 2,007. **Document type:** government publication.
●Also available online.
    Formerly (until 1977): Ministerialtidende for Kongeriget Danmark. Afdeling A (ISSN 0901-5000)
    Description: Official organ for promulgating Departmental circulars and Departmental orders, etc., which may not require promulgation by law.

350 340   US
MINNESOTA ADMINISTRATIVE PROCEDURE. 1987. base vol. (plus suppl.). $75. Butterworth Legal Publishers (Salem) (Subsidiary of: Reed Elsevier plc), 8 Industrial Way, Bldg. C, Salem, NH 03079. TEL 800-548-4001. FAX 603-898-9858. Ed.Bd.
    Description: Explanation of state administrative procedure in Minnesota, with special attention to the contested case, the adjudicative process and how rules are made by state agencies.

350   US
MINNESOTA GOVERNMENT REPORT. 1978. s-w. $250. Box 441, Willernie, MN 55090. TEL 612-426-6339. Ed. Jean L. Dawson.
    Description: Covers Minnesota state government, including appellate court activity.

340   US   ISSN 1061-0987
JK6130
MINNESOTA GUIDEBOOK TO STATE AGENCY SERVICES. 1977. quadrennial. $16.90 (effective 1995). Department of Administration, Print Communications Division, 117 University Ave., St. Paul, MN 55155. TEL 612-297-3000. Ed. Robin PanLener. index. circ. 12,500.

MINNESOTA PUBLIC EMPLOYEE. see *LABOR UNIONS*

MINNESOTA RULES. SUPPLEMENT. see *LAW — Judicial Systems*

MINNESOTA STATE REGISTER. see *LAW*

MONITOR (ATLANTA). see *POLITICAL SCIENCE — Civil Rights*

350 320   US
MONITOR (RANCHO PALOS VERDE); we the people and our two cents worth. 1988. q. $6 (overseas $10). E T S Research Inc., 80 Narcissa Dr., Rancho Palos Verde, CA 90274. TEL 310-377-7608. FAX 310-377-2178. Ed. Erica Stuart. circ. 5,000. **Document type:** newsletter.
    Description: Contains investigative reporting on local government and court. Also analyzes present and future political events.

350   US
MONTANA. DEPARTMENT OF COMMERCE. PROFESSIONAL AND OCCUPATIONAL LICENSING BUREAU. PUBLIC SAFETY DIVISION. BIENNIAL REPORT. biennial. Department of Commerce, Professional and Occupational Licensing Bureau, Public Safety Division, 111 N. Jackson, Helena, MT 59620-0407. TEL 406-444-3737. FAX 406-444-1667. **Document type:** government publication.
    Formerly: Montana. Department of Business Regulation. Annual Report (ISSN 0093-8246)

MONTANA. OFFICE OF THE LEGISLATIVE AUDITOR. STATE OF MONTANA BOARD OF INVESTMENTS. REPORT ON EXAMINATION OF FINANCIAL STATEMENTS. see *BUSINESS AND ECONOMICS — Investments*

350   BG
MONTHLY PRATIRODHA. 1976. s-m. Tk.36. Ministry of Home Affairs, Jatiya Gram Pratirakaha Committee, Khilgoan, Dhaka 1219, Bangladesh. Ed. Jahangir Habibullah. adv.; bk.rev.
    Formerly: Pakshika Pratirodha.

351 340   US
MUNICIPAL GOVERNMENT PERMITS AND LICENSES. 1992. m. $81 (effective 1993). Quinlan Publishing Co., Inc., 23 Drydock Ave., Boston, MA 02210-2387. TEL 617-542-0048; 800-229-2084. FAX 617-345-9646. index. (looseleaf format; back issues avail.) **Document type:** newsletter.
    Description: Covers recent decisions on laws defining permits and licenses granted, revoked, denied or amended, on topics ranging from tax assessment and landfill operations to liquor violations and adult entertainment businesses.

350   US
N A C R C BULLETIN. q. membership. National Association of County Recorders and Clerks, c/o National Association of Counties, 440 First St., N.W., 8th Fl., Washington, DC 20001. TEL 202-393-6226. circ. 900 (controlled). **Document type:** newsletter.
    Formerly: N A C R C News.
    Description: Contains legislative updates and conference notes.

N A S A O NEWSLETTER. (National Association of State Aviation Officials) see *AERONAUTICS AND SPACE FLIGHT*

350 330.9   US
N A S D A DIRECTORY OF DEVELOPMENT AGENCIES AND OFFICIALS. q. National Association of State Development Agencies, 750 First St., N.E., Ste. 710, Washington, DC 20002. TEL 202-898-1302. **Document type:** directory.
    Description: Aimed at state economic development directors and commissioners.

350 330.9   US
N A S D A LETTER. irreg. (6-9/yr.). National Association of State Development Agencies, 750 First St., N.E., Ste. 710, Washington, DC 20002. TEL 202-898-1302. **Document type:** newsletter.
    Description: Aimed at state economic development directors and commissioners.

350 330.9   US
N A S D A STATE ECONOMIC DEVELOPMENT EXPENDITURES AND SALARY SURVEY. s-a. National Association of State Development Agencies, 750 First St., N.E., Ste. 710, Washington, DC 20002. TEL 202-898-1302.
    Description: Aimed at state economic development directors and commissioners.

350 330.9   US
N A S D A STATE ENTERPRISE ZONE ROUNDUP. a. National Association of State Development Agencies, 750 First St., N.E., Ste. 710, Washington, DC 20002. TEL 202-898-1302.
    Description: Aimed at state economic development directors and commissioners.

350   US
N C L G FOCUS. 1982. q. (National Conference of Lieutenant Governors) Gail B. Manning, Ed. & Pub., 3560 Iron Works Pike, Box 11910, Lexington, KY 40578-1910. (Co-sponsor: Council of State Governments) circ. 550. **Document type:** newsletter.
    Formerly (until 1993): N C L G Newsletter.
    Description: Covers issues of interest to senior state officials.

350.6 663.1   US
N C S L A MINUTES of ANNUAL MEETING. 1937. a. $25. National Conference of State Liquor Administrators, 301 Centennial Mall, S., Lincoln, NE 68509. TEL 402-471-2571. Ed. Randy Yarbrough. circ. 100.

350.6 663.1   US
N C S L A OFFICIAL DIRECTORY. a. $5. National Conference of State Liquor Administrators, 300 Centennial Mall, S., Lincoln, NE 68509. TEL 402-471-2571. Ed. Randy Yarbrough. circ. 100. **Document type:** directory.
    Description: Directory of all state agencies administrating alcoholic beverage laws.

350   US   ISSN 0899-5052
N C S L CONFERENCE REPORT. q. $20 (Canada $22.50). National Conference of State Legislatures, 1560 Broadway, Ste. 700, Denver, CO 80202-5140. TEL 303-830-2200. FAX 303-863-8003. **Document type:** newsletter.
    Description: Communicates to legislators, staff, and those wanting to keep abreast of the many varied services and activities of the NCSL.

350   ISSN 0898-4298
N C S L FEDERAL UPDATE. 1975. 15/yr. $35 (Canada $37.50). National Conference of State Legislatures, 1560 Broadway, Ste. 700, Denver, CO 80202. TEL 303-830-2200. FAX 303-863-8003. **Document type:** newsletter.
    Former titles (until 1987): Capital to Capital; Dateline Washington.
    Description: Informs legislators and legislative staff on key federal issues.

350   UK   ISSN 0951-6611
N H S ECONOMIC REVIEW (YEAR). (National Health Service) 1983. a. £10. Birmingham Research Park, Vincent Dr., Birmingham B15 2SQ, England. TEL 021-471 4444. FAX 021-414-1120. circ. 750. (back issues avail.)
    Description: Sets in context the economic issues confronting the National Health Service (NHS) by taking a broad look at the activities and staffing of the health service, along with the challenges in health care for the present and coming years.

N S F BULLETIN. (U.S. National Science Foundation) see *SCIENCES: COMPREHENSIVE WORKS*

352.7   TS
NASHRAT AL-ISKAN WAL-ASHGHAL/WORKS AND HOUSING BULLETIN. (Text in Arabic) 1988. m. free. Wizarat al-Ashgal al-Aamah wal-Iskan, Al-Lajnah al-I'lamiyyah - Ministry of Pulbic Works and Housing, Information Committee, P.O. Box 878, Abu Dhabi, United Arab Emirates. TEL 651778. FAX 665598. TELEX 23833 EM. Ed. Muhammad Yusuf al-Awadi. adv.; illus.; stat. circ. 1,000.
    Formerly: United Arab Emirates. Ministry of Public Works and Housing. News Bulletin.
    Description: News of ministry activities.

NATIONAL ARCHIVES OF ZAMBIA. CALENDARS OF THE DISTRICT NOTEBOOKS. see *HISTORY — History Of Africa*

NATIONAL ASSOCIATION OF BLACKS WITHIN GOVERNMENT. NEWSLETTER. see *ETHNIC INTERESTS*

350   US   ISSN 1060-5029
HT392
NATIONAL ASSOCIATION OF REGIONAL COUNCILS. REGIONAL REPORTER. 1989. m. membership only. National Association of Regional Councils, 1700 K St. N.W., Washington, DC 20006. TEL 202-296-0710. FAX 202-296-9352. Ed. Beverly Nykwest. circ. 2,000. **Document type:** newspaper.
    Incorporates (1986-1989): National Association of Regional Councils. News and Notes (ISSN 0897-1536); Which supersedes: Director's News; Incorporates (1975-1989): National Association of Regional Councils. Washington Report (ISSN 0196-4003); Which supersedes: National Service to Regional Councils. Special Reports (ISSN 0028-0135); Which incorporates: Regional Review Quarterly (ISSN 0034-3382)

363.6 352   US   ISSN 0027-8645
HD2766.A3
NATIONAL ASSOCIATION OF REGULATORY UTILITY COMMISSIONERS. BULLETIN. Short title: N A R U C Bulletin. Variant title: Blue Bulletin. 1916. w. $110. National Association of Regulatory Utility Commissioners, 1102 Interstate Commerce Commission Bldg., Box 684, Washington, DC 20044-0684. TEL 202-898-2200. FAX 202-898-2213. Ed. Paul Rodgers. index. circ. 2,000. **Document type:** bulletin.
    Formerly: National Association of Railroad and Utilities Commissioners. Bulletin.

PUBLIC ADMINISTRATION

353.008 US ISSN 0077-3387
HE2715
NATIONAL ASSOCIATION OF REGULATORY UTILITY COMMISSIONERS. PROCEEDINGS. 1889. a. $45. National Association of Regulatory Utility Commissioners, 1102 Interstate Commerce Commission Bldg., Box 684, Washington, DC 20044-0684. TEL 202-898-2200. FAX 202-898-2213. **Document type:** proceedings.
Formerly: National Association of Railroad and Utilities Commissioners. Proceedings.

NATIONAL ASSOCIATION OF STATE BOARDS OF ACCOUNTANCY. STATE BOARD REPORT. see *BUSINESS AND ECONOMICS — Accounting*

350 US
NATIONAL BALLOT ISSUES MONITOR.* 1989. m. $300. Ballot Monitor Corporation, 7145 Melstone Valley Way, Marriottsville, MD 21104. TEL 202-337-0061. Ed. Richard Glaub. **Document type:** newsletter.
Description: Provides latest information on important initiative and referenda measures throughout the United States.

350 346.013 US
NATIONAL BLACK COALITION OF FEDERAL AVIATION EMPLOYEES. UPDATE.* s-a. National Black Coalition of Federal Aviation Employees, 132 Francisco Ter., Oak Park, IL 60302-2615.
Description: Promotes professionalism and equal opportunities for African-American and other minority employees at the U.S. Federal Aviation Administration.

353 US ISSN 1046-1841
JK2459
NATIONAL CONFERENCE OF LIEUTENANT GOVERNORS. BIOGRAPHICAL SKETCHES AND PORTRAITS. biennial. $30. The Council of State Governments, 3560 Iron Works Pike, Box 11910, Lexington, KY 40578-9989. TEL 606-244-8000. FAX 606-244-8001.

NATIONAL CONFERENCE ON PUBLIC RETIREMENT SYSTEMS. PROCEEDINGS RECORD. see *BUSINESS AND ECONOMICS — Labor And Industrial Relations*

NATIONAL CONTRACT MANAGEMENT JOURNAL. see *BUSINESS AND ECONOMICS — Management*

350 US
NATIONAL COUNCIL OF ELECTED COUNTY EXECUTIVES.* 1990. m. membership. Griffin Media Group, Box 203, New York, NY 10009-0203. TEL 212-481-4188. FAX 212-481-7239. Ed. Earl Wells. adv.; illus.; circ. 2,500 (controlled). (tabloid format) **Document type:** newspaper.
Description: Contains articles on national issues affecting local government operations, profiles of elected executives, and a legislative update.

350 AT ISSN 1030-6641
JQ4021
NATIONAL GUIDE TO GOVERNMENT; and the bureaucracy. 1983. q. Aus.$320. Information Australia, 45 Flinders Lane, Melbourne, Vic. 3000, Australia. TEL 03-654-2800. FAX 03-650-5261. Ed. Petra Torner. circ. 1,400. **Document type:** directory.

350 610 US ISSN 0270-6768
NATIONAL INTELLIGENCE REPORT; the biweekly on Medicare policy for laboratories, blood banks & physician services. 1979. fortn. $220. Washington G-2 Reports, 1111 14th St., N.W., Ste. 500, Washington, DC 20005. TEL 202-789-1034; 800-LAB-REGS. FAX 202-289-4062. Ed. Jim Curren; Pub. Dennis W. Weissman. charts. circ. 2,000. (looseleaf format; back issues avail.) **Document type:** newsletter.
Description: Covers third-party payment and billing news, C.L.I.A. developments, system fraud and abuse. Aimed at laboratory and hospital administrators, attorneys, physicians, and blood bank directors.

350 UK ISSN 0957-8978
HD8005.2.G7
NATIONAL UNION OF CIVIL AND PUBLIC SERVANTS. JOURNAL. 1923. m. £15 (foreign £25). National Union of Civil and Public Servants, 124-130 Southwark St., London SE1 0TU, England. TEL 0171-928-9671. FAX 0171-401-2693. Ed. Nick Wright. adv.; bk.rev.; illus. circ. 130,000. **Document type:** newsletter.
Incorporates: Whip (ISSN 0043-485X); Former titles (until 1987): Opinion; Civil Service Opinion (ISSN 0009-8027)

336.782 US
NEBRASKA. DEPARTMENT OF ADMINISTRATIVE SERVICES. ANNUAL FISCAL REPORT. Cover title: State of Nebraska Annual Fiscal Report. 1966. a. free. Department of Administrative Services, Lincoln, NE 68509. TEL 402-471-3593. illus.; stat. circ. 350.
Former titles: Nebraska. Accounting Division. Annual Fiscal Report; Nebraska. Accounting Division. Annual Report of Receipts and Disbursements (ISSN 0090-628X)

350 346.013 US
THE NETWORKER (WASHINGTON).* q. National Black Coalition of Federal Aviation Employees, P.O. Box 9306, Albuquerque, NM 87119-9306.
Description: Promotes professionalism and equal opportunities for African-American and other minority employees at the U.S. Federal Aviation Administration.

NEUE MITTE; Stimme der Katholiken in Wirtschaft und Verwaltung. see *RELIGIONS AND THEOLOGY — Roman Catholic*

353.9 US
NEVADA. OFFICE OF LEGISLATIVE AUDITOR. BIENNIAL REPORT. (Subseries of: Nevada. Legislative Counsel Bureau. Bulletin) 1974. biennial. Office of Legislative Auditor, Carson City, NV 89710. TEL 702-885-5622. stat.
Formerly: Nevada. Office of Fiscal Analyst. Annual Report (ISSN 0092-6841)

350 US
NEW DIRECTIONS IN PUBLIC ADMINISTRATION RESEARCH. 1987. s-a. $33. Florida Atlantic University, College of Urban and Public Affairs, 220 S.E. Second Ave., Fort Lauderdale, FL 33301. TEL 305-355-5219. Ed. Jay Mendell. circ. 300. (back issues avail.) **Indexed:** Int.Polit.Sci.Abstr., P.A.I.S.
Description: Covers new methods and research fields in public administration.

NEW HAMPSHIRE REGISTER: STATE YEARBOOK AND LEGISLATIVE MANUAL. see *PUBLIC ADMINISTRATION — Municipal Government*

NEW JERSEY. LEGALIZED GAMES OF CHANCE CONTROL COMMISSION. REPORT. see *LEISURE AND RECREATION*

350 US
NEW JERSEY COMPREHENSIVE ANNUAL FINANCIAL REPORT. a. Department of the Treasury, Division of Budget and Accounting, Office of Management and Budget, CN 221, Trenton, NJ 08625. **Indexed:** SRI. **Document type:** government publication.
Formerly: State of New Jersey Annual Financial Report.

350 US ISSN 0300-6069
KFN2240
NEW JERSEY REGISTER. 1969. fortn. $75. Office of Administrative Law, CN 301, Trenton, NJ 08625. TEL 609-588-6601. Ed. N. Olsson. cum.index. circ. 2,900.

NEW RESOURCES. see *BIBLIOGRAPHIES*

NEW SOUTH WALES. DEPARTMENT OF AGRICULTURE. ANNUAL REPORT. see *AGRICULTURE*

350 US ISSN 0743-7668
KFN5752
NEW YORK (STATE). OPINIONS OF THE COMPTROLLER. Key Title: Opinions of the New York State Comptroller. 1979. m. $88. Lenz & Riecker, Inc., 1 Columbia Pl., Albany, NY 12207. TEL 518-426-8647. FAX 518-436-0939. cum.index 1979-1990. (looseleaf format; back issues avail.)
Description: Contains official decisions of the comptroller.

NEW YORK EMPLOYER'S ALERT. see *BUSINESS AND ECONOMICS — Labor And Industrial Relations*

NEW YORK EMPLOYER'S GUIDE. see *BUSINESS AND ECONOMICS — Labor And Industrial Relations*

350 US ISSN 0196-4623
JK3430
NEW YORK RED BOOK. 1895. biennial. $50. New York Legal Publishing Corp., 6 Charles Park, Guilderland, NY 12084. TEL 800-541-2681. FAX 518-456-0828. Ed. George A. Mitchell. circ. 15,000.

353.9 US
NEW YORK SEA GRANT INSTITUTE. ANNUAL REPORT. 1973-1986; resumed 1992. a. New York Sea Grant Institute, Dutchess Hall, State University of New York at Stony Brook, Stony Brook, NY 11794-5001. TEL 516-632-6905. adv.; bk.rev.; illus. circ. 1,500.
Formerly: New York State Sea Grant Program. Annual Report (ISSN 0360-3326)

353.97 US ISSN 0883-1548
Q224.3.U62
NEW YORK STATE MUSEUM. BIENNIAL REPORT. biennial. free. New York State Museum, 3140 Cultural Education Center, Albany, NY 12230. circ. 1,000. **Document type:** government publication.
Formerly: New York State Science Service. Biennial Report.

338.9 US ISSN 0077-9423
NEW YORK STATE URBAN DEVELOPMENT CORPORATION. ANNUAL REPORT. 1969-1975; resumed 1977. a. free. Urban Development Corporation, 1515 Broadway, New York, NY 10036. TEL 212-930-0305. FAX 212-930-0444. circ. controlled.

354.9 NZ ISSN 1171-302X
NEW ZEALAND INSTITUTE OF PUBLIC ADMINISTRATION. RESEARCH PAPERS. 1979. irreg. price varies. New Zealand Institute of Public Administration, P.O. Box 5032, Lambton Quay, Wellington, New Zealand. TEL 64-4-389-8776. adv.; bk.rev. (back issues avail.) **Document type:** academic/scholarly publication.
Formerly (until 1991): Public Sector Research Papers (ISSN 0111-1523)

350.814 US
NEWS FROM CONGRESSIONAL BLACK ASSOCIATES. q. Congressional Black Associates, 1504 Longworth, Washington, DC 20515. TEL 202-225-5865.
Description: Informs members of the black community of federal government activities.

NGUOI DAI BIEU NHAN DAN/PEOPLE'S DEPUTY. see *POLITICAL SCIENCE*

350 BE
NIEUW KLIMAAT. (Text in Dutch) 1958. bi-m. 300 Fr. Verbond Vlaams Overheidspersoneel, Rykeklazenstraat, 45, B-1000 Brussels, Belgium. Ed. P. Stoppie. adv.; bk.rev. circ. 6,500.

NIEUWSBRIEF SOCIALE VERNIEUWING. see *SOCIAL SERVICES AND WELFARE*

350 JA
NIPPON GYOSEI KENKYU NENPO/JAPANESE SOCIETY FOR PUBLIC ADMINISTRATION. ANNALS.* (Text in Japanese) a. Nippon Gyosei Gakkai - Japanese Society for Public Administration, c/o Faculty of Law, University of Tokyo, Tokyo Daigaku Hogakubu, Motofuji-cho, Bunkyo-ku, Tokyo 113, Japan. bibl.

350 KE
NON GOVERNMENTAL ORGANIZATIONS REGULATIONS (YEAR). irreg. latest 1992. KShs.55. Government Press, Haile Selaissie Ave., P.O. Box 30128, Nairobi, Kenya. TEL 254-2-334075. **Document type:** government publication.

354.4 DK ISSN 0029-1285
NORDISK ADMINISTRATIVT TIDSSKRIFT. (Text in Danish, Norwegian and Swedish) 1919. q. DKK 225. Nordiske Administrative Forbund, c/o Indenrigsministeriet, Christiansborg Stotsplads 1, DK-1218 Copenhagen K, Denmark. Ed. Marius Ibsen. adv.; bk.rev.; bibl.; charts; stat. circ. 2,400. **Indexed:** Amer.Hist.& Life, ELLIS, Hist.Abstr., Int.Polit.Sci.Abstr.

PUBLIC ADMINISTRATION

NORDRHEIN-WESTFAELISCHE VERWALTUNGBLAETTER; Zeitschrift fuer Oeffentliches Recht und Oeffentliche Verwaltung. see *LAW*

350   GW
NORDRHEIN-WESTFALEN. FINANZMINISTERIUM. FINANZ REPORT. 1991. 2/yr. Finanzministerium des Landes Nordrhein-Westfalen, Jaegerhofstr. 6, 40479 Duesseldorf, Germany. TEL 0211-49722325. FAX 0211-49722300. TELEX 2114101-FMNRW-D. Ed.Bd. circ. 40,000. **Document type:** government publication.

350 330   NX
NORFOLK ISLAND GOVERNMENT GAZETTE. 1942. w. Norfolk Island Administration, Kingston, 2899, Norfolk Island, South Pacific. TEL 22001. FAX 23177. (back issues avail., reprint service avail.) **Document type:** newspaper.

350   US
NORTH CAROLINA. SECRETARY OF STATE. DIRECTORY OF STATE AND COUNTY OFFICIALS. 1936. a. $8. Secretary of State, 300 N. Salisbury St., Raleigh, NC 27603-5909. TEL 919-733-7355. Ed. Lisa Marcus. circ. 10,000 (controlled). **Document type:** directory, government publication.

350   US
NORTH CAROLINA MANUAL. 1901. biennial. $14.37. Secretary of State, 300 N. Salisbury St., Raleigh, NC 27603-5909. TEL 919-733-7355. Ed. Lisa Marcus. circ. 5,000 (controlled). **Document type:** government publication.

NORTH KOREA DIRECTORY (YEAR); comprehensive guide to North Korean organizations and leadership. see *POLITICAL SCIENCE — International Relations*

NORTHWEST PUBLIC POWER BULLETIN. see *ENERGY*

350 200   US   ISSN 0883-3648
K14
NOTRE DAME JOURNAL OF LAW, ETHICS & PUBLIC POLICY. 1984. s-a. $16. University of Notre Dame, Thomas J. White Center on Law and Government, Notre Dame Law School, Rm. 341, Notre Dame, IN 46556. TEL 219-631-5913. FAX 219-631-6371. Ed. Jeff Senkleski. adv. contact: Kelly A. Smith. circ. 1,000. (also avail. in microform from WSH; reprint service avail. from WSH) **Indexed:** C.L.I., Leg.Per. **Document type:** academic/scholarly publication.
—BLDSC (6175.405000); Faxon; UnCover.
Description: Applies normative and ethical concerns to public policy and legal issues.

354   CN
NOVA SCOTIA. DEPARTMENT OF ECONOMIC DEVELOPMENT. ANNUAL REPORT. 1971. a. free. Department of Economic Development, P.O. Box 519, Halifax, NS B3J 2R7, Canada. TEL 902-424-8922. FAX 902-424-5739. TELEX 019-22548. Ed. Linda Laffin. circ. 300 (controlled). **Former titles:** Nova Scotia. Department of Industry, Trade and Technology. Annual Report; Nova Scotia. Department of Development. Annual Report.

354.716   CN   ISSN 0380-5670
NOVA SCOTIA. OFFICE OF THE OMBUDSMAN. ANNUAL REPORT. 1971. a. free. Office of the Ombudsman, Lord Nelson Bldg., Ste. 300, 5675 Spring Garden Rd., P.O. Box 2152, Halifax, NS B3J 3B7, Canada. TEL 902-424-6780. FAX 902-424-6675. Ed. Gerald F. Deyoung. circ. 500. **Document type:** government publication.

O A G OFFICIAL TRAVELER FLIGHT GUIDE. see *TRAVEL AND TOURISM*

O A G OFFICIAL TRAVELER TRAVEL GUIDE. see *TRAVEL AND TOURISM*

350   FR
O E C D SOCIAL POLICY STUDIES SERIES. irreg, no.7, 1990. price varies. Organization for Economic Cooperation and Development, 2 rue Andre-Pascal, 75775 Paris Cedex 16, France. (U.S. orders to: O.E.C.D. Publications and Information Center, 2001 L St., N.W., Ste. 700, Washington, DC 20036-4910. TEL 202-785-6323) (also avail. in microfiche)

350   US
O M B WATCHER. (Office of Management and Budget) 1983. bi-m. $35 to individuals & community organizations; national & governmental organizations $100. O M B Watch, 1731 Connecticut Ave., N.W., Washington, DC 20009-1146. TEL 202-234-8494. FAX 202-234-8584. Ed. Gary D. Bass. **Document type:** newsletter.
Description: News of OMB activities.

O T A BROCHURE. (Office of Technology Assessment) see *SCIENCES: COMPREHENSIVE WORKS*

350 690   NE   ISSN 0923-9871
O T B WERKDOCUMENTEN. 1988. irreg., latest 1995. price varies. (Onderzoeksinstituut Technisch Bestuurskunde) Delft University Press, Stevinweg 1, 2628 CN Delft, Netherlands. TEL 31-15-2783254. FAX 31-15-2781661. (back issues avail.) **Document type:** monographic series.

349   GW   ISSN 0029-859X
DIE OEFFENTLICHE VERWALTUNG; Zeitschrift fuer oeffentliches Recht und Verwaltungswissenschaft. 1948. s-m. DM.438 (students DM.350.40). W. Kohlhammer GmbH, Hessbruehlstr. 69, 70565 Stuttgart, Germany. TEL 0711-7863-1. FAX 0711-7863263. Ed. Heinrich Siedentopf. adv.; bk.rev.; abstr. **Indexed:** Dok.Str., ELLIS. **Document type:** trade publication.
—BLDSC (6236.900000); SWETS. **CCC.**

354.4   AU   ISSN 0029-8581
DAS OEFFENTLICHE HAUSHALTSWESEN IN OESTERREICH. 1961. q. S.240($12) Gesellschaft fuer das Oeffentliche Haushaltswesen, Schenkenstr. 4, A-1010 Vienna, Austria. Ed. Walter Schwab. adv.; bk.rev. circ. 600. **Document type:** bulletin.

350   GY   ISSN 0030-0314
OFFICIAL GAZETTE OF GUYANA. 1966. w. $533. Ministry of Information, Public Communications Agency, 18 Brickdam, P.O. Box 1023, Georgetown, Guyana. adv.; stat. circ. 1,156. (looseleaf format)

350   US   ISSN 0471-1688
OFFICIAL MICHIGAN. 1949. w. $24.95 (effective 1995). Sanilac Publishing, Inc., 3078 S. Main St., Marlette, MI 48453. TEL 517-635-3000. Ed. Don Kilts; Pub. John D. Johnson. adv. **Document type:** newspaper.

350 320 792   IT   ISSN 0390-3079
OGGI E DOMANI. 1973. m. L.40000. EDIARS S.A.S., Via C. Battisti 162, Pescara, Italy. FAX 3985-381298. Ed. Edoardo Tiboni. adv.; bk.rev. circ. 5,000.
Description: Includes articles on relevant issues in the field of public administration, political sciences and economics.

388.324   US
OHIO GOVERNMENT DIRECTORY - OHIO TRUCKING TIMES. 1950. biennial. $5. Ohio Trucking Association, 50 W. Broad St., Ste. 1111, Columbus, OH 43215. TEL 614-221-5375. FAX 614-221-3717. Ed. David F. Bartosic. adv.; bk.rev.; illus. circ. 8,000.
Former titles: Ohio Truck Times; (until 1974): Ohio Trucking News (ISSN 0030-1191)

350   US   ISSN 0163-0008
OHIO MONTHLY RECORD. (Supplement to: Ohio Administrative Code, Approved Edition) 1977. m. $350. Banks - Baldwin Law Publishing Co., University Center, Box 1974, Cleveland, OH 44106. TEL 216-721-7373. FAX 216-721-8055. cum.index. (looseleaf format)
Description: Contains the full text of new administrative agency rules, with research aids--including notes to recent Ohio and federal court decisions and agency opinions.

350   US
OHIO STATE UNIVERSITY. SCHOOL OF PUBLIC ADMINISTRATION. WORKING PAPER SERIES. 1972. irreg. free. Ohio State University, Administrative Science Research, 1775 College Rd., Columbus, OH 42310. TEL 614-422-8696. circ. controlled. **Document type:** monographic series.

OHIO UNITED WAY. ADMINISTRATIVE REPORT. see *SOCIAL SERVICES AND WELFARE*

350   US
OKLAHOMA ALMANAC. 1907. biennial. $12. Oklahoma Department of Libraries, 200 N.E. 18th St., Oklahoma City, OK 73105. TEL 405-521-2502. FAX 405-525-7804. Ed. Ann Hamilton. circ. 7,500. **Document type:** government publication, directory.
Supersedes (in 1992): Directory of Oklahoma.

350 020   US
OKLAHOMA GOVERNMENT PUBLICATIONS; a checklist. 1977. q. free. Oklahoma Department of Libraries, 200 N.E. 18th St., Oklahoma City, OK 73105. TEL 405-521-2502. FAX 405-525-7804. Ed. Vicki Sullivan. circ. 450. **Document type:** government publication, bibliography.
Formerly: Oklahoma Government Documents.

350   US
OKLAHOMA STATE AGENCIES, BOARDS, COMMISSIONS, COURTS, INSTITUTIONS, LEGISLATURE AND OFFICERS. 1953. a. free. Oklahoma Department of Libraries, Legislative Reference Division, 200 N.E. 18th St., Oklahoma City, OK 73105. TEL 405-521-2502. FAX 405-525-7804. Ed. Susan Gilley. circ. 1,000. **Document type:** government publication, directory.
Description: Contact directory of state government agencies, entities and personnel.

350   CN   ISSN 0227-3268
ONTARIO. FEDERAL CABINET. ORDERS-IN-COUNCIL. w. Can.$390. Carswell, One Corporate Plaza, 2075 Kennedy Rd., Scarborough, ON M1T 3V4, Canada. TEL 416-609-8000. FAX 416-298-5094.

350   CN   ISSN 0318-0743
JS1721.058
ONTARIO. PROVINCIAL-MUNICIPAL AFFAIRS SECRETARIAT. MUNICIPAL DIRECTORY. French edition (ISSN 0832-6363) (Text in English and French) 1948. a. Can.$7.50. Ministry of Municipal Affairs and Housing, Provincial-Municipal Affairs Secretariat, 777 Bay St., 13th Fl., Toronto, Ont. M5G 2E5, Canada. TEL 416-585-4286. charts; stat.; index. **Document type:** directory.

350   NE   ISSN 0925-7322
OPENBAAR BESTUUR. 1991. m. fl.170 (effective 1995). Samsom H.D. Tjeenk Willink B.V. (Subsidiary of: Wolters Kluwer N.V.), Postbus 316, 2400 AH Alphen aan den Rijn, Netherlands. TEL 31-1720-66822. FAX 31-1720-66639. (Editorial addr.: Postbus 8, 3956 ZR Leersum, netherlands. TEL 31-3434-56653) Ed. Peter F. van Oosten de Boer. adv.; bk.rev.; index; circ. 2,800 (paid). (back issues avail.) **Document type:** academic/scholarly publication.
—SWETS.
Formed by the merger of: Tijdschrift voor Openbaar Bestuur (ISSN 0165-1226) & Bestuur (ISSN 0167-6733); Which was formerly: Centraal Instituut Vorming en Opleiding Bestuursdiensten-blad (ISSN 0922-3045)
Description: Articles of interest to civil servants at the central, provincial and municipal levels, as well as to scholars of public administration.
Refereed Serial

350   UK   ISSN 0030-3852
OPPORTUNITIES. 1963. w. Lind House Magazines Ltd., Link House, Dingwall Rd., Croydon CR9 2TA, England. circ. 53,000. (tabloid format)

OPSTINA; casopis za teoriju i praksu razvoja opstine. see *POLITICAL SCIENCE*

ORAL HISTORY SERIES. see *HISTORY — History Of North And South America*

350   US
OREGON. SECRETARY OF STATE. ADMINISTRATIVE RULE COMPILATION. 10 base vols. (plus irreg. updates). $350 (base vols. $500). Secretary of State, Archives Bldg., 800 N.E. Summer St., Salem, OR 97310. TEL 503-373-0701. FAX 503-378-4118. Ed. Dorothy Horton. **Document type:** government publication.

PUBLIC ADMINISTRATION

350 US ISSN 0196-4577
JK9031
OREGON BLUE BOOK. 1904. biennial. $12 (effective through Apr. 1997). Secretary of State, 225 Capitol St. N.E., Ste. 180, Salem, OR 97310. TEL 503-986-2235. FAX 503-378-4991. circ. 25,000. **Document type:** government publication.
 Description: Provides a record of Oregon's government, businesses, and people. Chronicles its society, providing a sense of how Oregonians live their lives.

350 US
OREGON BULLETIN. m. $50. Secretary of State, Archives Bldg., 800 N.E. Summer St., Salem, OR 97310. TEL 503-373-0701. FAX 503-378-4118. Ed. Dorothy Horton. **Document type:** bulletin, government publication.

350 GW ISSN 0323-3049
ORGANISATION; Zeitschrift fuer Leitungs- und Verwaltungsorganisation der sozialistischen Staatsorgans. 1967. bi-m. DM.30. Staatsverlag der DDR, Otto-Grotewohl Str. 17, 10117 Berlin, Germany.

354 TH ISSN 0475-2015
ORGANIZATIONAL DIRECTORY OF THE GOVERNMENT OF THAILAND.* (Text in English and Thai) irreg. (Translation & Secretarial Office) Office of the Prime Minister, Government House, Nakhon Pathom Rd., Bangkok 10300, Thailand. **Document type:** directory.

OTTAWA LETTER. see BUSINESS AND ECONOMICS — Economic Situation And Conditions

350 320 CN ISSN 0840-9196
OTTAWA WEEKLY UPDATE. 1986. w. Can.$700. (Informetrica Limited) Publinet, P.O. Box 828, Sta. B, Ottawa, Ont. K1P 5P9, Canada. TEL 613-238-4831. FAX 613-238-7698. Eds. Kelly Thomas, Steve Hall; Pub. Michael McCracken. adv. contact: Stephen Hall. (looseleaf format; back issues avail.) **Document type:** newsletter.
 ●Also available online.
 Description: Reports the status of federal legislation and government operations. Includes coverage of Parliamentary Committee activity and overall reaction from opposition parties and non-governmental organizations.

OUTLOOK ON SCIENCE POLICY. see SCIENCES: COMPREHENSIVE WORKS

354.669 NR
OYO STATE. ESTIMATES INCLUDING BUDGET SPEECH AND MEMORANDUM. Short title: Oyo State of Nigeria Estimates. a. £N40. Government Printer, Ibadan, Nigeria.
 Formerly: Western State. Estimates Including Budget Speech and Memorandum.

340.05
OYO STATE OF NIGERIA GAZETTE. (Supplements accompany some numbers) irreg. £N30. Government Printer, Ibadan, Nigeria. TEL 411216.
 Formerly: Western State. Gazette.

350 NE ISSN 0920-4865
P B O BLAD. (Publiek Rechtelijke Organisaties) Key Title: PBO-blad. 1950. w. Sociaal-Economische Raad, Postbus 90405, 2509 LK The Hague, Netherlands. TEL 31-70-3499499. FAX 31-70-3832535. circ. 500. **Indexed:** Key to Econ.Sci.
 Formerly (until 1987): Mededelingen- en Verordeningblad Bedrijfsorganisatie (ISSN 0920-4857); Which was formed by the 1984 merger of: Verordeningenblad Bedrijfsorganisatie (ISSN 0489-2534); Mededelingenblad Bedrijfsorganisatie (ISSN 0025-6862)

350 331.1 US ISSN 0732-1988
P E R B NEWS. 1968. m. $25. Public Employment Relations Board, 80 Wolf Rd., Albany, NY 12205. FAX 518-457-2664. Ed. R. Rosen. circ. 400. **Document type:** newsletter.

P S A REPORTER. (Public Service Association of New South Wales) see LABOR UNIONS

350.6 UK ISSN 0144-4212
HD4645
P S L G. (Public Service & Local Government) 1977. m. £8.50. Patey Doyle (Publishing) Ltd., Wilmington House, Church Hill, Wilmington, Dartford DA2 7EF, England. Ed. Alan Pickstock. illus. circ. 20,000.
 —BLDSC (6969.230000).

P T R C TRAFFEX CONFERENCE REPORTS. (Planning and Transport Research and Computation) see TRANSPORTATION — Roads And Traffic

350 PK ISSN 0078-8333
PAKISTAN. NATIONAL ASSEMBLY. DEBATES. OFFICIAL REPORT. (Text in English) 1962. irreg. Rs.0.50. National Assembly, Islamabad, Pakistan. (Dist. by: Manager of Publications, Government of Pakistan, 2nd Fl., Ahmad Chamber, Tariq Rd., P.E.C.H.S., Karachi 29, Pakistan)

350 PN
PANAMA. TRIBUNAL ELECTORAL. MEMORIA. irreg. Tribunal Electoral, Panama, Panama.

354 PP
PAPUA NEW GUINEA. PUBLIC SERVICE COMMISSION. REPORT. a. free. Public Service Commission, P.O. Ward Strip, NCD, Papua New Guinea. TEL 675-271285. FAX 675-259564. Ed. Karo Rupa. **Document type:** government publication.
 Formerly: Papua New Guinea. Public Service Board. Report (ISSN 0078-9399)

353.2 FR ISSN 0296-1830
PARIS. BULLETIN MUNICIPAL OFFICIEL - BULLETIN DEPARTEMENTAL OFFICIEL. Key Title: Bulletin Municipal Officiel de la Ville de Paris, Bulletin Departemental Officiel du Departement de Paris. 1882. 104/yr. 170 F. Ville de Paris, Cabinet du Maire, Service des Publications Administratives, Hotel de Ville, Annexe Napoleon, Bureau 242, 75004 Paris, France. TEL 42-76-52-61. FAX 42-76-64-89. Ed. P. Ribeyrolles. circ. 4,500. **Document type:** bulletin.
 Formed by the 1985 merger of: Paris (Departement). Bulletin Departement Officiel - Arrets (ISSN 0762-4689); Paris (City). Bulletin Municipal Officiel (ISSN 0152-0377); Which was formerly: Paris (City). Bulletin Municipal Officiel. Deliberations du Conseil de Paris (ISSN 0151-8267)

PARKS AND RECREATION; journal of park and recreation management. see LEISURE AND RECREATION

350 UK
PARLIAMENTARY BULLETIN FOR LOCAL GOVERNMENT EXECUTIVES. 1949. w. £38. Parliamentary and Common Market News Services, 19 Kingsdown Rd., Surbiton KT6 6JZ, England.

350 UK ISSN 1351-6183
PARLIAMENTARY MONITOR. 1993. w. £209 (Europe £240; elsewhere £280) (effective 1996). Parliamentary Communications Ltd., 10 Little College St., Westminster, London SW1P 3SH, England. TEL 0171-233-1388. FAX 0171-976-0422. Ed. Patrick Cormack; Pub. Keith Young. **Document type:** bulletin.

350 UK
PARLIAMENTARY YEAR BOOK.* 1979. a. £14.95($27) Blake's (Parliamentary Division) Ltd., 12-14 High Road Ln., London N2 9JP, England. TEL 44-171-450 9322. Ed. Joyce Blake. adv.; bk.rev. circ. 5,500.

350 BX
PELITA BRUNEI. (Text in Malay) 1956. w. free. Information Department, Prime Minister's Office, Bandar Seri Begawan 2041, Brunei Darussalam. circ. 45,000. **Document type:** newspaper, government publication.

350 US
PENNSYLVANIA CHAMBER OF BUSINESS AND INDUSTRY. LEGISLATIVE DIRECTORY.* a. $8 to non-members; members $4. Pennsylvania Chamber of Business and Industry, 417 Walnut St., Harrisburg, PA 17101. TEL 800-326-3252. FAX 717-255-3298. **Document type:** directory.
 Description: Provides information and addresses of Pennsylvania elected officials at state and federal levels.

PENTRU PATRIE. see CRIMINOLOGY AND LAW ENFORCEMENT

350 BL
PERFIL DA ADMINISTRACAO FEDERAL. 1974. s-a. $12 per no. Editora Visao Ltda., Rua Alvaro de Carvalho, 354, 1o andar, 01050 Sao Paulo, Brazil. TEL 256-5011. FAX 258-1919. adv. circ. 31,000.

354.8 BL ISSN 0006-9469
PERNAMBUCO. SECRETARIA DO SANEAMENTO, HABITACAO E OBRAS. BOLETIM TECNICO. bi-m. free. Secretaria do Saneamento, Habitacao e Obras, Av. Cruz Cabuga 1111, Recife, Pernambuco, Brazil. adv.; bk.rev.; charts; illus.; stat.

PERSIAN GULF REVIEW; information for veterans who served in Desert Storm. see MILITARY

PERSPECTIVES ON POLITICAL SCIENCE. see POLITICAL SCIENCE

350 PH ISSN 0031-7675
JA26
PHILIPPINE JOURNAL OF PUBLIC ADMINISTRATION. 1957. q. P.120($25) University of the Philippines, College of Public Administration, PARDEC-SAAC Building, P.O. Box 198, Don Mariano Marcos Ave., Diliman, Quezon City, Philippines. TEL 95-13-53. TELEX CPAUP. Ed. Victoria A. Bautista. bk.rev.; bibl.; charts; index. circ. 420. (also avail. in microform from UMI; reprint service avail. from UMI) **Indexed:** A.B.C.Pol.Sci. (until 1988), Amer.Hist.& Life, Asian-Pac.Econ.Lit., Hist.Abstr., Ind.Phil.Per., Lang.& Lang.Behav.Abstr.
 —UMI; UnCover.
 Formerly: University of the Philippines. College of Public Administration. (Publication) (ISSN 0079-9254)

350 PH
PHILIPPINES. DEPARTMENT OF PUBLIC INFORMATION. POLICY STATEMENTS. irreg., no.13, 1977. Department of Public Information, c/o Bureau of National and Foreign Information, U P L Building, PO Box 3396, Intramuros, Manila, Philippines.

350 020.6 PH
PHILIPPINES. NATIONAL PRINTING OFFICE. ITEMIZATION OF PERSONAL SERVICES AND ORGANIZATIONAL CHARTS. a. National Printing Office, Boston St., Port Area, Manila, Philippines.

350 PH
PHILIPPINES. PUBLIC INFORMATION OFFICE. OFFICIAL GAZETTE. 1905. w. P.1300($98.75) National Printing Office, Boston St., Port Area, Manila, Philippines. Ed. Elpidio de Peralta. circ. 1,400. (back issues avail.)

350 362 UK
POLICY ANALYSIS RESEARCH UNIT. DISCUSSION PAPER. 1980. irreg., no. 24. £3 per no. Glasgow Caledonian University, Policy Analysis Research Unit, Cowcaddens Rd., Glasgow G4 0BA, Scotland. TEL 0141-331-3319. FAX 0141-331-3293. E-mail: a.hutton@g.cal.uk.ac. Ed. Stephen J. Bailey. **Document type:** academic/scholarly publication, monographic series.
 Refereed Serial

POLICY AND POLITICS. see HOUSING AND URBAN PLANNING

350 US
POLICY FORUM. 1988. q. free. University of Illinois at Urbana-Champaign, Institute of Government and Public Affairs, 1007 W. Nevada St., Urbana, IL 61801. TEL 217-333-3340. FAX 217-244-4817. E-mail: ANNAM@IGPA.UIUC.edu. Ed. Anna J. Merritt. **Document type:** academic/scholarly publication.
 Description: Analysis of current Illinois policy issues.
 Refereed Serial

350 320 CN ISSN 0226-5893
JL1
POLICY OPTIONS/OPTIONS POLITIQUES. (Text in English, French) 1979. 10/yr. Can.$34.95 (US Can.$44.95; elsewhere Can.$49.95). Institute for Research on Public Policy, 1470 Peel St., Ste. 200, Montreal, PQ H3A 1T1, Canada. TEL 514-985-2461. FAX 514-985-2559. E-mail: cycy@musica.mcgill.ca. Ed. Mathew Horsman. bk.rev. circ. 2,500. **Indexed:** Can.B.P.I., Can.Per.Ind., CMI. **Document type:** bulletin.
 —BLDSC (6543.326650).
 Description: Forum for views on Canadian public policy.

PUBLIC ADMINISTRATION

350   US   ISSN 0163-108X
H1
POLICY STUDIES REVIEW ANNUAL. 1977. biennial. $89.95. Transaction Publishers, Transaction Periodicals Consortium, Department 3092, Rutgers University, New Brunswick, NJ 08903. TEL 908-445-2280. FAX 908-445-3138. Ed. W.N. Dunn. bibl. **Indexed:** Int.Polit.Sci.Abstr. **Document type:** academic/scholarly publication.
—BLDSC (6543.329500); Faxon.
    Description: Presents research and analysis in a wide variety of policy areas, including defense and national security, health care cost containment, work and labor information, the environment, immigration, and poverty.

350   US   ISSN 8756-9248
JK8701
POLITICAL PULSE. 1985. fortn. $255. Political Pulse, 926 J St., Rm. 1218, Sacramento, CA 95814. TEL 916-446-2048. FAX 916-446-5302. Ed. Bud Lembke; Pubs. Bud Lemke, Larry Lynch. circ. 700. **Document type:** newsletter.
    Description: News of California politics and government.

POLITICAL REPORT. see POLITICAL SCIENCE

353   US   ISSN 0362-4765
JA88.U6
POLITICAL SCIENCE UTILIZATION DIRECTORY. 1975. irreg. $5 to individuals; institutions $12. Policy Studies Organization, University of Illinois, 361 Lincoln Hall, Urbana, IL 61801. TEL 217-359-8541. Eds. Stuart Nagel, Marian Neef. bibl.; charts; stat.; index. circ. 2,400. (reprint service avail. from UMI) **Document type:** directory.
    Description: Describes how political science has been, and can be used in federal, state, and local government agencies.

POLITICS AND THE LIFE SCIENCES. see MEDICAL SCIENCES

POPULATION TRENDS AND PUBLIC POLICY. see POPULATION STUDIES

350   IT   ISSN 0391-7894
POTERE LOCALE. 1967. fortn. L.60000. Lega per le Autonomie ed i Poteri Locali, Via Cesare Balbo 43, 00184 Rome, Italy. TEL 39-6-4740041. TELEX 463360. Ed. Paolo Poeta. adv.: B&W page L.1900000, color page L.3400000. circ. 4,000.

350   II
PRASHASNIKA. (Text in English and Hindi) 1972. q. Rs.20($5) Harishchandra Mathur State Institute of Public Administration, Jaipur, Rajasthan, India. Ed. M.L. Mehta. bk.rev.; bibl.

350 340   SZ   ISSN 1017-8147
KKW19
DIE PRAXIS (BASEL). (Text in German) 1904. 11/yr. 190 SFr. Helbing und Lichtenhahn Verlag AG, Freie Str. 84, CH-4051 Basel, Switzerland. TEL 061-2721116. FAX 061-2721150. (Subscr. to: Sauerlaender AG, Laurenzenvorstadt 89, CH-5001 Aarau, Switzerland. TEL 064-268626) adv.: B&W page 750 SFr.; trim 112 x 185. **Document type:** academic/scholarly publication.
—CCC.
    Formerly (until 1991): Praxis des Bundesgerichts (ISSN 0254-9441)

PREVISIONS GLISSANTES DETAILLEES EN PERSPECTIVES SECTORIELLES (VOL39): SERVICES PUBLICS. see BUSINESS AND ECONOMICS — Economic Situation And Conditions

PRINCE EDWARD ISLAND. DEPARTMENT OF COMMUNITY AND CULTURAL AFFAIRS. ANNUAL REPORT. see ENVIRONMENTAL STUDIES

330   CN
PRINCE EDWARD ISLAND. DEPARTMENT OF ECONOMIC DEVELOPMENT AND TOURISM. ANNUAL REPORT. 1950. a. free. Department of Economic Development and Tourism, P.O. Box 2000, Charlottetown, PE C1A 7N8, Canada. TEL 902-368-4240. FAX 902-368-4224. TELEX 014-44154. stat. circ. 200.
    Former titles: Prince Edward Island. Department of Industry. Annual Report; Prince Edward Island. Department of Industry and Commerce. Annual Commerce.

338.9 380   CN
PRINCE EDWARD ISLAND. ISLAND REGULATORY & APPEALS COMMISSION. ANNUAL REPORT. 1961. a. free. Island Regulatory & Appeals Commission, P.O. Box 577, Charlottetown, PE C1A 7L1, Canada. TEL 902-892-3501. FAX 902-566-4076. Ed. Linda Webber. circ. 325.
    Formerly: Prince Edward Island. Public Utilities Commission. Annual Report (ISSN 0079-5151)

350   IT   ISSN 0391-2655
PROBLEMI DI AMMINISTRAZIONE PUBBLICA. 1976. q. L.130000. (Centro di Formazione e Studi per il Mezzogiorno) Societa Editrice Il Mulino, Strada Maggiore, 37, 40125 Bologna, Italy. TEL 39-51-256011. FAX 39-51-256034. Ed. Roberto Stampacchia. adv. circ. 1,900. (back issues avail.)

354.71   CN   ISSN 0318-0646
PROFESSIONAL INSTITUTE OF THE PUBLIC SERVICE OF CANADA. COMMUNICATIONS. (Text in English and French) 1975. bi-m. Professional Institute of the Public Service of Canada, 53 Auriga Dr., Nepean, Ont. K2E 8C3, Canada. TEL 613-228-6310. FAX 613-228-9048. circ. 29,000.

350.6   UK
PROFESSIONAL OFFICER. 1986. m. £5 to non-members. Federated Union of Managerial and Professional Officers, Terminus House, The High, Harlow, Essex CM20 1TZ, England. TEL 0274-434444. FAX 0279-451176. Ed. David Candler. adv.; bk.rev. circ. 14,000. (back issues avail.)

353.008   US
PROFILES OF REGULATORY AGENCIES IN THE U S AND CANADA. a. $50 (effective 1994). National Association of Regulatory Utility Commissioners, 1102 Interstate Commerce Bldg., Box 684, Washington, DC 20044-0684. TEL 202-898-2200. FAX 202-898-2213. Ed. Karen Bauer.
    Formerly: National Association of Regulatory Utility Commissioners. Annual Compilation of Profiles of Regulatory Agencies in the U S and Canada.

250   UK   ISSN 0956-4187
HT401
PROGRESS IN RURAL POLICY AND PLANNING. 1991. a. £39.50. John Wiley & Sons Ltd., Journals, Baffins Ln., Chichester, W. Sussex PO19 1UD, England. TEL 01243-779777. FAX 01243-776128. TELEX 86290-WIBOOK-G. **Document type:** academic/scholarly publication.
—BLDSC (6924.528500).

350   IT
PROVINCIA NUOVA. 1971. q. Amministrazione Provinciale, Corso V. Emanuele 17, 26100 Cremona, Italy. TEL 0372-406268. FAX 0372-456744. Ed. Dario Rceh. adv.; illus.; circ. 2,000 (controlled). **Document type:** bulletin.

350   CN   ISSN 0835-0329
PROVINCIAL LEGISLATIVE RECORD. 1983. m. Can.$210. C C H Canadian Ltd., 6 Garamond Ct., North York, ON M3C 1Z5, Canada. TEL 416-441-2292; 800-268-4522. FAX 416-444-9011. index. **Document type:** trade publication.
    Formerly: Provincial Pulse Newsletter (ISSN 0714-7015)
    Description: Complete reporting of the status of legislation for the Canadian provinces and territories, including all proclamations.

PSYCHOLOGY, PUBLIC POLICY, AND LAW. see PSYCHOLOGY

350   IT
PUBBLICA AMMINISTRAZIONE MANAGEMENT OGGI; il mensile della tecnologia e dell'innovazione. 1987. m. (10/yr.). L.150000 (effective 1994). Maggioli Editore, Viale Vespucci 12-n, Casella Postale 290, 47037 Rimini, Italy. TEL 0541-626777. FAX 0541-622020. Ed. Dario Tiengo. adv.: B&W page L.2000000, color page L.3100000; trim 195 x 265. circ. 9,376.
    Formerly (until 1993): Pubblica Amministrazione Oggi (ISSN 0394-8412)

350   UK   ISSN 0033-3298
       CODEN: PUADDD
PUBLIC ADMINISTRATION. 1923. q. £118($225) (foreign £140) (effective 1996). Basil Blackwell Ltd., 108 Cowley Rd., Oxford OX4 1JF, England. TEL 01865-791100. FAX 01865-791347. TELEX 837022 OXBOOK G. Ed. R.A.W. Rhodes. adv.; bk.rev.; index, cum.index 1953-1962. circ. 4,650. (also avail. in microform from UMI; reprint service avail. from UMI) **Indexed:** A.B.C.Pol.Sci., Account.& Data Proc.Abstr., Amer.Hist.& Life (until 1993), ASSIA, BPIA, Br.Hum.Ind., Curr.Cont., Educ.Admin.Abstr., Geo.Abstr., Hist.Abstr. (until 1993), INSPEC, Int.Polit.Sci.Abstr., Key to Econ.Sci., Manage.Cont., Mid.East: Abstr.& Ind., P.A.I.S., Pers.Lit., Polit.Sci.Abstr., PSI, Rural Recreat.Tour.Abstr., Soc.Sci.Ind., Sociol.Educ.Abstr., SSCI, Stud.Wom.Abstr., Tr.& Indus.Ind., World Agri.Econ.& Rural Sociol.Abstr.
—BLDSC (6962.400000); Faxon; Genuine Article; SWETS; UMI; UnCover. **CCC.**

350   US
PUBLIC ADMINISTRATION AND PUBLIC POLICY. 1978. irreg., vol.58, 1995. Marcel Dekker, Inc., 270 Madison Ave., New York, NY 10016. TEL 212-696-9000. FAX 212-685-4540. TELEX 1419.

350   US
PUBLIC ADMINISTRATION BRIEFING. 1990. m. Kentucky State University, School of Public Affairs, Center for Public Policy Research, Frankfort, KY 40601. TEL 502-227-6117. Ed. Manindra Mohapatra.

350   US   ISSN 0734-9149
JA1
PUBLIC ADMINISTRATION QUARTERLY. 1977. q. $31 to individuals; libraries $48. Southern Public Administration Education Foundation, c/o Dr. Jack Rabin, Pennsylvania State University at Harrisburg, Division of Public Affairs, Middletown, PA 17057. TEL 717-948-6363. FAX 717-540-1383. Eds. Jack Rabin, Thomas Vocino. bk.rev. circ. 1,300. (also avail. in microform from UMI; reprint service avail. from UMI) **Indexed:** ABI Inform, BPIA, INSPEC (1983-), Manage.Cont., Pers.Lit., Polit.Sci.Abstr., Sage Pub.Admin.Abstr., Sage Urb.Stud.Abstr. **Document type:** academic/scholarly publication.
●Also available online. Vendor(s): University Microfilms International.
—BLDSC (6962.595000); Faxon; SWETS; UMI.
    Formerly: Southern Review of Public Administration (ISSN 0147-8168)
    Refereed Serial

354.3   PK   ISSN 0033-3344
PUBLIC ADMINISTRATION REVIEW. (Text in English) 1963. 2/yr. Rs.100($30) National Institute of Public Administration, Regional Office, 190-Scotch Corner, Upper Mall, Lahore, Pakistan. Ed. Ahmad Iftikhar. bk.rev. (also avail. in microform from UMI; reprint service avail. from UMI) **Indexed:** A.B.C.Pol.Sci., Amer.Hist.& Life, Curr.Cont., Deep Sea Res.& Oceanogr.Abstr., Educ.Admin.Abstr., Fut.Surv., Hist.Abstr., L.R.I., Leg.Per., Pers.Lit., PSI, Soc.Sci.Ind., Tr.& Indus.Ind.
—UnCover.

350   US   ISSN 0033-3352
JK1
PUBLIC ADMINISTRATION REVIEW. 1940. bi-m. $80 (foreign $130). American Society for Public Administration, 1120 G St., N.W., Ste. 700, Washington, DC 20005. TEL 202-393-7878. FAX 202-638-4952. Ed. David Rosenbloom. adv.: B&W page $595. bk.rev.; index, irreg. cum.index. circ. 15,000. (also avail. in microform from MIM,UMI; reprint service avail. from UMI,KTO,WSH) **Indexed:** A.B.C.Pol.Sci., ABI Inform., Acad.Ind., ASSIA, B.P.I., Bk.Rev.Ind. (1965-), BPIA, C.L.I., Child.Bk.Rev.Ind. (1965-), Hum.Ind., Int.Polit.Sci.Abstr., L.R.I., Manage.Cont., Mid.East: Abstr.& Ind., P.A.I.S., Polit.Sci.Abstr., Sage Pub.Admin.Abstr., Sage Urb.Stud.Abstr., Soc.Sci.Ind., Soc.Work Res.& Abstr., SSCI, Tech.Educ.Abstr. **Document type:** academic/scholarly publication.
●Also available online. Vendor(s): University Microfilms International.
—BLDSC (6962.600000); Faxon; Genuine Article; SWETS; UMI. **CCC.**
    Description: Presents authoritative research and articles on current issues.

PUBLIC ADMINISTRATION

350 US ISSN 0033-3360
JK4601
PUBLIC ADMINISTRATION SURVEY. 1953. q. free to qualified personnel. University of Mississippi, Public Policy Research Center, University, MS 38677. TEL 601-232-5408. FAX 601-232-7808. Ed. D.B. Brammer. circ. 1,800. **Indexed:** P.A.I.S., Sage Pub.Admin.Abstr.
Description: Issue-oriented publication for the Mississippi governmental community.

350 US ISSN 0149-8797
JK1
PUBLIC ADMINISTRATION TIMES. 1978. m. $25 (foreign $35). American Society for Public Administration, 1120 G St., N.W., Ste. 700, Washington, DC 20005. TEL 202-393-7878. FAX 202-638-4952. Ed. Sheila McCormick. adv.: B&W page $4595. circ. 13,000. (reprint service avail. from UMI) **Indexed:** Pers.Lit.
Former titles (1951-1978): Public Administration News and Views (ISSN 0033-3328); A S P A News and Views (ISSN 0360-4233); Incorporates: Public Administration Recruiter (ISSN 0033-3336)
Description: Reports on current developments, innovative programs, and relevant issues in the field of public service.

PUBLIC AFFAIRS COMMENT. see *SOCIAL SCIENCES: COMPREHENSIVE WORKS*

PUBLIC BUDGETING AND FINANCE. see *BUSINESS AND ECONOMICS — Public Finance, Taxation*

PUBLIC EMPLOYEE NEWSLETTER. see *OCCUPATIONAL HEALTH AND SAFETY*

PUBLIC EMPLOYEE PRESS. see *LABOR UNIONS*

350 US
THE PUBLIC EYE (WASHINGTON). bi-m. Public Employees Roundtable, Box 14270, Ben Franklin Sta., Washington, DC 20044-4270. TEL 202-927-5000. FAX 202-927-5001. Ed. Gretchen Hakola. circ. controlled. **Document type:** newsletter.

350.7 GW ISSN 0033-3476
PUBLIC FINANCE/FINANCES PUBLIQUES. (Supplement avail.: International Institute of Public Finance. Papers and Proceedings (ISSN 0074-6533)) (Text in English) 1946. 3/yr. DM.190 to individuals; institutions DM.230 (effective 1995). (Foundation Journal Public Finance, NE) Foundation Journal Public Finance, Goethestr. 13, 61462 Koenigstein, Germany. TEL 06174-23370. Ed. Dieter Biehl. adv.; bibl.; charts; index. circ. 1,700. (reprint service avail. from SWZ,UMI) **Indexed:** ASSIA, Curr.Cont., J.of Econ.Lit., Mid.East: Abstr.& Ind., P.A.I.S., SSCI. **Document type:** academic/scholarly publication.
—BLDSC (6963.400000); Faxon; Genuine Article; SWETS; UnCover. **CCC.**
Description: Devoted to the study of public economics and policy and related problems.

350 UK ISSN 0963-5076
PUBLIC GENERAL ACTS & GENERAL SYNOD MEASURES. a. price varies. H.M.S.O., P.O. Box 276, London SW8 5DT, England. **Document type:** government publication.

PUBLIC INTEREST BRIEFS. see *LAW — Legal Aid*

353 US
PUBLIC LAWS. irreg. $160 (foreign £200) (effective 1995). U.S. Office of the Federal Register, National Archives and Records Administration, Eighth St. & Pennsylvania Ave., N.W., Washington, DC 20408. TEL 202-523-5240. (Subscr. to: Superintendent of Documents, U.S. Government Printing Office, Box 371954, Pittsburgh, PA 15250-7954. TEL 202-512-1800. FAX 202-512-2250) Ed. Gwen Henderson. **Document type:** government publication.
Description: Publishes federal laws once they are enacted.

350 US ISSN 1061-7639
JK1
THE PUBLIC MANAGER; the journal for practitioners. 1972. q. $27 to individuals; institutions $48. Bureaucrat, Inc., 12007 Titian Way, Potomac, MD 20854. TEL 301-279-9445. FAX 301-251-5872. Ed. T.W. Novotny. adv.; bk.rev.; index; circ. 5,500 (paid). **Indexed:** A.B.C.Pol.Sci., ABI Inform, B.P.I, BPIA, Bus.Ind., Curr.Cont., Human Resour.Abstr., Int.Polit.Sci.Abstr., Sage Pub.Admin.Abstr., Sage Urb.Stud.Abstr., SSCI, Tr.& Dev.Alert, Tr.& Indus.Ind., Urb.Aff.Abstr.
—BLDSC (6967.760000); Faxon; SWETS; UMI; UnCover. **CCC.**
Formerly (until Spring 1992): Bureaucrat (ISSN 0045-3544)
Refereed Serial

350 UK ISSN 0954-0962
HC251
PUBLIC MONEY AND MANAGEMENT; policy journal of the public sector. 1981. q. £130($240) (foreign £149) (effective 1996). (Public Finance Foundation) Basil Blackwell Ltd., 108 Cowley Rd., Oxford OX4 1JF, England. TEL 0865-791100. FAX 0865-791347. TELEX 837022-OXBOOK-G. (Subscr. addr.: c/o Marston Book Services, P.O. Box 87, Oxford OX2 0DT, England) Ed. M. Connolly. adv.; bk.rev.; illus. circ. 2,350. (back issues avail.) **Indexed:** ABI Inform., Cont.Pg.Manage., Curr.Cont., P.A.I.S., Soc.Sci.Ind.
—BLDSC (6967.781000); Genuine Article; SWETS; UMI. **CCC.**
Formerly: Chartered Institute of Public Finance and Accountancy. Public Money (ISSN 0261-1252)
Description: Directed to managers in the public services, consultants and advisors, students, teachers and other academics.
Refereed Serial

353.03 973 US ISSN 0079-7626
J80
PUBLIC PAPERS OF THE PRESIDENTS OF THE UNITED STATES. a. price varies. U.S. Office of the Federal Register, National Archives and Records Administration, Washington, DC 20408. TEL 202-523-5230. (Orders to: Superintendent of Documents, U.S. Government Printing Office, Box 371954, Pittsburgh, PA 15250-7954. TEL 202-783-3238. FAX 202-512-2233) index. (back issues avail.) **Document type:** government publication.

PUBLIC POLICY AND SOCIAL WELFARE. see *SOCIAL SERVICES AND WELFARE*

350 340 UK ISSN 0963-8245
K16
PUBLIC PROCUREMENT LAW REVIEW. 1992. bi-m. Sweet & Maxwell, South Quay Plaza, 7th Fl., 183 Marsh Wall, London E14 9FT, England. TEL 071-538-8686. FAX 071-538-9508. **Indexed:** Euro.LJI, LJI.
—BLDSC (6968.391000).

350 658 US ISSN 1044-8039
JF1411
PUBLIC PRODUCTIVITY AND MANAGEMENT REVIEW. 1975. q. $56 to individuals; institutions $115 (effective Sep. 1995). (American Society for Public Administration and the National Center for Public Productivity, Section on Management Science) Sage Publications, Inc., 2455 Teller Rd., Thousand Oaks, CA 91320. TEL 805-499-0721. FAX 805-499-0871. (Overseas subscr. to: Sage Publications Ltd., 6 Bonhill St., London EC2A 4PU, England; Sage Publications India Pvt. Ltd., P.O. Box 4125, New Delhi 110 048, India) Ed. Marc Holzer. bk.rev. circ. 1,450. (also avail. in microform from UMI; back issues avail.) **Indexed:** ABI Inform., Account.& Data Proc.Abstr., Anbar, B.P.I., BPIA, CINAHL, Pers.Lit., Pers.Manage.Abstr., Polit.Sci.Abstr., Sage Pub.Admin.Abstr., Sage Urb.Stud.Abstr., Urb.Aff.Abstr. **Document type:** academic/scholarly publication.
●Also available online. Vendor(s): University Microfilms International.
—BLDSC (6968.392000); Faxon; SWETS; UMI; UnCover.
Formerly (until 1990): Public Productivity Review (ISSN 0361-6681)
Description: Offers public and nonprofit sector professionals useful information on enhancing their organizations' productivity, case examples of successful practices and updates on public administration research and legislation.
Refereed Serial

352 368 US ISSN 0891-7183
PUBLIC RISK. 1986. 10/yr. $125. Public Risk Management Association, 1815 Fort Myer Dr., Ste. 1020, Arlington, VA 22209-1805. TEL 703-528-7701. FAX 703-528-7966. Ed. Lisa Gidley. adv.; bk.rev.; index. circ. 2,200. (back issues avail.) **Document type:** trade publication.
Description: Provides news and features on public sector risk management topics. Covers association business, pooling issues and legislation.

PUBLIC ROADS. see *ENGINEERING — Civil Engineering*

354.9 NZ ISSN 0110-5191
PUBLIC SECTOR. 1978. q. NZ.$67.50 (foreign NZ.$67.50) (effective 1994). New Zealand Institute of Public Administration, P.O. Box 5032, Lambton Quay, Wellington, New Zealand. TEL 64-4-389-8776. adv.; bk.rev.; charts; cum.index. circ. 1,135. (also avail. in microform) **Indexed:** Int.Polit.Sci.Abstr., P.A.I.S. **Document type:** academic/scholarly publication.
—Faxon; UnCover. **CCC.**
Formerly (until vol.40, 1978): New Zealand Journal of Public Administration (ISSN 0028-8357)

350 CN ISSN 0700-2092
PUBLIC SECTOR. 1977. w. Can.$497. Ottawa Bureau Inc., 9 Antares Dr., Nepean, ON K2E 7V5, Canada. TEL 613-226-6491. FAX 613-521-2520. Ed. Peter Menyasz. quarterly index.

350 338 US
PUBLIC SECTOR. 1976. q. free. Auburn University, Center for Governmental Services, 2232 Haley Center, Auburn University, Auburn, AL 36849. TEL 205-844-1913. FAX 205-844-1919. Ed. Charles Spindler. bibl.; charts; illus.; stat.; circ. 3,000 (controlled). (back issues avail.) **Indexed:** A.B.C.Pol.Sci.
Description: Covers current issues of interest to government officials such as: growth management, tax reform, economic development and solid waste management.

354.7 CN ISSN 0380-3988
PUBLIC SECTOR MANAGEMENT/MANAGEMENT ET SECTEUR PUBLIC. (Text in English, French) 1979. 4/yr. Can.$20 (foreign Can.$25). Institute of Public Administration of Canada - Institut d'Administration Publique du Canad, 150 Eglinton Ave. E., No. 305, Toronto, ON M4P 1E8, Canada. TEL 416-932-3666. FAX 416-932-3667. Ed.Bd. circ. 3,500.
Formerly (until 1990): Institute of Public Administration of Canada. Bulletin.

350 UK ISSN 1360-1830
PUBLIC SECTOR PROCUREMENT AND FINANCE. (Supplements avail.) 1990. 10/yr. £48 (foreign £55) (effective 1996) (includes supplements). Government Group Publications, Southbank House, Black Prince Rd., London SE1 7SJ, England. TEL 0171-582-9191. FAX 0171-587-1810. E-mail: gov.group@dial.pipex.com. (Subscr. to: 5 Woodland Grove, Weybridge, Surrey KT13, England) Ed. Jonathan Ball; Douglas/Holmes. adv.: B&W page $1385, color page $1840; trim 297 x 420; adv. contact: Trevor Hull. bk.rev.; circ. 11,480 (controlled). (back issues avail.) **Document type:** trade publication.
—BLDSC (4206.025700).
Formerly (until Jun. 1995): Government Purchasing (ISSN 0959-3721)
Description: Helps public-sector purchasers and managers responsible for buying goods and services keep abreast of new products and technologies and of the latest purchasing techniques and government initiatives.

350 IE ISSN 0790-1232
PUBLIC SECTOR TIMES. 1983. 12/yr. (Irish Public & Civil Service) Bradan Publishing Ltd., 1 Eglinton Rd., Bray, Co. Wicklow, Ireland. TEL 01-2869111. FAX 01-2869074. Ed. James D. Fitzmaurice. circ. 17,500. **Document type:** newspaper.

PUBLIC ADMINISTRATION

350 SA ISSN 0033-376X
HD8013.S6
PUBLIC SERVANT/STAATSAMPTENAAR. (Text in Afrikaans, English) 1920. bi-m. R.1.60 per no. Public Servants Association of South Africa - Vereniging van Staatsamptenare van Suid-Afrika, P.S.A. Bldg., 563 Belvedere St., P.O. Box 40404, Arcadia 0007, South Africa. TEL 012-323-4481. FAX 012-325-7434. Ed. J.C. Olivier. adv. contact: S. Frisby. bk.rev.; circ. 101,000 (controlled). **Indexed:** Ind.S.A.Per.

350.6 GY
PUBLIC SERVANT. vol.4, 1977. m. Guyana Public Service Union, 160 Regent Rd. & New Garden St., Georgetown, Guyana. TEL 2-61770.

350.6 331.8 NZ ISSN 0110-6945
PUBLIC SERVICE ASSOCIATION JOURNAL. Short title: P S A Journal. 1913. 10/yr. free to members. New Zealand Public Service Association, Private Bag, Wellington, New Zealand. TEL 64-4-4942000. FAX 64-4-4942019. Ed. Pat Martin. adv.; bk.rev.; rec.rev. **Document type:** newspaper.
Description: Covers economic and social issues, international trade union news, personality profiles, health and safety, and PSA news.

350 AT ISSN 0033-3786
PUBLIC SERVICE REVIEW. 1888. m. Aus.$10. Public Service Association of South Australia Inc., 122 Pirie St., Adelaide, S.A. 5000, Australia. TEL 61-8-205-3200. FAX 61-8-232-1438. Ed. Hendrik gout. adv. contact: Julie Ritchie. bk.rev.; illus. circ. 25,200. **Document type:** newspaper.

350 UK ISSN 1350-6943
PUBLIC SERVICES YEARBOOK. 1986. a. £19.99. (Public Finance Foundation) Chapman & Hall, 2-6 Boundary Row, London SE1 8HN, England. TEL 0171-865-0066. FAX 0171-522-9623. TELEX 290164 CHAPMA G. E-mail: journal.chall.mhs.compuserve.com. (Dist. by: International Thomson Publishing Services Ltd., Cheriton House, North Way, Andover, Hants. SP10 5BE, England. TEL 01264-342713. FAX 01264-342807; N. American orders to: Chapman & Hall, One Penn Plaza, 41st Fl., New York, NY 10019. TEL 212-564-1060. FAX 212-564-1505) Ed. Michael Lavender. adv.; bibl.; charts. circ. 2,000. (back issues avail.) **Document type:** trade publication.
—BLDSC (6969.315000).
Formerly (until 1992): Public Domain (ISSN 0952-7095)
Description: Reviews finance and policy trends in public services.

PUBLIC UTILITIES FORTNIGHTLY. see *ENGINEERING — Electrical Engineering*

PUBLIC UTILITIES LAW ANTHOLOGY. see *LAW*

PUBLIC UTILITIES NEWSLETTER. see *OCCUPATIONAL HEALTH AND SAFETY*

PUBLIC WORKS HISTORICAL SOCIETY NEWSLETTER. see *HISTORY — History Of North And South America*

350 SZ ISSN 0080-7249
PUBLICUS; Schweizer Jahrbuch des Oeffentlichen Lebens. (Text in French and German) 1958. a. 78 SFr. (with CD-ROM 248 SFr.). Schwabe und Co. AG, Steinentorstr. 13, CH-4010 Basel, Switzerland. TEL 061-2725523. FAX 061-2725573. Ed. Bernard Hess. adv.; index. circ. 6,500. **Document type:** consumer publication.
●Also available on CD-ROM.
—CCC.
Description: Summaries include science and culture, sports, economic and political organizations in Switzerland.

PUBLIUS; the journal of federalism. see *POLITICAL SCIENCE*

350 PR
PUERTO RICO. OFICINA DE PRESUPUESTO Y GERENCIA. PRESUPUESTO (YEARS). a. free. Oficina de Presupuesto - Office of Budget and Management, Box 3228, San Juan, PR 00902. TEL 809-725-9420. FAX 809-723-7308. circ. controlled. **Document type:** government publication.
Former titles: Puerto Rico. Oficina de Presupuesto y Gerencia. Resoluciones Conjuntas del Presupuesto General y de Presupuestos Especiales & Puerto Rico. Negociado del Presupuesto. Resoluciones Conjuntas del Presupuesto General y de Presupuestos Especiales (ISSN 0079-7863)

354.6 NR ISSN 0001-8333
QUARTERLY JOURNAL OF ADMINISTRATION; an international journal of administration management & policy. Short title: Q J A. 1966. q. £N1000($65) to institutions (foreign £35). Obafemi Awolowo University, Faculty of Administration, University P.O. Box 1044, Ile-Ife, Osun State, Nigeria. TEL 234-36-230290-9. FAX 234-2-2410000. TELEX IFEVARSITY IFE. Ed. Jide Owoeye. adv.: B&W page N£2000 ($200); adv. contact: Jide Owoeye. bk.rev.; abstr.; bibl.; charts; illus.; stat.; index; circ. 2,000 (paid). (also avail. in microform from UMI; back issues avail.; reprint service avail. from UMI) **Indexed:** Documentatieblad, Int.Lab.Doc., Int.Polit.Sci.Abstr., Int.Polit.Sci.Abstr., Mid.East. Abstr.& Ind., Rural Recreat.Tour.Abstr., World Agri.Econ.& Rural Sociol.Abstr. **Document type:** academic/scholarly publication.
—UMI.
Formerly: Administration.
Description: Devoted to the study, research, dissemination, and exchange of knowledge and information on all aspects of administration, management, and policy studies.
Refereed Serial

QUESTE ISTITUZIONI; cronache del sistema politico. see *POLITICAL SCIENCE*

QUORUM REPORT. see *POLITICAL SCIENCE*

R A NEWS. (Recreation Association of the Public Service of Canada) see *CLUBS*

350 UK ISSN 0144-6525
R I P A REPORT. 1980. q. membership. Royal Institute of Public Administration, 3 Birdcage Walk, London SW1H 9JH, England. TEL 071-222-2248. FAX 071-222-2249. Ed. Ivor Shelley. circ. controlled. **Indexed:** BPIA, Nutr.Abstr.

354.611 TI
R T A P. (Revue Tunisienne d'Administration Public) (Text in Arabic and French) 1967-1976; resumed 1985. s-a. $40. Ecole Nationale d'Administration, Centre de Recherches et d'Etudes Administratives, 24 Ave. du Dr. Calmette, Mutuelleville, 1060 Tunis, Tunisia. TEL 288-300. FAX 787-205. abstr.; stat. circ. 2,000. (tabloid format; back issues avail.)
Formerly: Servir (ISSN 0035-4120)
Description: Covers administration activities, such as modernization and reformation and innovations in public services.

R T A P TRAINING RESOURCES CATALOG FOR RURAL AND SPECIALIZED TRANSIT SYSTEMS. (Rural Transit Assistance Program) see *TRANSPORTATION*

350 DK ISSN 0107-8747
RASP. 1981. irreg. DKK 45 per no. (Aalborg Universitetscenter) Aalborg Universitetsforlag, Aalborg, Denmark.

RATING AND VALUATION REPORTER. see *LAW*

350 347 GW
RECHT DES OEFFENTLICHEN DIENSTES BRANDENBURG. 4/yr. DM.58. Walhalla Fachverlag, Dolomitenstr. 1, 93057 Regensburg, Germany. TEL 0941-696710. FAX 0941-68568. (looseleaf format) **Document type:** government publication.

350 347 GW
RECHT DES OEFFENTLICHEN DIENSTES MECKLENBURG-VORPOMMERN. 4/yr. DM.58. Walhalla Fachverlag, Dolomitenstr. 1, 93057 Regensburg, Germany. TEL 0941-696710. FAX 0941-68568. (looseleaf format) **Document type:** government publication.

350 347 GW
RECHT DES OEFFENTLICHEN DIENSTES SACHSEN. 4/yr. DM.58. Walhalla Fachverlag, Dolomitenstr. 1, 93057 Regensburg, Germany. TEL 0941-696710. FAX 0941-68568. (looseleaf format) **Document type:** government publication.

350 347 GW
RECHT DES OEFFENTLICHEN DIENSTES SACHSEN-ANHALT. 4/yr. DM.58. Walhalla Fachverlag, Dolomitenstr. 1, 93057 Regensburg, Germany. TEL 0941-696710. FAX 0941-68568. **Document type:** government publication.

350 347 GW
RECHT DES OEFFENTLICHEN DIENSTES THUERINGEN. 4/yr. DM.58. Walhalla Fachverlag, Dolomitenstr. 1, 93057 Regensburg, Germany. TEL 0941-696710. FAX 0941-68568. (looseleaf format) **Document type:** government publication.

350 UK ISSN 0034-2076
RED TAPE. 1911. m. £5. Civil and Public Services Association, 160 Falcon Rd., London SW11 2LN, England. TEL 0171-924-2727. FAX 0171-924-1847. Ed. A. Campbelln. adv.; bk.rev. circ. 135,000. **Document type:** trade publication, directory.

RED TAPE. see *LABOR UNIONS*

350 US
REFERENCE GUIDES TO THE STATE CONSTITUTIONS OF THE UNITED STATES. 1990. irreg. price varies. Greenwood Press (Subsidiary of: Greenwood Publishing Group Inc.), 88 Post Rd. W., Box 5007, Westport, CT 06881-5007. TEL 203-226-3571. FAX 203-222-1502. **Document type:** directory.

350 VE ISSN 1315-2378
JA5
▼**REFORMA Y DEMOCRACIA.** (Text in Spanish; abstracts in English) 1994. s-a. Bs.2000 (Latin America $25; elsewhere $30) (effective 1995). Centro Latinoamericano de Administracion para el Desarrollo, Calle Herrera Toro, Qta. CLAD, Sector Los Naranjos, Las Mercedes, Apdo. Postal 4181, Caracas 1010-A, Venezuela. TEL 582-92-28-95. FAX 582-91-84-27. E-mail: clad@dino.conicit.ve. Ed. Carlos Blanco.

350 FR ISSN 0337-7091
JN2301
REGARDS SUR L'ACTUALITE; mensuel de la vie publique en France. 1974. 10/yr. 280 F. (Europe 365 F., elsewhere 475 F.). Documentation Francaise, 29-31 Quai Voltaire, 75340 Paris Cedex 7, France. TEL 1-40-15-70-00. FAX 40-15-70-00. TELEX 215 666 DOCFRAN. (Subscr. to: 124 rue Henri Barbusse, 93308 Aubervilliers Cedex, France. TEL 48-39-56-00. FAX 48-39-56-01) bibl. (also avail. in microfiche from DFR) **Indexed:** ELLIS, Int.Polit.Sci.Abstr. **Document type:** government publication.
—BLDSC (7336.440000); SWETS.

350 340 SW ISSN 0345-9896
REGERINGSRAETTENS AARSBOK. Variant title: R Aa. 1909. a. SEK 530 (effective 1991). (Domstolsverket) Fritzes, S-106 47 Stockholm, Sweden. TEL 46-8-690-90-90. FAX 46-8-205021.
Incorporates (in 1978): Raettsfall och Notiser fraan Regeringsraetten.

REGIONAL AND INDUSTRIAL RESEARCH SERIES. see *BUSINESS AND ECONOMICS*

REGIONAL SCIENCE REVIEW. see *HOUSING AND URBAN PLANNING*

350 US
▼**THE REGIONALIST.** 1995. q. $30 to individuals; institutions $50. (National Association of Regional Councils, Institute for the Regional Community) Institute of Community and Area Development, University of Georgia, 1234 S. Lumpkin St., Athens, GA 30602-3552. TEL 706-542-3350. FAX 706-542-6189. E-mail: atkins@narc.org. Eds. Joe Epling, Joe Whorton. **Document type:** academic/scholarly publication.
Description: Features works that illuminate regional concepts and approaches across the social, physical, and economic sectors of metropolitan and rural America.
Refereed Serial

PUBLIC ADMINISTRATION

REGIONE ABRUZZO. see *SOCIAL SERVICES AND WELFARE*

350 IT ISSN 0393-7437
REGIONE E GOVERNO LOCALE. 1980. bi-m. Maggioli Editore, Viale Vespucci 12-n, Casella Postale 290, 47037 Rimini, Italy. TEL 0541-626777. FAX 0541-622020. adv.: B&W page L.1200000, color page L.1800000; trim 115 x 180. circ. 5,000.

350 SW ISSN 0280-1647
REGISTER OVER GAELLANDE S F S-FOERFATTNINGAR. a. Fritzes AB, S-106 47 Stockholm, Sweden. TEL 46-8-6909090. FAX -468-205021.

350 329.9 US
RENMIN ZHENGXIE BAO/C P P C C GAZETTE. (Text in Chinese) 3/w. $102.25. (Zhongguo Renmin Zhengzhi Xieshang Huiyi, CC - Chinese People's Political Consultative Conference) China Books & Periodicals, Inc., 2929 24th St., San Francisco, CA 94110. TEL 415-282-2994. FAX 415-282-0994.

350 SP ISSN 0408-3407
RENTA NACIONAL DE ESPANA; y su distribucion provincial (year). 1955. irreg. Banco de Bilbao, Servicio de Estudios, Apartado 21, Bilbao, Spain. charts; stat.

350 FR
REPERTOIRE DE L'ADMINISTRATION FRANCAISE. 1945. a. 190 F. (effective 1995). Documentation Francaise, 29-31 Quai Voltaire, 75340 Paris, France. TEL 1-40-15-70-00. FAX 40-15-72-30. TELEX 215 666 DOCFRAN. (Subscr. to: 124 rue Henri Barbusse, 93308 Aubervilliers Cedex, France. TEL 48-39-56-00. FAX 48-39-56-01) circ. 10,000. (also avail. in microfiche) **Document type:** government publication.
  Former titles: Repertoire Permanent de l'Administration Francaise; France. Delegation Generale a la Recherche Scientifique et Technique. Repertoire Permanent de l'Administration Publique (ISSN 0080-1186)

350 RE
REPERTOIRE DES TEXTES LEGISLATIFS ET REGLEMENTAIRES ET DES REPONSES AUX QUESTIONS ECRITES CONCERNANT LA REUNION. 1975. a. 100 F. Centre Universitaire de la Reunion, Center d'Etudes Administratives, 24, 26 av. de la Victoire, Saint-Denis, Reunion. circ. 150.

350 340 US
REPORT FROM STATE CIRCLE. 1968. 7/yr. $25 to non-members; members $15. League of Women Voters of Maryland, 200 Duke of Gloucester St., Annapolis, MD 21401. TEL 301-269-0232. circ. 300. (back issues avail.) **Document type:** newsletter.
  Formerly (until 1985): Legislative News Service.

350 NZ ISSN 0111-6053
REPORT OF THE ADMINISTRATOR OF TOKELAU. a. NZ.$7.75. Ministry of Foreign Affairs and Trade, Private Bag 18-901, Wellington, New Zealand. TEL 64-4-472-8877. FAX 64-4-473-7412. **Document type:** government publication.

350 US
REPORTS REQUIRED BY CONGRESS: C I S GUIDE TO EXECUTIVE COMMUNICATIONS. q. $595. Congressional Information Service, Part of the Reed Elsevier group, 4520 East-West Hwy., Bethesda, MD 20814. TEL 301-654-1550; 800-638-8380. FAX 301-654-4033. Ed. Jane M. McBrian.
  Description: Provides access to federal department and agency reports required by law.

350 SI
REPUBLIC OF SINGAPORE GOVERNMENT GAZETTE. (Text in English) w. Singapore National Printers Ltd., 303 Upper Serangoon Road, P.O. Box 485, Singapore 1334, Singapore. TEL 2820611. FAX 2854894. TELEX 24462.

RESEARCH IN PUBLIC POLICY ANALYSIS AND MANAGEMENT. see *SOCIOLOGY*

350 US ISSN 0734-371X
JK765
REVIEW OF PUBLIC PERSONNEL ADMINISTRATION. 1980. q. $40. University of South Carolina, Institute of Public Affairs, Columbia, SC 29208. TEL 803-777-8157. (Co-sponsor: American Society for Public Administration) Ed. Nicholas P. Lavich, Jr; Pub. L. Douglas Dobson. (back issues avail.) **Indexed:** A.B.C.Pol.Sci., ABI Inform., P.A.I.S., Pers.Lit., Pers.Manage.Abstr., Sage Pub.Admin.Abstr., Sage Urb.Stud.Abstr., Urb.Aff.Abstr. **Document type:** academic/scholarly publication.
  ●Also available online. Vendor(s): University Microfilms International.
  —BLDSC (7794.164000); Faxon; UMI; UnCover.
  Description: Focuses on the study and practice of personnel management in public organizations.

350 CR ISSN 1018-0680
REVISTA CENTROAMERICANA DE ADMINISTRACION PUBLICA. 1981. irreg., no.24, 1993. price varies. Instituto Centroamericano de Administracion Publica, Apdo. Postal 10025, 1000 San Jose, Costa Rica. TEL 5062-34-1011. FAX 5062-25-2049. TELEX 2180 ICAP CR. Ed. Rethelny Figueroa de Jain. **Document type:** academic/scholarly publication.

350 BL ISSN 0034-7612
JA5
REVISTA DE ADMINISTRACAO PUBLICA. (Text in Portuguese; summaries in English) 1967. q. $60 (effective 1995-96). Fundacao Getulio Vargas, C.P. 62591, 22272-970 Rio de Janeiro, R.J., Brazil. FAX 55-21-551-7801. TELEX 21-36811. Ed. Ana Maria Marquesini. bk.rev.; bibl. circ. 2,000.
  —Faxon.
  Description: Reviews administrative matters and issues. Analyzes theories and practices.

350 PR ISSN 0034-7620
JA5
REVISTA DE ADMINISTRACION PUBLICA. 1964. s-a. $4. Universidad de Puerto Rico, Escuela Graduada de Administracion Publica, Apartado 21839, Estacion U.P.R., Rio Piedras, PR 00931. TEL 809-764-0000. FAX 809-763-7510. Ed. Emerito Rivera Torres. bk.rev. circ. 1,000. **Indexed:** A.B.C.Pol.Sci., ELLIS. **Document type:** academic/scholarly publication.
  Description: Promotes the study, research and dissemination of information in the field of public affairs and public administration.

350 SP ISSN 0034-7639
K19
REVISTA DE ADMINISTRACION PUBLICA. 1950. 3/yr. 4800 ptas.($61) (Centro de Estudios Constitucionales) Libreria Europa, Plaza de la Marina Espanola 9, Apdo. de Correos 50877, 28013 Madrid, Spain. TEL 91-5325069. Ed.Bd. bk.rev.; abstr.; bibl.; index, cum.index. circ. 2,300. **Indexed:** A.B.C.Pol.Sci., Int.Polit.Sci.Abstr., P.A.I.S.For.Lang.Ind.
  —SWETS.

354.4 658 FR ISSN 0035-0672
JA11
REVUE ADMINISTRATIVE. 1948. bi-m. 735 F. (foreign 850 F.)(effective 1995). Bureau 203, 2 rue de Viarmes, 75001 Paris, France. TEL 42-36-23-90. FAX 42-36-23-90. Dir. Francois Monnier. adv.; bk.rev.; bibl.; rec.rev.; tr.lit.; index. (also avail. in microform from SWZ; reprint service avail. from SCH) **Indexed:** Int.Polit.Sci.Abstr., P.A.I.S.For.Lang.Ind. —BLDSC (7882.700000); SWETS.

REVUE BELGE DE SECURITE SOCIALE. see *SOCIAL SERVICES AND WELFARE*

350 FR ISSN 0245-9469
REVUE DE DROIT SANITAIRE ET SOCIAL. 1958. q. 570 F. (foreign 665 F.) (effective 1995). Editions Sirey, 11 rue Soufflot, 75240 Paris Cedex 05, France. TEL 40-51-54-54. FAX 45-87-37-48. TELEX 206 446 F. (Subscr. to: 35, rue Tournefort, 75240 Paris Cedex 05, France. TEL 40-51-54-35) Ed. M. Elie Alfandari. bk.rev.; index. (reprint service avail. from SCH) **Document type:** academic/scholarly publication.
  —BLDSC (7956.790000). CCC.
  Former titles (until 1980): Revue Trimestrielle de Droit Sanitaire et Social (ISSN 0035-4325); (until 1965): Revue de l'Aide Sociale (ISSN 0998-5077)

350 340 FR ISSN 0337-7393
REVUE DE JURISPRUDENCE FISCALE. 1832. m. 848 F. Editions Francis Lefebvre, 42 rue de Villiers, 92300 Levallois, France. TEL 41-05-22-00. FAX 41-05-22-30.

350 FR
REVUE DES COMMUNES ET DES ETABLISSEMENTS PUBLICS. 1908. 11/yr. Ed. P. Maraval, 34200 Saint-Pons, France. TEL 67-97-01-10. TELEX 485 181. adv. circ. 22,500.

350 FR ISSN 0152-7401
JS41
REVUE FRANCAISE D'ADMINISTRATION PUBLIQUE. 1967. q. 325 F. (Europe 410 F., elsewhere 478 F.). Institut International d'Administration Publique - International Institute of Public Administration, 2 av. de l'Observatoire, 75006 Paris, France. TELEX 204826 DOCFRAN. (Subscr. to: La Documentation Francaise, 29-31 quai Voltaire, 75340 Paris Cedex 07, France. TEL 48-39-56-00. FAX 48-39-56-01) Eds. Jacques Ziller, M.C. Meininger. adv.; bk.rev.; abstr.; bibl. circ. 2,500. (also avail. in microfiche from DFR) **Indexed:** A.B.C.Pol.Sci., ELLIS, Int.Polit.Sci.Abstr., Rural Recreat.Tour.Abstr., SCIMP (1982-), World Agri.Econ.& Rural Sociol.Abstr. **Document type:** academic/scholarly publication.
  —BLDSC (7902.240000); SWETS.
  Formerly (until 1977): Institut International d'Administration Publique. Bulletin (ISSN 0020-2355)
  Description: Details on all aspects of comparative public administration: broadcasting, city management and international cooperation, defense administration, immigration and health, civil servants, telecommunications, and the environment.

RISK, DECISION AND POLICY. see *BUSINESS AND ECONOMICS — Management*

RISKWATCH. see *INSURANCE*

350 IT ISSN 0391-190X
JA18
RIVISTA TRIMESTRALE DI SCIENZA DELL'AMMINISTRAZIONE. (Text in English, French and Italian) 1954; N.S. 1972. q. L.100000 (foreign L.130000) (effective 1993). Franco Angeli Editore, Viale Monza 106, 20127 Milan, Italy. TEL 02-28-27-651. Ed. Giorgio Freddi. adv.; bk.rev.; bibl.; charts; illus.; index. circ. 1,500. **Indexed:** Int.Polit.Sci.Abstr.
  Formerly (until 1972): Scienza e la Tecnica della Organizzazione nella Pubblica Amministrazione (ISSN 0036-8873)

ROLE OF STATE LEGISLATURES IN THE FREEDOM STRUGGLE. see *POLITICAL SCIENCE*

353.9 US
ROSTER - CALIFORNIA STATE, COUNTY, CITY AND TOWNSHIP OFFICIALS STATE OFFICIALS OF THE UNITED STATES. Variant title: California Roster. a. $14. Office of Procurement, c/o Secretary of State, 1500 11th St., Sacramento, CA 95814. TEL 916-445-3441. circ. 25,000. **Document type:** government publication.

351 RW
RWANDA. DIRECTION GENERALE DE LA STATISTIQUE. RAPPORT ANNUEL. a. Direction Generale de la Statistique, B.P. 46, Kigali, Rwanda.
  Formerly: Rwanda. Direction Generale de la Documentation et de la Statistique. Rapport Annuel (ISSN 0080-5033)

354.6 SA ISSN 0036-0767
JA26
S A I P A; journal of public administration - tydskrif vir publieke administrasie. (Text in Afrikaans, English; summaries in English) 1965. a. R.28 (effective 1994). South African Institute of Public Administration - Suid-Afrikaanse Instituut vir Publieke Administrasie, P.O. Box 2752, Pretoria 0001, South Africa. TEL 27-12-202-2851. FAX 27-12-326-5362. TELEX 321710. Ed. A. Viljoen. bk.rev. circ. 2,300. **Indexed:** A.B.C.Pol.Sci., Ind.S.A.Per., Int.Polit.Sci.Abstr. **Document type:** academic/scholarly publication.

SAIGAI NO JITTAI TO SHOBO NO GENKYO/ANNUAL REPORT OF FIRE AND DISASTER PREVENTION. see *FIRE PREVENTION*

350 320 XM
ST. VINCENT GOVERNMENT INFORMATION SERVICE NEWS BULLETIN. vol.6, 1974. m. free. Government Information Service, Kingstown, St. Vincent and the Grenadines, W.I.

PUBLIC ADMINISTRATION

350   BE   ISSN 0773-6991
SAISONS. (Text in Dutch and French) 10/yr. C A S, 146 rue Jourdan, 1060 Brussels, Belgium. adv. circ. 5,000.
    Formerly (until 1985): Informat (ISSN 0773-7092)

350   SM   ISSN 0036-4223
SAN MARINO (REPUBBLICA) BOLLETTINO UFFICIALE. 1924. 12/yr. L.20000. Dipartimento Affari Istituzionali, San Marino. bk.rev.; index. circ. 1,100.

350 327   SM
SAN MARINO (REPUBBLICA). DIPARTIMENTO AFFARI ESTERI. NOTIZIA. 1978. m. free. Dipartimento Affari Esteri, Ufficio Stampa, San Marino. Ed. Pier Roberto De Biagi. **Document type:** government publication.
    Formerly: San Marino (Repubblica). Segreteria di Stato per gli Affari Esteri. Notizia; Supersedes (1959-1978): San Marino (Repubblica). Segreteria di Stato per gli Affari Esteri. Notiziario (ISSN 0558-4477)

338 381   CN   ISSN 0080-6498
SASKATCHEWAN. DEPARTMENT OF INDUSTRY AND COMMERCE. REPORT FOR THE FISCAL YEAR.* 1957. a. free. Government Printing Co., 2005 8th St., Regina, Sask. S4P 3V7, Canada. TEL 306-566-9393.

SCHIEDSAMTSZEITUNG. see *LAW*

350   GW   ISSN 0343-8228
SCHRIFTEN ZUR OEFFENTLICHEN VERWALTUNG UND OEFFENTLICHEN WIRTSCHAFT. (Text in German; summaries in English, French, Russian) 1974. irreg. price varies. Nomos Verlagsgesellschaft mbH und Co. KG, Waldseestr. 3-5, 76530 Baden-Baden, Germany. TEL 07221-21040. FAX 07221-210427. (Subscr. to: Postfach 610, 76484 Baden-Baden, Germany) Eds. P. Eichhorn, P. Friedrich. **Document type:** monographic series.

350.6   GW   ISSN 0342-7722
SCHWARTZSCHE VAKANZEN-ZEITUNG. 1871. 3/m. DM.72. Verlag Otto Schwartz und Co., Annastr. 7, 37075 Goettingen, Germany. TEL 0551-31051. FAX 0551-372812. **Document type:** bulletin.

354.4   SZ
SCHWEIZERISCHES ZENTRALBLATT FUER STAATS- UND VERWALTUNGSRECHT. m. 123 SFr. (foreign 146 SFr.). Schulthess Polygraphischer Verlag AG, Zwingliplatz 2, CH-8022 Zurich, Switzerland. TEL 01-2519336. FAX 01-2616394. Ed.Bd. circ. 1,750. **Document type:** bulletin.
—CCC.
    Formerly: Schweizerisches Zentralblatt fuer Staats- und Gemeindeverwaltung (ISSN 0036-7990)

SCIENCE AND GOVERNMENT REPORT. see *POLITICAL SCIENCE*

SCIENCE AND PUBLIC POLICY. see *SCIENCES: COMPREHENSIVE WORKS*

350   UK   ISSN 0305-6562
JS4101
SCOTLAND'S REGIONS. 1933. a. £2. William Culross & Son Ltd., Queen St., Coupar Angus, Perthshire, Scotland.
    Incorporates: County and Municipal Year Book for Scotland (ISSN 0070-1300)

350 500   US   ISSN 1061-0340
JK468.S4
SECRECY & GOVERNMENT BULLETIN. 1991. m. $20 (free to libraries). Federation of American Scientists, 307 Massachusetts Ave., N.E., Washington, DC 20002. TEL 202-546-3300. FAX 202-675-1010. Ed. Steve Aftergood. **Document type:** bulletin.
    Description: Challenges excessive secrecy in government and research, and promotes public oversight and free exchange of information in science and technology research in government, defense and intelligence.

SENATE HISTORY. see *HISTORY — History Of North And South America*

350   SG   ISSN 0850-2307
SENEGAL D'AUJOURD'HUI. 1963. m. Ministry of Culture and Communications, 58 blvd. de la Republique, B.P. 4027, Dakar, Senegal. circ. 5,000. **Document type:** government publication.

350.1   GW   ISSN 0722-5725
SENIOREN ZEITSCHRIFT. 1974. q. Stadt Frankfurt, Dezernat Soziales, Jugend und Wohnungswesen, Eschenheimer Landstr. 42-44, 60322 Frankfurt a.M., Germany. TEL 069-21233405. Ed. Maria Schuster. (back issues avail.) **Document type:** government publication.

350.6   FR
SERVICE ECONOMIQUE FONCTIONNAIRE. 1961. q. 132 av. Jules Cantini, 13008 Marseille, France. TEL 9179-4138. Ed. Rene Monduel.
    Formerly: Fonctionnaire National.

SEYCHELLES. MINISTRY OF FINANCE. BUDGET ADDRESS. see *BUSINESS AND ECONOMICS — Public Finance, Taxation*

SHEPARD'S CLEAN AIR ACT REPORTER. see *ENVIRONMENTAL STUDIES — Pollution*

353   US
SHEPARD'S - MCGRAW-HILL. FEDERAL REGULATORY PUBLICATIONS. irreg. price varies. Shepard's - McGraw-Hill, Inc., Box 35300, Colorado Springs, CO 80935-3530. TEL 800-525-2474. (back issues avail.) **Document type:** trade publication.

350   US
SHEPARD'S - MCGRAW-HILL. REGULATORY MANUAL SERIES. irreg. price varies. Shepard's - McGraw-Hill, Inc., Box 35300, Colorado Springs, CO 80935-3530. TEL 800-525-2474. (back issues avail.) **Document type:** trade publication.

353.9   US   ISSN 0037-3672
JK3501
SHIELD; Civil Service news. 1935. w. $21.25. (New Jersey Civil Service Association) New Jersey Shield Publishing Co., Inc., Box 505, Fairview, NJ 07022-0505. FAX 201-945-3490. Ed. Ronald Page. adv.; bk.rev. circ. 30,000. (tabloid format)
Indexed: DM & T.

350   TS
AL-SIJIL AL-SHAHRI LI-AHDATH DAWLAT AL-IMARAT AL-ARABIYYAH AL-MUTTAHIDAH/MONTHLY RECORD FOR THE EVENTS OF THE UNITED ARAB EMIRATES. (Text in Arabic) 1979. m. Ministry of Information and Culture, Information Department, P.O. Box 17, Abu Dhabi, United Arab Emirates. TEL 453000. circ. 1,000 (controlled).
    Description: Reports activities of the rulers of the U.A.E., legislative, civil service, cabinet, and economic developments, and international concerns.

350   SI   ISSN 0129-3109
SINGAPORE GOVERNMENT DIRECTORY. 1960. biennial. S.$14.42 (foreign S$.42). Ministry of Information and the Arts, Publicity Division, PSA Bldg., 30th Fl., 460 Alexandra Rd., Singapore 0511, Singapore. TEL 3757833. FAX 3757860. TELEX RS 22428 MITA SI. circ. 12,000. **Document type:** government publication, directory.

350   US   ISSN 8756-3886
SINGLE AUDIT INFORMATION SERVICE. 1985. m. $274. Thompson Publishing Group, 1725 K St., N.W., Washington, DC 20006. TEL 202-872-4000. FAX 202-296-1091. Ed. Denise Lamoreaux. **Document type:** trade publication.
    Description: Publishes audit requirements for federal grantees (local and state governments, universities, and nonprofit organizations).

350   YU   ISSN 0037-7147
SLUZBEN VESNIK NA SOCIJALISTICKA REPUBLIKA MAKEDONIJA. (Text in Macedonian) 1945. irreg. 380 din. Socijalisticki Savez Radnog Naroda SR Makedonije, 29 Noemvri 10a, Skopje, Yugoslavia. Ed. Petar Janevski.

354 954   II   ISSN 0037-9786
SOCIETY FOR THE STUDY OF STATE GOVERNMENTS. JOURNAL. 1968. q. Society for the Study of State Governments, Kopparti Pl., Karaundi, Varanasi 221005, Uttar Pradesh, India. **Indexed:** Int.Polit.Sci.Abstr.
    Description: Covers the political and constitutional developments of India.

SOCIETY OF GOVERNMENT ECONOMISTS. BULLETIN. see *BUSINESS AND ECONOMICS*

350   UK   ISSN 0038-0121
HD82
SOCIO-ECONOMIC PLANNING SCIENCES; the international journal of public sector decision-making. 1967. q. £252($401) (effective 1996). Elsevier Science Ltd., Pergamon, P.O. Box 800, Kidlington, Oxford OX5 1DX, England. TEL 44-1865-843000. FAX 44-1865-843010. (Subscr. in U.S. and Canada to: Elsevier Science, 660 White Plains Rd., Tarrytown, NY 10591-5153. TEL 914-524-9200. FAX 914-333-2444) Ed. Barnett R. Parker. adv.: B&W page $550, color page $1350. bk.rev.; charts; illus.; stat.; index. circ. 1,700. (also avail. in microfiche from MIM; microfilm from UMI; back issues avail.) **Indexed:** A.B.C.Pol.Sci., Abstr.Health Care Manage.Stud., ASCA, ASSIA, BPIA, Bus.Ind., C.I.J.E., C.R.E.J., Cont.Pg.Manage., Curr.Cont., Educ.Admin.Abstr., Excerp.Med., Geo.Abstr., IDA, Int.Polit.Sci.Abstr., J.Cont.Quant.Meth., Lang.& Lang.Behav.Abstr., Manage.Cont., Med.Care Rev., Mid.East: Abstr.& Ind., Oper.Res.Manage.Sci., P.A.I.S., Qual.Contr.Appl.Stat., Risk Abstr., Rural Devel.Abstr., Rural Recreat.Tour.Abstr., Sage Pub.Admin.Abstr., Sage Urb.Stud.Abstr., SSCI, Tech.Educ.Abstr., Tr.& Indus.Ind., W.R.C.Inf., World Agri.Econ.& Rural Sociol.Abstr. **Document type:** academic/scholarly publication.
—BLDSC (8319.576000); Faxon; Genuine Article; SWETS; UMI; UnCover. **CCC.**
    Description: Devoted to the application of quantitative analysis to interdisciplinary decision problems arising in the area of socio-economic planning and development.
    Refereed Serial

SOLID WASTE TECHNOLOGIES; recycling, composting, waste-to-energy, landfilling, landfill gas-to-energy. see *ENERGY*

350   SO
SOMALI INSTITUTE OF PUBLIC ADMINISTRATION NEWSLETTER.* (Text in English) 1969. q. Somali Institute of Public Administration, Mogadishu, Somalia. bibl.

SORKINS' DIRECTORY OF BUSINESS & GOVERNMENT (CHICAGO EDITION). see *BUSINESS AND ECONOMICS — Production Of Goods And Services*

350   US   ISSN 0730-1154
KF165
SOURCE BOOK OF AMERICAN STATE LEGISLATION. 1976. biennial. $120. American Legislative Exchange Council, 910 17th St., N.W., 5th Fl., Washington, DC 20006. TEL 202-466-3800. FAX 202-466-3801. Ed. Samuel A. Brunelli. circ. 7,500.
    Description: Compendium of model state legislation, with analysis in the areas of: tax and fiscal policy, education, health care, energy, environment, labor, housing, welfare, civil justice, criminal justice, substance abuse, agriculture, telecommunications, transportation, and insurance.

354.9   AT   ISSN 0038-2906
SOUTH AUSTRALIAN GOVERNMENT GAZETTE. 1839. w. Aus.$142 (typically set in Jun.). Government Printer, 282 Richmond Rd., P.O. Box 210, Plympton, S.A. 5038, Australia. TEL 08-226-4701. FAX 08-226-4729. adv.; charts; stat.; s-a. index. circ. 1,850. **Indexed:** AESIS. **Document type:** government publication.

350 320   US
JK4201
SOUTH CAROLINA POLICY FORUM. 1990. q. $19.75. University of South Carolina, Institute of Public Affairs, Gambrell Hall, Columbia, SC 29208. TEL 803-777-8156. Ed. Charlie B. Tyer; Pub. L. Douglas Dobson. **Document type:** consumer publication.
    Formerly (until 1991): South Carolina Forum (ISSN 1055-2901)
    Description: Covers public policy issues and practical government problems in South Carolina.

PUBLIC ADMINISTRATION

350   US
JS39
SOUTH DAKOTA COUNTY COMMENT. 1953. m. $10. South Dakota Association of Counties, 207 E. Capitol, Ste. 203, Pierre, SD 57501. TEL 605-224-4554. Ed. Dennis Hanson. adv. contact: Dennis Hanson. bk.rev. circ. 1,000. **Document type:** newsletter, directory.
Former titles: South Dakota Counties County Government; (until 1992): S D A C C County Comment (ISSN 1049-7838); (until vol.36, no.5, 1990): South Dakota Journal of County Government.

350   UK
SOUTHAMPTON CITY NEWS. 1973. m. Southampton City Council, Civic Centre, Southampton SO9 4XR, England. TEL 0703-223855. FAX 0703-234537. TELEX 477915. adv.; circ. 92,000 (controlled).
Formerly: Now in Southampton.

350   US   ISSN 0362-3475
SOUTHEAST MICHIGAN COUNCIL OF GOVERNMENTS. ANNUAL REPORT. Key Title: Annual Report - Southeast Michigan Council of Governments. 1970. a. free. Southeast Michigan Council of Governments, 660 Plaza Dr., No. 1900, Detroit, MI 48226. TEL 313-961-4266. FAX 313-961-4869. Ed. Alma W. Simmons. illus. circ. 11,000. **Document type:** corporate report.

350   SP
SPAIN. BOLETIN OFICIAL DEL ESTADO. 1936. d. (except Sun.). 26931 ptas. (foreign 47250 ptas.)(effective 1992). Boletin Oficial del Estado, Trafalgar, 29, 28071 Madrid, Spain. TEL 5382100. FAX 5382348. index. (also avail. in microfilm from BHP,KTO; microfiche)
●Also available online.
Formerly: Spain. Ministerio de Relaciones con las Cortes y de la Secretaria del Gobierno. Boletin Oficial del Estado (ISSN 0212-033X)

363.6   SP
SPAIN. MINISTERIO DE LA VIVIENDA. SERIE 3: VIVIENDA. 1974 (no. 1010). irreg. Ministerio de la Vivienda, Secretaria General Tecnica, Madrid, Spain.

354   SP   ISSN 1130-9563
SPAIN. MINISTERIO DE OBRAS PUBLICAS Y TRANSPORTES. REVISTA. 1957. m. 300 ptas. Ministerio de Obras Publicas y Transportes, Secretaria General Tecnica, Paseo de la Castellana 67, 28071 Madrid, Spain. illus.; index.
Former titles (until 1991): Spain. Ministerio de Obras Publicas y Urbanismo. Revista (ISSN 0212-7148); (until 1983): Spain. Ministerio de Obras Publicas y Urbanismo. Boletin de Informacion (ISSN 0211-0504); (until 1978): Spain. Ministerio de Obras Publicas. Boletin de Informacion (ISSN 0490-334X)

352   US   ISSN 1067-8530
JK2403
SPECTRUM (LEXINGTON); journal of state government. 1927. q. $45 (foreign $50). Council of State Governments, 3560 Iron Works Pike, Box 11910, Lexington, KY 40578-1910. TEL 606-244-8000. FAX 606-244-8001. bk.rev.; index. circ. 9,000. (also avail. in microfilm from PMC; microfiche from WSH) **Indexed:** A.B.C.Pol.Sci. (1994-), Amer.Hist.& Life, ASCA, BPIA, Bus.Ind., Curr.Cont., Fut.Surv., Hist.Abstr., Manage.Cont., P.A.I.S., Polit.Sci.Abstr., Sage Pub.Admin.Abstr., Soc.Sci.Ind., SSCI, Tr.& Indus.Ind. **Document type:** academic/scholarly publication, trade publication.
●Also available online. Vendor(s): University Microfilms International.
—BLDSC (8411.167500); Faxon; Genuine Article; UMI; UnCover.
Formerly (until 1992): Journal of State Government (ISSN 0039-0097)
Description: Covers all aspects of state government; provides analysis of policies, programs and ideas for the student of state government and state government practitioners.

350.6   CE
SRI LANKA GOVERNMENT GAZETTE. (Text in English) 1802. w. Government Press, P.O. Box 507, Colombo, Sri Lanka. TEL 1-93611. circ. 54,000. **Description:** Official government bulletin.

350   GW   ISSN 0938-2100
STAATSWISSENSCHAFTEN UND STAATSPRAXIS; rechts-, wirtschafts- und sozialwissenschaftliche Beitraege zum staatlichen Handeln. 1990. q. DM.149. Nomos Verlagsgesellschaft mbH und Co. KG, Waldseestr. 3-5, 76530 Baden-Baden, Germany. TEL 07221-2104-0. FAX 07221-210427. TELEX 781201. (Subscr. to: Postfach 610, 76484 Baden-Baden, Germany) **Document type:** bulletin.
—BLDSC (8425.769500).

350   GW   ISSN 0942-3672
STADT DUISBURG. GESCHAEFTSBERICHT (YEAR). 1963. a. free. Amt fuer Statistik, Stadtforschung und Europaangelegenheiten, Der Oberstadtdirektor, 47049 Duisburg, Germany. TEL 0203-2833085. FAX 0203-2834404. **Document type:** government publication.
Formerly (until 1989): Stadt Duisburg. Verwaltungsbericht (ISSN 0932-8955)

354.43   GW   ISSN 0940-0990
STADT UND GEMEINDE. 1946. m. DM.132. (Deutscher Staedte- und Gemeindebund) Verlag Otto Schwartz und Co., Annastr. 7, 37075 Goettingen, Germany. TEL 0551-31051. FAX 0551-372812. adv.; bk.rev.; index; circ. 7,000 (controlled). **Document type:** bulletin.
Former titles: Staedte- und Gemeindebund (ISSN 0342-7706); Staedtebund (ISSN 0038-903X)

STADTGEMEINDE DEUTSCHLANDSBERG. MITTEILUNGEN. see *GENERAL INTEREST PERIODICALS — Austria*

331.795   NO   ISSN 0800-658X
STAFO-NYTT. 1925. m. (8/yr.). Statstjenestemannsforbundet, Postbox 9038, M-0134 Oslo 1, Norway. Ed. Tryque Christensen. adv. circ. 15,000.
—CCC.
Formerly: Statstjenestemannen.

350   US   ISSN 0561-8630
STATE ADMINISTRATIVE OFFICIALS: CLASSIFIED BY FUNCTION. (Supplement to: Book of the States) 1957. annual. $45. The Council of State Governments, 3560 Iron Works Pike, Box 11910, Lexington, KY 40578-1910. TEL 606-244-8000. FAX 606-244-8001. **Document type:** directory.
Formerly: Administrative Officials Classified by Functions (ISSN 0191-9458)
Description: Lists names, titles, addresses, and telephone numbers of thousands of administrators in more than 130 areas of state government.

350 317   US   ISSN 1047-3394
HA203
STATE AND LOCAL STATISTICS SOURCES. 1990. biennial. $145 (effective 1993). Gale Research Inc., 835 Penobscot Bldg., Detroit, MI 48226-4094. TEL 313-961-2242; 800-877-4253. FAX 313-961-6083. TELEX 810-221-7086. Eds. M. Balachandran, S. Balachandran.
Description: Contains more than 41,000 citations to state and local statistics sources.

STATE ARTS AGENCY DIRECTORY. see *BUSINESS AND ECONOMICS — Trade And Industrial Directories*

STATE BUDGET AND TAX NEWS. see *BUSINESS AND ECONOMICS — Public Finance, Taxation*

350   US
STATE CAPITOLS REPORT; the weekly briefing on news from the 50 states. w. $1200. (Information for Public Affairs, Inc.) State Net, 2101 K St., Sacramento, CA 95816. TEL 916-444-0840. FAX 916-446-5369. Ed. Steve Scott. (also avail. by fax) **Document type:** newsletter.
●Also available online.
Description: Reports on the legislation, leadership, politics, personalities of all 50 state capitols.

350   US   ISSN 0585-1173
JK5330
STATE DIRECTORY OF KENTUCKY. 1965. a. $16 to individuals; libraries $13 (effective 1994). Directories, Inc., Box 187, Pewee Valley, KY 40056. TEL 502-241-8256. Ed. Mary McKay Wright. circ. 5,000 (controlled). **Document type:** directory, government publication.

350   US   ISSN 0191-9466
JK2403
STATE ELECTIVE OFFICIALS AND THE LEGISLATURES. (Supplement to: Book of the States) a. $45. The Council of State Governments, 3560 Iron Works Pike, Box 11910, Lexington, KY 40578-1910. TEL 606-244-8000. FAX 606-244-8001. **Document type:** directory.
Former titles (until 1976): Selected State Officials and the Legislatures (ISSN 0191-944X); (until 1975): State Elective Officials and the Legislatures (ISSN 0191-9431)
Description: Lists names, parties, addresses, and districts of state legislators, as well as elected officials with state-wide jurisdiction.

350   US   ISSN 1051-7278
STATE-FEDERAL ISSUE BRIEFS. 1986. irreg., vol.5, no.2, 1992. $6.50 per issue. National Conference of State Legislatures, 1560 Broadway, Ste. 700, Denver, CO 80202-5140. TEL 303-830-2200. FAX 303-863-8003. **Document type:** newsletter.
Description: Describes congressional, White House, and federal agency issues that affect state legislatures.

350 320   US   ISSN 0888-8590
JK2403
STATE GOVERNMENT (WASHINGTON); guide to current issues and activities. 1985. a. $19.95. Congressional Quarterly Inc., 1414 22nd St., N.W., Washington, DC 20037. TEL 202-887-8500. FAX 202-887-6706. Ed. Thad L. Beyle.
Description: Collection of articles concerning state government reprinted from various publications. Topics include closed primaries, school reform, legislature, and ethics.

STATE GOVERNMENT NEWS; the monthly magazine covering all facets of state government. see *POLITICAL SCIENCE*

328 353.9   US   ISSN 0190-6623
STATE GOVERNMENT RESEARCH CHECKLIST. 1947. bi-m. $20 (foreign $30). The Council of State Governments, 3560 Iron Works Pike, Box 11910, Lexington, KY 40578-1910. TEL 606-244-8000. FAX 606-244-8001. bibl. circ. 1,800. (reprint service avail. from ISI,UMI) **Indexed:** C.L.I., Leg.Per., Manage.Cont. **Document type:** bibliography.
Formerly (until 1979): Legislative Research Checklist (ISSN 0024-0486)
Description: Lists reports by legislative research agencies, other study committees and commissions in the states, and independent organizations that have published material appropriate for review by state agencies.

STATE HOUSE WATCH. see *SOCIAL SERVICES AND WELFARE*

350   US   ISSN 0195-6639
JK2495
STATE LEGISLATIVE LEADERSHIP, COMMITTEES AND STAFF. (Supplements Book of States) a. $45 (effective 1995 & 1996). Council of State Governments, Iron Works Pike, Box 11910, Lexington, KY 40578-1910. TEL 606-244-8000. FAX 606-244-8001. circ. 8,000. **Document type:** directory.
Formerly: Principal Legislative Staff Offices.
Description: Supplies the names, telephone numbers, and organizational patterns of state legislative leaders, legislative committees and chairpersons, principal legislative staff officers, and staff members.

350   US   ISSN 0735-8733
KF85
STATE LEGISLATIVE REPORT. 1980. irreg., (12-16/yr.), vol.17, no.5, 1992. $5 per issue. National Conference of State Legislatures, 1560 Broadway, Ste. 700, Denver, CO 80202. TEL 303-830-2200. FAX 303-863-8003. Ed. Karen Hansen. **Document type:** newsletter.
Description: Reports on issues of current interest to state legislatures in the areas of natural resources and the environment, legislative management, health, education and fiscal issues.

STATE LEGISLATIVE SOURCEBOOK; a resource guide to legislative information in the fifty states. see *LAW*

PUBLIC ADMINISTRATION

350   US   ISSN 1065-9730
JK2495
STATE LEGISLATIVE STAFF DIRECTORY (YEAR). 1993. a. $35 (effective 1993). National Conference of State Legislatures, 1560 Broadway, Ste. 700, Denver, CO 80202. TEL 303-830-2200. FAX 303-863-8003. Eds. Denise Griffin, Linda Murakami. **Document type:** directory.
   Description: Identifies legislative policy analysts in 19 issue areas from agriculture to telecommunications.

STATE LEGISLATURES. see *POLITICAL SCIENCE*

350   US   ISSN 0099-2410
Z1223.5.L7
STATE OF LOUISIANA PUBLIC DOCUMENTS. Key Title: Public Documents (Baton Rouge, La.). 1948. s-a. free. State Library, Recorder of Documents, State Library of Louisiana, Box 131, Baton Rouge, LA 70821. TEL 504-342-4929. FAX 504-342-3547. Ed. Grace Moore. circ. 300. **Document type:** government publication.

STATE POLICY REPORTS. see *BUSINESS AND ECONOMICS — Public Finance, Taxation*

350   US   ISSN 0899-2207
JK2403
STATE YELLOW BOOK; who's who in the executive, and legislative branches of the 50 State Governments. 1973. q. $235 (foreign $285). Leadership Directories, Inc., 104 Fifth Ave., 2nd Fl., New York, NY 10011. TEL 212-627-4140. FAX 212-645-0931. Ed. Imogene Akins. circ. 3,800. **Document type:** directory.
● Also available on CD-ROM.
—CCC.
   Formerly: State Information Book.
   Description: Reflects the most recent changes in elected and appointed government personnel at the state level. Includes Executive and Legislative Branches, profiles of all 50 states and their counties.

331.7   US   ISSN 0091-1402
JK6655
STATEHOUSE OBSERVER. 1972. m. free. State Personnel Department, Box 94905, Lincoln, NE 68509. TEL 402-471-4112. Ed. Greg I. Votava. stat.; illus. circ. 18,000. (also avail. in microfiche) **Document type:** newsletter.

336.340 948.9   DK   ISSN 0902-6681
HJ56
STATENS LAANTAGNING OG GAELD. English edition: Danish Government Securities (ISSN 0909-0487) 1924. a. free. (Finansministeriet, Budgetdepartementet - Ministry of Finance) Danmarks Nationalbank, Havnegade 5, DK-1093 Copenhagen K, Denmark. TEL 45-33-14-14-11. FAX 45-33-14-14-04. TELEX 16140 DEBTDN. circ. 2,400.
   Formerly: Danske Statslaan (ISSN 0105-4554)
   Description: Reports on the Danish government's borrowing and debt.

STATUTORY TIME LIMITATIONS: WASHINGTON STATE. see *LAW*

STEDELIJKE EN REGIONALE VERKENNINGEN. see *HOUSING AND URBAN PLANNING*

STEINE SPRECHEN. see *CONSERVATION*

350   AU   ISSN 0039-1050
STEIRISCHE GEMEINDE-NACHRICHTEN. 1948. m. Steiermaerkischer Gemeindebund, Burgring 18, A-8010 Graz, Austria. Ed. Dr. Hermine Jarz. adv.; bk.rev.; charts; stat.; index.

350   UK   ISSN 0266-0172
STRATHCLYDE REGIONAL COUNCIL. ANNUAL REPORT & FINANCIAL STATEMENT. 1980. a. free. Strathclyde Regional Council, Public Relations Department, Strathclyde House, 20 India St., Glasgow G2 4PF, Scotland. Ed. Neil McIntosh. circ. 10,000.
   Formerly: Strathclyde's Budget (ISSN 0260-8065)

350   GW
STUDIENFUEHRER. 1979. s-a. Fachhochschule des Bundes fuer Oeffentliche Verwaltung, Willy-Brandt-Str. 1, 50321 Bruehl, Germany. TEL 02232-929-0. FAX 02232-9295100. **Document type:** bulletin.

354.624   SJ
SUDAN. MINISTRY OF FINANCE AND NATIONAL ECONOMY. ANNUAL BUDGET SPEECH, PROPOSALS FOR THE GENERAL BUDGET AND THE DEVELOPMENT BUDGET. a. Ministry of Finance and National Economy, Box 298, Khartoum, Sudan. **Document type:** government publication.

354.624   SJ
SUDAN. MINISTRY OF FINANCE AND NATIONAL ECONOMY. GENERAL BUDGET: REVIEW, PRESENTATION AND ANALYSIS. irreg. Ministry of Finance and National Economy, Box 298, Khartoum, Sudan. **Document type:** government publication.

350   SJ
SUDAN JOURNAL OF ADMINISTRATION AND DEVELOPMENT. (Text in Arabic or English) 1965. a. Institute of Public Administration, P.O. Box 1492, Khartoum, Sudan.

353.9   US   ISSN 0070-1157
KF165
SUGGESTED STATE LEGISLATION. 1941. a. $49. The Council of State Governments, 3560 Iron Works Pike, Box 11910, Lexington, KY 40578-1910. TEL 606-244-8000. FAX 606-244-8001. cum.index. circ. 5,500. (also avail. in microfiche from WSH; microfilm from PMC; reprint service avail. from WSH) Indexed: C.L.I., Leg.Per. **Document type:** directory.
   Description: Provides a source of legislative ideas and drafting assistance for state government officials.

SURVEY OF ARTS ADMINISTRATION TRAINING. see *ART*

SURVEY OF STATE RETIREMENT SYSTEMS. see *BUSINESS AND ECONOMICS — Labor And Industrial Relations*

354   SQ
SWAZILAND. MINISTRY OF FINANCE. RECURRENT ESTIMATES OF PUBLIC EXPENDITURE. (Report year ends Mar. 31.) a. Ministry of Finance Office, Box 443, Mbabane, Swaziland.
   Formerly: Swaziland. Central Statistical Office. Recurrent Estimates of Public Expenditure.

350 370   US   ISSN 0049-2752
HQ799.7
SYNERGIST.* 1971. 3/yr. free. American Industrial Hygiene Association, 2700 Prosperity Ave.., Ste. 250, Fairfax, VA 22031-4307. (Affiliate: ACTION) Ed.Bd. bk.rev.; bibl.; charts; illus.; index; cum.index 1971-1981. circ. 40,000. (also avail. in microform) **Indexed:** Ind.U.S.Gov.Per., Rehabil.Lit.
—BLDSC (8585.934200).

T I P R O TARGET NEWSLETTER. see *PETROLEUM AND GAS*

354.4   FR   ISSN 0039-8462
T P ANNALES. (Travaux Publics) 1881. m. 600 F. (Federation Nationale des Travaux Publics et des Syndicats Affilies) Centre de l'Industrie Francaise des Travaux Publics, 3 rue de Berri, 75008 Paris, France. adv.; bk.rev.; bibl.; illus. circ. 1,600.

354.3   II   ISSN 0039-9310
TAMIL NADU INFORMATION. (Text in English and Tamil) 1947. m. Rs.225. Director of Information and Public Relations, Fort St. George, Madras 9, India. adv.; bk.rev.; illus. circ. 6,000.
   Formerly: Madras Information.

350 330   IQ
TANMIAT AL-RAFIDAIN/RAFIDAIN DEVELOPMENT. Cover title: Journal of Tanmiat al-Rafidain. (Text in Arabic, English; summaries in English) 1978. 4/yr. ID.10000. (Mosul University, Faculty of Administration and Economics) Majallat Tanmiat al-Rafidain, P.O. Box 78, Mosul, Iraq. TEL 814433. TELEX 8011. Ed. Salem T. Al-Najafi. adv.; abstr. **Document type:** academic/scholarly publication.
   Description: Publishes research papers in the fields of administration, economics, accountancy and statistics and computer science.
   Refereed Serial

350   TZ   ISSN 0856-0323
TANZANIA OFFICIAL GAZETTE. (Text in English and Swahili) 1940. w. Sh.33300 (overseas). Ministry of Information and Broadcasting, The Government Bookshop, P.O. Box 1801, Dar es Salaam, Tanzania. TEL 255-51-32038. TELEX GOVTSHOP. Ed. H. Hadji. circ. 6,000. (tabloid format) **Document type:** government publication, newspaper.

350 015   GW   ISSN 0082-1829
DD15.5
TASCHENBUCH DES OEFFENTLICHEN LEBENS; Deutschland. 1950. a. DM.132. Festland Verlag GmbH, Postfach 200561, 53135 Bonn, Germany. TEL 0228-362021. FAX 0228-351771. Ed. Heinz H. Hey. adv. circ. 23,000. **Document type:** directory.

354.9   AT   ISSN 0039-9795
TASMANIAN GOVERNMENT GAZETTE. 1836. w. Aus.$330 (effective July 1994). Tasmanian Government Printer, G.P.O. Box 307-C, Hobart, Tas. 7001, Australia. adv. circ. 1,400. **Document type:** newspaper.

TAYLOR'S ENCYCLOPEDIA OF GOVERNMENT OFFICIALS, FEDERAL AND STATE. see *POLITICAL SCIENCE*

350   US
TEACHING GEORGIA GOVERNMENT. 1979. q. free. University of Georgia, Carl Vinson Institute of Government, 201 N. Milledge Ave., Athens, GA 30602. TEL 706-542-2736. FAX 706-542-9301. Eds. Edwin L. Jackson, Inge Whittle.
   Description: News of current developments and issues in Georgia government. Provides a forum for teachers to share ideas about teaching citizenship and government.

TEACHING PUBLIC ADMINISTRATION. see *EDUCATION — Teaching Methods And Curriculum*

TECHNISCH-BESTUURSKUNDIGE VERKENNINGEN. see *ENVIRONMENTAL STUDIES*

TELCO COMPETITION REPORT. see *COMMUNICATIONS — Abstracting, Bibliographies, Statistics*

350   US
TENNESSEE COUNTY NEWS. 1980. bi-m. $10. Tennessee County Services Association, 226 Capitol Blvd., Ste. 700, Nashville, TN 37219. Ed. Kelly Thompson; Pub. Bob Worksley. adv. contact: Kelly Thompson. circ. 4,000. **Document type:** newspaper.

350   US   ISSN 0194-1240
THE TENNESSEE JOURNAL. 1974. w. $187. M. Lee Smith Publishers & Printers LLC, 162 Fourth Ave., N., Box 198867, Nashville, TN 37219-8867. TEL 615-242-7395; 800-274-6774. FAX 615-256-6601. Ed. Bradford N. Forrister; Pub. M. Lee Smith. circ. 1,400. **Document type:** newsletter.
   Description: Gives an insider's view of Tennessee government and politics.

350 320   US
TEXAS AGENDA. 1989. s-m. $95. Decision - Strategies Group, Inc., Box 90422, Austin, TX 78709. TEL 512-892-6995. Ed. Hilary Hylton.
   Description: Covers Texas government, politics and business.

TEXAS GOVERNMENT NEWSLETTER. see *POLITICAL SCIENCE*

353   US   ISSN 0040-4640
TEXAS PUBLIC EMPLOYEE. 1946. m. $5. Texas Public Employees Association, Drawer 12217, Capitol Sta., Austin, TX 78711. TEL 512-476-2691. Ed. Randy Roberts. adv.; illus. circ. 20,000. (tabloid format) **Document type:** newsletter.

348   US   ISSN 0362-4781
KFT1236
TEXAS REGISTER. 1976. s-w. $95 (on diskette $90). Secretary of State, Texas Register Division, Box 13824, TX 78711-3824. TEL 512-463-5561. FAX 512-463-5569. E-mail: dprocter@SOS.texas.gov. Dir. Dan Procter. circ. 4,700. (also avail. in diskette format; back issues avail.) **Document type:** government publication, bulletin.
   Description: Acts as the notice bulltin for the state of Texas agency rules, meeting notices, Attorney General, and Ethics Commission opinions, appointments, and executive orders. Includes requests for proposals.

PUBLIC ADMINISTRATION

353   US   ISSN 0363-7530
JK4830
TEXAS STATE DIRECTORY. 1940. a. $26.95 (effective 1995-1996). Texas State Directory Press, Box 12186, Austin, TX 78711. TEL 512-477-5698; 800-388-8075. FAX 512-473-2447. Ed. Julie F. Sayers; Pub. Julie F. Sayers. adv. circ. 20,000. **Document type:** directory.
Description: Lists personnel at all levels of government in Texas.

352   US   ISSN 0040-473X
JS39
TEXAS TOWN & CITY. 1914. m. $20. Texas Municipal League, 1821 Rutherford Ln., No. 400, Austin, TX 78754-5128. TEL 512-719-6300. FAX 512-719-6391. Ed.Bd. adv.: B&W page $650, color page $1325; adv. contact: Regina Tharp. bk.rev.; illus.; index. circ. 11,800. **Indexed:** Sage Pub.Admin.Abstr., Sage Urb.Stud.Abstr. **Document type:** government publication.

TEXAS WEEKLY. see POLITICAL SCIENCE

354.3   TH   ISSN 0040-5353
THAI JOURNAL OF DEVELOPMENT ADMINISTRATION. (Text in English and Thai) 1960. q. $15. National Institute of Development Administration, Research Center, Klongchan, Bangkok 24, Thailand. Ed. Juree Vichit-Vadakan. adv.; bk.rev.; abstr.; charts; illus.; stat.; index. circ. 1,500.
Formerly: Thai Journal of Public Administration.

THINK TANK DIRECTORY; guide to independent nonprofit public policy research organizations. see BUSINESS AND ECONOMICS — Trade And Industrial Directories

THIS WEEK IN WASHINGTON. see SOCIAL SERVICES AND WELFARE

331.795   NO
TJENESTEMANNSBLADET. 10/yr. Norsk Tjenestemannslag, Hammersborg Torg 1, Oslo 1, Norway. adv. circ. 34,561.

TOPICAL ISSUES IN PROCUREMENT SERIES. see BUSINESS AND ECONOMICS — Marketing And Purchasing

350   NE   ISSN 0018-1129
HET TORENTJE; personeelsblad van het Ministerie van Binnenlandse Zaken. 1947. m. free. Ministerie van Binnenlandse Zaken - Ministry of the Interior, Schedeldoekshaven 200, 2500 EA The Hague, Netherlands. bk.rev.; illus.; index. circ. 6,000. **Document type:** government publication.

350   MP
TORIYN MEDEELEL/STATE INFORMATION. (Text in Mongolian) 1991. bi-m. varies. State Great Hural - Parliament of Mongolia, c/o Parliamentary Secretariat, State House, Ulaanbaatar - 12, Mongolia. TEL 976-1-327016. FAX 976-1-310011. TELEX 79309 GOVER MH. Ed. N. Rinchindorj. **Document type:** government publication.
Description: Covers presidential and governmental decrees, state laws, and parliamentary news.

354   NZ
TOTALISATOR AGENCY BOARD. ANNUAL REPORT. 1951. a. free. Totalisator Agency Board, 106-110 Jackson St., Petone, New Zealand. TEL 644-576-6999. FAX 644-576-6942. Ed. G.T. Maguren. illus.; circ. 1,600 (controlled). **Document type:** corporate report.

350   AT
TOWN PLANNING LAW AND PRACTICE. 1987. 2 base vols. (plus updates 4/yr.). Aus.$330 with updates. Law Book Co. Ltd., 44-50 Waterloo Rd., North Ryde, N.S.W. 2113, Australia. TEL 02-936-6444. FAX 02-888-2229. TELEX ASBOOK 27995. Eds. D.J. Gifford, K.H. Gifford. (looseleaf format)
Description: A comprehensive guide to town planning law and practice in Australia.

350 330.9   US
TRADE MONITOR. q. National Association of State Development Agencies, 750 First St., N.E., Ste. 710, Washington, DC 20002. TEL 202-898-1302.
Description: Aimed at state economic development directors and commissioners.

TRENTINO; rivista della provincia autonoma di Trento. see ENVIRONMENTAL STUDIES

350   TR
TRINIDAD AND TOBAGO GAZETTE. 1962. w. T.T.$18. Government Printer, 121 Victoria Ave., Port-of-Spain, Trinidad & Tobago, W.I. (also avail. in microfilm from UMI)

350 624   IT   ISSN 0394-8293
L'UFFICIO TECNICO; rivista mensile di tecnica edilizia e urbanistica per amministrazioni pubbliche, professionisti e costruttori. 1979. m. (11/yr.). L.110000 to individuals; institutions L.198000 (effective 1994). Maggioli Editore, Viale Vespucci 12-n, Casella Postale 290, 47037 Rimini, Italy. TEL 0541-626777. FAX 0541-622020. Dir. Ermete Dalprato. adv.: B&W page L.1950000, color page L.3000000; trim 115 x 195. circ. 7,858.

350 320   SW
UMEAA STUDIES IN POLITICS AND PUBLIC ADMINISTRATION. (Text in English or Swedish; summaries in English) 1978. irreg., no.9, 1984. price varies. Liber Forlag, S-205 10, Malmo, Sweden. Ed. Sten Berglund.

U.S. DEFENSE LOGISTICS AGENCY. D O D HAZARDOUS MATERIALS INFORMATION SYSTEM: HAZARDOUS ITEM LISTING. see PUBLIC HEALTH AND SAFETY

355.03   US   ISSN 0091-6919
UA23.2
U.S. DEPARTMENT OF DEFENSE. DEFENSE DEPARTMENT REPORT;* a statement by the Secretary of Defense to the Congress on the budget and defense programs. Key Title: Statement of Secretary of Defense Before the House Armed Services Committee on the Defense Budget and Program. 1968. a. price varies. U.S. Department of Defense, The Pentagon, Washington, DC 20301. TEL 202-545-6700. (Orders to: Supt. of Documents, Washington, DC 20402) (also avail. in microfiche) **Indexed:** C.I.S. Ind. **Document type:** government publication.

363.6   US
U.S. DEPARTMENT OF HEALTH AND HUMAN SERVICES. GRANTS ADMINISTRATION MANUAL. 1988. base vol. plus. irreg. updates. $38 (foreign $47.50). U.S. Department of Health and Human Services, Hubert H. Humphrey Bldg., 200 Independence Ave., S.W., Washington, DC 20201. TEL 202-619-0257. (Subscr. to: Superintendent of Documents, U.S. Government Printing Office, Box 371954, Pittsburgh, PA 15250-7954. TEL 202-512-1800. FAX 202-512-1800) (looseleaf format) **Document type:** government publication.
Description: Provides guidelines on the fiscal and administrative aspects of grant management to all H.H.S. granting agencies for all persons involved in this work.

U.S. DEPARTMENT OF HOUSING AND URBAN DEVELOPMENT. SECRETARY'S ESSAYS. see HOUSING AND URBAN PLANNING

U.S. DEPARTMENT OF JUSTICE. ATTORNEY GENERAL OF THE UNITED STATES. ANNUAL REPORT. see LAW

U.S. DEPARTMENT OF STATE DISPATCH. see POLITICAL SCIENCE — International Relations

353.3 338.2 367.73
340   US
U.S. DEPARTMENT OF THE INTERIOR. A L J DECISIONS. $100. U.S. Department of the Interior, Office of Hearings and Appeals, 4015 Wilson Blvd., Arlington, VA 22203. TEL 703-235-3799. **Document type:** government publication.
Description: Discusses Interior Department decisions regarding the Surface Mining Control and Reclamation Act.

353.3   US   ISSN 0011-7331
HD181
U.S. DEPARTMENT OF THE INTERIOR. DECISIONS. Key Title: Decisions of the Department of the Interior. 1955. m. $6 (foreign £7.50) (effective 1995). U.S. Department of the Interior, Office of Hearings and Appeals, c/o Printing Clerk, 4015 Wilson Blvd., Arlington, VA 22203. TEL 703-235-3799. (Subscr. to: Superintendent of Documents, U.S. Government Printing Office, Box 371954, Pittsburgh, PA 15250-7954. TEL 202-512-1800. FAX 202-512-2250) (also avail. in microform from PMC) **Document type:** government publication.

353.3 363.73 340   US
U.S. DEPARTMENT OF THE INTERIOR. I B I A CITATOR - DESCRIPTIVE WORD INDEX. base vol. plus irreg. updates. $50. U.S. Department of the Interior, Office of Hearings and Appeals, 4015 Wilson Blvd., Arlington, VA 22203. TEL 703-235-3799.
Document type: government publication.

353.3 340   US
U.S. DEPARTMENT OF THE INTERIOR. INTERIOR BOARD OF CONTRACT APPEALS. base vol. plus irreg. updates. $115 for base vol. U.S. Department of the Interior, Office of Hearings and Appeals, 4015 Wilson Blvd., Arlington, VA 22203. TEL 703-235-3799. **Document type:** government publication.

353.5 323.4 340   US
U.S. DEPARTMENT OF THE INTERIOR. INTERIOR BOARD OF INDIAN APPEALS. base vol. plus irreg. updates. $110. U.S. Department of the Interior, Office of Hearings and Appeals, 4015 Wilson Blvd., Arlington, VA 22203. TEL 703-235-3799. **Document type:** government publication.

353.5 338.2 340
363.73   US
U.S. DEPARTMENT OF THE INTERIOR. INTERIOR BOARD OF LAND APPEALS. base vol. (plus irreg. updates). $495 for base vol. U.S. Department of the Interior, Office of Hearings and Appeals, 4015 Wilson Blvd., Arlington, VA 22203. TEL 703-235-3799. **Document type:** government publication.

353.3 340   US
U.S. DEPARTMENT OF THE INTERIOR. LISTING OF APPEALS DOCKETED BY THE BOARD OF LAND APPEALS. m. $75. U.S. Department of the Interior, Office of Hearings and Appeals, 4015 Wilson Blvd., Arlington, VA 22203. TEL 703-235-3799. **Document type:** government publication.

U.S. EXPORT ADMINISTRATION REGULATIONS. see BUSINESS AND ECONOMICS — International Commerce

U.S. FEDERAL TRANSIT ADMINISTRATION. REPORT ON FUNDING LEVELS AND ALLOCATION OF FUNDS. see TRANSPORTATION

338.973   US
HC110.P63
U.S. GENERAL SERVICES ADMINISTRATION. CATALOG OF FEDERAL DOMESTIC ASSISTANCE. Key Title: Catalog of Federal Domestic Assistance. 1971. a. base vol. plus irreg. updates. $53 (foreign $66.25) (effective 1995). U.S. General Services Administration, Publications, 18th and F Sts., N.W., DC 20405. TEL 202-501-1794. FAX 202-501-4281. (Subscr. to: Superintendent of Documents, U.S. Government Printing Office, Box 371954, Pittsburgh, PA 15250-7954. TEL 202-512-1800. FAX 202-512-2250) (looseleaf format; also avail. in magnetic tape; diskette format) **Document type:** government publication, catalog.
●Also available online.
Former titles: U.S. Office of Management and Budget. Catalog of Federal Domestic Assistance (ISSN 0097-7799); U.S. Office of Economic Opportunity. Catalog of Federal Domestic Assistance.
Description: Summarizes financial and nonfinancial federal programs, projects, and activities that provide assistance or other benefits to the American public.

U.S. HOUSING MARKET CONDITIONS. see HOUSING AND URBAN PLANNING

U.S. LIBRARY OF CONGRESS. CONGRESSIONAL RESEARCH SERVICE. DIGEST OF PUBLIC GENERAL BILLS AND RESOLUTIONS. see LAW

U. S. NUCLEAR REGULATORY COMMISSION. ANNUAL REPORT TO CONGRESS. see ENERGY — Nuclear Energy

PUBLIC ADMINISTRATION 5559

328.73 US ISSN 0095-2109
T174.5
U.S. OFFICE OF TECHNOLOGY ASSESSMENT ANNUAL REPORT TO THE CONGRESS. Key Title: Annual Report to the Congress by the Office of Technology Assessment. 1974. a. free. U.S. Office of Technology Assessment, Washington, DC 20510.
TEL 202-224-8996. FAX 202-228-6098. (Subscr. to: National Technical Information Service, 5285 Port Royal Rd., Springfield, VA 22161. TEL 703-487-4650. FAX 703-321-8547) Ed. Martha Dexter. circ. 5,000. **Document type:** government publication.

350 US ISSN 0511-4187
J80
U.S. OFFICE OF THE FEDERAL REGISTER. WEEKLY COMPILATION OF PRESIDENTIAL DOCUMENTS. 1965. w. $75 (foreign $93.75) (effective 1995). U.S. Office of the Federal Register, National Archives and Records Administration, Eighth St. and Pennsylvania Ave., N.W., Washington, DC 20408.
TEL 202-523-5230. (Subscr. to: Superintendent of Documents, U.S. Government Printing Office, Box 371954, Pittsburgh, PA 15250-7954. TEL 202-512-1800. FAX 202-512-2250) index. circ. 7,000. (back issues avail.) Indexed: P.A.I.S.
Document type: government publication.
—UMI.
Description: Makes available to the public transcripts of the President's news conferences, messages to Congress, public speeches and statements, and other presidential materials released by the White House.

353 US ISSN 0092-1904
JK421 CODEN: USGMD9
UNITED STATES GOVERNMENT MANUAL. 1934. a. $30. U.S. Office of the Federal Register, National Archives and Records Administration, Eighth St. and Pennsylvania Ave., N.W., Washington, DC 20408. TEL 202-523-5230. (Dist. by: Bernan, 4611-F Assembly Dr., Lanham, MD 20706. TEL 301-459-7666. FAX 301-459-0056; Also avail. from: Superintendent of Documents, U.S. Government Printing Office, Box 371954, Pittsburgh, PA 15250-7954. TEL 202-512-1800. FAX 202-512-2250) circ. 61,000. (also avail. in microform from UMI,BHP; diskette format; microfilm from BHP) **Document type:** directory, government publication.
—CASDDS; UMI.
Former titles (until 1973): United States Government Organization Manual (ISSN 0083-1174); (until 1948): United States Government Manual (ISSN 0892-9149)
Description: Enables business managers locate the bureaus, divisions, services, offices, and departments that may need the products of services their firms sell.

350 658 CK ISSN 0465-4773
UNIVERSIDAD DE MEDELLIN. FACULTAD DE CIENCIAS ADMINISTRATIVAS. REVISTA. 1973. q. Universidad de Medellin, Facultad de Ciencias Administrativas, Calle 31, No. 83b-150, Medellin, Colombia. Ed. Orlando Vasquez Castro. charts; illus.

350 PN
UNIVERSIDAD DE PANAMA. FACULTAD DE ADMINISTRACION PUBLICA Y COMERCIO. REVISTA. q. Universidad de Panama, Facultad de Administracion Publica y Comercio, Panama, Panama. illus.

UNIVERSIDAD DE SEVILLA. INSTITUTO GARCIA OVIEDO. PUBLICACIONES. see LAW

350 AG
UNIVERSIDAD NACIONAL DEL LITORAL. FACULTAD DE CIENCIAS DE LA ADMINISTRACION. REVISTA. 1969. a. Universidad Nacional del Litoral, Facultad de Ciencias de la Administracion, 25 de Mayo, 1783, Santa Fe, Argentina.

UNIVERSITAET HOHENHEIM. AMTLICHE MITTEILUNGEN. see EDUCATION — Higher Education

350 ZR
UNIVERSITE NATIONALE DU ZAIRE, KINSHASA. INSTITUT DE RECHERCHES ECONOMIQUES ET SOCIALES. DOCUMENT DU MOIS. (Text in French) 1974. q. $15. Universite Nationale du Zaire, Kinshasa, Institut de Recherches Economiques et Sociale, B.P. 257, Kinshasa 11, Zaire. Ed.Bd.

350 320 010 US ISSN 0041-9443
UNIVERSITY OF CALIFORNIA. INSTITUTE OF GOVERNMENTAL STUDIES LIBRARY. ACCESSIONS LIST. 1963. m. free. University of California at Berkeley, Institute of Governmental Studies, 109 Moses Hall, Berkeley, CA 94720.
TEL 510-642-8274. FAX 510-642-3020. Ed. Terry Dean. circ. 250. (processed; reprint service avail. from UMI) **Document type:** bibliography.

350 US ISSN 0194-2670
UNIVERSITY OF NEW MEXICO. DIVISION OF GOVERNMENT RESEARCH. MONOGRAPH SERIES. 1946. irreg., vol.86, 1981. free. University of New Mexico, Division of Government Research, Albuquerque, NM 87131-6025.
TEL 505-277-3305. FAX 505-277-6540. Ed. Robert U. Anderson. bk.rev.; abstr. circ. 600. **Document type:** academic/scholarly publication, government publication, monographic series.

UNIVERSITY OF TEXAS, AUSTIN. LYNDON B. JOHNSON SCHOOL OF PUBLIC AFFAIRS. POLICY RESEARCH PROJECT REPORT SERIES. see POLITICAL SCIENCE

350 US
UNIVERSITY OF TEXAS, AUSTIN. LYNDON B. JOHNSON SCHOOL OF PUBLIC AFFAIRS. WORKING PAPER SERIES. vol.5, 1976. irreg. University of Texas at Austin, Lyndon B. Johnson School of Public Affairs, Austin, TX 78713-7450. TEL 512-471-4962. **Document type:** monographic series.

350 PH
UNIVERSITY OF THE PHILIPPINES. COLLEGE OF PUBLIC ADMINISTRATION. PUBLIC ADMINISTRATION OCCASIONAL PAPERS AND SPECIAL STUDIES SERIES. (Text in English) irreg. price varies. University of the Philippines, College of Public Administration, PARDEC-SAAC Building, P.O. Box 198, Don Mariano Marcos Avenue, U.P. Diliman, Quezon City, Philippines. TEL 95-13-53. TELEX CPAUP. **Document type:** monographic series.
Formerly: University of the Philippines. College of Public Administration. Public Administration Special Studies Series.

350 320 US ISSN 0042-0271
UNIVERSITY OF VIRGINIA NEWS LETTER.* 1925. m. $42. University of Virginia, Center for Public Service, 918 Emmet St., N., Ste. 300, Charlottesville, VA 22903-4832. TEL 804-924-3396.
FAX 804-924-4538. Ed. Sandra H. Wiley. circ. 4,300. (looseleaf format) **Indexed:** P.A.I.S., Vert.File Ind.
Description: Focuses on specific public policy issues and their impact on state or local government in Virginia.

UNIVERSITY URBAN PROGRAMS. see EDUCATION — Higher Education

350 US
UNSUNG HEROES. 1985. q. free. Public Employees Roundtable, Box 14270, Washington, DC 20044-4270. TEL 202-927-5000.
FAX 202-927-5001. Ed. Gretchen Hakola. circ. 10,000.
Description: Provides information on programs designed to enhance the image of public employees.

350 GW ISSN 0042-0611
UNTERRICHTSBLAETTER FUER DIE BUNDESWEHRVERWALTUNG; Zeitschrift fuer Ausbildung, Fortbildung und Verwaltungspraxis. 1961. m. DM.134 (foreign DM.147). (Bundesministerium der Verteidigung) R. v. Decker's Verlag, G. Schenck GmbH, Im Weiher 10, 69121 Heidelberg, Germany. TEL 06221-489281.
FAX 06221-489279. Eds. H. Schellknecht, D.H. Vogt. adv.; bk.rev.; bibl.; charts; illus.; stat.; index. circ. 6,000. **Document type:** government publication.

URBAN AND RURAL PLANNING THOUGHT. see ARCHITECTURE

URBAN LAWYER; the national quarterly on urban law. see LAW

350 UY
URUGUAY. CONSEJO DE ESTADO. DIARIO DE SESIONES.* 1974. irreg. Consejo de Estado, Office of the President, Edif. Libertad, Montevideo, Uruguay.

342.792 US ISSN 0882-4738
KFU440.A73
UTAH. DIVISION OF ADMINISTRATIVE RULES. UTAH STATE BULLETIN. (Formerly issued by: Utah State Archives and Research Service) 1973. s-m. $135 (prices typically set in July). Division of Administrative Rules, Archives Bldg., Salt Lake City, UT 84114. TEL 801-538-3011.
FAX 801-538-3844. Ed. Randy J. Fisher. circ. 500.
Former titles (until 1985): Utah. State Archives and Records Service. Utah State Bulletin; Utah. State Archives and Records Service. Administrative Rule Making Bulletin (ISSN 0093-8955)
Description: Contains the administrative rules and executive branch notices of the state government.

363.6 US ISSN 0162-1718
UTILITIES LAW REPORTS. 3 base vols. (plus w. updates). $2050. Commerce Clearing House, Inc., 4025 W. Peterson Ave., Chicago, IL 60646. TEL 312-583-8500.

353.008 US
UTILITY REGULATORY POLICY IN THE UNITED STATES AND CANADA. a. $70 (effective 1994). National Association of Regulatory Utility Commissioners, 1102 Interstate Commerce Commission Bldg., Box 684, Washington, DC 20044-0684.
TEL 202-898-2200. FAX 202-898-2213. Ed. Karen Bauer.
Formerly: National Association of Regulatory Utility Commissioners. Annual Compilation of Utility Regulatory Policy.

350 GW ISSN 0170-7140
V O P - FACHZEITSCHRIFT FUER DIE OEFFENTLICHE VERWALTUNG. (Verwaltungsfuehrung - Organisation - Personal) 1978. bi-m. DM.132. F B O - Fachverlag fuer Buero- und Organisationstechnik GmbH, Hermannstr. 2, 76530 Baden-Baden, Germany. TEL 07221-271066. FAX 07221-33228. Ed. Norbert Thom. adv.; bk.rev. circ. 5,000. (reprint service avail. from UMI) **Document type:** trade publication.

VACHER'S EUROPEAN COMPANION. see POLITICAL SCIENCE

350 UK ISSN 0958-0328
VACHER'S PARLIAMENTARY COMPANION. 1832. q. £23. Vacher's Publications, 113 High St., Berkhamsted, Herts. HP4 2DJ, England.
TEL 01442-876135. FAX 01442-870148. Ed. Elizabeth Gunn. adv. contact: A.S. Kerswill. (also avail. in microform from UMI) **Document type:** directory.
—BLDSC (9138.700000).
Description: Lists personnel of the British government, and national organizations in the U.K.

350 MG
VAOVAO. (Text in French and Malagasy) 1985. w. Ministry of Information, B.P. 271, 101 Antananarivo, Madagascar. TEL 21193. Ed. Marc Rakotonoely. circ. 5,000.

VERMONT BAR JOURNAL AND LAW DIGEST. see LAW

352 US ISSN 1071-3379
KFV36
VERMONT GOVERNMENT REGISTER. 1991. m. $258 (effective 1995). Weil Publishing Co., 3 Wade St., Augusta, ME 04330. FAX 207-622-4437. Ed. Teri Brayall; Pub. Gordon L. Weil. **Document type:** government publication.
Description: Covers executive orders of the Governor, Attorney General opinions, public laws enacted, public utility and environmental orders enacted, emergency rules, and gubernatorial appointments of state officials and board - commission members.

VERMONT YEAR BOOK. see BUSINESS AND ECONOMICS — Trade And Industrial Directories

VERSIYA. see MILITARY

PUBLIC ADMINISTRATION

350   GW   ISSN 0042-4498
JA44
DIE VERWALTUNG; Zeitschrift fuer Verwaltungswissenschaft. (Supplement avail.) 1968. q. DM.148. Duncker und Humblot GmbH, Postfach 410329, 12113 Berlin, Germany. TEL 030-7900060. FAX 030-79000631. Ed.Bd. adv.; bk.rev.; index. circ. 800. **Indexed:** A.B.C.Pol.Sci, Int.Polit.Sci.Abstr., P.A.I.S.For.Lang.Ind. **Document type:** academic/scholarly publication.
—SWETS. **CCC**.

350   AU
DIE VERWALTUNG DER STADT WIEN. 1863. a. S.200. Statistisches Amt der Stadt Wien, Volksgartenstr. 3, 1016 Vienna, Austria. TEL 4000-88611. FAX 4000-9988610. illus.; index. circ. 400. (back issues avail.) **Document type:** government publication.

VERWALTUNGSARCHIV; Zeitschrift fuer Verwaltungslehre, Verwaltungsrecht und Verwaltungspolitik. see *LAW*

VERZEICHNIS RHEINLAND-PFAELZISCHER RECHT- UND VERWALTUNGSVORSCHRIFTEN. see *LAW*

354.9   AT   ISSN 0042-5095
VICTORIA GOVERNMENT GAZETTE.* 1851. w. Law Printer, P.O. Box 292, S. Melbourne, Vic. 3205, Australia. TEL 61-3-2424600. FAX 61-3-2424699. adv.; bibl.; index. circ. 1,700.

VICTORIAN ADMINISTRATIVE LAW. see *LAW*

350   AT   ISSN 0158-1589
JQ5321
VICTORIAN GOVERNMENT DIRECTORY. 1971. a. Aus.$45 (typically set in Mar.). Information Victoria, 318 Little Bourke St., Melbourne, Vic. 3000, Australia. TEL 61-3-651-4100. FAX 61-3-651-4111. Ed. Nancy Tsaklazis. circ. 4,000. **Document type:** directory, government publication.
Formerly: Victoria, Australia. Directory of Government Departments and Authorities (ISSN 0310-8546)
Description: Guide to state government departments, agencies, and contact officers.

352   FR   ISSN 0042-5400
VIE COMMUNALE ET DEPARTEMENTALE; revue mensuelle de l'activite locale. 1923. m. 340 F. 35 rue Marbeuf, 75008 Paris, France. TEL 43-59-27-41. Ed. Vivianne d'Andigne. adv.; bk.rev.; bibl.; charts; illus.; stat.
Incorporates: Revue des Finances Communales (ISSN 0035-208X)

VIE DES AFFAIRES; bulletin consacre a l'analyse des avis emis par les dirigeants d'entreprise a l'egard du droit economique et des politiques gouvernementales. see *BUSINESS AND ECONOMICS — Management*

350   US
▼**VINSON INSTITUTE LINK.** 1994. q. free. University of Georgia, Carl Vinson Institute of Government, 201 N. Milledge Ave., Athens, GA 30602. TEL 706-542-2736. FAX 706-542-9301. Ed. Ann Allen.
Description: Reports on current programs and activities at the Vinson Institute.

350   VI   ISSN 0882-0023
JL1161.A11
VIRGIN ISLANDS OF THE UNITED STATES BLUE BOOK. 1981. biennial. $5. Division of Libraries, Archives and Museums, Department of Planning and Natural Resources, 23 Dronningens Gade, St. Thomas, VI 00802. TEL 809-774-3407. FAX 809-775-1887. Ed. Jeannette Allis Bastian.
Formerly: Virgin Island Blue Book.

340   US   ISSN 0092-1270
VIRGIN ISLANDS REGISTER. 1960. irreg., latest 1984. price varies. Equity Publishing Corporation, R.R. 1, Box 3, Orford, NH 03777. TEL 603-353-4351. FAX 603-353-9556. (looseleaf format)

350   IT
VOCE DI MONASTEROLO. 1968. s-a. free. Via Tridentina 5, I-24100 Bergamo, Italy. Dir. Bellini Aldo. circ. 800. (looseleaf format)

350   FR
VOIX DES CADRES DE LA FONCTION PUBLIQUE. 1963. 6/yr. 100 F. (effective 1995). Union Federale des Cadres des Fonctions Publiques (U.F.C.F.P.), 30 rue de Gramont, 75002 Paris, France. TEL 1-40-15-05-99. FAX 1-42-96-15-98. Ed. Perre Avignon. adv. contact: Pierre Avignon. bk.rev.; charts; illus.; stat. circ. 10,000. **Document type:** bulletin.

350   US   ISSN 0738-0798
KFN7481
WAKE FOREST UNIVERSITY SCHOOL OF LAW. CONTINUING LEGAL EDUCATION. ANNUAL REVIEW, NORTH CAROLINA. 1980. a. $90. Wake Forest University School of Law, Continuing Legal Education, Box 7206, Reynolda Sta., Winston-Salem, NC 27109-7206. TEL 910-759-4550. FAX 910-759-4632. James C. Cook, Dir. circ. 700. **Document type:** trade publication.
Description: Provides a comprehensive review and update of North Carolina and federal law in all significant areas, as well as new casses and legislation and the year's review.

WASHINGTON (STATE). DEPARTMENT OF NATURAL RESOURCES. ANNUAL REPORT. see *ENVIRONMENTAL STUDIES*

WASHINGTON (STATE). EMPLOYMENT SECURITY DEPARTMENT. AFFIRMATIVE ACTION INFORMATION. see *BUSINESS AND ECONOMICS — Labor And Industrial Relations*

350   US
WASHINGTON (STATE). JOINT BOARD OF LEGISLATIVE ETHICS. ANNUAL REPORT. 1968. a. Joint Board of Legislative Ethics, Box 40482, Olympia, WA 98504-0482. TEL 206-786-7501. FAX 206-786-7520. circ. 500. **Document type:** government publication.

328.797   US   ISSN 0091-8253
JK9230
WASHINGTON (STATE) LEGISLATURE. PICTORIAL DIRECTORY. Key Title: Pictorial Directory - Washington State Legislature. 1909. irreg., published each distinct legislation session. free. Legislature, Olympia, WA 98504. TEL 206-786-7550. FAX 20-786-7520. illus. circ. 19,000. **Document type:** government publication, directory.

353.9   US
WASHINGTON (STATE) RESEARCH COUNCIL. NOTEBOOK.* 1932. m. $50. Washington Research Council, 1301 Fifth Ave., Ste. 350, Seattle, WA 98101-2603. TEL 206-357-6643. FAX 206-754-2193. Ed. John S. Archer. charts; stat.; index; circ. 2,500 (controlled). (looseleaf format; back issues avail.) **Document type:** newsletter.
Former titles: Washington State Research Council Report; Washington State Research Council Monthly Report (ISSN 0043-0803)
Description: Focus is on Washington state public policy issues.

350 340   US
WASHINGTON ADMINISTRATIVE LAW PRACTICE MANUAL. 1991. base vol. (plus a. supplement). $85. Butterworth Legal Publishers (Salem) (Subsidiary of: Reed Elsevier plc), 8 Industrial Way, Bldg. C, Salem, NH 03079. TEL 800-548-4001. FAX 603-898-9858. Ed.Bd. (looseleaf format)

WASHINGTON ENVIRONMENTAL PROTECTION REPORT; twice-monthly letter on contracting opportunities, legislation, research & development, and rules & regulations for the nation's environmental programs. see *ENVIRONMENTAL STUDIES*

WASHINGTON MEMO (NEW YORK). see *MEDICAL SCIENCES — Obstetrics And Gynecology*

WASHINGTON RECREATION AND PARK ASSOCIATION. SYLLABUS. see *CONSERVATION*

350 330   US   ISSN 1042-0142
WASHINGTON REGULATORY REPORT. 1989. 10/yr. $150. Clark - Boardman - Callaghan Company Ltd., 375 Hudson St., New York, NY 10014. TEL 212-929-7500. FAX 212-924-0460. Eds. Steve Errick, Larry Selby.
Description: Reports on congressional and administrative agency activity affecting business.

350   US   ISSN 0192-060X
JK1118
WASHINGTON REPRESENTATIVES. 1977. a. $80. Columbia Books Inc., 1212 New York Ave., N.W., Ste. 330, Washington, DC 20005. TEL 202-898-0662. (Dist. by: Reference Press, Inc., 6448 Hwy. 290 E., Ste. E-104, Austin, TX 78723. TEL 512-454-7778. FAX 512-454-9401) Ed. Arthur C. Close. **Document type:** directory.
Formerly (until 1979): Directory of Washington Representatives of American Associations and Industry (ISSN 0147-216X)
Description: Compilation of over 14,000 Washington lobbyists, lawyers, government relations counselors, registered foreign agents, and other advocates, organized alphabetically by person and organization.

WASHINGTON STATE LABOR MARKET AND ECONOMIC REPORT (YEAR). see *BUSINESS AND ECONOMICS — Labor And Industrial Relations*

WATER ENVIRONMENT REGULATION WATCH. see *ENVIRONMENTAL STUDIES — Pollution*

350   US   ISSN 0193-4716
WAYS & MEANS; reporting on innovative approaches to state and local government. 1976. 4/yr. $30. Center for Policy Alternatives, 1875 Connecticut Ave., N.W., Ste. 710, Washington, DC 20009. TEL 202-387-6030. FAX 202-986-2539. Ed. Sandra Martin. bk.rev.; bibl.; charts; illus. circ. 2,000. **Indexed:** Urb.Aff.Abstr.
Formerly: Conference on Alternative State and Local Public Policies. Newsletter.
Description: Reports on policy issues such as toxic wastes, election law, small businesses, health care, corporate crime, prison construcion, worker safety, and tax reform.

350 320   US
WEEKLY REVIEW. 1970. w. $200. Louisiana News Bureau, Inc., Box 44212, Baton Rouge, LA 70804. TEL 504-342-1240. Eds. Kevin Morgan, Michael Courtney.
●Available only online.
Description: Review of Louisiana government and politics.

352   II   ISSN 0049-7193
WEST BENGAL. 1969. fortn. Rs.12. Department of Information and Cultural Affairs, Writers' Buildings, Calcutta 700001, India. Eds. A. Bhattachanya, S.N. Roy. adv.; illus. circ. 6,000.

350   US
WEST VIRGINIA. LEGISLATURE. COMMISSION ON SPECIAL INVESTIGATIONS. REPORT TO THE WEST VIRGINIA LEGISLATURE. 1981. a. free. Legislature, No. 1 Players Club Dr., Ste. 501, Charleston, WV 25311-1626. TEL 304-558-2345. Ed. Gary W. Slater. circ. 300. **Document type:** government publication.
Formerly: West Virginia. Legislature. Purchasing Practices and Procedures Commission. Report to the West Virginia Legislature.

350   US   ISSN 0363-356X
WESTCHESTER PLANNING. 1973. q. free. Westchester County Department of Planning, 432 County Office Bldg., White Plains, NY 10601. TEL 914-682-2564. Ed. Mary R.S. Carlson. bk.rev.; illus. circ. 2,000.
Formerly: Westchester Planning Newsletter.
Description: Covers planning and allied fields such as architecture, landscape architecture, law, political science, statistics and urban studies as they relate to Westchester.

354.9   AT   ISSN 0043-3489
WESTERN AUSTRALIA. GOVERNMENT GAZETTE. 1842. s-w. Aus.$458 (overseas Aus.$649) (effective 1994). Western Australia Government Printing Office, 22 Station St., Wembley, W.A. 6014, Australia. TEL 09-383-8811. FAX 09-382-1079. circ. 1,200. **Document type:** government publication.
Description: Publishes notices of a legal nature as required by Acts of Parliament.

WEST'S FEDERAL RULES DECISIONS. see *LAW*

PUBLIC ADMINISTRATION

350 US
WHEELER REPORT.* 1974. d. (during session); fortn. (during interim). $900. Wheeler News Service, 121 E. Main St., Ste. 300, Madison, WI 53703-3315. TEL 608-257-2614. Ed. Richard Wheeler.
Description: Reports on action taken in Wisconsin Legislature, including bill status information. Also covers attorney general opinion, agency appointments and interim committee activity.

350 320 US ISSN 0737-9218
E839.5
WHITE HOUSE WEEKLY. 1981. 48/yr. $495 (effective 1995). White House Weekly, Inc., 611 Pennsylvania Ave., S.E., Ste. 219, Washington, DC 20003. TEL 301-322-4350. Pub. M.A. McHugh. **Document type:** newsletter.
Description: Covers the White House, including president and staff.

354.1 UK ISSN 1352-7452
THE WHITEHALL COMPANION. 1992. a. £145 (effective 1995). Dod's Publishing and Research (DPR) Ltd., 33 John St., London WC1N 2AT, England. TEL 0171-753-7760. FAX 0171-753-7761. Ed. Dee O'Sullivan; Pub. Hilary Muggridge. **Document type:** directory.

350 US
WHO IS WHO IN THE OKLAHOMA LEGISLATURE. 1963. biennial. $3. Oklahoma Department of Libraries, 200 N.E. 18th St., Oklahoma City, OK 73105. TEL 405-521-2502. FAX 405-525-7804. Ed. Ann Hamilton. circ. 4,500. **Document type:** government publication, directory.
Description: Biographical sketches of Oklahoma state legislators.

336 US ISSN 0085-8226
WISCONSIN. DEPARTMENT OF ADMINISTRATION. ANNUAL FISCAL REPORT. 1950. a. free. Department of Administration, Bureau of Financial Operations, Box 7864, Madison, WI 53707. TEL 608-266-1694. Ed. W.J. Raftery. circ. 1,000. (also avail. in microfiche from CIS) **Indexed:** SRI.

350 US
WISCONSIN. STATE ELECTIONS BOARD. BIENNIAL REPORT. 1975. biennial. $15. State Elections Board, 132 E. Wilson St., 3rd Fl., Ste. 300, Madison, WI 53702. TEL 608-266-8005. FAX 608-267-0500. circ. 100. **Document type:** government publication.
Description: Lists political financial activity for two-year periods in Wisconsin.

350 US
WISCONSIN BLUE BOOK. biennial. $8.15. Department of Administration, Document Sales, 202 S. Thornton Ave., Box 7840, Madison, WI 53707. TEL 608-266-3358. Ed. Lawrence Barish. **Indexed:** SRI.
Refereed Serial

350 US
WISCONSIN ISSUES.* 1985. m. $50 (prices set in Jan.). Public Expenditure Research Foundation, 2114 N. Sherman Ave., Madison, WI 53704-3969. TEL 608-255-6767. FAX 608-256-0333. Ed. Robert C. Brunner. circ. 3,000.
Description: Policy issues related to Wisconsin state and local government.

350 336 US ISSN 0043-6720
HJ2441
WISCONSIN TAXPAYER. 1932. m. $8. Wisconsin Taxpayer Alliance, 335 W. Wilson St., Madison, WI 53703-3694. TEL 608-255-4581. Ed. Todd A. Berry.
Description: Analyzes and comments on issues dealing with Wisconsin state and local government.

WOMEN IN GOVERNMENT. see WOMEN'S INTERESTS

WOMEN IN PUBLIC SERVICE BULLETIN. see WOMEN'S INTERESTS

WORD FROM WASHINGTON (SAN ANTONIO). see BUSINESS AND ECONOMICS — Labor And Industrial Relations

350 US ISSN 0886-9162
KFO342.A15
WORKERS' COMPENSATION JOURNAL OF OHIO. Short title: W C J O. 1986. bi-m. $125. Banks - Baldwin Law Publishing Co., University Center, 1904 Ansel Rd., Box 1974, Cleveland, OH 44106. TEL 216-721-7373. FAX 216-721-8055. Ed. Jerald D. Harris. bk.rev.
Description: Reviews judicial, legislative, and administrative developments in Ohio workers' compensation and intentional tort law.

WORLD RESOURCE REVIEW. see ENVIRONMENTAL STUDIES

WORLDWIDE GOVERNMENT DIRECTORY. see BUSINESS AND ECONOMICS — Trade And Industrial Directories

350 320 US ISSN 1065-1098
WORLDWIDE GOVERNMENT REPORT. m. $247 (effective 1995). Worldwide Goverment Directories, Inc., 7979 Old Georgetown Rd., Ste. 900, Bethesda, MD 20814. TEL 301-718-8770. FAX 301-718-8494. **Document type:** newsletter.
Description: Contains news about events and personnel changes affecting governments in 195 countries.

350 US
JK7636
WYOMING. DEPARTMENT OF ADMINISTRATION AND INFORMATION. STATE LIBRARY. ANNUAL REPORT DIGEST. Key Title: Wyoming Annual Report Digest. 1973. a. Department of Administration and Information, State Library, Supreme Court Bldg., Cheyenne, WY 82002. TEL 307-777-7281. FAX 307-777-6289. stat.; circ. controlled. **Document type:** government publication.
Formerly (until 1992): Wyoming. Department of Administration and Information. State Library. Annual Report (ISSN 0094-3924)

YALE JOURNAL ON REGULATION. see LAW

YEARBOOK OF MARYLAND LEGISLATORS. see POLITICAL SCIENCE

351 BE ISSN 0771-7962
YEARBOOK OF THE EUROPEAN COMMUNITIES AND OF THE OTHER EUROPEAN ORGANIZATIONS/ANNUAIRE DES COMMUNAUTES EUROPEENNES ET DES AUTRES ORGANISATIONS EUROPEENNES/JAHRBUCH DER EUROPAEISCHEN GEMEINSCHAFTEN UND DER ANDEREN EUROPAEISCHEN ORGANISATIONEN. (Text in English, French, German) 1977. a. 5900 BEF (effective 1995). Editions Delta, Rue Scailquin 55, B-1030 Brussels, Belgium. TEL 32-2-217-55-55. FAX 32-2-217-93-93. (Dist. by: Unipub, 4611-F Assembly Dr., Lanham MD, 20706-4391) Ed. G.F. Seingry. adv.; index. circ. 8,000. **Document type:** directory.
—BLDSC (9384.371000).
Description: Provides information on the structure and operation of the European Communities and on about 1000 other European organizations, whether public or private, which contribute to European integration: political, economic, scientific, technical, and military.

350 320 US
YELLOW SHEET REPORT. 1906. 3/wk.(between legislative sessions). $149 per month. Arizona News Service, 14 N. 18th Ave., Phoenix, AZ 85007. TEL 602-258-7026. FAX 602-258-7026. Ed. Ned Creighton.
Description: Covers Arizona interim legislative committee activity and other state political and governmental news.

354.3 II ISSN 0044-0515
DS401 CODEN: YOJAE5
YOJANA. (Editions in Assamese, Bengali, English, Gujarati, Hindi, Telugu, Malayalam, Marathi, Tamil) 1957. fortn. (Eng., Hindi, Tamil, Talugu eds.); m. (other eds.). Rs.60 for Eng., Hindi eds.; Rs.40 for Tamil, Telugu eds.; Rs.30 for other eds. Ministry of Information & Broadcasting, Publications Division, Patiala House, Tilak Marg, New Delhi 110001, India. TEL 11-3710473. (Subscr. in U.S. to: M-S Inter Culture Associates, Thompson, CT 06277) Ed. D.K. Bharadwaj. adv.; bk.rev.; charts; illus.; stat. circ. 150,000. **Indexed:** Abstr.Rural Dev. Trop., Acid Rain Abstr., Acid Rain Ind., Rural Recreat.Tour.Abstr., World Agri.Econ. & Rural Sociol.Abstr. **Document type:** government publication.
Description: Serves as an intellectual forum on the problems and achievements of the planning and development of India.

350 US
YOUR WISCONSIN GOVERNMENT. 1972. w. (during session); s-m. (during interim). $45. Wisconsin Taxpayer Alliance, 335 W. Wilson St., Madison, WI 53703. TEL 608-255-4581. Ed. Todd A. Berry.
Description: Covers Wisconsin legislative issues, as well as state and local government.

YOUTH POLICY. see CHILDREN AND YOUTH — About

YOUTH RECORD; the semi-monthly report on federal youth-related policy. see CHILDREN AND YOUTH — About

ZAMBIA. CENTRAL STATISTICAL OFFICE. NATIONAL ACCOUNTS. see BUSINESS AND ECONOMICS — Public Finance, Taxation

342 ZA
ZAMBIA. COMMISSION FOR INVESTIGATIONS. ANNUAL REPORT. 1975. a. K.10. Commission for Investigations, Old Bank of Zambia Bldg., 3rd Fl., P.O. Box 50494, Ridgeway, Lusaka 10101, Zambia. (Dist. by: Government Printer, Box 136, Lusaka, Zambia) circ. 500. **Document type:** government publication.

ZEITSCHRIFT FUER BEAMTENRECHT. see LAW

350 334 GW ISSN 0344-9777
ZEITSCHRIFT FUER OEFFENTLICHE UND GEMEINWIRTSCHAFTLICHE UNTERNEHMEN. 1978. q. DM.112. Nomos Verlagsgesellschaft mbH und Co. KG, Waldseestr. 3-5, 76530 Baden-Baden, Germany. TEL 07221-21040. FAX 07221-210427. (Subscr. to: Postfach 610, 76484 Baden-Baden, Germany) Eds. Peter Eichhorn, Achim von Loesch. adv.; bk.rev. **Document type:** newsletter.
—BLDSC (9475.595000). **CCC.**
Incorporates (in 1984): Oeffentliche Wirtschaft und Gemeinwirtschaft (ISSN 0343-1479); Which was formerly (until 1973): Oeffentliche Wirtschaft (ISSN 0029-8603)

ZEITSCHRIFT FUER PARLAMENTSFRAGEN. see POLITICAL SCIENCE

350 AU
ZEITSCHRIFT FUER VERWALTUNG. 1976. bi-m. S.2850. Orac Zeitschriftenverlag GmbH, Schoenbrunnerstr. 59-61, A-1050 Vienna, Austria. TEL 01-54621-0. FAX 01-5462114. Ed. Heinz Peter Rill. adv.: B&W page S.9200; trim 167 x 249; adv. contact: Margot Stockhammer. circ. 5,300. **Document type:** trade publication.

350 FR ISSN 0298-2285
ZERO - UN INFORMATIQUE (HEBDOMADAIRE).*
(Supplements avail.: Zero - Un Informatique (Mensuel) (ISSN 0985-2999); Zero - Un References (ISSN 0997-654X); Telecommunications (ISSN 1152-9180)) 1969. w. 530 F. Groupe Tests, 26 rue d'Oradour sur Glance, 75504 Paris Cedex 15, France. TEL 42-40-22-01. FAX 42-45-59-43. TELEX GRTESTS 215 205 F. **Indexed:** Pt.de Rep. (Feb.1989-).
—CCC.
Formerly (until 1987): Zero - Un Hebdo (ISSN 0398-1169)

350 CC
ZHONGGUO XINGZHENG GUANLI/CHINESE ADMINISTRATION MANAGEMENT. (Text in Chinese) m. Zhongguo Xingzheng Guanli Zazhishe, No. 22, Xi'anmen Dajie, Beijing 100017, People's Republic of China. TEL 6012886. Ed. Liu Yichang.

PUBLIC ADMINISTRATION — ABSTRACTING, BIBLIOGRAPHIES, STATISTICS

350   US
ZHONGHUA RENMIN GONGHEGUO. QUANGUO RENDA CHANGWEIHUI GONGBAO/CHINA, PEOPLE'S REPUBLIC. NATIONAL PEOPLE'S CONGRESS. STANDING COMMITTEE. BULLETIN. (Text in Chinese) irreg. $28.25. (Quanguo Renmin Daibiao Dahui, Changwu Weiyuanhui, CC) China Books & Periodicals, Inc., 2929 24th St., San Francisco, CA 94110. TEL 415-282-2994. FAX 415-282-0994.
Document type: government publication.

350   US
ZHONGHUA RENMIN GONGHEGUO GUOWUYUAN GONGBAO/CHINA, PEOPLE'S REPUBLIC. STATE COUNCIL. BULLETIN. (Text in Chinese) irreg. $66.30. (Guowuyuan, CC) China Books & Periodicals, Inc., 2929 24th St., San Francisco, CA 94110. TEL 415-282-2994. FAX 415-282-0994. **Document type:** government publication.

350   CC   ISSN 1005-099X
ZHONGWAI KEJI ZHENGCE YU GUANLI/SCIENCE AND TECHNOLOGY POLICY AND MANAGEMENT. (Text in Chinese) 1986. m. $48. Zhongguo Kexueyuan, Wenxian Qingbao Zhongxin - Chinese Academy of Sciences, Documentation Information Center, 8 Kexueyuan Nanlu, Zhongguancun, Beijing 100080, People's Republic of China. TEL 2558446. FAX 2566846. Ed. Jia Baoqi. circ. 2,200.
Formerly: Zhongguo Keji Zhengce yu Guanli - Chinese Policy and Administration of Science and Technology.

350   RH
ZIMBABWE GOVERNMENT GAZETTE. w. with a. cum. $228. Department of Printing and Stationery, P.O. Box 8062, Causeway, Zimbabwe. TEL 706161.
Document type: government publication.

350.6   GW   ISSN 0177-1965
ZIVILDIENST; Zeitschrift fuer die Zivildienst-Leistenden. 1973. 10/yr. DM.12. Bundesamt fuer den Zivildienst, Sibille-Hartmann-Str. 2, 50969 Cologne, Germany. TEL 0221-3673520. FAX 0221-3673281. bk.rev. circ. 120,000. (reprint service avail.) **Document type:** government publication.
—CCC.

50 STATE LEGISLATIVE REVIEW. see *POLITICAL SCIENCE*

PUBLIC ADMINISTRATION — Abstracting, Bibliographies, Statistics

A B C POL SCI; a bibliography of contents: political science and government. see *POLITICAL SCIENCE — Abstracting, Bibliographies, Statistics*

350 016   AT   ISSN 0727-8926
Z7165.A8
A P A I S: AUSTRALIAN PUBLIC AFFAIRS INFORMATION SERVICE; subject index to current literature. 1945. m. (with a. cumulation). Aus.$190 (Aus.$90 for a. cum.) (effective 1995). National Library of Australia, Publications Section, Cultural and Educational Services Division, Canberra, A.C.T. 2600, Australia. TEL 61-6-262-1365. FAX 61-6-273-4493. index. circ. 1,250. (reprint service avail. from ISI,UMI) **Indexed:** AESIS, Bibl.Engl.Lang.& Lit. **Document type:** abstracting/indexing.
●Also available online.
—BLDSC (1818.400000).
Formerly: Australian Public Affairs Information Service (ISSN 0005-0075)
Description: Indexes periodical literature in social sciences and humanities published in or relating to Australia.

350 016   US
ABSTRACT NEWSLETTER: PROBLEM-SOLVING INFORMATION FOR STATE AND LOCAL GOVERNMENTS. s-m. $95 (foreign $135). U.S. National Technical Information Service, 5285 Port Royal Rd., Springfield, VA 22161. TEL 703-487-4630. FAX 703-321-8547. TELEX 64617. index. (back issues avail.)
Former titles: Weekly Abstract Newsletter: Problem-Solving Information for State and Local Governments; Weekly Government Abstracts. Problem-Solving Information for State and Local Governments (ISSN 0364-6459); Weekly Government Abstracts. Problem Solving Technology for State and Local Governments.

338.91   US
ABSTRACTS OF PUBLIC ADMINISTRATION, DEVELOPMENT AND ENVIRONMENT. 1988. a. $20. Indiana University, School of Public and Environmental Affairs, Bloomington, IN 47405. Ed. Michael Parrish. circ. 300. (back issues avail.)
Document type: abstracting/indexing.
Formerly: Abstracts of Development Studies.
Description: Abstracts of books published in English during the previous year on problems of development and developing countries.

350   TS
ABU DHABI. DEPARTMENT OF PLANNING. STATISTICAL YEARBOOK/ABU DHABI. DA'IRAT AL-TAKHTIT. AL-KITAB AL-IHSA'I AL-SANAWI. 1969. a. Department of Planning, Statistical Section, P.O. Box 12, Abu Dhabi, United Arab Emirates. TEL 727200. FAX 2-727749. TELEX 23194 PLANCO EM.
Formerly: Abu Dhabi. Department of Planning. Statistical Abstract and Yearbook.
Description: Includes statistics on climate, demographics, labor, industry, trade, transport and finance.

AFFIRMATIVE EMPLOYMENT STATISTICS. see *BUSINESS AND ECONOMICS — Abstracting, Bibliographies, Statistics*

312   US   ISSN 0095-3431
HA221
ALABAMA'S VITAL EVENTS. 1971. a. $10. Department of Public Health, Center for Health Statistics, Montgomery, AL 36130. TEL 205-261-5510. FAX 205-240-3097. Ed. Dale Quinney. illus. circ. 450. (also avail. in microfiche from CIS) **Indexed:** SRI. **Document type:** government publication.

350   CN   ISSN 0840-4976
Z1373.5.A57
ALBERTA GOVERNMENT PUBLICATIONS. q. (with a. cumulations). Alberta Public Affairs Bureau, Publication Services, 11510 Kingsway Ave., Edmonton, AB T5G 2Y5, Canada. TEL 403-427-4387. FAX 403-452-0668. **Document type:** bibliography, government publication.

350 310   US
AMERICAN STATISTICAL ASSOCIATION. GOVERNMENT STATISTICS SECTION. PROCEEDINGS. a., 4th ed. $27 to non-members; members $18. American Statistical Association, 1429 Duke St., Alexandria, VA 22314-3402. TEL 703-684-1221. FAX 703-684-2037. **Indexed:** Curr.Ind.Stat. **Document type:** proceedings.

316   AO   ISSN 0066-5193
ANGOLA. DIRECCAO DOS SERVICOS DE ESTATISTICA. ANUARIO ESTATISTICO. 1933. a. Esc.100. Direccao dos Servicos de Estatistica, C.P. 1215, Luanda, Angola. circ. 1,000.

316   AO
ANGOLA. DIRECCAO DOS SERVICOS DE ESTATISTICA. INFORMACOES ESTATISTICAS. 1970. a. free. Direccao dos Servicos de Estatistica, Ministerio do Planeamento e Coordenacao Economica, C.P. 1215, Luanda, Angola. stat. circ. 7,000.

350 572   MX
ARCHIVO HISTORICO DIOCESANO DE SAN CRISTOBAL DE LAS CASAS. SERIE TECNICA. 1981. irreg., vol.4, no.4, 1991. $45. Instituto de Asesoria Antropologica para la Region Maya, Archivo Historico Diocesano, Apdo. Postal 6, San Cristobal de las Casas, 29200 Chiapas, Mexico. **Document type:** abstracting/indexing.
Description: Indexes official papers from civil and religious governments concerning Chiapas and colonial government in general. Covers 1596-1930.

350   AT   ISSN 1031-0533
AUSTRALIA. BUREAU OF STATISTICS. APPARENT CONSUMPTION OF FOODSTUFFS AND NUTRIENTS, AUSTRALIA. 1947. a. Aus.$38. Australian Bureau of Statistics, P.O. Box 10, Belconnen, A.C.T. 2616, Australia. FAX 062-516009. TELEX 062-527911. circ. 443. (processed) **Document type:** government publication.
Description: Presents a general overview of the supply and utilization of approximately 130 basic foodstuffs, levels of nutrient intake and estimated supply of selected types of nutrients available for consumption.

350 319.4   AT   ISSN 0158-2496
AUSTRALIA. BUREAU OF STATISTICS. APPARENT CONSUMPTION OF SELECTED FOODSTUFFS, AUSTRALIA, PRELIMINARY. 1978. a. Aus.$11. Australian Bureau of Statistics, P.O. Box 10, Belconnen, A.C.T. 2616, Australia. circ. 285.
Document type: government publication.
Description: Presents preliminary details of the apparent consumption and per capita consumption of selected food items.

350   AT   ISSN 1032-805X
Z7554.A77
AUSTRALIA. BUREAU OF STATISTICS. CATALOGUE OF PUBLICATIONS AND PRODUCTS. 1967. a. Aus.$5 (foreign Aus.$20). Australian Bureau of Statistics, P.O. Box 10, Belconnen, A.C.T. 2616, Australia. circ. 2,105. (also avail. in diskette format) **Document type:** government publication.
Formerly: Catalogue of Publications, Australia (ISSN 0727-1417)
Description: Lists publications and other standard products issued by the ABS, including frequency, date of first issue, price and content.

350   AT   ISSN 1037-7921
AUSTRALIA. BUREAU OF STATISTICS. CHILD CARE, AUSTRALIA. 1969. 3/yr. Aus.$25. Australian Bureau of Statistics, P.O. Box 10, Belconnen, A.C.T. 2616, Australia. TEL 062-527911. FAX 062-527911. circ. 234. **Document type:** government publication.
Former titles: Child Care Arrangements, Australia (ISSN 0728-6368); (until 1980): Child Care (Canberra) (ISSN 0728-6376)
Description: Focuses on the family unit with children ages 0-11 years classified by type and hours of childcare, multiplicity of care, day-frequency of care, number and age of children, weekly cost of care and other areas.

350 319.4   AT
AUSTRALIA. BUREAU OF STATISTICS. DIRECTORY OF ENERGY RELATED STATISTICS. 1981. irreg., latest 1992. Aus.$30. Australian Bureau of Statistics, Ground Floor, Wing 5, Cameron Offices, Belconnen, A.C.T. 2617, Australia.
Formerly: Directory of A B S Energy Statistics.
Description: Contains details and descriptions of energy related statistics available from both private and public sector organizations and is intended to assist those interested in the subject of energy to locate relevant statistical information.

350 319.4   AT   ISSN 0156-4722
AUSTRALIA. BUREAU OF STATISTICS. PUBLICATIONS ADVICE. 1969. s-w. Aus.$0.60 per no. Australian Bureau of Statistics, P.O. Box 10, Belconnen, A.C.T. 2616, Australia. TEL 062-527911. FAX 062-516009. circ. 334. **Document type:** government publication.
Description: Lists publications released by all ABS offices on the day of issue of the Advice and those expected to be released on the following two working days. Also lists publications expected to be released by the Central Office on the three subsequent working days.

350 319.4   AT   ISSN 1031-0673
AUSTRALIA. BUREAU OF STATISTICS. PUBLICATIONS ISSUED IN (MONTH). 1961. m. Aus.$1 per no. Australian Bureau of Statistics, P.O. Box 10, Belconnen, A.C.T. 2616, Australia. TEL 062-527911. FAX 062-516009. circ. 457. **Document type:** government publication.
Description: Provides a complete list of publications issued by the ABS (Central and State Offices) during each month.

352   AT   ISSN 1031-2528
AUSTRALIA. BUREAU OF STATISTICS. QUEENSLAND OFFICE. LOCAL GOVERNMENT, QUEENSLAND. 1974. a. Aus.$21. Australian Bureau of Statistics, Queensland Office, 313 Adelaide St., Brisbane, Qld. 4000, Australia. TEL 07-222-6022. FAX 07-229-6171: TELEX AA 40271. **Document type:** government publication.
Description: Covers all local government areas: general summary, finance, all funds, ordinary services, roads, water supply, sewerage, length of roads normally open to traffic, water consumption, population served and locality supplied.

PUBLIC ADMINISTRATION — ABSTRACTING, BIBLIOGRAPHIES, STATISTICS

350 319.4   AT   ISSN 1035-3461
AUSTRALIA. BUREAU OF STATISTICS. SCHOOLS, AUSTRALIA. a. Aus.$23. Australian Bureau of Statistics, P.O. Box 10, Belconnen, A.C.T. 2616, Australia. TEL 062-527911. FAX 062-516009. circ. 399. **Document type:** government publication.
Formerly: National Schools Statistics Collection (ISSN 0819-5323); Formed by the merger of: National Schools Collection: Government Schools & Non-Government Schools.
Description: Covers statistics on schools, students, teaching and non-teaching staff involved in the provision or administration of primary and secondary education, in government and non-government schools.

350 319.4   AT   ISSN 1034-5671
AUSTRALIA. BUREAU OF STATISTICS. SCHOOLS, AUSTRALIA, PRELIMINARY. 1984. a. Aus.$11. Australian Bureau of Statistics, P.O. Box 10, Belconnen, A.C.T. 2616, Australia. TEL 062-527911. FAX 062-516009. circ. 277. **Document type:** government publication.
Formerly: National Schools Statistics Collection, Australia, Preliminary (ISSN 0816-1356)
Description: Contains preliminary summary statistics of primary and secondary schools, students and staff, classified by state or territory, type of school and year of education.

350 319.4   AT
AUSTRALIA. BUREAU OF STATISTICS. SOCIAL INDICATORS, AUSTRALIA. (Supplement avail.) 1976. irreg., latest 1992. Aus.$55. Australian Bureau of Statistics, P.O. Box 10, Belconnen, A.C.T. 2616, Australia. TEL 062-527911. FAX 062-516009. charts. circ. 845. **Document type:** government publication.
Description: A selection of social indicators and other statistics providing a broad background to social issues in Australia. Presents information under the following headings: Population, Families, Health, Education, Working Life, Income, Crime and Justice, Housing, and Welfare.

350   AU
AUSTRIAN POLITICIANS INDEX. a. S.880($84) Presseverlag Wien, Frimmelgasse 41, A-1190 Vienna, Austria. TEL 01-371577. FAX 01-374693. Ed. Peter Hoffer; Pub. Peter Hoffer. **Document type:** directory.

BADEN - WUERTTEMBERG. STATISTISCHES LANDESAMT. STATISTISCH-PROGNOSTISCHER BERICHT; Daten - Analysen - Perspektiven. see *STATISTICS*

BADEN - WUERTTEMBERG. STATISTISCHES LANDESAMT. STATISTISCHE BERICHTE. see *STATISTICS*

312   BB
BARBADOS. REGISTRATION OFFICE. REPORT ON VITAL STATISTICS & REGISTRATIONS. a., latest ed. 1981. free. Registration Office, Bridgetown, Barbados, W.I. stat. circ. 100. **Document type:** government publication.

BOCHUM. AMT FUER STATISTIK, STADTFORSCHUNG UND WAHLEN. REIHE "WAHLEN IN BOCHUM". see *POLITICAL SCIENCE — Abstracting, Bibliographies, Statistics*

BOCHUM. AMT FUER STATISTIK, STADTFORSCHUNG UND WAHLEN. SONDERBERICHTE. see *HOUSING AND URBAN PLANNING — Abstracting, Bibliographies, Statistics*

BOCHUM. AMT FUER STATISTIK, STADTFORSCHUNG UND WAHLEN. STATISTICAL YEARBOOK. see *HOUSING AND URBAN PLANNING — Abstracting, Bibliographies, Statistics*

BOCHUM. AMT FUER STATISTIK, STADTFORSCHUNG UND WAHLEN. VERWALTUNGSBERICHT. see *HOUSING AND URBAN PLANNING — Abstracting, Bibliographies, Statistics*

BOCHUM. AMT FUER STATISTIK, STADTFORSCHUNG UND WAHLEN. ZUR STADTENTWICKLUNG. see *HOUSING AND URBAN PLANNING — Abstracting, Bibliographies, Statistics*

350 350   BO
BOLIVIA. INSTITUTO NACIONAL DE ESTADISTICA. ESTADISTICAS REGIONALES DEPARTAMENTALES. 1976. a. $12. Instituto Nacional de Estadistica, Casilla de Correo No. 6129, La Paz, Bolivia.

310   BL
BRAZIL. SERVICO SOCIAL DO COMERCIO. ANUARIO ESTATISTICO. 1962. a. free. Servico Social do Comercio, Assessoria de Divulgacao e Promocao Institucional, Rua Voluntarios da Patria 169, 22270 Rio de Janeiro, Brazil. stat.

352.7   CN
BRITISH COLUMBIA. MINISTRY OF MUNICIPAL AFFAIRS, RECREATION AND HOUSING. MUNICIPAL STATISTICS, INCLUDING REGIONAL DISTRICTS. 1951. a. Can.$27. Ministry of Municipal Affairs, Recreation and Housing, Victoria, B.C., Canada. TEL 604-387-4063. FAX 604-387-1873. (Subscr. to: Crown Publications, 546 Yates St., Victoria, B.C. V8W 1K8, Canada. TEL 604-386-4636) circ. 1,250. **Document type:** government publication.
Former titles: British Columbia. Ministry of Municipal Affairs, Recreation and Culture. Municipal Statistics, Including Regional Districts; British Columbia. Ministry of Municipal Affairs. Municipal Statistics, Including Regional Districts (ISSN 0702-6641); Which supersedes: British Columbia. Ministry of Municipal Affairs. Municipal Statistics (ISSN 0521-0348)
Description: Contains financial and statistical information relating to municipalities and regional districts.

011 350   US   ISSN 0741-2878
KF70
C I S FEDERAL REGISTER INDEX. 1984. w. $675. Congressional Information Service, Part of the Reed Elsevier group, 4520 East-West Hwy., Bethesda, MD 20814-3389. TEL 301-654-1550; 800-638-8380. FAX 301-654-4033. Ed. James Shields. cum.index. (back issues avail.) **Document type:** abstracting/indexing.
Description: Provides access to virtually all regulatory items published in the Federal Register

328 016   US
C I S INDEX INDEX. (Supplement to: C I S Index to Publications of the United States Congress (ISSN 0007-8514)) 1970. m. Congressional Information Service, Part of the Reed Elsevier group, 4520 East-West Hwy., Bethesda, MD 20814. TEL 301-654-1550. FAX 301-654-4033. Ed. Aaron Lerner. **Document type:** abstracting/indexing.

328 016   US   ISSN 0007-8514
C I S INDEX TO PUBLICATIONS OF THE UNITED STATES CONGRESS. Variant title: C I S Index. CD-ROM edition: Congressional Masterfile 2 (ISSN 1064-4679) (In 2 sections: C I S Index Abstracts; C I S Index Index) 1970. m. (with q. and a. and multi-year cumulations). price varies. Congressional Information Service, Part of the Reed Elsevier group, 4520 East-West Hwy., Bethesda, MD 20814. TEL 301-654-1550; 800-638-8380. FAX 301-654-4033. E-mail: info@cispubs.com. Ed. Aaron Lerner. abstr.; index, cum.index: 1970-74; 1975-78; 1979-82; 1983-86; 1987-1990; 1991-1994. **Indexed:** Mid.East: Abstr.& Ind. **Document type:** abstracting/indexing.
●Also available online. Vendor(s): Knight-Ridder, Inc. (File no.101).
Also available on CD-ROM.
—BLDSC (3267.637500).
Description: Abstracts and indexes to information published by congressional committees.

C O S S A WASHINGTON UPDATE. (Consortium of Social Science Associations) see *SOCIAL SCIENCES: COMPREHENSIVE WORKS — Abstracting, Bibliographies, Statistics*

333.79 011   US   ISSN 0738-6435
C S I CONGRESSIONAL RECORD ABSTRACTS: ENERGY EDITION. d. following session of Congress. $495. (Capitol Services, Inc.) National Standards Association, 1200 Quince Orchard Blvd., Gaithersburg, MD 20878. **Document type:** abstracting/indexing.

350 011   US   ISSN 0738-6451
C S I CONGRESSIONAL RECORD ABSTRACTS: FOREIGN AFFAIRS EDITION. d. following session of Congress. $495. (Capitol Services, Inc.) National Standards Association, 1200 Quince Orchard Blvd., Gaithersburg, MD 20878. **Document type:** abstracting/indexing.

350 011   US   ISSN 0738-6443
C S I CONGRESSIONAL RECORD ABSTRACTS: MASTER EDITION. d. following session of Congress. $725. (Capitol Services, Inc.) National Standards Association, 1200 Quince Orchard Blvd., Gaithersburg, MD 20878. **Document type:** government publication.
●Also available online. Vendor(s): Ovid Technologies, Knight-Ridder, Inc.

350   US   ISSN 0738-6486
C S I CONGRESSIONAL RECORD ABSTRACTS: NATIONAL DEFENSE EDITION. d. following session of Congress. $525. (Capitol Services, Inc.) National Standards Association, 1200 Quince Orchard Blvd., Gaithersburg, MD 20878. **Document type:** abstracting/indexing.

350 011   US   ISSN 0738-646X
C S I FEDERAL REGISTER ABSTRACTS: MASTER EDITION. 1981. d. $725. (Capitol Services, Inc.) National Standards Association, 1200 Quince Orchard Blvd., Gaithersburg, MD 20878. **Document type:** abstracting/indexing.
●Also available online. Vendor(s): Ovid Technologies (FREG), Knight-Ridder, Inc., Orbit Search Service.

350 336   CM   ISSN 0258-0942
CAMEROON. DIRECTION DE LA STATISTIQUE ET DE LA COMPTABILITE NATIONAL. BULLETIN TRIMESTRIEL DE CONJONCTURE. 1982. q. free. Direction de la Statistique et de la Comptabilite Nationale - Department of Statistics and National Accounts, B.P. 660, Yaounde, Cameroon. TEL 22-07-88.

CENSUS CATALOG AND GUIDE. see *POPULATION STUDIES — Abstracting, Bibliographies, Statistics*

352   US   ISSN 0082-9358
CENSUS OF GOVERNMENTS (FINAL REPORTS). (Avail. in 6 vols.: Vol. 1 - Government Organization; Vol. 2 - Taxable Poperty Values and Assessmemt States; Vol. 3 - Public Employment; Vol. 4 - Government Finances; Vol. 5 - Tropical Studies; Vol. 6 - Guide to the Census of Governments) 1850. quinquennial since 1957, latest 1992. price varies. U.S. Bureau of the Census, Data User Services Division, Washington, DC 20233. TEL 301-457-4100. FAX 301-457-4714. (Orders to: Superintendent of Documents, U.S. Government Printing Office, Box 371954, Pittsburgh, PA 15250-7954. TEL 202-512-1800. FAX 202-512-2250; Or: Bernan, 4611-F Assembly Dr., Lanham, MD 20706. TEL 301-459-7666. FAX 301-459-0056) stat. (also avail. in microform from BHP; microfilm from BHP; back issues avail.) **Document type:** government publication.
●Also available online. Vendor(s): CompuServe, Inc., Knight-Ridder, Inc.
Description: Covers finance, taxes, and employment of state and local governments

350   UK   ISSN 0260-9762
HJ9041
CHARTERED INSTITUTE OF PUBLIC FINANCE AND ACCOUNTANCY. LOCAL GOVERNMENT COMPARATIVE STATISTICS. ESTIMATES. 1981. a. £60. Chartered Institute of Public Finance and Accountancy, Statistical Information Service, 3 Robert St., London WC2N 6BH, England. TEL 0171-895-8823. FAX 0171-895-8825. (back issues avail.)
—BLDSC (5290.014000).

350   UK   ISSN 0260-7603
CHARTERED INSTITUTE OF PUBLIC FINANCE AND ACCOUNTANCY. WASTE COLLECTION STATISTICS. ACTUALS. (Not avail. for circ. outside U.K. local authorities.) 1977. a. £68. Chartered Institute of Public Finance and Accountancy, Statistical Information Service, 3 Robert St., London WC2N 6BH, England. TEL 0171-895-8823. FAX 0171-895-8825. (back issues avail.)

350 628   UK   ISSN 0140-0150
CHARTERED INSTITUTE OF PUBLIC FINANCE AND ACCOUNTANCY. WASTE DISPOSAL STATISTICS. ACTUALS. (Not avail. for circ. outside U.K. authorities.) 1979-199?; resumed. a. £68. Chartered Institute of Public Finance and Accountancy, Statistical Information Service, 3 Robert St., London WC2N 6BH, England. TEL 0171-895-8823. FAX 0171-895-8825. (back issues avail.)

PUBLIC ADMINISTRATION — ABSTRACTING, BIBLIOGRAPHIES, STATISTICS

011 350　　　US　　ISSN 0146-0838
Z1223.5.N55
CHECKLIST OF OFFICIAL NEW JERSEY PUBLICATIONS. 1965. bi-m. free. New Jersey State Library, CN-520, Trenton, NJ 08625-0520. TEL 609-292-6294. Ed. Robert Lupp. circ. 300. (processed) **Indexed:** P.A.I.S. **Document type:** bibliography.

353.9 015　　　US　　ISSN 0077-9296
Z1223.5.N57
CHECKLIST OF OFFICIAL PUBLICATIONS OF THE STATE OF NEW YORK. (Title varies: Vols. 1-15 as Official Publications of the State of New York; Supplement avail.) 1947. m. $6 (foreign $12.50); or exchange basis. New York State Library, Collection, Acquisitions and Processing, Albany, NY 12230. author index: vols.1-23. circ. 1,500. **Document type:** bibliography.
　　Description: Monthly listing of monographs and serials published within the most recent two years received and catalogued by the New York State Library.

350　　　　　　CF
CONGO. CENTRE NATIONAL DE LA STATISTIQUE ET DES ETUDES ECONOMIQUES. ANNUAIRE STATISTIQUE. 1959. a. 12000 Fr.CFA. Centre National de la Statistique et des Etudes Economiques, B.P. 2031, Brazzaville, Congo. TEL 83-36-94.

350　　　　　　CF
CONGO. CENTRE NATIONAL DE LA STATISTIQUE ET DES ETUDES ECONOMIQUES. BULLETIN DE STATISTIQUE. 1977. q. Centre National de la Statistique et des Etudes Economiques, B.P. 2031, Brazzaville, Congo. TEL 83-36-94. Ed. Marcel Mouele.

350 330　　　　CF
CONGO. CENTRE NATIONAL DE LA STATISTIQUE ET DES ETUDES ECONOMIQUES. BULLETIN TRIMESTRIEL DE LA CONJONCTURE. q. 13500 Fr.CFA. Centre National de la Statistique et des Etudes Economiques, B.P. 2031, Brazzaville, Congo. TEL 83-36-94.

350　　　　IT　　ISSN 0390-6574
CONTI DEGLI ITALIANI. 1967. a. L.19000 (effective 1993). Istituto Nazionale di Statistica, Via Cesare Balbo 16, 00100 Rome, Italy. FAX 06-46735198. **Document type:** government publication.

353 310　　　　CY
CYPRUS. DEPARTMENT OF STATISTICS AND RESEARCH. FUNCTIONS AND SERVICES. (Text in English) 1981. irreg. free. Ministry of Finance, Department of Statistics and Research, 13 Lord Byron Ave., Nicosia, Cyprus. TEL 357-2-302349. FAX 357-2-456712. **Document type:** government publication.
　　Description: Brings information about the function and services of the Cyprus Department of Statistics and Research.

355　　　　　　US
▼**D L A P S.** (Defense Logistics Agency Publishing System) 1995. q. $92 (foreign $115). U.S. Defense Logistics Agency, Cameron Sta., Alexandria, VA 22314. (Subscr. to: Superintendent of Documents, U.S. Government Printing Office, Box 371954, Pittsburgh, PA 15250. TEL 202-512-1800. FAX 202-512-2250) (back issues avail.) **Document type:** bibliography, government publication.
●Available only on CD-ROM.
　　Description: Contains all D.L.A. regulatory publications and a selection of other Department of Defense titles.

DATABASES FOR ENVIRONMENTAL ANALYSIS: PROVINCIAL AND TERRITORIAL GOVERNMENTS. see ENVIRONMENTAL STUDIES — Abstracting, Bibliographies, Statistics

352.17109489　　DK　　ISSN 0106-9802
HJ9056
DENMARK. DANMARKS STATISTIK. KOMMUNALE FINANSER. (Text in Danish and English) 1981. a. DKK 73.77. Danmarks Statistik, Sejroegade 11, 2100 Copenhagen OE, Denmark. TEL 31-298222. FAX 31-184801. TELEX 16236.
　　Formerly: Denmark. Danmarks Statistik. Kommunale Finanser for Regnskabsaaret.

339.3489　　　DK　　ISSN 0108-8173
HC360.I5
DENMARK. DANMARKS STATISTIK. NATIONALREGNSKABSSTATISTIK. (Text in Danish and English) 1983. a. DKK 180. Danmarks Statistik, Sejroegade 11, DK-2100 Copenhagen OE, Denmark. TEL 45-31-29-82-22. FAX 45-31-18-48-01. TELEX 16236.

DIRECTORY OF POLITICAL NEWSLETTERS. see POLITICAL SCIENCE — Abstracting, Bibliographies, Statistics

350 316　　　　FT
DJIBOUTI. DIRECTION NATIONALE DE LA STATISTIQUE. BULLETIN DE STATISTIQUE ET DE DOCUMENTATION. 1970. q. 500 F. Ministere du Commerce, des Transports et du Tourisme, Direction Nationale de la Statistique, B.P. 1846, Djibouti, Djibouti.
　　Former titles: Djibouti. Service de Statistique et de Documentation. Bulletin de Statistique et de Documentation; (until 1976): French Territory of the Afars and Issas. Service de Statistique et de Documentation. Bulletin de Statistique et de Documentation.

016 350　　　II　　ISSN 0377-7081
Z7164.A2
DOCUMENTATION IN PUBLIC ADMINISTRATION. (Text in English) 1973. q. Rs.15($5) Indian Institute of Public Administration, Indraprastha Estate, Ring Rd., New Delhi 110002, India. Ed. T.N. Chaturvedi. bibl. —BLDSC (3611.165000).
　　Supersedes: Public Administration Abstracts and Index of Articles (ISSN 0033-331X)

357　　　　GW　　ISSN 0945-2702
DUISBURG. AMT FUER STATISTIK, STADTFORSCHUNG UND EUROPAANGELEGENHEITEN. MITTEILUNGEN. 1978. m. DM.6 per no. Amt fuer Statistik, Stadtforschung und Europaangelegenheiten, Der Oberstadtdirektor, 47049 Duisburg, Germany. TEL 0203-283-3085. FAX 0203-2834404. TELEX 8551214. index. circ. 450. (back issues avail.) **Document type:** government publication.
　　Former titles (until 1995): Statistischer Monatsbericht; Duisburg. Amt fuer Statistik und Stadtforschung. Statistischer Monatsbericht (ISSN 0173-8925)

EDUCATIONAL LEGISLATION INDEX. see EDUCATION — Abstracting, Bibliographies, Statistics

350 016　　　US　　ISSN 1046-3631
Z7165.U5
FEDERAL INDEX; covering the Congressional Record, Federal Register, Presidential Documents, U S Law Week. 1977. m. $695. (Capitol Services, Inc.) National Standards Association, 1200 Quince Orchard Blvd., Gaithersburg, MD 20878. index. **Document type:** abstracting/indexing.
●Also available online. Vendor(s): Knight-Ridder, Inc. (File no.20).
　　Former titles (until 1985): C S I Federal Index (ISSN 0738-6478); (until 1983): Federal Index Monthly (ISSN 0148-5512)

350 340　　　AT　　ISSN 1039-950X
FEDERAL STATUTES ANNOTATIONS. 2/yr. $290. Butterworths, Division of Reed International Books Australia Pty. Ltd. (Subsidiary of: Reed Elsevier Australia Pty. Ltd.), 271-273 Lane Cove Rd., North Ryde, N.S.W. 2113, Australia. TEL 02-335-4444. FAX 02-335-4678. **Document type:** abstracting/indexing.
　　Former titles: Federal Legislation Annotations (ISSN 1036-3661); Annotations to the Acts and Regulations of the Australian Parliament.

350 016　　　FJ　　ISSN 0015-0916
FIJI. GOVERNMENT PRINTING DEPARTMENT. PUBLICATIONS BULLETIN. s-a. free. Government Printing Department, P.O. Box 98, Suva, Fiji. circ. 1,000. **Document type:** government publication.

314 352　　　FI　　ISSN 0355-2217
FINLAND. TILASTOKESKUS. KUNNALLISVAALIT/FINLAND. STATISTIKCENTRALEN. KOMMUNALVALEN/FINLAND. CENTRAL STATISTICAL OFFICE. MUNICIPAL ELECTIONS. (Section XXIX B of Official Statistics of Finland) (Text in English, Finnish and Swedish) 1931. irreg; latest 1984. FIM 65. Tilastokeskus, Annankatu 44, SF-00100 Helsinki 10, Finland.

352　　　　GW
GELSENKIRCHEN IM SPIEGEL DER STATISTIK. 1982. s-a. Stadt Gelsenkirchen, Amt fuer Informationsverarbeitung, Vattmannstr. 11, 45877 Gelsenkirchen, Germany. TEL 0209-1692101. circ. 350.

GEOGRAPHICAL CODE OF GREECE; by department, eparchy, municipality, commune and locality. see GEOGRAPHY — Abstracting, Bibliographies, Statistics

352　　　　GW
GOETTINGER STATISTIK. 1950. q. Stadt Goettingen, Amt fuer Statistik und Stadtforschung, Postfach 3831, 37028 Goettingen, Germany. TEL 0551-4002353. circ. 600.

GOVERNMENT ACCOUNTING AND AUDITING UPDATE. see BUSINESS AND ECONOMICS — Accounting

354.710　　　CN　　ISSN 1181-6651
NX513.A1
GOVERNMENT EXPENDITURES ON CULTURE/DEPENSES PUBLIQUES AU TITRE DE LA CULTURE; (year) culture statistics. 1985. a. Can.$17 (US $20, elsewhere $24). Statistics Canada, Publications Division, Ottawa, ON K1A 0T6, Canada. TEL 416-951-7276. FAX 613-951-1582. **Document type:** government publication.
　　Former titles (until 1989): Government Expenditures on Culture in Canada (ISSN 0847-1258); (until 1988): Culture Statistics. Government Expenditures on Culture in Canada, Preliminary Statistics (ISSN 0832-9486)
　　Description: Contains survey highlights and statistical tables on government expenditures on libraries, heritage activities, performing arts, literary arts, visual arts and crafts, broadcasting, film and video.

016 500　　　US　　ISSN 0097-9007
Z7916　　　　　　　CODEN: GRAIDA
GOVERNMENT REPORTS ANNOUNCEMENTS & INDEX. Short title: G R A & I Journal. (Supplement avail.: Government Reports Annual Index (ISSN 0145-532X)) 1946. s-m. $535 (overseas $725); with Government Reports Annual Index $1105 (overseas $1435). U.S. National Technical Information Service, 5285 Port Royal Rd., Springfield, VA 22161. TEL 703-487-4630. FAX 703-321-8547. TELEX 64617. index. (also avail. in microform from UMI,PMC; reprint service avail. from UMI; back issues avail.) **Indexed:** MEDOC, Sh.& Vib.Dig. **Document type:** abstracting/indexing, government publication.
●Also available online. Vendor(s): Ovid Technologies, CEDOCAR, CISTI, Data-Star, Knight-Ridder, Inc. (File no.6), European Space Agency, JICST, Orbit Search Service (NTIS), STN International (NTIS). —BLDSC (4206.045000); CASDDS; UMI.
　　Former titles (until 1975): Government Reports Announcements (ISSN 0096-0799); (until 1971): U.S. Government Research and Developments Reports (ISSN 0099-9156); (until 1964): U.S. Government Research Reports (ISSN 0041-7696); (until 1954): Bibliography of Technical Reports (ISSN 0096-8897); (until 1949): Bibliography of Scientific and Technical Reports (ISSN 0097-370X).
　　Description: Multidisciplinary current awareness resource. Announces more than 60,000 R & D and engineering results annually.

GOVERNMENT REPORTS ANNUAL INDEX. see ENGINEERING — Abstracting, Bibliographies, Statistics

352 336　　　UK　　ISSN 0308-1745
GREAT BRITAIN. DEPARTMENT OF THE ENVIRONMENT. LOCAL GOVERNMENT FINANCIAL STATISTICS: ENGLAND AND WALES. (Joint publication with the Welsh Office) a. price varies. (Department of the Environment) H.M.S.O. Books, Publications Centre, 51 Nine Elms Ln., London SW8 5DR, England. TEL 071-873-0011. FAX 071-873-8463. (Subscr. to: H.M.S.O. Books, P.O. Box 276, London SW8 5DT, England. TEL 071-873-9090. FAX 071-873-8200) **Document type:** government publication.
　　—CCC.

PUBLIC ADMINISTRATION — ABSTRACTING, BIBLIOGRAPHIES, STATISTICS

350.6 UK ISSN 0267-095X
GREAT BRITAIN. H M TREASURY. CIVIL SERVICE STATISTICS. 1971. a. H.M.S.O. Books, 51 Nine Elms Ln., London SW8 5DR, England. TEL 0171-873-0011. FAX 0171-873-8463. (Subscr. to: H.M.S.O. Publication Centre, P.O. Box 276, London SW8 5DT, England. TEL 0171-873-9090. FAX 0171-873-8200) **Document type:** government publication.
—BLDSC (3273.876000).

016 US ISSN 0092-3168
Z1223.Z7
GUIDE TO U S GOVERNMENT PUBLICATIONS. a. $325. Documents Index, Inc., 7900 Sudley Rd., Ste. 405, Manassas, VA 22110-2806. TEL 703-257-4844. Ed. John L. Andriot. **Document type:** abstracting/indexing.

352 GW ISSN 0172-360X
HANDBUCH DER FINANZSTATISTIK. 1953. a. DM.22. Statistisches Landesamt Rheinland-Pfalz, Postfach, 53604 Bad Ems, Germany. TEL 02603-71245. stat. (back issues avail.)

INDEX TO CURRENT URBAN DOCUMENTS. see *HOUSING AND URBAN PLANNING* — *Abstracting, Bibliographies, Statistics*

011 350 US ISSN 0198-9014
KF70.A34
INDEX TO THE CODE OF FEDERAL REGULATIONS. 1977. a. with q. supplements. $745. Congressional Information Service, Part of the Reed Elsevier group, 4520 East-West Hwy., Bethesda, MD 20814-3389. TEL 301-654-1550; 800-638-8380. FAX 301-654-4033. Ed. Lewin Chan. index, cum.index: 1977-79. **Document type:** abstracting/indexing.
Description: Subject and geographic indexes to all 50 Code of Federal Regulations titles.

350 SP
INSTITUTO NACIONAL DE ADMINISTRACION PUBLICA. SERVICIO DE BIBLIOTECA Y DOCUMENTACION. BOLETIN DE INFORMACION BIBLIOGRAFICA. 1959. m. free. Instituto Nacional de Administracion Publica, Servicio de Biblioteca y Documentacion, C. Atocha 106, 28012 Madrid, Spain. Ed. Enrique Orduna Rebollo. **Document type:** bibliography.
Former titles: Instituto Nacional de Administracion Publica. Biblioteca. Boletin Informativo; (until 1977): Antigua Universidad de Cisneros. Instituto Nacional de Administracion Publica. Biblioteca. Boletin Informativo.

350 SZ
INVENTARAUFNAHME DER KANTONALEN DATEN UEBER DIE GESUNDHEITSBERUFE/INVENTAIRE DES DONNEES CANTONALES SUR LES PROFESSIONS DE LA SANTE/INVENTARIO DEI DATI CANTONALI SULLE PROFESSIONI SANITARIE. (Text in French, German, Italian) 1986. biennial. 30 SFr. Bundesamt fuer Statistik, Schwarztorstr. 96, CH-3003 Bern, Switzerland. TEL 031-3236011. FAX 031-3236061. **Document type:** government publication.

IOWA OFFICIAL REGISTER. see *POLITICAL SCIENCE* — *Abstracting, Bibliographies, Statistics*

350 IT
ITALY. ISTITUTO NAZIONALE DI STATISTICA. STATISTICHE SULLA AMMINISTRAZIONE PUBBLICA. irreg. L.21000 (effective 1991). Istituto Nazionale di Statistica, Via Cesare Balbo 16, 00100 Rome, Italy. FAX 06-46735198. **Document type:** government publication.

350 IV ISSN 0444-9746
IVORY COAST. DIRECTION DE LA STATISTIQUE. BULLETIN MENSUEL DE STATISTIQUES. 1948. m. Direction de la Statistique, 01 B.P. V55, Abidjan 01, Ivory Coast. TEL 21-15-38.

070.5950968 SA
J8
JUTA - STATE LIBRARY INDEX TO THE GOVERNMENT GAZETTE. 1979. q. (annual cum.) R.256 (R.168 for annual only). Juta & Co. Ltd., P.O. Box 14373, Kenwyn 7790, South Africa. TEL 27-21-7975101. FAX 27-21-7615010. circ. 504. (also avail. in microfiche from PSL; back issues avail.)
Formerly (until 1990): Government Gazette Index (ISSN 0379-6078).
Description: Alphabetical index of acts, proclamations, regulations, notices and legal advertisements in the Government Gazette of South Africa.

350 SZ
KANTONE UND STAEDTE DER SCHWEIZ/CANTONS ET VILLES SUISSES. (Text in French, German) 1991. a. 34 SFr. Bundesamt fuer Statistik, Schwarztorstr. 96, CH-3003 Bern, Switzerland. TEL 031-3236011. FAX 031-3236061. (also avail. in diskette format) **Document type:** government publication.

352 GW ISSN 0451-4874
KASSELER STATISTIK. 1970. q. Stadt Kassel, Statistisches Amt und Wahlamt, Untere Karlsstr. 8, 34117 Kassel, Germany. TEL 0561-7872299. FAX 0561-7872124.

357 GW ISSN 0933-632X
KOELNER STATISTISCHE NACHRICHTEN. SONDERHEFTE. 1979. irreg. Amt fuer Statistik und Einwohnerwesen, Athener Ring 4, 50765 Cologne, Germany. TEL 0221-221-1887. FAX 0221-2211900. circ. 1,000. (back issues avail.) **Document type:** government publication.

350 KO
KUKHOE HOEUIROK SAEGIN/INDEX TO THE NATIONAL ASSEMBLY DEBATES. Variant title: Kuk Hoe Hoe Eu Rok Saegin. (Text in Korean) 1975. irreg. free. National Assembly Library - Kukhoe Tosogwan, 1 Yoido-dong, Seoul, S. Korea. FAX 02-788-4194. circ. 1,000. **Document type:** abstracting/indexing.

350 016 UK ISSN 0023-6349
L O G A. (Local Government Annotations) 1966. bi-m. £5.90. (Association of London Chief Librarians) Havering Central Library. London Borough, St. Edwards Way, Romford, Essex RM1 3AR, England. Ed. Brian D. Evans. index. circ. 750. **Indexed:** P.A.I.S.
Formerly: LOGA-Local Government Abstracts.

352 GW
LANDESHAUPTSTADT KIEL. VIERTELJAHRESBERICHTE. 1955. q. DM.12. Landeshauptstadt Kiel, Fleethorn 9, 24103 Kiel, Germany. TEL 0431-9011104. circ. 500.

LEGISLATIVE TRENDS; recent acquisitions received in the New York State Library. see *LAW* — *Abstracting, Bibliographies, Statistics*

350 SZ
LIST OF BOOKS AND ARTICLES CATALOGUED. 1965. a. free. Inter-Parliamentary Union, Place du Petit-Saconnex, CH-1211 Geneva 19, Switzerland. TEL 022-7344150. FAX 022-733-3141. TELEX 289784 IPUCH. **Document type:** bibliography.

600 PH
M P W BULLETIN. 1956. q. free. Ministry of Public Works, MPW Bldg., 2nd Fl., Port Area, Manila, Philippines. Ed. Nicolas R. Velas. charts; illus.; stat. circ. 20,000. **Document type:** government publication.
Former titles: D P W & C Bulletin; Manila. Department of Public Works. Communications Technical Statistical Review (ISSN 0040-0998)

330 MM ISSN 0377-4503
MALTA. DEPARTMENT OF INFORMATION. REPORTS ON THE WORKING OF GOVERNMENT DEPARTMENTS. 1905. a. Department of Information, 3 Castille Place, Valletta, Malta. **Document type:** government publication.

015 US ISSN 0195-3443
Z1223.5.M3
MARYLAND DOCUMENTS. 1977. m. $15. Department of Legislative Reference, Legislative Sales, 90 State Circle, Annapolis, MD 21401. TEL 410-841-3885. Ed. Carol A. Carman. circ. 800. **Document type:** government publication.
Description: Lists all state and local publications catalogued by the state's Department of Legislative Reference.

MASSACHUSETTS TAXPAYERS FOUNDATION. STATE BUDGET TRENDS. see *BUSINESS AND ECONOMICS* — *Abstracting, Bibliographies, Statistics*

350 011 AT ISSN 1031-704X
MINISTERIAL DOCUMENT SERVICE. 1973. d. Aus.$1000 for 229 issues. Australian Government Publishing Service, G.P.O. Box 84, Canberra, A.C.T. 2601, Australia. TEL 61-6-295-4411. FAX 61-6-295-4455. TELEX AA62013. bibl.; index, cum.index. **Indexed:** INIS Atomind. **Document type:** government publication, abstracting/indexing.
—CCC.
Supersedes: Commonwealth Record (ISSN 0313-5136); (Until 1976): Australian Government Weekly Digest (ISSN 0312-3545); (Until 1975): Australian Government Digest (ISSN 0310-5229)
Description: Contains ministerial statements about policies and programs, speeches made to national and international forums, media releases regarding proposed and new legislation, major government contracts and more.

015 US ISSN 0091-6633
Z1223.5.M7
MISSOURI STATE GOVERNMENT PUBLICATIONS. 1972. m. $7 (free to state residents). State Library, Box 387, Jefferson City, MO 65102. TEL 314-751-3615. circ. 500. **Document type:** bibliography.
Supersedes: Missouri State Government Documents.

353 016 US ISSN 0362-6830
Z1223
MONTHLY CATALOG OF UNITED STATES GOVERNMENT PUBLICATIONS. m. $229 for print edition (foreign $286.25); microfiche edition $41 (foreign $51.25). U.S. Government Printing Office, Superintendent of Documents, Washington, DC 20402-9341. (Subscr. to: Superintendent of Documents, U.S. Government Printing Office, Box 371954, Pittsburgh, PA 15250-7954. TEL 202-512-1800. FAX 202-512-2250; Or: Bernan, 4611-F Assembly Dr., Lanham, MD 20706.) index. (also avail. in microform from UMI,PMC; microfiche; back issues avail.) **Indexed:** Fluidex. **Document type:** government publication.
•Also available online. Vendor(s): Ovid Technologies, Knight-Ridder, Inc. (File no.66).
Also available on CD-ROM. Producer(s): SilverPlatter Information, Inc., H.W. Wilson.
—BLDSC (5936.000000); Genuine Article; UMI.
Description: Lists publications printed, sold, and distributed to depository libraries by the U.S. Government Printing Office.

350 GW ISSN 0173-8895
MUELHEIMER STATISTIK. 1949. q. DM.16. Amt fuer Statistik und Stadtforschung, Von-Graefe-Str. 37, 45470 Muelheim, Germany. TEL 0208-4557243.

350 016 US
N T I S ALERTS: ADMINISTRATION AND MANAGEMENT. 1974. w. $125 175. U.S. National Technical Information Service, 5285 Port Royal Rd., Springfield, VA 22161. TEL 703-487-4630. FAX 703-321-8547. TELEX 64617. index. (back issues avail.)
Former titles: Abstract Newsletter: Administration and Management; Weekly Abstract Newsletter: Administration and Management; Weekly Government Abstracts. Administration and Management; Weekly Government Abstracts. Administration (ISSN 0364-7986)
Description: Contains summaries of the latest government-sponsored projects and their findings for professionals.

350 SZ ISSN 1012-6325
JN8931
NATIONALRATSWAHLEN (YEAR)/ELECTIONS AU CONSEIL NATIONAL (YEAR). (Text in French and German) 1943. every 4 yrs. 19 SFr. Bundesamt fuer Statistik, Schwarztorstr. 96, CH-3003 Bern, Switzerland. TEL 031-3236011. FAX 031-3236061. **Document type:** government publication.

371.82 US ISSN 0097-9325
HA491
NEBRASKA STATISTICAL HANDBOOK. biennial. $15. Department of Economic Development, Division of Research, Box 94666, Lincoln, NE 68509. TEL 402-471-3111. circ. 1,000. **Indexed:** SRI. **Document type:** government publication.

PUBLIC ADMINISTRATION — ABSTRACTING, BIBLIOGRAPHIES, STATISTICS

324   NE   ISSN 0168-5732
NETHERLANDS. CENTRAAL BUREAU VOOR DE STATISTIEK. STATISTIEK DER VERKIEZINGEN. PROVINCIALE STATEN/NETHERLANDS. CENTRAL BUREAU OF STATISTICS. ELECTION STATISTICS. PROVINCIAL COUNCILS. (Text in Dutch and English) 1946. irreg. Centraal Bureau voor de Statistiek, Prinses Beatrixlaan 428, Voorburg, Netherlands. (Dist. by: SDU - Publishers, Christoffel Plantijnstraat, The Hague, Netherlands) **Document type:** government publication.

015.715   CN   ISSN 0548-4006
NEW BRUNSWICK GOVERNMENT DOCUMENTS/PUBLICATIONS GOUVERNEMENTALES DU NOUVEAU-BRUNSWICK. 1955. a. Legislative Assembly - Assemblee Legislative, Legislative Library, 766 King St., P.O. Box 6000, Fredericton, NB E3B 5H1, Canada. TEL 506-453-2338. FAX 506-453-7154. E-mail: jmcneil@unb.ca. Ed. Janet McNeil. **Document type:** bibliography, government publication.
  Description: Checklist of New Brunswick government documents received at the Legislative Library during the calendar year.

015.715   CN   ISSN 0830-1085
NEW BRUNSWICK GOVERNMENT PUBLICATIONS QUARTERLY LIST/PUBLICATIONS DU GOUVERNEMENT DU NOUVEAU-BRUNSWICK LISTE TRIMESTRIELLE. 1986. q. Government Documents Service, Legislative Library - Service des Publications Gouvernementales, Bibliotheque de l'Assemblee Legislative, P.O. Box 6000, Fredericton, NB E3B 5H1, Canada. TEL 506-453-2338. FAX 506-444-5889. **Document type:** government publication.

352   NO   ISSN 0332-8023
NORWAY. STATISTISK SENTRALBYRAA. KOMMUNESTYREVALGET/NORWAY. CENTRAL BUREAU OF STATISTICS. MUNICIPAL AND COUNTY ELECTIONS. (Subseries of its Norges Offisielle Statistikk) (Text in English and Norwegian) 1902. quadrennial. NOK 75. Statistisk Sentralbyraa, P.O. Box 8131 Dep., N-0033 Oslo 1, Norway. TEL 47-22-864500. FAX 47-22-864976. circ. 2,300. **Document type:** government publication.
  Formerly (until 1975): Norway. Statistisk Sentralbyraa. Kommunevalget (ISSN 0333-0605)

324.6   NO   ISSN 0802-9067
HA1501
NORWAY. STATISTISK SENTRALBYRAA. STORTINGSVALG/NORWAY. CENTRAL BUREAU OF STATISTICS. PARLIAMENTARY ELECTIONS. (Subseries of its Norges Offisiele Statistikk) 1894. quadrennial. NOK 80. Statistisk Sentralbyraa, P.O. Box 8131-Dep., N-0033 Oslo, Norway. TEL 47-22-864500. FAX 47-22-864976. circ. 1,800. **Document type:** government publication.

352   GW   ISSN 0944-1506
NUERNBERGER STATISTIK AKTUELL. 1974. m. Stadt Nuernberg, Amt fuer Stadtforschung und Statistik, Unschlittplatz 7a, 90403 Nuernberg, Germany. TEL 0911-2312843. FAX 0911-2312844. circ. 600. **Document type:** government publication.

350 317   CN   ISSN 0841-0798
ONTARIO PUBLIC SECTOR; of official personnel in federal, provincial and municipal governments in the province of Ontario. 1988. a. Can.$185. 210-2175 Sheppard Ave. E., Willowdale, ON M2J 1W8, Canada. TEL 416-495-0700. FAX 416-495-1887. Ed. B. Hodding; Pub. S.R. Hyman. adv. contact: H.B. Hyman. circ. 2,500. **Document type:** directory.

380   US
HD2767.07
OREGON. PUBLIC UTILITY COMMISSIONER. OREGON UTILITY STATISTICS. 1970. a. free. Public Utility Commissioner, 351 W. Summer St., N.E., Salem, OR 97310-0335. TEL 503-378-4373. FAX 503-373-7752. stat. circ. 350. **Indexed:** SRI.
  Supersedes: Oregon Public Utility Commissioner. Statistics of Electric, Gas, Steam Heat, Telephone, Telegraph and Water Companies (ISSN 0091-6465)

PARLIAMENTARY YEAR BOOK. see *PUBLIC ADMINISTRATION*

PERSONNEL LITERATURE. see *BUSINESS AND ECONOMICS — Abstracting, Bibliographies, Statistics*

PIRMASENS ZAHLEN UND FAKTEN: STATISTISCHE JAHRBUCH STADT PIRMASENS. see *STATISTICS*

350   CN
PROFILE OF ELECTORAL DISTRICTS. irreg. Can.$60. Ministry of Government Services, B C Stats, 553 Superior St., Victoria, BC V8V 1X4, Canada. TEL 604-387-1502. FAX 604-387-0329.
  Description: Provides detailed data on the 75 provincial electoral districts in B.C., based on the most recent Canadian Census data.

659.132094   DK   ISSN 0904-2105
PROVINSENS DISTRIKTSBLADE. (Includes supplement: Daekningsnoeglen) 1973. irreg. DKK 388. Provinsens Distriktsblade, Kastelsvej 7, DK-2100 Copenhagen Oe, Denmark. (looseleaf format)
  Formerly (until 1982): Haandbog for Provinsens Distriktsblade (ISSN 0105-7162)

350 319   QA
QATAR YEARBOOK. (Text in English) 1976. a. free. Ministry of Information & Culture, Information Affairs Department, P.O. Box 5147, Doha, Qatar. TEL 427333. FAX 432850. TELEX 4552 QPRESS DH - DOHA. illus.; stat. circ. 10,000. **Document type:** government publication.
  Description: Covers the various activities of all ministries and public institutions in Qatar, as well as many private sector industrial and commercial enterprises.

352 016   GW   ISSN 0341-2512
Z7164.R33
REFERATEBLATT ZUR RAUMENTWICKLUNG. 1968. q. DM.72. Bundesforschungsanstalt fuer Landeskunde und Raumordnung, Am Michaelshof 8, 53177 Bonn, Germany. TEL 0228-826-0. FAX 0228-826266. Ed. Ingrid Idolski. adv.; abstr.; bibl. circ. 400. (back issues avail.) **Indexed:** P.A.I.S.For.Lang.Ind. **Document type:** abstracting/indexing, government publication.
  Formerly: Referateblatt zur Raumordnung (ISSN 0034-2246)
  Description: Contains abstracts on urban and regional planning, regional geography and housing.

363.6   UK
REGULATORY REVIEW (YEAR). 1993. a. £15 to non-members; members £12 (effective 1994). Chartered Institute of Public Finance and Accountancy, Centre for the Study of Regulated Industries, 3 Robert St., London WC2N 6BH, England. TEL 0171-895-8823. FAX 0171-895-8825. **Document type:** trade publication.
  Description: Reviews the year's important issues concerning the regulation of industries in the U.K.

350   US
REPORTS AND TESTIMONY: (MONTH - YEAR). m. $2 per no. U.S. General Accounting Office, Office of Public Affairs, 441 G St., N.W., Washington, DC 20548-0001. TEL 202-512-4448. (Subscr. to: U.S. General Accounting Office, Box 6015, Gaithersburg, MD 20884-6015. TEL 202-512-6000. FAX 301-258-4066) **Document type:** government publication.
  Description: Summarizes reports available through G.A.O.

016 350   US
REVIEW - S W A P.* (Sharing with a Purpose) 1972. bi-m. free. American Society for Public Administration, Section on Personnel Administration and Labor Relations, Rider College, Graduate Program for Administrators, 1120 G St., N.W., Ste. 500, Washington, DC 20005. Ed. Jack Rabin. bk.rev.; abstr. circ. 2,200. **Document type:** abstracting/indexing.
  Formerly: S W A P.
  Description: Abstracts of civil service literature relating to personnel selection research.

352   GW   ISSN 0174-2914
RHEINLAND-PFALZ. STATISTISCHES LANDESAMT RHEINLAND-PFALZ. STATISTISCHE MONATSHEFTE. 1958. m. DM.40. Statistisches Landesamt Rheinland-Pfalz, Postfach, 56130 Bad Ems, Germany. TEL 02603-71245. stat. (back issues avail.)

352   GW   ISSN 0174-2876
RHEINLAND-PFALZ HEUTE. 1977. a. DM.1. Statistisches Landesamt Rheinland-Pfalz, Postfach, 56130 Bad Ems, Germany. TEL 02603-71245. stat. (back issues avail.)

350 016   UK   ISSN 0140-4768
HN49.C6
RURAL DEVELOPMENT ABSTRACTS. 1978. q. £160($290) (effective 1996). CAB International, Wallingford, Oxon. OX10 8DE, England. TEL 01491-832111. FAX 01491-833508. TELEX 847964 COMAGG G. E-mail: cabi@cabi.org. (U.S. subscr. to: CAB International, North American Office, 845 N. Park Ave., Tucson, AZ 85719. TEL 800-528-4841) circ. 500. (also avail. in diskette format; back issues avail.) **Indexed:** E.I. **Document type:** abstracting/indexing.
  ●Also available online. Vendor(s): CISTI, DIMDI, European Space Agency, Knight-Ridder, Inc., Ovid Technologies (ECON).
  —BLDSC (8052.422200).
  Description: Contains abstracts from world literature relating to main aspects of rural development in the Third World.

750   US   ISSN 0094-6958
JA1
SAGE PUBLIC ADMINISTRATION ABSTRACTS. 1974. q. $108 to individuals; institutions $325 (effective Sep. 1995). Sage Publications, Inc., 2455 Teller Rd., Thousand Oaks, CA 91320. TEL 805-499-0721. FAX 805-499-0871. E-mail: libraries@sagepub.com. (Overseas subscr. to: Sage Publications Ltd., 6 Bonhill St., London EC2A 4PU, England; Sage Publications India Pvt. Ltd., P.O. Box 4215, New Delhi 110 048, India) Ed. Paul McDowell. adv.; index. circ. 750. (back issues avail.; reprint service avail.) **Document type:** abstracting/indexing.
  —UMI. **CCC.**
  Description: Abstracts articles from the recent literature on all aspects of public administration.

319   SE
SEYCHELLES. DEPARTMENT OF FINANCE. NATIONAL ACCOUNTS. a. R.5. Department of Finance, Statistics Division, P.O. Box 206, Independence House, Victoria, Republic of Seychelles.

350   SI   ISSN 0129-9786
HD9987.S57
SINGAPORE. DEPARTMENT OF STATISTICS. REPORT ON THE SURVEY OF SERVICES (YEAR). a. S.$20.40. Department of Statistics, 8 Shenton Way 10-01 Treasury Bldg., Singapore 0106, Singapore. TEL 3209702. FAX 3209689. TELEX RS 63001 STAT. **Document type:** government publication.

316.8   SA
SOUTH AFRICA. CENTRAL STATISTICAL SERVICE. FINAL SOCIAL ACCOUNTING MATRIX FOR SOUTH AFRICA. (Report No. 04-03-02) irreg., latest 1988. R.6 (foreign R.6.60) (diskette R.15). Central Statistical Service - Sentrale Statistiekdiens, Private Bag X44, Pretoria 0001, South Africa. TEL 27-12-310-8911. (Orders to: Government Printing Works, Private Bag X85, Pretoria 0001, South Africa) (also avail. in diskette format) **Document type:** government publication.

352.1 316.8   SA
SOUTH AFRICA. CENTRAL STATISTICAL SERVICE. FINANCIAL STATISTICS OF LOCAL GOVERNMENTS. (Report No. 91-14-01) irreg., latest for years 1988-1989. R.11 (foreign R.13.75). Central Statistical Service - Sentrale Statistiekdiens, Private Bag X44, Pretoria 0001, South Africa. TEL 27-12-310-8911. FAX 27-12-310-8500. (Orders to: Government Printing Works, Private Bag X85, Pretoria 0001, South Africa) **Document type:** government publication.

352   SA
SOUTH AFRICA. CENTRAL STATISTICAL SERVICE. LOCAL GOVERNMENT STATISTICS. (Report No. 91-05-01) a., latest 1987. R.4.40 (foreign R.5.50). Central Statistical Service - Sentrale Statistiekdiens, Private Bag X44, Pretoria 0001, South Africa. TEL 27-12-310-8911. FAX 27-12-310-8500. (Orders to: Government Printing Works, Private Bag X85, Pretoria 0001, South Africa) **Document type:** government publication.
  Formerly: South Africa. Department of Statistics. Local Government Statistics.

PUBLIC ADMINISTRATION — ABSTRACTING, BIBLIOGRAPHIES, STATISTICS

351.7 316.8   SA
SOUTH AFRICA. CENTRAL STATISTICAL SERVICE. STATISTICAL RELEASE. CENTRAL GOVERNMENT: REVENUE OF THE STATE REVENUE AND OTHER REVENUE ACCOUNTS. (No. P9119.1) a. free. Central Statistical Service - Sentrale Statistiekdiens, Private Bag X44, Pretoria 0001, South Africa. TEL 27-12-310-8911. FAX 27-12-310-8500. **Document type:** government publication.

351.7 316.8   SA
SOUTH AFRICA. CENTRAL STATISTICAL SERVICE. STATISTICAL RELEASE. EXCHEQUER ACCOUNT - FINAL. (No. P9151.2) m. free. Central Statistical Service - Sentrale Statistiekdiens, Private Bag X44, Pretoria 0001, South Africa. TEL 27-12-310-8911. FAX 27-12-310-8500. **Document type:** government publication.

351.7 316.8   SA
SOUTH AFRICA. CENTRAL STATISTICAL SERVICE. STATISTICAL RELEASE. EXCHEQUER ACCOUNT (FIRST PUBLICATION). (No. P9151.1) m. free. Central Statistical Service - Sentrale Statistiekdiens, Private Bag X44, Pretoria 0001, South Africa. TEL 27-12-310-8911. FAX 27-12-310-8500. **Document type:** government publication.

351.7 316.8   SA
SOUTH AFRICA. CENTRAL STATISTICAL SERVICE. STATISTICAL RELEASE. EXPENDITURE BY THE GENERAL GOVERNMENT. (No. P9141) a., latest for years 1990-1991. free. Central Statistical Service - Sentrale Statistiekdiens, Private Bag X44, Pretoria 0001, South Africa. TEL 27-12-310-8911. FAX 27-12-310-8500. **Document type:** government publication.
Description: Economic and functional classification of the consolidated expenditure by the total general government sector.

351.7 316.8   SA
SOUTH AFRICA. CENTRAL STATISTICAL SERVICE. STATISTICAL RELEASE. EXPENDITURE OF THE CENTRAL GOVERNMENT. (No. P9141.2) a., latest for years 1991-1992. free. Central Statistical Service - Sentrale Statistiekdiens, Private Bag X44, Pretoria 0001, South Africa. TEL 27-12-310-8911. FAX 27-12-310-8500. **Document type:** government publication.

352.1 316.8   SA
SOUTH AFRICA. CENTRAL STATISTICAL SERVICE. STATISTICAL RELEASE. FINANCIAL STATISTICS OF BLACK LOCAL AUTHORITIES. (No. P9107.1) a., latest for years 1988-1989. free. Central Statistical Service - Sentral Statistiekdiens, Private Bag X44, Pretoria 0001, South Africa. TEL 27-12-310-8911. FAX 27-12-310-8500. **Document type:** government publication.
Formerly: South Africa. Central Statistical Service. Statistical News Release. Statistics of Local Authorities for Blacks.

352.1 316.8   SA
SOUTH AFRICA. CENTRAL STATISTICAL SERVICE. STATISTICAL RELEASE. FINANCIAL STATISTICS OF LOCAL AUTHORITIES AND REGIONAL SERVICES COUNCILS AND JOINT SERVICES BOARDS. (No. P9144) q. free. Central Statistical Service - Sentrale Statistiekdiens, Private Bag X44, Pretoria 0001, South Africa. TEL 27-12-310-8911. FAX 27-12-310-8500. **Document type:** government publication.

352.1 316.8   SA
SOUTH AFRICA. CENTRAL STATISTICAL SERVICE. STATISTICAL RELEASE. FINANCIAL STATISTICS OF LOCAL GOVERNMENTS (YEAR). (No. P9114.1) irreg., latest for years 1988-1989. free. Central Statistical Service - Sentrale Statistiekdiens, Private Bag X44, Pretoria 0001, South Africa. TEL 27-12-310-8911. FAX 27-12-310-8500. **Document type:** government publication.

352.1 316.8   SA
SOUTH AFRICA. CENTRAL STATISTICAL SERVICE. STATISTICAL RELEASE. FINANCIAL STATISTICS OF PROVINCIAL ADMINISTRATIONS. (No. P9142.2) a. free. Central Statistical Service - Sentrale Statistiekdiens, Private Bag X44, Pretoria 0001, South Africa. TEL 27-12-310-8911. FAX 27-12-310-8500. **Document type:** government publication.

352.1   SA
SOUTH AFRICA. CENTRAL STATISTICAL SERVICE. STATISTICAL RELEASE. STATISTICS OF DEVELOPMENT BOARDS. (No. P9107) irreg., latest for years 1984-1986. free. Central Statistical Service - Sentrale Statistiekdiens, Private Bag X44, Pretoria 0001, South Africa. TEL 27-12-310-8911. FAX 27-12-310-8500. **Document type:** government publication.
Supersedes (in 1986): South Africa. Central Statistical Service. Statistics of Development Boards; Which was formerly: South Africa. Department of Statistics. Statistics of Administration Boards; (until 1977): South Africa. Department of Statistics. Statistics of Bantu Affairs Administration Boards.

352.1 316.8   SA
SOUTH AFRICA. CENTRAL STATISTICAL SERVICE. STATISTICAL RELEASE. STATISTICS OF DEVELOPMENT BOARDS. (No. P9107) irreg. free. Central Statistical Service - Sentrale Statistiekdiens, Private Bag X44, Pretoria 0001, South Africa. TEL 27-12-310-8911. FAX 27-12-310-8500. **Document type:** government publication.

352.1 316.8   SA
SOUTH AFRICA. CENTRAL STATISTICAL SERVICE. STATISTICS OF DIVISIONAL COUNCILS. (Report No. 91-06-01) a., latest 1989. R.4.40 (foreign R.5.50). Central Statistical Service - Sentrale Statistiekdiens, Private Bag X44, Pretoria 0001, South Africa. TEL 27-12-310-8911. FAX 27-12-310-8500. (Orders to: Government Printing Works, Private Bag X85, Pretoria 0001, South Africa) **Document type:** government publication.

350   GW
STADT DUISBURG. DATEN UND INFORMATION. 1975. irreg. Amt fuer Statistik, Stadtforschung und Europaangelegenheiten, Der Oberstadtdirektor, 47049 Duisburg, Germany. TEL 0203-283-3085. FAX 0203-2834404. circ. 600. (back issues avail.) **Document type:** government publication.
Formerly: Duisburg. Amt fuer Statistik und Stadtforschung. Daten und Information (ISSN 0172-4541)

352   GW   ISSN 0940-9009
STADT DUISBURG. MATERIALEN ZUR STADTFORSCHUNG. 1977. irreg. Amt fuer Statistik, Stadtforschung und Europaangelegenheiten, Der Oberstadtdirektor, 47049 Duisburg, Germany. TEL 0203-2833085. FAX 0203-2834404. **Document type:** government publication.

350   GW   ISSN 0172-4533
STADT DUISBURG. STATISTISCHES JAHRBUCH. 1951. a. Amt fuer Statistik, Stadtforschung und Europaangelegenheiten, Der Oberstadtdirektor, 47049 Duisburg, Germany. TEL 0203-2833085. FAX 0203-2834404. **Document type:** government publication.

350   GW   ISSN 0946-4883
▼**STADT DUISBURG. WAHLEN (YEAR).** 1994. irreg. Amt fuer Statistik, Stadtforschung und Europaangelegenheiten, Der Oberstadtdirektor, 47049 Duisburg, Germany. TEL 0203-2833085. FAX 0203-2834404. **Document type:** government publication.

352
STADT FREIBURG IM BREISGAU. AMT FUER STATISTIK UND EINWOHNERWESEN. JAHRESHEFT. 1977. a. DM.18. Amt fuer Statistik und Einwohnerwesen, Wilhelmstr. 20A, 79098 Freiburg im Breisgau, Germany. FAX 0761-2013299. stat. circ. 400. (back issues avail.) **Document type:** government publication.
Description: Studies the development of social and economic life within municipality of Freiburg.

352   GW
STADT MANNHEIM. VIERTELJAHRESBERICHT. 1972. q. DM.8. Stadt Mannheim, Amt fuer Statistik und Stadtforschung, Postfach 103051, 68030 Mannheim, Germany. TEL 0621-2933810. FAX 0621-2932868. (back issues avail.)

350   GW   ISSN 0934-5868
HT110
STADTFORSCHUNG UND STATISTIK; Zeitschrift des Verbandes Deutscher Staedtestatistiker. 1987. s-a. DM.28. Verband Deutscher Staedtestatistiker, c/o Stadt Oberhausen, Bereich Statistik und Wahlen, 46045 Oberhausen, Germany. TEL 0208-8252387. FAX 0208-8255120. Ed. Horst-Juergen Wienen. adv. contact: Hubert Harfst. **Document type:** corporate report.

353.9   US
STATISTICAL REVIEW OF GOVERNMENT IN UTAH. 1958. a. $11. Utah Foundation, 10 W. 100 S., No. 323, Salt Lake City, UT 84101-1544. TEL 801-364-1837. Ed. Michael Christensen. circ. 1,000. (also avail. in microfiche from CIS) **Indexed:** SRI.
Description: Contains most-used financial and statistical information about state and local governments in Utah.

352 310   CN   ISSN 0702-0988
HJ9014.B7
STATISTICS RELATING TO REGIONAL AND MUNICIPAL GOVERNMENTS IN BRITISH COLUMBIA. a. Can.$15.45. Ministry of Municipal Affairs, Recreation and Housing, Victoria, B.C., Canada. (Subscr. to: Crown Publications, 546 Yates St., Victoria, B.C. V8W 1K8, Canada. TEL 604-386-4636)
Description: Provides statistics on population, area of districts, incorporation dates and financial information.

350   SZ
STATISTISCHE INFORMATION/INFORMATIONS STATISTIQUES. (Text in French, German) 1986. a. free. Bundesamt fuer Statistik, Schwarztorstr. 96, CH-3003 Bern, Switzerland. TEL 031-3236011. FAX 031-3236061. **Document type:** government publication.
Formerly: Publikationsverzeichnis.

352 310   GW   ISSN 0947-7373
STATISTISCHE MONATSHEFTE SCHLESWIG-HOLSTEIN. 1948. m. DM.40. Statistisches Landesamt Schleswig-Holstein, Froebelstr. 15-17, 24113 Kiel, Germany. TEL 0431-6895-0. FAX 0431-6895698. bk.rev. circ. 650. **Document type:** government publication.

352 352.7 330.9   GW   ISSN 0944-1492
STATISTISCHE NACHRICHTEN DER STADT NUERNBERG. 1946. q. Amt fuer Stadtforschung und Statistik, Unschlittplatz 7a, 90403 Nuernberg, Germany. TEL 0911-2312843. Ed.Bd. circ. 700. (back issues avail.) **Document type:** government publication.
Description: Reports on population, housing, local economy, education and welfare.

352 310   GW
STATISTISCHER BERICHT DER STADT FRANKENTHAL. 1965. a. Stadtverwaltung Frankenthal, Postfach 2023, 67225 Frankenthal, Germany. TEL 06233-89-0. FAX 06233-89400. TELEX 465232-STFT-D. (back issues avail.) **Document type:** government publication.
Description: Provides statistical data about the city of Frankenthal.

352 310   GW   ISSN 0930-3782
STATISTISCHER VIERTELJAHRESBERICHT HANNOVER. 1896. q. DM.55. Landeshauptstadt Hannover, Abteilung Statistik, Prinzenstr. 6, 30159 Hannover, Germany. TEL 0511-1682422. FAX 0511-1685129. circ. 2,400. (back issues avail.) **Document type:** government publication.

352 310   GW   ISSN 0178-160X
STATISTISCHES JAHRBUCH DER STADT KOELN. 1911. a. DM.30. Amt fuer Statistik und Einwohnerwesen, Athener Ring 4, 50765 Cologne, Germany. TEL 0221-2211887. FAX 0221-2211900. **Document type:** government publication.

352 352.7 330.9   GW   ISSN 0944-1514
STATISTISCHES JAHRBUCH DER STADT NUERNBERG. 1977. a. DM.30. Amt fuer Stadtforschung und Statistik, Unschlittplatz 7a, 90403 Nuernberg, Germany. TEL 0911-2312843. stat. circ. 750. (back issues avail.) **Document type:** government publication.
Description: Contains tables on population, housing, local economy, education and welfare, plus selected data on the metropolitan area.

PUBLIC ADMINISTRATION — COMPUTER APPLICATIONS

352 310   GW   ISSN 0081-5349
STATISTISCHES JAHRBUCH DEUTSCHER GEMEINDEN. 1890. a. DM.120. Deutscher Staedtetag, Lindenallee 13-17, 50942 Cologne, Germany. TEL 0221-3771-155. FAX 0221-3771-128. **Document type:** abstracting/indexing.

314   DK   ISSN 0107-6744
HA1489.C6
STATISTISK TIAARS-OVERSIGT FOR KOEBENHAVNS KOMMUNE. English edition: Statistical Ten-Year Review of the Municipality of Copenhagen. 1981. biennial. DKK 20. Statistisk Kontor, Vester Voldgade 87, 1552 Copenhagen V, Denmark. illus.

315.61   TU
TURKEY. DEVLET ISTATISTIK ENSTITUSU. BUTCELER - BELEDIYELER, IL OZEL IDARLER VE KOYLER/TURKEY. STATE INSTITUTE OF STATISTICS. BUDGETS - MUNICIPAL AND SPECIAL PROVINCIAL ADMINISTRATIONS AND VILLAGES. (Text in English, Turkish) 1931. a., latest 1990. $25. Devlet Istatistik Enstitusu - State Institute of Statistics, Necatibey Caddesi No. 114, 06100 Ankara, Turkey. TEL 90-312-4185027. FAX 90-312-4170432. circ. 1,028. **Document type:** government publication.

315.61   TU
TURKEY. DEVLET ISTATISTIK ENSTITUSU. KESIN HESAPLAR - BELEDIYELER VE IL OZEL IDARELERI/TURKEY. STATE INSTITUTE OF STATISTICS. FINAL ACCOUNTS - MUNICIPALITIES AND SPECIAL PROVINCIAL ADMINISTRATIONS. (Text in Turkish) 1969. a., latest 1990. $25. Devlet Istatistik Enstitusu - State Institute of Statistics, Necatibey Caddesi No. 114, 06100 Ankara, Turkey. TEL 90-312-4185027. FAX 90-312-4170432. circ. 1,030. **Document type:** government publication.

TURKEY. DEVLET ISTATISTIK ENSTITUSU. MAHALLI IDARELER SECIMI SONUCLARI/TURKEY. STATE INSTITUTE OF STATISTICS. RESULTS OF ELECTIONS OF LOCAL ADMINISTRATIONS. see *POLITICAL SCIENCE — Abstracting, Bibliographies, Statistics*

THE U K REGULATED INDUSTRIES: FINANCIAL FACTS (YEAR). see *BUSINESS AND ECONOMICS — Abstracting, Bibliographies, Statistics*

THE U K WATER INDUSTRY: CHARGES FOR WATER SERVICES (YEAR). see *WATER RESOURCES — Abstracting, Bibliographies, Statistics*

THE U K WATER INDUSTRY: WATER SERVICES & COSTS (YEAR). see *WATER RESOURCES — Abstracting, Bibliographies, Statistics*

U S GOVERNMENT PERIODICALS INDEX. see *ABSTRACTING AND INDEXING SERVICES*

333   US   ISSN 0082-9110
HD183
U.S. BUREAU OF LAND MANAGEMENT. PUBLIC LAND STATISTICS. Key Title: Public Land Statistics. 1816. a. $3.75. U.S. Department of the Interior, Bureau of Land Management, Branch of Records and Library, Denver Service Center (D-553B), Denver Federal Center, Bldg. 50, Box 25047, Denver, CO 80225-0047. TEL 303-236-6638. (Avail. from: Superintendent of Documents, U.S. Government Printing Office, Box 371954, Pittsburgh, PA 15250-7954. TEL 202-783-3238. FAX 202-512-2233) Ed. R.E. Woerner. stat. circ. 4,000. (also avail. in microfiche) **Document type:** government publication.

350 016   US   ISSN 0364-8265
U.S. GENERAL ACCOUNTING OFFICE. MONTHLY LIST OF G A O REPORTS. vol.18, no.10, 1984. m. free to qualified personnel. U.S. General Accounting Office, Office of Public Affairs, Box 6015, Gaithersburg, MD 20877. TEL 202-275-6241. bibl. **Document type:** government publication.
   Description: Includes legal decisions and opinions of the U.S. Comptroller General.

353 015   US   ISSN 0027-0288
Z1223.5.A1
U.S. LIBRARY OF CONGRESS. MONTHLY CHECKLIST OF STATE PUBLICATIONS. 1910. m. $32 (foreign $40) (free to U.S. agencies that send state publications to L.C. Exchange annd Gift Division). U.S. Library of Congress, Exchange and Gift Division, Washington, DC 20540. TEL 202-707-9468. (Subscr. to: Superintendent of Documents, U.S. Government Printing Office, Box 371954, Pittsburgh, PA 15250-7954. TEL 202-783-3238. FAX 202-512-2233) index. circ. 5,000. **Document type:** bibliography, government publication.
  —UMI.
  Supersedes: Monthly List of State Publications (ISSN 0090-0087)

350 614.7 011   UK
URBAN ABSTRACTS. 1974. 12/yr. £102 (overseas £117). London Research Centre, Research Library, 81 Black Prince Rd., London SE1 7SZ, England. TEL 0171-735-4250. FAX 0171-627-9606. Ed. Jennifer Binnie. adv. contact: Annabel Davies. circ. 700. (back issues avail.) **Document type:** abstracting/indexing.
  ●Also available online. Vendor(s): European Space Agency.
  Also available on CD-ROM.
  —BLDSC (9123.146000).
  Formerly issued as two parts: Urban Abstracts Series 1: Policy; Urban Abstracts Series 2: Technical; Which superseded in part: Urban Abstracts (ISSN 0305-103X)
  Description: Examines new books, reports, and journal articles about urban affairs.

352   US   ISSN 0300-6859
HT123
URBAN AFFAIRS ABSTRACTS. 1971. m. (with a. cumulation). $300 (city governments & agencies $250; outside US $350) (effective 1995). (National League of Cities) Center for Urban and Economic Research, College of Business Administration, University of Louisville, Louisville, KY 40292. TEL 502-852-6626. Ed. Vernon Smith. bibl.; index. circ. 400. (processed) **Document type:** abstracting/indexing.
  Description: Summarizes articles about urban affairs from over 300 journals.

352   UK   ISSN 0140-4482
HJ9041
WELSH LOCAL GOVERNMENT FINANCIAL STATISTICS. 1977. a. Welsh Office, Statistical Directorate, New Crown Bldg., Cathays Park, Cardiff CF1 3NQ, Wales. TEL 01222-825054. FAX 01222-825350. **Document type:** government publication.
  —BLDSC (9294.660000).

350 015   US   ISSN 0364-507X
Z1223.5.W6
WISCONSIN PUBLIC DOCUMENTS. 1916. q. free. State Historical Society of Wisconsin, 816 State St., Madison, WI 53706. TEL 608-264-6527. Ed. Janet Monk. index. circ. 500. (also avail. in microfiche from BHP) **Document type:** newsletter.

350   SZ
WORLD-WIDE BIBLIOGRAPHY ON PARLIAMENTS. 1978. triennial. 48 SFr. Inter-Parliamentary Union, Place du Petit-Saconnex, CH-1211 Geneva, Switzerland. TEL 022-7344150. FAX 022-7333141. TELEX 414217-IPU-CH. **Document type:** monographic series.

350 314   YU
YUGOSLAVIA. SAVEZNI ZAVOD ZA STATISTIKU. KOMUNALNI FONDOVI U GRADSKIM NASELJIMA. (Subseries of: Statisticki Bilten) irreg. 4 din. Savezni Zavod za Statistiku, Kneza Milosa 20, Belgrade, Yugoslavia. TEL 38-11-681999. **Document type:** government publication.

350 316   ZA
ZAMBIA. CENTRAL STATISTICAL OFFICE. FINANCIAL STATISTICS OF GOVERNMENT SECTOR (ECONOMIC AND FUNCTIONAL ANALYSIS). 1964. a. $4.50. Central Statistical Office, P.O. Box 31908, Lusaka, Zambia. TEL 260-1-211231. **Document type:** government publication.
  Formerly: Zambia. Central Statistical Office. Government Sector Accounts (Economic and Functional Analysis) (ISSN 0084-4527)

PUBLIC ADMINISTRATION — Computer Applications

ADMINISTRATORS' COMPUTER LETTER. see *EDUCATION — School Organization And Administration*

350   FR
BANQUES DE DONNEES UTILES AUX COLLECTIVITES LOCALES ET TERRITORIALES. 1989. irreg. 498.12 per no. Editions F L A Consultants, 27 rue de la Vistule, 75013 Paris, France. TEL 45-82-75-75. FAX 45-82-46-04. Eds. Beatrice Riou, Francois Libmann. **Document type:** directory.
  Description: Presents databases useful to local and regional public bodies and the companies and organizations dealing with them.

COMPUTERS, ENVIRONMENT AND URBAN SYSTEMS; an international journal. see *ENVIRONMENTAL STUDIES — Computer Applications*

350 001.6 621.381   US   ISSN 0893-052X
FEDERAL COMPUTER WEEK; the newspaper for the government systems community. 1987. w. (36/yr.). $95. I D G Communications - F C W Publishing, 3110 Fairview Park Dr., Ste. 1040, Falls Church, VA 22042-4599. TEL 703-876-5100. FAX 703-876-5126. Ed. Anne A. Armstrong. adv.; bk.rev. circ. 64,000. (tabloid format) **Indexed:** Comput.Dtbs., Tel.Abstr., Tel.Alert. **Document type:** newspaper.
  —BLDSC (3901.873900); UMI.
  Description: Covers the government's use of information technology and the policy governing its acquisition.

350   US   ISSN 0738-4300
GOVERNMENT COMPUTER NEWS; the newspaper serving computer users throughout the Federal Government. 1982. 26/yr. $95.90 (Canada $129.90; Mexico $119.90; elsewhere $169.90); free to qualified personnel. Cahners Publishing Company (Silver Spring), Division of Reed Elsevier Inc., 8601 Georgia Ave., Ste. 300, Silver Spring, MD 20910. TEL 301-650-2000. FAX 301-650-2111. (Subscr. to: 44 Cook St., Denver, CO 80206-5800. TEL 800-662-7776) Ed. Thomas R. Temin; Pub. Gary R. Squires. adv.; bk.rev. circ. 80,298. (tabloid format; also avail. in microform from UMI) **Indexed:** CAD CAM Abstr., Comput.Dtbs., Comput.Lit.Ind., PCR2, Pers.Lit., Tel.Abstr., Tel.Alert. **Document type:** newspaper, trade publication.
  ●Also available online. Vendor(s): Knight-Ridder, Inc. Also available on CD-ROM.
  —BLDSC (4203.928000); UMI. **CCC.**
  Description: For computer managers and professionals associated with computer products and services in the Federal government. Provides information on the latest technologies, computer graphics, office automation and management.

350   UN
GOVERNMENT COMPUTERIZATION NEWSLETTER. s-a. United Nations Economic and Social Commission for Asia and the Pacific (ESCAP), Statistics Division, United Nations Bldg., Rajadamnern Ave., Bangkok 10200, Thailand. TEL 2829161. FAX 2829602. **Document type:** newsletter.

350   UK   ISSN 0951-7537
GOVERNMENT COMPUTING AND INFORMATION MANAGEMENT. 1987. 10/yr. £48 (foreign £55) (effective 1996). Government Group Publications, Southbank House, Black Prince Rd., London SE1 7SJ, England. TEL 0171-582-9191. FAX 0171-587-1810. E-mail: gov.group@dial.pipex.com. (Subscr. to: 5 Woodland Grove, Weybridge, Surrey KT13 9EQ, England) Ed. Peter Springett; Pub. Phil Windsor. adv.; bk.rev.; circ. 11,445 (controlled). (back issues avail.) **Document type:** bulletin.
  —BLDSC (4203.935200).
  Formerly (until May 1994): Government Computing.
  Description: Fosters debate between and among central government and computer industry professionals on the effective application and procurement of information technology, information services, information management, and communications in providing public services.

GOVERNMENT IMAGING; the national newspaper for government imaging technology. see *COMMUNICATIONS — Video*

PUBLIC ADMINISTRATION — MUNICIPAL GOVERNMENT

350   US   ISSN 1043-9668
JK2445.A8
GOVERNMENT TECHNOLOGY; solutions for state and local government in the information age. 1987. m. free to qualified personnel. G T Publications, Inc., 9719 Lincoln Village Dr., No. 500, Sacramento, CA 95827-3303. TEL 916-363-5000. FAX 916-363-5197. Ed. Dennis McKenna. adv. contact: Sherese Graves. circ. 56,000 (controlled). (tabloid format) **Document type:** trade publication.
    Description: For executives in state, county and local government involved in buying, managing and using information technology. Emphasis is on governmental applications of computer and telecommunications technologies.

350 384   NE   ISSN 0928-9038
INFORMATIZATION DEVELOPMENTS AND THE PUBLIC SECTOR. (Text in English) 1990. irreg., vol.3, 1995. price varies. I O S Press, Van Diemenstraat 94, 1013 CN Amsterdam, Netherlands. TEL 31-20-6382189. FAX 31-20-6203419. E-mail: marie-louise.kok@ios.nl. (In N. America: Box 10558, Burke, VA 22009-0558. TEL 703-323-5554. FAX 703-250-4705) **Document type:** monographic series.
    Description: Covers developments in informatization policies and the effect of informatization on public administration.

J I C S T ONLINE INFORMATION SYSTEM. (Japanese Information Center of Science and Technology) see *SCIENCES: COMPREHENSIVE WORKS — Computer Applications*

350   FR   ISSN 0768-9136
LETTRE INFORMATIQUE ET COLLECTIVITES LOCALES. 1985. bi-m. 1750 F. (foreign 1780 F.). Publications du Moniteur, 17 rue d'Uzes, 75002 Paris, France. TEL 1-40-13-30-30. FAX 1-40-26-20-94. TELEX UPRESSE 680876F. Ed. Hubert d'Erceville. circ. 800.

THE S I G C A T FOUNDATION COMPENDIUM OF C D - R O MS. (Special Interest Group on C D - R O M Applications & Technology) see *BIBLIOGRAPHIES*

SOCIAL SCIENCE COMPUTER REVIEW. see *EDUCATION — Computer Applications*

350   CN
▼**TECHNOLOGY IN GOVERNMENT;** the journal for managers and users of information systems in government. 1994. 5/yr. Can.$80 (in US Can.$115, elsewhere Can.$155). Plesman Publications Ltd., 2005 Sheppard Ave. E., 4th Fl., Willowdale, ON M2J 5B1, Canada. TEL 416-497-9562. FAX 416-497-9427. adv.: B&W page Can.$5100, color page Can.$6195; trim 10 3/4 x 15. circ. 25,000. (tabloid format)

350   CN
TRAFFIC REPORT/NOUVELLE OPTIQUE. (Text in English, French) bi-w. free. Department of Economic Development and Tourism, P.O. Box 6000, Fredericton, NB E3B 5H1, Canada. TEL 506-457-7340. E-mail: mauricel@gov.nb.ca. Ed. Maurice Lavigne. (avail. by fax) **Document type:** government publication.
    ●Also available online.
    Description: Discusses the latest technology available in the New Brunswick area.

350 333.7   US   ISSN 1066-8756
WISCONSIN LAND INFORMATION NEWSLETTER. 1984. s-a. free. University of Wisconsin-Madison, Land Information & Computer Graphics Facility, B102 Steenbock Library, 550 Babcock Dr., Madison, WI 53706. TEL 608-263-5534. FAX 608-262-2500. E-mail: LICGF@macc.wisc.edu. Ed. Bernard J. Niemann, Jr. bk.rev.; circ. 13,000 (controlled). **Document type:** academic/scholarly publication.
    Description: Aims to inform land records users and professionals; local, state, and federal policymakers; utilities; private-sector professionals about the most recent research activities, results, and applications pertaining to land records automation, integration, and modernization.

PUBLIC ADMINISTRATION — Municipal Government

see also Housing and Urban Planning

352   US   ISSN 1062-6514
A A C O G REGION. 1974. m. free. Alamo Area Council of Governments, 118 Broadway, Ste. 400, San Antonio, TX 78205. TEL 210-225-5201. FAX 210-225-5937. Ed. Nancy A. Roth-Roffy. illus. circ. 3,500. **Document type:** newsletter.
    Supersedes: A A C O G Newsletter; Which was formerly: A A C O G Highlights.

352   UK
A D C REVIEW. 1895. bi-m. £10.20 (overseas £15) (effective Apr. 1995). Association of District Councils, 26 Chapter St., London SW1P 4ND, England. TEL 0171-233-6868. FAX 0171-233-6551. Ed. Antony Roberts. adv.; bk.rev.; illus.; stat.; index; circ. 6,500 (paid). **Indexed:** Geo.Abstr., RICS.
    —BLDSC (7785.944500).
    Formerly: D C R. District Councils Review (ISSN 0953-4784); (until 1988): District Councils Review (ISSN 0306-3240); (until 1972): Rural District Review (ISSN 0036-0015)

A R C ACTION. (Atlanta Regional Commission) see *HOUSING AND URBAN PLANNING*

ACROSS THE TABLE. see *BUSINESS AND ECONOMICS — Labor And Industrial Relations*

AGENDA (NEW BRUNSWICK). see *COLLEGE AND ALUMNI*

352 336   US
ALABAMA. DEPARTMENT OF REVENUE. ANNUAL REPORT. 1985. a. free. Department of Revenue, Commissioner's Office, Box 327001, Montgomery, AL 36132-7001. TEL 334-242-1175. FAX 334-242-0550. Ed. Carla A. Snellgrove. circ. 1,000. **Document type:** government publication.
    Description: Provides a four-year compilation of state taxes and fees collected by the Revenue Dept.

352 336   US
ALABAMA. DEPARTMENT OF REVENUE. GENERAL SUMMARY OF STATE TAXES. 1985. a. free. Department of Revenue, Commissioner's Office, Box 327001, Montgomery, AL 36132-7001. TEL 334-242-1175. FAX 334-242-0550. Ed. Carla A. Snellgrove. **Document type:** government publication.
    Description: Provides a summary of state taxes and fees administered by the Revenue Department.

352 336   US
ALABAMA. DEPARTMENT OF REVENUE. REVENUE REVIEW NEWSLETTER. 1985. q. free. Department of Revenue, Commissioner's Office, Box 327001, Montgomery, AL 36132-7001. TEL 334-242-1390. FAX 334-242-0550. Ed. Carolyn Blackstock. circ. 5,300. **Document type:** government publication, newsletter.
    Description: Standard features include the Department of Revenue's administrative rules and regulations, an abstract of taxes administered by the department, and a tax calendar of both required monthly and quarterly - annual tax activity.

352   US   ISSN 0002-4309
ALABAMA MUNICIPAL JOURNAL. 1943. m. $12. Alabama League of Municipalities, 535 Adams Ave., Box 1270, Montgomery, AL 36102. TEL 334-262-2566. FAX 334-263-0200. Ed. Ann Christensen. adv. contact: Edye Goertz. illus. circ. 4,500.
    Description: Devoted to municipal government, its problems, solutions, trends, legal information, news of city and town governments statewide.

352   US   ISSN 0363-4167
JS451.A43
ALASKA MUNICIPAL OFFICIALS DIRECTORY. 1958. a. $50. Alaska Municipal League, 217 Second St., Ste. 200, Juneau, AK 99801-1267. FAX 907-463-5480. Ed. Kevin C. Ritchie. circ. 1,500. **Document type:** directory.
    Description: Provides addresses, telephone and fax numbers, and names and titles of government officials for each of Alaska's incorporated municipalities. Other information for each municipality includes population, sales tax rate and type (if any), type and form of government, and municipally owned utilities.

352   SP   ISSN 0211-8408
ALCALDE. 1967. 11/yr. San Agustin 15, bajo, 28014 Madrid, Spain. TEL 1-429-24-23. Ed. Alfredo Blanco Carro. circ. 6,000.

352   II   ISSN 0024-5623
JS7001
ALL INDIA INSTITUTE OF LOCAL SELF GOVERNMENT. QUARTERLY JOURNAL. (Text in English) 1930. q. Rs.100($30) to non-members (effective 1994). All India Institute of Local Self Government, Sthanikraj Bhavan, C.D. Barfiwala Marg, Andheri (West), Bombay 400 058, India. TEL 91-22-6206716. FAX 91-22-2620766. TELEX 78201 ALSG. Ed. K.R. Khalolkav. adv.; bk.rev.; charts. circ. 1,000. **Indexed:** P.A.I.S.

352 808.8   US
ALLIED ARTS NEWSLETTER. bi-m. Allied Arts of Seattle, 107 S. Main St., Ste. 201, Seattle, WA 98104. TEL 206-624-0432. **Document type:** newsletter.

ALTERNATIVE KOMMUNALPOLITIK; Fachzeitschrift fuer gruene und alternative Politik. see *PUBLIC ADMINISTRATION*

AMERICAN BAR ASSOCIATION. UTILITY SECTION. NEWSLETTER. see *LAW*

352   US   ISSN 0149-337X
HT101   CODEN: ACCOD3
AMERICAN CITY & COUNTY; administration, engineering, and operations in relation to local government. 1909. m. $58 (foreign $118). Argus Inc., 6151 Powers Ferry Rd., N.W., Atlanta, GA 30339-2941. TEL 404-955-2500. FAX 404-955-0400. Ed. Janet Ward. adv.: B&W page $4595, color page $6045. bk.rev.; charts; illus.; mkt.; tr.lit.; index. circ. 71,355. (also avail. in microform (ISSN 0364-9814) from UMI; back issues avail.; reprint service avail. from UMI) **Indexed:** A.S.& T.Ind., Avery Ind.Archit.Per., Bk.Rev.Ind. (1965-1990), Chem.Abstr., Child.Bk.Rev.Ind. (1965-1990), Eng.Ind., Excerp.Med., HRIS, Ind.Sci.Rev., Mag.Ind., Ocean.Abstr., Polit.Sci.Abstr., Pollut.Abstr., R.G, Repindex, Soc.Sci.Ind. (1994-), Tr.& Indus.Ind., W.R.C.Inf. **Document type:** trade publication.
    ●Also available online. Vendor(s): LOGIN Information Services, University Microfilms International.
    —BLDSC (0812.510000); Ei; Faxon; SWETS; UMI; UnCover. CCC.
    Formerly: American City (ISSN 0002-7936)
    Description: Covers the issues, concepts and trends of local government and public works, including the activities and concerns of engineers and administrators of municipal, township, county and special district governments, consulting and sanitary engineers and private firms performing public services.

352.16   US   ISSN 0077-2151
AMERICAN CITY & COUNTY MUNICIPAL INDEX; purchasing guide for city officials and consulting engineers. 1924. a. $64.95 (foreign $89.95). Argus Inc., 6151 Powers Ferry Rd., N.W., Atlanta, GA 30339-2941. TEL 404-955-2500. FAX 404-955-0400. Ed. Barbara Katinsky. adv. circ. 71,355. **Document type:** trade publication.

352.0489   DK
AMT OG KOMMUNE BLADET. m. Fag-Tek, Glostrup Torv 6, DK-2600 Glostrup, Denmark. Ed. Tommy Christiansen. circ. 22,000.
    Incorporates (1969-1976): Dansk Bygge Journal (ISSN 0045-9593)

PUBLIC ADMINISTRATION — MUNICIPAL GOVERNMENT

352.125   DK   ISSN 0109-7822
AMTERNES OEKONOMI. a. DKK 115. Amtsraadsforeningen i Danmark - Association of County Councils in Denmark, Landemaerket 10, P.O. Box 1144, DK-1010 Copenhagen K, Denmark. TEL 45-33-91-21-61. FAX 45-33-11-21-15. Ed. Birgit Skoedt. illus. circ. 1,000.
Former titles (until 1984): Amtskommunernes Oekonomi (ISSN 0105-8509); (until 1978): Oekonomisk Oversigt for Amtskommunerne.
Description: Reports on the budget of the 14 Danish counties. Provides information about income and expenditure.

352   GW
AMTLICHER SCHULANZEIGER FUER DEN REGIERUNGSBEZIRK UNTERFRANKEN; amtliches Mitteilungsblatt fuer die Volks-, Sonder- und Berufsschulen. 1871. m. DM.36. Unterfranken Regierung, Peterplatz 9, 97070 Wuerzburg, Germany. TEL 0931-3801307. FAX 0931-3802911. TELEX 068757-REGULR-D. adv.; bk.rev. circ. 2,500. (looseleaf format; back issues avail.) **Document type:** government publication.

352   GW   ISSN 0003-2131
AMTLICHES KREISBLATT FUER DEN KREIS HERZOGTUM LAUENBURG. 1883. m. DM.2.20 per no. Luebecker Nachrichten GmbH, Koenigstr. 51, 23552 Luebeck, Germany. circ. 350.

352 370 360   AU
AMTLICHES MITTEILUNGSBLATT DER MARKTGEMEINDE LEOBERSDORF. 1958. q. (Amtliche Berichterstattung der Marktgemeinde Leobersdorf) Druck- und Verlagsanstalt Gutenberg, Rathausplatz 1, 2700 Wiener Neustadt, Austria. Ed. Franz Gobec. adv. circ. 1,600. (back issues avail.)

352   GW
AMTSBLATT DER GEMEINDE WILHELMSFELD. 1960. w. (Buergermeisteramt) Druckerei Odenwaelder Buchen Wallduern, Karl-Tranzer-Str. 2, 74722 Buchen, Germany. TEL 06281-9211. (back issues avail.)

352   AU   ISSN 0038-8971
AMTSBLATT DER LANDESHAUPTSTADT LINZ. 1921. s-m. S.10 per no. Landeshauptstadt Linz, Pfarrgasse 9, A-4041 Linz, Austria. TEL 0732-2393-1341. FAX 0732-784427. Ed. Karin Frohner. adv.; bk.rev.; illus.; stat.; index. circ. 1,000. **Document type:** government publication.
Former titles: Stadt Linz; Amtsblatt der Landeshauptstadt Linz.

352   GW
AMTSBLATT DER LANDESHAUPTSTADT MUENCHEN. 1952. 3/m. DM.37. Kommunalschriften-Verlag, Postfach 801940, 81619 Munich, Germany. TEL 089-416006-52. Ed. Wolfgang Quadflieg.

352   AU   ISSN 0003-2239
AMTSBLATT DER STADT KAPFENBERG. 1947. q. free. Stadtgemeinde Kapfenberg, 8605 Kapfenberg, Austria. Ed. Nikolaus Prieschl.

252   GW   ISSN 0172-2522
AMTSBLATT DER STADT KOELN. 1970. w. DM.52. Stadt Koeln, Presse und Informationsamt, Laurenzplatz 4, 50667 Cologne, Germany. TEL 0221-2074. FAX 0221-6486. circ. 1,000. **Document type:** government publication.
Description: Lists decisions and announcements of the town government concerning construction, planning and roads.

252   GW
AMTSBLATT DER STADT KORNTAL - MUENCHINGEN. 1978. w. Nussbaum Verlag, Postfach 1340, 71261 Weil, Germany. TEL 07033-525-0. adv.; bk.rev.; play rev, illus. circ. 10,000. **Document type:** bulletin.

352   GW
AMTSBLATT DES KREISES WESEL; Amtliches Verkuendungsblatt. 1975. w. Kreiseigene Druckerei, Reeser Landstr. 31, 46483 Wesel, Germany. TEL 0281-2070. circ. 1,700.

352   GW   ISSN 0943-9064
AMTSBLATT FUER BERLIN. 1951. w. DM.160. (Senatsverwaltung fuer Inneres) Kulturbuch Verlag GmbH, Postfach 470449, 12313 Berlin, Germany. TEL 030-6618484. FAX 030-6617828. circ. 6,500. (back issues avail.) **Document type:** government publication.

352   AU   ISSN 0003-2271
AMTSBLATT FUER DAS LAND VORARLBERG. 1946. w. S.125. Landesregierung, Roemerstr. 15, A-6901 Bregenz, Austria. TEL 05574-511-0. FAX 05574-511-80. Ed. Klaus Rossmann. bk.rev. circ. 1,740. **Document type:** government publication.

352   GW
AMTSBLATT FUER DEN LANDKREIS ROSENHEIM. 1868. s-m. DM.30. Landratsamt Rosenheim, Wittelsbacherstrasse 53, 83022 Rosenheim, Germany. circ. 400.

352   GW
AMTSBLATT FUER DEN STADT- UND LANDKREIS HEILBRONN. 1945. w. DM.32.80. Stadt Heilbronn Pressestelle, Rathaus, Postfach 3440, 74024 Heilbronn, Germany. TEL 07131-562288. FAX 07131-563169. Ed. Klaus Koenninger. circ. 1,800. (looseleaf format; back issues avail.) **Document type:** government publication.

352   GW
AMTSBLATT FUER SCHLESWIG-HOLSTEIN. 1946. w. DM.72($40) Innenministerium, Duesternbrooker Weg 92, 24105 Kiel, Germany. TEL 0431-5961. FAX 0431-596-3131. circ. 4,000. (looseleaf format)

352   GW
AMTSBLATT - STADT AUGSBURG. 1746. w. DM.30. Amt fuer Oeffentlichkeitsarbeit, Maximilianstr. 4, 86150 Augsburg, Germany. TEL 0821-324-2170. FAX 0821-3242193. TELEX 533501. circ. 730. **Document type:** government publication.

352   GW   ISSN 0003-9209
JS41
ARCHIV FUER KOMMUNALWISSENSCHAFTEN. (Text in English, French, German) 1962. s-a. DM.128. (Deutsches Institut fuer Urbanistik) W. Kohlhammer GmbH, Hessbruehlstr. 69, 70565 Stuttgart, Germany. TEL 0711-7863-1. FAX 0711-7863263. Ed.Bd. adv.; bk.rev.; abstr.; bibl.; charts; stat.; index. circ. 1,200. Indexed: A.B.C.Pol.Sci., Amer.Hist.& Life, Hist.Abstr., P.A.I.S.For.Lang.Ind. **Document type:** academic/scholarly publication.
—SWETS. **CCC.**

352   IT   ISSN 0390-0606
ARCHIVIO AMMINISTRATIVO ED URBANISTICO SUBALPINO. 1974. m. Via Fratelli di Dio 26, 28026 Omegna, Italy. Ed. Giuseppe Ravasio.

ARTS AND CULTURE FUNDING REPORT. see ART

352.008   MF   ISSN 0304-6451
JS7659.M3
ASSOCIATION OF URBAN AUTHORITIES. ANNUAL BULLETIN. Added title: Local Government in Mauritius. (Text in English and French) 1962. a. Association of Urban Authorities, City Hall, Port Louis, Mauritius. circ. 200. **Document type:** bulletin.

ATLANTA REGIONAL COMMISSION. ANNUAL REPORT. see HOUSING AND URBAN PLANNING

AUDIT COMMISSION. HEALTH & PERSONAL SOCIAL SERVICES. BULLETIN. see BUSINESS AND ECONOMICS — Banking And Finance

AUDIT COMMISSION. REPORT & ACCOUNTS (YEAR). see BUSINESS AND ECONOMICS — Banking And Finance

352   AT   ISSN 0004-9808
AUSTRALIAN MUNICIPAL JOURNAL. 1921. m. Aus.$35. Municipal Association of Victoria, G.P.O. Box 4326PP, Melbourne, Vic. 3001, Australia. TEL 61-3-8235555. FAX 61-3-8248404. Ed. Alicia Patterson. adv.; bk.rev.; illus. circ. 3,500. Indexed: Aus.P.A.I.S., Aus.Rd.Ind. **Document type:** government publication.
—UnCover.
Description: Reports on local government issues and events with focus on Victorian councils.

352   US
B O C A RESEARCH REPORT. q. Building Officials and Code Administrators International, 4051 W. Flossmoor Rd., Country Club Hills, IL 60478-5795. TEL 708-799-2300. FAX 708-799-4981.
Description: Discusses topics of interest to municipal officials responsible for building, housing, and zoning regulations.

352   TS
BALADIAH RAS AL-KHAIMAH/RAS AL-KHAIMAH MUNICIPALITY. (Text in Arabic) 1977. m. Municipal Government, P.O. Box 4, Ras al-Khaimah, United Arab Emirates. TEL 32422. Ed. Saud bin Saghir al-Qusaimi. circ. 3,000.
Description: News of municipal activities and other matters of local concern.

352   TS
AL-BALADIAT/MUNICIPALITIES. (Text in Arabic) 1980. m. General Secretariat of Municipalities, P.O. Box 3774, Abu Dhabi, United Arab Emirates. TEL 331500. FAX 214430. TELEX 23147. Ed. Muhyi al-Din A. Nafeh. circ. 2,000.

BANQUES DE DONNEES UTILES AUX COLLECTIVITES LOCALES ET TERRITORIALES. see PUBLIC ADMINISTRATION — Computer Applications

352   GW   ISSN 0174-8386
BAYERISCHES JAHRBUCH; das grosse Auskunfts- und Adressenwerk. 1887. a. DM.178. Carl Gerber Verlag GmbH, Muthmannstr. 4, 80939 Munich, Germany. TEL 089-32393-280. FAX 089-32393325. adv. circ. 2,000. **Document type:** directory.
Description: Directory of Bavarian authorities.

352   GW
BEHOERDEN SPIEGEL; Zeitung fuer Kommunen, Laender und Europabehoerden. 1988. m. DM.39. ProPress Verlag GmbH, Am Buschhof 8, 53227 Bonn, Germany. TEL 0228-970970. FAX 0228-444296. Ed. R. Uwe Proll. bibl. circ. 134,000. **Document type:** newspaper.

352   US
BERKELEY - LEON SISTER CITY NEWSLETTER. 1991. q. $2. Berkeley - Leon Sister City Association, Box 1004, Berkeley, CA 94701. Ed. Rick Lewis. circ. 1,000. **Document type:** newsletter.
Description: Covers current political, economic, and educational situations in Nicaragua, with emphasis on Leon.

352   GW
BERLINER BEHOERDEN SPIEGEL; unabhaengige Zeitung fuer den oeffentlichen Dienst. 1984. m. DM.39. ProPress Verlag GmbH, Am Buschhof 8, 53227 Bonn, Germany. TEL 0228-970970. FAX 0228-444296. circ. 30,500. **Document type:** newspaper.

352   SZ
BERNISCHE STAATSPERSONAL ZEITUNG. 11/yr. Bernische Staatspersonal Verband, Postgasse 60, CH-3011 Bern, Switzerland. TEL 031-221166. Ed. Kurt Niklaus. circ. 7,800.

352   GW
BETRIFFT. 1986. q. Stadt Nuernberg, Presse- und Informationsamt, Rathaus, 90317 Nuernberg, Germany. TEL 0911-2312372. FAX 0911-2313660. Ed. Norbert Schuergers. circ. 15,000. **Document type:** government publication.
Formerly: Wir Bei Der Stadt.

352   SW   ISSN 0345-1143
BLAAMAERKET; tidning foer Landstinget i Oestergoetland. 1973. 10/yr. Oestergoetlands Laens Landsting, Landstingets Kansli, S-581 01 Linkoeping, Sweden.

352   GW
BLAETTER ZUR GESCHICHTE DES COBURGER LANDES. 1972. q. DM.16. Eisenacher Str. 25, 8631 Lauterta 2, Germany. TEL 09561-66922. Ed. Walter Eichhorn. circ. 1,000.

352   SW   ISSN 0281-5680
BLEKINGETINGET; personaltidning foer Landstinget Blekinge. 1968. bi-m. Landstinget Blekinge, S-371 81 Karlskrona, Sweden.

352   SA   ISSN 0006-4939
BLOEMFONTEIN NUUSBRIEF/BLOEMFONTEIN NEWSLETTER. (Text in Afrikaans, English) 1965. m. free. Public Relations Officer, P.O. Box 639, Bloemfontein, South Africa. illus.; stat.; tr.lit.; index. circ. 30,500. **Document type:** newsletter.

PUBLIC ADMINISTRATION — MUNICIPAL GOVERNMENT

352   IT
BOLOGNA. 1915. m. L.1500. Comune di Bologna, Direzione dei Servizi d'Informazione, Palazzo d'Accursio, Piazza Maggiore 6, Bologna, Italy. FAX 51-228500. TELEX 51-226353 ESTERI I. Dir. Giancarlo Roversi. adv.; bk.rev.; illus. circ. 25,000. Indexed: Abstr.Bull.Inst.Pap.Chem. **Document type:** government publication.
   Formerly: Comune di Bologna. Notiziario Mensile (ISSN 0010-4949)

352   GW
BONNER BEHOERDEN SPIEGEL; unabhaengige Zeitung fuer den oeffentlichen Dienst. 1984. m. DM.39. ProPress Verlag GmbH, Am Buschhof 8, 53227 Bonn, Germany. TEL 0228-970970. FAX 0228-444296. bibl. circ. 27,000. (looseleaf format; back issues avail.)

352   US   ISSN 0006-7946
BOSTON CITY RECORD. 1898. w. $50. One City Hall Plaza, City Hall, Rm. 808A, Boston, MA 02201. TEL 617-725-4188. FAX 617-723-6141. Ed. William D. Stanton. adv.; charts. circ. 52.
   Description: Presents municipal news, public notices and advertisements of invitations for sealed bids and proposals for all purchases of materials and services estimated to exceed $2,000 in value.

352   AU   ISSN 0006-8225
BOTE FUER TIROL; Amtsblatt der Behoerden Aemter und Gerichte Tirols. 1817. w. S.74. Amt der Tiroler Landesregierung, Landhaus, A 6010 Innsbruck, Tyrol, Austria. Ed. Johann Kainz. index. circ. 2,250.

352   II
BRIHANMUMBAI MAHANAGARPALIKA PATRIKA. (Text in English and Marathi) 1954. m. Rs.10. Municipal Corporation of Greater Bombay, Public Relations Dept., Municipal Extension Bldg., Mahapalika Marg, Bombay 400001, India. Ed. Shri J.B. Mahajan. adv.; bk.rev. circ. 2,000.
   Formerly: Bomaby Civic Journal (ISSN 0524-0166)

352   CN
BRITISH COLUMBIA. MINISTRY OF MUNICIPAL AFFAIRS, RECREATION AND HOUSING. MUNICIPAL MANUAL. base vol. (plus irreg. supplements). Can.$52. Ministry of Municipal Affairs, Recreation and Housing, Victoria, B.C., Canada. (Subscr. to: Crown Publications, 546 Yates St., Victoria, B.C. V8W 1K8, Canada. TEL 604-386-4636) (looseleaf format) **Document type:** government publication.
   Formerly: British Columbia. Ministry of Municipal Affairs, Recreation and Culture. Municipal Manual.

BRITISH COLUMBIA DECISIONS - MUNICIPAL LAW CASES. see LAW

352   GW
BUERGERBLATT DER GEMEINDE ROHRDORF. 1961. s-m. DM.10.40. O. Nussbaum Presse- und Wirtschaftsverlag, Postfach 1340, 71257 Weil der Stadt, Germany. TEL 07033-2001. circ. 470.

352.9   US   ISSN 0007-3547
BUILDING OFFICIAL AND CODE ADMINISTRATOR. 1967. bi-m. $18. Building Officials and Code Administrators International, 4051 W. Flossmoor Rd., Country Club Hills, IL 60478-5795. Ed. William J. Even. adv.; bk.rev.; charts; illus.; stat.; index, cum.index. circ. 13,000.
   Formerly: Building Official.

352   US
C Q'S WASHINGTON ALERT. d. Congressional Quarterly Inc., 1414 22nd St., N.W., Washington, DC 20037. TEL 800-432-2250. FAX 202-728-1863.
   ●Also available online.
   Description: Online database service for breaking legislation and for issues before the US Congress.

C R P C INFO. (Capital Region Planning Commission) see HOUSING AND URBAN PLANNING

352   II   ISSN 0008-0675
CALCUTTA MUNICIPAL GAZETTE. (Text in Bengali and English) 1924. fortn. Rs.12. Calcutta Municipal Corporation, Superintendent of Printing, 5 Surendranath Banarjee Rd., Calcutta 13, India. Ed. Shri Rabindra N. Bhatta Charyya.

352   US
CALENDAR AND BUYERS AND SERVICES GUIDE FOR LOCAL GOVERNMENTS (YEAR). a. free. Colorado Municipal League, 1660 Lincoln St., Ste. 2100, Denver, CO 80264. TEL 303-831-6411. FAX 303-860-8175. **Document type:** directory.
   Description: Lists firms that provide products and services to local governments. Includes the firm name, address, phone, contact person, and services performed.

CALIFORNIA CABLETTER; current community perspectives and directions. see COMMUNICATIONS

352   US
CALIFORNIA STATE ASSOCIATION OF COUNTIES LEGISLATIVE BULLETIN. w. $30 to non-members; members $10. California State Association of Counties, 1100 K St., Ste. 101, Sacramento, CA 95814. TEL 916-327-7500. **Document type:** bulletin.
   Description: Offers current information on key legislation affecting counties. Reports on both state and federal legislative issues and also provides information on upcoming meetings.

352   IT
CARPI CITTA. 1964. bi-m. free. Comune di Carpi, Corso Alberto Pio 91, 41012 Carpi, Italy. TEL 059-649234. FAX 59-649200. (Co-sponsor: Carpi Municipal Government) Ed. Claudio Bergianti. adv. circ. 23,500. **Document type:** government publication.
   Formerly (until 1988): Comune di Carpi.

352   US
    JS414
CARROLL'S COUNTY DIRECTORY. s-a. $150. Carroll Publishing, 1058 Thomas Jefferson St., N.W., Washington, DC 20007. TEL 202-333-8620. FAX 202-337-7020. (also avail. in diskette format) **Document type:** directory.
   ●Also available on CD-ROM.
   Formerly: County Executive Directory (ISSN 0742-1702)
   Description: Directory of county officials and administrators listed by state.

352   US
    JS363
CARROLL'S MUNICIPAL COUNTY DIRECTORY (YEAR) LIBRARY EDITION. a. $137. Carroll Publishing Company, 1058 Thomas Jefferson St., N.W., Washington, DC 20007. TEL 202-333-8620. FAX 202-337-7020. **Document type:** directory.
   Formerly: Municipal - County Executive Directory Annual (ISSN 0743-6211)
   Description: Provides detailed listings of officials and administrators in over 3,100 counties with population over 25,000 and cities - over 15,000 population.

352   US
    JS363
CARROLL'S MUNICIPAL DIRECTORY. s-a. $150. Carroll Publishing, 1058 Thomas Jefferson St., N.W., Washington, DC 20007. TEL 202-333-8620. FAX 202-337-7020. (also avail. in diskette format) **Document type:** directory.
   ●Also available on CD-ROM.
   Formerly: Municipal Executive Directory (ISSN 0742-1710)
   Description: Directory of more than 35,000 key officials in the municipal governments of the United States.

338   US
    JK2482.E94
CARROLL'S STATE DIRECTORY. 1980. 3/yr. $180. Carroll Publishing, 1058 Thomas Jefferson St., N.W., Washington, DC 20007. TEL 202-333-8620. FAX 202-337-7020. (also avail. in diskette format) **Document type:** directory.
   ●Also available on CD-ROM.
   Formerly: State Executive Directory (ISSN 0276-7163)
   Description: Directory of more than 37,000 key officials in executive and legislative branches of state governments in the United States.

338   US
    JK2482.E94
CARROLL'S STATE DIRECTORY (YEAR) EDITION. a. $137. Carroll Publishing Company, 1058 Thomas Jefferson St., N.W., Washington, DC 20007. TEL 202-333-8620. FAX 202-337-7020. **Document type:** directory.
   Formerly: State Executive Directory Annual (ISSN 1056-7011)
   Description: Includes more than 37,200 contacts with name, office address and phone number in the executive and legislative branches of state government.

352   IT
CASTELBOLOGNESE NOTIZIE. 1981. 3/yr. free. Amministrazione Comunale, Piazza Bernardi 1, 48014 Castel Bolognese, Italy. TEL 39-546-652411. FAX 39-645-55973. Ed. Francesco Marchi. circ. 3,300 (paid). cols./p.: 4; pp./issue: 12. (tabloid format; back issues avail.) **Document type:** newspaper.
   Description: Presents information on the local administration and its activities.

CAYMAN GAZETTE. see LAW

352   UK   ISSN 0264-2751
HT119
CITIES. 1983. bi-m. £293($466) (effective 1996). Butterworth - Heinemann, Part of the Reed Elsevier group, Linacre House, Jordan Hill, Oxford OX2 8DP, England. TEL 0865-310366. FAX 0865-310898. TELEX 83111 BHPOXF G. (Subscr. to: Elsevier Science Ltd., P.O. Box 800, Kidlington, Oxford OX5 1DX, England. TEL 44-865-843000. FAX 44-865-843010; Subscr. in U.S. and Canada to: Elsevier Science, 660 White Plains Rd., Tarrytown, NY 10591-5153. TEL 914-524-9200. FAX 914-333-2444) Ed. Penny Street. adv.; bk.rev.; abstr.; illus.; index. (also avail. in. microform from UMI; back issues avail.) Indexed: Avery Ind.Archit.Per., Environ.Abstr., Geo.Abstr., IDA, P.A.I.S. **Document type:** academic/scholarly publication.
   —BLDSC (3267.792160); CIS; Faxon; Genuine Article; SWETS; UMI; UnCover. CCC.
   Description: Focuses on the policies and technologies affecting urban environments and on the social, psychological and physical impact of planning policies.
   Refereed Serial

CITIES AND VILLAGES. see HOUSING AND URBAN PLANNING

330   US   ISSN 0009-756X
CITIZENS' BUSINESS. 1910. irreg. $50 membership. Pennsylvania Economy League, Eastern Division, 1211 Chestnut St., Ste. 600, Philadelphia, PA 19107-4103. TEL 215-864-9562. Ed.Bd. stat. circ. 3,000. (processed)

352   US
CITIZENS UNION FOUNDATION. OCCASIONAL PAPER SERIES. 1977. irreg. Citizens Union Foundation, Inc., 198 Broadway, New York, NY 10038. TEL 212-227-0342. FAX 212-227-0345. Dir. Jeannette Kahlenberg. **Document type:** monographic series.
   Formerly: Citizens Union Research Foundation. Occasional Paper Studies.

352   US
CITIZENS UNION REPORTS; citizens union news and comment on New York City. 1946. 4/yr. $20 to non-members. Citizens Union of the City of New York, 198 Broadway, New York, NY 10038. TEL 212-227-0342. FAX 212-227-0345. Ed. Jeannette Kahlenberg. circ. 3,000. (processed)
   Formerly: Across from City Hall (ISSN 0001-5059)
   Description: News articles and announcements on the legislative, political, and policy issues that affect the civic activities of this New York City people's lobby.

PUBLIC ADMINISTRATION — MUNICIPAL GOVERNMENT

352   US   ISSN 0193-8371
JS303.A8
CITY & TOWN (NORTH LITTLE ROCK). 1947. m. $15 (effective 1995 & 1996). Arkansas Municipal League, Box 38, North Little Rock, AR 72115. TEL 501-374-3484. FAX 501-374-0541. Ed. Don Zimmerman. adv. contact: John K. Woodruff. bk.rev.; circ. 6,700 (paid). **Document type:** government publication.
    Formerly: Arkansas Municipalities (ISSN 0004-1866)
    Description: Contains articles, information, documents, laws and other data about cities. Educates and informs municipal leaders, elected officials, supervisors about municipal affairs to help them govern, operate and administer cities and towns.

352   US
CITY CLUB GADFLY. 1959. m. free. City Club of New York, 33 W. 42nd St., New York, NY 10036. TEL 212-921-9870. bk.rev.; circ. 2,500 (controlled).
    Formerly (until May 1978): City Club Comments (ISSN 0009-7721)

350   US
CITY FISCAL CONDITIONS IN (YEAR). 1983. a. $34. National League of Cities, 1301 Pennsylvania Ave. N.W., Washington, DC 20004. TEL 202-626-3150. (back issues avail.) **Indexed:** SRI.
    Description: Survey of trends in city revenues and expenditures.

352   SW
CITY OF STOCKHOLM. ANNUAL FINANCIAL REPORT (YEAR). a. City of Stockholm Kammarkontor, City Hall, S-105 35 Stockholm, Sweden. TEL 46 8 785 91 83.

352   US
CITY RECORD; official journal of the City of New York. d. (M-F). $100. Department of General Services, 2223 Municipal Bldg., New York, NY 10007. TEL 212-566-4446. Ed. Virginia Bull. charts; stat.

CITYSCAPE. see HOUSING AND URBAN PLANNING

352   SP   ISSN 1133-4762
CIUDAD Y TERRITORIO: ESTUDIOS TERRITORIALES. 1993. q. 5000 ptas. (foreign 7000 ptas.) (effective 1993). Ministerio de Obras Publicas, Transportes y Medio Ambiente, Direccion General para la Vivienda, el Urbanismo y la Arquitectura, Paseo de la Castellana, 67, 28071 Madrid, Spain. TEL 34-1-5975883. FAX 34-1-5975884. Dir. Javier Garcia-Bellido. bk.rev.; bibl.; illus.; circ. 2,400 (paid). **Document type:** government publication.
    —CCC.
    Formed by the merger of (1970-1993): Ciudad y Territorio (ISSN 0210-0487); (1981-1993): Estudios Territoriales (ISSN 0211-6871)
    Refereed Serial

352   II   ISSN 0009-7772
CIVIC AFFAIRS. (Text in English) 1953. m. Rs.72($9) Citizen Publications, Box 188, Bhargova Estate, Kanpur 1, India. Ed. S.P. Mehra. adv.; bk.rev.; illus. circ. 3,500.
    —UnCover.

352   CN   ISSN 0829-772X
JS1701
CIVIC PUBLIC WORKS. 1949. bi-m. Can.$36. Maclean-Hunter Ltd., Business Publication Division, Maclean-Hunter Bldg., 777 Bay St., Toronto, ON M5W 1A7, Canada. TEL 416-596-5953. FAX 416-593-3193. Ed. Alex Jenkins; Pub. David J. Fidler. adv.; bk.rev.; bibl.; charts; illus.; mkt.; tr.lit.; index. circ. 13,500. **Indexed:** Can.B.P.I.
    —CCC.
    Formerly: Civic Administration (ISSN 0009-7764); Incorporates: Civic Public Works Reference Manual and Buyer's Guide; Which was formerly: Civic Municipal Reference Manual and Purchasing Guide (ISSN 0069-4258); Civic Administration's Municipal Reference Manual and Purchasing Guide.

331.1   US
COLORADO JOB FINDER. 1979. s-m. $40. Colorado Municipal League, 1660 Lincoln St., Ste. 2100, Denver, CO 80264. TEL 303-831-6411. FAX 303-860-8175. Ed. Barbara Major. circ. 360. (back issues avail.) **Document type:** government publication.
    Description: Lists administrative, technical and professional job openings in state and local government throughout Colorado.

352   US
COLORADO LAWS ENACTED AFFECTING MUNICIPAL GOVERNMENTS. a. $40 to non-members; members $20. Colorado Municipal League, 1660 Lincoln St., Ste. 2100, Denver, CO 80264. TEL 303-831-6411. **Document type:** government publication.
    Description: Presents selected laws of broad municipal interest that were enacted by the Colorado General Assembly.

352   US   ISSN 0010-1664
JS39
COLORADO MUNICIPALITIES. 1925. bi-m. $15 to non-members. Colorado Municipal League, 1660 Lincoln St., Ste. 2100, Denver, CO 80264. TEL 303-831-6411. FAX 303-860-8175. Ed. Kay Mariea. adv.; bk.rev.; illus.; index, cum.index. circ. 4,500. **Indexed:** P.A.I.S.
    —UnCover.
    Description: Presents articles on current interests and concerns of municipal officials, activities of Colorado municipalities and individuals involved in municipal government.

352   FR   ISSN 0573-0910
COMMUNES DE FRANCE. 1959. m. 400 F. Societe de Presse des Collectivites (SOPRECO), 12 cite Malesherbes, 75009 Paris, France. TEL 45-26-50-50. FAX 42-82-94-08. Ed. Claude-Emile Guerin. adv.; bk.rev. circ. 13,000.

352 634.9   FR   ISSN 1142-5083
COMMUNES FORESTIERES DE FRANCE. 1931. q. 130 F. (effective 1993). Federation Nationale des Communes Forestieres de France, 13 rue du General Bertrand, 75007 Paris, France. TEL 45-67-47-98. FAX 45-67-25-99. Ed. Brigitte Deshaires. adv. circ. 11,000.
    Former titles (until 1974): Federation Nationale des Communes Forestieres de France. Bulletin Officiel (ISSN 1142-5091); (until 1972): Federation des Communes Forestieres Francaises. Bulletin Officiel (ISSN 1142-5105); (until 1959): Federation des Associations de Communes Forestieres Francaises. Bulletin Officiel (ISSN 1142-5113)

352   US   ISSN 1044-6222
COMMUNITY LEADER BRIEFINGS. 1989. m. free. City Leaders Institute, 52 E. Franklin Rd., Meridian, ID 83642. TEL 208-887-6326. FAX 208-887-6015. Ed. Wayne S. Forrey. bk.rev.; index. circ. 500. (looseleaf format; back issues avail.)
    Description: Management and technical information to help mayors and council members govern cities.
    Refereed Serial

352   IT
COMPENDIO DATI; patrimoniali, economici, finanziari, tecnici, produttivi e del personale. 1974. a. L.80000. Confederazione Italiana dei Servizi Pubblici degli Enti Locali, Piazza Cola di Rienzo n.80-a, I-00192 Rome, Italy.

COMPENSATION (WASHINGTON, 1982); an annual report on local government executive salaries and fringe benefits. see BUSINESS AND ECONOMICS — *Personnel Management*

352   IT   ISSN 0010-4930
COMUNE DEMOCRATICO; rivista delle autonomie locali. 1945. bi-m. L.30000. Agenda della Lega per le Autonomie e i Poteri Locali, Via Cesare Balbo 43, 00184 Rome, Italy. Ed. Enzo Modica. adv.; bk.rev.; illus. circ. 6,000.

352   IT   ISSN 0010-4973
COMUNI D'EUROPA. 1952. m. L.30000 to individuals; institutions L.150000 (foreign L.40000). Associazione Italiana per il Consiglio dei Comuni d'Europa, Piazza di Trevi 86, 00187 Rome, Italy. TEL 6840461. FAX 6793275. Ed. Umberto Serafini. circ. 14,000. **Indexed:** ELLIS.

352   IT
CONFEDERAZIONE ITALIANA DEI SERVIZI PUBBLICI DEGLI ENTI LOCALI. ANNUARIO. 1961? a. L.80000. Confederazione Italiana dei Servizi Pubblici degli Enti Locali, Piazza Cola di Rienzo, 80, 00192 Rome, Italy. stat.

CONGRESSIONAL LEGISLATIVE REPORTING. see LAW

352   SP
CONSULTOR DE LOS AYUNTAMIENTOS. 26/yr. Coloreros 2, Apdo. 94, 28013 Madrid, Spain. TEL 1-266-01-06. FAX 1-265-97-44. Ed. Manuel Abella Poblet. circ. 117,000.

CONTAC. see BUSINESS AND ECONOMICS — *Trade And Industrial Directories*

352   AT   ISSN 0728-5582
COUNCIL AND COMMUNITY. 1981. bi-m. free. Local Government Association of South Australia, G.P.O. Box 2693, Adelaide, S.A. 5001, Australia. TEL 08-223-3468. FAX 08-223-2659. TELEX 87138. Ed. Katie Thorp. adv.; bk.rev. circ. 3,200. (back issues avail.)
    —UnCover.

350   EI
COUNCIL OF EUROPE. STUDY SERIES: LOCAL AND REGIONAL AUTHORITIES IN EUROPE. 1972. irreg. price varies. Council of Europe, Publishing and Documentation Service, 67075 Strasbourg Cedex, France. FAX 88-41-27-81. TELEX 870 943 F. (Dist. in U.S. by: Manhattan Publishing Co., 225 Lafayette St., New York, NY 10012) Ed.Bd. charts; stat.
    Former titles: Council of Europe. Steering Committee on Regional and Municipal Matters. Study Series: Local and Regional Authorities in Europe; Council of Europe. Committee on Cooperation in Municipal and Regional Matters. Study Series: Local and Regional Authorities in Europe.

352   UK   ISSN 0964-2544
JS3260
COUNTY NEWS. 1908. m. £30 (overseas £50). Association of County Councils, Eaton House, 66A Eaton Sq., London SW1W 9BH, England. TEL 0171-201-1500. FAX 0171-235-8458. Ed. Michael Baker. adv.; bk.rev.; abstr.; charts; illus.; stat.; index. circ. 6,750. **Indexed:** Geo.Abstr., RICS. **Document type:** newspaper.
    —BLDSC (3482.240000).
    Formerly (until 1991): County Councils Gazette (ISSN 0011-0310)

352   US   ISSN 0744-9798
COUNTY NEWS. vol.3, 1970. fortn. $82.50 (effective 1993). National Association of Counties, 440 First St., N.W., Washington, DC 20001. TEL 202-393-6226. FAX 202-393-2630. Ed. Beverly Schlotterbeck. adv.; charts; illus.; stat.; circ. 27,000 (controlled). (tabloid format) **Document type:** newspaper.
    Formerly: N A C O News and Views (ISSN 0027-5743)

658   FR   ISSN 1249-6936
LE COURIER DU MAIRE. 1990. s-m. 390 F. (foreign 480 F.). Publications du Moniteur, 17 rue d'Uzes, 75002 Paris, France. TEL 1-40-13-30-30. FAX 1-40-26-20-94. TELEX UPRESSE 680876F. Ed. Philippe Parmantier. circ. 15,000.
    Formed by the 1993 merger of: Lettre du Moniteur des Villes (ISSN 1241-4751) & Moniteur des Villes (ISSN 1156-6434)

352   IT   ISSN 0394-6088
CROCEVIA; mensile di polizia municipale, stradale, amministrativa e sanitaria per i Vigili Urbani d'Italia. 1946. m. (11/yr.). L.55000 to individuals; institutions L.110000 (effective 1992). Maggioli Editori, Via Crimes, 1, Casella Postale 290, 47037 Rimini, Italy. TEL 0541-626777. FAX 0541-622020. Ed. Valerio Lessi. adv.: B&W page L.900000, color page L.1400000; trim 170 x 260. circ. 6,452.

352   SP
CUNAL. 12/yr. National Local Administration Body, Carretas 14, 3o, 28012 Madrid, Spain. TEL 1-521-18-25. FAX 1-521-18-93. Ed. E. Castillo Zubia. circ. 44,000.

PUBLIC ADMINISTRATION — MUNICIPAL GOVERNMENT

352   US   ISSN 0011-3727
CURRENT MUNICIPAL PROBLEMS. Annual cumulation (ISSN 0161-5122) 1959. q. (plus a. cum.). $160. Clark - Boardman - Callaghan Company, Inc., 155 Pfingsten Rd., Deerfield, IL 60015. TEL 800-323-1336. Ed. Jim Fegen. bk.rev.; charts; cum.index. circ. 761. (also avail. in microfiche from UMI) **Indexed:** C.L.I., L.R.I., Leg.Cont., Sel.Water Res.Abstr., SSCI.
—Faxon; UMI; UnCover.

352 340   US   ISSN 0740-1744
KFD1240
D.C. CODE UPDATER. 1981. m. $300. David W. Lang, Ed. & Pub., P.O. Box 3107, Crofton, MD 21114. TEL 301-858-0127. charts; cum.index. circ. 40. (back issues avail.)
Description: Lists current changes to District of Columbia code and rules and regulations.

352   US
D G S DIGEST. 1989. 4/yr. free. Department of General Services, Office of Communications, Manhattan Municipal Bldg., 17th Fl. S., 1 Centre St., New York, NY 10007. TEL 212-669-7140. FAX 212-669-4664. circ. 3,500.
Formerly: D G S Reporter.
Description: Reports on agency's personnel activities, projects, achievements and awards.

352   US
D G S GREENTHUMB. 1981. 4/yr. free. Department of General Services, Office of Communications, Manhattan Municipal Bldg., 17th Fl. S., 1 Centre St., New York, NY 10007. TEL 212-669-7140. FAX 212-669-4664. Ed.Bd. circ. 3,000.
Description: Reports on Operation Greenthumb personnel, community gardens, achievements and awards.

352   US
D G S POWERLINES. 1989. s-a. free. Department of General Services, Office of Communications, Manhattan Municipal Bldg., 17th Fl. S., 1 Centre St., New York, NY 10007. TEL 212-669-7140. FAX 212-669-4664. Ed. Andrea Patterson. circ. 1,000.
Formerly: D G S Energy Manager.
Description: Reports on OEC personnel, conservation projects, achievements and awards.

352   DK   ISSN 0011-6106
DANMARKS AMTSRAAD. 1970. fortn. DKK 340. Amtsraadsforeningen i Danmark, Landemarket 10, P.O. Box 1144, DK-1010 Copenhagen K, Denmark. FAX 33-146115. Ed. Ib Bjoernbak. adv.; bk.rev.; charts. circ. 3,776.

352   DK   ISSN 0011-6572
DANSKE KOMMUNER. 1970. w. DKK 442. Kommunernes Landsforening - National Association of Local Authorities in Denmark, Gyldenloevesgade 11, 1600 Copenhagen V, Denmark. TEL 45-31-122788. FAX 45-31-122785. Ed. Jens Hoche. adv.; bk.rev.; illus.; stat.; index. circ. 11,500.
Supersedes: Koebstadforeningens Tidsskrift & Kommunal Tidende.

352   SP
DEBATS. 4/yr. Pl. Alfons el Magnanim 1 1o, 46003 Valencia, Spain. TEL 6-352-79-94. FAX 6-351-49-75. Ed. Mario Garcia Bonafe. circ. 13,000.

352   GW   ISSN 0011-8303
DEMOKRATISCHE GEMEINDE; die Monatszeitschrift fuer Kommunalpolitik. 1949. m. DM.120. Vorwaerts Verlag GmbH, Suedstr. 133, 53175 Bonn, Germany. TEL 0228-95113-0. FAX 0228-9511316. Ed. Ansgar Burghof. adv.; bk.rev.; abstr.; illus.; index. circ. 15,000. (also avail. in microform) **Document type:** newsletter.

352   EC
DESARROLLO LOCAL. 1987. irreg. Centro de Capacitacion y Desarrollo de los Gobiernos Locales, Av. Diez de Agosto 4612 y Juan Pablo Sanz, Casilla Postal 1109, Correo Central, Quito, Ecuador. TEL 435205. TELEX 21026 IULA ED. Ed. Maria Arboleda.

352   US   ISSN 0090-1989
JS451.N93
DIRECTORY: NORTH DAKOTA CITY OFFICIALS. 35rd ed. 1994. biennial. $15. North Dakota League of Cities, Box 2235, Bismarck, ND 58502. TEL 701-223-3518. Ed. Robert E. Johnson. adv. **Document type:** directory.

350   US   ISSN 1046-2686
JS39
DIRECTORY OF CITY POLICY OFFICIALS. 1984. a. $44. National League of Cities, 1301 Pennsylvania Ave. N.W., Washington, DC 20004. TEL 202-636-3150. (back issues avail.) **Document type:** directory.
Description: Lists names of mayors and council members in American cities of over 30,000 people and league member cities. Includes city hall address and telephone number, population and form of government.

352   US
DIRECTORY OF GEORGIA MUNICIPAL OFFICERS AND ASSOCIATE MEMBERS. a. $40 (effective July 1992). Georgia Municipal Association, 201 Pryor St., S.W., Atlanta, GA 30303. TEL 404-688-0472. FAX 404-577-6663. (back issues avail.) **Document type:** directory, government publication.

352   US   ISSN 0148-7442
JS303.M5
DIRECTORY OF MICHIGAN MUNICIPAL OFFICIALS. s-a. $36 per no. Michigan Municipal League, 1675 Green Rd., Box 1487, Ann Arbor, MI 48106. TEL 313-662-3246. FAX 313-662-8083. **Document type:** directory.

352   US   ISSN 0890-1651
JS451.M65
DIRECTORY OF MINNESOTA CITY OFFICIALS. 1986. a. $25. League of Minnesota Cities, 3490 Lexington Ave. N, St. Paul, MN 55126-8044. TEL 612-490-5600. Ed. Tim Busse. adv. contact: Gayle Brodt. circ. 3,500. **Document type:** government publication, directory.
Formerly: Directory of Minnesota Municipal Officials.

352   US
DIRECTORY OF MUNICIPAL AND COUNTY OFFICIALS IN COLORADO (YEAR). a. $40 to non-members; members $20. Colorado Municipal League, 1660 Lincoln St., Ste. 2100, Denver, CO 80264. TEL 303-831-6411. FAX 303-860-8175. **Document type:** directory.
Description: Lists names, titles, official addresses and telephone numbers of elected and appointed municipal and county officials. Also includes listings of selected federal and state offices and organizations, the Colorado congressional delegation, the councils of government, and the regional planning commissions.

352   US
DIRECTORY OF NORTH CAROLINA MUNICIPAL OFFICIALS. a. $30. North Carolina League of Municipalities, Box 3069, 215 N. Dawson St., Raleigh, NC 27602. TEL 919-715-4000. FAX 919-733-9519. Ed. Margot F. Christensen. circ. 1,500. **Document type:** directory.

352   BL   ISSN 0419-3911
DIRIGENTE MUNICIPAL. 1966. m. $70. Editora Visao Ltda., Rua Alvaro de Carvalho, 350, 2o andar, C.P. 3082, 01050 Sao Paulo, Brazil. TEL 256-5011. FAX 258-1919. TELEX 1121436. Ed. Hamilton Lucas de Oliveira. adv.; bk.rev. circ. 15,600.

352   IT   ISSN 0012-4737
DOCUMENTI DI VITA COMUNALE.* 1961. irreg., (approx. 3/yr.) free. Sindacato di Mogliano, Piazza Caduti 1, 31021 Magliano Veneto, Treviso, Italy. Ed. Dir. Giuseppe Marton. adv.; bk.rev.; abstr.; illus.; stat.; tr.lit. circ. 5,500 (controlled).

352   GW
DORTMUNDER BEKANNTMACHUNGEN; Amtsblatt der Stadt. 1945. w. DM.33. Krueger Verlag, Postfach 102452, 44024 Dortmund, Germany. TEL 0231-5401-180. **Document type:** government publication.

352   GW
DRESDENER BEHOERDEN SPIEGEL; unabhaengige Zeitung fuer den oeffentlichen Dienst. 1991. m. DM.36. ProPress Verlag GmbH, Am Buschhof 8, 53227 Bonn, Germany. TEL 0228-970970. FAX 0228-444296. circ. 6,000. **Document type:** newspaper.

352   GW   ISSN 0012-7019
DUESSELDORFER AMTSBLATT. 1946. w. DM.39. Landeshauptstadt Duesseldorf, Oberstadtdirektor Presseamt, Postfach 101120, 40002 Duesseldorf, Germany. TEL 0211-899-3131. FAX 0211-8994179. Ed. Hans-Joachim Neisser. adv.; bk.rev. circ. 5,500. **Document type:** government publication.

352   GW   ISSN 0939-4508
E C PUBLIC CONTRACT LAW. (European Community); public procurement in theory and practice. (Text in English, French, German and Italian) 1991. bi-m. DM.216. ProPress Verlag GmbH, Am Buschhof 8, 53227 Bonn, Germany. TEL 0228-970970. FAX 0228-444296. circ. 6,000. **Document type:** bulletin.

EDINBURGH COLLEGE OF ART - HERRIOT-WATT UNIVERSITY. RESEARCH PAPER. see HOUSING AND URBAN PLANNING

352   FR
ELU D'AUJOURD'HUI. 1975. 11/yr. 180 F. 10 rue Parmentier, 93100 Montreuil, France. TEL 48-51-78-78. FAX 48-51-92-62. Ed. Emile Clet. adv. circ. 34,500.

352 310   IT   ISSN 0013-6891
EMPOLI;* rassegna di vita cittadina e bollettino di statistica. 1959. s-a. L.100 per no. Casa Editrice la Toscografica, Via Pontorme 20, Empoli, Italy. Dir. Assessore G. Lombardi. adv.; charts; illus.; stat.

352   CN   ISSN 1182-6274
ENCYCLOPEDIA OF CANADIAN MUNICIPAL GOVERNMENTS. 1990. a. Municipal Publishers (Subsidiary of: Quaere Data Resources Inc.), 4583 Neville St., Burnaby, B.C. V5J 2G9, Canada. TEL 604-431-9808. Ed. Vian Andrews.

ENVIRONMENTAL AND URBAN ISSUES. see ENVIRONMENTAL STUDIES

ENVIRONMENTAL POLICY & PRACTICE. see ENVIRONMENTAL STUDIES — Pollution

352.7 628   UK
ESSEX COUNTY COUNCIL. PLANNING. APPLICATIONS & DECISIONS (WASTE & MINERALS). q. £7. Essex County Council, Planning, County Hall, Chelmsford, Essex CM1 1LF, England. TEL 01245-258353. FAX 01245-258353. **Document type:** government publication.

352.7   UK
ESSEX COUNTY COUNCIL. PLANNING. SUBJECT MONITORING REPORTS. 1986. a. price varies. Essex County Council, Planning, County Hall, Chelmsford, Essex CM1 1LF, England. TEL 01245-492211. FAX 01245-258353. (back issues avail.) **Document type:** government publication.

352.7 331   UK
ESSEX COUNTY COUNCIL. PLANNING. SUBJECT MONITORING REPORTS. EMPLOYMENT. 1984. irreg., latest June 1992. price varies. Essex County Council, Planning, County Hall, Chelmsford, Essex CM1 1LF, England. TEL 01245-492211. FAX 01245-258353. (back issues avail.) **Document type:** government publication.

352.7   UK
ESSEX COUNTY COUNCIL. PLANNING. SUBJECT MONITORING REPORTS. HOUSING LAND. 1988. irreg., latest Mar. 1994. £25. Essex County Council, Planning, County Hall, Chelmsford, Essex CM1 1LF, England. TEL 01245-492211. FAX 01245-258353. (back issues avail.) **Document type:** consumer publication.

352.7   UK
ESSEX COUNTY COUNCIL. PLANNING. SUBJECT MONITORING REPORTS. RETAILING. 1984. irreg., latest Oct. 1994. £20. Essex County Council, Planning, County Hall, Chelmsford, Essex CM1 1LF, England. TEL 01245-492211. FAX 01245-258353. (back issues avail.) **Document type:** government publication.

PUBLIC ADMINISTRATION — MUNICIPAL GOVERNMENT

352.7 — UK
ESSEX COUNTY COUNCIL. PLANNING. SUBJECT MONITORING REPORTS. RURAL AREAS. 1988. a. £20. Essex County Council, Planning, County Hall, Chelmsford, Essex CM1 1LF, England. TEL 01245-492211. FAX 01245-258353. (back issues avail.) **Document type:** consumer publication.

352.7 387.736 — UK
ESSEX COUNTY COUNCIL. PLANNING. SUBJECT MONITORING REPORTS. STANSTEAD AIRPORT. 1992. a. £5. Essex County Council, Planning, County Hall, Chelmsford, Essex CM1 1LF, England. TEL 01245-492211. FAX 01245-258353. (back issues avail.) **Document type:** government publication.

629 352.7 — UK
ESSEX DEVELOPMENT PLANS INDEX (YEAR). irreg. Essex County Council, Planning, County Hall, Chelmsford, Essex CM1 1LF, England. TEL 01245-492211. FAX 01245-258353. Ed. P.O. Milton.
Formerly: Essex County Council. Planning. Local Plan Scheme.
Description: Covers planning issues at the county level; includes findings from the Essex County Environmental Committee.

352.7 628 — UK
ESSEX GUIDE TO ENVIRONMENTAL ASSESSMENT. 1992. base vol. plus irreg. updates. £10 for base vol.; updates £5. Essex County Council, Planning, County Hall, Chelmsford, Essex CM1 1LF, England. TEL 01245-492211. FAX 01245-258353. **Document type:** government publication.

352.7 — UK
ESSEX PLANNING COUNCIL. PLANNING LEGISLATION UPDATE. q. £15. Essex County Council, Planning, County Hall, Chelmsford, Essex CM1 1LF, England. TEL 01245-492211. FAX 01245-259353. **Document type:** consumer publication.
Description: Gives up-to-date information on new U.K. Department of the Environment circulars, statutory instruments, and other documents.

352 — EI — ISSN 0252-0990
EUROPEAN REGIONAL PLANNING STUDY SERIES. French edition: Amenagement du Territoire Europeen. Serie Etudes (ISSN 0252-0982) 1977. irreg. price varies. Council of Europe, Publications Sections, 67075 Strasbourg Cedex, France. (Dist. in U.S. by: Manhattan Publishing Co., Box 650, Croton, NY 10520)
—BLDSC (3829.879000).

FEDERAL ELECTION CAMPAIGN FINANCING GUIDE. see *BUSINESS AND ECONOMICS — Banking And Finance*

352 — US
FINANCIAL CONDITION OF COLORADO MUNICIPALITIES. a. $30 to non-members; members $15. Colorado Municipal League, 1660 Lincoln St., Ste. 2100, Denver, CO 80264. TEL 303-831-6411. **Document type:** government publication.
Description: Reports on municipal fiscal health and what cities and towns are doing to cope with fiscal problems.

FINANCING LOCAL GOVERNMENT. see *BUSINESS AND ECONOMICS — Public Finance, Taxation*

352 — US
FLORIDA BAR. LOCAL GOVERNMENT LAW SECTION NEWSLETTER. irreg. (3-4/yr.). membership. Florida Bar, 650 Apalachee Pkwy., Tallahassee, FL 32399-2300. TEL 904-561-5631. circ. 1,040. **Document type:** newsletter.

352 — SP — ISSN 0210-1807
FUNCIONARIO MUNICIPAL. 1960. 11/yr. Dr. Sanchez Sivera 19 6o, 46008 Valencia, Spain. TEL 6-3259247. Ed. F. de las Marinas Alvarez. circ. 1,700. **Document type:** academic/scholarly publication.

352 — BL
FUNDACAO DE ASSISTENCIA AOS MUNICIPIOS DO ESTADO DO PARANA. BOLETIM INFORMATIVO. *
1975. irreg. free. Fundacao de Assistencia aos Municipios, Rua Mariano Torres 135, 8000 Curitiba, Parana, Brazil.

352 — GW — ISSN 0016-2779
DIE FUNDSTELLE; Erlaeuterungen zu allen wichtigen Vorschriften fuer die Bayerische Kommunalverwaltungen. 1947. s-m. DM.444. Richard Boorberg Verlag (Stuttgart), Scharrstr. 2, 70563 Stuttgart, Germany. TEL 0711-7385-0. Ed. Wolfram Zwick. bk.rev.; tr.lit.; index. circ. 3,500. (processed) **Document type:** bulletin.
—CCC.

352 — GW — ISSN 0721-1406
FUNDSTELLE FUER DIE KOMMUNALVERWALTUNG IN BADEN-WUERTTEMBERG. 1948. bi-w. DM.390. Richard Boorberg Verlag (Stuttgart), Scharrstr. 2, 70563 Stuttgart, Germany. TEL 0711-7385-0. Eds. Werner Frasch, Wilfried Rump. (back issues avail.) **Document type:** bulletin.

352 — GW — ISSN 0721-135X
FUNDSTELLE FUER DIE KOMMUNALVERWALTUNG IN HESSEN. 1948. 24/yr. DM.417.60. Richard Boorberg Verlag (Stuttgart), Scharrstr. 2, 70563 Stuttgart, Germany. TEL 0711-7385-0. Ed. Michael Althaus. **Document type:** bulletin.

354 — US — ISSN 1051-6964
G F O A NEWSLETTER. 1949. s-m. $50 includes Government Finance Review. Government Finance Officers Association, 180 N. Michigan Ave., Ste. 800, Chicago, IL 60601. TEL 312-977-9700. FAX 312-977-4806. Ed. Bd. bk.rev.; tr.lit. circ. 13,500. (looseleaf format) **Document type:** newsletter.
Formerly: Municipal Finance News Letter (ISSN 0027-3481)
Description: Provides information on legislative and regulatory issues, summarizes trends and events in the public finance field, lists current training seminars, and contains employment notices.

352 — NE — ISSN 0016-6049
GEMEENTEBLAD VAN AMSTERDAM. 1858. s-w. fl.400. Stadsuitgeverij, Voormalige Stadstimmertuin 4 - 6, 1018 ET Amsterdam, Netherlands. TEL 31-20-5522213. index; circ. 700 (paid). **Document type:** government publication.
Description: Municipal publication containing all new ordinances and the minutes of the Amsterdam City Council.

352 — GW — ISSN 0340-3653
DIE GEMEINDE. 1949. m. DM.112. (Schleswig-Holsteinischer Gemeindetag) Deutscher Gemeindeverlag GmbH (Kiel), Jaegersberg 17, 24105 Kiel, Germany. TEL 0431-554857. Eds. Hartmund Borchert, Wolfgang Ottens. circ. 1,700. **Document type:** bulletin.
—CCC.

352 — GW
GEMEINDE SCHOENAICH - RUECKSPIEGEL. 1975. a. free. Gemeinde Schoenaich, Buehlstr. 10, 71101 Schoenaich, Germany. TEL 07031-6390. FAX 07031-63999. Ed. Hans-Joerg Weinbrenner. (looseleaf format; back issues avail.) **Document type:** newsletter.

352 — AU — ISSN 0016-609X
GEMEINDEBOTE. 1963. irreg. (4-6/yr.). free. Marktgemeinde Hinterbruehl. Gemeindeamt, Hauptstr. 66, A-2371 Hinterbruehl, Austria. Ed. G. Tartarotti. stat. circ. 1,200.

352 — GW — ISSN 0340-3645
DER GEMEINDEHAUSHALT. 1900. m. DM.195. W. Kohlhammer GmbH, Hessbruehlstr. 69, 70565 Stuttgart, Germany. TEL 0711-7863-1. FAX 0711-7863263. Ed. Johannes Werner Schmidt. (reprint service avail.) **Document type:** bulletin.
—CCC.

352 — GW — ISSN 0016-612X
DIE GEMEINDEKASSE; das Blatt des Kassenverwalters fuer das Haushalts-, Kassen- und Rechnungswesen. 1950. m. DM.270. Richard Boorberg Verlag (Stuttgart), Scharrstr. 2, 70563 Stuttgart, Germany. TEL 0711-7385-0. Eds. Heinrich Albers, H.-P. Suermann. bk.rev.; tr.lit.; index. circ. 2,500. (processed) **Document type:** bulletin.
—CCC.

352 — GW — ISSN 0016-6170
GEMEINDEVERWALTUNG IN RHEINLAND - PFALZ. 1957. s-m. DM.309.60. Richard Boorberg Verlag (Stuttgart), Scharrstr. 2, 70563 Stuttgart, Germany. TEL 0711-7385-0. Eds. Walter Bogner, Hans Guenther Dehe. adv. **Document type:** bulletin.
—CCC.

352 — GW — ISSN 0016-6200
GEMEINSAMES AMTSBLATT DES LANDES BADEN-WUERTTEMBERG. 1953. irreg., approx. 40/yr. DM.100. Innenministerium, Dorotheenstr. 6, Postfach 102443, 70173 Stuttgart, Germany. Ed. W. Schmidt. bk.rev.; index. **Indexed:** Dok.Str., INIS Atomind.

352 — US
JS39
GEORGIA'S CITIES. 1951. 12/yr. $30. Georgia Municipal Association, 201 Pryor St., S.W., Atlanta, GA 30303-3606. TEL 404-688-0472. FAX 404-577-6663. Ed. Charles C. Craig. adv.; bk.rev. circ. 6,000. **Document type:** government publication.
Former titles: Urban Georgia (ISSN 0042-0875); Georgia Municipal Journal.

352 — GW — ISSN 0342-3557
GESETZ- UND VERORDNUNGSBLATT FUER DAS LAND HESSEN. 1945. DM.70. (Staatskanzlei) A. Bernecker Verlag, Unter dem Schoeneberg 1, 34212 Melsungen, Germany. TEL 05661-731-0. FAX 05661-73189. index. circ. 8,000. **Indexed:** Dok.Str., INIS Atomind. **Document type:** government publication.

352 — GW — ISSN 0016-9129
GESETZ- UND VERORDNUNGSBLATT FUER SCHLESWIG-HOLSTEIN. 1947. 27/yr. DM.40. Innenministerium, Duestenbrooker Weg 92, 24105 Kiel, Germany. FAX 0431-596-3131. circ. 4,000. **Indexed:** Dok.Str.

352 — SZ
GESTION ET SERVICES PUBLICS. (Text in French) 6/yr. Verlag Forum Press AG, Franklinstr. 21, CH-8050 Zurich, Switzerland. TEL 01-3115353. FAX 01-3115370. Ed. Werner Hochuli. circ. 3,400. **Document type:** trade publication.

352 — SP
GETAFE. AYUNTAMIENTO. BOLETIN INFORMATIVO. 12/yr. Ayuntamiento - Town Council, Pza. de la Constitucion 1, 28901 Getafe (Madrid), Spain. TEL 1-6811453. Ed. Pedro Castro Vazquez.

352 — IT
GIUSSANO. 1980. m. L.500 per no. Comune di Giussano, Via Milano, 60, I-20034 Giussano, Italy. Ed.Bd. adv. contact: Giulio Cassina. circ. 1,000. **Document type:** government publication.

352 — SW — ISSN 0280-8803
GOETEBORGS KOMMUNALKALENDER. 1929. a. SEK 190. Goeteborgs Stadskansli, S-404 82 Goeteborg, Sweden. TEL 46-31-61-11-03. FAX 46-31-13-12-48. Ed. Rolf Claesson. circ. 3,000. **Document type:** government publication.

352 — US — ISSN 0894-3842
JK2403
GOVERNING; the states and localities. 1987. m. $29.95. 2300 N St., N.W., Ste. 760, Washington, DC 20037. TEL 202-862-8802. FAX 202-862-0032. (Subscr. to: Box 420092, Palm Coast, FL 32142-9823) Ed. Peter A. Harkness. adv. contact: Mary Thoms. bk.rev.; index. circ. 85,000. (also avail. in microfilm) **Document type:** trade publication.
●Also available online. Vendor(s): Lexis-Nexis, LOGIN Information Services.
—Faxon; UMI; UnCover. **CCC.**
Description: Covers emerging trends and issues in policy and politics for state and local elected, appointed and career officials.

PUBLIC ADMINISTRATION — MUNICIPAL GOVERNMENT

352 606 US ISSN 0883-8690
HC110.P63
GOVERNMENT ASSISTANCE ALMANAC. 1985. a. $105. Omnigraphics, Inc., 2500 Penobscot Bldg., Detroit, MI 48226. TEL 313-961-1340; 800-234-1340. FAX 313-961-1383. Ed. J. Robert Dumouchel. stat.; index. **Document type:** directory.
Description: Data base of information on more than 1,200 domestic financial and non-financial assistance programs, with a cross-referenced index, application guidelines, funding summary tables, and more than 4,000 addresses and telephone numbers for federal program headquaters and field offices.

352 US ISSN 0882-6587
GOVERNMENT MICROCOMPUTER LETTER. 1983. bi-m. $19. Innovation Groups, Inc., Box 16645, Tampa, FL 33687. TEL 813-622-8484. FAX 813-664-0051. Ed. Alicia Lewis. adv. contact: Elizabeth Diaz. abstr.; bibl.; tr.lit. circ. 4,000. (tabloid format; back issues avail.) **Document type:** newsletter.
Description: For local governments using computer systems.

352 US
GOVERNMENTAL AFFAIRS REVIEW (ALBANY). m. Office of the State Comptroller, Division of Municipal Affairs, Smith State Office Bldg., Albany, NY 12236. TEL 518-474-5505. **Indexed:** Rehabil.Lit.

GREAT BRITAIN. AUDIT COMMISSION. LOCAL GOVERNMENT REORGANISATION PAPER. see BUSINESS AND ECONOMICS — Banking And Finance

GREAT BRITAIN. DEPARTMENT OF THE ENVIRONMENT. LOCAL GOVERNMENT FINANCIAL STATISTICS: ENGLAND AND WALES. see PUBLIC ADMINISTRATION — Abstracting, Bibliographies, Statistics

352 US ISSN 0199-1728
GREATER PORTLAND MAGAZINE.* 1956. bi-m. $9.97. Greater Portland Publications Inc., 51 Congress St., Portland, ME 04101-3667. TEL 207-773-5000. Ed. Shirley Jacks. adv. circ. 7,000. (back issues avail.)

352 FR
GREFFIER MUNICIPAL. 4/yr. Valeille, 42110 Feurs, France. TEL 77-28-94-42. Ed. Marc Chabrier. circ. 7,000.

352 360 US ISSN 1055-596X
HJ275
GUIDE TO FEDERAL FUNDING FOR GOVERNMENTS AND NONPROFITS. (Semi-monthly supplement avail.: Federal Grant Deadline Calendar) 1976. a. $349.95. Government Information Services, 4301 Fairfax Dr., Ste. 875, Arlington, VA 22203-1627. TEL 703-528-1000. FAX 703-528-6060. Ed.Bd. (looseleaf format)
—CCC.
Former titles (until 1990): Federal Funding Guide (ISSN 0273-4435); (until 1980): Federal Funding Guide for Local Governments (ISSN 0362-4285)
Description: Details more than 360 federal aid programs available to state, county and municipal government, tribal governments and non-profit groups. Provides information on eligibility requirements, outlook for funding, application deadlines, allowable uses of funds and program contacts (including telephone numbers).

352 AU
GUMPOLDSKIRCHNER NACHRICHTEN. 1982. q. Marktgemeinde Gumpoldskirchen, Gemeindeamt, A-2352 Gumpoldskirchen, Austria. TEL 02252-62101. FAX 02252-6210133. circ. 1,500. **Document type:** government publication, newsletter.

323 US ISSN 0073-1137
JK9349.O4
HAWAII. OFFICE OF THE OMBUDSMAN. REPORT. 1971. a. free. Office of the Ombudsman, Kekuanaoa Bldg., 4th Fl., 465 S. King St., Honolulu, HI 96813. TEL 808-587-0770. Ed. Yen L. Lew. stat.; circ. controlled. **Document type:** government publication.
Description: Annual report to the State Legislature; contains subject chapters, statistics, and case summaries.

352 GW
HEIDELBERGER STADTBLATT. 1946. w. Amt fuer Presse- und Oeffentlichkeitsarbeit, Postfach 105520, 69045 Heidelberg, Germany. TEL 06221-581200. FAX 06221-581290. Ed. Heike Diesselberg. circ. 60,000. **Document type:** government publication, newspaper.
Formerly (until 1993): Heidelberger Amtsanzeiger.

352 GW ISSN 0932-9757
HEIMAT DORTMUND; Stadtgeschichte in Bildern und Berichten. 1986. q. DM.24. Klartext Verlag, Dickmannstr. 2-4, 45143 Essen, Germany. TEL 0201-8620631. FAX 0201-8620622. Ed. Martina Horstendahl. **Document type:** bulletin.

352 GW
HEIMATBRIEFE DER STADT PIRMASENS. 1937. s-a. Stadtverwaltung Pirmasens, Rathaus am Exerzierplatz, 66953 Pirmasens, Germany. TEL 06331-842222. FAX 06331-842540. circ. 3,000. **Document type:** government publication.

HERNE IN ZAHLEN. JAHRBUCH (YEAR). see BUSINESS AND ECONOMICS — Abstracting, Bibliographies, Statistics

HERNE IN ZAHLEN. MONATSBERICHT. see BUSINESS AND ECONOMICS — Abstracting, Bibliographies, Statistics

HERNE IN ZAHLEN. VIERTELJAHRESBERICHTE. see BUSINESS AND ECONOMICS — Abstracting, Bibliographies, Statistics

352 GW
HESSEN - REPORT. 1988. m. Hessische Landesregierung, Bierstadter Str. 2, 65189 Wiesbaden, Germany. TEL 06121-320. circ. 28,000.

HIV PREVENTION AND SERVICES TECHNICAL ASSISTANCE REPORTS. see PUBLIC HEALTH AND SAFETY

HIV PREVENTION CASE STUDY SERIES. see PUBLIC HEALTH AND SAFETY

352 US
HONOLULU EMPLOYEE JOURNAL. vol.9, 1971. bi-m. free. Office of Information & Complaint, City Hall, Honolulu, HI 96813. TEL 808-527-5782. FAX 808-523-4386. Ed. Francis A. Marzen. bk.rev.; charts; illus. circ. 10,000. **Document type:** newsletter.
Description: For and about city workers.

352 US ISSN 0047-0651
I C M A NEWSLETTER. 1919. bi-w. $115. International City - County Management Association, 777 N. Capitol St., N.E., Ste. 500, Washington, DC 20002-4201. TEL 202-962-3624. FAX 202-962-3500. Ed. Kathleen Karas. bk.rev.; charts; tr.lit. circ. 8,600. **Document type:** newsletter.
Description: Covers the association's activities and local government position vacancies and appointments.

352 US
IDAHO CITIES. 1964. m. $18. Association of Idaho Cities, 3314 Grace St., Boise, ID 83703. TEL 208-344-8594. FAX 208-344-8677. Ed. Matt Hanzel. adv.; bk.rev.; circ. 2,250 (controlled). (processed)
Supersedes: Gem City News (ISSN 0300-8355)

352 US
IDEAS IN ACTION: GUIDE TO LOCAL GOVERNMENT INNOVATIONS. 1977. q. $65. International City - County Management Association, 777 North Capitol St., N.E. Ste. 500, Washington, DC 20002-4201. TEL 202-962-3620; 800-745-8780. FAX 202-962-3500. Ed. Christine Ulrich. index. circ. 700. **Document type:** bulletin.
Former titles: Guide to Management Improvement Projects in Local Government; Guide to Productivity Improvement Projects; **Supersedes:** Jurisdictional Guide to Productivity Improvement Projects.
Description: Describes projects aimed at improving services and reducing costs.

352 TU
ILLER VE BELEDIYELER; aylik ilim ve meslek dergisi. 1945. m. TL.1000000. Turk Belediyecilik Dernegi, Mithat Pasa Caddesi 45-2, Ankara, Turkey. Ed. Argun Ersoz. adv.; index. circ. 3,500.

352 US ISSN 0019-1949
ILLINOIS COUNTY AND TOWNSHIP OFFICIAL. 1940. m. (11/yr.). $15. (Township Officials of Illinois) Stevens Publishing Company, Box 455, Astoria, IL 61501. TEL 309-329-2101. FAX 309-329-2133. (Alt. addr.: 817 LaPorte Ave., Melrose Park, IL 60164. TEL 708-562-8290) Ed. George H. Miller. adv.: page $400; adv. contact: Bryan E. Smith. illus. circ. 13,000.
Description: Provides items of interest and general information for local government officials, particularly those representing townships.

352 US ISSN 0019-2139
JS39
ILLINOIS MUNICIPAL REVIEW;* the magazine of the municipalities. 1922. m. membership. Illinois Municipal League, Box 3387, Springfield, IL 62708. TEL 217-525-1220. Ed. Steven Sargent. adv.; illus.; index. circ. 10,000.

352 IT ISSN 0019-3003
IMPRESA PUBBLICA; municipalizzazione. (Monthly supplement avail.: Notiziario Interfederale) 1956. m. L.140000 (effective 1994). (Confederazione Italiana dei Servizi Pubblici degli Enti Locali) Maggioli Editore, Viale Vespucci 12-n, Casella Postale 290, 47037 Rimini, Italy. TEL 0541-626777. FAX 0541-622020. Ed. Renzo Santini. adv.: B&W page L.1300000, color page L.2100000; trim 180 x 270. bk.rev.; charts; illus.; stat.; index. circ. 2,272. **Indexed:** P.A.I.S.For.Lang.Ind.

352 CN
IMPROVEMENT DISTRICT MANUAL. base vol. (plus irreg. supplements). Can.$50.75. Ministry of Municipal Affairs, Recreation and Housing, Victoria, B.C., Canada. (Subscr. to: Crown Publications, 546 Yates St., Victoria, B.C. V8W 1K8, Canada. TEL 604-386-4636)
Description: Provides a comprehensive outline on some of the common procedures that are carried out under the Municipal Act.

352 IT ISSN 0394-8331
INFORMATICA ED ENTI LOCALI; rivista trimestrale di metodologie e tecnologie avanzate. 1984. q. L.180000 (effective 1994). Maggioli Editore, Viale Vespucci, 12-n, Casella Postale 290, 47037 Rimini, Italy. TEL 0541-626777. FAX 0541-622020. Ed. Donato Limone. adv.: B&W page L.1800000, color page L.2700000; trim 210 x 297. circ. 2,991.

352 GW
INFORMATION FUER ORMESHEIM. Short title: I F O. 1983. s-a. Sozialdemokratische Partei Deutschlands (SPD), Ortsverein Ormesheim, Mozartstr. 4, 66399 Mandelbachtal, Germany. TEL 06893-3996. Ed. Rainer Barth. (looseleaf format) **Document type:** newsletter.

INFORMATIONEN ZUR MODERNEN STADTGESCHICHTE (I M S). see HOUSING AND URBAN PLANNING

352 GW
INFORMATIONEN ZUR STADTENTWICKLUNG LUDWIGSHAFEN. 1972. irreg. Stadt Ludwigshafen, Amt fuer Stadtentwicklung, Rathausplatz 20, 67069 Ludwigshafen, Germany. TEL 0621-5042218. FAX 0621-5043453. Ed. Harald Kuehne. adv. contact: Antje Louis. circ. 1,000. **Document type:** government publication.

INFOTECH REPORT. see COMPUTERS — Microcomputers

352 US
INNOVATIVE MUNICIPAL PROGRAMS (YEAR). a. $30 to non-members; members $15. Colorado Municipal League, 1660 Lincoln St., Ste. 2100, Denver, CO 80264. TEL 303-831-6411. **Document type:** government publication.
Description: Information on innovative programs submitted for judging in CML's annual Innovative Program Awards. Contains a program description and contact person for each program.

INTERNATIONAL PERSPECTIVES IN URBAN STUDIES SERIES. see HOUSING AND URBAN PLANNING

PUBLIC ADMINISTRATION — MUNICIPAL GOVERNMENT

352   US   ISSN 0892-3795
IOWA COUNTY. 1972. m. $10. Iowa State Association of Counties, 701 E. Court Ave., Des Moines, IA 50309. TEL 515-244-7181. Ed. Tricia Fazzini. adv.; bk.rev. circ. 2,000. (back issues avail.)
Formerly: County (Des Moines) (ISSN 0199-7793)
Description: Promotes efficient and economically sound county government for the citizens of Iowa.

352   US   ISSN 0021-0595
JS303.I55
IOWA MUNICIPALITIES.* 1945. bi-m. $11.50. League of Iowa Municipalities, 317 6th Ave., Bldg. 1400, Des Moines, IA 50309-4122. TEL 515-244-7282. FAX 515-244-0740. Ed. Joy M. Newcom. adv.; bk.rev. circ. 10,400.

336   IS
ISRAEL. KNESSET. HA-VA'ADA LE-INYANEI BIKORET HA-MEDINA. SIKUMEHA VE-HATSA'OTEHA SHEL HA-VA'ADA LE-INYANEI BIKORET HA-MEDINA LE-DIN VE-KHESHBON SHEL MEVAKER HA-MEDINA.* 1973. a. Knesset, State Control Committee, Jerusalem, Israel. Ed. Aharon Berkner. circ. controlled. (processed)

352   US   ISSN 1074-956X
J O B. 1989. fortn. $15. International City - County Management Association, 777 North Capitol St., N.E., Ste. 500, Washington, DC 20002-4201. TEL 202-962-3662. FAX 202-962-3500. Ed. Deitra Crawley. circ. 12,000. **Document type:** newsletter.
Description: Assists communities in broadening their outreach to minority and female professionals.

352   GW
JAHRBUCH BRANDENBURG; das grosse Auskunfts- und Adressenwerk. 1991. a. DM.48. Carl Gerber Verlag, Muthmannstr. 4, 80939 Munich, Germany. TEL 089-32393280. FAX 089-3231269. circ. 1,000. **Document type:** bulletin.

352   GW
JAHRBUCH BUNDESREPUBLIK; das grosse Auskunfts- und Adressenwerk. 1992. a. DM.28. Carl Gerber Verlag, Muthmannstr. 4, 80939 Munich, Germany. TEL 089-32393280. FAX 089-3231269. **Document type:** directory.

352   GW
JAHRBUCH MECKLENBURG-VORPOMMERN; das grosse Auskunfts- und Adressenwerk. 1993. a. DM.48. Carl Gerber Verlag, Muthmannstr. 4, 80939 Munich, Germany. TEL 089-32393280. FAX 089-3231269. **Document type:** directory.

352   GW
JAHRBUCH SACHSEN; das grosse Auskunfts- und Adressenwerk. 1992. a. DM.48. Carl Gerber Verlag, Muthmannstr. 4, 80939 Munich, Germany. TEL 089-32393280. FAX 089-3231269. **Document type:** directory.

JAHRBUCH SACHSEN-ANHALT; grosses Auskunfts- und Adressenwerk. see BUSINESS AND ECONOMICS — Trade And Industrial Directories

352   GW
JAHRBUCH THUERINGEN; das grosse Auskunfts- und Adressenwerk. 1991. a. DM.48. Carl Gerber Verlag, Muthmannstr. 4, 80939 Munich, Germany. TEL 089-32393280. FAX 089-3231269. circ. 1,000. **Document type:** directory.

352   FR   ISSN 1157-0377
JOURNAL D'ADMINISTRATION DES COMMUNES RURALES. 1901. m. 480 F. Publications Paul Dupont, 38 rue Croix des Petits Champs, 75001 Paris, France. TEL 42-36-06-87. FAX 40-39-01-23. Ed. Rene Dubail. adv.

352   FR   ISSN 0021-8030
JOURNAL DES COMMUNES. 1828. m. 500 F. Publications Paul Dupont, 38 rue Croix des Petits Champs, 75001 Paris, France. TEL 42-36-06-87. FAX 40-39-01-23. Ed. Rene Dubail.

352   FR   ISSN 1013-2457
JOURNAL DES COMMUNES ET REGIONS D'EUROPE. 1956. q. 80 F. Association Francaise du Conseil des Communes et Regions d'Europe, 30 rue d'Alsace-Lorraine, 45000 Orleans, France. TEL 38-77-83-83. Ed. S. Gaumer. adv.; bk.rev. circ. 10,000.
Formerly (until 1985): Communes d'Europe (ISSN 0414-1105)

352   FR   ISSN 0294-8095
JOURNAL DES MAIRES; et des conseillers municipaux. 1857. m. (11/yr.). 360 F. SETAC, 22 rue Cambaceres, 75008 Paris, France. TEL 42-65-58-94. FAX 47-42-87-57. Ed. Jean-Luc Varin. adv. circ. 12,000.
Formerly (until 1863): Supplement Trimestriel du Secretaire de Mairie (ISSN 1146-9099)

JOURNAL OF WASTE MANAGEMENT & RESOURCE RECOVERY. see ENVIRONMENTAL STUDIES — Waste Management

JUSTICE OF THE PEACE AND LOCAL GOVERNMENT LAW. see LAW — Criminal Law

352   DK   ISSN 0903-6237
K C NYT. 1983. q. membership. Foreningen af Kommunale Chefer (KC), Leongangstraede 25, 4, 1468 Copenhagen K, Denmark. TEL 33-14-48-38. FAX 33-13-71-14. illus.
Former titles: F A K E Nyt (ISSN 0109-0925); Foreningen af Kommunale Embedsmaend. Medlemsny.

352   AU   ISSN 0022-7552
KAERNTNER GEMEINDEBLATT. 1926. irreg. S.973. (Amt der Kaerntner Landesregierung) Kaerntner Druck- und Verlags-Gesellschaft mbH, Viktringer Ring 28, A-9010 Klagenfurt, Austria. FAX 0463-536-32007. bk.rev.; stat.; index. (also avail. in microform)

352   AU   ISSN 0022-7579
KAERNTNER LANDES-ZEITUNG. 1949. w. S.156. Amt der Kaerntner Landesregierung, Arnulfplatz 1, A-9010 Klagenfurt, Austria. Ed. Eduard Schober.

352   US   ISSN 0022-8613
KANSAS GOVERNMENT JOURNAL. 1914. m. $26. League of Kansas Municipalities, 300 S.W. Eigth St., Topeka, KS 66603. TEL 913-354-9565. FAX 913-354-4186. Ed. Paula Drummond. adv.: B&W page $300. bk.rev.; illus.; stat.; index. circ. 7,000.

352   UK
KEMPS LOCAL AUTHORITY AND PUBLIC SERVICE YEARBOOK. a. £73. Kemps Publishing Ltd., 11 The Swan Courtyard, Charles Edward Rd., Birmingham B26 1BU, England. TEL 0121-765-4144. FAX 0121-706-5941. **Document type:** corporate report.

352   US   ISSN 0453-5677
JS39
KENTUCKY CITY. 1929. m. (11/yr.). $11. Kentucky League of Cities, 2201 Regency Rd., Ste. 100, Lexington, KY 40503. TEL 606-277-2886. FAX 606-278-5766. Ed. Judy Love. adv.; illus. circ. 4,500. (tabloid format)

352   AU   ISSN 0023-2017
KLAGENFURT; Mitteilungsblatt der Landeshauptstadt. 1951. fortn. S.120($5) Magistrat der Landeshauptstadt Klagenfurt, Rathaus, A-9010 Klagenfurt, Austria. FAX 0463-516990. Ed. Veronika Meissnitzer. adv. contact: Ludmilla Dreier. bk.rev.; bibl.; illus.; index. circ. 44,000. **Document type:** government publication.

352   GW
KOBLENZER BEHOERDEN SPIEGEL. 1984. m. DM.39. ProPress Verlag GmbH, Am Buschhof 8, 53227 Bonn, Germany. TEL 0228-970970. FAX 0228-444296. Ed. R. Uwe Proll. circ. 15,000. **Document type:** bulletin.

352   GW
KOELNER BEHOERDEN SPIEGEL; unabhaengige Zeitung fuer den oeffentlichen Dienst. 1984. m. DM.39. ProPress Verlag GmbH, Am Buschhof 8, 53227 Bonn, Germany. TEL 0228-970970. FAX 0228-444296. Ed. R. Uwe Proll. circ. 20,500. **Document type:** newspaper.

352   SW   ISSN 0347-5484
KOMMUN-AKTUELT/MUNICIPAL NEWS. 1978. w. SEK 280. Svenska Kommunfoerbundet - Swedish Association of Local Authorities, Hornsgatan 15, 116 47 Stockholm, Sweden. adv.; bk.rev.; charts; illus. circ. 46,000. (tabloid format)
Formed by the merger of: Paa Fritid (ISSN 0346-6159) & Kommunal Tidskrift (ISSN 0023-3072) & Kommunal Skoltidning (ISSN 0023-3064) & Socialt Forum (ISSN 0049-0970) & Hygien och Miljoe; Hygien och Miljoe formerly titled (until 1974): Hygienisk Revy (ISSN 0018-8255); Kommunal Tidskrift formerly titled: Kommuneras Tidskrift; Socialt Forum formerly titled: Svenska Socialvaardsfoerbundets Tidskrift.

352   DK   ISSN 0900-1484
KOMMUNAL AARBOG.* 1930. a. DKK 447.75. Kommunal Aarbog, Vedbaek, Denmark.

352.1   SW   ISSN 0282-0099
KOMMUNAL EKONOMI. 1969. 6/yr. SEK 300. Foereningen Sveriges Kommunalekonomer, Theres Svenssons Gata 10, S-417 55 Goeteborg, Sweden. TEL 46-31-23-45-89. FAX 46-31-22-86-00. Ed. Aake Wessman; Pub. Inger Nilsson. adv.: B&W page SEK 12000, color page SEK 17800; adv. contact: Evert Stroem. circ. 3,000. pp./issue: 32.
Formerly (until 1982): Kommunalekonomen (ISSN 0345-6315)

352   SZ
KOMMUNALMAGAZIN. 11/yr. Verlag Forum Press AG, Franklinstr. 21, CH-8050 Zurich, Switzerland. TEL 01-3115353. FAX 01-3115370. Ed. Werner Hochuli. circ. 5,040. **Document type:** consumer publication.

352   DK
KOMMUNEN; information om dansk kommunalstyre. 1958. fortn. Kommunen, Solvaenget 1, 2100 Copenhagen, Denmark. TEL 31 18 00 55. FAX 31-18-04-05. Ed. Erik Malling-Jensen. adv. circ. 7,800.

352   SZ
KORRESPONDENZBLATT. m. Matthof 18, CH-6014 Littau, Switzerland. TEL 041-574206. Ed. Pius Kost. circ. 4,100.

352   XV   ISSN 1318-0746
KRANJCAN. (Text in Slovenian) 1982. m. Skupscina Obcine Kranj, Trg Revolucije 1, 64000 Kranj, Slovenia. TEL 064 25661. circ. 6,700. (back issues avail.)

352   GW
KREISAMTSBLATT DES LANDKREISES UND LANDRATSAMTES KRONACH. 1900. w. DM.30. Landratsamt Kronach, Guetterstr. 18, 96317 Kronach, Germany. TEL 09261-90-0. FAX 09261-90211. circ. 400. (looseleaf format; back issues avail.) **Document type:** government publication.
Formerly: Landkreis Kronach. Amtsblatt.

352   GW
KREISPOSTILLE. 1967. q. free. Kreis Neuss, Lindenstr. 2-16, 41515 Grevenbroich, Germany. TEL 02181-6011130. FAX 02181-6012630. circ. 6,000.

352   FI   ISSN 1236-0066
JS6291.A1
KUNTALEHTI. (Text in Finnish) 1916. 22/yr. FIM 280. Suomen Kuntaliitto - Association of Finnish Local Authorities, Toinen Linja 14, 00530 Helsinki, Finland. TEL 358-90-7711. FAX 358-90-771-2486. Ed. Olli Havu. adv. contact: Heikki Macklin. bk.rev.; charts; illus.; stat.; index. circ. 16,700.
Formerly (until 1993): Suomen Kunnallislehti (ISSN 0039-5544)
Description: Covers municipal legislation, economy, local government, education, social welfare, cultural activities, the Parliament, and the European Community.

PUBLIC ADMINISTRATION — MUNICIPAL GOVERNMENT

352 II ISSN 0023-5660
KURUKSHETRA. (Editions in English and Hindi) 1952. fortn. Rs.5($2.40) Ministry of Information & Broadcasting, Publications Division, Patiala House, Tilak Marg, New Delhi 110001, India. (Subscr. in U.S. to: M-S Inter Culture Associates, Thompson, CT 06277) Ed. B.K. Dhusia. adv. contact: B.N. Rajbhar. bk.rev.; charts; illus.; cum.index. circ. 18,000. **Indexed:** Geo.Abstr., Rural Devel.Abstr., Rural Recreat.Tour.Abstr., Soils & Fert., World Agri.Econ. & Rural Sociol.Abstr. **Document type:** government publication.
—BLDSC (5131.412000); UnCover.
Incorporates (in June 1970): Panchayati Raj (New Delhi) (ISSN 0553-0946)
Description: Devoted of all aspects of rural reconstruction and village democracy. Features rural industrialisation, farm revolution, co-operative progress and problems of district and village administration.

LAND CONTAMINATION & RECLAMATION. see ENVIRONMENTAL STUDIES — Pollution

352 AU ISSN 0023-7884
LANDESGESETZBLATT FUER DAS LAND SALZBURG. 1945. irreg. S.450. Landesregierung Salzburg, Chiemseehof, A-5010 Salzburg, Austria. TEL 0662-80422047. FAX 0662-80422161. index. circ. 2,000. (looseleaf format) **Document type:** government publication.

352 SW ISSN 0282-4485
LANDSTINGSVAERLDEN. 1914. 20/yr. SEK 360 (effective 1994). Landstingsfoerbundet - Federation of Swedish County Councils, P.O. Box 70491, S-107 26 Stockholm, Sweden. FAX 08-702-4505. Ed. Erik Trillkott. adv.; bk.rev.; illus.; index. circ. 11,200. **Document type:** newspaper.
Former titles (until 1985): Landstingens Tidskrift (ISSN 0023-8074); (until 1966): Sveriges Landstings Tidskrift.

LEASE AUCTION NOTICE. see REAL ESTATE

352 GW
LEIPZIGER BEHOERDEN SPIEGEL; unabhaengige Zeitung fuer den oeffentlichen Dienst. 1990. m. DM.36. ProPress Verlag GmbH, Am Buschhof 8, 53227 Bonn, Germany. TEL 0228-970970. FAX 0228-444296. circ. 6,000. **Document type:** newspaper.

352 FR
LETTRE DES COMMUNES, DES DEPARTEMENTS ET DES REGIONS D'EUROPE. 6/yr. Association Francaise du Conseil des Communes et Regions d'Europe, 30 rue d'Alsace-Lorraine, 45000 Orleans, France. TEL 38-77-83-83. Ed. S. Gaumer.
Formerly: Lettre des Regions d'Europe (ISSN 0996-4231)

352 FR ISSN 1165-9394
LETTRE DU CADRE TERRITORIAL. 10/yr. S E P T, B.P. 215, 38506 Voiron Cedex, France. TEL 76-65-71-36. FAX 76-66-12-85. Ed. Claude Mauves. circ. 10,500.
Formerly (until 1994): Lettre du Cadre Territorial de Claude Mauves (ISSN 0767-0346)

352 FR
LETTRE EUROPEENNE DES JUMELAGES. irreg. (5-6/yr.). Association Francaises du Conseil des Communes et Regions d'Europe, 30 rue d'Alsace-Lorraine, 45000 Orleans, France. TEL 38-77-83-83. Ed. S. Gaumer.

354 LB ISSN 0304-730X
HN831.L54
LIBERIA. MINISTRY OF LOCAL GOVERNMENT, RURAL DEVELOPMENT & URBAN RECONSTRUCTION. ANNUAL REPORT.* (Report year ends Sept. 30) 1972. a. Ministry of Rural Development, P.O. Box 9030, Monrovia, Liberia.
Formerly: Liberia. Department of Internal Affairs. Annual Report.

352 UK ISSN 0958-3823
LOCAL AND CENTRAL GOVERNMENT RELATIONS RESEARCH FINDINGS. 1989. irreg. no.31, 1994. Joseph Rowntree Foundation, The Homestead, 40 Water End, York YO3 6LP, England. TEL 01904-629241. FAX 01904-620072. **Document type:** bulletin.
—BLDSC (5289.400000).

352 EI
LOCAL AND REGIONAL AUTHORITIES IN EUROPE. STUDY SERIES. (Text in English or French) 1972. irreg. (2-3/yr.). price varies. Council of Europe, Activities of the Steering Committee for Local and Regional Authorities, Publishing and Documentation Service, 67075 Strasbourg Cedex, France. (Dist. in U.S. by: Manhattan Publishing Co., Box 650, Croton, NY 10520)

352 UK
LOCAL AUTHORITY BUILDING & MAINTENANCE. 10/yr. Regal House Ct., Regal Way, Watford, Herts. WD2 4YJ, England. TEL 01923-37799. FAX 01923-246901. TELEX 025859 ELWOOD G. Ed. J. Dobbyn. circ. 17,165. **Document type:** trade publication.
Description: Concerns technical materials and methods.

352 328 NZ ISSN 0111-9087
LOCAL AUTHORITY MANAGEMENT. 1975. q. NZ.$45($88) New Zealand Society of Local Government Managers, c/o Graham W.A. Bush, Ed., University of Auckland, Private Bag 92019, Auckland, New Zealand. TEL 09-3737999. FAX 09-3737449. adv.; bk.rev.; circ. 700 (paid). **Document type:** academic/scholarly publication.
Formerly (until 1981): Local Authority Administration (ISSN 0110-6066)

352 UK
LOCAL AUTHORITY PLANT & VEHICLES. 1982. 10/yr. £36 (rest of Europe £50; elsewhere £60). Cedargreen House, Bentinck Rd., W. Drayton, Mddx. UB7 7RF, England. TEL 01895-421111. FAX 01895-431252. Ed. Malcolm Bates. adv. contact: Simon Turton. bk.rev. circ. 6,240. **Document type:** trade publication.
Description: Directed to local authority and public utility executives responsible for specifying and purchasing plant vehicles and equipment.

LOCAL AUTHORITY WASTE & ENVIRONMENT. see ENVIRONMENTAL STUDIES — Waste Management

352 UK ISSN 0308-3594
JS3001
LOCAL COUNCIL REVIEW. 1950. bi-m. £7.50. National Association of Local Councils, 109 Great Russell St., London WC1B 3LD, England. TEL 0171-637-1865. Ed. Paul Smith. adv. contact: L.A. Smith. bk.rev.; illus. circ. 25,000. **Indexed:** Geo.Abstr., RICS. **Document type:** bulletin.
—BLDSC (5290.011000).
Formerly: Parish Councils Review (ISSN 0031-2061)

352 PK
LOCAL GOVERNMENT. (Text in English) vol.5, 1974. m. Rs.25. Pakistan Group for the Study of Local Government, 14 Japan Mansion, Preedy St., Karachi, Pakistan. Ed. Malik M. Siddiq. adv.; bk.rev.

352 UK ISSN 0267-2022
LOCAL GOVERNMENT ADMINISTRATORS' OFFICIAL SOURCE BOOK. 1985. a. £25. Millbank Publications Ltd., 25 Catherine St., London WC2B 5JW, England. TEL 071-379-3036. FAX 071-240-6840. adv. circ. 3,000. **Document type:** directory.

352 UK ISSN 0968-2430
LOCAL GOVERNMENT AND LAW. 1991. £119 (foreign £141). Monitor Press, Rectory Rd., Great Waldingfield, Sudbury, Suffolk CO10 0TL, England. TEL 01787-378607. FAX 01787-880201. Ed. Richard Clutterbuck. **Indexed:** Euro.LJI, LJI. **Document type:** newsletter.
Description: Reviews developments in the law as they affect those who are engaged in local government.

352 PH ISSN 0024-5526
JS7301.A1
LOCAL GOVERNMENT BULLETIN. 1966. bi-m. P.90($15) University of the Philippines, College of Public Administration, Local Government Center, PARDEC-SAAC Building, Don Mariano Marcos Avenue, P.O. Box 198, Diliman, Quezon City, Philippines. TEL 99-39-14. Eds. Alex Brillantes, Jr., Vicente Mariano. bk.rev.; illus.; stat. circ. 1,000. **Indexed:** Ind.Phil.Per.

352 UK ISSN 0024-5534
LOCAL GOVERNMENT CHRONICLE. 1855. w. £71 (effective Jul. 1993). E M A P - Business Publishing Ltd., 33-39 Bowling Green Ln., London EC1R 0DA, England. TEL 0171-837-1212. FAX 0171-278-9509. Ed. David Pead. adv. contact: Marie Rogers. bk.rev.; illus.; index. circ. 8,407. (also avail. in microform from UMI; reprint service avail.) **Indexed:** Account.& Data Proc.Abstr., ASSIA, Euro.LJI, Geo.Abstr., LJI, RICS.
●Also available online.
—BLDSC (5290.013000); UMI.

352 UK ISSN 0305-0130
LOCAL GOVERNMENT COMPANION. 1974. a. £12. 18 Lincoln Green, Chichester, W. Sussex PO19 4DN, England. TEL 01243-787272. Ed. E.P. Craig. **Document type:** directory.

352 UK ISSN 1350-2719
LOCAL GOVERNMENT EXECUTIVE. 1991. bi-m. £32. Tempus House of Publishers, Fourways House, 57 Hilton St., Manchester M1 2EJ, England. TEL 0161-237-1007. FAX 0161-237-1004. Ed. David Honour; Pub. Kevin Hill. adv. contact: Kevin Brennan. bk.rev. circ. 3,800. **Document type:** government publication, trade publication.
Description: Covers finance, communications, information technology, and news of conferences and exhibitions.

352 363.6 SA ISSN 1015-0048
JS7531.A1
LOCAL GOVERNMENT IN SOUTHERN AFRICA/PLAASLIKE REGERING IN SUIDELIKE AFRIKA. (Text in Afrikaans, English) 1916. bi-m. R.24. (South African Association of Municipal Employees) Target Communications, P.O. Box 3445, Randburg 2125, South Africa. TEL 27-11-8864583. FAX 27-11-8864568. Ed. Ron Bull. adv.; bk.rev.; illus. circ. 3,200. **Indexed:** Excerp.Med., Ind.S.A.Per., W.R.C.Inf.
Former titles: Municipal Administration and Engineering (ISSN 0027-3422); Municipal Affairs.

352 SA
LOCAL GOVERNMENT LIBRARY BULLETIN/BULLETIN VAN DIE PLAASLIKE REGERINGSBIBLIOTEEK. (Text in Afrikaans, English) 1938. m. free. Johannesburg Public Library, Market Square, Johannesburg 2001, South Africa. TEL 27-11-836-3787. FAX 27-11-836-6607. circ. 300. (back issues avail.) **Document type:** abstracting/indexing.
Formerly (until 1992): Municipal References Library Bulletin - Bulletin van die Munisipale Naslaanbiblioteek.
Description: Current-awareness information on local government and municipal services in South Africa and elsewhere.

352 AT ISSN 0727-7342
LOCAL GOVERNMENT MANAGEMENT. Short title: L.G.M. 1957. bi-m. Aus.$37.50 (effective July 1991). Institute of Municipal Management, P.O. Box 409, S. Melbourne, Vic. 3205, Australia. TEL 03-696-5799. FAX 03-690-4217. Ed. Barrie Beattie. adv.; index; circ. 5,000 (controlled). (tabloid format; back issues avail.) **Indexed:** Aus.P.A.I.S.
—UnCover.
Formerly (until 1984): Local Government Administration (ISSN 0024-5518)
Description: Provides articles in relation to new manament technique applicable to local government senior managers.

352 UK ISSN 0261-5185
LOCAL GOVERNMENT NEWS. 1979. m. £40 (foreign £50). B & M Publications (London) Ltd., Box 13, Hereford House, Bridle Path, Croydon, Surrey CR9 4NL, England. TEL 0181-681-6000. FAX 0181-680-4200. FAX 0181-681-5049. Ed. P. Cooper. stat.; tr.lit. circ. 21,322. (back issues avail.)
—BLDSC (5290.019000).

PUBLIC ADMINISTRATION — MUNICIPAL GOVERNMENT

352   UK   ISSN 0264-2050
LOCAL GOVERNMENT POLICY MAKING. 1974. 5/yr. £110 (foreign £125). (University of Birmingham, Institute of Local Government Studies) Pitman Publishing, 128 Long Acre, London WC2E 9AN, England. TEL 0171-379-7383. FAX 0171-240-5771. Ed. John Benington. adv.; bk.rev.; index. (also avail. in microfilm; back issues avail.) **Indexed:** Bus.Ind., Cont.Pg.Manage. **Document type:** academic/scholarly publication.
—BLDSC (5290.022000); UMI. **CCC.**
  Former titles (until 1981): Corporate Planning Journal; (until 1979): Corporate Planning (ISSN 0305-3695)
  Description: Aims to contribute to both the theory and the practice of local government policy making and strategic management, under conditions of continuous change and uncertainty. Attempts to develop a better theoretical understanding of the role and potential of the local state.
Refereed Serial

352   JA   ISSN 0288-7622
JS7371.A1
LOCAL GOVERNMENT REVIEW IN JAPAN. (Text in English) 1973. a. free. General Center for Local Autonomy - Jichi Sogo Centre, Toranomon Bldg., 8th Fl., 1-7-1 Nishi-Shinbashi, Minato-ku, Tokyo 105, Japan. TEL 03-3504-0841. FAX 03-3504-0872. TELEX 02228505-JALTAS-J. Ed. Katsuomi Ohbayashi. circ. 600.
  Formerly: Local Government Review (ISSN 0449-0193)
  Description: Introduces problems faced by Japanese local governments. Contains articles selected and translated from publications of the bureaus of the Ministry of Home Affairs (Minister's Secretariat, Local Bureau, Local Autonomy College, and Fire Defense Agency.) Aims to promote mutual exchange between Japanese local governments and those abroad.

LOCAL GOVERNMENT REVIEW REPORTS. see *LAW*

352   UK   ISSN 0300-3930
JS40
LOCAL GOVERNMENT STUDIES. 1971. q. £145($195) to institutions (effective 1996). Frank Cass, Newbury House, 890-900 Eastern Ave., Newbury Park, Ilford, Essex 1G2 7HH, England. TEL 44-181-599-8866. FAX 44-181-599-0984. E-mail: 100067,1576@compuserve.com. Eds. Kieron Walsh, Chris Skelcher. adv.; B&W page £195 ($275); adv. contact: Anne Kidson. bk.rev.; index. circ. 1,000. (back issues avail.) **Indexed:** Account.& Data Proc.Abstr., ASSIA, Br.Hum.Ind., Curr.Cont., Geo.Abstr., IDA, Int.Polit.Sci.Abstr., Sage Urb.Stud.Abstr., SSCI. **Document type:** academic/scholarly publication.
—BLDSC (5290.029000); Genuine Article; SWETS.
  Description: Covers the study of politics, administration, and the management of local affairs.
Refereed Serial

LOCAL HEALTH OFFICERS NEWS. see *PUBLIC HEALTH AND SAFETY*

352   II   ISSN 0024-5615
LOCAL SELF-GOVERNMENT.* (Text in English) 1956. m. Rs.20.($4.) 1750 Sohanganj, Subzimandi, Delhi, India. Ed. H.C. Banjahi. adv.; charts; illus.

352.0763   US   ISSN 0164-3622
JS39
LOUISIANA MUNICIPAL REVIEW. 1938. m. $12. Louisiana Municipal Association, Box 4327, Baton Rouge, LA 70821. TEL 504-344-5001. FAX 504-344-3057. Eds. L. Gordon King, Thomas B. Darensbourg, Jr. adv. contact: Kay Jackson. bk.rev. circ. 3,300. **Document type:** newsletter.
  Description: Devoted to municipal government issues in Louisiana, the U.S., and intergovernmental relations.

352   SZ
LUZERNER KANTONSBLATT. 1975. w. 55 Fr. (Staatskanzlei) Raeber AG, Frankenstr. 7-9, Lucerne, Switzerland. Ed.Bd. adv. circ. 7,050.

352   US
M A P A REGIONAL DIRECTORY OF PUBLIC OFFICIALS. a. $10. Omaha - Council Bluffs Metropolitan Area Planning Agency, 2222 Cumming St., Omaha, NE 68102-4328. TEL 402-444-6866. FAX 402-342-0949. circ. 1,000. **Document type:** directory.

352   US   ISSN 0047-5262
M I S REPORTS. (Management Information Service) (Included in M I S subscription, which consists of data and inquiry services) 1946. m. price varies. International City - County Management Association, 777 N. Capitol St., N.E., Ste. 500, Washington, DC 20002-4201. TEL 202-962-3620; 800-745-8780. FAX 202-962-3500. Ed. Christine Ulrich. charts. circ. 1,000. (back issues avail.) **Indexed:** P.A.I.S., Sage Pub.Admin.Abstr., Urb.Aff.Abstr. **Document type:** bulletin.
  Description: Covers development, implementation, delivery and evaluation of local government programs and services.

352   US
THE (YEAR) M T A S SALARY AND FRINGE BENEFIT SURVEY. a. free. University of Tennessee at Knoxville, Municipal Technical Advisory Service, 600 Henley, Ste. 120, Knoxville, TN 37996-4105. TEL 615-974-0411. charts; stat.
  Formerly (until 1994): Salary and Fringe Benefits Survey of Tennessee Municipalities.
  Description: Monitors the salaries and benefits earned by Tennessee municipal employees.

MCQUILLIN MUNICIPAL LAW REPORT; a monthly review for lawyers, administrators and officials. see *LAW*

352 350   US   ISSN 0145-9597
JK2830
MAINE REGISTER: STATE YEARBOOK AND LEGISLATIVE MANUAL. 1822. a. $95. Tower Publishing Co., 588 Saco Rd., Standish, ME 04084-6239. TEL 207-642-5400; 800-969-8693. FAX 207-642-5463. adv.; index. circ. 1,400. (also avail. in diskette format) **Document type:** directory.
  Description: Contains information on state and county officials, with complete listing of municipal, business and professional directories and organizations.

352   US   ISSN 0025-0791
JS39
MAINE TOWNSMAN. 1939. m. $15 to non-members. Maine Municipal Association, Local Government Center, 37 Community Drive, Augusta, ME 04330. TEL 207-623-8428. FAX 207-626-5947. Ed. Michael L. Starn. adv.; B&W page $373, color page $673. bk.rev.; illus.; index. circ. 4,500.

352   FR
MAIRES DE FRANCE. 1952. m. 476 F. Association des Maires de France, 41 Quai d'Orsay, 75343 Paris cedex 07, France. TEL 44-18-14-14. FAX 44-18-14-16. Ed. Marie-Therese Poitevin. adv.; bk.rev.; abstr.; index. circ. 27,000. (tabloid format)
—BLDSC (3553.575000).
  Formerly: Departementes et Communes (ISSN 0045-9984)

352   GW
MANNHEIMER HEFTE. 1952. s-a. DM.5. Hauptamt, Postfach 10 30 51, 68030 Mannheim, Germany. TEL 0621-2931. FAX 0621-101452. Ed. Hansjoerg Probst. circ. 2,500. (back issues avail.)

352   US   ISSN 0361-2090
JS451.M47
MASSACHUSETTS MUNICIPAL ASSOCIATION DIRECTORY. (Supplement to: Municipal Advocate) 1964. a. $24. Massachusetts Municipal Association, 60 Temple Place, Boston, MA 02111. TEL 617-426-7272. FAX 612-695-1314. Ed. Sunny Edmunds. adv.; bk.rev. circ. 4,200. **Document type:** directory.
  Description: Lists local governments and officials in the commonwealth, including city and county governments and state professional organizations.

352   II
MAYORS' NEWSLETTER. (Text in English) 1973. q. Rs.6. All India Council of Mayors, 48-B Municipal Colony, Azadpur, Delhi 110 033, India. Ed. Hira Lall Mathur. adv.; bk.rev. circ. 2,000. **Document type:** newsletter.

352   US
THE MAYORS OF AMERICA'S PRINCIPAL CITIES. s-a. $16 to non-members; members $8. U.S. Conference of Mayors, Office of Public Affairs, 1620 Eye St., N.W., Washington, DC 20006. TEL 202-293-7330. **Document type:** directory.

352 360   AT
MELBOURNE. PORT COUNCIL NEWS. 1985. irreg. (3-4/yr.) free. City Council, Port Melbourne, Town Hall, Bay St., Port Melbourne, Vic. 3207, Australia. TEL 03-647-9500. FAX 03-646-4839. Ed. David Graham. circ. 4,000.
  Description: Current information about council services for residents.

MESSAGE. see *MEETINGS AND CONGRESSES*

352   US   ISSN 0076-8014
MICHIGAN MUNICIPAL LEAGUE. MUNICIPAL LEGAL BRIEFS. 1961. bi-m. $60. Michigan Municipal League, 1675 Green Rd., Box 1487, Ann Arbor, MI 48106. TEL 313-662-3246. Ed. William L. Steude. circ. 700. (reprint service avail.)

352   US   ISSN 0026-2331
JS39
MICHIGAN MUNICIPAL REVIEW. 1928. 10/yr. $24. Michigan Municipal League, 1675 Green Rd., Box 1487, Ann Arbor, MI 48106. TEL 313-662-3246. Ed. Judi L. Campbell. adv.; bk.rev.; charts; illus.; mkt.; index. circ. 9,200. (also avail. in microfilm from UMI; reprint service avail. from UMI) **Indexed:** Mich.Mag.Ind., P.A.I.S.
—UMI.

352   US   ISSN 0148-8546
JS39
MINNESOTA CITIES. (Supplement avail.: Loss Control Quarterly) 1916. m. $18. League of Minnesota Cities, 3490 Lexington Ave. N., St. Paul, MN 55126-8044. TEL 612-490-5600. Ed. Tim Busse. adv.; B&W page $800, color page $1200; adv. contact: Gayle Brodt. bk.rev.; charts; illus.; stat.; index. circ. 9,900. **Indexed:** P.A.I.S., Sage Pub.Admin.Abstr. **Document type:** government publication.
  Formerly: Minnesota Municipalities (ISSN 0026-5578)
  Description: Covers taxes, finances from the legislator's viewpoint, legislative programs, labor relations and court decisions.

352   CN
MIRROR (WINNIPEG). q. Manitoba Association of Urban Municipalities, 200-611 Corydon Ave., Winnipeg, MB R3L OP3, Canada. TEL 204-982-6286. FAX 204-478-1005. Ed. Rochelle Zimberg. circ. 700. **Document type:** newsletter.

352   US   ISSN 0026-6337
JS303.M7
MISSISSIPPI MUNICIPALITIES. 1955. m. $16. Mississippi Municipal Association, 200 N. State St., Jackson, MS 39201. TEL 601-353-5854. Ed. James B. Borsig. adv.; illus.; tr.lit. circ. 3,300. **Document type:** government publication, academic/scholarly publication, bulletin.

352   US   ISSN 0026-6647
JS39
MISSOURI MUNICIPAL REVIEW. 1936. 10/yr. $18. Missouri Municipal League, 1727 Southridge Dr., Jefferson City, MO 65109. TEL 314-635-9134. FAX 314-635-9009. Ed. Dolores Schulte. adv.; B&W page $330. bk.rev.; charts; illus.; index. circ. 5,600.

352   AU
MITTEILUNGSBLATT DER STADT VILLACH. 1947. s-m. $115.50. Magistrat der Stadt Villach, Pressestelle, Rathaus, A-9500 Villach, Austria. FAX 04242-22465. TELEX 45-516-MAGVIL-A. adv.; bk.rev. circ. 24,500. **Document type:** bulletin.

350   US   ISSN 0026-9980
MONTANA LEAGUE OF CITIES & TOWNS. NEWSLETTER. no.139, 1975. irreg. (3-4/yr.) free. Montana League of Cities & Towns, Box 1704, Helena, MT 59624. TEL 406-442-8768. Ed. Alec Hansen. adv. contact: Debbie Jones. illus. circ. 1,200. **Document type:** newsletter.
  Formerly: Montana Municipal League. Newsletter.

352   BE
MOUVEMENT COMMUNAL. (Text in French) 1919. m. 3000 BEF. Union des Villes et Communes de Wallonie, Rue d'Arlon 53, B4, B-1040 Brussels, Belgium. Ed. Louise-Marie Bataille. adv.; bk.rev.; bibl.; illus. circ. 5,100. **Document type:** bulletin.

PUBLIC ADMINISTRATION — MUNICIPAL GOVERNMENT

352 371.42 SP
MUFACE. 12/yr. General Mutual Society of Civil Servants, Po. Juan XXIII, 26, 28040 Madrid, Spain. TEL 1-346-08-67. FAX 5352172. Ed. A. Fernandez Burgos. circ. 6,100,000.

352 CN
MUNICIPAL ACT AND INDEX TO LOCAL GOVERNMENT LEGISLATION MANUAL. base vol. (plus irreg. supplements). Can.$37.50. Ministry of Municipal Affairs, Recreation and Housing, Victoria, B.C., Canada. (Subscr. to: Crown Publications, 546 Yates St., Victoria, B.C. V8W 1K8, Canada. TEL 604-386-4636) (looseleaf format)
Description: A consolidation of the Municipal Act and an Index to Local Government Legislation.

352 US ISSN 1046-2422
MUNICIPAL ADVOCATE. 1980. q. $40. Massachusetts Municipal Association, 60 Temple Pl., Boston, MA 02111. TEL 617-426-7272. FAX 617-695-1314. Ed. Adam Auster. adv. circ. 4,525.
Formerly (until **1988**): Municipal Forum (ISSN 1041-6021)
Description: Articles, news and information on municipal law, insurance, finance, public safety, land use and public works for mayors, town and city managers, finance committee chairmen, treasurers and other officials with purchasing authority.

352 AT ISSN 0085-3585
MUNICIPAL ASSOCIATION OF TASMANIA. SESSION. MINUTES OF PROCEEDINGS. 1912. a. Aus.$10 to non-members. Municipal Association of Tasmania, 34 Patrick St., Hobart, Tas. 7000, Australia. TEL 002-310666. FAX 002-240086. Ed. Sue Mecklenburgh. index; circ. 200 (controlled).

352 AT ISSN 0077-2143
MUNICIPAL ASSOCIATION OF VICTORIA. MINUTES OF PROCEEDINGS OF ANNUAL SESSION. 1879. a. Aus.$42. Municipal Association of Victoria, G.P.O. Box 4326PP, Melbourne, Vic. 3001, Australia. TEL 64-3-8235555. FAX 64-3-8248404. Ed. bruce Whelam. index. circ. 4,000. **Document type:** proceedings.

MUNICIPAL ATTORNEY. see *LAW*

352 US
MUNICIPAL ELECTION CALENDAR. biennial. $20 to non-members; members $10. Colorado Municipal League, 1660 Lincoln St., Ste. 2100, Denver, CO 80264. TEL 303-831-6411. **Document type:** government publication.
Description: Checklist of action required by the Municipal Election Code to be performed before, during and after elections.

MUNICIPAL FINANCE JOURNAL. see *BUSINESS AND ECONOMICS — Public Finance, Taxation*

352 340 US ISSN 0895-8912
KF1302.A2
MUNICIPAL IMMUNITY LAW BULLETIN. 1987. m. $60 (effective 1993). Quinlan Publishing Co., Inc., 23 Drydock Ave., Boston, MA 02210-2387. TEL 617-542-0048; 800-229-2084. FAX 617-345-9646. index. (looseleaf format; back issues avail.) **Document type:** newsletter.
—UMI. CCC.
Description: Covers issues relating to immunity in lawsuits brought against municipalities, including official misconduct, injuries on city property, street maintenance, civil rights violations, wrongful prosecution or arrest, and similar issues.

352 363.6 UK ISSN 0143-4187
TD1
MUNICIPAL JOURNAL; British public services, local government administrator, contractors' guide, public works engineer, local government journal and new technology weekly. 1893. w. £60. Municipal Journal Ltd., 32 Vauxhall Bridge Rd., London SW1V 2SS, England. Ed. Michael Burton. charts; film rev.; illus.; mkt.; stat.; index. circ. 10,668. **Indexed:** Br.Tech.Ind., HRIS, P.A.I.S., RICS. **Document type:** bulletin.
—BLDSC (5984.400000).
Formerly: Municipal and Public Services Journal (ISSN 0027-3430); Which incorporated: Municipal Engineering (ISSN 0027-3457); Municipal Journal (ISSN 0027-349X)

340 US ISSN 0278-1301
KF5304.A75
MUNICIPAL LITIGATION REPORTER. 1981. m. $342. Strafford Publications, Inc., 590 Dutch Valley Rd., N.E., Drawer 13729, Atlanta, GA 30324-0729. TEL 404-881-1141. FAX 404-881-0074. Pub. Richard M. Ossoff. cum.index: 1981-1991. (back issues avail.) **Document type:** trade publication.
Description: Covers full spectrum of litigation involving local government entities in all 50 states and U.S. territories and possessions.

352 US ISSN 0196-9986
MUNICIPAL MARYLAND. 1948. 10/yr. $21. Maryland Municipal League, Inc., 1212 West St., Annapolis, MD 21401. TEL 410-268-5514. Ed. Karen A. Liskey. adv.; bk.rev. circ. 2,000.
Formerly: Maryland Municipal News (ISSN 0025-4304)
Description: Articles on the economic, legislative, law-enforcement, and social issues that affect the state's cities and towns.

352 CN ISSN 1191-906X
MUNICIPAL MONITOR. 1967. 6/yr. Can.$36 (foreign Can.$42). (Association of Municipal Clerks and Treasurers of Ontario) Kenilworth Publishing Inc., 80 W. Beaver Creek, Ste. 18, Richmond Hill, ON L4B 1H3, Canada. TEL 905-771-7333. FAX 905-771-7336. Ed. Dennis Mellersh. adv.: B&W page Can.$1215; trim 8 1/8 x 10 3/4. circ. 2,240.
—CCC.

352 US
MUNICIPAL PLANNER AND BUYER'S GUIDE. a. $30. Georgia Municipal Association, 201 Pryor St., S.W., Atlanta, GA 30303. TEL 404-688-0472. FAX 404-577-6663. (back issues avail.)

352 UK ISSN 0261-5118
MUNICIPAL REVIEW AND A M A NEWS. 1930. 10/yr. £18 (foreign £36). Association of Metropolitan Authorities, 35 Great Smith St., London SW1P 3BJ, England. TEL 071-222-8100. FAX 071-222-0878. Ed. Peter Smith. adv.; bk.rev.; illus.; stat.; index. circ. 7,800. **Indexed:** RICS, Sage Pub.Admin.Abstr.
—BLDSC (5985.080000); UnCover.
Formerly: Municipal Review (ISSN 0027-3562)

352 US ISSN 0027-3589
MUNICIPAL WORLD. 1891. m. Can.$39.63. Municipal World Inc., Box 399, St. Thomas, ON N5P 3V3, Canada. TEL 519-633-0031. FAX 519-633-1001. Ed. Michael J. Smither. adv.: B&W page $1654, color page $2573; adv. contact: Nasreine Canaran. bk.rev.; illus.; index. circ. 7,400. (also avail. in microfiche) **Document type:** trade publication.
Description: Reviews management and planning strategies of municipalities, redistribution of jurisdictions and financial responsibilities between the province and municipal governemnts, energy conservation, environment, business development, roads and highways, housing, human rights, role of the media in municipal reporting, heritage conservation, urban planning, law enforcement, transportation, waste disposal, zoning, legal articles, opinions to municipal questions from readers.

352 US ISSN 0077-2186
JS344.C5
MUNICIPAL YEAR BOOK. 1922. a. $79.95. International City - County Management Association, 777 N. Capitol, N.E., Ste. 500, Washington, DC 20002-4201. TEL 202-289-4262. FAX 202-962-3500. Ed. Evelina Moulder. bk.rev. circ. 16,000. Indexed: SRI. **Document type:** bulletin.
—BLDSC (5985.412000).
Formerly: City Manager Yearbook.
Description: Provides information on local government management issues and trends, intergovernmental subjects, staffing and compensation.

352 UK ISSN 0305-5906
JS3003
MUNICIPAL YEAR BOOK. Variant title: Municipal Yearbook. 1897. a. (in 2 vols.). £155 (foreign £165). Municipal Journal Ltd., 32 Vauxhall Bridge Rd., London SW1V 2SS, England. TEL 0171-973-6402. FAX 0171-233-5056. Ed. David Ricketts. adv. contact: Adrian Clarke. circ. 7,000 (paid). (also avail. in microfiche from BHP) **Document type:** directory.
—BLDSC (5985.415000).
Description: Comprehensive guide to U.K. central and local government and public services.

352 US ISSN 1054-4062
JS39
MUNICIPAL YELLOW BOOK; who's who in the leading city and county governments and local authorities. 1992. s-a. $180 (foreign $230). Leadership Directories, Inc., 104 Fifth Ave., 2nd Fl., New York, NY 10011. TEL 212-627-4140. FAX 212-645-0931. **Document type:** directory.
●Also available on CD-ROM.
—CCC.
Description: Includes nearly 25,000 key elected and administrative officials in local government.

352 SP
MUNICIPALIA; revista de administracion local. 1944. m. (combined July-Aug.). 15000 ptas. Municipalia, S.A., Serrano, 7, 28001 Madrid, Spain. TEL 34-91-4356101. FAX 34-91-4310570. (Subscr. to: Apdo No. 103, F.D. Madrid, Spain) Dir. Hipolito Lafuente Xicola. adv.; bk.rev.; charts; illus.; stat. circ. 1,200,000.
Description: Essays and news on local jurisprudence in Spain.

352 US ISSN 0027-3597
MUNICIPALITY. 1900. m. $18 membership. League of Wisconsin Municipalities, 202 State Street, Ste. 300, Madison, WI 53703. TEL 608-267-2380. FAX 608-267-0645. Ed. Dan Thompson. adv. contact: John O. Kirkpatrick. bk.rev.; charts; index. circ. 9,682. **Indexed:** P.A.I.S. **Document type:** government publication.
—UnCover.
Description: Aims to assist municipal officials in their fields.

352 SA ISSN 0024-5577
MUNISIPALE EN OPENBARE DIENSTE/MUNICIPAL AND PUBLIC WORK SERVICES. (Includes supplement: Consulting Engineer Africa) (Text in Afrikaans, English) 1960. m. R.120 (foreign R.180) (effective 1995). Malnor (Pty) Ltd., Private Bag X20, Auckland Park 2006, South Africa. TEL 27-11-7263081. FAX 27-11-7263017. Ed. Donald Koch. adv.; bk.rev.; illus. circ. 4,100. **Document type:** trade publication.

352 US ISSN 0735-9691
N A T A T'S REPORTER. 1977. bi-m. $36. National Association of Towns and Townships, National Center for Small Communities, 1522 K St. N.W., Ste. 600, Washington, DC 20005. TEL 202-737-5200. Ed. Ronnie J. Kweller. adv.: B&W page $1035, color page $1210. bk.rev. circ. 15,000. (tabloid format; back issues avail) **Document type:** newspaper.
Formerly: N A T A T's National Community Reporter.
Description: Covers issues concerning America's grassroots governments, including management of small towns, and federal policies affecting town governments.

352 NE ISSN 0924-4816
JS5931
N G MAGAZINE. Key Title: N G. 1947. w. fl.175. V N G Uitgeverij, P.O. Box 30435, 2500 GK The Hague, Netherlands. TEL 31-70-3738888. FAX 31-70-3469201. Ed.Bd. adv.; illus. circ. 28,000. **Indexed:** ELLIS, Key to Econ.Sci. **Document type:** trade publication.
—SWETS.
Formerly (until 1990): Nederlandse Gemeente (ISSN 0166-8927)

352 AU
NACHRICHTEN DER STADTGEMEINDE LIEZEN. 1966. q. free. Stadtgemeinde Liezen, Rathaus, A-8940 Liezen, Austria. TEL 03612-22881. FAX 03612-22881-3. Ed. Herbert Waldeck. adv. contact: Rudolf Kaltenboeck. circ. 3,500. **Document type:** newsletter.

352 GW
NACHRICHTENBLATT FUER DAS UNTERE HAERTSFELD. 1961. w. DM.35. Gemeinde Dischingen, Marktplatz 9, 89561 Dischingen, Germany. FAX 07327-8140. adv. (looseleaf format; back issues avail.)

352 II ISSN 0027-7584
NAGARLOK; urban affairs quarterly. (Text in English) 1969. q. Rs.30($15) (Centre for Urban Studies) Indian Institute of Public Administration, Indraprastha Estate, Ring Rd., New Delhi 110002, India. Ed. P.R. Dubhashi. bk.rev.; bibl.; charts; stat. (back issues avail.)
—UnCover.

PUBLIC ADMINISTRATION — MUNICIPAL GOVERNMENT

352 US ISSN 0027-9013
JS39
NATIONAL CIVIC REVIEW. 1912. q. $30 in U.S. & Canada; elsewhere $33. National Civic League, Inc., 1445 Market St., Ste. 300, Denver, CO 80202-1728. TEL 303-571-4343. Ed. David Lampe. adv.; bk.rev.; charts; index. circ. 4,000. (also avail. in microfiche from WSH,PMC; microfilm from WSH; reprint service avail. from UMI,WSH) Indexed: A.B.C.Pol.Sci., Amer.Hist.& Life, Bk.Rev.Ind. (1965-), C.L.I., Child.Bk.Rev.Ind. (1965-), Fut.Surv., Hist.Abstr., Leg.Per., P.A.I.S., Polit.Sci.Abstr., Sage Pub.Admin.Abstr., So.Pac.Per.Ind., Soc.Sci.Ind (1994-).
• Also available online. Vendor(s): University Microfilms International.
Also available on CD-ROM. Producer(s): University Microfilms International.
—Faxon; SWETS; UMI; UnCover.
Formerly: National Municipal Review (ISSN 0190-3799)

352 US ISSN 1049-0973
JS451.N75
THE NATIONAL MUNICIPAL GAZETTEER. NEW YORK. 1990. a. $90.25. Target Exchange, Inc., 203 Champlain Dr., Plattsburgh, NY 12901-4203. TEL 518-563-0701. Pub. Henry G. McComb. circ. 5,000. **Document type:** directory.
Description: Provides data on the state, all its political subdivisions and their elected and appointed officials. Includes address and phone-fax information, salary data, land areas, assessed values, population data, per capita income data, municipal finance data, financial ranking data, local histories, and more.

352 US ISSN 0164-5935
NATION'S CITIES WEEKLY. 1978. w. $96. National League of Cities, 1301 Pennsylvania Ave., N.W., Washington, DC 20004. TEL 202-626-3040. Ed. Alan Beals. adv.; bk.rev.; charts; illus.; index. circ. 28,200. (tabloid format; also avail. in microform from UMI; reprint service avail. from UMI) Indexed: Bus.Ind., Curr.Cont., Hlth.Ind., Mag.Ind., P.A.I.S., PSI, Soc.Sci.Ind., Tr.& Indus.Ind., Urb.Aff.Abstr.
—UMI.
Incorporates (in 1978): City Weekly (ISSN 0164-5595); **Supersedes (1963-1978):** Nation's Cities (ISSN 0028-0488)
Description: Discusses how national developments affect cities, with case studies on how local governments solve problems.

352 US ISSN 0028-1905
NEBRASKA MUNICIPAL REVIEW. 1930. m. $30. League of Nebraska Municipalities, 1335 L St., Lincoln, NE 68508. TEL 402-476-2829. Ed. Lynn Marienau. adv.: B&W page $491. illus.; stat. circ. 3,300. Indexed: P.A.I.S. **Document type:** government publication.
Description: Contains news and feature articles on local, state and federal government issues of interest to municipal officials.

352 CN ISSN 0841-1352
NEW BRUNSWICK PUBLIC EMPLOYEES ASSOCIATION. NEWSLINE - BULLETIN. French edition: Association des Employes de la Fonction Publique du Nouveau-Brunswick (ISSN 0841-1360) (Editions in English, French) 1970. irreg. free to qualified personnel. New Brunswick Public Employees Association, 238 King St., Fredericton, NB E3B 4Y2, Canada. TEL 506-458-8440. FAX 506-450-8481. Ed. David MacDonald. circ. 6,000. **Indexed:** Refug.Abstr. **Document type:** newsletter.
Formerly: New Brunswick Public Employees Association. News Letter (ISSN 0381-7970)
Description: Union publication informing, educating, and promoting the goals of the union and its membership.

352 330.9 US ISSN 0749-016X
H96 CODEN: NEJPFU
NEW ENGLAND JOURNAL OF PUBLIC POLICY. 1984. s-a. $20 to individuals and libraries; institutions $100. John W. McCormack Institute of Public Affairs, University of Massachusetts at Boston, Harbor Campus, Boston, MA 02125. TEL 617-287-5550. FAX 617-287-5544. Ed. Padraig J. O'Mally. circ. 600. (back issues avail.)
—BLDSC (6084.008000); Faxon.

350 US
NEW HAMPSHIRE MUNICIPAL PRACTICE SERIES. VOL. 2: MUNICIPAL FINANCE AND TAXATION. (Series consists of 4 vols.; Vols. 1 and 1A: Land Use Planning and Zoning; Vol. 2: Municipal Finance and Taxation; Vol. 3: Public Health, Safety and Highways) base vol. (plus a. supplement). $70 (4-vol. set $225). Butterworth Legal Publishers (Salem) (Subsidiary of: Reed Elsevier plc), 8 Industrial Way, Bldg. C, Salem, NH 03079. TEL 800-548-4001.
FAX 603-898-9858. Ed. Peter J. Loughlin. (looseleaf format)
Description: Details information for municipal officials and lawyers concerning appropriations, budgets, funds, taxation, tax abatements, and exemptions.

350 US
NEW HAMPSHIRE MUNICIPAL PRACTICE SERIES. VOL. 3: PUBLIC HEALTH, SAFETY AND HIGHWAYS. (Series consists of 4 vols.; Vols. 1 and 1A: Land Use Planning and Zoning; Vol. 2: Municipal Finance and Taxation; Vol. 3: Public Health, Safety and Highways) base vol. (plus a . supplement). $70 (4-vol. set $225). Butterworth Legal Publishers (Salem) (Subsidiary of: Reed Elsevier plc), 8 Industrial Way, Bldg. C, Salem, NH 03079. TEL 800-548-4001.
FAX 603-898-9858. Ed. Peter J. Loughlin. (looseleaf format)
Description: Analyzes law and regulations concerning health and sanitation, sewage disposal and water supplies, housing standards and codes, and the layout and administration of highways, roads and streets.

350 US
NEW HAMPSHIRE MUNICIPAL PRACTICE SERIES. VOLS. 1 AND 1A: LAND USE AND PLANNING. (Series consists of 4 vols.; Vols. 1 and 1A: Land Use Planning and Zoning; Vol. 2: Municipal Finance and Taxation; Vol. 3: Public Health, Safety and Highways) 2 base vols. (plus a. supplement). $140 (4-vol. set $225). Butterworth Legal Publishers (Salem) (Subsidiary of: Reed Elsevier plc), 8 Industrial Way, Bldg. C, Salem, NH 03079. TEL 800-548-4001.
FAX 603-898-9858. Ed. Peter J. Loughlin. (looseleaf format)
Description: Discusses topics such as master plan, ordinance, enforcement, growth control, appeals and judicial review, variances, procedures of boards, and other state and federal controls.

352 US
NEW HAMPSHIRE PRACTICE SERIES. VOLS. 13 AND 14: LOCAL GOVERNMENT LAW. (Series consists of 14 vols.; Vols. 1 and 2: Criminal Practice and Procedure; Vol. 3: Family Law; Vols. 4, 5 and 6: Civil Practice and Procedure; Vol. 7: Wills, Trusts and Gifts; Vols. 8 and 9: Personal Injury - Tort and Insurance Practice; Vols. 10, 11 and 12: Probate Law and Procedure; Vols. 13 and 14: Local Government Law) 1990. 2 base vols. (plus a. supplement). $120 (14-vols. set $575). Butterworth Legal Publishers (Salem) (Subsidiary of: Reed Elsevier plc), 8 Industrial Way, Bldg. C, Salem, NH 03079. TEL 800-548-4001.
FAX 603-898-9858. Ed. Peter J. Loughlin. (looseleaf format)
Description: Provides comprehensive coverage of the law and practice relating to cities, towns, public officials, records and meetings, municipal power and liabilities, and elections.

352 350 US
NEW HAMPSHIRE REGISTER: STATE YEARBOOK AND LEGISLATIVE MANUAL. 1768. a. $95. Tower Publishing Co., 588 Saco Rd., Standish, ME 04084-6239. TEL 207-642-5400; 800-969-8693. FAX 207-642-5463. adv. circ. 800. (also avail. in diskette format)
Description: Reports information on state and county officials and organizations. Contains complete municipal, business and professional directories.

352 US ISSN 0028-5846
JS39
NEW JERSEY MUNICIPALITIES. 1917. m. (Oct.-Jun.). $12 to non-members; members $9 (foreign $20). New Jersey State League of Municipalities, 407 W. State St., Trenton, NJ 08618. TEL 609-695-3481. FAX 609-695-0151. Ed. William G. Dressel, Jr. adv. contact: Michael J. Darcy. bk.rev.; illus.; index. circ. 8,400. Indexed: P.A.I.S., Sage Fam.Stud.Abstr., Sage Urb.Stud.Abstr.
Description: Discusses legislative and economic issues affecting New Jersey cities and towns and contains articles on managing municipal affairs.

352 347 US
NEW JERSEY PRACTICE SERIES. LOCAL GOVERNMENT LAW. 1992? a. West Publishing Corp., 620 Opperman Dr., Eagan, MN 55123.
TEL 612-687-8000; 800-328-9352.
FAX 621-687-7302.
Description: Analyzes virtually every type of New Jersey municipal law and practice.

352 US ISSN 0028-6257
NEW MEXICO MUNICIPAL LEAGUE. MUNICIPAL REPORTER. 1959. m. $20. New Mexico Municipal League, 1229 Paseo de Peralta, Box 846, Santa Fe, NM 87504-0846. Ed. William F. Fulginiti. adv.; bk.rev. circ. 1,700.

352.12 US ISSN 0094-7547
HJ9013.N5e
NEW YORK (CITY). SCHEDULES SUPPORTING THE EXECUTIVE BUDGET. 1955. a. Office of Management and Budget, 75 Park Pl., 6th Fl., New York, NY 10007. TEL 212-788-5807. circ. 500.

352 US ISSN 0737-1314
JK3430
NEW YORK STATE DIRECTORY. 1983. a. $129. Walker's Western Research, 1650 Borel Pl., Ste. 130, San Mateo, CA 94402. TEL 415-341-1110.
FAX 415-341-2351. Ed.Bd. **Document type:** directory.
Description: Provides access to more than 10,000 persons from the executive, legislative, and judicial branches of New York State Government, as well as local government officials and private sector experts concerned with New York State affairs.

352 US
NEW YORK STATE MUNICIPAL BULLETIN. 1934. bi-m. $25. Conference of Mayors and Other Municipal Officials, 119 Washington Ave., Albany, NY 12210. TEL 518-463-1185. Ed. Patricia Giannola. adv. circ. 6,000. **Document type:** government publication, bulletin.

353.9 US ISSN 0197-2472
KFN5036
NEW YORK STATE REGISTER. 1928. w. $40. Department of State, Office of Public Affairs & Information Services, 162 Washington Ave., Albany, NY 12231. TEL 518-474-6957.
FAX 518-473-9055. adv. circ. 2,500. (also avail. in microform from PMC; microfiche from WSH)
Document type: government publication.
Supersedes (in 1979): New York State Bulletin (ISSN 0028-7555)

352 NZ ISSN 0028-8403
NEW ZEALAND LOCAL GOVERNMENT; the magazine for local authority decision makers. 1964. m. NZ.$60. T.P.L. Media (Trade Publications), 308 Great South Rd., 1st Fl., Greenlane, Auckland, New Zealand. TEL 64-9-529-3000. FAX 64-9-529-3001. Ed. Malcolm Wall. adv.: B&W page NZ.$1360, color page NZ.$2009; adv. contact: Andre Dromgool. bk.rev.; illus. circ. 2,400.
Formerly (until 1972): Local Body Review (ISSN 0459-6587)

352 NZ ISSN 0110-7763
NEW ZEALAND LOCAL GOVERNMENT YEARBOOK. 1964. a. NZ.$25. T.P.L. Media (Trade Publications), 308 Great South Rd., 1st Fl., Greenlane, Auckland, New Zealand. TEL 64-9-529-3000. FAX 64-9-529-3001. Ed. M. Wall. adv.: B&W page NZ.$1428, color page NZ.$2048; trim 190 x 125. bk.rev.; bibl.; illus. circ. 2,344.
Description: Includes a complete listing of city and regional councils, area health boards, energy supply authorities, galleries and museums, libraries, licensing trusts and central government departments. Also includes a complete list of industry suppliers and a glossary of articles published annually in the NZ Local Government magazine.

NEW ZEALAND RESOURCE MANAGEMENT APPEALS. see HOUSING AND URBAN PLANNING

352 GW ISSN 0028-9779
NIEDERSAECHSISCHE GEMEINDE; Monatsschrift fuer kommunale Selbstverwaltung. 1949. m. DM.82. Niedersaechsischer Staedte-und Gemeindebund, Seelhorststr. 18, 30175 Hannover, Germany. TEL 0511-280720. FAX 0511-854107. Ed. W. Haack. adv.; bk.rev.; stat.; index; picture. circ. 12,700 (controlled).

PUBLIC ADMINISTRATION — MUNICIPAL GOVERNMENT

352   GW   ISSN 0178-4226
NIEDERSAECHSISCHER STAEDTETAG; Nachrichten fuer kreisfreie und kreisangehoerige Staedt, Gemeinden und Samtgemeinden. 1972. m. DM.30. Verlag Otto Schwartz und Co., Annastr. 7, 37075 Goettingen, Germany. TEL 0551-31051. FAX 0551-372812. Ed. Eckehart Peil. circ. 6,450. **Document type:** newsletter.

352   NE   ISSN 0928-0723
NIEUWSBRIED GEMEENTERAADSLEDEN. 1992. bi-w. Samsom H.D. Tjeenk Willink B.V. (Subsidiary of: Wolters Kluwer N.V.), Postbus 316, 2400 AH Alphen aan den Rijn, Netherlands. TEL 31-1720-66822. FAX 31-1720-66639. **Document type:** newsletter.

NIEUWSBRIEF VOLKSHUISVESTING. see *HOUSING AND URBAN PLANNING*

352   NO   ISSN 0802-5177
NORSK KOMMUNEFORBUND. FAGBLAD.* 10/yr. Norsk Kommuneforbund, c/o Per Sletholt, Postboks 57, Tveita, Oslo 6, Norway. adv. circ. 116,548.
   Formerly (until 1987): Norsk Kommuneforbunds Fagblad (ISSN 0800-2290); Which was formed by the 1927 merger of: Kommunearbeideren (ISSN 0800-2525); Tidsskrift for Kommunale Tjenestemaend (ISSN 0800-2533); Which was formerly (1917-1920): Vor By (ISSN 0800-2541)

352   US   ISSN 0279-800X
JS451.N95
NORTH DAKOTA LEAGUE OF CITIES BULLETIN. 1969. 10/yr. $15. North Dakota League of Cities, Box 2235, Bismarck, ND 58502. TEL 701-223-3518. Ed. Robert E. Johnson. adv.; charts; illus. circ. 2,850. **Document type:** bulletin.

O D. see *LIBRARY AND INFORMATION SCIENCES*

352   XV
ODLOCANJE/DECISION. (Text in Slovenian) 1981. m. free. Skupscina Obcine Ravne na Koroskem, Cecovje 12-a, 62390 Ravne na Koroskem, Slovenia. TEL 062 861-821. circ. 1,200. (looseleaf format; back issues avail.)

352   AU
OE B Z. vol.25, 1972. m. S.1200 (foreign S.1400). Zeitungsverlag Kuhn und Co. GmbH, Kutschkergasse 42, A-1180 Vienna, Austria. TEL 01-47686. FAX 01-4768621. Ed. Gerd-Volker Weege. adv.: B&W page S.42000, color page S.60900; trim 265 x 185; adv. contact: Werner Deutsch. bk.rev.; illus. circ. 20,084. **Document type:** bulletin.
   Formerly: Oesterreichische Buergermeister Zeitung (ISSN 0048-1424)

DER OEFFENTLICHE DIENST. see *LAW*

352   AU   ISSN 0029-912X
JS4501
OESTERREICHISCHE GEMEINDE-ZEITUNG. 1934. m. S.418. (Oesterreichischer Staedtebund) J & V Edition Wien Dachs Verlag GmbH, Rainergasse 38, A-1050 Vienna, Austria. TEL 0222-5458210. FAX 0222-545821027. adv.; bk.rev.; stat. circ. 6,000. **Document type:** newspaper.

OFFICIAL (LOS ANGELES). see *HEATING, PLUMBING AND REFRIGERATION*

383   SA
OFFICIAL SOUTH AFRICAN MUNICIPAL YEARBOOK/AMPTELIKE SUID-AFRIKAANSE MUNISIPALE JAARBOEK; official South Africa. (Text in Afrikaans and English) 1909. a. R.145. (South African Association of Municipal Employees) Gafny Group, P.O. Box 812, Northlands 2116, South Africa. circ. 3,000.
   Formerly: Municipal Yearbook.

ONTARIO. PROVINCIAL-MUNICIPAL AFFAIRS SECRETARIAT. MUNICIPAL DIRECTORY. see *PUBLIC ADMINISTRATION*

352   US
OUTREACH (COLLEGE PARK). 1982. 5/yr. free. Institute for Governmental Service, University of Maryland, 4511 Knox Rd., Ste.205, College Park, MD 20740. TEL 301-403-4610. FAX 301-403-4222. Ed. Elizabeth Watts. circ. 1,130. (back issues avail.) **Document type:** newsletter.

P A R ANALYSIS. (Public Affairs Research Council of Louisiana, Inc.) see *POLITICAL SCIENCE*

352   US
P A R LEGISLATIVE BULLETIN. 1951. w. (during state legislative session). $100. Public Affairs Research Council of Louisiana, Inc., Box 14776, Baton Rouge, LA 70898-4776. TEL 504-926-8414. FAX 504-926-8417. **Document type:** bulletin.
   Description: Reports on various topics being considered by the Louisiana Legislature.

352 370   US
P P F BULLETIN. 1913. irreg. (8-18/yr.). $50. Public Policy Forum, 633 W. Wisconsin Ave., Milwaukee, WI 53203-1918. TEL 414-276-8240. FAX 414-276-9962. Ed. Jean B. Tyler. charts; stat. circ. 1,500.
   Formerly: C G R B Bulletin (Citizen's Governmental Research Bureau).
   Description: Covers the 5 county Milwaukee area.

352   FR
PAROLE EST AUX MAIRES. 3/yr. 103 rue Bechevelin, B.P. 7235, 69354 Lyon Cedex 07, France. TEL 78-72-13-08. FAX 72-72-98-37. circ. 5,000.

352   US   ISSN 0162-5160
PENNSYLVANIA TOWNSHIP NEWS. 1948. m. $27 (effective 1994). Pennsylvania State Association of Township Supervisors, 3001 Gettysburg Rd., Camp Hill, PA 17011. TEL 717-763-0930. FAX 717-763-9732. Ed. Ginni Linn. adv.; bk.rev. circ. 12,000. **Document type:** trade publication.
   Description: Keeps township officials informed about new laws, legislation, rules and regulations, current issues, and the day-to-day operation of township government.

352   US   ISSN 0031-4714
JS39
PENNSYLVANIAN; the magazine of local governments. 1962. m. $18. Local Pennsylvanian, Inc., Local Government Center, 2941 N. Front St., Harrisburg, PA 17110. TEL 717-236-9526. FAX 717-236-8164. (Co-sponsors: Pennsylvania State Association of Boroughs; Pennsylvania Local Governmental Secretaries Association; Assessors' Association of Pennsylvania) Ed. Susanne L. Kelly. adv.: B&W page $402, color page $852; trim 7 x 10. bk.rev.; charts; illus. circ. 7,500. (also avail. in microfilm from UMI; reprint service avail. from UMI) **Document type:** government publication.
—UMI.
   Description: Articles, directories, indexes and announcements on governmental units at the borough and township level of the state, for governmental secretaries, administrators and clerks, county assessors, borough mayors and councilmembers.

352   BL   ISSN 0100-8781
PERFIL MUNICIPAL. 1979. a. Fundacao Sistema Estadual de Analise de Dados, Av. Casper Libero 464, Caixa Postal 8223, 01033 Sao Paulo SP, Brazil. TEL 229-2433. TELEX 011-31390 SEAD. circ. 2,000.

PLANNING & ZONING NEWS. see *HOUSING AND URBAN PLANNING*

PLANNING COMMISSIONERS JOURNAL; for North America's municipal & county planning boards. see *HOUSING AND URBAN PLANNING*

352   SP
PLAZA DE LA CONSTITUCION. 1979. 6/yr. free. Ayuntamiento, Plaza de la Constitucion, 28700 San Sebastian de los Reyes, Spain. TEL 1-6526200. Ed. Luis Manuel Candil Martin. adv.: B&W page $60990 ptas. bk.rev.; circ. 15,000 (paid); 15,000 (controlled).

352   NQ
POPOL-NA; revista para la promocion y el desarrollo municipal. 1992. q. Col.40 (Latin America $20, elsewhere $25). Fundacion Popol-Na para la Promocion y el Desarrollo Municipal, Apdo. Postal 4611, Plaza Espana, 3 1/2 abajo, Managua, Nicaragua. TEL 660605. FAX 660133.

352   FR   ISSN 0998-8289
POUVOIRS LOCAUX. 1989. 4/yr. 350 F. to individuals; institutions 500 F.; students 250 F. Institut de la Decentralisation, 2 rue des Longs-Pres, 92100 Boulogne-Billancourt, France. TEL 47-61-92-48. FAX 47-61-92-47. Ed. Jean-Marc Ohnet. adv. contact: Herve Poulet. bk.rev. circ. 10,000. **Document type:** academic/scholarly publication.
   Description: Covers public policy, autonomy of cities, local authority, new territories.

352   SP
PREGONERO. 26/yr. Ayuntamiento - Town Council, Capitulares 1, Cordoba, Spain. TEL 57-47-2000. FAX 57-48-8050. Ed. R. Rodriguez Aparicio. circ. 120,000.

PRIVATIZATION WATCH. see *POLITICAL SCIENCE*

352 340   US   ISSN 0893-2573
KFM4225
PUBLIC AND LOCAL ACTS OF THE LEGISLATURE OF THE STATE OF MICHIGAN. 1835. a. price varies. Legislative Council, Legislative Service Bureau, 124 W. Allegan, MNT, 4th Fl., Box 30036, Lansing, MI 48909. TEL 517-373-0170. FAX 517-373-0171. Ed. Roger W. Peters. index. circ. 2,000. (back issues avail.) **Document type:** government publication.

352 361.6   UK   ISSN 0306-0470
PUBLIC AUTHORITIES DIRECTORY. 1975. a. £84. L G C Communications, 33-39 Bowling Green Ln., London EC1R ODA, England. TEL 0171-837-1212. FAX 0171-278-9509. adv. circ. 1,200. **Document type:** directory.
—BLDSC (6962.797500).
   Description: Reference for anyone who works in, or comes into contact with, local authorities, new towns, and health authorities.

352.1   UK   ISSN 1352-9250
HJ9701   CODEN: PUFIEK
PUBLIC FINANCE. 1896. w. £65 to non-members (overseas £85). Chartered Institute of Public Finance and Accountancy, 3 Robert St., London WC2N 6BH, England. TEL 0171-895-8823. FAX 0171-895-8825. Ed. Douglas Broom. adv.; bk.rev.; charts; illus.; stat.; index. circ. 13,000. (also avail. in microform; back issues avail.) **Indexed:** Account.& Data Proc.Abstr., Account.Ind. (1974-), BPIA, Bus.Ind., Cont.Pg.Manage., Hlth.Ind., INSPEC, RICS, Tr.& Indus.Ind.
—BLDSC (6963.399600); SWETS.
   Former titles (until Oct. 1993): Public Finance and Accountancy (ISSN 0305-9014); Local Government Finance (ISSN 0024-5542)

352   US   ISSN 0033-3611
JS344
PUBLIC MANAGEMENT; devoted to the conduct of local government. 1918. m. $30. International City - County Management Association, 777 North Capitol, N.E., Ste. 500, Washington, DC 20002-4201. TEL 202-962-3619. FAX 202-962-3500. Ed. Beth Payne. adv.: B&W page $1150. bk.rev.; bibl. circ. 14,000. (also avail. in microform from MIM,UMI; back issues avail.) **Indexed:** Account.& Data Proc.Abstr., B.P.I., BPIA, Bus.Ind., Chic.Per.Ind., Geo.Abstr., Mag.Ind., Mid.East: Abstr.& Ind., P.A.I.S., Pers.Lit., Sage Pub.Admin.Abstr., Soc.Sci.Ind. **Document type:** bulletin.
•Also available online. Vendor(s): University Microfilms International.
—BLDSC (6967.700000); Faxon; SWETS; UMI; UnCover.
   Description: Includes editorial commentary and selected departments.

352   US   ISSN 0033-3840
TD1   CODEN: PUWOAH
PUBLIC WORKS; city, county and state. 1896. 13/yr. $45 includes Public Works Manual (foreign $75) (effective 1994). Public Works Journal Corporation, 200 S. Broad St., Ridgewood, NJ 07451. TEL 201-445-5800. FAX 201-445-5170. Ed. E.B. Rodie. adv.: B&W page $4400, color page $5070. bk.rev.; abstr.; bibl.; charts; illus.; tr.lit.; index. circ. 55,000. (also avail. in microform from UMI,PMC; reprint service avail. from UMI) **Indexed:** A.S.& T.Ind., Chem.Abstr., Energy Res., Eng.Ind., Geotech.Abstr., HRIS, Repindex, Sel.Water Res.Abstr., Tr.& Indus.Ind., W.R.C.Inf. **Document type:** trade publication.
—BLDSC (6969.780000); Ei; Faxon; SWETS; UMI; UnCover.

PUBLIC ADMINISTRATION — MUNICIPAL GOVERNMENT

628 US ISSN 0163-9730
PUBLIC WORKS MANUAL; and catalog file. Special issue of: Public Works (ISSN 0033-3840) 1977. a. $30 (effective 1994). Public Works Journal Corporation, 200 S. Broad St., Ridgewood, NJ 07451. TEL 201-445-5800. FAX 201-445-5170. Ed. E.B. Rodie. adv. circ. 55,000. (reprint service avail. from UMI) **Document type:** trade publication.
Formed by the merger of: Environmental Wastes Control Manual (ISSN 0071-0946); Street and Highway Manual (ISSN 0081-5977); Water Works Manual (ISSN 0083-7717)

352 AT ISSN 0048-6078
Q I M A. 1950. q. Institute of Municipal Administration, Queensland Division, 151 Porteus Dr., Seven Hills, Brisbane, Qld. 4170, Australia. **Indexed:** Aus.P.A.I.S.

352 US ISSN 0892-4171
JS39
QUALITY CITIES. 1928. m. (11/yr.) $20. Florida League of Cities, Inc., Box 1757, Tallahassee, FL 32302. TEL 904-222-9684. FAX 904-222-3806. Ed. Cecka Trueblood; Pub. Raymond C. Sittig. adv. contact: Priscilla Dawson. bk.rev. circ. 5,300. **Document type:** government publication.
Formerly: Florida Municipal Record (ISSN 0015-4164)
Description: Covers subjects of interest to Florida municipal officials.

350 US ISSN 0033-6483
QUILL (PRINCETON). 1954. q. free. Municipal Clerks Association of N.J. Inc., Princeton Township, 369 Witherspoon St., Princeton, NJ 08540-3284. Ed. Patricia C. Shuss. circ. 1,500. (processed)

352 FR ISSN 0985-5645
QUOTIDIEN DU MAIRE. 45/yr. 30 rue Alexandre, 92238 Genevilliers Cedex, France. TEL 47-93-25-25. FAX 47-93-10-54. Ed. Bernard Soubrier. circ. 15,000.

352 GW
DAS RATHAUS; Zeitschrift fuer Kommunalpolitik. m. DM.79.20. Schmidt-Roemhild Verlag, Mengstr. 16, 23522 Luebeck, Germany. TEL 0451-1605-0. FAX 0451-1605253. **Document type:** bulletin.

352 CN
REDBOOK (NORTH BURNABY). 1949. a. Can.$68.10. Journal of Commerce Ltd. (Subsidiary of: Southam Business Communications Inc.), P.O. Box 82230, N. Burnaby, B.C. V5C 6E7, Canada. TEL 604-433-8164. FAX 604-433-9549. adv.: B&W page Can.$1113, color page Can.$1696; trim 8 1/2 x 11. circ. 20,308. **Document type:** directory.
Description: Directory of municipal government in British Columbia.

REGIE AUTONOME DES TRANSPORTS PARISIENS. BULLETIN DE DOCUMENTATION ET D'INFORMATION. see TRANSPORTATION

352 GW ISSN 0405-0665
REGIERUNG VON OBERBAYERN. AMTSBLATT. m. DM.53.80. (Regierung von Oberbayern) Verlagsgruppe Jehle - Rehm, Einsteinstr. 172, 81675 Munich, Germany. TEL 089-416006-0. FAX 089-4706998. **Document type:** bulletin.

352 CN
REGIONAL DISTRICT LEGISLATION; a resource manual. base vol. (plus irreg. supplements). Can.$37.80. Ministry of Municipal Affairs, Recreation and Housing, Victoria, BC, Canada. (Subscr. to: Crown Publications, 546 Yates St., Victoria, BC V8W 1K8, Canada. TEL 604-386-4636) (looseleaf format; back issues avail.)
Description: Assists regional district officials with the implementation of Bill 19.

352 UK
REGIONAL STUDIES ASSOCIATION. REGIONAL POLICY AND DEVELOPMENT. irreg., no. 7. Jessica Kingsley Publishers, 116 Pentonville Rd., London N1 9JB, England. TEL 071-833-2307. FAX 071-837-2917. (Dist. by: Kogan Page Ltd., 120 Pentonville Rd., London N1 9JN, England. TEL 071-278-0433. FAX 071-837-6348) **Document type:** monographic series.
Description: Tackles a wide range of policy relevant issues.

352 US ISSN 0277-0121
HT321
RESEARCH IN URBAN ECONOMICS. 1981. a. $63.50 to institutions. J A I Press Inc., 55 Old Post Rd., No. 2, Box 1678, Greenwich, CT 06836-1678. TEL 203-661-7602. Ed. Bob Ebel. —BLDSC (7774.037000); UnCover.

352 BL ISSN 0034-7604
REVISTA DE ADMINISTRACAO MUNICIPAL. 1954. q. $40 (effective 1995 & 1996). Instituto Brasileiro de Administracao Municipal, Largo IBAM 1, 22271-070 Rio de Janeiro, RJ, Brazil. FAX 021-5371262. TELEX 21-22638 INBM BR. Ed. Francois E.J. de Bremaeker. adv.; bk.rev.; bibl.; illus.; stat.; index, cum.index: 1965-1994. circ. 3,500.

352 SP ISSN 0213-4675
REVISTA DE ESTUDIOS DE ADMINISTRACION LOCAL Y AUTONOMICA. q. 1000 ptas.($3.60) Instituto Nacional de Administracion Publica, Biblioteca, C. Atocha 106, 28012 Madrid, Spain. Ed. Francisco Sosa Wagner. bk.rev.; bibl.; index. circ. 3,500. **Indexed:** Int.Polit.Sci.Abstr. **Document type:** academic/scholarly publication.
Formerly: Revista de Estudios de la Vida Local (ISSN 0034-8163)

352 FR ISSN 0755-3269
REVUE DES COLLECTIVITES LOCALES ET L'EQUIPEMENT. 1949. 11/yr. 460 F. (foreign 520 F.). 38 rue Claude Terrasse, 75016 Paris, France. TEL 44-14-60-60. FAX 44-14-60-61. Ed. Bernard Marx. adv.; bk.rev. circ. 10,200.

RHEINLAND-PFALZ. STATISTISCHES LANDESAMT RHEINLAND-PFALZ. STATISTISCHE MONATSHEFTE. see PUBLIC ADMINISTRATION — Abstracting, Bibliographies, Statistics

352 IT ISSN 0394-8439
RIVISTA DEL PERSONALE DELL'ENTE LOCALE; bimestrale di normativa e giurisprudenza. 1987. bi-m. L.185000 (effective 1994). Maggioli Editore, Viale Vespucci 12-n, Casella Postale 290, 47037 Rimini, Italy. TEL 0541-626777. FAX 0541-622020. Ed. Carlo Talice. adv.: B&W page L.1300000, color page L.2100000; trim 113 x 190.

352 352.7 IT ISSN 0394-8420
RIVISTA GIURIDICA DI URBANISTICA; trimestrale di giurisprudenza, dottrina e legislazione. 1985. q. L.118000 to individuals; institutions L.160000 (effective 1994). Maggioli Editore, Viale Vespucci 12-n, Casella Postale 290, 47037 Rimini, Italy. TEL 0541-626777. FAX 0541-622020. Eds. Leopoldo Mazzarolli, Gherardo Bergonzini. adv.: B&W page L.1600000; trim 115 x 125.

352 GW
ROSDORFER MITTEILUNGEN; fuer die Gemeinde Rosdorf. 1965. w. (Gemeinde Rosdorf) Verlag Otto Schwartz und Co., Annastr. 7, 37075 Goettingen, Germany. TEL 0551-51051. FAX 0551-372812. adv.: B&W page DM.490; trim 262 x 180. **Document type:** newspaper.

350.1 331.1 SW ISSN 0280-6975
S K T F! TIDNINGEN. 1955. 20/yr. SEK 200. Sveriges Kommunaltjaenstemannafoerbund, PO Box 7825, S-103 97 Stockholm, Sweden. TEL 46-8-789-63-00. FAX 46-8-789-64-79. Ed. Kent Kaellqvist. adv.: B&W page SEK 24600, color page SEK 34600; trim 460 x 290. circ. 186,700.
Formerly (until 1982): Kommunaltjaenstemannen (ISSN 0345-6323)

352 AU
ST. STEFANER GEMEINDENACHRICHTEN. 1977. q. Gemeinde St. Stefan ob Leoben, Gemeindeamt, A-8713 St. Stefan ob Leoben 148, Austria. TEL 03832-2250. FAX 03832-2250-7. Ed. Peter Pechan. circ. 750. (back issues avail.) **Document type:** government publication.

357 US
SALARIES AND FRINGE BENEFITS: BENCHMARK EMPLOYEE COMPENSATION REPORT. a. $75 to non-members; members $38. Colorado Municipal League, 1660 Lincoln St., Ste. 2100, Denver, CO 80264. TEL 303-831-6411. FAX 303-860-8175. **Document type:** government publication.
Description: Computerized report of employee compensation in municipalities of 3,000 population and over, as well as other jurisdictions, with comparative data of more than 59 key job classifications. Contains data on salaries, monetary fringe benefits and fringe benefit policies.

352 US
SALARIES AND FRINGE BENEFITS IN COLORADO CITIES AND TOWNS UNDER 3,000 POPULATION. a. $30 to non-members; members $15. Colorado Municipal League, 1660 Lincoln St., Ste. 2100, Denver, CO 80264. TEL 303-831-6411. FAX 303-860-8175. **Document type:** government publication.
Description: Survey of municipalities of under 3,000 population providing comparative data in tabular form on positions commonly found in cities and towns of this size. Statistical material is provided in three sections: basic municipal data, salaries, and fringe benefits.

352 US
SALARIES AND FRINGE BENEFITS: MANAGEMENT COMPENSATION REPORT. a. $50 to non-members; members $25. Colorado Municipal League, 1660 Lincoln St., Ste. 2100, Denver, CO 80264. TEL 303-831-6411. FAX 303-860-8175. **Document type:** government publication.
Former titles: Salaries and Fringe Benefits: Management Compensation Report for Colorado Municipalities; Salaries and Fringe Benefits: Management Compensation Report for Colorado Cities.
Description: Survey of Colorado municipalities of over 3,000 population, as well as other jurisdictions, providing comparative data in tabular form on more than 30 executive and administrative positions in three sections: general municipal information; salaries and fringe benefits; and job characteristics.

352 US
SALARIES AND WAGES FOR MICHIGAN MUNICIPALITIES OVER 1,000 POPULATION. 1942. a. $50. Michigan Municipal League, 1675 Green Rd., Box 1487, Ann Arbor, MI 48106. TEL 313-662-3246.
Formed by the merger of: Salaries and Wages for Michigan Municipalities over 4,000 Population; Which was formerly: Salaries, Wages, and Fringe Benefits in Michigan Municipalities over 4,000 Population (ISSN 0080-5548) & Salaries and Wages for Michigan Municipalities under 4,000 Population; Which was formerly: Salaries and Wages for Michigan Villages and Cities 1,000-4,000 Population; Salaries, Wages and Fringe Benefits for Michigan Villages and Cities 1,000-4,000 Population (ISSN 0077-216X).

352 SP
SAN FERNANDO. 6/yr. Ayuntamiento de San Fernando de Henares, Libertad 1, 28830 San Fernando de Henares (Madrid), Spain. TEL 1-672-65-11. FAX 1-672-48-63. Ed. A. Martinez Escribano. circ. 10,000. **Document type:** government publication.

352 CN ISSN 0581-8435
JS1721.S3
SASKATCHEWAN MUNICIPAL DIRECTORY. 1909. a. Can.$10. Saskatchewan Municipal Government, 1855 Victoria Ave., Regina, Sask. S4P 3V7, Canada. TEL 306-787-8282. FAX 306-787-4181. Ed. Jean Lazar. circ. 5,000. **Document type:** directory.

SCANDINAVIAN ATLAS OF HISTORIC TOWNS. see HISTORY — History Of Europe

352 SZ
DIE SCHWEIZER GEMEINDE. 11/yr. Solothurnstr. 22, CH-3322 Schoenbuehl, Switzerland. TEL 031-8583116. FAX 031-8583115. circ. 5,000. **Document type:** bulletin.

352 SZ
SCHWEIZERISCHE BEAMTEN ZEITUNG. (Text in German) 1912. 20/yr. Personal Verband Bundesverwaltung, Bahnhofstr. 20, CH-3072 Ostermundigen, Switzerland. TEL 031-9316061. FAX 031-9316065. adv.: B&W page 2288 SFr.; trim 290 x 440. circ. 11,882. **Document type:** trade publication.

PUBLIC ADMINISTRATION — MUNICIPAL GOVERNMENT

357 US
SEARCHLIGHT ON THE CITY COUNCIL. 7/yr. $60 includes membership. Citizens Union Foundation, Inc., 198 Broadway, New York, NY 10038. TEL 212-227-0342. FAX 212-227-0345. Dir. Jeannette Kahlenberg. circ. 12,000 (paid). **Document type:** newsletter.

SEMINARS DIRECTORY; a guide to approximately 10,000 seminars and workshops held in the United States and Canada on subjects of interest to business, industry, and government. see BUSINESS AND ECONOMICS — Trade And Industrial Directories

352 SZ
SERVICE ET COMMUNAUTE. (Text in French, German, Italian) w. Hopfenweg 21, CH-3007 Bern, Switzerland. TEL 031-455562. Ed. Robert Andenmatten. circ. 18,529.

352 FR
SERVICE PUBLIC INFORMATION. m. C G T, Case 547, 263 rue de Paris, 93515 Montreuil Cedex, France. TEL 48-51-83-74. circ. 150,000.

352 SZ
SERVICES PUBLICS. 23/yr. 60 SFr. (foreign 100 SFr.). Case Postale 1360, CH-1001 Lausanne, Switzerland. TEL 021-3238833. FAX 021-3209345. Ed. Lola Rens. adv. contact: Lola Rens. circ. 12,000. **Document type:** corporate report.

352 IT
SERVIZI PUBBLICI LOCALI. 1972. 11/yr. L.40000. Confederazione Italiana dei Servizi Pubblici degli Enti Locali, Piazza Cola di Rienzo 80, Rome 00192, Italy. bk.rev.; bibl.
Formerly (until Jan. 1978): Notiziario Interfederale.

352 US
SISTER CITY NEWS. 1961. bi-m. $27. (Sister Cities International) Town Affiliation Association of the U.S., Inc., 120 S. Payne St., Alexandria, VA 22314. TEL 703-836-3535. FAX 703-836-4815. TELEX 4015655. Ed. Nancy-Lynne Trentham. adv. contact: Nancy-Lynn Trentham. bk.rev.; stat. circ. 30,000. (tabloid format) **Document type:** newspaper.
Formerly: T A A Newsletter (ISSN 0300-6166)

352 CI ISSN 0037-7104
SLUZBENE NOVINE OPCINE KARLOVAC. 1964. irreg. Skupstina Opcine Karlovac, Banjavciceva 9, Karlovac, Croatia. Ed. Vladimir Funduk.

352 CI ISSN 0037-7120
SLUZBENI GLASNIK OPCINE ROVINJ. (Text in Croatian, Italian) 1964. irreg. Skupstina Opcine Rovinj, Ul. Matteotti 1-1, Rovinj, Croatia. Ed. Marija Matosovic.

352 CI ISSN 0037-7155
SLUZBENI VJESNIK OPCINE BUJE, NOVIGRAD I UMAG. (Text in Croatian, Italian) 1965. fortn. Socijalisticki Savez Radnog Naroda Opcine Buje Novigrad i Umag, Partizanska 2, Buje, Croatia. Ed. Nada Silic.

352 CI ISSN 0037-7163
SLUZBENI VJESNIK OPCINE KRIZEVCI. 1965. a? Skupstina Opcine Krizevci, Ivana Zakmardija Dinakovveckog 12, Krizevci, Croatia. Ed. Branko Tinodi. circ. 200.

352 SZ
SOLOTHURNISCHE STAATSPERSONAL. 1933. m. 6.50 SFr. (foreign 30 SFr.). Solothurnischer Staatspersonal Verband, Dammstr. 21, CH-4500 Solothurn, Switzerland. TEL 065-222279. FAX 065-223211. Ed. P. Bischof. adv.; bk.rev. circ. 3,000. **Document type:** government publication.

352.1 SA ISSN 0038-2779
HJ9103
SOUTH AFRICAN TREASURER/SUID-AFRIKAANSE TESOURIER. (Text in Afrikaans, English) 1929. m. R.48 (effective 1993). Institute of Municipal Treasurers and Accountants, P.O. Box 8652, Johannesburg 2000, South Africa. TEL 27-11-4918274. FAX 27-11-491-8346. Ed. J.R.J. Bosch. adv.; B&W page R.1100; bleed 280 x 210; adv. contact: N.J. du Bruyn. bk.rev.; charts; illus.; mkt.; pat.; tr.mk.; index. circ. 1,500. **Indexed:** Ind.S.A.Per.
Description: Promotes the interest of local government in the financial and allied fields.

352 US ISSN 0300-6182
SOUTH DAKOTA MUNICIPALITIES. 1934. m. $20. South Dakota Municipal League, 214 E. Capitol, Pierre, SD 57501. TEL 605-224-8654. Ed. Marla J. Gienger. adv. contact: Marla J. Gienger. bk.rev. circ. 2,700. **Document type:** newsletter.

352 US ISSN 0361-7130
SOUTHERN CITY. a. $6. North Carolina League of Municipalities, Box 3069, 215 N. Dawson St., Raleigh, NC 27602. TEL 919-715-4000. FAX 919-733-9519. Ed. Margot F. Christensen. adv.; charts; illus. circ. 6,200.

SPEKTRUM (MAINZ); Veranstaltungs- und Kongressinformation der Landeshauptstadt Mainz. 1973. q. free. Congress Centrum Mainz GmbH, Rheinstr. 66, 55116 Mainz, Germany. TEL 06131-242-110. FAX 06131-242105. adv. contact: Heidrun Dietze. circ. 10,000. **Document type:** government publication.

352 US ISSN 0038-7711
SPOKANE, WASHINGTON. OFFICIAL GAZETTE. 1910. w. $4.25 outside Spokane County $10.50. City of Spokane, Washington, City Clerk, Municipal Bldg., 5th Fl., W. 808 Spokane Falls Blvd., Spokane, WA 99201-3342. TEL 509-625-6354. FAX 509-625-6217. Ed. Marilyn J. Montgomery. circ. 450. **Document type:** government publication.

352 AU
DER STAATSBEAMTE. q. Hiligenstaedterstr. 131-1-3, A-1190 Vienna, Austria. TEL 01-372163. FAX 01-374117. Ed. F.C. Fetty.

352 AU ISSN 0038-8939
STADLINGER POST. 1952. a. S.10. Gemeindeamt, A-4651 Stadl-Paura, Austria. Ed. Friedrich Urbanek. adv.; abstr.; stat. circ. 900.

STADSBYGGNAD. see ENGINEERING — Civil Engineering

352 SZ
STADT. 6/yr. Schweizerischer Staedteverband, Junkerengasse 56, CH-3011 Bern, Switzerland. TEL 031-227785. FAX 031-227786. Ed. U. Geissmann. circ. 2,200.

352 GW
STADT BAMBERG. MITTEILUNGSBLATT; Amtsblatt der Stadt Bamberg. 1945. s-m. DM.33.60. St. Otto Verlag GmbH, Laubanger 23, 96052 Bamberg, Germany. TEL 0951-79020. Ed. Stefan Neuhaus. adv. contact: Helmut Treml. circ. 2,200. **Document type:** government publication.

STADT HERNE. ARBEITSMARKTBERICHT. see BUSINESS AND ECONOMICS — Abstracting, Bibliographies, Statistics

352 GW ISSN 0038-9048
JS41
DER STAEDTETAG; Zeitschrift fuer Praxis und Wissenschaft der kommunalen Verwaltung. 1948. m. DM.219.60. (Verband Kommunaler Abfallwirtschaft und Stadtreinigung e.V.) W. Kohlhammer GmbH, Hessbruehlstr. 69, 70565 Stuttgart, Germany. TEL 0711-7863-1. FAX 0711-7863263. adv.; bk.rev.; charts; illus.; index, cum.index. circ. 4,200. **Indexed:** Dok.Str., Excerp.Med., P.A.I.S.For.Lang.Ind. **Document type:** bulletin.
—BLDSC (8426.275000). CCC.

352 GW
DER STAEDTISCHE. m. V P O D, Stauffacherstr. 60, CH-8004 Zurich, Switzerland. circ. 7,500.

350 320 US ISSN 0160-323X
JK2403
STATE AND LOCAL GOVERNMENT REVIEW; a journal of research and viewpoints on state and local government issues. 1968. 3/yr. $14 to individuals; institutions $20. University of Georgia, Carl Vinson Institute of Government, 201 N. Milledge Ave., Athens, GA 30602. TEL 706-542-2736. FAX 706-542-9301. Ed. Richard W. Campbell. circ. 1,000. (back issues avail.) **Indexed:** A.B.C.Pol.Sci., Int.Polit.Sci.Abstr., P.A.I.S., Polit.Sci.Abstr., Sage Pub.Admin.Abstr., Sage Urb.Stud.Abstr. **Document type:** academic/scholarly publication.
—BLDSC (8437.603000); Faxon; UnCover.
Supersedes: Georgia Government Review (ISSN 0016-8289)

352 US ISSN 0898-8374
STATE MUNICIPAL LEAGUE DIRECTORY. a. $34 to non-members. National League of Cities, 1301 Pennsylvania Ave., N.W., Washington, DC 20004. TEL 202-626-3150. FAX 202-626-3043. **Document type:** directory.
Description: Guide to the operations and functions of state municipal associations.

STATISTICS RELATING TO REGIONAL AND MUNICIPAL GOVERNMENTS IN BRITISH COLUMBIA. see PUBLIC ADMINISTRATION — Abstracting, Bibliographies, Statistics

STATISTISCHE MONATSHEFTE SCHLESWIG-HOLSTEIN. see PUBLIC ADMINISTRATION — Abstracting, Bibliographies, Statistics

STATISTISCHER BERICHT DER STADT FRANKENTHAL. see PUBLIC ADMINISTRATION — Abstracting, Bibliographies, Statistics

STATISTISCHER VIERTELJAHRESBERICHT HANNOVER. see PUBLIC ADMINISTRATION — Abstracting, Bibliographies, Statistics

STATISTISCHES JAHRBUCH DER STADT KOELN. see PUBLIC ADMINISTRATION — Abstracting, Bibliographies, Statistics

STATISTISCHES JAHRBUCH DEUTSCHER GEMEINDEN. see PUBLIC ADMINISTRATION — Abstracting, Bibliographies, Statistics

352 SW ISSN 0039-0712
STATSANSTAELLD. 1955. fortn. SEK 90. Statsanstaelldas Foerbund, P.O. Box 1102, S-111 81, Stockholm, Sweden. TEL 08-7914100. FAX 08-211694. Ed. Ingvar Ygeman. adv.; bk.rev.; charts; illus.; tr.lit. circ. 210,941.

352 UK
STRATHCLYDER. 1974. 10/yr. Strathclyde Regional Council, Public Relations Department, Strathclyde House, 20 India St., Glasgow G2 4PF, Scotland. Ed. Henry D.M. Dutch. adv. circ. 953,234. (tabloid format; back issues avail.)
Formerly: Strathclyde Report.

350 US
SUMMARY OF PUBLIC ACTS OF INTEREST TO MUNICIPAL OFFICIALS. a. $15. University of Tennessee at Knoxville, Municipal Technical Advisory Service, 600 Henley, Ste. 120, Knoxville, TN 37996-4105. TEL 615-974-0411.
Summary of New Laws (ISSN 1049-605X)

352.7 US ISSN 0743-2585
SUMMERVILLE POST. 1976. q. $10. Summerville Neighborhood Association Inc., Box 12212, Augusta, GA 30914-2212. Ed. J. Marsella Shurtleff. adv.; illus. circ. 2,365. **Document type:** newsletter.
Description: Provides information about the activities of the Neighborhood Association and about events affecting the neighborhoood.

352 IC ISSN 0255-8459
SVEITARSTJORNARMAL. 1941. bi-m. Samband Islenskra Sveitarfelaga, Haaleitisbraut 11-13, Reykjavik, Iceland. TEL 354-581-3711. adv. circ. 4,800.

352 FR
SYNDICALISME - FONCTION PUBLIQUE. 6/yr. 13 rue des Ecluses St Martin, 75483 Paris Cedex 10, France. TEL 42-03-13-15. Ed. Nicole Prud'Homme. circ. 30,000.

352 GW
SZENE REMSCHEID. m. DM.24. J.F. Ziegler KG Druckerei und Verlag, Konrad-Adenauer-Str. 2-4, 42853 Remscheid, Germany. TEL 02191-909-0. FAX 02191-909266. bk.rev. circ. 10,000. (back issues avail.) **Document type:** newsletter.

PUBLIC ADMINISTRATION — MUNICIPAL GOVERNMENT

363.61 FR ISSN 0299-7258
CODEN: TSMREA
TECHNIQUES - SCIENCES - METHODES. GENIE URBAIN RURAL. (Text in French; summaries in English) 1905. m. 470 F. (foreign 525 F.). Association Generale des Hygienistes et Techniciens Municipaux, 9 rue de Phalsbourg, 75017 Paris Cedex 17, France. TEL 44-15-15-50. FAX 43-80-65-90. Ed. J. Gillet. adv.; bk.rev.; abstr.; illus.; index. circ. 4,000. (tabloid format; back issues avail.) **Indexed:** Acid Pre.Dig., Acid Rain Abstr., Acid Rain Ind., Energy Info.Abstr., Environ.Abstr., Fluidex, Geo.Abstr., Ocean.Abstr., Pollut.Abstr., Repindex, W.R.C.Inf. —BLDSC (8745.345000); CASDDS; Ei; SWETS.
Formerly (until 1986): Techniques et Sciences Municipales Eau (ISSN 0151-6973)

352 US
TENNESSEE GOVERNMENT OFFICIALS DIRECTORY. 1985. a. $37. M. Lee Smith Publishers & Printers LLC, 162 Fourth Ave. N., Nashville, TN 37219-8867. TEL 615-242-7395; 800-274-6774. FAX 615-256-6601. Ed. Joseph L. White; Pub. M. Lee Smith. **Document type:** directory.
Description: Lists all state, county, and city officials, including government officials and chambers of commerce, Tennessee colleges and universities, business and professional associations, lobbyists, Capitol Hill press corps and Tennessee newspapers, magazines, and radio and TV stations.

352 US ISSN 0892-5380
HD3890.T2
TENNESSEE PUBLIC WORKS. 1983. bi-m. $18. Images Publications, 501 Mulberry St., Loudon, TN 37774. TEL 615-458-3560. FAX 615-458-4095. Ed. Frank Kirk. adv.: B&W page $500. circ. 1,900.

352 US ISSN 0040-3415
JS39
TENNESSEE TOWN AND CITY. 1950. s-m. $15. Tennessee Municipal League, 226 Capitol Blvd., Nashville, TN 37219. TEL 615-255-6416. FAX 615-255-4752. Ed. Beverly Bruninga; Pub. Joseph Sweat. adv. contact: Nelle Gruelich. bk.rev.; bibl.; illus.; index. circ. 5,072. **Indexed:** P.A.I.S. **Document type:** newspaper.
Description: Covers municipal and state government and politics.

352 711 FR ISSN 0991-2428
TERRITOIRES; la revue des acteurs locaux. 1958. m. 330 F. to individuals; institutions 450 F.; students 200 F. Association pour la Democratie et l'Education Locale et Sociale, 108, rue Saint-Maur, 75011 Paris, France. TEL 43-55-40-05. Ed. Sylvie Barrezet. adv.; bk.rev.; bibl.; cum.index: 1968-1993. circ. 6,000. (also avail. in microfiche) **Document type:** newspaper.
Formerly (until 1988): Correspondance Municipale (ISSN 0223-5951)
Description: For elected officials, social workers and interested citizens.

352 330.9 JA
TOKYO INDUSTRY; a graphic overview. (Text in English) 1990. a. Tokyo Metropolitan Government, Bureau of Citizens and Cultural Affairs, International Communication Division, Liaison and Protocol Section, 8-1 Nishishinjuku 2-chome, Shinjuku-ku, Tokyo 163-01, Japan. TEL 03-5388-3172. FAX 03-5388-1329. charts; stat.
Description: Provides information on characteristics and trends in the Tokyo economy, structural adjustment, manufacturing, wholesale, retail, and service industries, and agriculture, forestry, and fishing.

352 JA ISSN 0916-7951
DS896
TOKYO METROPOLITAN NEWS. Chinese edition: Dongjing Dumin Tongxun (ISSN 0910-1020); French edition: Nouvelles Municipales de Tokyo (ISSN 0910-1039) 1951. q. free to qualified personnel. Tokyo Metropolitan Government, Bureau of Citizens and Cultural Affairs, Liaison and Protocol Section, 8-1 Nishishinjuku 2-chome, Shinjuku-ku, Tokyo 163-01, Japan. TEL 03-5388-3172. FAX 03-5388-1329. Ed.Bd. charts; illus.; stat. circ. 5,000. **Indexed:** Geo.Abstr., P.A.I.S.
Formerly (until 1991): Tokyo Municipal News (ISSN 0040-893X)

352 600 JA
CODEN: TSMREA
TOKYO-TO SHIKEN KENKYU KIKAN NO KENKYU KEIKAKU. (Text in Japanese) a. Tokyo-to Somu-kyoku, Somu-bu - Tokyo Metropolitan Government, Bureau of General Affairs, General Affairs Division, 5-1 Marunouchi 3-chome, Chiyoda-ku, Tokyo 100, Japan.
Description: Publicizes the plans of research institutions under the Tokyo Metropolitan Government.

352 US ISSN 0040-9065
TOLEDO CITY JOURNAL. 1916. w. $18. One Government Ctr., Ste. 2140, Toledo, OH 43604. TEL 419-245-1065. Ed. Sandra L. Brown. adv. circ. 1,000. **Document type:** government publication, newspaper.

352 JA ISSN 0387-3382
TOSHI MONDAI/MUNICIPAL PROBLEMS. (Text in Japanese) 1925. m. 7800 Yen. Tokyo Institute for Municipal Research, Hibiya Koen 1-3, Chiyoda-ku, Tokyo 100, Japan. TEL 03-3591-1201. FAX 03-3591-1209. Ed. Akira Yamagata. adv. contact: Yosikatu Kono. bk.rev.; bibl. circ. 2,800. **Document type:** academic/scholarly publication. —BLDSC (5984.800000); UnCover.

352 US
TOTAL COMPENSATION REPORT. a. $20 to non-members; members $10. Colorado Municipal League, 1660 Lincoln St., Sta. 2100, Denver, CO 80264. TEL 303-831-6411. **Document type:** government publication.
Description: Computerized report of employee compensation plus monetary fringe benefits and the dollar value of non-monetary fringe benefits. Contains comparative data for 59 key job classifications in municipalities of 3,000 population and over and other jurisdictions.

352 US ISSN 0748-5883
TOWN CRIER. 1984. q. National Association of Towns and Townships, National Center for Small Communities, 1522 K St., N.W., Ste. 600, Washington, DC 20005. TEL 202-737-5200. Ed. Ronnie Kweller. **Document type:** newsletter.
Description: News about the research and educational programs for America's grassroots governments offered by the center.

352 AT ISSN 0040-9995
TOWN PLANNING AND LOCAL GOVERNMENT GUIDE. 1956. m. Aus.$370. Law Book Co. Ltd., Head Office, 44-50 Waterloo Rd., North Ryde, N.S.W. 2113, Australia. TEL 02-936-6444. FAX 02-888-2229. TELEX ASBOOK 27995. Ed. Ken Gifford. bk.rev.
Description: Includes notes on administration, bulding control, environment, local government, pulic health, town planning, traffic and valuations.

TRIBUNA DELL'IRPINIA; settimanale di attualita. see BUSINESS AND ECONOMICS

352 SZ
U N SPECIAL. m. Publicite Generale, 34 rue de l'Athene, Postfach 145, CH-1211 Geneva 12, Switzerland. TEL 022-473388. FAX 022-462047. circ. 10,000.

352 US ISSN 1049-2119
JS39
U S MAYOR. 1934. s-m. $35. United States Conference of Mayors, 1620 Eye St., N.W., Washington, DC 20006. TEL 202-293-7330. Ed. Nicole Klimov. illus. circ. 5,000. (tabloid format; back issues avail.) **Document type:** newspaper.
Former titles: Mayor; United States Municipal News (ISSN 0041-7955)

U.S. NATIONAL RENEWABLE ENERGY LABORATORY. CITIES AND COUNTIES PROJECT. ENERGY TODAY FACT SHEET. see ENERGY

352 US
UNITED STATES CONFERENCE OF MAYORS. ANNUAL MEETING; official policy resolutions. a. $10. United States Conference of Mayors, 1620 Eye St., N.W., Washington, DC 20006. TEL 202-293-7330.

352 US
UNITED STATES CONFERENCE OF MAYORS. PROJECTS AND SERVICES. irreg. free to qualified personnel. United States Conference of Mayors, 1620 Eye St., N.W., Washington, DC 20006. TEL 202-293-7330.
Description: Offers a variety of services, news and information covering a wide range of issues.

327.045 FR
UNITED TOWNS NEWS NEWSLETTER. (Text in English, French, German, Italian, Spanish) bi-m. 100 F. World Federation of United Towns, 22, rue d'Alsace, 92300 Levallois, France. TEL 47-39-36-86. FAX 47-39-36-85. **Document type:** newsletter.
Formerly: U T O News (United Towns Organization).

352 PH
UNIVERSITY OF THE PHILIPPINES. COLLEGE OF PUBLIC ADMINISTRATION. LOCAL GOVERNMENT STUDIES. (Text in English) 1962. irreg. University of the Philippines, College of Public Administration, Local Government Center, PARDEC-SAAC Building, P.O. Box 198, Don Mariano Marcos Avenue, U.P.Diliman, Quezon City, Philippines. TEL 95-13-65. TELEX CPAUP.

352 XV ISSN 0042-0778
URADNI VESTNIK OBCIN ORMOZ IN PTUJ. (Text in Slovenian) 1964. irreg. free. Radio-Tednik, Raiceva 6, Ptuj, Slovenia. FAX 062-771-223. Ed. Marica Fajt. circ. 11,000.

342.73 US ISSN 0195-7686
KF5300
URBAN, STATE, AND LOCAL LAW NEWSLETTER. 1978. 4/yr. $30 (foreign $35). American Bar Association, Urban, State, and Local Government Law Section, 750 N. Lake Shore Dr., Chicago, IL 60611. TEL 312-988-5000. FAX 312-988-6281. Ed. Frederick W. Leonhardt. (reprint service avail.) **Indexed:** C.L.I., L.R.I. **Document type:** newsletter.
Formerly (1978 only): State, Local, and Urban Law Newsletter (ISSN 0163-2922)
Description: Informs members on the section's activities and legal issues.

352 US ISSN 0884-6421
KFU38
UTAH STATE DIGEST. 1985. s-m. $30. Department of Administrative Services, Division of Administrative Rules, Salt Lake City, UT 84114. Ed. Randy J. Fisher. circ. 400. **Document type:** government publication.
●Also available online.

352 NE ISSN 1380-5398
V G S NIEUWSBRIEF. 1992. 6/yr. membership. (Vereniging van Gemeentesecretarissen) Vuga Uitgeverij B.V., Postbus 16400, 2500 BK The Hague, Netherlands. TEL 31-70-3614011. FAX 31-70-3625468. (Editorial addr.: Secretariaat VGS, c/o Janny Lens-Mobach, Postbus 30435, 2500 GK The Hague, Netherlands. TEL 31-70-3738777) adv. **Document type:** newsletter.

352 SZ
V P O D ZEITUNG DER OEFFENTLICHE DIENST. 23/yr. Verband des Personals Oeffentlicher Dienste, Sonnenbergstr. 83, CH-8030 Zurich, Switzerland. TEL 01-2519935. FAX 01-2514316. Ed. Christina Beglinger. circ. 30,000. **Document type:** bulletin.

352 GW
VERBANDSGEMEINDE EDENKOBEN. AMTSBLATT. 1980. w. free. Verbandsgemeinde Edenkoben, c/o Manfred Horn, Am Bachweg 3, 6732 Edenkoben, Germany. TEL 06323-80826. FAX 06323-80899. adv. circ. 8,000. (back issues avail.)

VEREIN FUER DIE GESCHICHTE BERLINS. MITTEILUNGEN. see HISTORY — History Of Europe

352 SP
VETUSTA. 12/yr. Ayuntamiento - Town Council, Pza. de la Constitucion, 33009 Oviedo, Spain. TEL 85-21-89-49. Ed. Carlos Fuente.

352 AT ISSN 0049-6170
VICTORIAN MUNICIPAL DIRECTORY. 1866. s.a. Aus.$16. per no. Arnall & Jackson Pty. Ltd., 390 Barkly St., Brunswick, Vic. 3056, Australia. **Document type:** directory.

352 FR ISSN 0049-6294
VIE PUBLIQUE; le journal des elus et des administrateurs locaux. 1972. m. (11/yr.). 300 F. 13 rue d'Uzes, 75002 Paris, France. TEL 45-08-95-94. FAX 42-33-78-83. TELEX 215 741 JORMAN. Ed. Dennis Jeambar. adv.; bk.rev.; charts; illus.; tr.lit. circ. 10,500. —BLDSC (9235.350000).

352 US ISSN 0732-9156
JS39
VIRGINIA REVIEW. 1924. bi-m. $14. Review Publications, Inc., Box 860, Chester, VA 23831-0860. TEL 804-748-6351. FAX 804-796-6931. Ed. A. Taylor-White; Pub. Roger Habeck. adv.; bk.rev.; illus. circ. 5,000.
  Formerly (until 1981): Virginia Municipal Review (ISSN 0042-6660)

352 US ISSN 0042-6784
JS39
VIRGINIA TOWN & CITY. 1966. m. $8. Virginia Municipal League, Box 12164, Richmond, VA 23241-0164. TEL 804-649-8471. FAX 804-343-3758. Ed. Christine A. Everson. adv.: B&W page $441, color page $1413. bk.rev.; charts; illus. circ. 5,000.
  Description: Features include commentary and a marketplace, product and service guide, environmental counsel, professional directory, and legal guidelines.

352 FR
VOIX DES COMMUNES DES DEPARTMENTS ET DES REGIONS. Short title: Voix des Communes. 1966. m. 290 F.($70) Publications Periodique Professionnelles, 38 rue Claude Terrasse, 75016 Paris, France. TEL 44-14-60-60. FAX 44-14-60-61. Ed. Bernard Marx. adv.; bk.rev. circ. 10,700. (tabloid format; back issues avail.)

WELSH HOUSING QUARTERLY. see HOUSING AND URBAN PLANNING

352 US ISSN 0279-5337
TD1
WESTERN CITY. 1925. m. $34 to individuals; students $23 (foreign $45). League of California Cities, 1400 K St., Sacramento, CA 95814. TEL 916-444-5790. Ed. Victoria E. Clark. adv. contact: Jehan Flagg. bk.rev.; illus.; index. circ. 9,500. **Indexed:** Amer.Hist.& Life, Cal.Per.Ind. (1978-), Hist.Abstr., P.A.I.S., Urb.Aff.Abstr. **Document type:** government publication, trade publication.
  —UnCover.

352 US
WHAT'S HAPPENING FOR COMMUNITY LEADERS. (Includes irreg. supplements) 1976. m. free. Omaha - Council Bluffs Metropolitan Area Planning Agency, 2222 Cuming St., Omaha, NE 68102-4328. TEL 402-444-6866. FAX 402-342-0949. circ. 1,000. **Document type:** newsletter.
  Description: Regional data, development and public interest news for Douglas, Sarpy and Washington counties in Nebraska, Mills and Pottawattamie counties in Iowa.

352 AU
WIENER NEUSTADT. AMTSBLATT DER STATUTARSTADT. 1921. m. S.210. Magistrat, Rathaus, A-2700 Wiener Neustadt, Austria. Ed. Franz Pinczolits. adv. circ. 19,595. **Document type:** government publication.
  Formerly: Wiener Neustadt. Amtsblatt der Stadt (ISSN 0003-2255)
  Description: Local government publication covering news and information, politics, education, commerce and industry, culture and sport. Includes reports and announcements of events and exhibitions.

352 SZ
WIR STAEDTISCHEN. 10/yr. Stauffacherstr. 60, CH-8026 Zurich, Switzerland. TEL 01-2412674. circ. 7,500.

352 US ISSN 0749-6818
WISCONSIN COUNTIES. 1938. m. $24. Wisconsin Counties Association, 100 River Pl., Ste. 101, Madison, WI 53716-4016. TEL 608-224-5330. FAX 608-224-5325. Ed. Mark M. Rogacki. adv.: B&W page $415. circ. 3,450. **Document type:** government publication.

352 US
YOUR REGION. 1967. m. free. North Central Texas Council of Governments, P.O. Drawer COG, Arlington, TX 76005-5888. TEL 817-640-3300. FAX 817-640-7806. Ed. Edwina J. Shires. bk.rev.; bibl. circ. 5,000.
  Formerly: Your Region in Action (ISSN 0049-8432)
  Description: Covers activities of the Council in the 16 county Dallas-Forth Worth region.

352 SZ
Z V INFORMATION.* 1988. 11/yr. (Zentralverband des Staats- und Gemeindepersonals der Schweiz) Kocher Info, Tulpenweg 18, CH-4153 Reinach, Switzerland. Ed. Paul Vogel. circ. 23,000.

352 GW
ZEILBERG-ECHO. 1977. w. DM.24.80. (Marktgemeinde Maroldsweisach) Linus-Wittich Verlag, Peter-Henlein-Str. 1, 92342 Forchheim, Germany. TEL 09191-1624.

352 SZ
ZEITSCHRIFT FUER ZIVILSTANDSWESEN. (Text in French, German, Italian) 11/yr. Departem des Innern, Sektion Buergerrecht und Personenstand, CH-5001 Aarau, Switzerland. TEL 064-211561. Ed. W. Heussler. circ. 3,000.

352 FR ISSN 0245-3185
36000 COMMUNES. 1971. 10/yr. 300 F. Federation Nationale des Maires Ruraux, 26 rue de la Part-Dieu, B.P. 3144, 69406 Lyon Cedex 03, France. TEL 72-61-77-20. FAX 72-61-79-97. Ed. Helene Mira. adv.: B&W page 12200 F., color page 21000 F.; 210 x 297. circ. 9,000.

PUBLIC FINANCE, TAXATION

see Business and Economics–Public Finance, Taxation

PUBLIC HEALTH AND SAFETY

see also Birth Control; Fire Prevention; Funerals

614 US
A A W H QUARTERLY. 1953. q. $25 includes membership to individuals; libraries $250. American Association for World Health, 1129 20th St., N.W., Ste. 400, Washington, DC 20036. TEL 202-265-0286. Ed. William L. Wittenberg. bk.rev. circ. 1,000. (back issues avail.)
  Former titles: World Health News; American Association for World Health News.
  Description: Focuses on current international health issues.

A C P M NEWS. (American College of Preventive Medicine) see MEDICAL SCIENCES

614 UN ISSN 0250-8621
A F R O TECHNICAL PAPERS. French edition: Cahiers Techniques A F R O (ISSN 0250-8397) 1970. irreg., 2-4/yr. World Health Organization, Regional Office for Africa - Organisation Mondiale de la Sante. Bureau Regional de l'Afrique, B.P. No.6, Brazzaville, Congo. **Indexed:** Rural Recreat.Tour.Abstr., World Agri.Econ.& Rural Sociol.Abstr.

614 UN ISSN 0250-8443
A F R O TECHNICAL REPORT SERIES. French edition: Serie de Rapports Techniques A F R O (ISSN 0250-8567) 1976. irreg., 3-4/yr. World Health Organization, Regional Office for Africa - Organisation Mondiale de la Sante. Bureau Regional de l'Afrique, P.O. Box 6, Brazzaville, Congo.

A H C A NOTES. (American Health Care Association) see SOCIAL SERVICES AND WELFARE

614.8 360 US ISSN 0275-8407
A M S STUDIES IN MODERN SOCIETY. 1972. irreg., no.24, 1994. price varies. A M S Press, Inc., 56 E. 13th St., New York, NY 10003. TEL 212-777-4700. FAX 212-995-5413. (back issues avail.)
  Description: Monographs, reference works and bibliographies on contemporary social issues.

614.8 301.16 US ISSN 0001-2165
A P C O BULLETIN. 1935. m. $100 (foreign $200). Association of Public-Safety Communications Officials International, Inc., 2040 S. Ridgewood Ave., Daytona Beach, FL 32119-8437. TEL 904-322-2500. FAX 904-322-2501. Ed. Alan Chase; Pub. Alan W. Chase. adv. contact: Terry D. Diehl. bk.rev.; circ. 12,500 (controlled). (back issues avail.) **Document type:** trade publication.
  Description: For public safety personnel who operate, maintain, install, and design the emergency communications systems used to answer the public's calls for police, fire and EMS services.

A S D A NEWS. (American Sleep Disorders Association) see MEDICAL SCIENCES — Psychiatry And Neurology

614.8 AT ISSN 1037-3403
ABORIGINAL AND ISLANDER HEALTH WORKER JOURNAL; a national resource journal for Aboriginal and Islander community education workers. 1977. 6/yr. Aus.$26 to individuals; institutions Aus.$30. (Human Services and Health Department) Aboriginal and Islander Health Worker, P.O. Box 502, Matraville, N.S.W. 2036, Australia. TEL 02-311-2593. FAX 02-311-2814. Ed. Donnaleen Campbell. adv.: B&W page $800; adv. contact: Donnaleen Campbell. circ. 11,000. (back issues avail.)
  —UnCover.
  Former titles: Aboriginal and Islander Health Worker & Aboriginal Health Worker (ISSN 0155-0357)

614.8 UK ISSN 0001-4575
HV675.A1 CODEN: AAPVB5
ACCIDENT ANALYSIS & PREVENTION. 1969. bi-m. £484($770) (effective 1996). Elsevier Science Ltd., Pergamon, P.O. Box 800, Kidlington, Oxford OX5 1DX, England. TEL 44-1865-843000. FAX 44-1865-843010. E-mail: nlinfo-f@elsevier.nl; usinfo-f@elsevier.com; forinfo-kyf04035@niftyserve.or.jp; Site addr.: http://www.elsevier.nl/. (Subscr. in U.S. and Canada to: Elsevier Science, 660 White Plains Rd., Tarrytown, NY 10159-5153. TEL 919-524-9200. FAX 914-333-2444) Ed. Frank A. Haight. adv.; bk.rev.; charts; illus. (also avail. in microform from UMI; back issues avail.) **Indexed:** Abstr.Crim.& Pen., ASCA, Biol.Abstr., C.I.S.Abstr., Curr.Cont., Ergon.Abstr., Excerp.Med., HRIS, Intl.Civil Eng.Abstr., Psychol.Abstr. (1969-), Psyscan, Risk Abstr., Soft.Abstr.Eng., SSCI. **Document type:** academic/scholarly publication.
  —BLDSC (0573.130000); Ei; Faxon; Genuine Article; SWETS; UMI; UnCover. CCC.
  Description: Discusses industrial safety.
  Refereed Serial

614.8 US ISSN 0148-6039
HA217
ACCIDENT FACTS. a. $18.95. National Safety Council, Statistics Department, 1121 Spring Lake Dr., Itasca, IL 60143. TEL 708-285-1121. Ed. Alan F. Hoskin. (also avail. in microfiche from CIS) **Indexed:** SRI.
  Description: Compendium of statistical information relating to accidents.

ACTA HYDROCHIMICA ET HYDROBIOLOGICA; jpurnal for water and wastewater research. see WATER RESOURCES

ACUTE TOXICITY DATA. see PHARMACY AND PHARMACOLOGY

ADMINISTRATION AND POLICY IN MENTAL HEALTH. see MEDICAL SCIENCES

614 551.5 NE
ADVANCES IN NATURAL AND TECHNOLOGICAL HAZARDS RESEARCH. 1993. irreg., vol.2, 1993. Kluwer Academic Publishers, Postbus 17, 3300 AA Dordrecht, Netherlands. TEL 31-78-392392. FAX 31-78-392254. TELEX 29245 KAPG NL. (Dist. by: Kluwer Academic Publishers Group, P.O. Box 322, 3300 AH Dordrecht, Netherlands. TEL 31-78-392392. FAX 31-78-546474; N. America dist. addr.: Box 358, Accord Sta., Hingham, MA 02018-0358. TEL 617-871-6600. FAX 617-871-6528) Ed. Mohammed I. El-Sabh. (back issues avail.) **Document type:** proceedings.
  Refereed Serial

AFRICA MEDICINE AND HEALTH. see MEDICAL SCIENCES

PUBLIC HEALTH AND SAFETY

AIDS & HEALTH NEWS. see *MEDICAL SCIENCES — Communicable Diseases*

AIDS & PUBLIC POLICY JOURNAL. see *MEDICAL SCIENCES — Communicable Diseases*

AIDS & T B WEEKLY ARTICLE SUMMARIES. see *MEDICAL SCIENCES — Abstracting, Bibliographies, Statistics*

AIDS BULLETIN. see *MEDICAL SCIENCES — Communicable Diseases*

AIDS INFORMATION EXCHANGE. see *MEDICAL SCIENCES — Communicable Diseases*

614 616.9   UK   ISSN 1356-9880
THE AIDS LEADER. 1992. bi-m. £85($150) (effective 1996). Modus Operandi, P.O. Box 346, Bradford BD7 2DB, England. TEL 01274-521511. FAX 01274-521512. E-mail: aidslead@modus-op.demon.co.uk. Ed. Adam Christie. bk.rev.; circ. 500 (paid). (back issues avail.) **Document type:** newsletter.
●Also available on CD-ROM.
 Formerly: Digest of Organisational Responses to AIDS and HIV (ISSN 0965-5840)

AIDS POLICY AND LAW; the bi-weekly newsletter on legislation, regulation, and litigation concerning AIDS. see *LAW*

AIDS THERAPIES. see *MEDICAL SCIENCES — Communicable Diseases*

AIDS WEEKLY; a complete weekly report privately circulated. see *MEDICAL SCIENCES — Communicable Diseases*

614   GW   ISSN 0172-2131
AKADEMIE FUER OEFFENTLICHES GESUNDHEITSWESEN. SCHRIFTENREIHE. 1973. irreg. price varies. Akademie fuer Oeffentliches Gesundheitswesen, Auf'm Hennekamp 70, 40225 Duesseldorf, Germany. **Document type:** academic/scholarly publication.
 Formerly: Akademie fuer Staatsmedizin, Duesseldorf. Jahrbuch (ISSN 0065-5392)

613   US   ISSN 0145-6857
ALABAMA'S HEALTH. 1967. m. free. Department of Public Health, 434 Monroe St., Montgomery, AL 36130-3017. TEL 334-613-5300. FAX 334-240-3097. Ed. Arrol Sheehan. bk.rev. circ. 3,250.
 Description: Describes events and topics of interest to public health professionals.

ALERT; maandblad voor rampenbestrijding en crisisbeheersing. see *CIVIL DEFENSE*

AMBIENTE RISORSE SALUTE; scienza, tecnica e cultura per uno sviluppo di qualita. see *ENVIRONMENTAL STUDIES*

AMBIENTE SALUTE TERRITORIO. see *ENVIRONMENTAL STUDIES*

AMERICAN COLLEGE OF TOXICOLOGY. JOURNAL. see *ENVIRONMENTAL STUDIES — Toxicology And Environmental Safety*

AMERICAN HEALTH CARE ASSOCIATION. PROVIDER. see *SOCIAL SERVICES AND WELFARE*

AMERICAN HOSPITAL ASSOCIATION GUIDE TO THE HEALTH CARE FIELD. see *HOSPITALS — Abstracting, Bibliographies, Statistics*

613.2   US   ISSN 0890-1171
     CODEN: AJHPED
AMERICAN JOURNAL OF HEALTH PROMOTION. Short title: A J H P. 1986. bi-m. $69 to individuals (Canada $96.30; elsewhere $90); institutions $89 (Canada $117.70; elsewhere $110) (effective 1996). Mosby - Year Book, Inc. (Subsidiary of: Times Mirror Company), 11830 Westline Industrial Dr., St. Louis, MO 63146-3318. TEL 314-872-8370. FAX 314-432-1380. Ed. Michael P. O'Donnell. adv.: B&W page $1125, color page $2030; trim 8 1/2 x 11; adv. contact: Donna Ricko. bk.rev.; film rev.; abstr.; charts; stat. circ. 4,567. (back issues avail.) **Indexed:** ABI Inform., Access, CINAHL, Excerp.Med., Human Resour.Abstr., PSI, Psychol.Abstr. (1986-), Sage Fam.Stud.Abstr. **Document type:** academic/scholarly publication.
 —BLDSC (0824.760000); Faxon; SWETS; UnCover.
 Description: Covers the science and art of helping people change their lifestyle to move toward a state of optimal health.
 Refereed Serial

AMERICAN JOURNAL OF PHARMACY; and the sciences supporting public health. see *PHARMACY AND PHARMACOLOGY*

AMERICAN JOURNAL OF PREVENTIVE MEDICINE. see *MEDICAL SCIENCES*

614   US   ISSN 0090-0036
RA421   CODEN: AJHEAA
AMERICAN JOURNAL OF PUBLIC HEALTH. 1911. m. $100 to individuals (foreign $140); institutions $160 (foreign $200) (effective 1996). American Public Health Association, 1015 15th St., N.W., Washington, DC 20005. TEL 202-789-5600. Ed. Dr. Michael Ibrahim. adv.; charts; illus.; index. circ. 35,000. (also avail. in microform from UMI,PMC) **Indexed:** Abstr.Anthropol., Abstr.Health Care Manage.Stud., Abstr.Hyg., Abstr.Soc.Geront., Acad.Ind., AIM, ASSIA, Behav.Med.Abstr., Bibl.Dev.Med.& Child Neur., Biol.Abstr., Biol.Dig., C.I.J.E., C.I.N.L., C.I.S. Abstr., Chem.Abstr., CLOA, Curr.Adv.Cancer Res., Curr.Adv.Ecol.Sci., Curr.Cont., Curr.Lit.Fam.Plan., Curr.Tit.Dent., Dairy Sci.Abstr., Deep Sea Res.& Oceanogr.Abstr., Dent.Abstr., Dent.Ind., Diar.Dis.Res., Dok.Arbeitsmed., Environ.Abstr., Environ.Per.Bibl. (1972-), Excerp.Med., Food Sci.& Tech.Abstr., Gen.Sci.Ind., Helminthol.Abstr., Hlth.Ind., Hosp.Lit.Ind., HRIS, Human Resour.Abstr., I.P.A., Ind.Med., Ind.Sci.Rev., Ind.Vet., INIS Atomind., Int.Nurs.Ind., Irr.& Drain.Abstr., Kidney, Med.& Surg.Dermat., Med.Care Rev., Medsoc, Mult.Ed.Abstr., NRN, Nucl.Sci.Abstr., Nutr.Abstr., Ocean.Abstr., P.A.I.S., Phys.Ed.Ind., Popul.Ind., Protozool.Abstr., Psychol.Abstr. (1991-), Res.High.Educ.Abstr., Risk Abstr., Rural Recreat.Tour.Abstr., Saf.Sci.Abstr., Sage Fam.Stud.Abstr., Sci.Cit.Ind., Sel.Water Res.Abstr., Small Anim.Abstr., Soc.Sci.Ind., Soc.Work Res.& Abstr., Sp.Ed.Needs Abstr., SRI, SSCI, Stud.Wom.Abstr., Tech.Educ.Abstr., Trop.Dis.Bull., Vet.Bull., W.R.C.Inf., World Agri.Econ.& Rural Sociol.Abstr. **Document type:** academic/scholarly publication.
●Also available online. Vendor(s): Ovid Technologies, University Microfilms International.
 —BLDSC (0835.900000); CASDDS; CIS; EMDOCS; Faxon; Genuine Article; SWETS; UMI; UnCover. **CCC.**
 Supersedes in part (in 1971): American Journal of Public Health and the Nation's Health (ISSN 0002-9572); Which was formed by the 1927 merger of: American Journal of Public Health (ISSN 0271-4353); Nation's Health (ISSN 1076-0704).
 Description: Contains reports of original research, demonstrations, evaluations, and other articles covering current aspects of public health.
 Refereed Serial

614   US   ISSN 0273-4737
AMERICAN SOCIETY OF SAFETY ENGINEERS. SOCIETY UPDATE. 1974. m. included in subscr. to Professional Safety. American Society of Safety Engineers, 1800 E. Oakton St., Des Plaines, IL 60018-2187. TEL 708-692-4121. FAX 708-296-3769. Ed. Tamara Burke. circ. 30,000. (back issues avail.) **Document type:** bulletin.
 Description: ASSE members in the news; chapter and division highlights; society activities and new programs.

628   US   ISSN 0066-068X
AMERICAN SOCIETY OF SANITARY ENGINEERING. YEAR BOOK. 1906. a. $10 each per 2-part book. American Society of Sanitary Engineering, c/o Gael H. Dunn, Ed., Box 40362, Bay Village, OH 44140. TEL 216-835-3040. FAX 216-835-3488. adv.; cum.index: 1906-1950, 1951-1963, 1963-1970. circ. 2,700.

614.85   US
AMERISURE SAFETY NEWS. 1921. q. free to policyholders. Michigan Mutual Insurance Co., 28 W. Adams, Detroit, MI 48226. TEL 313-965-8600. FAX 313-965-7787. (Co-sponsor: Amerisure Companies) adv. contact: Judith Willis. circ. 14,500. (tabloid format; back issues avail.)
 Former titles: Michigan Mutual Safety News; Amerisure Companies Safety News; Shopman.
 Description: Provides safety tips for use in the home, on the road and at the workplace.

AMTSBLATT DES KREISES WESEL; Amtliches Verkuendungsblatt. see *PUBLIC ADMINISTRATION — Municipal Government*

614.8   AO
ANGOLA. SECRETARIA PROVINCIAL DE SAUDE, TRABALHO. PREVIDENCIA E ASSISTENCIA. SINTESE DA ACTIVIDADE DOS SERVICOS E ORGANISMOS.★ 1963. irreg. (approx. a.). free. Secretaria Provincial de Saude, Trabalho, Previdencia e Assistencia, Luanda, Angola. circ. controlled. (tabloid format)

614   IT   ISSN 0021-3071
ANNALI DELLA SANITA PUBBLICA. vol.23, 1970. m. L.52000. Ministero della Sanita, Piazzale del Industria, Rome, Italy. Ed. Dr. Fausto Federici. bk.rev. circ. 3,000. **Indexed:** Biol.Abstr., Chem.Abstr., Helminthol.Abstr., INIS Atomind., Trop.Dis.Bull.

614   US   ISSN 1047-2797
RA648.5   CODEN: ANNPE3
ANNALS OF EPIDEMIOLOGY. 1990. bi-m $265 to institutions (effective 1996). (American College of Epidemiology) Elsevier Science Inc., 655 Ave. of the Americas, New York, NY 10010. TEL 212-989-5800. FAX 212-633-3990. TELEX 420643 AEP UI. (Subscr. to: Box 882, Madison Sq. Sta., New York, NY 10159-0882) Eds. Charles H. Hennekens, Julie E. Buring. (also avail. in microform from UMI) **Indexed:** Diar.Dis.Res., Excerp.Med. (1992-), Ind.Med. (1993-), Med.& Surg.Dermat. **Document type:** academic/scholarly publication.
 —BLDSC (1040.470000); SWETS; UnCover. **CCC.**
 Description: Provides reports of original research in epidemiology of chronic and acute diseases that are of interest to clinicians as well as public health researchers.
 Refereed Serial

628   US
ANNUAL CONFERENCE ON ACTIVATED SLUDGE PROCESS CONTROL. PROCEEDINGS. 1981. a. Arthur Technology, Inc., Box 1236, Fond du Lac, WI 54935-6836. Ed. Robert M. Arthur. **Document type:** proceedings.

614   US   ISSN 0163-7525
RA421   CODEN: AREHDT
ANNUAL REVIEW OF PUBLIC HEALTH. 1980. a. $52 (foreign $57) (effective Jan. 1995). Annual Reviews Inc., 4139 El Camino Way, Box 10139, Palo Alto, CA 94303-0139. TEL 415-493-4400; 800-523-8635. FAX 415-855-9815. E-mail: annrevu@class.org. Ed. Gilbert S. Omenn. bibl.; index, cum.index. (also avail. in microfilm from UMI; back issues avail.; reprint service avail.) **Indexed:** Abstr.Health Care Manage.Stud., Abstr.Hyg., Adol.Ment.Hlth.Abstr., CINAHL, Curr.Cont., Deep Sea Res.& Oceanogr.Abstr., Dok.Arbeitsmed., Ind.Med., Risk Abstr., SSCI. **Document type:** academic/scholarly publication.
 —BLDSC (1528.450000); ADONIS; CASDDS; Faxon; Genuine Article; SWETS; UMI; UnCover. **CCC.**
 Description: Original critical reviews of the significant primary literature and current developments in public health.

628   IT   ISSN 1122-861X
ANNUARIO SANITARIO ITALIANO/ITALIAN SANITARY DIRECTORY. 1952. a. L.220000 (effective 1996). Guida Monaci S.p.A., Via Vitorchiano 107, 00187 Rome, Italy. TEL 06-3288805. FAX 06-3275693. TELEX 623234 MONACI. **Document type:** directory.
 Formerly: Guida Monaci. Annuario Sanitario (ISSN 0390-9263); (until 1974): Rome Sanitaria.
 Description: Directory of all Italian public health organizations and bodies, medical products and equipment manufacturers.

APPLIED OCCUPATIONAL & ENVIRONMENTAL HYGIENE. see *OCCUPATIONAL HEALTH AND SAFETY*

614   LE   ISSN 0257-3202
ARAB HEALTH. (Text in Arabic, English) 1985. 4/yr. $60. Chatila Publishing House, P.O. Box 135121, Chouran, Beirut, Lebanon. TEL 961-1-352413. FAX 961-1-352419. Ed. Dr. Abdul Salam Chatila. adv.; bk.rev. circ. 12,741. **Document type:** trade publication.
 Description: Covers articles of interest to importers and distributors of health care products and equipment, to hospital workers, and to ministries of health in the Middle East, Anglophone Africa and other countries.

613.62   GW   ISSN 0944-6052
RC963   CODEN: ASOUE
ARBEITSMEDIZIN, SOZIALMEDIZIN, UMWELTMEDIZIN; Zeitschrift fuer Praxis, Klinik, Forschung, Begutachtung. (Supplement avail. (ISSN 0944-6419)) 1965. m. DM.273 (foreign DM.305.40) (effective 1995). (Deutsche Gesellschaft fuer Arbeitsmedizin) Verlagsgemeinschaft Gentner Verlag - Strobel Verlag, Forststr. 131, 70193 Stuttgart, Germany. TEL 0711-63672-0. FAX 0711-6367211. (Co-sponsor: Oesterreichische Gesellschaft fuer Arbeitsmedizin) Eds. Dr. Georg Zerlett, Dr. Gerhard Triebig. adv. contact: Gernot Keuchen. bk.rev.; abstr.; charts; illus.; index. circ. 4,000. **Indexed:** Abstr.Hyg., Biol.Abstr., C.I.S. Abstr., Curr.Cont., Excerp.Med., INIS Atomind., Lab.Haz.Bull., Nutr.Abstr., Trop.Dis.Bull. **Document type:** academic/scholarly publication.
 —Genuine Article; SWETS.
 Former titles (until 1993): Arbeitsmedizin, Sozialmedizin, Praeventivmedizin (ISSN 0300-581X); Arbeitsmedizin, Sozialmedizin, Arbeitshygiene (ISSN 0003-7753)

613.62   GW   ISSN 0944-6419
                        CODEN: AUMSE
ARBEITSMEDIZIN, SOZIALMEDIZIN, UMWELTMEDIZIN. SUPPLEMENT. 1966. irreg. (Deutsche Gesellschaft fuer Arbeitsmedizin) Verlagsgemeinschaft Gentner Verlag - Strobel Verlag, Forststr. 131, 70193 Stuttgart, Germany. TEL 0711-63672-0. FAX 0711-6367211. **Indexed:** Excerp.Med. (1995-). **Document type:** monographic series.
 —BLDSC (1587.402755).
 Former titles: Arbeitsmedizin, Sozialmedizin, Praeventivmedizin. Sonderheft (ISSN 0720-0013); Arbeitsmedizin, Sozialmedizin, Arbeitshygiene. Sonderheft (ISSN 0570-5878)

614.85   SW   ISSN 0003-7834
ARBETSMILJOE. 1970. 12/yr. SEK 180. Foereningen foer Arbetarskydd - Swedish Work Environment Association, P.O. Box 17550, S-118 91 Stockholm, Sweden. TEL 46-8-668-14-60. FAX 46-8-668-25-05. Ed. Rolf Wikstroem. adv.; bk.rev.; charts; illus. circ. 133,000. **Indexed:** C.I.S. Abstr.
 —BLDSC (1588.080000).
 Formerly: Arbetarskyddet.

362.1 616   BE   ISSN 0003-9578
                        CODEN: ABMHAM
ARCHIVES BELGES DE MEDECINE SOCIALE, HYGIENE, MEDECINE DU TRAVAIL ET MEDECINE. (Summaries in English, Flemish, French) 1938. 6/yr. (1200 F.($38) Archives de Medecine Sociale et d'Hygiene, Cite Administrative de l'Etat, Quartier Esplanade, No.6, 1010 Brussels, Belgium. bk.rev.; abstr.; bibl.; charts; index. **Indexed:** Abstr.Hyg., Biol.Abstr., C.I.S. Abstr., Chem.Abstr., Dairy Sci.Abstr., Excerp.Med., Food Sci.& Tech.Abstr., Ind.Med., INIS Atomind., Nutr.Abstr., Trop.Dis.Bull.
 —CASDDS.
 Former titles (until 1947): Archives Belges de Medecine Sociale et d'Hygiene (ISSN 0365-4648); (until 1938): Revue de Pathologie et de Physiologie du Travail (ISSN 0771-6192); (until 1931): Revue de Medecine et de Chirurgie des Accidents de Travail et des Maladies Professionnelles (ISSN 0771-1301)

ARCTIC MEDICAL RESEARCH. see *MEDICAL SCIENCES*

353.9   US   ISSN 0362-1421
RA21
ARIZONA. DEPARTMENT OF HEALTH SERVICES. ANNUAL REPORT. Key Title: Annual Report of the Arizona Department of Health Services. 1974. a. free. Department of Health Services, 1740 W. Adams St., Phoenix, AZ 85007. TEL 602-542-1001. FAX 602-542-1062. Ed. Brad Christensen. illus.; circ. 500 (controlled). **Document type:** government publication.

614 360   US
ARIZONA MEDICINE. 1990. m. $36.47. Arizona Medical Association, 810 W. Bethany Home Rd., Phoenix, AZ 85013. TEL 602-246-8901. FAX 602-242-6283. Ed. Marshall B. Block. adv. contact: Linda Brown. cum.index. circ. 4,300. (tabloid format) **Document type:** newspaper.

ARIZONA RADIATION REGULATORY AGENCY. ANNUAL REPORT. see *ENERGY — Nuclear Energy*

ARZT IN NIEDEROESTERREICH. see *MEDICAL SCIENCES*

ASBESTOS & LEAD ABATEMENT REPORT; inspection, analysis, removal, maintenance, alternatives. see *ENVIRONMENTAL STUDIES*

ASIAN ENVIRONMENT; journal of environmental science and technology for balanced development. see *ENVIRONMENTAL STUDIES*

614 362.2   US   ISSN 1055-260X
ASSOCIATION OF MENTAL HEALTH ADMINISTRATORS. NEWSLETTER. 1963. m. membership. Association of Mental Health Administrators, 60 Revere Dr., Ste. 500, Northbrook, IL 60062. TEL 708-480-9626. Ed. James Rayball. adv.; bk.rev.; circ. 1,800 (controlled). **Document type:** newsletter.

614   UK   ISSN 0140-4563
ASSOCIATION OF NATIONAL HEALTH SERVICE SUPPLIES OFFICERS. REFERENCE BOOK & BUYER'S GUIDE. a. £30. Sterling Publications Ltd., 86-88 Edgware Rd., London, W2 2YW, England. TEL 01-258 0066. adv.

AUSTRALIAN DOCTOR. see *MEDICAL SCIENCES*

AUSTRALIAN FLUORIDATION NEWS. AQUA-PURA. see *WATER RESOURCES*

616.9   AT   ISSN 1035-7319
HV88   CODEN: AJPHET
AUSTRALIAN JOURNAL OF PUBLIC HEALTH. 1977. bi-m. Aus.$120 to individuals; libraries and institutions Aus.$185. Public Health Association of Australia, G.P.O. Box 2204, Canberra, A.C.T. 2601, Australia. TEL 06-285-2373. FAX 06-282-5438. E-mail: austjnl@pub.health.su.oz.au. Ed. Charles Kerr. adv.; bk.rev. circ. 2,500. (also avail. in microfilm from UMI; reprint service avail. from UMI) **Indexed:** Aus.P.A.I.S., Curr.Cont., Dent.Ind., Excerp.Med., IMFL, Ind.Med., NRN, Risk Abstr., Soc.Sci.Ind., SSCI. **Document type:** academic/scholarly publication.
 —BLDSC (1811.650000); Genuine Article; SWETS; UMI; UnCover. CCC.
 Formerly (until Dec. 1990): Community Health Studies (ISSN 0149-2047)
 Description: Publishes research reports, reviews and letters on epidemiology, health policy, health services and health promotion.
 Refereed Serial

362.1042505   AT   ISSN 1038-5282
AUSTRALIAN JOURNAL OF RURAL HEALTH. 1992. q. Aus.$170($170) (effective 1996). (Association for Australian Rural Nurses) Blackwell Science Pty Ltd, P.O. Box 378, Carlton South, Vic. 3053, Australia. TEL 61-3-93470300. FAX 61-3-93493016.

AUSTRALIAN MEDICINE. see *MEDICAL SCIENCES*

614   AT   ISSN 0067-2165
AUSTRALIAN STUDIES IN HEALTH SERVICE ADMINISTRATION. 1968. irreg., nos.72-74, 1992. University of New South Wales, School of Health Services Management, Sydney 2052, Australia. FAX 02-385-2591. circ. 300. **Document type:** monographic series.
 —BLDSC (1821.800000).

614   AT   ISSN 1032-6138
RA371
AUSTRALIA'S HEALTH. 1988. biennial. price varies. (Australian Institute of Health and Welfare) Australian Government Publishing Service, G.P.O. Box 84, Canberra, A.T.C. 2601, Australia. TEL 61-6-2954411. FAX 61-6-2954455. TELEX AA62013.

614.5   US
B M F T RISIKO- UND SICHERHEITSFORSCHUNG. 1982. irreg., latest 1986. price varies. (Bundesministerium fuer Forschung und Technologie, GW) Springer-Verlag, 175 Fifth Ave., New York, NY 10010. TEL 212-460-1500. FAX 212-473-6272. (Also: Berlin, Heidelberg, Tokyo and Vienna) **Indexed:** Chem.Abstr. **Document type:** monographic series.

614   US   ISSN 1070-5414
B N A CALIFORNIA HEALTH CARE REPORTER.* 1993. bi-w. $495. M. Lee Smith Publishers & Printers, 162 Fourth Ave., Box 198867, Nashville, TN 37219-8867. TEL 615-242-7395. FAX 615-256-6601. (Subscr. to: 9435 Key West Ave., Rockville, MD 20850. TEL 800-372-1033) Ed. Barrett McBride. (back issues avail.)
 Description: Features comprehensive coverage of laws, regulations and litigation affecting California's health care industry.

B N A'S FEDERAL ENVIRONMENT & SAFETY REGULATORY MONITORING REPORT. see *ENVIRONMENTAL STUDIES*

614   US
▼**B N A'S HEALTH CARE FACILITIES GUIDE.** 1994. m. $695 (effective July 1995). The Bureau of National Affairs, Inc., 1231 25th St., N.W., Washington, DC 20037. TEL 202-452-4200. FAX 202-822-8092. TELEX 285656 BNAI WSH. (Subscr. to: 9435 Key West Ave., Rockville, MD 20850) Ed. Randy Kubetin. (looseleaf format; back issues avail.) **Document type:** newsletter.

614   US   ISSN 1068-1213
B N A'S HEALTH CARE POLICY REPORT. 1993. w. $716 (effective July 1995). The Bureau of National Affairs, Inc., 1231 25th St., N.W., Washington, DC 20037. TEL 202-452-4200. FAX 202-822-8092. TELEX 285656 BNAI WSH. (Subscr. to: 9435 Key West Ave., Rockville, MD 20850. TEL 800-372-1033) Ed. Paul Albergo. s-a. index. (back issues avail.)
 —CCC.
 Description: Covers federal, state and private sector efforts to reform and manage the U.S. health care system.

B N A'S STATE ENVIRONMENT & SAFETY REGULATORY MONITORING REPORT. see *ENVIRONMENTAL STUDIES*

B T - L M & S. (Building Technology - Land Management & Safety) see *BUILDING AND CONSTRUCTION*

BAD TOELZ AKTUELL. see *TRAVEL AND TOURISM*

610   BB
BARBADOS. MINISTRY OF HEALTH. CHIEF MEDICAL OFFICER. ANNUAL REPORT. 1972. a. free. Ministry of Health, Bridgetown, Barbados, W.I. FAX 426-5570. Ed.Bd. charts; illus.; stat. circ. 300. **Document type:** government publication.
 Former titles: Barbados. Ministry of Health and Community Services. Chief Medical Officer. Annual Report; Barbados. Ministry of Health and Welfare. Chief Medical Officer. Annual Report.

614 613   GW   ISSN 0067-5083
                        CODEN: BHEPAP
BEITRAEGE ZUR HYGIENE UND EPIDEMIOLOGIE.* 1943. irreg., vol. 25, 1981. price varies. Johann Ambrosius Barth, Postfach 102869, 69018 Heidelberg, Germany. TEL 06221-489281. FAX 06221-489205. Eds. H. Habs, H. Rische. (back issues avail.) **Indexed:** Excerp.Med., Ind.Med. **Document type:** academic/scholarly publication.

614   BE
BELGIUM. MINISTERE DE LA SANTE PUBLIQUE ET DE LA FAMILLE. BULLETIN. (Text in Dutch and French) 1936. 2/yr. 600 Fr. Ministere de la Sante Publique et de la Famille - Ministerie van Volksgezondheid en van het Gezin, Cite Administrative de l'Etat, Bibliotheque, Quartier Vesale, 1010 Brussels, Belgium. Ed.Bd. charts. **Indexed:** Trop.Dis.Bull.

PUBLIC HEALTH AND SAFETY

BELGIUM. MINISTERE DE LA SANTE PUBLIQUE ET DE LA FAMILLE. RAPPORT ANNUEL. see *SOCIAL SERVICES AND WELFARE*

BEZPECNOST A HYGIENA PRACE/SAFETY AND HYGIENE OF WORK. see *LABOR UNIONS*

362.1 333.792　　PL　ISSN 0867-4752
BEZPIECZENSTWO JADROWE I OCHRONA RADIOLOGICZNA. 1989. q. (Panstwowy Dozor Bezpieczenstwa Jadrowego i Ochrony Radiologicznej) Panstwowa Agencja Atomistyki, Ul. Krucza 36, 00-525 Warsaw, Poland. TEL 48-22-298593. FAX 48-22-290164. Ed. Leszek Mlynarczyk.

614　　SZ　ISSN 0006-4629
BLAUE KREUZ. 1896. fortn. 60 SFr. (Blue Cross of Switzerland) Blaukreuz Verlag, Lindenrain 5A, CH-3001 Bern, Switzerland. TEL 031-3015866. FAX 031-3014154. Ed.Bd. bk.rev.; illus. circ. 3,700. (looseleaf format) **Document type:** newsletter.

628　　VE　ISSN 0798-037X
BOLETIN DE SALUD PUBLICA. 1941. a. Ministerio de Sanidad y Asistencia Social, Direccion de Salud Publica, Caracas, Venezuela. (Co-sponsor: Venezuela. Oficina de los Servicios Regionales de Salud) Ed.Bd. charts; illus. **Document type:** government publication.
Supersedes: Uruguay. Consejo de Salud Publica. Boletin.

614　　MX
BOLETIN EPIDEMIOLOGICO. 1973. a. free. Instituto Mexicano del Seguro Social, Subdireccion General Medica, Jefatura de Servicios de Medicina Preventiva, Apdo. Postal 12976, 03001 Mexico, D.F., Mexico. stat. circ. 2,000.
Formerly: Boletin Epidemiologico Anual.

614　　US
BORDER EPIDEMIOLOGICAL BULLETIN/BOLETIN EPIDEMIOLOGICO FRONTERIZO. (Text in English, Spanish) 1975. bi-m. $75 includes all organization publications; corporate rate $500. Pan American Health Organization, El Paso Field Office, 6006 N. Mesa, Ste. 600, El Paso, TX 79912. TEL 915-581-6645. FAX 915-833-4768. E-mail: vilchish@paho.org. Ed. Dr. Hugo Vilchis-licon. **Document type:** bulletin.
Description: Covers U.S.-Mexico border public health and epidemiology issues.

614　　US
BORDER HEALTH/SALUD FRONTERIZA. (Text in English, Spanish) 1984. q. $75 includes all organization publications; corporate rate $500. (United States - Mexico Border Health Association) Pan American Health Organization, El Paso Field Office, 6006 N. Mesa, Ste. 600, El Paso, TX 79912. TEL 915-581-6645. FAX 915-833-4768. E-mail: vilchish@paho.org. Ed. Dr. Hugo Vilchis-Licon. circ. 2,500. **Document type:** academic/scholarly publication.
Description: Covers U.S.-Mexico border public health and environmental issues.
Refereed Serial

BOTSWANA. CENTRAL STATISTICS OFFICE. HEALTH STATISTICS REPORT. see *MEDICAL SCIENCES — Abstracting, Bibliographies, Statistics*

616.9　　BS　ISSN 0258-8846
BOTSWANA. MINISTRY OF HEALTH. EPIDEMIOLOGICAL BULLETIN. Key Title: Botswana Epidemiological Bulletin. 1982. q. Ministry of Health, Epidemiological Unit, Private Bag 0038, Gaborone, Botswana. TEL 267-352000. (Dist. by: Government Printer, Box 87, Gaborone, Botswana) **Document type:** academic/scholarly publication, government publication.

614　　BS　ISSN 0253-5629
RA352.B6
BOTSWANA. MINISTRY OF HEALTH. REPORT. a. Ministry of Health, Private Bag 0038, Gaborone, Botswana. TEL 267-352000. **Document type:** government publication.
Former titles (until 1974): Botswana. Department of Health. Report (ISSN 0377-3949); (until 1963): Bechuanaland Protectorate. Director of Medical Services. Medical and Sanitary Report for (Year) (ISSN 0258-4530); (until 1961): Bechuanaland Protectorate. Director of Medical Services. Annual Medical and Sanitary Report for (Year) (ISSN 0258-4549)

BRIEFINGS ON HOSPITAL SAFETY; the newsletter for hospital safety committees. see *HOSPITALS*

614.8　　CN　ISSN 0706-4810
RA185.B7
BRITISH COLUMBIA. MINISTRY OF HEALTH. ANNUAL REPORT. 1975. a. free. Ministry of Health, Victoria, B.C., Canada. TEL 604-387-2323. circ. 4,000. **Document type:** government publication.
Formerly: British Columbia. Department of Health. Annual Report (ISSN 0701-5372)

614　　GW　ISSN 0007-5914
BUNDESGESUNDHEITSBLATT. 1958. fortn. DM.148. (Bundesgesundheitsamt) Carl Heymanns Verlag KG, Luxemburgstr. 449, 50939 Cologne, Germany. TEL 0221-94373-0. FAX 0221-94373901. adv.; bk.rev.; bibl.; charts; stat.; index. circ. 2,300. **Indexed:** Biol.Abstr., C.I.S. Abstr., Dairy Sci.Abstr., Dok.Arbeitsmed., Excerp.Med., Food Sci.& Tech.Abstr., Ind.Vet., INIS Atomind., Int.Packag.Abstr., Nutr.Abstr., Packag.Sci.Tech., Sugar Ind.Abstr., Vet.Bull. **Document type:** government publication.
—BLDSC (2930.200000); SWETS.

614.4　　US　ISSN 1077-8373
RA644.6
C D P FILE. (Chronic Disease Prevention) Variant title: C D P File on C D - R O M. (In 6 parts: Health Promotion and Education; AIDS School Health Education; Cancer Prevention and Control; a combination of the first 3 parts; Chronic Disease Prevention Directory; State Profile.) 1991. s-a. $41 (foreign $51.25). U.S. Centers for Disease Control, National Center for Chronic Disease Prevention and Health Promotion, 4770 Burford Hwy., N.E., MS K-50, Atlanta, GA 30341-3724. TEL 404-488-5705. FAX 404-488-5739. (Orders to: Superintendent of Documents, U.S. Government Printing Office, Box 371954, Pittsburgh, PA 15250-9754. TEL 202-512-1800. FAX 202-512-2250; Alt. addr.: U.S. Centers for Disease Control, MS K-12, 1660 Clifton Rd., N.E., Atlanta, GA 30333) (back issues avail.) **Document type:** government publication, abstracting/indexing, directory.
●Available only on CD-ROM.
Description: Contains information on federal, state, and local public-health programs, abstracts information from published and unpublished documents, and lists key contacts in the field.

C D R REVIEW. (Communicable Disease Report) see *MEDICAL SCIENCES — Communicable Diseases*

C D R SUPPLEMENT. (Communicable Disease Report) see *MEDICAL SCIENCES — Communicable Diseases*

C D R WEEKLY. (Communicable Disease Report) see *MEDICAL SCIENCES — Communicable Diseases*

C F O - MAGAZINE; league issue for nurses and other people working the health and social welfare field. (Christelijke Federatie Overheidspersoneel) see *MEDICAL SCIENCES — Nurses And Nursing*

C H R I A NEWS. (Committee for Health Rights in the Americas) see *BUSINESS AND ECONOMICS — International Development And Assistance*

614　　UK　ISSN 0964-7902
C H S S OCCASIONAL PAPER. irreg., latest no.4. Centre for Health Services Studies, University of Warwick, Warwick Business School, Coventry CV4 7AL, England. TEL 01203-523985. **Document type:** monographic series.

C O N C A W E REVIEW. see *ENVIRONMENTAL STUDIES*

613.7　　CN　ISSN 0703-5624
C P H A HEALTH DIGEST. French edition: A C S P Selection Sante. (Text in English) 1977. q. free to members. Canadian Public Health Association, 1565 Carling Ave., Ste. 400, Ottawa, ON K1Z 8R1, Canada. TEL 613-725-3769. FAX 613-725-9826. Ed. Gerald Dafoe. circ. 3,200 (3,000 English ed.; 200 French ed.). **Document type:** newsletter.

C S P DIRECTORY. (Board of Certified Safety Professionals) see *OCCUPATIONAL HEALTH AND SAFETY*

CAHIERS D'ETUDES ET DE RECHERCHES FRANCOPHONES SANTE. see *MEDICAL SCIENCES*

CAHIERS DE SOCIOLOGIE ET DE DEMOGRAPHIE MEDICALES. see *POPULATION STUDIES*

CALIFORNIA FIRE SERVICE. see *FIRE PREVENTION*

614.8　　US
CAMPUS SAFETY NEWSLETTER. 1956. 4/yr. $19 to non-members; members $15. National Safety Council, Periodicals Department, 1121 Spring Lake Dr., Itasca, IL 60143. TEL 708-775-2281. Ed. Kathy Henderson; Pub. Kevin H. Axe. abstr.; illus.; stat. circ. 5,000. **Document type:** newsletter.
Formed by the merger of: Campus Safety; College and University Newsletter; **Formerly:** College and University Safety Newsletter (ISSN 0010-0943)

614 610　　CN　ISSN 1188-4169
　　　　　　　　CODEN: CDWSE9
CANADA COMMUNICABLE DISEASE REPORT/RELEVE DES MALADIES TRANSMISSIBLES AU CANADA. (Supplement avail.) (Text in English and French) 1975. bi-m. Can.$75($97.50) Department of National Health and Welfare, Laboratory Centre for Disease Control, Ottawa, ON K1A 0L2, Canada. TEL 613-957-1788. Ed. Eleanor Paulson. charts; illus.; stat.; index. circ. 2,500. **Indexed:** Abstr.Hyg., Biodet.Abstr., Curr.Adv.Ecol.Sci. **Document type:** government publication, newsletter.
—BLDSC (3016.417400).
Former titles (until 1992): Canada Diseases Weekly Report (ISSN 0382-232X); Epidemiological Bulletin (ISSN 0425-1474) - Bulletin Epidemiologique (ISSN 0382-2311).

CANADIAN HEALTH FACILITIES LAW GUIDE. see *LAW*

CANADIAN JOURNAL OF COMMUNITY MENTAL HEALTH/REVUE CANADIENNE DE SANTE MENTALE COMMUNAUTAIRE. see *PSYCHOLOGY*

CANADIAN JOURNAL OF INFECTION CONTROL. see *MEDICAL SCIENCES — Communicable Diseases*

614　　CN　ISSN 0008-4263
　　　　　　CODEN: CJPEA4
CANADIAN JOURNAL OF PUBLIC HEALTH/REVUE CANADIENNE DE SANTE PUBLIQUE. 1910. bi-m. Can.$77($93) (elsewhere $118) (effective 1996). Canadian Public Health Association, 1565 Carling Ave., Ste. 400, Ottawa, ON K1Z 8R1, Canada. TEL 613-725-3769. FAX 613-725-9826. TELEX 21-053-3841. Dr. Stephen Corber (Scientific Editor). adv. contact: Karen Craven. bk.rev.; charts; illus. circ. 3,000. (also avail. in microform from UMI,PMC; reprint service avail. from UMI) **Indexed:** Abstr.Hyg., Bibl.Dev.Med.& Child Neur., Biol.Abstr., Biol.Dig., Can.B.P.I., Chem.Abstr., CINAHL, CMI, Curr.Cont., Dairy Sci.Abstr., Dent.Ind., Dok.Arbeitsmed., Excerp.Med., Food Sci.& Tech.Abstr., Ind.Med., Ind.Vet., INIS Atomind., Med.Care Rev., NRN, Nutr.Abstr., Ocean.Abstr., Pollut.Abstr., Protozool.Abstr., Rev.Med.& Vet.Mycol., Rev.Plant Path., Risk Abstr., Sel.Water Res.Abstr., Small Anim.Abstr., Sportsearch (1977-), SSCI, Trop.Dis.Bull., Vet.Bull., W.R.C.Inf. **Document type:** government publication.
—BLDSC (3035.000000); Faxon; Genuine Article; SWETS; UMI; UnCover. **CCC.**
Description: Covers all aspects of public health.
Refereed Serial

CANADIAN MENTAL HEALTH ASSOCIATION. ANNUAL REPORT/ASSOCIATION CANADIENNE POUR LA SANTE MENTALE. RAPPORT ANNUEL. see *PSYCHOLOGY*

CANADIAN NURSE - L'INFIRMIERE CANADIENNE. see *MEDICAL SCIENCES — Nurses And Nursing*

614.88　　UK　ISSN 0008-7580
CASUALTY SIMULATION; to simulate realism in first aid, nursing and rescue training. 1946. 4/yr. £4 (in the US £5.50). Casualties Union, 293 Lonsdale Dr., Rainham, Gillingham, Kent ME8 9JJ, England. TEL 0634-235760. Ed.Bd. adv.; bk.rev.; charts; illus.; index, cum.index. circ. 2,000. **Document type:** newsletter.

PUBLIC HEALTH AND SAFETY

614.49   XR   ISSN 1210-7778
RA421   CODEN: CEHJE
CENTRAL EUROPEAN JOURNAL OF PUBLIC HEALTH. (Text in English, French, German, Spanish) 1956. 2/yr. (Ceska Lekarska Spolecnost J.E. Purkyne - Czech Medical Society) Nakladateske Stedisko C L S J.E. Purkyne, Sokolska 31, 120 26 Prague 2, Czech Republic. TEL 42-2-202788. (Co-sponsor: Statni Zdravotni Ustav) Ed. Dr. B. Rosicky. adv.; bk.rev.; bibl.; charts; illus.; index. circ. 900. **Indexed:** Abstr.Hyg., Biol.Abstr., Biotech.Abstr., C.I.S. Abstr., Chem.Abstr., Curr.Adv.Ecol.Sci., Curr.Cont., Dairy Sci.Abstr., Excerp.Med., Helminthol.Abstr., Ind.Med., Ind.Vet., INIS Atomind., Poult.Abstr., Protozool.Abstr., Rev.Appl.Entomol., Rev.Plant Path., Soils & Fert., Trop.Dis.Bull., Vet.Bull. **Document type:** academic/scholarly publication.
—BLDSC (3106.138200); CASDDS; EMDOCS; Faxon; SWETS; UnCover.
Formerly (until 1993): Journal of Hygiene, Epidemiology, Microbiology and Immunology (ISSN 0022-1732)
Description: Covers epidemiology and immunology.

614   UN   ISSN 0009-0131
CENTRO PAN-AMERICANO DE FEBRE AFTOSA. BOLETIN. 1963. q. free. World Health Organization, Centro Pan Americano de Febre Aftosa, Pan American Health Organization, CP 589-Z 000, 20000 Rio de Janeiro, Brazil. Ed.Bd. circ. 1,500. **Indexed:** Biol.Abstr., Vet.Bull.
—BLDSC (2162.050000).
Formerly: Centro Pan-Americano de Febre Aftosa. Cuadernos.
Description: Covers foot and mouth disease.

CEYLON JOURNAL OF MEDICAL SCIENCE. see MEDICAL SCIENCES

THE CHALLENGE. see MEDICAL SCIENCES — Respiratory Diseases

CHARTERED INSTITUTE OF PUBLIC FINANCE AND ACCOUNTANCY. ENVIRONMENTAL HEALTH STATISTICS. ACTUALS. see PUBLIC HEALTH AND SAFETY — Abstracting, Bibliographies, Statistics

CHARTERED INSTITUTION OF WATER AND ENVIRONMENTAL MANAGEMENT. JOURNAL. see WATER RESOURCES

CHILD SAFETY REVIEW. see CHILDREN AND YOUTH — About

CLEVELAND FOUNDATION. ANNUAL REPORT. see SOCIAL SERVICES AND WELFARE

COMBUSTION SCIENCE AND TECHNOLOGY. see CHEMISTRY — Physical Chemistry

COMMON SENSE PEST CONTROL QUARTERLY. see BIOLOGY — Entomology

614   UK   ISSN 1354-103X
▼**COMMUNITY CARE MARKET NEWS.** 1994. m. (10/yr.). £195 (financial institutions £250). Laing & Buisson, Lymehouse Studios, 38 Georgiana St., London NW1 0EB, England. TEL 0171-284-1268. FAX 0171-267-8269. Ed. Vincent Jones. **Document type:** newsletter.
Description: Dedicated to bringing news and informed comment and analysis to senior managers and decision makers within the rapidly changing community care market and its supporting services.

COMMUNITY DENTISTRY AND ORAL EPIDEMIOLOGY. see MEDICAL SCIENCES — Dentistry

614   SA   ISSN 0258-9931
COMMUNITY HEALTH IN S.A/VOLKSGESONDHEID IN S.A.. (Text in Afrikaans and English) 1934. m. R.24. (Institute of Public Health) Royal Publications (Pty) Ltd., P.O. Box 1157, Edenvale 1610, South Africa. Ed. M.D. Pretorius. adv.; bk.rev.; charts. circ. 2,100. **Indexed:** Curr.Lit.Fam.Plan., Ind.Med, Ind.S.A.Per.
Formerly (until 1979): Volksgesondheid (ISSN 0033-3492)

614.8   US
COMPLIANCE PROGRAM GUIDANCE MANUALS. (Series of: Food and Cosmetics, Drugs and Biology, Veterinary Medicine, Medical and Radiological Devices) irreg. $425 for series in the U.S., Canada, Mexico; elsewhere $850. U.S. Food and Drug Administration, Office of Public Affairs, 5600 Fisher's Ln., Rockville, MD 20857. TEL 301-443-3220. (Orders to: National Technical Information Service, 5285 Port Royal Rd., Springfield, VA 22161. TEL 703-487-4650. FAX 703-321-8547) **Document type:** government publication.
Description: Provides latest information on and helps maintain program plans and instructions directed to F.D.A. field operations. These plans and instructions are surveillance or compliance-oriented and provide the needed direction from headquarters offices and bureaus in accomplishing F.D.A. regulatory obligations.

614.8 388.3   SP
CONCIENCIA VIAL. 12/yr. Boter 10 intra. Sr. de Thorson, 08002 Barcelona, Spain. TEL 3-207-19-73. Ed. Fernando Rubio Mila.

628   US   ISSN 0069-8474
CONFERENCE OF STATE SANITARY ENGINEERS. REPORT OF PROCEEDINGS. 1920. a. U.S. Public Health Service, Department of Health and Human Services, Washington, DC 20201. TEL 202-245-6761.

363   US   ISSN 1040-4376
CONTEMPORARY ISSUES IN RISK ANALYSIS. 1986. irreg., vol.5, 1991. price varies. (Society for Risk Analysis) Plenum Publishing Corp., 233 Spring St., New York, NY 10013-1578. TEL 212-620-8000. FAX 212-463-0742. TELEX 23-421139. (back issues avail.) **Document type:** proceedings.
—BLDSC (3425.184446).
Refereed Serial

CONTINUUM (SAN FRANCISCO); developments in ambulatory mental health care. see MEDICAL SCIENCES — Psychiatry And Neurology

614.49   SZ   ISSN 0377-3574
      CODEN: CEPBDV
CONTRIBUTIONS TO EPIDEMIOLOGY AND BIOSTATISTICS. (Text in English) 1977. irreg. (approx. a.). price varies. S. Karger AG, Allschwilerstr. 10, P.O. Box, CH-4009 Basel, Switzerland. TEL 061-3061111. FAX 061-3061234. E-mail: karger@karger.ch. Ed. J. Wahrendorf. (reprint service avail. from ISI) **Indexed:** Biol.Abstr. **Document type:** academic/scholarly publication.
—BLDSC (3458.410000); CASDDS. CCC.
Description: Problems of public health studied through the integrated use of epidemiologic and biostatistical methods.
Refereed Serial

614   IT
CORRIERE A V I S. 1956. s-a. free. Associazione Volontari Italiani del Sangue (Turin), Via P. Baiardi, 5, 10126 Turin, Italy. TEL 011-658095. FAX 011-678831. Eds. Sandro Fisso, Piero Onida. adv. circ. 45,000.
Description: Includes news and articles on medical subjects related to blood transfusions.

614.8   CI   ISSN 0350-8765
COVJEK I PROMET. (Text in Serbo-Croatian; summaries in English) 1975. q. $25 to individuals; institutions $50. Istrazivacki Centar za Medicinu i Psihologiju Prometa, Sarengradska 3, 41000 Zagreb, Croatia. TEL 041 562-325. Ed. Ivo Jelcic. circ. 1,000.

614 610   CU   ISSN 1013-2821
CUADERNOS DE HISTORIA DE LA SALUD PUBLICA. 1952. a. $10 in America; elsewhere $12. Ministerio de Salud Publica, Consejo Nacional de Sociedades Cientificas, Centro Nacional de Informacion de Ciencias Medicas, Calle 23 No. 177 e-N y O, La Rampa, Vedado, Apdo. No. 6520, Havana, Cuba. TEL 809-32-5338. (Dist. by: Ediciones Cubanas, Obispo No. 461, Apdo. 605, Havana, Cuba) Ed. Jose Antonio Fidalgo. circ. 1,300. **Indexed:** Biol.Abstr.

614.3   UK
CURRENT PROBLEMS IN PHARMACOVIGILANCE. m. Department of Health, Medicines Control Agency, Market Towers, Rm. 1023, 1 Nine Elms Ln., London SW8 5NQ, England. TEL 0171-273-0254. FAX 0171-273-0675. (Co-sponsor: Committee on Safety of Medicines) Ed. Dr. P. Waller. **Document type:** government publication.

614.8
D E S ACTION VOICE; a focus on diethylstilbestrol exposure. 1979. q. $30. D E S Action USA, 1615 Broadway, Ste. 510, Oakland, CA 94612. TEL 510-465-4011. FAX 510-465-4815. E-mail: desact.well.sf.ca.us. Ed. Pat Cody. bk.rev.; abstr.; circ. 300 (paid). (back issues avail.) **Document type:** newsletter.
Description: Covers latest medical and legal information for D E S mothers, daughters and sons.

614.8 628.44   US   ISSN 0164-1875
350.755
D R C BOOK & MONOGRAPH SERIES. 1968. irreg., no.24, 1990. price varies. University of Delaware, Disaster Research Center, Newark, DE 19716. TEL 302-831-6618. FAX 302-831-2091. TELEX 70 99 85. **Document type:** monographic series.
Formerly: Ohio State University. Disaster Research Center. D R C - T R (ISSN 0078-4109)

613   US   ISSN 1043-3546
SF257   CODEN: DFESEC
DAIRY, FOOD AND ENVIRONMENTAL SANITATION; a publication for sanitarians and fieldmen. 1980. m. $100. International Association of Milk, Food and Environmental Sanitarians, Inc., 6200 Aurora Ave., Ste. 200 W, Des Moines, IA 50322. TEL 515-276-3344. FAX 515-276-8655. Ed. Steven K. Halstead. adv.; bk.rev.; abstr.; charts; illus.; index. circ. 3,500. (also avail. in microform from UMI; reprint service avail. from UMI) **Indexed:** Biodet.Abstr., Curr.Adv.Ecol.Sci., Dairy Sci.Abstr., Food Sci.& Tech.Abstr., Ind.Vet. **Document type:** trade publication.
—BLDSC (3514.712000); Faxon; SWETS; UMI.
Former titles: Dairy and Food Sanitation (ISSN 0273-2866); Food and Fieldmen.

DENMARK. DANMARKS STATISTIK. FAERDSELSUHELD. see POPULATION STUDIES — Abstracting, Bibliographies, Statistics

362   NE   ISSN 0927-4987
DEVELOPMENTS IN HEALTH ECONOMICS AND PUBLIC POLICY. (Text in English) 1992. irreg., vol.2, 1992. price varies. Kluwer Academic Publishers, Postbus 17, 3300 AA Dordrecht, Netherlands. TEL 31-78-392392. FAX 31-78-392254. TELEX 29245 KAPG NL. (Dist. by: Kluwer Academic Publishers Group, P.O. Box 322, 3300 AH Dordrecht, Netherlands. TEL 31-78-392392. FAX 31-78-546474; N. American dist. addr.: Box 358, Accord Sta., Hingham, MA 02018-0358. TEL 617-871-6600) (back issues avail.) **Document type:** monographic series.
—BLDSC (3579.075100).

614   IT   ISSN 0012-2653
      CODEN: DISOAJ
DIFESA SOCIALE. (Text in Italian; summaries in English and Italian.) 1922. bi-m. free. Istituto Italiano di Medicina Sociale, Via Pasquale Stanislao Mancini 28, 00196 Rome, Italy. TEL 06-3200641. Ed. Giovanni Maria Pirone. bk.rev.; abstr.; index. circ. 4,500. **Indexed:** Biol.Abstr., C.I.S. Abstr., Excerp.Med., Psychol.Abstr. **Document type:** government publication.
—BLDSC (3584.000000).
Description: Provides a forum to cover the social issues of medicine. Includes articles on the socialization of people with handicaps, pollution issues, drug addiction and alcoholism, and the elderly.

614   UK
DIRECTORATE OF PUBLIC HEALTH. OCCASIONAL PAPERS IN GOOD PRACTICE. 1990. irreg. price varies. Directorate of Public Health, Yorkshire Health, Park Parade, Harrogate HG1 5AU, England. TEL 0423-500066. Ed. Frada Eskin. bk.rev. circ. 1,000.

DIRITTO SANITARIO MODERNO. see HOSPITALS

PUBLIC HEALTH AND SAFETY

614 UK ISSN 0961-1428
DISASTER MANAGEMENT. q. £201($364.50) (foreign £235). M C B University Press Ltd., 60-62 Toller Ln., Bradford, W. Yorks. BD8 9DY, England. TEL 01274-499821. FAX 01274-547143. TELEX 51317 MCBUNI G. Ed. Norman Anderson. **Indexed:** Environ.Abstr. Document type: academic/scholarly publication.
Description: Covers issues in contingency planning for large-scale emergencies.

614 UN ISSN 0251-4486
DISASTER PREPAREDNESS AND MITIGATION IN THE AMERICAS; news and information for the international disaster community. q. Pan American Health Organization, Pan American Sanitary Bureau, Regional Office of the World Health Organization, 525 23rd St., N.W., Washington, DC 20037. TEL 202-861-6096. FAX 202-775-4578. circ. 18,000. Document type: newsletter.

614.84 JA ISSN 0006-7873
DISASTER PREVENTION/BOSAI. (Text in Japanese) 1947. bi-m. 780 Yen. Tokyo Consolidated Fire Prevention Association - Tokyo Rengo Boka Kyokai, c/o Tokyo Shobo-cho, 3-5, Otemachi Ichome, Chiyoda-ku, Tokyo 100, Japan. Ed. Bunkichi Sawaguri. adv. circ. 12,000. **Indexed:** Abstr.J.Earthq.Eng., Geo.Abstr.

614 UK ISSN 0965-3562
DISASTER PREVENTION AND MANAGEMENT. 1992. 5/yr. £479($669) (effective 1996). M C B University Press Ltd., 60-62 Toller Ln., Bradford, W. Yorks BD8 9BY, England. TEL 01274-777700. FAX 01274-785200. Document type: academic/scholarly publication.

DISEASES AND PEOPLE. see *CHILDREN AND YOUTH — For*

628 IT
DISINFESTAZIONE. 1984. bi-m. L.100000. MO.ED.CO. s.r.l., Via Paolo da Cannobio 9, 20122 Milan, Italy. TEL 02-878577. FAX 0289010728. adv. circ. 5,000.
Description: Concerned with pest control.

DRINKING WATER & BACKFLOW PREVENTION. see *ENGINEERING — Civil Engineering*

DRUG G M P REPORT. see *PHARMACY AND PHARMACOLOGY*

DRUG NEWSLETTER. see *PHARMACY AND PHARMACOLOGY*

DRUG RESISTANCE WEEKLY. see *PHARMACY AND PHARMACOLOGY*

614.8 US
DRUGS AND BIOLOGY GUIDANCE MANUAL. (Subseries of: Compliance Program Guidance Manuals) irreg. $135 in U.S., Canada, Mexico; elsewhere $270. U.S. Food and Drug Administration, Office of Public Affairs, 5600 Fisher's Ln., Rockville, MD 20857. TEL 301-443-3220. (Orders to: National Technical Information Service, 5285 Port Royal Rd., Springfield, VA 22161. TEL 703-487-4650. FAX 703-321-8547) Document type: government publication.
Description: Provides the latest information on and helps maintain program plans and instructions directed to F.D.A. field operations. These plans and instructions are surveillance or compliance oriented and provide the needed direction from headquarters offices and bureaus in accomplishing F.D.A. regulatory obligations.

DRUGS AND DEVICE RECALL BULLETIN. see *PHARMACY AND PHARMACOLOGY*

E H P SUPPLEMENTS. (Environmental Health Perspectives) see *ENVIRONMENTAL STUDIES*

628.5 US
E M A NEWS. q. Environmental Management Association, 4350 DiPaolo Center, Ste. C, Glenview, IL 60025. TEL 708-699-6362. FAX 708-699-6369. Document type: newsletter.

E M F HEALTH & SAFETY DIGEST. (Electric and Magnetic Field) see *OCCUPATIONAL HEALTH AND SAFETY*

614.8 EI ISSN 1010-8149
E S R A NEWSLETTER. m. (European Safety and Reliability Association) Commission of the European Communities, Joint Research Center, I-21020 Ispra, Italy. Document type: newsletter.
—BLDSC (3811.662550).

ECOTOXICOLOGY AND ENVIRONMENTAL SAFETY. see *ENVIRONMENTAL STUDIES — Toxicology And Environmental Safety*

628 SP
EDUCACION SANITARIA. 1983. irreg., no.3, 1986. price varies. (Universidad de Navarra, Facultad de Medicina) Ediciones Universidad de Navarra, S.A., Apdo. 396, 31080 Pamplona, Spain. TEL 94 825 6850.

EDUCATION SANITAIRE ET NUTRITIONNELLE D'AFRIQUE CENTRALE. see *NUTRITION AND DIETETICS*

614.8 IT ISSN 0013-2071
EDUCAZIONE ALLA SICUREZZA. 1950. q. L.600. Ente Nazionale per la Prevenzione degli Infortuni, Via Alessandria 200-E, Rome, Italy. illus.; stat. circ. 38,000.

EGESZSEGNEUELES; educatio sanitaria. see *PHYSICAL FITNESS AND HYGIENE*

614 HU ISSN 0073-4012
EGESZSEGNEVELES SZAKKONYVTARA. 1967. irreg. price varies. Medicina Kiado, Beloiannisz u. 8, 1054 Budapest, Hungary.

614 UA ISSN 0013-2446
CODEN: JEGPAY
EGYPTIAN PUBLIC HEALTH ASSOCIATION JOURNAL. vol.45, 1970. 6/yr. $18. Egyptian Public Health Association, Shousha Bldg., Bloc A, Apt. 116, 31 Sharia 26 July, Cairo, Egypt. Ed. Dr. S. el-Kholy. circ. 750. **Indexed:** Biol.Abstr., Chem.Abstr., Excerp.Med., Ind.Med.
—CASDDS.

614 JA ISSN 0077-4715
RA421 CODEN: ESKHA5
EISEI SHIKENJO HOKOKU/NATIONAL INSTITUTE OF HEALTH SCIENCES. BULLETIN. (Text in Japanese; summaries in English) 1886. a. free. National Institute of Health Sciences, 1-18-1 Kamiyoga, Setagaya-ku, Tokyo 158, Japan. TEL 03-3700-1141. FAX 03-3700-7592. E-mail: kaminuma@nihs.go.jp. Ed. Tadao Terao. adv. contact: Tsugutika Kaminuma. circ. 1,000. **Indexed:** Biol.Abstr., Chem.Abstr., Dairy Sci.Abstr., Excerp.Med., Field Crop Abstr., Food Sci.& Tech.Abstr., Hort.Abstr., Ind.Med., INIS Atomind., Rev.Med.& Vet.Mycol., Rev.Plant Path., Triticale Abstr., Trop.Dis.Bull. Document type: academic/scholarly publication, bulletin.
—CASDDS; EMDOCS.
Description: Disseminates research activities of NIHS.

ELELMISZERVIZSGALATI KOZLEMENYEK. see *FOOD AND FOOD INDUSTRIES*

614.8 614.86 US ISSN 0747-816X
T55.3.H3
EMERGENCY RESPONSE GUIDEBOOK. a. U.S. Department of Transportation, Materials Transportation Bureau, Washington, DC 20590.
Description: Provides information for police and fire personnel on steps to be taken in the first critical minutes after a hazardous materials transportation accident.

ENVIRONMENT ADVISOR; monthly information report on congressional and regulatory activity to control, monitor or eliminate hazards created by hazardous and toxic substances. see *ENVIRONMENTAL STUDIES — Waste Management*

ENVIRONMENT & ASSESSMENT. see *ENVIRONMENTAL STUDIES*

ENVIRONMENT AND SAFETY BRIEFING. see *ENVIRONMENTAL STUDIES*

ENVIRONMENT INTERNATIONAL; a journal of science technology, health, monitoring and policy. see *ENVIRONMENTAL STUDIES*

ENVIRONMENTAL COMPLIANCE & LITIGATION STRATEGY. see *LAW*

614 UK ISSN 0013-9270
ENVIRONMENTAL HEALTH. 1895. m. £82 (includes w. Environmental Health News). (Chartered Institute of Environmental Health) Chadwick House Group Ltd., Chadwick Court, 15 Hatfields, London SE1 8DJ, England. TEL 0171-928-6006. FAX 0171-827-9930. Ed. Claire Brown. adv.: B&W page £600, color page £1050; 270 x 190; adv. contact: Paul Prior. bk.rev.; bibl.; charts; illus.; stat.; tr.lit.; index. circ. 11,725. (also avail. in microform from UMI; reprint service avail. from UMI) **Indexed:** Abstr.Hyg., Art.Hosp.& Tour., ASSIA, Biol.Abstr., C.I.S. Abstr., Curr.Adv.Ecol.Sci., Dairy Sci.Abstr., Diar.Dis.Res., Environ.Abstr., Environ.Per.Bibl., Excerp.Med., Helminthol.Abstr., Ocean.Abstr., Pollut.Abstr., RICS, Risk Abstr., Sport Fish.Abstr., Trop.Dis.Bull., W.R.C.Inf., Wild.Rev. Document type: trade publication.
—BLDSC (3791.481000); Faxon; UMI; UnCover.
Formerly: Public Health Inspector.
Description: Includes articles about food hygiene, health and safety, housing, pest control, pollution, waste management, and noise pollution.

614 614.85 UK ISSN 0964-914X
ENVIRONMENTAL HEALTH BRIEFING. (Editions in English, Scottish) 1989. w. £675. Barbour Index, New Lodge Drift Rd., Windsor, Berks. SL4 4RQ, England. TEL 01344-884121. FAX 01344-884112. Ed. D. Denton. bk.rev. (also avail. in diskette format) Document type: bulletin, abstracting/indexing.
●Also available on CD-ROM.
Description: Provides concise summaries of newly published U.K. and E.C. legislation, reports, and important information concerning environmental control, health, safety, housing, and food safety.

ENVIRONMENTAL HEALTH CRITERIA. see *ENVIRONMENTAL STUDIES*

ENVIRONMENTAL HEALTH PERSPECTIVES. see *ENVIRONMENTAL STUDIES*

614.7 CN ISSN 0319-6771
ENVIRONMENTAL HEALTH REVIEW.* (Text in English) 1956. q. Can.$28 (foreign $35). Canadian Institute of Public Health Inspectors, 1151 Bronte Road, Oakville, ON L6M 3O1, Canada. TEL 905-825-6211. FAX 905-825-8588. Ed. Anthony Amalfa. adv.; bk.rev. circ. 1,500.
—BLDSC (3791.501700); Faxon.

628.5 US
ENVIRONMENTAL MANAGEMENT NEWS. 1969. 4/yr. free to members. Environmental Management Association, 4350 Di Paolo Center, Ste. C, Glenview, IL 60025. TEL 708-699-6362. FAX 708-699-6369. Ed. Carl Wangman. index. **Indexed:** Energy Info.Abstr., Environ.Abstr., Ocean.Abstr., Pollut.Abstr., Sport Fish.Abstr., Wild.Rev. Document type: newsletter.
Former titles: Environmental Management (Englewood) (ISSN 1051-2837); Professional Sanitation Management (ISSN 0033-0191)
Description: Includes articles on facilities planning and design, internal building systems, maintenance and operations and building services.

ENVIRONMENTAL RADIATION SURVEILLANCE IN WASHINGTON STATE. ANNUAL REPORT. see *ENVIRONMENTAL STUDIES*

ENVIRONMENTAL TOXICOLOGY AND CHEMISTRY. see *ENVIRONMENTAL STUDIES — Toxicology And Environmental Safety*

628 US
EPI-GRAM. m. Department of Human Services, Division of Disease Control, State House, Sta. 11, Augusta, ME 04333. FAX 207-289-4172.

EPIDEMIOLOGICAL BULLETIN. see *MEDICAL SCIENCES*

EPIDEMIOLOGICAL SURVEILLANCE OF RABIES FOR THE AMERICAS. see *VETERINARY SCIENCE*

PUBLIC HEALTH AND SAFETY   5591

614.4 US ISSN 1044-3983
RA648.5 CODEN: EPIDEY
EPIDEMIOLOGY. 1990. bi-m. $119 to individuals; institutions $159 (effective 1995). (Epidemiology Resources Inc.) Williams & Wilkins, 428 E. Preston St., Baltimore, MD 21202. TEL 410-528-4000. FAX 410-528-4312. Ed. Kenneth J. Rothman. adv. contact: Carol Stockton. circ. 1,671. **Indexed:** Curr.Cont., Ind.Med. **Document type:** trade publication.
—BLDSC (3793.574000); Faxon; Genuine Article; SWETS; UnCover. **CCC.**
Description: Targets epidemiologists, public health investigators, and other practicing health professionals interested in scientific discussion on principles and methods in data analysis.

ERUUL MEND/HEALTH. see PHYSICAL FITNESS AND HYGIENE

616.009 305.8 UK ISSN 1355-7858
▼**ETHNICITY AND HEALTH.** Announced for publication in 1996. 4/yr. £46 to individuals; institutions £112 (effective 1996). Carfax Publishing Co., P.O. Box 25, Abingdon, Oxon. OX14 3UE, England. TEL 44-1235-555335. FAX 44-1235-553559. (N. American subscr. to: Carfax Publishing Co., 875-81 Massachusetts Ave., Cambridge, MA 02139) **Document type:** academic/scholarly publication.

EUROPE DRUG & DEVICE REPORT. see PHARMACY AND PHARMACOLOGY

EUROPEAN JOURNAL OF EPIDEMIOLOGY. see MEDICAL SCIENCES

EUROPEAN JOURNAL OF HEALTH LAW. see MEDICAL SCIENCES

614 UK ISSN 1101-1262
RA483
EUROPEAN JOURNAL OF PUBLIC HEALTH. 1991. q. £85($140) (effective 1996). (Stichting Journals for Public Health and Science, NE) Oxford University Press, Oxford Journals, Walton St., Oxford OX2 6DP, England. TEL 01865-267907. FAX 01865-267773. TELEX 837330-OXPRES-G. E-mail: jnlorders@oup.co.uk. (U.S. subscr. to: Oxford University Press Inc., 2001 Evans Rd., Cary, NC 27513. TEL 919-677-0977. FAX 919-677-0977) Ed. Per-Gunnar Svensson. circ. 200. **Document type:** academic/scholarly publication.
—BLDSC (3829.738030); SWETS.
Description: Provides a forum for the discussion and debate of current public health issues in the European region.

EUROPEAN PARLIAMENT. RESEARCH AND DOCUMENTATION PAPERS; resolutions of the European Parliament in the field of environment, public health and consumer protection. see ENVIRONMENTAL STUDIES

362.1 UK
EUROPEAN SAFETY NEWSLETTER. Abbreviated title: E S N. 1993. 11/yr. £65. Unit 3, St. George's Industrial Estate, White Hart Ln., London N22 5QL, England. TEL 0181-888-2734. FAX 0181-365-7855. Ed. John Manos. video rev.; circ. 1,500 (paid). **Document type:** newsletter.

614.4 664 US
▼**F D A HOTLINE.** 1994. s-w. $287. Hotline Printing and Publishing, Box 161132, Altamonte Springs, FL 32716. TEL 407-628-1377. FAX 407-628-9935. Ed. Dennis Blank. circ. 200. **Document type:** newsletter.

614 US ISSN 1069-5109
F D A NEWS. (Food and Drug Administration); drugs, cosmetics, devices, and biologics. 1993. m. $190 (foreign $220). (Association of Food and Drug Officials) Technomic Publishing Co., Inc., 851 New Holland Ave., Box 2525, Lancaster, PA 17604. TEL 717-291-5609. FAX 717-295-4538. TELEX 230 753565 (TECHNOMIC UD). Ed. Y.H. Hui. circ. 90 (paid). **Document type:** newsletter.
—**CCC.**

614.8 II
F R C H NEWSLETTER. (Text in English) 1986. bi-m. $25. Foundation for Research in Community Health, 84-A, R.G. Thadani Marg, Worli, Bombay 400 018, India. TEL 22-4938601. Ed. Vaijayanti Aphale. bk.rev. circ. 1,500. **Document type:** newsletter.
Description: Carries articles related to health, including general interest features and specific informative articles.

FACTS AND ADVICE FOR AIRLINE PASSENGERS. see TRANSPORTATION — Air Transport

614 370 TG
FAMILLE ET DEVELOPPEMENT.* 1975. q. 750 Fr.CFA. Association Africaine d'Education pour le Developpement, B.P. 3907, Lome, Togo. Ed. Pierre Pradervand. adv.; bk.rev.; illus. circ. 40,000. **Indexed:** HR Rep.

610 US ISSN 0160-6379
RA421
FAMILY AND COMMUNITY HEALTH; the journal of health promotion and maintenance. 1978. q. $104 (foreign $125). Aspen Publishers, Inc., 200 Orchard Ridge Dr., Gaithersburg, MD 20878. TEL 301-417-7500. FAX 301-417-7550. (also avail. in microform from UMI; reprint service avail. from UMI) **Indexed:** Abstr.Hyg., CINAHL, FAMLI, IMFL, NRN, Nurs.Abstr., Psychol.Abstr. (1982-).
—BLDSC (3865.558000); Faxon; SWETS; UMI; UnCover. **CCC.**

614.42 CN ISSN 0830-0305
FAMILY HEALTH.* 1985. bi-m. Can.$13.64 (in US Can.$14.75, elsewhere Can.$16.75). Box 2421, Edmonton, AB T5J 2S6, Canada. adv.
Description: Informs and increases health consciousness of Albertans through professional information.

FAMILY PLANNING TODAY. see BIRTH CONTROL

614.8 US ISSN 0749-310X
TX150
FAMILY SAFETY & HEALTH. 1961. q. $19 to non-members; members $15. National Safety Council, 1121 Spring Lake Dr., Itasca, IL 60143. TEL 708-285-1121. (Subscr. to: Box 558, Itasca, IL 60143-0558. TEL 800-621-7619) Ed. Laura Coyne. illus. circ. 1,200,000. (also avail. in microform from UMI; reprint service avail. from UMI) —UMI; UnCover.
Formerly (until 1984): Family Safety (ISSN 0014-7397)

628 642.9 UK ISSN 0143-0645
FAR EAST HEALTH. 1980. 10/yr. £60. Reed Business Publishing Group, Carew Division (Subsidiary of: Reed International PLC), Quadrant House, The Quadrant, Sutton, Surrey SM2 5AS, England. TEL 081-661-3500. TELEX 859500. Ed. Wendy Clare. adv. circ. 5,875. **Indexed:** ASSIA.
—BLDSC (3865.810000).

610 US
FEDERAL HEALTH MONITOR.* 1988. w. $85. National Health Lawyers Association, 1120 Connecticut Ave., N.W., Ste. 950, Washington, DC 20036-3921. TEL 202-833-1100. circ. 1,000. **Document type:** newsletter.

614 US ISSN 1070-9029
FEDERAL PHYSICIAN. 1979. bi-m. $37.50. Federal Physicians Association, Box 45150, Washington, DC 20026. TEL 703-455-5947. FAX 703-455-8282. Ed. Dennis W. Boyd. adv. contact: Nick Cordovana. circ. 1,000 (controlled). (back issues avail.) **Document type:** newsletter.
Description: Covers changes in federal physician pay and benefits, updates on changes affecting federal employees, news of federal health programs.

FEDERAL VETERINARIAN. see VETERINARY SCIENCE

FILM AUSTRALIA HEALTH & WELFARE CATALOGUE. see MOTION PICTURES

FIRE FOCUS. see FIRE PREVENTION

614 JA ISSN 0917-3625
FIRUMU BADJI NYUSU/FILM BADGE NEWS. (Text in Japanese) 1985. m. 400 Yen per no. Chiyoda Hoan Yohin K.K. - Chiyoda Safety Appliance Co., Ltd., 3-40-11 Hongo, Bunkyo-ku, Tokyo 113, Japan. Ed. Michihiko Watanabe. adv. contact: Tadashi Matsutani.

FLIGHT SAFETY FOUNDATION. ANNUAL INDEX. see TRANSPORTATION — Air Transport

614.8 US ISSN 1045-9758
RA447.F6
FLORIDA JOURNAL OF PUBLIC HEALTH.* 1982. 3/yr. $36 (foreign $72). Florida Public Health Association, Box 10547, Tallahassee, FL 32302-2547. TEL 904-681-6555. FAX 904-894-1156. Glenda Wood. adv.; bk.rev. circ. 1,100. **Document type:** academic/scholarly publication.
Description: Reports on programs surveys and research in public health medicine.

FLYING SAFETY. see AERONAUTICS AND SPACE FLIGHT

614 PH ISSN 0046-4317
FOCUS ON MENTAL HEALTH. (Text in English, Filipino) 1951. q. $3.60 to individuals; institutions $37. Philippine Mental Health Association, P.O. Box 1040, 1100 Quezon City, Philippines. Ed. Loreto Paras-Sulit. charts; illus.; stat. circ. 1,500. (tabloid format) **Document type:** newsletter.
Description: Covers public health and safety, community mental health, psychology and psychiatry, social work and social development.

614 CN ISSN 0015-5195
FOCUS: SOCIAL AND PREVENTIVE MEDICINE. 1964. 4/yr. Can.$20. Community Health Services Association, 455-2nd Ave. N., Saskatoon, SK S7K 2C2, Canada. TEL 306-664-4289. FAX 306-664-4120. Ed. Ingrid Larson. bk.rev.; illus. circ. 5,300. **Document type:** newsletter.
Refereed Serial

FOOD & BEVERAGE NEWSLETTER. see OCCUPATIONAL HEALTH AND SAFETY

614.8 US
FOOD AND COSMETICS GUIDANCE MANUAL. (Subseries of: Compliance Program Guidance Manuals) irreg. $140 in the U.S., Canada, Mexico; elsewhere $280. U.S. Food and Drug Administration, Office of Public Affairs, 5600 Fisher's Ln., Rockville, MD 20857. TEL 301-443-3220. (Orders to: National Technical Information Service, 5285 Port Royal Rd., Springfield, VA 22161. TEL 703-487-4650. FAX 703-321-8547) **Document type:** government publication.
Description: Provides the latest information on and helps maintain surveillance or compliance-oriented program plans and instructions directed to F.D.A. field operations, providing needed direction from headquarter offices and bureaus in accomplishing the F.D.A. regulatory obligations.

613 JA ISSN 0015-6426
RA601 CODEN: SKEZAP
FOOD HYGIENIC SOCIETY OF JAPAN. JOURNAL/SHOKUHIN EISEIGAKU ZASSHI. (Text in English or Japanese) 1960. bi-m. $72 to individuals; institutions $180 (membership only). Food Hygienic Society of Japan - Nihon Shokuhin Eisei Gakkai, 2-6-1 Jingumae, Shibuya-ku, Tokyo 150, Japan. FAX 03-3470-2933. adv.; bk.rev.; abstr.; charts; illus.; index; circ. 3,000 (paid). **Indexed:** Apic.Abstr., Biol.Abstr., Chem.Abstr., Curr.Adv.Ecol.Sci., Dairy Sci.Abstr., Excerp.Med., Field Crop Abstr., Food Sci.& Tech.Abstr., Ind.Vet., Maize Abstr., Nutr.Abstr., Poult.Abstr., Rev.Med.& Vet.Mycol., Sugar Ind.Abstr., Triticale Abstr., Vet.Bull. **Document type:** academic/scholarly publication.
—BLDSC (4754.400000); CASDDS; Genuine Article.
Refereed Serial

613 US ISSN 0884-0806
CODEN: FPREEP
FOOD PROTECTION REPORT. 1985. m. $135. Charles Felix Associates, Box 1581, Leesburg, VA 22075. TEL 703-777-7448. FAX 703-777-4453. Ed. Charles W. Felix. bk.rev. **Document type:** newsletter.
—BLDSC (3981.865100).

363.19 UK ISSN 0968-1647
FOOD SAFETY CONCERNS BULLETIN. 1991. m. £175 (effective 1996). Leatherhead Food R.A., Randalls Rd., Leatherhead, Surrey KT22 7RY, England. TEL 01372-376761. FAX 01372-386228. E-mail: hbennett@lfra.co.uk. **Document type:** trade publication.

P Q

PUBLIC HEALTH AND SAFETY

363.19 640   US   ISSN 1050-1843
FOOD SAFETY NOTEBOOK. 1990. 10/yr. $55 in U.S., Canada and Mexico; elsewhere $65. Lyda Associates, Inc., Box 700, Palisades, NY 10964. TEL 914-359-8282. FAX 914-359-1229. Ed. Lillian Langseth. circ. 1,000. (looseleaf format; back issues avail.) **Document type:** newsletter.
—BLDSC (3982.770000).
Description: Publishes comprehensive reports on national and international food safety issues.

FORUM NEWS. see *HOSPITALS*

614   FR   ISSN 0245-7466
FRANCE. MINISTERE CHARGE DE LA SANTE. BULLETIN EPIDEMIOLOGIQUE HEBDOMDAIRE. Abbreviated title: B E H. w. 260 F. (Europe 360 F., elsewhere 560 F.). (Ministere Charge de la Sante) Imprimerie Nationale, 25 rue de la Convention, 75732 Paris Cedex 15, France. (Subscr. to: 124 rue Henri Barbusse, 93308 Aubervilliers Cedex, France. TEL 48-39-56-00. FAX 48-39-56-01) circ. 650.
Former titles: France. Ministere des la Sante et de la Famille. Bulletin Hebdomdaire d'Information Epidemiologique (ISSN 0245-7474); France. Ministere des Affaires Sociales et de la Solidarite Nationale. Bulletin Epidemiologique; France. Ministere de la Sante et de la Famille. Bulletin Epidemiologique; France. Ministere de la Sante et de la Famille. Bulletin Epidemiologique.
Description: For the practitioner; provides practical information, covers new diseases and recommendations for travelers.

614   FR   ISSN 0755-3374
RA407.5.F7
FRANCE. MINISTERE DE LA SANTE ET DE LA SECURITE SOCIALE. ANNUAIRE DES STATISTIQUES SANITAIRES ET SOCIALES. 1971. a., latest 1992. newsstand price: 200 F. Documentation Francaise, 29-31 Quai Voltaire, 75344 Paris Cedex 07, France. TEL 1-40-15-70-00. FAX 40-15-70-00. TELEX 215 666 DOCFRAN. (Subscr. to: 124 rue Henri Barbusse, 93308 Aubervilliers Cedex, France. TEL 48-39-56-00. FAX 48-39-56-01) (Co-sponsor: Ministere de la Sante) **Document type:** government publication.
Supersedes: France. Ministere de la Sante et de la Securite Sociale. Tableaux Statistiques "Sante et Securite Sociale; France. Ministere de la Sante. Tableaux Sante et Securite Sociale; France. Ministere de la Sante Publique et de la Securite Sociale. Annuaire Statistique de la Sante et de l'Action Sociale (ISSN 0071-8866)

614   FR
FRANCE. MINISTERE DE LA SANTE ET DE LA SECURITE SOCIALE. BULLETIN OFFICIEL. w. 110 F. Ministere de la Sante et de la Securite Sociale, 8 Av. de Segur, 75700 Paris, France.

614   FR
FRANCE. MINISTERE DE LA SANTE ET DE LA SECURITE SOCIALE. NOTES D'INFORMATION. 1969. irreg., no.145, 1980. free. Ministere de la Sante et de la Securite Sociale, Service de Press, 8 Ave. de Segur, 75700 Paris, France.
Former titles: France. Ministere de la Sante. Note d'Information (ISSN 0071-8882); (until 1969): France. Ministere des Affaires Sociales. Information Actualites.

FRANCE. MINISTERE DE LA SOLIDARITE, DE LA SANTE ET DE LA PROTECTION SOCIALE. BULLETIN OFFICIEL. see *BIBLIOGRAPHIES*

FRANCE. MINISTERE DES AFFAIRES SOCIALES DE LA SANTE ET DE LA VILLE. BULLETIN OFFICIEL. see *PUBLIC ADMINISTRATION*

614.86   SZ
FREIE FAHRT/ROUTE LIBRE. (Text in French and German) 1923. m. 10 SFr. Schweizerischer Abstinenten-Verkehrsverband - Association Suisse des Conducteurs Abstinents, Zentralsekretariat, Langwiesstr. 22, CH-8050 Zurich, Switzerland. TEL 01-3115880. Ed. Peter Ritschard-Inaunen. adv.; illus. circ. 2,000. **Document type:** bulletin.
Former titles: Strasse und Nuechternheit (ISSN 0039-2170); Abstinenter Rad- und Motorfahrer.

FROM THE STATE CAPITALS. ENVIRONMENTAL REGULATION. see *ENVIRONMENTAL STUDIES — Waste Management*

FROM THE STATE CAPITALS. PUBLIC ASSISTANCE AND WELFARE TRENDS. see *SOCIAL SERVICES AND WELFARE*

614   US   ISSN 0734-1156
FROM THE STATE CAPITALS. PUBLIC HEALTH. Variant title: Public Health from the State Capitals. 1946. w. $215 (foreign $235). Wakeman-Walworth, Inc., 300 N. Washington St., Alexandria, VA 22314. TEL 703-549-8606. FAX 703-549-1372. (processed)
—CCC.
Description: Covers state and local action throughout the US in health and related fields.

FROM THE STATE CAPITALS: PUBLIC SAFETY AND JUSTICE POLICIES. see *FIRE PREVENTION*

614.8 614.7   JA   ISSN 0287-1254
FUKUOKA-KEN EISEI KOGAI SENTA NENPO/FUKUOKA ENVIRONMENTAL RESEARCH CENTER. ANNUAL REPORT. 1974. a. free. Fukuoka-ken Eisei Senta - Fukuoka Environmental Research Center, Fukuoka 818-01, Japan. Ed.Bd. circ. 500. (back issues avail.)

THE FUTURE OF CHILDREN. see *CHILDREN AND YOUTH — About*

363.6 352.628 690   GW   ISSN 0932-6200
CODEN: GHBUEG
G I - GESUNDHEITS INGENIEUR. 1877. m. DM.238 (effective 1996). R. Oldenbourg Verlag GmbH, Rosenheimerstr. 145, 81671 Munich, Germany. TEL 089-45051-0. FAX 089-45051207. adv.; bk.rev.; abstr.; bibl.; charts; illus.; pat.; index. circ. 4,000. **Indexed:** Biol.Abstr., Chem.Abstr., Eng.Ind., Excerp.Med., Ind.Med., INIS Atomind., W.R.C.Inf. **Document type:** trade publication.
—CASDDS; SWETS. **CCC.**
Former titles (until 1985): Haustechnik, Bauphysik, Umwelttechnik (ISSN 0172-8199); Gesundheits-Ingenieur (ISSN 0016-9277)

610   SP   ISSN 0213-9111
GACETA SANITARIA. (Text in Spanish; summaries in English) 1982. bi-m. 6800 ptas. to individuals; institutions 13600 ptas.; foreign $100 (effective 1995). (Sociedad de Salud Publica y Administracion Sanitaria) Editorial Garsi, S.A., Grupo Masson, Principe de Asturias 20, 08012 Barcelona, Spain. TEL 34-3-4154544. FAX 34-3-4161220. Ed. Dr. Fernando Rodriguez Artalejo. adv.; bk.rev.; bibl.; charts; index. 3,000. **Indexed:** Abstr.Hyg., Ind.Med.Esp. **Document type:** academic/scholarly publication.
—BLDSC (4066.169000). **CCC.**
Former titles (until 1986): Gaseta Sanitaria de Barcelona (ISSN 0212-0542); (1888-1910): Gaceta Sanitaria de Barcelona (ISSN 0212-2030)

GENETIC RESOURCE. see *BIOLOGY — Genetics*

614   US   ISSN 1077-131X
▼**GEORGIA HEALTH LAW UPDATE.** 1994. m. $177. (Arnall Golden & Gregory) M. Lee Smith Publishers & Printers LLC, 162 Fourth Ave., N., Box 198867, Nashville, TN 37219-8867. TEL 615-242-7395; 800-274-6774. FAX 615-256-6601. Ed.Bd; Pub. M. Lee Smith. **Document type:** newsletter.
Formerly (until 1995): Georgia Health Law Alert (ISSN 1073-0559)
Description: Reports state-specific new public health laws that affect companies in Georgia.

GERONTOLOSKO DRUSTVO S R SRBIJE. see *GERONTOLOGY AND GERIATRICS*

614   SZ
GESUNDHEITSPOLITISCHE INFORMATIONEN/POLITIQUE DE LA SANTE: INFORMATIONS. Short title: G P I. 1977. 4/yr. 70 SFr.($50) Schweizerische Gesellschaft fuer Gesundheitspolitik - Societe Suisse pour la Politique de la Sante (Swiss Society for Health Policy), Haldenweg 10A, CH-3074 Muri, Switzerland. TEL 031-9526655. FAX 031-952-6800. Ed. Gerhard Kocher. bk.rev.; abstr.; bibl.; charts; stat. circ. 2,000. **Document type:** bulletin.
Description: Examines health policies, medical sociology, patients' legal and human rights as well as related economic topics.

613   GW   ISSN 0016-9307
GESUNDHEITSPOLITISCHE UMSCHAU. 1948. m. DM.79. Albert Amann Verlag, Richterstr. 2, 63916 Amorbach, Germany. TEL 09373-971415. FAX 09373-971444. Ed. Hans Volkhardt. adv. contact: Susanne Grimm. bk.rev. circ. 3,500. **Document type:** bulletin.

614   GW   ISSN 0941-3790
DAS GESUNDHEITSWESEN; Sozialmedizin, Gesundheits-System-Forschung, Public Health, Oeffentlicher Gesundheitsdienst, Medizinischer Dienst. 1939. m. DM.234. (Bundesverband der Aerzte des Oeffentlichen Gesundheitsdienstes e.V.) Georg Thieme Verlag, Ruedigerstr. 14, 70469 Stuttgart, Germany. TEL 0711-8931-0. FAX 0711-8931298. (Subscr. to: Postfach 104853, 70042 Stuttgart, Germany) (Co-sponsors: Bundesverband der Vertrauens- und Rentenversicherungsaerzte e.V.; Zentralkomitee zur Bekaempfung der Tuberkulose; Deutsche Gesellschaft fuer Sozialhygiene und Prophylaktische Medizin) Ed.Bd. adv.; bk.rev.; abstr.; charts; illus.; index. circ. 6,400. (also avail. in microform from UMI; reprint service avail. from UMI) **Indexed:** Abstr.Hyg., C.I.S. Abstr., Curr.Cont., Helminthol.Abstr., Ind.Med., Ind.Vet., Nutr.Abstr., Sci.Cit.Ind., Trop.Dis.Bull., Vet.Bull. **Document type:** academic/scholarly publication.
—BLDSC (4165.078500); SWETS; UMI. **CCC.**
Former titles (until 1992): Oeffentliche Gesundheitswesen (ISSN 0029-8573); Oeffentliche Gesundheitsdienst.

GOLDENE GESUNDHEIT. see *MEDICAL SCIENCES*

GOOD PRACTICE SERIES. see *SOCIAL SERVICES AND WELFARE*

614.8   UK   ISSN 0262-5229
GREAT BRITAIN. DEPARTMENT OF EDUCATION AND SCIENCE. SAFETY IN EDUCATION. 1981. irreg. free. Department of Education and Science, Elizabeth House, York Road, London SE1 7PH, England. TEL 01-934-9000. Ed. Bernard McDonnell. bk.rev.; bibl.; charts; illus.; stat. circ. 100,000. (back issues avail.)
—BLDSC (8065.748000). **CCC.**
Description: Accounts of local governments' good practice in educational building and management.

614 362.11   UK   ISSN 0072-6036
GREAT BRITAIN. DEPARTMENT OF HEALTH AND SOCIAL SECURITY. HOSPITAL IN-PATIENT INQUIRY. 1960. irreg. price varies. H.M.S.O., P.O. Box 276, London SW8 5DT, England. (reprint service avail. from UMI) **Document type:** government publication.
—CCC.

614   UK   ISSN 0072-6087
RA241
GREAT BRITAIN. DEPARTMENT OF HEALTH AND SOCIAL SECURITY. ON THE STATE OF THE PUBLIC HEALTH. (Annual Report of the Chief Medical Officer of the Department of Health and Social Security) 1921. a. price varies. H.M.S.O., P.O. Box 276, London SW8 5DT, England. (reprint service avail. from UMI) **Document type:** government publication.
—CCC.

614.3   UK
GREAT BRITAIN. MEDICINES COMMISSION. ANNUAL REPORT. 1971. a. price varies. Department of Health, Medicines Commission, Markets Towers, 1 Nine Elms Ln., London SW8 5NQ, England. TEL 0171-273-0393. FAX 0171-273-0387. circ. 600. **Document type:** government publication.
Formerly: Great Britain. Committee on Safety of Medicines. Report.
Description: Contains the reports of the Medicines Commission, the Committee on Safety of Medicines, the Veterinary Products Committee, the British Pharmacopoeia Commission, the Committee on the Review of Medicines and the Committee on Dental and Surgical Materials.

GUIDE TO FEDERAL FUNDING FOR HOSPITALS & HEALTH CENTERS. see *HOSPITALS*

GUILDER. see *HANDICAPPED — Hearing Impaired*

PUBLIC HEALTH AND SAFETY

614   PH
H E A P JOURNAL. 1961. q. P.2($1.25) (Health Education Association of the Philippines) Philippine Normal College, Community-School Health Education Center, Taft Ave., Manila, Philippines. Ed. Carmen F. del Rosario. bk.rev. circ. 100.
Formerly: School Health Bulletin (ISSN 0048-9417)

H M C R I FOCUS. (Hazardous Materials Control Resources Institute) see *ENVIRONMENTAL STUDIES — Waste Management*

HANDGUN CONTROL. SEMI-ANNUAL PROGRESS REPORT. see *LAW*

628   GW
HARTMANNBUND IN BADEN - WUERTTEMBERG. 1949. q. Hartmannbund - Verband der Aerzte Deutschlands e.V., Godesberger Allee 54, 53175 Bonn, Germany. TEL 0228-8104-0. **Document type:** trade publication.

614   II   ISSN 0017-8241
RA312.H37
HARYANA HEALTH JOURNAL. (Text in English) 1970. q. free. State Health Education Bureau, Directorate of Health Services, 36 Madhaya Marg, Sector 7C, Chandigarh, Haryana, India. Ed. G.G. Saxena. charts; illus.; circ. controlled.
Description: Presents information about developments in medical and health services, oriented to health care professionals.

HAWAII. DEPARTMENT OF HEALTH. MENTAL HEALTH SERVICES FOR CHILDREN AND YOUTH; children's MH services branch. see *SOCIAL SERVICES AND WELFARE*

614   US   ISSN 1053-9662
HAWAII HEALTH MESSENGER. 1941. q. free. Department of Health, Communication Office, Box 3378, Honolulu, HI 96801. TEL 808-586-4442. FAX 808-586-4444. Ed. Barbara Hastings. charts; illus.; circ. 5,500 (controlled). **Document type:** newsletter.

614   US
HAWAII HEALTH PLANNING NEWS. 1969. bi-m. free. State Health Planning and Development Agency, Box 3378, Honolulu, HI 96801. TEL 808-548-4050. Ed. Jane Pang. circ. controlled.

614.8   US   ISSN 0743-8826
TA169.7
HAZARD PREVENTION. 1965. q. $45 to non-members. System Safety Society, Inc., Technology Trading Park, 5 Export Drive., Ste. A, Sterling, VA 22170-4421. TEL 703-444-6520. Ed. Sonya Kaiser. adv.; bk.rev. circ. 1,700. (also avail. in microfiche; back issues avail.)
—BLDSC (4274.386000); Faxon.
Description: Technical information and news of topical interest to those associated with the practice of system and product safety.

HAZARD TECHNOLOGY. see *CIVIL DEFENSE*

614.85   US   ISSN 0889-3454
HAZARDOUS MATERIALS NEWSLETTER. 1980. bi-m. $47 (foreign $50) (effective through 1996). Hazardous Materials Publishing, Box 204, Barre, VT 05641. TEL 802-479-2307. Ed. John R. Cashman. adv.; bk.rev.; abstr.; bibl.; tr.lit.; circ. 620 (paid). (looseleaf format; back issues avail.) **Document type:** newsletter.
Description: Addresses leak, fire, spill control for incident commanders and experienced responders, including incident causes, prevention, and remedial action.

HAZARDOUS SUBSTANCES & PUBLIC HEALTH. see *ENVIRONMENTAL STUDIES — Waste Management*

HAZARDOUS WASTE CONSULTANT. see *ENVIRONMENTAL STUDIES — Waste Management*

614 658.3   UK   ISSN 0966-906X
HAZARDS IN THE OFFICE. 1993. bi-m. £57($115) in E.C. nations; elsewhere £62 (effective 1996). The Royal Society of Chemistry, Thomas Graham House, Science Park, Milton Rd., Cambridge CB4 4WF, England. TEL 01223-420066.
FAX 01223-423429. E-mail: rsc1@rsc.org. (Dist. by: Turpin Distribution Services Ltd., Blackhorse Rd., Letchworth, Herts. SG6 1HN, England. TEL 01462-672555. FAX 01462-480947) Ed. Becky Allen. **Document type:** abstracting/indexing.
Description: Source of information on the hidden hazards in the office environment and the vital safety procedures to be adopted to prevent injury.

HAZARDS MAGAZINE. see *OCCUPATIONAL HEALTH AND SAFETY*

614   JO
HEALTH/SIHHAH. (Text in Arabic) 1966. m. Ministry of Health, P.O. Box 86, Amman, Jordan. Ed. Dr. Ahmad al-Nabulsi.

614   NZ   ISSN 0017-887X
HEALTH. 1948. 3/yr. free. Ministry of Health, P.O. Box 5013, Wellington, New Zealand. Ed. Nancy Consaul. charts; illus. circ. 50,000. **Document type:** government publication.
—CCC.
Description: Covers health news and articles on a variety of health topics.

614.8 368.382   US   ISSN 0278-2715
RA410.A1
HEALTH AFFAIRS; the policy journal of the health sphere. 1981. q. $54 to individuals; institutions $85. Project Hope, 7500 Old Georgetown Rd., No. 600, Bethesda, MD 20814-6133.
TEL 301-656-7401. FAX 301-654-2845. Ed. John K. Iglehart. bk.rev.; circ. 10,000 (paid). (also avail. in microform from UMI; reprint service avail. from UMI) **Indexed:** Abstr.Health Care Manage.Stud., Biostat., BPIA, Curr.Cont., Excerp.Med., Hosp.Lit.Ind., Int.Polit.Sci.Abstr., Manage.Cont., P.A.I.S., PSI.
Document type: academic/scholarly publication.
●Also available online. Vendor(s): University Microfilms International.
—BLDSC (4274.710000); Faxon; Genuine Article; SWETS; UMI; UnCover.

362.1 323   US   ISSN 1079-0969
▼**HEALTH AND HUMAN RIGHTS.** 1995. q. $36 to individuals (Canada $41.20; elsewhere $44); institutions $80 (Canada $85.20; elsewhere $88). Harvard School for Public Health, Francois-Xavier Bagnoud Center for Health and Human Rights, 677 Huntington Ave., Boston, MA 02115. (Subscr. to: Box 519, Shrub Oak, NY 10588-0519. TEL 914-962-6297. FAX 914-962-1338) (Co-sponsor: Association Francois-Xavier Bagnoud) **Document type:** academic/scholarly publication.
Description: Examines the impacts of health policies, programs, and practices on human rights and the effects of human rights violations on public health.

614   UK   ISSN 0140-2986
RA421   CODEN: HEHYDD
HEALTH AND HYGIENE. 1977. q. £38 to Europe; rest of world £42. Royal Institute of Public Health and Hygiene, 28 Portland Pl., London W1N 4DE, England. TEL 0171-580-2731.
FAX 0171-580-6157. Ed. A.M.B. Golding. adv.; bk.rev. circ. 2,600. (back issues avail.) **Indexed:** Abstr.Hyg., Curr.Adv.Ecol.Sci., Excerp.Med., Ind.Vet., Trop.Dis.Bull. **Document type:** academic/scholarly publication.
—BLDSC (4274.815000); Faxon; UMI.
Description: Contains information on environmental health, health education, laboratory science, the scientific side of the food industry, as well as the teaching, nursing and medical professions.

614   UK
HEALTH AND PERSONAL SOCIAL SERVICES STATISTICS. a. H.M.S.O., P.O. Box 276, London SW8 5DT, England. (reprint service avail. from UMI) **Document type:** government publication.
Formerly: Digest of Health Statistics for England and Wales (ISSN 0070-4849)

HEALTH & PLACE; an international journal. see *GEOGRAPHY*

628 621.3   UK   ISSN 0142-5021
HEALTH & SAFETY NEWSLINE; for the engineering industry (UK). 1968. bi-m. £50. Engineering Employers' Federation, Broadway House, Tothill St., London SW1H 9NQ, England. TEL 0171-222-7777. FAX 0171-222-2782. Ed. P.J. Reeve. bk.rev.; film rev.; circ. 8,000 (controlled). (looseleaf format) **Document type:** trade publication.
Formerly (until 1984): Industrial Health and Safety.
Description: Keeps company management abreast of occupational health, safety and environmental developments in the U.K.

HEALTH AND SAFETY SCIENCE ABSTRACTS. see *PUBLIC HEALTH AND SAFETY — Abstracting, Bibliographies, Statistics*

362.1 363.1   UK
HEALTH & SAFETY SPECIFIERS; health, safety and environmental safety. 1974. 6/yr. £24. Portland Communications Ltd., 32 Portland St., Cheltenham, Glos. GL52 2PB, England. TEL 01242-236336. FAX 01242-222331. Ed. D.G. Constantine. adv. contact: Deborah Preece. bk.rev. circ. 13,433. **Document type:** trade publication.
Former titles: Health and Safety Specifications; Caution Magazine.

614   UK   ISSN 0966-0410
CODEN: HSCCEL
HEALTH AND SOCIAL CARE IN THE COMMUNITY. 1993. bi-m. £37 to individuals (outside Europe £41($66)); institutions £111 (outside Europe £122.50($197) (effective 1996). Blackwell Science Ltd., Osney Mead, Oxford OX2 0EL, England.
TEL 01865-240201. FAX 01965-721205. TELEX 83355 MEDBOK G. Ed. Karen A. Luker. adv.; bk.rev.; bibl.; index. circ. 550. (also avail. in microform from UMI; back issues avail.) **Document type:** academic/scholarly publication.
—BLDSC (4274.874000); UMI. **CCC.**
Refereed Serial

614 360   CN   ISSN 1184-650X
HEALTH AND SOCIAL SERVICE WORKFORCE IN ALBERTA. 1979. a. Health and Social Service Disciplines Committee, Kensington Place, 5th Fl., 10011-109th St., Edmonton, Alta. T5J 3S8, Canada.
TEL 403-427-2655. (back issues avail.)
Former titles (until 1990): Health and Social Service Personnel Working in Alberta (ISSN 1184-6496); (until 1986): Survey of Health and Social Service Personnel Working in Alberta (ISSN 1184-6488); (until 1984): Survey of Employers of Health and Social Service Personnel in Alberta (ISSN 1184-647X); (until 1981): Survey of the Major Employers of Health and Social Service Personnel (ISSN 1184-6461); (until 1980): Semi-Annual Surveys of the Major Employers of Health and Social Service Personnel (ISSN 0225-9834)
Description: Contains data and information on the health and social services of employers and self-employed professionals.

HEALTH & SOCIAL WORK. see *SOCIAL SERVICES AND WELFARE*

338.43 362.1   US   ISSN 1057-9389
HEALTH CARE FINANCING REVIEW. SUPPLEMENT. (Supplement to: Health Care Financing Review (ISSN 1057-9389)) 1979. a. $21 (foreign $26.25) (effective 1995). U.S. Health Care Financing Administration, Department of Health and Human Services, Oak Meadows Bldg., Rm. 1A9, 6325 Security Blvd., Baltimore, MD 21207.
TEL 410-966-6572. FAX 410-966-6511. (Subscr. to: Superintendent of Documents, U.S. Government Printing Office, Box 371954, Pittsburgh, PA 15250-7954. TEL 202-512-1800. FAX 202-512-2250; Or: National Technical Information Service, 5285 Port Royal Rd., Springfield, VA 22161. TEL 703-487-4650. FAX 703-321-8547; Alt. addr.: Hubert H. Humphrey Bldg., 200 Independence Ave., S.W., Rm. 314G, Washington, DC 20201. TEL 202-245-6726) Ed. Linda F. Wolf. (also avail. in microform from UMI; microfiche from CIS; back issues avail.; reprint service avail. from CIS) **Indexed:** ABI Inform., Abstr.Health Care Manage.Stud., Amer.Stat.Ind. (1979-), CLOA, Excerp.Med., Hosp.Lit.Ind., Ind.U.S.Gov.Per., Med.Care Rev., MEDOC, PROMT, Soc.Work Res.& Abstr., World Bibl.Soc.Sec. **Document type:** government publication.

PUBLIC HEALTH AND SAFETY

614.8   US   ISSN 1041-0236
R118   CODEN: HECOER
HEALTH COMMUNICATION. 1989. q. $35 to individuals (foreign $60); institutions $180 (foreign $205). Lawrence Erlbaum Associates, Inc., 10 Industrial Dr., Mahwah, NJ 07430-2262. TEL 201-236-9500. FAX 201-236-0072. Ed. Teresa L. Thompson. adv.: page $575; 5 x 8. bk.rev. **Indexed:** Psychol.Abstr. (1989-). **Document type:** academic/scholarly publication.
—BLDSC (4274.953900); Faxon; UnCover.
Description: Features articles from scholars in communication, psychology, medicine, nursing and allied health fields.
Refereed Serial

362.1 360   UK   ISSN 1350-6102
HEALTH DIRECTOR. 1993. 10/yr. £35. National Association of Health Authorities and Trusts, Birmingham Research Park, Vincent Dr., Birmingham B15 2SQ, England. TEL 0121-471-4444. FAX 0121-414-1120. Ed. Barbara Connah. adv. contact: Theresa Westwood. **Document type:** bulletin.
—BLDSC (4274.964900).

614   UK
HEALTH ECHO. 1988. q. free. Lincolnshire Publishing Ltd., Brayford Wharf East, Lincoln LN5 9HA, England. TEL 01522-525252. FAX 01522-521600. Ed. Cliff Smith. adv. contact: Lorraine Wadsley. circ. 40,000. **Document type:** newspaper.

HEALTH ECONOMICS. see *MEDICAL SCIENCES*

614.8   US   ISSN 0193-5232
HEALTH EDUCATION REPORTS. 24/yr. $198. Feistritzer Publications, 4401-A Connecticut Ave., N.W., Ste. 212, Washington, DC 20008. TEL 202-362-3444. FAX 202-362-3493. **Document type:** newsletter.
Description: Covers health promotion and disease prevention. Reports on policy and legislation, reviews literature and meetings.

HEALTH FACILITIES DIRECTORY. see *SOCIAL SERVICES AND WELFARE*

613   US   ISSN 0749-4742
RA395.A3
HEALTH FREEDOM NEWS. 1955. m. $36 to individuals; senior citizens $24. National Health Federation, 212 W. Foothill, Monrovia, CA 91016. TEL 818-357-2181. FAX 818-303-0642. (Subscr. to: Box 688, Monrovia, CA 91016) Ed. James F. Scheer. adv.; bk.rev.; charts; illus.; stat. circ. 25,000. (tabloid format; back issues avail.)
Former titles (until 1982): Public Scrutiny (ISSN 0743-5053); National Health Federation. Bulletin (ISSN 0027-9420).
Description: Covers educational, legislative and legal topics related to health.

HEALTH GRANTS & CONTRACTS WEEKLY; selected federal project opportunities. see *PUBLIC ADMINISTRATION*

616.9   KE   ISSN 0140-5071
HEALTH INFORMATION BULLETIN. (Text in English) 1977. q. free. Ministry of Health, Division of Communicable Diseases Control and Epidemiology, Box 20781, Nairobi, Kenya. circ. 500. **Document type:** bulletin.

614 610 340   US   ISSN 0549-804X
HEALTH LAW BULLETIN. 1958. irreg. Institute of Government - North Carolina, UNC - Knapp Bldg. CB3330, Chapel Hill, NC 27599-3330. TEL 919-966-4119. FAX 919-962-2707. Eds. Anne M. Dellinger, Jeffrey C. Koeze. bibl. **Document type:** bulletin.
Description: Each issue deals with a current legal issue in the health care field. Reports the results of recent litigation and the effects of newly enacted legislation.

HEALTH LEGISLATION. see *MEDICAL SCIENCES*

HEALTH LETTER (WASHINGTON). see *MEDICAL SCIENCES*

HEALTH LITERATURE REPORTS. see *MEDICAL SCIENCES*

614   US   ISSN 0735-9683
HEALTH MARKETING QUARTERLY. 1978. q. $285 (foreign $399) (effective Mar. 1995). Haworth Press, Inc., 10 Alice St., Binghamton, NY 13904. TEL 607-722-5857; 800-342-9678. FAX 607-722-1424. TELEX 4932599 HAWORTH. Ed. William J. Winston. adv.; bk.rev.; abstr.; bibl. circ. 334. (also avail. in microfiche from HAW; back issues avail.; reprint service avail. from HAW)
Indexed: ABI Inform., Abstr.Health Care Manage.Stud., Abstr.Soc.Work, Chicago Psychoanal.Lit.Ind., Excerp.Med., Hosp.Abstr., Hosp.Lit.Ind., Med.Care Rev., Psychol.Abstr.
—BLDSC (4275.052850); Faxon; Haworth; UnCover.
Former titles (until 1984): Topics in Strategic Planning for Health Care (ISSN 0731-714X); Topics in Health Care; Health and Medical Care Services Review (ISSN 0160-7618)
Description: Each issue is devoted to a select health service, and serves as a basic resource for marketing the selected service. Covers group practice marketing, mental health marketing, and long-term care marketing.
Refereed Serial

HEALTH ORGANIZATIONS OF THE U.S., CANADA AND THE WORLD; a directory of voluntary associations, professional societies and other groups concerned with health and related fields. see *MEDICAL SCIENCES*

613   US
HEALTH - P A C BULLETIN.* 1968. q. $35 to individuals; institutions $45. Health Policy Advisory Center, 237 Thompson St., New York, NY 10012-1017. TEL 212-614-1660. FAX 212-614-1665. Ed. Ellen Bilofsky. adv.; bk.rev.; charts; illus.; stat.; tr.lit.; index. circ. 1,100. (also avail. in microform from UMI; back issues avail.)
Indexed: Alt.Press Ind., Med.Care Rev. **Document type:** bulletin.
—BLDSC (4275.086000); UMI; UnCover. **CCC.**
Supersedes (in 1987): Health and Medicine; Formerly: Health-Pac (ISSN 0017-9051)
Description: Analysis and commentary on health care and health policy advocating decent, accessible health care for all.

614 370   IE   ISSN 0168-8510
HEALTH POLICY. (Supplement avail.) (Text in English) 1979. m. I£568($897) (effective 1996). (European Health Policy Forum) Elsevier Science Ireland Ltd., P.O. Box 85, Limerick, Ireland. TEL 353-61-471944. FAX 353-61-472144. (Subscr. in U.S. and Canada to: Elsevier Science Inc., Box 882, Madison Sq. Sta., New York, NY 10159. TEL 212-989-5800. FAX 212-633-3990) Ed. J.E. Blanplain. (reprint service avail. from ISI,SWZ)
Indexed: Abstr.Health Care Manage.Stud., Adol.Ment.Hlth.Abstr., ASCA, ASSIA, Cont.Pg.Educ., Curr.Cont., Excerp.Med., Hosp.Lit.Ind., P.A.I.S., Risk Abstr., Sci.Cit.Ind., SSCI. **Document type:** academic/scholarly publication.
—BLDSC (4275.102700); Faxon; Genuine Article; SWETS; UnCover. **CCC.**
Incorporates (in 1986): Effective Health Care (ISSN 0167-871X); Formerly (until 1984): Health Policy and Education (ISSN 0165-2281)
Description: Forum for discussion of health policy issues among health policy researchers, legislators, decision makers and other professionals.
Refereed Serial

614   UK   ISSN 0268-1080
RA441.5
HEALTH POLICY AND PLANNING; a journal on health in development. 1986. q. £100($180) (effective 1996). (London School of Hygiene and Tropical Medicine) Oxford University Press, Oxford Journals, Walton St., Oxford OX2 6DP, England. TEL 01865-267907. FAX 01865-267773. TELEX 837330-OXPRES-G. E-mail: jnlorders@oup.co.uk. (U.S. subscr. to: Oxford University Press Inc., 2001 Evans Rd., Cary, NC 27513. TEL 919-677-0977. FAX 919-677-1714) Eds. Anne Mills, Gill Walt. adv.; bk.rev. circ. 900. **Indexed:** ASSIA, Curr.Adv.Ecol.Sci., Curr.Cont., Diar.Dis.Res., Excerp.Med., Refug.Abstr., Rural Devel.Abstr., Sel.Water Res.Abstr., Sociol.Abstr., World Agri.Econ.& Rural Sociol.Abstr. **Document type:** academic/scholarly publication.
—BLDSC (4275.103300); Faxon; Genuine Article; SWETS; UMI; UnCover. **CCC.**
Description: Covers issues in health policy, planning, management and evaluation in the developing world.

614   NE   ISSN 0927-5436
HEALTH POLICY MONOGRAPHS. (Supplement to: Health Policy (ISSN 0168-8510)) (Text in English) 1992. irreg., vol.2, 1992. price varies. Elsevier Science B.V., Books Division, P.O. Box 211, 1000 AE Amsterdam, Netherlands. TEL 31-20-4853911. FAX 31-20-4853705. TELEX 18582 ESPA NL. E-mail: nlinfo-f@elsevier.nl; usinfo-f@elsevier.com; forinfo-kyf04035@niftyserve.or.jp; Site addr.: http://www.elsevier.nl/. (Subscr. in U.S. and Canada to: Elsevier Science Inc., Box 882, Madison Sq. Sta., New York, NY 10159. TEL 212-989-5800) **Document type:** monographic series.
Description: In-depth analysis of issues at the forefront of the health policy debate.
Refereed Serial

614   US   ISSN 0732-7439
HEALTH POLICY WEEK. 1971. w. $395. United Communications Group, 11300 Rockville Pike, Ste. 1100, Rockville, MD 20852-3030. TEL 301-816-8950. FAX 301-816-8945. Ed. Burt Schorr. **Document type:** newsletter.
—CCC.
Description: Offers an inside look at federal and state government actions affecting the financing and delivery of health care services.

HEALTH PROFESSIONS REPORT; the independent bi-weekly newsletter on the education & training of medical, nursing and health professionals. see *EDUCATION*

614   CN   ISSN 1195-6747
RA440.3.C2
HEALTH PROMOTION IN CANADA. French Edition: Promotion de la Sante au Canada (Text in English and French) 1962. q. free. Health Canada, Ottawa, ON K1A 1B4, Canada. TEL 613-954-8842. FAX 613-990-7097. Ed. Kay Rawlings. bk.rev.; film rev.; circ. 14,000 (controlled) (10,000 English ed.; 4,000 French ed.). **Indexed:** Can.B.P.I., Can.Per.Ind.
—BLDSC (4275.105182).
Former titles (until 1993): Health Promotion (ISSN 0833-7594); Health Education (ISSN 0017-8950)

614   UK   ISSN 0957-4824
RA427.8   CODEN: HPINET
HEALTH PROMOTION INTERNATIONAL. 1986. q. £105($190) (effective 1996). Oxford University Press, Oxford Journals, Walton St., Oxford OX2 6DP, England. TEL 01865-267907. FAX 01865-267773. TELEX 837330-OXPRES-G. E-mail: jnlorders@oup.co.uk. (U.S. subscr. to: Oxford University Press Inc., 2001 Evans Rd., Cary, NC 27513. TEL 919-677-0977. FAX 919-677-1714) Ed. John Catford. adv.; bk.rev. circ. 900. **Indexed:** ASSIA, Excerp.Med., Psychol.Abstr. (1993-). **Document type:** academic/scholarly publication.
—BLDSC (4275.105183); Genuine Article; SWETS; UMI; UnCover. **CCC.**
Formerly (until 1989): Health Promotion (ISSN 0268-1099)
Description: Presents original articles, major reviews, and an editorial concerned with major health promotion themes.

HEALTH PSYCHOLOGY. see *PSYCHOLOGY*

614,8   UK
HEALTH, SAFETY ENVIRONMENT BULLETIN. 1976. m. £90 (foreign £100). Eclipse Group Ltd., 18-20 Highbury Pl., London N5 1QP, England. TEL 0171-354-5858. FAX 0171-359-4000. Ed. Rose Riddell. circ. 3,300. (reprint service avail. from UMI) **Indexed:** Br.Ceram.Abstr., Cadscan, Euro.LJI, Lab.Haz.Bull., Lead Abstr., LJI, World Surf.Coat., Zincscan. **Document type:** trade publication.
—BLDSC (4274.852000).
Formerly: Health and Safety Information Bulletin (ISSN 0142-9086)

HEALTH SERVICES MANAGEMENT RESEARCH. see *MEDICAL SCIENCES*

HEALTH SERVICES RESEARCH. see *HOSPITALS*

658 658   US   ISSN 0361-0195
HEALTH SYSTEMS MANAGEMENT.* 1974. irreg., no.18, 1985. S P Medical & Scientific Books, Inc. (Subsidiary of: Spectrum Publications, Inc.), c/o Fisher, 200 Park Ave. S., New York, NY 10003-1503. Ed. Dr. Samuel Levey.

HEALTH TRENDS. see *MEDICAL SCIENCES*

PUBLIC HEALTH AND SAFETY

614 360   CN   ISSN 1195-7506
RA410.9.C2
HEALTH WORKFORCE IN ALBERTA. ANNUAL REPORT. 1977. a. free. Alberta Health, Practitioner Services Division, 10025 Jasper Ave., 16th Fl., Edmonton, AB T5J 2N3, Canada. TEL 403-427-3276. FAX 403-422-2880. Ed. D. Chesley. circ. 500. **Document type:** government publication.
   Formerly (until 1993): Alberta. Health and Social Services Disciplines Committee. Annual Report (ISSN 0707-1434)
   Description: Contains the results of the annual survey of health employers in Alberta concerning the number of personnel employed, their status, vacancy and turnover rates, and recruitment difficulties.

614.8   US   ISSN 0886-1986
HEALTHACTION; * for a productive life. 1985. m. (10/yr.). (Kelly Group, Ltd.) Kelly Communications, RR 13, Box 28, Charlottsville, VA 22901-7927. TEL 804-296-5676. FAX 804-296-3972. Ed. Polly Turner. circ. 550,000. (back issues avail.)
   Description: Educates readers about nutrition, fitness, safety and overall wellness.

HEALTHCARE ADVERTISING REVIEW; creative forum for the people who plan and create healthcare advertising programs. see *ADVERTISING AND PUBLIC RELATIONS*

HEALTHCARE SYSTEMS STRATEGY REPORT. see *HOSPITALS*

614   US
HEALTHCARE 1500. 1991. a. $175 (effective 1995). Faulkner & Gray, Healthcare Information Center (Subsidiary of: Thomson Publishing Group), 1133 15th St., N.W., Ste. 450, Washington, DC 20005. TEL 202-828-4150. FAX 202-828-2352. Ed. Catherine Tokarski. **Document type:** directory.
   Former titles: HealthCare 1000; (until 1992): HealthCare 500.
   Description: Profiles influential federal and state health policy makers, advisors, lobbyists and health industry leaders, with addresses and telephone numbers. Also includes a review of health care budgets at the state level.

HEALTHFACTS. see *MEDICAL SCIENCES*

610   US   ISSN 0736-7929
HEALTHLINE; helping keep well people well. 1981. m. $24 (foreign $36). Healthline Publishers Inc., 830 Menlo Ave., Ste. 100, Menlo Park, CA 94025. TEL 800-325-4177. FAX 415-325-6457. Ed. Paul Insel. cum.index. circ. 11,000. (back issues avail.) **Indexed:** CHNI.
   —BLDSC (4275.247978).
   Description: Offers current information on health and wellness, written in nontechnical language by health care professionals and medical journalists.

362.1 614.4   UK   ISSN 0969-336X
HEALTHLINES; the Health Education Authority's magazine for everyone involved in health promotion. (Supplement avail.: Healthlines Plus (ISSN 0969-3378)) 1993. 10/yr. £20. Health Education Authority, Hamilton House, Mabledon Pl., London WC1H 9TX, England. TEL 0171-413-1920. (Subscr. to: Healthlines, Hazleton Industrial Park, Lakesmere Rd., Horndean, Hants. PO8 9JU, England. TEL 01705-571085) Ed. Sue Jelley. bk.rev. circ. 5,000. **Document type:** trade publication.
   Description: Discusses various aspects of health promotion and provides updates on research, publications, and events.

613   US   ISSN 1043-2779
S605.5
HEALTHY HARVEST. 1985. biennial. (National Institute for Science, Law, and Public Policy) Potomac Valley Press, 1424 16th St. N.W., Ste. 105, Washington, DC 20036.

614.8   US   ISSN 1064-5497
HEALTHY HOME & WORKPLACE; timely help for quality living in the 90's. 1990. q. $12. Healthy Home & Workplace, 248 Lafayette St., New York, NY 10012. TEL 212-226-5152. Ed. Mimi Weisbord. index. circ. 1,000. (back issues avail.) **Document type:** newsletter.
   Description: Offers help for dealing with indoor air pollution in the home, school, office, airplane, hotel room. Cautions about products and common workplace situations detrimental to health. Provides alternative non-toxic solutions which support healthful lifestyle.

HEALTHY LIFE NEWS. see *NUTRITION AND DIETETICS*

361   NO
HELSENYTT FOR ALLE; et popuaervitenskaplig medisinsk tidsskrift. 1910. bi-m. NOK 120. Nasjonalforeningen for Folkehelsen, P.O. Box 7139, Homansbyen, N-0307 Oslo 1, Norway. Ed. Terje Fugelli.
   —CCC.
   Former titles (until 1970): Helsenytt (ISSN 0018-0157); (until 1963): Nasjonalforeningen mot Tuberkulosen for Folkehelsen (ISSN 0333-287X)
   Description: Deals with medical issues in easy lay terms. Each issue has a main theme which is dealt with thoroughly.

HEPATITIS B COALITION NEWS. see *MEDICAL SCIENCES — Allergology And Immunology*

614   BU   ISSN 0018-8247
     CODEN: KHZDAN
HIGIENA I ZDRAVEOPAZVANE. (Text in Bulgarian; summaries in English and Russian) 1958. bi-m. 24 lv.($10) (Ministerstvo na Narodnoto Zdrave) Izdatelstvo Meditsina i Fizkultura, 11, Pl. Slaveikov, Sofia, Bulgaria. (Co-sponsor: Nauchno Druzhestvo po Higiena i Organizacia na Zdraveopazvaneto) Ed. E. Efremov. adv.; bk.rev.; abstr.; charts; illus.; stat.; index. circ. 1,402. **Indexed:** Abstr.Bulg.Sci.Med.Lit., Biol.Abstr., Chem.Abstr., Excerp.Med. (until 1993), INIS Atomind., Nutr.Abstr.
   —CASDDS.

614 352   US
HIV PREVENTION AND SERVICES TECHNICAL ASSISTANCE REPORTS. (Human Immunodeficiency Virus) irreg. free. U.S. Conference of Mayors, Office of Public Affairs, 1620 Eye St., N.W., Washington, DC 20006. TEL 202-293-7330. **Document type:** monographic series.

614 352   US
HIV PREVENTION CASE STUDY SERIES. (Human Immunodeficiency Virus) irreg. $5 per no. U.S. Conference of Mayors, Office of Public Affairs, 1620 Eye St., N.W., Washington, DC 20006. TEL 202-293-7330. **Document type:** monographic series.

614.8 374   JA   ISSN 0912-1420
HOKEN KANRI SENTA DAYORI. (Text in Japanese) 1975. 3/yr. Nara Joshi Daigaku, Hoken Kanri Senta - Nara Women's University, Health Administration Center, Kita-Uoya-Higashi-cho, Nara-shi 630, Japan. Ed. Kimihiro Yamamoto. circ. 3,000. **Document type:** bulletin.
   Description: Contains news of the center.

610   MX   ISSN 0185-2140
HOMBRE Y TRABAJO; boletin de medicina, seguridad e higiene. 1976. m. Secretaria del Trabajo y Prevision Social, Direccion General de Seguridad e Higiene en el Trabajo, Calzada Azcapotzalco-La Villa No. 209, Junto Metro Ferreria, 02020 Mexico D.F., Mexico. TEL 3943344. Dir. Dr. Juan Antonio Legaspi Velasco. charts; illus.; stat. circ. 4,000.
   Description: Covers regulations, agreements, and official standards of security, hygiene and work environment in Mexico.

HOPE HEALTH LETTER. see *PHYSICAL FITNESS AND HYGIENE*

614   US
HOPE NEWS. 1963. 2/yr. free. People-to-People Health Foundation, Inc., Project Hope Health Sciences Education Center, Millwood, VA 22646. TEL 703-837-2100. FAX 703-837-7813. Ed. Laura Petrosian. circ. 100,000. **Document type:** newsletter.

HUANJING YU JIANKANG ZAZHI/JOURNAL OF ENVIRONMENT AND HEALTH. see *ENVIRONMENTAL STUDIES*

HUMAN ECOLOGY (PARK RIDGE). see *HOSPITALS*

HUMAN RESOURCES ADMINISTRATOR. see *HOSPITALS*

628 614.8   FI   ISSN 1236-3081
HYVA TERVEYS. 1985. 9/yr. FIM 235. Helsinki Media Magazines, P.O. Box 107, 000381 Helsinki, Finland. TEL 358-0-1201. FAX 358-0-1205599. Ed. Jali Ruuskanen. adv.: B&W page FIM 7950, color page FIM 10900; 194 x 248. circ. 38,710 (paid). **Document type:** consumer publication.
   Formerly (until 1993): Terveys 2000 (ISSN 0782-3789)
   Description: Results of research in health care and medical research.

I A F C ON SCENE. (International Association of Fire Chiefs) see *FIRE PREVENTION*

I B F A N NEWS. (International Baby Food Action Network) see *CHILDREN AND YOUTH — About*

I P M PRACTITIONER; monitoring the field of pest management. (Integrated Pest Management) see *AGRICULTURE*

614   US   ISSN 1054-7053
I S S A TODAY. 1975. m. $75. International Sanitary Supply Association, Inc., 7373 N. Lincoln Ave., Lincolnwood, IL 60646. TEL 708-982-0800. FAX 708-982-1012. Ed. Lisa Veeck. adv.; circ. 4,000 (controlled). (back issues avail.)

I Z A. (Illustrierte Zeitschrift fuer Arbeitssicherheit) see *OCCUPATIONAL HEALTH AND SAFETY*

IDAHO. DEPARTMENT OF HEALTH AND WELFARE. RESEARCH AND STATISTICS SECTION. QUARTERLY WELFARE STATISTICAL BULLETIN. see *SOCIAL SERVICES AND WELFARE — Abstracting, Bibliographies, Statistics*

614   IT   ISSN 0019-1639
     CODEN: ISPRA2
IGIENE E SANITA PUBBLICA. (Text in Italian; summaries in English, French, German and Italian) 1945. bi-m. L.160000 (effective 1996). Nebo Sas Editore, Casella Postale 4238, Roma Appio, 00100 Rome, Italy. TEL 39-6-70300693. Ed. Augusto Pana; Pub. Giuseppe Cananzi. adv. contact: Giuseppe Cananzi. bk.rev.; charts; illus.; index. circ. 2,000. (also avail. in microform from UMI) **Indexed:** Abstr.Hyg., Biol.Abstr., Chem.Abstr., Curr.Adv.Ecol.Sci., Excerp.Med., INIS Atomind., Trop.Dis.Bull. **Document type:** academic/scholarly publication.
   —CASDDS; UMI. **CCC.**

IGIENE MENTALE. see *PSYCHOLOGY*

614   US   ISSN 1077-1328
▼**ILLINOIS HEALTH LAW UPDATE.** 1994. m. $177. (Vedder, Price, Kaufman & Kammholz) M. Lee Smith Publishers & Printers LLC, 162 Fourth Ave., N., Box 198867, Nashville, TN 37219-8867. TEL 615-242-7395; 800-274-6774. FAX 615-256-6601. Ed. Anne M. Murphy; Pub. M. Lee Smith. **Document type:** newsletter.
   Formerly (until 1995): Illinois Health Law Alert (ISSN 1073-0435)
   Description: Reports state-specific new public health laws that affect companies in Illinois.

613 310   US   ISSN 0885-9914
RA448.5.I5
INDIAN HEALTH TRENDS AND SERVICES. 1969. irreg. free. U.S. Public Health Service, Resources and Services Administration, 5600 Fishers Ln., Rm. 6A-30, Rockville, MD 20857. TEL 202-545-6700. (Orders to: Supt. of Documents, Washington, DC 20402) stat. circ. 15,000.

614   II   ISSN 0367-827X
RA565.A1   CODEN: IJEHBP
INDIAN JOURNAL OF ENVIRONMENTAL HEALTH. (Text in English) 1959. q. National Environmental Engineering Research Institute, Documentation and Library Services, Nehru Marg, Nagpur 440 020, India. (Affiliate: Council of Scientific and Industrial Research) Ed. S.B. Dabadghao. adv.; bk.rev.; bibl.; charts; illus.; tr.lit. circ. 1,200. **Indexed:** Biol.Abstr., Chem.Abstr., Curr.Leather Lit., Environ.Per.Bibl., Excerp.Med., INIS Atomind., Ocean.Abstr., Pollut.Abstr., Soils & Fert., W.R.C.Inf.
   —BLDSC (4412.100000); CASDDS.
   Formerly: Environmental Health (ISSN 0013-9289)

PUBLIC HEALTH AND SAFETY

614   II   ISSN 0019-557X
RA421   CODEN: IPBHAH
INDIAN JOURNAL OF PUBLIC HEALTH. (Text in English) 1956. q. Rs.100($30) Indian Public Health Association, 110 Chittaranjan Ave., Calcutta 700 073, India. Ed. A.K. Chakraborty. adv.; bk.rev.; abstr.; charts; illus.; stat.; index. circ. 2,500. Indexed: Abstr.Hyg., Biol.Abstr., Chem.Abstr., Diar.Dis.Res., Ind.Med., Ind.Vet., Small Anim.Abstr., Vet.Bull.
—BLDSC (4420.400000).

THE INDIAN PRACTITIONER; a monthly journal of medicine, surgery & public health. see *MEDICAL SCIENCES*

614   IO   ISSN 0216-3527
INDONESIAN JOURNAL OF PUBLIC HEALTH/MAJALAH KESEHATAN MASYARAKAT INDONESIA. (Text and summaries in English and Indonesian) 1969. m. Rps.3500 per no. Indonesian Public Health Association - Ikatan Ahli Kesehatan Masyarakat Indonesia, Pegangsaan Timur 16, Jakarta, Indonesia. Ed. Azrul Azwar. adv.; bk.rev.; charts; illus.; stat. circ. 10,000.
Former titles: Indonesian Public Health Association. Journal; Indonesian Journal of Public Health.

613.5 697   DK   ISSN 0905-6947
                           CODEN: INAIE5
INDOOR AIR; international journal of indoor air quality and climate. (Includes supplement: Indoor Air. Supplementum (ISSN 0908-5920)) (Text in English) 1991. q. DKK 1200 (effective 1996). (International Society of Indoor Air Quality and Climate) Munksgaard International Publishers Ltd., 35 Noerre Soegade, P.O. Box 2148, DK-1016 Copenhagen K, Denmark. TEL 45-33-12-70-30. FAX 45-33-12-93-87. Ed. David Grimsrud. adv.; charts; illus. circ. 600. (reprint service avail.) **Document type:** academic/scholarly publication.
—BLDSC (4438.046530); CASDDS; Genuine Article. **CCC**.
    Refereed Serial

INDOOR AIR QUALITY UPDATE; a guide to the practical control of indoor air problems. see *ARCHITECTURE*

INDOOR AIR REVIEW. see *ENVIRONMENTAL STUDIES*

INFECTION CONTROL WEEKLY. see *MEDICAL SCIENCES — Communicable Diseases*

INFORMAZIONE INNOVATIVA; agenzia quindicinale di documentazione internazionale servizio di informazione innovativa scientifica tecnologica legislativa per la produzione, l'ambiente, la sanita. see *ENVIRONMENTAL STUDIES*

628   IT   ISSN 0394-5871
                           CODEN: IGEABH
INGEGNERIA AMBIENTALE. (Text in Italian; summaries in English, Italian) 1972. 9/yr. L.105000 (foreign L.200000) (effective 1994). (Centro di Ingegneria per la Protezione dell'Ambiente) C I P A s.r.l., Via Palladio, 26, 20135 Milan, Italy. TEL 02-58301528. FAX 02-58301550. Ed.Bd. adv.; bk.rev. circ. 1,800. Indexed: Chem.Abstr., Pollut.Abstr.
—BLDSC (4500.650000); CASDDS.
Formerly (until 1986): Ingegneria Ambientale Inquinamento e Depurazione (ISSN 0302-7775)

628   IT
INGEGNERIA AMBIENTALE QUADERNI. (Text in Italian; summaries in English, Italian) 1984. 2/yr. L.80000. (Centro di Ingegneria per la Protezione dell'Ambiente) C I P A s.r.l, Via Palladio, 26, 20135 Milan, Italy. TEL 02-58301528. FAX 02-58301550. Indexed: Chem.Abstr., Pollut.Abstr. **Document type:** monographic series.
Formerly: Ingegneria Ambientale Inquinamento e Depurazione Quaderni.

628   IT
INGEGNERIA SANITARIA AMBIENTALE; rivista tecnica bimestrale. 1952; N.S. 1989. bi-m. L.90000 (effective 1994). (Associazione Nazionale di Ingegneria Sanitaria) Maggioli Editore, Viale Vespucci 12-n, Casella Postale 290, 47037 Rimini, Italy. TEL 0541-626777. FAX 0541-622020. Dir. Luigi Mendia. adv.; B&W page L.1600000, color page L.2500000; trim 160 x 270. bk.rev.; abstr.; bibl.; charts; illus. circ. 3,800. Indexed: Chem.Abstr., INIS Atomind.
Formerly (until 1990): Ingegneria Sanitaria (ISSN 0020-0980)

628   BL   ISSN 0446-2424
TD4
INGENIERIA SANITARIA. (Text in English, French, Portuguese and Spanish) 1946. q. $16. Interamerican Association of Sanitary and Environmental Engineering, Rua Nicolau Gagliardi, 354, 05429 Sao Paulo, Brazil. TEL 011-212-4080. FAX 011-814-2441. TELEX 11-81453. Ed. Osvaldo Rey. adv.; bk.rev. circ. 8,000. Indexed: Pollut.Abstr., Repindex.

614 610   FR   ISSN 0755-4168
INSTITUT NATIONAL DE LA SANTE ET DE LA RECHERCHE MEDICALE. ACTUALITES. Key Title: INSERM Actualites. 1950. m. free. Institut National de la Sante et de la Recherche Medicale, 101 rue de Tolbiac, 75654 Paris Cedex 13, France. TEL 44-23-60-00. FAX 44-23-60-99. stat. circ. 1,400.
Former titles: Institut National de la Sante et de la Recherche Medicale. Bulletin d'Information; Institut National de la Sante et de la Recherche Medicale. Bulletin (ISSN 0015-9603)

614   JA
INSTITUTE OF PUBLIC HEALTH. ANNUAL REPORT/KOKURITSU KOSHU EISEI-IN NENPO. (Text in Japanese) 1948. a. Institute of Public Health - Kokuritsu Koshu Eisei-in, 4-6-1 Shiroganedai, Minato-ku, Tokyo 108, Japan.

614   JA   ISSN 0020-3106
RA421   CODEN: KEKHA7
INSTITUTE OF PUBLIC HEALTH. BULLETIN/KOKURITSU KOSHU EISEI-IN KENKYU HOKOKU. (Text in English or Japanese) 1952. q. free or exchange basis. Institute of Public Health - Kokuritsu Koshu Eisei-in, 4-6-1 Shiroganedai, Minato-ku, Tokyo 108, Japan. Ed. Dr. Takeshi Suzuki. abstr.; bibl.; charts; illus.; index. circ. 1,200. Indexed: Abstr.Hyg., Biol.Abstr., Chem.Abstr., Excerp.Med., Ind.Vet., INIS Atomind., Trop.Dis.Bull., Vet.Bull. **Document type:** bulletin.
—CASDDS.

614   II   ISSN 0251-110X
TD1   CODEN: JEEEDS
INSTITUTION OF ENGINEERS (INDIA). ENVIRONMENTAL ENGINEERING DIVISION. JOURNAL. (Text in English) 1920. s-a. Rs.40($5) Institution of Engineers (India), Environmental Engineering Division, 8 Gokhale Rd., Calcutta 700 020, India. TEL 033-288334. FAX 033-288345. TELEX 0217885 IEIC IN. Ed. S.P. Misra. adv.; charts; illus.; index. circ. 8,000. Indexed: INIS Atomind., Ocean.Abstr., Pollut.Abstr. **Document type:** academic/scholarly publication.
—BLDSC (4794.021000); CASDDS; Ei.
Formerly: Institution of Engineers (India). Public Health Engineering Division. Journal (ISSN 0020-3416)

616.988   PO   ISSN 0303-7762
                           CODEN: AIHTDH
INSTITUTO DE HIGIENE E MEDICINA TROPICAL. ANAIS. (Text and summaries in English, French and Portuguese) 1943. irreg., vol.10, 1984. price varies. Instituto de Higiene e Medicina Tropical, Centro de Documentacao e Informacao Cientifica, Rua da Junqueira, 96, Lisbon 3, Portugal. bk.rev. circ. 1,000. Indexed: Abstr.Hyg., Biol.Abstr., Excerp.Med., Helminthol.Abstr., Ind.Med., Ind.Vet., Rev.Appl.Entomol., Trop.Dis.Bull., Vet.Bull.
Formerly: Lisbon. Escola Nacional de Saude de Medicina Tropical. Anais (ISSN 0075-9767)

589.9   CL   ISSN 0716-1387
RA465   CODEN: BICHDZ
INSTITUTO DE SALUD PUBLICA DE CHILE. BOLETIN. (Text in Spanish; summaries in English) 1942. 2/yr. $6. Instituto de Salud Publica de Chile, Marathon 1000, Casillo 48, Santiago, Chile. Eds. J. Hernan Lobos R., Julio Garcia M. adv.; bk.rev.; bibl.; charts; illus. circ. 628. Indexed: Biol.Abstr., Chem.Abstr., Ind.Med., Trop.Dis.Bull.
—CASDDS.
Formerly: Instituto Bacteriologico de Chile. Boletin (ISSN 0374-6224)

614   MX
INSTITUTO MEXICANO DEL SEGURO SOCIAL. BOLETIN ESTADISTICO. 1972. a. free. Instituto Mexicano del Seguro Social, Subdireccion General Medica, Jefatura de Servicios de Medicina Preventiva, Apdo. Postal 12976, 03001 Mexico, D.F., Mexico. circ. 2,000.

614   MX
INSTITUTO MEXICANO DEL SEGURO SOCIAL. BOLETIN SOBRE MORBILIDAD HOSPITALARIA. 1982. a. free. Instituto Mexicano del Seguro Social, Subdireccion General Medica, Jefatura de Servicios de Medicina Preventiva, Apdo. Postal 12976, 03001 Mexico, D.F., Mexico. circ. 2,000.

614   MX
INSTITUTO MEXICANO DEL SEGURO SOCIAL. BOLETIN SOBRE MORTALIDAD. 1977. a. free. Instituto Mexicano del Seguro Social, Subdireccion General Medica, Jefatura de Servicios de Medicina Preventiva, Apdo. Postal 12976, 03001 Mexico, D.F., Mexico. circ. 2,000.

614   MX
INSTITUTO MEXICANO DEL SEGURO SOCIAL. BOLETIN SOBRE MOTIVOS DE CONSULTA. 1980. a. free. Instituto Mexicano del Seguro Social, Subdireccion General Medica, Jefatura de Servicios de Medicina Preventiva, Apdo. Postal 12976, 03001 Mexico D.F., Mexico. circ. 2,000.

INSTYTUT BADAN JADROWYCH. ZAKLAD RADIOBIOLOGII I OCHRONY ZDROWIA. PRACE DOSWIADCZALNE. see *MEDICAL SCIENCES — Radiology And Nuclear Medicine*

614.86   US   ISSN 0018-988X
HE5614
INSURANCE INSTITUTE FOR HIGHWAY SAFETY. STATUS REPORT. 1961. m. free. Insurance Institute for Highway Safety, 1005 North Glebe Rd., Arlington, VA 22201. TEL 703-247-1500. Ed. Ann Fleming. index. circ. 17,000. (also avail. in microform from UMI; reprint service avail. from UMI) **Document type:** newsletter.
—Faxon; UMI; UnCover.
Formerly: I I H S Report.

INTEGRO; Gesundheits- und Sozialmagazin des V.P.O.D. see *SOCIAL SERVICES AND WELFARE*

INTERFACE (BETHESDA). see *COMPUTERS*

614   UN   ISSN 0074-1892
HD7269.A6   CODEN: SSAEAW
INTERNATIONAL ATOMIC ENERGY AGENCY. SAFETY SERIES. (Text in English, French, Russian or Spanish) 1960. irreg. price varies. International Atomic Energy Agency, Wagramerstr. 5, P.O. Box 100, A-1400 Vienna, Austria. TEL 43-1-209-2360. FAX 43-1-209-5302. E-mail: fossett@adp01.iaea.or.at. (Dist. in U.S. by: Unipub, 4611-F Assembly Dr., Lanham, MD 20706-4391) Indexed: Biol.Abstr., Pollut.Abstr. **Document type:** monographic series.
● Also available on CD-ROM.

362.1   US
INTERNATIONAL CLASSIFICATION OF DISEASES. CLINICAL MODIFICATION: CODING MANUAL. Short title: I C D - 9 - C M: Coding Manual. 1978. base vol. plus irreg. updates. $25 (foreign $31.25). U.S. Public Health Service, Parklawn Bldg., 5600 Fishers Ln., Rockville, MD 20857. (Subscr. to: National Technical Information Service, 5285 Port Royal Rd., Springfield, VA 22161. TEL 703-487-4650. FAX 703-321-8547; Or: Superintendent of Documents, U.S. Government Printing Office, Box 371954, Pittsburgh, PA 15250-7954. TEL 202-512-1800. FAX 202-512-2250) (Co-sponsor: U.S. Department of Health and Human Services. Health Care Financing Administration) (looseleaf format) **Document type:** government publication.
Description: Presents guidelines that provide general assistance in coding and reporting medical conditions

PUBLIC HEALTH AND SAFETY

614 UN ISSN 0020-6563
INTERNATIONAL DIGEST OF HEALTH LEGISLATION. French edition: Recueil International de Legislation Sanitaire (ISSN 0250-8583) 1949. q. 209 Fr.($167) World Health Organization, Distribution and Sales, CH-1211 Geneva 27, Switzerland. TEL 41-22-791-2476. FAX 41-22-791-4857. TELEX 27821-OMS. bibl.; charts; index. circ. 3,600 (2,600 English edition; 1,000 French edition). **Indexed:** Adol.Ment.Hlth.Abstr., Biol.Abstr., Cadscan, Curr.Adv.Ecol.Sci., Dairy Sci.Abstr., Food Sci.& Tech.Abstr., I.P.A., INIS Atomind., Lead Abstr., Mult.Ed.Abstr., NRN, Zincscan. **Document type:** academic/scholarly publication.
—BLDSC (4539.600000); SWETS; UMI.
 Description: Allows readers to follow worldwide developments in laws and regulations designed to protect public health and the human environment.

INTERNATIONAL ENVIRONMENT AND SAFETY. see *ENVIRONMENTAL STUDIES*

INTERNATIONAL FOOD SAFETY NEWS. see *FOOD AND FOOD INDUSTRIES*

INTERNATIONAL JOURNAL FOR CONSUMER SAFETY. see *CONSUMER EDUCATION AND PROTECTION*

INTERNATIONAL JOURNAL OF EPIDEMIOLOGY. see *MEDICAL SCIENCES*

614 UK ISSN 0965-8335
INTERNATIONAL JOURNAL OF HEALTH INFORMATICS. 1992. q. P M H Publications Ltd., P.O. Box 100, Chichester, Sussex PO19, England. Ed. Chris Dowd; Pub. Joe Ridge. adv. contact: Linda Cozens. **Document type:** bulletin.
—BLDSC (4542.277000).

614 US ISSN 0020-7314
RA421 CODEN: IJUSC3
INTERNATIONAL JOURNAL OF HEALTH SERVICES. 1970. q. $127 (effective 1996). Baywood Publishing Co., Inc., 26 Austin Ave., Box 337, Amityville, NY 11701. TEL 516-691-1270. FAX 516-691-1770. Ed. Dr. Vicente Navarro. bk.rev.; abstr.; illus. (back issues avail.) **Indexed:** Abstr.Health Care Manage.Stud., Abstr.Hosp.Manage.Stud., Abstr.Hyg., ASSIA, Biol.Abstr., C.I.S. Abstr., CINAHL, Curr.Cont., Diar.Dis.Res., Excerp.Med., Geo.Abstr., Hosp.Lit.Ind., I.P.A., IDA, IMFL, Ind.Med., INIS Atomind., Med.Care Rev., Mid.East: Abstr.& Ind., Polit.Sci.Abstr., Risk Abstr., Rural Devel.Abstr., SSCI, Trop.Dis.Bull. **Document type:** academic/scholarly publication.
●Also available online.
—BLDSC (4542.278000); EMDOCS; Faxon; SWETS; UnCover.
 Description: Contains current and authoritative information on the development of the health care industry worldwide.
 Refereed Serial

INTERNATIONAL JOURNAL OF HYGIENE AND NUTRITION IN FOOD SERVICE AND CATERING. see *FOOD AND FOOD INDUSTRIES*

INTERNATIONAL JOURNAL OF INFECTIOUS DISEASES. see *MEDICAL SCIENCES — Communicable Diseases*

INTERNATIONAL JOURNAL OF MASS EMERGENCIES AND DISASTERS. see *SOCIOLOGY*

INTERNATIONAL JOURNAL OF MENTAL HEALTH. see *PSYCHOLOGY*

INTERNATIONAL JOURNAL OF OCCUPATIONAL MEDICINE AND ENVIRONMENTAL HEALTH. see *OCCUPATIONAL HEALTH AND SAFETY*

INTERNATIONAL JOURNAL OF PEST MANAGEMENT. see *AGRICULTURE — Crop Production And Soil*

INTERNATIONAL NARCOTICS CONTROL BOARD. REPORT FOR (YEAR). see *PHARMACY AND PHARMACOLOGY*

INTERNATIONAL PEST CONTROL; crop protection, public health, wood preservation. see *BIOLOGY — Entomology*

613 US ISSN 0272-684X
RA440.A1
INTERNATIONAL QUARTERLY OF COMMUNITY HEALTH EDUCATION. 1981. q. $127 (effective 1996). Baywood Publishing Co., Inc., 26 Austin Ave., Box 337, Amityville, NY 11701. TEL 516-691-1270. FAX 516-691-1770. Ed. Dr. George P. Cernada. bk.rev.; abstr.; illus. (back issues avail.) **Indexed:** Curr.Lit.Fam.Plan., Mult.Ed.Abstr., NRN, Psychol.Abstr. (1993-), Sociol.Educ.Abstr., Tech.Educ.Abstr. **Document type:** academic/scholarly publication.
—BLDSC (4545.510000); Faxon; SWETS; UnCover.
 Description: Focuses on the systematic application of social science and health education theory and methodology to public health problems. Applies consumer-directed approaches to control preventive and curative health services.
 Refereed Serial

614.8 US
INTERNATIONAL SYSTEM SAFETY CONFERENCE. PROCEEDINGS. 1971. biennial. $75. System Safety Society, Inc., Technology Trading Park, 5 Export Dr., Ste. A, Sterling, VA 22170-4421. TEL 703-444-6520. Ed.Bd. circ. 550. (back issues avail.) **Document type:** proceedings.
 Description: Technical papers on system and product safety.

614 UN ISSN 1020-0169
RA638
INTERNATIONAL TRAVEL AND HEALTH: VACCINATION REQUIREMENTS AND HEALTH ADVICE. French edition: Voyages Internationaux et Sante. Vaccinations Exigees et Conseils d'Hygiene. (Editions in English, French, German) a. 15 SFr.($13.50) World Health Organization, Distribution and Sales, CH-1211 Geneva 27, Switzerland. TEL 41-22-791-2111. FAX 41-22-791-4857. TELEX 27821-OMS. circ. 15,000.
—BLDSC (4551.308370); SWETS.
 Former titles: Vaccination Certificate Requirements and Health Advice for International Travel (ISSN 0257-912X); Vaccination Certificate Requirements for International Travel and Health Advice to Travellers (ISSN 0254-296X); Vaccination Certificate Requirements for International Travel (ISSN 0512-3011)
 Description: Serves to alert physicians, health authorities and airline and shipping companies to changes in required and recommended vaccinations for travellers to every country in the world.

INTERNATIONAL UNION AGAINST TUBERCULOSIS AND LUNG DISEASE. CONFERENCE PROCEEDINGS. see *MEDICAL SCIENCES — Respiratory Diseases*

614 360 CN
RA410.9.C2
INVENTORY OF HEALTH WORKFORCE IN ALBERTA. 1978. a. free. Alberta Health, Practitioner Services Division, 10025 Jasper Ave., 16th Fl., Edmonton, AB T5J 2N3, Canada. TEL 403-427-3276. FAX 403-422-2880. Ed. D. Chesley. circ. 500. (back issues avail.) **Document type:** government publication.
 Former titles (until 1992): Inventory of Health & Social Service Personnel (ISSN 0848-7332); Health and Social Service Manpower in Alberta (ISSN 0714-1904)
 Description: Contains the results of the annual survey of professional associations in Alberta concerning information and statistical data on the number of personnel registered with each association.

614 IR ISSN 0304-4556
 CODEN: IJPHCD
IRANIAN JOURNAL OF PUBLIC HEALTH/MAJALLE-YE BEHDASHT-E IRAN. (Text and summaries in English and Persian) 1972. q. Rs.1000($25) Iranian Public Health Association, University of Teheran, Teheran, Iran. Ed. D. Farhud. illus.; index. circ. 2,000. **Indexed:** Abstr.Hyg., Biol.Abstr., Chem.Abstr., Entomol.Abstr., Excerp.Med., ExtraMED, Helminthol.Abstr., Nutr.Abstr., Protozool.Abstr., Rev.Appl.Entomol., Trop.Dis.Bull. **Document type:** academic/scholarly publication.
●Also available on CD-ROM.
—BLDSC (4567.529200); CASDDS.

614 IS
ISRAEL. MINISTRY OF HEALTH. DIVISION OF EPIDEMIOLOGY. INFECTIOUS DISEASES SURVEILLANCE. (Text in English) s-a. Ministry of Health, Division of Epidemiology, 107 Hebron Rd., Jerusalem 91000, Israel. **Document type:** government publication.

614 IS
ISRAEL. MINISTRY OF HEALTH. DIVISION OF EPIDEMIOLOGY. WEEKLY EPIDEMIOLOGICAL RECORD. (Text in English) w. Ministry of Health, Division of Epidemiology, 107 Hebron Rd., Jerusalem 91000, Israel. **Document type:** government publication.

610 636.089 IT ISSN 0021-2571
R61 CODEN: AISSAW
ISTITUTO SUPERIORE DI SANITA. ANNALI. (Text and summaries in English or Italian) 1965. q. L.75000 (foreign L.90000) (effective 1995). Istituto Superiore di Sanita, Viale Regina Elena 299, 00161 Rome, Italy. TEL 39-6-49901. FAX 39-6-4469938. TELEX 610071 ISTSAN I. (Subscr. to: Istituto Poligrafico e Zecca dello Stato, Direzione Commerciale - Settore Abbonamenti, Piazza Verdi 10, 00100 Rome, Italy.. TEL 06-85081) Ed. Vilma Alberani. bk.rev.; abstr.; bibl.; illus.; index, cum.index. circ. 1,000. (back issues avail.) **Indexed:** Biol.Abstr., Chem.Abstr., Dairy Sci.Abstr., Excerp.Med., Food Sci.& Tech.Abstr., Ind.Med., Ind.Vet., INSPEC (1980-), Nutr.Abstr., Protozool.Abstr., Rev.Appl.Entomol., Rev.Med.& Vet.Mycol., Trop.Dis.Bull., Vet.Bull. **Document type:** academic/scholarly publication.
—BLDSC (1008.045000); CASDDS; EMDOCS; Faxon; Genuine Article; SWETS; UnCover.
 Formerly: Istituto Superiore di Sanita. Rendiconti.
 Description: Original articles, monographs, proceedings and technical notes on health issues in many areas of public health.

614 BG ISSN 1012-8697
J O P S O M. (Journal of Preventive and Social Medicine) 1982. s-a. Tk.150 to individuals; institutions TK.200; foreign $20. National Institute of Preventive and Social Medicine, Mohakhali, Dhaka 1212, Bangladesh. Ed. M. Mobarak Ali. adv. circ. 500. (back issues avail.) **Indexed:** Diar.Dis.Res.

JAHRBUCH KRITISCHE MEDIZIN. see *MEDICAL SCIENCES*

362.1 JA ISSN 1340-2676
 CODEN: GHKKEV
JAPAN. GIFU PREFECTURAL HEALTH AND ENVIRONMENT RESEARCH CENTER. REPORT. (Text in Japanese) 1972. a. Gifu Prefectural Health and Environment Research Center, 6-3, Noishiki 4-chome, Gifu 500, Japan. **Document type:** government publication.
—BLDSC (7491.130000); CASDDS.
 Formerly (until 1993): Japan. Gifu Prefectural Institute of Public Health. Report (ISSN 0385-1575)

628.2 JA ISSN 0021-4639
TD511 CODEN: GSKSAQ
JAPAN SEWAGE WORKS ASSOCIATION. JOURNAL/GESUIDO KYOKAISHI. (Text in Japanese) 1964. m. newsstand price: 1000Yen. Japan Sewage Works Association - Nihon Gesuido Kyokai, 6-2, Otemachi 2-chome, Chiyoda-ku, Tokyo 102, Japan. TEL 81-3-5200-0816. FAX 81-3-5200-0847. Ed. Shogo Saito; Pub. Tsugio Furusawa. adv. contact: Yasuhiko Tanaka. bibl.; charts; illus.; mkt.; tr.lit.; index. circ. 12,000. **Indexed:** Chem.Abstr., Geo.Abstr., INIS Atomind. **Document type:** academic/scholarly publication.
—BLDSC (4805.900000).

JAPANESE JOURNAL OF SANITARY ZOOLOGY/EISEI DOBUTSU. see *BIOLOGY — Zoology*

JAPANESE JOURNAL OF TOXICOLOGY AND ENVIRONMENTAL HEALTH. see *ENVIRONMENTAL STUDIES — Toxicology And Environmental Safety*

PUBLIC HEALTH AND SAFETY

614.8   **US**   **ISSN 0277-8327**
JOINT COMMISSION PERSPECTIVES. 1952. bi-m. $80 (foreign $90). (Joint Commission on Accreditation of Healthcare Organizations) Mosby-Yearbook, Inc., 11830 Westline Dr., St. Louis, MO 63146-3318. TEL 800-453-4351. FAX 314-432-1380. Ed. Ruth Carol. cum.index: 1983-1986. circ. 22,718. (back issues avail.)
●Also available online. Vendor(s): Lexis-Nexis.
—BLDSC (4672.252490); Faxon; UMI. **CCC.**
Formerly: J C A H Perspectives.
Description: Informs readers of new and revised Joint Commission standards, scoring guidelines and new and revised policies and procedures; covers the organization's quality improvement initiatives.

614   **UN**   **ISSN 0449-122X**
TX537
JOINT F A O - W H O CODEX ALIMENTARIUS COMMISSION. REPORT OF THE SESSION. (Editions in English, French, Spanish) 1963. irreg., 20th, 1993, Geneva, Switzerland. $15. Food and Agriculture Organization of the United Nations, c/o UNIPUB, 4611-F Assembly Dr,, Lanham, MD 20706-4391. TEL 301-459-7666. FAX 301-459-0056. **Document type:** government publication.

614   **US**   **ISSN 0090-7421**
R690
JOURNAL OF ALLIED HEALTH. 1972. q. $75 to non-members (foreign $92) (typically set in Jul.). (American Society of Allied Health Professions) University of Illinois at Chicago, College of Associated Health Professions (M-C 518), 808 S. Wood St., Chicago, IL 60612. TEL 312-413-9180. FAX 312-413-0086. Ed. Dr. Leopold Secker. adv.: B&W page $350; 6 x 9. bk.rev.; abstr.; circ. 2,000 (paid). (also avail. in microform from UMI,MIM; reprint service avail. from UMI; back issues avail.) **Indexed:** Biol.Abstr., C.I.J.E., C.I.N.L., Dent.Ind., Ind.Med. **Document type:** academic/scholarly publication.
—BLDSC (4927.150000); Faxon; UMI; UnCover.
Description: Publishes scholarly papers, reports and findings related to research and development in allied health education, practice, history and current trends.
Refereed Serial

JOURNAL OF AMERICAN HEALTH POLICY. see *MEDICAL SCIENCES*

JOURNAL OF CLINICAL EPIDEMIOLOGY; including pharmacoepidemiology reports; devoted to the problems and management of chronic illness in all age groups. see *MEDICAL SCIENCES*

JOURNAL OF COMMUNITY HEALTH; the publication for health promotion and disease prevention. see *MEDICAL SCIENCES*

JOURNAL OF ENVIRONMENTAL HEALTH. see *ENVIRONMENTAL STUDIES*

JOURNAL OF ENVIRONMENTAL PATHOLOGY, TOXICOLOGY AND ONCOLOGY. see *ENVIRONMENTAL STUDIES — Toxicology And Environmental Safety*

JOURNAL OF ENVIRONMENTAL SCIENCE AND HEALTH. PART A: ENVIRONMENTAL SCIENCE AND ENGINEERING. see *ENVIRONMENTAL STUDIES*

JOURNAL OF ENVIRONMENTAL SCIENCE AND HEALTH. PART B: PESTICIDES, FOOD CONTAMINANTS, AND AGRICULTURAL WASTES. see *ENVIRONMENTAL STUDIES*

JOURNAL OF EPIDEMIOLOGY & COMMUNITY HEALTH. see *MEDICAL SCIENCES*

613   **US**   **ISSN 0362-028X**
SF221   **CODEN: JFPRDR**
JOURNAL OF FOOD PROTECTION. 1937. m. $135. International Association of Milk, Food and Environmental Sanitarians, Inc., 6200 Aurora Ave., Ste. 200 W, Des Moines, IA 50322. TEL 515-276-3344. FAX 515-276-8655. Ed. Lloyd Bullerman. adv.; bk.rev.; charts; illus.; index. circ. 3,500. (also avail. in microform from UMI,PMC; reprint service avail. from UMI) **Indexed:** Apic.Abstr., Biol.Abstr., Biol.& Agr.Ind., Chem.Abstr., Curr.Adv.Ecol.Sci., Curr.Cont., Curr.Pack.Abstr., Dairy Sci.Abstr., Excerp.Med., Food Sci.& Tech.Abstr., Ind.Sci.Rev., Ind.Vet., Int.Packag.Abstr., Maize Abstr., Microbiol.Abstr., Nutr.Abstr., Packag.Sci.Tech., Pig News & Info., Poult.Abstr., Rev.Med.& Vet.Mycol., Rev.Plant Path., Rice Abstr., Risk Abstr., Sci.Cit.Ind., Soils & Fert., Triticale Abstr., Vet.Bull., Weed Abstr.
—BLDSC (4984.550000); CASDDS; Faxon; Genuine Article; SWETS; UMI; UnCover.
Formerly (until 1977): Journal of Milk and Food Technology (ISSN 0022-2747)
Refereed Serial

JOURNAL OF GENDER, CULTURE AND HEALTH. see *MEDICAL SCIENCES*

JOURNAL OF HEALTH AND HUMAN SERVICES ADMINISTRATION. see *HOSPITALS*

JOURNAL OF HEALTH & SOCIAL POLICY. see *SOCIAL SERVICES AND WELFARE*

614   **NE**   **ISSN 0167-6296**
JOURNAL OF HEALTH ECONOMICS. (Text in English) 1982. bi-m. fl.765($466) (effective 1996). North-Holland (Subsidiary of: Elsevier Science B.V.), P.O. Box 211, 1000 AE Amsterdam, Netherlands. TEL 31-20-4853911. FAX 31-20-4853598. TELEX 18582 ESPA NL. (Subscr. in U.S. and Canada to: Elsevier Science Inc., Box 882, Madison Sq. Sta., New York, NY 10159. TEL 212-989-5800. FAX 212-633-3990) Ed. Joseph P. Newhouse. adv.; bk.rev. (also avail. in microform from UMI; back issues avail.; reprint service avail. from SWZ) **Indexed:** ABI Inform., Abstr.Health Care Manage.Stud., Abstr.Hyg., ASSIA, C.R.E.J., Excerp.Med., J.of Econ.Lit., Med.Care Rev., Sage Fam.Stud.Abstr., Sage Pub.Admin.Abstr., SSCI. **Document type:** academic/scholarly publication.
—BLDSC (4996.750000); Faxon; Genuine Article; SWETS; UMI; UnCover. **CCC.**
Description: Publishes articles related to the economics of health and medical care.
Refereed Serial

614.8 360   **US**   **ISSN 0092-8623**
JOURNAL OF MENTAL HEALTH ADMINISTRATION. 1972. q. $56 to individuals; institutions $110 (effective Sep. 1995). (Association of Mental Health Administrators) Sage Publications, Inc., 2455 Teller Rd., Thousand Oaks, CA 91320. TEL 805-499-0721. FAX 805-499-0871. E-mail: libraries@sagepub.com. (Overseas subscr. to: Sage Publications Ltd., 6 Bonhill St., London EC2A 4PU, England; Sage Publications India Pvt. Ltd., Box 4215, New Delhi, India) Ed. Bruce Lubotsky Levin. adv. contact: Merlin Hellner. bk.rev.; charts; illus.; stat.; index. circ. 2,000. (also avail. in microfilm from UMI; back issues avail.; reprint service avail.) **Indexed:** ABI Inform., Abstr.Health Care Manage.Stud., Excerp.Med. (1993-), Hosp.Lit.Ind., Human Resour.Abstr., P.A.I.S., PSI, Psychol.Abstr. (1986-), Sage Fam.Stud.Abstr., Sage Pub.Admin.Abstr., Sociol.Abstr., SOPODA. **Document type:** academic/scholarly publication.
—BLDSC (5017.685000); EMDOCS; UMI; UnCover. **CCC.**
Description: Publishes original research on the organization, financing and delivery of mental health services and substance abuse treatment services.
Refereed Serial

628   **US**   **ISSN 0884-0946**
JOURNAL OF NATURAL HYGIENE; the science and philosophy of natural hygiene. 1985. bi-m. $19 (Canada $20; elsewhere $30). Natural Hygiene, Inc., Box 2132, Huntington, CT 06484. TEL 203-929-1557. Ed. Jo Willard. adv.; bk.rev.; abstr.; circ. 3,200 (paid). (back issues avail.)
Description: Covers the laws of nature and provides information on ways of maintaining or regaining health.

JOURNAL OF PESTICIDE REFORM. see *ENVIRONMENTAL STUDIES*

JOURNAL OF PHARMACOEPIDEMIOLOGY; innovations in research and practice. see *PHARMACY AND PHARMACOLOGY*

613   **IT**   **ISSN 1121-2233**
   CODEN: GIMPAP
JOURNAL OF PREVENTATIVE MEDICINE AND HYGIENE. (Text in English) 1969. q. L.70000($90) (effective Jan. 1993). (Universita degli Studi di Genova, Istituto di Igiene) Medical Systems S.p.A., Via Rio Torbido, 40, 16165 Genova, Italy. TEL 010-83401. FAX 010-804661. TELEX 270310 IDEAL I. Ed. Dr. Sergio Rassu. adv.; charts; stat. **Indexed:** Abstr.Hyg., Biol.Abstr., C.I.S. Abstr., Chem.Abstr., Curr.Adv.Ecol.Sci., Dairy Sci.Abstr., Excerp.Med., Food Sci.& Tech.Abstr., Ind.Med., INIS Atomind., Trop.Dis.Bull.
—CASDDS.
Formerly (until 1978): Giornale di Igiene e Medicina Preventiva (ISSN 0017-0313)
Description: Includes research and studies conducted in the fields of hygiene and preventive medicine.

JOURNAL OF PUBLIC HEALTH DENTISTRY. see *MEDICAL SCIENCES — Dentistry*

362.1 658 368.382   **US**
▼**JOURNAL OF PUBLIC HEALTH MANAGEMENT.** 1995. q. $189 to institutions. Aspen Publishers, Inc., 200 Orchard Ridge Dr., Gaithersburg, MD 20873. TEL 301-417-7500. FAX 301-417-7550. **Document type:** academic/scholarly publication.
Description: Addresses public health administration and profiles local programs and initiatives.
Refereed Serial

JOURNAL OF PUBLIC HEALTH MEDICINE. see *SOCIAL SERVICES AND WELFARE*

614.8 178 658   **US**   **ISSN 0197-5897**
RA421   **CODEN: JPPODK**
JOURNAL OF PUBLIC HEALTH POLICY. 1980. q. $120 (foreign $120) (effective 1993). Journal of Public Health Policy, Inc., 208 Meadowood Dr., South Burlington, VT 05403. TEL 802-658-0136. FAX 802-862-4011. Ed. Dr. Milton Terris. adv.; bk.rev. circ. 1,800. (back issues avail.) **Indexed:** Abstr.Health Care Manage.Stud., Curr.Cont., Diar.Dis.Res., Dok.Arbeitsmed., Environ.Abstr., Environ.Per.Bibl. (1991-), Excerp.Med., Ind.Med., P.A.I.S., Sociol.Abstr. **Document type:** academic/scholarly publication.
—BLDSC (5043.570000); CIS; Faxon; SWETS; UnCover.
Refereed Serial

JOURNAL OF RURAL HEALTH. see *MEDICAL SCIENCES*

613   **US**   **ISSN 0022-4391**
LB3401   **CODEN: JSHEA2**
JOURNAL OF SCHOOL HEALTH. 1930. m. (Aug.-May). $85 to individuals; institutions $100 (effective 1996). American School Health Association, Box 708, Kent, OH 44240. TEL 216-678-1601. FAX 216-678-4526. Ed. R. Morgan Pigg, Jr. adv. contact: Rick Gabler. bk.rev.; abstr.; bibl.; charts; stat.; index, cum.index every 10 yrs. circ. 10,000. (also avail. in microform from UMI; reprint service avail. from UMI) **Indexed:** Acad.Ind., Adol.Ment.Hlth.Abstr., Biog.Ind., Biol.Abstr., C.I.J.E., C.I.N.L., Cont.Pg.Educ., Curr.Cont., Curr.Lit.Fam.Plan., Dent.Ind., Diar.Dis.Res., Educ.Ind., Except.Child.Educ.Abstr., Hlth.Ind., IMFL, Ind.Med., Int.Nurs.Ind., Mult.Ed.Abstr., Nurs.Abstr., Phys.Ed.Ind., Psychol.Abstr., Res.High.Educ.Abstr., Risk Abstr., Sp.Ed.Needs Abstr., Sportsearch (1976-), SSCI, Stud.Wom.Abstr., Tech.Educ.Abstr. **Document type:** academic/scholarly publication.
●Also available online. Vendor(s): University Microfilms International.
—BLDSC (5052.650000); Faxon; Genuine Article; SWETS; UMI; UnCover.
Formerly: School Physicians Bulletin.
Refereed Serial

JOURNAL OF SUDDEN INFANT DEATH SYNDROME AND INFANT MORTALITY. see *MEDICAL SCIENCES — Pediatrics*

JOURNAL OF TOXICOLOGY AND ENVIRONMENTAL HEALTH. see *ENVIRONMENTAL STUDIES — Toxicology And Environmental Safety*

JOURNAL OF TRAFFIC SAFETY EDUCATION. see *TRANSPORTATION — Automobiles*

JOURNAL OF TROPICAL MEDICINE. see *MEDICAL SCIENCES — Communicable Diseases*

JOURNAL OF VECTOR ECOLOGY. see *BIOLOGY — Entomology*

JUGENDROTKREUZ. see *CHILDREN AND YOUTH — For*

KANKYO EISEI/ENVIRONMENTAL SANITATION. see *ENVIRONMENTAL STUDIES*

KEEPING THE TRUST. see *SOCIAL SERVICES AND WELFARE*

613   JA   ISSN 0022-9938
KENKO KYOIKU/PUBLIC HEALTH EDUCATION. (Text in Japanese) 1956. q. free. Kawai Pharmaceutical Co., Ltd. - Kawai Seiyaku K.K., 2-51-8 Arai, Nakano-ku, Tokyo 165, Japan. FAX 03-3385-3118. Ed. Dr. T. Shimizu. bibl. circ. 20,000. (processed)

KEY STATISTICAL INDICATORS FOR HEALTH IN WALES/DANGOSYDDION YSTADEGOL ALLWEDDOL AR GYFER LECHYD YNG NGHYMRU. see *PUBLIC HEALTH AND SAFETY — Abstracting, Bibliographies, Statistics*

KIDSAFE. see *CHILDREN AND YOUTH — About*

KOKORO TO SHAKAI/MIND AND SOCIETY. see *PSYCHOLOGY*

614.8   JA
KOKUTETSU CHUO HOKEN KANRIJOHO; health control. (Text and summaries in English, Japanese) 1955. a. free. Japanese National Railways, Central Health Institute, 2-1 Yoyogi, Shibuyaku, Tokyo 151, Japan. circ. 1,000. (back issues avail.)

614   KO   ISSN 0023-401X
RA421   CODEN: KOPOAL
KOREAN JOURNAL OF PUBLIC HEALTH/BO KUN HAK NON ZIP. Key Title: Gonjun Bogen Jabji. (Text in English and Korean) 1964. s-a. free. Seoul National University, School of Public Health, 28 Yunkun-dong, Chongro-ku, Seoul, S. Korea. TEL 02-762-9101. Ed. Moonshik Zong. circ. 1,000. Indexed: Biol.Abstr.
    Description: Contains research articles on public health and population.

628   JA   ISSN 0368-5187
KOSHU EISEI/JOURNAL OF PUBLIC HEALTH PRACTICE. (Text in Japanese) 1946. m. 21240 Yen($163) Igaku-Shoin Ltd., 5-24-3 Hongo, Bunkyo-ku, Tokyo 113-91, Japan. TEL 03-3817-5718. Ed. Shunichi Araki. circ. 3,500.

614 697   JA   ISSN 0386-4081
KUKI CHOWA EISEI KOGAKU/HEATING, AIR-CONDITIONING AND SANITARY ENGINEERING. (Text in Japanese; summaries in English, Japanese) 1917. m. $218. Kuki Chowa Eisei Kogakkai - Society of Heating, Air-Conditioning and Sanitary Engineering of Japan, 8-1, Kitashinjuku 1-chome, Shinjuku-ku, Tokyo 160, Japan. (Dist by: Intercontinental Marketing Corp., I.P.O. Box 5056, Tokyo 100-30, Japan. TEL 81-3-3661-7458. FAX 81-3-3667-9646)
    —BLDSC (5120.600000).

614   IS
KUPAT-HOLIM. INFORMATION SERIES AND SPECIAL STUDIES AND SURVEYS ON MEDICAL MANPOWER SOCIOLOGY AND MEDICAL ECONOMICS. (Summaries in English) 1962. q. (Kupat-Holim Health Insurance Institution, Research Department) Kupat Holim Center, P.O. Box 16250, Tel Aviv, Israel. TEL 972-3-6923532. FAX 972-3-433474. Ed. Dr. Nelu Shavitt. bk.rev.; stat. circ. 150. (processed) **Document type:** academic/scholarly publication.
    Former titles: Kupat Holim. Information Series: Special Studies on Medical Manpower and Sociology; Kupat-Holim. Information Series: Special Studies and Surveys on Medical Sociology and Health Economics; (until 1973): Kupat-Holim. Information Series. "Meida" on Medical Sociology and Health.

614   IS   ISSN 0301-4843
         CODEN: SFYBAI
KUPAT-HOLIM YEARBOOK. (Editions in English and Hebrew) 1971. a. free. Kupat Holim, Health Insurance Institution of Histadrut, 101 Arlosoroff St., Tel Aviv, Israel. Indexed: Biol.Abstr., Chem.Abstr.
    —CASDDS.

614   JA   ISSN 0454-7675
TA495   CODEN: DPKBAN
KYOTO UNIVERSITY. DISASTER PREVENTION RESEARCH INSTITUTE. BULLETIN/KYOTO DAIGAKU BOSAI KENKYUJO KIYO. (Text in English) 1951. q. exchange basis. Kyoto University, Disaster Prevention Research Institute - Kyoto Daigaku Bosai Kenkyujo, Gokasho, Uji 611, Japan. Ed.Bd. circ. 650. Indexed: GeoRef, J.of Ferroc. **Document type:** bulletin.
    —BLDSC (2488.000000); UnCover.

L S T NYT. see *FOOD AND FOOD INDUSTRIES*

614.83   US   ISSN 0277-9196
LAURISTON S. TAYLOR LECTURE SERIES. 1977. a. $20 (effective Dec. 1995). National Council on Radiation Protection and Measurements, 7910 Woodmont Ave., Ste. 800, Bethesda, MD 20814. TEL 301-657-2652. Ed. W. Roger Ney. (back issues avail.)

LEAD DETECTION AND ABATEMENT CONTRACTOR. see *ENVIRONMENTAL STUDIES*

LEAD POISONING REPORT. see *ENVIRONMENTAL STUDIES*

614   LB
LIBERIA. MINISTRY OF HEALTH AND SOCIAL WELFARE. ANNUAL REPORT.* a., latest 1975. Ministry of Health and Social Welfare, Monrovia, Liberia.

614.8   CN   ISSN 0714-5896
LIVING SAFETY. French edition: Famille Avertie. 1983. q. Can.$7.95. Canada Safety Council, 1020 Thomas Spratt Pl., Ottawa, ON K1G 5L5, Canada. TEL 613-739-1535. FAX 613-739-1566. Ed. Jack A. Smith. circ. 100,000 (80,000 English edition; 20,000 French edition). **Document type:** consumer publication.

614 352   US
LOCAL HEALTH OFFICERS NEWS. bi-m. $35. U.S. Conference of Mayors, Office of Public Affairs, 1620 Eye St., N.W., Washington, DC 20006. TEL 202-293-7330. **Document type:** newsletter.
    Description: Offers mayors and municipal health officials updates on policy, legislation, meetings, and other items of interest.

614   UK
LONDON MONITOR. irreg. £7. King's Fund, 14 Palace Ct., London W2 4HT, England. Ed. Sean Boyle. **Document type:** bulletin.

614.86   US   ISSN 0741-4439
LOUISIANA. DEPARTMENT OF PUBLIC SAFETY. SUMMARY OF MOTOR VEHICLE TRAFFIC ACCIDENTS. KENNER. 1971. s-a. free. Department of Public Safety, Traffic Records Unit, Box 66614, Baton Rouge, LA 70896. TEL 504-925-6348. charts; stat. circ. 350. (also avail. in microfilm; microfiche from CIS) Indexed: SRI. **Document type:** government publication.
    Supersedes in part: Louisiana. Department of Public Safety. Summary of Motor Vehicle Accident Reports.

614.86   US   ISSN 0741-434X
LOUISIANA. DEPARTMENT OF PUBLIC SAFETY. SUMMARY OF MOTOR VEHICLE TRAFFIC ACCIDENTS. RURAL. 1981. s-a. free. Department of Public Safety, Traffic Records Unit, Box 66614, Baton Rouge, LA 70896. TEL 504-925-6348. Indexed: SRI. **Document type:** government publication.
    Supersedes in part: Louisiana Department of Public Safety. Summary of Motor Vehicle Accident Reports.

614.86   US   ISSN 0741-4382
LOUISIANA. DEPARTMENT OF PUBLIC SAFETY. SUMMARY OF MOTOR VEHICLE TRAFFIC ACCIDENTS. SHREVEPORT. s-a. free. Department of Public Safety, Traffic Records Unit, Box 66614, Baton Rouge, LA 70896. TEL 504-925-6348. Indexed: SRI. **Document type:** government publication.
    Supersedes in part: Louisiana. Department of Public Safety. Summary of Motor Vehicle Accident Reports.

614.86   US   ISSN 0741-4358
LOUISIANA. DEPARTMENT OF PUBLIC SAFETY. SUMMARY OF MOTOR VEHICLE TRAFFIC ACCIDENTS. STATEWIDE. s-a. free. Department of Public Safety, Traffic Records Unit, Box 666614, Baton Rouge, LA 70896. TEL 504-925-6348. **Document type:** government publication.
    Supersedes in part: Louisiana. Department of Public Safety. Summary Motor Vehicle Accident Reports.

362.1   ZA
LUSAKA. MEDICAL OFFICER OF HEALTH. ANNUAL REPORT. 1966. a. free. Health and Welfare Department, Medical Officer of Health, Public Health Department, Box 789, Lusaka, Zambia. stat. circ. 300.

M E - TIDNINGEN. see *BUILDING AND CONSTRUCTION*

352.3   US
M F D REGISTER. (Milwaukee Fire Department) 1961. m. $10. Milwaukee Fire Department Athletic Association, 711 W. Wells St., Milwaukee, WI 53233. TEL 414-276-5656. Ed. Carl W. Klitzke. circ. controlled.
    Description: News, articles, and announcements on issues of interest to the Milwaukee Fire Department, its retirees and affiliated organizations.

M S CANADA. (Multiple Sclerosis Society of Canada) see *MEDICAL SCIENCES — Allergology And Immunology*

MAISONS D'ENFANTS ET D'ADOLESCENTS DE FRANCE. ALBUM-ANNUAIRE NATIONAL; publication documentaire illustree des establissements de vacances, de repos, de soins, de cure et de prevention pour enfants et adolescents. see *CHILDREN AND YOUTH — About*

613   IR
MAJALLE-YE BEHDASHT-E JAHAN. Persian translation of: World Health (UN ISSN 0043-8502) 1974. q. $5. Iranian Public Health Association, Box 1310, Teheran, Iran. Ed. Iran Roboubi.

613   NE   ISSN 0920-8216
MAJOR HEALTH ISSUES. (Text in English) 1987. irreg., vol.2, 1987. price varies. Elsevier Science B.V., Books Division, P.O. Box 211, 1000 AE Amsterdam, Netherlands. TEL 31-20-4853911. FAX 31-20-4853705. TELEX 18582 ESPA NL. E-mail: nlinfo-f@elsevier.nl; usinfo-f@elsevier.com; forinfo-kyf04035@niftyserve.or.jp; Site addr.: http://www.elsevier.nl/. (Subscr. in U.S. and Canada to: Elsevier Science Inc., Box 882, Madison Sq. Sta., New York, NY 10159. TEL 212-989-5800) (back issues avail.) **Document type:** monographic series. *Refereed Serial*

MASS CYCLIST. see *SPORTS AND GAMES — Bicycles And Motorcycles*

614.8   US   ISSN 1058-0778
MASTER CROSS REFERENCE LIST, PART 1. Short title: M C R L - 1. q. $2500 for 1600 bpi in US, Canada, Mexico; elsewhere $5000. (Department of Defense, Defense Logistics Services) U.S. National Technical Information Service, 5825 Port Royal Rd., Springfield, VA 22161. TEL 703-487-4630. (magnetic tape)
    Description: Master list of logistics reference numbers cross-referenced to their applicable national stock number(s) in the federal catalog system.

614.8   US   ISSN 1058-0786
MASTER CROSS REFERENCE LIST, PART 2. Short title: M C R L - 2. q. $2200 for 1600 bpi in U.S., Canada, Mexico; elsewhere $4400. (Department of Defense, Defense Logistics Services) U.S. National Technical Information Service, 5825 Port Royal Rd., Springfield, VA 22161. TEL 703-487-4630. (magnetic tape)
    Description: Master list of national stock number(s) cross-referenced to their applicable logistics reference number(s) in the federal catalog system.

PUBLIC HEALTH AND SAFETY

614.8 US ISSN 1058-0794
MASTER CROSS REFERENCE LIST, PART 3. Short title: M C R L - 3. q. $2000 for 1600 bpi in U.S., Canada, Mexico; elsewhere $4000. (Department of Defense, Defense Logistics Services) U.S. National Technical Information Service, 5825 Port Royal Rd., Springfield, VA 22161. TEL 703-487-4630. (magnetic tape)
Description: Master list of manufacturers codes cross-referenced to their applicable logistics reference number(s) in the federal catalog system.

614 MF
MAURITIUS. MINISTRY OF HEALTH. ANNUAL REPORT. (Text in English) a. Government Printing Office, Elizabeth II Ave., Port Louis, Mauritius.

MEDECINS DES HOPITAUX PUBLICS. see *MEDICAL SCIENCES*

MEDICAL ADMINISTRATION EXECUTIVE. see *MEDICAL SCIENCES*

614.8 US
MEDICAL AND RADIOLOGICAL DEVICES GUIDANCE MANUAL. (Subseries of: Compliance Program Guidance Manuals) irreg. $140 in the U.S., Canada, Mexico; elsewhere $280. U.S. Food and Drug Administration, Office of Public Affairs, 5600 Fisher's Ln., Rockville, MD 20857. TEL 301-443-3220. (Orders to: National Technical Information Service, 5285 Port Royal Rd., Springfield, VA 22161. TEL 703-487-4650. FAX 703-321-8547) **Document type:** government publication.
Description: Provides the latest information on and helps maintain program plans and instructions directed to F.D.A. field operations. These plans and instructions are surveillance or compliance oriented and provide the needed direction from headquarters offices and bureaus in accomplishing F.D.A. regulatory obligations.

MEDICAL CARE. see *MEDICAL SCIENCES*

614.8 619 US
MEDICAL DEVICE ESTABLISHMENT REGISTRATION MASTER FILE. q. $360 in the U.S., Canada, Mexico; elsewhere $720. U.S. Food and Drug Administration, Office of Public Affairs, 5600 Fisher's Ln., Rockville, MD 20857. TEL 301-443-3220. (Subscr. to: National Technical Information Service, 5285 Port Royal Rd., Springfield, VA 22161. TEL 703-487-4630. FAX 703-321-8547) (magnetic tape) **Document type:** government publication.
Description: Contains information required to be submitted by owner-operators of medical device establishments in accordance with Section 510 of the Federal Food, Drug, and Cosmetics Act.

614.8 619 US
MEDICAL DEVICE PROBLEMS REPORT FROM THE D E N: REPORTS FROM MEDICAL DEVICE USERS. (Device Experience Network) m. $225 in the U.S., Canada, Mexico; elsewhere $450. U.S. Food and Drug Administration, Office of Public Affairs, 5600 Fisher's Ln., Rockville, MD 20857. TEL 301-443-3220. (Subscr. to: National Technical Information Service, 5285 Port Royal Rd., Springfield, VA 22161. TEL 703-487-4630. FAX 703-321-8547) **Document type:** government publication.
Description: Reports are arranged by specific medical specialty such as anaesthesia, cardiovascular or by general health areas. Each report is divided into six parts: accession number, date of report, product name, manufacturer name, serial number, and report narrative.

614.8 619 US
MEDICAL DEVICE REPORTING FROM THE D E N: REPORTS FROM MEDICAL DEVICE MANUFACTURERS. (Device Experience Network) m. $450 in the U.S., Canada, Mexico; elsewhere $900. U.S. Food and Drug Administration, Office of Public Affairs, 5600 Fisher's Ln., Rockville, MD 20857. TEL 301-443-3220. (Subscr. to: National Technical Information Service, 5285 Port Royal Rd., Springfield, VA 22161. TEL 703-487-4630. FAX 703-321-8547) **Document type:** government publication.
Description: Arranged by specific medical specialty such as anaesthesia, cardio-vascular or general health areas such as general hospital. Each report is divided into six parts: accession number, date of report, product name, manufacturer name, serial number, and report narrative.

614.8 GW ISSN 0724-8172
CODEN: MEFOET
MEDICAL FOCUS; international trade journal for medical, laboratory and hospital supplies. (Editions in Chinese and English) 1983. q. DM.70($46) Beta Verlag GmbH, Postfach 140121, 53056 Bonn, Germany. TEL 0228-252061. FAX 0228-252067. TELEX 8869536-BETA-D. Ed. Gerlinde Pape. adv.: B&W page DM.6400; trim 270 x 190; adv. contact: Una Hecker. circ. 24,714 (controlled). **Document type:** academic/scholarly publication.
—CCC.

MEDIKAMENT & MEINUNG; Zeitschrift fuer Arzneimittel- und Gesundheitswesen. see *MEDICAL SCIENCES*

MENSEN OP STRAAT. see *TRANSPORTATION — Roads And Traffic*

614 US
MENTAL HEALTH DIRECTORY. 1971. quinquennial. $24. U.S. Substance Abuse and Mental Health Services Administration, Center for Mental Health Services, 5600 Fishers Ln., Rockville, MD 20857. TEL 301-443-2792. (Subscr. to: Superintendent of Documents, U.S. Government Printing Office, New Orders, Box 371954, Pittsburgh, PA 15250-7954. TEL 202-512-1800. FAX 202-512-2250; Or: Bernan, 4611-F Assembly Dr., Lanham, MD 20706. TEL 301-459-7666. FAX 301-459-0056) Ed. Ronald W. Manderscheid. **Document type:** directory, government publication.

MENTAL HEALTH IN AUSTRALIA. see *MEDICAL SCIENCES — Psychiatry And Neurology*

MENTAL HEALTH MATTERS. see *PSYCHOLOGY*

MENTAL HEALTH STATISTICS FOR ILLINOIS. see *SOCIAL SERVICES AND WELFARE*

614 AU ISSN 0026-010X
MERKUR MAGAZIN FUER VOLKSGESUNDHEIT. 1958. q. free. Merkur Wechselseitige Versicherungsanstalt, Neutorgasse 57, A-8010 Graz, Austria. adv.; charts; illus.; mkt.; stat. circ. 200,000. (tabloid format)

614.8 US ISSN 0275-6595
CODEN: MIWNE3
MICROWAVE NEWS. 1981. bi-m. $285 (foreign $315). Box 1799, Grand Central Sta., New York, NY 10163. TEL 212-517-2800. Ed. Louis Slesin. adv.; bk.rev. (back issues avail.) **Document type:** newsletter.
—BLDSC (5761.220800); CASDDS. CCC.

614 UK ISSN 0309-2003
MIDDLE EAST HEALTH. 1977. 10/yr. £60. P D S Ltd., 71 Luaderdale Tower, The Barbican, London EC2Y 8YB, England. TEL 071-920-0723. Ed. David Powell. adv. circ. 5,875. **Document type:** trade publication.
—BLDSC (5761.375800).
Incorporates (from 1986): Middle East Dentistry; **Formerly:** Middle East Health Supply and Services.

THE MILBANK QUARTERLY. see *POLITICAL SCIENCE*

614 363.7 SW ISSN 1100-9535
MILJOEMEDICIN/ENVIRONMENTAL MEDICINE. 1987. 4/yr. free. Institutet foer Miljoemedicin (IMM) - Institute of Environmental Medicine, P.O. Box 210, S-171 77 Stockholm, Sweden. TEL 46-8-728-64-00. FAX 46-8-33-69-81. **Document type:** newsletter.

MISSOURI. DIVISION OF HIGHWAY SAFETY (YEAR). HIGHWAY SAFETY PLAN. see *TRANSPORTATION — Roads And Traffic*

MITIGATION AND ADAPTATION STRATEGIES FOR GLOBAL CHANGE; an international journal devoted to scientific, engineering, socio-economic and policy responses to global environmental change. see *ENVIRONMENTAL STUDIES*

614 JA ISSN 0917-3331
CODEN: MEKNEH
MIYAZAKIKEN EISEI KANKYO KENKYUJO NENPO/MIYAZAKI PREFECTURAL INSTITUTE FOR PUBLIC HEALTH AND ENVIRONMENT. ANNUAL REPORT. (Text in Japanese; summaries in English) 1991. a. Miyazakiken Eisei Kankyo Kenkyujo, 3-2, Gakuen Kibanadai Nishi 2-chome, Miyazaki-shi, Miyazaki-ken 889-21, Japan. TEL 0985-58-0930. FAX 0985-58-1410.
—BLDSC (1355.370000); CASDDS.
Formed by the merger of: Miyazakiken Kogai Senta Nenpo & Miyazakiken Eisei Kenkyujoho.

614.8 GW ISSN 0544-7119
MODERNE UNFALLVERHUETUNG. 1956. a. DM.38. Vulkan-Verlag GmbH, Postfach 103962, 45039 Essen, Germany. TEL 0201-82002-0. FAX 0201-82002-40. adv.; bk.rev. circ. 3,500. (back issues avail.) **Document type:** trade publication.
—BLDSC (5900.090000).

MONATSBERICHT ANGEZEIGTER FLUGUNFAELLE. see *TRANSPORTATION — Air Transport*

614.4 574 US ISSN 0740-0845
CODEN: MEBIEP
MONOGRAPHS IN EPIDEMIOLOGY AND BIOSTATISTICS. 1981. irreg. price varies. Oxford University Press, 200 Madison Ave., New York, NY 10016. TEL 212-679-7300. **Document type:** monographic series.
—BLDSC (5915.431000).
Refereed Serial

614.8 US
MONTHLY IMPORT DETENTION LIST. m. $350 in the U.S., Canada, Mexico; elsewhere $700. U.S. Food and Drug Administration, Office of Public Affairs, 5600 Fisher's Ln., Rockville, MD 20857. TEL 301-443-3220. (Subscr. to: National Technical Information Service, 5285 Port Royal Rd., Springfield, VA 22161. TEL 703-487-4630. FAX 703-321-8547) (also avail. in microfiche from CIS; reprint service avail. from CIS) **Indexed:** Amer.Stat.Ind. (1976-). **Document type:** government publication.
Description: Detentions are arranged by: product code, sample number, the product, district and port of entry, manufacturer's and shipper's names, city and country of origin, the primary and secondary reasons for detention, unit type and quantity, and value.

MONTHLY PRESCRIBING REFERENCE. see *MEDICAL SCIENCES*

614 UY
MORBILIDAD. irreg. Ministerio de Salud Publica, Departamento de Estadistica, Montevideo, Uruguay. stat.

614 UK ISSN 1357-6275
▼**MORTALITY.** Announced for publication in 1996. 3/yr. £32 to individuals; institutions £88 (effective 1996). Carfax Publishing Co., P.O. Box 25, Abingdon, Oxon. OX14 3UE, England. TEL 44-1235-555335. FAX 44-1235-553559. (N. American subscr. to: Carfax Publishing Co., 875-81 Massachusetts Ave., Cambridge, MA 02139) **Document type:** academic/scholarly publication.

614.862 US ISSN 0191-488X
TL242
MOTOR VEHICLE SAFETY; a report on activities under the National Traffic and Motor Vehicle Safety Act of 1966. 1966. a. U.S. National Highway Traffic Safety Administration, 400 Seventh St., N.W., Washington, DC 20590. (Prepared with: U.S. Federal Highway Administration) **Document type:** government publication.

628 GW ISSN 0027-2957
CODEN: MUABD8
MUELL UND ABFALL; Fachzeitschrift fuer Behandlung und Beseitigung von Abfaellen. 1969. m. DM.196.80 (students DM.148.80). Erich Schmidt Verlag GmbH & Co. (Berlin), Genthiner Str. 30G, 10785 Berlin, Germany. TEL 030-2500850. FAX 030-25008521. Ed. M. Ferber. adv.; bk.rev. **Indexed:** Chem.Abstr., Repindex. **Document type:** trade publication.
—BLDSC (5982.650000); CASDDS; SWETS. CCC.
Description: Emphasis is on sanitary engineering.

N A C A NEWS. (National Animal Control Association) see *PETS*

PUBLIC HEALTH AND SAFETY

614.84 UK
N A F O MAGAZINE. 1975. q. membership. National Association of Fire Officers, Hayes Court, W. Common Rd., Bromley, Kent BR2 7AU, England. circ. 5,000.

614 UK
N A H A T FINANCIAL SURVEY. a. National Association of Health Authorities and Trusts, Birmingham Research Park, Vincent Dr., Birmingham B15 2SQ, England. TEL 0121-471-4444. FAX 0121-414-1120. **Document type:** corporate report.
Formerly: N A H A T Healthcare Economic Review.

614 UK ISSN 0962-4791
N A H A T NETWORK. 1990. q. £20. National Association of Health Authorities and Trusts, Birmingham Research Park, Vincent Dr., Birmingham B15 2SQ, England. TEL 0121-471-4444. FAX 0121-414-1120. Ed. Chris Vellonoweth. **Document type:** newsletter.

614 UK
N A H A T SAFETY NET. q. £15. National Association of Health Authorities and Trusts, Birmingham Research Park, Vincent Dr., Birmingham B15 2SQ, England. TEL 0121-471-4444. FAX 0121-414-1120. Ed. Chris Vellenoweth. **Document type:** newsletter.

614 US
N A H S E'S RESUME.* 1972. q. $5. National Association of Health Services Executives, 8630 Fenton St., Ste. 328, Silver Spring, MD 20910-3803. adv.; bk.rev.; stat. circ. 1,500. (back issues avail.)

N A T O ADVANCED SCIENCE INSTITUTES SERIES D: BEHAVIOURAL AND SOCIAL SCIENCES. (North Atlantic Treaty Organization) see *SOCIAL SCIENCES: COMPREHENSIVE WORKS*

THE N A WAY MAGAZINE. (Narcotics Anonymous) see *DRUG ABUSE AND ALCOHOLISM*

614.8 US ISSN 0890-3417
N C A H F NEWSLETTER. quality in the health marketplace. 1977. bi-m. $15 (libraries $18). National Council Against Health Fraud, Inc., Box 1276, Loma Linda, CA 92354. TEL 909-824-4690. FAX 909-824-4838. Ed. William T. Jarvis. bk.rev.; index; circ. 2,000 (paid). (looseleaf format; also avail. in microform from UMI; back issues avail.) Indexed: Hlth.Ind. **Document type:** newsletter.
—UMI.
Description: Contains contributions from health professionals, educators, researchers and attorneys who actively oppose misinformation, fraud and quackery.

614.8 US ISSN 1063-9918
N C C E M BULLETIN. 1983. m. $85. National Coordinating Council on Emergency Management, 7297 Lee Highway, Ste. N, Falls Church, VA 22042. TEL 703-533-7672. FAX 703-241-5603. Ed. Shari Coffin. adv. circ. 1,500. **Document type:** bulletin.
Formerly: N C C E M's Official Monthly Newsletter.

614.83 US
N C R P COMMENTARY. 1980. irreg., no.7, 1991. price varies. National Council on Radiation Protection and Measurements, 7910 Woodmont Ave., Ste. 800, Bethesda, MD 20814. TEL 301-657-2652. Ed. W. Roger Ney.

614.839 621.48 US
N C R P NEWS. 1966. irreg. free to qualified personnel. National Council on Radiation Protection and Measurements, 7910 Woodmont Ave., Ste. 800, Bethesda, MD 20814. TEL 301-657-2652. Ed. W. Roger Ney. circ. controlled.

614.8 355.23 US ISSN 0083-209X
CODEN: NCRDBG
N C R P REPORT. 1931. irreg., no.116, 1993. price varies. National Council on Radiation Protection and Measurements, 7910 Woodmont Ave., Ste. 800, Bethesda, MD 20814. TEL 301-657-2652. Ed. W. Roger Ney. Indexed: Biol.Abstr., Energy Info.Abstr., Environ.Abstr., Excerp.Med., GeoRef.
—BLDSC (6067.817100); EMDOCS.

614.83 US
N C R P SYMPOSIUM PROCEEDINGS. 1982. irreg. $30. National Council on Radiation Protection and Measurements, 7910 Woodmont Ave., Ste. 800, Bethesda, MD 20814. TEL 301-657-2652. Ed. W. Roger Ney. **Document type:** proceedings.

614.8 US
N E I S S DATA HIGHLIGHTS. (National Electronic Injury Surveillance System) 1973. a. free. (U.S. Consumer Product Safety Commission) National Injury Information Clearinghouse, 5401 Westbard Ave., Rm.625, Washington, DC 20207. TEL 301-504-0424. FAX 301-504-0124. charts; index. circ. 3,000. **Document type:** government publication.
Formerly: N E I S S News (ISSN 0364-6475)

614 UK
N H S HEALTH ADVISORY SERVICE. ANNUAL REPORT OF THE DIRECTOR. a. £14.95. National Health Service, Health Advisory Service, Sutherland House, 29-37 Brighton Rd., Sutton, Surrey. (Subscr. to: H.M.S.O. Publications Centre, P.O. Box 276, London SW8 5DT, England. TEL 0171-873-9090. FAX 0171-873-8200) **Document type:** government publication, corporate report.
Formerly: N H S Health Advisory Service. Annual Report.

614 UK ISSN 1354-2362
N H S NEWS. m. National Health Service, Executive Communications Unit, Quarry House, Rm. 8E39, Quarry Hill, Leeds LS2 7UE, England. TEL 0532-546217. Ed. Geoff Wilson. **Document type:** bulletin.
Formerly (until 1994): N H S Management Executive News (ISSN 0963-5688)

N I P H ANNALS. (National Institute for Public Health) see *MEDICAL SCIENCES — Communicable Diseases*

614.8 374 JA ISSN 0287-9549
NARA JOSHI DAIGAKU HOKEN KANRI SENTA NENPO/NARA WOMEN'S UNIVERSITY. HEALTH ADMINISTRATION CENTER. ARCHIVES OF HEALTH CARE. (Text in Japanese; table of contents in English) 1978. a. Nara Joshi Daigaku, Hoken Kanri Senta - Nara Women's University, Health Administration Center, Kita-Uoya-Higashi-cho, Nara-shi 630, Japan. Ed. Kimihiro Yamamoto. charts. circ. 500. **Document type:** academic/scholarly publication.
Formerly (until 1983): Nara Joshi Daigaku Hoken Kanri Senta Kiyo (ISSN 0286-505X)

614.8 II
NATIONAL CONFERENCE ON SAFETY. PROCEEDINGS. 1970. a. Rs.10. National Safety Council, Central Labour Institute Bldg., Sion, Bombay 22, India. Ed. A.A. Krishnan. charts. circ. 2,000. **Document type:** proceedings.

614.83 355.23 US ISSN 0195-7740
CODEN: PNRME9
NATIONAL COUNCIL ON RADIATION PROTECTION AND MEASUREMENTS. PROCEEDINGS OF THE ANNUAL MEETING. 15th, 1979. a. price varies. National Council on Radiation Protection and Measurements, 7910 Woodmont Ave., Ste. 800, Bethesda, MD 20814. TEL 301-657-2652. **Document type:** proceedings.
—CASDDS.

NATIONAL DIRECTORY OF SAFETY CONSULTANTS. see *ENGINEERING*

614.8 US ISSN 0896-6923
NATIONAL HEALTH CARE EXPENDITURES STUDY. DATA PREVIEW. 1980. irreg. free. U.S. Department of Health and Human Services, National Center for Health Services Research, Research and Health Care Technology Assessment, 5600 Fishers Ln., 18A55, Rockville, MD 20857. Ed. Daniel C. Walden. circ. 6,500.

595.7 371.7 US
NATIONAL PEDICULOSIS ASSOCIATION. PROGRESS. 1984. q. $60 (effective 1992). National Pediculosis Association, Box 149, Newton, MA 02161. TEL 617-449-6487. FAX 617-449-8129. Eds. Deborah L. Altschuler, Linda Menditto. film rev.; bibl.; illus. (back issues avail.) **Document type:** newsletter.
Description: Newsletter reporting on health and prevention issues concerning head lice in schoolchildren.

614.8 SA ISSN 0028-0097
NATIONAL SAFETY/NASIONALE VEILIGHEID; and occupational hygiene - en Beroepshigiene. (Text mainly in English; occasionally in Afrikaans) 1938. bi-m. R.25 (foreign R.35) (effective 1995). Safety First Association, 7 Pitcairn Rd., Blairgowrie, Johannesburg 2194, South Africa. TEL 27-11-7827698. (Subscr. to: P.O. Box 400, Pinegowrie, Transvaal 2123, South Africa) Ed. Debbie Myer. adv.; bk.rev.; illus.; stat.; tr.lit.; circ. 3,200 (controlled). Indexed: C.I.S. Abstr. **Document type:** trade publication.
—BLDSC (6032.640000).
Description: Aims to prevent accidents by promoting an awareness of accident situations as they exist in day-to-day living among members of the community.

371 US ISSN 0270-4234
RE1
NATIONAL SOCIETY TO PREVENT BLINDNESS. ANNUAL REPORT. Key Title: Annual Report - National Society to Prevent Blindness. a. National Society to Prevent Blindness, 500 E. Remington Rd., Schaumburg, IL 60173. TEL 708-843-2020. FAX 708-843-8458.
Formerly: National Society for the Prevention of Blindness. Report.

362.4 614 US
NATIONAL SOCIETY TO PREVENT BLINDNESS. MEMBER NEWS. 1951. 4/yr. $25 membership. National Society to Prevent Blindness, 500 E. Remington Rd., Schaumburg, IL 60173. TEL 708-843-2020. FAX 708-843-8458. illus. circ. 25,000. (tabloid format) **Document type:** newsletter.
Former titles: Insight (Schaumburg); Prevent Blindness News (ISSN 0032-8014); Incorporates: Wise Owl News (ISSN 0043-6755)

614 US ISSN 0028-0496
RA421
THE NATION'S HEALTH. 1911. 11/yr. $15 to non-members (foreign $18) (effective 1995). American Public Health Association, 1015 15th St., N.W., Washington, DC 20005. TEL 202-789-5600. FAX 202-789-5661. Ed. Kathryn Foxhall. adv.; bk.rev.; charts; illus. circ. 35,000. (tabloid format; also avail. in microform from UMI; reprint service avail. from UMI) Indexed: Biol.Dig., Curr.Adv.Ecol.Sci., Hlth.Ind., Med.Care Rev., Rehabil.Lit., Telegen.
—UMI. CCC.
Supersedes in part (in 1971): American Journal of Public Health and the Nation's Health (ISSN 0002-9572); Which was formed by the 1927 merger of: American Journal of Public Health (ISSN 0271-4353); Nation's Health (ISSN 0028-0496).
Description: Covers public health policy, including legislative and other federal action.

614.88 NE ISSN 0925-6040
NEDERLANDS TIJDSCHRIFT VOOR E H B O EN REDDINGWEZEN. 1912. 6/yr. fl.35 (effective 1995). (Koninklijke Nationale Bond voor Reddingwezen en Eerste Hulp bij Ongelukken "Het Oranje Kruis") S M D Educatieve Uitgevers, P.O. Box 63, 2300 AB Leiden, Netherlands. FAX 31-71-323340. Ed.Bd. adv.: B&W page fl.645. bk.rev.; bibl.; charts; illus. circ. 5,700.
—SWETS.
Formerly: Reddingwezen (ISSN 0034-2114)

NEEDLE TIPS. see *MEDICAL SCIENCES — Allergology And Immunology*

614.05 NE
NETHERLANDS. RIJKSINSTITUUT VOOR DE VOLKSGEZONDHEID. MEDEDELINGEN. irreg. Ryksinstituut voor Volksgezondheid en Milieuhygiene - National Institute of Public Health and Environmental Protection, Bilthoven, Netherlands. FAX 30-742971. TELEX 47215 RIVBH NL. illus.

614 CN ISSN 0838-3693
RA450.N5
NEW BRUNSWICK. DEPARTMENT OF HEALTH AND COMMUNITY SERVICES. ANNUAL REPORT. (Text in English and French) 1918. a. free. Department of Health and Community Services, Box 5100, Fredericton, NB E3B 5G8, Canada. TEL 506-453-2536. FAX 506-453-3983. Ed. Gerald Weseen. stat. circ. 700. **Document type:** government publication.
Formerly: New Brunswick. Department of Health. Annual Report.

NEW JERSEY STATE FIRE CODE. see *FIRE PREVENTION*

PUBLIC HEALTH AND SAFETY

NEW SOLUTIONS; a journal of environmental and occupational health policy. see OCCUPATIONAL HEALTH AND SAFETY

NEW SOUTH WALES. DEPARTMENT OF INDUSTRIAL RELATIONS AND TECHNOLOGY. SAFETY. see BUSINESS AND ECONOMICS — Labor And Industrial Relations

614 US
NEW YORK (CITY). HEALTH SYSTEMS AGENCY. PERSPECTIVES. 1969. bi-m. free. Health Systems Agency of New York City, 275 7th Ave., 27th Fl., New York, NY 10001. TEL 212-741-8880. FAX 212-741-8305. Ed. Giri Vuppala. circ. 5,000. **Document type**: newsletter, government publication.
Former titles: New York (City). Health Systems Agency. Quarterly Bulletin; (until 1985): F Y I (New York); (until 1977): Health Planning.
Description: Provides information on New York City health care system, including medical services, primary, secondary and long term care, medical facilities planning, home health care, and substance abuse.

614 US
NEW YORK (STATE). HEALTH PLANNING COMMISSION. ADMINISTRATIVE PROGRAM FOR HEALTH PLANNING AND DEVELOPMENT. a. Health Planning Commission, Empire State Plaza, Tower Bldg. Rm. 1683, Albany, NY 12237.

353.9 US ISSN 0361-4018
RA981.N7
NEW YORK (STATE). MEDICAL CARE FACILITIES FINANCE AGENCY. ANNUAL REPORT. Key Title: Annual Report - New York State Medical Care Facilities Finance Agency. 1974. a. Medical Care Facilities Finance Agency, 641 Lexington Ave., New York, NY 10022. TEL 212-688-4000. charts; illus. **Document type**: government publication.

614 US ISSN 1077-1344
▼**NEW YORK HEALTH LAW UPDATE**. 1994. m. $177. (DeForest & Duer) M. Lee Smith Publishers & Printers LLC, 162 Fourth Ave., N., Box 198867, Nashville, TN 37219-8867. TEL 615-242-7395; 800-274-6774. FAX 615-256-6601. Ed.Bd; Pub. M. Lee Smith. **Document type**: newsletter.
Formerly (until 1994): New York Health Law Alert (ISSN 1073-0443)
Description: Reports state-specific new public health laws that affect companies in New York.

614 310 NZ
NEW ZEALAND. HEALTH STATISTICAL SERVICES. CLIENT SERVICES NEWSLETTER. m. Health Statistical Services, P.O. Box 5013, Wellington, New Zealand. TEL 04-496-2049. FAX 04-496-2050. **Document type**: newsletter.

614 NZ ISSN 0112-0212
NEW ZEALAND JOURNAL OF ENVIRONMENTAL HEALTH. 1952. q. membership. (New Zealand Institute of Environmental Health) Percival Publishing Co. Ltd., P.O. Box 52-024, Kingsland, Auckland, New Zealand. Ed. Rodney Giddnes. adv.; bk.rev.; charts; illus. circ. 750.
—CCC.
Former titles: New Zealand Environmental Health Inspector (ISSN 0110-4969); New Zealand Sanitarian (ISSN 0048-0142)

614 JA ISSN 0546-1766
CODEN: NKEZA4
NIHON KOSHU EISEI ZASSHI/JAPANESE JOURNAL OF PUBLIC HEALTH. (Text in Japanese; summaries in English, Japanese) 1954. m. 1000 Yen per no. Nihon Koshu Eisei Gakkai - Japanese Society of Public Health, 29-8, Shinjuku 1-chome, Shinjuku-ku, Tokyo 160, Japan. TEL 03-3352-4281. FAX 03-3352-4605. adv. **Indexed**: Chem.Abstr., INIS Atomind., Jap.Per.Ind.
—BLDSC (4658.400000); CASDDS; UnCover.

NIPPON NOYAKU GAKKAISHI. see ENGINEERING — Chemical Engineering

NON-SMOKERS' UPDATE. see POLITICAL SCIENCE — Civil Rights

NORSK V V S. see HEATING, PLUMBING AND REFRIGERATION

NORWAY. DIREKTORATET FOR BRANN OG EKSPLOSJONSVERN. AARSBERETNING. see FIRE PREVENTION

NUCLEAR LEMONS; an assessment of America's worst commercial nuclear reactors. see ENERGY — Nuclear Energy

NUCLEAR PLANT JOURNAL. see ENERGY — Nuclear Energy

NUCLEAR REACTOR SAFETY. see ENERGY — Nuclear Energy

614 UK
NUFFIELD INSTITUTE FOR HEALTH. WORKING PAPERS. irreg. University of Leeds, Nuffield Institute for Health, 71-75 Clarendon Rd., Leeds LS2 9PL, England. TEL 0532-459034. **Document type**: academic/scholarly publication.

O S L A NEWSLETTER. (Ontario Association of Speech - Language Pathologists and Audiologists) see EDUCATION — Special Education And Rehabilitation

614.8 US ISSN 0146-3632
OCCUPATIONAL SAFETY AND HEALTH SERIES (NEW YORK). 1976. irreg., vol.25, 1994. price varies. Marcel Dekker, Inc., 270 Madison Ave., New York, NY 10016. TEL 212-696-9000. FAX 212-658-4540. TELEX 421419.
—BLDSC (6231.150000). CCC.
Refereed Serial

614 UN ISSN 0030-0632
CODEN: BOSPA8
OFICINA SANITARIA PANAMERICANA. BOLETIN. (Text in Portuguese or Spanish; summaries in English) 1922. 12/yr. (in 2 vols.). $28. Pan American Health Organization, Pan American Sanitary Bureau, Regional Office of the World Health Organization, 525 23rd St., N.W., Washington, DC 20037. TEL 202-293-8130. FAX 202-338-0869. bk.rev.; abstr.; bibl.; illus.; index. circ. 16,500. (also avail. in microfiche from CIS; back issues avail.) **Indexed**: Abstr.Hyg., Biodet.Abstr., Biol.Abstr., Chem.Abstr., Curr.Adv.Ecol.Sci., Dairy Sci.Abstr., Dent.Ind., Geo.Abstr., IDA, IIS, Ind.Med., Ind.Vet., INIS Atomind., Nutr.Abstr., Protozool.Abstr., Repindex, Rev.Med.& Vet.Mycol., Rural Devel.Abstr., Trop.Dis.Bull., Vet.Bull., World Bibl.Soc.Sec.
—BLDSC (2186.000000); Faxon; SWETS.

OKLAHOMA. DEPARTMENT OF HEALTH. MONTHLY VITAL STATISTICS REPORT. see POPULATION STUDIES

614.8 BE ISSN 0771-2588
OPERATIE VEILIGHEID. French edition: Objectif Prevention (ISSN 0771-2634) 1964. m. (10/yr.). 880 BEF (effective 1994). Nationale Vereniging tot Voorkoming van Arbeidsongevallen (NVVA), Gachardstraat, 88, bus 4, B-1050 Brussels, Belgium. TEL 32-2-6480337. FAX 32-2-6486867. Ed. B. Schoenmaekers. adv.; bk.rev.; illus. circ. 27,000.

OPHTHALMIC EPIDEMIOLOGY. see MEDICAL SCIENCES — Ophthalmology And Optometry

613.9 US ISSN 0737-3732
OUTLOOK (SEATTLE); drug regulation and reproductive health. (Editions in Chinese, English, Portuguese, Russian, Spanish) 1983. q. $20 (free to developing countries). Program for Appropriate Technology in Health, 4 Nickerson St., Seattle, WA 98109. TEL 206-285-3500. FAX 206-285-6619. TELEX 4740049 PATH UI. E-mail: dlachman@path.org. Ed. Jacqueline Sherris. circ. 25,000 (5,000 each language ed.). (back issues avail.)
—BLDSC (6314.495000).

OVERVIEW (OLYMPIA). see SOCIAL SERVICES AND WELFARE

P H L S LIBRARY BULLETIN. (Public Health Laboratory Service) see MEDICAL SCIENCES — Communicable Diseases

P H L S MICROBIOLOGY DIGEST. (Public Health Laboratory Service) see MEDICAL SCIENCES — Communicable Diseases

614.8 327 US
P S R MONITOR. 1984. q. membership. Physicians for Social Responsibility, 1101 14th St., N.W., Ste. 700, Washington, DC 20005-5601. TEL 202-898-0150. Ed. Meg Duskin. circ. 5,000. **Document type**: monographic series.
Description: Covers health dangers of nuclear arms testing and social and environmental costs of nuclear arms race. Recommends legislative action.

614.8 US ISSN 0894-6264
P S R REPORTS. 1979. 4/yr. membership. Physicians for Social Responsibility, 1101 14th St., N.W., Ste. 700, Washington, DC 20005-5601. TEL 202-898-0150. Ed. Meg Duskin. adv.; bk.rev. circ. 25,000. **Document type**: newsletter.
Formerly: P S R Newsletter.
Description: Articles on the health and environmental impact of nuclear war, the nuclear arms race and military spending.

614 PK ISSN 0030-9834
PAKISTAN JOURNAL OF HEALTH. 1951. q. Rs.100. College of Community Medicine, 6 Birdwood Rd., Lahore, Pakistan. TEL 92-42-7583945. FAX 92-42-7586395. Ed. Dr. I.A. Naveed. adv.; bk.rev.; charts; illus.; stat.; circ. 1,000 (paid). **Indexed**: Biol.Abstr., Chem.Abstr., ExtraMED. **Document type**: academic/scholarly publication.
●Also available on CD-ROM.

614 UN ISSN 0085-4638
RA10
PAN AMERICAN HEALTH ORGANIZATION. BULLETIN. 1967. q. $26. Pan American Health Organization, Pan American Sanitary Bureau, Regional Office of the World Health Organization, 525 23rd St., N.W., Washington, DC 20037. TEL 202-293-8129. FAX 202-338-0869. bk.rev.; abstr.; charts; stat.; index. circ. 6,000. (also avail. in microfiche from CIS; back issues avail.) **Indexed**: Abstr.Health Care Manage.Stud., Biol.Abstr., Curr.Adv.Ecol.Sci., Diar.Dis.Res., Environ.Abstr., Excerp.Med., Helminthol.Abstr, IIS, Ind.Med., Ind.Vet., INIS Atomind., NRN, Nutr.Abstr., Protozool.Abstr., Repindex, Rev.Appl.Entomol., Rev.Med.& Vet.Mycol., Trop.Dis.Bull., Vet.Bull. **Document type**: bulletin.
—EMDOCS; SWETS; UnCover.

614 IE ISSN 0738-3991
R727.3
PATIENT EDUCATION AND COUNSELING; an interdisciplinary journal for patient education researchers and managers. 1978. 9/yr. I£351($555) (effective 1996). Elsevier Science Ireland Ltd., P.O. Box 85, Limerick, Ireland. TEL 353-61-471944. FAX 353-61-472144. (Subscr. in U.S. and Canada to: Elsevier Science Inc., Box 882, Madison Sq. Sta., New York, NY 10159. TEL 212-989-5800. FAX 212-633-3990) Eds. C. Herbert, A. Visser. **Indexed**: Abstr.Health Care Manage.Stud., Behav.Med.Abstr., CINAHL, Cont.Pg.Educ., Curr.Cont., Educ.Tech.Abstr., Excerp.Med., FAMLI, Hosp.Lit.Ind., I.P.A., Ind.Med., Int.Nurs.Ind., Psychol.Abstr. (1985-), Res.High.Educ.Abstr., SSCI. **Document type**: academic/scholarly publication.
●Also available online.
—BLDSC (6412.864600); Faxon; Genuine Article; SWETS; UnCover. CCC.
Formerly (until vol.5, 1983): Patient Counselling and Health (ISSN 0190-2040); Incorporates (as of 1986): Patient Education Reports; Which was formerly titled: Patient Education Newsletter.
Description: For patient education researchers, managers, clinicians, and others involved in patient education and counseling services and administration.
Refereed Serial

614 US
PENNSYLVANIA CHAMBER OF BUSINESS AND INDUSTRY. CHECKLIST.* m. $165 to non-members; members $115. Pennsylvania Chamber of Business and Industry, 417 Walnut St., Harrisburg, PA 17101. TEL 800-326-3252. FAX 717-255-3298.
Description: Provides updates on legislative, regulatory and legal activities affecting environmental policy matters.

614 635 US ISSN 1067-4276
PEOPLE PLANT CONNECTION. 1973. m. free to members. American Horticultural Therapy Association, 362A Christopher Ave., Gaithersburg, MD 20879-3660. TEL 301-948-3010. FAX 301-869-2397. Ed. Steven H. Davis. circ. 1,000. **Document type**: newsletter.
Description: Designed to further the aims of A.H.T.A. by reviewing and communicating developments in the field of horticultural therapy. Aimed at medical professionals and interested individuals.

PERSIAN GULF REVIEW; information for veterans who served in Desert Storm. see MILITARY

PUBLIC HEALTH AND SAFETY

628 SP ISSN 0188-0012
PERSPECTIVAS EN SALUD PUBLICA. (Text in English, Spanish) 1987. irreg. Instituto Nacional de Salud Publica, Ave. Universidad 665, Col. Santa Maria Ahuacatitlan, C.P. 62508, Cuernavaca, Morelos, Mexico. TEL 13-17-89. FAX 13-88-90. circ. 2,000.

PERSPECTIVE (CLEVELAND). see *SOCIAL SERVICES AND WELFARE*

PERU. POLICIA NACIONAL. REVISTA DE LA SANIDAD. see *MEDICAL SCIENCES*

614.8 628.96
PESTICIDE ANALYTICAL MANUAL. irreg. $274 (foreign $548). U.S. Food and Drug Administration, Office of Public Affairs, 5600 Fisher's Ln., Rockville, MD 20857. TEL 301-443-3220. (Subscr. to: National Technical Information Service, 5285 Port Royal Rd., Springfield, VA 22161. TEL 703-487-4650. FAX 703-321-8547) **Document type:** government publication.

614 UN ISSN 0587-5943
PESTICIDE RESIDUES IN FOOD. 1966. 3/yr. price varies. Food and Agriculture Organization of the United Nations, c/o UNIPUB, 4611-F Assembly Dr., Lanham, MD 20706-4391. TEL 301-459-7666. FAX 301-459-0056. **Document type:** monographic series.
 Formerly: Codex Committee on Pesticide Residues. Report on the Meeting.

PHARMACY HEALTH-LINE. see *PHARMACY AND PHARMACOLOGY*

614 PH ISSN 0048-380X
PHILIPPINE JOURNAL OF MENTAL HEALTH. (Text in English and Filipino) 1970-1980. s-a. P.24($3.50) Philippine Mental Health Association, Box 40, 18 East Ave., Quezon City, Philippines. Ed. Diwata Goce-Minimo. adv.; bibl.; illus.; stat. circ. 1,000. **Indexed:** Psychol.Abstr. **Document type:** newsletter.

POLITEKNIKA WROCLAWSKA. INSTYTUT INZYNIERII OCHRONY SRODOWISKA. PRACE NAUKOWE. MONOGRAFIE. see *ENVIRONMENTAL STUDIES*

POLLUTION TECHNOLOGY REVIEW. see *ENVIRONMENTAL STUDIES — Pollution*

POLSKA AKADEMIA NAUK. KOMITET GOSPODARKI WODNEJ. PRACE I STUDIA. see *WATER RESOURCES*

362.1 US ISSN 1075-5705
RC607.A26
▼**POZ.** 1994. bi-m. $19.95 to individuals; institutions $79.95. Box 1965, Danbury, CT 06813. (back issues avail.) **Document type:** consumer publication.
 Description: Addresses the human medical and social concerns of persons affected with H.I.V. and their families. Profiles well-known persons whose lives have been touched by the tragedy and covers court trials, films, and benefits dealing with AIDS.

PRAKTIKAN. see *MEDICAL SCIENCES — Dentistry*

648 363.72 NO ISSN 0805-0368
PRAKTISK SANITAERTEKNIKK. 1993. 4/yr. Skarland Press A-S, P.O. Box 5042 Maj., N-0301 Oslo 3, Norway. TEL 47-22-60-13-90.
FAX 47-22-60-13-90. Ed. Jan Bache-Wiig. **Document type:** bulletin.

PREHOSPITAL AND DISASTER MEDICINE; an international journal. see *MEDICAL SCIENCES*

614.8 SP ISSN 0034-8732
PREVENCION. 1962. q. membership. Asociacion para la Prevencion de Accidentes, Echaide 4, 2 Piso, 20005 San Sebastian, Spain. TEL 43-42-56-45.
FAX 43-42-91-32. Ed. Ramon Zamanillo Tellitu. adv.; bk.rev. circ. 6,326. **Indexed:** C.I.S. Abstr.
 Formerly (until 1975): Revista de Prevencion (ISSN 1132-3140)

614.44 610 UK ISSN 0300-2659
RA421
PREVENT; the journal for all who would prevent disease. 1973. bi-m. £5. Fitzken Publishers, 3 Alma Square, London NW8 6QD, England. Ed. Dr. J. McMurdoch. bibl.; illus.

614.8 FR ISSN 0032-8022
PREVENTION ROUTIERE. 1957. m. 5 F.($2) Chancerel Editions, 4 rue Aumont- Thieville, 75017 Paris, France. adv.; illus.; stat.; tr.lit. circ. 290,181.

614.8 FR ISSN 0032-8030
PREVENTION ROUTIERE DANS L'ENTREPRISE.* vol. 18, 1970. bi-m. 105 F. 32 rue Alexandre Dumas, 75543 Paris Cedex 11, France. TEL 43-67-03-62. FAX 43-67-28-43. Ed. Monique Anquetil. adv.; charts; illus. circ. 52,000.

PREVENTIVE MEDICINE; an international journal devoted to practice and theory. see *MEDICAL SCIENCES*

628 SP ISSN 0213-6457
PREVISION SANITARIA NACIONAL. 12/yr. Villanueva 11, 28001 Madrid, Spain. TEL 1-435-51-18.
FAX 1-575-50-97. Ed. M. Duque Garcia. circ. 137,686.

PREVOYANCE. see *OCCUPATIONAL HEALTH AND SAFETY*

614 NE ISSN 0926-9827
PRIMARY HEALTH CARE PUBLICATIONS. (Text in English) 1990. irreg., vol.2, 1990. price varies. (Vrije Universiteit Amsterdam) V U Boekhandel-Uitgeverij B.V., De Boelelaan 1105, 1081 HV Amsterdam, Netherlands.
TEL 31-20-6444355. FAX 31-20-6462719. **Document type:** monographic series.
—BLDSC (6612.908980).

354 614 CN
PRINCE EDWARD ISLAND. DEPARTMENT OF HEALTH AND SOCIAL SERVICES. ANNUAL REPORT. a. Department of Health and Social Services, Box 2000, Charlottetown, P.E.I. C1A 7N8, Canada. TEL 902-368-4900. FAX 902-368-4969. Ed. George Mason. circ. 300. **Document type:** government publication.
 Formerly: Prince Edward Island. Department of Health. Annual Report (ISSN 0317-4530)

614 US
PRIORITIES: FOR LONG LIFE AND GOOD HEALTH. 1989. q. $25. American Council on Science and Health, 1995 Broadway, 2nd Fl., New York, NY 10023-5560. TEL 212-362-7044.
FAX 212-362-4919. Ed. Dr. Elizabeth Whelan. adv. circ. 7,000. (reprint service avail.)
 Formerly: A C S H News and Views.
 Description: Consumer education magazine concerned with issues related to food nutrition, chemicals, pharmaceuticals, lifestyles, the environment and health.

614 RU ISSN 0869-866X
PROBLEMY SOTSIALNOI GIGIENY I ISTORIYA MEDITSINY. (Text in Russian; summaries in English) 1942. bi-m. $64. (Ministerstvo Zdravookhraneniya) Izdatel'stvo Meditsina, Petroverigskii pereulok 6-8, 101000 Moscow, Russia. Ed. O.P. Shchepin. adv. contact: T.D. Scheglova. bk.rev.; abstr.; bibl.; charts; illus.; stat.; index. (microform) **Indexed:** Abstr.Hyg., Biol.Abstr., C.I.S. Abstr., Chem.Abstr., Curr.Dig.Sov.Press, Dent.Ind., Ind.Med., Trop.Dis.Bull., World Bibl.Soc.Sec.
 Formerly (until 1994): Sovetskoe Zdravookhranenie (ISSN 0038-5239)
 Description: Discusses theoretical problems of social hygiene and public health organization, the main trends in the development of the socialist system of health protection, scientific bases of planning, prognosticating and management in public health service.

643 US ISSN 0092-7732
KF3945.A73
PRODUCT SAFETY & LIABILITY REPORTER; a weekly review of consumer safety developments. 1973. w. $1031 (effective July 1995). The Bureau of National Affairs, Inc., 1231 25th St., N.W., Washington, DC 20037. TEL 202-452-4200.
FAX 202-822-8092. TELEX 285656 BNAI WSH. (Subscr. to: 9435 Key West Ave., Rockville, MD 20850. TEL 800-372-1033) Ed. Gary A. Weinstein. index. (looseleaf format; back issues avail.)
—CCC.
 Description: Notification and reference service providing coverage of current administrative, legislative, judicial, and industry developments relating to product safety and product liability.

600 US ISSN 0098-7530
PRODUCT SAFETY LETTER. 1972. w. $797. Washington Business Information, Inc., c/o Karen Harrington, 1117 N. 19th St., Ste. 200, Arlington, VA 22209. TEL 703-247-3434. FAX 703-247-3421. Ed. Nick Wakeman. bk.rev.; charts; index. (looseleaf format) **Document type:** newsletter.
●Also available online. Vendor(s): NewsNet (GB52).
—CCC.
 Description: Contains information for executives concerned with government regulation of consumer products

614 US
TN119.R6 CODEN: CHMJBP
PRODUCT SAFETY NEWS. 1973. m. $120. Institute for Product Safety, Box 1931, Durham, NC 27702. TEL 919-489-2356. FAX 919-490-4954. Ed. Verne L. Roberts. bk.rev.; abstr.; charts; illus.; stat.; cum.index: 1973-1990. circ. 350. (looseleaf format; back issues avail.)

658.56 US ISSN 0091-8954
TS175
PRODUCT SAFETY UP TO DATE. 1973. bi-m. $19 to non-members; members $15. National Safety Council, Periodicals Department, 1121 Spring Lake Dr., Itasca, IL 60143. TEL 708-775-2281. Ed. Kathleen Henderson; Pub. Kevin H. Axe. illus. circ. 11,000. **Document type:** newsletter.

628 US
PROFESSIONAL SANITARIAN. irreg. (1-2/yr.). National Society of Professional Sanitarians, 1224 Hoffman Dr., Jefferson City, MO 65101.

900 US
PROGRESS (COLUMBUS). 1984. 5/yr. free to qualified personnel. Department of Health, Box 118, Columbus, OH 43215. TEL 614-462-8562. charts; illus. circ. 3,000.

618 613 CN ISSN 0715-4356
PROLIFE NEWS. 1971. m. Can.$16.50 (typically set in Feb.). Alliance Action, B1-90 Garry St., Winnipeg, MB R3C 4H1, Canada. TEL 204-943-5273.
FAX 204-943-9283. Ed. Mary Lamont. adv. contact: Ingrid Krueger. bk.rev.; cum.index: 1985-1993. (back issues avail.) **Document type:** newsletter.
 Description: Covers developments in the areas of abortion, infanticide, euthanasia from a pro-life perspective.

600 FR
PROMOTION ET EDUCATION; international journal of health education. (Text in English, French, Spanish) 1958. q. 205 F.($45) Union Internationale de Promotion de la Sante et d'Education pour la Sante - International Union of Health Promotion and Education, 15-21 rue de l'Ecole de Medecine, 75270 Paris Cedex 06, France. TEL 43-26-90-82. FAX 43-29-33-15. Ed. Anne W. Bunde-Birouste. adv.; bk.rev.; bibl.; charts; illus.; stat.; biennial index. circ. 4,000. (also avail. in microfilm from UMI; reprint service avail. from UMI) **Indexed:** Adol.Ment.Hlth.Abstr., Biol.Abstr., C.I.S. Abstr., Curr.Cont., Excerp.Med., FAMLI, NRN, SSCI, Trop.Dis.Bull.
—BLDSC (6925.172000); UMI; UnCover.
 Former titles: Hygie (ISSN 0751-7149); (until 1982): International Journal of Health Education (ISSN 0020-7306)
 Description: Presents theoretical research and practical papers on experiences, opinions and research leading to applications for health education internationally.

PROVIDERS; the journal of long term care. see *MEDICAL SCIENCES — Nurses And Nursing*

614.49 PL ISSN 0033-2100
PRZEGLAD EPIDEMIOLOGICZNY. (Text in Polish; summaries in English) 1947. q. $104 (effective 1995 & 1996). Panstwowy Zaklad Higieny - National Institute of Hygiene, Ul. Chocimska 24, 00-791 Warsaw, Poland. TEL 48-22-49-40-51. FAX 48-22-49-74-84. TELEX 81-67-12. (Dist. by: Ars Polona-Ruch, Krakowskie Przedmiescie 7, Warsaw, Poland) Ed. D. Naruszewicz - Lesiuk. adv.; bk.rev.; abstr.; charts; illus.; index, cum.index. circ. 1,080. **Indexed:** Abstr.Hyg., Biol.Abstr., Chem.Abstr., Dent.Ind., Dok.Arbeitsmed., Excerp.Med., Helminthol.Abstr., Ind.Med., Trop.Dis.Bull.
—BLDSC (6940.100000).
 Description: Discusses epidemiology, bacteriology, parasitology, pathology and clinical aspects of infectious diseases.

PUBLIC HEALTH AND SAFETY

614 — JA
PUBLIC CLEANSING SERVICES IN TOKYO/SEISO JIGYO GAIYO. (Text in English) 1965. a. exchange basis. Bureau of Public Cleansing - Tokyo-to Seiso-kyoku Somu-bu, 3-8-1 Marunouchi, Chiyoda-ku, Tokyo 100, Japan. Ed.Bd. circ. 500.

PUBLIC HEALTH. see *MEDICAL SCIENCES*

614 — UG
PUBLIC HEALTH AND HYGIENE.* vol.4, 1972. a. Public Health Inspectors' Association, Box 46, Kampala, Uganda. Ed. Wazarwahi Bwengye. adv.; bibl.; illus.

PUBLIC HEALTH LABORATORY SERVICE BOARD. BIENNIAL REPORT. see *MEDICAL SCIENCES — Communicable Diseases*

614 — US — ISSN 0079-7596
PUBLIC HEALTH MONOGRAPH.* no.3, 1951. irreg. U.S. Public Health Service, Dept. of Health Education and Welfare, Bethesda, MD 20014. TEL 301-444-6656.
Indexed: Biol.Abstr., Ind.Med.
Continues: Public Health Technical Monograph.

614 — UK — ISSN 0959-2946
PUBLIC HEALTH NEWS. 1989. m. £106($190) (effective 1996). CAB International, Wallingford, Oxon. OX10 8DE, England. TEL 01491-832111. FAX 01491-833508. TELEX 847964 COMAGG G. E-mail: cabi@cabi.org. (U.S. subscr. to: CAB International, 845 N. Park Ave., Tucson, AZ 85719. TEL 800-528-4241. FAX 520-621-3816) (back issues avail.) **Document type:** newsletter.

614 — US — ISSN 0090-2918
RA11 — CODEN: HSRPAT
PUBLIC HEALTH REPORTS; official journal of the U.S. Public Health Service. (Supplements avail.) 1878. bi-m. $14 (foreign $17.50). U.S. Public Health Service, Department of Health and Human Services, J.F.K. Federal Bldg., Rm. 1826, Boston, MA 02203. TEL 617-565-1442. FAX 617-565-4260. (Subscr. to: Superintendent of Documents, U.S. Government Printing Office, Box 371954, Pittsburgh, PA 15250-7954. TEL 202-512-1800. FAX 202-512-2250) Ed. Dr. Anthony Robbins. bibl.; charts; illus.; stat.; index. circ. 8,000. (also avail. in microform from UMI,PMC; microfiche from CIS; back issues avail.; reprint service avail. from CIS,UMI)
Indexed: Abstr.Health Care Manage.Stud., Abstr.Hyg., Acad.Ind., AIM, Amer.Stat.Ind. (1973-), Bibl.Dev.Med.& Child Neur., Biotech.Abstr., C.I.N.L., Chem.Abstr., Curr.Adv.Ecol.Sci., Curr.Cont., Dent.Abstr., Diar.Dis.Res., Dok.Arbeitsmed., Eng.Ind., Excerp.Med., Gen.Sci.Ind., Helminthol.Abstr., Hlth.Ind., Hosp.Lit.Ind., Ind.Hyg.Dig., Ind.Med., Ind.U.S.Gov.Per., Mid.East: Abstr.& Ind., Nutr.Abstr., P.A.I.S., Risk Abstr., Sci.Cit.Ind., Sel.Water Res.Abstr., Soc.Work Res.& Abstr., SSCI, W.R.C.Inf. **Document type:** government publication.
●Also available online. Vendor(s): Lexis-Nexis, University Microfilms International.
—BLDSC (6965.000000); EMDOCS; Faxon; Genuine Article; SWETS; UMI; UnCover.
Former titles (until 1974): Health Services Reports; (until 1972): H S M H A Health Reports; (until 1970): Public Health Reports (ISSN 0033-3549)
Description: Reports on research, activities in public health.

614 — IS — ISSN 0301-0422
CODEN: PBHRAM
PUBLIC HEALTH REVIEWS; an international quarterly. 1972. q. $130 (effective 1995). Technosdar Ltd., P.O. Box 31684, Tel Aviv 61316, Israel. TEL 972-3-5607418. FAX 972-3-5604932. TELEX 341667 RMYM. Ed. Sigmund Geller. adv.; bk.rev.; abstr.; bibl.; index, cum.index. **Indexed:** Biol.Abstr., C.I.N.L., Curr.Adv.Ecol.Sci., Curr.Cont., Energy Ind., Energy Info.Abstr., Excerp.Med., Hosp.Lit.Ind., Ind.Med., SSCI. **Document type:** academic/scholarly publication.
—BLDSC (6966.300000); Faxon; Genuine Article; SWETS; UnCover.
Description: Presents reviews and critical evaluations of topics in public health, including epidemiology, environmental and occupational health. Publishes concise reports of research, surveys, long-term studies, and trends in morbidity and mortality. Also publishes proceedings and abstracts of conferences.
Refereed Serial

PUBLIC RISK. see *PUBLIC ADMINISTRATION*

628 — IT — ISSN 0393-1072
PULIZIA INDUSTRIALE E SANIFICAZIONE. 1968. m. L.100000. MO.ED.CO. s.r.l., Via Paolo da Cannobio 9, 20122 Milan, Italy. TEL 02-878577. FAX 02-89040728. adv. circ. 5,500.

QUALITY OF LIFE NEWS LETTER. see *MEDICAL SCIENCES*

R F L (Rundschau Fleischhygiene und Lebensmittelueberwachung) see *FOOD AND FOOD INDUSTRIES*

614 340 — GW — ISSN 0948-3209
▼ **R P G.** (Recht und Politik im Gesundheitswesen) 1995. q. DM.198($143) (effective 1996). Springer-Verlag, Heidelberger Platz 3, 14197 Berlin, Germany. TEL 030-8207-0. FAX 030-8214091. (Subscr. in N. America to: Springer-Verlag New York, Inc., 44 Hartz Way, Secaucus, NJ 07096-2491. TEL 201-348-4033. FAX 201-348-4505)

614 — UK — ISSN 0143-3377
R S P A BULLETIN. 1971. m. £20. Royal Society for the Prevention of Accidents, Cannon House, The Priory Queensway, Birmingham B4 6BS, England. TEL 021-200-2461. FAX 021-200-1254. Ed. Elizabeth Herbert. **Document type:** bulletin.
—BLDSC (8024.580000).
Formerly: Industrial Accident Prevention Bulletin.

R T E C S. (Registry of Toxic Effects of Chemical Substances) see *OCCUPATIONAL HEALTH AND SAFETY*

RADIATION PROTECTION DOSIMETRY. see *PHYSICS — Nuclear Physics*

RADIATION PROTECTION MANAGEMENT; the journal of applied health physics. see *OCCUPATIONAL HEALTH AND SAFETY*

LA RADIOACTIVITE DES PRINCIPALES SOURCES D'EAU MINERALE EN BELGIQUE. ETUDE. see *WATER RESOURCES*

RAUMPLANUNG UND UMWELTSCHUTZ IM KANTON ZURICH. see *HOUSING AND URBAN PLANNING*

614 — MG
RAVINTSARA. (Text in French; summaries in English, French) 2/yr. 54 F.($9) Centre d'Information et de Documention Scientifique et Technique, B.P. 6224, Antananarivo 101, Madagascar. TEL 33288.

614.8 — DK — ISSN 0108-254X
REDNINGSHISTORISK FORENINGS INFORMATION. 1976. bi-m. membership. Redningshistorisk Forening, Postbox 101, 2770 Kastrup, Denmark. Ed. Jacob Stoppel. adv.; bk.rev.; illus. circ. 300.
Formerly (until 1981): Redningshistorisk Forening. Information (ISSN 0108-2531)

614 — CK
REGISTRO DE ORGANISMOS DE SALUD. 1976. a. Departamento Administrativo Nacional de Estadistica, Banco Nacional de Datos, Apdo. Aereo 80043, Bogota, D.E., Colombia.

REGULATORY UPDATE; government regulations related to plastics industry. see *PLASTICS*

614 — US — ISSN 0275-0902
REGULATORY WATCHDOG SERVICE. 1975. w. $997 ($695 to subscribers of Washington Business Information newsletters). Washington Business Information, Inc., c/o Karen Harrington, 1117 N. 19th St., Ste. 200, Arlington, VA 22209. TEL 703-247-3434. FAX 703-247-3421. Ed. Nick Wakeman. bk.rev.; index. (looseleaf format) **Document type:** newsletter.
—CCC.
Former titles: Regulatory Safety Watchdog Service; Product Safety Watchdog Service (ISSN 0146-4639)
Description: Reports on government documents available from Congress, FDA, and other federal agencies.

RENT I DANMARK. see *BUSINESS AND ECONOMICS — Management*

614 — UN — ISSN 0085-5529
RA8
REPORT ON THE WORLD HEALTH SITUATION. Spanish edition: Informe sobre la Situacion Sanitaria Mundial (ISSN 1010-027X); French edition: Rapport sur la Situation Sanitaire dans le Monde (ISSN 1010-0296); Chinese edition: Shijie Weisheng Zhuang Kuang Baogao (ISSN 1010-030X); Russian edition: Obzor Sostojanija Zdravoohranenija v Mire (ISSN 1010-0288); Arabic edition: Taqrir 'an al-Hala al-Sihhiyyah fil-'Alam (ISSN 1010-0318) 1959. every 6 yrs. World Health Organization, Distribution and Sales, CH-1211 Geneva 27, Switzerland. TEL 41-22-791-2476. FAX 41-22-791-4857. TELEX 27821-OMS. circ. 6,200. **Document type:** monographic series.

616 551.48 — JA
REPORTS OF INVESTIGATIONS ABOUT LAKE BIWA. (Text in English) 1984. irreg. Shiga Prefectural Institute of Public Health and Environmental Science - Shiga Kenritsu Eisei Kankyo Senta, 13-45, Gotenhama, Otsu-shi, Shiga-ken 520, Japan.

616.89 150 — US — ISSN 0192-0812
RA790.A1
RESEARCH IN COMMUNITY AND MENTAL HEALTH; an annual compilation of research. 1979. a. $58.50 to institutions. J A I Press Inc., 55 Old Post Rd., No. 2, Box 1678, Greenwich, CT 06836-1678. TEL 203-661-7602. Ed. Roberta G. Simmons.
Indexed: Chic.Per.Ind., Psychol.Abstr.
—BLDSC (7736.700000); Faxon. CCC.

RESEARCH IN THE SOCIOLOGY OF HEALTH CARE; a research annual. see *MEDICAL SCIENCES*

614 — BE — ISSN 0773-7777
RESEAU AUTOMATIQUE BELGE DE LA POLLUTION ATMOSPHERIQUE. (Text in Dutch, French) 1978. a. $7. Instituut voor Hygiene en Epidemiologie (IHE), Juliette Wytsmanstraat 14, B-1050 Brussels, Belgium. Ed.Bd. circ. 250.

REVIEWS ON ENVIRONMENTAL HEALTH. see *ENVIRONMENTAL STUDIES*

614 — BL — ISSN 0100-0233
RA464.B33
REVISTA BAIANA DE SAUDE PUBLICA. (Text in Portuguese; summaries in English) 1974. q. exchange basis. Secretaria da Saude do Estado da Bahia, Centro Administrativo da Bahia 4a, Av. Plataforma 06, Caixa Postal 631, 40000 Salvador, Bahia, Brazil. TEL (071)370-4273. TELEX 7136. Ed.Bd. bibl.; charts; stat. circ. 1,000. **Indexed:** Abstr.Hyg.

614.4 — CU — ISSN 0253-1151
CODEN: RCHEDF
REVISTA CUBANA DE HIGIENE Y EPIDEMIOLOGIA. (Text in Spanish; summaries in English, French, Spanish) 1963. s-a. $30 in S. America; N. America $32; elsewhere $34. Ministerio de Salud Publica, Centro Nacional de Informacion de Ciencias Medicas, Calle E No. 452, e-19 y 21, Plaza de la Revolucion, Apdo. 6520, Havana, Cuba. TEL 809-32-5338. (Dist. by: Ediciones Cubanas, Obispo No. 527, Apdo. 605, Havana, Cuba) Ed. Haydee Alfonso. abstr.; bibl.; charts; illus.; index. circ. 1,400. **Indexed:** Abstr.Hyg., Biol.Abstr., Chem.Abstr., Dairy Sci.Abstr., Excerp.Med., Ind.Med., Repindex, Trop.Dis.Bull.
—CASDDS.
Formerly: Boletin de Higiene y Epidemiologia (ISSN 0006-629X)

614 — CU — ISSN 0864-3466
RA456.C7
REVISTA CUBANA DE SALUD PUBLICA. (Text in Spanish; summaries in English, Spanish) 1975. s-a. $26 in S. America; N. America $28; elsewhere $30. Ministerio de Salud Publica, Centro Nacional de Informacion de Ciencias Medicas, Calle E No. 452, e-19 y 21, Plaza de la Revolucion, Apdo. 6520, Havana, Cuba. TEL 809-32-5338. (Dist. by: Ediciones Cubanas, Obispo No. 527, Apdo. 605, Havana, Cuba) Ed. Maria Julia Zamorano. bibl.; charts; illus.; index. circ. 1,500. **Indexed:** Abstr.Hyg., Curr.Adv.Ecol.Sci., Ind.Med., Popul.Ind.
—BLDSC (7852.150000).
Formerly: Revista Cubana de Administracion de Salud (ISSN 0252-1903)
Description: Covers the field of social medicine and organization and administration of the Cuban health system.

REVISTA DE IGIENA, BACTERIOLOGIE, VIRUSOLOGIE, PARAZITOLOGIE, PNEUMOFTIZIOLOGIE. BACTERIOLOGIE, VIRUSOLOGIE, PARAZITOLOGIE, EPIDEMIOLOGIE. see BIOLOGY — Microbiology

614   SP
REVISTA ESPANOLA DE SALUD PUBLICA. (Text in Spanish; summaries in English) 1927. 6/yr. 2000 ptas. Ministerio de Sanidad y Consumo, Paseo del Prado 18-20, 28071 Madrid, Spain. TEL 34-3-5964175. FAX 34-3-5964195. Ed. Juan Jose Artells Herrero. bk.rev.; abstr.; bibl.; charts; illus. circ. 5,000. **Indexed:** Abstr.Hyg., Biol.Abstr., Chem.Abstr., Helminthol.Abstr., Ind.Med., Ind.Med.Esp., Protozool.Abstr., Rev.Appl.Entomol., Trop.Dis.Bull.
—BLDSC (7870.600000); Faxon.
    Formerly (until 1995): Revista de Sanidad e Higiene Publica (ISSN 0034-8899)

REVISTA INTERNACIONAL DEL TRABAJO. see BUSINESS AND ECONOMICS — Labor And Industrial Relations

614   MZ   ISSN 0254-5705
REVISTA MEDICA DE MOCAMBIQUE. 1982. 4/yr. $100. Ministerio da Saude, Instituto Nacional de Saude, Universidade Eduardo Mondlane, Faculdade de Medicina, C.P. 264, Maputo, Mozambique. TEL 427131. FAX 258-1-423-726. Eds. Dr. Rui Gama Vaz, Dr. Joao Schwalbach. adv. circ. 1,500. **Indexed:** ExtraMED. **Document type:** academic/scholarly publication.
●Also available on CD-ROM.
—BLDSC (7864.325000).

614   BL   ISSN 0104-1290
            CODEN: RSPUB9
REVISTA SAUDE E SOCIEDAD. (Text in English, Portuguese or Spanish; summaries in English and Portuguese) 1967. s-a. $20 or on exchange basis (effective 1996). Universidade de Sao Paulo, Faculdade de Saude Publica, Av. Dr. Arnaldo 715, 01246-904 Sao Paulo, Brazil. TEL 55-11-2809163. E-mail: bibfsp@org.usp.br. Ed. Dr. Oswaldo Paulo Forattini. bk.rev.; bibl.; charts; illus.; index. circ. 1,500. **Indexed:** Abstr.Hyg., Biol.Abstr., C.I.S. Abstr., Curr.Cont., Dent.Ind., Entomol.Abstr., Excerp.Med., Helminthol.Abstr., Ind.Med., Ind.Vet., Microbiol.Abstr., Nutr.Abstr., Protozool.Abstr., Rev.Appl.Entomol., Rev.Med.& Vet.Mycol., Saf.Sci.Abstr., Soyabean Abstr., SSCI, Trop.Dis.Bull., Vet.Bull., Virol.Abstr. **Document type:** academic/scholarly publication.
—BLDSC (7870.635000); CASDDS; EMDOCS; Genuine Article; UMI.
    Formerly (until 1992): Revista de Saude Publica (ISSN 0034-8910); **Supersedes:** Universidade de Sao Paulo. Faculdade de Higiene e Saude Publica. Archivos.
    Description: Reflects scientific advances in the public health field through original research prepared by specialists, both domestic and foreign.
    Refereed Serial

614   VE   ISSN 0035-0583
RA421
REVISTA VENEZOLANA DE SANIDAD Y ASISTENCIA SOCIAL. (Text in Spanish; summaries in several languages) 1936. q. free. Ministerio de Sanidad y Asistencia Social, Oficina de Publicaciones, Biblioteca y Archivo, Centro Simon Bolivar, Edificio Sur, Caracas, Venezuela. Ed. Manuel Boet. charts; illus.; stat.; index. circ. 3,000. **Indexed:** Biol.Abstr., Chem.Abstr., Ind.Med., Nutr.Abstr., Rev.Appl.Entomol.

614   FR   ISSN 0398-7620
            CODEN: RESPDF
REVUE D'EPIDEMIOLOGIE ET DE SANTE PUBLIQUE. (Text in French; summaries in English) 1953. bi-m. 1070 F. (foreign 1270 F.) (effective 1996). Masson - Periodiques, Villa Laromiguiere, 75005 Paris, France. TEL 1-40-46-62-00. FAX 1-40-46-62-01. Ed. Ducimetiere. bk.rev.; illus.; index. circ. 1,300. (also avail. in microform from UMI; reprint service avail. from ISI) **Indexed:** Abstr.Hyg., Bibl.Dev.Med.& Child Neur., Biol.Abstr., C.I.S. Abstr., Curr.Adv.Ecol.Sci., Curr.Cont., Excerp.Med., Helminthol.Abstr., Ind.Med., Ind.Vet., Med.Care Rev., Trop.Dis.Bull., Vet.Bull. **Document type:** academic/scholarly publication.
—BLDSC (7900.109000); Genuine Article; SWETS; UMI. **CCC.**
    Former titles (until 1976): Revue d'Epidemiologie, Medecine Sociale et Sante Publique (ISSN 0035-2438); Revue d'Hygiene et de Medecine Sociale.
    Description: Publishes work on contagious diseases, together with research on cardiovascular disease, cancer, suicide, and other topics that affect public health.

REVUE INTERNATIONALE DU TRAVAIL. see BUSINESS AND ECONOMICS — Labor And Industrial Relations

REVUE MEDICALE RWANDAISE. see MEDICAL SCIENCES

614   US   ISSN 1073-8673
K22
RISK: HEALTH, SAFETY & ENVIRONMENT. 1990. q. $30 to individuals; institutions $55. Franklin Pierce Law Center, 2 White St., Concord, NH 03301. TEL 603-228-1541. FAX 603-224-3342. (Co-sponsor: Risk Assessment and Policy Association) Ed. Thomas G. Field, Jr. adv. contact: Carol Ruh. bk.rev.; circ. 315 (paid). (also avail. in diskette format; reprint service avail. from WSH) **Indexed:** Energy Abstr., Environ.Abstr., Environ.Per.Bibl. (1990-), L.R.I., P.A.I.S., Pollut.Abstr., Risk Abstr. **Document type:** academic/scholarly publication.
●Also available online. Vendor(s): West Services, Inc.
—BLDSC (7972.576000); CIS; UnCover.
    Formerly (until Jan. 1994): Risk, Issues in Health and Safety (ISSN 1047-0484)
    Description: Explores public and private efforts to manage science and technology for net reduction in the probability, severity and aversive quality of health, safety and environmental impacts.
    Refereed Serial

614.8   IT   ISSN 0035-6891
RIVISTA ITALIANA DI PREVIDENZA SOCIALE. 1948. bi-m. Via Nicola Marchese, 20, Rome, Italy. Ed. U. Chiapelli.

ROHSTOFF RUNDSCHAU; Fachblatt des gesamten Handels mit Alt- und Abfallstoffen. see TECHNOLOGY: COMPREHENSIVE WORKS

ROUTE. see TRANSPORTATION — Automobiles

614.8   UK   ISSN 0968-7726
THE ROYAL LIFE SAVING SOCIETY. LIFEGUARD. 1965. q. £10.50. Royal Life Saving Society UK, Mountbatten House, Studley, Warwickshire B80 7NN, England. TEL 01527-853943. FAX 01527-854453. Ed. Stephen Lear. adv.; bk.rev. circ. 13,000. **Indexed:** Sportsearch. **Document type:** trade publication.
    Former titles: Royal Life Saving Society U.K. Lifesaver U.K; Royal Life Saving Society - U.K. Quarterly Journal (ISSN 0048-8704)

ROYAL SOCIETY OF HEALTH JOURNAL. see SOCIAL SERVICES AND WELFARE

614   US
RURAL HEALTH F Y I. 1978. bi-m. $75. National Rural Health Association, 1 W. Armour Blvd., Ste. 301, Kansas City, MO 64111. TEL 816-756-3140. FAX 816-756-3144. Ed. Jenifer Bockelman Dick. circ. 3,600.
    Formerly: Rural Health Care.
    Description: Information on rural health issues, policy and projects.

614   RW
RWANDA. MINISTERE DE LA SANTE PUBLIQUE. RAPPORT ANNUEL. a. Ministere de la Sante Publique, B.P. 84, Kigali, Rwanda. circ. 200.

S A H O NEWS. (Saskatchewan Association of Health Organizations) see HOSPITALS

S B Z - SANITAER, HEIZUNGS- UND KLIMATECHNIK. see HEATING, PLUMBING AND REFRIGERATION

S S P C LEAD PAINT BULLETIN. (Steel Structures Painting Council) see PAINTS AND PROTECTIVE COATINGS

SAFETY AND HEALTH; the international safety, health and environmental magazine. see OCCUPATIONAL HEALTH AND SAFETY

614.8   UK   ISSN 0265-4792
            CODEN: SAFPDZ
THE SAFETY & HEALTH PRACTITIONER. m. £45. Paramount Publishing Ltd., 17-21 Shenley Rd., Borehamwood, Herts. WD6 1RT, England. TEL 081-207-5599. FAX 081-207-2598. Ed. J. Balian. adv.; bk.rev. circ. 13,000. (also avail. in microform from UMI) **Indexed:** Br.Ceram.Abstr., C.I.S. Abstr., Ind.Vet., Lab.Haz.Bull., Mgmt.& Market.Abstr., World Surf.Coat. **Document type:** bulletin.
    Formerly: Safety Practitioner; **Supersedes:** Safety Surveyor and Protection.

614
SAFETY AND RESCUE. 1959. m. £1($7) British Safety Council, Chancellors Rd., Hammersmith, London W6 9RS, England. Ed. James Tye. adv.; bk.rev. circ. 75,000. **Indexed:** C.I.S. Abstr.

614.8 350.78   US   ISSN 0036-245X
SAFETY BRIEFS. 1938. 4/yr. free. New Jersey State Safety Council, 6 Commerce Dr., Cranford, NJ 07016-3597. TEL 201-272-7712. FAX 201-276-6622. Ed. James F. Hughes. bk.rev.; charts; stat. circ. 19,000.

614.862   CN   ISSN 0048-8968
SAFETY CANADA. French edition: Prevention au Canada. 1957. q. free. Canada Safety Council, 1020 Thomas Spratt Pl., Ottawa, ON K1G 5L5, Canada. TEL 613-739-1535. FAX 613-739-1566. Ed. Jack A. Smith. bk.rev. circ. 12,000 (10,000 English edition; 2,000 French edition). **Document type:** newsletter.
    Formerly: Highway Safety News.

614   UK
SAFETY EDUCATION. 1966. 3/yr. £10 to non-members; members £4.50. Royal Society for the Prevention of Accidents, Cannon House, The Priory Queensway, Birmingham B4 6BS, England. TEL 021-200-2461. FAX 021-200-1254. Ed. Carole Peart. adv.; bk.rev. circ. 15,000. **Document type:** academic/scholarly publication.
    Description: News items, reviews, informational articles, case studies, and technical advice on instruction to children and young adults in the adoption of safety practices.

614   UK
▼**SAFETY EXPRESS.** 1995. bi-m. £13.50. Royal Society for the Prevention of Accidents, Cannon House, The Priory Queensway, Birmingham B4 6BS, England. TEL 0121-200-2461. FAX 0121-200-1254. Ed. Stephanie Lennon. adv. contact: Andy Taylor. video rev.; stat.; tr.lit.; circ. 5,000 (paid). (tabloid format; back issues avail.) **Document type:** government publication.

363.1 372.3   US
SAFETY IS ELEMENTARY. 1991. 3/yr. $10. Laboratory Safety Workshop, 192 Worcester Rd., Natick, MA 01760. TEL 508-647-1900. FAX 508-647-0062. Ed. James A. Kaufman. circ. 50. **Document type:** newsletter.
    Description: Deals with safety in the teaching of science.

SAFETY SCIENCE. see OCCUPATIONAL HEALTH AND SAFETY

614   CN
SAFETY UPDATE.* q. free. Ontario Safety League, 21 Four Seasons Place, Etobicoke, Ont. M9B 6J8, Canada. TEL 416-593-2670.
    Formerly: Ontario Safety League. News (ISSN 0700-9844)

614.88   UK
ST. JOHN WORLD. 1927. m. $30. Order of St. John, 1 Grosvenor Crescent, London SW1X 7EF, England. TEL 01-235-5231. FAX 01-235-0796. Ed. Anne Reilly. adv. contact: Sheila Merrett. bk.rev.; film rev.; illus. circ. 10,000. **Document type:** consumer publication.
    Formerly: St. John Review (ISSN 0036-2883)

PUBLIC HEALTH AND SAFETY

628 JA
SAITAMA-KEN EISEI TOKEI NENPO/ANNUAL REPORT OF PUBLIC HEALTH, SAITAMA PREFECTURE. (Text in Japanese) 1950. a. free. Saitama-ken, Eisei-bu - Saitama Prefecture, Bureau of Public Health, 15-1 Takasago 3-chome, Urawa-shi, Saitama-ken 336, Japan.

628 MX ISSN 0036-3634
SALUD PUBLICA DE MEXICO/PUBLIC HEALTH OF MEXICO. (Includes special issue) (Text in Spanish; summaries in English and Spanish) 1959. bi-m. Mex.$100($50) (outside Latin America $70) to individuals; students Mex.$80($40) (outside Latin America $55) (effective 1994). Instituto Nacional de Salud Publica, Secretaria de Salud, Av. Universidad, 665, Planta Baja, Col. Santa Maria Ahuacatitlad, 62508 Cuernavaca, Morelos, Mexico. TEL 52-73-110111. FAX 52-73-175529. Dir. Dr. Jose Gomez de Leon Cruces. bk.rev.; bibl. circ. 2,000. **Indexed:** Abstr.Hyg., Biol.Abstr., C.I.S. Abstr., Dairy Sci.Abstr., Excerp.Med., Helminthol.Abstr., Ind.Med., Nutr.Abstr., Rev.Med.& Vet.Mycol., Trop.Dis.Bull.
—BLDSC (8071.800000); Genuine Article; SWETS.
Incorporates (in 1977): Investigacion en Salud Publica.

614.8 RM
SANATATEA. 1952. m. National Council of the Red Cross, Str. Biserica Amzei 29, Bucharest, Rumania. Ed. Gheorghe M. George. circ. 140,000.

628 IT ISSN 0393-4101
SANITA PUBBLICA; rivista mensile amministrativa per gli operatori della sanita. 1981. m. (10/yr.). L.120000 to individuals; institutions L.230000 (effective 1994). Maggioli Editore, Viale Vespucci 12-n, Casella Postale 290, 47037 Rimini, Italy. TEL 0541-626777. FAX 0541-622020. Dir. Fabio Alberto Roversi-Monaco. adv.: B&W page L.1450000, color page L.2300000; trim 115 x 195.

SANITAER UND HEIZUNGS REPORT. see *HEATING, PLUMBING AND REFRIGERATION*

628 US ISSN 0036-4436
HD9999.S383
SANITARY MAINTENANCE; the journal of the sanitary supply industry. 1943. m. $49. Trade Press Publishing Corp., 2100 W. Florist Ave., Milwaukee, WI 53209. TEL 414-228-7701. FAX 414-228-1135. Ed. Austin Weber. adv.; illus.; tr.lit.; index. circ. 16,000. (also avail. in microfilm from UMI; reprint service avail. from UMI) **Document type:** trade publication.
—UMI.
Description: Serves the needs of distribution executives in the sanitary supply industry by covering market trends, product news, application methods, and management.

614 AE
SANTE. (Text in French) 1956. bi-m. Federation Nationale de la Sante, Maison du Peuple, Place du 1 Mai, Algiers, Algeria.

614 RM ISSN 0048-9107
SANTE PUBLIQUE.* (Editions also in English, German, Russian) 1958. q. 80 lei($12) Editura Medicala, c/o ILEXIM, Str. 13 Decembrie Nr. 3, P.O. Box 136-137, Bucharest, Rumania. Ed. Dr. Gh. Cadariu. bk.rev.; abstr.; bibl.; illus. circ. 650. **Indexed:** Abstr.Hyg., Biol.Abstr., C.I.S. Abstr., Excerp.Med., Ind.Med., Trop.Dis.Bull.
—BLDSC (8075.350000).

614 FR ISSN 0995-3914
CODEN: SPBQA
SANTE PUBLIQUE. 1978. bi-m. (Ecole Nationale de la Sante Publique) Societe Francaise de la Sante Publique, B.P. 7, 2, av. du Doyen J. Parisot, 54501 Vandoeuvre-les-Nancy Cedex, France. **Indexed:** Excerp.Med. (1993-). **Document type:** academic/scholarly publication.
—BLDSC (8075.350100).
Formed by the 1988 merger of: Revue Francaise de la Sante Publique (ISSN 0182-8819); Ecole Nationale de la Sante Publique. Cahiers (ISSN 0984-9289)

600 FR ISSN 0294-0337
CODEN: SSSAEC
SCIENCES SOCIALES ET SANTE. q. 350 F. to individuals (foreign 390 F.); institutions 580 F. (foreign 620 F.); students 250 F. (foreign 290 F.) (effective 1995). John Libbey Eurotext, 127 av de la Republique, 92120 Montrouge, France. TEL 1-46-73-06-60. FAX 1-40-84-09-99. (Subscr. to: A T E I, 23-25 rue Fernand Combette, 93100 Montreuil sous Bois, France. TEL 48-59-58-11. FAX 48-59-57-99) Ed. Gerard de Pouvourville. **Document type:** academic/scholarly publication.
Description: Serves as an information exchange between all health care fields.

614.8 US
SEARCHLINES. 1979. bi-m. $25. International Association of Dive Rescue Specialists, Box 5259, San Clemente, CA 92674-5259. TEL 714-489-2004. FAX 714-489-5955. Ed. Steven J. Linton. adv.; bk.rev. circ. 2,375. **Document type:** trade publication.
Formerly: Dive Rescue Specialist.
Description: Covers techniques, equipment and experiences pertinent to the job of public safety diver. For professional dive rescue specialists.

614.85 IT ISSN 0037-0657
SECURITAS; rivista di studi e documentazione sulla sicurezza nel lavoro. 1914. m. L.8000. Ente Nazionale per la Prevenzione degli Infortuni, Via Alessandria 220, Rome, Italy. Ed. Carlo Borrini. adv.; bk.rev.; abstr.; charts; illus.; stat.; tr.lit.; index. circ. 6,000. **Indexed:** Chem.Abstr., Trop.Dis.Bull.

SECURITY SPECIFIER. see *CRIMINOLOGY AND LAW ENFORCEMENT — Security*

614.8 PO ISSN 0049-0059
SEGURANCA. 1965. 4/yr. Esc.2200. Associacao Portuguesa de Seguradores, Av. Jose Malhoa, 1674-4 Piso, 1000 Lisbon Codex, Portugal. TEL 01-7268123. FAX 01-7262290. adv. circ. 3,500. **Indexed:** C.I.S. Abstr.

SEGURIDAD SOCIAL. see *SOCIAL SERVICES AND WELFARE*

SEIKATSU TO KANKYO/LIFE AND ENVIRONMENT. see *ENVIRONMENTAL STUDIES*

614 DK ISSN 0901-9685
SEX OG SUNDHED/SEX AND HEALTH; om sexualitet, praevention og sexuelt overfoerbare sygdomme. 1986. s-a. free. Danish Family Planning Association, Aurehoejvej 2, DK-2900 Hellerup, Denmark. Ed. Marianne Soendergaard. illus. circ. 10,000.
Former titles: Mer om Sex og Sikkerhed (ISSN 0108-7851); Mer om Koenssygdomme (ISSN 0108-7843)

613 AA
SHENDETI.* bi-m. $6.16. Ministere de la Sante Publique, Tirana, Albania.

SHONI NO HOKEN/OSAKA CHILDREN'S MEDICAL CENTER. JOURNAL. see *CHILDREN AND YOUTH — About*

SICHERHEIT ZUERST. see *TRANSPORTATION — Railroads*

614.8 CI ISSN 0350-6886
SIGURNOST/SAFETY. (Text in Croatian; summaries and contents page in English) 1959. 4/yr. $120. Zavod za Instrazivanje i Razvoj Sigurnosti - Institute of Safety Research and Development, Proleterskih Brigada 68, 41000 Zagreb, Croatia. TEL 41-512494. FAX 41-516012. (Co-sponsor: Ministartvo Znanosti, Tehnologije i Informatike Republike Hrvatske) Ed.Gordana Baraba. adv.; bk.rev.; charts; illus.; index, cum.index. circ. 1,500. **Indexed:** C.I.S. Abstr.
—BLDSC (8276.480000).
Formerly (until 1972): Sigurnost u Pogonu (ISSN 0037-508X)

614.8 DK ISSN 0108-6650
SIKKERHED. (Supplement to: Socialpaedagogernes Landsforbund. T R Information) 1981. irreg. free. Socialpaedagogernes Landsforbund, Brolaeggerstraede 9 St., DK-1211 Copenhagen K, Denmark. illus. **Document type:** consumer publication.

SINNETS HELSE. see *PSYCHOLOGY*

614 DK ISSN 0900-1980
SOCIAL ADMINISTRATION; lovsamling for praktikere og tilstudiebrug. 1984. a. DKK 195.20. Forlag for Social- og Sundhedssektor, Vibeholms Alle 11-15, 2605 Bronoby, Denmark.

362.1 UK ISSN 1352-4127
▼SOCIAL SCIENCES IN HEALTH. 1995. q. £28($50) to individuals; institutions £63 ($113) (effective 1996). Arnold (Subsidiary of: Hodder Headline plc.), 338 Euston Rd., London NW1 3BH, England. TEL 0171-873-6000. FAX 0171-873-6325. (Subscr. to: Turpin Distribution Services Ltd., Blackhorse Rd., Letchworth, Herts. SG6 1HN, England. TEL 01462-672555. FAX 01462-480947) adv.; bk.rev. **Document type:** academic/scholarly publication.
—BLDSC (8318.190800).
Description: Shows how the social sciences interact with the nursing while exploring current theories and models, topical issues and the role of the social sciences in the practice of health care, management, and research.

SOCIAL WORK IN HEALTH CARE; quarterly journal of medical & psychiatric social work. see *SOCIAL SERVICES AND WELFARE*

614 UK ISSN 0037-8119
SOCIALISM AND HEALTH. 1960. bi-m. £15 membership. Socialist Health Association, 16 Charles Sq., London N1 6HP, England. TEL 0171-490-0057. Eds. Joy Mostyn, Rosemary Ross. bk.rev. circ. 1,500. (looseleaf format; back issues avail.) **Document type:** bulletin.
—BLDSC (8318.243750).

613 NR ISSN 0037-9905
SOCIETY OF HEALTH OF NIGERIA. JOURNAL.* 1966. q. $7. Nigeria Medical Council, Plot PC 13, 25 Ahmed Onidudo St., Victoria Island, P.M.B. 12611, Lagos, Nigeria. adv.

614 NL ISSN 1013-9915
SOUTH PACIFIC COMMISSION. INFORMATION CIRCULAR. French edition: Commission de Pacifique Sud. Circulaire d'Information (ISSN 1017-981X) (Text in English) 1968. irreg., no.147, 1992. free. South Pacific Commission, B.P. D5, Noumea, Cedex, New Caledonia. **Indexed:** So.Pac.Per.Ind. **Document type:** monographic series.
—BLDSC (4491.450000).

SOUTHEAST ASIAN JOURNAL OF TROPICAL MEDICINE AND PUBLIC HEALTH. see *MEDICAL SCIENCES — Communicable Diseases*

614 SP
SPAIN. MINISTERIO DE SANIDAD Y CONSUMO. MONOGRAFIAS. 1988. irreg. price varies. Ministerio de Sanidad y Consumo, Paseo del Prado 18, 28014 Madrid, Spain. **Document type:** monographic series, government publication.

SPEAKING OF ENVIRONMENTAL RISK. see *INSURANCE*

363.1 US
SPEAKING OF SAFETY. 3/yr. $12.50. Laboratory Safety Workshop, 192 Worcester Rd., Natick, MA 01760-4723. TEL 508-647-1900. FAX 508-647-0062. Ed. James A. Kaufman. circ. 2,000. **Document type:** newsletter.

STAT! (DAYTON); serving the greater Dayton medical and health care community. see *PHARMACY AND PHARMACOLOGY*

614 US
STATE HEALTH NOTES. 1979. s-m. $227 to private sector; government, non-profit & university $147. Intergovernmental Health Policy Project, 2021 K St., N.W., Ste. 800, Washington, DC 20006. TEL 202-872-1445. Ed. Linda Demkovich. charts; stat. circ. 2,000. (tabloid format; back issues avail.) **Document type:** newsletter.
Description: Identifies and analyzes important health-related trends and innovations within state government.

614 SW ISSN 0085-6738
STATUS. 1938. 8/yr. SEK 75. Riksfoerbundet foer Hjaert- och Lungsjuka - Swedish Heart and Lung Association, P.O. Box 9090, 102 72 Stockholm, Sweden. TEL 08-669-0960. FAX 08-6682385. adv.; bk.rev. circ. 30,000.

354.489 DK ISSN 0905-0035
RA257
STATUS OG VISIONER - SUNDHEDSSTYRELSEN. 1978. a. free. Sundhedsstyrelsen, P.O. Box 2020, 1012 Copenhagen K, Denmark.
Formerly (until **1988**): Sundhedsstyrelsen. Aarsberetning (ISSN 0105-5151)

614.85 UK
STAYING ALIVE. 1968. q. Royal Society for the Prevention of Accidents, Cannon House, The Priory Queensway, Birmingham B4 6BS, England. TEL 021-200-2461. FAX 021-200-1254. bk.rev.; charts; illus. circ. 3,000. **Indexed:** ASSIA. **Document type:** consumer publication.
Former titles (until **1994**): Care in the Home (ISSN 0300-5909); Home Safety Journal (ISSN 0018-4136)
Description: Discusses issues relating to safety in and around the home.

363.17 616.9 NO ISSN 0804-4910
STRAALEVERNRAPPORT. Variant title: Norwegian Radiation Protection Authority Report. Parallel title: NRPA Report. (Text in various languages) 1979. irreg. free. Statens Straalevern - Norwegian Radiation Protection Authority, Oesterndalen 25, P.O. Box 55, N-1345 Oesteraas, Norway. TEL 47-67-14-41-90. FAX 47-67-14-74-07. Dir. Georg Thommesens.
—BLDSC (8470.450000).
Former titles (until **1994**): Statens Straalevern. Rapport (ISSN 0804-2098); (until 1993): S I S Rapport (ISSN 0800-4137)

STRAHLENTELEX; unabhaengiger Informationsdienst zu Radioaktivitaet, Strahlung und Gesundheit. see ENVIRONMENTAL STUDIES — Toxicology And Environmental Safety

614 BE
STUDIE VAN DE LUCHTKWALITEIT IN BELGIE. ZWAVEL-ROOK MEETNET. Short title: Zwavel-Rook Meetnet. (Text in Dutch, French) 1968. a. $5. Instituut voor Hygiene en Epidemiologie (IHE), Juliette Wytsmanstraat 14, B-1050 Brussels, Belgium. charts; stat. circ. 600.
Formerly: Instituut voor Hygiene en Epidemiologie. Zwavel-Rook Meetnet (ISSN 0378-892X)

STUDIES ON CURRENT HEALTH PROBLEMS. see MEDICAL SCIENCES

614 VN
SUC KHOE/HEALTH. fortn. Ministry of Public Health, 138 A Giang Vo St., Hanoi, Socialist Republic of Vietnam. TEL 43144. Ed. Phung Truc Phong.

614 II ISSN 0586-1179
SWASTH HIND. (Text in English) 1957. m. Rs.6($5) Ministry of Health and Family Welfare, Central Health Education Bureau, Kotla Rd., New Delhi 110 002, India. TEL 3315032. Ed. M.L. Mehta. adv.; bk.rev.; charts; illus.; stat.; index. circ. 8,500.

614 SW ISSN 0346-8445
SWEDEN. SJUKVAARDENS OCH SOCIALVAARDENS PLANERINGS- OCH RATIONALISERINGSINSTITUT. S P R I INFORMERAR. Short title: S P R I Informerar. 1968. 10/yr. free. Sjukvaardens och Socialvaardens Planerings- och Rationaliseringsinstitut - Swedish Planning and Rationalization Institute of the Health and Social Services, P.O. Box 70487, S-107 26 Stockholm, Sweden. TEL 08-702-4600. FAX 08-7024799. **Document type:** bulletin.
—BLDSC (8424.060000).

614 SW ISSN 0586-1691
SWEDEN. SJUKVAARDENS OCH SOCIALVAARDENS PLANERINGS- OCH RATIONALISERINGSINSTITUT. S P R I RAPPORT. Short title: S P R I Rapport. (Text in Swedish) 1968. irreg. price varies. Sjukvaardens och Socialvaardens Planerings- och Rationaliseringsinstitut - Swedish Planning and Rationalization Institute of the Health and Social Services, Box 70487, S-107 26 Stockholm, Sweden. TEL 08-702-4600. FAX 08-702-4799. **Indexed:** Abstr.Health Care Manage.Stud. **Document type:** monographic series.

SWIMMING POOLS TODAY. see SPORTS AND GAMES — Outdoor Life

614.8 US
SYSTEM SAFETY SOCIETY. DIRECTORY OF CONSULTANTS. a. $50 to non-members; members $10. System Safety Society, Inc., Technology Trading Park, 5 Export Dr., Ste. A, Sterling, VA 22170-4421. TEL 703-444-6520. circ. 1,100. **Document type:** directory.
Description: Lists consultants in system and product safety.

T B WEEKLY. (Tuberculosis) see MEDICAL SCIENCES — Communicable Diseases

614 US
TAKING SIDES: CLASHING VIEWS ON CONTROVERSIAL ISSUES IN HEALTH AND SOCIETY. 1993. irreg. $13.95. Dushkin Publishing Group, Sluice Dock, Guilford, CT 06437-9989. TEL 203-453-4351. FAX 203-453-4351. Ed. Eileen Daniel; Pub. Mimi Egan. illus. **Document type:** academic/scholarly publication.

TECHNIQUES HOSPITALIERES; la revue des technologies de la sante. see HOSPITALS

TECHNIQUES - SCIENCES - METHODES. GENIE URBAIN RURAL. see PUBLIC ADMINISTRATION — Municipal Government

614 IT ISSN 0392-8144
TECNICA SANITARIA E MEDICINA DI COMUNITA. 1963. bi-m. L.60000($45) (Associazione Nazionale Ufficiali Sanitari Medici Igienisti) Tecnisan s.r.l., Via Giardini 818, 41100 Modena, Italy. TEL 39-59-343785. Dir. Ferruccio Vivoli. adv.; bk.rev.; abstr.; bibl.; charts; illus.; stat.; index. circ. 1,000. **Indexed:** Food Sci.& Tech.Abstr.
—BLDSC (8762.575000).
Formerly (until **1976**): Tecnica Sanitaria (ISSN 0040-1897)

TEHNOLOGIJA MESA/MEAT TECHNOLOGY; casopis industrije mesa Jugoslavije. see AGRICULTURE — Poultry And Livestock

TEMAS DE POBLACION. see POPULATION STUDIES

614 BE ISSN 1370-0650
▼**TEST SANTE.** Dutch edition: Test Gezondheid (ISSN 1370-0847) (Text in French) 1994. 4/yr. 828 BEF in Belgium and Luxemburg (elsewhere 964 BEF). Association des Consommateurs - Verbruikersunie, Rue de Hollande 13, 1060 Brussels, Belgium. TEL 32-2-5423211. FAX 32-2-5423250. TELEX 26771. **Document type:** consumer publication.

614 US
TEXAS. DEPARTMENT OF HEALTH. ANNUAL REPORT. a. free. Department of Health, 1100 W. 49th St., Austin, TX 78756. TEL 512-458-7761. FAX 512-458-7476.
Formerly: Texas. Department of Health Resources. Biennial Report (ISSN 0163-1667)

TEXAS WATER UTILITIES JOURNAL. see WATER RESOURCES

TIJDSCHRIFT VOOR GEZONDHEID EN POLITIEK. see MEDICAL SCIENCES

614 340 NE ISSN 0165-0874
CODEN: TGEZD
TIJDSCHRIFT VOOR GEZONDHEIDSRECHT. 1977. bi-m. Samsom H.D. Tjeenk Willink B.V. (Subsidiary of: Wolters Kluwer N.V.), Postbus 316, 2400 AH Alphen aan den Rijn, Netherlands. TEL 31-1720-66822. FAX 31-1720-66639. circ. 1,200. (paid). **Indexed:** ELLIS, Excerpt.Med. (until 1992).
—BLDSC (8841.650000); SWETS.

TIJDSCHRIFT VOOR SOCIALE GEZONDHEIDSZORG; gezondheid & samenleving. see MEDICAL SCIENCES

TOKYO-TORITSU EISEI KENKYUJO KENKYU NENPO/TOKYO METROPOLITAN RESEARCH LABORATORY OF PUBLIC HEALTH. ANNUAL REPORT. see MEDICAL SCIENCES

614 TO ISSN 0082-4895
TONGA. MINISTER OF HEALTH. REPORT. (Text in English and Tongan) 1951. a. $25. Government Printer, Nuku'alofa, Tongatapu, Tonga. circ. 660.

TOURING. see TRANSPORTATION — Automobiles

604.7 368.5 US
TOXIC TORTS; litigation of hazardous substance cases. (2nd edition; subseries of: Trial Practice Series) 1984. irreg. $190. Shepard's - McGraw-Hill, Inc., Box 35300, Colorado Springs, CO 80935-3530. TEL 800-525-2474. Ed. G.Z. Nothstein. **Document type:** trade publication.
Description: Covers the specific hows, whys and wherefores for successfully handling chemical and hazardous waste litigation.

TOYAMA-KEN EISEI TOKEI NENPO/TOYAMA PREFECTURE. ANNUAL REPORT OF PUBLIC HEALTH. see PUBLIC HEALTH AND SAFETY — Abstracting, Bibliographies, Statistics

614.8 US ISSN 0275-844X
QD139.T7 CODEN: TANAD7
TRACE ANALYSIS. 1981. irreg., vol.4, 1985. Academic Press, Inc., 525 B St., Ste. 1900, San Diego, CA 92101-4495. TEL 619-231-0926. FAX 619-699-6715. (Subscr. to: Order Dept., 6277 Sea Harbor Dr., 4th Fl., Orlando, FL 32887. TEL 800-321-5068) Ed. James F. Lawrence. (reprint service avail. from ISI)
—CASDDS.
Refereed Serial

TRACE SUBSTANCES IN ENVIRONMENTAL HEALTH. see ENVIRONMENTAL STUDIES — Toxicology And Environmental Safety

614.8 380.5 US ISSN 8756-4408
TRANSPORTATION SAFETY RECOMMENDATIONS. m. price varies. (U.S. Department of Transportation, National Transportation Safety Board) U.S. National Technical Information Service, 5825 Port Royal Rd., Springfield, VA 22161. TEL 703-487-4630. FAX 703-321-8547. **Document type:** government publication.
Description: Reports on the board's safety oversight and accident prevention activities are provided. The safety reports inform on important transportation problems, issues, and activities.

614.8 US
TRANSPORTATION SAFETY SPECIAL REPORTS. 5/yr. $250 in the U.S., Canada, Mexico; elsewhere $500. (U.S. Department of Transportation, National Transportation Safety Board) U.S. National Technical Information Service, 5825 Port Royal Rd., Springfield, VA 22161. TEL 703-487-4630. FAX 703-321-8547. **Document type:** government publication.
Description: Includes safety studies and reports, accident investigation reports, as well as highway and railroad accident reports.

614 US
TRENDS (WASHINGTON, 1969).* 1969. m. $55. Association of Schools of Allied Health Professions, 1730 M St., N.W. 500, Washington, DC 20036-4505. TEL 202-857-1150. FAX 202-223-4579. Ed. Thomas W. Elwood. adv.; bk.rev. circ. 800. **Document type:** newsletter.
Formerly: Allied Health Trends.

PUBLIC HEALTH AND SAFETY

616.988 UK ISSN 1360-2276
TROPICAL MEDICINE & INTERNATIONAL HEALTH. 1996. bi-m. £249 in Europe; elsewhere £275($443) (effective 1996). Blackwell Science Ltd., Osney Mead, Oxford OX2 0EL, England. TEL 44-1865-206206. FAX 44-1865-206219. (Co-sponsors: Bernhard Nacht Institut, Hamburg; Foundation Tropical and Geographical Medicine, Amsterdam; Belgian Institute of Tropical Medicine, Antwerp; London School of Hygiene & Tropical Medicine) adv.; bk.rev. (also avail. in microform from UMI) **Indexed:** Abstr.Hyg., Abstr.Rural Dev.Trop., ASCA, Biol.Abstr., Biotech.Abstr., Chem.Abstr., Curr.Adv.Ecol.Sci., Curr.Cont., Dent.Ind., Diar.Dis.Res., Dok.Arbeitsmed., E.I., Excerp.Med., Geo.Abstr., Helminthol.Abstr., IDA, Ind.Med., Ind.Sci.Rev., Ind.Vet., Inf.Nurs.Ind., Med.& Surg.Dermat., Nutr.Abstr., Pig News & Info., Protozool.Abstr., Rev.Appl.Entomol., Rev.Med.& Vet.Mycol., Rev.Plant Path., Sci.Cit.Ind., Sel.Water Res.Abstr., So.Pac.Per.Ind., Trop.Dis.Bull., Vet.Bull. **Document type:** academic/scholarly publication.
—BLDSC (5071.000000); ADONIS; CASDDS; EMDOCS; Faxon; Genuine Article; SWETS; UMI; UnCover. **CCC.**
Formed by the merger of (1898-1995): Journal of Tropical Medicine and Hygiene (ISSN 0022-5304); (1948-1995): Tropical and Geographical Medicine (ISSN 0041-3232); Which incorporates (1926-1991): Acta Leidensia (ISSN 0065-1362); (1985-1995): Tropical Medicine and Parasitology (ISSN 0177-2392); (1972-1995): Societe Belge de Medecine Tropicale. Annales (ISSN 0772-4128); Which was formerly titled (until 1972): Annales des Societes Belges de Medecine Tropicale, de Parasitologie et de Mycologie (ISSN 0037-9638); (until 1971): Annales des Societes Belges de Medecine Tropicale, de Parasitologie et de Mycologie Humaine et Animale (ISSN 0373-2487); (1920-1964): Societe Belge de Medecine Tropicale. Annales (ISSN 0365-6527); Tropical Medicine and Parasitology was formerly titled (until 1985): Tropenmedizin und Parasitologie (ISSN 0303-4208); (1950-1974): Zeitschrift fuer Tropenmedizin und Parasitologie (ISSN 0044-359X).
Description: Covers all aspects of tropical medicine.
Refereed Serial

361.941 UK ISSN 1351-9492
U N I S O N MAGAZINE. 1906. m. Confederation of Health Service Employees, 1 Marbledon Pl., London WC1H 9AJ, England. TEL 071-388-2366. FAX 071-387-6692. Dir. John Marks. adv.; bk.rev.; illus. circ. 220,000. **Indexed:** ASSIA. **Document type:** trade publication.
Formed by the 1993 merger of: N A L G O Annual Report (ISSN 0077-4456); (1951-1993): N U P E Journal (ISSN 0266-8165) & C O H S E Journal (ISSN 0961-3781); Which was formerly (1912-1989): Health Services Journal (ISSN 0017-9116)

U Z MAGAZINE. (Universitaire Ziekenhuis) see *MEDICAL SCIENCES*

614.8 AU ISSN 0049-5131
UMWELTSCHUTZ. 1963. m. S.743. Bohmann Druck und Verlag GmbH & Co. KG, Leberstr. 122, A-1110 Vienna, Austria. TEL 0222-74095-0. FAX 0222-74095-183. TELEX 132312. adv.; bk.rev.; illus. circ. 14,000. **Indexed:** Biol.Abstr. **Document type:** bulletin.
—BLDSC (9083.500000).

614 TS
UNITED ARAB EMIRATES. WIZARAT AL-SIHHAH. IDARAT AL-TIBB AL-WAQA'I. AL-TAQRIR AL-SANAWI/UNITED ARAB EMIRATES. MINISTRY OF HEALTH. PREVENTIVE MEDICINE DEPARTMENT. ANNUAL REPORT. (Text in Arabic, English) 1981. a. Wizarat al-Sihhah, Idarat al-Tibb al-Waqa'i - Ministry of Health, Preventive Medicine Department, P.O. Box 344, Abu Dhabi, United Arab Emirates. TEL 333485. stat.; circ. 1,000. (controlled).
Description: Comprehensive review of the department's activities, including communicable disease control, health education, maternal and children's health services.

U.S. BUREAU OF MINES. ANNUAL RESEARCH REPORT. see *MINES AND MINING INDUSTRY*

U.S. CENTERS FOR DISEASE CONTROL. ABORTION SURVEILLANCE. ANNUAL SUMMARY. see *BIRTH CONTROL*

U.S. CENTERS FOR DISEASE CONTROL. DIPHTHERIA SURVEILLANCE REPORT. see *MEDICAL SCIENCES — Communicable Diseases*

615.9 US ISSN 0098-6623
RC143
U.S. CENTERS FOR DISEASE CONTROL. FOODBORNE & WATERBORNE DISEASE OUTBREAKS. ANNUAL SUMMARY. Key Title: Foodborne & Waterborne Disease Outbreaks. Annual Summary. a. U.S. Centers for Disease Control, 1600 Clifton Rd., NE, Atlanta, GA 30333. TEL 404-639-3311. **Document type:** government publication.
Formerly: U.S. Centers for Disease Control. Foodborne Outbreaks. Annual Summary.

U.S. CENTERS FOR DISEASE CONTROL. LEPROSY SURVEILLANCE REPORT. see *MEDICAL SCIENCES — Communicable Diseases*

U.S. CENTERS FOR DISEASE CONTROL. MALARIA SURVEILLANCE REPORT. see *MEDICAL SCIENCES — Communicable Diseases*

614.4 US ISSN 0149-2195
RA407.3
U.S. CENTERS FOR DISEASE CONTROL. MORBIDITY AND MORTALITY WEEKLY REPORT. Key Title: Morbidity and Mortality Weekly Report. 1950. w. $85 (foreign $106.25). U.S. Department of Health and Human Services, Centers for Disease Control (MS: A28), Epidemiology Program Office, 1600 Clifton Rd. N.E., Atlanta, GA 30333. TEL 800-843-6356. (Subscr. to: MMS Publications, C.S.P.O. Box 9120, Waltham, MA 02254; And: Superintendent of Documents, U.S. Government Printing Office, Box 371954, Pittsburgh, PA 15250-7954. TEL 202-512-1800. FAX 202-512-2250) Ed. Dr. Richard A. Goodman. circ. 84,000. (also avail. in microform from UMI; microfiche from CIS; back issues avail.; reprint service avail. from CIS) **Indexed:** Abstr.Hyg., Amer.Stat.Ind. (1974-), Curr.Lit.Fam.Plan., Curr.Tit.Dent., Diar.Dis.Res., Environ.Abstr., Hlth.Ind., I.P.A., Ind.Med., Ind.Vet., Med.& Surg.Dermat., MEDOC, Protozool.Abstr., Trop.Dis.Bull., Vet.Bull. **Document type:** government publication, newsletter. •Also available online. Vendor(s): Ovid Technologies, NewsNet.
—BLDSC (5966.650500); Faxon; Genuine Article; UMI.
Formerly (until 1976): U.S. National Communicable Disease Center. Morbidity and Mortality (ISSN 0091-0031)
Description: Provides an account of communicable diseases, ranging from AIDS to malaria, on a state, regional, and national basis.

628 312 US ISSN 1057-5987
RA407.A1
U.S. CENTERS FOR DISEASE CONTROL. MORBIDITY AND MORTALITY WEEKLY REPORT. RECOMMENDATIONS AND REPORT. Key Title: Morbidity and Mortality Weekly Report. Recommendations and Report. 1989. irreg. U.S. Department of Health and Human Services, Centers for Disease Control (MS: A28), Epidemiology Program Office, 1600 Clifton Rd. N.E., Atlanta, GA 30333. TEL 800-843-6356. (Orders to: Superintendent of Documents, Government Printing Office, Washington, DC 20402)

614 US
U.S. CENTERS FOR DISEASE CONTROL. SALMONELLA SURVEILLANCE. ANNUAL SUMMARY. 1962. a. free. U.S. Centers for Disease Control, Bureau of Epidemiology. Bacterial Disease Division, 1600 Clifton Rd., NE, Atlanta, GA 30333. TEL 404-639-3311. charts; stat. circ. 3,000. **Document type:** government publication.

628 US
U.S. DEFENSE LOGISTICS AGENCY. D O D HAZARDOUS MATERIALS INFORMATION SYSTEM: HAZARDOUS ITEM LISTING. irreg. (base. vol. plus updates). $155 (foreign $193.75) (effective 1994). U.S. Defense Logistics Agency, Cameron Sta., Alexandria, VA 22314. TEL 703-545-6700. (Subscr. to: Superintendent of Documents, U.S. Government Printing Office, Box 371954, Pittsburgh, PA 15250. TEL 202-512-1800. FAX 202-512-2250) (microfiche) **Document type:** government publication.
Description: Provides data elements for items included in the Department of Defense Materials Information System, primarily for Defense officials to use to comply with the regulatory controls established for hazardous materials.

362 US
U.S. NATIONAL CENTER FOR HEALTH STATISTICS. VITAL AND HEALTH STATISTICS. SERIES 13. DATA ON HEALTH RESOURCES UTILIZATION. 1966. irreg., latest no.119. price varies. U.S. National Center for Health Statistics, Data Dissemination Branch, 6525 Belcrest Rd., Hyattsville, MD 20782. TEL 301-436-8500. (Orders to: Superintendent of Documents, U.S. Government Printing Office, Box 371954, Pittsburgh, PA 15250-7954. TEL 202-512-1800. FAX 202-512-2250) **Indexed:** Excerp.Med. **Document type:** government publication.
Incorporates: U.S. National Center for Health Care Statistics. Vital and Health Statistics. Series 12. Data from the Institutional Population Surveys (ISSN 0083-1964); Formerly: U.S. National Center for Health Care Statistics. Vital and Health Statistics. Series 13. Data from the Hospital Discharge Survey (ISSN 0083-2006)

614 US
UNITED STATES - MEXICO BORDER HEALTH ASSOCIATION. NEWS - NOTICIAS. 1976. q. $75 includes all organization publications; corporate rate $500. Pan American Health Organization, El Paso Field Office, 6006 N. Mesa, Ste. 600, El Paso, TX 79912. TEL 915-581-6645. FAX 915-833-4768. E-mail: vilchish@paho.org. Ed. Dr. Hugo Vilchis-Licon. circ. 2,500.
Description: Reports on the activities of the Association and its membership.

628 GT
UNIVERSIDAD DE SAN CARLOS. FACULTAD DE INGENIERIA. ESCUELA REGIONAL DE INGENIERIA SANITARIA. CARTA PERIODICA. 1966. irreg. Universidad de San Carlos de Guatemala, Escuela Regional de Ingenieria Sanitaria, Ciudad Universitaria, Zona 12, Guatemala. Ed. Arturo Acajabon Mendoza. bibl.; charts; illus.
Formerly: Brujula.

UNIVERSIDAD INDUSTRIAL DE SANTANDER. REVISTA - SALUD. see *MEDICAL SCIENCES*

614 350 US
UNIVERSITY OF DELAWARE. DISASTER RESEARCH CENTER. DISSERTATIONS. 1965. irreg., no.29, 1985. $25. University of Delaware, Disaster Research Center, Newark, DE 19716. TEL 302-831-6618. FAX 302-831-2091. TELEX 70 99 85. **Document type:** academic/scholarly publication.

614 350 US
UNIVERSITY OF DELAWARE. DISASTER RESEARCH CENTER. FINAL PROJECT REPORTS. no.6, 1967. irreg., no.37, 1989. price varies. University of Delaware, Disaster Research Center, Newark, DE 19716. TEL 302-831-6618. FAX 302-831-2091. TELEX 70 99 85. **Document type:** monographic series.

614.8 628.44
350.755 US
UNIVERSITY OF DELAWARE. DISASTER RESEARCH CENTER. MISCELLANEOUS REPORTS. no.20, 1978. irreg., no.47, 1992. University of Delaware, Disaster Research Center, Newark, DE 19716. TEL 302-831-6618. FAX 302-831-2091. TELEX 70 99 85. **Document type:** monographic series.
Formerly: Ohio State University, Columbus. Disaster Research Center. Miscellaneous Reports.

614 350 US
UNIVERSITY OF DELAWARE. DISASTER RESEARCH CENTER. PRELIMINARY PAPERS. no.5, 1973. irreg., no.187, 1992. price varies. University of Delaware, Disaster Research Center, Newark, DE 19716. TEL 302-451-6618. FAX 302-451-2838. **Document type:** monographic series.

614.8 628.44
350.755 US
UNIVERSITY OF DELAWARE. DISASTER RESEARCH CENTER. REPORT SERIES. 1968. irreg., no.19, 1989. University of Delaware, Disaster Research Center, Newark, DE 19716. TEL 302-831-6618. FAX 302-831-2091. TELEX 70 99 85. **Document type:** monographic series.
Formerly: Ohio State University. Disaster Research Center. Report Series (ISSN 0078-4133)
Refereed Serial

UNIVERSITY OF OCCUPATIONAL AND ENVIRONMENTAL HEALTH. JOURNAL. see *OCCUPATIONAL HEALTH AND SAFETY*

PUBLIC HEALTH AND SAFETY

UNSCHEDULED EVENTS; research committee on disasters newsletter. see *SOCIOLOGY*

393.1   AU   ISSN 0042-0581
UNTERNEHMER. 1960. m. S.350. (Bundeskammer der Gewerblichen Wirtschaft) Oesterreichischer Wirtschaftsverlag, Nikolsdorfer Gasse 7-11, 1051 Vienna, Austria. TEL 0222-555585. TELEX 1-11669. Ed. Ernst Hofbauer. circ. 16,500.

614   SA
URBANISATION AND HEALTH NEWSLETTER. 1989. q. free. Medical Research Council, National Urbanisation and Health Research Programme, P.O. Box 19070, Tygerberg 7505, South Africa. TEL 27-21-938-0417. FAX 27-21-938-0342. Eds. Dr. John Seager, Michelle Galloway. circ. 750.
Document type: newsletter.
Description: Contains information about urbanization and related health matters of interest to community health groups and organizations involved in urban policy formulation.

363.11 004.7   US   ISSN 0742-938X
CODEN: VDTNEI
V D T NEWS. (Video Display Terminal); the computer health and safety report. 1984. bi-m. $147 (foreign $170). Microwave News, Box 1799, Grand Central Station, New York, NY 10163. TEL 212-517-2802. Ed. Louis Slesin. (back issues avail.) **Document type:** newsletter.
—BLDSC (9150.294270); CASDDS. CCC.

V F D B: ZEITSCHRIFT FUER FORSCHUNG UND TECHNIK IM BRANDSCHUTZ. (Vereinigung zur Foerderung des Deutschen Brandschutzes e.V.) see *ENGINEERING — Chemical Engineering*

VACCINE WEEKLY. see *PHARMACY AND PHARMACOLOGY*

614   SW   ISSN 1101-5888
HN571
VAEL & VE. 1968. 10/yr. SEK 280 (effective 1993). Socialstyrelsen - National Board of Health & Welfare, Sweden. (Subscr. to: Titel Data, S-112 86 Stockholm, Sweden) Ed. Leif-Rune Strandell. bk.rev.; charts; illus.; stat.; tr.lit. circ. 6,000. (also avail. in audio cassette)
Formed by the 1990 merger of: Socialnyt (ISSN 0037-7619) & Vigoer (ISSN 0346-4423)

VERKEHRSPSYCHOLOGISCHER INFORMATIONSDIENST. see *TRANSPORTATION — Roads And Traffic*

614.8   US
VETERINARY MEDICINE GUIDANCE MANUAL. (Subseries of: Compliance Program Guidance Manuals) irreg. $80 in the U.S., Canada, Mexico; elsewhere $160. U.S. Food and Drug Administration, Office of Pulic Affairs, 5600 Fisher's Ln., Rockville, MD 20857. TEL 301-443-3220. (Orders to: U.S. National Technical Information Service, 5285 Port Royal Rd., Springfield, VA 22161. TEL 703-487-4650. FAX 703-321-8547) **Document type:** government publication.
Description: Provides the latest information on and helps maintain surveillance or compliance-oriented plans and instructions directed to F.D.A. field operations, providing the needed direction from headquarters offices and bureaus in accomplishing F.D.A. regulatory obligations.

VIGILANCIA EPIDEMIOLOGICA DE LA RABIA PARA LAS AMERICAS. see *VETERINARY SCIENCE*

614.8   US   ISSN 0199-1345
VIRGINIA'S HEALTH. 1970. bi-m. free. Department of Health, Office of Health Education and Information, Box 2448, Ste. 245, Richmond, VA 23218. TEL 804-786-3552. FAX 804-371-6152. Ed. Dudley Olsson. circ. 6,000.

355.02   US
VITAL SIGNS (CAMBRIDGE). q. $25. International Physicians for the Prevention of Nuclear War, 126 Rogers St., Cambridge, MA 02142. TEL 617-868-5050. FAX 617-868-2560. Ed. Margaret Hewitt. bk.rev.; film rev.; charts; illus. circ. 30,000. (back issues avail.)
Description: Unites an international federation of 80 physicians' organizations worldwide practicing global social responsibility.

628   RU   ISSN 0321-4044
CODEN: VSTEAO
VODOSNABZHENIE I SANITARNAYA TEKHNIKA. 1913. m. $117 (effective 1996). Gosstroi, Moscow, Russia. (Dist. by: Mezhdunarodnaya Kniga, B. Yakimanka 39, 117049 Moscow, Russia) Ed. A.N. Radzivan. bk.rev.; bibl.; index. circ. 17,000. **Indexed:** C.I.S. Abstr., Chem.Abstr., Int.Build.Serv.Abstr., Pollut.Abstr.
—BLDSC (0041.000000); CASDDS.

614   US
VOLUNTEERS' VOICE FOR COMMUNITY SAFETY AND HEALTH. 1985. bi-m. $19 to non-members; members $15. National Safety Council, 1121 Spring Lake Dr., Itasca, IL 60143. TEL 708-285-1121. Ed. Kathy Henderson; Pub. Kevin H. Axe. illus.

614.8   UN   ISSN 1010-9609
CODEN: WDINE8
W H O DRUG INFORMATION. (French edition: Informations Pharmaceutiques O M S (ISSN 1011-5706) ceased 1993) q. 66 SFr.($53) World Health Organization, Distribution and Sales, 1211 Geneva 27, Switzerland. TEL 41-22-791-2475. FAX 41-22-791-4875. TELEX 27821-OMS. circ. 1,848. **Document type:** academic/scholarly publication.
—BLDSC (9311.903000); CASDDS; SWETS; UnCover.
Description: Communicates medicinal drug information that is either developed and issued by WHO or transmitted to WHO by research and regulatory agencies throughout the world.

W H O TECHNICAL REPORT SERIES. (World Health Organization) see *MEDICAL SCIENCES*

W N Y F. (With New York Firefighters) see *FIRE PREVENTION*

WALK. see *TRANSPORTATION — Roads And Traffic*

614   IO
WARTA DINAS KESEHATAN. m. Dinas Kesehatan, Jl. Kesehatan 10, Jakarta, Indonesia. illus.
Formerly: Warta Kesehatan (ISSN 0377-6549)

WARY CANARY; a news network for allergics, "sensitive birds," & environmental health advocates. see *ENVIRONMENTAL STUDIES*

WASHINGTON (STATE) DEPARTMENT OF SOCIAL AND HEALTH SERVICES. INCOME MAINTENANCE, COMMUNITY SOCIAL SERVICES AND MEDICAL ASSISTANCE. see *SOCIAL SERVICES AND WELFARE*

WATER SEWAGE AND EFFLUENT. see *WATER RESOURCES*

614   UN   ISSN 0049-8114
RA651
WEEKLY EPIDEMIOLOGICAL RECORD. (Text in English and French) 1925. w. 190 Fr.($167) World Health Organization, Distribution and Sales, CH-1211 Geneva 27, Switzerland. TEL 41-22-791-2476. FAX 41-22-791-4857. TELEX 27821-OMS. bibl.; charts; illus.; stat.; index. circ. 7,000. (also avail. in microfiche from CIS; back issues avail.) **Indexed:** Abstr.Hyg., Diar.Dis.Res., Excerp.Med., IIS, Ind.Vet., Irr.& Drain.Abstr., Protozool.Abstr., Rev.Appl.Entomol., Trop.Dis.Bull. **Document type:** trade publication.
—BLDSC (9284.780000); Faxon; SWETS.
Description: Provides an essential instrument for the collation and dissemination of data, including global number of AIDS cases, useful in disease surveillance and control on a global level.

614.8 658   UK
WHO'S WHO IN THE EMERGENCY & RESCUE SERVICES (YEAR). 1988. a. £21.50. Lincoln Publications, 28 Centre Point House, St. Giles High St., London WC2 8LW, England. TEL 0171-240-5562. FAX 0171-497-2811. Ed. James Hardwick. (back issues avail.) **Document type:** directory.

WISCONSIN. DEPARTMENT OF NATURAL RESOURCES. BIENNIAL WATER QUALITY REPORT TO CONGRESS. see *WATER RESOURCES*

628   GW   ISSN 0342-5967
WOHNMEDIZIN. 1962. bi-m. DM.55. Deutsche Gesellschaft fuer Wohnmedizin und Bauhygiene e.V., Postfach 368, 7513 Spoeck, Germany. TEL 07249-6932. bk.rev. (back issues avail.)
Document type: academic/scholarly publication.

614.85   SW   ISSN 1101-6930
WORKING ENVIRONMENT; arbetsmiljoee international. (Text in English) 1977. a. free. Foereningen foer Arbetarskydd - Swedish Work Environment Association, P.O. Box 17550, S-118 91 Stockholm, Sweden. TEL 46-8-668-14-60. FAX 46-8-668-25-05. Ed. Rolf Wikstroem. adv.; illus. circ. 20,000. **Indexed:** Biol.Dig., C.I.S. Abstr., Ergon.Abstr.

614 658.3   US   ISSN 1053-492X
WORKSITE WELLNESS WORKS. 1986. q. $20 (effective 1995-1996). Wellness Councils of America, 7101 Newport Ave., Ste. 311, Community Health Plaza, Omaha, NE 68152. TEL 402-572-3590. FAX 402-572-3594. Ed. Sandra Wendel. circ. 12,000. (back issues avail.) **Document type:** newsletter.
Description: Provides a forum for corporate health promotion and wellness programs, cost-benefits of health promotion programs, information from the Wellness Council National Network, and names the healthiest companies in the U.S.

614 361   NE   ISSN 0929-0850
WORLD DISASTERS REPORT. (Text in English; editions avail. in Arabic, French, Spanish) 1993. a. price varies. (International Federation of Red Cross and Red Crescent Societies) Martinus Nijhoff Publishers, Human Rights and International Law (Subsidiary of: Kluwer Academic Publishers Group), Postbus 163, 3300 AD Dordrecht, Netherlands. TEL 31-78-334911. FAX 31-78-334254. TELEX 29245 KAPG NL. (Dist. by: Kluwer Academic Publishers Group, P.O. Box 322, 3300 AH Dordrecht, Netherlands. TEL 31-78-524400. FAX 31-78-524474; N. America dist. addr.: Box 358, Accord Sta., Hingham, MA 02018-0358. TEL 617-871-6600. FAX 617-871-6528)
—BLDSC (9354.235000).

WORLD FEDERATION FOR MENTAL HEALTH. ANNUAL REPORT. see *PSYCHOLOGY*

WORLD FEDERATION FOR MENTAL HEALTH. NEWSLETTER. see *PSYCHOLOGY*

614   UN   ISSN 0043-8502
WORLD HEALTH. Spanish edition: Salud Mundial (ISSN 0250-9318); French edition: Sante du Monde (ISSN 0250-9326); Russian edition: Zdorov'e Mira (ISSN 0252-9270); Arabic edition: Al-Sihhah al-'Alamiyyah (ISSN 0250-9296) (German edition, Weltgesundheit (ISSN 0722-6209), ceased 1994.) 1948. bi-m. 30 SFr.($25) World Health Organization - Organisation Mondiale de la Sante, Distribution and Sales, CH-1211 Geneva 27, Switzerland. TEL 022-791-2111. FAX 41-22-791-4857. TELEX 27821-OMS. illus. (also avail. in microform from UMI; back issues avail.) **Indexed:** Abstr.Hyg., ASSIA, Biol.Abstr., Biol.Dig., CINAHL, Curr.Adv.Ecol.Sci., Curr.Adv.Genetics & Molec.Biol., Diar.Dis.Res., Environ.Abstr., Environ.Per.Bibl., Gdlns, Geo.Abstr., Helminthol.Abstr., Hlth.Ind., HR Rep., Mag.Ind., Mid.East: Abstr.& Ind., Pt.de Rep. (1979-), R.G., Repindex, So.Pac.Per.Ind., Telegen, Trop.Dis.Bull. **Document type:** consumer publication.
●Also available online. Vendor(s): Knight-Ridder, Inc., University Microfilms International.
Also available on CD-ROM. Producer(s): University Microfilms International.
—BLDSC (9356.040000); Faxon; SWETS; UMI; UnCover.
Description: A popular magazine illustrating the human side of efforts to improve world health.

PUBLIC HEALTH AND SAFETY

614 UN ISSN 0301-0740
RA8
WORLD HEALTH ORGANIZATION. HANDBOOK OF RESOLUTIONS AND DECISIONS OF THE WORLD HEALTH ASSEMBLY AND THE EXECUTIVE BOARD.. Arabic edition: Munazzamat al-Sihhiyyah al-'Alamiyyah. Dalil Qararat Jam'iyyah al-Sihhiyyah wal-Majlis al-Tanfidhi (ISSN 1010-0202); Chinese edition: Shijie Weisheng Dahui Ji Zhixing Weiyuanui Jueyi e Jueding Shouce (ISSN 1010-0245); French edition: Recueil des Resolutions et Decisions de l'Assemblee Mondiale de la Sante et du Conseil Executif (ISSN 1010-0229); Russian edition: Vsemirnaya Assambleya Zdravookhraneniya i Ispolnitel'nogo Komiteta. Sbornik Rezolyucii i Reshenii (ISSN 1010-0237); Spanish edition: Asamblea Mundial de la Salud y del Consejo Ejecutivo. Manual de Resoluciones y Decisiones (ISSN 1010-0210) 1948. biennial. World Health Organization, Distribution and Sales, CH-1211 Geneva 27, Switzerland. TEL 41-22-791-2476. FAX 41-22-791-4857. TELEX 27821-OMS. circ. 8,000.
—SWETS.

614 UN
WORLD HEALTH ORGANIZATION. REGIONAL OFFICE FOR AFRICA. REPORT OF THE REGIONAL COMMITTEE. 1959. a. World Health Organization, Regional Office for Africa - Organisation Mondiale de la Sante. Bureau Regional de l'Afrique, B.P. No. 6, Brazzaville, Congo. (also avail. in microfiche from CIS) **Indexed:** IIS.
Formerly: World Health Organization. Regional Office for Africa. Report of the Regional Committee. Minutes of the Plenary Session (ISSN 0512-3070)

614 UN ISSN 0510-8837
WORLD HEALTH ORGANIZATION. REGIONAL OFFICE FOR AFRICA. REPORT OF THE REGIONAL DIRECTOR. 1951. a. World Health Organization, Regional Office for Africa - Organisation Mondiale de la Sante. Bureau Regional de l'Afrique, B.P. No. 6, Brazzaville, Congo.

614 UN
WORLD HEALTH ORGANIZATION. REGIONAL OFFICE FOR THE EASTERN MEDITERRANEAN. ANNUAL REPORT OF THE REGIONAL DIRECTOR. 1950. a. free to qualified personnel. World Health Organization, Regional Office for the Eastern Mediterranean, P.O. Box 1517, Alexandria, Egypt. FAX 4838916. TELEX 54028. circ. 3,000. (also avail. in microfiche from CIS) **Indexed:** IIS.
Former titles (until 1989): World Health Organization. Regional Office for the Eastern Mediterranean. Biennial Report of the Regional Director; (until 1979): World Health Organization. Regional Office for the Eastern Mediterranean. Annual Report of the Regional Director (ISSN 0512-3089)

614 UN ISSN 0512-4921
WORLD HEALTH ORGANIZATION. REGIONAL OFFICE FOR THE WESTERN PACIFIC. ANNUAL REPORT OF THE REGIONAL DIRECTOR TO THE REGIONAL COMMITTEE FOR THE WESTERN PACIFIC. 1951. a. free. World Health Organization, Regional Office for the Western Pacific, P.O. Box 2932, Manila, Philippines. TEL 521-8421. FAX 521-1036. TELEX 63260. Ed. Alison Rowe. circ. 800.

614 UN
WORLD HEALTH REPORT. Key Title: Work of W H O. Spanish edition: Actividades de la O M S (ISSN 0250-8435); French edition: Activite de l'O M S (ISSN 0250-8427); Chinese edition: Shijie Weisheng Zuzhi Gongzuo (ISSN 0251-8724); Russian edition: Rabota V O Z (ISSN 0250-8745); Arabic edition: A'mal Munazzamat al-Sihhiyyah al-'Alamiyyah (ISSN 0250-8753) 1948. a. 15 SFr.($13.50) World Health Organization, Distribution and Sales, CH-1211 Geneva 27, Switzerland. TEL 41-22-791-2476. FAX 41-22-791-4857. TELEX 27821-OMS. circ. 8,000. (also avail. in microfiche from CIS) **Indexed:** IIS.
—BLDSC (9348.440000).
Formerly (until 1995): World Health Organization. Work of W H O (ISSN 0509-2558)

614.4 US ISSN 0740-0918
WORLDWIDE REPORT: EPIDEMIOLOGY. irreg. (approx. 30/yr.). $7 per no. (foreign $14 per no.). U.S. Joint Publications Research Service, Box 12507, Arlington, VA 22209. TEL 703-487-4630. (Orders to: NTIS, Springfield, VA 22161)
Former titles: World Epidemiology Review; Epidemiology Reports from the World Press.

353.9 US
WYOMING. DEPARTMENT OF HEALTH. ANNUAL REPORT. 1975. a. Department of Health, 135 Hathaway Bldg., Cheyenne, WY 82002. TEL 307-777-7959. FAX 307-777-5402. Ed. Helen G. Levine. circ. 500. **Document type:** government publication.
Formerly: Wyoming. Department of Health and Social Services. Annual Report (ISSN 0098-6984)

614.7 JA ISSN 0915-0498
CODEN: YEKHET
YAMAGUCHIKEN EISEI KOGAI KENKYU SENTA GYOSEKI HOKOKU. (Text in Japanese; titles and table of contents in English) 1958. a. exchange basis. Yamaguchiken Eisei Kogai Kenkyu Senta - Yamaguchi Prefectural Research Institute of Health, 5-67, Aoi 2-chome, Yamaguchi-shi, Yamaguchi-ken 753, Japan. TEL 0839-22-7630. FAX 0839-22-7632. charts; bibl.
—CASDDS.
Supersedes (in 1988): Yamaguchiken Eisei Kenkyujo Gyoseki Hokoku (ISSN 0513-4757)
Description: Contains original papers and research results on public health and medical issues.

628 333.91 US
YEARS AHEAD. 1982. q. $10. Pure Water of New England, 103 Union St., Watertown, MA 02172. TEL 617-924-0959. Ed. Patrick E. Mertens. circ. 10,000.

628 JA ISSN 0912-2826
YOKOHAMA CITY INSTITUTE OF HEALTH. ANNUAL REPORT. (Text in Japanese; summaries in English) 1962. a. Yokohama City Institute of Health, 2-17, 1-chome, Takigashira, Isogo-ku, Yokohama-shi 235, Japan. circ. 300.

YOKOHAMA MEDICAL JOURNAL. see MEDICAL SCIENCES

614 YU ISSN 0409-0314
ZAVOD ZA ZDRAVSTVENU ZASTITU S R SRBIJE. GLASNIK; casopis za preventivnu i socijalnu medicinu sa organizacijom zdravstvene. (Text in Serbo-Croatian; summaries in English, French and Russian) 1952. q. 120 din.($40) Zavod za Zdravstvenu Zastitu SR Srbije, Dr. Subotica 5, 11000 Belgrade, Yugoslavia. **Indexed:** Excerp.Med., Ind.Med.

614 RU ISSN 0044-1945
CODEN: ZDRVA4
ZDOROV'E. 1955. m. $76 (effective 1996). (Ministerstvo Zdravookhraneniya) Izdatel'stvo Pressa, Ul. Pravdy, 24, Moscow 125047, Russia. (Dist. in U.S. by: Victor Kamkin Inc., 4956 Boiling Brook Pkwy, Rockville, MD 20852. TEL 301-881-5973) Ed. M. Piradova. bk.rev.; bibl.; index. **Indexed:** Chem.Abstr.

614 BW ISSN 0044-1961
CODEN: ZDBEA9
ZDRAVOOKHRANENIE BELORUSSII. 1924-1941; resumed 1955. m. 46.50 Rub. (Ministerstvo Zdravookhraneniya) Izdatel'stvo Polymya, Ul. Zakharova 19, Minsk, Belarus. TEL 238-46-00. FAX 230-21-17. TELEX 411160. Ed. N.K. Deryugo. adv.; bk.rev.; charts; illus.; index. circ. 11,000. **Indexed:** Biol.Abstr., Chem.Abstr.
—CASDDS.
Former titles (until 1941): Meditsinsky Zhurnal B.S.S.R; (until 1938): Belorusskaya Meditsinskaya Mysl.

570 RU ISSN 0044-197X
ZDRAVOOKHRANENIE ROSSIISKOI FEDERATSII/PUBLIC HEALTHCARE OF THE RUSSIAN FEDERATION. 1957. bi-m. $80. (Ministerstvo Zdravookhraneniya i Meditsinnkoi Promyshlennosti Rossii) Izdatel'stvo Meditsina, Petroverigskii pereulok 6-8, 101000 Moscow, Russia. (Dist. by: Mezhdunarodnaya Kniga, B. Yakimanka 39, 117049 Moscow, Russia. TEL 7-095-2384600. FAX 7-095-2384634) Ed. A.I. Potapov. adv.; T.M./Kurushina. **Indexed:** Biol.Abstr., Ind.Med., Int.Aerosp.Abstr.
Description: Publishes scientific and practical materials on the health status of the population and on the development of public health services in autonomous republics, territories, regions and districts of the RSFSR.

614 XR ISSN 0044-1996
ZDRAVOTNICKE NOVINY;* tydenik pracovniku ve zdravotnictvi. 1955. w. $52.40. Strategie, s r.o., Drtinova 8, 150 00 Prague 5, Czech Republic. (Subscr. to: Artia, Ve Smeckach 30, 111 27 Prague 1, Czech Republic) Ed. Jiri Matous. circ. 35,000.

614 PL ISSN 0044-2011
RA421
ZDROWIE PUBLICZNE. 1885. m. $150. Ministerstwo Zdrowia i Opieki Spolecznej - Ministry of Health and Social Welfare, Ul. Miodowa 15, 00-923 Warsaw, Poland. TEL 48-22-312144. FAX 48-22-6359245. (Dist. by: Ars Polona-Ruch, Krakowskie Przedmiescie 7, Warsaw, Poland) bk.rev.; abstr.; charts; illus.; stat.; index. circ. 2,377. **Indexed:** Biol.Abstr., Excerp.Med., Ind.Med.
Description: Deals with social medicine, health care organization and health policy.

614 GW ISSN 0943-1853
ZEITSCHRIFT FUER GESUNDHEITSWISSENSCHAFTEN/JOURNAL OF PUBLIC HEALTH. (Text in English, German) 1993. q. DM.106 (foreign DM.118). Juventa Verlag GmbH, Ehretstr. 3, 69469 Weinheim, Germany. TEL 06201-61035. FAX 06201-13135. Ed.Bd. adv.; bk.rev.; circ. 500 (paid). **Document type:** academic/scholarly publication.

ZEITSCHRIFT FUER LAERMBEKAEMPFUNG. see PHYSICS — Sound

614.44 610 GW ISSN 0934-8859
QR46 CODEN: ZHUMEO
ZENTRALBLATT FUER HYGIENE UND UMWELTMEDIZIN. irreg. (6 nos./vol.). DM.1060 (foreign DM.1080). Gustav Fischer Verlag, Wollgrasweg 49, 70599 Stuttgart, Germany. TEL 0711-458030. FAX 0711-4580334. TELEX 7111488-FIBUCH. (Subscr. to: Postfach 720143, 70577 Stuttgart, Germany; U.S. address: VCH Publishers, Inc., 303 N.W. 12th Ave., Deerfield Beach, FL 33442-1788) Ed. E. Thofern. (also avail. in microfilm from VCI,PMC) **Indexed:** Biol.Abstr., Deep Sea Res.& Oceanogr.Abstr., Dent.Ind., Excerp.Med., Helminthol.Abstr., Ind.Med., Nutr.Abstr., Rev.Med.& Vet.Mycol. **Document type:** academic/scholarly publication.
—BLDSC (9508.530000); CASDDS; Faxon; Genuine Article; SWETS; UMI. **CCC.**
Incorporates: Zentralblatt fuer die Gesamte Hygiene und Ihre Grenzgebiete (ISSN 0049-8610); Former titles: Zentralblatt fuer Bakteriologie, Parasitenkunde, Infektionskrankenheiten und Hygiene. Series B: Krankenhaushygiene - Praeventive Medizin - Betriebshygiene (ISSN 0174-3015); Zentralblatt fuer Bakteriologie, Parasitenkunde, Infektionskrankheiten und Hygiene. Orginale Reihe B: Hygiene - Praeventive Medizin.

614 CC ISSN 1004-1257
ZHIYE YU JIANKANG/OCCUPATION AND HEALTH. (Text in Chinese) 1985. bi-m. Y19.80. Tianjin Institute of Labor Hygiene and Occupational Diseases, 221, Machangdao Street, Tianjin 300204, People's Republic of China. TEL 3283432. Ed. Zhang Yinde. circ. 100,000 (controlled). **Document type:** academic/scholarly publication.
Description: Popular science magazine for medical workers and safety-control technicians in industrial companies.
Refereed Serial

ZHONGGUO FUNU JIANKANG/CHINA WOMEN'S HEALTH. see MEDICAL SCIENCES — Obstetrics And Gynecology

614 CC ISSN 1001-0580
ZHONGGUO GONGGONG WEISHENG/CHINA'S PUBLIC HEALTH. (Text in Chinese) 1985. m. $19.20. Zhonghua Yufang Yixuehui (Shenyang) - China Preventive Medical Society (Shenyang), Jixian Jie, Heping Qu, Shenyang, Liaoning 110005, People's Republic of China. TEL 363643. (Dist. overseas by: Guoji Shudian - China International Book Trading Corp., P.O. Box 399, Beijing 100044, P.R.C.. TEL 8413063) Ed. Dai Zhicheng. adv.; B&W page $300, color page $500; adv. contact: Xiying Li. circ. 10,000.

614 CC ISSN 1001-0572
CODEN: ZGWXEQ
ZHONGGUO GONGGONG WEISHENG XUEBAO/CHINESE JOURNAL OF PUBLIC HEALTH. (Text in Chinese) 1982. bi-m. $12. Zhonghua Yufang Yixuehui (Shenyang) - China Preventive Medical Society (Shenyang), Jixian Jie, Heping Qu, Shenyang, Liaoning 110005, People's Republic of China. TEL 363643. (Dist. overseas by: Guoji Shudian - China International Book Trading Corp., P.O. Box 399, Beijing 100044, P.R.C.. TEL 8413063) Ed. Kan Xuegui. adv.: B&W page $300, color page $500; adv. contact: Xiying Li. circ. 3,000. —CASDDS.

ZIVOT I ZDRAVIJE; obitelski casopis za proucavanje i promicanje prirodnih zdravstvenih nacela. see *MEDICAL SCIENCES*

PUBLIC HEALTH AND SAFETY —
Abstracting, Bibliographies, Statistics

614.8 310 US
ADVANCES IN RISK ANALYSIS. 1983. irreg., vol.9, 1991. (Society for Risk Analysis) Plenum Publishing Corp., 233 Spring St., New York, NY 10013-1578. TEL 212-620-8000. FAX 212-463-0742. TELEX 23-421139. Ed.Bd. (back issues avail.) **Document type:** monographic series.
Refereed Serial

AIDS & T B WEEKLY ABSTRACTS FROM CONFERENCE PROCEEDINGS. see *MEDICAL SCIENCES — Abstracting, Bibliographies, Statistics*

614 600 US ISSN 1058-675X
AMERICAN PETROLEUM INSTITUTE. HEALTH AND ENVIRONMENTAL SCIENCES DEPARTMENT. REPORTS AND OTHER PUBLICATIONS, INDEX AND ABSTRACTS. 1978. irreg. free. American Petroleum Institute, Central Abstracting & Information Services, 275 Seventh Ave., New York, NY 10001-6708. Indexed: API Catal., API Hlth.& Environ., API Oil., API Pet.Ref., API Pet.Subst., API Transport. **Document type:** abstracting/indexing.
Former titles: American Petroleum Institute. Health and Environmental Sciences Department. Research Reports; American Petroleum Institute. Medicine and Biological Science Department. Medical Research Reports; American Petroleum Institute. Committee of Medicine and Environmental Health. Medical Research Reports.

312 BE ISSN 0522-7690
RA407.5.B5
ANNUAIRE STATISTIQUE DE LA SANTE PUBLIQUE/STATISTISCH JAARBOEK VAN VOLKSGEZONDHEID. (Text in Dutch) 1950. a. free. Ministere de la Sante Publique et de la Famille, Centre de Traitement de l'Information - Ministerie van Volksgezondheid en van het Gezin, Cite Administrative de l'Etat, Quartier Vesale, 1010 Brussels, Belgium. illus.; stat.

APPLIED HEALTH PHYSICS ABSTRACTS AND NOTES. see *PHYSICS — Abstracting, Bibliographies, Statistics*

614 318 AG
ARGENTINA. MINISTERIO DE SALUD Y ACCION SOCIAL. PROGRAMA NACIONAL DE ESTADISTICAS DE SALUD. BOLETIN. vol. 6, 1976. irreg. Ministerio de Salud y Accion Social, Direccion de Estadisticas de Salud, Alsina 301, Buenos Aires, Argentina.
Formerly: Argentina. Secretaria de Estado de Salud Publica. Programa Nacional de Estadisticas de Salud. Boletin.

614.86 BE ISSN 0770-237X
HE5614.5.B4
BELGIUM. INSTITUT NATIONAL DE STATISTIQUE. ACCIDENTS DE LA CIRCULATION SUR LA VOIE PUBLIQUE AVEC TUES ET BLESSES. Key Title: Accidents de la Circulation sur la Voie Publique avec Tues et Blesses. Dutch edition: Verkeersongevallen op de Openbare Weg met Doden of Gewonden (ISSN 0771-0577) (Text in Dutch, French) 1954. a. 220 BEF (foreign 275 BEF) (effective 1993). Institut National de Statistique, 44 rue de Louvain, B-1000 Brussels, Belgium. TEL 32-2-5486211. FAX 32-2-5486367. **Document type:** government publication.
Former titles (until 1973): Belgium. Institut National de Statistique. Statistique des Accidents de la Circulation sur la Voie Publique (ISSN 0067-5504); (until 1962): Belgium. Institut National de Statistique. Statistique des Accidents de Roulage (ISSN 0067-5512)

310 BE
BELGIUM. MINISTERE DE LA SANTE PUBLIQUE ET DE L'ENVIRONNEMENT. ADMINISTRATION DES ETABLISSEMENTS DE SOINS. ANNUAIRE STATISTIQUE DES HOPITAUX/BELGIUM. MINISTERIE VAN VOLKSGEZONDHEID EN LEEFMILIEU. BESTUUR VOOR DE VERZORGINGSINSTELLINGEN. STATISTISCH JAARBOEK VAN DE ZIEKENHUIZEN. (In 8 parts: Liste d'Adresses; Rapport Annuel; Activite dans les Hopitaux; Origine des Patients; Duree de Sejour Detaille; Activite des Medecins Hopitaliers; Personnel des Hopitaux; List d'Adresses des M R S) (Text in Dutch, French) 1962. a. free. Ministere de la Sante Publique et de l'Environnement, Administration des Etablissements de Soins, Service d'Etudes - Ministerie van Volksgezondheid en Leefmilieu, Bestuursafdeling voor de Verzorgingsinstellingen, Studiedienst, Cite Administrative de l'Etat, Quartier Vesale, B-1010 Brussels, Belgium. TEL 32-2-210-45-11. circ. 1,500. **Document type:** government publication.
Former titles: Belgium. Ministere de la Sante Publique et de la Famille. Annuaire Statistique des Hopitaux; Belgium. Ministere de la Sante et de la Famille. Premiers et Principaux Resultats Statistiques de l'Enquete dans les Etablissements de Soins.

614 016 YU ISSN 0350-0306
BILTEN DOKUMENTACIJE. ZASTITA NA RADU/BULLETIN OF DOCUMENTATION. SAFETY PRECAUTIONS. 1974. bi-m. $264. Jugoslovenski Centar za Tehnicku i Naucnu Dokumentaciju - Yugoslav Center for Technical and Scientific Documentation (YCTSD), Sl. Penezica-Krcuna 29-31, Box 724, 11000 Belgrade, Yugoslavia. Ed. Ljiljana Kojic-Bogdanovic.

304.6 CN ISSN 1188-1437
BRITISH COLUMBIA. DIVISION OF VITAL STATISTICS. QUARTERLY DIGEST. 1991. q. free. Ministry of Health, Division of Vital Statistics, 818 Fort St., Victoria, BC V8W 1H8, Canada. TEL 604-952-2558. FAX 604-952-2587. Ed. Julie M. Macdonald. **Document type:** government publication.
Description: Presents current statistical data for selected health status indicators on a regional basis, and discusses public health issues affecting British Columbia.

614.7 US ISSN 1047-8213
CODEN: CSIPEZ
C A SELECTS. INDOOR AIR POLLUTION. 1988. s-w. $220 to non-members; members $65 (effective 1996). Chemical Abstracts Service (Subsidiary of: American Chemical Society), 2540 Olentangy River Rd., Box 3012, Columbus, OH 43210-0012. TEL 614-447-3600. FAX 614-447-3713. TELEX 6842086. **Document type:** abstracting/indexing.
Formerly (until 1989): BIOSIS CAS Selects: Indoor Air Pollution.
Description: Covers the air pollution of indoor environments. Includes pollution from chemical contaminants, particulates, and biological agents.

614 UK ISSN 0957-4956
RA630.G73
CHARTERED INSTITUTE OF PUBLIC FINANCE AND ACCOUNTANCY. CEMETERIES STATISTICS. ACTUALS. 1982. a. £44. Chartered Institute of Public Finance and Accountancy, Statistical Information Service, 3 Robert St., London WC2N 6BH, England. TEL 0171-895-8823. FAX 0171-895-8825. (back issues avail.)
—BLDSC (3102.180000).
Supersedes in part (in 1989): Chartered Institute of Public Finance and Accountancy. Cemeteries and Crematoria Statistics. Actuals (ISSN 0263-2969); Which was formed by the merger of (1956-1982): Chartered Institute of Public Finance and Accountancy. Crematoria Statistics. Actuals (ISSN 0534-2104); (1979-1982): Chartered Institute of Public Finance and Accountancy. Cemeteries Statistics. Actuals (ISSN 0260-9959)

614 UK ISSN 0956-1439
RA630.G73
CHARTERED INSTITUTE OF PUBLIC FINANCE AND ACCOUNTANCY. CREMATORIA STATISTICS. ACTUALS. 1982. a. £34. Chartered Institute of Public Finance and Accountancy, Statistical Information Service, 3 Robert St., London WC2N 6BH, England. TEL 0171-895-8823. FAX 0171-895-8825. (back issues avail.)
Supersedes in part (in 1989): Chartered Institute of Public Finance and Accountancy. Cemeteries and Crematoria Statistics. Actuals (ISSN 0263-2969); Which was formed by the merger of (1956-1982): Chartered Institute of Public Finance and Accountancy. Crematoria Statistics. Actuals (ISSN 0534-2104); (1979-1982): Chartered Institute of Public Finance and Accountancy. Cemeteries Statistics. Actuals (ISSN 0260-9959)

614.8 UK ISSN 0266-9552
RA566.5.G7
CHARTERED INSTITUTE OF PUBLIC FINANCE AND ACCOUNTANCY. ENVIRONMENTAL HEALTH STATISTICS. ACTUALS. 1984. a. £44. Chartered Institute of Public Finance and Accountancy, Statistical Information Service, 3 Robert St., London WC2N 6BH, England. TEL 0171-895-8823. FAX 0171-895-8825.

CHARTERED INSTITUTE OF PUBLIC FINANCE AND ACCOUNTANCY. WASTE DISPOSAL STATISTICS. ACTUALS. see *PUBLIC ADMINISTRATION — Abstracting, Bibliographies, Statistics*

614 CL
CHILE. INSTITUTO NACIONAL DE ESTADISTICAS. ESTADISTICAS DE SALUD. RECURSOS Y ATENCIONES. 1965. a. Esc.1300 (US $8.50; elsewhere $9.10) (effective 1994). Instituto Nacional de Estadisticas, Av. Bulnes 418, Casilla 498, Correo 3 Santiago, Chile.

614 NE
COMPENDIUM GEZONDHEIDSSTATISTIEK NEDERLAND/COMPENDIUM HEALTH STATISTICS OF THE NETHERLANDS. (Text in Dutch and English) 1974. irreg. Centraal Bureau voor de Statistiek, Prinses Beatrixlaan 428, Voorburg, Netherlands. (Orders to: SDU-Publishers, Christoffel Plantijnstraat, The Hague, Netherlands) (Co-sponsor: Ministry of Public Health and Environmental Hygiene) circ. 2,000. **Document type:** government publication.

614 CY
CYPRUS. MINISTRY OF HEALTH. ANNUAL REPORT. (Text in Greek) 1920. a. Ministry of Health, Nicosia, Cyprus. FAX 357-2-303498. TELEX 5734. Ed. Dr. G. Malliotis. charts; stat. circ. 200. **Document type:** government publication.
Supersedes (in 1991): Cyprus. Ministry of Health. Department of Medical and Public Health Services. Annual Report; And the reports of the other departments: Psychiatric Services, Dental Services, General State Laboratory, and Pharmaceutical Services.

DOEDSAARSAGERNE/CAUSES OF DEATH IN DENMARK. see *POPULATION STUDIES — Abstracting, Bibliographies, Statistics*

DOKUMENTATION PUBLIC HEALTH, OEFFENTLICHES GESUNDHEITSWESEN, GESUNDHEITSWISSENSCHAFT. see *MEDICAL SCIENCES — Abstracting, Bibliographies, Statistics*

E C M T STATISTICAL REPORT ON ROAD ACCIDENTS. (European Council of Ministers of Transport) see *TRANSPORTATION — Abstracting, Bibliographies, Statistics*

610　　　　　　　　　　　　JA
EISEI TOKEI KARA MITA AICHI-KEN NO SUGATA. 1985. a. Aichi-ken Eiseibu Somu-Ka, 1-2, 3-chome, Sannomaru, Naka-ku, Nagoya-shi, Japan. circ. 200.

614 016　　　　NE　　ISSN 0924-5723
CODEN: EMPHA
EXCERPTA MEDICA. SECTION 17: PUBLIC HEALTH, SOCIAL MEDICINE & EPIDEMIOLOGY. 1955. 24/yr. fl.3426($2089) (effective 1996). Excerpta Medica (Subsidiary of: Elsevier Science B.V.), P.O. Box 548, 1000 AM Amsterdam, Netherlands. TEL 31-20-4853911. FAX 31-20-4853598. TELEX 18582 ESPA NL. (Dist. by: Elsevier Science Ireland Ltd., P.O. Box 85, Limerick, Ireland. TEL 353-61-471944. FAX 353-61-472144; Subscr. in U.S. and Canada to: Elsevier Science Inc., Box 882, Madison Sq. Sta., New York, NY 10159. TEL 212-989-5800. FAX 212-633-3990) adv.; index, cum.index. **Indexed:** Chem.Abstr., Popul.Ind. **Document type:** abstracting/indexing.
●Also available online. Vendor(s): Ovid Technologies, DIMDI, Data-Star, Knight-Ridder, Inc., JICST. Also available on CD-ROM. Producer(s): SilverPlatter Information, Inc.
—BLDSC (3835.875700). **CCC.**
 Formerly: Excerpta Medica. Section 17: Public Health, Social Medicine and Hygiene (ISSN 0014-4215)
 Description: Covers all aspects of public health and social medicine, and includes health planning and education, epidemiology and prevention of communicable disease, public health aspects of risk populations, food and nutrition and environmental radiation, medical ethics, the influence of life style on health and the epidemiological aspects of water supply and purification.

EXCERPTA MEDICA. SECTION 35: OCCUPATIONAL HEALTH AND INDUSTRIAL MEDICINE. see *MEDICAL SCIENCES — Abstracting, Bibliographies, Statistics*

EXCERPTA MEDICA. SECTION 46: ENVIRONMENTAL HEALTH AND POLLUTION CONTROL. see *ENVIRONMENTAL STUDIES — Abstracting, Bibliographies, Statistics*

GEORGIA VITAL STATISTICS REPORT. see *POPULATION STUDIES — Abstracting, Bibliographies, Statistics*

GREECE. NATIONAL STATISTICAL SERVICE. SOCIAL WELFARE AND HEALTH STATISTICS. see *SOCIAL SERVICES AND WELFARE — Abstracting, Bibliographies, Statistics*

HEALTH AND PERSONAL SOCIAL SERVICES STATISTICS FOR WALES. see *SOCIAL SERVICES AND WELFARE — Abstracting, Bibliographies, Statistics*

614.8 016　　US　　ISSN 0892-9351
HD7260
HEALTH AND SAFETY SCIENCE ABSTRACTS. 1973. 4/yr. $695 (foreign $745). (Institute of Safety and Systems Management) Cambridge Scientific Abstracts, 7200 Wisconsin Ave., 6th Fl., Bethesda, MD 20814. TEL 301-961-6750. FAX 301-961-6720. E-mail: market@csa.com. Ed. Evelyn Beck; Pub. Ted Caris. bk.rev.; abstr.; bibl.; tr.lit.; index, cum.index. (also avail. in magnetic tape; back issues avail.) **Indexed:** Oncol.Abstr. **Document type:** abstracting/indexing.
●Also available online. Vendor(s): Orbit Search Service (ORBIT).
Also available on CD-ROM. Producer(s): NISC, SilverPlatter Information, Inc. (PolTox1).
 Former titles: Safety Science Abstracts Journal (ISSN 0160-1342); Safety Science Abstracts (ISSN 0092-542X)
 Description: Abstracts journal on public health, occupational safety, and industrial hygiene.

362.10973　　US　　ISSN 1065-1403
RA407.3
HEALTH CARE STATE RANKINGS; health care in the 50 United States. 1993. a. $43.95. Morgan Quitno Corporation, Box 1656, Lawrence, KS 66044. TEL 913-841-3534. FAX 913-841-3568. Ed. Kathleen O'Leary Morgan.
 Description: Provides detailed, comparative statistical information on health care and health care finance in more than 470 categories for each of the 50 states.01873799xxx

312 614 360　　US　　ISSN 0362-9279
HA331
IDAHO. DEPARTMENT OF HEALTH AND WELFARE. ANNUAL SUMMARY OF VITAL STATISTICS. Key Title: Annual Summary of Vital Statistics (Boise). Cover title: Vital Statistics, Idaho. 1946. a. free. Department of Health and Welfare, Center for Vital Statistics and Health Policy, Statehouse, Boise, ID 83720. TEL 208-334-0685. FAX 208-334-0685. Ed. Janet Wick. stat.illus. circ. 800. (also avail. in microfiche from CIS) **Indexed:** SRI. **Document type:** government publication.
 Description: Covers statistics of Idaho. Includes population census, natality, mortality, marriages and divorces, induced abortions and more.

614　　US　　ISSN 1077-1212
HN51
INDEX OF SOCIAL HEALTH. a. Fordham Institute for Innovation in Social Policy, Fordham Graduate Center, Tarrytown, NY 10591.

INTERNATIONAL NARCOTICS CONTROL BOARD. STATISTICS ON PSYCHOTROPIC SUBSTANCES FOR (YEAR). see *PHARMACY AND PHARMACOLOGY — Abstracting, Bibliographies, Statistics*

368.384　　IT　　ISSN 0075-188X
ITALY. ISTITUTO NAZIONALE DI STATISTICA. STATISTICA DEGLI INCIDENTI STRADALI. 1953. a. L.23000 (effective 1992). Istituto Nazionale di Statistica, Via Cesare Balbo 16, 00100 Rome, Italy. FAX 06-46735198. **Document type:** government publication.

614　　IT　　ISSN 1121-1008
RA407.5.I8
ITALY. ISTITUTO NAZIONALE DI STATISTICA. STATISTICHE DELLA SANITA. 1958. a. L.27000 (effective 1992). Istituto Nazionale di Statistica, Via Cesare Balbo 16, 00100 Rome, Italy. FAX 06-46735198. circ. 1,150. **Document type:** government publication.
 Former titles (until 1989): Italy. Istituto Centrale di Statistica. Statistiche Sanitarie (ISSN 1121-0990); (until 1985): Italy. Istituto Centrale di Statistica. Annuario di Statistiche Sanitarie (ISSN 0075-1758)

628 360　　JA　　ISSN 0911-8403
HV411
JAPAN. MINISTRY OF HEALTH AND WELFARE. STATISTICS AND INFORMATION DEPARTMENT. HANDBOOK OF HEALTH AND WELFARE STATISTICS. Key Title: Kosei Tokei Yoran. English edition: Health and Welfare Statistics in Japan. (Text in Japanese) 1969. a. 2575 Yen (English ed. 2369 Yen). Ministry of Health and Welfare, Statistics and Information Department - Koseisho Daijin Kanbo Tokei Johobu, 7-3 Ichigaya-Honmura-cho, Shinjuku-ku, Tokyo 162, Japan. TEL 03-3260-3181. FAX 03-3269-8824. (Subscr. to: Health & Welfare Statistics Association, 5-13-14 Roppongi, Minato-ku, Tokyo, Japan. TEL 03-3586-3361. FAX 03-3584-4710) **Document type:** government publication.

614 312.3　　JA　　ISSN 0911-8489
JAPAN. MINISTRY OF HEALTH AND WELFARE. STATISTICS AND INFORMATION DEPARTMENT. STATISTICAL REPORT ON COMMUNICABLE DISEASES. Key Title: Densenbyo Tokei. (Text in English, Japanese) a. 2100 Yen. Ministry of Health and Welfare, Statistics and Information Department - Koseisho Daijin Kanbo Tokei Johobu, 7-3 Ichigaya Honmura-cho, Shinjuku-ku, Tokyo 162, Japan. TEL 03-3260-3181. FAX 03-3269-8824. (Subscr. to: Health & Welfare Statistics Association, 5-13-14 Roppongi, Minato-ku, Tokyo, Japan. TEL 03-3586-3361. FAX 03-3584-4710) **Document type:** government publication.
 Supersedes in part (in 1981): Japan. Ministry of Health and Welfare. Statistics and Information Department. Statistical Report on Communicable Diseases and Food Poisonings.

614　　JA　　ISSN 0911-8497
JAPAN. MINISTRY OF HEALTH AND WELFARE. STATISTICS AND INFORMATION DEPARTMENT. STATISTICAL REPORT ON FOOD POISONINGS. Key Title: Shokuchudoku Tokei. (Text in English, Japanese) a. 2987 Yen. Ministry of Health and Welfare, Statistics and Information Department - Koseisho Daijin Kanbo Tokei Johobu, 7-3 Ichigaya-Honmura-cho, Shinjuku-ku, Tokyo 162, Japan. TEL 03-3260-3181. FAX 03-3269-8824. (Subscr. to: Health and Welfare Statistics Association, 5-13-14 Roppongi, Minato-ku, Tokyo, Japan. TEL 03-3586-3361. FAX 03-3584-4710) **Document type:** government publication.
 Supersedes in part (in 1981): Japan. Ministry of Health and Welfare. Statistics and Information Department. Statistical Report on Communicable Diseases and Food Poisonings.

614 315　　JA　　ISSN 0448-3952
JAPAN. MINISTRY OF HEALTH AND WELFARE. STATISTICS AND INFORMATION DEPARTMENT. STATISTICAL REPORT ON PUBLIC HEALTH ADMINISTRATION AND SERVICES/EISEI GYOSEI GYOMU HOKOKU. (Text in Japanese) 1960. a. 4738 Yen. Ministry of Health and Welfare, Statistics and Information Department - Koseisho Daijin Kanbo Tokei Johobu, 7-3 Ichigaya Honmura-cho, Shinjuku-ku, Tokyo 162, Japan. TEL 03-3260-3181. FAX 03-3269-8824. (Subscr. to: Health & Welfare Statistics and Association, 5-13-14 Roppongi, Minato-ku, Tokyo, Japan. TEL 03-3586-3361. FAX 03-3584-4710) **Document type:** government publication.
 Formerly: Eisei Nenpo.

614.1　　US
KENTUCKY. CABINET FOR HUMAN RESOURCES. VITAL STATISTICS REPORT. Key Title: Kentucky Annual Vital Statistics Report. 1911. a. $10. Cabinet for Human Resources, Division of Vital Records & Health Development, 275 E. Main St., Frankfort, KY 40621. TEL 502-564-2757. circ. 600. **Indexed:** SRI. **Document type:** government publication.
 Former titles: Kentucky. Department for Human Resources. Selected Vital Statistics and Planning Data (ISSN 0145-5990); Kentucky Vital Statistics (ISSN 0098-6739); Kentucky Vital Statistics Report.

628　　UK　　ISSN 0969-3084
RA412.5.G7
KEY STATISTICAL INDICATORS FOR HEALTH IN WALES/DANGOSYDDION YSTADEGOL ALLWEDDOL AR GYFER LECHYD YNG NGHYMRU. 1983; N.S. 1993. a. £5. Welsh Office, Statistical Directorate, New Crown Buildings, Cathays Park, Cardiff CF1 3NQ, Wales. TEL 01222-285044. FAX 01222-825350. TELEX 498228. Ed. E. Swires-Hennessy. stat. circ. 750. (back issues avail.) **Document type:** government publication.
—BLDSC (5091.824600). **CCC.**
 Formerly (until 1993): Key Statistical Indicators for National Health Service Management in Wales (ISSN 0264-6714)

614　　NE　　ISSN 0075-6954
RA412.5.N4
KOSTEN EN FINANCIERING VAN DE GEZONDHEIDZORG IN NEDERLAND/COST OF HEALTH CARE IN THE NETHERLANDS. (Text in Dutch and English) 1953. irreg. Centraal Bureau voor de Statistiek, Prinses Beatrixlaan 428, Voorburg, Netherlands. (Orders to: SDU-Publishers, Christoffel Plantijnstraat 2, 2500 EA The Hague, Netherlands) **Document type:** government publication.

610　　FR　　ISSN 0298-8682
MEDEXPRES. m. 450 F. (foreign 550 F.). (Ministere de la Recherche et de la Technologie (D.I.S.T.)) Editions la Simarre, Z.I. No. 2 - rue Joseph-Cugnot, 37300 Joue-les-Tours, France. TEL 47-53-53-66. FAX 47-67-45-05. (Co-sponsor: Association pour la Promotion des Publications Medicales d'Expression Francaise (A.P.P.M.F.)) bibl.
 Description: Publishes summaries of French health journals.

PUBLIC HEALTH AND SAFETY — ABSTRACTING, BIBLIOGRAPHIES, STATISTICS

614 016 US ISSN 1077-5587
RA410.A1 CODEN: MDCRB
MEDICAL CARE RESEARCH AND REVIEW. 1944. q. $59 to individuals; institutions $110 (effective Sep. 1995). (Foundation of the American College of Healthcare Executives) Sage Publications, Inc., 2455 Teller Rd., Thousand Oaks, CA 91320. TEL 805-499-0721. FAX 805-499-0871. E-mail: libraries@sagepub.com. (Overseas subscr. to: Sage Publications Ltd., 6 Bonhill St., London EC2A 4PU, England) Ed. Thomas Rice. bibl. circ. 1,300. (also avail. in microform from UMI; back issues avail.; reprint service avail. from UMI) **Indexed:** Abstr.Health Care Manage.Stud., Hosp.Lit.Ind., I.P.A., Psychol.Abstr. (1992-). **Document type:** academic/scholarly publication.
—BLDSC (5526.908000); Faxon; SWETS; UMI; UnCover. **CCC.**
Former titles (until Mar. 1995): Medical Care Review (ISSN 0025-7087); Public Health Economics and Medical Care Abstracts.
Description: Analyzes, critiques, and synthesizes literature and research in the field of health care. *Refereed Serial*

MEDIZIN IM UMWELTSCHUTZ. see *MEDICAL SCIENCES — Abstracting, Bibliographies, Statistics*

614 310 US ISSN 0539-7413
RA407.4.M5
MICHIGAN HEALTH STATISTICS. 1898. a. $11. Department of Public Health, Office of State Registrar and Division for Health Statistics, 3423 N. Logan St., Box 30195, Lansing, MI 48909. TEL 517-335-8705. FAX 517-335-8711. Ed. Dr. Janet Eyster. illus. circ. 350. (also avail. in microfiche)
Formerly: Michigan Public Health Statistics.
Description: Longitudinal and annual natality, mortality, marriage and divorce for the state of Michigan.

312 US ISSN 0094-5641
RA407.4.M6
MINNESOTA HEALTH STATISTICS. 1950. a. $12.60. Department of Health, Center for Health Statistics, 717 Delaware St., S.E., Box 9441, Minneapolis, MN 55440-9441. TEL 612-623-5000. FAX 612-623-5043. Ed. Linda Salkowicz. circ. 900. **Indexed:** SRI. **Document type:** government publication.

MISSOURI MONTHLY VITAL STATISTICS. see *POPULATION STUDIES — Abstracting, Bibliographies, Statistics*

312 US ISSN 0098-1974
HA471
MISSOURI VITAL STATISTICS. a. free. Department of Health, Center for Health Statistics, Box 570, Jefferson City, MO 65102. TEL 314-751-6272. Ed. Garland Land. circ. 900. (also avail. in microfiche from CIS) **Indexed:** SRI. **Document type:** government publication.
Description: Contains tables and graphs.

614 US ISSN 0077-1198
HA481
MONTANA VITAL STATISTICS. 1954. a. free. Department of Health and Environmental Sciences, Bureau of Records & Statistics, Cogswell Bldg., Helena, MT 59620. TEL 406-444-2614. FAX 406-444-2606. Ed. Sam H. Sperry. circ. 850. **Indexed:** SRI. **Document type:** government publication.
Former titles: Montana. State Department of Health. Annual Statistical Supplement (ISSN 0097-9120); Montana State Board of Health. Annual Statistical Supplement (ISSN 0097-9112)

NARCOTIC DRUGS: ESTIMATED WORLD REQUIREMENTS FOR (YEAR). see *PHARMACY AND PHARMACOLOGY — Abstracting, Bibliographies, Statistics*

NETHERLANDS. CENTRAAL BUREAU VOOR DE STATISTIEK. JAARSTATISTIEK VAN DE BEVOLKING/NETHERLANDS. CENTRAL BUREAU OF STATISTICS. ANNUAL POPULATION STATISTICS. see *POPULATION STUDIES — Abstracting, Bibliographies, Statistics*

312.267 US ISSN 0085-428X
RA407.4.N8
NORTH CAROLINA COMMUNICABLE DISEASE MORBIDITY STATISTICS. 1918. a., latest 1988. free. Department of Environment, Health and Natural Resources, Division of Epidemiology, Box 27687, Raleigh, NC 27611-7687. TEL 919-733-3419. FAX 919-733-0490. stat. circ. 600. **Document type:** government publication.

NORTH CAROLINA VITAL STATISTICS. see *POPULATION STUDIES — Abstracting, Bibliographies, Statistics*

362.1021 NO ISSN 0332-7906
HA1501
NORWAY. STATISTISK SENTRALBYRAA. HELSESTATISTIKK/HEALTH STATISTICS. (Subseries of its Norges Offisielle Statistikk) (Text in Norwegian; summaries in English) 1962. a. NOK 75. Statistisk Sentralbyraa, P.O. Box 8131-Dep., N-0033 Oslo 1, Norway. TEL 47-22-864500. FAX 47-22-864976. circ. 1,200. **Document type:** government publication.

613 616 FR ISSN 1013-8293
NUTRICION EN SALUD PUBLICA. French edition: Nutrition de Sante Publique (ISSN 1013-8056); English edition: Public Health Nutrition (ISSN 1013-8285) (Text in Spanish) 1980. 2/yr. 240 F. for 2 yrs. Centre International de l'Enfance - International Children's Center, Chateau de Longchamp, Bois de Boulogne, 75016 Paris, France. TEL 1-45-20-79-92. FAX 1-45-25-73-67.
Formerly (until 1989): Produccion Alimentaria - Nutricion.
Description: Covers nutritional requirements, breast-feeding, types of diet, food, studies of dietary intake and nutritional status, indicators for nutritional surveillance, diseases and their effects, nutrition education, personnel training.

613 616 FR ISSN 1013-8056
NUTRITION DE SANTE PUBLIQUE. English edition: Public Health Nutrition (ISSN 1013-8285); Spanish edition: Nutricion en Salud Publica (ISSN 1013-8293) 1980. 2/yr. 240 F. for 2 yrs. Centre International de l'Enfance - International Children's Center, Chateau de Longchamp, Bois de Boulogne, 75016 Paris, France. TEL 1-45-20-79-92. FAX 1-45-25-73-67.
Formerly (until 1989): Production Alimentaire - Nutrition.
Description: Covers nutritional requirements, breast-feeding, types of diet, food, studies of dietary intake and nutritional status, indicators for nutritional surveillance, nutritional diseases, education, personnel training and programs.

614 DK ISSN 0906-3013
NYHEDSINFORMATION FOR SOCIAL-, SYGEHUS- OG SUNDHEDSSEKTOR. 1982. m. DKK 320. Forlag for Social- og Sundhedssektor, Vibeholms Alle 11-15, 2605 Bronoby, Denmark. TEL 43-43-43-80. FAX 43-43-60-29. illus.
Former titles (until 1990): Informationstidsskrift for Social- og Sundhedssektor (ISSN 0901-8565); (until 1984): Informationskatalog for Social- og Sundhedssektor (ISSN 0109-3487)

312 US ISSN 0098-5651
RA407.4.O6
OKLAHOMA HEALTH STATISTICS. a. free. Department of Health, Public Health Statistics Division, Box 53551, Oklahoma City, OK 73105. TEL 405-271-5600. illus.
Formerly (1943-1971): Public Health Statistics, State of Oklahoma (ISSN 0099-118X)

312 614
OREGON PUBLIC HEALTH STATISTICS REPORT.* Cover title: Oregon Health Division, Vital Statistics Annual Report. Variant title: Oregon Vital Statistics. 1960. a. $10. State Health Division, 800 N.E. Oregon St., Portland, OR 97232-2109. TEL 503-229-5897. stat. circ. 600. **Indexed:** SRI.

PREVENTION IN HUMAN SERVICES; summaries, reviews & index to the world's literature in community mental health. see *PSYCHOLOGY — Abstracting, Bibliographies, Statistics*

614 US ISSN 0079-7588
PUBLIC HEALTH CONFERENCE ON RECORDS AND STATISTICS. PROCEEDINGS. no.2, 1950. irreg., latest 1993. U.S. National Center for Health Statistics, 6525 Belcrest Rd., Hyattsville, MD 20782. TEL 301-436-8500. **Document type:** government publication, proceedings.

613 616 FR ISSN 1013-8285
PUBLIC HEALTH NUTRITION. French edition: Nutrition de Sante Publique (ISSN 1013-8056); Spanish edition: Nutricion en Salud Publica (ISSN 1013-8293) (Text in English) 1980. 2/yr. 240 F. for 2 yrs. Centre International de l'Enfance - International Childern's Center, Chateau de Longchamp, Bois de Boulogne, 75016 Paris, France. TEL 1-45-20-79-92. FAX 1-45-25-73-67.
Formerly (until 1989): Food Production - Nutrition.
Description: Covers nutritional requirements, breast-feeding, types of diet, food, studies of dietary intake and nutritional status, indicators for nutritional surveillance, nutritional diseases, education, personnel training, programs.

614.8 333.79 US
PUBLIC USE ENERGY STATISTICAL DATA BASE. Short title: P U E S D B. m. $200 per issue in US, Canada, Mexico; elsewhere $400. (U.S. Department of Energy, Energy Information Administration) U.S. National Technical Information Service, 5825 Port Royal Rd., Springfield, VA 22161. TEL 703-487-4630. (magnetic tape)
Description: Provides a machine-readable "mirror image" of published energy-related information to the analyst in an efficient and concise way.

614 360 PR
PUERTO RICO. DEPARTMENT OF HEALTH. BOLETIN ESTADISTICO. (Text in Spanish) 1979. irreg. free. Department of Health, Auxiliary Secretariat of Planning, Evaluation and Statistics, Division of Statistics, Box 70184, San Juan, PR 00936. TEL 809-274-7875. FAX 809-274-7877. circ. 500. **Document type:** government publication.

614.42 310 PR
PUERTO RICO. DEPARTMENT OF HEALTH. INFORME ANUAL DE ESTADISTICAS INSTITUCIONALES. (Text in Spanish) 1974. a. Department of Health, Auxiliary Secretariat of Planning, Evaluation and Statistics, Division of Statistics, P.O. Box 70184, San Juan, PR 00936. TEL 809-274-7875. FAX 809-274-7877. charts. circ. 900. (back issues avail.) **Document type:** government publication.
Former titles: Puerto Rico. Department of Health. Annual Health Services Report; Puerto Rico. Statistics, Analysis and Control of Information. Annual Vital Statistics Report.
Description: Information on patients, facilities, and services by municipality and region.

REFERATIVNYI ZHURNAL. ORGANIZATSIYA I BEZOPASNOST' DOROZHNOGO DVIZHENIYA. see *TRANSPORTATION — Abstracting, Bibliographies, Statistics*

614.84 016 RU ISSN 0202-9898
TH9111
REFERATIVNYI ZHURNAL. POZHARNAYA OKHRANA. 1971. m. $262 (effective 1996). Vsesoyuznyi Institut Nauchno-Tekhnicheskoi Informatsii (VINITI), Baltiiskaya ul., 14, Moscow A-219, Russia. (Subscr. to: Mezhdunarodnaya Kniga, Dimitrova ul. 39, 113095 Moscow, Russia) **Document type:** abstracting/indexing.

614 UK ISSN 0264-1178
SCOTTISH HOME AND HEALTH DEPARTMENT. STATISTICAL BULLETIN. 1983. q. Scottish Home and Health Department, New St. Andrew's House, Rm. 5-52, Edinburgh EH1 3TG, Scotland. TEL 031-244-4991. **Document type:** government publication.

614 US
▼**SISTER COMMUNITIES HEALTH PROFILES OF THE U S - MEXICO BORDER/PERFILES DE SALUD DE LAS COMUNIDADES HERMANAS DE LA FRONTERA MEXICO - ESTADOS UNIDOS.** (Text in English, Spanish) 1994. a. $75 includes all organization publications; corporate rate $500. (United States Mexico Border Health Association) Pan American Health Organization, El Paso Field Office, 6006 N. Mesa, Ste. 600, El Paso, TX 79912. TEL 915-581-6645. FAX 915-833-4768. E-mail: vilchish@paho.org. Ed. Dr. Hugo Vilchis-Licon. **Document type:** monographic series.

PUBLIC HEALTH AND SAFETY — ABSTRACTING, BIBLIOGRAPHIES, STATISTICS

610 015 SW ISSN 0036-1879
SWEDEN. SJUKVAARDENS OCH SOCIALVAARDENS PLANERINGS- OCH RATIONALISERINGSINSTITUT. S P R I LITTERATURTJAENST. Short title: S P R I Litteraturtjaenst. (Text and summaries in English and Swedish) 1968. 10/yr. SEK 350. Sjukvaardens och Socialvaardens Planerings- och Rationaliseringsinstitut - Swedish Planning and Rationalization Institute of the Health and Social Services, Spris Bibliotek, P.O. Box 70487, 107 26 Stockholm, Sweden. TEL 08-702-4600. FAX 08-702-4799. bibl.; index. **Document type:** abstracting/indexing.
 Supersedes: C S B Literaturtjaenst.

614.8 610 SW ISSN 0346-8992
RA407.5.S8
SWEDEN. STATISTISKA CENTRALBYRAAN. STATISTISKA MEDDELANDEN. SUBGROUP HS (PUBLIC HEALTH AND MEDICAL CARE). (Text in Swedish; summaries in English) 1976. irreg. SEK 500 (effective 1992). Statistiska Centralbyraan, Publishing Unit, S-701 89 Oerebro, Sweden. **Document type:** abstracting/indexing.

614 JA
TOYAMA-KEN EISEI TOKEI NENPO/TOYAMA PREFECTURE. ANNUAL REPORT OF PUBLIC HEALTH. (Text in Japanese) 1949. a. free. Toyama-ken Kosei-bu - Toyama Prefecture, Welfare Department, 1-7 Shin-Sogawa, Toyama 930, Japan. circ. 400.

312 US ISSN 0147-3956
RA407.3 CODEN: NADADR
U.S. NATIONAL CENTER FOR HEALTH STATISTICS. ADVANCE DATA FROM VITAL AND HEALTH STATISTICS. no.47, 1979. irreg. U.S. National Center for Health Statistics, 6525 Belcrest Rd., Hyattsville, MD 20782. TEL 301-436-8500. **Indexed:** Nutr.Abstr. **Document type:** government publication.

317 016 US ISSN 0278-4912
Z7553.M43
U.S. NATIONAL CENTER FOR HEALTH STATISTICS. CATALOG OF PUBLICATIONS. a. free. U.S. National Center for Health Statistics, 6525 Belcrest Rd., Hyattsville, MD 20782. TEL 301-436-8500. **Document type:** government publication, catalog.
 Formerly: U.S. National Center for Health Statistics. Current Listing and Topical Index to the Vital and Health Statistics Series (ISSN 0092-7287)

312 US ISSN 0083-2014
RA409
U.S. NATIONAL CENTER FOR HEALTH STATISTICS. VITAL AND HEALTH STATISTICS. SERIES 1. PROGRAMS AND COLLECTION PROCEDURES. 1963. irreg., latest no.34. price varies. U.S. National Center for Health Statistics, Data Dissemination Branch, 6525 Belcrest Rd., Hyattsville, MD 20782. TEL 301-436-8500. (Orders to: Superintendent of Documents, U.S. Government Printing Office, Box 371954, Pittsburgh, PA 15250-7954. TEL 202-512-1800. FAX 202-512-2250) **Indexed:** Chic.Per.Ind., Excerp.Med. **Document type:** government publication, monographic series.

312 US ISSN 0083-2057
 CODEN: VHSBA
U.S. NATIONAL CENTER FOR HEALTH STATISTICS. VITAL AND HEALTH STATISTICS. SERIES 2. DATA EVALUATION AND METHODS RESEARCH. 1963. irreg., latest no.121. price varies. U.S. National Center for Health Statistics, Data Dissemination Branch, 6525 Belcrest Rd., Hyattsville, MD 20782. TEL 301-436-8500. (Orders to: Superintendent of Documents, U.S. Government Printing Office, Box 371954, Pittsburgh, PA 15250-7954. TEL 202-512-1800. FAX 202-512-2250) **Indexed:** Excerp.Med., Popul.Ind. **Document type:** government publication.

312 US ISSN 0083-2065
U.S. NATIONAL CENTER FOR HEALTH STATISTICS. VITAL AND HEALTH STATISTICS. SERIES 3. ANALYTICAL STUDIES. 1964. irreg., latest no.29. price varies. U.S. National Center for Health Statistics, Data Dissemmination Branch, 6525 Belcrest Rd., Hyattsville, Hyattsville, MD 20782. TEL 301-436-8500. (Orders to: Superintendent of Documens, U.S. Government Printing Office, Box 371954, Pittsburgh, PA 15250-7954. TEL 202-512-1800. FAX 202-512-2250) **Indexed:** Excerp.Med. **Document type:** government publication.

312 US ISSN 0083-2073
HA37
U.S. NATIONAL CENTER FOR HEALTH STATISTICS. VITAL AND HEALTH STATISTICS. SERIES 4. DOCUMENTS AND COMMITTEE REPORT. 1965. irreg., latest no.29. price varies. U.S. National Center for Health Statistics, Data Dissemination Branch, 6525 Belcrest Rd., Hyattsville, MD 20782. TEL 301-436-8500. (Orders to: Superintendent of Documents, U.S. Government Printing Office, Box 371954, Pittsburgh, PA 15250-7954. TEL 202-512-1800. FAX 202-512-2250) **Indexed:** Excerp.Med. **Document type:** government publication.

312 US ISSN 0892-8959
U.S. NATIONAL CENTER FOR HEALTH STATISTICS. VITAL AND HEALTH STATISTICS. SERIES 5. COMPARATIVE INTERNATIONAL VITAL AND HEALTH STATISTICS REPORTS. 1984. irreg, no.5. price varies. U.S. National Center for Health Statistics, Data Dissemination Branch, 6525 Belcrest Rd., Hyattsville, MD 20782. TEL 301-436-8500. (Orders to: Superintendent of Documents, U.S. Government Printing Office, Box 371954, Pittsburgh, PA 15250-7954. TEL 202-512-1800. FAX 202-512-2250) **Indexed:** Excerp.Med. **Document type:** government publication, monographic series.
 Description: Comprises analytical and descriptive reports comparing U.S. vital and health statistics with those of other countries.

312 150 US
U.S. NATIONAL CENTER FOR HEALTH STATISTICS. VITAL AND HEALTH STATISTICS. SERIES 6. COGNITION AND SURVEY MEASUREMENT. 1989. irreg., no.7. price varies. U.S. National Center for Health Statistics, Data Dissemination Branch, 6525 Belcrest Rd., Hyattsville, MD 20782. TEL 301-436-8500. (Orders to: Superintendent of Documents, U.S. Government Printing Office, Box 371954, Pittsburgh, PA 15250-7954. TEL 202-512-1800. FAX 202-512-2250) **Indexed:** Excerp.Med. **Document type:** government publication, monographic series.
 Description: Comprises research from the National Laboratory for Collaborative Research in Cognition and Survey Measurement, using methods of cognitive science to design, evaluate, and test survey instruments,

614 US ISSN 0083-1972
U.S. NATIONAL CENTER FOR HEALTH STATISTICS. VITAL AND HEALTH STATISTICS. SERIES 10. DATA FROM THE HEALTH INTERVIEW SURVEY. 1963. irreg., no.191. price varies. U.S. National Center for Health Statistics, Data Dissemination Branch, 6526 Belcrest Rd., Hyattsville, MD 20782. TEL 301-436-8500. (Orders to: Superintendent of Documents, U.S. Government Printing Office, Box 371954, Pittsburgh, PA 15250-7954. TEL 202-512-1800. FAX 202-512-2250) **Indexed:** Excerp.Med. **Document type:** government publication.

614 US
U.S. NATIONAL CENTER FOR HEALTH STATISTICS. VITAL AND HEALTH STATISTICS. SERIES 11. DATA FROM THE HEALTH AND NUTRITION EXAMINATION SURVEY. Title varies: Data from the National Health Examination Survey and the National Health and Nutrition Examination Survey. 1964. irreg., latest no.242. price varies. U.S. National Center for Health Statistics, Data Dissemination Branch, 6525 Belcrest Rd., Hyattsville, Hyattsville, MD 20782. TEL 301-436-8500. (Orders to: Superintendent of Documents, U.S. Government Printing Office, Box 371954, Pittsburgh, PA 15250-7954. TEL 202-512-1800. FAX 202-512-2250) **Indexed:** Excerp.Med. **Document type:** government publication.
 Formerly: U.S. National Center for Health Statistics. Vital and Health Statistics. Series 11. Data from the Health Examination Survey (ISSN 0083-1980)

614 US
U.S. NATIONAL CENTER FOR HEALTH STATISTICS. VITAL AND HEALTH STATISTICS. SERIES 14. DATA ON HEALTH RESOURCES. 1968. irreg., latest no.34. price varies. U.S. National Center for Health Statistics, Data Dissemination Branch, 6525 Belcrest Rd., Hyattsville, MD 20782. TEL 301-436-8500. (Orders to: Superintendent of Documents, U.S Government Printing Office, Box 371954, Pittsburgh, PA 15250-7954. TEL 202-574-1800. FAX 202-574-2250) **Indexed:** Excerp.Med. **Document type:** government publication.
 Formerly: U.S. National Center for Health Statistics. Vital and Health Statistics. Series 14. Data on Health Resources: Manpower and Facilities (ISSN 0083-1999)

614 US ISSN 0083-2022
U.S. NATIONAL CENTER FOR HEALTH STATISTICS. VITAL AND HEALTH STATISTICS. SERIES 20. DATA ON MORTALITY. 1965. irreg., latest no.25. price varies. U.S. National Center for Health Statistics, Data Dissemination Branch, 6525 Belcrest Rd., Hyattsville, MD 20782. TEL 301-436-8500. (Orders to: Superintendent of Documents, U.S. Government Printing Office, Box 371954, Pittsburgh, PA 15250-7954. TEL 202-512-1800. FAX 202-512-2250) **Indexed:** Excerp.Med. **Document type:** government publication.
 Incorporates in part: U.S. National Center for Health Statistics. Vital and Health Statistics. Series 22. Data on Natality and Mortality Surveys (ISSN 0083-2049)

312 US ISSN 0083-2030
U.S. NATIONAL CENTER FOR HEALTH STATISTICS. VITAL AND HEALTH STATISTICS. SERIES 21. DATA ON NATALITY, MARRIAGE, AND DIVORCE. 1964. irreg., latest no.51. price varies. U.S. National Center for Health Statistics, Data Dissemination Branch, 6525 Belcrest Rd., Hyattsville, MD 20782. TEL 301-436-8500. (Orders to: Superintendent of Documents, U.S. Government Printing Office, Box 371954, Pittsburgh, PA 15250-7954. TEL 202-512-1800. FAX 202-512-2250) **Indexed:** Excerp.Med., Popul.Ind. **Document type:** government publication.
 Incorporates in part: U.S. National Center for Health Statistics. Vital and Health Statistics. Series 22. Data on Natality and Mortality Surveys (ISSN 0083-2049)

312 US ISSN 0278-5234
U.S. NATIONAL CENTER FOR HEALTH STATISTICS. VITAL AND HEALTH STATISTICS. SERIES 23. DATA FROM THE NATIONAL SURVEY OF FAMILY GROWTH. 1976. irreg., latest no.15. U.S. National Center for Health Statistics, Data Dissemination Branch, 6525 Belcrest Rd., Hyattsville, MD 20782. TEL 301-436-8500. (Subscr. to: Superintendent of Documents, U.S. Government Printing Office, Box 371954, Pittsburgh, PA 15250-7954. TEL 202-512-1800. FAX 202-512-2250) **Indexed:** Popul.Ind. **Document type:** government publication.

312 US
U.S. NATIONAL CENTER FOR HEALTH STATISTICS. VITAL AND HEALTH STATISTICS. SERIES 24. COMPILATIONS OF DATA ON NATALITY, MORTALITY, DIVORCE, AND INDUCED TERMINATIONS OF PREGNANCY. 1989. irreg., no.4. price varies. U.S. National Center for Health Statistics, Data Dissemination Branch, 6525 Belcrest Rd., Hyattsville, MD 20782. TEL 301-436-8500. (Orders to: Superintendent of Documents, U.S. Government Printing Office, Box 371954, Pittsburgh, PA 15250-7954. TEL 202-512-1800. FAX 202-512-2250) **Indexed:** Excerp.Med. **Document type:** government publication, monographic series.
 Description: Reports on trends of births, deaths, marriages and divorces, along with abortions.

614.109 US ISSN 0083-6710
HA203
VITAL STATISTICS OF THE UNITED STATES. (In 4 vols: Vol.1 Natality; Vol.2 (2 vols.) Mortality; Vol.3 Marriage and Divorce) 1937. a. price varies. U.S. National Center for Health Statistics, Data Dissemination Branch, 6525 Belcrest Rd., Hyattsville, MD 20782. TEL 301-436-8500. (Orders to: Superintendent of Documents, U.S. Government Printing Office, Box 371954, Pittsburgh, PA 15250-7954. TEL 202-512-2250; Or: Bernan, 4611-F Assembly Dr., Lanham, MD 20706. TEL 301-459-7666. FAX 301-459-0056) **Document type:** government publication.

628 016   UN   ISSN 0083-761X
WASTE MANAGEMENT RESEARCH ABSTRACTS. (Text in English) 1965. biennial. free. International Atomic Energy Agency, Wagramerstr. 5, P.O. Box 100, A-1400 Vienna, Austria. TEL 43-1-209-2360. FAX 43-1-209-5302. E-mail: fossett@adp01.iaea.or.at. circ. 650. **Document type:** abstracting/indexing.

614   UN   ISSN 0250-3794
RA651
WORLD HEALTH STATISTICS ANNUAL. Russian edition: Ezegodnik Mirovoj Sanitarnoj Statistiki (ISSN 0250-8664) (Text in English, French) a. $90. World Health Organization, Distribution and Sales, 1211 Geneva 27, Switzerland. TEL 41-22-791-2476. FAX 41-22-791-4857. TELEX 27821-OMS. circ. 4,800. (also avail. in microfiche from CIS) **Indexed:** IIS.
—BLDSC (9356.050000); SWETS.
Formerly (until 1965): Annual Epidemiological and Vital Statistics (ISSN 0509-2531)
Description: Contains life tables, changing morbidity and mortality rates for virtually every country in the world.

614   UN   ISSN 0379-8070
RA651   CODEN: WHSQDQ
WORLD HEALTH STATISTICS QUARTERLY/RAPPORT TRIMESTRIEL DE SANITARES MONDIALES. (Text in English or French) 1947. q. $88. World Health Organization, Distribution and Sales, 1211 Geneva 27, Switzerland. TEL 41-22-791-2476. FAX 41-22-791-4857. TELEX 27821-OMS. circ. 4,500. (also avail. in microfiche from CIS) **Indexed:** Abstr.Hyg., Child Devel.Abstr., Dent.Ind., Diar.Dis.Res., Environ.Abstr., Excerp.Med., IDA, IIS, Ind.Med., Popul.Ind., Repindex, Trop.Dis.Bull.
—BLDSC (9356.054500); EMDOCS; Faxon; SWETS; UMI; UnCover.
Former titles: World Health Statistics Report (ISSN 0043-8510); (until 1967): Epidemiological and Vital Statistics Report.
Description: Provides fundamental health guidance based on statistical data drawn from global sources.

614.7 310   JA   ISSN 0915-048X
CODEN: YKSNDQ
YAMAGUCHIKEN EISEI KOGAI KENKYU SENTA NENPO. (Text in Japanese) 1958. a. exchange basis. Yamaguchiken Eisei Kogai Kenkyu Senta - Yamaguchi Prefectural Research Institute of Health, 5-67, Aoi 2-chome, Yamaguchi-shi, Yamaguchi-ken 753, Japan. TEL 0839-22-7630. FAX 0839-22-7632. circ. 500. **Indexed:** Abstr.Hyg., Anal.Abstr.
—CASDDS.
Formed by the merger of (1958-1987): Yamaguchiken Eisei Kenkyujo Nenpo (ISSN 0288-7436); (1974-1987): Yamaguchi (ISSN 0914-031X)
Description: Annual report of the center. Reports on pollution control for air, water, noise, vibration, and offensive odors, as well as food safety and public health-related issues.

PUBLISHING AND BOOK TRADE

see also Bibliographies; Journalism; Patents, Trademarks and Copyrights; Printing

070.5 011   US   ISSN 0277-3104
Z475
A B A BOOK BUYER'S HANDBOOK (YEAR). a. membership only. American Booksellers Association, Inc., 828 S. Broadway, Tarrytown, NY 10591. TEL 914-591-2665. Ed.Bd. adv. circ. 8,500. (also avail. in diskette format) **Document type:** directory.
Formerly: Book Buyer's Handbook.
Description: Lists publishers, distributors and wholesalers of trade books; includes addresses, telephone numbers, discount and payment policies, return policies, freight policies, sales representation.

070.5   US   ISSN 8756-0267
Z479
A B B W A JOURNAL; the trade publication of the Black book industry. 1986. q. $30 to individuals (foreign $40); institutions $50 (foreign $60). American Black Book Writers Association, Inc., Box 10548, Marina Del Rey, CA 90295. TEL 213-822-5195. Ed. Toyomi Igus. adv.; bk.rev. circ. 50,000. (back issues avail.) **Document type:** trade publication.
—Faxon; UnCover.
Description: Covers Black books and reviews; Black writers; Black book publishing, and African-American literature.

658.896   US   ISSN 0001-0340
Z999.A1
A B BOOKMAN'S WEEKLY. (Antiquarian Bookman); for the specialist book world. (Yearbook avail.) 1948. w. $80 (includes A B Bookman's Yearbook). Specialist Book World, Box AB, Clifton, NJ 07015. TEL 201-772-0020. FAX 201-772-9281. Ed. Jacob L. Chernofsky. adv.; bk.rev.; bibl.; illus.; tr.lit.; index, cum.index every 10 yrs. circ. 10,000. **Indexed:** Bibl.Ind., Bk.Rev.Ind. (1987-), Child.Bk.Rev.Ind. (1987-), Child.Lit.Abstr., Lib.Lit. **Document type:** trade publication.
—Faxon; UnCover.
Formerly (until 1967): Antiquarian Bookman.

070.5   US   ISSN 0065-0005
Z990
A B BOOKMAN'S YEARBOOK. (Antiquarian Bookman); specialist book trade annual. 1949. a. $25. Specialist Book World, Box AB, Clifton, NJ 07015. TEL 201-772-0020. FAX 201-772-9281. Ed. Jacob L. Chernofsky. adv.; bk.rev.; index, cum.index. circ. 10,000.
—UnCover.

659.1   US
A B C BLUE BOOK: U S AND CANADIAN BUSINESS PUBLICATIONS. s-a. $110 to members only. Audit Bureau of Circulations, 900 N. Meacham Rd., Schaumburg, IL 60173. TEL 708-605-0909. FAX 708-605-0483.

659.1   US
A B C BLUE BOOK: U S AND CANADIAN MAGAZINES. s-a. $200 to members only. Audit Bureau of Circulations, 900 N. Meacham Rd., Schaumburg, IL 60173. TEL 708-605-0909. FAX 708-605-0483.
Formerly: A B C Blue Book: U S and Canadian Magazines and Farm Publications.
Description: Includes publishers' circulation statements.

A B C CIRCULATION REVIEW. see *JOURNALISM*

070.5   AT   ISSN 1321-4640
A B P A DIRECTORY OF MEMBERS. a. Aus.$15. Australian Book Publishers Association, 89 Jones St., Ultimo, N.S.W. 2007, Australia. TEL 61-2-281-9788. FAX 61-2-281-1073. **Document type:** directory.
Description: Contains the names and addresses and types of publishing activity of the members of the association.

A M P A NEWSLETTER. (American Medical Publishers' Association) see *MEDICAL SCIENCES*

070.5   US
A S P I F NEWSLETTER. 1983. s-a. $25. Association of Small Presses in Florida, 429 Hope St., Tarpon Springs, FL 34689. Ed. John Pyros. circ. 100.

686.09489   DK   ISSN 0108-1810
Z170.D3
AARETS BOGARBEJDE. 1981. a. membership. (Komiteen for Aarets Bogarbejde) Forening for Boghaandvaerk, c/o Grafisk Hoejskole, Glentevej 67, DK-2400 Copenhagen NV, Denmark. illus.
Formerly: Godt Bogarbejde.

ABBEY NEWSLETTER; bookbinding and conservation. see *LIBRARY AND INFORMATION SCIENCES*

027.7   US   ISSN 1069-1219
Z1035
ACADEMIA; a monthly magazine of academic titles and information. 1974; N.S. 1993. m. $36 (effective 1994). Baker & Taylor, Inc., Box 734, Somerville, NJ 08876. TEL 908-218-0400; 800-775-1800. FAX 908-218-3980. Ed. M. Jane McAuthur; Pub. Michael Struss. adv.; bk.rev.; illus. (also avail. in microfiche)
—UnCover.
Former titles (until 1993): Directions (Bridgewater) (ISSN 0360-473X); Supersedes: Current Books for Academic Libraries (ISSN 0011-3352)
Description: News and information on developments in academic publishing, including bibliographic data for new and forthcoming titles available through Baker and Taylor.

ACADEMIC LIBRARY BOOK REVIEW. see *LIBRARY AND INFORMATION SCIENCES*

070.5 378   US
▼**ACADEMIC TEXT REVIEW.** 1994. bi-m. during school yr. free to qualified personnel. Kay Ward & Associates, 2666 Shrewsbury Rd., Columbus, OH 43221. TEL 614-325-5735. FAX 614-459-9273. Ed. Amber Lacey; Pub. Kay Ward. adv.: B&W page $1285; trim 8 1/2 x 11. bk.rev.; circ. 5,000 (controlled).
Description: Publishes long and short reviews of college textbooks, non-print college teaching materials, and scholarly works.

070.5   CN   ISSN 1182-3968
ACTIVE VOICE. 10/yr. membership. Editors' Association of Canada, 35 Spadina Rd., Toronto, ON M5R 2S9, Canada. TEL 416-975-1379. FAX 416-975-1839. Ed. Claudette Reed Upton. **Document type:** newsletter.

AD MEDIA. see *ADVERTISING AND PUBLIC RELATIONS*

658.8   GW   ISSN 0065-2032
Z282
ADRESSBUCH FUER DEN DEUTSCHSPRACHIGEN BUCHHANDEL. 1839. a. DM.160. Buchhaendler-Vereinigung GmbH, Postfach 100442, 60004 Frankfurt a.M., Germany. TEL 069-13060. FAX 069-1306201. TELEX 413573-BUCHV-D. adv. circ. 4,500. **Document type:** directory.

ADVANCE; editorial features directory. see *ADVERTISING AND PUBLIC RELATIONS*

070.5   SI
ADVANCE BOOK INFORMATION. m. World Scientific Publishing Co. Pte. Ltd., P.O. Box 128, Singapore. TEL 3825663. FAX 3825919. TELEX RS 28561 WSPC. (U.S. addr.: 1060 Main St., Ste.1B, River Edge, NY 07661; U.K. addr.: 73 Lynton Mead, Totteridge, London N20 8DH, England)
Description: Provides information about books that World Scientific will be publishing and distributing in the near future.

070.5   CN   ISSN 0844-4404
ADVERTISER. 1879. s-w. Can.$64.50 (foreign $159.50) (effective June 1995). Kentville Publishing, P.O. Box 430, Kentville, NS B4N 3X4, Canada. TEL 902-678-2121. Ed. Paul Sparkes; Pub. Garnet Austen. adv. contact: Wayne Smith. circ. 11,073. (back issues avail.)

070.5   US
AFRICAN BOOK WORLD AND PRESS: A DIRECTORY. (Text in English and French) 1977. irreg., latest 1989. $135. Hans Zell Publishers (Subsidiary of: Bowker - Saur Ltd.), P.O. Box 56, Oxford OX1 2SJ, England. TEL 01865-511428. FAX 01865-311534. (Dist. in the U.S. by: K.G. Saur, A part of Reed Reference Publishing, 121 Chanlon Rd., New Providence, NJ 07974. TEL 800-521-8110) Ed. Hans M. Zell. adv. circ. 1,500. **Document type:** directory.
Description: Comprehensive information on libraries, publishers and the retail book trade, magazines, periodicals and major newspapers, and printing industries throughout Africa.

ALKALINE PAPER ADVOCATE. see *PAPER AND PULP*

002.075 809   SW   ISSN 1104-2974
ALLA TIDERS BOECKER; tidskrift foer boeckelskare. 1993. q. SEK 175 (foreign SEK 225). Tryckerifoerlaget, P.O. Box 7093, Tumstocksvaegen 19, S-183 07 Taaby, Sweden.

ALTERNATIVE PRESS REVIEW. see *LITERARY AND POLITICAL REVIEWS*

PUBLISHING AND BOOK TRADE

070.5 US ISSN 0065-759X
AMERICAN BOOK TRADE DIRECTORY. 1915. a., 41st edition, 1995. $235. R.R. Bowker, A Reed Reference Publishing company, 121 Chanlon Rd., New Providence, NJ 07974. TEL 908-464-6800. FAX 908-665-6688. TELEX 138 755. (Subscr. to: Order Dept., Box 31, New Providence, NJ 07974-9903. TEL 800-521-8110) index. (also avail. in magnetic tape) **Document type:** directory.
● Also available on CD-ROM. Producer(s): Bowker - Reed Reference Electronic Publishing.
—BLDSC (0810.860000). **CCC.**
 Description: Lists bookstores, antiquarians, wholesalers, distributors, jobbers, importers, exporters, language specialists, organized by geographic location and name. Firms are classified by the major category of books they sell.

070.5
Z477 US ISSN 0148-5903
AMERICAN BOOKSELLER. 1977. m. $49.99 to non-members; members $34.99. American Booksellers Association, 828 S. Broadway, Tarrytown, NY 10591-5112. TEL 800-637-0037. Ed. Kirsten Ruble. adv.: page $1625; adv. contact: Lisa Phelps. index. circ. 10,416. **Document type:** trade publication.

658.809
Z1035.1 US ISSN 0065-9959
AMERICAN REFERENCE BOOKS ANNUAL. 1970. a. $95. (Literary Guild) Libraries Unlimited, Inc., Box 6633, Englewood, CO 80155-6633. TEL 800-237-6124. FAX 303-220-8843. Ed. David Weitscher. bk.rev.; index, cum.index every 5 yrs. **Indexed:** Bibl.Ling., Bk.Rev.Ind. (1977-), Chic.Per.Ind., Child.Bk.Rev.Ind. (1977-), Leg.Info.Manage.Ind., Ref.Sour.
—BLDSC (0853.540000).
 Formerly: Preview (ISSN 0024-4538)
 Description: Contains approximately 1,700 titles covering general reference, history, humanities, education, business, science and technology; features increased coverage of CD-Rom products.

AMERICAN SOCIETY OF BOOKPLATE COLLECTORS AND DESIGNERS. YEAR BOOK. see *HOBBIES*

AMONG FRIENDS. see *LIBRARY AND INFORMATION SCIENCES*

686.3 747.5
Z116.A3 US ISSN 0740-5804
AMPERSAND. 1980. q. $40 to institutions. Pacific Center for the Book Arts, Box 424431, San Francisco, CA 94142-4431. E-mail: ajpoltroon@aol.com. Ed. Alastair Johnston. bk.rev. **Document type:** newspaper.

001.5
Z990 CN ISSN 0003-200X
AMPHORA. 1967. q. Can.$35. Alcuin Society, Box 3216, 8737 212th St., No. 150, Vancouver, BC V1M 2C. TEL 604-872-2326. Ed. Geoff Spencer. adv.; bk.rev.; illus. circ. 275. (also avail. in microfiche) **Indexed:** Br.Archaeol.Abstr., Can.Per.Ind.
 Description: Publishes articles on book art, book collecting, typography, private press publishing and related topics.

028.3 FR ISSN 0294-1090
UN AN DE NOUVEAUTES. 1981. a. Livres Hebdo, 35 rue Gregoire de Tours, 75006 Paris, France. TEL 44-41-28-00. FAX 44-41-28-64. **Document type:** trade publication.
 Formed by the 1982 merger of: Un An de Nouveautes (Edition avec Prix Cession de Base) (ISSN 0223-5218); Un An de Nouveautes (Edition Destine a l'Etranger) (ISSN 0223-5226)

070.5
Z990 UK ISSN 0306-7475
ANTIQUARIAN BOOK MONTHLY. 1974. m. £28 (rest of Europe £36; elsewhere £44). Countrywide Ediitons Ltd., 1 Park Parade, Park Rd., Farnham Royal, Bucks. SL2 3AV, England. TEL 01753-645999. FAX 01753-645255. Ed. Colin Hynson. adv. contact: Jan Richford. bk.rev.; bibl. circ. 2,000. **Indexed:** Child.Lit.Abstr. **Document type:** academic/scholarly publication, bibliography.
—BLDSC (1549.853900); UnCover.

658.896 AU ISSN 0042-3610
ANZEIGER DES VERBANDES DER ANTIQUARE OESTERREICHS. 1948. 4/yr. S.300. Hauptverband des Oesterreichischen Buchhandels, Gruenangergasse 4, A-1010 Vienna, Austria. TEL 0222-5121535. FAX 0222-5128482. adv.; bk.rev. circ. 1,700. **Document type:** trade publication.

658.8
Z2105 AU
ANZEIGER - DIE FACHZEITSCHRIFT DES OESTERREICHISCHEN BUCHHANDELS. 1866. 24/yr. S.1760. Hauptverband des Oesterreichischen Buchhandels, Gruenangergasse 4, A-1010 Vienna, Austria. TEL 0222-5121535. FAX 0222-5128482. adv.; bk.rev.; charts; illus.; index. circ. 1,700. **Document type:** trade publication.
 Former titles: Buchanzeiger des Oesterreichischen Buchhandels; Anzeiger des Oesterreichischen Buchhandels (ISSN 0003-6277); Anzeiger des Oesterreichischen Buch-, Kunst- und Musikalienhandels.

028.5
Z7401 US ISSN 0003-7052
APPRAISAL; science books for young people. 1967. q. $44 (foreign $56) (effective 1995). (Boston University, School of Education) Children's Science Book Review Committee, 605 Commonwealth Ave., Boston, MA 02215. TEL 617-353-4150. FAX 617-353-3924. Ed. Diane Holzheimer. bk.rev.; index, cum.index. circ. 2,600. **Indexed:** Bk.Rev.Ind. (1975-), Child.Bk.Rev.Ind. (1975-), Child.Lit.Abstr. **Document type:** academic/scholarly publication.
—UnCover.
 Description: Reviews science books for children and young adults.

APPRAISAL INSTITUTE PUBLICATIONS CATALOGUE. see *REAL ESTATE*

ARBIDO-B; offizielles Mitteilungsorgan - bulletin d'information officiel - bollettino d'informazioni officiale. see *LIBRARY AND INFORMATION SCIENCES*

ARBIDO-R; Fachorgan - revue professionnelle - rivista professionale. see *LIBRARY AND INFORMATION SCIENCES*

655
Z4 GW ISSN 0066-6327
ARCHIV FUER GESCHICHTE DES BUCHWESENS. (Summaries in English, French and German) 1956. s-a. (Boersenverein des Deutschen Buchhandels) Buchhaendler-Vereinigung GmbH, Postfach 100442, 60004 Frankfurt a.M., Germany. TEL 069-13060. FAX 069-1306201. TELEX 413573-BUCHV-D. **Indexed:** M.L.A. **Document type:** academic/scholarly publication.

070.5 US
ARIZONA AUTHORS NEWSLETTER. 1978. bi-m. $25. Arizona Authors' Association, 3509 E. Shea Blvd., Ste. 117, Phoenix, AZ 85028-3339. TEL 602-867-9001. FAX 602-978-6624. Ed. Sharon Saunders. adv.: page $60; adv. contact: Iva Lee Martin. bk.rev. circ. 500. **Document type:** newsletter.
 Description: Articles by writers, agents, book publishers and editorials on subjects related to writing or being in business related to writing for publication.

ART LINE; international art news. see *ART*

ARTHUR RACKHAM SOCIETY NEWSLETTER. see *ART*

686 GW ISSN 0935-7653
ARTIKEL 5; das Wirtschaftsmagazin der Printmedien. 1987. q. DM.126. Artikel 5 Verlagsgesellschaft mbH, Eidelstedteweg 22, 20255 Hamburg, Germany. TEL 040-565031. FAX 040-5602920. TELEX 2162603. Ed. Guenther Baehr. adv.; bk.rev. circ. 3,500. (back issues avail.)

ASIAN ADVERTISING AND MARKETING; the magazine for communication executives. see *ADVERTISING AND PUBLIC RELATIONS*

070.5 II ISSN 0254-6183
ASIAN LITERARY MARKET REVIEW; the international magazine of book, magazine and audiovisual publishing. (Text in English) 1975. q. Rs.100($10) Jaffe Publishing Management Service, Kunnuparambil Bldgs., Kurichy, Kottayam 686 549, India. TEL 04826-470. FAX 481-563057. Ed. K.P. Punnoose. adv.; bk.rev. circ. 3,150. (back issues avail.)

070.5 UN ISSN 0916-7838
ASIAN - PACIFIC BOOK DEVELOPMENT. Key Title: A B D Asian-Pacific Book Development. (Text in English) 1969. q. $13. Asian Cultural Centre for Unesco, 6, Fukuro-machi, Shinjuku-ku, Tokyo 162, Japan. TEL 269-4435. (Dist. by: Intercontinental Marketing Corp., I.P.O. Box 5056, Tokyo 100-30, Japan. TEL 81-3-3661-7458. FAX 81-3-3667-9646) Ed. Taichi Sasaoka. bk.rev.; charts; illus.; stat. circ. 2,000.
 Former titles (until 1989): Asian Book Development (ISSN 0388-5593); (until 1979): Tokyo Book Development Centre. Newsletter (ISSN 0049-4046)
 Description: Concerned with the situation and current events related to publishing and book promotion as well as with the common interests for the book-related personnel of the countries in Asia and the Pacific.

011 028 FR ISSN 0004-5365
ASSOCIATION DES BIBLIOTHECAIRES FRANCAIS. BULLETIN D'INFORMATIONS. 1907; N.S. 1956. q. 400 F. (foreign 420 F.). Association des Bibliothecaires Francais, 7 rue des Lions-Saint-Paul, 75004 Paris, France. TEL 48-87-97-87. FAX 42-87-97-13. Ed. Jacqueline Gascuel; Pub. Claudine Belayche. bk.rev.; bibl. **Indexed:** Lib.Lit., LISA. **Document type:** bulletin, trade publication.
—BLDSC (2862.220000).
 Description: Offers practical advice and opinion for booksellers.

070.5
Z477 US ISSN 0276-5349
ASSOCIATION OF AMERICAN PUBLISHERS. ANNUAL REPORT. Key Title: Annual Report - Association of American Publishers. a. Association of American Publishers, Inc., 71 Fifth Ave., New York, NY 10003-3004. TEL 212-255-0200. FAX 212-255-7007. **Document type:** corporate report.
 Description: Summary of the Association's activities for the previous year.

071 US ISSN 0147-0310
ASSOCIATION OF AMERICAN PUBLISHERS. EXHIBITS DIRECTORY. 1967. a. $100 to non-members; members $75. Association of American Publishers, Inc., 71 Fifth Ave., New York, NY 10003-3004. TEL 212-255-0200. FAX 212-255-7007. Ed. Marlene Scheuermann. circ. 700. **Document type:** directory.
 Formerly: Directory of Exhibit Opportunities.

070.5
Z475 US ISSN 0739-3024
ASSOCIATION OF AMERICAN UNIVERSITY PRESSES DIRECTORY. 1961. a. $14.95. Association of American University Presses, Inc., 584 Broadway, Ste. 410, New York, NY 10012. TEL 212-941-6610. Ed. Chris Terry. index; circ. controlled.

070.5 US
ASSOCIATION PUBLISHING. 1965. bi-m. membership. Society of National Association Publications, 1650 Tysons Blvd., Ste. 200, McLean, VA 22102. TEL 703-506-5285. FAX 202-833-1308. Ed. Karl Taylor. adv. circ. 1,000. **Document type:** trade publication.
 Former titles (until 1994): Snapshot; S N A P Bulletin.

070.5 800
Z473.R33 US ISSN 1062-0036
AT RANDOM; books and bookpeople from Random House. 1992. 3/yr. free. Random House, 201 E. 50th St., New York, NY 10022. TEL 212-872-8155. FAX 212-572-4949. Ed. Helen Morris; Pub. Harold Evans. adv.; bk.rev.; circ. 100,000 (controlled). (back issues avail.) **Document type:** consumer publication.
 Description: News, articles from the publishing world, including author interviews, photo essays and excerpts from forthcoming books.

PUBLISHING AND BOOK TRADE 5617

028.1   **CN**   ISSN 1192-3652
ATLANTIC BOOKS TODAY. 1974. q. Can.$10. Atlantic Provinces Book Review Society, 2085 Maitland St., Halifax, NS B3K 2Z8, Canada. TEL 902-420-5716. Ed. Elizabeth Eve. adv.; bk.rev.; circ. 30,000 (controlled). (tabloid format; back issues avail.) **Indexed**: Bk.Rev.Ind. (1982-), Can.Lit.Ind., Can.Per.Ind., Child.Bk.Rev.Ind. (1982-). **Document type**: consumer publication.
   Formerly (until 1992): Atlantic Provinces Book Review (ISSN 0316-5981)

659.1   **US**
AUDIT BUREAU OF CIRCULATIONS. BYLAWS AND RULES. (Editions in English, French) a. membership only. Audit Bureau of Circulations, 900 N. Meacham Rd., Schaumburg, IL 61073. TEL 708-605-0909. FAX 708-605-0483.

070.5   **US**
AUDIT REPORTS. a. Audit Bureau of Circulations, 900 N. Meacham Rd., Schaumburg, IL 60195. TEL 708-885-0909. FAX 708-605-0483.

028   **US**   ISSN 1043-352X
AUGSBURG FORTRESS BOOK NEWSLETTER. 1944. bi-m. free. Augsburg Fortress, Publishers, 426 S. Fifth St., Box 1209, Minneapolis, MN 55440-1209. TEL 612-330-3402. FAX 612-330-3455. Ed. Roderick D. Olson. bk.rev.; bibl.; illus.; index. circ. 38,000.
   Formerly (until 1985): Book News Letter (ISSN 0006-7296)
   Description: Book reviews of recent Augsburg Fortress publications for adult readers in theology, Bible studies, devotional, pastoral care and counseling, and church history.

070.5   **GW**
AUSLANDSINFO FUER DEN DEUTSCHEN VERLAGSBUCHHANDEL. q. free. Ausstellungs- und Messe GmbH, Reineckstr. 3, 60313 Frankfurt a.M., Germany. TEL 069-2102-0. FAX 069-2102227. (Subscr. to: Postfach 100116, 60001 Frankfurt a.M., Germany) Ed. Peter Weidhaas. adv.; charts; illus.; stat.; tr.lit.; circ. 2,000 (paid). (back issues avail.) **Document type**: newsletter, trade publication.

070.5 330   **US**
AUSTIN BOOK OF LISTS. 1986. a. Austin Business Journal, 1301 Capital of Texas Hwy., Ste. B-224, Austin, TX 78746. TEL 512-328-0180. FAX 512-328-7304. **Document type**: directory.

070.5   **AT**   ISSN 0045-026X
PN101
AUSTRALIAN AUTHOR. 1969. q. Aus.$24. Australian Society of Authors Ltd., P.O. Box 1566, Strawberry Hills, N.S.W. 2012, Australia. TEL 61-2-318-0877. FAX 61-2-318-0530. Ed. Dominic O'Grady. adv. contact: Ray Koppe. circ. 3,000. **Indexed**: Bibl.Engl.Lang.& Lit., Child.Lit.Abstr.
—UnCover.

028.1   **AT**   ISSN 0155-2864
Z4014.B6
AUSTRALIAN BOOK REVIEW. 1962. m. $48 to individuals; institutions Aus.$52 (foreign Aus.$70). National Book Council, 21 Drummond Pl., Ste. 3, Carlton 3053, Australia. TEL 61-3-96638657. FAX 61-3-96638658. Ed. Helen Daniel. adv.: page $560; 176 x 236. bk.rev.; bibl.; illus. circ. 4,000. **Indexed**: Bibl.Engl.Lang.& Lit., Bk.Rev.Ind. (1991-), Child.Bk.Rev.Ind. (1991-), Child.Lit.Abstr. **Document type**: consumer publication.

658.8   **AT**   ISSN 0004-8763
AUSTRALIAN BOOKSELLER AND PUBLISHER. 1921. m. (except Dec.-Jan. combined). Aus.$49. D.W. Thorpe, A part of Reed Reference Publishing, 18 Salmon St., Port Melbourne, Vic. 3207, Australia. TEL 03-245-7370. FAX 03-245-7395. Ed. John Nieuwenhuizen. adv.: B&W page Aus.$620; adv. contact: July Hille. bk.rev.; bibl. circ. 8,000. **Indexed**: Child.Lit.Abstr.
—BLDSC (1798.050000). **CCC**.
   Formerly: Ideas Book Trade Journal.
   Description: Reports news of the Australian and regional book trades.

AVERAGE PRICES OF BRITISH ACADEMIC BOOKS. see *LIBRARY AND INFORMATION SCIENCES*

B C BOOKWORLD. see *LITERATURE*

BARRY R. LEVIN SCIENCE FICTION & FANTASY LITERATURE. see *LITERATURE* — Science Fiction, Fantasy, Horror

020 940 090   **GW**   ISSN 0067-5091
Z240
BEITRAEGE ZUR INKUNABELKUNDE. DRITTE FOLGE. 1965. irreg., vol.9, 1993. price varies. (Deutsche Staatsbibliothek Berlin) Akademie Verlag GmbH, Muehlenstr. 33-34, 13187 Berlin, Germany. TEL 030-47889348. FAX 030-47889357. **Document type**: monographic series.

BELLES LETTRES (NORTH POTOMAC); a review of books by women. see *LITERATURE*

800   **US**
BERKELEY REVIEW OF BOOKS. 1989-1990; resumed 1995. 2/yr. $20. Deserted X, 1731 10th St., Ste. A, Berkeley, CA 94710. TEL 415-528-8713. Ed. H.D. Moe; Pub. Jerry Bass. adv.; bk.rev. circ. 1,000.

070   **GW**   ISSN 0005-9455
BERTELSMANN BRIEFE. 1960. 2/yr. free. Bertelsmann Fachzeitschriften GmbH, Postfach 120, 33311 Guetersloh, Germany. TEL 05241-801807. FAX 05241-806602. Ed. Matthias Rath. adv.; abstr.; bibl.; charts; stat.; index. circ. 15,000. **Document type**: newsletter.
—BLDSC (1941.400000).

070.5   **US**   ISSN 1046-8242
HF5801
BEST IN ADVERTISING. (Subseries of: Print Casebooks) 1975. biennial. R C Publications, Inc., 104 Fifth Ave., 19th Fl., New York, NY 10011. TEL 212-463-0600. FAX 212-989-9891. (Subscr. to: 3200 Tower Oaks Blvd., Rockville, MD 20852. TEL 301-770-2900) Ed. Martin Fox; Pub. Howard Cadel. illus.
   Formerly: Best in Advertising Campaigns (ISSN 0360-8263)
   Description: Explores commercial art, photography and graphics.

070.5   **US**   ISSN 0360-8743
HG4028.B2
BEST IN ANNUAL REPORTS. (Subseries of: Print Casebooks) 1975. biennial. R C Publications, Inc., 104 Fifth Ave., 19th Fl., New York, NY 10011. TEL 212-463-0600. FAX 212-989-9891. (Subscr. to: 3200 Tower Oaks Blvd., Rockville, MD 20852. TEL 301-770-2900) Ed. Martin Fox; Pub. Howard Cadel. illus. **Document type**: trade publication.

741.6   **US**
BEST IN COVERS AND POSTERS. (Subseries of: Print Casebooks) 1975. biennial. $27.95. R C Publications, Inc., 104 Fifth Ave., 19th Fl., New York, NY 10011. TEL 212-463-0600. FAX 212-989-9891. (Subscr. to: 3200 Tower Oaks Blvd., Rockville, MD 20852. TEL 301-770-2900) Ed. Martin Fox; Pub. Howard Cadel. illus. **Document type**: trade publication.
   Formed by the 1977 merger of: Best in Covers (ISSN 0361-2066); Best in Posters (ISSN 0360-8085)

070.5   **US**   ISSN 0360-8271
NC998.5.A1
BEST IN ENVIRONMENTAL GRAPHICS. (Subseries of: Print Casebooks) 1975. biennial. $27.95. R C Publications, Inc., 104 Fifth Ave., 19th Fl., New York, NY 10011. TEL 212-463-0600. FAX 212-989-9891. (Subscr. to: 3200 Tower Oaks Blvd., Rockville, MD 20852. TEL 301-770-2900) Ed. Martin Fox; Pub. Howard Cadel. illus. **Document type**: trade publication.

070.5   **US**   ISSN 1048-2644
T391
BEST IN EXHIBITION DESIGN. (Subseries of: Print Casebooks) 1977. biennial. R C Publications, Inc., 104 Fifth Ave., 19th Fl., New York, NY 10011. TEL 212-463-0600. FAX 212-989-9891. Ed. Martin Fox; Pub. Howard Cadel. illus. **Document type**: trade publication.

070.5   **US**   ISSN 0360-8689
TS195.A1
BEST IN PACKAGING. (Subseries of: Print Casebooks) 1975. biennial. R C Publications, Inc., 104 Fifth Ave., 19th Fl., New York, NY 10011. TEL 212-463-0600. FAX 212-989-9891. (Subscr. to: 3200 Tower Oaks Blvd., Rockville, MD 20852. TEL 301-770-2900) Ed. Martin Fox; Pub. Howard Cadel. illus. **Document type**: trade publication.

070.5   **CC**   ISSN 1003-6687
BIANJI ZHI YOU/COMPILERS' AND EDITORS' FRIEND. (Text in Chinese) 1985. bi-m. Y9.6($27) (effective in Jan. 1991). (Shanxi News and Publishing Bureau) Shuhai Chubanshe - Shuhai Press, 11 Bingzhou Beilu, Taiyuan, Shanxi, People's Republic of China. TEL 440440-95. (Dist. by: China International Book Trading Corporation, P.O. Box 399, Beijing, P.R.C.; Dist. in US by: China Books & Periodicals, Inc., 2929 24th St., San Francisco, CA 94110) (Co-publisher: Shanxi Renmin Chubanshe) Eds. Zhang Ansai, Du Houqin. bk.rev. circ. 9,300. (back issues avail.)
   Formerly (until Jan. 1985): Editors' and Authors' Friend.
   Description: Covers the fields of editing and publishing. Contains articles on editors' craft and techniques, researches laws in news and publishing, and comments on developments in China's publishing industry.

090   **IT**
BIBLIO; arte, storia e cultura del libro. 1986. s-a. L.90000 (deluxe edition L.180000) (effective 1995 & 1996). Ex Libris Museum, Via C. Porta 13, 20094 Corsico (MI), Italy. TEL 39-2-45100246. Ed. Giuseppe Mirabella. adv.: B&W page L.600000. circ. 500. **Document type**: bibliography.
   Formerly (until 1995): Ex Libris (ISSN 1120-785X)

020.75   **US**   ISSN 0006-128X
Z1008.B51
BIBLIOGRAPHICAL SOCIETY OF AMERICA. PAPERS. 1904. q. $40. Bibliographical Society of America, Box 397, Grand Central Station, New York, NY 10163. TEL 212-647-9171. E-mail: bibsocamer@aol.com. Ed. Trevor Howard-Hill. adv. contact: Marjory Zaik. bk.rev.; index. circ. 1,300. (also avail. in microfilm from KTO; reprint service avail. from KTO) **Indexed**: Abstr.Engl.Stud., Amer.Hist.& Life, Arts & Hum.Cit.Ind., Bibl.Engl.Lang.& Lit., Bk.Rev.Ind. (1965-), Child.Bk.Rev.Ind. (1965-), Curr.Cont., Hist.Abstr., Hum.Ind., Ind.Bk.Rev.Hum., Lib.Lit. **Document type**: academic/scholarly publication.
—BLDSC (6370.550000); UnCover.

070.5   **AT**   ISSN 0084-7852
BIBLIOGRAPHICAL SOCIETY OF AUSTRALIA AND NEW ZEALAND. BULLETIN. 1970. q. Aus.$30 to individuals (foreign Aus.$32); institutions Aus.$40 (foreign Aus.$48) (effective 1996). Bibliographical Society of Australia & New Zealand, c/o State Library of Victoria, 328 Swanston St., Melbourne, Vic. 3000, Australia. TEL 61-3-565-2953. FAX 61-3-565-2952. Ed. Brian Hubber. adv.; bk.rev. circ. 300. **Indexed**: Aus.P.A.I.S. **Document type**: academic/scholarly publication.
—UnCover.
   Description: Covers the history of printing, publishing, bookselling, typefounding, papermaking, bookbinding, palaeography and codicology, and textual bibliography.
   Refereed Serial

BIBLIOGRAPHY NEWSLETTER. see *LIBRARY AND INFORMATION SCIENCES*

070.5 809   **BE**
BIBLIOLOGIA; elementa ad librorum studia pertinentia. (Text mainly in French, occasionally in English) 1983. irreg., vol.12, 1992. N.V. Brepols, Steenweg op Tielen 68, 2300 Turnhout, Belgium. TEL 32-14-402500. FAX 32-14-428919. Ed. J. Vercruysse. (back issues avail.) **Document type**: monographic series.
   Description: Publishes scholarly studies deriving from all scientific disciplines that deal with books.

070.573   **AT**   ISSN 0157-3276
BIBLIONEWS AND AUSTRALIAN NOTES AND QUERIES; journal for book collectors. 1947. q. Aus.$20 (foreign Aus.$25) (effective 1995 & 1996). Book Collectors' Society of Australia, 16 Edwin St., Croydon, N.S.W. 2132, Australia. TEL 61-2-798-8984. FAX 61-2-798-8984. Ed. Brian Taylor. adv.; bk.rev.; index, cum.index: 1947-79 (nos.1-245), 1979-83 (nos.246-260). circ. 400. (back issues avail.) **Document type**: academic/scholarly publication.
—UnCover.
   Description: For all interested in the art and craft of the book.

PUBLISHING AND BOOK TRADE

090 070.5 686   HU   ISSN 0067-8007
BIBLIOTHECA HUNGARICA ANTIQUA. 1960. irreg., vol.24, 1991. price varies. (Magyar Tudomanyos Akademia) Akademiai Kiado, Publishing House of the Hungarian Academy of Sciences, P.O. Box 245, H-1519 Budapest, Hungary. TEL 181-2134. FAX 166-6466. TELEX 22-6228 AKNYO H.

686   SW   ISSN 0430-8417
BIBLIS. 1957. a. SEK 200 membership (effective 1995). Foereningen foer Bokhantverk, Kungl. Biblioteket, P.O. Box 5039, S-102 41 Stockholm, Sweden. Ed. Gunilla Jonsson. circ. 1,000. **Document type:** academic/scholarly publication.

090.75   US
BIG LITTLE TIMES. 1981. bi-m. $12 includes membership. (Big Little Book Club of America) Educational Research Corporation, Box 1242, Danville, CA 94526. TEL 510-837-2086. Ed. Lawrence Lowery. adv.; bk.rev. circ. 700. **Document type:** newsletter.
    Description: Serves as a conduit among collectors and dealers interested in children's books which preceded the comic book format.

655.7   GW   ISSN 0342-3573
BINDEREPORT; internationale Fachzeitschrift fuer Buchherstellung und Druckverarbeitung. 1886. m. DM.162 (foreign DM.188). Schluetersche Verlagsanstalt GmbH und Co., Hans-Boeckler-Allee 7, 30173 Hannover, Germany. TEL 0511-8550-0. FAX 0511-8550-100. (Subscr. to: Postfach 5440, 30054 Hannover, Germany) Ed. Matthias Will. adv.; bk.rev.; charts; illus.; pat.; tr.lit.; index. circ. 5,196. **Indexed:** Print.Abstr. **Document type:** trade publication.
    —CCC.
    Formerly: Allgemeiner Anzeiger fuer Buchbindereien; Incorporates: Narichten der Fachorganisationen (ISSN 0002-5984)

655.7   SZ   ISSN 1019-4657
BINDETECHNIK/RELIURE. (Text in French and German) 1979. m. (11/yr.). 90 SFr. Verband der Buchbindereien und Druckausrustbetriebe der Schweiz, Seestr. 71, Postfach, CH-8712 Staefa, Switzerland. TEL 01-9261176. FAX 01-9282628. (Co-sponsors: Gewerkschaft Druck und Papier; Berufsamt fuer das Schweizerische Buchbindergewerbe) Pub. H. Meier. adv. contact: T. Holenstein. abstr.; illus.; index. **Indexed:** Print.Abstr. **Document type:** trade publication.
    Supersedes (1890-1979): Schweizerische Fachschrift fuer Buchbindereien (ISSN 0036-7583)
    Description: Concerns bookbinding.

658.8 Z2435   NE   ISSN 0167-4765
BOEKBLAD; nieuwsblad voor het boekenvak. 1834. w. fl.599 (foreign fl.599). Koninklijke Vereeniging ter Bevordering van de Belangen des Boekhandels, Frederiksplein 1, Postbus 15007, 1001 MA Amsterdam, Netherlands. TEL 31-20-6253131. FAX 31-20-6220908. (Co-publisher: Boekblad bv, Postbus 6438, 3002 AK Rotterdam, Netherlands. TEL 31-10-4255944. FAX 31-10-4780904) Ed. F. Spek. adv.; bk.rev.; bibl.; stat.; index; circ. 5,500 (paid). **Indexed:** Key to Econ.Sci. **Document type:** trade publication.
    —SWETS.
    Formerly: Nieuwsblad voor de Boekhandel (ISSN 0028-9965)
    Description: Articles and news for the Dutch book trade.

027.8 Z671   DK   ISSN 0006-7792
BOERN OG BOEGER. (Text in Danish; summaries in English) 1948. 8/yr. DKK 583 (effective 1974). Danmarks Skolebiblioteksforening - Danish School Library Association, Vesterbrogade 20, DK-1620 Copenhagen V, Denmark. TEL 33-25-32-22. FAX 33-25-32-23. Ed. Niels Jacobsen. adv.; bk.rev.; illus.; index. circ. 3,500.

015.489038   DK   ISSN 0107-5195
BOG OG BAAND. (Supplement avail.) 1980. a. DKK 414.40 (supplement DKK 119.60) (effective 1996). Dansk BiblioteksCenter as, Tempovej 7-11, DK-2750 Ballerup, Denmark. TEL 45-44-97-40-00. FAX 45-44-68-24-42.

070.509489   DK   ISSN 0903-7195
Z2553
BOGMARKEDET. (Includes weekly supplement: Dansk Bogfortegnelse) 1854. w. DKK 530 (foreign DKK 700) (typically set in Jan.). Danske Bogmarked, Landemaerket 5, 3., DK-1119 Copenhagen K, Denmark. TEL 33-150844. FAX 33-156203. (Co-sponsors: Danske Forlaggerforening; Danske Boghandlerforening) Ed. Pia Rink. adv.; bk.rev.; illus. circ. 3,700.
    Formerly (until 1988): Danske Bogmarked (ISSN 0011-6556)

658.809   DK   ISSN 0006-5706
BOGORMEN. 1903. 4/yr. DKK 100. Danske Boghandlermedhjaelperforening (BMF), Siljangade 6-8, DK-2300 Copenhagen S, Denmark. Eds. Jesper Soeholm, Arvid Honore. adv.; bk.rev.; illus.; index. circ. 2,300. **Document type:** trade publication.
    Description: Oriented towards booksellers' assistants as well as other members of the book trade.

658.8   DK   ISSN 0006-5749
BOGVENNEN. 1893. a. DKK 200. Forening for Boghaandvaerk, c/o Graphic College of Denmark, Glentevej 67, DK-2400 Copenhagen NV, Denmark. TEL 01-12 21 14. Ed.Bd. bk.rev.; illus.; index. circ. 2,000.

028   BG   ISSN 0006-5773
BOI. 1965. m. Tk.60($2) National Book Centre of Bangladesh, Grantha Bhaban 5, Bangabandhu Ave., Dhaka 1000, Bangladesh. Ed. Fazle Rabbi. adv.; bk.rev.; abstr.; charts; illus.; stat.; index. circ. 5,000.

070.5   SW   ISSN 0283-5193
BOKFOERMEDLAREN; en tidning om stora boecker fraan smaa foerlag. 1986. q. SEK 160 membership (effective 1991). Bokfoermedlaren, Fornminnesv. 14, S-417 22 Goeteborg, Sweden.

658.8 Z1007   SW   ISSN 0006-5846
BOKVAENNEN. 1946. 6/yr. SEK 150. Saellskapet Bokvaennerna, Bokvaennen, P.O. Box 10285, S-100 55 Stockholm, Sweden. Ed. Lars-Ove Pollack. adv.; bk.rev.; bibl.; illus.; index. circ. 2,000. **Indexed:** M.L.A.

BONNIERS LITTERAERA MAGASIN. see *LITERARY AND POLITICAL REVIEWS*

BOOGIE WOOGIE AND BLUES COLLECTOR. see *MUSIC*

090.75   US   ISSN 0740-8439
THE BOOK; newsletter of the program in the history of the book in American culture. 1983. 3/yr. free. American Antiquarian Society, 185 Salisbury St., Worcester, MA 01609. TEL 508-755-5221. Eds. John B. Hench, Robert Gross. bk.rev.; illus. circ. 2,500. **Document type:** newsletter.
    Description: Contains the program, scholarly research notes, articles on research collections concerning the book in American history and culture to 1876. Also includes Society activities.

070.5   US   ISSN 0733-3005
BOOK ALERT (BRIDGEWATER). 1979. m. $36. Baker and Taylor, Inc., Box 734, Somerville, NJ 08876. TEL 908-218-0400. FAX 908-218-3980. adv.; bk.rev.; illus.
    Incorporates: Paperback Alert.
    Description: Prepublication announcement magazine for booksellers and librarians of adult, children's, and young adult hardcover and paperback (mass and trade) titles and spoken-word audio.

020.75   UK   ISSN 0952-8601
BOOK AND MAGAZINE COLLECTOR. 1984. m. $51. Daimond Publishing Group Ltd., 45 St. Mary's Rd., Ealing, London W5 5RQ, England. TEL 0181-579-1082. FAX 0181-566-2024. Ed. Crispin Jackson; Pub. John Dean. adv. contact: Steve Goodwin. bibl.; cum.index. (back issues avail.) **Indexed:** Child.Lit.Abstr. **Document type:** consumer publication.

070.5   UK   ISSN 0068-0095
BOOK AUCTION RECORDS. 1902. a. £77. Dawson UK Ltd., Cannon House, Folkestone, Kent CT19 5EE, England. TEL 01303-850101.
FAX 01303-850440. Ed. Wendy Y. Heath. adv.; cum.index every 5 yrs. **Document type:** directory.
    —BLDSC (2248.008000).
    Description: Provides a priced and annotated record of books auctioned worldwide.

658.809 Z1008   US   ISSN 0006-7202
BOOK CLUB OF CALIFORNIA. QUARTERLY NEWS-LETTER. 1933. q. $55 includes membership. Book Club of California, 312 Sutter St., Ste. 510, San Francisco, CA 94108. TEL 415-781-7532. FAX 415-781-7537. Ed. Harlan Kessel. adv.; bk.rev.; cum.index. circ. 1,000. (back issues avail.) **Document type:** newsletter.

BOOK COLLECTING WORLD. see *HOBBIES*

020.75   US
BOOK COLLECTORS' HANDBOOK OF VALUES. irreg. price varies. G. P. Putnam's Sons, 200 Madison Ave., New York, NY 10016. TEL 212-576-8900.

658.8   US
BOOK DEALERS WORLD; direct mail marketplace for book dealers and self-publishers and writers. 1980. q. $30. North American Bookdealers Exchange, Box 606, Cottage Grove, OR 97424. TEL 503-942-7455. FAX 503-942-7455. Ed. Al Galasso. adv.; bk.rev. circ. 20,000. (back issues avail.) **Document type:** trade publication.

070.5 001.3 AS30   US   ISSN 0094-9426
BOOK FORUM.* 1974. irreg. (approx. q.). $18 to individuals; institutions $24. Crescent Publishing Co., Inc., 37 Sunset Ave., Niantic, CT 06357-3314. TEL 203-739-9497. Ed. Clarence Driskill. adv.; bk.rev.; bibl.; index. circ. 5,200. (back issues avail.) **Indexed:** Abstr.Engl.Stud., Amer.Bibl.Slavic & E.Eur.Stud., Amer.Hum.Ind., Arts & Hum.Cit.Ind., Bk.Rev.Ind. (1976-), Child.Bk.Rev.Ind. (1976-), Curr.Cont., M.L.A., Mid.East: Abstr.& Ind.

658.8 Z477   US   ISSN 0160-970X
BOOK INDUSTRY TRENDS. Represents: Book Industry Study Group. Research Report. 1977. a. $500. Book Industry Study Group, Inc., 160 Fifth Ave., New York, NY 10010. TEL 212-929-1393. FAX 212-989-7542.
    —CCC.

BOOK MARK; children's literature in review with related activities for preschoolers through young adults. see *CHILDREN AND YOUTH — About*

070.5 658.8   US   ISSN 0891-8813
BOOK MARKETING UPDATE. 1986. m. $60 (foreign $98). Open Horizons Publishing, Box 205, Fairfield, IA 52556-0205. TEL 515-472-6130. FAX 515-472-1560. E-mail: JohnKremer@aol.com. Ed. John Kremer. adv.; bk.rev.; bibl.; charts; illus.; stat.; index; circ. 3,000 (paid). (back issues avail.) **Document type:** newsletter.
    —CCC.
    Description: Features ideas, tips, resources, case histories, and articles on book marketing, publicity, and promotions for large and small book publishers and authors.

070.5   US
BOOK NEWS. 1980. 10/yr. American Book Producers Association, 160 Fifth Ave., Ste. 604, New York, NY 10010. TEL 212-645-2368. FAX 212-989-7542. Ed. Sarah Stewart. circ. 75. **Document type:** newsletter.

020.75 Z1007.B7166   US   ISSN 0006-730X
BOOK-OF-THE-MONTH CLUB NEWS. 1926. 15/yr. membership. Book-Of-The-Month Club, Time & Life Bldg., 1271 Ave. of the Americas, New York, NY 10020. TEL 212-522-4200. Ed. Tracy Brown. bk.rev.; bibl, illus. circ. 1,000,000.

020   US
BOOK PAGE. 1988. m. $18. ProMotion, Inc., 2501 21st Ave., S., Ste. 5, Nashville, TN 37212-5626. TEL 615-292-8926. FAX 615-292-8249. E-mail: ann_shayne@bookpage.com. Ed. Ann Meador Shayne. adv. contact: Cathey Clark. bk.rev.; illus.; circ. 800,000 (paid). (tabloid format) **Document type:** consumer publication.
    Description: Features book reviews, author interviews and news of the world of books.

BOOK PARADE/BOEKPARADE. see *LIBRARY AND INFORMATION SCIENCES*

PUBLISHING AND BOOK TRADE

070.5 US ISSN 1049-4456
BOOK PROMOTION HOTLINE. 1989. w. $150. Ad-Lib Publications, 51 1-2 W. Adams, Box 1102, Fairfield, IA 52556-1102. TEL 800-669-0773. FAX 515-472-3186. Ed. Marie Kiefer. **Document type:** trade publication.
—CCC.
  Formerly (until 1990): Book Information Hotline.
  Description: Lists 75 to 100 key media and book marketing contacts.

BOOK PUBLISHING CAREER DIRECTORY. see *OCCUPATIONS AND CAREERS*

070 US ISSN 0145-9457
CODEN: IPUNEW
BOOK PUBLISHING REPORT; on the business of book publishing. 1974. w. (50/yr.) $456 (foreign $506) (effective 1995). SIMBA Information Inc., 213 Danbury Rd., Box 7430, Wilton, CT 06897-7430. TEL 203-834-0033. FAX 203-834-1771. E-mail: simba99@aol.com. Ed. Stephanie Oda; Pub. Alan Brigish. **Document type:** newsletter.
●Also available online. Vendor(s): Knight-Ridder, Inc., NewsNet (PB19).
—CASDDS; Genuine Article. CCC.
  Incorporates (1983-1989): International Publishing Newsletter (ISSN 0740-7513) & Audio Publishing Report (ISSN 0888-4498)
  Description: Monitors, analyzes, and reports on trends and developments in book publishing.

659.1 070.5 US
Z475
BOOK PUBLISHING RESOURCE GUIDE. 1986. biennial. $25. Ad-Lib Publications, 51 1-2 W. Adams, Box 1102, Fairfield, IA 52556-1102. TEL 515-472-6617. FAX 515-472-3186. Ed. Marie Kiefer. bibl.; index. circ. 2,000. (Avail. in database format for IBM-PC, Macintosh, or compatibles) **Document type:** trade publication.
  Formerly: Book Marketing Opportunities: A Directory (ISSN 0894-1785)
  Description: Includes major wholesalers, bookstore chains, clubs, catalogues and over 2,000 media contacts.

028.1 US
THE BOOK READER. bi-m. $20. Jay Bail, Ed. & Pub., 245 Mt. Hermon Rd., Ste. 256, Scotts Valley, CA 95066-4035. TEL 408-475-3412. **Document type:** newspaper.

028.1 US ISSN 0145-627X
BOOK TALK (ALBUQUERQUE). 1971. irreg. (approx. 5/yr.). $15 (effective 1996). New Mexico Book League, 8632 Horacio Pl., N.E., Albuquerque, NM 87111. TEL 505-299-8940. FAX 505-294-8032. Ed. Carol A. Myers. adv.; bk.rev.; circ. 550 (paid). (back issues avail.) **Document type:** consumer publication.
  Description: Contains articles of interest to Southwestern booksellers and librarians. Includes reviews of 20-25 new titles having a Southwestern appeal.

070.025 CN ISSN 0700-5296
Z485
BOOK TRADE IN CANADA/INDUSTRIE DU LIVRE AU CANADA. (Text in English, French) 1975. a. $57.50. Ampersand Communications Inc., 5606 Scobie Crescent, Manotick, ON K4M 1B7, Canada. TEL 613-692-2080. FAX 613-692-1419. Ed. Eunice A. Thorne. circ. 2,000. **Document type:** trade publication, directory.
—BLDSC (2248.280000).
  Formerly (until 1976): Book Publishers in Canada.
  Description: Covers the Canadian book industry; information on publishers, their programs and types of books published, on bookstores in Canada and on foreign publishers represented in Canada.

028.1 US ISSN 0006-7369
BOOK WORLD. Variant title: Washington Post Book World. 1972. w. $26 (foreign $31.20). Washington Post Co., 1150 15th St., N.W., Washington, DC 20071. TEL 202-334-6000. FAX 202-334-5059. TELEX 80-9522. Ed. Leonard Downie, Jr; Donald E. Graham. adv. contact: Stephen P. Hills. bk.rev.; illus.; circ. 1,153,822 (paid). (tabloid format; also avail. in microform from RPI,UMI) **Indexed:** Amer.Bibl.Slavic & E.Eur.Stud., Bibl.Engl.Lang.& Lit., Bk.Rev.Ind. (1967-), Child.Bk.Rev.Ind. (1967-), Mid.East: Abstr.& Ind. **Document type:** newspaper.
●Also available online. Vendor(s): Knight-Ridder, Inc.
—UMI.

686.3 US
BOOKARTS CLASSIFIED. m. $18. 2718 S.W. Kelly, Ste. 222, Portland, OR 97201. Ed. Tom Bannister. **Document type:** directory.

BOOKBIRD; world of Children's books. see *CHILDREN AND YOUTH — For*

658.8 UK
BOOKDEALER; the trade weekly for books wanted and for sale. 1971. w. £44 (foreign £58). Werner Shaw Ltd., 26 Charing Cross Rd., Ste. 34, London WC2H 0DH, England. TEL 0171-240-5991. FAX 0171-379-5770. Ed. Barry Shaw. adv.; bk.rev. circ. 2,300. **Document type:** trade publication.

BOOKENDS. see *LIBRARY AND INFORMATION SCIENCES*

020 US
BOOKLOVER. 1983. m. $10 to individuals; institutions $20. Reading Rage Publishing Co., 151 W. 75th St., New York, NY 10023. TEL 212-362-8096. Ed. Elizabeth Timmerman. adv.; bk.rev. circ. 50,000.

658.8 BG
BOOKMAN. (Text in Bengali or English) 1979. q. Tk.10($2) per no. Bangladesh Books International Ltd., Ittefaq Bhaban, 1 Ramkrishna Mission Rd., POB 377, Dhaka 3, Bangladesh. TEL 2-256071. bibl. (also avail. in microfilm from UMI; reprint service avail. from UMI)

070.5 US ISSN 0068-0133
BOOKMAN'S GUIDE TO AMERICANA. 1960. irreg., 9th ed., 1986. price varies. Scarecrow Press, Inc., 52 Liberty St., Box 4167, Metuchen, NJ 08840. TEL 800-537-7107. circ. 3,000. **Document type:** bibliography, directory.
  Description: Alphabetically arranged compilation of quotations transcribed from recent out-of-print booksellers' catalogs. Provides the bookseller or book buyer with a record of prices asked for out-of-print titles in the comprehensive field of Americana, including factual or fictional works.

070.5 US ISSN 0068-0141
Z1000
BOOKMAN'S PRICE INDEX; guide to the values of rare and other out-of-print books. 1964. irreg., vol.41, 1990. $199 per vol. Gale Research Inc., 835 Penobscot Bldg., Detroit, MI 48226. TEL 313-961-2242. FAX 313-961-6083. TELEX 810-221-7086. Ed. Daniel F. McGrath.
  Description: Price guide to out-of-print and rare books.

686 UK ISSN 0264-3693
BOOKPLATE JOURNAL. 1983. s-a. £30($50) (includes Bookplate Society Newsletter and annual members' book). Bookplate Society, 11 Nella Rd., London W6 9PB, England. (Subscr. to: c/o Mr. Gordon Smith, "Stancroft," 125 Brampton Rd., Carlisle, Cumbria, CA3 9AP, England) Ed. Brian North Lee. adv.; bk.rev. circ. 300. **Document type:** academic/scholarly publication.
  Description: Deals with all aspects of the history, making and collecting of bookplates.

686 UK ISSN 0309-7935
BOOKPLATE SOCIETY NEWSLETTER. 1972. q. included in subscr. to Bookplate Journal. Bookplate Society, 11 Nella Rd., London W6 9PB, England. Ed. Bryan Welch. **Document type:** newsletter.

070 UK ISSN 0952-987X
Z2005
BOOKS. bi-m. £21($40) Publishing News Ltd., 43 Museum St., London WC1A 1LY, England. TEL 0171-404-0304. FAX 0171-242-0762. adv.; illus. circ. 100,000. **Indexed:** Abstr.Engl.Stud., Bk.Rev.Ind. (1965-), Child.Bk.Rev.Ind. (1965-), Diab.Cont. **Document type:** trade publication.
—BLDSC (2250.120000).
  Formerly: Books and Bookmen (ISSN 0006-744X); Supersedes (in 1987): Book Choice (ISSN 0261-4227)
  Description: Contains reviews of general books.

070.5 NR ISSN 0794-8603
Z468.N5
BOOKS. 1987. q. Booklinks Ltd., 15, Obafemi Awolowo Way, P.O. Box 2547, Ikeja, Nigeria.

028.1 JA
BOOKS AND ESSAYS/TOSHO. (Text in Japanese) 1938. m. Iwanami Shoten Publishers, 2-5-5 Hitotsubashi, Chiyoda-ku, Tokyo 101, Japan. (Overseas Distributor: Japan Publications Trading Co., Ltd., Box 5030, Tokyo International, Tokyo 100-31, Japan; or 1255 Howard St., San Francisco, CA 94103)
  Description: To stimulate an interest in reading.

BOOKS AND LIBRARIES AT THE UNIVERSITY OF KANSAS. see *LIBRARY AND INFORMATION SCIENCES*

BOOKS AT IOWA. see *LIBRARY AND INFORMATION SCIENCES*

070.5 CN
BOOKS FOR EVERYBODY. a. Key Publishers Co. Ltd., 70 The Esplanade, 4th Fl., Toronto, ON M5E 1R2, Canada. TEL 416-360-0044. FAX 416-941-9038. Ed. Ted Mumford; Pub. Sharon McAuley. circ. 400,000. **Document type:** catalog.

020.75 UK ISSN 0143-909X
BOOKS FOR KEEPS. 1980. 6/yr. £15 (foreign £22). School Bookshop Association Ltd., 6 Brightfield Rd., Lee, London SE12 8QF, England. TEL 0181-852-4953. Ed. Chris Powling. adv. contact: Richard Hill. bk.rev.; bibl.; index. circ. 8,200. **Indexed:** Bk.Rev.Ind. (1980-), Child.Bk.Rev.Ind. (1980-), Child.Lit.Abstr. **Document type:** consumer publication.
  Incorporates (1983-1988): British Book News Children's Books (ISSN 0264-5637) & School Bookshop News.
  Description: Contains reviews, articles and interviews on children's books.

028.1 CN ISSN 0045-2564
Z1369
BOOKS IN CANADA. 1971. m. (9/yr.). Can.$22.98 to individuals (US $35, elsewhere $46); institutions Can.$29.98 (US $42, elsewhere $53). Canadian Review of Books Ltd., 130 Spadina Ave., Ste. 603, Toronto, ON M5V 2L4, Canada. TEL 416-601-9880. FAX 416-340-9813. Ed. Paul Stuewe. adv. contact: Anita Miecznikowski. bk.rev.; bibl.; illus.; index. circ. 10,000. (also avail. in microfiche from MMP; back issues avail., reprint service avail. from MMP) **Indexed:** Bk.Rev.Ind. (1979-), Can.B.P.I., Can.Lit.Ind., Can.Per.Ind., Child.Bk.Rev.Ind. (1979-), CMI. **Document type:** consumer publication.
—Faxon; UnCover.
  Description: A national consumer book review magazine.

028.1 UK ISSN 0143-1285
BOOKS IN SCOTLAND. 1978. q. £9.95 (foreign £10.95). Ramsay Head Press, 15 Gloucester Pl., Edinburgh EH3 6EE, Scotland. TEL 0131-225-5646. Ed. Conrad Wilson. adv. contact: Christine Wilson. bk.rev. circ. 3,000. **Document type:** academic/scholarly publication.
  Description: Articles on Scottish writers and writing, reviews of new books by Scottish writers, books about Scots and Scotland, and books in general.

070.5 380 UK ISSN 0961-2203
BOOKS IN THE MEDIA. 1979. w. £90($230) to members; non-members £97.50); newsstand price: £1.50. Bookwatch Ltd., 15-Up East St., Lewins Yard, Chesham, Bucks. HP5 1HQ, England. TEL 01494-792269. FAX 01494-784850. (Alt. addr.: 6 Green Ln., Chesham, Bucks. HP6 5LN, England. TEL 01494-727719) Ed. Sophie Walker; Pub. Peter W. Harland. adv.: page £375; adv. contact: Peter W. Harland. bk.rev.; circ. 1,500 (paid). **Document type:** newsletter.
  Description: Lists all book titles linked to U.K. television, radio, film, and video programmes; all titles reviewed in the press; and bestseller lists. Also provides industry news.

PUBLISHING AND BOOK TRADE

070.5   IE   ISSN 0376-6039
Z331.7
BOOKS IRELAND. (Text in English and Gaelic) 1976. 9/yr. $22. Jeremy Addis Ltd., 11 Newgrove Ave., Dublin 4, Ireland. TEL 0353-12692185. (U.S. subscr. to: Irish Books & Media, 1433 Franklin Ave. E., Minneapolis, MN 55404-2135. TEL 612-871-3505) Ed. Jeremy Addis. adv.; bk.rev.; tr.lit.; index. circ. 3,180. (also avail. in diskette format) **Document type:** trade publication.
—BLDSC (2250.201000); Faxon.
    Description: Provides bibliography listings and reviews of all Irish-interest and Irish-author books, with news of Irish publishing.

070.5 658.8   UK
BOOKS: THE INTERNATIONAL MARKET. (Subseries of: Market Direction reports) a. £1595($3190) (effective 1996). Euromonitor, 60-61 Britton St., London EC1M 5NA, England. TEL 0171-251-8024. FAX 0171-608-3149. (Addr. in N. America: Euromonitor International, 122 S. Michigan Ave., Ste. 1200, Chicago, IL 60603. TEL 312-922-1115. FAX 312-922-1157) **Document type:** trade publication.
    ●Also available online. Vendor(s): Data-Star, Knight-Ridder, Inc.
    Description: Analyzes book publishing in France, Germany, Italy, Spain, the U.K., the U.S., and Japan.

658.8   PK   ISSN 0006-7547
BOOKSELLER. 1968. m. Rps.60 (foreign $30). Bookseller (International), 26, Paisa Akbar, P.O. Box 2387, Lahore 54000, Pakistan. TEL 92-42-7232415. FAX 92-42-6360955. Ed. Muhammad Saeed Shaikh. adv.; bk.rev. circ. 17,000. **Document type:** trade publication, newsletter, catalog.

658.8   UK   ISSN 0006-7539
BOOKSELLER; the organ of the book trade. 1858. w. £125. J. Whitaker & Sons Ltd., 12 Dyott St., London WC1A 1DF, England. TEL 071-836-8911. FAX 071-836-2909. Ed. Louis Baum. adv.; bibl.; illus. circ. 16,200. (also avail. in microform from UMI) **Indexed:** Br.Ceram.Abstr., Br.Hum.Ind., Child.Lit.Abstr., Int.Lab.Doc., LISA, Print.Abstr. **Document type:** trade publication.
—BLDSC (2250.220000); UMI; UnCover. **CCC.**

070.5   US
BOOKSELLER. 1971. s-m. $36. Bookseller, Box 8183, Ann Arbor, MI 48107. TEL 313-930-0450. Ed. Raymond L. Hough. adv.; bk.rev. circ. 1,200. **Document type:** newsletter.
    Description: Trade paper for out-of-print bookdealers.

070.5   UK   ISSN 0952-1666
BOOKSELLERS ASSOCIATION OF GREAT BRITAIN AND IRELAND. DIRECTORY OF MEMBERS. a. Booksellers Association of Great Britain and Ireland, 272 Vauhall Bridge Rd., London SW1V 1BA, England. TEL 0171-834-5477. FAX 0171-834-8812. index. **Document type:** directory.
    Former titles: Booksellers Association of Great Britain. List of Charter Members (ISSN 0142-8934); (until 1985): Booksellers Association of Great Britain and Ireland. List of Members (ISSN 0068-0249)

070.5   UK   ISSN 0268-246X
BOOKSELLING. q. £25 to non-members. Booksellers Association of Great Britain and Ireland, 272 Vauxhall Bridge Rd., London SW1V 1BA, England. TEL 0171-834-5477. FAX 0171-834-8812. Ed. Meryl Halls. circ. 3,600. (back issues avail.) **Document type:** trade publication.

070.5   US
BOOKSELLING THIS WEEK. 1916. w. $50 to non-members; members $30. American Booksellers Association, 828 S. Broadway, Tarrytown, NY 10591. TEL 914-591-2665; 800-637-0037. FAX 914-591-2720. Ed. Gabrielle Quaranta. adv. contact: Aiyisha Bridges. circ. 8,800. (tabloid format) **Document type:** newsletter.
    Supersedes (in Apr. 1994): A B A Newswire; (in Feb. 1973): A B A Bulletin.

658.8 282   US   ISSN 0006-7563
Z479
BOOKSTORE JOURNAL. 1968. m. $45. (Christian Booksellers Association) C B A Service Corporation, 2620 Venetucci Blvd., Box 200, Colorado Springs, CO 80901. TEL 719-576-7880.
FAX 719-576-0795. Ed. Todd Hafer. adv. contact: Carlton Dunn. bk.rev.; illus. circ. 7,500.
    Description: Trade magazine for the Christian retail industry. Provides articles on retail management, industry news, and product information.

070.5 301.412   US   ISSN 0163-1128
BOOKWOMAN.* 1936. 3/yr. membership. Women's National Book Association, 5040 Cannon Bluff Dr., Woodbridge, VA 22192-5740. TEL 212-675-7805. Ed. Nancy Lutz. bk.rev. circ. 1,200.

077   YU
BORBIN INFORMATOR; list radnih ljudi NIGP Borba. m. Borba, Trg Marksa i Engelsa 7, Belgrade, Yugoslavia. Ed. Zivodar Zivkovic.

028.1 800   US   ISSN 0734-2306
BOSTON REVIEW. 1975. 6/yr. $15 to individuals; institutions $18. Boston Critic, Inc., c/o MIT, 77 Massachusetts Ave., No. E53-407, Cambridge, MA 02139-4307. TEL 617-253-3642.
FAX 617-252-1549. E-mail: bostonreview@MIT.EDU. Ed. Joshua Cohen. adv.: page 800; 10 x 14; adv. contact: John Thompson. bk.rev.; film rev.; play rev.; illus.; index. circ. 20,000. (tabloid format; also avail. in microfilm from UMI) back issues avail.; reprint service avail. from UMI) **Indexed:** Alt.Press Ind., Bk.Rev.Ind. (1978-), Child.Bk.Rev.Ind. (1978-), M.L.A.
—BLDSC (2251.827600); UMI.
    Formerly (until 1982): New Boston Review (ISSN 0361-168X)
    Description: Includes literary and political essays.

BOVE & RHODES INSIDE REPORT ON DESKTOP PUBLISHING AND MULTIMEDIA. see COMPUTERS — Microcomputers

THE BOWKER ANNUAL LIBRARY AND BOOK TRADE ALMANAC; facts, figures and reports. see LIBRARY AND INFORMATION SCIENCES

BRAILLE BOOK REVIEW (LARGE PRINT EDITION). see HANDICAPPED — Visually Impaired

BRANDYWINE DOCUMENTS ON THE HISTORY OF BOOKS & PRINTING. see PRINTING

BRANDYWINE KEEPSAKE. see PRINTING

070.5   BE
BREPOLS PUBLISHERS NEWSLETTER. (Text in English, French) irreg., no.27, 1994. free. N.V. Brepols, Steenweg op Tielen 68, 2300 Turnhout, Belgium. TEL 32-14-402500. FAX 32-14-418919. **Document type:** newsletter.
    Description: Provides news of recent and forthcoming scholarly publications from Brepols, including medieval studies, the arts, Latin literature, and religion.

BUCH UND BIBLIOTHEK. see LIBRARY AND INFORMATION SCIENCES

658.8   GW   ISSN 0007-2796
BUCHHAENDLER HEUTE. 1947. m. DM.55. Triltsch Druck und Verlag GmbH und Co. KG, Herzogstr. 53, 40215 Duesseldorf, Germany. adv.; bk.rev.; charts; illus.; index. circ. 4,000.
    Formerly: Jungbuchhandel.

070.5   SZ
BUCHHAENDLERIN. 5/yr. 20 SFr. Angestelltenverband des Schweizer Buchhandels, Franziskanerplatz 8, CH-6003 Luzern, Switzerland. TEL 041-235520. FAX 041-230278. Ed. Karin Vollrath. circ. 1,900. **Document type:** trade publication.

070.5   GW   ISSN 0170-5105
BUCHHANDELSGESCHICHTE. ZWEITE FOLGE; Aufsaetze, Rezensionen und Berichte zur Geschichte des Buchwesens. 1979. irreg. (approx. 4/yr.). DM.42. (Historische Kommission des Boersenvereins des Deutschen Buchhandels e.V.) Buchhaendler-Vereinigung GmbH, Postfach 100442, 60004 Frankfurt a.M., Germany. TEL 069-13060. FAX 069-1306201. TELEX 413573-BUCHV-D. bk.rev. **Document type:** academic/scholarly publication.
—SWETS.

686   GW   ISSN 0724-7001
BUCHWISSENSCHAFTLICHE BEITRAEGE AUS DEM DEUTSCHEN BUCHARCHIV MUENCHEN. 1950. irreg., no.48, 1994. price varies. Harrassowitz Verlag, Taunusstr. 14, 65183 Wiesbaden, Germany. TEL 0611-530-0. FAX 0611-530570. TELEX 4186135. (Subscr. to: Postfach 2929, 65019 Wiesbaden, Germany) Eds. Ludwig Delp, Ursula Neumann. **Document type:** monographic series.
    Formerly: Buchwissenschaftliche Beitraege (ISSN 0407-5439)

070.5   AU
BUECHER AUS OESTERREICH. 1947. a. Hauptverband des Oesterreichischen Buchhandels, Gruenangergasse 4, A-1010 Vienna, Austria. TEL 0222-5121535. FAX 0222-5128482. **Document type:** trade publication.
    Formerly (until 1993): Oesterreichische Buch (ISSN 0078-3455)

655   GW   ISSN 0007-3032
BUECHERGILDE. 1924. q. free. Buechergilde Gutenberg Verlagsgesellschaft mbH, Untermainkai 66, Postfach 60064, 60329 Frankfurt a.M., Germany. FAX 069-27390824. Ed. Karin Hirschfeld. bk.rev.; illus. circ. 200,000. **Document type:** trade publication.

028.1   SZ   ISSN 1016-9431
BUECHERPICK; das aktuelle Buchmagazin. (Text in German) 1982. q. 14 SFr. Buecherpick Verlag AG, Postfach 146, CH-3322 Urtenen, Switzerland. TEL 031-852233. Ed. Juerg Altwegg. adv.; bk.rev. circ. 120,000.

011   FR
BULLETIN DU BIBLIOPHILE (PARIS, 1920). 1920. s-a. 395 F. Editions du Cercle de la Librairie, 35 rue Gregoire-de-Tours, 75006 Paris, France. (Co-sponsor: Association Internationale de Bibliophilie) adv.; bibl.
    Formerly: Librairie Ancienne et Moderne. Bulletin (ISSN 0024-2128)

015 028   FR   ISSN 0399-9742
BULLETIN DU BIBLIOPHILE (PARIS, 1965). (Supplement avail.: Association Internationale de Bibliophilie. Nouvelles (ISSN 0220-388X)) (Text in English, French and German) 1965. 4/yr. membership. (Association Internationale de Bibliophilie) Bibliotheque Nationale de France, 58 rue Richelieu, 75020 Paris, France. Ed. Claude Guerin. bk.rev.
—BLDSC (2834.970000).
    Formed by the 1969 merger of: Bulletin du Bibliophile et du Bibliothecaire (ISSN 0152-0571); Bibliophilie (ISSN 0006-1603)

BULLETIN JUGEND UND LITERATUR. see LIBRARY AND INFORMATION SCIENCES

091   ET
BULLETIN OF ETHIOPIAN MANUSCRIPTS. (Text in English or Ethiopian) a. Ethiopian Manuscript Microfilm Library, Box 30274, Addis Ababa, Ethiopia.

BUREAU INTERNATIONAL DES SOCIETES GERANT LES DROITS D'ENREGISTREMENT ET DE REPRODUCTION MECANIQUE. BULLETIN. see PRINTING

BUSINESS BOOK REVIEW. see BUSINESS AND ECONOMICS

070.5 658.8   UK   ISSN 0261-7463
BUSINESS RATIO REPORT: BOOK PUBLISHERS; an industry sector analysis. a. I C C Business Ratios Ltd., Freepost, Field House, Hampton, Mddx. TW12 1BR, England. TEL 081-783-0977.
FAX 081-783-1940. charts; stat. **Document type:** trade publication.
    Supersedes in part (in 1978): Business Ratio Report: Book and Periodical Publishers.

070.5 658.8   UK   ISSN 0261-7471
BUSINESS RATIO REPORT: BOOKSELLERS; an industry sector analysis. 1980. a. I C C Business Ratios Ltd., Freepost, Field House, Hampton, Mddx. TW12 1BR, England. TEL 081-783-0977. FAX 081-783-1940. charts; stat. **Document type:** trade publication.
—BLDSC (2250.241000).

PUBLISHING AND BOOK TRADE

070.5 658.8   UK   ISSN 0261-9342
BUSINESS RATIO REPORT: PERIODICAL PUBLISHERS; an industry sector analysis. a. I C C Business Ratios Ltd., Freepost, Field House, Hampton, Mddx. TW12 1BR, England. TEL 081-783-0977. FAX 081-783-1940. charts; stat. **Document type:** trade publication.
   Supersedes in part (in 1978): Business Ratio Report: Book and Periodical Publishers.

658.8   US   ISSN 0732-6599
Z475
BUY BOOKS WHERE, SELL BOOKS WHERE; a directory of out of print booksellers and collectors and their author and subject specialties. 1978. irreg., 9th ed. 1994. $34.95 (libraries $31.45); $36 in Canada (libraries $32.40) (effective 1994). Ruth E. Robinson Books, Rt. 7, Box 162A, Morgantown, WV 26505. TEL 304-594-3140. Ed. Ruth E. Robinson. adv. circ. 3,000. **Document type:** directory.
   Description: Lists more than 2000 active dealers and collectors in the out of print book field in the U.S. and Canada, with names, addresses and pertinent information concerning the books they buy and/or sell.

658.8   AT
C B A A NEWS. 1982. m. membership. Christian Bookselling Association of Australia Inc., P.O. Box 576, Caringbah, N.S.W. 2229, Australia. TEL 61-2-524-3347. FAX 61-2-540-3001. Ed. Margaret Tembo. adv. contact: Jan Holt. bk.rev.; illus.; tr.lit. circ. 350. (back issues avail.) **Document type:** newsletter, trade publication.

028.5   US
C B C FEATURES; containing news of the children's book world. 1945. 2/yr. $50. Children's Book Council, Inc., 568 Broadway, New York, NY 10012-3225. TEL 212-966-1990. Ed. Maria Juarez. bibl. circ. 40,000. **Indexed:** Child.Lit.Abstr.
   Formerly: Calendar (ISSN 0008-0721)
   Description: Lists of titles and materials, profiles of authors and publications, and feature articles pertaining to children's literature.

574 700   US
C B E VIEWS. 1978. bi-m. $38. Council of Biology Editors Inc., 11 S. La Salle St., Ste. 1400, Chicago, IL 60603-1210. TEL 312-201-0101. Ed. Martha Tacker. adv. contact: Cindy Clark. bk.rev. circ. 1,200. **Document type:** newsletter.
   —BLDSC (3095.311000).
   Formerly (until 1977): Council of Biology Editors. Newsletter (ISSN 0164-5609)
   Description: Forum for the exchange of information among authors, editors, and publishers in the life sciences.

028.5   UK
C B H S NEWSLETTER. s-a. Children's Books History Society, 2 Courtney Crescent, Carshalton Beeches, Surrey SM5 4LZ, England. **Indexed:** Child.Lit.Abstr.
   Description: Promotes an appreciation of children's books, and the study of their history, bibliography and literary content.

070.5 028.5   CN   ISSN 0319-0080
PN1009.A1
C C L/LITTERATURE CANADIENNE POUR LA JEUNESSE. (Canadian Children's Literature) (Text in English, French) 1975. q. $28 (effective 1995-1996). Canadian Children's Press, University of Guelph, Department of English, Guelph, ON N1G 2W1, Canada. FAX 519-837-1315. Eds. Mary Rubio, Daniel Chouinard. adv. contact: Gay Christofides. bk.rev.; bibl.; circ. 900 (paid). (back issues avail.) **Indexed:** Bk.Rev.Ind. (1980-), Can.B.P.I., Can.Lit.Ind., Can.Per.Ind., Child.Bk.Rev.Ind. (1980-), Child.Lit.Abstr., CMI. **Document type:** academic/scholarly publication.
   —BLDSC (3019.405000).
   Description: Presents reviews and criticism of Canadian books for children and young adults. Examines the history of Canadian children's literature and contains in-depth reviews of recently published Canadian books and plays for young readers and ongoing interviews with writers and illustrators.

070.5 020   CK   ISSN 0121-1242
Z490
C E R L A L C: EL LIBRO EN AMERICA LATINA Y EL CARIBE. 1972. q. $18 in Latin America and the Caribbean; elsewhere $22. Centro Regional para el Fomento del Libro en America Latina y el Caribe, Calle 70 No. 9-52, Apdo. Aereo 57438, Bogota, Colombia. TEL 212-60-56. FAX 255-46-14. TELEX 44637 CERLA CO. Ed. Jose Arteaga. adv. circ. 1,000.
   Incorporates (1974-1987): Boletin Bibliografico C E R L A L (ISSN 0120-1204); **Former titles (until 1981):** C E R L A L C: Noticias sobre el Libro y Bibliografia (ISSN 0120-0887); And (until 1978): Revista de Noticias sobre el Libro y Bibliografia (1018-239X); (until 1978): Noticias C E R L A L C (1018-2381); (until 1977): Noticias C E R L A L (0120-1158).

070.5   SP   ISSN 0214-4123
C L I J. (Cuadernos de Literatura Infantil y Juvenil) 1988. 11/yr. $75. Editorial Fontalba, S.A., Valencia 359, 6o, 1a, 08009 Barcelona, Spain. TEL 93-458-5508. FAX 93-458-6602. TELEX 97835 FON E.

070.5   US
C L M PAGES. 1967-1990; resumed 1991. q. Council of Literary Magazines and Presses, 154 Christopher St., Ste. 3C, New York, NY 10014-2839. TEL 212-741-9110. FAX 212-741-9112. Ed. Celia O'Donnell. adv.; bk.rev. circ. 2,800. **Document type:** newsletter.
   Former titles: C L M P Newsletter; C C L M News (ISSN 0273-3315); C C L M. Newsletter (ISSN 0192-9887)
   Description: Contains technical and information articles, interviews, profiles and listings about literary publishing, and information about CLMP's activities.

070.5   CN
C M: A REVIEWING JOURNAL OF CANADIAN MATERIALS FOR YOUNG PEOPLE. 1971-1994 (Dec.). 6/yr. Can.$42($45) Canadian Library Association, 200 Elgin St., Ste. 602, Ottawa, ON K2P 1L5, Canada. TEL 613-232-9625. FAX 613-563-9895. Ed. Elizabeth Morton. adv.; bk.rev.; film rev.; bibl.; illus.; index. circ. 2,000. (back issues avail.) **Indexed:** Bk.Rev.Dig., Bk.Rev.Ind. (1988-), Can.Per.Ind., Child.Bk.Rev.Ind. (1988-), CMI, Media Rev.Dig. **Document type:** trade publication.
   Former titles: C M: Canadian Materials for Schools and Libraries (ISSN 0821-1450); Canadian Materials (ISSN 0317-4654)

070.5   CN   ISSN 0315-6621
C M P A NEWSLETTER. no.63, 1981. 6/yr. Can.$15($15) (typically set in Jun.). Canadian Magazine Publishers Association, 2 Stewart St., Toronto, ON M5V 1H6, Canada. TEL 416-362-2546. FAX 416-362-2547. adv. circ. 600. **Document type:** newsletter.
   —UMI.

C N I D A INFORMA; boletin bimestral de informacion autoral. (Centro Nacional de Informacion - Direccion General del Derecho de Autor) see *BIBLIOGRAPHIES*

655.4   US   ISSN 1064-4482
C O S M E P NEWSLETTER. (Committee of Small Magazine Editors & Publishers) 1969. m. $65 to non-members (effective Jan. 1995). C O S M E P, Inc., Box 420703, San Francisco, CA 94142-0703. TEL 415-922-9490. FAX 415-922-5566. e-mail: 74217.1707@compuserve.com. Ed. Richard Morris. bk.rev.; circ. 2,000 (paid). (back issues avail.) **Document type:** newsletter, trade publication.
   Former titles (until Feb. 1981): Independent Publisher; (until June 1980): C O S M E P Newsletter (ISSN 0007-8832)
   Description: For publishers, especially book publishers.

028.1   US   ISSN 0590-711X
C P D A NEWS. 1956. m. Council for Periodical Distributors Associations, 60 E. 42nd St., Ste. 2122, New York, NY 10165. TEL 212-818-0234. FAX 212-983-4699. Ed. Tilly McCardell Young. adv.: B&W page $2350; trim 8 1/8 x 10 7/8. circ. 4,900 (controlled). **Document type:** trade publication.
   Formerly: C I D News.
   Description: International association of local independent wholesaler distributors of magazines, paperback books, comics, trading cards, audiotapes, and newspapers in the United States and Canada.

070.5   US   ISSN 1066-5870
C R O W QUARTERLY REVIEW. (Capsule Review of Original Work); a new review of unpublished manuscripts. q. $20 (free to qualified personnel) (effective 1993). C R O W, 147 Vera Marie Ln., Box 170, Rollinsville, CO 80474. TEL 303-258-3851. Ed. Kevin McCarthy. adv.; circ. 800 (paid); 700 (controlled). **Document type:** consumer publication, trade publication.
   Formerly (until 1991): C R O W Newsletter.
   Description: Manuscript reviews, essays and evaluation tools of interest to writers, editors, agents and producers.

CABIRION: GAY BOOKS BULLETIN. see *HOMOSEXUALITY*

028.1   FR   ISSN 0338-7208
PQ1141
CAHIERS BLEUS. 1975. 3/yr. 210 F. (foreign 350 F.). Amis des Cahiers Bleus, Espace Argence, 10000 Troyes, France. TEL 25-73-77-13. FAX 25-80-16-59. Ed. Dominique Daguet. circ. 1,500.
   Description: Features reviews of books hot off the press.

CAHIERS D'ACTION LITTERAIRE. see *LITERATURE*

655.5 800   CN   ISSN 1193-9974
CANADIAN AUTHOR. 1919. q. Can.$15 to individuals; institutions Can.$25. Canadian Authors Association, 275 Slater St., 5th Fl., Ottawa, ON K1P 5H9, Canada. TEL 613-233-2846. FAX 613-235-8237. Ed. Welwyn Katz. adv.; illus. circ. 4,500. (also avail. in microfilm from CML) **Indexed:** Amer.Hum.Ind., Can.B.P.I., Can.Lit.Ind., Can.Per.Ind., CMI, Ind.Bk.Rev.Hum., M.L.A. **Document type:** academic/scholarly publication.
   Former titles: Canadian Author and Bookman (ISSN 0008-2937); Bookman; Incorporates (in 1968): Canadian Poetry.
   Description: Provides market updates on writing in Canada.

CANADIAN AUTHORS ASSOCIATION NEWSLINE. see *LITERATURE*

070.5   CN   ISSN 0576-470X
CANADIAN BOOK PRICES CURRENT. 1955. irreg. price varies. McClelland & Stewart, 481 University Ave., Ste. 900, Toronto, Ont. M5G 2E9, Canada. TEL 416-598-1114. FAX 416-598-7764.

028.1   CN   ISSN 0383-770X
F1001
CANADIAN BOOK REVIEW ANNUAL. 1975. a. Can.$104.95 (effective 1995 & 1996). 44 Charles St., W., Ste. 3205, Toronto, ON M4Y 1R8, Canada. TEL 416-961-8537. FAX 416-961-1855. Ed. Joyce M. Wilson; Pub. Joyce M. Wilson. bk.rev. circ. 1,500. **Document type:** consumer publication, bibliography.
   Description: Original short reviews of most Canadian trade, scholarly, reference and children's titles published that year; full bibliographic information: comprehensive subject, author, title index.

686.3 747.5   CN   ISSN 0822-9538
CANADIAN BOOKBINDERS & BOOK ARTISTS GUILD NEWSLETTER. 1983. q. Can.$35. Canadian Bookbinders & Book Artists Guild, 35 McCaul St., Ste. 221, Toronto, ON M5T 1V7, Canada. TEL 416-581-1071. Ed. Richard Miller. adv. contact: Richard Miller. bk.rev.; illus.; cum.index: 1983-1993; circ. 540 (paid). (back issues avail.) **Document type:** newsletter.
   Description: Contains technical articles, listings of events, publications, suppliers.

658.8   CN   ISSN 0225-2392
CANADIAN BOOKSELLER; the magazine of book retailing. 1978. 10/yr. Can.$74.90 to non-members in Canada; $80 to non-members in U.S.; Can.$100 to non-members elsewhere. Canadian Booksellers Association, 301 Donlands Ave., Toronto, Ont. M4J 3R8, Canada. TEL 416-467-7883. FAX 416-467-7886. Ed. Ken Larone. adv.: B&W page Can.$795, color page Can.$1620; trim 8 1/8 x 10 3/4; adv. contact: Jan Marriot. circ. 1,941. **Indexed:** Can.B.P.I.
   —CCC.
   Formerly: Net 30 (ISSN 0225-6622)
   Description: For owners, managers and staff of trade, college and independent bookstores.

PUBLISHING AND BOOK TRADE

655.4   CN   ISSN 0008-4859
CANADIAN PUBLISHERS DIRECTORY. (Supplement to: Quill & Quire) 1935. 2/yr. (included with subscr. to Quill and Quire). Key Publishers Co. Ltd., 70 The Esplanade, 4th Fl., Toronto, ON M5E 1R2, Canada. TEL 416-360-0044. FAX 416-941-9038. Ed. Marie Campbell. adv. contact: June Dickenson. circ. 8,000. **Document type:** directory.

070.5   659.1   US   ISSN 0736-9077
CODEN: CCIREV
CAPELL'S CIRCULATION REPORT; the newsletter of magazine circulation. 1982. 20/yr. $345. Daniel Capell, Ed. & Pub., 60 E. 42nd St., Ste. 3810, New York, NY 10165. TEL 212-697-5753, ext. 118. bk.rev. (back issues avail.) **Document type:** newsletter.
—CCC.
   Description: Provides current information on what's happening in circulation trends, strategies, tactics and analyses.

CARDOZO ARTS & ENTERTAINMENT LAW JOURNAL. see *LAW*

070.5   UK
CARFAX NEWS. 1981. a. free. Carfax Publishing Co., Box 25, Abingdon, Oxon.OX14 3UE, England. TEL 01235-555335. FAX 01235-553559. (Dist in N. America by: Carfax Publishing Co., 875-81 Massachusetts Ave., Cambridge, MA 02139) **Document type:** newsletter.
   Description: Includes new titles by subject and subscription rates.

800   JM   ISSN 1018-2926
F2155
CARIBBEAN REVIEW OF BOOKS. q. $10 to individuals (foreign $16); institutions $20 (foreign $30). (University of the West Indies Publishers' Association) U W I Publishers Association, P.O. Box 42, Mona, Kingston 7, Jamaica, W.I. TEL 809-977-2659. FAX 809-977-2660. Ed. Samuel Bandara. adv. contact: Annie Paul. bk.rev.; illus. circ. 400. (back issues avail.) **Document type:** academic/scholarly publication.
   Supersedes (1986-1991): U W I P A Newsletter.
   Description: Presents the latest information on books published in, about or relevant to the Caribbean; includes information on authors, publishers and the book trade.

070.5   UK
CASSELL AND PUBLISHERS ASSOCIATION DIRECTORY OF PUBLISHING IN THE UNITED KINGDOM, COMMONWEALTH AND OVERSEAS. 1960. a. £40. Cassell plc., Villiers House, 41-47 Strand, London WC2N 5JE, England. (Subscr. to: Stanley House, Fleets Ln., Poole, Dorset BH15 3AJ, England; Dist. in the U.S. by: Cassell, PCS Data Processing Inc., 360 W. 31st St., New York, NY 10001) Ed.Bd. adv.; index. circ. 5,000. **Document type:** directory.
   Former titles (until 1990): Cassell and Publishers Association Directory of Publishing in Great Britain, the Commonwealth, Ireland, South Africa and Pakistan; Cassell's Directory of Publishing in Great Britain, the Commonwealth, Ireland, South Africa and Pakistan (ISSN 0308-7018); Cassell's Directory of Publishing in Great Britain, The Commonwealth, Ireland and South Africa (ISSN 0069-097X)
   Description: Gives current details of all publishers in Great Britain and overseas: name, address, imprints, type of books published, key personnel, number of new titles published yearly.

CASSELL, PUBLISHERS ASSOCIATION AND THE FEDERATION OF EUROPEAN PUBLISHERS ASSOCIATIONS. DIRECTORY OF PUBLISHING IN CONTINENTAL EUROPE. see *BUSINESS AND ECONOMICS — Trade And Industrial Directories*

CATALOG AGE. see *ADVERTISING AND PUBLIC RELATIONS*

070.5   IT
CATALOGO DEGLI EDITORI ITALIANI. a. L.80000 (effective 1995). Editrice Bibliografica s.r.l., Viale Vittorio Veneto 24, 20124 Milan, Italy. TEL 39-2-29006965. FAX 39-2-654624. circ. 2,000. **Document type:** directory.
   Description: Lists Italian book publishers and distributors.

THE CATHOLIC. see *RELIGIONS AND THEOLOGY — Roman Catholic*

070.5   282   US   ISSN 1077-6656
CATHOLIC BOOK PUBLISHERS ASSOCIATION DIRECTORY. 1990. biennial. $25. Catholic Book Publishers Association, 333 Glen Head Rd., Old Brookville, NY 11545. TEL 516-671-9342. FAX 516-759-4227. Ed. Charles A. Roth. circ. 2,200 (controlled). **Document type:** directory.
   Description: Provides information about each publisher member of the Association for bookstore owners and managers.

CENTER FOR CHILDREN'S BOOKS. BULLETIN. see *BIBLIOGRAPHIES*

002   090   NE   ISSN 0069-1984
CENTRE NATIONAL D'ARCHEOLOGIE ET D'HISTOIRE DU LIVRE. PUBLICATION. 1965. irreg., vol.2, no.3-4, 1994. price varies. (Centre National d'Archeologie et d'Histoire du Livre, BE) De Graaf Publishers, P.O. Box 6, 2420 AA Nieuwkoop, Netherlands. TEL 31-1725-71461. **Document type:** monographic series.

070.5   BE
CERCLE BELGE DE LA LIBRAIRIE. ANNUAIRE.* 1926. a. 1060 Fr. Cercle Belge de la Librairie (CBL), 140 Blvd. Lanbermont, 1030 Brussels, Belgium.

070.5   US
CHICAGO GUIDES TO WRITING, EDITING, AND PUBLISHING. 1971. irreg., latest 1990. price varies. University of Chicago Press, 5801 S. Ellis Ave., Chicago, IL 60637. TEL 312-702-7899. (Subscr. to: 11030 Langley Ave., Chicago, IL 60628)
   Refereed Serial

070.5   028.5   US   ISSN 1073-7596
CHILDREN'S BOOK INSIDER; your monthly guide to children's writing success. 1990. m. $34. Children's Book Insider, Box 1030, Fairplay, CO 80440-1030. TEL 719-836-0394. E-mail: JB558@aol.com. Ed. Jon Bard; Pub. Laura Backes. index. circ. 3,000. (back issues avail.) **Document type:** newsletter.
   Description: Provides market news, writing tips, interviews with top authors and editors for writers of children's literature.

028.5   CN   ISSN 0705-0038
CHILDRENS BOOK NEWS. 1979. 4/yr. Can.$25 (membership). Canadian Children's Book Centre, 35 Spadina Rd., Toronto, ON M5R 2S9, Canada. TEL 416-975-0010. FAX 416-975-1839. bk.rev.; illus. circ. 35,000. Indexed: Bk.Rev.Ind. (1987-), Child.Bk.Rev.Ind. (1987-).
   Former titles (until 1983): Book News Times; Book Times (ISSN 0706-1064)

028.5   US   ISSN 0090-7987
Z1037.A1
CHILDREN'S BOOK REVIEW SERVICE. 1972. m. (plus two supplements). $40 (effective Sep. 1994). Children's Book Review Service Inc., 220 Berkeley Pl., No. 1-D, Brooklyn, NY 11217. TEL 718-622-4036. Ed. Ann L. Kalkhoff. bk.rev.; circ. 300 (paid). (looseleaf format) Indexed: Bk.Rev.Ind. (1979-), Child.Bk.Rev.Ind. (1979-). **Document type:** newsletter.

070.5   US   ISSN 0069-3472
Z1037.A2
CHILDREN'S BOOKS: AWARDS AND PRIZES. 1969. irreg. $85 hardcover; paper $57.50. Children's Book Council, Inc., 568 Broadway, New York, NY 10012-3225. TEL 212-966-1990. Ed. John Donovan. index. circ. 5,000.
   Description: International compilation of 191 children's book awards, with sponsor's address, description of award and winners, title and person indices, awards classification appendix and list of information resources.

028.5   UK   ISSN 0266-4232
CHILDREN'S BOOKS OF THE YEAR. 1971. a. £1. Young Book Trust, Book House, 45 East Hill, Wandsworth, London SW18 2QZ, England. TEL 0181-870-9055. FAX 0181-874-4790. **Document type:** directory.
   Description: Offers an independent selector's choice of the best children's books.

CHILDREN'S BOOKS OF THE YEAR. see *CHILDREN AND YOUTH — For*

070.5   US
CHILDREN'S BOOKS: ONE HUNDRED TITLES FOR READING AND SHARING. 1911. a. $3. New York Public Library, Office of Branch Libraries, 455 Fifth Ave., New York, NY 10016. TEL 212-340-0892. FAX 212-689-3193.
   Former titles: Children's Books and Recordings: Suggested as Holiday Gifts; Children's Books: Suggested as Holiday Gifts (ISSN 0069-3502)

070.5   808.068   700   US   ISSN 0897-9790
PN147.5
CHILDREN'S WRITER'S AND ILLUSTRATOR'S MARKET. a. $22.99. F & W Publications, Inc., 1507 Dana Ave., Cincinnati, OH 45207. TEL 513-531-2222. FAX 513-531-4744. Ed. Christine Martin. illus.
   Description: Provides information on book publishing and magazine markets for both writers and illustrators of children's publishing. Contains advice to help market one's work.

070.5   CC
CHINA BOOKS. (Text in Chinese and English) 1981. q. Guiji Shudian, Qikan Bu - China International Book Trading Corp., P.O. Box 339, Beijing 100044, People's Republic of China. bk.rev.

CHRISTIAN LIBRARIAN. see *LIBRARY AND INFORMATION SCIENCES*

658.8   200   US   ISSN 0749-2510
BV2369
CHRISTIAN RETAILING; the trade magazine of religious retailing. 1955. m. $30. Strang Communications Co., 600 Rinehart Rd., Lake Mary, FL 32746. TEL 407-333-0600. Ed. Carol Stertzer. adv.; bk.rev. circ. 9,800. (reprint service avail. from UMI) **Document type:** trade publication.
   Formerly: Christian Bookseller (ISSN 0009-5273)

070.5   CC   ISSN 1001-9316
CHUBAN FAXING YANJIU/PUBLISHING RESEARCH. (Text in Chinese) 1985. bi-m. Y2.80 per no. (Zhongguo Chuban Kexue Yanjiusuo) China Book Publishing House, No. A-7, Xirongxian Hutong, Xicheng-qu, Beijing 100031, People's Republic of China. TEL 010-6059539. Ed. Yuan Lian. adv. contact: Zhang Li. circ. 100,000 (paid). **Document type:** academic/scholarly publication.
   Refereed Serial

070.5   CC   ISSN 1001-2680
CHUBAN GONGZUO/PUBLISHING AFFAIRS. (Text in Chinese) m. Xinwen Chubanshu, No. 85, Dongsi Nandajie, Beijing 100703, People's Republic of China. TEL 555415. Ed. Teng Mingdao.

070.5   CC
CHUBAN SHILIAO/HISTORICAL MATERIAL ON PUBLISHING. (Text in Chinese) 1982. q. $10. Shanghai Chuban Gongzuozhe Xiehui - Shanghai Publishers Association, 5 Shaoxing Road, Shanghai 200020, People's Republic of China. TEL 4370176. FAX 86-21-433245. Eds. Song Yuanfang, Zhao Jiabi. bk.rev. circ. 2,500.

028.1   015   KO   ISSN 1227-1985
Z464.K67
CH'ULPAN MOONWHA/KOREAN BOOK JOURNAL. (Text in Korean) 1948. m. 2000 Won($3) Korean Publishers Association, 105-2 Sagan-dong, Chongno-ku, Seoul 110-190, S. Korea. TEL 02-735-2701. FAX 02-738-5414. Ed. Kim Nark-Joon. adv.; bk.rev.; bibl. circ. 2,000.

070.5   US   ISSN 0888-8191
PN4784.C6   CODEN: CIRMEZ
CIRCULATION MANAGEMENT. 1986. m. $32 to individuals; free to qualified personnel (foreign $89). Ganesa Corporation, 611 Broadway, Ste. 401, New York, NY 10012-2608. TEL 212-989-2133. FAX 212-620-0396. Ed. Karlene Lukovitz. adv.; bk.rev.; circ. 10,000 (controlled). (reprint service avail.) Indexed: INSPEC (1988-). **Document type:** trade publication.
—BLDSC (3265.288000). **CCC.**
   Description: For circulation executives and publishers in the magazine and newsletter publishing industry. Covers subscriptions, renewals, controlled circulation, ABC, BPA, postal, fulfillment and more.

028.1   BL
CIRCULO - REVISTA DO LIVRO. 1973. bi-m. free. Circulo do Livro Ltda., Caixa Postal 7413, CEP 01310 Sao Paulo, Brazil. Ed. Richard Civita. adv.; bk.rev.; illus. circ. 1,100,000.
   Formerly: Revista do Livro (Sao Paulo).

CIVIL AND MILITARY REVIEW. see *MILITARY*

COLE PAPERS; technology, journalism, publishing. see *TECHNOLOGY: COMPREHENSIVE WORKS*

658.8 UK ISSN 0268-3407
COLE'S REGISTER OF BRITISH ANTIQUARIAN & SECONDHAND BOOKDEALERS. 1986. a. £22. Clique, Ltd., 7 Pulleyn Dr., York YO2 2DY, England. TEL 01904-631752. FAX 01904-651325. **Document type:** directory.
—BLDSC (3297.450000).

070.5 686 US ISSN 1055-9701
Z48
COLOR PUBLISHING. 1991. 6/yr. $19 (foreign $28). PennWell Publishing Co. (Nashua), 10 Tara Blvd., 5th Fl., Nashua, NH 03062-2801. TEL 603-891-9168. FAX 603-891-0539. (Subscr. to: Box 2709, Tulsa, OK 74101. TEL 918-831-9537) Ed. Tom McMillan. adv.; illus.; circ. 24,000 (controlled). **Document type:** trade publication.
—CCC.
  Description: Covers new developments in color publishing technology for the technical professional.

070.5 US
COLORADO BOOK GUIDE; a directory of the Colorado book community. 1991. biennial. $8.95. Owaissa Communications Company, Inc., Box 8928, Denver, CO 80201. TEL 303-892-0260. FAX 303-892-5620. Pub. Tom Auer. adv. **Document type:** directory.
  Description: Lists Colorado libraries, bookstores, publishers, literary agents, book manufacturers, writing and book organizations, and literacy programs.

070.5 686 US
COLOUR.* 1991. m. free to qualified personnel. Ulick Publishing Co., 150 Houston St., Ste. 308, Batavia, IL 60510-1953. TEL 708-406-8330. Ed. Terry Ulick. adv.; illus.; circ. 80,000 (controlled).
  Description: Covers news of emerging color publishing technologies and new products for the technical professional.

COMIC ART STUDIES. see *LIBRARY AND INFORMATION SCIENCES*

COMICS JOURNAL; the magazine of news & criticism. see *ART*

070.5 IT
COMIX; il giornale dei fumetti. w. L.1500 per no. Frenco Cosimo Panini Editore S.p.A., Via Corassori 24, 41100 Modena, Italy. TEL 059-345294. FAX 059-345302. Ed. Giuseppe Cottafavi. **Document type:** consumer publication.

COMMUNIQUE (INDIANAPOLIS). see *INSURANCE*

659.1 US
COMPARABILITY UPDATE. bi-m. B P A International, 270 Madison Ave., New York, NY 10016-0699. TEL 212-779-3200. FAX 212-752-1721.

COMPUTER BOOK REVIEW. see *COMPUTERS*

COMPUTERITER; microcomputer news and views for the writer-editor. see *COMPUTERS — Personal Computers*

CONCEPTS IN COMMUNICATION INFORMATICS AND LIBRARIANSHIP. see *LIBRARY AND INFORMATION SCIENCES*

070.5 792 SA
CONTACTS/KONTAKTE. (Text in English) 1978. a. R.10. Limelight Publications C.C., P.O. Box 760, Randpark Ridge 2156, South Africa. TEL 27-11-7937231. FAX 27-11-7922679. Ed. Jennifer van Staden. adv. circ. 5,000.
  Formerly (until 1983): Limelight Contacts - Limelight Kontakte (ISSN 0250-2003)

CONTEMPORARY IMPRESSIONS. see *ART*

CONTEMPORARY JAPANESE BOOKS. see *BIBLIOGRAPHIES*

CONTRAPUNCT. see *JOURNALISM*

THE CORNERSTONE (NEW PROVIDENCE). see *BIBLIOGRAPHIES*

070.5 CK ISSN 0121-1390
CORREO EDITORIAL; revista informativa de la C C L. 1989. q. free. Camara Colombiana del Libro, Carrera 17A, No. 37-27, Bogota, Colombia. TEL 2886188. FAX 2873320. adv.; bk.rev.; abstr.; illus.; stat.

070.5 CR
COSTA RICA Y LOS LIBROS. 1990? q. Camara Costarricense del Libro, Apdo. Postal 1571, 1002 San Jose, Costa Rica. TEL 34-9020. FAX 506-24-3607. bibl.

070.5 US
CREATIVITY CONNECTION; a newsletter for writers. 1990. q. $8. University of Wisconsin at Madison, Division of University Outreach, Department of Communication Programs, 610 Langdon St., Rm. 224, Madison, WI 53703. TEL 608-262-4911. FAX 608-265-2329. E-mail: marshall.cook@mail.admin.wisc.edu. Ed. Marshall J. Cook; Pub. Marshall J. Cook. bk.rev.; tr.lit. circ. 750. (back issues avail.) **Document type:** newsletter.
  Description: Contains how-to articles, personal profiles, publishing information, and listings of adult-education opportunities of interest to freelance writers.

CRITICAL REVIEW; an interdisciplinary journal. see *LITERARY AND POLITICAL REVIEWS*

028.1 FR ISSN 0011-1600
Z1007
CRITIQUE; revue generale des publications francaises et etrangeres. 1946. m. 504 F. (foreign 650 F.). Editions de Minuit, 7 rue Bernard-Palissy, 75006 Paris, France. TEL 44-39-39-20. FAX 45-44-82-36. Ed. Jean Piel. adv.; bk.rev.; play rev.; charts; index. **Indexed:** Arts & Hum.Cit.Ind., Ind.Bk.Rev.Hum., Lang.& Lang.Behav.Abstr., M.L.A. **Document type:** academic/scholarly publication.
—BLDSC (3487.490000); Faxon; SWETS.

CUMULATIVE BOOK INDEX. see *BIBLIOGRAPHIES*

070.5 US ISSN 1063-9012
CURRENT BOOKS MAGAZINE. 1992. q. $14.95. Capital Communications Group LLC, Box 34468, Bethesda, MD 20827. TEL 301-530-8200. FAX 301-530-8201. Ed. Edwin S. Grosvenor. adv.: B&W page $1600; adv. contact: Joshua Dinman. bk.rev. circ. 36,000. (back issues avail.)
  Description: Excerpts new and recently published fiction and nonfiction books, covering such topics as history, biography, travel, business, current issues, archaeology, arts, humor and poetry.

028.1 CN ISSN 0316-9448
CURRENT CANADIAN BOOKS/LIVRES CANADIENS COURANTS. 1971. m. Can.$36. John Coutts Library Services Ltd., 6900 Kinsmen, P.O. Box 1000, Niagara Falls, ON L2E 7E7, Canada. TEL 905-356-6382. FAX 905-356-5064. TELEX 061-5299. Ed. John R. Grantier. circ. 100 (controlled). **Document type:** bibliography.
  Formerly: Current Canadian Imprints Catalogued.
  Description: Presents topical listings of bibliographic citations which represent new Canadian books, books published abroad which have association value, and books which must be ordered direct.

070.5 US
CURTIS LINE. 1935. bi-m. Curtis Circulation Co., 2500 McClellan Ave., Pennsauken, NJ 08109-4660. TEL 609-488-5700. FAX 609-488-2219. Ed. Patricia Lennon. circ. 2,400 (controlled).
  Description: For Curtis' publishers, wholesalers and retailers.

D K NEWSLETTER; a journal of news and reviews of Indian publications in English. see *BIBLIOGRAPHIES*

070.5 658.8 GW ISSN 0343-5598
D N V. (Der Neue Vertrieb) 1949. m. DM.173.34 (foreign DM.168). Presse Fachverlag, Eidelstedteweg 22, 20255 Hamburg, Germany. TEL 040-565031. FAX 040-5602920. adv.; bk.rev.; illus.; mkt.; tr.lit. circ. 1,800. **Document type:** trade publication.
  Description: Trade publication for paperback book, magazine, and newspaper businesses, featuring news, reports of events, and market information.

070.5 SP ISSN 0214-2694
DELIBROS; revista professional del libro. (Supplements avail.) (English summary avail.) 1988. m. (11/yr.). 7000 ptas. (foreign 12000 ptas.). Delibros, S.A., Goya, 115, 1o, 28009 Madrid, Spain. TEL 34-91-3090352. FAX 34-91-3091188. Ed. Jaime Brill. adv.; bk.rev.; bibl.; illus. circ. 18,000.
  Description: Offers information and analysis on the world of books; reflects trends, includes articles of opinion, and contemplates national and international culture.

DESKTOP PUBLISHING TODAY. see *PUBLISHING AND BOOK TRADE — Computer Applications*

070.5 GW ISSN 0344-7278
KK7013
DEUTSCHER PRESSERAT. JAHRBUCH. 1956. a. DM.15. Deutscher Presserat, Traegerverein, Thomas-Mann-Str. 54, 53111 Bonn, Germany. circ. 4,000 (paid). **Document type:** bulletin.
  Formerly (until 1978): Deutscher Presserat. Taetigkeitsbericht (ISSN 0418-9523)

070.5 GW
DEUTSCHES VERLAGSREGISTER; Verlage mit ihrem periodischen Schrifttum. 1970. irreg. DM.52. Stamm Verlag GmbH, Goldammerweg 16, 45143 Essen, Germany. TEL 0201-84300-0. FAX 0201-472590. Ed. Willy Stamm. adv.; bibl. circ. 1,500. **Document type:** directory.

070.5 GW ISSN 0940-5593
Z317
DEUTSCHSPRACHIGE VERLAGE; Deutschland - Oesterreich - Schweiz. 1950. a. DM.136. Verlag der Schillerbuchhandlung Hans Banger, Guldenbachstr. 1, 50935 Cologne, Germany. TEL 0221-431641. FAX 0221-4303271. **Document type:** directory.
  Formerly (until 1991): Anschriften Deutscher Verlage und Auslaendischer Verlage mit Deutschen Auslieferungen (ISSN 0066-4596)

090.75 US ISSN 0012-2874
PS374.D5
DIME NOVEL ROUND-UP; devoted to the collecting, preservation and literature of the old time dime and nickel novels, libraries and popular story papers. 1931. bi-m. $10. Edward T. LeBlanc, Ed. & Pub., 87 School St., Fall River, MA 02720. TEL 508-672-2082. adv.; bk.rev.; cum.index every 5 yrs. circ. 400. **Indexed:** M.L.A.
  Formerly: Reckless Ralph's Dime Novel Round-Up.

960 028 016 UK
DIPLOMATIC BOOKSHELF & REVIEW. 1957. m. £2. Arthur H. Thrower Ltd., 44-46 S. Ealing Rd., London W5, England. Ed. Arthur H. Thrower. adv.; bk.rev.; charts; illus.; tr.lit.; bibl. (also avail. in microform from UMI; back issues avail.; reprint service avail. from UMI)
  Former titles: Diplomatic Bookshelf (ISSN 0012-3080); African Bookshelf (ISSN 0001-995X)

380 011 070.5 US ISSN 0894-346X
Z286.D57
DIRECTORY MARKETPLACE. 1987. q. $25 (foreign $30). Todd Publications, 18 N. Greenbush Rd., W. Nyack, NY 10994. TEL 914-358-6213. Ed. Barry T. Klein. adv.; bk.rev. circ. 25,000. (back issues avail.) **Document type:** newsletter.
  Description: Reports on new directories and reference books of interest to business and to libraries.

DIRECTORY OF AMERICAN POETS AND FICTION WRITERS. see *LITERATURE — Poetry*

070.5 US
Z475
DIRECTORY OF BOOK PRINTERS (YEAR). 1984. biennial. $14.95. Ad-Lib Publications, 51 1-2 W. Adams, Box 1102, Fairfield, IA 52556-1102. TEL 515-472-6617. FAX 515-472-3186. Ed. Marie Kiefer. adv.; bibl.; charts; index. circ. 3,000. (back issues avail.) **Document type:** directory.
  Former titles (until 1991): Directory of Book, Catalog, and Magazine Printers (ISSN 0895-139X); Directory of Short-Run Book Printers.
  Description: Includes over 900 U.S. and Canadian printers. Pinpoints specializations: quantities, sizes and bindings.

PUBLISHING AND BOOK TRADE

070.5 UK
DIRECTORY OF BOOK PUBLISHERS, DISTRIBUTORS AND WHOLESALERS. a. Booksellers Association of Great Britain and Ireland, 272 Vauxhall Bridge Rd., London SW1V 1BA, England. TEL 0171-834-5477. FAX 0171-834-8812. adv. circ. 3,000. Document type: directory.
  Former titles: Directory of Book Publishers and Wholesalers; Directory of Book Publishers, Wholesalers and Their Terms.
  Description: Provides comprehensive details about 1,600 U.K. publishers, wholesalers, distributors, remainder dealers, and audio book suppliers, including trade terms.

070.5 JA
DIRECTORY OF JAPANESE PUBLISHING INDUSTRY. (Text in English) 1970. biennial. free. Publishers Association for Cultural Exchange, 1-2-1 Sarugaku-cho, Chiyoda-ku, Tokyo 101, Japan. TEL 03-3291-5685. FAX 03-3233-3645. Ed. Hiroyasu Ochiai. Document type: directory.
  Formerly: Guide to Publishers and Related Industries in Japan.

659.1 US
DIRECTORY OF MARKET COMPARABILITY PROGRAMS & MEMBERSHIP. a. B P A International, 270 Madison Ave., New York, NY 10016-0699. TEL 212-779-3200. FAX 212-725-1721. Document type: directory.
  Description: Serves as a guide to BPA's Market Comparability Programs and Market Classifications.

070.5 US
DIRECTORY OF MICHIGAN LITERARY PUBLISHERS. s-a. Poetry Resource Center of Michigan, 111 E. Kirby, Detroit, MI 48202. Ed. Leonard Kniffeld. Document type: directory.
  Description: Directory of literary publishers in Michigan.

070.5 011 II ISSN 0970-9266
Z6958.I4
DIRECTORY OF PERIODICALS PUBLISHED IN INDIA. (Text in English and regional languages) 1988. biennial. Rs.750($100) (effective thru 1996). Sapra & Sapra Publishers Distributors Pvt. Ltd., 51 Ring Road, Lajpat Nagar III, New Delhi 110 024, India. TEL 683-7040. circ. 500. Document type: directory.
  Description: Provides information on approximately 9,000 journals, bulletins, video magazines, a few widely circulated newspapers, proceedings and transactions of the learned bodies and government departments.

DIRECTORY OF POETRY PUBLISHERS. see LITERATURE — Poetry

020.75 US ISSN 1062-8010
PN162
DIRECTORY OF PUBLICATIONS RESOURCES. 1981. biennial. $18. Editorial Experts, Inc. (EEI), 66 Canal Center Plaza, Ste. 200, Alexandria, VA 22314-5570. TEL 703-683-0683. FAX 703-683-4915. Ed. Linda Jorgewsen; Pub. Daniel Horowitz. adv. contact: Everet Arnold. Document type: directory.
  Formerly (until 1991): Directory of Editorial Resources (ISSN 0731-4426)
  Description: Lists the best courses, books, periodicals, competitions, software, tools, and organizations for professional publications people.

DIRECTORY OF PUBLISHING: A PRACTICAL GUIDE. see BUSINESS AND ECONOMICS — Trade And Industrial Directories

338.47 070.5 UK ISSN 0957-3615
DIRECTORY OF PUBLISHING IN SCOTLAND. 1988. a. £6.99. Scottish Publishers Association, 137 Dundee St., Edinburgh EH11 1BG, Scotland. TEL 0131-228-6866. FAX 0131-228-3220. (Dist. by: Albany Publishers' Distribution, 32 Finlas St., Glasgow G22 5DU, Scotland. TEL 0141-558-5012. FAX 0141-557-0189) adv.: page £240; trim 198 x 128; adv. contact: Susanne Dickson. bibl.; circ. 1,000 (paid). Document type: directory.

070.5 SA ISSN 1018-7626
DIRECTORY OF SOUTH AFRICAN PUBLISHERS; with addresses and ISBN identifiers. (Text in Afrikaans, English) 1991. a. State Library - Staatsbiblioteek, P.O. Box 397, Pretoria 0001, South Africa. TEL 27-12-218931. FAX 27-12-325-5984. TELEX 3-22171 SA. E-mail: rhona@statelib.pwv.gov.za. Document type: directory.

658.8 UK
DIRECTORY OF SPECIALIST BOOKDEALERS IN THE UK HANDLING MAINLY NEW BOOKS. 1978. triennial. £15. Peter Marcan Publications, P.O. Box 3158, London SE1 4RA, England. TEL 0171-357-0368. adv. circ. 750. Document type: directory.
  Description: Subject classified annotated guide to specialist book outlets throughout the UK.

070.5 296 IS
DIRECTORY OF WORLD JEWISH PRESS AND PUBLICATIONS. (Text in English) 1984. a. $23. P.O. Box 7699, Jerusalem 91 076, Israel. Ed. Yitzhak Rogow. adv. circ. 2,000. (reprint service avail.) Document type: directory.

658.809 US ISSN 0012-5261
DOLPHIN BOOK CLUB NEWS. 1956. 15/yr. membership. Book-Of-The-Month Club, Time & Life Bldg., 1271 Ave. of the Americas, New York, NY 10020. TEL 212-522-4200. Dir. Laura Folden. adv.; bk.rev. circ. 50,000.

DRAGON'S BREATH; international small press review and monthly newsletter. see LITERARY AND POLITICAL REVIEWS

070.5 686.2 US ISSN 0741-6547
DUNN REPORT; electronic publishing & prepress systems news & views. 1983. m. $295. Dunn Technology, Inc., 1855 E. Vista Way, No. 1, Vista, CA 92084. TEL 619-758-5401. Ed. Patrice M. Dunn. (back issues avail.) Indexed: Print.Abstr. —CCC.
  Description: Focus on technological developments for the graphic arts and corporate publishing industries.

070.5 US ISSN 1042-3737
CODEN: EPNWEE
E P S I G NEWS. 4/yr. $50 or membership fee. Electronic Publishing Special Interest Group, c/o GCARI, Box 25707, Alexandria, VA 22313-5707. TEL 703-519-8184. FAX 703-548-2667. E-mail: mern@well.st.ca.us. Ed. Morion Ellege. bk.rev. circ. 300. Document type: newsletter.
  —BLDSC (3794.398100); CASDDS.
  Description: Covers new product announcements, user information, meeting announcements, and case studies from organizations and individuals using the Electronic Manuscript Standard for a variety of publishing ventures.
  Refereed Serial

070.5 GW
E S V SORTIMENTER INFORMATIONEN RECHT - WIRTSCHAFT - TECHNIK - UMWELT - PHILOLOGIE. (Erich Schmidt Verlag); titel und termine. 1950. m. free. Erich Schmidt Verlag GmbH & Co. (Bielefeld), Viktoriastr. 44a, 33602 Bielefeld, Germany. TEL 0521-583080. (Subscr. to: Postfach 102451, 33524 Bielefeld, Germany) adv. circ. 2,000. Document type: trade publication.
  Formerly: E S V Programmbereiche Recht - Wirtschaft - Technik - Umwelt.

070.5 BE
LES EDITEURS BELGES DE LANGUE FRANCAISE. (Text in French) 1960. a. free. Association des Editeurs Belges, 140 Bd. Lambermont, Bte. 1, B-1030 Brussels, Belgium. TEL 32-2-2416580. FAX 32-2-2167131. adv. circ. 4,000. Document type: directory.
  Former titles: Editeurs Belges de Langue Francaise et Leurs Livres; Livres Belges de Langue Francaise; Livres Belges.
  Description: Lists information on French language publishers in Belgium, including senior personnel, overseas distributors and areas of specialization.

EDITIO; internationales Jahrbuch fuer Editionswissenschaft. see LITERATURE

070.5 US ISSN 0193-7383
CODEN: EDEYDQ
THE EDITORIAL EYE; focusing on publications standards and practices. 1978. 12/yr. $87. Editorial Experts, Inc. (EEI), 66 Canal Center Plaza, Ste. 200, Alexandria, VA 22314-5570. TEL 703-683-0683. FAX 703-683-4915. Ed. Linda Jorgensen. bk.rev.; index. circ. 3,000. (looseleaf format; back issues avail.) Indexed: Graph.Arts Lit.Abstr. Document type: newsletter.
  —CASDDS; Faxon. CCC.
  Description: Covers editing, proofreading, publications management and language usage. Includes reviews of publishing software.

070.5 AT
EDITORIAL PROFILES MONTHLY. m. Aus.$48. Deslea Judd Publishing, P.O. Box 552, Wahroonga, NSW 2076, Australia. Ed. Deslea Judd. Document type: bulletin.

EDITORS' ASSOCIATION OF CANADA. DIRECTORY OF MEMBERS. see BUSINESS AND ECONOMICS — Trade And Industrial Directories

070.5 NR ISSN 0794-5655
EDITORS' FORUM; focusing on publications standards & practices. (Text in English) 1986. q. £N50($20) Codat Publications, P.O. Box 9400, U.I. Ibadan, Nigeria. TEL 022-314411. Ed. C.O. Adejuwon. circ. 1,000.

070.5 UK ISSN 0268-7542
EDITORS MEDIA DIRECTORIES. VOL. 1: NATIONAL MEDIA. m. £145 (£415 for all 6 vols.). P R Newslink, 9-10 Great Sutton St., London EC1V 0BX, England. TEL 0171-251-9000. FAX 0171-251-3738. Ed. Helen Buckhurst. adv. Document type: directory.

070.5 UK ISSN 0268-7569
EDITORS MEDIA DIRECTORIES. VOL. 3: PROVINCIAL NEWSPAPERS & TOWN GUIDE. 3/yr. £145 (£415 for all 6 vols.). P R Newslink, 9-10 Great Sutton St., London EC1V 0BX, England. TEL 0171-251-9000. FAX 0171-251-3738. Ed. Helen Buckhurst. adv. Document type: directory.

070.5 UK ISSN 0268-7577
EDITORS MEDIA DIRECTORIES. VOL. 4: CONSUMER & LEISURE MAGAZINES. q. £120 (£415 for all 6 vols.). P R Newslink, 9-10 Great Sutton St., London EC1V 0BX, England. TEL 0171-251-9000. FAX 0171-251-3738. Ed. Helen Buckhurst. adv. Document type: directory.

070.5 UK
EDITORS MEDIA DIRECTORIES. VOL. 6: FREELANCERS, WRITERS' GUILDS & LONDON CORRESPONDENTS OF FOREIGN PRESS. a. £95 (£415 for all 6 vols.). P R Newslink, 9-10 Great Sutton St., London EC1V 0BX, England. TEL 0171-251-9000. FAX 0171-251-3738. Ed. Helen Buckhurst. adv. Document type: directory.
  Formerly: Editors Media Directories. Vol. 6: Writers' Guilds and London Correspondents of Foreign Press (ISSN 0268-7631)

EDPRESS MEMBERSHIP ROSTER AND FREE-LANCE DIRECTORY. see EDUCATION

EDUCATIONAL MARKETER. see EDUCATION — Teaching Methods And Curriculum

ELSEVIER SCIENCE. CATALOGUE - BOOKS. see SCIENCES: COMPREHENSIVE WORKS

ELSEVIER SCIENCE. CATALOGUE - JOURNALS. see SCIENCES: COMPREHENSIVE WORKS

ELSEVIER SCIENCE. CATALOGUE ON C D - R O M. see SCIENCES: COMPREHENSIVE WORKS

ELSEVIER SCIENCE. DISPATCH LIST FOR JOURNALS, BOOK SERIES AND PROCEEDINGS. see SCIENCES: COMPREHENSIVE WORKS

ELSEVIER SCIENCE. NEW AND FORTHCOMING PUBLICATIONS. see SCIENCES: COMPREHENSIVE WORKS

ENTERTAINMENT LAW REPORTER; motion pictures, television, radio, music, theater, publishing, sports. see LAW

ENTERTAINMENT, PUBLISHING AND THE ARTS HANDBOOK. see COMMUNICATIONS — Television And Cable

090.78 US ISSN 0734-3337
EPHEMERA NEWS. 1981. q. $25. Ephemera Society of America, c/o Richard Friz, Box 472, Peterborough, NH 03458. adv.; bk.rev.; bibl.; illus. circ. 600. (tabloid format; back issues avail.)

PUBLISHING AND BOOK TRADE

070.483 US
EROTIC WRITER'S AND COLLECTOR'S MARKET. 1988. s-a. $14.95 per no. Michael Drax, Ed. & Pub., Box 20593, Sun Valley, NV 89433. adv.; index. circ. 1,000.
Description: Market listing of publishers and producers of erotic and sexual publications, videos, audios, software and clubs.

070 IT ISSN 0392-9752
ESOPO; rivista trimestrale di bibliofilia. 1979. q. L.160000. Edizioni Rovello, Via Rovello 1, 20121 Milan, Italy. FAX 02-72022884. Ed. Mario Scognamiglio. adv.; bk.rev. circ. 4,750.

070.5 GW ISSN 0943-206X
DER EULENHOF BERATERBRIEF. 1982. 4/yr. DM.40. Heinold Personal- und Unternehmensberatung GmbH, Eulenhof, 24616 Hardebek, Germany. TEL 04324-8978-0. FAX 04324-8146. Ed. Ehrhardt Friedrich Heinold; Pub. Wolfgang Ehrhardt Heinold. adv.: B&W page DM.1380, color page DM.2360; trim 190 x 265; adv. contact: Rainer Ott. bk.rev. circ. 4,100. **Document type:** newsletter.
Former titles: Eulenhof Basterbrief; Eulenhof Information; Eulenhof-Brief.

070.5 GW ISSN 0938-166X
EURO-KURIER. 1990. q. DM.15. Grabert Verlag GmbH, Am Apfelberg 18, 72076 Tuebingen, Germany. TEL 07071-69590. FAX 07071-68014. Ed. Wigbert Grabert. adv.; bk.rev. **Document type:** trade publication.

070.5 658.8 UK
Z1003.5.G7
THE EUROMONITOR BOOK REPORT (YEAR). 1975. biennial. £450($990) (effective 1996). Euromonitor, 60-61 Britton St., London EC1M 5NA, England. TEL 0171-251-8024. FAX 0171-608-3149. (Addr. in N. America: Euromonitor International, 122 S. Michigan Ave., Ste. 1200, Chicago, IL 60603. TEL 312-922-1115. FAX 312-922-1157) (back issues avail.) **Document type:** trade publication.
●Also available online.
Former titles: U K Book Report; Book Report (ISSN 0142-7628)
Description: Offers market analysis of the buying, selling, and reading of books in the U.K.

EUROPEAN SPECIALIST PUBLISHERS DIRECTORY. see BUSINESS AND ECONOMICS — Trade And Industrial Directories

070.5 EI ISSN 1016-0183
EUROSTAT CATALOGUE; publications and electronic services. 1986. a. (EUROSTAT) Office for Official Publications of the European Communities, 2985 Luxemburg, Luxembourg.
—BLDSC (3830.433800).

016 028 GW ISSN 0014-391X
EX LIBRIS; Aktueller Buchdienst fuer Studenten und Dozenten der Rechts, Wirtschafts, und Informatik. 1963. s-a. DM.50. Ex Libris-Verlag, Schwalbenweg 21, 52269 Frechen, Germany. TEL 02234-63580. FAX 02234-63886. bk.rev.; bibl. circ. 10,000.

070.5 900 US ISSN 1042-6647
EX LIBRIS (CONCORD). 1988. bi-m. $35. New Hampshire Writers & Publishers Project, Box 2693, Concord, NH 03302-2693. TEL 603-226-6649. Ed. Patricia Scholz-Cohen. adv.; bk.rev. circ. 600. (back issues avail.) **Document type:** newsletter.
Description: Articles and network by and for New Hampshire writers and publishers. Includes listings, leads and calendars

020.75 740 790.132 FR ISSN 0395-269X
EX-LIBRIS FRANCAIS. (Text in French; summaries in English, German, Italian, Spanish) 1939. q. 200 F. Association Francaise pour la Connaissance de l'Ex-Libris, Bibliotheque Municipale, 43 rue Stanislas, 54042 Nancy Cedex, France. Ed. L. Demezieres. adv.; bk.rev.; illus. circ. 325. **Document type:** bulletin.

097 DK ISSN 0014-4681
EXLIBRIS-NYT. 1960. 4/yr. membership. Dansk Exlibris Selskab - Danish Bookplate Society, Postbox 1519, DK-2700 Copenhagen, Denmark. Ed. Keld Larsen. illus. circ. 400.

070.5 II
EXPORT NEWS. (Text in English) vol.9, 1978. bi-m. Rs.30($15) People's Publishing House Private Ltd., 5E Rani Jhansi Rd., New Delhi 110055, India. bk.rev. Indexed: Key to Econ.Sci., So.Pac.Per.Ind.

FACHLITERATUR ZUM BUCH- UND BIBLIOTHEKSWESEN/INTERNATIONAL BIBLIOGRAPHY OF THE BOOK TRADE AND LIBRARIANSHIP. see LIBRARY AND INFORMATION SCIENCES

028.1 US ISSN 0890-6823
Z6941
FACTSHEET 5; the definitive guide to the zine revolution. 1982. 6/yr. $20 to individuals; institutions $40; Canada $35; Europe $45. Box 170099, San Francisco, CA 94117-0099. TEL 415-668-1781. Ed. R. Seth Friedman. adv.: B&W page $425; trim 8 1/4 x 10 3/4. bk.rev.; music rev.; illus.; circ. 15,000 (paid). **Document type:** directory.
Description: Comprehensive review of the underground and alternative press, also covering music and comic zines, poetry and small press publications. Covers more than 1200 publications per issue.

070.5 AG
FEDERACION ARGENTINA DE PERIODISTAS. GACETA.* 1970. a. Federacion Argentina de Periodistas, Esmeralda 356, 1035 Buenos Aires, Argentina. illus.

070.5 US
FEDERAL PUBLISHERS COMMITTEE. REPORTS OF MEETING. m. Federal Publishers Committee, c/o John H. Weiner, U.S. Energy Information Administration, EI-23, 1000 Independence Ave., S.W., Washington, DC 20585. TEL 202-586-6537. FAX 202-586-0114.
Description: Promotes the cost-effective management of the writing, editorial, and production aspects of publishing in the U.S. federal government.

070.5 US
FEDERAL PUBLISHERS COMMITTEE. SPECIAL REPORTS - TASK FORCE. irreg. Federal Publishers Committee, c/o John H. Weiner, U.S. Energy Information Administration, EI-23, 1000 Independence Ave., S.W., Washington, DC 20585. TEL 202-586-6537. FAX 202-586-0114.
Description: Promotes the cost-effective management of the writing, editorial, and production of publishing in the U.S. federal government.

070.5 II
FEDERATION OF PUBLISHERS AND BOOKSELLERS ASSOCIATIONS IN INDIA. NEWSLETTER. (Text in English) 1981. q. free. Federation of Publishers and Booksellers Associations in India, 4833-24 Govind Ln., Ansari Rd., New Delhi-110002, India. Ed. Vindo Kumar. adv.; bk.rev.; index. circ. 2,000.

323.4 305.4157 070.5 US ISSN 0741-6555
FEMINIST BOOKSTORE NEWS. 1976. bi-m. Can.$79($70) (foreign $19) (effective Dec. 1993). Box 882554, San Francisco, CA 94188. TEL 415-626-1556. FAX 415-626-8970. Ed. Carol Seajay. adv.; bk.rev.; bibl.; stat.; tr.lit. circ. 650. (back issues avail.) **Document type:** trade publication.
—UnCover.
Formerly: Feminist Bookstores Newsletter.
Description: News briefs, feature articles, and reader correspondence pertaining to feminist bookselling and publishing. Reviews over 300 titles per issue.

FEMINIST COLLECTIONS; a quarterly of women's studies resources. see WOMEN'S STUDIES

070.5 686 011 IT
FIERA DEL LIBRO. bi-m. Edizioni Pegaso s.a.s., Galleria Mazzini, 3-13, 16121 Genoa, Italy. Ed. Marina Seveso.

FILLERS FOR PUBLICATIONS; the editorial tool that eliminates deadline pressures. see JOURNALISM

070.5 658.3 US
FIRST DRAFT. 1992. m. $139 (effective Jan. 1994). Ragan Communications, 212 W. Superior St., Ste. 200, Chicago, IL 60610. TEL 800-878-5331. FAX 312-335-9583. Ed. Susan Kammeyer. circ. 1,000 (paid). **Document type:** newsletter.
Description: Contains clip art and articles for use in employee publications.

FIRST SOURCE; a CD-ROM newsletter for Bowker-Saur customers. see COMMUNICATIONS — Computer Applications

090.75 US ISSN 1066-5471
Z1033.F53
FIRSTS: COLLECTING MODERN FIRST EDITIONS.* 1991. m. $35 (Canada & Mexico $50; elsewhere $75). Firsts Magazine, Inc., Box 65168, Tucson, AZ 85728-5168. TEL 213-962-1469. Ed. Robin H. Smiley. adv.; bk.rev. **Document type:** consumer publication.

FIVE OWLS; a publication for readers, personally and professionally involved in children's literature. see CHILDREN AND YOUTH — About

070.5 US
FLASH MARKET NEWS. 1940. bi-m. $50 to non-members. National Writers Association, 1450 S. Havana, Ste. 424, Aurora, CO 80012. TEL 303-751-7844. FAX 303-751-8593. Ed. Sandy Whelchel. circ. 1,500. **Document type:** bulletin.

028 NE ISSN 0015-3540
DE FLEANENDE KRIE. (Text in Frisian) 1954. 3/yr. membership. Kristlik Fryske Folks Bibleteek, Hid Heroplantsoen 1, 8701 BS Bolsward, Friesland, Netherlands. Ed.Bd. adv.; bk.rev.; bibl.; illus.

658.809 UK ISSN 0015-5772
FOLIO. 1947. q. membership. Folio Society Ltd., 202 Great Suffolk St., London SE1 1PR, England. TEL 071-407-7411. FAX 071-378-6684. Ed. Sue Bradbury. adv.; bk.rev.; illus. circ. 48,000. (also avail. in microfilm from UMI; reprint service avail. from UMI)

655.5 US ISSN 0046-4333
PN4734 CODEN: FMMMD2
FOLIO (STAMFORD); the magazine for magazine management. 1972. s-m. $96 (Canada and Mexico $116; elsewhere $199). Cowles Business Media (Subsidiary of: Cowles Media Company), Six River Bend Center, 911 Hope St., Box 4949, Stamford, CT 06907-0949. TEL 203-358-9900. FAX 203-349-3848. Ed. Anne Russell. adv.: B&W page $4150, color page $5590; 8 1/8 x 10 7/8. bk.rev.; index. circ. 10,383. (also avail. in microform from UMI; back issues avail.; reprint service avail. from UMI) Indexed: SRI, Tr.& Indus.Ind. **Document type:** trade publication.
●Also available online. Vendor(s): Knight-Ridder, Inc., University Microfilms International.
—BLDSC (3974.395000); CASDDS; Faxon; SWETS; UMI; UnCover.
Incorporates (1988-1993): Folio's Publishing News (ISSN 1053-4563); Which was formerly: Publishing News (ISSN 1043-8688).

655.5 US
FOLIO: SOURCE BOOK. (Special issue of Folio magazine) a. Folio Publishing Corp. (Subsidiary of: Cowles Media Company), 911 Hope St., Six River Bend Center, Box 4949, Stamford, CT 06907-0949. Ed. Barbara Love.

070.5 IT
FONDAZIONE FELTRINELLI. QUADERNI. 4/yr. L.100000 (foreign L.130000) (effective 1993). Franco Angeli Editore, Viale Monza, 106, Casella Postale 17175, 20100 Milan, Italy. TEL 02-2895762.

FOOTPRINTS (TEMPE). see CLUBS

020 US ISSN 0098-213X
FORECAST (BRIDGEWATER); a prepublication announcement journal of hardcover and trade-paper titles (adult and children's) for public libraries. 1969. m. $24. Baker & Taylor, Inc., Box 734, Somerville, NJ 08876. TEL 908-218-0400. FAX 908-218-3980. adv.; bk.rev.; illus.
Formerly: New Books Preview Bulletin.
Description: Announcement journal of new and forthcoming adult and children's hardcover and trade paperback titles.

070.5025489 DK ISSN 0109-405X
FORLAGSVEJVISER. (Supplements avail.) 1984. a. DKK 425 (effective 1996). Dansk BiblioteksCenter as, Tempovej 7-11, DK-2750 Ballerup, Denmark. TEL 45-44-97-40-00. FAX 45-44-68-24-42.

PUBLISHING AND BOOK TRADE

655   FR   ISSN 0078-9666
FRANCE. IMPRIMERIE NATIONALE. ANNUAIRE. 1962. a. Imprimerie Nationale, B.P. 514, 59505 Douai Cedex, France. TEL 27-93-70-90. FAX 27-93-70-96. TELEX 120 389 F.

FRANCE GRAPHIQUE. see *PRINTING*

070.5 020
FREE MAGAZINES FOR LIBRARIES. a. McFarland & Company, Inc., Box 611, Jefferson, NC 28640. Ed. Adeline Smith. **Document type:** academic/scholarly publication.

070.5   US   ISSN 1062-3477
FREE PAPER PUBLISHER. Short title: F P P. 1990. m. $24. Free Paper Publisher, Inc., 1099 Granville Pike, Lancaster, OH 43130-1028. TEL 614-681-1660. FAX 614-681-1657. Ed. Howard Alspach. adv. contact: Sonna Whitney. bk.rev. circ. 2,000. (back issues avail.) **Document type:** trade publication.
Description: Trade magazine exclusively serving the free paper industry; provides sales, training, technical, and management information.

FREEDOM TO READ FOUNDATION NEWS. see *LIBRARY AND INFORMATION SCIENCES*

FREELANCE. see *LITERATURE*

070.5   US
FREELANCE EDITORIAL ASSOCIATION. NEWS. vol.6, 1990. q. membership. Freelance Editorial Association, Box 380835, Cambridge, MA 02238-0835. TEL 617-643-8626. adv. contact: Ruth Rautenberg. bk.rev. **Document type:** newsletter.
Description: Contains articles of interest to free lancers in the editorial field.

070.5   US
FREELANCE EDITORIAL ASSOCIATION YELLOW PAGES AND CODE OF FAIR PRACTICE. 1988. a. $47.50. Freelance Editorial Association, Box 380835, Cambridge, MA 02238-0835. TEL 617-729-8164. (back issues avail.) **Document type:** directory.
Description: Lists the services of hundreds of editorial freelancers.

FREELANCE WRITER'S REPORT. see *JOURNALISM*

070.5   US
THE FREELANCER. 1977. bi-m. $20. Editorial Freelancers Association, Inc., 71 W. 23rd St., Ste. 1504, New York, NY 10010. TEL 212-929-5400. FAX 212-929-5439. adv. contact: David Bell. bk.rev. circ. 1,300. (looseleaf format; back issues avail.) **Document type:** newsletter.
Formerly: E F A Newsletter.

070.5 371.42 659.1 658   US
FREELANCERS OF NORTH AMERICA. 1984. biennial. $59.95. Research Associates International, 340 E. 52nd St., New York, NY 10022. TEL 212-980-9179. Ed. Leonie Rosenstiel. adv.

FRIDAY MEMO. see *COMPUTERS*

FRIENDS OF THE NATIONAL LIBRARIES. ANNUAL REPORT. see *LIBRARY AND INFORMATION SCIENCES*

658.8   PO
GAZETA LITERARIA. 6/yr. Rua Rodrigues Sampaio 140, Porto, Portugal.

655   SY   ISSN 0072-0690
GENERAL DIRECTORY OF THE PRESS AND PERIODICALS IN JORDAN AND KUWAIT.* a. $15. Syrian Documentation Papers, P.O. Box 2712, Damascus, Syria. **Document type:** directory.

655   SY   ISSN 0072-0704
GENERAL DIRECTORY OF THE PRESS AND PERIODICALS IN SYRIA.* a. $15. Syrian Documentation Papers, P.O. Box 2712, Damascus, Syria. **Document type:** directory.
Description: Consists of advertising rates and names of institutions and officials concerned with media printing and circulation.

070.5 791.4   US   ISSN 0148-7566
GET READY SHEET. 1976. bi-w. $28. Mid-York Library System, c/o S.V. Wawrzazek, Ed., 1600 Lincoln Ave., Utica, NY 13502. TEL 315-735-8328. adv. circ. 1,300. **Document type:** bibliography.

070.5   US
GILA QUEEN'S GUIDE TO THE MARKETS. 1988. m. $24. Kathryn Ptacek, Ed. & Pub., Box 97, Newton, NJ 07860-0097.
Description: Provides news of the publishing marketplace, including book publishers, anthologies, magazines, and other information of interest to writers in all genres.

GNOMON; kritische Zeitschrift fuer die gesamte klassische Altertumswissenschaft. see *CLASSICAL STUDIES*

028.1   UK
THE GOOD BOOK GUIDE. 1977. m. £22 (rest of Europe £26; elsewhere £31). Good Book Guide Ltd., 24 Seward St., London EC1V 3GB, England. TEL 0171-490-9900. FAX 0171-490-9908. Ed. Bonnie Falconer; Pub. Peter Braithwaite. bk.rev.; circ. 40,000 (paid). **Document type:** consumer publication.
Description: An independent selection of books published in the U.K., including fiction, biography, arts, travel, and children's books accompanied by brief reviews.

028 011   US
GOOD READING; a guide for serious readers. irreg., 23rd edition, 1990. $44. R.R. Bowker, A Reed Reference Publishing company, 121 Chanlon Rd., New Providence, NJ 07979. TEL 908-464-6800. FAX 908-665-6688. TELEX 138 755. (Subscr. to: Order Dept., Box 31, New Providence, NJ 07974-9903. TEL 800-521-8110) **Document type:** directory.
Description: Recommends 3,000 enduring nonfiction and fiction titles.

DE GRAFISKE FAG. see *PRINTING*

GRAPHIC COMMUNICATIONS WORLD; the Monday morning briefing for senior management. see *PRINTING*

GRAPHIC NEWS. see *PRINTING*

028.5 Z1037.A1   UK   ISSN 0046-6506
GROWING POINT. 1962. 6/yr. £5($12.50) Growing Point, c/o Margery Fisher, Ed., Ashton Manor, Northampton NN7 2JL, England. TEL 0604 862277. bk.rev.; illus.; index. (back issues avail.) **Indexed:** Bk.Rev.Ind. (1975-), Child.Bk.Rev.Ind. (1975-).

658.8   BL
GUIA DAS LIVRARIAS E PONTOS DE VENDA DE LIVROS NO BRASIL. 1976. irreg. Sindicato Nacional dos Editores de Livros, Av. Rio Branco 37, s-1503-06, 20090-003 Rio de Janeiro R.J., Brazil.

070.5   SP   ISSN 0072-7903
GUIA DE EDITORES Y DE LIBREROS DE ESPANA. 1983. irreg; no. 89-90. price varies. (Federacion de Gremios de Editores de Espana) CRISOL, S.A., c/o Juan Ramon Jimenez, 45-9 Iz., 28036 Madrid, Spain. FAX 91-5639276. TELEX 48457 FGEE. circ. 5,000.

GUIA DE LA DISTRIBUCION EN ESPANA; libros y publicaciones. see *BUSINESS AND ECONOMICS — Trade And Industrial Directories*

070.5   BL
GUIA DOS EDITORES ASSOCIADOS. 1978. irreg. Sindicato Nacional dos Editores de Livros, Av. Rio Branco 37, s-1503-06, 20090-003 Rio de Janeiro R.J., Brazil. TEL 021-233-6481. FAX 021-253-8502.
Formerly: Guia das Editoras Brasileiras.

070.5 700 PN163   US   ISSN 1055-6087
GUIDE TO LITERARY AGENTS AND ART - PHOTO REPS. a. $21.99. F & W Publications, Inc., 1507 Dana Ave., Cincinnati, OH 45207. TEL 513-531-2222. FAX 513-531-4744. Ed. Kirsten Holm.
Description: Contains over 400 listings of agents and representatives across North America.

GUIDE TO MICROFORMS IN PRINT. AUTHOR - TITLE. see *BIBLIOGRAPHIES*

860   PR
GUIDE TO REVIEWS OF BOOKS FROM AND ABOUT HISPANIC AMERICA/GUIA A LAS RESENAS DE LIBROS DE Y SOBRE HISPANOAMERICA. (Text in English, Portuguese, Spanish) 1965. a. $165. A M M Editions, Box 151, Sta. 6, Ponce, PR 00732. TEL 313-841-2000. Ed. Antonio Matos. bk.rev. circ. 150. (back issues avail.) **Document type:** abstracting/indexing, bibliography.
Description: Contains summaries of reviews covering Latin America and the Caribbean. Includes coverage of Latin Americans in Canada, the U.S. and Great Britain. Fully indexed.

070.5   US   ISSN 0730-3203
GUILD OF BOOK WORKERS. NEWSLETTER. 1975. bi-m. $40. Guild of Book Workers, Inc., 521 Fifth Ave., 17th Fl., New York, NY 10175. TEL 212-757-6454. Ed. Margaret Johnson. adv.; bk.rev. circ. 800. (looseleaf format; back issues avail.) **Document type:** newsletter.

686.3 Z1008   US   ISSN 0434-9245
GUILD OF BOOK WORKERS JOURNAL. 1962. s-a. $40. Guild of Book Workers, Inc., 521 Fifth Ave., 17th Fl., New York, NY 10175. TEL 212-757-6454. bk.rev. circ. 800. **Indexed:** Art & Archaeol.Tech.Abstr.

090.75   BE   ISSN 0777-5067
GULDEN PASSER/COMPAS D'OR. (Text in Dutch, English, French, German) 1878. a. 800 BEF($25) Vereeniging der Antwerpsche Bibliophielen - Antwerp Bibliophile Society, Museum Plantin-Moretus, Vrijdagmarkt 22-23, B-2000 Antwerp, Belgium. TEL 32-3-233-02-94. FAX 32-3-226-25-16. Eds. Francine de Nave, Marcus De Schepper. bk.rev. circ. 1,000. (reprint service avail. from KTO) **Document type:** academic/scholarly publication, bulletin.
Formerly (until 1923): Maatschappij der Antwerpsche Bibliophilen. Uitgave (ISSN 0777-4451)

GUTENBERG-GESELLSCHAFT. KLEINE DRUCKE. see *PRINTING*

070.5   JA
HAMBAI KAKUSHIN. (Text in Japanese) 1963. m. 26900 Yen($250) Shyogyokai Publishing Company Ltd., 4-9, Azabudai 2-chome, Minato-ku, Tokyo 106, Japan. TEL 03-3224-7484. FAX 03-3589-1024. Ed. Kiyoshi Ito. circ. 85,000. (back issues avail.) **Document type:** trade publication.

HANDBOEK VAN DE NEDERLANDSE PERS EN PUBLICITEIT. see *ADVERTISING AND PUBLIC RELATIONS*

686   US
HANDBOOK OF CIRCULATION MANAGEMENT. irreg., latest 2nd ed. $69.95. Cowles Business Media (Subsidiary of: Cowles Media Company), Six River Bend Center, 911 Hope St., Box 4949, Stamford, CT 06907-0949. TEL 203-358-9900. FAX 203-357-9014. Ed.Bd. **Document type:** trade publication.

658.8   US
HANDBOOK OF MAGAZINE PRODUCTION. irreg., latest 2nd ed. $69.95. Cowles Business Media, Six River Bend Center, 911 Hope St., Box 4949, Stamford, CT 06907-0949. TEL 203-358-9900. Ed. Jeffery Parnau. **Document type:** trade publication.

686   US
HANDBOOK OF MAGAZINE PUBLISHING. irreg., latest 3rd ed. $79.95. Cowles Business Media (Subsidiary of: Cowles Media Company), Six River Bend Center, 911 Hope St., Box 4949, Stamford, CT 06907-0949. TEL 203-358-9900. FAX 203-357-9014. **Document type:** trade publication.

655   GW   ISSN 0073-0165
HANDBUCH FUER DEN WERBENDEN BUCH- UND ZEITSCHRIFTENHANDEL.* 1939. a. DM.20. Bundesverband des Werbenden Buch- und Zeitschriftenhandels e.V., Pecherhaupt Str. 2C, 5307 Wachtberg, Germany.

HEARTLAND CRITIQUES. see *LITERARY AND POLITICAL REVIEWS*

PUBLISHING AND BOOK TRADE

808.836 US ISSN 1070-0544
HERO ILLUSTRATED. 1993. m. $19.95. Warrior Communications (Subsidiary of: Sendai Publishing Group), 1920 Highland Ave., Ste. 222, Lombard, IL 60148. TEL 708-916-7222. FAX 708-916-7227. Ed. John Danovich. adv. circ. 250,000. **Document type:** consumer publication.
— **Description:** Reviews comic books and contains a price guide for collectors.

658 917.3 US ISSN 0894-2358
HISPANIC BOOKS BULLETIN. 2/yr. $8 to individuals; institutions $15; foreign $20. Hispanic Books Distributors, Inc., 1665 W. Grant Rd., Tucson, AZ 85745. TEL 602-882-9484. Ed. Arnulfo D. Trejo.

HISTORY: REVIEWS OF NEW BOOKS. see HISTORY

070.5 UK ISSN 0143-3237
HOME OFFICE LIST OF PUBLICATIONS. 1978. a. Home Office, 50 Queen Anne's Gate, London SW1H 9AT, England. TEL 071-273-2208. circ. 1,500. **Document type:** government publication.
—BLDSC (4326.105000).

028.5 US ISSN 1044-405X
HORN BOOK GUIDE TO CHILDREN'S AND YOUNG ADULT BOOKS. 1990. 2/yr. $50. Horn Book, Inc., 11 Beacon St., Ste. 1000, Boston, MA 02108-3017. TEL 617-227-1555. FAX 617-523-0299. Ed. Hanna B. Zeiger. adv. contact: Eden Edwards. bk.rev. circ. 5,500. (back issues avail.)
— **Description:** Contains reviews and ratings of all hardcover trade children's books published in the previous publishing season.

028.5 US ISSN 0018-5078
Z1037.A1
HORN BOOK MAGAZINE; recommending books for children and young adults. 1924. bi-m. $35 to individuals; institutions $42. Horn Book, Inc., 11 Beacon St., Ste. 1000, Boston, MA 02108-3017. TEL 617-227-1555; 800-325-1170. FAX 617-523-0299. Ed. Anita Silvey. adv. contact: Eden Edwards. bk.rev.; illus.; index. circ. 22,500. (also avail. in microform from UMI; reprint service avail. from UMI) **Indexed:** Acad.Ind., Access (1980-), Artbibl.Mod., Bk.Rev.Dig., Bk.Rev.Ind. (1965-), C.I.J.E., Child.Bk.Rev.Ind. (1965-), Child.Lit.Abstr., Gdlns, Ind.Child.Mag., Lib.Lit., Lib.Lit., Mag.Ind., Media Rev.Dig., PMR, R.G. **Document type:** trade publication.
—BLDSC (4328.200000); Faxon; UMI; UnCover.
— **Description:** Covers juvenile literature.

HORROR; the news magazine of the horror & dark fantasy field. see LITERATURE — Science Fiction, Fantasy, Horror

070.5 US
HOT PICKS. 1988. m. free. Baker & Taylor, Inc., 652 E. Main St., Box 6920, Bridgewater, NJ 08807-0920. TEL 908-218-0400. FAX 908-218-3980. adv.; bk.rev.
— **Incorporates:** Sound Buys.
— **Description:** Announcement journal of mass-market and trade paperback and spoken-word audio titles for booksellers and public libraries.

070.5 338 US ISSN 0738-7415
HOW TO BE YOUR OWN PUBLISHER UPDATE. 1986. triennial. $6.95. Bibliotheca Press, c/o Prosperity & Profits Unlimited, Distribution Services, Box 416, Denver, CO 80201-0416. TEL 303-575-5676. Ed. A. Doyle. circ. 2,000. (looseleaf format; reprint service avail.) **Document type:** newsletter.
— **Description:** Covers areas of promotion, wholesale printing, and mailing approaches.

HUBEI FANGZHI. see JOURNALISM

070.5 US
HUENEFELD REPORT; for managers and planners in modest-sized book publishing houses. 1973. forth. $88 (foreign $110). Huenefeld Company, Inc., 41 North Rd., Ste. 201, Bedford, MA 01730. TEL 617-275-1070. Ed. John Huenefeld. circ. 975. (back issues avail.) **Document type:** newsletter.
— **Description:** Focuses on the ups and downs of the small to modestly sized publisher.

028.1 US ISSN 0887-5499
HUNGRY MIND REVIEW; a Midwestern book review. 1986. q. $13. 1648 Grand Ave., St. Paul, MN 55105. TEL 612-699-2610. FAX 612-699-0970. Ed. Bart Schneider. adv.; bk.rev. circ. 45,000. **Indexed:** Bk.Rev.Ind. (1989-), Child.Bk.Rev.Ind. (1989-).
— **Description:** Each issue contains theme-based book reviews.

070.5 DK ISSN 0333-3620
Z286.S37
I A S P NEWSLETTER. (Text in English) 1980. 6/yr. $60. (International Association of Scholarly Publishers) Aarhus University Press, Building 170, Aarhus University, DK-8000 Aarhus C, Denmark. TEL 45-86-19-70-33. FAX 45-86-19-84-33. Ed. Toennes Bekker-Nielsen. **Document type:** newsletter.
—CCC.

028.5 SZ
I B B Y CONGRESS PROCEEDINGS. biennial. 20 SFr. International Board on Books for Young People, Nonnenweg 12, Postfach, CH-4003 Basel, Switzerland. TEL 061-2722917. FAX 061-2722757. **Document type:** proceedings.

I G F - JOURNAL; journal of the printing, bookbinding and paper workers in all countries. (International Graphical Federation) see PRINTING

070.5 GW ISSN 0938-3727
I G MEDIEN FORUM. (Industriegewerkschaft) 1862. 11/yr. Industriegewerkschaft Medien, Postfach 102451, 70020 Stuttgart, Germany. TEL 0711-2018-0. FAX 0711-2018262. Ed. Hermann Zoller. illus. circ. 30,000. **Indexed:** Print.Abstr. **Document type:** trade publication.
— **Former titles (until 1991):** Kontrapunkt; Druck und Papier (ISSN 0012-6470); Incorporates: Forum und Technik (ISSN 0015-7708)

070.5 UK
I P C NEWS. m. free. I P C Magazines, Press Office (Subsidiary of: Reed Elsevier group), King's Reach Tower, Stamford St., London SE1 9LS, England. TEL 0171-261-6575. FAX 0171-261-6393. **Document type:** newsletter.
— **Description:** Contains news and features on the company and staff.

020 GW ISSN 1015-9991
Z464.T357
I S B N NEWSLETTER. (International Standard Book Number) (Text in English) 1990. irreg., latest no.8, Oct. 1994. International I S B N Agency, Staatsbibliothek zu Berlin, Preussischer Kulturbesitz, 10772 Berlin, Germany. TEL 030-2662338. FAX 030-2662378. Ed. Hartmut Walravens. **Document type:** newsletter.
— **Description:** Covers agency activities, current news of ISBN and efforts to encourage ISBN use around the world.

029 070.5 GW ISSN 0342-4634
I S B N REVIEW. (International Standard Book Number) (Text in English and German) 1977. a. price varies. (International I S B N Agency) Staatsbibliothek zu Berlin, Preussischer Kulturbesitz, 10772 Berlin, Germany. TEL 030-266-2338. FAX 030-2662378. TELEX 183160-STAAB-D. adv.; bk.rev. circ. 300. **Indexed:** Nutr.Abstr. **Document type:** academic/scholarly publication.
—BLDSC (4582.772000).

IMAGE WORLD; careers in graphic communications. see OCCUPATIONS AND CAREERS

070.5 UK
IMMEDIATE ARTS - WRITERS' DIRECTORY; independent & small press publishers. a. £2.50 (Amiga diskette edition £3.50). Immediate Arts, 26 Lyndhurst Gardens, Glasgow G20 6QY, Scotland. TEL 0141-946-5798. Ed. James Morrison. **Document type:** directory.
— **Description:** Contains information on and lists the addresses of more than 300 magazine and book publishers seeking poetry, short stories, music reviews, comic strips, graphic art, and photographs.

658 FR
IMPAC. m. 263 rue de Paris, 93100 Montreuil Cedex, France. TEL 45-51-80-24. circ. 89,000.

IMPRIMERIE SYNDICALISTE. see LABOR UNIONS

IN-PLANT REPRODUCTIONS. see PRINTING

800 US
INDEPENDENT (ARLINGTON); a monthly notice of small press periodicals, books and ideas. 1978. m. $10 to individuals; institutions $12. c/o Leonard J. Andersen, 156 Pleasant St., Arlington, MA 02174. Ed.Bd. adv.; bk.rev. circ. 800. (also avail. in microfilm from UMI; reprint service avail. from UMI)
— **Supersedes (1975-1976):** Butt.

658.8 US
INDEPENDENT BOOKSELLING TODAY!. 1993. m. $65. Paz & Associates, 2106 20th Ave. S., Nashville, TN 37212-4312. TEL 615-298-2303. FAX 615-298-9864. Ed. Donna Paz. bk.rev.; circ. 400 (controlled). **Document type:** newsletter.
— **Description:** Covers retail management issues for owners and managers of independent bookstores. Helps them develop their business operations and meet the challenges of the changing market. Features include a manager's checklist, marketing and display ideas, and sideline recommendations.

028.1 US ISSN 1051-1261
INDEPENDENT SMALL PRESS REVIEW. 1989. s-a. $3 per no. Independent Small Press Review (I.S.P.R.), No. 91336 Victoria Court, Santa Barbara, CA 93190-1336. TEL 805-687-4087. FAX 805-964-3337. Ed. Janice Smythe. adv.; bk.rev. circ. 2,000.
● Also available online.
— **Description:** Reviews all titles published by independent publishers or self-published writers.

070 US
INDEX TO MARQUIS WHO'S WHO PUBLICATIONS. a. $95. Marquis Who's Who, A Reed Reference Publishing company, 121 Chanlon Rd., New Providence, NJ 07974. TEL 908-464-6800. FAX 908-665-6688. TELEX 138 755. (Subscr. to: Order Dept., Box 31, New Providence, NJ 07974-9903. TEL 800-521-8110) (also avail. in magnetic tape) **Document type:** directory.
— **Former titles:** Index to Marquis Who's Who Books; (until 1988): Index to Who's Who Books; Index to All Books.
— **Description:** Directs you to more than 320,000 biographies listed in the latest editions of most Marquis Who's Who publications.

655 II ISSN 0019-4433
INDIAN BOOK INDUSTRY; book production and distribution journal. (Text in English) 1969. m. Rs.100($25) (typically set in Oct.). Sterling Publishers Pvt. Ltd., L-10 Green Park Extention, New Delhi 110 016, India. TEL 11-669560. FAX 11-6875545. TELEX 031-72366 SITC IN. Ed. Om Parkash Ghai. adv.; bk.rev.; bibl.; charts; illus.; tr.lit. circ. 2,000.

028.1 II ISSN 0019-4441
INDIAN BOOK REVIEW SUPPLEMENT. 1968. q. Rs.75($20) Delhi Library Association, Box 1270, c/o Hardinge Public Library, Queen's Garden, Delhi 6, India. Ed. Shri C.P. Vashisth. bk.rev.

011 070.5 IT ISSN 0393-3903
Z1035.4
L'INDICE.* 1984. m. L.70400 (foreign L.90000) (effective 1994). Indice Coop. A.r.l., Via Madama Cristina 16, 10125 Turin, Italy. TEL 39-11-6698156. FAX 39-11-6699082. (Subscr. to: Via R. Grazioli Lante 15-A, 00195 Rome, Italy. TEL 39-6-37516199. FAX 39-6-37514390) Ed. Filippo Maone. adv.; B&W page L.4900000. circ. 31,000. (tabloid format) **Document type:** newspaper.
— **Description:** Reviews about 1400 books per year.

070.5 GW
INDUSTRIEGEWERKSCHAFT MEDIEN. SCHRIFTENREIHE FUER BETRIEBSRATE. 1969. irreg. exchange basis. Industriegewerkschaft Medien, Postfach 102451, 70020 Stuttgart, Germany. TEL 0711-2018-0. FAX 0711-2018262. Ed.Bd. charts; illus. **Document type:** trade publication.
— **Formerly:** Industriegewerkschaft Druck und Papier. Schriftenreihe fuer Betriebsrate (ISSN 0170-3463)

INFO PRESSE COMMUNICATIONS; le magazine des medias et de la publicite. see ADVERTISING AND PUBLIC RELATIONS

PUBLISHING AND BOOK TRADE

070.5   GW   ISSN 0723-4929
INFORMATION FUER DEN G M B H - GESCHAEFTSFUEHRER. (Gesellschaft mit beschraenkter Haftung); Persoenliches - Beratung - Steuern - Recht - Geld. 1982. w. DM.300. Information Verlag, Hindenburgstr. 67, 79102 Freiburg, Germany. TEL 0761-3683-150. Ed. L. Volkelt.

070.5   **338.025**   US   ISSN 1065-0393
HD9999.I493
INFORMATION MARKETPLACE DIRECTORY. 1992. irreg., no.2, 1995. $295 (effective 1995). SIMBA Information Inc., 213 Danbury Rd., Box 7430, Wilton, CT 06897-7430. TEL 203-834-0033. FAX 203-834-1771. E-mail: simba99@aol.com. **Document type:** directory.
   Description: Lists publishers (along with key personnel) of directories, databases, reference books, business newsletters, research reports, looseleaf publications and magazines.

070.5   US   ISSN 1058-4730
Z479
INFORMATION PUBLISHING: BUSINESS - PROFESSIONAL MARKETS & MEDIA. irreg., no.2, 1994 (Mar.). $1001 (Canada and Mexico $1015; elsewhere $1031) (effective 1994-1995). SIMBA Information Inc., 213 Danbury Rd., Box 7430, Wilton, CT 06897-7430. TEL 203-834-0033. FAX 203-834-1771. E-mail: simba99@aol.com. charts. **Document type:** trade publication.
   Description: Shows how publishers are profiting from leveraging their content in other media.

INFORMATION SOURCES (YEAR). see COMPUTERS

020   US   ISSN 1041-0031
Z678.85   CODEN: ISQUEK
INFORMATION STANDARDS QUARTERLY. Abbreviated title: I S Q. 1989. q. $65 (foreign $85). National Information Standards Organization (NISO), Box 1056, Bethesda, MD 20827. TEL 301-975-2814. FAX 301-869-8071. Ed. Pat Ensor. bk.rev. circ. 1,000. (looseleaf format; processed; back issues avail.) **Indexed:** LISA. **Document type:** newsletter.
—BLDSC (4496.323000); CASDDS; UnCover.
   Supersedes (in 1988): Voice of Z-39 (ISSN 0163-626X); Which was formerly (1965-1977): News About Z-39 (ISSN 0028-8942)
   Description: Reports on the activities of the organization. Includes regular status reports on standards being developed and revised, and reports news of standards activities.

070   US
INK (CHICAGO). 10/yr. Association of Free Community Papers, 401 N. Michigan Ave., Chicago, IL 60611-4267. TEL 312-644-6610. FAX 312-321-6869. TELEX 24-4703 SBA. adv. circ. 600. **Document type:** trade publication.
   Description: Provides news on the free-paper publishing industry.

686.36   US   ISSN 0894-0479
Z271.3.M37
INK & GALL; the marbling journal. 1987. 3/yr. $35 (foreign $40). Dexter Ing, Pub., Box 1469, Taos, NM 87571. TEL 505-586-1607. Ed. Polly Fox. adv.; bk.rev. circ. 1,500. **Document type:** trade publication.
—Faxon.
   Description: Devoted to furthering the art of marbling; both traditional & modern techniques.

332.6   US   ISSN 1075-3281
INSIDE EXPORT; a guide to growing international markets for the U.S. publishing industry. 1990. bi-m. $50. Association of American Publishers, Inc., International Division, 71 Fifth Ave., New York, NY 10003-3004. TEL 212-255-0200. FAX 212-255-7007. Ed. Fred Kobrak; Pub. Barbara Meredith. bk.rev. **Document type:** newsletter.
   Description: News on developments in international book markets. Includes regional reports, intellectual property news, services, market opportunities, calendar of events.

INSIDE MEDIA; for media department of advertising. see ADVERTISING AND PUBLIC RELATIONS

070.5   US   ISSN 1052-0120
Z475
INSIDER'S GUIDE TO BOOK EDITORS AND PUBLISHERS. 1991. a. Prima Publications and Communications, Box 1260JH, Rocklin, CA 85677.

INTER DOCUMENTATION COMPANY. CATALOGUE OF CATALOGUES. see BIBLIOGRAPHIES

028.1   FR   ISSN 0242-035X
INTERNATIONAL ASSOCIATION OF LITERARY CRITICS. REVUE. 1969. s-a. membership. International Association of Literary Critics, 38 rue du Faubourg, St. Jacques, 75014 Paris, France. TEL 40-51-33-00. FAX 43-54-92-99. TELEX SCAM SGL 206963 F. Dir. Robert Andre. adv.; bk.rev.; abstr.; bibl. circ. 850. **Document type:** academic/scholarly publication, bulletin.
   Formerly: International Association of Literary Critics. Bulletin.

INTERNATIONAL BOOK TRADE DIRECTORY; Europe, Australia, Oceania, Latin America, Africa, and Asia. see PUBLISHING AND BOOK TRADE — Abstracting, Bibliographies, Statistics

070.5   US   ISSN 0074-6827
           CODEN: ILMPD3
INTERNATIONAL LITERARY MARKET PLACE; the directory of the international book publishing industry. Variant title (1975-76, 1977-78): European Literary Market Place. 1966. a., 28th edition, 1994. $179.95. R.R. Bowker, A Reed Reference Publishing company, 121 Chanlon Rd., New Providence, NJ 07974. TEL 908-464-6800. FAX 908-665-6688. TELEX 138 755. (Subscr. to: Order Dept., Box 31, New Providence, NJ 07974-9903. TEL 800-521-8110) index. (also avail. in magnetic tape) **Document type:** bibliography, directory.
   •Also available on CD-ROM. Producer(s): Bowker - Reed Reference Electronic Publishing.
—BLDSC (4543.020000); CASDDS. **CCC.**
   Description: Arranged by function and country, lists publishers, book trade organizations, trade reference publications, agents, international events, major booksellers and libraries, and translation agencies in more than 170 countries. Indexed by institution name.

070.5   UK
THE INTERNATIONAL PRESS DIRECTORY. (Text in English, French, German, Italian, Spanish) 1992. a. £15. The Magazine Business Ltd., 8 Tottenham Mews, London W1P 9PJ, England. TEL 0171-436-5211. FAX 0171-436-5290. E-mail: magbus@demon.co.uk. Ed. Chris Mounce; Pub. Carey Labovitch. adv.; adv./page £2250; trim 297 x 210; adv. contact: Corinne Fe'devieille. charts; illus.; stats.; circ. 12,500. (back issues avail.) **Document type:** directory.
   Description: Directory listing the top 4,000 magazines and newspapers exported worldwide.

070.5   SZ   ISSN 0074-7556
INTERNATIONAL PUBLISHERS ASSOCIATION. PROCEEDINGS OF CONGRESS. 1896. quadrennial, 24th, 1992, New Delhi. 60 SFr.($54) International Publishers Association - Union Internationale des Editeurs (Internationale Verleger-Union), Ave. Miremont 3, CH-1206 Geneva, Switzerland. TEL 022-3463018. FAX 022-3475717. circ. 1,100. **Document type:** proceedings.
   Description: Provides insights into the concerns of the international publishing community. Addresses such issues as copyright, piracy, censorship, world trends in education and electronic publishing.

070.5   SZ   ISSN 0256-6613
INTERNATIONAL PUBLISHERS BULLETIN. 3/yr. International Publishers Association, Ave. Miremont 3, CH-1206 Geneva, Switzerland. TEL 022-3463018. FAX 022-3475717. Ed. J.A. Koutchoumow. **Document type:** bulletin.
—BLDSC (4545.425000).

686.209 070   IS
ISRAEL BIBLIOPHILES NEWSLETTER. (Text in English and Hebrew) 1980. a. $5. Israel Bibliofiles, P.O. Box 4368, 91043 Jerusalem, Israel. Ed. Leila Avrin. **Document type:** newsletter.

070.5   IS   ISSN 0333-6018
ISRAEL BOOK TRADE DIRECTORY; a guide to publishers, printers, booksellers and the book trade in Israel. (Text in English) 1967. biennial. $10. P.O. Box 7705, Jerusalem 91076, Israel. TEL 972-2-432147. FAX 972-3-380626. Ed. Asher Weill. adv. contact: Asher Weill. circ. 3,000. **Document type:** directory.
   Former titles: Israel Book Trades Directory: A Select List; Publishers and Printers of Israel: A Select List (ISSN 0079-7820)
   Description: Provides descriptions of each company, addresses, telephone and fax numbers for Israeli publishers, printers, booksellers, agents and publishers' representatives.

J B I A DIRECTORY. (Japan Book Importers Association) see BUSINESS AND ECONOMICS — Trade And Industrial Directories

070.5 011   JA   ISSN 0387-3927
J P G LETTER; news on English publishing in Japan and South-East Asia. (Text in English) 1973. m. 20000 Yen($200) Japan Publications Guide Service, 5-5-13 Matsushiro, Tsukuba-shi, Ibaraki-ken 305, Japan. TEL 81-3-3661-7458. FAX 81-3-3667-9646. (Subscr. to: Intercontinental Marketing Corp., IPO Box 5056, Tokyo 100-31, Japan. TEL 81-3-3661-7458) Ed. Warren E. Ball. adv.; bk.rev.; illus. circ. 600.
—BLDSC (5073.683300). **CCC.**
   Supersedes: Asia Notebook (ISSN 0004-4490)
   Description: Lists new or updated publication titles in Japan and in Southeast/East Asian countries. Also includes comments on publishers and other information sources.

JAHRBUCH DER AUKTIONSPREISE FUER BUECHER, HANDSCHRIFTEN UND AUTOGRAPHEN; Ergebnisse der Auktionen in Deutschland, den Niederlanden, Oesterreich und der Schweiz. see MUSEUMS AND ART GALLERIES

070.5   JA   ISSN 0287-9530
HD2429.J3
JAPAN DIRECTORY OF PROFESSIONAL ASSOCIATIONS. (Abridged diskette edition avail.) (Text in English) 1984. irreg., 3rd ed., 1995. 30000 Yen (foreign $300). Japan Publications Guide Service, 5-5-13 Matsushiro, Tsukuba-shi, Ibaraki-ken 305, Japan. FAX 81-3-3667-9646. (Subscr. to: Intercontinental Marketing Corp., IPO Box 5056, Tokyo 100-31, Japan. TEL 81-3-3661-7458) Ed. Warren E. Ball. adv.; stat.; tr.lit. circ. 2,000. (also avail. in diskette format) **Document type:** directory.
—**CCC.**
   Description: Lists all types of associations, as well as selected institutes.

070.5   JA   ISSN 0918-9580
JAPANESE BOOK NEWS. (Text in English) q. Japan Foundation, Publications Department, Ark-Mori Bldg., 1-12-32 Akasaka, Minato-ku, Tokyo 107, Japan. TEL 03-5562-3532. FAX 03-5562-3501. Ed. Yasuda Fumio.
   Description: Contains the latest trends in Japanese publishing and selected new titles with brief descriptions of the content.

686   IS
JERFAIR NEWS; the Jerusalem International Book Fair newsletter. (Text in English) 1975. irreg. free. Jerusalem International Book Fair, P.O. Box 775, Jerusalem 91007, Israel. TEL 972-2-240663. FAX 972-2-243144. circ. 5,000. **Document type:** newsletter.

070.5   FR   ISSN 1156-5977
JERICHO. 1984. a. 100 F. (membership). Club des Lecteurs de Presse et Livres Meconnus, 114 rue Louis Ranvier, 42300 Roanne, France. Ed. Jacqueline Grolleau. index. circ. 100. (back issues avail.)
   Formerly: Bulletin Annuel d'Information et de Liaison entre C.L.P.L.M. (ISSN 0765-328X)
   Description: Helps to recognize and promotes the usage of innovative but unknown works.

070.5   US
JERRY BUCHANAN'S BETTER LIFE JOURNAL. q. (Jerry Buchanan Advertising Agency) Towers Club, U.S.A., Inc., Box 2038, Vancouver, WA 98665. TEL 206-574-3084. FAX 206-576-8969. Ed. Jerry Buchanan.

PUBLISHING AND BOOK TRADE 5629

070.5   IS
JERUSALEM FELLOW. 1989. irreg. free. Jerusalem International Book Fair, P.O. Box 775, Jerusalem 91007, Israel. TEL 972-2-240663. FAX 972-2-243144. circ. 5,000.
Description: Publishing and book trade news of interest to alumni of the Jerusalem Editorial Fellows Program.

016.90904
JEWISH BOOK WORLD. a. $20 to non-members. (Jewish Welfare Board) J W B Jewish Book Center, 15 E. 26 St., New York, NY 10010. TEL 212-532-4949. FAX 212-481-4174. **Document type:** directory.
Formerly: Directory of Jewish Community Centers. **CCC.**
Description: Contains an annotated listing of books in the Jewish Book Center.

JOURNAL OF INFORMATION SCIENCE - PRINCIPLES AND PRACTICE. see *LIBRARY AND INFORMATION SCIENCES*

686 020   US   ISSN 0265-5942
PN4699
JOURNAL OF NEWSPAPER AND PERIODICAL HISTORY. 1984. 2/yr. $75 (effective Oct. 1990). Greenwood Press, Inc., Subscription Publications (Subsidiary of: Greenwood Publishing Group Inc.), 88 Post Rd. W., Box 5007, Westport, CT 06881-9990. TEL 203-226-3571. FAX 203-222-1502. Ed. Michael Harris. adv.; bk.rev.; index. circ. 300. (also avail. in microfilm; back issues avail.) **Indexed:** Hist.Abstr. (until 1994), RILM.
—Faxon; UnCover.

011 655   CN
Z286.S37
JOURNAL OF SCHOLARLY PUBLISHING. 1969. q. $30 to individuals; institutions $58; students $20. University of Toronto Press, Journals Department, 5201 Dufferin St., Downsview, ON M3H 5T8, Canada. TEL 416-667-7781. FAX 416-667-7881. (U.S. addr.: 340 Nagel Dr., Cheektowaga, NY 14225) Ed. Hamish Cameron. adv.; bk.rev.; illus.; index. circ. 2,159. (also avail. in microfiche from UMI) **Indexed:** Amer.Hist.& Life, C.L.I., Can.B.P.I., Curr.Cont., Hist.Abstr., Leg.Per., Lib.Lit., LISA, M.L.A., SSCI. **Document type:** academic/scholarly publication.
—Genuine Article; SWETS; UMI; UnCover. **CCC.**
Formerly: Scholarly Publishing (ISSN 0036-634X)

070.5   US   ISSN 0737-7436
JOURNAL OF THE PRINT WORLD. 1978. q. $10 to non-profit institutions in U.S.; others $15; elsewhere $20. Meredith, NH 03253-9599. TEL 603-279-6479. FAX 603-279-1337. Ed. Charles Stuart Lane. adv. contact: Sophia Lane. bk.rev. circ. 8,000. **Document type:** newspaper.

028 296 016   US   ISSN 0022-5754
Z6367
JUDAICA BOOK NEWS.* 1969. s-a. $9.50. Book News, Inc. (New York), 75 Hook Rd., Bayonne, NJ 07002-5006. TEL 212-691-3817. FAX 212-633-9731. Ed. Ernest L. Weiss. adv.; bk.rev.; bibl. circ. 18,000. (also avail. in microform from UMI; reprint service avail. from UMI)
—UMI.
Description: Devoted entirely to new and forthcoming books of Jewish interest.

028.5   UK   ISSN 0022-6505
Z1037.A1
JUNIOR BOOKSHELF; a review of children's books. 1936. 6/yr. £10.50 (elsewhere £12.80) (effective 1996). Marsh Hall, Thurstonland, Huddersfield, Yorkshire HD4 6XB, England. TEL 01484-661811. FAX 01484-510237. Ed. Diana Morrell. adv.; bk.rev.; illus.; index. circ. 1,500. (also avail. in microform from UMI; back issues avail.; reprint service avail. from UMI) **Indexed:** Bk.Rev.Ind. (1975-), Child.Bk.Rev.Ind. (1975-), Child.Lit.Abstr., Lib.Lit., Lib.Sci.Abstr. **Document type:** bibliography.
—BLDSC (5075.120000); UMI; UnCover.
Description: Offers authoritative reviews of the best new books for children.

070.5   CC   ISSN 1001-5272
KEJI CHUBAN/SCIENCE AND TECHNOLOGY PUBLISHING. (Text in Chinese) bi-m. Zhongguo Chuban Gongzuozhe Xiehui - China Publishers Association, 1 Banwanzhuang Nanjie, Beijing 100037, People's Republic of China. TEL 8317766. Ed. Zhao Deming.

070.5   UK
KEY NOTE MARKET REVIEW: U K PUBLISHING. Variant title: U K Publishing. irreg. £375. Key Note Publications Ltd., Field House, 72 Oldfield Rd., Hampton, Middlesex TW12 2HQ, England. TEL 0181-783-0755. FAX 0181-783-1720. **Document type:** trade publication.
●Also available online.
Also available on CD-ROM.

070.5   UK   ISSN 0268-4446
KEY NOTE REPORT: BOOK PUBLISHING. Variant title: Book Publishing. irreg. £185. Key Note Publications Ltd., Field House, 72 Oldfield Rd., Hampton, Middlesex TW12 2HQ, England. TEL 0181-783-0755. FAX 0181-783-1720. **Document type:** trade publication.
●Also available online.
Also available on CD-ROM.
—BLDSC (2248.186500).

070.5   UK   ISSN 0957-7882
KEY NOTE REPORT: BOOKSELLING. Variant title: Bookselling. irreg. £185. Key Note Publications Ltd., Field House, 72 Oldfield Rd., Hampton, Middlesex TW12 2HQ, England. TEL 0181-783-0755. FAX 0181-783-1720. **Document type:** trade publication.
●Also available online.
Also available on CD-ROM.
—BLDSC (2250.243000).

070.5   UK   ISSN 0951-6719
KEY NOTE REPORT: CONSUMER MAGAZINES. Variant title: Consumer Magazines. 1983. irreg. £185. Key Note Publications Ltd., Field House, 72 Oldfield Rd., Hampton, Middlesex TW12 2HQ, England. TEL 0181-783-0755. FAX 0181-783-1720. **Document type:** trade publication.
●Also available online.
Also available on CD-ROM.
—BLDSC (3424.315600).

KEY NOTE REPORT: NEWSPAPERS. see *JOURNALISM*

070.5 808   US
KEYSTROKES. 1979. 3/yr. $10. Writers Alliance, 12 Skylark Ln., Stonybrook, NY 11790. TEL 516-751-7080. Ed. Howard Austerlitz; Pub. Kiel Stuart. adv.; bk.rev. circ. 250. (back issues avail.) **Document type:** newsletter.
Formerly: Writers Alliance Newsletter.
Description: Directed to fiction, poetry, journalism, and research writers with information about markets and computer use.

070.5   FI   ISSN 0047-343X
Z374.7
KIRJAKAUPPALEHTI. 1897. m. FIM 400 in Scandinavia; in Europe FIM 430; elsewhere FIM 490. Kirjakauppalehden Julkaisu Oy, Eerikinkatu 15-17D, 00100 Helsinki, Finland. FAX 90-6944900. Ed. Olli Erakivi. adv.; bk.rev.; illus.; index. circ. 2,000. **Document type:** trade publication, newspaper.
Formerly: Suomen Kirjakauppalehti - Finsk Bokhandelstidning.

028.1   US   ISSN 0042-6598
Z477
KIRKUS REVIEWS; adult, young adult and children's book reviews. 1933. s-m. price varies. Kirkus Associates, LP, 200 Park Ave. S., New York, NY 10003. TEL 212-777-4554. Ed. Anne Larsen. bk.rev.; index. circ. 5,000. (also avail. in microform from UMI) **Indexed:** Bk.Rev.Ind. (1965-), Child.Bk.Rev.Ind. (1965-).
—UMI.

070.5   US
KITCHEN SINK PIPELINE.* 1983. m. free to qualified personnel. Kitchen Sink Press, Inc., 320 Riverside Dr., Northampton, MA 01060-2717. TEL 414-295-6922. FAX 414-295-6878. Ed. Denis Kitchen. circ. 16,000. (looseleaf format; back issues avail.) **Document type:** newsletter.
Description: Discusses Kitchen Sink Press publishing projects and forthcoming releases.

KLEIO. see *HISTORY*

028.1 011   US   ISSN 1065-8602
Z1037
KLIATT; reviews of selected of current paperbacks, audiobooks, and educational software. 1967. 6/yr. $36 (foreign $38). 33 Bay State Rd., Wellesley, MA 02181-3244. TEL 617-237-7577. FAX 617-237-7577. Ed. Claire Rosser. adv. contact: Paula Rohrlick. bk.rev.; index. circ. 2,300. (also avail. in microform from UMI; reprint service avail. from UMI) **Indexed:** Bk.Rev.Ind. (1977-), Child.Bk.Rev.Ind. (1977-).
—UMI.
Former titles: Kliatt Young Adult Paperback Book Guide (ISSN 0199-2376); Kliatt Paperback Book Guide (ISSN 0023-2114)

070.5 947   RU
KNIGA ISSLEDOVANIYA. 1959. 2/yr. Izdatel'stvo Kniga, 50, Gorky St., 125047 Moscow, Russia. bibl.; cum.index every 2 yrs.

070.5   XO
KNIHA. (Text in Slovak; summaries in English, German and Russian) 1976. a. price varies. Matica Slovenska, Slovenska Narodna Kniznica, Ul. L. Novomeskeho 32, 036 52 Martin, Slovakia. TEL 0842-313-71. FAX 0842-324-54. TELEX 075 331. Ed. Miroslava Domova.
Formerly: Knizna Kultura.

070.5   RU   ISSN 0869-6039
KNIZHNOE DELO. 1992. bi-m. $91 (effective 1996). Izdatel'stvo Progress, Zubovskii blv. 17, 119847 Moscow, Russia. TEL 246-0624. FAX 095-230-2403. TELEX 411800-KEGL-U. (Dist. by: Mezhdunarodnaya Kniga, B. Yakimanka 39, 117049 Moscow, Russia) Ed. S.S. Nosov. adv. circ. 10,000.
Formerly: Knizhone Delo v Rossii.
Description: News and trends of interest to publishers, booksellers and librarians.

028.1   RU   ISSN 0023-2378
Z372
KNIZHNOE OBOZRENIE; review of newly published books. 1966. w. $6. (Gosudarstvennyi Komitet Soveta Ministrov po Pechati) Izdatel'stvo Kniga, 50, Gorky St., 125047 Moscow, Russia. TEL 251-19-31. Ed. A.I. Ovsyannikov. (also avail. in microform) **Indexed:** Curr.Dig.Sov.Press.

070.5   XV
KNJIZEVNI GLASNIK MOHORJEVE DRUZBE. (Text in Slovanian) 1981. s-a. free. Mahorjeva Druzba Celje, Zidanskova 7, YU-63000 Celje, Slovenia. adv.; bk.rev. circ. 37,000.

THE KOBRIN LETTER; concerning children's books about real people, places and things. see *LITERATURE*

070.5 015   KO   ISSN 1227-1977
KOREAN PUBLICATIONS YEARBOOK/HANKUK CH'ULPAN YONGAM. 1963. a. 75000 Won($100) Korean Publishers Association, 105-2 Sagan-dong, Chongno-ku, Seoul 110-190, S. Korea. TEL 02-735-2701. FAX 02-738-5414. circ. 2,000. (back issues avail.)

070.5   BE
KREATIF JAARBOOK. (Text in Flemish) a. C E D Samsom (Subsidiary of: Wolters Samsom Belgie n.v.), Kouterveld 14, B-1831 Diegem, Belgium. TEL 32-2-7231111.
Description: Covers free-lancing in Belgium for copywriters, artists, graphic designers, photographers and illustrators.

070   PL   ISSN 0137-4060
KSIEGARZ. vol.19, 1975. q. $16. Stowarzyszenie Ksiegarzy Polskich, Ul. Mokotowska 4-6, 00-641 Warsaw, Poland. (Dist. by: Ars Polona-Ruch, Krakowskie Przedmiescie 7, 00-068 Warsaw, Poland) Ed. Tadeusz Hussak. adv.; bk.rev.; bibl.; illus.; index. circ. 3,500.

070.5   AG   ISSN 0326-226X
Z519.7
L E A. (Libros de Edicion Argentina) 1982. m. $30 (foreign $100). Camara Argentina del Libro, Av. Belgrano 1580, 6 Piso, 1093 Buenos Aires, Argentina. TEL 38-8383. Ed. Jose Naveiro. adv.; illus. circ. 4,000.

LAMBDA BOOK REPORT; a review of contemporary gay and lesbian literature. see *HOMOSEXUALITY*

PUBLISHING AND BOOK TRADE

070.5   US   ISSN 1056-0327
LAUGHING BEAR NEWSLETTER. 1976. m. $12 (Canada $14; elsewhere $22). Laughing Bear Press, Box 36159, Denver, CO 80236. TEL 303-744-3624. Ed. Tom Person. adv.; bk.rev.; illus.; tr.lit.; index. circ. 150. (back issues avail.) **Document type:** newsletter.
—CCC.
    Description: Contains practical information for independent publishers.

070.5   UK   ISSN 0953-1513
Z286.S37
LEARNED PUBLISHING: A L P S P BULLETIN. 1977. q. £75($135) to non-members (effective 1996). Association of Learned and Professional Society Publishers, 48 Kelsey Ln., Beckenham, Kent BR3 3NE, England. TEL 0181-658-0459. (Subscr. to: Turpin Distribution Services Ltd., Blackhorse Rd., Letchworth, Herts. SG6 1HN, England. TEL 01462-672555. FAX 01462-480947) Ed. Hazel K. Bell. adv.; B&W page £150; adv. contact: Hazel K. Bell. bk.rev. circ. 350. **Document type:** trade publication.
—BLDSC (5179.325650).
    Formerly (until 1988): A L P S P Bulletin (ISSN 0260-9428)

018.1 860   US   ISSN 0732-8001
Z1039.M5
LECTOR. 1982. s-a. $50. Floricanto Press, 16161 Ventura Blvd., Ste. 830, Encino, CA 91436-2504. TEL 818-990-1885. Ed. Roberto Cabello-Argandona. adv.; bk.rev. circ. 3,000. **Indexed:** Chic.Per.Ind.
    Description: Features English language reviews and information about Spanish language books published in Spain, Latin America and the US which are of interest to Hispanics in America.

070.5   US
LEE HOWARD NEWSLETTER; for small publishers and mail order book dealers. 1979. q. $10 for 3 nos. Selective Books, Inc., Box 1140, Clearwater, FL 34617. TEL 813-447-0100. Ed. Lee Howard. adv.; circ. 5,500 (controlled). **Document type:** trade publication.
    Formerly: Book Business Mart.
    Description: Focuses on the self-publishing book market and mail-order book selling.

070.5   GW   ISSN 0940-1954
Z4
LEIPZIGER JAHRBUCH ZUR BUCHGESCHICHTE. (Text in English, French, German) 1991. a. DM.98. Harrassowitz Verlag, Taunusstr. 14, 65183 Wiesbaden, Germany. TEL 0611-530-0. FAX 0611-530570. Eds. Mark Lehmstedt, Lothar Poethe. bk.rev.; circ. 400 (paid). (back issues avail.) **Document type:** academic/scholarly publication.

LIBRARIANS' CHRISTIAN FELLOWSHIP NEWSLETTER. see LIBRARY AND INFORMATION SCIENCES

LIBRARIAN'S WORLD. see LIBRARY AND INFORMATION SCIENCES

011 090   GW   ISSN 0024-2152
Z990
LIBRARIUM. (Text in English, French, German and Italian) 1958. 3/yr. 150 SFr.($60) Schweizerische Bibliophilen-Gesellschaft, SZ , Herzog August Bibliothek, Postfach 1364, 38299 Wolfenbuettel, Germany. TEL 05331-808228. FAX 05331-808266. Ed. Martin Bircher. adv.; bk.rev.; illus.; index. circ. 750. **Indexed:** M.L.A. **Document type:** bulletin.
    Description: Covers all aspects of collecting books, graphic art and autographs.

658.896   US   ISSN 0024-2217
THE LIBRARY BOOKSELLER; books wanted by college and university libraries. 1945. m. $50 to individuals (foreign $60); libraries $50 (foreign $60). Scott Saifer, Ed. & Pub., Box 9544, Berkeley, CA 94709-0544. TEL 510-540-6951. adv. contact: Scott Saifer. circ. 150. **Document type:** trade publication.

LIBRARY INTELLIGENCER. see LIBRARY AND INFORMATION SCIENCES

LIBRARY JOURNAL. see LIBRARY AND INFORMATION SCIENCES

028.1 015.45   IT   ISSN 0024-2683
LIBRI E RIVISTE D'ITALIA; rassegna bibliografica mensile. English edition: Italian Books and Periodicals (ISSN 0021-2881) (Editions in French, German, Italian, Spanish) 1950. m. L.22000. Istituto Poligrafico Dello Stato, Piazza Verdi 10, Rome, Italy. bk.rev.; bibl.; index. **Indexed:** M.L.A.

070.5 806   MX   ISSN 0186-2243
Z497
LIBROS DE MEXICO. 1985. q. $40 (outside America $50). Camara Nacional de la Industria Editorial Mexicana, Holanda 13, Col. San Diego Churubusco, 04120 Coyoacan, Mexico. TEL 688-7122. FAX 604-3147. Ed. Federico Krafft Vera. adv.; bibl. circ. 6,000. **Document type:** trade publication, bibliography.
    Description: Covers trade and industry in Mexico, as well as its history.

070.5   US
LIFTOUTS; a review of books and language work. 1983. a. $5. Preludium Publishers, 1414 S. Third St., Ste. 102, Minneapolis, NM 55454-1173. TEL 612-321-9044. FAX 612-831-1693. Ed. Barry Casselman. adv.; bk.rev.; film rev.; play rev. circ. 2,000. (tabloid format; back issues avail.)
    Description: Features new poetry and fiction, and recent work in translation from around the world.

070.5   BE
LIJSTENBOEK. 1929. a. 1060 BEF($8) Vereniging ter Bevordering van het Vlaamse Boekwezen - Flemish Book Trade Organisation, Hof ter Schrieklaan 17, B-2600 Berchem (Antwerp), Belgium. index. circ. 1,500.

028.1   GW   ISSN 0179-7417
LISTEN; Zeitschrift fuer Leserinnen und Leser. 1985. q. DM.30($28) Jordanstr. 14, 60486 Frankfurt a.M., Germany. TEL 069-775592. FAX 069-702056. (U.S. addr.: M. Rosenberg Inc., 1841 Broadway, New York, NY 10023) Ed K. Piberhofer. adv.; bk.rev. circ. 15,000. (back issues avail.) **Document type:** bibliography.

LITERARY AGENTS OF NORTH AMERICA. see LITERATURE

070.5   US   ISSN 0000-1155
PN161   CODEN: LTYMA4
LITERARY MARKET PLACE; the directory of American book publishing industry. Abbreviated title: L M P. 1940. a., 55th edition, 1994. $165. R.R. Bowker, A Reed Reference Publishing company, 121 Chanlon Rd., New Providence, NJ 07974. TEL 908-464-6800. FAX 908-665-6688. TELEX 138 755. (Subscr. to: Order Dept., Box 31, New Providence, NJ 07974-9903. TEL 800-521-8110) index. (also avail. in magnetic tape) **Document type:** bibliography, directory.
●Also available on CD-ROM. Producer(s): Bowker - Reed Reference Electronic Publishing.
—BLDSC (5276.650000); CASDDS. CCC.
    Formerly (until 1988): Literary Market Place with Names and Numbers (ISSN 0161-2905); Formed by the 1972 merger of: Literary Market Place (ISSN 0161-2891); Names and Numbers (ISSN 0075-9899); Which was formerly (until 1961): Book Industry Register (ISSN 0000-1171)
    Description: Lists publishing and publishing-related businesses, including distributors, literary agents, small presses, events, editorial and art services, printers and binders. Also lists recent mergers and acquisitions and company reportage of publishers, i.e., divisions, subsidiaries and imprints.

LITERARY SKETCHES; a magazine of interviews, reviews and memorabilia. see LITERATURE

070.5   PO
LIVRARIA FIGUEIRINHAS CATALOGO. 1898. a. free. Editora Figueirinhas Lda., Rua do Almada, 47, 4000 Porto, Portugal. FAX 325907. circ. 5,000.

010   BE   ISSN 0024-533X
Z990
LE LIVRE ET L'ESTAMPE. (Text in French) 1954. s-a. 1750 BEF. Societe Royale des Bibliophiles et Iconophiles de Belgique, 4 Bd. de l'Empereur, B-1000 Brussels, Belgium. Ed. A. Grisay. adv.; bk.rev.; cum.index: 1954-1985. circ. 350.

658.8   FR   ISSN 0294-0019
LIVRES DE FRANCE. (Supplement avail.: Service Ile-de-France (ISSN 1162-4469)) m. 580 F. Livres Hebdo, 35 rue Gregoire de Tours, 75006 Paris, France. TEL 44-41-28-00. FAX 44-41-28-64. Ed. Jean-Marie Doublet. adv.; bk.rev.; bibl.; illus.; stat. circ. 7,000. **Document type:** trade publication.
    Formed by the 1982 merger of: Livres de France (Edition avec Prix Cession de Base) (ISSN 0223-4831); Livres de France (Edition Destine a l'Etranger) (ISSN 0223-484X); Livres de France (Edition sans Prix) (ISSN 0223-4823); All of which supersede in part (1959-1979): Bulletin du Livre (ISSN 0007-456X); (1972-1979): Bibliographie de la France. Biblio (ISSN 0335-5675); Which was formed by the merger of (1933-1971): Biblio (Mensuel) (ISSN 1147-6710); (1814-1971): Bibliographie de la France (ISSN 0006-1344); Which was formerly: Bibliographie de l'Empire Francais (ISSN 1147-6680); (until 1811): Journal General de l'Imprimerie et de la Libraire (ISSN 1147-6672); (1797-1810): Journal Typographique et Bibliographique (ISSN 1147-6664). Former supplement (1973-1975): Connaissance et Formation.

658.8   FR   ISSN 0294-0027
LES LIVRES DU MOIS. (Supplement to: Livres Hebdo (ISSN 0294-0000)) 1979. m. Livres Hebdo, 35 rue Gregoire de Tours, 75006 Paris, France. TEL 44-41-28-00. FAX 44-41-28-64. **Document type:** trade publication.
—SWETS.
    Formed by the 1982 merger of: Livres du Mois (Edition avec Prix Cession de Base) (ISSN 0223-498X); Livres du Mois (Edition Destine a l'Etranger) (ISSN 0223-5005); Livres du Mois (Edition sans Prix) (ISSN 0223-4998)

015.46   PO   ISSN 0870-5259
Z2715
LIVROS DE PORTUGAL. 1940. m. $50 (typically set in Jan.). Associacao Portuguesa de Editores e Livreiros, Av. dos Estados Unidos da America, 97 6 Esq, 1700 Lisbon, Portugal. TEL 1-8489136. FAX 1-8489377. (Subscr. to: Dinalivro, Travessa do Convento de Jesus, 15 r-c, 1200, Lisbon, Portugal) Dir. Henrique Pavao. adv.; bk.rev.; bibl. circ. 1,500.
    Description: Covers news about the world book trade, includes interviews with publishers and book sellers, and lists a bibliography of new books and other printed materials from the previous month.

LOCUS (OAKLAND); the newspaper of the science fiction field. see LITERATURE — Science Fiction, Fantasy, Horror

070.5   UK   ISSN 0957-9656
Z284   CODEN: LGOSEL
LOGOS; the professional journal of the book world. 1990. q. £42($75) to individuals; institutions £65($110) (effective 1996). Whurr Publishers Ltd., 19b Compton Terrace, London N1 2UN, England. TEL 0171-359-5979. FAX 0171-226-5290. (Subscr. to: Turpin Distribution Services Ltd., Blackhorse Rd., Letchworth, Herts. SG6 1HN, England. TEL 01462-672555. FAX 01462-480947) Ed. Gordon Graham. adv. contact: Sarah Vicary. (reprint service avail. from SCH) **Document type:** trade publication.
—BLDSC (5292.404000).
    Description: For publishers, booksellers, librarians, and others in the international book community.

028.1   US
LOS ANGELES TIMES BOOK REVIEW. w. Los Angeles Times Inc., Times Mirror Sq., Los Angeles, CA 90053. TEL 213-237-7778. Ed. Shelley Coffney, III; Pub. Dick Schlosberg,III. bk.rev.; index. (also avail. in microform from UMI) **Indexed:** Bk.Rev.Ind. (1982-), Child.Bk.Rev.Ind. (1982-). **Document type:** newspaper.

070.5   UK
THE M D B MAGAZINE DIRECTORY. 1985. s-a. £25. The Magazine Business Ltd., 8 Tottenham Mews, London W1P 9PJ, England. TEL 0171-430-5211. FAX 0171-430-5290. Ed. Chris Mounce; Pub. C. Labovitch. adv.; color page £2155; trim 297 x 210; adv. contact: Tina Zanelli. illus.; mkt.; stat.; circ. 55,350. (back issues avail.) **Document type:** directory.
    Description: Lists magazines and periodicals available for retail sale in the U.K.

070.5 NE
M N I COURANT. s-a. free. Martinus Nijhoff International, P.O. Box 269, 2501 AX The Hague, Netherlands. TEL 31-79-3684400. FAX 31-79-3615698. (U.S. addr.: Box 562, Marshfield Hills, MA 02051. TEL 800-MNI-1853) **Document type:** newsletter.
  Description: News of the company, with book and serial publishing updates.

M P A NEWSLETTER OF RESEARCH. (Magazine Publishers of America) see *ADVERTISING AND PUBLIC RELATIONS*

MAC PUBLISHING AND PRESENTATIONS. see *COMPUTERS — Microcomputers*

658.8 US
MAGA SCENE. m. Ingram Periodicals Inc., 1226 Heil Quaker Blvd., Box 7000, La Vergne, TN 37086-7000. TEL 615-793-5522. (tabloid format) **Document type:** newsletter.
  Description: Provides features on magazine merchandising, tips on improving the profitability of magazine programs, and industry trends.

686 658.8 US
THE MAGAZINE; everything you need to know to make it in the magazine business. irreg., latest 3rd ed. $19.95. Cowles Business Media (Subsidiary of: Cowles Media Company), Six River Bend Center, 911 Hope St., Box 4949, Stamford, CT 06907-0949. TEL 203-358-9900. FAX 203-357-9014. Ed. Leonard Mogel. **Document type:** trade publication.

028.1 US ISSN 0744-3102
Z284
MAGAZINE & BOOKSELLER; mass market retailers' and publishers' guide. 1946. 8/yr. $49 (foreign $71) (effective 1994). North American Publishing Co. (New York), 322 Eighth Ave., 3rd Fl., New York, NY 10001. TEL 212-620-7330. FAX 212-620-7335. TELEX 215-494-6735 NAPCOPHL. E-mail: editor@mb.napco.com. (Subscr. to: 401 N. Broad St., Philadelphia, PA 19108. TEL 215-238-5300) Ed. Patricia H. McCarthy; Pub. Chris Gordon. adv.; bk.rev.; stat.; circ. 22,549 (controlled). (also avail. in microfiche from UMI) **Document type:** trade publication.
  —UMI. CCC.
  Formed by the 1982 merger of: Profitways; Marketing Bestsellers (ISSN 0164-9876); Which was formerly: Bestsellers (ISSN 0005-9730)
  Description: Directed to the marketing and distribution of magazines, paperback books, comic books, juvenile products and trading cards through retail outlets. Explores the important "how-to's" of magazine and paperback marketing.

070.5 UK
THE MAGAZINE BUSINESS WEEKLY REPORT. 1992. w. £275 (fax £225). The Magazine Business Ltd., 8 Tottenham News, London W1P 9PJ, England. TEL 0171-436-5211. FAX 0171-436-5290. E-mail: magbus@demon.co.uk. Ed. Chris Mounce; Pub. Simon Tesler. adv. contact: Alan MacFarlane. (back issues avail.) **Document type:** trade publication.
  Description: Digest of news from the British magazine publishing and distribution industry.

070.5 US ISSN 0899-7039
Z286.P4
MAGAZINE ISSUES. 1982. bi-m. $20. Feredonna Communications, Box 9808, Knoxville, TN 37940. TEL 615-584-1918. Ed. Michael Scott Ward. adv.; bk.rev. circ. 13,000. **Indexed:** ABI Inform.
  Formerly (until 1988): Publishing Trade (ISSN 0730-6741)
  Description: Serves publishers and key management personnel at magazine companies with circulations up to 500,000.

070.5 US
MAGAZINE PUBLISHERS ASSOCIATION. NEWSLETTER OF CIRCULATION. q. Magazine Publishers of America, 919 Third Ave., New York, NY 10022. TEL 212-872-3700.

070.5 US
MAGAZINE PUBLISHERS OF AMERICA. bi-m. Magazine Publishers of America, 919 Third Ave., New York, NY 10022. TEL 212-872-3700.

MAGAZINES CAREER DIRECTORY. see *OCCUPATIONS AND CAREERS*

MAGILL'S LITERARY ANNUAL. see *LITERATURE*

MAINE ENTRY. see *LIBRARY AND INFORMATION SCIENCES*

070.5 016 US ISSN 1045-5388
Z1000
MANDEVILLE'S USED BOOK PRICE GUIDE. 1962. triennial, latest 1994. $90. Price Guide Publishers, Box 82525, Kenmore, WA 98028-0525. TEL 206-783-7855. Ed. Richard L. Collins.
  Formerly: Used Book Price Guide (ISSN 0083-4807)
  Description: Assists in the evaluation of rare, scarce, old, and used books. Provides the background for determining the current market value of books.

MANUSCRIPTS. see *HOBBIES*

THE MAP REPORT. see *GEOGRAPHY*

070.5 CN ISSN 0832-512X
MASTHEAD; the magazine about magazines. 1987. 10/yr. Can.$39 (foreign Can.$49). North Island Sound Ltd., 1606 Sedlescomb Dr., Unit 8, Mississauga, ON L4X 1M6, Canada. TEL 905-625-7070. FAX 905-625-4856. E-mail: Masthead_Magazine@Magic.ca. Ed. Doug Bennet; Pub. Alexander Donald. adv.: B&W page $1732, color page $2657; trim 8 1/2 x 11; adv. contact: Andrew Luke. stat.; circ. 4,504 (controlled). (back issues avail.) **Document type:** trade publication.
  Description: Covers news, events and issues in the Canadian periodical publishing industry.

MEDIA; Asia's media & marketing newspaper. see *ADVERTISING AND PUBLIC RELATIONS*

MEDIA ASIA. see *COMMUNICATIONS*

MEDIA CALENDAR DIRECTORY. see *BUSINESS AND ECONOMICS — Trade And Industrial Directories*

MEDIA-DATEN ANNUALS. see *ADVERTISING AND PUBLIC RELATIONS*

MEDIA MERGERS & ACQUISITIONS. see *COMMUNICATIONS*

MEDIA MOVES; the PR industry guide to changes in the media and financial sectors. see *COMMUNICATIONS — Television And Cable*

MEDIA POCKET BOOK. see *COMMUNICATIONS*

MEDIENWISSENSCHAFT; Zeitschrift fuer Rezensionen ueber Veroeffentlichungen zu saemtlichen Medien. see *COMMUNICATIONS — Television And Cable*

020.75 US
MERC. 1970. m. $10. Mercantile Library Association of the City of New York, 17 E. 47th St., New York, NY 10017. TEL 212-755-6710. Ed. Harold Augenbraum. bk.rev. circ. 1,600.

MICROFORM REVIEW. see *LIBRARY AND INFORMATION SCIENCES*

MINIATURE BOOK NEWS. see *HOBBIES*

070.5 GW
MOHR KURIER. 3/yr. Verlag J.C.B. Mohr (Paul Siebeck), Wilhelmstr. 18, 72074 Tuebingen, Germany. TEL 07071-923-0. FAX 07071-51104. TELEX 7262872-MOHR-D. (Subscr. to: Postfach 2040, 72010 Tuebingen, Germany) Ed. Sabine Bacher. **Document type:** catalog.

070.5 US
MULTICULTURAL PUBLISHING AND EDUCATION COUNCIL. NEWSLETTER. 1989. bi-m. $48 (effective 1992). Multicultural Publishing and Education Council, c/o Rennie Mau, President, 2280 Grass Valley Hwy., No.181, Auburn, CA 95603. TEL 916-889-4438. FAX 916-888-0690. adv.; bk.rev.; tr.lit.; circ. 1,500 (controlled). (looseleaf format; also avail. in diskette format; back issues avail.) **Document type:** newsletter.
  Formerly: Multicultural Publishers Exchange Newsletter (ISSN 1049-5428)
  Description: News of the minority publishing industry in the U.S., covering marketing and distribution issues, and news of book fairs.

MUZIEKUITGEVERS NOOT. see *MUSIC*

MYSTERY SCENE. see *LITERATURE — Mystery And Detective*

070.5 SI ISSN 0129-9239
N B D C S NEWS. (Text in English) 1981. q. National Book Development Council of Singapore, NBDCS Secretariat, Bukit Merah Branch Library, Bukit Merah Central, Singapore 0315, Singapore. TEL 2732730. Ed. Vasantha Kumaree Siva. charts; illus. circ. 4,000. (back issues avail.)
  Description: Contains news of relevance to Singapore's book industry as well as educational institutions and libraries.

N O B S NEWSLETTER. (Northern Ohio Bibliophilic Society) see *HOBBIES*

N S K NEWS BULLETIN. (Nihon Shinbun Kyokai) see *JOURNALISM*

NANDE REKO; cuaderno de literatura popular. see *LITERATURE*

NASHR-I DANISH. see *HUMANITIES: COMPREHENSIVE WORKS*

070.5 US
NATIONAL ASSOCIATION OF SELECTIVE DISTRIBUTORS. NEWSLETTER.* m. National Association of Selective Distributors, c/o Dean Campbell, 5230 Stanton Dr., Kansas City, MO 64133. TEL 816-358-0589.

NATIONAL BRAILLE PRESS RELEASE. see *HANDICAPPED — Visually Impaired*

NATIONAL INFORMATION STANDARDS SERIES. see *LIBRARY AND INFORMATION SCIENCES*

070.5 UK
NATIONAL READERSHIP SURVEY. 1989. a. National Readership Surveys Ltd., Garden Studios, 11-15 Betterton St., London WC2H 9BP, England. TEL 0171-379-0344. FAX 0171-240-4399. **Document type:** trade publication.
  —BLDSC (6029.985000).

070.5 NE ISSN 1382-4627
▼**NETWORK;** news from Swets. (Text in English) 1995. s-a. free. Swets & Zeitlinger B.V., P.O. Box 830, 2160 SZ Lisse, Netherlands. TEL 31-2521-35111. FAX 31-2521-15888. E-mail: infoho@swets.nl; Site addr.: http://www.swets.nl. illus. **Document type:** newsletter.
  Description: Reports on new developments and concerns relating to subscriptions, activities of the different offices and divisions of Swets, and other matters of interest to Swets customers.

DIE NEUE BUECHEREI; Zeitschrift fuer die oeffentlichen Buechereien in Bayern. see *LIBRARY AND INFORMATION SCIENCES*

070.5 GW ISSN 0935-7866
NEUMANN - HANDBUCH FUER DEN PRESSEVERTRIEB. 1974. a. DM.68. Presse Fachverlag, Eidelstedteweg 22, 20255 Hamburg, Germany. TEL 040-565031. FAX 040-5602920. Ed. Hans van Treeck. circ. 2,900.

NEW AGE RETAILER; books, music, merchandise. see *NEW AGE PUBLICATIONS*

070.5 950 US ISSN 1075-2951
NEW ASIA REVIEW. (Supplements avail.) q. $36 (foreign $56). 10 Bay St., Westport, CT 06880. TEL 203-222-9734. Ed.Bd. bk.rev. **Document type:** trade publication.
  Description: Announces trends in publishing, new books, multimedia developments, and forecasts of publishing in Asia.

686.3 UK ISSN 0261-5363
THE NEW BOOKBINDER; journal of designer bookbinders. 1981. a. £24($48) to non-member individuals; institutions £38 ($75) (effective 1994). Designer Bookbinders Publications Ltd., Sales & Distribution, Warden's Cottage, Leintwardine, Shrops. SY7 OLL, England. TEL 054-73443. FAX 054-73488. G.C. Nicholson. adv. contact: S. Whiteaker. bk.rev. (back issues avail.) **Indexed:** DAAI, Print.Abstr. **Document type:** newsletter, catalog.
  —BLDSC (6082.280000).

NEW BOOKS QUARTERLY ON ISLAM & THE MUSLIM WORLD. see *RELIGIONS AND THEOLOGY — Islamic*

5632   PUBLISHING AND BOOK TRADE

NEW LAW BOOKS REVIEWER. see LAW

028.1   US
NEW LETTERS REVIEW OF BOOKS. Issued with: New Letters. q. University of Missouri at Kansas City, 5100 Rockhill Rd., Kansas City, MO 64110. Ed. Lawrence Alton. (tabloid format)

THE NEW LIBRARY SCENE. see LIBRARY AND INFORMATION SCIENCES

070.5   US   ISSN 0271-8197
Z477
NEW PAGES; alternatives in print & media. 1979. 3/yr. $12. New Pages Press, Box 438, Grand Blanc, MI 48439. TEL 313-743-8055. FAX 313-743-2730. Ed.Bd. adv.; bk.rev.; circ. 5,000 (controlled). **Indexed:** Alt.Press Ind., Bk.Rev.Ind. (1984-), Child.Bk.Rev.Ind. (1984-).
—UnCover.

NEW RELEASES PUBLICATIONS LIST. see LAW

028.1   US   ISSN 0028-7504
AP2
NEW YORK REVIEW OF BOOKS. 1963. 20/yr. $49.50. N Y R E V, Inc., 250 W. 57th St., New York, NY 10107. TEL 212-757-8070. FAX 212-333-5374. (Subscr. to: Box 420384, Palm Coast, FL 32142-0384) Eds. Robert Silvers, Barbara Epstein. adv.: B&W page $5400, color page $6200. bk.rev.; illus. circ. 115,000. (tabloid format; also avail. in microform from UMI; reprint service avail. from UMI) **Indexed:** Acad.Ind., Alt.Press Ind., Amer.Bibl.Slavic & E.Eur.Stud., Anthropol.Lit., Art & Archaeol.Tech.Abstr., Arts & Hum.Cit.Ind., Bk.Rev.Dig., Bk.Rev.Ind. (1965-), Can.Lit.Ind., Child.Bk.Rev.Ind. (1965-), Child.Lit.Abstr., Curr.Cont., Film Lit.Ind. (1973-), Fut.Surv., Ind.Bk.Rev.Hum., M.L.A., Mag.Ind., Mid.East: Abstr.& Ind., R.G., RILA, RILM.
●Also available online. Vendor(s): University Microfilms International.
—BLDSC (6089.700000); Faxon; Genuine Article; SWETS; UMI.
Description: Commentary and opinion on politics, science and culture by eminent writers.

028 655   US   ISSN 0028-7806
AP2
NEW YORK TIMES BOOK REVIEW. (Supplement to: New York Times (ISSN 0362-4331)) 1896. w. $52 (foreign $65) (effective 1995). New York Times Company, 229 W. 43rd St., New York, NY 10036. TEL 212-556-1234. (Subscr. to: Box 9564, Uniondale, NY 11555. TEL 800-631-2580) Ed. Charles McGrath. adv. contact: Leroy Baylor. bk.rev.; bibl.; illus.; circ. 1,770,500 (paid). (tabloid format; also avail. in microform from UMI) **Indexed:** Amer.Bibl.Slavic & E.Eur.Stud., Bibl.Engl.Lang.& Lit., Bk.Rev.Ind. (1965-), Can.Lit.Ind., Child.Bk.Rev.Ind. (1965-), Child.Lit.Abstr., Curr.Cont., Gard.Lit.(1992-), Ind.Bk.Rev.Hum., Mag.Ind., R.G., TOM. **Document type:** consumer publication.
—BLDSC (6089.766000); Faxon; Genuine Article; SWETS; UMI.
Description: Presents extended reviews of noteworthy books, short reviews, essays and articles on topics and trends in publishing, literature, culture and the arts. Includes lists of best sellers (hardcover and paperback).

051   US
THE NEW YORK TIMES BOOK REVIEW (MICROFORM EDITIONS). (Includes supplements) w. $88 vesicular; silver halide $103.60. (New York Times Company) U M I Company, 300 N. Zeeb Rd., Ann Arbor, MI 48106. TEL 313-761-4700; 800-521-0600. FAX 313-761-1203. (microform; back issues avail.) **Indexed:** Arts & Hum.Cit.Ind.

070.5 330   US
NEW YORK UNIVERSITY BUSINESS MAGAZINE PUBLISHING SERIES. 1987. irreg. price varies. New York University Press, 70 Washington Square S., New York, NY 10012. TEL 212-998-2575; 800-996-3833. FAX 212-995-3833. TELEX 235128 NYU UR. Ed. Albert Greco. **Document type:** monographic series.

028.1   CN   ISSN 0380-2817
NEWEST REVIEW; a journal of culture and current events in the West. 1975. bi-m. Can.$16.05. NeWest Publishers Ltd., Box 394, R.P.O. University, Saskatoon, SK S7N 4J8, Canada. TEL 306-934-1444. adv. contact: Doris Larson. bk.rev.; illus. circ. 1,000. **Indexed:** Can.B.P.I., Can.Lit.Ind., Can.Per.Ind., CMI. **Document type:** consumer publication.

070.5   US
NEWS FROM HOLT.* q. free. (Library Services Department) Holt, Rinehart and Winston, Inc., c/o Harcourt Brace Jovanovich, Orlando, FL 32887. TEL 407-345-2500.

070.5 658   US   ISSN 1043-7452
PN4899.N42
NEWS INC. 1989. fortn. $395 (foreign $445) (effective 1995). SIMBA Information Inc., 213 Danbury Rd., Box 7430, Wilton, CT 06897-7430. TEL 203-834-0033. FAX 203-834-1771. E-mail: simba99@aol.com. Ed. Carl Mercurio. adv.; bk.rev. circ. 18,000. (back issues avail.) **Document type:** newsletter.
—UnCover.
Description: Brings business news and opinion about the newspaper and related industries.

NEWSLETTER ON INTELLECTUAL FREEDOM. see LIBRARY AND INFORMATION SCIENCES

NEWSLETTER ON SERIALS PRICING ISSUES. see LIBRARY AND INFORMATION SCIENCES

070.5   CN   ISSN 1185-5088
NEWSLETTER TRENDS; a newsletter about newsletters. 1991. m. $97. Sterling Communications Inc., 1920 Ellesmere Rd., Ste. 104, Scarborough, ON M1H 3G1, Canada. TEL 416-512-2218. Ed. Barbara A. Fanson. adv.; bk.rev. (back issues avail.) **Document type:** newsletter.
Description: Discusses newsletter writing, editing, design, production, photography, and distribution.

NEWSPAPER PUBLISHERS HANDBOOK. see JOURNALISM

NEWSPAPERS CAREER DIRECTORY. see OCCUPATIONS AND CAREERS

070.5   NE   ISSN 0048-0355
NIEUWE POCKETS EN PAPERBACKS. 1961. bi-m. fl.7.50. Het Nederlandse Boek, Prinsengracht 1065, 1017 JG Amsterdam, Netherlands. TEL 31-20-6233187. Ed. Wim J. Simons. adv.; bk.rev.; bibl. circ. 20,000.

070.5   GW
NIGELNAGELNEU. s-a. K. Thienemanns Verlag, Blumenstr. 36, 70182 Stuttgart, Germany. TEL 0711-21055-0. FAX 0711-2105539. **Document type:** bibliography.

NIGERIAN LIBRARIES. see LIBRARY AND INFORMATION SCIENCES

NONGYE TUSHU QINGBAO XUEKAN/JOURNAL OF LIBRARY AND INFORMATION SCIENCES IN AGRICULTURE. see LIBRARY AND INFORMATION SCIENCES

655   DK   ISSN 0029-1323
NORDISK EXLIBRIS TIDSSKRIFT. Short title: N E T. (Text in Danish, English or German) 1946. 4/yr. membership. Dansk Exlibris Selskab - Danish Bookplate Society, Box 1519, DK-2700 Copenhagen, Denmark. Ed. Klaus Roedel. adv.; bk.rev.; illus.; cum.index every 2 yrs. **Indexed:** Artbibl.Mod.
Description: Facts about book plates.

020.75   NO   ISSN 0029-148X
Z671
NORDISK TIDSKRIFT FOER BOK- OCH BIBLIOTEKSVAESEN/SCANDINAVIAN JOURNAL OF LIBRARIES. (Text in Danish, Norwegian, Swedish; summaries in English) 1914. 2/yr. NOK 420 in Nordic countries; elsewhere $71 (effective 1996). Scandinavian University Press, P.O. Box 2959 Toeyen, N-0608 Oslo, Norway. TEL 47-22-57-54-00. FAX 47-22-57-53-53. (U.S. addr.: Scandinavian University Press, 200 Meacham Ave., Elmont, NY 11003. TEL 516-352-7377) Ed. Per S. Ridderstad. adv.; bk.rev.; charts; illus.; index, cum.index. circ. 750. **Indexed:** Lib.Lit., Lib.Sci.Abstr., LISA, MLA.
Description: Contains articles on Scandinavian bibliography and library science related to history of learning and cultural history.

NOTES AND QUERIES; for readers and writers, collectors and librarians. see LITERATURE

090   FR   ISSN 0335-752X
Z4
NOUVELLES DU LIVRE ANCIEN. 1974. q. free. C.N.R.S.(Centre National de Recherche Scientifique), Section de l'Humanisme, C.N.R.S., 40 Ave. d'Iena, 75013 Paris, France. FAX 47-23-89-39. (Co-sponsor: Bibliotheque Nationale de France) Ed.Bd. adv. contact: Louis Holtz. bk.rev.; bibl. circ. 3,100. **Document type:** newsletter.
Description: Studies the history of books. Covers ancient works as well as works in progress.

011   GW   ISSN 0029-4993
NOVA; Vorankuendigungen-forthcoming books-livres en preparation. (Table of contents and subtitles in English, German and Russian) 1957. s-m. free. Expolibri GmbH Leipzig, Zentrum fuer Buchwerbung & Ausstellungen, Grimmaischestr. 13-15, 04109 Leipzig, Germany. TEL 271514. FAX 293594.
Description: Annotated list of forthcoming books from German publishers (formerly East German), which can be ordered from abroad. Subjects include: social sciences, technology, agriculture, medicine, literature, art and sport.

070.5   GW
NOVITAET. s-a. Weitbrecht Verlag, Blumenstr. 36, 70182 Stuttgart, Germany. TEL 0711-21055-0. FAX 0711-2105539. **Document type:** bibliography.

070.5   BL
NOVO LIVROS.* vol.2, 1979. m. Cr.$18000($40) Companhia Editora Jorues Ltda., Rua Cardeal Arcoverde 2958, 05408 Sao Paulo, SP, Brazil. Ed. Virginia Pinheiro. adv.; bk.rev.; bibl.; illus. circ. 25,000. (tabloid format)
Formerly: Leia Livros.

002.060489   DK   ISSN 0109-0208
NYT FOR BOGVENNER. 1980. q. membership. Forening for Boghaandvaerk, Antoinettevej 5, DK-2500 Valby, Denmark.

070.5   US   ISSN 0078-2882
O.P. MARKET. (Out of Print) 1948. a. $25. (Antiquarian Bookman) A B Bookman Publications, Inc., Box AB, Clifton, NJ 07015. TEL 201-772-0020. FAX 201-772-9281. Ed. Jacob L. Chernofsky. adv.; bk.rev. circ. 10,000.
Description: Covers the out-of-print book market.

070.5 384.3   UK   ISSN 1356-5702
▼**OASIS;** the multimedia assets trade magazine. 1995. q. (Oasis Consortium) Pira International, Randalls Rd., Leatherhead, Surrey KT22 7RU, England. TEL 01732-376161. FAX 01732-377526. E-mail: oasis@pira.co.uk. Ed. Willem Bulthuis; Pub. Roberto Minio. **Document type:** trade publication.

070 384.55   US
OBSCURE PUBLICATIONS AND VIDEO. 1989. q. $2 per no. Box 1334, Milwaukee, WI 53201. TEL 414-257-2339. Ed. Jim Romenesko.
Description: Contains news and reviews from the small press, as well as interviews with publishers.

070.5   US   ISSN 0896-5730
OHIO WRITER. 1987. bi-m. $12 to individuals; institutions $18. (Ohio Writer) Poets' League of Greater Cleveland, Box 91801, Cleveland, OH 44101. TEL 216-932-8444. Ed. Linda L. Rome. adv.: B&W page $260; adv. contact: Darlene Montonaro. bk.rev./ circ. 650 (paid). **Document type:** newsletter.
  Description: Covers writing and writers with an Ohio connection. Includes calendar of Ohio events.

070.5760 659.1   US
OKLAHOMA PUBLISHER. m. $5. Oklahoma Press Association, 3601 N. Lincoln, Oklahoma City, OK 73105-5400. TEL 405-524-4421. Ed. Ben Blackstock. charts. circ. 1,200. (tabloid format) **Document type:** trade publication, newspaper.
  Description: For Oklahoma newspaper publishers; includes news of journalism, and public relations.

020   US
ON THE ROAD (FORDS). 1989. q. $12. On the Road - Library Outreach Reporter Publications, 148 Liberty St., Fords, NJ 08863-2042. TEL 908-738-5183. Ed. Cathi Alloway. adv.; illus.
  Description: Gives practical advice on how to get an author's work out to the public.

070.5   US   ISSN 1071-2526
ONCE UPON A TIME. 1990. q. $19 (Canada $24; elsewhere $29) (effective May 1995). Audrey Baird, Ed. & Pub.; 553 Winston Ct., St. Paul, MN 55118. TEL 612-457-6223. Ed. Auorey B. Baird. adv.: page $140. circ. 1,000. **Document type:** trade publication.
  Description: For children's writers and illustrators and those interested in children's literature.

686 900   FI   ISSN 0358-5581
Z829.A1
OPUSCULUM; kirja- ja oppihistoriallinen aikakauskirja. Bok- och laerdomshistorisk tidskrift. (Text in Finnish and Swedish; summaries in English) 1981. q. FIM 120($23) Helsingin Yliopiston Kirjasto - Helsinki University Library, Box 15, Unioninkatu 36, SF-00014, University of Helsinki, Finland. FAX 358-0-19122719. Ed. Esko Haekli. bk.rev.; illus.; index. circ. 350. (back issues avail.)
  Description: Contains articles on books, library history, and the history of learning.

070   US   ISSN 0745-6379
OREGON PUBLISHER. 1932. m. membership. Oregon Newspaper Publishers Association, 7150 S.W. Hampton St., Ste. 111, Portland, OR 97223. TEL 503-624-6397. FAX 503-639-9009. Ed. Lori Haskins. adv. contact: Fred Board. circ. 400 (controlled). (tabloid format; back issues avail.) **Document type:** newspaper.
  Description: Covers industry news and issues of concern to newspaper publishers in Oregon.

028.1   UK
ORIGO. 1979-1980; resumed 1995. q. £30. Genesis Publications Ltd., 9 Pilgrim House, Quarry St., Guildford, Surrey GU1 3XY, England. TEL 01483-37431. FAX 01483-304709. Ed. Kay Williams. bk.rev.; illus. circ. 8,000. **Document type:** newsletter.
  Description: Contains details of fine limited editions published by genesis publications, as well as related features, photos, guest celebrity columns, and reviews.

070.5   UK   ISSN 0048-2528
OVERSEAS BOOKS. vol.8, 1971. m. £17($55) per no. New Product Newsletter Co. Ltd., 1A Chesterfield St., London W.1., England. Ed. H.R. Vaughan. adv. circ. 7,000.

070.5   UK   ISSN 0078-7159
OVERSEAS NEWSPAPERS AND PERIODICALS. (Issued in 2 vols.: Vol. 1: Markets in Europe; Vol. 2: Markets outside Europe) 1952. biennial. £17($50) per vol. New Product Newsletter Co. Ltd., 1A Chesterfield St., London W.1, England. Ed. H.R. Vaughan. adv. circ. 5,000. (also avail. in microfilm from UMI)

P A T E F A NEWS BULLETIN. (Printing & Allied Trades Employers Federation of Australia) see PRINTING

070.5   US   ISSN 1058-4102
P M A NEWSLETTER. 1982. m. $40 membership. Publishers Marketing Association, 2401 Pacific Coast Hwy., Ste. 102, Hermosa Beach, CA 90254. TEL 310-372-2732. FAX 310-374-3342. Ed. Jan Nathan. adv. contact: Rick Stoff. bk.rev. circ. 6,000. **Document type:** newsletter.
  Description: Provides news of industry trends, publisher profiles and cooperative marketing ideas and information for small to medium-sized independent publishers.

P N P A PRESS. (Pennsylvania Newspaper Publishers Association) see JOURNALISM

070.5   US
P S P BULLETIN. vol.6, no.2, 1992. q. free to members. Association of American Publishers, Inc., Professional & Scholarly Publishing Division, 71 Fifth Ave., New York, NY 10003-3004. TEL 212-255-0200. FAX 212-255-7007. Ed. Janice E. Kuta. **Document type:** bulletin.

070.5 658.8   US
P S R S. (Publishing Sales Representative's Source) 1992. m. Marshall - Branch Publishing, 60 Holden St., Attleboro, MA 02703. TEL 508-226-1205. FAX 508-222-2580. Ed. Philip Marshall. adv.: B&W page $1555, color page $1975; trim 8 3/8 x 10 7/8. circ. 5,000.
  Description: Provides access to issues that affect sales success.

PAGES; editorial and filler service. see JOURNALISM

028.5   IT
PAGINE GIOVANI. 1977. q. L.30000. Gruppo di Servizio per la Letteratura Giovanile, Piazza Cardinal Ferrari 4, 00167 Rome, Italy. TEL 39-6-66000998. Ed. Maria Rosaria Lombardo. bk.rev. circ. 2,000. **Document type:** bulletin.
  Description: Addresses topics concerning literature for youths. Promotes reading and literature. Includes activities of the association.

028.1   IT   ISSN 0030-9435
Z1007
PAIDEIA; rivista letteraria di informazione bibliografica. (Text in English, French, German and Italian) 1946. 2/yr. L.55000 (effective 1994). Paideia Editrice, Via Corsica 130, 25125 Brescia, Italy. TEL 030-222094. FAX 030-223269. Ed.Bd. bk.rev.; rec.rev.; index. Indexed: Bibl.Ling., M.L.A. —SWETS.

070.5 011 020   PK
PAKISTAN'S BOOKS & LIBRARIES; the only monthly magazine of its kind. (Text in English) 1989. m. Rs.200($25) M. Nayeem Siddiqui, Ed. & Pub., 305-15, F.B. Area, Karachi 75950, Pakistan. TEL 21-685858. FAX 21-200678. TELEX 23898 CROWN PK. adv.; bk.rev.; bibl. circ. 2,000.
  Description: Covers the book trade and libraries in Pakistan.

070.5   NR   ISSN 0189-1049
PAN AFRICAN BOOK WORLD. 1981. irreg. Fourth Dimension Publishing Co. Ltd., House 16, Fifth Ave., P.M.B. 01164, City Layout, New Haven, Enugu State, Nigeria. TEL 234-42-39969. TELEX 513-FDPUBS-NG.

PANURGE. see LITERATURE

PAPERBACK INFERNO. see LITERATURE — Science Fiction, Fantasy, Horror

020.75 808.838   US
PAPERBACK PARADE. 1986. bi-m. $30 (foreign $36) (effective 1995-96). Gryphon Publications, Box 290, Brooklyn, NY 11228-0209. adv. contact: Gary Lovisi. bk.rev.; bibl.; illus. circ. 1,000. (back issues avail.) **Document type:** consumer publication.
  Description: Covers the hobby of collectible - rare paperbacks and books, authors, and artists.

PAPERBACK PREVIEWS. see LITERATURE

PAPUA NEW GUINEA NATIONAL BIBLIOGRAPHY. see BIBLIOGRAPHIES

070.5 028.5   VE
PARAPARA BOLETIN INFORMATIVO. 1980. 3/yr. Bs.1637.50($25) for all 3 Paraparas. Banco del Libro, Apdo. 5893, Caracas 1010-A, Venezuela. TEL 58-2-2661566. FAX 58-2-2663621. circ. 300.
  Supersedes in part (in 1990): Parapara.
  Description: Contains information about personalities, prizes, seminars, congresses and fairs in the world of children's literature.

070.5 028.5   VE   ISSN 0798-1619
PARAPARA SELECCION DE LIBROS PARA NINOS Y JOVENES. 1980. 3/yr. Bs.1637.50($25) includes all 3 Paraparas. Banco del Libro, Apdo. 5893, Caracas 1010A, Venezuela. TEL 58-2-2661566. FAX 58-2-2663621. bk.rev. circ. 1,000.
  Supersedes in part (in 1990): Parapara.
  Description: Offers a selection of books for children and young people, covering a different theme each issue.

070.5   SP   ISSN 1133-5556
PAUTAS/GUIDELINES. 1991. q. 2000 ptas. Asociacion de Revistas Culturales de Espana - Association of Cultural Magazines from Spain, C. Hortaleza, 75, 28004 Madrid, Spain. TEL 34-1-3086066. FAX 34-1-3199267. Ed. Enrique Helguera; Pub. Manuel Ortuno. **Document type:** bulletin.
  Description: Gathers new developments about culture and previews the content of associated magazines.

PEN IN HAND. see JOURNALISM

070.5   US   ISSN 0737-7843
Z6945.A2
PERIODICAL TITLE ABBREVIATIONS; covering periodical title abbreviations in science, the social sciences, the humanities, law, medicine, religion, library science, engineering, education, business, art, and many other fields. (In 3 Vols; Vol.1: By Abbreviation; Vol.2: By Title; Vol.3: New Abbreviation) 1969. irreg., 8th ed., 1991. $185 for vol.1 and vol.2; vol.3 $140. Gale Research Inc., 835 Penobscot Bldg., Detroit, MI 48226. TEL 313-961-2242. FAX 313-961-6083. TELEX 810-221-7086. Ed. Leland G. Alkire, Jr. —BLDSC (6426.040000).
  Description: Encyclopedia of periodical title abbreviations.

PERSPECTIVES ON POLITICAL SCIENCE. see POLITICAL SCIENCE

010 760   GW   ISSN 0031-7969
Z990
PHILOBIBLON. 1957. q. DM.120. (Maximilian-Gesellschaft e.V.) Dr. Ernst Hauswedell und Co. Verlag, Rosenbergstr. 113, 70193 Stuttgart, Germany. FAX 0711-6369010. Ed. Reimar W. Fuchs. adv.: B&W page DM.880; trim 182 x 121. bibl.; illus.; tr.lit.; index. circ. 1,800. **Indexed:** M.L.A. **Document type:** trade publication. —Faxon; SWETS. CCC.

PHILOSOPHICAL BOOKS. see PHILOSOPHY

PIMS BUSINESS, INVESTOR AND GOVERNMENT RELATIONS DIRECTORY. see BUSINESS AND ECONOMICS — Banking And Finance

PIMS EUROPEAN TRADE & TECHNICAL DIRECTORY. see BUSINESS AND ECONOMICS — Trade And Industrial Directories

658.8 380.1   UK
PIMS U K A-Z TOWNS. 1984. q. £195. PIMS (UK) Ltd., PIMS House, Mildmay Ave., London N1 4RS, England. TEL 0171-226-1000. FAX 0171-704-1360. (Subscr. to: 1133 Broadway, New York, NY 10010, U.S.A.) **Document type:** directory.
  Formerly: Pims Media Townslist (ISSN 0959-9525)
  Description: Media identified for over 1100 U.K. towns and cities.

PUBLISHING AND BOOK TRADE

658.8 380.1   UK
PIMS U K MEDIA DIRECTORY. 1981. m. £240. PIMS (UK) Ltd., PIMS House, Mildmay Ave., London N1 4RS, England. TEL 0171-226-1000. FAX 0171-704-1360. (Subscr. to: 1133 Broadway, New York, NY 10010, U.S.A.) **Document type:** directory.
—BLDSC (6501.345000).
Formerly: Pims Media Directory (ISSN 0261-5169)
Description: Lists contacts, addresses, telephone numbers for all U.K. media.

028.1   US   ISSN 1064-4741
PLANT'S REVIEW OF BOOKS. 1992. q. free. 3635 S.E. Alder, Box 14081, Portland, OR 97214-0081. TEL 503-234-4036. FAX 503-234-4036. E-mail: DPlant@aol.com. Ed. Darrel Plant. adv.; illus. circ. 6,000. (tabloid format)

POLICY PUBLISHERS AND ASSOCIATIONS DIRECTORY. see *POLITICAL SCIENCE*

POLIGRAFIYA. see *PRINTING*

070.5   JA
PRACTICAL GUIDE TO PUBLISHING IN JAPAN. (Text in English) 1990. a. free. Publishers' Association for Cultural Exchange, 2-1, Sarugaku-cho 1-chome, Chiyoda-ku, Tokyo 101, Japan. TEL 03-3233-3645. FAX 03-3233-3645. Ed. Tanio Yokote.

PRE-. see *PRINTING* — Computer Applications

PRESSE-PORTRAETS; das Angebot des Pressehandels. see *BIBLIOGRAPHIES*

658.8   GW   ISSN 0341-8073
PRESSE REPORT; Magazin fuer den Presseeinzelhandel. Short title: P R (Supplement avail.: Presse-Portraets) 1975. m. DM.58. Presse Fachverlag, Eidelstedteweg 22, 20255 Hamburg, Germany. TEL 040-565031. FAX 040-5602920. circ. 75,000.
Formerly (1951-1974): Zeitungs- und Zeitschriftenhandel (ISSN 0044-3832)
Description: Publication for the paperback book, magazine, and newspaper retail trade, featuring the latest news, sales strategies, businesses for sale, and new publications.

070   AU
PRESSEHANDBUCH (YEAR). 1953. a. S.957. Verband Oesterreichischer Zeitungsherausgeber und Zeitungsverleger, Schreyvogelgasse 3, A-1010 Vienna, Austria. TEL 01-5336178. FAX 01-5336178-22. Ed. Robert Keilhauer. adv.; bk.rev.; mkt.; tr.lit.; index. circ. 3,000. **Document type:** abstracting/indexing.
Formerly: Oesterreichs Presse, Werbung, Graphik (ISSN 0030-0040)

070.5 028.5   SP
PRIMERAS NOTICIAS LITERATURA INFANTIL Y JUVENIL. 8/yr. Cerdena 259, 08013 Barcelona, Spain. TEL 3-207-50-52. Ed. J. Aliaga Serrnao.

PRINT; America's graphic design magazine. see *COMPUTERS* — Computer Graphics

070.5 686.2   SZ
PRINT.* (Text in French, German and Italian) vol.100, 1975. w. 45 Fr. Schweizerischer Buchdruckerverein - Societe Suisse des Maitres-Imprimeurs, Gubelstr. 28, Postfach 8391, CH-8050 Zurich, Switzerland. Ed. E. Mueller. adv.; charts; illus. circ. 13,300.
Formerly: Schweizerische Buchdrucker-Zeitung.

PRINT AND PRODUCTION MANUAL. see *PRINTING*

PRINT PUBLISHING FOR THE SCHOOL MARKET: REVIEW, TRENDS & FORECAST. see *EDUCATION* — Teaching Methods And Curriculum

PRINTING AND BOOKBINDING TRADE REVIEW; equipment - materials - production. see *PRINTING*

070.5   US
PRINTING & PUBLISHING: LATIN AMERICAN INDUSTRIAL REPORT. (Avail. for each of 22 Latin American countries) 1985. a. $435 per country report. Aquino Productions, Box 15760, Stamford, CT 06901. TEL 203-325-3138. Ed. Andres C. Aquino.

PRINTING HISTORY. see *PRINTING*

PRIVATE LIBRARY. see *LIBRARY AND INFORMATION SCIENCES*

PROLIFIC FREELANCER. see *JOURNALISM*

PROVIDENT BOOK FINDER. see *RELIGIONS AND THEOLOGY* — Protestant

PUB. see *ADVERTISING AND PUBLIC RELATIONS*

070.5   BE
PUB NEWSLETTER. (Text in Flemish, French) 2/wk. 15455 BEF. Kluwer Business Press (Subsidiary of: Wolters Kluwer N.V.), Kouterveldstraat 2, B-1831 Diegem, Belgium. TEL 32-2-7231523. FAX 32-2-7231591. Ed. Jean-Michel Stichelbaut. adv.: B&W page 51000 BEF; adv. contact: Gerda Bourdeaud'hui. circ. 300. **Document type:** newsletter.
Description: Covers advertising, marketing, and media.

070.5   UK   ISSN 0033-3263
PUBDISCO NEWS. 1964. m. £17($50) each ed. New Product Newsletter Co. Ltd., 1A Chesterfield St., London W.1., England. Ed. H.R. Vaughan. adv.; bibl.; illus. circ. 7,000. (also avail. in microfilm from UMI)

PUBLICATION DESIGN ANNUAL. see *ART*

PUBLICATION PROFILES. see *ADVERTISING AND PUBLIC RELATIONS*

070.5   CH   ISSN 1015-2652
PUBLICATIONS YEARBOOK, REPUBLIC OF CHINA; including catalogs of books and records. 1977. a. NT.$700. China Publishing Company, Box 337, Taipei, Taiwan, Republic of China.

070.5   CN   ISSN 0380-8025
PUBLISHER. 1919. 10/yr. Can.$25. Canadian Community Newspapers Association, 90 Eglinton Ave., E., Ste. 206, Toronto, ON M4P 2Y3, Canada. TEL 416-482-1090. FAX 416-482-1908. Ed. Dave de Jong. adv. contact: Maureen de Jong. bk.rev. circ. 1,269. (tabloid format) **Document type:** trade publication.
Supersedes: Canadian Community Publisher (ISSN 0045-4583); Canadian Weekly Publisher (ISSN 0008-5316)

070   NZ
PUBLISHER. 1977. bi-m. membership. Book Publishers Association of New Zealand Inc., P.O. Box 386, Auckland 1, New Zealand. TEL 64-9-309-2561. FAX 64-9-309-7798. Ed. Fiona Mackenzie. adv.; circ. 150 (paid). **Document type:** newsletter.
—CCC.
Formerly: New Zealand Publishing News (ISSN 0111-834X)
Description: Provides members with trade information, advertising, local and overseas book trade news and calendar events.

070.5   NR   ISSN 0331-7714
THE PUBLISHER. 1985. a.? £N150($3.95) Nigerian Publishers' Association, 14 Awosika Ave., Nue Bodija Estate, G.P.O. Box 2541, Ibadan, Nigeria. TEL 234-22-411557. Ed. Damola Ifaturoti. adv. circ. 2,000. (back issues avail.) **Document type:** trade publication.

070.5   US   ISSN 0742-0501
Z475
PUBLISHERS DIRECTORY. 1977. a. $275 (effective 1994). Gale Research Inc., 835 Penobscot Bldg., Detroit, MI 48226. TEL 313-961-2242; 800-877-4253. FAX 313-961-6083. TELEX 810-221-7086. Ed. Wendy Van de Sande. (also avail. in magnetic tape; diskette format) **Document type:** directory.
●Also available online. Vendor(s): Knight-Ridder, Inc.
—BLDSC (7156.067900).
Former titles (until 1984): Book Publishers Directory (ISSN 0196-0903); Book Publishers of the U.S. and Canada.
Description: Lists 18,000 book publishers of the U.S. and Canada.

PUBLISHERS, DISTRIBUTORS & WHOLESALERS OF THE UNITED STATES; a directory of publishers, distributors, associations, wholesalers, software producers and manufacturers listing editorial and ordering addresses, and an ISBN publisher prefix index. see *BUSINESS AND ECONOMICS* — Trade And Industrial Directories

070.5   UK   ISSN 0079-7839
PUBLISHERS IN THE UNITED KINGDOM AND THEIR ADDRESSES. 1946. a. £14. J. Whitaker & Sons Ltd., 12 Dyott St., London WC1A 1DF, England. TEL 071-836-8911. FAX 071-836-2909. adv. **Document type:** directory.

PUBLISHERS INFORMATION BUREAU REPORT; magazine advertising expenditures. (Publishers' Information Bureau Inc.) see *ADVERTISING AND PUBLIC RELATIONS*

070.5   II
PUBLISHERS' MONTHLY. (Text in English and Hindi) 1959. m. Rs.10. S. Chand & Co. Ltd., Ravindra Mansion, Ram Nagar, New Delhi 5, India. Ed. R.C. Kumar. adv.; bk.rev.; bibl. circ. 10,000.

070.5   US   ISSN 0884-3090
PUBLISHER'S REPORT. 1985. bi-m. $40. National Association of Independent Publishers, Box 430, Highland City, FL 33846-0430. TEL 813-648-4420. FAX 813-648-4420. E-mail: naip@aol.com. Ed. Betsy Lampe. adv.; bk.rev. circ. 500. **Document type:** newsletter.
—CCC.
Description: Furthers the visibility of independent publishing and provides a clearinghouse for information of interest to independent and self publishers.

658.8   US   ISSN 0000-0019
Z1219   CODEN: PWEEAD
PUBLISHERS WEEKLY; the international news magazine of book publishing. 1872. 51/yr. $139 (Canada $187, foreign $270) (fax version $745). Cahners Publishing Company (New York), Printing and Publishing Division, Division of Reed Elsevier Inc., 249 W. 17th St., New York, NY 10011. TEL 212-645-0067. FAX 212-242-7216. TELEX 12-7703. (Subscr. to: Box 6457, Torrance, CA 90504. TEL 800-278-2991) Ed. Nora Rawlinson; Pub. Fred Ciporen. adv.; bk.rev.; bibl.; illus.; stat. circ. 37,894. (also avail. in microform from UMI; microfiche from CIS; reprint service avail. from UMI; also avail. by fax) **Indexed:** Acad.Ind., B.P.I, Bk.Rev.Ind. (1965-), Chic.Per.Ind., Child.Bk.Rev.Ind. (1965-), Child.Lit.Abstr., Curr.Lit.Fam.Plan., Gard.Lit. (1992-), Graph.Arts Lit.Abstr., Hlth.Ind., LHTN, Lib.Lit., LISA, Mag.Ind., Mid.East: Abstr.& Ind., PMR, R.G., SRI, Tr.& Indus.Ind. **Document type:** trade publication.
—BLDSC (7156.080000); CASDDS; Genuine Article; SWETS; UMI; UnCover. **CCC.**
Description: News and trends of interest to publishers, booksellers and librarians, including author interviews, advance book reviews, marketing and book design and manufacturing articles.

070.5 686   US   ISSN 1048-3055
Z284.   CODEN: PPEXEP
PUBLISHING & PRODUCTION EXECUTIVE. vol.2, 1988. q. $55. North American Publishing Co., 401 N. Broad St., Philadelphia, PA 19108. TEL 215-238-5300. FAX 215-238-5457. Ed. Rose Blessing. adv. circ. 33,300. **Document type:** trade publication.
—Ei; UMI; UnCover. **CCC.**
Formerly (until Nov. 1989): Publishing Technology.
Description: For printing buyers and production professionals who buy paper, prepress, printing and electronic publishing systems for book, magazine and catalogue publishers. Focuses on equipment, production techniques, computer hardware and software and related products and services.

PUBLISHING FOR THE COLLEGE MARKET: REVIEW, TRENDS & FORECAST. see *EDUCATION* — Higher Education

PUBLISHING AND BOOK TRADE

070.5   UK   ISSN 0309-2445
Z280
PUBLISHING HISTORY. 1977. s-a. £67 to institutions; individuals £33. Chadwyck-Healey Ltd., The Quorum, Barnwell Rd., Cambridge CB5 8SW, England. TEL 01223-215512. FAX 01223-215513. TELEX 93121 02281 CH G. E-mail: mail@chadwyck.co.uk. (U.S. subscr. to: Chadwyck-Healey Inc., 1101 King St., Alexandria, VA 22314. TEL 800-752-0515) Ed. Peter Cockton. adv.; bk.rev. circ. 500. (also avail. in microform; back issues avail.) **Indexed:** Amer.Hist.& Life, Arts & Hum.Cit.Ind., Bibl.Engl.Lang.& Lit., Child.Lit.Abstr., Curr.Cont., Hist.Abstr. **Document type:** academic/scholarly publication.
—BLDSC (7156.093000); Faxon; Genuine Article; UnCover. **CCC.**
    Description: Devoted to the socioeconomic and literary history of books, newspaper and magazine publishing.

070.5   UK   ISSN 0261-5398
PUBLISHING NEWS; weekly for people in the book trade. (Former name of issuing body: Gradegate Ltd.) 1979. w. £70 (rest of Europe £80; elsewhere £95). Publishing News Ltd., 43 Museum St., London WC1A 1LY, England. TEL 071-404-0304. Ed. Fred Newman. adv.: B&W page £1950, color page $2400. bk.rev.; illus. **Document type:** trade publication.
    Former titles: Book Buyer; Paperback Buyer.

PUBLISHING POYNTERS; book marketing news and ideas from Dan Poynter. see *BUSINESS AND ECONOMICS — Marketing And Purchasing*

070.5   US   ISSN 1053-8801
Z1003   CODEN: PREQEI
PUBLISHING RESEARCH QUARTERLY. 1986. q. $48 to individuals (foreign $80); institutions $96 (foreign $129) (effective Aug. 1995). Transaction Publishers, Transaction Periodicals Consortium, Department 3092, Rutgers University, New Brunswick, NJ 08903. TEL 908-445-2280. FAX 908-445-3138. Ed. Albert Henderson. bk.rev. circ. 3,000. **Indexed:** Child.Lit.Abstr. **Document type:** academic/scholarly publication.
—BLDSC (7156.094550); Faxon; UMI; UnCover. **CCC.**
    Formerly (until 1991): Book Research Quarterly (ISSN 0741-6148)
    Description: Publishes research on or about books, the publishing and book distribution process, and the social, political, economic, and technological conditions that help shape this process.

070.5   US
PUBLISHING SYSTEMS.* 1987. bi-m. $12. Technical Data Publishing Corporation, 393 Howard Blvd., Mt. Arlington, NJ 07856-1113. TEL 201-770-2633. Ed. William M. Rowe. circ. 20,000.

070.5   UK   ISSN 1351-0177
PUBLISHING TECHNOLOGY REVIEW. 1993. m. £175. Pira International, Randalls Rd., Leatherhead, Surrey KT22 7RU, England. TEL 01372-376161. FAX 01372-360104. Ed. Roberto Mirio; Pub. Marie Rushton. bk.rev.; software rev.; circ. 200 (paid). **Document type:** newsletter.
●Also available online.
    Description: Provides technological information for publishing professionals with little or no technical background.
    Refereed Serial

070.5 658   US   ISSN 1061-6780
Z479
PUBLISHING TRENDS AND TRENDSETTERS. 1978. 10/yr. $245. Oxbridge Communications, Inc., 150 Fifth Ave., New York, NY 10011. TEL 212-741-0231. FAX 212-633-2938. Ed. Jim Mann. bk.rev. circ. 320. (back issues avail.) **Document type:** newsletter.
    Formerly (until 1991): Media Management Monographs (ISSN 0192-7663)
    Description: Contains interviews with magazine publishing executives, analysis of publishing industry trends.

002   NE   ISSN 0014-9527
QUAERENDO; a quarterly journal from the Low Countries devoted to manuscripts and printed books. (Text mainly in English; occasionally in French and German) 1971. 4/yr. fl.98($63) to individuals; institutions fl.150($97) (effective 1996). E.J. Brill, P.O. Box 9000, 2300 PA Leiden, Netherlands. TEL 31-71-5353500. FAX 31-71-5317532. TELEX 39296 BRILL NL. E-mail: ejborders@ejbrill.com. (In N. America: E.J. Brill, 24 Hudson St., Kinderhook, NY 12106. TEL 800-962-4406. FAX 518-758-1959) Ed. A.R.A. Croiset van Uchelen. adv.; bk.rev.; illus.; index, cum.index: vols.1-16. circ. 750. (back issues avail.) **Indexed:** Bibl.Engl.Lang.& Lit., RILA. **Document type:** academic/scholarly publication.
—**CCC.**
    Refereed Serial

686.3 747.5   AT   ISSN 1035-1817
QUEENSLAND BOOKBINDERS' GUILD. NEWSLETTER. 1980. q. Aus.$25 (effective Mar. 1993). Queensland Bookbinders' Guild Inc., P.O. Box 73, Annerley, Qld. 4103, Australia. TEL 61-7-848-3774. circ. 110. (back issues avail.) **Document type:** newsletter.
    Description: To promote, foster and practise the arts of bookbinding, graphic arts and kindred arts.

658.8   CN   ISSN 0033-6491
Z487
QUILL AND QUIRE; Canada's magazine of book news and reviews. 1935. m. Can.$48.15 (foreign Can.$55) (effective 1991). Key Publishers Co. Ltd., 70 The Esplanade, 4th Fl., Toronto, ON M5E 1R2, Canada. TEL 416-360-0044. FAX 416-941-9038. Ed. Ted Mumford. adv. contact: June Dickenson. bk.rev.; bibl.; illus.; stat. circ. 7,000. (tabloid format; also avail. in microfiche) **Indexed:** Bk.Rev.Ind. (1980-), Can.B.P.I., Can.Lit.Ind., Can.Per.Ind., Child.Bk.Rev.Ind. (1980-), CMI. **Document type:** directory.
—**CCC.**
    Incorporates (in 1989): Books for Young People (ISSN 0045-2556)
    Description: For booksellers, librarians and publishers.

R N I B RHETORIC. see *HANDICAPPED — Visually Impaired*

070.5 808.8 011   UK   ISSN 0144-1779
RADICAL BOOKSELLER. (Includes: Radical Books of the Months) 1980. 8/yr. £15($30) Radical Bookseller Ltd., 265 Seven Sisters Rd., London N4 2DE, England. Ed. J.F. Nicol. adv.; bk.rev. circ. 300.
    Description: Trade news, literature and publications abstracts, article excerpts, and directory of small publishers of books and periodicals pertaining to avant-garde thought in economic, industrial and social politics, literature, science and education, and lifestyle, and of workshops dealing in such literature.

028   IT   ISSN 0033-8648
Z1007
RAGGUAGLIO LIBRARIO; rassegna mensile bibliografica culturale. 1933. m. L.60000 (effective 1993). Associazione Arte e Cultura, Via Terruggia 14, 20162 Milan, Italy. TEL 02-6473600. Dir. Giulio Madurini. adv.; bk.rev.; bibl.; illus. **Indexed:** M.L.A.

028.1   US   ISSN 1061-6861
Z1035.A1
RAPPORT; the West Coast review of books, arts & entertainment. 1974. bi-m. $11.97. Rapport Publishing Co., Inc., 5265 Fountain Ave., Upper Terrace, No.6, Los Angeles, CA 90029. TEL 213-660-0433; 800-397-1266. FAX 213-660-0434. Ed. David Dreis. adv. contact: Glen Kenyon. bk.rev. circ. 50,000. **Indexed:** Bk.Rev.Ind. (1977-), Child.Bk.Rev.Ind. (1977-). **Document type:** consumer publication.
—UnCover.
    Formerly (until 1991): West Coast Review of Books (ISSN 0095-3555)
    Description: Extended reviews of current books and CDs, as well as articles and interviews with writers and musicians.

090.75   IT   ISSN 1122-8148
▼**RARA VOLUMINA;** rivista di studi sull'editoria di pregio e il libro illustrato. 1994. s-a. L.56000 (foreign L.86000). Maria Pacini Fazzi Editore, Piazza S. Romano 16, Casella Postale 173, 55100 Lucca, Italy. TEL 39-583-55530. FAX 39-583-418245. Ed. Marco Paoli. adv.: page L.680000.

028.1   CN
READERS SHOWCASE. m. Can.$6. Suggitt Publishing Ltd., 17317-107 Ave., Edmonton, AB T5S 1E5, Canada. TEL 403-486-5802. FAX 403-481-9276. Ed. Dave Suggitt. adv.: B&W page Can.$1995, color page Can.$2535; trim 8 1/8 x 10 3/4; adv. contact: Rob Suggitt. circ. 40,000. **Document type:** bulletin.

028.1 800   US
READING WOMAN. 1993. q. $15 (effective 1995-1996). Box 19116, Minneapolis, MN 55419. TEL 612-822-1271. FAX 612-882-1271. E-mail: wienc002@maroon.tc.umn.edu. Ed. Chris Wiencke. circ. 1,000 (paid). **Document type:** newsletter.

READINGS; a journal of reviews and commentary in mental health. see *MEDICAL SCIENCES — Psychiatry And Neurology*

THE READMORE NEWSLETTER. see *LIBRARY AND INFORMATION SCIENCES*

READMORE REPORTER. see *LIBRARY AND INFORMATION SCIENCES*

028.1 364   US
REAL CRIME BOOK DIGEST. 1993. bi-m. $15. Presto Pub. Co., 1017 W. Wilson Ave., Chicago, IL 60640. Ed. Jim Agnew. adv.; bk.rev.; illus. **Document type:** consumer publication.

050   AG   ISSN 0325-1942
REDACCION; revista lider de opinion. m. (10/yr.). Arg.$80($100) Editorial Redaccion S.A., Bme. Mitre 1970, 2o piso, Buenos Aires, Argentina. TEL 953-4355. FAX 953-8455. Eds. Hugo Gambini, Emiliana Lopez Saavedra. illus.

REDACTUEL. see *JOURNALISM*

REDAKTIONS ADRESS. see *BUSINESS AND ECONOMICS — Trade And Industrial Directories*

070.5   US   ISSN 0735-1534
REFERENCE REPORT.* m. $78. Educational Materials Distributors, 28 Greenbriar, Grosse Point Shores, MI 48230. Ed. E.M. Dawson.

070.5   HK
REFLECTIONS; news from Springer-Verlag Hong Kong. (Text in English) 1991. s-a. free. Springer-Verlag Hong Kong, Ltd., 701 Mirror Tower, 61 Mody Rd., Tsim Sha Tsui, Kowloon, Hong Kong. TEL 852-723-9698. FAX 852-724-2366. Ed. Maurice C. Kwong. circ. 5,000 (controlled).
    Description: Features major academic activities in Asia and science-related articles.

658.8   CM
REGIONAL CENTRE FOR BOOK PROMOTION IN AFRICA. BULLETIN OF INFORMATION/CENTRE REGIONAL DE PROMOTION DU LIVRE EN AFRIQUE. BULLETIN D'INFORMATION. 1978. q. Regional Centre for Book Promotion in Africa, Box 1646, Yaounde, Cameroon.

658.8   IT   ISSN 0034-4176
REMAINDERS' BOOK ITALIANO; il servizio internazionale per l'acqisto del libro a meta del prezzo di copertina. no.3, 1967. q. Libreria Internazionale Guida, Via Port'Alba 20-21-24, Naples, Italy. adv.; illus.

655   FR   ISSN 0337-470X
REPERTOIRE INTERNATIONAL DES EDITEURS ET DIFFUSEURS DE LANGUE FRANCAISE. a. 430 F. Editions du Cercle de la Librairie, 35 rue Gregoire de Tours, 75279 Paris Cedex 06, France. circ. 5,000.
    Formerly: Livre de Langue Francaise - Repertoire des Editeurs (ISSN 0076-0110)

RESOURCES IN AGING; an international newsletter featuring new developments in aging. see *GERONTOLOGY AND GERIATRICS*

RETAIL NEWSAGENT TOBACCONIST CONFECTIONER. see *TOBACCO*

028.1   AG
REVISTA LIBROS ELEGIDOS. 1975. m. Editorial Atlantida, S.A., Azopardo 579, Buenos Aires, Argentina. Ed. Costancio C. Vigil. adv.; bk.rev.; illus. circ. 40,000.
    Description: Contains book reviews.

PUBLISHING AND BOOK TRADE

028.5 028.1   FR   ISSN 0398-8384
REVUE DES LIVRES POUR ENFANTS. 1965. bi-m. 240 F. (foreign 265 F.) (effective 1995). (Centre National du Livre pour Enfants) Joie par les Livres, 8 rue Saint-Bon, 75004 Paris, France. TEL 48-87-61-95. FAX 48-87-08-52. Ed. Francoise Ballanger. adv. contact: Genevieve Patte. bk.rev. circ. 5,000. (back issues avail.) Indexed: Child.Lit.Abstr.
   Formerly: Bulletin d'Analyses de Livres pour Enfants.
   Description: Reviews recently published children's books and publishes articles about children's literature and libraries.

REVUE FRANCAISE D'HISTOIRE DU LIVRE. see *LIBRARY AND INFORMATION SCIENCES*

RHODE ISLAND. DEPARTMENT OF STATE LIBRARY SERVICES. NEWSLETTER. see *LIBRARY AND INFORMATION SCIENCES*

RIGHTS AND LIABILITIES OF PUBLISHERS, BROADCASTERS, AND REPORTERS. see *LAW — Civil Law*

028.1   IT
RIVISTA DEI LIBRI. 1991. m. L.88000. New York Review of Books, Via De Lamberti 1, 50123 Florence, Italy. TEL 39-55-219624. FAX 39-55-295427. Ed. Pietro Corsi. adv.: page L.11500000; adv. contact: Flavio Biondi. circ. 15,000. Document type: consumer publication.

015.498   RM   ISSN 0035-8045
ROMANIAN BOOKS. (Editions in English, French, German, Russian) 1964. q. $5. (Consiliul Culturii si Educatiei Socialiste) Centrala Editoriala, Piata Scinteii Nr. 1, 79715 Bucharest, Rumania. (Subscr. to: ICECOOP-ILEXIM, 3 Str. Decembrie, POB 1-136, 1-137, 70116 Bucharest, Rumania.) Ed. Hristu Candroveanu. adv.; bk.rev.; bibl.; illus. circ. 6,000. (tabloid format)

070.5   IT
ROMANO; catalogo alfabetico dell'editoria di interesse scolastico. biennial? Libreria Romano, Casella Postale 11-114, Montesacro, Rome, Italy. TEL 39-6-8123033. FAX 39-6-8108634. Document type: directory.

ROMANTIC TIMES MAGAZINE; for readers of romantic and contemporary fiction. see *LITERATURE — Adventure And Romance*

ROMANTIC TRAVELING. see *TRAVEL AND TOURISM*

070.5   US
ROUND TABLE (ANDERSON). 1952. bi-m. free. Protestant Church-Owned Publishers Association, 1200 E. 5th St., Box 2499, Anderson, IN 46018. Ed. Richard Grant. circ. 500.

RUSS COCHRAN NEWSLETTER. see *ART*

RUSS VON HOELSCHER PUBLISHING REPORT. see *JOURNALISM*

070.5   US
S C B W I BULLETIN. 1971. bi-m. $50 membership (effective 1995). Society of Children's Book Writers & Illustrators, 22736 Vanowen St., Ste. 106, West Hills, CA 91307. TEL 818-888-8760. Ed. Stephen Mooser. bk.rev.; circ. 10,200 (paid). Document type: newsletter.
   Formerly: S C B W Bulletin.
   Description: Discusses the writing and illustration of children's books.

070   UK   ISSN 0960-5533
S E E P DIRECTORY. 1990. a. £8 (foreign £10). Society of Freelance Editors and Proofreaders, 38 Rochester Rd., London NW1 9JJ, England. TEL 0171-813-3113. circ. 2,500. Document type: directory.

S H A R P NEWS. (Society for the History of Authorship, Reading and Publishing) see *LITERATURE*

070.5   PO   ISSN 0870-3124
B5
S O D I LIVROS. ANALISE. 1984. q. (Sociedade Distribuidora de Livros e Publicacoes) Editorial Fragmentos, Lda. Travessa Estevao Pinto, 6-A, 1000 Lisbon, Portugal.

070.5   US   ISSN 0730-2223
S P E X. (Small-Publishers Exchange) 1981. bi-m. $40 membership only. Marin Small Publishers Association, Box E, Corte Madera, CA 94976. TEL 415-257-8275. Ed. Janet Andrews. adv.; bk.rev. circ. 250. Document type: newsletter.
   Description: News, letters, notes, announcements, reviews, articles and book lists pertaining to the activities of independent authors, publishers, and printers.

S R I S NEWSLETTER. (Science Reference and Information Service) see *LIBRARY AND INFORMATION SCIENCES*

070.5   US
SANDIA REVIEW OF BOOKS. 1986. m. $25. (Lange Foundation) Sandia Communications, Inc., 1208 Nakomis Ave., N.E., Ste. B, Albuquerque, NM 87112-6053. TEL 505-299-5245. bk.rev.; abstr.; illus.; circ. 12,500 (paid). (back issues avail.) Document type: trade publication.

070.5   US
SAUR NEWSLINE. 1986. irreg. free. K.G. Saur, A part of Reed Reference Publishing, 121 Chanlon Rd., New Providence, NJ 07974. TEL 908-665-3576. FAX 908-771-7792. Ed. Valerie Berk.

SCANDINAVIAN PUBLIC LIBRARY QUARTERLY. see *LIBRARY AND INFORMATION SCIENCES*

SCHEDARIO; periodico di letteratura giovanile. see *EDUCATION*

070.5 740   SZ   ISSN 0080-6838
SCHOENSTE SCHWEIZER BUECHER. (Text in English, French, German and Italian) 1943. a. free. Schweizerischer Buchhaendler- und Verleger-Verband, Postfach 9045, CH-8050 Zurich, Switzerland. TEL 01-3186444. FAX 01-3186462. (Co-sponsor: Eidgenoessisches Departement des Innern) Ed. Peter Oprecht. adv. contact: Harry Heusser. bk.rev. Document type: bibliography.

070.5   GW   ISSN 0941-8504
DIE SCHOENSTEN DEUTSCHEN BUECHER (YEAR). a. DM.10. Buchhaendler-Vereinigung GmbH, Postfach 100442, 60004 Frankfurt a.M., Germany. TEL 069-13060. FAX 069-1306201. Ed. Ingrid Ott. Document type: catalog.
   Formed by the 1991 merger of: Schoensten Buecher der Bundesrepublik Deutschland (ISSN 0722-284X); Schoensten Buecher der Deutschen Demokratischen Republik (ISSN 0323-4959); Which was formerly: Spiegel Deutscher Buchkunst (ISSN 0081-3702)
   Description: Report on the year's best books.

SCHOOL LIBRARY JOURNAL; the magazine of children, young adults & school librarians. see *LIBRARY AND INFORMATION SCIENCES*

658.8   SZ   ISSN 0036-732X
Z2771
SCHWEIZER BUCH. 1943. s-m. 300 SFr. (foreign 400 SFr.). Schweizerischer Buchhaendler- und Verleger-Verband, Postfach 9045, CH-8050 Zurich, Switzerland. TEL 01-3186400. FAX 01-3186462. (Co-sponsor: Schweizerische Landesbibliothek) adv.; bk.rev.; index. circ. 1,000. Document type: trade publication.
—BLDSC (8111.204000).

658.8   SZ   ISSN 0036-7338
SCHWEIZER BUCHHANDEL/LIBRAIRIE SUISSE/LIBRERIA SVIZZERA. 1943. 21/yr. 185 SFr. Schweizerischer Buchhaendler- und Verleger-Verband, Postfach 9045, CH-8050 Zurich, Switzerland. TEL 01-3186444. FAX 01-3186462. Ed. Franziska Schlaepfer. adv. contact: Urs Guenther. bk.rev.; bibl.; charts; index. circ. 3,300. Indexed: Key to Econ.Sci. Document type: trade publication.
   Description: Includes association news, reports of events, trade information, announcements of new publications, award presentations, list of events and exhibitions, letters from readers, list of advertisers, and positions available.

070.5   SZ   ISSN 0080-7230
SCHWEIZER BUCHHANDELS-ADRESSBUCH. 1966. a. 66 SFr. Schweizerischer Buchhaendler- und Verleger-Verband, Postfach 9045, CH-8050 Zurich, Switzerland. TEL 01-3186420. FAX 01-3186462. Ed. Thomas Rathgeb. adv. contact: Urs Guenther. Document type: directory.

SCIENCE FICTION CHRONICLE; the monthly science fiction and fantasy newsmagazine. see *LITERATURE — Science Fiction, Fantasy, Horror*

020.75   UK   ISSN 0954-8769
SCOTTISH BOOK COLLECTOR. 1987. bi-m. £11($30) (rest of Europe £13.50, N. America £15; Australia and Japan £16. 36 Lauriston Pl., Edinburgh EH3 9EZ, Scotland. TEL 0131-228-4837. Ed. Jennie Renton. adv. contact: Jennie Renton. bk.rev. circ. 1,000. Document type: consumer publication.
   Description: Covers Scottish books, modern literature and trade profiles from a collector's and librarian's perspective.

091   BE   ISSN 0036-9772
Z108
SCRIPTORIUM; international review of manuscript studies. (Text in several languages) 1947. s-a. 3800 Fr. Centre d'Etudes des Manuscrits, 4 bd. de l'Empereur, B-1000 Brussels, Belgium. (Dist. by: Casa Editrice Leo S. Olschki, Viuzzo del Pozzetto, 50126 Florence, Italy. TEL 39-55-6530684. FAX 39-55-6530214) Ed.Bd. bk.rev.; bibl.; charts; illus.; index. circ. 900. Indexed: Bibl.Engl.Lang.& Lit., New Test.Abstr., RILA, RILM.
—BLDSC (8213.235000); Faxon; SWETS.

070.5   IT
SCRIVERE; per farsi leggere. m. (11/yr.) L.70000. Edizioni Studio Kit, Via Aosta 2, 20155 Milan, Italy. TEL 02-33100413. FAX 02-33104726. Document type: trade publication.

070.5   US
SELECT (NEW YORK). 1919. q. Select Magazine, 101 Park Ave., New York, NY 10178-0002. TEL 212-696-7300. Ed. Nancy Cooper. circ. 2,000.
   Formerly: S - M News.
   Description: Contains magazine industry news.

658.8   FR   ISSN 1162-4469
SERVICE ILE-DE-FRANCE. (Supplement to: Livres de France (ISSN 0294-0019); Livres Hebdo (ISSN 0294-0000)) 1984. irreg. (Agence de Cooperation pour le Livre et la Lecture en Ile-de-France, Paris) Livres Hebdo, 35 rue Gregoire de Tours, 75006 Paris, France. TEL 44-41-28-00. FAX 44-21-28-64. Document type: trade publication.

SEYBOLD REPORT ON DESKTOP PUBLISHING. see *COMPUTERS — Microcomputers*

028.5   IT   ISSN 1120-253X
SFOGLIALIBRO; la biblioteca dei ragazzi. 1988. 6/yr. L.75000 (foreign L.130000). Editrice Bibliografica s.r.l., Viale Vittorio Veneto 24, 20124 Milan, Italy. TEL 39-2-29006965. FAX 39-2-654624. Ed. Massimo Belotti. adv.; bk.rev. circ. 3,000. Document type: trade publication.
   Description: Covers juvenile literature and children's libraries. Includes a bibliography of Italian books for children.

070.5   UK   ISSN 0950-0715
Z327
SHEPPARD'S BOOK DEALERS IN BRITISH ISLES. 1951. a. £24($48) Richard Joseph Publishers Ltd., Unit 2, Monks Walk, Farnham, Surrey GU9 8HT, England. TEL 01252-734347. FAX 01252-734307. Ed. M. Goulding. adv. circ. 2,000. (back issues avail.) Document type: directory.
   Formerly: Directory of Dealers in Secondhand and Antiquarian Books in the British Isles (ISSN 0070-5411)

070.5   UK
SHEPPARD'S BOOK DEALERS IN INDIA AND THE ORIENT. 1977. irreg. $48. Richard Joseph Publishers Ltd., Unit 2, Monks Walk, Farnham, Surrey GU9 8HT, England. TEL 01252-734347. FAX 01252-734307. Document type: directory.
   Formerly: Bookdealers in India, Pakistan and Sri Lanka (ISSN 0143-0270)

070.5   UK
▼**SHEPPARD'S BOOK DEALERS IN JAPAN.** 1994. irreg. £24. Richard Joseph Publishers Ltd., Unit 2, Monks Walk, Farnham, Surrey GU9 8HT, England. TEL 01252-734347. FAX 01252-734307. Document type: directory.

PUBLISHING AND BOOK TRADE

658.8   UK   ISSN 0962-2764
SHEPPARD'S BOOKDEALERS IN AUSTRALIA AND NEW ZEALAND. 1990. triennial. $48. Richard Joseph Publishers Ltd., Unit 2, Monks Walk, Farnham, Surrey GU9 8HT, England. TEL 01252-734347. FAX 01252-734307. adv. circ. 1,000. (back issues avail.) **Document type:** directory.
    Description: Directory of dealers in secondhand and antiquarian books.

070.5   UK   ISSN 0963-0171
Z291.5
SHEPPARD'S BOOKDEALERS IN EUROPE; a directory of dealers in secondhand and antiquarian books on the continent of Europe. 1966. biennial. $48. Richard Joseph Publishers Ltd., Unit 2, Monks Walk, Farnham, Surrey GU9 8HT, England. TEL 01252-734347. FAX 01252-734307. adv. circ. 1,500. (back issues avail.) **Document type:** directory.
    Former titles (until 1991): Sheppard's European Book Dealers (ISSN 0954-2590); European Bookdealers (ISSN 0071-2523)

070.5   UK   ISSN 0269-1469
Z475
SHEPPARD'S BOOKDEALERS IN NORTH AMERICA. 1954. biennial. $48. Richard Joseph Publishers Ltd., Unit 2, Monks Walk, Farnham, Surrey GU9 8HT, England. TEL 01252-734347. FAX 01252-734307. adv.; index. circ. 3,000. (back issues avail.) **Document type:** directory.
    —BLDSC (8256.432100).
    Formerly: Bookdealers in North America (ISSN 0068-0109)

070.5   UK
▼**SHEPPARD'S INTERNATIONAL DIRECTORY OF EPHEMERA DEALERS.** 1994. irreg. £24. Richard Joseph Publishers Ltd., Unit 2, Monks Walk, Farnham, Surrey GU9 8HT, England. TEL 01252-734347. FAX 01252-734307. **Document type:** directory.

070.5 020   CC   ISSN 1000-0097
Z284
SHIJIE TUSHU/WORLD BOOKS. (Text in Chinese) 1956. m. $80 (effective 1996). China National Publications Import and Export Corporation, P.O. Box 88, Beijing 100020, People's Republic of China. TEL 861-506-3067. FAX 861-506-3101. TELEX 22313 CPC CN. Ed. Zhu Fuzheng. adv.; bk.rev. circ. 10,000. **Document type:** trade publication.

665   JA   ISSN 0037-3788
SHINKAN NEWS FOR READERS/SHINKAN NYUSU. 1959. m. 2232 Yen($17) Tokyo Shuppan Hanbai Co., Ltd., 6-24 Higashigoken-cho, Shinjuku-ku, Tokyo 162, Japan. FAX 03-3267-3781. Ed. Hiromasa Kohtaki. adv.; bk.rev.; bibl. circ. 150,000.
    Description: Covers forthcoming books.

070.5   US   ISSN 1061-5709
SIGNATURE; a newsletter for the publishing industry. 1985. q. free. Griffin Printing and Lithograph, Co., Inc., 544 W. Colorado St., Glendale, CA 91204-1102. TEL 818-244-2128. FAX 818-242-1172. Ed. Larry Davis. adv.; bk.rev.; circ. 6,500 (controlled). (back issues avail.) **Document type:** newsletter.
    Description: Provides the small press and publishing community with a forum for the exchange of useful information and ideas.

070.5 338.025   US
SIMBA REPORT ON DIRECTORY PUBLISHING. 1987. m. $145 (foreign $170) (effective 1995). SIMBA Information Inc., 213 Danbury Rd., Box 7430, Wilton, CT 06897-7430. TEL 203-834-0033. FAX 203-834-1771. E-mail: simba99@aol.com. Ed. Victor Rubell; Pub. Chris Elwell. circ. 1,000. (back issues avail.) **Document type:** newsletter.
    •Also available online. Vendor(s): Knight-Ridder, Inc. (File no.636), NewsNet (PB30).
    —CCC.
    Formerly (until vol.4, no.11, 1994): Morgan Report on Directory Publishing (ISSN 0890-9512)
    Description: Provides news on contemporary legislative and business issues affecting the informational publishing industry.

SINDICATO NACIONAL DOS EDITORES DE LIVROS. INFORMATIVO BIBLIOGRAFICO. see *BIBLIOGRAPHIES*

070.5   BL
SINDICATO NACIONAL DOS EDITORES DE LIVROS. JORNAL. 1984. bi-m. Sindicato Nacional dos Editores de Livros, Av. Rio Branco 37, s-1503-06, 20090-003 Rio de Janeiro RJ, Brazil. TEL 021-233-6481. FAX 021-253-8502.

070.5   SI   ISSN 0080-9659
Z464.S55
SINGAPORE BOOK WORLD. (Text in Chinese, English and Malay) 1970. a. $10. National Book Development Council of Singapore, NBDCS Secretariat, Bukit Merah Branch Library, Bukit Merah Central, Singapore 0315. TEL 2732730. Ed. Hedwig Anuar. adv.; bk.rev. circ. 3,000. (back issues avail.) **Indexed:** Lib.Sci.Abstr.
    —BLDSC (8285.460000); UnCover.
    Description: Features articles on book trade.

020.75   MX
SISTEMA NACIONAL DE ARCHIVOS. INVENTARIOS. 1989. irreg. Archivo General de la Nacion, E. Molina y Albaniles, 15350 Mexico DF, Mexico.

658.8   FR   ISSN 0294-0043
SIX MOIS DE NOUVEAUTES. (Supplement to: Livres Hebdo (ISSN 0294-0000)) 1975. s-a. Livres Hebdo, 35 rue Gregoire de Tours, 75006 Paris, France. TEL 44-41-28-00. FAX 44-41-28-64. **Document type:** trade publication.
    Formed by the 1982 merger of: Six Mois de Nouveautes (Edition avec Prix Cession de Base) (ISSN 0223-5013); Six Mois de Nouveautes (Edition Destine a l'Etranger) (ISSN 0223-5021); Both of which superseded (in 1979): Repertoires du Livre (ISSN 0397-1120)

070.5   US   ISSN 0000-0485
Z231.5.L5
SMALL PRESS; the magazine of independent publishing. 1983. q. $29. Small Press, Inc., Kymbolde Way, Wakefield, RI 02879. TEL 401-789-0074. FAX 401-789-3793. Ed. Martha Smith; Pub. Britt Bell. adv.: page $1075; adv. contact: Sarah Mosher. bk.rev.; illus. circ. 9,000. (also avail. in microform from UMI) **Indexed:** Bk.Rev.Ind. (1988-), Child.Bk.Rev.Ind. (1988-), Graph.Arts Lit.Abstr., LHTN, Lib.Lit. **Document type:** trade publication.
    —BLDSC (8310.105000); Faxon; UnCover.
    Description: Dedicated to serving the independent publishing industry through articles, excerpts, and new title announcements.

028.1   US   ISSN 8756-7202
Z1215
SMALL PRESS BOOK REVIEW. 1985. q. Greenfield Press, Box 176, Southport, CT 06490. TEL 203-332-7629. E-mail: henryberry@aol.com. Ed. Henry Berry. adv.; bk.rev.; circ. 3,000 (controlled). (back issues avail.) **Indexed:** Bk.Rev.Ind. (1987-), Child.Bk.Rev.Ind. (1987-). **Document type:** trade publication.
    •Also available online.
    Description: Contains brief descriptive, critical reviews of all types of books published by small presses and periodicals from independent presses. Includes a children's book section and news notes.

070.5   US
SMALL PRESS NEWS. 1981-1985; resumed 1994. 4/yr. $15 (includes Stony Hills). Diane Kruchkow, Ed. & Pub., c/o Stony Hills Productions, RR 1, Box 780-11, New Sharon, ME 04955. TEL 207-778-4699. adv.; bk.rev.; bibl. (back issues avail.) **Document type:** newsletter.

016   US
SMALL PRESS REVIEW - SMALL MAGAZINE REVIEW. (Supplement to: International Directory of Little Magazines and Small Presses (ISSN 0092-3974)) 1967. m. $25 to individuals; institutions $31. Dustbooks, Box 100, Paradise, CA 95967. TEL 916-877-6110; 800-477-6110. FAX 916-877-0222. Ed. Len Fulton. adv.: B&W page $150; 7 x 9. bk.rev. circ. 3,500. **Indexed:** ACCESS, Bk.Rev.Ind. (1980-), Child.Bk.Rev.Ind. (1980-), New Per.Ind.
    Formerly (until Feb. 1994): Small Press Review (ISSN 0037-7228); Incorporates (1993-1994): Small Magazine Review (ISSN 1068-7742)
    Description: News, reviews, and articles on small press publishing worldwide. Includes interviews with small press or small magazine publishers and editors, advice on starting a small press and reaching a wider audience.

070.5   UK   ISSN 0956-9847
SMALL PRESS YEARBOOK. 1988. a. £9.95. Small Press Group of Britain, The Small Press Centre, Middlesex University, White Hart Ln., London N17 8HR, England. TEL 0181-362-6058. **Document type:** bibliography.
    —BLDSC (8310.117500).

070.5   US
SMALL PUBLISHER. 1993. m. $18 (foreign $36). Nigel Maxey, Ed. & Pub., Box 1620, Pineville, WV 24874-1620. adv.: B&W page $200. bk.rev. circ. 5,500. (tabloid format) **Document type:** newspaper.
    Description: Contains articles for persons at small companies publishing books, periodicals, and audio and video tapes. Also profiles successful self-publishers and small publishers and offers professional advice.

655 090   FR   ISSN 0081-0878
SOCIETE DES FRANCS-BIBLIOPHILES. ANNUAIRE. 1948. a. membership. 39 rue Raynouard, 75016 Paris, France.

070.5   US
SOCIETY FOR SCHOLARLY PUBLISHING NEWSLETTER. bi-m. $60 membership. Society for Scholarly Publishing, 10200 W. 44th St., Ste. 304, Wheat Ridge, CO 80033. TEL 303-422-3914. FAX 303-422-8894. **Document type:** newsletter.

SOLANUS. see *LIBRARY AND INFORMATION SCIENCES*

SOUTH AFRICA. STATE LIBRARY. CATALOGUE OF PUBLICATIONS/SOUTH AFRICA. STAATSBIBLIOTEEK. KATALOGUS VAN PUBLIKASIES. see *LIBRARY AND INFORMATION SCIENCES*

SOUTHERN AFRICAN BOOKS IN PRINT. see *BIBLIOGRAPHIES*

658.8 025.2   US
▼**SOUTHERN BOOK TRADE;** for book professionals. 1994. m. $12 to individuals. 4137 Princess Place Dr., Wilmington, NC 28405. TEL 910-343-8001. FAX 910-646-3355. (Alt. addr.: 201 Lyndon Ave., Wilmington, NC 28405. TEL 910-763-9573) Ed. Jack E. Fryar; Pub. Jack E. Fryar. adv.: B&W page $1000; adv. contact: Richard G. Sibley. bk.rev.; charts; illus. circ. 8,760. (tabloid format) **Document type:** newspaper, trade publication.
    Description: Provides bookstore managers and library professionals with reviews of new and noteworthy books of all kinds, news, and features.

070.5 282   US   ISSN 1077-6648
SPIRIT OF BOOKS. 1988. s-a. Catholic Book Publishers Association, 333 Glen Head Rd., Old Brookville, NY 11545. TEL 516-671-9342. FAX 516-759-4227. Ed. Charles A. Roth. adv. contact: Barbara Curran. circ. 150,000 (paid). **Document type:** catalog.
    Description: Catalog of popular books of interest to Catholic bookstore customers.

016 260   US   ISSN 0038-7606
SPIRITUAL BOOK NEWS. 1958. 8/yr. (Spiritual Book Associates) Ave Maria Press, Notre Dame, IN 46556. TEL 219-287-2838. FAX 219-239-2904. Ed. Robert Hamma. bk.rev. circ. 9,000. **Document type:** newsletter.
    Description: Contains feature reviews of book club selections, as well as notices and reviews of other current books available in the field of spiritual reading.

658.8   UK
SPOKEN WORD CATALOGUE. 1960. a. Retail Entertainment Data Publishing Ltd., Paulton House, 8 Shepherdess Walk, London N1 7LR, England. TEL 0171-490-0049. FAX 0171-253-1308. circ. 1,000. **Document type:** catalog.
    Former titles: Gramophone Spoken Word Catalogue (ISSN 0262-0812); Gramophone Spoken Word and Miscellaneous Catalogue.
    Description: Lists recordings of spoken word on cassettes, LPs, and CDs generally available in the U.K.

PUBLISHING AND BOOK TRADE

658.8 NZ
SPOTLIGHT; journal for the books, gifts, greeting cards, office products, stationery and toy trades of N.Z. 1965. m. NZ.$36. City Communications Ltd., P.O. Box 37-567, Parnell, New Zealand. TEL 09-357-6319. FAX 09-357-6318. Ed. Narena Olliver. adv.; bk.rev. circ. 4,000. (tabloid format) —CCC.
Formerly (until 1978): Spotlight: trade journal on the book, stationery, magazine, greeting cards, games and toy trade in New Zealand (ISSN 0038-8386).

STAR TRACK. see *LIBRARY AND INFORMATION SCIENCES*

686 US
STRATEGIC PLANNING FOR MAGAZINE EXECUTIVES; how to take the guesswork out of magazine publishing decisions. irreg., latest 2nd ed. $59.95. Cowles Business Media (Subsidiary of: Cowles Media Company), Six River Bend Center, 911 Hope St., Box 4949, Stamford, CT 06907-0949. TEL 203-358-9900. FAX 203-357-9014. Ed. Richard M. Koff. **Document type:** trade publication.

070.5 UK
STUDIES ON PUBLISHING. 1992. irreg., no.2, 1994. price varies. Hans Zell Publishers, An imprint of Bowker-Sauer (Subsidiary of: Reed Elsevier group), Maypole House, Maypole Rd., E. Grinstead, W. Sussex RH19 1HH, England. TEL 0342-330100. FAX 0342-330191. (back issues avail.) **Document type:** monographic series.

070.5 US
SUBSCRIPTION MARKETING. m. $295. Box 59859, Boulder, CO 80322-9859. TEL 800-462-0213. FAX 508-443-9728. Pub. Don Nicholas. **Document type:** trade publication.

070.5 658 UK ISSN 1357-4426
SUBSCRIPTIONS STRATEGY; the direct marketing newsletter for publishers. 1993. bi-m. £150. P.O. Box 2, Mullion, Helston, Cornwall TR12 7AA, England. TEL 01326-240039. FAX 01326-240039. Ed. Peter Hobday; Pub. Peter Hobday. bk.rev.; tr.lit.; cum.index: 1993-1994; circ. 300 (paid). (back issues avail.) **Document type:** newsletter.
Description: Contains information on how to plan and execute a subscriptions marketing program, with reviews of the best current examples of publishers direct mail, page advertising and loose inserts.

SUECANA EXTRANEA; boecker om Sverige och svensk skoenlitteratur paa fraemmande spraak. see *BIBLIOGRAPHIES*

070.502548 SW ISSN 0039-6451
Z407
SVENSK BOKHANDEL. Abbreviated title: SvB. 1952. fortn. (Jan.-Jul.); w. (Aug.-Dec.). SEK 850. (Svenska Bokfoerlaeggarefoereningen - Swedish Publishers' Association) Tidnings AB Svensk Bokhandel, P.O. Box 6888, S-113 86 Stockholm, Sweden. TEL 46-8-7361950. FAX 46-8-7361955. (Co-sponsor: Svenska Bokhandlarefoereningen - Swedish Booksellers Association) Ed. Anders Loewenbergon. adv. contact: Maj-Britt Sunnerholm. index. circ. 4,700. **Indexed:** Child.Lit.Abstr. **Document type:** trade publication.
Formed by the merger of: Svensk Bokhandelstidning; Bokhandlaren - Sortimentaren.

028.1 UK ISSN 0265-8119
PT9368
SWEDISH BOOK REVIEW. 1983. s-a. £12($20) Swedish-English Literary Translators Association, University of Wales, Lampeter SA48 7ED, Wales. TEL 01570-422351. FAX 01570-423782. (U.S. subscr. addr.: 260 E. St. Jose Ave., Claremont, CA 91711) Ed. Laurie Thompson. adv.; bk.rev.; illus. circ. 1,000. **Document type:** bibliography.
—BLDSC (8573.857600).
Description: Articles on Swedish writers, translations of their work, bibliographies and news of forthcoming books.

070.5 FR ISSN 1142-4443
SYNDICAT NATIONAL DE LA LIBRAIRIE ANCIENNE ET MODERNE. REPERTOIRE DES MEMBRES. 1930. a. 30 F. Syndicat National de la Librairie Ancienne et Moderne, 4 rue Git le Coeur, 75006 Paris, France. TEL 43-29-46-38. **Document type:** directory.
Former titles: Guide a l'Usage des Amateurs de Livres (ISSN 0224-6821); Guide du Livre Ancien et du Livre d'Occasion (ISSN 0294-8737); Syndicat National de la Librairie Ancienne et Moderne. Repertoire (ISSN 0080-1100).

070.5 US
T A R C WRITERS REPORT. (Only avail. by E-mail and Fax) 1984. d., w., m. $60 (foreign $70). The Authors Resource Center, 4725 E. Sunrise Dr., Ste. 219, Tucson, AZ 85718-4534. TEL 520-577-7751. FAX 520-577-3994. E-mail: TARCMG@aol.com. Ed. Martha R. Gore. bk.rev. **Document type:** newsletter.
Description: Provides business and professional news of publishing industry and publishing trends for writers.

T L S. (Times Literary Supplement) see *LITERATURE*

028.1 800 US
▼**TALKING BOOK REVIEW.** 1994. m. $30. 119 S. Sumner St., Wheaton, IL 60187-5516. Ed. Kurt Luchs. **Document type:** newsletter.

028 US
TARTAN BOOK SALES CATALOG. 1940. 12/yr. free. Brodart Co., 500 Arch St., Williamsport, PA 17705. TEL 800-233-8467. FAX 717-326-6769. Ed. Rob Ekblom. adv.; bk.rev.; bibl.; illus. index. circ. 8,000. **Document type:** catalog.
Supersedes: Tartan Book News; Book News (ISSN 0006-7288)

TASCHENBUCH DER FRAUENPRESSE. see *WOMEN'S STUDIES*

070.5 US ISSN 0894-9581
Z286.E43
TELEPUBLISHING REPORT. 1987. bi-m. $240 (effective 1995). Telepublishing Consultants International, 284 Harvard St., Ste. 62, Cambridge, MA 02139. TEL 617-354-3919. Ed. Lawrence Kingsley; Pub. Lawrence Kingsley. bk.rev. **Document type:** newsletter.
Description: Reviews trends and developments in telecommunications, publishing, and multimedia.

686 AT ISSN 1033-6885
THOMSON'S PRINT PRODUCTION DIRECTORY. 1989. q. Aus.$345. Thomson Business Publishing, 47 Chippen St., Chippendale, N.S.W. 2008, Australia. TEL 02-699-2411. FAX 02-698-3920. Ed. Michael Raffery. (looseleaf format)
Description: For ad agencies, printers, graphic artists, national and retail companies.

070.5 AT ISSN 1034-487X
THORPE'S BOOK TRADE FAX DIRECTORY. 1992. w. Aus.$25. D.W. Thorpe, A part of Reed Reference Publishing, 18 Salmon St., Port Melbourne, Vic. 3207, Australia. TEL 03-245-7370. FAX 03-245-7395. **Document type:** directory.
Description: Cumulates fax numbers used daily by publishers, booksellers, distributors and libraries.

070.5 BE ISSN 0778-1318
TIJDINGEN; tijdschrift voor het boekbedrijf. 1929. 17/yr. 2400 BEF. Vereniging ter Bevordering van het Vlaamse Boekwezen - Flemish Book Trade Organisation, Hof ter Schrieklaan 17, B-2600 Berchem (Antwerp), Belgium. adv.; bibl. circ. 2,000.

070.5 US
Z649.F35
TITLES AND FEES. 1978. s-a. Copyright Clearance Center, Inc., 222 Rosewood Dr., Danvers, MA 01923. TEL 508-750-8400. FAX 508-750-4744. **Document type:** catalog.
Former titles: Catalog of Publisher Information (ISSN 1065-7916) & Publishers' Photocopy Fee Catalog (ISSN 0887-2929); Permissions to Photocopy: Publishers' Fee List.
Description: Directory of titles registered with the Copyright Clearance Center by participating publishers. Provides registered users with information needed to report photocopying activity.

070.5 US ISSN 1070-3179
TOWERS CLUB INFO MARKETING REPORT. Variant titles: Info Marketing Report. Monthly Info Marketing Report. 1974. 10/yr. $195. (Jerry Buchanan Advertising Agency) Towers Club, U.S.A., Inc., Box 2038, Vancouver, WA 98668-2038. TEL 206-574-3084. FAX 206-576-8969. (Alt. addr.: c/o Jerry Buchanan, Ed., 9107 N.W. 11th Ave., Vancouver, WA 98665) Ed. Jerry Buchanan. adv.; bk.rev. circ. 5,700. (looseleaf format; back issues avail.)
Former titles: Jerry Buchannan's Info Marketing Report (ISSN 1066-5250); (until Jan. 1993): Towers Club U S A Newsletter (ISSN 0193-4953)
Description: Serving direct response marketing community information providers; insider news, tips, and sources especially for home-based entrepreneurs, as well as mail order miniclinics, success stories of self-publishers and marketers. Includes letters to the editor.

070.5 US
TRADE BOOK PUBLISHING: REVIEW, FORECAST AND SEGMENT ANALYSIS. irreg., no.2, 1995 (Mar.). $895. SIMBA Information Inc., 213 Danbury Rd., Box 7430, Wilton, CT 06897-7430. TEL 203-834-0033. FAX 203-834-1771. E-mail: simba99@aol.com. **Document type:** trade publication.
Description: Reviews the current state of trade book publishing, covering market size and structure, distribution outlets, and audio publishing. Analyzes market segments.

TRANSLATION REVIEW. see *LINGUISTICS*

655 BE ISSN 0041-1876
LE TRAVAILLEUR DU LIVRE. Dutch edition: De Boekarbeider (ISSN 0774-2797) 1945. bi-m. membership only. Centrale de l'Industrie du Livre et du Papier - Centrale der Boek- en Papiernijverheid, Galerie du Centre, Bloc 2, B-1000 Brussels, Belgium. FAX 02-2230023. Ed. Roger Sagon. charts. circ. 14,200 (Dutch ed. 5,400; French ed. 8,800). **Document type:** bulletin.

TRAVEL BOOKS WORLDWIDE; he travel book review. see *TRAVEL AND TOURISM*

070.5 SZ ISSN 0255-3570
TREFFPUNKT BIBLIOTHEK. 1984. a. 15 SFr. Kantonale Kommission fuer Gemeinde- und Schulbibliotheken Zuerich, Steigstr. 4, CH-8610 Uster, Switzerland. TEL 01-9409977. FAX 01-9400326. Ed. E. Wilhelm. bk.rev. circ. 2,000. **Document type:** bulletin, government publication.

070.5 UK ISSN 0958-5354
TRENDS IN JOURNAL SUBSCRIPTIONS. 1983. a. £100 to non-members; members £50 (effective 1995). Council of Academic and Professional Publishers, The Publishers Association, 19 Bedford Sq., London WC1B 3HJ, England. TEL 0171-580-6321. FAX 0171-636-5375. Ed. Priscilla Oakeshott. circ. 200. (back issues avail.)
—BLDSC (9049.640500).
Description: Analyzes the state of subscriptions to journals from an annual survey of publishers.

658.8 FR ISSN 0294-0035
TROIS MOIS DE NOUVEAUTES. (Supplement to: Livres Hebdo (ISSN 0294-0000)) 1980. q. Livres Hebdo, 35 rue Gregoire de Tours, 75006 Paris, France. TEL 44-41-28-00. FAX 44-41-28-64. **Document type:** trade publication.
Formed by the 1982 merger of: Trois Mois de Nouveautes (Edition avez Prix Cession de Base) (ISSN 0245-7237); Trois Mois de Nouveautes (Edition Destine a l'Etranger (ISSN 0245-7229)

055.1 IT ISSN 0390-4873
TUTTOLIBRI. 1975. w. L.1000. Editrice la Stampa S.p.A., Via Marenco 32, 10100 Turin, Italy. TEL 65681. TELEX 221121. bk.rev.; illus.

686 US ISSN 1042-105X
TYPE & PRESS. 1974. q. $4. Press of the Golden Unicorn, 24667 Heather Court, Hayward, CA 94545. Ed. Fred C. Williams. adv.; bk.rev. circ. 1,000. (back issues avail.)

PUBLISHING AND BOOK TRADE

070.5 US
TYPOGRAPHY DESIGN & USE. 1992. q. $12. Doron and Associates, 1213 Ridgecrest, Denton, TX 76205. TEL 817-566-1366. Ed. Tom Doron. bk.rev. circ. 5,430. (looseleaf format) **Document type:** newsletter.
Description: Covers typography design, use, supplies, guidelines and trends.

079.7 CU
U P E C. bi-m. $10 in N. America; S. America $13; Europe $15; elsewhere $21. (Union de Periodistas de Cuba) Ediciones Cubanas, Obispo No. 527, Apdo. 605, Havana, Cuba. illus.

070.5 US
U S B E BACK ISSUES SHELF LIST. a. $150 membership. United States Book Exchange, Periodicals and Serials Division, 2969 W. 25th St., Cleveland, OH 44113. Ed. Jeanette O'Brien.

U S B E: FOR MEMBERS ONLY. (United States Book Exchange) see LIBRARY AND INFORMATION SCIENCES

U S REAL ESTATE REGISTER. see REAL ESTATE

070.5 UN ISSN 0258-6142
UNESCO. STUDIES ON BOOKS AND READING. (Text in English; occasionally in Arabic, French, Spanish and Russian) irreg. free. Unesco, Division for Book Promotion, Audiovisual Archives and International Exchanges, 7 place de Fontenoy, 75700 Paris, France. TEL 45-68-10-00. charts. circ. 2,500.
Indexed: IIS.

658.8 FR ISSN 0398-5369
UNION PRESSE. 11/yr. 16 Place de la Republique, 75010 Paris, France. TEL 42-40-27-15. FAX 42-40-47-78. Ed. Isabelle Calabre. circ. 35,000.

028.5 US
UNITED STATES BOARD ON BOOKS FOR YOUNG PEOPLE. NEWSLETTER. 1976. s-a. $25 membership. United States Board on Books for Young People, Inc., c/o International Reading Association, 800 Barksdale Rd., Box 8139, Newark, DE 19714-8139. TEL 302-731-1600. Ed. Mary Jo Aman. circ. 1,250.
Indexed: Child Lit.Abstr. **Document type:** newsletter.
Formerly (until 1984): Friends of I B B Y Newsletter (International Board on Books for Young People).
Description: Source of information about books and related activities for children worldwide.

027.7 US ISSN 0041-9265
L11
UNIVERSITY BOOKMAN; a quarterly review. 1960. q. $10. Educational Reviewer, Inc., Box 367, Mecosta, MI 49332. TEL 616-972-7655. Ed. Annette Kirk. bk.rev.; index. circ. 4,000. (also avail. in microform from UMI) **Indexed:** Bk.Rev.Ind. (1986-), Child.Bk.Rev.Ind. (1986-). **Document type:** academic/scholarly publication.
—UMI.
Description: Multidisciplinary essays and reveows on problems of American education and culture.

UNIVERSITY OF IBADAN. LIBRARY. LIBRARY RECORD. see LIBRARY AND INFORMATION SCIENCES

655 NE ISSN 0042-1367
UT DE SMIDTE FAN DE FRYSKE AKADEMY. (Text in Frisian) 1966. q. free to contributors. Fryske Akademy, Doelestrjitte 8, 8911 DX Ljouwert-Leeuwarden, Netherlands. TEL 31-58-131414. FAX 31-58-131409. adv.; bk.rev.; charts; illus. circ. 3,250.

V MIRE KNIG. see LIBRARY AND INFORMATION SCIENCES

VERBREITUNGSDATEN DER SCHWEIZER PRESSE. see ADVERTISING AND PUBLIC RELATIONS

070.5 NE
VERENIGDE NEDERLANDSE UITGEVERSBEDRIJVEN. ANNUAL REPORT. a. Verenigde Nederlandse Uitgeversbedrijven (VNU), 5-25 Ceylonpoort, 2037 AA Haarlem, Netherlands. TEL 31-23-304304. TELEX 41549. **Document type:** corporate report.

658.8 NE ISSN 0042-4412
VERTEGENWOORDIGER.* 1935. 3/yr. fl.5. Vereniging van Uitgevers Vertegenwoordigers., Westerstraat 62, Wormerveer, Netherlands. Eds. P. Kluft, W. De Koning.

028.1 UK ISSN 0954-0881
VIGIL. 1988. 3/yr. £2.50. Vigil Publications, 12 Priory Mead, Bruton, Somers. BA10 ODZ, England. TEL 01749-813349. Ed. John Howard-Greaves. adv.; bk.rev.; illus. circ. 250. **Document type:** newsletter.
Incorporates (1979-1988): Period Piece and Paperback (ISSN 0260-5333)
Description: Focuses on the art and technique of poetry and other imaginative forms of writing. Publishes new work from contributors.

W E S AUTHORS' AND PUBLISHERS' SERVICE NEWSLETTER. (Watman Educational Services) see EDUCATION

070.5 US
W P A NEWS. bi-m. membership. Western Publications Association, 5000 Van Nuys Blvd., Ste. 300, Sherman Oaks, CA 91403. TEL 818-995-7338. FAX 818-995-0878. Ed. Jane Slbering. adv.; circ. 2,200. (back issues avail.) **Document type:** newsletter.
Formerly: Issue.

658.8 070.5 AT ISSN 0812-7042
WEEKLY BOOK NEWSLETTER. 1972. w. Aus.$195. D.W. Thorpe, A part of Reed Reference Publishing, Port Melbourne, Vic. 3207, Australia, Australia. TEL 03-245-7370. FAX 03-245-7395. Ed. Michael Webster. circ. 2,000. (processed) **Document type:** newsletter.
—CCC.
Description: Covers publishing and bookselling industry news in Australia.

WHAT IS TO BE READ. see LITERATURE

WHAT'S WORKING IN DIRECT MARKETING AND FULFILLMENT. see BUSINESS AND ECONOMICS — Marketing And Purchasing

070.5 GW ISSN 0170-7213
WHO'S WHO AT THE FRANKFURT BOOK FAIR; an international publishers' guide. 1969. a. price varies. (Frankfurt Book Fair) K.G. Saur Verlag KG, A part of Reed Reference Publishing, Ortlerstr. 8, 81373 Munich, Germany. TEL 089-76902-0. FAX 089-76902150. (Subscr. to: Postfach 701620, 81316 Munich, Germany; N. America subscr. to: K.G. Saur, 121 Chanlon Rd., New Providence, NJ 07974, USA. TEL 908-665-3576) Ed. Peter Weidhaas. adv. **Document type:** directory.
Description: Includes up-to-date facts on 13000 persons from 5000 companies - publishers, managers, editors, heads of press and production departments, rights and license officers and publishers' representatives and agents.

070.5 658.048 US
WHO'S WHO IN ASSOCIATION PUBLISHING. a. $150 to non-members. Society of National Association Publications, 1650 Tysons Blvd., Ste. 200, McLean, VA 22102. TEL 703-506-3285. FAX 703-506-3266. adv. circ. 700. **Document type:** directory.
Formerly: Who's Who in S N A P; **Incorporates** (in 1994): S N A P Buyers' Guide.

070.5 600 500 US ISSN 1063-0686
CODEN: WLINEU
WILEY LIBRARIANS' NEWSLETTER. 1962. q. free. John Wiley & Sons, Inc., Journals, 605 Third Ave., 4th Fl., New York, NY 10158-0012. TEL 212-850-6000. FAX 212-850-6088. TELEX 12-7063. circ. 25,000. **Document type:** newsletter.
Formerly (until 1991): Librarians' Newsletter (ISSN 0194-0112).
Description: Strives to keep librarians, book wholesalers, bookstores and individuals aware of newly published books and journals by John Wiley & Sons, Inc.

070.5 GW ISSN 0341-2253
Z119
WOLFENBUETTELER NOTIZEN ZUR BUCHGESCHICHTE. 1976. 2/yr. DM.80. (Wolfenbutteler Arbeitskreis fuer Geschichte des Buchwesens) Harrassowitz Verlag, Taunusstr. 14, 65183 Wiesbaden, Germany. TEL 0611-530-0. FAX 0611-530570. TELEX 4186135. (Subscr. to: Postfach 2929, 65019 Wiesbaden, Germany) Eds. Werner Arnold, Erdmann Weyrauch. circ. 750. **Document type:** academic/scholarly publication.
—CCC.

070.5 NE
WOLTERS KLUWER JAARVERSLAG/WOLTERS KLUWER ANNUAL REPORT. (Editions in Dutch, English) a. free. Wolters Kluwer N.V., Public Relations Department, P.O. Box 818, 1000 AV Amsterdam, Netherlands. TEL 31-20-6070400. **Document type:** corporate report.
Description: Reports on activities of the company and its legal, medical, scientific and academic publishing subsidiaries in Belgium, France, Germany, Italy, The Netherlands, Spain, Sweden, the UK and the US.

WORD WRAP. see LITERATURE

070.5 UK ISSN 0084-2664
PN12
WRITERS' AND ARTISTS' YEARBOOK; a directory for writers, artists, playwrights, writers for film, radio and television, photographers and composers. 1907. a. £9.99. A. & C. Black (Publishers) Ltd., Howard Rd., Eaton Socon, Huntingdon, Cambs. PE19 3EZ, England. TEL 01480-212666. FAX 01480-405014. index. **Document type:** directory.
Description: Provides a reference for writers, artists, journalists, and publishers.

070.5 AT ISSN 0084-2680
WRITERS' AND PHOTOGRAPHERS' MARKETING GUIDE; DIRECTORY OF AUSTRALIAN AND NEW ZEALAND LITERARY AND PHOTO MARKETS. 1945. a. Aus.$15 (typically set in Jan.). Australian Writers' Professional Service, Stott House, 140 Flinders St., Melbourne, Vic. 3000, Australia. TEL 613-650-9648. Ed. J. Thornton. **Document type:** directory.
Description: Directory for freelance writers and photographers.

070.5 070 US ISSN 0749-2014
WRITERS CONNECTION. (Steve/Lester) 1983. m. $25. Writers Connection, Box 24770, San Jose, CA 95154-4770. TEL 408-445-3600. FAX 408-445-3609. E-mail: writerscxn@aol.com. Ed. Jan Stiles. adv.: page $325; trim 7 3/8 x 9 1/4. bk.rev. circ. 1,500. (back issues avail.) **Document type:** directory, newsletter.
Description: Contains articles on writing nonfiction, fiction, business writing, self-publishing and publishing. Regular columns cover writers' markets, contests, events, and news for writers.

070.5 IS
WRITERS INFORMATION NETWORK; the professional association for Christian writers. 1983. bi-m. $25. Box 11337, 5359 Ruby Pl., N.E., Bainbridge Island, WA 98110. TEL 206-842-9103. FAX 206-842-0536. Ed. Elaine Wright Colvin. bk.rev. circ. 1,000. (back issues avail.) **Document type:** newsletter.
Description: Covers news and trends in the writing profession and offers advice on the editing, ethical, and marketing aspects of writing.

070.5 808 US
WRITERS INK. 1975. irreg. (2-4/yr.). $8 per no. (Writers Unlimited Agency, Inc.) Writers Ink Press, Box 698, Centereach, NY 11720-0698. TEL 516-736-6439. (Alt. addr.: Dr. David B. Axelrod, Suffolk College, 533 College Rd., Selden, NY 11784) Ed. David B. Axelrod; Pub. David B. Axelrod. bk.rev.; illus. circ. 2,000. (back issues avail.) **Document type:** newsletter.
Description: Informs the public about the services this school offers.

070.5 CN ISSN 0225-610X
WRITER'S LIFELINE. 1974. 3/yr. $18. Box 1641, Cornwall, ON K6H 5V6, Canada. TEL 613-932-2135. FAX 613-932-7735. Ed. Stephen Gill. adv.; bk.rev. circ. 1,500.
Formerly: Lifeline (Cornwall) (ISSN 0316-0602)

070.5 US ISSN 0084-2729
PN161
WRITER'S MARKET. 1926. a. $26.95. F & W Publications, Inc., 1507 Dana Ave., Cincinnati, OH 45207. TEL 513-531-2222. FAX 513-531-4744. Ed. Mark Garvey. index. (reprint service avail. from UMI)
—BLDSC (9364.738000).
Description: Provides information on where to sell articles, books, fillers, gags, greeting cards, novels, plays, scripts and short stories.

5640 PUBLISHING AND BOOK TRADE — ABSTRACTING, BIBLIOGRAPHIES, STATISTICS

686 US ISSN 0895-898X
WRITER'S N W; news and reviews for the community of the printed word. 1987. q. $10 (Canada $12). Media Weavers (Subsidiary of: Blue Heron Publishing, Inc.), 24450 N.W Hansen Rd., Hillsboro, OR 97124. TEL 503-621-3911. Eds. Linny Stovall, Dennis Stovall. adv.; bk.rev.; circ. 75,000 (controlled). (tabloid format; back issues avail.) **Document type:** newspaper.
 Formerly: Writer's Northwest Newsletter.
 Description: Lists N.W. publishing and writing markets and events; includes articles on writing and publishing, author interviews, new books and software reviews.

686 US ISSN 0896-7946
PN147
WRITER'S NORTHWEST HANDBOOK; comprehensive guide to writing and publishing in Oregon, Washington, Idaho, Montana, Alaska, and British Columbia. 1986. biennial. $18.95 softcover. Media Weavers (Subsidiary of: Blue Heron Publishing, Inc.), 24450 N.W. Hansen Rd., Hillsboro, OR 97124. TEL 503-621-3911. Eds. Linny Stovall, Dennis Stovall. adv. circ. 20,000. **Document type:** directory.
 Description: Lists 2,800 N.W. markets with editorial guidelines, and advertising resources, essays and interviews for writers and publishers.

070.5 800 US ISSN 0084-2737
WRITER'S YEARBOOK. 1930. a. $4.95. F & W Publications, Inc., 1507 Dana Ave., Cincinnati, OH 45207. TEL 513-531-2222. FAX 513-531-4744. Ed. Bruce Woods. adv. circ. 75,000. (also avail. in microform from UMI; reprint service avail. from UMI) —UMI.
 Description: Articles on how and where to sell writing.

WRITING FOR MONEY; where to sell what you write. see *LITERATURE*

070.5 420 US ISSN 1062-8770
WRITING RIGHT. 1992. m. $30. Elmwood Park Publishing Co., P.O. Box 35132, Elmwood Park, IL 60635. TEL 708-453-5023. Ed. John C. Biardo. bk.rev. **Document type:** newsletter.
 Description: Newsletter with the sole focus on helping writers and publishers with their careers. Features writing tips, researching, promotion and publicity, book reviews, writer's conventions, book exhibit news, and sources for writers.

028.5 UK
YOUNG BOOK TRUST NEWSLETTER; for all those interested in children and what they read. 1987. 3/yr. £10 membership. Children's Book Foundation, Book House, 45 East Hill, Wandsworth, London SW18 2QZ, England. TEL 0181-870-9055. FAX 0181-874-4790. Ed. Marsha Cawthorne. **Document type:** newsletter.
 Former titles: C B F News; C C B News (ISSN 0266-4216).
 Description: Presents information, reviews, and opinions to all matters concerning children and what they read.

028 AU ISSN 0044-2089
DIE ZEIT IM BUCH. 1947. q. S.140. Arbeitsgemeinschaft fuer Buch- und Schrifttum der Katholischen Aktion Oesterreichs, Stephans Platz 6-V, A-1010 Vienna, Austria. Ed. Margarete Schmid. adv.; bk.rev.; bibl.

070 384 PL ISSN 0555-0025
ZESZYTY PRASOZNAWCZE. (Text in Polish; summaries in English, French, Russian) 1960. q. $50. Uniwersytet Jagiellonski, Osrodek Badan Prasoznawczych - Jagiellonian Univerity, Press Research Center, Ul. Wislna 2, 31-007 Krakow, Poland. TEL 48-12-220644. FAX 48-12-226306. TELEX 332297 UJPL. E-mail: UWPISARE@cyr-kr.edu.pl. Ed. Walery Pisarek. adv.; illus.
 Formerly (until 1960): Prasa Wspolczesna i Dawna (ISSN 0551-8946).

070.5 CC ISSN 1001-8859
ZHONGGUO CHUBAN NIANJIAN/CHINA PUBLISHING YEARBOOK. (Text in Chinese) 1980. a. Y38. (China Research Institute of Publishing Science) Chinese Book Publishing House, 7A Xi Rong Xian Hu Tong, Xi Cheng District, Beijing 100031, People's Republic of China. TEL 6059534. (Co-sponsor: Publishing Association of China) Ed. Fang Houshu. adv. circ. 5,000. **Document type:** directory.
 Description: Contains articles on developments in China's publishing industry. Lists publishing companies and new publications; includes addresses, telephone and telegraph numbers, and personnel.

070.5 CC
ZHONGGUO KEJI QIKAN YANJIU/CHINESE SCIENCE AND TECHNOLOGY PERIODICALS RESEARCH. (Text in Chinese) q. Zhongguo Kexueyuan, Ziran Kexue Qikan Bianji Yanjiuhui - Chinese Academy of Sciences, Natural Science Periodicals Editing Society, Zhongguancun, Beijing 100080, People's Republic of China. TEL 284303. Ed. Su Shisheng.

028.1 895.1 CC ISSN 1002-235X
ZHONGGUO TUSHU PINGLUN/CHINA BOOK REVIEW. (Text in Chinese) 1987. bi-m. $23.70. Liaoning Renmin Chubanshe, Tushu Pinglun Bianjibu - Liaoning People's Publishing House, 108 Beiyi Malu, Heping-qu, Shenyang, Liaoning 110001, People's Republic of China. TEL 86-24-3861304. FAX 86-24-3871472. (Dist. in US by: China Books & Periodicals, Inc., 2929 24th St., San Francisco, CA 94110. TEL 415-282-2994) Ed. Xu Liyi. adv. contact: Li Keke. bk.rev. **Document type:** academic/scholarly publication.

070.5 CC ISSN 1000-6095
ZHONGWAI SHUZHAI/DIGEST OF CHINESE AND FOREIGN BOOKS. (Text in Chinese) 1985. bi-m. Y27. Shanghai Renmin Chubanshe, Qikan Bu, 54 Shaoxing Road, Shanghai 200020, People's Republic of China. TEL 021-4335250. FAX 021-4331665. Ed. Yu Chunde. circ. 55,000.

070.5 GW
ZWIEBEL. 1965. a. Verlag Klaus Wagenbach, Ahornstr. 4, 10787 Berlin, Germany. TEL 030-2115069. FAX 030-2116140. **Document type:** trade publication.

070.5 SI
8 DAYS. (Text in English) 1990. w. $1.20 per no. No. 21-02-05 Goldhill Plaza, 51 Newton Rd., Singapore 1130, Singapore. TEL 2556288. FAX 2568921. TELEX 39265. Ed. Agatha Koh. circ. 75,000.

PUBLISHING AND BOOK TRADE — Abstracting, Bibliographies, Statistics

070.5 UK
A A B'S BIBLIOGRAPHY OF RARE & OUT-OF-PRINT TITLES TRACED. (Published in 4 parts: Part 1: By Authors; Part 2: By Titles; Part 3: By Subjects; Part 4: By Categories) 1985. a £39.95 for each part (foreign £39.95). A A B British Book Search Services (Oxford), Editorial Research Centre, P.O. Box 342, Oxford OX1 1NN, England. TEL 01865-792610. FAX 01865-792611. E-mail: 100432,3602@csi.compuserve.com. Ed. L. Gigliotti. circ. 15,000. **Document type:** bibliography, academic/scholarly publication.
 ●Also available online.
 Former titles: A A B's Bibliography of Available Out-of-Print and Rare Italian Publications Published or Distributed in Great Britain; (until 1990): Bibliography of Italian Publications Published or Distributed in Great Britain.
 Description: Lists books printed or distributed in the U.K. and books about Italy in English and other languages available in the U.K.

070.5 UK ISSN 0966-2413
A A B'S REGISTER OF WANTED PUBLICATIONS; updated daily. (Avail. in 4 parts: Part 1: By Authors; Part 2: By Titles, Part 3: By Subjects, Part 4: By Categories) 1980. m. £29.95 for each part (foreign £39.95). A A B British Book Search Services (Oxford), Editorial Research Centre, P.O. Box 342, Oxford OX1 1NN, England. TEL 01865-792610. FAX 01865-792611. E-mail: 100432,3602@csi.compuserve.com. Ed. L. Gigliotti. **Document type:** bibliography, directory.
 ●Also available online.
 Formerly (until 1992): Book and Journals Wanted List.
 Description: Offers publishers, book distributors, librarians, second-hand booksellers, antiquarians, libraries and other reference researchers a book-referral service.

011 US
ABRIDGED MAGAZINE INDEX. m. $975. Information Access Company (Subsidiary of: Thomson Corporation), 362 Lakeside Dr., Foster City, CA 94404. TEL 415-378-5200; 800-227-8431. FAX 415-378-5369. (microform) **Document type:** abstracting/indexing.
 Description: Covers 6 years of data, indexing approximately 100 general-interest periodicals.

015.6 070.5 UK ISSN 0306-0322
Z465.7
AFRICAN BOOK PUBLISHING RECORD. (Text in English, occasionally in French) 1975. q. £100($165) (effective 1994). Hans Zell Publishers (Subsidiary of: Bowker - Saur Ltd.), P.O. Box 56, Oxford OX1 2SJ, England. TEL 01865-511428. FAX 01865-311534. (Subscr. to: World Wide Subscription Services Ltd., Unit 4, Gibbs Reed Farm, Ticehurst, E. Sussex TN5 7HE, England. TEL 01580-200657. FAX 01580-200616; Dist. in U.S. by: K.G. Saur, A part of Reed Reference Publishing, 121 Chanlon Rd., New Providence, NJ 07974. TEL 800-521-8110) Eds. Hans Zell, Cecile Lomer. adv.; bk.rev.; bibl.; illus.; stat.; circ. 800 (controlled). (back issues avail.) Indexed: Curr.Cont.Africa, Documentatieblad, M.L.A. **Document type:** trade publication, bibliography.
 —BLDSC (0732.360000). CCC.
 Description: Current bibliography of African published materials. Includes features, articles, reports and news about African publishing and book development.

070 015 US ISSN 0091-9357
Z1000
AMERICAN BOOK PRICES CURRENT. a. price varies. Bancroft - Parkman, Inc., Box 1236, Washington, CT 06793. TEL 212-737-2715. FAX 203-868-0080. circ. 3,000.

070 015 US ISSN 0091-9357
AMERICAN BOOK PRICES CURRENT. FOUR YEAR INDEX. 1899. quadrennial. $495. Bancroft - Parkman, Inc., Box 1236, Washington, CT 06793. TEL 212-737-2715. FAX 203-868-0080. Ed. Katharine Kyes Leab. adv.
 Formerly: American Book Prices Current. Five Year Index.

070 011 US ISSN 0002-7707
Z1219
AMERICAN BOOK PUBLISHING RECORD; arranged by Dewey Decimal Classification and indexed by author, title and subject. Short title: A B P R. 1960. m. with a. cumulations. $275 (effective 1995). R.R. Bowker, A Reed Reference Publishing company, 121 Chanlon Rd., New Providence, NJ 07974. TEL 908-464-6800. FAX 908-665-6688. TELEX 138 755. (Subscr. to: Order Dept., Box 31, New Providence, NJ 07974-9903. TEL 800-521-8110) index, cum.index. circ. 4,000. (also avail. in magnetic tape) Indexed: Abstr.Bull.Inst.Pap.Chem., Bibl.Engl.Lang.& Lit. **Document type:** directory.
 —Genuine Article; UMI. CCC.
 Description: Catalog records. Includes separate adult fiction and juvenile fiction sections. Included in each entry: main entry, title (italics), subtitle, author statement, publication place, publisher, publication date, collation, series statement, general note or contents note, LC Classification numbers, LC card numbers and subject tracings.

AUSTRALIAN SOCIETY OF INDEXERS NEWSLETTER. see *LIBRARY AND INFORMATION SCIENCES — Abstracting, Bibliographies, Statistics*

ULRICH'S INTERNATIONAL PERIODICALS DIRECTORY 1996

PUBLISHING AND BOOK TRADE — ABSTRACTING, BIBLIOGRAPHIES, STATISTICS 5641

655 011   IO   ISSN 0216-1273
Z3271
BERITA BIBLIOGRAFI; Indonesian book news. 1954. m. Rps.6000($10) Yayasan Idayu - Idayu Foundation, Gedung Kebangkitan Nasional, J1 Abdulrakhman Saleh 26, P.O. Box 48-Jkt, Jakarta 10410, Indonesia. TEL 361261. TELEX 45255-SATRIA-IA. Ed. Djusna Asif. adv.; bk.rev.; bibl. circ. 500. **Indexed:** E.I.
   Formerly: Berita Idayu Bibligrafi; Which was formed by the merger of: Berita Bibliografi (ISSN 0005-9129) & Berita Idayu.

020 010   IT   ISSN 0006-0941
Z1007
BIBLIOFILIA; rivista di storia del libro e di bibliografia. (Text in English, French, German and Italian) 1899. 3/yr. L.95000 (foreign L.118000) (effective 1995) US $79 (effective 1996). Casa Editrice Leo S. Olschki, Casella Postale 66, 50100 Florence, Italy. TEL 39-55-6530684. FAX 39-55-6530214. Ed. Luigi Balsamo. adv.; bk.rev.; illus. circ. 1,000. **Indexed:** Lib.Lit., Lib.Sci.Abstr., M.L.A. **Document type:** academic/scholarly publication.

BIBLIOGRAFIA NAZIONALE ITALIANA. see *BIBLIOGRAPHIES*

655 020 015   FR   ISSN 1142-3250
Z2165   CODEN: BIFRA9
BIBLIOGRAPHIE NATIONALE FRANCAISE. LIVRES; journal officiel du livre francais. 1811. 26/yr. (CD-ROM q.) 2615 F. (foreign 2905 F.) (effective 1995). Bibliotheque Nationale de France, 58 rue de Richelieu, 75002 Paris, France. TEL 47-03-86-10. FAX 47-03-85-86. adv.; bk.rev.; index. circ. 600. (also avail. in microfilm from PMC; reprint service avail. from KTO) **Document type:** bibliography.
●Also available on CD-ROM.
   Former titles (until 1990): Bibliographie de la France. Livres (ISSN 0150-1402); (until 1977): Bibliographie de la France. 1ere Partie, Bibliographie Officielle (ISSN 0335-5667); Supersedes in part: Bibliographie de la France, Biblio (ISSN 0335-5675)

020.6   AU   ISSN 0006-2022
BIBLOS; Beitraege zu Buch, Bibliothek und Schrift. (Text in English and German) 1952. 2/yr. S.300 (foreign S.340). (Gesellschaft der Freunde der Oesterreichischen Nationalbibliothek) Boehlau Verlag GmbH & Co.KG., Sachsenplatz 4-6, A-1201 Vienna, Austria. TEL 0222-3302427-0. FAX 0222-3302432. Ed.Bd. adv.; bk.rev.; bibl.; charts; illus.; index, cum.index every 10 yrs. circ. 1,200. **Indexed:** Amer.Hist.& Life, Art & Archaeol.Tech.Abstr., Hist.Abstr., Lib.Lit., Lib.Sci.Abstr., P.A.I.S.For.Lang.Ind. **Document type:** academic/scholarly publication.
—BLDSC (2022.000000); SWETS.
   Description: Covers library and information science news, technical information, news from Austrian libraries, events and meetings.

658.8   NO   ISSN 0800-0778
BOK OG SAMFUNN. 1879. 24/yr. NOK 990 (effective 1996). Norske Bokhandlerforening - Norwegian Booksellers' Association, Oevre Vollgt. 15, 0158 Oslo 1, Norway. adv.; bibl.; index.
—BLDSC (2121.460000).
   Formed by the 1981 merger of: Bok og Samfunn. A-Utgave (ISSN 0332-5946); Bok og Samfunn. B-Utgave (ISSN 0332-995X); Formerly (until 1976): Norske Bokhandlertidende (ISSN 0029-1889)

BOLETIN BIBLIOGRAFICO BOLIVIANO. see *BIBLIOGRAPHIES*

BOLETIN BIBLIOGRAFICO MEXICANO. see *BIBLIOGRAPHIES*

BOOK COLLECTOR. see *HOBBIES — Abstracting, Bibliographies, Statistics*

655 011   UK   ISSN 0006-7245
BOOK EXCHANGE. 1948. m. £3($8) 9 Chandler Close, Bath BA1 4EG, England. TEL 0225-20773. Ed. F.F. Taylor. adv.; bk.rev. circ. 1,000.

028.1   US   ISSN 0524-0581
BOOK REVIEW INDEX; indexes all reviews in over 500 periodicals. 1965. bi-m. $202 (effective 1993). Gale Research Inc., 835 Penobscot Bldg., Detroit, MI 48226. TEL 313-961-2242. FAX 313-961-6083. TELEX 810-221-7086. Eds. Neil E. Walker, Beverly Baer. circ. 3,000. (also avail. in microfiche) **Document type:** abstracting/indexing.
●Also available online. Vendor(s): Knight-Ridder, Inc. (File no.137).
   Description: Compendium of book reviews from various periodicals.

028.1   US   ISSN 0524-0581
Z1035.A1
BOOK REVIEW INDEX: ANNUAL CLOTHBOUND CUMULATIONS. 1965. a. $202 (effective 1993). Gale Research Inc., 835 Penobscot Bldg., Detroit, MI 48226. TEL 313-961-2242. FAX 313-961-6083. TELEX 810-221-7086. Eds. Neil E. Walker, Beverly Baer. (back issues avail.) **Document type:** abstracting/indexing.
   Description: Annual compendium of book reviews from various periodicals.

655 020 011   US   ISSN 0006-7385
Z1035.A1
BOOKLIST. 1905. 22/yr. $65 (foreign $80). American Library Association, 50 E. Huron St., Chicago, IL 60611-2795. TEL 800-545-2433. FAX 312-440-9374. Ed. Bill Ott. adv.; bk.rev.; bibl.; index, s-a. cum.index. circ. 31,168. (also avail. in microform from UMI; back issues avail.; reprint service avail. from UMI) **Indexed:** Amer.Bibl.Slavic & E.Eur.Stud., Bk.Rev.Ind. (1965-), Chic.Per.Ind., Child.Bk.Rev.Ind. (1965-), Child.Lit.Abstr., Gard.Lit. (1992-), Leg.Info.Manage.Ind., Lib.Lit., Media Rev.Dig., Microcomp.Ind., Mid.East: Abstr.& Ind., PCR2, Ref.Sour.
—BLDSC (2250.068000); Genuine Article; SWETS; UMI; UnCover. **CCC.**
   Incorporates: Reference Books Bulletin; **Formerly:** Booklist and Subscription Books Bulletin.
   Description: Reviews of recommended library materials for adults, young adults and children; print and non-print.

015 948   FI   ISSN 0006-7490
Z2520
BOOKS FROM FINLAND. (Text in English) 1967. q. FIM 150. Helsingin Yliopiston Kirjasto - Helsinki University Library, Box 15, Unioninkatu 36, SF-00014, University of Helsinki, Finland. FAX 358-0-1357942. Ed. Erkka Lehtola. bibl.; illus. circ. 4,000. **Indexed:** M.L.A.
   Description: Covers modern Finnish literature and writers.

BOOKS FROM KOREA. see *BIBLIOGRAPHIES*

943.8 057.85   UK   ISSN 0006-7512
BOOKS IN POLISH OR RELATING TO POLAND. 1950. q. £21. Polish Library, 238-246 King St., London W6 ORF, England. TEL 0181-741-0474. Ed. J. Szmidt. bibl.; index. circ. 150. (processed) **Document type:** bibliography.
—BLDSC (2250.208000).

973 015   US   ISSN 0006-7520
Z1251.S8
BOOKS OF THE SOUTHWEST; a critical checklist of current Southwestern Americana. 1957. m. $24 to individuals; institutions $36. Books West Southwest, 2452 N. Campbell, Tucson, AZ 85719. TEL 602-326-3533. Ed. W. David Laird. bk.rev.; bibl. circ. 400.
   Description: Publishes reviews of all books and other published items about the American Southwest and northern Mexico.

BRANDYWINE BIBLIOGRAPHY. see *PRINTING — Abstracting, Bibliographies, Statistics*

070.5   GW   ISSN 0068-3051
Z313
BUCH UND BUCHHANDEL IN ZAHLEN. 1952. a. DM.29. Boersenverein des Deutschen Buchhandels e.V., Grosser Hirschgraben 17-21, 60311 Frankfurt a.M., Germany. FAX 069-1306-396. Ed. Eva Martin. circ. 3,500. **Document type:** trade publication.
   Description: Statistical publication of the book trade. Lists book production, book prices, translations and licenses, foreign trade, magazine production, sales and costs, and readership.

070.5 015   AU
BUECHER NEWS. 1949. a. Hauptverband des Oesterreichischen Buchhandels, Gruenangergasse 4, A-1010 Vienna, Austria. TEL 0222-5121535. FAX 0222-5128482. adv.; bk.rev. **Document type:** trade publication.
   Former titles: Buecher Trend; Buecher; Buecher fuer Sie (ISSN 0067-0634); Aus der Schatzkammer der Buecher.

840 028.1 011   FR   ISSN 0007-4209
BULLETIN CRITIQUE DU LIVRE FRANCAIS. English edition: New French Books. 1945. m. 600 F. (foreign 800 F.). Association pour la Diffusion de la Pensee Francaise, 12 rue Pierre et Marie Curie, 75005 Paris, France. TEL 43-26-41-59. FAX 46-34-52-65. adv.; bk.rev.; index, cum.index. circ. 5,600. (also avail. in diskette format; back issues avail.)
   Description: New French books, quarterly editions.

CANADA. STATISTICS CANADA. PRINTING, PUBLISHING AND ALLIED INDUSTRIES. see *PRINTING — Abstracting, Bibliographies, Statistics*

020.75   UK   ISSN 0142-1980
Y CASGLWR. 3/yr. £3. Cymdeithdas Bob Owen, c/o Richard H. Lewis, 40 Maes Ceiro, Bow Street, Dyfed SY24 5BG, Wales. circ. 1,300.
   Description: Covers all aspects of book collecting and bibliography.

070.5   AG
CATALOGO COLECTIVO DE PUBLICACIONES PERIODICAS EXISTENTES EN BIBLIOTECAS CIENTIFICAS Y TECNICAS ARGENTINA. 1942; 2nd edt. 1962. irreg., suppl. 1972, 1981. $80. Consejo Nacional de Investigaciones Cientificas y Tecnicas, Moreno 433, 1091 Buenos Aires, Argentina.

011   SP
CATALOGO DE LIBROS ANTIGUOS Y MODERNOS. s-a. 300 ptas. Diego Gomez Florez, Ed. & Pub., Travesera de las Cortes, 305, Barcelona, 14, Spain. bibl.; illus. circ. 3,000.

CHILDREN'S LITERATURE ABSTRACTS. see *CHILDREN AND YOUTH — Abstracting, Bibliographies, Statistics*

028.1 011   US   ISSN 0009-4978
Z1035   CODEN: CHOIEZ
CHOICE (MIDDLETOWN); current reviews of academic books. 1963. m. (11/yr.). $165 (foreign $187). (Association of College and Research Libraries) Choice, 100 Riverview Ctr., Middletown, CT 06457. TEL 203-347-6933. FAX 203-346-8586. (Affiliate: American Library Association) Ed. Francine Graf; Pub. Francine Graf. adv.: B&W page $1575; adv. contact: Stewart Foster. bk.rev.; bibl.; index. circ. 4,800. (also avail. in cards; microfilm from UMI) **Indexed:** Bibl.Ind., Bk.Rev.Dig., Bk.Rev.Ind. (1965-), Chic.Per.Ind., Child.Bk.Rev.Ind. (1965-), Leg.Info.Manage.Ind., Lib.Lit. **Document type:** academic/scholarly publication.
●Also available online.
Also available on CD-ROM. Producer(s): SilverPlatter Information, Inc.
—BLDSC (3181.535000); UMI; UnCover. **CCC.**

070.5 011   UK   ISSN 0140-1939
CLOVER INFORMATION INDEX. 1974. q. £52 (foreign £68). Clover Publications, 32 Ickwell Road, Northill, Biggleswade, Beds. SG18 9AB, England. TEL 01767-627363. **Document type:** abstracting/indexing.
—BLDSC (3287.023000).
   Description: A subject guide to popular periodicals.

655 011   US   ISSN 0010-2237
Z1601
COMENTARIOS BIBLIOGRAFICOS AMERICANOS.* (Text in English, Spanish) 1969. q. $62. E. Darino, Ed. & Pub., 222 Park Ave S., Apt. 2A, New York, NY 10003. adv.; bk.rev.; bibl.; stat.; index. circ. 10,000. (looseleaf format; back issues avail.)
   Description: Presents book reviews published in Latin America and Spain.

CORREO EDITORIAL; revista informativa de la C C L. see *PUBLISHING AND BOOK TRADE*

PUBLISHING AND BOOK TRADE — ABSTRACTING, BIBLIOGRAPHIES, STATISTICS

028.1 016   II   ISSN 0378-7494
CREATIVE BOOK SELECTION INDEX. (Text in English) 1972. m. Rs.144($30) K.K. Roy (Private) Ltd., 55 Gariahat Rd., P.O. Box 10210, Calcutta 700 019, India. Ed. Dr. K.K. Roy. bk.rev.; index. circ. 2,280. (looseleaf format; reprint service avail. from UMI)
   Description: Reviews current fiction appearing in Indian periodicals and newspapers.

070.5 011   JA
CURRENT JAPANESE PERIODICALS FOR (YEAR). a. Japan Publications Inc., 2-1 Sarugaku-cho 1-chome, Chiyoda-ku, Tokyo 101, Japan. TEL 03-2958411. FAX 03-2958416. Ed. A. Takeuchi.
   Description: Lists both English- and Japanese-language periodicals that are available by subscription overseas, main title alpha list with U.S. dollar prices, index by category.

070.5   GW
DEUTSCHE NATIONALBIBLIOGRAPHIE. C D - R O M EDITION. 1989. 4/yr. DM.3000. (Deutsche Bibliothek) Buchhaendler-Vereinigung GmbH, Postfach 100442, 60004 Frankfurt a.M., Germany. TEL 069-1306-243. FAX 069-1306201. TELEX 413573-BUCHV-D. **Document type:** bibliography.
   ●Available only on CD-ROM.
   Formerly: Deutsche Bibliographie. C D - R O M Edition.

070.5 015   GW
Z2221
DEUTSCHE NATIONALBIBLIOGRAPHIE. FUENFJAHRES-VERZEICHNIS. 1945. irreg. price varies. (Deutsche Bibliothek) Buchhaendler-Vereinigung GmbH, Postfach 100442, 60004 Frankfurt a.M., Germany. TEL 069-13060. FAX 069-1306201. TELEX 413573-BUCHV-D. bibl.; index. **Document type:** bibliography.
   Formerly: Deutsche Bibliographie. Fuenfjahres-Verzeichnis (ISSN 0418-8233)

013 378   GW
Z5055.G29
DEUTSCHE NATIONALBIBLIOGRAPHIE. HOCHSCHULSCHRIFTEN-VERZEICHNIS. 1972. m. price varies. (Deutsche Bibliothek) Buchhaendler-Vereinigung GmbH, Postfach 100442, 60004 Frankfurt a.M., Germany. TEL 069-13060. FAX 069-1306201. TELEX 413573-BUCHV-D. bibl.; index. **Document type:** bibliography.
   Incorporates: Deutsche Nationalbibliographie. Reihe C: Dissertationen und Habilitationsschriften (ISSN 0012-0545); **Formerly:** Deutsche Bibliographie. Hochschulschriften-Verzeichnis (ISSN 0301-4665)

070.5 015   GW
Z2221
DEUTSCHE NATIONALBIBLIOGRAPHIE. REIHE A. MONOGRAPHIEN UND PERIODIKA DES VERLAGSBUCHHANDELS. 1947. w. DM.2172. (Deutsche Bibliothek) Buchhaendler-Vereinigung GmbH, Postfach 100442, 60004 Frankfurt a.M., Germany. TEL 069-13060. FAX 069-1306201. TELEX 413573-BUCHV-D. bibl.; index. **Document type:** bibliography.
   Former titles: Deutsche Nationalbibliographie. Wochentliches Verzeichnis. Ausgabe 1 Amtsblatt der Deutschen Bibliothek; Deutsche Bibliographie. Woechentliches Verzeichnis. Ausgabe 1 Amtsblatt der Deutschen Bibliothek (ISSN 0170-1037)

DIRECTORY OF COMPANY HISTORIES OF THE BOOK INDUSTRIES/VERZEICHNIS VON JUBILAEUMSSCHRIFTEN DER GRAPHISCHEN INDUSTRIE. see *PRINTING — Abstracting, Bibliographies, Statistics*

808   US   ISSN 0095-6414
PN4820
DIRECTORY OF SMALL MAGAZINE - PRESS EDITORS AND PUBLISHERS. 1970. a. $23.75. Dustbooks, Box 100, Paradise, CA 95967. TEL 916-877-6110; 800-477-6110. FAX 916-877-0222. Ed. Len Fulton. **Document type:** directory.
   Description: Lists editors and publishers of small presses and magazines with addresses and phone numbers.

070.5   BE   ISSN 0777-0006
DONNEES STATISTIQUES SUR LE LIVRE BELGE DE LANGUE FRANCAISE. (Text in French) a., latest 1992 (for the year 1990). free. Association des Editeurs Belges, 140 Bd. Lambermont, Bte. 1, B-1030 Brussels, Belgium. TEL 32-2-2416580. FAX 32-2-2167131. **Document type:** corporate report.
   Formerly (until 1983): Livre en Belgique en... (ISSN 0776-9997)
   Description: Statistical review of the state of French language publishing in Belgium.

070.5 016   US
EARTH GUILD MAIL ORDER CATALOG. 1974. s-a. $2 per no. Earth Guild Inc., Hot Springs, NC 28743. TEL 704-622-3258. adv.; bk.rev.; charts; illus. circ. 24,000.
   Formerly: Earth Guild - Grateful Union Mail Order Catalog.

070.5   FR
ELECTRE BIBLIO. (Former name of issuing body: Editions du Cercle de la Librairie) m. (11/yr.) or q. 16129.60 F. m. (foreign 13600 F.); q. 10258.90 F. (foreign 8650 F.). Electre, 35 rue Gregoire-de-Tours, 75006 Paris, France. TEL 44-41-28-00. FAX 44-41-28-65. Ed. P. Fouche. **Document type:** bibliography.
   ●Available only on CD-ROM.

THE EUROMONITOR BOOK REPORT (YEAR). see *PUBLISHING AND BOOK TRADE*

655 011   IT   ISSN 0017-0216
GIORNALE DELLA LIBRERIA. 1888. m. L.105000 to individuals; libraries L.84000 (foreign L.160000). (Associazione Italiana Editori) Editrice Bibliografica s.r.l., Viale Vittorio Veneto, 24, 20124 Milan, Italy. TEL 39-2-29006965. FAX 39-6-654624. Ed. Giancarla Re Mursia. adv.; bk.rev.; charts; stat.; index. circ. 5,000. **Document type:** trade publication.
   Description: Covers book publishing, book trade. Includes a bibliography of books published in Italy.

015   PK
ILMI A'INO. (Text in Sindhi) a. Rs.2. University of Sind, Institute of Sindhology, Jamshoro, Hyderabad 6, Pakistan.
   Description: Lists books, periodicals, publishers, cultural and literary organizations in Sind.

070.5 015.968   SA   ISSN 0379-0584
CODEN: ISAPDQ
INDEX TO SOUTH AFRICAN PERIODICALS. Short title: I S A P. (Print edition ceased in 1986) (Text in Afrikaans, English) 1945. a. R.2400 for CD-ROM (updates 3/yr.). State Library - Staatsbiblioteek, P.O. Box 397, Pretoria 0001, South Africa. TEL 27-12-21-8931. FAX 27-12-325-5984. E-mail: askatze@statelib.pwv.gov.za. circ. 350. (microfiche; back issues avail.) **Document type:** abstracting/indexing.
   ●Also available online.
   Also available on CD-ROM.
   —CASDDS.
   Description: Provides citations of more than 136000 articles from 400 South African periodicals from 1940 to the present.

655 015   II   ISSN 0019-445X
Z3201
INDIAN BOOKS. (Text in English) 1968. m. Rs.95($24) Mukherjee Library, 1 Gopi Mohan Dutta Ln., Calcutta 700003, India. Ed.Bd. adv.; bk.rev.; bibl.; index. circ. 500.

070.5   GW   ISSN 0344-6190
INTERNATIONAL BOOK TRADE DIRECTORY; Europe, Australia, Oceania, Latin America, Africa, and Asia. (Text in English and German) 1978. irreg., 2nd ed., 1989. DM.498($275) K.G. Saur Verlag KG, A part of Reed Reference Publishing, Ortlerstr. 8, 81373 Munich, Germany. TEL 089-76902-0. FAX 089-76902150. (Subscr. to: Postfach 701620, 81316 Munich, Germany; N. America subscr. to: K.G. Saur, 121 Chanlon Rd., New Providence, NJ 07974. TEL 908-665-3576) Ed. Michael Sachs. **Document type:** directory.
   Description: Lists 70,000 booksellers, bookstores, and wholesalers outside the US. Includes subject index.

070.5 016   US
INTERNATIONAL DIRECTORY OF CHILDREN'S LITERATURE. 1973. biennial. $34.95. George Kurian Reference Books, Box 519, Baldwin Place, NY 10505. TEL 914-962-3287. Ed. Mary Beth Dunhouse. bk.rev. circ. 3,500. **Document type:** directory.
   Formerly: Children's Literary Almanac (ISSN 0093-0431)

070   US   ISSN 0092-3974
Z6944.L5
INTERNATIONAL DIRECTORY OF LITTLE MAGAZINES AND SMALL PRESSES. (Supplement avail.: Small Press Review - Small Magazine Review) 1965. a. $44.95 cloth; paper $28.95 (for 30th ed.). Dustbooks, Box 100, Paradise, CA 95967. TEL 916-877-6110; 800-477-6110. FAX 916-877-0222. Ed. Len Fulton. adv. circ. 10,000. **Document type:** directory.
—BLDSC (4539.651000).
   Formerly: Directory of Little Magazines, Small Presses and Underground Newspapers (ISSN 0084-9979)
   Description: Lists 5200 independent publishers, with full data on each.

011.44   UK
▼**INTERNATIONAL RARE BOOK PRICES - CHILDREN'S BOOKS.** 1994. a. £18. Clique, Ltd., 7 Pulleyn Dr., York YO2 2DY, England. TEL 01904-631752. FAX 09104-651325.

090.75   UK   ISSN 0953-2838
INTERNATIONAL RARE BOOK PRICES - EARLY PRINTED BOOKS. 1987. a. £18. Clique, Ltd., 7 Pulleyn Dr., York YO2 2DY, England. TEL 01904-631752. FAX 01904-651325. **Document type:** bibliography.
   Description: Contains bibliographic information about rare books, prices and availability.

090.75   UK   ISSN 0968-882X
INTERNATIONAL RARE BOOK PRICES - LITERATURE. 1989. a. £22. Clique, Ltd., 7 Pulleyn Dr., York YO2 2DY, England. TEL 01904-631752. FAX 0904-651325. (back issues avail.) **Document type:** bibliography.
   Formerly: International Rare Book Prices - 19th Century Literature (ISSN 0968-9494)
   Description: Provides bibliographic information about rare literary books, along with their prices and availability.

090.75 011   UK   ISSN 0952-2972
INTERNATIONAL RARE BOOK PRICES - MODERN FIRST EDITION. 1987. a. £22. Clique, Ltd., 7 Pulleyn Dr., York YO2 2DY, England. TEL 01904-631752. FAX 01904-651325. **Document type:** bibliography.
   Description: Provides bibliographical information on rare first-edition books and includes prices and availability.

090.75 011   UK   ISSN 0952-2999
INTERNATIONAL RARE BOOK PRICES - SCIENCES & MEDICINE. 1987. a. £22. Clique, Ltd., 7 Pulleyn Dr., York YO2 2DY, England. TEL 01904-631752. FAX 01904-651325. **Document type:** bibliography.
   Description: Supplies bibliographic information on rare scientific and medical books, along with prices and availability.

090.75 011   UK   ISSN 0952-2964
INTERNATIONAL RARE BOOK PRICES - THE ARTS & ARCHITECTURE. 1987. a. £22. Clique, Ltd., 7 Pulleyn Dr., York YO2 2DY, England. TEL 01904-631752. FAX 01904-651325. **Document type:** bibliography.
   Description: Provides bibliographic information about rare books on the arts and architecture, along with prices and their availability.

090.75 011   UK   ISSN 0952-2980
INTERNATIONAL RARE BOOK PRICES - VOYAGES, TRAVEL & EXPLORATION. 1987. a. £22. Clique, Ltd., 7 Pulleyn Dr., York YO2 2DY, England. TEL 01904-631752. FAX 01904-651325. (back issues avail.) **Document type:** bibliography.
   Description: Provides bibliographic information about rare travel books, with prices and their availability.

PUBLISHING AND BOOK TRADE — ABSTRACTING, BIBLIOGRAPHIES, STATISTICS

070.5   IT   ISSN 0444-8677
HA40.C8
ITALY. ISTITUTO NAZIONALE DI STATISTICA. STATISTICHE CULTURALI. 1959. a. L1800 (effective 1993). Istituto Nazionale di Statistica, Via Cesare Balbo 16, 00100 Rome, Italy. FAX 06-46735198. circ. 1,200. **Document type:** government publication.
   Formerly: Italy. Istituto Centrale di Statistica. Annuario delle Statistiche Culturali (ISSN 0075-1677)

070.5 010   AE   ISSN 0066-5630
AL-KITAB AL-ARABI FI AAM/ARAB BOOK ANNUAL. (Text in Arabic; summary in English) 1961. a. £E1800($8.70) Entreprise National du Livre, 3 bd. Zirout Youcef, B.P. 49, Algiers, Algeria. TEL 2-63-97-12. TELEX 53845.

970 980 016   II   ISSN 0023-8740
LATIN AMERICAN BOOKS NEWSLETTER. (Text in English) 1970. m. R.200($58) K.K. Roy (Private) Ltd., 55 Gariahat Rd., P.O. Box 10210, Calcutta 700 019, India. Ed. John G. Aillard. bk.rev.; bibl.; index. circ. 980.

090.75 011   IT
LIBRI RARI; collezione di ristampe con nuovi apparati. 1977. irreg., latest 1987. price varies. Edizioni Il Polifilo, Via Borgonuovo 2, 20121 Milan, Italy.

655 011   FR   ISSN 0024-5348
LIVRES; bulletin bibliographique mensuel. 1949. 9/yr. 250 F. (foreign 280 F.). Centre National de Documentation Pedagogique, 29 rue d'Ulm, 75230 Paris Cedex 05, France. (Subscr. to: C.N.D.P., Abonnement, B.P. 21, Square St. Charles, 75012 Paris, France) adv.; abstr.; bibl.; index.

070.5 011   FR   ISSN 0294-0000
LIVRES HEBDO. (Supplements avail.: Livres du Mois (ISSN 0294-0027); Trois Mois de Nouveautes (ISSN 0294-0035); Six Mois de Nouveautes (ISSN 0294-0043); Un An de Nouveautes (ISSN 0294-1090); Service Ile-de-France (ISSN 1162-4469)) 1979. 44/yr. 2060 F. Livres Hebdo, 35 rue Gregoire de Tours, 75006 Paris, France. TEL 44-41-28-00. FAX 44-41-28-64. Ed. Jean-Marie Doublet. adv.; bk.rev.; bibl.; illus.; stat. circ. 9,000. **Document type:** trade publication.
—SWETS. CCC.
   Formed by the 1982 merger of: Livres Hebdo (Edition avec Prix Cession de Base) (ISSN 0223-4807); Livres Hebdo (Edition Destine a l'Etranger) (ISSN 0223-4815); Livres Hebdo (Edition sans Prix) (ISSN 0223-4793); All of which supersede in part (1959-1979): Bulletin du Livre (ISSN 0007-456X); (1972-1979): Bibliographie de la France. Biblio (ISSN 0335-5675); Which was formed by the merger of (1933-1971): Biblio (Mensuel) (ISSN 1147-6710); (1814-1971): Bibliographie de la France (ISSN 0006-1344); Which was formerly: Bibliographie de l'Empire Francais (ISSN 1147-6680); (until 1811): Journal General de l'Imprimerie et de la Libraire (ISSN 1147-6672); (1797): Journal Typographique et Bibliographique (ISSN 1147-6664).

655 011   UK   ISSN 0024-5437
LLAIS LLYFRAU/BOOKS IN WALES. (Text in English and Welsh) 1964. q. £5 (foreign £6.50). Welsh Books Council, Castell Brychan, Aberystwyth, Dyfed SY23 2JB, Wales. TEL 01970-624151. FAX 01970-625385. Ed. R. Gerallt Jones. adv. contact: D. Philip Davies. bk.rev.; bibl.; illus. circ. 3,000. **Indexed:** Child.Lit.Abstr. **Document type:** consumer publication.
   Description: List of all books published in Wales during previous three months, plus reviews and articles on the Welsh literary scene.

070.5 012   US
MAGAZINE INDEX. m. $2880 on CD-ROM. Information Access Company (Subsidiary of: Thomson Corporation), 362 Lakeside Dr., Foster City, CA 94404. TEL 415-378-5200; 800-227-8431. FAX 415-378-5369. (microform) **Document type:** abstracting/indexing.
   ●Also available online. Vendor(s): Ovid Technologies (MAGS), Knight-Ridder, Inc. (File no.47), Lexis-Nexis. Also available on CD-ROM.
   Description: Comprehensive guide to more than 350 general-interest periodicals. Covers over 4 years of data.

655 016   US   ISSN 0026-4377
MILWAUKEE READER. 1942. m. $5. Milwaukee Public Library, 814 W. Wisconsin Ave., Milwaukee, WI 53233. TEL 414-278-3031. FAX 414-278-2137. Ed. Lorelei Starck. bk.rev. circ. 4,500. (processed) **Document type:** newsletter.

NATIONAL BIBLIOGRAPHY OF BOTSWANA. see *BIBLIOGRAPHIES*

DAS NEUE BUCH; Buchprofile fuer die Katholische Buechereiarbeit. see *RELIGIONS AND THEOLOGY — Abstracting, Bibliographies, Statistics*

500 655   NE
NIJHOFF INFORMATION, NEW PUBLICATIONS FROM GERMANY, AUSTRIA AND SWITZERLAND. (Text in English) 1988. m. free. Martinus Nijhoff International, P.O. Box 269, 2501 AX The Hague, Netherlands. TEL 31-79-3684400. FAX 31-79-3615698. (U.S. addr.: Box 562, Marshfield Hills, MA 02051. TEL 800-MNI-1853) adv.; bk.rev.; index. circ. 2,500.
   Formerly: Nijhoff Information, New Publications from West Germany, Austria and Switzerland.
   Description: Bibliographic information on all new and forthcoming scientific journals, books, monographic titles and microfiches published in Germany, Austria and Switzerland.

655 015   NE   ISSN 0029-0459
NIJHOFF INFORMATION, NEW PUBLICATIONS FROM THE NETHERLANDS. (Text in English) 1965. m. free. Martinus Nijhoff International, P.O. Box 269, 2501 AX The Hague, Netherlands. TEL 31-79-3684400. FAX 31-79-3615698. (U.S. addr.: Box 562, Marshfield Hills, MA 02051. TEL 800-MNI-1853) adv.; bk.rev.; index. circ. 2,500.
   Description: Bibliographic information on all new and forthcoming scientific journals, books, monographic titles and microfiches published in the Netherlands.

655 011   IT   ISSN 0029-6317
NUOVO BOLLETTINO BIBLIOGRAFICO SARDO;* archivio tradizioni popolari. 1955. bi-m. L.6000. Via S. Giovanni 402, Cagliari, Italy. Ed. Dr. Giuseppe Della Maria. bk.rev.; bibl.; index.

P E N INTERNATIONAL. BULLETIN OF SELECTED BOOKS. see *LITERATURE*

070.5 310   BW
PECHAT BELARUSI/BYELORUSSIAN PUBLICATIONS. (Text in Byelorussian) 1976. a. 30 Rub. Nationalnaya Knizhnaya Palata Belarusi., Prospect Mazherova, 11, 220600 Minsk, Belarus. Eds. T.G. Rabushko, A.I. Voronko. circ. 300.
   Formerly: Pechat Belorusskoi S.S.R.
   Description: Contains statistical information on all publications coming out in Belarus.

070.5 070   US   ISSN 1054-1985
Z6951
PROGRESSIVE PERIODICALS DIRECTORY. 1981. irreg. $16. Progressive Education, Box 120574, Nashville, TN 37212. Ed. Craig T. Canan. index. circ. 1,500. **Document type:** bibliography, directory.
   Formerly: U S Progressive Periodicals Directory.
   Description: Reviews and details on 600 national social concerns periodicals.

070.5   GW
Z282
PUBLISHERS' INTERNATIONAL I S B N DIRECTORY (YEAR). (International Standard Book Number) (In 3 vols.) (Text in English and German) 1989. a., 22nd ed., 1995. DM.548($325) (International ISBN Agency, Berlin) K.G. Saur Verlag KG, A part of Reed Reference Publishing, Ortlerstr. 8, 81373 Munich, Germany. TEL 089-76902-0. FAX 089-76902150. (Subscr. to: Postfach 701620, 81316 Munich, Germany; N. America subscr. to: K.G. Saur, 121 Chanlon Rd., Box 31, New Providence, NJ 07974-9903. TEL 908-665-3576) adv. **Document type:** directory.
   ●Also available on CD-ROM. Producer(s): K.G. Saur Verlag.
   Formed by the merger of (1962-1989): Internationales Verlagsadressbuch mit I S B N - Register (ISSN 0074-9877); International I S B N Publishers' Directory.
   Description: Verified listings for publishers in 189 countries, indexed alphabetically, geographically, and numerically by ISBN. Includes microfilm, video and computer software publishers.

QUANGUO XIN SHUMU/NEW BOOKS CATALOG OF P R C. see *BIBLIOGRAPHIES*

028.1 016   US   ISSN 0090-7324
Z1035.1
R S R. (Reference Services Review) 1972. q. $45 to individuals; institutions $75. Pierian Press, Box 1808, Ann Arbor, MI 48106. TEL 313-434-5530. FAX 313-434-6409. Ed. Ilene Rockman. adv.; bk.rev.; bibl.; index. circ. 2,000. (back issues avail.) **Indexed:** Amer.Hist.& Life, Bk.Rev.Ind. (1973-), CALL, Child.Bk.Rev.Ind. (1973-), Hist.Abstr., Leg.Info.Manage.Ind., LHTN, Lib.Lit., LISA, Ref.Sour., Tr.& Indus.Ind.
—BLDSC (7331.920000); Faxon; SWETS; UMI; UnCover.
   Description: Devoted to the enrichment of reference knowledge and to the advancement of services in libraries.
   Refereed Serial

RADICAL BOOKSELLER. see *PUBLISHING AND BOOK TRADE*

070.5   PL   ISSN 0511-1196
RUCH WYDAWNICZY W LICZBACH/POLISH PUBLISHING IN FIGURES. 1955. a. 5 Zl.($8) (Biblioteka Narodowa, Instytut Bibliograficzny) Biblioteka Narodowa, Al. Niepodleglosci 213, 00-973 Warsaw, Poland. TEL 48-22-259271. FAX 48-22-255251. TELEX 813702 BN PL. (Dist. by: P.P. CHZ Ars Polona, ul. KrakowskiePrzedmiescie 7, 00-068 Warsaw, Poland) Ed. Krystyna Bankowska-Bober. circ. 350. **Document type:** abstracting/indexing.
   Description: Offers official statistical data concerning books and periodicals characterized by sheets, titles, copies, subject fields and publishers.

690 016   AG   ISSN 0037-2099
Z1007
SENALES; revista bibliografica. 1949. q. A50($18) Casilla 2484-Correo Central, 1000 Buenos Aires, Argentina. Ed. Amy Dominguez Murray. adv.; bk.rev.; bibl. circ. 2,000.

070.5   UK   ISSN 0963-9721
SHEPPARD'S INTERNATIONAL DIRECTORY PRINT & MAP SELLERS. 1987. irreg., vol.2. $48. Richard Joseph Publishers Ltd., Unit 2, Monks Walk, Farnham, Surrey GU9 8HT, England. TEL 01252-734347. FAX 01252-734307. **Document type:** directory.

SMALL PRESS RECORD OF BOOKS IN PRINT. see *BIBLIOGRAPHIES*

070.5 011   JA
SOUTHEAST - EAST ASIAN ENGLISH PUBLICATIONS IN PRINT. (Text in English) 1987. irreg. 25000 Yen($210) Japan Publications Guide Service, 5-5-13 Matsushiro, Tsukuba-shi, Ibaraki-ken 305, Japan. FAX 81-3-3667-9646. (Subscr. to: Intercontinental Marketing Corp., IPO Box 5056, Tokyo 100-31, Japan. TEL 81-3-3661-7458) adv. circ. 1,000. (also avail. in diskette format) **Document type:** directory.
   Description: Covers the publications in Brunei, Burma, China, Hong Kong, Indonesia, Korea, Macao, Malaysia, Philippines, Singapore, Taiwan, Thailand and Vietnam.

015   CE   ISSN 0253-8229
Z3211
SRI LANKA NATIONAL BIBLIOGRAPHY. (Text in English, Sinhalese, Tamil) 1962. m. Rs.240 (foreign $35). National Library of Sri Lanka, P.O. Box 1764, No. 14 Independence Ave., Colombo 07, Sri Lanka. TEL 941-698847. FAX 941-685201. circ. 1,000. **Document type:** bibliography.
—BLDSC (8425.117000).
   Formerly (until 1973): Ceylon National Bibliography (ISSN 0009-0883)

020 296.7 016   US   ISSN 0039-3568
Z7070
STUDIES IN BIBLIOGRAPHY AND BOOKLORE; devoted to research in the field of Jewish bibliography. (Text in English, Hebrew and other languages) 1953. irreg. price varies. Hebrew Union College - Jewish Institute of Religion (Cincinnati), 3101 Clifton Ave., Cincinnati, OH 45220. TEL 513-221-1875. FAX 513-221-0519. E-mail: gilnerdj@ucbeh.san.uc.edu. Ed.Bd. bk.rev.; bibl.; cum.index: vols. 1-11. circ. 1,100. **Indexed:** Amer.Hist.& Life, Child.Lit.Abstr., Hist.Abstr., Ind.Jew.Per., Mid.East: Abstr.& Ind. **Document type:** academic/scholarly publication.
—BLDSC (8489.660000).

5644 PUBLISHING AND BOOK TRADE — COMPUTER APPLICATIONS

SWAZILAND NATIONAL BIBLIOGRAPHY. see *BIBLIOGRAPHIES*

ULRICH'S INTERNATIONAL PERIODICALS DIRECTORY. see *BIBLIOGRAPHIES*

ULRICH'S ON MICROFICHE. see *BIBLIOGRAPHIES*

ULRICH'S PLUS; the complete International Serials database on compact laser disc. see *BIBLIOGRAPHIES*

ULRICH'S UPDATE. see *BIBLIOGRAPHIES*

860 011   AG
VIENTIN BIBLIOGRAPHIC SERVICE.* 1972. bi-m. Vientin S.A., Talcahuano 487, Buenos Aires, Argentina. bibl.

011   UK   ISSN 0953-041X
Z2005
WHITAKER'S BOOK LIST. 1924. a. £70. J. Whitaker & Sons Ltd., 12 Dyott St., London WC1A 1DF, England. TEL 071-836-8911. FAX 071-836-2909. **Document type:** bibliography.
     Formerly: Whitaker's Cumulative Book List (ISSN 0140-4229)

500 016   GW   ISSN 0341-8723
Z7403
WISSENSCHAFTLICHER LITERATURANZEIGER. 1961. s-a. DM.16. Verlag M. Veit M.A., Erlenweg 10, 33428 Harsewinkel, Germany. TEL 05247-5466. Ed. Manfred Veit. adv.; bk.rev. circ. 4,000. (back issues avail.) **Document type:** abstracting/indexing.

ZIMPEL. TEIL 2: ZEITSCHRIFTEN. see *BIBLIOGRAPHIES*

070.5   GW   ISSN 0946-3968
▼**ZIMPEL. TEIL 4: FACHZEITSCHRIFTEN.** 1995. m. Verlag Dieter Zimpel, Angererstr. 36, 80796 Munich, Germany. TEL 089-3073445. FAX 089-302409. Ed. Ingrid Finsterwald. **Document type:** directory.

296 016   IS   ISSN 0044-4774
ZIONIST LITERATURE. (Text in English and Hebrew) 1936. a. free. World Zionist Organization, Central Zionist Archives, P.O. Box 92, Jerusalem 91920, Israel. Ed. Ms. S. Palmor. circ. 1,000. **Document type:** bibliography.
     Description: Bibilography of publications on Zionism and the land of Israel in recent times.

PUBLISHING AND BOOK TRADE — Computer Applications

BEFORE & AFTER; how to design cool stuff. see *COMPUTERS — Computer Graphics*

070.5   SW
C A P. (Computer Assisted Publishing) 1987. 6/yr. C W - Communications AB, Soedra Hamnvagen 22, Stockholm 115 41, Sweden. TEL 665-10-37. FAX 663-78-73. adv.; B&W page 28600 SEK, color page 32600 SEK; trim 8.38 x 11.22. circ. 8,000.
     Description: Covers presentation, multimedia and design.

070.5   US
C D PUBLISHER NEWS. (Compact Disc) 1986. q. free. Meridian Data, Inc., 5615 Scotts Valley Dr., Scotts Valley, CA 95066. TEL 408-438-3100. FAX 408-438-6816. TELEX 998330. Ed. Monica Meyer. circ. 9,000.
     Description: In-house newsletter highlights applications, industry news and upcoming events in the CD-ROM industry.

070.5   US   ISSN 1075-9123
Z286.E43   CODEN: OPDIEW
C D - R O M FINDER. 1986. irreg., 6th ed., 1994. $69.50. Learned Information, Inc., 143 Old Marlton Pike, Medford, NJ 08055-8750. TEL 609-654-6266. FAX 609-654-4309. Eds. Joseph Webb, James Sheldon. **Document type:** directory.
     Former titles (until 1993): Optical Publishing Directory (ISSN 0896-9841); (until 1987): Optical-Electronic Publishing Directory (ISSN 0893-0317)
     Description: Lists more than 1,400 compact disc titles, product content, hardware requirements, and market data.

CHRIS DICKMAN'S COREL DRAW JOURNAL. see *COMPUTERS — Computer Graphics*

COMPUTER MEDIA DIRECTORY. see *COMPUTERS — Computer Industry Directories*

070.5   US   ISSN 0740-6231
COMPUTER PUBLISHING & ADVERTISING REPORT; the biweekly newsletter for publishing & advertising executives in the computer field. 1983. fortn. $498 (foreign $548) (effective 1995). SIMBA Information Inc., 213 Danbury Rd., Box 7430, Wilton, CT 06897-7430. TEL 203-834-0033. FAX 203-834-1771. E-mail: simba99@aol.com. Ed. Linda Kopp; Pub. Chris Elwell. bk.rev.; circ. 395 (paid). **Document type:** newsletter.
—CCC.
     Formerly: Classified Advertising Report.
     Description: Provides a source for keeping abreast of the $4 billion computer publishing and advertising industries.

070.5   US
COMPUTER PUBLISHING MARKET FORECAST (YEAR). 1985. biennial. $1795 (effective 1995). SIMBA Information Inc., 213 Danbury Rd., Box 7430, Wilton, CT 06897-7430. TEL 203-834-0033. FAX 203-834-1771. E-mail: simba99@aol.com. **Document type:** trade publication.
     Description: Covers the computer publication market and analyzes each segment.

070.5   SP
CREATIVE. 10/yr. Mallorca 219, 5o 2a, 08008 Barcelona, Spain. TEL 3-323-75-54. FAX 3-323-74-63.
     Description: Covers desk-top publishing.

070.5 004.16 686.2   NE   ISSN 0928-6985
D T P & P. (DeskTop Publishing & Presentations) 1993. 11/yr. fl.95. Nanton Press B.V., Leyenseweg 115C, 3721 BC Bilthoven, Netherlands. TEL 31-30-290644. FAX 31-30-286224. (Subscr. to: Postbus 93, 3720 AB Bilthoven, Netherlands) Ed. Anton Kriegsman. adv. contact: Anton Kriegsman.

DESKTOP COMMUNICATIONS. see *COMPUTERS — Microcomputers*

070.5 686.2   US   ISSN 0897-4764
Z286.D47
DESKTOP PUBLISHERS FORUM. 1987. m. $48. National Association of Desktop Publishers, 462 Old Boston St., Topsfield, MA 01983-1232. TEL 508-887-7900. FAX 508-887-6117. Ed. Noel Ward. adv.; bk.rev.; illus. circ. 80,000. (back issues avail.) **Document type:** trade publication.
     Description: How-to-do-it reports, some elementary, others technical. Dedicated to fostering growth in the desktop publishing industry. Provides a forum for user feedback to manufacturers, developers and vendors.

070.5 686.2 004.16   DK   ISSN 0906-5016
DESKTOP PUBLISHING. (Text in Danish) 1991. 8/yr. DKK 190. Specialbladsforlaget ApS, Finsensvej 80, DK-200-Frederiksberg, Denmark. TEL 45-38-88-32-22. FAX 45-38-88-30-38. Ed. Svend Erik Pedersen.
     Description: Concentrates on news about desktop publishing techniques and the people using them.

070.5   US
DESKTOP PUBLISHING JOURNAL. 1988. m. $12.99. Linda Hanson, Ed. & Pub., 4017-C Rucker Ave., Ste. 821, Everett, WA 98201. TEL 206-568-2950. circ. 40,000. (tabloid format)

070.5   UK   ISSN 0952-9012
                       CODEN: DPTOE9
DESKTOP PUBLISHING TODAY. Short title: D.P.T. Today. 1986. m. £100 (foreign £150). Andrew Bond, Ed. & Pub., Vine House, East St., Harrietsham, Maidstone, Kent ME17 1HJ, England. TEL 01732-359990. FAX 01732-770049. adv.; bk.rev.; circ. 10,500 (controlled). **Indexed:** INSPEC (1992-), Intl.Polym.Sci.& Tech., RAPRA.

070.5   US
DESKTOP PUBLISHING USERS' REPORT.* m. $115. Communications Concepts, Inc., 7481 Huntsman Blvd., Ste. 720, Springfield, VA 22153-1648. TEL 703-643-2200. FAX 703-643-2329. Ed. Bill Londino. **Document type:** trade publication.
     Description: Monographs on specific aspects of desktop publishing, from staffing and training to scheduling and internal SOPs.

DIGITAL IMAGING & PUBLISHING. see *COMPUTERS — Microcomputers*

070.5 621.381   US
DIGITAL IMAGING REPORT; the industry newsletter for electronic publishing vendors. 1984. m. $295. Micro Publishing, 21150 Hawthorne Blvd., Ste. 104, Torrance, CA 90503. TEL 310-371-5787. FAX 310-542-0849. Ed. James Cavuoto. adv. contact: Nancy Whelan. bk.rev. (back issues avail.) **Indexed:** Comput.Lit.Ind. **Document type:** newspaper.
     Formerly: Micropublishing Report (ISSN 0889-9533); **Incorporates:** Corporate Publishing.
     Description: Provides detailed analysis of market and industry trends, vendor profiles, show reports, personnel and financial briefs.

070.5 338   US   ISSN 1059-0080
HD99999.I49   CODEN: IIBUEB
DIGITAL INFORMATION GROUP'S INFORMATION INDUSTRY BULLETIN.* 1985. w. $395. Digital Information Group, Box 110235, Stamford, CT 06911-0235. TEL 203-348-2751. Ed. Maureen Fleming. charts. **Document type:** bulletin.
—CASDDS.
     Formerly: Information Industry Bulletin (ISSN 0885-7660)
     Description: News and analysis for executives in the business of publishing information. Includes financial and competitive statistics.

070.5 384   UK   ISSN 0954-3244
E P JOURNAL. 1987? 10/yr. £260. Electronic Publishing Services Ltd., 104A St. John St., London EC17 4EH, England. TEL 0171-490-1185. FAX 0171-490-4706. Ed. Hugh E. Look. bk.rev. (back issues avail.) **Document type:** newsletter.
—BLDSC (3793.170000).
     Description: Contains news and articles on all aspects of the use of electronic media to disseminate information. Aimed at a professional audience in publishing, the media, and related fields.

070.5   US
▼**ECONOMICS OF MULTIMEDIA TITLE PUBLISHING.** 1994. a. $745. SIMBA Information Inc., 213 Danbury Rd., Box 7430, Wilton, CT 06897-7430. TEL 203-834-0033. FAX 203-834-1771. E-mail: simba99@aol.com. stat. **Document type:** trade publication.
     Description: Addresses pertinent items about new media development, providing in-depth market analysis, industry statistics, and descriptions of choices multimedia publishers face in the business, consumer, and education markets.

070.5   FR   ISSN 1165-2594
EDITEUR ELECTRONIQUE. m. 1800 F. A Jour, 11 rue du Marche St. Honore, 75001 Paris, France. TEL 42-96-67-22. FAX 40-20-07-75. Ed. Nathalie Bloch-Sitbon.

070.5   CN   ISSN 0838-9535
Z253.53
ELECTRONIC COMPOSITION & IMAGING. 1987. bi-m. Can.$28.95. Youngblood Communications Corp., 2240 Midland Ave., Ste. 201, Scarborough, ON M1P 4R8, Canada. TEL 416-299-6007. FAX 416-299-6674. Ed. Scott Olson. adv.; bk.rev.; tr.lit. circ. 30,000. (back issues avail.) **Indexed:** Can.B.P.I.
—Faxon.
     Description: How-to magazine for people using desktop publishing to produce brochures, newsletters and advertising. Covers PC and Macintosh electronic prepress.

ELECTRONIC EDUCATION REPORT. see *EDUCATION — Computer Applications*

070.5   US
ELECTRONIC INFORMATION DELIVERY: INFORMATION DELIVERY AND MULTIMEDIA SOLUTIONS. 1986. 2 base vols. (plus m. updates). $851 to new subscr.; renewals $764 (effective 1996). Datapro Information Services Group (Subsidiary of: McGraw-Hill, Inc.), 600 Delran Pkwy., Delran, NJ 08075. TEL 609-764-0100; 800-328-2776.
     Formerly (until 1993): Datapro Reports on Electronic Publishing Systems.

ELECTRONIC MEDIA FOR THE SCHOOL MARKET: REVIEW, TRENDS & FORECAST. see *EDUCATION — Computer Applications*

PUBLISHING AND BOOK TRADE — COMPUTER APPLICATIONS

070.5   UK   ISSN 0894-3982
Z286.E43   CODEN: EPODEU
ELECTRONIC PUBLISHING; origination, dissemination and design. 1988. q. $375 (foreign $375) (effective 1996). John Wiley & Sons Ltd., Journals, Baffins Ln., Chichester, W. Sussex PO19 1UD, England. TEL 01243-779777. FAX 01243-776128. TELEX 86290 WIBOOK G. (Subscr. in the Americas to: John Wiley, Inc., 605 Third Ave., New York, NY 10158. TEL 212-850-6645. FAX 212-850-6021) Eds. D. Brailsford, R. Furuta. circ. 187. (also avail. in microform from UMI; back issues avail.; reprint service avail. from SWZ) **Indexed:** Abstr.Hum.Comp.Inter., Comput.Abstr., INSPEC (1988-), LISA. **Document type:** trade publication.
—BLDSC (3702.753200); Ei; Faxon; SWETS; UMI. **CCC.**
    Description: Encompasses areas such as structured editors, authoring tools, hypermedia, document bases, production concordances and indexes, document display on workstations, electronic documents over networks, integration of text and illustrations, typeface design and imaging hardware.
    Refereed Serial

686.2   US
ELECTRONIC PUBLISHING & TYPEWORLD; the first newspaper for digital publishing professionals. 1977. 18/yr. $30 (foreign $165) (effective 1994). Pennwell Publishing Co. (Nashua), 10 Tara Blvd., 5th Fl., Nashua, NH 03062-2801. TEL 603-891-9159. FAX 603-891-0539. (Subscr. to: Box 2709, Tulsa, OK 74101. TEL 918-831-9537) Ed. Keith Hevenor. adv. contact: Paul McPherson. bk.rev.; charts; illus.; circ. 52,500 (controlled). (tabloid format) **Indexed:** Graph.Arts Lit.Abstr., PROMT, Resour.Ctr.Ind. **Document type:** trade publication.
—UMI.
    Formerly (until Sep. 1992): TypeWorld (ISSN 0194-4851)

070.5   US   ISSN 1048-3403
FAXON REPORT. q. Faxon Company, Inc., 15 Southwest Park, Westwood, MA 02090. TEL 617-329-3350. FAX 617-461-1862. TELEX 681-7238. **Document type:** newsletter.
    Formerly: Faxletter (ISSN 0882-231X)
    Description: Provides news briefs and informational articles of interest to the clients of and representatives from the Faxon Company, an information-communications corporation.

G C A REVIEW. (Graphic Communications Association) see *PRINTING — Computer Applications*

070.5 686.2   US
GOVERNMENT PUBLISHER. 1981. a. $66. G P Inc., Box 170, Salem, NH 03079. TEL 603-898-2822. FAX 603-898-3393. Ed. W. Bunnell. adv.; bk.rev. circ. 11,000. **Document type:** trade publication.
    Description: Applications of electronic publishing by federal and state governments.

070.5   US   ISSN 1059-731X
HE7761
INFORMATION & INTERACTIVE SERVICES REPORT; the biweekly newsletter for the information industry. 1980. bi-w. $495 (outside N. America $531). Telecommunications Reports (Subsidiary of: Business Research Publications, Inc.), 1333 H St., N.W., 2nd Fl.-W., Washington, DC 20005. TEL 202-842-1875. FAX 202-842-3047. Ed. Rod Kuckro; Pub. Adam Goldstein. bk.rev.; index. (back issues avail.) **Document type:** newsletter.
    ●Also available online. Vendor(s): NewsNet (TE41).
    Formed by the Mar. 1991 merger of: Electronic Shopping News (ISSN 0893-0333); Which was formerly (until 1987): TeleServices Report (ISSN 0730-0263); Interactivity Report (ISSN 0893-0325); Which was formerly (until 1987): International Videotex Teletext News (ISSN 0197-677X)
    Description: Tracks major developments in the information industry, follows on-line services and interactive TV and video businesses, and reports targeting trends in these fast-changing markets. Alerts readers to new on-line services and the promotional strategies to market them.

004.7   US   ISSN 1054-3724
LASERJET JOURNAL.* 1987. 6/yr. $49. 850 Asbury Dr., Buffalo Grove, IL 60089-4557. TEL 800-323-2686. (reprint service avail.)

004.7   US
LASERS IN GRAPHICS: ELECTRONIC PUBLISHING IN THE 90'S. CONFERENCE PROCEEDINGS. (In 2 vols.) 1979. a. $95 per vol. Dunn Technology, Inc., 1855 E. Vista Way, No. 1, Vista, CA 92084. FAX 619-758-5401. Ed. Patrice M. Dunn. (back issues avail.) **Indexed:** Graph.Arts Lit.Abstr. **Document type:** proceedings.
    Formerly: Lasers in Graphics: Electronic Publishing in the 80's. Conference Proceedings.
    Description: Focus on the markets and the technology for commercial electronic design, pre-press and publishing.

070.5   CN
LIQUID IMAGE MULTIMEDIA. 1993. m. Youngblood Communications Corp., 2240 Midland Ave., Ste. 201, Scarborough, ON M1P 4R8, Canada. TEL 416-299-6007. FAX 416-299-6674.

070.5   IS
MAKINTOSH. 1988. m. $135. Israel Peled Publishing, Pinsker 64, Tel Aviv 61 332, Israel. TEL 3-295146. FAX 3-295144. circ. 5,000.

500   US   ISSN 1064-0479
Z7401
N T I S BIBLIOGRAPHIC DATA BASE. (Supplement avail.: Subject Headings Booklet) s-m. price varies. U.S. National Technical Information Service, 5285 Port Royal Rd., Springfield, VA 22161. TEL 703-487-4630. index.
    ●Also available online. Vendor(s): Ovid Technologies, Data-Star, Knight-Ridder, Inc., Orbit Search Service, STN International.
    Also available on CD-ROM. Producer(s): Knight-Ridder, Inc., OCLC, SilverPlatter Information, Inc.
    Description: Multidisciplinary coverage of engineering as well as research and development results of scientific and technical research of the U.S. government, its contractors and foreign governments.

686.2 070.5   US   ISSN 0897-6503
Z286.D47
NATIONAL ASSOCIATION OF DESKTOP PUBLISHERS. JOURNAL. Spine title: N A D T P Journal. (Supplement avail.: Desktop Publishers Forum (ISSN 0897-4767)) 1987. m. $48 to non-members; newsstand price: $4. (National Association of Desktop Publishers) Desktop Publishing Institute, 462 Old Boston St., Topsfield, MA 01983-1232. TEL 508-887-7900. FAX 508-887-6117. E-mail: America Online: NADTP; Compuserve: 74064, 2334. Ed. Noel Ward; Pub. Barry Jarrigan. adv.; B&W page $5400. illus.; software rev.; tr.lit. circ. 60,000. (back issues avail.) **Document type:** trade publication.
    Description: Serves as a prime resource for product and trend information on desktop publishing, graphic design and multimedia publishing.

NEWSLETTER DESIGN. see *JOURNALISM*

070.5 621.381   US   ISSN 0896-8209
Z286.D47
P C PUBLISHING AND PRESENTATIONS;* desktop publishing. 1987. m. $36 (Canada and Mexico $48; elsewhere $96). International Desktop Communications, Ltd., 342 Madison Ave., Ste. 622, New York, NY 10173-0002. TEL 212-768-7666. FAX 212-768-0288. Ed. Robert Mueller. adv. circ. 50,000.
—CCC.
    Formerly (until 1991): P C Publishing.
    Description: For IBM PC and compatible users. Feature articles cover diverse topics in desktop publishing: applications, hardware and software.

070.5   US   ISSN 0196-4127
PERSONAL COMPOSITION REPORT; the newsletter for users of desktop and electronic publishing, typesetting, and word & information processing. Short title: P C R. 1979. 10/yr. $100 (foreign $125). Graphic Dimensions, 134 Caversham Woods, Pittsford, NY 14534-2834. TEL 716-381-3428. Ed. Michael L. Kleper. bk.rev. (back issues avail.) **Document type:** newsletter.
    Formerly: Digest of Information on Phototypesetting.
    Description: Covers all aspects of electronic publishing and imaging through news, reviews, and analysis.

004   NE   ISSN 0928-6500
PREPRESS COMPUTING MAGAZINE. 11/yr. fl.1135. Nanton Press B.V., Leyenseweg 115C, 3721 BC Bilthoven, Netherlands. TEL 31-30-290644. FAX 31-30-286224. (Subscr. to: Postbus 93, 3720 AB Bilthoven, Netherlands) Ed. Anton Kriegsman. adv. contact: Anton Kriegsman.
—SWETS.
    Formerly (until 1991): PrePress Magazine (ISSN 0925-0999)

PUBLISH; the how-to magazine of desktop publishing. see *COMPUTERS — Microcomputers*

070.5   SP
PUBLISH. 12/yr. Principe de Vergara 136, 1o, 28002 Madrid, Spain. TEL 1-564-13-13. FAX 1-564-27-40. Ed. Jose M. Cerezo.
    Description: Covers desk-top publishing.

070.5   US   ISSN 1070-2962
REALLY, A FREE NEWSLETTER; publishing tips from Mary Bold. 1989. q. free. Bold Productions, Box 152281, Arlington, TX 76015. TEL 817-468-9924. Ed. Mary Bold. bk.rev. circ. 1,000. (looseleaf format; back issues avail.) **Document type:** newsletter, trade publication.
    Description: Covers desktop publishing tools and techniques; small press marketing issues.

070.5   US
▼**REED ELSEVIER TECHNOLOGY NEWSLETTER.** 1994. q. Reed Elsevier Technology, Part of the Reed Elsevier group, 155 Commerce Dr., Ft. Washington, PA 19034. TEL 215-542-2070. FAX 215-542-2060. Ed. Paul Piombino. **Document type:** newsletter.
    Description: Focuses on the technology issues that are increasingly impacting information markets.

001.6 070 651.8   US   ISSN 0736-7260
Z286.E43   CODEN: SRPSD9
SEYBOLD REPORT ON PUBLISHING SYSTEMS. 1971. s-m. $365 (Canada $377; elsewhere $401). Seybold Publications, 428 E. Baltimore Ave., Box 644, Media, PA 19063. TEL 610-565-2480; 800-325-3830. FAX 610-656-1858. Ed. Stephen Edwards; Pub. Jonathan Seybold. bk.rev.; charts; illus.; index, cum.index. **Indexed:** Comput.Cont., Graph.Arts Lit.Abstr., INSPEC, P.I.R.A. **Document type:** trade publication.
—BLDSC (8254.494000); CASDDS; Faxon. **CCC.**
    Former titles: Seybold Report (ISSN 0364-5517); Editing Technology (ISSN 0046-1261)
    Description: Chronicles developments in typesetting, page make-up facilities, and related electronic prepress systems.

SOFT.LETTER; trends & strategies in software publishing. see *COMPUTERS — Software*

070.5   US   ISSN 1055-2774
    CODEN: SBSDE4
STEP-BY-STEP ELECTRONIC DESIGN; the how-to newsletter for electronic designers. 1989. m. $48. 6000 N. Forest Park Dr., Peoria, IL 61614-3592. TEL 309-688-2300. FAX 309-688-8515. Ed. Talitha Harper; Pub. Nancy Aldrich-Ruenzel. bk.rev.; charts, illus, tr.lit.; index. circ. 12,000. (back issues avail.) **Document type:** newsletter.
    Description: Geared toward electronic designers and production professionals; contains how-to articles with step-by-step artwork for beginners as well as experienced desktop graphic designers.

WORLD PUBLISHING MONITOR. see *COMPUTERS — Abstracting, Bibliographies, Statistics*

070.5 686.2   US
THE YELLOWSTONE DESKTOP PUBLISHING LETTER.* 1988. bi-m. $49.95 (foreign $89.95). Yellowstone Information Services, 605 Brady Ave., Steubenville, OH 43952-1459. TEL 304-965-5548. FAX 304-965-7785. Ed. Roger C. Thibault. index, cum.index. circ. 1,000. (back issues avail.)
    Formerly (until 1991): Desktop Publisher (Elkview).
    Description: Covers desktop publishing software and hardware, applications, and product and business news.

RADIO

see Communications-Radio

RADIOLOGY AND NUCLEAR MEDICINE

see Medical Sciences-Radiology and Nuclear Medicine

RAILROADS

see Transportation-Railroads

REAL ESTATE

see also Architecture; Building and Construction; Business and Economics-Investments; Housing and Urban Planning

A L I - A B A ESTATE PLANNING COURSE MATERIALS JOURNAL. see LAW

333.33 US
A L T A CAPITAL COMMENT. 1907. m. $16. American Land Title Association, 1828 L St. N.W., Washington, DC 20036-5182. TEL 202-296-3671. Ed. Robin Keeney. circ. 4,300 (controlled).

333.33 US
A M O PERSPECTIVES. q. $50 to non-members; members $35. Institute of Real Estate Management, Accredited Management Organization, 420 N. Michigan Ave., Chicago, IL 60611. TEL 312-329-6056. FAX 312-661-0217. Ed. Nancy Pekala. charts; illus. **Document type:** newsletter.
   Description: Covers marketing, management, strategic planning, personnel management and business operations.

333.33 US
A O M A NEWSLETTER; profile of the multi-family housing industry. 1967. m. $125 to non-members. Apartment Owners and Managers Association of America, 65 Cherry Plaza, Box 238, Watertown, CT 06795-0238. TEL 203-274-2589. FAX 203-274-2580. Ed. Robert McGough. adv.; bk.rev.; abstr.; charts; illus. circ. 8,618. **Document type:** trade publication.

333.33 US ISSN 1056-9715
A R M NEWS. (Accredited Residential Manager) 7/yr. $30. Institute of Real Estate Management, 430 N. Michigan Ave., Chicago, IL 60611. TEL 312-329-6056. FAX 312-661-0217. TELEX 312-025-3742. Ed. Nancy Pekala. charts; illus. **Document type:** newsletter.
   Description: Provides residential managers with practical, hands-on information for smoothly run, efficient, cost-effective properties. Articles highlight methods, techniques, and tips for cost savings and optimal professional performance.

333.5 352.7 II
ACCOMMODATION TIMES. (Text in English) 1986. fortn. Rs.96; newsstand price: Rs.5. Murari Chaturvedi, Ed. & Pub., Radha Bhavan, First Ln., T.P.S. III, Golibar Rd., Santacruz, Bombay 400055, India. TEL 611-42-21. FAX 610-2482. adv.: B&W page Rs.14500, color page Rs.26000. circ. 20,000.

333.3 US
ACQUISITION COLUMBUS. m. $24 (free to qualified personnel). Acquisition Columbus, 2910 Brookdown Dr., Colombus, OH 43235-2704. TEL 614-841-0085. Ed. Rufus Jones; Pub. Rufus Jones. circ. controlled. **Document type:** newspaper.
   Description: For professionals in commercial and industrial real estate.

333.3 US
ACQUISITION, NORTHEASTERN OHIO. * m. Widener Publications, Inc., 36413 Derby Downs Dr., Cleveland, OH 44139-2657. TEL 216-425-4375. FAX 216-425-4306. Ed. Jeff Davis. adv. circ. 18,000.

333.33 US ISSN 1063-3405
ACQUISITION OF GREATER DAYTON; the Dayton area's commercial real estate source since 1985. (Supplement to: Dayton Business Reporter (ISSN 1063-3413)) 1985. m. $21 includes Dayton Business Reporter. Hannover Publishing Co., Inc., 6356 Far Hills Ave., Dayton, OH 45459-2782. TEL 513-291-1100. FAX 513-436-3426. Ed. Gene Fox. adv.: B&W page $2268, color page $2818; trim 11 3/8 x 15; adv. contact: Tina Rhodus. circ. 12,000.
●Also available online.
Also available on CD-ROM. Producer(s): University Microfilms International.
—UMI. **CCC.**
   Description: Covers area commercial - industrial real estate and economic development.

333.33 FR ISSN 0764-5066
ACTIVITE IMMOBILIERE. 1944. m. 350 F. Consortium d'Edition et de Publicite du Sud-Ouest, 26, avenue de Suffren, 75015 Paris, France. adv. circ. 5,000. (looseleaf format)
   Formerly: Activite Immobiliere Commerciale et Industrielle.

L'ACTUALITE JURIDIQUE: DROIT ADMINISTRATIF. see LAW

333.33 FR ISSN 0767-9939
ADMINISTRER. 1971. m. 18 F. per no. 53 rue du Rocher, 75008 Paris, France. TEL 42-93-60-55. FAX 43-87-07-95. Eds. Georges Duthil, Jean Robert Bouyeure. adv. circ. 4,000.

333.33 US
ADVISOR (TRENTON). vol.15, 1977. q. free. Real Estate Commission, Dept. of Insurance, 20 W. State St., CN 328, Trenton, NJ 08625. TEL 609-292-7053. **Document type:** government publication, newsletter.
   Formerly: New Jersey Advisor.

343.73 347.3 US ISSN 1042-5845
KF6535
AGGRESSIVE TAX AVOIDANCE FOR REAL ESTATE INVESTORS. 1981. a. $23.95. John T. Reed, Ed. & Pub., 342 Bryan Dr., Danville, CA 94526. TEL 510-820-6292. FAX 510-820-1259. circ. 4,000 (paid). **Document type:** catalog.

333.33 630 CN ISSN 0701-7502
HD319.A4
AGRICULTURAL REAL ESTATE VALUES IN ALBERTA. 1971. q. Alberta Agriculture, Food & Rural Development, Production Economics Branch, 3rd Fl., 7000 113th St., Edmonton, AB T6H 5T6, Canada. TEL 403-427-4005. FAX 403-427-5220. circ. 1,400. **Document type:** government publication.
   Formerly: Rural Real Estate Values in Alberta (ISSN 0383-3585)

333.33 GW
ALLGEMEINE IMMOBILIEN-ZEITUNG; Fachzeitschrift fuer Immobilienwirtschaft und Immobilienrecht. 1924. m. DM.92. (Ring Deutscher Makler e.V.) R D M Verlags GmbH, Moenckebergstr. 27, 20095 Hamburg, Germany. Ed. Gerhard Feldmann. adv.; bk.rev.; stat. circ. 8,900. **Document type:** trade publication.
   Formerly: A I Z (ISSN 0001-1673)

333.3 US
AMERICAN REAL ESTATE AND URBAN ECONOMICS ASSOCIATION NEWSLETTER. s-m. American Real Estate and Urban Economics Association, 2500 S. State St., Ann Arbor, MI 48109. TEL 313-769-1004. FAX 313-769-7653. (Subscr. to: Indiana University, School of Business, 10th St. and Fee Ln., Rm. 428, Blommington, IN 47045. TEL 812-855-7794. FAX 812-855-8679) **Document type:** newsletter.
   Description: Provides announcements of upcoming meetings, past meeting highlights, member activities, placement announcements, industry notes, dissertation competitions and other current information.

AMERICAN SOCIETY OF APPRAISERS. NEWSLINE. see BUSINESS AND ECONOMICS — Banking And Finance

APARTMENT AGE; the voice of the industry. see HOUSING AND URBAN PLANNING

333.33 US ISSN 0744-9143
APARTMENT MANAGEMENT NEWSLETTER; wealth building techniques for apartment owners & their managers. 1975. m. $95. Apartment Management Publishing Co., Inc., 122 E. 42nd St., Ste. 1700, New York, NY 10168-0002. TEL 212-551-1166. Ed. Helene Mandelbaum. bk.rev.; charts; tr.lit.; index. circ. 5,000. (back issues avail.) **Document type:** newsletter.

333.33 US
APARTMENT MANAGEMENT REPORT; for managers of apartments. 1975. m. $85. Apartment Owners and Managers Association of America, 65 Cherry Plaza, Box 238, Watertown, CT 06795-0238. TEL 203-274-2589. FAX 203-274-2580. **Document type:** trade publication.

333.33 US ISSN 0191-8826
APARTMENT OWNER; San Fernando Valley - Ventura County - Santa Clarita - Antelope Valley. 1969? m. $50. Apartment Association, 14550 Archwood St., Van Nuys, CA 91405. TEL 818-374-3240. FAX 818-781-6018. Ed. MaryEllen Hughes. adv.: B&W page $588; adv. contact: Jill McDonald. circ. 3,000 (controlled). **Document type:** trade publication.

333.332 CN ISSN 0003-7079
APPRAISAL INSTITUTE DIGEST. vol.4, 1970. 4/yr. included in Canadian Appraiser. Appraisal Institute of Canada, 1111 Portage Ave., Winnipeg, MB R3G 0S8, Canada. TEL 204-782-2224. FAX 204-785-5575. charts; illus. circ. 8,200. (also avail. in microfilm from MML)

333.33 070.5 US
APPRAISAL INSTITUTE PUBLICATIONS CATALOGUE. 1950. a. Appraisal Institute, 875 N. Michigan Ave., Ste. 2400, Chicago, IL 60611-1980. TEL 312-335-4100. FAX 312-335-4400. **Document type:** catalog.
   Description: Lists books, periodicals and videotapes published by the institute.

333.332 US ISSN 0003-7087
HD251 CODEN: APPJA5
APPRAISAL JOURNAL. 1932. q. $35 to non-members (foreign $40); students $30 (foreign $35). Appraisal Institute, 875 N. Michigan Ave., Ste. 2400, Chicago, IL 60611-1980. TEL 312-335-4100. FAX 312-353-4400. Ed. Jennifer Roberts. bk.rev.; abstr.; charts; illus.; stat.; index. circ. 36,000. (also avail. in microform from UMI; reprint service avail. from UMI,KTO) **Indexed:** AAR, ABI Inform, Account.Ind. (1974-), B.P.I., BPIA, Bus.Ind., Manage.Cont., Noise Pollut.Publ.Abstr., P.A.I.S., RICS, Tr.& Indus.Ind.
●Also available online. Vendor(s): University Microfilms International.
—BLDSC (1580.130000); Faxon; SWETS; UMI; UnCover.
   Description: Provides perspectives of professors, practitioners, and acknowledged authorities on all areas of real estate appraisal: residential, commercial, industrial, and rural.
   Refereed Serial

333.332 US
APPRAISAL REVIEW. q. membership. National Association of Independent Fee Appraisers, 7501 Murdoch Ave., St. Louis, MO 63119. TEL 314-781-6688. Ed. Pierce Hollingsworth. circ. 80,000. **Document type:** trade publication.
   Description: Subjects of interest to members of appraisal organizations.

333.33 US ISSN 0195-4407
HD1387
APPRAISAL REVIEW AND MORTGAGE UNDERWRITING JOURNAL. 1978. q. $45. (National Association of Review Appraisers & Mortgage Underwriters) Todd Publishing, Inc., 8383 E. Evans Rd., Scottsdale, AZ 85260. TEL 602-998-7743. FAX 602-998-8022. adv. circ. 10,000. **Document type:** trade publication.

333.33 US
THE APPRAISAL TIMES. q. National Association of Real Estate Appraisers, 8383 E. Evans Rd., Scottsdale, AZ 85260. TEL 602-948-8000. FAX 602-998-8022. Ed. David M. Brown; Pub. E. Kenneth Twichell. **Document type:** newsletter.
   Former titles: National Association of Real Estate Appraisers Newsletter; N A R E A Real Estate Appraisal Newsletter.

REAL ESTATE

333.332 US
APPRAISER GRAM. 1966. m. National Association of Independent Fee Appraisers, 7501 Murdoch Ave., St. Louis, MO 63119. TEL 314-781-6688. Ed. Donna Walter. circ. 5,800. (looseleaf format) **Document type:** newsletter.
Description: Information for members of the organization.

333.332 US ISSN 1054-5999
HD251
APPRAISER NEWS. 1959. m. $25 (foreign $30). Appraisal Institute, 875 N. Michigan Ave., Ste. 2400, Chicago, IL 60611-1980. TEL 312-335-4100. FAX 312-335-4400. Ed. Jennifer McLavin. charts; illus.; stat. circ. 37,000.
Formerly (until 1991): Appraiser (ISSN 0003-7095)
Description: Covers events, trends and opinions in real estate appraisal practice and related legislative, regulatory, financial and economic affairs.

ARCHIVIO DELLE LOCAZIONI E DEL CONDOMINIO. see LAW

ARIZONA BUSINESS MAGAZINE. see BUSINESS AND ECONOMICS — Office Equipment And Services

333.33 US ISSN 0199-9206
HD266.A7
ARIZONA REALTOR DIGEST. 1979. bi-m. $6. Arizona Association of Realtors, 4414 N. 19th Ave., No. R, Phoenix, AZ 85015. TEL 602-248-7787. FAX 602-351-2474. Ed. Sue Scholz. adv. contact: Sue Scholz. circ. 19,000. **Document type:** trade publication.

333.33 UK
ARREARS MANAGEMENT MANUAL. base vol. (plus irreg. updates). £85 to members only (effective 1994-1995). Building Societies Association, 3 Savile Row, London W1X 1AF, England. TEL 0171-437-0655. FAX 0171-287-0109. (Co-sponsor: Council of Mortgage Lenders) stat. (looseleaf format) **Document type:** trade publication.
Description: Provides an overview of mortgage arrears and possessions, along with their causes and characteristics. Also covers the handling of arrears and possessions, the possessions register, income support for mortgage interest, mortgage rescue schemes, and political commentary.

ASOCIACION NACIONAL DE PROMOTORES CONSTRUCTORES DE EDIFICIOS URBANOS. ANNUAL REPORT. see HOUSING AND URBAN PLANNING

ASOCIACION NACIONAL DE PROMOTORES CONSTRUCTORES DE EDIFICIOS URBANOS. PROMOCION. see HOUSING AND URBAN PLANNING

333.332 US ISSN 1073-8568
ASSESSMENT JOURNAL. 1994. bi-m. $200 to non-members. International Association of Assessing Officers, 130 E. Randolph, Ste. 850, Chicago, IL 60601. TEL 312-819-6110. Ed. Annie Aubrey. adv.: B&W page $950, color page $1985; trim 8 1/2 x 11; adv. contact: Patrick Edwards. bk.rev. circ. 8,450. (also avail. in microform from UMI; reprint service avail. from UMI) Indexed: ABI Inform., P.A.I.S. **Document type:** trade publication.
—Faxon; UMI; UnCover.
Formed by the 1994 merger of: Assessment and Valuation Legal Reporter (ISSN 0090-6352) & I A A O Update; Which was formerly (until 1987): International Association of Assessing Officers. News Bulletin (ISSN 0741-4609) & Property Tax Journal (ISSN 0731-0285); Which was formerly (until 1982): Assessors Journal (ISSN 0004-5071); Which was formerly: Assessment Digest (ISSN 0731-0277); International Assessor; I A A O Newsletter; Assessors News Letter - A N L (ISSN 0004-508X).
Description: Contains information on property tax assessment, law and policy, appraisal.
Refereed Serial

ASSISTED HOUSING ACCOUNTS & AUDITS INSIDER. see BUSINESS AND ECONOMICS — Accounting

333.33 340 US ISSN 1072-009X
ASSISTED HOUSING MANAGEMENT INSIDER. m. $245. Brownstone Publishers, Inc., 149 Fifth Ave., New York, NY 10010-6801. TEL 212-473-8200. FAX 212-473-8786. Ed. David B. Klein. **Document type:** newsletter.
Description: Covers regulatory requirements for federally-assisted housing, and gives advice on how to stay in compliance.

526.9 CN ISSN 0318-2126
TA527.N4
ASSOCIATION OF NEW BRUNSWICK LAND SURVEYORS. ANNUAL REPORT. 1955. a. free. Association of New Brunswick Land Surveyors, 535 Beaverbrook Ct. No. 120, Fredericton, NB E3B 1X6, Canada. TEL 506-458-8266. FAX 506-458-8267. Ed. Douglas Morgan. adv. contact: Claire Quigley. circ. 250 (controlled).

AUDIO ESTATE PLANNER. see LAW — Estate Planning

333.33 352.7 US
AUSTIN HOME FINDER. 1974. bi-m. free. Southeast Publishing Ventures, 528 East Blvd., Charlotte, NC 28203-5110. (Orders to: 1106 Clayton Ln., Ste. 528 W., Austin, TX 78723-1034. TEL 512-451-5777. FAX 512-451-5779) Ed. Angela Jones. adv.: page $1400; trim 5 3/8 x 8 3/8; adv. contact: Angela Jones. bk.rev.; maps; circ. 25,000 (controlled). (back issues avail.) **Document type:** consumer publication, directory.
Former titles: Home Finder Guidebook; (until 1987): Austin Living (ISSN 0741-5478)

AUSTRALIAN TENANCY PRACTICE & PRECEDENTS. see LAW

333.33 UK ISSN 0267-2901
AVERAGE YIELDS. 1984. q. £8 per no. Hillier Parker, 77 Grosvenor St., London W1A 2BT, England. TEL 0171-629-7666. FAX 0174-409-3016. Ed. Kiran Patel. (back issues avail.) **Document type:** trade publication.

B N A'S ENVIRONMENTAL DUE DILIGENCE GUIDE. see LAW

333.33 658 US ISSN 0738-2170
TX980
B O M A EXPERIENCE EXCHANGE REPORT; income - expense analysis for office buildings. 1920. a. $195. Building Owners and Managers Association International, 1201 New York Ave., N.W., Ste. 300, Washington, DC 20005. TEL 202-408-2662. FAX 202-321-0181. Eds. Ellen Ku, Deidre Schexnayder. circ. 8,000. (back issues avail.) Indexed: SRI.
Formerly (until vol.2, 1988): Trends (Washington, 1987).

333.33 AT ISSN 0816-0856
B O M A NEWS.* 1984. q. free. Building Owners & Managers Association of Australia Ltd., 98-102 Elizabeth St., Block Arcade, 3rd Fl., Melbourne, Vic. 3000, Australia. Ed. A.W. Larnach-Jones. adv. circ. 400. (back issues avail.)

B S A ANNUAL REPORT. (Building Societies Association) see BUILDING AND CONSTRUCTION

333.33 UK
B S A - C M L BOOKSHOP DATAFAX SERVICE. ARREARS AND POSSESSIONS. (Avail. only by fax) irreg. Building Societies Association - Council of Mortgage Lenders, Bookshop, 3 Savile Row, London W1X 1AF, England. TEL 0171-437-0655. FAX 0171-287-0109. **Document type:** trade publication.

333.33 UK
B S A - C M L BOOKSHOP DATAFAX SERVICE. BUILDING SOCIETY SAVINGS AND LENDING FIGURES. (Avail. only by fax) m. Building Societies Association - Council of Mortgage Lenders, Bookshop, 3 Savile Row, London W1X 1AF, England. TEL 0171-437-0655. FAX 0171-287-0109. **Document type:** trade publication.

333.33 UK
B S A - C M L BOOKSHOP DATAFAX SERVICE. HOUSING PRICES. (Avail. only by fax) irreg. Building Societies Association - Council of Mortgage Lenders, Bookshop, 3 Savile Row, London W1X 1AF, England. TEL 0171-437-0655. FAX 0171-287-0109. **Document type:** trade publication.

333.3 332 352.7 UK
B S A - C M L PARLIAMENTARY CUTTING SERVICE. w. £117 (effective 1994-1995). Building Societies Association, 3 Savile Row, London W1X 1AF, England. TEL 0171-437-0655. FAX 0171-287-0109. (Co-sponsor: Council of Mortgage Lenders) **Document type:** trade publication.
Description: Presents relevant excerpts from both houses of Parliament regarding the mortgage and housing market.

333.3 332 352.7 UK ISSN 0265-0479
B S A DIRECTORY OF MEMBERS. irreg., latest Oct. 1994. £5 to non-members; members £3 (effective 1994-1995). Building Societies Association, 3 Savile Row, London W1X 1AF, England. TEL 0171-437-0655. FAX 0171-287-0109. **Document type:** directory.
Description: Describes the association and its activities; lists member societies and their senior executives.

BAALMAN & WELL'S LAND TITLES OFFICE PRACTICE. see LAW

BANCASSURANCE REPORT. see INSURANCE

333.33 GW
BAYERISCHE HAUSBESITZER-ZEITUNG. m. Zentralverband der Deutschen Haus-, Wohnungs- und Grundeigentuemer, Landesverband Bayerischer Haus- und Grundbesitzer, Sonnenstr. 13, 80331 Munich, Germany.

333.33 NE ISSN 0165-2540
BEHEER EN ONDERHOUD. 1975. m. Misset (Subsidiary of: Reed Elsevier N.V.), Postbus 4, 7000 BA Doetinchem, Netherlands. TEL 31-8340-49911. FAX 31-8340-43839. TELEX 45481. Ed. W. Pasman. (looseleaf format) **Document type:** monographic series.
Description: Cost and management information for the management of real estate.

333.33 CC
BEIJING FANGDICHAN/BEIJING REAL ESTATE. (Text in Chinese) 1987. m. Y42. Beijing Fangdichang Guanliju - Beijing Real Estate Administration, 1 Nanwanzi, Nanheyan, Dongcheng-qu, Beijing 100006, People's Republic of China. TEL 5225481. FAX 5225481. Ed. Liang Bingliang. adv.: color page Y4000; adv. contact: Sunwei Wang. circ. 10,000.
Description: Covers the real estate market, property management, and related policies and regulations in China.

333.33 GW ISSN 0938-8893
BELLEVUE. 1990. m. DM.96; newsstand price: DM.8.50. Verlagsgruppe Milchstrasse, Milchstr. 1, 20148 Hamburg, Germany. TEL 040-441980. FAX 040-458519. Ed. Claus-Peter Haller; Pubs. Joerg Altendorf, Dirk Manthey. adv. contact: Christel Horsthemke. circ. 39,375. **Document type:** consumer publication.

333.33 GW
BERLINER HAUS- UND GRUNDBESITZ. 1963. m. DM.39.60. Verlag Adalbert Bestgen, Spessartstr. 13, Abholfach, 14197 Berlin, Germany. Ed. A. Bestgen. adv.; bk.rev. circ. 4,000. (back issues avail.)

333.33 SZ
BERNER HAUSEIGENTUEMER. 8/yr. Schwarzhallstr. 31, CH-3000 Bern 14, Switzerland. TEL 031-256008. Ed. Daniel Rutsch. circ. 8,000.

333.33 FR ISSN 1246-225X
BERTRAND VACANCES. 2/yr. price varies. Editions Indicateur Bertrand, 43 bd. Barbes, 75018 Paris, France. TEL 1-49-25-26-27. FAX 1-49-25-26-00. adv. contact: Jean-Michel Moncurps. illus. circ. 235,000.
Former titles (until 1988): Bertrand Locations Vacances (ISSN 0990-5944); Vacances.
Description: Advertisements for the renting of vacation homes from real estate agencies and private owners.

333.33 AU
BESSER WOHNEN; die oesterreichische Wohnzeitschrift. 1966. 12/yr. S.260. Verein Besser Wohnen, Bauernmarkt 9-3-X, A-1010 Vienna, Austria. TEL 01-5350300. FAX 01-53503009. Ed. Franz Klar. adv.: B&W page S.48400, color page S.82000; trim 185 x 265; adv. contact: Peter Schriefl. circ. 101,666. **Document type:** consumer publication.

REAL ESTATE

333.33 US
BETTER HOMES AND GARDENS NEW HOME PLANNING GUIDE. a. Meredith Corporation, Special Interest Publications, 1716 Locust St., Des Moines, IA 50336. TEL 515-284-3000. Pub. Steve Levinson. adv.: B&W page $20025, color page $28775; adv. contact: Pat Tomlinson. circ. 450,000.

333.33 US
BIRMINGHAM COMMERCIAL REAL ESTATE REVIEW & FORECAST ANNUAL.* 1990. a. $8.95. First Publishing Inc., Box 380545, Birmingham, AL 35238-0545. TEL 205-733-1970. FAX 205-733-1974. Ed. Charlie Cox. adv. circ. 18,100. (back issues avail.)
Description: Tracks and reports commercial real estate activities and trends.

333.33 US
BLACK'S BROKER TENANT GUIDE: SOUTH FLORIDA - TREASURE COAST.* 1986. s-a. $124.95. Black's Guide, Inc., 818 W. Diamond Ave., Ste. 300, Gaithersburg, MD 20878-1417. Ed. Sheila Holzberger. adv. **Document type:** directory.

333.33 US
BLACK'S BROKER TENANT GUIDE: TAMPA BAY - SOUTHWEST FLORIDA.* 1986. s-a. $124.95. Black's Guide, Inc., 818 W. Diamond Ave., Ste. 300, Gaithersburg, MD 20878-1417. Ed. Sheila Holzberger. adv. **Document type:** directory.

333.33 US
BLACK'S BROKER TENANT GUIDE: THE GREATER BALTIMORE AREA.* 1992. s-a. $124.95. Black's Guide, Inc., 818 W. Diamond Ave., Ste. 300, Gaithersburg, MD 20878-1417. Ed. Sheila Holzberger. adv. **Document type:** directory

333.33 US
BLACK'S GUIDE TO THE OFFICE SPACE MARKET: PHILADELPHIA - SOUTH NEW JERSEY - DELAWARE.* 1981. a. $99.95. Black's Guide, Inc., 818 W. Diamond Ave., Ste. 300, Gaithersburg, MD 20878-1417. Ed. Sheila Holzberger. adv. **Document type:** directory.
Formerly: Black's Guide to the Office Space Market: Philadelphia and Suburbs.

333.33 US
BLACK'S METRO RICHMOND GUIDE.* 1992. a. $49.95. Black's Guide, Inc., 818 W. Diamond Ave., Ste. 300, Gaithersburg, MD 20878-1417. Ed. Sheila Holzberger. **Document type:** directory.

333.33 US
BLACK'S OFFICE AND INDUSTRIAL GUIDE: HOUSTON.* 1982. a. $94.95. Black's Guide, Inc., 818 W. Diamond Ave., Ste. 300, Gaithersburg, MD 20878-1417. Ed. Sheila Holzberger. adv. **Document type:** directory.
Formerly: Black's Guide to the Office Space Market: Houston.

333.33 US
BLACK'S OFFICE LEASING GUIDE: ATLANTA.* 1993. s-a. $124.95. Black's Guide, Inc., 818 W. Diamond Ave., Ste. 300, Gaithersburg, MD 20878-1417. Ed. Sheila Holzberger. **Document type:** directory.

333.33 US
BLACK'S OFFICE LEASING GUIDE: CONNECTICUT - NEW YORK SUBURBS.* 1983. a. $94.95. Black's Guide, Inc., 818 W. Diamond Ave., Ste. 300, Gaithersburg, MD 20878-1417. Ed. Sheila Holzberger. adv. **Document type:** directory.
Formerly (until 1992): Black's Guide to the Office Space Market: Connecticut - New York Suburbs.

333.33 US
BLACK'S OFFICE LEASING GUIDE: DALLAS - FORT WORTH.* 1984. s-a. $149.95. Black's Guide, Inc., 818 W. Dimaond Ave., Ste. 300, Gaithersburg, MD 20878-1417. Ed. Sheila Holzberger. adv. **Document type:** directory.
Formerly (until 1985): Black's Guide to the Office Space Market: Dallas - Fort Worth.

333.33 US
BLACK'S OFFICE LEASING GUIDE: METRO DENVER - BOULDER - COLORADO SPRINGS.* 1982. a. $94.95. Black's Guide, Inc., 818 W. Diamond Ave., Ste. 300, Gaithersburg, MD 20878-1417. Ed. Sheila Holzberger. adv. **Document type:** directory.
Formerly: Black's Guide to the Office Space Market: Denver.

333.33 US
BLACK'S OFFICE LEASING GUIDE: NORTHERN NEW JERSEY.* 1976. s-a. $149.95. Black's Guide, Inc., 818 W. Diamond Ave., Ste. 300, Gaithersburg, MD 20878-1417. Ed. Sheila Holzberger. adv. **Document type:** directory.
Formerly: Black's Guide to the Office Space Market: Northern New Jersey.

333.33 US
BLACK'S OFFICE LEASING GUIDE: ORLANDO - CENTRAL FLORIDA.* 1993. a. $94.95. Black's Guide, Inc., 818 W. Diamond Ave., Ste. 300, Gaithersburg, MD 20878-1417. **Document type:** directory.

333.33 US
BLACK'S OFFICE LEASING GUIDE: SAN FRANCISCO BAY AREA - SACRAMENTO.* 1984. s-a. $124.95. Black's Guide, Inc., 818 W. Diamond Ave., Ste. 300, Gaithersburg, MD 20878-1417. Ed. Sheila Holzberger. adv. **Document type:** directory.
Formerly: Black's Guide to the Office Space Market: San Francisco Bay Area.

333.33 US
BLACK'S OFFICE LEASING GUIDE: THE GREATER LOS ANGELES AREA.* 1982. s-a. $149.95. Black's Guide, Inc., 818 W. Diamond Ave., Ste. 300, Gaithersburg, MD 20878-1417. Ed. Sheila Holzberger. adv. **Document type:** directory.
Formerly: Black's Guide to the Office Space Market: Greater Los Angeles Area.

333.33 US
BLACK'S WASHINGTON METROPOLITAN AREA GUIDE.* 1978. q. $349.95. Black's Guide, Inc., 818 W. Diamond Ave., Ste. 300, Gaithersburg, MD 20878-1417. Ed. Sheila Holzberger. adv. **Document type:** directory.
Former titles (until 1992): Black's Broker - Tenant Guide: Washington - Baltimore; (until 1991): Black's Guide to the Office Space Market: Washington - Baltimore.

333.33 GW
BREMISCHE HAUSBESITZERZEITUNG. m. Zentralverband der Deutschen Haus-, Wohnungs- und Grundeigentuemer, Landesverband Bremischer Haus- und Grundbesitzervereine e.V., Am Dobben 3, 28203 Bremen, Germany. TEL 0421-328205.

333.33 FR
BRETAGNE IMMOBILIERE. 1919. m. 5 F. per no. Federation des Associations des Proprietaires Urbains et Ruraux de la Bretagne et de l'Ouest de la France, 6. R. Saint-Louis, 35000 Rennes, France. Ed. Maitre Bellenger. adv. circ. 11,000.

BRITAIN'S TOP 300 PROPERTY DEVELOPERS. see BUSINESS AND ECONOMICS — Trade And Industrial Directories

BRITISH COLUMBIA POPULATION FORECAST. see POPULATION STUDIES

333.33 340 CN
BRITISH COLUMBIA REAL ESTATE LAW GUIDE. m. Can.$560. C C H Canadian Ltd., 6 Garamond Ct., North York, ON M3C 1Z5, Canada. TEL 416-441-2992; 800-268-4522. FAX 416-444-9011. Ed.Bd. **Document type:** trade publication.
Description: Covers laws governing real estate transactions in B.C.

333.33 UK ISSN 0261-0035
BRITISH SHOPPING CENTRE DEVELOPMENT MASTER LIST. SUPPLEMENT. 1979. a. £25. Hillier Parker, 77 Grosvenor St., London W1A 2BT, England. TEL 0171-629-7666. FAX 0171-409-3016. Ed. Clare Andrews. (back issues avail.) **Document type:** trade publication.

BROKER-DEALERS AND SECURITIES MARKETS; a guide to the regulatory process. see LAW

333.33 340 US
BRONX COOP CONDO CONVERSION DIGEST. 1979. base vol. (plus irreg. updates, 2-4/yr.) $255. Yale Robbins, Inc., 31 E. 28th St., New York, NY 10016. TEL 212-683-5700. FAX 212-545-0764. Ed. George Kelly. (looseleaf format)

333.33 US
BRONX REALTOR NEWS. 1927. bi-w. membership. Bronx Board of Realtors, Inc., 1867 Williamsbridge Rd., Bronx, NY 10461-6205. Ed, Nunzio DelGreco. adv.; bk.rev.; charts; illus.; stat. circ. 1,000.
Formerly (until 1980): Bronx Real Estate and Building News (ISSN 0007-2265)

333.33 340 US
BROOKLYN COOP CONDO CONVERSION DIGEST. 1979. base vol. (plus irreg. updates, 2-4/yr.) $290. Yale Robbins, Inc., 31 E. 28th St., New York, NY 10016. TEL 212-683-5700. FAX 212-545-0764. Ed. George Kelly. (looseleaf format)

333.33 US
THE BROWNSTONER. q. $35 to new subscr.; renewal $25. Box 577, New York, NY 10113. circ. 1,200. **Document type:** newsletter.

333.33 SI
BUILDING AND ESTATE MANAGEMENT SOCIETY. PROCEEDINGS. s-a. Building and Estate Management Society, c/o Faculty of Architecture and Building, National University of Singapore, Kent Ridge, Singapore 0511. TEL 7756666.

333.33 690 CN ISSN 1191-9841
BUILDING MANAGEMENT & DESIGN; for the design, construction, facilities & building management industry. 1986. 6/yr. Can.$27.82 (foreign Can.$32). (Resident Managers Training Institute) Southam Magazine Group, 1450 Don Mills Rd., Don Mills, ON M3B 2X7, Canada. TEL 416-442-2055. FAX 416-442-2229. Ed. Cindy Woods. circ. 30,000. (back issues avail.)
Formerly (until 1992): Building Owner and Property Manager (ISSN 1189-6264)
Description: News for building owners-developers, property managers and real estate developers.

333.3 332 352.7 UK
BUILDING SOCIETIES YEARBOOK. (Supplement avail: Building Societies Yearbook Updating Service) a. £60 (effective 1994-1995). Building Societies Association, 3 Savile Row, London W1X 1AF, England. TEL 0171-437-0655. FAX 0171-287-0109. (Co-sponsor: Council of Mortgage Lenders) stat. **Document type:** directory.
Incorporates: Council of Mortgage Lenders Yearbook.
Description: Lists directors and senior managers of member societies and compiles key statistics. Also provides addresses of building society members and a listing of surveyors.

333.33 UK
BUILDING SOCIETY ACTIVITIES SURVEY. a. £295 to non-members; members £175 (effective 1994-1995). Building Societies Association, 3 Savile Row, London W1X 1AF, England. TEL 0171-437-0655. FAX 0171-287-0109. (Co-sponsor: Council of Mortgage Lenders) **Document type:** trade publication.
Description: Reviews the nonmortgage activities of each U.K. building society.

333.3 332 352.7 UK
BUILDING SOCIETY ANNUAL ACCOUNTS DATA. a. £40 to non-members (diskette version £100); members £20 (diskette version £50) (effective 1994-1995). Building Societies Association, 3 Savile Row, London W1X 1AF, England. TEL 0171-437-0655. FAX 0171-287-0109. stat. (also avail. in diskette format) **Document type:** trade publication.
Description: Features data drawn from the published reports and accounts of building societies.

BUILDING SOCIETY ANNUAL ACCOUNTS MANUAL. see BUILDING AND CONSTRUCTION

333.33 UK
BUILDING SOCIETY LEAGUE TABLES (FINANCIAL). a. £295 to non-members; members £175 (effective 1994-1995). Building Societies Association, 3 Savile Row, London W1X 1AF, England. TEL 0171-437-0655. FAX 0171-287-0109. (Co-sponsor: Council of Mortgage Lenders) **Document type:** trade publication.
Description: Provides comprehensive information on U.K. building societies from a financial standpoint and ranks them in descending order of value.

REAL ESTATE 5649

333.33 UK
BUILDING SOCIETY LEAGUE TABLES (OPERATIONAL). a. £295 to non-members; members £175 (effective 1994-1995). Building Societies Association, 3 Savile Row, London W1X 1AF, England. TEL 0171-437-0655. FAX 0171-287-0109. (Co-sponsor: Council of Mortgage Lenders) **Document type:** trade publication.
  Description: Features operational data on U.K. building societies.

BUILDING SOCIETY MORTGAGE ARREARS AND LOSSES REPORT. see *BUSINESS AND ECONOMICS — Banking And Finance*

333.33 UK
BUILDING SOCIETY PEER GROUPS (FINANCIAL). a. £375 to non-members; members £225 (effective 1994-1995). Building Societies Association, 3 Savile Row, London W1X 1AF, England. TEL 0171-437-0655. FAX 0171-287-0109. (Co-sponsor: Council of Mortgage Lenders) **Document type:** trade publication.
  Description: Provides comprehensive information, allowing for the comparison of the financial performance of each U.K. building society with its peers.

333.33 UK
BUILDING SOCIETY PEER GROUPS (OPERATIONAL). a. £295 to non-members; members £175 (effective 1994-1995). Building Societies Association, 3 Savile Row, London W1X 1AF, England. TEL 0171-437-0655. FAX 0171-287-0109. (Co-sponsor: Council of Mortgage Lenders) **Document type:** trade publication.
  Description: Provides comprehensive information, allowing for the comparison of the operational performance of each U.K. building society with its peers for both the current and preceeding years.

333.33 UK
BUILDING SOCIETY RESULTS SUMMARIES (FINANCIAL). a. £295 to non-members; members £175 (effective 1994-1995). Building Societies Association, 3 Savile Row, London W1X 1AF, England. TEL 0171-437-0655. FAX 0171-287-0109. (Co-sponsor: Council of Mortgage Lenders) **Document type:** trade publication.
  Description: Shows the financial performance of each U.K. building society, providing both preceeding and current year figures for comparison.

333.33 UK
BUILDING SOCIETY RESULTS SUMMARIES (OPERATIONAL). a. £295 to non-members; members £175 (effective 1994-1995). Building Societies Association, 3 Savile Row, London W1X 1AF, England. TEL 0171-437-0655. FAX 0171-287-0109. (Co-sponsor: Council of Mortgage Lenders) **Document type:** trade publication.
  Description: Shows the operational performance of each U.K. building society for both the current and preceeding years.

BUILDING SOCIETY TAXATION MANUAL. see *LAW — Estate Planning*

333.33 SZ ISSN 0007-4675
BULLETIN IMMOBILIER. 1918. 10/yr. 60 SFr. Federation Romande Immobiliere, Case postale 2560, CH-1002 Lausanne, Switzerland. TEL 021-3110942. FAX 021-3110946. Ed. Claudine Amstein. adv.: B&W page 2240 SFr., color page 3190 SFr.; trim 195 x 276. stat.; mkt. circ. 12,000. **Document type:** consumer publication.

333.33 US ISSN 0746-0023
HC101
BUSINESS FACILITIES. 1968. m. $30. Group C Communications, 121 Monmouth St., Box 2060, Red Bank, NJ 07701. TEL 800-524-0337. FAX 908-758-6634. Ed. Eric Peterson. adv. contact: Susan L. Coene. charts; illus.; stat.; tr.lit. circ. 40,000. (back issues avail.) **Document type:** trade publication.
  Formerly: A I P R (American Industrial Properties Report) (ISSN 0193-7308)

BUSINESS FIRST MAGAZINE. see *BUSINESS AND ECONOMICS — Economic Situation And Conditions*

BUSINESS OPPORTUNITIES JOURNAL. see *BUSINESS AND ECONOMICS — Investments*

333.3 US
BUSINESS PROPERTIES. q. Southeast Publishing Ventures, 528 E. Blvd., Charlotte, NC 28203-5110. TEL 704-373-0051. Ed. Tobin Roberts. circ. 15,000.

333.33 658.8 UK ISSN 0955-7547
BUSINESS RATIO REPORT: ESTATE AGENTS; an industry sector analysis. 1989. a. I C C Business Ratios Ltd., Freepost, Field House, Hampton, Mddx. TW12 1BR, England. TEL 081-783-0977. FAX 081-783-1940. charts; stat. **Document type:** trade publication.
  —BLDSC (3812.537230).

333.33 658.8 UK
BUSINESS RATIO REPORT: PROPERTY DEVELOPERS, INVESTORS AND DEALERS; an industry sector analysis. a. I C C Business Ratios Ltd. (Subsidiary of: I C C Business Ratios Ltd.), Freepost, Field House, Hampton, Mddx. TW12 1BR, England. TEL 081-783-0977. FAX 081-783-1940. charts; stat. **Document type:** trade publication.
  Formerly (until 1989): Property Developers (ISSN 0950-8406)

BUSINESS VALUATION REVIEW. see *BUSINESS AND ECONOMICS — Banking And Finance*

BUTTERWORTHS PROPERTY LAW SERVICE. see *LAW*

333.33 US
BUYING, SELLING & OWNING YOUR HOME; the guide to the American dream. 1991. s-a. E C V L.P., 333 Sylvan Ave., Ste. 400, Englewood Cliffs, NJ 07632. TEL 201-568-4600. FAX 201-568-3646. adv.: B&W or color page $22060; trim 8 1/8 x 10 7/8. circ. 375,000. **Document type:** consumer publication.

BYGGREFERAT; Nordiskt litteraturindex. see *HOUSING AND URBAN PLANNING*

332.1 US ISSN 8755-3732
C A A S NEWS; newsletter on computer-assisted appraisal. 1984. 4/yr. membership. International Association of Assessing Officers, Computer-Assisted Appraisal Section, 130 E. Randolph St., Ste. 850, Chicago, IL 60601. TEL 312-819-6107. FAX 312-819-6149. Ed. Jenney Kroft. circ. 800. **Document type:** newsletter.
  Supersedes (1981-1982): E D P.
  Description: Covers computer-assisted appraisal, new technological advances in the field and solutions to problems in mass appraisal.

333.3 US
C E A NEWS.* m. California Escrow Association, 530 Bercut Dr., Ste. G, Sacramento, CA 95814-0101. TEL 213-461-7383. Ed. Geraldine Cassidy. adv. circ. 4,500.

333.3 332 352.7 UK
C M L ANNUAL REPORT. a. £5 (effective 1994-1995). Council of Mortgage Lenders, 3 Savile Row, London W1X 1AF, England. TEL 0171-437-0655. FAX 0171-287-0109. **Document type:** corporate report, directory.
  Description: Reviews the activities of C.M.L. in all matters concerning housing and housing finance. Includes directory.

333.3 332 352.7 UK ISSN 0967-7151
C M L - B S A MORTGAGE WEEKLY. w. £75 to non-members; members £25 (effective 1994-1995). Council of Mortgage Lenders, 3 Savile Row, London W1X 1AF, England. TEL 0171-437-0655. FAX 0171-287-0109. **Document type:** newsletter.
  Description: Provides a weekly digest of news stories covering the housing and mortgage markets and the organizations that operate them.

333.3 332 352.7 UK
C M L DIRECTORY OF MEMBERS. irreg., latest Feb. 1994. £5 to non-members; members £3 (effective 1994-1995). Council of Mortgage Lenders, 3 Savile Row, London W1X 1AF, England. TEL 0171-437-0655. FAX 0171-287-0109. **Document type:** directory.
  Description: Describes the association and its activities; lists member organizations.

333.3 332 352.7 UK
C M L JOURNALS INDEX. m. £150 to non-members; members £85 (effective 1994-1995). Council of Mortgage Lenders, 3 Savile Row, London W1X 1AF, England. TEL 0171-437-0655. FAX 0171-287-0109. **Document type:** bibliography, abstracting/indexing.
  Description: Lists and abstracts journal articles indexed in the C M L Library database.

333.3 332 352.7 UK
C M L LIBRARY BULLETIN. m. £65 to non-members; members £45 (effective 1994-1995). Council of Mortgage Lenders, 3 Savile Row, London W1X 1AF, England. TEL 0171-437-0655. FAX 0171-287-0109. **Document type:** bulletin, bibliography.
  Description: Provides bibliographic details of the documents and publications received at the C.M.L. Library; reports current library information services. Includes information on hard-to-find or unusual sources of information on housing finance.

333.3 332 352.7 UK
C M L MARKET BRIEFING. m. £120 to non-members; members £60 (effective 1994-1995). Council of Mortgage Lenders, 3 Savile Row, London W1X 1AF, England. TEL 0171-437-0655. FAX 0171-287-0109. stat. **Document type:** trade publication.
  Description: Provides members with a wide range of statistical and economic information on the economy and the mortgage and housing markets.

333.3 332 352.7 UK
C M L NEWS UPDATE. 1981. m. £6 to members; non-members £12. Council of Mortgage Lenders, 3 Savile Row, London W1X 1AF, England. TEL 0171-437-0655. FAX 0171-287-0109. **Document type:** newsletter.
  Former titles (until 1995): Mortgage Finance Monthly (ISSN 0957-1388); (until 1989): Savings and Loan Monthly (ISSN 0955-5870); Building Society News (ISSN 0261-5304)
  Description: Reports events, trends, and developments in the housing finance industry.

333.3 UK
C M L NEWS UPDATE. m. £18 to non-members; members £9 (effective 1994-1995). Council of Mortgage Lenders, 3 Savile Row, London W1X 1AF, England. TEL 0171-437-0655. FAX 0171-287-0109. charts. **Document type:** newsletter.
  Formerly: Mortgage Monthly.
  Description: Includes opinions and perspectives on current issues in the mortgage market.

333.33 352.7 US ISSN 0199-7653
C P M ASPECTS. (Certified Property Manager) 1968. bi-m. membership. Institute of Real Estate Management, 430 N. Michigan Ave., Chicago, IL 60611. TEL 312-329-6055. FAX 312-661-0217. TELEX 312-025-3742. Ed. Pamela M. Chwedyk. charts; illus. circ. 12,800. (back issues avail.) **Document type:** newsletter.
  Description: Includes news and features on industry trends, IREM policies and programs, legislation affecting property management, HUD, and a jobs bulletin.

333.33 US ISSN 1058-8205
KFC811.A59
CALIFORNIA LAND USE LAW AND POLICY REPORTER. 1991. m. $200. Shepard's - McGraw-Hill, Inc., Box 35300, Colorado Springs, CO 80935-3530. TEL 719-488-3000. FAX 800-525-0053. Ed. Robert M. Schuster. **Document type:** newsletter.

CALIFORNIA PLANNING AND DEVELOPMENT REPORT. see *PUBLIC ADMINISTRATION*

333.33 US ISSN 0008-1450
CALIFORNIA REAL ESTATE. 1920. m. $12. California Association of Realtors, 525 S. Virgil Ave., Los Angeles, CA 90020. TEL 213-739-8320. FAX 213-480-7724. Ed. Ann Framroze. adv.: B&W page $3880, color page $5000. bk.rev.; bibl.; charts; illus.; mkt.; stat.; index. circ. 110,700. Indexed: Cal.Per.Ind. (1985-).
  Former titles (until 1975): California Real Estate Magazine (ISSN 0732-2194); (until 1929): California Real Estate (ISSN 0732-3832)

5650 REAL ESTATE

333.33 US
CALIFORNIA REAL ESTATE JOURNAL. bi-m. Daily Journal Corporation (Los Angeles), 915 E. First St., Los Angeles, CA 90012-4092. TEL 213-625-2141. FAX 213-680-3682. Ed. Roger Vincent. adv. circ. 25,000.

333.33 330 US ISSN 1046-3844
KFC140.B452
CALIFORNIA REAL ESTATE REPORTER. 1986. m. $235. Matthew Bender & Co., Inc., 11 Penn Plaza, New York, NY 10001. TEL 212-967-7707. Ed. David W. Walters. (looseleaf format)

346.04 US ISSN 1052-2921
K3
CALIFORNIA REAL PROPERTY JOURNAL. 1982. q. $40 membership. State Bar of California, Real Property Law Section, 555 Franklin St., San Francisco, CA 94102-4498.

333.33 SP
CAMARA OFICIAL DE LA PROPIEDAD URBANA DE LA PROVINCIA DE MALAGA. HOJA INFORMATIVA. 1970. m. Camara Oficial de la Propiedad Urbana de la Provincia, Carreteria, 7, Malaga, Spain.

333.33 CN ISSN 0383-6649
CANADIAN APPRAISER/EVALUATEUR CANADIEN. 1943; N.S. 1956. 4/yr. Can.$25. Appraisal Institute of Canada, 1111 Portage Ave., Winnipeg, MB R3G 0S8, Canada. TEL 204-783-2224. FAX 204-785-5575. adv.; bk.rev. circ. 6,000. **Indexed:** ABI Inform., Can.B.P.I., RICS.
—UMI.
Formerly: A I M.

333.33 340 CN
CANADIAN COMMERCIAL REAL ESTATE MANUAL. q. Can.$470. Carswell, One Corporate Plaza, 2075 Kennedy Rd., Scarborough, ON M1T 3V4, Canada. TEL 416-609-8000. FAX 416-298-5094. index. (looseleaf format)
Description: Addresses the unique requirements of the commercial real estate industry. Covers the critical stages of development from acquisition through property management.

CANADIAN REAL ESTATE INCOME TAX GUIDE. see BUSINESS AND ECONOMICS — Public Finance, Taxation

333.33 CN ISSN 1193-8021
CANADIAN REALTOR NEWS; official organ of organized real estate in Canada. (Text in English and French) 1955. m. Can.$40. Canadian Real Estate Association, Place de Ville, Tower A, 320 Queen St., 21st Fl., Ottawa, ON K1R 5A3, Canada. TEL 613-237-7111. FAX 613-234-2567. Ed. James B. McCarthy. adv.: B&W page $2415. bk.rev.; charts; illus.; stat.; index; circ. 80,000 (controlled). (also avail. in microfilm from UMI; reprint service avail. from UMI) **Indexed:** Can.B.P.I., RICS. **Document type:** newspaper, trade publication.
—UMI.
Formerly: Canadian Real Estate (ISSN 0823-8197); Supersedes: C R E A Reporter (ISSN 0315-3843); Canadian Realtor (ISSN 0008-4905)

CARLSONREPORT FOR SHOPPING CENTER MANAGEMENT. see BUSINESS AND ECONOMICS — Management

333.33 US ISSN 0742-5678
CAROLINA REAL ESTATE JOURNAL. 1981. q. $55. Shaw Publishing Inc., 128 S. Tryon St., Ste. 2200, Charlotte, NC 28202. TEL 704-371-3269. Ed. Scott Smith; Pub. Sam Rogers. **Document type:** trade publication.

333.33 US
CHARLESTON TRIDENT COMMERCE MAGAZINE. 1987. s-a. $10. A P G, Inc., Box 61719, Charleston, SC 29419-1719. TEL 803-747-0025. FAX 803-744-0816. Ed. Nancy Jones. adv.: B&W page $1880, color page $3580; adv. contact: Scott Shellhaas. circ. 8,000.
Formerly: Charleston Real Estate Report.

333.33 US ISSN 1047-1413
CHARLOTTE COUNTY FLORIDA LAND OWNER. 1989. m. $24. C.F. Cline, Ed. & Pub., 3279 Eldorado Ln., Pt. Charlotte, FL 33948. adv. circ. 5,000.
Description: Records deeds from the previous month - who bought what, who sold what, and for how much. Includes information on county functions and profiles of county business people.

CHENGXIANG JIANSHE/URBAN AND RURAL CONSTRUCTION. see HOUSING AND URBAN PLANNING

333.33 HK ISSN 1021-6332
CHINA PROPERTY REVIEW. (Text in Chinese, English) 1992. 10/yr. HK.$2250($295) (effective Jan. 1994). Asia Law & Practice Ltd., 2-F, 29 Hollywood Rd., Central, Hong Kong. TEL 852-544-9918. FAX 852-543-7617. Ed. Chris Hunter. circ. 3,000. (back issues avail.)
Description: Contains updates and comprehensive analysis of the real property market in P.R. China.

333.33 IT
CITTA (MILAN). m. L.18000. Altra Casa S.r.l., Via Cornelio Tacito 6, 20137 Milan, Italy. TEL 02-65-99-590. Ed. Ivan Rizzi. circ. 50,000.

THE CLAYTON-FILLMORE REPORT; perspectives on economics and real estate. see BUSINESS AND ECONOMICS — Economic Situation And Conditions

CLOSING OFFICER'S GUIDE. see LAW

COLLIER REAL ESTATE TRANSACTIONS AND THE BANKRUPTCY CODE. see BUSINESS AND ECONOMICS — Banking And Finance

333.33 US ISSN 1061-138X
COMMERCIAL INC.; the magazine for commercial real estate. 1988. m. $18. Commercial Inc., 138 N. Saginaw, Pontiac, MI 48342-2112. TEL 810-332-9770. FAX 810-332-3003. Ed. Bonnie M. Taube. circ. 37,000. (back issues avail.) **Document type:** trade publication.
Description: Provides comprehensive, current offerings of commercial real estate and business opportunities for sales or lease in Michigan and reports the latest commercial real estate news, trends, and professional "how-to" articles.

333.33 332.6 US ISSN 0887-4778
HD1361
COMMERCIAL INVESTMENT REAL ESTATE JOURNAL. 1982. 5/yr. $32. Commercial Investment Real Estate Institute, 430 N. Michigan Ave., Chicago, IL 60611-4092. TEL 312-321-4470. FAX 312-321-4530. E-mail: csimpson@cirei.mhs.compuserve.com. Ed. Catherine A. Simpson; Pub. Kimberly Farmer. adv.; index; circ. 9,000 (controlled). (back issues avail.) **Indexed:** ABI Inform. **Document type:** trade publication.
—BLDSC (3336.963650); UMI.
Description: Practical information for professionals on all aspects of commercial real estate.
Refereed Serial

333.33 340 US ISSN 0736-0517
KF593.C6
COMMERCIAL LEASE LAW INSIDER; the practical, plain-English, monthly newsletter for owners, managers, attorneys and other real estate professionals. 1982. m. $236. Brownstone Publishers, Inc., 149 Fifth Ave., New York, NY 10010-6801. TEL 212-473-8200. FAX 212-473-8786. Ed. Nicole Lefton. index. (back issues avail.) **Document type:** newsletter.
Description: Nationwide review of new legal developments and leasing techniques for major owners and tenants.

COMMERCIAL LEASES. see BUSINESS AND ECONOMICS — Investments

333.3 US ISSN 0898-5634
KF593.C6
COMMERCIAL LEASING LAW AND STRATEGY. 1988. m. $1995. New York Law Publishing Co., 345 Park Ave. S., New York, NY 10010. TEL 212-545-6170. FAX 212-696-1848. Ed. Stephanie McEvily. index. (looseleaf format; back issues avail.) **Document type:** newsletter.
Description: Provides latest developments, strategies and techniques on the business and legal aspects of commercial leasing.

333.33 US ISSN 1043-1675
COMMERCIAL PROPERTY NEWS; the national newspaper for commercial property professionals. 1987. s-m. $89 (Canada & Mexico $115; elsewhere $225). Miller Freeman Inc. (New York) (Subsidiary of: United Newspapers Group), 1515 Broadway, New York, NY 10036. TEL 212-869-1300. FAX 212-302-6273. Ed. Mark Klionsky. adv.: B&W page $4225, color page $4450. circ. 35,521 (controlled). **Document type:** newspaper.
Formerly (until 1989): Real Estate Times (ISSN 0893-1968)

333.33 US ISSN 1073-0370
COMMERCIAL REALTY REVIEW. 1987. bi-m. $45. J & C Publishing, 430 E. Lancaster Ave., Ste. B7, St. Davids, PA 19087. TEL 610-644-3144. FAX 610-993-0536. E-mail: R. Ed. Colleen Mogil; Pub. Henry J. Stursberg. adv. contact: Ida Marie Higgins. circ. 7,000. (back issues avail.) **Document type:** trade publication.
Description: Covers trends in commercial real estate industry in NJ, DE, PA.

333.33 US ISSN 0885-6133
COMMON GROUND (ALEXANDRIA); the magazine for community associations. 1984. bi-m. $59 to non-members; members $39. Community Associations Institute, 1630 Duke St., Alexandria, VA 22314. TEL 703-548-8600. FAX 703-684-1581. (Subscr. to: Box 26506, Richmond, VA 23260-6506) Ed. Ken Budd. adv.: B&W page $1430; adv. contact: Jeff Sandersen. circ. 25,000. **Document type:** trade publication.
Description: For volunteer board members, professional managers, accountants and attorneys who work with condominiums, townhouses and other forms of common interest ownership property.

333.33 332.6 330.9 US ISSN 0893-9136
COMMONWEALTH LETTERS; for investors in single family homes. 1978. m. $70 (foreign $82). (National Capital Corporation) CommonWealth Press, Inc., Box 21172, Tampa, FL 33622. TEL 619-538-0151. FAX 619-454-7496. Ed. Jack Miller. adv. contact: Chris Miller. circ. 2,000. (looseleaf format; back issues avail.) **Document type:** newsletter.
Formerly: Jack Miller's CommonWealth Letters.
Description: A practical guide for small investors in income-producing houses with appropriate background data in tax-economics.

333.33 US ISSN 0199-9028
COMMUNIQUE (CHICAGO). 1955. 8/yr. $25 to non-members. Women's Council of Realtors, 430 N. Michigan Ave., Chicago, IL 60611. TEL 312-329-5967. FAX 312-329-3290. Ed. Jean M. Lukow. adv.; bk.rev.; tr.lit.; index. circ. 15,000. **Document type:** trade publication.
Description: Covers real estate sales techniques, management, finance and personal development.

333.33 US
COMMUNITIES MAGAZINE. 1978. bi-m. free. 200 Galleria Pkwy., Ste. 1700, Atlanta, GA 30339-5946. TEL 404-644-7575. FAX 404-644-7585. Ed. Laura Hearron; Pub. Gid Dickey. adv. contact: Laura Hearron. circ. 75,000. **Document type:** consumer publication.
Description: Metro Atlanta's complete guide to all new home subdivisions and condominiums.

COMMUNITY ENTERPRISE. see BUSINESS AND ECONOMICS — Banking And Finance

333.33 US
COMMUNITY LIVING OF CALIFORNIA. 6/yr. $32 (members $24). Community Associations Institute, 1630 Duke St., Alexandria, VA 22314. TEL 703-548-8600. Ed. Erin Eckles. **Document type:** newsletter.
Description: Professional, legislative, legal issues unique to FL condominium and homeowner associations.

333.33 US
COMMUNITY LIVING OF FLORIDA. 9/yr. $32 (members $24). Community Associations Institute, 1630 Duke St., Alexandria, VA 22314. TEL 703-548-8600. Ed. Erin Eckles. adv.: B&W page $890. circ. 3,115. **Document type:** newsletter.
Description: Professional, legislative and legal issues unique to FL condominium and homeowner associations.

REAL ESTATE 5651

COMPILATION OF NATIONALLY AVERAGED RENTAL RATES. see HOUSING AND URBAN PLANNING

333.33 US ISSN 8750-1236
CONDO SALES REPORT. 1982. m. $450. Yale Robbins, Inc., 31 E. 28th St., New York, NY 10016. TEL 212-683-5700. Ed. Yale Robbins. (looseleaf format; back issues avail.)
  Description: Reviews condo sales transactions with analysis of each sale.

333.33 CN
CONDOMINIUM MANAGER. 1979. 4/yr. Can.$25. (Association of Condominium Managers of Ontario) B B & C, 1 Eva Rd., Ste. 409, Etobicoke, ON M9C 4Z5, Canada. TEL 416-626-7895. FAX 416-620-5392. Ed. Bill Thompson. adv.: B&W page Can.$985; trim 8 1/4 x 10 7/8. circ. 2,117.

333.33 US
CONNECTICUT REAL ESTATE JOURNAL. 1972. m. East Coast Publications, Inc., Box 55, Accord, MA 02081. TEL 617-878-4540; 800-654-4993. FAX 617-871-1853. Ed. David Denelle; Pub. Kristine fernald. adv. contact: Kristine Fernald. (tabloid format; back issues avail.) Document type: trade publication, newspaper.
  Description: Covers commercial, industrial, and investment real estate.

333.33 340 US
KFC3712.A15
CONNECTICUT REAL ESTATE LAW JOURNAL. 6/yr. $55. Butterworth Legal Publishers (Salem) (Subsidiary of: Reed Elsevier plc), 8 Industrial Way, Bldg. C, Salem, NH 03079. TEL 800-548-4001. FAX 603-898-9858. Ed. Susan Sjostrom. cum.index. (looseleaf format; back issues avail.) Document type: newsletter.
  Description: Includes case comments and Connecticut Superior Court decisions.

CONNECTICUT REAL PROPERTY STATUTES. see LAW

333.33 US
CONNECTICUT REALTOR. 1977. 8/yr. free to members. Connecticut Association of Realtors, 316 Farmington Ave., Hartford, CT 06105. TEL 203-522-7255. FAX 203-549-5934. Ed. Brad R. Durrell. adv.: B&W page $1000; adv. contact: Lisa Governale. circ. 13,000. (tabloid format) Document type: trade publication.
  Description: Covers legislative issues affecting industry, primarily association related materials, including general issues relating to real estate.

333.33 IT ISSN 0010-7050
CONSULENTE IMMOBILIARE. 1957. s-m. L.190000($120) Pirola Editore S.p.A., Via Parabiago 19, Casella Postale 10444, 20110 Milan, Italy. TEL 2-30-221. FAX 2-380-11-205. bk.rev.; stat.; index, cum.index. circ. 13,000.

333.33 CN
CONSUMERS GUIDE.* 1990. 6/yr. Thompson Newspapers Co. Ltd., 44 Pitt. St., Cornwall, Ont. K6J 3P3, Canada. TEL 416-286-3113. FAX 416-286-4071. adv. circ. 727,964.

333.33 CN ISSN 0838-018X
CONTACT (MONTREAL). 1982. 4/yr. Can.$19 (effective Jan. 1990). Association des Courtiers et Agents Immobiliers du Quebec, 500 Rene-Levesque Ouest, Bur. 700, Montreal, PQ H2Z 1W7, Canada. TEL 514-842-0783. FAX 514-842-1346. Ed. Serge Cayer. adv. contact: Claude Lafreniere. circ. 11,000.

340 UK ISSN 0010-8200
CONVEYANCER AND PROPERTY LAWYER. 1936. bi-m. £72. Sweet & Maxwell, South Quay Plaza, 7th Floor, 183 Marsh Wall, London E14 9FT, England. TEL 071-538-8686. FAX 071-538-9508. Ed.Bd. adv. contact: Jackie Wood. bk.rev.; index. (reprint service avail. from RRI,WSH) Indexed: C.L.I., L.R.I., Leg.Cont., Leg.Per., LJI. Document type: bulletin.
  —Faxon; UnCover. CCC.

333.33 US ISSN 1042-9115
CORPORATE REAL ESTATE EXECUTIVE. 1986. 9/yr. $65 (foreign $95). International Association of Corporate Real Estate Executives, 440 Columbia Dr., W. Palm Beach, FL 33409-6685. TEL 407-683-8111. FAX 407-697-4853. Ed. Kathleen B. Dempsey. bk.rev.; tr.lit.; index. circ. 3,468. (back issues avail.) Document type: trade publication.
  Formerly: Corporate Real Estate Journal.
  Description: Educational and informative articles on topics of interest to heads of real estate departments in large corporations.

333.33 US ISSN 1048-7948
CORRIDOR REAL ESTATE JOURNAL. 1989. w. $52. Adler Group, Inc., 8601 Georgia Ave., Ste. 400, Silver Springs, MD 20910. TEL 301-587-4097. FAX 301-588-2574. (Affiliate: Lionmark Publications, Inc.) Ed. Mark Heschmeyer. adv. contact: Suzan Jagels. circ. 5,500. Document type: newspaper.
  Description: Provides real estate information in order to assist readers to advance their careers and improve their job performance.

333.33 UK ISSN 0011-0159
COUNTRY LANDOWNER. 1907. m. £12. Country Landowners Association, 16 Belgrave Sq., London SW1X 8PQ, England. TEL 071-824-8681. FAX 071-730-1390. Ed. John Kendall. adv.; bk.rev.; index. circ. 49,272. (tabloid format) Indexed: Forest.Abstr., Forest Prod.Abstr., Geo.Abstr., RICS, World Agri.Econ.& Rural Sociol.Abstr.
  —BLDSC (3481.880000).

COURRIER DES EMPLOYES D'IMMEUBLES. see BUSINESS AND ECONOMICS

333.33 BE
CRI. 10/yr. 1250 BEF. Syndicat National des Proprietaires, Rue du Lombard 76, B-1000 Brussels, Belgium. TEL 32-2-512-62-87. FAX 32-2-512-44-61.

CRITTENDEN GOLF INC.. see SPORTS AND GAMES — Ball Games

333.33 US ISSN 0888-9139
CRITTENDEN REAL ESTATE BUYERS. 1984. w. $387. Crittenden Publishing, Inc., 250 Bel Marin Keys, Bldg. A, Novato, CA 94949. TEL 415-382-2400. (Subscr. to: Box 1150, Novato, CA 94948-1150)

387 332 US ISSN 0736-0339
CRITTENDEN REPORT REAL ESTATE FINANCING. 1975. w. $395. Crittenden Research, Inc., Box 1150, Novato, CA 94948. TEL 415-382-2400. FAX 415-382-2476. Ed. John N. Goodwin. index. circ. 2,500. (back issues avail.) Document type: newsletter.

333 NE
CURRENT ISSUES IN REAL ESTATE FINANCE & ECONOMICS. (Text in English) irreg. price varies. Kluwer Academic Publishers, Postbus 17, 3300 AA Dordrecht, Netherlands. TEL 31-78-392392. FAX 31-78-392254. TELEX 29245 KAPG NL. (Dist. by: Kluwer Academic Publishers Group, P.O. Box 322, 3300 AH Dordrecht, Netherlands. TEL 31-78-392392. FAX 31-78-546474; N. America dist. addr.: Box 358, Accord Sta., Hingham, MA 02018-0358. TEL 617-871-6600. FAX 617-871-6528) Document type: monographic series.

333.33 340 US ISSN 0738-6931
D.C. REAL ESTATE REPORTER. 1979. m. $265. Land Development Institute, Ltd., 1401 16th St., N.W., Washington, DC 20036. TEL 202-232-2144. FAX 202-232-4757. Ed.Bd. index. circ. 250. (back issues avail.) Document type: newsletter.
  Description: Covers legislative and judicial decisions affecting land use-zoning, home ownership and rental housing in D.C.

333.33 US ISSN 0279-4195
DAILY COMMERCE. 1917. d. (Mon.-Fri.). $182. Daily Journal Corporation (Los Angeles), 915 E. First St., Los Angeles, CA 90012. TEL 213-229-5300. FAX 213-680-3682. Ed. Darrel Lippman. adv.; bk.rev. circ. 3,000. (tabloid format; also avail. in microfilm) Document type: newspaper.
  Former titles: Journal of Commerce Review; Journal of Commerce and Independent Review (ISSN 0021-9835)

333.33 US
DAILY TRANSCRIPT. 5/w. $95. Pioneer Printing and Publishing, 22 N. Sierra Madre, Colorado Springs, CO 80903. TEL 719-634-1593. FAX 719-632-0762. Ed. Dennis Ingmire; Pub. Fred Bernheim. adv. contact: Michael Murt. circ. 650. Document type: newspaper.

333.33 352.7 US ISSN 0894-0258
DALLAS - FORT WORTH HOME BUYER'S GUIDE. 1972. bi-m. free. Home Buyer's Guide (Dallas), 5501 LBJ Frwy., Ste. 300, Dallas, TX 75240-6202. TEL 214-239-2399. Ed.Bd. adv.; bk.rev.; charts; illus.; circ. 75,000 (controlled). Document type: consumer publication.
  Former titles (until 1987): Living (Dallas - Fort Worth Edition) (ISSN 0741-5494); (until 1983): Dallas - Fort Worth Living (ISSN 0192-8546)
  Description: New-home housing map-guide for the Dallas-Fort Worth Metroplex.

333.33 UK ISSN 0011-5894
DALTONS WEEKLY; houses, shops & businesses for sale; hotel guest house & self-catering holiday accommodation advertiser. 1870. w. £1 (in U.S. £4.24). Daltons Weekly plc., C.I. Tower, St. George's Sq., New Malden, Surrey KT3 4JA, England. TEL 0181-949-6199. FAX 0181-949-2718. Kate Kaegler, Dir. adv.; illus.; index; circ. 40,115 (paid). Document type: consumer publication.

DAYTON BUSINESS REPORTER. see BUSINESS AND ECONOMICS

333.33 US
THE DEAL MAKERS. 1979. w. $197. T K O - Real Estate Advisory Group, Box 2630, Mercerville, NJ 08690. TEL 609-587-6200. FAX 609-587-3511. E-mail: deal.makers@property.com. Pub. Ann O'Neal. adv.; bk.rev. circ. 6,000. (also avail. in diskette format) Document type: newsletter.
  Formerly (until 1991): Retail Leasing Reporter.
  Description: For retail real estate executives. Covers retailers' expansion plans, developments planned and under way, current construction and rehabilitation of existing centers, listings of property for sale.

659.1 720 FR ISSN 0291-1191
DEMEURES ET CHATEAUX. (Text and descriptions in English, French) 1978. 8/yr. 510 F. (rest of Europe 680 F.; elswhere 900 F.). Edinot, B.P. 17, 19230 Pompadour, France. TEL 55-73-32-37. Ed. Jean-Michel Reillier. adv. contact: Patrick Garnier. bk.rev.; illus.; tr.lit. circ. 25,000. Document type: consumer publication.
  Formerly: Demeures et Chateaux en France (ISSN 0180-3905)
  Description: Presents illustrated advertisements for castles, country seats and manors.

333.33 352.7 US
DENVER HOUSING GUIDE. 1974. bi-m. $12. Baker Publications, 2323 S. Troy, Ste. 103, Aurora, CO 80014. TEL 303-695-8440. FAX 303-695-8449. Ed. Patt Dodd. adv.; bk.rev.; circ. 70,000 (controlled).
  Former titles: Living - The Denver Housing Guide & Living (Denver Edition) (ISSN 0741-5508); Denver Living (ISSN 0192-9100)

333.33 GW ISSN 0724-6617
DEUTSCHE WOHNUNGSWIRTSCHAFT. 1949. m. DM.60. (Zentralverband der Deutschen Haus, Wohnungs und Grundeigentuemer e.V.) Verlag Deutsche Wohnungswirtschaft GmbH, Cecilienallee 45, 40474 Duesseldorf, Germany. TEL 0211-47817-0. FAX 0211-4781723. adv.; bk.rev.; charts; illus.; index. circ. 7,000. Document type: trade publication.

333.33 GW ISSN 0012-1371
DEUTSCHES VOLKSHEIMSTAETTENWERK. INFORMATIONSDIENST. 1946. s-m. DM.102. Deutsches Volksheimstaettenwerk e.V., Neefestr. 2a, 53115 Bonn, Germany. bk.rev.; stat.; index. circ. 4,800.
  Incorporates: So Planen und Bauen.

333.33 AT ISSN 0012-1525
DEVELOPER.* vol. 8, 1970. q. membership (non-members Aus.$8.40). Urban Development Institute of Australia, Ste. 11, 283 Alfred St., N. Sydney, N.S.W. 2060, Australia. TEL 02-954-5500. FAX 02-954-5544. Ed. E.J. Burger. adv.; stat.

DEVELOPMENT (HERNDON). see BUILDING AND CONSTRUCTION

ULRICH'S INTERNATIONAL PERIODICALS DIRECTORY 1996

5652 REAL ESTATE

333.33 352.7   UK
DEVELOPMENT PLANS IN THE PIPELINE. s-a. Hillier Parker, 77 Grosvenor St., London W1A 2BT, England. TEL 0171-629-7666. FAX 0171-409-3016. Ed. Joe McClenaghan. (back issues avail.) **Document type:** trade publication.

DEVELOPMENTS; news magazine for the resort-recreational real estate and community development industries. see *HOUSING AND URBAN PLANNING*

DICTIONNAIRE PERMANENT: GESTION IMMOBILIERE. see *BUSINESS AND ECONOMICS — Management*

DIGEST, BUSINESS & LAW JOURNAL. see *BUSINESS AND ECONOMICS — Banking And Finance*

333.33   US
DIRECT SOURCE. 1992. s-a. $49.95. Metro America Office Guides, 921 S.W. Morrison St., No. 407, Portland, OR 97205. TEL 503-223-0304. FAX 503-221-6544. adv. circ. 9,000. **Document type:** trade publication.
   Description: Contains listings of office buildings and parks in the Detroit, Michigan area. Covers real estate trends and features people, products and services.

333.33 690   SP   ISSN 1133-7990
DIRECTIVOS CONSTRUCCION. (Includes q. supplements TecniOcio and UrbaTec) 1985. 11/yr. 36977 ptas. Grupo Especial Directivos, C. Orense 39 2o D, 28020 Madrid, Spain. TEL 1-556-64-11. FAX 1-555-41-18. TELEX 43016 GED E. Ed. Javier Martin. adv.: B&W page 180000 ptas., color page 250000 ptas; trim 185 x 272; adv. contact: Juan Manuel Castro. circ. 7,000.

DIRECTORY OF FOREIGN INVESTMENT IN THE U S; real estate and business. see *BUSINESS AND ECONOMICS — Trade And Industrial Directories*

333.33   HK
DIRECTORY OF HONG KONG LAND AND INVESTMENTS.* a. HK.$200. Hong Kong Trade and Industry Promotion Centre, c/o Hong Kong Trade Development Council, 36th-39th Fl., Office Tower, Convention Plaza, 1 Harbor Rd., Wanchai, Hong Kong. TEL 3-882708. FAX 3-7716438.

DIRECTORY OF INTELLECTUAL PROPERTY ATTORNEYS. see *LAW*

333 658.7   US   ISSN 0732-5983
HF5430.3
DIRECTORY OF MAJOR MALLS. 1977. a. $385 (foreign $405). Jomurpa Publishing Inc., Box 1708, 7 S. Myrtle Ave., Spring Valley, NY 10977. TEL 914-426-0040. FAX 914-426-0802. (Also: 430 Mallard Dr., Santa Rosa, CA 95401. TEL 707-528-3631) Ed. Murray Shor. adv.; maps. —CCC.
   Description: Lists existing and planned shopping centers in the United States and Canada, over 250,000 sq.ft. of gross leasable area; includes portfolios of 48 leading owner-developers and over 250 top retailers seeking mall space. Computerized version, mailing labels, custom report services also available.

DIRECTORY OF PROFESSIONAL APPRAISAL SERVICES. see *BUSINESS AND ECONOMICS — Trade And Industrial Directories*

DIRECTORY OF PROPERTY INVESTORS AND DEVELOPERS. see *BUSINESS AND ECONOMICS — Trade And Industrial Directories*

DISTRESSED BUSINESS AND REAL ESTATE NEWSLETTER. see *LAW*

333.33   US   ISSN 1048-2938
DISTRESSED PROPERTY INVESTOR'S MONTHLY.* 1988. m. $70. Real Estate Publications, Inc. (Tampa), 322 W. Rio Vista Ct., Tampa, FL 33604-6941. TEL 800-356-2317. Ed. Thomas J. Lucier. bk.rev.; index. circ. 1,500. (looseleaf format; back issues avail.)
   Formerly: Diamonds in the Rough (ISSN 0896-0542)
   Description: Provides news of investment opportunities: foreclosures, probate sales, IRS tax-seized sales, and other types of distressed property.

DISTRESSED REAL ESTATE LAW ALERT. see *LAW*

333.33   US   ISSN 0070-704X
HF5430.3
DOLLARS AND CENTS OF SHOPPING CENTERS. (Supplemental special report avail.) 1961. triennial. $225 to non-members; members $180. Urban Land Institute, 625 Indiana Ave., N.W., Ste. 400, Washington, DC 20004-2930. TEL 202-624-7000. FAX 202-624-7140. Ed. Michael Beyard. (reprint service avail. from UMI) **Indexed:** SRI. **Document type:** trade publication.

DOMUS MAGAZIN. see *BUSINESS AND ECONOMICS — Investments*

333.33   US
DOUGLAS PROPERTIES INTERNATIONAL. 1989. 3/yr. $50. Jon Douglas Company, 11900 W. Olympic Blvd., Ste. 400, Los Angeles, CA 90064. TEL 310-442-8002. FAX 310-447-6435. Ed. Judy Kleinberg. adv.; circ. 20,000 (controlled). **Document type:** consumer publication.
   Description: Targets homeowners in the affluent areas of Santa Barbara, Ventura, Los Angeles Westside and the San Fernando Valley. Showcases the company's homes.

333.33   SZ
DROIT AU LOGEMENT. (Text in French) 1975. bi-m. 10 SFr. Association Suisse des Locataires Federation Romande, Rue de la Borde 28, CH-1018 Lausanne, Switzerland. TEL 021-9079494. FAX 021-9079437. Ed. Philippe Bieler. circ. 72,000.

333.33   US   ISSN 0160-9629
HD255
E-R-C DIRECTORY. 1964. a. $35. Employee Relocation Council, 1720 N St., N.W., Washington, DC 20036. TEL 202-857-0857. FAX 202-467-4012. Ed. Tina Lung. circ. 16,000. **Document type:** directory.
   Formerly: E R E A C Directory (ISSN 0071-0113)
   Description: Lists real estate brokers and appraisers.

333.33   UK
E S P C WEEKLY LIST. 1992. Edinburgh Solicitors' Property Centre, 85 George St., Edinburgh EH2 2ES, Scotland. TEL 031-226-3891. FAX 031-225-4980. adv.; illus. (tabloid format) **Document type:** newspaper.
   Description: Covers the eastern Scotland real estate market.

333.33   SZ
ECONOMIA FONDIARIA. (Text in Italian) m. Camera Ticinese dell'Economia Fondiaria, Via Dufour 1, CH-6901 Lugano, Switzerland. TEL 091-529171. Ed. Stelio Pesciallo. circ. 15,000.

333.33   NO
EIENDOMSMEGLEREN.* m. Norges Eiendomsmeglerforbund, Prinsensgt. 21, 0258 Oslo 2, Norway. TEL 02-447953.

333.33   DK   ISSN 0013-2896
EJENDOMSMAEGLEREN. 1934. m. DKK 396.50. (Foreningen at Statsautoriserede Ejendomsmaeglere) Ejendomsmaeglerens Forlag, Stormgade 16, 1470 Copenhagen K, Denmark. (Co-sponsor: Dansk Ejendomsmaeglerforening) Ed. Knud Pedersen. adv.; bk.rev.; abstr.; illus.; stat. circ. 7,000. (tabloid format)
   Former titles (until 1985): Ejendomshandleren (ISSN 0900-8276); (until 1949): Ejendomskommissionaeren; Incorporates (in 1990): D E H Bladet (ISSN 0900-8373)

333.33   US   ISSN 0279-6112
EMPIRE STATE REALTOR. 1970. 12/yr. $12 to non-members. New York State Association of Realtors, 130 Washington Ave., Albany, NY 12210-2298. TEL 518-463-0300. FAX 518-462-5474. Ed. Jill M. Tribula. adv.: B&W page $1230, color page $12237. bk.rev. circ. 35,000. **Document type:** trade publication, newspaper.
   Description: Provides information about current events in the real estate industry and association activities and programs.

EQUITABLE DISTRIBUTION OF PROPERTY. see *LAW*

333.33   UK
ESTATE AGENCY NEWS. 1986. m. £12.50. Estates Press Ltd., Keenans Mill, Lords St., St. Annes on Sea, Lancs. FY8 2DF, England. TEL 0253-722142. FAX 0253-714020. Ed. David F. Perkins. adv.: B&W page £1,785; color page £2,523; adv. contact: C.F. Wilson. bk.rev.; charts; illus. circ. 14,000. (tabloid format; back issues avail.) **Document type:** newspaper, trade publication.
   Description: Serves residential real estate agents with news, views, and informed commentary.

333.33   UK   ISSN 0260-1001
THE ESTATE AGENT; voice of the practical estate agent. 1980. 8/yr. £24. National Association of Estate Agents, 21 Jury St., Warwick CV34 4EH, England. FAX 0926-403958. Ed. Peter Cliff. adv.; bk.rev. circ. 11,000. **Indexed:** Ind.S.A.Per. **Document type:** trade publication.
   Description: For realtors in the UK: dealing with residential practice and procedures.

333.33   US
ESTATE AND PERSONAL FINANCIAL PLANNING NEWSLETTER. m. Clark - Boardman - Callaghan Company Ltd., 375 Hudson St., New York, NY 10014. TEL 212-929-7500; 800-221-9428. FAX 212-924-0460. **Document type:** newsletter.

333.33 690   IE
ESTATE & PROPERTY NEWS. 1976. m. £25. Keltic Enterprises Ltd., 45 Lower Baggot St., Dublin 2, Ireland. Ed. Leo T. Mooney. charts; illus.; stat. (back issues avail.)

333.33   UK   ISSN 0967-1862
ESTATES EUROPE; the European property newsletter. (Supplement avail.: Estates Europe Directory) 1992. m. £150 includes a. supplement. Estates Gazette Ltd., 151 Wardour St., London W1V 4BN, England. TEL 0171-437-0141. FAX 0171-437-2432. **Document type:** trade publication.
   Description: Briefs senior real estate executives on legal developments in the field.

333.33 332.04   UK   ISSN 0014-1240
ESTATES GAZETTE; devoted to land, commercial, industrial, residential and agricultural properties. (Supplement avail.: Estates Gazette Directory) 1858. w. £102 (rest of Europe £152) (includes m. directory; a. supplement). Estates Gazette Ltd., 151 Wardour St., London W1V 4BN, England. TEL 0171-437-0141. FAX 0171-437-2432. Ed. Helen Pearce. adv.; bk.rev.; mkt.; index. circ. 29,710. **Indexed:** Euro.LJI, Geo.Abstr., LJI, RICS, World Agri.Econ. & Rural Sociol.Abstr. **Document type:** trade publication.
   ●Also available online.
   —BLDSC (3812.538000).
   Incorporates: Property Market Review.
   Description: Provides authoritative information on all aspects of real and estate law.

333.3 332.04   UK   ISSN 0951-9289
ESTATES GAZETTE LAW REPORTS. s-a. price varies. Estates Gazette Ltd., 151 Wardour St., London W1V 4BN, England. TEL 0171-437-0141. FAX 0171-437-2432. Ed. Barry Denyer-Green. **Document type:** trade publication.
   Supersedes (in 1985): Estates Gazette Digest of Land and Property Cases (ISSN 0071-1586)
   Description: Contains reports on various aspects of real estate law.

333.33 352.7   UK   ISSN 0954-1977
ESTATES GAZETTE PLANNING LAW REPORTS. 1988. 3/yr. Estates Gazette Ltd., 151 Wardour St., London W1V 4BN, England. TEL 0171-437-0141. FAX 0171-437-2432. **Document type:** trade publication.
   Description: Offers a comprehensive and specialist series of law reports devoted exclusively to town and country planning cases.

333.33   UK   ISSN 0014-1259
ESTATES TIMES. 1968. w. £82($160) Morgan-Grampian Publishers Press (Subsidiary of: Morgan-Grampian plc), Morgan-Grampian House, 30 Calderwood St., London SE18 6QH, England. TEL 0181-855-7777. FAX 0181-854-7476. Ed. Derek Penfold. adv. contact: Martin Austen. circ. 27,848. (tabloid format; also avail. in microform from UMI; reprint service avail. from UMI) **Indexed:** RICS. **Document type:** bulletin.
   —BLDSC (3812.548000); UMI.
   Incorporates: Commercial Property Advertiser.

333.3 332 352.7   UK
EUROPEAN COMMUNITY MORTGAGE BULLETIN. bi-m. £15 to members only (effective 1994-1995). Council of Mortgage Lenders, 3 Savile Row, London W1X 1AF, England. TEL 0171-437-0655. FAX 0171-287-0109. (Co-sponsor: Building Societies Association) circ. (controlled). **Document type:** bulletin.
   Description: Alerts members to policy developments at the E.C. level that could affect mortgage lending institutions in the U.K.

333.33   UK   ISSN 1352-626X
EUROPEAN PROPERTY BULLETIN. 1991. q. £8 per no. Hillier Parker, 77 Grosvenor St., London W1A 2BT, England. TEL 0171-629-7666. FAX 0171-409-3016. Ed. Jenny Mottram. (back issues avail.)

EUROPROPERTY. see BUSINESS AND ECONOMICS — Investments

333.33   US   ISSN 0896-0763
EXECUTIVE GUIDE TO SPECIALISTS IN INDUSTRIAL AND OFFICE REAL ESTATE. a. $70. Society of Industrial and Office Realtors, 700 11th St., N.W., Ste. 510, Washington, DC 20001-4511. TEL 202-737-1150. circ. 8,000. **Document type:** directory.
   Description: For industrial and office real estate brokers worldwide.

333   US   ISSN 0191-2208
HD7287.67.U5
EXPENSE ANALYSIS: CONDOMINIUMS, COOPERATIVES AND PLANNED UNIT DEVELOPMENTS. a. $136.95. Institute of Real Estate Management, 430 N. Michigan Ave., Chicago, IL 60611. TEL 312-661-1953. Ed. Kay McGuire. **Indexed:** SRI.
   Supersedes in part: Income - Expense Analysis: Apartments, Condominiums and Cooperatives (ISSN 0161-5262)
   Description: Reports median costs for condominiums throughout the U.S.

333.33   US
EXTRA EQUITY FOR HOMEBUYERS.* 1984. 3/yr. free. Smart Marketing, Home & Land Publishing, Inc., Box 475, Southport, CT 06490-0475. TEL 203-225-0855. FAX 203-259-0724. circ. 250,000 (controlled). **Document type:** consumer publication.
   Description: Features promotional offers from national advertisers for persons buying a single-family home.

333.33   FR   ISSN 0767-0192
F I A B C I PRESS. (Editions in English, French, German, Spanish) 1985. 5/yr. free. International Real Estate Federation (FIABCI) - Federation Internationale des Professions Immobiliers, 23 ave. Bosquet, 75007 Paris, France. TEL 45-50-45-49. FAX 45-50-42-00. Ed. Andrew Irvine. adv.; bk.rev. circ. 6,000. **Document type:** newsletter.
   Description: Provides news of the Federation.

333.33 640.73   US   ISSN 0274-9882
F M O NEWS. 1964. 8/yr. $10. Federation of Mobile Home Owners of Florida, 4020 Portsmouth Rd., Largo, FL 34641. TEL 813-530-7539. FAX 813-535-9427. Ed. Steven Germain. adv. circ. 126,000.
   Description: Reports on the federation's lobbying and legal efforts. Contains lifestyle-oriented information.

333.33 338.1   US   ISSN 1076-3856
F M R A NEWS. 1955. bi-m. $22. American Society of Farm Managers and Rural Appraisers, 950 S. Cherry St., Ste. 508, Denver, CO 80222. TEL 303-758-3513. FAX 303-758-0190. Ed. Alan L. Yoder. circ. 4,000.
   Description: Contains articles of interest to farm managers, rural appraisers, agricultural consultants, and other agricultural professionals.
   Refereed Serial

FACILITIES PLANNING HANDBOOK. see ARCHITECTURE

FACILITIES PLANNING NEWS. see ARCHITECTURE

333.33   US   ISSN 0191-2704
HG2040.5.U5
FANNIE MAE ANNUAL REPORT. a. Federal National Mortgage Association, 3900 Wisconsin Ave., N.W., Washington, DC 20016. TEL 202-752-4322. FAX 202-752-4933.

333.33   SW   ISSN 0345-3278
FASTIGHETSMAEKLAREN/REAL ESTATE BROKER. 1942. q. SEK 25($6) Maeklarsamfundet - Swedish Association of Real Estate Brokers, P.O. Box 1487, 171 28 Solna, Sweden. Ed. Anders Engstroem. adv. circ. 9,000.(controlled). **Document type:** trade publication.

333.33   SW   ISSN 0348-5552
FASTIGHETSTIDNINGEN. Variant title: Svensk Fastighetstidning. (Text in Swedish) 1909. 20/yr. SEK 480. (Sveriges Fastighetsaegarefoerbund) Fastighedstidningen, P.O. Box 1707, Regeringsgatan 67, 8 tr., S-111 87 Stockholm, Sweden. TEL 46-8-613-57 40. FAX 46-8-10-09-60. Ed. Olle Vaevare. adv.: B&W page SEK 13900, color page SEK 21900; trim 185 x 270; adv. contact: Aasa Friberg. illus.; index. circ. 23,045. (back issues avail.) **Document type:** trade publication, consumer publication.
   Former titles (until 1978): Svensk Fastighetstidning; (until 1948): Sveriges Fastighetstidning; (until 1917): Byggnadsvaerlden. Uppl. B, Fastighetsaegartidningen; (until 1915): Byggnadsvaerlden; (until 1914): Nyhaeter fraan Byggnadsvaerlden.

FEDERAL HOME LOAN BANK OF ATLANTA. ANNUAL REPORT. see BUSINESS AND ECONOMICS — Banking And Finance

333.33   US
FEDERAL INCOME TAXATION OF REAL ESTATE. base vol. (plus updates 3/yr). $110 (for base vol. and supplement) (foreign $143) (effective 1994). Warren, Gorham & Lamont, One Penn Plaza, New York, NY 10119. TEL 212-971-5000. FAX 212-971-5113. (Subscr. to: The Park Square Bldg., 31 St. James Ave., Boston, MA 02116-4112. TEL 800-950-1207) (looseleaf format) **Document type:** trade publication.
   Formerly: Robinson Federal Income Taxation of Real Estate.

333.33 340   FR
FEDERATION NATIONALE DE L'IMMOBILIERS. INFORMATIONS F N A I M: JURIDIQUES ET TECHNIQUES. m. Federation Nationale de l'Immobiliers, 129 rue du Faubourg St.-Honore, 75008 Paris, France. TEL 44207700.
   Formerly: Federation Nationale des Agents Immobiliers, Mandataires en Vente de Fonds de Commerce, Administrateurs de Bien, Syndics de Copropriete et Experts. Informations Juridiques.

333.33   UK
FEDERATION OF PRIVATE RESIDENTS ASSOCIATIONS LTD. NEWSLETTER. 1980? q. £2.50 per no. to non-members. Federation of Private Residents Associations, 62 Bayswater Rd., London W2 3PS, England. TEL 0171-402-1581. Ed. T.G. Buckeridge. circ. 250. **Document type:** newsletter.

FINANCE, INSURANCE AND REAL ESTATE U S A. see BUSINESS AND ECONOMICS — Abstracting, Bibliographies, Statistics

FINANCIAL FREEDOM REPORT; the magazine for high profit investors. see BUSINESS AND ECONOMICS — Banking And Finance

333.33   CN
▼**FIRST HOME BUYER'S GUIDE.** 1994. q. Can.$12. Homes Publishing Group, 178 Main St., Unionville, ON L3R 2G9, Canada. TEL 905-479-4663. FAX 905-479-4482. Ed. Rise Levy. adv.; circ. 100,000 (paid). **Document type:** consumer publication.
   Description: Treats all areas of purchasing, financing, designing, decorating, and renovating a first home.

333.3   US   ISSN 0272-8230
HD251
FIRST TUESDAY.* 1979. m. $109. Realty Publications, Inc., Box 200068, Riverside, CA 92516. TEL 714-781-7300. Ed. Fred Crane. adv.: B&W page $570. circ. 5,000.

333.33   US
HG2040.5.U5
FLEET'S GUIDE: DEBT & EQUITY SOURCEBOOK. 1988. s-a. $375. KaraCo Publishing Group, 15020 Shady Grove Rd., Ste. 500, Rockville, MD 20850-3364. TEL 301-279-6800. Ed. Robert K. Hendel. adv.: B&W page $1650. **Document type:** directory.
   Formerly: Fleet's Guide: Commercial Real Estate Financing Sourcebook (ISSN 0899-9147)
   Description: Provides current information regarding sources of financing for income property.

FLORIDA COMMERCIAL LANDLORD - TENANT LAW. see LAW

FLORIDA CONDOMINIUM LAW MANUAL. see LAW

FLORIDA MORTGAGE BROKER. see BUSINESS AND ECONOMICS — Banking And Finance

FLORIDA PREMISES LIABILITY. see LAW

333.33   US   ISSN 0887-3208
FLORIDA REAL ESTATE AND DEVELOPMENT UPDATE; news and background information about Florida real estate, construction, development and building activities. 1986. m. $100 (foreign $135). Hank Boerner, Ed. & Pub., Box 1052, Port Washington, NY 10050. TEL 516-741-8877.

FLORIDA REAL ESTATE CLOSINGS. see LAW

333.33 340   US
FLORIDA REAL ESTATE CONTRACTS. 1987. base vol. (plus suppl.). $80. Butterworth Legal Publishers (Salem) (Subsidiary of: Reed Elsevier plc), 8 Industrial Way, Bldg. C, Salem, NH 03079. TEL 800-548-4001. FAX 603-898-9858. (looseleaf format)

FLORIDA REAL ESTATE PRINCIPLES, PRACTICES AND LAW. see LAW

FLORIDA REAL ESTATE PRINCIPLES, PRACTICES AND LAW. INSTRUCTOR'S MANUAL. see LAW

FLORIDA REAL ESTATE PRINCIPLES, PRACTICES AND LAW. SALESMAN REVIEW OUTLINE & EXAM GUIDE. see LAW

333.33 340   US
FLORIDA REAL ESTATE TRANSACTIONS. 1982. 3 base vols. (plus suppl. 2-3/yr.). $195. Butterworth Legal Publishers (Salem) (Subsidiary of: Reed Elsevier plc), 8 Industrial Way, Bldg. C, Salem, NH 03079. TEL 800-548-4001. FAX 603-898-9858. (looseleaf format)

333.33   US   ISSN 0199-5839
FLORIDA REALTOR. 1925. m. $15. Florida Association of Realtors, Box 725025, Orlando, FL 32872-5025. TEL 407-438-1400. FAX 407-438-1411. E-mail: mageditor@aol.com. Ed. Pam Littlefield. adv. contact: Tracey Lawton. tr.lit. circ. 60,000. **Document type:** trade publication.
   Description: Provides real estate professionals with a useful combination of practical information trend analysis and insights into the industry.

FLORIDA RESIDENTIAL LANDLORD - TENANT LAW MANUAL. see LAW

FLORIDA RETIREMENT LIFESTYLES. see GERONTOLOGY AND GERIATRICS

333.33   UK
FOCUS ON FRANCE; the UK's largest French property classified. 1987. q. £12 (effective 1995). Amberstock Ltd., 532 Kingston Rd., Raynes Park, London SW20 8DT, England. TEL 0181-542-9088. FAX 0181-542-2737. Ed. Mr. G. Batgent. adv. contact: G. Larkin. circ. 30,000. **Document type:** consumer publication.
   Description: Lists French real estate for sale, along with legal and financial services.

333.33   US
▼**FOR SALE BY FAX.** 1994. m. $197. T K O Real Estate Advisory Group, Box 2630, Mercerville, NJ 08690. TEL 609-587-6200. FAX 609-587-3511. E-mail: deal.makers@property.com. **Document type:** bulletin.

FORECAST OF HOUSING ACTIVITY. see BUSINESS AND ECONOMICS — Economic Situation And Conditions

REAL ESTATE

333.33 — GW — ISSN 0016-0784
DIE FREIE WOHNUNGSWIRTSCHAFT. 1946. 6/yr. DM.82. (Bundesverband Freier Wohnungsunternehmen e.V.) Abiszet Gesellschaft fuer Werbung und Verkaufsfoerderung mbH, Neue Weyerstr. 1-3, 50676 Cologne, Germany. circ. 3,000.

333.33 — UK
FRENCH PROPERTY NEWS. 1989. m. £11 (Europe £14; rest of world £16). Wisefile Ltd., 2A Lambton Rd., London SW20 OLR, England. TEL 0181-944-5500. FAX 0181-944-5293. Ed. Emma Matovu. adv. contact: R.M.B. Schrader. bk.rev.; stat.; tr.lit.; circ. 18,000 (paid). (tabloid format; back issues avail.) Document type: consumer publication.
   Description: Matters relating to the purchase of property in France.

333.33 — US
FROM THE CLIPBOARD. 1977. bi-m. membership. American Association of Certified Appraisers, 800 Compton Rd., Ste. 10, Cincinnati, OH 45231. TEL 800-543-2222. FAX 513-729-1401. Ed. Thomas Sherman. circ. 2,000. Document type: newsletter.

FULL COLLECTION. see BUILDING AND CONSTRUCTION

G D W INFORMATIONEN. (Gemeinschaft der Wohnungseigentuemer) see BUILDING AND CONSTRUCTION

333.33 340 — US
GEORGIA CONDOMINIUM LAW MANUAL. 1985. base vol. (plus a. suppl.). $50. Butterworth Legal Publishers (Salem) (Subsidiary of: Reed Elsevier plc), 8 Industrial Way, Bldg. C, Salem, NH 03079. TEL 800-548-4001. FAX 603-898-9858. (looseleaf format)

333.33 340 — US
GEORGIA LANDLORD - TENANT LAW. 1987. base vol. (plus a. suppl.). $50. Butterworth Legal Publishers (Salem) (Subsidiary of: Reed Elsevier plc), 8 Industrial Way, Bldg. C, Salem, NH 03079. TEL 800-548-4001. FAX 603-898-9858. (looseleaf format)

GEORGIA REAL ESTATE LAW LETTER. see LAW

333.33 — FR
GERANT POLITIQUES IMMOBILIERES. 6/yr. Societe des Publications du Gerant, 79 Av. de Wagram, 75017 Paris, France. TEL 47-63-44-44. FAX 48-88-94-76. Ed. Beatrice Saccardi. circ. 13,900.

333.33 796.352 — US
GOLF PROPERTY. 1991. bi-m. $18. Golf Living Inc., Box 809, Hendersonville, NC 28793. TEL 800-248-6994. Ed. John Woodbury. circ. 125,000.
   Description: Covers golf course communities, resorts and properties.

333.33 — US
GORDON OFFICE MARKET REPORT. q. Edward S. Gordon Co., Inc., 200 Park Ave., New York, NY 10166. TEL 212-984-8000.

333.33 — US
GREATER PHILADELPHIA & SOUTHERN NEW JERSEY OFFICE BUILDINGS. a. $49. Yale Robbins, Inc., 31 E. 28th St., New York, NY 10016. TEL 212-683-5700. Ed. Yale Robbins.
   Description: Annual review of Greater Philadelphia and southern New Jersey office buildings.

333.33 — GW — ISSN 0722-6918
GRUNDBESITZ. m. Landesverband Hamburg, Postfach 62 04 24, D-2000 Hamburg 62, Germany. TEL 040-5239193.

DAS GRUNDEIGENTUM; Zeitschrift fuer die gesamte Grundstuecks-, Haus- und Wohnungswirtschaft. see BUILDING AND CONSTRUCTION

333.33 — GW — ISSN 0938-0175
GRUNDSTUECKSMARKT UND GRUNDSTUECKSWERT. bi-m. DM.258. Luchterhand Verlag, Heddesdorferstr. 31, 56564 Neuwied, Germany. TEL 02631-801-0. FAX 02631-801210. Document type: bulletin.

333.33 — US
GUARANTOR (CHICAGO). 1956. q. Chicago Title and Trust Co., 171 N. Clark St., Chicago, IL 60601. TEL 312-223-2000. Ed. Stephen Flanagan. tr.lit.; index. circ. 70,000. (back issues avail.) Document type: trade publication.

HABITABEC MONTREAL; pour mieux se loger - everything about the house. see HOUSING AND URBAN PLANNING

HABITABEC QUEBEC; pour mieux se loger. see HOUSING AND URBAN PLANNING

333.33 — US — ISSN 1079-7068
HABITAT (NEW YORK CITY EDITION). 1982. 10/yr. $34.95. Carol Group Ltd., 928 Broadway, New York, NY 10010. TEL 212-505-2030. FAX 212-254-6795. Ed. Carol J. Ott. adv.; charts; illus.; stat.; circ. 10,000. (back issues avail.) Document type: trade publication.
   Formerly (until 1994): N Y Habitat (ISSN 0745-0893); **Incorporates:** Loft Letter.

333.33 — US
HABITAT (REGIONAL EDITION). 10/yr. $34.95. Carol Group Ltd., 928 Broadway, Ste. 1105, New York, NY 10010. TEL 212-505-2030. FAX 212-254-6795. Ed. Carol J. Ott. circ. 8,000 (controlled). (back issues avail.) Document type: trade publication.

333.33 — SZ
HABITER. bi-m. Case Postale 880, CH-1001 Lausanne, Switzerland. TEL 021-6529941. FAX 021-6527323. Ed. Claude Rastello. circ. 20,000.

333.33 — US
HAMPTON STYLE. bi-m. $11.90. Parents Guide Network, Corp., 419 Park Ave. S., 13th Fl., New York, NY 10016. TEL 212-213-8840. Ed. Leslie Elgort. Document type: consumer publication.
   Description: For homeowners in the Hamptons, New York.

333.33 — GW — ISSN 0944-2219
HAUS- UND GRUND IN DEUTSCHLAND (AUSGABE FUER WESTFALEN). 1976. m. Zentralverband der Deutschen Haus-, Wohnungs- und Grundeigentuemer, Landesverband Westfaelischer Haus-, Wohnungs- und Grundeigentuemer e.V., Dahlenkampstr. 5, 58095 Hagen, Germany.
   Formerly (until 1992): Haus- und Grundeigentuemer (ISSN 0343-8821)

333.33 — GW
HAUS- UND GRUNDBESITZ. 1948. m. DM.20 (foreign DM.30). (Landesverband der Hessischen Haus-, Wohnungs- und Grundeigentuemer e.V.) Verlag Haus- und Grundbesitz, Niedenau 61-63, 60325 Frankfurt a.M., Germany. TEL 069-729458. FAX 069-172635. Document type: bulletin.

333.33 — SZ
HAUSBESITZER. m. Kanonengasse 23, CH-4051 Basel, Switzerland. TEL 061-237117. FAX 061-237137. Ed. Edi Borer. circ. 24,600.

333.33 — AU
HAUSBESITZER ZEITUNG. m. Zentralverband der Hausbesitzer von Wien und den Laendern Oesterreichs, Landesgerichtsstr. 6, A-1010 Vienna, Austria. TEL 01-4063318. Ed. Friedrich Noszek. circ. 12,000. Document type: newsletter.

333.3 — US — ISSN 0895-8556
HAWAII REALTOR JOURNAL. s-m. $24. P M P Company, Ltd., 1134 Kilani Ave., Ste. 108, Wahiawa, HI 96786-2274. TEL 808-621-8200. FAX 808-622-3025. Ed. Peggi Murchison. adv. circ. 11,000. Document type: trade publication, newspaper.

333.33 340 — UK
HILL & REDMAN'S LAW OF LANDLORD & TENANT. 3 base vols. (plus updates 3/yr.). £260($520) Butterworth & Co. (Publishers) Ltd., Part of the Reed Elsevier group, Halsbury House, 35 Chancery Ln., London WC2A 1EL, England. TEL 071-400-2500. FAX 071-400-2842. (U.S. addr.: Butterworth Legal Publishers, 90 Stiles Rd., Salem, NH 03079-9981. TEL 603-898-9664) Ed. Michael Barnes. (looseleaf format) Document type: trade publication.
   Description: Covers general law, business tenancies, the Rent Acts, public-sector residential tenancies, long leases and agricultural tenancies.

333.33 — US
HOMEFINDERS GUIDE. 1974. m. Travel Publications, Inc., Alta Loma, CA 91701. FAX 714-944-9274. bk.rev.; circ. 55,000 (controlled). Document type: consumer publication.

333.33 — CN — ISSN 0820-490X
HOMEOWNERS' GUIDE.* 1978. m. Target Market Group, 65 The East Mall, Toronto, Ont., Canada. adv. Document type: consumer publication.

333.33 — US — ISSN 1052-4711
HOMES & REAL ESTATE MAGAZINE - GREAT FALLS, MONTANA. 1985. m. Real Estate Publications, Inc. (Billings), Box 30516, Billings, MT 59107-0516. TEL 406-259-3534. FAX 406-259-1676. Ed. G.L. Dangerfield. adv. Document type: consumer publication.
   Description: Lists real estate for sale in Greater Great Falls area.

333.33 — CN
HOMES MAGAZINE. 1985. 8/yr. $24. Homes Publishing Group, 178 Main St., Unionville, ON L3R 2G9, Canada. TEL 905-479-4663. FAX 905-479-4482. Ed. Rise Levy. adv. circ. 100,000.
   Description: Focuses on all areas of home ownership, including buying and selling, finance, design, decor, renovation and new-home buyers guide.

333.33 — HK
HONG KONG PROPERTY REVIEW; a summary of supply, forecast supply, vacancies, rentals and purchase prices. (Text in Chinese and English) 1970. a. HK.$150. Rating and Valuation Department, 500 Hennessy Rd., Hennessy Centre, 26th Fl., Causeway Bay, Hong Kong. FAX 5776916. (Subscr. to: Director of Information Services, Information Services Department, 4 & 4A Queens's Rd. Central, Beaconsfield House, Hong Kong. TEL 8428777. FAX 8459078) circ. 1,000. Document type: government publication.
   Formerly (until 1995): Property Review.

333.33 — UK — ISSN 0018-6473
HOUSE BUYER. 1955. m. £25. Brittain Publications, 137 George Ln., S. Woodford, London E18 1AJ, England. TEL 081-530-7555. FAX 081-530-7609. Ed. Con Crowley. adv.; charts; illus.; mkt.; tr.lit. Document type: consumer publication.
   Formerly: Houses and Estates.

HOUSING CHEAP OR ON A BUDGET NEWSLETTER. see CONSUMER EDUCATION AND PROTECTION

HOUSING ECONOMICS. see BUSINESS AND ECONOMICS — Economic Situation And Conditions

333.3 332 352.7 — UK — ISSN 0955-3800
HOUSING FINANCE. 1975. q. £20 to members; non-members £60 (effective 1994-1995). Council of Mortgage Lenders, 3 Savile Row, London W1X 1AF, England. TEL 0171-437-0655. FAX 0171-287-0109. Ed. Adrian Coles. stat. Indexed: World Bank.Abstr. Document type: trade publication.
   —BLDSC (4335.098829).
   Formerly (until 1989): B S A Bulletin (ISSN 0261-6394)
   Description: Publishes the latest developments in building and housing market activity, including savings and lending statistics.

HOUSING LEGISLATION MANUAL. see PUBLIC ADMINISTRATION

HOUSING POLICY DEBATE. see HOUSING AND URBAN PLANNING

HOW TO BUY AND SELL BUSINESS OPPORTUNITIES. see BUSINESS AND ECONOMICS — Investments

333.33 — NE
HUIS; koopwoning- en interieurgidsen. 1985. 3/yr. fl.20.85. Service Pers B.V., Postbus 9044, 1800 GA Alkmaar, Netherlands. TEL 31-72-158084. FAX 31-72-157540. Ed. P. Hagtingius. adv. circ. 80,000. Document type: consumer publication.
   Description: Covers all aspects of purchasing a house or apartment, from financing to furnishing and remodeling.

REAL ESTATE 5655

346.04 SW ISSN 0018-8360
HYRESGAESTEN. 1962. 7/yr. free. Hyresgaesternas Riksfoerbund, P.O. Box 7514, S-103 92 Stockholm, Sweden. TEL 8-791-0200. FAX 8-205324. Ed. Peder Palmstierna. illus. circ. 23,000.

333.3 US ISSN 1074-5424
▼**I A A O OPPORTUNITIES FOR EDUCATION AND EMPLOYMENT.** 1994. s-m. membership. International Association of Assessing Officers, 130 E. Randolph, Ste. 850, Chicago, IL 60601. TEL 312-819-6110. Ed. Tim Nelson.
Description: Contains education calendar, want ads, and member news.

333.33 US ISSN 1043-5395
HF5429.7
I C S C RESEARCH QUARTERLY. 1986-1990; resumed 1994. q. International Council of Shopping Centers, 665 Fifth Ave., New York, NY 10022. TEL 212-421-8181. FAX 212-486-0849. stat.; circ. 5,500 (controlled). pp./issue: 24. (looseleaf format) **Document type:** trade publication.
Description: Presents articles of topical interest to members of the industry. Reports on research projects undertaken by I.C.S.C.

333.33 UK ISSN 0961-804X
I R R V JOURNAL. 1928. m. £41 (effective 1995). Institute of Revenues, Rating and Valuation, 41 Doughty St., London WC1N 2LF, England. TEL 0171-831-3505. FAX 0171-831-2048. Ed. Kate Miller. adv. contact: Kate Miller. bk.rev.; abstr.; tr.lit.; index. circ. 6,000. **Indexed:** RICS. **Document type:** newsletter.
Former titles (until **1991**): R R V Monthly (ISSN 0959-6097); (until 1990): R V A Monthly (ISSN 0959-4094); (until 1989): Rating and Valuation (ISSN 0483-9889); (until 1960): Rating and Valuation Association. Journal.

333.33 SZ
IMMOBILIA. 1933. m. 45 SFr. Schweizerische Verband der Immobilien-Treuhaender, Buchmattweg 4, CH-8057 Zurich, Switzerland. Ed. Albert Petermann. **Document type:** bulletin.

333.33 AU
IMMOBILIEN BAZAAR. w. Mayerhofgasse 1, A-1040 Vienna, Austria. TEL 01-501470. FAX 01-5056059.

333.33 GW ISSN 0934-5639
IMMOBILIEN-BERATER; Handbuch fuer den wirtschaftlichen Erfolg mit Haus- mit Wohnungsbesitz. 1988. 8/yr. DM.298. Verlag Norman Rentrop, Theodor-Heuss-Str. 4, 53177 Bonn, Germany. TEL 0228-8205-0. FAX 0228-364411. TELEX 17228309. Ed. H.J. Oberhettinger. (looseleaf format) **Document type:** bulletin.

IMMOBILIEN MANAGER. see BUILDING AND CONSTRUCTION

333.33 GW ISSN 0935-2759
IMMOBILIEN WIRTSCHAFT HEUTE; der aktuelle Branchenbrief fuer den Immobilien - Insider. 1987. bi-w. DM.211. G W Verlag Henning Grabener, Parkwinkel 13, 24229 Schwedeneck, Germany. TEL 04308-1470. Ed. Henning Grabener. **Document type:** newsletter.

333.33 FR
IMMOBILIER MAGAZINE. 1961. q. 180 F. Federation Nationale des Promoteurs-Constructeurs (F.N.P.C.), 106 rue de l'Universite, 75007 Paris, France. TEL 47-05-44-36. FAX 47-53-92-73. Ed. Sylvie Charvin. adv.; bk.rev.; bibl.; charts; illus.; stat. circ. 7,500. **Document type:** corporate report.
Formerly: Promotion Immobiliere.

690 US ISSN 1046-8234
HD7287.6.U5
INCOME - EXPENSE ANALYSIS: CONVENTIONAL APARTMENTS. 1954. a. $157.95. Institute of Real Estate Management, Box 109025, Chicago, IL 60610-9025. TEL 312-661-1953. Ed. Kay McGuire. **Indexed:** SRI.
Formerly: Income - Expense Analysis: Apartments (ISSN 0194-1941); Supersedes in part: Income - Expense Analysis: Apartments, Condominiums and Cooperatives (ISSN 0161-5262); (until 1973): Apartment Building Income - Expense Analysis (ISSN 0084-6651).
Description: Detailed analysis of the financial operations of multi-family properties.

333.33 690 US
INCOME - EXPENSE ANALYSIS: FEDERALLY ASSISTED APARTMENTS. a. $136.95. Institute of Real Estate Management, 430 N. Michigan Ave., Chicago, IL 60610-9025. TEL 312-661-1953. FAX 312-661-0217.
Description: Summarizes the operating experience of apartment buildings across the US that receive subsidies under one of five federal programs, drawing on a sample of over 1500 buildings.

333 US
INCOME - EXPENSE ANALYSIS: OFFICE BUILDINGS, DOWNTOWN AND SUBURBAN. 1976. a. $157.95. Institute of Real Estate Management, Box 109025, Chicago, IL 60610-9025. TEL 312-661-1930. Ed. Kay McGuire. **Indexed:** SRI.
Supersedes: Income - Expense Analysis: Suburban Office Buildings.
Description: Analysis of office building revenues and expenses.

333.33 690 US
INCOME - EXPENSE ANALYSIS: SHOPPING CENTERS, OPEN AND ENCLOSED. a. $157.95. Institute of Real Estate Management, Box 109025, Chicago, IL 60610-9025. TEL 312-661-1953. FAX 312-661-0217. **Document type:** trade publication.
Description: For real estate professionals. Provides income and expense data for open shopping centers and enclosed malls.

333.33 UK
INDEPENDENT ESTATE AGENTS' PROPERTY GUIDE; west Yorkshire. 1990. m. Organiza Services, Guardian House, Mill St. E., Dewsbury, W. Yorks WF12 9AH, England. TEL 01924-459301. FAX 01924-457145. Ed. R.A. Dixon. adv. contact: R.A. Dixon. circ. 10,000. (tabloid format) **Document type:** newspaper.

333.33 US
INDIANAPOLIS REAL ESTATE NEWS. q. Real Estate News Corp., 2600 W. Peterson Ave., Chicago, IL 60659. TEL 312-465-5151. FAX 312-465-7218. Ed. Steven Polydoris. adv.: B&W page $776; 7 1/2 x 10. circ. 2,442. **Document type:** trade publication.

333.33 FR ISSN 0247-8609
INDICATEUR BERTRAND MIDI - MEDITERRANEE. m. 15 F. Editions Indicateur Bertrand, 43 bd. Barbes, 75018 Paris, France. TEL 1-49-25-26-27. FAX 1-49-25-26-00. adv. contact: Guy Coponat. charts; illus. circ. 30,000. **Document type:** consumer publication.
Formerly: Indicateur Bertrand Mediterranee.
Description: Advertisements for the sale of houses and apartments on the Mediterranean.

333.33 FR ISSN 0290-1528
INDICATEUR BERTRAND OUEST - SUD-OUEST. m. 15 F. per no. Editions Indicateur Bertrand, 43 bd. Barbes, 75018 Paris, France. adv.: B&W page 11200 F.; trim 270 x 210; adv. contact: Michel Joubert. charts; illus.; stat. circ. 25,000. **Document type:** consumer publication.
Former titles: Indicateur Bertrand Ouest; Indicateur Bertrand Normandie (ISSN 0751-2759)
Description: Advertisements for the sale of houses and apartments in the Western and South-western regions of France.

333.33 FR
INDICATEUR BERTRAND PARIS - BANLIEU. 1905. s-m. 20 F. per no. Editions Indicateur Bertrand, 43 bd. Barbes, 75018 Paris, France. adv.: B&W page 19000 F., color page 41000 F.; trim 270 x 210; adv. contact: Jean-Pierre Dubos. circ. 30,000. **Document type:** consumer publication.
Formerly: Indicateur Bertrand (ISSN 0151-2943)
Description: Advertisements for the sale of houses and apartments in Paris and its suburbs.

333.33 FR ISSN 0980-8744
INDICATEUR BERTRAND RHONE-ALPES. 1986. m. 15 F. per no. Editions Indicateur Bertrand, 43 bd. Barbes, 75018 Paris, France. TEL 1-49-25-26-27. FAX 1-49-25-26-00. adv.: color page 21000 F.; trim 270 x 210; adv. contact: Didier Cassin. circ. 25,000. **Document type:** consumer publication.
Description: Advertisements for the sale of houses and apartments in the Rhone-Alpes region of France.

333.33 JA ISSN 0073-7186
INDICES OF URBAN LAND PRICES AND CONSTRUCTION COST OF WOODEN HOUSES IN JAPAN. (Text in Japanese) s-a. price varies. Japan Real Estate Institute - Nihon Fudosan Kenkyusho, Kangin-Fujiya Bldg., 1-3-2 Toranomon, Minato-ku, Tokyo, Japan.

333.33 CN
INDUSTRIAL & COMMERCIAL PROPERTY - WINDSOR - ESSEX. 1959. s.a. free. Windsor-Essex County Development Commission, City Centre, Ste. 215, 333 Riverside Dr. W., Windsor, ON N9A 5K4, Canada. TEL 519-255-9200. FAX 519-255-9987. Ed. Lina Williams. circ. 600. **Document type:** trade publication.
Former titles: Industrial Property - Windsor - Essex; Industrial Buildings - Windsor - Essex.
Description: Listings of industrial and commercial properties available in the Windsor, Essex counties and the Town of Tilbury area.

333.33 FR ISSN 0046-936X
INFORMATION IMMOBILIERE. 1968. m. 165 F. Presse Immobiliere, 11 quai Anatole-France, 75007 Paris, France. TEL 47-05-90-30. FAX 45-56-03-17. Ed. Andre Lorieux. adv.; bk.rev. circ. 93,964. **Document type:** trade publication.

333.33 FR ISSN 1153-2432
INFORMATIONS F.N.A.I.M. 1973. m. 105 F. Federation Nationale des Agents Immobiliers et Administrateurs de Biens-Syndics d'Immeubles, 129 rue du Faubourg St. Honore, 75008 Paris, France. TEL 42-25-24-26. adv.; bk.rev. circ. 7,000.

333.33 FR ISSN 0750-8042
INFORMATIONS RAPIDES DE LA COPROPRIETE. 1960. 12/yr. Particulier Editions, 21 bd. Montmartre, 75002 Paris, France. TEL 40-20-70-00. FAX 40-20-70-10. Ed. C. Michalopoulos. circ. 5,000.
Formerly (until 1963): Informations Rapides des Cahiers de la Copropriete (ISSN 0998-5719)

333.33 647.9 US
INNSIDE ISSUES. 1984. q. free. Hotel & Motel Brokers of America, 10220 N. Executive Hills Blvd., Ste. 610, Kansas City, MO 64153-2312. TEL 816-891-7070; 800-821-5191. FAX 816-891-7071. Eds. Patrick H. Ford, Jerry Daly; Pub. Robert Kralicek. circ. 28,000. (looseleaf format) **Document type:** newsletter.
Description: Focuses on hotel and motel real estate brokerage.

INSIDE MORTGAGE SECURITIES. see BUSINESS AND ECONOMICS — Banking And Finance

INSTITUTE ON ADVANCED TAX PLANNING FOR REAL PROPERTY TRANSACTIONS. see BUSINESS AND ECONOMICS — Public Finance, Taxation

INSTITUTE ON PLANNING, ZONING AND EMINENT DOMAIN. PROCEEDINGS. see LAW

333.33 UK
INTERNATIONAL PROPERTY BULLETIN. a. £35. Hillier Parker, 77 Grosvenor St., London W1A 2BT, England. TEL 0171-629-7666. FAX 0171-409-3016. Ed. Jenny Mottram. (back issues avail.) **Document type:** trade publication.

333.33 US ISSN 8755-6138
HD1361
INTERNATIONAL REAL ESTATE JOURNAL. 1980. 6/yr. $75. (International Real Estate Institute) Todd Publishing, Inc., 8383 E. Evans Rd., Scottsdale, AZ 85260. TEL 602-998-7743. FAX 602-998-8022. Ed. Troy E. Johnson. adv. circ. 19,000. (back issues avail.) **Document type:** trade publication.
—Faxon; UnCover.
Description: Covers investment, development, finance, valuation sales and property management.

INVESTMENT ADVISER. see BUSINESS AND ECONOMICS — Investments

333.33 US ISSN 0882-1879
ISLAND PROPERTIES REPORT. 1983. m. $44. Island Properties Report, Box 8029, Naples, FL 33941. Ed. Glenn Thornbill. bk.rev. circ. 10,210. (back issues avail.) **Document type:** newsletter.
Description: Reports on Caribbean Island economy, politics, taxes and purchase regulations. Also lists properties for sale.

REAL ESTATE

333.33 346.043   AT
JESSUP'S LANDS TITLES OFFICE PRACTICE S.A.. 1989. 2/yr. Aus.$215 with updates. Law Book Co. Ltd., 44-50 Waterloo Rd., North Ryde, N.S.W 2113, Australia. TEL 02-887-0177. FAX 02-888-9706. TELEX ASBOOK-27995. Ed. R.J. White. (looseleaf format)
   Description: Reflects the current practice of the Lands Titles Office in S.A. to assist the conveyancer in matters which arise in the course of document preparation.

333.33   US   ISSN 0887-1922
JOHN T. REED'S REAL ESTATE INVESTOR'S MONTHLY. 1986. m. $125. John T. Reed, Ed. & Pub., 342 Bryan Dr., Danville, CA 94526. TEL 510-820-6292. FAX 510-820-1259. E-mail: JohnTReed@aol.com. (Subscr. to: Box 2587, Berkeley, CA 94702. TEL 800-635-5425) bk.rev.; charts; stat.; circ. 650 (paid). (looseleaf format; back issues avail.) **Document type:** newsletter.
   Description: Includes articles on real estate investment and strategy, finance, management, tax laws, and other pertinent non-tax court decisions.

JOURNAL OF FINANCIAL SERVICES RESEARCH. see *BUSINESS AND ECONOMICS — Banking And Finance*

JOURNAL OF HOUSING RESEARCH. see *HOUSING AND URBAN PLANNING*

333.33   UK   ISSN 0958-868X
                   CODEN: JPFIEL
JOURNAL OF PROPERTY FINANCE. 1990. q. £339($539) (effective 1996). M C B University Press Ltd., 60-62 Toller Ln., Bradford, W. Yorks BD8 9BY, England. TEL 01274-499821. FAX 01274-547143. TELEX 51317-MCBUNI-G. bk.rev. (reprint service avail. from SWZ) **Indexed:** Euro.LJI, LJI. **Document type:** academic/scholarly publication.
   —BLDSC (5042.778000). **CCC**.

333.33   US   ISSN 0022-3905
TX955
JOURNAL OF PROPERTY MANAGEMENT. 1934. bi-m. $38.95 (foreign $77.90). Institute of Real Estate Management, 430 N. Michigan Ave., Box 109025, Chicago, IL 60610-9025. TEL 312-329-6073. FAX 312-661-0217. adv.; charts; illus.; tr.lit.; index. (back issues avail.) **Indexed:** Account.Ind. (1974-), BPIA, Bus.Ind., Hospit.Ind., Manage.Cont., P.A.I.S., Sage Urb.Stud.Abstr., Tr.& Indus.Ind.
●Also available online. Vendor(s): University Microfilms International.
   —BLDSC (5042.780000); Faxon; SWETS; UMI; UnCover. **CCC**.
   Incorporates: Operating Techniques and Products Bulletin.
   Description: Provides a forum for sharing ideas and discussing new trends that affect the asset management of investment real estate. Articles may address the management of apartments, office buildings, shopping and strip centers, mixed use properties, office-industrial properties, condominiums, and special-purpose real estate.

333.33   UK   ISSN 0960-2712
HD1387
JOURNAL OF PROPERTY VALUATION AND INVESTMENT. 1982. 5/yr. £239($549) (effective 1996). M C B University Press Ltd., 60-62 Toller Ln., Bradford, W. Yorks BD8 9BY, England. TEL 01274-499821. FAX 01274-547143. TELEX 51317-MCBUNI-G. Ed. Nick French. bk.rev. (reprint service avail. from SWZ) **Document type:** academic/scholarly publication.
   —BLDSC (5042.781500).
   Formerly: Journal of Valuation (ISSN 0263-7480)

333.33 332   US   ISSN 0895-5638
HG2040   CODEN: JREEEI
JOURNAL OF REAL ESTATE FINANCE AND ECONOMICS. 1988. bi-m. fl.657 to institutions; $421 to institutions in U.S. (effective 1996). Kluwer Academic Publishers Boston, Box 358, Accord Sta., Hingham, MA 02018-0358. TEL 617-871-6600. FAX 617-871-6528. TELEX 20090. (Dist. outside N. America by: Kluwer Academic Publishers Group, P.O. Box 322, 3300 AH Dordrecht, Netherlands. TEL 31-78-392392. FAX 31-78-546474) Eds. James Kau, C.F. Sirmans. adv. (also avail. in microform from UMI; reprint service avail. from SWZ,UMI) **Indexed:** J.of Econ.Lit. **Document type:** academic/scholarly publication.
   —BLDSC (5047.750000); Faxon; Genuine Article; SWETS; UMI; UnCover. **CCC**.
   Description: Publishes empirical and theoretical research in real estate finance and economics.
Refereed Serial

333.33   US   ISSN 0927-7544
JOURNAL OF REAL ESTATE LITERATURE. 1993. s-a. fl.265 to institutions; $170 to institutions in U.S. (effective 1996). (American Real Estate Society) Kluwer Academic Publishers Boston, Box 358, Accord Sta., Hingham, MA 02018-0358. TEL 617-871-6300. FAX 617-871-6528. TELEX 200190. (Dist. outside N. America by: Kluwer Academic Publishers Group, P.O. Box 322, 3300 AH Dordrecht, Netherlands. TEL 31-78-392392. FAX 31-78-546474) Eds. James B. Kau, C.F. Sirmans. adv.; bk.rev.; abstr.; stat. circ. 1,500. (also avail. in microform from UMI; back issues avail.) **Document type:** academic/scholarly publication.
   —BLDSC (5047.755000); Faxon; UMI. **CCC**.
   Description: Publishes research, dissertations, and works in progress, including information on software and data bases for the researcher and publishing case studies to support the classroom instruction of real estate.
Refereed Serial

333.33   US
▼**JOURNAL OF REAL ESTATE PORTFOLIO MANAGEMENT**. 1995. s-a. $85 to individuals; institutions $300. American Real Estate Society, c/o James R. Webb, Exec. Dir., Cleveland State University, University Center, Rm. 592A, Cleveland, OH 44115. TEL 216-687-4732. FAX 216-687-9354. adv.; circ. 1,400 (paid). **Document type:** academic/scholarly publication.
Refereed Serial

333.33   US   ISSN 0896-5803
JOURNAL OF REAL ESTATE RESEARCH. 1986. q. $95 to individuals & libraries; institutions $350 (effective 1996). American Real Estate Society, c/o James R. Webb, Cleveland State University, Dept. of Finance, College of Busines, University Center, Rm. 592A, Cleveland, OH 44115. TEL 216-687-4732. FAX 216-687-9354. Ed. G. Donald Jud. adv. contact: James R. Webb. circ. 1,500. **Document type:** academic/scholarly publication.
   —BLDSC (5047.770000); Faxon; SWETS; UMI; UnCover.
Refereed Serial

333.33 336.2   US   ISSN 0093-5107
HJ4181.A1
JOURNAL OF REAL ESTATE TAXATION. 1973. q. $146.50 (overseas $225.95) (effective 1995). Warren, Gorham & Lamont, One Penn Plaza, New York, NY 10119. TEL 212-971-5000. FAX 212-971-5113. (Subscr. to: The Park Square Bldg., 31 St. James Ave., Boston, MA 02116-4112. TEL 800-950-1205) Ed. John Delaney. bk.rev.; bibl. (also avail. in microform from UMI; reprint service avail. from RRI,UMI,WSH) **Indexed:** ABI Inform, Account.Ind. (1974-), BPIA, Bus.Ind., C.L.I., L.R.I., Leg.Cont., Leg.Per., PROMT, PSI, SSCI. **Document type:** trade publication.
   —BLDSC (5047.800000); Faxon; Genuine Article; UMI; UnCover. **CCC**.
   Description: Covers all aspects of real estate tax planning. Written by leading attorneys, tax accountants, and real estate authorities.

333.33   US
▼**LAKE HOME**. 1994. bi-m. $19.95; newsstand price: $4.95. Blue Water Communications, Inc., 137 N. Main St., West Bend, WI 53095. TEL 414-334-2501. Ed. David Rank; Pub. Frank Raimo. adv.; B&W page $1696. circ. 5,000. **Document type:** consumer publication.

323.4   UK   ISSN 0023-7574
HD591.A1
LAND AND LIBERTY; bi-monthly journal for land value taxation and free trade. 1894. bi-m. £12($20) Land and Liberty International Ltd., 177 Vauxhall Bridge Rd., London SW1V 1EU, England. TEL 071-834-4266. FAX 071-834-4979. Ed. Fred Harrison. adv.; bk.rev.; charts; index; circ. 2,000 (controlled). (back issues avail.) **Indexed:** P.A.I.S., RICS. **Document type:** trade publication.
   —BLDSC (5146.760000).

LAND USE & ENVIRONMENT FORUM; a journal of law, policy, and practice. see *LAW*

347.2   US   ISSN 0094-7598
K30
LAND USE LAW AND ZONING DIGEST. (Monthly supplement avail.: Zoning News) 1948. m. $240. American Planning Association, 1313 E. 60th St., Chicago, IL 60637. TEL 312-955-9100. FAX 312-955-8312. (And: 1776 Massachusetts Ave., N.W., Washington, DC 20036. TEL 202-872-0611) Ed. Rodney Cobb. index. circ. 1,800. (also avail. in microform from UMI; back issues avail.; reprint service avail. from UMI)
   —Faxon; UMI; UnCover.
   Formerly: Zoning Digest (ISSN 0084-5566)

333.33   NE   ISSN 0166-5839
DE LANDEIGENAAR; maandblad voor beheer van het buitengebied. 1953. m. fl.102 to non-members (effective 1995). Uitgeverij de Landeigenaar b.v., Laan van Beek en Royen 1a, 3701 AH Zeist, Netherlands. TEL 31-3404-33945. FAX 31-3404-33794. (Subscr. to: Vuga Uitgeverij B.V., P.O. Box 16400, 2500 BK The Hague, Netherlands. TEL 31-70-3305252. FAX 31-70-3305290) Co-sponsors: Nederlandse Vereniging voor de Landelijke Eigendom; Vereniging Het Friesch Grondbezit; Nederlandse Vereniging van Boseigenaren) Ed. G.R. van Woudenberg. adv.: B&W page fl. 1505, color page fl.3630; trim 210 x 297. bk.rev. circ. 3,500. **Document type:** trade publication.
   Description: Covers topics of interest to landowners, forest owners, and persons concerned with the economic and environmental aspects of land ownership.

333.33 330.9 352.7   AT   ISSN 0310-320X
LANDLINE IN AUSTRALIA. 1973. q. Real Estate Institute of Australia, P.O. Box 234, Deakin West, A.C.T. 2602, Australia. TEL 61-6-282-4277. FAX 61-6-285-2444. Ed. Keith Conley. circ. 14,500. (back issues avail.) **Indexed:** AESIS.
   Description: Advocate journal on real estate industry issues.

LANDLORD REMEDIES IN FLORIDA. see *LAW — Civil Law*

LANDLORD TENANT LAW BULLETIN. see *LAW — Civil Law*

333.33   US   ISSN 0163-951X
LANDOWNER. 1979. s-m. $79. (Professional Farmers of America) Oster Communications, Inc., 219 Main St., Cedar Falls, IA 50613. TEL 319-277-1278. FAX 319-277-5803. Ed. Jerry Carlson.
   Description: Provides information on the land market. Includes safe, creative ways to buy, sell or rent farm property. Also covers regional price trends and environmentally sound methods of farmland stewardship to enhance land productivity.

333.33   US   ISSN 0272-7161
LAWYERS TITLE NEWS. 1937. q. free. Lawyers Title Insurance Corporation, Box 27567, Richmond, VA 23261. TEL 804-281-6700. FAX 804-282-5453. Ed. Eleanor R. Anders. circ. 80,000. **Document type:** trade publication.

333.33   US
LEASE AUCTION NOTICE. Cover title: City of New York Lease Auction. irreg. (2-3/yr.) Bureau of Commercial Leasing, Division of Real Property, 2 Lafayette St., New York, NY 10007. TEL 212-374-3136. **Document type:** government publication.

333.33   DK
VI LEJERE. 1969. q. membership. Lejernes Landsorganisation, Reventlowsgade 14,4, 1651 Copenhagen V, Denmark. TEL 45-31-22-68-69. FAX 45-31-22-37-87. Ed. Jens Reiermann. adv. circ. 100,000.
   Formerly (until 1985): Bolignyt (ISSN 0006-6524)

REAL ESTATE

333.33 332.6   UK
LIFESTYLE AND LONDON LIVING. 1983. m. £25. Reed Publishing Services, 7-11 St. Johns Hill, London SW11, England. TEL 0171-228-3344. FAX 0171-924-3408. Ed. N. Keith. adv.; bk.rev. circ. 50,000.
   Incorporates: Property and Investment; *Formerly:* London Gentleman.

LIVING FRANCE. see *TRAVEL AND TOURISM*

333.33 910.09   US
LOAN-A-HOME DIRECTORY. 1968. s-a. (plus 2 supplements). $35. Muriel Gould, Ed.& Pub., 2 Park Ln., 6E, Mt. Vernon, NY 10552-3443. TEL 914-664-7640. (looseleaf format) **Document type:** directory.
   Description: Residential listing service for members of the international academic, business and retired communities who need temporary long-term housing worldwide.

333.33   FR   ISSN 0024-5674
LOCATIONS VACANCES. a. 32 F. Editions Indicateur Bertrand, 43 bd. Barbes, 75018 Paris, France. TEL 1-49-25-26-27. FAX 1-49-25-26-00. adv.; bk.rev. **Document type:** consumer publication.
   Description: Advertisements for the renting of vacation homes from private owners in France and elsewhere.

LOUISIANA LANDLORD & TENANT LAW. see *LAW — Civil Law*

M I R A S LENDERS MANUAL. see *BUSINESS AND ECONOMICS — Banking And Finance*

333.3   CN
M R E ACTION. 1980. m. free. Manitoba Real Estate Association, 1240 Portage Ave., 2nd Fl., Winnipeg, Man. R3G 0T6, Canada. TEL 204-772-0405. FAX 204-775-3781. Ed. Thomas E. Lewicki. charts; stat. circ. 2,100. (looseleaf format)

333.33 658   US
MANAGER'S REPORT; journal for community association management. 1987. m. $18. Ivor Thomas & Associates, Inc., 1700 Southern Blvd., West Palm Beach, FL 33406. TEL 407-687-4700. Ed. Ivor Thomas. adv. contact: Vince Rossi. circ. 10,000. **Document type:** trade publication.
   Description: News and feature articles dealing with areas of interest to individuals responsible for the management and purchasing activities of condominium, homeowner and co-operative associations.

MANAGING MORTGAGES. see *BUSINESS AND ECONOMICS — Banking And Finance*

MANAGING THE FLORIDA CONDOMINIUM. see *LAW*

333.33 340   US
MANHATTAN COOP CONDO CONVERSION DIGEST. 1979. base vol. (plus irreg. updates, 2-4/yr.). $540. Yale Robbins, Inc., 31 E. 28th St., New York, NY 10016. TEL 212-683-5700. FAX 212-545-0764. Ed. George Kelly. (looseleaf format)

333.33   US   ISSN 0886-2737
HD1393.55
MANHATTAN OFFICE BUILDINGS: DOWNTOWN. a. $39. Yale Robbins, Inc., 31 E. 28 St., New York, NY 10016. TEL 212-683-5700. Ed. Yale Robbins. adv.
   Description: Annual review of Manhattan's downtown office buildings.

333.33   US   ISSN 0886-3725
HD1393.55
MANHATTAN OFFICE BUILDINGS: MIDTOWN. a. $39. Yale Robbins, Inc., 31 E. 28 St., New York, NY 10016. TEL 212-683-5700. Ed. Yale Robbins. adv.
   Description: Annual review of Manhattan's midtown office buildings.

333.33   US   ISSN 1046-8943
HD1393.55
MANHATTAN OFFICE BUILDINGS: MIDTOWN SOUTH. a. 25. Yale Robbins, Inc., 31 E. 28th St., New York, NY 10016. TEL 212-683-5700.
   Description: Annual review of Manhattan's midtown south office buildings.

333.33   IT
MANUTENZIONE E RESTAURO. s-a. Protogesco s.r.l., Via Molino 1, 25010 Pozzolengo (BS), Italy. TEL 030-918260. FAX 030-918454. adv.: B&W page L.2000000, color page L.3800000; trim 185 x 265. circ. 5,449.

333.332   US   ISSN 1055-5579
MARKETSOURCE. 1991. q. $150 to non-members; members $100. Appraisal Institute, 875 N. Michigan Ave., Ste. 2400, Chicago, IL 60611-1980. TEL 312-335-4100. FAX 312-335-4400. Ed. Joy M. White. circ. 2,000.
   Description: Features real estate market forecasts and data.

333.33 690   US   ISSN 0732-815X
TH435
MEANS SQUARE FOOT COSTS (YEAR); residential, commercial, industrial, institutional. 1980. a. $91.95. R.S. Means Company, Inc., 100 Construction Plaza, Box 800, Kingston, MA 02364-0800. TEL 800-334-3509. FAX 617-585-7466. Ed. Philip R. Waier. (also avail. in microform)
   Formerly: Appraisal Manual (ISSN 0272-0051)

333.33   FR   ISSN 0995-5194
MEDITERRANEE (PARIS). (Text in English, French and German) 1970. m. 225 F. Publi Ric, 8 rue Richelieu, 75001 Paris, France. Ed. Gerard Lacape. circ. 25,000.
   Formerly (until 1989): Mediterranee Immobiliere (ISSN 0395-8833)

333.33   US   ISSN 0891-7698
MERCER COUNTY BOARD OF REALTORS. NEWSLINE. 1986. 11/yr. $5. Mercer County Board of Realtors, 1428 Brunswick Ave., Box 5455, Trenton, NJ 08638. TEL 609-392-3666. FAX 609-394-3939. Ed. Linda M. Mottin. adv. circ. 2,500. **Document type:** newsletter, trade publication.
   Description: For realtors, realtor associates, and affiliate members of the Board. Covers real estate and related industries and association topics.

METRO CHICAGO OFFICE GUIDE. see *BUSINESS AND ECONOMICS — Office Equipment And Services*

333.33   US   ISSN 0893-0775
METRO CHICAGO REAL ESTATE. 1913. bi-w. $38. Law Bulletin Publishing Co., 415 N. State St., Chicago, IL 60610-4674. TEL 312-644-7800. Ed. Jennifer Harris. adv.; bk.rev. circ. 10,476. (also avail. in microfilm)
   Former titles: Real Estate Magazine (ISSN 0746-164X); Chicagoland's Real Estate Advertiser (ISSN 0009-3769)

METRO PHOENIX BLUE CHIP ECONOMIC FORECAST. see *BUSINESS AND ECONOMICS — Economic Situation And Conditions*

333.33   CN
METROTRENDS. 1958. a. Can.$35. Real Estate Board of Greater Vancouver, 1101 W. Broadway, Vancouver, BC V6H 1G2, Canada. TEL 604-736-4551. FAX 604-734-1778. Ed. Ray A. Nelson. stat. circ. 1,000. (looseleaf format)
   Formerly (until 1984): Real Estate Trends in Metropolitan Vancouver (ISSN 0085-5405)

333.33   US   ISSN 0893-2719
MIDWEST REAL ESTATE NEWS. 1984. m. $40 (foreign $100). Argus Inc., 6151 Powers Ferry Rd., N.W., Atlanta, GA 30339-2941. TEL 404-955-2500. FAX 404-955-0400. (And: 35 E. Wacker Dr., Chicago, IL 60601-2198. TEL 312-726-7277) Ed. Roger Nadolny. circ. 17,144. (tabloid format; also avail. in microform from UMI; reprint service avail. from UMI) **Document type:** trade publication.
   —UMI. **CCC.**
   Description: Covers commercial and industrial real estate activity in 10 Midwestern states: Illinois, Indiana, Iowa, Kansas, Michigan, Minnesota, Missouri, Nebraska, Ohio, and Wisconsin.

333.33   GW   ISSN 0723-3418
MIETER MAGAZIN. m. Berliner Mieterverein, Spichernstr. 12, 10777 Cologne, Germany. TEL 030-2115099.

333.33   SZ
MIETER ZEITUNG. 11/yr. Postfach, CH-5001 Aarau, Switzerland. TEL 064-249449. Ed. Josef Beck. circ. 56,000.

MIETRECHTLICHE ENTSCHEIDUNGEN. see *LAW — Civil Law*

333.33   US
MILWAUKEE REAL ESTATE NEWS. q. Real Estate News Corp., 2600 W. Peterson Ave., Chicago, IL 60659. TEL 312-465-5151. FAX 312-465-7218. Ed. Steven Polydoris. adv.: B&W page $880; 7 1/2 x 10. circ. 2,685. **Document type:** trade publication.

MINIAPPARTAMENTI. see *HOUSING AND URBAN PLANNING*

333.3   US   ISSN 0893-2255
MINNESOTA REAL ESTATE JOURNAL. 1985. fortn. $59. Minnesota Real Estate Journal Inc., 8900 Wentworth Ave., S. Bloomington, MN 55420. TEL 612-885-0815. FAX 612-885-0818. Ed. John Share. adv.; bk.rev. circ. 7,200.

MINNESOTA REAL ESTATE LAW JOURNAL. see *LAW*

MINNESOTA RESIDENTIAL REAL ESTATE. see *LAW — Civil Law*

333.33   US
MISSOURI REALTOR. 1937. 8/yr. $6. Missouri Association of Realtors, 2601 Bernadette Pl., Box 1327, Columbia, MO 65205. TEL 314-445-8400. FAX 314-445-7865. Ed. Victoria Shahan. adv. contact: Victoria Shahan. circ. 18,000. **Document type:** bulletin.
   Description: News digest of Missouri real estate and activities of the Missouri Association of Realtors.

333.33   US
MOBILEHOME PARKS REPORT; the monthly report devoted to investment and ownership. 1980. m. $135. Parks Publishing Company, 3807 Pasadena Ave., Ste.100, Sacramento, CA 95821. TEL 916-971-0489. Ed. Thomas P. Kerr. bk.rev. circ. 300. (back issues avail.) **Document type:** newsletter.
   Formerly: Kerr Report (ISSN 0273-2726)
   Description: Reports on legislation, issues and trends important to owners and developers of manufactured housing communities.

333.331   US   ISSN 0195-8194
HF5549.5.R47
MOBILITY (WASHINGTON). 1980. 12/yr. $48. Employee Relocation Council, 1720 N St., N.W., Washington, DC 20036. TEL 202-857-0857. Ed. Jerry Holloman. adv.; bk.rev.; index. circ. 12,500.

333.33   US
MONITOR'S INSIDER. 1986. w. $262.50. Trade Dimensions, 263 Tresser Blvd., 5th Fl., Stamford, CT 06901-3202. TEL 203-977-7636. FAX 203-977-7645. Ed. Lynda Beatty; Pub. Garrett Van Siclen. index. circ. 1,000. (back issues avail.) **Document type:** newsletter.
   Description: Provides up-to-the-minute news on retailer expansion plans, shopping center developments, acquisitions and related issues.

333.33   US   ISSN 0887-0470
HF5429.3
MONITOR'S RETAIL TENANT DIRECTORY. 1978. a. $325. Trade Dimensions, 263 Tresser Blvd., Stamford, CT 06901. TEL 203-977-7600. FAX 203-977-7645. Ed. Adrienne Toth; Pub. Garrett Van Siclen. circ. 2,000. (also avail. in diskette format) **Document type:** directory.
   Formerly: Retail Tenant Directory.
   Description: Profiles retail tenants and their expansion lease requirements.

333.33   US   ISSN 1052-469X
MONTANA LAND MAGAZINE. 1982. q. $15 (foreign $30). Real Estate Publications, Inc. (Billings), Box 30516, Billings, MT 59107-0516. TEL 406-259-3534. FAX 406-259-1676. Ed. G.L. Dangerfield. adv. (back issues avail.) **Document type:** consumer publication.
   Description: Lists real estate for sale throughout Montana.

REAL ESTATE

333.33 US ISSN 0047-813X
MORTGAGE AND REAL ESTATE EXECUTIVES REPORT. 1969. s-m. $159.75 (overseas $223.20) (effective 1995). Warren, Gorham & Lamont, One Penn Plaza, New York, NY 10119. TEL 212-971-5000. FAX 212-971-5113. (Subscr. to: The Park Square Bldg., 31 St. James Ave., Boston, MA 02116-4112. TEL 800-950-1207) Ed. Alvin L. Arnold. charts; illus.; stat. (also avail. in microfilm; microform from UMI) **Indexed:** Bank.Lit.Ind. **Document type:** newsletter. —UMI. **CCC.**
    Incorporates (in Sep. 1976): Condominium Report; (in Jul. 1976): Real Estate Investors Report.
    Description: Provides ideas and new updates, including analysis and forecasts of important trends and developments, investment opportunities, and other money-making ideas.

MORTGAGE BANKING. see *BUSINESS AND ECONOMICS — Banking And Finance*

MORTGAGE FINANCE GAZETTE. see *BUSINESS AND ECONOMICS — Banking And Finance*

MORTGAGE LENDER DIRECTORY. see *BUSINESS AND ECONOMICS — Trade And Industrial Directories*

332.7 US
MORTGAGE NEWS. 1987. m. $30. Leader Observer, 80-34 Jamaica Dr., Woodhaven, NY 11421. TEL 718-296-2660. FAX 718-296-5372. Ed. Susan Pechman. circ. 15,000. (tabloid format) **Document type:** trade publication.

333.33 GW
MOSAIK (SCHWAEBISCH HALL). q. Bausparkasse Schwaebisch Hall AG, Crailsheimerstr. 52, 74523 Schwaebisch Hall, Germany. TEL 0791-462869. FAX 0791-464166. Ed. Klaus Latteman. adv. contact: Juergen Weise. circ. 3,068,208. **Document type:** bulletin.

333.33 917 CN ISSN 0713-8369
MOVING TO & AROUND ALBERTA. a. Can.$7.95. Moving Publications Ltd., 44 Upjohn Rd., Don Mills, ON M3B 2W1, Canada. TEL 416-441-1168. FAX 416-441-1641. Ed. Lorraine Hunter. adv. contact: Anita Wood. **Document type:** consumer publication.

333.33 917 CN ISSN 0228-7153
MOVING TO & AROUND MARITIMES & NEWFOUNDLAND. biennial. Can.$4.95. Moving Publications Ltd., 44 Upjohn Rd., Don Mills, ON M3B 2W1, Canada. TEL 416-441-1168. FAX 416-441-1641. Ed.Bd. adv. contact: Anita Wood. **Document type:** consumer publication.

333.33 917.124 CN ISSN 0713-8385
MOVING TO & AROUND SASKATCHEWAN. 1980. s-a. Can.$7.95. Moving Publications Ltd., 44 Upjohn Rd., Don Mills, ON M3B 2W1, Canada. TEL 416-441-1168. FAX 416-441-1641. Ed. Lorraine Hunter. adv. contact: Anita Wood. illus. **Document type:** consumer publication.
    Formerly (until 1983): Moving to Saskatchewan (ISSN 0225-5383)

333.33 917.13 CN ISSN 0713-8377
MOVING TO & AROUND TORONTO & AREA. 1974. a. Can.$7.95. Moving Publications Ltd., 44 Upjohn Rd., Don Mills, ON M3B 2W1, Canada. TEL 416-441-1168. FAX 416-441-1641. Ed. Lorraine Hunter. adv. contact: Anita Wood. **Document type:** consumer publication.
    Former titles: Moving to Toronto and Area (ISSN 0226-7829); Moving to Toronto (ISSN 0702-9179)

333.33 917.11 CN ISSN 0713-8407
MOVING TO & AROUND VANCOUVER & B.C. 1977. a. Can.$7.95. Moving Publications Ltd., 44 Upjohn Rd., Don Mills, ON M3B 2W1, Canada. TEL 416-441-1168. FAX 416-441-1641. Ed. Lorraine Hunter. adv. contact: Anita Wood. illus. **Document type:** consumer publication.
    Former titles: Moving to Vancouver and B.C; Moving to Vancouver - Victoria (ISSN 0702-9187)

333.33 917 CN ISSN 0825-2432
MOVING TO & AROUND WINNIPEG & MANITOBA. s-a. Can.$7.95. Moving Publications Ltd., 44 Upjohn Rd., Don Mills, ON M3B 2W1, Canada. TEL 416-441-1168. FAX 416-441-1641. Ed. Lorraine Hunter. adv. contact: Anita Wood. **Document type:** consumer publication.

333.33 CN
MOVING TO GREATER HAMILTON, C.T.T., BRANTFORD & NIAGARA. s-a. Can.$6.95. Moving Publications Ltd., 44 Upjohn Rd., Don Mills, ON M3B 2W1, Canada. TEL 416-441-1168. FAX 416-441-1641. Ed. Frank Stephan. adv. contact: Anita Wood. **Document type:** consumer publication.
    Formerly: Moving to Greater Hamilton and the Golden Triangle (ISSN 0843-9214)

333.33 917.13 CN
MOVING TO METRO OTTAWA - HULL. (Text in English and French) 1977. a. Can.$7.95. Moving Publications Ltd., 44 Upjohn Rd., Don Mills, ON M3B 2W1, Canada. TEL 416-441-1168. FAX 416-441-1641. Ed. Lorraine Hunter. adv. contact: Anita Wood. illus. **Document type:** consumer publication.
    Former titles (until 1995): Moving to Ottawa - Hull (ISSN 0226-7837); (until 1978): Emanager a Ottawa - Hull (ISSN 0702-9063)

333.33 CN ISSN 0702-9225
MOVING TO MONTREAL/EMMENAGER A MONTREAL. (Text in English, French) s-a. Can.$6.95. Moving Publications Ltd., 44 Upjohn Rd., Ste. 100, Don Mills, ON M3B 2W1, Canada. TEL 416-441-1168. FAX 416-441-1641. Ed. Frank Stephan. adv. contact: Anita Wood. **Document type:** consumer publication.

333.33 US
MR. LANDLORD; the survival newsletter for landlords and landladies. 1985. m. $59. Home Rental Publishing, Box 64442, Virginia Beach, VA 23467. TEL 804-495-5809. FAX 804-467-1427. Ed. Jeffrey E. Taylor. adv.; bk.rev. circ. 15,000. (looseleaf format; back issues avail.) **Document type:** newsletter.
    Description: Aims to help landlords to attain and maintain maximum cashflow, control and gain cooperation from tenants, and to serve as a forum for rental owners to share ideas and concerns.

MULTI-HOUSING NEWS. see *BUILDING AND CONSTRUCTION*

MULTI-HOUSING NEWSLETTER. see *BUILDING AND CONSTRUCTION*

333.33 AT
MULTILIST REALTOR. fortn. Real Estate Institute of Queensland, P.O. Box 1555, Coorparoo DC, Brisbane, Qld. 4151, Australia. Ed. Monique Belousoff. **Document type:** catalog.

333.33 CN
MUSKOKA REAL ESTATE GUIDE. w. Muskoka Publications Group, Box 1600, Bracebridge, ON P1L 1V6, Canada. TEL 705-645-4463. FAX 705-645-3928. adv. **Document type:** consumer publication.

333.33 368 US
N A I F A CONVENTION. PROCEEDINGS. a. National Association of Independent Fee Appraisers, 7501 Murdoch St., St. Louis, MO 63119. TEL 314-781-6688. **Document type:** proceedings.

333.33 US
N A R E A APPRAISAL GUIDELINE. bi-m. National Association of Real Estate Appraisers, 8383 E. Evans Rd., Scottsdale, AZ 85260. TEL 602-948-8000. FAX 602-998-8022.

333.33 US
N A R E E NEWS. 1947. m. $75 to nonmembers; members free. National Association of Real Estate Editors, Box 10057, Columbia, MO 65205-4001. TEL 314-499-0934. FAX 314-499-0898. Ed. Bruce Beck. bk.rev.; bibl.; charts; illus.; stat. circ. 600. **Document type:** newsletter.
    Description: Covers journalism, real estate, housing and urban planning and consumer education and protection.

333.33 AT
N.S.W. REALTY AUCTIONEER. (New South Wales) m. Aus.$215. Ian Huntley Pty. Ltd., P.O. Box 90, Cremorne, N.S.W. 2090, Australia. TEL 61-2-953-5788. Ed. Sandy Wilson. (back issues avail.)
    Description: Reports on the real estate market in New South Wales, Australia.

333.33 US
N.Y. REAL PROPERTY LAW JOURNAL. 1973. 4/yr. $40 (effective 1995). New York State Bar Association, Real Property Section, 1 Elk St., Albany, NY 12207-1096. TEL 518-463-3200. FAX 518-487-5699. Ed.Bd. adv.; circ. 4,600 (controlled). **Document type:** academic/scholarly publication.
    Formerly (until 1995): New York State Bar Association. Real Property Law Section. Newsletter (ISSN 0147-135X)

333.33 352.7 US ISSN 1059-3071
NATIONAL HOUSING REGISTER. 1991. irreg., approx. q. free to qualified personnel. William D. Diemer, Ed. & Pub., 27239 Meadowbrook Dr., Davis, CA 95616-5049. TEL 916-757-6403. FAX 916-753-1768. E-mail: wddiemer@wheel.ucdavis.edu. circ. 50 (controlled). (back issues avail.) **Document type:** newsletter.
    Description: Discusses the need for a National Housing Register listing every structure in the United States, strategies and measures appropriate to the design, development and maintenance of this list, and serves as a clearinghouse for information of interest to professionals and government officials.

333.33 US
NATIONAL MORTGAGE BROKER. 1985. m. $59.95 (foreign $69.95). National Association of Mortgage Brokers, 706 E. Bell Rd., Ste. 101, Phoenix, AZ 85022. TEL 602-992-6181. FAX 602-493-8711. Ed. John Ruzan. adv. contact: Laurie Patterson. bk.rev.; charts; illus.; stat.; tr.lit. circ. 6,500. **Document type:** trade publication.
    Description: Covers developments and news affecting the mortgage brokering community, including legislative matters, industry automation, human resources, business management and other concerns.

333.33 US ISSN 0027-9994
HD251
NATIONAL REAL ESTATE INVESTOR. 1958. m. (plus a. Directory). $72 (foreign $132). Argus Inc., 6151 Powers Ferry Rd., N.W., Atlanta, GA 30339-2941. TEL 404-955-2500. FAX 404-955-0400. Ed. Ben Johnson. adv.; bk.rev.; illus.; mkt.; stat.; tr.lit. circ. 33,708. (also avail. in microfilm from UMI; reprint service avail. from UMI) **Indexed:** ABI Inform., B.P.I, BPIA, Bus.Ind., P.A.I.S., PSI, Tr.& Indus.Ind. **Document type:** trade publication.
    ●Also available online. Vendor(s): University Microfilms International.
    —BLDSC (6030.030000); Faxon; UMI; UnCover. **CCC.**
    Description: Covers the development, investment, financing and management of commercial real estate and its allied fields.

333.33 US ISSN 0731-8693
NATIONAL REAL ESTATE INVESTOR. DIRECTORY ISSUE. a. $76.95. Argus Inc., 6151 Powers Ferry Rd., N.W., Atlanta, GA 30339-2941. TEL 404-955-2500. FAX 404-955-0400. Ed. Barbara Katinsky. adv. circ. 33,000. **Document type:** directory.
    Former titles: National Real Estate Handbook and Directory (ISSN 0547-8383); (until 1962): National Real Easte Investor Directory (ISSN 0196-7789)

333.3 US
HD253
NATIONAL REFERRAL ROSTER. 1962. a. $30 to real estate agents; others $75. Stamats Communications Inc., c/o Guy Wendler, Pub., 427 Sixth Ave., S.E., Box 1888, Cedar Rapids, IA 52406. TEL 319-364-6032. FAX 319-365-5421. Ed. Candy Holub. adv. contact: Guy Wendler. illus. circ. 14,000. **Document type:** directory.
    Formerly (until 1994): National Roster of Realtors (ISSN 0090-1741)

333.33 US ISSN 1079-0292
NATIONAL REVIEW OF REAL ESTATE MARKETS. 1990. q. $889. Local Market Monitor, 34 Crescent St., Wellesley, MA 02181. TEL 617-431-7151. Ed. Ingo Winzer. circ. 150 (paid). pp./issue: 200. (back issues avail.) **Document type:** bulletin.
    Former titles (until 1993): Cohane Rafferty's National Review of Real Estate Markets (ISSN 1069-4986); (until 1992): Local Market Monitor (ISSN 1056-0475)
    Description: Review of economic and real estate conditions in 150 local markets across the US, with emphasis on economic growth, home prices, and foreclosing risk.

NATIONAL SECOND MORTGAGE ASSOCIATION. LEGISLATIVE REPORT. see *BUSINESS AND ECONOMICS — Banking And Finance*

NATIONWIDE BUILDING SOCIETY. HOUSE PRICES. see *BUILDING AND CONSTRUCTION*

333 UK ISSN 0950-3382
NATIONWIDE PROPERTIES. 1984. m. £32 (rest of Europe £56; elsewhere £80). Grosvenor Publishing Ltd., Stone House Studios, Drury Ln., Minsterley, Shrops. SY5 OEL, England. TEL 01743-791887. FAX 01743-790708. (Dist. by: S. M. Magazine Distribution Ltd., 6 Leigham Court Rd., Streatham, London SW16 2PG, England) Ed. Imelda Zygmund. adv.: B&W page £550; color page £950; adv. contact: Stephen T. Wild. bk.rev. (back issues avail.) **Document type:** consumer publication.
 Description: Provides information about property matters from cottages to castles ranging in price from less than 30,000 pounds to more than 2 million, both in the U.K. and abroad.

NEIGHBORING PROPERTY OWNERS. see *LAW — Civil Law*

NELSON'S DIRECTORY OF INSTITUTIONAL REAL ESTATE. see *BUSINESS AND ECONOMICS — Trade And Industrial Directories*

333.3 US ISSN 0028-4890
NEW ENGLAND REAL ESTATE JOURNAL. 1962. w. $96. East Coast Publications, Inc., Box 55, Accord, MA 02081. TEL 617-878-4540; 800-654-4993. FAX 617-871-1853. Ed. David Denelle; Pub. Roland Hopkins. adv. contact: Patty Stone-Coleman. bk.rev. (tabloid format) **Document type:** trade publication.
 Description: Covers commercial, industrial, and investment real estate.

333.3 US
NEW ENGLAND REAL ESTATE JOURNAL - SHOPPING CENTERS. (Supplement to: New England Real Estate Journal) 1984. m. East Coast Publications, Inc., Box 55, Accord, MA 02081. TEL 617-878-4540; 800-654-4993. FAX 617-871-1853. Pub. Linda Christman. adv.; bk.rev. (tabloid format; back issues avail.) **Document type:** trade publication.

333.3 US
NEW HAMPSHIRE LAND SALES DISCLOSURE AND CONDOMINIUM LAWS AND RULES. a. $15. Butterworth Legal Publishers (Salem) (Subsidiary of: Reed Elsevier plc), 8 Industrial Way, Bldg. C, Salem, NH 03079. TEL 800-548-4001. FAX 603-898-9858. Ed.Bd.
 Description: For attorneys, real estate professionals, municipal boards and private developers; contains both the New Hampshire laws relating to land sales disclosure and the administrative rules.

333.33 US
NEW HAMPSHIRE LANDLORD AND TENANT LAW. a. $15. Butterworth Legal Publishers (Salem) (Subsidiary of: Reed Elsevier plc), 8 Industrial Way, Bldg. C, Salem, NH 03079. TEL 800-548-4001. FAX 603-898-9858. Ed.Bd.
 Description: Covers landlord and tenant law as well as related laws dealing with manufactured housing and requirements of the New Hampshire Human Rights Commission.

333.33 CN
▼**NEW HOMES**; Manitoba's guide to new housing. 1995. m. Can.$36. (Manitoba Home Builders' Association) Canadian Publishers, 1465 St. James St., Winnipeg, MB R3H 0W9, Canada. Ed. Bruce Nairn; Pub. Gerald L. Dorge. adv. contact: M. Cheryl Hunt. cols./p.: 5; pp./issue: 20. (tabloid format) **Document type:** consumer publication, newspaper.
 Description: Covers real estate and remodeling in Winnipeg and throughout Manitoba.

333.33 US ISSN 0192-4893
NEW HOMES MAGAZINE;* for the Twin Cities and suburbs. 1973. m. free. New Homes, Inc., 7643 W. 85th St., Bloomington, MN 55438-1308. FAX 612-933-6310. Ed. Wendy B. Danks. adv.; circ. 60,000 (controlled).
 Description: Consumer resource on Twin Cities housing with information on the effect of national trends, laws and viewpoints on the city.

333.33 UK
NEW HOMES MAGAZINE. s-a. included as supplement in real-estate magazines. Custom Publishing Company Ltd. (Subsidiary of: Glendower Holdings Ltd.), 54 Station Rd., Reddhill, Surrey RH1 1QH, England. TEL 0737-767213. FAX 0737-771662. Ed. David Hoppit. adv.: color page £1250; adv. contact: John Bailey. circ. 300,000 (paid). **Document type:** consumer publication.
 Description: Furnishes information regarding new property developments throughout the U.K. and overseas.

333.33 US
NEW JERSEY. DEPARTMENT OF THE TREASURY. LOCAL PROPERTY BRANCH NEWS. 1953. 6/yr. (plus annual report). free. Department of the Treasury, Division of Taxation, Local Property Branch, 50 Barrack St., Trenton, NJ 08646. TEL 609-984-3276. Ed. Gary R. Dal Corso. index. circ. 2,300. **Document type:** government publication.
 Formerly (until Dec. 1984): New Jersey. Department of the Treasury. Local Property and Public Utility Branch News.

333.33 US ISSN 1056-0165
NEW JERSEY OFFICE BUILDINGS. a. $49. Yale Robbins, Inc., 31 E. 28th St., New York, NY 10016. TEL 212-683-5700. Ed. Yale Robbins.
 Incorporates: Central New Jersey Office Buildings.
 Description: Annual review of New Jersey office buildings.

333.33 US ISSN 0028-5919
NEW JERSEY REALTOR. vol.12, 1970. m. $10. New Jersey Association of Realtors, 295 Pierson Ave., Edison, NJ 08837. TEL 908-494-5616. Ed. Peter L. Mosca; Pub. Robert F. Ferguson. adv. contact: Meredith Swanson. illus. circ. 38,000. **Document type:** trade publication.

333.33 US
NEW JERSEY STATE BAR ASSOCIATION. REAL PROPERTY, PROBATE AND TRUST LAW SECTION. NEWSLETTER. 1966. New Jersey State Bar Association, Real Property, Probate and Trust Law Section, One Constitution Sq., New Brunswick, NJ 08901-1500. TEL 908-249-5000. FAX 908-828-0034. Ed. Amy Franco. bk.rev. circ. 2,000. **Document type:** newsletter.

NEW MEXICO REAL ESTATE LAW REPORTER. see *LAW*

333.33 340 US ISSN 0898-2961
KFX2022
NEW YORK APARTMENT LAW INSIDER. 1979. m. $159. Brownstone Publishers, Inc., 149 Fifth Ave., New York, NY 10010-6801. TEL 212-473-8200. FAX 212-473-8786. Ed. Susan R. Lipp. index. (looseleaf format; back issues avail.) **Document type:** newsletter.
 Description: Covers new laws, cases, and regulations for New York apartment building owners.

NEW YORK CITY. REAL PROPERTY TAX. ANNUAL REPORT. see *BUSINESS AND ECONOMICS — Public Finance, Taxation*

333.33 747 US ISSN 1061-1436
THE NEW YORK COOPERATOR. 1981. 10/yr. free. Manhattan Cooperator Publications, Inc., 301 E. 45th St., Ste. 5C, New York, NY 10017-3422. Ed. Vicki Chesler. adv.; bk.rev. circ. 60,000. (tabloid format; back issues avail.) **Document type:** consumer publication.
 Formerly: Manhattan Cooperator (ISSN 0889-9878)

333.33 340 US ISSN 0883-0746
KFX2022
NEW YORK LANDLORD V. TENANT. Key Title: Landlord vs. Tenant - N Y C. 1985. m. $349. Brownstone Publishers, Inc., 149 Fifth Ave., New York, NY 10010-6801. TEL 212-473-8200. FAX 212-473-8786. Ed. Andrew O. Shapiro; Pub. John M. Striker. (back issues avail.) **Document type:** newsletter.
 Description: Tracks and summarizes judgements in landlord-tenant disputes in the New York City metropolitan area.

333.3 US ISSN 1057-2104
NEW YORK REAL ESTATE JOURNAL. 1989. s-m. $48. East Coast Publications, Inc., Box 55, Accord, MA 02081. TEL 617-878-4540; 800-654-4993. FAX 617-871-1853. Ed. David Denelle; Pub. Linda Christman. adv. contact: Linda Christman. bk.rev. (tabloid format; back issues avail.) **Document type:** trade publication, newspaper.
 Description: Comprehensive coverage of commercial, industrial, and investment real estate matters.

NEW YORK REAL ESTATE REPORTER. see *LAW*

333.32 NZ ISSN 0113-0315
NEW ZEALAND VALUERS' JOURNAL. 1942. q. NZ.$50 (effective 1995). New Zealand Institute of Valuers, P.O. Box 27-146, Willis St., Wellington, New Zealand. TEL 64-4-385-8436. FAX 64-4-382-9214. (Subscr. to: P.O. Box 27146, Wellington, New Zealand) Ed. W.O. Harrigton. adv.; bk.rev.; index, cum.index: 1942-1988. circ. 2,400. **Document type:** academic/scholarly publication.
 —BLDSC (6099.810000).
 Formerly: New Zealand Valuer (ISSN 0027-7282)
 Description: Contains articles on valuation principles and methodology and topical issues relevant to the profession in New Zealand.
 Refereed Serial

333.33 GW
NORDDEUTSCHE HAUSBESITZER-ZEITUNG. m. Verband Schleswig-Holsteinischer Haus-, Wohnungs- und Grundeigentuemer e.V., Sophienblatt 3, 24103 Kiel, Germany.

333 US
NORTH SHORE HOMES. Times - Beacon - Record Newspapers, 185 Rte. 25-A, Box 707, Setauket, NY 11733. TEL 516-571-7744. FAX 516-751-4165. Ed. Leah D. Dunaief. adv. contact: Kathryn Mandracchia. **Document type:** newspaper.
 Description: Covers local real estate; included as a supplement in many local papers.

333.33 US
NORTHERN NEW ENGLAND REAL ESTATE JOURNAL. 1973. m. $48. East Coast Publications, Inc., Box 55, Accord, MA 02081. TEL 617-878-4540; 800-654-4993. FAX 617-871-1853. Ed. David Denlle; Pub. Jim Coleman. adv. contact: Jim Coleman. bk.rev. (tabloid format; back issues avail.) **Document type:** trade publication, newspaper.
 Description: Covers commercial, industrial, and investment real estate in Maine, New Hampshire, and Vermont.

333.33 CN
NOVA SCOTIA REAL PROPERTY PRACTICE MANUAL. 1988. 3/yr. Can.$200. Butterworths Canada Ltd., Part of the Reed Elsevier group, 75 Clegg Rd., Markham, ON L6G 1A1, Canada. TEL 905-479-2665. FAX 905-479-2826. Ed. Charles W. MacIntosh. (looseleaf format) **Document type:** trade publication.
 Description: Treats the practice and procedure of Nova Scotia real property law.

333.33 AU
OESTERREICHISCHE IMMOBILIEN-ZEITUNG. bi-w. Landesinung Wien der Immobilien- und Vermoegenstreuhaender, Salesianergasse 1, A-1030 Vienna, Austria. TEL 725611.

333.33 US ISSN 0733-1266
OFFICE GUIDE TO ORLANDO;* a guide to office space, products and services. 1982. q. $30. Zink Media Group, Ltd., Box 915077, Longwood, FL 32791-5077. TEL 407-426-9446. FAX 407-426-9276. Ed. Sherry L. Valle. adv. circ. 12,026. **Document type:** trade publication.
 Description: Office and industrial space directory listing available square footage, costs maps, and leasing contacts. Telecommunications, interior design, office equipment, and new products and services are featured regularly, as well as articles on health and stress in the office, employee motivators, and stress and management skills and techniques.

OLD-HOUSE JOURNAL. see *BUILDING AND CONSTRUCTION*

OLD-HOUSE JOURNAL DIRECTORY. see *BUILDING AND CONSTRUCTION*

ONTARIO REAL ESTATE LAW GUIDE. see *LAW*

REAL ESTATE

333.33 CN
ONTARIO RESIDENTIAL REAL ESTATE PRACTICE MANUAL. q. Can.$165. Butterworths Canada Ltd., Part of the Reed Elsevier group, 75 Clegg Rd., Markham, ON L6G 1A1, Canada. TEL 905-479-2665. FAX 905-479-2826. Ed.Bd. **Document type:** trade publication.

333.33 US ISSN 0747-3435
ORANGE COUNTY APARTMENT NEWS. 1961. m. $36. (Apartment Association of Orange County) Orange County Multi-Housing Service Corporation, 12822 Garden Grove Blvd., Ste D, Garden Grove, CA 92643. TEL 714-638-6013. FAX 714-638-6042. Ed. Erica C. /Pierce. adv. contact: Erica C. Pierce. bk.rev.; charts; stat.; tr.lit. circ. 4,000. **Document type:** trade publication.
  Formerly: Orange County Apartment House News (ISSN 0030-4247)

ORANGE COUNTY REPORT. see BUSINESS AND ECONOMICS — Domestic Commerce

333.33 CN ISSN 0843-3836
OTTAWA REAL ESTATE NEWS.* 1988. m. O R E N Publishing Ltd., P.O. Box 3884, Sta. C, Ottawa, Ont. K1Y 4M5, Canada. TEL 613-232-2661. FAX 613-232-2922. Ed. Mark Buckshon. adv. contact: Kim Davidson. circ. 3,500. (tabloid format)

P M A DIRECTORY. (Property Management Association) see BUSINESS AND ECONOMICS — Trade And Industrial Directories

P W V HOME OWNER BUILDING & IMPROVEMENTS BUYERS GUIDE. (Pretoria - Witwatersrand - Vaal) see BUILDING AND CONSTRUCTION

333.33 690 US
PERSPECTIVE (INDIANAPOLIS). 1985. bi-m. free to qualified personnel. Resort Condominiums International, Inc., Box 80229, Indianapolis, IN 46280-0229. TEL 317-871-9641. FAX 317-871-9507. Ed. Laurie Borman. adv.; circ. 7,000 (controlled). **Document type:** trade publication.
  Description: Reports on events and trends in the resort-condominium development, vacation-ownership, and or exchange and travel industries on an international, federal and state-wide basis.

333.33 FR
PERSPECTIVES IMMOBILIERES. bi-m. (5/yr.). 350 F. (foreign 500 F.). Federation Nationale de l'Immobilier, 129, rue du Faubourg Saint-Honore, 75008 Paris, France. TEL 44-20-77-00. FAX 1-42-25-80-84. Ed. Catherine Vergnolle. adv.; bk.rev.
  Description: Covers the activities of the National Federation of Real Estate Agents, new innovations, interviews, etc.

PLACES RATED ALMANAC. see HOUSING AND URBAN PLANNING

PLANNING TAX-DEFERRED PROPERTY TRANSACTIONS. see LAW — Estate Planning

PLANS DE MAISONS DU QUEBEC. see INTERIOR DESIGN AND DECORATION

THE PRACTICAL REAL ESTATE LAWYER. see LAW

333.33 US
PRIME REAL ESTATE.* 1987. bi-m. $19.95. Prime Publishing Company, Inc., 123 W. Padre St., B, Santa Barbara, CA 93105-3960. Ed. Michael Colin. adv. circ. 40,000.
  Description: Features luxury residential real estate in the US. Provides localized feature articles and pertinent market information for consumers and brokers.

333 GW ISSN 0171-3523
PRIVATES EIGENTUM. 1960. m. membership. Vereinigung der Haus-, Grund- und Wohnungseigentuemer Frankfurt am Main e.V., Niedenau 61, 60325 Frankfurt a.M., Germany. TEL 069-720221. FAX 069-172384. adv.; bk.rev. circ. 20,000. **Document type:** bulletin.
  Formerly (until 1974): Private Haus- und Grundbesitz (ISSN 0171-3582)

PROBATE & PROPERTY. see LAW — Estate Planning

333.3 US ISSN 1071-4960
PROBLEM ASSET REPORTER. 1993. s-m. $398 (effective 1994). Dorset Group, Inc., 212 W. 35th St., 13th Fl., New York, NY 10001. TEL 212-563-4405. FAX 212-563-8879. Ed. Stan Strachan. adv. contact: Jim Hollander. circ. 620. (back issues avail.) **Document type:** newsletter.
  ● Also available online.
  Formed by the merger of (1989-1993): Resolution Trust Reporter (ISSN 1045-0130); (1991-1993): Bank Resolution Reporter (ISSN 1056-7232)
  Description: Documents sale of problem assets by banks, savings and loans, and the U.S. government. Focuses on the influences of government regulations on the market place.

333.33 340 US ISSN 0891-2599
PROFESSIONAL APARTMENT MANAGEMENT. 1986. m. $168. Brownstone Publishers, Inc., 149 Fifth Ave., New York, NY 10010-6801. TEL 212-473-8200. FAX 212-473-8786. Eds. Glenn Demby, Marion Walsh. index. (looseleaf format; back issues avail.)
  Description: Covers how to successfully manage an apartment community. Includes legal advice on leasing, maintenance, and employee relations.

333.33 US
HD1361
PROFESSIONAL RELOCATION & REAL ESTATE SERVICES; directory of professional relocation services and professionals. 1980. a. $95. Relocation Information Service, Inc., 50 Water St., Norwalk, CT 06854-3061. TEL 203-855-1234. Ed. Peter S. Featherston. adv.; bk.rev.; index. circ. 35,000. (back issues avail.) **Document type:** directory.
  Formerly: National Relocation and Real Estate Directory (ISSN 1056-9723)

333.33 US ISSN 1067-4764
PROFESSIONAL REPORT OF INDUSTRIAL AND OFFICE REAL ESTATE. 1991. bi-m $40 (foreign $45). Society of Industrial and Office Realtors, 700 11th St., N.W., Ste. 510, Washington, DC 20001-4511. TEL 202-737-1150. Ed. Linda Nasvaderani. circ. 2,500. **Document type:** trade publication.
  Description: Reports industry news in the fields of industrial and office real estate.

333.33 US ISSN 0033-1287
PROPERTIES. 1937. m. $15. Properties Magazine Publishing Co., 4900 Euclid Ave., Cleveland, OH 44103. TEL 216-431-7666. Ed. Gene E. Bluhm. adv.; bk.rev.; charts; illus.; stat.; tr.lit.; index. circ. 2,100. (tabloid format) **Document type:** trade publication.

333.33 FR
PROPERTIES DE FRANCE. 6/yr. 50 F. per no. Editions Indicateur Bertrand, 43 bd. Barbes, 75018 Paris, France. TEL 1-49-25-26-27. FAX 1-49-25-26-00. adv.: color page 15200 F. circ. 50,000.
  Description: Advertises luxury houses and apartments for sale or rent in France.

333.33 US
PROPERTY DIGEST AND LITERATURE REVIEW. 1991. 2/yr. Barry Inc., Box 551, Wilmington, MA 01887-0551. TEL 508-658-0441. FAX 508-657-8691. adv.: B&W page $1990, trim 8 x 10 7/8. circ. 6,000. **Document type:** trade publication.

PROPERTY FINANCE & DEVELOPMENT. see LAW

333.33 UK
PROPERTY GUIDE. 1978. m. free. Clarendon Advertising Ltd., Burley Hill House, Burley Rd., Leeds LS4 2PX, England. FAX 0532-744740. Ed. R.J. Fletcher. adv. circ. 40,000.
  Formerly: Property Fortnightly.
  Description: Describes property in the North of England.

333.33 UK ISSN 0033-1309
K16
PROPERTY JOURNAL. 1970. 6/yr. £12.80. British Property Federation, 35 Catherine Pl., London S.W.1, England. TEL 071-828-0111. FAX 071-834-3442. Ed. Helen McCarthy. adv.; bk.rev.; index. circ. 2,000. **Indexed:** RICS.
  —BLDSC (6927.307000).

PROPERTY LAW AND PRACTICE IN QUEENSLAND. see LAW

333.33 UK ISSN 0263-7472
HD1394.5.G7
PROPERTY MANAGEMENT. 1982. q. £219($349) (effective 1996). M C B University Press Ltd., 60-62 Toller Ln., Bradford, W. Yorks BD8 9BY, England. TEL 01274-499821. FAX 01274-547143. TELEX 51317-MCBUNI-G. Ed. Brenda Rouse. bk.rev. (reprint service avail. from SWZ) **Document type:** bulletin.
  —BLDSC (6927.309700).

333.33 658 US
PROPERTY MANAGEMENT ASSOCIATION. BULLETIN. 1975. m. $100. Property Management Association, 8811 Colesville Rd., Ste. G106, Silver Spring, MD 20910. TEL 301-587-6543. Ed. John P. Bachner. adv. contact: Stacy Johnson. circ. 1,200. **Document type:** bulletin.
  Description: Covers property management, association activities, and business management personnel.

333.33 US ISSN 1049-2372
HD1394
PROPERTY MANAGEMENT MONTHLY; serving decision-makers of income-producing properties. 1984. m. $18 (effective Feb. 1991). Adler Group, 8601 Georgia Ave., Ste. 400, Silver Spring, MD 20910. TEL 301-588-0681. FAX 301-588-6314. Ed. Laura O. Zaner. adv.; bk.rev. circ. 6,000. (back issues avail.)
  Formerly: Apartment and Office Management News.
  Description: Provides information to anyone involved in the management of commercial and residential real estate.

333.33 CN ISSN 1194-9554
PROPERTY MANAGEMENT NEWS. 1992. bi-m. Can.$20.33. K-Rey Publishing Inc., 789 W. Pender St., Ste. 920, Vancouver, BC V6C 1H2, Canada. TEL 604-669-7671. FAX 604-681-9535. Ed. Kelly Reynolds; Pub. Steve Munday. adv. contact: Kelly Piket. circ. 8,007. (back issues avail.) **Document type:** trade publication.

333.33 UK
PROPERTY MARKET VALUES. q. £8 per no. Hillier Parker, 77 Grosvenor St., London W1A 2BT, England. TEL 0171-629-7666. FAX 0171-409-3016. Ed. Kiran Patel. (back issues avail.) **Document type:** trade publication.

333.33 SA
THE PROPERTY PROFESSIONAL; the magazine for real estate sales and management. 1992. m. (10/yr.). R.63.20. Pretoria Publishing, P.O. Box 5262, Rivonia 2128, South Africa. illus. **Document type:** trade publication.

333.33 UK
PROPERTY REGISTER. 1978. m. £250. Tophill Press, 49 High St., Sevenoaks, Kent TN13 1L8, England. TEL 0732-743300. FAX 0732-743006. Ed. Arthur Hill. adv.; circ. controlled.
  Formerly: Commercial Property Register.

333.33 UK ISSN 0961-2815
PROPERTY RESEARCH SUMMARIES. s-a. £10 per no. Hillier Parker, 77 Grosvenor St., London W1A 2BT, England. TEL 0171-629-7666. FAX 0171-409-3016. (back issues avail.) **Document type:** trade publication.

333.33 352.7 UK ISSN 0966-8225
PROPERTY REVIEW. 1992. m. £285 includes a. index. Cardinal Publications Ltd., 24 Bankside Ct., Kidlington, Oxon. OX5 1JE, England. TEL 0865-842013. FAX 0865-842012. Ed.Bd; Pub. Andrew Dent. bk.rev.; index. **Document type:** trade publication.
  —BLDSC (6927.311700).
  Description: Explores the economic and legal aspects of urban planning and real-estate development.

333 IE ISSN 0790-1658
THE PROPERTY VALUER. 1982. 4/yr. I£20. Irish Auctioneers and Valuers Institute (IAVI), 38 Merrion Sq. E., Dublin 2, Ireland. TEL 01-6611794. FAX 01-6611797. Ed. Niall Fallon. adv.: B&W page I£500, color page I£750; adv. contact: Valerie Bourke. bk.rev. circ. 3,000. **Document type:** trade publication.
  Description: Contains national and international news.

REAL ESTATE 5661

333.33   UK
PROPERTY WEEK. 1868. w. £85 (overseas £100) (effective 1995). Builder Group plc., Builder House, 1 Millharbour, London E14 9RA, England. TEL 0171-537-2222. FAX 0171-537-2007. (Subscr. to: Building, Freepost (LE6522), Leicester LE87 4DH, England. TEL 01858-468811) Ed. Penny Guest; Pub. Trevor Barratt. adv. contact: John Scharfli. bk.rev.; charts; illus.; index. circ. 37,955. (also avail. in microfilm from UMI; reprint service avail. from UMI) **Indexed:** Bibl.Cart., Br.Tech.Ind., Build.Manage.Abstr., Eng.Ind., Forest.Abstr., Forest Prod.Abstr., Geo.Abstr., Intl.Civil Eng.Abstr., LJI, RICS, Soft.Abstr.Eng., World Agri.Econ.& Rural Sociol.Abstr. **Document type:** trade publication.
—UMI.
    Former titles (until Feb. 1994): C S W - The Property Week (ISSN 0969-7594); (until 1992): Chartered Surveyor Weekly (ISSN 0264-049X); (until 1982): Chartered Surveyor (ISSN 0009-1936); Which was formed by the 1955 merger of: Royal Institution of Chartered Surveyors. Transactions (ISSN 0309-6491); Royal Institution of Chartered Surveyors. Journal; Chartered Surveyors Institution. Journal.

333.33   IT
PROPRIETA EDILIZIA DI PUGLIA. 12/yr. Via N. de Nicolo 37, 70123 Bari, Italy. TEL 080-5235467. Ed. Felice Giovine. circ. 2,000. **Document type:** trade publication.

333.33   IT   ISSN 0033-1422
PROPRIETA EDILIZIA LOMBARDA. 1901. m. L.3500 per no. Federazione Lombarda Proprieta Edilizia, Via Meravigli 3, 20121 Milan, Italy. TEL 39-2-8056643. Ed. G. Carone. adv.: B&W page L.1200000, color page L.1900000. circ. 25,000.

333.33 001.6
621.381   US   ISSN 1052-5521
THE QUARTERLY BYTE. 1985. q. $35 (foreign $40). Appraisal Institute, 875 N. Michigan Ave., Ste. 2400, Chicago, IL 60611-1980. TEL 312-335-4100. FAX 312-335-4400. Ed. Mary J. Dum. circ. 3,000. **Indexed:** Comput.Lit.Ind.
    Formerly (until 1988): Appraisal Institute Quarterly (ISSN 0884-7649)
    Description: Articles and software reviews for the computer-using real estate appraiser.

333.33 340   US
QUEENS COOP CONDO CONVERSION DIGEST. 1979. base vol. (plus irreg. updates, 2-4/yr.). $390. Yale Robbins, Inc., 31 E. 28th St., New York, NY 10016. TEL 212-683-5700. FAX 212-545-0764. Ed. George Kelly. (looseleaf format)

333.33 747   US
QUEST: MANHATTAN PROPERTIES & COUNTRY ESTATES. 1987. m. $15 (free to qualified personnel). Quest Magazines, Inc., 1046 Madison Ave., New York, NY 10021-0137. FAX 212-288-4536. Ed. Heather Cohane. circ. 97,000 (controlled). **Document type:** consumer publication.
    Description: Contains advertisements for real estate and interior design, celebrity interviews, photos of social events, with focus on Manhattan.

333.33   US   ISSN 1051-0737
R E D I REALTY REPORT. (Real Estate Data Inc.) 1868. w. & q. $530. T R W R E D I Property Data, 1200 Harbor Blvd., 10th Fl., Weehawken, NJ 07087-6728. TEL 201-330-9600. Ed. Venice Kelly. circ. 1,300. **Document type:** directory.
    Formerly: Real Estate Record and Builder's Guide (ISSN 0034-0774)

333.33   US
R E E ACTION. m. membership. Real Estate Educators Association, 11 S. La Salle St., Ste. 1400, Chicago, IL 60603-1210. adv.; bk.rev. circ. 1,200. (looseleaf format)
    Description: Articles on real estate education. Includes association news.

333.33   US
R E I S REPORT: INDUSTRIAL MARKET SERVICE. (Real Estate Information Service) 1980. irreg. price varies. R E I S Reports, Inc., 11 E. 36th St., 7th fl., New York, NY 10016-3318. TEL 212-481-8500. FAX 212-481-9892. Ed. Lloyd Lynford.

333.3   US
R E I S REPORT: RESIDENTIAL MARKET SERVICE. (Real Estate Information Service) 1980. irreg. price varies. R E I S Reports, Inc., 11 E. 36th St., 7th fl., New York, NY 10016-3318. TEL 212-481-8500. FAX 212-481-9892. Ed. Lloyd Lynford. stat. (also avail. in looseleaf format; back issues avail.)

333.3   US
R E I S REPORTS: OFFICE MARKET SERVICE. (Real Estate Information Service) 1980. irreg. price varies. R E I S Reports, Inc., 11 E. 36th St., 7th fl., New York, NY 10016-3318. TEL 212-481-8500. FAX 212-481-9892. Ed. Lloyd Lynford. stat. (looseleaf format; back issues avail.)

333.33   US
R E I S REPORTS: RETAIL MARKET SERVICE. (Real Estate Information Service) 1980. irreg. price varies. R E I S Reports, Inc., 11 E. 36th St., 7th fl., New York, NY 10016. TEL 212-481-8500. FAX 212-481-9892. Ed. Lloyd Lynford. stat. (back issues avail.)

332.6 333.33   US
HG5095
R.E.I.T. BASIC FACTS. 1974. irreg. $25. National Association of Real Estate Investment Trusts, Inc., 1129 20th St., N.W., Ste. 305, Washington, DC 20036. TEL 202-785-8717. Eds. Victoria J. Baker, Karen T. White. illus. circ. 3,500.
    Formerly (until 1995): R.E.I.T. Fact Book (ISSN 0095-1374)

333.33 332.6   US
R.E.I.T. REPORT. 1981. q. membership. National Association of Real Estate Investment Trusts, Inc., 1129 20th St., N.W., Ste. 305, Washington, DC 20036. TEL 202-785-8717. Ed. Victoria J. Baker. adv.; bk.rev. circ. 2,800.

333.33 340   IT
RASSEGNA DELL'EQUO CANONE; locazioni e condominio. 1979. q. L.90000 (foreign L.110000) (effecttive 1995). Casa Editrice Dott. Antonio Milani, Via Jappelli 5-6, 35121 Padua, Italy. TEL 39-49-656677. FAX 39-49-8752900. Ed. Giuseppe Spagnuolo. index. circ. 1,500.

RATES AND TERMS ON CONVENTIONAL HOME MORTGAGES. see *BUSINESS AND ECONOMICS — Banking And Finance*

333.33 330.9   US   ISSN 0882-9144
HD251
REAL ESTATE ANALYSIS AND PLANNING SERVICE. s-a. $20000. F.W. Dodge - McGraw-Hill, 24 Hartwell Ave., Lexington, MA 02173. TEL 617-863-5100. FAX 617-860-6884. TELEX 200 284.
    Description: Forecasts market supply and demand for users looking to target real estate markets for investment, expansion, site location or construction.

333.33   US   ISSN 0744-642X
HD1361
REAL ESTATE BUSINESS. 1982. q. $20 membership. Realtors National Marketing Institute, Real Estate Brokerage Council, Residential Sales Council, Box 300, Wheaton, IL 60189-0300. TEL 708-752-0500. FAX 708-752-0525. Ed. Pierce Hollingsworth. adv.; bk.rev.; circ. 31,000 (controlled). (back issues avail.)
    Description: News and educational articles for designated realtors.

333.3   US
REAL ESTATE CENTER LAW LETTER. 1986. q. $50. Texas A & M University, Real Estate Center, College Station, TX 77843-2115. TEL 409-845-2031. FAX 409-845-0460. Ed. Shirley E. Bovey; Pub. R. Malcolm Richards. circ. 6,500. (back issues avail.) **Document type:** newsletter.
    Description: Covers new laws, relevant court cases and rulings with impact on Texas real estate.

333.33 621.381   US   ISSN 0742-5600
REAL ESTATE COMPUTER REVIEW. m. 1564 A Fitzgerald Dr., Ste. 404, Pinole, CA 94088. TEL 415-799-6156. Ed. Michael J. Hanrahan. circ. 1,200.

333.33   US
REAL ESTATE COORDINATOR. (In 8 vols.) bi-w. $775. Research Institute of America, Inc., 90 Fifth Ave., New York, NY 10011. TEL 212-645-4800. FAX 212-337-4279. (Subscr. to: 117 E. Stevens Ave., Valhalla, NY 10595) (looseleaf format)
    Description: Presents planning guidance and tax analysis for real estate transactions.

333.3   US   ISSN 0098-8936
HD268.N5
REAL ESTATE DIRECTORY OF MANHATTAN. a. $745. T R W R E D I Property Data, 1200 Harbor Blvd., 10th Fl., Weehawken, NJ 07087-6728. TEL 201-330-9600. **Document type:** directory.
    Formerly: Real Estate Directory of the Borough of Manhattan.

333.3   US   ISSN 1080-8620
HD251
REAL ESTATE ECONOMICS. 1973. q. $75 (foreign $80) (effective 1996). (American Real Estate and Urban Economics Association) Edward Bros., 2500 S. State St., Ann Arbor, MI 48106. TEL 313-769-1004. FAX 313-769-7653. E-mail: shshenry@ucs.indiana.edu. (Subscr. to: Indiana University, School of Business, Room 428, Bloomington, IN 47401) Ed.Bd. adv. contact: Dinnis Capozza. bk.rev.; index, cum.index: 1973-1987. circ. 1,500. (also avail. in microfiche from UMI; back issues avail.; reprint service avail. from UMI) **Indexed:** ABI Inform, ASCA, B.P.I, J.of Econ.Lit., Risk Abstr., SSCI, Tr.& Indus.Ind. **Document type:** academic/scholarly publication.
—BLDSC (7303.280140); Faxon; Genuine Article; SWETS; UMI; UnCover. CCC.
    Former titles (until 1995): American Real Estate and Urban Economics Association. Journal (ISSN 1067-8433); (until 1992): A R E U A Journal (ISSN 0270-0484); (until 1977): American Real Estate and Urban Economics Association. Journal (ISSN 0092-914X)
    Description: Publishes research and scholarly studies of current and emerging real estate issues. *Refereed Serial*

333.33   US
REAL ESTATE EDUCATORS ASSOCIATION. JOURNAL. 1988. a. membership. Real Estate Educators Association, 11 S. La Salle St., Ste. 1400, Chicago, IL 60603-1210. adv. circ. 1,200.
    Description: Articles on real estate education. Includes a membership directory.

333.33   US
REAL ESTATE EDUCATORS ASSOCIATION. PROCEEDINGS. 1985. a. $10. Real Estate Educators Association, 11 S. La Salle St., Ste. 1400, Chicago, IL 60603-1210. (back issues avail.) **Document type:** proceedings.
    Description: Academic research papers on a wide variety of real estate topics.

333.33   US   ISSN 1070-5171
REAL ESTATE ENTREPRENEUR. 1992. m. $45 (effective 1995). Bryan Wittenmyer, Ed. & Pub., Box 13246, Reading, PA 19612. TEL 610-371-9977. adv. circ. 150. (back issues avail.) **Document type:** newsletter.
    Description: Provides national news and advice on buying and selling real estate, with particular emphasis on rental houses and apartments for individual investors.

REAL ESTATE - ENVIRONMENTAL LIABILITY NEWS; the bi-weekly report on litigation, regulation, and industry practice. see *LAW*

333.33   US   ISSN 0748-318X
HD1361
REAL ESTATE FINANCE. 1984. q. $98. Federal Research Press - Standard Publishing, 155 Federal St., 13th fl., Boston, MA 02110. Ed. Barbara Grzincic. bk.rev.; illus. circ. 1,800. **Indexed:** ABI Inform.
    ●Also available online. Vendor(s): University Microfilms International.
—BLDSC (7303.280150); Faxon; UMI; UnCover.
    Incorporates (1984-198?): Real Estate Leasing Report (ISSN 0748-3163); (1985-1986): Real Estate Finance Law Journal (ISSN 0882-3413)

REAL ESTATE

330 US ISSN 0898-0209
HD1361
REAL ESTATE FINANCE JOURNAL. 1903. q. $130.98 (overseas $206.45) (effective 1995). Warren, Gorham & Lamont, One Penn Plaza, New York, NY 10119. TEL 212-971-5000. FAX 212-971-5113. (Subscr. to: The Park Square Bldg., 31 St. James Ave., Boston, MA 02116-4112. TEL 800-950-1207) Ed. William Zucker. adv. **Indexed:** ABI Inform. **Document type:** trade publication. —BLDSC (7303.280180); Faxon; UMI; UnCover. **CCC.**
  Formerly (until 1993): Real Estate Finance Update (ISSN 0891-9852)
  Description: Provides analysis of current real estate financing events and issues, giving forecasts on important regulatory trends.

333.33 US ISSN 0742-0021
REAL ESTATE FINANCE TODAY. 1984. fortn. $95. Mortgage Bankers Association of America, 1125 15th St., N.W., Washington, DC 20005-2766. TEL 202-861-6555. Ed. Richard Helgerson. adv.; illus. circ. 16,000. (also avail. in microform from UMI)
  •Also available online. Vendor(s): University Microfilms International.
  —UMI. **CCC.**

333.33 US ISSN 0034-0707
REAL ESTATE FORUM.* 1946. m. $65. Real Estate Forum, Inc., 111 Eighth Ave., No. 1511, New York, NY 10011-5201. TEL 212-563-6460. FAX 212-967-1498. Ed. Michael Desiato. adv.; bk.rev.; charts; illus.; circ. 3,000 (paid); 24,000 (controlled). **Document type:** trade publication.
  Description: Provides national coverage of real estate investment and development news.

333.33 US ISSN 0034-0715
REAL ESTATE INSIDER; weekly newsletter. 1968. bi-w. $225. Walker Communications Inc., 1541 Morris Ave., Bronx, NY 10457-8702. TEL 718-583-8060. FAX 718-583-8258. Ed. Suzie Mitchell; Pub. Beverly Walker. bk.rev.; charts; tr.lit. circ. 1,000. (reprint service avail. from UMI) **Document type:** newsletter.
  —**CCC.**
  Description: Aimed at owners, managers and brokers of real estate firms.

333.33 AT
REAL ESTATE INSTITUTE OF QUEENSLAND. ANNUAL REPORT. no.62, 1981. a. Real Estate Institute of Queensland, P.O. Box 1555, Coorparoo DC, Brisbane, Qld. 4151, Australia. circ. 4,500.

333.33 US ISSN 0145-1022
REAL ESTATE INVESTING LETTER. 1976. m. $96. Orm Publishing Co., Inc.c., 861 Lafayette Rd., Hampton, NH 03842. bk.rev.; charts. (back issues avail.) **Document type:** newsletter.
  Formerly: Real Estate Investor Letter.

333.33 US ISSN 0034-0723
REAL ESTATE INVESTMENT IDEAS.* s-m. $69. Macmillan Information Company Inc., 90 Fifth Ave., New York, NY 10011-7629. TEL 800-562-0245. FAX 201-816-3569. adv.; bk.rev.

333.33 332.6 US
REAL ESTATE INVESTMENT TRUSTS HANDBOOK; a pass-through entity to make mortgage loans and operate real estate. a. $97.50. Clark - Boardman - Callaghan Company Ltd., 375 Hudson St., New York, NY 10014. TEL 212-929-7500; 800-221-9428. FAX 212-924-0460. Ed.Bd.
  Description: Offers fundamental information, analysis, and procedural guidance for making full use of real estate investment trusts.

333.33 US ISSN 0146-0595
HD251
REAL ESTATE ISSUES. vol.2, 1976. s-a. $27 to individuals; university faculty and students $21; foreign $29. Counselors of Real Estate, 430 N. Michigan Ave., Chicago, IL 60611. TEL 312-329-8427. FAX 312-329-8881. Ed. Halbort Smith. adv.; bk.rev.; index. circ. 2,000. (also avail. in microform from UMI) **Indexed:** ABI Inform. **Document type:** trade publication.
  •Also available online. Vendor(s): University Microfilms International.
  —BLDSC (7303.280330); Faxon; UMI; UnCover.
  Description: Offers in-depth articles by leading authors on the restructuring of the real estate industry.

333.33 JM
REAL ESTATE JAMAICA. 1985. bi-m. J.$30($2.10) per issue. Financial & Economic Resources Ltd., 12 Merrick Ave., Kingston 10, Jamaica, W.I. TEL 809-929-2993. FAX 809-968-1188. Ed. Marilyn DeLisser. adv.

333.33 AT ISSN 0048-685X
REAL ESTATE JOURNAL (BRISBANE). 1963. m. Aus.$66. Real Estate Institute of Queensland, P.O. Box 1555, Coorparoo DC, Brisbane, Qld. 4151, Australia. E.d Ross Elliott. adv. circ. 4,800. **Document type:** trade publication.

333.33 AT ISSN 0034-074X
REAL ESTATE JOURNAL (SYDNEY SOUTH). 1923. bi-m. Aus.$40. Real Estate Institute of New South Wales, P.O. Box A624, Sydney South, N.S.W. 2000, Australia. Ed. Danielle McDonald. adv.: B&W page $Aus.$990; trim 297 x 210. bk.rev.; illus.; tr.lit.; index. circ. 4,500. (tabloid format) **Document type:** trade publication.
  —BLDSC (7303.280500).

REAL ESTATE LAW DIGEST (SUPPLEMENT). see *LAW*

REAL ESTATE LAW JOURNAL. see *LAW*

REAL ESTATE LAW REPORT. see *LAW*

333.33 US
REAL ESTATE NEWS. 1927. m. $30. Real Estate News Corp., 2600 W. Peterson Ave., Chicago, IL 60659. FAX 312-465-7218. Ed. Steven Polydoris. adv.; bk.rev. circ. 9,500.
  Description: Magazine for real estate, building, financing and investment.

333.33 CN ISSN 0225-2783
REAL ESTATE NEWS. 1970. w. Can.$96.30($127.50) Toronto Real Estate Board, 1400 Don Mills Rd., North York, ON M3B 3N1, Canada. TEL 416-443-8113. FAX 416-443-9185. Ed. Laura Morrison. adv. contact: Ed Yeo. bk.rev.; charts; illus.; stat. circ. 74,438. **Document type:** newspaper.
  Formerly (until 1979): Toronto Real Estate (ISSN 0225-2775); (until 1971): Toronto Homes for Sale (ISSN 0225-2767)
  Description: Geared to home buyers and sellers.

333.33 352.7 CN
REAL ESTATE NEWS AND BUYERS GUIDE. 1977. w. free. Conni Robinson, Pub., 333 Arvin Ave., Stoney Creek, ON L8E 2M6, Canada. TEL 416-523-5800. FAX 416-664-3102. Ed. Judi Pattison. adv. circ. 57,000. (back issues avail.) **Document type:** newspaper, trade publication.

333.33 US
REAL ESTATE NEWSLETTER (BURLINGTON). m. National Research Bureau, Box 1, Burlington, IA 52601-0001. TEL 319-752-5415. FAX 319-752-3421. Ed. Barbara Boeding; Pub. Michael Darnall. **Document type:** newsletter.
  Description: Real estate news and trends for realtors, developers, title companies and financial personnel.

333.33 US
REAL ESTATE NEWSLETTER (MANHASSET).* (In 2 editions: Suburban and Manhattan and Outer Boroughs) 1969. w. $109 per ed. L L & I L Publishing, Inc., 125A Service Rd., Jericho, NY 11753-1008. Ed. Ivan Levine. adv.; tr.lit. circ. 3,710. (reprint service avail.) **Indexed:** ABI Inform. **Document type:** newsletter.

333.3 US ISSN 0749-8640
REAL ESTATE NEWSLINE. 1984. m. free. Kenneth Leventhal & Co., 2049 Century Park, Ste. 2300, Los Angeles, CA 90067. TEL 310-277-0880. Ed. Stan Ross. index. circ. 17,000. pp./issue: 8. **Document type:** newsletter.

333 US
HD251
REAL ESTATE OUTLOOK: MARKET TRENDS & INSIGHTS. 1976. m. $135 to non-members; members $95 (effective 1994). National Association of Realtors, Research Group, 777 14th St., N.W., Washington, DC 20005. TEL 202-383-1110. FAX 202-383-7568. Ed. Lisa Cole. circ. 1,400. (looseleaf format; also avail. in microfiche from CIS) **Indexed:** SRI. **Document type:** newsletter.
  •Also available online.
  Formed by the 1993 merger of: Real Estate Outlook & Home Sales (ISSN 1063-0511); Which was formerly titled: National Association of Realtors. Existing Home Sales (ISSN 0161-5882); National Association of Realtors. Department of Economics and Research. Existing Home Sales Series, Annual Report.

333.33 US ISSN 0079-9890
HD251
REAL ESTATE REPORTS. 1966. irreg., no.36, 1982. price varies. University of Connecticut, Center for Real Estate & Urban Economic Studies, U-41 RE, Rm. 426, 368 Fairfield Rd., Storrs, CT 06269. TEL 203-486-3227. FAX 203-486-0349. Ed. Katherine A. Stadtmueller. circ. 500. (also avail. in microfiche; Braille) **Document type:** academic/scholarly publication.

333 JA ISSN 0532-7776
REAL ESTATE RESEARCH/FUDOSAN KENKYU. (Text in Japanese) 1959. q. Japan Real Estate Institute - Nihon Fudosan Kenkyusho, Kangin-Fujiya Bldg., 1-3-2 Toranomon, Minato-ku, Tokyo, Japan.

333.33 NE
▼**REAL ESTATE RESEARCH ISSUES.** (Text in English) 1994. irreg. (American Real Estate Society) Kluwer Academic Publishers, Postbus 17, 3300 AA Dordrecht, Netherlands. TEL 31-78-392392. FAX 31-78-392254. TELEX 29245 KAPG NL. (Dist. by: Kluwer Academic Publishers Group, P.O. Box 322, 3300 AH Dordrecht, Netherlands. TEL 31-78-392392. FAX 31-78-546474; N. America dist. addr.: Box 358, Accord Sta., Hingham, MA 02018-0358. TEL 617-871-6600. FAX 617-871-6528) **Document type:** monographic series. *Refereed Serial*

333.33 US ISSN 0034-0790
HD251
REAL ESTATE REVIEW. 1971. q. $104.48 (overseas $173.30) (effective 1995). Warren, Gorham & Lamont, One Penn Plaza, New York, NY 10119. TEL 212-971-5000. FAX 212-971-5240. (Subscr. to: The Park Square Bldg., 31 St. James Ave., Boston, MA 02116-4112. TEL 800-950-1207) Ed. Norman Weinberg. adv.; bk.rev. (also avail. in microform from UMI; reprint service avail. from RRI,UMI,WSH) **Indexed:** ABI Inform, B.P.I, Bank.Lit.Ind., BPIA, Bus.Ind., C.L.I., Curr.Cont., Leg.Per., Manage.Cont., P.A.I.S., RICS, Risk Abstr., SSCI, Tr.& Indus.Ind. **Document type:** trade publication.
  —BLDSC (7303.281500); Faxon; Genuine Article; UMI; UnCover. **CCC.**
  Description: Provides expert advice from the leaders of the real estate field who share the insights, opinions, and techniques that have made significant changes in the industry. *Refereed Serial*

333.33 336 US ISSN 8756-3835
KF6535.A15
REAL ESTATE TAX DIGEST. 1983. m. $260 (effective 1995). Matthew Bender & Co., Inc., 11 Penn Plaza, New York, NY 10001. TEL 212-216-8582. FAX 212-216-8302. Ed. Robert Lopatin; Pub. Lawrence Kaplan. adv. contact: Gary Goldstein. index; circ. 371 (paid); 50 (controlled). (looseleaf format) **Document type:** newsletter.
  —**CCC.**
  Description: Contains articles and analyses of regulations, cases and IRS pronouncements on federal tax matters affecting real estate activities. *Refereed Serial*

333.33 336 US
REAL ESTATE TAX GUIDE. a. $89.50. Clark - Boardman - Callaghan Company Ltd., 375 Hudson St., New York, NY 10014. TEL 212-929-7500; 800-221-9428. Ed.Bd.
  Description: Covers the latest developments in real property tax principles, rules, and the consequences of an array of real estate transactions.

REAL ESTATE

333.33 US ISSN 0162-7538
REAL ESTATE TAX IDEAS. 1971. m. $125.25 (overseas $180.95) (effective 1995). Warren, Gorham & Lamont, One Penn Plaza, New York, NY 10119. TEL 212-971-5000. FAX 212-971-5113. (Subscr. to: The Park Square Bldg., 31 St. James Ave., Boston, MA 02116-4112. TEL 800-950-1205) Eds. Gerald J. Robinson, Stephen L. Owen. (looseleaf format; also avail. in microform from UMI) **Indexed:** Bus.Ind. **Document type:** newsletter.
—UMI. **CCC.**
Description: Provides expert analysis of the current marketplace and regulatory agencies. Shows how to make use of the existing tax structure and achieve the most profitable tax treatment possible.

333.33 HK ISSN 1012-3253
REAL ESTATE TIMES/FANGDICHAN DAO BAO. (Text in Chinese) m. HK.$172. Economic Information & Agency, 342 Hennessy Road, 10th Fl., Hong Kong. TEL 852-573-8217. FAX 852-838-8304. TELEX 86990 EIA HXX.

333.33 US ISSN 0034-0804
HD251
REAL ESTATE TODAY. 1968. 10/yr. $38. National Association of Realtors (Chicago), 430 N. Michigan Ave., Chicago, IL 60611. TEL 312-329-8458. FAX 312-329-5978. Ed.Bd. adv.; bk.rev.; charts; illus.; index. circ. 775,855. (also avail. in microform from UMI; reprint service avail. from UMI) **Indexed:** B.P.I., Bus.Ind., Mag.Ind., Tr.& Indus.Ind.
—Faxon; UMI; UnCover.
Description: Serves as a forum of ideas, opinions, and practical applications in all areas of residential, commercial-investment, and brokerage-management real estate. Also covers association activities and interests.

333.33 US
REAL ESTATE TRANSACTIONS; tax planning and consequences. 1973. irreg. West Publishing Corp., 620 Opperman Dr., Eagan, MN 55123. TEL 612-687-7000; 800-328-9352. FAX 612-687-7302. **Document type:** trade publication.

333.33 US
REAL ESTATE U S A. 1988. q. free to qualified personnel. Great Western Financial Corporation, Corporate Communications, 9200 Oakdale Ave., Chatsworth, CA 91311. bk.rev. circ. 37,000.
Formerly: Great Western Real Estate Digest.
Description: Aimed at real estate professionals. Covers residential real estate issues, news, trends, statistics.

333.3 CN
REAL ESTATE VICTORIA. 1977. w. Can.$103. Circulation Department, 1609 Blanshard St., Victoria, BC V8V 2J5, Canada. TEL 604-382-9171. FAX 604-382-9172. Ed. Glenda Turner. adv. circ. 20,000. **Document type:** consumer publication.

333.33 US
REAL ESTATE WEEKLY. 1957. w. $49. Hagedorn Communications Corp., One Madison Ave., 35th Fl., New York, NY 10010. TEL 212-679-1234. Ed. Therese Fitzgerald. adv.; charts; illus.; tr.lit. circ. 7,450.

333.33 US
REAL ESTATE WORKOUTS AND ASSET MANAGEMENT. 1992. m. $157.25 (overseas $212.50). Warren Gorham Lamont, One Penn Plaza, New York, NY 10119. TEL 212-971-5000. (Subscr. to: The Park Square Bldg., 31 St. James Ave., Boston, MA 02116-4112. TEL 800-950-2107) Ed. Howard A. Zuckerman. (looseleaf format; also avail. in microform from UMI) **Document type:** newsletter.
Description: Offers solutions to real-estate workout problems.

333.33 US
REAL ESTATEMENT; what's new with the Idaho Real Estate Commission. 1978. s-a. free. Idaho Real Estate Commission, 633 N. Fourth St., Boise, ID 83702. TEL 208-334-3285. FAX 208-334-2050. (Subscr. to: Statehouse Mail, Boise, ID 83720-6000) Ed. Jim Faust. bk.rev.; charts; stat. circ. 8,000. (tabloid format) **Document type:** government publication.

333.33 US ISSN 0445-4278
REAL PROPERTY. 1955. 4/yr. $16. Illinois State Bar Association, Illinois Bar Center, Springfield, IL 62701. TEL 217-525-1760. FAX 217-525-0712. Ed. Gary Gehlbach. circ. 5,750. (looseleaf format) **Document type:** newsletter.

REAL PROPERTY INSTITUTE; troubled projects: workout techniques and litigation strategies. see LAW

REAL PROPERTY LAW REPORTER. see LAW

333.33 US
REAL PROPERTY, PROBATE AND TRUST LAW NEWSLETTER. 2/yr. Pennsylvania Bar Association, 100 South St., Harrisburg, PA 17108. TEL 717-238-6715. FAX 717-238-7182. **Document type:** newsletter.

333.33 CN ISSN 0703-4687
REAL PROPERTY REPORTS. 1977. 12/yr. (in 6 vols.). Can.$118. Carswell, One Corporate Plaza, 2075 Kennedy Rd., Scarborough, ON M1T 3V4, Canada. TEL 416-609-8000. FAX 416-298-5094. Ed. John Mascarin. adv. contact: M. Lalani. **Indexed:** C.L.I., Ind.Can.L.P.L., L.R.I.
Description: Features all important decisions in real property law from all Canadian jurisdictions selected by experts in the field. Includes cases on Registry Acts and Land Titles legislation, agreements of purchase and sale, and damages for breach thereof.

333.33 US
REALIST FLYER.* m. National Association of Real Estate Brokers, 1629 K St. NW, Ste. 605, Washington, DC 20006. TEL 202-785-4477.

333.33 US ISSN 0279-6309
REALTOR NEWS. 1980. bi-w. $12. National Association of Realtors (Chicago), 430 N. Michigan Ave., Chicago, IL 60611. TEL 312-329-8449. Ed. Bill Adkinson. adv.; charts; stat. circ. 116,545. (tabloid format; back issues avail.)
Description: Provides current news and information on the real estate industry.

333.33 US ISSN 1057-4808
THE REALTOR VOICE. 1920. m. $15 to non-members. Metropolitan Indianapolis Board of Realtors, 1912 N. Meridian St., Indianapolis, IN 46202. TEL 317-926-1912. FAX 317-921-3295. Eds. Stephen J. Sullivan, Meg C. Schamp. adv. circ. 5,000. **Document type:** newsletter.
Formerly (until 1991): Metropolitan Indianapolis Realtor (ISSN 0887-1620)
Description: For realtors and affiliate members of the trade association.

333.33 US ISSN 0888-5427
REALTORS LAND INSTITUTE. (Consists of: Journal Edition and News Edition, numbered consecutively) 1944. bi-m. $24 to non-members. Realtors Land Institute, 430 N. Michigan Ave., Chicago, IL 60611. TEL 312-329-8440. FAX 312-329-8633. Ed. Paddy Buratto. adv. circ. 2,500. **Document type:** trade publication.
Formerly: Farm and Land Realtor.
Description: Focuses on land sales, brokerage management, and land development.

333.33 US ISSN 0481-9004
REALTY. 1950. fortn. $22. Leader Observer, Inc., 80-34 Jamaica Ave., Woodhaven, NY 11421. TEL 718-296-2233. Ed. Lester A. Sobel. adv.; bk.rev.; illus. circ. 8,000. (tabloid format)
Formerly: Realty and Chain Store Renting Leads (ISSN 0034-1053)

333.33 IT
REALTY; le piu belle case da ammirare e da acquistare. (Text in Italian, English, French, German, Spanish) 1989. s-a. L.50000 (foreign L.80000). F C Editore S.r.l., Via Vivaio, 24, 20122 Milan, Italy. TEL 02-76009001. FAX 02-781346. Ed. Fabrizio Capsoni. adv.; B&W page L.5000000, color page L.8000000. circ. 30,000. **Document type:** consumer publication.
Description: Depicts real estate, art, and antiques for sale in Europe.

333.33 US ISSN 0034-1045
HG1
REALTY AND BUILDING. 1888. w. $35. Realty and Building, Inc., 11 E. Hubbard St., Ste. 300, Chicago, IL 60611-3536. TEL 312-467-1888. FAX 312-467-0225. Ed. John C. Cutler. adv. contact: Pamela Goettsch. bk.rev.; illus. circ. 9,000. **Document type:** trade publication.
Description: Covers real estate ownership finance, construction, sale, and management, primarily in the greater Chicago metropolitan area.

333 US ISSN 0090-399X
HD253
REALTY BLUEBOOK. (In 2 vols.: Vol.1 Real Estate; Vol.2 Financing Tables) 1966. a. $26.50 (prices typically set. in Jan.). Professional Publishing Corp., 122 Paul Dr., San Rafael, CA 94903. TEL 800-288-2006; 415-472-1964. FAX 415-472-2069. Ed. R.W. de Heer. circ. 100,000.
Description: Covers real estate and amortization. including sales techniques, financing, checklists, contract clauses and tax information.

RECHTSPFLEGER - STUDIENHEFTE. see LAW

333.33 US ISSN 1067-0521
REGISTRY REVIEW. 1978. w. $148. Real Data Corporation, 36 Bay St., Box 240, Manchester, NH 03105. TEL 603-669-3822. FAX 603-645-0072. Ed. Mary Lazzar. adv.; index. (tabloid format) **Document type:** newspaper.
Description: Real estate and credit information for New Hampshire.

THE RELOCATION REPORT. see BUSINESS AND ECONOMICS — Personnel Management

333.33 UK ISSN 0143-6473
RENT INDEX. 1977. q. £8 per no. Hillier Parker, 77 Grosvenor St., London W1A 2BT, England. TEL 0171-629-7666. FAX 0171-409-3016. Ed. Kiran Patel. circ. 2,000. (back issues avail.) **Document type:** trade publication.

333.33 352.7 UK ISSN 0263-7499
K18
RENT REVIEW AND LEASE RENEWAL. 1980. q. £219($339) (effective 1996). M C B University Press Ltd., 60-62 Toller Ln., Bradford, W. Yorks BD8 9BY, England. TEL 01274-499821. FAX 01274-547143. TELEX 51317-MCBUNI-G. Ed. Brenda Rouse. bk.rev. (reprint service avail. from SWZ) **Indexed:** Euro.LJI, LJI. **Document type:** bulletin.
—BLDSC (7364.255200).
Formerly (until 1982): Rent Review (ISSN 0260-907X)

333.33 CN
RENTERS NEWS.* w. 21 Apex Rd., Toronto, Ont. M6A 1V6, Canada. TEL 416-784-3311.

333.33 US ISSN 0731-7999
HD251
RESEARCH IN REAL ESTATE. 1981. a. $63.50 to institutions. J A I Press Inc., 55 Old Post Rd., No. 2, Box 1678, Greenwich, CT 06836-1678. TEL 203-661-7602. Ed. C.F. Sirmans.

333.3 US
RESORT DEVELOPMENT & OPERATION. 10/yr. C H B Company, Inc., Box 5627, Bellingham, WA 98227-5627. TEL 206-676-4146. Ed. Carl Burlingame. adv. circ. 4,000. **Indexed:** Hospit.Ind.

RESORT DEVELOPMENT LAW REPORTER. see LAW

333.33 UK
RETAIL WAREHOUSE PARKS DEVELOPMENT MASTER LIST. SUPPLEMENT. a. £8. Hillier Parker, 77 Grosvenor St., London W1A 2BT, England. TEL 071-629-7666. FAX 071-409-3016. Ed. Clare Andrews. (back issues avail.) **Document type:** trade publication.

333.33 UK
RETAIL WAREHOUSE PARKS IN THE PIPELINE. q. £8 per no. Hillier Parker, 77 Grosvenor St., London W1A 2BT, England. TEL 0171-629-7666. FAX 0171-409-3016. Ed. Clare Andrews. (back issues avail.) **Document type:** trade publication.

REAL ESTATE

333.33   301.435
RETIREMENT COMMUNITY BUSINESS. 1992. bi-m. Great River Publishing, Inc., 4715 Spottswood Ave., Memphis, TN 38117-4818. TEL 901-762-0329. FAX 901-762-0718. Ed. Sherry Campbell. adv.: B&W page $1640; trim 8 1/2 x 11; adv. contact: am Inman. circ. 10,000. **Document type:** trade publication.
   Description: Provides news of management decisions, marketing tactics, legal concerns, product news and profiles of executives, construction and development.

333.33   FR   ISSN 0180-9849
REVUE DE DROIT IMMOBILIER. 1979. q. 610 F. (foreign 740 F.) (effective 1995). Editions Sirey, 11 rue Soufflot, 75240 Paris Cedex 05, France. TEL 40-51-54-54. FAX 45-87-37-48. TELEX 206 446 F. (Subscr. to: 35 rue Tournefort, 75240 Paris Cedex 05, France. TEL 40-51-54-35) Ed. Philippe Malinvaud. (reprint service avail. from SCH) **Document type:** trade publication.
—SWETS. **CCC.**

333.33   FR   ISSN 0048-7953
REVUE DE L'HABITAT FRANCAIS. 1959. m. 156 F. Societe Parisienne d'Editions et de Publications Immobilieres, 274 bd. Saint-Germain, 75007 Paris, France. Ed. Jean Leveque. adv.; stat. circ. 24,630.

RHODE ISLAND LAWYERS WEEKLY. see *LAW*

333.33   US
RHODES REAL ESTATE REVIEW.* 1989. 10/yr. $79. 50 Broadway, Hawthorne, NY 10532-1245. TEL 800-253-1005. Ed. Chris Maffucci. bk.rev. circ. 3,500.
   Description: Covers zoning and planning law, environmental law, and real property law.

333.33   US   ISSN 0035-5275
RIGHT OF WAY; the magazine for the right of way professional. 1954. bi-m. $16. International Right of Way Association, 13650 S. Gramercy Place, Gardena, CA 90249-2465. TEL 213-538-0233. FAX 213-538-1471. adv.; bk.rev.; charts; illus.; cum.index: 1954-1984. circ. 9,500. Indexed: Energy Info.Abstr., Environ.Abstr.
—CIS.
   Description: Technical articles covering subjects of interest to right of way professionals in acquisition management of real estate for the public sector.

ROCKY MOUNTAIN MINERAL LAW INSTITUTE. PROCEEDINGS. see *MINES AND MINING INDUSTRY*

333.33   US
RURAL PROPERTY BULLETIN; national marketplace for rural property. 1981. m. $16. Rural Property Bulletin, Box 37-PD, Sparks, NE 69220. TEL 402-376-2985. Ed. Bruce A. Weaver. adv.; bk.rev. circ. 16,000. **Document type:** newspaper.
   Description: Lists all types of rural real estate and businesses for sale throughout the US.

333.33   US
RURAL PROPERTY INVESTOR; electronic cottage connector. 1985. q. $28 (foreign $40) (effective 1995). Greener Pastures Institute, Box 2190, Pahrump, NV 89041-2190. TEL 702-382-4847; 800-688-6352. Ed. William L. Seavey. adv.; bk.rev.; index. circ. 1,000. (back issues avail.) **Document type:** newsletter.
   Formerly (until 1994): Greener Pastures Gazette (ISSN 0884-4089)
   Description: Profiles small towns, real estate listings, information resources for individuals and families considering relocating from urban centers to small cities and towns throughout the US.

333.33   US
S F (WOBURN). (Square Foot) 1987. m. $38. Mass High Tech, 500 W. Cummings Park, Ste.3500, Woburn, MA 01801-6514. TEL 617-935-1100. Ed. John Heymann. circ. 7,000.

333.33   SZ
ST. GALLER HAUSEIGENTUEMER. bi-m. Rosenbergstr. 51, CH-9000 St. Galler, Switzerland. TEL 071-231823. FAX 071-231846. Ed. Bert Gruendler. circ. 12,500.

333.33   US
ST. LOUIS REAL ESTATE NEWS. 1927. q. Real Estate News Corp., 2600 W. Peterson, Chicago, IL 60659. TEL 312-465-5151. FAX 312-465-7218. Ed. Steven Polydoris. adv.: B&W page $1047; 7 1/2 x 10. circ. 3,297. **Document type:** trade publication.

SAN JOSE POST-RECORD; daily legal, & commercial real estate & financial news. see *LAW*

333.33
SCHEDULED RETAIL WAREHOUSE PARK OPENINGS. a. £8. Hillier Parker, 77 Grosvenor St., London W1A 2BT, England. TEL 0171-629-7666. FAX 0171-409-3016. (back issues avail.) **Document type:** trade publication.

333.33   SZ
SCHWEIZERISCHE HAUSEIGENTUEMER. bi-w. Schweizerischer Hauseigentuemerverband, Muehlebachstr. 70, CH-8008 Zurich, Switzerland. **Document type:** newsletter.

333.33   SZ
SCHWEIZERISCHER BURGENVEREIN. (Text in German) vol.45, 1972. bi-m. Association Suisse Chateaux et Ruines, Balderngasse 9, CH-8039 Zurich, Switzerland. charts; illus.

333.33   US
SEA SHELTERS.* 1982. m. Coastland Times, P.O. Drawer 400, Manteo, NC 27954. TEL 919-473-2105. Ed. Darel LaPrade. adv. circ. 20,000.

SEALES CAYMAN LETTER; an investment, economic and real estate review of the tax-free Cayman Islands. see *BUSINESS AND ECONOMICS — Investments*

SECONDARY MORTGAGE MARKET GUIDE. see *BUSINESS AND ECONOMICS — Banking And Finance*

SECONDARY MORTGAGE MARKETS. see *BUSINESS AND ECONOMICS — Banking And Finance*

333.33   UK
SECONDARY PROPERTY. 1986. s-a. Hillier Parker, 77 Grosvenor St., London W1A 2BT, England. TEL 0171-629-7666. FAX 0171-409-3016. Ed. Kiran Patel. (back issues avail.) **Document type:** trade publication.

333.33   US   ISSN 1073-4465
▼**SELF-STORAGE LEGAL REVIEW.** 1994. q. $85. D. Carlos Kaslow, Ed. & Pub., 2203 Los Angeles Ave., Berkeley, CA 94707. TEL 510-528-0630. circ. 1,200 (paid). **Document type:** newsletter.
   Description: Covers legal issues of interest to owners and operators of self-storage facilities.

333.33   FR
SEMAINE IMMOBILIERE. (Bi-m. supplement avail.) 1962. w. 10 F. per no. Editions Indicateur Bertrand, 43 bd. Barbes, 75018 Paris, France. TEL 1-49-25-26-27. FAX 1-49-25-26-00. adv.: B&W page 10500 F.; trim 320 x 210; adv. contact: J.P. Dubos. bk.rev. circ. 40,000. (looseleaf format)
   Former titles: Locations and Ventes (ISSN 0024-5666); Locations.
   Description: Advertisements for the sale and renting of houses and apartments in Paris and its suburbs.

333.33   US
SHEPARD'S - MCGRAW-HILL. REAL ESTATE PUBLICATIONS. irreg., no.3, 1993. Shepard's - McGraw-Hill, Inc., Box 35300, Colorado Springs, CO 80935-3530. TEL 800-525-2474. (back issues avail.) **Document type:** trade publication.

333.33   UK
SHOP EXPANSION PLANS. q. £8 per no. Hillier Parker, 77 Grosvenor St., London W1A 2BT, England. TEL 0171-629-7666. FAX 0171-409-3016. Ed. Oliver Boucke. (back issues avail.) **Document type:** trade publication.

333.33   US   ISSN 0885-209X
SHOPPING CENTER DIGEST; the locations newsletter. 1973. s-m. $164 (foreign $179). Jomurpa Publishing Inc., Box 1708, 7 S. Myrtle Ave., Spring Valley, NY 10977. TEL 914-426-0040. FAX 914-426-0802. (Also: 430 Mallard Dr., Santa Rosa, CA 95401. TEL 707-528-3631) Ed. Murray Shor. adv.; tr.lit. **Document type:** trade publication.
   Description: Provides detailed information on new and expanding shopping centers in U.S. and Canada, existing centers with space available, expansion plans of retail chains.

SHOPPING CENTER WORLD. see *BUSINESS AND ECONOMICS — Marketing And Purchasing*

333.33   UK   ISSN 0269-9168
SHOPPING CENTRES IN THE PIPELINE. 1986. q. £8 per no. Hillier Parker, 77 Grosvenor St., London W1A 2BT, England. TEL 0171-629-7666. FAX 0171-409-3016. Ed. Clare Andrews. (back issues avail.) **Document type:** trade publication.

333.33   FR   ISSN 1150-7691
SITES COMMERCIAUX. 10/yr. 300 F. Editions du Sites, 43 rue Liancourt, 75014 Paris, France. TEL 40-47-00-75. FAX 40-47-00-75. circ. 15,000.

333.33   US   ISSN 1061-9933
SMALL TOWN OBSERVER.* 1992. q. $24. 515 N.W. Congress St., Bend, OR 97701-2509. TEL 800-535-8853. Pub. Tom Evons. (tabloid format) **Document type:** newspaper.
   Formerly: Northwest Relocation News.
   Description: Features interviews with residents of towns in Oregon, Idaho and Washington and detailed information on respective communities.

SNAKE RIVER BASIN ADJUDICATION DIGEST. see *LAW*

SOUTH AFRICAN HOME OWNER. see *ARCHITECTURE*

333.33   US   ISSN 0192-1630
HD266.A13
SOUTHEAST REAL ESTATE NEWS. 1972. m. $40 (foreign $100). Argus Inc., 6151 Powers Ferry Rd., N.W., Atlanta, GA 30339-2941. TEL 404-955-2500. FAX 404-955-0400. Ed. Coles P. McKagen. adv.; illus. circ. 19,532. (tabloid format; also avail. in microform from UMI; reprint service avail. from UMI) **Document type:** trade publication.
●Also available online.
—UMI. **CCC.**
   Description: Covers commercial and industrial real estate activity in Alabama, Florida, Georgia, Kentucky, Maryland, Mississippi, North Carolina, South Carolina, Tennessee, Virginia, West Virginia, and Washington, D.C.

333.33   US
SOUTHERN COMMERCIAL REAL ESTATE REVIEW AND FORECAST.* 1992. a. First Publishing Inc., Box 380545, Birmingham, AL 35238-0545. TEL 205-733-1970. FAX 205-733-1974.
   Description: Tracks and reports commercial real estate activities and trends.

333.33   US   ISSN 0192-9194
SOUTHWEST REAL ESTATE NEWS. 1973. bi-m. $38 (foreign $78). Argus Inc., 6151 Powers Ferry Rd., N.W., Atlanta, GA 30339-2941. TEL 404-955-2500. FAX 404-955-0400. (And: 310 E. I-30, Ste. 240, Garland (Dallas), TX 75403-4047. TEL 214-226-1339) Ed. Jim Mitchell. adv.; illus. circ. 13,000. (tabloid format; also avail. in microform from UMI; reprint service avail. from UMI) **Document type:** trade publication.
●Also available online.
—UMI. **CCC.**
   Formerly: Texas Real Estate News.
   Description: Serves the field of commercial real estate in a nine-state geographic area, including Arizona, Arkansas, Colorado, Louisiana, New Mexico, Oklahoma, California, Nevada and Texas. All aspects of commercial real estate markets are covered.

SPAN (LIVONIA). see *HOUSING AND URBAN PLANNING*

333.33   AU
SPAREN - PLANEN - BAUEN. 3/yr. Piaristengasse 16, Postfach 170, A-1081 Vienna, Austria. TEL 01-432643425. FAX 01-42558927. TELEX 114968. Ed. Sonja Hochreiter. circ. 750,000.

REAL ESTATE

333.33   UK   ISSN 0269-9605
SPECIALISED PROPERTY. 1986. s-a. £8 per no. Hillier Parker, 77 Grosvenor St., London W1A 2BT, England. TEL 0171-629-7666. FAX 0171-409-3016. Ed. Kiran Patel. (back issues avail.) **Document type:** trade publication.

STRUCTURING FOREIGN INVESTMENT IN U.S. REAL ESTATE. see *LAW*

333.33   US
SUBURBAN LIFESTYLE. 1990. q. $14. Progressive Publishing, 125 E. Lake St., Ste. 103, Bloomingdale, IL 60108. TEL 708-582-8888. FAX 708-852-8895. Ed. Arley Harriman. adv.: B&W page $2160, color page $2560; trim 8 1/2 x 11. circ. 48,500. **Document type:** consumer publication.

SUPERINTENDENT OF INSURANCE ANNUAL REPORT. see *INSURANCE*

333.33   AT
THE SYDNEY MORNING HERALD, HOME PRICE GUIDE. 1989. irreg. Aus.$34.95. H W W Pty. Ltd. (Horan Wall & Walker), 15-19 Prospect St., Surry Hills, N.S.W. 2010, Australia. TEL 61-2-331-6600. FAX 61-2-380-5533. **Document type:** consumer publication, trade publication.
    Formerly: Real Estate Price Guide (ISSN 1033-3363)

333.33   US
TAX MANAGEMENT REAL ESTATE. (Subseries of: Tax Management Real Estate Series) 1984. m. $731 (includes Tax Management Real Estate Journal). Tax Management, Inc. (Subsidiary of: The Bureau of National Affairs, Inc.), 1250 23rd St., N.W., Washington, DC 20037-1166. TEL 202-833-7240. FAX 202-833-7297. TELEX 285656-BNAI-WSH. (Subscr. to: 9435 Key West Ave., Rockville, MD 20850. TEL 800-372-1033) Ed. Glenn B. Davis. **Document type:** trade publication.
    ●Also available online. Vendor(s): West Services, Inc. (Files TM-RE, TM-RE-OLD, TM-REJ).
    Description: Real estate tax reference service consisting of a series of portfolios written by tax practitioners, with a monthly journal covering developments in the field.

333.33   US   ISSN 8755-0628
KF6535.A15
TAX MANAGEMENT REAL ESTATE JOURNAL. (Subseries of: Tax Management Real Estate Series) 1984. m. $327. Tax Management, Inc. (Subsidiary of: The Bureau of National Affairs, Inc.), 1250 23rd St., N.W., Washington, DC 20037-1166. TEL 202-833-7240. FAX 202-833-7297. TELEX 285656-BNAI-WSH. (Subscr. to: 9435 Key West Ave., Rockville, MD 20850. TEL 800372-1033) Ed. Glenn B. Davis. index. (back issues avail.) **Indexed:** Account.Ind. (1984-), C.L.I. **Document type:** trade publication.
    ●Also available online. Vendor(s): University Microfilms International, West Services, Inc. (File TM-REJ).
    —UMI. **CCC.**
    Description: Covers judicial, legislative, and administrative developments in the real estate area.

346.04 301.54   US   ISSN 0040-3083
TENANT/INQUILINO. (Text in English and Spanish) 1971. m. (11/yr.). $2.50 to individuals; institutions $5. Met Council, Inc., 102 Fulton St., Ste. 302, New York, NY 10038-2525. TEL 212-693-0550. FAX 212-693-0555. Ed. Judy Pasternak. adv.; bk.rev.; charts; illus. circ. 3,500. **Document type:** newspaper.

333.5 352.7   CN   ISSN 1195-423X
TENANTS' BULLETIN. 1976. q. Can.$15 membership. Federation of Metro Tenants' Associations, 344 Bloor St., W., Toronto, ON M5S 3A7, Canada. TEL 416-921-9494. FAX 416-921-4177. Ed. Peter Bruer. adv. contact: Peter Bruer. circ. 22,000. (tabloid format) **Document type:** consumer publication, newspaper.
    Description: Provides information for and about residential tenants and tenancy in the Greater Toronto area.

TENNESSEE REAL ESTATE LAW LETTER. see *LAW*

333.33   US   ISSN 0274-9491
TENNESSEE REALTOR. 1970. q. $5. Tennessee Association of Realtors, Inc., Box 121980, Nashville, TN 37212-1980. TEL 615-321-0515. FAX 615-320-0452. Ed. Stephen Harding. adv. circ. 12,000. **Document type:** trade publication.

TEXAS CONDOMINIUM LAW MANUAL. see *LAW*

TEXAS MUNICIPAL ZONING LAW. see *LAW*

TEXAS REAL ESTATE LAW REPORTER. see *LAW*

333.33   US   ISSN 1068-1248
TEXAS REALTOR. 1948. 10/yr. $15. Texas Association of Realtors, Box 2246, Austin, TX 78768-2246. TEL 512-480-8200. FAX 512-370-2390. Ed. Rachel Farabee. adv.: B&W page $1,590; trim 8 1/4 x 10 7/8; adv. contact: Tricia Vaughan. circ. 44,767. **Document type:** trade publication.

TEXAS RESIDENTIAL LANDLORD - TENANT LAW. see *LAW — Civil Law*

333.33   CN
THUNDER BAY REAL ESTATE NEWS. 1983. w. Can.$100($60) North Superior Publishing Inc., 1145 Barton St., Thunder Bay, ON P7B 5N3, Canada. TEL 807-623-2348. FAX 807-623-7515. Ed. Scott A. Sumner. circ. 31,000. (tabloid format; back issues avail.) **Document type:** consumer publication.

333.33   US   ISSN 1070-0234
TIERRA GRANDE. 1987. q. $25. Texas A & M University, Real Estate Center, Texas A&M University, College Station, TX 77843-2115. TEL 409-845-0369. Ed. David S. Jones; Pub. R. Malcolm Richards. illus. circ. 50,000. **Document type:** trade publication.
    Former titles (until 1993): Real Estate Center Journal (ISSN 0164-5781); Which superseded (1979-1986): Tierra Grande.

TORRENS SYSTEM IN N.S.W.. see *LAW*

TRESPASS TO TRY TITLE. see *LAW*

333.33   US   ISSN 8750-5088
TRI-STATE REAL ESTATE JOURNAL. 1984. w. $84. Adler Group, Inc., 4002 Linclon Drive West, Ste. G, Marlton, NJ 08053. TEL 609-988-0092. FAX 609-988-0093. Ed. Stefanie P. Mis. adv.: B&W page $545; trim 10 x 13 3/4. circ. 7,000 (controlled). (tabloid format)
    Description: Devoted to commercial, industrial and residential real estate in New Jersey, Pennsylvania, and Delaware.

333.33   CN   ISSN 0835-6386
U - CHOOSE: A GUIDE TO HOMES FOR SENIORS IN CANADA (EASTERN - ATLANTIC PROVINCE EDITION). biennial. Moving Publications Ltd., 44 Upjohn Rd., Don Mills, ON M3B 2W1, Canada. TEL 416-441-1168. FAX 416-441-1641. adv. contact: Anita Wood. **Document type:** consumer publication.

333.33   CN   ISSN 0835-6378
U - CHOOSE: A GUIDE TO HOMES FOR SENIORS IN CANADA (ONTARIO EDITION). biennial. Can.$12.95. Moving Publications Ltd., 44 Upjohn Rd., Don Mills, ON M3B 2W1, Canada. TEL 416-441-1168. FAX 416-441-1641. adv. contact: Anita Wood. **Document type:** consumer publication.

333.33   CN   ISSN 0835-6394
U - CHOOSE: A GUIDE TO HOMES FOR SENIORS IN CANADA (WESTERN EDITION). biennial. Can.$12.95. Moving Publications Ltd., 44 Upjohn Rd., Don Mills, ON M3B 2W1, Canada. TEL 416-441-1168. FAX 416-441-1646. adv. contact: Anita Wood. **Document type:** consumer publication.

333.33   UK
U K DIRECTORY OF PROPERTY DEVELOPERS, INVESTORS & FINANCIERS. 1986? a. Building Economics Bureau Ltd., 5 Carlton Chambers, Station Rd., Shortlands, Bromley, Kent BR2 0EY, England. TEL 081-464-5418. **Document type:** directory.
    Formerly (until 1990): Directory of Property Developers, Investors & Financiers.

333.33   US   ISSN 0894-6108
HD251
U L I MARKET PROFILES. 1986. a. $285 to non-members; members $230. Urban Land Institute, 625 Indiana Ave., N.W., Ste. 400, Washington, DC 20004-2930. TEL 202-624-7000. FAX 202-624-7170. Ed. J. Thomas Black. charts; illus.; stat. **Document type:** monographic series.
    —CCC.

333.33 659.1   US   ISSN 8755-1608
HD1394
U S REAL ESTATE REGISTER. 1967. a. $62.50. Barry Inc., Box 551, Wilmington, MA 01887-0551. TEL 508-658-0441. FAX 508-657-8691. Ed. Joan L. Carrns. adv. contact: Therese DiBlasi. circ. 11,000. **Document type:** directory, trade publication.
    Formerly: Industrial-Commercial Real Estate Managers' Directory.
    Description: Designed to help corporate real estate managers and all others in the real estate industryfind the site, properties and services (appraisal, investment, construction, etc.) they need when they realize need.

333.33   SI   ISSN 0129-3680
UNIBEAM. a. Building and Estate Management Society, c/o Faculty of Architecture and Building, National University of Singapore, Kent Ridge, Singapore 0511, Singapore. TEL 7756666.

333.33   US
UNIFORM REAL PROPERTY ACTS. irreg., latest 1990. West Publishing Corp., 620 Opperman Dr., Eagan, MN 55123. TEL 612-687-8000; 800-328-9352. FAX 612-687-7302. **Document type:** trade publication.

333.33   BE
UNION DES PROFESSIONS IMMOBILIERES DE BELGIQUE. BULLETIN MENSUEL - MAANDBLAD. m. Union des Professions Immobilieres de Belgique, Ave. Albert I 29, B-1060 Brussels, Belgium. TEL 3445768.

333.33   US   ISSN 0747-7465
HD1390.5
UNIQUE HOMES; the national magazine of luxury real estate. 1973. 8/yr. $27.97. Unique Homes, Inc., 801 Second Ave., No.11, New York, NY 10017-4706. TEL 212-599-3377. Ed. Rick Goodwin. adv. circ. 70,746. (back issues avail.)

333.33   US
UNITEDLAND. 1946. m. free. United National Real Estate, Inc., 4700 Belleview, Kansas City, MO 64112. TEL 816-753-4212. Ed. Jack R. Waln. circ. 1,500.
    Formerly: United Way.

333.33   US   ISSN 0068-5968
UNIVERSITY OF CALIFORNIA AT BERKELEY. CENTER FOR REAL ESTATE AND URBAN ECONOMICS. REPRINT SERIES. 1948. irreg., no.99, 1993. price varies. University of California at Berkeley, Center for Real Estate and Urban Economics, 156 Barrows Hall, Berkeley, CA 94720. (back issues avail.) **Document type:** monographic series.

333.3   US
UNIVERSITY OF CALIFORNIA AT BERKELEY. CENTER FOR REAL ESTATE AND URBAN ECONOMICS. WORKING PAPER. 1950. irreg., no.229, Dec. 1994. price varies. University of California at Berkeley, Center for Real Estate and Urban Economics, 156 Barrows Hall, Berkeley, CA 94720. (back issues avail.) **Document type:** monographic series.
    Formerly: University of California at Berkeley. Center for Real Estate and Urban Economics. Research Report (ISSN 0068-5976)

333.33   US   ISSN 0589-381X
HD251
UNIVERSITY OF CONNECTICUT. CENTER FOR REAL ESTATE AND URBAN ECONOMIC STUDIES. ANNUAL REPORT. 1965. a. University of Connecticut, Center for Real Estate and Urban Economic Studies, U-41 RE, Rm. 426, 368 Fairfield Rd., Storrs, CT 06269. TEL 203-486-3227. FAX 203-486-0349. **Document type:** academic/scholarly publication.

REAL ESTATE

333.33 US ISSN 0069-9047
HD251
UNIVERSITY OF CONNECTICUT. CENTER FOR REAL ESTATE AND URBAN ECONOMIC STUDIES. GENERAL SERIES. 1968. irreg., no.18, 1985. price varies. University of Connecticut, Center for Real Estate and Urban Economic Studies, U-41 RE, Rm. 426, 368 Fairfield Rd., Storrs, CT 06269.
TEL 203-486-3227. FAX 203-486-0349. Ed. Katherine A. Stadtmueller. circ. 300. **Document type:** academic/scholarly publication.

333.33 UK
UNIVERSITY OF ULSTER. SCHOOL OF THE BUILT ENVIRONMENT. REAL ESTATE STUDIES UNIT. OCCASIONAL PAPER. irreg., no.2, 1994. £3. University of Ulster, School of the Built Environment, Real Estate Studies Unit, Coleraine BT52 1SA, N. Ireland. **Document type:** monographic series.
—BLDSC (6224.177735).

URBAN LAND INSTITUTE PROJECT REFERENCE FILE. see *HOUSING AND URBAN PLANNING*

VALUATION. see *BUSINESS AND ECONOMICS — Banking And Finance*

333.332 UK ISSN 0042-2428
VALUER. 1927. 10/yr. £30 (overseas £45) (effective 1994-1996). I V S A, Incorporated Society of Valuers & Auctioneers, 3 Cadogan Gate, London SW1X 0AS, England. TEL 0171-235-2282. FAX 0171-235-4390. Ed. Margaret Powley-Baker. adv. contact: Richard Gresham. bk.rev.; charts; illus.; index. circ. 9,000. **Indexed:** RICS. **Document type:** trade publication.
Incorporates: Land and Property - Auctions.

333.332 AT
VALUER AND LAND ECONOMIST. 1930. q. Aus.$65. Australian Institute of Valuers and Land Economists, 6 Campion St., Deakin, A.C.T. 2600, Australia. TEL 61-6-2822411. FAX 61-6-28521944. Ed. Yvonne Watkinson. adv.; bk.rev.; charts; cum.index every 2 yrs. circ. 7,400. **Indexed:** Aus.P.A.I.S., Aus.Rd.Ind., RICS. **Document type:** trade publication.
Formerly: Valuer (ISSN 0042-241X)

333.33 NE ISSN 0166-4204
VASTGOED. 1926. 11/yr. fl.142.50. Nederlandse Bond van Makelaars in Onroerende Goederen (NVM), Postbus 2222, 3430 DC Nieuwegein, Netherlands. TEL 31-3402-85176. adv.; bk.rev.; abstr.; stat.; index. circ. 8,000. **Indexed:** Key to Econ.Sci. **Document type:** trade publication.
—SWETS.
Formerly (until 1973): Vaste Goederen (ISSN 0042-286X)

VASTGOEDMARKT. see *BUILDING AND CONSTRUCTION*

333.33 340 GW ISSN 0930-8369
VERBRAUCHER UND RECHT. 1986. bi-m. DM.114. Werner-Verlag GmbH, Karl-Rudolf-Str. 172, 40215 Duesseldorf, Germany. TEL 0211-38798-0. FAX 0211-383104. **Document type:** bulletin.

333.33 AT ISSN 0815-3132
VICTORIAN REAL ESTATE JOURNAL. 1938. q. Aus.$20. Real Estate Institute of Victoria Ltd., P.O. Box 443, Camberwell, Vic. 3124, Australia.
TEL 03-882-9188. FAX 03-882-8112. Ed. Graham Stanley. adv.; bk.rev.; abstr.; stat.; index, cum.index; circ. 2,500 (controlled). **Indexed:** RICS. **Document type:** trade publication.
Formerly: Real Estate and Stock Journal (ISSN 0034-0669)

346.04 728 690 SW ISSN 0346-444X
VILLAEGAREN. 1953. 6/yr. SEK 185 membership (effective 1991); newsstand price: SEK 35. Villaaegarnas Riksfoerbund, P.O. Box 1712, S-111 87 Stockholm, Sweden. TEL 46-8-24-54-25. Ed. Bo Seijmer; Pub. Nils Schirren. adv.; illus.: B&W page SEK 1200, color page SEK 31000; trim 185 x 270. circ. 104,500. cols./p.: 3. **Document type:** consumer publication.

VIRGINIA CONDOMINIUM LAW. see *LAW*

VIRGINIA RESIDENTIAL LANDLORD AND TENANT LAW. see *LAW*

VOORRAADBEHEER EN WONINGMARKTONDERZOEK. see *HOUSING AND URBAN PLANNING*

333.33 GW ISSN 0179-7948
W I - WOHNUNGSWIRTSCHAFTLICHE INFORMATIONEN. 1949. w. DM.120. Gesamtverband der Wohnungswirtschaft e.V., Bismarkstr. 7, 50672 Cologne, Germany. TEL 0221-57989-0.
FAX 0221-5798999. bk.rev. circ. 4,000. **Document type:** bulletin.

333.33 US
WASHINGTON REAL ESTATE NEWS. 1953. q. free to qualified personnel. Department of Licensing, Real Estate Division, Box 9015, Olympia, WA 98507. TEL 206-753-3194. FAX 206-586-0998. Ed. Nancy K. Botaitis. bibl.; illus.; circ. 60,000 (controlled). **Document type:** newsletter, government publication.

333.33 US
WASHINGTON STATE BAR ASSOCIATION. REAL PROPERTY, PROBATE AND TRUST SECTION. NEWSLETTER. 1974. q. $15. 500 Westin Bldg., 2001 Sixth Ave., Seattle, WA 98121.
TEL 206-727-8239. FAX 206-727-8300. circ. 1,715. (looseleaf format; back issues avail.) **Document type:** newsletter.

333.33 690 SA
WEEKEND PROPERTY HOME FINDER. 1974. w. free. Devonshire Pl., P.O. Box 950, Durban 4000, South Africa. FAX 305-7568. Ed. Colin Vineall. adv.; bk.rev. circ. 63,000.

333.33 US
WELCOME HOMEOWNER. 1987. q. $12. Welcome Homeowner, Inc., 12444 Victory Blvd., Ste. 316, N. Hollywood, CA 91606. TEL 818-508-1202. Ed. Ellen Tuck Meli. adv. circ. 200,000.
Description: Publication for all new homeowners in southern California within two weeks of escrow closing.

333.33 US
WESTCHESTER - CONNECTICUT OFFICE BUILDINGS. a. $49. Yale Robbins, Inc., 31 E. 28th St., New York, NY 10016. TEL 212-683-5700. Ed. Yale Robbins. adv.
Formed by the merger of: Westchester Office Buildings & Connecticut Office Buildings.
Description: Annual review of Westchester County and Connecticut office buildings.

333.33 US ISSN 0043-339X
WESTCHESTER REALTOR. 1926. m. $10. Westchester County Board of Realtors, Inc., 59 S. Broadway, White Plains, NY 10601. TEL 914-681-0833.
FAX 914-681-6044. Ed. Glenn J. Kalinoski. adv.; bk.rev.; charts; illus. circ. 4,500.

333.33 GW
WESTDEUTSCHER TUERMER. m. Haus-, Wohungs- und Grundeigentuermerverband Ruhr e.V., Huyssenallee 50, 45128 Essen, Germany.

333.33 US ISSN 0043-4124
WESTERN REAL ESTATE NEWS. 1964. s-m. $80. (Business Extension Bureau) B E B Publications, 500 S. Airport Blvd., S. San Francisco, CA 94080. TEL 415-737-5700. FAX 415-737-9080. Ed. Leila K. Moavero. adv.; bk.rev.; charts; illus. circ. 12,500. (also avail. in microform from UMI; reprint service avail.) **Document type:** trade publication.
—UMI.

333.33 US ISSN 0511-8719
WHERE TO RETIRE ON A SMALL INCOME. biennial. $4.95. Harian Publications, One Vernon Ave., Floral Park, NY 11001. TEL 516-437-3440. Ed. Norman D. Ford. charts; illus.

333.33 US
WISCONSIN COUNTY LANDS.* 1967. 10/yr. $25. Box 311, Lake Delton, WI 53940-0311. Ed. Sheila R. Whaley. adv.; illus. circ. 2,000.

333.33 SZ
WOHNEIGENTUM. fortn. Schweizerische Zentralstelle fuer Eigenheim- und Wohnbaufoerderung, Stampfenbachstr. 69, CH-8035 Zurich, Switzerland. TEL 01-3632240. **Document type:** newsletter.

333.33 GW
WOHNEN IM EIGENEN HEIM. q. free. B H W Bausparkasse AG, Lubahnstr. 2, 31789 Hameln, Germany. TEL 05151-18-0. FAX 05151-182616. Ed. Heiko Barner. adv. contact: Eva Hartwig. circ. 1,796,780. **Document type:** bulletin.

333.33 AU
WOHNEN IN WIEN. 6/yr. Falkestr. 3, A-1010 Vienna, Austria. TEL 01-525360. Ed. Herbert Dobrovolny. circ. 10,000.

DER WOHNUNGSEIGENTUEMER. see *BUILDING AND CONSTRUCTION*

333.33 GW ISSN 0939-625X
HD9715.A1
WOHNUNGSWIRTSCHAFT. 1948. m. DM.108. Nordweststr. 50, 63128 Dietzenbach, Germany. adv.; bk.rev. circ. 3,100. **Document type:** trade publication.
—BLDSC (9342.603000).
Former titles (until 1990): Gemeinnuetziges Wohnungswesen (ISSN 0179-745X); (until 1949): Gemeinnuetzige Wohnungswirtschaft (ISSN 0179-7468)

333.33 SZ
WOHNWIRTSCHAFT. bi-m. Aargauischen Hauseigentuemer Verband, Badstr. 36, CH-5400 Baden, Switzerland. TEL 056-29683. Ed. Edwin Thoma.

333.33 340 US
WORKOUTS AND TURNAROUNDS LAW REPORT. m. $250. Clark - Boardman - Callaghan Company Ltd., 375 Hudson St., New York, NY 10014.
TEL 212-929-7500; 800-221-9428.
FAX 212-924-0460. Ed. R. Kenneth Keim. **Document type:** newsletter.
Description: Offers the latest business and legal news involving workout law and distressed properties.

333.33 UK
WORLD OF PROPERTY MAGAZINE; the UK's largest overseas property classified. 1986. q. £12 (effective 1995). Amberstock Ltd., 532 Kingston Rd., Raynes Park, London SW20 8DT, England.
TEL 0181-542-9088. FAX 0181-542-2737. Ed. Mr. G. Batgent. adv. contact: G. Larkin. circ. 30,000. **Document type:** consumer publication.
Description: Lists property for sale and related services in Cyprus, Florida, Greece, Italy, Portugal, Spain, and other tourist regions throughout the world.

WORLDWIDE INSURANCE AND REAL ESTATE. see *INSURANCE*

333.33 US ISSN 8756-0259
YANKEE HOMES.* 1985. 12/yr. $25. Yankee Publishing, Inc., Box 520, Dublin, NH 03444-0520. TEL 603-563-8111. Ed. Jim Collins. circ. 35,000. (back issues avail.)

YOUR MORTGAGE MAGAZINE. see *BUSINESS AND ECONOMICS — Banking And Finance*

333.33 GW ISSN 0340-7497
ZEITSCHRIFT FUER MIET- UND RAUMRECHT. 1948. m. DM.240. Werner-Verlag GmbH, Karl-Rudolf-Str. 172, 40215 Duesseldorf, Germany. TEL 0211-38798-0. FAX 0211-383104. Eds. Dr. Groothold, Helga Lehmann. **Document type:** bulletin.
—BLDSC (9472.500000); SWETS. **CCC.**

333.33 CC
ZHONGGUO FANGDI XINXI/CHINA REAL ESTATE NEWS. (Text in Chinese) m. Zhongguo Fangdi Chanye Xiehui - China Real Estate Society, A-3 Congshanli, Xidan, Beijing 100031, People's Republic of China. TEL 6013301. Ed. Han Lidong.

333.33 CC
ZHONGGUO FANGDICHAN/CHINESE REAL ESTATE. (Text in Chinese) m. Tianjin-shi Fangdichan Guanli-ju - Tianjin Municipal Administration of Real Estate, 50 Munan Dao, Heping Qu, Tianjin 300050, People's Republic of China. TEL 399464. Ed. Kang Tianjin.

333.33 US ISSN 0514-7905
ZONING BULLETIN. 1954. s-m. $83. Quinlan Publishing Co., Inc., 23 Drydock Ave., 2nd Fl., Boston, MA 02210-2387. TEL 800-229-2084.
FAX 617-345-9646. index. (looseleaf format; also avail. in microform from UMI; back issues avail.) **Document type:** newsletter.
—UMI. **CCC.**
Description: Summarizes current cases addressing zoning issues for zoning administrators, enforcement officials and land developers.

ZONING NEWS. see *HOUSING AND URBAN PLANNING*

333.33   SZ
ZUERCHER HAUSEIGENTUEMER. m. Albisstr. 152, CH-8060 Zurich, Switzerland. TEL 01-4815000. FAX 01-4829719. Ed. Hannes Ringger. circ. 24,500.

333.33   US
30 DAY NOTICE - TENANT TATTLER. q. $3. Seattle Tenants Union, 3902 D. Ferdinand, c/o Col. Cong. Church, Seattle, WA 98118-1740. TEL 206-722-6848. Ed. Bill Butler. circ. 2,000.

REAL ESTATE — Abstracting, Bibliographies, Statistics

333.33   AT   ISSN 1034-1897
AUSTRALIA. BUREAU OF STATISTICS. HOUSE PRICE INDEXES: EIGHT CAPITAL CITIES. 1989. q. Aus.$27 per no. Australian Bureau of Statistics, P.O. Box 10, Belconnen, A.C.T. 2616, Australia. **Document type:** government publication, abstracting/indexing.
Description: Provides estimates of changes in housing prices for each of the eight capital cities of Australia.

333.33 310   AT
AUSTRALIA. BUREAU OF STATISTICS. REAL ESTATE AGENTS INDUSTRY, AUSTRALIA. 1987. irreg., lates 1993. Aus.$20. Australian Bureau of Statistics, P.O. Box 10, Belconnen, A.C.T. 2616, Australia. **Document type:** government publication.

B S A MONTHLY STATISTICS DIGEST (PRESS RELEASE). see *BUILDING AND CONSTRUCTION — Abstracting, Bibliographies, Statistics*

333.33   AT
BONDI JUNCTION CITYSCOPE. 1988. 3/yr. Aus.$505. Cityscope Publications Pty. Ltd., P.O. Box 807, Manly, N.S.W. 2095, Australia. TEL 02-976-2233. FAX 02-976-2263. Ed. Neil Speirs. adv.; maps. (looseleaf format) **Document type:** abstracting/indexing.
Description: Contains complete property index of all buildings within the Bondi Junction - Double Bay business districts in eastern Sydney. Includes descriptions, historical information, developments, ownership, prices, sales histories, exact boundaries, and more.

333.33   AT
BRISBANE CITYSCOPE. 1986. 3/yr. Aus.$665. Cityscope Publications Pty. Ltd., P.O. Box 807, Manly, N.S.W. 2095, Australia. TEL 02-976-2233. FAX 02-976-2263. Ed. Neil Speirs. adv.; maps. (looseleaf format) **Document type:** abstracting/indexing.
●Also available online. Vendor(s): Info-One International Pty Ltd.
Description: Contains complete property index of all buildings within the Brisbane Central Business District. Includes descriptions, historical information developments, ownership, prices, sales histories, exact boundaries, and more.

BUILDING, CONSTRUCTION AND REAL ESTATE SECTORS. SURVEY. see *BUILDING AND CONSTRUCTION — Abstracting, Bibliographies, Statistics*

333.33   AT
BURKE ROAD CITYSCOPE. 1988. 3/yr. Aus.$475. Cityscope Publications Pty. Ltd., P.O. Box 807, Manly, N.S.W. 2095, Australia. TEL 02-976-2233. FAX 02-976-2263. Ed. Neil Speirs. maps. **Document type:** abstracting/indexing.
Description: Contains complete property index of all buildings within the Camberwell Juction District Centre in eastern Melbourne. Includes descriptions, historical information, developments, ownership, tenancies, prices, sales history, exact boundaries, and more.

333.33   AT
CANBERRA CITYSCOPE. 1991. 3/yr. Aus.$635. Cityscope Publications Pty. Ltd., P.O. Box 807, Manly, N.S.W. 2095, Australia. TEL 02-976-223. FAX 02-976-2263. Ed. Neil Speirs. adv.; maps. (looseleaf format) **Document type:** abstracting/indexing.
Description: Contains a complete property index of all buildings within the Canberra City Centre, plus the outlying Town Centre districts of Woden, Belconnen and Tuggeranong. Includes descriptions, historical information, developments, ownership, prices, sales histories, exact boundaries, and more.

333.33   AT
CHATSWOOD CITYSCOPE. 1987. 3/yr. Aus.$545. Cityscope Publications Pty. Ltd., P.O. Box 807, Manly, N.S.W. 2095, Australia. TEL 02-976-2233. FAX 02-976-2263. Ed. Neil Speirs. adv.; maps. (looseleaf format) **Document type:** abstracting/indexing.
Description: Contains complete property index of all commercial buildings within the Chatswood Central Business District and the Willoughby municipality in northern Sydney. Includes descriptions, historical information, developments, ownership, prices, sales histories, exact boundaries and more.

333.33   US   ISSN 1066-0933
HD1393.5
COMPARATIVE STATISTICS OF INDUSTRIAL OFFICE REAL ESTATE MARKETS. 1980. a. $75. Society of Industrial and Office Realtors, 700 11th St., N.W., Ste. 510, Washington, DC 20001-4511. TEL 202-737-1150. Ed. Linda Nasvaderani. stat. circ. 7,000. (also avail. in microfiche) Indexed: SRI. **Document type:** trade publication.
Former titles (until 1991): Guide to Industrial and Office Real Estate Markets (ISSN 1048-2784); Industrial Real Estate Market Survey (ISSN 0730-0131)

COMPENDIUM OF HOUSING FINANCE STATISTICS. see *HOUSING AND URBAN PLANNING — Abstracting, Bibliographies, Statistics*

333.33   AT
GOLD COAST CITYSCOPE. 1989. 3/yr. Aus.$630. Cityscope Publications Pty. Ltd., P.O. Box 807, Manly, N.S.W. 2095, Australia. TEL 02-976-2233. FAX 02-976-2263. Ed. Neil Speirs. adv.; maps. (looseleaf format) **Document type:** abstracting/indexing.
Description: Contains a complete property index of the commercial centers of the Gold Coast towns in southern Queensland. Includes descriptions, historical information, developments, ownership, prices, sales histories, exact boundaries, and more.

333.33   AT   ISSN 0816-6153
HOME LOAN AFFORDABILITY IN AUSTRALIA. 1985. q. Aus.$30. Real Estate Institute of Australia, P.O. Box 234, Deakin West, A.C.T. 2602, Australia. TEL 61-6-282-4277. FAX 61-6-285-2444. Ed. Nadar Mirfakhrai. circ. 2,000.
Description: Examines ratio between average monthly home loan repayments and median family income.

333.33 310   MH
MACAO. DIRECCAO DOS SERVICOS DE ESTATISTICA E CENSOS. ESTATISTICAS DE CONSTRUCAO/MACAO. CENSUS AND STATISTICS DEPARTMENT. CONSTRUCTION STATISTICS. (Text in Chinese, Portuguese) 1984. a. free. Direccao dos Servicos de Estatistica e Censos, Rua Inacio Baptista, No. 4-6, P.O. Box 3022, Macao. TEL 853-3995311. FAX 853-307825. **Document type:** government publication.
Former titles: Macao. Direccao dos Servicos de Estatistica e Censos. Estatisticas de Construcao Civil e Operacoes sobre Imoveis; (until 1989): Macao. Direccao dos Servicos de Estatistica e Censos. Relatorio Anual da Construcao Civil - Construction in Macao (Annual Report).
Description: Provides a convenient source of information for those engaged in analyzing the housing market, including information on the structure and operating characteristics of all buildings.

333.33   MH
MACAO. DIRECCAO DOS SERVICOS DE ESTATISTICA E CENSOS. ESTATISTICAS DAS SOCIEDADES/MACAO. CENSUS AND STATISTICS DEPARTMENT. STATISTICAL DATA CONCERNING COMPANIES. (Text in Chinese, Portuguese) 1986. q. free. Direccao dos Servicos de Estatistica e Censos, Rua Inacio Baptista, No.4-6, P.O. Box 3022, Macao. TEL 853-3995311. FAX 853-307825. **Document type:** government publication.
Supersedes in part (in 1994): Macao. Direccao dos Servicos de Estatistica e Censos. Indicadores Estatisticos - Operacoes sobre Imoveis e Sociedades.

333.33   MH
MACAO. DIRECCAO DOS SERVICOS DE ESTATISTICA E CENSOS. OPERACOES SOBRE IMOVEIS/MACAO. CENSUS AND STATISTICS DEPARTMENT. TRANSACTIONS CONCERNING REAL ESTATE. (Text in Chinese, Portuguese) 1986. q. free. Direccao dos Servicos de Estatistica e Censos, Rua Inacio Baptista, No. 4-6, P.O. Box 3022, Macao. TEL 853-3995311. FAX 853-307825. **Document type:** government publication.
Supersedes in part (in 1994): Macao. Direccao dos Servicos de Estatistica e Censos. Indicadores Estatisticos - Operacoes sobre Imoveis e Sociedades.

333.33   AT   ISSN 0818-1152
MARKET FACTS. 1973. m. Aus.$220 (includes Annual Review of Major Residential Property Markets in Australia). Real Estate Institute of Australia, P.O. Box 234, Deakin West, A.C.T. 2602, Australia. TEL 61-6-282-4277. FAX 61-6-285-2444. Ed. Julian Roberston. circ. 1,000. (back issues avail.)
Incorporates: Market Facts (Brisbane) (ISSN 0811-3564); Market Facts (Adelaide) (ISSN 0811-3513); Market Facts (Melbourne) (ISSN 0811-3556); Market Facts (Perth) (ISSN 0811-353X); Markets Facts (Hobart-Launceston); Market Facts (Canberra) (ISSN 0811-3521); Market Facts (Newcastle) (0811-3270); Market Facts (Sydney) (ISSN 0811-3548).
Description: Reports the state of residential propertie markets in major Australian cities.

352.7   AT
MARKET FACTS (NORTHERN TERRITORY: DARWIN - ALICE SPRINGS). 1986. q. Aus.$60. Real Estate Institute of Australia, P.O. Box 234, Deakin West, A.C.T 2602, Australia. TEL 61-6-282-4277. FAX 61-6-285-2444. circ. 250. (back issues avail.)

333.33   AT
MELBOURNE CITYSCOPE. 1976. 3/yr. Aus.$1140 (renewals Aus.$980). Cityscope Publications Pty. Ltd., P.O. Box 807, Manly, N.S.W. 2095, Australia. TEL 02-976-2233. FAX 02-976-2263. Ed. Neil Speirs. adv.; charts; illus.; maps. (looseleaf format) **Document type:** abstracting/indexing.
●Also available online. Vendor(s): Info-One International Pty Ltd.
Description: Contains complete property index of all commercial buildings within the Melbourne Central Business District. Includes descriptions, historical information, developments, ownership, prices, sales histories, exact boundaries, and more.

333.33   AT
MELBOURNE CITYSCOPE UNIT REPORT. 1993. 3/yr. Aus.$495. Cityscope Publications Pty. Ltd., P.O. Box 807, Manly, N.S.W. 2095, Australia. TEL 02-976-2233. FAX 02-976-2263. Ed. Neil Speirs. adv.; maps. (looseleaf format) **Document type:** abstracting/indexing.
Description: Contains a complete property index of all residential apartments within the Melbourne Central Business District. Includes descriptions, historical information, developments, ownership, prices, sales histories, exact boundaries, and more.

333.33   US   ISSN 1061-8546
HG4655
MORTGAGE MARKET STATISTICAL ANNUAL. 1987. a. $295. Inside Mortgage Finance Publications, Box 42387, Washington, DC 20015. TEL 301-951-1240. FAX 301-656-1709.
Description: Compilation of mortgage-related statistics.

RELIGIONS AND THEOLOGY

333.33 AT
NORTH RYDE CITYSCOPE. 1989. a. Aus.$300. Cityscope Publications Pty. Ltd., P.O. Box 807, Manly, N.S.W. 2095, Australia. TEL 02-976-2233. FAX 02-976-2263. Ed. Neil Speirs. adv.; maps. (looseleaf format) **Document type:** abstracting/indexing.
   Description: Contains complete index of all industrial properties within the Ryde municipality of Sydney. Includes descriptions, improvements, occupants, ownership, prices, sales histories, exact boundaries, zoning, and more.

333.33 AT
NORTH SYDNEY CITYSCOPE. 1980. 3/yr. Aus.$750. Cityscope Publications Pty. Ltd., P.O. Box 807, Manly, N.S.W. 2095, Australia. TEL 02-976-2233. FAX 02-976-2263. Ed. Neil Speirs. adv.; charts; illus. (looseleaf format) **Document type:** abstracting/indexing.
   ●Also available online. Vendor(s): Info-One International Pty Ltd.
   Description: Contains complete property index of all commercial buildings within the North Sydney municipality. Includes descriptions, sales history, developments, ownership, historical information, prices, exact boundaries, and more.

333.33 AT
PARRAMATTA CITYSCOPE. 1982. 3/yr. Aus.$615. Cityscope Publications Pty. Ltd., P.O. Box 430, Milsons Point, N.S.W. 2061, Australia. TEL 02-976-2233. FAX 02-976-2263. Ed. Neil Speirs. adv.; charts; illus.; maps. (looseleaf format) **Document type:** abstracting/indexing.
   Description: Contains complete property index of all buildings within the Parramatta Central Business District in western Sydney. Includes descriptions, historical information, developments, ownership, prices, sales histories, exact boundaries, and more.

333.33 AT
ST. KILDA ROAD CITYSCOPE. 1984. 3/yr. Aus.$530. Cityscope Publications Pty. Ltd., P.O. Box 870, Manly, N.S.W. 2095, Australia. TEL 02-976-2233. FAX 02-976-2263. Ed. Neils Speirs. adv.; charts; illus.; maps. (looseleaf format) **Document type:** abstracting/indexing.
   ●Also available online. Vendor(s): Info-One International Pty Ltd.

333.33 316.8 SA
SOUTH AFRICA. CENTRAL STATISTICAL SERVICE. CENSUS OF ESTATE AGENCIES, RENT COLLECTORS, APPRAISERS AND VALUERS. (Report No. 05-03-02) irreg., latest 1990. R.10 (foreign R.11). Central Statistical Service - Sentrale Statistiekdiens, Private Bag X44, Pretoria 0001, South Africa. TEL 27-12-310-8911. FAX 27-12-310-8500. (Orders to: Government Printing Works, Private Bag X85, Pretoria 0001, South Africa) **Document type:** government publication.

333.33 SA
SOUTH AFRICA. CENTRAL STATISTICAL SERVICE. CENSUS OF LETTING OF OWN FIXED PROPERTY. (Report No. 83-02-01) irreg., latest 1986. R.4.40 (foreign R.4.80). Central Statistical Service - Sentrale Statistiekdiens, Private Bag X44, Pretoria 0001, South Africa. TEL 27-12-310-8911. FAX 27-12-310-8500. (Orders to: Government Printing Works, Private Bag X85, Pretoria 0001, South Africa) **Document type:** government publication.

333.33 316.8 SA
SOUTH AFRICA. CENTRAL STATISTICAL SERVICE. STATISTICAL RELEASE. CENSUS OF LETTING OF OWN FIXED PROPERTY (YEAR). (No. P8302) irreg., latest 1986. free. Central Statistical Service - Sentrale Statistiekdiens, Private Bag X44, Pretoria 0001, South Africa. TEL 27-12-310-8911. FAX 27-12-310-8500. **Document type:** government publication.

333.33 316.8 SA
SOUTH AFRICA. CENTRAL STATISTICAL SERVICE. STATISTICAL RELEASE. CENSUS OF TOWNSHIP DEVELOPERS. (No. P8304) irreg., latest 1988. free. Central Statistical Service - Sentrale Statistiekdiens, Private Bag X44, Pretoria 0001, South Africa. TEL 27-12-310-8911. FAX 27-12-310-8500. **Document type:** government publication.

333.33 SA
SOUTH AFRICA. CENTRAL STATISTICAL SERVICE. STATISTICAL RELEASE. TRANSFERS OF RURAL IMMOVABLE PROPERTY. (No. P1141) a., latest for years 1992-1993. Central Statistical Service, Private Bag X44, Pretoria 0001, South Africa. TEL 27-12-310-8911. FAX 27-12-310-8500. **Document type:** government publication.
   Former titles: South Africa. Central Statistical Service. Transfers of Rural Immovable Property; South Africa. Department of Statistics. Transfers of Rural Immovable Property.

333.33 AT
SOUTHBANK CITYSCOPE. 1991. 3/yr. Aus.$560. Cityscope Publications Pty. Ltd., P.O. Box 807, Manly, N.S.W. 2095, Australia. TEL 02-976-2233. FAX 02-976-2263. Ed. Neil Speirs. adv.; maps. (looseleaf format) **Document type:** abstracting/indexing.
   Description: Contains a complete property index of all buildings within the Southbank commercial area across the Yarra River from the City of Melbourne. Includes descriptions, historical information, developments, ownership, prices, sales histories, exact boundaries, and more.

333.33 AT
SPRING HILL CITYSCOPE. 1990. 3/yr. Aus.$550. Cityscope Publications Pty. Ltd., P.O. Box 807, Manly, N.S.W. 2095, Australia. TEL 02-976-2233. FAX 02-976-2263. Ed. Neil Speirs. adv.; maps. (looseleaf format) **Document type:** abstracting/indexing.
   Description: Contains a complete property index of all buildings within the commercial centers of Spring Hill, Fortitude Valley and Coronation Drive, adjoining Brisbane city. Includes descriptions, historical information, developments, ownership, prices, sales histories, exact boundaries, and more.

333.33 AT
SYDNEY CITYSCOPE. 1975. 3/yr. Aus.$975. Cityscope Publications Pty. Ltd., P.O. Box 807, Manly, N.S.W. 2095, Australia. TEL 02-976-2233. TELEX 02-976-2263. Ed. Neil Speirs. adv.; charts; illus.; maps. (looseleaf format) **Document type:** abstracting/indexing.
   ●Also available online. Vendor(s): Info-One International Pty Ltd.
   Description: Contains complete property index of all commercial buildings within the Sydney Central Business District. Includes descriptions, ownership, historical information, developments, prices, sales histories, exact boundaries, and more.

333.33 AT
SYDNEY CITYSCOPE UNIT REPORT. 1989. 3/yr. Aus.$495. Cityscope Publications Pty. Ltd., P.O. Box 807, Manly, N.S.W. 2095, Australia. TEL 02-976-2233. FAX 02-976-2263. Ed. Neil Speirs. adv.; maps. (looseleaf format) **Document type:** abstracting/indexing.
   Description: Contains a complete property index of all residential apartments within the Sydney Central Business District. Includes descriptions, historical information, developments, ownership, prices, sales histories, exact boundaries, and more.

TITLE NEWS. see *INSURANCE — Abstracting, Bibliographies, Statistics*

RELIGIONS AND THEOLOGY

see also Religions and Theology–Buddhist; Religions and Theology–Eastern Orthodox; Religions and Theology–Islamic; Religions and Theology–Judaic; Religions and Theology–Protestant; Religions and Theology–Roman Catholic; Religions and Theology–Other Denominations and Sects

200 KE
A A C C BULLETIN. (Text in English and French) 1983. q. EAs.36($2.10) All Africa Conference of Churches, P.O. Box 14205, Nairobi, Kenya. Ed. Maxime V. Rafransoa. adv.; bk.rev. circ. 1,000. **Indexed:** HR Rep. **Document type:** bulletin.
   Formed by the 1983 merger of: A A C C Quarterly Bulletin; A A C C Newsletter.

268 US ISSN 0277-1071
A A R ACADEMY SERIES. 1974. irreg. (American Academy of Religion) Scholars Press, Box 15399, Atlanta, GA 30333-0399. TEL 404-727-2320. FAX 404-727-2348. Ed. Barbara Holdrege. **Document type:** monographic series.
   —BLDSC (0570.590500).
   Formerly: A A R Dissertation Series.
   Description: Monographs on a wide range of subjects within the academic study of religion.

200 US ISSN 0084-6287
A A R STUDIES IN RELIGION. 1970. irreg., no.34, 1984. (American Academy of Religion) Scholars Press, Box 15399, Atlanta, GA 30333-0399. TEL 404-727-2320. FAX 404-727-2348. Ed. D. Klemm. **Document type:** monographic series.
   —BLDSC (8491.431000).
   Description: Monographs on a wide variety of topics in the academic study of religion.

200 US
A C P NEWSLOG. 1960. q. membership only. Associated Church Press, Box 30215, Phoenix, AZ 85046-0215. TEL 602-569-6371. FAX 602-569-6180. Ed. John Stapert. circ. 700.
   Description: Covers association news, awards, management features, and member publication information.

200 UK ISSN 0968-6045
A C T. 1970. irreg. (1-2/yr.). £2 per no. Ashram Community Trust, 178 Abbeyfield Rd., Sheffield S4 7AY, England. TEL 01742-436688. Ed. Rev. John Vincent.
   Description: Studies radical Christian discipleship, community living, Bible study.

200 621.38 US ISSN 0300-7022
BL1
A D R I S NEWSLETTER. 1971-1992; resumed 1995. q. $20 to individuals; corporates $50; students & seniors $10. Association for the Development of Religious Information Services, Box 210735, Nashville, TN 37221-0735. TEL 615-662-5189. FAX 615-662-5251. E-mail: adris@telalink.net. Ed. Edward W. Dodds. bk.rev.; abstr.; bibl.; index. circ. 425. **Indexed:** CERDIC. **Document type:** newsletter.
   Description: Aims to provide current and retrospective bibliographical and informational control in religion-theology and related fields. Includes calendar of events, news about recent reference materials in religion, and listings of recent articles.

200 AT ISSN 1031-8453
A.D. 2000. Variant title: A.D. Two Thousand. 1988. 11/yr. Aus.$30 (foreign Aus.$45). Freedom Publishing Co., 582 Queensberry St., N. Melbourne, Vic. 3051, Australia. TEL 61-3-326-5757. FAX 61-3-328-2877. Ed. B.A. Santamaria. circ. 7,000.

283 276 KE ISSN 0250-4650
BX1675.A1
A F E R; African ecclesiastical review. 1959. bi-m. KShs.360($31) (AMECEA Pastoral Institute) Gaba Publications, P.O. Box 4002, Eldoret, Kenya. Ed. A. Raboli. bk.rev.; index. circ. 2,500. (back issues avail.) **Indexed:** Canon Law Abstr., Cath.Ind., New Test.Abstr., P.L.E.S.A. (1990-), Rel.Ind.One.
   —BLDSC (0731.235000).
   Formerly (until 1975): African Ecclesiastical Review (ISSN 0001-1134)
   Description: Examines scripture, religion and development.

200 US
A I INSIDE INFORMATION. bi-m. membership. Alban Institute, 4550 Montgomery Ave., Ste. 433 N, Bethesda, MD 20814. TEL 301-718-4407. circ. 8,100. **Document type:** bulletin.
   Description: Covers institute activities and upcoming items of interest.

RELIGIONS AND THEOLOGY

266 276 US ISSN 0884-6316
A I M INTERNATIONAL. 1896. q. free. Africa Inland Mission International, Box 178, Pearl River, NY 10965. TEL 914-735-4014. FAX 914-735-1814. Ed. Glen Peterson; Pub. Ted Barnett. bk.rev.; illus.; circ. 30,000 (controlled). (also avail. in microfilm) **Document type:** newsletter.
—UMI.
Former titles: Inland Africa (ISSN 0020-1464); (until 1916): Hearing and Doing.
Description: Covers the mission's ministries, its personnel and the national church through which it serves.
Refereed Serial

A L M INTERNATIONAL ANNUAL REPORT. see *MEDICAL SCIENCES — Communicable Diseases*

200 US
A M S STUDIES IN RELIGIOUS TRADITION. 1993. irreg., no.2, 1994. (Abrahams Magazine Service) A M S Press, Inc., 56 E. 13th St., New York, NY 10003. TEL 212-477-4700. FAX 212-995-5413. **Document type:** academic/scholarly publication, monographic series.

200 KE
A P S BULLETIN. (All Africa Press Service); a pan-African news and features service. (Text in English) 1979. w. EAs.600($75) Africa Church Information Service, P.O. Box 14205, Nairobi, Kenya. TEL 2542-44215. FAX 2542-742352. TELEX 22175-NAIROBI. bk.rev. circ. 350. **Document type:** bulletin.
Description: Covers church and secular events with integrity, giving news an African perspective. Includes the continent's leading news and in-depth feature articles that probe behind the headlines in religion, socio-economics, culture, political development and even environmental issues.

200 US
A T L A MONOGRAPH SERIES. no.22, 1985. irreg., latest no.27. (American Theological Library Association) Scarecrow Press, Inc., 52 Liberty St., Box 4167, Metuchen, NJ 08840. TEL 800-537-7107. Ed. Dr. Kenneth E. Rowe. **Document type:** monographic series.

284.1489 266 DK ISSN 0905-071X
AARBOG (YEAR) FOR KIRKELIG FORENING FOR DEN INDRE MISSION I DANMARK. 1906. a. DKK 48. (Kirkelig Forening) Lohses Forlag, Korskaervej 25, 7000 Fredericia, Denmark. TEL 75 93 44 55. FAX 0045-75926146. Ed. K. Lindhardt Jensen. adv.; illus.
Formerly (until 1988): Nye Aar (ISSN 0108-8297)
Description: Contains reports of Den Kirkelige Forening for den Indre Mission i Danmark.

274.81 NO ISSN 0400-227X
BX8037
AARBOK FOR DEN NORSKE KIRKE. 1951. a. NOK 108. Kirkens Informationstjeneste - Church of Norway Information, P.O. Box 5913, N-0308 Oslo, Norway. TEL 47-22-93-27-50. FAX 47-22-93-28-28. Eds. Dag Stange, Gunnar Westermoen. adv.; stat.; index. circ. 4,000. **Document type:** directory.
—CCC.
Description: Events within the Church of Norway, with a full account of the clerical districts and church organizations and institutions.

ABINGDON CLERGY INCOME TAX GUIDE. see *BUSINESS AND ECONOMICS — Public Finance, Taxation*

252 US ISSN 1047-5486
ABINGDON PREACHER'S ANNUAL. 1991. a. $19.95. Abingdon Press, 201 Eighth Ave., S., Box 801, Nashville, TN 37202-0801. TEL 800-251-3320. FAX 615-749-6522.

ACADEMIA; Zeitschrift fuer Politik und Kultur. see *LITERARY AND POLITICAL REVIEWS*

200 US ISSN 0894-9034
BV3750
ACADEMY FOR EVANGELISM IN THEOLOGICAL EDUCATION. JOURNAL. 1986. a. $10. Academy for Evangelism in Theological Education, c/o Richard J. Armstrong, Ed., Princeton Theological Seminary, Box 821, Princeton, NJ 08542. TEL 609-942-2997. FAX 609-924-2973. (Subscr. to: David S. Young, 107 Valley Dr., West Chester, PA 19382) bk.rev.; cum.index: 1986-1994. circ. 400. (back issues avail.) **Document type:** academic/scholarly publication.
Description: Scholarly forum and medium for the responsible sharing of ideas among those engaged in the teaching of evangelism, primarily at the seminary level, as well as those whose ministries involve them in serious research and writing in the field.
Refereed Serial

ACADEMY OF RELIGION AND PSYCHICAL RESEARCH. PROCEEDINGS. see *PARAPSYCHOLOGY AND OCCULTISM*

ACCEPTANCE NEWSLETTER. see *HOMOSEXUALITY*

ACCION; revista Paraguaya de reflexion y dialogo. see *SOCIAL SCIENCES: COMPREHENSIVE WORKS*

249 US ISSN 0001-5083
ACT. 1947. m. (bi-m. Nov.-Dec., Jul.-Aug.). $8. Christian Family Movement, 525 Sixth St., Rm. 202, Box 272, Ames, IA 50010. TEL 515-232-7432. FAX 515-232-7432. Ed. Lauri Przybysz. bk.rev. circ. 2,500. (looseleaf format) **Document type:** monographic series.
Description: For family life network; covers topics of importance to families and has a Christian and social justice orientation.

205 DK ISSN 0106-0945
ACTA JUTLANDICA. TEOLOGISK SERIE/ACTA JUTLANDICA. THEOLOGY SERIES. Variant title: Teologisk Serie. (Subseries of: Acta Jutlandica) (Text in various languages) 1935. s-a. (Laerde Selskab i Aarhus) Aarhus University Press, Building 170, DK-8000 Aarhus, Denmark. TEL 45-86-19-70-33. FAX 45-86-19-84-33.

200 NE ISSN 0065-1672
ACTA THEOLOGICA DANICA. (Text in English and German) 1958. irreg., vol.24, 1988. price varies. E.J. Brill, P.O. Box 9000, 2300 PA Leiden, Netherlands. TEL 31-71-5353500. FAX 31-71-5317532. TELEX 39296 BRILL NL. (In N. America: E.J. Brill, 24 Hudson St., Kinderhook, NY 12106. TEL 800-962-4406. FAX 518-758-1959) Ed.Bd. (back issues avail.) **Document type:** monographic series.
Refereed Serial

266 284 AT ISSN 1033-1913
ACTION AFRICA. 1987. q. free. Africa Evangelical Fellowship, P.O. Box 100, 4 Morgan St., Kingsgrove, N.S.W. 2208, Australia. (U.K. addr.: 35 Kingfisher Court Hambridge Rd., Newbury Berks RG14 5SJ, England) Ed. Rev. William A. Walker. circ. 4,500. (tabloid format; back issues avail.)
Description: Christian missions in Africa, especially South of the Sahara, targeted to the Christian community.

ACTION NEWSLETTER. see *COMMUNICATIONS*

ACTION SOCIALE. see *POLITICAL SCIENCE*

200 CN ISSN 1184-7204
ACTUALITES BIBLIQUES. English edition: Canadian Bible Society. Newsletter. 1976. 2/yr. free. Canadian Bible Society - Societe Biblique Canadienne, 10 Carnforth Rd., Toronto, ON M4A 2S4, Canada. TEL 416-757-4171. FAX 416-757-3376. Ed. Serge Rheaume. circ. 15,000. **Document type:** newsletter.
Former titles (until 1990): Bulletin de Nouvelles Bibliques (ISSN 0834-1842); (until 1984): Nouvelles Bibliques (ISSN 0225-0489)

ADVENT. see *HOMOSEXUALITY*

200 KE
AFRICAN CHALLENGE BOOK SERIES. (Text in English and French) q. All Africa Conference of Churches, P.O. Box 14205, Westlands, Nairobi, Kenya. TEL 441483. FAX 2542-443241. TELEX 22175 AACC. **Indexed:** HR Rep.
Former titles (until 1989): A A C C Magazine (ISSN 1010-1071); (until 1982): A A C C Newsletter (ISSN 1017-6977)

200 KE
AFRICAN CHRISTIAN. fortn. African Church Information Service, P.O. Box 14205, Nairobi, Kenya. TEL 62974. TELEX 22175.
Description: Covers church news and developments in Africa.

200 282 NR ISSN 0795-7602
AFRICAN JOURNAL OF BIBLICAL STUDIES. 1986. s-a. $20. Nigerian Association for Biblical Studies, c/o Department of Religious Studies, University of Ibadan, Oyo State, Nigeria. Ed. S.O. Oyin Abogunrin. adv.; bk.rev. circ. 500. **Indexed:** Bibl.Ling.

266 GW
AHA; Gossner Mission fuer Kinder und Jugendliche. a. Gossner Mission, Fennstr. 31, 1190 Berlin-Schoeneweiche, Germany. TEL 00372-6351198. circ. 7,000. (back issues avail.)

267 NE ISSN 0002-3744
AKTIE; maandblad voor jongeren. 1951. 11/yr. fl.42. Stichting Youth for Christ Nederland, Postbus 273, 3970 AG Diebergen, Netherlands. FAX 03438-15674. Ed. Leo Blokhuis. adv.; bk.rev. circ. 8,000.
Formerly: Jeugd in Aktie.
Description: Christian youth magazine.

200 GR
AKTINES/BEAM. (Text in Greek) 1938. m. Christian Union, Odos Karytsi, 105 61 Athens, Greece. TEL 02-3235023. circ. 10,000.
Description: Promotes Christian civilization.

200 GW
AKTION; Zeitung junger Arbeiter. 1949. m. DM.11.40. Christliche Arbeiter-Jugend, Huettmannstr. 52, 45143 Essen, Germany. TEL 0201-621065. adv.; bk.rev. **Document type:** newsletter.
Former titles: C A J Christliche Arbeiter-Jugend; Junge Christliche Arbeitnehmer. Befreiung (ISSN 0022-622X)

200 UK ISSN 0951-2667
ALCUIN. 1897. q. $30. Alcuin Club, 11 Abbey St., Chester, Ches. CH1 2JF, England. TEL 01244-347811. FAX 01244-347823. Ed. T.R. Barker. bk.rev. circ. 900. **Document type:** academic/scholarly publication.
—BLDSC (0786.808220).

200 NE ISSN 0002-5267
ALGEMEEN MACONNIEK TIJDSCHRIFT. 1946. m. membership only. Grand East of the Netherlands, Plantsoen 20, 3755 HJ Eemnes, Netherlands. Ed. Wim G. Ket. adv.; bk.rev.; illus. circ. 6,800.
Description: Masonic review of the Netherlands.

266 KE
ALL AFRICA CONFERENCE OF CHURCHES. REFUGEE DEPARTMENT. PROGRESS REPORT. irreg., latest 1974. All Africa Conference of Churches, Refugee Department, Pioneer House, Government Rd., P.O. Box 20301, Nairobi, Kenya.

266 KE
ALL AFRICA CONFERENCE OF CHURCHES. REFUGEE DEPARTMENT. PROJECT LIST. irreg., latest 1977. All Africa Conference of Churches, Refugee Department, Pioneer House, Government Rd., P.O. Box 20301, Nairobi, Kenya.

ALLIANCE REVIEW. see *EDUCATION*

266 MX ISSN 0002-628X
ALMAS. 1950. m. $5. (Misioneros de Guadalupe) Editora Escalante, Cordoba 17, Apdo. 24-550, Mexico 7, D. F., Mexico. FAX 5-533-6564. Ed. Jose Chavez Calderon. illus. circ. 225,000. **Document type:** newspaper.
Description: Covers missionary work overseas.

RELIGIONS AND THEOLOGY

200 SP
ALTERNATIVA 2000. 1990. bi-m. 2500 ptas.($25) (effective 1995) $30 (effective 1996). Juan Antonio Monroy, Ed. & Pub., Apdo. 2029, 28080 Madrid, Spain. TEL 91-5721862. circ. 3,000.

200 US
ALTERNATIVE MODELS NEWSLETTER.* 1989. q. $10. Catechetical Renewal Network, Box 634, Dayton, OH 45475-0634. Ed. Robert L. Humphrey. bk.rev. circ. 950. **Document type:** newsletter.

200 GW
ALTOETTINGER LIEBFRAUENBOTE. w. (Sun.) DM.81.60 (foreign DM.100.80). Altoettinger Liebfrauenbote Verlagsgesellschaft mbH, Neuoettingerstr. 5, 84503 Altoetting, Germany. TEL 08671-12005. FAX 08671-13630. Ed. Peter Becker. adv. contact: Bernhard Neumeier. circ. 38,601. **Document type:** bulletin.

213 US ISSN 0882-2123
AMBASSADOR REPORT. 1977. q. $20. Box 60068, Pasadena, CA 91116. TEL 818-798-6112. Ed. John Trechak. bk.rev.; circ. 2,000 (paid). (back issues avail.) **Document type:** newsletter.
Description: Provides reports about regligious cults

200 US
AMERICAN ACADEMY OF RELIGION. ANNUAL MEETING. a. Scholars Press, Box 15399, Atlanta, GA 30333-0399. TEL 404-727-2320. FAX 404-727-2348. (Co-sponsor: Society of Biblical Literature) **Document type:** proceedings.
Description: Discusses events at the annual meeting of the American Academy of Religion and Society of Biblical Literature.

200 US ISSN 0002-7189
BV1460
AMERICAN ACADEMY OF RELIGION. JOURNAL. 1933. q. $60. (American Academy of Religion) Scholars Press, Box 15399, Atlanta, GA 30333-0399. TEL 404-727-2320. FAX 404-727-2348. Ed. Glen Yokum. adv.; bk.rev.; bibl.; index, cum.index: 1933-1979. circ. 7,600. (also avail. in microform from UMI; microfiche) **Indexed:** Amer.Hist.& Life, Arts & Hum.Cit.Ind., Bibl.Ind., Bk.Rev.Ind. (1990-), CERDIC, Child.Bk.Rev.Ind. (1990-), Curr.Cont., Hist.Abstr., Hum.Ind., Mid.East: Abstr.& Ind., New Test.Abstr., Old Test.Abstr., Rel.& Theol.Abstr. (1968-), Rel.Ind.One, Rel.Per., SSCI. **Document type:** academic/scholarly publication.
—BLDSC (4683.740000); Faxon; Genuine Article; SWETS; UMI; UnCover.
Formerly: Journal of Bible and Religion.
Description: Gives various religious topics a scholarly treatment.

AMERICAN ATHEIST; a journal of atheist news and thought. see *PHILOSOPHY*

220 US ISSN 0006-0801
BV2370
AMERICAN BIBLE SOCIETY RECORD. 1818. m. $3 donation. American Bible Society, 1865 Broadway, New York, NY 10023. TEL 212-408-1480. FAX 212-408-1456. Ed. Clifford P. Macdonald. adv.; illus.; index. circ. 270,000. **Document type:** consumer publication.
Formerly: Bible Society Record.
Description: Contains news and articles concerning worldwide Bible mission.

200 US ISSN 1065-8068
E98.R3
▼**AMERICAN INDIAN RELIGIONS.** 1994. q. $30 to individuals; institutions $50. Center for Academic Publication, Stanford University Branch Box 5097, Standford, CA 94309-5097. TEL 805-683-1676. FAX 805-683-1077. Ed.Bd. adv.; bk.rev.; circ. 300 (paid). **Document type:** academic/scholarly publication.
Description: Devoted to the study and advancement of the religious traditions of American Indians.

200 100 US ISSN 0194-3448
BR1
AMERICAN JOURNAL OF THEOLOGY & PHILOSOPHY. 1980. 3/yr. $18 to individuals; institutions and foreign $30. United Theological Seminary, 1810 Harvard Blvd., Dayton, OH 45406-4599. TEL 513-278-5817. FAX 513-278-1218. (Subscr. to: Box 2009, Highlands, NC 28741) (Co-sponsor: Indiana University at South Bend) Ed. Tyron Inbody. adv.; bk.rev.; index. circ. 450. (back issues avail.) **Indexed:** Phil.Ind., Rel.& Theol.Abstr. (1989-), Rel.Ind.One. **Document type:** academic/scholarly publication.
—BLDSC (0838.700000); UMI; UnCover.
Description: Provides a forum for the discussion of issues in American theology and its dialogue with philosophy.

291.2 US ISSN 0740-0446
AMERICAN UNIVERSITY STUDIES. SERIES 7. THEOLOGY AND RELIGION. 1984. irreg. Peter Lang Publishing, Inc., 62 W. 45th St., 4th Fl., New York, NY 10036. TEL 212-302-6740. Ed. Christopher Myers. **Document type:** academic/scholarly publication, monographic series.
—BLDSC (0858.078100).

200 US ISSN 0894-9999
AMERICAN WALDENSIAN SOCIETY. NEWSLETTER. 1906. s-a. membership. American Waldensian Society, 475 Riverside Dr., Rm. 1850, New York, NY 10115. TEL 212-870-2671. Ed. Rev. Frank G. Gibson, Jr. bk.rev. circ. 2,500. **Document type:** newsletter.
Formerly: American Waldensian Aid Society. Newsletter (ISSN 0517-5798)
Description: Updates on Waldensian ministry in Italy, Argentina and Uruguay, and ministry exchanges between Waldensian and US churches.

200 IT ISSN 0003-1739
AMICIZIA EBRAICO-CRISTIANA DI FIRENZE. BOLLETTINO. 1951. q. free. Amicizia Ebraico-Cristiana di Firenze, Casella Postale 282, 50100 Florence, Italy. Ed. Ines Zilli Gay. bk.rev.; bibl. circ. 500.

AMICO DELL'ARTE CRISTIANA. see *ART*

200 FR ISSN 0003-1909
AMITIES SPIRITUELLES. BULLETIN. 1919. q. 50 F. (foreign 55 F.). Association de Amities Spirituelles, 42 ter, rue de la Foucotte, 54000 Nancy, France. TEL 83-96-10-36. (Subscr. to: B.P. 236, 75624 Paris Cedex 13, France) Ed. Jacques Sardin. bk.rev. circ. 1,200. **Document type:** bulletin, catalog.
Description: Objective is to shed light on issues in Christianity and spirituality.

200 UK ISSN 0003-2018
AMPLEFORTH JOURNAL. 1895. s-a. £10. Ampleforth Abbey, c/o Rev. J. Felix Stephens, Ed., York YO6 4EN, England. TEL 01439-788798. FAX 01439-788182. adv.; B&W page £120; adv. contact: B. Davies. bk.rev.; charts; illus. circ. 4,000. (back issues avail.) **Document type:** academic/scholarly publication.
—BLDSC (0859.470000).
Description: Presents news about the Ampleforth Abbey and surrounding community, in addition to religious articles and commentary.

200 US
ANAHATA NADA/SOUNDLESS SOUND. 1974. q. $1. (Sri Chinmoy Centre) AUM Publications, 85-42 160th St., Jamaica, NY 11432. TEL 718-523-1166. (Subscr. to: Box 32433, Jamaica, NY 11431) Ed. David Burke. bk.rev.; illus.

209 BE ISSN 0003-2468
BX4655
ANALECTA BOLLANDIANA; revue critique d'hagiographie - journal of critical hagiography. (Text in English, French, German, Italian, Latin; summaries in English) 1882. s-a. 3000 BEF. Societe des Bollandistes, 24 bd. Saint-Michel, B-1040 Brussels, Belgium. TEL 32-2-7393338. bk.rev.; index, cum.index every 20 yrs. (vols.1-100). circ. 1,100. **Indexed:** CERDIC, M.L.A. **Document type:** academic/scholarly publication.
—Faxon; SWETS.
Description: Studies about saints' lives up to 1500.

271.71 AU ISSN 0253-1593
ANALECTA CARTUSIANA; review for Carthusian history and spirituality. (Text in various languages) 1970. irreg., no.132, 1995. DM.65 per no. Universitaet Salzburg, Institut fuer Englische Sprache, Akademiestr. 24, A-5020 Salzburg, Austria. Ed. James Hogg. circ. 300. (back issues avail.) **Indexed:** M.L.A. **Document type:** academic/scholarly publication.

271 940 BE ISSN 0517-6735
ANALECTA PRAEMONSTRATENSIA. (Text in Dutch, English, French, German, Latin) 1925. 2/yr. 1226 BEF (Europe 1415 BEF; $50 in US; elsewhere 1500 BEF) (effective 1996). Praemonstratensia V.z.w., Abdij van Averbode, Abdijstraat 1, B-3271 Averbode, Belgium. bk.rev.; cum.index: 1925-1967. **Indexed:** CERDIC. **Document type:** academic/scholarly publication.
—SWETS.
Description: Publishes studies relating to the history of the Norbertine Order.

207.11 US ISSN 0003-2980
ANDREWS UNIVERSITY SEMINARY STUDIES. (Text in English, French, German) 1963. 2/yr. $18 to individuals (foreign $21); institutions $24 (foreign $27); students $15 (foreign $18) (effective thru 1996). Andrews University Press, Berrien Springs, MI 49104. TEL 616-471-6023. FAX 616-471-6202. E-mail: auss@andrews.edu. (Subscr. to: Seminary Hall 132, Andrews University, Berrien Springs, MI 49104. TEL 616-471-6023) Ed. Nancy J. Vyhmeister. bk.rev.; charts; illus.; index. circ. 750. **Indexed:** CERDIC, Mid.East: Abstr.& Ind., New Test.Abstr., Old Test.Abstr., Rel.& Theol.Abstr. (1969-), Rel.Ind.One, Rel.Per. **Document type:** academic/scholarly publication.
—BLDSC (0900.420000).
Description: Contains articles on biblical studies, biblical archaeology, historical, theological studies, and research on applied theology.
Refereed Serial

200 FR ISSN 0751-6460
ANGE GARDIEN. 1891. 6/yr. 130 F.($26) Association de l'Ange Gardien, 21 montee Saint Laurent, 69005 Lyon, France. TEL 78-38-02-72. Ed. Louis Chauffour. circ. 4,800. **Document type:** bulletin.

291.2 US ISSN 1063-8962
ANGELWATCH. 1992. bi-m. $16. AngelWatch Foundation, Inc., Box 1397, Mountainside, NJ 07092. TEL 908-232-5240. FAX 908-233-1339. Ed. Eileen E. Freeman. bk.rev.; circ. 1,500 (paid). (back issues avail.) **Document type:** newsletter.
Description: Covers news, reviews and features concerning angels in history, literature, music, culture, and religion and contemporary society.

200 209 US ISSN 0003-3286
BR1
ANGLICAN THEOLOGICAL REVIEW. 1918. q. $23 to individuals; institutions $30 (effective 1995 & 1996). Anglican Theological Review, Inc., 600 Haven St., Evanston, IL 60201. TEL 708-864-6024. FAX 708-328-9624. Ed. James E. Griffiss. adv.; bk.rev.; abstr.; index, cum.index every 10 yrs.; circ. 1,600 (paid). (also avail. in microform from UMI; reprint service avail. from UMI) **Indexed:** Amer.Hist.& Life, Bull.Signal, CERDIC, Hist.Abstr., New Test.Abstr., Old Test.Abstr., Rel.& Theol.Abstr. (1968-), Rel.Ind.One. **Document type:** academic/scholarly publication.
—BLDSC (0902.770000); Faxon; UMI.
Refereed Serial

200 BE
ANNUA NUNTIA LOVANIENSIA. (Text in English, French, German) 1960. a., vol.38, 1994. price varies. (Katholieke Universiteit Leuven, Faculty of Divinity) Éditions Peeters s.p.r.l., Bondgenotenlaan 153, 3000 Leuven, Belgium. TEL 32-16-235170. FAX 32-16-228500. (back issues avail.) **Document type:** monographic series.

200 FR ISSN 0066-2860
ANNUAIRE DES INSTITUTS DE RELIGIEUSES EN FRANCE. 1959. irreg., latest 1980. 50 F. Service National des Vocations Francais, 106 rue du Bac, 75341 Paris, France.

ANNUAL REVIEW OF WOMEN IN WORLD RELIGIONS. see *WOMEN'S STUDIES*

RELIGIONS AND THEOLOGY 5671

209   GW   ISSN 0003-5157
ANNUARIUM HISTORIAE CONCILIORUM; Internationale Zeitschrift fuer Konziliengeschichtsforschung. (Text in English, French, German, Italian & Spanish) 1969. s-a. DM.152. Verlag Ferdinand Schoeningh GmbH, Postfach 2540, 33055 Paderborn, Germany. TEL 05251-127665. FAX 05251-127860. adv.; bk.rev. **Indexed:** CERDIC. **Document type:** academic/scholarly publication.
—SWETS. CCC.

200   GW   ISSN 0003-519X
DIE ANREGUNG (NETTETAL); Seelsorglicher Dienst in der Welt von heute. 1948. m. DM.4 per no. Steyler Verlag, Bahnhofstr. 9, 41334 Nettetal, Germany. TEL 02157-1202-20. FAX 02157-120222. Ed.Bd. bk.rev. **Document type:** bulletin.

260   GW   ISSN 0003-5270 (should be checked)
ANRUF. 1896. bi-m. DM.15. (Deutscher Verband der Jugenbuende fuer Entschiedenes Christentum e.V.) Born-Verlag, Leuschnerstr. 72-74, 34134 Kassel, Germany. TEL 0561-40950. FAX 0561-4095-112. Ed. Walter Lohrey. adv.; bk.rev.; illus. circ. 16,000. **Document type:** bulletin.

248.83   GW   ISSN 0721-2291
ANSAETZE; E S G - Nachrichten. 1953. 8/yr. DM.35. Evangelische Studentinnengemeinde in der Bundesrepublik Deutschland, Tunisstr. 3, 50667 Cologne, Germany. TEL 0221-2577455. FAX 0221-256674. (Co-sponsors: Bundesministerium fuer Familie, Senioren, Frauen und Jugend) Ed. Friedhelm Quade. adv.; bk.rev. circ. 600. (processed) **Document type:** bulletin.
Formerly: E S G - Nachrichten (ISSN 0012-7981)

207.11   GW   ISSN 0003-5270
ANSTOESSE; aus der Arbeit der Evangelischen Akademie Hofgeismar. 1954. 4/yr. DM.16. Evangelische Akademie von Kurhessen-Waldeck, Schloesschen Schoenburg, 34369 Hofgeismar, Germany. bk.rev.; index. circ. 2,000.

270   SP   ISSN 0214-7165
ANTIGUEDAD Y CRISTIANISMO. (Text in English, Spanish) 1984. a. 5000 ptas. Universidad de Murcia, Secretariado de Publicaciones e Intercambio Cientifico, Santo Cristo 1, 30001 Murcia, Spain. TEL 34-68-363014. FAX 34-68-363414. Ed. Rafael Gonzalez Fernandez. **Document type:** academic/scholarly publication.
Description: Approaches subjects of history and material cultures of Late Antiquity.

200   GW   ISSN 0003-6285
ANZEIGER DES REICHES DER GERECHTIGKEIT; Menschenfreundliche Zeitung fuer Jedermann. (Summaries in Dutch, English, French, Italian, Portuguese and Spanish) 1938. m. DM.16. (Menschenfreundliche Gesellschaft) Verlag der Engel des Herrn, Baeckerweg 12, 60316 Frankfurt, Germany. Ed. Miss Roulin. circ. 120,000.

229   BE   ISSN 1155-3316
APOCRYPHA. 1990. a. 1750 BEF (effective 1995). (Association pour l'Etude de la Litterature Apocryphe Chretienne) N.V. Brepols, Steenweg op Tielen 68, 2300 Turnhout, Belgium. TEL 32-14-402500. FAX 32-14-428919. (back issues avail.) **Document type:** academic/scholarly publication.
Description: Publishes studies exploring aspects of apocryphal literature preserved in Christian and Jewish communities in Europe, Africa and Asia.

266   FR   ISSN 1144-164X
APPEL DE L'AFRIQUE. 1967. q. free. Societe des Missions Africaines, 36 rue Miguel Hidalgo, 75019 Paris, France. TEL 42-78-42-15. FAX 42-78-46-76. Ed. Gerard Sagnol. circ. 24,000. **Document type:** bulletin.
Formerly: Almanach Noir.

APPLICATIO. see LINGUISTICS — Computer Applications

ARBEITEN ZUR GESCHICHTE DES ANTIKEN JUDENTUMS UND DES URCHRISTENTUMS. see RELIGIONS AND THEOLOGY — Judaic

200   GW
ARBEITEN ZUR GESCHICHTE DES PIETISMUS. 1979. irreg. Vandenhoeck und Ruprecht, Robert-Bosch-Breite 6, 37079 Goettingen, Germany. TEL 0551-6959-0. FAX 0551-695917. (Subscr. to: 37070 Goettingen, Germany) Ed.Bd. **Document type:** monographic series.

200   GW
ARBEITEN ZUR KIRCHLICHEN ZEITGESCHICHTE. REIHE B; Darstellungen. 1975. irreg. Vandenhoeck und Ruprecht, Robert-Bosch-Breite 6, 37079 Goettingen, Germany. TEL 0551-6959-0. FAX 0551-695917. (Subscr. to: 37070 Goettingen, Germany) Ed.Bd. **Document type:** monographic series.

200   GW   ISSN 0570-5517
ARBEITEN ZUR PASTORALTHEOLOGIE. 1962. irreg. Vandenhoeck und Ruprecht, Robert-Bosch-Breite 6, 37079 Goettingen, Germany. TEL 0551-6959-0. FAX 0551-695917. (Subscr. to: 37070 Goettingen, Germany) Ed.Bd. **Document type:** monographic series.

200   GW   ISSN 0066-5711
ARBEITEN ZUR THEOLOGIE. REIHE 1. 1960. irreg., vol.71, 1994. price varies. Calwer Verlag, Scharnhauserstr.44, 70599 Stuttgart, Germany. TEL 0711-16722-0. FAX 0711-1672277. **Document type:** monographic series.

200   GW   ISSN 0723-2446
ARBEITSGEMEINSCHAFT NEUE RELIGIOESE GRUPPEN. FORUM; Materialen und Beitraege zum religioesen Dialog. 1981. a. DM.4. Arbeitsgemeinschaft Neue Religioese Gruppen e.V., Stahlburgstr. 38, 60318 Frankfurt a.M., Germany. TEL 069-285502. FAX 069-296260. Ed. Kurt-Helmuth Elmuth. (back issues avail.) **Document type:** academic/scholarly publication.
Description: Provides information and reports on new religious movements and cults in Germany, with an emphasis on Frankfurt.

ARCANA; inner dimensions of spirituality. see RELIGIONS AND THEOLOGY — Other Denominations And Sects

243   GW   ISSN 0066-6386
BX1970.A1
ARCHIV FUER LITURGIEWISSENSCHAFT. 1950. a. DM.218. Abt-Herwegen-Institut fuer Liturgische und Monastische Forschung, Abtei Maria Laach, 56653 Maria Laach, Germany. Ed. Emmanuel v. Severus. bk.rev. circ. 800. **Indexed:** CERDIC, New Test.Abstr., Rel.Ind.One.

209   GW   ISSN 0066-6432
BR857.R5
ARCHIV FUER MITTELRHEINISCHE KIRCHENGESCHICHTE. 1949. a. DM.60. Gesellschaft fuer Mittelrheinische Kirchengeschichte, Karmeliterstr. 1, 56068 Koblenz, Germany. TEL 06131-253531. FAX 06131-253397. (Dist. by: Vertriebsstelle beim Bistumsarchiv, Jesuitenstr. 13b, 54290 Trier, Germany) Ed. Friedhelm Juergensmeier. circ. 2,500. **Indexed:** Bibl.Cart. **Document type:** academic/scholarly publication.

291.64   GW   ISSN 0341-8375
ARCHIV FUER REFORMATIONGESCHICHTE. LITERATURBERICHT/ARCHIVE FOR REFORMATION HISTORY. LITERATURE REVIEW. 1907. a. $28.50. (Society for Reformation Research, US) Guetersloher Verlagshaus Chr. Kaiser, Carl-Bertelsmann-Str. 270, 33311 Guetersloh, Germany. TEL 05241-7405-0. FAX 05241-740548. Eds. Gottfried Krodel, Hans Guggisberg. bk.rev. circ. 480. **Document type:** academic/scholarly publication.
Description: Contains articles and reviews on the religious and church history of the Reformation era.

270   GW   ISSN 0003-9381
BR300
ARCHIV FUER REFORMATIONSGESCHICHTE/ARCHIVE FOR REFORMATION HISTORY; Internationale Zeitschrift zur Erforschung der Reformation und ihrer Weltwirkungen. (Text in English and German) 1904. s-a. DM.115. (Verein fuer Reformations Geschichte) Guetersloher Verlagshaus Chr. Kaiser, Carl-Bertelsmann-Str. 270, 33311 Guetersloh, Germany. TEL 05241-7405-0. FAX 05241-740548. (Co-sponsor: Society for Reformation Research, US) Ed.Bd. bk.rev. circ. 800. (also avail. in microform from PMC; reprint service avail. from KTO) **Indexed:** Amer.Hist.& Life, Arts & Hum.Cit.Ind., Hist.Abstr., M.L.A., Rel.& Theol.Abstr. (1970-), Rel.Ind.One, Rel.Per. **Document type:** academic/scholarly publication; Genuine Article; SWETS.
—BLDSC (1640.700000).

200 150   GW   ISSN 0084-6724
ARCHIV FUER RELIGIONSPSYCHOLOGIE. vol.4, 1929. irreg. price varies. (Internationale Gesellschaft fuer Religionspsychologie und Religionswissenschaft) Vandenhoeck und Ruprecht, Robert-Bosch-Breite 6, 37079 Goettingen, Germany. TEL 0551-6959-0. FAX 0551-695917. (Subscr. to: 37070 Goettingen, Germany) Ed.Bd. **Document type:** monographic series.

260   IT   ISSN 0066-6688
ARCHIVIO ITALIANO PER LA STORIA DELLA PIETA. (Text in language of contributor) 1951; N.S. 1970. irreg., vol.8, 1980. price varies. Edizioni di Storia e Letteratura s.r.l., Via Lancellotti 18, 00186 Rome, Italy. TEL 65-40-556. FAX 06-6872567. Ed. Romana Guarnieri.

200   HK   ISSN 1011-8101
AREOPAGUS; a living encounter with today's religious world. 1987. q. $24. Tao Fang Shan Christian Centre, P.O. Box 33, Shatin, New Territories, Hong Kong. TEL 852-691-1904. FAX 852-694-0354. Ed. John G. LeMond. adv. contact: Eric Boseu. bk.rev. circ. 1,000. (also avail. in microform from UMI) **Indexed:** Rel.Ind.One. **Document type:** academic/scholarly publication.
—UMI.
Incorporates (in 1987): Update (Aarhus) (ISSN 0108-7029); New Religious Movements Up-Date (ISSN 0105-9998)
Description: Provides a forum for communication between the good news of Jesus Christ and the people of faith both in major world religions and new religious movements.

200 949.5   GR   ISSN 1105-008X
ARISTOTELION PANEPISTEMION THESSALONIKES. THEOLOGIKE SCHOLE. EPISTEMONIKE EPETERIS. 1953. a. Aristotelion Panepistemion Thessalonikes, Theologike Schole, Serron 39, Triandria, Thessaloniki, Greece. **Indexed:** Chem.Abstr. **Document type:** monographic series.

207.114891   DK   ISSN 0107-363X
ARKEN. 1979. bi-m. DKK 10 per no. (Teologiske Fakultet) Forlaget Arken, Koebmagergade 44-46, DK-1150 Copenhagen K, Denmark. Ed. Peter Grane. illus. **Document type:** newsletter.
Formerly: Teologiske Fakultet. Bladet.

205   DK   ISSN 0107-4520
ARKEN-TRYK. 1981. irreg. price varies. (Teologiske Fakultet) Forlaget Arken, Koebmagergade 44-46, DK-1150 Copenhagen K, Denmark. Ed. Rasmus Noejgaard. **Document type:** academic/scholarly publication.

ARMARIUM CODICUM INSIGNIUM. see HISTORY — History Of Europe

ARMONIA DI VOCI. see MUSIC

ARMY CHAPLAINCY. see MILITARY

ARTE CRISTIANA; rivista internazionale di storia dell'arte e di arti liturgiche. see ART

200   US   ISSN 1044-6494
ASHLAND THEOLOGICAL JOURNAL. 1968. a. $6. Ashland Theological Seminary, 910 Center St., Ashland, OH 44805. TEL 419-289-5177. FAX 419-289-5969. E-mail: dbaker@aashland.edu. Ed. David. W. Baker. bk.rev. (back issues avail.) **Document type:** academic/scholarly publication.
—BLDSC (1742.057500).
Formerly (until 1981): Ashland Theological Bulletin (ISSN 0888-2185)
Description: Articles of interest to seminary alumni in ministry and to theological academic community.

200 950   II
ASIAN CHURCH TODAY. (Text in English) 1984. q. Evangelical Fellowship of Asia, c/o EFI 4-1-826, J N Rd., Victoria Chambers, 2nd Fl., Hyderabad 500 001, India. TEL 40-553646. FAX 40-222-483. Ed. Rev. Francis Sunderaraj. circ. 2,000.

200 800   DK   ISSN 0905-7749
ASLAN. 1989. q. DKK 40. Aslan amba, Liljevej 8, DK-3600 Frederikssund, Denmark. TEL 45-42313213. Ed. Gunhild Lindstroem. bk.rev. circ. 400.
Description: Focuses on books with religious and ethical relevancy for children, youth and adults.

ASOCIACION. see CHILDREN AND YOUTH — About

RELIGIONS AND THEOLOGY

200 060   FR   ISSN 0066-8907
ASSOCIATION DES AMIS DE PIERRE TEILHARD DE CHARDIN. BULLETIN. 1966. a. Association des Amis de Pierre Teilhard de Chardin, 38 rue Geoffroy-Saint-Hilaire, 75005 Paris, France. bibl. **Document type:** bulletin.

378   US
ASSOCIATION FOR PROFESSIONAL EDUCATION FOR MINISTRY. REPORT OF THE BIENNIAL MEETING. 1950. biennial. $10. Association for Professional Education for Ministry, c/o Oliver Williams, Pres., University of Notre Dame, Notre Dame, IN 46556. TEL 219-239-5000. (Subscr. to: Joseph Kelly, Treas., St. Bernard's Seminary, 2260 Lake Ave., Rochester, NY 14612) Ed. Gaylord Noyce. circ. 400.

230   IT   ISSN 0587-1999
ASSOCIATION INTERNATIONALE D'ETUDES PATRISTIQUES. BULLETIN D'INFORMATION ET DE LIAISON. (Text in English, French) 1968. irreg. (1-2/yr.). 80 F. per no. for libraries only. Brepols Publisher, c/o A. Di Berardino, Sec. Gen., Institutum Patristicum Augustinianum, Via Paolo VI, 25, 00193 Rome, Italy. TEL 39-6-680069. FAX 39-6-68006298. (Subscr. to: B. Gain, 14 rue Saint Louis, 57158 Montigny-Les-Metz, France) Ed. A. di Berardino. bk.rev.; bibl. circ. 800. **Document type:** bulletin.

ASSOCIATION OF BRITISH THEOLOGICAL AND PHILOSOPHICAL LIBRARIES. BULLETIN. see *LIBRARY AND INFORMATION SCIENCES*

268   US   ISSN 0362-1472
BV4019
ASSOCIATION OF THEOLOGICAL SCHOOLS IN THE UNITED STATES AND CANADA. BULLETIN. 1937. biennial. $27. Association of Theological Schools, 10 Summit Park Dr., Pittsburgh, PA 15275-1103. TEL 412-788-6505. Ed. Nancy Merrill. circ. 2,000. **Document type:** bulletin.
Formerly: American Association of Theological Schools in the United States and Canada. Bulletin (ISSN 0065-7360)

268   US   ISSN 0362-1472
ASSOCIATION OF THEOLOGICAL SCHOOLS IN THE UNITED STATES AND CANADA. DIRECTORY. 1918. a. $7.25. Association of Theological Schools, 10 Summit Park Dr., Pittsburgh, PA 15275-1103. TEL 412-788-6505. Ed. Nancy Merrill. **Document type:** directory.
Formerly: American Association of Theological Schools in the United States and Canada. Directory (ISSN 0065-7379)

200   US   ISSN 0190-4280
AT EASE. bi-m. (General Council of the Assemblies of God) Gospel Publishing House, 1445 Boonville Ave., Springfield, MO 65802-1894. TEL 417-862-2781. FAX 417-862-8558. (Subscr. to: Division of Home Missions, Chaplaincy Dept., 1445 Boonville Ave., Springfield, MO 65802-1894) Ed. Lemuel McElyea. circ. 26,000.
Description: Religious publication geared towards motivating and uplifting military personnel.

291 301.15   IO
ATMA JAYA RESEARCH CENTRE. SOCIO-RELIGIOUS RESEARCH REPORT/PUSAT PENELITIAN ATMA JAYA. LAPORAN PENELITIAN KEAGAMAAN. 1977. irreg. Atma Jaya Research Centre - Pusat Penelitian Atma Jaya, Jalan Jenderal Sudirman 51, P.O. Box 2639, Jakarta 10001, Indonesia. Ed. Paul W. Kartono. circ. controlled. **Document type:** monographic series.

967.5 200   BD   ISSN 0563-4245
AU COEUR DE L'AFRIQUE. 1961. 4/yr. 1500 Fr.CFA (Africa $30; elsewhere $35). Association des Conference des Ordinaires du Rwanda et Burundi, B.P. 1390, Bujumbura, Burundi. TEL 22-32-63. FAX 257-22-32-70. Ed. Adrien Ntabona. adv.; bk.rev. circ. 1,000. **Indexed:** CERDIC. **Document type:** bulletin.
Description: Contains research on cultural, socio-political, theological and pastoral issues.

200   UK   ISSN 0004-7481
AUDENSHAW PAPERS. 1967. bi-m. £6.25 (foreign £11) (effective until Oct. 1996). Hinksey Centre, Westminster College, Oxford OX2 9AT, England. Ed. Linda Lear. bk.rev. circ. 3,000. **Indexed:** CERDIC.
Supersedes: Christian Comment.

260   GW
AUFTRAG UND WEG. 1915. bi-m. DM.18. (Deutscher Verband der Jugenbuende fuer Entschiedenes Christentum e.V.) Born-Verlag, Leuschnerstr. 72-74, 34134 Kassel, Germany. TEL 0561-40950. FAX 0561-4095-112. Ed. Klaus Matthiesen. bk.rev. circ. 4,000. **Document type:** bulletin.

200   GW
AUFWAERTS (GIESSEN); die Zeitschrift mit den guten Nachrichten. 1909. m. DM.6. Brunnen Verlag GmbH, Postfach 100143, 35331 Giessen, Germany. TEL 0641-6059-0. FAX 0641-605940. Ed. Ralf Tibusek. bk.rev. **Document type:** consumer publication.

AUGSBURG FORTRESS BOOK NEWSLETTER. see *PUBLISHING AND BOOK TRADE*

200   GW
DIE AUSLESE; vierteljaehrliche Informationsschrift fuer Kirche und Friedhof. 1958. 4/yr. DM.6.20. Dr. Krueger Verlag, Am Schiessberg 19, 35745 Herborn, Germany. TEL 02772-2427. FAX 02772-2420. Ed. Hans-Joachim Krueger. adv.; B&W page DM.2550; trim 261 x 180. bk.rev.; circ. 26,000 (controlled). **Document type:** newsletter.

200   AT   ISSN 0588-3237
AUSTRALIAN & NEW ZEALAND SOCIETY FOR THEOLOGICAL STUDIES. COLLOQUIUM. 1964. s-a. Aus.$35. Australian and New Zealand Society for Theological Studies, c/o Dr. Gregory C. Jenks, St. Francis' Theological College, 233 Milton Rd., P.O. Box 1261, Australia. TEL 07-369-4286. FAX 61-7-369-4691. Ed. James Haire. adv.; bk.rev. circ. 500. (back issues avail.) **Indexed:** Aus.P.A.I.S., Rel.& Theol.Abstr., Rel.Ind.One.
—UnCover.
Description: Features issues in biblical studies, theology, ethics, church history.

200   AT   ISSN 1022-3347
AUSTRALIAN BEACON. 1968. m. Aus.$25 (foreign Aus.$35) (effective 1995). P.O. Box 88, Para Hills, S.A. 5096, Australia. TEL 08-2637156. Ed. John S. MacKenzie. adv. circ. 1,000.
Description: For Christians concerned with the state of the Church today.

220   AT   ISSN 0045-0308
BS410
AUSTRALIAN BIBLICAL REVIEW. 1951. a. Aus.$10 per issue. Fellowship for Biblical Studies, c/o Joint Theological Library, Ormond College, Parkville, Vic. 3052, Australia. Eds. M. O'Brien, D. Lee. bk.rev. circ. 375. **Indexed:** CERDIC, New Test.Abstr., Old Test.Abstr., Rel.& Theol.Abstr. (1976-), Rel.Ind.One. **Document type:** academic/scholarly publication.
—BLDSC (1797.800000).

AUSTRALIAN CHURCHES OF CHRIST HISTORICAL SOCIETY. DIGEST. see *HISTORY — History Of Australasia And Other Areas*

200   AT   ISSN 1030-617X
AUSTRALIAN JOURNAL OF LITURGY. 1987. s-a. Aus.$15. Australian Academy of Liturgy, G.P.O. Box 282, Brisbane, Qld. 4001, Australia. TEL 07-224-3332. FAX 07-221-1705. adv.; bk.rev.; index. circ. 250. (back issues avail.) **Document type:** academic/scholarly publication.
Description: Christian liturgy and worship with particular reference to Australia. Ecumenical in scope.

AUSTRALIAN RADIO TIMES. see *COMMUNICATIONS — Radio*

266 370   BE   ISSN 0776-2461
AVIMO INFO. Variant title: Audio-visuele Missie en Ontwikkelingswerken Info. (Text in Dutch) 1981. q. 350 BEF. Avimo v.z.w., Kardinaal Mercierplein 3, 3000 Louvain, Belgium. TEL 32-16-234293. FAX 32-16-293165. Ed. Anne Vansteelandt. adv.; film rev. circ. 5,500. (back issues avail.) **Document type:** catalog.
Description: Covers audio-visual materials relating to mission, education and development issues in the Third World, spirituality and world religions.

200   UK
AWARE. 1900. bi-m. £17.95 (foreign £19.75). The Paternoster Press, P.O. Box 300, Kingstown Broadway, Carlisle, Cumbria CA3 0QS, England. TEL 0228-512512. FAX 0228-514949. (Dist. in U.S. & Canada by: Paternoster Press, P.O. Box 11127, Birmingham, AL 35201-1127) Ed. John Allan. adv.; bk.rev.; illus. circ. 1,500. (tabloid format; also avail. in microform from UMI; microfilm from WMP) **Document type:** newsletter.
—UMI. **CCC.**
Former titles: Aware Harvester; Harvester (ISSN 0017-8217); Incorporates: Witness.
Description: Publishes contemporary articles and practical input for local church life.

200 700   US   ISSN 0067-3129
BAMPTON LECTURES IN AMERICA. 1949. irreg., no.29, 1994. price varies. Columbia University Press, 562 W. 113th St., New York, NY 10025. TEL 212-666-1000. **Document type:** monographic series.

200 950   II   ISSN 0253-9365
BANGALORE THEOLOGICAL FORUM. (Text in English) 1968. q. Rs.25($10) United Theological College, 17 Miller's Rd., Bangalore, S. India 560 046, India. TEL 575844. Ed. Eric J. Lott. adv.; bk.rev.; abstr. circ. 550. (also avail. in microform from UMI; back issues avail.) **Indexed:** New Test.Abstr., Rel.& Theol.Abstr. (1989-), Rel.Ind.One.
—UMI.

BARTIMAEUS REVIEW. see *HANDICAPPED — Visually Impaired*

BASIS. see *MILITARY*

BASIS: CHRISTENE SCHOOL. see *EDUCATION*

200   SZ   ISSN 0005-6189
BASLER PREDIGTEN; eine monatliche Predigtfolge. 1936. m. 24.80 SFr. Friedrich Reinhardt Verlag, Missionsstr. 36, CH-4012 Basel, Switzerland. Ed.Bd. circ. 3,500.

200   GW   ISSN 0005-6618
DAS BAUGERUEST: Mitarbeiterzeitschrift fuer ausserschul. Jugendbildung. 1949. 4/yr. DM.30. Verein zur Foerderung Evangelischer Jugendarbeit e.V., Hummelsteiner Weg 100, 90459 Nuernberg, Germany. TEL 0911-4304-0. FAX 0911-4304201. Ed. Volker Lehmann. bk.rev.; bibl.; tr.lit.; index. circ. 2,100. (avail. on records) **Document type:** bulletin.

200   GW   ISSN 0005-707X
DER BAYERISCHE KRIPPENFREUND. 1917. q. DM.25. (Verband Bayerischer Krippenfreunde) Anton H. Konrad Verlag, Schulstr. 5, 89264 Weissenhorn, Germany. TEL 07309-2657. Ed. Erich Lidel. circ. 5,000. (back issues avail.) **Document type:** bulletin.

200   NE   ISSN 0005-7312
DE BAZUIN. 1911. w. fl.180. Stichting De Bazuin, P.O. Box 2456, 3500 GL Utrecht, Netherlands. TEL 31-80600164. FAX 31-80601337. Ed. Lambert van Gelder. adv.; bk.rev.; illus.; circ. 5,000 (controlled). (also avail. in microfiche from IDC) **Indexed:** CERDIC. **Document type:** newspaper.
Description: Covers Church issues and their context in society.

BEACON (NEW YORK). see *PHILOSOPHY*

333.7 289.6   US   ISSN 1050-0332
BEFRIENDING CREATION. 1985. 11/yr. $20 (effective 1995). Friends Committee on Unity with Nature, 179 N. Prospect St., Burlington, VT 05401-1607. TEL 802-658-0308. E-mail: fcun@together.org. (Ed. addr.: 2757 N.E. 96th St., Seattle, WA 98115) Ed. Nancy Wick. bk.rev. circ. 500. **Document type:** newsletter.
Formerly (until 1988): Unity with Nature Newsletter.
Description: Provides news and information to members about our spiritual relations with the environment.

280   GW
DIE BEIDEN TUERME; Niederaltaicher Rundbrief. 1965. s-a. free. Benediktinerabtei Niederaltaich, 94557 Niederaltaich, Germany. Ed. P. Bonifaz Pfister. circ. 4,500.

BEITRAEGE ZUR GESCHICHTE DER PHILOSOPHIE UND THEOLOGIE DES MITTELALTERS. NEUE FOLGE. see *PHILOSOPHY*

266 GW ISSN 0342-1341
BEITRAEGE ZUR GESCHICHTE DES ALTEN MOENCHTUMS UND DES BENEDIKTINERORDENS. 1912. irreg. price varies. Aschendorffsche Verlagsbuchhandlung, Soesterstr. 13, 48155 Muenster, Germany. TEL 0251-690-0. FAX 0251-690143. Ed. Emmanuel v. Severus. **Document type:** monographic series.

200 GW ISSN 0522-6619
BX1538.R37
BEITRAEGE ZUR GESCHICHTE DES BISTUMS REGENSBURG. 1967. a. DM.30. Verein fuer Regensburger Bistumsgeschichte e.V., Petersweg 11-13, 93047 Regensburg, Germany. TEL 0941-58813. **Indexed:** RILM.

230 GW ISSN 0067-5172
BEITRAEGE ZUR OEKUMENISCHEN THEOLOGIE. 1967. irreg., vol.20, 1981. price varies. Verlag Ferdinand Schoeningh GmbH, Postfach 2540, 33055 Paderborn, Germany. TEL 05251-127665. FAX 05251-127860. Ed. Heinrich Fries. circ. 500. **Document type:** academic/scholarly publication.
   Description: Scholarly publication about the ecumenical movement in the Catholic Church and the beliefs of contemporary theologians. Each issue covers a distinctive topic.

THE BELTANE PAPERS; a journal of women's mysteries. see WOMEN'S INTERESTS

BENJAMIN; evangelische Monatszeitschrift fuer Maedchen und Jungen. see CHILDREN AND YOUTH — For

220 UK
BEREAN EXPOSITOR. 1909. bi-m. £5 (rest of Europe £6; elsewhere £12). Berean Publishing Trust, 4 Orchard Ave., Whetstone, London N20 0JA. TEL 0181-446-2762. Ed. Stuart Allen. circ. 600. **Document type:** academic/scholarly publication.
   Description: General Bible subjects for Bible students.

200 US ISSN 0005-8890
BEREAN SEARCHLIGHT. 1940. m. (except Jul.). free. Berean Bible Society, 7609 W. Belmont Ave., Chicago, IL 60635. TEL 708-456-7889. Ed. Paul M. Sadler. bk.rev.; charts; illus. circ. 22,500. (also avail. in microfilm from UMI; reprint service avail.) **Document type:** academic/scholarly publication.

252 US ISSN 1041-6382
BV4241
BEST SERMONS. 1988. a. Harper Collins Publishers, 10 E. 53rd St., New York, NY 10022. TEL 800-242-7737.

220 296 IS ISSN 0005-979X
BS410
BET MIKRA. (Text in Hebrew) 1956. q. $50 (effective 1996). World Jewish Bible Center, P.O. Box 7024, Jerusalem 93557, Israel. TEL 972-2-254851. Ed. David Hacohen. bk.rev. circ. 1,400. **Indexed:** Ind.Heb.Per., Rel.& Theol.Abstr. (1977-). **Document type:** academic/scholarly publication.
   Description: Publishes Bible studies and research.

220 418.02 AT
BEYOND WORDS. 1986. a. $8. Wycliffe Bible Translators Australia, Graham Rd., Kangaroo Ground, Vic. 3097, Australia. TEL 03-712-2777. FAX 61-3-712-2799. Ed. Bruce Grayden. bk.rev. circ. 9,500. **Document type:** bulletin.

220 IT ISSN 0006-0585
BS410
BIBBIA E ORIENTE; rivista per la conoscenza della Bibbia. (Supplements avail.) 1959. q. $72. (Centro Studi Arti Grafiche) Editrice Sardini, 25040 Bornato (Brescia), Italy. TEL 030-725123. FAX 030-7254348. Ed. Fausto Sardini. adv.; bk.rev.; illus.; index. **Indexed:** New Test.Abstr., Old Test.Abstr., Rel.& Theol.Abstr.

220 GW
BIBEL IM JAHR. 1964. a. DM.14.80. Katholisches Bibelwerk e.V., Silberburgstr. 121, 70176 Stuttgart, Germany. TEL 0711-6192050. FAX 0711-6192077. Ed. F.J. Ortkemper. adv.; bk.rev.; illus.; index. **Document type:** bulletin.

220 SW ISSN 0006-0607
BIBEL-JOURNALEN; bibel och vaeckelsetidskrift. 1952. bi-m. SEK 50. Ryska Bibelsaellskapet - Russian Bible Society, P.O. Box 1801, S-701 18 Oerebro, Sweden. FAX 019-360807. Ed. Ingemar Hallzon. illus. circ. 6,000.

220 GW ISSN 0006-0615
BIBEL UND GEMEINDE. 1900. q. DM.28($25) Bibelbund e.V., Narzissenweg 11, 35447 Reiskirchen, Germany. TEL 0228-638784. Ed. Dr. Thomas Schirrmacher. bk.rev.; circ. 3,500 (controlled). **Document type:** academic/scholarly publication.
   —BLDSC (1947.808000).
   Description: Theological journal of German evangelical fundamentalism.

220 282 GW ISSN 0006-0623
BIBEL UND KIRCHE. 1946. q. DM.35. Katholisches Bibelwerk e.V., Silberburgstr. 121, 70176 Stuttgart, Germany. TEL 0711-6192050. FAX 0711-6192077. Ed. F.J. Ortkemper. adv.; bk.rev.; abstr.; index. circ. 22,000. **Indexed:** CERDIC, New Test.Abstr., Old Test.Abstr. **Document type:** academic/scholarly publication.
   —BLDSC (1947.810000).

220 GW ISSN 0006-064X
BIBEL UND LITURGIE. 1926. q. DM.47 (foreign DM.58). Patmos Verlag GmbH, Am Wehrhahn 100, 40211 Duesseldorf, Germany. TEL 0211-16795-0. FAX 0211-1679575. (Subscr. to: Cornelsen Verlaskontor, Kammerratsheide 66, 33609 Bielefeld, Germany) (Co-sponsor: Oesterreichisches Katholisches Bibelwerk) Ed. Norbert W. Hoeslinger. adv.; bk.rev.; abstr.; bibl.; tr.lit.; index. circ. 3,000. **Indexed:** CERDIC, New Test.Abstr., Old Test.Abstr. **Document type:** bulletin.

220 US
BIBELLEKTIONEN. (Text in German) 1919. q. $4. (German Church of God in U.S.A.) Christian Unity Press, 2211 Lincoln Ave., Box 527, York, NE 68467. TEL 402-362-5133. Ed. Rev. Fritz Friedrich. circ. 2,480. (processed) **Document type:** academic/scholarly publication.
   Formerly: Internationale Bibellektionen.

200 GW ISSN 0933-9949
BIBELREPORT. 1968. q. DM.6. Deutsche Bibelgesellschaft, Balinger Str. 31, 70567 Stuttgart, Germany. TEL 0711-7181-0. FAX 0711-7181-250. TELEX 7255299-BIBL-D. Ed. Christian Pruefer. bk.rev.; illus. circ. 74,000. (back issues avail.) **Document type:** bulletin.
   Description: Magazine of the Bible societies in Germany and Austria.

266 SW ISSN 0006-0658
BIBELTROGNA VAENNERS MISSIONSTIDNING. 1912. m. SEK 150. Missionssaellskapet Bibeltrogna Vaenner, P.O. Box 6160, S-102 33 Stockholm, Sweden. TEL 08-736-6010. FAX 08-345818. Ed. Rune Karlsson. bk.rev.; index. circ. 2,200.

200 US ISSN 0746-0104
BIBLE ADVOCATE. 1863. m. free. (Church of God (Seventh Day), General Conference) Bible Advocate Press, Box 33677, Denver, CO 80233. TEL 303-452-7973. FAX 303-452-0657. (Canada addr.: Box 67010, Northland Village P.O., Alta. T2L 2L2, Canada) Ed. Roy A. Marrs. index. circ. 12,700. (back issues avail.) **Document type:** consumer publication.
   Description: Features articles on Bible doctrine, current issues in today's world, and other material that will enrich the spirtual lives of those who seek to know about God.

BIBLE AND SPADE. see ARCHAEOLOGY

220 UK
BIBLE EXPLORATION MATERIAL AND ANNUAL PROJECT. a. £2.95. National Christian Education Council, Robert Denholm House, Nutfield, Redhill, Surrey RH1 4HW, England. TEL 0737-822411. FAX 0737-822116. Ed. D. Trenaman. circ. 2,000. **Document type:** bulletin.
   Former titles: Bible Exploration Material and Annual Scripture Project; Scripture Examination Material and Annual Scripture Project.

220 US ISSN 0006-0739
BIBLE FRIEND; of Biblical faith and Christ's teaching. 1903. m. $4. Osterhus Publishing House, Inc., 4500 W. Broadway, Minneapolis, MN 55422. TEL 612-537-8335. Ed. Mrs. Cyrus Osterhus. illus. circ. 10,000. **Document type:** newspaper.

220 US ISSN 0278-0259
BIBLE-IN-LIFE FRIENDS. w. David C. Cook Publishing Co., 850 N. Grove Ave., Elgin, IL 60120. TEL 708-741-2400. Ed. Ramona Warren.
   Description: Aimed at children aged 6-8.

220 SW ISSN 0347-2787
BIBLE RESEARCHER. (Text in Arabic, English, French, German, Polish and Swedish; summaries in English) 1975. m. SEK 120($20) European Human Rights, Marknadsvagen 289, S-183 34 Taby, Sweden. TEL 08-7681398. Ed. Ditlieb Felderer. bk.rev. circ. 1,000. (back issues avail.) **Document type:** newsletter.

200 US ISSN 8755-6316
BS410
BIBLE REVIEW. 1985. bi-m. $14.97 (foreign $20.97). Biblical Archaeology Society, 4710 41st St., N.W., Washington, DC 20016. TEL 202-364-3300. FAX 202-364-2636. (Subscr. to: Box 7027, Red Oak, IA 51591) Ed. Hershel Shanks. adv.; bk.rev.; cum.index: 1985-1987. circ. 40,000. (also avail. in talking book; back issues avail.) **Indexed:** Old Test.Abstr.
   —BLDSC (1947.824660); Faxon; UnCover.
   Description: Articles written by scholars and edited for an audience on Bible interpretation, and exegesis.

220 US
BIBLE - SCIENCE NEWS. 1963. 9/yr. $25 (foreign $40). Bible - Science Association Inc., Box 33220, Minneapolis, MN 55433-0220. TEL 612-755-8606. FAX 612-755-8606. Ed. Jan E. Reeser. bk.rev.; illus. circ. 3,500. **Document type:** consumer publication.
   Formerly (until Jan. 1992): Bible - Science Newsletter (ISSN 0164-5587)
   Description: Non-technical publication of Bible and science issues for a Christian audience.

200 US ISSN 0006-081X
BIBLE STANDARD AND HERALD OF CHRIST'S KINGDOM. French edition: Etendard de la Bible et Heraut du Royaume de Christ. (Editions also in Brazilian, Danish, German, Ukrainian and Polish) 1920. m. $1. Laymen's Home Missionary Movement, Box 67, Chester Springs, PA 19425. TEL 610-827-7665. Ed. Bernard W. Hedman. circ. 4,000. **Indexed:** CERDIC.
   Description: Highlights doctrines, signs of the times.

200 UK
BIBLE STUDY MONTHLY. 1924. bi-m. free to members. Bible Fellowship Union, 4 Manor Gardens, Barnstone, Nottingham NG13 9JL, England. bk.rev. circ. 1,700.
   Description: Covers Bible history, archaeology, prophecy, exposition, and devotional from a premillennial advent perspective.

220 US ISSN 0006-0836
BIBLE TODAY; a periodical promoting understanding and appreciation of scripture for life & ministry. 1962. bi-m. $22 (foreign $26). Liturgical Press, St. John's Abbey, Collegeville, MN 56321. TEL 612-363-2213. FAX 800-445-5899. Ed. Rev. Leslie J. Hoppe. adv. contact: Michelle Verkuilen. bk.rev.; illus.; index. circ. 8,000. (also avail. in microform from UMI; back issues avail.; reprint service avail. from UMI) **Indexed:** Cath.Ind., New Test.Abstr., Old Test.Abstr.
   —UMI.

266 US
BIBLES FOR THE WORLD NEWS. 1966. q. free to donors. Bibles for the World, Inc., Box 805, Wheaton, IL 60189. TEL 708-668-7733. FAX 708-668-6348. Ed.Bd. bk.rev. circ. 35,000. **Document type:** newsletter.
   Description: Focuses on missions and missionary work.

BIBLICAL ARCHAEOLOGIST. see ARCHAEOLOGY

BIBLICAL ARCHAEOLOGY REVIEW. see ARCHAEOLOGY

RELIGIONS AND THEOLOGY

220 US
BIBLICAL ERRANCY; a national periodical focusing on Biblical errors, contradictions and fallacies, while providing a hearing for apologists. 1983. m. $12 in U.S.; Canada $14 (effective May 1991). Dennis McKinsey, Ed. & Pub., 3158 Sherwood Park Dr., Springfield, OH 45505. TEL 513-323-6146. circ. 350. (back issues avail.) **Document type:** academic/scholarly publication, newsletter.
Description: Exposes and critiques fallacies and contradictions in the Bible. Includes letters from readers and critics.

220.6 NE ISSN 0927-2569
BS410
BIBLICAL INTERPRETATION; a journal of contemporary approaches. (Text in English) 1993. 3/yr. fl.115($74) to individuals; institutions fl.162($105) (effective 1993). E.J. Brill, P.O. Box 9000, 2300 PA Leiden, Netherlands. TEL 31-71-5353500. FAX 31-71-5317532. TELEX 39296 BRILL NL. E-mail: ejborders@ejbrill.com. (In N. America: E.J. Brill, 24 Hudson St., Kinderhook, NY 12106. TEL 800-962-4406. FAX 518-758-1959) Eds. J. Cheryl Exum, Mark G. Brett. bk.rev. (back issues avail.) **Document type:** academic/scholarly publication. —SWETS. **CCC.**
Description: Provides an interdisciplinary forum for fresh Biblical interpretation and critical analysis in a variety of styles, including post-structuralism, semiotics, feminism, liberation hermeneutics, and for theoretical discussions of such interpretations.
Refereed Serial

220.6 809.935 NE ISSN 0928-0731
BIBLICAL INTERPRETATION SERIES. (Text in English) 1993. irreg., vol.9, 1995. price varies. E.J. Brill, P.O. Box 9000, 2300 PA Leiden, Netherlands. TEL 31-71-5353500. FAX 31-71-5317532. TELEX 39296 BRILL NL. (In N. America: E.J. Brill, 24 Hudson St., Kinderhook, NY 12106. TEL 800-962-4406. FAX 518-758-1959) (back issues avail.) **Document type:** monographic series.
Description: Publishes contemporary Biblical scholarship and studies of related issues in Biblical interpretation, providing a vehicle for experimental work from a whole range of newer perspectives, including feminist readings, semiotic and post-structuralist approaches, ecological, psychological and many other types of readings.
Refereed Serial

220 IS ISSN 0792-4739
BIBLICAL POLEMICS. (Text in English) 1988. bi-m. $25 (effective 1995 & 1996). Jerusalem Institute of Biblical Polemics, P.O. Box 9773, Jerusalem 91091, Israel. TEL 972-2-414299. FAX 972-2-414522. E-mail: m-debate@jerusalem1.dataspv.co.il. Ed. Shmuel Golding. adv. contact: Josh Adler. bk.rev. circ. 1,000. **Document type:** academic/scholarly publication.
Description: Attempts to educate and present information to refute Christian missionaries.

220 US ISSN 0067-6535
BS410
BIBLICAL RESEARCH. 1956. a. $10 (effective 1996). (Chicago Society of Biblical Research) Covenant Press, 5105 Francisco, Chicago, IL 60625. TEL 312-784-3000. Ed. David E. Aune. index. circ. 700. (also avail. in microform from UMI; back issues avail.) **Indexed:** CERDIC, New Test.Abstr., Old Test.Abstr., Rel.& Theol.Abstr. (1967-), Rel.Ind.One. **Document type:** academic/scholarly publication. —BLDSC (1947.855000); UMI.

200 US ISSN 0277-0474
BIBLICAL SCHOLARSHIP IN NORTH AMERICA. irreg. (Society of Biblical Literature) Scholars Press, Box 15399, Atlanta, GA 30333-0399. TEL 404-727-2320. FAX 404-727-2348. Ed. Kent Harold Richards. **Document type:** monographic series. —BLDSC (1947.855400).
Description: Monographs on important biblical scholars in the United States.

230 IE ISSN 0006-0917
BIBLICAL THEOLOGY. 1950. s-a. $3. Donegal Democrat, Ballyshannon, Co. Donegal, Ireland. Eds. Rev. Dr. J. Thompson, Rev. R.D. Drysdale. bk.rev. circ. 250.

220 US ISSN 0146-1079
BS410
BIBLICAL THEOLOGY BULLETIN. 1971. 4/yr. $18 to individuals (foreign $22); institutions and libraries $30. Biblical Theology Bulletin, Inc., Seton Hall University, S. Orange, NJ 07079. TEL 201-761-9770. FAX 201-325-7136. E-mail: bossmada@lanmail.shu.edu. Eds. David M. Bossman, Leland J. White. adv. contact: Veronica Classen. bk.rev.; bibl.; index, cum.index; circ. 1,800 (paid). (also avail. in microform from UMI,WMP; reprint service avail. UMI) **Indexed:** Bk.Rev.Ind. (1982-), CERDIC, Child.Bk.Rev.Ind. (1982-), New Test.Abstr., Old Test.Abstr., Rel.& Theol.Abstr. (1977-), Rel.Ind.One, Rel.Per. **Document type:** academic/scholarly publication.
—BLDSC (1947.856000); SWETS; UMI. **CCC.**
Description: Covers Bible and theology for clergy, educators in religion and social sciences, college and seminary students, and libraries.
Refereed Serial

230 US ISSN 0006-0925
BIBLICAL VIEWPOINT. 1967. s-a. $4 (foreign $6). Bob Jones University, Greenville, SC 29614. TEL 803-242-5100. Ed. Stewart Custer. bk.rev.; bibl. circ. 1,500. **Indexed:** Chr.Per.Ind., Rel.& Theol.Abstr. (1968-). **Document type:** academic/scholarly publication.
—UMI.
Description: Exposition on the books of the Bible.

220 SW ISSN 0345-1453
BIBLICUM; tidskrift foer biblisk tro och forskning. 1972. q. (plus 3 supplements). SEK 100. Stiftelsen Biblicum, c/o C. Peterson, Norra Stationsg. 29, 287 00 Trarÿd, Sweden. FAX 031-116230. TELEX 018-506925. Ed. Ingemar Furberg. bk.rev. circ. 1,000.
Supersedes: Foer Biblisk Tro (ISSN 0015-5217)

200 SP ISSN 0067-740X
BIBLIOTECA DE TEOLOGIA. 1964. irreg., no.18, 1987. price varies. (Universidad de Navarra, Facultad de Teologia) Ediciones Universidad de Navarra, S.A., Apdo. 396, 31080 Pamplona, Spain. TEL 94 825 6850.

200 SW
BIBLIOTECA THEOLOGIAE PRACTICAE. (Text in Swedish; summaries in English or German) 1957. irreg. price varies. A W I International AB, P.O. Box 4627, S-116 91 Stockholm, Sweden. TEL 468-640-8800. FAX 468-641-1180. Eds. Carl-Gustaf Andren, Aake Andren.

209 PL ISSN 0519-8658
BIBLIOTEKA PISARZY REFORMACYJNYCH. (Text in Latin and Polish) 1958. irreg., vol.16, 1988. price varies. Polska Akademia Nauk, Instytut Filozofii I Socjologii, Nowy Swiat 72, 00-330 Warsaw, Poland. Ed. L. Szczucki. circ. 350.

BIBLIOTHECA DISSIDENTIUM. see *BIBLIOGRAPHIES*

200 BE
BIBLIOTHECA EPHEMERIDUM THEOLOGICARUM LOVANIENSIUM. (Supplement to: Ephemerides Theologicae Lovanienses (ISSN 0013-9513)) 1954. irreg. (4-6 /yr.), vol.117, 1995. Leuven University Press, Krakenstraat 3, B-3000 Leuven, Belgium. TEL 32-16-324175. FAX 32-16-323782. (back issues avail.) **Indexed:** Rel.Ind.Two. **Document type:** monographic series.

200 NE
BIBLIOTHECA HUMANISTICA & REFORMATORICA. (Text in English, French or German) 1971. irreg., vol.52, 1992. price varies. De Graaf Publishers, P.O. Box 6, 2420 AA Nieuwkoop, Netherlands. TEL 31-1725-71461. **Document type:** monographic series.

BIBLIOTHECA VICTORINA; subsidia ad historiam canonicorum regularium investigandam. see *HISTORY — History Of Europe*

281.7 299.932 BE ISSN 0824-9555
BIBLIOTHEQUE COPTE DE NAG HAMMADI. (Text in Coptic, English, French) 1977. irreg., vol.20, 1993. price varies. (Universite de Laval) Editions Peeters s.p.r.l., Bondgenotenlaan 153, 3000 Leuven, Belgium. TEL 32-16-235170. FAX 32-16-228500. (Co-publisher: Presses Universitaires de Laval) (back issues avail.) **Document type:** monographic series.
Description: Publishes studies on topics relating to gnosticism, early Christianity and the Coptic texts uncovered and Nag Hammadi, Egypt.

281.9 932 UA ISSN 1110-0001
BIBLIOTHEQUE D'ETUDES COPTES. (Text in French) 1919. irreg., vol.15, 1979. price varies. Institut Francais d'Archeologie Orientale du Caire, P.O. Box 11562 Kasr-el-Aini, 37 Sharia Sheikh Aly Youssef, Mounira, Cairo, Egypt. TEL 20-2-3548245. FAX 20-2-3544635. (Dist. by: Boustany's Arab Publishing House, 29 Faggalah St., 11271 Cairo, Egypt. TEL 20-2-4177915. FAX 20-2-3404905; In France: Imprimerie Nationale - D A C F, 27 rue de la Convention, 75732 Paris Cedex 15, france. TEL 33-1-40583292. FAX 33-1-40583057) (back issues avail.) **Document type:** monographic series.
Description: Scholarly studies of historical and linguistic topics relating to Coptic Egypt.

200 BE ISSN 0067-8279
BIBLIOTHEQUE DE LA REVUE D'HISTOIRE ECCLESIASTIQUE. (Text in Dutch, English, French and Italian) 1928. irreg. Universite Catholique de Louvain, Bureau de la Revue d'Histoire Ecclesiastique, Bibliotheque, College Erasmè, B-1348 Louvain-la-Neuve, Belgium. circ. 500. **Document type:** academic/scholarly publication, monographic series.

220 SZ ISSN 0582-1673
BIBLISCHE BEITRAEGE. 1961. irreg., no.13, 1977. price varies. Universitaetsverlag Freiburg, Perolles 42, CH-1705 Fribourg, Switzerland. TEL 037-864311. FAX 037-864300. adv.; illus. circ. 1,750. **Document type:** monographic series.

220 GW ISSN 0523-5154
BIBLISCHE UNTERSUCHUNGEN. 1967. irreg., vol.21, 1990. price varies. Verlag Friedrich Pustet, Gutenbergstr. 8, 93051 Regensburg, Germany. TEL 0941-92022-0. FAX 0941-948652. Eds. Jost Eckert, Josef Hainz. circ. 800. **Document type:** monographic series.

220 GW ISSN 0006-2014
BS410
BIBLISCHE ZEITSCHRIFT. N.S. 1957. s-a. DM.70. Verlag Ferdinand Schoeningh GmbH, Postfach 2540, 33050 Paderborn, Germany. TEL 05251-127665. FAX 05251-127860. Eds. J. Schreiner, R. Schnackenburg. adv.; bibl.; index. circ. (also avail. in microform from UMI; reprint service avail. from UMI) **Indexed:** Arts & Hum.Cit.Ind., Bibl.Ling., CERDIC, Curr.Cont., New Test.Abstr., Old Test.Abstr., Rel.& Theol.Abstr. (1968-), Rel.Ind.One, Rel.Per. **Document type:** academic/scholarly publication.
—BLDSC (2020.800000); Genuine Article; SWETS; UMI. **CCC.**
Description: Collection of articles concerning the Old and the New Testament. Includes reviews and criticisms.

220 GW
BIBLISCHES SEMINAR. 1967. irreg. price varies. Calwer Verlag, Scharnhauserstr. 44, 70599 Stuttgart, Germany. TEL 0711-16722-0. FAX 0711-1672277. **Document type:** monographic series.

266 338.91 NE ISSN 0006-2308
BIJEEN; opinieblad over mondiale samenleving. 1968. m. (11/yr.). fl.62.50. Bijeen Derde Wereld Informatiehuis, Postbus 750, 5201 AT 's-Hertogenbosch, Netherlands. FAX 31-73-218512. Ed.Bd. adv.; bk.rev.; film rev.; play rev.; charts; illus. circ. 30,000. (also avail. in microfiche) **Indexed:** CERDIC.

200 US ISSN 0195-265X
BILLY JAMES HARGIS' CHRISTIAN CRUSADE; international Christian newspaper. 1969. m. free. Church of Christian Crusade, Box 977, Tulsa, OK 74102. TEL 918-438-4234. Ed. Billy James Hargis. bk.rev. circ. 55,000. (also avail. in microfilm from UMI) **Document type:** newspaper.
—UMI.
Formerly: Christian Crusade Weekly; **Supersedes:** Weekly Crusader (ISSN 0509-9498)

RELIGIONS AND THEOLOGY

291.5642 174.2 NE ISSN 0926-261X
R725.55
BIOETHICS YEARBOOK. (Text in English) 1991. a. fl.200 (for 1993 Yearbook). (Center for Ethics, Medicine and Public Issues) Kluwer Academic Publishers, Postbus 17, 3300 AA Dordrecht, Netherlands. TEL 31-78-392392. FAX 31-78-392254. TELEX 29245 KAPG NL. (Dist. by: Kluwer Academic Publishers Group, P.O. Box 322, 3300 AH Dordrecht, Netherlands. TEL 31-78-392392. FAX 31-78-546474; N. America dist. addr.: Box 358, Accord Sta., Hingham, MA 02018-0358. TEL 617-871-6600. FAX 617-871-6528) Document type: monographic series.
—BLDSC (2072.122500).
Description: Discusses and interprets recent theological issues, governmental policies, and general bioethics concerns.
Refereed Serial

270 940 GW ISSN 0341-9479
BLAETTER FUER WUERTTEMBERGISCHE KIRCHENGESCHICHTE. 1886. a. DM.70. Verein fuer Wuerttembergische Kirchengeschichte, Gaensheidestr. 4, 70184 Stuttgart, Germany. FAX 0711-2149236. Eds. Martin Brecht, Hermann Ehmer. bk.rev.; index. circ. 1,250. (reprint service avail. from SCH) Indexed: Amer.Hist.& Life, Hist.Abstr. Document type: academic/scholarly publication.

200 GW ISSN 0179-3012
BLAUES KREUZ. 1897. m. DM.39.60. (Blaues Kreuz in Deutschland e.V.) Blaukreuz Verlag, Freiligrathstr. 27, 42289 Wuppertal, Germany. Ed. Alexander Schubert. circ. 5,300.

BOA SEMENTE. see CHILDREN AND YOUTH — For

200 NE ISSN 0006-5439
BODE VAN HET HEIL IN CHRISTUS. 1858. m. fl.42.50. Uitgeverij H. Medema, Box 113, 8170 AC Vaassen, Netherlands. TEL 31-5788-74995. FAX 31-5788-73099. Ed. H.P. Medema. bk.rev. circ. 2,700. Document type: bulletin.
Formerly: Bode des Heils.

200 SP
BOLETIN OFICIAL ECLESIASTICO DEL ARZOBISPADO CASTRENSE DE ESPANA. 1950. bi-m. 5000 ptas. (effective 1996). Arzobispado Castrense de Orpana, C. Nuncio 13, 28005 Madrid, Spain. TEL 34-1-366-8228. FAX 34-1-366-8225. Dir. Jose Martin Sanz. bk.rev.; bibl.; index; circ. 700 (controlled). Document type: bulletin.
Formerly (until Jan. 1986): Boletin Oficial de la Jurisdiccion Eclesiastica Castrense.
Description: Contains documents of the Holy See, the Spanish Episcopal Conference, and the Military Archbishopric. Includes religious news and comuniques, official military orders, and an obituary column.

268 IT ISSN 0300-4589
BOLLETTINO DI COLLEGAMENTO; fra comunita cristiane in Italia. 1969. m. c/o Tony Sansone, Via delle Cascine 22, 50144 Florence, Italy. Eds. Maurizio Matteuzzi, Tony Sansone. bk.rev.; film rev.; bibl.; index. circ. 3,000.

200 282 IT ISSN 0394-1841
BOLLETTINO STORICO DELLA BASILICATA. 1985. a. L.33000. Edizioni di Storia e Letteratura s.r.l., Via Lancellotti, 18, 00186 Rome, Italy. TEL 6540556. Ed. Vincenzo Verrastro. bk.rev.

BOLLINGEN SERIES. see PHILOSOPHY

200 US
BOOKS OF ORAL TRADITION. (Text in Arabic, English, Hebrew) 1980. irreg. Quantal Publishing, 375 Moreton Bay Ln., No. 3, Goleta, CA 93117-6245. TEL 805-964-7293. Ed. Ken Bartlett; Pub. Albert Schutz. circ. 3,000. (back issues avail.)
Description: Basic guidance to practical psychotherapy of religions and mythologies.

BOOKSTORE JOURNAL. see PUBLISHING AND BOOK TRADE

200 100 US
BOSTON UNIVERSITY STUDIES IN PHILOSOPHY AND RELIGION. 1980. irreg., latest no.15. price varies. University of Notre Dame Press, Notre Dame, IN 46556. TEL 219-631-6346. FAX 219-631-8148. (Orders to: 11030 S. Langley Ave, Chicago, IL 60628. TEL 800-621-2736. FAX 800-621-8476; Overseas orders to: Eurospan University Press Group, Order Dept., 3 Henrietta St., London WC2E 8LU, England) Ed. Leroy S. Rouner. Indexed: Rel.Ind.Two. Document type: monographic series.

200 GW ISSN 0068-0443
BOTSCHAFT DES ALTEN TESTAMENTS; Erlauterungen Alttestamentlicher Schriften. 1958. irreg., vol.25, 1993. price varies. Calwer Verlag, Scharnhauserstr. 44, 70599 Stuttgart, Germany. TEL 0711-16722-0. FAX 0711-1672277. Document type: monographic series.

200 GW ISSN 0176-8573
BOTSCHAFT HEUTE. m. DM.114. Bergmoser und Hoeller Verlag GmbH, Karl-Friedrich-Str. 76, 52072 Aachen, Germany. TEL 0241-9388821. FAX 0241-9388834. circ. 4,000. (looseleaf format; back issues avail.) Document type: newsletter.
Description: Publication of interest to preachers. Features ideas for hymns, songs, psalms, prayers, Bible excerpts, and liturgical texts for sermons on all Sundays and special celebrations.

200 US ISSN 0006-9655
BRETHREN JOURNAL.* 1902. m. Rt. 3, Box 558N, Brenham, TX 77833. TEL 409-830-8762.

200 US
BRETHREN PEACE FELLOWSHIP NEWSLETTER. 1968. bi-m. Brethren Peace Fellowship, Box 455, New Windsor, MD 21776. TEL 410-775-2254. Ed. Dale Aukerman. bk.rev. circ. 750. (looseleaf format) Document type: newsletter.
Description: Deals with issues of Christian peacemaking and resistance to war.

200 HK ISSN 1018-8983
BRIDGE; church life in China today. (Editions in English, Chinese) 1983. bi-m. $19. Christian Study Centre on Chinese Religion & Culture, 6-F Kiu Kin Mansion, No. 566, Nathan Rd., Kowloon, Hong Kong. TEL 852-7703310. FAX 852-7826869. Ed. Deng Zhaoming. Indexed: Rel.Ind.One. Document type: bulletin.
Description: Covers church in China today from an ecumenical perspective.

377 200 UK ISSN 0141-6200
BRITISH JOURNAL OF RELIGIOUS EDUCATION. 1934. 3/yr. £24 (overseas £30). Christian Education Movement (C E M), Royal Bldgs., Derby DE1 1GW, England. TEL 01332-296655. Ed. John M. Hall. adv. contact: Rev. Colin Johnson. bk.rev.; charts; index. circ. 4,000. (also avail. in microform from UMI; back issues avail.; reprint service avail. from UMI) Indexed: Abstr.Musl.Rel., Br.Educ.Ind., CERDIC, Cont.Pg.Educ., Mult.Ed.Abstr., Rel. & Theol.Abstr, Sociol.Educ.Abstr. Document type: academic/scholarly publication.
—BLDSC (2324.200000); UMI.
Supersedes (in 1978): Learning for Living (ISSN 0023-9704) & Religion in Education.
Description: Contains the latest research findings that explore the philosphy of religious education worldwide.
Refereed Serial

207 268.8 US ISSN 0068-2721
BROADMAN COMMENTS; INTERNATIONAL SUNDAY SCHOOL LESSONS. 1945. q. $4.99. Broadman & Holman Publishers, 127 Ninth Ave., N., Nashville, TN 37234. TEL 615-251-2533. Ed. Robert J. Dean. circ. 14,000.
Description: Supplementary reading on International Sunday School lessons for adults.

266 US ISSN 0007-2494
BROWN GOLD. 1943. m. New Tribes Mission Publications, 1000 E. First St., Sanford, FL 32771-1487. TEL 407-323-3430. FAX 407-330-0376. Ed. Macon G. Hare. illus. circ. 46,000. Document type: newsletter.

266 GW
BRUECKENSCHLAG; Berichte aus der Mission fuer Dankopferringe und Kollektenvereine. 1990. q. Vereinigte Evangelische Mission, Rudolfstr. 137, 42285 Wuppertal, Germany. TEL 0202-89004-0. FAX 0202-89004-79.

BUDDHIST - CHRISTIAN STUDIES. see RELIGIONS AND THEOLOGY — Buddhist

266 FR ISSN 0007-4330
BULLETIN DE L'OEUVRE APOSTOLIQUE. 1913. q. 100 F. Oeuvre Apostolique pour les Missions de Fondation Francaise a l'Etranger, 8 av. Daniel Lesueur, 75007 Paris, France. TEL 43-06-44-37. Ed. L. Fromy. circ. 1,000. Document type: bulletin.

200 FR ISSN 0337-7148
BULLETIN DE SAINT-SULPICE. 1953. a. foreign US $20. Compagnie des Pretres de Saint-Sulpice, 6 rue du Regard, 75006 Paris, France.
Formerly (until 1970): Compagnie de Saint Sulpice. Bulletin du Comite des Etudes.

230 BE ISSN 0007-442X
BULLETIN DE THEOLOGIE ANCIENNE ET MEDIEVALE. 1929. a. 1000 BEF($30) (Abbaye du Mont-Cesar) Editions Peeters s.p.r.l., Bondgenotenlaan 153, B-3000 Louvain, Belgium. TEL 32-16-235170. FAX 32-16-228500. Ed. E. Manning. bk.rev.; bibl.; index. (also avail. in microfiche from IDC; back issues avail.) Document type: bulletin.

200 GO
BULLETIN EVANGELIQUE D'INFORMATION ET DE PRESSE. m. B.P. 80, Libreville, Gabon.

220 US ISSN 1065-223X
BULLETIN FOR BIBLICAL RESEARCH. 1991. a. Institute for Biblical Research, Box 275, Winona Lake, IN 46590-0275. Ed. Bruce Chilton.
—BLDSC (2834.523000).

220 GR ISSN 1012-2311
BULLETIN OF BIBLICAL STUDIES. (Text in English, French, German, and Greek) 1971; N.S. 1980. s-a. $10. Artos Zoes Publications, 12 Efranoros St., 116 35 Athens, Greece. TEL 30-1-7015-379. Ed. Savas Agouridis. bk.rev. circ. 1,000. Indexed: New Test.Abstr. Document type: academic/scholarly publication, bulletin.
—BLDSC (2834.526000).

200 US ISSN 0898-8463
PQ9189.A44
BULLETIN OF THE CANTIGUEIROS. 1987. a. $10 to individuals; institutions $20. Society of the Cantigueiros de Santa Maria, Department of Romance Languages - ML 377, University of Cincinnati, Cincinnati, OH 45221. TEL 513-556-1836. FAX 513-556-2577. E-mail: Connie.Scarborough@UC.edu. Eds. John E. Keller, Connie Scarborough. adv.; bk.rev. circ. 210. (back issues avail.) Document type: academic/scholarly publication.
—Faxon.
Description: Examines Medieval literature in relation to the Virgin Mary.
Refereed Serial

BUNYAN STUDIES. see LITERATURE

230 SP ISSN 0521-8195
BR7
BURGENSE; collectanea scientifica. (Text in French, Latin and Spanish) 1960. s-a. 3500 ptas.($40) (Facultad de Teologie) Ediciones Aldecoa, Martinez del Campo, 10, Apartado 50, 09003 Burgos, Spain. TEL 947-26700. FAX 947-260245. Ed. Nicolas Lopez Martinez. bk.rev.; bibl. circ. 600. Indexed: CERDIC, New Test.Abstr., Old Test.Abstr.
—BLDSC (2931.623000).

BURIED HISTORY. see ARCHAEOLOGY

200 US ISSN 0007-6309
BURNING BUSH. 1902. bi-m. $3 (foreign $3.50). Metropolitan Church Association, 323 Broad St., Lake Geneva, WI 53147. TEL 414-248-6786. Ed. Eva L. Adams. circ. 600.
Description: Contains sermons, editorials, seasonal poetry, religious articles, children's stories, and news from missions abroad.

C A L C REPORT. (National Clergy and Laity Concerned) see POLITICAL SCIENCE — International Relations

5676 RELIGIONS AND THEOLOGY

200 150 US
C A P S REPORT NEWSLETTER; fellowship, personal news, membership, convention. 1956. s-a. membership. Christian Association for Psychological Studies, Inc., Box 310400, New Braunfels, TX 78131-0400. TEL 210-629-2277. FAX 210-629-2342. Ed. Randolph K. Sanders. bibl. circ. 2,500. (looseleaf format) **Document type:** newsletter.
  Formerly: EnCAPSulate Newsletter.
  Description: Covers information about and schedules of conventions, activities and decisions of the board; applying Christian beliefs to psychological professions; human interest about noteworthy members.

C B M FREUNDESBRIEF. (Christoffel-Blindenmission e.V.) see *MEDICAL SCIENCES*

200 SZ
C C I A BACKGROUND INFORMATION. 1975. irreg. (approx. 2/yr.). $20. World Council of Churches, Commission of the Churches on International Affairs, 150 route de Ferney, Box 2100, CH-1211 Geneva 2, Switzerland. TEL 022-7916111. FAX 022-7910361. TELEX 415730-OIK-CH. circ. 2,000. **Document type:** bulletin.

200 US
C E S NEWSLETTER.* m. $12. Church of the Eternal Source, Box 371353, San Diego, CA 92137-1353. **Document type:** newsletter.

200 297 GW ISSN 0932-3945
C I B E D O - BEITRAEGE ZUM GESPRAECH ZWISCHEN CHRISTEN UND MUSLIMEN. 1978. bi-m. DM.30. (Provinz der Weissen Vaeter) C I B E D O, Postfach 170427, 60078 Frankfurt a.M., Germany. TEL 069-726491. FAX 069-723052. bk.rev. circ. 1,000. (back issues avail.) **Document type:** bibliography.
  Formed by the 1987 merger of: C I B E D O - Texte (ISSN 0721-0035); C I B E D O - Dokumentation (ISSN 0721-0027)

C L S QUARTERLY. see *LAW*

200 GW ISSN 0935-0373
C-MAGAZIN. 1987. q. DM.28($19) Gemeinschaft Immanuel e.V., Postfach 1460, 88483 Ravensburg, Germany. TEL 0751-17036. FAX 0751-23899. Ed. Michael Rathgeb. adv. contact: Margarete Dorm. bk.rev.; film rev.; play rev.; illus. circ. 4,300. **Document type:** consumer publication.
  Description: Reports and news about worldwide events in Christian churches.

200 US
C R E E D NEWS. 1980. q. free. Christian Renewal Effort for Emerging Democracies, 787 Princeton Kingston Rd., Princeton, NJ 08540. TEL 609-497-0224. FAX 609-497-0622. Ed. Ernest Gordon. bk.rev. circ. 4,500. (looseleaf format)
  Description: To witness to and for the persecuted church, and to encourage letter writing, and exchange visits.

200 US ISSN 1063-0872
C R I S CHAPLAIN'S CRAFT. 1988. q. $12. Council for Religion in Independent Schools, 4405 East-West Hwy., Ste. 506, Bethesda, MD 20814. TEL 301-657-0912. FAX 301-657-0915. (Subscr. to: Box 40613, Washington, DC 20016. TEL 202-342-1661) Eds. Robert Rokusek, James Goodmann. **Document type:** academic/scholarly publication.
  Description: A journal of theological reflection for school chaplains and others concerned about the moral and spiritual life of schools.

200 US ISSN 1063-0864
C R I S NEWSLETTER. m. (10/yr.). $25 membership. Council for Religion in Independent Schools, 4405 East-West Hwy., Ste. 506, Bethesda, MD 20814. TEL 301-657-0912. FAX 301-657-0915. (Subscr. to: Box 40613, Washington, DC 20016. TEL 202-342-1661) Ed. James M. Goodmann. circ. 1,200. **Document type:** newsletter.
  Description: Aims to help schools to initiate, evaluate and improve their teaching of religion and ethics.

200 US
C S S R BULLETIN. 4/yr. $18 to individuals; libraries $24; foreign $30. Council of Societies for the Study of Religion, CSSR Executive Office, Valparaiso University, Valparaiso, IN 46383. TEL 219-464-5515. Ed. Rick Busse. circ. 6,000. **Document type:** bulletin.
  Description: Serves as a clearing house for information about specific activities in the field of religious studies; includes news from various societies, general announcements, information on grants, program announcements, calendar of events.

266 UK ISSN 0308-5252
C W I HERALD; a quarterly record of Christian Witness to Israel. 1976. q. $10. Christian Witness to Israel, 166 Main Rd., Sunridge, Sevenoaks, Kent TN14 6EL, England. TEL 0959-565955. FAX 0959-565966. Ed. M.T. Moore. bk.rev. circ. 12,000. (also avail. in microform from UMI; reprint service avail. from UMI)
  —UMI.
  Former titles: Herald; Immanuel's Witness (ISSN 0019-2759)

C W R MEMBERSHIP NEWSLETTER. (Center for Women and Religion) see *WOMEN'S STUDIES*

250 FR ISSN 0008-0063
CAHIERS D'ETUDES CATHARES. 1948. q. 200 F. (foreign 250 F.). Societe du Souvenir et des Etudes Cathares, Chateau de Ferrieres, 81260 Ferrieres, France. TEL 63-74-03-53. bk.rev.; index. circ. 650. **Indexed:** CERDIC. **Document type:** bulletin.

281.7 299.932 BE
CAHIERS DE LA BIBLIOTHEQUE COPTE. (Text in French, occasionally in other languages) 1983. irreg., no.9, 1995. price varies. Editions Peeters s.p.r.l., Bondgenotenlaan 153, 3000 Leuven, Belgium. TEL 32-16-235170. FAX 32-16-228500. (back issues avail.) **Document type:** monographic series, proceedings.

200 FR ISSN 1167-1114
CAHIERS DE LA FORMATION. q. 110 F. (foreign 140 F.). Armee du Salut, 60, rue de Freres Flavien, 75976 Paris Cedex 20, France. TEL 1-43-62-25-00. **Document type:** academic/scholarly publication.
  Description: Studies the Bible, the history of the Church and the ethical positions of the Salvation Army.

200 CN ISSN 0710-4693
CAHIERS DE RECHERCHE ETHIQUE. (Text in French) 1977. irreg. price varies. Editions Fides, 165, rue Deslaurier, Ville St.-Laurent, PQ H4N 2S4, Canada. TEL 514-745-4290. FAX 514-745-4299. **Indexed:** CERDIC.

243 FR ISSN 0222-9714
CAHIERS EVANGILE. (Supplement avail.) 1951. q. 100 F. (foreign 140 F.); with supplement 180 F. (foreign 244 F.). (Service Biblique Evangile et Vie) Editions du Cerf, 29 bd. Latour Maubourg, 75340 Paris Cedex 07, France. TEL 43-26-38-32. (Subscr. to: 6 av. Vavin, 75006 Paris, France) Ed. Philippe Gruson. bk.rev.; abstr. circ. 16,000. **Indexed:** Old Test.Abstr., Pt.de Rep.
  Formerly: Cahiers Bibliques Trimestriels (ISSN 0007-960X)

261 FR ISSN 0987-2213
CAHIERS POUR CROIRE AUJOURD'HUI. 1933. s-m. 285 F. (foreign 400 F.). Assas Editions, 14 rue d'Assas, 75006 Paris, France. TEL 44-39-48-48. FAX 40-49-01-92. Ed. Luc Pareydt. index. circ. 22,000. **Indexed:** CERDIC.
  Formerly (until 1987): Cahiers de l'Actualite Religieuse et Sociale (ISSN 0007-9669)

266 US
CALL TO PRAYER. 1919. m. (10/yr.). $10 donation. World Gospel Mission, 3783 State Road 18 East, Box WGM, Marion, IN 46952. TEL 317-664-7331. Ed. Dr. Thomas H. Hermiz. circ. 40,000. (tabloid format)

220 GW ISSN 0342-8052
CALWER THEOLOGISCHE MONOGRAPHIEN. REIHE A: BIBELWISSENSCHAFT. 1972. irreg., no.15, 1993. price varies. Calwer Verlag, Scharnhauserstr. 44, 70599 Stuttgart, Germany. TEL 0711-16722-0. FAX 0711-1672277. Eds. Peter Stuhlmacher, Claus Westermann. **Document type:** monographic series.
  Superseded in part (1962-1969): Arbeiten zur Theologie. Reihe 2 (ISSN 0066-572X)

230 GW ISSN 0342-8060
CALWER THEOLOGISCHE MONOGRAPHIEN. REIHE B: SYSTEMATISCHE THEOLOGIE UND KIRCHENGESCHICHTE. 1973. irreg., no.11, 1994. price varies. Calwer Verlag, Scharnhauserstr. 44, 70599 Stuttgart, Germany. TEL 0711-16722-0. FAX 0711-1672277. Ed.Bd. **Document type:** monographic series.
  Superseded in part (1962-1969): Arbeiten zur Theologie. Reihe 2 (ISSN 0066-572X)

200 GW ISSN 0342-8079
CALWER THEOLOGISCHE MONOGRAPHIEN. REIHE C: PRAKTISCHE THEOLOGIE UND MISSIONSWISSENSCHAFT. 1973. irreg., vol.23, 1994. price varies. Calwer Verlag, Scharnhauserstr. 44, 70599 Stuttgart, Germany. TEL 0711-16722-0. FAX 0711-1672277. Eds. S.H. Buekle, M. Seitz. **Document type:** monographic series.
  Superseded in part (1962-1069): Arbeiten zur Theologie. Reihe 2 (ISSN 0066-572X)

291 UK
CAMBRIDGE STUDIES IN RELIGIOUS TRADITIONS. 1992. irreg., vol.2, 1992. price varies. Cambridge University Press, Edinburgh Bldg., Shaftesbury Rd., Cambridge CB2 2RU, England. TEL 01223-312393. FAX 01233-315052. TELEX 851817256. (N. American addr.: Cambridge University Press, Journals Dept., 40 W. 20th St., New York, NY 10011. TEL 212-924-3900. FAX 212-691-3239) Eds. John Clayton, Nicholas de Lange. (back issues avail.) **Document type:** monographic series.

CAMPANIA SACRA; rivista di storia sociale e religiosa del Mezzogiorno. see *HISTORY — History Of Europe*

200 CN ISSN 1192-6805
CANADIAN BIBLE SOCIETY NEWSLETTER. French edition: Actualites Bibliques (ISSN 1184-7204) 1960. 3/yr. free. Canadian Bible Society - Societe Biblique Canadienne, 10 Carnforth Rd., Toronto, ON M4A 2S4, Canada. TEL 416-757-4171. FAX 416-757-3376. Ed. Michele Owens. circ. 134,000. **Document type:** newsletter.
  Formerly: Canadian Bible Society Quarterly Newsletter (ISSN 0832-1590)
  Description: Demonstrates how the Society translates, publishes and distributes the Word of God to those in need.

270 CN ISSN 0008-3208
BR570
CANADIAN CHURCH HISTORICAL SOCIETY JOURNAL. 1950. s-a. Can.$20($20) Canadian Church Historical Society, c/o Archives, Anglican Church of Canada, 600 Jarvis St., Toronto, ON M4Y 2J6, Canada. TEL 416-924-9192. FAX 416-968-7983. Ed. Richard Virr. bk.rev.; cum.index. circ. 300. (also avail. in microform from UMI) **Indexed:** Amer.Hist.& Life, CERDIC, Hist.Abstr., Rel.Ind.One, Rel.Per. **Document type:** academic/scholarly publication.
  Refereed Serial

277.1 CN ISSN 0701-4309
CANADIAN COUNCIL OF CHURCHES. RECORD OF PROCEEDINGS. 1944. triennial. Canadian Council of Churches - Conseil Canadien des Eglises, 40 St. Clair Ave., E., Toronto, ON M4T 1M9, Canada. TEL 416-921-4152. FAX 416-921-7478.

266 CN ISSN 0316-2907
CANADIAN GIDEON. (Text in English and French) 1955. bi-m. Can.$8.50. Gideons International in Canada, 501 Imperial Rd. N., Guelph, ON N1H 7A2, Canada. TEL 519-823-1140. FAX 519-767-1913. Ed. Neil Bramble. illus. circ. 4,200.
  Supersedes: Torch and Trumpet (ISSN 0316-2915)

200 CN ISSN 0316-8743
CANADIAN RELIGIOUS CONFERENCE. BULLETIN. French edition: Conference Religieuse Canadienne. Bulletin (ISSN 0316-8751) (Editions in English and French) 1955. q. Canadian Religious Conference, 324 Laurier Ave. E., Ottawa, ON K1N 6P6, Canada. TEL 613-236-0824. FAX 613-236-0825. Ed. Richard Renshaw. **Document type:** bulletin.

RELIGIONS AND THEOLOGY

220 CN ISSN 0068-970X
CANADIAN SOCIETY OF BIBLICAL STUDIES. BULLETIN/SOCIETE CANADIENNE DES ETUDES BIBLIQUES. BULLETIN. (Not issued 1960-1963) 1935. a. membership. Canadian Society of Biblical Studies, Faculty of Theology, c/o Dr. Lyle Eslinger, Ed., Department of Rel. Stud., University of Calgary, Calgary, AB T2N 1N4, Canada. TEL 403-220-5886. circ. 300. **Document type:** bulletin.
—BLDSC (2434.192000).

200 CN ISSN 0527-9860
CANADIAN UNITARIAN. 1957. q. free. Canadian Unitarian Council, 188 Eglinton Ave. E., Ste. 706, Toronto, ON M4P 2X7, Canada. TEL 416-489-4121. FAX 416-489-9010. Ed. Liz Kind. bk.rev. circ. 5,000. **Document type:** newsletter.
Description: Provides information, opinion, profiles of members.

CANNON. see COLLEGE AND ALUMNI

200 US ISSN 1077-842X
CAREGIVER JOURNAL. 1983. 4/yr. College of Chaplains, Inc., 1701 E. Woodfield Rd., Ste. 311, Schaumburg, IL 60173. TEL 708-240-1014. FAX 708-240-1015. Eds. George Fitchett, Margaret Brennan. adv.: page $200; adv. contact: Mary Ann Browning. circ. 3,000. (back issues avail.)
Description: Covers topics related to pastoral care.

266 JM ISSN 0008-6436
CARIBBEAN CHALLENGE. 1959. m. $7. Christian Literature Crusade Inc., 55 Church St., P.O. Box 186, Kingston, Jamaica, W.I. TEL 908-92-27878. Ed.Bd. adv. circ. 20,000. (tabloid format)
Description: Christian magazine designed primarily to reach the "man in the street".

268 JM ISSN 0253-066X
BR1
CARIBBEAN JOURNAL OF RELIGIOUS STUDIES. 1975. s-a. J.$80($12) United Theological College of the West Indies, Golding Ave., P.O. Box 136, Mona, Kingston 7, Jamaica, W.I. TEL 809-927-2868. FAX 809-977-0812. Ed. Howard K. Gregory. bk.rev.; bibl. circ. 400. **Indexed:** Rel.Ind.One. **Document type:** academic/scholarly publication.
—UnCover.
Description: Forum for discussion of religious and pastoral issues affecting the life of Caribbean people.

260 GW
CARITAS-KALENDER. 1924. a. DM.6.50. (Deutscher Caritasverband) Lambertus-Verlag GmbH, Woelflinstr. 4, 79104 Freiburg, Germany. TEL 0761-36825-25. FAX 0761-37064. Ed. Bodo Brasching. adv. circ. 55,000. **Document type:** bulletin.

CARL NEWELL JACKSON LECTURES. see FOLKLORE

200 US ISSN 0008-672X
CAROLINA CHRISTIAN. 1959. m. $8. Carolina Christian Publications, Inc., Box 5423, Sta. B, Greenville, SC 29606. Ed. Johnny Melton. adv.; bk.rev. circ. 2,200.

200 323.4 FR ISSN 1169-9019
CATACOMBES; messager supraconfessionel de l'Eglise du silence. 1971. m. 90 F. Sergiu Grossu, Ed. & Pub., B.P. 98, 92405 Courbevoie, France. bk.rev. circ. 10,000. (tabloid format) **Indexed:** HR Rep.

CATALOGUE OF CONFERENCES, SEMINARS, WORKSHOP. see EDUCATION — Adult Education

377.8 US ISSN 0008-7726
CATECHIST. 1967. 7/yr. $19.95 (effective 1995-96). Peter Li, Inc., 330 Progress Rd., Dayton, OH 45449. TEL 513-847-5900. FAX 513-847-5910. Ed. Carl Fischer. bk.rev.; film rev.; illus. circ. 47,537. **Indexed:** Cath.Ind., CERDIC.
—UMI.
Description: Articles, announcements, and services pertaining to Catholic education.

240 SP ISSN 0528-2772
CATEQUETICA. 4/yr. 2400 ptas.($25) (effective 1994). Editorial Sal Terrae, Calle Guevara, 20, 39080 Santander, Spain. TEL 942-369198. FAX 942-369201.

200 US
CATHEDRAL COLLEGE OF THE LAITY NEWSLETTER. 1980. q. free. Cathedral College of the Laity, Washington Cathedral, Mount Saint Alban, Washington, DC 20016. TEL 202-537-6562. FAX 202-364-6605. Ed. Diane Amussen. bk.rev. circ. 9,000.

222 US ISSN 1044-6427
CATHOLIC BIBLE QUARTERLY MONOGRAPH SERIES. 1971. irreg. price varies. Catholic Biblical Association of America, Catholic University of America, Washington, DC 20064. TEL 202-319-5519. Ed. Michael Barrel. circ. 1,000. **Indexed:** Cath.Ind., New Test.Abstr., Old Test.Abstr., Rel.Per. **Document type:** monographic series, academic/scholarly publication.

CATHOLIC HEALTH ASSOCIATION MEMBERS (YEAR). see HOSPITALS

CATHOLIC HEALTH WORLD. see HOSPITALS

320 US
CENTRAL AMERICA REPORT. 1980. bi-m. $10 to individuals; institutions $15. Religious Task Force on Central America, 1747 Connecticut Ave., N.W., Washington, DC 20009. TEL 202-387-7652. Ed. Margaret Swedish. bk.rev.; illus. (tabloid format)
Description: Covers religious, political, social and economic developments in Central America, as well as relevant US policies on human rights issues.

CENTRO CAMUNO DI STUDI PREISTORICI. BOLLETTINO. see ARCHAEOLOGY

CENTRO CAMUNO DI STUDI PREISTORICI. SYMPOSIA. see ART

200 FR ISSN 0411-5562
BR23
CERCLE ERNEST RENAN. CAHIERS. 1954. bi-m. 70 F. membership. Cercle Ernest Renan, 3 rue Recamier, 75341 Paris Cedex 07, France. Ed. J. Coryne. bk.rev.; bibl. circ. 1,000. **Indexed:** CERDIC, Int.Z.Bibelwiss., New Test.Abstr.
Incorporates: Cercle Ernest Renan. Bulletin.

200 IT
CERTEZZE; rivista dei gruppi biblici universitari. 1953. m. L.20000 to individuals (foreign L.26000); students L.17000. Gruppi Biblici Universitari, Via Michelangelo Poggioli 9-17, 00161 Rome, Italy. TEL 06 495 7964. Ed. M. Fanelli. bk.rev.; charts; illus. circ. 500. (back issues avail.)
Description: Presents Christian messages. Includes dialogues and interviews on meaning and its power to transform our thoughts and actions.

200 100 US ISSN 1053-9018
BT1211
CHALCEDON REPORT. 1965. m. donation basis. Chalcedon, Inc., Box 158, Vallecito, CA 95251. TEL 209-728-3510. FAX 209-736-0536. Ed. Rev. Andrew Sandlin; Pub. Rev. Dr. R.J. Rushdoony. adv. contact: John Upton. bk.rev. circ. 11,000. (also avail. in microfiche; back issues avail.; reprint service avail.)
Description: Scholarly, serious laymen, broad analysis of international social and cultural affairs from biblical perspectives.

200 UK ISSN 0009-1014
CHALLENGE (SANDBACH); the magazine of St. Mary's Church, Sandbach. 1964. m. £2.40. St. Mary's Parochial Church Council, 55 Cookesmere Ln., Sandbach, Ches. CW11 9BQ, England. TEL 0270-763033. FAX 0270-764719. Eds. John & Nora Williams. adv.; bk.rev.; charts; illus. circ. 450. **Document type:** newsletter.

CHANNELS OF BLESSING. see HANDICAPPED — Visually Impaired

200 726 FR ISSN 0009-160X
LES CHANTIERS DU CARDINAL. 1963. q. 15 F. 106 rue du Bac, 75341 Paris Cedex 07, France. TEL 42-22-46-86. Ed. M. Poirson. adv.; illus. circ. 75,000.

200 DK ISSN 0108-4453
CHAOS; Dansk-Norsk tidsskrift for religionshistoriske studier. 1982. s-a. DKK 97 per no. Koebenhavns Universitet, Institut for Religionshistorie, Copenhagen, Denmark. (Subscr. to: Museum Tusculanums Forlag, Njalsgade 94, DK-2300 Copenhagen S, Denmark) (Co-sponsor: Religionshistorisk Forening) Ed. J. Podemann Soerensen. illus. **Document type:** academic/scholarly publication.

200 US ISSN 0895-7916
CHAPLAINCY TODAY; the newsletter for professional chaplains. 10/yr. $20. College of Chaplains, Inc., 1701 E. Woodfield Rd., Ste. 311, Schaumburg, IL 60173. TEL 708-240-1014. FAX 708-240-1015. Ed. Frank Moyer. bk.rev.; circ. 550 (paid). **Document type:** newsletter.
Description: Geared to professional chaplains, and individuals in pastoral care, counseling and education.

200 US ISSN 0279-0424
CHARISMA; the magazine about Spirit-led living. 1975. m. $19.97. Strang Communications Co., 600 Rinehart Rd., Lake Mary, FL 32746. TEL 407-333-0600. Ed. Stephen Strang. adv.; bk.rev. circ. 200,000. **Indexed:** Chr.Per.Ind., G.Soc.Sci.& Rel.Per.Lit. **Document type:** consumer publication.
—UMI.

CHART AND COMPASS INTERNATIONAL. see SOCIAL SERVICES AND WELFARE

200 CN ISSN 0843-1736
CHASTITY AND HOLINESS MAGAZINE; Christ and integrity. 1988. s-a. Can.$15($17) (effective June 1995). (Christianiac Poetic Ministry) C J L Poetic Empire Art Co., 22006 Thorncliffe Stn., Toronto, ON M4H 1N9, Canada. TEL 416-696-2350. Ed. Cecil Justin Lam; Pub. Cecil Justin Lam. adv. contact: Janet King. bk.rev.; index. circ. 1,000. (looseleaf format; back issues avail.)
Description: Covers evangelism, integrity, purity and love, chastity and hope.
Refereed Serial

200 US
CHICAGO HISTORY OF AMERICAN RELIGION. 1973. irreg., latest 1981. price varies. University of Chicago Press, 5801 S. Ellis Ave., Chicago, IL 60637. TEL 312-702-7899. Ed. Martin E. Marty. adv.; bk.rev. (reprint service avail. from UMI,ISI)
Refereed Serial

200 US ISSN 0739-5124
BV4070
CHICAGO THEOLOGICAL SEMINARY REGISTER. 1908. 3/yr. $4. Chicago Theological Seminary, 5757 University Ave., Chicago, IL 60637. TEL 312-752-5757. Ed. Perry LeFevre. bk.rev. circ. 4,000. **Indexed:** Rel.& Theol.Abstr. (1989-), Rel.Ind.One.

200 IT
LA CHIESA NEL TEMPO; rivista quadrimestrale di vita edicultura. 1985. 3/yr. L.20000. Arcidiocesi di Reggio Calabria, Via T. Campanella, 63, 89100 Reggio Calabria, Italy. TEL 0965-21037. Ed. Antonio Denisi.

CHILDREN'S MINISTRY. see CHILDREN AND YOUTH — About

CHILDWORLD. see CHILDREN AND YOUTH — About

200 GW ISSN 0932-6855
CHINA HEUTE; Informationen ueber Religion und Christentum im Chinesischen Raum. 1982. bi-m. China-Zentrum e.V., Arnold-Janssen-Str. 22, 53754 Sankt Augustin, Germany. TEL 02241-237432. FAX 02241-205841. TELEX 889559-STEYL-D. Ed. Roman Malek. bk.rev. circ. 1,600. (back issues avail.) **Document type:** newsletter.

| 291 | UK | ISSN 0956-4314 |

CHINA STUDY JOURNAL. 1986. 3/yr. £12 to individuals (rest of Europe £17 ($44); elsewhere £20 ($50)); institutions £18 (rest of Europe £22 ($34); elsewhere £25 ($40)) (effective 1995). Council of Churches for Britain and Ireland, China Department, 35-41 Lower Marsh, London SE1 7RL, England. TEL 0171-620-4444. FAX 0171-928-0010. Ed. Edmond Tang. circ. 300. **Document type:** academic/scholarly publication.
 Description: Contains academic articles about religion in China by Chinese and European researchers, documentation of China source materials, and translations of Church documents.

| 200 | US | ISSN 0896-7660 |

CHINESE THEOLOGICAL REVIEW. 1985. a. $10. Foundation for Theological Education in Southeast Asia, 2390 Orchard, Holland, MI 49424. TEL 616-399-9585. Ed. Janice Wickeri; Pub. Marvin Hoff. circ. 1,200. (back issues avail.) **Document type:** academic/scholarly publication.
 —BLDSC (3181.122200).

| 291 | HK | ISSN 0009-4668 |

CHING FENG; a journal on Christianity and Chinese relition and culture. (Text in English) 1957. q. $30. Christian Study Centre on Chinese Religion & Culture, 6-F Kiu Kin Mansion, 566 Nathan Rd., Kowloon, Hong Kong. TEL 7703310. FAX 7826869. Ed. Peter K.H. Lee. adv.; bk.rev. circ. 1,200. (also avail. in microform from NBI,UMI; reprint service avail.) **Indexed:** Rel.& Theol.Abstr. (1987-), Rel.Ind.One. **Document type:** academic/scholarly publication.
 ●Also available online. Vendor(s): Knight-Ridder, Inc., Ovid Technologies.
 —UMI.
 Formerly (until 1964): Quarterly Notes on Christianity and Chinese Religion.

| 266 | US | ISSN 0199-6487 |

CHINMAYA MISSION WEST NEWS. m. $7. Chinmaya Mission West, Box 129, Piercy, CA 95587. TEL 707-247-3488. FAX 707-247-3422. Ed. Viji Sundaram.

| 200 | SZ | ISSN 0009-4994 |

CHOISIR; revue de reflexion chretienne. 1959. m. 74 Fr. Society of Jesus, 18 Rue Jacques-Dalphin, CH-1227 Carouge-Geneve, Switzerland. TEL 022-429880. FAX 022-429269. TELEX 421325-CHOICH. Ed.Bd. adv.; bk.rev.; index. circ. 4,300.

| 200 | UK | ISSN 0964-0886 |

CHRISM. 1965. q. £5 (typically set in Jan.). Guild of St. Raphael, The Vicarage, Skirwith, Penrith, Cumbria CA10 1RQ, England. TEL 01768-88663. Ed. Martin Dudley. bk.rev. circ. 1,600. **Document type:** academic/scholarly publication.
 Formerly: St. Raphael Quarterly.

| 200 | US | ISSN 0889-8901 |

CHRIST FOR THE NATIONS. vol.44, no.11, 1992. m. Christ for the Nations, Inc., 3404 Conway St., Dallas, TX 75224. TEL 214-376-1711. (Subscr. to: Box 769000, Dallas, TX 75376-9000; Canadian addr.: Christ for the Nations (Canada), Inc., P.O. Box 272, Surrey, B.C. V3T 4W8) Ed. Mrs. Gordon Lindsay.

| 200 | GW | ISSN 0009-5087 |

CHRIST UND BUCH; eine Hilfe fuer die Auswertung und Andwendung des gedruckten Wortes. 1960. q. membership. Evangelische Buchhilfe e.V., Alte Hauptstr. 14, 34246 Vellmar, Germany. Ed. Oskar Schnetter. bk.rev. circ. 10,000.

| 200 | NE | ISSN 0009-5141 |

CHRISTELIJK OOSTEN. (Text in Dutch; summaries in English, French, German) 1948. s-a. fl.70 to individuals; institutions fl.75. Instituut voor Oosters Christendom te Nijmegen, Erasmusplein 1, 6525 HT Nijmegen, Netherlands. TEL 31-80-615603. Ed. A. Davids. adv.; bk.rev.; bibl.; illus.; index, cum.index. circ. 450. **Indexed:** CERDIC. **Document type:** academic/scholarly publication.
 Description: Review on Christianity in Eastern Europe and the Middle East.

| 200 | GW | ISSN 0009-5184 |

DIE CHRISTENGEMEINSCHAFT; Monatsschrift zur religioesen Erneuerung. 1924. m. DM.58. Verlag Urachhaus Johannes M. Mayer GmbH, Urachstr. 41, 70190 Stuttgart, Germany. FAX 0711-281379. adv.; bk.rev.; index. circ. 10,000. (processed) **Indexed:** CERDIC. **Document type:** proceedings.

| 266 | UK | ISSN 0263-7715 |

CHRISTIAN ACTION JOURNAL. q. £10. Christian Action, 125 Kennington Rd., London SE11 6SF, England. TEL 0171-735-2372. Ed. Rev. Canon Eric James. adv.; bk.rev. circ. 1,000. (back issues avail.)
 —BLDSC (3181.779050).

CHRISTIAN ADVERTISING FORUM. see *ADVERTISING AND PUBLIC RELATIONS*

CHRISTIAN ANTI-COMMUNISM CRUSADE. NEWSLETTER. see *POLITICAL SCIENCE*

CHRISTIAN BIOETHICS; non-ecumenical studies in medical morality. see *MEDICAL SCIENCES*

| 262 | US | ISSN 0009-5281 |
| BR1 | | |

CHRISTIAN CENTURY; an Ecumenical weekly. 1900. w. $35. Christian Century Foundation, 407 S. Dearborn St., Chicago, IL 60605. TEL 312-427-5380. Ed. James M. Wall. adv.; bk.rev.; s-a. index. circ. 33,000. (also avail. in microform from UMI) **Indexed:** Acad.Ind., Amer.Hist.& Life, Bk.Rev.Dig., Bk.Rev.Ind. (1965-), CCR, Child.Bk.Rev.Ind. (1965-), Film Lit.Ind. (1973-), G.Soc.Sci.& Rel.Per.Lit., Hist.Abstr., Hlth.Ind., Mag.Ind., Media Rev.Dig., Mid.East: Abstr.& Ind., PMR, R.G., Rel.& Theol.Abstr. (1968-), Rel.Ind.One, Rel.Per., TOM. **Document type:** academic/scholarly publication, trade publication.
 ●Also available online. Vendor(s): University Microfilms International.
 Also available on CD-ROM. Producer(s): University Microfilms International.
 —Faxon; SWETS; UMI; UnCover.

CHRISTIAN CHIROPRACTOR. see *MEDICAL SCIENCES — Chiropractic, Homeopathy, Osteopathy*

CHRISTIAN CHIROPRACTORS ASSOCIATION JOURNAL. see *MEDICAL SCIENCES — Chiropractic, Homeopathy, Osteopathy*

| 200 | US | |

THE CHRISTIAN CHRONICLE; an international newspaper for members of Churches of Christ. 1943. m. $10. Oklahoma Christian University of Science and Arts, Box 11000, Oklahoma City, OK 73136-1100. TEL 405-425-5070. FAX 405-425-5076. Ed. Howard W. Norton. adv. contact: Paul Cook. bk.rev.; illus. circ. 103,000. (tabloid format) **Document type:** newspaper.
 Description: National and international news, features, and announcements pertaining to the members and activities of the Churches of Christ.

CHRISTIAN CIVIC LEAGUE RECORD. 1900. m. $10 (effective 1995). Christian Civic League of Maine, 70 Sewall St., Box 5459, Augusta, ME 04332. TEL 207-622-7634. FAX 207-622-7635. Ed. Michael Heath. circ. 5,500. (back issues avail.) **Document type:** newsletter.

| 200 | US | ISSN 0892-9300 |

CHRISTIAN CONQUEST. 1969. m. $10 institutional contribution. Charles Simpson Ministries, Box Z, Mobile, AL 36616. TEL 205-633-7900. FAX 205-633-7080. illus. circ. 92,000.
 Formerly (until 1987): New Wine (ISSN 0194-438X)

| 266 | US | ISSN 0739-8913 |
| BV1460 | | |

CHRISTIAN EDUCATION JOURNAL. 1980. 3/yr. $10 (foreign $12). S P Ministries, Box 650, Glen Ellyn, IL 60138. TEL 708-260-6440. FAX 708-668-3806. Ed. Leslie H. Stobbe; Pub. V. Gilbert Beers. bk.rev.; circ. 2,400. (paid). (also avail. in microfiche from UMI; microfilm from UMI; back issues avail.) **Indexed:** CERDIC, Chr.Per.Ind., Rel.& Theol.Abstr. (1980-), Rel.Ind.One. **Document type:** academic/scholarly publication.
 —UMI.
 Formerly: Journal of Christian Education (ISSN 0277-9935)
 Description: Promotes growth and advancement in Christian education.

| 268 | US | |

CHRISTIAN EDUCATORS JOURNAL. 1961. q. $7.50 to non-members (foreign $11). Christian Educators Journal Association, c/o Peter Boogaart, Bus.Mgr., 1828 Mayfair N.E., Grand Rapids, MI 49503. Ed. Lorna Van Gilst. adv.; bk.rev.; illus. circ. 5,000. (back issues avail.) **Indexed:** Chr.Per.Ind., G.Soc.Sci.& Rel.Per.Lit.

| 200 | US | ISSN 0009-5338 |
| BV1420 | | |

THE CHRISTIAN ENDEAVOR WORLD; the voice of Christian Endeavor. 1886. a. membership. Christian Endeavor International, 3575 Valley Rd., Box 820, Liberty Corner, NJ 07938-0820. TEL 908-604-9440. FAX 908-604-6075. Ed. David G. Jackson. bk.rev.; illus. circ. 4,200. (also avail. in microfilm)

CHRISTIAN FAMILY CATALOG. see *GIFTWARE AND TOYS*

| 200 | MW | |

CHRISTIAN FORUM. (Text in Chichewa or English) q. Christian Council of Malawi, Lilongwe, Malawi. (Dist. by: Christian Literature Association in Malawi, Box 503, Blantyre, Malawi)

| 200 | UK | ISSN 0953-4385 |

CHRISTIAN HERALD. 1866. w. £36 for 6 mos. Herald House Ltd., 96 Dominion Rd., Worthing, W. Sussex BN14 8JP, England. TEL 01903-821082. FAX 01903-821081. Ed. B. Hardy. adv.; bk.rev.; circ. 20,000. (paid). **Indexed:** Access, CCR, G.Soc.Sci.& Rel.Per.Lit., Mag.Ind. **Document type:** newspaper.
 Description: Contains news and articles of interest to a Christian audience.

| 200 900 | US | ISSN 0891-9666 |
| BR140 | | |

CHRISTIAN HISTORY MAGAZINE. 1982. q. $19.95. Christianity Today, Inc., 465 Gundersen Dr., Carol Stream, IL 60188. TEL 708-260-6200. FAX 708-260-0114. E-mail: edit@aol.com. (Subscr. to: CDS, Box 11618, Des Moines, IA 50340. TEL 800-873-6986) Ed. Mark Galli. adv. contact: Linda Schambach. bk.rev.; illus. circ. 90,000. (back issues avail.) **Document type:** consumer publication.
 —Faxon; UMI; UnCover.
 Description: Covers major persons, events, issues in the history of the Christian Church.

| 377.8 | US | ISSN 0009-5389 |

CHRISTIAN HOME & SCHOOL. 6/yr. $11.95. Christian Schools International, 3350 E. Paris Ave., S.E., Grand Rapids, MI 49512. TEL 616-957-1070. Ed. Gordon L. Bordewyk. adv. contact: Lori Feenstra. bk.rev. circ. 58,000. **Document type:** academic/scholarly publication.
 Description: Aimed at contemporary Christian families. Focuses on family life and educational issues.

| 266 | CN | ISSN 0844-5699 |

CHRISTIAN INFO NEWS. 1982. m. Can.$16. Christian Info (Vancouver - Lower Mainland) Society, Ste. 200, 20316 56 Ave., Langley, BC V3A 3Y7, Canada. TEL 604-534-1444. FAX 604-534-2970. Ed. Flyn Ritchie. adv.; bk.rev.; film rev.; play rev. circ. 27,000. (tabloid format; back issues avail.)
 Formerly: Christian Info (ISSN 0838-8547)

| 294.6 | II | |

CHRISTIAN INSTITUTE FOR RELIGIOUS STUDIES. BULLETIN. (Text in English) vol.18, 1989. 2/yr. Rs.201. Christian Institute for Religious Studies, Baring Union Christian College, Batala 143505 (Punjab), India. TEL 01871-40011. Ed. Clarence O. Mcmullen. bk.rev. **Document type:** bulletin.
 Formerly (until 1990): Christian Institute of Sikh Studies. Bulletin.
 Description: Discusses Sikh culture and theology from a Christian perspective, and fosters dialogue between Sikhs and Christians.

CHRISTIAN IRELAND TODAY. see *SOCIOLOGY*

| 260 051 | US | ISSN 0009-5435 |

CHRISTIAN LIVING; a magazine about people and faith today. 1954. 8/yr. $19.95. Mennonite Publishing House, 616 Walnut Ave., Scottdale, PA 15683-1999. TEL 412-887-8500. FAX 412-887-3111. Ed. Steve Kriss. adv.; bk.rev.; illus.; index. circ. 5,200.

CHRISTIAN MANAGEMENT REPORT. see *BUSINESS AND ECONOMICS — Management*

RELIGIONS AND THEOLOGY

CHRISTIAN MEDICAL & DENTAL SOCIETY JOURNAL. see *MEDICAL SCIENCES*

CHRISTIAN MEDICAL ASSOCIATION OF INDIA. JOURNAL. see *MEDICAL SCIENCES*

250   US   ISSN 0033-4138
BV4000
THE CHRISTIAN MINISTRY; a professional journal for clergy. vol.40, 1969. bi-m. $14. Christian Century Foundation, 407 S. Dearborn St., Chicago, IL 60605-1111. TEL 312-427-5380. FAX 312-427-1302. Ed. James M. Wall. adv.; bk.rev.; index. circ. 8,000. (also avail. in microform from UMI; back issues avail.) **Indexed:** G.Soc.Sci.& Rel.Per.Lit., Rel.Ind.One. **Document type:** academic/scholarly publication, trade publication.
—UMI.
Formerly: Pulpit.

200   US   ISSN 0744-4052
CHRISTIAN MISSIONS IN MANY LANDS. vol.33, 1970. m. (11/yr.). free. Christian Missions in Many Lands, Inc., Box 13, Spring Lake, NJ 07762. TEL 908-449-8880. Ed.Bd. bk.rev.; illus. circ. 14,000.
Formerly: Fields (ISSN 0015-0762)

248   US
CHRISTIAN MOTHER (PITTSBURGH). 1942? q. $3. Archconfraternity of Christian Mothers, 220 37th St., Pittsburgh, PA 15201. TEL 412-683-2400. Ed. Rev. Bertin Roll. circ. 30,000.

CHRISTIAN MUSIC DIRECTORIES: RECORDED MUSIC. see *MUSIC*

200   US   ISSN 0899-7292
CHRISTIAN NEW AGE QUARTERLY; a bridge supporting dialogue. 1989. q. $12.50 (effective Jan.1, 1991). Bethsheva's Concern, Box 276, Clifton, NJ 07011-0276. Ed. Catherine Groves. adv.; bk.rev. (back issues avail.) **Document type:** newsletter, academic/scholarly publication.
Description: Probes the common ground and distinctions of Christianity and the New Age movement - a forum for dialogue between the two ideologies.

200   IS   ISSN 0009-5532
BR1110
CHRISTIAN NEWS FROM ISRAEL. (Editions in English, French and Spanish) 1949. s-a. $5. Ministry of Religious Affairs, Box 1167, 30 Jaffa St., Jerusalem, Israel. Ed. Shalom Ben-Zakkai. adv.; bk.rev.; bibl.; illus.; index. circ. 10,000. (also avail. in microform from UMI; reprint service avail. from UMI) **Indexed:** New Test.Abstr., Old Test.Abstr.
—UMI.

266   US   ISSN 1040-8088
CHRISTIAN PARENTING TODAY.* 1988. 6/yr. $16.97 (foreign $21.37) (effective Jan. 1992). Good Family Magazine, Box 36630, Colorado Springs, CO 80936-3663. TEL 503-549-8261. FAX 503-549-0153. adv.; bk.rev. circ. 200,000.
Description: Provides parents with expert, biblically sound advice that covers every aspect of child development from birth through the teen years.

CHRISTIAN PATHWAY. see *CHILDREN AND YOUTH — For*

200   US
CHRISTIAN RANCHMAN. 1976. m. Cowboys for Christ, Box 7557, Ft. Worth, TX 76111. TEL 817-834-6841. Ed. Ted K. Pressley. bk.rev. circ. 38,000. (tabloid format; back issues avail.) **Document type:** newspaper.
Description: Outreach ministry to livestock industry. Provides testimonies of what God has done in livestock people's lives.

266   US
CHRISTIAN READER. 1963. 6/yr. $17.50. Christianity Today, Inc., 465 Gundersen Dr., Carol Stream, IL 60188-2498. TEL 708-260-6200. FAX 708-260-0114. E-mail: creditoria@aol.com. (Subscr. to: Christian Reader, Box 1913, Marion, OH 43305. TEL 800-347-6969) Ed. Bonne Steffen. adv. contact: Linda Schambach. bk.rev.; illus. circ. 234,000. **Document type:** consumer publication.
Description: Digest of the best in Christian reading.

CHRISTIAN RECORD TALKING MAGAZINE. see *HANDICAPPED — Visually Impaired*

207   US
CHRISTIAN RESEARCH JOURNAL. 1975. q. $20 (Canada $24; elsewhere $36) (effective 1995). Christian Research Institute, Box 500, San Juan Capistrano, CA 92693-0500. TEL 714-855-9926. FAX 714-855-9927. (Subscr. in Canada to: CRI Canada, Box 3216, Station B, Calgary, AB T2M 4L7, Canada) Ed. Elliot Miller. adv. contact: Melanie M. Codgill. bk.rev.; bibl.; circ. 40,000 (paid). **Document type:** academic/scholarly publication.
Former titles: Forward (San Juan Capistrano); Christian Research Institute. Newsletter (ISSN 0045-6845)
Description: Specializes in in-depth, cutting-edge research of cults, the occult (including new age), religions, controversial new religious movements, and ethics from the perspective of evangelical Christianity.

CHRISTIAN RETAILING; the trade magazine of religious retailing. see *PUBLISHING AND BOOK TRADE*

200   US   ISSN 0017-2251
BR1
CHRISTIAN SCHOLAR'S REVIEW; a Christian quarterly of the arts and sciences. 1970. q. $19 to individuals (foreign $23); libraries $24 (foreign $28). c/o Calvin College, Grand Rapids, MI 49546. (Subscr. to: Circulation Department, Calvin College, Grand Rapids, MI 49546) Ed. William Hasker. adv.; bk.rev.; abstr.; bibl.; index, cum.index. circ. 4,200. (also avail. in microform from UMI; microfiche; back issues avail.) **Indexed:** Abstr.Engl.Stud., Amer.Hist.& Life, Bibl.Engl.Lang.& Lit., CERDIC, Chr.Per.Ind., G.Soc.Sci.& Rel.Per.Lit., Hist.Abstr., M.L.A., Mid.East: Abstr.& Ind., New Test.Abstr., Rel.& Theol.Abstr. (1971-), Rel.Ind.One. **Document type:** academic/scholarly publication.
—BLDSC (3181.920000); Faxon; UMI; UnCover.
Description: Peer articles, essays, and publication reviews pertaining to Christian thought and the interrelationship between Christian thought and all areas of scientific, theological, philosophical, cultural, and social scholarly interest.
Refereed Serial

CHRISTIAN SCHOOL ADMINISTRATOR. see *EDUCATION — School Organization And Administration*

CHRISTIAN SCHOOL BUILDER. see *EDUCATION — Teaching Methods And Curriculum*

200   MW
CHRISTIAN SERVICE COMMITTEE OF THE CHURCHES IN MALAWI. ANNUAL REPORT. (Text in English) a. free. Christian Service Committee of the Churches in Malawi, Box 51294, Limbe, Malawi. TEL 265-642877. FAX 265-642616. TELEX 44365-CSC-MI.

CHRISTIAN SINGLES NEWS. see *SINGLES' INTERESTS AND LIFESTYLES*

CHRISTIAN SOCIALIST. see *POLITICAL SCIENCE*

200   US   ISSN 0009-5656
CHRISTIAN STANDARD. 1866. w. $19. Standard Publishing, 8121 Hamilton Ave., Cincinnati, OH 45231. TEL 513-931-4050. FAX 513-931-0904. Ed. Sam E. Stone. bk.rev.; illus.; index, cum.index: 1866-1966. circ. 61,000. (also avail. in microfilm) **Indexed:** G.Soc.Sci.& Rel.Per.Lit.
—UMI.

261 300   US   ISSN 0009-5664
HN51
CHRISTIAN STATESMAN. 1867. bi-m. $15. National Reform Association, Box 97086, Pittsburgh, PA 15229-0086. TEL 412-244-0337. E-mail: 76060.3620@compuserve.com. Ed. Niles S. Campbell. adv.; bk.rev. circ. 1,000. (also avail. in microform; reprint service avail. from UMI) **Document type:** academic/scholarly publication.
—UMI.

200   US
CHRISTIAN VANGUARD. 1971. m. $25. New Christian Crusade Church, Box 426, Metairie, LA 70004. TEL 504-279-5940. (back issues avail.) **Document type:** newsletter.

200   US   ISSN 0009-5702
CHRISTIAN WOMAN. 1933. 6/yr. $16.98. Gospel Advocate Company, 1006 Elm Hill Pike, Nashville, TN 37210. TEL 615-254-8781. FAX 615-254-7411. Ed. Sandra Humphrey. adv.; bk.rev.; illus.; index. circ. 30,000.
Description: Features poetry, fiction, lessons, and information on issues pertaining to contemporary family life, self-improvement, motivation, parenting, and marriage for the practicing female Christian, married or single, with advice and opinion columns.

267   AT
CHRISTIAN WOMAN. 1954. 6/yr. Aus.$15 (effective Nov.1, 1991). Christian Women Communicating International, P.O. Box 650, Punchbowl, N.S.W. 2196, Australia. TEL 61-2-740-6355. FAX 61-2-750-5330. Ed. Sanna Wilson. adv. contact: Janice Derley. bk.rev. circ. 9,900.

200   FR   ISSN 0009-5729
CHRISTIANISME AU VINGTIEME SIECLE. 1872. w. 685 F. (Association le Christianisme au 20th Siecle) Mereau, 175 bd. Anatole France, 93208 Saint-Denis, France. TEL 48-13-38-58. FAX 48-13-09-08. Ed. F. Delgorge. adv.; bk.rev.; bibl.; film rev.; illus.; play rev. circ. 7,000.

201 296   US
CHRISTIANITY AND JUDAISM IN ANTIQUITY. 1988. irreg., latest vol.9, 1995. price varies. University of Notre Dame Press, Notre Dame, IN 46556. TEL 219-631-6346. FAX 219-631-8148. (Orders to: 11030 S. Langley Ave., Chicago, IL 60628. TEL 800-621-2736. FAX 800-621-2736; Overseas orders to: Eurospan University Press Group, Order Dept., 3 Henrietta St., London WC2E 8LU, England) Ed. Charles Kannengiesser. **Document type:** academic/scholarly publication.

CHRISTIANITY AND LITERATURE. see *LITERARY AND POLITICAL REVIEWS*

200   US   ISSN 0009-5753
BR1
CHRISTIANITY TODAY. 1956. 14/yr. $24.95. Christianity Today, Inc., 465 Gundersen Dr., Carol Stream, IL 60188. TEL 708-260-6200. FAX 708-261-0114. E-mail: ctedit@aol.com. (Subscr. to: CDS, Box 11618, Des Moines, IA 50340. TEL 800-999-1704) Ed. David Neff. adv. contact: Linda Schambach. bk.rev.; bibl.; index. circ. 180,000. (also avail. in microform from UMI) **Indexed:** Acad.Ind., Biog.Ind., Bk.Rev.Ind. (1990-), CCR, Chic.Per.Ind., Child.Bk.Rev.Ind. (1990-), Chr.Per.Ind., G.Soc.Sci.& Rel.Per.Lit., Mag.Ind., Mid.East: Abstr.& Ind., New Test.Abstr., Old Test.Abstr., Peace Res.Abstr., PMR, R.G., Rel.& Theol.Abstr. (1968-), Rel.Ind.One, Rel.Per. **Document type:** consumer publication.
●Also available online. Vendor(s): University Microfilms International.
—Faxon; UMI; UnCover.
Description: To keep thoughtful persons and Christian leaders informed, challenged and motivated.

200   US
CHRISTIANITY UNDER STRESS. 1988. irreg. Duke University Press, Box 90660, Durham, NC 27708. TEL 919-687-3600. FAX 919-688-4574. Ed. Sabrina Ramet.

200 323.4   US   ISSN 1044-5846
CHRISTIANS IN CRISIS. 1985. bi-m. free. Christian Forum Research Foundation, 1111 Fairgrounds Rd., Grand Rapids, MN 55744. TEL 218-326-2688. Ed. Sidney Reiners. circ. 1,000 (controlled). **Document type:** newsletter.
Description: Covers religious freedom and church-state issues internationally.

268   AU   ISSN 0009-5761
CHRISTLICH-PAEDAGOGISCHE BLAETTER; Zeitschrift fuer den katechetischen Dienst. 1887. q. S.320. (Oesterreichische Schulamtsleiterkonferenz) Verlag Herder, Wollzeile 33, A-1010 Vienna, Austria. TEL 01-5121413. Ed. Kurt Zisler. adv.; bk.rev.; abstr.; index. circ. 3,800. **Indexed:** Canon Law Abstr. **Document type:** academic/scholarly publication.

RELIGIONS AND THEOLOGY

200   AU   ISSN 0009-5796
CHRISTLICHE INNERLICHKEIT; Schrift fuer Gebet und gelebtes Christentum. 1965. bi-m. S.70($5) Werk Christliche Innerlichkeit, Karmelweg 1, A-8630 Mariazell, Austria. (Affiliate: Order of Discalced Carmelite Fathers in Austria) Ed. P. Suitbert Siedl. bk.rev. circ. 5,000.

200 051   US
CHRISTMAS (MINNEAPOLIS). 1931. a. $10.95 paper. Augsburg Fortress, Publishers, 426 S. Fifth St., Box 1209, Minneapolis, MN 55440.
TEL 612-330-3402; 800-328-4648.
FAX 612-330-3455.

266   US   ISSN 8755-6901
CHRISTOPHER NEWS NOTES. 1945. 10/yr. free. Christophers, Inc., 12 E. 48th St., New York, NY 10017. TEL 212-759-4050. FAX 212-838-5073. Ed. Stephanie Raha. circ. 600,000. **Document type:** newsletter.
Description: Discusses family, spiritual and personal issues.

200   US
CHRISTOPHER WORLD. 1976. a. free. Christophers, Inc., 12 E. 48th St., New York, NY 10017.
TEL 212-759-4050. FAX 212-838-5073. Ed. Stephanie Raha. circ. 200,000 (controlled).
Description: Happenings at the Christophers including upcoming publications, since the last Christopher World.

220   US   ISSN 0009-630X
CHURCH ADVOCATE. 1835. m. $10.25. Churches of God, General Conference, Box 926, Findlay, OH 45839. TEL 419-424-1961. FAX 419-424-3433. Ed. Linda Draper. bk.rev.; charts; illus.; circ. 6,600 (paid). (also avail. in microfilm) **Indexed:** CERDIC.
Formerly (until 1889): Gospel Publisher.
Description: Encourages an informed people to be the Church.
Refereed Serial

261 323   US   ISSN 0009-6334
BR516
CHURCH & STATE.* 1948. m. (Sep.-July). $18 (foreign $25). Americans United for Separation of Church and State, 1816 Jefferson Pl. N.W., Washington, DC 20036-2505. TEL 301-589-3707.
FAX 301-495-9173. Ed. Joseph L. Conn. bk.rev.; illus.; index. circ. 25,000. (also avail. in microform from UMI; reprint service avail. from UMI) **Indexed:** CERDIC, Mid.East: Abstr.& Ind., P.A.I.S., Polit.Sci.Abstr. **Document type:** newsletter.
—BLDSC (3189.733000); Faxon; UMI; UnCover.
Formerly (until 1951): Church and State Newsletter.
Description: Reviews church-state news and analysis; focuses on the U.S. with some international reports.

CHURCH AND SYNAGOGUE LIBRARIES. see *LIBRARY AND INFORMATION SCIENCES*

200   UK
CHURCH ARMY. SHARE IT. 1906. q. free. Church Army, Independents Rd., Blackheath, London SE3 9LG, England. Ed. S. Barnes. bk.rev. circ. 60,000. **Document type:** newsletter.
Former titles (until 1992): Church Army. Frontline News; (until 1985): Church Army. Review; New Review; (until 1983): Church Army Review (ISSN 0009-6350)
Description: Reports on the activities of the Church Army and reviews evangelism within the Church of England.

266   US
CHURCH AROUND THE WORLD. m. donation. U S Center for World Mission, Frontier Fellowship, 1605 Elizabeth St., Pasadena, CA 91104.
TEL 818-398-2241. FAX 0818-398-2263.

200 690   CN   ISSN 1198-1156
CHURCH BUSINESS. PRODUCTS & TECHNOLOGY. 1992. bi-m. Can.$18($30) Momentum Media Management, 4040 Creditview Rd., Unit 11, Box 1800, Mississauga, ON L5C 348, Canada.
TEL 905-569-1800. FAX 905-569-1818. Ed. Hugh Parkinson. adv.: B&W page Can.$1915, color page Can.$2750; trim 8 x 11; adv. contact: Hugh Parkinson. bk.rev. circ. 12,400. **Document type:** trade publication.
Former titles (until 1994): Church Business Magazine (ISSN 1195-8642) & Church Business (ISSN 1183-2339)
Description: Covers the administration and facility management of churches for clergy, administration and property managers.

CHURCH COMPUTING NEWS. see *COMPUTERS — Microcomputers*

200   UK   ISSN 0268-7658
CHURCH GROWTH DIGEST. 1979. 4/yr. £5. B C G A, 59 Warrington Rd., Harrow, Middlesex HA1 1SZ, England. TEL 01-863-4495.
Description: Examines church growth in all its dimensions: numerical, spiritual, organizational and incarnational.

270   US   ISSN 0009-6407
BR140
CHURCH HISTORY. 1932. q. $50 (effective 1996). American Society of Church History, Box 8517, Red Bank, NJ 07701-8517. Ed.Bd. adv.; bk.rev.; bibl.; index, cum.index. circ. 3,400. (also avail. in microform) **Indexed:** Amer.Bibl.Slavic & E.Eur.Stud., Amer.Hist.& Life, Arts & Hum.Cit.Ind., Bibl.Engl.Lang.& Lit., Bk.Rev.Ind. (1965-), CERDIC, Child.Bk.Rev.Ind. (1965-), Chr.Per.Ind., Curr.Cont., Hist.Abstr., Hum.Ind., Lang.& Lang.Behav.Abstr., Old Test.Abstr., Rel.& Theol.Abstr. (1968-), Rel.Ind.One, Rel.Per., RILA. **Document type:** academic/scholarly publication.
●Also available online. Vendor(s): University Microfilms International.
—BLDSC (3189.768000); Faxon; SWETS; UMI; UnCover.

CHURCH LADS' AND CHURCH GIRLS' BRIGADE. ANNUAL REPORT. see *CHILDREN AND YOUTH — About*

CHURCH LAW & TAX REPORT. see *LAW*

200   US   ISSN 8750-8613
CHURCH LIFE. 1887. m. $1. Episcopal Diocese of Ohio, 2230 Euclid Ave., Cleveland, OH 44115.
TEL 216-771-4815. FAX 216-623-0735. Ed. Dana C. Speer. adv.; bk.rev. circ. 23,000. (back issues avail.)

254   US   ISSN 0009-6431
BV652.A1
CHURCH MANAGEMENT. Variant title: Clergy Journal. 1924. 10/yr. $27 (foreign $33); newsstand price: $3.50. Logos Productions Inc., Box 240, South St. Paul, MN 55075-0240. Ed. Clyde J. Steckel; Pub. Pete Velander. adv. contact: Steve Truran. bk.rev. circ. 15,000. (also avail. in microform from UMI; back issues avail.) **Indexed:** CCR. **Document type:** consumer publication.
—UMI.

THE CHURCH MUSIC REPORT. see *MUSIC*

CHURCH OF SCOTLAND BRAILLE MAGAZINE. see *HANDICAPPED — Visually Impaired*

268   UK
CHURCH POCKET BOOK AND DIARY. a. £5.99. Society for Promoting Christian Knowledge, Holy Trinity Church, Marylebone Rd., London NW1 4DU, England. TEL 071-387-5282. FAX 071-388-2352. Ed. Rachel Boulding. circ. 7,000. **Document type:** bulletin.
Formerly: Churchman's Pocket Book and Diary (ISSN 0069-4029)

252   UK   ISSN 0069-4002
CHURCH PULPIT YEAR BOOK (YEAR); sermon outlines. 1903. a. £12.75. Chansitor Publications Inc., St. Mary's Works, St. Mary's Pl., Norwich, Norfolk NR3 3BH, England. TEL 01603-616563.
FAX 01603-624483. adv.; index. circ. 3,000.

200   US   ISSN 0009-6601
CHURCH WORLD. 1930. w. $25. Diocese of Portland, Maine, Box 698, Brunswick, ME 04011.
TEL 207-729-8753. FAX 207-729-5728. Ed. Claire M. Bastien. adv.; bk.rev.; film rev.; play rev.; illus. circ. 6,848. (tabloid format) **Document type:** newspaper.

200   US   ISSN 1043-9609
CHURCHES SPEAK. q. $99. Gale Research Inc., 835 Penobscot Bldg., Detroit, MI 48226.
TEL 800-877-4253. FAX 313-961-6815. TELEX 810-221-7086.

267.4   US   ISSN 0009-6598
BV4415
CHURCHWOMAN. 1934. bi-m. $8. Church Women United, 475 Riverside Dr., Rm. 812, New York, NY 10115. TEL 212-870-2347. FAX 212-870-2338. Ed. Margaret Schiffert. bk.rev.; illus. circ. 7,000.
Description: Addresses the concerns of today's women of faith: children, peacemaking, the discovery of gifts, health and wholeness, inclusive language, partnerships of empowerment, worship, land, homelessness, criminal justice, and poverty of women and children.

271   US   ISSN 0578-3224
BX3401
CISTERCIAN STUDIES QUARTERLY. 1966. q. $20. Cistercian Studies Quarterly, Santa Rita Abbey, HC 1, Box 929, Sonoita, AZ 85637-9705.
TEL 520-455-5595. Ed. Fr. Charles Cummings. adv. contact: Sr. Sheryl Chen. bk.rev. circ. 1,500. (also avail. in microform; back issues avail.) **Document type:** academic/scholarly publication.
Description: Review combining historical and critical studies of Western and Eastern spirituality in both monastic and lay commitment.

200   US   ISSN 0009-7527
AS36
CITHARA; essays in Judaeo-Christian tradition. 1961. s-a. $6. Saint Bonaventure University, Box BC, St. Bonaventure, NY 14778. TEL 716-375-2000. Ed. Scott Colvin; Pub. Robert Wickenheiser. adv. contact: Mary Sokolowski. bk.rev.; cum.index every 2 vols. circ. 700. (also avail. in microfilm from UMI) **Indexed:** Abstr.Engl.Stud., Amer.Hist.& Life, Arts & Hum.Cit.Ind., Bibl.Engl.Lang.& Lit., Cath.Ind., Curr.Cont., Hist.Abstr., M.L.A. **Document type:** newspaper.
—BLDSC (3267.792080); Faxon; Genuine Article; UMI; UnCover.

200 700   IT   ISSN 0009-7632
CITTA DI VITA; bimestrale di religione arte e scienza. 1946. bi-m. L.30000 (foreign L.50000) (effective 1993). Piazza S. Croce 16, 50122 Florence, Italy. TEL 055-242783. Ed. Massimiliano G. Rosito. adv.; bk.rev.; bibl.; illus.; index. circ. 6,000. **Indexed:** M.L.A.

200 900   BE   ISSN 0774-7241
CLAIRLIEU: TIJDSCHRIFT GEWIJD AAN DE GESCHIEDENIS DER KRUISHEREN. (Editions in Dutch, English, French and German) 1943. a. 18.50. Geschiedkundige Kring "Clairlieu", Pelserstraat 33, B-3680 Maaseik, Belgium. Ed. C. Brasseur. bk.rev. **Indexed:** Amer.Hist.& Life, Hist.Abstr. **Document type:** bulletin.
Description: Covers history of the crosiers and spirituality.

200   US
CLOSER WALK; to develop a heart for God. 1981. m. $18. Walk Thru the Bible Ministries, Inc., 4201 N. Peachtree Rd., Box 80587, Atlanta, GA 30341-1362. TEL 404-458-9300. Ed. Paula Kirk. circ. 9,299. (reprint service avail.)
Formerly: Timeless Insights.

CLUBS & ORGANIZATIONS. see *CLUBS*

200 301.412   US   ISSN 0896-0038
CO-LABORER MAGAZINE. 1961. bi-m. $5.75. Women Nationally Active for Christ, Box 5002, Antioch, TN 37011-5002. TEL 615-731-6812.
FAX 615-731-0771. Ed. Suzanne Franks. bk.rev. circ. 14,000.
Description: Seeks to promote missions and deepen the spiritual life of women.

200   AG
COLECCION AMANECE.* no.4, 1976. irreg. Editora Patria Grande, Rivadavia 6374, 1406 Buenos Aires, Argentina. **Document type:** monographic series.

RELIGIONS AND THEOLOGY

200   SP   ISSN 0069-505X
COLECCION CANONICA. 1959. irreg., no.102, 1989. price varies. (Universidad de Navarra, Facultad de Derecho Canonico) Ediciones Universidad de Navarra, S.A., Apdo. 396, 31080 Pamplona, Spain. TEL 94 825 6850.
   Description: Discusses canon law.

200   CK
COLECCION COMUNICACION.* 1977. irreg. Ediciones Paulinas, Transversal 40 A, No. 43, Apdo. 100383, Bogota, Colombia.

COLLABORATION. see *PHILOSOPHY*

230   FR   ISSN 1158-7032
COLLECTION DES ETUDES AUGUSTINIENNES. SERIE ANTIQUITE. 1954. irreg., vol.143, 1994. price varies. Institut d'Etudes Augustiniennes, 3 rue de l'Abbaye, 75006 Paris, France. (Subscr. in France to: Editions Brepols, 23 rue des Grands Augustins, 75006 Paris, France. TEL 1-44-41-20-00. FAX 1-43-26-23-77; Elsewhere to: N.V. Brepols, Steenweg op Tielen 68, 2300 Turnhout, Belgium. TEL 32-14-415463. FAX 32-14-428919) Dir. Jean-Claude Fredouille. (back issues avail.) **Document type:** monographic series.

230   FR   ISSN 1159-4888
COLLECTION DES ETUDES AUGUSTINIENNES. SERIE MOYEN AGE ET TEMPS MODERNES. 1964. irreg., vol.29, 1994. price varies. Institut d'Etudes Augustiniennes, 3 rue de l'Abbaye, 75006 Paris, France. (Subscr. in France to: Editions Brepols, 23 rue des Grands Augustins, 75006 Paris, France. TEL 1-44-41-20-00. FAX 1-43-26-23-77; Elsewhere to: N.V. Brepols, Steenweg op Tielen 68, 2300 Turnhout, Belgium. TEL 32-14-415463. FAX 32-14-428919) Dir. Jean-Claude Fredouille. (back issues avail.) **Document type:** monographic series.

200   AT
COLLECTIONS OF RELIGION AND THEOLOGY IN AUSTRALIA AND NEW ZEALAND. Abbreviated title: C O R T I A N Z. irreg. (4-5/yr.). Aus.$32. Auslib Press, P.O. Box 622, Blackwood, S.A. 5051, Australia. TEL 61-8-278-4363. FAX 61-8-278-4000. E-mail: Alan@dBundy@Unisa.edu.au. circ. 450. **Document type:** directory.

261   US
COLORADO KAIROS. 1965. irreg. (3-4/yr.). $5. Colorado Council of Churches, 1234 Bannock St., Denver, CO 80204-3631. abstr.; bibl.; illus. circ. 2,000.
   Formerly (until 1982): Colorado Councillor (ISSN 0010-1540); Supersedes: Rocky Mountain Churchman.
   Description: Lists events and membership news.

220   CN   ISSN 0316-3040
COME AND SEE. 1974. bi-m. free. Nathanael Literature Distributors, 64 Hills Rd., Ajax, ON L1S 2W4, Canada. Ed. John van Dijk. circ. 8,100.

220 375   UK   ISSN 0950-7191
COME LEARN BEGINNERS. q. £0.55. Go Teach Publications, 2 Radford Rd., Leamington Spa CV31 1LX, England. TEL 0926-26573.
   Description: Children's activity workbook for use with: Go Teach Beginners.

220 375   UK   ISSN 0950-7213
COME LEARN JUNIORS. q. £0.55. Go Teach Publications, 2 Radford Rd., Leamington Spa CV31 1LX, England. TEL 0926-26573.
   Description: Children's activity workbook for use with: Go Teach Juniors.

220 375   UK   ISSN 0950-7205
COME LEARN PRIMARIES. q. £0.55. Go Teach Publications, 2 Radford Rd., Leamington Spa CV31 1LX, England. TEL 0926-26573.
   Description: Children's activity workbook for use with: Go Teach Primaries.

COMMON BOUNDARY; exploring spirituality, psychotherapy and creativity. see *PSYCHOLOGY*

200   UK   ISSN 0010-325X
COMMON GROUND. 1946. 3/yr. £10 to non-members; members free. Council of Christians and Jews, 1 Dennington Park Rd., London NW6 1AX, England. FAX 0171-431-3500. Ed. Rev. Jonathan Gorky. adv.; bk.rev.; illus. circ. 5,000. (also avail. in microform from UMI) **Indexed:** CERDIC. **Document type:** consumer publication.
   —UMI.
   Description: Seeks to encourage appreciation of the Jewish and Christian religious and interfaith understanding.

COMMUNAL COMPUTING NEWS. see *COMPUTERS — Microcomputers*

230   SP   ISSN 0010-3705
COMMUNIO; commentarii internationales de ecclesia et theologia. 1968. 3/yr. 3000 ptas.($40) Estudio General Dominicano, Provincia Betica (Espana), Apdo. 820, 41080 Seville, Spain. FAX 8-904367. Ed. Miguel de Burgos. bk.rev.; cum.index. circ. 500. **Indexed:** CERDIC, New Test.Abstr., Old Test.Abstr., Rel.& Theol.Abstr.
   —BLDSC (3363.543400).

291 301   US   ISSN 1052-1135
COMPARATIVE STUDIES IN RELIGION & SOCIETY. 1987. irreg., vol.6, 1993. price varies. University of California Press, 2120 Berkeley Way, Berkeley, CA 94720. TEL 510-642-4247. FAX 510-643-7127. (Orders to: California-Princeton Fulfillment Services, 1445 Lower Ferry Rd., Ewing, NJ 08618. TEL 800-777-4726. FAX 800-999-1958) Ed. Mark Juergensmeyer. (back issues avail.) **Document type:** monographic series.
   Description: Discusses Eastern and Western religious traditions in various sociopolitical contexts. *Refereed Serial*

200   FR   ISSN 1140-7654
CONCILIUM; revue international de theologie. 1965. 6/yr. 310 F. (foreign 390 F.). Editions Beauchesne, 72 rue des Saints Peres, 75007 Paris, France. TEL 45-48-80-28. FAX 42-22-59-79. **Indexed:** CERDIC.

200   UK   ISSN 0010-5236
CONCILIUM; international review of theology. 1965. bi-m. $60 to individuals; institutions $75. S C M Press, 26-30 Tottenham Rd., London N1 4BZ, England. TEL 0171-249-7262. FAX 0171-249-3776. (U.S. subscr. to: Orbis Books, Maryknoll, NY 10545-0308. TEL 914-941-7636) adv. circ. 1,000. **Indexed:** Canon Law Abstr., CERDIC. **Document type:** academic/scholarly publication.
   Description: Promotes theological discussion.

200   NE   ISSN 0167-1200
CONCILIUM. 6/yr. fl.124.50. Gooi en Sticht, Postbus 133, 3740 AC Baarn, Netherlands. TEL 31-2154-15320. FAX 31-2154-20658. circ. 2,250.
   —SWETS.

200   GW   ISSN 0588-9804
CONCILIUM; internationale Zeitschrift fuer Theologie. 1964. bi-m. DM.93 (foreign DM.96) (effective 1996). (Stichting Concilium, NE) Matthias Gruenewald Verlag GmbH, Max-Hufschmidt-Str. 4a, 55130 Mainz, Germany. TEL 06131-839055. FAX 06131-834322. Ed. Bruno Kern. adv. contact: Andrea Buchauer. circ. 3,000. (back issues avail.) **Document type:** academic/scholarly publication.

200   IT
CONCILIUM; rivista internazionale di teologia. 1965. bi-m. L.70000 (foreign L.90000) (effective 1996). Editrice Queriniana, Via Piamarta 6, 25187 Brescia, Italy. TEL 39-30-294653. FAX 39-30-3756375. Ed. Rosino Gibellini. adv. contact: Mario De Risio. bk.rev. (back issues avail.)

200   US   ISSN 0145-7233
BX8001
CONCORDIA JOURNAL. q. $10 (foreign $14). (Concordia Seminary) Ovid Bell Press, Inc., 801 Demun, Clayton, MO 63105. TEL 314-721-5934. FAX 314-721-5902. Ed. Quentin Wesselschmidt. adv.; bk.rev. circ. 9,000. (also avail. in microform from UMI; back issues avail.) **Indexed:** CERDIC, Chr.Per.Ind., Int.Z.Bibelwiss., New Test.Abstr., Old Test.Abstr., Rel.& Theol.Abstr. (1978-), Rel.Ind.One. **Document type:** academic/scholarly publication.
   —BLDSC (3399.477200); UMI.
   Former titles (until 1975): C T M (ISSN 0090-9823); (Until 1973): Concordia Theological Monthly (ISSN 0010-5279); Which was formed by the merger of (1855-1929): Lehre und Wehre (ISSN 0360-6155); (1921-1929): Theological Monthly (ISSN 0360-6201); (1877-1929): Pastoraltheologie (ISSN 0360-6163)
   Description: Official theological organ issued by the faculty of Concordia Seminary in St. Louis.

207.11   US   ISSN 0884-2825
CONCORDIA THEOLOGICAL QUARTERLY. N.S. 1959. q. $10. Concordia Theological Seminary, 6600 N. Clinton St., Fort Wayne, IN 46825. TEL 219-452-2100. FAX 219-452-2121. Ed. Hejno O. Kadai. adv.; bk.rev.; cum.index: 1959-1964. circ. 9,000. (also avail. in microfilm from UMI; reprint service avail. from UMI) **Indexed:** CERDIC, New Test.Abstr., Old Test.Abstr., Rel.& Theol.Abstr. (1983-), Rel.Ind.One, Rel.Per. **Document type:** academic/scholarly publication.
   —BLDSC (3399.478300); UMI.
   Formerly (until vol.40, no.2, 1976): Springfielder (ISSN 0038-8610)

200   UY
CONFEDERACION LATINOAMERICANA DE ASOCIACIONES CRISTIANAS DE JOVENES. CONFEDERACION. 1982. q. free. Confederacion Latinoamericana de Asociaciones Cristianas de Jovenes - Latin American Confederation of YMCAs, Colonia 1884, p.1, Montevideo, Uruguay. Ed. Edgardo G. Crovetto.

200   UY
CONFEDERACION LATINOAMERICANA DE ASOCIACIONES CRISTIANAS DE JOVENES. CONTACTO. 1982. m. free. Confederacion Latinoamericana de Asociaciones Cristianas de Jovenes - Latin American Confederation of YMCAs, Colonia 1884, p.1, Montevideo, Uruguay. Ed. Edgardo G. Crovetto.

369.4   UY
CONFEDERACION LATINOAMERICANA DE ASOCIACIONES CRISTIANAS DE JOVENES. CARTA. (Editions in English and Spanish) irreg. free. Confederacion Latinoamericana de Asociaciones Cristianas de Jovenes, Casilla 172, Montevideo, Uruguay.
   Formerly: Federacion Sudamericana de Asociaciones Cristianas de Jovenes. Noticias (ISSN 0428-1039)

200   NP
CONFIDENT CHRISTIAN. (Text in English) 1982. s-a. $100 (foreign $120). Siveast Consultants, Inc., USA, c/o Dr. C.V. Ramasastry, Ed., P.O. Box 8510, Kathmandu, Nepal. (UK Subscr. to: Dr. Ramasastry, c/o Overseas Customer Service, Midland Bank plc., Poultry & Princes St., London EC2, England) adv.; bk.rev. circ. 200. **Document type:** newsletter.
   Description: Covers religion and contains fictional serial stories.

200   SW   ISSN 0069-8946
CONIECTANEA BIBLICA. NEW TESTAMENT SERIES. (Text in English and French) 1966. irreg. price varies. A W I International AB, P.O. Box 4627, S-116 91 Stockholm, Sweden. TEL 468-640-8800. FAX 468-641-1180. Eds. Birger Gerhardson, Lars Hartman.
   Former titles: Acta Seminarii Neotestamentici Upsaliensis & Coniectanea Neotestamentica.

200   SW   ISSN 0069-8954
CONIECTANEA BIBLICA. OLD TESTAMENT SERIES. 1967. irreg. price varies. A W I International AB, P.O. Box 4627, S-116 91 Stockholm, Sweden. TEL 468-640-8800. FAX 468-641-1180. Eds. Tryggve Mettinger, Helmer Ringgren.

CONNECTICUT HISTORICAL SOCIETY. BULLETIN. see *HISTORY — History Of North And South America*

RELIGIONS AND THEOLOGY

200   IT   ISSN 0035-600X
CONSACRAZIONE E SERVIZIO; rivista delle religiose. 1952. m. L.33000 (effective 1996). Unione Superiore Maggiori d'Italia, Via Zanardelli 32, 00186 Rome, Italy. TEL 39-6-68802316. FAX 39-6-68801935. Dir. Teresa Magliano. bk.rev.; index. circ. 12,000.
    Formerly: Rivista delle Religiose.

CONSCIENCE ET LIBERTE. see *POLITICAL SCIENCE — Civil Rights*

200   US
CONSULTATION ON CHURCH UNION. DIGEST. 1962. irreg., latest 1988. $15. Consultation on Church Union, Research Park, 151 Wall St., Princeton, NJ 08540-1514. Ed. Daniell C. Hamby. **Document type:** proceedings.
  —BLDSC (3588.240000).
    Former titles: Consultation on Church Union. Official Record (ISSN 0272-8958); Consultation on Church. Digest (ISSN 0589-4867)

200 610   SZ
CONTACT. (Text in English, French, Portuguese and Spanish) bi-m. 24 SFr.($15) World Council of Churches, C M C - Churches' Action for Health, 150 route de Ferney, P.O. Box 2100, CH-1211 Geneva 2, Switzerland. TEL 022-791-6111. FAX 022-791-0361. TELEX 415730-OIK-CH. Ed. Diana Smith. circ. 30,000. **Document type:** bulletin.

200   UK
CONTACT (ALDERSHOT). 1920. q. £1 per no. Officers' Christian Union, Havelock House, Barrack Rd., Aldershot GU11 3NP, England. TEL 01252-311221. FAX 01252-311222. Ed. Sqn. Ldr. Mike Warwood. bk.rev. circ. 3,000. **Indexed:** CERDIC. **Document type:** newsletter.
    Formerly: Practical Christianity (ISSN 0032-6364)
    Description: Inspirational articles, profiles, and announcements of conferences and affiliations pertaining to the activities of Christian officers in the British armed forces.

200   FR   ISSN 0045-8325
CONTACTS (PARIS, 1949); revue Francaise de l'Orthodoxie. 1949. q. 215 F.($37) Centre Ecumenique Enotikon, c/o John J. Balzon, 43 rue du Fer-a-Moulin, 75005 Paris, France. TEL 535-80-98. Ed. John J. Balzon. bk.rev.; bibl.; index. circ. 3,000. **Indexed:** CERDIC.
  —BLDSC (3425.025000).

CONTEMPORARY CHRISTIAN MUSIC. see *MUSIC*

200   US   ISSN 0361-8854
CONTEXT; a commentary on the interaction of religion and culture. 1972. 22/yr. $29.95. Claretian Publications, 205 W. Monroe St., Chicago, IL 60606. TEL 312-236-7782. FAX 312-236-7320. Ed. Rev. Mark J. Brummel. circ. 7,326. (reprint service avail. from UMI) **Indexed:** Numis.Lit.
  —UMI.

220   NE   ISSN 0926-6097
CONTRIBUTIONS TO BIBLICAL EXEGESIS AND THEOLOGY. (Text in English) 1990. irreg., vol.6, 1993. price varies. Kok Pharos Publishing House, Postbus 5019, 8260 AG Kampen, Netherlands. TEL 31-5202-92555. FAX 31-5202-27331. (Dist. in U.S. and Canada by: Books International, Inc., Box 605, Herndon, VA 22070-0605. TEL 800-377-7192. FAX 703-689-0660) (back issues avail.) **Document type:** monographic series.
    Description: Scholarly monographs on Jewish and Christian theological issues.
    Refereed Serial

200   US   ISSN 0196-7053
CONTRIBUTIONS TO THE STUDY OF RELIGION. 1981. irreg. price varies. Greenwood Press, Inc. (Subsidiary of: Greenwood Publishing Group Inc.), 88 Post Rd. W., Box 5007, Westport, CT 06881-5007. TEL 203-226-3571. FAX 203-222-1502. Ed. Henry W. Bowden.
  —BLDSC (3461.455000).

200   US   ISSN 8750-4812
CONVENTION HERALD. 1955. bi-m. $5. Inter-Church Holiness Convention, 3589 New Garden Rd., Salem, OH 44460. Ed. Leonard Sankey. adv.; bk.rev. circ. 12,500.

200   US   ISSN 0275-2743
CORNERSTONE (CHICAGO). 1972. irreg. $15 for 8 nos. Cornerstone Communications, Inc., 939 W. Wilson Ave., Chicago, IL 60640. TEL 312-561-2450 ext. 2080. FAX 312-989-2076. Ed. Dawn Mortimer. adv. contact: China Thompson. bk.rev. circ. 45,000. **Document type:** consumer publication.
    Description: Avant garde evangelical publication dealing with social issues, scriptural truths, and cultural change.

CORPUS CHRISTIANORUM. LINGUA PATRUM. see *LINGUISTICS*

200   BE
CORPUS CHRISTIANORUM. SERIES GRAECA. 1977. irreg. (2-3/yr.), vol.30, 1994. (Centrum voor Hellenisme en Kristendom, Leuven) N.V. Brepols, Steenweg op Tielen 68, 2300 Turnhout, Belgium. TEL 32-14-402500. FAX 32-14-428919. (Co-publisher: Leuven University Press) (back issues avail.) **Document type:** monographic series.

CORPUS SACRAE SCRIPTURAE NEERLANDICAE MEDII AEVII. see *LITERATURE*

COUNSELOR (WHEATON). see *CHILDREN AND YOUTH — For*

COURAGE IN THE STRUGGLE FOR JUSTICE AND PEACE. see *SOCIOLOGY*

COURTENAY LIBRARY OF REFORMATION CLASSICS. see *HISTORY — History Of Europe*

289.9   SA   ISSN 0259-028X
COVENANT MESSAGE; a journal of good news. 1954. 3/yr. free. Federation of the Covenant People, P.O. Box 830, Honeydew 2040, South Africa.

200 500   UK
CREATION. (Former name of issuing body: Evolution Protest Movement) 1971. bi-m. £6 to individuals; students £4 (foreign £8) (effective 1996). Creation Science Movement, 50 Brecon Ave., Portsmouth, Hants. PO6 2AW, England. TEL 01705-293988. (Co-sponsor: Evangelical Alliance) bk.rev. circ. 2,100.
    Description: Argues that scientific facts are best explained by the Biblical account of creation.

CREATION - EVOLUTION; the journal of evolution and science education which explores aspects of evolution and antievolutionism. see *SCIENCES: COMPREHENSIVE WORKS*

200 500   AT   ISSN 0819-1530
CREATION EX NIHILO. 1978. q. Aus.$19.50($22) Creation Science Foundation Ltd., P.O. Box 6302, Acacia Ridge D.C., Qld. 4110, Australia. TEL 617-273-7650. FAX 617-273-7672. (Dist. addr. in U.S.: P.O. Box 6330, Florence, KY 41022) Ed. R.J. Doolan. adv.; bk.rev.; cum.index. circ. 50,000.
    Description: Presents scientific and biblical evidence for creationism and related subjects in a popular, easy-to-read format.

200 500   AT   ISSN 1036-2916
CREATION EX NIHILO TECHNICAL JOURNAL. 1984. s-a. Aus.$25. Creation Science Foundation Ltd., P.O. Box 6302, Acacia Ridge D.C., Qld. 4110, Australia. TEL 617-273-7650. FAX 617-273-7672. Ed. A.A. Snelling. abstr.; charts; illus. circ. 2,000. (back issues avail.) **Document type:** academic/scholarly publication.
    Formerly: Ex Nihilo Technical Journal (ISSN 0814-6764)
    Description: Technical study of the sciences as they relate to the study of biblical creation and Noah's flood.

CREATION RESEARCH SOCIETY QUARTERLY. see *SCIENCES: COMPREHENSIVE WORKS*

200   US   ISSN 1053-9891
BL624
CREATION SPIRITUALITY. q. $24 (foreign $32) (effective 1994). Friends of Creation Spirituality, Inc., Box 20369, Oakland, CA 94620. TEL 510-547-0711. Ed. Matthew Fox. adv. contact: Cliff Atkinson.
  —UMI.
    Formerly: Creation (ISSN 8756-3088)

CREATOR; the bimonthly magazine of balanced music ministries. see *MUSIC*

267 301   NO   ISSN 0804-7529
CREDO. 1933. 10/yr. NOK 250. Credo Forlag AS, P.O. Box 6707 St. Olovs Plass, N-0130 Oslo, Norway. Eds. Haakon Soedal, Jens-Petter Johnsen. bk.rev.
    Description: Concerned with the relationship between Church and society, Christianity and science, and new religiousness.

280   IT   ISSN 0393-3598
BR140
CRISTIANESIMO NELLA STORIA; ricerche storiche esegetiche teologiche. (Text in English, French, German, Italian and Spanish; summaries in English) 1980. 3/yr. L.59000 (foreign L.71000) (effective 1994). (Istituto per le Scienze Religiose) Centro Editoriale Dehoniano, Via Nosadella 6, 40123 Bologna, Italy. TEL 051-306811. FAX 051-341706. Ed. Prof. Giuseppe Alberigo. bk.rev.; bibl.; index. circ. 1,700. (back issues avail.) **Indexed:** Canon Law Abstr., CERDIC, New Test.Abstr., Old Test.Abstr., Rel.& Theol.Abstr.

200   AG   ISSN 0011-1457
CRISTIANISMO Y SOCIEDAD. 1963. q. Arg.$20000($15) Apdo. Postal 15067, Guayaquil, Ecuador. Ed. Julio Barreiro. **Indexed:** Hisp.Amer.Per.Ind. (1984-), Rel.& Theol.Abstr. (1989-), Rel.Ind.One.

200   UK
CRISTION. 1983. bi-m. £5 (overseas £6.50) (effective Jan. 1994). Cristion Publishing Company, 3 Maes Lowri, Aberystwyth, Dyfed SY23 2AU, Wales. TEL 0970-612925. Ed. Rev. E. ap Nefydd Roberts. adv.: page £110. bk.rev. circ. 2,250. **Document type:** consumer publication.
    Description: Covers all aspects of religious life.

200   US
CROSS AND QUILL; the Christian writers newsletter. 1976. bi-m. $18 to non-members (foreign $21); members $35 (foreign $40). Christian Writers Fellowship International, Rt. 3, Box 1635, Jefferson Davis Rd., Clinton, SC 29325. TEL 803-697-6035. E-mail: CWFI@aol.com. Ed. Sandy Brooks. bk.rev.; index. (looseleaf format) **Document type:** newsletter.
    Incorporates (in Oct. 1989): Christian Writers Newsletter.
    Description: Information, writing tips and marketing news for writers of freelance material for the Christian market.

260 378   US   ISSN 0011-1953
BR1
CROSS CURRENTS (NEW ROCHELLE). 1950. q. $25 to individuals; libraries $32.50. Association for Religion and Intellectual Life, College of New Rochelle, New Rochelle, NY 10805-2308. TEL 914-654-5425. FAX 914-654-5925. Ed. Nancy Malone; Pub. Teresa Phodes McLee. adv. contact: Ronnie Carpini. bk.rev. circ. 5,000. (also avail. in microform; magnetic tape) **Indexed:** Per.Islam. (1991-), Rel.& Theol.Abstr. (1979-), Rel.Ind.One. **Document type:** academic/scholarly publication.
●Also available online.
Also available on CD-ROM.
  —BLDSC (3488.850000); Faxon; SWETS; UMI; UnCover.
    Former titles (until 1990): Religion and Intellectual Life (ISSN 0741-0549); (until 1983): N I C M Journal for Jews and Christians in Higher Education (ISSN 0362-0794)

200   FR   ISSN 1147-2081
CROYANTS EN LIBERTE. q. 120 F. (foreign 150 F.) Societe de Presse et d'Edition, 49 rue du Faubourg-Poissionniere, 75009 Paris, France. TEL 1-42-46-37-50. FAX 1-48-24-33-67. TELEX 290 562. (Subscr. to: B.P. 63, F 77932 Perthes Cedex, France. TEL 1-64-38-01-55)

CRUSADER. see *CHILDREN AND YOUTH — For*

200   CN   ISSN 0011-2186
CRUX; a quarterly journal of Christian thought and opinion. 1966. q. Can.$14($14) Regent College, 5800 University Blvd., Vancouver, BC V6T 2E4, Canada. TEL 604-224-3245. FAX 604-224-3097. Ed. Donald M. Lewis. adv.; bk.rev.; bibl.; charts; illus.; stat.; index, cum.index. circ. 1,000. (microform) **Indexed:** New Test.Abstr., Old Test.Abstr., Rel.& Theol.Abstr. (1970-), Rel.Ind.One.
  —BLDSC (3490.132000); UnCover. **CCC**.

RELIGIONS AND THEOLOGY

282 US ISSN 0591-2296
CRUX OF THE NEWS. 1965. w. $79.50. Gabriel Publishing Co., Inc., 3 Enterprise Dr., Albany, NY 12204. TEL 518-465-4591. FAX 518-465-4597. Ed. Richard A. Dowd. adv.; bk.rev. circ. 3,400. **Document type:** newsletter.

CRUZADA EUCARISTICA. see *CHILDREN AND YOUTH — For*

CUADERNOS PARA LA HISTORIA DE LA EVANGELIZACION EN AMERICA LATINA. see *HISTORY — History Of North And South America*

CULT OBSERVER; toward an awareness of cultism in society. see *SOCIOLOGY*

CULTIC STUDIES JOURNAL; a journal on cults and manipulative techniques of social influence. see *SOCIOLOGY*

200 VC ISSN 1022-8675
CULTURES AND FAITH. (Text in English, French, Spanish) 1966. q. $30 (effective Sep. 1993). Pontifical Council for Culture, 00120 Vatican City (Rome), State of the Vatican City. TEL 396-6988-7321. FAX 396-6988-7368. TELEX 2013 CULTVAT VA. Ed. Paul Poupard. circ. 1,000. **Document type:** academic/scholarly publication.
  Supersedes (in Sep. 1993): Atheism and Faith; Which was formerly: Atheism and Dialogue; Incorporates: Church and Cultures.
  Description: Contains articles on modern atheism and religious indifference, dialogue between faith and culture, and science-faith relationships, with a greater emphasis on cultural issues.

200 SZ
CURRENT DIALOGUE. (Text in English) 2/yr. $15. World Council of Churches, Office on Inter-Religious Relations, 150 route de Ferney, P.O. Box 2100, CH-1211 Geneva 2, Switzerland. TEL 022-791-6111. FAX 022-791-0361. TELEX 415730-OIK-CH. **Indexed:** Abstr.Musl.Rel. **Document type:** bulletin.
  Formerly: Church and the Jewish People.

CURRENTS IN SCIENCE, TECHNOLOGY AND SOCIETY. see *SCIENCES: COMPREHENSIVE WORKS*

200 AU ISSN 0011-4057
CURSILLO; fuer ein erlebtes Evangelium. 1964. m. S.180. Arbeitsgemeinschaft der Dioezesansekretariate der Cursillo-Bewegung, Bennogasse 21, A-1080 Vienna, Austria. TEL 0222-4055318. FAX 0222-4081015. Ed. Josef G. Cascales. bk.rev.; bibl. **Document type:** consumer publication.
  Formerly: Karat.

270 GW ISSN 0070-2234
CUSANUS-GESELLSCHAFT. BUCHREIHE. 1964. irreg. price varies. Aschendorffsche Verlagsbuchhandlung, Soesterstr. 13, 48155 Muenster, Germany. TEL 0251-690-0. FAX 0251-690143. Ed.Bd. **Document type:** monographic series.

280 US ISSN 0011-5525
DAILY WORD. Spanish edition: Palabra Diaria. 1924. m.; cassette bi-m. $6.95 for inkprint edition; large-print $6.95; Braille and cassette free. Unity School of Christianity, Unity Village, MO 64065. TEL 816-524-3550. Ed. Colleen Zuck. circ. 1,223,000 (large-print 30,000; cassette 1,000). (also avail. in microform from UMI; Braille; audio cassette; large-print edition in 18 pt.)
  —UMI.
  Formerly: Unity Daily Word (ISSN 0041-8188)
  Description: Covers daily devotional readings, with articles and poetry on spiritual inspiration, human relations, and everyday living.

274.89 DK ISSN 0105-7383
DANSK KIRKEHILSEN. 1927. bi-m. DKK 65. Dansk Kirke i Udlandet, Noerrevaenget 43B, P.O. Box 83, DK-5100 Odense C., Denmark. TEL 45-66-13-95-31. FAX 45-66-13-96-69. Ed. Egon Christiansen. adv. contact: Laila Christiansen. circ. 5,000. **Document type:** newsletter.
  Formerly (until 1976): Dansk Kirke i Udlandet (ISSN 0105-7375)
  Description: Brings the latest news of the Danish churches outside Denmark, also of the Danish organisation which is responsible for collection of funds for support of the Danish churches in Argentina, Canada, Australia and Europe.

266.023489 DK ISSN 0011-6378
DANSK MISSIONSBLAD. 1834. 8/yr. DKK 135 (typically set in Dec.). Danske Missionsselskab - Danish Missionary Society, Strandagervej 24, DK-2900 Hellerup, Denmark. FAX 45-01-62-02-06. Ed. Rev. Inge Tranholm-Mikkelsen. adv.; bk.rev.; abstr.; illus.; index. circ. 9,000. **Indexed:** CERDIC. **Document type:** newsletter.

200 DK ISSN 0105-3191
DANSK TEOLOGISK TIDSSKRIFT. 1938. 4/yr. DKK 220. Anis Forlag, Frederiksberg Alle 10-A, 1820 Frederiksberg C, Denmark. TEL 45-31-24-92-50. FAX 45-33-25-06-07. Ed. Mogens Mueller. adv.; bk.rev. circ. 650. **Indexed:** New Test.Abstr., Old Test.Abstr., Rel.& Theol.Abstr. (1990-), Rel.Ind.One. **Formerly** (until 1938): Teologisk Tidsskrift for den Danske Folkekirke (ISSN 0909-3265)

220 DK ISSN 0109-5846
DANSKE BIBELSELSKABS AARBOG. 1966. a. DKK 75. Danske Bibelselskab, Frederiksborggade 50, DK-1360 Copenhagen K, Denmark.
  Formerly: Danske Bibelselskabs Aarsberetning.

DARSHANA INTERNATIONAL; an international quarterly of philosophy, psychology, sociology, psychical research, religion and mysticism. see *PHILOSOPHY*

DAUGHTERS OF SARAH. see *WOMEN'S INTERESTS*

266 UK
DAY ONE DIARY. 1928. a. £1.30. Lord's Day Observance Society, 6 Sherman Rd., Bromley, Kent BR1 3JH, England. Ed. J.G. Roberts. circ. 85,000. **Document type:** bulletin.
  Formerly: Happy Day Diary.
  Description: Pocket diary with daily Bible verse based upon a theme.

296.155 933 NE ISSN 0929-0761
BM487.A62
▼**DEAD SEA DISCOVERIES;** a journal of current research on the scrolls and related literature. (Text in English) 1994. 3/yr. fl.110($71) to individuals; institutions fl.175($113) (effective 1996). E.J. Brill, Postbus 9000, 2300 PA Leiden, Netherlands. TEL 31-71-5353500. FAX 31-71-5317532. TELEX 39296 BRILL NL. E-mail: ejborders@ejbrill.com. (In N. America: E.J. Brill, 24 Hudson St., Kinderhook, NY 12106. TEL 800-962-4406. FAX 518-758-1959) Ed. Lawrence H. Schiffman. bk.rev.; abstr.; bibl. (back issues avail.) **Document type:** academic/scholarly publication.
  Description: Publishes original research arising from the recent release of photographs of the previously unpublished Dead Sea Scrolls, and discusses the significance of the Qumran finds for the study of Palestinian Judaism and the history and ideas of early Christianity.
  Refereed Serial

200 SZ
DECADE LINK. irreg. World Council of Churches, 150 route de Ferney, P.O. Box 2100, CH-1211 Geneva 2, Switzerland. TEL 022-7916111. FAX 022-7981346. TELEX 415730-OIK-CH. **Document type:** bulletin.

200 SW ISSN 0283-5762
DEKANALEN. 1979. q. Uppsala University, P.O. Box 1604, S-751 46 Uppsala, Sweden.

200 FR
DEMAIN D'AVANTAGE QU'HIER.* 15/yr. 200 F. Nouvelles Editions Latines, 1 rue Palatine, 75006 Paris, France. bk.rev.; bibl.

200 US ISSN 0193-6883
DENOMINATIONS IN AMERICA. 1985. irreg. price varies. Greenwood Press, Inc. (Subsidiary of: Greenwood Publishing Group Inc.), 88 Post Rd. W., Box 5007, Westport, CT 06881-5007. TEL 203-226-3571. FAX 203-222-1502. Ed. Harry Bowden.

200 GW ISSN 0174-786X
DEUTSCHE WALDENSER. q. DM.20. (Deutsche Waldenservereinigung) Quell Verlag, Furtbachstr. 12A, 70178 Stuttgart, Germany. TEL 0711-60100-0. circ. 1,500. **Document type:** bulletin.

200 MY ISSN 0012-1746
DHARMA; a quarterly devoted to universal religion, righteousness & culture. (Not issued in 1976) (Text in English) 1949. q. M.$6. Pure Life Society - Persatuan, Batu 6, Jalan Puchong, Jalan Kelang Lama P.O., 58200 Kuala Lumpur, Malaysia. TEL 03-792-9391. FAX 03-792-8303. Ed. Mother A. Mangalam. bk.rev.; illus. circ. 3,000. **Indexed:** Per.Islam. (1991-).
  Description: Promotes the study of comparative theology and philosophy in its widest form. Promotes inter-cultural relations and spiritual values.

200 110 070 US
DHARMA COMBAT; a magazine about spirituality, metaphysics, reality and other conspiracies. 1988. q. $10. Keith, Ed. & Pub., Box 20593, Sun Valley, NV 89433. adv.; bk.rev. circ. 3,000.

200 410 US ISSN 0167-9554
DIA REGNO/DIVINE KINGDOM: CHRISTIAN ESPERANTO MAGAZINE; Kristana Esperanto-Gazeto. (Text in Esperanto) 1908. m. $16 membership (effective 1994). Kristana Esperantista Ligo Internacia, c/o Edwin C. Harler Jr., 47 Hardy Rd., Levittown, PA 19056. (Alt. addr.: 26 Rue de Pre Ventnet, F-86430 Nouaille-Mauperturs, France) Ed. Philippe Cousson. adv.; bk.rev. circ. 1,100. (back issues avail.)
  Description: Aims to spread the international language Esperanto among Evangelical Christians and to use Esperanto to make Jesus Christ and His message known among Esperantists.

240 GW ISSN 0341-9592
DIAKONIA; internationale Zeitschrift fuer praktische Theologie. 1966. bi-m. DM.99 (students DM.80.40) (effective 1996). Matthias Gruenewald Verlag GmbH, Max-Hufschmidt-Str. 4a, 55130 Mainz, Germany. TEL 06131-839055. FAX 06131-834322. Ed. Helmut Erharter. adv.; bk.rev.; bibl.; stat.; index. circ. 4,000. **Indexed:** Cath.Ind.
  Description: Reflections and reports of church and parish life, practical theology and the influence of social changes on parishes and theology.

200 AU
DIAKONIE; Zeitschrift fuer Freunde und Mitarbeiter des Evangelischen Diakoniewerkes Gallneukirchen. 1875. bi-m. S.90. Evangelisches Diakoniewerk Gallneukirchen, Martin-Boos-Str. 4, A-4210 Gallneukirchen, Austria. TEL 07235-63251. FAX 07235-63251201. Eds. Gerhard Gaebler, Andrea Kloesch. adv.; bk.rev. circ. 5,000. **Document type:** newsletter.
  Formerly: Gallneukirchner Bote (ISSN 0016-4143)

200 GW
DIAKONIESCHWESTER. 1904. m. DM.75. Ev. Diakonieverein e.V., Glockenstr. 8, 14163 Berlin, Germany. TEL 030-8018091. FAX 030-8022452. Ed. Rainer Sommer. bk.rev.; circ. 3,500 (controlled). (back issues avail.) **Document type:** newsletter.

200 GW
DIALOG (HANNOVER). 1973. 3/yr. membership. Ev.-Luth. Landeskirche Hannover, Informations- und Pressestelle, Rote Reihe 5, 30169 Hannover, Germany. TEL 0511-1241399. FAX 0511-18200. Eds. Uwe Arnhold, Armin Pollehn. bk.rev. circ. 24,000. **Document type:** bulletin.
  Formerly (until 1992): D I A.

230 US ISSN 0012-2033
BR1
DIALOG (ST. PAUL); a journal of theology. 1962. q. $21 to individuals; students and senior citizens $14. Dialog, Inc., 2481 Como Ave., St. Paul, MN 55108. TEL 612-641-3482. FAX 612-641-3280. Ed. Ted F. Peters. adv. contact: Ruth E. Taylor. bk.rev. circ. 2,300. (also avail. in microform from UMI; reprint service avail. from UMI) **Indexed:** CERDIC, New Test.Abstr., Old Test.Abstr., Rel.& Theol.Abstr. (1968-), Rel.Ind.One, Rel.Per.
  —BLDSC (3579.730000); Faxon; UMI; UnCover.
  Description: Publishes a wide range of theological articles.

200 US
DIALOG (WILMINGTON). 1966. w. $15. Diocese of Wilmington, 1925 Delaware Ave., Wilmington, DE 19806. TEL 302-573-3109. FAX 302-573-2397. Ed. Robert Johnston. adv.; bk.rev. circ. 48,000. (tabloid format) **Document type:** newspaper.

RELIGIONS AND THEOLOGY

240 GW ISSN 0939-5539
DIALOG DER RELIGIONEN. 1991. 2/yr. DM.61.50 (foreign DM.65.50). Guetersloher Verlagshaus Chr. Kaiser, Carl-Bertelsmann-Str. 270, 33311 Guetersloh, Germany. TEL 05241-7405-0. FAX 05241-740548. Ed. Regina von Brueck. adv.: B&W page DM.900; trim 108 x 192. circ. 1,000. **Document type:** academic/scholarly publication.

200 SP ISSN 0210-2870
DIALOGO ECUMENICO; revista cuatrimestral de teologia ecumenica. 1966. 3/yr. 2500 ptas.($39) Universidad Pontificia, Departamento de Ediciones y Publicaciones, Apdo. de Correos 541, 37080 Salamanca, Spain. TEL 923-215140. FAX 923-213450. Dir. Adolfo Gonzalez-Montes. adv.; bk.rev. circ. 400. **Indexed:** CERDIC.

200 ISSN 0891-5881
BL1
DIALOGUE & ALLIANCE. 1987. 2/yr. $10 to individuals; institutions $15; foreign $20. International Religious Foundation, Inc. (IRF), 4 W. 43rd St., New York, NY 10036. TEL 212-869-6023. FAX 212-869-6424. TELEX 499 1393 NWERA. Ed. Thomas Walsh. adv.: page $200; adv. contact: Frank Lagrotteria. bk.rev. circ. 2,000. (also avail. in microform; back issues avail.) **Indexed:** Per.Islam. (1991-), Rel.& Theol.Abstr. (1988-), Rel.Ind.One, Rel.Per. **Document type:** academic/scholarly publication.
—BLDSC (3579.775210); UnCover.
Description: Explores interreligious topics for purposes of promoting dialogue, understanding and peace between religions.
Refereed Serial

378 268 US ISSN 0012-2289
DIALOGUE ON CAMPUS; linking the religious and the higher education systems. 1950. 4/yr. $5. Association for the Coordination of University Religious Affairs, Executive Committee, c/o Robert L. Johnson, Cornell United Religious Work, Anabel Taylor Hall, Ithaca, NY 14882. TEL 607-255-6004. FAX 607-255-9412. adv.; bk.rev.; bibl. circ. 300. (looseleaf format; back issues avail.) **Indexed:** ERIC, High.Educ.Abstr.

221 GW
DIELHEIMER BLAETTER ZUM ALTEN TESTAMENT UND SEINER REZEPTION IN DER ALTEN KIRCHE. 1972. s-a. DM.7. Wissenschaftlich-Theologisches Seminar der Universitaet Heidelberg, Kisselgasse 1, 69117 Heidelberg, Germany. Eds. Bernd Jorg Diebner, Claudia Nauerth. bk.rev. circ. 250.
Formerly: Dielheimer Blaetter zum Alten Testament.

200 GW ISSN 0012-2572
DIENENDER GLAUBE; Zeitschrift fuer Ordensfrauen. 1924. m. DM.58. Butzon und Bercker Verlag, Hoogeweg 71, 47623 Kevekaer, Germany. TEL 02832-2906. FAX 02832-40321. Ed. Sister Christeta Hess. adv.; bk.rev. circ. 3,300.
Formerly: An Heiligen Quellen.

200 US
DIRECTORY OF DEPARTMENTS AND PROGRAMS OF RELIGIOUS STUDIES IN NORTH AMERICA. 1978. a. $22.95. Council of Societies for the Study of Religion, CSSR Executive Office, Valparaiso University, Valparaiso, IN 46383. TEL 219-464-5515. Ed. David G. Truemper. **Document type:** directory.

266 UK
DIRECTORY OF ENGLISH-SPEAKING CHURCHES ABROAD. 1966. irreg. £2. Intercontinental Church Society, 175 Tower Bridge Rd., London SE1 2AQ, England. TEL 071-407-4588. FAX 071-378-0541. circ. 3,000. **Document type:** directory.

200 US
DIRECTORY OF FACULTY OF DEPARTMENTS AND PROGRAMS OF RELIGIOUS STUDIES IN NORTH AMERICA; contains biographical information on over 3,200 faculty members. (Suppl. to: Directory of Departments and Programs of Religious Studies in North America) 1988. irreg., 1992. $55. Council of Societies for the Study of Religion, CSSR Executive Office, Valparaiso University, Valparaiso, IN 46383. TEL 219-464-5515. Ed. David G. Truemper. **Document type:** directory.

DIRECTORY OF RELIGIOUS MEDIA. see *BUSINESS AND ECONOMICS — Trade And Industrial Directories*

133 CN ISSN 0848-3760
DIRECTORY TO CANADIAN PAGAN RESOURCES. 1988. a. Can.$4. Obscure Pagan Press, P.O. Box 2205, Clearbrook, BC V2T 3X8, Canada. TEL 604-855-8893. Ed. Samuel Wagar.
Description: Covers all types of Pagan and occult resources available in Canada - witchcraft, Druid, womanspirit and feminist spirituality, Asatru and ceremonial magickal groups, bookstores, gatherings and newsletters and groups providing resources or services to these communities.

262.9 IT
DIRITTO ECCLESIASTICO E RASSEGNA DI DIRITTO MATRIMONIALE. (Text in Italian and Latin) 1889. q. L.90000 (foreign L.135000). Casa Editrice Dott. A. Giuffre, Via Busto Arsizio 40, 20151 Milan, Italy. TEL 02-38000905. FAX 02-38009582. Ed. S. Bianconi. bk.rev.; bibl.; index. circ. 800. **Indexed:** CERDIC. **Document type:** directory.
Formerly: Diritto Ecclesiastico (ISSN 0012-3455)

200 US ISSN 0092-8372
BX7301
DISCIPLE (ST. LOUIS). 1862. m. $15.95. Christian Board of Publication, 1316 Convention Plaza, St. Louis, MO 63103. TEL 314-231-8500; 800-366-3383. FAX 314-231-8524. (Subscr. to: Box 179, St. Louis, MO 63166-0179) Ed. Robert L. Friedly; Pub. James C. Suggs. adv. contact: Fred A. Jones. bk.rev.; charts; illus.; index; circ. 33,000 (paid). (reprint service avail. from UMI) **Indexed:** CERDIC. **Document type:** consumer publication.
—UMI.
Supersedes: World Call (ISSN 0043-8308); Formerly (until 1974): Christian (ISSN 0009-5206)
Description: Features, departments, profiles, and announcements pertaining to the evangelical, congregational, ministerial, and missionary work of the Christian Church (Disciples of Christ.)

200 100 US
DISTANT DRUMS. 1979. irreg. (3-5/yr.), latest vol.15, 1993. $18 for 6 issues (foreign $25). 4106 Degardner Cir., St. Francis, MN 55070. Ed. Ronald S. Miller. circ. 100. (looseleaf format; back issues avail.) **Document type:** newsletter.
Description: Discusses syncretism in religion, education, and national and international affairs.

230 100 IT ISSN 0012-4257
DIVUS THOMAS; commentarium de philosophia et theologia. (Text in English, French, Italian, Latin, German and Spanish) 1880. 3/yr. L.45000 (foreign L.90000) (effective 1995). (Collegio Alberoni) Edizioni Studio Domenicano, Via Osservanza 72, 40136 Bologna, Italy. TEL 39-51-582034. FAX 39-51-331583. Ed. Enzo Panzacchi. bk.rev.; index. circ. 600. **Indexed:** CERDIC, M.L.A., New Test.Abstr., Old Test.Abstr. **Document type:** academic/scholarly publication, monographic series.
Description: Offers scholarly study in theology and philosophy, chiefly in the field of Thomistic research.

266 IV
DJELIBA; le journal des jeunes chretiens. 1974. 5/yr. 1500 F.($3) Eglise Catholique en Cote d'Ivoire, 01 B.P. 1287, Abidjan 01, Ivory Coast. TEL 21-69-79. Ed. Pierre Trichet; Pub. Pierre Trichet. adv. circ. 7,200. (back issues avail.) **Document type:** bulletin.

271 BE ISSN 0378-424X
DOCUMENTATION CISTERCIENNE. (Text in French, Latin) 1968. a., vol.22, 1993. price varies. N.V. Brepols, Steenweg op Tielen 68, 2300 Turnhout, Belgium. TEL 32-14-402500. FAX 32-14-428919. **Document type:** monographic series.
Description: Publishes scholarly editions and translations of documents relating to the history of the Cistercian order.

200 SP ISSN 1133-715X
DOCUMENTS D'ESGLESIA. (Text in Catalan) 1966. fortn. 4950 ptas. (Europe 6500 ptas.; elsewhere $75). Publicacions de l' Abadia de Montserrat, Ausias March 92-98, Apdo. 244, 08013 Barcelona, Spain.

200 CN ISSN 0318-0123
DONUM DEI. French edition (ISSN 0318-0131) (Editions in English and French) 1958. a. price varies. Canadian Religious Conference, 324 Laurier Ave. E., Ottawa, ON K1N 6P6, Canada. TEL 613-236-0824. FAX 613-236-0825. Ed. Richard Renshaw. circ. 6,000 (both editions). **Document type:** proceedings.

220 FR ISSN 0761-7267
DOSSIERS DE LA BIBLE. 1984. 5/yr. 110 F. (foreign 130 F.). Editions du Cerf, 29 bd. Latour Maubourg, 75340 Paris Cedex 07, France. TEL 45-50-34-07. FAX 45-56-04-17. (Subscr. to: Service Abonnements, 3 chemin des Prunais, 94350 Villier-sur-Marne, France) Ed. Philippe Gruson. bk.rev.; rec.rev.; charts; illus.; cum.index. circ. 15,000. (tabloid format) **Indexed:** Pt.e Rep. (1984-).
Formerly (until 1984): Bible et Son Message (ISSN 0006-0704)

DOUAI MAGAZINE. see *COLLEGE AND ALUMNI*

200 110 US
DOUBLE HEARTLINE. 1981. q. $10 (effective Jan. 1991). Teaching of the Inner Christ, Inc., 3150 Main St., Lemon Grove, CA 91945-2428. TEL 619-697-3900. Ed. R. Zito. circ. 6,000. (tabloid format; back issues avail.)
Description: Seeks to inspire and offer spiritual insights and education to all New Age seekers of Truth through regular features and a series of daily lessons.

291 US ISSN 1062-7359
DOVETAIL (BOULDER). 1992. bi-m. $24.99 (foreign $35). Dovetail Publishing, P.O. Box 19945, Kalamazoo, MI 49019-0945. TEL 616-342-2900. E-mail: hawxhurst@aol.com. Ed. Joan C. Hawzhurst. **Document type:** newsletter.
Description: Aimed at interfaith Jewish - Christian families.

200 US
DOVETAIL (DES MOINES). 1977. q. $10. Iowa Peace Network, 4211 Grand Ave., Des Moines, IA 50312. TEL 515-255-7114. Eds. Nancy and Gary T. Guthrie. bk.rev. circ. 3,000. (looseleaf format; back issues avail.) **Document type:** newsletter.
Formerly (until Sep. 1991): Dovetail - Peaces; Which was formed by the merger of: Peaces; Dovetail.
Description: Provides information on issues of conscience (concientious objection to war, war tax resistance) and updates on peace efforts, especially in Iowa.

200 291.3 US
DREAD TIMES; news for the Nazarite. 1991. q. $5. Identity by Mail, 4-771 Kuhio Hwy. C-7, Kapaa, HI 96746. TEL 808-823-6100. FAX 808-823-6101. Ed. Jimmy Dread. bk.rev.; charts; illus. circ. 500. (looseleaf format; back issues avail.) **Document type:** newsletter.

DREAMS & VISIONS; new frontiers in Christian fiction. see *LITERATURE*

200 AU ISSN 0012-6764
DRUZINA IN DOM. (Text in Slovene) m. S.2($8) Druzba Sv. Mohorja, Viktringer Ring 26, A-9020 Klagenfurt, Austria.

200 AT
E.C.M. NEWS. 1965. bi-m. free. European Christian Mission (Australian Section) Inc., P.O. Box 15, Croydon, N.S.W. 2132, Australia. TEL 61-2-7475446. FAX 61-2-7475509. E-mail: 100351.1065@compuserve.com. Ed. Rev. Jim Bosma. adv.; bk.rev. circ. 5,000. (also avail. in diskette format)

200 GW ISSN 0175-7695
E M W - INFORMATIONEN. 1978. irreg. free. Evangelisches Missionswerk in Deutschland, Normannenweg 17-21, 20537 Hamburg, Germany. TEL 040-25456-0. FAX 040-2542987. Ed. Brunhild Christmann. circ. 2,000. **Document type:** monographic series.

200 GW ISSN 0344-9106
E Z W - TEXTE; Informationen - Impulse - Arbeitstexte. 1970. 3/yr. (in 2 vols.). free. (Evangelische Kirche in Deutschland) Evangelische Zentralstelle fuer Weltanschauungsfragen, Hoelderlinplatz 2A, 70193 Stuttgart, Germany. TEL 0711-2262281. FAX 0711-2261331. adv. circ. 11,000. (back issues avail.) **Document type:** monographic series.

EARTHKEEPING ONTARIO. see *AGRICULTURE*

RELIGIONS AND THEOLOGY

291   II   ISSN 0012-8384
EAST AND WEST SERIES; an interpreter of the life of the spirit. (Text in English) 1954. m. Rs.3.($2) Gita Publishing House, 10 Sadhu Vaswani Rd., Mira Nagar, Poona 1, India. Ed. J.P. Vaswani. bk.rev.; bibl. (back issues avail.)

266   US   ISSN 1069-5664
EAST-WEST CHURCH & MINISTRY REPORT. 1993. q. $39 (foreign $49). Institute for East-West Christian Studies, Billy Graham Center, Wheaton College, Wheaton, IL 60187-5593. TEL 708-752-5917. FAX 708-752-5555. E-mail: iewcs@david.wheaton.edu. Eds. Mark Elliott, Wil Triggs. circ. 400 (paid). **Document type:** newsletter.
   Description: Seeks to encourage Western Christian ministry in East Central Europe and the former Soviet Union that is effective, culturally sensitive, and cooperative. Also serves as a forum for the exploration of a variety of issues relating to Christianity's presences in Europe's formerly Marxist states.

266   UK   ISSN 1354-0580
▼**EASTERN CHURCHES JOURNAL.** 1994. s-a. $25 u.S and Canada; elsewhere £20 ($30). Society of St. John Chrysostom, 22 Binney St., London W1Y 1YN, England. Ed. Serge Keleher. circ. 500. **Document type:** academic/scholarly publication.

262.9   UK   ISSN 0956-618X
K5
ECCLESIASTICAL LAW JOURNAL. 1987. s-a. Ecclesiastical Law Society, 1 The Sanctuary, Westminster, London SW1 JT, England. (reprint service avail. from WSH) **Indexed:** Euro.LJI, LJI. **Document type:** academic/scholarly publication.

284   FR   ISSN 0397-0736
ECHANGES; journal de l'eglise reformee...Provence, Cote d'Azur, Corse. 1955. m. 130 F. (typically set in Jan.). Association Echanges, 34 bvd des Platanes, 13009 Marseille, France. TEL 91-26-17-49. Ed. Eric Trocme. adv.; bk.rev.; film rev.; illus. circ. 4,000. **Indexed:** Geo.Abstr., Pt.de Rep.
   Formerly: Eglise Reformee Vous Parle.
   Description: News about the protestant religion and theology. Provides chronilces of the parishes of Provence-Cote d'Azur.

200   GW
ECHO AUS AFRIKA UND ANDERN ERDTEILEN. 1888. 10/yr. St. Petrus Claver Sodalitaet, Billerstr. 20, 86154 Augsburg, Germany. TEL 0821-414077. circ. 26,000. **Document type:** newsletter.

266   CN   ISSN 0318-9872
ECHO MISSIONAIRE/MISSION NEWS. (Text in English or French) 1975. bi-m. free. Comboni Missionaries, 79 Moore Ave., Kitchener, ON N2H 3S4, Canada. TEL 519-744-4680. Ed. Luigi Marcolongo. circ. 6,000. **Document type:** newsletter.

266 276   NE
ECHO UIT AFRIKA EN ANDERE WERELDDELEN. 1933. bi-m. fl.15. Missiezusters van St. Petrus Claver - Missionary Sisters of St. Peter Claver, Bouillonstraat 4, 6211 LH Maastricht, Netherlands. TEL 31-43-3212158. Ed. Zr.M. Jeanine van Ooteghem. charts; illus. circ. 18,000.
   Formerly: Echo uit Afrika (ISSN 0012-9305)

268   SZ
ECHOES; justice, peace and creation news. 2/yr. World Council of Churches, Unit III, 150 route de Ferney, P.O. Box 2100, CH-1211 Geneva 2, Switzerland. TEL 022-791-6111. FAX 022-791-0361. TELEX 415730-OIK-CH. circ. 7,000. **Document type:** bulletin.

200   IT
L'ECO DELLE VALLI VALDESI. 1848. w. L.110000. Edizioni Protestanti, s.r.l., Via Pio V 15, bis., 10125 Turin, Italy. TEL 011-655278. FAX 011-657542. Dir. Giorgio Gardiol. circ. 5,000.

200   BE
ECOLE DES HAUTES ETUDES SCIENCES RELIGIEUSES. BIBLIOTHEQUE. (Text in French) 1940. irreg., (2-3/yr.), vol.101, 1994. price varies. Editions Peeters s.p.r.l., Bondgenotenlaan 153, 3000 Leuven, Belgium. TEL 32-16-235170. FAX 32-16-228500. (back issues avail.) **Document type:** monographic series.

200   FR   ISSN 0070-8860
ECRITS LIBRES. 1955. irreg., no.16, 1973. Librairie Fischbacher, 33 rue de Seine, 75006 Paris, France. TEL 43-26-84-87. FAX 43-26-48-87.

200   US   ISSN 0013-0761
ECUMENICAL COURIER. 1941. irreg., (2-4/yr.). $15 donations. United States Conference for the World Council of Churches, 475 Riverside Dr., No. 915, New York, NY 10115. TEL 212-870-2533. FAX 212-870-2528. bk.rev. circ. 10,000.

200   SZ
ECUMENICAL LETTER ON EVANGELISM. (Editions in English, French, German) 1956. irreg. 12 SFr. World Council of Churches, Unit II - Desk on Evangelism, 150 route de Ferney, P.O. Box 2100, CH-1211 Geneva 2, Switzerland. TEL 022-791-6111. FAX 022-791-0361. TELEX 415730-OIK-CH. Ed. Samuel Kokou Ada. circ. 4,000 (all eds.). **Indexed:** CERDIC. **Document type:** newsletter.
   Formerly (until 1994): Monthly Letter on Evangelism.

200   IO
ECUMENICAL NEWS.* 1973. m. Council of Churches in Indonesia, Jalan Selemba Raya 10, Jakarta, Indonesia. (processed)

200   SZ
ECUMENICAL NEWS INTERNATIONAL. (Text in English, French) 24/yr. 85 SFr. Ecumenical News International, 150 route de Ferney, P.O. Box 2100, CH-1211 Geneva 2, Switzerland. TEL 022-7916178. FAX 022-7981346. Eds. Edmond Doogue, Stephen Brown. **Document type:** bulletin.

200   SZ   ISSN 0013-0796
BX1
ECUMENICAL REVIEW. 1948. q. 43.50 SFr.($32.50) World Council of Churches, Publications Office, 150 route de Ferney, P.O. Box 2100, CH-1211 Geneva 2, Switzerland. TEL 022-791-6111. FAX 022-791-0361. TELEX 415730-OIK-CH. Ed. Raiser Konrad. adv.; bk.rev.; index. circ. 4,000. (also avail. in microform from UMI; reprint service avail. from UMI) **Indexed:** Arts & Hum.Cit.Ind., Bk.Rev.Ind. (1965-), CERDIC, Child.Bk.Rev.Ind. (1965-), Curr.Cont., Hum.Ind., IMFL, Mid.East: Abstr.& Ind., New Test.Abstr., Old Test.Abstr., Rel.& Theol.Abstr. (1989-), Rel.Ind.One, Rel.Per. **Document type:** bulletin.
   ●Also available online. Vendor(s): University Microfilms International.
   —BLDSC (3659.700000); Faxon; SWETS; UMI; UnCover.

200   US   ISSN 0360-9073
ECUMENICAL TRENDS. 1972. 11/yr. $10. 475 Riverside Dr., Rm. 528, New York, NY 10115-0050. (Subscr. to: Graymoor Ecumenical Institute, Garrison, NY 10524) Ed. Patrick J. Cogan. bk.rev. circ. 2,300. (also avail. in microform from UMI; reprint service avail. from UMI) **Indexed:** Cath.Ind., Rel.Ind.One.
   —BLDSC (3659.702000); UMI.
   Description: Provides news, opinion, documentation and features in the area of ecumenical and inter-religious activity. Directed towards those involved in ecumenism and church leadership.

200   CN   ISSN 0383-431X
ECUMENISM. French edition: Oecumenisme (ISSN 0383-4301) 1966. q. Can.$15($17.50) Canadian Centre for Ecumenism, 2065 Sherbrooke St. W., Montreal, PQ H3H 1G6, Canada. TEL 514-937-9176. FAX 514-935-5497. Ed.Bd. adv.; bk.rev.; circ. 1,600 (paid). (also avail. in microfilm from UMI) **Indexed:** Rel.& Theol.Abstr., Rel.Ind.One.
   —UMI.

200   SA
ECUNEWS. (Not published 1990-1992) 1975. q. free. South African Council of Churches, Khotso House, 62 Marshall St., P.O. Box 4921, Johannesburg 2000, South Africa. FAX 27-11-492-1448. Ed. Bernard Spong. bk.rev. circ. 6,000.

200   NE   ISSN 0165-4268
DE EERSTE DAG. 1978. q. fl.62.50. Boekencentrum B.V., P.O. Box 29, 2700 AA Zoetermeer, Netherlands. TEL 31-79-615481. FAX 31-79-615489. Ed. Klaas Touwen.
   Description: Ecumenical liturgical schedule with suggestions for psalms and hymns, exegetic study, and ideas for children in the church.

200   CN   ISSN 0013-2322
L'EGLISE CANADIENNE; documents et informations. (Text in French) 1968. 11/yr. Can.$30. Revue L'Eglise Canadienne Inc., 6255 rue Hutchison, Bur. 103, Montreal, PQ H2V 4C7, Canada. TEL 514-278-3025; 800-668-2547. FAX 514-278-3030. Ed. Rolande Parrot. adv.; bk.rev.; index. circ. 5,000. **Indexed:** CERDIC, Pt.de Rep. (1979-).
   Description: Features studies and information on theological questions. Also covers life in the church in a general sense.

260   CN   ISSN 0013-2349
EGLISE ET THEOLOGIE. (Text in English and French) 1970. 3/yr. Can.$37.45 (foreign $35). Saint Paul University, Faculty of Theology, 223 Main St., Ottawa, ON K1S 1C4, Canada. TEL 613-236-1393. FAX 613-782-3005. Ed. Leo Laberge. bk.rev.; index. (also avail. in microform from UMI; reprint service avail. from UMI) **Indexed:** Bull.Signal., Canon Law Abstr., CERDIC, Int.Z.Bibelwiss., New Test.Abstr., Old Test.Abstr., Rel.& Theol.Abstr. (1974-), Rel.Ind.One, Rel.Per.
   —BLDSC (3664.215500); SWETS; UMI.

EGLISE QUI CHANTE. see *MUSIC*

200   IT
EKUMENISMO; trimonata internacia gazeto pri ekumenaj temoj kaj aferoj. (Text in Esperanto) 1985. q. L.10000($10) Tutmonda Ekumena Ligo, Via Francesco Berni 9, 00185 Rome, Italy. TEL 39-6-7000323. Ed. Angelo Duranti.

200   US   ISSN 8756-1336
ELISABETH ELLIOT NEWSLETTER. 1982. bi-m. $7 donation. (Servant Ministeries) Servant Publications, Box 8617, Ann Arbor, MI 48107-8617. TEL 313-761-8505. FAX 313-761-1577. Ed. Peggy Morgan. bk.rev. circ. 13,000. (back issues avail.) **Document type:** newsletter.
   Description: Publishes inspirational articles for Christians.

200   NE   ISSN 0013-6212
ELISABETHBODE. 1929. w. fl.29. Stichting Elisabethbode, Postbus 2, 7260 AA Ruurlo, Netherlands. circ. 160,000.

EMERGE!; a journal for Christian Scientists supporting lesbians, bisexuals, and gay men. see *HOMOSEXUALITY*

266   IT   ISSN 0013-6697
EMIGRATO ITALIANO.* 1903. m. L.1000($4) Congregazione dei Missionari di S. Carlo, Via Scalabrini 3, 36061 Bassano del Grappa (Vicenza), Italy. Ed. P.G.B. Saraggi. adv.; charts; stat.; index. circ. 5,000.

266   US   ISSN 0194-5246
EMPHASIS ON FAITH AND LIVING. 1969. bi-m. donations. Missionary Church, Inc., Box 9127, Ft. Wayne, IN 46899. TEL 219-747-2027. FAX 219-747-5331. Ed. Robert L. Ransom. adv.; bk.rev. circ. 13,000. **Indexed:** G.Soc.Sci.& Rel.Per.Lit.
   Description: Communicates message and ministry of the Missionary Church.

200 283   UK   ISSN 0958-2797
ENCOUNTER. q. £4. United Society for the Propagation of the Gospel, Partnership House, 157 Waterloo Rd., London SE1 8XA, England. TEL 0171-928-8681. FAX 0171-928-2371. circ. 5,000. **Document type:** bulletin.
   Incorporates (in 1990): United Society for the Propagation of the Gospel. Quarterly Intercession Paper.
   Description: Includes prayer and liturgical material.

RELIGIONS AND THEOLOGY

200   US   ISSN 0013-7081
BR1
ENCOUNTER (INDIANAPOLIS, 1956). 1956. q. $18. Christian Theological Seminary, 1000 W. 42nd St., Indianapolis, IN 46208. TEL 317-924-1331. Ed. Clark M. Williamson. adv.; bk.rev.; index. circ. 650. (also avail. in microfilm from UMI; reprint service avail. from UMI) **Indexed:** Amer.Hist.& Life, Arts & Hum.Cit.Ind., G.Soc.Sci.& Rel.Per.Lit., Hist.Abstr., Hum.Ind., Int.Z.Bibelwiss., New Test.Abstr., Old Test.Abstr., Rel.& Theol.Abstr., Rel.Ind.One. **Document type:** academic/scholarly publication.
—BLDSC (3738.540000); UMI; UnCover.
Description: Discusses creative theological scholarship among believers in Christ and people of other faiths.

200   US   ISSN 1066-1212
ENCYCLOPEDIA OF AMERICAN RELIGIONS. 1987. irreg., 4rd ed., 1992. $175. Gale Research Inc., 835 Penobscot Bldg., Detroit, MI 48226. TEL 800-877-4253. FAX 313-961-6083. TELEX 810-221-7086. Ed. J. Gordon Melton.
Description: Details approximately 1,600 religious groups of North America, ranging from Adventists to Zen Buddhists. Divided into two sections: essays and directory listings.

200   US
ENCYCLOPEDIA OF AMERICAN RELIGIONS: RELIGIOUS CREEDS. irreg. $125. Gale Research Inc., 835 Penobscot Bldg., Detroit, MI 48226. TEL 800-877-4253. FAX 313-961-6083. TELEX 810-221-7086. Ed. J. Gordon Melton.
Description: Presents 464 religious creeds, statements of faith, and summaries of doctrine associated with the many branches of Christian, Jewish, Islamic, Hindu, and other religions practiced in United States.

200   SP
ENSENANZA DE LA RELIGION. 1982. irreg., no.2, 1986. price varies. (Universidad de Navarra, Facultad de Teologia) Ediciones Universidad de Navarra, S.A., Apdo. 396, 31080 Pamplona, Spain. TEL 94 825 6850.

250   CN
ENTRE - NOUS. (Editions in English, French) 1970. irreg. (2-3/yr.). donation. Canadian Council of Churches, 40 St. Clair Ave. E., Ste. 201, Toronto, ON M4T 1M9, Canada. TEL 416-921-4152. FAX 416-921-7478. Ed. Jim Hodgson. bk.rev. circ. 3,000. **Document type:** newsletter.
Formerly (until 1990): Canadian Council of Churches. Council Communicator (ISSN 0045-4605)
Description: News and views from across Canada about the work of the CCC, its member churches, overseas partners and inter-church coalitions.

200   AU   ISSN 0017-4602
ENTSCHLUSS; Zeitschrift fuer Praxis und Theologie. 1946. m. S.420. Lainzerstr. 138, A-1130 Vienna, Austria. TEL 0222-8049742. FAX 0222-8049743. Ed. Gustav Schoerghofer. adv.; bk.rev.; rec.rev.; bibl.; charts; index. circ. 8,000. **Indexed:** CERDIC. **Document type:** academic/scholarly publication.
Formerly: Grosse Entschluss.

262   IT   ISSN 0013-9505
EPHEMERIDES LITURGICAE; commentarius bimestre de re liturgica. (Text in various languages) 1887. 5/yr. L.35000 (Europe L.45000; elsewhere L.55000 ($48,60)) (effective 1994). (Centro Liturgico Vincenziano) C L V Edizioni Liturgiche, Via Pompeo Magno, 21, 00192 Rome, Italy. TEL 00396-3216114. FAX 00396-3221078. (Co-sponsor: Vincentian Fathers) adv.; bk.rev. circ. 1,500. **Indexed:** Canon Law Abstr., CERDIC, New Test.Abstr.
—BLDSC (3793.475000); SWETS.

262   IT
EPHEMERIDES LITURGICAE. COLLECTIO SUBSIDIA. 1974. irreg., no.67, 1991. price varies. (Centro Liturgico Vincenziano) C L V Edizioni Liturgiche, Via Pompeo Magno, 21, 00192 Rome, Italy. TEL 00396-3216114. FAX 00396-3221078.

200   US   ISSN 0273-6969
BV4485
EPIPHANY JOURNAL; a journal of faith and insight. 1980. q. $22.50 (foreign $28.50). (Christ the Saviour Brotherhood) Epiphany Press, Box 2250, S. Portland, ME 04116-2250. Ed. F. Michael Crowley. bk.rev. circ. 1,800. (also avail. in microform from UMI; back issues avail.) **Indexed:** Rel.& Theol.Abstr. (1988-), Rel.Ind.One. **Document type:** academic/scholarly publication.
●Also available online. Vendor(s): Ovid Technologies, Knight-Ridder, Inc.
—UMI.
Formerly: Epiphany.
Description: An Orthodox journal proclaiming the living Gospel of Jesus Christ in the contemporary world.

200 901   US   ISSN 0149-3043
BL41
EPOCHE; journal of the history of religions at U.C.L.A. 1972. a. $6. University of California at Los Angeles, Graduate Student Association, 301 Kerchoff Hall, 308 Westwood Plaza, Los Angeles, CA 90024. (Subscr. to: Department of History, UCLA, Los Angeles, CA 90024) Ed. Rick Talbott. cum.index: 1972-82. circ. 850. (back issues avail.)
Formerly (until 1976): History of Religions Newsletter (ISSN 0360-6147)

ERASMUS OF ROTTERDAM SOCIETY YEARBOOK. see PHILOSOPHY

200   GW   ISSN 0014-0201
ERMLANDBRIEFE. 1946. q. DM.15. Apostolischer Visitator fuer Klerus und Glaeubige des Ermlandes, Ermlandweg 22, 48159 Muenster, Germany. TEL 0251-211477. FAX 0251-260517. Ed. Johannes Schwalke. bk.rev.; illus. circ. 31,000. **Document type:** newsletter.

ERRANT NEWS. see ART

ESPIRITU. see PHILOSOPHY

200   FR   ISSN 0014-0775
ESPRIT ET VIE. (In 2 Parts: Doctrine; Pastorale) 1879. w. 400 F. (for both parts)(foreign 460 F.). B.P. 4, 52200 Langres, France. TEL 25-87-02-26. FAX 25-87-45-66. bk.rev.; bibl.; index. circ. 5,000. **Indexed:** CERDIC, New Test.Abstr.
Formerly: Ami du Clerge.
Description: Discusses readings, the Holy Scripture, theology, philosophy, liturgy, the history of literature, morals.

240   FR   ISSN 0396-969X
ESPRIT SAINT; revue de spiritualite. 1952. q. 35 F. Congregation du Saint-Esprit, Fraternites du Saint-Esprit, 30 rue Lhomond, 75005 Paris, France. Ed. Michel Picard. bk.rev.; bibl.; cum.index. circ. 6,000.
Formerly: Devotion au Saint-Esprit (ISSN 0012-1711)

220   SP   ISSN 0014-1437
BS410
ESTUDIOS BIBLICOS. (Text in English, French, German, Italian, Spanish) 1941. q. 4000 ptas. (foreign 5500 ptas.) (effective 1996). Centro de Estudios Teologicos "San Damaso", San Buenaventura, 9, 28005 Madrid, Spain. TEL 91-3652404. FAX 91-3642882. (Co-sponsor: Asociacion Biblica Espanola) Ed. Alfonso de la Fuente. bk.rev.; bibl. circ. 600. **Indexed:** New Test.Abstr., Old Test.Abstr., Rel.Ind.One.

200   SP   ISSN 0210-1610
ESTUDIOS ECLESIASTICOS; revista de teologia. 1922. q. 4600 ptas.($43) (Europe $58; Latin America & Africa $60; US $68; Asia $75) (effective 1995). (Compania de Jesus, Facultades de Teologia) Centro Loyola de Estudios y Comunicacion Social, Pablo Aranda 3, 28006 Madrid, Spain. FAX 341-5634073. Ed.Bd. bk.rev.; bibl. **Indexed:** Amer.Hist.& Life, Canon Law Abstr., CERDIC, Hist.Abstr., New Test.Abstr., Old Test.Abstr.

200   SP   ISSN 0210-0363
ESTUDIOS TRINITARIOS. 1967. 3/yr. 4175 ptas.($55) Ediciones Secretariado Trinitario, Filiberto Villalobos, 82, 37007 Salamanca, Spain. TEL 235602. Ed. P. Nereo Silanes. bk.rev. **Indexed:** CERDIC.

200   FR   ISSN 0245-9329
ETENDARD DE LA BIBLE ET HERAUT DU ROYAUME DE CHRIST. English edition: Bible Standard and Herald of Christ's Kingdom (ISSN 0006-081X) 1957. bi-m. 15 F. Mouvement Missionnaire Interieur Laique, c/o Gilbert Hermetz, 2 rue du Dr. Capiaux, 62620 Barlin, France. TEL 21-25-94-86. FAX 21-27-26-50. Ed. Bernard Hedman. circ. 500.

ETHICS & POLICY. see SOCIOLOGY

ETHICS AND PUBLIC POLICY CENTER NEWSLETTER. see POLITICAL SCIENCE

200   SZ
ETHOS - DIE ZEITSCHRIFT FUER DIE GANZE FAMILIE. 1983. m. 90.40 Fr. Foerderung Christlicher Publizistik, Postfach 263, CH-9435 Heerbrugg, Switzerland. TEL 0711-724358. Ed. Bruno Schwengeler. circ. 30,000.
Description: Family oriented magazine of Bible study.

ETUDES GREGORIENNES; revue de musicologie religieuse. see MUSIC

ETUDES SCHWEITZERIENNES; revue annuelle d'ethique, de theologie et de philosophie. see PHILOSOPHY

200 060   FR   ISSN 0082-2612
ETUDES TEILHARDIENNES/TEILHARDIAN STUDIES. 1969. irreg. price varies. Editions du Seuil, 27 rue Jacob, 75261 Paris Cedex 06, France. Ed. J.P. DeMoulin. **Indexed:** Rel.Ind.One.
—CCC.

EUNTES DOCETE. see RELIGIONS AND THEOLOGY — Roman Catholic

266   US
EUROPE TODAY. 1971. q. free. Greater Europe Mission, 18950 Base Camp Rd., Monument, CO 80132-8009. TEL 719-488-8008. FAX 719-488-8019. E-mail: devere@gemusa.org. Ed. Devere K. Curtiss. adv.; bk.rev. circ. 40,000. **Document type:** newsletter.
Former titles (until 1992): Europe Report (ISSN 0274-8037); (until vol.18, no.5, 1988): G E M's Europe Report; Greater Europe Report.
Description: Reports the activities of GEM missionaries and national Christians to the Missions's supporting constituency in North America.

200   NE
EUROPEAN SOCIETY OF WOMEN IN THEOLOGICAL RESEARCH. YEARBOOK/EUROPAEISCHE GESELLSCHAFT FUER DIE THEOLOGISCHE FORSCHUNG VON FRAUEN. JAHRBUCH. (Text in English, French, German) 1993. a. fl.39.50($25) (effective 1993). Kok Pharos Publishing House, Postbus 5019, 8260 AG Kampen, Netherlands. TEL 31-5202-92565. FAX 31-5202-27331. (Dist. in U.S. and Canada by: Books International, Inc., Box 605, Herndon, VA 22070-0605. TEL 800-377-7192. FAX 703-689-0660) (Co-publisher: Matthias Gruenewald Verlag GmbH, GW) Eds. Luise Schottroff, Annette Esser. **Document type:** academic/scholarly publication.
Description: Discusses issues relating to feminist theology and the current state of scholarship in Europe.

EUROPEAN STUDIES JOURNAL. see HISTORY — History Of Europe

261   UK   ISSN 0265-4547
EVANGEL. 3/yr. £11.85 (foreign £12.35). The Paternoster Press, P.O. Box 300, Kingstown Broadway, Carlisle, Cumbria CA3 0QS, England. TEL 0228-512512. FAX 0228-514949. (Dist. in U.S. by: The Paternoster Press, Box 11127, Birmingham, AL 35201-1127) Ed. Stephen Dray. **Document type:** newsletter.
Description: Interdenominational evangelical review.

243
EVANGELICAL & ECUMENICAL WOMEN'S CAUCUS. 1980. q. $30 (students $15). Ecumenical & Evangelical Women's Caucus, Box 9989, Oakland, CA 94613-0989. TEL 510-696-2406. Ed. Letha Dawson Scanzoni. bk.rev. circ. 425. (back issues avail.) **Document type:** newsletter.
Formerly (until 1992): Evangelical Women's Caucus. Update.

200 974 US
EVANGELICAL & REFORMED HISTORICAL SOCIETY NEWSLETTER. 1970. s-a. membership. Evangelical & Reformed Historical Society, Philip Schaff Library, Lancaster Theological Seminary, 555 W. James St., Lancaster, PA 17603. Ed. John B. Payne. circ. 1,500. (back issues avail.) **Document type:** newsletter.
 Description: News about society meetings, papers presented and members' activities.

200 US
EVANGELICAL CATHOLIC. 1977. bi-m. $20 (foreign $30). Episcopal Synod of America, 6300 Ridglea Place, Ste. 910, Ft. Worth, TX 76116. TEL 412-741-8843. Ed. David Peter Mills. circ. 3,000. (back issues avail.)
 Description: Addresses the clergy and laity. Covers theological issues in the Episcopal Church.

200 UK ISSN 0014-3367
BR1
EVANGELICAL QUARTERLY. 1929. q. £17 (foreign £18.05). The Paternoster Press, P.O. Box 300, Kingstown Broadway, Carlisle, Cumbria CA3 0QS, England. TEL 0228-512512. FAX 0228-514949. (Dist. in U.S. & Canada by: The Paternoster Press, P.O. Box 11127, Birmingham, Alabama 35201-1127) Ed. I. Howard Marshall. bk.rev.; index. circ. 1,100. (also avail. in microfilm from UMI; reprint service avail. from UMI) **Indexed:** CERDIC, Chr.Per.Ind., New Test.Abstr., Old Test.Abstr., Rel.& Theol.Abstr. (1969-), Rel.Ind.One, Rel.Per. **Document type:** academic/scholarly publication.
 —BLDSC (3830.700000); UMI; UnCover. **CCC.**
 Description: Articles on a variety of biblical and theological topics.

200 UK ISSN 0144-8153
EVANGELICAL REVIEW OF THEOLOGY. 1977. q. £18 (foreign £19.35). The Paternoster Press, P.O. Box 300, Kingstown Broadway, Carlisle, Cumbria CA3 0QS, England. TEL 0228-512512. FAX 0228-514949. (Dist. in U.S. & Canada by: The Paternoster Press, P.O. Box 11127, Birmingham, Alabama 35201-1127) Ed. Bruce Nicholls. bk.rev. circ. 1,000. (also avail. in microform from UMI; reprint service avail. from UMI) **Indexed:** CERDIC, Rel.& Theol.Abstr. (1989-), Rel.Ind.One. **Document type:** academic/scholarly publication.
 —BLDSC (3830.702000); UMI. **CCC.**
 Description: Interprets the Christian faith for contemporary living.

266 SP
EVANGELIO Y MISION. 1964. m. donation. Compania de Jesus, Plaza de San Marcos, 1, 24001 Leon, Spain. TEL 22 85 78. Ed. J. Pedraz. illus. circ. 5,000.
 Formerly: Boletin Intimo de Compania.

DER EVANGELISCHE ERZIEHER; Zeitschrift fuer Paedagogik und Theologie. see *EDUCATION*

EVANGELISCHE IMPULSE; Zeitschrift fuer die Arbeit mit alten Menschen. see *GERONTOLOGY AND GERIATRICS*

200 GW ISSN 0300-4236
EVANGELISCHE KOMMENTARE; Monatsschrift zum Zeitgeschehen in Kirche und Gesellschaft. 1968. m. DM.118.80. Kreuz-Verlag Zeitschriften GmbH, Breitwiesenstr. 30, 70565 Stuttgart, Germany. TEL 0711-78803. Ed.Bd. adv.; bk.rev. circ. 8,500. **Document type:** bulletin.
 —BLDSC (3830.730000); SWETS. **CCC.**

200 GW
EVANGELISCHE SAMMLUNG. m. Foerderverein Evangelische Sammlung Berlin e.V., Motzstr. 52, 10777 Berlin, Germany. TEL 030-242252.

240 GW ISSN 0014-3502
BR4
EVANGELISCHE THEOLOGIE. 1934. bi-m. DM.87 (students DM.59). Guetersloher Verlagshaus Chr. Kaiser, Carl-Bertelsmann-Str. 270, 33311 Guetersloh, Germany. TEL 05241-7405-0. FAX 05241-740548. Eds. Regina Hunziker-Rodewald, Olaf Wassmuth. adv.; B&W page DM.900; trim 108 x 192. circ. 2,500. (also avail. in microform from UMI; reprint service avail. from UMI) **Indexed:** CERDIC, New Test.Abstr., Old Test.Abstr., Rel.& Theol.Abstr. (1991-), Rel.Ind.One, Rel.Per. **Document type:** academic/scholarly publication.
 —SWETS. **CCC.**

200 053.1 GW ISSN 0177-185X
EVANGELISCHER DIGEST. 1951. m. DM.97.20. Verlag Axel B. Trunkel, Landhausstr. 22, 70190 Stuttgart, Germany. Ed. Andrea Przyklenk. circ. 14,800. (back issues avail.)
 Description: General interest subjects for senior citizens.

200 GW ISSN 0174-3376
EVANGELISCHES SONNTAGSBLATT AUS BAYERN. w. (Sun.). DM.58.80. Gebr. Holstein GmbH und Co. KG, Erlbacherstr. 104, 91541 Rothenburg, Germany. TEL 09861-5028. FAX 09861-7722. Ed. Burkhard Stark. circ. 39,878. **Document type:** newsletter.

243 UK
EVANGELISM TODAY. 1972. m. £8.50 (overseas £9.50-15). 320 Ashley Down Rd., Bristol BS7 9BQ, England. TEL 0117-924-1679. Ed. Bill Spencer. adv.; bk.rev.; circ. 4,500. (paid).
 Description: Reports news and topics on prayer of interest to supporters of evangelism and outreach.

200 IT
EVANGELIZZARE; mensile per animatori di catechesi. 1974. m. L.27000 (foreign L.42000) (effective 1994). Centro Editoriale Dehoniano, Via Nosadella 6, 40123 Bologna, Italy. TEL 051-306811. FAX 051-341706. adv.; bk.rev.

262.9 SP ISSN 0214-3100
EXCERPTA E DISSERTATIONIBUS IN IURE CANONICO. 1983. irreg., no.5, 1987. 3000 ptas. (Universidad de Navarra, Facultad de Derecho Canonico) Servicio de Publicaciones de la Universidad de Navarra, S.A., Apdo. 177, 31080 Pamplona, Spain. TEL 94 25 2700.

266 NE ISSN 0166-2740
EXCHANGE; a journal of missiological and ecumenical research. (Text in English) 1972. 3/yr. fl.70($45) to individuals; institutions fl.115($74) (effective 1996). (Interuniversitair Instituut voor Missiologie en Oecumenica, Leiden) E.J. Brill, Postbus 9000, 2300 PA Leiden, Netherlands. TEL 31-71-5353500. FAX 31-71-5317532. TELEX 39296 BRILL NL. E-mail: ejborders@ejbrill.com. (In N. America: E.J. Brill, 24 Hudson St., Kinderhook, NY 12106. TEL 800-962-4406. FAX 518-758-1959) Ed. K. Steenbrink. **Document type:** academic/scholarly publication.
 Refereed Serial

200 UK ISSN 0014-5246
BS410
THE EXPOSITORY TIMES. 1889. m. £14.95 (U.S. $29.95; Canada Can.$39.95; Australia Aus.$39.95; elsewhere £17.50). T & T Clark, 59 George St., Edinburgh EH2 2LQ, Scotland. TEL 0131-225-4703. FAX 0131-220-4260. Ed. Rev. C.S. Rodd. adv.; bk.rev.; index. circ. 6,000. (also avail. in microform from WMP) **Indexed:** Arts & Hum.Cit.Ind., Br.Hum.Ind., Curr.Cont., New Test.Abstr., Old Test.Abstr., Rel.& Theol.Abstr. (1968-), Rel.Ind.One.
 —BLDSC (3843.370000); Genuine Article; SWETS.
 Description: Interdenominational articles, sermons and book reviews for ministers, scholars and theological students.

200 AT
F A C T. (Faith and Atheism in Communist Territories) 1979. m. free. Voice of Peace Ltd. (Inc. in N.S.W.), P.O. Box 339, Cronulla, N.S.W. 2230, Australia. TEL 02-527-2387. FAX 02-527-3335. circ. 1,800.

200 301.4157 051 US
F L G C NEWSLETTER. 1976. q. $10. Friends for Lesbian and Gay Concerns, Box 222, Sumneytown, PA 18084. TEL 215-234-8424. Ed. Bruce Grimes. bk.rev. circ. 830. (looseleaf format) **Document type:** newsletter.
 Description: Carries articles of special interest to lesbian and gay Quakers, including current topics in same-sex marriage among Quakers.

200 US ISSN 0363-7735
BV4025
FACT BOOK ON THEOLOGICAL EDUCATION. 1969. a. $24.75. Association of Theological Schools, 10 Summit Park Dr., Pittsburgh, PA 15275-1103. TEL 412-788-6505. Ed. Gary Gilbert. circ. 700. (also avail. in microfiche from CIS) **Indexed:** SRI.
 Description: Provides comprehensive statistical data useful for planning by theological institutions.

200 UK
FAITH. 1968. bi-m. £8($17) (Europe and Ireland £20). Faith - Magazine, 7 St. Brides Close, Erith, Kent DA18 4DT, England. TEL 0181-776-8399. (Subscr. to: Paul Butcher, 16a Off Conniston Ave., Reigate, Surrey RH2 OLN, England. TEL 01737-770016. FAX 01737-766907) Ed. Rev. Timothy Finigan. adv.; bk.rev. circ. 1,200. **Document type:** academic/scholarly publication.

200 UK ISSN 0014-701X
FAITH AND FREEDOM; a journal of progressive religion. 1947. 2/yr. £10($20) 41 Bradford Dr., Ewell, Epsom, Surrey KT19 0AQ, England. TEL 0181-393-9122. Ed. Rev. Peter Godfrey. adv.; bk.rev. circ. 600. (also avail. in microform from UMI; reprint service avail. from UMI) **Indexed:** CERDIC, Rel.& Theol.Abstr. (1989-), Rel.Ind.One. **Document type:** academic/scholarly publication.
 —BLDSC (3865.510600); UMI.

200 UK ISSN 0140-0266
FAITH AND HERITAGE. 1977. s-a. £2.50 (foreign £3.50). Prayer Book Society, 36 The Drive, Northwood, Middlesex HA6 1HP, England. TEL 01923-824278. (Subscr. to: John Skinner, 59A Kings End, Ruislip, Middlesex HA4 7DD, England) Ed. Anthony Kilmister. bk.rev. circ. 7,000. **Document type:** bulletin.

200 SZ ISSN 0512-2589
FAITH AND ORDER PAPERS. 1949. irreg., no.170, 1995. price varies. World Council of Churches, Publications Office, 150 route de Ferney, P.O. Box 2100, CH-1211 Geneva 2, Switzerland. TEL 022-791-6111. FAX 022-791-0361. TELEX 415730-OIK-CH. (Dist. in U.S. by: World Council of Churches Distribution Center, Rt. 111 & Sharadin Rd., Box 346, Kutztown, PA 19530-0346) cum.index: 1910-70. **Indexed:** Rel.Ind.Two. **Document type:** monographic series.

FAITH AND PHILOSOPHY. see *PHILOSOPHY*

230.05 US ISSN 0098-5449
BR1
FAITH & REASON (FRONT ROYAL). 1975. q. $20. (Christendom College) Christendom Press, 134 Christendom Dr., Front Royal, VA 22630. FAX 703-636-1655. Ed. James McLucas. bk.rev. circ. 500. **Indexed:** Cath.Ind., CERDIC. **Document type:** academic/scholarly publication.

200 UK ISSN 0309-1627
FAITH & WORSHIP. 1976. s-a. £1.25. Prayer Book Society, 36 The Drive, Northwood, Middlesex HA6 1HP, England. TEL 01923-824278. (Subscr. to: John Skinner, 59A Kings End, Ruislip, Middlesex HA4 7DD, England. TEL 018956-37429) bk.rev. circ. 7,000. **Document type:** bulletin.

200 IT ISSN 0014-7095
FAMIGLIA CRISTIANA. 1931. w. L.142800. Periodici San Paolo S.r.l., Via Giotto 36, 20145 Milan, Italy. TEL 39-2-48071. Ed. Leonardo Zega. adv.; B&W page L.64000000, color page L.77000000; adv. contact: Corrado Minnella. bk.rev.; film rev.; play rev.; charts; illus.; stat.; index, cum.index every 5 yrs. circ. 1,084,000. (tabloid format)

FAMILIA CRISTA; revista da paz e do amor - revista mensal para a familia. see *SOCIOLOGY*

FAMILIA Y SOCIEDAD. see *SOCIOLOGY*

200 GW ISSN 0936-8043
FAMILIEN UND JUGEND - GOTTESDIENSTE. m. DM.96. Bergmoser und Hoeller Verlag GmbH, Karl-Friedrich-Str. 76, 52072 Aachen, Germany. TEL 0241-9388821. FAX 0241-9388834. circ. 5,200. (looseleaf format) **Document type:** consumer publication.
 Formerly: Gottesdienste mit Kindern und Jugendlichen (ISSN 0176-8581)
 Description: For use in preparing Sunday services for children and youth.

268 US
FAMILY RADIO NEWS. 1966. q. free. Family Stations, Inc., 290 Hegenberger Rd., Oakland, CA 94621. TEL 800-543-1495. FAX 510-633-7983. Ed. Richard Homeres. charts; illus. circ. 100,000.
 Description: Contains articles about the ministry of Family Radio as well as the program guide for the stations served.

RELIGIONS AND THEOLOGY

200 155.4 US
FAMILY SPIRIT; dedicated to the spiritual well-being of parent and child. 1980. q. $14. Family Spirit Publ., Box 82503, Albuquerque, NM 87198. TEL 505-266-5492. Ed. Pat Harvey. adv.; bk.rev. circ. 1,000. (back issues avail.)
Former titles: Spiritual Mothering Journal (ISSN 0886-3156); Spiritual Mothering Newsletter.

200 NO ISSN 0014-8733
FAST GRUNN. 1948. bi-m. NOK 210 (foreign NOK 295). Lunde Forlag, Grensen 19, N-0159 Oslo 1, Norway. TEL 47-22-42-91-30. FAX 47-22-42-10-49. Ed. Jon Kvalbein. adv.; bk.rev.; illus.; index. circ. 3,200.
—CCC.
Description: Aimed at laymen leaders in the Church, the periodical features articles on theology, Church life, society and ethics; carries reviews of Church debate.

200 US
FELLOWSHIP LIFE & LIFESTYLES. 1975. q. Fellowship of the Inner Light, 620 14th St., Virginia Beach, VA 23451. TEL 703-896-3673. FAX 804-428-6648. Eds. Myrrh and Stephen Haslam.

200 UK
FELLOWSHIP OF RECONCILIATION. ANNUAL REPORT; nonviolence: peace in action. a. free. Fellowship of Reconciliation, 40-46 Harleyford Rd., Vauxhall, London SE11 5AY, England. TEL 0171-582-9054. FAX 0171-582-9180. **Document type:** corporate report.
Description: News of the fellowship's work.

FEMINIST THEOLOGY. see *WOMEN'S STUDIES*

260 FR ISSN 0015-0371
FETES ET SAISONS. 1945. 10/yr. 185 F. (foreign 232 F.). Editions du Cerf, 29 bd. Latour Maubourg, 75340 Paris Cedex 07, France. TEL 44-18-12-12. FAX 45-56-04-27. (Subscr. to: Service Abonnements, 3 chemin des Prunais, 94350 Villiers-sur-Marne, France) Ed. Marc Sevin. illus. circ. 40,000. **Indexed:** Pt.de Rep. (1979-).
Description: Studies Christian life, sacraments, the lives of saints, questions of education and morals, happenings in the Church.

FIDES ET HISTORIA. see *HISTORY*

200 IT
FILOSOFIA DELLA RELIGIONE. TESTI E STUDI. 1977. irreg., latest no.3. price varies. Paideia Editrice, Via Corsica 130, 25125 Brescia, Italy. TEL 030-222094. FAX 030-223269.

207.11 IT ISSN 0015-2528
FIORI DI S. ANTONIO. 1951. s-m. free. Convento di Giaccherino, 51030 Pontelungo, Italy. Ed. P. Lorenzo Lazzeri. illus. circ. 17,000.

200 US ISSN 1047-5141
BL2525
FIRST THINGS; a monthly journal of religion and public life. 1990. m. (10/yr.). $29 (effective Jan. 1994; typically set in Sept.). Institute of Religion & Public Life, 156 Fifth Ave., Ste. 400, New York, NY 10010. TEL 212-627-2288. FAX 212-627-2184. (Subscr. to: Department FT, Box 3000, Denville, NJ 07834-9847. TEL 800-875-2997) Ed. Richard John Neuhaus. adv. contact: Richard Vaughan. bk.rev.; index; circ. 27,000. (paid). (also avail. in microfilm; microfiche; back issues avail.; reprint service avail.) **Indexed:** Rel.Ind.One. **Document type:** consumer publication.
● Also available online.
—BLDSC (3934.466700); UnCover.
Description: Examines issues arising at the crossroads of religion and public life today.

FLASH. see *HANDICAPPED — Visually Impaired*

FLAT EARTH NEWS; the last iconoclast. see *HUMANITIES: COMPREHENSIVE WORKS*

200 US
FLOODTIDE; literature evangelism. 1948. bi-m. free. Christian Literature Crusade, Inc., Box 1449, Fort Washington, PA 19034. TEL 215-542-1242. Ed. Leona Hepburn. bk.rev. circ. 6,500.

914.606 200 SP
FOC NOU; revista al servei dels Cristians. (Text in Catalan) 1974. m. 4500 ptas. (foreign 5300 ptas.). Publicaciones de el Ciervo, S.A., Calvet 56, 08021 Barcelona, Spain. Ed. Roser Bofill Portabella. adv.; bk.rev.; illus. circ. 3,000.

200 UK
FOCUS (WARWICKSHIRE). 1975. q. £0.30. Christian Endeavour Union of Great Britain and Ireland, Wellesbourne House, Walton Rd., Wellesbourne, Warks. CV35 9JB, England. TEL 01789-470439. Ed. Sandra O'Nions. adv.; bk.rev. circ. 1,500. **Document type:** newsletter.
Formerly: Ascent.

200 UK ISSN 0950-9720
FOCUS ON CHRISTIAN - MUSLIM RELATIONS. Arabic edition: Al-Adwa. 1978. 12/yr. £10 to individuals (foreign £18); institutions £12 (foreign £20). Islamic Foundation, Markfield Dawah Centre, Ratby Lane, Markfield, Leicester LE6 0RN, England. TEL 0530-244944. FAX 0530-244946. Ed. A. Siddiqui. **Indexed:** Per.Islam. (1991-). **Document type:** academic/scholarly publication, newsletter.
Description: Examines Christian-Muslim relations in all the dimensions; provides Muslims with information from Christian sources.

200 US ISSN 0894-3346
FOCUS ON THE FAMILY. 1980. m. free. Focus on the Family, Inc., 8605 Explorer Dr., Colorado Springs, CO 80920-1051. TEL 719-531-3400. FAX 719-531-3499. Ed. Mike Yorkey. circ. 2,000,000 (controlled).
Description: Presents articles intended to strengthen families and reinforce traditional Judeo-Christian values.

254 SW ISSN 1100-8636
FOERSAMLINGS- OCH PASTORATSFOERVALTNING. 1947. 5/yr. SEK 165 (effective 1991). Svenska Kyrkans Foersamlings- och Pastoratsfoerbund, St. Eriksg. 63, S-112 34 Stockholm, Sweden. Ed. Per Olof Nilsson. adv.; illus.; stat. circ. 17,000.
Formerly (until 1966): Tidskrift foer Pastoratsfoervaltning.
Description: Covers church administration.

200 FR ISSN 0152-139X
FOI AUJOURD'HUI. 1977. m. 397 F. (outside EC 444 F.). Bayard Presse, 3 rue Bayard, 75393 Paris Cedex 08, France. TEL 44-35-60-60. FAX 44-35-60-91. TELEX 648 094 F. circ. 40,000.
Description: Helps people to live their faith and better understand how to share it with those around them.

200 054.1 FR ISSN 0015-5357
FOI ET VIE. 1898. 5/yr. 220 F. Association des Amis de Foi et Vie, 139 bd. Montparnasse, 75006 Paris 6, France. Ed. Olivier Millet. adv.; bk.rev.; bibl.; charts; illus.; index. circ. 1,200. **Indexed:** CERDIC, New Test.Abstr., Rel.& Theol.Abstr. (1989-), Rel.Ind.One, Rel.Per.
—BLDSC (3964.385000).
Description: A religious and theological publication with protestant tendencies.

250 IT ISSN 0015-5802
FOLIUM DIOCESANUM BAUZANENSE-BRIXINENSE. (Text in German, Italian and Latin) 1964. m. L.5000. Curia Episcopalis Bauzanensis-Brixinensis, 39100 Bolzano, Italy. index. circ. 800. (tabloid format)

FOOTPRINTS (TEMPE). see *CLUBS*

200 UK
FOR CHRIST AND PEACE. 1951. irreg. $10. Loverseed Press, 141 Woolacombe Rd., Blackheath, London SE3, England. circ. 1,500.

200 GW ISSN 0532-2154
FORSCHUNGEN ZUR KIRCHEN- UND DOGMENGESCHICHTE. 1954. irreg. Vandenhoeck und Ruprecht, Robert-Bosch-Breite 6, 37079 Goettingen, Germany. TEL 0551-6959-0. FAX 0551-695917. (Subscr. to: 37070 Goettingen, Germany) **Document type:** monographic series.

200 GW
FORSCHUNGEN ZUR RELIGION UND LITERATUR DES ALTEN UND NEUEN TESTAMENTS. 1930. irreg. Vandenhoeck und Ruprecht, Robert-Bosch-Breite 6, 37079 Goettingen, Germany. TEL 0551-6959-0. FAX 0551-695917. (Subscr. to: 37070 Goettingen, Germany) Eds. Wolfgang Schrage, Rudolf Smend. **Document type:** monographic series.

232 US ISSN 0883-4970
BS410
FORUM (SANTA ROSA); foundations & facets. 1985. q. $30. (Westar Institute) Polebridge Press, 2120 Bluebell Dr., Box 6144, Santa Rosa, CA 95406. TEL 707-523-1323. FAX 707-523-1350. Ed. Philip Sellew. (back issues avail.) **Document type:** academic/scholarly publication.
—BLDSC (4025.281500).
Description: Publishes current research in biblical and acognate studies, including the historical Jesus, social phenomena of first- and second-century Palestine, and the myths manifested in American culture.
Refereed Serial

200 370.196 CN ISSN 1201-558X
FORUM FOCUS. 1991. s-a. Can.$15. Canadian Churches' Forum for Global Ministries, 11 Madison Ave., Toronto, ON M5R 2S2, Canada. TEL 416-924-9351. FAX 416-924-5356. E-mail: ccforum@web.apc.org. Ed. Robert Faris. bk.rev. circ. 750. (back issues avail.) **Document type:** newsletter.
Formerly (until 1991): Fish-Eye Lens (ISSN 0835-6521)

200 US ISSN 1060-8559
FORUM NEWSLETTER. 1974. q. membership. National Catholic Educational Association, Department of Religious Education, 1077 30th St., N.W., Ste. 100, Washington, DC 20007. TEL 202-337-6232. FAX 202-333-6706. Ed. Michael Carotta. bk.rev. circ. 5,702. (reprint service avail. from UMI)

200 GW ISSN 0343-7744
FORUM RELIGION. 1975. q. DM.32.80. Kreuz-Verlag Zeitschriften GmbH, Breitwiesenstr. 30, 70565 Stuttgart, Germany. TEL 0711-78803. Ed.Bd. bk.rev. circ. 3,700. **Document type:** bulletin.
—CCC.

FORWARD. see *SOCIAL SERVICES AND WELFARE*

200 UK ISSN 0144-378X
FOUNDATIONS. 1978. biennial. £2. British Evangelical Council, 113 Victoria St., St. Albans, Herts. AL1 3TJ, England. TEL 01727-855655. Pub. Alan Gibson. bk.rev. **Indexed:** Rel.& Theol.Abstr. (1989-). **Document type:** academic/scholarly publication.
Description: Contains articles and reviews on contemporary theological issues: biblical theology, church history and apologetics.

FOUNDER'S SOUNDER. see *MUSIC*

FOUR AND FIVE. see *CHILDREN AND YOUTH — For*

205 232 US
FOURTH R; an advocate for religious literacy. 1981. bi-m. $18. (Westar Institute) Polebridge Press, 2120 Bluebell Dr., Box 6144, Santa Rosa, CA 95406. TEL 707-523-1323. FAX 707-523-1350. Ed. Culver H. Nelson. bk.rev. circ. 1,500. (back issues avail.) **Document type:** consumer publication.
Formerly: Westar Magazine (ISSN 0893-1658)
Description: Addresses a broad range of questions about the Christian religion, past and present.

200 FR ISSN 0015-9239
FOYERS MIXTES; informations et reflexions pour un oecumenisme vecu. 1968. q. 175 F.($30) (effective Jan. 1994). Centre Saint Irenee, 2 place Gailleton, 69002 Lyon, France. TEL 78-38-05-07. FAX 78-42-11-00. Ed. Rene Beaupere. adv.; bk.rev.; index. circ. 1,800. **Document type:** bulletin.

200 US
FR. SERAPHIM ROSE FOUNDATION NEWSLETTER. 1992. q. Fr. Seraphim Rose Foundation, Box 1656, Forestville, CA 95436.

FRANKFURTER KIRCHLICHES JAHRBUCH. see *HISTORY — History Of Europe*

RELIGIONS AND THEOLOGY

200 — GW — ISSN 0722-8120
FRAU UND MUTTER. 1918. m. DM.17.40. (Arbeitsgemeinschaft Frau und Mutter) Kreuz-Verlag Zeitschriften GmbH, Breitwiesenstr. 30, 70565 Stuttgart, Germany. TEL 0711-78803. circ. 55,000. (looseleaf format) **Document type:** bulletin.

200 — US
FREE GRACE BROADCASTER. no.129, 1989. q. free. (Mt. Zion Bible Church) Mt. Zion Publications, 2306 W. Wright St., Pensacola, FL 32505. TEL 904-438-6666. Ed. L.R. Shelton, Jr.

FREETHINKER. see *PHILOSOPHY*

200 — US — ISSN 0882-8512
FREETHOUGHT TODAY. 1983. 10/yr. $20. Freedom from Religion Foundation, Box 750, Madison, WI 53701. TEL 608-256-5800. FAX 608-256-1116. Ed. Annie Laurie Gaylor. adv.; circ. 3,800 (paid); 700 (controlled). (tabloid format) **Document type:** newspaper.
   Description: Chronicles freethought activism, critiques religion and monitors state-church separation.

261 — GW — ISSN 0016-0776
FREIE RELIGION; Monatsschrift fuer religioese Selbstbestimmung. 1962. m. DM.18. (Freireligioese Landesgemeinde Baden) Freireligioese Verlagsbuchhandlung, L 10, 4-6, 68161 Mannheim, Germany. TEL 0621-22805. Ed. Dr. Eckhart Pilick. bk.rev.; abstr.; illus. circ. 5,000. (processed) **Indexed:** CERDIC.

291 100 — GW
FREIRELIGIOESE RUNDSCHAU. 1990. q. DM.10. Freireligiose Landesgemeinde Wuerttemberg, Oberer Kirchhaldenweg 59, 70195 Stuttgart, Germany. TEL 0711-692119. bk.rev.; bibl.; illus.; music rev. (back issues avail.) **Document type:** academic/scholarly publication.

200 — UK — ISSN 0016-1292
FRIENDLY COMPANION. 1857. m. £6($15) Gospel Standard Publications, 12B Roundwood Ln., Harpenden, Herts. AL5 3DD, England. TEL 01582-765488. FAX 01582-469148. Ed. B.A. Ramsbottom. circ. 1,650 (paid).
   Description: Focuses on scriptural teaching and everyday experiences for children and teens.

200 — GW — ISSN 0340-6091
FROHE BOTSCHAFT; Andachten fuer jeden Sonntag. bi-m. DM.31. Vandenhoeck und Ruprecht, Robert-Bosch-Breite 6, 37079 Goettingen, Germany. TEL 0551-6959-26. FAX 0551-695917. (Subscr. to: 37070 Goettingen, Germany) Ed. H. Waehrisch. **Document type:** bulletin.

266 — US
FRONTIERSCAN. m. $25 or donation per 50 copies. U S Center for World Mission, Frontier Fellowship, 1605 Elizabeth St., Pasadena, CA 91104. TEL 818-398-2241. FAX 818-398-2263. (back issues avail.) **Document type:** bulletin.
   Description: Condenses material published in Global Prayer Digest.

266 — DK — ISSN 0108-1357
GAMLE EVANGELIUM.* Variant title: Gamle Evangelium er Lige Nyt i Dag. 1981. bi-m. free. Kristen Mission, Abildgade 13/5, 8200 Aarhus N, Denmark. illus.

200 — NE — ISSN 0922-405X
GEEST EN LEVEN; tijdschrift voor informatie, bezinning en gesprek. 1923. bi-m. fl.32.50. St. Goedelestraat 2, 5643 MK Eindhoven, Netherlands. (Subscr. to: Postbus 90109, 5000 LA Tilburg, Netherlands) Ed. Nico Tromp. bk.rev.; bibl. circ. 1,000. **Indexed:** CERDIC.
   Formerly (until 1988): Ons Geestelijk Leven (ISSN 0030-2678)

200 149.3 200 — GW — ISSN 0016-5921
BV5015
GEIST UND LEBEN. 1927. bi-m. DM.69 (students DM.48). Echter-Verlag, Postfach 5560, 97005 Wuerzburg, Germany. Ed. Franz-Josef Steinmetz. adv. contact: Thomas Hauessner. bk.rev. circ. 3,000. **Indexed:** CERDIC, New Test.Abstr. **Document type:** bulletin.

200 — NE — ISSN 0016-6065
GEMEENTELEVEN. 1956. m. fl.25. Remonstrantse Gemeente Groningen, Coehoornsingel 14, 9711 BS Groningen, Netherlands. TEL 31-50-130771. adv.; bk.rev. circ. 500.

220 — GW — ISSN 0344-2233
GEMEINDEBIBELSCHULE; Mitarbeiterzeitschrift. 1977. m. DM.19.20. Oncken Verlag GmbH, Muendener Str. 13, 34123 Kassel, Germany. TEL 0561-52005-0. Ed. Bo Riedel. circ. 11,000. (back issues avail.) **Document type:** newsletter.

200 — NE — ISSN 0016-6324
GENADEKLANKEN; nieuws voor nu. 1947. s-m. fl.5. Stichting Ga Uit, Postbus 61, 7090 AB Dinxperlo, Netherlands. circ. 80,000.

200 — CN — ISSN 1183-3491
BL458
GENDER IN WORLD RELIGIONS. 1990. a. $15. McGill University, Faculty of Religious Studies, 3520 University St., Montreal, PQ H3A 2A7, Canada. TEL 514-398-6138. Ed.Bd. **Document type:** academic/scholarly publication.
   Description: Publishes scholarly articles bearing on the role of gender in world religions.

200 — US
GENERAL CONVENTION OF THE NEW JERUSALEM. JOURNAL. 1817. a. $15. General Convention of the New Jerusalem, 48 Sargent St., Newton, MA 02158. Ed. Patte Levan. circ. 150.
   Description: Contains a directory of officers, bylaws of church and school, minutes of annual meeting, and a directory of churches.

266 — IT — ISSN 0016-6960
GENTES. 1927. m. L.30000. Lega Missionaria Studenti, Via M. Massimo, 7, 00144 Rome, Italy. TEL 39-6-5439628. FAX 39-6-5910803. Dir. Massimo Nevola. bk.rev.; bibl.; illus.; stat.; index. circ. 3,000. **Document type:** monographic series.
   Refereed Serial

200 — SZ — ISSN 0016-9021
GESCHAEFTSMANN UND CHRIST. 1960. m. (10/yr.). 32 Fr. Internationale Vereinigung Christlicher Geschaeftsleute, Gruppe Zurich, Box 29, 8034 Zurich, Switzerland. FAX 01-2527242. Ed.Bd. bk.rev.; illus. circ. 15,000.
   Description: Devoted to Christianity's role in the business world, and the problem of applying Christian principles to the business community. Includes list of events.

240 — GW
GESTERN, HEUTE UND MORGEN. w. DM.20.35. Guetersloher Verlagshaus Chr. Kaiser, Carl-Bertelsmann-Str. 270, 33311 Guetersloh, Germany. TEL 05241-7405-0. FAX 05241-740548. Ed. Ingrid Ryssel. **Document type:** newsletter.

248.83 — IT — ISSN 0017-0542
GIOVENTU EVANGELICA. 1947. q. L.40000. Consiglio della Federazione della Gioventu Evangelica Italiana, Via L. Porro Lambertenghi 28, 20159 Milan, Italy. Eds. Giorgio Quelmani, Michele Rostan. adv.; bk.rev.; illus. circ. 3,000.

271 — IT — ISSN 0072-4548
GIOVENTU PASSIONISTA/PASSIONIST YOUTH; rivista di formazione e d'informazione passionista. (Text in various languages; summaries in English) 1955. irreg., no.3, 1960. $3. Edizioni E C O, 64048 S. Gabriele (Teramo), Italy. Ed. P. Natale Cavatassi.

200 100 — US — ISSN 0732-7781
GIST. (Former name of issuing body: University of Healing Press) 1975. m. $20 (overseas $30) (effective 1995-1996). U N I Press, 1101 Far Valley Rd., Campo, CA 91906. TEL 619-478-5111. FAX 619-478-5013. Ed. Herbert L. Beierle. circ. 3,000. **Document type:** consumer publication.
   Description: Expresses the theme of the absolute archetypal nature of humanity in first person, present tense, positive.

200 — GW
GLAUBE HOFFNUNG LIEBE. 1947. m. Weidenweg 21, 52074 Aachen, Germany. TEL 0241-872552. FAX 0241-875968. Ed. Horst Krueger; Pub. Horst Krueger. circ. 3,100. **Document type:** newsletter.

200 323.4 — SZ — ISSN 0254-4377
GLAUBE IN DER 2. WELT; Zeitschrift fuer Religionsfreiheit und Menschenrechte. 1973. m. 65 SFr. Institut Glaube in der 2. Welt, Bergstr. 6, Postfach 9, CH-8702 Zollikon-Zurich, Switzerland. TEL 01-3913747. FAX 01-3914426. Ed. Erich Bryner. (back issues avail.) **Document type:** bulletin.

200 — GW — ISSN 0935-8889
GLAUBE UND LEBEN. 1947. w. (Sun.). DM.120. (Bistum Mainz) Verlag Josef Knecht, Ludwig-Corden-Str. 3, 65549 Limburg, Germany. TEL 06131-9113-0. FAX 06131-911337. Ed. Ernst Schloegel. adv. contact: Sylvia Ehrengard. circ. 30,229. **Document type:** newsletter.

200 — GW — ISSN 0179-3551
GLAUBE UND LERNEN; Zeitschrift fuer theologische Urteilsbildung. s-a. DM.42. Vandenhoeck und Ruprecht, Robert-Bosch-Breite 6, 37079 Goettingen, Germany. TEL 0551-6959-26. FAX 0551-695917. (Subscr. to: 37070 Goettingen, Germany) Ed.Bd. **Indexed:** Rel.& Theol.Abstr. (1989-). **Document type:** academic/scholarly publication.

266 — US — ISSN 0746-3022
GLENMARY CHALLENGE. 1937. q. Glenmary Home Missioners, Box 465618, Cincinnati, OH 45246-5618. TEL 513-874-8900. FAX 513-874-1690. Ed. Rev. Paul Fredette; Pub. Rev. Robert Dalton. charts; illus.; stat.; circ. 100,000 (controlled). **Document type:** trade publication.
   Formerly: Glenmary's Challenge (ISSN 0017-1182)
   Description: Discusses Catholic mission work in the states.

266 — US — ISSN 1045-9731
GLOBAL PRAYER DIGEST. (Text in English, Spanish) 1982. m. $9 (Canada and Mexico $18; overseas $30). U S Center for World Mission, Frontier Fellowship, 1605 Elizabeth St., Pasadena, CA 91104. TEL 818-398-2241. FAX 818-398-2263. Ed. Keith Carey. index; circ. 10,000 (paid). (back issues avail.)

200 — US
GLOW INTERNATIONAL. 1966. q. $22. Glow International, 599 Edison Dr., E. Windsor, NJ 08520-5207. TEL 609-426-4345. Ed. Naosherwan Anzar. adv.; bk.rev. circ. 1,000. (back issues avail.)

200 — GW — ISSN 0017-1409
GNADE UND HERRLICHKEIT. 1949. bi-m. DM.40. Paulus-Verlag Karl Geyer, Goethestr. 38, 74074 Heilbronn, Germany. TEL 07131-172090. FAX 07131-953105. Ed. Heinz Schumacher. **Indexed:** CERDIC. **Document type:** bulletin.

220 375 — UK — ISSN 0950-7221
GO TEACH BEGINNERS. q. £2.30. Go Teach Publications, 2 Radford Rd., Leamington Spa CV31 1LX, England. TEL 0926-26573.
   Description: Teachers' book for teaching scripture lessons to 3-5 year olds.

220 375 — UK — ISSN 0950-7248
GO TEACH JUNIORS. q. £2.30. Go Teach Publications, 2 Radford Rd., Leamington Spa CV31 1LX, England. TEL 0926-26573.
   Description: Teachers' book for teaching scripture lessons to 8-12 year olds.

220 375 — UK — ISSN 0142-5935
GO TEACH PRIMARIES. q. £2.30. Go Teach Publications, 2 Radford Rd., Leamington Spa CV31 1LX, England. TEL 0926-26573. illus.
   Description: Teachers' book for teaching scripture lessons to 5-8 year olds.

220 375 — UK — ISSN 0950-7256
GO TEACH YOUNG TEENS. q. £2.30. Go Teach Publications, 2 Radford Rd., Leamington Spa CV31 1LX, England. TEL 0926-26573.
   Description: Teachers' book for teaching scripture lessons to over 12 year olds.

251 — GW — ISSN 0340-6083
GOETTINGER PREDIGTMEDITATIONEN. 1946. q. DM.80. Vandenhoeck und Ruprecht, Robert-Bosch-Breite 6, 37079 Goettingen, Germany. TEL 0551-6959-26. FAX 0551-695917. (Subscr. to: 37070 Goettingen, Germany) Ed. F. Merkel. adv.; index. circ. 4,900. **Document type:** academic/scholarly publication.

RELIGIONS AND THEOLOGY

266 UK ISSN 1353-8101
GOING PLACES. 1962. 3/yr. membership. Intercontinental Church Society, 175 Tower Bridge Rd., London SE1 2AQ, England. TEL 071-407-4588. FAX 071-378-0541. bk.rev.; circ. 5,000 (controlled). **Document type:** consumer publication.
Former titles (until 1994): Intercon (ISSN 0264-0961); (until 1982): Intercom (London) (ISSN 0020-5265)

266 SA ISSN 0017-2146
GOOD NEWS/GOEIE NUUS; the magazine with a message. (Editions in Afrikaans and English) 1951. q. R.10($5) Good News Missionary Society, Box 7848, Johannesburg, South Africa. TEL 011-729-9581. Ed. Sean O'Sullivan. circ. 5,000 (Eng. ed.); 2,500 (Afrikaans ed.).

266 UK ISSN 0262-2874
GOOD NEWS (BIRMINGHAM). 1837. s-a. £0.20 per no. Additional Curates Society for England and Wales, Bordon Browning House, 8 Spitfire Rd., Birmingham B24 9PB, England. TEL 0121-328-0749. FAX 0121-327-7951. Ed. Fr. Stephen Bond. adv. contact: David W. Streeter. bk.rev.; illus.; circ. 20,000 (controlled). (also avail. in microform)
Formerly (until vol.48, 1981): Home Mission News.
Description: Contains news and features of the Additional Curarates Society, which seeks to assist Anglican parishes, especially in deprived areas of England and Wales, by paying for assistant priests.

266 UK ISSN 0954-562X
GOOD NEWS (EXETER). 1939. m. £35.70 (foreign £39.65). The Paternoster Press, Sta. A, Box 300, Kingstown Broadway, Carlisle, Cumbria CA3 0QS, England. TEL 0228-512512. FAX 0228-514949. (Dist. in U.S. & Canada by: The Paternoster Press, Box 11127, Birmingham, AL 35201-1127) Ed. Robert Beale. circ. 30,000. **Document type:** newsletter.
—CCC.
Formerly (until 1988): Emergency Post (ISSN 0305-005X)
Description: Evangelistic monthly for local churches.

251 US ISSN 1047-2320
GOOD NEWS (NEW BERLIN). 1972. m. $59. Liturgical Publications Inc., 2875 South James Dr., New Berlin, WI 53151. TEL 414-785-1188. FAX 414-785-9567. Ed. Rev. Joseph T. Nolan. (looseleaf format) **Indexed:** Rehabil.Lit.
Description: Inter-denominational homily, sermon resource for ministers and priests.

200 CN
GOOD TIDINGS. 1944. m. Can.$10($15) (effective 1992). (Pentecostal Assemblies of Newfoundland) Good Tidings Press, P.O. Box 8895, Sta. A, St. John's, NF A1B 3T2, Canada. TEL 709-753-6314. FAX 709-753-4945. Ed. Roy D. King. adv.; bk.rev. circ. 7,500. (back issues avail.) **Document type:** bulletin.
Description: Covers the Bible, church news, missions, and Christian service.

200 US ISSN 0195-1297
GOSPEL ADVOCATE. 1855. m. $16.98 (effective 1995). Gospel Advocate Company, 1006 Elm Hill Pike, Nashville, TN 37210. TEL 615-254-8781. FAX 615-254-7411. (Subscr. to: Box 150, Nashville, TN 37202) Ed. F. Furman Kearley. adv.; index. circ. 23,000.
Description: Devotional and educational material for church leaders and members.

200 CN ISSN 0829-4666
GOSPEL HERALD. 1936. m. Can.$11($17.50) Gospel Herald Foundation, 4904 King St., Beamsville, ON L0R 1B6, Canada. TEL 905-563-7503. FAX 905-563-7503. Ed. Wayne Turner; Pub. Eugene C. Perry. adv. contact: Eugene C. Perry. bk.rev. circ. 1,415. (also avail. in microfilm from CML,UMI; reprint service avail. from UMI) —UMI.
Description: Articles promoting New Testament Christianity, including teaching material for youth and women, and features history, news, and family life.

291 377.8 US ISSN 0746-0880
THE GOSPEL HERALD AND SUNDAY SCHOOL TIMES. 1902. q. Union Gospel Press, Box 6059, Cleveland, OH 44101. TEL 216-749-2100. FAX 216-749-2205. Ed. Beryl C. Bidlen. circ. 50,000. **Document type:** consumer publication.
Formerly: Sunday School Times and Gospel Herald.

GOSPEL MESSENGER. see HANDICAPPED — Visually Impaired

266 US
GOSPEL OUTREACH. 1949. q. $2. Concordia Gospel Outreach, Box 201, St. Louis, MO 63166-0201. TEL 314-268-1363. FAX 314-268-1329. Ed. Annette Frank. circ. 12,000 (controlled). **Document type:** newsletter.
Formerly (until 1994): Worldwide Evangelist.

200 UK ISSN 0017-2367
GOSPEL STANDARD. 1835. m. £9.60($20) Gospel Standard Publications, 12B Roundwood Ln., Harpenden, Herts. AL5 3DD, England. TEL 01582-765448. FAX 01582-469148. Ed. B.A. Ramsbottom. bk.rev.; circ. 2,500 (paid). **Indexed:** CERDIC.
Description: Presents information relating to the Gospel Standard Societies; includes free grace sermons and articles concerning the doctrines of grace and experince of the Truth.

GOSPEL TODAY; America's leading gospel news magazine. see MUSIC

266 GW
GOSSNER MISSION. 1852. bi-m. Gossner Mission, Fennstr. 31, 1190 Berlin-Schoeneweiche, Germany. TEL 00372-6351198. circ. 7,000. (back issues avail.)

200 GW ISSN 0017-2480
GOTTES WORT. 3/yr. DM.72. Echter-Verlag, Postfach 5560, 97005 Wuerzburg, Germany. Ed. Rainer Rack. adv. contact: Thomas Haeussner. **Document type:** bulletin.

200 GW ISSN 0343-8732
GOTTESDIENST; Information und Handreichung der Liturgischen Institute Deutschlands, Oesterreichs und der Schweiz. 1967. s-m. DM.55.20. Verlag Herder GmbH & Co. KG, Hermann-Herder-Str. 4, 79104 Freiburg, Germany. TEL 0651-94808-0. FAX 0651-94808-33. Ed. Eduard Nagel. adv. contact: Bettina Wegmann. bk.rev. circ. 12,500. (back issues avail.) **Document type:** newsletter.

250 PO ISSN 0017-2758
GRACAS DO SERVO DE DEUS: PADRE CRUZ. 1949. bi-m. Cr.$150. Causa Beatificaciao do Padre Cruz, Rua da Madalena 179, Apdo. 2661, 1117 Lisbon Codex, Portugal. Dir. P. Manuel Baptista. adv.; bk.rev. circ. 26,200.

200 PO
GRACAS PADRE CRUZ, S.J.. q. $750. Vice Postulacao - Causa do Padre Cruz, Rua da Madalena, 179-RC. Ap. 2661, 1117 Lisbon Codex, Portugal. TEL 872100. Ed. Antonio Reis.

286 UK ISSN 0046-6239
GRACE. 1833. m. £6. Grace Magazine Trust, Bethesda Baptist Church, Bury St., Stowmarket, Suffolk, England. (Subscr. to: 4-6 Beechwood Rd., Caterham, Surrey CR3 6NA, England) Ed. N. Lacey. adv.; bk.rev. circ. 1,900.

GRACE TIDINGS. see COLLEGE AND ALUMNI

200 CN ISSN 0828-4083
GRAIL: AN ECUMENICAL JOURNAL. 1985. q. Can.$20($20) to individuals; institutions Can.$30($30). NOvalis, Saint Paul University, 223 Main St., Ottawa, ON K1S 1C4, Canada. TEL 613-236-1393. FAX 613-782-3004. Ed. Christopher Humphrey. bk.rev.; illus. circ. 1,500. **Document type:** academic/scholarly publication.
Description: Promotes dialogue, debate, and understanding among scholars and educated readers.
Refereed Serial

230 BL ISSN 0046-6271
GRANDE SINAL. 1947. 6/yr. $65. Editora Vozes Ltda., Rua Frei Luis 100, Caixa Postal 90023, 25689-900 Petropolis, RJ, Brazil. TEL 0242-43-5112. FAX 0242-42-0692. Ed. Jose Arlovaldo da Silva. bk.rev.; abstr.; bibl.; illus.; stat.; index. circ. 2,900. (tabloid format)

GREAT BRITAIN. ROYAL ARMY CHAPLAINS' DEPARTMENT. JOURNAL. see MILITARY

200 UK ISSN 0957-8935
THE GREATER WORLD NEWSLETTER. 1928. q. free. Greater World Christian Spiritualist Association, Greater World Spiritual Centre, c/o Mrs. B. Scott, Sec., 3-5 Conway St., London W1P 5HA, England. TEL 0171-436-7555. Ed. A. Clifton. adv. contact: J. Lee. bk.rev. circ. 6,000. **Document type:** newsletter.
Formerly (until 1989): Greater World (ISSN 0046-6352)
Description: Disseminates spiritual teachings based on Christian Spiritualism.

200 400 GW ISSN 0232-2900
GRIECHISCHEN CHRISTLICHEN SCHRIFTSTELLER DER ERSTEN JAHRHUNDERTE. (Text in English, German, Greek or Latin) 1953. irreg. Akademie Verlag GmbH, Muehlenstr. 33-344, 13187 Berlin, Germany. TEL 030-47889348. FAX 030-47889357. (also avail. in microfiche from IDC) **Document type:** monographic series.

GROUP (LOVELAND); the youth ministry magazine. see CHILDREN AND YOUTH — About

200 GW
GRUSS DER GROSSHEPPACHER SCHWESTERNSCHAFT; Kind und Schwester. s-a. Stiftung Grossheppacher Schwesternschaft, Postfach 1124, 71365 Weinstadt, Germany. TEL 07151-9934-0. FAX 07151-993450. Ed. Willi Duerring. circ. 6,000. **Document type:** newsletter.

268 260 US
GUIDE PAK OF CHRISTIAN CAMPS AND CONFERENCE CENTERS. 1981. a. $10.95. Christian Camping International, Box 62189, Colorado Springs, CO 80962-2189. TEL 719-260-9400. FAX 719-260-6398. Ed. Dean Ridings. adv. circ. 100,000.
Former titles: Official Guide to Christian Camps and Conference Centers; Guide to Christian Camps; Christian Camping International Directory (ISSN 0069-3855); (until 1969): Christian Camp and Conference Association. International Directory.

200 US ISSN 0017-5331
BV4800
GUIDEPOSTS; a practical guide to successful living. 1945. m. $10.97 (effective Jan. 1991). Guideposts Associates, Inc., 16 E. 34th St., New York, NY 10016. TEL 212-251-8100. Eds. Fulton Oursler, Jr. circ. 4,000,000. (also avail. in Braille; audio cassette; talking book; diskette format; large print edition in 18 pt.) **Document type:** consumer publication.

GUIDEPOSTS FOR KIDS. see CHILDREN AND YOUTH — For

200 GW ISSN 0017-5730
GUSTAV-ADOLF-BLATT. 1955. q. DM.12.80. (Gustav-Adolf-Werk e.V. Diasporawerk der Evangelischen Kirche in Deutschland) Verlag des Gustav-Adolf-Werks e.V., Pistorisstr. 6, 04229 Leipzig, Germany. TEL 0341-4906218. FAX 0341-4906266. Ed. Evelin Hoehne. bk.rev. circ. 20,000. **Document type:** consumer publication.
Description: Provides general information about minority Protestant churches.

200 GW
GUTE BESSERUNG. 1977. m. Bergmoser und Hoeller Verlag GmbH, Karl-Friedrich-Str. 76, 52072 Aachen, Germany. TEL 0241-9388821. FAX 0241-9388834. Ed. Paul Ostermann. circ. 50,000. **Document type:** consumer publication.
Description: Publication concerned with giving strength and information to those who are ill, by means of religion and humor.

RELIGIONS AND THEOLOGY

200 GW
H M K KURIER - STIMME DER MAERTYRER; Nachrichten der Hilfsaktion Maertyrerkirche. 1969. m. DM.12. Hilfsaktion Maertyrerkirche e.V., Postfach 1160, 88683 Uhldingen, Germany. TEL 07556-6508. FAX 07556-8618. Ed. Hans Martin Braun. circ. 38,000 (controlled). (back issues avail.) **Document type:** newsletter.
Formed by 1993 merger of: Stimme der Maertyrer & H M K Kurier; Which was formerly: H M K Kirche.
Description: Publication devoted to Christian mission of the Communist world. Supports and aids suppressed Christians and brings evangelism to former Communist countries. Focus on Bible study and radio missions.

200 CN
HALLELUJAH (TORONTO); Ontario's Christian news source. 1986. q. Can.$5. D. Bruce Arnold Publications, Box 25, Ste. 0116, 65 Front St. W., Toronto, ON M5J 1E6, Canada. TEL 416-778-8042. FAX 416-368-0104. Ed. Bruce Arnold. adv.: B&W page Can.$400. bk.rev.; circ. 2,000 (paid). (tabloid format) **Document type:** newspaper.
Description: General interest news, music reviews, radio and TV reviews, editorial comment on subjects of interest to the Christian community.

268 US ISSN 0072-9787
HANDBOOK OF DENOMINATIONS IN THE U S. quinquennial. $13.95. Abingdon Press, 201 Eighth Ave., S., Box 801, Nashville, TN 37202-0801. TEL 800-251-3320. FAX 615-749-6522.
Description: Reference describing many religious bodies in the US, with information on their historical background and doctrines.

HAPPENINGS. see *SOCIAL SERVICES AND WELFARE*

HARMONY (SAN FRANCISCO); voices for a just future. see *POLITICAL SCIENCE — Civil Rights*

230 US ISSN 0017-8047
BV4070
HARVARD DIVINITY BULLETIN. 1935. q. free. Harvard Divinity School, 45 Francis Ave., Cambridge, MA 02138. TEL 617-496-9147. FAX 617-496-3668. bk.rev.; illus. circ. 23,000. **Indexed:** Rel.Per.
Document type: academic/scholarly publication.
Description: Scholarly articles in the field of religious studies and news of the School

HARVARD SEMITIC MONOGRAPHS, see *LINGUISTICS*

230 US ISSN 0017-8160
BR1
HARVARD THEOLOGICAL REVIEW. 1908. q. $25 to individuals; institutions $45. Harvard Divinity School, 45 Francis Ave., Cambridge, MA 02138. TEL 617-496-5786. FAX 617-495-9489. Ed. Helmut Koester. adv.; charts. circ. 1,900. (also avail. in microfiche; reprint service avail. from KTO) **Indexed:** Amer.Hist.& Life, Arts & Hum.Cit.Ind., CERDIC, Curr.Cont., Hist.Abstr., Hum.Ind., M.L.A., New Test.Abstr., Old Test.Abstr., Rel.& Theol.Abstr. (1971-), Rel.Ind.One, Rel.Per. **Document type:** academic/scholarly publication.
—BLDSC (4270.690000); Faxon; SWETS; UnCover.
Description: Scholarly articles in the field of religious studies.

201 US ISSN 0073-0726
HARVARD THEOLOGICAL STUDIES. 1916. irreg., no.34, 1982. price varies. (Harvard Divinity School) Fortress Press, 426 S. 5th St., Box 1209, MN 55440. TEL 612-330-3300; 800-328-4648. FAX 612-330-3455. Ed. Marshall Johnson. adv. contact: Kirsten Feste. (reprint service avail. from KTO) **Document type:** monographic series, academic/scholarly publication.

615.852 283 282 UK ISSN 0962-0893
HEALING AND WHOLENESS. 1991. q. £9.60 (rest of Europe £11; elsewhere £12) (effective 1995). Monarch Magazines, Broadway House, The Broadway, Crowborough, E. Sussex TN6 1HQ, England. TEL 01892-652364. FAX 01892-663329. Ed. John Gunstone. adv.: B&W page £565, color page £825; trim 297 x 210; adv. contact: Helen Nicholson. bk.rev. circ. 9,500. **Document type:** newsletter.
Description: Provides news and information on the Christian healing ministry and related topics.

266 UK ISSN 0017-8829
HEALING HAND. 1950. 3/yr. free. Edinburgh Medical Missionary Society, Seven Washington Ln., Edinburgh EH11 2HA, Scotland. TEL 0131-313-3828. FAX 0131-313-4662. Ed. Fred Aitken. adv.; bk.rev. circ. 2,000. **Document type:** consumer publication.
Description: News of activities of the society, articles on medical missions.

200 AU ISSN 0017-9620
HEILIGER DIENST. 1947. q. S.250. (Oesterreichisches Liturgisches Institut) Verlag St. Peter, Postfach 113, A-5010 Salzburg, Austria. TEL 0662-844576-84. FAX 0662-844576-80. Ed. P. Winfried Bachler. adv.: B&W page S.2150. bk.rev. circ. 900. **Indexed:** CERDIC. **Document type:** bulletin.
Description: Covers liturgy and liturgical practice.

200 GW
HEINRICHSBLATT. w. (Sun.). DM.80.40 (foreign DM.137.40). (Erzbischoefliches Ordinariat Bamberg) St. Otto Verlag GmbH, Laubanger 23, 96052 Bamberg, Germany. TEL 0951-7902-0. FAX 0951-790279. Ed. Marion Krueger. circ. 46,549. **Document type:** newsletter.

266.023489 DK ISSN 0908-066X
EN HEL VERDEN. 1993. q. free. Danske Missionsselskab, Strandagervej 24, DK-2900 Hellerup, Denmark. TEL 31-62-99-11. FAX 31-62-02-06. Ed. Anne Slinger. illus. circ. 33,000. **Document type:** newsletter.

266 SW ISSN 1102-0105
HELA JORDEN. 1846. bi-m. SEK 75 in Sweden; Nordic and Baltic countries SEK 110; elsewhere SEK 120. Lunds Missionssaellskap, Roerbaecksv. 41 B, S-757 57 Uppsala, Sweden. (Subscr. to: PROGEK, P.O. Box 31003, S-400 32 Goeteborg, Sweden. TEL 46-31-24-34-25) (Co-sponsors: Luthershjaelpen, Svenska Kyrkans Mission)
Former titles (until 1991): Missionsorientering; (until 1972): Evangeliska Missionen; (until 1921): Lunds Missions-tidning.

200 SW ISSN 0018-0335
HEMMETS VAEN. den alkristna rikstidning. 1897. w. SEK 329($40) (effective 1990). Evangeliipress, P.O. Box 1712, S-701 17 Oerebro, Sweden. Ed. Stig Hallzon. adv.; bk.rev.; illus. circ. 45,000. (tabloid format)
Supersedes: Missionsblad foer Kronobergs Laen.

200 US
HERALD OF HIS COMING. 1941. m. free. Gospel Revivals, Inc., Box 886, Newton, KS 67114. TEL 316-283-7747. FAX 316-284-2311. Ed. Lois J. Stucky; Pub. Elmer G. Klassen. circ. 120,000. (tabloid format) **Document type:** newspaper.
Description: Articles on practical examples of living out and putting into practice Bible teaching, with prayers and scripture.

200 CU
HERALDO EPISCOPAL. 1938. q. $6. Iglesia Episcopal Cubana, Centro Diocesano, Calle 13, no.874 e-4 y 6, Vedado, Havana, Cuba. TEL 7-32-1120. Ed. Rev. Juan Quevedo. bk.rev. circ. 2,000.
Description: Channels communication between the Anglican and Christian Cuban communities and the world church.

200 NE ISSN 0165-2397
TER HERKENNING (ZOETERMEER); tijdschrift voor Joden en Christenen. q. fl.56. Boekencentrum B.V., Postbus 29, 2700 AA Zoetermeer, Netherlands. TEL 31-79-615481. FAX 31-79-615489. Ed. C.M.L. Verdegaal.

200 IT
HERMENEUTICA. 1981. a. L.30000. (Universita di Urbino, Istituto Superiore di Scienze Religiose) Edizioni Quattroventi, Via Dini 16, Casella Postale 156, 61029 Urbino, Italy. TEL 0722-2588. FAX 0722-320998. Ed. Italo Mancini.

200 GW ISSN 0440-7180
HERMENEUTISCHE UNTERSUCHUNGEN ZUR THEOLOGIE. (Text in English, German) irreg., vol.31, 1993. price varies. J.C.B. Mohr (Paul Siebeck), Wilhelmstr. 18, 72074 Tuebingen, Germany. TEL 07071-923-0. FAX 07071-51104. TELEX 7262872-MOHR-D. (Subscr. to: Postfach 2040, 72010 Tuebingen, Germany) Ed.Bd. **Document type:** monographic series.

266 NE
HERNHUTTER SURINAME ZENDING. 1834. q. free. Zendingsgenootschap der Evangelische Broedergemeente, Box 19, 3700 AA Zeist, Netherlands. TEL 03404-17424. Ed.Bd. bk.rev.; illus. circ. 150,000.
Formerly: Suriname Zending (ISSN 0039-6141)

284 NE ISSN 0018-0939
HERVORMD NEDERLAND. 1944. w. fl.138. Box 84410, The Hague, Netherlands. FAX 070-3584761. Ed. B. van Duyn. adv.; bk.rev.; illus. circ. 26,500. **Indexed:** CERDIC.

200 SA ISSN 0259-9422
HERVORMDE TEOLOGIESE STUDIES. (Supplement avail.) (Text in Afrikaans, Dutch, English, German; summaries in English) 1942. q. $25 (effective 1995). Universiteit van Pretoria, Fakulteit Teologie, Afdeling A - University of Pretoria, Faculty of Theology, Section A, Pretoria 0002, South Africa. TEL 27-12-4203156. FAX 27-12-420-2887. E-mail: Vanaarde@ccnet.up.ac.za. Ed. A.G. van Aarde. adv.; bk.rev. circ. 1,000. **Indexed:** New Test.Abstr., Old.Test.Abstr., Rel.& Theol.Abstr. (1989-). **Document type:** academic/scholarly publication.
—BLDSC (4300.390000).
Description: Features articles on topics in all the theological disciplines including Bible study.
Refereed Serial

100 200 UK ISSN 0018-1196
BX801
HEYTHROP JOURNAL; a review of philosophy and theology. 1960. q. £55($97) (foreign £60) (effective 1996). Basil Blackwell Ltd., 108 Cowley Rd., Oxford OX4 1JF, England. TEL 0865-791100. FAX 0865-791347. TELEX 830722 OXBOOK G. Ed. Thomas J. Deidun. adv.; bk.rev.; bibl.; charts; illus.; index. circ. 950. (also avail. in microform from UMI; back issues avail.) **Indexed:** Arts & Hum.Cit.Ind., Canon Law Abstr., Cath.Ind., CERDIC, Curr.Cont., Int.Z.Bibelwiss., New Test.Abstr., Old Test.Abstr., Phil.Ind., Rel.& Theol.Abstr. (1979-). **Document type:** academic/scholarly publication.
—BLDSC (4303.100000); Faxon; Genuine Article; SWETS; UMI; UnCover. **CCC**.
Description: Features contemporary philosophical and theological issues, including Bible, ecclesiastical history and the sociology of religion.

200 NE
HIER EN GINDER. m. fl.16. Missiethuisfront, Akkerstraat 12, 6617 BA Bergharen, Netherlands. Ed. J. van Gelder. bk.rev. circ. 1,250.

HINDU - CHRISTIAN STUDIES BULLETIN. see *RELIGIONS AND THEOLOGY — Hindu*

209 SP ISSN 0018-215X
BR1020
HISPANIA SACRA. 1948. s-a. 4500 ptas. (foreign 6000 ptas.). Centro de Estudios Historicos (CSIC), Duque de Medinaceli, 6, 28016 Madrid, Spain. FAX 34-1-585-61-97. (Distr. by: Consejo Superior de Investigaciones Cientificas, Apdo. 14458, Vitruvio 8, 28006 Madrid, Spain) Ed. Jose Andres-Gallego. adv.; bk.rev.; illus. circ. 800. (also avail. in microfilm; reprint service avail.) **Indexed:** Amer.Hist.& Life, Hist.Abstr., Rel.Ind.One, Rel.Ind.Two. **Document type:** academic/scholarly publication.
—BLDSC (4315.765000); SWETS.

200 974 US ISSN 0439-2191
HISTORIAN'S DIGEST. 1959. q. $22. United Methodist Church, General Commission on Archives & History, Box 127, Madison, NJ 07940. TEL 201-408-3189. FAX 201-408-3909. Ed. Charles Yrigoyen, Jr. circ. 800. (looseleaf format; back issues avail.) **Document type:** newsletter.

RELIGIONS AND THEOLOGY

291 209   US   ISSN 0018-2710
BL1
HISTORY OF RELIGIONS; an international journal for comparative historical studies. 1961. q. $30 to individuals; institutions $64; students $21. University of Chicago Press, Journals Division, 5720 S. Woodlawn Ave., Chicago, IL 60637. TEL 312-753-3347. FAX 312-753-0811. TELEX 25-4603. (Subscr. to: Box 37005, Chicago, IL 60637) Ed.Bd. adv.; bk.rev.; index. circ. 1,800. (also avail. in microform from PMC; reprint service avail. from UMI,ISI) **Indexed**: A.I.C.P., Amer.Hist.& Life, Anthropol.Lit., Arts & Hum.Cit.Ind., CERDIC, Curr.Cont., E.I., G.Soc.Sci.& Rel.Per.Lit., Hist.Abstr., Hum.Ind., Int.Z.Bibelwiss., Mid.East Abstr.& Ind., New Test.Abstr., Old Test.Abstr., Rel.& Theol.Abstr. (1968-), Rel.Ind.One, Rel.Per. **Document type**: academic/scholarly publication.
—BLDSC (4318.420000); Faxon; Genuine Article; SWETS; UMI; UnCover. **CCC**.
    Refereed Serial

200   NE   ISSN 0925-8426
HOLLANDISCHE MISSION - I G V C. 1950. 5/yr. free. Internationale Gemeenschap van Christenen, Postbus 102, 5280 AC Boxtel, Netherlands. TEL 31-4116-73077. (In Austria: Hollaendische Mission, Postfach 2, A-9585 Goedersdorf, Austria. TEL 43-4257-2810) Eds. Jan Dirk, Eta Brouwer. bk.rev.; illus. circ. 1,450. **Document type**: newsletter.
    Formerly (until Nov. 1988): Oorspronkelijk Christendom (ISSN 0030-3267)

200 933   IS
HOLY PLACES OF PALESTINE. (Text in various languages) 1970. irreg., latest 1993. Franciscan Printing Press, P.O. Box 14064, Jerusalem 91140, Israel. TEL 972-2-286594. FAX 972-2-272274.

200   US   ISSN 1042-5888
HOME ALTAR; meditations for families with children. 1939. q. $4.60. Augsburg Fortress, Publishers, 426 S. Fifth St., Box 1209, Minneapolis, MN 55440. TEL 612-330-3402; 800-328-4648. Ed. Elaine M. Dunham. circ. 71,000.

249   UK   ISSN 0018-3946
HOME AND FAMILY. 1886. q. £4.50 (foreign £5.50). Mothers' Union, Mary Sumner House, 24 Tufton St., Westminster, London SW1P 3RB, England. TEL 0171-222-5533. FAX 0171-222-1591. Ed.Bd. adv.; bk.rev.; illus. circ. 90,000. **Document type**: newsletter.

HOME SCHOOL GAZETTE. see *JOURNALISM*

251   SP   ISSN 0439-4208
HOMILETICA; revista de predicacion liturgica. 6/yr. 3400 ptas. (Europe $40; elsewhere $45) (effective 1994). Editorial Sal Terrae, Guevara, 20, 39080 Santander, Spain. TEL 942-369198. FAX 942-369201.

251   GW   ISSN 0018-4276
HOMILETISCHE MONATSHEFTE. 1925. m. DM.102. Vandenhoeck und Ruprecht, Robert-Bosch-Breite 6, 37079 Goettingen, Germany. TEL 0551-6959-26. FAX 0551-695917. (Subscr. to: 37070 Goettingen, Germany) Ed. Wolf Dietrich Berner. adv.; bk.rev.; index. circ. 4,200. **Document type**: bulletin.
—**CCC**.

200   US
HOMILY HELPS. 62/yr. $30. St. Anthony Messenger Press, 1615 Republic St., Cincinnati, OH 45210. TEL 513-241-5615. FAX 513-241-0399. Ed. Rev. Hilarion Kistner. circ. 6,700. (looseleaf format)
    Description: Aid to preaching for Catholic clergy.

264   US   ISSN 0732-1872
HOMILY SERVICE; an ecumenical resource for sharing the word. 1968. m. $55. Liturgical Conference, 8750 Georgia Ave., No.123, Silver Spring, MD 20910-3621. TEL 301-495-0885. FAX 301-495-5945. Ed. Virginia Sloyan. adv. **Document type**: academic/scholarly publication.
    Description: Ecumenical resource for sharing scripture. Includes exegetical analysis of scriptural readings.

200   FR   ISSN 0018-4322
HOMME NOUVEAU. 1946. bi-m. 350 F.($60) 10 rue Rosenwald, 75015 Paris, France. TEL 45-32-10-80. FAX 45-32-10-84. Ed. M. Marcel Clement; Pub. Marcel Clement. bk.rev. circ. 40,000. **Document type**: newspaper.
    Description: Analyzes the news in the light of the Gospel.

200   US
HONOR THE PROMISE. 1979. irreg. $5. National Christian Leadership Conference for Israel, 134 E. 39th St., New York, NY 10016. TEL 212-213-8636. FAX 212-683-3475. Ed. Nancy G. Carroll, Rose Thering. circ. 10,000. **Document type**: newsletter.

220   US   ISSN 0195-9085
BS543.A1
HORIZONS IN BIBLICAL THEOLOGY. 1979. s-a. $12 to individuals; institutions $15; students $8. Pittsburgh Theological Seminary, 616 N. Highland Ave., Pittsburgh, PA 15206. TEL 412-362-5610. FAX 412-363-3260. Ed.Bd. adv.; bk.rev. circ. 500. (back issues avail.) **Indexed**: New Test.Abstr., Old Test.Abstr., Rel.& Theol.Abstr. (1979-), Rel.Ind.One. **Document type**: academic/scholarly publication.
—BLDSC (4326.794500); UMI.

200   NE   ISSN 0018-7119
HUIZER KERKBLAD. 1935. w. fl.16. J. Bout en Zoon, Ceintuurbaan 32-34, Huizen, Netherlands. adv.; bk.rev. circ. 2,400.

150 301 200   US
HUMAN KINDNESS FOUNDATION NEWSLETTER; a little news. 1974. q. free. Human Kindness Foundation, Rt. 1, Box 201-N, Durham, NC 27705. TEL 919-942-2138. Ed. Bo Lozoff. circ. 21,000. (looseleaf format) **Document type**: newsletter.
    Formerly: Prison - Ashram Project Newsletter.

200 301   US
BX5800
HUMAN QUEST. 1804. bi-m. $10. (Churchman Associates, Inc.) Churchman Company, Inc., 1074 23rd Ave., N., St. Petersburg, FL 33704-3228. TEL 813-894-0097. Ed. Edna Ruth Johnson. adv.; bk.rev.; bibl. circ. 10,000. (also avail. in microform from UMI; back issues avail.) **Indexed**: Amer.Hist.& Life, CERDIC, Chr.Per.Ind., Hist.Abstr., Rel.Ind.One. —UMI.
    Former titles (until Dec. 1989): Churchman's Human Quest (ISSN 0897-8786); Churchman (ISSN 0009-6628)
    Description: Dedicated to educating the public in humanistic religion, peace activism, disarmament, and separation of church and state.

HUMANITIES, CHRISTIANITY AND CULTURE. see *HUMANITIES: COMPREHENSIVE WORKS*

HYMN; a journal of congregational song. see *MUSIC*

200   US   ISSN 1051-2772
I C S A NEWSLETTER. 1983. a. free. (International Christian Studies Association) Institute for Interdisciplinary Research, 2828 Third St., Ste. 11, Santa Monica, CA 90405-4150. TEL 310-396-0517. Ed. Oskar Gruenwald. adv. circ. 1,200. (tabloid format; back issues avail.) **Document type**: newsletter.
    Description: Covers Association, conferences, research and publishing news.

I C S NEWSLETTER. (International Catacomb Society) see *ART*

I N R O ADS. (International Network for Religion and Animals) see *ANIMAL WELFARE*

200 600   US   ISSN 1073-5976
I T E S T BULLETIN. 1969. q. $35 membership. Institute for Theological Encounter with Science and Technology, 221 N. Grand Blvd., St. Louis, MO 63103. TEL 314-658-2703. FAX 314-977-7211. Ed. Marianne Postiglione. bk.rev. circ. 1,000. (back issues avail.) **Document type**: academic/scholarly publication.

200 600   US
I T E S T CONFERENCE PROCEEDINGS. 1970. irreg. (approx. 2/yr.). $12.95. Institute for Theological Encounter with Science and Technology, 221 N. Grand Blvd., St. Louis, MO 63103. TEL 314-658-2703. Ed. Robert Brungs. circ. 1,000. (back issues avail.) **Document type**: proceedings.
    Description: Contains edited versions of meetings on topics such as artificial intelligence, bio-technology, and law, the environment, Christian and Jewish perspectives on creation, sci-tech education in Church-related colleges and universities and the human genome project

266   ZA
ICENGELO; Christian magazine in Bemba. (Text in Bemba) 1970. m. K.120($5) Mission Press, Box 71581, Ndola, Zambia. TEL 680456. FAX 680484. TELEX CAMIFF ZA 30054. Ed. Rev. Umberto Davoli. circ. 73,000.
    Description: Covers religious, social and health topics.

DEN ICONOGRAPHISKE POST; Nordisk tidskrift foer bildtolkning - Nordic iconographic review. see *ART*

ICONOGRAPHY OF RELIGIONS. see *ART*

ICONOGRAPHY OF RELIGIONS. SECTION 24, CHRISTIANITY. see *ART*

ICONOGRAPHY OF RELIGIONS. SUPPLEMENTS. see *ART*

IGAKU TO FUKUIN/MEDICINE AND GOSPEL. see *MEDICAL SCIENCES*

200   GW   ISSN 0019-2597
IM LANDE DER BIBEL. 1955. 4/yr. DM.20. (Jerusalemsverein) Berliner Missionswerk, Handjery Str. 19, 12159 Berlin, Germany. FAX 030-8593011. TELEX 186655-BLNMW-D. Ed. Rev. Michael Deckwerth. bk.rev.; bibl.; illus. circ. 15,000. **Document type**: newsletter.

200   GW   ISSN 0176-8565
IMAGE; Pfarrbriefmaterial. 1970. m. (11/yr.). DM.150. Bergmoser und Hoeller Verlag GmbH, Karl-Friedrich-Str. 76, 52072 Aachen, Germany. TEL 0241-9388821. FAX 0241-9388834. circ. 7,000. (looseleaf format; back issues avail.) **Document type**: bulletin.

266   IS   ISSN 0302-8127
BM1
IMMANUEL; religious thought and research in Israel. (Text in English) 1972. a. $19 (£14 in UK; 720 BEF in Belgium; fl.40 in Netherlands; elsewhere $21) (effective Mar. 1993). Ecumenical Theological Research Fraternity in Israel, P.O. Box 249, Jerusalem 91002, Israel. TEL 972-2-254941. FAX 972-2-254961. Ed. Malcolm F. Lowe. adv.; bk.rev.; bibl. circ. 1,000. (back issues avail.) **Indexed**: CERDIC, Curr.Cont., Ind.Artic.Jew.Stud., New Test.Abstr., Old Test.Abstr., Rel.& Theol.Abstr. (1990-), Rel.Ind.One. **Document type**: academic/scholarly publication.
    Description: Presents translations and summaries of recent academic, religious, and theological studies originally published in Hebrew, for an international audience.

IMPACT; Asian magazine for human transformation. see *SOCIAL SCIENCES: COMPREHENSIVE WORKS*

266   GW
IMPULSE (GIESSEN); fuer missionarisches christsein. 1978. q. DM.16. Campus für Christus, Am Unteren Rain 2, 35394 Giessen, Germany. TEL 0641-975180. FAX 0641-9751840. Ed. Karin Herm. adv.; bk.rev. circ. 12,000. **Document type**: newsletter.

200   US   ISSN 0363-5058
IN COMMON. 1971. q. $2. Consultation on Church Union, Research Park, 151 Wall St., Princeton, NJ 08540-1514. Ed. Daniell C. Hambly. circ. 10,000. **Document type**: newsletter.

RELIGIONS AND THEOLOGY

200 NE ISSN 0019-3151
IN DE RECHTE STRAAT. Spanish edition: En la Calle Recta. 1958. m. (Dutch ed.); bi-m. (Spanish ed.). fl.22.75 for Dutch ed. (Spanish ed. free to Catholics). Stichting In de Rechte Straat, Boulevard 11, 6881 HN Velp, Netherlands. TEL 31-85-646050. Ed. Ev. J.W.N. van Dooijeweert. bk.rev.; illus. circ. 14,000. **Indexed:** CERDIC.
Description: Discusses dialogue and witness with the Catholic Church and helps ex-priests who left their church for reasons of conscience.

200 NE ISSN 0019-316X
IN DE WAAGSCHAAL.* 1945. fortn. fl.17. Amaco, C/o C.E. Bakker Delvaux, Van Humboldtstr. 89, 3514 GN Utrecht, Netherlands. Ed. Prof. Dr. K.H. Miskotte. circ. 2,000. **Indexed:** CERDIC.
—SWETS.

266 GW
IN DIE WELT - FUER DIE WELT. bi-m. DM.12. Vereinigte Evangelische Mission, Postfach 201963, 42219 Wuppertal, Germany. TEL 0202-89004-0. FAX 0202-89004179. **Document type:** bulletin.

220 US ISSN 0279-3172
IN OTHER WORDS. 1943. bi-m. free to U.S. subscribers. Wycliffe Bible Translators, Inc., Box 2727, Huntington Beach, CA 92647. TEL 714-969-4600. FAX 714-969-4661. TELEX 284682. Ed. Mack Timm. illus.; circ. 300,000 (controlled). **Document type:** newsletter.
—UMI.
Superseded: Translation (ISSN 0041-1221)
Description: Communicates with the supporting constituency regarding the work of Wycliff Bible Translators for recruiting, prayer, and financial support and to minister to the spiritual needs of the readers.
Refereed Serial

200 UK ISSN 0019-3283
IN TOUCH (PINNER). 1969. q. £5 (typically set in Jan.). (Grail) The Grail, 125 Waxwell Ln., Pinner, Middsx., England. TEL 0181-866-0505. FAX 0181-866-4016. Ed. Mary Grasar. bk.rev.; play rev.; illus. circ. 1,100. (tabloid format) **Document type:** bulletin.
Formerly: Mosaic.

IN TOUCH (TORONTO). see *HANDICAPPED — Visually Impaired*

200 US
IN TUNE; the quarterly newsletter of 970 DJ. vol.6, 1990. q. W W D J, Box 970, Hackensack, NJ 07602.

200 US
INDEPENDENT LESSON SERMON QUARTERLY. q. $10. Plainfield Christian Science Church (Independent), 905 Prospect Ave., Box 5619, Plainfield, NJ 07060. TEL 908-756-4669.

209 II ISSN 0019-4530
BR1150
INDIAN CHURCH HISTORY REVIEW. (Text in English) 1967. s-a. $5. Church History Association of India, Mackin-Chan Hall, Wilson College, Bombay 7, India. Ed. Dr. H. Grafe. bk.rev.; index. circ. 500. (back issues avail.) **Indexed:** Rel.& Theol.Abstr. (1989-), Rel.Ind.One, Rel.Per.
—SWETS; UnCover.

230 II ISSN 0019-5685
BR1
INDIAN JOURNAL OF THEOLOGY. (Text in English) 1952. s-a. $10. Serampore College, Theology Department, c/o D.K. Sahu, Ed., Serampore, Hooghly District, West Bengal 712201, India. TEL 033-662-2322. adv.; bk.rev.; bibl.; index. circ. 500. **Indexed:** Excerp.Med., New Test.Abstr., Old Test.Abstr., Rel.& Theol.Abstr., Rel.Ind.One, Rel.Per. **Document type:** academic/scholarly publication.
Description: Encourages efforts to reinterpret Christian theology. Serves as a link between the East and West theological thinking.

200 GW ISSN 0942-4822
INFORMATIONES THEOLOGIAE EUROPAE. (Text in English, French, German) 1993. a. DM.77. Peter Lang GmbH Europaeischer Verlag der Wissenschaften, Eschborner Landstr. 42-50, 60489 Frankfurt a.M., Germany. TEL 069-780705-0. FAX 069-785893. Ed. Ulrich Nembach. (back issues avail.) **Document type:** academic/scholarly publication.

INNER PATHS. see *NEW AGE PUBLICATIONS*

200 UK ISSN 0020-1723
INQUIRER. 1842. fortn. £12.50($30) Inquirer Publishing Co. Ltd., 1-6 Essex St., London W.C.2, England. Ed. Rev. K. Gilley. adv.; bk.rev.; illus. circ. 2,500. (also avail. in microfilm from WMP)

INSIGHT (TORONTO). see *HANDICAPPED — Visually Impaired*

200 US
INSIGHTS FOR PREACHERS; a publication for parish pastors providing sermon resources on common lectionary texts. 1973. 4/yr. $22. King Publications, 5697 Applebutter Hill Rd., Coopersburg, PA 18036-9560. TEL 610-967-3901. FAX 610-967-2128. Ed. Richard H. Stough, Sr. adv. contact: Joan L. Stough. circ. 1,000. **Indexed:** Rel.& Theol.Abstr. (1988-). **Document type:** consumer publication.
Former titles: Insights into Preaching; Insights (Springfield) (ISSN 0164-7709); Incorporates (1981-198?): Kerygma.

INSOUND. see *HANDICAPPED — Visually Impaired*

INSTITUT CATHOLIQUE DE PARIS. REVUE. see *GENERAL INTEREST PERIODICALS — France*

200 UY
INSTITUTO TEOLOGICO DEL URUGUAY MONSENOR MARIANO SOLER. LIBRO ANUAL. 1974. a. Instituto Teologico del Uruguay Monsenor Mariano Soler, San Fructuoso 1019, Montevideo, Uruguay. TEL 598-2-200289. circ. 500. **Document type:** academic/scholarly publication.
Description: Contains articles on philosophy and theology. Covers conferences.

INSTRUMENTA LEXICOLOGIA LATINA. see *CLASSICAL STUDIES*

281 BE
INSTRUMENTA PATRISTICA. (Text in various European languages) vol.2, 1962. irreg., vol.25, 1992. price varies. (St. Pietersabdij, Steenbrugge) N.V. Brepols, Steenweg op Tielen 68, 2300 Turnhout, Belgium. TEL 32-14-402500. FAX 32-14-428919. (back issues avail.) **Document type:** monographic series, academic/scholarly publication.
Description: Scholarly monographs on early and modern Christian theology, history and texts.

INTERCESSOR. see *ADVERTISING AND PUBLIC RELATIONS*

200 AT ISSN 0047-0430
INTERCHANGE; papers on Biblical and current questions. 1967. 2/yr. Aus.$20. Australian Fellowship of Evangelical Students, Graduate Fellowship of Australia, The Business Manager, 16 Mill Hill Rd., Bondi Junction, N.S.W. 2022, Australia. TEL 02-369-1688. FAX 02-369-1688. Ed. Peter Inman. bk.rev. circ. 700. (back issues avail.) **Indexed:** Phil.Ind. **Document type:** academic/scholarly publication.
—BLDSC (4532.600000).

200 US
INTERCHANGE (CINCINNATI). 1971. 8/yr. $10 to non-members. Episcopal Diocese of Southern Ohio, 412 Sycamore St., Cincinnati, OH 45202-4179. TEL 513-421-0311. FAX 513-421-0315. Ed. Michael R. Barwell. adv.; bk.rev.; illus.; stat. circ. 13,500. (tabloid format; back issues avail.)

230.05 US ISSN 0092-6558
BR1
INTERDENOMINATIONAL THEOLOGICAL CENTER, ATLANTA. JOURNAL. Key Title: Journal of the Interdenominational Theological Center. 1973. s-a. $6 to individuals; institutions $8. Interdenominational Theological Center, 671 Beckwith St., Atlanta, GA 30314. TEL 404-527-7727. Ed. John C. Diamond Jr. bk.rev. circ. 2,500. **Indexed:** CERDIC, New Test.Abstr., Rel.& Theol.Abstr. (1990-), Rel.Ind.One, Rel.Per.
—BLDSC (4802.064000); UMI.

200 US ISSN 0020-5575
INTERLIT. 1964. q. $2.50 (free to qualified personnel). David C. Cook Foundation, 850 N. Grove Ave., Elgin, IL 60120. TEL 708-741-2400. Ed. Gladys J. Peterson. bk.rev. circ. 7,000. **Indexed:** CERDIC.

INTERNATIONAL ASSOCIATION FOR THE DEVELOPMENT OF CONSCIOUSNESS. INFORMATION BULLETIN. see *PHILOSOPHY*

367 US
INTERNATIONAL ASSOCIATION OF LIBERAL RELIGIOUS WOMEN. NEWSLETTER.* 1949. a. membership. International Association of Liberal Religious Women, c/o Tina Jas, Sec., 43 Coolidge Ave., Lexington, MA 02173. (Edit. addr.: Havikhorst 17hs, Amsterdam 1083 TM, Netherlands) Ed. Gusta Greve. **Document type:** newsletter.
Former titles: International Union of Liberal Christian Women. Newsletter; International League of Liberal Christian Women. Newsletter (ISSN 0074-6746)

INTERNATIONAL BIOGRAPHICAL DICTIONARY OF RELIGION; an encyclopedia of more than 4000 leading personalities. see *BIOGRAPHY*

200 US
INTERNATIONAL COMMISSION ON ENGLISH IN THE LITURGY. NEWSLETTER. 1975. s-a. free. International Commission on English in the Liturgy, 1275 K St., N.W., Ste. 1202, Washington, DC 20005. TEL 202-347-0800. Ed. James Schellman. circ. 2,500. **Document type:** newsletter.

201 NE ISSN 0020-7047
BL51 CODEN: IJPREB
INTERNATIONAL JOURNAL FOR PHILOSOPHY OF RELIGION. (Text in English) 1970. bi-m. fl.397 to institutions; $255 to institutions in U.S. (effective 1996). Kluwer Academic Publishers, Postbus 17, 3300 AA Dordrecht, Netherlands. TEL 31-78-392392. FAX 31-78-392254. TELEX 29245 KAPG NL. E-mail: SERVICES@WKAP.NL. (Dist. by: Kluwer Academic Publishers Group, P.O. Box 322, 3300 AH Dordrecht, Netherlands. TEL 31-78-392392. FAX 31-78-546474; N. America dist. addr.: Box 358, Accord Sta., Hingham, MA 02018-0358. TEL 617-871-6600. FAX 617-871-6528) Eds. Eugene T. Long, Frank R. Harrison III. bk.rev.; bibl. (also avail. in microform from UMI; back issues avail.; reprint service avail. from SWZ) **Indexed:** Arts & Hum.Cit.Ind., ASCA, Curr.Cont., Hum.Ind., Mid.East: Abstr.& Ind., Phil.Ind., Rel.& Theol.Abstr. (1979-), Rel.Ind.One. **Document type:** academic/scholarly publication.
—BLDSC (4542.455000); Faxon; Genuine Article; SWETS; UMI; UnCover. **CCC.**
Description: Provides a non-sectarian and independent forum for the exposition, development and criticism of philosophical insights and theories relevant tot religion in any of its varied forms.
Refereed Serial

200 150 US ISSN 1050-8619
BL53.A1 CODEN: IPRLEB
INTERNATIONAL JOURNAL FOR THE PSYCHOLOGY OF RELIGION. 1991. q. $35 to individuals (foreign $60); institutions $145 (foreign $170). Lawrence Erlbaum Associates, Inc., 10 Industrial Dr., Mahwah, NJ 07430-2262. TEL 201-236-9500. FAX 201-236-0072. Ed.Bd. adv.: page $425; 5 x 8. bk.rev. **Indexed:** Psychol.Abstr. (1991-). **Document type:** academic/scholarly publication.
—BLDSC (4542.506200); Faxon; UnCover.
Description: Forum for reporting specific results and encouraging discussion of the methods, theories, and applications of psychological research, in the broadest sense, to religions.
Refereed Serial

268 US ISSN 0074-6770
BV1560
INTERNATIONAL LESSON ANNUAL; commentary and teaching suggestions on the International Sunday School lessons. 1956. a. $9.95. Abingdon Press, 201 Eighth Ave., S., Box 801, Nashville, TN 37202-0801. TEL 800-251-3320. FAX 615-749-6522. Ed. Horace R. Weaver.
Description: Detailed explanations of the Bible for every Sunday session.

200 US ISSN 0743-5614
INTERNATIONAL PARTNERS IN PRAYER TRUMPETING NEWS.* 1984. a. $.50. International Partners in Prayer, Box 416, Denver, CO 80201-0416. Ed. A.C. Doyle. circ. 1,600. (looseleaf format; also avail. in microfiche; back issues avail.)
Formerly: Trumpeting News.

RELIGIONS AND THEOLOGY

266   SZ   ISSN 0020-8582
BV2351
INTERNATIONAL REVIEW OF MISSION. 1911. q. 43.50 SFr.($32.50) World Council of Churches, CWME - Unit II: Churches in Mission, 150 route de Ferney, P.O. Box 2100, CH-1211 Geneva 2, Switzerland. TEL 022-791-6111. FAX 022-791-0361. TELEX 415730-OIK-CH. Ed. Christopher Duraisingh. adv.; bk.rev.; bibl.; index; cum.index: 1912-1990. circ. 4,000. (also avail. in microform from UMI; reprint service avail. from UMI,KTO) **Indexed:** A.I.C.P., Abstr.Musl.Rel., Amer.Hist.& Life, Br.Hum.Ind., CERDIC, Chr.Per.Ind., Hist.Abstr., Mid.East: Abstr.& Ind., Rel.& Theol.Abstr. (1968-), Rel.Ind.One, Rel.Per., So.Pac.Per.Ind. **Document type:** bulletin.
●Also available online. Vendor(s): University Microfilms International.
—BLDSC (4547.380000); Faxon; SWETS; UMI; UnCover.

290 150   NE   ISSN 0925-4153
INTERNATIONAL SERIES IN THE PSYCHOLOGY OF RELIGIONS. 1990. irreg. price varies. Editions Rodopi B.V., Keizersgracht 302-304, 1016 EX Amsterdam, Netherlands. TEL 31-20-6227507. FAX 31-20-6380948. E-mail: F.van.der.Zee@Rodopi.nl. (In N. America: 233 Peachtree St., N.E., Ste. 404, Atlanta, GA 30303-1504. TEL 800-225-3998. FAX 404-522-7116) Ed. Jaap van Belsen. (back issues avail.) **Document type:** monographic series.

200   UK
INTERNATIONAL SOCIETY FOR THE SOCIOLOGY OF RELIGION. DIRECTORY. 1948. biennial. International Society for the Sociology of Religion, Dept. of Sociology, Univ. of Exeter, Rennes Dr., Exeter EX4 4RJ, England. TEL 44-1342-263276. FAX 44-1392-263285. bk.rev. **Document type:** directory.
Formerly: International Conference for the Sociology of Religion. Directory (ISSN 0074-297X)

200 300   UK
INTERNATIONAL SOCIETY FOR THE SOCIOLOGY OF RELIGION. NEWSLETTER - BULLETIN. s-a. £38. International Society for the Sociology of Religion, Dept. of Sociology, Univ. of Exeter, Rennes Dr., Exeter EX4 4RJ, England. TEL 44-1392-263276. FAX 44-1392-263285. **Document type:** bulletin.

INTERNATIONAL UNION OF GOSPEL MISSIONS MEMBERSHIP DIRECTORY & RESOURCE GUIDE. see SOCIAL SERVICES AND WELFARE

200   SZ   ISSN 0020-9252
INTERNATIONALE KIRCHLICHE ZEITSCHRIFT. 1911. q. 70 SFr. Staempfli und Cie AG, Hallerstr. 7-9, CH-3001 Bern, Switzerland. TEL 031-3006666. FAX 031-3006688. Ed. Hans Frei. bk.rev.; bibl.; index. circ. 700. (tabloid format; reprint service avail. from SCH) **Indexed:** CERDIC, New Test.Abstr., Old Test.Abstr. **Document type:** bulletin.
—CCC.

200   BE   ISSN 0776-2488
INTER-PRESSE; relations internationales dialogue interreligieux. 1984. q. 1000 BEF. Centre d'Inter-Action Culturelle, Rue de la Procession, 4, B-1331 Rosieres, Belgium. TEL 32-2-653-53-24. FAX 32-2-654-19-08. Ed. Pierre Houart. adv.; bk.rev.
Formerly (until 1988): Dialogue Interreligieux (ISSN 0775-5325)
Description: Focuses on all interreligious themes worldwide. Celebrates the universality of religion and addresses human rights.

200   NE   ISSN 0929-015X
INTERPRETATIE; tijdschrift voor bijbelse theologie. 1993. 8/yr. fl.98.50 (students & senior citizens fl.75). Boekencentrum B.V., P.O. Box 29, 2700 AA Zoetermeer, Netherlands. TEL 31-79-615481. FAX 31-79-615489. Ed. Dirk Monshouwer. **Document type:** academic/scholarly publication.
Description: Provides a forum for interpretation of the Bible.

INTERPRETATION (FLUSHING); a journal of political philosophy. see POLITICAL SCIENCE

220 230   US   ISSN 0020-9643
BR1
INTERPRETATION (RICHMOND); a journal of Bible and theology. 1947. q. $18.50 to individuals (foreign $20); institutions $25 (effective 1996). Union Theological Seminary in Virginia, 3401 Brook Rd., Richmond, VA 23227. TEL 804-278-4296. FAX 804-355-3919. Ed. Jack D. Kingsbury. adv.; bk.rev.; bibl.; index, cum.index: 1972-1981; 1982-1986; 1987-1991. circ. 10,500. (also avail. in microform from UMI; back issues avail; reprint service avail. from UMI) **Indexed:** Bk.Rev.Ind. (1965-), Child.Bk.Rev.Ind. (1965-), Chr.Per.Ind., G.Soc.Sci.& Rel.Per.Lit., Hum.Ind., Ind.Artic.Jew.Stud., Int.Z.Bibelwiss., New Test.Abstr., Old Test.Abstr., Rel.& Theol.Abstr. (1967-), Rel.Ind.One, Rel.Per., Soc.Sci.Ind. **Document type:** academic/scholarly publication.
—BLDSC (4557.347000); Faxon; SWETS; UMI; UnCover.
Description: Publishes articles and essays of biblical and theological interpretation for scholars, clergy, and laity of all denominations.

200   HK
INTER-RELIGIO; a network of Christian organizations for interreligious encounter in east Asia. (Text in English) 1982. s-a. $8 free to qualified personnels. Christian Study Center on Chinese Religion and Culture, 6-F Kiu Kin Mansion, 556 Nathan Rd., Kowloon, Hong Kong. TEL 852-2770-3310. FAX 852-2782-6869. Ed. Brian Lawless. bk.rev.; index. circ. 700. (back issues avail.) **Document type:** newsletter.
Description: Contains articles on inter-religious dialogues, news events and publications.

267   JM   ISSN 0020-5087
INTER-SCHOOL & INTER-VARSITY CHRISTIAN FELLOWSHIP; for prayer and praise. m. free. Students Christian Fellowship and Scripture Union, 22 Hagley Park Plaza, Box 281, Kingston 10, Jamaica, W.I. Ed. Sam McCook. bk.rev. circ. 800. (processed)
Formerly: Inter-School and Inter-Varsity Christian Fellowship of the West Indies.

255   BE   ISSN 0021-0978
BX1
IRENIKON. 1926. q. 1270 BEF($40) (effective 1994). Monastere de Chevetogne, 5590 Chevetogne, Belgium. TEL 32-83-211763. FAX 32-83-216045. Ed. Emmanuel Lanne. adv.; bk.rev.; bibl.; index. circ. 1,600. **Indexed:** CERDIC, Ind.Med., New Test.Abstr., Rel.Ind.One, Rel.Per. **Document type:** academic/scholarly publication.
—SWETS.

200   IE   ISSN 0332-4427
IRISH BIBLICAL ASSOCIATION. PROCEEDINGS. 1976. a. I£7. Columba Press, 93 The Rise, Mt. Merrion, Blackrock, Dublin, Ireland. TEL 01-2832954. FAX 01-2883770. Ed.Bd. adv. circ. 250. (back issues avail.) **Indexed:** New Test.Abstr., Old Test.Abstr., Rel.& Theol.Abstr. (1989-). **Document type:** proceedings.
—BLDSC (6740.700000).
Description: Presents academic papers on Scripture studies with a particular interest in Hiberno-Latin studies.

220   UK   ISSN 0268-6112
BS543
IRISH BIBLICAL STUDIES. 1979. q. £26. Irish Biblical Studies, 26 College Green, Belfast BT7 1JT, Northern Ireland. TEL 01232-325374. FAX 01232-325397. E-mail: jc.mccullough@uk.ac.qub.v2. Ed. J.C. CcCollough. bk.rev. circ. 400. **Indexed:** Rel.& Theol.Abstr. (1990-). **Document type:** academic/scholarly publication.
—BLDSC (4570.400000).
Description: Covers the Old and New Testaments and related material.

500   UK   ISSN 0264-6579
IRISH CHRISTIAN STUDY CENTRE. JOURNAL. 1983. a. £2.50 to individuals; institutions £10. Irish Christian Study Centre, Glenburn House, Glenburn Rd. S., Dunmurry, Belfast BT17 9JP, Northern Ireland. TEL 602264. FAX 01232-301523. bk.rev. circ. 400. **Document type:** academic/scholarly publication.
Description: Provides encouragement for the development of Christian scholarship and research.

200   IE   ISSN 0021-1400
IRISH THEOLOGICAL QUARTERLY. 1906. q. £16.12. St. Patrick's College, Faculty of Theology, Maynooth, Co. Kildare, Ireland. TEL 01-285-222. Ed.Bd. bk.rev.; index. circ. 1,000. (also avail. in microform from UMI; reprint service avail. from UMI) **Indexed:** Canon Law Abstr., Cath.Ind., New Test.Abstr., Old Test.Abstr., Rel.& Theol.Abstr. (1968-).
—BLDSC (4574.870000); Faxon; UMI.

200   VC   ISSN 0392-7288
ISLAMOCHRISTIANA/DIRASAT ISLAMIYYA MASIHIYYA. 1975. a. L.38000($30) (effective 1994). Pontificio Istituto di Studi Arabi e d'Islamistica, Palazzo S. Callisto, 00120 Vatican City (Rome), State of the Vatican City. (Subscr. to: Viale di Trastevere 89, 00153 Rome, Italy. TEL 39-6-5882676. FAX 39-6-5882595) Ed. Maurice Borrmans. bk.rev. **Document type:** academic/scholarly publication.
Description: Publishes articles, documents and materials concerned with the theoretical and practical aspects, past and present, of the Muslim-Christian dialogue.

281   FR   ISSN 0021-2423
BX1781
ISTINA. 1954. q. 335 F. (typically set in Sep.). Centre d'Etudes Istina, 45 rue de la Glaciere, 75013 Paris, France. TEL 45-35-37-04. (Affiliate: Centre National de la Recherche Scientifique, Paris) Dir. B.D. Dupuy. bk.rev.; index. circ. 1,100. (also avail. in microfilm from UMI; back issues avail.; reprint service avail. from UMI) **Indexed:** Bull.Signal., CERDIC, New Test.Abstr., Rel.Ind.One, Rel.Per. **Document type:** academic/scholarly publication.
—UMI.

262.9   SP   ISSN 0021-325X
IUS CANONICUM. (Text in Spanish; summaries in English and Latin) 1961. 2/yr. 6000 ptas.($60) (Universidad de Navarra, Instituto Martin de Azpilcueta) Servicio de Publicaciones de la Universidad de Navarra, S.A., Apdo. 177, 31080 Pamplona, Spain. TEL 94 25 2700. Ed. Tomas Rincon. bk.rev. circ. 1,000. **Indexed:** Canon Law Abstr., CERDIC.
Description: Discusses canon law.

J P; paper for boys and girls. see CHILDREN AND YOUTH — For

200   GW   ISSN 0342-6505
JA; mit das taegliche Wort. 1953. m. DM.67.80. (Unity School of Christianity) Frick Verlag GmbH, Postfach 447, 75104 Pforzheim, Germany. TEL 07231-102842. FAX 07231-357744. Ed. Thea Jung. circ. 12,000. **Document type:** bulletin.

200   GW   ISSN 0342-6513
JA, DAS WORT FUER ALLE. 1982. m. DM.17.40. (Berliner Stadtmission) Kreuz-Verlag Zeitschriften GmbH, Breitwiesenstr. 30, 70565 Stuttgart, Germany. TEL 0711-78803. circ. 21,000. (looseleaf format) **Document type:** bulletin.

291   SW   ISSN 0283-3484
JABBOK. Variant title: Tidskriften Jabbok. 1985. q. SEK 110. Stiftelsen Jabbok, P.O. Box 2017, S-128 21 Stockholm, Sweden. TEL 46-8-604-25-89.

200   GW   ISSN 0341-9126
JAHRBUCH DER HESSISCHEN KIRCHENGESCHICHTLICHEN VEREINIGUNG. 1949. a. DM.40. Hessische Kirchengeschichtliche Vereinigung, Ahastr. 5a, 64285 Darmstadt, Germany. TEL 06151-405493. FAX 06151-405494. TELEX 4197176-EKYN-D. Ed. Martin Sauer. index. circ. 700. (back issues avail.) **Indexed:** RILM. **Document type:** academic/scholarly publication.

270   GW   ISSN 0075-2541
BR128.A2
JAHRBUCH FUER ANTIKE UND CHRISTENTUM. 1958. a. price varies. (Universitaet Bonn, Franz Joseph Doelger-Institut) Aschendorffsche Verlagsbuchhandlung, Soesterstr. 13, 48155 Muenster, Germany. TEL 0251-690-0. FAX 0251-690143. bk.rev. **Indexed:** Br.Archaeol.Abstr., New Test.Abstr., RILA, RILM. **Document type:** academic/scholarly publication.

RELIGIONS AND THEOLOGY

270   GW   ISSN 0075-2568
BR857.B8
JAHRBUCH FUER BERLIN-BRANDENBURGISCHE KIRCHENGESCHICHTE. vol.55, 1985. a. DM.28. (Arbeitsgemeinschaft fuer Berlin-Brandenburgische Kirchengeschichte) Wichern Verlag GmbH, Bachstr. 1-2, 10555 Berlin, Germany. TEL 030-3915075. FAX 030-3936047. circ. 850. **Document type:** bulletin.
—BLDSC (4630.380000).
   Supersedes: Jahrbuch fuer Brandenburgische Kirchengeschichte.

JAHRBUCH FUER CHRISTLICHE SOZIALWISSENSCHAFTEN. see *SOCIOLOGY*

264 245   GW   ISSN 0075-2681
ML3168
JAHRBUCH FUER LITURGIK UND HYMNOLOGIE. 1955. a. price varies. (International Fellowship of Research in Hymnology - Internationale Arbeitsgemeinschaft fuer Hymnologie) Lutherisches Verlagshaus GmbH, Knochenhauerstr. 38-40, 30159 Hannover, Germany. TEL 0511-1241-733. Ed.Bd. bk.rev. circ. 1,000. **Indexed:** CERDIC, RILM. **Document type:** bulletin.
—BLDSC (4631.640000).

270   GW   ISSN 0075-2762
BR857.S6
JAHRBUCH FUER SCHLESISCHE KIRCHENGESCHICHTE. 1882. a. DM.44. (Verein fuer Schlesische Kirchengeschichte e.V.) Jan Thorbecke Verlag GmbH und Co., Postfach 546, 72482 Sigmaringen, Germany. TEL 07571-728-100. FAX 07571-728-287. Ed. Dietrich Meyer. bk.rev. **Indexed:** RILM. **Document type:** academic/scholarly publication.
—BLDSC (4632.270000).

JAHRBUCH FUER WESTFAELISCHE KIRCHENGESCHICHTE. see *HISTORY — History Of Europe*

260   GW   ISSN 0931-248X
JAHRBUCH MISSION. 1969. a. DM.9.80. (Verband Evangelischer Missionskonferenzen) Missionshilfe Verlag, Normannenweg 17-21, 20537 Hamburg, Germany. Ed. Klaus Schaefer. bk.rev. circ. 8,000. **Document type:** bulletin.
   Formerly: Evangelische Mission Jahrbuch (ISSN 0531-4798)

268   FR   ISSN 0399-4600
J'AIME LIRE. 1977. m. 399 F. (outside EC 450 F.). Bayard Presse, 3 rue Bayard, 75393 Paris Cedex 08, France. TEL 44-35-60-60. FAX 44-35-60-91. TELEX 648 094 F. (Subscr. to: B.P. 15, 99505 Paris Entreprises, France. TEL 46-30-38-00. FAX 46-30-31-67) circ. 180,000.
   Description: Promotes the love of reading in children 7 years and older.

200   JA   ISSN 0021-4353
JAPAN CHRISTIAN ACTIVITY NEWS. (Text in English) 1952. q. 2000 Yen($20) National Christian Council in Japan, Japan Christian Center, Rm. 24, 2-13-18 Nishi-Waseda, Shinjuku-ku, Tokyo 160, Japan. FAX 03-204-9495. TELEX J-27890-CCRAI. (Overseas subscr. to: Cherie Emery, JCAN Subscr. Liaison, 6800 Broadway Terrace, Oakland, CA 94611) Ed.Bd. bk.rev. circ. 600. (processed) **Indexed:** I.C.U.I.S.Abstr. **Document type:** newsletter.

266   JA   ISSN 0021-4361
BV3440
JAPAN CHRISTIAN QUARTERLY. (Text in English) 1925. q. $32. (Fellowship of Christian Missionaries) Japan Publications Trading Co., Ltd., Box 5030, Tokyo International, Tokyo 100-31, Japan. circ. 5,000. **Indexed:** M.L.A., Rel.& Theol.Abstr. (1989-), Rel.Ind.One, Rel.Per.
—UMI; UnCover.
   Description: Discusses mission work in the country.

266   JA   ISSN 0910-7118
JAPAN MISSION JOURNAL/FUKUIN SENKYO. (Text in English) 1947. q. 4120 Yen($35) (effective Jan. 1994). Oriens Institute for Religious Research, 28-5 Matsubara, 2-chome, Setagaya-ku, Tokyo 156, Japan. TEL 03-3322-7601. FAX 03-3325-5322. Ed. M. Christiaens. adv.; bk.rev.; charts; illus.; index. circ. 1,500. pp./issue: 72. **Document type:** academic/scholarly publication.
—UnCover.
   Formerly (until 1985): Japan Missionary Bulletin - Fukyo (ISSN 0021-4531)
   Description: Provides theological and cultural articles on Japanese Christianity.

200   UK   ISSN 0307-3033
JAPAN NEWS. 1965. 4/yr. £3.60. Japan Evangelistic Band, 275 London Rd., North End, Portsmouth, Hants. PO2 9HE, England. TEL 01705-666151. FAX 01705-666151. Ed. Maureen Smith. circ. 2,000. **Document type:** newsletter.
   Formerly: Japan Evangelistic Band Magazine.

291   JA   ISSN 0448-8954
BL2202
JAPANESE RELIGIONS. (Text in English) 1959. s-a. 3600 Yen($30) (foreign $27) for 2 yrs. National Christian Council of Japan, Center for the Study of Japanese Religions, Karasuma-Shimotachiuri, Kamikyo-ku, Kyoto-shi 602, Japan. FAX 075-432-1945. Ed. Martin Repp. bk.rev. circ. 500. (also avail. in microfilm from WMP; back issues avail.) **Indexed:** Rel.& Theol.Abstr. (1967-), Rel.Ind.One.
—BLDSC (4661.600000); SWETS; UnCover.

200   FR   ISSN 1167-4571
JARDIN DES DRAGONS; a la recherche des heritages traditionnels. 1991. q. 500 F. for 6 nos. Editions du Prieure, Le Prieure, 27120 Rouvray, France. TEL 32-26-24-05. FAX 32-26-24-04. **Document type:** bulletin.

200   IT
JESUS. 1979. m. L.60000 (effective July 1995). Periodici San Paolo S.r.l., Via Liberazione, 4, 12051 Alba (CN), Italy. TEL 39-173-296292. FAX 39-173-296431. Ed. D. Stefano Andreatta. adv.: B&W page L.7000000, color page L.10000000.

JESUS MAESTRO. see *CHILDREN AND YOUTH — For*

220   IS   ISSN 0792-3910
BS410
JEWISH BIBLE QUARTERLY. (Text in English) 1972. q. $24 (effective 1993). Jewish Bible Association, P.O. Box 29002, Jerusalem 93801, Israel. TEL 972-2-759144. FAX 972-759144. E-mail: backon@VMS.HUJI.AC.IL. Ed. Shimon Bakon. adv.; bk.rev. circ. 1,400. (also avail. in microfiche) **Indexed:** Ind.Jew.Per., Old Test.Abstr., Rel.& Theol.Abstr. (1977-). **Document type:** academic/scholarly publication.
—BLDSC (4668.351280); UnCover.
   Former titles: Dor le-Dor (ISSN 0334-2166); Bible Readers' Union Bulletin (ISSN 0006-0771)
   Description: Publishes original articles and translations from scholarly Hebrew journals on biblical themes.

220 371.911
JOHN MILTON ADULT LESSONS QUARTERLY. 1950. 4/yr. free. John Milton Society for the Blind, 475 Riverside Dr., Rm. 455, New York, NY 10115. TEL 212-870-3335. Ed. Darcy Quigley. circ. Braille ed. 1,450; cassette ed. 1,400. (Braille; also avail. in audio cassette) **Document type:** academic/scholarly publication.
   Formerly: John Milton Sunday School Quarterly.
   Description: Biblical studies based on the Cooperative Uniform Lesson Series.

JOHN MILTON MAGAZINE. see *HANDICAPPED — Visually Impaired*

JOHN MILTON TALKING BOOK MAGAZINE. see *HANDICAPPED — Visually Impaired*

200   NE   ISSN 0021-7395
JONGE KERK. 1917. m. fl.15. Apostolaat van het Gebed, Postbus 418, 6500 AK Nijmegen, Netherlands. TEL 31-80-222-495. FAX 31-80-222-593. Ed. Chr. Swueste. adv.; bk.rev.; index. circ. 10,000.

255   US   ISSN 0021-7603
JOSEPHITE HARVEST. 1888. q. $2. Society of St. Joseph of the Sacred Heart, 1130 N. Calvert St., Baltimore, MD 21202. TEL 410-727-3386. FAX 410-385-2331. Ed. Earle A. Newman. adv. circ. 46,000.

200   US   ISSN 0021-8294
BL1   CODEN: JSSRBT
JOURNAL FOR THE SCIENTIFIC STUDY OF RELIGION. 1961. q. $45 to non-members. Society for the Scientific Study of Religion, c/o Ralph Hood, Department of Psychology, University of Tennessee, Chattanooga, TN 37403. TEL 317-494-6286. Ed. Ralph Hood. adv. contact: Anna Davidson. bk.rev.; charts; stat.; index, cum.index: 1961-1981. circ. 3,500. (also avail. in microform from UMI; reprint service avail. from UMI,KTO) **Indexed:** Abstr.Anthropol., Amer.Bibl.Slavic & E.Eur.Stud., Amer.Hist.& Life, Arts & Hum.Cit.Ind., CERDIC, Chic.Per.Ind., Curr.Cont., G.Soc.Sci.& Rel.Per.Lit., Hist.Abstr., Hum.Ind., Lang.& Lang.Behav.Abstr., Mid.East. Abstr.& Ind., Old Test.Abstr., PSI, Psychol.Abstr. (1961-), Rel.& Theol.Abstr. (1967-), Rel.Ind.One, Rel.Per., Sociol.Abstr. (1961-), SSCI. **Document type:** academic/scholarly publication.
● Also available online. Vendor(s): University Microfilms International.
—BLDSC (5061.500000); Faxon; Genuine Article; SWETS; UMI; UnCover.
   Refereed Serial

291   SA   ISSN 1011-7601
JOURNAL FOR THE STUDY OF RELIGION. (Text in English) 1980; N.S. 1988. 2/yr. R.25 (outside Africa $35) (effective 1994). Association for the Study of Religion in Southern Africa, c/o Dept. of Religious Studies, University of Natal, Pietermaritzburg 3201, South Africa. TEL 27-331-2605571. Eds. M.H. Prozesky, P.S. Maxwell. adv.; bk.rev.; abstr.; bibl.; charts; stat.; biennial index. circ. 240. (back issues avail.) **Indexed:** Ind.S.A.Per., Rel.Ind.One. **Document type:** academic/scholarly publication.
—BLDSC (5066.928000).
   Formerly (until 1988): Religion in Southern Africa.
   Description: Forum for scholarly contributions on topics of contemporary significance in the academic study of religion.
   Refereed Serial

200   UK   ISSN 0142-064X
BS410
JOURNAL FOR THE STUDY OF THE NEW TESTAMENT. 1978. 4/yr. $39.50 to individuals; institutions $120. Sheffield Academic Press Ltd., Mansion House, 19 Kingfield Rd., Sheffield S11 9AS, England. TEL 44-171-267-4466. FAX 44-171-482-2293. E-mail: admin@sheffac.demon.co.uk. **Indexed:** Bibl.Ling., New.Test.Abstr., Rel.& Theol.Abstr. (1979-), Rel.Ind.One. **Document type:** academic/scholarly publication.
—BLDSC (5066.917000); Faxon; UMI; UnCover.

200   UK   ISSN 0143-5108
JOURNAL FOR THE STUDY OF THE NEW TESTAMENT. SUPPLEMENT SERIES. irreg. price varies. Sheffield Academic Press Ltd., Mansion House, 19 Kingfield Rd., Sheffield S11 9AS, England. TEL 44-171-267-4466. FAX 44-171-482-2293. E-mail: admin@sheffac.demon.co.uk. **Indexed:** New Test.Abstr. **Document type:** academic/scholarly publication.
—BLDSC (5066.918000).

221   UK   ISSN 0309-0892
BS410
JOURNAL FOR THE STUDY OF THE OLD TESTAMENT. 1976. 4/yr. $39.50 to individuals; institutions $120. Sheffield Academic Press Ltd., Mansion House, 19 Kingfield Rd., Sheffield S11 9AS, England. TEL 44-171-267-4466. FAX 44-171-482-2293. E-mail: admin@sheffac.demon.co.uk. Ed.Bd. **Indexed:** Bibl.Ling., Bull.Signal, Int.Z.Bibelwiss, New.Test.Abstr., Old Test.Abstr., Rel.& Theol.Abstr. (1977-), Rel.Ind.One, Rel.Ind.Two, Rel.Per. **Document type:** academic/scholarly publication.
—BLDSC (5066.920000); Faxon; SWETS; UMI; UnCover.

RELIGIONS AND THEOLOGY

221   UK   ISSN 0309-0787
JOURNAL FOR THE STUDY OF THE OLD TESTAMENT. SUPPLEMENT SERIES. irreg. price varies. Sheffield Academic Press Ltd., Mansion House, 19 Kingfield Rd., Sheffield S11 9AS, England. TEL 44-171-267-4466. FAX 44-171-482-2293. E-mail: admin@sheffac.demon.co.uk. Ed.Bd. Indexed: Old Test.Abstr. **Document type:** monographic series.
—BLDSC (5066.920100).

200   UK   ISSN 0951-8207
JOURNAL FOR THE STUDY OF THE PSEUDOEPIGRAPHA. 1988. 2/yr. $29.50 to individuals; institutions £85. Sheffield Academic Press Ltd., Mansion House, 19 Kingfield Rd., Sheffield S11 9AS, England. TEL 44-171-267-4466. FAX 44-171-482-2293. E-mail: admin@sheffac.demon.co.uk. Ed. James Charlesworth. adv.; bk.rev. **Document type:** academic/scholarly publication.
—BLDSC (5066.925000).

291   UG   ISSN 1018-8592
JOURNAL OF AFRICAN RELIGION AND PHILOSOPHY; a journal of religion and philosophy in Africa. 1988. 2/yr. £12 per no. Sun Publishers, P.O. Box 16144, Wandegeya, Kampala, Uganda. Ed. L. Njinya-Mujinya. adv.; bk.rev. circ. 5,000. **Indexed:** Documentatieblad, P.L.E.S.A. (1989-). **Document type:** academic/scholarly publication.
Formerly (until 1989): African Mind.
Description: Publishes comparative studies on African religions, and related theological, sociological, and philosophical issues.

200   UK
JOURNAL OF BELIEFS AND VALUES. 1980. 2/yr. £6. National Association of Teachers in Further and Higher Education, Religious Studies Section, c/o Deirdre Burke, University of Wolverhampton, Walsall Campus, Walsall WS1 3BD, England. TEL 0902-323200. adv.; bk.rev. **Document type:** academic/scholarly publication.
Description: Aimed at teachers of religious education and religious studies in higher and continuing education.

200 150   US   ISSN 1063-2166
JOURNAL OF BIBLICAL COUNSELING. 1978. 3/yr. $18 to individuals (foreign $23); libraries $24 (foreign $29). Christian Counseling & Educational Foundation, 1803 E. Willow Grove Ave., Glenside, PA 19038. TEL 215-884-7676. FAX 215-884-9435. Ed. David Powlison. adv. contact: Sharon Covington. bk.rev. circ. 1,000. (back issues avail.) **Indexed:** Chr.Per.Ind., Past.Care & Couns.Abstr.
Formerly (until vol.11, no.1, 1992): Journal of Pastoral Practice (ISSN 0196-9072)
Description: Publishes articles that both advance biblical counseling theoretically and provide concrete "how-to's" for pastors and laymen.

JOURNAL OF BIBLICAL ETHICS IN MEDICINE. see MEDICAL SCIENCES

220   US   ISSN 0021-9231
BS410
JOURNAL OF BIBLICAL LITERATURE. 1881. q. $50 to non-members. (Society of Biblical Literature) Scholars Press, Box 15399, Atlanta, GA 30333-0399. TEL 404-727-2320. FAX 404-727-2348. Ed. Jouette Bassler. adv.; bk.rev.; index. circ. 8,000. (also avail. in service from UMI,PMC; microfiche; reprint service avail. from UMI) **Indexed:** Arts & Hum.Cit.Ind., Bibl.Ling., Bk.Rev.Ind. (1977-), CERDIC, Child.Bk.Rev.Ind. (1977-), Curr.Cont., G.Soc.Sci.& Rel.Per.Lit., Hum.Ind., Ind.Jew.Per., Mid.East: Abstr.& Ind., New Test.Abstr., Old Test.Abstr., Rel.& Theol.Abstr. (1968-), Rel.Ind.One, Rel.Per. **Document type:** academic/scholarly publication.
—BLDSC (4951.550000); Faxon; Genuine Article; SWETS; UMI; UnCover.
Description: Publishes academic papers on biblical scholarship and interpretation.

377.8   AT   ISSN 0021-9657
JOURNAL OF CHRISTIAN EDUCATION. 1958. 3/yr. Aus.$30 to individuals; institutions Aus.$40 (effective 1996). Australian Christian Forum on Education Inc., P.O. Box 139, Lidcombe, N.S.W. 2141, Australia. TEL 61-2-7642084. FAX 61-2-7462710. Ed. N. Holm. bk.rev.; bibl.; cum.index every 3 yrs. circ. 650. (also avail. in microform from UMI; back issues avail) **Indexed:** Aus.Educ.Ind., Aus.P.A.I.S., Chr.Per.Ind., Cont.Pg.Educ., Educ.Ind., Rel.& Theol.Abstr. (1970-), Rel.Ind.One. **Document type:** academic/scholarly publication.
—BLDSC (4958.270000); UnCover.
Description: Considers the implications of the Christian faith for the entire field of education and to examine its contribution to the solution of educational problems.

JOURNAL OF CHRISTIAN JURISPRUDENCE. see LAW

JOURNAL OF CHRISTIAN NURSING. see MEDICAL SCIENCES — Nurses And Nursing

230.05   US   ISSN 0360-1420
BR1
JOURNAL OF CHRISTIAN RECONSTRUCTION. 1974. s-a. $18 to individuals (foreign $20.50); libraries $16 (foreign $18.50). Chalcedon, Inc., Box 158, Vallecito, CA 95251. TEL 209-728-3510. FAX 209-736-0536. Ed. Rev. Andrew Sandlin; Pub. Rev. Dr. R.J. Rushdoony. adv. contact: John Upton. bk.rev. circ. 2,000. (also avail. in microform from UMI; reprint service avail.) **Indexed:** Chr.Per.Ind.
—BLDSC (4958.280000); UMI.
Description: Scholarly and lay articles on the revitalization of the intellectual and cultural heritage of Christians in terms of standards set in the Old and New Testaments.

322 261   US   ISSN 0021-969X
BV630.A1
JOURNAL OF CHURCH AND STATE. 1959. q. $20 to individuals (foreign $25); institutions $35 (foreign $40). Baylor University, J.M. Dawson Institute of Church-State Studies, Box 97308, Waco, TX 76798-7308. TEL 817-755-1510. FAX 817-755-1571. E-mail: DAVIS D@BAYLOR.EDU. Ed. Derek H. Davis. adv.; bk.rev.; index. circ. 1,700. (also avail. in microform from WSH,PMC; microform from UMI; reprint service avail. from WSH) **Indexed:** Abstr.Bk.Rev.Curr.Leg.Per., Amer.Bibl.Slavic & E.Eur.Stud., Amer.Hist.& Life, Arts & Hum.Cit.Ind., Bk.Rev.Ind. (1980-), C.L.I., CERDIC, Child.Bk.Rev.Ind. (1980-), Chr.Per.Ind., Educ.Admin.Abstr., Hist.Abstr., L.R.I., Mid.East: Abstr.& Ind., P.A.I.S., Polit.Sci.Abstr., Rel.& Theol.Abstr. (1968-), Rel.Ind.One, Rel.Per. **Document type:** academic/scholarly publication.
—BLDSC (4958.365000); Faxon; SWETS; UMI; UnCover.

291   CN   ISSN 1023-0440
▼ **JOURNAL OF COMPARATIVE RELIGION.** 1994. a. $50. (International Centre for Religious Studies) S T C, P.O. Box 7305, Ottawa, ON K1L 8E4, Canada. TEL 613-831-1052. FAX 613-831-8452. Ed. Amarjit S. Sethi. adv.; bk.rev. **Document type:** academic/scholarly publication.
Description: Examines, encourages and publishes studies on comparative religion and intercultural research.
Refereed Serial

JOURNAL OF COMPARATIVE SOCIOLOGY AND ETHICS. see SOCIOLOGY

200   UK   ISSN 1353-7903
JOURNAL OF CONTEMPORARY RELIGION. 1984. 3/yr. £22 to individuals; institutions £94 (effective 1996). (Centre for New Religious Movements) Carfax Publishing Co., P.O. Box 25, Abingdon, Oxon. OX14 3UE, England. TEL 01235-555335. FAX 01235-553559. E-mail: elaineh@carfax.com. (Subscr. in N. America to: 875-81 Massachusetts Ave., Cambridge, MA 02139) Ed. Peter B. Clarke. adv.; bk.rev. circ. 500. **Indexed:** ASSIA. **Document type:** academic/scholarly publication.
—BLDSC (4965.240300). CCC.
Formerly (until 1995): Religion Today (ISSN 0267-1700)
Description: Provides a forum for discussion and analysis of new religions and trends and developments within mainstream churches.
Refereed Serial

JOURNAL OF COPTIC STUDIES. see HISTORY — History Of The Near East

291   II   ISSN 0253-7222
BL1
JOURNAL OF DHARMA; an international quarterly of world religions. 1975. q. Rs.80($28) (effective 1992). (Dharma Research Association) Dharmaram College, Centre for the Study of World Religions, Bangalore 560 029, India. TEL 80-5536866. FAX 80-5536046. Ed. Thomas Manninezhath; Pub. J.B. Chethimattam. adv.; bk.rev.; circ. 1,800 (paid). (also avail. in microfilm from UMI; reprint service avail. from ISI,UMI) **Indexed:** Arts & Hum.Cit.Ind., Curr.Cont., Phil.Ind., Rel.& Theol.Abstr. (1989-), Rel.Ind.One. **Document type:** academic/scholarly publication.
—BLDSC (4969.403000); Genuine Article; SWETS; UMI; UnCover.
Description: Serves as a forum for the exchange of ideas and experience regarding the approaches and methods to the problems related to man's religious quest.
Refereed Serial

209   US   ISSN 1067-6341
BR66
JOURNAL OF EARLY CHRISTIAN STUDIES. 1981; N.S. 1993. q. $33 to individuals (foreign $39.90); institutions $56 (foreign $62.90) (effective 1995). (North American Patristics Society) Johns Hopkins University Press, Journals Publishing Division, 2715 N. Charles St., Ste. 750, Baltimore, MD 21218-4319. TEL 410-516-6987; 800-548-1784. FAX 410-516-6968. Eds. Elizabeth A. Clark, Everett Ferguson. adv. contact: Tara Dorai-Berry. bk.rev. circ. 1,000. **Indexed:** IBR, Int.Z.Bibelwiss., New Test.Abstr., Rel.& Theol.Abstr. (1981-), Rel.Ind.One (1981-). **Document type:** academic/scholarly publication.
—BLDSC (4970.703000); Faxon; Genuine Article; UMI; UnCover.
Supersedes (in 1993): Second Century (ISSN 0276-7899); Incorporates (1972-1993): Patristics (ISSN 0360-652X)
Description: Publishes original scholarly studies on the early history and theology of the Christian church up to 600 CE.

209   UK   ISSN 0022-0469
BR140
JOURNAL OF ECCLESIASTICAL HISTORY. 1953. q. £99($175) (effective 1996). Cambridge University Press, Edinburgh Bldg., Shaftesbury Rd., Cambridge CB2 2RU, England. TEL 01223-312393. FAX 01223-315052. TELEX 851817256. (N. American addr.: Cambridge University Press, Journals Dept., 40 W. 20th St., New York, NY 10011. TEL 212-924-3900. FAX 212-691-3239) Eds. Diarmid McColloch, Martin Brett. adv.; bk.rev.; bibl.; index. (also avail. in microform from UMI; back issues avail.) **Indexed:** Amer.Hist.& Life, Arts & Hum.Cit.Ind., Br.Archaeol.Abstr., Br.Hum.Ind., CERDIC, Curr.Cont., G.Soc.Sci.& Rel.Per.Lit., Hist.Abstr., Hum.Ind., New Test.Abstr., Rel.& Theol.Abstr. (1967-), Rel.Ind.One, Rel.Per. **Document type:** academic/scholarly publication.
—BLDSC (4971.700000); Faxon; Genuine Article; SWETS; UMI; UnCover. CCC.
Description: Contains material on the history of the Christian Church as an institution and its relations with other religions and society.

260   US   ISSN 0022-0558
BX1
JOURNAL OF ECUMENICAL STUDIES. 1964. 4/yr. $27 (foreign $30). Temple University, 022-38, Philadelphia, PA 19122. TEL 215-204-7714. FAX 215-204-4569. Ed. Leonard Swidler. adv. contact: Nancy Krody. bk.rev.; abstr.; index. circ. 1,750. (also avail. in microfilm from WSH,PMC; reprint service avail. from WSH) **Indexed:** Amer.Bibl.Slavic & E.Eur.Stud., Amer.Hist.& Life, Arts & Hum.Cit.Ind., C.L.I., Cath.Ind., CERDIC, Curr.Cont., G.Soc.Sci.& Rel.Per.Lit., Hist.Abstr., Hum.Ind., Int.Z.Bibelwiss, Leg.Per., Mid.East: Abstr.& Ind., New Test.Abstr., Old Test.Abstr., Rel.& Theol.Abstr. (1970-), Rel.Ind.One, Rel.Per. **Document type:** academic/scholarly publication.
—BLDSC (4973.096000); Faxon; SWETS; UnCover.
Description: Scholarly and grassroots concern for interreligious and interideological dialogue worldwide, including English-language coverage of the literature and events from six continents.

RELIGIONS AND THEOLOGY

230   NE   ISSN 0922-2936
JOURNAL OF EMPIRICAL THEOLOGY. Key Title: J E T. Journal of Empirical Theology. (Text in English) 1988. 2/yr. fl.82.50($54) (effective 1994). (Universiteit van Nijmegen, Theologisch Instituut) Kok Pharos Publishing House, Postbus 5019, 8260 AG Kampen, Netherlands. TEL 31-5202-92565. FAX 31-5202-27331. (Dist. in U.S. and Canada by: Books International, Inc., Box 605, Herndon, VA 22070-0605. TEL 800-377-7192. FAX 703-689-0660) Ed.Bd. **Document type:** academic/scholarly publication.
    Description: Publishes theological articles which are directly or indirectly based on empirical research and empirical methodology, and which contribute to a deeper understanding of religion in modern times, in relation to the Christian tradition.

JOURNAL OF EUROPEAN STUDIES. see HISTORY — History Of Europe

JOURNAL OF FEMINIST STUDIES IN RELIGION. see WOMEN'S STUDIES

JOURNAL OF HEALTH CARE CHAPLAINCY. see PHYSICAL FITNESS AND HYGIENE

220 809   US   ISSN 1075-7139
▼**THE JOURNAL OF HIGHER CRITICISM.** 1994. s-a. $30 to individuals; institutions $50 (effective 1995). Institute for Higher Critical Studies, Drew University Theological School, 36 Madison Ave., Madison, NJ 07940. TEL 201-408-3000. Ed. Robert M. Price. adv.: B&W page $300; adv. contact: Robert M. Price. bk.rev. circ. 350. (back issues avail.) **Indexed:** New Test.Abstr. **Document type:** academic/scholarly publication.
    Description: Critical study of Old and New Testaments and related writings, from a radical methodological standpoint. Provides biblical scholars with a forum for fresh, controversial theories.
    Refereed Serial

JOURNAL OF HUMANISM & ETHICAL RELIGION. see PHILOSOPHY

JOURNAL OF LAW AND RELIGION. see LAW

200 157.63   US   ISSN 1053-8755
BV4460.3   CODEN: JMARE2
▼**JOURNAL OF MINISTRY IN ADDICTION & RECOVERY.** 1994. s-a. $75 (foreign $105) (effective 1996). Haworth Press, Inc., 10 Alice St., Binghamton, NY 13904. TEL 607-722-5857; 800-342-9678. FAX 607-722-1424. TELEX 4932599. Ed. Robert H. Albers. bk.rev. (also avail. in microfilm from UMI; reprint service avail. from HAW) **Indexed:** G.Soc.Sci.& Rel.Per.Lit., Human Resour.Abstr., IMFL, Past.Care & Couns.Abstr., Ref.Zh.
—Haworth.
    Description: Offers pastoral caregivers and others in the addiction field innovative approaches to treating a variety of addictive behaviors.
    Refereed Serial

658   US   ISSN 1057-1523
▼**JOURNAL OF MINISTRY MARKETING & MANAGEMENT.** 1995. s-a. $48 (foreign $67.20) (effective 1996). Haworth Press, Inc., 10 Alice St., Binghamton, NY 13904. TEL 607-722-5857; 800-342-9678. FAX 607-722-1424. Eds. David Loudon, Robert E. Stevens. adv.: page $300. bk.rev. (also avail. in microfiche from UMI)
—Haworth.
    Description: Provides practical information on marketing and management issues in all types of church and ministry settings.
    Refereed Serial

250   US   ISSN 0022-3409
BV4000   CODEN: JPACA8
THE JOURNAL OF PASTORAL CARE. 1947. q. $22.95 to individuals (foreign $25.25): institutions $27.95 (foreign $30.75). Journal of Pastoral Care Publications, Inc., 1549 Clairmont Rd., Ste. 103, Decatur, GA 30033-4611. TEL 404-320-0195. FAX 404-320-0849. (Subscr. to: Journal of Pastoral Care, Subscription Dept., c/o Kutztown Publishing Co., Box 346, Kutztown, PA 19530) Ed. Orlo Strunk. adv. contact: Janet H. Emerson. bk.rev.; index. circ. 10,500. (also avail. in microfilm from UMI; reprint service avail. from UMI) **Indexed:** ASSIA, CERDIC, Mid.East: Abstr.& Ind., Past.Care & Couns.Abstr., Psychol.Abstr., Rel.& Theol.Abstr. (1968-), Rel.Ind.One, Rel.Per., Soc.Work Res.& Abstr. **Document type:** academic/scholarly publication.
—BLDSC (5029.500000); UMI; UnCover.
    Description: Includes articles that reflect the cutting edges of clinical pastoral education and the pastoral counseling movements.

JOURNAL OF PSYCHOLOGY AND CHRISTIANITY. see PSYCHOLOGY

JOURNAL OF PSYCHOLOGY AND THEOLOGY; an evangelical forum for the integration of psychology and theology. see PSYCHOLOGY

200   US   ISSN 0022-4189
BR1
JOURNAL OF RELIGION. 1882. q. $24 to individuals; institutions $48; students $18. University of Chicago Press, Journals Division, 5720 S. Woodlawn Ave., Chicago, IL 60637. TEL 312-753-3347. FAX 312-753-0811. TELEX 25-4603. (Subscr. to: Box 37005, Chicago, IL 60637) Ed.Bd. adv.; bk.rev.; index. circ. 2,200. (also avail. in microform from MIM,UMI,PMC; reprint service avail. from UMI,ISI) **Indexed:** Acad.Ind., Amer.Hist.& Life, Arts & Hum.Cit.Ind., Bibl.Engl.Lang.& Lit., Bk.Rev.Dig., Bk.Rev.Ind. (1965-), Child.Bk.Rev.Ind. (1965-), Curr.Cont., G.Soc.Sci.& Rel.Per.Lit., Hist.Abstr., Hum.Ind., Int.Z.Bibelwiss., Mid.East: Abstr.& Ind., New Test.Abstr., Old Test.Abstr., Rel.& Theol.Abstr. (1971-), Rel.Ind.One, Rel.Per., SSCI. **Document type:** academic/scholarly publication.
—BLDSC (5049.200000); Faxon; Genuine Article; SWETS; UMI; UnCover. **CCC.**
    Refereed Serial

200 150   US   ISSN 0022-4197
RC321   CODEN: JRHEAT
JOURNAL OF RELIGION AND HEALTH. 1961. q. $240 (foreign $280) (effective 1996). (Institute of Religion) Human Sciences Press, Inc. (Subsidiary of: Plenum Publishing Corp.), 233 Spring St., New York, NY 10013-1578. TEL 212-620-8000. FAX 212-463-0742. TELEX 12-421139. (Co-sponsor: Institute of Health) Eds. Ann & Barry Ulanov. adv.; bk.rev.; charts; index. circ. (also avail. in microform from UMI; reprint service avail. from ISI,UMI) **Indexed:** Arts & Hum.Cit.Ind., Curr.Cont., Excerp.Med., G.Soc.Sci.& Rel.Per.Lit., Ind.Jew.Per., Mid.East: Abstr.& Ind., Past.Care & Couns.Abstr., Psychol.Abstr., Rel.& Theol.Abstr. (1969-), Rel.Ind.One, SSCI. **Document type:** academic/scholarly publication.
—BLDSC (5049.350000); Faxon; Genuine Article; SWETS; UMI; UnCover. **CCC.**
    Description: Explores contemporary modes of religious thought with emphasis on its relevance to current medical and psychological research.
    Refereed Serial

JOURNAL OF RELIGION & PSYCHICAL RESEARCH; a scholarly quarterly dealing with religion, psychical research, and related topics. see PARAPSYCHOLOGY AND OCCULTISM

291   NE   ISSN 0022-4200
BL2400
JOURNAL OF RELIGION IN AFRICA. (Supplement avail.: Studies on Religion in Africa (ISSN 0169-9814)) (Text in English and French) 1967. 4/yr. fl.148($95) to individuals; institutions fl.200($129) (effective 1996). E.J. Brill, P.O. Box 9000, 2300 PA Leiden, Netherlands. TEL 31-71-5353500. FAX 31-71-5317532. TELEX 39296 BRILL NL. E-mail: ejborders@ejbrill.com. (In N. America: E.J. Brill, 24 Hudson St., Kinderhook, NY 12106. TEL 800-962-4406. FAX 518-758-1959) Ed. Adrian Hastings. bk.rev.; bibl.; charts; illus. **Indexed:** Amer.Hist.& Life (until 1992), Arts & Hum.Cit.Ind., CERDIC, Curr.Cont., Curr.Cont.Africa, Documentatieblad, Hist.Abstr. (until 1992), Rel.& Theol.Abstr. (1989-), Rel.Ind.One, Rel.Per. **Document type:** academic/scholarly publication.
—Faxon; SWETS; UnCover. **CCC.**
    Description: Studies of the forms and history of religion on the African continent, with particular emphasis on sub-Saharan Africa and the relationships between Christianity and Islam in the region.
    Refereed Serial

200 362.4   US   ISSN 1059-9258
BV4460   CODEN: JRDRFJ
JOURNAL OF RELIGION IN DISABILITY & REHABILITATION; innovations in ministry for independent living. 1993. q. $75 (foreign $105) (effective 1996). Haworth Press, Inc. (Subsidiary of: Haworth Pastoral Press), 10 Alice St., Binghamton, NY 13904-1580. TEL 607-722-5857; 800-342-9678. FAX 607-722-1424. Eds. William A. Blair, Dana Y. Davidson. adv.: B&W page $300. bk.rev. (also avail. in microfiche; microform from UMI) **Indexed:** Abstr.Anthropol., ASSIA, CINAHL, Human Resour.Abstr., IMFL, Past.Care & Couns.Abstr., Per.Islam., Sage Fam.Stud.Abstr. **Document type:** academic/scholarly publication.
—BLDSC (5049.352200); Haworth.
    Description: Informs religious professionals about developments in the field of disability and rehabilitation in order to facilitate greater contributions on the part of pastors, religious educators, and pastoral counselors.
    Refereed Serial

200   US   ISSN 1045-5876
BV4012
JOURNAL OF RELIGION IN PSYCHOTHERAPY. 1952. q. $60 (foreign $84) (effective Mar. 1995). (Princeton Theological Seminary) Haworth Press, Inc., 10 Alice St., Binghamton, NY 13904. TEL 607-722-5857; 800-342-9678. FAX 607-722-1424. TELEX 4932599. Ed. William M. Clements. adv.; bk.rev. (also avail. in microform from HAW,UMI; reprint service avail. from HAW,ISI,UMI) **Indexed:** CCR, CERDIC, Curr.Cont., G.Soc.Sci.& Rel.Per.Lit., Past.Care & Couns.Abstr., Psychol.Abstr., Rel.& Theol.Abstr. (1987-), Rel.Ind.One, Rel.Per., Soc.Work Res.& Abstr., SSCI. **Document type:** academic/scholarly publication.
—BLDSC (5029.820000); Haworth.
    Formerly (until 1990): Journal of Pastoral Psychotherapy (ISSN 0886-5477)
    Description: For therapists and researchers who are interested in the role and dynamic of religion in the healing process of psychotherapy.
    Refereed Serial

200   US   ISSN 1047-7845
Z7753   CODEN: JRTIE3
JOURNAL OF RELIGIOUS & THEOLOGICAL INFORMATION. 1993. s-a. $48 (foreign $67.20) (effective 1996). Haworth Press, Inc., 10 Alice St., Binghamton, NY 13904-1580. TEL 607-722-5857; 800-342-9678. FAX 607-722-1424. TELEX 4932599. Ed. William C. Miller. (also avail. in microform from UMI; reprint service avail. from HAW) **Indexed:** Abstr.Anthropol., Educ.Admin.Abstr., G.Soc.Sci.& Rel.Per.Lit., Human Resour.Abstr., Inform.Sci.Abstr., INSPEC (1993-), LISA, New Test.Abstr., Past.Care & Couns.Abstr., Ref.Zh., Rel.& Theol.Abstr.
—BLDSC (5049.352700); Haworth; UnCover.
    Description: Presents articles pertaining to the production, dissemination, preservation, & bibliography of religious and theological information.
    Refereed Serial

RELIGIONS AND THEOLOGY

200 US ISSN 0384-9694
BJ1
JOURNAL OF RELIGIOUS ETHICS. 1973. s-a. $18 to individuals; institutions $24. (Religious Ethics, Inc.) Scholars Press, Box 15399, Atlanta, GA 30333-0399. TEL 404-727-2320. FAX 404-727-2348. Ed. Diane Yeager. circ. 1,200. (also avail. in microform from UMI; reprint service avail. from UMI) **Indexed:** Arts & Hum.Cit.Ind., CERDIC, Curr.Cont., Hum.Ind., Old Test.Abstr., Phil.Ind., Rel.& Theol.Abstr. (1978-), Rel.Ind.One, Rel.Per. **Document type:** academic/scholarly publication.
—BLDSC (5049.353000); Faxon; Genuine Article; UMI; UnCover.
Description: Explores various aspects of religious ethics.

JOURNAL OF RELIGIOUS GERONTOLOGY. see GERONTOLOGY AND GERIATRICS

209 UK ISSN 0022-4227
BR140
JOURNAL OF RELIGIOUS HISTORY. 1960. s-a. £67($108) (foreign £67) (effective 1996). (Association for the Journal of Religious History, AT) Basil Blackwell Ltd., 108 Cowley Rd., Oxford, OX4 1JF, England. Ed. A.E. Cahill. bk.rev.; bibl.; index, cum.index every 2 yrs. circ. 700. (also avail. in microform) **Indexed:** Amer.Hist.& Life, Arts & Hum.Cit.Ind., Aus.P.A.I.S., CERDIC, Curr.Cont., Hist.Abstr., Mid.East: Abstr.& Ind., Rel.& Theol.Abstr. (1978-), Rel.Ind.One, Rel.Per. **Document type:** academic/scholarly publication.
—BLDSC (5049.355000); Faxon; Genuine Article; SWETS; UMI; UnCover. **CCC.**

200 CN ISSN 1183-3262
JOURNAL OF RELIGIOUS PLURALISM. 1991. a. $15. McGill University, Faculty of Religious Studies, 3520 University St., Montreal, PQ H3A 2A7, Canada. TEL 514-398-6138. Eds. Kathleen M. Dugan, Arvind Sharma.
Description: Provides a forum for the discussion of religious pluralism as represented by plurality of religious traditions, a plurality of methods of studying religions, and a plurality of new religious movements.

200 II ISSN 0047-2735
BL1
THE JOURNAL OF RELIGIOUS STUDIES. (Text and summaries in English) 1969. s-a. Rs.100. Punjabi University, Department of Religious Studies, c/o S. Tirath Singh, Registrar, Punjabi University, Patiala, India. TEL 78561. Ed. Nirbhai Singh. bk.rev. circ. 800. **Indexed:** New Test.Abstr., Rel.Ind.One.
—UnCover.
Description: Covers religion, theology and philosophy.

200 US ISSN 0193-3604
JOURNAL OF RELIGIOUS STUDIES. 1972. s-a. $4. Cleveland State University, Department of Religion, Cleveland, OH 44115. Ed. Frederick Holck. adv.; bk.rev.; illus. circ. 1,200. (back issues avail.) **Indexed:** CERDIC, New Test.Abstr., Rel.Ind.One, Rel.Per.
—BLDSC (5049.356000).
Formerly: Ohio Journal of Religious Studies (ISSN 0094-5668)

700 US ISSN 0022-4235
BR1
JOURNAL OF RELIGIOUS THOUGHT. 1943. s-a. $12 to individuals; institutions $14; students $22. (Howard University, School of Divinity) Howard University Press, 1240 Randolph St., N.E., Washington, DC 20017. TEL 202-806-4935. FAX 202-806-4946. Ed. Cain H. Felder. adv.; bk.rev.; bibl.; cum.index. circ. 1,500. (also avail. in microform from UMI; reprint service avail. from UMI) **Indexed:** Amer.Hist.& Life, Hist.Abstr., Ind.Sel.Per., Mid.East: Abstr.& Ind., New Test.Abstr., Rel.& Theol.Abstr. (1966-), Rel.Ind.One, Rel.Per.
●Also available online. Vendor(s): University Microfilms International.
—BLDSC (5049.360000); Faxon; UMI; UnCover.
Description: Contains articles from persons of varied theological and ethnic backgrounds.

JOURNAL OF SPIRITUAL HEALTH. see ALTERNATIVE MEDICINE

377.8 US ISSN 0160-7774
BV4012
JOURNAL OF SUPERVISION AND TRAINING IN MINISTRY. 1978. a. $20 (foreign $25). Journal of Pastoral Care Publications, Inc., 1549 Clairmont Rd., Ste. 103, Decatur, GA 30033-4611. TEL 404-320-0195. FAX 404-320-0849. Ed. George Fitchett. adv.; bk.rev. circ. 1,000. **Indexed:** Rel.Ind.One, Rel.Per. **Document type:** academic/scholarly publication.
—BLDSC (5067.120000).
Description: Covers issues related to the training and supervision of ministers and chaplains.

200 150 CN ISSN 1192-3830
JOURNAL OF THE PSYCHOLOGY OF RELIGION. 1992. a. Can.$15. McGill University, Faculty of Religious Studies, 3520 University St., Montreal, PQ H3A 2A7, Canada. TEL 514-398-6138. Eds. Kaisa Puhakka, Arvind Sharma. **Document type:** academic/scholarly publication.
Description: Forum for drawing impartially on all branches of psychology to shed light on religious phenomena to overcome current compartmentalizations.

230 UK ISSN 0022-5185
BR1
JOURNAL OF THEOLOGICAL STUDIES. 1899. s-a. £82($160) (effective 1996). Oxford University Press, Oxford Journals, Walton St., Oxford OX2 6DP, England. TEL 01865-267907. FAX 01865-267773. TELEX 837330-OXPRES-G. E-mail: jnlorders@oup.co.uk. (U.S. subscr. to: Oxford University Press Inc., 2001 Evans Rd., Cary, NC 27513. TEL 919-677-0977. FAX 919-677-1714) Ed.Bd. adv. contact: Jane Parker. bk.rev.; abstr.; bibl.; charts; illus.; index. circ. 1,550. (also avail. in microform from UMI) **Indexed:** Arts & Hum.Cit.Ind., Bibl.Ling., Br.Hum.Ind., CERDIC, Curr.Cont., M.L.A., New Test.Abstr., Old Test.Abstr., Rel.& Theol.Abstr. (1968-), Rel.Ind.One, Rel.Per. **Document type:** academic/scholarly publication.
—BLDSC (5069.070000); Faxon; Genuine Article; SWETS; UMI; UnCover. **CCC.**
Description: Academic study of Christian theology: Old and New Testaments, Church history, philosophy of religion and ethics.

200 SA ISSN 0047-2867
BR1
JOURNAL OF THEOLOGY FOR SOUTHERN AFRICA. 1972. q. R.25 to individuals (Africa $15; elsewhere R.40 or $35); institutions and libraries R.30 (Africa $20; elsewhere R.60 or $55) (effective 1995). c/o University of Cape Town, Department of Religious Studies, Rondebosch 7700, South Africa. TEL 27-21-650-3453. FAX 27-21-650-3761. E-mail: NAN@SOCSCI.UCT.AC.ZA. Ed. John W. de Gruchy. adv.; bk.rev.; abstr.; index. circ. 1,000. (also avail. in microfilm from UMI,WMP) **Indexed:** CERDIC, Ind.S.A.Per., New Test.Abstr., Old Test.Abstr., Rel.& Theol.Abstr. (1989-), Rel.Ind.One. **Document type:** academic/scholarly publication.
—BLDSC (5069.074000); UMI.
Refereed Serial

JOURNAL OF TRANSLATION AND TEXTLINGUISTICS. see LINGUISTICS

JOURNAL OF WOMEN AND RELIGION. see WOMEN'S STUDIES

JR. HIGH MINISTRY MAGAZINE. see CHILDREN AND YOUTH — About

JUDAICA BOHEMIAE. see ETHNIC INTERESTS

200 100 BN ISSN 0350-6398
JUKIC; zbornik radova. (Text in Croatian) 1971. a. 5500 din.($7) Zbor Franjevackih Bogoslova "Jukic", Aleja Branka Bujica 111, 71000 Sarajevo, Bosnia Hercegovina. TEL 071-453-266. circ. 1,000. (back issues avail.)

JUL I FAMILIEN. see CHILDREN AND YOUTH — For

268 AU ISSN 0022-6289
JUNGE GEMEINDE. 1948. q. S.20. Evangelisches Jugendwerk in Oesterreich, Liechtensteinstr. 20, A-1090 Vienna, Austria. FAX 0222-34926716. Ed. Thomas Dasek. adv.; bk.rev.; abstr. circ. 2,600. (tabloid format) **Document type:** consumer publication.
Description: Contains information of interest to those involved in evangelical work with Austrian youth. Includes readers' letters, reports and announcements of events.

200 GW ISSN 0022-6319
BX8001
JUNGE KIRCHE; Zeitschrift europaeischer Christinnen und Christen. 1933. m. DM.66. Verlag Junge Kirche, Mathildenstr. 86, 28203 Bremen, Germany. TEL 0421-71648. FAX 0421-71939. Ed.Bd. adv.; bk.rev.; index. circ. 6,800. **Indexed:** CERDIC. **Document type:** academic/scholarly publication.
Description: Christian socialist publication with articles about religion, politics, ecumenical isseues, justice, peace and the integrity of creation.

268 GW ISSN 0022-6467
JUNGSCHARHELFER; Mitarbeiterhilfe fuer Jungen- und Maedchenarbeit. 1954. q. DM.25.60. (Gemeindejugendwerk) Oncken Verlag GmbH, Muendener Str. 13, 34123 Kassel, Germany. TEL 0561-52005-0. Ed. Kay Moritz. bk.rev. circ. 2,100. (tabloid format) **Document type:** bulletin.
—CCC.

200 UK ISSN 0306-7645
JUSTPEACE. 1936. 8/yr. £12 to individuals; institutions £20. Pax Christi, Christian Peace Education Centre, 9 Henry Rd., London N4 2LH, England. TEL 0181-800-4612. FAX 0181-802-3223. Ed. Brian Wicker. adv.; bk.rev. circ. 2,000. **Document type:** newsletter.
Formerly: Pax Bulletin (ISSN 0031-3319)
Description: News items, letters, and calendar of events pertaining to Christian pacifism and the activities and members of the international Catholic peace movement.

200 MW
KACHERE TEXTS. 1979-1993; N.S. 1995. irreg. price varies. Chancellor College, Department of Theology and Religious Studies, Box 280, Zomba, Malawi. FAX 265-50-522046. TELEX 44742 CHANCOLL MI. circ. 500 (controlled).
Former titles (until 1993): Sources for the Study of Religion in Malawi; (until 1980): Chancellor College. Department of Religious Studies. Staff Seminar Paper.

KACIC. see HISTORY — History Of Europe

200 AU ISSN 0022-7757
BL1
KAIROS; Zeitschrift fuer Religionswissenschaft und Theologie. 1959. q. S.380. Otto Mueller Verlag, Postfach 167, A-5021 Salzburg, Austria. TEL 0662-881974-0. FAX 0662-872387. Ed.Bd. adv.; bk.rev.; bibl.; index. circ. 700. **Indexed:** CERDIC, New Test.Abstr., Rel.Ind.One, Rel.Per. **Document type:** academic/scholarly publication.
—BLDSC (5081.400000).

200 GW ISSN 0022-779X
KAISERSWERTHER MITTEILUNGEN. 1836. 3/yr. free. Diakoniewerk Kaiserswerth, Alte Landstr. 179, 40489 Duesseldorf, Germany. TEL 0211-4093718. FAX 0211-4092111. Eds. J. Degen, M. Klaemmt. bk.rev.; illus. circ. 26,000.

200 II ISSN 0022-8028
KALYAN. (Text in Hindi) 1927. m. Rs.38($7) Gita Press, Sagdesh Psesad Jalan, Gorakhpur, India. Ed.Bd.

KANDELAAR. see EDUCATION

KANON. see LAW

RELIGIONS AND THEOLOGY

200 VC
KANONIKA. (Text in English, French, German, Greek, Italian) 1992. irreg., no.7, 1992. price varies. (Pontificium Institutum Studiorum Orientalium, Facultas Iuris Canonici - Pontifical Oriental Institute, Canon Law Faculty) Edizioni Orientalia Cristiana, Piazza S. Maria Maggiore, 7, 00185 Rome, Italy. TEL 06-446-5589. FAX 06-446-5576. Ed. George Nedungatt, S.J. circ. 1,000. **Document type:** monographic series.
   Description: Covers the law of the Eastern Churches.

200 GW ISSN 0022-9245
KASSELER SONNTAGSBLATT; christliches Familienblatt fuer Deutschland. 1879. w. DM.102. Kasseler Sonntagsblatt Verlagsgesellschaft mbH, Werner-Heisenberg-Str. 7, 34123 Kassel, Germany. TEL 0561-959250. FAX 0561-9592568. Ed. Rolf Schwarz. adv.; bk.rev.; illus.; mkt. circ. 40,000. (tabloid format) **Document type:** newsletter.

200 GW ISSN 0939-3137
KATHOLISCHER ARBEITSKREIS FUER ZEITGESCHICHTLICHE FRAGEN. OST-WEST INFORMATIONSDIENST. 1961. q. Katholischer Arbeitskreis fuer Zeitgeschichtliche Fragen e.V., Hochkreuzallee 246, 53175 Bonn, Germany. Ed. Michael Albus. circ. 1,600. **Document type:** bulletin.
   Formerly: Katholischer Arbeitskreis fuer Zeitgeschichtliche Fragen. Informationsdienst (ISSN 0176-5493)

KATOLIKUS MAGYAROK VASARNAPJA/CATHOLIC HUNGARIANS' SUNDAY. see *RELIGIONS AND THEOLOGY — Roman Catholic*

200 952 JA ISSN 0917-818X
KENKYUJOHO. Variant title: Nanzan Shukyo Bunka Kenkyujo Kenkyujoho. (Text in Japanese) 1991. a. free. Nanzan University, Nanzan Institute for Religion and Culture, 18 Yamazato-cho, Showa-ku, Nagoya-shi, Aichi-ken 466, Japan. TEL 052-832-3111. FAX 052-832-6157. **Document type:** academic/scholarly publication.

200 NE ISSN 0165-2346
KERK EN THEOLOGIE. 1950. q. fl.90 (students fl.72). Boekencentrum B.V., P.O. Box 29, 2700 AA Zoetermeer, Netherlands. TEL 31-79-615481. FAX 31-79-615489. Ed. A.S. van der Woude. **Document type:** academic/scholarly publication.
   Formerly: Onder Eigen Vaandel.
   Description: Publishes articles on exegesis, hermeneutics, theological praxis and related topics.

230 NE ISSN 0922-9086
KERK EN THEOLOGIE IN CONTEXT. (Text in English, French) 1988. irreg., vol.24, 1994. price varies. Kok Pharos Publishing House, Postbus 5019, 8260 AG Kampen, Netherlands. TEL 31-5202-92565. FAX 32-5202-27331. (Dist. in U.S. and Canada by: Books International, Inc., Box 605, Herndon, VA 22707-0605. TEL 800-377-7192. FAX 703-689-0660) (back issues avail.) **Document type:** monographic series, proceedings.
   Description: Publishes studies of contemporary issues in Christian theology, with a focus on regional, cultural and non-Western concerns.

200 327 NE ISSN 0924-5596
KERK EN VREDE. 1925. 6/yr. fl.55. Kerk en Vrede, Postbus 2119, 3500 GC Utrecht, Netherlands. Ed. Henk Eisma. adv.; bk.rev.; abstr. circ. 3,100. **Indexed:** CERDIC.
   Formerly: Militia Christi (ISSN 0026-4156)
   Description: Discusses theological aspects of nonviolence through the subjects of social justice, confession, conscientious objection and peace education.

270 NE ISSN 0169-8451
KERKHISTORISCHE BIJDRAGEN. 1970. irreg., vol.17, 1995. price varies. E.J. Brill, P.O. Box 9000, 2300 PA Leiden, Netherlands. TEL 31-71-5353500. FAX 31-71-5317532. TELEX 39296 BRILL NL. (In N. America: E.J. Brill, 24 Hudson St., Kinderhook, NY 12106. TEL 800-962-4406. FAX 518-758-1959) (back issues avail.) **Document type:** monographic series.
   Refereed Serial

200 NE ISSN 0023-0685
KERUGMA. 1957. 6/yr. fl.52.25. Gooi en Sticht, Postbus 133, 3740 AC Baarn, Netherlands. TEL 31-2154-15320. FAX 31-2154-20658. Eds. B. Robben, A. Willems. **Indexed:** CERDIC.

200 GW ISSN 0023-0707
BR4
KERYGMA UND DOGMA; Zeitschrift fuer theologische Forschung und kirchliche Lehre. 1955. q. DM.84. Vandenhoeck und Ruprecht, Robert-Bosch-Breite 6, 37079 Goettingen, Germany. TEL 0551-6959-26. FAX 0551-695917. (Subscr. to: 37070 Goettingen, Germany) Ed.Bd. adv.; bk.rev.; index. circ. 1,300. **Indexed:** CERDIC, New Test.Abstr., Old Test.Abstr., Rel.& Theol.Abstr. (1970-), Rel.Ind.One, Rel.Per. **Document type:** academic/scholarly publication.
—BLDSC (5090.370000); Faxon; SWETS. **CCC.**

KEY TO CHRISTIAN EDUCATION. see *EDUCATION*

268 NE ISSN 0023-1444
KIND EN ZONDAG. 1930. m. fl.78. Nederlandse Zondagsschool Vereeniging, Bloemgracht 65, 1016 KG Amsterdam, Netherlands. Ed. C.M. Wigmans. adv.; bk.rev. circ. 20,000.

200 GW ISSN 0341-7190
KINDERGOTTESDIENST/LASS MICH HOEREN. 1890. q. DM.30.30. Guetersloher Verlagshaus Chr. Kaiser, Carl-Bertelsmann-Str. 270, 33311 Guetersloh, Germany. TEL 05241-7405-0. FAX 05241-740548. (Subscr. to: Bechauf Verlag, Friedrichstr. 48, 33615 Bielefeld, Germany) **Document type:** bulletin.

200 US ISSN 0023-1614
KINGDOM DIGEST.* vol.29, 1968. m. $10. Box 171345, Irving, TX 75017-1345. bk.rev.; bibl. **Indexed:** CERDIC.

KINSHIP. see *SOCIAL SERVICES AND WELFARE*

200 TZ
KIPALAPALA LEO. (Text in English, Swahili) vol.29, 1989. a. $1. St. Paul's Senior Seminary, P.O. Box 325, Tabora, Tanzania. TEL 255-51-2532. Ed. Deac. John Tenamwenye. **Indexed:** P.L.E.S.A. **Document type:** academic/scholarly publication.
   Description: Offers scholarly commentary on the African Synod in Tanzania.

KIRCHE IN MARBURG; Mitteilungen der evangelischen und Katholischen Gemeinden. see *RELIGIONS AND THEOLOGY — Roman Catholic*

200 GW ISSN 0453-929X
KIRCHE UND KONFESSION. 1962. irreg. (Konfessionskundliche Institut des Ev. Bundes) Vandenhoeck und Ruprecht, Robert-Bosch-Breite 6, 37079 Goettingen, Germany. TEL 0551-6959-0. FAX 0551-695917. (Subscr. to: 37070 Goettingen, Germany) **Document type:** monographic series.

KIRCHE UND RECHT. see *LAW*

KIRCHENMUSIKALISCHE NACHRICHTEN. see *MUSIC*

DER KIRCHENMUSIKER. see *MUSIC*

KIRCHLICHE ZEITGESCHICHTE; Internationale Halbjahresschrift fuer Theologie und Geschichtswissenschaft. see *HISTORY — History Of Europe*

200 GW ISSN 0023-1827
KIRCHLICHES AMTSBLATT FUER DAS BISTUM ESSEN. 1958. s-m. DM.34. Bischoefliches Generalvikariat Essen, Zwoelfling 16, 45127 Essen, Germany. index. circ. 2,200. (looseleaf format)

200 GW
KIRCHLICHES AMTSBLATT FUER DAS BISTUM TRIER. 1853. s-m. DM.30. Bischoefliches Generalvikariat Trier, Hinter dem Dom 6, 54290 Trier, Germany. TEL 0651-71050. FAX 0651-7105498. index. circ. 3,000. (back issues avail.) **Document type:** newsletter.
   Description: Provides official documentation of Diocesan regulations and laws.

058.82 NO ISSN 0023-186X
AP45
KIRKE OG KULTUR. 1894. bi-m. NOK 450 in Nordic countries; elsewhere $87 (effective 1996). Scandinavian University Press, P.O. Box 2959 Toeyen, N-0608 Oslo, Norway. TEL 47-22-57-54-00. FAX 47-22-57-53-53. (Dist. in U.S. by: Scandinavian University Press, 200 Meacham Ave., Elmont, NY 11003. TEL 516-352-7300) Ed. Inge Loenning. adv.; bk.rev.; index. circ. 2,500. (back issues avail.) **Indexed:** Bibl.Engl.Lang.& Lit, M.L.A.
   Formerly: For Kirke og Kultur.
   Description: Presents essays and debate on topics within culture, ethics, religion, philosophy and society.

280.4 DK ISSN 0107-9824
KIRKEFONDETS AARBOG. 1929. a. DKK 50. Kirkefondet, Pile Alle 3, 2000 Frederiksberg, Denmark. TEL 31-233-355. adv.; illus. circ. 6,000.
   Formerly: Koebenhavnske Kirkefondets Aarbog.

280.4 DK ISSN 0900-1433
KIRKENS UNDERVISNING; tidskrift for medarbejdere. 1985. 4/yr. DKK 100. Evangelisk Paedagogisk Samvirke, Religionspedagogisk Center, Frederiksberg Alle 10A, DK-1820 Frederiksberg C, Denmark. TEL 45-31-24-92-50. FAX 45-33-25-06-07. Ed. Henning Noerhoej. adv.; bk.rev. **Document type:** trade publication.
   Formerly: Episkopet (ISSN 0105-6867)

KIZITO; a children's magazine. see *CHILDREN AND YOUTH — For*

KNANAYAMITHRAM; a Christian magazine for children. see *CHILDREN AND YOUTH — For*

209 DK ISSN 0105-4821
KOEBENHAVNS UNIVERSITET. INSTITUT FOR RELIGIONSHISTORIE. SKRIFTER. 1976. irreg. Koebenhavns Universitet, Institut for Religionshistorie, Copenhagen, Denmark. **Document type:** academic/scholarly publication.

284 SA ISSN 0023-270X
KOERS; bulletin vir Christelike wetenskap - bulletin for Christian scholarship. (Text in Afrikaans, English; summaries in English) 1934. 4/yr. R.36($16) (DM.24). (Potchefstroom University for Christian Higher Education - Potchefstroomse Universiteit vir Christelike Hoer Onderwys) Buro vir Wetenskaplike Tydskrifte - Bureau for Scholarly Journals, Private Bag X6001, Potchefstroom 2520, South Africa. TEL 27-148-2991769. FAX 27-148-2991562. E-mail: BWTMV@Puknet.Puk.AC.ZA. (Co-sponsor: Die Koersvereniging) Ed. Annette L. Combrink. bk.rev.; abstr.; index. circ. 350. **Indexed:** Ind.S.A.Per. **Document type:** academic/scholarly publication.
   Refereed Serial

KORRESPONDENZBLATT EVANGELISCHER SCHULEN UND HEIME. see *EDUCATION*

299.93 DK ISSN 0107-7902
KOSMOS. English edition (ISSN 0107-7929); German edition (ISSN 0107-7937); Swedish edition (ISSN 0107-7910) 1978. m. (Danish and Swedish eds.); 6/yr. (English and German eds.) DKK 320($16) Martinus Institut, Mariendalsvej 94, DK-2000 Frederiksberg, Denmark. TEL 45-38-34-62-80. FAX 45-38-34-61-80. Ed.Bd. bk.rev. circ. 1,770 (900 Danish ed., 100 English ed., 70 German ed., 700 Swedish ed.). **Indexed:** Chem.Abstr.
   Formerly: Contact with the Martinus Institute of Spiritual Science.
   Description: Includes articles on spiritual science based on the work of the Danish writer, Martinus.

200 NE ISSN 0023-4389
KRACHT VAN OMHOOG. 1937. 6/yr. fl.25. Postbus 84, 4200 AB Gorinchem, Netherlands. Ed. P. Bronsveld. bk.rev.; illus.; tr.lit. circ. 2,500.

200 XR ISSN 0023-4613
KRESTANSKA REVUE. 1927-1939; resumed 1946. 10/yr. 50 Kc.($20) Oikumene Akademicka Y M C A, Na Porici 12, 115 30 Prague 1, Czech Republic. Ed. Jan Simsa. bk.rev. circ. 1,800. **Indexed:** CERDIC.

205 DK ISSN 0106-6749
KRITISK FORUM. 1980. q. DKK 175. (Religionspaedagogisk Center) Anis Forlag, Frederiksberg Alle 10A, DK-1820 Frederiksberg C, Denmark. TEL 45-31-24-92-50. FAX 45-33-25-06-07.

5700 RELIGIONS AND THEOLOGY

200 NE
KRUISTOCHT. m. Nationaal Kruisleger, Nieuwe Boteringestraat 73, 9712 PK Groningen, Netherlands. TEL 31-50-3181520. bk.rev. circ. 10,000.

200 II
KUNDALINI; a quarterly magazine of international spiritual & scientific progress. (Text in English) 1977. q. Rs.16($8) Kundalini Research and Publication Trust, D-291 Sarvodaya Enclave, New Delhi 110017, India. Ed. Anil Vidyalankar. adv.; bk.rev. circ. 4,000. (back issues avail.) **Indexed:** Ind.India.
Formerly (until 1979): Spiritual India.

200 GW
KURIER (LIESBORN); der christlichen Mitte. 1988. m. DM.30. Christliche Mitte, Lippstaedterstr. 42, 59329 Liesborn, Germany. TEL 02523-8388. FAX 02523-6138. Ed. Adelgunde Mertensacker. bk.rev. circ. 19,000. **Document type:** newsletter.

266 KO
KUSEGONGBO. (Text in Korean) 1909. m. $1. Salvation Army, C.P.O. Box 1192, Seoul 100, S. Korea. Eds. Captain Han, Kwang-Soo. circ. 15,000. **Document type:** newspaper.

KVINNOR OCH FUNDAMENTALISM. see WOMEN'S INTERESTS

262.9 340.5 SW ISSN 0023-6136
KYRKOFOERFATTNINGAR. 1957. bi-m. SEK 252 (effective 1995). Verbum Foerlag AB, P.O. Box 15169, S-104 65 Stockholm, Sweden. TEL 46-8-743-65-00. FAX 46-8-641-45-85. Ed. Ulla Granarp. charts; index; circ. 2,000. (controlled).
—BLDSC (5134.981000).
Description: Publishes new ecclesiastical law and ordinances for the Church of Sweden; also some common law.

209 SW ISSN 0085-2619
BR140
KYRKOHISTORISK AARSSKRIFT. (Text in English, Swedish; summaries in English, French, German) 1900. a. SEK 175. (Svenska Kyrkohistoriska Foereningen) Uppsala Universitet, Teologiska Institutionen, Box 1604, S-751 46, Sweden. FAX 46-18-12-68-75. Ed. Harry Lenhammar. adv.; bk.rev. circ. 1,000. **Indexed:** Amer.Hist.& Life, Hist.Abstr., NAA.

KYRKOMUSIKERNAS TIDNING. see MUSIC

200 PE ISSN 0360-3350
BX1425.A1
L A D O C. (Text in English) 1970. bi-m. $10 (Latin America $20; elsewhere $25) (effective 1995). Latin American Documentation, Apdo. 18-0964, Lima 18, Peru. TEL 51-14-475210. FAX 51-14-45681. Ed. Maeve O'Driscoll. adv. contact: Henry Sanchez. circ. 850. (also avail. in microform) **Indexed:** Cath.Ind., CERDIC, HR Rep. —UMI.
Description: Selects materials representative of the broad range of issues facing the Latin American people from their churches' magazines and documents.

200 IT
LABRYS. (Text in Italian; summaries in English) 1980. a. L.15000($18) Istituto di Studi Tradizionali, Via Roscetto 22, 06100 Perugia PG, Italy. Ed. Marco Pucciarini. adv.; bk.rev. **Document type:** academic/scholarly publication, bibliography.

266 SW ISSN 0345-7842
LAERARNAS MISSIONSFOERENING. MEDDELANDE TILL L M F.. (Text in Danish, Norwegian, and Swedish) 1902. bi-m. SEK 60. Laerarnas Missionsfoerening, Chapmansgatan 6, S-414 54 Goeteborg, Sweden. TEL 031-125440. Eds. Margareta Burgen, Margareta Hoverstam. bk.rev.; illus. circ. 2,200.
Formerly: Laerarinnornas Missionsfoerening. Meddelande till L M F. (ISSN 0023-6322)

LANDMARK STUDIES. see ARCHAEOLOGY

248 US ISSN 0896-002X
LAST DAYS MAGAZINE. q. free. Last Days Ministries, Box 40, Lindale, TX 75771-0040. TEL 903-963-8671. FAX 903-882-7709. Ed.Bd.

200 VC ISSN 1010-7215
BX800.A1
LATERANUM. 1976. 3/yr. $65. Pontificia Universita Lateranense, Piazza S. Giovanni in Laterano 4, 00120 Vatican City, State of the Vatican City. Ed. Marcello Bordoni. bk.rev. **Indexed:** CERDIC, Old Test.Abstr.

200 CR ISSN 1012-2982
LATIN AMERICAN PASTORAL ISSUES. 1988. a. $6. Centro Evangelico Latinoamericano de Estudios Pastorales, Apdo. 1710, 01901 Guatemala City, Guatemala. FAX 502-2-513688. E-mail: celep@nicarao.apc.org. (Subscr. to: Box 59-1796, Miami, FL 33159-1796) Ed. Dennis A. Smith. bk.rev.

200 301 PE ISSN 0254-203X
LATINAMERICA PRESS. Spanish edition: Noticias Aliadas. (Text in English) 1969. w. (48/yr.) $60 to individuals; institutions $85 (effective 1996). Noticias Aliadas, Apdo. 18-0964, Lima 18, Peru. TEL 51-14-475210. FAX 51-14-454681. E-mail: postmaster@acna.org.pe. Ed.Bd; Pub. Brian Goonan Costelloe. bk.rev.; index, cum.index. circ. 2,500. **Indexed:** HR Rep. (1985-), I.C.U.I.S.Abstr. **Document type:** bulletin.
Description: Focuses on issues involving the church, women's rights, grassroots organizations, indigenous issues, the environment and neoliberal economic programs in Latin America.

LAVAL THEOLOGIQUE ET PHILOSOPHIQUE. see PHILOSOPHY

LAW & JUSTICE. see LAW

200 SZ
LAY AND STUDY CENTRES NEWSLETTER. (Text in English) irreg. World Council of Churches, 150 route de Ferney, P.O. Box 2100, CH-1211 Geneva 2, Switzerland. TEL 022-7916111. FAX 022-7981346. TELEX 415730-OIK-CH. **Document type:** newsletter.

200 US ISSN 1041-4460
LEADER (ANDERSON); a resource for Christian leadership. 1939. bi-m. $7. Church of God, Board of Christian Education, 1303 E. Fifth St., Box 2458, Anderson, IN 46018-2458. TEL 317-642-0257. Ed. Joseph L. Cookston. adv. contact: David Pappas. circ. 4,000. **Document type:** trade publication.
Formerly: Christian Leadership.

200 UK
LEADER (STOCKPORT). 1985. q. free to qualified personnel. Covenanters, 11-33 Lower Hillgate, Stockport, Ches. SK1 1JQ, England. TEL 0161-474-1262. FAX 0161-474-1300. Ed. Heather Smith. adv.; bk.rev.; circ. 4,300 (controlled).
Formerly: Leaders' Digest. Covenanter and Juco Leader.

266 UG ISSN 0047-424X
LEADERSHIP; a magazine for Christian leaders in Africa. 1956. bi-m. $2 (typically set in Jan.). (Comboni Missionaries) Leadership Publications, Box 2522, Kampala, Uganda. TEL 256-41-221358. FAX 256-41-221576. Ed. Rev. Raphael Dellagiacoma. bk.rev.; illus.; stat.; circ. 8,000 (paid). **Indexed:** Rel.& Theol.Abstr. (1980-). **Document type:** newspaper.
Description: Examines social, moral and religious issues for the purposes of forming and informing Christian youth and adults.

200 SZ
LEBEN; Monatszeitschrift der Fokolar-Bewegung in der Schweiz. (Text in German) 1974. m. 20 Fr. (Fokolar-Bewegung) Verlag Neue Stadt, Seestrasse 426, Postfach 435, Ch-8038 Zurich, Switzerland. FAX 01-4826017. circ. 2,600. (back issues avail.)

200 GW
LEBENDIGE SEELSORGE UND LEBENDIGE KATCHESE. 1949. bi-m. DM.63 (students DM.47). Echter-Verlag, Postfach 5560, 97005 Wuerzburg, Germany. Eds. Lothar Roos, Werner Ruck. adv.; bk.rev. circ. 5,000. **Document type:** bulletin.

209 US ISSN 0075-8531
LECTURES ON THE HISTORY OF RELIGIONS. NEW SERIES. no.6, 1963. irreg., latest 1990. Columbia University Press, 562 W. 113th St., New York, NY 10025. TEL 212-666-1000. **Document type:** monographic series.

200 NE ISSN 0024-0427
LEGIOEN VAN MARIA. 1945. q. fl.6. Senaat van Het Legioen van Maria in Nederland, Pb. 77, 5000 AB Tilburg, Netherlands. illus.

200 TZ ISSN 0039-9655
LENGO/TARGET. (Text in Swahili) 1968. fortn. Sh.960 (Europe Sh.3720; America Sh.4320). East African Venture (Tanzania), PO Box 9290, Dar es Salaam, Tanzania. TEL 25825. Ed. Nancy Mrwendamseke. adv.; bk.rev.; charts; illus. circ. 30,000. **Document type:** newspaper.

266.025 UK ISSN 0075-8809
LEPROSY MISSION, LONDON. ANNUAL REPORT. 1874. a. free. Leprosy Mission, 80 Windmill Rd., Brentford, Middlesex TW8 0QH, England. TEL 0181-569-7292. FAX 0181-569-7808. Ed. Donna Bowers. circ. 20,000. **Document type:** corporate report.
Formerly: Mission to Lepers, London. Annual Report.

200 LO
LESELINYANA LA LESOTHO/LESOTHO CHRISTIAN NEWSPAPER. (Text in Sesotho; articles occasionally in English) 1863. fortn. Lesotho Evangelical Church, P.O. Box 7, Morija 190, Lesotho. TEL 244-360244. Ed. A.B. Thoahlane. circ. 15,000.

200 US
LETTER FROM PLYMOUTH ROCK. 1980. m. $25. Plymouth Rock Foundation, 26 McKinley Circle, Box 425, Marlborough, NH 03455. TEL 603-876-4685. FAX 603-876-4128. Ed. Rus Walton. bk.rev.; charts; illus.; stat. circ. 15,000. (looseleaf format; back issues avail.) **Document type:** newsletter.
Description: Looks at life from a biblical perspective.

391 US
LETTERS OF PAUL; Hilarion speaks to the new spiritual world view. 1990. irreg. Triad Publishers, 2401 College Ave., Weed, CA 96094-9534. Ed. L. Durham.

266 FR ISSN 0024-1490
LEVANT MORGENLAND. (Text in French and German) 1923. 4/yr. 30 F. (effective 1996). Action Chretienne en Orient, 7 rue du General-Offenstein, Strasbourg, France. TEL 88-39-11-55. FAX 88-40-27-98. Ed. Pasteur E. Reichert. bk.rev.; illus. circ. 10,000. **Document type:** newsletter.
Description: Contains news on partner churches in the Middle East (Lebanon, Syria, Egypt, Iran, Algeria) and on Christian - Muslim relations.

207.11 US ISSN 0160-8770
LEXINGTON THEOLOGICAL QUARTERLY. 1964. q. free to qualified personnel or on exchange basis. Lexington Theological Seminary, 631 S. Limestone St., Lexington, KY 40508. FAX 606-281-6042. Ed. Philip N. Dare. bk.rev.; circ. 2,300 (controlled). (also avail. in microfilm from UMI) **Indexed:** CERDIC, New Test.Abstr., Old Test.Abstr., Rel.& Theol.Abstr. (1968-), Rel.Ind.One. **Document type:** academic/scholarly publication.
—BLDSC (5185.720000); UMI.
Formerly: College of the Bible Quarterly (ISSN 0024-1628)
Refereed Serial

200 UK ISSN 0953-7805
LIBERTARIAN ALLIANCE. RELIGIOUS NOTES. 1990. irreg. £15($30) Libertarian Alliance, 25 Chapter Chambers, Esterbrooke St., London SW1P 4NN, England. TEL 0171-821-5502. FAX 0171-834-2031. E-mail: liberty@capital.demon.co.uk. **Document type:** monographic series.

261 US ISSN 0024-2055
BX6101
LIBERTY (HAGERSTOWN); a magazine of religious freedom. 1888. bi-m. $6.95. (International Religious Liberty Association) Review and Herald Publishing Association, 55 W. Oak Ridge Dr., Hagerstown, MD 21740. TEL 301-791-7000. Ed. Clifford Goldstein. adv.; bk.rev.; illus.; index, cum.index. circ. 240,000. (also avail. in microform from UMI; reprint service avail. from UMI) **Indexed:** CCR, HR Rep. (1988-). —Faxon; UMI; UnCover.

LIBRARY LINES. see LIBRARY AND INFORMATION SCIENCES

RELIGIONS AND THEOLOGY

200 US
LIBRARY OF RELIGIOUS PHILOSOPHY. 1989. irreg., vol.10, 1994. price varies. University of Notre Dame Press, Notre Dame, IN 46556. TEL 219-631-6346. FAX 219-631-8148. (Orders to: 11030 S. Langley Ave., Chicago, IL 60628. TEL 800-621-2736. FAX 800-621-8476; Overseas orders to: Eurospan University Press Group, Order Dept., 3 Henrietta St., London WC2E 8LU, England) Ed. Thomas V. Morris. **Document type:** academic/scholarly publication.

266 GW ISSN 0945-4179
LICHT IM OSTEN. English edition: Light in the East News. 1920. bi-m. free. Licht im Osten, Missionsbund, Zuffenhauserstr. 37, 70825 Korntal-Muenchingen, Germany. TEL 0711-839908-0. FAX 0711-8399084. Ed. E. Damson. bk.rev.; bibl.; illus. circ. 27,900. **Document type:** newsletter.
Formerly: Dein Reich Komme (ISSN 0011-7692)

200 US
LIFEGLOW. 1983. q. free to legally blind people. Christian Record Services, 4444 South 52nd St., Lincoln, NE 68516. TEL 402-488-0981. Ed. Richard Kaiser. circ. 23,400. (large print edition in 22 pt.)
Description: Inspirational, devotional articles and stories for adults, especially senior citizens.

268 II ISSN 0970-2571
LIGHT OF LIFE; all India magazine of Christian growth. (Text in English) 1957. m. $15. Christian Digest Society of India, 21 YMCA Rd., Bombay 400 008, India. TEL 3076941. FAX 3076941. Ed. P. Abraham. adv. contact: Regi George. bk.rev.; illus. circ. 5,000.

THE LIGHTHOUSE (STATE COLLEGE); shining light on today's Christian music. see MUSIC — Abstracting, Bibliographies, Statistics

LINGUISTICA BIBLICA; Interdisziplinaere Zeitschrift fuer Theologie, Semiotik und Linguistik. see LINGUISTICS

200 800 US ISSN 0732-1929
PN49
LITERATURE AND BELIEF. 1981. a. $5 (foreign $7). Brigham Young University, College of Humanities, Center, Study of Christian Values in Literature, 3076F Jesse Knight Bldg., Provo, UT 84604-9989. TEL 801-378-3073. FAX 801-378-4720. E-mail: cracrftr@JKHBHRC.byu.edu. Eds. Richard H. Cracroft, John J. Murphy. bk.rev. circ. 1,000. (also avail. in microfiche) **Indexed:** Abstr.Engl.Stud., LCR, M.L.A. **Document type:** academic/scholarly publication, monographic series.
—BLDSC (5276.712750); Faxon.
Description: Focuses on the moral-religious aspects of literature through scholarly critical articles, short fiction, interviews, personal essays, reviews and poetry.
Refereed Serial

LITERATURE AND THEOLOGY. see LITERATURE

200 US ISSN 0460-1297
BL624
LITTLE LAMP; a journal for leading the spiritual life through the practice of meditation. 1967. q. $18. (Blue Mountain Center of Meditation) Nilgiri Press, Box 256, Tomales, CA 94971. TEL 707-878-2369. FAX 707-878-2375. Ed. Christine Easwaran. circ. 1,000. (back issues avail.)

264 NE
LITURGIA CONDENDA. 1993. irreg., vol.2, 1994. price varies. Kok Pharos Publishing House, Postbus 5019, 8260 AG Kampen, Netherlands. TEL 31-5202-92565. FAX 31-5202-27331. (Dist. in U.S. and Canada by: Books International, Inc., Box 605, Herndon, VA 22070-0605. TEL 800-377-7192. FAX 703-689-0660) (back issues avail.) **Document type:** monographic series.
Description: Publishes current scholarship in liturgical research, with particular emphasis on innovation in methods, and explorations of new questions.

200 GW ISSN 0344-9092
LITURGIE KONKRET. 1978. m. DM.53.50. Verlag Friedrich Pustet, Gutenbergstr. 8, 93051 Regensburg, Germany. TEL 0941-92022-0. FAX 0941-948652. Ed.Bd. **Document type:** newsletter.

200 GW ISSN 0076-0048
LITURGIEWISSENSCHAFTLICHE QUELLEN UND FORSCHUNGEN. 1919. irreg. price varies. Aschendorffsche Verlagsbuchhandlung, Soesterstr. 13, 48155 Muenster, Germany. TEL 0251-690-0. FAX 0251-690143. Ed. W. Heckenbach. **Document type:** monographic series.

264 GW ISSN 0024-5100
LITURGISCHES JAHRBUCH. 1951. 4/yr. DM.70. (Deutsches Liturgisches Institut Trier) Aschendorffsche Verlagsbuchhandlung, Soesterstr. 13, 48155 Muenster, Germany. TEL 0251-690-0. FAX 0251-690143. Ed. Andreas Heinz. adv.; bk.rev.; index. **Indexed:** Rel.& Theol.Abstr. (1989-), Rel.Ind.One. **Document type:** academic/scholarly publication.
—SWETS. CCC.

264 US ISSN 0458-063X
BV169
LITURGY. 1955; N.S. 1980. q. $42. Liturgical Conference, Inc., 8750 Georgia Ave., Ste. 123, Silver Spring, MD 20910-1621. TEL 301-496-0885. FAX 301-495-5945. Ed. Blair Gilmer Meeks. adv.; bk.rev.; bibl. circ. 25. (back issues avail.) **Indexed:** Cath.Ind., CERDIC, Rel.& Theol.Abstr. (1980-). **Document type:** academic/scholarly publication.
—UMI.
Description: Resource for parish leaders to promote liturgical renewal and ecumenism. Includes essays, guidelines, rituals, prayers.

264 UK ISSN 0309-4308
LITURGY. 1976. bi-m. £12 (outside Europe £13) (effective Oct. 1994). Bishops' Conference of England and Wales, Liturgy Office, 39 Eccleston Sq., London SW1V 1PL, England. TEL 0171-821-0553. FAX 0171-630-5166. Ed. Martin Foster. bk.rev. circ. 1,200. **Document type:** newsletter.
Description: For priests and parish liturgy committees.

200 US ISSN 0190-3845
LIVE (SPRINGFIELD); to live is Christ. 1928. w. $5.20. Gospel Publishing House, 1445 Boonville Ave., Springfield, MO 65802-1894. TEL 417-862-2781. circ. 160,000.

LIVE AND LET LIVE. see PHILOSOPHY

200 US ISSN 0193-5968
BX809.F6
LIVING CITY. 1967. m. $15. Focolare Movement, Inc., Women's Branch, 99-28 64th Rd., Rego Park, NY 11374. TEL 212-904-1898. FAX 212-892-0419. (Subscr. to: Box 837, Bronx, NY 10465) Ed. Sharry Silvi. circ. 9,000. (back issues avail.)
Description: News of a world striving for unity.

200 US ISSN 0890-5568
LIVING PRAYER. 1968. bi-m. $17 (foreign $22). Living Prayer, Inc., Beckley Hill, Barre, VT 05641. TEL 802-476-8362. Ed. Rose Page. bk.rev.; circ. 6,500 (paid). (also avail. in microform from UMI) **Indexed:** Cath.Ind.
—UMI.
Formerly (until Sep. 1986): Contemplative Review (ISSN 0193-8452)
Refereed Serial

200 UK ISSN 0024-5445
Y LLAN; newyddiadur yr Eglwys yng Nghymru. (Text in Welsh) 1976. s-m. £16.65. (Church of Wales, Education and Communications Centre) Board of Mission Publications, Woodland Place, Penarth, S. Glam CF64 2EX, Wales. TEL 01222-708234. FAX 01222-712413. Ed. Rev. Gwyn Ap Gwilym. adv.; bk.rev. circ. 1,000. (looseleaf format) **Document type:** newspaper.
Description: Directed to clergy and those interested in the activities of the Church of Wales.

LONERGAN STUDIES NEWSLETTER. see PHILOSOPHY

LOOKOUT (NEW YORK). see SOCIAL SERVICES AND WELFARE

230 BE ISSN 0024-6964
BX801
LOUVAIN STUDIES. 1966. q. 1000 BEF($30) (effective 1996). Katholieke Universiteit Leuven, Faculty of Theology, St. Michielsstraat 2, B-3000 Leuven, Belgium. TEL 32-16-283894. FAX 32-16-283858. Ed. Joseph A. Selling. bk.rev.; index. circ. 1,500. (also avail. in microform from UMI; back issues avail.) **Indexed:** Canon Law Abstr., Cath.Ind., CERDIC, New Test.Abstr., Old Test.Abstr., Rel.& Theol.Abstr. (1979-). **Document type:** academic/scholarly publication.
—BLDSC (5296.360000); UMI.

200 BE
LOUVAIN THEOLOGICAL AND PASTORAL MONOGRAPHS. (Text in English) 1990. irreg. (2-3/yr.), vol.16, 1994. price varies. (Katholieke Universiteit Leuven, Faculty of Divinity) Editions Peeters s.p.r.l., Bongenotenlaan 153, 3000 Leuven, Belgium. TEL 32-16-235170. FAX 32-16-228500. (Co-publisher: Wm. B. Eerdmans, US) (back issues avail.) **Document type:** monographic series.

200 US
LUIS PALAU LETTER. 1964. m. Luis Palau Evangelistic Association, Box 1173, Portland, OR 97207. TEL 503-643-0777. FAX 503-643-6851. Ed. David Sanford.
Description: Shares ministry vision and results with supporters.

220 264 FR ISSN 0024-7359
LUMIERE ET VIE; revue de formation et de reflexion theologiques. 1951. 5/yr. 240 F. (foreign 270 F.) (effective 1996). Association Lumiere et Vie, 2 place Gailleton, 69002 Lyon, France. TEL 78-42-66-83. FAX 78-37-23-82. Ed. Christian Duquoc. adv.; bk.rev.; index. circ. 5,000. **Indexed:** Cath.Ind., CERDIC, New Test.Abstr.
—BLDSC (5304.770000).

241 SW ISSN 1102-769X
LUND STUDIES IN ETHICS AND THEOLOGY. (Text in English, Swedish) 1992. irreg. price varies. Lund University Press, P.O. Box 141, S-221 00 Lund, Sweden. TEL 46-46-31-20-00. FAX 46-46-30-53-38. E-mail: Order@Studli.se. Ed. G. Bexell. **Document type:** academic/scholarly publication, monographic series.

159.9 SW ISSN 1103-5757
LUND STUDIES IN PSYCHOLOGY OF RELIGION. (Text in English) 1993. irreg. price varies. Lund University Press, P.O. Box 141, S-221 00 Lund, Sweden. TEL 46-46-31-20-00. FAX 46-46-30-53-38. E-mail: order@studli.se. Ed. K. Bergling. **Document type:** academic/scholarly publication.

220 IT
LUX BIBLICA; rivista teologica. 1990. s-a. L.20000 (foriegn L.25000). Istituto Biblico Evangelico Italiano, Via del Casale Corvio 50, 00132 Rome, Italy. TEL 39-6-20762293. FAX 39-6-2070151. Ed. Luigi Fausto Dettori. bk.rev. circ. 550. **Document type:** academic/scholarly publication, monographic series.
Description: Consists of one monographic issue and one theological journal issue per year.

266 US ISSN 0740-6460
M A R C NEWSLETTER. q. free. (Mission Advanced Research & Communication Center) M A R C (Subsidiary of: World Vision International), 121 E. Huntington Dr., Monrovia, CA 91016-3400. TEL 818-303-8811. FAX 818-301-7786. E-mail: marc@wvi.org. Ed. John A. Kenyon. adv. contact: Steve Singley. **Indexed:** CERDIC. **Document type:** newsletter.
Description: News and articles on strategic planning for world evangelization by Christian mission agencies.

200 US ISSN 1049-152X
M A R GOSPEL MINISTRIES NEWSLETTER. (Middle Atlantic Regional) 1989. s-a. free. (Middle Atlantic Regional Gospel Ministries) Middle Atlantic Regional Press, 100 Bryant St., N.W., Washington, DC 20001. TEL 202-265-7609. Ed. E. Myron Noble. bk.rev. **Document type:** newsletter.
Description: Covers African American church and current events of M A R Gospel Ministries.

M E T E M - INTERNATIONAL SOCIETY OF TORONTO FOR HUNGARIAN CHURCH HISTORY. NEWSLETTER/M E T E M. HIREK. see HISTORY — History Of Europe

RELIGIONS AND THEOLOGY

200 US ISSN 0362-0808
M S S.* (Master Sermon Series) 1970. m. $25. Cathedral Publishers, Box 129, Royal Oak, MI 48068-0129. Ed. Carl G. Howie. (looseleaf format)

200 IT ISSN 0024-9599
MADONNA DI CASTELMONTE. 1913. m. L.13000($20) (foreign L.22000). Frati Minori Cappuccini Veneti, 33040 Castelmonte (UD), Italy. TEL 32-731094. Ed. Aurelio Blasotti. illus. circ. 60,000.

266 028.5 US ISSN 8756-4564
MAGAZINE FOR CHRISTIAN YOUTH!. 1985. m. $18 (Canada $20); newsstand price: $2. United Methodist Publishing House, 201 Eighth Ave. S., Box 801, Nashville, TN 37202. TEL 615-749-6319. FAX 615-749-6079. film rev.; illus. circ. 30,000.
Document type: consumer publication.
Description: Contains religious articles for a teenage audience.

MAGYAR EGYHAZTORTENETI VAZLATOK/ESSAYS IN CHURCH HISTORY IN HUNGARY. see *HISTORY — History Of Europe*

200 FR ISSN 0025-0937
MAISON - DIEU; revue specialisee de liturgique. 1945. 4/yr. 230 F. (foreign 285 F.). (Centre National de Pastorale Liturgique) Editions du Cerf, 29 bd. Latour Maubourg, 75340 Paris Cedex 07, France. TEL 45-50-34-07. FAX 45-56-04-27. (Subscr. to: Service Abonnements, 3 chemin des Prunais, 94350 Villiers-sur-Marne, France) Ed. Pierre-Marie Gy. adv.; bk.rev.; index. circ. 2,600. **Indexed:** CERDIC, New Test.Abstr.
—SWETS.

266 CN ISSN 0225-7068
MANDATE. 1969. 6/yr. Can.$7.50. United Church of Canada, 3250 Bloor St. W., Etobicoke, ON M8X 2Y4, Canada. TEL 416-231-5931. FAX 416-231-3103. Ed. Rebekah Chevalier. circ. 31,000. **Document type:** consumer publication.
Description: Covers mission and justice work in Canada and overseas.

266 CN ISSN 0225-7068
MANDATE "SPECIAL". 1977. a. Can.$1.95 per no. United Church of Canada, 3250 Bloor St. W., Etobicoke, ON M8X 2Y4, Canada. TEL 416-231-5931. FAX 416-231-3103. Ed. Rebekah Chevalier. charts; illus. circ. 34,000. (back issues avail.) **Document type:** consumer publication.
Formerly: Mission Magazine (ISSN 0706-5590)
Description: Focus is annual United Church mission study theme.

200 JM
MANNA. q. Jam.$70. University and Colleges Christian Fellowship, 22 Hagley Park Plaza, Box 281, Kingston 10, Jamaica, W.I. circ. 2,000.

200 SP ISSN 0214-2457
MANRESA; revista de investigacion e informacion ascetica y mistica. 1925. q. 3800 ptas.($36) (Europe $45; Latin America $47; US $50; Asia $60) (effective 1995). Centro Loyola de Estudios y Comunicacion Social, Pablo Aranda 3, 28006 Madrid, Spain. FAX 341-5634073. adv.; bk.rev. circ. 1,000. **Indexed:** Amer.Hist.& Life, CERDIC, Hist.Abstr., New Test.Abstr.

200 GW ISSN 0542-657X
MARBURGER THEOLOGISCHE STUDIEN. 1963. irreg., no.32, 1992. DM.82. N.G. Elwert Verlag, Reitgasse 7-9, 35037 Marburg, Germany. TEL 06421-25023. FAX 06421-15487. **Document type:** monographic series.

200 AU ISSN 0025-2999
MARIAHILFER PFARRBOTE. 1924. q. contribution. Pfarramt Mariahilf, Barnabitengasse 14, 1060 Vienna, Austria. Ed. Waldemar Posch. bk.rev.; abstr.; charts; illus.; stat.; index. circ. 3,000.

266 232 AU ISSN 0025-3022
MARIANNHILL. bi-m. S.30. Missionare von Mariannhill, Riedegg 1, A-4210 Gallneukirchen, Austria. Eds. Br. Franziskus Puehringer, P.A. Balling. bk.rev. circ. 45,000. (tabloid format)

282 US
MARKINGS. 1971. 11/yr. $37.95. Thomas More Association, 205 W. Monroe St., 6th Fl., Chicago, IL 60606. TEL 312-609-8880. circ. 3,000.
Description: Homily service for priests.

200 US ISSN 1052-181X
MARTIN LUTHER KING, JR. MEMORIAL STUDIES IN RELIGION, CULTURE AND SOCIAL DEVELOPMENT. irreg. Peter Lang Publishing, Inc., 62 W. 45th St., 4th Fl., New York, NY 10036. TEL 212-302-6740. FAX 212-302-7574. Ed. Mozella G. Mitchell.
Document type: academic/scholarly publication, monographic series.
Description: Promotes scholarly research and writing in areas that reflect the interrelatedness of religion and social-cultural-political development both in the American society and in the world.

260 II ISSN 0376-6608
PK2030
MASIHI AVAZA. (Text in Hindi) vol.45, 1972. m. Rs.5. 277 Angrahpuri, Gaya, Bihar, India. bibl.; illus.

266 UK
MASTER AND THE MULTITUDE. 1853. q. £1. Open-Air Mission, 19 John St., London WC1N 2DL, England. TEL 0171-405-6135. Ed. Alan J. Greenbank. illus. circ. 5,000. **Document type:** newsletter.
Description: Mission work in the British Isles.

200 GW ISSN 0721-2402
MATERIALDIENST. 1937. m. DM.53. (Evangelische Zentralstelle fuer Weltanschauungsfragen) Quell Verlag, Furtbachstr. 12A, 70178 Stuttgart, Germany. TEL 0711-60100-0. circ. 5,000.
Document type: bulletin.

200 GW
MATHILDE-ZIMMER-STIFTUNG. BLAETTER. 1906. bi-m. DM.11. (Mathilde-Zimmer-Stiftung e.V.) Christlicher Zeitschriftenverlag, Bachstr. 1-2, 1000 Berlin 21, Germany. Ed. E. Zimmer. adv.; bk.rev. circ. 2,000.

MEDIA & VALUES. see *COMMUNICATIONS*

MEDIA DEVELOPMENT. see *COMMUNICATIONS*

266 610 UK ISSN 0025-7370
MEDICAL MISSIONARY NEWS. 1946. q. £2. Medical Mission Sisters, 3 Blakesley Ave., Ealing, London WC5 2DN, England. Ed. Kathleen Brown. illus. circ. 1,000. **Document type:** newsletter.
Description: Mission work, mainly in the Third World.

200 901 US ISSN 1056-7917
MEDIEVAL AND EARLY MODERN MYSTICISM. irreg. price varies. Peter Lang Publishing, Inc., 62 W. 45th St., 4th Fl., New York, NY 10036. TEL 212-302-6740. Ed. Teresa Howe. **Document type:** academic/scholarly publication, monographic series.
Description: Covers studies of Christian, Jewish, and Islamic mystical figures and their works from the 9th to the 17th centuries.

MEDIEVAL PHILOSOPHY AND THEOLOGY. see *PHILOSOPHY*

200 GW ISSN 0171-3841
MEDITATION; Anstoesse fuer den Christlichen Vollzug. 1975. q. DM.24. Verlag Christianopolis, Hechenbergstr. 13, 82362 Weilheim, Germany. Ed. Wolf von Fritsch. bk.rev.; bibl.; illus.; index. (back issues avail.)

294.5 158.12 US ISSN 1075-9727
▼**MEDIATOR'S NEWSLETTER.** 1994. m. $5 (effective 1994). Seaport Poets & Writers Press, Orchard Hill Rd., Harriman, NY 10926. TEL 914-783-8154. Eds. Daryl & George Bailin. (also avail. in diskette format) **Document type:** newsletter.
Description: Publishes essays, poetry and letters discussing issues of interest to meditators and spiritual seekers, including comparative examination of traditional approaches to self-realization with current psychology, and other topics relating to the contemplative life.

200 US ISSN 0194-7826
MEGIDDO MESSAGE. 1914. m. $5. Megiddo Church, 481 Thurston Rd., Rochester, NY 14619-1697. TEL 716-436-1614. FAX 716-436-3627. Ed. Newton H. Payne. index, cum.index: 1915-1994. circ. 14,000. (also avail. in looseleaf format; reprint service avail. from UMI)
—UMI.

200 GW
MEHR FREUDE MAGAZIN. 1979. q. DM.8. Jugend fuer Christus Deutschland e.V., Postfach 1180, 64355 Muethal, Germany. TEL 06151-145194. FAX 06151-144399. Ed. Bernd Schweinfurth. adv.; bk.rev. circ. 24,500.

240 GW
MEINE WELT. w. DM.13.30. Guetersloher Verlagshaus Chr. Kaiser, Carl-Bertelsmann-Str. 270, 33311 Guetersloh, Germany. TEL 05241-7405-0. FAX 05241-740548. Ed. Ingrid Ryssel. **Document type:** newsletter.

283 UK
MELANESIA NEWS. 1977. q. £20. Melanesian Mission, 2 Harpsden Way, Henley-on-Thames, Oxon RG9 1NL, England. TEL 01941-573401. circ. 1,200.
Document type: newsletter.
Description: Contains news from the Church of the Province of Melanesia (Anglican).

200 PP ISSN 0256-856X
MELANESIAN JOURNAL OF THEOLOGY. (Text in English) 1985. s-a. $10. Melanesian Association of Theological Schools, c/o Martin Luther Seminary, P.O. Box 80, Lae, Papua New Guinea. TELEX 422699. Ed. Christopher Garland. adv.; bk.rev. circ. 600. (back issues avail.) **Indexed:** Rel.& Theol.Abstr. (1990-).

200 212.5 MM ISSN 1012-9588
BX804
MELITA THEOLOGICA. (Supplement avail.) (Text in English, French, Italian) 1947. 2/yr. $27. Theology Students' Association, University of Malta, Msida MSD 04, Malta. TEL 356-333998. (Subscr. to: Foundation for Theological Studies, Tal Virtu, Rabat RBT 09, Malta. TEL 356-455497) (Co-sponsor: University of Malta, Faculty of Theology) Ed. Rev. Dr. Anthony Abela. adv.; bk.rev.; index. circ. 600.
Indexed: New Test.Abstr., Old Test. Abstr., Rel.& Theol.Abstr. (1968-). **Document type:** academic/scholarly publication.
—BLDSC (5544.700000).
Description: Contains articles in dogmatic and moral theology, fundamental theology, holy scripture, canon law, spiritual theology, liturgy, patrology, ecclesiastical history, Christian archaeology, philosophy and sociology.

200 MM
MELITA THEOLOGICA SUPPLEMENTARY SERIES. 1991. irreg., approx. a., vol.2, 1992. price varies. Theology Students' Association, University of Malta, Msida MSD 04, Malta. TEL 356-333998. (Subscr. to: Foundation for Theological Studies, Tal Virtu, Rabat RBT 09, Malta. TEL 356-455497) (Co-sponsor: University of Malta, Faculty of Theology) (back issues avail.) **Document type:** monographic series.
Description: Publishes monographic studies and collections of essays on topics in theology and related issues.
Refereed Serial

MEMORIE DOMENICANE. see *HISTORY*

254.041489 DK ISSN 0904-8545
MENIGHEDSRAADENES BLAD. 1922. m. (11/yr.). DKK 260. Landsforeningen af Menighedsraadsmedlemmer, Vesterport 3, DK-8000 Aarhus C, Denmark. TEL 45-86-19-70-77. FAX 45-86-19-80-40. Ed. Niels Erik Kjaer-Larsen. adv. contact: Inge Litrup. circ. 24,000. **Document type:** newsletter.
Description: Contains articles and information of interest to the members of the association of local Danish church councils.

200 SP ISSN 0211-6561
MENSAJERO; del corazon de Jesus. 1866. m. 2500 ptas.($33.50) (effective Jan. 1993). Ediciones Mensajero S.A., Sancho de Azpeitia, 2, Apdo. 73, 48080 Bilbao, Spain. TEL 94-447-0358. FAX 94-447-2630. Ed. Angel Perez Gomez. adv.; bk.rev.; illus. circ. 25,000. (back issues avail.)
Description: Covers religious and family subjects. Includes some political, social and cultural issues.

RELIGIONS AND THEOLOGY

200   AU   ISSN 0026-0126
MERLEG; folyoiratok es konyvek szemleje. (Text in Hungarian; summaries in English and German) 1965. q. S.400. Pastorale Ungarnhilfe der Oesterreichischen Bischofskonferenz, Boltzmanngasse 14, A-1090 Vienna, Austria. (Dist. addr.: Distelfinkweg 21, 81249 Munich, Germany. TEL 089-8644424. FAX 089-8643573) Ed. Janos Boor. adv.; bk.rev.; abstr.; bibl.; index. circ. 4,500. **Indexed:** Old Test.Abstr. **Document type:** consumer publication.

MERTON ANNUAL: STUDIES IN THOMAS MERTON, RELIGION, CULTURE, LITERATURE, AND SOCIAL CONCERNS. see *LITERATURE*

200 800   US   ISSN 0899-4927
THE MERTON SEASONAL: A QUARTERLY REVIEW. 1976. q. $20 (effective Apr. 1994). Thomas Merton Center, Bellarmine College, Newburg Rd., Louisville, KY 40205-0671. TEL 502-452-8187. FAX 502-452-8038. (Co-sponsor: International Thomas Merton Society) Ed. Robert E. Daggy. bk.rev.; bibl.; illus. circ. 1,846. (looseleaf format; back issues avail.)
    Formerly: Merton Seasonal.
    Description: Studies in Thomas Merton, religion, culture, literature and social concerns.

200   US   ISSN 0026-0231
BX6101
MESSAGE (HAGERSTOWN). 1934. bi-m. $12.95. Review and Herald Publishing Association, 55 W. Oak Ridge Dr., Hagerstown, MD 21740. TEL 301-791-7000. Ed. Stephen Ruff. bk.rev.; illus.; rec.rev.; index. circ. 68,000. **Indexed:** CCR.
    Formerly: Message Magazine (ISSN 0162-6019)

200   US   ISSN 0746-0635
MESSAGE OF THE CROSS. 1950. q. free. Bethany Fellowship Inc., 6820 Auto Club Rd., Minneapolis, MN 55438. TEL 612-829-2492. FAX 612-829-2753. Ed. George R. Foster. adv.; bk.rev.
    Description: Communication vehicle for college and church community.

220   US   ISSN 0889-4159
MESSAGE OF THE OPEN BIBLE. 1920. 6/yr. $9.75. Open Bible Standard Churches, Open Bible Publishers, 2020 Bell Ave., Des Moines, IA 50315-1096. TEL 515-288-6761. FAX 515-288-2510. Ed. Delores A. Winegar. circ. 4,000 (paid).
    Description: To inform, inspire and educate members of the denomination.

200   US   ISSN 0026-0363
MESSENGER (KANSAS CITY)/MESSAGGERO.* (Text in English, Italian) 1921. m. $1. Messenger Publishing Co. (Kansas City), Box 30300h, Kansas City, MO 64112-3300. Ed. Dr. J.B. Bisceglia. adv.; bk.rev.; bibl.; illus. circ. 1,000. (tabloid format; also avail. in microform)

200   UK
BV2619
THE MESSIANIC JEW (AND HEBREW CHRISTIAN). 1928. q. £3($4) in U.S.; Canada $5. International Messianic Jewish (Hebrew - Christian) Alliance, Shalom, Brockenhurst Rd., Ramsgate CT11 8ED, England. TEL 01843-589756. Ed. Rev. Ronald H. Lewis. bk.rev. circ. 6,000. (microfiche) **Indexed:** CERDIC. **Document type:** academic/scholarly publication, newsletter.
    Formerly: Hebrew Christian (ISSN 0017-9477)
    Description: Advocates the pastoral care and material support (where necessary) of Jewish believers in Jesus as Messiah who are members of a recognized fellowship.

200   GW   ISSN 0943-3058
METHOD AND THEORY IN THE STUDY OF RELIGION. 1993. 4/yr. DM.154. (North American Association for the Study of Religion) Walter de Gruyter und Co., Mouton de Gruyter, Genthiner Str. 13, 10785 Berlin, Germany. TEL 030-26005-0. FAX 030-26005251. TELEX 184027. (U.S. addr.: 200 Saw Mill River Rd., Hawthorne, NY 10532. TEL 914-747-0110) Ed. Ann Baranowski. bk.rev. **Document type:** academic/scholarly publication.
—BLDSC (5745.620000). **CCC.**

METHOD: JOURNAL OF LONERGAN STUDIES. see *PHILOSOPHY*

200   CN   ISSN 0317-8498
MICHAEL; for the triumph of the Immaculate. 1955. 6/yr. Can.$10 for 2 yrs. Louis Even Institute, 1101 Principale St., Rougemont, Que. J0L 1M0, Canada. TEL 514-469-2209. Ed. Gilberte Cote-Mercier. circ. 35,000.
    Description: Promotes the application of the teachings of the Roman Catholic Church in every aspect of social life, especially in economics with the social credit philosophy of Scottish engineer, Clifford Hugh Douglas.

MIGRANTI-PRESS. see *POLITICAL SCIENCE*

MILITARY CHAPLAIN. see *MILITARY*

200 100   IE   ISSN 0332-1428
BR1
MILLTOWN STUDIES. 1977. 2/yr. I£10.50 (foreign I£12($20)). Milltown Institute of Theology & Philosophy, Milltown Park, Dublin 6, Ireland. TEL 01-2698802. FAX 01-2692528. Ed. Gervase Corcoran. adv.; bk.rev. circ. 200. **Indexed:** New Test.Abstr., Old Test.Abstr. **Document type:** academic/scholarly publication.
—BLDSC (5774.350000).

500   PH   ISSN 0115-2742
DS688.S9
MINDANAO JOURNAL. (Text in English) 1974. q. $10. Mindanao State University, Mamitua Saber Research Center, P.O. Box 5594, Iligan City 9200, Philippines. Ed. Raymond Llorca. circ. 500. **Indexed:** Ind.Phil.Per. **Document type:** academic/scholarly publication.
—UnCover.

267 270   ZA
MINDOLO WORLD. 1961. 2/yr. K.20($5) Mindolo Ecumenical Foundation, P.O. Box 21493, Kitwe, Zambia. TEL 260-2-214572. FAX 260-2-211001. Ed. Chris Akufuna. adv. circ. 1,000. **Document type:** newsletter.
    Formerly: Mindolo News Letter (ISSN 0076-8901)

200   SZ   ISSN 0255-8777
BV4019
MINISTERIAL FORMATION. (Text in English) q. $10. World Council of Churches, Ecumenical Theological Education, 150 route de Ferney, P.O. Box 2100, CH-1211 Geneva 2, Switzerland. TEL 022-791-6111. FAX 022-791-0361. TELEX 415730-OIK-CH. Ed. Judo Poerwowidagdo. circ. 1,600. **Indexed:** Rel.Ind.One. **Document type:** newsletter.

200   US   ISSN 0894-3966
MINISTER'S MANUAL (YEAR);* preaching and worship planning. a. $21.95. Church Management, Inc., 6160 Carmen Ave. E., Inver Grove Heights, MN 55076-4420. Ed. Manfred Holck.

200   GW   ISSN 0937-9886
MINISTRANTENPOST. Key Title: Minipost. m. DM.18. Patmos Verlag GmbH, Am Wehrhahn 100, 40211 Duesseldorf, Germany. TEL 0211-16795-0. FAX 0211-1679575. **Document type:** bulletin.

200   US   ISSN 0891-5725
BV4000
MINISTRIES TODAY; the magazine for Christian leaders. 1983. bi-m. $29.95. Strang Communications Co., 600 Rinehart Rd., Lake Mary, FL 32746. TEL 407-333-0600. Ed. J. Buchan. circ. 30,000. **Indexed:** CCR. **Document type:** trade publication.
—UMI.
    Formerly: Ministries.

266   US
MINISTRY TODAY. 1991. bi-m. donations. Missionary Church, Inc., Box 9127, Ft. Wayne, IN 46899. TEL 219-747-2027. FAX 219-747-5331. Ed. Robert L. Ransom. circ. 5,000.
    Description: Communicates message and ministry of the Missionary Church to people 20 to 40 years of age.

200 110   US   ISSN 1061-3927
MIRACLES MAGAZINE. 1991. q. $21.95. Miracles Community Network, Box 418, Santa Fe, NM 87504. TEL 505-989-3656. FAX 505-982-4159. Ed. Paul Ferrini; Pub. Paul Ferrini. adv.; B&W page $1250; trim 8 3/8 x 10 7/8; adv. contact: Carol Fritz. bk.rev. (back issues avail.) **Document type:** bulletin.
    Description: Publishes articles for persons seeking a deeper spiritual meaning in their lives.

200 100 370.1 150   SP   ISSN 0210-9522
BX880
MISCELANEA COMILLAS; revista de teologia y ciencias humanas. 1943. s-a. $50. Universidad Pontificia Comillas de Madrid, Facultades de Filosofia y Letras y Teologia, 28049 Madrid, Spain. FAX 341-7344570. Ed. Jose Joaquin Alemany. adv.; bk.rev. circ. 400. **Indexed:** Amer.Hist.& Life, CERDIC, Hist.Abstr., New Test.Abstr.
—BLDSC (5811.840000).

296 282   IS   ISSN 0792-0474
BV2619
MISHKAN; a forum on the gospel and the Jewish people. (Text in English) 1984. s-a. £9($15) United Christian Council in Israel, P.O. Box 116, Jerusalem 91000, Israel. TEL 972-2-256095. FAX 972-2-251933. (Co-sponsor: Caspari Center for Biblical and Jewish Studies) Ed. Kai Kjaer-Hansen. adv.; bk.rev. circ. 700. **Indexed:** Rel.& Theol.Abstr. (1990-). **Document type:** academic/scholarly publication.
    Description: Covers Biblical and theological debate on issues relating to Jewish evangelism, Hebrew-Christian and Messianic-Jewish identity, and Jewish-Christian relations.

266   SP
MISIONEROS JAVERIANOS. 1963. m. free. Monserrat, 9, 28008 Madrid, Spain. illus. circ. 48,000. (tabloid format)

200   FR   ISSN 0026-5977
MISSI; magazine d'information spirituelle et de solidarite internationale. 1935. 10/yr. 160 F.($32) (foreign 175 F.). 6 rue d'Auvergne, 69287 Lyon Cedex 2, France. TEL 78-37-86-30. Ed. Pierre Gerard. bk.rev.; index. circ. 15,000. **Indexed:** CERDIC.

MISSIOLOGY; an international review. see *ANTHROPOLOGY*

266   CN   ISSN 1198-0400
MISSION; journal of mission studies. (Text in English, French) 1967. s-a. Can.$25.68 (foreign $25). Saint Paul University, Institute of Mission Studies, 223 Main St., Ottawa, ON K1S 1C4, Canada. TEL 613-236-1393. FAX 613-782-3005. Ed. Martin Roberge. bk.rev. circ. 250. **Indexed:** New Test.Abstr. **Document type:** academic/scholarly publication.
    Formerly (until 1994): Kerygma (ISSN 0023-0693)

266   DK   ISSN 0106-5610
MISSION; nordisk missionstidsskrift. 1889. q. $25 (foreign $47). Dansk Missionsraad - Danish Missionary Council, Skt. Lukas Vej 13, DK-2900 Hellerup, Denmark. TEL 45-31-61-27-77. Ed. Mogens Jenssen. bk.rev.; charts; stat.; index. circ. 800.
    Formerly (until 1970): Nordisk Missionstidsskrift (ISSN 0029-1447)

200   US
MISSION. q. $3. Sisters of the Blessed Sacrament, 1663 Bristol Pike, Bensalem, PA 19020-8502. TEL 215-244-9900. Ed. Christa McGill. circ. 4,000.
    Description: Provides information about the activities of the congregation which is dedicated to the interracial apostolate in the U.S. and Haiti.

266   US   ISSN 0889-9436
MISSION FRONTIERS. 1979. bi-m. $4. U S Center for World Mission, Frontier Fellowship, 1605 Elizabeth St., Pasadena, CA 91104. TEL 818-398-2241. FAX 818-398-2263. **Document type:** bulletin.

266   FR   ISSN 0026-6124
MISSION MESSAGES. 1920. bi-m. 40 F. Procure des Missions du Levant, 32 rue Boissonade, 75014 Paris, France. TEL 16-1-43-22-42-08. FAX 16-1-45-38-97-83. Ed. Joseph Coz. bk.rev.; illus.; stat. circ. 4,500.

260   AT   ISSN 0158-0531
MISSION PROBE. irreg. free. Uniting Church in Australia, Commission for Mission, 222 Pitt St., 5th Fl., Sydney, N.S.W. 2000, Australia. TEL 02-287-0900. FAX 02-287-0999. (Subscr. to: P.O. Box E266, St. James, N.S.W. 2000, Australia) Ed. D. McRae McMahon. circ. 125,000. (back issues avail.)
    Description: Covers mission issues within the life of the Uniting Church.

RELIGIONS AND THEOLOGY

MISSION TO MILITARY GARRISONS NEWS. see *MILITARY*

266   US   ISSN 0161-7133
MISSIONARY MONTHLY. 1896. m. (9/yr.). $14 in the U.S.: Canada and Mexico $16; elsewhere $17. Missionary Monthly, Inc., 4595 Broadmoor Ave., S.E., Ste. 237, Grand Rapids, MI 49512-5365. TEL 616-698-8393. FAX 616-698-3080. Ed. Dick L. Van Halsema. adv.; bk.rev. circ. 4,000.
   Description: Coverage of missionary efforts worldwide, and the political and social issues facing them and their message.

266   CN   ISSN 0026-6116
MISSIONS-ETRANGERES. (Text in French) 1941. bi-m. Can.$5. Societe des Missions-Etrangeres, 160 Place Juge-Desnoyers, Pont-Viau, Ville de Laval, PQ H7G 1A4, Canada. TEL 514-667-4190. Ed. Jean Greffard. charts; illus.; stat. circ. 40,000.

266   GW   ISSN 0076-9428
MISSIONSWISSENSCHAFTLICHE FORSCHUNGEN. 1962. irreg. price varies. Guetersloher Verlagshaus Chr. Kaiser, Carl-Bertelsmann-Str. 270, 33311 Guetersloh, Germany. TEL 05241-7405-0. FAX 05241-740548. **Document type:** monographic series.

200   GW   ISSN 0939-9186
BL256
MITTEILUNGEN FUER ANTHROPOLOGIE UND RELIGIONSGESCHICHTE. (Text in English, French, German) 1973. a. Ugarit-Verlag, Ricarda-Huch-Str. 6, 48161 Muenster, Germany. TEL 02534-1590. FAX 0251-832662. (Dist. by: BDK Buecherdienst GmbH, Koelnerstr. 248, 51149 Cologne, Germany. TEL 02203-100292. FAX 02203-100284) Ed. M.L.G. Dietrich. **Document type:** academic/scholarly publication.
   Formerly (until 1991): Jahrbuch fuer Anthropologie und Religionsgeschichte (ISSN 0341-0684)

268   TZ   ISSN 0047-7583
MLEZI/EDUCATOR; a journal for preaching and teaching religion. (Text in Swahili) 1970. bi-m. Sh.360($18) (effective 1994). Peramiho Publications, P.O. Box 41, Peramiho, Tanzania. TEL 255-1-580-8236. TELEX 21540. Ed. Vitus Ndunguru. adv.; bk.rev.; illus.; circ. 18,000 (paid). **Document type:** academic/scholarly publication.
   Description: Covers research on problems facing those teaching in the church.

200   UK   ISSN 0026-7597
BX5011
MODERN CHURCHMAN. 1911. q. £6 to non-members. Modern Churchpeople's Union, School House, Leysters, Leominster, Herefordshire HR6 0HB, England. Ed A.O. Dyson. adv.; bk.rev.; index. circ. 1,200. (also avail. in microfilm from UMI) **Indexed:** CERDIC, Mid.East: Abstr.& Ind., New Test.Abstr., Rel.& Theol.Abstr. (1989-), Rel.Ind.One, Rel.Per.

264   US   ISSN 0363-504X
BV169
MODERN LITURGY. 1973. 10/yr. $40. Resource Publications, Inc., 160 E. Virginia St., San Jose, CA 95112. TEL 408-286-8505. FAX 408-287-8748. Ed. Nick Wagner. adv.: B&W page $898, color page $1378; 8 3/8 x 10 7/8. bk.rev. circ. 12,000. (also avail. in microform from UMI / reprint service avail. from UMI) **Indexed:** Cath.Ind., CERDIC, Music Artic.Guide, Music Ind. **Document type:** trade publication.
   —BLDSC (5888.200000); UMI.
   Formerly: Folk Mass and Modern Liturgy (ISSN 0094-775X); Incorporates (in Sep. 1979): Worship Times.
   Description: Professional growth magazine for church leaders, with an emphasis on liturgical resources devoted to planning worship with help from the arts.

200   UK   ISSN 0266-7177
MODERN THEOLOGY. 1984. q. £104($188) (foreign £125) (effective 1996). Basil Blackwell Ltd., 108 Cowley Rd., Oxford OX4 1JF, England. TEL 0865-791100. FAX 0865-791347. TELEX 837022-OXBOOK-G. Ed.Bd. adv.; bk.rev. circ. 800. (also avail. in microform; reprint service avail. from SWZ) **Indexed:** Rel.& Theol.Abstr. (1986-).
   —BLDSC (5898.210000); Faxon; SWETS; UMI; UnCover. **CCC.**

MONDE DE LA BIBLE; archeologie & histoire. see *ARCHAEOLOGY*

200   NE   ISSN 0928-2742
MORALITY AND THE MEANING OF LIFE. (Text in English, German) 1992. irreg. price varies. Kok Pharos Publishing House, Postbus 5019, 8260 AG Kampen, Netherlands. TEL 31-5202-92565. FAX 31-5202-27331. (Dist. in U.S. and Canada by: Books International, Inc., Box 605, Herndon, VA 22070-0605. TEL 80-377-7192. FAX 703-689-0660) **Document type:** monographic series.

MOREANA; time trieth truth. see *HISTORY — History Of Europe*

200   GW
MORGENROTE. 1877. q. membership. Frei-religioese Gemeinde, Schillerplatz 1, 63067 Offenbach a.M., Germany. TEL 069-885275. FAX 069-64826409. circ. 2,100. **Document type:** newsletter.
   Description: Trends in liberal theology; humanistic, ethical and counseling issues.

MOUNTAIN PATH. see *PHILOSOPHY*

200   MG
MPANOLOTSAINA. (Text in Malagasy) q. B.P. 623, 101 Antananarivo, Madagascar. TEL 26845. Ed. Paul Solohery.

200   CN
MULTIFAITH NEWS. 1976. 5/yr. Can.$5. Multifaith Action Society, 385 Boundary Rd., Vancouver, BC V5K 4S1, Canada. TEL 604-291-1865. Ed. Joan Craker. adv.; bk.rev.; illus. circ. 2,000.
   Former titles: Canadian Ecumenical News (ISSN 0227-8243); B.C. Ecumenical News.
   Description: An inter-faith publication aimed at promoting understanding between different faith groups, social action in perspective.

200   US
MUNDI MEDICINA. 1989. 3/yr. (Order of the Holy Cross) Holy Cross Monastery, Box 99, West Park, NY 12493. TEL 914-384-6660.
   Description: Covers news of the Monastic community.

266   SP   ISSN 1134-7074
MUNDO NEGRO; revista misional africana. 1960. m. 1900 ptas. Misioneros Combonianos, Congregacion Misionera, Arturo Soria, 101, 28043 Madrid, Spain. FAX 91-5192550. Ed. Antonio Villarino Rodriguez. adv.; bk.rev.; illus.; stat.; index; circ. 100,000 (controlled). (back issues avail.) **Document type:** consumer publication.
   Description: Contains general information about the African continent (politics, economics, religion) and about Blacks in America.

200   UG
MUNNO. (Text in Luganda) 1911. m. EAs.1200. P.O. Box 4027, Kampala, Uganda. Ed. J. Kayondo. adv. circ. 6,500. **Document type:** newspaper.
   Formerly: Musizi (ISSN 0541-4385)

LE MUSEON; revue d'etudes orientales. see *ORIENTAL STUDIES*

226   PK   ISSN 0254-7856
AL-MUSHIR/COUNSELOR. (Text in English or Urdu) 1959. q. Rs.75($18) Christian Study Centre, 126-B Murree Rd., P.O. Box 579, Rawalpindi, Pakistan. TEL 92-51-567412. FAX 92-51-584594. Ed. Charles Amjad-Ali. bk.rev. circ. 650. **Document type:** academic/scholarly publication.
   Description: Discusses Christian-Muslim relations; Islamic, Christian theology and cultural, social issues in the context of Pakistan.

MUSIK UND KIRCHE. see *MUSIC*

MUZIEKBODE. see *MUSIC*

200   CK   ISSN 0027-5638
BX1751A1
MYSTERIUM. 1946. q. Col.$50. Provincia Occidental Claretianos de Colombia, Apdo Aereo 51-841, Medellin, Colombia. bk.rev.; bibl.; index. (tabloid format) **Indexed:** Amer.Hist.& Life, Hist.Abstr.

290 189   US   ISSN 0737-5840
BV5077.G7
MYSTICS QUARTERLY. 1974. q. $15 to individuals (foreign $20); institutions $20 (foreign $25). University of Cincinnati, Department of English, Cincinnati, OH 45221. TEL 519-556-3937. FAX 519-556-0142. Ed. Elizabeth Armstrong. bk.rev.; bibl.; index. circ. 450. (back issues avail.) **Indexed:** M.L.A. **Document type:** academic/scholarly publication.
   Formerly (until 1984): Fourteenth Century English Mystics Newsletter.
   Description: Publishes literary and historic research on mysticism, particularly that of medieval England and the rest of Europe.

N A O S; notes and materials for the linguistic study of the sacred. see *LINGUISTICS*

261.7 320.531   SW   ISSN 0282-1184
NAALSOEGAT. 1980. q. SEK 60. Kristna foer Socialism i Sverige (KFS), C/o Karin Boberg, Rudeboksvaegen 640, S-226 55 Lund, Sweden. TEL 46-32-04-68.

266 610   GW   ISSN 0027-7398
NACHRICHTEN AUS DER AERZTLICHEN MISSION. 1950. q. free. Deutsches Institut fuer Aerztliche Mission - German Institute for Medical Mission, Paul-Lechler-Str. 24, 72076 Tuebingen, Germany. TEL 07071-206-512. FAX 07071-27125. Ed. Rainward Bastian. bk.rev.; illus. circ. 15,000. **Document type:** newsletter.

281.7 299.932   NE
NAG HAMMADI AND MANICHAEAN STUDIES. 1971. irreg., vol.37, 1995. price varies. E.J. Brill, P.O. Box 9000, 2300 PA Leiden, Netherlands. TEL 31-71-5353500. FAX 31-71-5317532. TELEX 39296 BRILL NL. (In N. America: E.J. Brill, 24 Hudson St., Kinderhook, NY 12106. TEL 800-962-4406. FAX 518-758-1959) Ed.Bd. (back issues avail.) **Document type:** monographic series.
   Formerly (until vol.36, 1994): Nag Hammadi Studies (ISSN 0169-9350); Supersedes: Coptic Gnostic Library (ISSN 0169-7749)
   Description: Scholarly discussions of Gnostic, Manichaean and early Christian religious topics based upon the papyrus Gospels found at Nag Hammadi, and Coptic and Manichaean texts from Dakhlah Oasis, Egypt. Includes translations, commentary on specific codices as well as analysis of textual and theological issues.
   Refereed Serial

200 952   JA   ISSN 0386-720X
NANZAN INSTITUTE FOR RELIGION AND CULTURE. BULLETIN. (Text in English) 1977. a. free. Nanzan University, Nanzan Institute for Religion and Culture, 18 Yamazato-cho, Showa-ku, Nagoya 466, Japan. TEL 052-832-3111. FAX 052-833-6157. Ed. James W. Heisig. circ. 1,200. (back issues avail.) **Document type:** bulletin.
   —BLDSC (2629.105000).

200   JA   ISSN 0387-3730
NANZAN JOURNAL OF THEOLOGICAL STUDIES. (Text in Japanese) 1979. a. free. Nanzan University, Faculty of Sacred Theology, 18 Yamazato-cho, Showa-ku, Nagoya-shi, Aichi-ken 466, Japan. TEL 052-832-3111. E-mail: nas@ic.nanzan-u.ac.jc.

200 296   US
NARROW WAY. (Text in English, Greek, Hebrew) 1970. bi-m. free. Assemblies of Yahweh, Box C, Bethel, PA 19507. TEL 717-933-4518. Ed. Jacob O. Meyer. circ. 1,200. (back issues avail.) **Document type:** newsletter.

291   US
NATIONAL AND INTERNATIONAL RELIGION REPORT. 1987. fortn. $49. Religion Today, Inc., Box 21505, Roanoke, VA 24018-0560. TEL 703-989-7500. FAX 703-989-0189. E-mail: CompuServe: 71736,702. circ. 7,800 (paid). **Document type:** newsletter.
   Description: Covers news of current events in and of interest to church.

RELIGIONS AND THEOLOGY

200 AT ISSN 0159-3242
NATIONAL OUTLOOK; Australian Christian monthly. 1979. m. Aus.$35 (foreign Aus.$48). Outlook Media Ltd., G.P.O. Box 2134, Sydney, N.S.W. 2001, Australia. TEL 61-2-3180918. FAX 61-2-6999182. E-mail: bill.neville@accnet.net.au. Ed. David Thomas. adv.; bk.rev. circ. 3,000. (back issues avail.)
Incorporates (1980-1995): Poverty Watch (ISSN 0810-5537)
Description: Independent, ecumenical magazine concerned with social ethics, theological developments, economics, and politics.

NAVY CHAPLAIN. see *MILITARY*

NAZAN STUDIES IN RELIGION & CULTURE. see *PHILOSOPHY*

200 IT ISSN 0028-1700
NAZARETH.* vol.90, 1970. bi-m. contributions. Via Filitteria 10, 06049 Spoleto, Italy. circ. 2,000 (controlled). (processed)

270 NE ISSN 0028-2030
NEDERLANDS ARCHIEF VOOR KERKGESCHIEDENIS/DUTCH REVIEW OF CHURCH HISTORY. 1900. 2/yr. fl.110($71) to individuals; institutions fl.128($83) (effective 1996). E.J. Brill, P.O. Box 9000, 2300 PA Leiden, Netherlands. TEL 31-71-5353500. FAX 31-71-5317532. TELEX 39296 BRILL NL. E-mail: ejborders@ejbrill.com. (In N. America: E.J. Brill, 24 Hudson St., Kinderhook, NY 12106. TEL 800-962-4406. FAX 518-758-1959) Ed. J. Trapman, E.G.E. van der Wall. bk.rev.; bibl. **Indexed:** Amer.Hist.& Life, CERDIC, Hist.Abstr., Rel.Ind.One. **Document type:** academic/scholarly publication.
—BLDSC (6069.350000); SWETS. **CCC.**
Description: Explores church history in the Netherlands.
Refereed Serial

230 NE ISSN 0028-212X
NEDERLANDS THEOLOGISCH TIJDSCHRIFT. vol.30, 1975. q. fl.80. Boekencentrum B.V., Postbus 29, 2700 AA Zoetermeer, Netherlands. TEL 31-79-615481. FAX 31-79-615489. Ed. K.A.D. Smelik. adv.; bk.rev.; bibl.; index. circ. 800. **Indexed:** CERDIC, New Test.Abstr., Old Test.Abstr., Rel.& Theol.Abstr. (1967-), Rel.Ind.One, Rel.Per.
—BLDSC (6071.380000); SWETS.

200 301 301 283 AT ISSN 0726-0458
NELEN YUBU. 1978. q. Aus.$15. Nelen Yubu Missiological Unit, P.O. Box 156, Drummoyne, N.S.W. 2047, Australia. TEL 61-2-819-7627. FAX 61-2-819-7626. (Subscr. to: 4-17 Jersey Ave, Leura, N.S.W. 2780, Australia) Ed. M.J. Wilson. bk.rev.; cum.index: 1978-1985. circ. 250. (back issues avail.)

205 DK ISSN 0108-3023
NEMALAH/MYREN. 1982. q. DKK 95 (foreign DKK 120). Dansk Bibel Institut, Frederiksborggade 1 B, 1, DK-1360 Copenhagen K, Denmark. TEL 45-33-13-55-00. Ed. Flemming H. Moeller. bk.rev. circ. 400. **Document type:** academic/scholarly publication.
Description: Directed to students at the Danish Bible Institute, pastors and lay preachers. Presents theological and spiritual guidance.

225 SA ISSN 0254-8356
NEOTESTAMENTICA. (Text in English) 1967. 2/yr. $30. New Testament Society of South Africa - Nuwe Testamentiese Werkgemeenskap van Suid-Afrika, c/o Department of New Testament, University of the Orange Free State, P.O. Box 339, Bloemfontein 9300, South Africa. TEL 27-51-4012667. FAX 27-51-489203. E-mail: TLGHC@RS.UOVS.AC.ZA. Ed. H.C. van Zyl. adv.; bk.rev. 430. (also avail. in microfiche; reprint service avail. from UMI) **Indexed:** Bull.Signal., Int.Z.Bibelwiss., New Test.Abstr., Rel.& Theol.Abstr. (1983-). **Document type:** academic/scholarly publication.
—BLDSC (6075.655000); Faxon. **CCC.**
Description: Contains literary, historical and theological reflections on New Testament texts.
Refereed Serial

266 US
NETWORK (ATLANTA). 1983. q. Presbyterian Church in America, Mission to the World, Box 29765, Atlanta, GA 30359. FAX 404-636-5733. Ed. Jud Lamos. bk.rev.; illus.; stat. circ. 85,000. (processed)
Supersedes (1957-1983): W P M Newsletter (World Presbyterian Missions) (ISSN 0042-9783)
Description: Covers foreign mission work of the church.

200 GW ISSN 0344-7022
NEUE STADT. 1957. m. DM.35. Verlag Neue Stadt, Postfach 8306567, 81706 Munich, Germany. TEL 08093-2091. FAX 08093-2096. adv. circ. 20,000. (back issues avail.) **Document type:** bulletin.

266 SZ ISSN 0028-3495
NEUE ZEITSCHRIFT FUER MISSIONSWISSENSCHAFT/NOUVELLE REVUE DE SCIENCE MISSIONNAIRE. (Text in English, French, German and Italian) 1945. q. 49.60 SFr. Verein zur Foerderung der Missionswissenschaft - Association for Promoting Mission Studies, CH-6405 Immensee, Switzerland. TEL 041-828192. FAX 041-814209. Ed. Fritz Kollbrunner. adv.; bk.rev.; bibl.; illus.; index. circ. 800. **Indexed:** CERDIC, Curr.Cont.Africa, E.I. **Document type:** newsletter.

201 GW ISSN 0028-3517
NEUE ZEITSCHRIFT FUER SYSTEMATISCHE THEOLOGIE UND RELIGIONSPHILOSOPHIE. 1959. 3/yr. DM.174 (students DM.65). Walter de Gruyter und Co., Genthiner Str. 13, 10785 Berlin, Germany. TEL 030-26005-0. FAX 030-26005251. TELEX 184027. (U.S. addr.: Walter de Gruyter, Inc., 200 Saw Mill River Rd., Hawthorne, NY 10532. TEL 914-747-0110) Ed. Oswald Bayer. adv.; bk.rev.; bibl.; index. **Indexed:** CERDIC, Rel.& Theol.Abstr. (1984-), Rel.Ind.One, Rel.Per. **Document type:** academic/scholarly publication.
—Genuine Article; SWETS. **CCC.**

200 GW ISSN 0720-3772
NEUERWERBUNGEN THEOLOGIE UND ALLGEMEINE RELIGIONSWISSENSCHAFT. 1973. m. DM.40. Universitaetsbibliothek Tuebingen, Theologische Abteilung, Postfach 2620, 72016 Tuebingen, Germany. TEL 07071-292587. FAX 07071-293123. circ. 650. (back issues avail.) **Document type:** academic/scholarly publication.

200 GW ISSN 0028-3665
NEUES LEBEN (MOERS). Christliches Monatsmagazin. 1956. m. DM.72.90. (Neues Leben Medien e.V) Brendow Verlag, Gutenbergstr. 1, 47443 Moers, Germany. TEL 02681-941250. FAX 02681-941100. Eds. Peter Schulte, Wilfried Schulte. adv.; bk.rev.; illus. circ. 25,000. **Document type:** consumer publication.

NEW ATHENAEUM/NEUES ATHENAEUM. see *LITERATURE*

200 US ISSN 0028-4254
NEW AURORA. (Text in English and Italian) 1903. m. (except July & Aug.). $5. Association of Evangelicals for Italian Missions, 314 Richfield Rd., Upper Darby, PA 19082. TEL 610-352-2396. Ed. Rev. Anthony F. Vasquez. adv. circ. 1,500.

200 PH
NEW CITY. 1966. m. P.90($4) (Focolare Movement for Men) New City Press, Box 332, Manila, Philippines. FAX 02-623956. Ed. Guido Mirti. adv.; circ. 10,000 (controlled).

200 UK ISSN 0142-7725
NEW CITY (LONDON). 1970. 11/yr. £13.50 (foreign £16). Mariapolis Ltd. Focolare Movement, 57 Twyford Ave., London W3 9PZ, England. TEL 0181-993-6944. Ed. Frank Johnson. adv. contact: Rumold van Geffen. bk.rev. circ. 1,200. (back issues avail.) **Document type:** newsletter.
Description: Examines religion and theology via the Focolare Movement.

200 UK ISSN 0140-5845
NEW CITY (SHEFFIELD). 1971. irreg. (1-2/yr.). £20. Urban Theology Unit, 210 Abbeyfield Rd., Sheffield S4 7AZ, England. TEL 01742-435342. **Document type:** bulletin.
—BLDSC (6082.686000).
Description: Covers urban issues, the ministry in the city, liberation theology, and theological education.

200 US ISSN 0360-0181
NEW CONVERSATIONS. 1975. 3/yr. $10. United Church Board for Homeland Ministries, 700 Prospect Ave., Cleveland, OH 44115-1100. TEL 216-736-3277. FAX 216-736-3263. Ed. Nanette M. Roberts. bk.rev.; circ. 1,500 (controlled).

266.025 UK
NEW DAY. 1896. 2/yr. free. Leprosy Mission, Goldhay Way, Orton Goldway, Peterborough PE2 5GZ, England. TEL 01733-3705052. FAX 01733-3709608. Ed. D. Chand. circ. 139,700. **Document type:** bulletin.
Former titles: Leprosy Mission in Action; Without the Camp (ISSN 0043-7018)

200 AT
NEW DAY INTERNATIONAL. 1980. 10/yr. Aus.$25 (foreign Aus.$38). House of Tabor, 7 Lynton Ave., Plympton, S.A. 5038, Australia. TEL 08-3710940. FAX 08-2977833. (Subscr. to.: P.O. Box 564, Plympton, S.A. 5038, Australia) Ed. Geoffrey Strelan. adv.; bk.rev.; film rev. circ. 3,000. (back issues avail.)
Formerly (until 1986): Australia's New Day.
Description: Covers teaching, inspirational - devotional material, news from a charismatic perspective with an emphasis on Christian unity.

220 AT ISSN 0812-9576
NEW DOCUMENTS ILLUSTRATING EARLY CHRISTIANITY. 1981. irreg. Aus.$30 to individuals; institutions Aus.$35. Ancient History Documentary Research Centre, Macquarie University, N.S.W. 2109, Australia. TEL 02-805-7512. FAX 02-805-8892. TELEX AA 122377 MACUNI. Ed. S.R. Llewelyn. index. circ. 2,000. (back issues avail.)
Description: Studies Greek texts, inscriptions and papyri.

200 II
NEW LEADER. (Text in English) 1887. w. 93 North Rd., St. Mary's Town, Bangalore 560 005, India. Ed. Rev. Herman D'Souza. circ. 10,000. **Indexed:** Polit.Sci.Abstr.

200 UK ISSN 0260-2792
NEW LIFE (LONDON, 1971); prison service chaplaincy review. 1971. a. Home Office, 50 Queen Anne's Gate, London SW1H 9AT, England. TEL 0522-533633. Ed. Rev. A.R. Duce. circ. 4,000. **Document type:** government publication.
—BLDSC (6084.455120).

200 305.31 US ISSN 1077-3959
HQ1090.3
▼**NEW MAN**. 1994. bi-m. $15. Strang Communications Co., 600 Rinehart Rd., Lake Mary, FL 32746. TEL 407-333-0600. Ed. Brian Peterson; Pub. Stephen Strang. circ. 200,000. **Document type:** consumer publication.
Description: Contains articles of a religious nature for men.

200 CN ISSN 0704-5883
NEW RELIGIONS NEWSLETTER. 1978. m. $10. c/o Prof. Herbert Richardson, 81 St. Mary's St., Toronto, ON M5S 1J4, Canada.

225 UK ISSN 0028-6885
BS410
NEW TESTAMENT STUDIES. (Text in English, French and German) 1954. q. £59($112) (effective 1996). (Studiorum Novi Testamenti Societas) Cambridge University Press, Edinburgh Bldg., Shaftesbury Rd., Cambridge CB2 2RU, England. TEL 01223-312393. FAX 01223-315052. TELEX 851817256. (N. American addr.: Cambridge University Press, Journals Dept., 40 W. 20th St., New York, NY 10011. TEL 212-924-3900. FAX 212-691-3239) Ed. A.J.M. Wedderburn. adv.; bk.rev. (also avail. in microform from UMI; back issues avail.; reprint service avail. from SWZ) **Indexed:** Arts & Hum.Cit.Ind., CERDIC, Curr.Cont., Hum.Ind., New Test.Abstr., Rel.& Theol.Abstr. (1968-), Rel.Ind.One, Rel.Per. **Document type:** academic/scholarly publication.
—BLDSC (6088.862000); Faxon; Genuine Article; SWETS; UMI; UnCover. **CCC.**
Description: Covers all aspects of the text and theology of the New Testament.

RELIGIONS AND THEOLOGY

220 NE ISSN 0077-8842
NEW TESTAMENT TOOLS AND STUDIES. 1960. irreg., vol.19, 1994. price varies. E.J. Brill, P.O. Box 9000, 2300 PA Leiden, Netherlands. TEL 31-71-5353500. FAX 31-71-5317532. TELEX 39296 BRILL NL. (In N. America: E.J. Brill, 24 Hudson St., Kinderhook, NY 12106. TEL 800-962-4406. FAX 518-758-1959) Ed. Bruce M. Metzger. **Document type:** monographic series, bibliography.
  Description: Presents studies of the New Testament, and bibliographies of research and commentary relevant to further study.
  Refereed Serial

NEW THOUGHT JOURNAL. see *PHILOSOPHY*

200 US
NEW WINE;* for Christians today. 1990. w. $12.95 (Canada $22.95; elsewhere $32.95). Chalice Press, Inc., 13 Oak Hill Cluster, Independence, MO 64050. TEL 800-762-4935. FAX 816-836-1942. adv.; bk.rev. circ. 10,000.

266 284.1 US ISSN 0043-8812
BV2550
NEW WORLD OUTLOOK; United Methodist missions. 1911; N.S. 1941. bi-m. $12. United Methodist Church, General Board of Global Ministries, 475 Riverside Dr., Rm. 1351, New York, NY 10115. TEL 212-870-3765. FAX 212-870-3940. Ed. Alma Graham. adv. contact: Ruth Kurtz. bk.rev.; illus.; index; circ. 30,000 (paid). (also avail. in microfilm) **Indexed:** CERDIC, Mid.East: Abstr.& Ind.
  Formerly: World Outlook.
  Description: Covers United Methodist Mission work in the United States and around the world.

200 US
NEW YORK CHRISTIAN TIMES; good news for a change! 1990. bi-w. $36. Harvest Press, 1061 Atlantic Ave., Brooklyn, NY 11238. TEL 718-638-6397. FAX 718-638-1810. circ. 28,000.

NEW YORK PEARL. see *POLITICAL SCIENCE*

200 323.4 US ISSN 1042-606X
NEWS NETWORK INTERNATIONAL. 1983. s-m. price varies. N N I, Inc., Box 28001, Santa Ana, CA 92799. TEL 714-775-4900. FAX 714-775-7315. E-mail: 75362,2573@compuserve.com. Ed. Kim Lawton. (looseleaf format; back issues avail.; reprint service avail.)
  Formerly: Open Doors News Service.
  Description: Religious freedom news and information.

200 UK ISSN 0263-7170
NEWS OF LITURGY. 1975. m. £6.50($18) Grove Books, Ltd., Bramcote, Nottingham NG9 3DS, England. TEL 0115-943-0786. FAX 0115-922-0134. Ed. Colin Buchanan. adv.; bk.rev. circ. 1,000. (looseleaf format; back issues avail.)

NEWS SPECIAL; & the messenger. see *GENERAL INTEREST PERIODICALS — Great Britain*

200 CN ISSN 0703-5888
NIAGARA ANGLICAN. 1954. m. (10/yr.). Can.$10. 67 Victoria Ave. S., Hamilton, ON L8N 2S8, Canada. TEL 905-521-9598. FAX 905-521-9598. Ed. Larry Perks. adv. contact: Roddie Gould-Perks. bk.rev. circ. 19,500. **Document type:** newspaper.

200 NR ISSN 0029-005X
BR1463.N5
NIGERIAN CHRISTIAN. (Text in English) 1967-1982; N.S. 1984. m. $12. (Christian Council of Nigeria) Daystar Press, Box 1261, Ibadan, Nigeria. Ed. Rachel Alao. adv.; bk.rev.; illus. circ. 1,500. **Indexed:** CERDIC.
  Description: Reports on matters of importance to Nigerian national life with critical references to Christianity in the region.

266 IT ISSN 0029-0173
BV3500
NIGRIZIA; fatti e problemi del mondo nero. 1883. m. L.30000. Missionari Comboniani, Vicolo Pozzo 1, 37129 Verona, Italy. Ed. Efrem Tresoldi. adv.; bk.rev.; illus.; stat.; index. circ. 50,000. **Indexed:** CERDIC, Curr.Cont.Africa.

200 NE ISSN 0169-930X
NISABA; religious texts translation series. 1973. irreg., vol.17, 1989. price varies. E.J. Brill, P.O. Box 9000, 2300 PA Leiden, Netherlands. TEL 31-71-5353500. FAX 31-71-5317532. TELEX 39296 BRILL NL. (In N. America: E.J. Brill, 24 Hudson St., Kinderhook, NY 12106. TEL 800-962-4406. FAX 518-758-1959) (back issues avail.) **Document type:** monographic series.
  Description: Collection of texts in English translation, illuminating the religions of the world for students.

230 NO ISSN 0029-2176
NORSK TEOLOGISK TIDSSKRIFT/NORWEGIAN THEOLOGICAL JOURNAL. 1900. q. NOK 390 in Nordic countries; elsewhere $74 (effective 1996). (Teologiske Fakultet) Scandinavian University Press, P.O. Box 2959 Tøyen, N-0608 Oslo, Norway. TEL 47-22-85-03-00. E-mail: aud.tonnessen@teologi.uid.no. (U.S. addr.: Scandinavian University Press, 200 Meecham Ave., Elmont, NY 11003. TEL 516-352-7300) Ed. Trygve Wyller. adv.; bk.rev.; abstr.; index. circ. 550. **Indexed:** Amer.Hist.& Life (until 1991), CERDIC, Hist.Abstr. (until 1991), New Test.Abstr., Old Test.Abstr., Rel.& Theol.Abstr. (1989-), Rel.Ind.One, Rel.Per.

266 NO ISSN 0029-2214
NORSK TIDSSKRIFT FOR MISJON/NORWEGIAN JOURNAL OF MISSION AND MISSIONARY QUESTIONS. q. $60. (Egede Institute, Oslo) Scandinavian University Press, P.O. Box 2959 Tøyen, N-0608 Oslo, Norway. TEL 47-22-57-54-00. FAX 47-22-57-53-53. (U.S. addr.: Scandinavian University Press, 200 Meacham Ave., Elmont, NY 11003. TEL 516-352-7300) Ed. Notto R. Thelle. adv.; bk.rev.; index. circ. 800. (back issues avail.) **Indexed:** CERDIC.

250 II
NORTH INDIA CHURCHMAN. (Text in English) 1971. m. Rs.10($9) North India Churchman Board, 16 Pandit Pant Marg, New Delhi 110 001, India. TELEX 3166763-UPC-IN. Ed. Harold Williams. adv.; bk.rev. circ. 1,200.

NOTES ON LITERATURE IN USE AND LANGUAGE PROGRAMS. see *LINGUISTICS*

200 301 PE
NOTICIAS ALIADAS. English edition: Latinamerica Press. w. $60 to individuals; institutions $85 (effective 1996). Noticias Aliadas, Apdo. 18-0964, Lima 18, Peru. TEL 51-14-475210. FAX 51-14-454681. E-mail: postmaster@acna.org.pe. Dir. George Ann Potter; Pub. Brian Goonan Costelloe. circ. 2,500. **Indexed:** HR Rep. **Document type:** bulletin.
  Description: Focuses on issues involving the church, women's rights, grassroots organizations, indigenous issues, the environment and neoliberal economic programs in Latin America.

266 NQ
NOTICIAS EVANGELICAS. bi-m. Comite Evangelico pro Ayudo al Desarrollo, Apdo. Postal 3091, Managua, Nicaragua.

NOTRE DAME JOURNAL OF LAW, ETHICS & PUBLIC POLICY. see *PUBLIC ADMINISTRATION*

230 BE ISSN 0029-4845
BX802
NOUVELLE REVUE THEOLOGIQUE. 1868. 6/yr. $73. (Centre de Documentation et de Recherche Religieuses) Casterman, S.A., 28 rue des Soeurs Noires, B-7500 Tournai, Belgium. (Dist. in N. America by: Aquinas Agency, 561 Fort Rd., St. Paul, MN 55102) Ed. A. Toubeau. bk.rev.; bibl.; index. circ. 4,000. **Indexed:** Canon Law Abstr., Cath.Ind., CERDIC, New Test.Abstr., Old Test.Abstr., Rel.& Theol.Abstr. (1970-). **Document type:** academic/scholarly publication.
  —BLDSC (6176.845000); SWETS.

225 NE ISSN 0048-1009
BS410
NOVUM TESTAMENTUM; an international quarterly for New Testament and related studies. (Supplement avail. (ISSN 0167-9732)) (Text in English, French and German) 1956. q. fl.128($83) to individuals; institutions fl.180($116) (effective 1996). E.J. Brill, P.O. Box 9000, 2300 PA Leiden, Netherlands. TEL 31-71-5353500. FAX 31-71-5317532. TELEX 39296 BRILL NL. E-mail: ejborders@ejbrill.com. (In N. America: E.J. Brill, 24 Hudson St., Kinderhook, NY 12106. TEL 800-962-4406. FAX 518-758-1959) Ed. H.J. de Jonge. cum.index: vols.1-35. (also avail. in microform from SWZ; reprint service avail. from SWZ) **Indexed:** Arts & Hum.Cit.Ind., Bibl.Ling., CERDIC, Curr.Cont., New Test.Abstr., Rel.& Theol.Abstr. (1968-), Rel.Ind.One, Rel.Per. **Document type:** academic/scholarly publication.
  —Faxon; Genuine Article; SWETS; UnCover. **CCC.**
  Description: International coverage of New Testament studies, including literary and textual criticism, critical interpretation, theology and the historical and literary background of the New Testament and early Christian literature. Includes a bibliographic section, Bibliographia Gnostica.
  Refereed Serial

225 NE ISSN 0167-9732
NOVUM TESTAMENTUM. SUPPLEMENTS. (Supplement to: Novum Testamentum (ISSN 0048-1009)) 1958. irreg., vol.78, 1995. price varies. E.J. Brill, P.O. Box 9000, 2300 PA Leiden, Netherlands. TEL 31-71-5353500. FAX 31-71-5317532. TELEX 39296 BRILL NL. (In N. America: E.J. Brill, Kinderhook, NY 12106. TEL 800-962-4406. FAX 518-758-1959) Ed.Bd. (back issues avail.) **Indexed:** Rel.Ind.One. **Document type:** monographic series.
  —BLDSC (6180.445200).
  Description: Scholarly studies on topics pertaining to the history of early Christianity and studies in the New Testament.
  Refereed Serial

268 028.5 DK
NU PA VEJ; en bibelnoegle for juniorer. 1985. q. DKK 20. Bibellaeser-Ringen, Korskaervej 25, 7000 Fredericia, Denmark. illus.
  Formerly: Paa Vej (ISSN 0900-3355)

200 DR ISSN 0029-5752
NUESTRO AMIGO. 1931. m. free. Iglesia Evangelica Dominicana, Apartado 727, Santo Domingo, Dominican Republic. Ed. Herman Gonzalez Roca. circ. 2,500. (tabloid format; also avail. in cards)

200 AG ISSN 0327-7097
BR7
NUEVO MUNDO. 1971. s-a. $10. Ediciones Castaneda, Centenario 1399, 1718 San Antonio de Padua, Buenos Aires, Argentina.

209 NE ISSN 0029-5973
BL1
NUMEN; international review for the history of religions. (Supplement avail. (ISSN 0169-8834)) (Text in English, French, German and Italian) 1954. 3/yr. fl.100($65) to individuals; institutions fl.150($97) (effective 1996). (International Association for the History of Religions) E.J. Brill, P.O. Box 9000, 2300 PA Leiden, Netherlands. TEL 31-71-5353500. FAX 31-71-5317532. TELEX 39296 BRILL NL. E-mail: ejborders@ejbrill.com. (In N. America: E.J. Brill, 24 Hudson St., Kinderhook, NY 12106. TEL 800-962-4406. FAX 518-758-1959) Ed. H.G. Kippenberg, E.T. Lawson. bk.rev.; bibl. (also avail. in microform from SWZ; back issues avail.; reprint service avail. from SWZ) **Indexed:** CERDIC, Curr.Cont., Mid.East: Abstr.& Ind., New Test.Abstr., Rel.& Theol.Abstr. (1980-), Rel.Ind.One, Rel.Per. **Document type:** academic/scholarly publication.
  —BLDSC (6184.650000); Faxon; Genuine Article; SWETS; UnCover. **CCC.**
  Description: Publishes original, international contributions reporting the results of investigations carried out in the history of religions.
  Refereed Serial

RELIGIONS AND THEOLOGY

291 NE ISSN 0169-8834
NUMEN SUPPLEMENTS; studies in the history of religions. Variant title: Numen Bookseries. (Supplement to: Numen (ISSN 0029-5973)) 1954. irreg., vol.64, 1994. price varies. (International Association for the History of Religions) E.J. Brill, P.O. Box 9000, 2300 PA Leiden, Netherlands. TEL 31-71-5353500. FAX 31-71-5317532. TELEX 39296 BRILL NL. (In N. America: E.J. Brill, 24 Hudson St., Kinderhook, NY 12106. TEL 800-962-4406. FAX 518-758-1959) Ed.Bd. (back issues avail.) **Indexed:** Rel.Ind.Two. **Document type:** monographic series, proceedings.
—BLDSC (8490.676000).
Formerly: Studies in the History of Religions (ISSN 0585-7260); **Supersedes:** Numen Supplements, Altera Series (ISSN 0169-8885)
Description: Publishes scholarly studies on topics in the history of specific ancient and modern religions throughout the world, comparative studies, and proceedings of conferences.
Refereed Serial

NUOVA EUROPA. see *ART*

200 IT
NUOVO LEOPARDI. irreg., no.32, 1990. L.5000 per no. (6 nos. L.25000). Associazione per la Ricerca Religiosa "S. Bernadino" Societa Coop. a r.l., Via S. Donato 1, 61029 Urbino, Italy. TEL 0722-320539. (Dist. by: Edizioni Quattroventi, Via Dini 16, 61029 Urbino, Italy. TEL 0722-2588) Ed. Gastone Mosci. circ. 1,500.

NURTURE; journal for home and school. see *EDUCATION — Teaching Methods And Curriculum*

NUTRAM. see *ETHNIC INTERESTS*

NY DAG. see *CHILDREN AND YOUTH — For*

200 DK ISSN 0109-3169
NYHEDSBREV. 1983. s-a. free. Aarhus Universitet, Teologiske Fakultet, Universitetsparken, 8000 Aarhus C, Denmark. TEL 45-89-42-11-11. Ed. Povl Lind-Petersen. bk.rev. circ. 2,000.
Formerly: T F Nyhedsbrev (ISSN 0108-8939)

220 DK ISSN 0108-898X
NYT FRA BIBELSELSKABET. 1982. q. free. Danske Bibelselskab, Frederiksborggade 50, 1360 Copenhagen K, Denmark. TEL 33-127835. FAX 33-93-21-50. illus.
Formerly: Danske Bibelselskab. Medlemsbrev.

255 SP
OBISPADO DE TORTOSA. BOLETIN OFICIAL. 1858. m. 3000 ptas. (effective 1990). Obispado de Tortosa, Cruera, 5, Tortosa, Spain. TEL 977-44-07-00. FAX 977-44-03-78. Ed. Jose Maria Ribes Herrero. adv.; bk.rev.; bibl.; index. circ. 350. **Document type:** bulletin.

266 US
OBLATES. 1943. 6/yr. membership. Missionary Association of Mary Immaculate, 15 S. 59th St., Belleville, IL 62223-4694. TEL 618-233-2238. Ed. Christine Portell. circ. 500,000 (controlled). (back issues avail.) **Document type:** newsletter.
Description: Articles and poetry espousing positive Christian direction for primarily middle-age to older Catholic adults.

282 CI ISSN 0351-3947
OBNOVLJENI ZIVOT/LIFE RENEWED; dvomjesecnik za religioznu kulturu. (Text in Croatian; summaries in English, French, German, Latin) 1919-1945; resumed 1971. bi-m. $50. Filozofsko-Teoloski Insitut Druzbe Isusove - Institute of Philosophy and Theology, S.J., Jordanovac 110, 41001 Zagreb, Croatia. TEL 041-216-266. Ed. Ivan Koprek. bk.rev.; abstr.; bibl.; stat.; index. circ. 1,600. (back issues avail.)

280 GW ISSN 0029-8654
OEKUMENISCHE RUNDSCHAU. 1952. q. DM.48. (Deutscher Oekumenischer Studienausschuss) Verlag Otto Lembeck, Leerbachstr. 42, 60322 Frankfurt a.M., Germany. TEL 069-5970988. FAX 069-5975742. Ed. Hans Vorster. adv. contact: Christina Gleichfeld. bk.rev.; index. circ. 1,600. **Indexed:** CERDIC. **Document type:** academic/scholarly publication.

200 GW ISSN 0179-9959
OEKUMENISCHER INFORMATIONSDIENST. 1982. q. DM.15. Oekumenische Gesellschaft fuer G F S, Rendeler Str. 9-11, 60385 Frankfurt a.M., Germany. TEL 05694-1417. Ed. Ulrich Schmitthenner. adv.; bk.rev. circ. 6,000. (back issues avail.) **Document type:** bulletin.

OESTERREICHISCHES ARCHIV FUER KIRCHENRECHT. see *LAW*

266 GW ISSN 0030-011X
OFFENE TUEREN. 1907. bi-m. Missionshaus Bibelschule Wiedenest e.V., Olper Str. 10, 51702 Bergneustadt, Germany. TEL 02261-4092-0. FAX 02261-4092155. Ed. Thomas Meyerhoefer. adv. contact: Klaus Brinkmann. bk.rev.; illus. circ. 11,000. **Document type:** newsletter.
Description: Focus on the work of German missionaries in various countries.

221 SA ISSN 1010-9919
BS410
OLD TESTAMENT ESSAYS. (Text mainly in English; occasionally in Afrikaans, Dutch, German) 1983-198?; N.S. 1988. q. $70. (Old Testament Society of South Africa) Serva Publishers, P.O. Box 30043, Sunnyside 0132, Transvaal, South Africa. (Co-sponsor: University of South Africa, Department of Old Testament) Ed. J. Burden. adv.; bk.rev. circ. 400. (back issues avail.) **Indexed:** Old Test.Abstr., Rel.& Theol.Abstr. (1989-). **Document type:** academic/scholarly publication.
Refereed Serial

377.8 UK ISSN 0268-8786
ONE TO ONE (LONDON, 1947). 1947. q. £5.20. Scripture Union Publishing, 130 City Rd., London EC1V 2NJ, England. TEL 0171-782-0013. FAX 0171-782-0014. (Subscr. to: 9-11 Clothier Rd., Bristol BS4 5RL, England) Ed. Jenny Hyatt. adv. contact: J. Bicknell. charts; illus. circ. 15,000. **Document type:** bulletin.
Formerly: Key Notes.

200 SZ ISSN 0303-125X
BR1
ONE WORLD. (Text in English) 1975. 10/yr. 39.90 SFr.($29.90) World Council of Churches, Publications Office, 150 route de Ferney, P.O. Box 2100, CH-1211 Geneva 2, Switzerland. TEL 022-791-6111. FAX 022-791-0361. TELEX 415730-OIK-CH. Ed. Mark Halton. illus. circ. 6,500. (also avail. in microform from UMI; reprint service avail. from UMI) **Indexed:** CERDIC, Rel.Ind.One, So.Pac.Per.Ind. **Document type:** bulletin.
—BLDSC (6260.246000); SWETS; UMI.

209 940 BE ISSN 0774-2827
BX806.D8
ONS GEESTELIJK ERF; tijdschrift voor de geschiedenis van de vroomheid in de Nederlanden. (Text in Dutch) 1927. 4/yr. 1800 BEF (effective 1995). (Universitaire Faculteiten Sint Ignatius te Antwerpen, Ruusbroecgenootschap) Editions Peeters s.p.r.l, Bondgenotenlaan 153, 3000 Leuven, Belgium. TEL 32-16-235170. FAX 32-16-228500. (back issues avail.) **Document type:** academic/scholarly publication.
—SWETS.
Description: Publishes contributions on the history of piety in the Netherlands, and related topics in religion and medieval studies.
Refereed Serial

OPEN VENSTER; maandblad voor ouderen. see *GERONTOLOGY AND GERIATRICS*

OPINION. see *PHILOSOPHY*

ORACLE. see *PARAPSYCHOLOGY AND OCCULTISM*

200 FR ISSN 0030-4352
ORATORIANA.* 1960. s-a. 10 F. Oratoire de France, 75 rue de Vaugirard, 75006 Paris, France. bk.rev.; bibl.; illus.

200 GW ISSN 0340-6407
ORIENS CHRISTIANUS; Hefte fuer die Kunde des christlichen Orients. 1911. a. DM.138. Harrassowitz Verlag, Taunusstr. 14, 65183 Wiesbaden, Germany. TEL 0611-530-0. FAX 0611-530570. TELEX 4186135. (Subscr. to: Postfach 2929, 65019 Wiesbaden, Germany) Eds. Julius Assfalg, Hubert Kaufhold. adv.; bk.rev. circ. 400. (back issues avail.) **Indexed:** Bibl.Ling., Rel.Ind.One. **Document type:** academic/scholarly publication.
—SWETS.

200 VC ISSN 0030-5375
BX100
ORIENTALIA CHRISTIANA PERIODICA; commentarii de re orientali aetatis christianae sacra et profana. (Text in English, French, German, Italian, Latin and Spanish) 1935. a. L.70000($60) (foreign L.70000) (effective 1996). (Pontificio Istituto Orientale) Edizioni Orientalia Cristiana, Piazza S. Maria Maggiore 7, 00185 Rome, Italy. TEL 39-6-446-5589. FAX 39-6-446-5576. Ed. Vincenzo Poggi. bk.rev.; charts; index. circ. 1,000. (back issues avail.) **Indexed:** Amer.Bibl.Slavic & E.Eur.Stud., Bibl.Ling., Bull.Signal., CERDIC, New Test.Abstr., Rel.& Theol.Abstr., Rel.Ind.One. **Document type:** academic/scholarly publication.
—Faxon; SWETS.
Description: Covers articles in theology, patrology, liturgy, history, canon law, archaeology and similar aspects of the Christian East.

200 IT ISSN 0472-0784
ORIENTAMENTI PASTORALI. 1953. m. L.39000 (foreign L.60000). (Centro di Orientamento Pastorale) Edizioni Dehoniane, Via Casale S. Pio V, 20, 00165 Rome, Italy. TEL 39-6-6634070. Ed. G. Bonicelli. adv.; page L.1500000. circ. 4,500. **Indexed:** CERDIC.
—BLDSC (6291.202000).

ORIGINS RESEARCH. see *SCIENCES: COMPREHENSIVE WORKS*

200 NR ISSN 0030-5596
BL80.2
ORITA; Ibadan journal of religious studies. (Text in English) 1967. s-a. $20. University of Ibadan, Department of Religious Studies, Ibadan, Nigeria. Ed. J. Kenny. adv.; bk.rev.; illus.; cum.index; circ. 500 (controlled). (tabloid format) **Indexed:** Documentatieblad, Mid.East: Abstr.& Ind. **Document type:** academic/scholarly publication.
—SWETS.
Description: Offers a mirror of Nigerian thinking on religion.

323.4 200 US ISSN 0145-7675
THE OTHER SIDE (PHILADELPHIA); justice rooted in discipleship. 1965. bi-m. $39.97 (foreign $48.97) (effective 1994). The Other Side, Inc., 300 W. Apsley St., Philadelphia, PA 19144. TEL 215-849-2178. E-mail: tos-pa@ecunet.org. Ed. Mark Olsen. adv.; bk.rev.; film rev.; illus.; circ. 15,000 (paid). (also avail. in microfiche from UMI; back issues avail.) **Indexed:** Chr.Per.Ind., Rel.Ind.One. **Document type:** consumer publication.
—UMI.
Formerly: Freedom Now.
Description: Deals with questions of peace, faith and justice from a compassionate Christian perspective.

200 CN
OTHER SIDE OF THE BOAT. 1990. irreg. donation. Canadian Council of Churches, Youth Working Group - Conseil Canadien des Eglises, 40 St. Clair Ave. E., Ste. 201, Toronto, ON M4T 1M9, Canada. TEL 416-921-4152. FAX 416-921-7478. circ. 500.

200 NE ISSN 0030-6746
OUDE PADEN.* 1937. s-m. fl.10. Dorpsstraat 19, Oegstgeest, Netherlands. Ed. Fr. Luitjes. circ. 1,200.

RELIGIONS AND THEOLOGY

220 NE ISSN 0169-7226
BS1192
OUDTESTAMENTISCHE STUDIEN. (Text in English and German) 1942. irreg., vol.31, 1995. price varies. E.J. Brill, P.O. Box 9000, 2300 PA Leiden, Netherlands. TEL 31-71-5353500. FAX 31-71-5317532. TELEX 39296 BRILL NL. (In N. America: E.J. Brill, 24 Hudson St., Kinderhook, NY 12106. TEL 800-962-4406. FAX 518-758-1959) Ed. A.S. van der Woude. **Indexed:** Bibl.Ling., Old Test.Abstr. **Document type:** monographic series.
—SWETS.
Description: Scholarly studies on linguistic, textual, historical and theological topics pertaining to the Old Testament.
Refereed Serial

OUR DAILY BREAD. see *HANDICAPPED — Visually Impaired*

200 II
OUR LINK. (Text in English) 1954. bi-m. Rs.50 (students Rs.20) (effective 1993). Union of Evangelical Students of India, 10 Millers Rd., Madras 600010, India. TEL 6241478. Ed. Prema Fenn. adv.; bk.rev. circ. 1,500.
Formerly (until Jan. 1977): Evangelical Student.

OUR LITTLE FRIEND. see *CHILDREN AND YOUTH — For*

200 US
OUT-REACH (SUMMERFIELD). 1974. 10/yr. membership. Spiritual Advisory Council, 14345 S.E. 103rd Terr., Summerfield, FL 34491-3724. TEL 904-288-6607. FAX 904-288-6744. Ed. Paul V. Johnson. bk.rev. circ. 2,000. (back issues avail.) **Document type:** newsletter.
Description: Discusses the Spiritual Advisory Council's religious and metaphysical philosophy and alerts readers to coming events.

266 UK
OXFORD MISSION NEWS. 1894. 2/yr. (May, Nov.). £4. Bocardo Press, 22 The Harrage, Romsey, Hants. SO51 8AE, England. TEL 01794-515004. Ed. G. Wilson. circ. 1,800. (processed) **Document type:** newsletter.
Formerly: Oxford Mission (ISSN 0048-2579)
Description: Contains letters from the superiors of the Oxford Mission stations in India and Bangladesh, describing their activities. Includes other articles of interest to mission supporters.

201 US ISSN 0078-7272
OXFORD THEOLOGICAL MONOGRAPHS. irreg. Oxford University Press, 200 Madison Ave., New York, NY 10016. TEL 212-679-7300. Ed.Bd. **Document type:** monographic series.

200 370 US ISSN 1048-4523
P A C E. (Professional Approaches for Christian Educators) 1970-1987 (no.18); resumed 1989. 8/yr. $95. Brown - Roa, 1170 Roosevelt Ext., Dubuque, IA 52001. TEL 800-922-7696. FAX 319-557-3719. Ed. Padraoc O'Hare; Pub. Matthew Thibeau. index, cum.index: vols.11-17. circ. 2,000. (looseleaf format; back issues avail.) **Document type:** academic/scholarly publication.

P C R INFORMATION; reports and background papers. (Programme to Combat Racism) see *POLITICAL SCIENCE — Civil Rights*

226 365 US
P F I WORLD REPORT. (Text in English, French, Spanish) 1981. bi-m. free. Prison Fellowship International, Box 17434, Washington, DC 20041. TEL 703-481-0000. FAX 703-481-0003. Ed. David Singer. circ. 6,500 (controlled). **Document type:** newsletter.
Former titles (until Oct. 1993): Jubilee International; (until 1991) Fellowship Communique (ISSN 0738-1530); (until 1983): Jubilee International (ISSN 0736-9662)
Description: Covers the worldwide activities of the Prison Fellowship ministries, with stories on the impact of ministry activities on prisoners' lives.

200 US ISSN 0889-8936
BL2525
P R R C: EMERGING TRENDS. 1979. 10/yr. $38. Princeton Religion Research Center, Inc., 47 Hulfish St., Ste. 215, Box 389, Princeton, NJ 08542. TEL 609-921-8112. FAX 609-924-0228. circ. 1,900. (looseleaf format; also avail. in microfiche from CIS; back issues avail.) **Indexed:** SRI. **Document type:** bulletin.
—Faxon.
Description: Presents the results of recent surveys on religious beliefs and practices, with commentary, based on studies by Gallup and other polling organizations.

268 SP
P S. 1899. m. 1000 ptas.($4) Editorial Perpetuo Socorro, Covarrubias, 19, 28010 Madrid, Spain. Ed. Jose Maria Lorca. adv.; bk.rev.; illus.; circ. 14,000 (controlled).

266 US
PACIFIC CHRISTIAN COLLEGE BULLETIN. 1928. 4/yr. Pacific Christian College, 2500 E. Nutwood Ave., Fullerton, CA 92631. TEL 714-879-3901. FAX 714-526-0231. Ed. Becky Ahlberg. (tabloid format) **Document type:** bulletin.
Description: Articles and faculty information for students and constituency of Pacific Christian College.

200 294.54 AT ISSN 1030-570X
PACIFICA; Australian theological studies. 1988. 3/yr. Aus.$35($32) to individuals; institutions Aus.$40($35) (effective 1995). Pacifica Theological Studies Association, P.O. Box 271, Brunswick East, Vic. 3057, Australia. TEL 613-347-6366. FAX 613-347-6371. (Co-sponsor: Melbourne College of Divinity) Ed. John Honner. adv. contact: Celia A. Phillips. bk.rev.; index; circ. 700 (paid). (also avail. in diskette format; back issues avail.) **Indexed:** Aus.P.A.I.S., New Test.Abstr., Old Test.Abstr., Rel.& Theol.Abstr. (1988-). **Document type:** academic/scholarly publication.
—BLDSC (6331.815000).
Description: Covers all areas of theology, with emphasis on theological work in Australasia and Pacific Region.

255 248 IT ISSN 0030-9214
PADRE SANTO; periodico dei Cappuccini liguri. 1912. m. Frati Minori Cappuccini, Provincia di Genova, Piazza Cappuccini 1, 16122 Genoa, Italy. Ed. Toso Domenico.

133.4 CN ISSN 0838-1550
PAGANS FOR PEACE. 1983. bi-m. Can.$10($10) (Pagans for Peace Network) Obscure Pagan Press, P.O. Box 2205, Clearbrook, BC V2T 3X8, Canada. TEL 604-855-8893. Ed. Samuel Wagar. adv.; bk.rev.; circ. 200 (paid). **Document type:** newsletter.

200 US ISSN 0475-4816
LA PALABRA DIARIA. English edition: Daily Word. (Text in Spanish) 1955. m. $6.95. Unity School of Christianity, Unity Village, MO 64065. TEL 816-524-3550. Ed. Colleen Zuck. circ. 58,000.
Description: Contains daily devotional readings, with poetry and articles on spiritual inspiration, human relations, and everyday living.

PALAESTINA ANTIQUA. see *ARCHAEOLOGY*

266 GW ISSN 0031-0395
PALLOTTIS WERK. 1949. q. free. (Provinzialat der Pallottiner) Lio Druck, Postfach 1162, 65531 Limburg, Germany. TEL 06431-401221. Ed. P.W. Schuetzeichel. bk.rev. circ. 60,000. **Document type:** bulletin.
Description: Catholic publication covering missionary work in Germany and abroad, especially Third World countries.

200 FR ISSN 0299-6898
PANORAMA; un regard Chretien. 1968. m. (11/yr.). 290 F. (outside EC 340 F.). Bayard Presse, 3 rue Bayard, 75393 Paris Cedex 08, France. TEL 44-35-60-60. FAX 44-35-60-91. TELEX 648 094 F. (Subscr. to: B.P. 12, 99505 Paris Entreprises, France. TEL 46-30-38-00. FAX 46-30-31-67) adv.; bk.rev.; film rev.; illus. circ. 96,000. **Indexed:** Pt.de Rep. (1979-).
Formerly (until 1986): Panorama Aujourd'hui (ISSN 0048-2838)
Description: Offers an in-depth look at people in the news.

PAPYROLOGY AND HISTORICAL PERSPECTIVES. see *HISTORY*

PARABOLA; the magazine of myth and tradition. see *FOLKLORE*

PARENTING FOR PEACE & JUSTICE NETWORK NEWSLETTER. see *EDUCATION — Adult Education*

200 UK ISSN 0968-9346
PARENTWISE. 1979. bi-m. £13.50. Elm House Christian Communications Ltd., 37 Elm Rd., New Malden, Surrey KT3 3HB, England. TEL 0181-942-9761. FAX 0181-949-2313. Ed. Clive Price. adv. contact: Jan Hurrell. bk.rev.; illus.; film rev.; circ. 10,000 (paid). (back issues avail.) **Document type:** consumer publication.
Former titles (until Apr. 1993): Christian Family (ISSN 0269-4689); (until 1986): Family (ISSN 0144-7696); Incorporated (in Aug. 1980): Life of Faith Monthly (ISSN 0141-2493); Which was (until Feb. 1979): Life of Faith (ISSN 0024-3175)
Description: Presents a popular Christian perspective on marriage, parenting, and home affairs.

PARMARTH; religious monthly. see *PHILOSOPHY*

200 LE ISSN 0258-8331
PAROLE DE L'ORIENT. (Text in English, French) 1970. s-a. $10 (outside Lebanaon $30) (effective 1995). Universite Saint Esprit Kaslik, B.P. 446, Jounieh, Lebanon. Ed. Pere Joseph Obeid. bk.rev. circ. 1,000. **Indexed:** Amer.Hist.& Life (1988-), Hist.Abstr. (1988-). **Document type:** academic/scholarly publication.
—BLDSC (6406.942000).
Description: Examines the theology, exegeses, patrology, liturgy and history of churches in the Near and Middle East.

250 UK ISSN 0031-2436
PARSON AND PARISH; National Church News. 1938. s-a. £6. English Clergy Association, 840 Walsall Rd., Birmingham B42 1ES, England. TEL 0121-357-1259. FAX 0121-357-8328. Ed. Rev. M.G. Smith. adv.; bk.rev. circ. 700.
Description: Covers current church affairs, articles of general theological and pastoral interest, and correspondence.

PARTNERS IN EDUCATION. see *EDUCATION — Teaching Methods And Curriculum*

250 GW ISSN 0031-2681
PASSAUER BISTUMSBLATT; Kirchenzeitung der Dioezese Passau. 1936. w. DM.10.30 per quarter. Diozese Passau, 57707, Ed. Konrad Haberger, Domplatz 3, 94030 Passau, Germany. adv.; bk.rev.; film rev.; abstr.; illus. circ. 35,000. **Document type:** newsletter.

250 US ISSN 0031-2762
PASTORAL LIFE; the magazine for today's ministry. 1952. m. $17. Society of St. Paul (Canfield), Box 595, Canfield, OH 44406-0595. TEL 216-533-5503. FAX 216-533-1076. Ed. Rev. Anthony Chenevey; Pub. Jeffrey Mickler. adv.; bk.rev.; illus.; index. circ. 3,200. (also avail. in microfilm from UMI; reprint service avail. from UMI) **Indexed:** Cath.Ind., CERDIC.
—UMI.

266 SP ISSN 0210-3559
PASTORAL MISIONERA. 1965. 6/yr. 2550 ptas.($22) (foreign 3100 ptas.($27)). Editorial Popular, S.A., Bola, 3 bajo, 28013 Madrid, Spain. FAX 91-559-00-64. TELEX 49416-PUBL-E. Ed. Fernando Urbina de la Quintana. bk.rev.

PASTORAL PSYCHOLOGY. see *PSYCHOLOGY*

250 GW ISSN 0031-2800
PASTORALBLAETTER. 1860. m. DM.63.60. Kreuz-Verlag Zeitschriften GmbH, Breitwiesenstr. 30, 70565 Stuttgart, Germany. TEL 0711-78803. Ed. Hans-Georg Lubkoll. adv. circ. 5,000. **Document type:** bulletin.
—CCC.

RELIGIONS AND THEOLOGY

200   GT
PASTORALIA. 1974. s-a. $6 in America; elsewhere $7. Centro Evangelico Latinoamericano de Estudios Pastorales, Apartado 1710, 01901 Guatemala City, Guatemala. FAX 502-2-513688. Dir. Plutarco Bonilla A. bk.rev. circ. 1,600.
    Supersedes (in 1977, vol.4, nos.1-2): C E L E P Ensayos Ocasionales.

250   GW   ISSN 0720-6259
PASTORALTHEOLOGIE - MONATSSCHRIFT FUER WISSENSCHAFT UND PRAXIS IN KIRCHE UND GESELLSCHAFT. 1904. m. DM.94. Vandenhoeck und Ruprecht, Robert-Bosch-Breite 6, 37079 Goettingen, Germany. TEL 0551-6959-26. FAX 0551-695917. (Subscr. to: 37070 Goettingen, Germany) Eds. Guenter Brakelmann, Peter Stolt. adv.; bk.rev.; index. circ. 3,000. **Indexed:** CERDIC. **Document type:** academic/scholarly publication.
    —CCC.
    Former titles: Wissenschaft und Praxis in Kirche und Gesellschaft (ISSN 0031-2827); Pastoraltheologie.

200 100   II
PATHWAY TO GOD; one God, one world, one humanity. (Text in English) 1966. q. Rs.25 (foreign Rs.100). Academy of Comparative Philosophy and Religion, Belgaum, Hindwadi, Belgaum 590 011, India. TEL 22231. Ed. P.D. Dharwarkar. adv.; bk.rev. circ. 1,000. **Document type:** academic/scholarly publication.

PATRISTIC AND BYZANTINE REVIEW. see *HISTORY — History Of Europe*

PATTERNS IN RECONCILIATION. see *POLITICAL SCIENCE — Civil Rights*

266   CN   ISSN 0031-3335
PAX REGIS. 1942. s-a. $3. Westminster Abbey Ltd., Mission, B.C. V2V 4J2, Canada. TEL 604-826-8975. Ed. Alban Riley. illus. circ. 1,500.
    Description: Articles and news for alumni of the Seminary of Christ the King, and for those interested in Roman Catholic seminary education.

364 200   US
PEACE AND JUSTICE SERIES. irreg. $5.95. Herald Press, 616 Walnut Ave., Scottdale, PA 15683-1999. TEL 412-887-8500. Ed. Michael King. bibl. (back issues avail.) **Document type:** monographic series.

200   UK
PEACELINKS. 1971. bi-m. £3 in the U.K. and abroad. Fellowship of Reconciliation, 40-46 Harleyford Rd., Vauxhall, London SE11 5AY, England. TEL 0171-582-9054. FAX 0171-582-9180. Ed. Ben Rees. bk.rev.; bibl.; illus. circ. 2,000. (also avail. in microform from UMI; back issues avail.) **Document type:** newsletter.
    Formerly: Newspeace (ISSN 0048-0304)
    Description: Presents a forum for news about the worldwide works of the Fellowship of Reconciliation (in England, Wales, Scotland and Northern Ireland).

200   FR   ISSN 0399-5755
PELERIN. 1873. w. 811 F. (outside EC 995 F.). Bayard Presse, 3 rue Bayard, 75393 Paris Cedex 08, France. TEL 44-35-60-60. FAX 44-35-60-91. TELEX 648 094 F. (Subscr. to: B.P. 12, 99505 Paris Entreprises, France. TEL 46-30-38-00. FAX 46-30-31-67) Eds. Henry Caro, Guy Mauratille. adv.; bk.rev.; film rev.; play rev.; bibl.; illus.; mkt. circ. 386,000.
    Former titles (until 1976): Pelerin du Vingtieme Siecle (ISSN 0031-4145); (until 1963): Pelerin (ISSN 0399-5747)
    Description: Presents world news from a Christian perspective as well as columns on health, law, education, house and garden.

200   AU   ISSN 0031-5141
PERCHTOLDSDORFER PFARRBOTE. 1950. m. contributions. Pfarramt Perchtoldsdorf, Marktplatz 14, A-2380 Perchtoldsdorf, Austria. Ed. Msgr. Karl Seemann. circ. 4,700.

200   US
PERE MARQUETTE THEOLOGY LECTURE SERIES. 1969. a. $10. Marquette University Press, Box 1881, Milwaukee, WI 53201-1881. TEL 414-288-1564. Ed. Andrew Tallon. **Document type:** academic/scholarly publication.
    Description: Annual public lectures by theologians.

270.1   FR   ISSN 0180-7439
LES PERES DANS LA FOI. 1977. irreg., vol.56, 1994. price varies. (Association Jacques Paul Migne) Editions Brepols, 23, rue des Grands Augustins, 75006 Paris, France. TEL 33-1-44412000. FAX 33-1-43212377. **Document type:** monographic series.
    Description: Publishes studies of historical figures, doctrines and practices of the early Christian church.

200   BL   ISSN 0031-5486
PERMANENCIA.* 1968. m. Cr.$50. Editora Permanencia, Rua Jardim Botanico 86, Rio de Janeiro, Brazil. Ed. Julio Fleichman.

PERSONA Y SOCIEDAD. see *SOCIAL SCIENCES: COMPREHENSIVE WORKS*

PERSPECTIVE. see *PHILOSOPHY*

268   US
PERSPECTIVE (WHEATON). Variant title: Pioneer Clubs Perspective. 1967. 3/yr. $5. Pioneer Clubs, 27W130 St. Charles Rd., Box 788, Wheaton, IL 60189. TEL 708-293-1600. FAX 708-293-3053. Ed. Rebecca Powell Parat. circ. 25,000. (back issues avail.)
    Description: Provides resources for club leaders to develop leadership and relationship skills.

215   US   ISSN 0892-2675
BL240.2
PERSPECTIVES ON SCIENCE AND CHRISTIAN FAITH. 1949. q. $25 to individuals; institutions $35. American Scientific Affiliation, Box 668, Ipswich, MA 01938. TEL 508-356-5656. FAX 508-356-4375. Ed. J.W. Haas, Jr. adv.; bk.rev.; abstr. circ. 3,400. (also avail. in microform from UMI; reprint service avail. from UMI) **Indexed:** CERDIC, Chr.Per.Ind., G.Soc.Sci.& Rel.Per.Lit., Rel.& Theol.Abstr. (1968-), Rel.Ind.One, Soc.Work Res.& Abstr. **Document type:** academic/scholarly publication.
    —Faxon; UMI; UnCover. **CCC.**
    Formerly: American Scientific Affiliation. Journal: Evangelical Perspectives on Science and Christian Faith (ISSN 0003-0988)
    Description: Academic articles related to issues involving the interaction of science and Christian faith.

PESHITTA INSTITUTE, LEIDEN. MONOGRAPHS. see *RELIGIONS AND THEOLOGY — Judaic*

PHENOMENOLOGICAL THEOLOGY. see *PHILOSOPHY*

PHILIPPINE STUDIES; quarterly publication of Philippine thought and culture. see *HUMANITIES: COMPREHENSIVE WORKS*

PHILIPPINE WITNESS. see *POLITICAL SCIENCE — Civil Rights*

200   NE   ISSN 0166-5030
PHILOSOPHIA PATRUM; interpretations of patristic texts. 1971. irreg., vol.8, 1986. price varies. E.J. Brill, P.O. Box 9000, 2300 PA Leiden, Netherlands. TEL 31-71-5353500. FAX 31-71-5317532. TELEX 39296 BRILL NL. (In N. America: E.J. Brill, 24 Hudson St., Kinderhook, NY 12106. TEL 800-962-4406. FAX 518-758-1959) Eds. J.H. Waszink, J.C.M. van Winden. (back issues avail.) **Document type:** monographic series.
    Refereed Serial

PHILOSOPHIA RELIGIONIS. see *PHILOSOPHY*

PHILOSOPHY AND RELIGION; a comparative yearbook. see *PHILOSOPHY*

PHILOSOPHY AND SOCIAL CRITICISM. see *HUMANITIES: COMPREHENSIVE WORKS*

PHILOSOPHY & THEOLOGY; Marquette University quarterly. see *PHILOSOPHY*

200   GR   ISSN 0031-8396
PHONI TOU EVANGELIOU/VOICE OF THE GOSPEL. 1944. m. Dr.1500($15) A M G International, 28 Emm. Benaki St., 105 61 Athens, Greece. TEL 30-1-362-3495. FAX 30-1-654-8506. Ed. Spiros Zodhiates. bk.rev.; abstr.; bibl.; illus.; index. circ. 6,500. **Document type:** academic/scholarly publication.
    Description: Family-oriented Christian magazine.

220   US   ISSN 1061-1010
BS587
PICKING THE "RIGHT" BIBLE STUDY PROGRAM. 1992. a. A C T A Publications, 4848 N. Clark St., Chicago, IL 60640.

200 028.5   GW
PICO; illustrierte Kinderzeitschrift ab 7 Jahre. 1990. m. DM.26.40. Steyler Missionare e.V., Bahnhofstr. 9, 41334 Nettetal, Germany. TEL 02157-1202-0. FAX 02157-1202-60. Ed. P.E. Schoppert. **Document type:** consumer publication.

266 301.2   IT
PIEMME. 1927. m. L.24000. Missionari Comboniani, Vicolo Pozzo 1, 37129 Verona, Italy. Ed. Gianni Albanese. adv.; bk.rev. circ. 120,000.
    Formerly: Piccolo Missionario (ISSN 0031-9600)

200   SA   ISSN 0031-9805
PILGRIM/PELGRIM. (Text in Afrikaans and English) 1930. bi-m. R.2. Africa Evangelistic Band, P.O. Box 73, Parow 7500, South Africa. Ed. S. J. Kettles. bk.rev.; illus. circ. 4,000. **Indexed:** CERDIC.

200   UK
PILGRIM POST. 1990. bi-m. £10 (foreign £13). Churches Together in England, Inter-Church House, 35-41 Lower Marsh, London SE1 7RL, England. TEL 0171-620-4444. FAX 0171-928-5771. (Subscr. to: Churches Together in England, Baptist House, 129 Broadway, Didcot, Oxon. OX11 8XD, England) Ed. Rev. Roger Nunn. adv.; bk.rev. circ. 1,500. **Document type:** bulletin.
    Formerly: Vision One.
    Description: Examines ecumenical Christianity.

PILGRIMAGE; reflections on the human journey. see *MEDICAL SCIENCES — Psychiatry And Neurology*

PLANET WALK. see *LITERATURE*

268   FR
POINTS DE REPERE. (Supplement avail.: Points de Depart) 1955. 7/yr. 185 F. (outside EC 205 F.). (Centre National de l'Enseignement Religieux (C.N.E.R.)) Bayard Presse, 3 rue Bayard, 75393 Paris Cedex 08, France. TEL 44-35-60-60. FAX 44-35-60-91. TELEX 648 094 F. (Subscr. to: B.P. 12, 99505 Paris Entreprises, France. TEL 46-30-38-00. FAX 46-30-31-67) circ. 60,000.
    Formerly: Catechistes d'Aujourd'hui (ISSN 0008-7742)

207 268.8   US   ISSN 0079-2543
POINTS FOR EMPHASIS; INTERNATIONAL SUNDAY SCHOOL LESSONS IN POCKET SIZE. (Large type edition also avail.) 1917. a. $3.50 (large type ed. $4.50). Broadman & Holman Publishers, 127 Ninth Ave., N., Nashville, TN 37234. TEL 615-251-2533. Ed. Frent C. Butler. circ. 33,000. **Document type:** consumer publication.
    Description: Supplementary reading on International Sunday School lessons for adults.

POLKA; Polish women's quarterly magazine. see *WOMEN'S INTERESTS*

200   VC
PONTE D'ORO. 1966. m. L.4500. Pontificia Opera della Santa Infanzia, Via di Propaganda 1, 00187 Rome, Italy. Ed. Giuliani Sandro. circ. 30,000.

200 360   IT   ISSN 0391-6901
POPOLO. 1922. w. L.5000. Giunta Diocesana di A.C., Piazza delle Cinque Lune 113, 00186 Rome, Italy. TEL 6-65-151. (Subscr. to: Il Popolo, Casella Postale 103, Pordenone, Italy) circ. 87,000.

A POSITIVE APPROACH; a national magazine for the physically challenged. see *HANDICAPPED — Physically Impaired*

POTCHEFSTROOM UNIVERSITY FOR CHRISTIAN HIGHER EDUCATION. WETENSKAPLIKE BYDRAES. REEKS B: NATUURWETENSKAPPE. SERIES. see *EDUCATION — Adult Education*

200   US   ISSN 0032-6003
POWER FOR LIVING. 1942. q. $9.95. Scripture Press Publications, Inc., 1825 College Ave., Wheaton, IL 60187. TEL 708-668-6000. FAX 708-668-3806. Ed. Don H. Alban, Jr. illus.

5710 RELIGIONS AND THEOLOGY

200 US ISSN 0032-6011
POWER FOR TODAY. 1955. q. $7.95. 20th Century Christian Foundation, 2809 Granny White Pike, Nashville, TN 37204. TEL 615-383-3842. Eds. Steven S. and Emily Y. Lemley. adv. circ. 50,000. (processed; also avail. in microfilm from UMI; reprint service avail. from UMI)

PRACTICAL PAPERS FOR THE BIBLE TRANSLATOR. see *LINGUISTICS*

205 DK ISSN 0106-6218
PRAESTEFORENINGENS BLAD. 1899. w. (50/yr.). DKK 504. Danske Praesteforening, Rosenvaengets Hovedvej 19, 2100 Copenhagen OE, Denmark. TEL 45-35-26-05-55. FAX 45-35-43-05-88. Ed. Jakob Grosboell. adv. contact: Dorothe Hansen. bk.rev. circ. 4,000.

266 AT
PRAISE & PRAYER CALENDAR. bi-m. Far East Broadcasting Co., Cnr. Banksia Rd. & Willarong Rd., P.O. Box 183, Caringbah, N.S.W. 2229, Australia. TEL 61-2-525-6460. FAX 61-2-526-1250. Ed. Mari Atkinson. circ. 8,500. (back issues avail.)
Description: Daily prayer guide.

240 GW
BV1
PRAKTISCHE THEOLOGIE; Zeitschrift fuer Religion, Gesellschaft und Kirche. 1966. q. DM.86 (foreign DM.90). Guetersloher Verlagshaus Chr. Kaiser, Carl-Bertelsmann-Str. 270, 33311 Guetersloh, Germany. TEL 05241-7405-0. FAX 05241-740548. Ed.Bd. adv.: B&W page DM.900; trim 108 x 192. bk.rev.; index. circ. 1,000. Indexed: CERDIC. Document type: newsletter.
Formerly (until 1993): Theologia Practica (ISSN 0049-3643)

PRAXIS JURIDIQUE ET RELIGION. see *LAW*

200 UK
PRAYER BOOK SOCIETY NEWSLETTER. 1975. 5/yr. membership. Prayer Book Society, 36 The Drive, Northwood, Middlesex HA6 1HP, England. TEL 01923-824278. (Subscr. addr.: c/o Col. H.D. Rogers, Redlynch Lodge, Redlynch, Salisbury, Wiltshire SP5 2NJ, England) Ed. Neil Inkley. bk.rev. circ. 10,500. Document type: newsletter.
Description: Campaigns for traditionalism in the Church of England and in particular for the 1662 Book of Common Prayer.

266 248.3 AT
PRAYER UNION. Abbreviated title: P U. bi-m. European Christian Mission (Australian Section) Inc., P.O. Box 15, Croydon, N.W.S. 2132, Australia. TEL 61-2-7475446. FAX 61-2-7475509. E-mail: 100351.1065@compuserve.com. Ed. Rev. Jim Bosma. circ. 5,000.

251 US ISSN 0274-600X
PRAYERS FOR WORSHIP. 1978. q. $25. Liturgical Publications Inc., 2875 South James Dr., New Berlin, WI 53151. TEL 414-785-1188. FAX 414-785-9567. Ed. Rev. L. Koopman. (looseleaf format)

200 US ISSN 0882-7036
PREACHING. 1985. bi-m. $24.95 (Canada $30.95, elsewhere $41.95). Preaching Resources, Inc., Box 7728, Louisville, KY 40257-0728. TEL 502-899-3119. FAX 502-893-5069. Ed. Michael Duduit. adv.; bk.rev.; circ. 10,000 (paid). (back issues avail.) Document type: trade publication.
—CCC.
Description: Practical articles on preaching, sermon manuscripts and homiletic helps.

200 GW ISSN 0079-4961
PREDIGTSTUDIEN. 1968. s-a. DM.36 per vol. Kreuz-Verlag, Breitwiesenstr. 30, 70565 Stuttgart, Germany. FAX 0711-7880310. Ed.Bd. adv. circ. 7,000.

200 CN ISSN 1188-5580
PRESENCE MAGAZINE. 1962. 8/yr. Can.$30 (foreign Can.$40). Ordre des Dominicains du Canada, 2715 Cote Ste-Catherine, Montreal, PQ H3T 1B6, Canada. TEL 514-739-9797. FAX 514-739-1664. Ed. Jean-Claude Breton. adv.: page Can.$480. bk.rev.; bibl. circ. 3,000. Indexed: CERDIC, Pt.de Rep. Document type: academic/scholarly publication.
●Also available online.
Former titles (until 1992): Nouveau Magazine Communaute Chretienne; Communaute Chretienne (ISSN 0010-3454)

200 CK
PRESENCIA. 1950. m. $14. Editorial Presencia Ltda., Calle 23 no. 24-20, Bogota D.E., Colombia. Ed. Maria Carrizosa de Umana. adv.; abstr.; bibl. circ. 15,000.

200 FR ISSN 0181-6578
PRIER. 1978. m. Malesherbes Publications, 163 bd. Malesherbes, 75017 Paris, France. TEL 48-88-46-00. FAX 48-88-46-01. TELEX 649 333 F. circ. 85,000.
Description: A review of modern prayer and contemplation.

268 US ISSN 0032-8278
PRIMARY DAYS; makes Bible truths live. vol.5, 1939. q. $9.95. Scripture Press Publications, Inc., 1825 College Ave., Wheaton, IL 60187. TEL 708-668-6000. FAX 708-668-3806. Ed. Janice K. Briton. charts; illus.
Description: Presents the teachings of the Bible for children ages 6-8.

200 AT
PRISM. 1968. 4/yr. Aus.$12. Openbook Publishers, 205 Halifax St., Adelaide, S.A. 5000, Australia. Ed. Mrs. P. Oster. circ. 1,315.

200 US ISSN 0887-5049
PRISM (NEW BRIGHTON); a theological forum for the United Church of Christ. 1985. 2/yr. $16. (United Church of Christ) Prism Publishers, 3000 Fifth St. N.W., New Brighton, MN 55112. TEL 612-633-4311. FAX 612-633-4315. Eds. Clyde Steckel, Elizabeth Nordbeck. circ. 2,500 (paid). Document type: academic/scholarly publication.

PRISMET; pedagogisk tidsskrift. see *EDUCATION*

209 956 IS ISSN 0032-9622
BR1070
PROCHE-ORIENT CHRETIEN. (Text in English and French) 1951. q. $20. Peres Blancs de Sainte-Anne de Jerusalem, B.P. 19079, Jerusalem, Israel. TEL 972-2-281992. FAX 972-2-280764. Ed. Frans Bouwen. bk.rev.; index, cum.index: 1951-1970. circ. 1,000. (also avail. in microfiche from IDC) Indexed: Bull.Signal., CERDIC, Rel.& Theol.Abstr. (1990-), Rel.Ind.One.

PROFESSIONAL CHRISTIAN COUNSELOR. see *PSYCHOLOGY*

282 CN ISSN 0033-054X
PROGRESS/POSTUP. (Editions in English, Ukrainian) 1959. w. Can.$30($35) (Ukrainian Catholic Archdiocese of Winnipeg) Progress Printing & Publishing Co. Ltd., 418 Aberdeen Ave., Winnipeg, MB R2W 1V7, Canada. TEL 204-582-1940. Ed. Rev. S. Izyk. adv. contact: Martha Gawick. bk.rev.; film rev.; play rev.; illus. circ. 4,500.
Description: Carries news items about the Ukranian Catholic Church in North America and Ukraine as well as items of general interest to the Ukranian community.

170 US
PROGRESS (MEDFORD). 1895. m. $2. International Reform Federation, 205 Tuckerton Rd., Ste. 200, Medford, NJ 08055-8805. TEL 609-985-7724. Ed. Samuel A. Jeanes. bk.rev. circ. 1,500. (back issues avail.) Document type: newsletter.

220 CN ISSN 0048-5578
PROPHETIC EXPOSITOR. 1964. m. membership. British Israel World Federation (Canada) Inc., 313 Sherbourne St., Toronto, ON, Canada. TEL 416-921-5996. Eds. D.C. Nesbit, M. McEwan. adv.; bk.rev.; abstr.; bibl.; charts; illus.; stat.; index. circ. 1,600. (processed)

200 RU
PROTESTANT. 1982. q. Mukomolni Proezd Dom 1 Korpus 2, 123290 Moscow, Russia. TEL 7-095-2599397. FAX 7-095-2926511.
Formerly: Samizdat Review.

200 SP ISSN 0478-6378
BX805
PROYECCION; teologia y mundo actual. 1954. q. $19 (effective 1995). Facultad de Teologia de Granada, Apartado 2002, 18080 Granada, Spain. TEL 34-58-160202. FAX 34-58-162559. Ed. Guillermo Rodriguez-Izquierdo; Pub. Enrique Borrego. adv.; bk.rev. circ. 2,100. (tabloid format; back issues avail.) Indexed: Old Test.Abstr. Document type: academic/scholarly publication.
—BLDSC (6938.323000).

200 PL ISSN 1230-4379
PRZEGLAD RELIGIOZNAWCZY. (Text in Polish; summaries in English, Russian) 1957. q. $25. Polskie Towarzystwo Religioznawcze, Ul. Jaracza 1, lok. 6, P.O. Box 151, 00-959 Warsaw, Poland. Ed. Zbigniew Stachowski. bk.rev.; bibl.; illus.; index. circ. 860. Document type: academic/scholarly publication.
Formerly (until 1992): Euhemer (ISSN 0014-2298)

220.48 NE ISSN 0079-7197
PSEUDEPIGRAPHA VETERIS TESTAMENTI GRAECE. 1964. irreg., vol.4, 1977. price varies. (Rijksuniversiteit te Leiden) E.J. Brill, P.O. Box 9000, 2300 PA Leiden, Netherlands. TEL 31-71-5353500. FAX 31-71-5317532. TELEX 39296 BRILL NL. (In N. America: E.J. Brill, 24 Hudson St., Kinderhook, NY 12106. TEL 800-962-4406. FAX 518-758-1959) Eds. A.M. Denis, M. de Jonge. (back issues avail.) Document type: monographic series.
Refereed Serial

PSYCHICAL STUDIES. see *PARAPSYCHOLOGY AND OCCULTISM*

200 150 US
PSYCHOLOGY FOR LIVING. 11/yr. Narramore Christian Foundation, Box 5000, Rosemead, CA 91770-0950. TEL 213-288-7000. Ed. Ruth Narramore. circ. 38,000.

200 GW ISSN 0343-1401
PUBLIK-FORUM. 1972. fortn. (Leserinitiative Publik e.V.) Publik Forum Verlagsgesellschaft mbH, Krebsmuehle, 61440 Oberursel, Germany. TEL 06171-70030. FAX 06171-700340. Ed. Harald Pawlowski. adv. contact: Barbara Wetzel. bk.rev. circ. 30,204. Document type: bulletin.

250 US ISSN 0160-838X
BV4200
PULPIT DIGEST. N.S. 1972. bi-m. $24.95 to individuals (foreign $29.95); institutions $49.90 (foreign $54.90) (effective 1994). HarperSanFrancisco (Subsidiary of: HarperCollins Publishers), 1160 Battery St., San Francisco, CA 94111-1213. TEL 415-477-4400. (Subscr. to: Box 2357, San Francisco, CA 94126; Editorial correspondence: c/o David A. Farmer, University Baptist Church, 3501 N. Charles St., Baltimore, MD 21218-2499) Ed. David A. Farmer. adv. contact: Julie Wunderlich. bk.rev.; index. circ. 12,000. (back issues avail.)
Formerly: New Pulpit Digest (ISSN 0145-7969); Which was formed by the merger of: Pulpit Digest (ISSN 0033-4146); Pulpit Preaching (ISSN 0160-3515)

200 US
PULPIT HELPS. 1975. m. $15. Advancing the Ministries of the Gospel International, 6815 Shallowford Rd., Chattanooga, TN 37422-1755. TEL 800-251-7206. FAX 615-894-6863. Ed. Spiros Zodhiates. adv.: B&W page $2776, color $3076. bk.rev.; illus. circ. 210,000. (back issues avail.) Indexed: CCR.
Former titles: Pulpit and Bible Study; (until 1992): Pulpit Helps (ISSN 0193-3914)
Refereed Serial

251 US ISSN 0195-1548
PULPIT RESOURCE. 1973. q. $35.95. Logos Productions Inc., 6160 Carmen Ave. East, Inver Grove Heights, MN 55076. TEL 612-451-9945. FAX 612-457-4617. Ed. William H. Willimon. circ. 8,000. (back issues avail.) Document type: consumer publication.
Description: Resource and illustrative material for preparation of sermons for ministers, priests, and rabbis and lay speakers.

RELIGIONS AND THEOLOGY

200   CE
PUTHIYA ULAHAM. (Text in Tamil) 1976. 6/yr. Centre for Better Society, 115, 4th Cross St., Jaffna, Sri Lanka. TEL 21-22627. Ed. Rev. S.J. Emmanuel. circ. 1,500.

200   IT
QUADERNI DE IL GALLO. 1946. m. L.33000($18) (foreign L.45000) (effective Jan. 1994). Associazione Il Gallo, Casella Postale 1242, 16100 Genoa, Italy. TEL 010-592819. Dir. Germano Beringheli. bk.rev.; index. circ. 3,000. (also avail. in microform from UMI; reprint service avail. from UMI) Indexed: CERDIC.
—UMI.
Formerly: Gallo (ISSN 0016-416X)

200 933   IS
QUADERNI DE "LA TERRA SANTA". (Text in various languages) 1963. irreg., latest 1991. Franciscan Printing Press, P.O. Box 14064, Jerusalem 91140, Israel. TEL 972-2-286594. FAX 972-2-272274. (back issues avail.)

262.9 340   IT   ISSN 1122-0392
QUADERNI DI DIRITTO E POLITICA ECCLESIASTICA. 1993. 3/yr. L.150000. Societa Editrice Il Mulino, Strada Maggiore, 37, 40125 Bologna, Italy. TEL 39-51-471237. FAX 39-51-256034. Ed. Silvio Ferrari. (back issues avail.)

266   US   ISSN 0033-6017
QUEEN OF ALL HEARTS; the true devotion magazine. 1950. bi-m. $17 (foreign $20) (effective Jul. 1995). Montfort Missionaries, 26 S. Saxon Ave., Bay Shore, NY 11706. TEL 516-665-0726. FAX 516-665-4349. Ed. J. Patrick Gaffney, S.M.M. bk.rev.; illus.; circ. 4,500 (paid). (back issues avail.)
Description: Religious forum covering Christianity and missionaries.

260   GW   ISSN 0079-9084
QUELLEN UND FORSCHUNGEN ZUR WUERTTEMBERGISCHEN KIRCHENGESCHICHTE. 1967. irreg., vol.12, 1994. Calwer Verlag, Scharnhauserstr. 44, 70599 Stuttgart, Germany. TEL 0711-16722-0. FAX 0711-1672277. Eds. Martin Brecht, Hermann Ehmer. Document type: monographic series.

200   US   ISSN 1070-244X
QUEST (BOSTON); a monthly for religious liberals. 1945. m. membership. Church of the Larger Fellowship, Unitarian Universalist, 25 Beacon St., Boston, MA 02108. TEL 617-742-2100. FAX 617-523-4123. E-mail: CLF@UUA.ORG. Eds. Scott Alexander, Nancy Engels. bk.rev.; circ. 3,000 (controlled). (also avail. in audio cassette) Document type: newsletter.

THE QUEST (WHEATON). see *NEW AGE PUBLICATIONS*

QUESTION DE. see *PARAPSYCHOLOGY AND OCCULTISM*

200   SP   ISSN 0214-7769
QUESTIONS DE VIDA CRISTIANA. (Text in Catalan) 5/yr. 4850 ptas. (Europe 6350 ptas.; elsewhere $75). Publicacions de l' Abadia de Montserrat, Ausias March 92-98, Apdo. 244, 08013 Barcelona, Spain.

260   BE   ISSN 0774-5524
QUESTIONS LITURGIQUES; studies on liturgy. (Text in various languages) 1910. 4/yr. 1000 BEF (effective 1995). (Liturgisch Instituut) Éditions Peeters s.p.r.l., Bondgenotenlaan 153, 3000 Leuven, Belgium. TEL 32-16-235170. (Co-sponsors: Abbaye de Mont Cesar; Katholieke Universiteit te Leuven, Fakulteit Godgeleerdheid) Ed.Bd. (back issues avail.) Document type: academic/scholarly publication.
Former titles (until 1971): Questions Liturgiques et Paroissiales (ISSN 0774-5532); (until 1914): Questions Liturgiques (ISSN 0779-2050)

220   US   ISSN 0744-4796
QUIET MIRACLE. 1923. q. Bible Literature International, 625 E.N. Broadway, Columbus, OH 43214-4133. TEL 614-267-3116. FAX 614-267-7110. Ed. Annette Vasulka. adv.; circ. 20,000 (controlled). Formerly: B L I Crusader.

200   PE   ISSN 1022-789X
QUINCENARIO SIGNOS. 1980. s-m. $50 in Latin America; elsewhere $55. Centro de Estudios y Publicaciones, Camilo Carrillo 479, Jesus Maria, Apdo. 11-0107, Lima 11, Peru. TEL 51-14-4336453. FAX 51-14-4331078. (Co-sponsor: Instituto Bartolome de Las Casas - Rimac)

261 322   US   ISSN 1061-656X
BR738.6
R C D A. (Religion in Communist Dominated Areas) 1962. q. $25 to individuals; institutions and foreign $28. Research Center for Religion & Human Rights in Closed Societies, Ltd., 475 Riverside Dr., Ste. 448, New York, NY 10115. TEL 212-870-2481. Ed. Olga S. Hruby. adv.; bk.rev.; illus.; index. circ. 3,000. (also avail. in microform from UMI; back issues avail.) Indexed: Mid.East: Abstr.& Ind., Rel.Ind.One.
—Faxon; UnCover.
Formerly (until 1990): R C D A - Religion in Communist Dominated Areas (ISSN 0034-3978)
Description: Covers issues pertaining to religion and human rights.

268   US
R C M A INSIGHTS. no.4, 1991. irreg., no.13, 1994. membership only. Religious Conference Management Association, 1 R C A Dome, Ste. 120, Indianapolis, IN 46225. TEL 317-632-1888. Dir. DeWayne S. Woodring. circ. 3,000. (looseleaf format)
Description: Informational materials designed to assist members in planning religious conferences.

R I. see *POLITICAL SCIENCE — Civil Rights*

200   US
R I A L UPDATE. 1949. q. free. Religion in American Life, 2 Queenston Pl., Rm. 200, Princeton, NJ 08540. TEL 609-921-3639. FAX 609-921-0551. Ed. Nicholas van Dyck. charts; illus.; stat.; circ. 2,500 (controlled). (tabloid format) Document type: newsletter.
Formerly: R I A L News.
Description: Provides general information on strengthening congregation from an inter-faith perspective.

R N A NEWSLETTER. (Religion Newswriters Association) see *JOURNALISM*

R N I B GLEANINGS. (Royal National Institute for the Blind) see *HANDICAPPED — Visually Impaired*

R P R C COUNSELOR. (Religious Public Relations Council) see *ADVERTISING AND PUBLIC RELATIONS*

RADAR. see *CHILDREN AND YOUTH — For*

201 301   US   ISSN 0275-0147
RADIX. 1969. q. $15 (foreign $17). Radix Magazine, Inc., Box 4307, Berkeley, CA 94704-0307. TEL 510-548-5329. Ed. Sharon Gallagher. adv.; bk.rev.; film rev.; illus.; circ. 5,000 (paid). Indexed: Soils & Fert. Document type: academic/scholarly publication.
Formerly (until 1976): Right On.
Description: Includes interviews with people who influence church and society, feature articles, reviews and editorials dealing with the interface of Christian faith and culture.

RASSEGNA DI LETTERATURA TOMISTICA. see *PHILOSOPHY*

200   IT   ISSN 0033-9644
RASSEGNA DI TEOLOGIA; rivista bimestrale per un aggiornamento cristiano teorico e pratico. 1960. bi-m. L.30000 to individuals; members and students L.15000. Editrice A.V.E, Via Aurelia 481, 00165 Rome, Italy. Ed. Antonio Barruffo. adv.; bk.rev.; bibl.; index. circ. 2,000. Indexed: CERDIC, New Test.Abstr.
Formerly: Digest Cattolico.

200   US   ISSN 1071-4294
RATIO;* essays in Christian thought. 1993. s-a. $20 (effective 1994). 350 Canner St., Apt. 405, New Haven, CT 06511-2254. Ed. Jeffrey Bearce. adv.; bk.rev. (back issues avail.) Document type: academic/scholarly publication.

THE RATIONALIST NEWS. see *PHILOSOPHY*

REACH (NEW HAVEN). see *EDUCATION*

200   US   ISSN 0034-0987
REALITY; a national monthly of Christian belief and opinion. 1965. m. free. Reality Inc., 1 Canyon Dr., Alexandria, VA 22305. TEL 703-836-0565. (Subscr. to: Box 50, Washington, DC 20044) Ed. Paul Rader. adv.; bk.rev.; charts; illus.; circ. 10,000 (controlled). (tabloid format; also avail. in microform from UMI; reprint service avail. from UMI) Document type: newsletter.
—UMI.
Formerly: Magazine of Reality.

230 189   FR   ISSN 0484-0887
BR65.A62
RECHERCHES AUGUSTINIENNES. 1958. irreg., vol.27, 1994. 2400 BEF. Institut d'Etudes Augustiniennes, 3 rue de l'Abbaye, 75006 Paris, France. (Subscr. in France to: Editions Brepols, 23 rue des Grands Augustins, 75006 Paris, France. TEL 33-1-44-41-20-00. FAX 33-1-43-26-23-77; Elsewhere to: N.V. Brepols, Steenweg op Tielen 68, 2300 Turnhout, Belgium. TEL 32-14-415463. FAX 32-14-428919) Dir. Jean-Claude Fredouille. (back issues avail.) Document type: academic/scholarly publication.

200   FR   ISSN 0034-1258
RECHERCHES DE SCIENCE RELIGIEUSE. 1910. q. 234 F. (foreign 272 F.). Association Recherches de Science Religieuse, 15 rue Monsieur, 75007 Paris, France. TEL 40-61-64-00. Ed. Joseph Moingt. bk.rev.; index, cum.index: 1910-1960. circ. 1,310. (reprint service avail. from SCH) Indexed: Bull.Signal., CERDIC, M.L.A., New Test.Abstr., Old Test.Abstr., Rel.Ind.One, Rel.Per.
—BLDSC (7309.160000); SWETS.

230   BE   ISSN 0034-1266
BX800.A1
RECHERCHES DE THEOLOGIE ANCIENNE ET MEDIEVALE; a journal of ancient and medieval Christian literature. (Text in English, French and German) 1929. a., vol.62, 1995. 1000 BEF. (Abbaye du Mont Cesar) Editions Peeters s.p.r.l., Bondgenotenlaan 153, 3000 Leuven, Belgium. TEL 32-16-235170. FAX 32-16-228500. Ed. E. Manning. adv.; bk.rev.; bibl.; index. (back issues avail.) Indexed: CERDIC, M.L.A., New Test.Abstr., Rel.& Theol.Abstr. (1979-). Document type: academic/scholarly publication.

262.9 200   FR
RECHERCHES INSTITUTIONNELLES. (In 4 series: Droit et Eglises (ISSN 0220-7818); Institutions et Histoire (ISSN 0243-2412); Culture et Religion (ISSN 0154-0416); Recherche Documentaire (ISSN 0244-6936)) irreg. no.21, 1995. 200 F. (effective 1995). CERDIC Publications, 2 rue Goethe, Palais Universitaire, 67083 Strasbourg, France. Eds. J. Schlick, M. Zimmerman. illus. circ. 2,000. Document type: monographic series.

RECORD (NEW YORK, 1976). see *HOMOSEXUALITY*

200   US
REFLECTIONS (NEW HAVEN). 1965. s-a. free. Yale University, Divinity School, 409 Prospect St., New Haven, CT 06511. TEL 203-432-5033. FAX 203-432-5756. (Co-sponsors: Berkeley Divinity School; Institute of Sacred Music) Ed. Robert Ford. circ. 7,500. (also avail. in microfilm) Document type: academic/scholarly publication.

280   US   ISSN 0034-303X
REFORMATION REVIEW. (Vol. 22 not published) 1953. q. $10. (International Council of Christian Churches) Christian Beacon Press, Collingswood, NJ 08108. TEL 609-858-0700. Ed. J.C. Maris. bk.rev.; index. circ. 850. Indexed: CERDIC.

230   AT   ISSN 0034-3072
REFORMED THEOLOGICAL REVIEW. 1942. 3/yr. Aus.$15 (effective 1996). P.O. Box 635, Doncaster, Vic. 3108, Australia. Eds. A.M. Harman, D.G. Peterson. bk.rev.; index. circ. 650. Indexed: CERDIC, Int.Z.Bibelwiss., New Test.Abstr., Rel.& Theol.Abstr. (1968-), Rel.Ind.One, Rel.Per.
—BLDSC (7332.530000).
Description: Contains biblical and theological articles.

REFUGEE REPORTS. see *POLITICAL SCIENCE — Civil Rights*

RELIGIONS AND THEOLOGY

248.82 AU
REGENBOGEN; Zeitung fuer Maedchen und Buben. 1946. w. S.150. Dioezesanhaus Klagenfurt, Tarviserstr. 30, A-9020 Klagenfurt, Austria. TEL 0463-5877551. FAX 0463-5877559. Ed. Martin Bliem. bk.rev.; illus. circ. 60,000. (looseleaf format) **Document type:** bulletin.
Formerly (until Mar. 1977): Gotteskinder (ISSN 0017-2510)

250 GW ISSN 0034-3250
REGENSBURGER BISTUMSBLATT. 1926. w. (Sun.). (Bischoeflicher Stuhl Regensburg) Verlag Regensburger Bistumsblatt, Koenigsstr. 2, 93047 Regensburg, Germany. TEL 0941-53068. FAX 0941-58179. Ed. Klaus Christian Reiter. adv. contact: Eduard Hertel. circ. 100,000. **Document type:** bulletin.

266 US
REGIONS BEYOND ADVANCE.* 1949. q. free. Regions Beyond Missionary Union International, 1431 Stuckert Rd., Warrington, PA 18976-1526. TEL 215-745-0680. FAX 215-742-3031. Ed. Joseph F. Conley. adv.; circ. 11,400 (controlled). **Document type:** newsletter.
Description: Reports progress and development of R.B.M.U. International overseas ministries.

200 IT ISSN 0009-000X
REGNO - DOCUMENTI. 1966. m. L.34000 (foreign L.48000) (effective 1994). Centro Editoriale Dehoniano, Via Nosadella 6, 40123 Bologna, Italy. TEL 051-306811. FAX 051-341706. adv. circ. 14,000. (looseleaf format)
Description: Covers religion and ecclesiastic issues.

200 GW
REGULAE BENEDICTI STUDIA. ANNUARIUM INTERNATIONALE. (Text in English, French and German) 1972. a. price varies. E O S Verlag, Erzabtei St. Ottilien, 86941 St. Ottilien, Germany. TEL 08193-71261. FAX 08193-6844. Eds. B. Jaspert, E. Manning. circ. 300. **Document type:** bulletin.

RELIGIEUSES DANS LES PROFESSIONS DE SANTE. see HOSPITALS

200 UK ISSN 0048-721X
BL1
RELIGION; the established journal of the history, structure and theory of religion and religions. 1970. q. £95 (effective 1996). Academic Press Ltd. (Subsidiary of: Harcourt Brace & Company Ltd.), 24-28 Oval Rd., London NW1 7DX, England. TEL 44-171-267-4466. FAX 44-171-482-2293. TELEX 25775 ACPRES G. (Subscr. to: Harcourt Brace & Company Ltd., Foots Cray High St., Sidcup, Kent DA14 5HP, England. TEL 44-181-300-3322. FAX 44-181-309-0807) Eds. Adrian Cunningham, Ivan Strenski. circ. 600. **Indexed:** Arts & Hum.Cit.Ind., CERDIC, Curr.Cont., Mid.East: Abstr.& Ind., New Test.Abstr., Old.Test.Abstr., Rel.Ind.One. **Document type:** academic/scholarly publication.
—BLDSC (7356.435000); Faxon; Genuine Article; SWETS; UnCover. CCC.
Description: Covers interdisciplinary and cross-cultural research in religious studies, including descriptive, explanatory, methodological, and critical studies about religion and the study of religion, with relevant contributions from the disciplines of anthropology, archaeology, history, philosophy of science, political theory, psychology, and sociology.
Refereed Serial

200 US ISSN 0273-2556
BL1
RELIGION. (Subseries of: S I R S Social Issues (ISSN 0740-3127)) 1977. a. price varies; a. supplement $17. Social Issues Resources Series, Box 2348, Boca Raton, FL 33427-2348. TEL 407-994-4704; 800-232-7477. FAX 407-994-4704. (looseleaf format; also avail. in microfiche; back issues avail.)
Description: Reprints articles that explore the major religions and sects, as well as religious perspectives on controversial issues.

200 US ISSN 1052-1151
BL65.C8
RELIGION AND AMERICAN CULTURE; a journal of interpretation. 1991. s-a. $30. Indiana University Press, Journal Division, 601 N. Morton St., Bloomington, IN 47404. TEL 812-855-9449. FAX 812-855-7931. Ed. Conrad Cherry; Pub. John Gallman. adv. contact: Kathryn Caras. circ. 1,100. (also avail. in microfilm; back issues avail.) **Document type:** academic/scholarly publication.
—Faxon; Genuine Article; UMI; UnCover.
Description: Explores the interplay between religion and other spheres of American culture.
Refereed Serial

RELIGION AND LITERATURE. see LITERATURE

RELIGION & PUBLIC EDUCATION. see EDUCATION

261 301 II ISSN 0034-3951
RELIGION AND SOCIETY. 1953. q. Rs.30($15) Christian Institute for the Study of Religion and Society, Publications Trust, Box 4600, 73 Miller's Rd., Bangalore 560046, India. TEL 0002981. FAX 3330335. Ed. Jean S. Augustine. adv.; bk.rev. circ. 1,250. (also avail. in microfilm; reprint service avail. from UMI) **Indexed:** CERDIC, G.Indian Per.Lit., Rel.Ind.One, Rel.Ind.Two, Rel.Per. **Document type:** bulletin.
—SWETS; UMI.
Description: Publishes articles on religious and social problems especially issues in social justice, and results of studies and discussions on these matters carried out by the institute.

200 US ISSN 0742-6984
THE RELIGION & SOCIETY REPORT. 1984. m. $24 ($36 outside U.S.). Rockford Institute, Center on Religion & Society, 934 N. Main St., Rockford, IL 61103-7061. TEL 815-964-5813. FAX 815-965-1826. (Subscr. to: Box 424, Mt. Morris, IL 61054; Editorial addr.: Trinity Evangelical Divinity School, 2275 Half Day Rd., Ste. 350, Deerfield, IL 60015-1274) Ed. Harold O.J. Brown. circ. 3,700. (back issues avail.) **Document type:** academic/scholarly publication.
Description: Covers religious issues and their effect on society, with special reports on timely topics.

200 SA ISSN 1023-0807
BR1
RELIGION & THEOLOGY/RELIGIE & TEOLOGIE. Abbreviated title: R & T. (Text in Afrikaans, English) 1968; N.S. 1994. 3/yr. R.18 (overseas $5.83) (effective 1996). University of South Africa, Faculty of Theology and Religious Studies, P.O. Box 392, Pretoria 0001, South Africa. FAX 27-12-429-2533. TELEX 350068. Ed. S. Maimela. adv.; bk.rev. circ. 3,457. (also avail. in microfilm from UMI) **Indexed:** Ind.S.A.Per., New Test.Abstr., Old.Test.Abstr., Rel.& Theol.Abstr. (1989-), Rel.Ind.One. **Document type:** academic/scholarly publication.
—BLDSC (7356.456100).
Formerly (until 1994): Theologia Evangelica (ISSN 0255-8858)

200 370.196 US
RELIGION FOR PEACE; newsletter on inter-religious dialogue and action for peace. 1974. 3/yr. $25. World Conference on Religion and Peace, International Division, 777 United Nations Plaza, New York, NY 10017. TEL 212-687-2163. Ed. William F. Vendley. circ. 4,000. (back issues avail.) **Document type:** newsletter.
Description: Includes youth page and reports from various committees of the conference.

200 GW ISSN 0722-9151
RELIGION HEUTE. 4/yr. DM.69.40 (foreign DM.72.60). Erhard Friedrich Verlag GmbH, Im Brande 17, 30926 Seelze, Germany. TEL 0511-40004-0. FAX 0511-4000444. (Subscr. to: Postfach 100150, 30917 Seelze, Germany) Ed.Bd. **Document type:** academic/scholarly publication.
—BLDSC (7356.463000).

RELIGION HEUTE: SUPPLEMENT. see EDUCATION

200 US
RELIGION IN AMERICA.* 1967. a. $30. Princeton Religion Research Center, Inc., 47 Hulfish St., Box 389, Princeton, NJ 08542. TEL 609-921-8112. (back issues avail.)

200 947 US ISSN 1069-4781
BR738.6
RELIGION IN EASTERN EUROPE. 1981. bi-m. $36. Christian Association for Relationships with Eastern Europe, c/o Rosemont College, Rosemont, PA 19010. TEL 215-527-0200. FAX 215-696-8970. E-mail: PMojzes@VM.Temple.Edu. Ed. Paul Mojzes. bk.rev. circ. 700. (looseleaf format; also avail. in microfilm; back issues avail.) **Document type:** academic/scholarly publication.
●Also available online. Vendor(s): Knight-Ridder, Inc., Ovid Technologies.
—BLDSC (7356.459000); UnCover.
Formerly: Occasional Papers on Religion in Eastern Europe (ISSN 0731-5465)

200 MW
RELIGION IN MALAWI. 1987. a. K.5. University of Malawi, Department of Theology and Religious Studies, P.O. Box 280, Zomba, Malawi. TEL 0265-522549. Ed. Joseph Chakanza. adv. contact: Joseph Chakanza. bk.rev.; circ. 500 (paid). (also avail. in diskette format; back issues avail.) **Document type:** academic/scholarly publication.
Description: Covers information and discussions in all fields of religion in Malawi.

200 US ISSN 0730-6350
Z695.1.T3
RELIGION INDEXES: THESAURUS. 1981. biennial. $70. American Theological Library Association, Religion Indexes, 820 Church St., Ste. 300, Evanston, IL 60201-5613. TEL 708-869-7788. FAX 708-869-8513. E-mail: atla@atla.com. Ed. Erica Treesh. **Document type:** abstracting/indexing.
●Also available on CD-ROM.

200 335 UK ISSN 0963-7494
BR738.6
RELIGION, STATE AND SOCIETY: THE KESTON JOURNAL. 1973. q. £37 to individuals; institutions £158 (effective 1996). (Keston Institute) Carfax Publishing Co., P.O. Box 25, Abingdon, Oxon. OX14 3UE, England. TEL 01235-555335. FAX 01235-555359. (Subscr. in N. America to: Carfax Publishing Co., 875-81 Massachusetts Ave., Cambridge, MA 02139) Ed. Philip Walters. adv.; bk.rev.; bibl.; index. circ. 2,000. (also avail. in microfilm from UMI; reprint service avail. from UMI) **Indexed:** Abstr.Musl.Rel., CERDIC, HR Rep. (1985-1990), Rel.Ind.One. **Document type:** academic/scholarly publication.
—BLDSC (7356.474500); Faxon; SWETS; UMI. CCC.
Formerly (until 1992): Religion in Communist Lands (ISSN 0307-5974)
Description: Presents articles on religious communities in communist and formerly communist countries, and social, cultural, ethical and religious issues influencing the emergence of the new Europe.
Refereed Serial

268 US ISSN 0034-401X
RELIGION TEACHER'S JOURNAL. 1967. 7/yr. $18.95. Twenty-Third Publications, Box 180, Mystic, CT 06355-0180. TEL 203-536-2611. FAX 203-572-0788. Ed. Gwen Costello. adv.: B&W page $1695, color page $2595; adv. contact: Julie McCabe. abstr.; illus.; index. circ. 36,000. (also avail. in microform from UMI; reprint service avail. from UMI) **Indexed:** Cath.Ind., CERDIC. **Document type:** consumer publication.
—UMI.
Description: Provides help for lay persons working as church educators and as a training vehicle for pastors to use with them.

200 301 IT ISSN 0391-853X
RELIGIONE E SOCIETA (ROME); storia della chiesa e dei movimenti cattolici. 1977. irreg., latest vol.21. price varies. Edizioni Studium, Via Cassiodoro 14, 00193 Rome, Italy. **Document type:** monographic series.

200 301 IT ISSN 0394-9397
RELIGIONI E SOCIETA (TURIN); rivista di scienze sociali della religione. 1986. 2/yr. L.65000 (Europe L.95000; elsewhere L.105000) (effective 1995). Rosenberg & Sellier, Via Andrea Doria 14, 10123 Turin, Italy. TEL 39-11-8127820. FAX 39-11-8127744. Ed.Bd. adv. circ. 1,000. **Indexed:** Sociol.Abstr. (1986-).
Description: Religious forum covering theology, philosophy and sociology of religions.

RELIGIONS AND THEOLOGY

200   CN
RELIGIONS AND BELIEFS/RELIGIONS ET CROYANCES. (Text in English, French) 1993. irreg. price varies. University of Ottawa Press, 542 King Edward, Ottawa, ON K1N 6N5, Canada. TEL 613-564-2270. FAX 613-564-9284. Ed. Robert Choquette.
   Description: Studies on various aspects of religion: the religions of America, religion in relation with ethics and the Bible and culture.

292 937   NE   ISSN 0927-7633
RELIGIONS IN THE GRAECO-ROMAN WORLD. 1961. irreg., vol.124, 1995. price varies. E.J. Brill, P.O. Box 9000, 2300 PA Leiden, Netherlands. TEL 31-71-5353500. FAX 31-71-5317532. TELEX 39296 BRILL NL. (In N. America: E.J. Brill, 24 Hudson St., Kinderhook, NY 12106. TEL 800-962-4406. FAX 518-758-1959) Eds. M.E.C. van Haaren, M.B. deBoer. (back issues avail.) Indexed: Rel.Ind.Two. **Document type:** monographic series.
   Formerly (until vol.114, 1992): Etudes Preliminaires aux Religions Orientales dans l'Empire Romain (ISSN 0531-1950)
   Description: Scholarly monographs on historical, bibliographical and archaeological aspects of Egyptian, Mithraic and Oriental religions in all parts of the Roman Empire and the Graeco-Roman world.
   Refereed Serial

RELIGIONSUNTERRICHT AN HOEHEREN SCHULEN. see *EDUCATION*

291   DK   ISSN 0108-1993
RELIGIONSVIDENSKABELIGT TIDSSKRIFT. (Text in Danish; summaries in English) 1982. s-a. DKK 148. Religionsvidenskab, Aarhus Universitet, DK-8000 Aarhus C, Denmark. TEL 45-8619-70-33. FAX 45-86-19-84-33. (Dist. by: Aarhus University Press, Aarhus Universitet, Bldg. 170, DK-8000 Aarhus C., Denmark. TEL 45-6615-8600) Eds. Carsten Riis, Jeppe Sinding Jensen. adv.; bk.rev. circ. 350. **Document type:** academic/scholarly publication.

200   GW   ISSN 0934-2192
RELIGIONSWISSENSCHAFTLICHE REIHE. 1988. a. Diagonal Verlag, Postfach 1248, 35002 Marburg, Germany. TEL 06421-681936. FAX 06421-681944. Ed.Bd. **Document type:** monographic series.

RELIGIOUS BROADCASTING. see *COMMUNICATIONS — Television And Cable*

268 658   US   ISSN 1050-2742
RELIGIOUS CONFERENCE MANAGER. 1972. q. $42 (foreign $64). (Religious Conference Management Association) Adams-Laux Company, Inc., 63 Great Rd., Maynard, MA 01754. TEL 508-897-5552. FAX 508-897-6824. Ed. Patricia Wargocki. adv. circ. 2,600.
   —CCC.
   Description: Provides religious planners with information to help them in arranging for and conducting meetings and conventions.

200   II
RELIGIOUS CONSULTANCY. 1978. 4/yr. Rs.135($27) K.K. Roy (Private) Ltd., 55 Gariahat Rd., P.O. Box 10210, Calcutta 700 019, India. Ed. K.K. Roy. adv.; abstr.; bibl.; index. circ. 980.

200 370   US   ISSN 0034-4087
BV1460   CODEN: RLEDAN
RELIGIOUS EDUCATION; a platform for the free discussion of issues in the field of religion and their bearing on education. 1906. q. $45 (foreign $48). Religious Education Association, 409 Prospect St., New Haven, CT 06511. TEL 203-865-6141. FAX 203-865-6142. Ed. H.A. Alexander. adv. contact: Barbara B. Ryan. bk.rev.; index. circ. 2,600. (also avail. in microform from UMI;PMC; reprint service avail. from UMI) Indexed: Bk.Rev.Ind. (1990-), CERDIC, Child.Bk.Rev.Ind. (1990-), Cont.Pg.Educ., Curr.Cont., Educ.Ind., IMFL, Ind.Jew.Per., Psychol.Abstr., Rel.& Theol.Abstr. (1967-), Rel.Ind.One.
   —BLDSC (7356.500000); Faxon; Genuine Article; SWETS; UMI; UnCover.
   Description: Brings together work by Jewish, Catholic, Orthodox, Protestant and other educators.

RELIGIOUS FREEDOM ALERT. see *POLITICAL SCIENCE — Civil Rights*

RELIGIOUS FUNDING RESOURCE GUIDE. see *SOCIAL SERVICES AND WELFARE*

200 920   US   ISSN 1057-2961
BL2525
RELIGIOUS LEADERS OF AMERICA. 1991. triennial. $79.95. Gale Research Inc., 835 Penobscot Bldg., Detroit, MI 48226. TEL 800-877-4253. FAX 313-961-6083. TELEX 810-221-7086. Ed. J. Gordon Melton.
   ●Also available online. Vendor(s): Lexis-Nexis.

200   UK   ISSN 0034-4125
BL1
RELIGIOUS STUDIES. 1965. q. £90($159) (effective 1996). Cambridge University Press, Edinburgh Bldg., Shaftesbury Rd., Cambridge CB2 2RU, England. TEL 01223-312393. FAX 01223-315052. TELEX 851817256. (N. American addr.: Cambridge University Press, Journals Dept., 40 W. 20th St., New York, NY 10011. TEL 212-924-3900. FAX 212-691-3239) Eds. P.A. Byrne, K. Ward. adv.; bk.rev.; index. (also avail. in microform from UMI; back issues avail.; reprint service avail. from SWZ) Indexed: Arts & Hum.Cit.Ind., Bk.Rev.Ind. (1981-), Br.Hum.Ind., CERDIC, Child.Bk.Rev.Ind. (1981-), Curr.Cont., Hum.Ind., Ind.Jew.Per., Mid.East: Abstr.& Ind., New Test.Abstr., Phil.Ind., Rel.& Theol.Abstr. (1968-), Rel.Ind.One, Rel.Per. **Document type:** academic/scholarly publication.
   —BLDSC (7356.550000); Faxon; Genuine Article; SWETS; UMI; UnCover. CCC.
   Description: Covers primarily the philosophy and history of religion.

200   PH   ISSN 0115-6349
BR1
RELIGIOUS STUDIES JOURNAL. (Text in English) 1978. a. P.30($3.20) (De La Salle University, Religious Studies Department) De La Salle University Press, 2401 Taft Ave., Manila, Philippines. TEL 2-59-48-32. FAX 632-521-9094. adv.; bk.rev. circ. 300. Indexed: Ind.Phil.Per. **Document type:** academic/scholarly publication.
   Description: Publishes scholarly articles reflecting significant quantitative or qualitative research. Includes speeches, research reports, and "state of the art" papers.

200   US   ISSN 0885-0372
RELIGIOUS STUDIES NEWS. irreg. $20. Scholars Press, Box 15399, Atlanta, GA 30333-0399. TEL 404-727-2320. FAX 404-727-2348. Ed. Heidi Nordberg. adv.; bk.rev. (tabloid format; back issues avail.)
   —UMI.

200   US   ISSN 0319-485X
BL1
RELIGIOUS STUDIES REVIEW; a quarterly review of publications in the field of religion and related disciplines. 1975. q. $36 to individuals (foreign $44); institutions $44 (foreign $53). Council of Societies for the Study of Religion, CSSR Executive Office, Valparaiso University, Valparaiso, IN 46383. TEL 219-464-5515. Ed.Bd. adv.; bk.rev.; bibl. circ. 3,500. Indexed: Bibl.Ling., Bk.Rev.Ind. (1980-), CERDIC, Chic.Per.Ind., Child.Bk.Rev.Ind. (1980-), Mid.East: Abstr.& Ind., New Test.Abstr., Old Test.Abstr., Rel.& Theol.Abstr. (1989-), Rel.Ind.One, Rel.Per. **Document type:** academic/scholarly publication.
   —BLDSC (7356.555000); Faxon; SWETS; UnCover.

200   CN   ISSN 0156-1650
RELIGIOUS TRADITIONS; a journal in the study of religion. 1978. a. Can.$15. McGill University, Faculty of Religious Studies, 3250 University St., Montreal, PQ H3A 2A7, Canada. TEL 514-398-6138. (Co-sponsor: University of Sydney, School of Studies in Religion, AT) Eds. Arvind Sharma, Ian Kesarcodi-Watson. adv.; bk.rev.; charts. circ. 300. Indexed: Rel.& Theol.Abstr. (1979-), Rel.Ind.One.
   —BLDSC (7356.570000); UMI.
   Description: Forum for discussion of the various religious traditions and methods of studying them.

RES MEDICAE. see *MEDICAL SCIENCES*

266   US   ISSN 1049-586X
RESCUE (KANSAS CITY). 1985. bi-m. free. International Union of Gospel Missions, 1045 Swift Ave., Kansas City, MO 64116-4127. TEL 816-471-8020. FAX 816-471-3718. E-mail: iugm@fileshop.com. Ed. Phil Rydman. adv.; bk.rev. circ. 3,500. **Document type:** newsletter.
   Formerly: Horizons.
   Description: For ministries and individuals ministering to the homeless addicted and urban poor in inner cities of North America and the world.

200 301.4   US   ISSN 1055-1158
RESEARCH IN RELIGION AND FAMILY: BLACK PERSPECTIVES. irreg. price varies. Peter Lang Publishing, Inc., 62 W. 45th St., 4th Fl., New York, NY 10036. TEL 212-302-6740. Ed. Noel Leo Erskine. **Document type:** academic/scholarly publication, monographic series.
   Description: Examines the goals of family and religion within the black tradition.

200   US
RESEARCH IN THE SOCIAL SCIENTIFIC STUDY OF RELIGION. 1989. a. (Abilene Christian University) J A I Press Inc., 55 Old Post Rd., No. 2, Box 1678, Greenwich, CT 06836-1678. TEL 203-661-7602.
   Description: Contains approximately 9 international articles examining religion and religious organizations from a variety of social science perspectives.
   Refereed Serial

THE RESHAPING OF PSYCHOANALYSIS; from Sigmund Freud to Ernest Becker. see *PSYCHOLOGY*

200   CN   ISSN 0708-2177
RESTORATION. 1947. 10/yr. Can.$6. Madonna House, Inc., Combermere, ON K0J 1L0, Canada. TEL 613-756-3713. Ed. Rev. David May. circ. 9,000. (also avail. in microform from UMI; reprint service avail. from UMI) **Document type:** newsletter.
   —UMI.

200   US   ISSN 0034-5830
RESTORATION HERALD. 1925. m. $8. Christian Restoration Association, 5664 Cheviot Rd., Cincinnati, OH 45247. TEL 513-385-0461. Ed. Thomas D. Thurman. adv.; bk.rev.; illus.; circ. 4,500 (controlled). (also avail. in audio cassette)

222   US   ISSN 0486-5642
RESTORATION QUARTERLY. 1958. q. $15 to individuals; institutions $20. Restoration Quarterly Corporation, ACU Station, Box 8227, Abilene, TX 79699. TEL 915-674-3781. FAX 915-674-3776. E-mail: RQ@BIBLE.ACU.EDU. Ed. James Thompson. adv.; B&W page $125. bk.rev. circ. 800. Indexed: CERDIC, New Test.Abstr., Old Test.Abstr., Rel.& Theol.Abstr. (1969-), Rel.Ind.One.
   —BLDSC (7777.850000); UMI.
   Description: Journal of Bible and religion with a special interest in articles dealing with the Campbell Stone Movement.
   Refereed Serial

266   CN   ISSN 0034-6284
REVEIL MISSIONNAIRE. 1966. bi-m. Can.$3. Missionnaires de la Consolata, 2505 W. bd. Gouin, Montreal, PQ H3M 1B5, Canada. TEL 514-334-1910. FAX 514-332-1940. Ed. Jean Pare. adv.; illus. circ. 20,000.

REVIEW (NEW YORK). see *HOMOSEXUALITY*

200   US   ISSN 0034-673X
BL1
REVIEW OF RELIGIOUS RESEARCH. 1959. q. $40. Religious Research Association, Marist Hall, Rm. 108, Catholic University of America, Washington, DC 20064. TEL 202-319-5447. (Editorial addr.: c/o D. Paul Johnson, Sociology Dept., Texas Tech. University, Lubbock, TX 79401) adv.; bk.rev.; abstr.; bibl.; stat.; index. cum.index: vols. 1-10. circ. 1,200. (also avail. in microform from UMI; reprint service avail. from UMI,WSH) Indexed: Arts & Hum.Cit.Ind., C.L.I., CERDIC, Curr.Cont., G.Soc.Sci.& Rel.Per.Lit., IMFL, Lang.& Lang.Behav.Abstr., Leg.Per., Mid. East: Abstr.& Ind., Past.Care & Couns.Abstr., Rel.& Theol.Abstr. (1968-), Rel.Ind.One, Rel.Per., Sociol.Abstr. (1972-), SSCI. **Document type:** academic/scholarly publication.
   —BLDSC (7794.195000); Faxon; Genuine Article; SWETS; UMI; UnCover.

RELIGIONS AND THEOLOGY

220   **AG**   ISSN 0034-7078
REVISTA BIBLICA. 1939. q. $35 in Latin America; N. America $38; Europe $40 (effective 1995). (Sociedad Argentina de Profesores de Sagrada Escritura) Editorial Guadalupe, Mansilla 3865, 1425 Buenos Aires, Argentina. TEL 54-1-8268587. FAX 54-1-8054112. Dir. P. Armando Levoratti. adv. contact: Elida Lila del Rio. bk.rev.; bibl.; index, cum.index. circ. 700. **Indexed:** Int.Z.Bibelwiss., New Test.Abstr., Rel.Ind.One.

200   **SP**   ISSN 0034-8147
BX805
REVISTA DE ESPIRITUALIDAD. 1941. q. 2000 ptas. (effective 1992). Padres Carmelitas Descalzos, Triana 9, 28016 Madrid, Spain. FAX 91-359-16-61. adv.; bk.rev.; bibl.; index. circ. 1,200. **Indexed:** New Test.Abstr.
—BLDSC (7854.420000).

220   **CR**   ISSN 1018-5763
BT83.57
REVISTA DE INTERPRETACION BIBLICA LATINOAMERICANA. Short title: R I B L A. (Editions in Portuguese and Spanish) 1988. 3/yr. $18 in Latin America; elsewhere $30. (Departamento Ecumenico de Investigaciones) Editorial D E I, Apdo. 390-2070 Sabanilla, San Jose, Costa Rica. TEL 53-0229. FAX 53-1541. TELEX 3472 ADEI CR. (For Portuguese ed. subscr. to: Editora Vozes, Rua Frei Luis 100, 25689 Petropolis RJ, Brazil) Ed.Bd.

200   **BL**
REVISTA ECLESIASTICA BRASILEIRA. 1941. q. $80. Editora Vozes Ltda., Rua Frei Luis 100, Caixa Postal 90023, 25689-900 Petropolis, RJ, Brazil. TEL 0242-43-5112. FAX 0242-42-0692. Ed. Eloi Dionisio Piva. adv.; bk.rev.; bibl. circ. 3,000. **Indexed:** Cath.Ind., New Test.Abstr., Old Test.Abstr.

262.9   **SP**   ISSN 0034-9372
K19   CODEN: REDCE4
REVISTA ESPANOLA DE DERECHO CANONICO. (Text in French, Italian, Latin, Spanish; summaries in English, Latin, Spanish) 1946. 2/yr. 5400 ptas.($63) (Consejo Superior de Investigaciones Cientificas (C.S.I.C.), Instituto de Derecho Canonico "San Raimundo de Penafort") Universidad Pontificia, Departamento de Ediciones y Publicaciones, Apdo. de Correos 541, 37080 Salamance, Spain. TEL 923-21-51-40. FAX 923-21-34-50. Ed. Antonio Garcia y Garcia. bk.rev.; bibl.; index, cum.index every 20 yrs. circ. 1,000. (tabloid format) **Indexed:** Canon Law Abstr., CERDIC.
Incorporates (in 1984): Colectanea de Jurisprudencia Canonica (ISSN 0210-0711)

200   **SP**   ISSN 0210-7112
BR7
REVISTA ESPANOLA DE TEOLOGIA. 1940. q. 3500 ptas. (foreign 5000 ptas.) (effective 1996). Centro de Estudios Teologicos "San Damaso", San Buenaventura, 9, 28005 Madrid, Spain. TEL 91-365-24-04. FAX 34-1-3642882. Ed. Manuel Gesteira. bk.rev.; bibl. circ. 600.
—SWETS.

200 800 100   **SP**   ISSN 0210-0525
REVISTA ESTUDIOS; revista trimestral publicada por los fraties de la orden de la merced. 1945. q. 2800 ptas.($55) or exchange basis (effective 1995). Provincial Merced Castilla, Belisana, 2, 28043 Madrid, Spain. TEL 34-1-3002972. FAX 34-1-3002994. Dir. Luis Vazquez Fernandez. adv. contact: Jose Amable Suarez. bk.rev. circ. 500. **Document type:** academic/scholarly publication.

200   **EC**
REVISTA MENSAJERO. 1884. m. (10/yr.). S/2500($13) Ediciones Mensajero, Apdo. 17-01-4100, Quito, Ecuador. Ed.Bd. circ. 5,000.
Description: Examines the concerns and issues of present-day Catholics living in Ecuador.

200 300   **CR**
REVISTA PASOS. bi-m. $12 in Latin America; elsewhere $18. (Departamento Ecumenico de Investigaciones) Editorial D E I, Apdo. 390-2070 Sabanilla, San Jose, Costa Rica. TEL 53-0229. FAX 53-1541. TELEX 3472 ADEI CR. Ed.Bd.

220   **FR**   ISSN 0035-0907
REVUE BIBLIQUE. 1892. q. 968 F. (foreign 1030 F.). (Ecole Biblique et Archeologique de Jerusalem, IS) J. Gabalda et Cie, 18, rue P. et M. Curie, 75006 Paris, France. Ed. R.P. deTarragon. bk.rev.; bibl.; charts; illus.; index, cum.index: 1892-1972; 1973-1993. (also avail. in microfiche from IDC) **Indexed:** Arts & Hum.Cit.Ind., Bibl.Ling., CERDIC, Curr.Cont., New Test.Abstr., Old Test.Abstr., Rel.& Theol.Abstr. (1975-), Rel.Ind.One, Rel.Per. **Document type:** academic/scholarly publication.
—BLDSC (7892.820000); Faxon; SWETS; UnCover.

274   **FR**   ISSN 0300-9505
BR840
REVUE D'HISTOIRE DE L'EGLISE DE FRANCE. 1910. s-a. 360 F. (2100 BEF) (effective 1995). Societe d'Histoire Religieuse de la France, 28 rue d'Assas, 75006 Paris, France. (Subscr. in France to: Editions Brepols, 23 rue des Grands-Augustins, 75006 Paris, France. TEL 1-44-41-20-00. FAX 1-43-26-23-77; Elsewhere to: N.V. Brepols, Steenweg op Tielen 68, 2300 Turnhout, Belgium. TEL 32-14-415463. FAX 32-14-428914) Ed. M. Venard. bk.rev. **Indexed:** Amer.Hist.& Life, CERDIC, Hist.Abstr. **Document type:** academic/scholarly publication.
—Faxon; SWETS.

209   **BE**   ISSN 0035-2381
BX940
REVUE D'HISTOIRE ECCLESIASTIQUE. 1900. q. 3500 BEF($76) Universite Catholique de Louvain, Bureau de la Revue d'Histoire Ecclesiastique, Bibliotheque, College Erasme, B-1348 Louvain-la-Neuve, Belgium. Ed. Claude Soetens. adv.; bk.rev.; bibl.; charts; index, cum.index every 15-20 yrs. circ. 250. (also avail. in microfiche from IDC; reprint service avail. from SCH) **Indexed:** Amer.Hist.& Life, Arts & Hum.Cit.Ind., Hist.Abstr., M.L.A., New Test.Abstr., Rel.& Theol.Abstr. (1967-), Rel.Ind.One, Rel.Per. **Document type:** academic/scholarly publication.
—Faxon; SWETS.

200   **FR**   ISSN 0035-2403
BR3
REVUE D'HISTOIRE ET DE PHILOSOPHIE RELIGIEUSES. 1921. q. 165 F. (foreign 200 F.). (Universite de Strasbourg II) Presses Universitaires de France, Departement des Revues, 14 av. du Bois-de-l'Epine, B.P.90, 91003 Evry Cedex, France. TEL 1-60-77-82-05. FAX 1-60-79-20-45. TELEX PUF 600 474 F. adv.; bk.rev.; charts; illus.; index, cum.index: 1920-1945, 1946-1974. circ. 1,800. (also avail. in microfilm from KTO; reprint service avail. from KTO,SCH) **Indexed:** Amer.Hist.& Life, Arts & Hum.Cit.Ind., Bibl.Ling., CERDIC, Curr.Cont., Hist.Abstr., New Test.Abstr., Rel.& Theol.Abstr. (1975-), Rel.Ind.One, Rel.Per., So.Pac.Per.Ind.
—Faxon; SWETS. **CCC.**
Description: Provides a scientific study of various biblical, historical, philosophical and dogmatic problems posed by the develoment of christian theological thought and its links with non-Christian thought.

209   **FR**   ISSN 0035-1423
BL3
REVUE DE L'HISTOIRE DES RELIGIONS. 1880. q. 400 F. (foreign 480 F.) (effective 1996). Presses Universitaires de France, Departement des Revues, 14 av. du Bois-de-l'Epine, B.P.90, 91003 Evry Cedex, France. TEL 1-60-77-82-05. FAX 1-60-79-20-45. TELEX PUF 600 474 F. Dirs. A. Guillaumont, Charles Amiel. bk.rev.; q. index. (also avail. in microfilm from BHP; reprint service avail. from KTO) **Indexed:** Amer.Hist.& Life, Arts & Hum.Cit.Ind., Curr.Cont., Hist.Abstr., New Test.Abstr., Rel.Ind.One, Rel.Per.
—Faxon; Genuine Article; SWETS. **CCC.**
Description: Encompasses the general history of religions as well as a more in depth focus on particular aspects of a different religion each issue.

221 296.155   **FR**   ISSN 0035-1725
BM487.A62
REVUE DE QUMRAN. (Text in English, French, German, Italian, Latin, Spanish) 1958. s-a. 680 F. J. Gabalda et Cie, 18 rue P.et M. Curie, 75005 Paris, France. Ed. Emile Puech. bk.rev. circ. 1,000. **Indexed:** Bibl.Ling., New Test.Abstr., Old Test.Abstr., Rel.& Theol.Abstr. (1968-), Rel.Ind.One, Rel.Per. **Document type:** academic/scholarly publication.
—SWETS.
Description: Examines the Dead Sea Scrolls.
Refereed Serial

230 100   **SZ**   ISSN 0035-1784
REVUE DE THEOLOGIE ET DE PHILOSOPHIE. 1868. q. 59 SFr. (foreign 63 SFr.) to individuals; institutions 75 SFr.(foreign 80 SFr.) A T A R, S.A., 11 rue de la Dole, CH-1211 Geneva 13, Switzerland. TEL 022-3446400. FAX 022-3446865. Ed. Pierre Buehler. bk.rev.; index. (also avail. in microfilm from BHP) **Indexed:** Bull.Signal., CERDIC, New Test.Abstr., Old Test.Abstr., Phil.Ind., Rel.Ind.One. **Document type:** academic/scholarly publication.
—BLDSC (7956.070000).

230 100   **SZ**   ISSN 0250-6971
REVUE DE THEOLOGIE ET DE PHILOSOPHIE. CAHIERS. 1977. irreg. (approx. a.). A T A R, S.A., 11 rue de la Dole, CH-1211 Geneva 13, Switzerland. TEL 022-3446400. FAX 022-3446865. Ed. Pierre Buehler. **Indexed:** New Test.Abstr., Rel.Ind.One. **Document type:** bulletin.

230 809   **FR**   ISSN 0035-2012
BX2901
REVUE DES ETUDES AUGUSTINIENNES. (Text in various languages; summaries in English, French) 1955. s-a. 400 F. (2400 BEF) (effective 1995). Institut d'Etudes Augustiniennes, 3 rue de l'Abbaye, 75006 Paris, France. (Subscr. in France to: Editions Brepols, 23 rue des Grands Augustins, 75006 Paris, France. TEL 1-44-41-20-00. FAX 1-43-26-33-77; Elsewhere to: N.V. Brepols, Steenweg op Tielen 68, 2300 Turnhout, Belgium. TEL 32-14-415463. FAX 32-14-428919) Dir. Jean-Claude Fredouille. bk.rev.; bibl.; illus.; index. circ. 1,000. **Indexed:** Bull.Signal., CERDIC, M.L.A., New Test.Abstr., Phil.Ind. **Document type:** academic/scholarly publication.
—Faxon; SWETS.
Formerly (until 1954): Annee Theologique Augustinienne.
Description: Publishes original scholarship in the areas concerning early Christianity and the High Middle Ages, including history, literature, philology, exegesis, philosophy and archaeology, as well as other related disciplines. Also publishes an annual systematic review of studies on Augustine.

REVUE MABILLON. see *RELIGIONS AND THEOLOGY — Roman Catholic*

200   **CN**   ISSN 0700-6500
REVUE NOTRE DAME DU CAP. (Text in French) 1892. 10/yr. Can.$9 (effective 1995). Corporation Revue Notre-Dame du Cap, 626 rue Notre Dame, Cap-de-la-Madelaine, PQ G8T 4G9, Canada. TEL 819-374-2441. FAX 819-374-2441. Ed. Jerome Martineau. adv. contact: Paul Arsenault. bk.rev.; circ. 95,000 (paid). **Document type:** newspaper.

230   **FR**   ISSN 0035-4295
BX802
REVUE THOMISTE; revue doctrinale de theologie et de philosophie. 1893. q. 380 F. (Europe 450 F.; elsewhere 480 F.) (effective 1995 & 1996). Association Culturelle de Publications, Dominicains de la Province de Toulouse, 1 Imp. Lacordaire, 31078 Toulouse Cedex, France. TEL 62-17-31-26. FAX 62-17-31-17. (Subscr. in US to: Kraus Reprint and Periodicals, Route 100, Milwood, NY 10546) Ed. Pere Serge-Thomas Bonino. adv.; bk.rev.; index. circ. 1,100. (also avail. in microfilm from BHP; reprint service avail. from KTO) **Indexed:** Bull.Signal., CERDIC, M.L.A., New Test.Abstr., Phil.Ind., Rel.& Theol.Abstr. **Document type:** academic/scholarly publication.
—Faxon; SWETS.
Description: Aims to promote theological wisdom and Christian humanism to today's culture.

RHEINISCHER MERKUR; Christ und Welt. see *GENERAL INTEREST PERIODICALS — Germany*

200   **AT**
RHEMA LIVE. 1986. bi-m. free. Rhema Publications, 1 Thorogood St., Victoria Park, Perth, W.A. 6100, Australia. TEL 61-9-4701256. FAX 61-9-4703670. Ed. Penny Webb. adv.; bk.rev. circ. 6,000. (back issues avail.)
Formerly: Rhema Life (ISSN 1030-0147)

200   **GW**
RHOEN BRIEF. q. free. Christliche Tagungsstaette Hohe Rhoen e.V., Fischzucht 1-3, 97653 Bischofsheim, Germany. TEL 09772-248. FAX 09772-8213. Ed. Fritz Schroth. **Document type:** newsletter.

RICERCHE DI STORIA SOCIALE E RELIGIOSA. see *SOCIOLOGY*

RELIGIONS AND THEOLOGY

200 282 IT ISSN 0391-8424
RICERCHE PER LA STORIA RELIGIOSA DI ROMA. 1977. irreg., vol.8, 1990. price varies. Edizioni di Storia e Letteratura s.r.l., Via Lancellotti, 18, 00186 Rome, Italy. TEL 65-40556. Ed.Bd. **Document type:** academic/scholarly publication.

200 IT ISSN 1120-8333
RICERCHE TEOLOGICHE. 1990. s-a. L.40000 (foreign L.50000). (Societa Italiana per la Ricerca Teologica) Edizioni Dehoniane Roma (Rome), Via Casale S. Pio V, 20, 00165 Rome, Italy. TEL 06-663-88-69. Ed. Angelo Amato.

RIGHT TO HOUSING REPORT. see *HOUSING AND URBAN PLANNING*

268 SZ ISSN 0254-3966
RISK BOOK SERIES. 1965. q. 43.50 SFr.($32.50) World Council of Churches, 150 Route de Ferney, P.O. Box 2100, CH-1211 Geneva 2, Switzerland. TEL 022-791-6111. FAX 022-791-0361. circ. 4,000. **Indexed:** CERDIC, Rel.Ind.One, Rel.Per. **Document type:** monographic series.
—BLDSC (7972.585000).
Formerly (until 1978): Risk (ISSN 0035-5585)

RITES EGYPTIENS. see *ARCHAEOLOGY*

264 IT ISSN 0035-6395
RIVISTA DI PASTORALE LITURGICA. 1962. bi-m. L.38000 (foreign L.59000) (effective 1996). Editrice Queriniana, Via Piamarta 6, 25187 Brescia, Italy. TEL 39-30-294653. FAX 39-30-3756375. Ed. Daniele Piazzi. adv. contact: Mario De Risio. **Document type:** trade publication.

274 900 IT ISSN 0035-6557
BR870
RIVISTA DI STORIA DELLA CHIESA IN ITALIA. (Text in English, French, German, Italian, Latin, Spanish) 1947. s-a. $100. Herder Editrice e Libreria s.r.l., Piazza Montecitorio 120, 00186 Rome, Italy. TEL 67 94 628. FAX 678-47-51. TELEX 621427 NATEL. Ed. Michele Maccarrone. bk.rev.; bibl.; charts; stat.; tr.lit.; index. (tabloid format) **Indexed:** Amer.Hist.& Life, Hist.Abstr. **Document type:** academic/scholarly publication.
—BLDSC (7992.880000); Faxon; SWETS.

209 IT ISSN 0035-6573
RIVISTA DI STORIA E LETTERATURA RELIGIOSA. (Text in English, French, German, Italian) 1965. 3/yr. L.78000 (foreign L.98000) (effective 1995) US $67.50 (effective 1996). (Universita di Torino, Biblioteca Erik Peterson) Casa Editrice Leo S. Olschki, Casella Postale 66, 50100 Florence, Italy. TEL 39-55-6530684. FAX 39-55-6530214. Ed.Bd. adv.; bk.rev. circ. 1,000. **Indexed:** CERDIC, M.L.A., New Test.Abstr. **Document type:** academic/scholarly publication.
—Genuine Article; SWETS.

209 IT ISSN 0392-016X
RIVISTA DI STORIA E LETTERATURA RELIGIOSA. BIBLIOTECA. STUDI. 1990. irreg., no.5, 1992. price varies. Casa Editrice Leo S. Olschki, Casella Postale 66, 50100 Florence, Italy. TEL 39-55-6530684. FAX 39-55-6530214. **Document type:** monographic series.

209 IT ISSN 0392-016X
RIVISTA DI STORIA E LETTERATURA RELIGIOSA. BIBLIOTECA. TESTI E DOCUMENTI. 1967. irreg., no.15, 1993. price varies. Casa Editrice Leo S. Olschki, Casella Postale 66, 50100 Florence, Italy. TEL 39-55-6530684. FAX 39-55-6530214. **Indexed:** Arts & Hum.Cit.Ind. **Document type:** monographic series.

205 IT ISSN 0391-108X
ROCCA. 1940. fortn. L.70000. Pro Civitate Christiana, Via Ancaiani 3, 06081 Assisi, Italy. TEL 075-813641. Ed. Gesuino Bulla. adv.: B&W page L.1500000. bk.rev. circ. 90,000.

200 US
THE ROCK (ELGIN). q. $10. David C. Cook Publishing Co., 850 N. Grove Ave., Elgin, IL 60120. TEL 708-741-2400. FAX 708-741-0595. Ed. Sharon Stultz.
Former titles: Sprint (Elgin) (ISSN 0277-0377); (until 1983): Looking Ahead (Elgin) (ISSN 0162-9549)
Description: Helps junior high students in Sunday school to develop a Christian perspective on life through faith in Jesus Christ.

200 US ISSN 1052-2204
ROCKWELL LECTURE SERIES. irreg. Peter Lang Publishing, Inc., 62 W. 45th St., 4th Fl., New York, NY 10036. TEL 212-302-6704. FAX 212-302-7574. Ed. Niels C. Nielsen. **Document type:** academic/scholarly publication, monographic series.

ROEMISCHE HISTORISCHE MITTEILUNGEN. see *HISTORY — History Of Europe*

200 GW ISSN 0035-7812
ROEMISCHE QUARTALSCHRIFT FUER CHRISTLICHE ALTERTUMSKUNDE UND KIRCHENGESCHICHTE. 1905. s-a. DM.228. Verlag Herder GmbH und Co. KG, Hermann-Herder-Str. 4, 79104 Freiburg, Germany. FAX 0761-2717-407. adv.; bk.rev.; charts; illus. circ. 350. (reprint service avail. from SCH) **Indexed:** Numis.Lit., RILA. **Document type:** newsletter.
—Faxon; SWETS.

THE ROLL; magazine of the Schola Contemplationis. see *PHILOSOPHY*

200 NE ISSN 0035-8169
ROND DE TAFEL; leerkrant liturgie. 1892; N.S. 1946. bi-m. fl.12. Grafische Bedrijven Berne B.V., Postbus 27, 5473 ZG Heeswijk-Dinther, Netherlands. TEL 31-4139-1394. FAX 31-4139-2270. bk.rev.; illus.; index. circ. 2,400. **Indexed:** CERDIC.
Formerly: Offer.

ROTTENBURGER JAHRBUCH FUER KIRCHENGESCHICHTE. see *HISTORY — History Of Europe*

200 US
ROUNDTABLE REPORT. 1980. bi-m. $25. 3295 Popular Ave., Box 11467, Memphis, TN 38111. TEL 901-458-3795. Ed. Donna Mooshian Striegel.
Formerly: Religious Round Table.

280 NE ISSN 0166-4069
RUIMZICHT. 1875. q. fl.40($19) Vereniging Hervormd Opleidingscentrum, J.W. Frisostraat 18, Postbox 14147, 3508 SE Utrecht, Netherlands. TEL 31-30-540248. bk.rev.; illus. circ. 1,100.
Formerly: Nieuw Ruimzicht (ISSN 0028-9841)

RUNDBRIEF EHEMALIGER SCHUELER UND FREUNDE DER SCHULBRUEDER. see *COLLEGE AND ALUMNI*

377.8 UK ISSN 0968-5375
THE S A L T PROGRAMME FOR 5 TO 7. q. £4 per no. Scripture Union Publishing, 130 City Rd., London EC1V 2NJ, England. TEL 0171-782-0013. FAX 0171-782-0014. Ed. Kathryn Copsey. adv. contact: J. Bicknell. illus. circ. 23,000. **Document type:** bulletin.
Former titles (until 1993): Learning Together with 5-7's; Teaching 5-7's; Teaching Primaries (ISSN 0040-0653)

377.8 UK ISSN 0968-5383
THE S A L T PROGRAMME FOR 8 TO 10. q. £4 per no. Scripture Union Publishing, 130 City Rd., London EC1V 2NJ, England. TEL 0171-782-0013. FAX 0171-782-0014. Ed. Judith Merrell. adv. contact: J. Bicknell. illus. circ. 26,000. **Document type:** bulletin.
Former titles (until 1993): Learning Together with 7-11's (ISSN 0963-4851); Teaching 7-10's; Teaching Juniors (ISSN 0040-0629)

377.8 UK ISSN 0968-5391
THE S A L T PROGRAMME FOR 11 TO 13. q. £4 per no. Scripture Union Publishing, 130 City Rd., London EC1V 2NJ, England. TEL 0171-782-0013. FAX 0171-782-0014. Ed. Jenny Hyatt. adv. contact: J. Bicknell. illus. circ. 13,000. **Document type:** bulletin.
Former titles (until 1993): Learning Together with 11-14's (ISSN 0308-356X); Teaching 10-13's; Teaching Teenagers (ISSN 0040-067X)

280 100 US ISSN 0883-1300
S C P JOURNAL. 1977. irreg. $25 donation (foreign $35). Spiritual Counterfeits Project, Inc., 2606 Dwight Way, Berkeley, CA 94704. TEL 510-540-0300. FAX 510-540-1107. Eds. Tal Brooke, Brooks Alexander; Pub. Tal Brooke. bk.rev. circ. 6,000. (back issues avail.) **Indexed:** Chr.Per.Ind. **Document type:** academic/scholarly publication.
Description: Interprets social, cultural, and spiritual trends from a Christian biblical viewpoint. Offers critical insight from a Christian perspective on the New Age movement, cults, the occult, and UFOs.

280 US ISSN 0883-1319
S C P NEWSLETTER. 1975. q. $10 suggested donation. Spiritual Counterfeits Project, Inc., 2606 Dwight Way, Berkeley, CA 94704. TEL 510-540-0330. FAX 510-540-1107. Eds. Tal Brooke, Brooks Alexander; Tal Brooke. bk.rev. circ. 18,000. **Indexed:** Chr.Per.Ind. **Document type:** newsletter.
—UMI.
Description: Offers critical insight from a Christian perspective on social, cultural, and spiritual trends, including the New Age movement, the occult, cults, and UFOs.

200 BL ISSN 0036-1267
S E D O C. (Servicio de Documentacao) 1968. 6/yr. $65. Editora Vozes Ltda., Rua Frei Luis 100, Caixa Postal 90023, 25689-900 Petropolis, RJ, Brazil. TEL 0242-43-5112. FAX 0242-42-0692. Ed. Antonio Moser. circ. 2,400.

266 UK
S G M NEWS. 1943. q. free. Scripture Gift Mission, Radstock House, 3 Eccleston St., London SW1W 9LZ, England. Ed. Eleanor Trotter. adv. contact: Bryan Stonehouse. illus. circ. 20,000. **Document type:** newsletter.
Formerly: S G M News Digest (ISSN 0048-9859)

200 IT
S I D I C. (Editions in English and French) 1968. 3/yr. L.30000($23) (effective 1996). Service International de Documentation Judeo-Chretienne, Via del Plebiscito 112, In 9, 00186 Rome, Italy. TEL 06-6795307. FAX 06-6786280. (Subscr. to: Dr. Eugene Fisher, Secretariat for Catholic-Jewish Relations, 1312 Massachusetts Ave., N.W., Washington, DC 20005) Ed.Bd. bk.rev.; bibl.; cum.index every 3 yrs. circ. 1,500. (back issues avail.) **Indexed:** Cath.Ind. **Document type:** academic/scholarly publication.
Description: Focuses on common interests to Jews and Christians; promotes knowledge, understanding and respect among Christian and Jewish communities.

266 CN ISSN 0711-6683
BV3500
S I M NOW. (Society for International Ministries) 1958. q. free in Canada and U.S. S I M International, 10 Huntingdale Blvd., Scarborough, ON M1W 2S5, Canada. TEL 416-497-2424. FAX 416-497-2444. (U.S. address: Box 7900, Charlotte, NC 28241) Ed. David W. Fuller. bk.rev. circ. 125,000. (reprint service avail. from UMI) **Indexed:** Curr.Cont.Africa.
—UMI.
Formerly (until Jan. 1982): Africa Now (ISSN 0044-6513)
Description: To inform of SIM activities and create interest in missions.

S T R A I G H T. (Society to Reform All Immoral Godless Homosexual Trash) see *POLITICAL SCIENCE*

200 IT
SACERDOZIO REGALE; centro sacerdozio regale and apostolato della Preghiera. 1954. m. free. Centro Sacerdozio Regale, Via Villanova, 14, Casa Betania, 33170 Pordenone, Italy. TEL 39-434-570019. Ed. Domenico Corelli. circ. 3,000 (controlled). **Document type:** bulletin.

200 100 IT ISSN 0036-2190
SACRA DOCTRINA. 1956. 5/yr. L.50000 (foreign L.90000) (effective 1995). Edizioni Studio Domenicano, Via dell'Osservanza, 72, 40136 Bologna, Italy. TEL 39-51-582034. FAX 39-51-331583. Ed. Enzo Panzacchi. adv. contact: P. Vincenzo Ottorino Benetollo. bk.rev.; bibl.; index. circ. 1,500. (tabloid format) **Indexed:** CERDIC, New Test.Abstr. **Document type:** academic/scholarly publication, trade publication.
—BLDSC (8062.730000).

RELIGIONS AND THEOLOGY

SACRED ART JOURNAL; Orthodox liturgical arts. see *ART*

SACRED DANCE GUILD JOURNAL. see *DANCE*

SACRED MUSIC NEWS & REVIEW. see *MUSIC*

282   BE   ISSN 0771-7776
BX800.A1
SACRIS ERUDIRI. 1948. a., vol.33, 1993. 2400 BEF (effective 1994). (Sint-Pietersabdij, Steenbrugge) N.V. Brepols, Steenweg op Tielen 68, 2300 Turnhout, Belgium. TEL 32-14-402500. FAX 32-14-428919. (back issues avail.) **Document type:** academic/scholarly publication.

220   SP
SAGRADA BIBLIA. 1976. irreg., no.12, 1989. price varies. (Universidad de Navarra, Facultad de Teologia) Ediciones Universidad de Navarra, S.A., Apdo. 396, 31080 Pamplona, Spain. TEL 94 825 6850.

ST. JOSEPH'S MESSENGER AND ADVOCATE OF THE BLIND. see *HANDICAPPED* — *Visually Impaired*

207.11   AT   ISSN 0036-3103
ST. MARK'S REVIEW. 1955. q. Aus.$25 (foreign Aus.$32). St. Mark's National Theological Centre, Library, P.O. Box E67, Canberra, A.C.T. 2600, Australia. TEL 06-273-1572. FAX 06-273-4067. Ed. Graeme Garrett. adv.; bk.rev.; cum.index; circ, 800 (paid). (also avail. in microform from UMI; reprint service avail. from UMI) **Indexed:** Aus.P.A.I.S., CERDIC, Rel.Ind.One. **Document type:** academic/scholarly publication.
—BLDSC (8070.191000); UMI; UnCover. **CCC**.

200   US   ISSN 0038-8815
ST. PAUL'S PRINTER. 1958. q. donation. Society of St. Paul (Palm Desert), Box 14350, Palm Desert, CA 92255-4350. TEL 619-568-2200. Ed. Rev. Andrew Rank. bk.rev.; illus.; stat. circ. 5,000. **Document type:** newsletter.

250   AU   ISSN 0036-3162
ST. POELTNER DIOEZESANBLATT. 1785. irreg. (approx. 12/yr.). S.400. Bischoefliches Ordinariat St. Poelten, Domplatz 1, A-3101 St. Poelten, Austria. Ed. Heinrich Fasching. bk.rev.; bibl.; charts. circ. 800. **Document type:** newsletter.

ST. WILLIBRORD STUDIES IN PHILOSOPHY AND RELIGION. see *PHILOSOPHY*

200   SP   ISSN 0211-4569
SAL TERRAE; revista de teologia pastoral. m. (11/yr.). 3800 ptas.($40) (effective 1994). Editorial Sal Terrae, Calle Guevara, 20, 39080 Santander, Spain. TEL 942-369198. FAX 942-369201. **Indexed:** Canon Law Abstr., CERDIC.

282   US   ISSN 0883-2587
SALT; for Christians who seek social justice. 1981. 10/yr. $18. Claretian Publications, 205 W. Monroe St., Chicago, IL 60606. TEL 800-328-6565. FAX 312-236-7230. Ed. Rev. Mark J. Brummel. adv.; B&W page $600. bk.rev.; illus. circ. 10,000.
Description: Explores the integral tie between scripture and justice.

200   AT   ISSN 0816-0031
SALT. 1985. 4/yr. Aus.$10. Australian Fellowship of Evangelical Students, 16 Mill Hill Rd., Bondi Junction, N.S.W. 2022, Australia. TEL 02-369-1688. Ed. Kerry Nagel. bk.rev.; illus.; tr.lit. circ. 3,000. (back issues avail.) **Document type:** newsletter.
Description: Prayer information on tertiary campus in Australia, while addressing issues relevant to students on those campuses.

200   IT   ISSN 0036-424X
SAN SALVATORE DA HORTA. 1927. bi-m. free. Chiesa Santa Rosalia, Cagliari 09124, Italy.

200   GW   ISSN 0342-1465
UNA SANCTA; Zeitschrift fuer oekumenische Bewegnung. 1946. q. DM.34. Kyrios Verlag, Postfach 15 45, 85315 Freising, Germany. index. circ. 2,000. (back issues avail.)

200   MX
SANTERIA CIENCIA Y RELIGION. 1993. bi-m. Jaripeo 115, Colinas del Sur, 01430 Mexico DF, Mexico. TEL 525-6436366. Ed. Jose Rodriguez Brenas. circ. 7,300.

200   BL   ISSN 0036-4614
SANTUARIO DE APARECIDA. 1900. w. $6.42 (foreign $45.55). (Congregacao do Santissimo Redentor) Editora Santuario, Rua Padre Claro Monteiro 342, 12570 Aparecida SP, Brazil. TEL 0125-362140. FAX 0125-362141. TELEX 125659 CSRE BR. Ed. Manoel Jose Paixao. adv.; bk.rev.; illus. circ. 40,000.

SAPIENZA; rivista internazionale di filosofia e di teologia. see *PHILOSOPHY*

SAT SANDESH; the message of the masters. see *PHILOSOPHY*

200   CN   ISSN 0315-7970
LE SAUVEUR. 1926. 6/yr. Can.$8. Sanctuaire de la Reparation au Sacre-Coeur, 3650, bd. de la Rousseliere, Montreal, PQ H1A 2X9, Canada. TEL 514-642-5391. FAX 514-642-5033. Ed. Yves Deschenes. circ. 10,000.

221   NO   ISSN 0901-8328
SCANDANAVIAN JOURNAL OF THE OLD TESTAMENT. s-a. NOK 380 in Nordic countries; elsewhere $77 (effective 1996). Scandinavian University Press, P.O. Box 2959 Toeyen, N-0608 Oslo, Norway. TEL 47-22-57-54-00. FAX 47-22-57-53-53. (U.S. addr.: Scandinavian University Press, 200 Meacham Ave., Elmont, NY 11003. TEL 516-352-7300) Eds. Knud Jeppesen, Niels Peter Lemche.
—BLDSC (8087.517700).
Description: Devoted to international Old Testament scholarship, with particular emphasis on Scandinavian O.T. scholarship.

266   CN   ISSN 0700-6802
SCARBORO MISSIONS. 1919. 9/yr. Can.$8. Scarboro Foreign Mission Society, 2685 Kingston Rd., Scarborough, ON M1M 1M4, Canada. TEL 416-261-7135. Ed. Rev. Gerald Curry. adv.; bk.rev. circ. 35,000. (back issues avail.)
Description: Presents a global vision of faith; one which promotes within the Canadian church a dialogue and understanding of the faiths, cultures and struggles of the people among whom the society works.

200   US
SCHLEIERMACHER STUDIES AND TRANSLATION. irreg., latest no.15. $49.95 per no. Edwin Mellen Press, 415 Ridge St., Box 450, Lewiston, NY 14092. TEL 716-754-2788. FAX 716-754-4056. **Document type:** monographic series.

SCHOLARS OF EARLY MODERN STUDIES. see *HISTORY* — *History Of Europe*

200   UK   ISSN 0261-5703
SCHOOLS OF PRAYER. 1980. 3/yr. £15 per copy. Diocese of Northampton, Religious Education Service, St. Mary's R.E. Centre, 118 Bromham Rd., Bedford MK40 2QR, England. Ed. J. Glen, K. McGinnell. bk.rev.; illus. circ. 200.

215   UK   ISSN 0954-4194
AS122
SCIENCE AND CHRISTIAN BELIEF. 1866. 2/yr. £13.90 (foreign £14.60). (Victoria Institute, Philosophical Society of Great Britain) The Paternoster Press, P.O. Box 300, Kingstown Broadway, Carlisle, Cumbria CA3 0QS, England. TEL 0228-512512. FAX 0228-514949. (Subscr. to: Paternoster Press, Box 11127, Birmingham, AL 35201-1127) Eds. Denis Alexander, A. Brian Robins. bk.rev.; bibl.; index, cum.index every 5 yrs. circ. 2,000. **Indexed:** CERDIC, Rel.& Theol.Abstr. (1989-). **Document type:** academic/scholarly publication.
—BLDSC (8131.830000); UMI.
Incorporates: Science and Faith (ISSN 0268-2885); Faith and Thought (ISSN 0014-7028)

SCIENCE ET ESPRIT. see *PHILOSOPHY*

SCIENCE OF RELIGION; abstracts and index of recent articles. see *RELIGIONS AND THEOLOGY* — *Abstracting, Bibliographies, Statistics*

200   UK
SCIENCE OF THOUGHT REVIEW. 1921. bi-m. £5($20) Science of Thought Press Ltd., Bosham House, Bosham, Chichester, W. Sussex PO18 8PJ, England. TEL 01243-572109. Ed. Stephanie Sorrell. adv. contact: Pat Willard. bk.rev. circ. 4,000. (back issues avail.) **Document type:** bulletin.
Former titles: Review; (until 1992): Science of Thought Review.
Description: Devoted to the spiritual life.

280   UK   ISSN 0264-5572
SCOTTISH CHURCH HISTORY SOCIETY. RECORDS. 1923. a. £10($22) Scottish Church History Society, 1 Denham Green Terrace, Edinburgh EH5 3PG, Scotland. TEL 0131-552-4059. Ed. James Kirk. bk.rev.; bibl.; index. circ. 280. (back issues avail.) **Document type:** academic/scholarly publication.
—BLDSC (7325.120000).
Description: Papers on history of church in Scotland including links abroad.

266   UK   ISSN 0048-9778
BV2100
SCOTTISH INSTITUTE OF MISSIONARY STUDIES BULLETIN. 1967. s-a. £2($5) Scottish Institute of Missionary Studies, Department of Missionary Studies, University of Aberdeen, King's College, Aberdeen AB9 2UB, Scotland. Ed. A. F. Walls. bk.rev. circ. 500. (processed; also avail. in microform from UMI; reprint service avail. from UMI) **Indexed:** CERDIC.
—UMI.

200   UK   ISSN 0143-8301
BL1
SCOTTISH JOURNAL OF RELIGIOUS STUDIES. 1980. 2/yr. £7 to individuals; institutions £15. University of Stirling, Department of Religious Studies, Stirling FK9 4LA, Scotland. TEL 01786-73171. FAX 01786-63000. Ed. Glyn Richards. adv.; bk.rev. circ. 200. **Indexed:** Rel.& Theol.Abstr. (1989-). **Document type:** academic/scholarly publication.
—BLDSC (8210.610000); SWETS; UMI.
Description: Critical investigation of major religious traditions of the world.

230   UK   ISSN 0036-9306
BR1
SCOTTISH JOURNAL OF THEOLOGY. 1948. 4/yr. £49.95 to institutions; individuals £24.95. T & T Clark, 59 George St., Edinburgh EH2 2LQ, Scotland. TEL 0131-225-4703. FAX 0131-220-4260. Eds. A.I.C. Heron, J. Houston. adv.; bk.rev.; index. circ. 1,200. (reprint service avail. from KTO) **Indexed:** Arts & Hum.Cit.Ind., CERDIC, Curr.Cont., New Test.Abstr., Old Test.Abstr., Rel.& Theol.Abstr. (1968-), Rel.Ind.One, Rel.Per. **Document type:** academic/scholarly publication.
—BLDSC (8210.630000); Faxon; Genuine Article; UnCover. **CCC**.
Description: Publishes contributions of major theological and philosophical interest from the world's leading scholars. Includes articles on biblical and applied theology intended to help the preacher and teacher.

SCREAMS OF ABEL. see *MUSIC*

200   FI   ISSN 0582-3226
SCRIPTA INSTITUTI DONNERIANI ABOENSIS. (Text in English, French, German) 1967. triennial. Fmk.200. Donner Institute for Research in Religious and Cultural History, Gezeliusgatan 2, P.O. Box 70, SF-20501 Turku, Finland. TEL 358-21-2654-315. FAX 358-21-2311-290. E-mail: Donner.Institute@abo.fi. (Dist. by: Almqvist & Wiksell International, P.O. Box 4627, S-11691, Stockholm, Sweden) Tore Ahlbaeck. circ. 550. **Indexed:** Arts & Hum.Cit.Ind. **Document type:** proceedings.

200   SP   ISSN 0036-9764
BR7
SCRIPTA THEOLOGICA. 1969. 3/yr. 6000 ptas.($85) (Universidad de Navarra, Facultad de Teologia) Servicio de Publicaciones de la Universidad de Navarra, S.A., Apdo. 177, 31080 Pamplona, Spain. TEL 94 25 2700. Ed. Pedro Rodriguez. bk.rev. **Indexed:** New Test.Abstr., Old Test.Abstr., Rel.& Theol.Abstr. (1978-).

200 028.5   IT   ISSN 0036-9950
SE VUOI. 1960. bi-m. L.17000 (foreign L.25000). Societa San Paolo, Via Mole 3, 00040 Castelgandolfo, Rome, Italy. TEL 06-932-03-56. FAX 06-936-07-00. (Co-sponsor: Istituto Regina degli Apostoli) Dir. Maria De Luca. bk.rev. circ. 7,500.
Description: Magazine for young people in search of God.

200   CN   ISSN 0704-1845
SECOND MILE. 1973. bi-m. $12. Lancelot Press Ltd., Box 425, Hantsport, NS B0P 1P0, Canada. TEL 902-684-9129. FAX 902-684-3685. Ed. William Pope. adv.; bk.rev.; circ. 800 (paid). **Document type:** trade publication.

RELIGIONS AND THEOLOGY

THE SECOND STONE; the national newspaper for gay and lesbian Christians. see *HOMOSEXUALITY*

200   US
SEEK. 1970. w. $10.99 for sets of five for 3 mos. Standard Publishing, 8121 Hamilton Ave., Cincinnati, OH 45231. TEL 513-931-4050. FAX 513-931-0904. Ed. Eileen H. Wilmoth. circ. 72,000.
    Description: Sunday school take-home paper for older teens and young adults.

201   IT   ISSN 0394-364X
SEGNI DEI TEMPI; rivista trimestrale per un cristianesimo migliore. 1921. q. L.32000 (effective 1996). Edizioni A.D.V., 1 Via Chiantigiana 30, Falciani, 50023 Imprunieta, Florence, Italy. TEL 055-2326291. Ed. Giuseppe Cupertino. index. circ. 10,000. **Document type:** monographic series.

230   SP   ISSN 0037-119X
SELECCIONES DE TEOLOGIA. 1962. q. 2250 ptas.($22.00) Instituto de Teologia Fundamental, Facultad de Teologia de Catalunya, Llaseres 30, Sant Cugat del Valles, Barcelona, Spain. TEL 93-301-23-50. (Subscr. to: Roger de Lluria 13, 08010 Barcelona, Spain) Ed. Xavier Alegre. adv.; index. circ. 5,000. **Indexed:** CERDIC.

131.3 200   US   ISSN 0037-1564
B132.Y6
SELF-REALIZATION. 1925. q. $3. Self-Realization Fellowship, Inc., 3880 San Rafael Ave., Los Angeles, CA 90065. TEL 213-225-2471. Ed. Irene Bartram. bk.rev.; illus.; index. circ. 26,000. (back issues avail.)
    Description: Features information on healing the body, mind and soul through the practical application of spriritual principles.

200   UK
SELLY OAK COLLEGES. OCCASIONAL PAPERS. 1990. irreg. £2. Selly Oak Colleges, Bristol Rd., Birmingham B29 6LQ, England. TEL 0121-472-4231. FAX 0121-472-8852. TELEX 334349-SELLYO-G. **Document type:** academic/scholarly publication.

200   US   ISSN 0095-571X
BS410
SEMEIA; an experimental journal for biblical criticism. (Text in English, Greek and Hebrew) 1974. q. $35. (Society of Biblical Literature) Scholars Press, Box 15399, Atlanta, GA 30333-0399. TEL 404-727-2320. FAX 404-727-2348. Ed. Daniel Patte. adv.; bk.rev.; bibl.; charts; illus.; cum.index. circ. 1,300. (also avail. in microfiche) **Indexed:** Arts & Hum.Cit.Ind., CERDIC, New Test.Abstr., Old Test.Abstr., Rel.& Theol.Abstr. (1977-), Rel.Ind.One. **Document type:** academic/scholarly publication.
—BLDSC (8237.840000); Faxon; Genuine Article; SWETS; UMI; UnCover.
    Description: Publishes academic papers on biblical criticism.

220 410   FR   ISSN 0154-6902
SEMIOTIQUE ET BIBLE. 1975. q. 100 F. Centre pour l'Analyse du Discours Religieux, 25 rue du Plat, 69002 Lyon Cedex, France. Ed. Jean Delorme. bk.rev. circ. 800. **Indexed:** CERDIC, New Test.Abstr.
—BLDSC (8239.502300).

252   US   ISSN 0037-248X
SERMON BUILDER;* preacher's professional periodical. 1953. m. $6. Church Extension Service, Inc., Box 209, Longmont, CO 80502-0209. TEL 303-279-1011. Ed. Glen Williamson. adv.; bk.rev. circ. 5,000.

200   US
SERRAN. 1951. bi-m. $5. Serra International, 65 E. Wacker Pl., No. 1210, Chicago, IL 60601-7203. TEL 312-782-2613. FAX 312-782-2358. Ed. Tari Brown. circ. 16,000. **Document type:** academic/scholarly publication.

291   US   ISSN 1076-6987
▼**SERVANT LIFE.** 1994. 12/yr. $29.95. Religion Today, Inc., Box 21505, Roanoke, VA 24018-0560. TEL 703-989-7500. FAX 703-989-0189. Ed. Cheryl L. Hoffman; Pub. Stephen M. Wike. circ. 3,500 (paid). **Document type:** newsletter.

200   IT   ISSN 0037-2773
SERVIZIO DELLA PAROLA. 1968. m. (10/yr.). L.60000 (foreign L.88000) (effective 1996). Editrice Queriniana, Via Piamarta 6, 25187 Brescia, Italy. TEL 39-30-294653. FAX 39-30-3756375. Ed. Chino Biscontin.

SERVIZIO MIGRANTI. see *POLITICAL SCIENCE*

200   IT
SETTE E RELIGIONI; rivista trimestrale di cultura religiosa. 1991. q. L.40000 (foreign L.90000) (effective 1995). (Gruppo di Ricerca e Informazione sulle Sette) Edizioni Studio Domenicano, Via Osservanza 72, 40136 Bologna, Italy. TEL 39-51-582034. (Edit. addr.: Via del Monte 5, 40126 Bologna, Italy. TEL 39-51-260244) Ed. Enzo Panzacchi. **Document type:** academic/scholarly publication, monographic series.

268   FR   ISSN 0985-5734
SEVE EGLISE AUJOURD'HUI. 1944. m. 210 F. (foreign 225 F.). Chretiens dans le Monde Rural, 9 rue du General Leclerc, 91230 Montgeron, France. TEL 1-69-03-09-09. FAX 1-69-83-23-24. Ed. Remy Fitterer. adv.; bk.rev. **Indexed:** CERDIC.
    Formerly: Eglise Aujourd'hui (ISSN 0223-5854)
    Description: For those who wish to prepare the future of the Church.

SHALOM. see *RELIGIONS AND THEOLOGY* — *Judaic*

266   UK
SHARE (TUNBRIDGE WELLS). (Includes: Partners' News) 1867. 4/yr. donations. South American Missionary Society, Allen Gardiner House, Pembury Rd., Tunbridge Wells, Kent TN2 3QU, England. TEL 01892-538647. FAX 01892-525797. Ed. Jean Marshall. bk.rev. circ. 16,000. **Indexed:** CERDIC. **Document type:** newsletter.
    Formerly: Sent (ISSN 0037-2269)

200   US   ISSN 0193-8274
SHARING THE PRACTICE. 1978. q. $25. Academy of Parish Clergy, Inc., 2330 Rose Garden Dr., Gastonia, NC 28054. TEL 704-864-6491. (Subscr. to: 13500 Shaker Blvd., Ste. 601, Cleveland, OH 44120. TEL 216-295-2006) Ed. Rev. Dr. Dennis R. Bolton. adv. contact: Dennis R. Bolton. bk.rev. circ. 350. (tabloid format; also avail. in microform from UMI) **Document type:** academic/scholarly publication.
—UMI.
    Formerly: Academy of Parish Clergy. News and Views.
    Description: For members of the Clergy to share their interests and experiences.

200 808.81   US   ISSN 0745-1245
SHARING THE VICTORY. 1982. m. $18. Fellowship of Christian Athletes, 8701 Leeds Rd., Kansas City, MO 64129. TEL 816-921-0909. FAX 816-921-8755. Ed. John Dodderidge; Pub. Dal Shealy. adv.; bk.rev. circ. 50,000. (back issues avail.) **Document type:** consumer publication.
    Formerly (until 1982): Christian Athlete (ISSN 0744-0227)
    Description: Christian publication aimed at individuals involved in athletics at any level.

200   CC   ISSN 1000-4289
BL9.C4
SHIJIE ZONGJIAO YANJIU/STUDIES ON WORLD RELIGION. (Text in Chinese) 1979. q. $25.50. (Zhongguo Shehui Kexueyuan, Shijie Zongjiao Yanjiusuo - Chinese Academy of Social Sciences, Institute of World Religion) Zhongguo Shehui Kexueyuan Chubanshe, Gulou Xidajie A 158, Beijing, People's Republic of China. (Distr. in US by: China Books & Periodicals, Inc., 2929 24th St., San Francisco, CA 94110. TEL 415-282-2994)

200   CC   ISSN 1000-4505
SHIJIE ZONGJIAO ZILIAO. (Text in Chinese) 1980. q. $12.30. (Zhongguo Shehui Kexueyuan, Shijie Zongjiao Yanjiusuo - Chinese Academy of Social Sciences, Institute of World Religion) Shehui Kexue Zazhishe, A-158 Gulou Xidajie, Beijing 100720, People's Republic of China. (Distr. in US by: China Books & Periodicals, Inc., 2929 24th St., San Francisco, CA 94110. TEL 415-282-2994)

200 919.306   PE   ISSN 0254-2021
F3429
SHUPIHUI. 1976. q. $18. Centro de Estudios Teologicos de la Amazonia, Putmayo 355, Iquitos, Peru. TEL 233552. FAX 23-31-90. Ed. Joaquin Garcia Sanchez. bk.rev. circ. 1,000.

SIAH MESHARIM; journal of Judaism, religion and state. see *RELIGIONS AND THEOLOGY* — *Judaic*

294.6   II   ISSN 0037-5128
BL2017
SIKH REVIEW; journal of enlightenment. (Text in English) 1953. m. Rs.100 for members; foreign $25 (typically set in Jan.). Sikh Cultural Centre, 116 Karnani Mansion, 25A Park St., Calcutta 700016, India. TEL 91-33-29-9656. FAX 91-33-242-0714. Ed. Saran Singh; Pub. N.P. Singh. adv.; bk.rev. circ. 5,000. **Document type:** academic/scholarly publication.
    Description: a theological and socio-cultural journal of Sikhism in global setting.

SINGLE ADULT MINISTRIES JOURNAL; ideas, resources and guidance for ministry with single adults. see *SINGLES' INTERESTS AND LIFESTYLES*

SINO-WESTERN CULTURAL RELATIONS JOURNAL. see *HISTORY*

291   SA
SKOTAVILLE BLACK THEOLOGY SERIES. irreg., latest no.6. Skotaville Publishers, P.O. Box 32483, Braamfontein 2017, South Africa. (Dist. outside Africa by: African Books Collective Ltd., The Jam Factory, 27 Park End St., Oxford OX1 1HU, England. TEL 0865-726686. FAX 0865-793298) **Document type:** monographic series.

200   SA   ISSN 0257-8891
SKRIF EN KERK. (Text in Afrikaans) 1980. 2/yr. R.30 to individuals; students R.20; overseas $30 (effective 1995). University of Pretoria, Theological Faculty (Section B), Pretoria 0002, South Africa. TEL 27-12-4202322. FAX 27-12-437431. E-mail: otnt@ccnet.up.ac.za. Ed. W.S. Prinsloo. bk.rev. circ. 500. **Document type:** academic/scholarly publication.
    Description: Stimulates theological debate through the publication of original articles in all theological disciplines.

266   AT
SKYWAVES. bi-m. Far East Broadcasting Co., Corner of Banksia & Willarong Rds., P.O. Box 183, Caringbah, N.S.W. 2229, Australia. TEL 61-2-525-6460. FAX 61-2-526-1250. Ed. Mari Atkinson. circ. 8,500. (back issues avail.) **Document type:** newsletter.
    Description: Covers the organization's projects and missionaries.

260   CI   ISSN 0037-7074
SLUZBA BOZJA; liturgijsko-pastoralna revija. 1961. q. $20. Franjevacka Visoka Bogoslovija, Makarska - Franciscan High School for Theology at Makarska, Zrtava Fasizma 1, 58300 Makarska, Croatia. TEL 059 612-259. Ed. Marko Babic. adv.; bk.rev.; index. circ. 1,400.

200   IT   ISSN 0037-7562
SOCCORSO PERPETUO DI MARIA. 1946. m. L.15000 (foreign L.25000). Santuario della Madonna del Perpetuo Soccorso, 37012 Bussolengo, Verona, Italy. illus. circ. 8,000.

SOCIAL COMPASS; international review of sociology of religion. see *SOCIOLOGY*

SOCIAL THOUGHT; journal of religion in the social services. see *SOCIAL SERVICES AND WELFARE*

200 500   US
SOCIETY FOR COMMON INSIGHTS. JOURNAL. 1976. s-a. $5 to individuals; institutions $6. Society for Common Insights, c/o Kurt Johnson, Dept. of Biology, City University of New York, Convent Ave. and 138th St., New York, NY 10031. (Affiliate: National Council for the Church and Social Action) Eds. Kurt Johnson, Eric L. Quinter. bk.rev.; charts; illus. (back issues avail.) **Indexed:** CERDIC.

225   UK   ISSN 0081-1432
SOCIETY FOR NEW TESTAMENT STUDIES. MONOGRAPH SERIES. 1965. irreg., no.57, 1986. price varies. Cambridge University Press, Edinburgh Bldg., Shaftesbury Rd., Cambridge CB2 2RU, England. TEL 01223-312393. FAX 01223-315052. TELEX 851817256. (N. American addr.: Cambridge University Press, Journals Dept., 40 W. 20th St., New York, NY 10011. TEL 212-924-3900. FAX 212-691-3239) Ed. G.N. Stanton. index. **Document type:** monographic series.

RELIGIONS AND THEOLOGY

221   UK
SOCIETY FOR OLD TESTAMENT STUDIES. MONOGRAPHS. 1972. irreg., no.6, 1980. price varies. Cambridge University Press, Edinburgh Bldg., Shaftesbury Rd., Cambridge CB2 2RU, England. TEL 01223-312393. FAX 01223-315052. TELEX 851817256. (N. American addr.: Cambridge University Press, Journals Dept., 40 W. 20th St., New York, NY 10011. TEL 212-924-3900. FAX 212-691-3239) **Document type:** monographic series.

200   US
SOCIETY FOR THE SCIENTIFIC STUDY OF RELIGION. MONOGRAPH SERIES. 1978. irreg., no.8, 1990. Society for the Scientific Study of Religion, Pierce Hall, No. 193, Purdue Univ., West Lafayette, IN 47907. TEL 317-494-6286. **Document type:** academic/scholarly publication, monographic series.
   Refereed Serial

220   US   ISSN 0145-2711
BS410
SOCIETY OF BIBLICAL LITERATURE. SEMINAR PAPERS (YEAR). a. $25. (Society of Biblical Literature) Scholars Press, Box 15399, Atlanta, GA 30333-0399. TEL 404-727-2320. FAX 404-727-2348. Ed. Greg Glover. (back issues avail.) **Indexed:** Rel.Ind.One. **Document type:** proceedings.
—BLDSC (8239.423670).
   Description: Publishes seminar papers to be given at the annual meeting of the Society of Biblical Literature meetings.

200   US   ISSN 0732-4928
BJ1188.5
SOCIETY OF CHRISTIAN ETHICS. ANNUAL. 1975. a. price varies. Georgetown University Press, 3619 O St., N.W., Washington, DC 20007. TEL 202-687-5889. FAX 202-687-6340. (Orders to: Box 4866, Hampden Sta., Baltimore, MD 21211-4866. TEL 410-516-6995. FAX 410-516-6998; Editorial addr.: c/o Religion Dept., Washington & Lee University, Lexington, VA 24450. TEL 703-463-8784) Ed. Harlan Beckley. adv. circ. 850. (also avail. in microfiche) **Indexed:** Rel.Ind.Two. **Document type:** proceedings.
—BLDSC (1073.837200); Genuine Article.
   Description: Scholarly articles targeted toward an audience that includes college professors in religion, the social sciences, and philosophy; professionals in law, medicine, politics, and human services; and the clergy and others working in Christian education and social action programs--with a section on professional resources available for teaching ethics.

266   FR
SOLIDAIRES - LUMIERE DU MONDE. 1920. q. 70 F. (foreign 120 F.). (Societe Presse et Publications Missionnaires) Oeuvre de la Propagation de la Foi, 5, rue Monsieur, 75007 Paris, France. TEL 47-83-67-95. Ed. Marie-Jo Hazard. adv. contact: Olivier de Berranger. abstr.; charts; illus.; stat. circ. 100,000. (also avail. in microfiche from BHP)
   Formed by the merger of: Lumiere du Monde (ISSN 0024-7340) & Solidaires (ISSN 0336-335X); Which was formerly: Annales de la Propagation de la Foi (ISSN 0003-4045)
   Description: Focuses on mission work in the country.

230   SZ   ISSN 0067-4907
SONDERBAENDE ZUR THEOLOGISCHEN ZEITSCHRIFT. 1966. irreg., no.11, 1992. price varies. Friedrich Reinhardt Verlag, Missionsstr. 36, CH-4012 Basel, Switzerland. (Dist. by: Albert J. Phiebig Books, Box 352, White Plains, NY 10602) Ed. B. Reicke. circ. 1,000.
   Formerly: Beihefte zur Theologischen Zeitschrift.

DER SONNTAGSBRIEF. see *GERONTOLOGY AND GERIATRICS*

SONNTAGSCHULMITARBEITER; religionspaedagogisches Monatsblatt. see *EDUCATION*

SOPHIA; a journal for philosophical theology and cross-cultural philosophy of religion. see *PHILOSOPHY*

200   KO
SOUND WORDS.* 1984. bi-m. $5. Glyn Taylor, Jr., Ed & Pub., 703-402 Mok Dong Yangchun-ku, Seoul 158-0501, S. Korea.

260 301   US   ISSN 0744-8333
SOURCE (SEATTLE). 1960. m. $12. Church Council of Greater Seattle, 4759 15 Ave., N.E., 3rd Fl., Seattle, WA 98105-4404. TEL 206-525-1213. FAX 206-525-1218. Ed. Margaret Lueders. adv.; bk.rev. circ. 7,500. (tabloid format) **Document type:** directory, newspaper.
   Supersedes (in 1976): Church Council of Greater Seattle Occasional News (ISSN 0010-9924); Formerly: Council in Action.

266   SA   ISSN 0038-2523
SOUTH AFRICAN OUTLOOK; a journal dealing with ecumenical and racial affairs. 1870. m. R.30($40) (effective 1995). Outlook Publications (Pty) Ltd., Box 245, Rondebosch 7700, South Africa. Ed. N. Barney Pityana. adv.; bk.rev.; index. circ. 1,400. (also avail. in microfilm from SAL,WMP) **Indexed:** CERDIC, HR Rep. (1986-), Ind.S.A.Per.
   Former titles (until 1922): Christian Express; (until 1876): Kaffir Express.

200   UK
SOUTHWELL AND OXFORD PAPERS ON CONTEMPORARY SOCIETY. 1984. 4/yr. £7. Oxford Institute for Church and Society, Ripon College, Oxford OX9 9EX, England. TEL 08677-4595.
   Formerly: Oxford Papers on Contemporary Society.
   Description: Covers all aspects of the interaction of Christian faith and contemporary society.

200 286   US   ISSN 0038-4828
BX6201
SOUTHWESTERN JOURNAL OF THEOLOGY. 1958. 3/yr. $19 (foreign $21). Southwestern Baptist Theological Seminary, Faculty, School of Theology, Box 22000 2E, Ft. Worth, TX 76122-0490. TEL 817-923-1921. Ed. Kenneth Hemphill. adv.; bk.rev. circ. 3,500. (also avail. in microform from UMI; reprint service avail. from UMI) **Indexed:** CERDIC, Chr.Per.Ind., New Test.Abstr., Old Test.Abstr., Rel.& Theol.Abstr. (1967-), Rel.Ind.One, Rel.Per., South.Bap.Per.Ind.
—BLDSC (8357.210000); UMI; UnCover.

200   SA   ISSN 0038-5980
THE SOWER. (Text in English) 1957. q. free. Bible Society of South Africa, P.O. Box 6215, Roggebaai, Cape Town 8012, South Africa. FAX 27-21-419-4846. Ed. Rev. N.N. Turley. illus.; circ. 68,000 (controlled). (also avail. in microfiche)

268   UK
SOWER. 1919. q. £6. Sower Ltd., 10-12 High St., Great Wakering, Essex SS3 0EQ, England. FAX 0702-216082. Ed.Bd. adv.; bk.rev. circ. 2,000.
   Formerly: New Sower; Which was formed by the 1978 merger of: Sower (ISSN 0049-1772); Christian Celebration.

200 360   AT   ISSN 0158-1090
SOWER. 1956. q. Aus.$15. Bible Society in Australia, G.P.O. Box 507, Canberra, A.C.T. 2601, Australia. TEL 062-485188. FAX 062-49618. TELEX 61642. Ed. Irene Voysey. illus. circ. 43,000. (back issues avail.)
   Description: Sows the seed of the Word of God through stories of Bible Society work in Australia and overseas; in translation; and production and distribution of the Scriptures.

266   UK
SPAN (LONDON). 1835. bi-m. contributions. London City Mission, 175 Tower Bridge Rd., London SE1 2AH, England. TEL 0171-407-7585. FAX 0171-403-6711. Ed. Peter Trainer. circ. 41,000. **Indexed:** Apic.Abstr., Fuel & Energy Abstr. **Document type:** newsletter.
   Formerly: London City Mission Magazine (ISSN 0047-5025)

200   KE
SPEARHEAD. (Text in English) 1969. 5/yr. EAs.121($17.60) (AMECEA Pastoral Institute) Gaba Publications, P.O. Box 4002, Eldoret, Kenya. Ed. Agatha Radol. circ. 2,500. (back issues avail.) **Indexed:** CERDIC.
   Formerly (until 1977): Gaba Pastoral Papers.

268   UK   ISSN 0305-7917
SPECTRUM (CARLISLE). 1969. s-a. £13.90 (foreign £14.40). (Association of Christian Teachers) The Paternoster Press, P.O. Box 300, Kingstown Broadway, Carlisle, Cumbria CA3 0QS, England. TEL 0228-512512. FAX 0228-514949. (Dist. in U.S. & Canada by: The Paternoster Press, Box 11127, Birmingham, AL 35201-1127) Ed. John Shortt. adv.; bk.rev.; illus.; cum.index: vols.1-6. circ. 600. (back issues avail.) **Indexed:** Abstr.Engl.Stud., Br.Educ.Ind., CERDIC, Excerp.Med., Mult.Ed.Abstr. **Document type:** academic/scholarly publication.
—BLDSC (8411.168000).
   Description: Provides a Christian viewpoint on education in both maintained and private-sector schools and colleges.

200 255   NE   ISSN 0038-7320
SPELING. 1948. q. fl.42. H. Gianotten B.V., Postbus 9228, 5000 HE Tilburg, Netherlands. TEL 31-13-425050. FAX 31-13-359175. bk.rev.; play rev.; illus. circ. 2,600. **Indexed:** CERDIC.
—SWETS.
   Formerly: Carmel.

200   GW   ISSN 0933-8985
SPIRITA; Zeitschrift fuer Religionswissenschaft. 1987. 2/yr. DM.18. Diagonal Verlag, Postfach 1248, 35002 Marburg, Germany. TEL 06421-681936. FAX 06421-681944. Eds. Thomas Schweer, Steffen Rink. (back issues avail.) **Document type:** academic/scholarly publication.

200   IT
SPIRITUALITA CRISTIANA. 1981. irreg., latest no.20. price varies. Edizioni Studium, Via Cassiodoro 14, 00193 Rome, Italy. **Document type:** monographic series.

266   FR   ISSN 0038-7665
SPIRITUS; experience et recherche missionnaires. 1959. q. 175 F. (foreign US $40) (effective 1996). Association de la Revue Spiritus, 40 rue La Fontaine, 75781 Paris Cedex 16, France. TEL 42-88-82-64. FAX 42-88-41-75. Ed. Joseph Gross. bk.rev.; abstr.; bibl.; index. circ. 3,500. **Indexed:** CERDIC.
   Description: Aims to advance the missionary vocation and improve communication among diverse churches.

200   IT   ISSN 0038-8769
SQUILLA DI S. GERARDO.* 1923. bi-m. free. Parrocchia S. Gerardo, Piedimonte Etneo 95017, Sicily, Italy.

266   GW
STADT GOTTES; Illustrierte Familienzeitschrift. 1878. m. DM.26.40. Steyler Missionare e.V., Bahnhofstr. 9, 41334 Nettetal, Germany. TEL 02157-1202-0. FAX 02157-1202-60. Ed. Joachim Burghardt. **Document type:** consumer publication.

268.8 374   US   ISSN 0081-4245
STANDARD LESSON COMMENTARY; international Sunday school lessons. 1954. a. $14.99 casebound; $11.99 kivar. Standard Publishing, 8121 Hamilton Ave., Cincinnati, OH 45231. TEL 513-931-4050. FAX 513-931-0904. Ed. James I. Fehl. circ. 200,000.
   Description: Sunday-school lesson manual for teachers of adults.

200   US
STARTHROWERS. 1977. m. $5. 615 Throwbridge, Box 192, Franklin, LA 70538.
   Formerly (until 1985): Agape (Franklin).

266   GW
STEFANUS; Werkbrief fuer taetige Christen in Kirche und Welt. 1949. 6/yr. DM.45. Stefanuswerk e.V., Am Muenster 10, 79400 Riedlingen, Germany. TEL 07371-18641. FAX 07371-18643. Ed. Werner Fiutak. illus.

200 052   KE
STEP. (Text in English) 1979. m. $33 to rest of Africa; USA, Australia & Far East $43; Europe & Asia $38 (typically set every 2 years). Youth for Christ, P.O. Box 58070, Nairobi, Kenya. Ed. Connie Kisuke. adv.; bk.rev. circ. 50,000.
   Description: Directed toward Christian Africans with news, insights, and regular features.

RELIGIONS AND THEOLOGY

266 GW ISSN 0722-6942
STEYLER MISSIONSCHRONIK. 1959. a. DM.20. (Steyler Missionswissenschafliches Institut) Steyler Verlag, Bahnhofstr. 9, 41334 Nettetal, Germany. TEL 02157-1202-20. FAX 02157-1202-22. **Document type:** bulletin.

200 GW ISSN 0039-1492
STIMMEN DER ZEIT. 1875. m. DM.144. Verlag Herder GmbH und Co. KG, Hermann-Herder-Str. 4, 79104 Freiburg, Germany. TEL 0761-2717407. Ed. Dr. Wolfgang Seibel. adv.; bk.rev. circ. 4,500. **Indexed:** Amer.Hist.& Life, Cath.Ind., CERDIC, Hist.Abstr., M.L.A., New Test.Abstr. **Document type:** newsletter. —SWETS.

200 IT
STORIA DELLE RELIGIONI. 1985. irreg., no.7, 1990. price varies. L'Erma di Bretschneider, Via Cassiodoro 19, 00193 Rome, Italy. TEL 06-687-41-27. FAX 06-687-41-29. Dirs. Ugo Bianchi, Guilia Piccaluga.

200 GW
STORMARNSPIEGEL. 1973. irreg. (6-8/yr.) Kirchenkreis Stormarn, Kirchenkreisvorstand, Rockenhof 1, 22359 Hamburg, Germany. TEL 040-603-143-28. bk.rev. circ. 1,320. (back issues avail.)

248.83 US
STRAIGHT. 1951. w. $10.99. Standard Publishing, 8121 Hamilton Ave., Cincinnati, OH 45231. TEL 513-931-4050. FAX 513-931-0904. Ed. Carla J. Crane. illus. circ. 50,000.
Formed in two parts by the 1980 merger of: Glad and Now; **Formerly** (until 1977): Straight (ISSN 0039-2081)
Description: An uplifting take-home newspaper for Christians teenagers with stories and feature articles.

STRAIGHT WORD; news for Aboriginal and Islander Bible translators. see LINGUISTICS

200 GW
STREIFLICHTER. bi-m. DM.12. C V J M Landesverband Baden, Friedrich-Naumann-Str. 33, 76187 Karlsruhe, Germany. TEL 0721-757077. FAX 0721-753763. Ed. Hermann Traub. circ. 3,000. (back issues avail.)

STROMATA; antigua ciencia y fe. see PHILOSOPHY

220 IT ISSN 0039-2898
STUDI BIBLICI; collezione di argomento biblico. 1968. q. L.84000 (foreign L.105000) (effective 1994). Paideia Editrice, Via Corsica 130, 25125 Brescia, Italy. TEL 030-222094. FAX 030-223269. Ed. Giuseppe Scarpat. bk.rev. **Document type:** monographic series.

200 IT ISSN 0393-8417
STUDI E MATERIALI DI STORIA DELLE RELIGIONI. (Text mainly in Italian; occasionally in English, French, German) 1925. s-a. L.38000 (foreign L.45000). Universita degli Studi di Roma "La Sapienza", Dipartimento di Studi Storico-Religiosi, Citta Universitaria, 00185 Rome, Italy. TEL 06-4957308. FAX 06-4453753. bk.rev.
Former titles (until 1982): Studi Storico-Religiosi (ISSN 0393-4128); (until 1976): Religioni e Civilta (ISSN 0393-8409); (until 1969): Studi e Materiali di Storia delle Religioni (ISSN 0036-1690)

200 940 IT ISSN 0394-0616
STUDI E RICERCHE SULL'ORIENTE CRISTIANO. (Text mainly in Italian; occasionally in Armenian, Greek) 1978. 3/yr. L.40000 (foreign L.64000) (effective 1994). Filoteo M. Sorge, Ed. & Pub., Via Panaro 11, 00199 Rome, Italy. TEL 06-860-2972. bk.rev. circ. 450. (back issues avail.) **Document type:** academic/scholarly publication.
Description: Features readings on research and study in Christianity.

270 IT ISSN 1122-0694
STUDI E TESTI PER LA STORIA RELIGIOSA DEL CINQUECENTO. 1986. irreg., no.5, 1994. price varies. Casa Editrice Leo S. Olschki, Casella Postale 66, 50100 Florence, Italy. TEL 39-55-6530684. FAX 39-55-6530214. **Document type:** monographic series.

200 IT ISSN 0393-3687
STUDI ECUMENICI. 1983. q. L.40000 (foreign L.45000) (effective Jan. 1995). (Istituto di Studi Ecumenici) Associazione Francescani Riuniti per Attivita Territoriali e Religiose, Castello 2786, 30122 Venice, Italy. TEL 39-41-5235341. FAX 39-41-5228323. Ed.Bd. bk.rev.; index. (back issues avail.)

220 NE ISSN 0169-801X
STUDIA AD CORPUS HELLENISTICUM NOVI TESTAMENTI. (Text in English, French and German) 1970. irreg., vol.6, 1980. price varies. E.J. Brill, P.O. Box 9000, 2300 PA Leiden, Netherlands. TEL 31-71-5353500. FAX 31-71-5317532. TELEX 39296 BRILL NL. (In N. America: E.J. Brill, 24 Hudson St., Kinderhook, NY 12106. TEL 800-962-4406. FAX 518-758-1959) Ed.Bd. (back issues avail.) **Document type:** monographic series.
Refereed Serial

221 NE ISSN 0169-9954
STUDIA BIBLICA. 1983. irreg., vol.4, 1990. price varies. E.J. Brill, P.O. Box 9000, 2300 PA Leiden, Netherlands. TEL 31-71-5353500. FAX 31-71-5317532. TELEX 39296 BRILL NL. (In N. America: E.J. Brill, 24 Hudson St., Kinderhook, NY 12106. TEL 800-962-4406. FAX 518-758-1959) (back issues avail.) **Document type:** monographic series.
Description: Scholarly studies of theology and history relating to Old and New Testaments.
Refereed Serial

262.9 CN ISSN 0039-310X
K23
STUDIA CANONICA; a Canadian canon law review. (Text in English, French, Latin) 1967. s-a. Can.$48.15($45) Saint Paul University, Faculty of Canon Law, 223 Main St., Ottawa, ON K1S 1C4, Canada. TEL 613-236-1393. FAX 613-782-3005. Ed. Michel Theriault. adv.; bk.rev. circ. 1,300. (also avail. in microfiche; reprint service avail. from WSH) **Indexed:** Bull.Signal., C.L.I., Canon Law Abstr., Cath.Ind., CERDIC, Ind.Can.L.P.I., Leg.Per. —UMI.

268
STUDIA EPHEMERIDIS AUGUSTINIANUM. 1967. irreg. Institutum Patristicum Augustinianum, Via S. Uffizio, 25, 00193 Rome, Italy. FAX 6-800-6298. (back issues avail.) **Document type:** academic/scholarly publication.

STUDIA HUMANITATIS. see HISTORY — History Of Europe

220 NE ISSN 0169-8125
BS1700
STUDIA IN VETERIS TESTAMENTI PSEUDEPIGRAPHA. 1970. irreg., vol.11, 1995. price varies. E.J. Brill, P.O. Box 9000, 2300 PA Leiden, Netherlands. TEL 31-71-5353500. FAX 31-71-5317532. TELEX 39296 BRILL NL. (In N. America: E.J. Brill, 24 Hudson St., Kinderhook, NY 12106. TEL 800-962-4406. FAX 518-758-1959) Eds. A.M. Denis, M. de Jonge. (back issues avail.) **Document type:** monographic series.
Description: Publishes texts, translations and critical studies on Old Testament pseudepigrapha and apocrypha.
Refereed Serial

100 GW ISSN 0081-6663
STUDIA IRENICA. (Text in English, German) 1968. irreg., no.36, 1993. Peter Lang GmbH Europaeischer Verlag der Wissenschaften, Eschborner Landstr. 42-50, 60489 Frankfurt a.M., Germany. TEL 069-7807050. FAX 069-785893. **Document type:** monographic series.
Formerly (until 1971): Frankfurt am Main. Universitaet. Institut fuer Wissenschaftliche Irenik. Schriften.

240 US ISSN 0039-3207
STUDIA LITURGICA; an international ecumenical review for liturgical research and renewal. (Text in English) 1962. s-a. $22.50 (effective 1995-1996). Societas Liturgica, Box 597, Notre Dame, IN 46556. Ed. Paul F. Bradshaw. bk.rev. circ. 1,000. (back issues avail.) **Indexed:** CERDIC, New Test.Abstr., Rel.& Theol.Abstr. (1979-), Rel.Ind.One, Rel.Per. **Document type:** academic/scholarly publication.
—BLDSC (8482.973000); SWETS.
Refereed Serial

271 900 SP ISSN 0039-3258
BX2400
STUDIA MONASTICA; commentarium ad rem monasticam historice investigandam. (Text in Catalan, English, French, German, Italian, Latin, Portuguese, Spanish) 1959. s-a. 8200 ptas. (Europe 11500 ptas., elsewhere $105). Publicacions de l' Abadia de Montserrat, Ausias March 92-98, Apdo. 244, 08013 Barcelona, Spain. Ed. Rev. Josep Massot Muntaner. adv.; bk.rev.; abstr.; bibl.; charts; illus.; index. circ. 800. **Indexed:** Amer.Hist.& Life, Arts & Hum.Cit.Ind., CERDIC, Hist.Abstr., M.L.A.
—BLDSC (8483.063000).

240 IT ISSN 0081-6736
STUDIA MORALIA. (Text in English, French, German, Italian, Spanish; summaries in English, French) 1963. s-a. L.50000($40) (effective 1995-96). Editiones Academiae Alfonsianae, Via Merulana 31, C.P. 2458, 00100 Rome, Italy. FAX 39-6-4465887. Ed. Real Trembley. bk.rev.; index. circ. 1,200. **Indexed:** CERDIC. **Document type:** academic/scholarly publication.
—Faxon.

200 956 IS
STUDIA ORIENTALIA CHRISTIANA. COLLECTANEA. (Text in Arabic, Coptic, English, French, Italian) 1956. a., vol.24, 1994 (for the year 1991). price varies. (Franciscan Centre of Christian Oriental Studies in Cairo, UA) Franciscan Printing Press, P.O. Box 14064, Jerusalem 91140, Israel. TEL 972-2-286594. FAX 972-2-272274. illus. (back issues avail.) **Document type:** academic/scholarly publication.
Description: Publishes scholarly articles on theological, historical, ethnological, and linguistic topics relating to Christianity in the Middle East.

281.5 956 IS
STUDIA ORIENTALIA CHRISTIANA. MONOGRAPHIAE. (Text in Arabic, Coptic, English, French, German, Italian, Latin) 1955. irreg., no.4, 1991. price varies. (Franciscan Centre of Christian Oriental Studies in Cairo, UA) Franciscan Printing Press, P.O. Box 14064, Jerusalem 91140, Israel. TEL 972-2-286594. FAX 972-2-272274. illus. **Document type:** monographic series.
Description: Publishes scholarly studies of theological, historical, ethnological, and linguistic topics relating to Christianity in the Middle East.

230 100 IT ISSN 0039-3304
STUDIA PATAVINA; rivista di scienze religiose. 1954. 3/yr. L.60000 (foreign L.75000) (effective 1995). Seminario Vescovile, Facolta Teologica, Via del Seminario 29, 35122 Padova, Italy. TEL 39-49-657099. FAX 39-49-8761934. Ed.Bd. adv.; bk.rev.; index. circ. 600. (back issues avail.) **Indexed:** CERDIC, New Test.Abstr., Old Test.Abstr. **Description:** Emphasizes the promotion of the study of all religious disciplines; organizes meetings from many cultural institutions.

281 BE
STUDIA PATRISTICA. (Text in English, French, German) 1954. irreg., vol.28, 1993. 3600 BEF. (Oxford University, UK) Editions Peeters s.p.r.l., Bondgenotenlaan 153, 3000 Leuven, Belgium. TEL 32-16-235170. FAX 32-16-228500. (back issues avail.) **Document type:** monographic series.

200 NE ISSN 0169-9717
STUDIA POST BIBLICA. (Text in English; occasionally in French, German) 1959. irreg., vol.46, 1995. price varies. E.J. Brill, P.O. Box 9000, 2300 PA Leiden, Netherlands. TEL 31-71-5353500. FAX 31-71-5317532. TELEX 39296 BRILL NL. (In N. America: E.J. Brill, 24 Hudson St., Kinderhook, NY 12106. TEL 800-962-4406. FAX 518-758-1959) Ed. P.A.H. deBoer. (back issues avail.) **Document type:** monographic series.
—BLDSC (8483.160000).
Description: Scholarly studies on textual, historical, cultural, religious and social aspects of Judaism and early Christianity.
Refereed Serial

R

RELIGIONS AND THEOLOGY

266   SP   ISSN 0210-8739
STUDIA SILENSIA. (Text in English, French, German, Portuguese and Spanish) 1975. a. price varies. Abadia de Santo Domingo de Silos, Libreria de la Abadia, 09610 Burgos, Spain. TEL 34-47-390068. FAX 34-47-390033. Ed. Clemente de la Serna Gonzalez. illus.; stat.; tr.lit.; index, cum.index. circ. 1,500. (back issues avail.) **Document type:** monographic series.
   Refereed Serial

230   NO   ISSN 0039-338X
BR1
STUDIA THEOLOGICA; Scandinavian journal of theology. (Text in English and German) 1946. s-a. NOK 315 in Nordic countries; elsewhere $63 (effective 1996). Scandinavian University Press, P.O. Box 2959 Toeyen, N-0608 Oslo, Norway. TEL 47-22-57-54-00. FAX 47-22-57-53-53. (Subscr. to: Academic Press Copenhagen (Akademisk Forlag), P.O. Box 54, DK-1002, Copenhagen K, Denmark. TEL 45-33-11-98-26) Ed. Carl-Henrik Grenholm. adv.; bk.rev.; bibl.; index, cum.index every 10 yrs. circ. 550. (also avail. in microform from UMI) **Indexed:** Arts & Hum.Cit.Ind., Bibl.Ling., CERDIC, Curr.Cont., M.L.A., New Test.Abstr., Rel.& Theol.Abstr. (1978-), Rel.Ind.One, Rel.Per. **Document type:** academic/scholarly publication.
   —BLDSC (8483.227000); SWETS; UMI.
   Description: Presents Scandinavian contributions to the field of international theology.

230   SW   ISSN 0491-2853
STUDIA THEOLOGICA LUNDENSIA. (Text in English, German, Swedish) 1952. irreg. price varies. Lund University Press, P.O. Box 141, S-221 00 Lund, Sweden. TEL 46-46-31-20-00. FAX 46-46-30-53-38. E-mail: Order@Studli.se. Ed. Goeran Gustafsson. **Document type:** academic/scholarly publication.

200   RM
STUDIA UNIVERSITATIS "BABES-BOLYAI". THEOLOGIA - ORTHODOXA. 1992. s-a. exchange basis. Universitatea "Babes-Bolyai", Biblioteca Centrala Universitara, Str. Clinicilor Nr. 2, Cluj-Napoca 3400, Rumania. TEL 36-64-197092. FAX 36-64-197633. Ed. I. Haiduc. **Document type:** academic/scholarly publication.
   Formerly: Studis Universitatis "Babes Bolyai". Theologia.

200   GW   ISSN 0938-5924
STUDIEN ZUR KIRCHENGESCHICHTE NIEDERSACHSENS. 1919. irreg. Vandenhoeck und Ruprecht, Robert-Bosch-Breite 6, 37079 Goettingen, Germany. TEL 0551-6959-0. FAX 0551-695917. (Subscr. to: 37070 Goettingen, Germany) Ed. Inge Mager. **Document type:** monographic series.

200   GW
STUDIEN ZUR UMWELT DES NEUEN TESTAMENTS. 1968. irreg. Vandenhoeck und Ruprecht, Robert-Bosch-Breite 6, 37079 Goettingen, Germany. TEL 0551-6959-0. FAX 0551-695917. (Subscr. to: 37070 Goettingen, Germany) Ed.Bd. **Document type:** monographic series.

200   US
STUDIES IN AMERICAN RELIGION. 1980. irreg., latest no.62. $49.95 per no. Edwin Mellen Press, 415 Ridge St., Box 450, Lewiston, NY 14092. TEL 716-754-2788. FAX 716-754-4056. Ed. Herbert Richardson. bibl.; index. **Document type:** monographic series.

STUDIES IN ART AND RELIGIOUS INTERPRETATION. see ART

222   US
STUDIES IN BIBLE AND EARLY CHRISTIANITY. 1982. irreg., latest no.37. $49.95 per no. Edwin Mellen Press, 415 Ridge St., Box 450, Lewiston, NY 14092. TEL 716-754-2788. FAX 716-754-4056. **Document type:** monographic series.

200   US   ISSN 0897-7828
STUDIES IN BIBLICAL GREEK. irreg. Peter Lang Publishing, Inc., 62 W. 45th St., 4th Fl., New York, NY 10036. TEL 212-302-6740. FAX 212-302-7574. Ed. D.A. Carson. **Document type:** academic/scholarly publication, monographic series.
   Description: Covers the latest research into biblical Greek (Old and New Testaments).

STUDIES IN CHRISTIAN ETHICS. see PHILOSOPHY

266   NE   ISSN 0924-9389
STUDIES IN CHRISTIAN MISSION. 1990. irreg., no.12, 1995. price varies. E.J. Brill, P.O. Box 9000, 2300 PA Leiden, Netherlands. TEL 31-71-5353500. FAX 31-71-5317532. TELEX 39296 BRILL NL. (In N. America: E.J. Brill, 24 Hudson St., Kinderhook, NY 12106. TEL 800-962-4406. FAX 518-758-1959) (back issues avail.) **Document type:** monographic series.
   —BLDSC (8489.909000).
   Description: Scholarly monographs on the history of Christian missionary activities and related theological issues.
   Refereed Serial

200 320   US
STUDIES IN CHURCH AND STATE. irreg. price varies. Princeton University Press, 41 William St., Princeton, NJ 08540. TEL 609-258-4900. FAX 609-258-6305. E-mail: jhardy@pupress.princeton.edu. Ed. John F. Wilson. **Document type:** monographic series.

200   US
STUDIES IN COMPARATIVE RELIGION. irreg., latest vol.5. $49.95 per no. Edwin Mellen Press, 415 Ridge St., Box 450, Lewiston, NY 14092. TEL 716-754-2788. FAX 716-754-4056. **Document type:** monographic series.

292   NE   ISSN 0169-9512
STUDIES IN GREEK AND ROMAN RELIGION. 1980. irreg., vol.7, 1991. price varies. E.J. Brill, P.O. Box 9000, 2300 PA Leiden, Netherlands. TEL 31-71-5353500. FAX 31-71-5317532. TELEX 39296 BRILL NL. (In N. America: E.J. Brill, 24 Hudson St., Kinderhook, NY 12106. TEL 800-962-4406. FAX 518-758-1959) Eds. H.S. Versnel, F.T. van Straten. (back issues avail.) **Document type:** monographic series.
   —BLDSC (8490.627500).
   Description: International studies in Hellenic and Roman theology.
   Refereed Serial

291   NE   ISSN 0926-2326
STUDIES IN INTERRELIGIOUS DIALOGUE. (Text in English) 1991. 2/yr. fl.83($53.50) (effective 1994). Kok Pharos Publishing House, Postbus 5019, 8260 AG Kampen, Netherlands. TEL 31-5202-92565. FAX 31-5202-27331. (Editorial addr.: c/o Henk Vroom - SID, Faculty of Theology, Free University, De Boelelaan 1105, 1081 HV Amsterdam, Netherlands; Dist. in U.S. and Canada by: Books International, Inc., Box 605, Herndon, VA 22070-0605. TEL 800-377-7192. FAX 703-689-0660) Ed.Bd. **Document type:** academic/scholarly publication.
   —BLDSC (8490.775600); UnCover.
   Description: Forum for academic discussion and comparative study of religious beliefs and philosophies of life, systematic and practical issues concerning interreligious relations, and other matters related to the modern situation of a pluralist culture.
   Refereed Serial

200   NE   ISSN 0585-6914
STUDIES IN MEDIEVAL AND REFORMATION THOUGHT. 1966. irreg., vol.55, 1995. price varies. E.J. Brill, P.O. Box 9000, 2300 PA Leiden, Netherlands. TEL 31-71-5353500. FAX 31-71-5317532. TELEX 39296 BRILL NL. (In N. America: E.J. Brill, 24 Hudson St., Kinderhook, NY 12106. TEL 800-962-4406. FAX 518-758-1959) Ed. H.A. Oberman. (back issues avail.) **Document type:** monographic series.
   Refereed Serial

STUDIES IN MORAL PHILOSOPHY. see PHILOSOPHY

230 190   NE   ISSN 1381-2025
STUDIES IN PHILOSOPHICAL THEOLOGY. (Text in English, German, other European languages) 1988. irreg., vol.8, 1993. price varies. Kok Pharos Publishing House, Postbus 5019, 8260 AG Kampen, Netherlands. TEL 31-5202-92565. FAX 31-5202-27331. (Dist. in U.S. and Canada by: Books International, Inc., Box 605, Herndon, VA 22070-0605. TEL 800-377-7192. FAX 703-689-0660) (back issues avail.) **Document type:** monographic series.
   Description: Publishes scholarly studies on philosophical issues in contemporary Christian theology.

STUDIES IN PHILOSOPHY AND RELIGION. see PHILOSOPHY

200   CN   ISSN 0008-4298
BL1
STUDIES IN RELIGION/SCIENCES RELIGIEUSES. (Text in English and French) 1971. q. Can.$45($49) (Canadian Corporation for Studies in Religion) Wilfrid Laurier University Press, 75 University Ave. W., Waterloo, ON N2L 3C5, Canada. TEL 519-884-0710. FAX 519-725-1399. E-mail: press@mach1.wlu.ca. Ed. Peter Richardson. adv.; bk.rev.; charts; index. circ. 1,350. **Indexed:** Arts & Hum.Cit.Ind., CERDIC, M.L.A., Mid.East: Abstr.& Ind., New Test.Abstr., Old Test.Abstr., Rel.& Theol.Abstr. (1974-), Rel.Ind.One, Rel.Per.
   —BLDSC (8491.430000); Faxon; Genuine Article; UMI; UnCover. **CCC.**
   Supersedes: Canadian Journal of Theology.
   Description: Offers articles covering the field of religious and theological studies as well as reviews and critical notes on recent publications.

200   US   ISSN 0894-7082
STUDIES IN RELIGION AND SOCIETY. 1981. irreg., latest no.30. $49.95 per no. Edwin Mellen Press, 415 Ridge St., Box 450, Lewiston, NY 14092. TEL 716-754-2788. FAX 716-754-4056. **Indexed:** Rel.Ind.Two. **Document type:** monographic series.
   —BLDSC (8491.433000).

291   NE   ISSN 0926-6453
STUDIES IN SPIRITUALITY. 1991. a. fl.90($58) (effective 1994). Kok Pharos Publishing House, Postbus 5019, 8260 AG Kampen, Netherlands. TEL 31-5202-92565. FAX 31-5202-27331. (Dist in U.S. and Canada by: Books International, Inc., Box 605, Herndon, VA 22070-0605. TEL 800-377-7192. FAX 703-689-0660) **Document type:** academic/scholarly publication.
   Description: Publishes multidisciplinary articles on spirituality and mysticism, including theoretical questions, fundamental aspects and phenomena of spiritual transformation, with the main focus on the Judeo-Christian tradition.

230   NE   ISSN 0081-8607
STUDIES IN THE HISTORY OF CHRISTIAN THOUGHT. 1966. irreg., vol.64, 1995. price varies. E.J. Brill, P.O. Box 9000, 2300 PA Leiden, Netherlands. TEL 31-71-5353500. FAX 31-71-5317532. TELEX 39296 BRILL NL. (In N. America: E.J. Brill, 24 Hudson St., Kinderhook, NY 12106. TEL 800-962-4406. FAX 518-758-1959) Ed. Heiko A. Oberman. (back issues avail.) **Document type:** monographic series.
   —BLDSC (8490.656000).
   Description: Covers topics in Christian theology.
   Refereed Serial

266.009   US
STUDIES IN THE HISTORY OF MISSIONS. irreg., latest no.12. $49.95 per no. Edwin Mellen Press, 415 Ridge St., Box 450, Lewiston, NY 14092. TEL 716-745-2788. FAX 716-754-4056. **Document type:** monographic series.

290 150   US
STUDIES IN THE PSYCHOLOGY OF RELIGION. irreg., latest no.7. $49.95 per no. Edwin Mellen Press, 415 Ridge St., Box 450, Lewiston, NY 14092. TEL 716-754-2788. FAX 716-754-4056. **Document type:** monographic series.

200 301.412   US
STUDIES IN WOMEN AND RELIGION. 1979. irreg., latest no.36. $49.95 per no. Edwin Mellen Press, 415 Ridge St., Box 450, Lewiston, NY 14092. TEL 716-754-2788. FAX 716-754-4056. **Document type:** monographic series.

291.2   UK   ISSN 1354-9901
▼**STUDIES IN WORLD CHRISTIANITY;** the Edinburgh review of theology and religion. 1995. s-a. £15 to individuals (outside the E.U. £16.50 ($30)); institutions £30 (outside the E.U. £33 ($50)) (effective 1996). Edinburgh University Press, 22 George Sq., Edinburgh EH8 9LF, Scotland. TEL 44-131-650-4689. FAX 44-131-662-0053. Ed. James Mackey; Pub. Vivian C. Stone. adv. contact: Kathryn MacLean. bk.rev. **Document type:** academic/scholarly publication.
   Description: Explores the new challenges and opportunities every branch of Christian theology and studies faces in a changing world.

RELIGIONS AND THEOLOGY 5721

STUDIES OF CLASSICAL INDIA. see *PHILOSOPHY*

200 NE ISSN 0169-9814
STUDIES ON RELIGION IN AFRICA. (Supplement to: Journal of Religion in Africa (ISSN 0022-4200)) 1970. irreg., vol.11, 1994. price varies. E.J. Brill, P.O. Box 9000, 2300 PA Leiden, Netherlands. TEL 31-71-5353500. FAX 31-71-5317532. TELEX 39296 BRILL NL. (In N. America: E.J. Brill, 24 Hudson St., Kinderhook, NY 12106. TEL 800-962-4406. FAX 518-758-1959) Ed. Adrian Hastings. bibl. (back issues avail.) **Document type:** monographic series.
—BLDSC (8491.432000).
Refereed Serial

STUDIES ON THE TEXTS OF THE DESERT OF JUDAH. see *RELIGIONS AND THEOLOGY — Judaic*

STUDIO; a journal of Christians writing. see *LITERATURE*

225 BE
STUDIORUM NOVI TESTAMENTI AUXILIA. (Text in English, French, German) 1965. a., vol.18, 1993. price varies. (Katholieke Universiteit Leuven, Faculty of Divinity) Editions Peeters s.p.r.l., Bondgenotenlaan 153, 3000 Leuven, Belgium. TEL 32-16-235170. FAX 32-16-228500. (back issues avail.) **Document type:** monographic series.

220 IS ISSN 0081-8909
STUDIUM BIBLICUM FRANCISCANUM. ANALECTA. (Text in various languages) 1962. irreg., no.38, 1995. price varies. Franciscan Printing Press, P.O. Box 14064, 91140 Jerusalem, Israel. TEL 972-2-286594. FAX 972-2-272274. circ. 1,000. **Document type:** monographic series.

220 VC
SUBSIDIA BIBLICA. 1972. irreg., no.17, 1994. price varies. (Pontificio Istituto Biblico - Pontifical Biblical Institute) Biblical Institute Press, Piazza della Pilotta 35, 00187 Rome, Italy. TEL 39-6-678-15-67. FAX 39-6-678-05-88.
Description: Contains various Biblical studies.

200 UK
SUDAN CHURCH REVIEW. 1949. 2/yr. membership. Sudan Church Association, 3 Marne Rd., Bitterne, Southampton SO18 6AJ, England. TEL 01703-470855. Ed. A. Oakley John. bk.rev. circ. 1,300. **Document type:** bulletin.
Description: News from church leaders and other workers in the Sudan. Includes news from supporting groups and organizations in UK.

200 US ISSN 0039-5188
SUNDAY DIGEST; selected reading for Christian adults. 1886. w. $3.50. David C. Cook Publishing Co., 850 N. Grove Ave., Elgin, IL 60120. TEL 312-741-2400. Ed. Judy Couchman. bk.rev.; illus. circ. 125,000. (tabloid format) **Indexed:** A.I.P.P.

200 FR ISSN 0750-1455
BJ2
LE SUPPLEMENT; revue d'ethique et de theologie morale. 1947. 4/yr. 210 F. (foreign 260 F.). Editions du Cerf, 29 bd. Latour Maubourg, 75340 Paris Cedex 07, France. TEL 45-50-34-07. FAX 45-56-04-27. (Subscr. to: Service Abonnements, 3 chemin des Prunais, 94350 Villiers-sur-Marne, France) Ed. Jean-Paul Durand. circ. 3,000. **Indexed:** Cath.Ind., CERDIC.
Description: Forum for exchange between theologians and theosophists.

SURPRISE ME. see *LITERATURE*

220 SW ISSN 1100-2298
BS410
SVENSK EXEGETISK AARSBOK. (Text in English or Swedish) 1936. a. SEK 120 (effective 1990). Uppsala Exegetiska Saellskap, P.O. Box 1604, S-751 46 Uppsala, Sweden. bk.rev.; illus. **Indexed:** New Test.Abstr., Old Test.Abstr., Rel.& Theol.Abstr. (1983-).

200 SW ISSN 0039-6699
SVENSK PASTORALTIDSKRIFT. 1959. w. SEK 425 in Sweden (students SEK 325); Nordic and Baltic countries SEK 455 (students SEK 355); elsewhere SEK 510. Stiftelsen Kyrkligt Forum, P.O. Box 2085, S-750 02 Uppsala 2, Sweden. TEL 46-18-510986. FAX 46-18-550986. Ed. Carl Strandberg. adv.; bk.rev. circ. 3,200.

230 SW ISSN 0039-6761
BR6
SVENSK TEOLOGISK KVARTALSKRIFT. Abbreviated title: S T K. 1925. q. SEK 115 (effective 1990). Liber Forlag, S-205 10, Malmoe, Sweden. (Subscr. to: Bloms Boktryckeri, Bytaregatan 6, 222 21 Lund, Sweden) Eds. Bengt Hagglund, P.E. Persson. adv.; bk.rev.; abstr.; index, cum.index every 10 yrs. circ. 1,000. **Indexed:** Bibl.Ling., CERDIC, New Test.Abstr., Old Test.Abstr., Rel.& Theol.Abstr. (1989-), Rel.Ind.One, Rel.Per.

266 SW ISSN 0039-6826
SVENSK VECKOTIDNING. Variant title: Nya Svensk Veckotidning. 1882. w. SEK 278 (effective 1990). Svenska Missionsfoerbundet, P.O. Box 6302, 113 81 Stockholm, Sweden. FAX 46-8-33-55-57. TELEX S-142 75. Ed. Leif Nilsson. adv.; bk.rev.; play rev. circ. 28,000. (tabloid format; also avail. in audio cassette)
Incorporates (in 1985): Missionstidningen Familjevaennen.

284.1 SW ISSN 0280-4603
SVENSKA KYRKANS TIDNING. 1982. w. SEK 429 (typically set in Oct.); newsstand price: SEK 12. (Svenska Kyrkan) Svenska Kyrkans Press AB, P.O. Box 342, S-191 30 Sollentuna, Djupdalsvaegen 7, SWeden. TEL 46-8-623-65-55. FAX 46-8-35-93-40. Ed. Lars B. Stenstroem. adv.: B&W page SEK 21200, color page SEK 26500; trim 249 x 360; adv. contact: Claes Waern. bk.rev.; illus. circ. 59,500. cols./p.: 6; pp./issue: 12. (tabloid format; also avail. in audio cassette) **Document type:** newspaper.

289.4 UK
SWEDENBORG SOCIETY MAGAZINE. 1986. irreg. £1 per no. Swedenborg Society, 20-21 Bloomsbury Way, London WC1A 2TH, England. TEL 0171-405-7986. Ed. Frederick Elphick. bk.review. circ. 800. (back issues avail.) **Document type:** bulletin.

200 US ISSN 0039-7547
SWORD OF THE LORD; America's foremost revival publication. 1934. bi-w. $12. Sword of the Lord Foundation, Box 1099, 224 Bridge Ave., Murfreesboro, TN 37133. TEL 615-893-6700. FAX 615-895-7447. Ed. Curtis Hutson. adv.; bk.rev.; index. circ. 100,000. (tabloid format)
Description: Features more than 100 sermons, tips on soul winning and getting converts down the aisle, Bible studies and answers to Bible questions, and reports of revivals from leading evangelists.

SYCAMORE TREE NEWSLETTER. see *EDUCATION — Teaching Methods And Curriculum*

200 GW ISSN 0939-5199
T A N Z. (Texte und Arbeiten zum Neutestamentlichen Zeitalter) 1989? irreg., vol.16, 1994. price varies. Francke Verlag GmbH, Postfach 2560, 72015 Tuebingen, Germany. TEL 07071-9797-0. FAX 07071-75288. **Document type:** monographic series.

300 NR ISSN 0794-7046
T C N N RESEARCH BULLETIN. 1978. s-a. $25 for 2 yrs. Theological College of Northern Nigeria, P.O. Box 64, Bukuru, Plateau State, Nigeria. Ed. Timothy Palmer. bk.rev. circ. 400. (back issues avail.) **Document type:** academic/scholarly publication.

266 US ISSN 0163-3422
BV2350
T E A M HORIZONS. 1925. 6/yr. $2. Evangelical Alliance Mission, Box 969, Wheaton, IL 60189-0969. TEL 708-653-1826. FAX 708-653-1826. Ed. Jack Kilgore. illus.; circ. 45,000. (controlled).

253 SA
T F M MONITOR. 1992. irreg., approx. q. Church of the Province of South Africa, Department of Training for Ministries, Pretoria Diocese, P.O. Box 1032, Pretoria 0001, South Africa. **Document type:** newsletter.

200 800 GW ISSN 0941-0570
T H L I. (Textwissenschaft Theologie Hermeneutik Literaturanalyse Informatik) 1991. irreg., vol.9, 1994. price varies. Francke Verlag GmbH, Postfach 2560, 72015 Tuebingen, Germany. TEL 07071-9797-0. FAX 07071-75288. Ed. Winfried Bader. **Document type:** monographic series.

200 CN ISSN 0704-6421
T R A C E. 1976. q. Can.$15. (Teachers of Religion and Christian Ethics) Saskatchewan Teachers' Federation, Box 1108, Saskatoon, SK S7K 3N3, Canada. Ed. Miles Myers. **Document type:** newsletter.
Formerly (until 1977): T R A C E Newsletter (ISSN 0701-192X)

266 US ISSN 1071-3468
T W RADIO. (Trans World Radio) 1980. q. free. Trans World Radio, Box 8700, Cary, NC 27512-8700. TEL 919-460-3700. FAX 919-460-3702. Ed. Marion L. Tunis. circ. 45,000. **Document type:** trade publication.
Formerly: T W R Magazine (ISSN 0274-9831)
Description: Missionary broadcasting magazine, concentrating on TWR's worldwide ministry.

200 UK ISSN 0039-8837
AP4
TABLET. 1840. w. £55. Tablet Publishing Co. Ltd., 1 King St. Cloister, Clifton Walk, London W6 0QZ, England. TEL 0181-748-8484. FAX 0181-748-1550. Ed. John Wilkins. adv. contact: Conor Taaffe. bk.rev.; film rev.; index. circ. 18,560. (also avail. in microform from UMI; reprint service avail. from UMI) **Indexed:** Cath.Ind., CERDIC, Rural Recreat.Tour.Abstr., World Agri.Econ.& Rural Sociol.Abstr. **Document type:** newspaper.
—BLDSC (8597.450000); SWETS; UMI; UnCover. CCC.
Description: Covers religion, politics, society, ethics and the arts.

296 US ISSN 0039-9213
TALKS AND TALES. (Editions in French, Hebrew, Italian, Spanish and Yiddish) 1942. m. $3. Merkos L'Inyonei Chinuch, Inc., 770 Eastern Parkway, Brooklyn, NY 11213. Ed. Nissan Mindel. index.

291 US
TANTRA: THE MAGAZINE. 1991. q. $18. Box 10268, Albuquerque, NM 87184. Ed. Susana Andrews; Pub. Alan Verdegraal. adv. contact: Danielle Isabelle. bk.rev.; illus. circ. 13,000. **Document type:** consumer publication.
Description: Devoted to tantric practices found throughout the world, including history, philosophy, rituals and life-styles.

268.8 US ISSN 0082-1713
TARBELL'S TEACHER'S GUIDE; to the International Sunday School Lessons. 1905. a. $7.95. David C. Cook Publishing Co., 850 N. Grove Ave., Elgin, IL 60120. TEL 708-741-2400. Ed. William P. Barker. circ. 2,300.
Description: Bible commentary using KJV and RSV for Sunday School teachers.

200 KE
TARGET. (Text in English) 1964. bi-m. P.O. Box 72839, Nairobi, Kenya. Ed. Rebeka Njau. circ. 17,000.

220 US ISSN 8755-8769
TEACH; a newsletter for Christian teachers and church leaders. 1985. q. $16.95 (effective 1995). Sweet Publishing, 4037 Scruggs Dr., Ft. Worth, TX 76180-8821. TEL 817-232-5661. FAX 817-232-2030. Ed. Mary Hollingsworth. bk.rev. circ. 9,000. **Document type:** newsletter.

TECHNICAL PAPERS FOR THE BIBLE TRANSLATOR. see *LINGUISTICS*

TEEN POWER; a powerline paper. see *CHILDREN AND YOUTH — For*

220 375 UK ISSN 0142-5943
TEEN-SEARCH. q. £0.55. Go Teach Publications, 2 Radford Rd., Leamington Spa CV31 1LX, England. TEL 0926-26573. illus.
Description: Young peoples' workbooks for use with: Go Teach Teens.

TEENQUEST. see *CHILDREN AND YOUTH — For*

TEENS TODAY (KANSAS CITY, 1969). see *CHILDREN AND YOUTH — For*

200 NE ISSN 0040-2133
TEGENWOORDIG.* 1946. bi-m. fl.5.25. St. Jozefslaan 56, 5817 AD Smakt, Netherlands. (Subscr. to: Karmel, Rijksweg N. 35, Geleen, Netherlands) Ed.Bd. bk.rev.; illus. circ. 17,000.
Formerly: Scapulier.

RELIGIONS AND THEOLOGY

200   UK
TEILHARD REVIEW - A JOURNAL FOR BRIDGING SCIENCE AND RELIGION. 1966. 3/yr. £20 (foreign £25). Teilhard Centre for the Future of Man, 3 Priory Farm Ct., Lavenham, Suffolk CO10 9RW, England. Ed. Thomas Baxter. adv.; bk.rev.; bibl.; charts; illus.; cum.index: 1966-1971, 1972-1977. circ. 1,000. (tabloid format; also avail. in microform from UMI; reprint service avail. from UMI) **Indexed:** Cath.Ind., CERDIC, Mid.East: Abstr.& Ind. **Document type:** academic/scholarly publication.
—UMI; UnCover.
Former titles: Teilhard Review and Journal of Cosmic Convergence (ISSN 0959-7069); Teilhard Review and Journal of Creative Evolution (ISSN 0952-6471); (until 1981): Teilhard Review (ISSN 0040-2184)
Description: Reprints of Teilhard's essays, and articles on Teilhard's work and related developments in science, philosophy and religion.

200   ZR   ISSN 1013-7769
BR3
TELEMA. (Text in French) 1975. q. $45. B.P. 3277, Kinshasa-Gombe, Zaire. Ed. Boka di Mpasi. adv.; bk.rev. circ. 4,000. **Indexed:** CERDIC, Curr.Cont.Africa, Old Test.Abstr.

200   US
TELLING THE TRUTH. m. Triple T Ministries, 12814 U.S. Hwy. 41 N., Evansville, IN 47711. TEL 812-867-2418. Ed. George Dooms. adv. circ. 2,000.

200   FI   ISSN 0497-1817
BL1.A1
TEMENOS (TURKU). (Text in English, French, German) 1965. a. FIM 150. Finnish Society for the Study of Comparative Religion, P.O. Box 70, FIN-20501 Turku, Finland. TEL 358-21-2311-290. FAX 358-21-2311-290. E-mail: Tore.Ahlback@abo.fi. (Dist. by: Academic Bookstore, Keskuskatu 1, FIN-00100 Helsinki, Finland) Ed. Tore Ahlbaeck. bk.rev. circ. 250. **Indexed:** Arts & Hum.Cit.Ind., Rel.Ind.Two. **Document type:** academic/scholarly publication.
—BLDSC (8789.760000); UnCover.

200   IT
TEMI DI PREDICAZIONE - OMELIE. 1957. m. L.45000($75) (foreign L.90000). Editrice Domenican Italian, Via L. Palmieri 19, 80133 Naples, Italy. Ed. P. Reginaldo Agostino Iannarone. adv. **Indexed:** CERDIC.

TEMOIGNAGE CHRETIEN. see *LITERARY AND POLITICAL REVIEWS*

200   SP   ISSN 0495-1549
BX2350.65
TEOLOGIA ESPIRITUAL. 1958. 3/yr. 3000 ptas. (foreign 4200 ptas.). Facultad de Teologia "San Vicente Ferrer", Seccion Dominicos, C. Pouet de Sant Vicent, 1, 46003 Valencia, Spain. TEL 96-352-84-81. FAX 96-394-12-11. bk.rev.; index. circ. 600.

200   SP   ISSN 0212-1964
TEOLOGIA Y CATEQUESIS. 1982. q. 3500 ptas. (foreign 4800 ptas.) (effective 1996). Centro de Estudios Teologicos "San Damaso", San Buenaventura, 9, 28005 Madrid, Spain. TEL 34-1-3652404. FAX 34-1-3642882. Ed. Eliseo Touron. bibl.; circ. 600.

230   FI   ISSN 0040-3555
TEOLOGINEN AIKAKAUSKIRJA/TEOLOGISK TIDSKRIFT. (Text in Finnish and Swedish) 1896. 6/yr. FIM 220 (typically set in Aug.). Teologinen Julkaisuseura r.y., P.O. Box 33, Aleksanderinkatu 7, FIN-00014 Helsinki University, Finland. TEL 90-174527. FAX 90-1913033. Ed. Juha Seppo. adv. contact: Anna Huotari. bk.rev.; charts; illus.; index, cum.index. circ. 3,000.

200   YU   ISSN 0497-2597
BX200
TEOLOSKI POGLEDI; versko naucni casopis. (Text in Serbian; summaries in English) 1968. q. $25. Srpska Patrijarsija, 7 Jula 5, 11000 Belgrade, Yugoslavia. Ed. Radovan Bigovic. bk.rev.; bibl. circ. 1,200.

200   US
TERRA UNA. 1972. s-a. $25. International Association for Religious Freedom, U S Chapter, 777 UN Plaza 7-D, New York, NY 10017. TEL 212-986-5165. bk.rev. circ. 500.
Formerly: Interdependence (ISSN 0362-4668)

262.9   IT
TESTIMONI NEL MONDO; pagine di vita spirituale. 1974. bi-m. L.34000. Edizioni O.R., Via Necchi 2, 20123 Milan, Italy. TEL 86453578. bk.rev. circ. 2,500.

TESTIMONIANZE; quaderni mensili. see *LITERARY AND POLITICAL REVIEWS*

200 465   GW   ISSN 0082-3589
BR45
TEXTE UND UNTERSUCHUNGEN ZUR GESCHICHTE DER ALTCHRISTLICHEN LITERATUR. 1952. irreg., vol.141, 1995. price varies. Akademie Verlag GmbH, Muehlenstr. 33-34, 13187 Berlin, Germany. TEL 030-47889348. FAX 030-47889357. (also avail. in microfiche from IDC) **Document type:** monographic series.

200   US
TEXTS AND STUDIES IN RELIGION. 1977. irreg., latest no.64. $49.95 per no. Edwin Mellen Press, 415 Ridge St., Box 450, Lewiston, NY 14092. TEL 716-754-2788. FAX 716-754-4056. **Document type:** monographic series.

220   IS   ISSN 0082-3767
BS410
TEXTUS; annual of the Hebrew University Bible Project. (Text in English; summaries in Hebrew) 1960. irreg., latest vol.17. price varies. (Hebrew University of Jerusalem) Magnes Press, Hebrew University, Jerusalem, P.O. Box 7695, Jerusalem 91076, Israel. TEL 972-2-660341. FAX 972-2-633370. (back issues avail.) **Document type:** monographic series.
—BLDSC (8813.785000).

200   GW   ISSN 0082-3775
TEXTUS PATRISTICI ET LITURGICI. 1964. irreg. price varies. (Institutum Liturgicum Ratisbonense) Verlag Friedrich Pustet, Gutenbergstr. 8, 93051 Regensburg, Germany. TEL 0941-92022-0. FAX 0941-948652. Ed. Klaus Gamber. circ. 1,000. **Document type:** monographic series.

268   UK   ISSN 0307-8388
THEMELIOS. 1964. 3/yr. £5.70($12) Universities and Colleges Christian Fellowship, 38 De Montfort St., Leicester LE1 7GP, England. TEL 0116-255-1700. FAX 0116-255-5672. (Co-sponsor: International Fellowship of Evangelical Students) Ed. Rev. Stephen Williams. bk.rev.; bibl. circ. 4,500. (back issues avail.) **Indexed:** Old Test.Abstr., Rel.& Theol.Abstr. (1975-), Rel.Ind.One.
—BLDSC (8814.477000); UMI.
Description: International journal for theology and religious studies students which espouses and defends the historic Christian faith.

200   GW   ISSN 0937-8766
THEMENHEFTE GEMEINDEARBEIT. 1990. a. DM.60. Bergmoser und Hoeller Verlag GmbH, Karl-Friedrich-Str. 76, 52072 Aachen, Germany. TEL 0241-9388821. FAX 0241-9388834. circ. 3,700. **Document type:** bulletin.

130   US   ISSN 0362-0085
THEOLOGIA 21. 1970. s-a. $15 to non-members. (Affiliated Christian Emortalists) Dominion Press, Box 4608, Salem, OR 97302-8608. TEL 503-362-9634. Ed. A. Stuart Otto. bibl.; charts; illus.; stat. circ. 100. (looseleaf format; also avail. in microform from UMI; back issues avail.; reprint service avail. from UMI)
—UMI.
Formerly: (until 1976): Immortality Newsletter (ISSN 0019-2783)
Description: Articles on metaphysical Christianity.

200   HU   ISSN 0133-7599
BR9.H8
THEOLOGIAI SZEMLE. 1925. 6/yr. $40.50. Magyarorszagi Egyhazak Okumenikus Tanacsa - Ecumenical Council of Churches in Hungary, Bimbo ut 127, 1088 Budapest, Hungary. TEL 361-138-2302. FAX 361-176-1210. Ed. Zoltan Bona. bk.rev. circ. 1,000. **Indexed:** Amer.Hist.& Life (until 1990), Hist.Abstr. (until 1990).

200   UK   ISSN 0954-2191
THEOLOGICAL BOOK REVIEW. 1988. 3/yr. £15($30) (typically set in Oct.). Feed the Minds, Robertson House, Leas Rd., Guildford, Surrey GU1 4QW, England. TEL 01483-577877. FAX 01483-301387. Ed. Rev. J.L. Houlden. adv.; bk.rev. circ. 600. **Document type:** catalog.
Description: For theological librarians and educators to aid them in current book selection.

207   US   ISSN 0040-5620
BV4019
THEOLOGICAL EDUCATION. 1964. 2/yr. $10 (foreign $11). Association of Theological Schools, 10 Summit Park Dr., Pittsburgh, PA 15275-1103. TEL 412-788-6505. Ed. James L. Warts. stat.; index. circ. 2,700. (also avail. in microform from UMI) **Indexed:** CERDIC, Curr.Cont., Rel.& Theol.Abstr. (1989-), Rel.Ind.One, Rel.Per. **Document type:** academic/scholarly publication.
—UMI.

268 377.9   US   ISSN 0198-6856
BR1
THEOLOGICAL EDUCATOR. 1968. s-a. $8 (foreign $11) (effective 1995). New Orleans Baptist Theological Seminary, 3939 Gentilly Blvd., New Orleans, LA 70126. TEL 504-286-3610. FAX 504-286-3639. Ed. Paul E. Robertson. adv.; bk.rev. circ. 2,500. **Indexed:** CERDIC, G.Soc.Sci.& Rel.Per.Lit., Rel.Ind.One, South.Bap.Per.Ind. **Document type:** academic/scholarly publication.
—BLDSC (8814.523050).

200   KO   ISSN 0260-3705
THEOLOGICAL NEWS. 1968. 4/yr. $8 (effective 1993). P.O. Box 94, Choong Jong No, Seoul 120-650, Korea. TEL 2-393-9895. FAX 2-393-8462. circ. 3,000. **Document type:** academic/scholarly publication, newsletter.
Description: News of interest to evangelical theologians and theological educators. Contains information about consultations, seminars and other worldwide activities.

230   US   ISSN 0040-5639
BX801
THEOLOGICAL STUDIES. 1940. q. $20 to individuals (foreign $27 (£20)); institutions $30 (foreign $36 (£25)) (effective 1996). (Theological Faculties of the Society of Jesus in the U S) Theological Studies, Inc., Georgetown University, 37th and O Sts., N.W., Washington, DC 20057. TEL 202-338-0754. FAX 202-687-7679. (Subscr. to: Theological Studies, Inc., Box 465, Hanover, PA 17331) Ed. Robert J. Daly. adv. contact: John R. Keating. bk.rev.; index, cum.index: vols.1-40; circ. 5,000 (paid). (also avail. in microform from UMI; back issues avail.) **Indexed:** Arts & Hum.Cit.Ind., Bk.Rev.Ind. (1984-), Canon Law Abstr., Cath.Ind., CERDIC, Child.Bk.Rev.Ind. (1984-), Curr.Cont., Hum.Ind., New Test.Abstr., Old Test.Abstr., Ref.Sour., Rel.& Theol.Abstr. (1969-), Rel.Ind.One, Rel.Per. **Document type:** academic/scholarly publication.
●Also available online. Vendor(s): University Microfilms International.
—BLDSC (8814.524000); Faxon; SWETS; UMI; UnCover.
Description: Publishes scholarly articles, bulletins, and notes in the various theological disciplines.
Refereed Serial

THEOLOGICAL TIMES. see *HANDICAPPED — Visually Impaired*

200   GW   ISSN 0342-1457
THEOLOGIE DER GEGENWART. 1957. q. DM.42. Butzon und Bercker Verlag, Hoogeweg 71, Postfach 215, 47623 Kevelaer, Germany. TEL 02832-2906. FAX 02832-40321. TELEX 812207-BBKEV. bk.rev. circ. 1,350.

230   GW
THEOLOGIE UND DIENST. 1973. irreg., latest no.30. price varies. (Prediger- und Missionsseminar St. Chrischona) Brunnen Verlag GmbH, Postfach 100143, 35331 Giessen, Germany. TEL 0641-6059-0. FAX 0641-605940. Ed.Bd. circ. 3,000. **Document type:** bulletin.

230   NE
THEOLOGIE & EMPIRIE. (Text in German, occasionally in English) irreg., vol.22, 1994. price varies. Kok Pharos Publishing House, Postbus 5019, 8260 AG Kampen, Netherlands. FAX 31-5202-92565. (Dist. in U.S. and Canada by: Books International, Inc., Box 605, Herndon, VA 22070-0605. TEL 800-377-7192. FAX 703-689-0660) (Co-publisher: Deutscher Studien Verlag, GW) (back issues avail.) Document type: monographic series.
   Description: Publishes studies addressing issues in practical theology.

230 100   GW   ISSN 0040-5655
BX803
THEOLOGIE UND PHILOSOPHIE. 1926. q. DM.228. Verlag Herder GmbH und Co. KG, Hermann-Herder-Str. 4, 79104 Freiburg, Germany. FAX 0761-2717-407. Ed. Hermann Josef Sieben. adv.; bk.rev.; bibl.; index. circ. 700. (reprint service avail. from SWZ) **Indexed:** Bibl.Ling., Canon Law Abstr., CERDIC, New Test.Abstr., Phil.Ind., Rel.& Theol.Abstr. Document type: newsletter.
   —SWETS.
   Formerly: Scholastik.

207   GW   ISSN 0040-5663
THEOLOGISCH-PRAKTISCHE QUARTALSCHRIFT. 1848. q. DM.58. (Theologische Hochschule der Dioezese Linz, AU) Verlag Friedrich Pustet, Gutenbergstr. 8, 93051 Regensburg, Germany. TEL 0941-92022-0. FAX 0941-948652. Ed.Bd. adv.; bk.rev. **Indexed:** Canon Law Abstr., CERDIC, New Test.Abstr. Document type: academic/scholarly publication.
   —BLDSC (8814.540000).

266   GW   ISSN 0342-2372
THEOLOGISCHE BEITRAEGE. 1970. bi-m. DM.49.50. Theologischer Verlag R. Brockhaus, Postfach 2220, 42766 Haan, Germany. TEL 02104-96860-0. FAX 02104-968601. Ed.Bd. adv.; bk.rev. circ. 4,000. **Indexed:** CERDIC, New Test.Abstr., Old Test.Abstr. Document type: academic/scholarly publication.
   Description: Non-denominational publication containing essays on religion, ethics, and evangelism.

230   SZ   ISSN 0082-3902
THEOLOGISCHE DISSERTATIONEN. (Editions in English and German; summaries in English or German) 1969. irreg., no.17, 1986. price varies. (Universitaet Basel, Theologische Fakultaet) Friedrich Reinhardt Verlag, Missionsstr. 36, CH-4012 Basel, Switzerland. (Dist. by: Albert J. Phiebig Books, Box 352, White Plains, NY 10602) Ed. Bo Reicke.

200   GW   ISSN 0040-5671
Z7753
THEOLOGISCHE LITERATURZEITUNG; Monatsschrift fuer das gesamte Gebiet der Theologie und Religionswissenschaft. 1876. m. DM.198 (foreign DM.228). Evangelische Verlagsanstalt GmbH, Burgstr. 1-5, 04109 Leipzig, Germany. TEL 0341-71141-0. FAX 0341-9603179. Ed. Dr. Ernst-Heinz Amberg. adv.; B&W page DM.1200; trim 255 x 175; adv. contact: Christine Herrmann. bk.rev.; index. circ. 1,600. **Indexed:** Bibl.Ling., CERDIC, New Test.Abstr., Old Test.Abstr., Rel.& Theol.Abstr. (1979-), Rel.Ind.One, Rel.Per. Document type: newspaper.
   —SWETS.

230   GW   ISSN 0040-5698
BR4
THEOLOGISCHE RUNDSCHAU. 1929. q. DM.138 to individuals, students DM.74. Verlag J.C.B. Mohr (Paul Siebeck), Wilhelmstr. 18, 72074 Tuebingen, Germany. TEL 07071-923-0. FAX 07071-51104. TELEX 7262872-MOHR-D. (Subscr. to: Postfach 2040, 72010 Tuebingen, Germany) Eds. J. Baur, L. Perlitt. adv.; bk.rev.; index. **Indexed:** Bibl.Ling., CERDIC, New Test.Abstr., Old Test.Abstr., Rel.& Theol.Abstr. (1980-), Rel.Ind.One, Rel.Per. Document type: academic/scholarly publication.
   —Faxon; SWETS. CCC.
   Description: Reports and reviews of problems and developments in all theological fields.

200   GW
THEOLOGISCHE TEXTE UND STUDIEN. 1992. irreg., vol.4, 1994. price varies. Georg Olms Verlag, Hagentorwall 7, 31134 Hildesheim, Germany. TEL 05121-1501-0. FAX 05121-150150. (U.S. subscr. to: 111 W. 57th St., New York, NY 10019. TEL 212-757-5237) Document type: monographic series.

230   SZ   ISSN 0040-5701
BR4
THEOLOGISCHE ZEITSCHRIFT. 1945. bi-m. 107 SFr. (Universitaet Basel, Theologische Fakultaet) Friedrich Reinhardt Verlag, Missionsstr. 36, CH-4012 Basel, Switzerland. Ed. K. Seybold. adv.; bk.rev.; abstr.; bibl.; cum.index. circ. 750. **Indexed:** Bibl.Ling., CERDIC, New Test.Abstr., Old Test.Abstr., Rel.& Theol.Abstr. (1975-), Rel.Ind.One.
   —BLDSC (8814.537000); SWETS.

200   UK   ISSN 0040-571X
BR1
THEOLOGY. 1920. bi-m. £15($30) Society for Promoting Christian Knowledge, Holy Trinity Church, Marylebone Rd., London NW1 4DU, England. TEL 071-387-5282. FAX 071-388-2352. Ed.Bd. adv.; bk.rev.; index. circ. 5,000. (also avail. in microform) **Indexed:** Br.Hum.Ind., New Test.Abstr., Rel.& Theol.Abstr. (1968-), Rel.Ind.One. Document type: bulletin.
   —BLDSC (8814.541000); UnCover.

200   US
THEOLOGY AND CULTURE NEWSLETTER. 1967. a. free. Andover Newton Theological School, 210 Herrick Rd., Newton Centre, MA 02159. TEL 617-964-1100. FAX 508-771-7919. Eds. Gabriel & Dorothy Fackre. circ. 3,000 (controlled). (back issues avail.) Document type: newsletter.
   Description: Trends in theology, church renewal - for clergy and active laity.

291.5642 174.2   NE   ISSN 0928-8783
THEOLOGY AND MEDICINE. (Text in English) 1992. irreg., vol.2, 1992. price varies. Kluwer Academic Publishers, Postbus 17, 3300 AA Dordrecht, Netherlands. TEL 31-78-392392. FAX 31-78-392254. TELEX 29245 KAPG NL. (Dist. by: Kluwer Academic Publishers Group, P.O. Box 322, 3300 AH Dordrecht, Netherlands. TEL 31-78-392392. FAX 31-78-546474; N. America dist. addr.: Box 358, Accord Sta., Hingham, MA 02018-0358. TEL 617-871-6600. FAX 617-871-6528) Document type: monographic series.
   Refereed Serial

261.8   US   ISSN 1052-9314
BJ1188.5
THEOLOGY & PUBLIC POLICY. 1989. s-a. $10 (foreign $3). Churches' Center for Theology and Public Policy, 4500 Massachusetts Ave. N.W., Washington, DC 20016-5690. TEL 202-885-8648. Ed. James A. Nash. circ. 1,200 (paid). Document type: academic/scholarly publication.
   —BLDSC (8814.541230).
   Refereed Serial

200 301   UK   ISSN 1355-8358
▼**THEOLOGY AND SEXUALITY.** 1994. 2/yr. $22.50 to individuals; institutions $45. Sheffield Academic Press Ltd., Mansion House, 19 Kingfield Rd., Sheffield S11 9AS, England. TEL 44-171-267-4466. FAX 44-171-482-2293. E-mail: admin@sheffac.demon.co.uk. Document type: academic/scholarly publication.
   Description: Forum for publication of new theological work on issues of sexuality and gender.

230   US   ISSN 0040-5728
BX801
THEOLOGY DIGEST. 1953. q. $12 (foreign $14). (Saint Louis University, Department of Theological Studies) Theology Digest, Inc., 3634 Lindell Blvd., St. Louis, MO 63108-3395. TEL 314-658-2859. (Subscr. to: Box 6036, Duluth, MN 55806) Ed. Bernhard Asen. adv. contact: Rosemary Jermann. bk.rev.; bibl.; cum.index: 1953-1973. circ. 4,000. (also avail. in microfilm from UMI; back issues avail.) **Indexed:** Cath.Ind., CERDIC, Int.Z.Bibelwiss., Old Test.Abstr., Rel.& Theol.Abstr. (1980-). Document type: academic/scholarly publication.
   —BLDSC (8814.543000); Faxon; UMI; UnCover.
   Description: Theology magazine with an international readership.

RELIGIONS AND THEOLOGY   5723

230   US   ISSN 0040-5736
BR1
THEOLOGY TODAY. 1944. q. $21. (Princeton Theological Seminary) Theology Today, Box 29, Princeton, NJ 08542. TEL 609-497-7714. FAX 609-924-2973. Eds. T. Long, P. Mlller. adv.; bk.rev.; index, cum.index every 10 yrs. circ. 14,000. (also avail. in microform from MIM,UMI; back issues avail.; reprint service avail. from UMI) **Indexed:** Arts & Hum.Cit.Ind., Bk.Rev.Ind. (1965-), Bk.Rev.Mo., CCR, CERDIC, Child.Bk.Rev.Ind. (1965-), Curr.Cont., G.Soc.Sci.& Rel.Per.Lit., Hum.Ind., Mid.East: Abstr.& Ind., New Test.Abstr., Old Test.Abstr., Rel.& Theol.Abstr. (1968-), Rel.Ind.One. Document type: academic/scholarly publication.
   —BLDSC (8814.545000); Faxon; SWETS; UMI; UnCover.

THEORIE UND PRAXIS DER SOZIALPAEDAGOGIK. see *CHILDREN AND YOUTH — About*

283   UK   ISSN 0143-8514
THINKING MISSION. 1972. q. £4. United Society for the Propagation of the Gospel, Partnership House, 157 Waterloo Rd., London SE1 8XA, England. TEL 0171-928-8681. FAX 0171-928-2371. Document type: bulletin.
   Description: Theological reflections on mission.

200   IT   ISSN 0040-6686
TI SALUTO, FRATELLO! 1946. m. free. Segretariato Diocesano Malati, Via Longhin, 7, Casa Toniolo, 31100 Treviso (Veneto), Italy. TEL 0422-411069. Ed. Sac. Giovanni Bordin. circ. 7,500. (processed)
   Description: Features letters of thanks from devoted Christians who have prayed for someone with an illness. Includes articles on religious community activities.

200   US   ISSN 1077-8403
THE TIE (SCHAUMBURG). bi-m. $20. College of Chaplains, Inc., 1701 E. Woodfield Rd., Ste. 311, Schaumburg, IL 60173. FAX 708-240-1015. Ed. Rev. Arne K. Jessen. adv. circ. 3,000.
   Description: Designed to let members know what is current in chaplaincy and what the association is doing at national and state levels.
   Refereed Serial

248.83   SA
TIENERKOMPAS. (Text in Afrikaans) 1951. q. R.7.50 (effective 1995). Afrikaanse Christen-Studentevereniging van Suid-Afrika, P.O. Box 25, Stellenbosch, South Africa. Ed. P.J.L. Brink. adv.; bk.rev. circ. 25,000.
   Former titles (until 1987): Tagtig; (until 1980): Ons Bou (ISSN 0030-2643)

TIERRA NUEVA. see *SOCIOLOGY*

808.81   US   ISSN 1074-2271
TIME OF SINGING; a magazine of Christian poetry. 1958. 3/yr. $12 (Canada $15; elsewhere $22.50). (High Street Community Church, Conneaut Lake) Time of Singing, Box 211, Cambridge Springs, PA 16403. TEL 814-382-5911. Ed. Charles A. Waugaman. circ. 300.

200   US   ISSN 0740-9680
TIMES OF RESTORATION. 1949. bi-m. free. Kingdom Press, 105 Chestnut Hill Rd., Amherst, NH 03031-1505. TEL 603-673-3208. (Subscr. to: Kingdom Press, 105 Chestnut Hill Rd., Amherst, NH 03031) Ed. Timothy F. Murray; Pub. Charles K. Sandford. bk.rev. circ. 700.
   Former titles (until 1985): Restoration Tidings; (until 1984): Standard (ISSN 0038-9404)
   Description: Articles encouraging Christian belief and practice.

266   KE
TODAY IN AFRICA. (Text in English) 1967. bi-m. KShs.170($5) (Africa Inland Church) Kesho Publications, P.O. Box 60, Kijabe, Kenya. TEL 254-154-64211. Ed. Mwaura Njoroge. adv.: B&W page KShs.6500; adv. contact: Joe Gacheru. bk.rev. circ. 13,000. (back issues avail.) **Indexed:** CERDIC. Document type: consumer publication.
   Formerly: Today (ISSN 0040-8387)
   Description: Aimed at singles 16 to 30 years old facing problems in decision making and family life. Discusses marriage and other relations, careers, religion, and health from a nondenominational Christian perspective.

TODAY'S CHRISTIAN WOMAN. see *WOMEN'S INTERESTS*

RELIGIONS AND THEOLOGY

TODAY'S SINGLE; serving the singles of America. see *SINGLES' INTERESTS AND LIFESTYLES*

200 370   NE   ISSN 0166-3461
TOERUSTING; tijdschrift voor kerk en educatie met werkmateriaal. 1961. 6/yr. fl.47.50. (Nederlandse Hervormde Kerk, Centrum voor Educatie) Boekencentrum B.V., P.O. Box 29, 2700 AA Zoetermeer, Netherlands. TEL 31-79-615481. FAX 31-79-615489. Ed. J.W. Breunese. **Document type:** bulletin.
Description: For church members and group leaders. Discusses educational issues.

266   UK   ISSN 0040-8824
TOILERS OF THE DEEP. 1886. 2/yr. £10 (effective Dec. 1991). Royal National Mission to Deep Sea Fishermen, 43 Nottingham Place, London W1M 4BX, England. TEL 071-487-5101. FAX 071-224-5240. Ed. David Saltiel. charts; illus. circ. 40,000.

200   CN   ISSN 0826-9831
TORONTO JOURNAL OF THEOLOGY. 1985. 2/yr. Can.$30. (Toronto School of Theology) Wilfrid Laurier University Press, Waterloo, ON N2L 3C5, Canada. TEL 519-884-0710. FAX 519-725-1399. E-mail: press@mach1.wlu.ca. bk.rev.; index. circ. 402. **Indexed:** Rel.& Theol.Abstr. (1988-). **Document type:** academic/scholarly publication.
—BLDSC (8868.760000).
Description: Covers historical, philosophical and systematic theology, ethics, biblical and pastoral studies, the history of Christianity, Christianity and culture, interreligious dialogue and related subjects.
Refereed Serial

200   US   ISSN 8756-7385
TORONTO STUDIES IN RELIGION. 1987. irreg. Peter Lang Publishing, Inc., 62 W. 45th St., 4th Fl., New York, NY 10036. TEL 212-302-6740. Ed. Donald Wiebe. **Document type:** academic/scholarly publication, monographic series.
—BLDSC (8868.785000).
Description: Contributes to the scholarly and academic understanding of religion.

200   US
TORONTO STUDIES IN THEOLOGY. 1978. irreg., latest vol.70. $49.95 per no. Edwin Mellen Press, 415 Ridge St., Box 450, Lewiston, NY 14092. TEL 716-754-2788. FAX 716-754-4056. **Document type:** monographic series.

200   IT
TRACCE - LITTERAE COMMUNIONIS. 1975. m. L.40000 (foreign L.80000). (Gruppi di Comunione e Liberazione) Cooperativa Editoriale Nuovo Mondo, Via Porpora 127, 20131 Milano, Italy. TEL 39-2-26823673. FAX 39-2-26823923. Ed. Alberto Savorana. adv.; bk.rev.
Former titles: Litterae Communionis; Comunione e Liberazione.

225 480   BE
TRADITIO EXEGETICA GRAECA. (Text in English, French, German, Greek) 1991. irreg., vol.2, 1993. (Universite Catholique de Louvain) Editions Peeters s.p.r.l., Bondgenotenlaan 153, 3000 Leuven, Belgium. TEL 32-16-235170. FAX 32-16-228500. (back issues avail.) **Document type:** monographic series.

200   UK   ISSN 0265-3788
TRANSFORMATION. 1984. q. £13.20 (foreign £13.90). The Paternoster Press, P.O. Box 300, Kingstown Broadway, Carlisle, Cumbria CA3 0QS, England. TEL 01228-512512. FAX 01228-514949. (Dist. in U.S. & Canada by: Transformation, 6 Lancaster Ave., Wynnewood, PA 19096) Ed.Bd. circ. 1,800. (tabloid format; back issues avail.; reprint service avail. from KTO) **Indexed:** Rel.& Theol.Abstr. (1984-). **Document type:** academic/scholarly publication.
—BLDSC (9020.593000); UMI.
Description: Provides a forum for discussion on economics, development, violence, family life and other ethical issues, with a focus on Christian social ethics.

TRANSFORMATION TIMES; new age journal. see *NEW AGE PUBLICATIONS*

260 144   RM   ISSN 0255-0539
TRANSILVANIA. 1868. 3/yr. $40 in Europe; elsewhere $50 (effective 1995). Casa de Presa si Editura Cultura Nationala, Str. Dr. Ion Ratiu nr.2, 2400 Sibiu, Rumania. TEL 40-24-69413377. Ed. Ion Mircea. adv. contact: Ion Metiu. bk.rev.; circ. 3,000 (controlled). **Document type:** academic/scholarly publication.
Description: Presents issues on themes of the theology and philosophy of culture. Interested in humanism.

283   UK   ISSN 0967-926X
TRANSMISSION (LONDON). 1992. q. United Society for the Propagation of the Gospel, Partnership House, 157 Waterloo Rd., London SE1 8XA, England. TEL 0171-928-8681. FAX 0171-928-2371. **Document type:** bulletin.

200   UK
TREASURY. 1976. m. £9.36. Calvinistic Methodist Book Agency, St. David's Rd., Caernarfon, Gwynedd LL55 1ER, Wales. TEL 01286-2018. FAX 01286-77823. adv.; bk.rev.
Description: Contains news from various churches.

200   US
TREE OF LIFE.* 1983. bi-m. $12. Tree of Life, 363 Oakland Ave., S.E., Atlanta, GA 30312-2232. TEL 404-624-9928. Ed. Rebecca Myers. circ. 700.

200   GW
TRIERER FORUM. 1968. q. DM.10. Bischoefliches Generalvikariat Trier, Hinter dem Dom 6, 54290 Trier, Germany. TEL 0651-7105-469. FAX 0651-7105511. circ. 4,800. (back issues avail.) **Document type:** newsletter.

230   GW   ISSN 0041-2945
BR4
TRIERER THEOLOGISCHE ZEITSCHRIFT. 1947. q. DM.64.80. (Theologische Fakultaet Trier) Paulinus-Verlag, Fleischstr. 62-65, 54292 Trier, Germany. TEL 0651-4604162. (Co-sponsor: Katholisch-Theologischer Fachbereich der Universitaet Mainz) bk.rev.; index; circ. 850 (paid). **Indexed:** Canon Law Abstr., New Test.Abstr., Old Test.Abstr. **Document type:** academic/scholarly publication.
—BLDSC (9050.610300); UMI.

220   UK   ISSN 0049-4712
TRINITARIAN BIBLE SOCIETY. QUARTERLY RECORD. 1859. q. £5($10) Trinitarian Bible Society, Tyndale House, Dorset Rd., London SW19 3NN, England. TEL 0181-543-7857. FAX 0181-543-6370. bk.rev. **Document type:** bulletin.
Incorporates: Trinitarian Bible Society. Annual Report.
Description: Reports on Scripture publication and distribution; includes articles on Bible translation and textual questions.

280   US   ISSN 0360-3032
BR1
TRINITY JOURNAL. 1971-1978; N.S. 1980. s-a. $10 to individuals (foreign $12); students $9. Trinity Evangelical Divinity School, 2065 Half Day Rd., Deerfield, IL 60015. TEL 708-945-8800. Ed. Douglas J. Moo. bk.rev. circ. 1,400. (back issues avail.) **Indexed:** Bk.Rev.Ind., Bk.Rev.Mo., Bull.Signal., Chr.Per.Ind., Curr.Bk.Rev.Cit., G.Soc.Sci.& Rel.Per.Lit., Int.Z.Bibelwiss., New Test.Abstr., Old Test.Abstr., Rel.& Theol.Abstr. (1980-), Rel.Ind.One. **Document type:** academic/scholarly publication.
—BLDSC (9050.662400); UMI.
Formerly: Trinity Studies (ISSN 0360-2915)

266   US
TRINITY MISSIONS. 1928. w. $5. Missionary Servants of the Most Holy Trinity, Box 7130, Silver Spring, MD 20907-7130. TEL 301-434-6761. Ed. Fr. Joseph, S.T. circ. 300,000.
Description: Portrays life and work of the missionaries and residents of regions served by Trinity Missionaries.

200   AT   ISSN 0813-796X
TROWEL AND SWORD. 1954. m. Aus.$30 (foreign Aus.$35.50). Reformed Churches Publishing House, 55 Maud Street, P.O. Box 6600, Blacktown, N.S.W. 2148, Australia. TEL 61-2-6714770. FAX 61-2-6212362. (Subscr. to: Trowel and Sword, POB 47, Geelong 3220, Australia) Ed. J. Westendorp. adv.; bk.rev. circ. 2,500.

200   GW
TUDUV-STUDIE. REIHE RELIGIONSWISSENSCHAFTEN. 1975. irreg. price varies. Tuduv Verlagsgesellschaft mbH, Gabelsbergerstr. 15, 8000 Munich 2, Germany.

207   UK   ISSN 0082-7118
TYNDALE BULLETIN. 1956. s-a. £5.95. Tyndale House, 36 Selwyn Gardens, Cambridge CB3 9BA, England. FAX 01223-566608. Ed. B.W. Winter. circ. 1,100. (back issues avail.) **Indexed:** New Test.Abstr., Old Test.Abstr., Rel.& Theol.Abstr. (1968-), Rel.Ind.One. **Document type:** bulletin.
—BLDSC (9077.455000). CCC.

UEBERBLICK; Zeitschrift fuer oekumenische Begegnung und internationale Zusammenarbeit. see *POLITICAL SCIENCE — International Relations*

200   HU   ISSN 0133-1205
UJ EMBER. 1945. w. $97. Kossuth Lajos u. 1, 1053 Budapest, Hungary. TEL 117-3933. FAX 117-3471. Ed. Laszlo Lukacs. circ. 100,000.

ULTIMATE REALITY AND MEANING; interdisciplinary studies in the philosophy of understanding. see *PHILOSOPHY*

266   SA   ISSN 0041-6274
UMAFRIKA; the Zulu weekly. (Text in Zulu) 1911. w. R.60. Mariannhill Mission Institute, The Monastery, P.O. Box 11002, Mariannhill 3601, South Africa. TEL 031-7002720. FAX 031-7003707. Ed. Cyril Madlada. adv.; bk.rev.; charts; illus. circ. 80,000. (also avail. in microfilm from PSL)
Description: Aims to offer a Christian-based perspective on contemporary society. Functions as an instrument of communication leading to reconciliation mainly among the Zulu-speaking population of South Africa.

200   GW   ISSN 0041-6444
UNAUSFORSCHLICHER REICHTUM; Zweimonatsschrift fuer Gott und sein Wort. 1932. bi-m. DM.15($8) (Freunde Konkordanter Wortvekuendigung e.V. Pforzheim) Konkordanter Verlag Pforzheim, Leipziger Str. 11, 75217 Birkenfeld, Germany. TEL 07231-485620. FAX 07231-485529. Eds. Herman H. Rocke, Heinz Hoffmann. adv.; bk.rev.; index, cum.index: 1932-1993. circ. 1,200. **Document type:** bulletin.

200   FR   ISSN 0396-2393
UNION DES SUPERIEURES MAJEURS DE FRANCE. ANNUAIRE. 1975. a. Union des Superieures Majeures des Instituts Religieux de France, 10 rue Jean-Bart, 75006 Paris, France.

207.11 371.8   US   ISSN 0041-7025
UNION SEMINARY QUARTERLY REVIEW. 1939. 4/yr. $21 to individuals; institutions $40. Union Theological Seminary, 3041 Broadway, New York, NY 10027. TEL 212-280-1361. FAX 212-280-1416. Ed.Bd. adv.; bk.rev.; bibl.; index. circ. 1,500. (also avail. in microfilm from UMI) **Indexed:** CERDIC, New Test.Abstr., Old Test.Abstr., Rel.& Theol.Abstr. (1969-), Rel.Ind.One, Rel.Per.

200   GW   ISSN 0932-0180
UNITARISCHE BLAETTER. 1950. bi-m. DM.65 (foreign DM.69.50). (Religionsgemeinschaft Deutsche Unitarier e.V.) Verlag Deutsche Unitarier, Birkenstr. 4, 88214 Ravensburg, Germany. TEL 0751-62596. FAX 0751-67201. Ed. Gunde Hartmann; Pub. Micha Ramm. adv.; bk.rev.; illus.; index. circ. 2,000. **Document type:** bulletin.
Formerly: Glaube und Tat (ISSN 0017-1123)

268   FR   ISSN 1248-9646
UNITE DES CHRETIENS; revue de formation et d'information oecumenique. 1971. q. 110 F. (foreign 125 F.). Secretariat National pour l'Unite des Chretiens, 80 rue de l'Abbe Carton, 75014 Paris, France. TEL 1-45-42-00-39. FAX 1-45-42-03-07. Ed. Guy Lourmande. circ. 5,000. (back issues avail.) **Indexed:** CERDIC.

220   UK   ISSN 0041-719X
BV2370
UNITED BIBLE SOCIETIES. BULLETIN. 1950. 2/yr. $10. United Bible Societies (Reading), Reading Bridge House, 7th Fl., Reading RG1 8PJ, England. TEL 01734-500200. FAX 01734-500857. circ. 3,000. (reprint service avail. from UMI) **Document type:** bulletin.
—UMI.

200   US   ISSN 0270-9287
BX8201
UNITED METHODIST BOARD OF HIGHER EDUCATION AND MINISTRY. QUARTERLY REVIEW; a scholarly journal for reflection on ministry. 1932. q. $16. (United Methodist Board of Higher Education and Ministry) United Methodist Publishing House, 201 Eighth Ave. S., Box 801, Nashville, TN 37202. TEL 615-749-6732. Ed. Sharon Hels. adv.; bk.rev.; index. **Indexed:** CERDIC, G.Soc.Sci.& Rel.Per.Lit., Hum.Ind., Old Test.Abstr., Rel.& Theol.Abstr., Rel.Ind.One, Rel.Per. **Document type:** academic/scholarly publication.
—BLDSC (7203.503100); UMI.
   Supersedes (in 1980): Religion in Life (ISSN 0034-3986)

266   UK
UNITED SOCIETY FOR THE PROPAGATION OF THE GOSPEL. YEARBOOK. 1704. a. United Society for the Propagation of the Gospel, Partnership House, 157 Waterloo Rd., London SE1 8XA, England. TEL 0171-928-8681. FAX 0171-928-2371. **Document type:** corporate report.
   Formerly: United Society for the Propagation of the Gospel. Annual Report - Review (ISSN 0144-9508)

200   SP   ISSN 0078-8759
UNIVERSIDAD DE NAVARRA. FACULTAD DE DERECHO CANONICO. MANUALES: DERECHO CANONICO. 1973. irreg., no.7, 1988. price varies. Ediciones Universidad de Navarra, S.A., Apdo. 396, 31080 Pamplona, Spain. TEL 94 825 6850.

200   CK
UNIVERSIDAD JAVERIANA. FACULTAD DE TEOLOGIA. COLECCION PROFESORES. irreg. price varies. Pontificia Universidad Javeriana, Facultad de Teologia, Apdo. Aereo 54-953, Bogota, 2 D.E., Colombia. FAX 571-2882335. Ed. German Neira. **Document type:** monographic series.

200 100   SP
UNIVERSIDAD PONTIFICIA COMILLAS DE MADRID. PUBLICACIONES. SERIE 1: ESTUDIOS. Theology section (ISSN 0211-2752); Philosophy section (ISSN 0211-2779); Canon section (ISSN 0211-2760) 1975. irreg., no.32, 1984. Universidad Pontificia Comillas de Madrid, Comision de Publicaciones, E-28049 Madrid, Spain. Ed. Antonio Vargas-Machuca.

230   AU   ISSN 0579-7780
UNIVERSITAET INNSBRUCK. THEOLOGISCHE FAKULTAET. STUDIEN UND ARBEITEN. (Subseries of: Universitaet Innsbruck. Veroeffentlichungen) 1968. irreg., vol.10, 1974. price varies. Oesterreichische Kommissionsbuchhandlung, Maximilianstrasse 17, A-6020 Innsbruck, Austria. Ed. Hans Bernhard Meyer.

UNIVERSITE CATHOLIQUE DE LOUVAIN. INSTITUT ORIENTALISTE. PUBLICATIONS. see HISTORY — History Of Asia

UNIVERSITE SAINT-JOSEPH. FACULTE DES LETTRES ET DES SCIENCES HUMAINES. RECHERCHES. SERIE B: ORIENT CHRETIEN. see ORIENTAL STUDIES

UNIVERSITY OF DAYTON REVIEW. see LITERARY AND POLITICAL REVIEWS

200 100   US
UNIVERSITY OF NOTRE DAME. STUDIES IN THE PHILOSOPHY OF RELIGION. 1979. irreg., no.7. price varies. University of Notre Dame Press, Notre Dame, IN 46556. TEL 219-631-6346. FAX 219-631-8148. (Orders to: 11030 S. Langley Ave., Chicago, IL 60628. TEL 800-621-2736. FAX 800-621-8476; Overseas orders to: Eurospan University Press Group, Order Dept., 3 Henrietta St., London WC2E 8LU, England) Ed. Frederick Crosson. **Document type:** academic/scholarly publication.

UNIVERSITY OF ST. THOMAS MAGAZINE. see COLLEGE AND ALUMNI

220   US   ISSN 0042-0476
UNSEARCHABLE RICHES. 1909. bi-m. $1. Concordant Publishing Concern, 15570 Knochaven Rd., Santa Clarita, CA 91350. TEL 805-252-2112. Ed. Dean H. Hough. index, cum.index every 10 yrs. circ. 2,000. **Document type:** academic/scholarly publication.
   Description: Directed to students of the scriptures.

200   GW   ISSN 0930-1313
UNTERWEGS (MUNICH). 1983. q. membership. Deutscher Katecheten Verein e.V., Preysingstr. 83c, 81667 Munich, Germany. TEL 089-48092242. FAX 089-48092237. Ed. Haerst Leopold. bk.rev. circ. 11,000. **Document type:** newsletter.

200   RW   ISSN 1019-8768
URUNANA. 1967. 3/yr. $30. Grand Seminaire de Nyakibanda, B.P. 85, Butare, Rwanda. TEL 30-792. Ed. Evariste Nambaje. bk.rev. circ. 800. **Document type:** bulletin.
   Description: Studies theology and philosophy; covers activities of the Seminary and Church.

V.C.F. NEWSLETTER. (Veterinary Christian Fellowship) see VETERINARY SCIENCE

V R B - INFORMATIE. (Vereniging van Religieus - Wetenschappelijke Bibliothecarissen) see LIBRARY AND INFORMATION SCIENCES

200   SW   ISSN 0042-2010
VAAR FANA. 1905. 30/yr. SEK 175 (effective 1990). Svenska Fraelsningsarmen, Ekonomiavdelingen, Kungsgatan 17, S-502 31 Boraas, Sweden. TEL 33-132770. FAX 33-132791. illus.
   Formerly (until vol.41, 1945): Svenska Fraelsningsarmens Tidning.

200   MG
VAOVAO F J K M. 10/yr.(Malagasy ed.); 5/yr.(French-English ed.). B.P. 623, 101 Antananarivo, Madagascar. TEL 30253. Ed. Edmond Razafimahefa.

200   NE   ISSN 0042-3262
VELUWS KERKBLAD. 1942. w. fl.48. Gereformeerde Kerken in Classis Harderwijk en Nijkerk, Redactie Raad, Hazeveld 21, 3862 XA Nijkerk, Netherlands. FAX 31-3420-13141. Ed. E.P. van der Veen. adv.; bk.rev. circ. 6,500.

VENTURE INWARD. see NEW AGE PUBLICATIONS

200 930   IT   ISSN 0391-8564
VERBA SENIORUM; collana di testi e studi patristici. irreg., latest no.12. price varies. Edizioni Studium, Via Cassiodoro 14, 00193 Rome, Italy. **Document type:** monographic series.

266   DK   ISSN 0109-0062
VERDEN RUNDT. 1982. bi-m. DKK 65. Laegmandsbevaegelsen for Ydre Mission, LYM-Landsformanden, Saxovej 11, 5210 Odense NV, Denmark. Ed. Simon Thorup. bk.rev.; illus.
   Formerly: Maend og Mission.

200   GW
VEREIN FUER RHEINISCHE KIRCHENGESCHICHTE. SCHRIFTENREIHE. 1953. irreg., no.115, 1994. Rheinland Verlag GmbH, Abtei Brauweiler, Postfach 2140, 50250 Pulheim, Germany. TEL 02234-8051. FAX 02234-82503. (Dist. by: Dr. Rudolf Habelt GmbH, Am Buchenhang 1, 53115 Bonn, Germany. TEL 0228-232016. FAX 0228-232017) **Document type:** monographic series.

266   GW   ISSN 0342-2410
BR4
VERKUENDIGUNG UND FORSCHUNG. Supplement to: Evangelische Theologie. 2/yr. DM.45. Guetersloher Verlagshaus Chr. Kaiser, Carl-Bertelsmann-Str. 270, 33311 Guetersloh, Germany. TEL 05241-7405-0. FAX 05241-740548. Ed. Annegrete Sauter. adv.: B&W page DM.900; trim 108 x 192. circ. 1,500. (reprint service avail. from UMI) **Indexed:** CERDIC, New Test.Abstr. **Document type:** academic/scholarly publication.
—BLDSC (9170.613000). **CCC.**

220   SZ
VESTIGIA BIBLIAE. 1979. a. 118 SFr. (Deutsche Bibelarchiv) Verlag Peter Lang AG, Jupiterstr. 15, CH-3000 Bern 15, Switzerland. TEL 031-9411122. FAX 031-9411131. adv.; bk.rev. **Document type:** academic/scholarly publication.

VETERA CHRISTIANORUM. see ARCHAEOLOGY

220   NE   ISSN 0042-4935
BS410
VETUS TESTAMENTUM. (Supplement avail. (ISSN 0083-5889)) (Text in English, French or German) 1951. 4/yr. fl.125($81) to individuals; institutions fl.200($129) (effective 1996). (International Organization for the Study of the Old Testament) E.J. Brill, P.O. Box 9000, 2300 PA Leiden, Netherlands. TEL 31-71-5353500. FAX 31-71-5317532. TELEX 39296 BRILL NL. E-mail: ejborders@ejbrill.com. (In N. America: E.J. Brill, 24 Hudson St., Kinderhook, NY 12106. TEL 800-962-4406. FAX 518-758-1959) Ed. J.A. Emerton. bk.rev.; bibl. (also avail. in microform from SWZ; back issues avail.; reprint service avail. from SWZ) **Indexed:** Arts & Hum.Cit.Ind., Bibl.Ling., Curr.Cont., New Test.Abstr., Old Test.Abstr., Rel.& Theol.Abstr. (1990-), Rel.Ind.One, Rel.Per. **Document type:** academic/scholarly publication.
—BLDSC (9231.470000); Faxon; Genuine Article; SWETS; UnCover. **CCC.**
   Description: Covers the whole range of Old Testament study, including history, literature, religion and theology, language, and relevant contributions from archaeology and the study of the ancient Near East.
Refereed Serial

221   NE   ISSN 0083-5889
VETUS TESTAMENTUM. SUPPLEMENTS. Key Title: Supplements to Vetus Testamentum. (Certain vols. constitute: Proceedings of the Triennial Congress) 1953. irreg., vol.56, 1994. price varies. (International Organization for the Study of the Old Testament) E.J. Brill, P.O. Box 9000, 2300 PA Leiden, Netherlands. TEL 31-71-5353500. FAX 31-71-5317532. TELEX 39296 BRILL NL. (In N. America: E.J. Brill, 24 Hudson St., Kinderhook, NY 12106. TEL 800-962-4406. FAX 518-758-1959) (back issues avail.) **Document type:** monographic series, proceedings.
—BLDSC (9231.475000).
   Description: Publishes scholarly studies on topics relating to the Old Testament, the history and culture of the ancient Near East.
Refereed Serial

200   BL   ISSN 0507-7184
VIDA PASTORAL. 1960. bi-m. free. (Pia Sociedade de Sao Paulo) Edicoes Paulinas, R. Dr. Pinto Ferraz, 183, 04117 Sao Paulo, SP, Brazil. Ed. Angelo Songego. adv.; bk.rev.; bibl.; illus. circ. 25,000.
   Former titles: Pastoral Popular; Vida Pastoral (ISSN 0042-5265)

230   BE   ISSN 0771-6842
VIE CONSACREE. 1925. bi-m. 600 BEF. Centre de Documentation et de Recherche Religieuses, Rue de Bruxelles 61, B-5000 Namur, Belgium. (Dist. by: N.V. Brepols, Steenweg op Tielen 68, 2300 Turnhout, Belgium. TEL 32-14-415463. FAX 32-14-428919; In France: Brepols-Paris, 23 rue des Grands Augustins, 75006 Paris, France. TEL (1)44412035. FAX (1)43262377) bk.rev.; bibl.; index. circ. 5,000. **Indexed:** Canon Law Abstr., CERDIC. **Document type:** monographic series.
   Formerly (until 1965): Revue des Communautes Religieuses.

VIEWS ON EDUCATION - NEWS OF EPISCOPAL COLLEGES. see EDUCATION — Higher Education

RELIGIONS AND THEOLOGY

209 NE ISSN 0042-6032
BR66
VIGILIAE CHRISTIANAE; a review of early Christian life and language. (Supplement avail. (ISSN 0920-623X)) (Text in various languages) 1947. 4/yr. fl.130($84) to individuals; institutions fl.195($126) (effective 1996). E.J. Brill, P.O. Box 9000, 2300 PA Leiden, Netherlands. TEL 31-71-5353500. FAX 31-71-5317532. TELEX 39296 BRILL NL. E-mail: ejborders@ejbrill.com. (In N. America: E.J. Brill, 24 Hudson St., Kinderhook, NY 12106. TEL 800-962-4406. FAX 518-758-1959) Ed. J. den Boeft. adv.; bk.rev.; index. (also avail. in microform from RPI,SWZ; reprint service avail. from SWZ) **Indexed:** Arts & Hum.Cit.Ind., Bibl.Ling., Curr.Cont., M.L.A., New Test.Abstr., Rel.& Theol.Abstr. (1968-), Rel.Ind.One, Rel.Per. **Document type:** academic/scholarly publication.
—BLDSC (9236.080000); Faxon; Genuine Article; SWETS; UnCover. **CCC**.
Description: Publishes articles and short notes of a cultural, historical, linguistic or philological nature on early Christian literature written after the New Testament, as well as on Christian epigraphy and archaeology.
Refereed Serial

209 NE ISSN 0920-623X
VIGILIAE CHRISTIANAE. SUPPLEMENT. (Text in English, French, German) 1987. irreg., vol.30, 1995. price varies. E.J. Brill, P.O. Box 9000, 2300 PA Leiden, Netherlands. TEL 31-71-5353500. FAX 31-71-5317532. TELEX 39296 BRILL NL. (In N. America: E.J. Brill, 24 Hudson St., Kinderhook, NY 12106. TEL 800-962-4406. FAX 518-758-1959) (back issues avail.) **Document type:** monographic series.
—BLDSC (9236.081000).
Description: Scholarly translations, commentary and critical studies of texts and issues relating to early Christianity.
Refereed Serial

VIRTUE. see *WOMEN'S INTERESTS*

200 NE ISSN 0169-5606
BL1
VISIBLE RELIGION; annual for religious iconography. (Text in English, French and German) 1982. irreg., vol.7, 1990. price varies. (Rijksuniversiteit te Groningen, Institute for Religious Iconography) E.J. Brill, P.O. Box 9000, 2300 PA Leiden, Netherlands. TEL 31-71-5353500. FAX 31-71-5317532. TELEX 39296 BRILL NL. (In N. America: E.J. Brill, 24 Hudson St., Kinderhook, NY 12106. TEL 800-962-4406. FAX 518-758-1959) Ed. H.G. Kippenberg. illus. (back issues avail.) **Document type:** academic/scholarly publication.
—**CCC**.
Refereed Serial

200 SA
VISION. (Text in English) 1983. q. R.22. Apostolic Faith Mission of South Africa, P.O. Box 89735, Lyndhurst 2106, South Africa. TEL 27-11-786-8550. FAX 27-11-887-1182. Ed. Edgar J. Gschwend. abstr. circ. 10,000. (back issues avail.)
Former titles (until Feb. 1992): Faith and Action; (until Jan. 1992): A F M Koinonia.

200 US
VISION (COSTA MESA). irreg. free. Full Gospel Business Men's Fellowship International, 3150 Bear St., Box 5050, Costa Mesa, CA 92626. TEL 714-754-1400. FAX 714-557-9916.
Description: Covers the work of the fellowship around the world.

200 US ISSN 0882-6609
VISION (PASADENA). 1953. m. $15 to individuals; institutions $50. Christian Educators Association, Box 50025, Pasadena, CA 91115. TEL 818-798-1124. Ed. Forrest Turpen. adv. circ. 5,000.
Description: Articles of interest to Christians serving in public and private schools.

200 US
VISTA (INDIANAPOLIS). 1907. w. $8. Wesleyan Publishing House, Box 50434, Indianapolis, IN 46250-0434. TEL 800-493-7539. FAX 317-577-4397. Ed. Kelly Trennpohl. circ. 80,000.

209 IT ISSN 0042-7330
VITA CONSACRATA; rivista mensile di studio e informazione per Istituti Religiosi e Secolari. 1964. m. L.35000 (Europe L.40000; America L.85000). Editrice Ancora Milano, Via G.B. Niccolini 8, 20154 Milan, Italy. TEL 02-33608941.
FAX 02-33608944. Dir. Giuliano Bertoldi. adv.; bk.rev.; bibl.; index. circ. 1,200. **Indexed:** Canon Law Abstr.
Formerly: Vita Religiosa.

200 CN ISSN 0507-1690
VITA EVANGELICA. French edition (ISSN 0315-5048) (Text in English) 1965. irreg., no.12, 1984. price varies. Canadian Religious Conference, 324 Laurier Ave. E., Ottawa, ON K1N 6P6, Canada. TEL 613-236-0824. FAX 613-236-0825. circ. 6,000 (3,500 English edition; 3,500 French edition). **Document type:** academic/scholarly publication.

200 IT ISSN 0042-7284
LA VITA IN CRISTO E NELLA CHIESA; mensile per l'animazione liturgica. 1951. m. L.33000 (foreign L.50000) (effective 1996). Congregazione Suore Pie Discepole del Divin Maestro, Via Portuense 739, 00148 Rome, Italy. TEL 39-6-6530213. FAX 39-6-6531973. Dir. G. Oberto. adv.; bk.rev.; illus.; index. circ. 17,000.
Description: Religious forum devoted to Christians. Includes articles on the church, liturgical art, ecumenism, prayer and observance of religious holidays in modern day context.

200 IT
VITA PASTORALE. 1912. m. (11/yr.) L.39000 (foreign L.45000) (effective 1995). Periodici San Paolo S.r.l., Via Liberazione 4, 12051 Alba (CN), Italy. TEL 39-173-296292. FAX 39-173-296431. Ed. Stefano Andreatta. adv.; B&W page L.2200000, color page L.5200000. circ. 36,000.

200 CI ISSN 0042-7659
VJESNIK NADBISKUPIJE SPLITSKO-MAKARSKE. (Text in Croatian) 1948. bi-m. Nadbiskupija Splitsko-Makarska, Zrinjsko-Frankopanska 14, 58001 Split, Croatia. Ed. Marijan Ivan Caglj. bk.rev. circ. 400.
Supersedes: Vjesnik Biskupije Splitske i Makarske.

200 GT
VOCES DEL TIEMPO; revista de religion y sociedad. 1992. q. Q.30 (Latin America $10; elsewhere $15). Sociedad para el Estudio de la Religion en Guatemala, 11 Calle, 9-44, 2o Nivel, Zona 1, Guatemala, Guatemala. TEL 29440.

200 US ISSN 0042-8159
VOICE OF LIBERTY. 1960. s-a. donation. Voice of Liberty Association, 692 Sunnybrook Dr., Decatur, GA 30033. TEL 404-633-3634. Ed. Martha O. Andrews. bk.rev.; charts; illus. circ. 3,500. (processed) **Indexed:** CERDIC. **Document type:** newsletter.

VOICE OF REASON. see *POLITICAL SCIENCE — Civil Rights*

200 US
VOICE OF THE MARTYRS. (Editions in several languages) 1967. m. free. Voice of the Martyrs, Inc., Box 443, Bartlesville, OK 74005-0443. TEL 918-337-8015. FAX 918-337-9287. Ed. Tom White. adv.: Steve/Cleary. bk.rev. circ. 1,000,000. **Document type:** newsletter.
Description: News on atrocities against and persecution of Christians and their families in communist countries, former couuminst nations and Muslim areas. Includes language-specific translations of the English newsletter.

266 FR ISSN 0293-9932
VOIX D'AFRIQUE (PARIS). (Text in French, German) 1923. 5/yr. 30. Peres Blancs Missionnaires d'Afrique, 49 rue de Romainville, 75019 Paris, France. TEL 42-08-92-46. circ. 9,500.
Description: Tries to give objective information about the country and news of White Fathers missionaries doing work in Africa.

200 GW ISSN 0083-6923
VORREFORMATIONSGESCHICHTLICHE FORSCHUNGEN. 1902. irreg. price varies. Aschendorffsche Verlagsbuchhandlung, Soesterstr. 13, 48155 Muenster, Germany. TEL 0251-690-0. FAX 0251-690143. Ed. Klaus Ganzer. **Document type:** monographic series.

200 UK ISSN 0263-6786
VOX EVANGELICA. 1959. a. £6.50 (foreign £6.75). (London Bible College) The Paternoster Press, P.O. Box 300, Kingstown Broadway, Carlisle, Cumbria CA3 0QS, England. TEL 0228-512512.
FAX 0228-514949. (Dist. in U.S. & Canada by: The Paternoster Press, Box 11127, Birmingham, AL 35201-1127) Ed. Antony Billington. circ. 600. (tabloid format; back issues avail.) **Indexed:** CERDIC, Old Test.Abstr., Rel.& Theol.Abstr. (1968-). **Document type:** academic/scholarly publication.
—**CCC**.

200 NE ISSN 0042-9155
VRIEND VAN OUD EN JONG; Christelijk weekblad. 1880. fortn. fl.54.25. Uitgeverij J.J. Groen en Zoon, Rooseveltstraat 12, Postbus 11031, 2301 EA Leiden, Netherlands. TEL 31-71-311661. FAX 31-71-323340. Ed. Mrs. H.W. Dekker; Pub. D.L. Aangeenbrug. adv.

200 320 NE ISSN 0928-8066
VRIJE UNIVERSITEIT AMSTERDAM. CENTER FOR THE STUDY OF RELIGION AND POLITICS. STUDIES. Key Title: CentREPOL-VU Studies. (Text in English) 1992. irreg., vol.2, 1993. price varies. V U Boekhandel-Uitgeverij B.V., De Boelelaan 1105, 1081 HV Amsterdam, Netherlands. TEL 31-20-6444355. FAX 31-20-6462719. **Document type:** monographic series.

VROUW EN WOORD; informatie en uitwisseling rond vrouw, geloot en samenleving. see *WOMEN'S INTERESTS*

200 SZ
W C C FOCUS. (Text in English) s-a. World Council of Churches, 150 route de Ferney, P.O. Box 2100, CH-1211 Geneva 2, Switzerland. TEL 022-7916111. FAX 022-7981346. TELEX 415730-OIK-CH. **Document type:** newsletter.

200 SZ
W C C HORIZONS. (Text in English, German, Spanish) irreg. World Council of Churches, 150 route de Ferney, P.O. Box 2100, CH-1211 Geneva 2, Switzerland. TEL 022-7916111.
FAX 022-7981346. TELEX 415730-OIK-CH. **Document type:** newsletter.

200 SZ
W C C PUBLICATIONS. s-a. World Council of Churches, 150 route de Ferney, P.O. Box 2100, CH-1211 Geneva 2, Switzerland. TEL 022-7916178. FAX 022-7981346. **Document type:** newsletter.

282 305.4 CN
W I C C NEWSLETTER. q. Women's Inter-Church Council of Canada, 815 Danforth Ave., Ste. 402, Toronto, ON M4J 1L2, Canada. TEL 416-462-2528. FAX 416-462-3915. bk.rev. circ. 11,000. **Document type:** newsletter.

266 NQ
WABUL. m? Comite Evangelico por Ayuda al Desarrollo, Centro de Historio y Cultura, Apdo. 3091, Puerto Cabezas, Nicaragua. Ed.Bd. circ. 1,500.

WALK AWAY; the newsletter for ex-fundamentalists. see *SOCIOLOGY*

WARRIOR. see *CHILDREN AND YOUTH — For*

200 GW ISSN 0341-7158
WAS UND WIE?; Arbeitshilfen zur religoesen Erzeihen der 3 bis 7 jahrigen. 1972. q. DM.49.80. Guetersloher Verlagshaus Chr. Kaiser, Carl-Bertelsmann-Str. 270, 33311 Guetersloh, Germany. TEL 05241-7405-0.
FAX 05241-740548. Ed. Burkhard Straeck. adv.: B&W page DM.950; trim 144 x 205. circ. 6,500. **Document type:** academic/scholarly publication.

200 UK ISSN 0043-1575
BX2350.A1
WAY; a quarterly review of Christian spirituality. 1961. q. £14.50($30) to individuals; institutions £17.50($34). (Society of Jesus) Way Publications, Heythrop College, Kensington Sq., London W8 5HQ, England. TEL 0171-499-7002.
FAX 0171-495-1673. Ed. Philip Endean. bk.rev. circ. 4,000. (also avail. in microform from UMI; back issues avail.) **Indexed:** Cath.Ind., CERDIC, New Test.Abstr., Old Test.Abstr. **Document type:** academic/scholarly publication.
—BLDSC (9280.780000); UMI.

RELIGIONS AND THEOLOGY

200   UK   ISSN 0307-5532
THE WAY SUPPLEMENT. 1965. 3/yr. £14.50($30) to individuals; institutions £17.50($34). Way Publications, Heythrop College, Kensington Sq., London W8 5HQ, England. TEL 0171-499-7002. FAX 0171-495-1673. Ed. Philip Endean. circ. 2,500. (back issues avail.) **Document type:** academic/scholarly publication.

200   US   ISSN 0890-6491
WEAVINGS; a journal of the Christian spiritual life. 1986. bi-m. $24. Upper Room, 1908 Grand Ave., Box 189, Nashville, TN 37202-0189. TEL 615-340-7254. FAX 615-340-7006. Ed. John S. Mogabgab. bk.rev. circ. 42,000.

200 028.5   US
WEE LAMBS. 1964. w. $6.50. Rod and Staff Publishers, Inc., State Rte. 172, Crockett, KY 41413. TEL 606-522-4348. Ed. Paul Landis. circ. 3,890.
   Description: For pre-school children and young readers.

268   US
WEEKLY BIBLE READER. 1965. w. $10.99 q. Standard Publishing, 8121 Hamilton Ave., Cincinnati, OH 45231. TEL 513-931-4050. FAX 513-931-0904. Ed. Ruth Davis. circ. 104,000.

261   GW
WEG UND ZIEL. 1948. w. DM.52. (Johannische Kirche) Verlag Weg und Ziel, Teutonenstr. 14, 14129 Berlin, Germany. TEL 030-8031075. FAX 030-8034479. Eds. Rainer Gerhardt, Hansjuergen Rohr. adv.; bk.rev. circ. 2,000. (back issues avail.) **Document type:** bulletin.
   Description: Information about the Johannische Church and related regional news.

200   GW
WEGE UND VISIONEN. 1985. bi-m. DM.30. (Centre of the World Religions e.V.) Sandila Import-Export Handels GmbH, Saegestr. 37, 79737 Herrischried, Germany. TEL 07764-1026. FAX 07764-6660. adv.; bk.rev. circ. 31,000. (back issues avail.) **Document type:** academic/scholarly publication.
   Former titles: Vision (ISSN 0941-8784); (until 1992): Universale Religion (ISSN 0179-0617)
   Description: Comparative study of religions.

200   GW   ISSN 0043-2040
WEGE ZUM MENSCHEN; Monatsschrift fuer Seelsorge und Beratung, heilendes und soziales Handeln. 1949. 8/yr. DM.110. Vandenhoeck und Ruprecht, Robert-Bosch-Breite 6, 37079 Goettingen, Germany. TEL 0551-6959-26. FAX 0551-695917. (Subscr. to: 37070 Goettingen, Germany) adv.; index. circ. 3,100. **Indexed:** CERDIC. **Document type:** academic/scholarly publication.
   —CCC.

200   GW
WEGGEFAEHRTE. 1963. s-a. DM.5. Bund Deutsch - Unitarischer Jugendliche, Hauptstr. 78, 52066 Aachen, Germany. Eds. Robert Roeber, Karsten Urban. circ. 100.

200 028.5   GW
WEITE WELT; illustrierte Kinderzeitschrift ab 10 Jahre. 1921. m. DM.26.40. Steyler Missionare e.V., Bahnhofstr. 9, 41334 Nettetal, Germany. TEL 02157-1202-0. FAX 02157-1202-60. Ed. Bernd Aretz. **Document type:** consumer publication.

200   UK
WELSH CHURCHMAN. 1960. m. £4. Church in Wales Publications, Woodland Place, Penarth, South Glam. CF6 2EX, Wales. Eds. Rev. Canon M.M. Davies, C. Davies. adv.; bk.rev. circ. 30,000.

266   GW
WELTWEITEN CHRISTLICHEN BEHINDERTENDIAKONTE. BERICHTE. 1908. bi-m. free. Christoffel-Blindenmission e.V., Nibelungenstr. 124, 64625 Bensheim, Germany. TEL 06251-131-0. FAX 06251-131122. (U.S. subscr. to: Christian Blind Mission International Inc., 450 E. Park Ave., Greenville, SC 29601. TEL 803-239-0065. FAX 803-239-0069) illus. circ. 500,000. **Document type:** bulletin.
   Former titles: Weltweiten Christlichen Armendiakonte. Bericht (ISSN 0723-1539); (until 1979): Weltweiten Christlichen Behindertenhilfe. Bericht (ISSN 0723-1512); Weltweiten Dienst Christlicher Blindennothilfe. Bericht (ISSN 0723-1490); Evangelische Missionsarbeit an Blinden und Augenkranken in Asien und Afrika. Bericht (ISSN 0723-1482); Evangelische Missionsarbeit an den Blinden im Asien und Afrika. Bericht (ISSN 0723-1474); Evangelische Missionsarbeit an den Blinden Irans. Bericht (ISSN 0723-1474); Christoffel-Blindenmission. Bericht (ISSN 0009-580X).
   Description: Covers Christian missionary work and medical aid to the blind, the handicapped, and the hungry in Third World countries.

266   NE   ISSN 0165-988X
BV3000
WERELD EN ZENDING; oecumenisch tijdschrift voor missiologie en missionaire praktijk. 1948. 4/yr. fl.52.50. Uitgeverij Kok, Postbus 130, 8260 AC Kampen, Netherlands. (Editorial addr.: Baantjebolwerk 1, 9101 NH Dokkum, Netherlands. TEL 31-5190-98104) (Co-sponsors: Nederlandse Missieraad; Nederlandse Zendingsraad; Verenigde Protestantse Kerk in Belgie; Comite van de Missionerende Instituten, BE) Ed. Rev. Ype Schaaf. adv.; bk.rev.; index. circ. 2,000. **Indexed:** CERDIC.
   Former titles (until 1972): Heerbaan (ISSN 0017-9531); Het Messiewerk.
   Description: Covers Protestant and Roman Catholic mission activities of interest to readers in the Netherlands and the Flemish portion of Belgium.

327 200   BE   ISSN 0779-6633
WERELDBRIEF. 1982. m. 600 BEF. V.Z.W. Wereldwijd, Arthur Goemaerelei 69, 2018 Antwerp, Belgium. Ed. Marc van Laere. circ. 1,000.
   Description: Covers issues relating to church and society.

266 327   BE   ISSN 0779-665X
WERELDWIJD; tijdschrift over evangelizatie en ontwikkeling. 1970. m. (10/yr.) 880 BEF. V.Z.W. Wereldwijd, Arthur Goemaerelei 69, B-2018 Antwerp, Belgium. Ed. Gie Goris. adv. circ. 22,000. **Indexed:** CERDIC.
   Description: Covers issues pertaining to evangelization and development in the Third World.

266   US   ISSN 0739-0440
WESLEYAN WORLD. 1968. m. donation. Wesleyan World Missions, 6060 Castleway West Dr., Box 50434, Box 50434, IN 46250-0434. TEL 317-595-4172. FAX 317-841-1125. Ed. Wayne MacBeth. circ. 36,000 (controlled). **Document type:** newsletter.
   Description: Informs and motivates on behalf of overseas Wesleyan World Missions.

270   NR   ISSN 0083-8187
BL2465
WEST AFRICAN RELIGION. 1963. s-a. £N3($8) per no. University of Nigeria, Department of Religion, Nsukka, Enugu State, Nigeria. Ed. O.U. Kalu. adv.; bk.rev. circ. 1,000. **Indexed:** CERDIC, Rel.Ind.One, Rel.Per. **Document type:** academic/scholarly publication.

230   GW
WESTFALIA SACRA; Quellen und Forschungen zur Kirchengeschichte Westfalens. 1948. irreg. price varies. Aschendorffsche Verlagsbuchhandlung, Soesterstr. 13, 48155 Muenster, Germany. TEL 0251-690-0. FAX 0251-690143. Ed. Alois Schroeer. **Document type:** monographic series.

230   US   ISSN 0043-4388
BR1
WESTMINSTER THEOLOGICAL JOURNAL. 1938. s-a. $20 to individuals (foreign $21); institutions $30 (foreign $31) (effective 1996). Westminster Theological Seminary, Chestnut Hill, Philadelphia, PA 19118. TEL 215-887-5511. FAX 215-887-5404. Ed. Moises Silva. bk.rev.; index, cum.index. circ. 1,200. (also avail. in microform from UMI; back issues avail.) **Indexed:** CERDIC, Chr.Per.Ind., Int.Z.Bibelwiss., New Test.Abstr., Old Test.Abstr., Rel.& Theol.Abstr. (1968-), Rel.Ind.One, Rel.Per. **Document type:** academic/scholarly publication. —BLDSC (9304.800000).
   Description: Advances Christian theological scholarship, with emphasis on biblical studies and Reformed theology.

266   US   ISSN 0889-0781
WHEREVER. 1976. 3/yr. $3 (free to qualified personnel). Evangelical Alliance Mission (TEAM), Box 969, Wheaton, IL 60189. TEL 708-653-5300. FAX 708-653-1826. Ed. Jack Kilgore. bk.rev.; charts; illus. circ. 14,000.

WHITE CRANE NEWSLETTER. see HOMOSEXUALITY

222   GW   ISSN 0512-1604
WISSENSCHAFTLICHE UNTERSUCHUNGEN ZUM NEUEN TESTAMENT. (Text in English and German) 1950. irreg. price varies. Verlag J.C.B. Mohr (Paul Siebeck), Wilhelmstr. 18, 72074 Tuebingen, Germany. TEL 07071-923-0. FAX 07071-51104. TELEX 7262872-MOHR-D. (Subscr. to: Postfach 2040, 72010 Tuebingen, Germany) Eds. Martin Hengel, Otfried Hofius. **Document type:** monographic series.

200 305.4   UK   ISSN 0962-2152
WOMAN ALIVE. 1982. m. £37. Herald House Ltd., 96 Dominion Rd., Worthing, W. Sussex BN14 8JP, England. TEL 01903-821082. FAX 01903-821081. Ed. E. Proctor. circ. 13,000 (paid). **Document type:** consumer publication.
   Formerly: Christian Woman (ISSN 0269-0616)
   Description: Covers Christian life-styles for women. Includes articles on food, leisure, health, and Christian theology.

250   US   ISSN 0043-7379
BV676
WOMAN'S PULPIT. 1922. q. $15 membership. International Association of Women Ministers, c/o 579 Main St., Stroudsburg, PA 18360. (Editorial addr.: 5227 Castor Ave., Philadelphia, PA 19124) Ed. Lavonne Althouse. bk.rev.; illus. circ. 550. **Document type:** newsletter.

WOMEN'S CONCERNS REPORT. see WOMEN'S INTERESTS

200   NE   ISSN 0165-2443
WOORD EN DIENST. 1952. fortn. fl.77.50. Boekencentrum B.V., Postbus 29, 2700 AA Zoetermeer, Netherlands. TEL 31-79-615481. FAX 31-79-615489. Ed. Theo. Klein. adv.; bk.rev.; illus.

WORD & DEED. see MEDICAL SCIENCES — Communicable Diseases

200   US
WORD AND WORK. 1908. m. $4. Word, 2518 Portland Ave., Louisville, KY 40212-1040. Ed. Alex Wilson. circ. 1,180.

200   UK
WORD IN ACTION. 1973. q. free. British and Foreign Bible Society, Stonehill Green, Westlea, Swindon, Wilts. SN5 7DG, England. TEL 01793-513713. FAX 01793-512539. TELEX 44283. Ed. Joy Aldred. charts; illus. circ. 170,000. (tabloid format) **Document type:** newspaper.
   Formerly: Bible Society News (ISSN 0006-0755)

200   US   ISSN 0279-6007
WORD IN SEASON. 1932. q. $5. Augsburg Fortress, Publishers, 426 S. 5th St., Box 1209, Minneapolis, MN 55440. TEL 612-330-3402; 800-328-4648. FAX 612-330-3455. Ed. Beth Ann Gaede. circ. 161,700. (also avail. in Braille)

200   US
WORD OF FAITH. 1968. m. free. Kenneth Hagin Ministries, Box 50126, Tulsa, OK 74150-0126. TEL 918-258-1588. Ed. Jayne Sleeter. circ. 313,000.

RELIGIONS AND THEOLOGY

200 US
WORD OF GOD. 1933. w. $6. Society of St. Paul (Staten Island), Staten Island, NY 10314-6603. TEL 212-761-0047. Ed. Rev. Contardo Omarini. circ. 10,000.
  Description: Explains the Sunday liturgy, the Church in the modern world and many other religious topics.

200 US
WORD OF LIFE QUARTERLY. 1990. q. Word of Life Fellowship, Rte. 9, Schroon Lake, NY 12870. TEL 518-532-7111. FAX 518-532-7421. Ed. Mark Ward, Sr. adv.; B&W page $1895, color page $2390. circ. 40,000 (paid); 50,000 (controlled).

200 AT ISSN 0813-7951
WORD OF SALVATION. 1955. m. Aus.$90. Reformed Churches Publishing House, P.O. Box 6600, Blacktown, N.W.S. 2148, Australia. TEL 61-2-6714770. FAX 61-2-6212362. (Subscr. to: P.O. Box 47, Geelong 3220, Australia) Ed. M.P. Geluk. circ. 100.

200 US
WORD ONE. 1973. 5/yr. free. Claretian Publications, 205 W. Monroe St., Chicago, IL 60606. TEL 312-236-7782. FAX 312-236-7230. Ed. Rev. Mark J. Brummel.

200 US
WORDS OF L I F E. 1984. irreg. membership. Living in Freedom Eternally, Inc., Box 353, New York, NY 10185. TEL 212-265-6044. Ed. Ronald Highley. circ. 2,100. **Document type:** newsletter.
  Description: Focuses on homosexuality in the context of Christianity.

200 AT ISSN 0728-912X
WORKING TOGETHER NATIONALLY. 1977. a. free. Uniting Church in Australia, National Assembly, 222 Pitt St., 5th Fl., Sydney N.S.W. 2000, Australia. TEL 02-287-0900. FAX 02-287-0999. (Subscr. to: P.O. Box E266, St. James, N.S.W. 2000, Australia) Ed. Rev. Gregor Henderson. circ. 5,500.
  Description: Life and work of the Uniting Church in Australia, nationally.

200 US ISSN 0743-2399
BV1430.I6
WORLD CHRISTIAN. 1980. 10/yr. $15. 21550 Oxnard St., Ste. 860, Woodland Hills, CA 91367. TEL 818-797-1907. FAX 818-797-1706. Ed. Verne Becker. adv.; bk.rev.; illus.; index. circ. 22,000. (also avail. in microfilm from UMI; reprint service avail. from UMI) **Indexed:** A.I.P.P., CERDIC, Chr.Per.Ind., G.Soc.Sci.& Rel.Per.Lit.
—UMI.
  Incorporates (1941-1989): U: For University and College Students (ISSN 0893-0201); Which was formerly titled (until Dec. 1986): His Magazine; (until Oct. 1985): His (ISSN 0018-2095)

200 SZ ISSN 0084-1676
WORLD COUNCIL OF CHURCHES. GENERAL ASSEMBLY. ASSEMBLY - REPORTS. (Text in English) 1948. irreg., 7th, 1991. price varies. World Council of Churches, Publications Office, 150 route de Ferney, P.O. Box 2100, CH-1211 Geneva 2. TEL 022-791-6111. FAX 022-791-0361. TELEX 415730-OIK-CH. (Dist. in U.S. by: World Council of Churches Distribution Center, Rt. 111 & Sharadin Rd., Box 346, Kutztown, PA 19530-0346) **Document type:** proceedings.

200 SZ ISSN 0084-1684
WORLD COUNCIL OF CHURCHES. MINUTES AND REPORTS OF THE CENTRAL COMMITTEE MEETING. (Text in English) 1948. irreg. (approx. a.), 45th, 1994. price varies. World Council of Churches, Publications Office, 150 route de Ferney, P.O. Box 2100, CH-1211 Geneva 2, Switzerland. TEL 022-791-6111. FAX 022-791-0361. TELEX 415730-OIK-CH. (Dist. in U.S. by: World Council of Churches, Distribution Center, Rt. 222 & Sharadin Rd., Box 346, Kutztown, PA 19530-0346) **Document type:** corporate report.

268 SZ
WORLD COUNCIL OF CHURCHES. OFFICE OF EDUCATION. EDUCATION NEWSLETTER. (Text in English) 1972. 2/yr. donations. World Council of Churches, Unit II - Life, Education and Mission, 150 route de Ferney, P.O. Box 2100, CH-1211 Geneva 2, Switzerland. TEL 022-791-6111. FAX 022-791-0361. TELEX 415730-OIK-CH. Ed. C. Payne. bk.rev.; film rev.; illus. circ. 4,000. **Document type:** newsletter.

204 UK ISSN 0968-7718
BL1
WORLD FAITHS ENCOUNTER. 1980. 3/yr. £10($25) World Congress of Faiths, The Rectory, Old Church St., Leicester LE2 8ND, England. Eds. K.L.S. Rao, Alan Race. adv.; bk.rev. circ. 850. **Indexed:** Chr.Per.Ind. **Document type:** academic/scholarly publication.
—BLDSC (9354.887000); UMI.
  Formerly (until 1991): World Faiths Insight (ISSN 0273-1266)
  Description: Covers historical and contemporary questions of inter-faith dialogue and cooperation between religions and ideologies.

266 AT ISSN 1033-2243
WORLD MISSION PARTNERS. 3/yr. free. Uniting Church in Australia, Uniting Church Word Mission, 222 Pitt St., 5th Fl., Sydney, N.S.W. 2000, Australia. TEL 02-287-0900. FAX 02-287-0999. (Subscr. to: P.O. Box E266, St. James, N.S.W. 2000, Australia) Ed. Rev. G. Brookes. circ. 25,000. (back issues avail.)
  Description: Stories of Uniting Church mission work overseas and partner churches.

266 US ISSN 1063-7931
WORLD PULSE. 1967. s-m. $24.95. Evangelical Missions Information Service, Box 794, Wheaton, IL 60189. TEL 708-653-2158. FAX 708-653-0520. Ed. James W. Reapsome. circ. 4,500. **Indexed:** Int.Nurs.Ind. **Document type:** newsletter.
—UMI.
  Former titles: Pulse (Wheaton) (ISSN 0747-8631); (until 1984): Europe Pulse.
  Description: Contains news and commentary about missions, politics and religion worldwide.

200 US
WORLD WIDE BARACA - PHILATHEA NEWS. 1913. bi-m. $5. World Wide Baraca-Philathea Union, Tower House, Mt. Vernon, VA 22121-9999. TEL 703-780-9806. Ed. Mary Hoskin. circ. 600 (controlled).

266 US
WORLD - WIDE MISSIONARY CRUSADER. 1943. q. $3. 2451 34th St., Lubbock, TX 79411. TEL 806-794-3406. Ed. Mark Duncan. circ. 10,000.

200 US ISSN 1058-4463
WORLDORAMA. 1967. 10/yr. free. Pentecostal Holiness Church, World Mission Department, Box 12609, Oklahoma City, OK 73157. TEL 405-787-7110. FAX 405-789-3957. Ed. Jesse D. Simmons. circ. 40,000.

248 US ISSN 0746-9241
WORLDWIDE CHALLENGE. 1974. bi-m. $12.95. Campus Crusade for Christ, Inc., 100 Sunport Ln., Dept. 1500, Orlando, FL 32809-7836. TEL 407-826-2383. FAX 407-826-2374. Ed. Diane McDougall. illus. circ. 110,000.
  Formerly (until Oct. 1974): World-Wide Impact.

WORLDWIND. see *CHILDREN AND YOUTH — For*

220 US ISSN 0043-941X
BV175
WORSHIP; concerned with the issues of liturgical renewal. 1926. bi-m. $26. Liturgical Press, St. John's Abbey, Collegeville, MN 56321. TEL 612-363-2213. Ed. Kevin Seasoltz. adv.; bk.rev.; index, cum.index every 25 yrs. circ. 6,000. (also avail. in microfilm from UMI; reprint service avail. from UMI) **Indexed:** Canon Law Abstr., Cath.Ind., CERDIC, New Test.Abstr., Old Test.Abstr., Rel.& Theol.Abstr. (1979-), Rel.Ind.One, Rel.Per.
—BLDSC (9364.450000); UMI.

200 US ISSN 1066-1247
WORSHIP LEADER MAGAZINE. 1992. bi-m. $14.95. C M Communications, 107 Kenner Ave., Nashville, TN 37205. TEL 615-386-3011. FAX 615-386-3380. adv.: B&W page $1995, color page $2395; trim 8 1/4 x 10 7/8. circ. 50,000.
  Description: Provides the tools, information, and resouces church leaders need to enhance the worship experience. Non-denominational.

200 US ISSN 0084-3644
YEARBOOK OF AMERICAN AND CANADIAN CHURCHES. 1916. a. $29.95. Abingdon Press, 201 Eighth Ave., S., Box 801, Nashville, TN 37202-0801. TEL 800-251-3320. FAX 615-749-6522. **Indexed:** SRI.
  Formerly: Yearbook of American Churches.
  Description: Index for gauging trends in American and Canadian churches.

266 UK ISSN 0951-726X
YES. 1960. q. £1.20 per no. Church Mission Society, 157 Waterloo Rd., London SE1 8UU, England. TEL 0171-928-8681. FAX 0171-401-3215. TELEX 934968 FAXTEL G CMS. Ed. Rev. Wallace Boulton. bk.rev.; illus. circ. 24,000. **Document type:** bulletin.
  Description: Presents news, views, and feature articles on mission and church life in those countries in which C.M.S. has a relationship with partner churches.

200 UK ISSN 0085-8374
YORK JOURNAL OF CONVOCATION. 1856. irreg. £5.50. Convocation of York, c/o Synodal Secretary, Church House, West Walls, Carlishe CA3 8UE, England. Ed. Canon D.T.I. Jenkins. circ. 400 (controlled). **Document type:** proceedings.

267.2 US ISSN 0020-2673
YOUNG MEN'S INSTITUTE. INSTITUTE JOURNAL. 1890. bi-m. $3. Young Men's Institute, 50 Oak St., San Francisco, CA 94102. TEL 415-621-4948. FAX 415-621-0963. Ed. Franklin Y. Nelson. adv.; bk.rev.; illus.; circ. 4,500 (controlled). **Document type:** newsletter.

254 US ISSN 0049-8394
BV652.A1
YOUR CHURCH. 1955. bi-m. free to churches. Christianity Today, Inc., 465 Gundersen, Carol Stream, IL 60188-2498. TEL 708-260-6200. FAX 708-260-0114. E-mail: yceditor@aol.com. (Subscr. to: Your Church, Box 901013, Fort Worth, TX 76101. TEL 800-632-2738) Ed. Richard Doebler. adv.: B&W page $5850; adv. contact: Linda Schambach. bk.rev.; circ. 150,000 (controlled). (also avail. in microform from UMI; reprint service avail. from UMI) **Document type:** trade publication.
—UMI.
  Description: Assists churches with the business side of ministry.

266 US ISSN 0044-1015
YOUR EDMUNDITE MISSIONS NEWS LETTER. 1943. bi-m. $2. (Society of Saint Edmund) Southern Missions, Inc., 1428 Broad St., Selma, AL 36701. TEL 334-875-2359. FAX 205-875-8189. Ed. Roger J. LaCharite. illus. circ. 54,500. **Document type:** newsletter.

280 US ISSN 1054-7126
YOUTH MINISTRY QUARTERLY (NEW HAMPTON). 1979. q. $23 (foreign $28). Fred B. Estabrook Company, Inc., Rte. 1, Box 142, New Hampton, NH 03256-9713. TEL 603-744-6316. FAX 603-744-6318. Ed. Nancy S. Couch. abstr.; stat. circ. 700. **Document type:** newsletter.
  Formerly: Catholic Youth Ministry (ISSN 0277-8165)
  Description: Religious articles, readings, program planning advice, discussion and lesson plans, news and historical sketches, and other suggestions pertaining to teenage life-style.

267.3 II
YOUTH OF INDIA. (Text in English) bi-m. Rs.10($2) National Council of YMCA's of India, P.O. Box No.14, New Delhi 110001, India. TEL 91-011-312859. FAX 91-011-312859. Ed. K.P. Philip. adv. circ. 2,500.
  Former titles: Yuvak (ISSN 0044-1414); Association Men.

220 US
YOUTHWALK. 1988. m. $18. Walk Thru the Bible Ministries, Inc., 4201 N. Peachtree Rd., Box 80587, Atlanta, GA 30341-1362. TEL 404-458-9300. Ed. Helen Ryser. circ. 104,000.

200 GW ISSN 0943-8610
Z F R - ZEITSCHRIFT FUER RELIGIONSWISSENSCHAFT. 1993. 2/yr. DM.70. (Deutsche Vereinigung fuer Religionsgeschichte) Diagonal Verlag, Postfach 1248, 35002 Marburg, Germany. TEL 06421-681936. FAX 06421-681944. Ed.Bd. (back issues avail.) **Document type:** academic/scholarly publication.

RELIGIONS AND THEOLOGY

200 301　　　AT　　ISSN 0156-7470
ZADOK CENTRE. SERIES NO.1. 1977. q. Aus.$50. Zadok Institute for Christianity & Society, Locked Bag 23, Kew, Vic. 3101, Australia. TEL 03-816-9367. Ed. Diaby Hannah. circ. 1,000. (back issues avail.)
　Description: Extended evaluations of specific political, cultural or economic issues that deal with the subject area within the context of Christian values and beliefs.

200 301　　　AT　　ISSN 0156-7489
ZADOK CENTRE. SERIES NO.2. 1977. q. Aus.$50. Zadok Institute for Christianity & Society, Locked Bag 23, Ken, Vic. 3101, Australia. TEL 06-816-9367. Ed. Diaby Hannah. circ. 1,000. (back issues avail.)
　Description: Evaluations of biblical and theological issues as well as papers of general interest to promote application of Biblical truth to everyday life.

200 301　　　AT　　ISSN 0156-7500
ZADOK CENTRE READING GUIDES. 1977. a. Aus.$50. Zadok Institute for Christianity & Society, Locked Bag 23, Ken, Vic. 3101, Australia. TEL 03-816-9361. Ed. Diaby Hannah. bk.rev.; bibl. circ. 1,000. (back issues avail.)
　Description: Introduces five or six significant books in a particular field to help people evaluate the subject and its implications to Christian faith.

200 301　　　AT　　ISSN 0810-9796
ZADOK PERSPECTIVES. 1983. q. Aus.$30. Zadok Institute for Christianity & Society, Locked Bag 23, Ken, Vic. 3101, Australia. TEL 03-816-9367. Ed. Diaby Hannah. bk.rev. circ. 1,000. (back issues avail.)
　Description: Examines contemporary issues within the context of Christian belief.

221　　　　　GW　　ISSN 0044-2526
BS410
ZEITSCHRIFT FUER DIE ALTTESTAMENTLICHE WISSENSCHAFT. (Text in several languages) 1881. 4/yr. DM.268 (students DM.107). Walter de Gruyter und Co., Genthiner Str. 13, 10785 Berlin, Germany. TEL 030-26005-0. FAX 030-26005251. TELEX 184027. (U.S. addr.: Walter de Gruyter, Inc., 200 Saw Mill River Rd., Hawthorne, NY 10532. TEL 914-747-0110) Eds. H.-Ch. Schmitt, G. Wanke. bk.rev.; abstr.; index. (also avail. in microform; microfiche from IDC) **Indexed:** Arts & Hum.Cit.Ind., Bibl.Ling., Curr.Cont., New Test.Abstr., Old Test.Abstr., Rel.& Theol.Abstr. (1969-), Rel.Ind.One, Rel.Per. **Document type:** academic/scholarly publication.
—BLDSC (9446.950000); Faxon; Genuine Article; SWETS. **CCC.**

225　　　　　GW　　ISSN 0044-2615
BS410
ZEITSCHRIFT FUER DIE NEUTESTAMENTLICHE WISSENSCHAFT UND DIE KUNDE DER AELTEREN KIRCHE. 1900. 2/yr. DM.154 (students DM.63). Walter de Gruyter und Co., Genthiner Str. 13, 10785 Berlin, Germany. TEL 030-26005-0. FAX 030-26005251. TELEX 184027. (U.S. addr.: Walter de Gruyter, Inc., 200 Saw Mill River Rd., Hawthorne, NY 10532) Ed. Erich Graesser. adv.; bk.rev.; bibl.; index, cum.index: vols. 1-37, 1900-1938. (also avail. in microform) **Indexed:** Bibl.Ling., CERDIC, New Test.Abstr., Rel.& Theol.Abstr. (1970-), Rel.Ind.One, Rel.Per. **Document type:** academic/scholarly publication.
—Faxon; Genuine Article; SWETS. **CCC.**

241 261　　　GW　　ISSN 0044-2674
ZEITSCHRIFT FUER EVANGELISCHE ETHIK. 1957. bi-m. DM.99.80. Guetersloher Verlagshaus Chr. Kaiser, Carl-Bertelsmann-Str. 270, 33311 Guetersloh, Germany. TEL 05241-7405-0. FAX 05241-740548. Ed. Joachim von Soosten. adv.: B&W page DM.900; trim 126 x 200. bk.rev.; bibl. circ. 1,500. **Indexed:** Arts & Hum.Cit.Ind., CERDIC, Curr.Cont., Rel.& Theol.Abstr., Rel.Ind.One, Rel.Per. **Document type:** bulletin.
—Genuine Article; SWETS.

200　　　　　GW
ZEITSCHRIFT FUER GOTTESDIENST UND PREDIGT. 1983. bi-m. DM.84.60. Guetersloher Verlagshaus Chr. Kaiser, Carl-Bertelsmann-Str. 270, 33311 Guetersloh, Germany. TEL 05241-7405-0. FAX 05241-740548. Ed. Horst Nitschke. adv.: B&W page DM.1400; trim 170 x 250. bk.rev. circ. 3,700. **Document type:** bulletin.

209　　　　　GW　　ISSN 0044-2925
BR140
ZEITSCHRIFT FUER KIRCHENGESCHICHTE. 1889. 3/yr. DM.256. W. Kohlhammer GmbH, Hessbruehlstr. 69, 70565 Stuttgart, Germany. TEL 0711-7863-1. FAX 0711-7863263. Ed. Joachim Mehlhausen. adv.; bk.rev.; abstr.; bibl.; index. circ. 950. (reprint service avail. from SCH) **Indexed:** Amer.Hist.& Life, CERDIC, Hist.Abstr., Rel.& Theol.Abstr. (1970-), Rel.Ind.One, Rel.Per. **Document type:** academic/scholarly publication.
—Faxon; Genuine Article; SWETS. **CCC.**

266　　　　　GW　　ISSN 0342-9423
ZEITSCHRIFT FUER MISSION. 1975. q. DM.32. Christliches Verlagshaus GmbH, Postfach 311141, 70471 Stuttgart, Germany. FAX 0711-83000-10. Ed. O. Schumann. adv.; bk.rev.; index. circ. 1,100. **Indexed:** CERDIC. **Document type:** bulletin.
　Formerly (until 1974): Evangelische Missionszeitschrift (ISSN 0014-3472)

266　　　　　GW　　ISSN 0044-3123
BV2130
ZEITSCHRIFT FUER MISSIONSWISSENSCHAFT UND RELIGIONSWISSENSCHAFT. (Text in English, French, German) 1911. 4/yr. DM.56. (Institut fuer Missionswissenschaftliche Forschungen) E O S Verlag, Erzabtei St. Ottilien, 86941 St. Ottilien, Germany. TEL 08193-71261. FAX 08193-6844. adv.; bk.rev.; index. **Indexed:** Canon Law Abstr., CERDIC, Rel.& Theol.Abstr. (1978-), Rel.Ind.One, Rel.Per. **Document type:** bulletin.
—SWETS. **CCC.**

200　　　　　GW　　ISSN 0943-7592
▼**ZEITSCHRIFT FUER NEUERE THEOLOGIEGESCHICHTE/JOURNAL FOR THE HISTORY OF MODERN THEOLOGY.** (Text in English, German) 1994. 2/yr. DM.168. Walter de Gruyter und Co., Genthiner Str. 13, 10785 Berlin, Germany. TEL 030-26005-0. FAX 030-26005251. (U.S. addr.: 200 Saw Mill River Rd., Hawthorne, NY 10532. TEL 914-747-0110) Ed.Bd. **Document type:** academic/scholarly publication.
—BLDSC (5001.010000).

291　　　　　NE　　ISSN 0044-3441
BL4
ZEITSCHRIFT FUER RELIGIONS- UND GEISTESGESCHICHTE/JOURNAL OF RELIGIOUS AND INTELLECTUAL HISTORY. (Supplement avail. (ISSN 0514-650X)) 1948. q. fl.115($74) to individuals; institutions fl.160($103) (effective 1996). E.J. Brill, P.O. Box 9000, 2300 PA Leiden, Netherlands. TEL 31-71-5353500. FAX 31-71-5317532. TELEX 39296 BRILL NL. E-mail: ejborders@ejbrill.com. (In N. America: E.J. Brill, 24 Hudson St., Kinderhook, NY 12106. TEL 800-962-4406. FAX 518-758-1959) Ed. J.H. Schoeps. adv.; bk.rev.; bibl.; cum.index: vols.1-39, 1948-1986. circ. 650. (reprint service avail. from SCH) **Indexed:** Amer.Hist.& Life, Arts & Hum.Cit.Ind., CERDIC, Hist.Abstr., New Test.Abstr., Phil.Ind., Rel.& Theol.Abstr. (1976-), Rel.Ind.One, Rel.Per. **Document type:** academic/scholarly publication.
—Faxon; Genuine Article; SWETS. **CCC.**
　Description: Publishes contributions relating to the history and comparison of religions, the history of German thought, and the history of ideas and ideologies.
　Refereed Serial

200　　　　　NE　　ISSN 0514-650X
BL4
ZEITSCHRIFT FUER RELIGIONS- UND GEISTESGESCHICHTE. BEIHEFTE. 1955. irreg., vol.31, 1989. price varies. E.J. Brill, P.O. Box 9000, 2300 PA Leiden, Netherlands. TEL 31-71-5353500. FAX 31-71-5317532. TELEX 39296 BRILL NL. (In N. America: E.J. Brill, 24 Hudson St., Kinderhook, NY 12106. TEL 800-962-4406. FAX 518-758-1959) Ed. H.J. Klimkeit. (back issues avail.) **Indexed:** Rel.& Theol.Abstr., Rel.Ind.One. **Document type:** monographic series.
　Description: Scholarly studies on topics in the religious and intellectual history of ancient, medieval and modern societies.
　Refereed Serial

209　　　　　SZ　　ISSN 0044-3484
ZEITSCHRIFT FUER SCHWEIZERISCHE KIRCHENGESCHICHTE/REVUE D'HISTOIRE ECCLESIASTIQUE SUISSE. (Text and title in French and German) 1907. a. 50 SFr. (Vereinigung fuer Schweizerische Kirchengeschichte) Editions Saint-Paul, Perolles 42, CH-1700 Fribourg, Switzerland. bk.rev.; bibl. (also avail. in microfiche from IDC) **Indexed:** CERDIC. **Document type:** academic/scholarly publication.

284　　　　　GW　　ISSN 0341-9630
Z7753
ZEITSCHRIFTENVERZEICHNIS THEOLOGIE. irreg. DM.35. Universitaetsbibliothek Tuebingen, Theologische Abteilung, Postfach 2620, 72016 Tuebingen, Germany. TEL 07071-292587. FAX 07071-293123. **Document type:** bibliography.

ZELOS. see CHILDREN AND YOUTH — For

ZHEXUE YANJIU/PHILOSOPHICAL RESEARCH. see PHILOSOPHY

ZHONGGUO ZHEXUESHI YANJIU. see PHILOSOPHY

220　　　　　SA　　ISSN 0028-3568
ZIONS FREUND. vol.9, 1969. q. R.10. Good News Missionary Society, P.O. Box 7848, Johannesburg 2000, South Africa. TEL 011-729-9581. Ed. Sean O'Sullivan. circ. 1,500.
　Formerly: Neuer Zions Freund.

277　　　　　CI　　ISSN 0353-0434
ZNACI VREMENA; obitelski casopis za kriscansku renesansu. (Text in Croatian and Serbian) 1969. q. $4. Centar za Istrazivanje Biblije Dokumentaciju i Informacije, Klaiceva 40, 41000 Zagreb, Croatia. Eds. Tomislav Stefanovic, Zdenko Hlisc-Bladt. circ. 6,500 (Croatian ed.); 9,000 (Serbian ed.).

200　　　　　PL　　ISSN 0044-488X
AP54
ZNAK. (Text in Polish; summaries in English, French) 1946. m. $36. Spoleczny Instytut Wydawniczy "Znak", Ul. Kosciuszki 37, 30-106 Krakow, Poland. TEL 21-89-20. FAX 21-98-14. Ed. Stefan Wilkanowicz. bk.rev.; index. circ. 7,500. **Indexed:** CERDIC, M.L.A.

200　　　　　NE　　ISSN 0044-5002
ZONDAGSMIS. 1951. 60/yr. fl.19. Grafische Bedrijven Berne B.V., Postbus 27, 5473 ZG Heeswijk-Dinther, Netherlands. TEL 31-4139-1394. FAX 31-4139-2270. circ. 120,000.

250　　　　　US　　ISSN 0084-5558
ZONDERVAN PASTOR'S ANNUAL. 1966. a. $14.99. Zondervan Publishing House, 5300 Patterson Ave. S.E., Grand Rapids, MI 49530. TEL 616-698-6900; 800-727-3480. FAX 616-698-3439. circ. 15,000. (reprint service avail. from UMI)
　Description: Contains planned and prepared sermons for every Sunday, Wednesday and special occasion of the year.

200　　　　　CC
ZONGJIAOXUE YANJIU/RELIGION RESEARCH. (Text in Chinese) q. Sichuan Daxue, Zongjiaoxue Yanjiusuo - Sichuan University, Religion Research Institute, Sichuan Daxue Nei, Jiugenqiao, Chengdu, Sichuan 610064, People's Republic of China. TEL 583875.

RELIGIONS AND THEOLOGY — ABSTRACTING, BIBLIOGRAPHIES, STATISTICS

215　　　　　　　US　　ISSN 0591-2385
BL240.2
ZYGON; journal of religion and science. 1966. 4/yr. $39.50 to individuals (outside N. America $48); institutions $62.50 (outside N. America $82.50). (Institute on Religion in an Age of Science) Blackwell Publishers, 238 Main St., Cambridge, MA 02142. FAX 617-547-0789. (Editorial addr.: c/o Chicago Center for Religion and Science, 1100 E. 55th St., Chicago, IL 60615. TEL 312-753-0670) Eds. Philip Hefner, Karl E. Peters. adv.: page $365; trim 4 1/4 x 7 1/2. bk.rev.; index, cum.index: vols.1-20. circ. 2,400. (also avail. in microfilm from UMI; back issues avail; reprint service avail. UMI) **Indexed:** Amer.Hist.& Life, Arts & Hum.Cit.Ind., Arts & Hum.Cit.Ind., Bk.Rev.Ind. (1977-), CERDIC, Child.Bk.Rev.Ind. (1977-), Curr.Cont., G.Soc.Sci.& Rel.Per.Lit., Hist.Abstr. (until 1990), Hum.Ind., New Test.Abstr., Old Test.Abstr., Phil.Ind., Psychol.Abstr., Rel.& Theol.Abstr. (1971-), Rel.Ind.One, Rel.Per., Sociol.Abstr., SSCI. **Document type:** academic/scholarly publication.
—BLDSC (9538.880000); Faxon; Genuine Article; SWETS; UnCover. **CCC.**
Description: Covers scholarly work that explores positive ways of relating contemporary scientific knowledge to the world's philosophical and religious heritage.
Refereed Serial

200 028.5　　　　　　　GW
17; illustrierte Monatzeitschrift fuer junge Christen. 1973. m. DM.26.40. Steyler Missionare e.V., Bahnhofstr. 9, 41334 Nettetal, Germany. TEL 02157-1202-0. FAX 02157-1202-60. Ed. Wolfgang Limberg. **Document type:** consumer publication.

240　　　　　　　US　　ISSN 0162-6418
20TH CENTURY CHRISTIAN. 1938. m. $10.95. 20th Century Christian Foundation, 2809 Granny White Pike, Nashville, TN 37204. TEL 615-383-3842. Ed. Mike Cope. circ. 18,000.

RELIGIONS AND THEOLOGY — Abstracting, Bibliographies, Statistics

200　　　　　　　US
A T L A BIBLIOGRAPHY SERIES. no.17, 1987. irreg., latest no.27. price varies. (American Theological Library Association) Scarecrow Press, Inc., 52 Liberty St., Box 4167, Metuchen, NJ 08840. TEL 800-537-7107. Ed. Kenneth E. Rowe. **Document type:** bibliography.

016.2　　　　　　　DK　　ISSN 0901-4497
AARHUS UNIVERSITET. TEOLOGISKE FAKULTET. BIBLIOGRAFI. Key Title: Bibliografi for Det Teologiske Fakultet ved Aarhus Universitet. 1984. a. free. Aarhus Universitet, Teologiske Fakultet, Nordre Ringgade 1, DK-8000 Aarhus C, Denmark. TEL 45-89-42-11-11. Ed. Thorkild C. Lyby.

253.5　　　　　　　US　　ISSN 0733-2599
BV4012.2
ABSTRACTS OF RESEARCH IN PASTORAL CARE AND COUNSELING. 1972. a. $30 (foreign $35) (typically set in Feb.) Loyola College in Maryland, Commission on Ministry in Specialized Settings, 7135 Minstrel Way, Ste.101, Columbia, MD 21045. TEL 410-290-5995. Ed. Joanne Greer. adv. contact: Susan Tincher. bk.rev. circ. 450. (back issues avail.) **Document type:** abstracting/indexing.
Formerly: Pastoral Care and Counseling Abstracts.
Description: Presents abstracts of all research published in English-language academic psychology journals in which psychology is a variable, or which relates religion and psychology, counseling, or mental health.

ACTUALIDAD BIBLIOGRAFICA DE FILOSOFIA Y TEOLOGIA; selecciones de libros. see *PHILOSOPHY — Abstracting, Bibliographies, Statistics*

200 314　　　　　　　VC　　ISSN 1010-6227
BX845
ANNUARIUM STATISTICUM ECCLESIAE/STATISTIQUE DE L'EGLISE/STATISTICAL YEARBOOK OF THE CHURCH. (Text in English, French, Latin) 1969. a. L.80000. (Segretaria di Stato, Ufficio Centrale di Statistica della Chiesa) Libreria Editrice Vaticana, 00120 Vatican City (Rome), State of the Vatican City. TEL 0036-6-6983532. FAX 0036-6-6984716. charts; stat.
Formerly: Raccolta di Tavole Statistiche.
Description: Statistics on the presence and Apostolic work of the Church in various countries and continents.

ARCHIVES DE SCIENCES SOCIALES DES RELIGIONS. see *SOCIAL SCIENCES: COMPREHENSIVE WORKS — Abstracting, Bibliographies, Statistics*

271　　　　　　　VC
ARCHIVUM BIBLIOGRAPHICUM CARMELI TERESIANI. (Text in Latin and modern languages) 1956. irreg. L.50000 (effective 1995). Edizioni del Teresianum, Piazza S. Pancrazio 5-A, 00152 Rome, Italy. TEL 39-6-58540250. FAX 39-6-58540300. Ed. Father Manuel Diego Sanchez. circ. 400. **Document type:** bibliography.
Formerly: Archivum Bibliographicum Carmelitanum (ISSN 0570-7242)

282　　　　　　　VC　　ISSN 0066-6785
BR1.A1
ARCHIVUM HISTORIAE PONTIFICAE. (Text in English, French, German, Italian, Latin or Spanish; summaries in Latin) 1963. a. L.110000($95) (effective 1995). (Pontificia Universita Gregoriana, Facolta di Storia Ecclesiastica - Pontifical Gregorian University, Faculty of Church History) Gregorian University Press, Piazza della Pilotta, 35, 00187 Rome, Italy. TEL 39-6-678-15-67. FAX 39-6-678-05-88. Ed. Paulius Rabikauskas, S.J. adv.; bk.rev.; bibl. circ. 750. (back issues avail.) **Document type:** bibliography.
—SWETS.
Description: Comprehensive bibliography of church history arranged chronologically and thematically.

ASSOCIATED CHURCH PRESS. DIRECTORY. see *BUSINESS AND ECONOMICS — Trade And Industrial Directories*

200 011　　　　　　　AT　　ISSN 1033-2626
Z7753
AUSTRALASIAN RELIGION INDEX. Short title: A R I. 1989. s-a. Aus.$70 to non-members; members Aus.$55; foreign Aus.$70 (effective 1996). Centre for Information Studies, Charles Sturt University - Riverina, Locked Bag 660, Wagga Wagga, N.S.W. 2678, Australia. TEL 61-69-332325. FAX 61-69-332733. E-mail: cis@csu.edu.au. (Co-sponsor: Australian and New Zealand Theological Library Association (ANZTLA)) **Document type:** abstracting/indexing.
Description: Author, subject and scriptural passage index to religious and theological serials and selected serials with religious and theological coverage published in Australia and New Zealand.

200　　　　　　　US
Z7755
BANGOR THEOLOGICAL SEMINARY. GENERAL THEOLOGICAL LIBRARY. BULLETIN. 1908. q. $15. Bangor Theological Seminary, 159 State St., Portland, ME 04101. TEL 207-874-2214. E-mail: portlib@btsgatep.caps.maine.edu. Ed. Clifton G. Davis. bk.rev. circ. 1,200. **Document type:** bulletin.
●Also available online.
Former titles (until 1991): General Theological Center of Maine. Bulletin (ISSN 1052-8202); (until 1988): General Theological Library. Bulletin (ISSN 0361-0837)
Description: Contains annotations and short reviews of 50-75 recently published books in the fields of theology and religion. Most issues include an article on a topic of current theological interest.

282　　　　　　　VC　　ISSN 0394-9869
Z7838.M6
BIBLIOGRAFIA MISSIONARIA. 1935. a. L.35000($40) (Pontificia Universita Urbaniana, Pontificia Biblioteca Missionaria della S.C. per l'Evangelizzazione dei Popoli) Urbaniana University Press, Via Urbano VIII, 16, 00165 Rome, Italy. FAX 39-6-8308363. Ed. Willi Henkel. bk.rev. circ. 1,000. **Document type:** bibliography.
Formerly (until 1987): Bibliographia Missionaria.

200 016　　　　　　　AG　　ISSN 0326-6680
BIBLIOGRAFIA TEOLOGICA COMENTADA DEL AREA IBEROAMERICANA. 1973. a. $70. Instituto Superior Evangelico de Estudios Teologicos, Camacua 282, 1406 Buenos Aires, Argentina. Ed. Eduardo Bierzychudek. bk.rev.; bibl. circ. 1,000. (back issues avail.)

255 011 920　　　　　　　IT
BIBLIOGRAPHIA FRANCISCANA. (Annual supplement to: Collectanea Franciscana) (Text in Latin) 1931. a. price varies. Frati Minori Cappuccini, Istituto Storico, Casella Postale 18283, Circonv. Occidentale 6850 (GRA km 65), 00163 Rome, Italy. TEL 39-6-66151958. FAX 39-6-66162401. circ. 800.

296 016　　　　　　　US　　ISSN 0067-6853
BIBLIOGRAPHICA JUDAICA. 1969. irreg., no.13, 1993. Hebrew Union College - Jewish Institute of Religion (Cincinnati), 3101 Clifton Ave., Cincinnati, OH 45220. TEL 513-221-1875. FAX 513-221-0519. E-mail: gilnerdj@ucbeh.san.uc.edu. Ed. Herbert C. Zafren. **Document type:** monographic series.

200　　　　　　　US　　ISSN 0742-6836
BIBLIOGRAPHIES AND INDEXES IN RELIGIOUS STUDIES. 1984. irreg. price varies. Greenwood Press, Inc. (Subsidiary of: Greenwood Publishing Group Inc.), 88 Post Rd. W., Box 5007, Westport, CT 06881-5007. TEL 203-226-3571. FAX 203-222-1502. Ed. Gary E. Gorman. **Document type:** abstracting/indexing, bibliography.
—BLDSC (1993.097500).

016.23096　　　　　　　SA
BIBLIOGRAPHY IN CONTEXTUAL THEOLOGY IN AFRICA. (Supplement avail.) 1993. a. R.8. (University of Natal, Pietermaritzburg, School of Theology) Cluster Publications, P.O. Box 2400, Pietermaritzburg 3200, South Africa. Ed.Bd. **Document type:** bibliography, catalog.

282　　　　　　　IT
BIBLIOTHECA ASCETICO-MYSTICA. (Text in various languages) 1932. irreg., no.7, 1995. price varies. Frati Minori Cappuccini, Istituto Storico, Casella Postale 18283, Circonv. Occidentale 6850 (GRA km 65), 00163 Rome, Italy. TEL 39-6-66151958. FAX 39-6-66162401. **Document type:** bibliography.

BOOKS AND ARTICLES ON ORIENTAL SUBJECTS PUBLISHED IN JAPAN. see *ORIENTAL STUDIES — Abstracting, Bibliographies, Statistics*

294.3 011　　　　　　　US　　ISSN 0360-6112
Z7860
BUDDHIST TEXT INFORMATION. 1974. q. $20. Institute for Advanced Studies of World Religions, Rd. 2, Route 301, Carmel, NY 10512. TEL 914-225-1445. FAX 914-225-1485. Ed. Richard A. Gard. index. circ. 350. (back issues avail.) **Document type:** academic/scholarly publication, bibliography.
Description: Cumulative bibliographic information for the study of Buddhist texts.

262.9 016　　　　　　　IE　　ISSN 0008-5650
CANON LAW ABSTRACTS; half-yearly review of periodical literature in canon law. 1959. s-a. £16($30) (effective 1994-1995). Canon Law Society of Great Britain and Ireland, Cathedral House, Ingrave Rd., Brentwood, Essex CM15 8AT, England. Ed. Rev. John Aveyard. bk.rev. circ. 1,000. **Indexed:** CERDIC, Old Test.Abstr. **Document type:** abstracting/indexing.
—UMI.

282 011　　　　　　　US　　ISSN 0008-8285
AI3
CATHOLIC PERIODICAL AND LITERATURE INDEX. 1930. q. with biennial cum. (service basis). Catholic Library Association, 9009 Carta, Allen Park, MI 48101. TEL 215-649-5250. Ed. Allen Gruenke. bk.rev.; abstr.; bibl. circ. 1,500. (also avail. in microfilm from UMI) **Document type:** abstracting/indexing.
Former titles: Catholic Periodical Index (ISSN 0363-6895); Guide to Catholic Literature (ISSN 0145-191X)

RELIGIONS AND THEOLOGY — ABSTRACTING, BIBLIOGRAPHIES, STATISTICS

200 011 FR ISSN 1157-7452
CENTRE PROTESTANT D'ETUDES ET DE DOCUMENTATION. LIBRESENS. 1944. 10/yr. 195 F. (foreign 260 F.). Centre Protestant d'Etudes et de Documentation, 46 rue de Vaugirard, 75006 Paris, France. FAX 46-33-13-91. (Co-sponsor: Federation Protestante de France) Ed. Geoffroy de Turckheim. adv.; bk.rev.; abstr.; bibl.; index. circ. 1,350. **Indexed:** CERDIC, New Test.Abstr.
 Former titles: Centre Protestant d'Etudes et de Documentation. Bulletin (ISSN 0181-7671); Federation Protestante de France. Centre d'Etudes et de Documentation. Bulletin (ISSN 0008-9842)

280 016 US ISSN 0069-3871
CHRISTIAN PERIODICAL INDEX; an index to subjects, authors and book reviews. 1959. 3/yr. $95 (including annual). Association of Christian Librarians Inc., Box 4, Cedarville, OH 45314. TEL 513-766-7842. FAX 513-766-2337. Ed. Douglas J. Butler. circ. 450. **Document type:** abstracting/indexing.

285 UK ISSN 0266-7088
CONGREGATIONAL YEAR BOOK. 1973. a. £7.50 (effective 1995). Congregational Federation, Congregational Centre, 4 Castle Gate, Nottingham NG1 7AS, England. TEL 01602-413801. FAX 01602-480902. Ed. Andrew Carter. stat.; index. circ. 750. **Document type:** directory.

016.2 US ISSN 0270-2347
Z7755
CURRENT CHRISTIAN BOOKS. 1975. a. $75. (Christian Booksellers Association) C B A Service Corporation, 2620 Venetucci Blvd., Box 200, Colorado Springs, CO 80901. TEL 719-576-0795. Ed. Carol Norris. circ. 2,000. (also avail. in microfiche) **Document type:** directory.
 Incorporating: Current Christian Books. Authors and Titles (ISSN 0098-5554); Current Christian Books. Titles, Authors, and Publishers (ISSN 0098-5562)
 Description: Lists titles currently available in the Christian market by title, author, and subject index.

200 US ISSN 1054-8688
BR1
CURRENT THOUGHTS & TRENDS. 1985. m. $36. Box 35004, Colorado Springs, CO 80935-3504. TEL 719-531-3585. FAX 719-598-7128. E-mail: 74104,2176@compuserve.com. Ed. Dennis Cone; Pub. Kent R. Wilson. adv. contact: Dave Wilson. bk.rev.; circ. 15,000 (paid). **Document type:** abstracting/indexing.
 ●Also available online.
 Formerly: Current Christian Abstracts (ISSN 0883-1440)
 Description: Summaries of articles from Christian and secular periodicals dealing with contemporary religious, ethical, theological, social, economic, political, educational, and psychological trends in the church and in society.

220 016 VC
ELENCHUS OF BIBLICA. a. L.180000($165) (effective 1995). (Pontificio Istituto Biblico - Pontifical Biblical Institute) Biblical Institute Press, Piazza della Pilotta 35, 00187 Rome, Italy. TEL 39-6-678-15-67. FAX 39-6-678-05-88. Ed. Robert North S.J. **Document type:** bibliography.
 —BLDSC (3729.147000).
 Formerly: Elenchus Bibliographicus Biblicus (ISSN 0392-7423)
 Description: Bibliography covering all areas of investigation which involve the scientific study of the Bible.

F R A N C I S. 519: PHILOSOPHIE. see *PHILOSOPHY — Abstracting, Bibliographies, Statistics*

200 016 FR ISSN 1157-3775
F R A N C I S. 527: HISTOIRE ET SCIENCES DES RELIGIONS. (Printed format ceased Jan. 1995) 1947. q. Centre National de la Recherche Scientifique, Institut de l'Information Scientifique et Technique, 2 allee de Brabois, 54514 Vandoeuvre-les-Nancy Cedex, France. TEL 83-50-46-00. FAX 83-50-46-50. adv. contact: Veronique Guinvarc'h. cum.index. **Document type:** bibliography.
 ●Also available online. Vendor(s): Telesystemes - Questel.
 Also available on CD-ROM.
 Former titles: Bulletin Signaletique. Part 527: Histoire et Sciences des Religions (ISSN 0180-9296); Bulletin Signaletique. Part 527: Sciences Religieuse (ISSN 0007-5620)

200 011 CE
GLEANINGS. (Text in English) 1982. q. Rs.16($4) Sioll School of Technology, 389 Battaramulla, Sri Lanka. (Subscr. to: Ecumenical Institute for Study & Dialogue, 490-5 Havelock Rd., Colombo 6, Sri Lanka) Ed. J.F. Newslan. circ. 400.

016 200 NE ISSN 0167-7470
GODSDIENST EN MAATSCHAPPIJ. 1981. bi-m. fl.30.50. Nederlands Bibliotheek en Lektuur Centrum, Postbus 93054, 2509 AB The Hague, Netherlands. Ed. F. Stein. bk.rev. circ. 1,000.
 Supersedes (1979-1980): Lektuurinformatie (ISSN 0920-8488)
 Description: Information for public librarians on religous literature and its relation to society.

GUIDE TO SOCIAL SCIENCE AND RELIGION IN PERIODICAL LITERATURE. see *SOCIAL SCIENCES: COMPREHENSIVE WORKS — Abstracting, Bibliographies, Statistics*

296 GW ISSN 0175-7016
DS101
HEBRAEISCHE BEITRAEGE ZUR WISSENSCHAFT DES JUDENTUMS; ein Referatenorgan. 1985. s-a. DM.81. (Lessing-Akademie) Verlag Lambert Schneider GmbH, Postfach 100123, 70826 Gerlingen, Germany. TEL 07156-4308-0. FAX 07156-430840. Ed. Thomas Reichert. **Document type:** abstracting/indexing.
 Description: Articles and summaries of works published in Israel for those who can't read the Hebrew language.

INDEX OF ARTICLES ON JEWISH STUDIES/RESHIMAT MA'AMARIM BE-MADA'E HA-YAHADUT. see *ETHNIC INTERESTS — Abstracting, Bibliographies, Statistics*

011 200 US ISSN 0887-1574
Z7753
INDEX TO BOOK REVIEWS IN RELIGION. Short title: I B R R. (Text in English, French, German) 1949. 3/yr. (plus a. cum.). $340 (foreign $355). American Theological Library Association, Religion Indexes, 820 Church St., Ste. 300, Evanston, IL 60201-5613. TEL 708-869-7788. FAX 708-869-8513. E-mail: atla@atla.com. Ed.Bd. bk.rev. circ. 475. **Document type:** abstracting/indexing.
 ●Also available on CD-ROM.

296.7 011 US ISSN 0019-4050
Z6367
INDEX TO JEWISH PERIODICALS. 1963. a. $90 (disk $125). Box 18570, Cleveland Heights, OH 44118. TEL 216-381-4846. FAX 216-381-4321. Ed. Lenore Pfeffer Koppel. adv. contact: Harold H. Koppel. bk.rev. circ. 350. (also avail. in diskette format) **Document type:** abstracting/indexing.
 Description: Studies articles, book reviews, feature stories and other English-language writings on Jewish topics which appear in periodicals from the US, England, Israel, South Africa and Australia.

289.3 016 US ISSN 0073-5981
INDEX TO PERIODICALS OF THE CHURCH OF JESUS CHRIST OF LATTER-DAY SAINTS. 1961. a. $2 (cum.index $8). Church of Jesus Christ of Latter-day Saints, Corporation of the President, 50 E. North Temple, Salt Lake City, UT 84150. TEL 801-240-5274. (Subscr. to: Salt Lake Distribution Center, 1999 West 1700 South, Salt Lake City, UT 84104) cum.index every 5 yrs. circ. 5,000. **Document type:** abstracting/indexing.
 Description: From 1986 on, includes the following periodicals: The Friend, Church News, Conference Reports, New Era, and the Ensign.

200 GW ISSN 0074-9745
Z7770
INTERNATIONALE ZEITSCHRIFTENSCHAU FUER BIBELWISSENSCHAFT UND GRENZGEBIETE/INTERNATIONAL REVIEW OF BIBLICAL STUDIES. 1951. a. DM.158. Universitaet Paderborn, Universitaet FB.1, Warburgerstr. 100, 33098 Paderborn, Germany. Ed. Bernhard Lang. adv.; bk.rev. circ. 1,000. **Document type:** abstracting/indexing.

284 ZA
LUTHERAN CHURCH OF CENTRAL AFRICA. STATISTICAL REPORT. (Text in English) 1970. a. $2. Lutheran Church of Central Africa, P.O. Box CH 195, Lusaka, Zambia. TEL 260-1-281593. FAX 260-1-281523. Ed. Rev. Joel Spaude. circ. 200.

M L B D NEWSLETTER; monthly of indological bibliography. (Motilal Banarsidass (Delhi)) see *ORIENTAL STUDIES — Abstracting, Bibliographies, Statistics*

220 US
MELLEN BIBLIOGRAPHIES FOR BIBLICAL RESEARCH. 1993. irreg. $49.95. Edwin Mellen Press, 415 Ridge St., Box 450, Lewiston, NY 14092. TEL 716-754-2788. FAX 716-754-4056. Ed. Watson Mills.

655 028.1 011 GW ISSN 0028-3118
DAS NEUE BUCH; Buchprofile fuer die Katholische Buechereiarbeit. 1925. bi-m. DM.45. Borromaeusverein, Wittelsbacherring 9, 53115 Bonn, Germany. (And: St. Michaelsbund, Herzog Wilhelmstr. 5, 80331 Munich, Germany) Eds. Herbert Stangl, Thomas Steinherr. bk.rev.; cum.index. circ. 10,000. **Document type:** bibliography.

220 016 US ISSN 0028-6877
BS410
NEW TESTAMENT ABSTRACTS; a record of current literature. 1956. 3/yr. $33 (foreign $36). Weston Jesuit School of Theology, 3 Phillips Place, Cambridge, MA 02138. TEL 617-492-1960. FAX 617-492-5833. E-mail: NTAweston@aol.com. (Subscr. to: Catholic Biblical Association of America, Catholic University of America, Washington, DC 20064) Ed. D.J. Harrington. adv.; bk.rev.; abstr.; index, cum.index: vols. 1-15 (1956-1970). circ. 2,250. (back issues avail) **Indexed:** Int.Z.Bibelwiss. **Document type:** abstracting/indexing.
 —BLDSC (6088.856000).

200 011 RU
TA418.24
NOVAYA LITERATURA PO SOTSIAL'NYM I GUMANITARNYM NAUKAM. RELIGIOVEDENIE; bibliograficheskii ukazatel' 1959. m. $46. Rossiiskaya Akademiya Nauk, Institut Nauchnoi Informatsii po Obshchestvennym Naukam, Ul. Krasikova 28-21, 117418 Moscow V-418, Russia. Ed. E.I. Serebryannaya. **Document type:** bibliography.
 Formerly (until 1992): Novaya Sovetskaya i Inostrannaya Literatura po Obshchestvennym Naukam. Problemy Ateizma i Religii (ISSN 0134-2932)

220 US ISSN 0364-8591
BS410
OLD TESTAMENT ABSTRACTS. 1978. 3/yr. $26. Catholic Biblical Association of America, Catholic University of America, Washington, DC 20064. TEL 202-319-5519. Ed. Christopher T. Begg. adv. contact: Joseph Jensen. circ. 2,050. **Document type:** abstracting/indexing.
 —UMI.
 Description: Summaries and bibliographical data on articles and books on the Old Testament.

PERIODICA ISLAMICA; an international contents journal. see *RELIGIONS AND THEOLOGY — Islamic*

PROVIDENT BOOK FINDER. see *RELIGIONS AND THEOLOGY — Protestant*

RELIGIONS AND THEOLOGY — BUDDHIST

200　　　　　　UK　　ISSN 1351-9220
QUADRANT. 1986. bi-m. £19. Christian Research, Vision Bldg., 4 Footscray Rd., Eltham, London SE9 2TZ, England. TEL 0181-294-1989. FAX 0181-294-0014. Eds. P.W. Brierley, H. Wright. adv.: page £495; adv. contact: Liz Knowles. bk.rev.; illus. circ. 3,500. (back issues avail.) Document type: academic/scholarly publication.
  Formerly (until 1993): Land M A R C (ISSN 0950-4249)
  Description: Publishes information on religious trends worldwide and reports news of church life.
  Refereed Serial

200 016　　　　US　　ISSN 0149-8428
Z7753
RELIGION INDEX ONE: PERIODICALS. Short title: R I O. (Text in English, French, German) 1949. s-a. (plus a. cum.). $455 (foreign $460). American Theological Library Association, Religion Indexes, 820 Church St., Ste. 300, Evanston, IL 60201-5613. TEL 708-869-7788. FAX 708-869-8513. E-mail: atla@arla.com. circ. 1,200. Document type: abstracting/indexing.
  •Also available on CD-ROM.
  —BLDSC (7356.464000).
  Formerly: Index to Religious Periodical Literature (ISSN 0019-4107)

200　　　　　　US　　ISSN 0149-8436
Z7751
RELIGION INDEX TWO: MULTI-AUTHOR WORKS. Short title: R I T. (Text in English, French, German) 1970. a. $370. American Theological Library Association, Religion Indexes, 820 Church St., Ste. 300, Evanston, IL 60201-5613. TEL 708-869-7788. FAX 708-869-8513. E-mail: atla@atla.com. Ed. Erica Treesh. circ. 500. Document type: abstracting/indexing.
  •Also available on CD-ROM.
  —BLDSC (7356.465000).

200 016　　　　US　　ISSN 0034-4044
BR1
RELIGIOUS & THEOLOGICAL ABSTRACTS. 1958. q. $50 to individuals (foreign $55); institutions $100 (foreign $105); CD-ROM $595 (updates $295) (effective 1995). Religious & Theological Abstracts Inc., 100 W. Park, Box 215, Myerstown, PA 17067. TEL 717-866-6734. FAX 717-866-9280. Ed. William S. Sailer. index. circ. 1,100. Document type: abstracting/indexing.
  •Also available on CD-ROM.
  —BLDSC (7356.480000).
  Description: Provides abstracts of articles from more than 400 scholarly periodicals in religion, including Christian, Jewish and other world religions, classified under Biblical, Theological, Historical or Practical headings.

200 016　　　　II　　ISSN 0034-4060
RELIGIOUS BOOK REVIEW INDEX. 1970. b-m. Rs.150.($63) K.K. Roy (Private) Ltd., 55 Gariahat Rd., P.O. Box 10210, Calcutta 700 019, India. Ed. John A. Gillard. adv.; bk.rev.; bibl. circ. 1,000. (looseleaf format) Document type: abstracting/indexing.
  —BLDSC (9050.211000).

200　　　　　　US
RESEARCH IN MINISTRY; an index to Doctor of Ministry project reports and theses. Short title: R I M. 1981. a. $60. American Theological Library Association, Religion Indexes, 820 Church St., Ste. 300, Evanston, IL 60201-5613. TEL 708-869-7788. E-mail: atla@atla.com. Ed. Barry Hopkins. abstr. circ. 175. (looseleaf format; also avail. in microfiche; back issues avail.) Document type: abstracting/indexing.
  •Also available on CD-ROM.

300 016　　　　US　　ISSN 0036-6358
SCHOLARS' CHOICE; significant current theological literature from abroad. 1960. s-a. $5 (effective 1995-1996). Union Theological Seminary in Virginia, Library, 3401 Brook Rd., Richmond, VA 23227. TEL 804-278-4296. FAX 804-355-3919. Ed. John B. Trotti. bibl. circ. 650. Document type: academic/scholarly publication.

200　　　　　　UK　　ISSN 0165-8794
SCIENCE OF RELIGION; abstracts and index of recent articles. 1976. q. £33($49) (effective 1995). Roots and Branches, 51 Searle St., Cambridge CB4 3DB, England. TEL 44-1223-355984. (Editorial addr.: Zur Hege 11, 35041 Marburg, Germany) Ed. Michael Pye. circ. 350. **Indexed:** E.I. Document type: abstracting/indexing.
  Formerly: Science of Religion Bulletin.

200　　　　　　UK　　ISSN 0081-1440
SOCIETY FOR OLD TESTAMENT STUDY. BOOK LIST. 1946. a. £15($27.50) (Society for Old Testament Study) W.S. Maney & Son Ltd., Hudson Rd., Leeds LS9 7DL, England. TEL 01532-497481. FAX 01532-486983. Ed. L. Grabbe. adv.; bk.rev.; index. circ. 1,200. Document type: bibliography.

316.8　　　　　SA
SOUTH AFRICA. CENTRAL STATISTICAL SERVICE. POPULATION CENSUS. RELIGION BY DEVELOPMENT REGION, STATISTICAL REGION AND DISTRICT. (Report No. 03-01-05) 1991. irreg. R.14 (foreign R.17.50). Central Statistical Service - Sentrale Statistiekdiens, Private Bag X44, Pretoria 0001, South Africa. TEL 27-12-310-8911. FAX 27-12-310-8500. (Orders to: Government Printing Works, Private Bag X85, Pretoria 0001, South Africa) Document type: government publication.

STUDIES IN BIBLIOGRAPHY AND BOOKLORE; devoted to research in the field of Jewish bibliography. see *PUBLISHING AND BOOK TRADE — Abstracting, Bibliographies, Statistics*

200　　　　　　US
TOPICS IN RELIGION: A BIBLIOGRAPHIC SERIES. irreg. price varies. Greenwood Press, Inc. (Subsidiary of: Greenwood Publishing Group Inc.), 88 Post Rd. W., Box 5007, Westport, CT 06881-5007. TEL 203-226-3571. FAX 203-222-1502. Ed. Gary E. Gorman.

200　　　　　　UK　　ISSN 0952-4061
U K CHRISTIAN HANDBOOK (YEAR). 1972. biennial. £29.99. Christian Research, Vision Bldg., 4 Footscray Rd., Eltham, London SE9 2TZ, England. TEL 0181-294-1989. FAX 0181-294-0014. Eds. P. Brierley, H. Wraight. adv. circ. 6,000. (back issues avail.) Document type: directory.
  —BLDSC (9082.655100).
  Description: Lists the addresses of 5,000 Christian organizations and information about church membership.

WORLD SURVEY OF ISLAMIC MANUSCRIPTS. see *RELIGIONS AND THEOLOGY — Islamic*

284　　　　　　GW　　ISSN 0340-8361
ZEITSCHRIFTENINHALTSDIENST THEOLOGIE; indices theologici. 1975. m. DM.40 (foreign DM.60). Universitaetsbibliothek Tuebingen, Theologische Abteilung, Postfach 2620, 72016 Tuebingen, Germany. TEL 07071-292587. FAX 07071-293123. (Co-sponsor: Deutsche Forschungsgemeinschaft) index. circ. 960. (also avail. in diskette format; back issues avail.) Document type: abstracting/indexing.

ZIONIST LITERATURE. see *PUBLISHING AND BOOK TRADE — Abstracting, Bibliographies, Statistics*

RELIGIONS AND THEOLOGY — Buddhist

see also Oriental Studies

294.3　　　　　US
AMERICAN BUDDHIST NEWS. 1980. m. $25 (effective Sep. 1991). (American Buddhist Movement) Buddhist Press, 301 W. 45th St., New York, NY 10036. TEL 212-489-1075. Ed. Kevin O'Neil. adv.; bk.rev. circ. 5,000. (looseleaf format; back issues avail.) Document type: newsletter.
  Former titles: American Buddhist; American Buddhist Newsletter (ISSN 0747-900X); (until 1984): American Buddhist News.
  Description: Covers Buddhism in the United States, Buddhism for beginners and advanced.

ARS BUDDHICA/BUKKYO GEIJUTSU. see *ART*

294.392 495.4　　US
ASIAN CLASSICS INPUT PROGRAM. 1991. irreg., no.3, 1993. $15 donation. Asian Classics Input Program, 1911 Marmary Rd., Gaithersburg, MD 20878-1839. TEL 301-948-5569. FAX 301-294-7870. (In Japan: c/o Linguistics Information Research Inc., 4-19-15 Koyoma, Shinagawa-ku, Tokyo, Japan. TEL 3783-9428. FAX 3788-6180) (also avail. in diskette format; back issues avail.) Document type: academic/scholarly publication.
  •Also available on CD-ROM.
  Description: Reports on international efforts to prepare electronic editions of the Kangyur and Tengyur Buddhist texts. Discusses Tibetan language software, and presents reference materials and bibliographic materials of interest to scholars.

294.3　　　　　KO
BEOP RYUN. (Text in Korean) 1968. m. 3000 Won($6) Beop Ryun Sa, 131-1 Pyoungchangdong, Jongro-Ku, Seoul, S. Korea. Ed. Park Wan III. adv.; bk.rev.; illus. circ. 20,000.

294.3　　　　　US
BLIND DONKEY. 1975. irreg. $24 for 4 nos. (foreign $32). California Diamond Sangha, Box 2915, Petaluma, CA 94953. TEL 707-874-1717. Ed. Joan Sutherland. bk.rev. circ. 1,000.

294　　　　　　CE　　ISSN 0520-3325
BODHI LEAVES. (Includes: Wheel) (Text in English) q. Rs.150($15) Buddhist Publication Society, P.O. Box 61, 54, Sangharaja Mawatha, Kandy, Sri Lanka. Ed. Venerable Bhikkhu Bodhi. (back issues avail.)

294.3 100　　　US
BUDDHA WORLD. 1973. q. $12. American Zen College Press, 16815 Germantown Rd., Germantown, MD 20874. TEL 301-428-0665. Ed. Barbara Abrams. circ. 1,000. (back issues avail.)
  Description: Zen Buddhist philosophy, theory, history, stories; events of the American Zen College.

294.3　　　　　CN　　ISSN 1181-8360
BUDDHISM AT THE CROSSROADS. 1981. irreg. $20 for 3 nos. Zen Lotus Society, 86 Vaughan Rd., Toronto, Ont. M6C 2M1, Canada. TEL 416-658-0137. FAX 416-658-5855. (Subscr. to: 1214 Packard Rd., Ann Arbor, MI 48104) Ed. Linda Klevnick. adv.; bk.rev. circ. 2,000. (back issues avail.)
  —CCC.
  Formerly: Spring Wind (ISSN 0825-799X)
  Description: Information about Buddhist culture and practice. Non-sectarian, each issue devoted to a single theme.

294.3 200　　　US　　ISSN 0882-0945
BR128.B8
BUDDHIST - CHRISTIAN STUDIES. 1981. a. $17 to individuals (foreign $19); institutions $20 (foreign $22). (Society for Buddhist-Christian Studies) University of Hawaii Press, Journals Department, 2840 Kolowalu St., Honolulu, HI 96822. TEL 808-956-8833. FAX 808-988-6052. Ed. Terry C. Muck. adv.; bk.rev.; illus. circ. 750. (back issues avail.; reprint service avail. from UMI) **Indexed:** Rel.& Theol.Abstr., Rel.Ind.One. Document type: academic/scholarly publication.
  —BLDSC (2357.252440); UMI; UnCover.
  Description: Focuses on Buddhism and Christianity and their historical and contemporary interrelationship.
  Refereed Serial

294.3　　　　　US　　ISSN 0507-6986
BQ2
THE BUDDHIST MONTHLY: VAJRA BODHI SEA/HAI TI PU KANG CHIN. Key Title: Vajra Bodhi Sea. (Text in Chinese, English) 1970. m. $40. (Dharma Realm Buddhist Association) Vajra Bodhi Sea Publication Society, City of 10,000 Buddhas, Box 217, Talmage, CA 95481-0217. TEL 707-462-0939. (Subscr. to: Gold Mountain Monastery, 800 Sacramento St., San Francisco, CA 94108) Ed. Bhikshuni Heng Syin. bk.rev.; illus.; index. circ. 4,000. (back issues avail.)
  Description: Specializes in the translation of classical Chinese philosophical and Buddhist texts.

RELIGIONS AND THEOLOGY — BUDDHIST

294.3 CE
BUDDHIST PUBLICATION SOCIETY NEWSLETTER. (Text in English) 1985. 3/yr. membership. Buddhist Publication Society, P.O. Box 61, 54, Sangharaja Mawatha, Kandy, Sri Lanka. Ed. Bhikkhu Bodhi. bk.rev. circ. 4,000. (back issues avail.) **Document type:** newsletter.
Description: Provides instruction, news, and information of relevance to members of the society.

294.3 II ISSN 0970-9754
BUDDHIST STUDIES. (Text in English, Hindi and Sanskrit) 1974. a Rs.40. University of Delhi, Department of Buddhist Studies, Delhi 110007, India. TEL 7257725. Ed. Sanghasen Singh. bk.rev. circ. 200.
—BLDSC (2357.253310).

294.37 UK ISSN 0265-2897
BQ2
BUDDHIST STUDIES REVIEW. 1976. 2/yr. £7.50 to individuals; institutions £12.50. Institut de Recherche Bouddhique Linh-Son, FR , 31 Russell Chambers, Bury Place, London WC1A 2JX, England. (Co-sponsor: Pali Buddhist Union) Ed. Russell Webb; Pub. Russell Webb. adv.; bk.rev. circ. 400. **Document type:** academic/scholarly publication.
—BLDSC (2357.253800).
Formerly (until 1983): Pali Buddhist Review (ISSN 0308-3756)

BUDDHIST TEXT INFORMATION. see *RELIGIONS AND THEOLOGY — Abstracting, Bibliographies, Statistics*

294.3 II
BUDDHIST TRADITION SERIES. (Text in English, Sanskrit, Tibetan) 1985. irreg.,vol.24, 1994. price varies. Motilal Banarsidass (Delhi), 41 U.A. Bungalow Rd., Jawahar Nagar, Delhi 110 007, India. TEL 91-11-2911985. FAX 91-11-2930689. Ed. Alex Waymen. bibl. (back issues avail.) **Document type:** monographic series.
Description: Publishes scholarly editions and translations of Buddhist texts in the Indian, Chinese and Tibetan traditions, and studies of cultural, historical and philosophical aspects of Buddhism.

294.3 GW
BUDDHISTISCHE MONATSBLAETTER. 1954. bi-m. DM.60. Buddhistische Gesellschaft e.V., Beisserstr. 23, 22337 Hamburg, Germany. TEL 040-6313696. FAX 040-6313690. bk.rev.; bibl.; tr.lit.; index; circ. 550. **Document type:** newsletter.

294.3 AT ISSN 0813-3573
CHORTEN. 1981. bi-m. Aus.$15. Atisha Centre Ltd., RMB 1530, Eaglehawk, Vic. 3556, Australia. FAX 61-54-426277. E-mail: 100036,2766@compuserve. Ed. I. Green. bk.rev. circ. 300. **Document type:** newsletter.
Description: Features teachings of Atisha Centre for Buddhist studies, and general Buddhist information.

299.51 CH
CHUNG-KUO FO CHIAO. (Text in Chinese) m. Shih Pu Temple, 140 Nanchang St. Sec. 2, Taipei, Taiwan, Republic of China. TEL 02-321-4734. Ed.Bd. charts; illus.
Description: Chinese Buddhist magazine.

294.392 US ISSN 0097-7209
BQ7662
CRYSTAL MIRROR; Tibetan Buddhism. 1971. irreg., latest vol.8. price varies. (Tibetan Nyingma Meditation Center) Dharma Publishing, 2425 Hillside Ave., Berkeley, CA 94704. TEL 510-548-5407. FAX 510-845-7540. illus. **Document type:** monographic series.

294.392 US ISSN 0894-2056
DENSAL; karma triyana dharmachakra's newsletter. 1979. q. $14. Karma Triyana Dharmachakra (K.T.D.), 352 Mead Mountain Rd., Woodstock, NY 12498. TEL 914-679-7541. FAX 914-679-4625. Ed. Naomi Schmidt. adv.; bk.rev.; tr.lit. circ. 2,000. (back issues avail.) **Document type:** newsletter.
Description: Teaching and news of the Karma Kagyu Lineage of Tibetan Buddhism.

299.56 294.3 JA ISSN 0387-5970
DHARMA WORLD. (Text in English) 1974. 6/yr. $22. Kosei Publishing Co. Ltd., Kosei Bldg., 2-7-1 Wada, Suginami-ku, Tokyo 166, Japan. TEL 03-53852319. FAX 03-53852331. Ed. Kazumasa Osaka. **Document type:** newsletter.
Description: For living Buddhism and interfaith dialogue.

294 TH
THE DHARMACHAKSU/DHARMA-VISION. (Text in Thai) 1894. m. Foundation of Mahamakut Rajavidyalaya, Phra Sumeru Road, Bangkok 10200, Thailand. Ed. Wasin Indasara. circ. 5,000.
Description: Covers Buddhism and related subjects.

294.3 MP
DHARMADUTA. (Text in English) 1979. q. $8. Asian Buddhist Conference for Peace (ABCP), Ulan Bator 51, Mongolia. TEL 976-1-53538. FAX 976-1-310014. Ed. B. Wangchindorj. illus. circ. 3,000.
Formerly: Buddhists For Peace.
Description: Contains organization news, articles on history, culture, and comparative religion, all concerning Buddhism.

294.3 II
DRELOMA. 1978. 2/yr. $10. Drepung Loseling Library Society, Lama Camp 2, Tibetan Col., Uttar Kannada 581 411, India. TEL 84202. Ed. Damdul Namgyal. adv.; bk.rev. circ. 1,000. **Document type:** academic/scholarly publication.

DUNHUANG YANJIU/DUNHUANG STUDIES. see *ARCHAEOLOGY*

294 100 JA ISSN 0012-8708
EASTERN BUDDHIST. N.S. 1965. s-a. 3000 Yen($25) Eastern Buddhist Society, Otani University, Koyama, Kita-ku, Kyoto 603, Japan. TEL 81-75-431-4390. (U.S., Canada & Europe subscr. to: Scholars Press, P.O. Box 15399, Decatur, GA 30333-0399) Ed.Bd. bk.rev.; illus. circ. 1,200. Indexed: Arts & Hum.Cit.Ind., Curr.Cont., M.L.A., Rel.Ind.One, Rel.Per. —Faxon; Genuine Article; SWETS; UnCover.
Refereed Serial

299.51 CC
FA YIN/DHARMAGOSO BIMONTHLY. (Text in Chinese) m. $49.50. Zhongguo Fojiao Xiehui - China Buddhism Society, 25 Fuchengmennei Dajie, Beijing 100034, People's Republic of China. (Dist. in US by: China Books & Periodicals, Inc., 2929 24th St., San Francisco, CA 94110. TEL 415-282-2994) Ed. Jing Hui.

294.3 100 UK
FRIENDLY WAY. 1966. q. £5. Buddhapadipa Temple, 14 Calonne Rd., Wimbledon, London SW19 5HJ, England. TEL 0181-946-1357. Ed. Phrakru Lom. bk.rev. circ. 200. **Document type:** academic/scholarly publication.
Description: Contains information on Vipassana, or insight meditation, and Buddhism.

294.3 US ISSN 1072-2971
BQ2
GASSHO. 1993. q. $15 (free in electronic format). Dharmanet International, Box 4951, Berkeley, CA 94704-4951. TEL 510-620-0936. E-mail: dharma@netcom.com. Ed. Barry Kapke. bk.rev. (back issues avail.) **Document type:** academic/scholarly publication.
● Also available online.
Description: Forum for the global Buddhist community.
Refereed Serial

294.392 US ISSN 0738-2294
GESAR; Buddhism in the West. 1973. 4/yr. $12. (Tibetan Nyingma Meditation Center) Dharma Publishing, 2425 Hillside Ave., Berkeley, CA 94704. TEL 510-548-5407. FAX 510-845-7540. Eds. Heslie Bradburn, Elizabeth Cook. bk.rev. circ. 3,000. (back issues avail.) **Document type:** trade publication.

294.3 821 US
GREAT TAO. 1986. q. $10 membership. American Taoist and Buddhist Association, 81 Bowery St., New York, NY 10002.

ICONOGRAPHY OF RELIGIONS. SECTION 12, EAST AND CENTRAL ASIA. see *ART*

ICONOGRAPHY OF RELIGIONS. SECTION 13, INDIAN RELIGIONS. see *ART*

294.3 JA ISSN 0287-1513
INSTITUTE FOR THE COMPREHENSIVE STUDY OF LOTUS SUTRA. JOURNAL/HOKKE BUNKA KENKYU. (Text in English or Japanese) 1975. a. price varies. Rissho University, Institute for the Comprehensive Study of Lotus Sutra - Rissho Daigaku Hokekyo Bunka Kenkyujo, 4-2-16 Osaki, Shinagawa-ku, Tokyo 141, Japan. TEL 03-5487-3253. FAX 03-5487-3352. Ed. Zuiryu Nakamura. bk.rev.; illus. **Document type:** academic/scholarly publication.

294.3 US ISSN 0193-600X
BQ2
INTERNATIONAL ASSOCIATION OF BUDDHIST STUDIES. JOURNAL. 1978. s-a. $25 to individuals; institutions $50; students $15. International Association of Buddhist Studies, c/o L. Lancaster, University of California, Department of Oriental, Berkeley, CA 94720. TEL 415-642-3480. Ed. Gregory Schopen. adv.; bk.rev. circ. 500. (also avail. in microform from UMI; back issues avail.; reprint service avail. from UMI)
—BLDSC (4802.071000); Faxon; UMI; UnCover.

294.3 US
INTERNATIONAL BUDDHIST MEDITATION CENTER. MONTHLY GUIDE. 1970. 12/yr. donation. International Buddhist Meditation Center, 928 S. New Hampshire Ave., Los Angeles, CA 90006. TEL 213-384-0850. FAX 213-386-6643. Ed. Rev. Sarika Dharma. circ. 1,000. (looseleaf format; back issues avail.) **Document type:** newsletter.
Formerly: International Buddhist Center. Monthly Guide.
Description: Covers temple news, calendar of events, Buddhist issues and spiritual writings.

JOURNAL OF CONTEMPLATIVE PSYCHOTHERAPY. see *PSYCHOLOGY*

291 JA ISSN 0019-4344
JOURNAL OF INDIAN AND BUDDHIST STUDIES/INDOGAKU BUNKKYOGAKU KENKYU. (Text in Japanese; title in English) 1952. s-a. 9000 Yen($14) Japanese Association of Indian and Buddhist Studies - Nihon Indogaku-Bukkyogakukai, c/o Dept. of Indian Philosophy and Sanskrit Philology, Faculty of Letters, University of Tokyo, 7-3-1 Hongo, Bunkyo-ku, Tokyo 113, Japan. Ed.Bd. bibl.; illus.; index. circ. 3,000.
—UnCover.

294.3 US
JOURNAL OF NICHIREN BUDDHISM. 1979. q. membership. (Institute of Nichiren Buddhism) American Buddhist Press, 301 W. 45th St., New York, NY 10036. Ed. Kevin R. O'Neil. adv.; bk.rev. circ. 500. **Document type:** academic/scholarly publication.

294 KO
KOREAN BUDDHISM. (Text in English) irreg. Lotus Lantern International Buddhist Center, 148-5 Sokyok-dong, Chongno-ku, Seoul 110 200, S. Korea. TEL 735-5347. FAX 720-7849. E-mail: mujin@soback.hana.nm.kr. Ed. Won-Myong Sunim.
Description: Book series.

294.3 US
KWAN UM ZEN SCHOOL NEWSLETTER. 3/yr. membership. Kwan Um School of Zen, 99 Pound Rd., Cumberland, RI 02864. TEL 401-658-1476. FAX 401-658-1188. **Document type:** newsletter.
Description: Facilitates communication among nearly 60 Kwan Um Zen centers and groups around the world.

294 KO
LOTUS LANTERN INTERNATIONAL BUDDHIST CENTER. NEWSLETTER. (Text in English) 1987. bi-m. $20. Lotus Lantern International Buddhist Center, 148-5 Sokyok-dong, Chongno-ku, Seoul 110 200, S. Korea. TEL 735-5347. FAX 720-7849. E-mail: mujin@soback.hana.nm.kr. Ed. Won-Myong Sunim. **Document type:** newsletter.

LUNGTA. see *POLITICAL SCIENCE — International Relations*

294.344 II ISSN 0025-0406
MAHA BODHI; international Buddhist monthly. (Text in English) 1892. m. Rs.12($4) Maha Bodhi Society of India, 4A Bankim Chatterjee St., Calcutta 73, India. Ed.Bd. adv.; bk.rev.; illus.; index. circ. 2,500.

RELIGIONS AND THEOLOGY — BUDDHIST

294.3   CE
MAHINDA. (Text in English) 1976. q. Rs.8($2) (Maha Mahinda International Dhammaduta Society) Buddhist English Speaking Society, 58 Sri Vipulasena Mawatha, Colombo 10, Sri Lanka.

294.3   US   ISSN 1075-4113
MANDALA. 6/yr. $15. Foundation for the Preservation of the Mahayana Tradition, Central Office, Box 1778, Soquel, CA 95073. TEL 408-476-8436. FAX 408-476-4823. E-mail: compuserve 75317,3335. Ed. Robina Courtin; Pub. Harvey Horrocks. **Document type:** consumer publication.
Incorporates: Mandala Newsletter (ISSN 1075-4121)
Description: International news and information of interest to modern-day Tibetan Buddhist students.

294.3   US
METTA. 1972. m. free. Honpa Hongwanji Mission of Hawaii, 1727 Pali Highway, Honolulu, HI 96813. TEL 808-522-9200. FAX 808-522-9209. Ed. Rev. Yoshiaki Fujitani. bk.rev. circ. 1,775. (looseleaf format) **Document type:** newsletter.
Description: Gives information and personal insights on Buddhism, especially Jodo Shinshu. Includes information on events concerning Buddhism in Hawaii.

294.344   UK   ISSN 0026-3214
MIDDLE WAY. 1926. q. £8.50 (foreign £12.50). Buddhist Society, 58 Eccleston Sq., London SW1V 1PH, England. TEL 071-834-5858. Ed. Desmond Bidoulph. adv.; bk.rev.; illus.; index. circ. 2,500. **Document type:** newsletter, academic/scholarly publication, directory.
—BLDSC (5761.407000); UnCover.

294.3   US   ISSN 0896-8942
MOUNTAIN RECORD. 1981. q. $14. Dharma Communications, Inc., S. Plank Rd., Box 197MR, Mt. Tremper, NY 12457. TEL 914-688-7993. FAX 914-688-7911. Ed. Bonnie Myotai Treace. adv.; bk.rev. circ. 5,000.
Description: Covers both Eastern and Western religious traditions especially reflecting the impact of Zen Buddhism on social action, ecology, art, science and health.

294.3   UK
NAMO BUDDHA NEWSLETTER. 1992. 2/yr. $10. Namo Buddha Seminar, Maytrees, Aylesbury Rd., Monks Risborough, Bucks. HP27 0JT, England. TEL 08444-3642. (U.S. addr.: Namo Buddha Seminar, 1390 Kalmia Ave., Boulder, CO 80304. TEL 303-449-6608) Ed. Cornelia Hwang. illus.; circ. 2,000 (controlled). **Document type:** newsletter.

299.51   HK
NEI MING. (Text in Chinese) m. free. Nei Ming Magazine Society, c/o Miu Fat Buddhist Monastery, 22 Mile, Castle Peak Rd., Lam Tei, Tuen Mun, N.T., Hong Kong. circ. 3,000.

294.3   CN
NOVA SCOTIA KARMA DZONG BANNER; news from the heart of the mandala. m. $25. Karma Dzong, 1084 Tower Rd., Halifax, N.S. B3H 2Y5, Canada. TEL 902-420-1118.
Description: Covers education, social and economic issues, and other news from a Buddhist perspective.

294.3   US   ISSN 0891-1177
BQ9460
ORDER OF BUDDHIST CONTEMPLATIVES. JOURNAL. 1970. q. $20 (foreign $23). Order of Buddhist Contemplatives, c/o Rev. Shiko Rom, Asst. Ed., 3612 Summit Dr., Box 199, Mt. Shasta, CA 96067. TEL 916-926-4208. FAX 916-926-5796. Ed. Rev. Choshin Passimore. circ. 560. (back issues avail.)
Former titles (until 1986): Shasta Abbey. Journal (ISSN 0732-8508); Zen Mission Society. Journal.
Description: Articles on the practical aspects of Buddhist meditation and training written by monks of the order and lay members of the congregation.

294.3   US   ISSN 0897-3962
QA431
PACIFIC WORLD. 1985. a. free. Institute of Buddhist Studies, 1900 Addison St., Berkeley, CA 94704. TEL 510-849-2383. FAX 510-849-2158. Ed. Richard Payne. bk.rev. circ. 3,000.
—Faxon; SWETS; UnCover.

294.3   US
PRIMARY POINT. 3/yr. $12 or membership. Kwan Um School of Zen, 99 Pound Rd., Cumberland, RI 02864. TEL 401-658-1476. FAX 401-658-1188. adv.
Description: Presents the practice of Zen Buddhism as taught by Zen Master Seung Sahn, and presents articles on contemporary issues in the Buddhist world.

294.3   US
PROPER DHARMA SEAL. (Text in Chinese) 1983. q. free. (Dharma Realm Buddhist Association) Vajra Bodhi Sea Publication Society, City of 10,000 Buddhas, Box 217, Talmage, CA 95481-0217. TEL 707-462-0939. Ed. Heng Ruei. circ. 10,000. (tabloid format; back issues avail.)
Description: Specializes in short articles on eastern and western ethics.

294.3   US
SEIKYO TIMES. (Text in English) 1981. m. $50. (Soka Gakkai International - U.S.A.) World Tribune Press, 525 Wilshire Blvd., Santa Monica, CA 90401. TEL 310-451-8811. FAX 310-451-3501. Ed. Fred M. Zaitsu. circ. 28,000.
Description: Publishes study material of the Soka Gakkai International and the Soka Gakkai International - USA, lay organizations that practice Nichiren Daishonin's Buddhism.

294.3   CN   ISSN 1190-7886
BQ2
SHAMBHALA SUN; creating enlightened society. (Text in English) 1978. bi-m. $20. Nalanda Foundation, 1084 Tower Road, Halifax, NS B3H 2Y5, Canada. TEL 902-422-8404. FAX 902-423-2701. E-mail: shambsun@ra.isisnet.com. (U.S. addr.: 1345 Spruce St., Boulder, CO 80302. TEL 303-440-8849. FAX 303-443-2975) Ed. Melvin McLeod. adv.: B&W page $686; adv. contact: Alex Gault. bk.rev.; illus. circ. 20,000. (tabloid format) **Document type:** trade publication, consumer publication.
Formerly (until Apr. 1992): Vajradhatu Sun (ISSN 0882-0813)
Description: Covers Buddhism and the contemplative world, presenting features on the arts, social issues, poetry, fiction, and news events.

294.392   US   ISSN 1059-3691
BQ7530
SNOW LION NEWSLETTER & CATALOG. 1986. q. free. Snow Lion Publications, Box 6483, Ithaca, NY 14851. TEL 607-273-8519. FAX 607-273-8508. E-mail: 75061,1026@CompuServe.com. Ed. Jeff Cox. adv. contact: Jeff Cox. circ. 18,000. **Document type:** newsletter, catalog.
Description: Contains up-to-date information on Tibetan Buddhist activities, Tibetan events, and the political situation in Tibet. Offers a large selection of books, audiotapes, videos, art, ritual items, and other cultural artifacts.

200 950   DK   ISSN 0904-2431
BQ1
STUDIES IN CENTRAL AND EAST ASIAN RELIGIONS. 1988. a. $24. Seminar for Buddhist Studies, Center for East- and Southeast Asian Studies, University of Copenhagen, Stockhusgade 5, DK-1317 Copenhagen K, Denmark. TEL 45-35-32-25-96. FAX 45-35-32-25-95. E-mail: ceseas@inet.uni-c.dk. Ed.Bd. adv.; bk.rev. circ. 200.
Description: Covers all aspects of religious life in Tibet, Central Asia, Mongolia, China, Korea and Japan from a variety of standpoints: philosophical, linguistic, sociological.
Refereed Serial

294.3   US
THE TEN DIRECTIONS. 1979. s-a. donation (foreign $15). (Kuroda Institute) Zen Center of Los Angeles, 923 S. Normandie Ave., Los Angeles, CA 90006. TEL 213-387-2351. FAX 213-387-2377. Ed. Wendy Egyoku Nakao. adv.; bk.rev. circ. 10,000.
Description: Covers current issues, social and cultural issues of Zen Buddhism in America.

294.392   GW   ISSN 0938-3506
TIBET UND BUDDHISMUS; Vierteljahresheft des Tibetischen Zentrums e.V. Hamburg. 1987. q. DM.32 (foreign DM.42). Tibetisches Zentrum e.V. Hamburg, Hermann-Balk-Str. 106, 22147 Hamburg, Germany. TEL 040-6443585. FAX 040-6443515. Ed. Birgit Stratmann. bk.rev. circ. 2,500. (back issues avail.) **Document type:** bulletin.
Formerly (until 1990): Zentrumsnachrichten.

299.51   II   ISSN 0254-9808
TIBETAN BULLETIN; the official journal of the Tibetan Administration. (Text in English) 1969. bi-m. free. Central Tibetan Administration of His Holiness the Dalai Lama, Department of Information and International Relations, Gangchen Kyishong, Dharamsala 176215, Himachal Pradesh, India. TEL 0091-1892-2457. FAX 0091-1892-4357. TELEX 31-66140-BDL-IN. Ed. Bhuchung K. Tsering. adv.; bk.rev.; music rev. circ. 3,500. **Indexed:** HR Rep. (1990-). **Document type:** bulletin.
Description: Covers events in Chinese occupied Tibet, activities within the Tibetan administration in exile, international human rights initiatives on behalf of Tibetans, as well as cultural and religious topics of general interest.

294.3 800   US   ISSN 1055-484X
BQ2
TRICYCLE; the Buddhist review. 1991. q. $20. Buddhist Ray, Inc., 163 W. 22nd St., New York, NY 10011. TEL 212-645-1143. FAX 212-645-1493. (Subscr. to: Department TRI, Box 3000, Denville, NJ 07834) Ed. Helen Tworkov. adv.; bk.rev.; illus. circ. 35,000. **Document type:** consumer publication.
Description: Independent cultural review illuminated by a Buddhist point of view. Publishes interviews, art, fiction, profiles, reports on international news, and discussions of the applications of Buddhism in contemporary American society.

294.39   FR   ISSN 0049-4739
TROISIEME CIVILISATION. 1971. m. 18 F. per no. Soka Gakkai France, 64 rue du Lycee, 92332 Sceaux Cedex, France. FAX 46-60-12-12. Ed. Eiichi Yamazaki. adv.; bk.rev.; charts; illus. circ. 7,000.
Description: Covers buddhism, peace, culture and education.

294.3   US   ISSN 1065-058X
BQ2
TURNING WHEEL. 1984. 4/yr. $35. Buddhist Peace Fellowship, Box 4650, Berkeley, CA 94704. TEL 510-525-8596. FAX 510-525-7973. Ed. Susan Moon. adv. contact: Lewis Woods. bk.rev. 4,500. **Document type:** bulletin.
Description: Publishes articles, reviews, poems, interviews and graphics relating to Buddhist peace and ecology work in all traditions.

299.51   CH
UNIVERSAL DOOR/P'U MEN; to promote humanistic Buddhism; to establish humanly pure land; of the public; international; of living. (Text mostly in Chinese; occasionally in English) m. NT.$800. 270 Hsin 2nd Rd., Keelung, Taiwan 20118, Republic of China. TEL 02-426-4724. FAX 02-423-8572. Ed. Yung Yun. adv.

294   AT   ISSN 1036-4471
VESAK. 1992. a. donations. Australian Buddhist Mission Inc., 16 Woodhouse Drive, Ambarvale, N.S.W. 2560, Australia. TEL 61-46-267420. FAX 61-2-4494657. Ed. Y.K. Yau. bk.rev.; circ. 2,000 (controlled). **Document type:** academic/scholarly publication.
Description: Publishes articles on Buddhist mental culture relevant to contemporary society. Reports on mission's activities in Australia, New Zealand, Singapore and Malaysia.

294.344   MY   ISSN 0042-8094
VOICE OF BUDDHISM. (Text mainly in English; occasionally in Chinese) 1963. s-a. M.$5($5) (£3). Buddhist Missionary Society, Buddhist Temple, 123 Jalan Berhala, Brickfields, 50470 Kuala Lumpur, Malaysia. TEL 3-2741141. Ed. Tan Teik Beng. adv.; bk.rev.; illus. circ. 6,500. (back issues avail.)
Description: Promotes the study and practice of Buddhism through articles and printed lectures. Also assists in the opening of schools and endowment funds.

200   US
WASHINGTON BUDDHIST. 1969. q. $6. Buddhist Vihara Society, 5017 16th St., N.W., Washington, DC 20011. TEL 202-723-0773. Ed. Rev. M. Dhamma. bk.rev. circ. 1,000.

299.5   UK   ISSN 0144-9818
WESTERN BUDDHIST. 1979. s-a. £1.90. Scientific Buddhist Association, 30 Hollingbourne Gdns., Ealing, London W13 8EN, England. Ed. Paul Ingram. adv.; bk.rev. circ. 550.

294.3 CE ISSN 0049-7541
WHEEL; a series of Buddhist publications. (Includes: Bodhi Leaves) (Text in English) 1958. q. Rs.150($15) Buddhist Publication Society, P.O. Box 61, 54, Sangharaja Mawatha, Kandy, Sri Lanka. Ed. Venerable Bhikkhu Bodhi. circ. 4,000. (back issues avail.)

294.3 US
WHEEL OF DHARMA. (Text in English, Japanese) 1973. m. $5. Buddhist Churches of America, 1710 Octavia St., San Francisco, CA 94109. TEL 415-776-5600. FAX 415-771-6293. Ed. Elson B. Snow. bk.rev. circ. 13,600. (tabloid format)
 Description: Propagation of Buddhism and Jodo-Shinshu religion; organizational and layman education.

294.392 US ISSN 0043-5708
WIND BELL. 1962. 2/yr. $6. (Zen Center (San Francisco)) Wheelwright Press, 300 Page St., San Francisco, CA 94102. TEL 415-863-3136. Ed.Bd. bk.rev. circ. 3,000. (processed)

294 TH ISSN 0084-1781
WORLD FELLOWSHIP OF BUDDHISTS. BOOK SERIES. 1965. irreg. price varies. World Fellowship of Buddhists, 33 Sukhumvit Rd., Bangkok 10-110, Thailand.

294.344 TH ISSN 0043-8464
WORLD FELLOWSHIP OF BUDDHISTS. REVIEW. q. B.160($8) World Fellowship of Buddhists, 33 Sukhumvit Rd., Between Soi 1-3, Bangkok 10-110, Thailand. Ed. Ambhorn Arunrangsi. adv.; bk.rev.; charts; illus. circ. 2,000.

294.3 US ISSN 0049-8165
WORLD TRIBUNE. 1964. w. $44. (Soka Gakkai International - U.S.A.) World Tribune Press, 525 Wilshire Blvd., Box 1427, Santa Monica, CA 90401. TEL 213-451-8811. FAX 213-451-3501. Ed. Fred M. Zaitsu. bk.rev.; illus. circ. 44,000.
 Description: Publishes news and study material about the Soka Gakkai International and Soka Gakkai International - USA, lay organizations that practice Nichiren Daishonon's Buddhism.

294.392 CC
XIZANG FOJIAO/TIBETAN BUDDHISM. (Text in Tibetan) s-a. Zhongguo Fojiaohui, Xizang Fenhui - Chinese Society of Buddhism, Tibetan Chapter, 11, Niangre Lu, Lhasa, Xizang (Tibet) 850000, People's Republic of China. TEL 22282. Ed. Yixi Wangqiu.

294.3 GW
YANA; Zeitschrift fuer Buddhismus u. Religioese Kultur auf Buddhistischer Grundlage. 1948. bi-m. DM.36. Altbuddhistische Gemeinde e.V., Zur Ludwigshoehe 30, 86917 Utting, Germany. TEL 08806-7507. bk.rev.; cum.index: 1948-1967, 1968-1988. circ. 550. **Document type:** newsletter.

294.3 SI
YOUNG BUDDHIST. (Text in Chinese and English) a. Singapore Buddhist Youth Organisations Joint Celebrations Committee, 83 Silat Rd., Singapore 3, Singapore. illus.

YOUNG EAST; a quarterly on Buddhism and Japanese culture. see *ORIENTAL STUDIES*

294.3 CN
ZANMAI. 1986. 4/yr. $26 for 3 nos. (White Wind Zen Community) Great Matter Publications, Box 203, Stn. A, Ottawa, ON K1N 8V2, Canada. TEL 613-232-7851. FAX 613-235-0472. adv.; bk.rev.; illus.
 Description: Contains transcripts of teisho and classes by the Sensei, essays, poetry, translations of classical texts.

294.3 GW ISSN 0921-8335
ZEN. Dutch edition (ISSN 0921-5174) 1927. q. DM.36 (Dutch edition fl.41). Huffertsheck 1, 54619 Lautzerath, Germany. TEL 06559-467. FAX 06559-1342. Ed. Adelheid Meutes-Wilsing. adv.; bk.rev. circ. 1,600. **Document type:** bulletin.

294.392 US
ZEN BOW; a publication of the Rochester Zen Center. 1967. q. $12 (foreign $16). Rochester Zen Center, 7 Arnold Park, Rochester, NY 14607. TEL 716-473-9180. FAX 716-473-6846. Ed. Richard von Sturmer. bk.rev. circ. 800. (processed) Indexed: New Per.Ind. **Document type:** newsletter.
 Formerly (until 1990): Zen Bow Newsletter; Supersedes (1967-1979): Zen Bow (ISSN 0044-3956)
 Description: Written by Rochester Zen Center members on Zen practice and current events at the center and its affiliates.

294.3 US
ZEN NOTES. 1954. 10/yr. $10. First Zen Institute of America, 113 E. 30th St., New York, NY 10016. TEL 212-686-2520. Ed. Armando Mendonca. bk.rev. circ. 600. (back issues avail.)

294.3 CN
ZHEN FO BAO/TRUE BUDDHA NEWS. (Text in Chinese) 1991. s-m. $30. True Buddha Publication, 357 East Hasting St. Ste 200, Vancouver, BC V6A 1P3, Canada. TEL 604-255-3811. FAX 604-255-8894. (Subscr. to: P.O. Box 88180, CPO, Vancouver, BC V6A 4A5, Canada) Pub. May Jean Pai. adv. contact: Xiao Ping Mon. circ. 210,000. **Document type:** newspaper.

RELIGIONS AND THEOLOGY — Eastern Orthodox

281.9 US ISSN 0885-9795
AGAIN; a call for the people of God to return to their roots in historic Orthodoxy once... 1978. q. $14.50 (foreign $16.50) (effective 1995). (Antiochion Evangelical Orthodox Mission) Conciliar Press, 10090 A Hwy. 9, Box 76, Ben Lomond, CA 95005-0076. TEL 408-336-5118. FAX 408-336-8882. Ed. Weldon M. Hardenbrook. circ. 4,000. (back issues avail.)
 Description: Contemporary journal of Eastern Orthodox thought, including history, theology, lives of saints, and contemporary issues.

281.9 CY
APOSTOLOS VARNAVAS. (Text in English and Greek) 1918. m. £C5($15) Orthodox Church of Cyprus, Archbishopric of Nicosia, Nicosia, Cyprus. TEL 357-2-474411. FAX 357-2-474180. Ed. Andreas Mitsides. bk.rev. circ. 1,500.

281.9 US ISSN 1059-1001
AUTOCEPHALOUS ORTHODOX CHURCHES. 1991. irreg., no.4, 1995. price varies. Borgo Press, St. Willibrord's Press, Box 2845, San Bernardino, CA 92406. TEL 909-884-5813. FAX 909-888-4942. Ed. Karl Pruter. **Document type:** monographic series.
 Description: Histories, indexes, chronologies, directories, and guides to the independent Eastern churches.

281.9 BH ISSN 0278-551X
AXIOS; the orthodox journal. 1980. q. $15 (effective through 1997). Axios Newsletter, Inc., 30-32 Macaw Ave., Belmopan, Belize. TEL 501-8-23284. FAX 501-8-23633. E-mail: father.daniel@belize.com.bz. Ed. Daniel John Gorham. adv.; bk.rev. circ. 10,506. **Document type:** newsletter.
 Description: Presents challenges in ethics and theology.
 Refereed Serial

281.9 US ISSN 0005-8327
BELARUSKAYA CARKVA. 1956. s-a. $4. Belaruskaja Vydaveckaja Siabrynia, 3006 Logan Blvd., Chicago, IL 60647. Ed. Vaclau Panucevic. bk.rev.; charts; illus.; index. circ. 500.

281.9 YU ISSN 0006-5714
BOGOSLOVLJE. (Text in Serbo-Croatian) 1926. s-a. $15. Pravoslavni Bogoslovski Fakultet u Beogradu, 7 Jula 2, Belgrade, Yugoslavia. TEL 011-630-268. FAX 182-780. Ed. B. Simic. bk.rev. circ. 1,200.
 Description: Presents articles by Orthodox and non-Orthodox theologians on various contemporary theological issues.

CHRISTELIJK OOSTEN. see *RELIGIONS AND THEOLOGY*

281.9 US ISSN 0734-0036
CHURCH MESSENGER/CERKOVNYJ VISTNIK. 1944. bi-m. $12. American Carpatho-Russian Orthodox Greek Catholic Diocese, 312 Garfield St., Johnstown, PA 15906. Ed. Rev. James S. Dutko. adv. contact: Rev. John A. Barnik, Jr. bk.rev.; film rev.; illus. circ. 7,200. **Document type:** newspaper.

281.9 YU
CRKVA/CHURCH; kalendar Srpske Pravoslavne Patrijarsije. (Text in Serbian) 1965. a. price varies. Sveti Arhijerejski Sinod, Sedmoga Jula 5, 11000 Belgrade, Yugoslavia. TEL 011 635-699. circ. 25,000.

281.9 US ISSN 1059-9738
DESERT VOICE. 1985. 5/yr. donations. (Monastery of St. Anthony the Great) St. Anthony the Great Orthodox Publications, Box 1432, Alamogordo, NM 88311-1432. (Subscr. to: 3044 N. 27th St., Phoenix, AZ 85016) Ed. Rev. Fr. Bessarion Agioantonides. adv.; bk.rev.; tr.lit. circ. 4,000. (tabloid format) **Document type:** newspaper.
 Formerly: Orthodox Southwest (ISSN 0897-7682)

ECU - LINK. see *RELIGIONS AND THEOLOGY — Protestant*

281.9 HU ISSN 0133-0047
EGYHAZI KRONIKA; keleti orthodox egyhazi folyoirat. 1952. bi-m. 120 Ft.($2) Magyar Orthodox Adminisztratura, Petofi ter 2, 1052 Budapest, Hungary. TEL 1-184-813. Ed. Dr. Feriz Berki. circ. 500. (back issues avail.) **Document type:** newspaper.
 Description: Contains ecclesiastical news and religious articles for Christian Orthodox people.

281.9 YU
GLAS ALMASKE PAROHIJE. 1975. irreg. Srpska Pravoslavna Parohija pri Hramu Sv. Tri Jerarha-Almaska, Almaska 11, 21000 Novi Sad, Yugoslavia. TEL 021 51-394. Ed. Mirko Tisma. circ. 500. (back issues avail.)
 Description: Provides news on religious education. Includes the history of the parish and parish church, as well as records of births, marriages and deaths.

281.9 CI
GLAS SVETIH RAVNOAPOSTOLA CIRILA I MATODIJA. (Text in Serbo-Croatian written in Cyrillic alphabet) 1974. irreg. $2. Srpska Pravoslavna Eparhija Zagrebacka - Serbian Orthodox Diocese of Zagreb, Prilaz JNA 4, 41000 Zagreb, Croatia. FAX 041-421-660. adv.; bk.rev. circ. 2,000. (back issues avail.)

281.9 YU ISSN 0017-0925
GLASNIK. 1920. m. $25. Sveti Arhijerejski Sinod Srpske Pravoslavne Crkve, 7 Jula 5, 11000 Belgrade, Yugoslavia. Ed. Dragan Milin. adv.; bk.rev. circ. 2,600.

281.9 US
GREEK ORTHODOX ARCHDIOCESE OF NORTH AND SOUTH AMERICA. ANNUAL REPORT. a. Greek Orthodox Archdiocese of North and South America, 8 E. 79th St., New York, NY 10021.

GREEK ORTHODOX CALENDAR. see *ETHNIC INTERESTS*

281.9 230 BX200 US ISSN 0017-3894
GREEK ORTHODOX THEOLOGICAL REVIEW. 1954. q. $22 (foreign $25). (Holy Cross Greek Orthodox School of Theology, Hellenic College) Holy Cross Orthodox Press, 50 Goddard Ave., Brookline, MA 02146. TEL 617-731-3500. Ed. Rev. Dr. N.M. Vaporis. adv.; bk.rev.; cum.index every 5 yrs. circ. 1,075. (also avail. in microform from UMI; reprint service avail. from UMI) Indexed: Amer.Bibl.Slavic & E.Eur.Stud., Amer.Hist.& Life, CERDIC, Hist.Abstr., New Test.Abstr., Old Test.Abstr., Rel.& Theol.Abstr. (1968-), Rel.Ind.One, Rel.Per.
 —BLDSC (4214.905000); Faxon; UMI.

281.9 UK
HERALD OF THE SERBIAN ORTHODOX CHURCH IN WESTERN EUROPE. 1951. 4/yr. Religious Brotherhood of the Serbian Orthodox Church, 89 Lancaster Rd., London W11 1QQ, England. TEL 01-727-8367.

RELIGIONS AND THEOLOGY — EASTERN ORTHODOX

281.9 US ISSN 0437-6749
HOLAS CARKVY/VOICE OF THE CHURCH. (Text in Byelorussian, English) 1955. s-a. $6. Byelorussian Autocephalous Orthodox Church, 401 Atlantic Ave., Brooklyn, NY 11217. TEL 908-873-8026. Ed. Borys Daniluk. circ. 500.
 Description: Byelorussian Christian-Orthodox theology, practices and traditions.

281.9 917.106 CN ISSN 0021-1761
ISKRA. (Text in English and Russian) 1943. fortn. Can.$40 (foreign $50). Soyuz Dukhovnykh Obshchin Krista - Union of Spiritual Communities of Christ, Box 760, Grand Forks, B.C. V0H 1H0, Canada. TEL 604-442-8252. FAX 604-442-3433. Ed. D.E. Popoff. adv.; bk.rev. circ. 1,300. (processed; also avail. in microfilm from KTO)
 Description: Focuses on the history, culture, beliefs and present day activities of the Doukhobors.

281.9 US
MODERN ORTHODOX SAINTS. 1971. irreg., vol.11,1993. price varies. Institute for Byzantine and Modern Greek Studies, 115 Gilbert Rd., Belmont, MA 02178. TEL 617-484-6595. Ed. Constantine Cavarnos. adv. contact: Asterios Gerostergios. bk.rev.; bibl.; illus.; index. circ. 1,000. **Document type:** trade publication, monographic series, academic/scholarly publication.
 Refereed Serial

281.9 US ISSN 0029-7143
O L O G O S. 1949. bi-m. $4. (Orthodox Lore of the Gospel of Our Savior Mission) St. Photios National Shrine, 41 St. George St., St. Augustine, FL 32085. TEL 800-222-6727. circ. 86,700.

281.9 US
O S A MESSENGER. (Former name of issuing body: United Russian Orthodox Brotherhood of America) 1925. bi-m. $3. Orthodox Society of America, 429 Forbes Ave., Ste. 1616, Pittsburgh, PA 15219-1604. TEL 412-261-4277. FAX 412-261-4277. Ed. George G. Lichvarik. circ. 3,000. (tabloid format) **Document type:** newspaper. **Former titles:** U R O B A Messenger (ISSN 0164-5978); Russian Messenger - Russkij Vistnik (ISSN 0036-0287)

281.9 US ISSN 0030-2503
ONE CHURCH/YEDINAYA TSERKOV. 1947. bi-m. $7.50. Patriarchal Parishes of the Russian Orthodox Church in the U.S.A., c/o Rt. Rev. Feodor Kovalchuk, Ed., 727 Miller Ave., Youngstown, OH 44502. TEL 216-788-0151. FAX 216-788-9361. bk.rev.; illus.; index. circ. 1,200. (also avail. in microform from UMI; reprint service avail. from UMI) **Indexed:** CERDIC.
 —UMI.

281.9 US ISSN 0890-099X
ORTHODOX AMERICA. 1980. 8/yr. $8 (Canada $10; foreign $12). (Russian Orthodox Church Outside of Russia) Nikodemos Orthodox Publication Society, Box 992132, Redding, CA 96099-2132. Ed. Mary Mansur. adv.; bk.rev. circ. 2,300. (tabloid format) **Document type:** newspaper.
 Description: Dedicated to traditional Eastern Orthodox Christianity containing articles on spiritual life, lives of saints, teachings of the Holy Fathers, contemporary issues and more.

281.9 US ISSN 0048-2269
BX496.A1
ORTHODOX CHURCH. 1965. m. $15. Orthodox Church in America, 7900 W. 120 St, Palos Park, IL 60464. TEL 708-361-1684. FAX 708-923-1706. Ed. V. Rev. John Matusiak. bk.rev.; charts; illus. circ. 34,000. (tabloid format) **Indexed:** CERDIC. **Document type:** newspaper.
 Description: Covers Orthodox and ecumenical church news. Includes feature articles and official annoucements.

281.9 US ISSN 0145-7950
BX496.A5
ORTHODOX CHURCH IN AMERICA. YEARBOOK AND CHURCH DIRECTORY. Key Title: Yearbook and Church Directory of the Orthodox Church in America. a. $15. Orthodox Church in America (Syosset), Box 675, Rte. 25A, Syosset, NY 11791. TEL 516-922-0550. FAX 516-922-0954. Ed. Gregory Havrilak. charts; illus.; stat. circ. 3,000. **Document type:** directory.
 Supersedes: Russian Orthodox Greek-Catholic Church of America. Yearbook (ISSN 0095-2257); Russian Orthodox Greek Catholic Church of America. Yearbook and Church Directory (ISSN 0557-532X)
 Description: Complete listing of parishes and clergy, bishops, officers of church administration, institutions and publications in U.S. and Canada.

281.9 US ISSN 0744-1495
ORTHODOX HERALD. 1952. m. $6. Orthodox Herald, Inc, Box 9, Hunlock Creek, PA 18621. TEL 717-256-7232. Ed. V. Rev. W. Basil Stroyen. bk.rev.; circ. 5,000 (paid). (looseleaf format) **Document type:** newsletter.
 Description: News about the Othodox Christian faith and church, and the traditions and culture of people whose ancestors came from the former Austro-Hungarian empire and Russia.

281.9 UK ISSN 0267-8470
ORTHODOX NEWS. 1979. m. St. George Orthodox Information Service, 64 Prebend Gardens, London W6 0XU, England. TEL 081-741-9624. Ed. Andrew Bond. adv.; bk.rev. circ. 2,500.
 Description: News service dealing with current affairs in the Orthododox Church.

281.9 US ISSN 0731-2547
ORTHODOX OBSERVER. (Text and summaries in English and Greek) 1971. m. $5.50. (Greek Archdiocese of North and South America) Greek Archdiocese Press, 154-23 22nd Ave., New York, NY 11357. TEL 212-628-2590. FAX 212-570-4005. Ed. Jim Golding. adv.; bk.rev. circ. 130,000. (tabloid format; also avail. in microfilm) **Document type:** newspaper.

281.9 UK ISSN 0950-8376
ORTHODOX OUTLOOK. 1986. bi-m. £14 (foreign £16). 42 Witwen's Ln., Wallasey, Wirral L45 7NN, Wales. TEL 0151-639-6509. Ed. Fr. Pancratius Sanders. adv. contact: Anna Sanders. bk.rev. circ. 1,000. **Document type:** newsletter.
 Description: News about the Orthodox Church in Britain and worldwide.

281 US ISSN 0030-5839
ORTHODOX WORD. 1965. bi-m. $15 (foreign $18). St. Herman of Alaska Brotherhood, Box 70, Platina, CA 96076. TEL 707-887-0525. FAX 707-857-9023. Ed. Monk Damascene. adv. contact: Fr. Theodore Niklasson. bk.rev.; illus.; index. circ. 2,500. (also avail. in microfilm from UMI; reprint service avail. from UMI) **Indexed:** CERDIC, Rel.Per. **Document type:** trade publication.
 —UMI.
 Description: Covers traditional Christianity from Apostolic times. Features the lives of saints, especially of modern holy men and women, and offers spiritual guidance from ascetics and visionaries. Includes discussions of contemporary issues from an Orthodox perspective.

281.9 GW ISSN 0933-8586
ORTHODOXES FORUM. (Text in English, French, German, Greek) 1987. 2/yr. DM.48. (Universitaet Muenchen, Institut fuer Orthodoxe Theologie) E O S Verlag, Erzabtei St. Ottilien, 86941 St. Ottilien, Germany. TEL 08193-71261. FAX 08193-6844. adv.; bk.rev.; bibl.; illus. circ. 600. (back issues avail.) **Document type:** bulletin.

281.9 SW ISSN 0283-4545
ORTODOX TIDNING. (Text in Danish, Norwegian, Swedish) 1961. m. SEK 200 (effective 1993). (Stockholms Ortodoxa Institut) Ortodoxa Bokhandeln, Tulegatan 3, P.O. Box 7677, S-103 95 Stockholm, Sweden. TEL 46-8-20-82-42. FAX 46-8-20-82-42. Ed.Bd. bk.rev. circ. 1,000.
 Former titles: (until 1985): Ortodox Orientering (ISSN 0281-9465); (until 1981): Ortodox Tidning; (until 1975): Ortodox Kyrkotidning (ISSN 0030-5952)

281.9 BE
PATROLOGIA SYRIACA ET ORIENTALIS. 1903. irreg., vol.45, fasc.2, 1992. N.V. Brepols, Steenweg op Tielen 68, 2300 Turnhout, Belgium. TEL 32-14-402500. FAX 32-14-428919. (also avail. in microfiche from IDC; back issues avail.) **Document type:** monographic series.

281.9 NE ISSN 0032-2415
POKROF; bi-monthly review about eastern Christianity. 1954. 5/yr. fl.22.50. Apostolaat voor de Oosterse Kerken, Dr. Nuijensstraat 4, 5014 RL Tilburg, Netherlands. TEL 31-13-368985. FAX 31-13-439510. Ed. P. Gabriel Muenninghoff. bk.rev.; illus.; index every 4 yrs. circ. 1,500. **Indexed:** CERDIC. **Document type:** academic/scholarly publication.

281.9 362.7 GR
POLYTECHNI OIKOGENEIA. q. Panhellenia Enosi Philon ton Polytechnon, Akademias 78D, 106 78 Athens, Greece. TEL 30-1-3838-586. FAX 30-1-3839-509.
 Description: Discusses activities of the Greek Orthodox church and activities for children.

281.9 YU
PRAVOSLAVLJE/ORTHODOXY; novine Srpske Patrijarsije. (Text in Serbian) 1967. s-m. $25. Srpska Patrijarsija, 7 Jula 5, 11000 Belgrade, Yugoslavia. TEL 011 635-699. FAX 011-630-865. (Co-sponsor: Sveti Arhijerijaki Sinod Srpske Provoslave Crkve) Ed. Slobodan Mileusnic. adv.; bk.rev. circ. 27,000.

281.9 US ISSN 0032-7018
BX460
PRAVOSLAVNAYA RUS'; tzerkovno-obshchestvennyi organ. (Monthly supplement avail.: Pravoslavnaya Zhyzn (ISSN 0032-6992)) (Text in Russian) 1928. fortn. $30 (including supplement). Holy Trinity Monastery, Box 36, Jordanville, NY 13361. TEL 315-858-0940. bk.rev. circ. 2,500. (tabloid format) **Indexed:** CERDIC. **Document type:** newspaper.

281.9 248 US ISSN 0032-6992
BX460
PRAVOSLAVNAYA ZHYZN/ORTHODOX LIFE. (Supplement to: Pravoslavnaya Rus' (ISSN 0032-7018)) (Text in Russian) 1950. m. $10. Holy Trinity Monastery, Box 36, Jordanville, NY 13361. TEL 315-858-0940. circ. 2,625. (tabloid format) **Indexed:** Amer.Bibl.Slavic & E.Eur.Stud., CERDIC.

281.9 YU ISSN 0032-700X
PRAVOSLAVNO MISAO. (Text in Serbo-Croatian) 1959. a. 100 din.($5) Udruzenje Pravoslavnog Svestenstva SFR Jugoslavije, Glavni Savez, Francuska 31-1, Belgrade, Yugoslavia. Ed. Dusan Strbac. bk.rev. circ. 1,600.

281.9 266 YU ISSN 0555-0122
PRAVSLAVNI MISIONAR/ORTHODOX MISSIONARY. (Text in Serbian) 1958. bi-m. 900 din.($10) Sveti Arhijerijski Sinod, Sedmog Jula 5, 11000 Belgrade, Yugoslavia. TEL 011 635-699. Ed. Irineus Bulovic. adv.; bk.rev. circ. 32,000.

281.9 US ISSN 0036-0317
BX496.A1
RUSSIAN ORTHODOX JOURNAL. 1927. 8/yr. $12. Federated Russian Orthodox Clubs of America, 10 Downs Dr. (Plains), Wilkes-Barre, PA 18705. TEL 717-825-3158. Ed. Nancy Gilbert. adv. contact: Michael Dorosh. bk.rev.; illus.; index. circ. 3,800. **Document type:** academic/scholarly publication.
 Description: Features articles about the organization's activities and members, and about the Orthodox faith.

281.9 RU ISSN 0044-4553
RUSSKAYA PRAVOSLAVNAYA TSERKOV'. MOSKOVSKAYA PATRIARKHIYA. ZHURNAL/JOURNAL OF THE MOSCOW PATRIARCHATE. (Editions in English and Russian) 1931. m. 12 Rub. Moskovskaya Patriarkhiya, Novodevichii pr., 1, Moscow G-435, Russia. Ed. Archbishop Pitirim. bibl.; illus. **Indexed:** CERDIC, Curr.Dig.Sov.Press, Rel.& Theol.Abstr. (1989-), Rel.Ind.One.
 —CCC.

RELIGIONS AND THEOLOGY — HINDU

281.9   US   ISSN 0222-1543
BX598.A1
RUSSKOE VOZROZHDENIE; nezavisimyi russkii pravoslavnyi natsional'nyi zhurnal. (Text in Russian) 1978. q. $28. St. Seraphim Foundation, 53 Duane Ln., Demarest, NJ 07627-1304. TEL 201-768-5424. FAX 201-768-3436. Ed. Miliza K. Holodny. adv.; bk.rev. circ. 1,500. (back issues avail.) **Indexed:** Amer.Bibl.Slavic & E.Eur.Stud.

281.9   US
ST. PAISIUS MISSIONARY SCHOOL. COURSES FOR (YEAR). a. St. Pasius Missionary School, 7777 Martinelli Rd., Forestville, CA 95436. TEL 707-887-9740. FAX 707-887-9023.
  Description: Details courses and workshops the school is running, discusses forthcoming conferences, and outlines the missionary's philosophy.

281.9   US   ISSN 0897-7690
ST. PETER THE ALEUT ORTHODOX EDUCATIONAL SERIES. 1983. bi-m. (Monastery of St. Anthony the Great) St. Anthony the Great Orthodox Publications, Box 1432, Alamogordo, NM 88311-1432. (Subscr. to: 3044 N. 27th St., Phoenix, AZ 85016) Ed. Rev. Fr. Bessarion Agioantonides. circ. 50,000. (back issues avail.) **Document type:** monographic series.

230   US   ISSN 0036-3227
BX460
ST. VLADIMIR'S THEOLOGICAL QUARTERLY. 1953; N.S. 1957. q. $25 (foreign $35). St. Vladimir's Orthodox Theological Seminary, 575 Scarsdale Rd., Crestwood, Tuckahoe, NY 10707. TEL 914-961-8313. FAX 914-961-4507. Ed. Rev. John Breck. adv.; bk.rev.; bibl.; illus.; index. circ. 1,800. (also avail. in microform from UMI; reprint service avail. from UMI) **Indexed:** CERDIC, New Test.Abstr., Old Test.Abstr., Rel.& Theol.Abstr. (1967-), Rel.Ind.One, Rel.Per. **Document type:** academic/scholarly publication.
  —BLDSC (8070.208000); Faxon; UMI; UnCover.
  Formerly: St. Vladimir's Seminary Quarterly.
  Description: Publishes scholarly articles on Orthodox theology. Includes the history, liturgy, ecclesiology, scripture and pastoral theology of East and West, from an Orthodox perspective.

281.9   UK   ISSN 0260-0382
THE SHEPHERD; an Orthodox Christian pastoral magazine. 1980. m. contributions. St. Edward Brotherhood, St. Cyprian's Ave., Brookwood, Woking, Surrey GU24 0BL, England. (U.S. subscr. to: Orthodox Benevolent Fund, Box 743, Rye, NH 03870-0743) Ed. Fr. Alexis (Pobjoy). adv.; bk.rev. circ. 750. **Document type:** bulletin.

281.9   YU   ISSN 0353-1805
SLATKI GROZDOVI VINOGRADA GOSPODNJEG. (Text in Serbo-Croatian) 1987. w. free. Uprava Parohije Uspenske, Sumadijska 3-III, 21000 Novi Sad, Yugoslavia. TEL 021 28-055. Ed. N. Petrovic.

281.9   AT
SLAVIC GOSPEL NEWS. 1970. bi-m. free. Slavic Gospel Association, P.O. Box 396, Noble Park, Vic. 3174, Australia. TEL 03-562-3434. Eds. Brian Harper, Ron Vogt. circ. 4,000.
  Description: Discusses and promotes Christianity in the former U.S.S.R. and other Slavic countries.

281.9   UK   ISSN 0144-8722
BX1
SOBORNOST. 1928. s-a. £15($32) to individuals; libraries £8 (U.S. $25; elsewhere £10) (effective 1995-1996). Fellowship of St. Alban & St. Sergius, 1 Canterbury Rd., Oxford OX2 6LU, England. TEL 01865-529913. Ed.Bd. adv.; bk.rev.; illus. circ. 1,300. (also avail. in microform from UMI; reprint service avail. from UMI) **Indexed:** Arts & Hum.Cit.Ind., Br.Hum.Ind., Cath.Ind., CERDIC, Curr.Cont., New Test.Abstr., Rel.& Theol.Abstr. (1979-), Rel.Ind.One, Rel.Per.
  —BLDSC (8318.020500); Genuine Article; SWETS; UMI.
  Incorporating (in 1979): Eastern Churches Review (ISSN 0012-8740)
  Description: Contains articles dealing with Orthodox theology and church history, with particular reference to parallels in Western (Anglican and Roman) milieux. Reports on ecumenical concerns within this area.

281.9   US   ISSN 0038-1039
SOLIA; the herald. (Text in English and Rumanian) 1936. m. $12 in U.S.; Canada $14; elsewhere $16. Romanian Orthodox Episcopate of America, Box 185, Grass Lake, MI 49240-0185. TEL 517-522-3656. FAX 517-522-5907. Ed. Rt. Rev. Bishop Nathaniel Popp. bk.rev. circ. 5,300. **Indexed:** CERDIC. **Document type:** newspaper.

281.9   US   ISSN 0950-2742
SOUROZH. 1980. 4/yr. £12($25) Russian Patriarchal Diocese of Sourozh, 94A Banbury Rd., Oxford OX2 6JT, England. TEL 0865-512701. (Subscr. to: 13 Carver Rd., Herne Hill, London SE24 9LS, England) Ed. Bishop Basil of Sergievo. bk.rev. circ. 700. **Document type:** academic/scholarly publication.
  Description: Covers Orthodox theology, current events, history, and ecumenical activities.

281.9   US   ISSN 0039-7156
SVIT/LIGHT.* (Text in English) 1910. bi-m. $3. Russian Orthodox Catholic Mutual Aid Society of U.S.A., 10 Down Dr., Wilkes Barre, PA 18705-3802. TEL 717-822-8591. adv. circ. 1,500. (tabloid format) **Indexed:** CERDIC.

281.9   GR   ISSN 0049-3635
THEOLOGIA. (Text in English, French, German, Greek or Italian) 1923. q. Dr.5100($40) Holy Synod of the Church of Greece, 14 Ioannou Gennadiou St., Athens 11521, Greece. TEL 30-1-72-18-327. Ed. Evangelos Theodorou. bk.rev.; bibl.; illus.; index. circ. 1,800. **Indexed:** Bibl.Ling., CERDIC. **Document type:** corporate report.

281.9   RU
TOMSKIE PRAVOSLAVNYE VEDOMOSTI. 1990. m. 1000 Rub. Novosibirskaya Eparkhiya, Blagochinie Pravoslavnykh Khramov Tomskoi Oblasti, Ul. Altaiskaya 47, 634029 Tomsk, Russia. TEL 23-41-23. bk.rev. circ. 10,000.
  Description: Presents the history and life of the Eastern Orthodox church in Tomsk region.

281.9   YU   ISSN 0042-4552
UDRUZENJE PRAVOSLAVNOG SVESTENSTVA S.F.R. JUGOSLAVIJE. GLAVNI SAVEZ. VESNIK. 1949. m. 500 din. Udruzenje Pravoslavnog Svestenstva S.F.R. Jugoslavije, Glavni Savez, Francuska 31-1, Belgrade, Yugoslavia. Ed. Stanislav Mirovic. adv.; bk.rev. circ. 3,000.

281.9   US
VINEYARD/VRESHTA. (Text in English, Albanian) 1970. bi-m. Albanian Orthodox Archdiocese in America, 523 E. Broadway, S. Boston, MA 02127-4415. TEL 617-268-7808. Ed. Nicholas Liolin. circ. 2,800. (tabloid format; back issues avail.)

281.9 949.7   YU   ISSN 0353-1783
VINOGRAD GOSPODNJI; list za duhovnu kulturu. (Text in Serbo-Croatian) 1978. 4/yr. free. Uprava Parohije Uspenske, Sumadijska 3-III, Novi Sad, Yugoslavia. TEL 021-28-055. Ed. Dusan Petrovic. (back issues avail.)
  Description: Examines the history of the Serbian Orthodox Church and its theology.

281.9   AT
VOICE OF ORTHODOXY. (Text in English and Greek) 1980. m. Aus.$20 (foreign Aus.$35) (effective 1995 & 1996). Greek Orthodox Archdiocese of Australia, 242 Cleveland St., Redfern, N.S.W 2016, Australia. TEL 61-2-6985066. FAX 61-2-6985368. Ed. Bishop Seraphim. bk.rev. circ. 3,500. **Document type:** bulletin.

RELIGIONS AND THEOLOGY — Hindu

see also Oriental Studies

ADVENT. see *PHILOSOPHY*

294.5   II
ANDHRA PATRIKA PANCHANGAM. a. Andhra Patrika, 14-14-21 Mallikarjuna Rao St., Gandhinagar, Vijayawada 520 003, India. TEL 61247. adv.
  Description: Almanac for Hindu families.

181.41 610   II
ARUT PERUM JOTHI. (Hindu philosophy and Siddha medicine) (Text in English and Tamil) vol.11, 1970. m. Rs.6. Arumbakkam, Madras 29, India. Ed.Bd. adv.

294.5   US   ISSN 0005-3643
BACK TO GODHEAD; magazine of the Hare Krishna movement. 1944. 6/yr. $24 in U.S. & Canada; elsewhere $27. Box 255, Sandy Ridge, NC 27046. TEL 800-800-3BTG. FAX 904-462-7893. (Subscr. to: BTG Subscriber Service Center, Box 16027, N. Hollywood, CA 91615-9900. TEL 619-272-7384) Ed. Jayadvaita Swami. adv. contact: Tom Chapa. bk.rev.; illus.; index. circ. 20,000. **Document type:** trade publication.
  —UMI; UnCover.
  Description: Promotes self-relization, spiritual culture, philosophical understanding, and devotion to Krishna, the supreme personality of godhead, as depicted in the Vedic literature of India.

BHAU VISHNU ASHETAR VEDIC RESEARCH SERIES. see *LINGUISTICS*

294.5   II
DAILY PANTH KHALSA. (Text in Punjabi) 1977. d. Guru Harkrishan Public School Bldg., Shere-Punjab Market, Patiala, India. Ed. Upkar Singh Bedi; Pub. Sarabjit Singh. adv. contact: Manpreet Singh. circ. 18,539. **Document type:** newspaper.

294   II   ISSN 0012-4206
DIVINE LIFE. (Text in English) vol.32, 1970. m. $4.50. Divine Life Society, Sivananda Nagar, Tehri-Garhwal 249192, Uttar Pradesh, India. Ed. Swami Krishnananda. bk.rev.; illus.; index.

294   II   ISSN 0012-4265
DIVYA VANI/DIVINE VOICE. (Text in English) 1961. m. $6. Avatar Meher Baba Mission, 1-8-7 Sriramanagar, Kakinada 3, Andhra Pradesh, India. Ed. Swami Satya Prakash Meheranada. bk.rev.; bibl. circ. 1,000.

294.5   II
ECSTASY; inter-disciplinary journal of cultural renaissance. 1984. q. Rs.150. (Nityanand Institute of Culture) Brahmavidyapeeth, 23-354 Azadnagar, Jaiprakash Rd., Andheri, Bombay 400 058, India. Ed. M.R. Sinha. adv.; bk.rev.; charts; illus.; index. circ. 3,500.

294   II
GURMAT SAGAR. (Text in Punjabi) 1964. m. Rs.12. Giani Balwaut Singh Saut Sipahi, Ed. & Pub., M-90 Raghuvir Nagar, Najaf Garh Rd., New Delhi 110027, India.

294.5   MF
HINDU. (Text in English and French) 1981. w. Hindi Publications House, 26, Av. Drapers, Quatre Bornes, Mauritius. Ed. Krishnaduth Bhorra.

291   CN   ISSN 0844-4587
HINDU - CHRISTIAN STUDIES BULLETIN. 1988. a. Can.$12($10) (effective 1994). Centre for Studies in Religion and Society, University of Victoria, P.O. Box 3045, Victoria, BC V8W 3P4, Canada. TEL 604-721-6325. FAX 604-721-6234. Ed. Harold Coward. bk.rev. (back issues avail.) **Document type:** academic/scholarly publication.
  Description: Provides a world-wide forum for Hindu-Christian scholarly studies and dialogue.

200   II
HINDU REGENERATION. (Text in English) 1971. q. Rs.10. Bharat Sevashram Sangha, Hyderabad Branch, Lower Tank Bund Rd., Hyderabad 500029, India. Ed. Swami Shantananda. adv. circ. 1,000.

294.5   US   ISSN 0896-0801
HINDUISM TODAY. South African edition (ISSN 1022-2154) (Asian, European, Dutch and Hindi editions also avail.) 1979. m. $27. Himalayan Academy, 107 Kaholale Rd., Kapaa, HI 96746. TEL 808-822-7032. FAX 808-822-4351. Ed. Rev. Palaniswami. adv.; bk.rev.; film rev.; video rev. circ. 55,000. **Document type:** newspaper.
  Description: International newspaper affirming the dharma and recording the modern history of nearly a billion members of a global religion.

INDIA CULTURES/SAMSKRITI. see *SOCIOLOGY*

INTERNATIONAL YOGA GUIDE. see *PHILOSOPHY*

294.5   II
JATRA. (Text in Marathi) 1963. w. newsstand price: Rs.4. Menaka Prakashan Pvt. Ltd., 2117 Sadashiv Peth, Pune 30, India. Ed. Purushottam Vishnu Beheray.

294.592 CN ISSN 0706-6449
JOURNAL OF STUDIES IN THE BHAGAVADGITA. 1981. irreg. Can.$10 to individuals; institutions Can.$15. McGill University, Faculty of Religious, Montreal, PQ H3A 2A7, Canada. Ed.Bd. adv.; bk.rev. circ. 100. (back issues avail.) Indexed: Rel.& Theol.Abstr. (1990-), Rel.Ind.One, Rel.Per.

294.1 US ISSN 0276-0444
B130
MANANAM PUBLICATION SERIES. (Text in English and Sanskrit) 1978. q. $20 (foreign $30). Chinmaya Mission West, Box 129, Piercy, CA 95587. TEL 707-247-3488. FAX 707-247-3422. Ed. Margaret Leuverink. adv.; bk.rev.; charts; illus. circ. 1,300. (back issues avail.)

MEDITATOR'S NEWSLETTER. see *RELIGIONS AND THEOLOGY*

294.6 UK ISSN 0969-7942
NAMA HATTA NEWSLETTER; newsletter of the Vaisnava Community. 1981. 6/yr. £8. (International Society for Krishna Consciousness) BBL Distribution Services Ltd., P.O. Box 324, Borehamwood, Herts. WD6 1NB, England. TEL 081-905-1244. FAX 081-905-1108. Ed. Kripamoya Das. adv.; bk.rev.; illus. circ. 1,500. Document type: newsletter.
  Former titles: F O L K Newsletter; F O L K Magazine (ISSN 0260-938X)
  Description: Contains local news, philosophy, and topics of interest to the members.

294.5 II ISSN 0027-7770
NANAK PRAKASH PATRIKA. (Text in English, Hindi, or Panjabi) 1969. m. Rs.3. Punjabi University, Patiala 4, Punjab, India. Ed. Taran Singh. bk.rev. circ. 600. (processed)

NANDAN KANAN. see *PHILOSOPHY*

294.5 II
NAVNEE HINDI DIGEST. (Text in Hindi) 1952. m. newsstand price: Rs.6. Bharatiya Vidya Bhavan, Kulapati K.M. Munshi Marg, Bombay 400 007, India. TEL 8110224. Ed. Girijashankar Trivedi; Pub. S. Ramakrishnan. adv.; B&W page Rs.1200; 140 x 190.

294.5 SA ISSN 1016-5320
NIDAN. (Text in English) 1989. a. R.5 in southern Africa; overseas $5. University of Durban-Westville, Department of Hindu Studies, Private Bag X54001, Durban 4000, South Africa. TEL 27-31-820-2657. FAX 27-31-820-2383. Ed. Anil Sooklal. abstr.; bibl. (back issues avail.) Document type: academic/scholarly publication.
  Description: Publishes original scholarly articles on topics of contemporary significance in the study of Hindu religion, philosophy and culture.
  Refereed Serial

294 II
OSHO TIMES INTERNATIONAL. (Text in English, French, German, Hindi, Italian, Japanese, Polish, Portuguese, Spanish, Tamil) 1982. s-m. Rs.600($60) Tao Publishing (Pvt.) Ltd., 50 Koregaon Park, Poona 411 001, Maharashtra, India. TEL 91-212-624181. FAX 91-212-624181. TELEX 0145 7474 LOVIN. (Dist. in N. America by: Osho Chidvilas Inc., Box 3849, Sedona, AZ 86340; Dist. in UK by: Osho Purnima Publications, Greenwise, Vange Park Rd., Basildon, Essex, SS6 5LA, England) Ed. Chaitanya Keerti. adv.; bk.rev. circ. 20,000. (tabloid format; back issues avail.)
  Formerly (until 1988): Rajneesh Times International.

295.6 II ISSN 0971-3786
PARSIANA. 1964. 10/yr. Rs.175. Parsiana Publications Pvt. Ltd., c/o H. L. Rochat, Navsari Chambers, 39 A.K. Nayak Marg, Fort, Bombay 400 001, India. TEL 2042915. FAX 2042922. TELEX 11-85710 RABO IN. E-mail: jimmy%dartnet@uunet.uu.net. Ed. Jehangir R. Patel. adv.; B&W page Rs.2200, color page Rs.6500; trim 210 x 275. bk.rev.; illus. circ. 3,800. Indexed: Ind.India.

294.6 II ISSN 0031-3467
PEACE. Telegu edition: Santi. (Text in English) 1928. m. Rs.15. Santi Asram - Mission of Peace, P.O. Totapalli Hills Pin 533446, Via Shankavaram, E. Godavari Dist., Andhra Pradesh, India. TEL 8644 P.C.O.007. Document type: academic/scholarly publication.
  Description: Aims to illuminate Hinduism as well as other religions through prayer, poetry, meditations and devotions. Also covers religious activities. Propagates individual and universal peace.

294.5 II ISSN 0032-6178
BL1100
PRABUDDHA BHARATA/AWAKENED INDIA. (Text in English) 1896. m. Rs.30 (U.S. & Canada $20; elsewhere £15). (Ramakrishna Order) Advaita Ashrama, 5 Dehi Entally Rd., Calcutta 700 014, India. TEL 91-33-244-0898. FAX 91-33-245-0050. Ed. Swami Atmaramananda. adv. contact: Swami Bodhasarananda. bk.rev.; charts; illus.; index. circ. 6,000. Document type: academic/scholarly publication.
  —BLDSC (6579.250000).
  Description: Universal religion and its application to daily life for followers of all religions and sects.

294.5 II
SAI SUDDHA. (Text in English, Tamil or Telugu) m. All India Sai Samaj, Madras 4, Tamil Nadu, India. illus.

294.5 II
SANTI. Variant spelling: Shanti. English edition: Peace (ISSN 0031-3467) (Text in Telugu) 1924. m. Rs.15. Santi Asram - Mission of Peace, P.O. Totapalli Hills Pin 533446, Via Shankavaram, E. Godavari Dist., Andhra Pradesh, India.
  Description: Aims to illuminate Hinduism as well as other religions through prayer, poetry, meditations, and devotion. Also covers religious activities. Advocates individual and universal peace.

294.5 II
SHREE GURUDEV ASHRAM NEWSLETTER. (Text in English) vol.7, 1978. m. Rs.10($6) (Shree Gurudev Ashram) Gurudev Siddhapeeth, P.O. Ganeshpuri District, Thana 401206, India. Ed. R. Pratap. illus. Document type: newsletter.

294.5 100 II ISSN 0251-1746
SHREE HARI KATHA/GOSPEL OF GOD. (Text in English and Hindi) 1974. m. Rs.51. Shiksha Sansthan, B5-73 Azad Apartments, Sri Aurobindo Marg, New Delhi 110016, India. TEL 11-6864836. FAX 11-89-22052. TELEX 598214. Ed. Surendra Agrawal. circ. 1,000. Document type: academic/scholarly publication.

294.5 II ISSN 0037-5950
SIVAM. (Text in Bengali) 1963. m. Rs.15. Swami Bholananda Seva Mandal, 1 Mahesh Choudhury Ln., Calcutta 25, India. Eds. Sachindra Kumar Bhattacharyya, Amulya Kishore Lodh. adv.; bk.rev. circ. 2,000. Indexed: Rel.& Theol.Abstr.

SUDHI SAHITYA; a bilingual literary monthly. see *PHILOSOPHY*

294.5 II ISSN 0971-3964
TAPOVAN PRASAD. (Text in English) 1962. m. Rs.60($20) Chinmaya Mission, No. 2, 13th Ave., Harrington Rd., Madras 600031, Tamil Nadu, India. TEL 8265641. (U.S. addr.: c/o Chinmaya Mission West, Box 129, Piercy, CA 95467. TEL 707-247-3488) Ed. C. Ammini Kutti. adv.; bk.rev.; circ. 5,000 (controlled). Document type: academic/scholarly publication.

294.5 UK ISSN 1355-6436
VEDANTA. 1952. bi-m. £6($12.50) Ramakrishna Vedanta Centre, Bourne End, Bucks. SL8 5LG, England. TEL 01628-526464. Ed. Swami Dayatmananda. bk.rev. circ. 600. Document type: newsletter.
  Formerly (until 1995): Vedanta for East and West (ISSN 0951-127X)

294.5 II ISSN 0042-2983
VEDANTA KESARI. (Text in English) 1914. m. Rs.45($20) (effective 1995). Sri Ramakrishna Math, 16 Ramakrishna Math Rd., Mylapore, Madras 600 004, India. FAX 91-44-493-4589. Ed. Swami Tyagananda. adv.; bk.rev.; charts; illus.; stat.; index, cum.index. circ. 3,500.
  Description: Exposition of Vedanta philosophy.

294.5 100 II ISSN 0377-6360
VEDIC LIGHT. (Text in English) vol.8, 1974. m. Rs.35 (effective 1990). International Aryan League - Sarvadishik Arya Pratinidhi Sabha, Dayanand Bhavan 3-5, Asaf Sli Road, New Delhi 110 002, India. TEL 3274771. Ed. S.C. Pathak. adv.; bk.rev. circ. 1,000.

294.5 US
VIVEKANANDA VEDANTA SOCIETY OF CHICAGO. BULLETINS. 1930. m. free. Vivekananda Vedanta Society, 5423 S. Hyde Park Blvd., Chicago, IL 60615. TEL 312-363-0027. Ed. Swami Chidananda. circ. 750. (looseleaf format; back issues avail.) Document type: bulletin.
  Description: Gives schedule of activities at the Vivekananda Vedanta Society and quotations from the society's teachings.

RELIGIONS AND THEOLOGY — Islamic

A I M. (Association of Indian Muslims of America) see *SOCIAL SCIENCES: COMPREHENSIVE WORKS*

AL-ADALAH/JUSTICE. see *LAW*

297 SL ISSN 0044-653X
AFRICAN CRESCENT. 1955. m. Le.4. Ahmadiyya Muslim Mission, P.O. Box 353, Freetown, Sierra Leone. Ed. Maulana Khalil Mobashir. adv.; bk.rev. circ. 1,000.

268 NR ISSN 0065-468X
AHMADU BELLO UNIVERSITY. CENTRE OF ISLAMIC LEGAL STUDIES. JOURNAL. 1966. irreg., vol.5, 1974. Ahmadu Bello University, Centre of Islamic Legal Studies, P.M.B. 1013, Zaria, Nigeria. (Foreign orders to: Wiley & Sons Ltd., Lincoln's Inn Archway, Carey St., London W.C. 2, England)

297.65 SU ISSN 1319-0725
AKHBAR AL-A'ALAM AL-ISLAMI. (Text in Arabic; summaries in English) 1966. w. $40. Muslim World League, P.O. Box 538, Makkah, Saudi Arabia. TEL 966-2-5447905. FAX 966-2-5448196. Document type: newspaper.

297 DK ISSN 0108-7290
AKTIV ISLAM. (Text in Danish) 1959. q. DKK 30 free to libraries. Nusrat Djahan Moske, Eriksminde Alle 2, 2650 Hvidovre, Denmark. TEL 45-31-75-35-05. FAX 45-75-00-07. Ed. Mansoor Ahmad Tariq. bk.rev. circ. 750.
  Description: Presents various different religious issues, with particular reference to the mission of the Ahmadiyya Movement in Islam.

297 SA
AL-BALAAGH; dedicated to the expounding of Islam in its pristine purity. (Text in English) vol.16, no.2, 1991. q. R.15 (UK £5; elsewhere $10). P.O. Box 1925, Lenasia 1820, South Africa. TEL 27-11-8527041. Ed. A.S.K. Joommal. circ. 5,000. (tabloid format) Indexed: Per.Islam. (1991-).
  Description: Forum for the discussion of topics of interest to Muslims throughout the world.

297 IO ISSN 0126-6357
AMANAH. fortn. Jalan Garuda 69, Kemayoran, Jakarta, Indonesia. TEL 021-410254. Ed. Maskun Iskandar. circ. 180,000.

300 297 US ISSN 0742-6763
BP1
AMERICAN JOURNAL OF ISLAMIC SOCIAL SCIENCES. 1984. q. $30 to individuals (foreign $55); institutions $45 (foreign $70). Association of Muslim Social Scientists, 555 Grove St., Box 669, Herndon, VA 22070. TEL 703-471-1133. FAX 703-471-3922. TELEX 901153 IIIT WASH. (Co-sponsor: International Institute of Islamic Thought) Ed. Sayyid M. Syeed. adv.; bk.rev.; charts; illus.; stat.; index, cum.index: 1985-1991. circ. 3,000. (back issues avail.; reprint service avail.) Indexed: Int.Bibl.Soc.Sci., Int.Polit.Sci.Abstr., P.A.I.S. (1990-), Per.Islam. (1991-), Polit.Sci.Abstr., Rel.Ind.One (1987-), Sociol.Abstr. (1985-). Document type: academic/scholarly publication.
  —Faxon; SWETS; UMI; UnCover.
  Formerly (until 1984): American Journal of Islamic Studies.
  Description: Devoted to serious research and development of a scientific approach in the fields of Islamic social sciences and human studies.
  Refereed Serial

RELIGIONS AND THEOLOGY — ISLAMIC

297 US
THE AMERICAN MUSLIM; a Muslim by conviction. 1989. q. $20 (foreign $30). American Muslim Support Group, Box 5670, Bel Ridge, MO 63121. TEL 314-291-3711. adv. contact: Sheila Musaji. bk.rev. **Indexed:** Per.Islam.

297 US
THE AMERICAN MUSLIM RESOURCE DIRECTORY. 1992. a. $25. American Muslim Support Group, Box 5670, Bel Ridge, MO 63121. TEL 314-291-3711. adv. contact: Sheila Musaji. **Indexed:** Per.Islam.

297 FR ISSN 1246-7731
ANNALES DE L'AUTRE ISLAM. 1993. a. 150 F. Institut National des Langues et Civilisations Orientales, Equipe de Recherche Interdisciplinaire sur les Societes Mediterraneennes Musulmanes Non-Arabes, 2 rue de Lille, 75343 Paris Cedex 07, France. TEL 44-08-89-68. FAX 44-08-89-79. Ed. Michel Bozdemir. **Document type:** academic/scholarly publication.

ANNALES ISLAMOLOGIQUES. see ORIENTAL STUDIES

ANNALES ISLAMOLOGIQUES. SUPPLEMENT. see ORIENTAL STUDIES

297 MK
AL-AQIDAH. (Text in Arabic) w. P.O. Box 4001, Ruwi, Muscat, Sultanate of Oman. TEL 701000. TELEX 3399. Ed. Said as-Samhan al-Kathiri. illus. circ. 5,000.

ARAB LAW QUARTERLY. see LAW — International Law

ARABIC SCIENCES AND PHILOSOPHY; a historical journal. see SCIENCES: COMPREHENSIVE WORKS

ARCHEOLOGIE ISLAMIQUE. see ARCHAEOLOGY

297 NE ISSN 0923-2044
ASFAR. 1977. irreg., vol.4, 1992. price varies. (Rijksuniversiteit te Leiden, Documentatiebureau Islam-Christendom) E.J. Brill, P.O. Box 9000, 2300 PA Leiden, Netherlands. TEL 31-71-5353500. FAX 31-71-5317532. TELEX 39296 BRILL NL. (In N. America: E.J. Brill, 24 Hudson St., Kinderhook, NY 12106. TEL 800-962-4406. FAX 518-758-1959) Ed. P. van Koningsveld. (back issues avail.) **Document type:** monographic series.

297 IR ISSN 1019-0368
ASHINA. (Text in Persian) 1991. m. $35 in Middle East; Europe, Asia $40; Americas $50. Islamic Thought Foundation, P.O. Box 14155-3899, Tehran, Iran. TEL 98-21-844092. FAX 98-21-898295.

297 TU
ATATURK UNIVERSITESI. ILAHIYAT FAKULTESI. DERGISI. 1982. a. Ataturk Universitesi, Ilahiyat Fakultesi - Ataturk University, Faculty of Theology, Erzurum, Turkey. **Indexed:** Per.Islam. (1992-). **Document type:** academic/scholarly publication.

297 AT ISSN 1039-2300
AUSTRALASIAN MUSLIM TIMES. (Text in Arabic, English, Persian, Turkish, Urdu) 1991. fortn. Aus.$30. (Australian Federation of Islamic Councils) Amust Publications Pty. Ltd., P.O. Box 331, Waterloo, N.S.W. 2017, Australia. TEL 61-2-823-8208. E-mail: zia@biochem.su.oz.au. (Subscr. to: P.O. Box 111, Bonnyrigg, N.S.W. 2177, Australia. TEL 61-2-823-3626) Ed. Qazi Ashfaq Ahmad. adv.: B&W page Aus.$350, color page Aus.$500; adv. contact: Manar Ahmad. circ. 7,500. **Indexed:** Per.Islam (1991-).
Formerly: Australian Muslim Times (ISSN 1036-899X)
Description: Presents international Muslim news for the Muslim community and Muslim business persons.

AWAL. see HISTORY — History Of Africa

059.915 297 IR ISSN 1023-7992
AYENEH-E PAZHOOHESH/MIRAT AL-TAHQIQ/MIRROR OF RESEARCH. (Text in Persian; summaries in Arabic, English) 1990. 6/yr. $30 in Europe & Arab countries; Asia & Africa $33; US & Australia $37.50. Daftar-i Tablighat-i Islami-i Hawzah-i 'Ilmiyah-i Qum, P.O. Box 37185-3693, Qum, Iran. TEL 98-251-37729. Ed. Mohammed Ali Mahdavi Raad. bk.rev.; bibl. circ. 7,000. **Document type:** academic/scholarly publication.
Description: Presents articles dealing with methodological issues and current research in Islamic culture, with extensive reviews of recent publications in the field, and news of research and translation projects underway.

297 GW ISSN 0174-2477
BERLINER ISLAMSTUDIEN. 1981. irreg., vol.5, 1992. price varies. (Institut fuer Islamwissenschaft der Freien Universitaet Berlin) Franz Steiner Verlag Wiesbaden GmbH, Birkenwaldstr. 44, 70191 Stuttgart, Germany. TEL 0711-2582-0. FAX 0711-2582390. (Subscr. to: Postfach 101061, 70009 Stuttgart, Germany) Ed.Bd. **Document type:** monographic series.

297 IO ISSN 0215-806X
BESTARI; edisi jurnal ilmiah. (Text in Bahasa Indonesia) vol.4, no.6, 1991. bi-m. Universitas Muhammadiyyah, Jalan Bandung No. 1, Malang 51253, Indonesia. **Indexed:** Per.Islam. (1991-).

956 297 GW ISSN 0170-3102
BIBLIOTHECA ISLAMICA. (Text in English and German) irreg., vol.42, 1995. price varies. (Deutsche Morgenlaendische Gesellschaft) Franz Steiner Verlag Wiesbaden GmbH, Birkenwaldstr. 44, 70191 Stuttgart, Germany. TEL 0711-2582-0. FAX 0711-2582390. (Subscr. to: Postfach 101061, 70009 Stuttgart, Germany) Ed.Bd. **Document type:** monographic series.

297 UA ISSN 0259-7373
BP1
BULLETIN CRITIQUE DES ANNALES ISLAMOLOGIQUES. (Supplement to: Annales Islamologiques (ISSN 0570-1716)) 1984. a. £E70 (overseas 200 F.). Institut Francais d'Archeologie Orientale du Caire, P.O. Box 11562 Kasr el-Aini, 37 Sharia Shaikh Aly Youssef, Mounira, Cairo, Egypt. TEL 20-2-3548245. FAX 20-2-3544635. (Dist. by: Boustany's Arab Publishing House, 29 Faggalah St., 11271 Cairo, Egypt. TEL 20-2-4177915. FAX 20-2-3404905; In France: Imprimerie Nationale - D A C F, 27 rue de la Convention, 75732 Paris Cedex 15, France. TEL 33-1-40583292. FAX 33-1-40583057; Editorial correspondence to: 27 rue Jacob, 75261 Paris Cedex 06, France) Eds. D. Gimaret, M.-Cl. Simeone-Senelle. bk.rev. circ. 800. (back issues avail.) **Indexed:** Bibl.Ling. **Document type:** academic/scholarly publication.
Description: Annual review of books recently published in the field of Islamic and Arabic studies throughout the world.

C I B E D O - BEITRAEGE ZUM GESPRAECH ZWISCHEN CHRISTEN UND MUSLIMEN. see RELIGIONS AND THEOLOGY

297 SU
CALL TO THE TRUTH. (Text in Arabic) m. $24 to individuals; institutions $30. World Muslim League, P.O. Box 538, Makkah, Saudi Arabia. TEL 966-2-544-1622. TELEX 440390.

297.65 CN ISSN 0707-2945
CANADIAN MUSLIM. (Text in Arabic and English) 1977. q. free. Ottawa Muslim Association, P.O. Box 2952, Sta. D, Ottawa, Ont. 51P 5W9, Canada. TEL 613-725-0004. Ed. Saeed Bokhari. adv.; bk.rev.; circ. 2,000 (controlled).

CENTRAL ASIA BRIEF. see POLITICAL SCIENCE

297 US ISSN 1051-0354
COMPARATIVE STUDIES ON MUSLIM SOCIETIES. 1987. irreg., no.17, 1993. price varies. University of California Press, 2120 Berkeley Way, Berkeley, CA 94720. TEL 510-642-4247. FAX 510-643-7127. (Orders to: California-Princeton Fulfillment Services, 1445 Lower Ferry Rd., Ewing, NJ 08618. TEL 800-777-4726. FAX 800-999-1958) Ed. Barbara D. Metcalf. (back issues avail.) **Document type:** monographic series.
—BLDSC (3363.834500).
Description: Publishes papers on a wide variety of historical and theological topics of Islam.
Refereed Serial

297 IT
COMUNITA ISLAMICA; Jihad periodico Islamico. (Text in French, German, Italian) 1980; N.S. 1990, Dec. bi-m. L.30000($10) (foreign L.50000). Edizioni Arktos, Via Gardezzana 57, 10022 Carmagnola, Italy. Ed. Giovanni Oggero. adv.; bk.rev.
Formerly: Jihad.

297 CN ISSN 0705-3754
DS35.3
CRESCENT INTERNATIONAL. 1972. s-m. $40 to individuals; institutions $60. Crescent Pak Inc., 300 Steelcase Rd. W., Unit 8, Markham, ON L3R 2W2, Canada. TEL 905-474-9292. FAX 905-474-9293. Ed. Zafar Bangash. adv. contact: S. Sharif Niazi. bk.rev. circ. 12,000. (tabloid format; also avail. in microfilm; back issues avail.) **Indexed:** Per.Islam. (1991-). **Document type:** newspaper.
Description: Covers the Islamic movements worldwide.

297 MF
LE CROISSANT. (Text in English, French) vol.5, 1991. fortn. Mauritian Islamic Mission, Rue Velore et Noor-e-Islam Mosque, Port Louis, Mauritius. **Indexed:** Per.Islam. (1991-).

DAILY JANG LONDON. see ETHNIC INTERESTS

DANSALAN QUARTERLY. see SOCIOLOGY

297 SU
AL-DA'WAH. (Text in Arabic) w. P.O. Box 626, Riyadh 11421, Saudi Arabia. TEL 966-2-4357249. Ed. Abdul Aziz Al-Eissa. **Document type:** consumer publication.
Description: Covers Islamic religious affairs.

297 LY
AL-DA'WAH AL-ISLAMIYYAH. (Text in Arabic, English, French) 1980. w. World Islamic Call Society, P.O. Box 2682, Tripoli, Libya. TEL 31021. TELEX 20407.

297 PK ISSN 0002-399X
BP1
AL-DIRASAT AL-ISLAMIYYAH. (Text in Arabic) 1965. q. Rs.100($30) Islamic Research Institute, International Islamic University, P.O. Box 1035, Islamabad 44000, Pakistan. TEL 92-51-850751. FAX 92-51-853360. TELEX 54068 IIU PK. Ed. Muhammad Al-Ghazali; Pub. Saeed Ahmad Shah. adv.; bk.rev.; index. circ. 3,000. (back issues avail.) **Document type:** academic/scholarly publication.
Description: Covers Islamic law, history, political theory and philosphy as well as other topics.

297 355 TS
DIR'U AL-ISLAM. (Text in Arabic) 1988. q. exchange basis. General Command for the Armed Forces, Administration for Spiritual Instruction, P.O. Box 907, Abu Dhabi, United Arab Emirates. TEL 447999. Ed. Ahmed Khalil. circ. 1,000.
Description: Covers Islamic topics, with an emphasis on fostering morale and Islamic customs and culture among members of the Armed Forces.

297 TS
AL-DIYA'. (Text in Arabic; supplements in English, Farsi, Urdu) 1978. q. Da'irat al-Awqaf wal-Shu'un al-Islamiyyah - Department of Endowments and Islamic Affairs, P.O. Box 3135, Dubai, United Arabi Emirates. TEL 695294. Ed. Isa Abdullah al-Mani' al-Hamadi. circ. 10,000.
Description: Covers topics related to the Qur'an, Hadith, and Sunna, as well as Islamic jurisprudence, literature, medicine, and interviews.

297 TU
DUNYA VE ISLAM. no.8, 1991. q. Yonelis Yayinlari, Lalali Cad. No. 11-3, 34480 Laleli, Istanbul, Turkey. **Indexed:** Per.Islam. (1992-).

5740 RELIGIONS AND THEOLOGY — ISLAMIC

297   IR   ISSN 1019-0775
ECHO OF ISLAM. (Text in English) m. $45. Islamic Thought Foundation, P.O. Box 14155-3899, Tehran, Iran. TEL 98-21-844092. FAX 98-21-898295. **Indexed:** Per.Islam. (1991-).
Description: Contains current news of interest to the Muslim world. Covers political developments, Islamic uprisings, general news and views.

297 034 960   FR   ISSN 1015-7344
ENCYCLOPEDIE BERBERE. 2/yr. 240 F. Edisud, La Calade - RN7, 13090 Aix-en-Provence, France. TEL 42-21-61-44. FAX 42-21-56-20.

297 034   FR   ISSN 0295-5245
DT193.5.B45
ETUDES ET DOCUMENTS BERBERES. a. 220 F. (foreign 240 F.). Edisud, La Calade - RN 7, 13090 Aix-en-Provence, France. TEL 42-21-61-44. FAX 42-21-56-20. **Indexed:** RILM.

297   LE
FAWAZIR. irreg. £L1000 per no. Dar al-Risalah al-Islamiyyah, P.O. Box 155063, 13-6173 Beirut, Lebanon. TEL 868661. FAX 831253. TELEX 207339 LE. Ed. Faysal al-Sammak. adv. circ. 10,000.
Description: Covers Islamic issues from around the world.

297   PK   ISSN 0430-4055
FIKR-O-NAZAR. (Text in Urdu) 1964. q. Rs.75($20) Islamic Research Institute, International Islamic University, P.O. Box 1035, Islamabad 44000, Pakistan. TEL 92-51-850751. FAX 92-51-853360. TELEX 54068 IIU PK. Ed. Sahibzada Sajid-ur-Rehman; Pub. Saeed Ahmad Shah. adv.; bk.rev.; index. (back issues avail.) **Document type:** academic/scholarly publication.
Description: Covers Islamic law, history, philosophy as well as other topics.

297   SU
FIQH COUNCIL JOURNAL. (Text in Arabic) 2/yr. $4 to individuals; instititutions $5. Muslim World League, P.O. Box 538, Makkah, Saudi Arabia. TEL 966-2-544-1622. TELEX 440390.

FREIBURGER ISLAMSTUDIEN. see *ORIENTAL STUDIES*

297   II
AL FURQAN. (Text in Urdu) 1933. m. Rs.25. 31 Naya Gaon West, Lucknow 226018, India.

GESCHICHTE DES ARABISCHEN SCHRIFTTUMS. see *HISTORY — History Of The Near East*

297   SU
HAJJ. (Text in Arabic, English) 1947. m. Ministry of Pilgrimage Affairs and Awqaf, Sharia Omar bin al-Khattab, Riyadh 11183, Saudi Arabia. TEL 966-1-4022200. TELEX 401603. Ed. Abdullah bin Abdul-Muttaleb Bogas. **Document type:** government publication.

297   PK
HAMDARD FOUNDATION. REPORT. 1980. biennial. free. Hamdard Foundation, Nazimabad No. 3, Karachi 74600, Pakistan. TEL 92-21-6616001. FAX 92-21-6641766. TELEX 24529 HAMD PK. circ. 2,000. **Document type:** corporate report.

297   PK   ISSN 0250-7196
BP1
HAMDARD ISLAMICUS. (Text in English) 1978. q. Rs.200($28) Hamdard Foundation, Nazimabad No. 3, Karachi 74600, Pakistan. TEL 92-21-6616001. FAX 92-21-6641766. TELEX 24529 HAMD PK. Ed. Hakim Mohammed Said. bk.rev. circ. 2,000. **Indexed:** Abstr.Musl.Rel., Amer.Hist.& Life, ExtraMED, Hist.Abstr., Mid.East: Abstr.& Ind., Per.Islam. (1991-), Rel.& Theol.Abstr. (1990-), Rel.Ind.One. **Document type:** academic/scholarly publication.
●Also available on CD-ROM.
—Faxon; UMI; UnCover.

297   NR
AL-HAQQ; a periodic Islamic newspaper. (Text in English) vol.2, no.3, 1991. bi-m. Hizbullah Movement of Nigeria, P.O. Box 5236, Marina, Lagos, Nigeria. **Indexed:** Per.Islam. (1992-). **Document type:** newspaper.

AL-HAQQ - SHARI'AH WA QANUN. see *LAW — Judicial Systems*

291 297   II   ISSN 0970-4698
BP1
HENRY MARTYN INSTITUTE OF ISLAMIC STUDIES. BULLETIN. 1930-1986; resumed in Jan. 1991. q. Rs.75($20) to individuals; institutions Rs.85 ($25). Henry Martyn Institute of Islamic Studies, c/o Diane D'Souza, Mng. Ed., P.O. Box 153, Hyderabad, A.P. 500 001, India. TEL 91-40-201134. Ed. Andreas D'Souza. bk.rev.; index. circ. 400. **Indexed:** Abstr.Musl.Rel., Per.Islam. (1991-), Rel.Ind.One. **Document type:** academic/scholarly publication.
—BLDSC (2554.779000).
Supersedes: Al-Basheer; Formerly: Christian Institutes of Islamic Studies Bulletin (ISSN 0009-5397)
Description: Aims to promote inter-faith understanding with a special focus on Islam.

297   BA
AL-HIDAYAH. (Text in Arabic) 1978. m. Ministry of Justice and Islamic Affairs, P.O. Box 450, Diplomatic Area, Manama, Bahrain. TEL 531333. Ed. Abd ar-Rahman bin Muhammad Rashid al-Khalifa.

297   IO   ISSN 0854-2414
AL-HIKMAH. (Text in Bahasa Indonesia) vol.4, 1991. q. Yayasan Mutthahhari, Jalan Kampus III-4, Bandung 40283, Indonesia. **Indexed:** Per.Islam. (1992-).

HOLY LAND REVIEW; illustrated quarterly of the Franciscan custody of the holy land. see *RELIGIONS AND THEOLOGY — Roman Catholic*

297   HK
HONG KONG MUSLIM HERALD. (Text in English) vol.14, 1992. m. P.O. Box 6488, G.P.O., Hong Kong. **Indexed:** Per.Islam. (1992-).

297   CM
AL HOUDA; islamic cultural review. q. P.O. Box 1638, Yaounde, Cameroon. Ed. Ndam Njoya Adamou.

297.38   JO
HUDA AL-ISLAM. (Text in Arabic) 1956. m. Ministry of Awqaf and Islamic Affairs, P.O. Box 659, Amman, Jordan. TEL 666141. TELEX 21559. Ed. Ahmad Muhammad Hulayyel.

ICONOGRAPHY OF RELIGIONS. SECTION 22, ISLAM. see *ART*

297   SA   ISSN 0258-932X
AL-ILM. (Text in English) 1981. a. University of Durban - Westville, Center for Research in Islamic Studies, Private Bag X54001, Durban 4000, South Africa. **Indexed:** Per.Islam. (1991-). **Document type:** academic/scholarly publication.

IMPACT (LONDON, 1971); international independent muslim news magazine. see *LITERARY AND POLITICAL REVIEWS*

297   US
INDIAN MUSLIM RELIEF COMMITTEE. ANNUAL REPORT. 1980. a. Islamic Society of North America, Indian Muslim Relief Committee, Box 0622, Freemont, CA 94537-0622. Ed. Manzoor Ghori. **Document type:** newsletter.
Description: Documents plight of under-privileged minority communities with a special emphasis on Indian muslims.

297   II
INTERACTION (HYDERABAD). (Text in English) s-a. Henry Martyn Institute of Islamic Studies, P.O. Box 153, Hyderabad, A.P. 500 001, India. Ed. Packiam T. Samuel. **Document type:** newsletter.
Description: Contains news, activities, and notes of the institute.

297   US
INVITATION. 1984. q. $10 (foreign $15). Islamic Information Center of America, Box 4052, Des Plaines, IL 60016. TEL 708-541-8141. FAX 708-824-8436. Ed. Musa Qutub. adv. contact: Husam Khateeb. bk.rev. circ. 8,000. **Document type:** academic/scholarly publication.
Refereed Serial

297   PK
IQRA. (Text in Urdu) w. Independent Newspapers Corp. Pvt. Ltd., Printing House, I.I. Chundrigar Rd., P.O. Box 52, Karachi (Sindh) 74200, Pakistan. TEL 92-21-2637111. FAX 92-21-2636066.

AL-IQTISAD AL-ISLAMI/ISLAMIC ECONOMY. see *BUSINESS AND ECONOMICS — Economic Situation And Conditions*

297   TS
ISHRAQAT JEEL. (Text in Arabic) 1984. a. Madrasat al-Qadisiyyah al-I'dadiyyah al-Thanawiyyah lil-Banat, Jama'at al-Tarbiyah al-Islamiyyah, P.O. Box 5246, Abu Dhabi, United Arab Emirates. TEL 477606. circ. 500.
Description: Covers topics relating to Islamic education for girls.

297   NE   ISSN 0021-180X
AL-ISLAAM. 1947. m. fl.35 (foreign fl.45). Ahmadiyya Moslim Missie Holland - Ahmadiyya Moslim Djamaat Nederland - Ahmadiyya Muslim Mission Holland, Oostduinlaan 79, 2596 JJ The Hague, Netherlands. TEL 31-70-3245902. FAX 31-70-3242881. Ed. A.H. van der Velden. adv.; bk.rev.; circ. 200 (paid). (also avail. in diskette format) **Document type:** bulletin.
Description: Covers the teachings of Islam and the discussion of current Islamic questions and concerns.

297   TS
AL-ISLAH/REFORM. (Text in Arabic) 1978. m. Jam'iyat al-Islah wal-Tawjih al-Ijtima'i - Society of Social Reform and Guidance, P.O. Box 4663, Dubai. TEL 665962. FAX 662071. Ed. Muhammed bin Rahma al-Aamiri. circ. 15,000.
Description: Presents an Islamic viewpoint on topics of interest to Muslims, including social, political, and cultural issues.

DER ISLAM; Zeitschrift fuer Geschichte und Kultur des Islamischen Orients. see *ORIENTAL STUDIES*

297   RE   ISSN 0151-7163
BP1
AL ISLAM. (Text in French) 1975. bi-m. 150 F. Centre Islamique de la Reunion, B.P. 437, 97459 Saint-Pierre, Reunion. TEL 25-19-65. Ed. A. Saeed Ingar. circ. 1,200. **Indexed:** So.Pac.Per.Ind.

297   IT   ISSN 0393-246X
ISLAM; storia e civilta. 1981. q. L.40000. Accademia della Cultura Islamica, Unione Islamica in Occidente, Corso Trieste, 90, 00198 Rome, Italy. FAX 85300712. (Edit. addr.: Via Archiano 4, 00199 Rome, Italy) Ed. Salvatore Bono. bk.rev. **Indexed:** RILM. **Document type:** academic/scholarly publication.

297   PK
AL-ISLAM. (Text in Urdu) 1973. w. Rs.400. c/o Jamiat Ahl-e-Hadith, 106 Ravi Rd., Lahore, Pakistan. FAX 042-54072. TELEX 46426 KARAM PK. Ed. Bashir Ansari. adv.; bk.rev.; circ. 4,000 (controlled).

297   UK   ISSN 0959-6410
BP172   CODEN: ICMREF
ISLAM AND CHRISTIAN - MUSLIM RELATIONS. 1990. 3/yr. £38 to individuals; institutions £104 (effective 1996). (Centre for the Study of Islam and Christian - Muslim Relations) Carfax Publishing Co., P.O. Box 25, Abingdon, Oxon. OX14 3UE, England. TEL 01235-555335. FAX 01235-553559. (Subscr. in N. America to: Carfax Publishing Co., 875-81 Massachusetts Ave., Cambridge, MA 02139) Ed. Joergen S. Nielsen. adv.; bk.rev. (also avail. in microfiche) **Indexed:** Bibl.Ling., Per.Islam. **Document type:** academic/scholarly publication.
—BLDSC (4583.014500); UMI; UnCover. **CCC.**
Description: Deals with Islam and Christian-Muslim relations worldwide, especially historical, regional or sociological themes.
Refereed Serial

297   II   ISSN 0021-1826
ISLAM AND THE MODERN AGE. (Text in English) 1970. q. $20. Zakir Husain Institute of Islamic Studies, Jamia Nagar, New Delhi 110025, India. Ed. Z.H. Faruqi. adv.; bk.rev. circ. 1,000. **Indexed:** Abstr.Musl.Rel., Ind.Islam., Int.Polit.Sci.Abstr.
—BLDSC (4583.015000); SWETS.

297 059.9435   IR   ISSN 1019-0813
ISLAM CAGRISI. (Text in Turkish) no.69, 1990. m. $25 in Middle East; $35 in Europe; $40 in N. America & Australasia. Islamic Thought Foundation - Islam Dusunceler merkezi, P.O. Box 1415-3899, Teheran, Iran.

ISLAM ET SOCIETES AU SUD DU SAHARA. see *HISTORY — History Of Africa*

RELIGIONS AND THEOLOGY — ISLAMIC

ISLAM INTERNATIONAL. see *POLITICAL SCIENCE*

297   GW
ISLAM NACHRICHTEN. 1927. w. DM.260. Zentralinstitut Islam-Archiv-Deutschland, Postfach 1528, 59475 Soest, Germany. TEL 02921-60702. FAX 02921-65417. Ed. M. Salim Abdullah. adv. contact: Wolf Ahmad Aries. circ. 100. **Document type:** consumer publication.
   Description: News of Islam and Muslims in Europe.

297   MR   ISSN 0851-1128
ISLAM TODAY/ISLAM AUJOURD'HUI. (Text in Arabic, English, French) 1983. 2/yr. $6. P.O. Box 755, Rabat, Morocco. FAX 002127. TELEX 31845M. Ed. Abdulaziz Bin Othman Altwaijri. circ. 15,000.

297 059.943   IR
ISLAMI BAYRLAYK. (Text in Azerbaijani) 1990. w. Hawzah-i Hunari Sazman-i Tablighat-i Islami, 213 Summaiyah St., P.O. Box 1677-15815, Teheran, Iran.

297   US
ISLAMIC AFFAIRS. (Text mainly in English; occasionally in Arabic) 1969. w. $25. (National Council on Islamic Affairs) Islamic Affairs, P.O. Box 416, New York, NY 10017. TEL 212-972-0460. FAX 212-682-1405. Ed. Dr. M. T. Mehdi. adv. contact: Ghazi Khankan. bk.rev.; charts; illus. circ. 15,000. (tabloid format) **Document type:** newspaper.
   Formerly (until 1992): Action (New York) (ISSN 0001-7388)

ISLAMIC CULTURE. see *ORIENTAL STUDIES*

297 956   NE
ISLAMIC HISTORY AND CIVILIZATION. (Text in English, French, German) 1991. irreg., vol.9, 1994. price varies. E.J. Brill, P.O. Box 9000, 2300 PA Leiden, Netherlands. TEL 31-71-5353500. FAX 31-71-5317532. TELEX 39296 BRILL NL. (In N. America: E.J. Brill, 24 Hudson St., Kinderhook, NY 12106. TEL 800-962-4406. FAX 518-758-1959) (back issues avail.) **Document type:** monographic series.
   Formerly (until vol.4, 1994): Arab History and Civilization (ISSN 0925-2908)
   Description: Publishes scholarly studies of topics relating to the history and culture of the Islamic world, including studies of institutions, historical figures, religious orders, architecture.

297   US   ISSN 8756-2367
BP1
ISLAMIC HORIZONS. 1963. bi-m. $24 (foreign $28). Islamic Society of North America, Box 38, Plainfield, IN 46168. TEL 317-839-8157. FAX 317-839-1840. adv.; bk.rev.; stat. circ. 30,000. **Document type:** bulletin.
   —UnCover.
   Incorporates (in 1995): I S N A Matters.

340.59   NE   ISSN 0928-9380
K9
▼**ISLAMIC LAW & SOCIETY.** (Text in English, French, German) 1994. 3/yr. fl.98($63) to individuals; institutions fl.220($142) (effective 1996). E.J. Brill, Postbus 9000, 23300 PA Leiden, Netherlands. TEL 31-71-5353500. FAX 31-71-5317532. TELEX 39296 BRILL NL. E-mail: ejborders@ejbrill.com. (In N. America: E.J. Brill, 24 Hudson St., Kinderhook, NY 12106. TEL 800-962-4406. FAX 518-758-1959) Ed.Bd. bk.rev.; abstr.; bibl.; index. (back issues avail.) **Document type:** academic/scholarly publication.
   Description: Forum for comparative research in the field of Islamic law in Muslim and non-Muslim countries, covering both theory and practice, from its emergence up to the present. Discusses historical, juridical and social-scientific perspectives on Islamic law, including current legal issues and legislation.
   Refereed Serial

297 181.07   NE   ISSN 0169-8729
ISLAMIC PHILOSOPHY, THEOLOGY AND SCIENCE; texts and studies. (Text in English, French, German) 1986. irreg., vol.20, 1994. price varies. E.J. Brill, P.O. Box 9000, 2300 PA Leiden, Netherlands. TEL 31-71-5353500. FAX 31-71-5317532. TELEX 39296 BRILL NL. (In N. America: E.J. Brill, 24 Hudson St., Kinderhook, NY 12106. TEL 800-962-4406. FAX 518-758-1959) Eds. H. Daiber, D. Pingree. (back issues avail.) **Document type:** monographic series.
   —BLDSC (4583.025950).
   Description: Publishes translations of medieval Islamic philosophical, theological scientific and medical texts, with commentary, as well as scholarly studies of aspects of Islamic philosophy, literature and ethics.
   Refereed Serial

ISLAMIC QUARTERLY; a review of Islamic Culture. see *ORIENTAL STUDIES*

297   PK   ISSN 0578-8072
BP1
ISLAMIC STUDIES. (Text in English) 1962. q. Rs.100($30) Islamic Research Institute, International Islamic University, P.O. Box 1035, Islamabad 44000, Pakistan. TEL 92-51-850751. FAX 92-51-853360. TELEX 54068 IIU PK. Ed. Zafar Ishaq Ansari; Pub. Saeed Ahmad Shah. adv.; bk.rev.; index. circ. 3,000. (back issues avail.; reprint service avail. from SCH) **Indexed:** Abstr.Musl.Rel. **Document type:** academic/scholarly publication.
   —Faxon; UnCover.
   Description: Covers Islamic law, history, political theory and philosophy as well as other topics.

297.07 500.9   PK
ISLAMIC THOUGHT AND SCIENTIFIC CREATIVITY. (Text in English) 1990. q. Rs.300 (foreign $60) (effective 1995 & 1996). Organization of Islamic Conference, Standing Committee on Scientific and Technological Co-operation, 3 Constitution Ave., Sector G-5, Islamabad, Pakistan. TEL 92-51-220681. FAX 92-51-220265. TELEX 54349 COMST PK. Ed. Muzaffar Iqbal. bk.rev. **Document type:** academic/scholarly publication.

297   II
THE ISLAMIC TIMES; the official organ of the Islamic Cultural Centre (India). (Text in English) 1992. q.? Rs.125($20) Islamic Cultural Centre (India), 317-321, Prospect Chambers Dr., Dr. D.N. Rd., Fort, Bombay 400 001, India. TEL 204-2493. FAX 204-3316. Ed. Ahmed B. Zakaria.
   Description: Aims to enhance understanding among the various religions in India and elsewhere.

ISLAMIC WORLD MEDICAL JOURNAL. see *MEDICAL SCIENCES*

297   SU
JAMI'AT AL-IMAM MUHAMMAD IBN SA'UD AL-ISLAMIYYAH. IMADAT AL-BAHTH AL-ILMI. MAJALLAH/ISLAMIC UNIVERSITY OF IMAM MUHAMMAD IBN SAUD. DEANERY OF ACADEMIC RESEARCH. JOURNAL. (Text in Arabic, English) q. SRI.10. Jami'at al-Imam Muhammad Ibn Sa'ud al-Islamiyyah, Imadat al-Bahth al-Ilmi - Islamic University of Imam Muhammad Ibn Saud, Deanery of Academic Research, P.O. Box 18011, Riyadh 11415, Saudi Arabia. TEL 966-1-2582051. FAX 966-1-2590469. circ. 6,000. **Document type:** academic/scholarly publication.
   Formerly (until 1989): Jami'at al-Imam Muhammad Ibn Saud al Islamiyyah. Markaz al-Buhuth. Majallah.

297   IS   ISSN 0334-4118
DS36
JERUSALEM STUDIES IN ARABIC AND ISLAM.* irreg. Hebrew University, Institute of Asian & African Studies, Mount Scopus, Jerusalem, Israel. Ed. S. Pines. **Indexed:** Bibl.Ling. **Document type:** monographic series.
   —BLDSC (4667.516900).
   Description: Scholarly monographs on topics in Islamic religion and history and Arabic linguistics.

297 572   UK   ISSN 0955-2340
DS35.3
JOURNAL OF ISLAMIC STUDIES. 1990. s-a. £54($98) (effective 1996). (Oxford Centre for Islamic Studies) Oxford University Press, Oxford Journals, Walton St., Oxford OX2 6DP, England. TEL 01865-267907. FAX 01865-267773. TELEX 837330-OXPRES-G. E-mail: jnlorders@oup.co.uk. (U.S. subscr. to: Oxford University Press Inc., 2001 Evans Rd., Cary, NC 27513. TEL 919-677-0977. FAX 919-677-1714) Ed. Farham Ahmad Nizami. adv. contact: Jane Parker. bk.rev. circ. 400. **Indexed:** Bibl.Ling. **Document type:** academic/scholarly publication.
   —BLDSC (5008.550000); SWETS; UMI. **CCC.**
   Description: Dedicated to the multi-disciplinary study of any aspect of Islam and the Islamic.

297 305.8   UK   ISSN 1360-2004
BP52.5
JOURNAL OF MUSLIM MINORITY AFFAIRS. (Text and summaries in English) 1979. s-a. £24($40) to individuals; institutions £78($96) (effective 1996). (Institute of Muslim Minority Affairs) Carfax Publishing Co., P.O. Box 25, Abingdon, Oxon. OX14 3UE, England. TEL 44-1235-555335. FAX 44-1235-553559. (N. American subscr. to: Carfax Publishing Co., 875-81 Massachusetts Ave., Cambridge, MA 02139) adv.; bk.rev. (back issues avail.) **Indexed:** Amer.Hist.& Life, ASSIA, Documentatieblad, Hist.Abstr., HR Rep., Int.Lab.Doc., Per.Islam. (1991-), Refug.Abstr., Rel.Ind.One, Sociol.Abstr., SOPODA. **Document type:** academic/scholarly publication.
   —BLDSC (4777.760000); UnCover.
   Formerly: Institute of Muslim Minority Affairs. Journal (ISSN 0266-6952)
   Description: Devoted to the social, economic and political affairs of the Muslim minority.

297   II   ISSN 0971-3220
JOURNAL OF OBJECTIVE STUDIES. 1992. s-a. $40. Institute of Objective Studies, P.O. Box 9725, Jamia Nagar, New Delhi 110 025, India. TEL 630989. FAX 6841104. Ed. F.R. Faridi. adv.; bk.rev.
   —BLDSC (5024.900000).

JUSUR; the U C L A journal of Middle Eastern studies. see *HISTORY — History Of The Near East*

297   IR   ISSN 1017-4176
KAYHAN ANDISHE. (Text in Persian) 1985. 6/yr. $102 to N. America (effective 1994). Kayhan Publications, Ferdowsi Ave., P.O. Box 11365-9631, Tehran, Iran. TEL 98-21-3110251. FAX 98-21-3114228. TELEX 212467. **Document type:** consumer publication.
   Description: Covers topics relating to Islam, Islamic philosophy, and Iranian literature.

297   SU
KING FAISAL CENTER FOR RESEARCH AND ISLAMIC STUDIES. NEWSLETTER. irreg. King Faisal Center for Research and Islamic Studies, P.O. Box 51049, Riyadh 11543, Saudi Arabia. TEL 4652255. FAX 4659993. TELEX 205470. **Document type:** newsletter.

297 370   SU
KING SAUD UNIVERSITY. JOURNAL. EDUCATIONAL SCIENCES AND ISLAMIC STUDIES/JAMI'AT AL-MALIK SA'UD. MAJALLAH. AL-'ULUM AL-TARBAWIYYAH WAL-DIRASAT AL-ISLAMIYYAH. (Other sections avail.: Administrative Sciences, Agricultural Sciences, Architecture and Planning, Arts, Computer and Information Sciences, Engineering Sciences, Science) (Text in Arabic, English) 1989. s-a. $10. King Saud University, University Libraries, P.O. Box 22480, Riyadh 11495, Saudi Arabia. TEL 966-1-4676148. FAX 966-1-4676162. TELEX 401019 KSU SJ. Ed. Mohammed A. Al-Mannie. charts; illus. circ. 2,000. **Document type:** academic/scholarly publication.
   Formerly: King Saud University. Journal. Educational Sciences (ISSN 1018-3620)
   Refereed Serial

297   UK   ISSN 0268-8352
LINK INTERNATIONAL: EDUCATIONAL NEWSLETTER. 1986. bi-m. £5 to individuals; institutions £7. Islamic Educational Publications, Muslim Community Studies, Post Box 139, Leicester LE2 2YH, England. TEL 01533-706714. **Document type:** newsletter.

297   UA
AL-LIWA' AL-ISLAMI/ISLAMIC STANDARD. (Text in Arabic) 1982. w. 11 Sharia Sharif Pasha, Cairo, Egypt. Ed. Muhammad Ali Sheta. circ. 30,000.
   Description: Covers topics relating to Islamic fundamentalism.

RELIGIONS AND THEOLOGY — ISLAMIC

297 955   IR   ISSN 0259-904X
LUQMAN. (Text in French) 1985. 2/yr. IRI.3000 (Middle East £11; Europe £13; elsewhere £14). Markaz-i Nashr-i Danishgahi - Iran University Press, 85 Park Ave., Dr. Bihishti Ave., P.O. Box 15875-4748, Tehran, Iran. TEL 98-21-8713232. FAX 98-21-8861749. TELEX 213636-8-D5300. Ed. Djavad Hadidi. circ. 1,000. (back issues avail.) **Document type:** academic/scholarly publication.
    Description: Publishes studies in Iranology and Islam.

M A A S JOURNAL OF ISLAMIC SCIENCE. (Muslim Association for the Advancement of Science) see *ORIENTAL STUDIES*

M A A S NEWSLETTER. (Muslim Association for the Advancement of Science) see *ORIENTAL STUDIES*

AL-MA'ARIF. see *ORIENTAL STUDIES*

297 181   IR   ISSN 1015-2822
DS251
MA'ARIF. (Text in Persian) 1984. 3/yr. IRI.4000 (Middle East £24; Europe £25; elsewhere £30). Markaz-i Nashr-i Danishgahi - Iran University Press, 85 Park Ave., Dr. Bihishti Ave., P.O. Box 18875-4748, Tehran, Iran. TEL 98-21-8713232. FAX 98-21-8861749. TELEX 213636-8-D5300. Ed. Nasrollah Pourjavady. circ. 3,000. (back issues avail.) **Document type:** academic/scholarly publication.
    Description: Publishes articles and comparative studies relating to Islamic history, philosophy, theology and mysticism.

297   IR   ISSN 1019-0767
MAHJUBAH. (Text in English) 1981. m. $50. Islamic Thought Foundation, P.O. Box 14155-3899, Tehran, Iran. TEL 98-21-844092. FAX 98-21-898295. Ed. Zahra Sepahi. circ. 30,000. **Indexed:** Per.Islam. (1991-). **Document type:** government publication.
    Description: For Muslim women.

297   UA
AL-MAJALLAH AL-'ILMIYYAH LI-KULLIYYAT USUL AL-DIN WAL-DA'WAH LIL-ZAGAZIG. (Text in Arabic) 1987. a? Al-Azhar University, Faculty of Islamic Theology in Zagazig, Zagazig, Egypt.

297   JO
MAJALLAT AL-SHARIA. (Text in Arabic) 1959. m. $20 to individuals; institutions $40 (effective 1992). League of Islamic Sciences, Yazid ben Abu Sufian St., P.O. Box 1829, Amman, Jordan. TEL 637203. FAX 819036. Ed. Hassan T. Zibian.
    Formerly: Theology - Sharia.
    Description: General interest articles focusing on Islam, religious and health matters, issues in Jordanian society, as well as educational and entertainment topics.

MAJALLAT AL-SHARI'AH WAL-QANUN. see *LAW*

297   TS
MANAAR AL-ISLAM. 1979. m. Ministry of Justice, Islamic Affairs and Endowments, P.O. Box 2922, Abu Dhabi, United Arab Emirates. TEL 212300. TELEX 22589 ISLAMI EM. Ed. Ali Muhammad al-Ajla. circ. 2,500.
    Description: Discusses Islamic guidance, Quranic studies, Sunna, Islamic history and literature, family issues, and news of the Islamic world.

297   KE
MAPENZI YA MUNGU. (Text in Swahili) 1943. m. K.25. East African Ahmadiyya Muslim Mission, PO Box 40554, Nairobi, Kenya. Ed. Jamil R. Rafiq. adv.; bk.rev. circ. 4,000.

AL-MASAQ; studia arabo-islamica mediterranea. see *HISTORY — History Of The Near East*

MEDIEVAL ENCOUNTERS; a journal of Jewish, Christian and Muslim culture in confluence and dialogue. see *HISTORY*

297   UK
THE MESSAGE. (Text in Arabic, English) 1972. bi-m. free. United Islamic Association (UK), 31 Crawley Rd., Wood Green, London N22 6AG, England. Ed. Salim Karim. circ. 1,000. (back issues avail.) **Document type:** newsletter.
    Formerly (until 1981): National Message.
    Description: Dedicated to delivering the message of Islam.

297   US   ISSN 1071-5215
BP1
THE MESSAGE (JAMAICA). 1989. m. $28 (effective 1993). Islamic Circle of North America, 166-26 89th Ave., Jamaica, NY 11432. TEL 718-658-5163. FAX 718-526-3645. (And: 100 McLevin Ave., No. 3A, Scarborough, ON M1B 2V5, Canada. TEL 416-609-2452) Ed. Muhammad Yunus. adv. contact: Tariq Ahmad Khan. illus. **Indexed:** Per.Islam (1991-). **Document type:** academic/scholarly publication.
    Formerly: Message International (ISSN 1046-1019)
    Description: Provides an overview of the current issues that face American Muslims and the Muslim world at large. Includes international news, discussions of anti-Muslim bias in Western print and broadcast media, in-depth coverage of conditions in specific countries, advice and guidance on aspects of Islam.

297.7   MF
LE MESSAGE DE L'AHMADIYYAT. (Text in French) 1965. m. $24. Ahmadiyya Muslim Association, P.O. Box 6, Rose Hill, Mauritius. TEL 230-464-1747. FAX 230-454-2223. Ed. Zafrullah Domun. bk.rev. circ. 3,000. **Document type:** newspaper.
    Formerly: Message.

297   IR   ISSN 1012-0734
LE MESSAGE DE L'ISLAM. (Text in French) 1981. m. $30 in Middle East; Europe $35; Americas $45. Islamic Thought Foundation - Fondation de la Pensee Islamique, P.O. Box 14155-3899, Tehran, Iran. TEL 98-21-844092. FAX 98-21-898295.

297   US   ISSN 0892-0559
THE MINARET. vol.13, 1991. m. $25. Islamic Center of Southern California, 434 S. Vermont Ave., Los Angeles, CA 90020. TEL 213-384-4570. FAX 213-384-9674. E-mail: mviqnetcom.com. Ed. Aslam Abdullah. adv. contact: Ifran Khan. bk.rev.; circ. 8,000 (paid). **Indexed:** Per.Islam (1991-). **Document type:** academic/scholarly publication.
    —UnCover.

297   PK
MINARET MONTHLY INTERNATIONAL. (Text in English) 1964. m. Rs.15 per no (Europe, Africa, Asia $11/yr.; elsewhere $20/yr.) (effective 1993). World Federation of Islamic Missions, Islamic Centre, Abdul Aleem Siddiqi Rd., Block B, N. Nazimabad, Karachi 74700, Pakistan. TEL 6644156. Ed. Muhammed Ja'fer. adv.; bk.rev. circ. 1,200. **Indexed:** Abstr.Musl.Rel.
    Formerly (until Sep. 1976): Minaret (ISSN 0026-4415)
    Description: Explores mission work in the country.

297   UA
MINBAR AL-ISLAM. (Text in Arabic, English, French, Spanish) 1942. m. $75 in N. America. (Al-Majlis al-A'la lil-Shu'un al-Islamiyyah - Supreme Council for Islamic Affairs) Mu'assassat al-Ahram, Sharia al-Galaa, Cairo, Egypt. TEL 02-7583333. FAX 02-745888. (In N. America: Al-Ahram International, 405 Lexington Ave., New York, NY 10174. TEL 212-972-6440. FAX 212-286-0285) bibl.; illus.

297   IR
AL-MISBAH. 1984. q. Astan-i Quds Islamic Research Foundation, P.O. Box 366-91735, Meshed, Iran. TEL 63031.

297 955   IR
MISHKAT. (Text in Persian) 1984. q. Astan-i Quds Islamic Research Foundation, P.O. Box 366-91735, Meshed, Iran. TEL 63031.
    Description: Publishes papers in Islamic studies.

297   GW   ISSN 0930-7338
BP1
MOSLEMISCHE REVUE. 1924. q. DM.45. Zentralinstitut Islam-Archiv-Deutschland, Postfach 1528, 59475 Soest, Germany. TEL 02921-60702. FAX 02921-65417. Ed. M. Salim Abdullah. adv. contact: Wolf Ahmad Aries. circ. 900. **Document type:** consumer publication.
    Description: Muslim theology, muslims and their life in Germany, dialogue between Christians and Moslem, news of the Islamic world.

297   UK   ISSN 0266-2183
B753.I24
MUHYIDDIN IBN ARABI SOCIETY. JOURNAL. 1982. 2/yr. £16.50 (effective 1993). Muhyiddin Ibn Arabi Society, 23 Oakthorpe Road, Oxford OX2 7BD, England. TEL 01865-511963. bk.rev. **Document type:** academic/scholarly publication.
    —BLDSC (4828.440000); UnCover.
    Description: Translations and studies of works of Ibn Arabi.

297   SA   ISSN 0027-4860
MUSLIM AFRICA. 1969. m. $10. Islamic Missionary Society, P.O. Box 54125, Vrededorp 2141, Transvaal, South Africa. FAX 27-11-834-8241. Ed. M.S. Laher. adv. circ. 5,000.
    Description: Highlights mission work in the country.

297   SA   ISSN 0027-4887
MUSLIM DIGEST; international magazine of Muslim affairs. 1950. bi-m. $15. Makki Publications, 100 Brickfield Rd., Durban, South Africa. adv.; illus.

297.7   UK   ISSN 0267-615X
MUSLIM EDUCATION QUARTERLY. 1983. q. £13.50 to individuals; institutions £19.50. The Islamic Academy, 23 Metcalfe Rd., Cambridge CB4 2DB, England. TEL 01223-350976. FAX 01223-350976. Ed. Syed Ali Ashraf. adv.; bk.rev. circ. 1,200. **Document type:** academic/scholarly publication.
    —BLDSC (5991.137100).
    Formerly (until 1983): Muslim Education (ISSN 0263-6247)
    Description: Provides a forum for the exchange of ideas on education and related issues among Muslim as well as non-Muslim scholars and educationalists. *Refereed Serial*

297   US   ISSN 0883-816X
MUSLIM JOURNAL. 1961. w. $45. Muslim Journal Enterprises, Inc., 910 W. Van Buren, Ste. 100, Chicago, IL 60607. TEL 312-243-7600. FAX 312-243-9778. Ed. Ayesha K. Mustafaa. adv. contact: Bilal Akbar. **Document type:** newspaper.
    Former titles (until 1985): A M Journal (ISSN 0744-7639); (until 1983): A M News (ISSN 0744-7647); (until 1982): World Muslim News (ISSN 0744-0014); (until 1981): Bilalian News (ISSN 0161-8644); (until 1975): Muhammad Speaks (ISSN 0027-3031)

297   UK   ISSN 0956-5027
THE MUSLIM NEWS. 1989. m. £17. Visitcrest Ltd., P.O. Box 380, Harrow, Middlesex HA2 6LL, England. TEL 0171-831-0428. FAX 0171-831-0830. Ed. Ahmed Versi. adv.: page £1000; trim 381 x 266; adv. contact: M. Versi. bk.rev.; circ. 50,000 (paid). (back issues avail.) **Document type:** newspaper.

297   II   ISSN 0027-4895
MUSLIM REVIEW. (Text in English) 1923. q. Rs.8. Idari Madrasatul Waizeen, Madrasatul Waizeen, 16 Canning St., Lucknow, India. Ed. Shaheed Safipuri. adv.; bk.rev. circ. 500. (also avail. in microfiche from IDC) **Indexed:** Per.Islam. (1991-).

297   SU
MUSLIM SOLIDARITY/MAJALLAT AL-TADAMUM AL-ISLAMI. (Text in Arabic and English) m. free. Ministry of Pilgrimage Affairs and Awqaf - Wizarat Shu'un al-Hajj wal-Awqaf, Sharia Omar bin al-Khattab, Riyadh 11183, Saudi Arabia. TEL 966-1-4022200. Ed. Abdullah bin Abdul-Muttaleb Bogas. bk.rev.; bibl. circ. 11,000. **Document type:** government publication.
    Formerly: Majallat al-Hajj.

297   US
MUSLIM STAR. 1953. m. $10. Federation of Islamic Associations in the United States and Canada, 25341 Five Mile Rd., Redford Township, MI 48239. TEL 313-534-3295. FAX 313-534-1474. Ed. Nihad Hamed. adv.; bk.rev.; illus.; circ. 10,000 (paid).

297   US
MUSLIM SUNRISE. q. $6. Ahmadiyya Movement in Islam, Inc., 15000 Good Hope Rd., Silver Spring, DC 20905-4120. TEL 202-232-3737. Ed. Mubasher Ahmad. bk.rev. circ. 1,000.
    Description: Provides a platform for public opinion on current problems confronting humanity and their solution. Features articles written by scholars discussing as well as topics relating to other religions.

RELIGIONS AND THEOLOGY — ISLAMIC

297　　　　　US　　ISSN 0027-4909
DS36
MUSLIM WORLD; a journal devoted to the study of Islam and Christian-Muslim relationships past and present. 1911. q. $20 individuals; institutions $30. (Duncan Black Macdonald Center) Hartford Seminary, 77 Sherman St., Hartford, CT 06105. TEL 203-232-4451. FAX 203-231-0348. Ed.Bd. adv.; bk.rev.; index, cum.index: vols.1-25 (1911-1935), vols.26-50 (1936-1960). circ. 1,200. (also avail. in microform from UMI; back issues avail.; reprint service avail. from KTO,UMI) **Indexed:** Amer.Bibl.Slavic & E.Eur.Stud, Amer.Hist.& Life, Curr.Cont., E.I., Hist.Abstr., Hum.Ind., Int.Polit.Sci.Abstr., M.L.A., Mid.East: Abstr.& Ind., Rel.& Theol.Abstr., Rel.Ind.One, Rel.Per. **Document type:** academic/scholarly publication.
—BLDSC (5991.150000); Faxon; Genuine Article; SWETS; UnCover.
　Formerly (until 1948): Moslem World (ISSN 0362-4641)

297.7　　　　UK　　ISSN 0260-3063
DS35.3
MUSLIM WORLD BOOK REVIEW. (Supplement avail.: Index of Islamic Literature) 1980. q. £20 to individuals (foreign £28); institutions £30 (foreign 38). Islamic Foundation, Markfield Dawah Centre, Ratby Lane, Markfield, Leicester LE6 0RN, England. TEL 0530-244944. FAX 0530-244946. TELEX 341539-ISLAMF-G. (Co-sponsor: International Institute of Islamic Thought, US) Ed. M.M. Ahsan. adv.; bk.rev.; bibl.; index. circ. 1,000. (back issues avail.) **Indexed:** Bibl.Ling. **Document type:** academic/scholarly publication.
—BLDSC (5991.160000); SWETS.
　Description: Lists and reviews books on Islam, comparative religion, and the Muslim world, and publishes critical analyses on topics of interest to scholars of religion and Islamic studies.

297　　　　　SU
MUSLIM WORLD LEAGUE JOURNAL. (Editions in Arabic, English) 1973. m. $20 to individuals; institutions $26. Muslim World League, Press and Publications Department - Rabitat al-Alam al-Islami, P.O. Box 538, Makkah, Saudi Arabia. TEL 2-544-1622. FAX 2-544-1622. TELEX 440390. Ed. Hamid Hassan Al-Radadi. index. circ. 30,000.
　Description: News and features of interest to Muslims throughout the world.

297　　　　　UK　　ISSN 1319-1128
AL-MUSLIMUN. (Text in Arabic) 1986. w. $80 (effective 1994). Saudi Research and Marketing, Arab Press House, 184 High Holborn, London WC1V 7AP, England. TEL 44-171-831-8181. FAX 44-171-831-2310. TELEX 889272. (And: P.O. Box 4556, Jeddah 21441, Saudi Arabia. TEL 966-2-6691888. FAX 966-2-6671650; Subscr. in U.S. to: Attache International, 3050 Broadway, Ste. 300, Boulder, CO 80304-1354. TEL 303-442-8900. FAX 303-442-7979) Ed. Dr. Abdul Qadir Tash. adv.: B&W page $4533; 14 x 21 3/16. cols./p.: 8. (broadsheet format) **Document type:** newspaper.
　Description: Provides news and information on events and personalities throughout the Islamic community, and provides an Islamic interpretation of local and world events.

297 070.5　　UK　　ISSN 0144-994X
BP1
NEW BOOKS QUARTERLY ON ISLAM & THE MUSLIM WORLD. 1982. q. £4. Islamic Council of Europe, 16 Grosvenor Crescent, London S.W.1., England. bk.rev.

297　　　　　US　　ISSN 0732-1848
BP1
NEW TREND; independent forum for the oppressed Muslim masses. 1977. m. $7.50. American Society for Education and Religion, Inc., Box 356, Kingsville, MD 21087. TEL 410-435-4046. Ed. Kaukab Siddique. bk.rev.; film rev. circ. 5,000. (tabloid format) **Indexed:** Per.Islam. **Document type:** newsletter.
　Description: Islamic perspective on change and conflict in the world.

297　　　　　UA
NIDA AL-ISLAM. m. £E60 per no. Dar al-Fikr Lil-Nashr Wa-al-Ilam, 58 Shari 26 Yuliyu, Cairo, Egypt.

297　　　　　LE
NOOR AL-ISLAM; thiqafiyyah islamiyyah - islamic cultural magazine. (Text in Arabic, English) 1988. bi-m. $40 to individuals (Europe $45; U.S. & Canada $50); institutions $55 (Europe $60; U.S. & Canada $70). Imam Hussain Charitable - Cultural Foundation - Muassasat al-Imam al-Husain al-Khairiyya al-Thiqafiyya, P.O. Box 25156, Beirut, Lebanon. TEL 961-1-823049. FAX 961-1-603379. TELEX 40512 KAMEC. Ed. Husain Al-Hakim. adv.: color page $350; adv. contact: Jihad Abdallah. bk.rev.; illus. circ. 10,000. (back issues avail.) **Document type:** academic/scholarly publication.
　Description: Discusses religious and cultural issues of interest to Muslims of all nations. Most issues include an article looking at the history and current status of Muslim communities within a particular country or ethnic group.

297　　　　　TU
NUR - THE LIGHT. (Text in English; summaries in Arabic, German, Turkish) vol.6, 1991. m. Nuruosmaniye Cad. Sorkun Han No. 28-3, 34410 Cagaloglu - Istanbul, Turkey. **Indexed:** Per.Islam. (1991-).

ORIENTATIONS. see ORIENTAL STUDIES

297　　　　　US
OUR ISLAM. 1980. q. $12 for 12 nos. (African Islamic Mission Inc.) A.I.M. Publications, 1390 Bedford Ave., Brooklyn, NY 11216. FAX 212-789-0530. Ed. Alhaji Obaba Muhammad. adv.; bk.rev. circ. 12,000. (tabloid format; back issues avail.)

297　　　　　MY　　ISSN 0128-3715
Z3499.9
PERIODICA ISLAMICA; an international contents journal. (Text in English) 1991. q. $40 to individuals; institutions $200. (Islamic Arts Foundation London) Berita Publishing, 22 Jalan Liku, 59100 Kuala Lumpur, Malaysia. TEL 60-3-282-5286. FAX 60-3-282-1605. TELEX 30259 NEW TIMES. E-mail: dranees@aol.com. (Dist. overseas by: Carfax Publishing Co., P.O. Box 25, Abingdon, Oxon. OX14 3UE, England. TEL 44-1235-555335. FAX 44-1235-553559) Ed. Munawar A. Anees. adv.; illus. (microfiche) **Document type:** abstracting/indexing.
—CCC.
　Description: Provides information on a broad spectrum of disciplines explicitly or implicitly related to Islamic issues.

QUELLEN ZUR GESCHICHTE DES ISLAMISCHEN AEGYPTENS. see HISTORY — History Of Africa

297　　　　　PK
QURANULHUDA. (Text in English and Urdu) 1976. m. Rs.170($40) S.M.S.A. Hayat, Ed. & Pub., P.O. Box 8677, 28 Qasr-e-Batool, Shahrah-e-Iraq, Karachi 74400, Pakistan. TEL 92-21-521292. adv.; bk.rev. circ. 31,000.
　Description: Presents texts from the Qur'an with exhaustive commentary.

297 340　　　II　　ISSN 0971-3212
RELIGION AND LAW REVIEW. 1992. s-a. $25. Institute of Objective Studies, P.O. Box 9725, Jamia Nagar, New Delhi 110 025, India. TEL 6309890. FAX 6841104. Ed. Tahir Mahmood. adv.; bk.rev.

REPERTOIRE CHRONOLOGIQUE D'EPIGRAPHIE ARABE. see ORIENTAL STUDIES

291　　　　　UK　　ISSN 0034-6721
REVIEW OF RELIGIONS. (Text in English) 1902. m. £15($30) Ahmadiyya Movement, The London Mosque, 16 Gressenhall Rd., London SW18 5QL, England. Ed. B.A. Rafiq; Pub. S.H. Abbasi. adv. contact: Naeem Memon. bk.rev.; index, cum.index. circ. 7,300. (also avail. in microform from UMI; reprint service avail. from UMI) **Document type:** bulletin.
—UMI.
　Description: Presents teachings of Islam, the discussion of Islamic affairs and religion in general.

REVUE DES ETUDES ISLAMIQUES. see ORIENTAL STUDIES

REVUE DU MONDE MUSULMAN DE LA MEDITERRANEE. see HUMANITIES: COMPREHENSIVE WORKS

297　　　　　BN　　ISSN 0353-779X
RIJASETA ISLAMSKE ZAJEDNICE. GLASNIK/SUPREME ISLAMIC AUTHORITIES. HERALD. (Text in Bosnian, summaries in Arabic, English) 1950. bi-m. Rijaseta Islamske Zajednice u Bosnia Hercegovina - Supreme Islamic Authorities in Bosnia Hercegovina, Save Kovacevica 2, 71000 Sarajevo, Bosnia Hercegovina. **Indexed:** Per.Islam. (1991-).
　Formerly (until 1990): Vrhovno Islamsko Starjesinstvo. Glasnik (ISSN 0504-8273)

297　　　　　TS
AL-RISALAH. (Text in Arabic) 1987. m. exchange basis. Islamic Information Office, Publications Section, P.O. Box 1731, Sharjah, United Arab Emirates. TEL 372544. circ. 1,000.
　Description: Covers topics of interest to Muslims.

297　　　　　LE
AL-RISALAH AL-ISLAMIYYAH. 1977. irreg. £L1000 per no. Dar al-Risalah al-Islamiyyah, P.O. Box 155063, 13-6173 Beirut, Lebanon. TEL 868661. FAX 831253. TELEX 207339 LE. Ed. Faysal Al-Sammak. adv.; bk.rev. circ. 10,000.
　Description: Covers Islamic issues all over the world.

297　　　　　MK
RISALAT AL-MASJID. (Text in Arabic) m. Diwan of Royal Court Affairs, Protocol Department, P.O. Box 6066, Muscat, Sultanate of Oman. TEL 704580. Ed. A. Kareem. illus. **Document type:** government publication.

297　　　　　LY
RISSALAT AL-JIHAD. (Text in Arabic, English, French) 1983. m. World Islamic Call Society, P.O. Box 2682, Tripoli, Lybia. TEL 31021. TELEX 20407.

297 305.6　　SW　　ISSN 0283-684X
SALAAM. 1986. 6/yr. SEK 150. Islamiska Informationsfoereningen, Goetagatan 103 A, S-116 62 Stockholm, Sweden. TEL 46-8-702-00-67. FAX 46-46-730-117. Ed. Soumaya Pernilla Onis. bk.rev. circ. 1,000. **Document type:** academic/scholarly publication, newsletter.
　Description: Publishes articles and newsitems on Islam and the Muslim world, particularly Muslims in Sweden.

SAMANYOLU; uc aylik egitim dergisi - quarterly magazine of the social sciences. see SOCIAL SCIENCES: COMPREHENSIVE WORKS

297　　　　　IR　　ISSN 1019-0783
SAUTI YA UMMA. (Text in Swahili) m. $40 in Africa & Europe; Americas $45. Islamic Thought Foundation, P.O. Box 14155-3899, Tehran, Iran. TEL 98-21-844092. FAX 98-21-898295.

297　　　　　IR　　ISSN 1019-0805
SAWT AL-WAHDAH. Key Title: Sawt al-Wahdat al-Islamiyyat. (Text in Arabic) 1981. m. $30 in Middle East; Europe, Asia $35; Africa $40; elsewhere $45. Islamic Thought Foundation - Mu'assasat al-Fikr al-Islami, P.O. Box 14155-3899, Tehran, Iran. TEL 98-21-844092. FAX 98-21-898295.

297　　　　　MP
SHARAPAT/COMPASSION. (Text in Kazakh) 1991. every 3 weeks. Mongolian Muslim Society, Ulan Bator, Mongolia.

297.38　　　JO
SHARI'AH. (Text in Arabic) 1959. fortn. Shari'ah College, P.O. Box 585, Amman, Jordan. circ. 5,000.

297　　　　　UK
SHIA WORLD. 1976. q. free. World Federation of Khoja Shia Ithnaasheri Muslim Communities, P.O. Box 60, Wood Lane, Stanmore, Middlesex HA7 4LQ, England. TEL 081-954-9881. FAX 081-954-9034. bk.rev. circ. 3,000. (back issues avail.) **Document type:** newsletter.

297.7　　　PK
SHIAH. (Text in Urdu) vol.56, 1977. w. Rs.12. Insaf Press, Railway Rd., Lahore, Pakistan.

SIMURGH. see LITERARY AND POLITICAL REVIEWS

RELIGIONS AND THEOLOGY — JUDAIC

297　　　　　　FR　　ISSN 0585-5292
BP1
STUDIA ISLAMICA. 1953. s-a. Editions Maisonneuve et Larose, 15 rue Victor Cousin, 75005 Paris, France. **Document type:** academic/scholarly publication. —BLDSC (8482.950000); SWETS; UnCover.

STUDIES IN LATE ANTIQUITY AND EARLY ISLAM. see HISTORY — History Of The Near East

297.4　　　　　　US
SUFI REVIEW. 1991. q. $12 (effective 1993). (Sufi Book Club) Pir Publications, Inc., Colonial Green, 256 Post Rd. E., Westport, CT 06880. TEL 203-221-7595. FAX 203-454-5873. Ed. Louis Rogers; Pub. Louis Rogers. adv. contact: Louis Rogers. bk.rev.; illus. circ. 30,000. (tabloid format) **Document type:** consumer publication, catalog.
Description: Discusses contemporary and classic Sufi mystical thought and teachings, and lists books available through the Sufi Book Club.

297　　　　　　IR　　ISSN 1019-0791
AL-TAHIRAH. (Text in Arabic) no.30, 1992. m. $25 in Middle East; Europe, Asia $30; Africa $35; elsewhere $40. Islamic Thought Foundation - Mu'assasat al-Fikr al-Islami, P.O. Box 14155-3899, Tehran, Iran. TEL 98-21-844092. FAX 98-21-898295.
Description: Discusses the stats and activities of women in an Islamic context.

297　　　　　　PK
TARJUMAN AL-HADITH. (Text in Urdu) 1969. m. Rs.300. Jamait E Ahl A Hadees Pakistan, 53 Lawrence Rd., Lahore, Pakistan. FAX 042-54072. TELEX 46424-KARAM-PK. Ed. Sajid Mir. circ. 2,000. (back issues avail.)

297　　　　　　IR　　ISSN 0267-968X
AL-TAWHID; a quarterly journal of Islamic thought and culture. (Text in English) 1983. q. $35 to individuals; institutions $60 (effective 1995-1996). Sazman-e Tablighat-e Islami, P.O. Box 37165-111, Qum, Islamic Republic of Iran. TEL 98-251-21588. FAX 98-251-21588. Ed. Ali Quli Qarai. **Indexed:** Rel.& Theol.Abstr. (1990-). **Document type:** academic/scholarly publication.
Description: Covers Quranic studies, hadith, Islamic law and jurisprudence, Islamic history and philosophy, mysticism, ethics, sociology, economics, political science and comparative religion.

TEXTES ARABES ET ETUDES ISLAMIQUES. see LINGUISTICS

TEXTES ET TRADUCTIONS D'AUTEURS ORIENTAUX. see LINGUISTICS

297　　　　　　NR　　ISSN 0331-5975
THE TRUTH; the Muslim weekly. (Text in English) 1951. w. £N52($5) (UK £3). Ahmadiyya Muslim Jamaat, 45 Idumagbo Ave., P.O. Box 418, Lagos, Nigeria. TEL 234-1-920105. FAX 234-1-668455. TELEX 26947 KESSAN NG. Ed. Alhaji M. Habbebu. adv.; bk.rev. circ. 5,000. (back issues avail.) **Document type:** newspaper.

297　　　　　　SA　　ISSN 0257-7062
BP1
TYDSKRIF VIR ISLAMKUNDE/JOURNAL FOR ISLAMIC STUDIES. (Text in Afrikaans, English) 1980. a. Rand Afrikaans University, Centre for Islamic Studies, P.O. Box 524, Johannesburg 2000, South Africa. **Indexed:** Per.Islam. (1991-). **Document type:** academic/scholarly publication.

297　　　　　　PK
UNIVERSAL MESSAGE. (Text in English) 1979. m. Rs.150($25) Islamic Research Academy, D-35, Block 5, Federal 'B' Area, Karachi 75950, Pakistan. TEL 681157. FAX 422827. Ed. Qadir Sharif. adv.; bk.rev.; bibl.; circ. 1,000 (controlled). (back issues avail.) **Document type:** academic/scholarly publication.
Description: Teaches a better understanding of the religion, culture and history of Islam.

297 400　　　　　　LE
UNIVERSITE SAINT-JOSEPH. FACULTE DES LETTRES ET DES SCIENCES HUMAINES. RECHERCHES. SERIE A: LANGUE ARABE ET PENSEE ISLAMIQUE. (Previously published by its Institut des Lettres Orientales in 4 series) 1956; N.S. 1971. irreg. price varies. Dar el-Mashreq S.A.R.L., 2 rue Huvelin, P.O. Box 946, Beirut, Lebanon. TEL 961-1-326469. (Subscr. to: Librairie Orientale, P.O. Box 946, Beirut, Lebanon) **Document type:** monographic series.

297　　　　　　PK　　ISSN 0042-8132
VOICE OF ISLAM. vol.16, 1968. m. Rs.10. Jamiyat-ul-Falah Karachi, PO Box 7141, Karachi 3, Pakistan. Ed. A.A. Alam. adv.; bk.rev. circ. 5,000.

297　　　　　　UG
VOICE OF ISLAM. m. Ahmaddiyya Muslim Association, PO Box 16085, Kampala, Uganda.

297　　　　　　MF
VOIX DE L'ISLAM. (Text in English and French) 1951. m. Rs.5. Abdool Azize Peeroo, Ed. & Pub., Parisot Rd., Mesnil, Phoenix, Mauritius. (back issues avail.)

297 800　　　　　　GW
WEISSES MINARETT. 1984. a. free. Verlag der Islam, Babenhaeuser Landstr. 25, 60599 Frankfurt a.M., Germany. TEL 069-681062. FAX 069-686504. Ed. Hadayatullah Huebsch. bk.rev. circ. 2,500. **Document type:** bulletin.

DIE WELT DES ISLAMS; internationale Zeitschrift fuer die Geschichte des Islams in der Neuzeit - international journal for the history of modern Islam. see ORIENTAL STUDIES

200　　　　　　PK　　ISSN 0084-2052
WORLD MUSLIM CONFERENCE. PROCEEDINGS. (Published in: Muslim World) (Text in English) biennial. World Muslim Congress - Motamar al-Alam al-Islami, Site 9-A, Gulsha-e-Iqbal, Karachi 75300, Pakistan. TEL 460712. FAX 466878. TELEX 24318-UMMAT-PK. **Document type:** proceedings.

297　　　　　　PK　　ISSN 0084-2060
WORLD MUSLIM GAZETTEER. (Text in English) 1964. quinquennial. $30. World Muslim Congress - Motamar Al-Alam al-Islami, Site 9-A, Block 7, Gulshan-e-Iqbal, Karachi 75300, Pakistan. TEL 460712. FAX 466878. Ed. Inamullah Khan.

297　　　　　　NE
WORLD SURVEY OF ISLAMIC MANUSCRIPTS. (Text in various languages) 1992. irreg., vol.4, 1994. fl.250($143) per vol. (effective 1995). (Al-Furqan Islamic Heritage Foundation) E.J. Brill, P.O. Box 9000, 2300 PA Leiden, Netherlands. TEL 31-71-5353500. FAX 31-71-5317532. TELEX 39296 BRILL NL. E-mail: ejborders@ejbrill.com. (In N. America: E.J. Brill, 24 Hudson St., Kinderhook, NY 12016. TEL 800-962-4406. FAX 518-758-1959) Ed. Geoffrey Roper. **Document type:** bibliography.
Description: Comprehensive bibliographical guide to collections of Islamic manuscripts in all Islamic languages in over 90 countries throughout the world.

297　　　　　　PK　　ISSN 0044-0213
YAQEEN INTERNATIONAL. (Text in Arabic and English) 1952. fortn. Rs.150 (Europe, Japan $20; Australia, America $30). Darut Tasnif, Iqbal Mansion, Off Shahrah-e-Liaquat, Near Naveed Clinic, Saddar, Karachi 74400, Pakistan. TEL 5684325. (Subscr. to: Darut Tasnif, Main Hub River Rd., Mujahidabad, Karachi 75760, Pakistan. TEL 226598) Ed. Hafiz Muhammad Adil. bk.rev.; bibl. circ. 5,000. (back issues avail.) **Indexed:** Abstr.Musl.Rel.
Description: Presents Islam as taught by the Quran and Sunnah.

297　　　　　　II
YOGASANA ALAYA VIJAYAM. (Text in English, Tamil) 1948. m. Rs.4. Yogazana Alayn, 462, T.H. Rd., Choolai Medu, Old Washermepet, Madras 600021, India. Ed. Pulavar B. Alwar. adv.; bk.rev. circ. 800.

YOUTH MIRROR. see CHILDREN AND YOUTH — For

RELIGIONS AND THEOLOGY — Judaic

see also Ethnic Interests

A J L NEWSLETTER. (Association of Jewish Libraries) see LIBRARY AND INFORMATION SCIENCES

A J S REVIEW. (Association for Jewish Studies) see ETHNIC INTERESTS

A O J T NEWS. (Association of Orthodox Jewish Teachers) see EDUCATION

AFRICAN JEWISH NEWSPAPER; Africa's only Yiddish newspaper. see ETHNIC INTERESTS

AGADA; an illustrated Jewish literary magazine. see ETHNIC INTERESTS

AGENDA: JEWISH EDUCATION; a journal of public policy magazine. see EDUCATION

AKRON JEWISH NEWS. see ETHNIC INTERESTS

ALGEMEINER JOURNAL. see ETHNIC INTERESTS

296.68　　　　　　IS
ALHAPEREK. q. (Ministry of Education and Culture) Shivtei Israel, Pedagogical Secretariat, 8 David Hamelech St., Jerusalem 91911, Israel. TEL 02-238377.

ALLGEMEINE JUEDISCHE WOCHENZEITUNG. see ETHNIC INTERESTS

296 200　　　　　　FR　　ISSN 0002-6050
ALLIANCE ISRAELITE UNIVERSELLE EN FRANCE. CAHIERS; paix et droit. 1947. irreg. (2-3/yr.) free to qualified personnel. Alliance Israelite Universelle en France, 45 rue de la Bruyere, 75009 Paris, France. Eds. Gerard Israel, Anne Grynberg. bk.rev.; bibl. circ. 5,000.

296.68　　　　　　IS
ALON SHVUT; bulletin of graduates. 1969. q. $3. Yeshivat Har Etzion, Alon Shvut, Gush Etzion 90433, Israel. TEL 972-2-931456. FAX 972-2-931298. Ed. Yosef Zvi Rimon. circ. 1,000. **Document type:** academic/scholarly publication.

296 956　　　　　　US
AMERICAN ACADEMY FOR JEWISH RESEARCH. MONOGRAPH SERIES. (Text in Arabic, English, French, German, Greek, Hebrew, Latin) irreg., vol.4, 1992. American Academy for Jewish Research, 3080 Broadway, New York, NY 10027. TEL 212-678-8864. FAX 212-678-8947. Ed. Nahum Sarna. **Document type:** monographic series.

296 956　　　　　　US　　ISSN 0065-6798
DS101
AMERICAN ACADEMY FOR JEWISH RESEARCH. PROCEEDINGS OF THE A A J R. (Text in Arabic, English, French, German, Greek, Hebrew, Latin) 1929. a. $30. American Academy for Jewish Research, 3080 Broadway, New York, NY 10027. TEL 212-678-8864. FAX 212-678-8947. Ed. Nahum M. Sarna. circ. 500. **Document type:** proceedings.

296 956　　　　　　US
AMERICAN ACADEMY FOR JEWISH RESEARCH. TEXT AND STUDIES SERIES. (Text in Arabic, English, French, German, Greek, Hebrew, Latin) irreg. American Academy for Jewish Research, 3080 Broadway, New York, NY 10027. TEL 212-678-8864. FAX 212-678-8947. **Document type:** monographic series.

296　　　　　　US　　ISSN 0741-465X
AMERICAN COUNCIL FOR JUDAISM. ISSUES. 1958. q. free. American Council for Judaism, Box 9009, Alexandria, VA 22304. TEL 703-836-2546. Ed. Allan C. Brownfeld. bk.rev. circ. 8,000. **Indexed:** C.L.I. **Document type:** bulletin.
Formerly (until 1979): Brief (ISSN 0006-9922)

296　　　　　　US　　ISSN 0740-8528
AMERICAN COUNCIL FOR JUDAISM. SPECIAL INTEREST REPORT; a digest of news items and articles in the area of the council's interest. 1968. m. American Council for Judaism, Box 9009, Alexandria, VA 22304. TEL 703-836-2546. Ed. Allan C. Brownfeld. circ. 8,000. (back issues avail.) **Document type:** bulletin.

AMERICAN ISRAELITE. see ETHNIC INTERESTS

AMERICAN JEWISH ARCHIVES; devoted to the preservation and study of the American Jewish experience. see ETHNIC INTERESTS

RELIGIONS AND THEOLOGY — JUDAIC

AMERICAN JEWISH CONGRESS. CONGRESS MONTHLY; a journal of opinion and Jewish affairs. see *ETHNIC INTERESTS*

AMERICAN JEWISH HISTORY. see *ETHNIC INTERESTS*

AMERICAN JEWISH TIMES OUTLOOK. see *ETHNIC INTERESTS*

AMERICAN JEWISH WORLD; voice of Minnesota Jewry. see *ETHNIC INTERESTS*

AMERICAN JEWISH YEAR BOOK. see *ETHNIC INTERESTS*

AMERICAN SEPHARDI. see *ETHNIC INTERESTS*

AMIT WOMAN. see *ETHNIC INTERESTS*

AMUDIM. see *ETHNIC INTERESTS*

ANTISEMITISM WORLD REPORT (YEAR). see *POLITICAL SCIENCE — Civil Rights*

296 NE ISSN 0169-734X
ARBEITEN ZUR GESCHICHTE DES ANTIKEN JUDENTUMS UND DES URCHRISTENTUMS. (Text in English, German) 1961. irreg., no.25, 1995. price varies. (Institutum Iudaicum, Tuebingen, GW) E.J. Brill, P.O. Box 9000, 2300 PA Leiden, Netherlands. TEL 31-71-5353500. FAX 31-71-5317532. TELEX 39296 BRILL NL. (In N. America: E.J. Brill, 24 Hudson St., Kinderhook, NY 12106. TEL 800-962-4406. FAX 518-758-1959) Ed.Bd. (back issues avail.) **Document type:** monographic series.
 Description: Scholarly studies of early Jewish and Christian history, including studies of theology, law, textual and related issues.
 Refereed Serial

296 NE ISSN 0169-7390
ARBEITEN ZUR LITERATUR UND GESCHICHTE DES HELLENISTISCHEN JUDENTUMS. (Text in English, French, German) irreg., vol.22, 1991. price varies. E.J. Brill, P.O. Box 9000, 2300 PA Leiden, Netherlands. TEL 31-71-5353500. FAX 31-71-5317532. TELEX 39296 BRILL NL. (In N. America: E.J. Brill, 24 Hudson St., Kinderhook, NY 12106. TEL 800-962-4406. FAX 518-758-1959) Ed. K.M. Rengstorf. **Document type:** monographic series.
 Description: Scholarly bibliographies and critical studies of literary figures, specific texts and historical issues pertaining to Judaism in the Hellenistic period.

ARBEITSINFORMATIONEN UEBER STUDIENPROJEKTE AUF DEM GEBIET DER GESCHICHTE DES DEUTSCHEN JUDENTUMS UND DES ANTISEMITISMUS. see *HISTORY — History Of Europe*

296 FR ISSN 0518-2840
ARCHE. 1957. m. 80 F. 14 rue Georges Berger, 75017 Paris, France. adv.

ARIZONA JEWISH POST. see *ETHNIC INTERESTS*

ASCHKENAS; Zeitschrift fuer Geschichte und Kultur der Juden. see *ETHNIC INTERESTS*

296 IS
ASPAKLARIA. (Text in English and Hebrew) 1982. q. $7 per no. Institute for Science and Halacha, 1 Hapisga St., Jerusalem, Israel. TEL 02-416505. Ed.Bd. adv.; bk.rev. **Indexed:** Ind.Heb.Per.

ASSIA. see *MEDICAL SCIENCES*

ASSIA - JEWISH MEDICAL ETHICS. see *MEDICAL SCIENCES*

ASSOCIATION FOR JEWISH STUDIES NEWSLETTER. see *ETHNIC INTERESTS*

ATLANTA JEWISH TIMES. see *ETHNIC INTERESTS*

AUFBAU/RECONSTRUCTION. see *ETHNIC INTERESTS*

AUSTRALIAN JEWISH HISTORICAL SOCIETY. JOURNAL. see *ETHNIC INTERESTS*

AUSTRALIAN JEWISH HISTORICAL SOCIETY. NEWSLETTER. see *ETHNIC INTERESTS*

AVOTAYNU. see *GENEALOGY AND HERALDRY*

296 US ISSN 0067-2742
B.G. RUDOLPH LECTURES IN JUDAIC STUDIES. 1963. a. free. Syracuse University, Jewish Studies Program, Syracuse, NY 13244-1170. TEL 315-443-3861. FAX 315-443-5390. Ed. Alan L. Berger. circ. 500 (controlled). **Document type:** academic/scholarly publication.

296 956 GW ISSN 0931-6418
BABYLON; Beitraege zur Juedischen Gegenwart. 1986. s-a. DM.20 per no. Verlag Neue Kritik KG, Kettenhofweg 53, 60325 Frankfurt a.M., Germany. TEL 069-727576. FAX 069-726585. Ed.Bd. (back issues avail.) **Document type:** academic/scholarly publication.

BALTIMORE JEWISH TIMES. see *ETHNIC INTERESTS*

296 300 IS ISSN 0067-4109
BM1
BAR-ILAN: ANNUAL OF BAR-ILAN UNIVERSITY. (Text in Hebrew; summaries in English) 1963. a. $26 (effective 1993). Bar-Ilan University Press, Ramat Gan 52900, Israel. TEL 03-5318401. Ed.Bd. (back issues avail.) **Indexed:** Ind.Heb.Per. **Document type:** monographic series.

296 IS ISSN 0334-1380
BARKAI. 1984. a. IS.30($15) Mifal Rabanim Ubnei Torah, c/o Mr. S.R. Sachs, P.O. Box 7720, Jerusalem, Israel. TEL 972-2-258833. Ed. Rabbi Shaul Yisraeli. circ. 2,000.

BATFUTZOT; newsletter on Jewish life in the Diaspora. see *ETHNIC INTERESTS*

BEER-SHEVA. see *ARCHAEOLOGY*

BET MIKRA. see *RELIGIONS AND THEOLOGY*

296 015 AG
BIBLIOGRAFIA TEMATICA SOBRE JUDAISMO ARGENTINO. (Text in English, Hebrew, Spanish, Yiddish) 1984. irreg. price varies. (Centro de Documentacion e Informacion sobre Judaismo "Marc Turkow") A.M.I.A., Pasteur 633, 1028 Capital Fed., Buenos Aires, Argentina. TEL 490518. FAX 953-5474. (Co-sponsor: American Jewish Committee) index. circ. 200.
 Description: Covers Jewish education in Argentina, antisemitism in Argentina and the Jewish labor movement in Argentina; includes socio-historical investigation.

296 US ISSN 1048-6054
BINAH: STUDIES IN JEWISH HISTORY, CULTURE, AND THOUGHT. 1989. irreg. price varies. Praeger Publishers (Subsidiary of: Greenwood Publishing Group Inc.), 88 Post Rd. W., Box 5007, Westport, CT 06881-5007. TEL 203-226-3571. FAX 203-222-1502. **Document type:** monographic series.

296 IS
BISHVILEI HAREFUAH. a. $3. Laniado Hospital, Netanya 42 150, Israel. TEL 053-21666. Ed. Rabbi Schwartz.

B'NAI B'RITH INTERNATIONAL JEWISH MONTHLY. see *ETHNIC INTERESTS*

B'NAI B'RITH MESSENGER. see *ETHNIC INTERESTS*

BOSTON JEWISH TIMES. see *ETHNIC INTERESTS*

296 900 NE ISSN 0926-2261
BRILL'S SERIES IN JEWISH STUDIES. 1991. irreg., vol.12, 1994. price varies. E.J. Brill, P.O. Box 9000, 2300 PA Leiden, Netherlands. TEL 31-71-5353500. FAX 31-71-5317532. TELEX 39296 BRILL NL. (In N. America: E.J. Brill, 24 Hudson St., Kinderhook, NY 12106. TEL 800-962-4406. FAX 518-758-1959) Ed. David S. Katz. (back issues avail.) **Document type:** monographic series.
 Description: Scholarly monographs covering topics in Jewish history, language, society and culture up to the present era.
 Refereed Serial

296 US ISSN 0007-2435
BROTHERHOOD. 1967. q. $1. National Federation of Temple Brotherhoods, 838 Fifth Ave., New York, NY 10021. TEL 212-570-0707. FAX 212-570-0960. Ed. Douglas Barden. adv.; bk.rev.; charts; illus.; circ. 60,000 (controlled).

BROWARD JEWISH WORLD. see *ETHNIC INTERESTS*

BUFFALO JEWISH REVIEW. see *ETHNIC INTERESTS*

296.81 BE ISSN 1148-6716
BULLETIN DES ETUDES KARAITES. 1988. a., vol.3, 1992. 1000 BEF (effective 1994). Editions Peeters s.p.r.l., Bondgenotenlaan 153, 3000 Leuven, Belgium. TEL 32-16-235170. FAX 32-16-228500. Ed.Bd. bk.rev. (back issues avail.) **Document type:** academic/scholarly publication.

296 UK ISSN 0954-1179
BULLETIN OF JUDAEO-GREEK STUDIES. 1987. s-a. £7 (typically set in Dec.). University of Cambridge, Faculty of Oriental Studies, Sidgwick Ave., Cambridge CB3 9DA, England. Eds. Nicholas de Lange, Judith Humphrey. bk.rev. circ. 150. (back issues avail.) **Document type:** academic/scholarly publication.
 Description: Studies Jews in Greek-speaking lands and surrounding areas (all periods). Emphasis is on the origins of Judeo-Byzantine culture and on Greek-speaking Jews under Christian rule (4th to 15th centuries).

296.4 US ISSN 1058-8760
BM197.A1
C C A R JOURNAL; a reform Jewish quarterly. 1953. q. $18. (Central Conference of American Rabbis) C C A R Press, 192 Lexington Ave., 7th Fl., New York, NY 10016. TEL 212-684-4990.
 FAX 212-689-1649. Ed. Lawrence Englander. adv.; bk.rev.; cum.index (25 yrs.). circ. 2,200. (also avail. in microform from UMI; reprint service avail. from UMI) **Indexed:** Ind.Artic.Jew.Stud., Ind.Jew.Per., Rel.& Theol.Abstr. (1982-).
 —BLDSC (3095.844000); Faxon; UMI; UnCover.
 Former titles (until summer 1991): Journal of Reform Judaism (ISSN 0149-712X); C C A R Journal (ISSN 0007-7976)
 Description: Contains articles about contemporary topics that pertain to the leading members of the rabbinical, scholarly, and lay communities.

C M J S CENTERPIECES. (Cohen Center for Modern Jewish Studies) see *ETHNIC INTERESTS*

THE CALL. see *ETHNIC INTERESTS*

CANADIAN JEWISH ARCHIVES (NEW SERIES). see *ETHNIC INTERESTS*

CANADIAN JEWISH HERALD. see *ETHNIC INTERESTS*

CANADIAN JEWISH NEWS. see *ETHNIC INTERESTS*

CANADIAN ZIONIST NEWSLETTER. see *POLITICAL SCIENCE*

CENTRAL ARCHIVES FOR THE HISTORY OF THE JEWISH PEOPLE NEWSLETTER/ARKHIYON HA-MERKAZI LE-TOLDOT HA-AM HA-YEHUDI. YEDIOT. see *HISTORY*

CENTRAL CALIFORNIA JEWISH HERITAGE. see *ETHNIC INTERESTS*

296.4 170 US ISSN 0069-1607
CENTRAL CONFERENCE OF AMERICAN RABBIS. YEARBOOK. 1890. a. $20. (Central Conference of American Rabbis) C C A R Press, 192 Lexington Ave., 7th Fl., New York, NY 10016.
 TEL 212-684-4990. FAX 212-689-1649. Ed. Elliot L. Stevens. cum.index. circ. 1,500. (also avail. in microfilm from AJP) **Indexed:** Rel.Ind.Two.
 Description: An indexed reference on modern Reform thought, including the annual summary of proceedings of C.C.A.R. conventions and conferences.

CHARLESTON JEWISH JOURNAL. see *ETHNIC INTERESTS*

CHARLOTTE JEWISH NEWS. see *ETHNIC INTERESTS*

CHICAGO J U F NEWS. see *SOCIAL SERVICES AND WELFARE*

CHICAGO JEWISH STAR. see *ETHNIC INTERESTS*

296 US
CHICAGO STUDIES IN THE HISTORY OF JUDAISM. 1981. a. price varies. University of Chicago Press, 5801 S. Ellis Ave., Chicago, IL 60637. TEL 312-702-7899. (Subscr. to: 11030 Langley Ave., Chicago, IL 60628) Ed. Jacob Neusner.
 Refereed Serial

RELIGIONS AND THEOLOGY — JUDAIC

CHRISTIANITY AND JUDAISM IN ANTIQUITY. see *RELIGIONS AND THEOLOGY*

THE CHRONICLE (SARASOTA). see *ETHNIC INTERESTS*

CLEVELAND JEWISH NEWS. see *ETHNIC INTERESTS*

296   FR   ISSN 0763-062X
CLUB DES HEBRAISANTS. (Text in French, Hebrew) 1984. q. 65 F.($7) Association pour la Lecture de la Bible Hebraique, 39 Grande rue, 94130 Nogent sur Marne, France. (Subscr. to: 7 route du Grand Morin, 77515 La-Celle-sur-Morin, France. TEL 64-20-02-42) Ed. Emile Nicole. adv. contact: Bernard Huck. bk.rev. circ. 250. (back issues avail.) Document type: academic/scholarly publication.
  Description: Philological notes on the Hebrew text of the Old Testament.

296   US
COALITION: THE TORAH ACTION JOURNAL. (Text in English, Yiddish) 1985. 5/yr. free. Agudath Israel of America, 84 William St., New York, NY 10038. TEL 212-797-9000. Ed. Rabbi A. Shafran. circ. 50,000. (tabloid format; back issues avail) Document type: newspaper.
  Description: Explores news and trends in the field of orthodox Jewish activism.

296   SP
COLECCION SENDA ABIERTA. SERIE 2 (AZUL): JUDAISMO. 1974. irreg. 150 ptas. (Centro de Estudios Judeo-Cristianos) Studium Ediciones, Bailen 19, Madrid 13, Spain.

COLLECTION DE LA REVUE DES ETUDES JUIVES. see *ETHNIC INTERESTS*

COMMENTARY; journal of significant thought and opinion on contemporary issues. see *LITERARY AND POLITICAL REVIEWS*

COMMUNITY (LOUISVILLE). see *ETHNIC INTERESTS*

COMMUNITY REVIEW (HARRISBURG). see *ETHNIC INTERESTS*

296   NE
COMPENDIA RERUM IUDAICARUM AD NOVUM TESTAMENTUM. sect.1, no.2, 1976. irreg., sect.3, no.3, 1993. price varies. Van Gorcum en Co. B.V., P.O. Box 43, 9400 AA Assen, Netherlands. TEL 31-5920-46846. FAX 31-5920-72064. Document type: monographic series.

296   AG
COMUNIDADES; periodico judio independiente. vol.5, 1991. 17/yr. Arg.$100000. Casilla de Correo 49, Sucursal Sarandi, 1872 Buenos Aires, Argentina. TEL 204-8801. Eds. Alberto Rotenberg, Natalio Steiner. Document type: newspaper.

CONFERENCE OF PRESIDENTS OF MAJOR AMERICAN JEWISH ORGANIZATIONS. ANNUAL REPORT. see *ETHNIC INTERESTS*

CONNECTICUT JEWISH LEDGER. see *ETHNIC INTERESTS*

296.4   US   ISSN 0010-6542
BM197.5
CONSERVATIVE JUDAISM. 1945. q. $20. Rabbinical Assembly, 3080 Broadway, New York, NY 10027. TEL 212-678-8060. FAX 212-749-9166. E-mail: rabassembly@jtsa.edu. (Co-sponsor: Jewish Theological Seminary of America) Ed. Benjamin Scolnic. bk.rev.; cum.index: 1955-1963, 1963-1976. circ. 2,000. Indexed: Amer.Bibl.Slavic & E.Eur.Stud., Ind.Jew.Per., Mid.East: Abstr.& Ind., Rel.& Theol.Abstr. (1968-).
—BLDSC (3418.500000); Faxon; UMI; UnCover. *Refereed Serial*

CONTEMPORARY JEWRY; a journal of sociol scientific inquiry. see *ETHNIC INTERESTS*

CONTRIBUTIONS TO THE SOCIOLOGY OF JEWISH LANGUAGES. see *LINGUISTICS*

COUNCIL OF JEWISH THEATRES NEWSLETTER. see *THEATER*

296   IS   ISSN 0334-4649
HM1   CODEN: CSRDD9
CROSSROADS; Halacha and the modern world. (Text in English) 1988. a. $18 (effective 1993). Zomet Institute, Alon Shvut, Gush Etzion 90940, Israel. TEL 972-2-931442. FAX 972-2-931889. Ed. Ezra Rosenfeld. circ. 3,000. Indexed: Int.Polit.Sci.Abstr. Document type: academic/scholarly publication. —Faxon.
  Description: Examines Jewish law and ethics as they relate to modern society. Includes questions of modern technology, medicine, social services, Zionism, and the Israeli army.

296   IS
DAF LITARBUT YEHUDIT. (Text in Hebrew) 1974. m. free. Ministry of Education and Culture, Department of Torah Culture, D'vora Hanevia 2, Jerusalem 91911, Israel. Ed. Arie Strikovsky. bk.rev. circ. 7,500. Document type: government publication.

DAVKE; revista Israelita. see *ETHNIC INTERESTS*

DAYTON JEWISH CHRONICLE. see *ETHNIC INTERESTS*

DEAD SEA DISCOVERIES; a journal of current research on the scrolls and related literature. see *RELIGIONS AND THEOLOGY*

DETROIT JEWISH NEWS. see *ETHNIC INTERESTS*

DIALOGUE (MONTREAL). see *ETHNIC INTERESTS*

DIMENSIONS: A JOURNAL OF HOLOCAUST STUDIES. see *HISTORY — History Of Europe*

DIRECTORY OF DAY SCHOOLS IN THE UNITED STATES AND CANADA. see *EDUCATION — Guides To Schools And Colleges*

EAST AND MAGHREB. see *ETHNIC INTERESTS*

EAST EUROPEAN JEWISH AFFAIRS; a journal on Jewish problems in Eastern Europe. see *POLITICAL SCIENCE — Civil Rights*

LE'ELA; a journal of judaism today. see *ETHNIC INTERESTS*

296   IS   ISSN 0303-7819
DS102.8
ENCYCLOPAEDIA JUDAICA YEAR BOOK. (Text in English) 1973. a. Keter Publishing House Ltd., Givat Shaul Industrial Area, P.O. Box 7145, Jerusalem, Israel.

ERENSIA SEFARDI/HERENCIA SEFARDI/HERITAGE SEPHARADE/SEPHARDIC HERITAGE. see *HISTORY — History Of Europe*

296   CN   ISSN 0827-8687
ETHIOPIAN JEWRY REPORT. s-a. Canadian Association for Ethiopian Jews, 788 Marlee Ave., Toronto, ON M6B 3K1, Canada. TEL 416-782-2546.

296   NE   ISSN 0169-815X
ETUDES SUR LE JUDAISME MEDIEVAL. 1968. irreg., vol.14, 1992. price varies. E.J. Brill, P.O. Box 9000, 2300 PA Leiden, Netherlands. TEL 31-71-5353500. FAX 31-71-5317532. TELEX 39296 BRILL NL. (In N. America: E.J. Brill, 24 Hudson St., Kinderhook, NY 12106. TEL 800-962-4406. FAX 518-758-1959) Ed. D.R. Blumenthal. (back issues avail.) Document type: monographic series.
  Description: Scholarly translation and discussion of texts and issues in medieval Judaism in Europe and the Middle East.
  Refereed Serial

296 940   UK   ISSN 0014-3006
BM1
EUROPEAN JUDAISM. 1966. s-a. $27 to individuals; institutions $86 (effective 1995). Carfax Publishing Co., P.O. Box 25, Abingdon, Oxon OX14 3 UE, England. TEL 01235-555335. FAX 01235-553559. (Subscr. in N. America to: Carfax Publishing Co., 875-81 Massachusetts Ave., Cambridge, MA 02139) (Co-sponsors: Leo Baeck College; Michael Goulston Educational Foundation) Eds. Albert Friedlander, Jonathan Magonet. adv.; bk.rev.; cum.index. circ. 1,000. (also avail. in microfilm from UMI; back issues avail.) Indexed: Ind.Jew.Per., Mid.East: Abstr.& Ind. Document type: academic/scholarly publication.
—BLDSC (3829.747500); UMI; UnCover. CCC.
  Description: Covers all aspects of contemporary European Jewish thought.
  Refereed Serial

FOCUS SOVIET JEWRY. see *POLITICAL SCIENCE — Civil Rights*

FORWARD (NEW YORK). see *ETHNIC INTERESTS*

296   US   ISSN 0886-1277
FOUR WORLDS JOURNAL. 1983. q. $18 to individuals; institutions $28. (Four Worlds Institute) Four Worlds Press, Box 695, Commack, NY 11725. TEL 516-864-1912. FAX 516-864-7429. Ed. Edward Hoffman; Pub. Edward Hoffman. adv. contact: Harvey Gitlin. bk.rev. circ. 500. Document type: academic/scholarly publication.
  Description: Inter-disciplinary journal devoted to Jewish mysticism from a contemporary perspective.

FRANKFURTER JUDAISTISCHE BEITRAEGE. see *ETHNIC INTERESTS*

296   GW   ISSN 0938-6408
FRIEDE UEBER ISRAEL; Zeitschrift fuer Kirche und Judentum. 1903. q. free. Evang. Luth. Zentralverein fuer Zeugnis und Dienst unter Juden und Christen e.V., Archivstr. 3, 30169 Hannover, Germany. TEL 0511-1241-434. FAX 0511-1241499. bk.rev. circ. 12,000. (back issues avail.)

296   IS
FRONTLINE. (Text in English) 1986. s-a. Chabad Mobile Centers, P.O. Box 1035, Upper Nazareth 17 110, Israel. TEL (06)571468.

DIE GEMEINDE. see *POLITICAL SCIENCE*

GESHER; semi-annual journal of Jewish affairs. see *ETHNIC INTERESTS*

296   US   ISSN 0016-9145
GESHER. (Text in English and Hebrew) a. $5. (Yeshiva University, Student Organization of Yeshiva) Rabbi Isaac Elchanan Theological Seminary, 500 W. 185th St., New York, NY 10033. TEL 212-960-5277. Ed.Bd.

HABINJAN; de opbouw. see *ETHNIC INTERESTS*

HABONE; le batisseur. see *ETHNIC INTERESTS*

296   IS   ISSN 0017-6508
HADASHOT MEHACHAIM HADATIYIM BEISRAEL. 1961. bi-m. $2. Hechal Shlomo, P.O. Box 7440, Jerusalem, Israel. Ed. Rabbi Aaron Pechenick. bk.rev. circ. 3,000. (looseleaf format)

HADASSAH MAGAZINE. see *ETHNIC INTERESTS*

HADOAR. see *LITERARY AND POLITICAL REVIEWS*

296.4   US   ISSN 0017-6532
HADOROM; a journal of Torah and Halakkic studies. (Text in Hebrew; contents page in English) 1957. a. $10. Rabbinical Council of America, 275 Seventh Ave., New York, NY 10001. TEL 212-807-7888. Ed. Rabbi Gedalia Schwartz. bk.rev. circ. 1,300.

296   US   ISSN 0017-7040
HAMEVASER. 1962. m. $10 (effective Oct. 1991). Yeshiva University, Jewish Studies Division, 500 W. 185 St, New York, NY 10033. TEL 212-960-5277. Ed. Mitchel Benuck. adv.; bk.rev.; index. circ. 5,000. (tabloid format)
  Description: A student journal of traditional thought.

HARVARD JUDAIC MONOGRAPHS. see *ETHNIC INTERESTS*

RELIGIONS AND THEOLOGY — JUDAIC

HEBRAEISCHE BEITRAEGE ZUR WISSENSCHAFT DES JUDENTUMS; ein Referatenorgan. see *RELIGIONS AND THEOLOGY — Abstracting, Bibliographies, Statistics*

HEBREW STUDIES; a journal devoted to Hebrew language and literature of all periods. see *LINGUISTICS*

HEBREW UNION COLLEGE ANNUAL. see *ETHNIC INTERESTS*

HEBREW UNION COLLEGE ANNUAL SUPPLEMENTS. see *ETHNIC INTERESTS*

296 US
HEBREW UNION COLLEGE - JEWISH INSTITUTE OF RELIGION. CHRONICLE. 1972. s-a. free. Hebrew Union College - Jewish Institute of Religion (New York), One W. Fouth St., New York, NY 10012. TEL 212-674-5300. Ed. Jean Rosensaft. bk.rev.; bibl.; illus. circ. 40,000.
Formerly (until 1977): Hebrew Union College - Jewish Institute of Religion. Reporter.

HEBREW WATCHMAN. see *ETHNIC INTERESTS*

296.67 US ISSN 0732-0914
HERITAGE (WALTHAM). 1968. s-a. $50 to members. American Jewish Historical Society, 2 Thornton Rd., Waltham, MA 02154. TEL 617-891-8110. FAX 617-899-9208. Ed. Stanley Remsberg. circ. 4,000. **Document type:** bulletin.
Former titles (until 1984): American Jewish Historical Society. Report; (until 1976): American Jewish Historical Society. News (ISSN 0065-8944)

HERITAGE FLORIDA JEWISH NEWS. see *ETHNIC INTERESTS*

HERITAGE - SOUTHWEST JEWISH PRESS. see *ETHNIC INTERESTS*

HIDDEN CHILD. see *HISTORY — History Of Europe*

HILLEL GATE. see *ETHNIC INTERESTS*

HOLOCAUST EDUCATION. see *HISTORY — History Of Europe*

HOLOCAUST STUDIES SERIES. see *HISTORY — History Of Europe*

HOLY LAND REVIEW; illustrated quarterly of the Franciscan custody of the holy land. see *RELIGIONS AND THEOLOGY — Roman Catholic*

296.3 US ISSN 0441-4195
BM1
HUMANISTIC JUDAISM. 1967. q. $18 domestic; Canada $24; foreign $36. Society for Humanistic Judaism, 28611 W. 12 Mile Rd., Farmington Hills, MI 48334. TEL 810-478-7610. FAX 810-477-9014. Eds. M. Bonnie Cousens, Ruth Duskin Feldman. bk.rev. circ. 2,500. **Indexed:** Ind.Jew.Per., Ind.Jew.Per.

I J A REPORTS. (Institute of Jewish Affairs) see *ETHNIC INTERESTS*

ICONOGRAPHY OF RELIGIONS. SECTION 23, JUDAISM. see *ART*

ILLIANA NEWS. see *ETHNIC INTERESTS*

INDEX TO JEWISH PERIODICALS. see *RELIGIONS AND THEOLOGY — Abstracting, Bibliographies, Statistics*

INDIANA JEWISH POST AND OPINION. see *ETHNIC INTERESTS*

INFORMATION JUIVE. see *ETHNIC INTERESTS*

INSIGHT (NEW YORK). see *WOMEN'S INTERESTS*

INSTITUTE FOR AGRICULTURAL RESEARCH ACCORDING TO THE TORAH. BULLETIN. see *AGRICULTURE*

296 US
INTERCOM (NEW YORK, 1960?). (Text mainly in English; occasionally in Hebrew) vol.14, 1973. s-a. $50 membership. Association of Orthodox Jewish Scientists, 3 W. 16th St., New York, NY 10011-6363. TEL 212-229-2340. FAX 212-229-2319. Ed. Rabbi Barry Freundel. bk.rev. circ. 1,400.
Description: Addresses issues of science and Jewish law. Seeks to reconcile and resolve conflicts and challenges of science and Jewish law.

INTERMOUNTAIN JEWISH NEWS. see *ETHNIC INTERESTS*

ISRAEL HORIZONS; the socialist Zionist journal. see *POLITICAL SCIENCE*

ISRAEL QUALITY. see *BUSINESS AND ECONOMICS — International Commerce*

ISSUES (SAN FRANCISCO). see *RELIGIONS AND THEOLOGY — Other Denominations And Sects*

J C C CIRCLE. (Jewish Community Centers Association of North America) see *ETHNIC INTERESTS*

J T A COMMUNITY NEWS REPORTER. (Jewish Telegraphic Agency) see *ETHNIC INTERESTS*

J T A DAILY NEWS BULLETIN. (Jewish Telegraphic Agency) see *POLITICAL SCIENCE*

J T A WEEKLY NEWS DIGEST. (Jewish Telegraphic Agency) see *POLITICAL SCIENCE*

296 IS ISSN 0333-7081
BM1
JERUSALEM STUDIES IN JEWISH THOUGHT. 1981. s-a. $30 paperbound (hardcover $40) (effective 1994). Jewish National and University Library, P.O. Box 34165, Jerusalem 91341, Israel. TEL 972-2-585039. FAX 972-2-586315. **Document type:** academic/scholarly publication.
Description: Jewish thought throughout history; medieval and modern Jewish philosophy and mysticism.

JEVREJSKI PREGLED. see *ETHNIC INTERESTS*

JEWISH ACTION. see *ETHNIC INTERESTS*

JEWISH ADVOCATE. see *ETHNIC INTERESTS*

JEWISH AFFAIRS. see *POLITICAL SCIENCE*

JEWISH ART. see *ART*

JEWISH BIBLE QUARTERLY. see *RELIGIONS AND THEOLOGY*

296.4 892.4 US ISSN 0075-3726
PN6067
JEWISH BOOK ANNUAL. (Text in English, Hebrew and Yiddish) 1942. a. $35. Jewish Book Council, 15 E. 26th St., New York, NY 10010. TEL 212-532-4949. Ed. Esther Nussbaum. bk.rev. circ. 1,200. (reprint service avail. from KTO) **Indexed:** Amer.Bibl.Slavic & E.Eur.Stud, Ind.Heb.Per.

JEWISH BOOK WORLD. see *PUBLISHING AND BOOK TRADE*

JEWISH BOOK WORLD. see *LITERARY AND POLITICAL REVIEWS*

JEWISH BRAILLE REVIEW. see *HANDICAPPED — Visually Impaired*

JEWISH BULLETIN OF NORTHERN CALIFORNIA. see *ETHNIC INTERESTS*

JEWISH CHRONICLE; the world's leading Jewish newspaper. see *LITERARY AND POLITICAL REVIEWS*

JEWISH CHRONICLE (WORCESTER). see *ETHNIC INTERESTS*

JEWISH CHRONICLE (YONKERS); serving Southern Westchester. see *LITERARY AND POLITICAL REVIEWS*

JEWISH CIVIC PRESS. see *ETHNIC INTERESTS*

JEWISH COMMUNITY ADVOCATE OF SOUTH BROWARD. see *ETHNIC INTERESTS*

JEWISH COMMUNITY NEWS. see *ETHNIC INTERESTS*

JEWISH COMMUNITY VOICE. see *ETHNIC INTERESTS*

JEWISH CURRENT EVENTS. see *ETHNIC INTERESTS*

JEWISH CURRENTS. see *ETHNIC INTERESTS*

296 US ISSN 1063-4614
JEWISH DENOMINATIONS IN AMERICA. 1988. irreg. price varies. Praeger Publishers (Subsidiary of: Greenwood Publishing Group Inc.), 88 Post Rd. W., Box 5007, Westport, CT 06881-5007. TEL 203-226-3571. FAX 203-222-1502. **Document type:** monographic series.

JEWISH EXPONENT. see *SOCIAL SERVICES AND WELFARE*

JEWISH FRONTIER. see *POLITICAL SCIENCE*

296 US
JEWISH GUARDIAN. 1974. bi-m. $4.50. Neturei Karta of U.S.A. - Guardians of the Holy City, P.O. Box 2143, Brooklyn, New York, NY 11202. Ed. Mordecai Weberman. adv.; bk.rev.; illus. circ. 10,000.

JEWISH HERALD-VOICE. see *ETHNIC INTERESTS*

JEWISH HISTORICAL SOCIETY OF ENGLAND. ANNUAL REPORT AND ACCOUNTS FOR THE SESSION. see *HISTORY — History Of Europe*

JEWISH HISTORICAL SOCIETY OF ENGLAND. BULLETIN. see *HISTORY — History Of Europe*

JEWISH HISTORICAL STUDIES. TRANSACTIONS. see *HISTORY — History Of Europe*

JEWISH HISTORY. see *ETHNIC INTERESTS*

JEWISH HORIZON. see *ETHNIC INTERESTS*

JEWISH JOURNAL (DEERFIELD BEACH). see *ETHNIC INTERESTS*

JEWISH JOURNAL (VALLEY STREAM). see *ETHNIC INTERESTS*

JEWISH JOURNAL (YOUNGSTOWN). see *ETHNIC INTERESTS*

JEWISH JOURNAL OF GREATER LOS ANGELES. see *ETHNIC INTERESTS*

JEWISH JOURNAL OF SAN ANTONIO. see *ETHNIC INTERESTS*

JEWISH JOURNAL OF SOCIOLOGY. see *SOCIOLOGY*

JEWISH JURISPRUDENCE SERIES. see *LAW*

JEWISH LAW ANNUAL. see *LAW*

JEWISH LAW IN CONTEXT. see *LAW*

JEWISH LEADER. see *ETHNIC INTERESTS*

JEWISH LEDGER. see *ETHNIC INTERESTS*

JEWISH LINGUISTIC STUDIES. see *LINGUISTICS*

JEWISH NEWS OF GREATER PHOENIX. see *ETHNIC INTERESTS*

JEWISH OBSERVER (DEWITT). see *ETHNIC INTERESTS*

296.4 US ISSN 0021-6615
BM1
JEWISH OBSERVER (NEW YORK). 1963. m. (Sep.-June). $22. Agudath Israel of America, 84 William St., New York, NY 10038. TEL 212-797-9000. FAX 212-269-2843. Ed. Rabbi Nisson Wolpin. adv.; bk.rev.; index. circ. 16,000. (also avail. in microform from UMI; reprint service avail. from UMI) **Indexed:** Ind.Jew.Per. **Document type:** academic/scholarly publication.
—UMI.
Description: Presents thought and opinion on Jewish affairs from an orthodox perspective.

JEWISH PARENT CONNECTION. see *CHILDREN AND YOUTH — For*

JEWISH POST. see *ETHNIC INTERESTS*

RELIGIONS AND THEOLOGY — JUDAIC

JEWISH POST AND NEWS. see *ETHNIC INTERESTS*

JEWISH POST OF NEW YORK. see *ETHNIC INTERESTS*

JEWISH PRESS (BROOKLYN). see *ETHNIC INTERESTS*

JEWISH PRESS (OMAHA). see *ETHNIC INTERESTS*

JEWISH PRESS OF PINELLAS COUNTY. see *ETHNIC INTERESTS*

JEWISH PRESS OF TAMPA. see *ETHNIC INTERESTS*

296.7   US   ISSN 0021-6682
DS101
JEWISH QUARTERLY REVIEW. 1909. q. $35 to individuals; institutions $50. University of Pennsylvania, Center for Judaic Studies, 420 Walnut St., Philadelphia, PA 19106. TEL 215-238-1290. FAX 215-238-1540. Ed.Bd. adv.; bk.rev.; bibl.; illus.; index. circ. 1,000. (also avail. in microfilm from UMI,PMC; reprint service avail. from UMI,KTO) **Indexed:** A.I.C.P., Amer.Hist.& Life, Arts & Hum.Cit.Ind., Bibl.Ling., Curr.Cont., Hist.Abstr., Ind.Jew.Per., M.L.A., Mid.East: Abstr.& Ind., New Test.Abstr., Old Test.Abstr., Rel.& Theol.Abstr. (1968-), Rel.Ind.One, Rel.Per., RILM. **Document type:** academic/scholarly publication.
—Faxon; Genuine Article; SWETS; UnCover.
  Description: Provides a forum for the study of religion, Judaica, Old and New Testaments, Semitic languages and ancient Near Eastern studies.

JEWISH RECORD. see *ETHNIC INTERESTS*

JEWISH REPORTER. see *ETHNIC INTERESTS*

296   UK
JEWISH REVIEW. 1946. q. £3.50($6) Mizrachi - Hapoel Hamizrachi Federation, 2B Golders Green Rd., London NW11 8LH, England. TEL 0181-455-2243. FAX 0181-458-7472. Ed. Arieh L. Handler. adv.; bk.rev.; film rev.; play rev.; rec.rev.; abstr.; illus.; stat. circ. 5,000. (tabloid format) **Document type:** newsletter.
  Former titles (until 1983): Religious Zionist Movement Newsletter; (until 1976): Jewish Review (ISSN 0021-6690)

296   US   ISSN 0898-7963
JEWISH SCIENCE INTERPRETER; a message of health and happiness through the Jewish Faith. 1922. 8/yr. $12. (Society of Jewish Science) Jewish Science Publishing Co., 54 Sunnyside Blvd., Plainview, NY 11803-1507. TEL 516-349-0022. FAX 516-349-0022. Ed. David Goldstein. adv.; bk.rev. circ. 1,000.

JEWISH SOCIAL STUDIES; history, culture and society. see *SOCIAL SCIENCES: COMPREHENSIVE WORKS*

296.7   US   ISSN 0021-6720
AP92
JEWISH SPECTATOR. 1935. q. $24. American Friends of the Center for Jewish Living and Values, 4391 Park Milano, Calabasas, CA 91302. TEL 818-591-7481. FAX 818-591-7267. Ed. Robert Bleiweiss. bk.rev. circ. 6,500. (also avail. in microform from AJP) **Indexed:** Ind.Jew.Per. **Document type:** academic/scholarly publication.
—Faxon; UMI; UnCover.
  Description: Contains scholarly articles, religious and political opinion, fiction and poetry of interest to Jews.

JEWISH SPORTS & FITNESS. see *PHYSICAL FITNESS AND HYGIENE*

JEWISH STANDARD. see *ETHNIC INTERESTS*

JEWISH STANDARD; New Jersey's oldest English-Jewish newspaper. see *ETHNIC INTERESTS*

JEWISH STAR. see *ETHNIC INTERESTS*

JEWISH STAR (SAN FRANCISCO); independent newspaper. see *ETHNIC INTERESTS*

296   IS   ISSN 0792-8467
JEWISH STUDIES. 1967. a. $3. Jerusalem Academy of Jewish Studies, P.O. Box 5454, Jerusalem, Israel. TEL 972-2-817647. FAX 972-2-825787. Ed. Rabbi A. Carmell. adv.; bk.rev. circ. 5,000. **Document type:** academic/scholarly publication.

JEWISH STUDIES QUARTERLY. see *ETHNIC INTERESTS*

JEWISH TELEGRAPH. see *ETHNIC INTERESTS*

296   US   ISSN 1059-4388
BM496.A1
JEWISH THOUGHT. 1990. s-a. Union of Orthodox Jewish Congregations of America, 333 Seventh Ave., 18th Fl., New York, NY 10001-5004. TEL 212-244-2011. FAX 212-268-4819.

JEWISH TIMES (HUNTINGDON VALLEY). see *ETHNIC INTERESTS*

296   SA
JEWISH TRADITION. (Text in English) 1954. m. R.36. Union of Orthodox Synagogues of South Africa, P.O. Box 27701, Yeoville 2143, South Africa. TEL 27-11-648-9136. FAX 27-11-648-4014. Ed. R.I. Reznik. adv.; bk.rev.; charts; illus. circ. 15,000. (tabloid format)
  Formerly: Federation of Synagogues of South Africa. Federation Chronicle (ISSN 0014-9314)
  Description: Official mouthpiece of South African Orthodox Jewry.

JEWISH TRANSCRIPT. see *ETHNIC INTERESTS*

JEWISH VETERAN; the patriotic voice of American Jewry. see *MILITARY*

THE JEWISH VOICE. see *ETHNIC INTERESTS*

JEWISH VOICE (DEAL PARK). see *ETHNIC INTERESTS*

JEWISH VOICE (NEW ORLEANS). see *ETHNIC INTERESTS*

THE JEWISH VOICE (WILMINGTON). see *ETHNIC INTERESTS*

296.7   US
JEWISH VOICE & OPINION. 1987. m. $15. 73 Dana Pl., Englewood, NJ 07631. TEL 201-569-2845. FAX 201-569-1739. Ed. Susan L. Rosenbluth. circ. 11,500. **Document type:** newsletter.

JEWISH WEEK. see *ETHNIC INTERESTS*

JEWISH WEEKLY NEWS. see *ETHNIC INTERESTS*

JEWISH WESTERN BULLETIN. see *ETHNIC INTERESTS*

JEWISH WORLD. see *ETHNIC INTERESTS*

296   UK   ISSN 0075-3769
JEWISH YEAR BOOK. 1896. a. £15. Jewish Chronicle Publications Ltd., 25 Furnival St, London EC4A 1JT, England. FAX 071-405-9040. TELEX 940-11415. Ed. Stephen Massil. adv.; bk.rev. circ. 5,000. (also avail. in microform)
—BLDSC (4668.381000).

JEWS AND THE JEWISH PEOPLE. EXCERPTS FROM THE SOVIET PRESS/EVREI I EVREISKII NAROD. MATERIALI IZ SOVIETSKOI PECATI. see *ETHNIC INTERESTS*

JEWS AND THE JEWISH PEOPLE - JEWISH SAMIZDAT/EVREI I EVREISKI NAROD - EVREISKII SAMIZDAT. see *ETHNIC INTERESTS*

JEWS FOR JESUS NEWSLETTER. see *RELIGIONS AND THEOLOGY — Other Denominations And Sects*

296   IS   ISSN 0334-0953
DS135.R92
JEWS OF THE SOVIET UNION; immigration and struggle in the 1980's. (Text in Hebrew) 1976. irreg. (Israel Public Council for Soviet Jewry, Scientist Committee) Magnes Press, Hebrew University, Jerusalem, P.O. Box 7695, Jerusalem 91076, Israel. TEL 972-2-660341. FAX 972-2-633370. Ed. David Prital. **Document type:** monographic series.
  Supersedes (in 1983): Jewish Intelligentsia in the USSR.

JOEDISK ORIENTERING. see *ETHNIC INTERESTS*

296   NE   ISSN 0047-2212
BM176
JOURNAL FOR THE STUDY OF JUDAISM IN THE PERSIAN, HELLENISTIC AND ROMAN PERIOD. 1970. q. fl.130($84) to individuals; institutions fl.210 ($135) (effective 1996). E.J. Brill, P.O. Box 9000, 2300 PA Leiden, Netherlands. TEL 31-71-5353500. FAX 31-71-5317532. TELEX 39296 BRILL NL. E-mail: ejborders@ejbrill.com. (In N. America: E.J. Brill, 24 Hudson St., Kinderhook, NY 12106. TEL 800-962-4406. FAX 518-758-1959) Ed A.S. van der Wonde. (back issues avail.) **Indexed:** Bibl.Ling., Mid.East: Abstr.& Ind., New Test.Abstr., Old Test.Abstr., Rel.& Theol.Abstr. (1979-), Rel.Ind.One, Rel.Per. **Document type:** academic/scholarly publication.
—Faxon; SWETS; UnCover. **CCC.**
  Formerly: Journal for the Study of Judaism.
  Description: International forum of scholarly discussions on the history, literature and religious ideas of Judaism in the Persian, Hellenistic and Roman period.
  Refereed Serial

JOURNAL OF JEWISH COMMUNAL SERVICE. see *SOCIAL SERVICES AND WELFARE*

JOURNAL OF JEWISH EDUCATION. see *EDUCATION*

JOURNAL OF JEWISH MUSIC AND LITURGY. see *MUSIC*

296   UK   ISSN 0022-2097
BM1
JOURNAL OF JEWISH STUDIES. (Text in English; occasionally in French) 1948. s-a. £21($40) Oxford Centre for Hebrew and Jewish Studies, 45 St. Giles, Oxford OX1 2LP, England. TEL 01865-311961. FAX 01865-735034. Ed. G. Vermes. adv.; bk.rev.; bibl.; index. circ. 1,000. (also avail. in microform from UMI; reprint service avail. from KTO) **Indexed:** Adol.Ment.Hlth.Abstr., Amer.Hist.& Life, Arts & Hum.Cit.Ind., Bibl.Ling., Br.Hum.Ind., Curr.Cont., Hist.Abstr., Ind.Jew.Per., Mid.East: Abstr.& Ind., New Test.Abstr., Old Test.Abstr., Rel.& Theol.Abstr. (1970-), Rel.Ind.One, Rel.Per. **Document type:** academic/scholarly publication.
—BLDSC (5009.600000); Faxon; Genuine Article; SWETS; UnCover.
  Description: Jewish history, literature and culture throughout the ages.

296   US   ISSN 1053-699X
BM1   CODEN: JJTPE2
JOURNAL OF JEWISH THOUGHT AND PHILOSOPHY. 2/yr. (in 1 vol.). 61 ECU (effective 1996). Harwood Academic Publishers, c/o International Publishers Distributor, 820 Town Center Dr., Langhorne, PA 19047. TEL 215-750-2642. FAX 215-750-6343. (Subscr. to: Internatjonal Publishers Distributor, PO Box 90, Reading, Berkshire, RG1 8JL, England. TEL 44-173-456-8316) Ed. Elliot R. Wolfson. (also avail. in microform) **Indexed:** Ind.Jew.Per. **Document type:** academic/scholarly publication.
—CCC.
  Description: Provides an international forum for Jewish thought, philosophy and intellectual history, with an emphasis on contemporary issues. Covers biblical studies, mysticism, literary criticism, political theory, sociology and anthropology.
  Refereed Serial

296   UK   ISSN 1352-4178
BM197
JOURNAL OF PROGRESSIVE JUDAISM. 1993. 2/yr. $15 to individuals; institutions $37.50. Sheffield Academic Press Ltd., Mansion House, 19 Kingfield Rd., Sheffield S11 9AS, England. TEL 44-171-267-4466. FAX 44-171-482-2293. E-mail: admin@sheffac.demon.co.uk. Ed. Seth Kunin. **Document type:** academic/scholarly publication.
—BLDSC (5042.746000).

JOURNAL OF PSYCHOLOGY AND JUDAISM. see *PSYCHOLOGY*

296   SZ   ISSN 0022-572X
DS101
JUDAICA; Beitraege zum Verstaendnis des juedischen Schicksals in Vergangenheit und Gegenwart. 1945. q. 42 SFr. (Stiftung fuer Kirche und Judentum) Judaica Verlag, Austr. 114, CH-4051 Basel, Switzerland. TEL 061-2719897. FAX 061-2719234. Ed. Nico Rubeli-Guthauser. adv.; bk.rev. circ. 600. **Indexed:** Amer.Hist.& Life, CERDIC, Hist.Abstr., Old Test.Abstr. **Document type:** academic/scholarly publication.
—SWETS.

RELIGIONS AND THEOLOGY — JUDAIC

JUDAICA BOOK NEWS. see *PUBLISHING AND BOOK TRADE*

296.4   US   ISSN 1061-0448
N7415
JUDAICA NEWS. 1989. q. Box 1130, Fair Lawn, NJ 07410. TEL 201-796-6151. FAX 201-796-6545. Ed. Terry Cohn. **Document type:** newsletter.

296.7   US   ISSN 0022-5762
BM1
JUDAISM; a quarterly journal of Jewish life and thought. 1952. q. $20 to individuals; libraries $35. American Jewish Congress, 15 E. 84th St., New York, NY 10028. TEL 212-879-4500. Ed. Murray Baumgarter. adv.; bk.rev.; index, cum.index (20 yr.). circ. 6,000. (also avail. in microform from UMI; reprint service avail. from UMI) **Indexed:** Acad.Ind., Amer.Bibl.Slavic & E.Eur.Stud, Arts & Hum.Cit.Ind., CERDIC, Curr.Cont., G.Soc.Sci.& Rel.Per.Lit., Ind.Jew.Per., Mid.East: Abstr.& Ind., New Test.Abstr., Rel.& Theol.Abstr. (1970-), Rel.Ind.One, Rel.Per., SSCI. **Document type:** academic/scholarly publication.
●Also available online. Vendor(s): University Microfilms International.
—BLDSC (5073.825000); Faxon; Genuine Article; SWETS; UMI; UnCover.

JUEDISCHER ALMANACH. see *ETHNIC INTERESTS*

JUSTICE. see *LAW*

296 100   IS   ISSN 0334-6994
BM526
KABBALAH; newsletter of current research in Jewish mysticism. (Text in English) 1985. 3/yr. $12.75 to individuals; institutions $32.75. 41 Palyam St., Jerusalem 97 890, Israel. TEL 02-817-876. Ed. Hananya Goodman. (back issues avail.) **Document type:** newsletter.

KADIMA. see *LITERARY AND POLITICAL REVIEWS*

KANSAS CITY JEWISH CHRONICLE. see *ETHNIC INTERESTS*

KASHRUS FAXLETTER. see *FOOD AND FOOD INDUSTRIES*

296   SA
KASHRUT GUIDE. 1977. a. free. Union of Orthodox Synagogues of South Africa, P.O. Box 4110, Johannesburg 2000, South Africa. TEL 27-11-648-9136. FAX 27-11-648-4014. Ed. Saul Emanuel. adv.; circ. 13,000 (controlled).
Description: Lists all Kosher food products and establishments under the supervision of the Johannesburg and Cape Town rabbinical authorities.

296   US   ISSN 0022-9644
KEEPING POSTED WITH N C S Y.* (Reporter and Leadership Editions) 1959. q. $6. National Conference of Synagogue Youth, 333 Seventh Ave., 19th Fl., New York, NY 10001-5004. TEL 212-244-2011. FAX 212-268-4819. (Co-sponsor: Union of Orthodox Jewish Congregations of America) Ed. Renee Straussand. adv.; bk.rev. circ. 20,000.

KENTUCKY JEWISH POST AND OPINION. see *ETHNIC INTERESTS*

296.7   US   ISSN 1068-6975
BM723
KEREM; creative explorations in Judaism. 1992. a. $8.50 individuals per no.; institutions $15. Jewish Study Center Press, Inc., 3035 Porter St., N.W., Washington, DC 20008-3272. TEL 202-364-3006. FAX 202-364-3806. Eds. Gilah Langner, Sara R. Horowitz. adv. circ. 2,000. **Indexed:** Ind.Jew.Per.
Description: Provides a forum for religious, spiritual and literary contributions on contemporary Judaism.

296   US
KEREM SHLOMO. (Text in Hebrew) 1977. irreg. (10-12/yr.). $15. Bobover Congregation, 1577 48th St., Brooklyn, NY 11219. TEL 718-438-2018. Ed. Shmerel Zitronenbaum. bibl.; index. circ. 2,500. (back issues avail.)

296   IS
KFAR CHABAD. w. IS.60($68) Chabad Association, P.O. Box 41, Kfar Chabad 60978, Israel. TEL 03-984959.

KIRYAT SEFER; bibliographical quarterly. see *BIBLIOGRAPHIES*

KOL HA-T'NUAH/VOICE OF THE MOVEMENT. see *ETHNIC INTERESTS*

296 327 028.5   UK   ISSN 0260-6585
KOLEINU. (Text mainly in English; occasionally in Hebrew) 1980. q. membership. Habonim-Dror Organization, 523 Finchley Rd., London NW3 7BD, England. TEL 01-435-9033. FAX 01-431-4503. (Co-sponsor: World Zionist Organisation. Youth and Hechalutz Department) Ed. Steven Brown. adv.; film rev. circ. 1,500. (back issues avail.)

296   IS   ISSN 0333-8584
KOLOT. 1981. irreg. free. Israel Movement for Progressive Judaism, 13 King David St., Jerusalem, Israel. TEL 02-203448. FAX 02-203446. Ed. Yehoram Mazor. bk.rev. circ. 2,500.

296.4   US
KOSHER DIRECTORY. a. $10. Union of Orthodox Jewish Congregations of America, Kashruth Division, 333 Seventh Ave., 18th fl., New York, NY 10001-5004. TEL 212-563-4000. FAX 212-564-9058. Ed. Zahava Fulda. adv. circ. 20,000.

KULTUR UN LEBN. see *ETHNIC INTERESTS*

LAMISHPAHA. see *LINGUISTICS*

LAS VEGAS ISRAELITE. see *ETHNIC INTERESTS*

296   US
LIBRARY OF JEWISH LAW AND ETHICS. irreg., vol.19, 1993. price varies. Yeshiva University Press - Ktaw Publishing House, Inc., 900 Jefferson St., No. 6249, Hoboken, NJ 07030-7205. TEL 201-963-9524. FAX 201-963-0102. Eds. Norman Lamm, Yaakov Elman. **Document type:** academic/scholarly publication, monographic series.

LIKUTIM; a journal of visual impairment and blindness. see *HANDICAPPED — Visually Impaired*

LILITH; the independent Jewish women's magazine. see *WOMEN'S INTERESTS*

THE LINK (ALBUQUERQUE). see *ETHNIC INTERESTS*

LONG ISLAND JEWISH WORLD. see *ETHNIC INTERESTS*

296   AG   ISSN 0024-7693
LUZ; la revista judia independiente. 1931. fortn. Arg.$30 for 6 mos. (America $120; elsewhere $140). Paso 684, Piso 2o A, 1031 Buenos Aires, Argentina. Ed. David Elnecave Jr. bk.rev.; bibl.; illus. circ. 25,000.

MAAJAN - DIE QUELLE. see *GENEALOGY AND HERALDRY*

MABUEY HANCHAL. see *ETHNIC INTERESTS*

296.68   US
MACHBERET HAMENAHEL. 1975. m. $6. National Conference of Yeshiva Principals, 160 Broadway, New York, NY 10038. TEL 212-406-4190. Ed. Rabbi Chaim Feuerman. bk.rev. circ. 900. (looseleaf format; back issues avail.)

296   IS
MACHSHEVET. 1971. bi-m. IS.12. P.O. Box 363, Bnei Brak, Israel. TEL 03-703186.

MAHUT. see *LITERATURE*

MANHATTAN JEWISH SENTINEL. see *ETHNIC INTERESTS*

296   UK   ISSN 0266-4003
MANNA. 1966. q. £9.75 (foreign £14). Manor House Society, Sternberg Centre for Judaism, The Manor House, 80 East End Rd., London N3 2SY, England. TEL 0181-346-2288. FAX 0181-349-0694. Ed. Rab. Tony Bayfield. adv.; bk.rev.; illus. circ. 2,000. **Indexed:** Ind.Jew.Per. **Document type:** bulletin.
Formerly (until 1983): Living Judaism (ISSN 0024-5267)
Description: Covers a wide range of topics of Jewish interest.

MARTYRDOM AND RESISTANCE. see *ETHNIC INTERESTS*

MEDIEVAL ENCOUNTERS; a journal of Jewish, Christian and Muslim culture in confluence and dialogue. see *HISTORY*

296   IS   ISSN 0334-8814
BS410
MEGADIM. 1986. 3/yr. $20. Yaacov Herzog Institute, Alon Shvut, Gush Etzion 90940, Israel. TEL 972-2-931451. FAX 972-2-931298. Eds. Yoseph Offer, Avraham Sham'ah. bk.rev. circ. 1,500. **Document type:** academic/scholarly publication.

MELTON JOURNAL. see *EDUCATION*

MENORAH. see *ETHNIC INTERESTS*

MENORAH REVIEW. see *ETHNIC INTERESTS*

296   UY
MENSAJE. vol.4, 1978. bi-m. Comite Central Israelita del Uruguay, Rio Negro 1308, Montevideo, Uruguay. Ed. Jorge Sztarcevsky. **Indexed:** Biol.Abstr.

296   IS
MESILOT; religious Zionism in action. (Editions in English and Hebrew) 1983. m. Society for the Advancement of Religious Zionism, Mesilot, c/o Mr. S.R. Sachs, P.O. Box 7720, Jerusalem, Israel. TEL 972-2-258833. FAX 972-2-257418. bk.rev. circ. 1,800.

HA-MESIVTA. see *LAW*

METROWEST JEWISH NEWS. see *ETHNIC INTERESTS*

METROWEST JEWISH REPORTER. see *SOCIAL SERVICES AND WELFARE*

MIAMI JEWISH TRIBUNE. see *ETHNIC INTERESTS*

MIDSTREAM; a monthly Jewish review. see *LITERARY AND POLITICAL REVIEWS*

MISHKAN; a forum on the gospel and the Jewish people. see *RELIGIONS AND THEOLOGY*

289   US   ISSN 1068-4379
MISHPOCHAH MESSAGE. 19?? q. Jews for Jesus, 60 Haight St., San Francisco, CA 94102. TEL 415-864-2600. FAX 415-552-8325. Ed. Ruth Rosen.
Description: Deals with issues of interest to Jewish believers in Jesus.

296   IS   ISSN 0541-5632
MITZION TETZEH TORAH. M.T.T.. 1968. irreg. (approx. 2/yr.). price varies. Mitzion Tetzeh Torah, Ltd., P.O. Box 29435, 9 Derech Haifa Rd., Tel-Aviv, Israel. Ed. G. Rachaman. adv.; bk.rev. circ. 1,000.

296.4   US
MITZVAH CONNECTION. a. Box 948, Avon, CT 06001. TEL 203-675-7763. Ed. C. Dianne Zweig.

MODERN JEWISH STUDIES ANNUAL. see *LITERATURE*

MODERN JUDAISM. see *ETHNIC INTERESTS*

MOMENT. see *ETHNIC INTERESTS*

MONITOR (WASHINGTON). see *POLITICAL SCIENCE — Civil Rights*

296 028.5   US
MOSHIACH TIMES. 1981. 7/yr. $10. Tzivos HaShem, 332 Kingston Ave., Brooklyn, NY 11213. TEL 718-467-6630. FAX 718-467-8527. Ed. David S. Pape. circ. 10,000. (back issues avail.)
Description: Contains stories, biographies, cartoon and humor, letters and games of contemporary and historical interest for Jewish children. Illustrated by top cartoon artists.

MUSEO SEFARDI. NOTICIAS. see *MUSEUMS AND ART GALLERIES*

MUSICA JUDAICA. see *MUSIC*

296   US
N A T A JOURNAL. 1981. s-a. free. National Association of Temple Administrators, 838 Fifth Ave., New York, NY 10021. TEL 312-525-4707. FAX 312-525-3502. Ed. Robert Mills. bk.rev. circ. 2,500.

RELIGIONS AND THEOLOGY — JUDAIC

296 US ISSN 0300-6689
N A T E NEWS. 1955. 6/yr. membership. National Association of Temple Educators, 707 Summerly Dr., Nashville, TN 37209-4253. TEL 615-352-6800. FAX 615-352-7800. Ed. Richard M. Morin. adv.; bk.rev. circ. 2,100. **Document type:** newsletter.

NA'AMAT WOMAN. see *POLITICAL SCIENCE*

NARROW WAY. see *RELIGIONS AND THEOLOGY*

NATIONAL JEWISH ADVOCATE. see *ETHNIC INTERESTS*

NATIONAL JEWISH NEWS. see *ETHNIC INTERESTS*

NATIONAL JEWISH POST AND OPINION. see *ETHNIC INTERESTS*

NEAR EAST REPORT; a Washington newsletter on American policy in the Middle East. see *POLITICAL SCIENCE — International Relations*

296.4 US ISSN 0883-0215
NEW MENORAH. 1979. q. $36 membership. Aleph: Alliance for Jewish Renewal, 7318 Germantown Ave., Philadelphia, PA 19119. TEL 215-247-9700. FAX 215-247-9703. E-mail: Alephajr@aol.com. Ed. Arthur Waskow. adv. contact: Rivkah Walton. bk.rev. circ. 1,000. **Document type:** academic/scholarly publication, newsletter.
Formerly (until 1985): Menorah.
Description: For networking the emerging liturgical, spiritual, and social action concerns that arise out of the loose coalition of individuals and groups of the Jewish Renewal movement.

296 NE ISSN 0028-9833
NIEUW GELUID. 1952. 7/yr. fl.25($10) Bond Nederlands Israel, Postbus 88, 9285 ZW Buitenpost, Netherlands. TEL 31-511-543053. FAX 31-511-542344. Ed. G. van der Laan. bk.rev.; index. circ. 800.

296 IS ISSN 0048-0460
NIV HAMIDRASHIA. (Text in English, French, Hebrew) 1963. irreg $20 per no. Friends of the Midrashia, Israel, 3, Achuzath Bayith St., Tel Aviv, Israel. Ed. Israel Sadan. adv.; bk.rev. circ. 5,000. **Indexed:** Ind.Heb.Per. **Document type:** academic/scholarly publication.

NOAH'S ARK; a newspaper for Jewish children. see *CHILDREN AND YOUTH — For*

NORTH SHORE JEWISH PRESS. JOURNAL. see *ETHNIC INTERESTS*

NOTRE VOIX. see *POLITICAL SCIENCE*

296 FR ISSN 0029-4705
LES NOUVEAUX CAHIERS. 1965. q. 220 F. (foreign 270F.). Alliance Israelite Universelle en France, 45 rue la Bruyere, 75009 Paris, France. Ed. Anne Grynberg. adv.; bk.rev.; bibl. circ. 3,000.
Description: Deals with Jewish history, philosophy, sociology and literature.

OBSERVER (NASHVILLE). see *ETHNIC INTERESTS*

OLAM HADASH. see *CHILDREN AND YOUTH — For*

296.4 US ISSN 0030-2139
OLOMEINU/OUR WORLD. (Text in English, Hebrew) 1945. m. (8/yr.) $10 (foreign $12). National Society for Hebrew Day Schools, 5723 18th Ave., Brooklyn, NY 11204. TEL 718-259-1223. FAX 718-259-1795. Eds. Rabbi Yaakov Fruchter, Rabbi Nosson Scherman. illus.; circ. 18,500 (paid). **Indexed:** Ind.Jew.Per. **Document type:** consumer publication.
Description: For students in elementary grades of Yeshiva day schools. Includes articles and short stories to supplement and enhance Torah studies and values.

ON CAMPUS. see *ETHNIC INTERESTS*

296 US ISSN 0362-2770
OPTIONS (WAYNE); the Jewish resources magazine. 1974. m. $21. Options Publishing Co., Box 311, Wayne, NJ 07474-0311. TEL 201-694-2327. Ed. Betty J. Singer. bk.rev.; index. (back issues avail.) **Document type:** newsletter.
Description: American Jewish resources: cultural, educational, religious and more.

296 IS ISSN 0333-6298
B'OR HA'TORAH; science, the arts and problems of modern life in the light of the Torah. (Editions in English and Hebrew) 1982. s-a. $11.50 per no. (effective 1995). Shamir, Association of Religious Professionals from the Former Soviet Union in Israel, 6 David Yellin St., P.O. Box 5749, Jerusalem, Israel. TEL 972-2-385702. FAX 972-2-385118. (U.S. addr.: Mishulovin, 309 Kingston Ave., Brooklyn, NY 11213) Ed. Herman Branover. bk.rev.; index. circ. 3,000. **Document type:** academic/scholarly publication.
Description: Contains poetry, critical articles, sources for study, and essays discussing contemporary situations and concerns and applications of Jewish law and ethics to these problems.
Refereed Serial

296 IS
ORACHOT. (Text in Hebrew) 1965. a. free. Haifa Religious Council, 4 Shmuel Ben Adia St., P.O. Box 2405, Haifa 31024, Israel. TEL 972-4-641186. FAX 972-4-667623. adv. circ. 3,000. **Document type:** bulletin.

296 IS ISSN 0333-9270
ORAITA; torah publication for Jewish thought and Halacha. (Text in Hebrew) 1977. s-a. IS.180($6) Rabbinical College Tifereth Netanya "Yad Moshe", P.O. Box 245, Netanya 42102, Israel. Ed. Rabbi Amihud Levine. adv.; bk.rev. circ. 2,000. (back issues avail.) **Document type:** academic/scholarly publication.

OTTAWA JEWISH BULLETIN. see *ETHNIC INTERESTS*

OUDTESTAMENTISCHE STUDIEN. see *RELIGIONS AND THEOLOGY*

296 155.451 267 US
OUR WAY.* 1970. irreg. (3-4/yr.) $6. (Union of Orthodox Jewish Congregations of America) National Conference of Synagogue Youth, 333 Seventh Ave., 19th Fl., New York, NY 10001-5004. TEL 212-244-2011. FAX 212-268-4819. Ed. Rabbi E. Lederfeind. adv. circ. 2,000.
Description: News and information about the Jewish deaf community, with emphasis on the youth.

OUTLOOK. see *ETHNIC INTERESTS*

OYFN SHVEL. see *ETHNIC INTERESTS*

DER PAKN TREGER/BOOK PEDDLER. see *LITERATURE*

PALM BEACH JEWISH WORLD. see *ETHNIC INTERESTS*

296 900 FR ISSN 0295-5652
DS112
PARDES.* (Text in French; summaries in English) 1985. s-a. 180 Fr. Editions Lattes, 24 bd. Saint-Michel, 75006 Paris, France. Eds. Shmuel Trigano, Annie Kriegel. adv.; bk.rev. circ. 2,000. (back issues avail.)

PASSAGES. see *ETHNIC INTERESTS*

296.4 US
PASSOVER DIRECTORY. 1923. a. Union of Orthodox Jewish Congregations of America, 333 Seventh Ave., 18th Fl., New York, NY 10001. TEL 212-563-4000. FAX 212-564-9058. Ed. Shelley Scharf.

PATTERNS OF PREJUDICE. see *POLITICAL SCIENCE — Civil Rights*

PE'AMIM; studies in Oriental Jewry. see *HISTORY — History Of The Near East*

296 221 NE ISSN 0169-9008
PESHITTA INSTITUTE, LEIDEN. MONOGRAPHS. Key Title: Monographs of the Peshitta Institute, Leiden. 1972. irreg., vol.7, 1994. E.J. Brill, P.O. Box 9000, 2300 PA Leiden, Netherlands. TEL 31-71-5353500. FAX 31-71-5317532. TELEX 39296 BRILL NL. (In N. America: E.J. Brill, 24 Hudson St., Kinderhook, NY 12106. TEL 800-962-4406. FAX 518-758-1959) (back issues avail.) **Document type:** monographic series.
Description: Scholarly studies on the Syriac translations of the Old and New Testaments.
Refereed Serial

PITTSBURGH JEWISH CHRONICLE. see *ETHNIC INTERESTS*

POINTS EAST (MENLO PARK). see *ETHNIC INTERESTS*

PORTLAND JEWISH REVIEW. see *ETHNIC INTERESTS*

296 US
PRAYER AND PRAISE. 1949. m. free. International Board of Jewish Missions, Box 3307, Chattanooga, TN 37404. TEL 615-698-3417. FAX 615-698-3418. Ed. O.L. Norwood. circ. 1,500. **Document type:** newsletter.

296.4 809 US ISSN 0272-9601
PJ5001
PROOFTEXTS; a journal of Jewish literary history. 1981. 3/yr. $25 to individuals (foreign $29.50); institutions $51.50 (foreign 56.40). Johns Hopkins University Press, Journals Publishing Division, 2715 N. Charles St., Baltimore, MD 21218. TEL 410-516-6987. FAX 410-516-6968. Eds. Alan Mintz, David G. Roskies. adv. contact: Tara Dorai-Berry. circ. 800. (also avail. in microform from UMI; back issues avail.; reprint service avail. from UMI) **Indexed:** Amer.Bibl.Slavic & E.Eur.Stud, Arts & Hum.Cit.Ind., Curr.Cont., Ind.Jew.Per., M.L.A., Old Test.Abstr., Rel.& Theol.Abstr. (1985-), Rel.Ind.One. **Document type:** academic/scholarly publication. —BLDSC (6927.075000); Faxon; Genuine Article; UMI. **CCC.**
Description: Covers Jewish literary heritage.

296.4 US
R C A RECORD. 1953. q. Rabbinical Council of America, 275 Seventh Ave., New York, NY 10001. TEL 212-807-7888. FAX 212-727-8452. Ed. Rabbi Mark Dratch.

296 UK
R S G B INFORM NEWSLETTER. 1973. q. Reform Synagogues of Great Britain, Manor House, 80 East End Rd., Finchley, London N3 2SY, England. TEL 0181-349-4731. FAX 0181-343-0901. Ed.Bd. adv.; illus. circ. 16,000. **Document type:** newsletter.

296 US ISSN 0079-936X
RABBINICAL ASSEMBLY, NEW YORK. PROCEEDINGS. (Text in English; occasionally in Hebrew, Yiddish) 1927-1970; resumed 1973. a. $11. Rabbinical Assembly, 3080 Broadway, New York, NY 10027. TEL 212-678-8060. FAX 212-749-9166. E-mail: rabassembly@jtsa.edu. cum.index: 1927-1968. circ. 1,500. **Document type:** proceedings.

296.6 US ISSN 1042-1807
BM735
RABBINICAL COUNCIL OF AMERICA. SERMON ANTHOLOGY. Cover title: R C A Sermon Anthology. (Text in English) 1969. a. Rabbinical Council of America, 275 Seventh Ave., New York, NY 10001. TEL 212-807-7888. FAX 212-727-8452.
Formerly (until 1985): Rabbinical Council of America. Sermon Manual (ISSN 0099-2488)

RAICES; revista judia de cultura. see *ETHNIC INTERESTS*

296 AG
RAICES; judaismo contemporaneo. 1991. q. $40. (A.M.I.A. Comunidad Judia de Buenos Aires) Editorial Agedit S.A., Parana 866, 1017 Buenos Aires, Argentina. TEL 812-5301. FAX 803-9944. Eds. Gustavo Borenstein, Alberto Iaccarino. adv.: B&W page $1300; color page $4300; 190 x 265; adv. contact: Alberto Iaccarino. circ. 10,000. **Document type:** consumer publication.

296 IT ISSN 0033-9792
DS101
RASSEGNA MENSILE DI ISRAEL. (Text in English, French, Italian) 1924. 3/yr. L.50000($65) Unione delle Comunita Israelitiche Italiane, Lungotevere Sanzio 9, Rome, Italy. Dir. Guido Fubini. bk.rev.; charts; illus.; index. circ. 1,000. **Document type:** academic/scholarly publication, bibliography.

200 NE ISSN 0034-1487
RECONSTRUCTION. 1947. m. $40.
Portugees-Israelietische Gemeente - Spanish and Portuguese Jewish Community at Amsterdam, Gerrit van der Veenstr. 141, 1077 DX Amsterdam, Netherlands. TEL 31-20-6762041. Ed. Dr. J.Z. Baruch. bk.rev. circ. 13,000.

RELIGIONS AND THEOLOGY — JUDAIC 5751

296.7 US ISSN 1072-3250
DS133
▼**RECONSTRUCTIONISM TODAY.** 1994. q. $12 (foreign $18) (effective 1995 & 1996). Federation of Reconstructionist Congregations and Havurot, Church Rd. & Greenwood Ave., Wyncote, PA 19095. TEL 215-887-1988. FAX 215-887-5348. Ed. Larry Bush; Pub. Mordecai Liebling. adv.; bk.rev.; index. circ. 10,500. (also avail. in microform from UMI; reprint service avail. from UMI) **Indexed:** HR Rep., Ind.Jew.Per., Mid.East: Abstr.& Ind. **Document type:** newsletter.
—UMI.

296.7 US ISSN 0034-1495
RECONSTRUCTIONIST. 1935-1993; N.S. 1995. s-a. $35 for 4 nos. (effective 1995). (Reconstructionist Rabbinical College) Reconstructionist Press, Church Rd. & Greenwood Ave., Wyncote, PA 19095. TEL 215-576-0800. FAX 215-576-6143. E-mail: gen@rrc.edu. circ. 2,500. **Indexed:** Ind.Jew.Per. **Document type:** academic/scholarly publication.

296.4 US ISSN 0482-0819
BM197
REFORM JUDAISM. 1955. q. $12. Union of American Hebrew Congregations, 838 Fifth Ave., New York, NY 10021. TEL 212-249-0100. Ed. Aron Hirt-Manheimer. illus. circ. 295,000. (also avail. in microfilm from AJP) **Indexed:** Ind.Jew.Per.
—UnCover.
Formerly (until 1972): Dimensions in American Judaism; **Incorporates:** Keeping Posted (ISSN 0022-9636)
Description: Links the institutions and affiliates of Reform Judaism with every Reform Jew. Covers developments within the Movement while interpreting world events and Jewish tradition from a Reform perspective. Conveys the creativity, diversity, and dynamism of Reform Judaism.

296 282 US
REMNANT OF ISRAEL. 1976. a. free. Remnant of Israel Publications, New Hope, KY 40052. TEL 502-325-3081. Ed. Arthur Klyber. circ. 15,000. (back issues avail.) **Document type:** newsletter.

RENEWAL MAGAZINE. see ETHNIC INTERESTS

THE REPORTER (NEW YORK, 1966). see SOCIAL SERVICES AND WELFARE

THE REPORTER (NEW YORK, 1972). see ETHNIC INTERESTS

296.6 US ISSN 0098-468X
BM60
RESHIMAT HAVRE HISTADRUT HA-RABANIM DA-AMERIKA/RABBINIC REGISTRY. (Text in English, Hebrew) irreg. Rabbinical Council of America, 275 Seventh Ave., New York, NY 10001. TEL 212-807-7888. FAX 212-727-8452.

RESPONSE (LOS ANGELES). see ETHNIC INTERESTS

RESPONSE (NEW YORK, 1967); a contemporary Jewish review. see ETHNIC INTERESTS

297 RM ISSN 0034-754X
REVISTA CULTULUI MOZAIC/REVIEW OF THE MOSAIC CREED. (Text in English, Hebrew, Rumanian) 1956. bi-m. $65 (effective Apr. 1992). Federatia Comunitatilor Evreiesti din Romania - Federation of Jewish Communities of Rumania, Str. Sf. Vineri nr.9-11, 70478 Bucharest, Rumania. TEL 6132538. FAX 3120869. TELEX 10798. Ed. Haim Rimer. adv.; bk.rev.; illus. circ. 9,000. **Document type:** newspaper.

296 BE ISSN 0035-2055
REVUE DES ETUDES JUIVES. (Supplement avail.: Collection de la Revue des Etudes Juives (ISSN 0777-785X)) (Text in French) 1880. q. 3000 BEF (effective 1995). (Societe des Etudes Juives, FR) Editions Peeters s.p.r.l., Bondgenotenlaan 153, 3000 Leuven, Belgium. TEL 32-16-235170. FAX 32-16-228500. Eds. G. Nahon, C. Touati. adv.; bk.rev.; charts; illus. circ. 1,800. (also avail. in microfiche from IDC; back issues avail.) **Indexed:** Amer.Hist.& Life, Bibl.Ling., Bull.Signal., Hist.Abstr., Lang.& Lang.Behav.Abstr., New Test.Abstr. **Document type:** academic/scholarly publication.
—BLDSC (7900.166000).
Description: Scholarly discussion of religious, cultural, social and historical issues in Jewish studies.

RHODE ISLAND JEWISH HISTORICAL NOTES. see ETHNIC INTERESTS

ROCKY MOUNTAIN JEWISH HISTORICAL NOTES. see ETHNIC INTERESTS

S.A. JEWISH TIMES. see ETHNIC INTERESTS

THE SAGARIN REVIEW; the St. Louis Jewish literary journal. see LITERATURE

ST. LOUIS JEWISH LIGHT; the newspaper of the Jewish community of Greater St. Louis. see ETHNIC INTERESTS

SAN DIEGO JEWISH PRESS HERITAGE. see ETHNIC INTERESTS

SAN DIEGO JEWISH TIMES. see ETHNIC INTERESTS

296 IS
SANZ. 1978. m. Igud Chasidei Sanz, P.O. Box 5032, Netanya 42 150, Israel.
Description: Topics of interest to the Sanz Jewish community.

SAVANNAH JEWISH NEWS. see ETHNIC INTERESTS

296 IS
SECULAR HUMANISTIC JUDAISM.* q. Israeli Association for Secular Humanistic Judaism, 8 Itamar Ben Avi St., P.O. Box 4512, Jerusalem 91044, Israel.

SEMANARIO ISRAELITA; unabhaengiges juedisches Wochenblatt. see ETHNIC INTERESTS

SEPHARDIC SCHOLAR. see ETHNIC INTERESTS

296 UY
SHAJAR; nuevo amanecer. 1990. q. Comunidad Israelita Sefaradi del Uruguay, C. Buenos Aires 234, Montevideo, Uruguay. TEL 96-11-36. Ed. Alejandro R. Moron.

SHALOM. see ETHNIC INTERESTS

200 UK
SHALOM. 1962. 3/yr. £5 (typcially set in Nov.). Church's Ministry Among the Jews, 30C Clarence Rd., St. Albans, Herts. AL1 4JJ, England. TEL 01727-833114. FAX 01727-848312. Ed. M. Perry. bk.rev.; illus. circ. 6,000.
Former titles: C M J Quarterly (ISSN 0007-8646); C.M.J. News.

296.68 IS ISSN 0582-9836
SHAMATIV. q. IS.12. Organization of Religious Teachers, Rehov Harav Hertzog 36, Bat Yam 59 461, Israel. TEL 03-862495. circ. 800.

SHIRIM; a Jewish poetry journal. see LITERATURE — Poetry

SH'MA; a journal of Jewish responsibility. see ETHNIC INTERESTS

296.8 US ISSN 0300-7960
SHMUESSEN MIT KINDER UN YUGENT. (Text in Yiddish) 1942. m. $3. Merkos L'Inyonei Chinuch, Inc., 770 Eastern Pkwy., Brooklyn, NY 11213. Ed. Nissan Mindel. illus.; index.

SHOFAR (CHATTANOOGA). see ETHNIC INTERESTS

SHOFAR (MELVILLE). see CHILDREN AND YOUTH — For

SHOMERNIK. see EDUCATION

SHVUT; Jewish problems in the USSR and Eastern Europe. see ETHNIC INTERESTS

296 IS ISSN 0334-7559
BM390
SIAH MESHARIM; journal of Judaism, religion and state. (Text in Hebrew) 1986. q. IS.25($15) 10 Harav Berlin St., Jerusalem 92503, Israel. TEL 972-2-632155. FAX 972-2-234127. E-mail: MSKRUPP@PLUTO.MSCC.HUJI.AC.IL. Ed. Z.W. Falk. bk.rev. circ. 500. **Document type:** academic/scholarly publication.
Description: Presents a forum for a pluralist discussion of Judaism, religion and state problems.

296 IS
SICHAT HASHAVUA; the weekly sheet for every Jew. (Text in Hebrew) w. Young Chabad Center, P.O. Box 14, Kfar Chabad 72915, Israel. TEL 03-985588. Ed. Menachem Barod.

296.68 IS ISSN 0334-6986
BM496.A1
SIDRA; a journal for the study of Rabbinic literature. (Text in Henbrew; summaries in English) 1985. a. $14. (Bar-Ilan University, Talmud Department) Bar-Ilan University Press, Ramat Gan 52900, Israel. TEL 972-3-5318575. Ed. Zvi Arie Steinfeld. (back issues avail.) **Document type:** academic/scholarly publication.
Description: Collection of research papers in various fields of Jewish oral law.

296 IS ISSN 0334-4304
SINAI. Key Title: Siynay. (Text in Hebrew) 1937. bi-m. $15. Rabbi Kook Foundation, P.O. Box 642, Jerusalem, Israel. TEL 972-2-526231. FAX 972-2-526968. Ed. Yitzchak Raphael. bk.rev. circ. 1,500. (back issues avail.) **Indexed:** Ind.Heb.Per.

SINO-JUDAICA OCCASIONAL PAPERS. see ETHNIC INTERESTS

296.4 US ISSN 0196-2183
BM40
SOLOMON GOLDMAN LECTURES; perspectives in Jewish learning. 1977. irreg., vol.6. $15 cloth. Spertus College of Judaica Press, 618 S. Michigan Ave., Chicago, IL 60605. TEL 312-922-9012. FAX 312-922-6406. Ed. Byron L. Sherwin. circ. 500. (back issues avail.) **Document type:** academic/scholarly publication.
—BLDSC (8327.590000).
Supersedes: Perspectives in Jewish Learning (ISSN 0079-1016)
Description: Represents the spectrum of Jewish studies.

SOURCES FOR THE HISTORY OF THE JEWS IN SPAIN. see HISTORY — History Of Europe

SOURCES OF CONTEMPORARY JEWISH THOUGHT/MEKEVOT. see LITERARY AND POLITICAL REVIEWS

SOUTHERN SHOFAR. see ETHNIC INTERESTS

296 IS ISSN 0333-6174
SRIDIM. 1982. a. $2.50. Standing Committee of the Conference of European Rabbis, P.O.B. 5324, Jerusalem 91 052, Israel. TEL 972-2-812859. FAX 972-2-810080. Ed. Rabbi Moshe Rose. circ. 1,000. **Document type:** academic/scholarly publication.
Description: Publishes scholarly articles and essays by rabbis and members of rabbinical courts on subjects pertaining to Jewish law and religion.

STARK JEWISH NEWS. see ETHNIC INTERESTS

296 IT ISSN 1122-0716
STORIA DELL'EBRAISMO IN ITALIA; studi e testi. 1980. irreg., vol.16, 1994. price varies. Casa Editrice Leo S. Olschki, Casella Postale 66, 50100 Florence, Italy. TEL 39-55-6530684. FAX 39-55-6530214. Ed. P. Joly Zorattini. **Document type:** monographic series.

296 US ISSN 1061-2858
STRAIGHTALK. 1991. q. $18. Foundation for Jewish Studies, Inc., 1531 S. Negley Ave., Pittsburgh, PA 15217. TEL 412-521-1959. FAX 412-521-2903. E-mail: 71535,1207@compuserve.com. Ed. Ronald A. Brauner. bk.rev.; circ. 4,500 (paid). **Document type:** newsletter.

STUDIA BIBLICA. see RELIGIONS AND THEOLOGY

STUDIA IN VETERIS TESTAMENTI PSEUDEPIGRAPHA. see RELIGIONS AND THEOLOGY

296 RM ISSN 1221-5163
DS135.R7
STUDIA JUDAICA. (Text in English) 1991. a. exchange basis. Universitatea "Babes-Bolyai", Moshe Carmilly Institute for Hebrew and Jewish History, Biblioteca Centrala Universitara, Str. Clinicilor Nr. 2, Cluj-Napoca, Rumania. TEL 40-64-197092. FAX 40-64-197633. Ed. Ladislau Gyemant. bk.rev.; illus. circ. 400. **Document type:** academic/scholarly publication.

RELIGIONS AND THEOLOGY — JUDAIC

STUDIA SEMITICA NEERLANDICA. see *LINGUISTICS*

STUDIES IN AMERICAN JEWISH HISTORY. see *ETHNIC INTERESTS*

STUDIES IN JUDAICA & THE HOLOCAUST. see *ETHNIC INTERESTS*

296   NE   ISSN 0169-961X
STUDIES IN JUDAISM IN LATE ANTIQUITY. 1973. irreg., vol.40, 1989. price varies. E.J. Brill, P.O. Box 9000, 2300 PA Leiden, Netherlands. TEL 31-71-5353500. FAX 31-71-5317532. TELEX 39296 BRILL NL. (In N. America: E.J. Brill, 24 Hudson St., Kinderhook, NY 12106. TEL 800-962-4406. FAX 518-758-1959) Ed. J. Neusner. (back issues avail.) **Document type:** monographic series.
—BLDSC (8490.805000).
Description: The history of Jews from the period of the Second Temple to the rise of Islam.
Refereed Serial

296   NE   ISSN 0169-9660
STUDIES IN JUDAISM IN MODERN TIMES. 1978. irreg., vol.10, 1992. price varies. E.J. Brill, P.O. Box 9000, 2300 PA Leiden, Netherlands. TEL 31-71-5353500. FAX 31-71-5317532. TELEX 39296 BRILL NL. (In N. America: E.J. Brill, 24 Hudson St., Kinderhook, NY 12106. TEL 800-962-4406. FAX 518-758-1959) Ed. J. Neusner. (back issues avail.) **Document type:** monographic series.
Description: Scholarly discussions of religious, historical, literary and cultural issues relating to Judaism in Europe, North Africa and the Middle East in the early modern and modern period.
Refereed Serial

296.155 221.44   NE   ISSN 0169-9962
STUDIES ON THE TEXTS OF THE DESERT OF JUDAH. (Text in English, French, German) 1957. irreg., vol.16, 1995. price varies. E.J. Brill, P.O. Box 9000, 2300 PA Leiden, Netherlands. TEL 31-71-5353500. FAX 31-71-5317532. TELEX 39296 BRILL NL. (In N. America: E.J. Brill, 24 Hudson St., Kinderhook, NY 12106. TEL 800-962-4406. FAX 518-758-1959) Ed. J. van der Ploeg. (back issues avail.) **Document type:** monographic series.
Description: Scholarly translation and evaluation of Biblical texts from the papyrii and manuscripts of Wadi Qumran and the Dead Sea Scrolls, and related bibliographic, linguistic, cultural and historical aspects of ancient Judaism and early Christianity.
Refereed Serial

SULLIVAN - ULSTER JEWISH STAR. see *ETHNIC INTERESTS*

296   US   ISSN 1044-0011
BM1
S'VARA. 1990. s-a. Columbia University, School of Law, 435 W. 116th St., New York, NY 10027.

296   GW   ISSN 0946-4484
▼**SYNAGOGEN RUNDSCHAU.** (Text in German, Russian) 1994. m. DM.35 (foreign DM.50). Arthur-Custos-Gedaechtnis-Archiv, Tinnagel 5, 47608 Geldern, Germany. TEL 02831-2759. FAX 02831-98537. E-mail: apfelbaum@kali.rhein-ruhr.de. Ed. Arie Apfelbaum; Pub. Aaron Apfelbaum. (back issues avail.) **Document type:** newsletter.
● Also available online.

296.4   US   ISSN 1067-7518
BM1
SYNAGOGUE LIGHT - KOSHER LIFE. 1933. q. (Kosher Food Institute) Synagogue Light, Inc., 47 Beekman St, New York, NY 10038. TEL 212-227-7543. Ed. Rabbi Meyer Hager. adv. contact: Mark Warshow. **Document type:** consumer publication.
Formerly: Synagogue Light (ISSN 0194-7109)
Description: Covers religious and current events, as well as cultural issues concerning the Jewish community and kosher life, including kosher food news, recipes, kosher restaurants, kosher travel, and kosher products available through mail-order catalogs.

296   IS   ISSN 0334-3650
956.94 DS101
TARBIZ; a quarterly for Jewish studies. (Text in Hebrew; summaries in English) 1929. q. $50. (Hebrew University of Jerusalem) Magnes Press, Hebrew University, Jerusalem, P.O. Box 7695, Jerusalem 91076, Israel. TEL 972-2-660341. FAX 972-2-633370. Ed.Bd. bk.rev.; index. circ. 700. (back issues avail.) **Indexed:** Bibl.Ling., M.L.A., Rel.& Theol.Abstr. (1968-). **Document type:** academic/scholarly publication.

296   CN   ISSN 0704-5905
BS709.4
TARGUMIC AND COGNATE STUDIES. NEWSLETTER. 1974. s-a. $5 (typically set in Jan.). University of Toronto, Department of Near Eastern Studies, Toronto, ON M5S 1A1, Canada. TEL 416-978-3184. FAX 416-978-5294. E-mail: eclark@epas.utoronto.ca. Ed. E.G. Clark. circ. 200. (back issues avail.) **Document type:** newsletter, bibliography.

296   US
TAUBMAN LECTURES IN JEWISH STUDIES. no.2, 1991. irreg., no.3, 1992. price varies. California University Press, 2120 Berkeley Way, Berkeley, CA 94720. TEL 510-643-7127. FAX 510-643-7127. (Orders to: California-Princeton Fulfillment Services, 1445 Lower Ferry Rd., Ewing, NJ 08618. TEL 800-777-4726. FAX 800-999-1958) Pub. James Clark. (back issues avail.) **Document type:** monographic series.
Description: Explores Old Testament and later Hebrew poetry.
Refereed Serial

296   IS   ISSN 0333-6883
BM520
TECHUMIM. (Text in Hebrew) 1980. a. $18 (effective 1993). Zomet Institute, Alon Shvut, Gush Etzion 90940, Israel. TEL 972-2-931442. FAX 972-2-931889. Ed. Ezra Rosenfeld. circ. 4,500. **Document type:** academic/scholarly publication, monographic series.
Description: Collection of monographs concerning modern society and Jewish law.

296   SA   ISSN 0040-2966
TEMPLE DAVID BULLETIN. 1969. s-m. free. Durban Progressive Jewish Congregation, 369 Ridge Rd., Durban, South Africa. FAX 27-31-292429. adv.; bk.rev. circ. 535. (tabloid format) **Document type:** bulletin.
Formerly: Temple David Review.

TEXAS JEWISH POST; the Southwest's leading English - Jewish weekly newspaper. see *ETHNIC INTERESTS*

296   GW   ISSN 0721-8753
TEXTE UND STUDIEN ZUM ANTIKEN JUDENTUM. (Text in English, French and German) 1981. irreg. price varies. Verlag J.C.B. Mohr (Paul Siebeck), Wilhelmstr. 18, 72074 Tuebingen, Germany. TEL 07071-923-0. FAX 07071-51104. TELEX 7262872-MOHR-D. (Subscr. to: Postfach 2040, 72010 Tuebingen, Germany) Eds. Martin Hengel, Peter Schaefer. **Document type:** monographic series.

296   NE   ISSN 0169-8370
THEOKRATIA: JAHRBUCH DES INSTITUTUM JUDAICUM DELITZSCHIANUM. 1967. irreg., vol.3, 1979. price varies. (Institutum Judaicum Delitzschianum) E.J. Brill, P.O. Box 9000, 2300 PA Leiden, Netherlands. TEL 31-71-5353500. FAX 31-71-5317532. TELEX 39296 BRILL NL. (In N. America: E.J. Brill, 24 Hudson St., Kinderhook, NY 12106. TEL 800-962-4406. FAX 518-758-1959) Ed. K.H. Rengstorf. **Document type:** monographic series.

TIKKUN MAGAZINE; a bi-monthly Jewish critique of politics, culture and society. see *ETHNIC INTERESTS*

TOLEDO JEWISH NEWS; the monthly newspaper for the Jewish community of greater Toledo. see *ETHNIC INTERESTS*

296   IS
TORAH EDUCATION. (Text in English) 1971. q. World Zionist Organization, Department for Torah Education and Culture in the Diaspora, P.O. Box 92, Jerusalem 91920, Israel. TEL 02-527156. FAX 02-533542. Ed. Avner Tomaschoff. bk.rev.; charts; illus. circ. 8,000.

296   US   ISSN 1050-4745
BM538.S3
TORAH U - MADDA JOURNAL. 1989. a. Yeshiva University, Torah U - Madda Project, 500 W. 185th St., New York, NY 10033. TEL 212-960-5277.
Indexed: Ind.Jew.Per.

296 305.3   US   ISSN 1068-6134
TORCHLIGHT. 1941. q. $2. Federation of Jewish Men's Clubs Inc., 475 Riverside Dr., Ste. 244, New York, NY 10115. TEL 212-749-8100. FAX 212-316-4271. Ed. Gordon Cooper. adv.; bk.rev.; illus. circ. 40,000. **Document type:** newspaper.
Formerly (until 1977): Torch (ISSN 0049-416X)

296.4   US   ISSN 0041-0608
BM1   CODEN: TRADD2
TRADITION (NEW YORK); a journal of Orthodox Jewish thought. 1958. q. $23 to individuals; institutions $66. Rabbinical Council of America, 275 Seventh Ave., New York, NY 10001. TEL 212-807-7888. FAX 212-727-8452. Ed. Rabbi Emmanuel Feldman. bk.rev. circ. 3,000. (also avail. in microform from UMI) **Indexed:** Arts & Hum.Cit.Ind., Ind.Jew.Per., Mid.East: Abstr.& Ind., Old Test.Abstr., Rel.& Theol.Abstr. (1969-), Rel.Ind.One. **Document type:** academic/scholarly publication.
—BLDSC (8881.070300); Faxon; Genuine Article; UMI.

TRENDS (NEW YORK). see *EDUCATION*

296   GW   ISSN 0041-2716
DS101
TRIBUENE; Zeitschrift zum Verstaendnis des Judentums. 1962. q. Tribuene Verlag, Habsburgerallee 72, 60385 Frankfurt a.M., Germany. Ed. Elisabeth Reisch. adv.; bk.rev.; stat. circ. 5,000. **Indexed:** Phil.Ind. **Document type:** newsletter.

296   FR   ISSN 1149-6630
TSAFON; revue d'etudes juives du Nord. 1990. q. 170 F. 1 place du Temple, 59000 Lille, France. Dir. J.-M. Delmaire. **Document type:** academic/scholarly publication.

TULSA JEWISH REVIEW. see *ETHNIC INTERESTS*

TZIVOS HASHEM CHILDREN'S NEWSLETTER. see *CHILDREN AND YOUTH — For*

U C S J MEMBERSHIP REPORT. (Union of Councils for Soviet Jews) see *ETHNIC INTERESTS*

U C S J MONITOR. see *ETHNIC INTERESTS*

U J F VIRGINIA NEWS. (United Jewish Federation) see *SOCIAL SERVICES AND WELFARE*

296 327   US   ISSN 0888-3440
ULTIMATE ISSUES. 1985. q. $24. Dennis Prager, Ed. & Pub., 6020 Washington Blvd., Ste. 2, Culver City, CA 90232. TEL 310-558-3958. FAX 310-558-4241. bk.rev.; bibl.; tr.lit. circ. 8,500. (looseleaf format; back issues avail.) **Indexed:** Ind.Jew.Per.

296.8   US   ISSN 0363-3810
BM21
UNION OF AMERICAN HEBREW CONGREGATIONS. STATE OF OUR UNION. biennial. Union of American Hebrew Congregations, 838 Fifth Ave., New York, NY 10021. TEL 212-249-0100.

296.4   US   ISSN 0041-8153
BM197.5
UNITED SYNAGOGUE REVIEW. 1943. biennial. $3. United Synagogue of Conservative Judaism, 155 Fifth Ave., New York, NY 10010. TEL 212-533-7800. FAX 212-353-9439. Ed. Lois Goldrich. adv. contact: Diana Stevens. bk.rev.; illus. circ. 255,000. **Indexed:** Ind.Jew.Per.
Description: Serves as a communication vehicle for the Conservative Movement in Judaism.

UNSER TSAIT. see *LITERARY AND POLITICAL REVIEWS*

VETUS TESTAMENTUM. see *RELIGIONS AND THEOLOGY*

VETUS TESTAMENTUM. SUPPLEMENTS. see *RELIGIONS AND THEOLOGY*

VISION MAGAZINE. see *ETHNIC INTERESTS*

VOICE OF THE DUTCHESS JEWISH COMMUNITY. see *ETHNIC INTERESTS*

296   CN   ISSN 0703-153X
VOICE OF THE VAAD. 1961. q. Jewish Community Council of Montreal, 5491 Victoria Ave., Ste. 117, Montreal, PQ H3W 2P9, Canada. TEL 514-739-6363. Ed. Rabbi I.L. Hechtman. adv.; bk.rev. (tabloid format)

VORWAERTS/FORWARD. see *ETHNIC INTERESTS*

WASHINGTON JEWISH WEEK. see *ETHNIC INTERESTS*

296   US   ISSN 0887-011X
WELLSPRINGS; a quarterly journal exploring the inner dimensions of Torah and Jewish life. 1984. q. $15. Lubavitch Youth Organization, Student Affairs Office, 770 Eastern Pkwy., Brooklyn, NY 11213. TEL 718-953-1000. FAX 718-771-6553. Ed. Baila Olidort. adv.; bk.rev.; tr.lit. circ. 15,000. (back issues avail.)
   Description: Explores issues of contemporary and social concern through a Hasidic perspective. Includes essays and dialogues on the arts and sciences.

WESTERN STATES JEWISH HISTORY. see *ETHNIC INTERESTS*

WINDSOR JEWISH FEDERATION. see *ETHNIC INTERESTS*

WISCONSIN JEWISH CHRONICLE. see *ETHNIC INTERESTS*

296.4   US   ISSN 0043-7557
WOMEN'S LEAGUE OUTLOOK. 1930. q. $8. Women's League for Conservative Judaism, 48 E. 74th St., New York, NY 10021. TEL 212-628-1600. FAX 212-772-3507. Ed. Janis Sherman Popp. adv.; bk.rev. circ. 120,000.

WOMEN'S WORLD. see *WOMEN'S INTERESTS*

WOMEN'S ZIONIST ORGANIZATION OF SOUTH AFRICA. NEWS AND VIEWS. see *POLITICAL SCIENCE*

296 020   CN
WORLD JEWISH DIRECTORY. 1991. biennial. Can.$36. J E S L Educational Products, 58 Glen Park Ave., Toronto, ON M6B 2C2, Canada. TEL 416-785-7941. FAX 416-782-2740. Ed. Edmond Y. Lipsitz. circ. 5,000. (also avail. in diskette format; back issues avail.) **Document type:** directory.
   Description: Serves as a tool for research and communications. Provides up-to-date comprehensive, worldwide listings of diaspora Jewish resources, including addresses, phone, fax numbers and contact names.

WORLD UNION OF JEWISH STUDIES. see *ETHNIC INTERESTS*

WORLD ZIONIST ORGANIZATION. GENERAL COUNCIL. ADDRESSES, DEBATES, RESOLUTIONS. see *POLITICAL SCIENCE*

296   IS   ISSN 0333-7596
YAD L'ACHIM WALL CALENDAR. (Text in English) 1970. bi-m. $15. Yad L'achim, 8 Nahum St., P.O. Box 5195, Jerusalem, Israel. TEL 972-2-371003. FAX 972-2-370043. Ed.Bd. adv.; circ. 3,000. (back issues avail.)

296   IS   ISSN 0084-3296
DS135.E83
YAD VASHEM STUDIES. (Text in English) 1957. a. $35 (effective 1993). (Yad Vashem Martyrs' and Heroes' Remembrance Authority, IS) Rubin Mass Ltd., P.O. Box 990, Jerusalem 91009, Israel. TEL 972-2-894634. FAX 972-2-894778. Ed. Aharon Weiss. bk.rev.; index, cum.index: vols.1-20 (1957-1990). circ. 750. (also avail. in microform; back issues avail.) **Indexed:** Amer.Hist.& Life, Hist.Abstr. **Document type:** academic/scholarly publication.
—UMI. **CCC.**
   Formerly (until 1976): Yad Vashem Studies on the European Jewish Catastrophe and Resistance. *Refereed Serial*

296   US   ISSN 0084-3369
YALE JUDAICA SERIES. 1948. irreg., no.27, 1992. price varies. Yale University Press, Box 209040, New Haven, CT 06520. TEL 203-432-0940. **Document type:** academic/scholarly publication.
—BLDSC (9370.100000).

296   IS
YEARBOOK OF RELIGIOUS ZIONISM. (Text in English and Hebrew) 1982. a. IS.30($15) Society for the Advancement of Religious Zionism, Mesilot, c/o Mr. S.R. Sachs, P.O. Box 7720, Jerusalem, Israel. TEL 972-2-258833. FAX 972-2-257418. adv. circ. 5,000.

YESHIVA UNIVERSITY. ANNUAL REPORT. see *EDUCATION — Higher Education*

YESHIVA UNIVERSITY SEPHARDIC BULLETIN. see *ETHNIC INTERESTS*

296   US   ISSN 0044-040X
DER YID; voice of American Orthodox Jewry. (Text in Yiddish) 1951. w. $43. (National Committee of Orthodox Jewish Communities) Der Yid Publishing, 13 Hooper St., Brooklyn, NY 11211. TEL 718-797-3900. FAX 718-797-1985. E-mail: DERYIDNEWS. Ed. Sender Deutsch. adv. contact: Aron Friedman. bk.rev. circ. 74,500. (tabloid format; also avail. in microfilm from AJP) **Document type:** newspaper.

YIDDISH. see *LINGUISTICS*

DI YIDDISHE HEIM/JEWISH HOME. see *ETHNIC INTERESTS*

YIDDISHE KULTUR. see *ETHNIC INTERESTS*

DOS YIDDISHE VORT. see *ETHNIC INTERESTS*

YIDDISHER KEMFER. see *ETHNIC INTERESTS*

DER YIDDISHER VEG. see *ETHNIC INTERESTS*

YIDISHE SHPRAKH/YIDDISH LANGUAGE. see *LINGUISTICS*

YIVO BLETER/YIVO PAGES. see *SOCIAL SCIENCES: COMPREHENSIVE WORKS*

296   FR   ISSN 0338-9316
DS101
YOD; revue des etudes hebraiques et juives modernes et contemporaines. 1975. s-a. 85 F. per no. Institut National des Langues et Civilisations Orientales, 2 rue de Lille, 75343 Paris Cedex 07, France. TEL 49-26-42-00. FAX 49-26-42-99. Ed. Mireille Hadas-Lebel. **Document type:** academic/scholarly publication.
●Also available on CD-ROM.
   Description: Studies the literature, history, and sociology of the Jewish people in Israel and the surrounding area in the 19th and 20th centuries.

296   IS
YOM HASHISHI. 1988. w. IS.250. 19 B Keren Hayesod St., Jerusalem 94188, Israel. TEL 972-2-251844. FAX 972-2-251637. Ed.Bd. adv.; bk.rev. circ. 40,000.

YOUNG ISRAEL VIEWPOINT. see *POLITICAL SCIENCE*

YOUNG JUDAEAN. see *ETHNIC INTERESTS*

YOUR CHILD. see *EDUCATION*

YUGNTRUF; Yiddish student quarterly. see *ETHNIC INTERESTS*

ZION; a quarterly for research in Jewish history. see *ETHNIC INTERESTS*

296   UK   ISSN 0951-0575
THE ZIONIST REVIEW. 1917. q. Zionist Federation, Balfour House, 741 High Rd., London N12 0BQ, England. TEL 0181-343-9756. FAX 0181-446-0639. Ed. Joe Finklestone. **Document type:** bulletin.

296   US
ZRAIM. (Text in English, Hebrew) 1972. q. $18. Bnei Akiva, National Office, 25 W. 26th St., 4th Fl., New York, NY 10010. TEL 212-889-5260. FAX 212-213-3053. Ed. Alex Bailey. circ. 2,500. (back issues avail.)
   Formerly: Akivon.

ZUKUNFT/FUTURE. see *LITERARY AND POLITICAL REVIEWS*

RELIGIONS AND THEOLOGY — Protestant

A A B C NEWSLETTER. (Accrediting Association of Bible Colleges) see *EDUCATION — Higher Education*

A A C S NEWSLETTER. (American Association of Christian Schools) see *EDUCATION — Guides To Schools And Colleges*

287   US   ISSN 1050-6039
A.M.E. CHRISTIAN RECORDER. 1848. bi-w. $18. African Methodist Episcopal Church, Drawer 24730, Nashville, TN 37202. TEL 615-256-8548. FAX 615-244-7604. Ed. R.H. Reid, Jr. circ. 8,000. (tabloid format) **Document type:** newspaper.

287   US   ISSN 0360-3725
A.M.E. CHURCH REVIEW. 1884. q. $10. African Methodist Episcopal Church, 500 Eighth Ave. S., Nashville, TN 37203. TEL 615-256-7020. FAX 615-244-7604. Ed. Jamye C. Williams. bk.rev.; bibl.; charts; illus.; stat. circ. 6,000. (also avail. in microform from UMI; back issues avail.)
—UMI.

284.14895   DK   ISSN 0107-5055
AALBORG STIFTSBOG. 1959. a. DKK 40. Aalborg Stifts Landemoede, Bispekontoret, Thulebakken 1, DK-9000 Aalborg, Denmark. illus. circ. 2,500.

284.148 948.9   DK   ISSN 0108-7940
AARHUS STIFTS AARBOEGER. 1908. a. DKK 120. Historisk Samfund for Aarhus Stift, Vester Alle 12, DK-8000 Aarhus C, Denmark. TEL 45-86-12-85-33. FAX 45-86-12-85-60. Ed. Erik Korr Johansen. **Indexed:** NAA.
   Formerly (until 1958): Aarboeger Udgivne af Historisk Samfund for Aarhus Stift (ISSN 0906-9763)

286 362.7   US   ISSN 0162-1955
ACCENT (BIRMINGHAM). (Avail. in Leadership and Member editions) 1970. m. (11/yr.). $14.95 for Leadership Edition; Membership Edition $13.95 (effective 1995-1996). Southern Baptist Convention, Woman's Missionary Union, Hwy. 280, E., 100 Missionary Ridge, Birmingham, AL 35242-5235. TEL 205-991-8100. (Subscr. to: Box 830711, Birmingham, AL 35283-0711. TEL 800-WMU-7301. FAX 205-995-4840) Ed. Jan Turrentine. circ. 93,000.
   Description: Publication of interest to members and leaders of Southern Baptist Acteens organizations.

286 362.7   US
ACTEENS ACCESSORIES. q. $30 (effective 1995-1996). Southern Baptist Convention, Woman's Missionary Union, Hwy. 280, E., 100 Missionary Ridge, Birmingham, AL 35242-5235. TEL 205-991-8100. (Subscr. to: Box 830711, Birmingham, AL 35283-7111. TEL 800-WMU-7301. FAX 205-995-4840)

ACTION AFRICA. see *RELIGIONS AND THEOLOGY*

283   AT   ISSN 0001-8147
ADELAIDE CHURCH GUARDIAN. 1906. m. Aus.$12. Anglican Church of Australia, Diocese of Adelaide, Anglican Church Office, P.O. Box 2667, Adelaide, S.A. 5001, Australia. TEL 618-211-231-2402. FAX 618-211-8748. E-mail: Robyn.Douglass@accnet.net.au. Ed. Robyn Douglass. adv. contact: Stewart Perkins. bk.rev. circ. 3,500. **Document type:** newspaper.

268
ADULT BIBLE LESSONS FOR THE DEAF. q. $14.25. Southern Baptist Convention, Sunday School Board, 127 Ninth Ave., N., Nashville, TN 37234. TEL 800-458-2772.

220   US   ISSN 0149-8347
ADULT BIBLE STUDIES. 1967. q. $13.25. (United Methodist Church, Board of Discipleship) United Methodist Publishing House, Cokesbury, 201 Eighth Ave. S., Nashville, TN 37203. TEL 615-749-6000. FAX 615-749-6079. Ed. Michael Russell. circ. 475,000 inkprint; 150,000 large print. (large print edition in 14 pt.)

RELIGIONS AND THEOLOGY — PROTESTANT

285   US
ADULT QUARTERLY. 1891. q. $3.20 (large print ed. $8). Associate Reformed Presbyterian Center, Office of Christian Education, 1 Cleveland St., Greenville, SC 29601. TEL 803-232-8297. Ed. W.H.F. Kuykendall. circ. 12,000 (paid). (large print edition in 16 pt.) **Document type:** bulletin.
  Description: Includes lesson topics, scripture portions, and daily Bible readings.

284   US
ADULT STUDY GUIDE. q. $2.95 per no. for teacher ed.; student ed. $1.65. Messenger Publishing House, Box 850, Joplin, MO 64802. TEL 417-624-7050. FAX 417-624-7102. illus. circ. 15,000.

268 375   US   ISSN 0400-5880
ADULT TEACHER. q. $12.50. Southern Baptist Convention, Sunday School Board, 127 Ninth Ave., N., Nashville, TN 37234. TEL 800-458-2772.

268 378   US   ISSN 0162-4148
ADVANCED BIBLE STUDY. q. $11.25. Southern Baptist Convention, Sunday School Board, 127 Ninth Ave., N., Nashville, TN 37234. TEL 800-458-2772.

286   NE   ISSN 0165-8603
ADVENT. 1899. m. (10/yr.) fl.3.50. (Zevende-Dags Adventisten - Seventh-Day Adventists) Stichting Uitgeverij "Veritas", Biltseweg 14, 3735 ME Bosch en Duin, Netherlands. FAX 31-30-281084. Ed. A.J. van der Kamp. illus. **Indexed:** CERDIC.
  Formerly: Adventbode (ISSN 0001-8767)

286   GW   ISSN 0179-7999
ADVENTECHO; Gemeindeblatt der Siebenten - Tags - Adventisten. 1895. m. DM.57.50. Advent Verlag GmbH, Luener Rennbahn 16, 21339 Lueneburg, Germany. TEL 04131-985522. FAX 04131-985502. Ed. F. Klingeberg. adv. contact: Margrit Rupp. bk.rev. circ. 10,000. **Document type:** bulletin.

286   JA
ADVENTIST LIFE. (Text in Japanese) m. 5520 Yen($42.46) Japan Union Conference of S.D.A., 846 Kamikawai-cho, Asahi-ku, Yokohama 241, Japan. FAX 045-921-2319.

286   US   ISSN 0161-1119
BX6101
ADVENTIST REVIEW. (Editions in English and Spanish) 1850. w. $44.97. Review and Herald Publishing Association (Silver Spring), 12501 Old Columbia Pike, Silver Spring, MD 20904-6600. TEL 301-680-6000. FAX 301-680-6638. Ed. William G. Johnsson. bk.rev.; index. circ. 43,000. (tabloid format; reprint service avail. from UMI)
  Former titles: Advent Review and Sabbath Herald (ISSN 0095-2397); Review and Herald (ISSN 0034-6381)

268   US   ISSN 0001-8783
ADVENTURE (NASHVILLE). m. (plus regular w. nos.). $23.95. Southern Baptist Convention, Sunday School Board, 127 Ninth Ave., N., Nashville, TN 37234. TEL 800-458-2772.

284   US   ISSN 0044-6467
AFFIRM; our eternal Christ and his word for our changing and urgent needs. 1971. bi-m. contributions. Balance, Inc., c/o Walther Memorial Lutheran Church, 4040 W. Fond du Lac Ave., Milwaukee, WI 53216. TEL 414-444-4133. (Subscr. to: Box 8390, St. Louis, MO 63132-0390) Ed. Rev. Thomas Baker. bk.rev. circ. 104,000.
  Description: Dedicated to preserving theological heritage while looking at related developments in the Lutheran church.

285   NR
AFRICA JOURNAL OF EVANGELICAL THEOLOGY. Abbreviated title: A J E T. 1982. s-a. $15. Scot Theological College, Box 49, Machakos, Kenya. Ed. Mark Shaw. bk.rev. circ. 350. **Document type:** academic/scholarly publication.
  Formerly (until 1988): East Africa Journal of Evangelical Theology.
  Description: Provides African evangelical theologians with information about theology and ministry.

284   TZ   ISSN 0856-0048
AFRICA THEOLOGICAL JOURNAL. 1968. 3/yr. $27 (foreign $25). All Africa Lutheran Churches Information and Coordination Centre, P.O. Box 314, Arusha, Tanzania. TELEX 42054 LUTHA TZ. Ed. Mutembe Gaetan. adv.; bk.rev. circ. 1,500. **Indexed:** CERDIC, New Test.Abstr., P.L.E.S.A. (1990-), Rel.& Theol.Abstr. (1988-), Rel.Ind.One.
  —BLDSC (0732.189700).

284   KE
AFROSCOPE. (Text in English and French) 1972. q. donation. Association of Evangelicals in Africa, P.O. Box 49332, Nairobi, Kenya. TEL 254-2-722769. FAX 254-2-710254. TELEX 23041 TRN KE. Ed. Gilbert Okoronkwo. circ. 3,500 (2,500 English edition; 1,000 French edition). **Document type:** newsletter.
  Description: Covers Christian evangelism in East Africa and Madagascar.

286 209   US   ISSN 0002-4147
ALABAMA BAPTIST HISTORIAN. 1964. s-a. $5. Alabama Baptist Historical Society, Samford University Library, Birmingham, AL 35229. Ed. Lee N. Allen. bk.rev.; bibl. circ. 250. **Indexed:** Amer.Hist.& Life, Hist.Abstr.
  —BLDSC (0786.488000).

200   US   ISSN 0891-8767
ALIVE NOW; devotional reading. 1971. bi-m. $115. (United Methodist Church, General Board of Discipleship) Upper Room, 1908 Grand Ave., Box 189, Nashville, TN 37202. TEL 615-340-7218. Ed. George Graham. bk.rev.; illus. circ. 70,000.

220   UK   ISSN 0963-2743
ALIVE TO GOD; bible guidelines for living by the spirit. 1984. q. £9.20. Scripture Union Publishing, 130 City Rd., London EC1V 2NJ, England. TEL 0171-782-0013. FAX 0171-782-0014. (Subscr. to: 9-11 Clothier Rd., Bristol BS4 5RL, England) Ed. Tony Hobbs. adv. contact: J. Bicknell. circ. 33,000.

266   NE   ISSN 0002-5666
ALLE DEN VOLCKE. 1907. bi-m. fl.10. Gereformeerde Zendingsbond in de Nederlandse Hervormde Kerk - Board of the Reformed Mission League in the Netherlands Reformed Church, Faunalaan 49, 3972 PP Driebergen, Netherlands. FAX 03438-21392. Ed. T. Eikelboom. bk.rev.; illus. circ. 44,000.

200   US   ISSN 1040-6794
ALLIANCE LIFE. 1882. fortn. (m. Jun.-Aug. & Dec.). $9.50 (Canada $16; elsewhere $13). Christian and Missionary Alliance, Box 35000, Colorado Springs, CO 80935-3500. TEL 719-599-5999. FAX 719-593-8692. Ed. Maurice R. Irvin. adv. contact: Michael Saunier. bk.rev.; illus.; index. circ. 65,000. (also avail. in microform from UMI; back issues avail.; reprint service avail. from UMI) **Indexed:** Chr.Per.Ind., G.Soc.Sci.& Rel.Per.Lit.
  —UMI.
  Formerly (until 1987): Alliance Witness (ISSN 0745-3256)
  Description: Journal of Christian life and missions.

284   DK   ISSN 0900-4726
ALLIANCEBLADET; unum corpus sumus in Christo. 1907. s-a. Evangelisk Alliance, c/o Frederik G. Soerensen, Ledjetoften 10, DK-2765 Smoerum, Denmark. illus.

284   US   ISSN 1052-2670
BR1
ALMANAC OF THE CHRISTIAN WORLD.* 1992. a. Tyndale House Publishers, Inc., 8959 E. Palm Ridge Dr., Scottsdale, AZ 85260-7535.

284   UK   ISSN 0961-6950
ALPHA (NEW MALDEN). 1991. m. £23.70. Elm House Christian Communications Ltd., 37 Elm Rd., New Malden, Surrey KT3 3HB, England. TEL 0181-942-9761. FAX 0181-949-2313. Ed. Dave Roberts. adv. contact: Jan Hurell. bk.rev.; charts; illus.; circ. 12,000 (paid). (back issues avail.) **Document type:** consumer publication.
  Formed by the merger of (1965-1991): 21st Century Christian (ISSN 0952-6269); Which was formerly: Buzz (ISSN 0045-3692); (1982-1991): Today (New Malden) (ISSN 0956-2648); Which had former titles (until Jan. 1989): Leadership Today (ISSN 0952-6277); And (until 1987): Today (London) (ISSN 0262-8023); (until 1982): Crusade (ISSN 0011-2127).
  Description: Covers Christian and social issues, including church leadership, personal teaching. Informs and challenges leaders of all areas in church.

AMERICAN ASSOCIATION OF CHRISTIAN SCHOOLS. DIRECTORY. see EDUCATION — Guides To Schools And Colleges

286   US   ISSN 0091-9381
BX6207
AMERICAN BAPTIST CHURCHES IN THE U S A DIRECTORY. 1971. biennial. $7. American Baptist Churches in the U S A, Box 851, Valley Forge, PA 19482-0851. TEL 610-768-2000. Ed. Patricia Schlosser. circ. 6,000. **Document type:** directory.
  Supersedes: American Baptist Convention. Directory (ISSN 0096-3380); American Baptist Convention. Yearbook.

286   US   ISSN 0092-3478
BX6207
AMERICAN BAPTIST CHURCHES IN THE U S A YEARBOOK. Key Title: Yearbook of the American Baptist Churches in the U S A. 1907. biennial. $7. American Baptist Churches in the U S A, Box 851, Valley Forge, PA 19482-0851. TEL 610-768-2000. Ed. Daniel E. Weiss. illus. circ. 3,500.
  Formerly: American Baptist Convention. Yearbook.

286 209   US   ISSN 0745-3698
BX6201
AMERICAN BAPTIST QUARTERLY; a Baptist journal of history, theology and ministry. 1958. q. $15. American Baptist Historical Society, Linfield College, McMinnville, OR 97128. (Subscr. to: Dr. William H. Brackney, Box 857, Valley Forge, PA 19482) Ed. Dr. William R. Millar. bk.rev. circ. 1,200. (also avail. in microform from UMI; reprint service avail. from UMI) **Indexed:** Amer.Hist.& Life, Hist.Abstr., Rel.& Theol.Abstr. (1982-), Rel.Ind.One, Rel.Per.
  —BLDSC (0810.725000); UMI; UnCover.
  Former titles (until vol.25, 1982): Foundations (ISSN 0015-8992); Chronicle (Greensburg) (ISSN 0360-5779)

286   US   ISSN 0191-0183
AMERICAN BAPTIST WOMAN. 1956. 3/yr. $6. American Baptist Women's Ministries, Box 851, Valley Forge, PA 19482-0851. TEL 610-768-2283. FAX 610-768-2275. adv.; bk.rev. circ. 8,000. **Document type:** bulletin.

286.31   US
BX6201
AMERICAN BAPTISTS IN MISSION. 1803. 6/yr. free. American Baptist Churches in the U S A, Box 851, Valley Forge, PA 19482-0851. TEL 610-768-2216. FAX 610-768-2320. Ed. Richard W. Schramm. adv.; bk.rev.; charts; illus. circ. 44,000.
  —UMI.
  Former titles: American Baptist (ISSN 0002-757X); (until 1970): Crusader; Mission.

RELIGIONS AND THEOLOGY — PROTESTANT

286 US ISSN 0886-5159
BX8935
AMERICAN PRESBYTERIANS: JOURNAL OF PRESBYTERIAN HISTORY. 1901. q. $15. Presbyterian Church (U.S.A), Presbyterian Historical Society, 425 Lombard St., Philadelphia, PA 19147. TEL 215-627-1852. FAX 215-627-0509. Ed. James H. Smylie. bk.rev.; abstr.; illus.; index, cum.index: 1901-1962. circ. 1,400. (also avail. in microfilm) Indexed: Amer.Hist.& Life, Arts & Hum.Cit.Ind., Bibl.Engl.Lang.& Lit., Curr.Cont., Hist.Abstr., Rel.& Theol.Abstr. (1966-), Rel.Ind.One, Rel.Per. **Document type:** academic/scholarly publication.
—Faxon; UMI.
Former titles (until 1984): Journal of Presbyterian History (ISSN 0022-3883); (until 1961): Presbyterian Historical Society Journal (ISSN 0147-3735)

AMERICAN PROTESTANT HEALTH ASSOCIATION. BULLETIN. see *HOSPITALS*

284 AT
ANCHOR. 1973. bi-m. Aus.$2. Redeemer Lutheran Church Waverley, 25 Cypress Ave., Glen Waverley, Vic. 3150, Australia. TEL 03-803-5715. circ. 200.
Description: Parish circular with items to challenge, inform, encourage and update members.

283 CN ISSN 0517-7731
ANGLICAN. 1958. m. Can.$5 (foreign Can.$8). Anglican Church of Canada, Diocese of Toronto, 135 Adelaide St. E., Toronto, Ont. M5C 1L8, Canada. TEL 416-363-6021. FAX 416-363-7678. Ed. Vivian Snead. adv.; bk.rev. circ. 46,000. **Indexed:** CERDIC.

283 US ISSN 1059-6763
ANGLICAN ADVANCE. 1875. 7/yr. $7 (free to Diocese residents). Episcopal Diocese of Chicago, 65 E. Huron St., Chicago, IL 60611. TEL 312-751-4200. FAX 312-787-4534. Ed. David P. Skidmore. bk.rev.; illus. circ. 18,000. **Indexed:** CERDIC. **Document type:** newspaper.
Formerly (until 1989): Advance (Chicago) (ISSN 0001-8562)
Description: Contains news of the Diocese, the Episcopal Church and the Anglican communion.

283 US ISSN 0896-8039
BX5800
ANGLICAN AND EPISCOPAL HISTORY. 1932. q. $30 to individuals; institutions $40. Historical Society of the Episcopal Church, c/o John F. Woolverton, Ed., Box 261, Center Sandwich, NH 03227. TEL 603-284-6584; 800-553-7745. FAX 512-282-6149. adv. contact: May Zofgreen. bk.rev.; bibl.; index. circ. 1,500. (also avail. in microfilm from UMI; reprint service avail. from UMI) **Indexed:** Amer.Hist.& Life, Bibl.Engl.Lang.& Lit., CERDIC, Hist.Abstr., Rel.Ind.One, Rel.Per. **Document type:** academic/scholarly publication.
—BLDSC (0902.769200); Faxon; UMI.
Formerly (until 1987): Historical Magazine of the Protestant Episcopal Church (ISSN 0018-2486)

266 CN ISSN 1193-9737
ANGLICAN CHURCH DIRECTORY. 1900. a. Can.$26.95. (Anglican Church of Canada) Anglican Book Centre, 600 Jarvis St., Toronto, Ont. M4Y 2J6, Canada. TEL 416-924-9192. FAX 416-924-2760. Ed. M. Lloyd. adv.; stat. circ. 1,000. **Document type:** directory.
Formerly (until 1993): Anglican Year Book (ISSN 0317-8765)

283 CN
ANGLICAN CHURCH OF CANADA. GENERAL SYNOD. JOURNAL. 1894. triennial. Anglican Church of Canada, 600 Jarvis St., Toronto, ON M4Y 2J6, Canada. TEL 416-924-9192. FAX 416-921-0211. circ. 450.
Formerly (until 1980): Anglican Church of Canada. General Synod. Journal of Proceedings (ISSN 0380-2469)

283 US ISSN 0003-3278
ANGLICAN DIGEST. 1958. bi-m. $15 donation. (Society for Encouraging and Promoting Christian Arts and Knowledge, Inc.) S P E A K, Inc., Hillspeak, Eureka Springs, AR 72632-9705. TEL 501-253-9701. Ed. Rev. C. Frederick Barbee. adv.; bk.rev. circ. 130,000. **Indexed:** CERDIC.
Description: Reflects the ministry of the faithful throughout the Anglican Communion.

283 AT ISSN 1032-9234
ANGLICAN ENCOUNTER. 1970. m. Aus.$13 (foreign Aus.$28) (effective 1994). Anglican Diocese of Newcastle, P.O. Box 817, Newcastle, N.S.W. 2300, Australia. TEL 61-49-26-3733. FAX 61-49-261968. Ed. Marion Willey. adv.: B&W page Aus.$600, color page Aus.$660; trim 270 x 380. bk.rev. circ. 7,100. (tabloid format) **Document type:** newspaper.
Description: Local and international news and teachings of interest to Anglican church members.

200 AT
ANGLICAN GAZETTE; magazine for the Anglican Church in Central Queensland. 1890. m. Aus.$9. Anglican Diocese of Rockhampton, P.O. Box 6158, Mail Centre, Rockhampton, Qld. 4702, Australia. TEL 079-273-188. FAX 079-224-562. adv.; bk.rev. circ. 2,500.
Formerly: Church Gazette.

283 CN ISSN 0847-978X
ANGLICAN JOURNAL/JOURNAL ANGLICAN. (Text in English, French) 1874. m (10/yr.). Can.$8 (foreign Can.$17). Anglican Church of Canada, Board of Trustees, 600 Jarvis St., Toronto, ON M4Y 2J6, Canada. TEL 416-924-9192. FAX 416-921-4452. Ed. Carolyn Purden. adv. contact: Brian Trotter. bk.rev.; film rev.; illus. circ. 270,600. (tabloid format; also avail. in microfilm from MML,UMI) **Indexed:** Can.B.P.I., Can.Per.Ind., CMI. **Document type:** newspaper.
Former titles (until 1989): Canadian Churchman (ISSN 0008-3216); Anglican Journal - Journal Episcopal.
Description: The national newspaper of the Anglican Church of Canada.

283 AT
ANGLICAN MESSENGER. 1969. m. Aus.$12. Anglican Church in Western Australia, East Vic Park, W.A. 6101, Australia. TEL 61-9-470-3825. FAX 61-9-470-5810. Ed. Canon Greg Harvey. adv.: B&W page Aus.$645; adv. contact: Coralie Wilson. bk.rev. circ. 6,000. (tabloid format) **Document type:** newspaper.

266 UK ISSN 0969-7373
ANVIL; an Anglican Evangelical journal for theology and mission. 1984. 3/yr. £15.25($35) (overseas £22.25 ($42)). Anvil Trust, The Rectory, 2 Short St., Bourn, Cambs. CB3 7SG, England. TEL 01954-719728. (Subscr. to: Mrs. J. Smith, 58 Yokecliffe Dr., Wirksworth, Matlock, Derbys. DE4 4EX, England) Ed. Rev. J.C.B. Pemberton. adv. contact: Rev. M. Slater. bk.rev. circ. 850. (also avail. in microform from UMI) **Document type:** academic/scholarly publication.
—BLDSC (1565.470000).

287 US ISSN 0003-6552
EL APOSENTO ALTO. English edition: Upper Room (ISSN 0042-0735) (Text in Spanish; editions in 44 languages) 1938. bi-m. $4.95 for inkprint; large print edition $6.95. (United Methodist Church, General Board of Discipleship) Upper Room, 1908 Grand Ave., Box 189, Nashville, TN 37202. TEL 615-340-7246. FAX 615-340-7006. Ed. Carmen M. Gaud. illus. circ. 68,000. (large print edition in 18 pt.)
Description: Contains meditation, suggested Scripture reference, and a thought for each day.

283 US ISSN 1041-3316
THE APOSTLE. 1892. m. $5. Episcopal Diocese of Alabama, 521 N. 20th St., Burmingham, AL 35203. TEL 205-328-8374. Ed. Kenneth L. Fields. circ. 13,500. **Document type:** newspaper.
Formerly (until 1988): Alabama Churchman (ISSN 8750-9679)

284 GW
ARBEITSHILFE ZUM WEITERGEBEN. 1947. q. DM.26. Evangelischen Frauenhilfe in Deutschland e.V., Alte Landstr. 179, Postfach 310206, 40489 Duesseldorf, Germany. TEL 0211-40648. FAX 0211-401268. Ed. Inge Heiling. bk.rev. circ. 10,000. (back issues avail.)
Formerly (until 1992): Zum Weitergeben (ISSN 0936-7136)

260 US ISSN 0890-5258
ARKANSAS EPISCOPALIAN. vol.49, 1975. 9/yr. $3 donation. Episcopal Diocese of Arkansas, Box 164668, Little Rock, AR 72216-4668. TEL 501-372-2168. Ed. Julie Keller. bk.rev.; circ. 8,000 (controlled). (tabloid format) **Document type:** newspaper.
Formerly (until 1985): Arkansas Churchman (ISSN 0199-4611)

287 US ISSN 1080-2819
ARKANSAS UNITED METHODIST. 1881. bi-w. $12.50 (effective 1995). (United Methodist Church, Arkansas Area) Arkansas Methodist, Inc., Box 3547, Little Rock, AR 72203-3547. TEL 501-324-8031. FAX 501-324-8018. Ed. Jane D. Dennis. adv. contact: Laura Organ. circ. 11,000. **Document type:** newspaper.
Formerly (until 1983): Arkansas Methodist.
Description: Contains news, features and opinions relating to the United Methodist Church in Arkansas and its constituents. Includes national and international news and features on topics and events affecting the religious community.

207.11 US
ASBURY THEOLOGICAL JOURNAL. 1946. s-a. $5 (foreign $8). Asbury Theological Seminary, 204 N. Lexington Ave., Wilmore, KY 40390-1199. TEL 606-858-3581. FAX 606-858-3581. Ed. Laurence Wood. bk.rev.; cum.index: 1946-66 in vol. 21. circ. 1,200. (also avail. in microform from UMI; reprint service avail. from UMI) **Indexed:** CERDIC, Chr.Per.Ind., Rel.& Theol.Abstr. (1988-), Rel.Ind.One. **Document type:** academic/scholarly publication.
—UMI.
Formerly (until vol.40): Asbury Seminarian (ISSN 0004-4253)
Description: Provides a scholarly forum for thorough discussion of issues relevant to Christian thought and faith, and to the nature and mission of the church. Addresses those concerns and ideas across the curriculum which interface with Christian thought, life and ministry.

051 US ISSN 1076-5778
BT732.4
ASPIRE. bi-m. $19.80. (Minirth-Meier Clinic) Publishing Directions, Inc., 5301 Wisconsin Ave., N.W., Ste. 620, Washington, DC 20015. TEL 202-364-8000. FAX 202-364-8910. (Subscr. to: Box 50475, Boulder, CO 80322-0475. TEL 800-228-3141) Eds. Frank Minirth, Paul Meier. adv.: B&W page $1995, color page $2695; trim 8 1/2 x 10 7/8; adv. contact: Nancy Howard. bk.rev.; illus. circ. 100,000. **Document type:** consumer publication.
Former titles (until 1994): Today's Better Life (ISSN 1071-586X); (until 1991): Christian Psychology for Today.
Description: Focuses on helping today's busy Christian family simplify life and achieve total health in all areas of life through exercise, faith, nutrition, and good mental health.

285 US ISSN 0362-0816
ASSOCIATE REFORMED PRESBYTERIAN. 1976. m. $15. Associate Reformed Presbyterian, Inc., General Synod of the Associate Reformed Presbyterian Church, One Cleveland St., Greenville, SC 29601. TEL 803-232-8297. Ed. Ben Johnston. adv. contact: Ben Johnston. bk.rev. circ. 6,200. (also avail. in microform from UMI; back issues avail.) **Document type:** bulletin.
—UMI.
Description: Devoted to the concerns of the Associate Reformed Presbyterian Church in relationship to its mission to the service of God.

284 UK ISSN 0952-6889
ASSOCIATION OF CHRISTIANS IN HIGHER EDUCATION. FORUM. a. £12. (Association of Christians in Higher Education) Universities and Colleges Christian Fellowship, 38 De Montfort St., Leicester LE1 7GP, England. TEL 0116-255-1700. FAX 0116-255-5672. Ed. Gwynne Davies. bk.rev. (back issues avail.) **Document type:** academic/scholarly publication.

RELIGIONS AND THEOLOGY — PROTESTANT

286   CN   ISSN 0004-6752
ATLANTIC BAPTIST. 1827. m. Can.$18.75. United Baptist Convention of the Atlantic Provinces, Board of Publication, Box 756, Kentville, NS B4N 3X9, Canada. TEL 902-681-6868. FAX 902-681-0315. Ed. Rev. Michael A. Lipe; Pub. Rev. Michael A. Lipe. adv.; bk.rev.; illus.; index; circ. 6,900 (paid). (back issues avail.)
    Description: Covers general religion and family life, devotional and social action.

284   GW   ISSN 0722-625X
AUFBRUCH; evangelische Kirchenzeitung fuer Baden. 1965. w. (Sun.). DM.66. Evangelischer Presseverband fuer Baden e.V., Postfach 2280, 76010 Karlsruhe, Germany. TEL 0721-9175930. FAX 0721-9175950. Eds. Veronika Besau, Hans-Peter Scheibel. adv. contact: Edeltrud Kieser. bk.rev.; film rev.; illus. circ. 33,345. **Document type:** newsletter.

200   SZ   ISSN 0004-7880
AUFTRAG. 1967. 6/yr. 20 SFr.($2) Kooperation Evangelischer Kirchen und Missionen, Missionstr. 21, CH-4003 Basel, Switzerland. TEL 061-2688289. FAX 061-2688268. Ed. Armin Mettler. illus. circ. 33,000. **Document type:** newsletter.
    Description: Covers missionary activities in Third World countries. Includes announcements of events.

284 282   GW
AUFTRAG; eine christliche Lehrzeitschrift. 1981. q. DM.21. Jugend mit einer Mission, Schlossgasse 1, 86857 Hurlach, Germany. FAX 030-8811932. Ed.Bd. adv.; bk.rev. circ. 26,000. (back issues avail.)

268   US   ISSN 0896-6990
AUGSBURG ADULT BIBLE STUDIES. LEADER GUIDE. 1968. q. $16. Augsburg Fortress, Publishers, 426 S. Fifth St., Box 1209, Minneapolis, MN 55440. TEL 612-330-3402. FAX 612-330-3455. circ. 8,000.
    Formerly (until 1987): A L C - L C A Augsburg Adult Bible Studies. Teacher's Guide.

268   US   ISSN 0896-6982
AUGSBURG ADULT BIBLE STUDIES. PARTICIPANT BOOK. 1968. q. $7.40. Augsburg Fortress, Publishers, 426 S. Fifth St., Box 1209, Minneapolis, MN 55440. TEL 612-330-3402; 800-328-4648. FAX 612-330-3455. circ. 75,000.
    Former titles (until 1987): A L C - L C A Augsburg Adult Bible Studies. Adult Quarterly; A L C - L C A Augsburg Adult Bible Studies.

268   US   ISSN 0896-808X
AUGSBURG HOME BIBLE STUDIES. 1968. q. $14.60. Augsburg Fortress, Publishers, 426 S. Fifth St., Box 1209, Minneapolis, MN 55440. TEL 612-330-3402; 800-328-4648. FAX 612-330-3455. circ. 750. (back issues avail.)
    Former titles (until 1987): A L C - L C A Augsburg Adult Bible Studies. Home Bible Studies; A L C - L C A Augsburg Home Bible Studies; A L C - L C A Augsburg Adult Bible Studies. Home Bible Studies.

285   MQ   ISSN 0986-1491
AUJOURD'HUI DIMANCHE. w. Presbytere de Belleuve, Fort-de-France, Martinique. TEL 714897. Ed. Pere Gauthier. circ. 12,000.

280   AT   ISSN 0004-8852
AUSTRALIAN CHRISTIAN; national journal of Churches of Christ. 1898. fortn. Aus.$28 (effective 1995). (Federal Conference of Churches of Christ) Australian Christian Board of Management, P.O. Box 101, Essendon North, Vic. 3041, Australia. TEL 03-379-1219. FAX 03-379-0015. Ed. C.R. Ambrose. adv.; bk.rev.; index; circ. 3,700 (paid). **Indexed:** CERDIC. **Document type:** newspaper.

283   AT   ISSN 0812-0811
AUSTRALIAN LECTIONARY (YEAR). 1978. a. Aus.$4.95. (Anglican Press Australia) A I O Press, St. Andrews House, 2nd Fl., Sydney South, N.S.W. 200, Australia. TEL 61-2-283-2638. FAX 61-2-283-3987. Ed. Pam Raff. adv. contact: Mamie Long. circ. 15,000. (back issues avail.) **Document type:** consumer publication.
—CCC.

285   AT
AUSTRALIAN PRESBYTERIAN LIVING TODAY. 1966. m. (except Jan.). Aus.$30 (foreign Aus.$43). Presbyterian Church of Australia, National Journal Committee, 156 Collins St., Melbourne, Vic. 3000, Australia. TEL 03-654-2765. FAX 03-654-2785. Ed. Rev. R. Humphreys. adv.; bk.rev.; film rev.; illus. circ. 3,500.
    Formerly: Australian Presbyterian Life (ISSN 0005-0059)

286 362.7   US   ISSN 0162-6833
AWARE. 1970. q. $12.95 for magazine; Picture Set $30; Resource Kit $30 (effective 1995-1996). Southern Baptist Convention, Woman's Missionary Union, Hwy. 280, E., 100 Missionary Ridge, Birmingham, AL 35242-5235. TEL 205-991-8100. (Subscr. to: Box 830711, Birmingham, AL 35283-0711. TEL 800-WMU-7301. FAX 205-995-4840) Ed. Barbara Massey. adv. contact: Also avail.: q. Aware Picture Set; q. Aware Resource Kit. circ. 36,500 (paid).
    Description: Publication of interest to leaders of Southern Baptist Girls in Action groups.

286   CN   ISSN 0833-4587
B.C. FELLOWSHIP BAPTIST. 1927. m. Can.$7. Fellowship of Evangelical Baptist Churches of British Columbia & Yukon, Box 800, Langley, BC V3A 8C9, Canada. TEL 604-888-3616. FAX 604-888-3601. Ed. Bruce Christiansen. bk.rev. circ. 10,000. **Document type:** newsletter.
    Formerly: B.C. Regular Baptist (ISSN 0702-1003)

286   CN
B C O Q DIRECTORY. a. Can.$20. Baptist Convention of Ontario and Quebec, 195 The West Mall, Ste. 414, Etobicoke, ON M9C 5K1, Canada. Ed. T. Cromwell. circ. 800. **Document type:** directory.
    Former titles: Baptist Directory; Baptist Yearbook.

284   GW
B I M S. (Blaukreuz Information - Meinungen - Szene) 1986. q. DM.10. Blaues Kreuz in der Evangelischen Kirche, Dietrichsstr. 17a, 30159 Hannover, Germany. TEL 0511-651917. Ed. Guenter Blueder. adv.; bk.rev. circ. 1,500.

285   US   ISSN 0005-5557
BANNER (GRAND RAPIDS). 1866. 45/yr. $35. (Christian Reformed Church) C R C Publications, 2850 Kalamazoo Ave. S.E., Grand Rapids, MI 49560. TEL 616-246-0725. FAX 616-246-0834. Ed. Rev. John Suk. adv.; illus.; index. circ. 38,500. (also avail. in microform from UMI; reprint service avail. from UMI) **Indexed:** CERDIC, G.Soc.Sci.& Rel.Per.Lit.
—UMI.
    Formerly: Banner of Truth.
    Description: Contains news pertaining to the life of the church, as well as feature articles that address the Christian faith and life of the members and readers.

285   UK   ISSN 0408-4748
BANNER OF TRUTH. 1955. m. (11/yr.). £10.50($20) (typically set in Jan.). Banner of Truth Trust Publishers, The Grey House, 3 Murrayfield House, Edinburgh EH12 6EL. TEL 0131-337-7310. FAX 0131-346-7484. (U.S. addr.: Box 621, Carlisle, PA 17013. TEL 717-249-5747) Rev. Iain H. Murray; Pub. Murdo MacLeod. bk.rev. circ. 6,000.
    Description: Exposition and application of the historic reformed Christian faith.

268 378   US   ISSN 0162-4180
BAPTIST ADULTS. q. $10.95. Southern Baptist Convention, Sunday School Board, 127 Ninth Ave., N., Nashville, TN 37234. TEL 800-458-2772.

286   US
BAPTIST AND REFLECTOR. 1835. w. $7.50. Tennessee Baptist Convention, c/o Executive Board, Box 728, Brentwood, TN 37027. TEL 615-371-2003. FAX 615-371-2080. Ed. W. Fletcher Allen. adv. contact: Lonnie Wilkey. circ. 67,000. **Document type:** newspaper.

286   US   ISSN 0005-5689
BAPTIST BULLETIN. 1933. m. (11/yr.). $10. General Association of Regular Baptist Churches, 1300 N. Meacham Rd., Schaumburg, IL 60173-4888. TEL 708-843-1600. FAX 708-843-3757. E-mail: 76520.553@compuserve.com. Ed. Norman Olson. adv.; bk.rev. circ. 25,000. **Indexed:** G.Soc.Sci.& Rel.Per.Lit. **Document type:** bulletin, academic/scholarly publication.
—UnCover.

286   US   ISSN 0005-5697
BAPTIST CHALLENGE; voice of independent Baptists. 1961. m. free. Central Baptist Church, c/o M.L. Moser, Ed., Box 25848, Little Rock, AR 72221-5848. TEL 501-868-7703; 800-594-4876. FAX 501-868-7622. adv.; bk.rev.; illus. circ. 7,500.

286   US   ISSN 0744-6985
BAPTIST COURIER. 1878. w. $8.50. Baptist Courier, Inc., Box 2168, Greenville, SC 29602. circ. 116,000.
    Description: Forum and news on religion.

286   US   ISSN 0005-5700
BAPTIST HERALD. 1923. m. (combined in Jan.-Feb. July-Aug.). $8 (Canada $10.50, elsewhere $16). North American Baptist Conference, 1 S. 210 Summit Ave., Oakbrook Terrace, IL 60181. TEL 708-495-2000. FAX 708-495-3301. Ed. Barbara J. Binder. adv.; illus. circ. 8,000. (also avail. in microfilm from UMI) **Indexed:** CERDIC.
—UMI.

286   US
BAPTIST HERITAGE UPDATE. 1985. q. $14.95 membership; students and seniors $10.95 (includes Baptist History and Heritage). Southern Baptist Convention, Historical Commission, 901 Commerce St., Ste. 400, Nashville, TN 37203-3630. TEL 615-244-0344. FAX 615-242-2153. Ed. Kim Medley. circ. 1,000 (paid). (looseleaf format; back issues avail.) **Document type:** newsletter.
    Description: Reports on the Historical Commission's efforts to foster Baptist history.

286 209   US   ISSN 0005-5719
BX6207
BAPTIST HISTORY AND HERITAGE. 1965. q. $10.95 (foreign $13.45) (with Baptist Heritage Update $14.95). Southern Baptist Convention, Historical Commission, 901 Commerce St., Ste. 400, Nashville, TN 37203-3630. TEL 615-244-0344. FAX 615-242-2153. Ed. Lynn E. May, Jr. bk.rev.; charts; illus.; index; circ. 1,100 (paid). (back issues avail.) **Indexed:** Amer.Hist.& Life, CERDIC, Hist.Abstr., Rel.& Theol.Abstr. (1989-), Rel.Ind.One, South.Bap.Per.Ind. **Document type:** academic/scholarly publication.
—Faxon; UMI.
    Description: Brings perspectives of the past to bear on issues on the present.

286 910.03   US
BAPTIST INFORMER. 1878. m. $5. G B S C of North Carolina, 603 S. Wilmington St., Raleigh, NC 27601. TEL 919-821-7466. FAX 919-836-0061. Ed. Paul L. Anderson. adv.; bk.rev. circ. 8,500. (tabloid format; back issues avail.) **Document type:** newspaper.
    Description: For and about African-American Baptists.

BAPTIST LEADER. see EDUCATION — Teaching Methods And Curriculum

286   US
BAPTIST LIFE. 1849. bi-m. $7.50. Baptist Convention of Maryland - Delaware, 10255 Old Columbia Rd., Columbia, MD 21046-1736. TEL 410-290-5290; 800-466-5290. FAX 410-290-6627. Ed. Ronald K. Chaney. adv.; illus.; stat. circ. 9,500. (tabloid format; also avail. in microfilm) **Document type:** newspaper.
    Former titles (until Jul. 1994): Baptist True Union (ISSN 0025-4169); (until 1985): Maryland Baptist; **Incorporates:** True Union.

RELIGIONS AND THEOLOGY — PROTESTANT

283 US ISSN 0744-9518
BAPTIST MESSENGER. 1912. w. $6. Baptist General Convention of Oklahoma, 3800 N. May Ave., Oklahoma City, OK 73112-6506. TEL 405-942-3800. FAX 405-947-7170. (Subscr. to: Box 12130, Oklahoma City, OK 73157) Ed. Glenn A. Brown. adv. contact: Dave Parker. circ. 101,838.
Description: Relates news of interest to Oklahoma Southern Baptists region.

266 US ISSN 0091-2743
BX6209.B37
BAPTIST MISSIONARY ASSOCIATION OF AMERICA. DIRECTORY AND HANDBOOK. Key Title: Directory and Handbook - Baptist Missionary Association of America. 1961. a. $5. Baptist News Service, Box 97, Jacksonville, TX 75766. TEL 903-586-2501. FAX 903-586-0378. Ed. James C. Blaylock. circ. 5,000. **Document type:** directory.

266.6 UK ISSN 0067-4079
BAPTIST MISSIONARY SOCIETY. DIRECTORY AND FINANCIAL REPORT. Key Title: Baptist Missionary Society. Official Report and Directory of Missiories. 1793. a. free. Baptist Missionary Society, P.O. Box 49, Baptist House, 129 Broadway, Didcot, Oxon. OX11 8XA, England. TEL 01235-512077. FAX 01235-511265. circ. 6,000. **Document type:** consumer publication.
Description: Lists missionaries, staff, and committee members and provides a financial report.

266 UK ISSN 0067-4060
BAPTIST MISSIONARY SOCIETY, DIDCOT. ANNUAL REPORT. 1792. a. free. Baptist Missionary Society, P.O. Box 49, Baptist House, 129 Broadway, Didcot, Oxon. OX11 8XA, England. TEL 01235-512077. FAX 01235-511265. circ. 24,000.
Description: Reports the work of the Baptist Missionary Society for the year.

286 US ISSN 0005-5751
BAPTIST PROGRESS. 1912. w. $15. Baptist Missionary Association of Texas, Box 2085, Waxahachie, TX 75165. TEL 214-923-0756. FAX 214-923-2679. Ed. Danny Pope. adv.; bk.rev.; circ. 12,000 (controlled). (also avail. in microfilm) **Document type:** newspaper.

286 US
BAPTIST PUBLIC RELATIONS ASSOCIATION NEWSLETTER.* 1953. m. membership. Baptist Public Relations Association, 1914 Valley Park Dr., Nashville, TN 37216. TEL 615-227-7836. Ed. Mary E. Speidel. bk.rev.; tr.lit.; circ. controlled. (looseleaf format) **Document type:** newsletter.

286 209 UK ISSN 0005-576X
BX6276.A1
BAPTIST QUARTERLY. N.S. 1922. q. £16 to individuals; libraries £20. Baptist Historical Society, 28 Dowthorpe Hill, Earls Barton, Northampton NN6 OPB, England. TEL 01604-811170. Ed. J.H.Y. Briggs. adv.; bk.rev.; illus.; index every 2 yrs. cum.index in 4 vols.: 1908-1921; 1922-1941; 1942-1964; 1965-1986. circ. 700. (also avail. in microfilm from UMI; reprint service avail. from UMI) **Indexed:** Amer.Hist.& Life, Br.Hum.Ind., CERDIC, Hist.Abstr., Hist.Abstr, Rel.& Theol.Abstr. (1968-), Rel.Ind.One, Rel.Per. **Document type:** academic/scholarly publication.
—BLDSC (1863.150000); UMI.
Refereed Serial

286 US ISSN 0005-5778
BAPTIST RECORD. 1877. w. $8.35. Mississippi Baptist Convention, Box 530, Jackson, MS 39205. TEL 601-968-3800. FAX 601-968-3928. Eds. Guy Henderson, William H. Perkins. adv. contact: Teresa Dickens. bk.rev.; charts; illus.; rec.rev. circ. 107,000. (also avail. in microfilm) **Indexed:** CERDIC. **Document type:** newspaper.

286 US
THE BAPTIST STANDARD. 1888. w. $10.05. Baptist Standard Publishing Company, Box 660267, Dallas, TX 75266-0267. TEL 214-630-4571. FAX 214-638-8535. adv.; bk.rev. circ. 234,820.

286 UK ISSN 0005-5786
BAPTIST TIMES. 1855. w. £30. Baptist Times Ltd., 129 The Broadway, Didcot, Oxon OX11 8XB, England. TEL 01235-512012. FAX 01235-512013. adv.; bk.rev.; illus.; music rev.; rec.rev. circ. 11,000. (also avail. in microfilm from WMP) **Document type:** newspaper.

284 LB
BAPTIST TIMES. 1993. w. $10. Liberia Baptist Missionary and Educational Convention, Inc., Ste. 217-128, ACDB Bldg., Careu and Warren Sts., P.O. Box 10-0390, Monrovia, Liberia. TEL 231-223269. Ed. Rev. Emil D.E. Sani Peal. **Document type:** newsletter.
Description: Reports on missionary news and contains words of inspiration.

286 US ISSN 0888-9074
BAPTIST TRUMPET. 1940. w. $14. Baptist Missionary Association of Arkansas, Box 192208, Little Rock, AR 72219-2208. TEL 501-565-4601. Ed. David Tidwell. adv. circ. 12,831. (tabloid format)

286.1 UK ISSN 0302-3184
BX6276.A1
BAPTIST UNION DIRECTORY. 1861. a. £9.50 (effective 1995). Baptist Union of Great Britain, P.O. Box 44, 129 Broadway, Didcot, Oxon. OX11 8RT, England. TEL 01235-512077. FAX 01235-811537. E-mail: 100442,1750@compuserve.com. Ed. Hilary Saunders. adv. circ. 2,500. **Document type:** directory.
Formerly: Baptist Handbook (ISSN 0067-4052)
Description: Contains details of accredited ministers and churches in membership with the Baptist Union of Great Britain.

286 CN ISSN 0067-4087
BX6252.W47
BAPTIST UNION OF WESTERN CANADA. YEARBOOK. 1907. a. Can.$20 (typically set in Sept.). Baptist Union of Western Canada, 605, 999 8 St., S.W., Calgary, AB T2R 1J5, Canada. TEL 403-228-9559. FAX 403-228-9048. Ed.Bd. circ. 700 (controlled). **Document type:** corporate report.

286 US ISSN 0005-5808
BAPTIST WORLD. 1954. q. donation. Baptist World Alliance, Division of Communications, 6733 Curran St., McLean, VA 22101-6005. TEL 703-790-8980. Ed. Wendy Ryan. illus. circ. 11,000. (also avail. in microform from UMI; reprint service avail. from UMI) —UMI.
Description: Informs Baptists about the work of the BWA and of what Baptists are doing worldwide.

286 US ISSN 0067-4095
BAPTIST WORLD ALLIANCE. CONGRESS REPORTS. 1905. quinquennial; 16th, 1990, Seoul (published in 1991). $11.50. Baptist World Alliance, Division of Communications, 6733 Curran St., McLean, VA 22101-6005. TEL 703-790-8980. circ. 15,000. **Document type:** proceedings.

284 GW ISSN 0005-7282
BAYREUTHER GEMEINDEBLATT. 1922. m. DM.10. Evang.-Luth. Kirchengemeinden Bayreuths, Hans-Meiser-Str. 1, 95447 Bayreuth, Germany. TEL 0921-61036. Ed. Gottfried Lindner. adv.; bk.rev.; abstr. circ. 5,500. (looseleaf format) **Document type:** bulletin.

268 US ISSN 0198-6201
BEGINNING (NASHVILLE). 1980. q. $9.25. Southern Baptist Convention, Sunday School Board, 127 Ninth Ave., N., Nashville, TN 37234. TEL 800-458-2772.

284 GW
BERLIN - BRANDENBURGISCHES SONNTAGSBLATT DIE KIRCHE; evangelische Wochenzeitung. 1946. w. (Sun.). DM.54. Wichern Verlag GmbH, Bachstr. 1-2, 10555 Berlin, Germany. TEL 030-3915075. FAX 030-3936047. Ed. Lutz Borgmann. adv. contact: Hans-Juergen Grundmann. circ. 12,859. **Document type:** newspaper.
Formed by the 1995 merger of: Kirche & Berlin - Brandenburgisches Sonntagsblatt (ISSN 0941-2735); Which was formed by 1991 merger of: Berliner Sonntagsblatt; Potsdamer Kirche (ISSN 0232-5020); Formerly: Potsdamer.

284 GW ISSN 0724-6137
BERLINER THEOLOGISCHE ZEITSCHRIFT. 1983. s-a. DM.46 (students DM.40). (Kirchliche Hochschule Berlin) Wichern Verlag GmbH, Bachstr. 1-2, 10555 Berlin, Germany. TEL 030-3915075. FAX 030-3936047. circ. 500. **Document type:** academic/scholarly publication.
Description: Discusses theoretical and scientific problems of theology.

A BETTER TOMORROW; the magazine for seniors with a future. see *GERONTOLOGY AND GERIATRICS*

268 371.3 US ISSN 0164-4440
BIBLE BOOK STUDY COMMENTARY. 1979. q. $22.95. Southern Baptist Convention, Sunday School Board, 127 Ninth Ave., N., Nashville, TN 37234. TEL 800-458-2772.

268 374 US ISSN 0162-4849
BIBLE BOOK STUDY FOR ADULTS. Chinese edition (ISSN 0897-0742); Korean edition (ISSN 0747-9514) q. $14.25. Southern Baptist Convention, Sunday School Board, 127 Ninth Ave., N., Nashville, TN 37234. TEL 800-458-2772.

268 374 US ISSN 0747-9514
BS410
BIBLE BOOK STUDY FOR ADULTS. KOREAN EDITION. English edition (ISSN 0162-4849); Chinese edition (ISSN 0897-0742) (Text in Korean) q. $14.25. Southern Baptist Convention, Sunday School Board, 127 Ninth Ave., N., Nashville, TN 37234. TEL 800-458-2772.

268 374 US ISSN 0162-4849
BIBLE BOOK STUDY FOR ADULTS. LARGE PRINT EDITION. q. $11.50. Southern Baptist Convention, Sunday School Board, Customer Service Department, 127 Ninth Ave., N., Nashville, TN 37234. TEL 800-458-2772. (large print in 18 pt.)

268 375 US ISSN 0162-4202
BIBLE BOOK STUDY FOR ADULTS. TEACHER. Chinese edition (ISSN 0897-0750) q. $16.50. Southern Baptist Convention, Sunday School Board, 127 Ninth Ave., N., Nashville, TN 37234. TEL 800-458-2772.

268 375 US ISSN 0897-0750
BIBLE BOOK STUDY FOR ADULTS. TEACHER. CHINESE EDITION. English edition (ISSN 0162-4849) q. $25.95. Southern Baptist Convention, Sunday School Board, 127 Ninth Ave., N., Nashville, TN 37234. TEL 800-458-2772.

268 028.5 US ISSN 0162-4822
BIBLE BOOK STUDY FOR YOUTH. q. $10.90. Southern Baptist Convention, Sunday School Board, 127 Ninth Ave., N., Nashville, TN 37234. TEL 800-458-2772.
Description: Written for adolescents ages 12-17.

268 375 US ISSN 0162-4830
BIBLE BOOK STUDY FOR YOUTH. TEACHER. q. $23.80. Southern Baptist Convention, Sunday School Board, 127 Ninth Ave., N., Nashville, TN 37234. TEL 800-458-2772.

248 286 US ISSN 0731-8391
BIBLE BOOK STUDY GUIDE. q. $14.25. Southern Baptist Convention, Sunday School Board, 127 Ninth Ave., N., Nashville, TN 37234. TEL 800-458-2772.

268 028.5 US ISSN 0162-4695
BIBLE DISCOVERERS. q. $10.50. Southern Baptist Convention, Sunday School Board, 127 Ninth Ave., N., Nashville, TN 37234. TEL 800-458-2772.
Description: Written for children ages 8 and 9.

268 375 US ISSN 0162-4687
BIBLE DISCOVERERS. TEACHER. q. $17.25. Southern Baptist Convention, Sunday School Board, 127 Ninth Ave., N., Nashville, TN 37234. TEL 800-458-2772.

384 286 US ISSN 1068-2775
BIBLE EXPRESS. 1993. q. $10.75. Southern Baptist Convention, Sunday School Board, 127 Ninth Ave., N., Nashville, TN 37234. TEL 800-458-2772. FAX 612-251-5933.
Description: Provides a devotional guide for boys and girls.

283 UK ISSN 0006-0763
BIBLE LANDS. 1899. s-a. donation. Jerusalem and the Middle East Church Association, 1 Hart House, The Hart, Farnham, Surrey GU9 7HA, England. TEL 01252-726994. FAX 01252-735558. Eds. Mrs. V. Wells, C. Williamson. adv.; bk.rev.; illus.; index. circ. 3,500. **Document type:** newsletter.

268 028.5 US ISSN 0162-4679
BIBLE LEARNERS. q. $10.50. Southern Baptist Convention, Sunday School Board, 127 Ninth Ave., N., Nashville, TN 37234. TEL 800-458-2772.
Description: Written for children ages 6-8.

268 375 US ISSN 0162-4660
BIBLE LEARNERS. TEACHER. q. $17.25. Southern Baptist Convention, Sunday School Board, 127 Ninth Ave., N., Nashville, TN 37234. TEL 800-458-2772.

RELIGIONS AND THEOLOGY — Protestant

283   UK   ISSN 0965-531X
BIBLE PUZZLER. 1987. q. £10.50. Herald House Ltd., 96 Dominion Rd., Worthing, W. Sussex BN14 8JP, England. TEL 01903-821082. FAX 01903-821081. Ed. Heather Thompson. circ. 4,000 (paid). **Document type:** consumer publication.
    Formerly: Christian Puzzler (ISSN 0958-3858)
    Description: Contains Bible-based puzzles to challenge persons of all ages.

268 371.3   US   ISSN 0006-078X
BIBLE SEARCHERS. 1970. q. $10.50. Southern Baptist Convention, Sunday School Board, 127 Ninth Ave., N., Nashville, TN 37234. TEL 800-458-2772.
    Supersedes: Sunday School Junior Pupil.

268 375   US   ISSN 0006-0798
BIBLE SEARCHERS. TEACHER. q. $17.25. Southern Baptist Convention, Sunday School Board, 127 Ninth Ave., N., Nashville, TN 37234. TEL 800-458-2772.

268 374   US   ISSN 0890-880X
BIBLE STORY TIME. OLDER PUPIL. q. $10.25. Southern Baptist Convention, Sunday School Board, 127 Ninth Ave., N., Nashville, TN 37234. TEL 800-458-2772.
    Description: Religious publication directed at children ages 3-5.

268 371.3   US   ISSN 0890-8788
BIBLE STORY TIME. TEACHER. q. $15.95. Southern Baptist Convention, Sunday School Board, 127 Ninth Ave., N., Nashville, TN 37234. TEL 800-458-2772.

268 028.5   US   ISSN 0890-8796
BIBLE STORY TIME. YOUNGER PUPIL. q. $10.25. Southern Baptist Convention, Sunday School Board, 127 Ninth Ave., N., Nashville, TN 37234. TEL 800-458-2772.
    Description: Religious publication directed at newborns to children age 2.

268 371.3   US   ISSN 0195-1351
BX6225
BIBLICAL ILLUSTRATOR. q. $13.50. Southern Baptist Convention, Sunday School Board, 127 Ninth Ave., N., Nashville, TN 37234. TEL 800-458-2772. **Indexed:** South.Bap.Per.Ind.
    Formerly: Sunday School Lesson Illustrator (ISSN 0162-4407)

266 285   US   ISSN 0006-0909
BIBLICAL MISSIONS. 1935. irreg. (3-6/yr.). $6. Independent Board for Presbyterian Foreign Missions, 246 W. Walnut Lane, Philadelphia, PA 19144. TEL 215-438-0511. FAX 215-438-0560. Ed. Rev. William R. LeRoy. adv.; bk.rev.; illus. circ. 3,000. **Indexed:** CERDIC.

286   US   ISSN 0279-8182
BIBLICAL RECORDER. 1833. w. $8. (Baptist State Convention of North Carolina) Biblical Recorder, Inc., Box 26568, Raleigh, NC 27611. TEL 919-847-2127. FAX 919-847-6939. (Subscr. to: Box 26568, Raleigh, NC 27511) Ed. R. Gene Puckett. adv. contact: R.G. Puckett. circ. 65,000. (tabloid format; also avail. in magnetic tape) **Document type:** newspaper.
    Description: Covers news of churches, ministries, church staff, and denominational events.

284 900   SW   ISSN 0346-5438
BIBLIOTHECA HISTORICO-ECCLESIASTICA LUNDENSIS. (Text in English and Swedish) 1972. irreg. price varies. Lund University Press, P.O. Box 141, S-221 00 Lund, Sweden. TEL 46-46-31-20-00. FAX 46-46-30-53-38. E-mail: Order@Studli.se. Ed. I. Brohed. **Document type:** academic/scholarly publication.

230   US   ISSN 0006-1921
BR1   CODEN: BSTQAA
BIBLIOTHECA SACRA; a theological quarterly. 1843. q. $18 (foreign $23) (effective 1991). Dallas Theological Seminary, 3909 Swiss Ave., Dallas, TX 75204. TEL 214-824-3094. FAX 214-841-3642. Ed. Roy B. Zuck. bk.rev.; abstr.; bibl.; index. circ. 9,000. (also avail. in microform from UMI; reprint service avail. from UMI) **Indexed:** CERDIC, Chr.Per.Ind., Int.Z.Bibelwiss., New Test.Abstr., Old Test.Abstr., Rel.& Theol.Abstr. (1967-), Rel.Ind.One, Rel.Per. **Document type:** academic/scholarly publication.
    ●Also available on CD-ROM.
    —BLDSC (2019.450000); UMI.
    Description: Provides biblical and theological instruction to biblical scholars, pastors, teachers and serious lay bible students.

284   NE   ISSN 0920-2331
BIBLIOTHECA UNITARIORUM. 1983. irreg., no. 3, 1994. price varies. De Graaf Publishers, P.O. Box 6, 2420 AA Nieuwkoop, Netherlands. TEL 31-1725-71461. Ed. Robert Dan. **Document type:** monographic series.

267   UK
BICENTENARY BROCHURE. (Each issue has distinctive title) 1993. biennial. £5. Council for World Mission, 11 Carteret St., London SW1H 9DL, England. TEL 0171-222-4214. FAX 0171-233-1747. Ed. Geoffrey Duncan. circ. 5,000. (back issues avail.) **Document type:** corporate report.
    Former titles (until 1995): Beyond Ourselves; **Supersedes:** C W M Report (ISSN 0069-8857)
    Description: Covers women's interests, environmental studies, religion and theology, and ethnic interests.

284   IC
BJARMI; kristilegt timarit. 1906. 8/yr. ISK 2450($45) Kristilega Skolahreyfingin, P.O. Box 4060, IS-124 Reykjavik, Iceland. TEL 354-567-8899. FAX 354-567-8840. (Co-sponsors: K F U M - K; S I K) Ed. Gunnar J. Gunnarsson. adv. circ. 1,000. (back issues avail.)

BLACK MINISTRIES. see *ETHNIC INTERESTS*

283   GW   ISSN 0341-9452
BLAETTER FUER PFAELZISCHE KIRCHENGESCHICHTE UND RELIGIOESE VOLKSKUNDE. 1925. a. DM.40. Verein fuer Pfaelzische Kirchengeschichte, Kirchstr. 3, 66501 Grossbundenbach, Germany. bk.rev.; index. (back issues avail.)

284   GW
BLICK IN DIE KIRCHE. 1965. m. free to qualified personnel. Evangelisches Informationszentrum Kurhessen-Waldeck, Heinrich-Wimmer-Str. 4, 34131 Kassel, Germany. TEL 0561-9307-0. FAX 0561-9307155. Ed. Otmar Schulz. bk.rev. circ. 19,000. **Document type:** newsletter.

284   GW
BLICKPUNKT GEMEINDE; Mitarbeiterzeitschrift. 1977. q. DM.19.20. Oncken Verlag GmbH, Muendener Str. 13, 34123 Kassel, Germany. TEL 0561-52005-0. Ed. Hinrich Schmidt. circ. 2,000. **Document type:** newsletter.

284.2   SA   ISSN 0006-4947
BLOEMHEUWEL-NUUS. (Text in Afrikaans) 1953. q. free. Nederduitse Gereformeerde Kerk, Bloemfontein - Dutch Reformed Church, Bloemfontein, Bloemheuwel, 15 General Hertzog Str., Bloemfontein 9300, South Africa. Ed. Rev. H. C. J. Flemming. adv.; bk.rev.; bibl. circ. 1,000. **Document type:** academic/scholarly publication.

205   DK
BOERNEBLADET. 1949. 20/yr. DKK 119. Danmarks Folkekirkelige Soendagsskoler og Boernegudstjenester, Korshaersvej 25, 7000 Fredericia, Denmark. TEL 45-75-92-61-00. Ed. Bente Graugaard Nielsen. circ. 4,824.

368 284   US   ISSN 0279-9111
BX8001
BOND. 1924. q. $4 to non-members. Lutheran Brotherhood, 625 Fourth Ave. S., Minneapolis, MN 55415. TEL 612-340-7000. Ed. Richard Hagen. illus.; circ. 540,000 (controlled).
    Description: Covers fraternal programs serving members, their families, churches and communities.

283 800   US
▼**BOOKS & CULTURE**. 1995. bi-m. $19.95. Christianity Today, 465 Gunderson Dr., Carol Stream, IL 60188. TEL 708-260-6200. FAX 708-261-0114. Ed. David Neff. (tabloid format) **Document type:** consumer publication.
    Description: Examines current books from a conservative Protestant perspective.

284   GW
BOTSCHAFT; Monatsschrift der Bruedergemeinden. 1853. m. DM.48. R. Brockhaus Verlag, Postfach, 42766 Haan, Germany. Ed. Manfred Klatt. adv.; bk.rev. circ. 16,000. (back issues avail.)
    Description: Christian evangelical publication covering religion and missionary work in Germany and abroad.

BRAILLE EVANGELISM BULLETIN. see *HANDICAPPED — Visually Impaired*

260   GW
BREMER KIRCHENZEITUNG. 1928. bi-w. DM.19.50. (Bremische Evangelische Kirche) Carl Ed. Schuenemann KG, Postfach 106067, 28060 Bremen, Germany. TEL 0421-36903-72. FAX 0421-36903-34. Ed. Peter Bick. circ. 19,000. **Document type:** bulletin.

284   US   ISSN 0747-4288
BRETHREN EVANGELIST. 1878. m. $14.50. Brethren Church, 524 College Ave., Ashland, OH 44805. TEL 419-289-1708. Ed. Richard C. Winfield. adv.; index. circ. 3,100. (back issues avail.)
    Description: Inspirational articles and news of the Church and its ministries.

250   UK
BRISTOL DIOCESAN NEWS. m. £1 for 100 copies. Diocese of Bristol, 23 Great George St., Bristol BS1 5QZ, England. Ed. Hugh Bunting. bk.rev. circ. 15,000.
    Formerly: Bristol Diocesan Gazette (ISSN 0045-2858)

200   FR   ISSN 0760-8365
BULLETIN D'INFORMATION PROTESTANT. Key Title: BIP. 1961. w. 495 F. Federation Protestante de France, Service d'Information, 47 rue de Clichy, 75009 Paris, France. TEL 44-53-47-12. FAX 42-81-40-01. Ed. Geoffroy de Turckheim. abstr. circ. 800. (processed) **Document type:** bulletin.
    Formerly: Service Protestant Francais de Presse et d'Information (ISSN 0760-8616)

280   UK   ISSN 0045-3536
BX4800
BULWARK. 1851. 6/yr. $6 (effective Jan. 1992). Scottish Reformation Society, The Magdalen Chapel, 39 Cowgate, Edinburgh EH1 1JR, Scotland. TEL 031-220-1450. Ed. A. Sinclair Horne. bk.rev. circ. 6,200. **Document type:** newsletter.

266 282   SX
C C N MESSENGER. 1980. m. R.1.50 per no. Council of Churches in Namibia, P.O. Box 41, Windhoek 9000, Namibia. Ed. D.J.K. Tjongarero. adv.; bk.rev. circ. 2,000. (back issues avail.)
    Supersedes (in 1991): C C N Information.

289   US
C J A NEWS. q. $20 membership. Christians for Justice Action, 233 North Country Rd., Mount Sinai, NY 11766. (Subscr. to: Fred Tilinski, 1822 Peach St., St. Charles MO 63303) Eds. John Nelson, Donna Schaper.
    Description: Covers justice and peace issues of interest to members of the United Church of Christ.

266   US
C O R LETTER. 1986. 4/yr. $10. (National Council of the Churches of Christ) Ecumenical Networks, 475 Riverside Dr., Rm. 868, New York, NY 10115. TEL 212-870-2157. FAX 212-870-2158. Ed. Kathleen Hurty. bk.rev. circ. 3,575. **Document type:** newsletter.

C P F I NEWSLETTER. (Christian Pharmacists Fellowship International) see *PHARMACY AND PHARMACOLOGY*

283   AT   ISSN 0007-9073
C S C NEWSLETTER. 1966. 3/yr. Aus.$10. Community of the Sisters of the Church, 62-422 Cardigan St., Carlton, Vic. 3053, Australia. TEL 61-3-93482284. Ed. Sister Audrey C.S.C. bk.rev. circ. 2,200. **Indexed:** CERDIC.
    Supersedes: Our Work.
    Description: For Anglican religious community.

283   CN   ISSN 0383-6509
CALEDONIA DIOCESAN TIMES. 1960. m. Anglican Church of Canada, Diocese of Caledonia, Box 278, Prince Rupert, BC V8J 3P6, Canada. TEL 604-624-6013. illus.

286   US   ISSN 0008-1558
CALIFORNIA SOUTHERN BAPTIST. 1941. bi-w. $9.50. California Southern Baptist Convention, 678 E. Shaw Ave., Fresno, CA 93710. TEL 209-229-9533. FAX 209-229-2824. Ed. Mark Wyatt. adv.; bk.rev.; illus.; index. circ. 12,500. **Document type:** newspaper.

284.2   NE   ISSN 0008-1787
CALVIJN. 1919. m. fl.5($3) Nederlandse Hervormde Vereniging Calvijn - Dutch Reformed Society, A. Paulownastraat 38, Dordrecht, Netherlands. Ed. G.J. Edelman. circ. 500.

RELIGIONS AND THEOLOGY — PROTESTANT

230 US ISSN 0008-1795
BR1
CALVIN THEOLOGICAL JOURNAL. 1966. s-a. $15. Calvin Theological Seminary, 3233 Burton St. S.E., Grand Rapids, MI 49546. TEL 616-957-6010. FAX 616-957-8621. E-mail: bltj@calvin.edu. Ed. John Bolt. adv. contact: Ina De Moor. bk.rev.; index. circ. 3,000. (also avail. in microform from UMI; reprint service avail. from UMI) **Indexed:** CERDIC, Chr.Per.Ind., Int.Z.Bibelwiss., New Test.Abstr., Old Test.Abstr., Rel.& Theol.Abstr. (1968-), Rel.Ind.One, Rel.Per. **Document type:** academic/scholarly publication.
—BLDSC (3015.800000); UMI.
Refereed Serial

284 CN ISSN 0832-0179
CANADA LUTHERAN (NATIONAL EDITION). 9/yr. Can.$17. Evangelical Lutheran Church in Canada, 1512 St. James St., Winnipeg, MB R3H 0L2, Canada. TEL 204-786-6707. FAX 204-783-7548. Ed. Kenn Ward. adv. contact: Irene Pomes. circ. 23,000 (paid).
Supersedes (in 1986): Shepherd (ISSN 0383-8544) & Western Canada Lutheran (ISSN 0382-0793) & Central Canada Lutheran (ISSN 0708-7969); Supersedes in part: Canada Lutheran (ISSN 0008-2716); Central Canada Lutheran was formerly (until 1978): Central Canada Lutheran Circle 'N Dot (ISSN 0705-8926); (until 1977): Circle 'N Dot (ISSN 0319-468X); (until 1968): Central Canada Lutheran (ISSN 0319-4671).

286 CN ISSN 0008-2988
CANADIAN BAPTIST. 1854. m. (10/yr.). Can.$18. Baptist Convention of Ontario and Quebec, 195 The West Mall, Ste. 414, Etobicoke, ON M9C 5K1, Canada. (Co-sponsor: Baptist Union of Western Canada) Ed. Dr. Larry Matthews. adv.; bk.rev.; index. circ. 11,000. (also avail. in microform) **Indexed:** Can.B.P.I., Can.Per.Ind.

283 UK ISSN 0950-6276
CANTERBURY CATHEDRAL CHRONICLE. 1928. a. £10 (foreign £15). Friends of Canterbury Cathedral, Cathedral House, 8 The Precincts, Canterbury, Kent CT1 2EE, England. TEL 01227-471000. FAX 01227-762897. Ed. Frank Fricker. **Document type:** newsletter.
Description: Contains articles about the cathedral and its environs, its history, stained glass and wall paintings.

CAREGIVING; a resource for Christian ministry. see SOCIAL SERVICES AND WELFARE

CATHEDRAL. see JOURNALISM

704.948 US ISSN 0008-7874
NA4830
CATHEDRAL AGE; an international magazine devoted to activities at and about Washington National Cathedral. 1925. q. $15 to non-members. Washington National Cathedral, Massachusetts & Wisconsin Aves., N.W., Washington, DC 20016. TEL 202-537-6247. FAX 202-364-6600. Ed. Sherwood Harris. adv.; bk.rev.; film rev.; illus. circ. 33,000. (also avail. in microform from UMI; reprint service avail. from UMI)
—UMI; UnCover.

CELEBRATE CHORAL MUSIC. see MUSIC

200 US
EL CENTINELA. French edition: Sentinelle. (Text in Spanish) 1896. m. $9.99. (Seventh-Day Adventists) Pacific Press Publishing Association, 1350 Kings Rd., Nampa, ID 83651. TEL 208-465-2500. FAX 208-465-2531. Ed. Tulio Peverini. circ. 140,000. (also avail. in microform from UMI)

284 FR ISSN 0753-4639
CENTRE DE GENEALOGIE PROTESTANTE. CAHIERS. 1977. irreg. 180 F. (foreign 230 F.). Societe de l'Histoire du Protestantisme Francais, Centre de Genealogie Protestante, 54 rue des Saints-Peres, 75007 Paris, France.
Former titles (until 1980): Cahier de Genealogie Protestante (ISSN 0753-4620); (until 1978): Genealogie Protestante (ISSN 0753-4612)

284 572 100 SZ
CENTRE PROTESTANT D'ETUDES DE GENEVE. BULLETIN. (Text in French) 1948. bi-m. 38 SFr. Centre Protestant d'Etudes de Geneve, Case Postale 3158, CH-1211 Geneva 3, Switzerland. Ed. Isabelle Graessle. adv. circ. 1,300. **Document type:** bulletin.
Description: Covers theological and ethical inquiries conducted in the different centers in French-speaking Switzerland, particularly in Geneva.

200 CE
CEYLON CHURCHMAN. (Text in English) 1867. bi-m. $10 or £8 (effective 1996). Dioceses of Colombo & Kurunagala, Diocesan Office, Bauddhaloka Mawatha, Colombo 7, Sri Lanka. Eds. Rev. Sydney Knight, N.Y. Casie Chetty. adv.; bk.rev. circ. 1,500.

283 UK ISSN 0009-0999
CHALLENGE (LONDON, 1961). 1961. bi-m. £2. Anglican Pacifist Fellowship, Walters Farmhouse, Brenchley, Tonbridge, Kent TN12 7NU, England. TEL 44-666-825249. FAX 44-532-755497. Ed. Rev. Robin Eastoe. adv.; bk.rev. circ. 1,500. **Indexed:** Acad.Ind. **Document type:** newsletter.
Formerly: Anglican Pacifist.

286
CHALLENGE (MEMPHIS); missions magazines for the high school Baptist young men. 1987. m. $2.82 per quarter (effective Aug. 1993). Southern Baptist Convention, Brotherhood Commission, 1548 Poplar Ave., Memphis, TN 38104. TEL 901-272-2461. FAX 901-726-5540.

285
CHALLENGER (PETALUMA). 1961. bi-m. free. Chinese Christian Mission, 1269 N. McDowell Blvd., Petaluma, CA 94975-0759. TEL 707-762-1314. FAX 707-762-1713. Ed. Cecilia Yau. circ. 11,000. (back issues avail.)

284 US
CHAPLAIR.* 1977? q. membership. Assembly of Episcopal Hospitals and Chaplains, Box 487, Chesapeake City, MD 21816. circ. 800.

286 GW
CHARISMA. 1974. q. contributions. Grafenberger Allee 51-55, 40237 Duesseldorf, Germany. TEL 0211-667575. FAX 0211-6912434. Eds. Gerhard Bially, Klaus-Dieter Passon. circ. 23,000. (back issues avail.) **Document type:** bulletin.
Description: Information about the Charismatic Renewal movement worldwide, with special emphasis on the German speaking regions of Europe.

CHARITY AND CHILDREN; the voice of child care in North Carolina. see CHILDREN AND YOUTH — About

266 AT ISSN 0311-0737
CHECKPOINT. 1972. q. for members only. Church Missionary Society of Australia, 93 Bathurst St., Sydney, N.S.W. 2000, Australia. TEL 61-2-284-6777. FAX 61-2-267-3626. Ed. David Claydon. bk.rev.; illus. circ. 8,400. **Document type:** newsletter.
Incorporates: Going On (ISSN 0705-2316) & Discovery (ISSN 0726-6286); **Supersedes:** C M S News (ISSN 0007-8689)
Description: Explores mission work in North Australia and overseas.

283 UK ISSN 0009-2126
CHEERING WORDS. 1851. m. £5.50 (foreign £6.50). 22 Victoria Rd., Stamford, Lincs. PE9 1HB, England. TEL 01780-63780. Ed. David Oldham; Pub. David Odham. bk.rev.; illus.; index. circ. 4,500. **Document type:** consumer publication.

200 UK
THE CHICHESTER LEAFLET. 1895. m. £4. Chichester Diocese, 9 Brunswick Sq., Hove, E. Sussex BN3 1EN, England. TEL 44-273-329023. FAX 44-273-821810. Ed. W.R. Pratt. bk.rev. circ. 33,000.
Former titles: Chichester News (ISSN 0009-3785); Chichester Diocesan Leaflet.

283 UK
CHICHESTER MAGAZINE. 1988. q. £4. Chichester Diocese, 9 Brunswick Sq., Hove, E. Sussex BN3 1EN, England. TEL 44-273-329023. FAX 44-273-821810. Ed. W.R. Pratt. circ. 7,200.

CHILDREN IN FOCUS. see SOCIAL SERVICES AND WELFARE

268 028.5 US ISSN 0273-3161
CHILDREN'S BIBLE STUDY. OLDER PUPIL. q. $10.25. Southern Baptist Convention, Sunday School Board, 127 Ninth Ave., N., Nashville, TN 37234. TEL 800-458-2772.
Description: Religious publication directed at children ages 9-11.

268 375 US ISSN 0273-3153
CHILDREN'S BIBLE STUDY. TEACHER. q. $15.95. Southern Baptist Convention, Sunday School Board, 127 Ninth Ave., N., Nashville, TN 37234. TEL 800-458-2772.

268 028.5 US ISSN 0273-317X
CHILDREN'S BIBLE STUDY. YOUNGER PUPIL. s-a. $10.25. Southern Baptist Convention, Sunday School Board, 127 Ninth Ave., N., Nashville, TN 37234. TEL 800-458-2772.
Description: Religious publication directed at children ages 6-8.

THE CHILDREN'S CHOIR. see MUSIC

285 US ISSN 1045-6147
CHINESE TODAY. (Text in Chinese) 1961. m. free. Chinese Christian Mission, 1269 N. McDowell Blvd., Petaluma, CA 94975-0759. TEL 707-762-1314. FAX 707-762-1713. Ed. Mandy Fung. circ. 40,000. (back issues avail.)
Formerly: Chinese Christians Today.

200 US ISSN 0412-2968
CHRIST IN OUR HOME; light for today. 1954. q. $5.10 for regular edition; large print, Braille and cassette $8.60. Augsburg Fortress, Publishers, 426 S. Fifth St., Box 1209, Minneapolis, MN 55440. TEL 612-300-3402; 800-328-4648. FAX 612-330-3455. Ed. Beth Ann Gaede. circ. 370,000. (also avail. in Braille; audio cassette; back issues avail.; large print edition in 20 pt.)

CHRISTEN HEUTE; Zeitung der Alt-Katholiken fuer Christen heute. see RELIGIONS AND THEOLOGY — Roman Catholic

268 282 GW ISSN 0009-5192
DIE CHRISTENLEHRE; Zeitschrift fuer den Katechetischen Dienst in Gemeinde und Schule. 1948. m. DM.84 (foreign DM.98). Evangelische Verlagsanstalt GmbH, Burgstr. 1-5, 04109 Leipzig, Germany. TEL 0341-71141-0. FAX 0341-9603179. Ed. Dieter Reiher. adv.: B&W page DM.800; trim 210 x 140; adv. contact: Christine Herrmann. bk.rev. circ. 1,500. **Document type:** bulletin.
Description: Contains discussions, curricula, teaching instructions and news.

283 UK ISSN 0263-4023
CHRISTIAN AID NEWS. 1969. q. free. (Council of Churches in Britain and Ireland) Christian Aid, P.O. Box 100, London SE1 7RT, England. TEL 0171-620-4444. FAX 0171-620-0719. Ed. Angela Burton. bk.rev. circ. 183,500. (tabloid format; back issues avail.) **Document type:** newspaper.
Description: Provides news of projects benefiting the poor in developing countries with funds from the British charity, Christian Aid. Also news of development-related world events and of fundraising initiatives by the charity's supporters.

286 US ISSN 0746-0171
THE CHRISTIAN BAPTIST. 1967. m. $10. Box 68, Atwood, TN 38220. TEL 901-662-7417. Ed. S.T. Tolley. bk.rev. circ. 3,200. **Document type:** newspaper.

285 US ISSN 0009-5265
CHRISTIAN BEACON. 1936. w. $12. Christian Beacon Press, 756 Haddon Ave., Collingswood, NJ 08108. TEL 609-858-0700. Ed. Carl McIntire. bk.rev.; illus. circ. 20,000. (tabloid format)

283 282 US ISSN 0890-6793
BX5800
CHRISTIAN CHALLENGE. 1962. 9/yr. $22 (Canada $25; foreign $30). Foundation for Christian Theology, 1215 Independence Ave., S.E., Washington, DC 20003. TEL 202-547-5409. FAX 202-543-8704. Ed. Auburn Faber Traycik. adv.; bk.rev. circ. 5,000. (also avail. in microfilm; back issues avail.)
Description: News, opinions and spirituality of Anglican and Episcopal Christianity from a traditional viewpoint.

RELIGIONS AND THEOLOGY — PROTESTANT

284 366 CN ISSN 1192-3415
CHRISTIAN COURIER. 1951. w. Can.$43.50. Calvinist Contact Publishing Ltd., 261 Martindale Rd., Unit 4, St. Catharines, ON L2W 1A1, Canada. TEL 905-682-8311. FAX 905-682-8313. Ed. Bert Witvoet. adv. contact: Stan de Jong. bk.rev.; film rev.; illus.; circ. 5,500 (paid). **Document type:** newspaper.
Former titles (until 1992): Calvinist Contact (ISSN 0410-3882); Contact (ISSN 0382-5949)

285 US ISSN 0362-0832
CHRISTIAN INDEX (ATLANTA). 1822. w. $10 (effective Jan. 1995). Georgia Baptist Convention, Executive Committee, 2930 Flowers Rd., S., Atlanta, GA 30341. TEL 404-936-5312. FAX 404-936-5260. Ed. William T. Neal. adv. contact: John D. Pierce. bk.rev.; circ. 65,000 (paid). (tabloid format; also avail. in microfilm; back issues avail.) **Document type:** newspaper.

287 US ISSN 0744-4060
CHRISTIAN INDEX (MEMPHIS). 1867. w. $25. Christian Methodist Episcopal Church, c/o Lawrence L. Reddick, III, Ed., Box 665, Memphis, TN 38101. TEL 901-345-1173. FAX 901-345-4108. Ed. Lawrence L. Reddick III; Pub. William E. George. adv.; bk.rev. circ. 7,000.
Description: Focuses on the predominantly Black, Christian Methodist Episcopal denomination.

285 UK
CHRISTIAN IRISHMAN. 1880. 10/yr. 55p. Irish Mission of the Presbyterian Church in Ireland, Church House, Fisherwick Pl., Belfast BT1 6DW, N. Ireland. TEL 01232-322284. FAX 01232-248377. Ed. Rev. David J. Temple. adv.: B&W page £160; color page £300, £350; adv. contact: Nehru M. Dass. bk.rev.; illus. circ. 10,000.
Description: Devotional magazine provides articles on Christian living, mission, church growth, conferences and more.

CHRISTIAN LIBRARIAN. see *LIBRARY AND INFORMATION SCIENCES*

CHRISTIAN LIBRARIAN. see *LIBRARY AND INFORMATION SCIENCES*

CHRISTIAN MAGNIFIER. see *HANDICAPPED — Visually Impaired*

285 GH ISSN 0009-5478
CHRISTIAN MESSENGER. (Text in English, Ga, Twi) 1883. m. $7.16 per no. Presbyterian Book Depot, Box 3075, Accra, Ghana. TELEX 2525 PRESBY GHANA. Ed. G.B.K. Owusu. adv.; bk.rev.; bibl.; illus.; stat. circ. 58,000. (tabloid format; also avail. in microfiche from IDC) **Indexed:** CERDIC.

285 US ISSN 8750-7765
CHRISTIAN MISSION; reporting what God is doing through indigenous missions. 1971. q. Christian Aid Mission, 3045 Ivy Rd., Charlottesville, VA 22903. TEL 804-977-5650. Ed. John M. Lindner. circ. 15,000. (back issues avail.)
Description: Covers missions work outside North America being done by non-North Americans.

284 US ISSN 0009-5494
CHRISTIAN MONTHLY. 1950. m. $12 (Canada $14; elsewhere $25). (Apostolic Lutheran Church of America) Apostolic Lutheran Book Concern, Box 2126, Battle Ground, WA 98604-2126. TEL 360-687-4416. Ed. Alvar Helmes. adv. contact: Neal Karlsen. circ. 1,900. **Document type:** newsletter.

284 US ISSN 0009-5516
CHRISTIAN NEWS. 1968. w. (except Aug.) $20 (foreign $24). Lutheran News, Inc., 3277 Boeuf Lutheran Rd., New Haven, MO 63068-9568. TEL 314-237-3110. FAX 314-237-3858. E-mail: OTTEN@AOL.COM. Ed. Rev. Herman J. Otten. bk.rev.; stat.; index. circ. 13,000. (tabloid format)
Formerly (1962-1967): Lutheran News.

285 US ISSN 0899-2584
CHRISTIAN OBSERVER. 1813. fortn. $27 (foreign $35). Christian Observer, Inc., 9400 Fairview Ave., Manassas, VA 22110-5802. TEL 703-335-2844. FAX 703-368-4817. Ed. E.P. Elliott, Jr. adv.: B&W page $305.00. bk.rev.; film rev.; play rev.; abstr.; bibl.; charts; illus.; tr.list; index. circ. 1,400. (back issues avail.) **Document type:** newspaper.
Description: Encourages and edifies God's people and strengthens the Christian family.

280 US ISSN 1072-4486
CHRISTIAN SCIENCE QUARTERLY (FULL TEXT LARGE TYPE EDITION). 1992. 4/yr. $90. Christian Science Publishing Society, Box 11389, Des Moines, IA 50340-1389. TEL 800-288-7090. (large print in 16 pt.)

280 US ISSN 0145-7365
BX6901
CHRISTIAN SCIENCE QUARTERLY (REGULAR EDITION); Bible lessons. Danish edition (ISSN 0145-739X); Dutch edition (ISSN 0145-742X); French edition (ISSN 0145-7438); German edition (ISSN 0145-7411); Greek edition (ISSN 0145-9503) Italian edition (US ISSN 0145-7373) Japanese edition (US ISSN 0145-7527) Norwegian edition (US ISSN 0145-7381) Polish edition (US ISSN 0145-7446) Full Text Edition, Print Version (ISSN 1053-251X); Full Text Large Type Edition (ISSN 1072-4486)) (Portuguese edition (ISSN 0145-7454); Spanish edition (ISSN 0145-7462); Swedish edition (ISSN 0145-7403) 1890. q. $12. Christian Science Publishing Society, Box 11389, Des Moines, IA 50340-1389. TEL 800-456-4851. (also avail. in diskette format (ISSN 1054-4550); audio cassette; Braille)

CHRISTIAN SINGLE. see *SINGLES' INTERESTS AND LIFESTYLES*

261 287 US ISSN 0897-0459
HN37.M4
CHRISTIAN SOCIAL ACTION. 1973. m. $13.50. United Methodist Church, General Board of Church and Society, 100 Maryland Ave. N.E., Washington, DC 20002. TEL 202-488-5621. FAX 202-488-5619. Ed. Lee Ranck; Pub. Thom White Wolf Fassett. adv. contact: Ruth Taylor. bk.rev.; illus.; index; circ. 2,500 (paid). (also avail. in microfilm from UMI; back issues avail.; reprint service avail. from UMI) **Indexed:** CERDIC, Meth.Per.Ind., Rel.Ind.One, Rel.Per.
—UMI.
Formerly (until 1988): Engage - Social Action (ISSN 0164-5528); Which was formed by the merger of (1968-1973): Engage (ISSN 0013-7618) & (1935-1973): Social Action (ISSN 0037-7635).

CHRISTIAN TALKING MAGAZINE. see *HANDICAPPED — Visually Impaired*

285 CN ISSN 0835-412X
CHRISTIAN WEEK; a window on Christian faith and life in Canada. 1987. bi-w. Can.$24.61 (foreign Can.$35). Fellowship for Print Witness Inc., Box 725, Winnipeg, MB R3C 2K3, Canada. TEL 204-943-1147. FAX 204-947-5632. Ed. Harold D. Jantz. adv. contact: Bryan Rempel. bk.rev.; illus. circ. 11,500. (tabloid format; also avail. in microfilm; back issues avail.) **Document type:** newspaper.
Description: News about Canadian churches and religious organizations, Christian response to issues of faith and life.

200 UK
CHRISTIAN WORDS. 1849. m. £7.08. Wesleyan Reform Union, Wesleyan Reform Church House, 123 Queen St., Sheffield S1 2DU, England. TEL 0114-272-1938. Ed. Rev. E. Downing. adv. circ. 1,800. **Document type:** newsletter.

282 GW
DIE CHRISTLICHE FAMILIE; eine Katholische Wochenschrift. 1885. w. (Sun.) Verlag Christliche Familie GmbH, Ruhrtalstr. 52-60, 45239 Essen, Germany. TEL 0201-8492400. FAX 0201-8492416. Ed.Bd; Pub. Albert Fischer. adv. contact: Michael Janscheidt. circ. 58,744. (back issues avail.) **Document type:** newspaper.

284 AT ISSN 0728-0351
CHRISTOPHANY; Christ displayed. 1949. q. Aus.$12. Perth Bible College, Private Bag 3, Karrinyup, W.A. 6018, Australia. TEL 61-0-448-0055. FAX 61-9-448-0487. Ed. Alan F. Meers. adv.; bk.rev.; illus. circ. 1,400. (back issues avail.) **Document type:** academic/scholarly publication, newsletter.

284 GW
CHRISTUS IST SIEGER. 1972. bi-m. DM.7. Gertrud Papst, Ed. & Pub., Kinzigstr. 36, 78112 St. Georgen, Germany. TEL 07724-7353. FAX 07724-5397. (Co-sponsors: Internationale Evangelikale Laiengemeinschaft; Laymen's Evangelical Fellowship (India)) circ. 7,000. (back issues avail.) **Document type:** consumer publication.

284 GW
CHRISTUSSTAAT. 1985. s-m. DM.64.80. Universelles Leben GmbH, Marienstr. 1, 97070 Wuerzburg, Germany. TEL 0931-17183. Eds. Hans Dienstknecht, Alfred Schulte. adv.; bk.rev. **Document type:** newsletter.

286 362.7 US ISSN 1056-358X
CHUAN DAO TIAN DI. Variant title: Chuandao Tiandi. English edition: Our Missions World (ISSN 0899-3823); Korean edition: Uri Ui Son' Gyo Segye (ISSN 1048-4973) (Text in Chinese) 1991. q. $12.95 (effective 1995-1996). Southern Baptist Convention, Woman's Missionary Union, Hwy. 280, E., 100 Missionary Ridge, Birmingham, AL 35242-5235. TEL 205-991-8100. (Subscr. to: Box 830711, Birmingham, AL 35283-7111. TEL 800-WMU-7301. FAX 205-995-4840)

268 379 US ISSN 0412-4553
CHURCH ADMINISTRATION. m. $25.50. Southern Baptist Convention, Sunday School Board, 127 Ninth Ave., N., Nashville, TN 37234. TEL 800-458-2772. FAX 615-251-5933. **Indexed:** South.Bap.Per.Ind. **Document type:** trade publication.
Description: Offers practical leadership advice for pastors, Sunday school staff, and other church leaders.

261 285 US ISSN 0037-7805
CHURCH & SOCIETY. 1908. 6/yr. $12. Presbyterian Church (U.S.A.), 100 Witherspoon St., Louisville, KY 40202-1396. TEL 502-569-5810. E-mail: KATHY__LANCASTER.parti@ecunet.org. Ed. Rev. Kathy Lancaster. bk.rev. circ. 5,000. (also avail. in microfilm from UMI; reprint service avail. from UMI) **Indexed:** CERDIC, Mid.East: Abstr.& Ind., Rel.Ind.One, Rel.Per.
—UnCover.
Formerly: Social Progress.

283 UK
CHURCH ARMY. ANNUAL REPORT. 1981. a. free. Church Army, Independents Rd., Blackheath, London SE3 9LG, England. illus. **Document type:** corporate report.
Former titles (until 1992): Church Army. Front Line Annual Report; Church Army. Front Line.
Description: Review of the year's work by the Church Army.

285 US ISSN 0009-6393
CHURCH HERALD. 1826. 11/yr. $15. (Reformed Church in America) Church Herald, Inc., 4500 60th St., S.E., Grand Rapids, MI 49512-9631. TEL 616-698-7071. Ed. Jeff Japinga. adv.; illus. circ. 110,000. (also avail. in microfilm; reprint service avail. from UMI) **Indexed:** G.Soc.Sci.& Rel.Per.Lit.
—UMI.

209 AT ISSN 0156-224X
CHURCH HERITAGE. 1978. s-a. Aus.$7. Church Records and Historical Society (NSW), P.O. Box 2395, North Parramatta, N.S.W. 2151, Australia. TEL 61-2-6833147. Ed. Malcolm David Prentis. bk.rev.; index; circ. 220 (paid). **Indexed:** So.Pac.Per.Ind. **Document type:** academic/scholarly publication.
Supersedes (in 1978): Australasian Methodist Historical Society. Journal and Proceedings (ISSN 0084-6988)
Description: Articles on Church history in Australia and South Pacific, Congregational, Methodist, Presbyterian, Uniting.

CHURCH MEDIA LIBRARY MAGAZINE. see *LIBRARY AND INFORMATION SCIENCES*

THE CHURCH MUSICIAN. see *MUSIC*

283 UK ISSN 0307-7225
CHURCH OF ENGLAND. GENERAL SYNOD. REPORT OF PROCEEDINGS. 1970. s-a. £26 (typically set in Jan.). Church of England, General Synod, Church House, Great Smith St., Westminster, London SW1P 3NZ, England. (Subscr. to: Church House, Bookshop, Great Smith St., London SW1P 3NZ, England) index. circ. 600. **Document type:** proceedings.
Description: Provides a verbatim report of the sessions of the General Synod of the Church of England.

RELIGIONS AND THEOLOGY — PROTESTANT

283 270   AT   ISSN 0009-6490
CHURCH OF ENGLAND HISTORICAL SOCIETY (DIOCESE OF SYDNEY). JOURNAL. 1956. q. Aus.$20 (effective 1993). Church of England Historical Society, G.P.O. Box 2902, Sydney, N.S.W. 2001, Australia. TEL 02-918-7179. Ed. J. Bunyan. bk.rev. circ. 250. (back issues avail.)

283   UK   ISSN 0964-816X
CHURCH OF ENGLAND NEWSPAPER. 1828. w. £39($100) (overseas £59) (effective 1995); newsstand price: £0.40. Parliamentary Communications Ltd., 10 Little College St., London SW1P 3SH, England. TEL 0171-976-7760. FAX 0171-976-0783. Ed. John K. Martin. adv.: page £745; adv. contact: Chris Turner. bk.rev.; film rev.; rec.rev.; illus.; circ. 11,600 (paid). cols./p.: 5; pp./issue: 20. (tabloid format) **Document type:** newspaper.
    Incorporates (1886-1991): Christian Week; Which was formerly (until 1987): British Weekly and Christian Record; Which was formed by the merger of: British Weekly and Christian World (ISSN 0007-1951) & Christian Record.
    Description: Provides news of the Church of England, of the Anglican Communion worldwide and on Christian charities and missionary organizations. Covers theological developments and how Christian faith applies to everyday life and problems.

283   UK   ISSN 0069-3987
CHURCH OF ENGLAND YEARBOOK. 1882. a. £19.50. Church House Publishing, Church House, Great Smith St., London SW1P 3NZ, England. TEL 0171-222-9011. FAX 0171-340-0281. Ed. Mrs. Jo Linzey. adv. circ. 3,000.
—BLDSC (3189.762000).
    Description: Official yearbook of the Church of England. Lists holders of office in the English dioceses with details of associated organizations.

283   US   ISSN 0745-6778
CHURCH OF GOD EVANGEL. 1910. m. (Jan., June, July, Aug., Dec.), fortn. $10. (Church of God) Pathway Press, Box 2250, Cleveland, TN 37320-2250. TEL 615-476-3361. FAX 615-478-7521. Ed. Homer G. Rhea. circ. 50,000. (also avail. in microform)

266 289.9   US   ISSN 0009-6504
CHURCH OF GOD MISSIONS. 1951. bi-m. $7. Church of God, Missionary Board, Box 2337, Anderson, IN 46018. TEL 317-642-0256. FAX 317-642-0279. Ed. E. Raymond Chin. adv.; bk.rev.; illus. circ. 9,000.

200   UK   ISSN 0009-6512
CHURCH OF IRELAND GAZETTE. 1850. w. 20p. Church of Ireland Press, 36 Bachelor's Walk, Lisburn BT28 1XN, Northern Ireland. Ed. Rev. C.W.M. Cooper. adv.; bk.rev. circ. 6,000.

285.241   UK   ISSN 0069-3995
CHURCH OF SCOTLAND. YEARBOOK. 1885. a. £10. St. Andrew Press, 121 George St., Edinburgh EH2 4YN, Scotland. TEL 0131-225-5722. FAX 0131-220-3113. Ed. Rev. James Black. adv. contact: David Carson. index. circ. 2,500. **Document type:** bulletin.
    Description: Guide to Church of Scotland for ministers and office bearers.

283   AT   ISSN 0009-6563
CHURCH SCENE; Australian National Anglican newspaper. 1971. w. Aus.$70 (effective 1995). Church Press Ltd., P.O. Box 358, Carnegie, 3163, Australia. TEL 61-3-95635311. FAX 61-3-95635991. E-mail: gerald.davis@accnet.net.au. Ed. Gerald Charles Davis. adv.: page Aus.$1132. bk.rev.; illus.; circ. 3,000 (paid). (tabloid format) **Document type:** newspaper.

283   UK   ISSN 0009-658X
CHURCH TIMES. 1863. w. £31 (foreign £38). G.J. Palmer & Sons Ltd., 33 Upper St., London N1 0PN, England. TEL 0171-359-4570. FAX 0171-226-3051. (Subscr. to: 16 Blyburgate, Beccles, Suffolk NR34 9TB, England. TEL 01502-711171) Ed. Paul Handley. adv. contact: Stephen Dutton. bk.rev.; illus.; index. circ. 37,850. (tabloid format; also avail. in microform from UMI; reprint service avail. from UMI) **Indexed:** Chr.Per.Ind. **Document type:** newspaper.
—UMI.

283 380   US   ISSN 1072-1975
CHURCHART PLUS ON DISK. 1993. m. $149.95. Communication Resources Inc., 4150 Belden Village St., Ste. 400, Canton, OH 44718-2502. TEL 800-992-2144. FAX 216-493-7897. Ed. Jeffrey Monter. (looseleaf format; also avail. in diskette format; back issues avail.) **Document type:** newsletter.
    Description: Provides layout and design ideas for church publications.

283   UK   ISSN 0009-661X
BX5011
CHURCHMAN; a journal of Anglican theology. 1879. 4/yr. £20. Church Society, Dean Wace House, 16 Rosslyn Rd., Watford, Herts. WD1 7EY, England. TEL 01923-235111. Ed. Gerald Bray. adv. contact: John Lindeck. bk.rev.; index. circ. 1,200. (also avail. in microfilm) **Indexed:** CERDIC, New Test.Abstr., Old Test.Abstr., Rel.Ind.One, Rel.Per. **Document type:** academic/scholarly publication.
—BLDSC (3189.930000); UMI. **CCC.**
    Description: Committed to a Reformational outlook with regard to Anglican affairs.

287   US   ISSN 0146-9924
BX8382.2.A1
CIRCUIT RIDER (NASHVILLE). 1976. m. $8 (free to United Methodist clergy). United Methodist Publishing House, 201 Eighth Ave. S., Box 801, Nashville, TN 37202. TEL 615-749-6319. Ed. Tony Peterson. circ. 40,000 (controlled).

287 940   UK   ISSN 0950-8732
CIRPLAN. 1955. 2/yr. £1.25. Society of Cirplanologists, 34 Fernhill Crescent, Stacksteads, Bacup, Lancs. OL13 8JU, England. Ed. Ken F. Bowden. bk.rev. circ. 120. (processed; back issues avail.) **Document type:** bulletin.
    Description: Provides current and historical information on Methodist circuit regulations, preaching appointments, and preaching plans.

CLARITY. see *WOMEN'S INTERESTS*

284   AT   ISSN 1036-4013
CLOSER CONTACT. 1987. m. Christian Radio Missionary Fellowship, P.O. Box 46, Blackburn South, Vic. 3130, Australia. TEL 61-3-890-2338. FAX 61-899-1921. Ed. Robin G. Cole. circ. 100. (back issues avail.) **Document type:** newsletter.
    Description: News and information about CRMF.

CLUBHOUSE. see *CHILDREN AND YOUTH — For*

285   UK
Y COFIADUR. 1923. a. £2. Undeb Yr Annibynwyr Cymraeg, c/o Ty John Penry, Abertawe, Morgannwg SA1 4AL, Wales. TEL 52542.
    Description: Covers the history of Welsh congregational churches and institutions.

200   US   ISSN 0883-6728
COLORADO EPISCOPALIAN. 1939. 6/yr. free. Diocese of Colorado, 1300 Washington St., Denver, CO 80203-2008. TEL 303-837-1173. FAX 303-837-1311. Ed. Nancy Kinney. bk.rev. circ. 19,000. (tabloid format) **Document type:** newspaper.
    Description: News about the Episcopal Church for members in Colorado.

266   US   ISSN 0010-3179
COMMISSION; Foreign Missions Journal. 1849. bi-m. $8.25. Southern Baptist Convention, Foreign Mission Board, 3806 Monument Ave., Box 6767, Richmond, VA 23230. TEL 804-353-0151. FAX 804-358-0504. Ed. Leland F. Webb. illus.; index. circ. 87,000. **Indexed:** South.Bap.Per.Ind.

COMMUNICATOR (BOSTON). see *WOMEN'S INTERESTS*

283   UK
COMMUNICATOR (WATFORD). m. South England Conference of Seventh-Day Adventists, Communication Department, 25 St. John's Rd., Watford, Herts. WD1 1PY, England. TEL 0293-232728. FAX 0923-250582. Ed. Keith Davidson. **Document type:** newspaper.
    Description: Reports on church activities and events.

284   XR   ISSN 0010-3713
BR1A1
COMMUNIO VIATORUM; a theological journal. (Text in English, French and German) 1958. 3/yr. 20 Fr. Charles University, Protestant Theological Faculty, Jungmannova 9, 110 00 Prague 1, Czech Republic. TEL 42-2-24221425. FAX 42-2-24226566. (Subscr. to: Communio Viatorum, Jungmannova 9, 110 00 Prague 1, Czech Republic) Ed. Petr Macek. bk.rev.; index. circ. 1,000. **Indexed:** New Test.Abstr., Rel.Ind.One, Rel.Per. **Document type:** academic/scholarly publication.

285   US
COMMUNIQUE (COLUMBUS, 1974); the newspaper of the Synod of the Covenant. 1974. m. (except Aug.). $3. Presbyterian Church (U.S.A.), Synod of the Covenant, 6172 Busch Blvd., Ste. 3000, Columbus, OH 43229. TEL 614-436-3310. FAX 614-846-5582. Ed. Doris Campbell. adv.; bk.rev. circ. 9,000. (tabloid format; back issues avail.) **Document type:** newspaper.

338.91 370.196   US
COMPASSION MAGAZINE (COLORADO SPRINGS). 1955. q. free. Compassion International, Box 7000, Colorado Springs, CO 80933. TEL 719-594-9900. FAX 719-536-9618. Ed. Jennifer L. Ball. circ. 158,000 (controlled). (back issues avail.)
    Formerly: Compassion Update (ISSN 1041-472X)
    Description: News, country reports and photo features covering child development work for ministry's US supporters and friends.

285   US
CONCILIATION QUARTERLY. q. $20 for 2 years. Mennonite Central Committee, 21 S. 12th St., Box 500, Akron, PA 17501-0500. TEL 717-859-3889. FAX 717-859-3875. Ed. James Stutzman. circ. 1,200. (back issues avail.)
    Description: Newsletter of Mennonite conciliation service for anyone interested in conflict resolution.

209 900   US   ISSN 0010-5260
BX8001
CONCORDIA HISTORICAL INSTITUTE QUARTERLY. 1928. q. $25. (Lutheran Church - Missouri Synod) Concordia Historical Institute, 801 DeMun Ave., St. Louis, MO 63105. TEL 314-721-5934. Ed. Dale Griffin. adv.; bk.rev.; charts; illus, tit.lit.; cum.index every 4 yrs. circ. 1,700. **Indexed:** Amer.Hist.& Life, Geneal.Per.Ind., Hist.Abstr., Rel.& Theol.Abstr. (1988-), Rel.Ind.One, Rel.Per. **Document type:** academic/scholarly publication.
—UMI; UnCover.

CONGREGATIONAL LIBRARY. BULLETIN. see *LIBRARY AND INFORMATION SCIENCES*

285   US   ISSN 0010-5856
BX7101
CONGREGATIONALIST. 1816. s-m. $8. National Association of Congregational Christian Churches, 6134 Kerry Ave., Cheyenne, WY 82009. TEL 313-393-9433. Ed. Mary K. Woolsey. adv.; bk.rev.; illus. circ. 6,500.

284 282   US
CONGREGATIONS: THE ALBAN JOURNAL; resources for people who care about congregations. 1975. bi-m. membership. Alban Institute, 4550 Montgomery Ave., Ste. 433 N, Bethesda, MD 20814. TEL 301-718-4407. Ed. Celia Allison Hahn. bk.rev.; illus.; index, cum.index. circ. 8,100. **Document type:** academic/scholarly publication.
    Formerly (until 1992): Action Information.

284   AT   ISSN 1030-7052
CONTACT (BLACKBURN SOUTH). 1986. q. free. Christian Radio Missionary Fellowship, P.O. Box 46, Blackburn South, Vic. 3130, Australia. TEL 61-3-890-2338. FAX 61-3-899-1921. Ed. Robin G. Cole. circ. 1,500. (back issues avail.) **Document type:** newsletter.
    Description: Provides information and news items about the work and the staff of the Christian Radio Missionary Fellowship.

200   NE
CONTACT (HUIS TER HEIDE); voor cursisten en oud-cursisten. 1948. q. free. (Zevende Dags Adventisten) E S D A Institute, Pr. Alexanderweg 1C, 3712 AD Huis Ter Heide, Netherlands. FAX 31-3404-33503. Dir. R.H. Dingjan. adv.; bk.rev. circ. 8,000. (microfilm) **Document type:** newsletter.
    Formerly: Contactblad (ISSN 0010-731X)

RELIGIONS AND THEOLOGY — PROTESTANT

CONTEMPORARY PRAISE. see MUSIC

CONTRAPUNKT; christliche Zweimonatszeitschrift fuer junge Leute. see CHILDREN AND YOUTH — For

287 UK ISSN 0574-1009
CORNISH METHODIST HISTORICAL ASSOCIATION JOURNAL. 1960. a. £3. c/o Barrie S. May, Pelmear Villa, Carharrack, Redruth, Cornwall TR16 5RB, England. TEL 01209-820381. bk.rev.; circ. 300 (controlled). **Document type:** academic/scholarly publication, newsletter.

230 940 UK
COURTENAY REFORMATION FACSIMILES. 1973. irreg. no.3. price varies. Sutton Courtenay Press, c/o Appleford Publishing Group, Appleford House, Appleford, Abingdon, Oxon. OX14 4PB, England. TEL 01235-848319. Ed. Gervase Duffield.
Document type: monographic series.
Formerly: Courtenay Facsimiles.
Description: Publishes rare texts of the Reformation with scholarly comments.

289 940 UK ISSN 0070-1408
COURTENAY STUDIES IN REFORMATION THEOLOGY. 1966. irreg., no.6. price varies. Sutton Courtenay Press, c/o Appleford Publishing Group, Appleford House, Appleford, Abingdon, Oxon. OX14 4PB, England. TEL 01235-848319. Ed. Gervase Duffield.
Document type: monographic series.
Description: Studies major figures of the Reformation.

287 US ISSN 1052-3790
COVENANT DISCIPLESHIP QUARTERLY. 1985. q. $10. (United Methodist Church, Board of Discipleship) United Methodist Publishing House, 201 Eighth Ave. S., Box 801, Nashville, TN 37202. TEL 615-749-6292. Ed. Ellen Bourne. bk.rev. circ. 900. (back issues avail.) **Document type:** newsletter.
Description: Designed to educate, encourage and empower covenant discipleship group members and class leaders in their daily Christian living, by reviewing resources, exploring issues and sharing information.

266 IT ISSN 0394-0284
IL CRISTIANO. 1888. m. L.15000. Associazione Stampe Pubblicazioni Evangeliche (A.S.P.E.), Via Campo della Fiera, 16, 52031 Anghiari (AR), Italy. Ed. Paolo Moretti. circ. 4,200.

286 FR ISSN 0755-7205
CROIRE ET SERVIR. 1946. m. 170 F. Federation des Eglises Evangelique Baptistes, 123 Av du Maine, 75014 Paris, France. TEL 40-47-06-19. Ed. Andre Thobois. bk.rev. circ. 20,000.

270 US ISSN 0011-1961
CROSS OF LANGUEDOC. 1960. s-a. $6 membership. National Huguenot Society, c/o Mrs. Edward Coleman, Ed., RD 1 Box 205C, Greensburg, PA 15601-9720. TEL 412-527-5650. bk.rev. circ. 4,000. (processed) **Document type:** newsletter.
Supersedes: National Huguenot Society Proceedings.

200 AT ISSN 1037-826X
CROSSLIGHT. 1977. m. Aus.$35. Uniting Church in Australia, Synod of Victoria, 130 Little Collins St., Melbourne, Vic. 3000, Australia. Ed. Bruce Best. adv.; bk.rev.; illus. circ. 3,600. (back issues avail.)
Former titles (until 1992): Church and Nation (ISSN 0314-6200); New Spectator (ISSN 0300-3736); Spectator.
Description: Emphasis on Uniting Church in Victoria and Tasmania.

285 NZ ISSN 0113-2024
CROSSLINK. 1987. m. NZ.$15 free to members. Presbyterian and Methodist Churches of New Zealand, P.O. Box 9049, Wellington, New Zealand. TEL 64-4-801-6000. FAX 64-4-801-6001. Ed. Rev. R.L.D. Wiig. adv. contact: Leigh Bredenkamp. bk.rev.; illus. circ. 53,000. **Document type:** newspaper.
Description: Seeks to relate the Christian gospel to contemporary life.

283.713 CN ISSN 0845-4795
CROSSTALK AND ANGLICAN JOURNAL EPISCOPAL. 1978. 10/yr. Can.$5. Anglican Church of Canada, Diocese of Ottawa, 71 Bronson Ave., Ottawa, ON K1R 6G6, Canada. TEL 613-232-1451. FAX 613-232-7088. Ed. Sue Becker Davidson; Pub. Rt. Rev. John Baycroft. adv. contact: Jamie Tomlinson. bk.rev. circ. 15,900. (tabloid format; back issues avail.) **Document type:** newspaper.
Formerly: Crosstalk (ISSN 0706-8069)

261 UK ISSN 0011-2100
CRUCIBLE (LONDON). 1962. q. £8. (Board for Social Responsibility of the General Synod) Church House Publishing, Church House, Great Smith St., London SW1P 3NZ, England. FAX 0171-233-2576. Ed. Margaret Jeffery. adv.; bk.rev.; index. circ. 800.
Indexed: CERDIC.
—BLDSC (3489.870000).
Description: Features industrial affairs, social problems, faith and morals.

286 US ISSN 0011-2151
CRUSADER (MEMPHIS). 1970. m. $2.55 for 3 mos. (typically set in Feb.). Southern Baptist Convention, Brotherhood Commission, 1548 Poplar Ave., Memphis, TN 38104. TEL 800-727-6466. Ed. James Warren. bk.rev.; illus. circ. 67,000. **Indexed:** South.Bap.Per.Ind.
Description: Provides missions education for boys 9-11 enrolled in Royal Ambassadors in Southern Baptist churches.

283 CN ISSN 0382-4314
CRUSADER (TORONTO). 1929. 2/yr. free. Church Army in Canada, 397 Brunswick Ave., Toronto, Ont. M5R 2Z2, Canada. TEL 416-924-9279. Ed. W. Marshall. illus. circ. 12,000.
Continues: Anglican Crusader (ISSN 0382-4306)

CRUSADER MAGAZINE (GRAND RAPIDS). see CHILDREN AND YOUTH — For

283 UK
CRUX. 1972. m. £0.10 per issue. (Diocese of Manchester) Board of Finance, 90 Deansgate, Manchester M3 2GH, England. TEL 061-833-9521. Ed. Rev. Tim Baynes. adv.; bk.rev. circ. 25,000. (back issues avail.)
Description: Covers local church life.

285 US ISSN 0011-2968
CUMBERLAND FLAG. 1915. m. $8. General Assembly Second Cumberland Presbyterian Church, 226 Church St., Huntsville, AL 38501. TEL 205-536-7481.

285 US ISSN 0011-2976
CUMBERLAND PRESBYTERIAN. 1829. 11/yr. $11. Cumberland Presbyterian Church, Office of the General Assembly, 1978 Union Ave., Memphis, TN 38104. TEL 901-276-4572. Ed. Rev. M. Jacqueline Warren. adv.: B&W page $470; trim 8 1/2 x 11. bk.rev.; illus. circ. 7,600.
Description: A denominational news and features magazine.

284 US ISSN 0098-2113
CURRENTS IN THEOLOGY AND MISSION. 1974. bi-m. $13.50. Lutheran School of Theology at Chicago, 1100 E. 55th St., Chicago, IL 60615. TEL 312-753-0751. FAX 312-753-0782. Ed. Ralph W. Klein. adv.; bk.rev. circ. 4,000. (also avail. in microform from UMI; reprint service avail. from UMI; back issues avail.) **Indexed:** CERDIC, indt.Z.Bibelwiss., New Test.Abstr., Old Test.Abstr., Rel.& Theol.Abstr. (1977-), Rel.Ind.One, Rel.Per.
—BLDSC (3505.203000); UMI.
Description: Contains articles and preaching helps for pastors and laity.

THE CUTTING EDGE (ORLANDO); unearthing the best in the underground. see MUSIC

284 UK ISSN 0143-0076
Y CYLCHGRAWN EFENGYLAIDD. 1948. q. £5.80. Evangelical Press of Wales, Bryntirion, Bridgend, Mid Glam. CF31 4DX, Wales. TEL 01656-655886. FAX 01656-656095. Ed. Gwyn Davies. adv.; bk.rev.; illus. circ. 900. (back issues avail.)
Description: Contains articles on a wide range of subjects relating to the historic evangelical faith of the Christian Church and news of the contemporary religious scene.

280 US
D R C MISSISSIPPI NEWSLETTER. 1972. q. free. Delta Resources Committee, Inc., 300 N. Edison St., Box 584, Greenville, MS 38702. TEL 601-335-3121. Ed. Roger A. Smith. circ. 1,500 (controlled). **Document type:** newsletter.

284.2 SA
D R C NEWS. (Dutch Reformed Church) (Text in English) 1958. q. R5. Nederduitse Gereformeerde Kerk in Suid-Afrika, Ecumenical Department, P.O. Box 4445, Pretoria 0001, South Africa. FAX 27-12-322-3803. Ed. P. Rossouw. bk.rev. circ. 2,000. **Document type:** newsletter.
Former titles: D R C Africa News (ISSN 0250-0353); (until 1976): D R C Newsletter (ISSN 0011-5118)

284 GW
DAHEIM UND DRAUSSEN. 1950. q. free. Herrnhuter Missionshilfe e.V., Badwasen 6, 73087 Bad Boll, Germany. TEL 07164-8010. FAX 07164-80199. Ed. Joerg Bayer. circ. 40,000. **Document type:** newsletter.
Former titles: Gruss aus der Weltweiten Brueder-Unitaet - Daheim und Draussen; Daheim und Draussen (ISSN 0177-1817); (until 1984): Herrnhuter Arbeit Daheim und Draussen (ISSN 0177-1825)
Description: Reports on mission work throughout the world.

220 US ISSN 0742-065X
DAILY BIBLE STUDY. 1984. q. $11. (United Methodist Church, Board of Discipleship) United Methodist Publishing House, Cokesbury, 201 Eighth Ave. S., Nashville, TN 37202. TEL 615-749-6417. FAX 615-749-6079. (large print edition in 14 pt.)

283 US ISSN 0011-538X
DAILY BLESSING. 1959. s-a. $5. Oral Roberts Evangelistic Association Inc., Box 2187, Tulsa, OK 74102-2187. TEL 918-495-7307. Ed. Oral Roberts.

283 UK ISSN 0963-4797
DAILY BREAD (LONDON); practical help from the Bible. 1937. q. £9.20. Scripture Union Publishing, 130 City Rd., London EC1V 2NJ, England. TEL 0171-782-0013. FAX 0171-782-0014. (Subscr. to: S.U. Mail Order Dept., 9-11 Clothier Rd., Bristol BS4 5RL, England) Ed. Tony Hobbs. circ. 80,000. (audio cassette; also avail. in Braille) **Document type:** bulletin.
Description: Bible study geared to the individual.

283 UK
DAILY BREAD (PETERBOROUGH). m. £0.38. Royal National Institute for the Blind, Bakewell Rd., Orton Southgate, Peterborough, Cambridgeshire PE2 0XU, England. TEL 0733-370777. FAX 0733-317555. circ. 70. (Braille) **Document type:** bulletin.

DAILY DEVOTIONS FOR THE DEAF. see HANDICAPPED — Hearing Impaired

284 US
DAILY WALK; a guide for dynamic Christian living. 1978. m. $18. Walk Thru the Bible Ministries, Inc., 4201 N. Peachtree Rd., Box 80587, Atlanta, GA 30341-1362. TEL 404-458-9300. Ed. Paula Kirk. abstr.; charts; illus. circ. 18,362. (reprint service avail.)

268 UK
DAILY WATCHWORDS; the Moravian textbook with almanack. 1722. a. £2. Moravian Union Inc., Book Room, 5 Muswell Hill, London N10 3TJ, England. TEL 01-883-3409. Ed. B. McLeavy. circ. 5,000. **Document type:** bulletin.

284 GW
DARUM; Evangelisches Missionswerk in Suedwestdeutschland. 1983. bi-m. DM.10. Evangelisches Missionswerk in Suedwestdeutschland e.V., Vogelsangstr. 62, 70197 Stuttgart, Germany. FAX 0711-63678-66. TELEX 723059-EMS-D. Ed. Klaus Zoeller. bk.rev. circ. 25,000. (back issues avail.) **Document type:** newsletter.
Description: Informations about mission and ecumenical matters concerning churches in Africa and Asia.

RELIGIONS AND THEOLOGY — PROTESTANT

254 US ISSN 0045-9771
THE DEACON. 1970. q. $11.75. Southern Baptist Convention, Sunday School Board, 127 Ninth Ave., N., Nashville, TN 37234. TEL 800-458-2772. cum.index every 3 yrs. **Indexed:** South.Bap.Per.Ind.
Description: Provides deacons and church staff with ongoing training and inspirational articles.

284 US ISSN 0011-7307
BV3750
DECISION (MINNEAPOLIS). 1960. m. (except Aug.) $9. Billy Graham Evangelistic Association, 1300 Harmon Place, Minneapolis, MN 55403. TEL 612-338-0500. (Or: Box 779, Minneapolis, MN 55440) Ed. Roger C. Palms. illus.; index, cum.index. circ. 1,600,000. **Indexed:** CCR, Chr.Per.Ind. —UMI; UnCover.
Description: Encourages, teaches and strengthens Christians; and reports on the crusade ministry of Billy Graham and associate evangelists.

283 UK ISSN 1350-9519
DEO. 1988. q. £19. Herald House Ltd., 96 Dominion Rd., Worthing, W. Sussex BN14 8JP, England. TEL 01903-821082. FAX 01903-821081. Ed. Jane Hicks. circ. 3,000 (paid). **Document type:** consumer publication.
Formerly (until 1993): Christian Music (ISSN 0958-2630)
Description: Intended to encourage and inform leaders of Christian worship while examining various aspects of music in worship.

283 UK ISSN 0953-9301
DERBY DIOCESAN NEWS. m. Diocese of Derby, Derby Diocesan Communications Committee, Derby Church House, Full St., Derby DE1 3DR, England. TEL 01332-382233. FAX 01332-292969. Ed. Bryan Harris. bk.rev. circ. 27,000. (looseleaf format) **Document type:** newsletter.

283 UK ISSN 0305-0874
DERBY DIOCESAN YEAR BOOK; and clergy list (year). 1927. a. £4.00 (typically set in Oct.). Diocese of Derby, Derby Diocesan Communications Committee, Derby Church House, Full St., Derby DE1 3DR, England. TEL 01332-382233. FAX 01332-292969. (Alt. addr.: The Vicarage, Pursglove Dr., Tideswell, Buxton, Derbys. SK17 8PA, England) Ed. M. Hulbert. adv. (looseleaf format; back issues avail.) **Document type:** directory.
Description: Contains a list of clergy readers, church wardens, secretary treasurers, and other church people in 270 parishes for the Derby Diocese.

270 GW ISSN 0012-0294
DER DEUTSCHE HUGENOTT. 1929. q. DM.25. Deutscher Hugenotten-Verein e.V., Hafenplatz 9a, 34385 Bad Karlshafen, Germany. TEL 05672-1433. Ed. Jochen Desel. bk.rev.; abstr.; bibl.; illus. circ. 1,500. **Indexed:** Amer.Hist.& Life, Hist.Abstr. **Document type:** academic/scholarly publication.

DEUTSCHER HUGENOTTEN-VEREIN E.V. GESCHICHTSBLAETTER. see HISTORY — History Of Europe

284 US
DEVOTIONS (CINCINNATI). 1957. q. $5.99 (large print $10.99). Standard Publishing, 8121 Hamilton Ave., Cincinnati, OH 45231. TEL 513-931-4050. FAX 513-931-0904. Ed. Eileen H. Wilmoth. circ. 167,500.

284 US
DIACONALOGUE. 1984. irreg. $5 donation. Lutheran Deaconess Association, Center for Diaconal Ministry, 1304 LaPorte Ave., Valparaiso, IN 46383. TEL 219-464-0909. Ed. Dot Nuechterlein. bk.rev. circ. 1,000. (back issues avail.)
Description: Articles affirming the daily ministries of Christian service among the laity in their work places, volunteer commitments and family life.

284.2 GW ISSN 0012-1975
DIAKONIE IM RHEINLAND. 1963. 6/yr. DM.20. Diakonisches Werk der Evangelischen Kirche im Rheinland, Lenaustr. 41, 40470 Duesseldorf, Germany. TEL 0211-6398219. FAX 0211-6398299. Ed. Kurt Holz. adv.; illus. **Document type:** bulletin.

DIALOGUE. see GENERAL INTEREST PERIODICALS — Africa

283 CN ISSN 1184-6283
DIALOGUE (KINGSTON). 1960. m. (10/yr.). Can.$6. Synod of the Diocese of Ontario, Dialogue Board of Directors, 90 Johnson St., Kingston, ON K7L 1X7, Canada. TEL 613-544-4774. FAX 613-547-3745. Ed. Brenda Thompson. adv. contact: Jane Miller. bk.rev. circ. 6,000. **Document type:** newspaper.
Formerly (until 1991): Ontario Churchman (ISSN 0030-2848)
Description: Provides news, opinion, features concerning interests of the Anglican parishes in Eastern Ontario.

287 SA ISSN 0046-0265
DIMENSION. 1970. m. $25. Methodist Church of Southern Africa, P.O. Box 34632, Jeppestown 2043, Transvaal, South Africa. TEL 27-11-614-6325. FAX 27-11-614-0624. Ed. Ruth Coggin. adv.: B&W page R.2600; adv. contact: Anne Robertson. bk.rev.; circ. 18,200 (paid). (tabloid format) **Indexed:** Cath.Ind. **Document type:** newspaper.
Description: Journal of the Methodist Church of Southern Africa, providing news of the activities of that Church.

286 362.7 US ISSN 0162-6825
DIMENSION (BIRMINGHAM). (Avail. in regular and Associational editions) 1970. q. $12.95 for regular edition; Associational Edition $13.95 (effective 1995-1996). Southern Baptist Convention, Woman's Missionary Union, Highway 280 E., 100 Missionary Ridge, Birmingham, AL 35242-5235. TEL 205-991-8100. (Subscr. to: Box 830711, Birmingham, AL 35283-0711. TEL 800-WMU-7301. FAX 205-995-4840) Ed. Judith Edwards. circ. 30,500 (paid).
Description: Publication of interest to pastors and W.M.U. missions organizations in Southern Baptist churches.

283 GY
DIOCESAN MAGAZINE. q. 144 Almond and Oronoque Sts., Queenstown, Georgetown, Guyana.
Description: Anglican interests.

200 CN ISSN 0382-9391
DIOCESAN TIMES. 1946. m. (except July-Aug.). Can.$5. (Anglican Diocese of Nova Scotia) Diocesan Times Publishing Co., 5732 College St., Halifax, N.S. B3H 1X3, Canada. TEL 902-423-8301. Ed. Lawrin C. Armstrong. adv. circ. 17,500.

284 UK
DIRECTION. 1919. m. donation (overseas £15). Elim Pentecostal Church, Box 38, Cheltenham. Glos. GL50 3HN, England. TEL 0151-691-2134. FAX 0151-691-2153. (Editorial address: McKennas Bldg., Dock Rd., Birkenhead, Wirral L41 1DQ, England) Ed. Derek J. Green. adv. contact: Barry Cooper. bk.rev. circ. 27,000. (also avail. in microfiche) **Document type:** consumer publication.
Formerly (until 1989): Elim Evangel (ISSN 0013-6182)
Description: Addresses current issues affecting the Christian Church in a lively manner for all ages.

DIRECTORY OF MINISTRIES IN HIGHER EDUCATION. see EDUCATION — Higher Education

284 US ISSN 0273-5865
BV4485
DISCIPLESHIP JOURNAL. 1981. bi-m. $18.97. Navigators, Box 35004, Colorado Springs, CO 80935. TEL 719-548-9222. FAX 719-598-7128. (Subscr. to: Box 54470, Boulder, CO 80323-4470) Ed. Susan Maycinik. adv.; index; circ. 100,000 (paid). **Indexed:** Chr.Per.Ind. **Document type:** consumer publication.
Incorporates: Small Group Letter (ISSN 0742-1737)
Description: Designed to help Christians understand and practice the teachings of the Bible.

286 US ISSN 0732-9881
BX7301
DISCIPLIANA. 1941. q. $15. Disciples of Christ Historical Society, 1101 Nineteenth Ave., S., Nashville, TN 37212. TEL 615-327-1444. FAX 615-327-1445. Ed. D. Newell Williams. bk.rev.; bibl. circ. 5,500. (also avail. in microfilm) **Document type:** academic/scholarly publication.

287 US ISSN 1052-3804
DISCIPULOS RESPONSABLES. (Text in Spanish) 1987. q. $8. (United Methodist Church, Board of Discipleship) United Methodist Publishing House, 201 Eighth Ave. S., Box 801, Nashville, TN 37202. TEL 615-749-6292. FAX 615-340-7565. Ed. Marigene Chamberlain. bk.rev. circ. 750. (back issues avail.) **Document type:** newsletter.
Description: Designed to inform and educate members of covenant discipleship groups and class leaders about issues of Christian discipleship. Reviews resources, shares information and empowers faithful Christians.

286 362.7 US ISSN 0162-198X
DISCOVERY (BIRMINGHAM). 1970. m. $12.95. Southern Baptist Convention, Woman's Missionary Union, Hwy. 280, E., 100 Missionary Ridge, Birmingham, AL 35242-5235. TEL 205-991-8100. (Subscr. to: Box 830711, Birmingham, AL 35283-0711. TEL 800-WMU-7301. FAX 205-995-4840) Ed. Barbara Massey. circ. 189,000 (paid).
Description: For girls, grades 1-6, who are members of Southern Baptist Girls in Action organization.

286 949.2 NE ISSN 0167-0441
DOOPSGEZINDE BIJDRAGEN. 1975. a. fl.37.50. Doopsgezinde Historische Kring, Singel 452, 1017 AW Amsterdam, Netherlands. FAX 31-20-6278919. (Subscr. to: Doopsgezinde Bijdragen, H. Smit, Elpermeer 27, 1025 AA Amsterdam, Netherlands. TEL 31-20-6369330) Ed. Sjouke Voolstra. bk.rev.; bibl.; illus. circ. 700. (also avail. in microfiche from IDC) **Indexed:** CERDIC. **Document type:** academic/scholarly publication.
Description: Covers the history of Mennonitism and Anabaptism and related fields.

284 US ISSN 1044-7512
THE DOOR. 1971. bi-m. $22.95. Youth Specialties, 1224 Greenfield Dr., El Cajon, CA 92021. TEL 916-842-2701. FAX 916-842-7729. (Subscr. to: Box 616, Mt. Morris, IL 61054. TEL 800-597-3667) Ed. Mike Yaconelli. bk.rev.; illus.; circ. 10,000 (paid). **Indexed:** Chr.Per.Ind. **Document type:** consumer publication.
Formerly: Wittenburg Door (ISSN 0199-8285)

282
THE DOOR; Diocese of Oxford Reporter. 1989. m. (Oxford Diocesan Board of Finance) Oxford Diocesan Publications Ltd., Diocesan Church House, North Hinksey, Oxford OX2 0NB, England. TEL 0865-244566. FAX 0865-790470. Ed. Christine Zwart. adv.; bk.rev. circ. 59,800. **Document type:** newsletter.
Formerly (until 1989): Oxford Diocesan Magazine.
Description: Covers Berkshire, Buckinghamshire and Oxfordshire. Includes church news, theological articles.

283 323.4 US
DOOR OF HOPE INTERNATIONAL. 1972. m. $25 donation. Door of Hope International Press, CA 91209. TEL 818-500-3939. FAX 819-500-9933. E-mail: DOHIUSA@DELPHI.COM. Ed. Paul Haralan Popov. adv. contact: Jeana Kendrick. bk.rev.; film rev.; play rev.; bibl.; tr.lit. circ. 25,000. **Document type:** newsletter.
Formerly: Door of Hope.

284 GW ISSN 0012-608X
DREIKOENIGSBOTE. 1951. m. free. Evangelisch-Lutherische Dreikoenigsgemeinde, Oppenheimer Str. 5, 60594 Frankfurt, Germany. bibl. circ. 800.

284 GW
DURCHBLICK UND DIENST. 1969. m. DM.21.60. Liebenzeller Gemeinschaftsverband, Postfach 1205, 75375 Bad Liebenzell, Germany. TEL 07052-17114. Ed. Rev. Alfred Gajan. circ. 5,200. (back issues avail.) **Document type:** newsletter.

DUTCH CHURCH TRANSCRIPTS. see GENEALOGY AND HERALDRY

284 028.5 US ISSN 1078-2788
▼**E C.** (Essential Connection) 1995. m. $19.50. Southern Baptist Convention, Sunday School Board, 127 Ninth Ave., N., Nashville, TN 37234. TEL 800-458-2772.
Description: Provides leisure-time reading and devotional articles for youth (grades 7-12).

RELIGIONS AND THEOLOGY — Protestant

284 GW ISSN 0342-1937
E M K AKTUELL. 1963. m. DM.32. (Evangelisch-Methodistische Kirche) Christliches Verlagshaus GmbH, Postfach 311141, 70471 Stuttgart, Germany. TEL 0711-8300051. FAX 0711-8300030. Ed. Ingo Stauch. circ. 2,600. **Document type:** bulletin.

266 GW
E M S - JAHRBUCH. 1984. a. free. Evangelisches Missionswerk in Suedwestdeutschland e.V., Vogelsangstr. 62, 70197 Stuttgart, Germany. TEL 0711-63678-0. FAX 0711-63678-66. TELEX 723059-EMS-D. Eds. Reinhilde Freise, Klaus Zoeller. circ. 5,000. **Document type:** bulletin.

200 US
E P F NEWSLETTER. 1939. q. $25 membership. Episcopal Peace Fellowship, Box 28156, Washington, DC 20038-8156. TEL 202-783-3380. bk.rev. circ. 3,000. **Document type:** newsletter.

266 US
EAST ASIA'S MILLIONS. 1892. q. $4. (Overseas Missionary Fellowship) O M F International, 10 W. Dry Creek Cir., Littleton, CO 80120-4413. TEL 800-422-5330. FAX 303-730-415. E-mail: pnelson@cproject.com. Ed. E. David Dougherty. bk.rev.; illus.; index. circ. 25,000. (also avail. in microfilm from UMI) **Indexed:** Helminthol.Abstr. —UMI.
Former titles: East Asia Millions (ISSN 0012-8406); China's Millions.
Description: Covers mission work in East Asia.

280 370.196 US ISSN 0898-9346
EASTERN CHALLENGE. 1962. q. free. International Missions, Inc., Box 14866, Reading, PA 19612-4866. TEL 610-375-0300. FAX 610-375-6862. Ed. Osborne Buchanan, Jr. bk.rev.; circ. 22,000 (controlled).
Description: Provides information and reports on ministries which establish churches in many lands, primarily among Asian-people groups.

284 CN ISSN 0831-4446
EASTERN SYNOD LUTHERAN. 1920. 10/yr. Can.$6.50($4) Evangelical Lutheran Church in Canada, Eastern Synod, 50 Queen St. N., Kitchener, ON N2H 6P4, Canada. FAX 519-743-4291. Ed. Jane Wahl. adv. contact: Michael Pryse. bk.rev. circ. 23,000. **Document type:** newsletter.
Supersedes in part: Canada Lutheran (ISSN 0008-2716)

286 UK
ECHOES. 1872. s-m. £10.25 (foreign 18.50). Echoes of Service, 1 Widcombe Crescent, Bath, Avon BA2 6AQ, England. TEL 01225-310893. FAX 01225-480134. Eds. J.H. Burness. circ. 9,000 (paid). **Document type:** newsletter.
Description: Stimulates interest in various aspects of missionary work of the Christian Brethren, worldwide.
Refereed Serial

284 US
ECU - LINK. 1986. 4/yr. $6. National Council of Churches, Communication Department, 475 Riverside Dr., Rm. 850, New York, NY 10115. TEL 212-870-2227. FAX 212-870-2030. Ed. Sarah Vilankulu. circ. 5,000. **Document type:** newsletter.
Description: An ecumenical newsletter to help create community among the Council's member communions. Includes news of NCC member denominations.

200 AT ISSN 0726-4143
EDITOR'S CLIP SHEETS. 1980. m. Aus.$42. Mediacom Associates Inc., P.O. Box 610, Unley, S.A. 5061, Australia. TEL 61-8-371-1399. FAX 61-8-297-8719. Ed. Rev. A.G. Nancarrow. adv. circ. 2,000. (looseleaf format) **Document type:** consumer publication.

EDUCATION NEWSLINE. see *EDUCATION*

266 GW ISSN 0949-216X
EINEWELT; Magazin aus Mission und Oekumene. 1915. bi-m. DM.15. (Evangelisches Missionswerk) Missionshilfe Verlag, Normannenweg 17-21, 20537 Hamburg, Germany. Ed.Bd. bk.rev.; illus.; index. circ. 12,000. **Document type:** bulletin.
Former titles: Weltmission (ISSN 0723-6204); Wort in der Welt (ISSN 0341-082X); Allgemeine Missionsnachrichten (ISSN 0002-5909)

ENCOUNTER. see *RELIGIONS AND THEOLOGY*

283 UK ISSN 0963-4819
ENCOUNTER WITH GOD; Bible studies for thought and action. 1923. q. £9.20. Scripture Union Publishing, 130 City Rd., London EC1V 2NJ, England. TEL 0171-782-0013. FAX 0171-782-0014. (Subscr. addr.: S.U. Mail Order Dept., 9-11 Clothier Rd., Bristol BS4 5RL, England) Ed. Tony Hobbs. circ. 33,000. **Document type:** bulletin.
Formerly (until 1994): Daily Notes.

ENGLISH CHURCHMAN & ST. JAMES'S CHRONICLE. 1843. fortn. £13 (foreign £20.50). English Churchman Trust Ltd., 22 Lesley Ave., Canterbury, Kent CT1 3LF, England. TEL 01227-781282. Ed. Rev. J. Lee Potter. adv. contact: Guy M. Longley. bk.rev. circ. 87. (back issues avail.) **Document type:** newspaper.
Formerly: English Churchman (ISSN 0013-8223)
Description: Discusses a variety of ethical and philosophical issues from a Christian perspective.

200 GW ISSN 0013-9092
ENTSCHEIDUNG. 1963. bi-m. DM.22.50 (foreign DM.34.50). (Billy Graham Evangelistic Association Deutschland e.V.) Friedrich Haenssler KG, Bismarkstr. 4, 73765 Neuhausen, Germany. TEL 07158-177-0. FAX 07158-177119. Ed. Irmhild Baerend. adv.; bk.rev.; bibl. circ. 50,000. **Document type:** bulletin.

284 GW ISSN 0343-6519
ENTWURF; religionspaedagogische Mitteilungen. 1970. 3/yr. DM.32. Fachgemeinschaft Evangelische Religionslehrer in Wuerttemberg, Grueningerstr. 25, 70599 Stuttgart, Germany. TEL 0711-45804-0. FAX 0711-45804-22. Ed. Walter Dietz. bk.rev.; cum.index. circ. 12,700. (back issues avail.) **Document type:** bulletin.

284 US
EPISCOPAL CLERICAL DIRECTORY. biennial. Church Hymnal Corporation, 800 Second Ave., New York, NY 10017.

283 US
EPISCOPAL DIOCESE OF MICHIGAN. 1952. m. $6. Episcopal Diocese of Michigan, 4800 Woodward Ave., Detroit, MI 48201-1310. TEL 313-832-4400. Ed. Jeanie Wylie. adv. circ. 10,000.

283 US ISSN 0013-9610
BX5800
EPISCOPAL RECORDER.* 1823. m. (except July-Aug.). $20. Reformed Episcopal Seminary, 7372 Henry Ave., Philadelphia, PA 19128-1401. Ed. Walter G. Truesdell. adv.; bk.rev. circ. 1,100. (also avail. in microfilm from UMI) **Indexed:** G.Soc.Sci.& Rel.Per.Lit.

250 UK ISSN 0308-0382
BR1
EPWORTH REVIEW. 1973. 3/yr. £6. Methodist Publishing House, 20 Ivatt Way, Peterborough, Cambs. PE3 7PG, England. TEL 01733-332202. FAX 01733-331201. Ed. Rev. Dr. Richard G. Jones. circ. 3,500. **Indexed:** Rel.& Theol.Abstr. (1991-). **Document type:** bulletin.
—BLDSC (3794.470000).

284 GW ISSN 0171-6204
ERNEUERUNG IN KIRCHE UND GESELLSCHAFT. 1977. q. DM.38. Westerhudestr. 38, 33154 Salzkotten, Germany. TEL 05258-4889. Ed. Richard Martin Schleyer. adv.; bk.rev. **Document type:** bulletin.

284 GW
ERNEUERUNG UND ABWEHR. 1966. m. Vorstand der Evangelischen Notgemeinschaft in Deutschland, Schulstr. 19C, 82234 Wessling, Germany. TEL 08153-3782. circ. 6,500.

284 GW ISSN 0179-1583
ERWECKLICHE STIMME. 1960. m. Geistliches Ruestzentrum Krelingen, Krelingen 37, 29664 Walsrode, Germany. TEL 05167-970-0. Ed. Wilfried Reuter. illus. circ. 22,000. **Document type:** newsletter.

280 FR
ESQUISSE D'UNE PHILOSOPHIE DE LA RELIGION. 1956. irreg., no.24, 1973. Librairie Fischbacher, 33 rue de Seine, 75006 Paris, France. TEL 43-26-84-87. FAX 43-26-48-87. **Indexed:** Canon Law Abstr.
Formerly: Esprit et Liberte (ISSN 0071-1330)

286 028.5 US ISSN 0890-3115
ESTUDIOS BIBLICOS PARA NINOS. ALUMNOS. (Text in Spanish) q. $10.25. Southern Baptist Convention, Sunday School Board, 127 Ninth Ave., N., Nashville, TN 37234. TEL 800-458-2772.

286 US ISSN 0890-3123
ESTUDIOS BIBLICOS PARA NINOS. MAESTROS. (Text in Spanish) q. $13.95. Southern Baptist Convention, Sunday School Board, 127 Ninth Ave., N., Nashville, TN 37234. TEL 800-458-2772.

230 FR ISSN 0014-2239
ETUDES THEOLOGIQUES ET RELIGIEUSES. 1926. q. 175 F. (effective 1994). Institut Protestant de Theologie, 13 rue Louis-Perrier, 34000 Montpellier, France. TEL 67-92-61-28. FAX 67-58-09-47. Ed. A. Gounelle. adv.; bk.rev.; bibl.; index. circ. 2,350. (also avail. in microfilm from UMI; reprint service avail. from UMI) **Indexed:** Arts & Hum.Cit.Ind., Bull.Signal., CERDIC, Curr.Cont., New Test.Abstr., Old Test.Abstr., Rel.Ind.One, Rel.Per.
—BLDSC (3822.310000); UMI.

284 UK
EUROPEAN ACTION REPORT; voice of the Church of God in Europe. (Text in English) 1976. q. 14 Clark's Mead, Bushey Heath, Herts., England. TEL 0181-950-6539. FAX 0181-950-7929. Ed. Douglas LeRoy. circ. 5,000. **Document type:** newsletter.

280 UK ISSN 0960-2720
EUROPEAN JOURNAL OF THEOLOGY; a new journal for a new Europe. 1992. 2/yr. £13.90 (foreign £14.70). The Paternoster Press, P.O. Box 300, Kingstown Broadway, Carlisle, Cumbria CA3 0QS, England. TEL 0228-512512. FAX 0228-514949. (Dist. in Germany by: Brunnen Verlag GmbH, Postfach 100143, 35331 Giessen, Germany. TEL 0641-6059-0. FAX 0641-605940; Dist. in U.S. & Canada by: Paternoster Press, Box 11127, Birmingham, AL 35201-1127) Ed. J. Gordon McConville. adv.; bk.rev. (reprint service avail. from IRC) **Document type:** academic/scholarly publication.
—BLDSC (3829.746500); UnCover.
Description: Seeks to reflect the variety of European evangelical theology.

287 US ISSN 0162-1890
EVANGEL. w. $6.50. (Free Methodist Church of North America) Free Methodist Publishing House, Box 535002, Indianapolis, IN 46253-5002. TEL 317-244-3660. FAX 317-244-1247. circ. 25,000. (back issues avail.)

286 CN ISSN 0014-3324
EVANGELICAL BAPTIST. 1953. m. Can.$12.95. Fellowship of Evangelical Baptist Churches in Canada, 679 Southgate Dr., Guelph, ON N1G 4S2, Canada. TEL 519-821-4830. FAX 519-821-9829. Ed. Rev. Terry Cuthbert. adv.; bk.rev.; illus. circ. 7,000.

286.1 CN ISSN 0317-266X
EVANGELICAL BAPTIST CHURCHES IN CANADA. FELLOWSHIP YEARBOOK. Key Title: Fellowship Yearbook. 1959. a. Fellowship of Evangelical Baptist Churches in Canada, 679 Southgate Dr., Guelph, ON N1G 4S2, Canada. TEL 519-821-4830. FAX 519-821-9829. illus.
Formerly: Missions Digest and Year Book (ISSN 0544-439X)

285.73 US ISSN 0014-3332
BX7548.A1
EVANGELICAL BEACON. 1931. 7/yr. $12. Evangelical Free Church of America, 901 E 78th St., Minneapolis, MN 55420. TEL 612-854-1300. Ed. Carol Madison. adv. contact: Jan Delay. bk.rev.; illus. circ. 33,000.
Description: Information, inspiration and evangelism for members.

RELIGIONS AND THEOLOGY — PROTESTANT

284 US
EVANGELICAL LUTHERAN CHURCH IN AMERICA (YEAR). Short title: E L C A Yearbook. 1961. a. $14.95. (Evangelical Lutheran Church in America) Augsburg Fortress, Publishers, 426 S. Fifth St., Box 1209, Minneapolis, MN 55440. TEL 612-330-3402; 800-328-4648. FAX 612-330-3455. adv. circ. 15,000.
Formed by the merger of: Lutheran Church in America. Yearbook & Yearbook of American Lutheran Church (ISSN 1050-477X)
Description: Roster listings of congregations, ordained ministers, associates in ministry and agencies, and more.

283 940 UK ISSN 0421-8094
EVANGELICAL MAGAZINE OF WALES. 1955. bi-m. £8.50 (foreign £10.50). Evangelical Press of Wales, Bryntirion, Bridgend, Mid Glam. CF31 4DX, Wales. TEL 01656-655886. FAX 01656-656095. Ed. Rev. Derek Swann. adv.; bk.rev.; bibl.; illus. circ. 2,000. (back issues avail.)
Description: Contains articles on a wide range of subjects relating to the historic evangelical faith of the Christian Church and news of the contemporary religious scene.

266 US ISSN 0014-3359
BV2350
EVANGELICAL MISSIONS QUARTERLY. 1964. q. $19.95. Evangelical Missions Information Service, Box 794, Wheaton, IL 60189. TEL 708-653-2158. FAX 708-653-0520. Ed. James W. Reapsome. adv.; bk.rev.; index. circ. 7,500. Indexed: CERDIC, Chr.Per.Ind., Rel.& Theol.Abstr. (1969-), Rel.Ind.One.
—UMI.
Description: Journal devoted to understanding evangelical Protestant missionary thought and practice.

285 US ISSN 0360-8808
BR21
EVANGELICAL THEOLOGICAL SOCIETY. JOURNAL. 1958. q. $20 (effective Jan. 1995). Evangelical Theological Society, c/o James Borland, Sec. Treas., 112 Russell Woods Dr., Lynchburg, VA 24502. TEL 804-237-1486. FAX 804-582-2575. Ed. Ronald Youngblood. adv.; bk.rev. circ. 2,950. pp./issue: 160. (also avail. in microform from UMI; reprint service avail. from UMI) Indexed: CERDIC, Chr.Per.Ind., New Test.Abstr., Old Test.Abstr., Rel.& Theol.Abstr. (1983-), Rel.Ind.One. **Document type:** academic/scholarly publication.
—BLDSC (4741.650000); UMI.
Formerly: E T S Bulletin (ISSN 0071-3171)
Description: Scholarly evangelical theological quarterly containing articles on Old and New Testament and theological issues.

286 US ISSN 0745-0486
EVANGELICAL VISITOR. 1887. m. $12 (Canada $14.50). (Brethren in Christ Church, Board for Media Ministries) Evangel Publishing House, 2000 Evangel Way, Box 166, Nappanee, IN 46550. TEL 219-773-3164. Ed. Glen A. Pierce. circ. 5,500. (back issues avail.) **Document type:** consumer publication.
Description: Promotes the doctrine, teaching and ministry of the Brethren in Christ Church.

284 UK
EVANGELICALS & SOCIETY FROM 1750 SERIES. irreg., no.4. $85 per vol. Sutton Courtenay Press, c/o Appleford Publishing Group, Appleford House, Appleford, Abingdon, Oxon. OX14 4PB, England. TEL 01235-848319. **Document type:** monographic series.
Description: Discusses the activities of the evangelical movement and individual evangelicals worldwide since 1750.

284 XR
EVANGELICKY CASOPIS CESKY BRATR. 1924. 18/yr. 432 Kc. Ceskobratrska Cirkev Evangelicka, Synodi Rada, Jungmannova 9, 111 21 Prague 1, Czech Republic. TEL 42-2-24222217. FAX 42-2-24222219. Ed. Lydie Roskovcova. bk.rev. circ. 4,600.
Formerly (until 1991): Cesky Bratr (ISSN 0009-0778)
Description: Provides articles on theological, ethical and educational subjects; includes information on the work of local congregations and church workers.

284 960 980 GW ISSN 0177-8706
EVANGELIKALE MISSIOLOGIE. 1985. q. DM.17. Arbeitskreis fuer Evangelikale Missiologie, Hindenburgstr. 36, 70825 Korntal, Germany. FAX 0611-409803. (Co-sponsor: Freie Hochschule fuer Mission) Ed. Klaus Fiedler. bk.rev.; index. circ. 1,000. (also avail. in diskette format; back issues avail.) **Document type:** academic/scholarly publication.
Description: Non-denominational publication covering information and discussions in all fields of missiology. Includes association news and events.

284 HU ISSN 0133-1302
EVANGELIKUS ELET. 1933. w. $40. Evangelical - Lutheran Church, Puskin u. 12, 1088 Budapest, Hungary. TEL 138-23-60. FAX 1382-302. (And: P.O. Box 500, 1447 Budapest, Hungary) Ed. Mihaly Toth-Szollos. circ. 12,000.

284 GW ISSN 0423-8346
EVANGELISCH-LUTHERISCHE LANDESKIRCHE SACHSENS. AMTSBLATT. 1949. s-m. DM.48.40. (Evangelisch-Lutherisches Landeskirchenamt Sachsens) Saechsisches Druck- und Verlagshaus GmbH, Tharandterstr. 23-27, 01159 Dresden, Germany. TEL 0351-4182203. FAX 0351-4182267. Ed.Bd. bk.rev.; play rev.; abstr.; index. circ. 2,500. **Document type:** bulletin.

266 GW
EVANGELISCH-LUTHERISCHES MISSIONSWERK IN NIEDERSACHSEN. JAHRBUCH (YEAR). 1954. a. DM.15. (Evangelisch-Lutherisch Missionswerk in Niedersachsen) Missionshandlung Hermannsburg, Postfach 1109, 29314 Hermannsburg, Germany. FAX 05052-69222. Ed. Ernst-August Luedemann. bk.rev.; index. circ. 5,000. (back issues avail.) **Document type:** bulletin.
Formerly (until 1979): Die Hermannsburger Mission im Jahre (Year).
Description: Articles about the work of the missionaries of the Missionswerk, and about the countries in which they work.

283 GW ISSN 0937-1729
EVANGELISCHE JUGEND IN BAYERN. NACHRICHTEN. 1958. s-a. DM.18. Amt fuer Evangelische Jugendarbeit, Hummelsteiner Weg 100, 90459 Nuernberg, Germany. TEL 0911-4304-0. FAX 0911-4304-201. Ed. Norbert Schneider. circ. 1,500. (back issues avail.) **Document type:** bulletin.

284 GW ISSN 0342-2763
EVANGELISCHE KINDERKIRCHE; Zeitschrift fuer Mitarbeiterinnen und Mitarbeiter im Kindergottesdienst. 1924. q. DM.25. (Wuerttemberg Evangelische Landesverband fuer Kindergottesdienst) Verlag Junge Gemeinde, Postfach 100355, 70747 Leinfelden-Echterdingen, Germany. TEL 0711-7978994. FAX 0711-7970660. circ. 50,000 (paid). **Document type:** newsletter.

284 340 GW ISSN 0232-6310
EVANGELISCHE KIRCHE DER KIRCHENPROVINZ SACHSEN. AMTSBLATT. 1945. m. DM.0.60. Evangelisches Konsistorium der Kirchenprovinz Sachsen, Am Dom 2, 39104 Magdeburg, Germany. circ. 2,000. **Document type:** bulletin.
Description: Events and information on evangelistic churches in western part of Germany.

284.2 GW ISSN 0014-343X
EVANGELISCHE KIRCHE IN DEUTSCHLAND. AMTSBLATT. 1946. m. DM.40. Kirchenamt der Evangelische Kirche in Deutschland, Herrenhaeuser Str. 12, 30149 Hannover, Germany. TEL 0511-7111463. Ed. Dr. J. Linnewedel. index. circ. 1,400. (tabloid format; back issues avail.) **Document type:** bulletin.

284 GW ISSN 0942-1513
EVANGELISCHE KIRCHENZEITUNG. 1946. w. (Sun.). Evangelischer Presseverband in Hessen und Nassau e.V., Neue Schlesingergasse 24, 60311 Frankfurt a.M., Germany. TEL 069-299884-0. FAX 069-299884-24. Ed. Hans Gerhard Gensch. adv. contact: Wilhelm Schmitz. bk.rev. circ. 16,470. **Document type:** newspaper.
Formerly (until Jan. 1989): Weg und Wahrheit (ISSN 0170-6136)

284 GW ISSN 0014-3529
EVANGELISCHE LANDESKIRCHE IN WUERTTEMBERG. AMTSBLATT. 1855. m. DM.50 (free to qualified personnel). Evangelischer Oberkirchenrat, Postfach 101342, 70012 Stuttgart, Germany. TEL 0711-2149-0. FAX 0711-2149236. index. circ. 3,600. **Document type:** bulletin.
Description: Focuses on church matters including changes in constitution, by-laws, regulations, obligations for pastors and congregations.

284 GW
EVANGELISCHE LUTHERISCHE KIRCHE IN BAYERN. PFARRER- UND PFARRERINNENVEREIN. KORRESPONDENZBLATT. 1876. m. DM.25. Evangelische Lutherische Kirche in Bayern, Pfarrer- und Pfarrerinnenverein, Kronacher Str. 16, 96215 Lichtenfels, Germany. TEL 09571-2077. Ed. Martin Ost. adv.; bk.rev.; index. circ. 3,100. (back issues avail.) **Document type:** newsletter.

284 GW ISSN 0014-326X
EVANGELISCHE-LUTHERISCHE KIRCHE IN THUERINGEN. AMTSBLATT. 1948. s-m. DM.0.50. (Evangelische-Lutherische Kirche in Thueringen, Landeskirchenrat) Wartburg Verlag GmbH, Marienstr. 14, 99423 Weimar, Germany. TEL 03643-246111. FAX 03643-246112. bk.rev. **Document type:** bulletin.

284 GW ISSN 0933-7857
EVANGELISCHER BUND; beitraege zur evangelischen Orientierung. 1954. q. DM.30. Evangelischer Bund, Konfessionskundliches Institut, Postfach 1255, 64602 Bensheim, Germany. TEL 06251-38000. FAX 06251-2045. Ed. Walter Fleischmann-Bisten. circ. 11,000. (back issues avail.) **Document type:** bulletin.

284 AU ISSN 0036-6943
EVANGELISCHER BUND IN OESTERREICH. SCHRIFTENREIHE. 1956. q. Evangelischer Bund in Oesterreich, Ungargasse 9, A-1030 Vienna, Austria. Ed. Paul Weiland. circ. 8,000.
Incorporates: Martin Luther.

284 GW
EVANGELISCHER INFORMATIONSDIENST FUER JUGEND- UND ERWACHSENBILDUNG AUF DEM LANDE. 1971. q. DM.10. Evangelische Landjugendakademie, Dieperzbergweg 13-17, 57610 Altenkirchen, Germany. TEL 02681-4377. FAX 02681-70206. bk.rev. (back issues avail.)
Formerly: Evangelischer Informationsdienst fuer Jugend- und Erwachsenbildung.

284 AU
EVANGELISCHER KIRCHENBOTE LINZ. 1952. 6/yr. S.120. Evangelischer Pfarrgemeinde Linz, Konrad-Vogel-Str. 2A, A-4021 Linz, Austria. TEL 0732-773260. FAX 0732-77326085. Ed. Helmuth Koehrer. adv.; bk.rev. circ. 6,400. **Document type:** newsletter.

284 GW ISSN 0014-360X
EVANGELISCHES GEMEINDEBLATT FUER WUERTTEMBERG. 1905. w. (Sun.). DM.74.40. (Evangelische Gesellschaft Stuttgart e.V.) Evangelische Gemeindepresse GmbH, Furtbachstr. 12a, 70178 Stuttgart, Germany. TEL 0711-60100-25. FAX 0711-60100-76. Ed. Andreas Roessler. adv. contact: Wolfgang Schmoll. bk.rev.; illus. circ. 132,035. **Document type:** newspaper.

371.3 369.4 200 US ISSN 0891-3846
EVANGELIZING TODAY'S CHILD. 1942. bi-m. $17.95 (effective 1995 & 1996). Child Evangelism Fellowship Inc., Box 348, Warrenton, MO 63383. TEL 314-456-4321. Ed. Elsie Lippy. adv. contact: Lydia Kaiser. bk.rev.; index; circ. 25,000 (paid). Indexed: Chr.Per.Ind. **Document type:** academic/scholarly publication.
Description: Designed to give Sunday school teachers and other Christian education workers instruction and tools to teach 5- to 12-year-olds the Bible.

284 FR
EVANGILE ET LIBERTE. 1885. m. 205 F. Association Evangile et Liberte, c/o Pasteur Christian Mazel, Les Genets, Residence St. Michel, 84400 Apt en Luberon, France. TEL 90-74-56-37. adv.; bk.rev.; bibl. **Document type:** academic/scholarly publication, newsletter, newspaper.

RELIGIONS AND THEOLOGY — PROTESTANT

284 YU ISSN 0014-3642
EVANJELICKY HLASNIK. 1965. m. 250 din. (effective 1992). Slovenska Evanjelicka A.V. Cirkva v SFR Juhoslavii, Karadziceva 2, 21000 Novi Sad, Yugoslavia. TEL 23 887-922. Ed. Rev. Ondrej Petkovsky. bk.rev. circ. 4,200.

EXALTATION. see *MUSIC*

283 UK
EXETER DIOCESAN DIRECTORY. 1946. a. £3.50 (effective 1995). Diocese of Exeter, Diocesan House, Palace Gate, Exeter, Dorset EX1 1HX, England. TEL 01392-72686. FAX 01392-499594. Ed. Paul Greener. adv. contact: Paul Greener. circ. 800. (back issues avail.) **Document type:** directory.

268 US ISSN 1077-3606
▼**EXPERIENCING GOD MAGAZINE.** 1994. m. $19.95. Southern Baptist Convention, 127 Ninth Ave., N., Nashville, TN 37234. TEL 800-458-2772.
Description: Contains inspirational articles from a Baptist perspective.

268 028.5 US ISSN 0745-032X
EXPLORING 1. q. $9.75. Southern Baptist Convention, Sunday School Board, 127 Ninth Ave., N., Nashville, TN 37234. TEL 800-458-2772.
Formerly (until 1982): Exploring A (ISSN 0162-4415).
Description: Religious publication directed at children ages 6-8.

268 US ISSN 0745-0346
EXPLORING 1 FOR LEADERS. q. $13.50. Southern Baptist Convention, Sunday School Board, 127 Ninth Ave., N., Nashville, TN 37234. TEL 800-458-2772.
Formerly (until 1982): Exploring A for Leaders (ISSN 0162-4423).

268 028.5 US ISSN 0745-0338
EXPLORING 2. q. $9.75. Southern Baptist Convention, Sunday School Board, 127 Ninth Ave., N., Nashville, TN 37234. TEL 800-458-2772.
Formerly (until 1982): Exploring C (ISSN 0162-4458)
Description: Religious publication directed at children in grades 4-6.

268 375 US ISSN 0745-0354
EXPLORING 2 FOR LEADERS. q. $13.50. Southern Baptist Convention, Sunday School Board, 127 Ninth Ave., N., Nashville, TN 37234. TEL 800-458-2772.
Formerly (until 1982): Exploring C for Leaders (ISSN 0162-4466)

286 AG ISSN 0014-522X
EXPOSITOR BAUTISTA. 1908. m. Arg.$24. Convencion Evangelica Bautista Argentina, Rivadavia 3461, 1203 Buenos Aires, Argentina. TEL 54-1-8642711. Ed. Raull Guzman. adv.; charts; illus.

266 US ISSN 1074-1712
FAITH AND FELLOWSHIP. 1933. 17/yr. $14. (Church of the Lutheran Brethren) Faith and Fellowship Press, Box 655, Fergus Falls, MN 56537. TEL 218-736-7357. FAX 218-736-2200. Ed. Rev. David Rinden. bk.rev. circ. 6,000.

286 US ISSN 0740-0659
FAITH AND MISSION. 1983. s-a. $9. Southeastern Baptist Theological Seminary, Inc., Wake Forest, NC 27587. TEL 919-556-3101. FAX 919-556-0998. Ed. David E. Lanier. adv.; bk.rev.; circ. 1,000. (controlled). (back issues avail.) **Indexed:** Rel.& Theol.Abstr. (1983-), Rel.Ind.One. —BLDSC (3865.510900); UMI.

284 052 CN ISSN 0832-1191
FAITH TODAY; Canada's evangelical news-feature magazine. 1983. bi-m. Can.$17.99($20.99) Evangelical Fellowship of Canada, Box 8800, Sta. B, Willowdale, ON M2K 2R6, Canada. TEL 905-479-5885. FAX 905-479-4742. Ed. Brian C. Stiller. adv. contact: Jerry Lewis. bk.rev. circ. 18,000. **Document type:** consumer publication.
Formerly (until 1986): Faith Alive.
Description: Informs Canadian Christians on issues facing church and society and on events and trends within the church community.

284 028.5 US
FAMILY WALK. 1983. m. $18. Walk Thru the Bible Ministries, Inc., 4201 N. Peachtree Rd., Box 80587, Atlanta, GA 30341-1362. TEL 404-458-9300. Ed. Paula Kirk. circ. 9,736.

286 370.196 US ISSN 0162-4504
LA FE BAUTISTA. (Text in Spanish) q. $9.95. Southern Baptist Convention, Sunday School Board, 127 Ninth Ave., N., Nashville, TN 37234. TEL 800-458-2772.

284 IT
FEDELTA; mensile di in-formazione. 1976. m. free. Via Vespucci 3-19, 50047 Prato (FI), Italy. TEL 39-574-42024. Ed. Mario Affuso. bk.rev. circ. 1,000. (back issues avail.)
Formerly: Fedelta Apostolica.

284 FR ISSN 0240-5164
FEDERATION PROTESTANTE DE FRANCE. ANNUAIRE. Key Title: Annuaire de la France Protestante. 1952. a. 200 F. Federation Protestante de France, c/o A. Nicolas, 47 rue de Clichy, 75009 Paris, France. TEL 48-74-15-08. FAX 42-81-40-01.
Formerly: France Prostestante (ISSN 0071-9064)

280 US ISSN 1045-3849
FELLOWSHIP TODAY.* 1963. m. $7.80. (Fellowship of Christian Assemblies) Fellowship Press, 2345 Sugar Lake Trl., Ste. 501A, Bass Brook, MN 55721. TEL 516-474-4862. Ed. James Mattson. adv.; bk.rev. circ. 5,000.
Formerly (until June 1989): Conviction Magazine.

284 GW ISSN 0015-0320
DER FESTE GRUND. 1850. m. DM.30.60. Evangelische Gesellschaft fuer Deutschland e.V., Kaiserstr. 78, 42329 Wuppertal, Germany. TEL 0202-784018. FAX 0202-7866318. Ed. Herbert Becker. adv.; bk.rev. circ. 7,000. **Document type:** bulletin.
Incorporates: Saemann.
Description: Evangelical publication covering various topics in Christianity and missionary work.

286 362.7 US
FIRST STEPS IN MISSIONS. a. $8 (effective 1995-1996). Southern Baptist Convention, Woman's Missionary Union, Hwy. 280, E., 100 Missionary Ridge, Birmingham, AL 25242-5235. TEL 205-991-8100. (Subscr. to: Box 830711, Birmingham, AL 35283-7111. TEL 800-WMU-7301. FAX 205-995-4840)

266 UK ISSN 0015-4822
FLYING ANGEL. 1958. q. £1. Missions to Seamen, St. Michael Paternoster Royal, College Hill, London EC4R 2RL, England. TEL 0171-248-5202. FAX 0171-248-4761. Ed. Gillian Ennis. illus. circ. 13,500. **Document type:** newsletter.

284 305.1 CN
FOCUS (BURLINGTON). 1992. 6/yr. free. Christian Service Brigade of Canada, 1254 Plains Rd. E., Burlington, ON L7S 1W6, Canada. TEL 416-634-1841. FAX 416-634-7643. Ed. Mark Clayton.

286 UK ISSN 0143-7925
FOCUS (GRANTHAM). 1979. q. £2.95 (foreign £5). Stanborough Press Ltd., Alma Park, Grantham, Lincs. NG31 9SL, England. TEL 01476-591700. FAX 01476-77144. Ed. D.N. Marshall; Pub. P. Hammond. adv. contact: Edward Johnson. illus. circ. 25,000. **Document type:** bulletin.

266 US
FOCUS ON MISSIONS. 1970. 3/yr. free. Fellowship of Missions, Box 136, Middletown, DE 19709-0136. TEL 302-378-1525. E-mail: compuserve 75541,21. Ed. Henry J. Heijermans. bk.rev.; circ. 23,000 (controlled). (back issues avail.) **Document type:** newsletter.
Description: Covers news on missions worldwide.

200 US
FORWARD (ERIE); a witness to the Good News of Jesus Christ in the Episcopal Church Diocese of Northwestern Pennsylvania. 1948. m. (10/yr.). Episcopal Diocese of Northwestern Pennsylvania, 145 W. Sixth St., Erie, PA 16501. TEL 814-456-4203. Ed. Rev. Dr. William S. Pugliese. circ. 3,800. **Document type:** newsletter.
Formerly: Forward in Erie (ISSN 0015-8623)

284 US ISSN 1058-6784
FORWARD DAY BY DAY; a manual of daily Bible reading and devotions. Spanish edition: Dia a Dia. 1935. q. $8 for inkprint for 2 yrs. (foreign $10); large print $12 (foreign $15); Braille & cassette free (effective Aug. 1995). Forward Movement Publications, 412 Sycamore St., Cincinnati, OH 45202. TEL 513-721-6659; 800-543-1813. FAX 513-421-0315. Ed. Edward Gleason. circ. 306,000. (also avail. in Braille; audio cassette; large print edition in 18 pt.) **Document type:** consumer publication.

139 FR
BX4843.A2
FRANCE PROTESTANTE ET LES EGLISES DE LANGUE FRANCAISE. 1922, 40th ed. a. Librairie Fischbacher, 33 rue de Seine, 75006 Paris, France. TEL 43-26-84-87. FAX 43-26-48-87.
Formerly: Annuaire Protestant: la France Protestante et les Eglises de Langue Francaise (ISSN 0066-362X)

283 UK ISSN 0532-579X
FRANCISCAN. 1959. 3/yr. £4.50. Society of St. Francis, The Friary, Hilfield, Dorchester, Dorset DT2 7BE, England. TEL 0300-341345. FAX 0300-341293. Ed. Tristam Holland. bk.rev. circ. 3,500. **Document type:** newsletter.
Former titles: Floweret; Franciscan News.

287 US
FREE METHODIST WORLD MISSION PEOPLE. 1897. $10 (talking book $18) (effective Sep. 1990). Free Methodist World Missions, 770 N. High School Rd., Indianapolis, IN 46214. TEL 317-244-3660. FAX 317-244-1247. (Subscr. to: Box 535002, Indianapolis, IN 46253-5002) Ed. Daniel V. Runyon. bk.rev.; circ. 8,000 (paid). (also avail. in talking book) **Document type:** trade publication.
Formerly (until 1995): Missionary Tidings (ISSN 1043-0725)
Description: Provides news and features about cross-cultural communication and world evangelization in the Free Methodist denomination.

284 GW ISSN 0931-3834
FREIES CHRISTENTUM; Auf der Suche nach neuen Wegen. 1949. bi-m. DM.30. Bund fuer Freies Christentum, Niederurseler Landstr. 116, 60439 Frankfurt a.M., Germany. TEL 069-583533. (Dist. By: Lore Zoller, Ulrich-von-Hutten-Str. 61, 70825 Korntal-Muenchingen, Germany. TEL 0711-831660) Ed. Jutta Reich. bk.rev.; circ. 500 (paid). (back issues avail.) **Document type:** bulletin.
Description: For persons looking for religious information and stimulation in a basic type of Christianity free from conventional dogmatic restraints.

FRIEDE UEBER ISRAEL; Zeitschrift fuer Kirche und Judentum. see *RELIGIONS AND THEOLOGY — Judaic*

284 GW
FRIEDE UND FREIHEIT. 1946. every 6 wks. DM.6. Evangelisch-Reformierte Kirche, Troendlinring 7, 04105 Leipzig, Germany. Ed.Bd. contr. 3,000.

284 GW
FRIEDENSBOTE. m. DM.7.60. Oncken Verlag GmbH, Muendener Str. 13, 34123 Kassel, Germany. TEL 0561-52005-0. Ed. Hinrich Schmidt. circ. 50,000. (back issues avail.) **Document type:** bulletin.

269 266 GW
FRIEDENSGLOCKE. 1893. s-m. DM.6. Evangelisch-Methodistische Kirche in der DDR, Wiener Str. 56, 01219 Dresden, Germany. Ed. G. Roegner.

266 285 AT ISSN 1033-2235
FRONTIER NEWS. 1930. 4/yr. free. Uniting Church in Australia, Uniting Church Frontier Services, 222 Pitt St., 5th Fl., Sydney, N.S.W. 2000, Australia. TEL 02-287-0900. FAX 02-287-0999. (Subscr. to: P.O. Box E266, St. James, N.S.W. 2000, Australia) Ed. Rev. Brian Smith. bk.rev.; charts; illus.; stat. circ. 20,000. (tabloid format; back issues avail.)
Description: Stories of Uniting Church mission work in the outback, isolated areas of Australia.

RELIGIONS AND THEOLOGY — PROTESTANT

284   GW   ISSN 0016-2434
FUER ARBEIT UND BESINNUNG. 1947. s-m. DM.80. (Evangelischer Oberkirchenrat) Quell Verlag, Furtbachstr. 12A, 70178 Stuttgart, Germany. TEL 0711-60100-0. adv.; bk.rev.; index. circ. 3,800. **Document type:** bulletin.

287   GW   ISSN 0016-2442
FUER HEUTE. 1968. w. DM.20.40. (Evangelisch-Methodistische Kirche) Christliches Verlagshaus GmbH, Postfach 311141, 70471 Stuttgart, Germany. TEL 0711-8300051. FAX 0711-8300030. circ. 15,000. **Document type:** bulletin.
    Formed by the 1968 merger of: Gute Botschaft; Friedensglocke.

284   US   ISSN 0896-5749
FUNDAMENTAL NEWS SERVICE. 1960. bi-m. $15.00. American Council of Christian Churches, Box 19, Wallingford, PA 19086. TEL 610-566-8154. Ed. Ralph Colas. bk.rev. circ. 15,000. **Document type:** newsletter.

286   US   ISSN 0016-2744
FUNDAMENTALIST. 1927. bi-m. $3 (foreign $3.50). World Baptist Fellowship, Box 13459, Arlington, TX 76094-0459. TEL 817-274-7161. Ed. Dr. Wendell Hiers. bk.rev. circ. 8,000. **Indexed:** CERDIC.
    Description: Promotional news from the World Baptist Fellowship.

284.1489   DK   ISSN 0107-8399
FYENS STIFTSBOG. 1969. a. DKK 65. Fyens Stifts Landemode, Stiftsoevrighedens Kontor, Klaregade 17, 5000 Odense, Denmark. TEL 45-66-12-53-02. Ed. Poul Erik Andersen. illus. circ. 2,400. (also avail. in diskette format) **Indexed:** NAA.

286   US
▼**G A WORLD.** (Girls in Action) 1995. m. $10.95. Woman's Missionary Union, Hwy. 280, E., 100 Missionary Ridge, Birmingham, AL 35242-5235. TEL 205-991-8100. (Subscr. to: Box 830010, Birmingham, AL 35283-0010. TEL 800-WMU-7301. FAX 205-995-4840) Ed. Barbara Massey.
    Description: For girls, grades 5 and 6, who are members of the Southern Baptist Girls in Action organization.

284   GW
DER GAERTNER. 1893. w. DM.72.50. Bundes-Verlag GmbH, Postfach 4065, 58426 Witten, Germany. TEL 02302-399-43. Ed. Erhard Diehl. adv.; bk.rev. circ. 10,000. (back issues avail.)

284   GW   ISSN 0016-6073
DIE GEMEINDE (KASSEL). 1946. w. DM.92. (Bund Evangelisch-Freikirchlicher Gemeinden) Oncken Verlag GmbH, Muendener Str. 13, 34123 Kassel, Germany. TEL 0561-52005-0. Ed. Reinhard Schwarz. adv.; bk.rev.; abstr.; illus.; index. circ. 15,000. (tabloid format) **Document type:** bulletin.
—CCC.

GEMEINDEBIBELSCHULE; Mitarbeiterzeitschrift. see *RELIGIONS AND THEOLOGY*

284   AU   ISSN 0016-6111
GEMEINDEBRIEF; fuer die gemeindemitglieder der evangelischen Pfarrgemeinde Melk-Scheibbs. 1956. bi-m. DM.46. Evangelisches Pfarramt Melk, Kirchenstr. 15, Postfach 9, A-3390 Melk, Austria. TEL 069-78972-0. Ed. Britta Hubener. illus.; index. circ. 8,500. (back issues avail.)

200   NE
GEREFORMEERD KERKHISTORISCH TIJDSCHRIFT. 1973. q. fl.12.50. Gereformeerd Historisch Instituut - Reformed Historical Institute, Zestienhovensekade 409, Rotterdam 3008, Netherlands. Ed. J. Lussenburg. adv.; bk.rev.

284 230   NE   ISSN 0016-8610
GEREFORMEERD THEOLOGISCH TIJDSCHRIFT. 1900. q. fl.61 (foreign fl.75) (effective 1995). Uitgeversmaatschappij J.H. Kok B.V., Postbus 130, 8260 AC Kampen, Netherlands. TEL 31-5202-92555. FAX 31-5202-27331. Ed. H.C. van der Sar. bk.rev./; index. **Indexed:** CERDIC, New Test.Abstr., Old Test.Abstr., Rel.& Theol.Abstr. (1968-). **Document type:** academic/scholarly publication.

284.2   SA   ISSN 0378-407X
GEREFORMEERDE VROUEBLAD. (Text in Afrikaans) 1947. m. R.25.20. Reformed Churches in South Africa - Gereformeerde Kerke in Suid-Afrika, P.O. Box 20008, Noordbrug 2522, Potchefstroom, South Africa. Ed. Mrs. A. de Bruyn. circ. 6,400.

GESELLSCHAFT FUER NIEDERSAECHSISCHE KIRCHENGESCHICHTE. JAHRBUCH. see *HISTORY — History Of Europe*

053.1   GW   ISSN 0016-934X
GETROSTER TAG/HOPEFUL DAY.* 1955. 3/yr. DM.9.90. Burckhardthaus-Laetare Verlag GmbH, Schumannstr. 161, 6050 Offenbach, Germany. circ. 35,000.

284 052   AT
GIPPSLAND ANGLICAN. 1930. m. Aus.$3.50 (typically set in Feb.). Anglican Diocese of Gippsland, Church News Board, 453 Raymond St., Sale, Vic. 3850, Australia. TEL 61-51-44-2044. FAX 61-51-44-7183. Ed. Rev. Phil Gale. adv. contact: Merle Sheean. bk.rev.; film rev. circ. 4,500. (tabloid format; back issues avail.) **Document type:** newspaper.
    Description: Regional Anglican newpaper for Anglicans in the Diocese of Gippsland.

285 266   CN   ISSN 0017-0720
GLAD TIDINGS. 1925. bi-m. Can.$8.50. Women's Missionary Society (WD), Presbyterian Church in Canada, 50 Wynford Dr., North York, ON M3C 1J7, Canada. TEL 416-441-1111. FAX 416-441-2825. Ed. L. June Stevenson. bk.rev.; illus.; index. circ. 8,000.
    Description: Covers mission work in the world.

GLASS (LEICESTER). see *LITERATURE*

284   GW   ISSN 0323-8202
BX9798.U5
GLAUBE UND HEIMAT; evangelische Wochenzeitung fuer Thueringen. 1946. w. DM.59. (Landeskirchenrat der Evangelisch-Lutherischen Kirche in Thueringen) Wartburg Verlag GmbH, Marienstr. 14, 99423 Weimar, Germany. TEL 03643-246111. FAX 03643-246112. Ed. Christine Laessig. adv. contact: Christian Machalet. bk.rev. circ. 19,000. **Document type:** bulletin.

GLORY SONGS. see *MUSIC*

283   UK   ISSN 0256-4726
GO. (Former name of issuing body: B M M F International) 1872. q. donation. Interserve, 325 Kennington Rd., London SE11 4QH, England. TEL 0171-735-8227. FAX 0171-587-5362. E-mail: 100014,2566 (CompuServe). (Dist. in U.S. by: Box 418, Upper Darby, PA 19082-0418; International addr.: P.O. Box 2140 Nicosia, Cyprus. TEL 357-2-452745) Ed. Martin Hickey; Pub. Richard Clark. bk.rev. circ. 13,000. (back issues avail.) **Document type:** newsletter.
    Description: Provides an international review of mission and development issues affect Interserve, missionaries serving in Asia and the Middle East, as well as the ethnic minorities in the U.K., the U.S. and Canada.

287   UK   ISSN 0017-1700
GOLEUAD/LIGHT. 1871. w. 20p. per no. (Presbyterian Church of Wales) Y Llyfrfa, St. David's Rd., Caernarvon, Gwynedd LL55 1ER, Wales. Ed. E.R. Lloyd-Jones. adv.; bk.rev. circ. 5,000. **Document type:** newspaper.

284   XV
GOLGOTSKA VEST. (Text in Slovenian) 1966. m. 500 SLT. Binkostna Cerkev, Celovska 70, 61000 Ljubljana, Slovenia. TEL 38-61-553-260. Ed. Mihael Kuzmic. circ. 500. (back issues avail.)

285   US   ISSN 0436-1563
GOOD NEWS (WILMORE). 1967. bi-m. $14.95. Forum for Scriptural Christianity, Inc., 308 E. Main St., Box 150, Wilmore, KY 40390. TEL 606-858-4661. FAX 606-858-4972. Ed. James V. Heidinger II. adv.; bk.rev. circ. 20,000. (back issues avail.)
    Description: Covers United Methodist related current issues, testimonies and inspirational pieces.

283   UK
GOSPEL MAGAZINE. 1766. bi-m. £5.50; newsstand price: (effective 1996). Gospel Magazine Trust, 9 Birtlespol Rd., Cheadle Hulme, Ches. SK8 5SZ, England. Ed. Rev. Maurice Handford. adv.: B&W page £22. bk.rev. (back issues avail.) **Document type:** newspaper.
    Incorporates: Protestant Beacon & British Protestant.
    Description: Covers a variety of religious, ethical, and moral issues from a Christian perspective.

286   UK
GRACE BAPTIST MISSION HERALD. 1900. q. free. Grace Baptist Mission, 12 Abbey Close, Abingdon, Oxon. OX14 3JD, England. TEL 0235 20147. Ed. J.C. Richards. circ. 6,000.

268 028.5   US   ISSN 0162-4512
GROWING (NASHVILLE). 1970. q. $10.25. Southern Baptist Convention, Sunday School Board, 127 Ninth Ave., N., Nashville, TN 37234. TEL 800-458-2772.

268   US   ISSN 1045-8948
GROWING CHURCHES. 1990. q. $22.30. Southern Baptist Convention, Sunday School Board, 127 Ninth Ave., N., Nashville, TN 37234. TEL 615-251-2991; 800-458-2772. FAX 615-251-5067. **Document type:** trade publication.
    Description: Encourages pastors and staff to consider the issues related to church growth.

268 375   US   ISSN 1047-9449
GROWING DISCIPLES. q. $21.25. Southern Baptist Convention, Sunday School Board, 127 Ninth Ave., N., Nashville, TN 37234. TEL 800-458-2772. **Indexed:** South.Bap.Per.Ind.
    Former titles: Discipleship Training; Church Training.

284   DK   ISSN 0107-4164
GRUNDTVIG STUDIER. 1948. a. DKK 150. Grundtvig-Selskabet af 8. September 1947, c/o Danske Boghandleres Anstalt, Siljangade 6, 2300 Copenhagen S, Denmark. TEL 33-13-76-70. (Subscr. to: Vartov, Farvergade 27, DK-1463 Copenhagen K, Denmark) Eds. J.H. Schoerring, Hellmut Toftdal. bk.rev. circ. 800. **Indexed:** M.L.A. **Document type:** academic/scholarly publication.

284   US
GUIDE FOR BIBLICAL STUDIES. 1885. q. $8. Church of the Brethren, General Board, 1451 Dundee Ave., Elgin, IL 60120. TEL 312-742-5100. FAX 708-742-6103. Ed. Julie L. Garber. adv. circ. 15,000. **Document type:** academic/scholarly publication.
    Description: Based on international Sunday school lessons for Christian teaching.

284.1489   DK   ISSN 0108-7541
HADERSLEV STIFTSBOG. 1946. a. (Haderslev Stiftsfond) J.D. Nielsens Forlag, 6100 Haderslev, Denmark.
    Formerly: Haderslav Stifts Aarbog.

HANDBELLS; for directors and ringers. see *MUSIC*

268   US
HAPPY TIMES. 1964. m. $7.50. (Lutheran Church - Missouri Synod, Board for Parish Services) Concordia Publishing House, 3558 S. Jefferson Ave., St. Louis, MO 63118. TEL 800-325-3381. Ed. Earl H. Gaulke. circ. 49,000. (also avail. in microfilm) **Document type:** consumer publication.
    Description: Stories and activities for 3 to 5 year old children.

283   US   ISSN 0274-7154
HAWAIIAN CHURCH CHRONICLE. 1910. 9/yr. $6 donation. Episcopal Church in Hawaii, 229 Queen Emma Square, Honolulu, HI 96813-2304. TEL 808-536-7776. FAX 808-536-2099. Ed.Bd. bk.rev. circ. 7,600. (tabloid format) **Document type:** newspaper.

286   US
HEARTBEAT (NASHVILLE). 1961. 6/yr. free. Free Will Baptist Foreign Missions, Box 5002, Antioch, TN 37011-5002. TEL 615-731-6812. FAX 615-731-5345. Ed. Don Robirds. circ. 45,000 (controlled).
    Description: News, profiles, and personal experiences pertaining to the foreign missionary work of Free Will Baptists.

RELIGIONS AND THEOLOGY — PROTESTANT

284   SZ
HEILSARMEE ZEITUNG. French edition: Journal de l'Armee du Salut. (Text in German) 1884. 24/yr. 35 SFr. Laupenstr. 5, Postfach 6575, CH-3001 Bern, Switzerland. TEL 031-3810591. FAX 031-3823302. Ed. Hedy Brenner. circ. 19,600. **Document type:** newsletter.
    Formerly: Kriegsruf.

HELFENDE HAENDE; Zeitschrift des diakonischen Werkes Westfalen. see *SOCIAL SERVICES AND WELFARE*

285   US
HELPING HAND IN BIBLE STUDY. 1884. q. $4.50. (Seventh Day Baptist Board of Christian Education) American Sabbath Tract & Communications Council, 3120 Kennedy Rd., Box 1678, Janesville, WI 53547-1678. TEL 608-752-5055. Ed. Linda Harris. circ. 2,200. (back issues avail.)
    Description: Bible study lessons, based on international Bible lessons for Christian teaching, for Seventh Day Baptists.

285   CU   ISSN 0864-0270
HERALDO CRISTIANO. bi-m. Iglesia Presbiteriana, Salud No. 222nd, Lealtad y Companario, Havana 2, Cuba. TEL 61-1558. Dir. Jacobo Guiribitey.

284   NE   ISSN 0018-0920
HERVORMD ARNHEM. 1905. w. fl.15. (Hervormde Gemeente Arnhem) J.C. Willemsen, Sibeliusstr. 2, 3816 MR Amersfoort, Netherlands. (Subscr. address: Breyers Boekhandel, Looierstraat 1, Arnhem, Netherlands) adv.; bk.rev.; film rev. (looseleaf format)

284   NE   ISSN 0018-0947
HERVORMD WAGENINGEN.* 1945. fortn. fl.6.75($2) Hervormde Gemeente Kerkelijk Bureau, Markt 17, Wageningen, Netherlands. adv.; bk.rev.; bibl. circ. 4,000.

284   SA   ISSN 0259-949X
DIE HERVORMER. (Text in Afrikaans) 1909. s-m. R.23 (typically set in Jan.). Nederduitsch Hervormde Kerk van Afrika, P.O. Box 5777, Pretoria 0001, South Africa. Ed. D.J.C. van Wyk. adv.; bk.rev. circ. 27,500.

284   GW   ISSN 0941-5475
HESSISCHES PFARRBLATT. 1971. bi-m. DM.15. Pfarrerinnen- und Pfarrerverein in der Evang. Kirche in Hessen und Nassau e.V., Melsunger Str. 8a, 60389 Frankfurt a.M., Germany. TEL 069-471820. FAX 069-479487. Ed. Martin Zentgraf. index. circ. 2,700. (back issues avail.) **Document type:** newsletter.
    Description: Covers church problems and matters of the pastoral profession.

200   SA   ISSN 0018-1684
HIGHWAY. (Text in Afrikaans, English) 1940. m. $12. Anglican Diocese of Kimberley and Kuruman, P.O. Box 45, Kimberley 8300, South Africa. FAX 531-812730. Ed. Canon Owen Franklin. adv.; bk.rev. circ. 2,100. (tabloid format) **Document type:** newspaper.

286   US   ISSN 0890-3247
HISTORIAS BIBLICAS PARA PREESCOLARES. ALUMNOS. (Text in Spanish) q. $10.25. Southern Baptist Convention, Sunday School Board, 127 Ninth Ave., N., Nashville, TN 37234. TEL 800-458-2772.

286 375   US   ISSN 0890-3158
HISTORIAS BIBLICAS PARA PREESCOLARES. MAESTROS. (Text in Spanish) q. $13.95. Southern Baptist Convention, Sunday School Board, 127 Ninth Ave., N., Nashville, TN 37234. TEL 800-458-2772.

284   US   ISSN 0360-9030
HISTORICAL FOOTNOTES (ST. LOUIS). 1955. q. $25 includes membership. Concordia Historical Institute, 801 De Mun Ave., St. Louis, MO 63105. TEL 314-721-5934. Ed. Daniel Preus. bk.rev.; bibl. circ. 1,700. **Indexed:** Amer.Hist.& Life, Hist.Abstr. **Document type:** newsletter.

287   US
HISTORICAL HIGHLIGHTS. 1971. s-a. $10. South Georgia Conference Commission on Archives and History of the United Methodist Church, Box 407, Arthur J. Moore Methodist Museum, St. Simons Island, GA 31522. TEL 912-638-4050. Ed. Marynell S. Waite. bk.rev.; cum.index every 4 yrs. circ. 275. **Document type:** academic/scholarly publication.
    Description: Written by scholars and amateur historians for the purpose of collecting and preserving the Methodist heritage, history of the region and its relations to its roots and current world sphere.

287 270   US
HISTORICAL MESSENGER. 1969. q. $4. United Methodist Church, Central Illinois Conference, Historical Society, Box 515, Bloomington, IL 61702-0515. TEL 309-828-5092. Ed. Vera Swantner. illus.; stat. circ. 1,200. **Indexed:** Amer.Hist.& Life, Hist.Abstr.
    Formerly: Central Illinois Historical Messenger (ISSN 0008-9419)

200   UK
HISTORICAL SOCIETY OF THE CHURCH IN WALES. JOURNAL. 1946. a. £2. Historical Society of the Church in Wales, c/o Owen W. Jones, The Vicarage, Builth Wells, Brec, Wales. Ed. Canon David Walker. charts; stat. **Indexed:** Br.Archaeol.Abstr.

940 200   UK
HISTORICAL SOCIETY OF THE PRESBYTERIAN CHURCH OF WALES. JOURNAL. (Text in English and Welsh) 1916. a. 50p. Historical Society of the Presbyterian Church of Wales, The Manse, Caradog Rd., Aberystwyth, Dyfed, Wales. Ed. Rev. Gomer M. Roberts. bk.rev. circ. 600.

286   US   ISSN 0018-3229
HOGAR CRISTIANO. (Text in Spanish) 1957. q. $9. Casa Bautista de Publicaciones, Box 4255, El Paso, TX 79914. TEL 915-566-9656. Ed. Exzequiel San Martin. illus. circ. 15,000.

285   US   ISSN 1040-8584
HOLINESS DIGEST. s-a. membership. Christian Holiness Association, Box 100, Wilmore, KY 40390. TEL 606-858-4091. FAX 606-858-4096. Eds. Steve Schellin, Patricia Walls. adv.; bk.rev. circ. 5,600.
    Description: Examines the idea of biblical holiness in a secular age.

283   US
HOLY CROSS. NEWSLETTER. vol.4, 1965. 3/yr. contributions. Order of the Holy Cross, Holy Cross Monastery, Box 99, West Park, NY 12493. TEL 914-384-6660. circ. 24,000. **Document type:** newspaper.
    Formerly (until 1978): Holy Cross News (ISSN 0018-3725)

284   US   ISSN 0738-0534
HOMILETIC; review of publications in religious communications. 1976. s-a. $9 to libraries. Religious Speech Communication Association, c/o Lutheran Theological Seminary, 61 W. Confederate Ave., Gettysburg, PA 17325. TEL 717-334-6286. FAX 717-334-3469. (Co-sponsor: Academy of Homiletics) Ed. Richard L. Thulin. adv.: page $150; trim 5 x 8; advis. comm.: Ed. Richard Thulin. bk.rev.; abstr.; bibl. circ. 1,500. (back issues avail.) **Document type:** academic/scholarly publication.
    Description: Interdisciplinary journal exploring disciplines related to religious communication, biblical interpretation, theology, worship, art and media, human sciences and culture, and communication theory.

283   US   ISSN 1040-6255
HOMILETICS; the art of writing and preaching sermons. 1989. q. $37.95. Communication Resources Inc., 4150 Belden Village St., Ste. 400, Canton, OH 44718-2502. TEL 800-992-2144. FAX 216-493-7897. Ed. Timothy Merrill. (also avail. in diskette format) **Document type:** trade publication.
    Description: Provides sermon resources for Protestant pastors.

HORIZON (NEPTUNE). see *GERONTOLOGY AND GERIATRICS*

285   US   ISSN 1041-5270
HORIZONS UNLIMITED. 1987. s-a. free. Redeeming Love Christian Center, 145 W. Rt. 59, Box 577, Nanuet, NY 10954-9963. TEL 914-623-9300. FAX 914-623-0521. Ed. Deborah D. Walker. circ. 44,000.
    Description: Biblically-based teachings by Clinton and Sarah Utterbach, fellowship's pastors and a variety of guest writers. Focus is on the result of practical application of biblical principles in the lives of individuals featured.

HUGUENOT TRAILS. see *HISTORY — History Of North And South America*

HUMAN DEVELOPMENT (HARTFORD). see *PSYCHOLOGY*

283   CN   ISSN 0018-7917
HURON CHURCH NEWS. 1950. 10/yr. Can.$10. Anglican Church of Canada, Diocese of Huron, 4-220 Dundas St., London, ON N6A 1H3, Canada. TEL 519-434-6893. FAX 519-673-4151. Ed. Rev. Kevin J. Dixon; Pub. Archbishop Percy O'Driscoll. adv. contact: Robert Browning. bk.rev.; illus. circ. 26,000. (tabloid format)

284 783   DK   ISSN 0106-4940
ML3142
HYMNOLOGISKE MEDDELELSER; tidsskrift om salmer. (Text in Danish, Norwegian and Swedish; summaries in English and German) 1972. q. DKK 150. Salmehistorisk Selskab, Koebenhavns Universitet, Institut for Kirkehistorie, Koebmagergade 44-46, DK-1150 Copenhagen K, Denmark. TEL 45-35-32-36-23. Ed. Peter Balslev-Clausen. bk.rev.; illus. circ. 700. (back issues avail.) **Indexed:** M.L.A.
    Description: Discusses hymnology and new hymns from Denmark, Norway, Sweden and Finland.

284   SZ
IDEA MAGAZIN. (Text in German) 1975. s-m. 98 SFr. (Informationsdienst der Schweizerischen Evangelischen Allianz) Idea Schweiz, Postfach 3320, CH-6002 Lucerne, Switzerland. TEL 041-236779. FAX 041-232904. TELEX 817585146-COM-CH. Ed. Fritz Imhof. adv.; bk.rev.; illus.; tr.lit. circ. 4,500. **Document type:** bulletin.
    Former titles: Idea Schweiz; Schweizerische Arbeitsgemeinschaft fuer Evangelisation.

284   GW   ISSN 0721-8796
IDEA-SPEKTRUM. English edition. 1979. w. DM.212 for German. ed.; English. ed. DM.60. Idea e.V., Postfach 1820, 35528 Wetzlar, Germany. TEL 06641-9014-0. FAX 06641-901444. Ed. Helmut Matthies. adv.; bk.rev. circ. 21,000. (back issues avail.) **Document type:** academic/scholarly publication.

283   ISSN 1075-1467
▼**IDEASOURCE;** enlightening ideas for the church, from the church. 1994. m. $39.95. Communication Resources Inc., 4150 Belden Village St., Ste.400, Canton, OH 44718-2502. TEL 800-992-2144. FAX 216-493-7897. Ed. Stan Purdum. (also avail. in looseleaf format; back issues avail.) **Document type:** newsletter.
    Description: Contains ideas churches have used in various areas to promote fellowship, stewardship and community service.

284   AG   ISSN 0019-1671
IGLESIA EVANGELICA DEL RIO DE LA PLATA. REVISTA PARROQUIAL.* (Text in German, Spanish) 1895. m. Arg.$300($10) Federacion Argentina de Iglesias Evangelicas, Jose Maria Moreno 873, 1424 Buenos Aires, Argentina. TEL 54-1-9225356. adv.; bk.rev. circ. 5,100.

284   TZ   ISSN 0856-1931
IJA WEBONERE. (Text in Haya, Swahili) vol.14, 1968. bi-m. Sh.300($30) Evangelical Lutheran Church in Tanzania, North Western Diocese, Box 277, Bukoba, Tanzania. TELEX 58387-ELCT-TZ. Ed. Rev. J. Kalugendo. adv.; stat. (looseleaf format)

286   US   ISSN 0019-1868
ILLINOIS BAPTIST. 1905. w. $6. Illinois Baptist State Association, Box 3486, Springfield, IL 62708. TEL 217-786-2638. Ed. Robert J. Hastings. bk.rev.; charts; illus.; stat. circ. 46,000. (tabloid format; also avail. in microform)

RELIGIONS AND THEOLOGY — PROTESTANT

284.2   SA   ISSN 0378-4088
IMBONGI YENKOSI. (Text in Zulu) 1952. m. (11/yr.). R.3. Reformed Churches in South Africa - Gereformeerde Kerke in Suid-Afrika, P.O. Box 59, Hammanskraal 0400, South Africa. Ed. Rev. W.L. Kurpershoek. circ. 2,150.

284   GW
IMMER GRUEN. 1911. a. DM.6.80. Quell Verlag, Fuertbachstr. 12A, 70178 Stuttgart, Germany. TEL 0711-60100-0. Ed. Johannes Burdinski. circ. 25,000. **Document type:** bulletin.

286   US   ISSN 0019-2821
IMPACT (WHEATON). 1943. 4/yr. $3. C B International, Box 5, Wheaton, IL 60189-0005. TEL 708-665-1200. Ed. Dennis Callaway. bk.rev.; film rev.; charts; illus.; stat.; tr.lit. circ. 40,375.
    Formerly: Conservative Baptist Impact.
    Description: Discusses mission work in the world.

284   SA   ISSN 1018-6441
IN DIE SKRIFLIG. (Text in Afrikaans, Dutch, English; summaries in English) 1966. 4/yr. R.30($30) (effective 1994). (Gereformeerde Teologiese Vereniging) Buro vir Wetenskaplike Tydskrifte - Bureau for Scholarly Journals, Private Bag X6001, Potchefstroom 2520, South Africa. TEL 27-148-2991769. FAX 27-148-2991562. E-mail: BWTMV@Puknet.puk.AC.ZA. Eds. J.H. van Wyk, Mariana Venter. adv.; bk.rev.; abstr.; circ. 350 (paid). **Document type:** academic/scholarly publication.
    Description: Publishes theological research articles in the Reformational tradition.
    Refereed Serial

284   US
IN PARTNERSHIP. 1978. q. free. Lutheran Social Services of Metropolitan New York, Inc., 27 Park Pl., New York, NY 10007-2502. FAX 212-406-9130. Ed. Dorothy M. Scholz. adv. circ. 16,000. **Indexed:** Bibl.& Ind.Geol.
    Former titles: On the Edge (New York); Which superseded: Focus (Brooklyn); Which was formerly: Our70's.
    Description: News and notes on Christian social mission from Lutheran social services in N.Y.

284   US
IN SEASON.* 1974. w. $25. Cathedral Publishers, Box 129, Royal Oak, MI 48068-0129. Ed. H. Dean Lueking. circ. 2,000.

284   II
INDIAN LUTHERAN NEWSLETTER. (Text in English) 1967. q. Rs.12. United Evangelical Lutheran Churches in India, No. 1 First St., Haddows Rd., Madras 600 006, India. TEL 91-44-827-1676. FAX 91-44-827-4557. TELEX 41-66-13 NIEO IN. Ed. Rev. J. Daniel Victor. adv.; bk.rev. circ. 1,200. **Document type:** newsletter.
    Former titles (until 1991): Indian Lutheran; (until 1980): Gospel Witness (ISSN 0017-2391)

287   II   ISSN 0019-6487
INDIAN WITNESS. 1871. s-m. Rs.10($6) to individuals; institutions Rs.15. Methodist Church in India, 25 Lodi Rd., New Delhi 110003, India. (U.S. subscr. address: c/o 1st United Methodist Church, 1589 W. Maple, Birmingham, MI 48010) Ed. Richard Renwick Smyth. adv.; bk.rev. circ. 2,500.
    Description: Church news and views.

284   IO
INDONESIA. DIREKTORAT JENDERAL BIMBINGAN MASYARAKAT KRISTEN-PROTESTAN LAPORAN TAHUNAN/INDONESIA. DIRECTORATE GENERAL OF PROTESTANT AFFAIRS. ANNUAL REPORT.* a. Directorate General of Protestant Affairs, Ministry of Religious Affairs, Jalan M.H. Thamrin 6, Jakarta Pusat, Indonesia.

286 248.83   US   ISSN 0020-1944
INSIGHT (HAGERSTOWN); a magazine of Christian understanding for young Adventists. 1970. w. $36.97. (General Conference of Seventh-day Adventists) Review and Herald Publishing Association, 55 W. Oak Ridge Dr., Hagerstown, MD 21740. TEL 301-791-7000. Ed. Lori Peckham. adv.; bk.rev.; illus. circ. 22,000. (reprint service avail. from UMI) **Indexed:** Chr.Per.Ind.
    Supersedes: Youth's Instructor.

286   CN   ISSN 0383-6061
INTERCOM (GUELPH). 1968. bi-m. Fellowship of Evangelical Baptist Churches in Canada, 679 Southgate Dr., Guelph, ON N1G 4S2, Canada. TEL 519-821-4830. FAX 519-821-9829.

266 026   US   ISSN 0272-6122
BV2350
INTERNATIONAL BULLETIN OF MISSIONARY RESEARCH. 1950; N.S. 1977. q. $18 (effective 1995-1996). Overseas Ministries Study Center, 490 Prospect St., New Haven, CT 06511-2196. TEL 203-624-6672. (Subscr. to: Box 3000, Denville, NJ 07834) Ed. Gerald H. Anderson. adv.; bk.rev.; bibl.; index, cum.index: 1977-1980, 1981-1984, 1985-1988, 1989-1992. circ. 6,000. (also avail. in microform from UMI; reprint service avail. from UMI) **Indexed:** CERDIC, Chr.Per.Ind., G.Soc.Sci.& Rel.Per.Lit., Rel.& Theol.Abstr. (1981-), Rel.Ind.One.
    —BLDSC (4538.080000); UMI; UnCover.
    Formed by the merger of: Gospel in Context (ISSN 0193-8320); Occasional Bulletin of Missionary Research (ISSN 0364-2178); Which was formerly (until 1977): Missionary Research Library. Occasional Bulletin (ISSN 0026-606X)
    Description: Covers the latest developments in Christian mission worldwide.

INTERNATIONAL DIRECTORY OF CHRISTIAN ARTS ORGANIZATIONS. see *ART*

286 371.3   US   ISSN 0162-4342
EL INTERPRETE. (Text in Spanish) q. $9.75. Southern Baptist Convention, Sunday School Board, 127 Ninth Ave., N., Nashville, TN 37234. TEL 800-458-2772. FAX 615-251-5933. **Indexed:** M.L.A.

286 375   US   ISSN 0740-0063
EL INTERPRETE. MAESTROS. (Text in Spanish) q. $15.25. Southern Baptist Convention, Sunday School Board, 127 Ninth Ave., N., Nashville, TN 37234. TEL 800-458-2772.

287   US   ISSN 0020-9678
INTERPRETER (NASHVILLE). 1957. 8/yr. $8. United Methodist Communications, 810 12th Ave. S., Nashville, TN 37203-4744. TEL 615-742-5400. FAX 615-742-5460. Ed. M. Garlinda Burton; Pub. Arvin R. Luchs. adv.; bk.rev.; charts; illus.; circ. 20,097 (paid); 264,903 (controlled). (also avail. in microfilm from UMI; back issues avail.) **Indexed:** Comput.Lit.Ind., Meth.Per.Ind.
    ●Also available online. Vendor(s): University Microfilms International.
    —UMI.
    Formed by the 1969 merger of: Spotlight and Methodist Story; Methodist Story.
    Description: Directed to local United Methodist Church leaders containing program ideas and resources.

285 371.2   US
INTERVARSITY. 1982. q. donation basis. Inter-Varsity Christian Fellowship of the United States of America, 6400 Schroeder Rd., Box 7895, Madison, WI 53707-7895. TEL 608-274-9001. FAX 608-274-7882. Ed. Neal Kunde. circ. 50,000. (back issues avail.)
    Description: Reports InterVarsity's activity on college campuses.

286   UK
IRISH BAPTIST. 1877. 11/yr. £10 (E.C. subscr. £13.20; elsewhere $20). Baptist Union of Ireland, 117 Lisburn Rd., Belfast BT9 7AF, N. Ireland. TEL 0232-663108. FAX 0232-663616. circ. 3,150.

286.0415   UK   ISSN 0075-0727
IRISH BAPTIST HISTORICAL SOCIETY. JOURNAL. 1969. a. £6($10) Baptist Union of Ireland, 117 Lisburn Rd., Belfast BT9 7AF, N. Ireland. TEL 0232-669157. FAX 0232-663616. Ed. Joshua Thompson. bk.rev.; cum.index: vols.1-20. circ. 250. **Document type:** academic/scholarly publication.

JAHRBUCH FUER DIE GESCHICHTE DES PROTESTANTISMUS IN OESTERREICH. see *HISTORY — History Of Europe*

283   JM   ISSN 0047-1720
JAMAICA CHURCHMAN. 1970. m. 75p.($1.10) Anglican Diocese of Jamaica, Anglican Church Office, Kingston 5, Jamaica, W.I. Ed. Barbara Gloudon. adv.; illus. circ. 6,000.

266   JA   ISSN 0021-440X
JAPAN HARVEST. (Text in English) 1951. q. $20. Japan Evangelical Missionary Association, 2-1 Kanda Surugadai, Chiyoda-ku, Tokyo 101, Japan. FAX 03-3295-6783. Ed. Don Wright. adv.; bk.rev.; charts; illus. circ. 1,200.
    Description: Discusses mission work in the country.

268   US
JOURNAL OF CHRISTIAN EDUCATION OF THE AFRICAN METHODIST EPISCOPAL CHURCH. 1936. q. $3. African Methodist Episcopal Church, Christian Education Department, 500 Eighth Ave. S., Nashville, TN 37203. TEL 615-256-7020. FAX 615-244-7604. Ed. Rev. Edgar L. Mack. adv.; bk.rev.; film rev.; rec.rev.; charts; illus. circ. 6,000. (also avail. in microform from UMI; reprint service avail. from UMI)
    —UMI.
    Former titles (until 1982): Journal of Religious Education of the African Methodist Episcopal Church (ISSN 0276-0770); (until 1980): Journal of Religious Education (ISSN 0022-4219)

289.809   CN   ISSN 0824-5053
BX8101
JOURNAL OF MENNONITE STUDIES. (Text in English, German) 1983. a. Can.$10. University of Winnipeg, Chair of Mennonite Studies, Winnipeg, Man. R3B 2E9, Canada. TEL 204-786-9104. FAX 204-786-1824. Eds. Harry Loewen, Al Reimer. adv.; bk.rev. circ. 600. (back issues avail.)

284   UK   ISSN 0966-7369
BR1644
JOURNAL OF PENTECOSTAL THEOLOGY. 1992. 2/yr. £15($20) to individuals; institutions £20($30). Sheffield Academic Press Ltd., Mansion House, 19 Kingfield Rd., Sheffield S11 9AS, England. TEL 44-171-267-4466. FAX 44-171-482-2293. E-mail: admin@sheffac.demon.co.uk. **Document type:** academic/scholarly publication.
    Description: Covers the areas of biblical studies, modern theology, ethics and practical theology.

200   US   ISSN 0361-1906
JOURNAL OF THEOLOGY. 1961. 4/yr. $9 (foreign $12). Immanuel Lutheran College, 501 Grover Rd., Eau Claire, WI 54701. TEL 715-836-6621. FAX 715-836-6634. (Subscr. to: 2750 Oxford St., N., Roseville, MN 55113) Ed. John Lau. bk.rev. circ. 280. **Document type:** academic/scholarly publication.

200   AT   ISSN 0314-6235
JOURNEY (BRISBANE). 1977. m. (except Jan.). Aus.$29($55) Uniting Church in Australia, Communications Services Unit, P.O. Box 674, Brisbane, Qld. 4001, Australia. TEL 07-377-9911. FAX 07-377-9796. Ed. Andrew Demack. adv. contact: Judy Taubner. bk.rev.; film rev.; charts; illus. circ. 3,200. (also avail. in microfilm; back issues avail.)
    Formerly: Life and Times.

268 305.4   US   ISSN 1073-4473
JOURNEY: A WOMAN'S GUIDE TO INTIMACY WITH GOD. m. $18.50. Southern Baptist Convention, Sunday School Board, 127 Ninth Ave., N., Nashville, TN 37234. TEL 800-458-2772.
    Description: Provides devotional readings for women.

284 301.412   US   ISSN 0164-4882
THE JOYFUL WOMAN. 1978. bi-m. $13. Joyful Woman Ministries, Box 90028, Chattanooga, TN 37412. TEL 615-698-7318. Ed. Elizabeth Handford. adv.; bk.rev. circ. 15,000.
    Description: Covers every facet of a Christian woman's life.

266   US   ISSN 0893-1607
JUBILEE; the monthly newsletter of Prison Fellowship. 1977. m. free. Prison Fellowship, Box 17500, Washington, DC 20041-0500. TEL 703-478-0100. FAX 703-478-0452. Ed. Becky Beane. circ. 180,000. **Document type:** newsletter.

280.4 028.5   AT   ISSN 1030-0287
JUNIOR CLUBHOUSE. 1975. m. (except Jan.). Aus.$10.50 (foreign Aus.$13.50). Mission Publications of Australia, 19 Cascade St., P.O. Box 21, Lawson, N.S.W. 2783, Australia. TEL 61-47-591003. FAX 61-47-591101. Ed. Marilyn Banks. circ. 2,000.
    Description: Christian magazine for children ages 5-12.

RELIGIONS AND THEOLOGY — PROTESTANT

285   CU   ISSN 0864-0254
JUPRECU. 3/yr. Iglesia Presbiteriana, Salud No. 222, Lealtad y Companario, Havana 2, Cuba. TEL 809 61-1558. Dir. Francisco Marrero.

287   US   ISSN 1073-8479
KALEIDOSCOPE (BALTIMORE); a magazine about today's Christians. 1993. bi-m. $18. 5124 Greenwich Ave., Baltimore, MD 21229. TEL 410-362-4700; 800-492-2525. FAX 410-362-4714. E-mail: umkaleido@aol.com. Ed. James E. Skillington. adv.: B&W page $2675, color page $3025; trim 8 1/4 x 10 7/8; adv. contact: Trisk Twentey. bk.rev. circ. 110,000. **Document type:** consumer publication.
   Description: Written for and about active Christians striving to make a positive difference in today's world.

284.2   SA   ISSN 0023-0596
KERKBLAD. (Text in Afrikaans) 1873. fortn. R.44. Reformed Churches in South Africa - Gereformeerde Kerke in Suid-Afrika, P.O. Box 20008, Noordbrug 2522, Potchefstroom, South Africa. Ed. G.T.C. Jordaan. adv.; bk.rev. circ. 9,300.

284   SA
DIE KERKBODE; amptelike blad van die Nederduitse Gereformeerde Kerk. (Text in Afrikaans) 1849. w. Nederduitse Gereformeerde Kerk in Suid-Afrika, P.O. Box 1444, Cape Town 8000, South Africa. Ed. G.S.J. Moller. adv.; bk.rev. circ. 19,000. (back issues avail.) **Document type:** newspaper.

284   NE   ISSN 0023-0618
KERKBODE VAN NEDERLANDS GEREFORMEERDE KERKEN. 1945. 17/yr. fl.46.75. Buijten en Schipperheijn, B.V., Valkenburgerstraat 106, 1011 NA Amsterdam, Netherlands. FAX 31-20-6263956. Ed.Bd. adv.; bk.rev. circ. 1,000. (tabloid format)
   Formerly (until 1979): Kerkbode van Gereformeerde Kerken in Noord en Zuid-Holland.

284   GW   ISSN 0173-4636
KIRCHE IM LAENDLICHEN RAUM. 1950. q. DM.26 (foreign DM.36). Evangelische Landjugendakademie, Dieperzbergweg 13-17, 57610 Altenkirchen, Germany. TEL 02681-9516-0. FAX 02681-70206. Ed. Hans-Heiner Heuser. circ. 900. (back issues avail.) **Document type:** bulletin.

284   GW   ISSN 0453-9273
KIRCHE IM OSTEN. 1958. irreg. (approx. 1/yr.). DM.95. (Studien zur Osteuropaeischen Kirchengeschichte und Kirchenkunde) Vandenhoeck und Ruprecht, Theaterstr. 13, 37073 Goettingen, Germany. Ed. Guenther Schulz. (back issues avail.) **Document type:** academic/scholarly publication.

284   GW   ISSN 0178-8906
KIRCHLICHER DIENST IN DER ARBEITSWELT; Zeitschrift fuer evangelische Arbeitnehmer und evangelische Industrie- und Sozialarbeit. 1959. bi-m. DM.26.50($15) (Kirchlicher Dienst in der Arbeitswelt) Verlag Stimme der Arbeit, Postfach 1113, 73085 Boll, Germany. TEL 07164-2008. FAX 07164-5798. Ed. Ruediger Weiser. adv.; bk.rev. circ. 3,500. (back issues avail.) **Document type:** corporate report.

274   GW   ISSN 0075-6210
KIRCHLICHES JAHRBUCH FUER DIE EVANGELISCHE KIRCHE IN DEUTSCHLAND. a. price varies. Guetersloher Verlagshaus Chr. Kaiser, Carl-Bertelsmann-Str. 270, 33311 Guetersloh, Germany. TEL 05241-7405-0. FAX 05241-740548. **Document type:** bulletin.

284.1   IC   ISSN 1021-8351
KIRKJURITID. 1935. q. Prestafelag Islands, Kirkjutorg 4, Reykjavik, Iceland. TEL 354-562-1525.

KOERS; bulletin vir Christelike wetenskap - bulletin for Christian scholarship. see *RELIGIONS AND THEOLOGY*

230.05   US   ISSN 1047-1057
BR1
KOINONIA; the Princeton Theological Seminary graduate forum. (Text in English, occasionally in French, German, Greek, Hebrew) 1989. 2/yr. $18 to individuals; institutions $24; students $12 (effective 1993). Princeton Theological Seminary, CN 821, Princeton, NJ 08540-0803. TEL 609-497-7788. FAX 609-924-2973. Ed. Gregory L. Glover. bk.rev.; bibl. circ. 600. (back issues avail.) **Indexed:** Rel.Ind.One. **Document type:** academic/scholarly publication.
   Description: Promotes interdisciplinary and interreligious discussion and explorations of new and emerging areas and issues in the study of religion.

284   GW
KREIS DER FREUNDE UND FOERDERER DER LUTHERISCHEN THEOLOGISCHEN HOCHSCHULE IN OBERURSEL. MITTEILUNGEN. 1960. 2/yr. Kreis der Freunde und Foerderer der Lutherischen Theologischen Hochschule in Oberursel e.V., Altkoenigstr. 150, 61440 Oberursel, Germany. Ed. Wilhelm Rothfuchs. **Document type:** newsletter.

289   GW
DER KRIEGSRUF. 1887. w. DM.60 (Europe DM.90). (Heilsarmee - Salvation Army) Heilsarmee Verlag, Salierring 23-27, 50677 Cologne, Germany. TEL 0221-208190. FAX 0221-2081943. Ed. Evelin Binsch. bk.rev. circ. 15,000. **Document type:** corporate report.
   Description: Official organ of the Salvation Army in Germany.

266   MW
KUUNIKA. (Text in Chichewa) 1909. m. 72 T. (Christian Literature Fund) Presbyterian Church of Central Africa, Nkhoma Synod, P.O. Nkhoma, Lilongwe, Malawi. Ed. Rev. M.C. Nkhalambayausi. bk.rev. circ. 6,000.

266   US
L I R S BULLETIN. 1964. 2/yr. free to qualified personnel. Lutheran Immigration and Refugee Service, 390 Park Ave. S., New York, NY 10016-8803. Ed. Lily R. Wu. circ. 3,500.
   Formerly: L I R S Information Bulletin.
   Description: Articles about immigration ranging from news of previous immigrants to why the church is involved in helping refugees. Updates on LIRS activities in resettlement and advocacy, and on developments in US immigration policy.

284 370.196   US
L P E A HEARTBEAT. 1988. 6/yr. Luis Palau Evangelistic Association, Box 1173, Portland, OR 97207. TEL 503-643-0777. FAX 503-643-6851. Ed. Mike Umlandt. circ. 15,000. (back issues avail.) **Document type:** newsletter.
   Description: Focuses primarily on Evangelistic ministry of LPEA worldwide.

284   GW   ISSN 0174-1764
BX8001
L W B DOKUMENTATION. REPORT. 1978. irreg. DM.24. (Lutheran World Federation - Geneva) Kreuz-Verlag Zeitschriften GmbH, Breitwiesenstr. 30, 70565 Stuttgart, Germany. TEL 0711-7880323. circ. 3,000. **Document type:** bulletin.
—CCC.

286   US   ISSN 0893-5262
LAD. 1987. m. Southern Baptist Convention, Brotherhood Commission, 1548 Poplar Ave., Memphis, TN 38104. TEL 800-727-6466.
   Description: For students in grades 1-3.

280   US
LATIN AMERICA EVANGELIST. 1921. q. free. Latin America Mission, Box 52-7900, Miami, FL 33152. TEL 305-884-8400. FAX 305-885-8649. Ed. Paul E. Pretiz. circ. 17,000. **Document type:** trade publication.
   Description: Focuses on Latin America and the Christian Church there.

280 370   US   ISSN 0895-1403
LEADER IN THE CHURCH SCHOOL TODAY. 1988. q. $14; newsstand price: $3.50. (United Methodist Church, Board of Discipleship) United Methodist Publishing House, Cokesbury, 201 Eighth Ave., S., Nashville, TN 37202. TEL 615-749-6292; 800-672-1789. FAX 615-749-6512. Ed. Marvin W. Cropsey; Pub. Robert K. Feaser. bk.rev.; index. circ. 14,000. **Document type:** consumer publication.
   Formerly (until 1988): Children's Leader (ISSN 0276-3427)
   Description: Nurtures and supports leaders in Christian education, equipping them with knowledge and skills, providing information about resources, training, and programs.

284   US   ISSN 0199-7661
BV4000
LEADERSHIP (CAROL STREAM); a practical journal for church leaders. 1980. 4/yr. $22. Christianity Today, Inc., 465 Gunderson Dr., Carol Stream, IL 60188. TEL 708-260-6200. FAX 708-260-0114. E-mail: leaderj@aol.com. (Subscr. to: CDS, Box 11618, Des Moines, IA 50340. TEL 800-777-3136) Ed. Kevin A. Miller. bibl.; illus. circ. 75,000. (also avail. in microfiche; back issues avail.) **Indexed:** CCR, Rel.& Theol.Abstr. (1980-). **Document type:** consumer publication.
—UMI.
   Description: Offers practical help for pastors and local church leaders for everyday ministry situations.

LEAPING; magazine of Christian dance fellowship of Australia. see *DANCE*

284   GW   ISSN 0173-4199
DIE LESEPREDIGT. 1967. a. (in 2 vols.). DM.29.50 per vol. Guetersloher Verlagshaus Chr. Kaiser, Carl-Bertelsmann-Str. 270, 33311 Guetersloh, Germany. TEL 05241-7405-0. FAX 05241-740548. **Document type:** bulletin.
—BLDSC (5183.570000).

269.2   CN
LIBERATION. 1972. q. Ken Campbell Evangelistic Association, Box 100, Milton, Ont. L9T 2Y3, Canada. TEL 416-878-8461. Ed. Ken Cambell. illus. circ. 35,000. **Indexed:** Arts & Hum.Cit.Ind., G.Soc.Sci.& Rel.Per.Lit.
   Formerly: Encounter (ISSN 0315-0097)

266.6   LB
LIBERIA BAPTIST MISSIONARY AND EDUCATIONAL CONVENTION. YEARBOOK.* (Text in English) a. Liberia Baptist Missionary and Educational Convention, Bentol City, Liberia. illus.

LIBRARIANS' CHRISTIAN FELLOWSHIP NEWSLETTER. see *LIBRARY AND INFORMATION SCIENCES*

284   GW   ISSN 0047-4584
LICHT UND LEBEN. 1889. m. DM.30.60. (Evangelische Gesellschaft fuer Deutschland e.V.) Verlag und Schriftenmission der Evangelischer Gesellschaft fuer Deutschland, Kaiserstr. 78, 42329 Wuppertal, Germany. TEL 0202-784018. FAX 0202-7866318. Ed. Volker Heckl. adv. contact: Herbert Becker. bk.rev. circ. 6,000. **Document type:** bulletin.
   Description: Aims to disseminate knowledge about the Bible and Christianity. Discusses missionary activities.

283   GW
LICHTSTRAHLEN; taegliche Bibellese. 1897. a. DM.7.50. (Deutscher E C-Verband) Born-Verlag, Leuschnerstr. 72-74, 34134 Kassel, Germany. TEL 0561-40950. FAX 0561-4095-112. circ. 50,000. **Document type:** bulletin.

284   GW
LIEBFRAUEN KALENDER. 1983. a. DM.5. Birken Verlag, 85399 Hallbergmoos-Birkeneck, Germany. FAX 0811-82119. Ed. Alois Linder.

274   UK   ISSN 0024-306X
LIFE AND WORK; the record of the Church of Scotland. 1879. m. £10. Church of Scotland, 121 George St., Edinburgh EH2 4YN, Scotland. FAX 0131-220-3133. Ed. Robin E. Hill. adv. contact: David Carson. bk.rev.; illus. circ. 70,800. **Indexed:** CERDIC.

RELIGIONS AND THEOLOGY — PROTESTANT

268 378 US
LIFE AND WORK DIRECTIONS: BIBLE STUDIES FOR ADULTS 18-24. 1970. q. $11.25. Southern Baptist Convention, Sunday School Board, 127 Ninth Ave., N., Nashville, TN 37234. TEL 800-458-2772.
 Supersedes in part (in 1995): Young Adult Bible Study (ISSN 0162-4814)

268 378 US ISSN 1076-5905
LIFE AND WORK DIRECTIONS: BIBLE STUDIES FOR ADULTS 25-34. 1970. q. $11.25. Southern Baptist Convention, Sunday School Board, 127 Ninth Ave., N., Nashville, TN 37234. TEL 800-458-2772.
 Supersedes in part (in 1995): Young Adult Bible Study (ISSN 0162-4814)

268 375 US ISSN 1076-593X
LIFE AND WORK DIRECTIONS: TEACHER EDITION. q. $19.75. Southern Baptist Convention, Sunday School Board, 127 Ninth Ave., N., Nashville, TN 37234. TEL 800-458-2772.
 Description: Provides guidelines for Sunday school teachers of students 18-24.

268 374 US ISSN 1076-5859
LIFE AND WORK PATHWAYS: BIBLE STUDIES FOR ADULTS 70 & UP. q. $11.25. Southern Baptist Convention, Sunday School Board, 127 Ninth Ave., N., Nashville, TN 37234. TEL 800-458-2772.
 Supersedes in part: Senior Adult Bible Study (ISSN 0162-4733)

268 374 US ISSN 1076-5883
LIFE AND WORK PURSUITS: BIBLE STUDIES FOR ADULTS 25-54. (American Indian edition (ISSN 1040-5086) & Vietnamese edition (ISSN 1040-5178) ceased in 1993) q. $11.25. Southern Baptist Convention, Sunday School Board, 127 Ninth Ave. N., Nashville, TN 37234. TEL 800-458-2772.
 Formerly: Adult Bible Study (ISSN 0162-4156)

286 US
LIFE AND WORK PURSUITS: BIBLE STUDIES FOR SINGLE ADULTS. q. $11.25. Southern Baptist Convention, Sunday School Board, 127 Ninth Ave. N., Nashville, TN 37234. TEL 800-458-2772.
 Former titles: Single Adult Bible Study (ISSN 0731-1478); (until 1982): Collegiate Bible Study (ISSN 0162-4571)

268 371.3 US ISSN 1076-5921
LIFE AND WORK PURSUITS: TEACHER EDITION. q. $11.29. Southern Baptist Convention, Sunday School Board, 127 Ninth Ave. N., Nashville, TN 37234. TEL 800-458-2772.
 Formerly: Adult Bible Teacher (ISSN 0162-4164)

268 375 US ISSN 1076-5913
LIFE AND WORK VENTURES AND PATHWAYS: TEACHER EDITION. q. $19.75. Southern Baptist Convention, Sunday School Board, 127 Ninth Ave. N., Nashville, TN 37234. TEL 800-458-2772.

268 374 US ISSN 1076-5867
LIFE AND WORK VENTURES: BIBLE STUDIES FOR ADULTS 55-69. q. $11.25. Southern Baptist Convention, Sunday School Board, 127 Ninth Ave. N., Nashville, TN 37234. TEL 800-458-2772.
 Supersedes in part: Senior Adult Bible Study (ISSN 0162-4733)

284 UK
LIFE INDEED. 1892. bi-m. £4.14. Faith Mission, 2 Drum St., Gilmerton, Edinburgh EH17 8QG, Scotland. TEL 0131-664-5814. FAX 0131-664-2260. Ed. Rev. Dr. Colin N. Peckham. adv. contact: Keith Percival. cum.index. circ. 8,500. (back issues avail.)

266 SA
DIE LIGDRAER - LIGSTRAAL. 1940. m. R.37,75 (effective 1995). Uniting Reformed Church in Southern Africa, Private Bag X1, Belhar 7507, South Africa. Ed. Dr. P.J.A. Fourie. adv.; bk.rev.; bibl.; illus.; stat.; index. circ. 25,000. **Document type:** newspaper.
 Formerly: Ligdraer (ISSN 0024-3272); Incorporates: Ligstraal.
 Description: Provides articles relevant to Christian daily life, news about the church at an international, national and congregational level.

287 US ISSN 0024-3299
LIGHT AND LIFE. 1896. m. $15 (effective 1995). (Free Methodist Church of North America) Free Methodist Publishing House, Box 535002, Indianapolis, IN 46253-5002. TEL 317-244-3660. FAX 317-244-1247. Ed. Robert Haslam. adv.; bk.rev. circ. 25,000. **Indexed:** G.Soc.Sci.& Rel.Per.Lit.
 Description: Articles about Christians involved in service ministries.

284 UK
LIGHT AND LIFE. 1935. 3/yr. U F M Worldwide, 47A Fleet St., Swindon, Wilts. SN1 1RE, England. TEL 01793-610515. FAX 01793-432255. Ed. Rev. P. Anderson. circ. 9,500. **Document type:** bulletin.
 Description: Contains articles, biographical sketches, and profiles of the missionary ministry of the U F M Worldwide.

266 AT
LIGHT AND LIFE; news-line. 1989. bi-m. Aus.$5. Asia Pacific Christian Mission, 345 Bell St., Preston, Vic. 3072, Australia. TEL 03-480-4722. FAX 03-480-4186. Ed. R.W. Averill. circ. 8,400. (back issues avail.)
 Description: Work of mission staff in partnership with nationals in the Asia-Pacific region. Informs supporters and those not involved in the work.

287 UK ISSN 0265-2226
LINCOLNSHIRE METHODIST HISTORY SOCIETY. JOURNAL. 1963. 2/yr. £3 to individual members; institutional members £5. Lincolnshire Methodist History Society, c/o J.S. English A.L.A., 1 Dorton Ave., Gainsborough, Lincs DN21 1UB, England. TEL 01427-615215. bk.rev. circ. 120. **Document type:** academic/scholarly publication.
 Description: Covers all aspects of the history of Methodism in Lincolnshire and South Humberside.

LINK & VISITOR; a magazine for Baptist women. see WOMEN'S INTERESTS

268 028.5 US ISSN 0162-4253
LIVING (NASHVILLE). q. $9.75. Southern Baptist Convention, Sunday School Board, 127 Ninth Ave. N., Nashville, TN 37234. TEL 800-458-2772.
 Description: Religious publication for preschool children ages 2-3.

283 US ISSN 0024-5240
LIVING CHURCH; an independent weekly record of the news of the Church and the views of Episcopalians. 1878. w. $39.50. Living Church Foundation, Inc., Box 92936, Milwaukee, WI 53202. TEL 414-276-5420. FAX 414-276-7483. Ed. David A. Kalvelage. adv. contact: Lila Thurber. bk.rev.; illus. circ. 9,000.

LIVING WITH TEENAGERS. see CHILDREN AND YOUTH — About

284 UK
LLANDAFF DIOCESAN DIRECTORY. a. £3. Llandaff Diocesan Board of Finance - Esgobaeth Llandaf Bwrdd Cyllid, Heol Fair, Llandaff, Cardiff CF5 2EE, Wales. TEL 01222-578899. FAX 01222-576198. Ed. M.J. Beasant. bibl.; index. circ. 1,000. **Document type:** directory.

287 UK ISSN 0024-5607
LOCAL PREACHERS MAGAZINE. 1850. q. membership. Methodist Local Preachers Mutual Aid Association, Head Office, Chorleywood Close, Rickmansworth, Herts. WD3 4EG, England. TEL 01923-775856. Ed. N. Clarkson. bk.rev. circ. 13,500. **Document type:** bulletin.

268 LB
LOMA WEEKLY PAPER.* (Text in English, Loca) 1951. w. $1. Lutheran Church in Liberia, Loma Literacy Center, Box 1046, Wozi, Monrovia, Liberia.

LOOK!; the juniors' magazine of the Baptist Missionary Society. see CHILDREN AND YOUTH — For

268 028.5 US ISSN 0162-4369
LOOK AND LISTEN. q. (plus regular w. nos.). $6.25. Southern Baptist Convention, Sunday School Board, 127 Ninth Ave. N., Nashville, TN 37234. TEL 800-458-2772.

284 US
THE LOOKOUT (CINCINNATI). 1894. w. $21. Standard Publishing, 8121 Hamilton Ave., Cincinnati, OH 45231. TEL 513-931-4050. Ed. Simon J. Dahlman. circ. 115,000.

286 US ISSN 0024-6743
LOUISIANA BAPTIST BUILDER. 1953. m. $6.50. Baptist Missionary Association of Louisiana, Box 1297, Denham Springs, LA 70727-1297. FAX 504-262-1808. Ed. Leroy Mayfield. adv.; bk.rev.; illus. circ. 1,665. (tabloid format) **Document type:** newspaper.
 Description: Provides information on mission work in the state.

284 GW ISSN 0340-6210
BR323.5
LUTHER. 1919. 3/yr. DM.36. (Luther-Gesellschaft) Vandenhoeck und Ruprecht, Robert-Bosch-Breite 6, 37079 Goettingen, Germany. TEL 0551-6959-26. FAX 0551-695917. (Subscr. to: 37070 Goettingen, Germany) adv.; bk.rev.; index. circ. 1,750. **Indexed:** CERDIC. **Document type:** academic/scholarly publication.
 —CCC.

284 AU
DIE LUTHER-KIRCHE. 1948. q. Evangelische Gemeinde A.B. Wien-Waehring, Martinstr. 25, A-1180 Vienna, Austria. TEL 01-4064534. FAX 01-4063638. Ed. Werner Puelz. circ. 4,000. **Document type:** bulletin.

284.1 US ISSN 0024-743X
BX8001
THE LUTHERAN; news magazine of the Evangelical Lutheran Church in America. 1860. 12/yr. $11.90. Augsburg Fortress (Chicago), 8765 Higgins Rd., Chicago, IL 60631. TEL 800-638-3522. FAX 312-380-2751. TELEX 4900009324 LUT. E-mail: lutheran-manazine.parl@ecunet.org. Ed. Edgar R. Trexler. adv. contact: Sigurd Hadland. bk.rev.; illus. circ. 800,000. (also avail. in microform from UMI) **Indexed:** CERDIC, G.Soc.Sci.& Rel.Per.Lit. **Document type:** consumer publication.
 —UMI; UnCover.
 Incorporates (as of 1987): Lutheran Standard (ISSN 0024-7545)
 Description: Contains news and activities of the Evangelical Lutheran Church in America, news of the world of religion, ethical reflections on issues in society, and personal Christian experience.

284 US
LUTHERAN ANNUAL. 1910. a. $9.25 for paper; spiral $11.75 (effective 1995). (Lutheran Church - Missouri Synod) Concordia Publishing House, 3558 Jefferson Ave., St. Louis, MO 63118. TEL 314-268-1000. Ed. Walter Rosin. adv. circ. 20,000. **Document type:** consumer publication.

284 AT ISSN 0726-4305
LUTHERAN CHURCH OF AUSTRALIA. YEARBOOK. 1967. a. Aus.$12. Openbook Publishers, 205 Halifax St., Adelaide, S.A. 5000, Australia. Ed. M. Oster. **Document type:** directory.
 Formed by the merger of: Australian Lutheran Almanac; Lutheran Almanac.

380 284 CN ISSN 0316-800X
BX8063.C2
LUTHERAN CHURCHES IN CANADA. DIRECTORY. 1954. a. Can.$7.50. Lutheran Council in Canada, 1512 St. James St., Winnipeg, MB R3H 0L2, Canada. TEL 204-786-6707. FAX 204-783-7548. Ed. L.C. Gilbertson. adv. circ. 1,600. **Document type:** directory.

280 US ISSN 0458-497X
BR1
LUTHERAN DIGEST. 1953. q. $20 for 2 years. Lutheran Digest, Inc., P.O. Box 4250, Hopkins, MN 55343. TEL 612-933-2820. FAX 612-933-5708. Ed. David L. Tank. circ. 150.000. (also avail. in Braille; large print) **Document type:** academic/scholarly publication.

LUTHERAN DIGEST (LARGE PRINT EDITION). see HANDICAPPED — Visually Impaired

LUTHERAN EDUCATION. see EDUCATION

RELIGIONS AND THEOLOGY — PROTESTANT

284.1 US ISSN 0024-7456
BX8001
LUTHERAN FORUM; an independent journal. (Supplement: Una Sancta) 1967. q. $22.50 (includes subscr. to Forum Letter). American Lutheran Publicity Bureau, Box 327, Delhi, NY 13753. TEL 607-746-7511. Ed. Rev. Leonard Klein. adv. contact: Martin A. Christiansen. bk.rev.; illus.; stat. circ. 3,500. (also avail. in microform from UMI; back issues avail.; reprint service avail. from UMI) **Indexed:** CERDIC, Rel.& Theol.Abstr. (1989-), Rel.Ind.One. **Document type:** bulletin.
—UMI.
Supersedes: American Lutheran Magazine.

284 US ISSN 0046-4732
LUTHERAN FORUM. FORUM LETTER. 1972. m. $22.50 (includes subscr. to Lutheran Forum). American Lutheran Publicity Bureau, Box 327, Delhi, NY 13753. TEL 607-746-7511. Ed. Russell E. Saltzman. bk.rev. circ. 3,500. (also avail. in microfilm from UMI; back issues avail.; reprint service avail. from UMI) **Indexed:** CERDIC. **Document type:** bulletin.
—UMI.
Description: Provides readers with information and viewpoints from all sides of Lutheranism.

285 977 US ISSN 0090-3817
BX8011.A1
LUTHERAN HISTORICAL CONFERENCE. ESSAYS AND REPORTS. 1964. biennial. $20 membership. Lutheran Historical Conference, c/o Concordia Historical Institute, 801 DeMun Ave., St. Louis, MO 63105. TEL 314-721-5934. E-mail: calc-mah@genie.geis.com. Ed. Marvin A. Huggins. circ. 350. **Indexed:** Rel.& Theol.Abstr. (1988-). **Document type:** proceedings.
Description: Contains papers presented at biennial meetings that are of interest to professional Lutheran historians, librarians, and archivists.

284 US ISSN 0460-0274
LUTHERAN HISTORICAL CONFERENCE NEWSLETTER. 1962. 3/yr. $20 to non-members. Lutheran Historical Conference, Trinity Lutheran Seminary, 8765 W. Higgins Rd., Chicago, IL 60631. TEL 312-380-2818. FAX 312-380-2977. Ed. Elisabeth Wittman. bk.rev. circ. 225. (back issues avail.) **Indexed:** Rel.Ind.One. **Document type:** newsletter.
Description: Contains items of interest to archivists, librarians and historians, plus technical notes and bibliographical resources. Conference is intended to foster effective cooperation among persons and institutions concerned with research, documentation, and preservation of the resources revealing experiences of Lutheranism in North America.

284 US
LUTHERAN HISTORICAL SOCIETY OF EASTERN PENNSYLVANIA. PERIODICAL. 1950. s-a. $7.50 membership. Lutheran Historical Society of Eastern Pennsylvania, Lutheran Theological Seminary, 7301 Germantown Ave., Philadelphia, PA 19119. Ed. Mahlon H. Hellerich. bk.rev. circ. 550. (back issues avail.) **Document type:** proceedings.
Formerly: Lutheran Historical Society of Eastern Pennsylvania.

285 US
LUTHERAN HOUR MESSAGES. 1930. w. contribution. Lutheran Layman's League, 2185 Hampton Ave., St. Louis, MO 63139. TEL 314-647-4900. (large print edition in 18 pt.; Braille ed. avail. on request) **Document type:** consumer publication.
Formerly: Lutheran Hour Sermons.
Description: Text of weekly sermons which have been broadcast.

284.1 US ISSN 0360-6945
BX8001
LUTHERAN JOURNAL. 1937. q. $15. Outlook Publishing, Inc., 7317 Cahill Rd., Edina, MN 55439. TEL 612-941-6830. FAX 612-941-6830. Ed. Rev. Armin U. Deye; Pub. John Leykom. adv.; bk.rev.; illus. circ. 125,000. **Indexed:** A.I.P.P. **Document type:** consumer publication.
Former titles (1943-1947): Northwest Lutheran Journal; Lutheran Home Journal.

284 US ISSN 0024-7464
LUTHERAN LAYMAN. 1929. 10/yr. $5. International Lutheran Laymen's League, 2185 Hampton, St. Louis, MO 63139. TEL 314-647-4900; 800-944-3450. FAX 314-647-6923. TELEX 590083. Ed. Gerald Perschbacher. adv.; bk.rev.; illus. circ. 85,000. (tabloid format)
Description: Contains religious news for Lutheran laity.

LUTHERAN LIBRARIES. see *LIBRARY AND INFORMATION SCIENCES*

LUTHERAN MESSENGER FOR THE BLIND. see *HANDICAPPED — Visually Impaired*

284 US ISSN 0885-9922
BX8001
LUTHERAN PARTNERS. 1985. bi-m. $10. (Augsburg Fortress) Augsburg Fortress, Publishers, 426 S. Fifth St., Box 1209, Minneapolis, MN 55440. TEL 612-330-3402; 800-328-4648. FAX 612-330-3455. (Co-sponsor: Evangelical Lutheran Church in America (ELCA), Division for Ministry) Ed. Carl E. Linder. adv.; bk.rev. circ. 21,500.

284.1 US ISSN 0024-7510
LUTHERAN SENTINEL. 1917. m. $7. Evangelical Lutheran Synod, 1176 Waterville Rd., Waterville, IA 52170-7518. TEL 515-424-4341. FAX 515-424-9687. (Dist. by: Stoyles Graphic Services, 19 8th St., S.E., Mason City, IA 50401) Ed. Paul G. Madson. bk.rev. circ. 6,000.

284.1 US ISSN 0024-7537
LUTHERAN SPOKESMAN. 1958. m. $6. Church of the Lutheran Confession (Minneapolis), 460 75th Ave., N.E., Minneapolis, MN 55432. TEL 414-425-6665. (Subscr. to: 2750 Oxford St., N, Roseville, MN 55113) Ed. Rev. Paul Fleischer. bk.rev. circ. 2,500.
Description: Testamentary commentary on issues relevant to the Church of the Lutheran Confession, with official notices and news pertaining to its activities.

284.1 AT ISSN 0024-7553
LUTHERAN THEOLOGICAL JOURNAL. 1966. 3/yr. Aus.$20. (Lutheran Church of Australia) Openbook Publishers, 205 Halifax St., Adelaide, S.A. 5000, Australia. Ed. J.G. Strelan. bk.rev. circ. 680. **Indexed:** CERDIC, New Test.Abstr., Old Test.Abstr., Rel.Ind.One. **Document type:** academic/scholarly publication.
—UMI; UnCover.

207.11 284 US ISSN 0362-0581
LUTHERAN THEOLOGICAL SEMINARY BULLETIN. 1921. q. free. Lutheran Theological Seminary, 61 N.W. Confederate Ave., Gettysburg, PA 17325. TEL 717-334-6286. FAX 717-334-3469. Ed. Richard D. Nelson. circ. 3,500. (also avail. in microform from UMI) **Indexed:** Rel.& Theol.Abstr. (1989-).
—UMI.
Formerly: Gettysburg Seminary Bulletin (ISSN 0016-9366)
Description: Discusses theological and ecclesiastical issues, primarily to its immediate constituency, but also to a broader readership of interested persons.

284.1 US ISSN 0024-757X
BX8001
LUTHERAN WITNESS. 1882. m. $7.50. (Lutheran Church - Missouri Synod) Concordia Publishing House, 3558 S. Jefferson Ave., St. Louis, MO 63118. TEL 314-268-1000. Ed. David Mahsman. bk.rev.; illus. circ. 330,000. (also avail. in Braille; audio cassette; large print) **Indexed:** G.Soc.Sci.& Rel.Per.Lit. **Document type:** consumer publication.
—UMI.

284.787 US
LUTHERAN WITNESS (LARGE PRINT EDITION). m. free. (Lutheran Church - Missouri Synod) Lutheran Library for the Blind, 1333 S. Kirkwood Rd., St. Louis, MO 63122. TEL 800-433-3954. (also avail. in Braille; audio cassette; large print in 22 pt.)

284.1 US ISSN 0896-209X
LUTHERAN WOMAN TODAY. 1908. m. (11/yr.). $10 for regular and large print ed. Augsburg Fortress, Publishers, 426 S. Fifth St., Box 1209, Minneapolis, MN 55440. TEL 800-328-4648. (Co-sponsor: Women of the Evangelical Lutheran Church in America (ELCA)) Ed. Nancy J. Stelling. bk.rev.; film rev.; illus.; index. (large print edition in 14 pt. avail.) **Indexed:** A.I.P.P.
Formed by the 1987 merger of: Lutheran Woman (ISSN 0024-7596); Scope (ISSN 0036-8997)

284 266 US
LUTHERAN WOMAN'S QUARTERLY; knowing Christ and making Him known. 1942. q. $2.50. Lutheran Church - Missouri Synod, Lutheran Women's Missionary League, 3558 S. Jefferson Ave., St. Louis, MO 63118-3910. TEL 314-664-7000. Ed. Patricia Beach. bk.rev. circ. 200,000. (also avail. in Braille; audio cassette; back issues avail.)

284.1 GW ISSN 0024-7618
BX8001
LUTHERISCHE MONATSHEFTE. 1962. m. DM.66. Lutherisches Verlagshaus GmbH, Knochenhauerstr. 38-40, 30159 Hannover, Germany. TEL 0511-1241-733. adv.; bk.rev.; bibl.; charts; index. circ. 9,500. **Indexed:** CERDIC. **Document type:** bulletin.

284 GW ISSN 0170-3846
LUTHERISCHE THEOLOGIE UND KIRCHE. 1977. q. DM.25. Lutherische Theologischen Hochschule in Oberursel e.V., Altkonigstr. 150, 61440 Oberursel, Germany. TEL 06171-24340. adv.; bk.rev. circ. 800. (back issues avail.) **Document type:** academic/scholarly publication.
Description: Studies Lutheran theology.

284 GW ISSN 0342-0914
LUTHERJAHRBUCH. 1919. a. price varies. (Luther-Gesellschaft) Vandenhoeck und Ruprecht, Robert-Bosch-Breite 6, 37079 Goettingen, Germany. TEL 0551-6959-0. FAX 0551-695917. (Subscr. to: 37070 Goettingen, Germany) Ed. Helmar Junghans. **Document type:** academic/scholarly publication.

284.1 AU ISSN 0024-7626
DIE LUTHERKIRCHE; Pfarrblatt. 1948. q. free. Evangelische Gemeinde A.B. Wien-Waehring, Martinstr. 25, A-1180 Vienna, Austria. TEL 01-4064534. FAX 01-4063638. Ed. Werner Puelz. circ. 4,500. **Document type:** bulletin.

268 SW ISSN 0345-7389
LUTHERSK BARNTIDNING. 1952. w. SEK 120. Missionssaellskapet Bibeltrogna Vaenner, P.O. Box 6160, 102 33 Stockholm, Sweden. TEL 08-736-6010. FAX 08-345818. Ed. Inga-Lisa Persson. circ. 3,000.

266 GW
M B K - MISSION. NACHRICHTEN. 1927. bi-m. M B K - Mission e.V., Postfach 560, 32067 Bad Salzuflen, Germany. FAX 05222-180557. circ. 3,000. (looseleaf format; back issues avail.) **Document type:** newsletter.
Description: Reports on social and missionary work in Japan and Hong Kong.

288 US
M S U U NEWSLETTER: GLEANINGS. 1974. q. membership only. Ministerial Sisterhood Unitarian Universalist, c/o Universalist Unitarian Church, 740 E. Main St., Santa Paula, CA 93060. TEL 805-525-8859. Ed. Rev. Marjorie Newlin Leaming. adv.; bk.rev.; circ. 300 (controlled). **Document type:** newsletter.
Formerly: M S U U Newsletter (ISSN 0360-7046)
Description: For Unitarian Universalist women ministers.

286 362.7 US ISSN 1047-1820
MAGAZETTE (BIRMINGHAM). 1989. q. $7.95 (effective 1995-1996). Southern Baptist Convention, Woman's Missionary Union, Hwy. 280, E., 100 Missionary Ridge, Birmingham, AL 35242-5235. TEL 205-991-8100. (Subscr. to: Box 830711, Birmingham, AL 35283-7111. TEL 800-WMU-7301. FAX 205-995-4840)

RELIGIONS AND THEOLOGY — PROTESTANT

283 US
MASTER THOUGHTS. 1972. q. $15. (Invisible Ministry) Dominion Press, Box 4608, Salem, OR 97302-8608. TEL 503-362-9634. Ed. Friend Stuart. circ. 100. (looseleaf format; also avail. in microfilm; back issues avail.)
Description: Presents analysis and interpretations of words of Jesus Christ from King James Version.

MATURE LIVING. see *GERONTOLOGY AND GERIATRICS*

MATURE YEARS. see *GERONTOLOGY AND GERIATRICS*

283 AT
MELBOURNE ANGLICAN. 1966. m. Aus.$15 (foreign Aus.$36). Anglican Media, Diocese of Melbourne, 1st Fl. Cathedral Buildings, 209 Flinders Ln., Melbourne, Vic. 3000, Australia. TEL 61-3-653-4221. FAX 61-3-650-5237. Ed. Angela Grutzner. adv.: page $1800; adv. contact: Eowyn Robertson. bk.rev.; film rev.; play rev.; illus. circ. 16,787. (tabloid format) Document type: newspaper.
Formerly: See (ISSN 0037-0754)
Description: Brings current issues in the Church into debate and scrutiny.

MEN OF ACTION. see *MEN'S INTERESTS*

289.709 CN ISSN 0380-0121
MENNONITE REPORTER. 1971. fortn. Can.$27.50 (foreign Can.$45). Mennonite Publishing Service, 3-312 Marsland Drive, Waterloo, ON N2J 3Z1, Canada. TEL 519-884-3810. FAX 519-884-3331. Ed. Ron Rempel. adv.; bk.rev.; index. circ. 12,000. (also avail. in microform from MML) Indexed: Can.B.P.I., CMI, CMI. Document type: newspaper.
Formerly (until 1972): Canadian Mennonite Reporter (ISSN 0380-013X)
Description: Independent inter-Mennonite news and comment.

289.709 GW ISSN 0342-1171
BX8101
MENNONITISCHE GESCHICHTSBLAETTER. 1936. a. DM.30. Mennonitischer Geschichtsverein, Weierhof, 67295 Bolanden, Germany. (Subscr. to: Christel Schultz, Blumenweg 28, 63128 Dietzenbach, Germany) Eds. Hans-Juergen Goertz, Christophe Wiebe. bk.rev. circ. 700. Document type: academic/scholarly publication.
Description: Studies the history of the Mennonite Church.

287 MX ISSN 0026-0185
MESIAS; boletin semanal de la iglesia Metodista. vol.8, 1971. w. Iglesia Metodista el Mesias, Balderas 47, Mexico D.F., Mexico.

284.2 FR ISSN 0026-0274
MESSAGER EVANGELIQUE. (Text in French, German) 1945. w. 240 F. Eglise de la Confession d'Ausburg, La quai Saint Thomas, F-67081 Strasbourg, France. (Co-sponsor: Eglise Reforme d'Alsace et de Lorraine) Ed. Fritz Westphal. adv.; bk.rev.; illus. circ. 20,000.

286 IT ISSN 0392-6346
MESSAGGERO AVVENTISTA. 1926. m. L.30000 (effective 1996). (Unione Italiana delle Chiese Cristiane Avventiste) Edizioni A.D.V., Via Chiantigiana 30, Falciani, 50023 Impruneta, Florence, Italy. TEL 055-2326291. Ed. Franco Evangelisti. circ. 1,600. Document type: newspaper.

286 UK ISSN 0309-3654
MESSENGER (GRANTHAM). 1895. fortn. £13 (foreign £27). Stanborough Press Ltd., Alma Park, Grantham, Lincs. NG31 9SL, England. TEL 01476-591700. FAX 01476-77144. Ed. D.N. Marshall; Pub. P. Hammond. adv. contact: Edward Johnson. bk.rev. circ. 10,000. Document type: bulletin.
Formerly: British Advent Messenger (ISSN 0045-2874)

286 US
THE MESSENGER (OMAHA). 1911. 6/yr. $1. American Baptist Churches of Nebraska, 6404 Maple St., Omaha, NE 68104. TEL 402-556-4730. FAX 402-556-1910. Ed. Rovert C. Molby. bk.rev.; illus. circ. 3,875. Document type: newsletter.
Formerly: Nebraska Baptist Messenger.

283 UK
MESSIANIC WITNESS. 1876. q. $15. Messianic Testimony, 93 Axe St., Barking, Essex IG11 7LZ, England. TEL 081-594-3072. Ed. D. Steiner. bk.rev. circ. 7,000. Document type: bulletin.

289 UK
METHODIST CONFERENCE. MINUTES AND YEARBOOK. 1932. a. Methodist Publishing House, 20 Ivatt Way, Peterborough PE3 7PG, England. TEL 01733-332202. FAX 01733-331201. circ. 7,000. Document type: proceedings.

691 UK
METHODIST DIARIES. 1850. a. Methodist Publishing House, 20 Ivatt Way, Peterborough PE3 7PG, England. TEL 01733-332202. FAX 01733-331201. circ. 5,000. Document type: bulletin.

287 209 US ISSN 0026-1238
BX8235
METHODIST HISTORY. 1962. q. $15. United Methodist Church, General Commission on Archives & History, Box 127, Madison, NJ 07940. TEL 201-708-3189. FAX 201-408-3909. Ed. Charles Yrigoyen, Jr. adv.; bk.rev.; charts; index. circ. 1,100. (also avail. in microfilm from UMI) Indexed: Amer.Hist.& Life, CERDIC, Hist.Abstr., Meth Per.Ind., Rel.& Theol.Abstr. (1970-), Rel.Ind.One, Rel.Per. Document type: academic/scholarly publication.
—BLDSC (5746.350000); Faxon; UMI; UnCover.

287 UK ISSN 0026-1262
METHODIST RECORDER. 1861. w. £27.50 (foreign £41). Methodist Newspaper Co. Ltd., 122 Golden Lane, London EC1Y 0TL, England. TEL 0171-251-8414. FAX 0171-608-3490. Ed. Michael Taylor. adv.; bk.rev.; play rev.; rec.rev.; charts; illus. circ. 25,803. (tabloid format; also avail. in microfilm from WMP) Document type: newspaper.

287 377.8 US
METHODIST THEOLOGICAL SCHOOL IN OHIO. STORY. 1989. s-a. free. Methodist Theological School in Ohio, Box 1204, Columbus Pike, Delaware, OH 43015-0931. TEL 614-363-1146. FAX 614-362-3235. Ed. Cassandra S. Clancy. (back issues avail.)
Description: Contains news for students, staff, faculty, alumni, and friends of the school.

287 SW ISSN 0543-6206
METODISTKYRKANS I SVERIGE AARSBOK; utgiven enligt konferensens beslut. 1908. a. SEK 100. Metodistkyrkan i Sverige - United Methodist Church in Sweden, P.O. Box 45130, S-104 30 Stockholm, Sweden. FAX 46-31-55-79. Ed. Rev. Haakan Englund. stat. circ. 400.
Formerly (until 1939): Metodist-Episkopal-Kyrkans i Sverige Aarsbok.
Description: Reports on the work of the Methodist Church in Sweden.

200 US ISSN 0026-2072
MICHIGAN CHRISTIAN ADVOCATE. 1873. 3/yr. (June, July, Aug.) $9. (United Methodist Church, West Michigan and Detroit Annual Conferences) Michigan Christian Advocate Publishing Co., 316 Springbrook Ave., Adrian, MI 49221. TEL 517-265-2075. Ed. Edward L. Duncan. adv.; bk.rev.; illus. circ. 21,000.

264 US
MICHIGAN LUTHERAN. 1922. m. $6. Lutheran Church - Missouri Synod, Michigan District, 3773 Geddes Road, Ann Arbor, MI 48105. TEL 313-665-3791. FAX 313-665-0255. Ed. Walt Rummel. adv.; bk.rev.; film rev.; circ. 76,000 (controlled).
Description: Presents the work of the Michigan District and its congregations to the membership of the church in the area, for information, motivation, and inspiration.

284 CN ISSN 1193-1825
MIERA DRAUDZES VESTIS. (Text in Latvian) 1953. bi-m. Can.$15. Peace Latvian Lutheran Church, 83 Main St., Ottawa, ON K1S 1B5, Canada. TEL 613-230-4085. Ed. Rev. Maris Ludviks. adv.; bk.rev. circ. 170. Document type: bulletin.
Formerly (until 1991): Draudzes Vestis (ISSN 0701-0214)
Description: News of events in the church, and articles and news of interest to the Latvian community.

285 US ISSN 0026-5314
BX6101
MINISTRY; international journal for clergy. 1928. m. $22. (General Conference of Seventh-day Adventists) Review and Herald Publishing Association, 55 W. Oak Ridge Dr., Hagerstown, MD 21740. TEL 301-791-7000. Ed. David Newman. adv.; bk.rev.; charts; illus.; index. circ. 70,000. (reprint service avail. from UMI) Indexed: CCR, CERDIC.
—UMI.
Description: Publishes theological and practical articles for ministers of all denominations.

384 US ISSN 1068-3151
BV2540.A1
MISSIO APOSTOLICA. 1993. s-a. Lutheran Society for Missiology, Box 5734, Fort Wayne, IN 46895.

266 UK
MISSION. 1922. 3/yr. Bible Churchmens Missionary Society (B.C.M.S.), 251 Lewisham Way, London SE4 1XF, England. Ed. Sue Knight. bk.rev. circ. 6,000. (back issues avail.)

266 284 US ISSN 1050-771X
BV2050
MISSION HANDBOOK: U S A - CANADA PROTESTANT MINISTRIES OVERSEAS. 1951. irreg. (every 3-5 yrs.). $39.95 (diskette version $99.95; both versions $119.95). (Mission Advanced Research and Communication Center) M A R C (Subsidiary of: World Vision International), 121 E. Huntington Dr., Monrovia, CA 91016-3400. TEL 818-303-8811; 800-777-7752. FAX 818-301-7786. Ed. John A. Siewert. index. circ. 1,500. (also avail. in diskette format)
Former titles: Mission Handbook: North American Protestant Ministries Overseas (ISSN 0093-8130); North American Protestant Ministries Overseas (ISSN 0078-1339)
Description: Presents detailed data on Canadian and U.S. Christian missionary agencies, cross-indexed by ministry, state, province, countries of services, and church tradition. Includes interpretive essays.

266 US ISSN 1051-3345
MISSION TODAY; for Baptist men and Baptist young men. vol.45, 1974. m. $10.56. Southern Baptist Convention, Brotherhood Commission, 1548 Poplar Ave., Memphis, TN 38104. TEL 800-727-6466. Ed. Jim Burton. circ. 32,000. (tabloid format) Indexed: South.Bap.Per.Ind.
Former titles: World Mission Journal (Baptist Men's Edition); Baptist Men's Journal.
Description: Provides missions education for men in Southern Baptist churches.

266 UK ISSN 0264-1372
MISSIONARY HERALD. 10/yr. £5. Baptist Missionary Society, P.O. Box 49, Baptist House, 129 Broadway, Didcot, Oxon OX11 8XA, England. TEL 01235-512044. FAX 01235-511265. Ed. Rev. D.E. Pountain. circ. 15,000. (back issues avail.)

266 US
MISSIONARY REPORTER. 1946. q. membership. (Seventh Day Baptist Missionary Society) Seventh Day Baptist Missionary Society, 119 Main St., Westerly, RI 02891. TEL 401-596-4326. FAX 401-348-9494. circ. 250. (looseleaf format) Document type: newsletter.
Description: Covers the minutes of the board meetings. Includes reports of workers on various missionary projects.

266 US
MISSIONS; update. 1975. m. free. (Seventh Day Baptist Missionary Society) American Sabbath Tract & Communication Council, Seventh Day Baptist General Conference, Box 1678, Janesville, WI 53547. TEL 608-752-5055. FAX 608-752-7711. (Subscr. to: Seventh Day Baptist Missionary Society, 119 Main St., Westerly, RI 02891. TEL 401-596-4326) Ed. Kirk Looper. circ. 200. (looseleaf format) Document type: newsletter.
Description: National and international coverage of the society's activities.

RELIGIONS AND THEOLOGY — PROTESTANT

266 362.7 US
BV2520.A1
MISSIONS MOSAIC. (Avail. in Member and Executive Editions) 1995. m. $14.95 for Member Edition; Executive Edition £15.95 (effective 1995-1996). Southern Baptist Convention, Woman's Missionary Union, Hwy. 280, E., 100 Missionary Ridge, Birmingham, AL 35242-5235. TEL 205-991-8100. (Subscr. to: Box 830711, Birmingham, AL 35283-0711. TEL 800-WMU-7301. FAX 205-995-4840) Ed. Cindy Dake. bk.rev.; illus.; circ. 270,000 (paid).
 Formed by the merger of (1970-1995): Contempo (ISSN 0162-1971) & Royal Service (ISSN 0035-9084); Which was formerly: Our Mission Fields.
 Description: Dedicated to members and leaders of Baptist women's missions organizations.

266 UK
MISSIONS TO SEAMEN ANNUAL REPORT. 1856. a. free. Missions to Seamen, St. Michael Paternoster Royal, College Hill, London EC4R 2RL, England. TEL 0171-248-5202. FAX 0171-248-4761. Ed. Gillian Ennis. index.
 Formerly: Missions to Seamen Handbook (ISSN 0076-9401)

266 US ISSN 0279-5345
BV2520.A1
MISSIONS U S A. 1930. 8/yr. $6.50. Southern Baptist Convention, Home Mission Board, 1350 Spring St., N.W., Atlanta, GA 30309. TEL 404-898-7520. FAX 404-898-7542. Ed. Phyllis Thompson. adv.; bk.rev.; illus.; index. circ. 95,000. **Indexed:** South.Bap.Per.Ind.
 Formerly: Home Missions (ISSN 0018-408X)

284 GW
MISSIONSBLATT; Lutherische Kirchenmission (Bleckmarer Mission). 1899. m. DM.42. Lutherische Kirchenmission e.V., Bleckmar 33, 29303 Bergen, Germany. TEL 05051-2098. FAX 05051-2845. Ed. Pastor Gerhard Heidenreich. bk.rev. circ. 4,000. (back issues avail.) **Document type:** bulletin.
 Description: Discusses mission and evangelistic work worldwide.

266 GW
MISSIONSGLOCKE DER LIEBENZELLER MISSION. 1909. m. DM.5. Liebenzell Mission, Postfach 1240, 75375 Bad Liebenzell, Germany. TEL 07052-17109. FAX 07052-17104. Ed. Rev. Albert Rechkemmer. illus. circ. 11,000. (back issues avail.) **Document type:** bulletin.

287 US
MISSISSIPPI UNITED METHODIST ADVOCATE. 1947. fortn. $9.50. United Methodist Church, Mississippi Conference, Box 1093, Jackson, MS 39215. TEL 601-354-0515. Ed. Rev. J.R. Woodrick. adv.; bk.rev.; circ. 15,000 (controlled). (tabloid format) **Document type:** newspaper.
 Formerly: Mississippi Methodist Advocate (ISSN 0026-6329)

284 GW
MITTEILEN. 1853. bi-m. DM.20. Evangelisch-Lutherisches Missionswerk in Niedersachsen, Georg-Haccius-Str. 9, 29320 Hermannsburg, Germany. TEL 05052-69233. FAX 05052-69222. Ed. Klaus-D. Hampe. bk.rev.; illus.; maps; circ. 17,500. (back issues avail.) **Document type:** proceedings.
 Formerly (until 1993): Hermannsburger Missionsblatt.

284.2 SA ISSN 0378-410X
MOLAETSA-MOLAETSA. (Text in South Suthu, Swana) 1957. 8/yr. R.3. Reformed Churches in South Africa - Gereformeerde Kerke in Suid-Afrika, P.O. Box 59, Hammanskraal 0400, South Africa. Ed. H.A. Louw. circ. 2,500.
 Formerly: Rugama.

284 GW ISSN 0540-6226
MONATSHEFTE FUER EVANGELISCHE KIRCHENGESCHICHTE DES RHEINLANDES. 1952. m. DM.40. (Rheinland Verlag GmbH) Dr. Rudolf Habelt GmbH, Am Buchenhang 1, 53115 Bonn, Germany. TEL 0228-232016. FAX 0228-232017. Ed.Bd. **Document type:** bulletin.
 —BLDSC (5904.200000).

285 US ISSN 0360-6171
MONDAY MORNING. 1936. s-m. (21/yr.) $12. Presbyterian Church (U.S.A.), Office of Communications, 100 Witherspoon St, Louisville, KY 40202-1396. TEL 502-569-5755. FAX 502-569-8073. E-mail: MONDAY_MORNING@pcusa.org. Ed. Stephen V. Moulton. adv.; bk.rev. circ. 22,000.
 Description: Forum for ministers to discuss relevant issues.

284 UK
MORAVIAN MESSENGER. m. £7.44. Moravian Union Inc., Book Room, 5 Muswell Hill, London N10 3TJ, England. TEL 01-883-3409. Ed. Rev. P. Gubi. bk.rev.; illus. circ. 900. **Document type:** bulletin.
 Formerly: Moravian Message.

268 028.5 US ISSN 0162-4288
MORE. m. (plus regular w. nos.) $10.80. Southern Baptist Convention, Sunday School Board, 127 Ninth Ave., N., Nashville, TN 37234. TEL 800-458-2772.
 Description: Religious publication directed at children ages 6-7.

MORE LIGHT UPDATE. see *HOMOSEXUALITY*

284 GW
MORGENLAND - ABENDLAND. 1968. bi-m. DM.60. Morgenland Verlag, Postfach 1146, 88678 Salem, Germany. **Document type:** bulletin.

MULOT'SCHEN FAMILIENVERBAND. ZEITSCHRIFT; genealogische Mitteilungen fuer Hugenotten- und Waldensernachkommen. see *GENEALOGY AND HERALDRY*

284.2 SA ISSN 0378-4126
MURUMIWA. (Editions in Tsonga and Venda) 1950. bi-m. R.1.50. Reformed Churches in South Africa, Synod Soutspansberg - Gereformeerde Kerke in Suid-Afrika, P.O. Box 496, Sibasa, Venda, South Africa. Ed. G.D. Affourtit.

THE MUSIC LEADER. see *MUSIC*

MUSIC MAKERS (NASHVILLE). see *MUSIC*

MUSIC TIME. see *MUSIC*

242 US ISSN 0027-5387
MY DEVOTIONS. 1958. m. $6.50. Concordia Publishing House, 3558 S. Jefferson Ave., St. Louis, MO 63118. TEL 800-325-3381. Ed. Don Hoeferkamp. illus. circ. 70,000. (also avail. in microfilm; Braille; large print) **Document type:** consumer publication.
 Description: Selected daily devotions and Bible readings for Christian children, ages 8-13.

284.787 US
MY DEVOTIONS (LARGE PRINT EDITION). m. free. Lutheran Library for the Blind, 1333 S. Kirkwood Ave., St. Louis, MO 63122. TEL 800-433-3954. (also avail. in Braille; large print in 22 pt.)
 Description: For ages 8-13.

284 GW
N M - NORDELBISCHE MISSION; Breklumer Sonntagsblat fuers Haus. 1974. m. DM.10. Nordelbisches Zentrum fuer Weltmission und Kirchlichen Weltdienst, Agathe-Lasch Weg 16, 22605 Hamburg, Germany. TEL 040-883000-0. FAX 040-883000-11. Ed. Martina Steinkuehler. bk.rev. circ. 11,000. **Document type:** newsletter.
 Description: Lutheran publication covering missionary work and development aid in all parts of the world, especially developing countries in the southern hemisphere. Includes letters from readers.

284 GW
NACHRICHTEN AUS DER BASLER MISSION. bi-m. free. Basler Mission Deutscher Zweig, Vogelsangstr. 62, 70197 Stuttgart, Germany. TEL 0711-63678-43. FAX 0711-63678-66. (Co-sponsor: Evangelisches Missionswerk in Suedwestdeutschland e.V.) circ. 85,000. (back issues avail.) **Document type:** newsletter.
 Description: Missionary and ecumenical affairs from Asia, Africa, Latin America; information for mission friends.

266 UK ISSN 0077-3557
NATIONAL BIBLE SOCIETY OF SCOTLAND. ANNUAL REPORT. (Supplement to: Word at Work) 1860. a. free. National Bible Society of Scotland, 7 Hampton Terrace, Edinburgh EH12 5XU, Scotland. FAX 0131-337-0641. circ. 1,000. **Document type:** corporate report.

284.2 SA ISSN 0024-8665
NEDERDUITSE GEREFORMEERDE KERK VAN NATAL GEMEENTE VRYHEID. MAANDBRIEF. 1965. m. free. Nederduitse Gereformeerde Kerk van Natal Gemeentevryheid, Smalstraat 82, Vryheid, Natal, South Africa. Ed. E. Oberholster. adv.; circ. 600 (controlled). (looseleaf format)

284.2 230 SA ISSN 0028-2006
BR9.A34
NEDERDUITSE GEREFORMEERDE TEOLOGIESE TYDSKRIF. 1959. q. R.77 in RSA & Namibia; elsewhere R.82 (effective 1995). (Nederduitse Gereformeerde Kerk in Suid-Afrika - Dutch Reformed Church in South Africa) Nederduitse Gereformeerde Kerk Uitgewers, P.O. Box 4539, Cape Town, South Africa. TEL 27-21-215540. FAX 27-21-4191865. Ed. D. Pienaar. bk.rev.; bibl.; index; circ. 1,800 (controlled). **Indexed:** CERDIC, Old Test.Abstr. **Document type:** academic/scholarly publication.
 —BLDSC (6069.150000).

200 DK ISSN 0901-649X
NEMLI'. Key Title: Nemli' (Fredericia). Variant title: Nemlig. 1981. 10/yr. DKK 118. Danmarks Folkekirkelige Soendagsskoler og Boernegudstjenester, Korskaervej 25, 7000 Fredericia, Denmark. TEL 45-75-92-61-00. Ed. Karen Bodil Leth-Madsen. circ. 1,602.
 Formerly (until 1986): Juniornyt (ISSN 0109-5137)

284 NZ ISSN 1172-9244
NEW DIRECTIONS; signposts to the living word. bi-m. NZ.$20. Bible College of New Zealand, Private Bag, Henderson, Auckland 1231, New Zealand. TEL 64-9-837-0675. FAX 64-9-837-4209. Ed. Victor Johnston. adv.; B&W page NZ.$150; adv. contact: Russell Ford. circ. 2,700.
 Description: Publishes devotional, expositional comments on selected passages of the Bible for every day of the year.

NEW HORIZONS (NEW YORK). see *EDUCATION — Higher Education*

285 US ISSN 0199-3518
NEW HORIZONS (WILLOW GROVE). 1935. 11/yr. $15 (foreign $20). Orthodox Presbyterian Church, Committee on Christian Education, P.O. Box P, Willow Grove, PA 19090-0920. TEL 215-830-0900. FAX 215-830-0350. Ed. Thomas E. Tyson. adv.; bk.rev.; illus. circ. 11,300. **Indexed:** CERDIC.
 Formerly (until 1980): Presbyterian Guardian (ISSN 0032-7522)

266 AT ISSN 1033-7903
NEW LIFE; Australia's weekly Christian newspaper. 1938. w. Aus.$40. New Life Australia Ltd., P.O. Box 267, Blackburn, Vic. 3130, Australia. TEL 61-3-877-4833. FAX 61-3-894-2240. Ed. Rev. Ross Prout. adv. contact: Wilma Zegelis. bk.rev. circ. 6,500. (tabloid format; back issues avail.) **Document type:** newspaper.
 Description: Features world and Australia news of Evangelical Christian activities.

287 AT ISSN 0726-2612
NEW TIMES. 1971. m. Aus.$21. (Uniting Church in Australia, Synod of South Australia) New Times Incorporated, Epworth Building, 33 Pirie St., Adelaide, S.A. 5000, Australia. TEL 61-8-212-4066. FAX 61-8-231-6013. Ed. Nicholas Kerr. adv. contact: Chris Wait. bk.rev.; illus. circ. 4,500. **Indexed:** CERDIC. **Document type:** newspaper.
 Former titles: Central Times (ISSN 0038-2949); South Australian Methodist.

NEW WORLD OUTLOOK; United Methodist missions. see *RELIGIONS AND THEOLOGY*

RELIGIONS AND THEOLOGY — PROTESTANT

286   NZ   ISSN 0027-7177
THE NEW ZEALAND BAPTIST. 1881. m. (except Jan.). NZ.$25. Baptist Union of New Zealand, P.O. Box 65-275, Auckland 1330, New Zealand. TEL 64-9-479-7603. FAX 64-9-479-7819. E-mail: jbelding@ccc.gen.nz. (Subscr. to: New Zealand Baptist, P.O. Box 97-543, South Auckland, New Zealand) Ed. Julie C. Belding. adv.; bk.rev.; music rev. circ. 11,900. (tabloid format) **Document type:** newspaper.
—CCC.
  Description: Contains news, reviews, and feature articles.

283   CN   ISSN 0549-0898
NEWFOUNDLAND CHURCHMAN. 1888. m. Can.$5($7.50) Anglican Church of Newfoundland, 19 Kingsbridge Rd., St. John's, Nfld. A1C 3K4, Canada. TEL 709-576-6697. Ed. Hollis Hiscock. adv.; bk.rev. circ. 33,000.

285   US   ISSN 0362-1510
NEWS FROM THE CONGREGATIONAL CHRISTIAN HISTORICAL SOCIETY. 1969. s-a. membership. Congregational Christian Historical Society, Inc., 14 Beacon St., Boston, MA 02108. TEL 617-523-0470. FAX 617-523-0491. Ed. Harold F. Worthley. bk.rev.; circ. 1,100 (paid). **Document type:** newsletter.
  Description: News and announcements pertaining to the members and activities of this Boston-based church historical society.

284   UK
NEWS TODAY CHURCH MAGAZINE OUTSET. 1980. £7.50 per month for 100 copies. Appleford Publishing Group, Appleford House, Appleford, Abingdon, Oxon. OX14 4PB, England. TEL 01235-848319. Ed. Gervase Duffield. adv. contact: E. Collie. bk.rev.; illus.; circ. 22,500 (paid). (back issues avail.) **Document type:** newsletter.
  Former titles: News Plus Church Magazine Outset; News Today Church Magazine Outset.

287   US   ISSN 1073-4910
NEWSCOPE; the national weekly for United Methodist leaders. 1973. w. $24.95. United Methodist Publishing House, 201 Eighth Ave. S., Box 801, Nashville, TN 37202. TEL 615-749-6732. FAX 615-749-6079. Ed. J. Richard Peck. circ. 8,000. (looseleaf format; back issues avail.) **Document type:** newsletter.
●Also available online.
  Description: Summary of United Methodist news from the U.S. and the world.

284   AT
NEWSFLASHES. q. Pocket Testament League of Australia (P T L), P.O. Box 253, Kingsgrove, N.S.W. 2208, Australia. TEL 02-502-2982.

283   US   ISSN 0885-6966
THE NEWSLETTER NEWSLETTER. 1979. m. $34.95. Communication Resources Inc., 4150 Belden Village St., Ste. 400, Canton, OH 44718-2502. TEL 800-992-2144. FAX 216-493-7897. Ed. Linda Arvin. (looseleaf format; back issues avail.) **Document type:** newsletter.
  Description: Contains editorial, production, design and distribution advice for church newsletter editors.

284 028.5   GW
NICKI - JESUS LIEBT KINDER. 1925. 3/yr. DM.15. (Deutscher E C-Verband) Born-Verlag, Leuschnerstr. 72-74, 34134 Kassel, Germany. TEL 0561-40950. FAX 0561-4095-112. circ. 8,000. **Document type:** bulletin.
  Formerly: Jesus Liebt Kinder.

284   GW
NIEDERSAECHSISCHE EVANGELISCHE ZEITUNG. 1946. w. DM.51.60. Lutherisches Verlagshaus GmbH, Knochenhauerstr. 38-40, 30159 Hannover, Germany. TEL 0511-1241733. FAX 0511-329730. Ed. Joachim Piper. adv.; bk.rev. circ. 57,000. **Document type:** newspaper.

284   NE   ISSN 0167-3602
NIEUW LEVEN. 1962. m. fl.20. Stichting Johan Maasbach Wereldzending, Apedoornselaan 2, 2573 The Hague, Netherlands. TEL 31-70-3469729. FAX 31-70-3107111. circ. 30,000. **Document type:** newspaper.
  Description: Inspirational and evangelical publication.

284   GW
NORDDEUTSCHE MISSION. MITTEILUNGEN. 1949. bi-m. free. Norddeutsche Mission, Vahrerstr. 243, 28329 Bremen, Germany. TEL 0421-4677038. FAX 0421-4677907. Ed. Antje Pult. **Document type:** newsletter.

284   GW   ISSN 0938-3697
NORDELBISCHE STIMMEN; Monatszeitschrift fuer haupt- und ehrenamtliche Mitarbeiter in Hamburg und Schleswig-Holstein. 1977. m. DM.48($30) Evangelischer Presseverband Nord e.V., Postfach 2060, 24019 Kiel, Germany. TEL 0431-5197-0. FAX 0431-5197292. Ed. Peter Moeller. adv.; bk.rev.; index. circ. 3,000. (back issues avail.) **Document type:** bulletin.

285   US
NOR'EASTER (SYRACUSE). 1985. bi-m. $10. Presbyterian Church (U.S.A.), Synod of the Northeast, 3049 E. Genesee St., Syracuse, NY 13224. TEL 315-446-5990. FAX 315-446-3708. Ed. Jane T. Mead. adv.; bk.rev. circ. 125,000. (tabloid format; back issues avail.) **Document type:** newspaper.
  Description: Covers Presbyterians in the Northeast US.

266   US
NORTH AMERICAN MISSIONS. 1950. 3/yr. free. Association of North American Missions, 3859 Nottingham Dr., Sarasota, FL 34235. TEL 941-955-8529. FAX 941-951-0805. Ed. Dr. Earl Parvin. bk.rev.; circ. 5,000 (controlled). **Document type:** newsletter.
  Formerly: Round Table (Sarasota).
Refereed Serial

200   US   ISSN 0029-2435
NORTH CAROLINA CHRISTIAN ADVOCATE. 1855. s-m. $10. (United Methodist Church, North Carolina Conference and Western North Carolina Conference) Methodist Board of Publication, Inc., Box 508, Greensboro, NC 27402-0508. TEL 919-272-1196. Ed. Kevin Rippin. adv.; bk.rev. circ. 16,637. (also avail. in microfiche)

280   US
NORTHEAST (PORTLAND). bi-m. Episcopal Diocese of Maine, 143 State St., Portland, ME 04357. TEL 207-772-1953. FAX 207-772-0095. Ed. Nellie Blagden. circ. 10,000. (tabloid format; back issues avail.) **Document type:** newspaper.
  Description: Covers news and issues of the church.

284   US   ISSN 0029-3512
NORTHWESTERN LUTHERAN. 1914. m. $9. (Wisconsin Evangelical Lutheran Synod) Northwestern Publishing House, 1250 N. 113th St., Milwaukee, WI 53226-3284. TEL 414-256-3230; 800-662-6093. FAX 414-256-3899. Ed. Rev. Gary P. Baumler. bk.rev.; index. circ. 60,000. **Indexed:** CERDIC.

284   AG   ISSN 0029-425X
NOTICIERO DE LA FE. 1935. m. $1.50. Revista Luterana, Simbron 4667, Buenos Aires, Argentina. Ed. Ernesto Weigandt. adv.; bk.rev.; illus. circ. 3,100.

286 362.7   US   ISSN 0469-1733
NUESTRA TAREA. (Text in Spanish) 1955. m. $15.95 (effective 1995-1996). Southern Baptist Convention, Woman's Missionary Union, Hwy. 280, E., 100 Missionary Ridge, Birmingham, AL 35242-5235. TEL 205-991-8100. (Subscr. to: Box 830711, Birmingham, AL 35283-0711. TEL 800-WMU-7301. FAX 205-995-4840) Ed. Elizabeth Rivera. circ. 4,000 (paid).
  Description: Publication of interest to Hispanic members and leaders of Southern Baptist women's organizations.

284 028.5 370.196   US   ISSN 0274-9459
O M S OUTREACH; official publication of O M S International. 1901. q. $10 donation. O M S International, Box A, Greenwood, IN 46142. TEL 317-881-6751. FAX 317-888-5275. Ed. Eleanor L. Burr. circ. 60,000. (back issues avail.)
  Description: Provides information on mission work in 16 countries.

OKAY; Schuelerkalender und taegliche Bibellese. see
CHILDREN AND YOUTH — For

284   IC
OKKAR A MILLI; kristilegt skolablad. 1944. a. free. (Kristileg Skolasamtoek) Sem Er Utgafa, Armuli 15, IS-108 Reykjavik, Iceland. TEL 354-581-2777. FAX 354-581-2776. Ed. Gigja Gretarsdottir. circ. 10,000.

286 976   US   ISSN 0889-745X
OKLAHOMA BAPTIST CHRONICLE. 1958. s-a. $2. (Baptist General Convention of Oklahoma, Historical Commission) Messenger Press (Oklahoma City), 2231 Gershwin Dr., Durant, OK 74701. TEL 405-924-7944. Ed. J.M. Gaskin. bk.rev. circ. 400.

283   AT   ISSN 0156-6296
ON BEING. 1974. 11/yr. Aus.$30. 36 Media Ltd., 2 Denham St., Hawthorn, Vic. 3122, Australia. TEL 03-8194755. FAX 03-8183515. Ed. Daniel Batt. adv. contact: Maureen Lim. bk.rev.; film rev.; index. circ. 6,400. (back issues avail.)
  Description: Aims to serve the Christian Church addressing social and spiritual issues of current concern.

284.2   NE   ISSN 0030-3356
OPBOUW; weekblad tot opbouw van het Gereformeerde leven. 1957. fortn. fl.119 (effective 1995). Gereformeerde Persvereniging Opbouw, Pluuthaven 7, 3891 AW Zeewolde, Netherlands. TEL 31-3242-2276. Ed.Bd. adv.; bk.rev.; circ. 2,800. **Document type:** consumer publication.

200   NE   ISSN 0030-3402
OPEN DEUR. 1936. m. fl.26. Boekencentrum B.V., Postbus 29, 2700 AA Zoetermeer, Netherlands. TEL 31-79-615481. FAX 31-79-615489. (Co-sponsors: Dutch Reformed Church; Lutheran Church; Roman Catholic Church; Geref. Foundation) Ed. Willem van der Merden. bk.rev.; illus.; circ. controlled.

284 301.4157   US   ISSN 0888-8833
OPEN HANDS; resources for ministries affirming the diversity of human sexuality. 1985. q. $20 ($25 outside U.S.). Reconciling Congregation Program Inc., 3801 N. Keeler, Chicago, IL 60641. TEL 312-736-5526. FAX 312-736-5475. (Co-sponsors: More Light, Open and Affirming, Reconciled in Christ programs) Ed. Mary Jo Osterman. adv.; bk.rev.; bibl. circ. 2,500. (back issues avail.) **Indexed:** IMFL.
  Formerly (until 1986): Manna for the Journey.

268   US   ISSN 0162-4296
BV4800
OPEN WINDOWS. q. $6.75. Southern Baptist Convention, Sunday School Board, 127 Ninth Ave., N., Nashville, TN 37234. TEL 800-458-2772.
  Description: Provides a daily devotional guide for adults.

OPEN WINDOWS. LARGE PRINT EDITION. see
HANDICAPPED — Visually Impaired

283   US   ISSN 1068-8811
OREGON EPISCOPAL CHURCH NEWS. 1861. 8/yr. $5. Episcopal Diocese of Oregon, 11800 S.W. Military Ln., Portland, OR 97214. TEL 503-636-5613. FAX 503-636-5616. Ed. Arlene Christianson Pickard. adv.; bk.rev.; illus.; stat. circ. 12,500. (tabloid format)
  Former titles: Oregon Episcopal Churchman; Oregon Churchman (ISSN 0030-4646)

286 362.7   US   ISSN 0899-3823
OUR MISSIONS WORLD. Chinese edition: Chuan Dao Tian Di (ISSN 1056-358X); Korean edition: Uri Ui Son' Gyo Segye (ISSN 1048-4973) 1982. q. $12.95 (effective 1995-1996). Southern Baptist Convention, Woman's Missionary Union, Hwy. 280, E., 100 Missionary Ridge, Birmingham, AL 35242-5235. TEL 205-991-8100. (Subscr. to: Box 830711, Birmingham, AL 35283-7111. TEL 800-WMU-7301. FAX 205-995-4840)

285   US   ISSN 0030-7238
OUTLOOK (WAKE FOREST). 1951. q. free. Southern Baptist Convention, Southeastern Baptist Theological Seminary, Inc., Wake Forest, NC 27587. TEL 919-556-3101. FAX 919-556-8550. Ed. C. Greg Kingry. bk.rev.; index; circ. 13,000 (controlled).

RELIGIONS AND THEOLOGY — PROTESTANT

283 UK
OXFORD DIOCESAN YEAR BOOK. 1857. a. £5.90. Oxford Diocesan Publications Ltd., Diocesan Church House, North Hinksey, Oxford OX2 0NB, England. TEL 0865-244566. FAX 0865-790470. Ed. Rev. Peter Green. adv. circ. 2,000. **Document type:** corporate report.

283 UK
P I O S A. 1982. 2/yr. £5. Province of the Indian Ocean Support Association, The Vicarage, Old Town, Brackley, Northants NN13 7BZ, England. TEL 01280-702767. Ed. P.C. Woodward. circ. 800. (back issues avail.) **Document type:** bulletin.

268 028.5 US
BV1620
PAIDEIA: TO PLAY, TO LEARN, TO GROW IN HIM. m. $60. Southern Baptist Convention, Sunday School Board, 127 Ninth Ave., N., Nashville, TN 37234. TEL 800-458-2772. **Indexed:** Sportsearch.
Former titles (until 1995): Church Recreation Magazine (ISSN 0162-4652); Church Recreation (ISSN 0529-7028)

PANORAMA (PITTSBURGH, 1960). see COLLEGE AND ALUMNI

284 US ISSN 0190-4639
PARACLETE. 1967. q. $5.50. (General Council of the Assemblies of God) Gospel Publishing House, 1445 Boonville Ave., Springfield, MO 65802-1894. TEL 417-862-2781. FAX 417-862-8558. Ed. David R. Bundrick. bk.rev.; index, cum.index every 2 yrs. circ. 4,750. (also avail. in microform from UMI) **Indexed:** CERDIC, Rel.& Theol.Abstr. (1989-), Rel.Ind.One.
—UMI.
Description: Covers the person and work of the Holy Spirit including Bible exposition, theology and history.

PARENTLIFE. see CHILDREN AND YOUTH — About

PARISH COMMUNICATION. see RELIGIONS AND THEOLOGY — Roman Catholic

284 US ISSN 0738-7962
PARISH TEACHER. 1977. m. (except July & Aug.) $6.75. Augsburg Fortress, Publishers, 426 S. Fifth St., Box 1209, Minneapolis, MN 55440. TEL 612-330-3402; 800-328-4648. FAX 612-330-3455. Ed. Rebecca Grothe. circ. 52,000.

282 283 SA ISSN 0031-2088
PARISHIONER. 1902. 10/yr. contribution. Cathedral of St. Mary the Virgin, P.O. Box 2029, Johannesburg 2000, South Africa. TEL 27-11-333-2537. FAX 27-11-29-0051. Ed. Lynda Wyngaard. adv.; bk.rev. circ. 1,500. **Document type:** newsletter.

268 UK ISSN 0079-0117
PARTNERS IN LEARNING; worship and learning resources for all ages. 1968. a. £12.90 (effective Oct. 1994). Methodist Church, Division of Education and Youth, 2 Chester House, Pages Ln., London N10 1PR, England. TEL 0181-444-9845. FAX 0181-365-2471. (And: National Christian Education Council, 1020 Bristol Rd., Selly Oak, Birmingham B29 6LB, England) Ed. Clare Amos. circ. 15,000. **Document type:** bulletin.

284 UK
PARTNERSHIP CHRISTIAN BRETHREN REVIEW. 1963. irreg. £15 (foreign £10). (Christian Brethren Research Fellowship) The Paternoster Press, P.O. Box 300, Kingstown Broadway, Carlisle, Cumbria CA3 0QS, England. TEL 01228-512512. FAX 01228-514949. (U.S. subscr. addr.: Box 11127, Birmingham, AL 35201-1127) Ed. Harold Rowdon. adv.; bk.rev. circ. 800. (back issues avail.) **Indexed:** Rel.& Theol.Abstr. (1980-). **Document type:** monographic series.
—UMI. CCC.
Formerly: Christian Brethren Review (ISSN 0263-466X)
Description: Contains articles on historical, ecclesiastical and theological subjects.

284 US
PASTOR'S TAX AND MONEY. 1992. q. $59.95. Pastor's Tax and Money, Box 50188, Indianapolis, IN 46250. TEL 317-674-3301; 800-877-3158. FAX 317-674-3302. Ed. Daniel Busby. circ. 6,000. **Document type:** newsletter.
Description: Provides sound, understandable tax and financial advice for ministers and churches.

284 282 US
PATHWAYS (LAS VEGAS).* 4/yr. New Order of Glastonbury, c/o Charlotte Schick, 2411 Llewellyn Dr., Las Vegas, NV 89102.

285 US
PEACE OFFICE NEWSLETTER. q. $10 suggested donation. Mennonite Central Committee, 21 S. 12th St., Box 500, Akron, PA 17501-0500. TEL 717-859-1151. FAX 717-859-2171. Ed. Gwen Groff. circ. 2,100. **Document type:** newsletter.
Description: For those desiring more specialized information on peace, justice and related issues.

PEDALPOINT. see MUSIC

287 MY
PELITA METHODIST. 1977. m. M.$10($2) Methodist Church in Malaysia - Gereja Methodist Malaysia, Methodist Headquarters, 65 Jalan 5-31, Petaling Jaya, Selangor, Malaysia. Ed. Rev. Ng Ee Lin. adv.; bk.rev. circ. 2,000. **Document type:** newsletter.
Former titles: Methodist Message (ISSN 0026-1254); Malaysia Methodist.

289.9 US ISSN 0031-4919
PENTECOSTAL MESSENGER. 1919. m. $11. Messenger Publishing House, Box 850, Joplin, MO 64802. TEL 417-624-7050. Ed. Don Allen. adv. circ. 8,000. **Indexed:** CERDIC.

289.9 CN ISSN 0031-4927
PENTECOSTAL TESTIMONY. 1920. m. $24. Pentecostal Assemblies of Canada, 6745 Century Ave., Mississauga, ON L5N 6P7, Canada. TEL 416-542-7400. FAX 416-542-7313. Ed. Rick P. Hiebert. adv. contact: Deanna Niles. bk.rev. circ. 27,000. **Indexed:** CERDIC.

200 US ISSN 0888-5281
PERSPECTIVES (ADA); a journal of reformed thought. 1986. 10/yr. $18 (foreign $21; in Canada Can.$26). Reformed Church Press, Box 470, Ada, MI 49301-0470. TEL 616-285-8074. Ed. Craig Stapert. bk.rev.; biennial index. circ. 3,000. (also avail. in microform from UMI) **Indexed:** CERDIC, Rel.& Theol.Abstr. (1989-), Rel.Ind.One. **Document type:** consumer publication.
—Faxon; UMI; UnCover.
Incorporates (1951-1991): Reformed Journal (ISSN 0486-252X)
Description: Expresses the Reformed faith theologically and engages issues that Reformed Christians meet in personal, ecclesiastical and societal life.

200 US ISSN 0093-531X
PERSPECTIVES IN RELIGIOUS STUDIES. 1974. q. $18 to individuals; libraries $25 (foreign $40). National Association of Baptist Professors of Religion, c/o Dr. Rollin Armour, Ed., Department of Christianity, Mercer University, Macon, GA 31207. TEL 912-752-2759. FAX 912-752-2384. E-mail: ARMOUR-RS@MERCER.PEACHNET.EDU. adv.; bk.rev.; abstr.; bibl.; charts; illus.; stat.; cum.index: 1974-1983. circ. 550. (also avail. in microform from UMI; back issues avail.) **Indexed:** Bk.Rev.Mo., CERDIC, New Test.Abstr., Old Test.Abstr., Rel.& Theol.Abstr. (1975-), Rel.Ind.One, Rel.Per. **Document type:** academic/scholarly publication.
—BLDSC (6428.163500); UMI.

284 GW ISSN 0172-6943
PIETISMUS UND NEUZEIT; Jahrbuch zur Geschichte des neueren Protestantismus. 1974. a. price varies. Vandenhoeck und Ruprecht, Robert-Bosch-Breite 6, 37079 Goettingen, Germany. TEL 0551-6959-0. FAX 0551-695917. index. (back issues avail.) **Document type:** bulletin.

285.834 US
PILGRIM STATE NEWS. 1951. bi-m. free. (United Church of Christ, Massachusetts Conference) Beacon Communications Corporation, 20 Main St., Acton, MA 01720. TEL 617-875-5233. Ed. Rosemary K. Agnew. bk.rev.; illus. circ. 4,500.
Former titles: Pilgrim State Newsletter (ISSN 0362-0557); (until 1974): Pilgrim States News.

289.9 SA ISSN 0031-9902
PINKSTER PROTESTANT/PENTECOSTAL PROTESTANT. (Text in Afrikaans, English) 1958. 3/yr. R.2. Pinkster Protestante Kerk - Pentecostal Protestant Church, P.O. Box 180, Isando, Transvaal, South Africa. TEL 27-11-974-1772. FAX 27-11-974-9135. Ed. Pastor Jannie Hough. adv.; bk.rev. circ. 5,500.

266 CN
PIONEER; Christian monthly. 1951. m. Can.$15. Council of the Reformed Church in Canada, R.R. 4, Cambridge, ON N1R 5S5, Canada. TEL 519-622-1777. Ed. Rev. Jeff Kingswood. adv. contact: Rita Thomas. bk.rev. circ. 3,000. (also avail. in microform) **Document type:** newsletter.

283 AT ISSN 1035-1035
THE PIONEER. 1931. q. donation. Church Army in Australia, 75 Hawkesbury Rd., Wetmead, N.S.W. 2145, Australia. TEL 61-2-6355669. Ed. Rev. W.M. Harris. bk.rev.; circ. 4,000 (controlled). (back issues avail.) **Document type:** newsletter.
Description: Evangelism of Church Army work and challenge to evangelism.

286 US ISSN 0893-5254
PIONEER (MEMPHIS). 1970. m. $2.64 for 3 mos. (typically set in Feb.). Southern Baptist Convention, Brotherhood Commission, 1548 Poplar Ave., Memphis, TN 38104. TEL 800-727-6466. Ed. Jeno Smith. illus. circ. 26,000. (also avail. in microform from UMI)
—UMI.
Former titles (until 1988): Pioneer Probe; (until 1984): Probe (Memphis) (ISSN 0032-9215)
Description: Provides missions education for boys 12-14 enrolled in Southern Baptist churches.

284 NE ISSN 0032-0056
DE PIONIER. 1939. m. free. (Stichting Alliance Zendings, Centrum Parousia) C A M A - Zending, Amersfoortseweg 44, 3951 LC Maarn, Netherlands. TEL 31-3432-3392. Ed. Rev. A.M. Verduijn. illus.; circ. 4,500 (controlled). **Document type:** newsletter.
Description: Missionary magazine.

284 028.5 SZ
▼**PLATTFORM**. 1995. q. free. Junge Kirche - Zwinglibund, Brauerstr. 60, CH-8004 Zurich, Switzerland. TEL 01-2410707. Ed. Bruno Sommer. bk.rev.; film rev.; music rev. (back issues avail.) **Document type:** newsletter.

289.7 300 US ISSN 0740-9125
THE PLOUGH (FARMINGTON). 1938-1958; resumed 1983. irreg. donation. (Hutterian Brethren Service Committee, Inc.) Plough Publishing House, Spring Valley Bruderhof, R.D. 2, Box 446, Farmington, PA 15437. TEL 412-329-1100; 800-521-8011. FAX 412-329-0942. (In U.K.: The Plough, Darvell Bruderhof, Robertsbridge, E. Sussex TN32 5DR, England. TEL 01580-881003) Ed. Christopher Zimmermann. bk.rev.; illus.; tr.lit.; index. circ. 5,500. (also avail. in Braille; back issues avail.)
Description: Covers urgent issues, including personal committment to Christ, children and education, community life, prison ministry, and racial justice.

269.4 US ISSN 0272-0965
BR1644
PNEUMA. 1979. s-a. $24. Society for Pentecostal Studies, Box 2671, Gaithersburg, MD 20886. TEL 301-990-2083. Ed. Murray W. Dempster; Pub. Murray W. Dempster. bk.rev. circ. 600. (back issues avail.) **Indexed:** Rel.Ind.One. **Document type:** academic/scholarly publication.
—BLDSC (6541.106000); UMI.

287 028.5 US ISSN 0278-565X
POCKETS. 1981. m. (except Jan.) $16.95. (United Methodist Church, General Board of Discipleship) Upper Room, 1908 Grand Ave., Box 189, Nashville, TN 37202. TEL 615-340-7333. FAX 615-340-7006. Ed. Janet R. Knight. circ. 91,000 (paid).
Description: Includes stories, scriptures, prayers, and games for children ages 6-12.

RELIGIONS AND THEOLOGY — PROTESTANT

248   US   ISSN 0032-4884
PORTALS OF PRAYER; daily devotions for adults. German edition: Taegliche Andachten (ISSN 0273-8562) 1937. q. $4.90. (Lutheran Church - Missouri Synod) Concordia Publishing House, 3558 S. Jefferson Ave., St. Louis, MO 63118. TEL 314-268-1000. Ed. Dr. Arnold Kuntz. circ. 900,000. (also avail. in microform; Braille; large print edition in 18 pt.) **Document type:** consumer publication.

287   PO   ISSN 0032-5066
PORTUGAL EVANGELICO. 1920. m. Esc.1000($12) (Igreja Evangelica Metodista Portuguesa) Rev. Ireneu da Silva Cunha, Ed. & Pub., Praca Coronel Pacheco 23, 4000 Porto, Portugal. TEL 02-2007410. FAX 02-2086961. (Co-sponsor: Presbyterian Church in Portugal) Ed. Jorge S. Barros Sousa. bk.rev.; illus. circ. 2,000. **Document type:** newspaper.

284   GW
POSENER STIMMEN. 1953. m. DM.38. Gemeinschaft Evangelischer Posener e.V., Bernhard-Riemann-Str. 30, 21335 Lueneburg, Germany. TEL 04131-43607. circ. 3,400. **Document type:** newsletter.

284   FR   ISSN 0032-5228
POSITIONS LUTHERIENNES. 1953. q. 180 F. Association "Positions Lutheriennes", 16 rue Chauchat, 75009 Paris, France. TEL 47.70.80.30. Ed. J.N. Peres. bk.rev.; bibl. circ. 550. **Indexed:** Bull.Signal., CERDIC.

289   US
POSSIBILITIES; the magazine of hope. 1983. bi-m. free. (Crystal Cathedral) Publishing Directions, Inc., 5301 Wisconsin Ave., N.W., Ste. 620, Washington, DC 20015. TEL 202-364-8000. FAX 202-364-8910. (Subscr. to: Box 100, Garden Grove, CA 92642) Ed. Jeanne Dunn. adv.; circ. 300,000 (controlled).

266   FR   ISSN 0751-5987
POUR LA VERITE. 1935. m. 110 F. Union des Eglises Evangeliques Libres de France, c/o Claude Baty, 3 rue Germain Dardan, 92120 Montrouge, France. TEL 46-57-38-09. (Subscr. to: c/o Marit Niemand, 28 bd. Emile Genevoix, 93230 Romainville, France. FAX 48-46-00-66) Ed. Mireille Boissonnat. bk.rev. circ. 1,000.

286 362.7   US
PRAYER PATTERNS. m. $7.95 (effective 1995-1996). Southern Baptist Convention, Woman's Missionary Union, Hwy. 280, E., 100 Missionary Ridge, Birmingham, AL 35242-5235. TEL 205-991-8100. (Subscr. to: Box 830711, Birmingham, AL 35283-7111. TEL 800-WMU-7301. FAX 205-995-4840)

285   US
PRAYERLINE; a guide to intercession for indigenous missions. 1983. m. Christian Aid Mission, 3045 Ivy Rd., Charlottesville, VA 22903. TEL 804-977-5650. Ed. Cheryl Chafee. circ. 16,500. (back issues avail.) **Description:** Covers mission work overseas conducted by non-North Americans.

284   NE   ISSN 0923-0343
PREDIKANT EN SAMENLEVING. 1923. 9/yr. fl.60. Bond van Nederlandse Predikanten, Cornelis Houtmanstraat 2, 3572 LV Utrecht, Netherlands. TEL 31-30-716133. FAX 31-30-733429. adv.; bk.rev. (back issues avail.)
●Also available online.
Description: News and information for Dutch predikants.

285   AT   ISSN 0729-3542
PRESBYTERIAN BANNER. 1846. m. (except Jan.). Aus.$20. Presbyterian Church of Eastern Australia, 9 Craiglea Close, Taree, N.S.W. 2430, Australia. TEL 61-65-521317. Ed. Rev. W.P. Gadsby. adv.; bk.rev. circ. 450. (back issues avail.) **Document type:** newsletter.
Description: Serves as a forum for edification of the Biblical Reformed faith.

285   US
PRESBYTERIAN CHURCH (U.S.A.). MINUTES OF THE GENERAL ASSEMBLY. a. $10 paperbound; $15 hardbound. Presbyterian Church (U.S.A.), 100 Witherspoon St., Louisville, KY 40202-1396. TEL 502-569-5810. circ. 16,000. **Document type:** proceedings.
Formerly: United Presbyterian Church in the United States of America. Minutes of the General Assembly (ISSN 0082-8548)

285   CN   ISSN 0079-4996
PRESBYTERIAN CHURCH IN CANADA. GENERAL ASSEMBLY. ACTS AND PROCEEDINGS. a. Can.$10. Presbyterian Church in Canada, General Assembly, 50 Wynford Dr., North York, ON M3C 1J7, Canada. TEL 416-441-1111. **Document type:** proceedings.

285   UK   ISSN 0032-7530
THE PRESBYTERIAN HERALD. 1943. 10/yr. £5; newsstand price: £0.60. Presbyterian Church in Ireland, Church House, Fisherwick Place, Belfast BT1 6DW, N. Ireland. TEL 0232-322284. FAX 0232-248377. Ed. Rev. Arthur Clarke. adv.: B&W page £335; trim 170 x 255; adv. contact: Winnie Cranston. bk.rev. circ. 17,000. **Indexed:** CERDIC. **Document type:** newsletter.
—UMI.
Description: Features articles on Christian ideas plus news and views from home and abroad.

285   CM
PRESBYTERIAN NEWSLETTER. (Text in English) q. B.P. 19, Buea, Cameroon. TELEX 5613.

285   US   ISSN 0032-7565
PRESBYTERIAN OUTLOOK. 1819. w. (43/yr.) $26.50. Presbyterian Outlook Foundation, Box 85623, Richmond, VA 23285-5623. TEL 804-359-8442. FAX 804-353-6369. Ed. Robert H. Bullock, Jr. adv. contact: George Whipple. bk.rev.; illus.; circ. 12,045 (paid). (also avail. in microform from UMI; reprint service avail. from UMI) **Document type:** newspaper.
—UMI.
Description: Independent national weekly serving the Presbyterian Church (U.S.A.)

285   CN   ISSN 0032-7573
BX8901
PRESBYTERIAN RECORD. 1876. m. Can.$11($17) Presbyterian Church in Canada, 50 Wynford Dr., North York, ON M3C 1J7, Canada. TEL 416-441-1111. FAX 416-441-2825. Ed. John Congram. adv.; bk.rev.; film rev.; index. circ. 637,541. (also avail. in microfilm) **Indexed:** Can.B.P.I., Can.Per.Ind.

285   US
PRESBYTERIAN SUN. 1954. m. (except Jan., Aug.). Synod of the Sun, 920 S.I.-35.E, Denton, TX 76205-7898. Ed. Carolyn J. Frazier. adv. contact: Carolyn J. Frazier. bk.rev.; illus.; circ. 117,000 (controlled). (tabloid format; also avail. in microfilm from UMI; reprint service avail. from UMI) **Indexed:** Chr.Per.Ind., Old Test.Abstr. **Document type:** newspaper.
Former titles: Presbyterian (ISSN 0893-4134); Texas Presbyterian (ISSN 0040-4616)

285 266   US   ISSN 0032-759X
BV2570.A1
PRESBYTERIAN SURVEY. 1867. m. $11 (effective 1994). Presbyterian Church (U.S.A.), 100 Witherspoon St., Louisville, KY 40202-1396. TEL 502-569-5637. FAX 502-569-5018. Ed. Catherine Cottingham. adv.; bk.rev.; charts; illus.; index. circ. 105,000. (also avail. in microform from UMI)
—UMI.
Incorporates: Missionary Survey (founded in 1911); Today in World Missions; Home Missionary (founded in 1890); Missionary (founded in 1862).
Description: Offers broad coverage and interpretation of the work of the church and other religious news, discussions of contemporary issues, information for both individuals and congregations.

285   US   ISSN 0193-6212
PRESBYTERION. 1975. s-a. $8.50. Covenant Theological Seminary, 12330 Conway Rd., St. Louis, MO 63141. TEL 314-434-4044. FAX 314-434-4819. Ed. V. Phillips Long. bk.rev.; circ. 400 (paid); 100 (controlled). (also avail. in microform) **Indexed:** CERDIC, Chr.Per.Ind., New Test.Abstr., Old Test.Abstr., Rel.& Theol.Abstr. (1978-), Rel.Ind.One. **Document type:** academic/scholarly publication.
—BLDSC (6609.673000); UMI.
Description: Covers all theological disciplines in a scholarly, yet readable manner.

268   US   ISSN 0732-9431
PRESCHOOL BIBLE TEACHER A. q. $15.95. Southern Baptist Convention, Sunday School Board, 127 Ninth Ave., N., Nashville, TN 37234. TEL 800-458-2772.
Formerly (until 1982): Guide A for Preschool Teachers (ISSN 0162-4474)

268   US   ISSN 0732-944X
PRESCHOOL BIBLE TEACHER B. q. $15.95. Southern Baptist Convention, Sunday School Board, 127 Ninth Ave., N., Nashville, TN 37234. TEL 800-458-2772.
Formerly (until 1982): Guide B for Preschool Teachers (ISSN 0162-4482)

268   US   ISSN 0732-9458
PRESCHOOL BIBLE TEACHER C. q. $15.95. Southern Baptist Convention, Sunday School Board, 127 Ninth Ave., N., Nashville, TN 37234. TEL 800-458-2772.
Formerly (until 1982): Guide C for Preschool Teachers (ISSN 0162-4490)

268 375   US   ISSN 1048-5279
PRESCHOOLERS AT CHURCH. TEACHER'S GUIDE. 1991. q. $14.25. Southern Baptist Convention, Sunday School Board, 127 Ninth Ave., N., Nashville, TN 37234. TEL 800-458-2772.

PRESCHOOLERS AT CHURCH AND HOME. see *CHILDREN AND YOUTH — About*

266   US   ISSN 0162-4326
PROCLAIM (NASHVILLE). q. $13.75. Southern Baptist Convention, Sunday School Board, 127 Ninth Ave., N., Nashville, TN 37234. TEL 800-458-2772. **Indexed:** South.Bap.Per.Ind.
Description: Provides pastors with seron aids and illustrations.

285   US   ISSN 1041-2689
PROCLAIM (PETALUMA). (Text in Chinese) 1988. bi-m. free. Chinese Christian Mission, 1269 N. McDowell Blvd., Petaluma, CA 94975-0759. TEL 707-762-1314. FAX 707-762-1713. Ed. Cecilia Yau. circ. 18,000. (back issues avail.)

200   UK   ISSN 1357-5155
PROTESTANT TRUTH. 1846. bi-m. £3.50. Protestant Truth Society Inc., 184 Fleet St., London EC4A 2HJ, England. TEL 0171-405-4960. Ed. W. John Cook. adv.; bk.rev.; illus. circ. 3,200. **Document type:** newsletter.
Formerly (until 1995): Churchman's Magazine (ISSN 0009-6636)

200 230   IT   ISSN 0033-1767
BR5
PROTESTANTESIMO. 1946. q. L.38000 (foreign L.48000) (effective 1996). Facolta Valdese di Teologia, Via Pietro Cossa 42, 00193 Rome, Italy. TEL 39-6-3210789. FAX 39-6-3201040. Ed. Sergio Rostagno. bk.rev.; bibl.; cum.index: 1946-1988. circ. 1,000. **Indexed:** Bull.Signal., CERDIC, Int.Z.Bibelwiss, Rel.Ind.One. **Document type:** academic/scholarly publication.

284 917.306   US
PROVIDENT BOOK FINDER. 1970. 4/yr. free. (Provident Bookstores) Mennonite Publishing House, 616 Walnut Ave., Scottdale, PA 15683. TEL 412-887-8500. FAX 412-887-3111. Ed. Ron Meyer. bk.rev. circ. 12,000. (back issues avail.) **Description:** Each issue contains over 100 reviews of new books concentrating on peace, social concerns, theology, ethics, children's books and family life.

RELIGIONS AND THEOLOGY — PROTESTANT

289.6   US   ISSN 0033-5096
QUAKER SERVICE BULLETIN. 1947. 2/yr. $10 contribution. American Friends Service Committee, Inc., 1501 Cherry St., Philadelphia, PA 19102. TEL 215-241-7051. FAX 215-241-7275. Ed. Melissa Elliott. illus. circ. 85,000. (also avail. in microform from UMI; reprint service avail. from UMI) **Indexed:** HR Rep.
—UMI.
Formerly (until 1960): Bulletin (Philadelphia) (ISSN 0033-510X)
Description: Program activities of the committee.

284   GW   ISSN 0341-9495
QUATEMBER; Vierteljahreshefte fuer Erneuerung und Einheit der Kirche. 1936. q. DM.32.80. Lutherisches Verlagshaus GmbH, Knochenhauer Str. 38-40, 30159 Hannover, Germany. TEL 0511-1241-739. Ed. Ulrich Wickert. circ. 1,400. **Document type:** bulletin.
—CCC.

284 300   GW   ISSN 0938-6130
QUERSCHNITTE. 1983. q. DM.10. Verlag fuer Kultur und Wissenschaft, Friedrichstr. 38, 53111 Bonn, Germany. TEL 0228-638784. FAX 0228-638784. Ed. Thomas Schirrmacher. adv.: page DM.1000; adv. contact: Carsten Hobolaur. bk.rev.; circ. 1,000. (back issues avail.) **Document type:** academic/scholarly publication.

284.2   SA   ISSN 0033-6637
QUO VADIS (POTCHEFSTROOM). (Text in Afrikaans) 1950. 10/yr. R.3.50. Gereformeerde Kerke in Suid-Afrika - Reformed Churches in South Africa, P.O. Box 20008, Noordbrug 2522, Potchefstroom, South Africa. circ. 7,000.

284   GW
R A B S. (Religionspaedagogik an Berufsbildenden Schulen) 1969. q. DM.36.80. Koesel-Verlag GmbH und Co., Flueggenstr. 2, 80639 Munich, Germany. TEL 089-17801-0. FAX 089-17801111. illus. circ. 2,400. **Document type:** academic/scholarly publication.

205   US
R E C MISSION BULLETIN. 1981. q. $5 (effective through 1996). Reformed Ecumenical Council, 2017 Eastern Ave., Ste. 201, Grand Rapids, MI 49507-3234. TEL 616-241-4424. E-mail: RVHREC@AOL.COM. Ed. Richard L. van Houten. circ. 700. **Document type:** newsletter.
Former titles: R E S Mission Bulletin; R E S World Diaconal Bulletin.

285   US
R E C NEWS EXCHANGE. 1964. m. $7 (effective through 1996). Reformed Ecumenical Council, 2017 Eastern Ave., Ste. 201, Grand Rapids, MI 49507-3234. TEL 616-241-4424. E-mail: RVHREC@AOL.COM. Ed. Richard L. van Houten. bk.rev. circ. 1,200. **Document type:** newsletter.
Formerly: R E S News Exchange (ISSN 0033-6904)

200   US
R E C THEOLOGICAL FORUM. 1973. q. $7 (effective through 1996). Reformed Ecumenical Council, 2017 Eastern Ave., Ste. 201, Grand Rapids, MI 49507-3234. TEL 616-241-4424. E-mail: RVHREC@AOL.COM. Ed. Pieter Potgieter. circ. 550. **Formerly:** R E S Theological Forum.

268   DK   ISSN 0105-7073
RAADGIVEREN; boerne og juniorlederen. 1891. 10/yr. DKK 199. Danmarks Folkekirkelige Soendagsskoler og Boernegudstjenester, Korshaervej 25, 7000 Fredericia, Denmark. TEL 75-92-61-00. Ed. Ejgil Bodilsen. circ. 1,829.

266   US
RAINBOW (LONDON). 1841. q. free. Methodist Church Overseas Division, 25 Marylebone Rd., London NW1 5JR, England. circ. 50,000. (also avail. in microfiche from IDC) **Document type:** bulletin.
Former titles (until 1993): Junkanoo; (until 1991): Window (ISSN 0306-9028); (until 1974): At Home and Abroad (ISSN 0044-9830)
Description: Children's interests.

266   US
REACH (GRAND RAPIDS). bi-m. (Christian Reformed Church of North America) Christian Reformed Home Missions, 2850 Kalamazoo Ave., S.E., Grand Rapids, MI 49560. TEL 616-246-0822. FAX 616-246-0834. Ed. Donald J. McCrory. circ. 12,500. (back issues avail.) **Document type:** newsletter.
Description: Deals with church growth issues for pastors and church leaders in the Christian Reformed Church of North America.

284   US   ISSN 0199-7777
BV4531.2.A1
REACH (OKLAHOMA CITY). 1980. q. International Pentecostal Holiness Church, Box 12609, Oklahoma City, OK 73157. (Subscr. to: Advocate Press, Box 98, Franklin Springs, GA 30639) **Document type:** bulletin.

260   UK   ISSN 0300-3469
READER. 1904. q. £3.20 up 29 93105 EE. Church of England, Central Readers' Conference, Church House, Great Smith St., London SW1P 3NZ, England. TEL 071-222-9011. FAX 0865-723884. Ed. C.A. Cull. adv. contact: G Brown. bk.rev. circ. 9,000.

READY. see MILITARY

284   NZ   ISSN 1172-9236
REALITY; Christian reflections on today's world. 1923. bi-m. NZ.$30 (foreign NZ$35). Bible College of New Zealand, Inc., Private Bag, Henderson, Auckland 1231, New Zealand. TEL 64-9-837-0675. FAX 64-9-837-4209. Ed. John Hitchen. adv.: B&W page NZ.$500; adv. contact: Russell Ford. bk.rev.; film rev.; music rev.; software rev. circ. 5,700. (tabloid format)
—CCC.
Formerly (until vol.75, no.6): Reaper (ISSN 0034-107X)
Description: Interdenominational, evangelical articles of topical and spiritual interest. Also news of the Bible College of New Zealand and its graduates.

200   UK   ISSN 0034-1479
RECONCILIATION QUARTERLY. 1924. q. £7 in U.K. and N. Ireland; rest of Europe £8 (elsewhere £10.50). Fellowship of Reconciliation, 40-46 Harleyford Rd., Vauxhall, London SE11 5AY, England. TEL 0171-582-9054. FAX 0171-582-9180. Ed. Ben Rees. adv.; bk.rev.; illus. circ. 950. (also avail. in microform from UMI; reprint service avail. from UMI) **Indexed:** CERDIC. **Document type:** academic/scholarly publication.
—UMI.
Description: Each issue covers a topic of social concern such as peace and disarmament and discusses the subject with notes, articles and reviews.

285   UK   ISSN 0306-7262
REFORM. 1972. m (11/yr.). £10.50. The United Reformed Church in the United Kingdom, 86 Tavistock Pl., London WC1H 9RT, England. Ed. David Lawrence. adv.; bk.rev.; film rev.; illus. circ. 14,500. **Document type:** bulletin.
Formed by the merger of: Congregational Monthly (ISSN 0010-583X); Outlook (ISSN 0030-7203)

286   UK   ISSN 0034-3048
REFORMATION TODAY. 1970. 6/yr. £10($15) 75 Woodhill Rd., Leeds LS16 7BZ, England. TEL 01532-612513. (Subscr. to: Stan Thompson, 200 Appley Ln. N., Appley Bridge, Wigan WN6 9DY, England) Ed. Erroll Hulse. bk.rev.; charts. circ. 3,000. **Indexed:** CERDIC. **Document type:** bulletin.
Supersedes: Christians Pathway.
Description: Presents bible study material, biographies, and news of Reformed churches worldwide.

284   GW   ISSN 0171-3469
REFORMATIONSGESCHICHTLICHE STUDIEN UND TEXTE. 1906. irreg., vol.130, 1991. price varies. Aschendorffsche Verlagsbuchhandlung, Soesterstr. 13, 48155 Muenster, Germany. TEL 0251-690-0. FAX 0251-690143. Ed. Klaus Ganzer. (also avail. in microform from BHP; microfiche from BHP) **Document type:** monographic series.

284   HU
REFORMATUS EGYHAZ. 1949. m. $35.50. Hungarian Reformed Church, Abonyi u. 21, 1146 Budapest, Hungary. TEL 122-7870. Ed. Ferenc Dusicza. circ. 1,600.

284   HU   ISSN 0482-086X
REFORMATUSOK LAPJA. 1957. w. $37. Reformed Church, POB 424, 1395 Budapest, Hungary. TEL 117-6809. Ed. Attila P. Komlos. circ. 40,000.

284   FR   ISSN 0223-5749
REFORME; chaque semaine un regard protestant sur l'actualite. 1945. w. 510 F. (foreign 625 F.). 53-55 Avenue du Maine, 75014 Paris, France. TEL 43-20-32-67. FAX 1-43-21-42-86. Ed. Michel Leplay. adv.; bk.rev.; illus. (tabloid format)

284   US   ISSN 0362-0476
BX9185
REFORMED LITURGY & MUSIC. 1963. q. $15. Division of Congregational Ministries of the Presbyterian Church, 100 Witherspoon St., Rm. 2616A, Louisville, KY 40202-1396. TEL 502-569-5331. FAX 502-569-5501. Ed. Dennis J. Hughes. bk.rev.; index. circ. 5,010. (also avail. in microfiche; back issues avail.) **Document type:** academic/scholarly publication.
—UMI; UnCover.
Description: Seeks to develop an understanding of reformed piety, corporate worship, and the role of music in the life of the church.

200   US   ISSN 0034-3064
REFORMED REVIEW. 1947. 3/yr. $15. Western Theological Seminary, 101 E. 13th St., Holland, MI 49423. TEL 616-392-8555. FAX 616-392-7717. Ed. James I. Cook. adv. contact: Norman Donkersloot. bk.rev.; bibl.; cum.index. circ. 2,900. (also avail. in microform from UMI; reprint service avail. from UMI) **Indexed:** CERDIC, Int.Z.Bibelwiss, New Test.Abstr., Rel.& Theol.Abstr. (1967-), Rel.Ind.One, Rel.Per. **Document type:** academic/scholarly publication.
—BLDSC (7332.520000); UMI.

284   SZ   ISSN 0034-3056
BX8901
REFORMED WORLD. 1971. q. 14 SFr.($9) World Alliance of Reformed Churches, P.O. Box 2100, 150, route de Ferney, CH-1211 Geneva 2, Switzerland. TEL 022-7916236. FAX 022-7916505. TELEX 415730-OIK-CH. Ed. Milan Opocensky. adv. contact: Paraic Reamonn. bk.rev.; index. circ. 11,500. (also avail. in microfilm from UMI; reprint service avail. from UMI) **Indexed:** CERDIC, Rel.& Theol.Abstr. (1971-), Rel.Ind.One, Rel.Per. **Document type:** bulletin.
—UMI.
Formerly: Reformed and Presbyterian World.

284   US   ISSN 0890-8583
REFORMED WORSHIP; resources in liturgy and music. 1986. q. $22. C R C Publications, Education Department, 2850 Kalamazoo S.E., Grand Rapids, MI 49560. TEL 800-333-8300. FAX 616-246-0834. Ed. Emily Brink. bk.rev.; circ. 3,500 (paid). (back issues avail.) **Document type:** consumer publication.

280   UK   ISSN 0034-3080
REFORMER. 1930. bi-m. £3. Protestant Alliance, 77 Ampthill Rd., Flitwick, Bedford MK45 1BD, England. TEL 01525-712348. Ed. Rev. Stephen Scott-Pearson. bk.rev.; illus. circ. 4,500. **Document type:** bulletin.

RELIGIONSUNTERRICHT UND KONFIRMANDENUNTERRICHT FUER GEHOERLOSE UND SCHWERHOERIGE; ein Informationsdienst. see HANDICAPPED — Hearing Impaired

200   US   ISSN 0738-7318
RELIGIOUS HERALD. 1828. w. $11.25. Religious Herald, Box 8377, Richmond, VA 23226-0377. TEL 804-672-7913. FAX 804-672-2051. Ed. Dr. Michael Clingenpeel. adv. circ. 32,000. **Document type:** newspaper.
Description: News for the Southern Baptist community in Virginia.

283 282   UK   ISSN 1351-4326
RENEWAL (CROWBOROUGH). 1966. m. £22. Monarch Magazines, Broadway House, The Broadway, Crowborough, E. Sussex TN6 1HQ, England. TEL 01892-652364. FAX 01892-663329. Ed. Rev. Wallace Boulton. adv. contact: Penelope Thomas. bk.rev.; circ. 11,600 (paid). (back issues avail.) **Document type:** bulletin.
Description: Informs people about the work of the Holy Spirit.

RELIGIONS AND THEOLOGY — PROTESTANT

285 US ISSN 1043-125X
RENEWAL NEWS. 1966. q. donation. (Presbyterian and Reformed Renewal Ministries International) Presbyterian Renewal Publications, Box 429, Black Mountain, NC 28711-0429. TEL 704-669-7373. Ed. Rev. Dr. Zeb Bradford Long. bk.rev.; circ. 12,000 (controlled). (tabloid format; back issues avail.)
Formerly (until 1980): Presbyterian Charismatic Communion Newsletter.
Description: Promotes an experience of the Holy Spirit through news, teaching, and testimony.

285 US
RENEWS (LOUISVILLE). q. Presbyterians for Renewal, 8134 New La Grange Rd., Ste. 227, Louisville, KY 40222-0069. **Document type:** newsletter.
Formerly (until 1989): Open Letter (ISSN 0194-7125)
Description: Provides resources for Presbyterian Church (U.S.A.).

286 US ISSN 0364-6661
REPORT FROM THE CAPITAL. 1946. 24/yr. $10. Baptist Joint Committee on Public Affairs, 200 Maryland Ave., N.E., Washington, DC 20002. TEL 202-544-4226. FAX 202-544-2094. Ed. Larry Chesser. bk.rev. circ. 10,000. (back issues avail.) **Indexed:** South.Bap.Per.Ind. **Document type:** newsletter.
Description: Provides news, views and articles about religious liberty and church-state separation.

284.1 US ISSN 0360-7119
REPORTER (ST. LOUIS). 1954. m. $12. Lutheran Church - Missouri Synod, 1333 S. Kirkwood Rd., St. Louis, MO 63122. TEL 314-965-9000. Ed. David Mahsman. (also avail. in microform from UMI) **Document type:** consumer publication.
Formerly (until 1975): Advance (St. Louis) (ISSN 0001-8570)

268.8 CN ISSN 0832-9354
RESOURCE; the national leadership magazine. 1986. bi-m. Can.$15($18) Pentecostal Assemblies of Canada, Church Ministries Department, 6745 Century Ave., Mississauga, ON L5N 6P7, Canada. TEL 905-542-7400. FAX 905-542-1624. Ed. Michael P. Horban. adv. contact: Rick Hiebert. bk.rev. circ. 10,500.
Former titles (until 1986): Source (ISSN 0229-4931); (until 1981): Pentecostal Assemblies of Canada. Cell Pak (ISSN 0707-1868)
Description: Topics of relevance to lay and ordained church leaders; relationships, authority, finances and specialized ministries.

287 US ISSN 0034-5725
RESPONSE (NEW YORK, 1969). 1969. m. (11/yr., combined Jul.-Aug.). $10. United Methodist Church, General Board of Global Ministries, Women's Division, 475 Riverside Dr., Rm. 13463, New York, NY 10115. TEL 212-870-3755. Ed. Dana E. Jones. illus.; index. circ. 70,500. **Indexed:** Mid.East: Abstr.& Ind.
Supersedes (1940-1969): Methodist Woman.

286 US ISSN 0034-6373
BX6201
REVIEW AND EXPOSITOR. 1904. q. $24 (foreign $30) (effective 1995). Southern Baptist Theological Seminary, Faculty Club, 2825 Lexington Rd., Louisville, KY 40280. TEL 502-897-4407. Ed. Can Stiver. adv. contact: Joel Drinkard. bk.rev.; index. circ. 6,000. (also avail. in microform from UMI) **Indexed:** CERDIC, New Test.Abstr., Old Test.Abstr., Rel.& Theol.Abstr. (1967-), Rel.Ind.One, Rel.Per., South.Bap.Per.Ind. **Document type:** academic/scholarly publication.
—BLDSC (7786.940000); UMI.
Formerly: Baptist Review and Expositor (ISSN 0190-5856)

283 NQ
REVISTA DE HISTORIA DEL PROTESTANTISMO NICARAGUENSE. 1990. a. C.$50($12) Centro Inter-Eclesial de Estudios Teologicos y Sociales, Instituto de Historia Protestante y Filosofia, Plaza el Sol, 1 c. al sur, 50 vrs. arriba, Apdo. RP-082, Managua, Nicaragua. TEL 506-2-673033. FAX 506-2-671010. Ed. Noel Gonzalez Garcia. **Document type:** academic/scholarly publication.

284.1489 DK ISSN 0108-0806
RIBE STIFTSBOG. 1970. a. DKK 35. Stiftsoevrigheds- og Bispekontoret, Korsbroedregade 7, 6760 Ribe, Denmark.
Formerly: Ribe Stift.

284 IT
RIFORMA; settimanale delle chiese battiste metodiste e valdesi. w. L.110000. Edizioni Protestanti, s.r.l., Via S. Pio V, no.15, bis., 10125 Turin, Italy. TEL 011-655278. FAX 011-657542. Dir. Giorgio Gardiol. circ. 5,000.
Formerly: Luce (Turin).

284 282 AT
THE ROCK (EPPING). 1945. bi-m. Aus.$12 (foreign Aus.$20). The Rock Newspaper Company, D.& C. Shelton, P.O. Box 551, Epping, N.S.W. 2121, Australia. TEL 02-868-4591. Ed. Rev. D.C. Shelton. (back issues avail.) **Document type:** newspaper.
Description: Articles and news critical of Roman Catholicism; promotes Protestant Christianity.

284 NE
RONDUIT MAGAZINE. 1989. 6/yr. fl.10. Evangelische Omroep, Postbus 21000, 1202 BJ Hilversum, Netherlands. Ed. L. de Jong. circ. 60,000.

286 US ISSN 0893-5246
ROYAL AMBASSADOR LEADERSHIP. q. Southern Baptist Convention, Brotherhood Commission, 1548 Poplar Ave., Memphis, TN 38104. TEL 800-727-6466. Ed. Tim Seanor.
Formerly (until 1986): Crusader Counselor (ISSN 0162-2579)

284 UK ISSN 1354-6422
▼**RUTHERFORD JOURNAL OF CHURCH AND MINISTRY.** 1994. s-a. £5($15); newsstand price: £3. Rutherford House, 17 Claremont Park, Edinburgh EH6 7PJ, Scotland. TEL 0131-554-1206. FAX 0131-555-1002. Ed. David Searle. circ. 600 (paid). **Document type:** academic/scholarly publication.

284 UK ISSN 0968-5405
THE S A L T PROGRAMME FOR ALL AGES. 1984. q. £4. Scripture Union Publishing, 130 City Rd., London EC1V 2NJ, England. TEL 0171-782-0013. Ed. Peter Graystone. circ. 9,500. **Document type:** bulletin.
Formerly (until 1993): Learning All Together.
Description: Church curriculum material for all-age and adult worship.

284 UK ISSN 0968-5367
THE S A L T PROGRAMME FOR 3 TO 4. 1984. q. £4 per no. Scripture Union Publishing, 130 City Rd., London EC1V 2NJ, England. TEL 0171-782-0013. FAX 0171-782-0014. Ed. Christine Wright. circ. 15,000. **Document type:** bulletin.
Formerly (until 1993): Learning Together with Under 5's.
Description: Church curriculum for children 3 to 4.

286 US ISSN 1081-8189
S B C LIFE. 1927. m. $10. Southern Baptist Convention, Executive Committee, 901 Commerce, Ste. 750, Nashville, TN 37203-3630. TEL 615-244-2355. FAX 615-742-8919. Ed. Jon Walker. adv. contact: Jon Walker. bk.rev.; illus.; index. circ. 70,000. (tabloid format; back issues avail.) **Indexed:** South.Bap.Per.Ind. **Document type:** newspaper.
Formerly (until Sept. 1993): Baptist Program (ISSN 0005-5743)
Description: Keeps readers informed about programs and plans.

289.9 US ISSN 0279-6716
S O W. (Save Our World) 1962. q. free. (Church of God World Missions) Pathway Press, Box 2250, Cleveland, TN 37320-2250. TEL 615-476-3361. FAX 615-478-7521. Ed. Christopher Moree. charts; illus.; stat. circ. 87,000.
Description: Provides news and feature articles on international missions, to promote interest in missionary work among the constituency of the Church of God.

284 AT ISSN 0725-6140
S.U. NEWS. q. Aus.$15 donation. Scripture Union (A.C.T.), Unit 5 Block 2, Shopping Centre, Cook, A.C.T. 2614, Australia. TEL 61-6-251-3677. FAX 61-6-251-2953. bk.rev. circ. 2,800. **Document type:** newsletter.

286 US ISSN 0036-214X
SABBATH RECORDER. 1844. m. free. (American Sabbath Tract and Communication Council) Seventh Day Baptist Center, Box 1678, Janesville, WI 53547. TEL 608-752-5055. FAX 608-752-7711. Ed. Kevin Butler. bk.rev.; illus. circ. 4,600. (also avail. in microfilm)
Description: Contains inspirational and informational news for and about Seventh Day Baptists.

286.73 US ISSN 0098-9517
BX6101
SABBATH WATCHMAN. 1926. bi-m. $12 (foreign $15) (effective 1994). Religious Liberty Publishing Association, 2877 E. Florence Ave., Huntington Park, CA 90255. TEL 310-862-5252. FAX 310-862-7166. (Co-sponsor: Seventh-Day Adventist Church Reform Movement, American Union) Ed. Branko Cholich. bk.rev.; illus. circ. 650. **Document type:** newsletter.

200 UK ISSN 0036-3111
ST. MARTIN'S REVIEW; the journal with the international outlook. 1893. m. £8 (foreign £10). St-Martin-In-The-Fields Church, 5 St. Martins Place, London WC2, England. TEL 0171-930-1862. Ed. Rev. Schuennemann. adv.; bk.rev.; play rev.; illus. circ. 1,500. **Document type:** bulletin.

283 UK
THE SARUM LINK. 1987. m. free. Diocese of Salisbury, Church House, Crane St., Salisbury, Wilts. SP1 2QB, England. TEL 01722-411988. FAX 01722-411990. Ed. Kevin Catchpole. adv. contact: Amanda Field. bk.rev.; charts; illus.; stat.; tr.lit. circ. 62,000. (back issues avail.) **Document type:** newspaper.
Description: Contains news and commentary relating to people and events in the Anglican Diocese of Salisubry for members of local churches.

283 KE
SAUTI NYIKANI. (Text in Swahili) 1964. bi-m. free. Evangel Publishing House, P.O. Box 28963, Nairobi, Kenya. TEL 254-2-802033. FAX 254-2-860840. circ. 20,000. **Document type:** newspaper.

283 TZ
SAUTI YA JIMBO. (Text in Swahili) q. Church of the Province of Tanzania, P.O. Box 899, Dodoma, Tanzania.
Description: Provides Anglican diocesan, provincial, and world news.

283 610 UK ISSN 0036-5106
SAVING HEALTH. 1962. q. £5 (effective 1994). Medical Missionary Association, 244 Camden Rd., London NW1 9HE, England. TEL 0171-485-2672. FAX 0171-485-2672. Ed. Dr. D. Glegg. adv.; bk.rev.; illus. circ. 1,000. **Indexed:** CERDIC. **Document type:** newsletter.
Description: Contains articles by Christian doctors, nurses, journalists and medical-health workers in the developing world working through church agencies.

283 362.7 GW
SCHNELLER-MAGAZIN. 1895. q. free. Evangelischer Verein fuer das Syrische Waisenhaus (Schneller-Schulen) e.V., Vogelsangstr. 62, 70197 Stuttgart, Germany. TEL 0711-63678-0. FAX 0711-63678-66. TELEX 723059-EMS-D. Ed.Bd. circ. 20,000. (back issues avail.) **Document type:** bulletin.
Former titles (until 1991): Schneller Bote (ISSN 0344-8525); (until 1969): Bote aus Zion (ISSN 0174-8491)
Description: Information on orphanages in Jordan and Lebanon and other Middle East issues.

284 GW ISSN 0170-6128
SCHOENBERGER HEFTE. 1970. q. DM.9. (Evangelische Kirche in Hessen und Nassau, Religionspaedagogische Studienzentrum) Evangelischer Presseverband in Hessen und Nassau e.V., Neue Schlesingergasse 24, 60311 Frankfurt a.M., Germany. TEL 069-299884-0. FAX 069-299884-24. Eds. Gerhard Brockmann, Hans Heller. bk.rev. circ. 12,000.
Description: Articles on Protestant religious education, aimed at teachers in German high schools.

SCHRIFTENREIHE FUER DIE EVANGELISCHE FRAU. see *WOMEN'S INTERESTS*

RELIGIONS AND THEOLOGY — PROTESTANT

286   UK   ISSN 0036-9136
SCOTTISH BAPTIST MAGAZINE. 1860. m. £4. Baptist Union of Scotland, c/o Rev. Robert Armstrong, Ed., Baptist Church House, 14 Aytoun Rd., Glasgow G41 5RT, Scotland. FAX 041-424-1422. adv.; bk.rev. circ. 4,000.

284   UK   ISSN 0265-4539
BR1
SCOTTISH BULLETIN OF EVANGELICAL THEOLOGY. 1983. s-a. £11.50. Rutherford House, 17 Claremont Park, Edinburgh EH6 7PJ, Scotland. TEL 0131-554-1206. FAX 0131-555-1002. (Co-sponsor: Scottish Evangelical Theology Society) Ed. David Wright. adv. contact: David Searle. bk.rev. circ. 800. (reprint service avail. from IRC) **Document type:** academic/scholarly publication.
—BLDSC (8206.542000).
   Former titles (until 1983): Scottish Evangelical Theology Society Bulletin; Scottish Tynedale Bulletin (ISSN 0262-1053)

283   UK   ISSN 1351-5349
SCOTTISH EPISCOPAL CHURCH REVIEW. s-a. £5. Scottish Episcopal Church, 21 Grosvenor Crescent, Edinburgh EH12 5EE, Scotland. TEL 0131-225-6357. FAX 0131-346-7247. Ed. Timm Engh. **Document type:** academic/scholarly publication.

267   UK   ISSN 0260-0617
BX5225
SCOTTISH EPISCOPAL CHURCH YEARBOOK. 1879. a. £6. Scottish Episcopal Church, 21 Grosvenor Crescent, Edinburgh EH12 5EE, Scotland. TEL 0131-225-6357. FAX 0131-346-7247. index. circ. 800. **Document type:** bulletin.

283   UK   ISSN 0969-4161
THE SCOTTISH EPISCOPALIAN. 1965. m. 30p. Scottish Episcopal Church, 21 Grosvenor Crescent, Edinburgh EH12 5EE, Scotland. TEL 0131-225-6357. FAX 0131-346-7247. adv.; bk.rev. circ. 6,500. (tabloid format) **Document type:** bulletin.
   Former titles: Newscan; Outlook (ISSN 0306-2295); Scan (ISSN 0036-5475)

284   SA   ISSN 0254-1807
SCRIPTURA; tydskrif vir Bybel en teologie in Suider-Afrika - journal of Bible and Theology in Southern Africa. (Text in Afrikaans and English) 1980. 6/yr. R.30 to individuals; libraries R.40 (effective 1994). University of Stellenbosch, Department of Biblical Studies - Universiteit van Stellenbosch, Departement Bybelkunde, 7600 Stellenbosch, South Africa. TEL 27-21-8082117. FAX 27-21-8082031. Ed. B.C. Lategan. bk.rev.; illus. circ. 340. (back issues avail.) **Indexed:** Ind.S.A.Per., New Test.Abstr., Rel.& Theol.Abstr. (1988-), Rel.Ind.One.
—BLDSC (8213.237300).
   Description: Publishes articles on the Bible and theology. Emphasizes contextual theological and ethical issues, in particular those relating to Southern Africa.
   Refereed Serial

284   IE   ISSN 0332-0618
SEARCH; Church of Ireland journal. 1978. 2/yr. I£5($10) Religious Education Resource Centre, Holy Trinity Church, Rathmines, Dublin 6, Ireland. TEL 01-4972821. Ed. M. Burrows. bk.rev. circ. 600. **Document type:** academic/scholarly publication.
—BLDSC (8213.809000).
   Description: For teachers in primary and secondary schools, people of responsibility in parishes, as well as the clergy.

286   US   ISSN 0739-2281
SEARCHING TOGETHER. 1972. q. $7. Word of Life Church, Box 548, St. Croix Falls, WI 54024. TEL 715-755-3560. FAX 612-465-5101. Ed. Jon Zens. adv.; bk.rev. circ. 3,000. (also avail. in microform from UMI; back issues avail.) **Indexed:** CERDIC, Rel.& Theol.Abstr. (1988-), Rel.Ind.One, Rel.Per. **Document type:** academic/scholarly publication.
—UMI.
   Formerly (until 1981): Baptist Reformation Review (ISSN 0276-7945)
   Description: Explores church issues and biblical teachings. Includes new publications information.

286   US   ISSN 0037-0606
BV4800
SECRET PLACE. 1938. q. $4 for inkprint; Braille $16; cassette $35; large print $6.50. American Baptist Churches in the U S A, Educational Ministries, Box 851, Valley Forge, PA 19482-0851. TEL 610-768-2000. (Cassette orders to: Shared Daily Devotions, Box 93734, Pasadena, CA 91109-9857) Ed. Kathleen Hayes. circ. 112,000. (also avail. in Braille; audio cassette; large print edition in 14 pt.)
   Description: A devotional guide to be used with the Bible at home.

SECRETARY: F Y I. see BUSINESS AND ECONOMICS — Office Equipment And Services

284   US   ISSN 0897-5663
SEEDS FOR THE PARISH. 1972. 6/yr. free to qualified personnel. Evangelical Lutheran Church in America, 8765 W. Higgins Rd., Chicago, IL 60631-4177. TEL 312-380-2949. FAX 312-380-2406. Ed. Marcia Erickson Bates. bk.rev.; circ. 200,000 (controlled). (tabloid format; also avail. in diskette format)
   Supersedes (in 1988): Congregation (ISSN 0361-8862)
   Description: Reports on new resources and services available on clergy and lay congregational leaders.

286   PO   ISSN 0037-1874
SEMEADOR BAPTISTA. 1926. m. Esc.1700 (effective 1995) Esc.1800 (effective 1996). Convencao Baptista Portuguesa - Portuguese Baptist Convention, Apdo. 3085, 2746 Queluz Codex, Portugal. TEL 351-1-4362718. FAX 351-1-4361833. Ed. Pedro Guedes. adv.; B&W page Esc. 30000. bk.rev.; illus. circ. 1,250. (tabloid format) **Document type:** newspaper.

SENIOR MUSICIAN. see MUSIC

284 305.3   CN
SERVANT LEADER. 1959. q. free. Christian Service Brigade of Canada, 1254 Plains Rd. E., Burlington, Ont. L7S 1W6, Canada. TEL 416-634-1841. FAX 416-634-7643. Ed. Mark Clayton. bk.rev. circ. 5,000. (looseleaf format; back issues avail.)
   Formerly: Torch Runner (ISSN 0316-2931)
   Description: For the leaders of men's and boys' programs of the Christian Service Brigade.

285   CN   ISSN 0848-1741
SERVANT MAGAZINE. 1989. 6/yr. donation. Prairie Bible Institute, Three Hills, AB T0M 2N0, Canada. TEL 403-443-5511. FAX 403-443-5540. Ed. Phil R. Callaway. bk.rev. circ. 25,000.
   Description: Features world news section related to the Church, moral issues, articles devoted to important figures, education and encouragement for today's Christian.

284   CM
SERVITEUR. m. B.P. 1405, Yaounde, Cameroon. Ed. Daniel Ako'o. circ. 3,000.

286   YU
SESTRINSKI LIST. (Text in Serbo-Croatian) 1955. m. $6. (Dobra Vest Union - Union of Baptist Churches) Rijeci Iskrene, Dravska 2, 42305 Puscine, Yugoslavia. TEL 021-369-882. Ed. Olga Dega. adv.; bk.rev. circ. 1,400.

283   US   ISSN 1059-9576
BR1
SEWANEE THEOLOGICAL REVIEW. 1957. q. $15 to individuals; libraries $20. University of the South, School of Theology, Sewanee, TN 37383-1000. TEL 615-598-1475. E-mail: JJONES@SERAPH1.SEWANEE.EDU. Ed. Christopher Bryan. adv.; bk.rev.; index, cum.index: 1956-1967, 1967-1977; circ. 1,350 (paid). (also avail. in microfilm from UMI; reprint service avail. from UMI) **Indexed:** CERDIC, New Test.Abstr., Old Test.Abstr, Rel.& Theol.Abstr. (1989-), Rel.Ind.One, Rel.Per. **Document type:** academic/scholarly publication.
—BLDSC (8254.252000); UMI.
   Former titles (until 1991): St. Luke's Journal of Theology (ISSN 0036-309X)
   Description: Engages readers in Anglican theological reflection.

SHINING STAR MAGAZINE. see CHILDREN AND YOUTH — For

SIGNAL (STREAMWOOD). see CHILDREN AND YOUTH — About

286   US
SIGNS OF THE TIMES (NAMPA). 1874. m. $12.95. (Seventh-Day Adventists) Pacific Press Publishing Association, 1350 Kings Rd., Nampa, ID 83651. TEL 208-465-2500. FAX 208-465-2531. Ed. R. Greg Brothers. circ. 290,000. (also avail. in microform from UMI)

283   TZ
SIKILIZA. q. $1.60 per no. (effective 1993). Seventh Day Adventist, P.O. Box 635, Morgoro, Tanzania. TEL 056-3338. FAX 056-4374. Ed. G.H. Mbwana. circ. 10,000.

SILVER WINGS; poems. see LITERATURE — Poetry

283 267.15   UK
SING TO THE LORD. 1886. 3/yr. Salvation Army, Territorial Headquarters, 101 Queen Victoria St., London EC4P 4EP, England. TEL 0171-387-3768. FAX 0171-236-3491. Ed. Richard Phillips. circ. 23,000. **Document type:** bulletin.
   Formerly (until 1994): Musical Salvationist (ISSN 0027-464X)

SINGLES SCENE - SPIRIT & LIFE. see SINGLES' INTERESTS AND LIFESTYLES

266   US   ISSN 0700-5202
SLAVNA NADEJE/GLORIOUS HOPE. (Text in English, Czech, Slovak) 1974. bi-m. Czechoslovak Baptist Convention of the United States and Canada, Rt. 1, Box 58D, Philippi, WV 26416. TEL 304-457-4287. FAX 304-457-3043. Ed. George Legierski. circ. 1,300. **Document type:** newsletter.

284.2   SA   ISSN 0037-685X
SLINGERVEL; publication for the youth. (Text in Afrikaans) 1959. m. R.17. Reformed Churches in South Africa - Gereformeerde Kerke in Suid-Afrika, P.O. Box 20008, Noordbrug 2522, Potchefstroom, South Africa. Ed. P.W. Buys. bk.rev. circ. 7,850.

284   XV
SNOPJE Z DOMACIH IN TUJIH NJIV KRSCANSKE MISLI. (Text in Slovenian) 1977. a. 500 SLT. Binkostna Cerkev, Celovska 76, 61000 Ljubljana, Slovenia. TEL 38-61-553-260. Ed. Mihael Kuzmic. circ. 500. (back issues avail.)

301   US   ISSN 0731-0234
SOCIAL QUESTIONS BULLETIN. 1911. bi-m. $13 to individuals; institutions $17. Methodist Federation for Social Action, 76 Clinton Ave., Staten Island, NY 10301. TEL 718-273-6372. Ed. Rev. George D. McClain. bk.rev. circ. 2,000. (also avail. in microform from UMI; back issues avail.; reprint service avail. from UMI) **Indexed:** CERDIC. **Document type:** newsletter.
—UMI.

284   FR   ISSN 0035-3884
BX9401
SOCIETE CALVINISTE DE FRANCE. REVUE REFORMEE. 1950. q. 170 F. (typically set in Dec.). Faculte de Theologie Reformee, 33 av. Jules Ferry, 13100 Aix-en-Province, France. TEL 33-42-26-1355. FAX 33-42-93-2263. Ed. Paul Wells. bk.rev.; index, cum.index every 10 yrs. circ. 1,300. **Indexed:** New Test.Abstr., Old Test.Abstr.
—BLDSC (7945.300000).

384   FR   ISSN 0037-9050
SOCIETE DE L'HISTOIRE DU PROTESTANTISME FRANCAIS. BULLETIN. 1852. q. 220 F. (foreign 300 F.). Societe de l'Histoire du Protestantisme Francais, 54 rue des Saints-Peres, 75007 Paris, France. Ed. Jean-Hugues Carbonnier. bk.rev.; bibl.; charts; illus.; stat.; index, cum.index. circ. 2,200. **Indexed:** Amer.Hist.& Life, CERDIC, Hist.Abstr. **Document type:** bulletin.
—SWETS.

269.4   US
SOCIETY FOR PENTECOSTAL STUDIES. NEWSLETTER. 1970. s-a. $6 to non-members; members free. Society for Pentecostal Studies, Box 2671, Gaithersburg, MD 20886. TEL 301-990-2083. Ed. Peter D. Hocken. bk.rev.; bibl. (back issues avail.) **Document type:** newsletter.

RELIGIONS AND THEOLOGY — PROTESTANT

286　　　　　DK　　ISSN 0109-2375
SOENDAGSKOLEKONTAKT. 1984. q. free. Danmarks Folkekirkelige Soendagsskoler og Boernegudstjenester, Korskaervej 25, DK-7000 Fredericia, Denmark. TEL 75-92-61-00 609. FAX 75-92-61-46. Ed. Bjarne Gertz Olsen. illus. circ. 7,000.

284　　　　　GW　　ISSN 0722-3145
SONNTAGSBLATT. 1929. w. DM.74.40. (Evangelisch-Lutherischer Landeskirchenrat) Evangelischer Presseverband fuer Bayern e.V., Birkerstr. 22, 80636 Munich, Germany. TEL 089-12172146. FAX 089-12172304. Ed. Johanna Haberer; Pub. Hartmut Joisten. adv. contact: H. Friedlhuber. bk.rev.; illus.; stat. circ. 54,966. **Document type:** newspaper.
Former titles (until 1981): Sonntagsblatt fuer die Evangelisch-Lutherische Kirche in Bayern. Ausgabe Oberfranken (ISSN 0014-3391); Evangelisches Gemeindeblatt fuer Hof und Umgebung.

284　　　　　GW　　ISSN 0940-5208
SONNTAGSGRUSS; Kraft fuer den Tag. 1928. w. DM.13.90. Christliche Verlagsanstalt GmbH, Andreas-Braem-Str. 18-20, 47506 Neukirchen-Vluyn, Germany. TEL 02845-392242. FAX 02845-392250. **Document type:** bulletin.

283　　　　　US　　ISSN 0194-8040
SOUNDINGS (MINNEAPOLIS). 1976. 9/yr. $10. Episcopal Diocese of Minnesota, 430 Oak Grove, Ste. 306, Minneapolis, MN 55403. TEL 612-871-5311. Ed. Walt Gordon. adv.: B&W page $600, trim 11 x 17. circ. 16,000.
Description: Provides news and current issues of concern to Episcopalians.

286　　　　　SA
SOUTH AFRICAN BAPTIST HANDBOOK. 1885. a. R.22($15) Baptist Union of Southern Africa, P.O. Box 1085, Roodepoort 1725, South Africa. TEL 011-760-3038. FAX 011-760-2685. circ. 1,200. (back issues avail.)

286　　　　　US　　ISSN 0146-0196
BX6248.S6
SOUTH CAROLINA BAPTIST HISTORICAL SOCIETY JOURNAL. 1975. a. $3. South Carolina Baptist Historical Society, Furman University Library, Greenville, SC 29613. TEL 803-294-2194. FAX 803-294-3004. Ed. J. Glenwood Clayton. bk.rev. circ. 200. (back issues avail.) **Document type:** academic/scholarly publication.
Description: Publishes articles dealing with Baptist history and especially South Carolina Baptist history.

287　　　　　US
SOUTH CAROLINA UNITED METHODIST ADVOCATE. 1837. w. $14.25 (effective Jan. 1992). (United Methodist Church, South Carolina Conference) Southern Christian Advocate, 4908 Colonial Dr., Columbia, SC 29203. TEL 803-786-9483. Ed. Willie S. Teague. adv.; bk.rev.; illus. circ. 12,000.
Former titles: South Carolina Methodist Advocate (ISSN 0038-3147); Southern Christian Advocate.

286 016　　　US　　ISSN 0081-3001
SOUTHERN BAPTIST CONVENTION. ANNUAL. 1845. a. $7.50. Southern Baptist Convention, 901 Commerce, Ste. 400, Nashville, TN 37203. TEL 615-244-2355. Ed. Martin Bradley. cum.index 1845-1953; 1954-1965. circ. 35,000. (also avail. in microfilm)

SOUTHERN BAPTIST CONVENTION. NATIONAL DRAMA SERVICE. see *THEATER*

377.8　　　　US　　ISSN 0038-3848
SOUTHERN BAPTIST EDUCATOR. vol.12, 1947. 10/yr. $8. Southern Baptist Convention, Education Commission, 901 Commerce St., Ste.600, Nashville, TN 37203-3632. TEL 615-244-2362. FAX 615-242-2153. Ed. Tim Fields. bk.rev.; bibl.; stat.; index. circ. 11,350. **Document type:** academic/scholarly publication.

283　　　　　AT　　ISSN 0313-5861
SOUTHERN CROSS; Anglican news magazine. 1961. 11/yr. Aus.$25. Anglican Media, P.O. Box Q190, Queen Victoria Building, Sydney, N.S.W. 2000, Australia. TEL 61-2-265-1505. FAX 61-2-261-2864. Ed. George James Fisher. adv. contact: George Fisher. bk.rev.; film rev. circ. 20,000. (back issues avail.)
Description: Studies applied theology, information and debate on current issues.

286　　　　　DK　　ISSN 0038-4917
SOUTHWESTERN NEWS. 1943. m. (Sep.-Jul.). free. Southwestern Baptist Theological Seminary, Box 22000 3E, Ft. Worth, TX 76122-0490. TEL 817-923-1921. Ed. John E. Seelig. circ. 38,000. (reprint service avail. from UMI) **Indexed:** South.Bap.Per.Ind.

286　　　　　US
SOUTHWESTERN UNION RECORD. 1902. m. $9 (typically Jan.). Southwestern Union Conference of Seventh Day Adventists, Box 4000, Burleson, TX 76028. TEL 817-295-0476. FAX 817-447-2443. E-mail: 74617,537@CompuServe.com. Ed. Jean Thomas. adv. contact: Sean Thomas. circ. 22,000.
Description: Focuses on news and promotion of Seventh-Day Adventists' churches and institutions in Arkansas, Louisiana, Oklahoma, Texas, and New Mexico.

SPARK. see *HANDICAPPED — Visually Impaired*

268 362.4 371.3　US　ISSN 1049-2828
SPECIAL EDUCATION. TEACHER. 1991. q. $52.75. Southern Baptist Convention, Sunday School Board, 127 Ninth Ave., N., Nashville, TN 37234. TEL 800-458-2772.

268 362.4　　　US　　ISSN 1049-281X
SPECIAL EDUCATION BIBLE STUDY. 1990. q. $11.75. Southern Baptist Convention, Sunday School Board, 127 Ninth Ave., N., Nashville, TN 37234. TEL 800-458-2772.

268 362.4　　　US
SPECIAL EDUCATION TODAY. q. $19.50. Southern Baptist Convention, Sunday School Board, 127 Ninth Ave., N., Nashville, TN 37234. TEL 800-458-2772.
Formerly (until 1995): Special Education Leadership (ISSN 0896-7784)
Description: Provides information and advice for parents, families, and church leaders with persons with handicaps.

286　　　　　US　　ISSN 1061-6160
SPECTRUM (WHEATON). 1992. bi-m. $5. (Conservative Baptist Association of America) C B A of America, Box 66, Wheaton, IL 60189. TEL 708-260-3800. FAX 708-653-5387. Ed. Robert Rummel. circ. 3,100. **Document type:** newsletter.
Description: Informative, inspirational, and educational, concerning national, home missions, and international missions.

SPIRITUAL LIGHT. see *HANDICAPPED — Visually Impaired*

200　　　　　US　　ISSN 0038-9382
STANDARD (ARLINGTON HEIGHTS). 1911. m. (10/yr.). $15.75. Baptist General Conference, 2002 S. Arlington Heights Rd., Arlington Heights, IL 60005. TEL 708-228-0200. FAX 708-228-5376. E-mail: GMBGCSTD@aol.com. Ed. Jodi Hanning. adv.; bk.rev.; charts; illus. circ. 14,000.

266　　　　　UK
STAR IN THE EAST; magazine of life and work in Bible lands. 1883. q. free. Bible Lands Society, The Old Kiln, Willow Chase, Off Amersham Rd., Hazlemere, High Wycombe, Bucks. HP15 7QU, England. TEL 01494-521351. FAX 01494-462171. Ed. M. Lampard. bk.rev. circ. 67,000. **Indexed:** Numis.Lit. **Document type:** newsletter.
Description: Concerned with the care of needy children in the lands of the Bible. Combines reports of this work with articles on aspects of life and living in the area covered by the Society's operations.

287　　　　　US　　ISSN 0038-9870
BX8450
STAR OF ZION. 1876. w. $22. African Methodist Episcopal Zion Church, Box 31005, Charlotte, NC 28231. TEL 704-377-4329. FAX 704-377-2809. Ed. Dr. Morgan W. Tann. adv.; bk.rev.; illus. circ. 8,000. (tabloid format; also avail. in microfilm from UMI; reprint service avail. from UMI) **Document type:** newspaper.

286　　　　　US　　ISSN 0162-6841
START (BIRMINGHAM). 1970. q $14.95 (effective 1995-1996). Southern Baptist Convention, Woman's Missionary Union, Highway 280, E., 100 Missionary Ridge, Birmingham, AL 35242-5235. TEL 205-991-8100. (Subscr. to: Box 830711, Birmingham, AL 35283-0711. TEL 800-WMU-7301. FAX 205-995-4840) Ed. Rhonda Reeves. circ. 31,200 (paid).
Description: For leaders of Mission Friends organizations.

285.241　　　UK
STEDFAST. 1930. m. £6.50. United Free Church of Scotland, 11 Newton Pl., Glasgow G3 7PR, Scotland. TEL 0141-332-3435. Ed. Rev. David Beatty. adv. contact: John Fulton. circ. 2,400 (paid). **Document type:** newsletter.

284　　　　　GW
STIFTSKIRCHE; Protestantisches Gemeindeblatt fuer das Dekanat Landau. 1930. m. DM.15. Bezirkskirchenrat des Kirchenbezirks Landau, Westring 3, 76829 Landau, Germany. TEL 06341-4091. Ed. Gerd Uhrig.

284.787　　　US
STRENGTH FOR THE DAY. m. free. Lutheran Library for the Blind, 1333 S. Kirkwood Rd., St. Louis, MO 63122. TEL 800-433-3954. (also avail. in Braille; large print edition in 22 pt.)
Description: Includes religious articles and light fiction.

284.2　　　　SA
STROOIDAK. (Text in Afrikaans) 1949. q. free. Nederduitse Gereformeerde Gemeente die Paarl - Dutch Reformed Church, Paarl, Hoofstraat 144, Paarl, South Africa. Eds. J.C.P.B. Nieuwoudt. circ. 1,000. (looseleaf format)
Formerly: Paarlse Padwyser (ISSN 0030-8455)

286 268　　　US　　ISSN 0039-2685
BX6205.B27
THE STUDENT (NASHVILLE). m. $15.40. Southern Baptist Convention, Sunday School Board, 127 Ninth Ave., N., Nashville, TN 37234. TEL 800-458-2772. —UMI.
Formerly: Baptist Student.
Description: Provides Bible study and leisure reading for college students.

STUDENT LEADERSHIP JOURNAL. see *EDUCATION*

284　　　　　AU
STUDIEN UND TEXTE ZUR KIRCHENGESCHICHTE UND GESCHICHTE. (Consists of two series) 1975. irreg., vol.4 (series 1), 1987. price varies. Boehlau Verlag GmbH & Co.KG., Sachsenplatz 4-6, Postfach 87, A-1201 Vienna, Austria. TEL 0222-3302427-0. FAX 0222-3302432. TELEX 114-506-SPRIW-A. Ed. Peter Barton. circ. 800. (back issues avail.) **Indexed:** Rel.Ind.Two. **Document type:** monographic series.

285　　　　　US　　ISSN 1048-8553
BX9354.2
STUDIES IN PURITAN AMERICAN SPIRITUALITY. a. $49.95. Edwin Mellen Press, 415 Ridge St., Box 450, Lewiston, NY 14092. TEL 716-754-2788. FAX 716-754-4056. Ed. Michael Schuldiner.
Description: Addresses spiritual concerns that existed in Puritan America.

268　　　　　US　　ISSN 0191-4219
BX6225
STUDYING ADULT LIFE AND WORK LESSON.. q. $19.50. Southern Baptist Convention, Sunday School Board, 127 Ninth Ave., N., Nashville, TN 37234. TEL 800-458-2772.

285　　　　　CU　　ISSN 0864-0262
SU VOZ. a. Iglesia Presbiteriana, Salud No. 22nd, Lealtad y Campanario, Havana 2, Cuba. TEL 809 61-1558. Dir. Francisco Marrero.

268　　　　　US　　ISSN 0162-4911
SUNDAY SCHOOL ADULTS. q. $6.95. Southern Baptist Convention, Sunday School Board, 127 Ninth Ave., N., Nashville, TN 37234. TEL 800-458-2772.

RELIGIONS AND THEOLOGY — Protestant

268 US
THE SUNDAY SCHOOL LEADER. 1980. m. $18.75. Southern Baptist Convention, Sunday School Board, 127 Ninth Ave., N., Nashville, TN 37234. TEL 800-458-2772. bk.rev.; charts; illus.; index. **Indexed:** South.Bap.Per.Ind.
—UMI.
Formed by the merger of: Sunday School Leader. Smaller Church Edition (ISSN 1056-2001); Which was formerly (until 1991): Youth Leadership (ISSN 0162-4709); And: Sunday School Leader. Larger Church Edition (ISSN 1056-201X); Which was formerly (until 1991): Sunday School Leadership (ISSN 0274-8568); Outreach (Nashville) (ISSN 0162-4318)
Description: Provides Sunday School leadership advice for churches large and small.

268 371.2 US
SUNDAY SCHOOL PLANNING & PROMOTION RESOURCE KIT. q. $54.95. Southern Baptist Convention, Sunday School Board, 127 Ninth Ave., N., Nashville, TN 37234. TEL 800-458-2772.

268 US ISSN 0585-9328
SUNDAY SCHOOL SENIOR ADULTS. q. $7.50. Southern Baptist Convention, Sunday School Board, 127 Ninth Ave., N., Nashville, TN 37234. TEL 800-458-2772.

268 US ISSN 0162-4903
SUNDAY SCHOOL YOUNG ADULTS. q. $10.50. Southern Baptist Convention, Sunday School Board, 127 Ninth Ave., N., Nashville, TN 37234. TEL 800-458-2772.

268 028.5 US ISSN 0731-0749
SUNDAY SCHOOL YOUTH. q. $10.90. Southern Baptist Convention, Sunday School Board, 127 Ninth Ave., N., Nashville, TN 37234. TEL 800-458-2772.
Formerly: Sunday School Youth A (ISSN 0162-4881)
Description: Provides young readers, grades 7-12, with Bible study based on international Sunday School lessons.

268 US ISSN 0736-9174
SUNDAY SCHOOL YOUTH. TEACHER. q. $11. Southern Baptist Convention, Sunday School Board, 127 Ninth Ave., N., Nashville, TN 37234. TEL 800-458-2772.
Formerly: Youth Teacher (ISSN 0162-4865)
Description: Provides Sunday school teachers with material for teaching youth, grades 7-12.

266 SW ISSN 0346-217X
SVENSK MISSIONSTIDSKRIFT. 1913. m. SEK 100 (students and seniors SEK 70). Svenska Missionsraadet, P.O. Box 1767, S-111 87 Stockholm, Sweden. TEL 46-8-453-68-80.

284 US ISSN 0273-8562
TAEGLICHE ANDACHTEN. English edition: Portals of Prayer (ISSN 0032-4884) (Text and summaries in German) 1937. q. $5.85. (Lutheran Church - Missouri Synod) Concordia Publishing House, 3558 S. Jefferson Ave., St. Louis, MO 63118. TEL 314-268-1000. Ed. Luther Poellot. circ. 16,000. (also avail. in microfilm) **Document type:** consumer publication.

200 US
TARGET (GARLAND). 1966. m. $10 donation. Tim Lee Ministries, Box 461674, Garland, TX 75046. TEL 214-276-3168. FAX 214-272-4052. Eds. Tim Lee, David L. Maulsby. adv.; bk.rev.; illus.; circ. 50,000 (controlled). (tabloid format)
Incorporates (in May 1993): Biblical Evangelist (ISSN 0740-7998)

286 AT ISSN 0815-6964
TASMANIAN BAPTIST ADVANCE. 1952. bi-m. Aus.$9 (effective Mar. 1995). Baptist Union of Tasmania, 22 Wellington St., Launceston, Tas. 7250, Australia. TEL 003-314104. FAX 003-313946. Ed. Laurence F. Rowston. adv.; bk.rev. circ. 800. (back issues avail.) **Document type:** newspaper, newsletter, bulletin.
Formerly (until 1984): Advance (ISSN 0815-6956)
Description: Covers church news, church history and general denominational interest.

284 US
TE DEUM; alumni newsletter. 1978. q. free. Trinity Lutheran Seminary, Office of Communications, 2199 E. Main St., Columbus, OH 43209. TEL 614-235-4136. FAX 614-238-0263. Ed. Ann Russell. illus. circ. 10,000. (back issues avail.) **Document type:** newsletter.
Description: Features articles about the Trinity Lutheran Seminary, its curriculum, faculty and alumni.

TEACHER'S INTERACTION; a magazine for Sunday school teachers. see EDUCATION

TEEN TIME (LARGE PRINT EDITION). see CHILDREN AND YOUTH — For

284 GW
THEO. 1986. q. DM.15($20) Besselweg 200, 48149 Muenster, Germany. TEL 0251-868653. FAX 0251-868653. E-mail: thomas_haendel@ms.maus.de. Ed. Thomas Haendel; Pub. Thomas Haendel. adv.; bk.rev.; film rev.; play rev. circ. 1,000. (back issues avail.) **Document type:** academic/scholarly publication.
Formerly: Bescheid.
Description: Aacademic publication for students of protestant theology at the University of Muenster.

284.2 NE ISSN 0040-5612
THEOLOGIA REFORMATA. 1958. 4/yr. fl.57.50 (students fl.46). (Gereformeerde Bond in de Hervormde Kerk) Drukkerij Oosterbaan en Le Cointre B.V., Postbus 25, 4460 AA Goes, Netherlands. TEL 08380-17091. Ed. J.M. Smit. adv.; bk.rev.; index; circ. 750 (controlled). **Indexed:** CERDIC.
—BLDSC (8814.510500).

THINKING MISSION. see RELIGIONS AND THEOLOGY

268 US
THIRD CENTURY METHODISM. 1962. irreg. (3-4/yr.). $10. United Methodist Historical Society of Baltimore Conference, Inc., 2200 St. Paul St., Baltimore, MD 21218. TEL 301-889-4458. FAX 410-889-1501. Ed. Rev. Edwin Schell. circ. 800 (paid). (looseleaf format; back issues avail.) **Document type:** newsletter.

284 UK ISSN 0309-3492
THIRD WAY (HARROW). 1977. 10/yr. £29 in U.K. and Europe; elsewhere £35. Third Way Trust Ltd., St. Peter's, Sumner Rd., Harrow, Middlesex HA2 9LN, England. TEL 0181-423-8494. FAX 0181-423-5367. Ed. Huw Spanner. adv. contact: David Ryde. bk.rev.; charts; illus. circ. 3,500. **Document type:** academic/scholarly publication.
—BLDSC (8820.144000); UMI.

283 CC ISSN 1006-1274
TIAN FENG/HEAVENLY WIND. (Text in Chinese) 1945. m. $30 (effective 1995). Zhongguo Jidujiao Xiehui - China Christian Council, 169 Yuanmingyuan Rd., 3rd Fl., Shanghai 200002, People's Republic of China. TEL 3210487. (Co-sponsor: National Committee of Protestant Three-self Patriotic Movement) Ed. Shen Cheng'en. circ. 100,000.

284 NO ISSN 0040-7194
BX8001
TIDSSKRIFT FOR TEOLOGI OG KIRKE; Norwegian periodical for Church and theology. (Text in Norwegian; summaries in English) 1930. q. NOK 390 in Nordic countries; elsewhere $74 (effective 1996). Scandinavian University Press, P.O. Box 2959 Toeyen, N-0608 Oslo, Norway. TEL 47-22-57-54-00. FAX 47-22-57-53-53. (U.S. addr.: Scandinavian University Press, 200 Meacham Ave., Elmont, NY 11003. TEL 516-352-7300) Ed. Magne Saeboe. adv.; bk.rev.; bibl.; index. circ. 1,000. (back issues avail.) **Indexed:** New Test.Abstr., Old Test.Abstr.
—BLDSC (8828.180000).
Description: Focuses on research in theology and the Church.

286 US ISSN 0040-7232
TIE (LOUISVILLE). 1929. q. free. Southern Baptist Theological Seminary, 2825 Lexington Rd., Louisville, KY 40280. TEL 502-897-4141. Ed. Michael Duduit. circ. 30,000. **Indexed:** South.Bap.Per.Ind. **Document type:** consumer publication.

TIJDSCHRIFT VOOR THEOLOGIE. see RELIGIONS AND THEOLOGY — Roman Catholic

280.4 028.5 AT ISSN 1030-0295
TODAY (LAWSON); family magazine. 1966. m. (except Jan.). free. Mission Publications of Australia, 19 Cascade St., P.O. Box 21, Lawson, N.S.W. 2783, Australia. TEL 61-47-591003. FAX 61-47-591101. Ed. Ian Lindsay. illus. circ. 8,000. **Document type:** bulletin.
Incorporates (1979-1992): Today's Young Life (ISSN 1030-0309); (1962-1992): Letterstick (ISSN 0727-5854)
Description: Family magazine for Australian aboriginal people. Includes stories, testimonies, Bible teaching and photos.

266 NR ISSN 0189-0557
TODAY'S CHALLENGE. (Text in English) 1951. bi-m. £N42($15) (Evangelical Church of West Africa) E C W A Productions Ltd., P.M. Bag 2010, Jos, Nigeria. TEL 073-52230. Ed. Jacob Shaibu Tsado. adv.; bk.rev.; charts; illus. circ. 20,000.
Formerly: African Challenge (ISSN 0001-9968)

268 UK ISSN 0307-5982
TOGETHER (LONDON, 1956). 1956. 9/yr. £12. National Society, Church House, Great Smith St., London SW1P 3NZ, England. TEL 0171-222-1672. FAX 0171-233-2592. Ed. Pam Macnaughton. adv.; bk.rev.; illus. circ. 3,000. **Indexed:** CCR, CERDIC, Curr.Cont. **Document type:** consumer publication.
Formerly: Church Teacher (ISSN 0009-6571)
Description: For those concerned with children's Christian education.

248.4 028.5 US
TOUCH. 1970. m. $12.50. Calvinettes, Box 7244, Grand Rapids, MI 49510-7244. TEL 616-241-5616. Ed. Jan Boone. circ. 17,000.
Description: For girls 9-14.

TRACT MESSENGER. see HANDICAPPED — Visually Impaired

280 380.5 CN ISSN 0714-8100
TRANSACTION. 1982. bi-m. free. Christian Transportation Inc., 2222 S. Sheridan Way, Unit 5, Bldg. 2, Mississauga, Ont. L5J 2M4, Canada. TEL 416-822-2700. Ed. Louis G. Voyer. circ. 29,000.
—CCC.
Supersedes: Postal Christian Witness; Christian Airman; Christian Bus Driver; Christian Railroader; Automotive Christian Witness.

TRANSMISSION (LONDON). see RELIGIONS AND THEOLOGY

280 380.5 CN ISSN 0229-4362
TRANSPORTEUR; au service du personnel dans le transport et les industries connexes. (Text in French) 1983. bi-m. free. Christian Transportation, Inc., 2222 S. Sheridan Way, Unit 5, Bldg. 2, Mississauga, Ont. L5J 2M4, Canada. TEL 416-822-2700. Ed. Louis G. Voyer. circ. 6,300.
Formerly: Bonne Nouvelle pour le Transporteur.

284 US ISSN 0744-9437
TRI-COUNTY LUTHERAN. 1941. m. $7. Lutheran Center Association of Southeastern Michigan, 579 E. 9 Mile Rd., Ferndale, MI 48220-1952. TEL 313-879-7610. Ed. Betty J. Mueller. adv.: B&W page $325. bk.rev. circ. 8,300. **Document type:** newspaper.
Former titles: Detroit and Suburban Lutheran (ISSN 0011-9660); Detroit Lutheran.

283 AT ISSN 0811-2304
TRINITY OCCASIONAL PAPERS. 1981. s-a. Aus.$22.50. Trinity Theological College, P.O. Box 683, Toowong, Qld. 4066, Australia. TEL 07-377-9950. FAX 07-377-9796. Ed.Bd. adv.; bibl. circ. 500. (back issues avail.)
Description: Information for ministers and church members; current theological issues.

TRINITY REVIEW. see PHILOSOPHY

284 GW ISSN 0930-732X
TUTZINGER BLAETTER. 1975. q. DM.7. Evangelische Akademie Tutzing, Postfach 1227, 82327 Tutzing, Germany. TEL 08158-251-112. FAX 08158-251-133. Ed. Axel Schwanebeck. circ. 10,000. **Document type:** newsletter.

RELIGIONS AND THEOLOGY — PROTESTANT

285 UK
TYST. (Text in Welsh) 1867. w. £27.42. Union of Welsh Independents, 11 St. Helen's Rd., Swansea SA1 4AL, Wales. TEL 01792-467040. FAX 01792-650647. Ed. Rev. Guto Gwynfor. adv.; bk.rev. circ. 1,500. **Document type:** newspaper.

U U M N NOTES. (Unitarian Universalist Musician's Network) see *MUSIC*

283 TZ
UHURU NA AMANI. (Text in Swahili) fortn. POB 3033, Arusha, Tanzania. TEL 3221. TELEX 42054. Ed. Elias G.B. Goroi. circ. 15,000.
Description: Evangelical-Lutheran publication.

284 NE ISSN 0041-5944
UITZICHT. 1964. m. free. (Reformed Presbyterian Fellowship in the Great Congregation (Ps.40,10)) Evangelisatie-Boekhandel en Uitgeverij Horizont, Box 77, 7900 AB Hoogeveen (Dr.), Netherlands. Ed. Rev. G. Taverne. bk.rev.; charts. circ. 400.

284.2 SA ISSN 0378-4134
UMTHOMBO WAMANDLA. (Text in Xhosa) 1972. bi-m. R.2. Reformed Churches in South Africa - Gereformeerde Kerke in Suid-Afrika, P.O. Box 400, Hammanskraal, South Africa. Ed. W.D. Graham. circ. 860.

288 UK ISSN 0049-531X
UNITARIAN. 1905. m. £1.44. Manchester and District Association of Unitarian & Free Christian Churches Inc., c/o Keith M. Noble, Elbon House, 69 Downs Drive, Tinperley, Altrincham, Cheshire, England. Ed. Rev. John Rowland. adv.; bk.rev. circ. 4,000.

267 UK
UNITARIAN AND FREE CHRISTIAN CHURCHES. HANDBOOK AND DIRECTORY OF THE GENERAL ASSEMBLY. 1890. a (directory); quinquennial (handbook). £5 each for Handbook or Directory. General Assembly of Unitarian Free Christian Churches, Essex Hall, 1-6 Essex St., Strand, London, WC2R 3HY, England. Ed. Matthew Smith. circ. 850.
Formerly: Unitarian and Free Christian Churches. Yearbook of the General Assembly (ISSN 0082-7797)

288 UK ISSN 0082-7800
BX9803
UNITARIAN HISTORICAL SOCIETY, LONDON. TRANSACTIONS. 1917. a. £7.50 to institutions. Unitarian Historical Society, c/o Hon. Treasurer, 58 Stoneygate Court, London Rd., Leicester LE2 2AJ, England. E-mail: dlw@leicester.ac.uk. Ed. Alan Ruston. adv.; bk.rev.; cum.index every 4 yrs.; circ. 325 (paid). **Indexed:** Amer.Hist.& Life, Br.Hum.Ind., Hist.Abstr. **Document type:** academic/scholarly publication.
Description: Publishes articles, notes, original documents and reveiws on the history of Unitarianism and its historical constituency (English Presbyterianism and General Baptists).

285 US ISSN 0362-0492
BX9801
UNITARIAN UNIVERSALIST CHRISTIAN. 1944. q. $30 (foreign $35). Unitarian Universalist Christian Fellowship, 110 Arlington St., Boston, MA 02116. TEL 508-365-2427. FAX 508-368-1616. (Subscr. to: Box 66, Lancaster, MA 01523) Ed. Rev. Thomas D. Wintle. bk.rev.; cum.index. circ. 1,100. (also avail. in microfilm; microfiche; back issues avail.) **Indexed:** Rel.& Theol.Abstr. (1988-), Rel.Ind.One. **Document type:** academic/scholarly publication.
—BLDSC (9090.790990); UMI.
Description: Contains theological and liturgical articles for liberal Protestant clergy and laity.

266 US ISSN 0082-7827
UNITARIAN UNIVERSALIST DIRECTORY. 1961. a. $19. Unitarian Universalist Association, Publications Department, 25 Beacon St., Boston, MA 02108. TEL 617-742-2100. FAX 617-367-3237. Ed. Myha Nguyen. adv. circ. 2,500. (also avail. in microform from UMI) **Document type:** directory.
—UMI.

288 900 US ISSN 0731-4078
UNITARIAN UNIVERSALIST HISTORICAL SOCIETY. PROCEEDINGS. 1925. irreg., approx. biennial, latest 1994. $10 per part (2 parts/vol.). Unitarian Universalist Historical Society, c/o Conrad Wright, Harvard Divinity School, Andover Hall, Cambridge, MA 02138. TEL 617-495-9766. bk.rev. circ. 400. **Document type:** academic/scholarly publication.
—BLDSC (6828.754000).
Formerly: Unitarian Historical Society. Proceedings (ISSN 0082-7819)
Description: Presents scholarly articles on American, British, and Continental Unitarianism and Universalism.

286 CN ISSN 0082-7843
UNITED BAPTIST CONVENTION OF THE ATLANTIC PROVINCES. YEARBOOK. 1963. a. price varies. United Baptist Convention of the Atlantic Provinces, 1655 Manawagonish Rd., Saint John, NB E2M 3Y2, Canada. TEL 506-635-1922. FAX 506-635-0366. Ed. Eugene M. Thompson. index. circ. 2,200.

286 US ISSN 0882-7214
UNITED CHURCH NEWS. 1985. m. (except Jan. & Aug.). $10. United Church of Christ, Office of Communication, 700 Prospect Ave., Cleveland, OH 44115-1100. TEL 216-736-2218. FAX 216-736-2223. Ed. Rev. W. Evan Golder. adv. contact: Charlene J. Smith. illus. circ. 90,000. (tabloid format; back issues avail.) **Document type:** newspaper.
Incorporates: Keeping You Posted (ISSN 0361-8668)
Description: News and features of the people, churches and agencies of The United Church of Christ.

287.92 CN ISSN 0041-7238
BX9881.A1
UNITED CHURCH OBSERVER. 1925. m. Can.$20. United Church of Canada, 478 Huron St., Toronto, ON M5R 2R3, Canada. TEL 416-960-8500. FAX 416-960-8477. Ed. Muriel Duncan. adv.; bk.rev.; film rev. circ. 160,000. (also avail. in microfilm from UMI) **Indexed:** Can.B.P.I., Can.Per.Ind., CMI. **Document type:** newsletter.
—UMI.

200 CN ISSN 0082-7878
UNITED CHURCH OF CANADA. GENERAL COUNCIL RECORD OF PROCEEDINGS. 1925. biennial. Can.$29.95. United Church of Canada, 3250 Bloor St. W., Etobicoke, ON M8X 2Y4, Canada. TEL 416-231-5931. FAX 416-231-3103. circ. 4,000. **Document type:** proceedings.
—BLDSC (7326.069000).

200 CN ISSN 0848-4449
UNITED CHURCH OF CANADA. YEAR BOOK AND DIRECTORY. 1925. a. Can.$29.95. United Church of Canada, 3250 Bloor St. W., Etobicoke, ON M8X 2Y4, Canada. TEL 416-231-5931. FAX 416-231-3103. circ. 4,000. **Document type:** directory.
Formerly: United Church of Canada. Year Book (ISSN 0082-7886)

200 US ISSN 0041-7270
UNITED EVANGELICAL ACTION. 1942. bi-m. membership only. National Association of Evangelicals, Box 28, Wheaton, IL 60189. TEL 708-665-0500. FAX 708-665-8575. Ed. Donald R. Brown. adv.: B&W page $500, color page $1100; adv. contact: Maxine Hummel. bk.rev.; illus. circ. 10,000. (also avail. in microform) **Indexed:** Chr.Per.Ind., G.Soc.Sci.& Rel.Per.Lit. **Document type:** trade publication.
—UMI.

285.241 UK ISSN 0082-7908
BX9089
UNITED FREE CHURCH OF SCOTLAND. HANDBOOK. 1930. biennial. £6.49. United Free Church of Scotland, 11 Newton Pl., Glasgow G3 7PR, Scotland. TEL 0141-332-3435. Ed. Rev. D.R. Beatty. bk.rev. circ. 600. **Document type:** bulletin.

284 US ISSN 0041-7300
UNITED LUTHERAN. (Text mainly in English; occasionally in Slovak) 1894. m. free. United Lutheran Society, Ross Mt. Park Rd., Box 947, Ligonier, PA 15658-0947. TEL 412-238-9505. FAX 412-238-9506. Ed. Paul M. Payerchin, Jr. adv.; bk.rev. circ. 5,000. (tabloid format; also avail. in microform)

287 US ISSN 0503-3551
BX8382.2.A1
UNITED METHODIST CHURCH. GENERAL MINUTES OF THE ANNUAL CONFERENCES. Key Title: General Minutes of the Annual Conferences of the United Methodist Church. 1968. a. $15.85 paperbound; cloth $21.60. United Methodist Church, General Council on Finance and Administration, 1200 Davis St., Evanston, IL 60201-4193. TEL 708-869-3345. FAX 708-869-6972. Ed. Daniel A. Nielsen. illus. circ. 2,500. (also avail. in microfiche from IDC) **Document type:** proceedings.
—BLDSC (4105.600000).
Description: Directory of the Churches and personnel of the United Methodist Church.

287.6 US ISSN 0503-356X
BX8382.2.A1
UNITED METHODIST DIRECTORY. irreg. United Methodist Publishing House, 201 Eithth Ave. S., Nashville, TN 37203. TEL 615-749-6334. (Subscr. to: Box 801, Nashville, TN 37202) Ed. Gwen Colvin.

287 US
UNITED METHODIST LIFE. 1957. 10/yr. $5 (free to all Iowa local officers). United Methodist Church, Iowa Conference, 1019 Chestnut St., Des Moines, IA 50309. TEL 515-283-1991. Ed. Karen J. Tisinger. adv.; illus. circ. 24,000. (tabloid format) **Document type:** newspaper.
Former titles (until 1995): Hawkeye (Des Moines) (ISSN 0887-0829); Hawkeye United Methodist (ISSN 0017-8632); Hawkeye Methodist.

287 US ISSN 0737-5581
UNITED METHODIST REPORTER. (Text in English and Spanish) 1847. w. $20 (typically set in Jan.). United Methodist Communications Council, Box 660275, Dallas, TX 75266. TEL 214-630-6495. FAX 214-630-0079. Ed. John A. Lovelace. adv.; bk.rev.; charts; illus. circ. 450,000. (also avail. in microfilm) **Document type:** newspaper.
Former titles: Texas Methodist - United Methodist Reporter; Texas Methodist (ISSN 0040-4489)

287 US
UNITED METHODIST REVIEW. w. $20. United Methodist Communications Council, Box 660275, Dallas, TX 75266. TEL 214-630-6495. FAX 214-630-0079. Ed. John A. Lovelace. circ. 23,000.

285 UK ISSN 0049-5433
BX9890.U25
UNITED REFORMED CHURCH HISTORY SOCIETY. JOURNAL. 1973. s-a. $18. United Reformed Church History Society, Church House, 86 Tavistock Pl., London WC1H 9RT, England. TEL 0171-916-2020. FAX 0171-916-2021. Ed. Clyde Binfield. bk.rev.; index. circ. 500. (also avail. in microform from UMI; reprint service avail. from KTO) **Indexed:** Amer.Hist.& Life, Br.Hum.Ind., CERDIC, Hist.Abstr. **Document type:** academic/scholarly publication.
—BLDSC (4910.640000); UMI.
Former titles: Congregational Historical Society. Transactions; Presbyterian Historical Society. Journal.

285 UK
UNITED REFORMED CHURCH IN THE UNITED KINGDOM. UNITED REFORMED CHURCH YEAR BOOK. 1973. a. £13.50. The United Reformed Church in the United Kingdom, 86 Tavistock Pl., London WC1H 9RT, England. adv. circ. 2,000.
Formerly: Congregational Church in England and Wales. Congregational Year Book (ISSN 0069-8849)

285 UK
UNITED REFORMED CHURCH POCKET DIARY. a. £3.25. The United Reformed Church in the United Kingdom, 86 Tavistock Pl., London WC1H 9RT, England. **Document type:** bulletin.

285 UK
UNITED REFORMED CHURCH, YORKSHIRE PROVINCE, PROVINCIAL HANDBOOK. 1973. a. £2. United Reformed Church (Yorkshire Province), 43 Hunslet Ln., Leeds LS10 1JW, England. TEL 0532-451267. FAX 0532-341145. Ed. Colin Mundy. adv. circ. 450. **Document type:** directory.
Description: Names and addresses of churches' officers and committees.

RELIGIONS AND THEOLOGY — PROTESTANT

284   GW
UNSERE KIRCHE - DER WEG - SONNTAGSGRUSS. 1935. w. Postfach 140380, 33623 Bielefeld, Germany. TEL 0521-9440-0. FAX 0521-9440181. **Document type:** newsletter.

242   US   ISSN 0042-0735
BV4800
UPPER ROOM; daily devotional guide, interdenominational, international. Spanish edition: El Aposento Alto (ISSN 0003-6552) (61 editions in 41 languages) 1935. bi-m. $5.95 for inkprint; large-print $6.95; cassette $35; Braille edition free; prices for editions in other languages vary. (United Methodist Church, General Board of Discipleship) Upper Room, 1908 Grand Ave., Box 189, Nashville, TN 37202. TEL 615-340-7250. FAX 615-340-7006. Ed. Mary Lou Redding. circ. 2,250,000. (also avail. in Braille; audio cassette; large print edition in 18 pt. avail.)

286 362.7   US   ISSN 1048-4973
URI UI SON' GYO SEGYE. Chinese edition: Chuan Dao Tian Di (ISSN 1056-358X); English edition: Our Missions World (ISSN 0899-3823) (Text in Korean) 1989. q. $12.95 (effective 1995-1996). Southern Baptist Convention, Woman's Missionary Union, Hwy. 280, E., 100 Missionary Ridge, Birmingham, AL 35242-5235. TEL 205-991-7301. (Subscr. to: Box 830711, Birmingham, AL 35283-7111. TEL 800-WMU-7301. FAX 205-995-4840)

266 284   NO
UT I ALL VERDEN. q. Norsk Luthersk Misjonssamband, Grensen 19, Oslo 1, Norway. adv.

284   GW
V E D D FORUM. 1913. bi-m. membership. Verband Evangelischer Diakonen- und Diakoninnen-Gemeinschaften in Deutschland e.V., Goethestr. 1, 33617 Bielefeld, Germany. **Document type:** newsletter.
Formerly: Diakon.

284   GW
V E L K D - INFORMATIONEN. 1969. q. Vereinigte Evangelisch - Lutherische Kirche Deutschlands, Lutherisches Kirchenamt, Postfach 510409, 30634 Hannover, Germany. TEL 0511-6261226. FAX 0511-6261211. Ed. Juergen Jeziorowski. bk.rev. circ. 4,500. **Document type:** newsletter.

283   UK
VALUES. 1889. m. £11.40. Salvation Army, 101 Queen Victoria St., London EC4P 4EP, England. TEL 0171-236-5222. FAX 0171-236-3491. Ed. Jean Bryant. adv. contact: Len Dormon. circ. 10,500. **Document type:** bulletin.
Formerly (until 1993): Deliverer (ISSN 0011-7897)

284.2   NE   ISSN 0167-2363
VANDAAR. 1902. 10/yr. fl.11. Gereformeerde Kerken in Nederland, Centrum voor Zending en Werelddiakonaat - Mission and World Service of the Reformed Churches in the Netherlands, P.O. Box 200, 3830 AE Leusden, Netherlands. TEL 31-33-960360. FAX 31-33-948707. (Co-sponsors: Netherlands Reformed Church; Interchurch Organisation for Development Cooperation) Ed.Bd. bk.rev.; illus.; index. circ. 140,000. **Document type:** bulletin, newsletter.
Formerly (until 1975): Zending (ISSN 0044-3972)
Description: Information on mission, world service and development cooperation.

284   US   ISSN 0042-2568
BT734
VANGUARD (MILWAUKEE, 1954). 1954. 6/yr. membership. Lutheran Human Relations Association, 2703 N. Sherman Blvd., Milwaukee, WI 53210. TEL 414-871-7300. Ed. Joyce Caldwell. bk.rev.; illus. circ. 10,000. (also avail. in microform from UMI; reprint service avail. from UMI) **Document type:** newspaper.
—UMI.
Description: Focuses on issues of justice.

266   SW   ISSN 1104-2702
VECKOMAGASINET PETRUS. 1993. w. (51/yr.). SEK 395 (effective 1991). (Helgelsefoerbundet) Veckomagasinet Petrus AB, S-105 36 Stockholm, Sweden. TEL 46-8-619-25-00. FAX 46-8-619-25-16. (Co-sponsors: Dagegruppen AB (Pingstroerelsen): Svenska Alliansmissionen; Oerebromissionen) Ed Haakan Arenius. adv.; bk.rev.; illus. circ. 27,700.
Formed by the merger of (1980-1993): Tro (ISSN 0349-9812); (1921-1993): Missionsbaneret (ISSN 0026-6132); (1916-1993): Evangelii Haerold (ISSN 0345-2980); (1890-1993): Trons Segrar (ISSN 0041-3178)

268   US   ISSN 0042-3459
VENTANA; missionary magazine for women. (Text in Spanish) 1931. q. $9. Casa Bautista de Publicaciones, Box 4255, El Paso, TX 79914. TEL 915-566-9656. Ed. Alicia Zorzoli. adv.; illus. circ. 13,000.

284.14895   DK   ISSN 0107-8925
VIBORG STIFTS AARBOG. 1942. a. free. Viborg Stiftsoevrighed, Sct. Mogensgade 35, DK-8800 Viborg, Denmark. Ed. Poul Nielsen. illus. circ. 3,800. **Document type:** government publication.

286   AT   ISSN 0726-4097
VICTORIAN BAPTIST WITNESS. 1931. m. Aus.$6.60 (effective 1995). Baptist Union of Victoria, 227 Burwood Rd., Hawthorn, Vic. 3122, Australia. TEL 61-3-818-0341. FAX 61-3-818-1041. Ed. Geoff Holland. adv.; bk.rev.; circ. 9,000 (paid). **Document type:** newspaper.
Formerly: Baptist Witness (ISSN 0005-5794)
Description: Includes news and features of interest to Baptist Church members.

269.2   US   ISSN 0745-9173
VICTORY (SAN DIEGO). Spanish edition (ISSN 8750-2534) 1964. bi-m. $6. Morris Cerullo World Evangelism, Box 85277, San Diego, CA 92186. TEL 619-277-2200. FAX 619-277-5111. Ed. Christine Wingard. circ. 130,000.
Formerly (until 1983): Deeper Life.

286   US   ISSN 0083-6311
BX6248.V8
VIRGINIA BAPTIST REGISTER. 1962. a. $4.50 to non-members. Virginia Baptist Historical Society, Box 34, University of Richmond, VA 23173. TEL 804-289-8437. FAX 804-829-8434. Ed. John S. Moore. bk.rev.; cum.index every 5 yrs.; circ. 450 (paid). (also avail. in microfilm) **Document type:** academic/scholarly publication.
Description: Covers early Virginia Baptist history.

200   US
VIRGINIA EPISCOPALIAN. 1922. m. (except Aug.). $5. Episcopal Diocese of Virginia, 110 W. Franklin, Richmond, VA 23220. TEL 804-643-8451. FAX 804-644-6928. Ed. Sarah Bartenstein. adv. contact: Patrick N. Getlein. bk.rev. circ. 28,000. (tabloid format) **Document type:** newspaper.
Formerly (until 1986): Virginia Churchman.
Refereed Serial

287   US   ISSN 0891-5598
VIRGINIA UNITED METHODIST ADVOCATE. 1832. bi-w. $10. (United Methodist Church, Virginia Conference) Virginia United Methodist Communications, Inc., 4016 W. Broad St., Richmond, VA 23230-3916. TEL 804-359-9451. FAX 804-359-5904. Ed. Alvin J. Horton. adv.; bk.rev. circ. 16,000.
Former titles (until 1984): Virginia Advocate (ISSN 0042-6458); Virginia Methodist Advocate.

284 384.5   NE   ISSN 0921-7711
VISIE. 1970. w. fl.61 (effective 1995). Evangelische Omroep, Postbus 21400, 1202 BJ Hilversum, Netherlands. Ed. L. de Jong. adv.; bk.rev. circ. 150,000.
Incoproates (1976-1984): Alpha (ISSN 0166-4182)

284   AT
VISION. 1950. q. Aus.$12. Australian Baptist Missionary Society, 597 Burwood Rd., Hawthorn, Vic. 3122, Australia. FAX 61-3-819-1004. Ed. Grace Munro. bk.rev.; index. circ. 7,000. (back issues avail.)
Description: Publishes articles about activities of the organization worldwide, issues related to mission.

284   GW   ISSN 0933-6117
DIE VOELKER RUFEN. m. DM.6. Liebenzell Mission, Postfach 1240, 75375 Bad Liebenzell, Germany. TEL 07052-17109. FAX 07052-17104. Ed. Rev. Albert Rechkemmer. circ. 20,500. **Document type:** bulletin.

287   US
VOICE (BIRMINGHAM). 1881. m. $15. North Alabama Conference of the United Methodist Church, Office of Communications, 898 Arkadelphia Rd., Birmingham, AL 35204-3498. TEL 205-226-7971. FAX 205-226-7991. Ed. Mel Campbell. adv.; bk.rev. circ. 6,000. **Document type:** newspaper.
Formerly: United Methodist Christian Advocate (ISSN 8750-7668)

282   US   ISSN 0277-2272
VOICE (NEWARK). 1878. m. (except Jul. & Aug.). contributions. Episcopal Diocese of Newark, Cathedral House, 24 Rector St., Newark, NJ 07102. TEL 201-622-4306. Ed. V. Dale Gruner. bk.rev.; charts; illus.; stat.; cum.index. circ. 17,500. **Document type:** newspaper.
Formerly: Newark Churchman (ISSN 0028-8853)

287   UK   ISSN 0042-8167
VOICE OF METHODISM. 1964. 3/yr. $2 to non-members. Voice of Methodism Association, 24 Eldon Rd., Winton, Bournemouth BH9 2RT, England. Ed. Oliver A. Beckerlegge. adv.; bk.rev. circ. 6,000. **Indexed:** CERDIC. **Document type:** bulletin.

266   US   ISSN 0042-8175
VOICE OF MISSIONS. 1898. irreg. $10. African Methodist Episcopal Church (New York), 475 Riverside Dr., Rm. 1926, New York, NY 07102-4512. TEL 212-870-2258. Ed. Anne Eliott. bk.rev.; illus. circ. 3,950.

284   US
VOICE OF PROPHECY NEWS. 1942. q. free to qualified personnel. Voice of Prophecy, Inc., Box 2525, Newbury Park, CA 91319. TEL 805-373-7657. FAX 805-373-7701. Ed. Eldyn Karr. circ. 30,000. (back issues avail.) **Document type:** consumer publication.
Description: Reports on the North American activities of the oldest, continuously aired religous radio broadcast since 1930.

284.2   SA   ISSN 0042-8728
DIE VOORLIGTER. (Text in Afrikaans) 1937. w. (Nederduitse Gereformeerde Kerk) Die Voorligter, P.O. Box 1444, Cape Town 8000, South Africa. Ed. F.M. Gaum. adv.; bk.rev.; illus. circ. 132,000. **Indexed:** CERDIC.

284   AT   ISSN 0728-0912
VOX REFORMATA; Australasian journal for Christian scholarship. 1962. a. $8.50. Reformed Theological College, Association for Christian Tertiary Education, 55 Maud St., Geelong, Vic. 3220, Australia. TEL 61-52-222155. FAX 61-52-221263. Ed. W. Berends. adv.; bk.rev.; index. circ. 275. (also avail. in microfiche; back issues avail.) **Indexed:** CERDIC. **Document type:** academic/scholarly publication. —UMI.
Description: Devoted to specific topics of theological, biblical and ecclesiastical interest.

WALKING WITH INTEGRITY. see *HOMOSEXUALITY*

WAS UNS BETRIFFT; Zeitschrift fuer Kriegsdienstverweigerer und Zivildienstleistende. see *POLITICAL SCIENCE — Civil Rights*

283   US   ISSN 0043-0544
WASHINGTON DIOCESE. 1933. 9/yr. $5 to non-members; members $3. Episcopal Diocese of Washington, Episcopal Church House, Mount Saint Alban, N.W., Washington, DC 20016-5094. TEL 202-537-5560. FAX 202-364-6605. adv.; bk.rev.; charts; illus.; stat. circ. 21,500. (tabloid format; also avail. in microfilm) **Indexed:** CERDIC. **Document type:** newspaper.

285   US
WASHINGTON MEMO (AKRON). bi-m. $18 for 2 yrs. Mennonite Central Committee, 21 S. 12th St., Box 500, Akron, PA 17501-0500. TEL 717-859-1151. FAX 717-859-2171. Ed. J. Daryl Byler. circ. 1,600. **Document type:** newsletter.
Description: Deals with US public policy issues. Includes issues of peacemaking and justice in domestic and international affairs.

RELIGIONS AND THEOLOGY — PROTESTANT

283 US
WASHINGTON REPORT TO PRESBYTERIANS. 1979. bi-m. $20. Presbyterian Church (U.S.A.), Washington Office, 110 Maryland Ave., N.E., Washington, DC 20002. TEL 202-543-1126. FAX 202-543-7755. Ed. Catherine A. Sunshine. circ. 1,000. **Document type:** newsletter.
  Description: Advocates the public policy positions of the General Assembly of the Presbyterian Church (U.S.A.)

284 UK ISSN 1351-4768
WATCHING AND WAITING. 1918. q. £3. Sovereign Grace Advent Testimony, 1 Donald Way, Chelmsford, Essex CM2 9JB, England. TEL 01245-268815. Ed. Stephen A. Toms. bk.rev. **Document type:** bulletin.

284 UK
WAYMARK. 1967. 10/yr. £15. St. Mark's Unitarian Church, Castle Terrace, Edinburgh EH1 2DP, Scotland. TEL 0131-667-4360. Ed. Andrew Hill. bk.rev. circ. 500. (tabloid format; back issues avail.) **Document type:** newsletter.

287 UK
WESLEY HISTORICAL SOCIETY. LANCASHIRE AND CHESHIRE BRANCH. JOURNAL. 1964. 2/yr. Wesley Historical Society, Lancashire and Cheshire Branch, 26 Roe Cross Green, Mottram, Hyde, Cheshire SK14 6LP, England.

287 270 UK ISSN 0043-2873
WESLEY HISTORICAL SOCIETY. PROCEEDINGS. 1897. 3/yr. £8 (foreign £10). Wesley Historical Society, 98 Chester Rd., Gresford, Wrexham, Clwyd LL12 8PA, Wales. Ed. E.A. Rose. adv.; bk.rev.; bibl.; charts; illus.; index, cum.index: vols.1-30 (1897-1958). circ. 900. **Indexed:** Amer.Hist.& Life, Br.Hum.Ind., CERDIC, Hist.Abstr. **Document type:** proceedings.
  —BLDSC (6832.400000).

287.1 US ISSN 0043-289X
WESLEYAN ADVOCATE. 1842. m. $12.50. (Wesleyan Church) Wesley Press, Box 50434, Indianapolis, IN 46250-0434. TEL 317-576-1313. Ed. Norman G. Wilson. adv.: B&W page $500, color page $750. bk.rev. circ. 21,000. (also avail. in microfilm; microfiche from IDC) **Indexed:** G.Soc.Sci.& Rel.Per.Lit.
  Formed by the merger of: Wesleyan Methodist (ISSN 0190-6100); Pilgrim Holiness Advocate.
  Description: Provides doctrinal, devotional, inspirational and practical articles.

200 US ISSN 0190-6097
WESLEYAN CHRISTIAN ADVOCATE. 1836. w. $14. (United Methodist Church, North and South Georgia Conferences) Jacob's Regligious List, 104 Ansel Dr., Clinton, SC 20325-2808. TEL 404-659-0002. FAX 404-659-1727. Ed. G. Ross Freeman. adv.; bk.rev. circ. 30,980.

287.1 US ISSN 0092-4245
BR1
WESLEYAN THEOLOGICAL JOURNAL.* 1966. s-a. $5. Wesleyan Theological Society, c/o William M. Arnett, Nazarene Theological Seminary, 1700 E. Meyer Blvd., Kansas City, MO 64131. Ed. Paul Bassett. adv.; bk.rev. circ. 1,200. (also avail. in microform from UMI; reprint service avail. from UMI) **Indexed:** CERDIC, Chr.Per.Ind., Rel.& Theol.Abstr. (1983-), Rel.Ind.One.
  —BLDSC (9298.673700); UMI.

286 US ISSN 0043-4132
WESTERN RECORDER. 1826. w. $10.60 to individuals; churches $8.50. (Kentucky Baptist Convention) Western Recorder, Inc., 10701 Shelbyville Rd., Box 43969, Middletown, KY 40253. TEL 502-244-6470. FAX 502-244-6474. E-mail: 70420.30.CompuServe.com. Ed. Marv Knox. adv. contact: Mauri Smith. circ. 50,000 (paid). (tabloid format; also avail. in microform) **Document type:** newspaper.

284 US
WHOLE EARTH NEWSLETTER. 1805. 3/yr. $2. United Church Board for World Ministries, 700 Prospect Ave., 6th Fl., Cleveland, OH 44115. TEL 216-736-3206. FAX 216-736-3259. Ed. Sandra J. Rooney. circ. 11,000. **Document type:** newsletter.
  Description: Contains news and views of mission activities.

280 US ISSN 0197-8896
BX5800
WITNESS (DETROIT). 1917. m. $25 (foreign $30) (effective Jan. 1995). Jeanie Wylie-Kellermann, Ed. & Pub., 1249 Washington Blvd., Ste. 3115, Detroit, MI 48226-1822. TEL 313-962-2650. FAX 313-962-1012. bk.rev.; illus.; circ. 6,000. (also avail. in microfiche; microfilm) **Indexed:** CERDIC, Rel.Ind.One. **Document type:** consumer publication.
  —UMI.
  Description: Concerned with peace and justice issues and the social mission of the Church and the Gospel message.

WONDER TIME. see *CHILDREN AND YOUTH — For*

286 US ISSN 0049-7959
WORD AND WAY. 1895. w. $9.15 to individuals; chures $6.20. Missouri Baptist Convention, 400 E. High St., Jefferson City, MO 65101. TEL 314-635-7931. FAX 314-659-7436. Ed. Bobby S. Terry. adv.; bk.rev.; illus. circ. 56,000. (tabloid format)
  Description: News of Missouri Baptist and Southern Baptist churches.

251 US ISSN 1047-2339
WORD & WITNESS. 1976. 6/yr. $49. Liturgical Publications Inc., 2875 S. James Dr., New Berlin, WI 53151. TEL 414-785-1188. FAX 414-785-9567. Ed. Rev. Paul Wilson. circ. 1,969. (looseleaf format) **Document type:** trade publication.
  Description: Homily resource for ministers preparing sermons.

284 US ISSN 0275-5270
BR1
WORD & WORLD; theology for Christian ministry. 1981. q. $18 to individuals; students and senior citizens $12. Luther Seminary, 2481 Como Ave., St. Paul, MN 55108. TEL 612-641-3482. Ed. Frederick J. Gaiser. adv. contact: Ruth E. Taylor. bk.rev.; index. circ. 3,000. (also avail. in microfilm from UMI; back issues avail.) **Indexed:** New Test.Abstr., Old Test.Abstr., Rel.& Theol.Abstr. (1981-), Rel.Ind.One. **Document type:** academic/scholarly publication.
  —BLDSC (9347.841200); UMI; UnCover.
  Description: Journal for pastors and scholars who seek to relate the work of theology to the ministry of the Christian church.

266 UK
WORD AT WORK. 3/yr. free. National Bible Society of Scotland, 7 Hampton Terrace, Edinburgh EH12 5XU, Scotland. FAX 0131-337-0641. Ed. Pauline Hurst. circ. 60,000. **Document type:** bulletin.

288 US ISSN 0892-2462
THE WORLD (BOSTON). 1970. 6/yr. $18. Unitarian Universalist Association, 25 Beacon St., Boston, MA 02108. TEL 617-742-2100. FAX 617-367-3237. Ed. Linda Beyer. adv.; bk.rev.; charts; illus. circ. 107,000.
  —UMI.
  Formerly (until 1986): Unitarian Universalist World (ISSN 0041-7122)

287 US
WORLD METHODIST HISTORICAL SOCIETY. HISTORICAL BULLETIN. 1961. q. $5. World Methodist Historical Society, Box 127, Madison, NJ 07940. TEL 201-822-2787. FAX 201-408-3909. bk.rev.; illus. circ. 200. (back issues avail.) **Document type:** newsletter.
  Formerly: World Methodist Historical Society. News Bulletin.

286 UK
WORLD OUTLOOK. 1918. q. £2.40. Baptist Men's Movement, Kingsley, Pontesbury, Shrewsbury, Shrops. SY5 0QH, England. TEL 01743-790377. Ed. Michael Putnam. adv.; bk.rev.; circ. 1,200 (controlled). (back issues avail.)

287 US ISSN 0043-8839
BX8201
WORLD PARISH. 1948. bi-m. free. World Methodist Council, Box 518, Lake Junaluska, NC 28745. TEL 704-456-9432. FAX 704-456-9433. Ed. Joe Hale; Pub. Joe Hale. bk.rev.; charts; illus. circ. 18,300. **Document type:** newsletter.

284 362.7 US ISSN 0043-9215
WORLD VISION. 1957. bi-m. free. World Vision Inc., Box 1131, Pasadena, CA 91301-0312. TEL 818-357-7979. FAX 818-357-0915. TELEX 6753411 WORVIS MROV. (Subscr. to: 919 W. Huntington Dr., Monrovia, CA 91016. TEL 800-777-5777) Ed. Terry Madison. bk.rev.; charts; illus.; stat.; circ. 100,651 (controlled). **Indexed:** Chr.Per.Ind.
  Description: Looks at relief, development, child sponsorship, human rights and injustice in the Third World from an Evangelical Christian perspective.

284 361 US
WORLD VISION PARTNERS. q. free to donors. World Vision Inc., Box 1131, Pasadena, CA 91301-0312. TEL 818-357-7979. FAX 818-357-0915. TELEX 6753411 WORVIS MROV. (Subscr. to: Partners, World Vision, 919 W. Huntington Dr., Monrovia, CA 91016. TEL 800-777-5777) Ed. Terry Madison. **Document type:** bulletin.
  Description: Describes the agency's efforts to serve God by helping people worldwide.

WORLDVIEW. see *CHILDREN AND YOUTH — For*

284 US
WORLDWIDE NEWS. 1917. 4/yr. free. The Pocket Testament League, 11 Toll Gate Rd., Box 800, Lititz, PA 17543-7026. TEL 717-636-1919. FAX 717-626-5553. Ed. Martha L. Kitchen. circ. 15,000. **Document type:** newsletter.
  Description: Information on The Pocket Testament League outreach, particularly Scripture distribution and evangelism worldwide.

250 UK ISSN 0032-7107
WORSHIP AND PREACHING. 1970. q. £9. Methodist Publishing House, 20 Ivatt Way, Peterborough PE3 7PG, England. TEL 01733-332202. FAX 01733-331201. Ed. Rev. Peter Barber. adv.; bk.rev.; index. circ. 6,000. **Document type:** bulletin.
  Supersedes: Preacher's Quarterly.

WORSHIP: RESOURCES FOR THE CHURCH MUSICIAN. see *MUSIC*

287 GW ISSN 0043-9444
WORT UND WEG; Sonntagsblatt der Evangelisch-Methodistischen Kirche. 1968. w. DM.86.40. (Evangelisch-Methodistische Kirche) Christliches Verlagshaus GmbH, Postfach 311141, 70471 Stuttgart, Germany. TEL 0711-8300051. FAX 0711-8300030. Ed. Ingo Stauch. adv.; bk.rev.; bibl.; illus.; stat. circ. 13,500. **Document type:** bulletin.
  Formed by the 1968 merger of: Evangelischer Botschaft; Evangelist.

284 028.5 AT
Y F C NEWSRELEASE. 1975. m. free. Geelong Youth for Christ, 58 McKillop St., Geelong, Vic. 3220, Australia. TEL 052-2144769. FAX 052-779614. Ed. Richard Brohier. circ. 800. (looseleaf format; back issues avail.)

200 US ISSN 0044-0388
YEVANHELSKYJ RANOK/EVANGELICAL MORNING. (Includes an English section: Ukrainian Christian Herald, Protestant monthly) 1905. q. $5. Ukrainian Evangelical Alliance of North America, 5610 Trowbridge Dr., Dunwoody, GA 30338. TEL 404-394-7795. Ed. Rev. W. Borowsky. adv.; bk.rev.; illus. circ. 500. (reprint service avail. from UMI, ISI)

YOUNG MUSICIANS. see *MUSIC*

YOUNG SOLDIER. see *CHILDREN AND YOUTH — For*

286 US ISSN 0196-0946
THE YOUTH DISCIPLE. q. $11.25. Southern Baptist Convention, Sunday School Board, 127 Ninth Ave., N., Nashville, TN 37234. TEL 800-458-2772.
  Description: Provides a discipleship curriculum for youth, grades 7-12.

264 028.5 US
YOUTH DISCIPLE LEADER'S PACKET. q. $69.75. Southern Baptist Convention, Sunday School Board, 127 Ninth Ave., N., Nashville, TN 37234. TEL 800-458-2772.
  Description: Contains discipleship leader material for youth, grades 7-12.

RELIGIONS AND THEOLOGY — ROMAN CATHOLIC

268 028.5 US ISSN 0162-4784
YOUTH IN ACTION. q. $11.25. Southern Baptist Convention, Sunday School Board, 127 Ninth Ave., N., Nashville, TN 37234. TEL 800-458-2772.

268 371.3 US ISSN 0162-4792
YOUTH IN ACTION. TEACHER. q. $17.75. Southern Baptist Convention, Sunday School Board, 127 Ninth Ave., N., Nashville, TN 37234. TEL 800-458-2772.

268 US ISSN 0162-4776
YOUTH IN DISCOVERY. q. $11.25. Southern Baptist Convention, Sunday School Board, 127 Ninth Ave., N., Nashville, TN 37234. TEL 800-458-2772.

268 371.3 US ISSN 0162-4768
YOUTH IN DISCOVERY. TEACHER. q. $17.75. Southern Baptist Convention, Sunday School Board, 127 Ninth Ave., N., Nashville, TN 37234. TEL 800-458-2772.

264 US
YOUTH MINISTRY UPDATE. m. $22.50. Southern Baptist Convention, Sunday School Board, 127 Ninth Ave., N., Nashville, TN 37234. TEL 800-458-2772.
Description: Contains up-to-date articles for youth ministers and leaders.

284 US ISSN 0747-3486
YOUTHWORKER JOURNAL. 1984. q. $25.95. Youth Specialties, 1224 Greenfield Dr., El Cajon, CA 92021. TEL 619-440-2333. FAX 619-440-4939. (Subscr. to: Box 616, Mt. Morris, IL 61054. TEL 800-769-7624) Ed. Tim McLaughlin. adv. circ. 9,000. **Document type:** trade publication.
Description: Covers vital youth ministry topics.

284 US ISSN 0889-5058
YOUTHWORKER UPDATE. 1986. m. $23.95. Youth Specialties, 1224 Greenfield Dr., El Cajon, CA 92021. TEL 619-440-2333. FAX 619-440-4939. (Subscr. to: Youthworker, Box 635, Mt. Morris, IL 61054. TEL 800-769-7624) Ed. Tim McLaughlin. **Document type:** newsletter.
Description: Provides information on the latest youth culture trends, research, resources, and news.

284 GW
ZEICHEN. 1972. q. DM.10. Aktion Suehnezeichen Friedensdienste e.V., Schottstr. 6, 10365 Berlin, Germany. TEL 030-55190310. FAX 030-55190376. bk.rev. circ. 12,000. (back issues avail.) **Document type:** bulletin.

282 GW ISSN 0044-2038
BR4
DIE ZEICHEN DER ZEIT. 1947. bi-m. DM.60 (foreign DM.75). Evangelische Verlagsanstalt GmbH, Burgstr. 1-5, 04109 Leipzig, Germany. TEL 0341-7114122. FAX 0341-9603179. Ed.Bd. adv.: B&W page DM.1200; trim 250 x 175. bk.rev.; index. circ. 3,500. **Indexed:** CERDIC. **Document type:** bulletin.
Description: Contains articles, essays, commentaries, sermons's Exegesis and news.

284 GW ISSN 0342-4316
ZEITSCHRIFT FUER BAYERISCHE KIRCHENGESCHICHTE. 1926. a. DM.36. Verein fuer Bayerische Kirchengeschichte, Veilhofstr. 28, 90489 Nuernberg, Germany. TEL 0911-550269. FAX 0911-5819683. Ed. Horst Weigelt. bk.rev. circ. 800. **Document type:** bulletin.

262.9 284 GW ISSN 0044-2690
ZEITSCHRIFT FUER EVANGELISCHES KIRCHENRECHT. 1951. q. DM.152. Verlag J.C.B. Mohr (Paul Siebeck), Wilhelmstr. 18, 72074 Tuebingen, Germany. TEL 07071-923-0. FAX 07071-51104. TELEX 7262872-MOHR-D. (Subscr. to: Postfach 2040, 72010 Tuebingen, Germany) Ed.Bd. adv.; bk.rev.; index. **Indexed:** CERDIC. **Document type:** academic/scholarly publication.
—CCC.
Description: Examines the problems of Protestant ecclesiastical law and the relation between church and state in Germany.

200 284 SZ ISSN 1017-7620
BR115.C8
ZEITSCHRIFT FUER KULTUR POLITIK KIRCHE. 1952. bi-m. 72 SFr. Verein Reformatio Zurich, Postfach 7650, CH-3001 Bern, Switzerland. TEL 031-3312431. FAX 031-3312407. (Subscr. to: Laenggass Druck AG, Postfach 7062, CH-3001 Bern, Switzerland) Eds. Hektor Leibundgut, Brigitte Schnegg. adv.: page 600 SFr. bk.rev.; index. circ. 1,600. (reprint service avail.) **Indexed:** Rel.Ind.One, Rel.Per. **Document type:** consumer publication.
Formerly: Reformatio (ISSN 0034-3021)

284 GW ISSN 0044-3549
BR4
ZEITSCHRIFT FUER THEOLOGIE UND KIRCHE. (Supplement avail.: Zeitschrift fuer Theologie und Kirche. Beiheft (ISSN 0513-9147)) 1891. q. DM.82 to individuals; students DM.56. Verlag J.C.B. Mohr (Paul Siebeck), Wilhelmstr. 18, 72074 Tuebingen, Germany. TEL 07071-923-0. FAX 07071-51104. TELEX 7262872-MOHR-D. (Subscr. to: Postfach 2040, 72010 Tuebingen, Germany) Ed. Eberhard Juengel. adv.; index. **Indexed:** Arts & Hum.Cit.Ind., CERDIC, Curr.Cont., Old Test.Abstr., Rel.& Theol.Abstr. (1975-), Rel.Ind.One, Rel.Per. **Document type:** academic/scholarly publication.
—Genuine Article; SWETS. **CCC.**
Description: Studies all areas of theological research and the teachings of the church.

284 GW
ZELTGRUSS. 1902. bi-m. Deutsche Zeltmission e.V., Postfach 223180, 57037 Siegen, Germany. TEL 0271-8800100. FAX 0271-8800150. Ed. Michael Hoehn. bk.rev.; bibl.; illus. circ. 25,000. (back issues avail.) **Document type:** bulletin.

284 266 NE
ZENDINGSBLAD; voor de Christelijke Gereformeerde Kerken in Nederland. 1906. 4/yr. fl.10. Christelijke Gereformeerde Kerken in Nederland - Mission of the Christian Reformed Churches in the Netherlands, Zendingshuis, Postbus 334, 3900 AH Veenendaal, Netherlands. TEL 31-8385-24916. FAX 31-8385-54130. Ed.Bd. adv.; bk.rev.; illus.; stat. circ. 29,000.
Former titles: Over en Weer; (until 1992): Uw Koninkrijk Kome: Zendingsblad (ISSN 0042-1650)
Description: Covers missionary activities Third world countries.

287.1 US ISSN 0098-9282
BX8201
ZION'S HERALD; a publication for New England United Methodists. 1823. bi-m. $15. United Methodist Church, 566 Commonwealth Ave., Boston, MA 02215-2510. TEL 617-266-3900. Ed. Ann Whiting. adv.; bk.rev. circ. 5,000. (tabloid format; back issues avail.) **Document type:** newspaper.
Incorporates (in 1994): Maine United Methodist (ISSN 0745-0273); Formerly (until 1974): Methodist Churchman.

284 GW ISSN 0722-3234
ZUVERSICHT UND STAERKE. 1982. bi-m. DM.42.80. (Ludwig-Hofacker-Vereinigung) Haenssler Verlag, Postfach 1220, 73762 Neuhausen, Germany. TEL 07158-177-114. FAX 07158-177119. Ed.Bd. circ. 3,000. (back issues avail.) **Document type:** academic/scholarly publication.

RELIGIONS AND THEOLOGY — Roman Catholic

200 FR ISSN 0758-8240
A I M MONASTIC BULLETIN; aide inter-monasteres pour les jeunes eglises. English ed.: I M A Bulletin (Inter Monastic Aid). (Editions in English, Spanish) 1965. s-a. 80 F.($12) Aide Inter-Monasteres Secretariat, 7 rue d'Issy, 92170 Vanves, France. TEL 46-64-60-05. (U.S. Center: Alliance for International Monasticism, c/o St. Scholastica Priory, 355 E. 9th St., Erie, PA 16503) Ed. Dom Marie-Bernard de Soos. bk.rev.; illus. circ. 1,800. **Document type:** bulletin.
—BLDSC (0773.203500).
Formerly: A I M Bulletin (ISSN 0007-4314)

282 BL ISSN 0005-1934
A M.* (Ave Maria) 1898. s-m. Cr.$15($6) Editora Ave Maria Ltda, Rua Martins Fontes 646, Caixa Postal, 615, 01000 Sao Paulo, Brazil. adv.; bk.rev.; illus.; circ. 50,000 (controlled).

271 US ISSN 0567-6630
ACADEMY OF AMERICAN FRANCISCAN HISTORY. BIBLIOGRAPHICAL SERIES. 1953. irreg., no.4, vol.1, 1978. price varies. Academy of American Franciscan History, 1712 Euclid Ave., Berkeley, CA 94709-1208. TEL 510-548-1755. **Document type:** bibliography.

271 US ISSN 0065-0633
ACADEMY OF AMERICAN FRANCISCAN HISTORY. DOCUMENTARY SERIES. 1951. irreg., vol.11, 1979. price varies. Academy of American Franciscan History, 1712 Euclid Ave., Berkeley, CA 94709-1208. TEL 510-548-1755. **Document type:** academic/scholarly publication.

271 US ISSN 0065-0641
ACADEMY OF AMERICAN FRANCISCAN HISTORY. MONOGRAPH SERIES. 1953. irreg., vol.13, 1981. price varies. Academy of American Franciscan History, 1712 Euclid Ave., Berkeley, CA 94709-1208. TEL 510-548-1755. **Document type:** monographic series.

271 US ISSN 0065-065X
ACADEMY OF AMERICAN FRANCISCAN HISTORY. PROPAGANDA FIDE SERIES. 1966. irreg., vol.11, 1988. price varies. Academy of American Franciscan History, 1712 Euclid Ave., Berkeley, CA 94709-1208. TEL 510-548-1755. Eds. Mathias Kiemen, Alexander Wyse. index. **Document type:** academic/scholarly publication.

282 US ISSN 0888-0247
ACADIANA CATHOLIC. (Supplements avail.) 1954. m. $12. Diocese of Lafayette, 1408 Carmel Ave., Lafayette, LA 70501. TEL 318-261-5513. FAX 318-261-5526. Ed. Barbara Gutierrez. adv. contact: Patrick Breaux. bk.rev. circ. 28,000. **Document type:** newspaper.

282 VC ISSN 0001-5199
BX850
ACTA APOSTOLICAE SEDIS. COMMENTARIUM OFFICIALE. (Text in Latin and European languages) 1909. m. L.100000 (foreign L.145000($114)) (effective 1996). (Secretariat of State) Libreria Editrice Vaticana, 00120 Vatican City (Rome), State of the Vatican City. index. circ. 6,000. (also avail. in microfiche from IDC) **Indexed:** Cath.Ind., CERDIC.
—Faxon; SWETS; UMI.
Description: Contains official commentary of the Holy See with information on Papal activites.

ACTA MEDIAEVALIA. see HISTORY — History Of Europe

270 VC ISSN 0065-1443
BX1528.A2
ACTA NUNTIATURAE GALLICAE. (Text in French) 1961. irreg., no.16, 1994. price varies. (Pontificia Universita Gregoriana, Facolta di Storia Ecclesiastica - Pontifical Gregorian University, Faculty of Church History) Gregorian University Press, Piazza della Pilotta, 35, 00187 Rome, Italy. TEL 39-6-678-15-67. FAX 39-6-678-05-88. (Co-sponsor: Ecole Francaise de Rome) Ed. Pierre Blet, S.J. circ. 1,000.
Description: Consists of critical editions of the correspondence of papal Nuncios to the French court during the XVI century.

282 IT ISSN 0001-6411
ACTA ORDINIS FRATRUM MINORUM. (Text in original languages) 1882. 3/yr. $12. Ordo Fratrum Minorum, Curia Generalis, Via S. Maria Mediatrice, 25, I-00165 Rome, Italy. TEL (06) 632241. Dir. Fr. Patrick McCloskey. index. cum.index; circ. controlled.
—BLDSC (0582.505000).

282 IT ISSN 0001-642X
ACTA ORDINIS SANCTI AUGUSTINI; commentarium officiale. (Triennial supplement avail.: Commentarium Officiale - Fasciculus Specialis) (Text in Latin and various languages) 1956. a. L.25000 (supplement L.30000) (effective 1992). Order of Saint Augustine, Economato Generale, Via Paolo VI, 25, 00193 Rome, Italy. FAX 6-800-6298. circ. 550. (back issues avail.) **Document type:** corporate report.

282 VC
ACTA ROMANORUM PONTIFICUM. 1977. irreg. no.7-8, 1985. price varies. Biblioteca Apostolica Vaticana, 00120 Vatican City (Rome), State of the Vatican City.

RELIGIONS AND THEOLOGY — ROMAN CATHOLIC

282   AG   ISSN 0587-4300
BX1425.A1
ACTUALIDAD PASTORAL; revista mensuel. (Includes special editions.) 1968. m. Arg.$70($70) (effective 1993). Abel Costa 261, C.C. 140, 1708 Moron, Argentina. TEL 627-2806. FAX 541-627-2806. Ed. Vicente Oscar Vetrano. adv.; bk.rev.; charts; illus.; index. circ. 5,000. (looseleaf format)
    Description: Covers Christianity around the world.

232   CN   ISSN 0823-552X
ACTUALITE DIOCESAINE. 1970. m. Can.$7. Eglise Catholique, Diocese de Saint-Jean-Longueuil, c/o Micheline le Royer, 740 bd. Ste-Foy, Longueuil, PQ J4K 4X8, Canada. TEL 514-679-1100. FAX 514-679-1102. adv.; bk.rev. circ. 8,000.
    Formerly (until 1983): Rythme de Notre Eglise (ISSN 0383-0152)

282   FR   ISSN 0757-3529
ACTUALITE RELIGIEUSE DANS LE MONDE. Abbreviated title: A R M. 1953. m. (11/yr.). 330 F. (foreign 365 F.). Malesherbes Publications, 163 bd. Malesherbes, 75859 Paris Cedex 17, France. TEL 48-88-46-00. FAX 48-88-46-01. TELEX 649 333 F. Ed. Jean-Claude Petit. adv.; bk.rev.; film rev.; bibl.; illus.; index. circ. 30,000. (tabloid format) **Indexed:** Pt.de Rep. (1983-).
    Former titles (until 1983): Informations Catholiques Internationales (ISSN 0020-0441); (until 1955): Actualite Religieuse dans le Monde (ISSN 0400-4620)
    Description: Examines the religious aspects of world events.

200   IT   ISSN 0001-8740
ADVENIAT. 1929. m. L.16000. Opera della Regalita' di N.S.G.C., Via L. Necchi 2, 20123 Milan, Italy. TEL 02-86453378. Ed.Bd. bk.rev. circ. 15,000.

282   KE   ISSN 1013-171X
AFRICAN CHRISTIAN STUDIES. Variant title: C H I E A African Christian Studies. 1985. q. KShs.400 (rest of Africa $40; Europe and Middle East $50; elsewhere $60) (effective 1996). (Catholic Higher Institute of Eastern Africa, Faculty of Theology) C U E A Publications, P.O. Box 24205, Karen, Nairobi, Kenya. TEL 254-2-891601. FAX 254-2-891261. **Indexed:** P.L.E.S.A.
  —BLDSC (0732.380000).

AFRICAN JOURNAL OF BIBLICAL STUDIES. see *RELIGIONS AND THEOLOGY*

282   IT
AGENDA. 1959. m. L.10000 (effective Oct. 1991). Azione Cattolica, Via del Monte 5, 40126 Bologna, Italy. FAX 51-239832. Ed. V. Prodi. circ. 3,000. (tabloid format)

282 255   IT   ISSN 0002-4066
AI NOSTRI AMICI. 1930. bi-m. L.1000. Gesuiti di Sicilia, Missioni Rettoria Casa Professa, 90134 Palermo, Italy. TEL 329-878. Ed. Carmelo Salv. Bentivegna, S.I. adv.; bk.rev.; bibl.; illus.; stat.; index. circ. 10,000.
    Description: Features missionary articles written by Jesuits of Sicily.

282 267   GW   ISSN 0002-3000
AKADEMISCHE MONATSBLAETTER. 1887. 10/yr. DM.65. Kartellverband Katholischer Deutscher Studentenvereine, Neubeckumerstr. 20, 59269 Beckum, Germany. TEL 02521-6695. FAX 02521-13197. bk.rev.; index. (tabloid format) **Document type:** bulletin.

282   US   ISSN 0272-7250
ALBANIAN CATHOLIC BULLETIN/BULETINI KATOLIK SHQIPTAR. (Text in Albanian, English) 1980. a. donations. Albanian Catholic Institute "Daniel Dajani, S.J.", University of San Francisco, Xavier Hall, San Francisco, CA 94117. TEL 415-666-6966. FAX 415-387-1867. Ed. Gjon Sinishta. bk.rev. circ. 1,500. (back issues avail.) **Document type:** academic/scholarly publication.
    Description: To assist the rebuilding of the Catholic Church in Albania and to promote the dissemination of knowledge of Albania's national, cultural and religious heritage.

282   CN   ISSN 0316-473X
ALBERTA CATHOLIC DIRECTORY. 1920. a. Can.$14. Western Catholic Reporter, 8421 - 101 Ave., Edmonton, AB T6A OL1, Canada. TEL 403-465-8030. FAX 403-465-8031. Ed. Glen Argan. adv. contact: Linda Keer. circ. 1,200 (paid). **Document type:** directory.
    Description: Lists all priests, parishes, religious orders and other Catholic organizations.

282   US
ALIVE AND WELL SAINT PATRICK'S CATHEDRAL. vol.56, 1976. m. $6. (St. Patrick's Parish House) Cathedral Publications (New York), 14 E. 51st St., New York, NY 10022. TEL 212-753-2261. Ed. Michael Hoffman. adv.; bk.rev.; illus. circ. 5,000.
    Former titles: Alive and Well and Living in New York City Saint Patrick's Cathedral; St. Patrick's Cathedral Bulletin.

ALLGEMEINER CAECILIEN-VERBAND. SCHRIFTENREIHE. see *MUSIC*

282   US   ISSN 1051-7286
ALMA MARIANA. (Text in Spanish) bi-m. $6. (World Apostolate of Fatima) Blue Army of Our Lady of Fatima, U S A, Inc., Mountain View Rd., Box 976, Washington, NJ 07882-0976. TEL 908-689-1700. FAX 908-689-6279.
    Description: Addresses the Spanish speaking community in the US and Latin American countries.

282   VC
ALOISIANA. irreg., no.27, 1994. price varies. (Pontificia Facolta Teologica dell'Italia Meridionale) Biblical Institute Press, Piazza della Pilotta 35, 00187 Rome, Italy. TEL 39-6-678-15-67. FAX 39-6-678-05-88.

282   GW
ALT UND JUNG METTEN. 1926. s-a. DM.10. Abtei Verlag Metten, Postfach 1180, 94523 Metten, Germany. TEL 0991-9108-141. Ed. P. Raban Schinabeck. bk.rev. circ. 3,000. **Document type:** bulletin.

282   NQ   ISSN 0254-1688
AMANECER; reflexion Cristiana en la nueva Nicaragua. 1981. 10/yr. $25. Centro Ecumenico Antonio Valdivieso, Apdo. 3205, Managua, Nicaragua. Ed. Jose Arguello. bk.rev. circ. 2,500.

282   US   ISSN 0002-7049
BX801
AMERICA. 1909. w. (bi-w. Jan., June-Aug.). $33 (effective 1993). America Press Inc., 106 W. 56th St., New York, NY 10019. TEL 212-581-4640. FAX 212-399-3596. Ed. George W. Hunt, S.J. adv. contact: Julia Sosa. bk.rev.; film rev.; play rev.; s-a. index. circ. 35,000. (also avail. in microform (ISSN 0364-989X) from UMI) **Indexed:** A.I.P.P., Acad.Ind., Biog.Ind., Bk.Rev.Dig., Bk.Rev.Ind. (1965-), Cath.Ind, CERDIC, Child.Bk.Rev.Ind. (1965-), Film Lit.Ind. (1973-), G.Soc.Sci.& Rel.Per.Lit., HR Rep. (1985-1989), Mag.Ind., Media Rev.Dig., Mid.East Abstr.& Ind., Old Test.Abstr., PMR, R.G.
•Also available online. Vendor(s): University Microfilms International.
Also available on CD-ROM. Producer(s): University Microfilms International.
  —BLDSC (0809.660000); Faxon; SWETS; UMI; UnCover.
    Description: Contains timely and thought-provoking articles written by prestigious writers and theologians.

200   PE
AMERICA LATINA. BOLETIN. no.15, Feb., 1978. irreg. Movimiento Internacional de Estudiantes Catolicos, Centro de Documentacion, Apartado 3564, Lima 100, Peru. illus.

282 207.11   US   ISSN 0002-7650
BX3001
AMERICAN BENEDICTINE REVIEW. 1950. 4/yr. $15. American Benedictine Review, Inc., Assumption Abbey, Box A, Richardton, ND 58652. TEL 701-974-3315. FAX 701-974-3317. Ed. Rev. Terrence Kardong. index. circ. 1,000. (also avail. in microform from UMI; reprint service avail. from UMI) **Indexed:** Amer.Hist.& Life, Cath.Ind., Hist.Abstr., M.L.A., New Test.Abstr., Rel.& Theol.Abstr. (1989-), Rel.Per. **Document type:** academic/scholarly publication.
  —BLDSC (0810.785000); Faxon; SWETS; UMI; UnCover.
    Description: Publishes research on the history and spirituality of the monastic movement, including its current issues.

282 209   US   ISSN 0002-7790
E184.C3
AMERICAN CATHOLIC HISTORICAL SOCIETY OF PHILADELPHIA. RECORDS. 1886. q. $15 (effective 1995 & 1996). American Catholic Historical Society of Philadelphia, 263 S. Fourth St., Box 84, Philadelphia, PA 19105. TEL 215-925-5752. Ed. Thomas R. Greene. adv.; bk.rev.; index, cum.index. circ. 850. (also avail. in microfiche from BHP; back issues avail.) **Indexed:** Amer.Hist.& Life, Cath.Ind., Hist.Abstr. **Document type:** academic/scholarly publication.
  —Faxon; UnCover.

AMERICAN CATHOLIC PHILOSOPHICAL ASSOCIATION. PROCEEDINGS. see *PHILOSOPHY*

282   US   ISSN 1081-4019
AMERICAN CATHOLIC STUDIES NEWSLETTER. 1975. s-a. $3. University of Notre Dame, c/o Cushwa Center for the Study of American Catholicism, 614 Hesburgh Library, Notre Dame, IN 46556. TEL 219-631-5441. FAX 219-631-8471. bibl. circ. 700. (tabloid format) **Document type:** newsletter.
    Description: Directed to scholars, graduate students, librarians and archivists with a research interest in the history of the U.S. Catholic church in any of its aspects.

282   US
AMERICAN MONASTIC NEWSLETTER. 1947. 3/yr. $5 to non-members. American Benedictine Academy, Mount St. Scholastica, 801 South 8th, Atchison, KS 66002. TEL 913-367-6110. FAX 913-367-3866. Ed. Judith Sutera. circ. 965. **Document type:** newsletter.
    Description: Includes news, commentaries, reviews of interest to members of monastic communities and others associated with monastic studies.

282 020   US
AMICI. 1983. q. membership. American Friends of the Vatican Library, 157 Lakeshore Rd., Grosse Pointe Farms, MI 48236. TEL 313-885-8855. Ed. Joy Blouin. bk.rev. circ. 1,500. (back issues avail.) **Document type:** newsletter.
    Description: News on the Vatican library and VAL activities.

282   IS
AMICI DI TERRA SANTA. (Text in Italian) 1972. 4/yr. (Associazione Amici di Terra Santa) Franciscan Printing Press, P.O. Box 14064, Jerusalem 91140, Israel. TEL 972-2-286594. FAX 972-2-272274. (Subscr. to: Centro di Propaganda e Stampa di erra Santa, Via Gherardini 7, 20145 Milan, Italy. TEL 39-2-311327)

282   DR
AMIGO DEL HOGAR. no.442, 1983. m. $12. Apdo. Postal 1104, Santo Domingo, Dominican Republic. Ed. Juan Rodriquez. circ. 23,000.

282   FR   ISSN 0998-2671
AMITIES. N.S. 1915. q. 100 F. Comite Catholique des Amities Francaises dans le Monde, 9-11 rue Guyton de Morveau, 75013 Paris, France. TEL 45-65-96-66. FAX 1-45-81-30-81. Ed. Dominique de la Motte. adv.; bk.rev.; bibl.; stat.; index. circ. 3,300. (tabloid format) **Document type:** bulletin.
    Formerly (until 1994): Amities Catholiques Francaises (ISSN 0003-1895)

RELIGIONS AND THEOLOGY — ROMAN CATHOLIC

282 GW ISSN 0003-2328
AMTSBLATT FUER DIE ERZDIOEZESE BAMBERG. (Text in German, Latin) 1878. s-m. DM.12. (Archdiocese Bamberg, Erzbischoefliches Ordinariat Bamberg) Sankt-Otto-Verlag GmbH, Laubanger 23, 96052 Bamberg, Germany. Ed. Alois Albrecht. bk.rev.; stat.; index. circ. 900.

AN SEANRUD. see *LITERATURE*

255 IT ISSN 0392-2855
ANALECTA AUGUSTINIANA. (Text in Latin & various languages) 1905. a. L.50000($45) (effective 1992). Order of Saint Augustine, Economato Generale, Via Paolo VI, 25, 00193 Rome, Italy. FAX 6-800-6298. circ. 550. (back issues avail.) **Document type:** academic/scholarly publication.

282 VC ISSN 0066-135X
ANALECTA BIBLICA. (Text in various languages) 1952. irreg., no.132, 1994. price varies. (Pontificio Istituto Biblico - Pontifical Biblical Institute) Biblical Institute Press, Piazza della Pilotta 35, 00187 Rome, Italy. TEL 39-6-678-15-67. FAX 39-6-678-05-88. Ed. Albert Vanhoye, SJ. circ. 300.
   Description: Most numbers are doctoral dissertations, some are critical editions of texts.

271 IT ISSN 0003-2476
ANALECTA CISTERCIENSIA. (Text in English, French, German and Italian) 1945. s-a. L.95000. (Curia Generalis Ordinis Cisterciensis) Edizioni Cisterciensi, Piazza Tempio di Diana 14, 00153 Rome, Italy. Ed. Armando Battista. bk.rev.; index. circ. 300. **Indexed:** M.L.A.
   —SWETS.
   Formerly: Analecta Sacri Ordinis Cisterciensis.

270 282 VC ISSN 0066-1376
ANALECTA GREGORIANA. (Text in English, French, German, Italian, Latin or Spanish) 1930. irreg., no.266, 1994. price varies. (Pontificia Universita Gregoriana - Pontifical Gregorian University) Gregorian University Press, Piazza della Pilotta, 35, 00187 Rome, Italy. TEL 39-6-678-15-67. FAX 39-6-678-05-88. Ed. Angel Anton.
   Description: Contains research studies on sacred scripture, theology, patristics, church law, philosophy, church history, ecumenism, non-Christian religions and more.

900 200 IT ISSN 0394-7726
ANALECTA ORDINIS CARMELITARUM. 1909. s-a. L.30000. (Institutum Carmelitanum) Edizioni Carmelitane, Via Sforza Pallavicini 10, 00193 Rome, Italy. TEL 06-68303513. FAX 06-68307200. Ed. Emanuele Boaga. adv. circ. 500. **Document type:** bulletin.
   Description: Official documents of the Carmelite Order; also news and brief historical articles.

282 BE ISSN 0066-1414
ANALECTA VATICANO-BELGICA. DEUXIEME SERIE. SECTION A: NONCIATURE DE FLANDRE. 1924. irreg. price varies. (Institut Historique Belge de Rome) N.V. Brepols, Steenweg op Tielen 68, 2300 Turnhout, Belgium. TEL 32-14-402500. FAX 32-14-428919. circ. controlled. **Document type:** monographic series.
   Description: Correspondence from and to nuncios in the Southern Low Countries during the 16th, 17th and 18th centuries.

274 BE ISSN 0066-1422
ANALECTA VATICANO-BELGICA. DEUXIEME SERIE. SECTION B: NONCIATURE DE COLOGNE. 1956. irreg. price varies. (Institut Historique Belge de Rome) N.V. Brepols, Steenweg op Tielen 68, 2300 Turnhout, Belgium. TEL 32-14-402500. FAX 32-14-428919. circ. controlled. **Document type:** monographic series.
   Description: Correspondence from and to nuncios in the Southern Low Countries during the 16th, 17th and 18th centuries.

282 BE ISSN 0066-1430
ANALECTA VATICANO-BELGICA. DEUXIEME SERIE. SECTION C: NONCIATURE DE BRUXELLES. 1956. irreg., vol.10, 1990. price varies. (Institut Historique Belge de Rome) N.V. Brepols, Steenweg op Tielen 68, 2300 Turnhout, Belgium. TEL 32-14-402500. FAX 32-14-428919. circ. controlled. **Document type:** monographic series.
   Description: Correspondence from and to nuncios in 19th century Belgium.

282 BE ISSN 0066-1449
ANALECTA VATICANO-BELGICA. PREMIERE SERIE: DOCUMENTS RELATIFS AUX ANCIENS DIOCESES DE CAMBRAI, LIEGE, THEROUANNE ET TOURNAI. 1906. irreg., vol.32, 1987. price varies. (Institut Historique Belge de Rome) N.V. Brepols, Steenweg op Tielen 68, 2300 Turnhout, Belgium. TEL 32-14-402500. FAX 32-14-428919. circ. controlled. **Document type:** monographic series.
   Description: Letters from and supplications to the Popes concerning the Southern Low Countries during the 14th and 15th centuries.

282 US
ANCHOR; Fall River Diocesan newspaper for Southeast Massachusetts, Cape Cod & the Islands. 1957. w. $11 (effective 1993). (Roman Catholic Diocese of Fall River) Anchor Publishing Co., 887 Highland Ave., Box 7, Fall River, MA 02722. TEL 508-675-7151. FAX 508-675-7048. Ed. Rev. John F. Moore. adv. contact: Rosemary Dussault. film rev.; illus. circ. 31,000. (tabloid format; also avail. in microfilm; back issues avail.) **Document type:** newspaper.

ANGELIC WARFARE DISPATCH. see *CHILDREN AND YOUTH — About*

ANGELICUM; periodicum trimestre pontificae studiorum universitatis a Santo Thoma Aquinate in Urbe. see *PHILOSOPHY*

282 255 GR
ANICHTI ORIZONTES - ANGHELIAFOROS. 1900. m. Dr.1500($10) Mone Pateron Iesouitons - Jesuit Fathers, 27 Smyrnis St., Athens 10439, Greece. Ed. Fr. Gabriel Marangos. adv.; bk.rev.; bibl. circ. 3,500.
   Former titles (until 1977): Anichti Orizontes; (until 1975): Angheliaforos (ISSN 1105-3496)

ANNO DOMINI; magazine pro mlade. see *CHILDREN AND YOUTH — For*

282 FR ISSN 0066-2488
ANNUAIRE CATHOLIQUE DE FRANCE. 1950. biennial. 730 F. Publicat, 17 bd. Poissonniere, 75082 Paris Cedex 02, France. adv. **Document type:** directory.

282.675 ZR
ANNUAIRE DE L'EGLISE CATHOLIQUE AU ZAIRE. a. Edition du Secretariat-General, Kinshasa-Combe, Zaire. illus.

282 FR ISSN 0153-3533
ANNUAIRE DU DIOCESE DE LYON. 1826. a. 100 F. Archeveche de Lyon, 1 Place de Fourviere, 69321 Lyon Cedex 05, France.
   Formerly (until 1972): Ordo et Annuaire de l'Archdiocese de Lyon.
   Description: Discusses departments, parishes, communities, and various groups of the Diocese.

266 IT ISSN 0066-4464
ANNUARIO CATTOLICO D'ITALIA. 1956. biennial. L.210000($130) Editoriale Italiana, Via Viglena 10, 00192 Rome, Italy. TEL 39-6-3212653. FAX 39-6-3211359. adv.: page L.1500000. index. circ. 8,000. **Document type:** directory.
   Description: Yearbook about the Catholic Church, Cadres and institutions in Italy.

ANNUARIO DELLE BIBLIOTECHE ECCLESIATICHE ITALIANE. see *LIBRARY AND INFORMATION SCIENCES*

282 US ISSN 1060-0345
BX3601
THE ANTHONIAN. 1927. q. $10. St. Anthony's Guild, Paterson, NJ 07509-2948. TEL 212-594-6224. FAX 212-594-2769. Eds. Fr. Cassian Miles, Janet Gianopoulos. circ. 90,000 (paid). **Document type:** consumer publication.
   Description: Promotes devotion to St. Anthony of Padua and presents the works of the Franciscans of Holy Name Province the along the eastern U.S. and abroad.

282 VC ISSN 0003-6064
ANTONIANUM. (Text in English, French, German, Italian, Latin, Spanish) 1926. q. L.135000($85) (effective 1995). (Pontificio Ateneo Antonianum) Edizioni Antonianum, Via Merulana 124, 00185 Rome, Italy. TEL 39-6-70373462. FAX 39-6-70373605. Ed. Marco Nobile. adv.; bk.rev.; abstr.; bibl.; index, cum.index. circ. 850. **Indexed:** Amer.Hist.& Life, CERDIC, Hist.Abstr., M.L.A., New Test.Abstr., Old Test.Abstr., Rel.& Theol.Abstr. (1968-).
   —SWETS.

282 GW ISSN 0721-1937
ANZEIGER FUER DIE SEELSORGE; Monatszeitschrift fuer die praktische Seelsorge. 1891. m. DM.34.80. Verlag Herder GmbH und Co. KG, Hermann-Herder-Str. 4, 79104 Freiburg, Germany. TEL 0761-2717407. FAX 0761-2717-407. Ed. Karl Schlemmer. circ. 26,000. (back issues avail.) **Document type:** newsletter.

APOLLINARIS. see *LAW — Civil Law*

282 CN ISSN 0706-9928
APOSTOLAT. (Text in French) 1929. bi-m. Can.$6($6) Missionary Oblates of Mary Immaculate, 8844 Notre-Dame Est, Montreal, PQ H1L 3M4, Canada. TEL 514-351-9310. FAX 514-351-1314. Ed. Rev. Claude St.-Laurent. circ. 21,000. **Document type:** newsletter.
   Description: Religious topics on the Roman Catholic home and missions abroad.

AQUINAS; rivista internazionale di filosofia. see *PHILOSOPHY*

282 CE
AQUINAS JOURNAL. (Text in English) 1984. s-a. Rs.75 (foreign $10). (Archbishop of Colombo) Aquinas College of Higher Studies, Colombo - 8, Sri Lanka. Ed. Rev. Don Gerald Chrispin Leo. bk.rev. circ. 500. **Document type:** academic/scholarly publication.

282 IT ISSN 0003-7559
ARALDO DI S. ANTONIO; incontri con Papa Giovanni. 1949. fortn. free. Orfanotrofio Antoniano dei PP. Rogazionisti, Viale Motta, 54, 25015 Desenzano del Garda (BS), Italy. TEL 39-30-9141743. FAX 39-30-9912306. Pub. Gaetano Tria. adv.; bk.rev.; illus. circ. 150,000. (tabloid format) **Document type:** newspaper.

282 US
ARCHDIOCESE OF CINCINNATI ALMANAC DIRECTORY AND BUYER'S GUIDE. 1959. a. $15. Catholic Telegraph, 100 E. Eighth St., Cincinnati, OH 45202. TEL 513-421-3131. Ed. James Stackpoole. adv.; stat. circ. 3,000. **Document type:** directory.

282 IT ISSN 0003-8296
ARCHIDIOCESI DI MONREALE. BOLLETTINO ECCLESIASTICO. 1908. m. L.12000. Curia Arcivescovile di Monreale, Palermo, Italy. Ed. Msgr. Francesco Sparacio. bk.rev.

200 SP
ARCHIDIOCESIS DE MADRID-ALCALA. BOLETIN OFICIAL. 1878. s-m. 1500 ptas.($13) Arzobispado de Madrid, Bailen 8, 28013 Madrid, Spain. Ed. J. Gonzalez Prado. adv.; bibl.; index. circ. 1,500. (back issues avail.)

282 209 GW ISSN 0003-9160
ARCHIV FUER KATHOLISCHES KIRCHENRECHT. (Text in German and Latin) 1857. s-a. DM.100 per no. Verlag Kirchheim und Co. GmbH, Kaiserstr. 41, 55116 Mainz, Germany. TEL 06131-96070-0. FAX 06131-9607070. adv.; bibl.; index. circ. 550. **Indexed:** Canon Law Abstr., CERDIC. **Document type:** academic/scholarly publication.

282 IT ISSN 0390-8240
ARCHIVIO PER LA STORIA DEL MOVIMENTO SOCIALE CATTOLICO IN ITALIA. BOLLETTINO. 1966. 3/yr. L.71000 (foreign L.111000($84)) (effective 1996). (Universita Cattolica del Sacro Cuore) Vita e Pensiero, Largo Gemelli 1, 20123 Milan, Italy. TEL 39-2-72342310. FAX 39-2-72342260. TELEX 321033 UCATMI 1. Ed. Alberto Cova. circ. 650. **Document type:** bulletin, academic/scholarly publication.
   Description: Covers history of the Social-Catholic movement in Italy.

RELIGIONS AND THEOLOGY — ROMAN CATHOLIC

900 282   IT   ISSN 0394-7734
ARCHIVIUM HISTORICUM CARMELITANUM. (Text in English, French, German, Italian, Latin, Spanish) 1961. irreg. price varies. (Order of Carmelites) Edizioni Carmelitane, Via Sforza Pallavicini 10, 00193 Rome, Italy. TEL 06-68803513. FAX 06-68307200. adv. circ. 500. **Document type:** monographic series.
    Description: Covers Carmelite history; an order in the Catholic religion.

200   SP   ISSN 0211-2035
ARCHIVO AGUSTINIANO. (Text in English, French, Italian, Spanish) 1914-1935; resumed 1950-1965; resumed 1976. a. 3500 ptas.($35) (effective Jan. 1995). Provincia Agustiniana del Santisimo Nombre de Jesus de Filipinas, Po. de Filipinos, 7, 47007 Valladolid, Spain. TEL 983-306800. FAX 983-397896. Eds. Carlos Alonso, Florentino Rubio. bk.rev.; cum.index: 1914-1927; 1928-1959. circ. 300. (back issues avail.) **Document type:** academic/scholarly publication.
    Formerly (until **1927**): Archivo Historico Hispano-Agustiniano (ISSN 0211-2019)

282   GT
ARCHIVO HISTORICO ARQUIDIOCESANO "FRANCISCO DE PAULA GARCIA PELAEZ". BOLETIN. 1990? s-a. Archivo Historico Arquidiocesano "Francisco de Paula Garcia Pelaez", Palacio Arzobispal, 7a Avda. 6-21, Zona 1, 01001 Guatemala, Guatemala. Dir. Ramiro Ordonez Jonama.

ARCHIVO IBERO-AMERICANO; revista de estudios historicos. see HISTORY — History Of Europe

271   IT   ISSN 0004-0665
BX3601
ARCHIVUM FRANCISCANUM HISTORICUM. (Text in English, French, German, Italian, Latin and Spanish) 1908. s-a. L.65000 (effective 1994). Collegio San Bonaventura, Commissione Storica, Via Vecchia di Marino 28-30, 00046 Grottaferrata (Rome), Italy. TEL 06-94315318. FAX 06-94-10-781. Ed. R.P. Victor Sanchez Gil. bk.rev.; bibl.; charts; illus.; cum.index: 1908-1957. circ. 600. **Indexed:** Amer.Hist.& Life, CERDIC, Hist.Abstr., M.L.A.
  —SWETS.
    Description: Contains studies, articles, and notes on Franciscan history, 13th-19th centuries.

ARCHIVUM HISTORIAE PONTIFICAE. see RELIGIONS AND THEOLOGY — Abstracting, Bibliographies, Statistics

271   IT   ISSN 0037-8887
ARCHIVUM HISTORICUM SOCIETATIS IESU. (Text and summaries in English, French, German, Italian, Latin, Portuguese, and Spanish) 1932. s-a. $50. Institutum Historicum Societatis Iesu - Jesuit Historical Institute, Via dei Penitenzieri 20, 00193 Rome, Italy. Ed. Laszlo Szilas. bk.rev.; bibl.; cum.index: 1932-1951, 1952-1961, 1962-1981. circ. 900. **Indexed:** Amer.Hist.& Life, Hist.Abstr., So.Pac.Per.Ind.
    Description: Contains research articles on history of Jesuits worldwide.

ARCHIWA, BIBLIOTEKI I MUZEA KOSCIELNE/ARCHIVA, BIBLIOTHECAE ET MUSEA ECCLESIASTICA. see HISTORY — History Of Europe

228   IT
ARCIDIOCESI DI REGGIO CALABRIA. RIVISTA PASTORALE. 1910. q. L.30000. Curia Metropolitana di Reggio Calabria, Via T. Campanella 63, 89100 Reggio Calabria, Italy. TEL 39-965-21037. FAX 39-965-330963. Ed. Sac. Umberto Giovanni Latella. adv.; illus.
    Formerly: Bollettino Ecclesiastico (ISSN 0006-6788)

282   US   ISSN 1057-8439
ARKANSAS CATHOLIC. 1911. w. $15. 2500 N. Tyler, Box 7417, Little Rock, AR 72217-7417. TEL 501-664-0340. FAX 501-664-9075. Ed. Malea Walters. adv. circ. 7,500. **Document type:** newspaper.

282   US   ISSN 0361-3712
BX801
ARLINGTON CATHOLIC HERALD. 1976. w. $14. Arlington Catholic Herald, Inc., 200 N. Glebe Rd., Ste. 614, Arlington, VA 22203. TEL 703-841-2590. Ed. Michael Flach. adv.; bk.rev.; illus. circ. 40,000. (also avail. in microfilm)
    Description: Local, national, international news and features of Catholic interest.

282   CL
ARZOBISPADO DE SANTIAGO. VICARIA DE LA SOLIDARIDAD. ESTUDIOS. 1978. irreg. Arzobispado de Santiago, Vicaria de la Solidaridad, Plaza de Armas 444, Casilla 30D, Santiago, Chile.

250   SP
ARZOBISPADO DE SEVILLA. BOLETIN OFICIAL ECLESIASTICO. 1854. m. 3000 ptas. Arzobispado de Sevilla, Oficina Diocesana de Informacion, Apdo. Postal 6, Sevilla, Spain. Ed. Antonio Fernandez Estevez. adv.; bk.rev. circ. 700.

282   IT
ASIA NEWS; agenzia quindicinale di informazioni. (Includes 2 quarterly supplements: Cina Oggi, Islam Oggi) 1987. fortn. (20/yr.). L.60000 (Europe L.80000, elsewhere L.100000). Pontificio Istituto Missioni Estere, Via Mose Bianchi 94, 20149 Milan, Italy. TEL 02-48-00-91-91. FAX 02-46-95-193. Ed. Fr. Piero Gheddo. adv.: B&W page L.1500000. circ. 2,200.
    Description: Covers the Roman Catholic Church, non-Christian religions, missionary work, human rights, refugees, and the environment in Asia.

282 209   IT   ISSN 0004-4970
ASPRENAS; rivista di scienze teologiche. 1953. q. L.65000($45) (effective 1994). (Facolta Teologica dell'Italia Meridionale, Sezione "S. Tommaso d'Aquino") Edizioni Dehoniane Roma, Viale Colli Aminei 2, 80131 Naples, Italy. FAX 39-81-7413041. Ed. Antonio Terracciano. adv. contact: Settimio Cipriani. bk.rev.; charts; illus. circ. 1,000. **Indexed:** CERDIC. **Document type:** academic/scholarly publication.
    Description: Contains studies and research on all aspects of theological science; Bible, patristics, systematic and practical theology, ecumenism, with particular attention to their cultural contexts and their relationship to the humanities.

ASSOCIATION OF JESUIT COLLEGES AND UNIVERSITIES AND JESUIT SECONDARY EDUCATION ASSOCIATION DIRECTORY. see EDUCATION — Higher Education

AUFTRAG; eine christliche Lehrzeitschrift. see RELIGIONS AND THEOLOGY — Protestant

282   US   ISSN 0094-5323
BR65.A9
AUGUSTINIAN STUDIES. (Text mainly in English) 1970. s-a. $24 (effective 1995). Villanova University, Augustinian Studies, Tolentine Hall, Villanova, PA 19085. TEL 215-519-7903. FAX 610-519-6306. E-mail: Fitzgeral@UCIS.VILL.edu. Ed. Allan D. Fitzgerald. bk.rev. circ. 500. (back issues avail.) **Indexed:** Cath.Ind., Phil.Ind. **Document type:** academic/scholarly publication.
  —SWETS.
    Description: Studies the life, work, philosophy, and influence of St. Augustine.
    Refereed Serial

271   BE   ISSN 0004-8003
AUGUSTINIANA; revue pour l'etude de Saint Augustin et de l'Ordre des Augustins. (Text in English, French, German, Latin) 1951. a-a. 1300 BEF. Augustijns Historisch Instituut - Institut Historique Augustinien, Pere August Pakenstraat 109, 3001 Heverlee-Louvain, Belgium. TEL 32-16-404440. FAX 32-16-405733. Ed. T. van Bavel. bk.rev.; bibl.; index. **Indexed:** CERDIC, M.L.A.
  —SWETS.

271   IT   ISSN 0004-8011
AUGUSTINIANUM. 1961. s-a. L.50000 (foreign L.60000) (effective 1992). Order of Saint Augustine, Economato Generale, Via Paolo VI, 25, 00193 Rome, Italy. FAX 6-800-6298. (Affiliate: Institutum Patristicum Augustinianum) Ed. V. Grossi. bk.rev.; index. circ. 850. (back issues avail.) **Indexed:** M.L.A., New Test.Abstr., Old Test.Abstr. **Document type:** academic/scholarly publication.
  —BLDSC (1791.700000); SWETS.

271   SP   ISSN 0004-802X
AUGUSTINUS. (Text in Spanish) 1956. q. 4500 ptas.($50) (effective 1995). Orden de Agustinos Recoletos, General Davila 5, Bajo D, 28003 Madrid, Spain. TEL 34-1-5342070. Dir. Jose Oroz Reta. adv. contact: Pablo Fortunato. bk.rev.; index. circ. 500. (processed) **Indexed:** CERDIC, M.L.A., Phil.Ind.
  —SWETS.
    Description: Studies on the life, doctrine, thought, spirituality and influence of St. Augustine.

282   AT   ISSN 0727-3215
AUSTRALASIAN CATHOLIC RECORD. 1924. q. Aus.$30. St. Patrick's College, Manly, N.S.W., Australia. Ed.Bd. adv.; bk.rev.; index. circ. 2,500. **Indexed:** Aus.P.A.I.S., Canon Law Abstr., Cath.Ind., New Test.Abstr., Rel.& Theol.Abstr.
  —UnCover.

282   LE   ISSN 0005-1950
AVEDIK.* 1932. m. £L10($4) Armenian Catholic Patriarchate, Place Debbas, Beirut, Lebanon. Ed. Fr. Vartan Tekeyan. illus.

282   US
AYLESFORD CARMELITE NEWSLETTER. 1984. q. $4. Lay Carmelite Office, 8501 Bailey Road, Darien, IL 60561. TEL 708-969-5050. FAX 708-969-5536. Ed. Rev. Aloysius Sieracki; Pub. Rev. Quinn Conners. bk.rev.; circ. 12,000 (controlled). (back issues avail.) **Document type:** newsletter.
    Description: Deals with Carmelite spirituality and recent trends in the involvement of the laity in Carmel.
    Refereed Serial

B D K J JOURNAL. (Bund der Deutschen Katholischen Jugend) see CHILDREN AND YOUTH — For

255   IT   ISSN 0005-3783
BADIA GRECA DI GROTTAFERRATA. BOLLETTINO. 1947. s-a. L.15000. (Monastero Esarchico di Grottaferrata) Badia Greca di Grottaferrata, 00046 Grottaferrata (Rome), Italy. bk.rev.; illus.; cum.index every 10 yrs. circ. 350. **Indexed:** CERDIC.

282 249   GW   ISSN 0005-7177
BAYERISCHES SONNTAGSBLATT FUER DIE KATHOLISCHE FAMILIE. 1879. w. (Sun.). DM.84.60. Bayerisches Sonntagsblatt Verlags GmbH, Nymphenburger Str. 156, 80634 Munich, Germany. TEL 089-164139. FAX 089-162133. Eds. Christian Freuel, Ursula Goldmann-Posch. adv. contact: Evelyne Zoeller. bk.rev.; film rev.; abstr.; illus. circ. 28,722. (looseleaf format) **Document type:** newspaper.

281   CN   ISSN 0382-6384
BEACON; Ukrainian rite bi-monthly. Ukrainian edition: Svitlo - Light (ISSN 0039-7164) (Text in English) 1966. bi-m. Can.$12. (Order of Saint Basil-The-Great in Canada) Basilian Press, 265 Bering Ave., Etobicoke, Ont. M8Z 3A5, Canada. TEL 416-234-1212. Ed. Rev. Ignatius Holowaychuk. adv.; bk.rev. circ. 1,300.
    Description: Covers news and theological articles as well as human interest articles in the life of the Ukrainian community.

282   IT   ISSN 0005-7436
BEATO ANGELO; organo culturale informativo. 1924. m. free. Frati Minori Cappuccini della Provincia Consentina, Parrocchia SS. Roberto e Biagio, 87052 Camigliatello Silano (CS), Italy. TEL 39-984-26592222. FAX 39-984-578018. Dir. P. Elio Vittorino Vivacqua. adv.; bk.rev.; illus. circ. 3,000.

200   NE   ISSN 0005-8734
BENEDICTIJNS TIJDSCHRIFT; voor Evangelische bezinning. 1937. q. fl.25 (effective 1995-1996). Sint-Adelbertabdij, Abdijlaan 26, 1935 BH Egmond-Binnen, Netherlands. adv.; bk.rev.; bibl. circ. 2,800. **Indexed:** CERDIC.

BENEDICTINA. see HISTORY — History Of Europe

271   UK   ISSN 0522-8883
BX3050.E9
BENEDICTINE YEARBOOK. 1863. a. £3 (effective 1995-1996). English Congregation of the Order of Saint Benedict, Ampleforth Abbey, York YO6 4EN, England. TEL 01772-35387. FAX 01772-35387. Ed. Rev. J. Gordon Beattie. adv. contact: Rev. J. Gordon Beattie. circ. 5,500. **Document type:** directory.
    Supersedes: Benedictine Almanac

RELIGIONS AND THEOLOGY — ROMAN CATHOLIC

282   US   ISSN 0005-8726
BENEDICTINES. 1946. s-a. $9. (Mount St. Scholastica Convent) Mount St. Scholastica, Inc., Atchison, KS 66002. TEL 913-367-6110. Ed. Sister Mary Alice Guilfoil. bk.rev.; illus.; cum.index: vols.1-9, 10-20, 21-30. circ. 800. (also avail. in microform from UMI; back issues avail.; reprint service avail. from UMI) **Indexed:** Bull.Signal., CERDIC.
—UMI.
Formerly (until 1966): Benedictine Review (ISSN 0148-947X)

282   GW
BERCKERS KATHOLISCHER TASCHENKALENDER. 1955. a. DM.9.80. Butzon und Bercker Verlag, Hoogeweg 71, Postfach 215, 47623 Kevelaer, Germany. TEL 02832-2906. FAX 02832-40321. circ. 20,000.
Former titles: Berckers Taschenkalender; Berckers Katholischer Taschenkalender.

282   IT
LA BIBBIA NELLA STORIA. 1984. irreg. Centro Editoriale Dehoniano, Via Nosadella 6, 40123 Bologna, Italy. TEL 051-306811. FAX 051-341706. Ed.Bd.

220 282   GW   ISSN 0006-0593
BIBEL HEUTE. 1965. q. DM.35. Katholisches Bibelwerk e.V., Silberburgstr. 121, 70176 Stuttgart, Germany. TEL 0711-6192050. FAX 0711-6192077. Ed. F.J. Ortkemper. adv.; bk.rev.; illus.; index, cum.index. circ. 25,000. **Indexed:** CERDIC. **Document type:** academic/scholarly publication.

282   GW
BIBELLESE PLAN. a. DM.2.50. Katholisches Bibelwerk e.V., Silberburgstr. 121, 70176 Stuttgart, Germany. TEL 0711-6192050. FAX 0711-6192077. Ed. Wolfgang Baur. **Document type:** bulletin.
Formerly: Leseplan Jahreslosung.

220   II   ISSN 0970-2288
BS410
BIBLEBHASHYAM; Indian Biblical quarterly. (Text in English) 1975. q. Rs.30($8) Bible Bhashyam Trust, Post Box No. 1, Vadavathoor, Kottayam 686010, India. Ed. Matthew Vellanickal. adv.; bk.rev. circ. 4,000. **Indexed:** New Test.Abstr., Old Test.Abstr.
—BLDSC (1947.821100).

282   BL
BIBLIA - GENTE. 1978. w. Cr.$100. (Pia Sociedade de Sao Paulo) Edicoes Paulinas, Via Raposo Tavares Km 18.5, C.P. 8107, 01051 Sao Paulo, Brazil. Ed. A.C. D'Elboux. illus. circ. 120,000.

220   VC   ISSN 0006-0887
BS410
BIBLICA. (Text in English, French, German, Italian, Latin or Spanish) 1920. q. L.75000($70) (effective 1995). (Pontificio Istituto Biblico - Pontifical Biblical Institute) Biblical Institute Press, Piazza della Pilotta 35, 00187 Rome, Italy. TEL 39-6-678-15-67. FAX 39-6-678-05-88. Ed. Horacio Simian Yofre, S.J. bk.rev.; index, cum.index: vols.1-25, vols.26-50. circ. 1,900. **Indexed:** Arts & Hum.Cit.Ind., Bibl.Ling., CERDIC, Curr.Cont., New Test.Abstr., Old Test.Abstr., Per.Islam. (1991-), Rel.& Theol.Abstr. (1977-), Rel.Ind.One, Rel.Per.
—Faxon; SWETS.
Description: Explores the scientific study of scripture.

282   VC
BIBLICA ET ORIENTALIA. 1928. irreg., no.44, 1993. price varies. (Pontificio Istituto Biblico - Pontifical Biblical Institute) Biblical Institute Press, Piazza della Pilotta 35, 00187 Rome, Italy. TEL 39-6-678-15-67. FAX 39-6-678-05-88.
Description: Covers aspects of the Bible which are directly related to the ancient Near Eastern background out of which the Bible came.

282   VC
BIBLIOTECA APOSTOLICA VATICANA. CATALOGHI E NORME DI CATALOGAZIONE. (In nine subseries: A: Cataloghi ed Inventari di Manoscritti; B: Bibliografia del Manoscritti; C: Cataloghi di Mostre; D: Cataloghi di Stampati; E: Norme di Catalogazione; F: Cataloghi di Pubblicazioni; G: Storia delle Biblioteche Pontificie; H: Quaderni della Scuola di Biblioteconomia; I: Capellae Aposolicae Sixtinaeque Collectanea Acta Monumenta) 1902. irreg. price varies. Biblioteca Apostolica Vaticana, 00120 Vatican City (Rome), State of the Vatican City.

282   VC
BIBLIOTECA APOSTOLICA VATICANA. EDIZIONI ILLUSTRATE. (In 3 subseries: A: Illustrazioni di Codici; B: Illustrazioni di Documenti; C: Illustrazioni di Monumenti) 1902. irreg. price varies. Biblioteca Apostolica Vaticana, 00120 Vatican City (Rome), State of the Vatican City.

282   VC
BIBLIOTECA APOSTOLICA VATICANA. STUDI E TESTI. 1900. irreg., no.342, 1991. price varies. Biblioteca Apostolica Vaticana, 00120 Vatican City (Rome), State of the Vatican City.

BIBLIOTHECA ASCETICO-MYSTICA. see *RELIGIONS AND THEOLOGY — Abstracting, Bibliographies, Statistics*

282   IT
BIBLIOTHECA INSTITUTI HISTORICI SOCIETATIS IESU. 1941. irreg., latest no.48, 1988. Institutum Historicum Societatis Iesu - Jesuit Historical Institute, Via dei Penitenzieri 20, 00193 Rome, Italy. (back issues avail.) **Document type:** monographic series.
Description: Contains research monographs on history of the Jesuits worldwide.

200   IT   ISSN 0067-8163
BIBLIOTHECA SERAPHICO-CAPUCCINA. SECTIO HISTORICA. (Multilingual text) 1932. irreg., no.47, 1995. price varies. Frati Minori Cappuccini, Istituto Storico, Cas. Postale 18283, Circonv. Occidentale 6850 (GRA km 65), 00163 Rome, Italy. TEL 39-6-66151958. FAX 39-6-66162401. index. circ. 500.

282   US
BIRMINGHAM ONE VOICE. 1971. w. $12. Birmingham Catholic Press, Inc., 8131 Fourth Ave., S., Birmingham, AL 35206. TEL 205-838-8305. Ed. Rev. John Igoe. adv. contact: Sam Ciulla. bk.rev. circ. 17,000. (tabloid format) **Document type:** newspaper.

282 340   GW
BISCHOEFLICHES ORDINARIAT AUGSBURG. RECHTSSAMMLUNG. 1990. a. Verlag Bischoefliches Ordinariat Augsburg, Postfach 110349, 86028 Augsburg, Germany. TEL 0821-3166291. FAX 0821-3166189. **Document type:** bulletin.

282   RM   ISSN 0257-4667
BISERICA ORTODOXA ROMANA. 1822. m. Romanian Patriarchate, Intrarea Patriarhiei 9, Bucharest, Rumania. TEL 234449. Ed. Rev. Dumitru Soare. circ. 10,000.

282   IT
BISERICA ROMANEASCA. (Text in Rumanian) 1976. q. L.12000($25) Comunita Ortodossa Romana in Italia, Via Meravigli 14, 20123 Milan, Italy. (Co-sponsor: Fondazione Europea Dragan) adv.; bk.rev.; illus. circ. 1,700.

282   XV   ISSN 0006-5722
BOGOSLOVNI VESTNIK. (Text in Slovenian) 1921-1944; resumed 1965. q. $20. Teoloska Fakulteta v Ljubljani, Poljanska 4, 61000 Ljubljana, Slovenia. FAX 061-329-793. Ed. Anton Stres. bk.rev. circ. 900.

282   PH   ISSN 0116-1830
BOLETIN ECLESIASTICO DE FILLIPINAS; official organ of the Catholic hierarchy of the Philippines. (Text in English) 1923. bi-m. $30 (effective 1994). (University of Santo Tomas) Santo Tomas University Press, Espana St., Manila 1008, Philippines. TEL 632-731-3101. FAX 632-732-7486. Ed. Honorato Castigador. adv.; bk.rev.; bibl.; index. circ. 1,800.

282   BO
BOLIVIA: GUIA ECLESIASTICA. 1977. irreg., latest 3rd ed. $15. Conferencia Episcopal Boliviana, Secretariado General, Casilla 7857, La Paz, Bolivia. TEL 377878. FAX 02-392326. illus. **Document type:** directory.
Formerly: Guia de la Iglesia.

282   IT   ISSN 0404-9462
BOLLETTINO DI S. NICOLA. (Text mainly in Italian; occasionally in other languages) 1906. m. L.5000($8) Padri Domenicani della Basilica di S. Nicola di Bari, Basilica di S. Nicola, 70122 Bari, Italy. Ed. P. Gerardo Cioffari. bk.rev.; bibl.; index. circ. 2,000. (back issues avail.)

282   IT   ISSN 0391-5867
BOLLETTINO SALESIANO; rivista fondata da San Giovanni Bosco. 1877. s-a. free. Direzione Generale Opere Salesiane, Via della Pisana 1111, 00163 Rome, Italy. Ed. Giuseppe Costa. (back issues avail.)

BOLLETTINO STORICO DELLA BASILICATA. see *RELIGIONS AND THEOLOGY*

266   IT   ISSN 0006-6907
BOLLETTINO VINCENZIANO. 1966. bi-m. L.20000. (Preti della Missione della Provincia di Roma) Centro Liturgico Vincenziano, Via Pompeo Magno 21, 00192 Rome, Italy. Ed. E. Fei. bk.rev.; charts; illus. circ. 2,000.

BONDINGS. see *HOMOSEXUALITY*

254.4   GW   ISSN 0006-7113
BONIFATIUSBLATT. 1849. q. DM.4. Bonifatiuswerk der Deutschen Katholiken e.V., Postfach 1169, 33041 Paderborn, Germany. TEL 05251-29960. FAX 05251-299688. Ed. Hand Dieter Huber. illus.; stat. circ. 350,000. (avail. in talking book ed.) **Document type:** newsletter.
Description: Reports on Catholic minorities, so-called "Diaspora-Church", in Germany and Scandinavian countries.

282   GW   ISSN 0935-8897
BONIFATIUSBOTE. 1884. w. (Sun.) DM.102. (Bischoeflicher Stuhl Fulda) Verlag Josef Knecht, Ludwig-Corden-Str. 3, 65549 Limburg, Germany. TEL 06431-9113-0. FAX 06431-191337. Ed. Ernst Schloegel. adv. contact: Sylvia Ehrengard. circ. 14,139. **Document type:** bulletin.

282   CN   ISSN 0225-0233
BONNE NOUVELLE. (Text in French) 1911. 10/yr. Can.$8. Secular Franciscan Order, 5730 bd. Pie 9, Montreal, Que. H1X 2B9, Canada. TEL 514-727-8483. Ed.Bd. adv.; bk.rev.; bibl.; charts; illus.; stat. circ. 4,000. (back issues avail.) **Indexed:** CERDIC.

282   NE   ISSN 0006-8349
BOUWEN AAN DE NIEUWE AARDE. 1953. bi-m. fl.20. Stichting Bouwen aan de Nieuwe Aarde, Prins Karelstraat 100, 5701 VM Helmond, Netherlands. TEL 31-4920-54644. Ed. K. Slijkerman. bk.rev. circ. 3,500.
Description: Promotes renewal of the Christian church by the power of the Holy Spirit.

282   XV
BOZJE OKOLJE. (Text in Slovenian; summaries in English) 1977. bi-m. 810 SLT($13.50) (Sovenske Rimskokatoliske Skofije) Druzina, Cankarjevo Nabrezje 3-I, 61101 Ljubljana, Slovenia. TEL 061 221324. Ed. France Orazem. circ. 2,500.

BRAUNAUER RUNDBRIEF. see *ETHNIC INTERESTS*

282   CN   ISSN 0821-168X
BREAD OF LIFE. 1977. bi-m. donation. C.C.S.O. Bread of Life Renewal Centre, 370 Main St. E., Ste. B1, Hamilton, ON L8N 1J6, Canada. TEL 416-529-4496. FAX 416-529-5373. Ed. Rev. Peter B. Coughlin. bk.rev. circ. 6,100. **Document type:** bulletin.
Description: Designed to encourage spiritual growth in areas of renewal in the Catholic Church today.

282   UK
BRIDGE (KINGSTON-UPON-THAMES). 1959. q. £3 (foreign £4). Sons of Divine Providence, 25 Lower Teddington Rd., Hampton Wick, Kingston-upon-Thames, Surrey KT1 4HB, England. TEL 0181-977-5130. FAX 0181-977-0105. Ed. Michael Moss. adv. contact: John Perrotta. circ. 5,500. (back issues avail.) **Document type:** newsletter.
Description: Provides international news of work of organization and personnel, including publicity, information, communication with friends and supporters.

RELIGIONS AND THEOLOGY — ROMAN CATHOLIC

282 UK ISSN 0308-0544
BRIEFING. 1970. m. £28. Catholic Media Office, Allington House, 39 Eccleston Sq., London SW1V 1BX, England. TEL 0171-828-8709. FAX 0171-931-7678. (Subscr. to: c/o Sister Mary Bernadette, Redemptorstine Convent, Back Gillmoss Lane, Liverpool L11 0AY, England) Ed. Kieran Conry. index. circ. 4,000. (back issues avail.)
Description: Documents bishops conferences in England, Scotland, and Wales.

282 US
BRINGING RELIGION HOME; the newsletter that helps teach religion in the home. 1976. 10/yr. $12. Claretian Publications, 205 W. Monroe St., Chicago, IL 60606. TEL 312-236-7782. FAX 312-236-7230. Ed. Rev. Mark J. Brummel. circ. 70,000. (reprint service avail. from UMI) **Document type:** newsletter.

282 CN ISSN 0007-0483
BRITISH COLUMBIA CATHOLIC. 1931. w. Can.$25 (foreign Can.$45). Vancouver Archdiocese, 150 Robson St., Vancouver, BC V6B 2A7, Canada. TEL 604-683-0281. FAX 604-683-8117. Ed. F.V. Hawkswell; Pub. Adam Exner. adv.; bk.rev.; film rev.; play rev.; illus. circ. 20,000. (tabloid format)

271 016 BE ISSN 0777-3331
BULLETIN D'HISTOIRE CISTERCIENNE/CISTERCIAN HISTORY ABSTRACTS. (Supplement to: Citeaux (ISSN 0774-4919)) 1987. biennial. Citeaux V.Z.W., Abdij O.L.Vr. van Nazareth, Abdijlaan 9, B-2960 Brecht, Belgium. (back issues avail.) **Document type:** abstracting/indexing.
Description: Provides a comprehensive overview of contemporary Cistercian studies, with abstract and complete references.

240 FR ISSN 0007-4322
BULLETIN DE LITTERATURE ECCLESIASTIQUE. 1899. q. 295 F.($55) (effective Jan. 1994). Institut Catholique de Toulouse, 31 rue de la Fonderie, 31068 Toulouse Cedex, France. TEL 61-36-81-00. Ed. Robert Cabie. bk.rev.; bibl.; index. circ. 850. (back issues avail.) **Indexed:** Bull.Signal., CERDIC, M.L.A., New Test.Abstr., Old Test.Abstr.

C A F O D MAGAZINE. (Catholic Fund for Overseas Development) see BUSINESS AND ECONOMICS — International Development And Assistance

C A F O D REPORT. (Catholic Fund for Overseas Development) see BUSINESS AND ECONOMICS — International Development And Assistance

282 US
C A R A FORMATION DIRECTORY FOR MEN AND WOMEN RELIGIOUS. 1990. biennial. $30. Center for Applied Research in the Apostolate, Georgetown University, Washington, DC 20057-1033. TEL 202-687-8080. FAX 202-687-8083. circ. 500. (back issues avail.) **Document type:** directory.

282 US
C A R A SEMINARY DIRECTORY; US Catholic institutions for the training of candidates for the priesthood. 1965. biennial. $30. Center for Applied Research in the Apostolate, Georgetown University, Washington, DC 20057-1033. TEL 202-687-8080. FAX 202-687-8083. Ed. C. Joseph O'Hara. circ. 500. (back issues avail.) **Document type:** directory.

282 UK ISSN 0262-6896
C A S BULLETIN. 1980. a. membership. Catholic Archives Society, c/o P. Bracken, 43 Garthland Dr., Glasgow G31 2RE, Scotland. circ. 280 (controlled). **Document type:** newsletter.
Description: Contains notes on seminars, local meetings and the society's annual conference.

C A V E NEWSLETTER. (Catholic Audio-Visual Educators) see EDUCATION — Teaching Methods And Curriculum

282 US
C C I C A ANNUAL. 1982. a. $12. Catholic Commission on Intellectual and Cultural Affairs, c/o La Salle University, Box 673, Philadelphia, PA 19141-1199. TEL 215-951-1221. Ed. Daniel Burke. circ. 350. (back issues avail.) **Document type:** proceedings.

C C N MESSENGER. (Council of Churches in Namibia) see RELIGIONS AND THEOLOGY — Protestant

C H A C INFO/INFO A C C S. (Catholic Health Association of Canada) see HOSPITALS

C H A C REVIEW. (Catholic Health Association of Canada) see HOSPITALS

C P F I NEWSLETTER. (Christian Pharmacists Fellowship International) see PHARMACY AND PHARMACOLOGY

282 360 US
C U S A N. 1948. s-a. membership. Catholics United for Spiritual Action, An Apostolate for Persons with Disabilities, 176 W. Eighth St., Bayonne, NJ 07002. TEL 201-437-0412. Ed. Lawrence Jadgfeld. bk.rev. circ. 1,100. (also avail. in magnetic tape; Braille)
Description: Articles by and for members. Focus is spiritual, practical or humorous in nature.

282 CN ISSN 0007-9774
BT690
CAHIERS DE JOSEPHOLOGIE. (Text in English and French) 1953. s-a. Can.$25. Oratoire Saint-Joseph du Mont-Royal, 3800 Chemin Reine-Marie, Montreal, PQ H3V 1H6, Canada. TEL 514-733-8211. FAX 514-733-9735. Ed. Roland Gauthier. bk.rev.; bibl.; illus.; index, cum.index: 1953-1972; 1973-1992. circ. 500. **Indexed:** Cath.Ind., New Test.Abstr., Old Test.Abstr., Rel.& Theol.Abstr. **Document type:** academic/scholarly publication.

282 CM
CAMEROON PANORAMA. (Text in English) 1962. m. B.P. 46, Buea, Cameroon. TEL 32-22-40. Ed. Sr. Mercy Horgan. circ. 4,000.

282 255 NE ISSN 0008-221X
CAMILLUSBODE. 1950. s-a. free. Provincialaat van de Camillianen, Heinsbergerweg 174, 6045 CK Roermond, Netherlands. TEL 31-4750-21985. Ed. P. Denneman. circ. 6,000. (tabloid format) **Document type:** bulletin.
Formerly: St. Camillusbode.

282 255 IT ISSN 0008-2260
CAMMINO; annali Francescani. 1869. m. $2. Viale Piave 2, Milan 20129, Italy. Ed.Bd. bk.rev.; film rev.; play rev.; illus. circ. 15,000.

282 CN ISSN 0703-1963
CANADIAN CANON LAW SOCIETY. (Text and summaries in Cajun, English, French) 1975. s-a. membership. Canadian Canon Law Society, 223 Main St., Ottawa, Ont. K1S 1C4, Canada. bk.rev. circ. 450. (looseleaf format; back issues avail.) **Document type:** newsletter.

282 CN ISSN 0827-1704
CANADIAN CATHOLIC HISTORICAL STUDIES. (Text in English, French) 1933. a. Can.$30. Canadian Catholic Historical Association, 355 Church Street, Toronto, ON M5B 1Z8, Canada. TEL 416-977-1500. FAX 416-977-6063. Eds. Paul Bator, Jeanne Beck. bk.rev. circ. 350. **Document type:** academic/scholarly publication.
Description: Features papers that were read at both the annual conferences.
Refereed Serial

282 CN ISSN 0714-7724
CANADIAN CATHOLIC REVIEW. 1983. 11/yr. Can.$25 (foreign $25). Canadian Catholic Review Corporation, 1437 College Dr., Saskatoon, SK S7N 0W6, Canada. TEL 306-966-8959. FAX 306-966-8904. Ed. Daniel Callam. adv. contact: Daniel Callam. bk.rev.; film rev.; index. circ. 1,000. (back issues avail.) **Indexed:** Cath.Ind. **Document type:** consumer publication.

200 CN
CANADIAN CONFERENCE OF CATHOLIC BISHOPS. NATIONAL BULLETIN ON LITURGY. Key Title: National Bulletin on Liturgy. 1965. 4/yr. Can.$10($12) (oustide US and Canada US$25). Canadian Conference of Catholic Bishops, Publications Service - Conference des Eveques Catholiques du Canada, 90 Parent Ave, Ottawa, ON K1N 7BI, Canada. TEL 613-241-9461. FAX 613-241-5090. Ed. J. Frank Henderson. bk.rev.; cum.index: 1965-77, 1978-85. circ. 3,500. (also avail. in microfilm from UMI; back issues avail.; reprint service avail. from UMI) **Document type:** bulletin.
—UMI.
Formerly: Canadian Catholic Conference. National Bulletin on Liturgy (ISSN 0084-8425)
Description: For parishes, schools, communities as they prepare, celebrate, and improve their life of worship and prayer. Primarily pastoral in scope.

282 CN ISSN 0835-2003
CARAVAN; a resource for those engaged in animating adult faith formation. 1987. q. Can.$16($18) (outside US and Canada US$24). Canadian Conference of Catholic Bishops, Publications Service - Conference des Eveques Catholiques du Canada, 90 Parent Ave., Ottawa, ON K1N 7B1, Canada. TEL 613-241-9461. FAX 613-241-5090. Ed. Joanne Chafe. bk.rev.; charts; illus.; stat. circ. 1,000. **Document type:** bulletin.
Description: News about workshops, research, upcoming conferences.

285 PH
CARDINAL BEA STUDIES. Short title: C B S. 1970. irreg., no.7, 1977. Cardinal Bea Institute for Ecumenical Studies, Box 4082, Manila, Philippines. Ed. Pedro S. de Achutegui, S.J. circ. 750.

282 US
CARING COMMUNITY. 1985. m. National Catholic Reporter Publishing Company, Inc., 115 E. Armour Blvd., Box 419281, Kansas City, MO 64141. TEL 816-531-0538; 800-333-7373. FAX 816-931-5082. Eds. Carolyn Hoff, Rich Heffren. illus. circ. 30,000. **Document type:** newsletter.
Description: Newsletter of support and inspiration for homebound and hospitalized Catholics.

282 LI ISSN 0236-2716
BX2347
CARITAS. 1989. m. $15. Lithuanian Caritas Federation, Vilniaus 29, Kaunas 233000, Lithuania. TEL 370-7-209683. FAX 370-7-205549. Ed. Albina Pribushauskaite. bk.rev. circ. 13,000.

255 IE ISSN 0008-6665
CARMEL. 1930. bi-m. £4.20. Discalced Carmelites, 55 Marlborough Rd., Donnybrook, Dublin 4, Ireland. Ed. Philip McParland, OCD. adv. circ. 11,000.
Description: Aims to help people to pray and discover the presence of God in their daily lives.

282 IT ISSN 0394-7742
CARMEL IN THE WORLD. (Text in English) 1961. 3/yr. L.17000($10) (Order of Carmelites) Edizioni Carmelitane, Via Sforza Pallavicini 10, 00193 Rome, Italy. TEL 06-68803513. FAX 06-68307200. Eds. Redemptus M. Valabek, O. Carm. adv. circ. 800. **Document type:** bulletin.
Description: Features readings on Carmelite spirituality, especially for laity.

282 IT ISSN 0394-7750
CARMEL IN THE WORLD PAPERBACKS. (Text in English) 1982. irreg. price varies. (Institutum Carmelitanum) Edizioni Carmelitane, Via Sforza Pallavicini 10, 00193 Rome, Italy. TEL 06-68803513. FAX 06-68307200. Eds. Redemptus M. Valabek, O. Carm. adv. circ. 1,000. **Document type:** monographic series.
Description: Forum includes Carmelite spirituality biography and popular treatment.

282 US ISSN 0887-123X
CARMELITE DIGEST. q. $15 (effective 1994). Discalced Carmelites, Box 3180, San Jose, CA 95156. TEL 408-286-8505. FAX 408-287-8748. adv.; B&W page $300; trim 5 1/2 x 8 1/2. circ. 2,500 (paid).

255 IT ISSN 0008-6673
BX3201
CARMELUS; commentarii ab Instituto Carmelitano editi. (Text in English, French, German, Italian, Latin and Spanish) 1954. 2/yr. L.55000. (Order of Carmelites) Edizioni Carmelitane, Via Sforza Pallavicini 10, 00193 Rome, Italy. TEL 06-68803513. FAX 06-68307200. Eds. Joachim Smet, O. Carm. adv.; bk.rev.; bibl.; index. circ. 580. (back issues avail.) **Document type:** academic/scholarly publication.
—SWETS; UnCover.
Description: Contains original articles on theology, with emphasis on spirituality and mariology and history.

282 US
CASA CRY. 1972. m. free. Casa Maria Catholic Worker, 1131 N. 21st St., Box 05206, Milwaukee, MI 53205. TEL 414-344-5745. Ed. Don Timmerman. circ. 1,750 (paid). (back issues avail.; reprint service avail.) **Document type:** newsletter.
Description: Update on work of Casa Maria Catholic Worker community.

RELIGIONS AND THEOLOGY — ROMAN CATHOLIC

CATALYST (ST. DAVIDS). see *SOCIAL SERVICES AND WELFARE*

282   IT   ISSN 0391-5433
CATECHESI. 1932. bi-m. (5/yr.) L.25000 (foreign L.36000) (effective 1996). (Centro Catechistico Salesiano) Editrice Elle Di Ci, Corso Francia 214, 10096 Leumann (TO), Italy. TEL 39-11-9591091. FAX 39-9572900. Ed. Pietro Damu. adv.: page L.350000. circ. 7,000. **Indexed:** CERDIC.

240   US
CATECHIST'S CONNECTION. 1984. 10/yr. National Catholic Reporter Publishing Company, Inc., 115 E. Armour Blvd., Box 419281, Kansas City, MO 64141. TEL 816-531-0538; 800-333-7373. FAX 816-931-5082. Ed. Jean Marie Hiesburger. adv.; bk.rev. circ. 38,000.
  Description: Articles supporting professional and volunteer teachers of Catholic religion.

282   US   ISSN 1040-659X
CATECHUMENE; a journal of Christian initiation. 1978. bi-m. $20. (Archdiocese of Chicago) Liturgy Training Publications, 1800 N. Hermitage Ave., Chicago, IL 60622-1101. TEL 312-486-8970. FAX 800-933-7094. Ed. Victoria Tufano. bk.rev.; index. circ. 6,100. (back issues avail.) **Document type:** academic/scholarly publication.
  Formerly (until 1978): Chicago Catechumenate.
  Description: Contains reflections and information for catechists of children and adults, parish staff, and parents.

282   UK
THE CATHOLIC. 1896. a. $20. Incorporated Catholic Truth Society, 192 Vauxhall Bridge Rd., London SW1V 1PD, England. TEL 0171-834 4392. FAX 0171-630-1124. Ed. Christopher Ralls. adv.; bk.rev.; bibl.; circ. 25,000 (controlled).
  Formerly (until Jul. 1989): The Catholic (ISSN 0411-275X)
  Description: Contains reports for members of the society detailing publishing work carried out and financial position.

282   US   ISSN 0745-399X
CATHOLIC ACCENT. 1961. w. $13.50 (effective 1993-94). Greensburg Catholic Accent and Communications, Inc., 723 E. Pittsburgh St., Greensburg, PA 15601. TEL 412-834-4010. FAX 412-836-5650. Ed. Carol Kalich. adv. circ. 48,735. (tabloid format) **Document type:** newspaper.

282   US   ISSN 0008-7904
CATHOLIC ADVANCE. 1901. w. $10 in Kansas; out of state $12. Catholic Diocese of Wichita, 424 N. Broadway, Wichita, KS 67202. TEL 316-269-3965. Ed. Christopher M. Riggs. adv.; bk.rev. circ. 30,000. (also avail. in microform) **Document type:** newspaper.
  Formerly: Advance.

282   US   ISSN 0045-5970
CATHOLIC AGITATOR. 1971. 8/yr. $1. (Ammon Hennacy House of Hospitality) Los Angeles Catholic Worker, 632 N. Brittania St., Los Angeles, CA 90033. TEL 213-267-8789. Ed. Jeff Dietrich. adv.; bk.rev. circ. 6,000.

CATHOLIC AID NEWS. see *INSURANCE*

282   US   ISSN 0069-1208
AY81.R6
CATHOLIC ALMANAC. 1904. a. $18.95. Our Sunday Visitor, Inc., 200 Noll Plaza, Huntington, IN 46750. TEL 219-356-8400. FAX 219-356-8472. Eds. Rev. Felician A. Foy, Rose M. Avato. index. (also avail. in microfiche from CIS) **Indexed:** SRI. **Document type:** directory.
  Formerly: National Catholic Almanac.
  Description: Names and addresses of all types of Catholic offices, organizations and facilities.

282   NR   ISSN 1115-8832
THE CATHOLIC AMBASSADOR. 1980. q. £N25($5) (effective 1992). (Missionary Society of St. Paul - Nigeria) Ambassador Publications, P.M.B. 2011, Iperu Remo, Osun State, Nigeria. Ed. Rev J.E. Otoide. adv.; bk.rev. circ. 20,000. (back issues avail.)
  Formerly: Ambassador.
  Description: Helps the faithful take an interest in the Universal Church. Contains news of activities and coverage of issues both in Nigeria and the world.

282   US   ISSN 1044-1581
THE CATHOLIC ANSWER. 1987. bi-m. $15. Our Sunday Visitor, Inc., 200 Noll Plaza, Huntington, IN 46750. TEL 219-356-8400. FAX 219-356-8472. Ed. Rev. Peter M.J. Stravinskas. adv. circ. 53,000.
  Description: Supplies Catholics with answers on what the church teaches, how to live their faith, and what their Catholic heritage is.

282   US
CATHOLIC ARCHDIOCESE OF LOUISVILLE. RECORD.* 1879. w. $12. Catholic Archdiocese of Louisville, 1200 S. Shelby St., Louisville, KY 40203-2600. TEL 502-587-1327. Ed. Joseph Duerr. adv.; circ. 61,700 (controlled).

282   UK   ISSN 0261-4316
CATHOLIC ARCHIVES. 1981. a. £5. Catholic Archives Society, c/o P. Bracken, 43 Garthland Dr., Glasgow G31 2RE, Scotland. circ. 400. **Indexed:** CERDIC.
  Description: Guide to the history and use of the archives of the Roman Catholic Church in the U.K. and Ireland.

220 282   US   ISSN 0008-7912
BS410
CATHOLIC BIBLICAL QUARTERLY. 1939. q. $25. Catholic Biblical Association of America, Catholic University of America, Washington, DC 20064. TEL 202-319-5519. Ed. Alfred Cody. adv. contact: Joseph Jensen. bk.rev.; index, cum.index. circ. 4,230. (also avail. in microfilm) **Indexed:** Arts & Hum.Cit.Ind., Bibl.Ling., Cath.Ind., CERDIC, Curr.Cont., Hum.Ind., Mid.East: Abstr.& Ind., New Test.Abstr., Old Test.Abstr., Rel.& Theol.Abstr. (1968-), Rel.Ind.One, Rel.Per. **Document type:** academic/scholarly publication.
  —BLDSC (3093.010000); Faxon; Genuine Article; SWETS; UMI; UnCover. **CCC.**
  Description: Articles and notices of a scholarly nature on the Scripture.

CATHOLIC BOOK PUBLISHERS ASSOCIATION DIRECTORY. see *PUBLISHING AND BOOK TRADE*

282   US
CATHOLIC BULLETIN. 1911. w. $26.95. St. Paul Catholic Bulletin, 244 Dayton Ave., St. Paul, MN 55102. TEL 612-291-4444. Ed. Robert Zyskowski. circ. 30,000. (tabloid format) **Document type:** newspaper.

CATHOLIC CEMETERY. see *FUNERALS*

282   US   ISSN 8756-7482
CATHOLIC CHALLENGE.* 1985. q. $15. Sanderleaf Publishing, Inc., 205 Mineola Blvd., Apt. 3l, Mineola, NY 11501-2552. TEL 516-488-7439. Ed. Rev. James P. Lisante.

282   US   ISSN 0008-7971
CATHOLIC CHRONICLE. 1934. bi-w. $19. (Catholic Diocese of Toledo) Catholic Chronicle, Inc., 2130 Madison Ave., Box 1866, Toledo, OH 43603. TEL 419-243-4178. FAX 419-243-4235. Ed. Patricia Lynn Morrison. adv. contact: James Pencheff. film rev. circ. 25,000. (also avail. in microfilm) **Document type:** newspaper.

282   XK
CATHOLIC CHRONICLE. 1957. m. EC$1. Archdiocese of Castries, c/o Benedictine Nuns, Box 778, Castries, St. Lucia, W.I. TEL 809-20790. Ed. Patrick A.B. Anthony. adv. circ. 2,500.
  Formerly: Castries Catholic Chronicle.

282   US   ISSN 0746-0511
THE CATHOLIC COMMENTATOR. 1962. fortn. $10. Roman Catholic Diocese of Baton Rouge, 1800 S. Acadian Thruway, Baton Rouge, LA 70808. TEL 504-387-0983. FAX 504-336-8710. (Subscr. to: Box 14746, Baton Rouge, LA 70898) Ed. Laura G. Deavers. adv. contact: Wanda Koch. circ. 53,000. (tabloid format) **Document type:** newspaper.
  Description: Covers local and world news, and diocesan communications.

280   FR
CATHOLIC COUNTER-REFORMATION IN THE XXTH CENTURY. (Text in English) 1970. m. $30. Contre Reforme Catholique, Maison Saint-Joseph, 10260-Saint-Parres-les-Vaudes, France. Ed. Frere Gerard Cousin. bk.rev. circ. 4,500.

282   US   ISSN 1054-2728
CATHOLIC COURIER. 1889. w. $20 (effective 1995). (Roman Catholic Diocese of Rochester, N.Y.) Rochester Catholic Press Association, 1150 Buffalo Rd., Rochester, NY 14624. TEL 716-328-4340. Ed. Karen M. Franz. adv. contact: Ray Frey. bk.rev.; circ. 50,234 (paid). (tabloid format; also avail. in microfilm) **Document type:** newspaper.
  Formerly: Courier-Journal.
  Description: Newspaper of the 12-county Rochester, NY diocese. Includes local, national and international church news, feature articles, columns, commentary and reviews.

282   US   ISSN 0008-7998
BX801
CATHOLIC DIGEST. 1936. m. $19.97. University of St. Thomas, Box 64090, St. Paul, MN 55164. TEL 612-962-6741. FAX 612-962-6755. Ed. Richard J. Reece. adv.; illus. circ. 575,000. (also avail. in microform from UMI,PMC; reprint service avail. from UMI) **Indexed:** Cath.Ind., CERDIC. **Document type:** consumer publication.

267   US   ISSN 0069-1224
CATHOLIC DIRECTORY. Variant title: Catholic Directory of England and Wales. 1837. a. £19.50. Gabriel Communications, St. James's Bldg., 1st Fl, Oxford St., Manchester M1 6FP, England. Ed. Monsig. George Leonard. adv. **Document type:** directory.

282   US
CATHOLIC DIRECTORY (SAN DIEGO). 1936. a. $15. Roman Catholic Diocese of San Diego, Box 81869, San Diego, CA 92138. TEL 619-490-8266. FAX 619-490-8355. Ed. Larry Montal; Pub. Bishop Robert Brom. adv. contact: Lee Haralson. circ. 3,500. **Document type:** directory.

282   US
CATHOLIC DIRECTORY (SAN FRANCISCO); Marin, San Francisco and San Mateo Counties. a. $12. Archdiocese of San Francisco, Catholic Communications Center, 441 Church St., San Francisco, CA 94114. TEL 415-565-3630. Ed. Charlotte Pace. adv.; stat. **Document type:** directory.

267   UK   ISSN 0306-5677
BX1497.A3
CATHOLIC DIRECTORY FOR SCOTLAND. 1828. a. £9.50. John S. Burns and Sons, 25 Finlas St., Possilpark, Glasgow, G22 5DS, Scotland. **Document type:** directory.
  —BLDSC (3093.019000).
  Formerly: Catholic Directory for the Clergy and Laity in Scotland (ISSN 0069-1232)

282   SA   ISSN 0379-4652
CATHOLIC DIRECTORY OF SOUTHERN AFRICA. 1906. biennial. R.20. Southern African Catholic Bishops' Conference, Office for Social Communications, P.O. Box 941, Pretoria 0001, South Africa. TEL 27-12-3236458. FAX 27-12-3266218. E-mail: SN0073@CNNECTINC.COM. adv.; stat.; index. circ. 1,500. **Document type:** directory.
  Description: Guide to all Catholic organizations and institutions comprising the ecclesiastical territories of South Africa, Botswana, Namibia, and Swaziland.

282   US
CATHOLIC DIRECTORY OF THE ARCHDIOCESE OF BALTIMORE. 1921. a. $11. (Archdiocese of Baltimore) Cathedral Foundation, 320 Cathedral St., Box 777, Baltimore, MD 21201. TEL 301-547-5314. Ed. Daniel Medinger. adv. circ. 1,900. **Document type:** directory.
  Formerly: Archdiocese of Baltimore. Directory.

282   US
CATHOLIC DIRECTORY OF THE DIOCESE OF ALBANY. 1957. a. $11. Albany Catholic Press Association, Inc., 40 N. Main Ave., Albany, NY 12203. TEL 518-453-6688. FAX 518-453-6793. Ed. James P. Breig; Pub. Bishop Howard J. Hubbard. adv. contact: Barbara R. Oliver. **Document type:** directory.
  Description: Lists churches, staff, agencies, organizations, and institutions of Albany Roman Catholic Diocese, covering 14 counties in upstate NY.

282 377.8   UK
CATHOLIC EDUCATION. 1960. biennial. £8. Catholic Education Service for England and Wales, 41 Cromwell Rd., London SW7 2DJ, England. FAX 0171-823-7545. Ed. M.M. Smart. circ. 2,000.

RELIGIONS AND THEOLOGY — ROMAN CATHOLIC

282 US
CATHOLIC EYE. w. $34.95. National Committee of Catholic Laymen, Inc., 150 E. 35th St., New York, NY 10016. **Document type:** newsletter.
Description: Examines U.S. and international news and issues from a Catholic perspective.

282 US ISSN 0008-8056
CATHOLIC FREE PRESS. (Supplements avail.) 1951. w. $19. (Roman Catholic Bishop of Worcester) Catholic Free Press, 47 Elm St., Worcester, MA 01609. TEL 508-757-6387. FAX 508-753-7180. Ed. Gerard E. Goggins. adv.; bk.rev.; illus. circ. 20,000. (also avail. in microfilm) **Document type:** newspaper.

282 UK ISSN 0008-8064
CATHOLIC GAZETTE. 1910. m. £1.10. Catholic Missionary Society, 114 W. Heath Rd., London NW3 7TX, England. FAX 0181-905-5780. Ed. John Breem. adv. contact: Graeme Dunne. bk.rev.; index. circ. 6,000. **Indexed:** CERDIC.

282 UK ISSN 0008-8072
CATHOLIC HERALD. 1884. w. 40 (effective 1994). Catholic Herald Ltd., Herald House, Lamb's Passage, Bunhill Row, London, England. TEL 44-71-588-3101. FAX 44-71-256-9728. Ed. Cristina Odone. adv.; bk.rev.; music rev.; index. circ. 25,000. (also avail. in microform from WMP) **Document type:** newspaper.
Description: Contains news, features, arts, and letters to the editor.

282 US
CATHOLIC HERALD (MILWAUKEE). 1869. w. $38. Milwaukee Catholic Press Apostolate, 3501 S. Lake Dr., Box 07913, Milwaukee, WI 53207-0913. TEL 414-769-3500. Ed. Thomas J. Smith. adv. contact: Ronald Lundean. circ. 87,616. **Document type:** newspaper.

282 US
CATHOLIC HERALD (SUPERIOR). 1952. w. $30. 1512 N. Second St., Superior, WI 54880. TEL 715-392-8268. (Subscr. to: Box 969, Superior, WI 54880) Ed. Sam M. Lucero. adv. circ. 21,100. (tabloid format) **Document type:** newspaper.

282 US ISSN 1057-929X
CATHOLIC HERITAGE. 1991. bi-m. $15 (foreign $17). Our Sunday Visitor, Inc., 200 Noll Plaza, Huntington, IN 46750. TEL 219-356-8400. FAX 219-356-8472. adv.; B&W page $330; trim 5 1/4 x 8. circ. 25,000.

282 270 US ISSN 0008-8080
BX1404
CATHOLIC HISTORICAL REVIEW. 1915. q. $35 (effective 1996). (American Catholic Historical Association) Catholic University of America Press, 620 Michigan Ave., N.E., Washington, DC 20064. TEL 202-319-5052. FAX 202-319-5802. Ed. Rev. Robert Trisco. adv.; bk.rev.; bibl.; index, cum.index: vols.1-20, 21-50. circ. 2,083. (also avail. in microfilm from UMI,PMC; reprint service avail. from KTO,UMI) **Indexed:** Amer.Bibl.Slavic & E.Eur.Stud., Amer.Hist.& Life, Arts & Hum.Cit.Ind., Bibl.Engl.Lang.& Lit., Bk.Rev.Ind. (1980-), Cath.Ind., Child.Bk.Rev.Ind. (1980-), Curr.Cont., Hist.Abstr., Hum.Ind., Mid.East: Abstr.& Ind., Old Test.Abstr., Rel.& Theol.Abstr. (1977-), RILA.
—BLDSC (3093.070000); Faxon; Genuine Article; SWETS; UMI; UnCover. **CCC.**
Description: Publishes articles, review articles in all areas of church history.

282 II
CATHOLIC INDIA. (Text in English) q. Catholic Bishop's Conference of India, CBCI Centre, 1 Ashok Place, Goldakkhana, New Delhi 110 001, India. TEL 11-344470. TELEX 3161366.

282 CN ISSN 1192-5671
CATHOLIC INSIGHT; a magazine for Canada in the universal Church. 1993. 10/yr. Can.$16($18) Life Ethics Information Centre, 1515 Bathurst St., Toronto, ON M5P 2H4, Canada. TEL 416-368-3558. FAX 416-368-8575. Ed. Alphonse de Valk. adv. contact: Lianne Laurence. circ. 3,100. **Document type:** academic/scholarly publication.
Description: Information and opinion on public, political, cultural and religious affairs in Canada and the universal Church.

CATHOLIC JOURNALIST. see JOURNALISM

282 US
CATHOLIC KEY. 1969. w. $18. Diocese of Kansas City, St. Joseph, 300 E. 36th St., Box 419037, Kansas City, MO 64141-6037. TEL 816-756-1850. FAX 816-756-0878. Ed. Albert de Zutter; Pub. Bishop Raymond J. Boland. adv. contact: Thomas de Zutter. bk.rev. circ. 17,200. (tabloid format; back issues avail.) **Document type:** newspaper.

CATHOLIC LAWYER. see LAW

CATHOLIC LIBRARY ASSOCIATION. NORTHERN ILLINOIS CHAPTER. NEWSLETTER. see LIBRARY AND INFORMATION SCIENCES

282 GW ISSN 0930-8679
CATHOLIC MEDIA COUNCIL. INFORMATION BULLETIN. 1972. q. free. Catholic Media Council, Publizistische Medienplanung fuer Entwicklungslaender e.V., Anton-Kurze-Allee 2, 52074 Aachen, Germany. TEL 0241-73081. FAX 0241-73462. Ed. Hans-Peter Gohla. bk.rev.; charts. circ. 850. **Document type:** bulletin.

CATHOLIC MEDICAL QUARTERLY. see MEDICAL SCIENCES

282 US ISSN 0008-8234
CATHOLIC MESSENGER. 1882. w. $20 (effective 1995). Roman Catholic Diocese of Davenport, 736 Federal St., Box 460, Davenport, IA 52805-0460. TEL 319-323-9959. FAX 319-323-6612. Ed. Rev. Francis C. Henricksen. adv. contact: Kathy Weiss. bk.rev.; circ. 22,726 (paid). (also avail. in microform) **Document type:** newspaper.

282 US
CATHOLIC MISSOURIAN. 1957. w. $11. Diocese of Jefferson City, Box 1107, Jefferson City, MO 65101. TEL 314-635-9127. FAX 314-635-2286. Ed. Father Hugh Behan. bk.rev.; illus. circ. 21,000. (tabloid format) **Document type:** newspaper.

282 US
THE CATHOLIC MOMENT. 1945. w. $17. Diocese of Lafayette-in-Indiana, Local Church of Northcentral Indiana, Box 1603, Lafayette, IN 47902-1603. TEL 317-742-2050. FAX 317-742-7513. Ed. Thomas A. Russell. adv.; B&W page $500, color page $628; trim 11 1/2 x 14/1/2. bk.rev. circ. 26,614. (tabloid format) **Document type:** newspaper.
Former titles (until Dec. 1994): Sunday Visitor; Lafayette Sunday Visitor.
Description: Addresses general social, religious, educational, health, and familial issues through a catholic perspective.

CATHOLIC MUSIC EDUCATOR. see MUSIC

282 US ISSN 0164-0674
BX1617
CATHOLIC NEAR EAST MAGAZINE. 1974. bi-m. $10. Catholic Near East Welfare Association, 1011 First Ave., New York, NY 10022-4195. TEL 212-826-1480. FAX 212-838-1344. TELEX 910 250 1440 NYK UQ. Ed. Michael La Civita. illus.; circ. 105,000 (controlled). **Document type:** trade publication.
Description: Informs members of ecumenical and interfaith endeavors, projects and programs developed by the church in the Near East and cultural and spiritual items.

200 CN ISSN 0701-0788
CATHOLIC NEW TIMES. 1976. 23/yr. Can.$20($30) New Catholic Times Inc., 80 Sackville St., Toronto, Ont. M5A 3E5, Canada. TEL 416-361-0761. FAX 1-416-361-0796. Ed. Anne O'Brien. adv.; bk.rev. circ. 11,000. (also avail. in microfiche) **Indexed:** Can.B.P.I., Can.Per.Ind.

282 US ISSN 0278-1174
CATHOLIC NEW YORK. 1981. w. $20. (Roman Catholic Diocese of New York) Ecclesiastical Communications Corp., 1011 First Ave., New York, NY 10022. TEL 212-688-2399. FAX 212-688-2642. Ed. Anne M. Buckley. adv.; bk.rev. circ. 131,406. (also avail. in microfiche)

282 TR
CATHOLIC NEWS. 1892. w. $50 (effective Jan. 1994). (Roman Catholic Archdiocese) Printing Services Ltd., 31 Independence Sq., Port of Spain, Trinidad, W.I. TEL 809-623-6093. Ed. Fr. Michel de Verteuil. adv.; circ. 13,000 (paid). (tabloid format; back issues avail.) **Document type:** newspaper.
Description: Contains news of the Church, locally and worldwide, social commentary, and spiritual reading.

282 US
CATHOLIC OBSERVER. (Supplement avail. annual directory) 1954. bi-w. $12. Diocese of Springfield, Massachusetts, 65 Elliott St., Springfield, MA 01105. TEL 413-732-3175. FAX 413-747-0273. Ed. Sharon A. Roulier. adv.; bk.rev. circ. 18,000. (tabloid format) **Document type:** newspaper.

282 US
CATHOLIC OUTLOOK. 1970. m. $10. Diocese of Duluth, 2830 E. Fourth St., Duluth, MN 55812. TEL 218-724-9111. FAX 218-724-1056. Ed. Molly Stein. adv.; bk.rev.; illus. circ. 33,000. (tabloid format) **Document type:** newspaper.

CATHOLIC PARENT. see CHILDREN AND YOUTH — About

282 US ISSN 0008-8277
CATHOLIC PEACE FELLOWSHIP BULLETIN. 1965. 2/yr. donation. Catholic Peace Fellowship, 339 Lafayette St., New York, NY 10012. TEL 212-673-8990. Ed. Bill Ofenloch. bk.rev.; illus. circ. 4,000.
Description: Reports on events and views in the peace and disarmament movement.

THE CATHOLIC PHARMACIST. see PHARMACY AND PHARMACOLOGY

282 UK ISSN 0008-8293
CATHOLIC PICTORIAL. 1962. w. £0.40 (effective Aug. 1992). Catholic Pictorial Ltd., Media House, Mann Island, Pier Head, Liverpool L3 1DQ, England. TEL 051-236-2191. FAX 051-236-2216. Ed. Rev. Paul F. Thomson. adv.; bk.rev.; illus. circ. 9,500. (tabloid format)

282 US
THE CATHOLIC POST. 1969. w. $14. Diocese of Peoria, 409 N.E. Monroe, Peoria, IL 61603. TEL 309-673-3603. FAX 309-673-0334. Ed. Tom Dermody. circ. 32,500. **Document type:** newspaper.

282 US
CATHOLIC QUOTE; instant inspiration. vol.37, 1974. m. $5. Rev. Jerome Pokorny, Ed. & Pub., Valparaiso, NE 68065. index. circ. 7,000. (back issues avail.)

282 CN ISSN 0383-1620
CATHOLIC REGISTER. 1893. w. (47/yr.) Can.$24($41.50) Canadian Register Ltd., 67 Bond St., Ste. 303, Toronto, ON M5B 1X6, Canada. TEL 416-362-6822. FAX 416-362-8652. Ed. Bernard M. Daly. adv.; bk.rev.; film rev.; abstr. circ. 28,000. (tabloid format) **Document type:** newspaper.
Formerly: Canadian Register (ISSN 0008-4913)

282 US
CATHOLIC REGISTER. 1918. bi-w. $10. Diocese of Altoona Johnstown, Box 413, Hollidaysburg, PA 16648. TEL 814-695-7563. FAX 814-695-7517. Ed. Rev. Timothy P. Stein. adv.; bk.rev.; illus. circ. 37,000. **Document type:** newspaper.

282 US ISSN 0008-8315
CATHOLIC REVIEW (BALTIMORE). 1913. w. $24. Cathedral Foundation, Inc., 320 Cathedral St., Box 777, Baltimore, MD 21203. TEL 410-547-5327. FAX 410-385-0113. Ed. Daniel Medinger. adv.; bk.rev. circ. 69,300. (also avail. in microfilm) **Document type:** newspaper.

282 US ISSN 0008-8323
CATHOLIC REVIEW (NEW YORK). 1943. 6/yr. free to qualified individuals. Xavier Society for the Blind, 154 E. 23rd St., New York, NY 10010. TEL 212-473-7800; 800-637-9193. FAX 212-473-7801. Ed. Ann Murray. circ. 3,200. (also avail. in Braille; audio cassette; large print edition in 20 pt.)
Description: Includes articles from Catholic periodicals.

RELIGIONS AND THEOLOGY — ROMAN CATHOLIC

200   AT   ISSN 0813-5827
CATHOLIC SCHOOL STUDIES. 1928. 2/yr. Aus.$16 (foreign Aus.$20) per no. Christian Brothers of the Australian and New Zealand Provinces, Treacy Centre, 156 The Avenue, Parkville, Vic. 3052, Australia. TEL 61-3-347-4111.
FAX 61-3-347-3112. Ed. R.S. Stewart. adv.; bk.rev. circ. 2,900. **Indexed:** Aus.Educ.Ind. **Document type:** academic/scholarly publication.
    Former titles: Christian Brothers of the Australian and New Zealand Provinces. Our Studies (ISSN 0045-6780); Christian Brothers Studies; Catholic School Studies.
    Description: Covers education for Australian and New Zealand Catholic schools.

282   US   ISSN 0162-2102
CATHOLIC SENTINEL (ARCHDIOCESE OF PORTLAND, OREGON). w. Oregon Catholic Press, 5536 N.E. Hassalo St., Portland, OR 97213.
TEL 503-281-1191. FAX 503-282-3486. **Document type:** newspaper.

282   US   ISSN 0162-0363
CATHOLIC SENTINEL (DIOCESE OF BAKER). w. $22. Oregon Catholic Press, 5536 N.E. Hassalo St., Portland, OR 97213. TEL 503-281-1191.
FAX 503-282-3486. Ed. Robert Pfohman. adv.; bk.rev.; film rev.; abstr.; illus. circ. 17,921. (tabloid format; also avail. in microform) **Document type:** newspaper.

282   US   ISSN 0896-2715
CATHOLIC SPIRIT (AUSTIN). (Text in English, Spanish) 1983. m. $12. Diocese of Austin, Box 13327, Austin, TX 78711. TEL 512-476-4888.
FAX 512-469-9537. Ed. Helen Osman. adv.; bk.rev. circ. 25,000. (tabloid format)
    Description: Provides news and religious education to families in the diocese.

200   US
CATHOLIC SPIRIT (WHEELING). 1934. bi-w. $15. Catholic Diocese of Wheeling-Charleston, Box 951, Wheeling, WV 26003-0119. TEL 304-233-0880. FAX 304-233-0890. Ed. Richard Cain. adv.; bk.rev.; film rev. circ. 4,600. (tabloid format; also avail. in microfiche)

282   UK   ISSN 0008-8366
CATHOLIC STANDARD. 1938. w. £40 (effective 1994). The Catholic Herald, Herald House, Lambs Passage, Bunhill Row, London EC1Y 8T2, England.
TEL 44-71-588-3101. FAX 44-71-256-9728. Ed. Cristina Odone. adv.; bk.rev.; illus. circ. 5,000. **Indexed:** CERDIC, HR Rep. **Document type:** newspaper.
    Description: Irish edition of Catholic Herald

282   GY
CATHOLIC STANDARD. 1905. w. 293 Oronoque St., Queenstown, POB 10720, Georgetown, Guyana. TEL 2-61540. Ed. Fr. Andrew Morrison. circ. 10,000.

282   US   ISSN 0411-2741
THE CATHOLIC STANDARD. 1951. w. $28. (Archdiocese of Washington) Carroll Publishing Co., Box 4464, Washington, DC 20017.
TEL 301-853-4599. FAX 301-853-3349. Ed. Joseph Sicciardi. adv. contact: Caryn Kruze. bk.rev.; illus. circ. 50,000. (tabloid format) **Document type:** newspaper.

282   US
CATHOLIC STAR HERALD. 1951. w. $17. Diocese of Camden, Inc., 1845 Haddon Ave., Camden, NJ 08103. TEL 609-756-7910. FAX 609-963-2655. Ed. Charles J. Giglio. adv. contact: Samuel A. Bonavita. bk.rev. circ. 41,000. **Document type:** newspaper.

282   US
CATHOLIC STUDY COUNCIL BULLETIN. 1985. m. $15. (National Center for Public Policy Research) Catholic Study Council, 300 Eye St., N.E., Ste. 2, Washington, DC 20002. TEL 202-543-1286. Ed. Michael G. Pauley. circ. 600.
    Description: Discusses the role of religion in social problems.

282   US   ISSN 0744-267X
CATHOLIC SUN. 1893. w. $20. Syracuse Catholic Press, Inc., 421 S. Warren St., Syracuse, NY 13202-2603. TEL 315-422-8153.
FAX 315-422-7549. Ed. Anne Checkosky. adv.; bk.rev. circ. 37,000. (tabloid format; also avail. in microfilm; back issues avail.) **Document type:** newspaper.
    Description: Publication for the Roman Catholic diocese of Syracuse.

282   US
CATHOLIC SUN (PHOENIX). 1985. s-m. $10 (outside AZ $15). Roman Catholic Diocese of Phoenix, 400 E. Monroe St., Phoenix, AZ 85004.
TEL 602-257-5565. FAX 602-258-6404. E-mail: CatholSun@aol.com. (Subscr. to: Box 13549, Phoenix, AZ 85002) Ed. Christopher Gunty. adv. contact: Lynn R. Wurth. bk.rev.; circ. 88,000 (paid). (tabloid format) **Document type:** newspaper.

282   US   ISSN 1073-6689
CATHOLIC TELEGRAPH. 1831. w. $22. (Archdiocese of Cincinnati) Catholic Telegraph, 100 E. 8th St., Cincinnati, OH 45202. TEL 513-421-3131.
FAX 513-381-2242. adv.; bk.rev.; film rev. circ. 32,000.

282   US   ISSN 0147-5959
BX1417.N4
CATHOLIC TELEPHONE GUIDE. a. $28. Catholic News Publishing Co., Inc. (Subsidiary of: School Guide Publications), 210 North Ave., New Rochelle, NY 10801. TEL 914-632-1220; 800-433-7771.
FAX 914-632-3412. Ed. Annette Miserendino; Pub. Myles Ridder. adv.: B&W page $2090; 7 x 10; adv. contact: Myles Ridder.

282   US   ISSN 0069-1267
CATHOLIC THEOLOGICAL SOCIETY OF AMERICA. PROCEEDINGS. 1946. a. $18 (foreign $20). Catholic Theological Society of America, c/o Dr. Maryanne Stevens, Department of Theology, Creighton University, 2500 California Plaza, Omaha, NE 68178-0116. TEL 402-280-2505. Ed. Paul Crowley. index, cum.index. circ. 1,600. (also avail. in microform from UMI; reprint service avail. from UMI) **Indexed:** Cath.Ind., CERDIC, New Test.Abstr. **Document type:** proceedings, academic/scholarly publication.
—UMI.

200 100   US   ISSN 1051-693X
CATHOLIC THOUGHT FROM LUBLIN. irreg. Peter Lang Publishing, Inc., 62 W. 45th St., 4th Fl., New York, NY 10036. TEL 212-302-6740.
FAX 212-302-7574. Ed. Andrew Woznicki. **Document type:** academic/scholarly publication, monographic series.

282   UK   ISSN 1351-7945
CATHOLIC TIMES. 1993. w. £0.40. Gabriel Communications, St. James's Bldg., 1st Fl., Oxford St., Manchester M1 6FP, England. Ed. Norman Cresswell. (also avail. in broadsheet format) **Document type:** newspaper.

282 051   US   ISSN 0745-6050
CATHOLIC TIMES (COLUMBUS). 1951. w. $18. Catholic Times, Inc., Box 636, Columbus, OH 43216.
TEL 614-224-5195. Ed. Fr. Kessler. adv. contact: Jim Fath. bk.rev.; film rev. circ. 32,145. (tabloid format; also avail. in microfilm; magnetic tape; back issues avail.) **Document type:** newspaper.
    Description: Newspaper of the Diocese of Columbus.

282   US
CATHOLIC TIMES (LANSING). 1991. w. $21.75. G.L.S. Diocesan Reports, Inc., 1520 Court St., Saginan, MI 48602. TEL 810-767-6525. Ed. Barbara Kelley. adv.; bk.rev. circ. 8,500. **Document type:** newspaper.

282   US
CATHOLIC TIMES (SPRINGFIELD).* (Supplements avail.) 1896. w. $11. Diocese of Springfield, Illinois, Box 3187, Springfield, IL 62708-3187.
TEL 217-523-4469. Ed. Ed Wojcicki. adv. contact: Carol Durbin. bk.rev. circ. 43,500. (tabloid format) **Document type:** newspaper.

282   US
CATHOLIC TRANSCRIPT. 1896. w. $25. Catholic Transcript, Inc., 785 Asylum Ave., Hartford, CT 06105-2886. TEL 203-527-1175;
800-726-2391. FAX 203-947-6397. Ed. Rev. John P. Gatzak; Pub. Rev. Daniel Cronin. adv. contact: Roy Rowland. bk.rev.; circ. 15,000 (paid). (tabloid format; also avail. in microfilm) **Document type:** newsletter.

282   US   ISSN 0273-6136
CATHOLIC TWIN CIRCLE.* 1965. w. $49.95 (Canada $65). Twin Circle Publishing Co., 15760 Ventura Blvd., Ste. 1201, Encino, CA 91436-3002.
TEL 800-421-3230. FAX 213-655-0344. Ed. Loretta Seyer. adv.; bk.rev.; film rev.; play rev.; illus. circ. 30,000. (tabloid format)
    Former titles: Catholic Twin Circle Weekly Magazine; Twin Circle Weekly Catholic Magazine; Twin Circle (ISSN 0041-4654)

282   US   ISSN 0162-7023
CATHOLIC UNIVERSE BULLETIN. 1873. bi-w. $21 (effective Jan. 1996). Catholic Universe Bulletin Pub. Co., Inc., 1027 Superior Ave., Cleveland, OH 44114-2556. TEL 216-696-6525.
FAX 216-696-6519. Ed. Patrick Hyland. adv. contact: David Sarosy. film rev.; circ. 40,000 (paid). (tabloid format) **Document type:** newspaper.
    Description: Contains world news and religious happenings, a recipe column, and church and social news.

CATHOLIC UNIVERSITY LAW REVIEW. see *LAW*

282   US
CATHOLIC UPDATE. m. $9. (Franciscan Friars of St. John the Baptist Province) St. Anthony Messenger Press, 1615 Republic St., Cincinnati, OH 45210.
TEL 513-241-5615. FAX 513-241-0399. Ed. Rev. Jack Wintz. circ. 200,000. **Document type:** newsletter.
    Description: Covers Roman Catholic concerns and practices.

282   US   ISSN 0008-8404
CATHOLIC VIRGINIAN. 1946. w. $10. Diocese of Richmond, c/o Most. Rev. Walter F. Sullivan, Bishop of Richmond, 800 Cathedral Pl., Box 26843, Richmond, VA 23261. TEL 804-359-5654. Ed. Charles E. Mahon. adv.; bk.rev.; film rev.; charts; illus. circ. 38,827. (tabloid format) **Document type:** newspaper.

266   GH   ISSN 0008-8412
CATHOLIC VOICE. 1926. m. $72. (Archdiocese of Cape Coast) Catholic Mission Press, Box 60, Cape Coast, Ghana. Ed. Rev. Gabriel D. Mensah. illus. circ. 6,000. **Indexed:** CERDIC.

282   US   ISSN 0744-9585
CATHOLIC VOICE. 1903. fortn. $17.50. (Catholic Archbishop of Omaha, Nebraska) Catholic Voice Publishing Co., 6060 N.W. Radial Highway, Box 4010, Omaha, NE 68104. TEL 402-558-6611.
FAX 402-558-6614. Ed. Stephen M. Kent. adv. contact: Jeff Quandt. bk.rev. circ. 69,023. (tabloid format; also avail. in microfiche; back issues avail.) **Document type:** newspaper.

282   US   ISSN 0279-0645
CATHOLIC VOICE. 1963. bi-w. $8. Diocese of Oakland, 2918 Lake Shore Ave., Oakland, CA 94610.
TEL 510-893-4711. Ed. Monica Clark. adv. contact: Tim Holden. bk.rev. circ. 92,500. (tabloid format) **Document type:** newspaper.

282   US   ISSN 1045-7496
CATHOLIC WEEK. 1934. w. $12 inside diocese; outside diocese $15. Box 349, Mobile, AL 36601.
TEL 205-432-3529. FAX 205-434-1547. Ed. Larry G. Wahl. adv.; bk.rev. circ. 14,300. (tabloid format) **Document type:** newspaper.

282   AT   ISSN 0008-8420
CATHOLIC WEEKLY. 1942. w. Aus.$46. Catholic Press Newspaper Co. Pty. Ltd., 2nd Fl., Mary Potter Wing, Ozaman Village, Cnr West & Thomas Sts., Lewisham, N.S.W. 2049, Australia.
TEL 02-550-9411. FAX 02-560-0542. Ed. Phil Pearman. adv.; bk.rev.; illus. circ. 19,000. **Document type:** newspaper.
    Description: Catholic family newspaper. Includes international, national and local news.

RELIGIONS AND THEOLOGY — ROMAN CATHOLIC

282   US   ISSN 0008-8439
CATHOLIC WEEKLY. 1942. w. $21.75. Catholic Dioceses of Saginaw & Gaylord, 1520 Court St., Box 1405, Saginaw, MI 48605. TEL 517-793-7661. FAX 517-793-7663. Ed. Kathleen Socha. adv. contact: Jean Milburn. bk.rev. circ. 12,600. (back issues avail.) **Document type:** newspaper.
   Description: Coverage of current local, national and world news from a Catholic perspective.

282   US   ISSN 0008-8447
CATHOLIC WITNESS. 1966. fortn. $9 to non-parish members. (Diocese of Harrisburg) Harrisburg Catholic Publishing Associates, Box 2555, 4800 Union Deposit Rd., Harrisburg, PA 17105. TEL 717-657-4804. FAX 717-657-7673. Ed. Rev. T.R. Haney. bk.rev.; illus. circ. 68,000. (also avail. in microfilm) **Document type:** newspaper.
   Description: Regional, national and international news of religious events.

322.1 282   US   ISSN 0008-8463
BX801
CATHOLIC WORKER. 1933. 7/yr. $0.25. Catholic Worker Movement, 36 E. First St., New York, NY 10003. TEL 212-777-9617. Ed. Jennifer Belisle. bk.rev. circ. 89,000. (tabloid format; also avail. in microform from UMI) **Indexed:** Alt.Press Ind., Cath.Ind., Peace Res.Abstr.
—UMI.

282   US   ISSN 0008-8471
CATHOLIC WORKMAN. vol.63, 1970. m. $5 to non-members. Box 47, New Prague, MN 56071. TEL 612-758-2229. FAX 612-758-6221. Ed. Mae Dvorak. stat.; circ. 8,500 (controlled). (tabloid format) **Document type:** newspaper.
   Description: Covers religious articles, news and activity calendar.
   Refereed Serial

282   US   ISSN 1042-3494
AP2
THE CATHOLIC WORLD. 1865. bi-m. $12. (Missionary Society of St. Paul the Apostle in the State of New York) Paulist Press, 997 Macarthur Blvd., Mahwah, NJ 07430. TEL 201-825-7300. FAX 201-825-8345. Ed. Laurie Felknor. bk.rev.; index. circ. 6,000. (also avail. in microform from UMI,PMC; reprint service avail. from UMI) **Indexed:** Access (1980-), Amer.Hist.& Life, Bk.Rev.Ind. (1965-), Cath.Ind., CERDIC, Chic.Per.Ind., Child.Bk.Rev.Ind. (1965-), G.Soc.Sci.& Rel.Per.Lit., Hist.Abstr., Mag.Ind., Mid.East: Abstr.& Ind., R.G. **Document type:** consumer publication.
●Also available online. Vendor(s): Information Access Co., University Microfilms International.
Also available on CD-ROM. Producer(s): University Microfilms International.
—Faxon; UMI; UnCover.
   Former titles: New Catholic World; Catholic World (ISSN 0008-848X)
   Description: Thematic coverage of key religious questions from different perspectives.

282   GW   ISSN 0008-8501
CATHOLICA; vierteljahresschrift fuer Oekumenische Theologie. 4/yr. DM.76. (Johann Adam Moehler-Institut Paderborn) Aschendorffsche Verlagsbuchhandlung, Soesterstr. 13, 48155 Muenster, Germany. TEL 0251-690-0. FAX 0251-690143. Eds. Hans Joerg Urban, Peter Blaeser. adv.; bk.rev.; bibl.; index. **Indexed:** New Test.Abstr., Rel.& Theol.Abstr. (1989-), Rel.Ind.One, Rel.Per. **Document type:** academic/scholarly publication.
—CCC.

282   FR
CATHOLICISME HIER, AUJOURD'HUI, DEMAIN. 1935. irreg. (approx. 3/yr.) 150 F. per vol. Letouzey et Ane Editeurs, 87 bd. Raspail, 75006 Paris, France. TEL 45-48-80-14. Ed.Bd.

282   CN   ISSN 0843-2538
CELEBRATE. 1940. bi-m. Can.$23($24.95) Novalis, St. Paul University, 223 Main St., Ottawa, ON K1S 1C4, Canada. TEL 613-236-1393.
FAX 613-782-3004. (Subscr. to: 49 Front St., E., 2nd Fl., Toronto, ON M5E 1B3, Canada. TEL 416-363-3303) Ed. Bernadette Gasslein. **Document type:** academic/scholarly publication.
   Formerly: Homiletic Service (ISSN 0381-7466)
   Description: For catechists, religion teachers, homilists and liturgy planners.

200   US   ISSN 0094-2421
CELEBRATION: A CREATIVE WORSHIP SERVICE. Key Title: Celebration (Kansas City). 1970. m. $64.95. National Catholic Reporter Publishing Company, Inc., 115 E. Armour Blvd., Box 414281, Kansas City, MO 64141. TEL 816-531-0538; 800-333-7373. Ed. William Freburger. adv.; bk.rev. circ. 10,500. (looseleaf format)
   Description: Resource packet for complete liturgy planning.

282   FR   ISSN 0240-4656
CELEBRER. (Supplements avail.) 10/yr. 215 F. (foreign 250 F.). (Centre National de Pastorale Liturgique) Editions du Cerf, 29 bd. Latour Maubourg, 75340 Paris Cedex 07, France. TEL 44-18-12-12. FAX 45-56-04-27. (Subscr. to: Service Abonnements, 3 chemin des Prunais, 94350 Villiers-sur-Marne, France)

CELEBRIAMO; rivista bimestrale di musica vocale per la liturgia. see MUSIC

CENTRE CATHOLIQUE DES INTELLECTUELS FRANCAIS. RECHERCHES ET DEBATS. see HUMANITIES: COMPREHENSIVE WORKS

CENTRUM JANA PAWLA II BIULETYN. see BIOGRAPHY

282   XV   ISSN 0009-0387
CERKEV V SEDANJEM SVETU. 1967. bi-m. 420 SLT($20) Slovenske Rimskokatoliske Skofije, Cankarjevo Nabrezje 3, 6100 Ljubljana, Slovenia. TEL 061-329-793. FAX 061-116152. TELEX 31776 DRUNA YU. Ed. Rafko Valencic. bk.rev.; bibl. circ. 2,500.

282   US
CHAP-LETT. 3/yr. $15. American Catholic Correctional Chaplains, Box 888, Ashland, KY 41101. TEL 606-928-6414. Ed. Rev. John P. Noe. circ. 350.

230.205   US   ISSN 0009-3718
BX801
CHICAGO STUDIES. 1962. 3/yr. $17.50. (Civitas Dei) Liturgy Training Publications, 1800 N. Hermitage Avenue, Chicago, IL 60622. TEL 312-486-8970. FAX 800-933-7094. Ed. Rev. George J. Dyer. adv.; bk.rev.; index. circ. 2,000. (also avail. in microform from UMI; reprint service avail. from UMI) **Indexed:** Canon Law Abstr., Cath.Ind., CERDIC, New Test.Abstr., Old Test.Abstr., Rel.& Theol.Abstr. (1979-).
—BLDSC (3172.730000); UMI.

282   GW   ISSN 0170-5148
CHRIST IN DER GEGENWART. 1948. w. DM.91. Verlag Herder GmbH und Co. KG, Hermann-Herder-Str. 4, 79104 Freiburg, Germany. TEL 0761-2717-276. FAX 0761-2717-407. Ed. Manfred Plate. index. circ. 36,000. (looseleaf format; back issues avail.) **Document type:** newsletter.

282 266   IT   ISSN 0011-1465
CHRIST TO THE WORLD/CHRIST AU MONDE; international review of Apostolic experiences. (Editions in English, French) 1955. 5/yr. L.35000($30) Christ to the World, Via di Propaganda 1c, 00187 Rome, Italy. TEL 06-6793226. Dir. Fr. Massimiliano M. Zangheratti. bk.rev. **Indexed:** Cath.Ind., CERDIC.

CHRISTELIJK OOSTEN. see RELIGIONS AND THEOLOGY

282   GW   ISSN 0930-5718
CHRISTEN HEUTE; Zeitung der Alt-Katholiken fuer Christen heute. 1873; N.S. 1956. m. DM.44. Katholisches Bistum der Alt-Katholiken in Deutschland, Gregor-Mendel-Str. 28, 53115 Bonn, Germany. TEL 0228-232285. (Subscr. to: Christen Heute, Postfach 27, 25843 Nordstrand, Germany. FAX 04842-1511) bk.rev. (back issues avail.) **Document type:** bulletin.
   Formerly: Alt-Katholiken Kirchenzeitung (ISSN 0002-6522)

CHRISTIAN CHALLENGE. see RELIGIONS AND THEOLOGY — Protestant

282   US   ISSN 0739-6422
CHRISTIAN LIFE COMMUNITIES HARVEST. 1967. q. $18. National Christian Life Community of the United States of America, 3601 Lindell Blvd., No. 421, St. Louis, MO 63108-3393. TEL 314-977-7370. Ed. Dorothy Zambito. adv.; bk.rev.; index. circ. 1,000. (back issues avail.) **Document type:** academic/scholarly publication.
—CCC.
   Formerly: Christian Life Communicator.

200   PK   ISSN 0009-5699
CHRISTIAN VOICE; a weekly newspaper and review. (Text in English) 1950. w. Rs.25. Archdiocese of Karachi, St. Patrick's High School, Sangster Rd., Saddar, Karachi 0328, Pakistan. Ed. Fr. Augustine P. Varkey. adv.; bk.rev.; bibl.; illus. circ. 1,200. **Document type:** newspaper.

CHRISTLICHE FRAU. see WOMEN'S INTERESTS

268 282   GW   ISSN 0009-5818
CHRISTOPHORUS. 1955. q. DM.50. Egenhoferstr. 16, 81243 Munich, Germany. TEL 089-887857. FAX 089-8349481. Ed. Klaus Goebel. adv.; bk.rev.; charts. **Document type:** newsletter.

200   FR   ISSN 0009-5834
CHRISTUS; revue de formation spirituelle. 1954. q. 195 F. (foreign 230 F.). Assas Editions, 14 rue d'Assas, 75006 Paris, France. TEL 44-39-48-48. FAX 40-49-01-92. Ed. C. Flipo. adv. circ. 6,000. **Indexed:** CERDIC, Refug.Abstr.

282   US   ISSN 1041-1984
CHRONICLE OF CATHOLIC LIFE. 1943. bi-m. $10. Bishop of Pueblo, Diocese of Pueblo, 1001 N. Grand Ave., Pueblo, CO 81003. TEL 719-544-9861. FAX 719-544-5202. Ed. John Pearring. adv. contact: Joanne Pearring. bk.rev. circ. 29,000. (tabloid format) **Document type:** newsletter.
   Formerly (until 1988): Catholic Crosswinds (ISSN 0888-1464)

282   PL   ISSN 0578-0594
CHRZESCIJANSKIE STOWARZYSZENIE SPOLECZNE. INFORMATION BULLETIN. (Text in English, French and German) 1957. m. $12 or on exchange basis. Chrzescijanskie Stowarzyszenie Spoleczne - Christian Social Association, Marszalkowska 4, 00-590 Warsaw, Poland. (Dist. by: RSW "Prasa-Ksiazka-Ruch" Centrala Kolportazu Prasy i Wydawnictw, Towarowa 28, 00-958 Warsaw) Ed.Bd. adv. circ. 950.

282   PL
CHRZESCIJANSKIE STOWARZYSZENIE SPOLECZNE. MATERIALY PROBLEMOWE. 1965. m. $10. Chrzescijanskie Stowarzyszenie Spoleczne - Christian Social Association, Marszalkowska 4, 00-590 Warsaw, Poland. Ed. Jan Pawel Henne. adv. circ. 5,000.

200 282   US   ISSN 0883-5667
CHURCH. 1985. q. $26. National Pastoral Life Center, 299 Elizabeth St., New York, NY 10012-2806. TEL 212-431-7825. FAX 212-274-9786. Ed. Karen Sue Smith. adv. contact: Mary Good. bk.rev.; circ. 8,600 (paid). (back issues avail.) **Document type:** trade publication.
   Description: For Catholic pastoral ministers. Publishes articles on theology, moral issues, scripture, liturgy, parish and staff administration, religious education, spirituality, and practical examples of successful parish programs.

CHURCH MESSENGER/CERKOVNYJ VISTNIK. see RELIGIONS AND THEOLOGY — Eastern Orthodox

282   UK   ISSN 0009-6482
CHURCH OBSERVER. 1948. 3/yr. £1 per no. (Church Union) Church Literature Association, Faith House, 7 Tufton St., London SW1P 3QN, England. TEL 0181-805-5107. FAX 0181-292-4520. Ed. Geoffrey Wright. adv.; bk.rev.; illus. circ. 8,000. (also avail. in microfilm from UMI) **Indexed:** CERDIC.
   Description: Catholics in the Church of England.

200   SP   ISSN 0210-0398
BX805
CIENCIA TOMISTA. 1910. 3/yr. $50 (effective 1996). Facultad Teologica de San Esteban, Convento de San Esteban, Apdo. 17, 37080 Salamanca, Spain. TEL 2150000. FAX 923-26-54-80. Ed. Luis Lago. bk.rev. circ. 700. **Indexed:** Cath.Ind., CERDIC, M.L.A. **Document type:** academic/scholarly publication.

RELIGIONS AND THEOLOGY — ROMAN CATHOLIC

CISTERCIENSER CHRONIK. see *ARCHITECTURE*

271   BE   ISSN 0774-4919
BX3401
CITEAUX; commentarii cistercienses. (Bibliographic supplement avail: Bulletin d'Histoire Cistercienne (ISSN 0777-3331)) (Text in Dutch, English, French, German, Italian, Portuguese, Spanish; summaries in English, French, German) 1950. 2/yr. $48 (effective 1995). Citeaux V.Z.W., Abdij O.L.Vr. van Nazareth, Abdijlaan 9, 2960 Brecht, Belgium. Ed. Terryl N. Kinder. bk.rev.; bibl.; illus.; index, cum.index: 1950-1974. (also avail. in microfiche) **Indexed:** Amer.Hist.& Life, Hist.Abstr., M.L.A. **Document type:** academic/scholarly publication.
    Description: Publishes articles concerning all aspects and periods of Cistercian history, art, archeology, law, economy, liturgy and spirituality.

271   BE
CITEAUX. COLLECTION STUDIA ET DOCUMENTA. irreg., latest 1995. price varies. Citeaux V.Z.W., Abdij O.L.Vr. van Nazareth, Abdijlaan 9, B-2960 Brecht, Belgium. (back issues avail.) **Document type:** monographic series.
    Description: Scholarly editions of texts and documents pertaining to the Cistercian order.

271   BE
CITEAUX. COLLECTION TEXTES ET DOCUMENTS. 1988. irreg., latest 1995. price varies. Citeaux V.Z.W., Abdij O.L.Vr. van Nazareth, Abdijlaan 9, B-2960 Brecht, Belgium. (back issues avail.) **Document type:** monographic series, proceedings.
    Description: Scholarly examinations of texts and issues in Cistercian history and life.

282 255   SP   ISSN 0009-7756
CIUDAD DE DIOS; revista Agustiniana. 1881. 3/yr. 4300 ptas.($52) (effective 1994). Ediciones Escurialenses, Real Monasterio del Escorial, 28200 San Lorenzo del Escorial, Madrid, Spain. TEL 91-890-50-11. FAX 91-890-54-21. bk.rev.; index. circ. 700. (also avail. in microfilm from UMI) **Indexed:** Amer.Hist.& Life, CERDIC, Hist.Abstr., M.L.A., New Test.Abstr.
    Description: Contains manuscripts on religion, philosophy and history.

282   IT   ISSN 0009-8167
AP37
CIVILTA CATTOLICA. 1850. s-m. L.80000($110) Compagnia di Gesu, Via di Porta Pinciana 1, 00187 Rome, Italy. TEL 39-6-6798351. FAX 39-6-69940997. Ed. Gian Paolo Salvini. adv.: page L.2000000; adv. contact: Giovanni Marchesi. bk.rev.; film rev.; play rev.; bibl.; index, cum.index: 1940-1960, 1960-1970, 1970-1980, 1980-1990, 1980-1990. circ. 20,000. **Indexed:** Amer.Hist.& Life, Cath.Ind., CERDIC, Hist.Abstr., Int.Polit.Sci.Abstr., New Test.Abstr.
    —SWETS.

282   VC   ISSN 0578-4182
CLARETIANUM; commentaria theologica. (Text in various European languages) 1961. a. L.50000($35) (effective Oct. 1994). Institutum Theologiae Vitae Religiosae, Largo Lorenzo Mossa 4, 00165 Rome, Italy. TEL 39-6-66-38-981. FAX 39-6-66-36-713. Ed. Bruno Proietti. bk.rev.; bibl. circ. 300. **Indexed:** Canon Law Abstr., CERDIC. **Document type:** academic/scholarly publication.
    Formerly (until 1993): Theologica.

282   MH
CLARIM. 1948. w. P.300. Diocese of Macau, Rua Central, 26 A, Macao. TEL 573860. FAX 307867. Ed. Albino Bento Pais. adv. contact: Mr. Pau. circ. 1,100. cols./p.: 6; pp./issue: 24. (tabloid format) **Document type:** newspaper.
    Description: Covers religion, education, social assistance, and government.

282   US
CLARION HERALD. (Supplements avail.) 1963. bi-w. $12 (out of state $14) (effective Jun. 1994). (Archdiocese of New Orleans) Clarion Herald Publishing Co., 1000 Howard Ave., Ste. 400, New Orleans, LA 70113. TEL 504-524-1618. FAX 504-596-3020. Ed. Peter Finney, Jr. adv. contact: Maureen Austin. bk.rev. circ. 56,048. (tabloid format; also avail. in microfilm) **Document type:** newspaper.

CLUBHOUSE. see *CHILDREN AND YOUTH — For*

282   IT
CODICE DEL VATICANO II. 1984. irreg. Centro Editoriale Dehoniano, Via Nosadella 6, 40123 Bologna, Italy. TEL 051-306811. FAX 051-341706.

282   SP
COLECCION HISTORIA DE LA IGLESIA. 1971. irreg., no.24, 1990. price varies. (Universidad de Navarra, Departamento de Historia de la Iglesia) Ediciones Universidad de Navarra, S.A., Apdo. 396, 31080 Pamplona, Spain. TEL 92 825 6850.

282   SP
COLECCION TEOLOGICA. 1970. irreg., no.69, 1990. price varies. (Universidad de Navarra, Facultad de Teologia) Ediciones Universidad de Navarra, S.A., Apdo. 396, 31080 Pamplona, Spain. TEL 94 825 6850.

282   SP
COLEGIO MAYOR P. FELIPE SCIO. PUBLICACIONES. 1975. irreg. price varies. Ediciones Calasancias, Paseo de Canalejas 75, Apdo. 206, Salamanca, Spain.

282   IT   ISSN 0069-5254
COLLANA RICCIANA. FONTI. 1963. irreg., no.12, 1975. price varies. Casa Editrice Leo S. Olschki, Casella Postale 66, 50100 Florence, Italy. TEL 39-55-6530684. FAX 39-55-6530214. Ed. P. di Agresti. circ. 1,000. **Document type:** monographic series.

282   IT   ISSN 0394-7769
COLLATIONES MARIALES INSTITUTI CARMELITANI. (Text in English, French, German, Italian, Latin and Spanish) 1960. irreg. price varies. (Order of Carmelites) Edizioni Carmelitane, Via Sforza Pallavicini 10, 00193 Rome, Italy. TEL 06-66803513. FAX 06-68307200. adv. circ. 500. **Document type:** monographic series.

282   VC
COLLECTANEA ARCHIVI VATICANI. 1970. irreg., no.38, 1995. price varies. Archivio Segreto Vaticano, 00120 Vatican City (Rome), State of the Vatican City. TEL 39-6-698-83595.

COLLECTANEA BIBLIOGRAPHICA CARMELITANA. see *BIBLIOGRAPHIES*

271   BE   ISSN 0378-4916
COLLECTANEA CISTERCIENSIA; revue trimestrielle de spiritualite monastique. (Text in French) 1934. q. 1000 BEF($30) (£21) (effective 1996). Abbaye N.D. de Soleilmont, B-6220 Fleurus, Belgium. (U.S. subscr. to: Sr. Sheryl Frances Chen, Santa Rita Abbey, HC 1 Box 929, Sonoita, AZ 85637-9705; U.K. subscr. to: Fr. Peter Claver Craddy, Mt. St. Bernard Abbey, Coalville, Leicester LE67 5UL, England) bk.rev.; bibl.; cum.index: 1934-1988. (also avail. in microform from UMI; back issues avail.) **Indexed:** Cath.Ind., CERDIC. **Document type:** academic/scholarly publication.
    —BLDSC (3299.400000); SWETS.
    Description: Publishes studies on the various monastic traditions, both oriental and occidental, information pertaining to the dialogue between Christian and non-Christian monasticism, and reports on events in the monastic world, including congresses, meetings, and relevant publications.

271   IT   ISSN 0010-0749
COLLECTANEA FRANCISCANA. (Annual supplement: Bibliographia Franciscana) (Text in English, French, German, Italian, Latin, Portuguese and Spanish) 1931. q. L.70000 (foreign L.85000($70)) (effective 1995). Frati Minori Cappuccini, Istituto Storico, Casella Postale 18283, Circonv. Occidentale 6850 (GRA km 65), Rome, Italy. TEL FAX 39-6-66151958. FAX 39-6-6262401. Ed. Vincenzo Criscuolo. bk.rev.; bibl.; index, cum.index: 1931-1970. circ. 800. **Indexed:** CERDIC.
    —SWETS.

266   US   ISSN 0095-4438
BV3410
COLUMBAN MISSION. 1918. 8/yr. $10. (St. Columban's Foreign Mission Society) Columban Fathers, St. Columbans, NE 68056. FAX 402-291-8693. Ed. Rev. Richard Steinhilber; Pub. Rev. Brendan O'Sullivan. adv. contact: William Zuerlein. bk.rev. circ. 100,000 (controlled).
    Formerly: Columban Fathers Mission.

282 249   US   ISSN 0010-1869
AP2
COLUMBIA (NEW HAVEN); America's largest Catholic family magazine. 1921. m. $6 (foreign $8). Knights of Columbus, 1 Columbus Plaza, New Haven, CT 06510-3326. TEL 203-772-2130. FAX 203-777-0114. Ed. Richard McMunn. adv.; bk.rev.; index. circ. 1,500,000. **Indexed:** Cath.Ind.
    Description: Provides features and columns demonstrating how groups and families can cooperate to improve society.

266   US   ISSN 0279-3652
COMBONI MISSIONS. 1948. q. $6. Comboni Missionaries of the Heart of Jesus, 8108 Beechmont Ave., Cincinnati, OH 45255. TEL 513-474-4997. FAX 513-474-0382. Ed. Jose Marques. illus.; circ. 25,000 (controlled).
    Former titles: Verona Missions (ISSN 0164-4211); Verona Fathers Missions (ISSN 0042-4234).
    Description: Informs readers about Third World situations and about the congregation's mission work.

262.9   IT   ISSN 0010-2598
COMMENTARIUM PRO RELIGIOSIS ET MISSIONARIIS. 1920. q. L.50000 (foreign L.55000). Institutum Iuridicum Claretianum - Claretian Juridical Institute, Via Giacomo Medici 5, 00153 Rome, Italy. Ed. Giuseppe Metteocci. bk.rev.; bibl.; index. circ. 5,000. (back issues avail.) **Indexed:** Canon Law Abstr., CERDIC.
    Description: Discusses canon law.

COMMONWEAL. see *LITERARY AND POLITICAL REVIEWS*

282 659.2   GW   ISSN 0010-3497
COMMUNICATIO SOCIALIS; Zeitschrift fuer Publizistik in Kirche und Welt. (Text in German; summaries in English, French and Spanish) 1968-1988; resumed. q. DM.60 (students DM.48) (effective 1996). Matthias Gruenewald Verlag GmbH, Max-Hufschmidt-Str. 4a, 55130 Mainz, Germany. TEL 06131-839055. FAX 06131-834322. Ed. Dr. Franz-Josef Eilers. adv. contact: Andrea Buchauer. bk.rev.; film rev. **Indexed:** CERDIC, Lang.& Lang.Behav.Abstr., So.Pac.Per.Ind. **Document type:** academic/scholarly publication.
    —CCC.
    Description: Catholic publication dealing with mass media and religion, the Catholic press, and communication in theology. Includes list of book and magazine references.

282   VC   ISSN 0393-0327
COMMUNICATIONES. Key Title: Communicationes - Pontificia Codici Iuris Canonici Recognoscendo. 1969. s-a. L.38000 (foreign L.48000($39)) (effective 1996). (Pontificia Commissio Codici Iuris Canonici Recognoscendo) Libreria Editrice Vaticana, 00120 Vatican City (Rome), State of the Vatican City. **Indexed:** Canon Law Abstr., Cath.Ind., CERDIC.
    Description: Organ of the Pontifical Commission for the right interpretation of the Code of Canon Law.

282   US   ISSN 0094-2065
BX801
COMMUNIO; international Catholic review. 1974. q. $23 to individuals (foreign $29); institutions $33 (effective 1995). Communio, Inc., Box 4557, Washington, IN 20017-0557. TEL 202-526-0251. FAX 202-526-1934. Ed. David L. Schindler. adv. contact: David D. Spesia. index, cum.index. circ. 2,700. (also avail. in microform from UMI; back issues avail.; reprint service avail. from UMI) **Indexed:** Cath.Ind., Old Test.Abstr., Rel.& Theol.Abstr. (1979-), Rel.Ind.One. **Document type:** academic/scholarly publication.
    —BLDSC (3363.543600); UMI.
    Description: Journal of theological and cultural reflection from a Catholic perspective by noted theologians, philosophers, and other scholars.
    Refereed Serial

282   CN
COMPANION MAGAZINE; to inspire today's catholics. 1937. m. (except Jul.-Aug. combined). Can.$16($17) Conventual Franciscan Friars, Box 535, Station "F", Toronto, ON M4Y 2L8, Canada. TEL 416-690-5611. FAX 416-690-3320. Ed. Rev. J. Richard Roccioli. adv.: B&W page Can.$350; trim 4 13/16 x 7 1/2; adv. contact: Mary-Rose Disimino. bk.rev.; illus. circ. 4,500.
    Formerly: Companion of St. Francis and St. Anthony (ISSN 0010-3985)

RELIGIONS AND THEOLOGY — ROMAN CATHOLIC

282 378 US ISSN 0886-1293
COMPANY; a magazine of the American Jesuits. 1983. q. free. 3441 N. Ashland Ave., Chicago, IL 60657. TEL 312-281-1534. FAX 312-281-2667. Ed. Martin McHugh. circ. 115,000 (controlled).

230.05 AT ISSN 1036-9686
COMPASS; a review of topical theology. 1967. q. Aus.$20 (efective 1995 & 1996). (Missionaries of the Sacred Heart) Chevalier Press, P.O. Box 13, Kensington, N.S.W. 2033, Australia. TEL 61-2-6627894. FAX 61-2-6621910. Ed. Fr. Peter Malone. bk.rev. circ. 1,500. **Document type:** academic/scholarly publication.
  Former titles (until 1990): Compass Theology Review (ISSN 0819-4602); (until 1973): Compass (ISSN 0311-1210).

282 SP
COMUNIDAD 2000; semanario de la Iglesia Diocesana, Salamanca. 1971. w. 2500 ptas. (effective 1995). Iglesia Diocesana, Iscar Peyra, 26, Obispado, 37002 Salamanca, Spain. TEL 34-23-218205. Ed. Manuel Cuesta Palomero. circ. 6,000 (controlled).

282 IT
COMUNITA E STORIA. 1974. bi-m. L.15000($10) Comunita e Storia, Via Mazzini 6a, 52100 Arezzo, Italy. Ed. Maria Grotti. bk.rev. circ. 500.

282 IT
CONFERENZA ITALIANA SUPERIORI MAGGIORI. NOTIZIARIO. 1960. bi-m. free. Conferenza Italiana Superiori Maggiori, Via degli Scipioni, 256B, 00192 Rome, Italy.

CONGREGATIONS: THE ALBAN JOURNAL; resources for people who care about congregations. see *RELIGIONS AND THEOLOGY — Protestant*

282 305 US ISSN 0740-6835
CONSCIENCE (WASHINGTON); a news journal of prochoice Catholic opinion. 1980. q. $10 (free to libraries). Catholics for a Free Choice, 1436 U St., N.W., Ste. 301, Washington, DC 20009-3997. Ed. Maggie Hume. adv.; bk.rev.; illus. circ. 10,000.

282 US ISSN 0884-7010
CONSECRATED LIFE. 1975. s-a. $20. Institute on Religious Life, Box 41007, Chicago, IL 60641. TEL 312-267-1195. FAX 312-267-2044. Ed. Fr. James Downey, O.S.B. circ. 2,000. (back issues avail.) **Document type:** bulletin.
  Description: Contains news and notices of religious activities, and statements of the Holy Father pertinent to religious life and decisions.

248 US ISSN 0010-8685
CORD. 1951. m. $20. Franciscan Institute, St. Bonaventure University, St. Bonaventure, NY 14778. TEL 716-375-2105. Ed. Sr. Elise Saggau. adv.; bk.rev.; bibl.; illus. circ. 1,700. **Indexed:** CERDIC.

282 GW ISSN 0070-0320
BR302
CORPUS CATHOLICORUM. 1919. irreg. price varies. Aschendorffsche Verlagsbuchhandlung, Soesterstr. 13, 48155 Muenster, Germany. TEL 0251-690-0. FAX 0251-690143. Ed. Klaus Ganzer. **Document type:** monographic series.

282 BE
CORPUS CHRISTIANORUM. CONTINUATIO MEDIAEVALIS. 1966. irreg. (5-10/yr.), vol.144, 1994. (Abbey of Steenbrugge) N.V. Brepols, Steenweg op Tielen 68, 2300 Turnhout, Belgium. TEL 32-14-402500. FAX 32-14-428919. Ed.Bd. (back issues avail.) **Document type:** monographic series.
● Also available on CD-ROM.
  Description: Publishes critical editions of mediaeval Christian texts from the eight to the fifteenth century.

282 BE
CORPUS CHRISTIANORUM. SERIES APOCRYPHORUM. 1983. irreg., vol.7, 1993. (Association pour l'Etude de la Litterature Apocrypha Chretienne) N.V. Brepols, Steenweg op Tielen 68, 2300 Turnhout, Belgium. TEL 32-14-402500. FAX 32-14-428919. (back issues avail.) **Document type:** monographic series.
  Description: Publishes critical editions of New Testament apocrypha.

282 BE
CORPUS CHRISTIANORUM. SERIES LATINA. 1952. irreg. (6-7/yr.). (Abbey of Steenbrugge) N.V. Brepols, Steenweg op Tielen 68, B-2300 Turnhout, Belgium. TEL 32-14-402500. FAX 32-14-428919. Ed.Bd. (back issues avail.) **Document type:** monographic series.
● Also available on CD-ROM.

282 IT
COSCIENZA. 1946. m. L.20000. Movimento Ecclesiale di Impegno Culturale, Via della Conciliazione 1, 00193 Rome, Italy. Ed. Romolo Pietrobelli. bk.rev.; illus.; index. circ. 4,500. **Indexed:** CERDIC.

282 CH
COSTANTINIAN; magazine for mature Catholics. (Index in English) 1951. bi-m. NT.$350($12) 73 Linsen N. Rd., Taipei 10420, Taiwan, Republic of China. Ed. John H. Liu. circ. 1,000.

377.8 371.4 US ISSN 0160-7960
LC461 CODEN: COVADQ
COUNSELING AND VALUES. 1956. 3/yr. $18 to individuals; institutions $24 (effective 1996). (Association for Religious and Value Issues in Counseling) American Counseling Association, 5999 Stevenson Ave., Alexandria, VA 22304-3300. TEL 703-823-9800. FAX 703-823-0252. (Subscr. to: Box 2513, Birmingham, AL 35201-2513. TEL 205-995-1567. FAX 205-995-1588) Ed. M. Harry Daniels. adv.; bk.rev. (also avail. in microform from UMI; reprint service avail. from UMI) **Indexed:** C.I.J.E., Cath.Ind., Psychol.Abstr. (1971-), Soc.Work Res.& Abstr.
—BLDSC (3481.320000); Faxon; SWETS; UMI; UnCover. **CCC.**
  Formerly: National Catholic Guidance Conference Journal (ISSN 0027-8912)
  Description: Focused on the role of values and religion in counseling and psychology.

282 IT ISSN 1123-3281
CREDEREOGGI. bi-m. L.32000 (foreign L.43000) (effective 1995). Editrice Grafiche Messaggero Sant' Antonio, Via Orto Botanico, 11, 35123 Padua, Italy. TEL 39-49-8225000. FAX 39-49-8225650. TELEX 430855 MSA PD I. (Subscr. to: Basilica del Santo, 35123 Padua, Italy) Ed. Ugo Sartorio. circ. 3,000. (back issues avail.) **Document type:** monographic series.

282 US
CRISIS (WASHINGTON); a journal of lay Catholic opinion. 1982. 11/yr. $25 (foreign $36). Brownson Institute, Inc., 1511 K St., N.W., No.525, Washington, DC 20005. TEL 219-234-3759. (Subscr. to: Crisis, Box 1006, Notre Dame, IN 46556) Ed. Scott Walter. adv. contact: Dean Carignan. bk.rev. circ. 10,000.
  Supersedes (in 1986): Catholicism in Crisis (ISSN 0884-1705)

282 IT
CRISTIANESIMO OGGI. 1969. m. (10/yr.). L.5000. Editrice Lanterna, Via Robino 71-A.R., 16142 Genova, Italy. adv. circ. 5,000.

282 US ISSN 0574-4350
THE CRITERION (INDIANAPOLIS). 1960. w. $20. Archdiocese of Indianapolis, 1400 N. Meridian St., Indianapolis, IN 46202. TEL 317-236-1570. (Subscr. to: Box 1717, Indianapolis, IN 46206) Ed. John F. Fink. adv. contact: Reed Yadon. bk.rev.; circ. 54,226 (paid). **Document type:** newspaper.

CRITIC (CHICAGO); a Catholic review of culture and the arts. see *HUMANITIES: COMPREHENSIVE WORKS*

282 IT ISSN 0011-1651
CROCE. 1952. w. Curia Vescovile, 40022 Comacchio (Ferrara), Italy.

282 FR ISSN 0242-6056
CROIX; l'evenement. 1880. d. 2450 F. (outside EC 2990 F.). Bayard Presse, 3 rue Bayard, 75393 Paris Cedex 08, France. TEL 44-35-60-60. FAX 44-35-60-91. TELEX 648 094 F. (Subscr. to: B.P. 12, 99505 Paris Entreprises, France. TEL 46-30-38-00. FAX 46-30-31-67) circ. 120,000. (tabloid format) **Document type:** newspaper.
  Description: Covers bioethics, education, the environment, religious news from a Catholic perspective.

282 DM
CROIX DE BENIN. 1946. fortn. B.P. 105, Cotonou, Benin. TEL 32-11-19. Ed. Barthelemy Cakpo Assogba.

282 366 PH
CROSS; national Catholic magazine. (Text in English) 1945. bi-m. P.6($1) Knights of Columbus in the Philippines, P.O. Box 510, Manila, Philippines. Ed. Ben S. De Castro. adv.; bk.rev. circ. 51,000.
  Former titles (until 1988): Crossline; (until 1986): Cross.

282 CK
CUADERNOS DE TEOLOGIA Y PASTORAL.* irreg. Ediciones Paulinas, Transversal 40 A, No. 43, Apdo. 100383, Bogota, Colombia.

282 BL
CULTURA E FE. 1978. q. $20. Instituto de Desenvolvimento Cultural, Av. Alberto Bins 467, 90030-142 Porto Alegre RS, Brazil. TEL 55-21-2240496. bk.rev.
  Description: Review of culture from a Roman Catholic point of view.

CURRENT ISSUES IN CATHOLIC HIGHER EDUCATION. see *EDUCATION*

D K K F - NYT. (Dansk Katolsk Kvinde-Forbund) see *WOMEN'S INTERESTS*

282 IT
DALLO SCOGLIO DI SANTA RITA. 1940. m. Santuario di Santa Rita, Vicolo Sinibaldi 1, 00186 Rome, Italy. TEL 06-687-71-80. Dir. Luigi Di Giannicola. bk.rev.

282 US
DANICA; hrvatski tjednik. (Text in Croatian; summaries in Croatian and English) 1921. w. $30. (Croatian Center Association) Croatian Franciscan Press, 4851 Drexel Blvd., Chicago, IL 60615. TEL 312-268-2819. Ed. Fr. Castimir Majic. adv.; bk.rev. circ. 5,000. (tabloid format)

282 US ISSN 0011-6637
DARBININKAS. (Text in Lithuanian) 1915. w. $30. Franciscan Fathers, 341 Highland Blvd., Brooklyn, NY 11207. TEL 718-827-1352. FAX 718-827-2964. Ed. Rev. Dr. Cornelius Bucmys. adv.; bk.rev.

282 SP ISSN 1130-5207
DELTA (EDICION EN CASTELLANO). Catalan edition: Delta (Edicio en Catalan) (ISSN 1130-5223) 1961. q. 1500 ptas. Instituto Catolico de Estudios Sociales de Barcelona, Enrique Granados, 2, 08007 Barcelona, Apartado de Correos 5217, Spain. Ed. Maria Martinell. bk.rev.; abstr. circ. 2,700.
  Former titles (until 1989): Cuadernos de Orientacion Familiar (ISSN 0011-2453); (until 1969): Delta (ISSN 0210-3869)

282 GW ISSN 0933-0771
DIACONIA CHRISTI. 1966. q. DM.35. Internationales Diakonatszentrum, Postfach 9, 72101 Rottenburg, Germany. TEL 07472-169491. FAX 07472-169607. adv. contact: Albert Biesinger. bk.rev.; bibl. circ. 900. (back issues avail.) **Document type:** newsletter.
  Formerly (until 1987): Diaconia XP (ISSN 0343-3218)

282 IT ISSN 0391-545X
DIAGROUP. bi-m. L.110000 (foreign L.135000) (effective 1996). Editrice Elle Di Ci, Corso Francia 214, 10096 Leumann (Turin), Italy. TEL 39-11-9591091. FAX 39-11-9572900. (photographic slide format)

282 NQ
DIAKONIA; servicio de la fe y promocion de la justicia. 1977. q. $25. Centro Ignaciano de Centro America, Apartado C-31, Managua, 13, Nicaragua. circ. 600. (back issues avail.) **Indexed:** CERDIC.
  Description: Religious publication that aids those involved in religion. Looks at problematic aspects that Christianity and other religions face in Latin America. Includes articles, research and other writings of sprituality.

RELIGIONS AND THEOLOGY — ROMAN CATHOLIC

282 388.3 **GW**
DIASPORA - M I V A; Verkehrshilfe des Bonifatiuswerkes. 1949. s-a. free. Bonifatiuswerk der Deutschen Katholiken e.V., Postfach 1169, 33041 Paderborn, Germany. TEL 05251-29960. FAX 05251-299688. Ed. Michael Henn. circ. 50,000. (back issues avail.) **Document type:** newsletter.

282 **PO** ISSN 0253-1674
BR7
DIDASKALIA. (Text in various European languages; summaries in English and French) 1971. s-a. $30. (Universidade Catolica Portuguesa, Faculdade de Teologia) Didaskalia Editora, Palma de Cima, 1600 Lisbon, Portugal. TEL 726-8187. FAX 7260546. TELEX 65094 UNICAP P. bk.rev. circ. 1,000. **Indexed:** CERDIC, New Test.Abstr., Old Test.Abstr., Rel.& Theol.Abstr. (1990-).

DIGNITY - U S A. see *HOMOSEXUALITY*

200 **BE** ISSN 0012-2866
DIMANCHE. (Text in French) 1935. w. 750 BEF($20) 20 Place de Vannes, B-7000 Mons, Belgium. TEL 3265-352885. FAX 3265-346370. Ed. Fr. Charles Delhez. adv.; bk.rev.; film rev. circ. 475,000.
Description: Chain of parish-weeklies covering local news.

282 **US** ISSN 1072-7922
DIOCESAN DIALOGUE; a newsletter for television Mass producers. 1986. s-a. $5. American Catholic Press, 16565 S. State St., S. Holland, IL 60473. TEL 708-331-5485. Ed. Rev. Michael Gilligon. adv. contact: Joan Termini. circ. 750. (back issues avail.) **Document type:** newsletter.
Description: Includes news about the work of offices of communication in various Roman Catholic dioceses in the US, especially those that produce religious services on television.

282 **UK**
DIOCESAN DIRECTORY (CARLISLE). 1879. a. £3($6) Carlisle Diocesan Board of Finance, Church House, West Walls, Carlisle, Lancs. CA3 8UE, England. TEL 01228-22573. FAX 01228-48469. circ. 600 (paid). (looseleaf format) **Document type:** directory.

282 **AU**
DIOZESE GURK. JAHRBUCH/KRSKE SKOFIJE. ZBORNIK. (Text in German, Slovenian) 1979. a. S.80($5) Bischoefliches Gurker Ordinariat, Mariannengasse 2, A-9020 Klagenfurt, Austria. FAX 0463-57770-87. Ed.Bd. adv.; bk.rev. circ. 7,000. (back issues avail.) **Document type:** bulletin.

282 **GW** ISSN 0341-9975
DIOZESE HILDESHEIM IN VERGANGENHEIT UND GEGENWART. 1927. a. DM.30. (Verein fuer Geschichte und Kunst in Bistum Hildesheim e.V.) Bernward Verlag, Domhof 24, 31134 Hildesheim, Germany. TEL 05121-16920. bk.rev. circ. 1,100. (back issues avail.)

DIRECT. see *CHILDREN AND YOUTH — For*

282 **GW**
DIRECTORIUM FUER DAS BISTUM TRIER. LITURGISCHER KALENDER. biennial. Paulinus Verlag GmbH, Fleischstr. 62, Postfach 3040, 54290 Trier, Germany. TEL 0651-4604-162. circ. 450.

282 **US**
DIRECTORY OF CATHOLIC DIOCESE OF SPOKANE. biennial. Catholic Diocese of Spokane, Box 48, Spokane, WA 99210-0048. TEL 509-456-7140. FAX 509-456-7108. **Document type:** directory.

220 **CN** ISSN 0018-912X
DISCOVER THE BIBLE. French edition: Feuillet Biblique. 1964. w. Can.$22 (foreign Can.$36). Discover the Bible, P.O. Box 2400, London, ON N6A 4G3, Canada. TEL 519-439-7211. FAX 519-439-0207. Ed. Guy Lajoie. bk.rev.; bibl.; index. circ. 4,500. **Document type:** consumer publication.
Formerly: I Discover the Bible.

282 **VC** ISSN 0012-4222
BR1.A1
DIVINITAS. 1957. 3/yr. $20. Pontificia Accademia Teologica Romana, Piazza S. Giovanni in Laterano 4, 00184 Rome, Italy. adv.; bk.rev.; cum.index every 10 yrs. **Indexed:** New Test.Abstr., Rel.& Theol.Abstr. (1967-).
—BLDSC (3604.276000).

282 **IE** ISSN 0012-446X
DOCTRINE AND LIFE. 1951. 10/yr. I£29.80($47.46) Dominican Publications, 42 Parnell Sq., Dublin 1, Ireland. TEL 01-8721611. FAX 01-8731760. Ed. Rev. Bernard Treacy. adv.; bk.rev.; index. circ. 5,000. (also avail. in microfilm from UMI; reprint service avail. from UMI) **Indexed:** Cath.Ind., CERDIC, New Test.Abstr., Old Test.Abstr. **Document type:** bulletin.
—BLDSC (3608.030000); UMI.

282 **FR** ISSN 0012-4613
BX802
DOCUMENTATION CATHOLIQUE. English edition: Catholic International. 1919. s-m. 416 F. (outside EC 484 F.). Bayard Presse, 3 rue Bayard, 75393 Paris Cedex 08, France. TEL 44-35-60-60. FAX 44-35-60-91. TELEX 648 094 F. (Subscr. to: B.P. 12, 99505 Paris Entreprises, France. TEL 46-30-38-00. FAX 46-30-31-67) Ed. P. Claude Musnier. adv.; index. circ. 31,000. **Indexed:** Cath.Ind., CERDIC.
—SWETS.
Description: Presents church texts in their entirety as a source of inspiration for study, reflexion and meditation.

282 **GW**
DOM. 1946. a. DM.7.20. (St. Godehards Werk, Hildesheim) Bernward Verlag GmbH, Domhof 24, 31134 Hildesheim, Germany. TEL 05121-1692-0. circ. 6,000. (back issues avail.)

282 **IT** ISSN 0012-5288
DOMENICA. 1921. w. Viale Tunisi 43-C, 96100 Siracuse, Italy. Ed. Pino Filippelli.

282 **BL**
DOMINGO. (Supplements avail.) 1932. w. $100. (Pia Sociedade de Sao Paulo) Edicoes Paulinas, Via Raposo Tavares Km 18.5, C.P. 8107, 01051 Sao Paulo, Brazil. Ed. Virgilio Ciaccio. circ. 253,000.

282 255 **NE** ISSN 0012-5504
DOORTOCHT; schakel tussen mensen met een Franciscaanse visie. 1963. 6/yr. fl.22.50 (effective 1995). Franciscaanse Tijdschriften, Volendamlaan 22, 2547 CH The Hague, Netherlands. TEL 31-70-3673117. bk.rev.; illus. circ. 5,500.

282 **IT**
DOSSIER CATECHISTA. m. (9/yr.) L.12000 (foreign L.22000) (effective 1995). Editore Elle Di Ci, Corso Francia 214, 10096 Leuman (TO), Italy. TEL 39-11-9591091. FAX 39-11-9572900.

282 **UK** ISSN 0012-5806
BX801
DOWNSIDE REVIEW; a quarterly of Catholic thought. 1880. q. £20($38) Downside Abbey, Stratton on the Fosse, Bath, Avon BA3 4RH, England. Ed. Dom Daniel Rees. adv.; bk.rev.; index. circ. 600. (also avail. in microfiche; reprint service avail. from KTO) **Indexed:** Cath.Ind., CERDIC, M.L.A., New Test.Abstr., Old Test.Abstr., Rel.& Theol.Abstr. (1968-), Rel.Ind.One, Rel.Per.
—BLDSC (3620.100000); Faxon; SWETS; UnCover.

DRAUGAS. see *ETHNIC INTERESTS*

282 **XV** ISSN 0416-3885
DRUZINA/FAMILY; verski tednik - Catholic weekly. 1952. w. 1300 SLT($60) Slovenske Rimskokatoliske Skofije, P.P. 95, 61001 Ljubljana, Slovenia. TEL 061 329-793. FAX 061-116152. TELEX 31776 DRUNA YU. Ed. Janez Gril. circ. 100,000. (back issues avail.)

266 **PH** ISSN 0116-0257
EAST ASIAN PASTORAL REVIEW; a quarterly with focus on Asia for all church ministers and theology in context, interested laity and theological students. 1979. q. $12 (effective 1992). East Asian Pastoral Institute, Box 221, U.P. Campus, Quezon City 1101, Philippines. FAX 02-924-4359. Ed. Rev. Geoffrey King, S.J. bk.rev. circ. 2,000. **Indexed:** Cath.Ind., Ind.Phil.Per.
Formed by the merger of: Teaching All Nations (ISSN 0040-0564); Good Tidings (ISSN 0436-1571); Amen.

282 **US** ISSN 0894-9786
EASTERN CATHOLIC LIFE. 1965. bi-w. $10. Eastern Catholic Life Press Association, 445 Lackawanna Ave., W. Paterson, NJ 07424. TEL 201-890-7794. FAX 201-890-7175. adv.; bk.rev. circ. 12,017. (also avail. in microform) **Document type:** newspaper.

282 **US**
EASTERN OKLAHOMA CATHOLIC. 1974. bi-w. $20 (effective Apr. 1994). Diocese of Tulsa, Box 520, Tulsa, OK 74101. TEL 918-587-3115. FAX 918-587-6692. Ed. Meg Kaiser. circ. 7,500. (tabloid format) **Document type:** newspaper.

282 **FR** ISSN 0766-6101
EAUX - VIVES. 1941. m. 40 F. 21 bd. Voltaire, 75011 Paris, France. adv.; illus.

282 **SP** ISSN 0012-9038
ECCLESIA. 1941. w. 7000 ptas.($121) (effective Jan. 1993). Conferencia Episcopal Espanola, Alfonso 11, No. 4, 28014 Madrid, Spain. TEL 91-5315400. FAX 91-5225561. Ed. Jose Antonio Carro Celada. adv.; bk.rev.; film rev.; bibl.; charts; illus.; index. circ. 25,000. **Indexed:** CERDIC.
Description: Covers religious information and documentation.

282 **IT**
ECCLESIA MATER. 1963. 3/yr. L.20000 (foreign L.25000) (effective 1995). Istituto Suore Figlie della Chiesa, Viale Vaticano 62, 00165 Rome, Italy. TEL 39-6-39376638. Dir. Maria Teresa Sotgiu. bk.rev.; illus. circ. 3,500. **Document type:** academic/scholarly publication.
Incorporates: Mater Ecclesiae (ISSN 0025-522X)

282 **IT**
ECCO TUA MADRE. 6/yr. L.10000 (foreign L.15000). Santuario "S. Maria Greca", Corso Garibaldi, 55, 70033 Corato, Italy.
Description: Catholic newsletter featuring articles on events in the church, prayers and interviews with missionaries.

282 **GW** ISSN 0252-2527
ECHO DER LIEBE. Dutch edition: Echo der Liefde (ISSN 0252-2543); English edition: Mirror (ISSN 0252-2535); Spanish edition: Boletin (ISSN 0252-256X); French edition: Bulletin (ISSN 0252-2519) (Editions in various languages) 1959. bi-m. DM.2($5) Kirche in Not - Ostpriesterhilfe e.V., Postfach 1209, 61452 Koenigstein, Germany. TEL 06174-291-0. FAX 06174-3423. TELEX 410654-KINI-D. circ. 600,000. (back issues avail.) **Document type:** newsletter.
Description: News about the persecuted Church and refugees in Eastern Europe and the Third World.

282 **SE**
L'ECHO DES ILES. (Text in Creole, English, French) fortn. POB 138, Victoria, Seychelles. Ed. P. Symphorien. circ. 2,800.
Description: Roman Catholic publication.

282 **US**
ECHO Z AFRYKI I INNYCH KONTYNENTOW. (Text in Polish) 1892. m. $5. Missionary Sisters of St. Peter Claver, St. Mary's Mission House, 265 Century Ave., St. Paul, MN 55125. Ed. Sr. Maria Moryl. circ. 8,000.

282 **CR**
ECO CATOLICO. 1931. w. Avda. 10, Calles 5 y 7, Apdo. 1064, San Jose, Costa Rica. TEL 22-5903. Dir. Armando Alfaro. circ. 20,000.

282 **IT**
L'ECO DI GIBILMANNA. 1919. bi-m. free. Provincia di Messina dei Frati Minori Cappuccini, Santuario Maria SS. di Gibilmanna, 90010 Gibilmanna, Cefalu Pa, Italy. TEL 0921-21835. Ed. P. Pasquale Di Bella. bk.rev. circ. 3,000.

282 **IT**
L'ECO DI SAN GABRIELE. 1913. m. L.30000 (foreign L.45000) (effective 1995). Editoriale Eco s.r.l., Via Santuario, 187, 64048 S. Gabriele (TE), Italy. TEL 39-861-975924. FAX 39-861-975655. Ed. Ciro Benedettini. circ. 130,000. **Document type:** consumer publication.

282 **IT**
L'ECO DI SAN GERMANO. 1957. m. free. Tipolitografia San. Lorenzo Tortona, Largo Paolo Savini, 1, 27057 Varzi, Italy. TEL 0383-52129. Ed. Don Giuseppe De Tommasi. adv. circ. 1,100. (tabloid format; back issues avail.)
Description: Covers in Italian, religious articles and news about parish and diocesan life. Also presents the conditions of the churches that are situated in the territory of little villages.

282 248.8 US ISSN 0013-1016
EDMUNDITE. 1959. m. $1. Society of St. Edmund, P.O. Box 399, Mystic, CT 06355-0399. TEL 203-536-7540. Ed. Rev. Joseph Hart. circ. 30,000. **Document type:** newsletter.
Refereed Serial

282 FR ISSN 0992-6887
EGLISE A LYON. (Supplement avail.) fortn. 110 F. Archeveche de Lyon, 1 Place de Fourviere, 69321 Lyon Cedex 5, France.
Former titles (until 1983): Eglise a Lyon et a Saint Etienne (ISSN 0996-3251); (until 1972): Eglise de Lyon (ISSN 0996-374X)
Description: Review of the diocese.

282 MG
EGLISE CATHOLIQUE A MADAGASCAR. Cover title: Annuaire de l'Eglise Catholique a Madagascar. (Text in French or Malagasy) a. Imprimerie Catholique, 127, Arabe Lenine Vladimir, Antananarivo, Malagasy Republic.

200 CN ISSN 0381-0380
EGLISE DE MONTREAL. (Text in French) 1882. w. Can.$21. Eglise de Montreal, 2000 ouest, rue Sherbrooke, Montreal, Que. H3H 1G4, Canada. Ed. Rev. Yvan Desrochers. adv.; bibl.; index. circ. 2,500.

282 FR ISSN 0013-2330
EGLISE EN ALSACE. 1967. m. 155 F. Office Diocesain d'Information, 16 rue Brulee, 67081 Strasbourg Cedex, France. TEL 88-32-76-25. FAX 88-23-26-18. adv.; bk.rev. **Indexed:** CERDIC.

282 371.3 GW ISSN 0344-2896
EICHSTAETTER HOCHSCHULREDEN. irreg., no.90. DM.12.80. (Universitaet Eichstaett) Verlag Friedrich Pustet, Gutenbergstr. 8, 93051 Regensburg, Germany. TEL 0941-92022-0. FAX 0941-948652. **Document type:** academic/scholarly publication, monographic series.

282 371.3 GW ISSN 0722-1010
EICHSTAETTER MATERIALIEN. irreg., vol.15. DM.64. (Universitaet Eichstaett) Verlag Friedrich Pustet, Gutenbergstr. 8, 93051 Regensburg, Germany. TEL 0941-92022-0. FAX 0941-948652. **Document type:** academic/scholarly publication, monographic series.

253 US ISSN 0013-6719
EMMANUEL; magazine of Eucharist spirituality. 1895. m. (except Jan.-Feb. & Jul.-Aug.) $19.95 (foreign $24.95). Congregation of Blessed Sacrament, 5384 Wilson Mills Rd., Cleveland, OH 44143. FAX 216-449-3862. Ed. Rev. Anthony Schueller. adv.; bk.rev.; bibl.; index. circ. 4,500. **Indexed:** New Test.Abstr.

282 CN ISSN 0317-851X
EN EGLISE. (Text in French) 1974. m. Can.$12. Eglise Catholique, Diocese de Chicoutimi, Office des Communications Sociales, 602, Racine Est., Chicoutimi, PQ G7H 6J6, Canada. TEL 418-543-0783. Ed. M. l'abbe Jacques Bouchard. bk.rev.; illus. circ. 1,450. **Document type:** newsletter.
Description: Contains information about Catholic members and diocese life.

206 FR
EN EQUIPE A C G F AU SERVICE DE L'EVANGILE. 1976. q. 90 F. Action Catholique Generale Feminine, 98 rue de l'Universite, 75007 Paris, France. TEL 40-62-65-13. FAX 40-62-65-18. Ed. Christiane Jourdain. **Document type:** bulletin.
Formerly: En Equipe au Service de l'Evangile (ISSN 0395-1766)

282 UK
ENGLISH BENEDICTINE CONGREGATION. ORDO. 1885. a. £1. Ampleforth Abbey, c/o Rev. R. Jones, Ed., St. Anne, 23 Prescot Rd., Ormskirk, Lancs. L39 4TG, England. circ. 1,400. **Document type:** directory.
Description: Directory of the Divine Office and Mass for use in the Abbeys and churches of this congregation.

ENVIRONMENT AND ART LETTER; a forum on architecture and the arts for the Parish. see *ARCHITECTURE*

262.9 IT ISSN 0013-9491
EPHEMERIDES IURIS CANONICI. (Text in various languages) 1945. q. L.4000($100) Officium Libri Catholici - Catholic Book Agency, Via dei Lucchesi 20, 00187 Rome, Italy. Ed. Pius Fedele. bk.rev.; index. **Indexed:** Canon Law Abstr., CERDIC.

266 SP ISSN 0425-1466
BT595
EPHEMERIDES MARIOLOGICAE; international revue of mariology. 1951. q. 3100 ptas.($32) (foreign 3750 ptas.) (effective Jan. 1994). (Ephemerides Mariologicae) Claretian Fathers, Calle Buen Suceso, 22, 28008 Madrid, Spain. TEL 91-248-66-01. FAX 91-248-21-01. adv.; bk.rev.; index. circ. 550. (back issues avail.) **Indexed:** CERDIC, New Test.Abstr.

262.9 900 BE ISSN 0013-9513
BR1.A1
EPHEMERIDES THEOLOGICAE LOVANIENSES; revue de theologie et de droit canon de Louvain/Leuvens tijdschrift voor theologie en kerkelijk recht/Louvain journal of theological and canonical studies. (Supplement avail.: Bibliotheca Ephemeridum Theologicarum Lovaniensium) (Text in English, French, German) 1924. q. 2000 BEF (effective 1994). (Katholieke Universiteit Leuven - Universite Catholique de Louvain) Editions Peeters s.p.r.l., Bondgenotenlaan 153, 3000 Leuven, Belgium. TEL 32-16-235170. FAX 32-16-228500. bibl.; index. (back issues avail.) **Indexed:** Bibl.Ling., CERDIC, New Test.Abstr., Old Test.Abstr., Rel.& Theol.Abstr. (1983-), Rel.Ind.One, Rel.Per. **Document type:** academic/scholarly publication.
—BLDSC (3793.500000); Faxon.
Description: Publishes articles reflecting the full scope of theological research, with an international calendar of meetings and congresses.

EQUIPES ST. VINCENT. see *SOCIAL SERVICES AND WELFARE*

282 255 GW ISSN 0013-9963
BX3001
ERBE UND AUFTRAG; Benediktinische Monatsschrift. 1919. bi-m. DM.42. Beuroner Kunstverlag GmbH, 88631 Beuron, Germany. TEL 07466-17228. FAX 07466-17209. Ed. B. Schwank. adv.; bk.rev.; abstr.; bibl.; illus.; index. circ. 2,100. **Indexed:** New Test.Abstr., Old Test.Abstr. **Document type:** bulletin.

ERNEUERUNG IN KIRCHE UND GESELLSCHAFT. see *RELIGIONS AND THEOLOGY — Protestant*

ESCOGE LA VIDA!. see *POPULATION STUDIES*

266 CN ISSN 0318-7551
ESKIMO. French edition (ISSN 0318-756X) (Editions in English and French) 1944. s-a. Can.$5. Diocese of Churchill Hudson Bay, P.O. Box 10, Churchill, MN ROB 0E0, Canada. TEL 204-675-2252. FAX 204-675-2140. Ed. Lorraine Brandson. bk.rev. circ. 5,400 (3,100 French ed., 2,300 English ed.). (back issues avail.) **Document type:** newsletter.
—BLDSC (3811.230000).
Description: Information about Inuit culture and religious activities.

200 SP ISSN 0425-340X
ESTUDIO AGUSTINIANO. (Text in English, French, Italian, Spanish) 1966. 3/yr. 3500 ptas.($35) (effective 1995). Estudio Teologico Agustiniano, Po. de Filipinos, 7, 47007 Valladolid, Spain. TEL 34-983-306900. FAX 34-983-397896. Eds. Pio De Luis, Tomas Marcos. bk.rev.; index. circ. 400. (back issues avail.) **Indexed:** Canon Law Abstr., CERDIC. **Document type:** academic/scholarly publication.
Formerly (until 1967): Archivo Teologico Agustiniano (ISSN 0211-2043)
Description: Publishes articles of philosophy and theology from the institute's professors.

282 SP ISSN 0210-7074
ESTUDIOS JOSEFINOS. 1947. s-a. $21. Centro Josefino Espanol, c/o Fray Jose Antonio Carrasco, San Benito, 3, 47003 Valladolid, Spain. TEL 923-33-01-69. bk.rev. circ. 600.

ETHICS AND MEDICS. see *PHILOSOPHY*

ETUDES. see *LITERARY AND POLITICAL REVIEWS*

268 US ISSN 0743-524X
EUCHARISTIC MINISTER. 1984. m. National Catholic Reporter Publishing Company, Inc., 115 E. Armour Blvd., Box 419281, Kansas City, MO 64141. TEL 816-531-0538; 800-333-7373. FAX 816-931-5082. Eds. Carolyn Hoff, Rich Heffren. circ. 65,000.
Description: Spiritual support and insights for the eucharistic minister.

282 200 VC ISSN 0394-9850
EUNTES DOCETE. 1948. 3/yr. L.40000($40) (Pontificia Universita Urbaniana) Urbaniana University Press, Via Urbano VIII, 16, 00165 Rome, Italy. TEL 39-6-868640. FAX 39-6-8308363. Ed. Thomas Thengumpallil. adv.; bk.rev. circ. 1,000. (back issues avail.) **Indexed:** CERDIC, New Test.Abstr. **Document type:** academic/scholarly publication.

282 GW ISSN 0939-3897
EUROPAEISCHE GESELLSCHAFT FUER KATHOLISCHE THEOLOGIE. BULLETIN. (Text in English, French, German) 1990. s-a. Europaeische Gesellschaft fuer Katholische Theologie, Liebermeisterstr. 12, 72076 Tuebingen, Germany. TEL 07071-295250. FAX 07071-295249. Ed.Bd. **Document type:** academic/scholarly publication.

282 US ISSN 0738-8489
EVANGELIST (ALBANY). 1926. w. $20. (Roman Catholic Diocese of Albany) Albany Catholic Press Association, Inc., 40 N. Main Ave., Albany, NY 12203. TEL 518-453-6688. FAX 518-453-6793. Ed. James P. Breig; Pub. Bishop Howard J. Hubbard. adv. contact: Barbara R. Oliver. bk.rev.; film rev.; bibl.; stat. circ. 59,500. (also avail. in microfilm)

282 SP ISSN 0214-6827
EXCERPTA E DISSERTATIONIBUS IN SACRA THEOLOGICA. 1975. irreg., no.13, 1987. 3000 ptas. (Universidad de Navarra, Facultad de Teologia) Servicio de Publicaciones de la Universidad de Navarra, S.A., Apdo. 177, 31080 Pamplona, Spain. TEL 94 25 2700.

282 US
▼**EXPLORING THE NEW CATECHISM.** 1994. m. $11. St. Anthony Messenger Press, 1615 Republic St., Cincinnati, OH 45210. TEL 513-241-5616. FAX 513-241-0399. Ed. John Bookser Feister. circ. 69,500. **Document type:** newsletter.
Description: Offers an overview of the new Catechism of the Catholic Church.

266 US
EXTENSION. 1906. 9/yr. free. Catholic Church Extension Society of the United States, 35 E. Wacker Dr., Chicago, IL 60601. TEL 312-236-7240. FAX 312-236-5276. Ed. Bradley Collins. circ. 85,000. **Indexed:** Cath.Ind., CERDIC. **Document type:** trade publication.
Description: Discusses mission work in the US.

282 US
FAIRFIELD COUNTY CATHOLIC. 1984. m. $15. Roman Catholic Diocese of Bridgeport, 238 Jewett Ave., Bridgeport, CT 06606. TEL 203-372-4301. FAX 203-374-2044. adv. circ. 90,000. **Document type:** newspaper.

282 IT ISSN 0393-3555
FAMIGLIA DOMANI. q. L.24000 (foreign L.30000) (effective 1996). Editore Elle Di Ci, Corso Francia 214, 10096 Leumann (TO), Italy. TEL 39-11-9591091. FAX 39-11-9572900.

282 MX
FAMILIA CRISTIANA. 1953. m. Mex.$45. Ediciones Paulinas, S.A., Apdo. 69-766, 04460 Coyoacan, Mexico D.F., Mexico. TEL 525-5491454. FAX 525-6709392. Dir. G. Emmanuel Hidalgo. adv. contact: Ezequiel Tovar. circ. 65,000. **Document type:** consumer publication.

282 US ISSN 0899-1529
THE FAMILY (BOSTON); a Catholic perspective. 1952. m. $12. Daughters of St. Paul, 50 St. Paul's Ave., Boston, MA 02130. TEL 617-522-8911. Ed. Sr. Theresa Frances Myers. circ. 10,000.
Description: Practical advice on Christian family life.

RELIGIONS AND THEOLOGY — ROMAN CATHOLIC

282   US
THE FAMILY DIGEST. 1945. bi-m. Box 40137, Ft. Wayne, IN 46804. Ed. Corine B. Erlandson. adv. circ. 150,000. **Document type:** consumer publication.
Formerly: Parish Family Digest.
Description: Publishes general-interest articles dedicated to the joy and fulfillment of Catholic family and parish life.

THE FAMILY FRIEND. see INSURANCE

282 360   AT
THE FAR EAST; mission magazine of the Columban fathers. 1920. 10/yr. Aus.$10. St. Columban's Mission Society, 69 Woodland St, North Essendon, Vic. 3041, Australia. TEL 03-379-3544. FAX 03-379-6040. Ed. John Colgan. circ. 28,000.

282   US   ISSN 0014-8814
FATHERS OF THE CHURCH. 1947. irreg., vol.89, 1993. price varies. Catholic University of America Press, 620 Michigan Ave., N.E., Washington, DC 20064. TEL 202-319-5052. FAX 202-319-5802. (Subscr. to: Box 4852, Hampden Sta., Baltimore, MD 21211. TEL 410-516-6953)
—CCC.

220   CN   ISSN 0225-2112
FEUILLET BIBLIQUE. (Editions in English, French) 1958. w. (except Jul. & Aug.) Can.$20. Archeveche de Montreal, Centre Biblique, 2000 ouest, rue Sherbrooke, Montreal, PQ H3H 1G4, Canada. TEL 514-931-7311. Ed. Rev. Yves Guillemette. bk.rev.; bibl.; index. circ. 11,800.
Formerly: Parole-Dimanche.

282   IT
FIACCOLA. 1916. m. L.20000 (typically set in Jan.). Associazione Amici del Seminario Arcivescovile, Segretariato per il Seminario, Piazza Duomo 16, 20122 Milan, Italy. (Subscr. to: Editrice Velar, via Torquato Tasso 10, 24020 Gorle (BG), Italy) bk.rev (also avail. in microfilm from KTO; back issues avail.)

282   US   ISSN 1041-7710
FIDELIS ET VERUS/FAITHFUL AND TRUE. 1985. q. $10 for 10 issues. Children of Mary, Box 350333, Ft. Lauderdale, FL 33335-0333. TEL 305-463-0649. Ed. John Walsh. adv.: B&W page $200; adv. contact: John Walsh. bk.rev. circ. 5,000. (tabloid format; back issues avail.) **Document type:** newspaper.
Description: Exposes infiltration of church by Masons and Communists. Teaches traditional Catholic doctrine and practices.

282   US   ISSN 0730-0271
BX801
FIDELITY MAGAZINE. m. (11/yr.). $25. Ultramontane Associates, Inc., 206 Marquette Ave., South Bend, IN 46617. TEL 219-289-9786. FAX 219-289-1461. Ed. E. Michael Jones. adv. contact: Phil Niswouger. bk.rev.; index. circ. 7,000. (back issues avail.) **Document type:** consumer publication.
Description: Focuses on events and issues concerning faith and morals, family, and culture from a Roman Catholic perspective.

282   US   ISSN 0275-6145
E184.S64
FIRST CATHOLIC SLOVAK UNION OF AMERICA. MINUTES OF ANNUAL MEETING.* Key Title: Minutes of the Annual Meeting of the First Catholic Slovak Union of the United States of America and Canada. a. First Catholic Slovak Union, 6611 Rockside Rd., Cleveland, OH 44131-2398.

FIT DURCH TIP. see CHILDREN AND YOUTH — For

282   FR   ISSN 0015-5365
FOI ET VIE DE L'EGLISE AU DIOCESE DE TOULOUSE; semaine catholique de Toulouse. 1860. bi-m. 45 F. Archeveche de Toulouse, 1 Place Stes Scarbes, 31000 Toulouse, France. Ed. Chanoine Ducasse. adv.; bk.rev.; bibl.; index. circ. 1,800.

FORUM; contactblad voor inrichtende machten, pedagogische begleiders en directies van het Katholieke Onderwijs. see EDUCATION

FRAENKISCHER HAUSKALENDER UND CARITASKALENDER. see BIOGRAPHY

282   FR   ISSN 0766-4125
FRANCE CATHOLIQUE. 1925. w. 480 F. (overseas 640 F.). Soceval, B.P. 25, 78117 Chateaufort, France. TEL 39-56-80-00. FAX 39-56-17-18. Ed. A. Chabadel. adv.; bk.rev. circ. 20,000. **Document type:** newspaper.
Former titles: France Catholique - Ecclesia (ISSN 0244-528X); France Catholique (ISSN 0015-9506)

271.3   US   ISSN 0080-5459
BX3601
FRANCISCAN STUDIES. 1941. a. $20. Franciscan Institute, St. Bonaventure University, Drawer F, St. Bonaventure, NY 14778. TEL 716-375-2105. Ed. Fr. Conrad L. Harkins. (also avail. in microform from UMI; reprint service avail. from UMI) **Indexed:** Cath.Ind., CERDIC, M.L.A., Phil.Ind., Rel.Ind.Two.
—BLDSC (4032.785000).

255   BE   ISSN 0015-9840
FRANCISCANA; bijdragen tot de geschiedenis van de Minderbroeders in de Nederlanden. 1946. s-a. 400 BEF. Instituut voor Franciskaanse Geschiedenis, Minderbroedersstraat 5, B-3800 Sint-Truiden, Belgium. Ed. A. Coenen. bk.rev.; bibl.; illus.; index, cum.index. circ. 250. **Indexed:** Amer.Hist.& Life, Hist.Abstr.
—SWETS.

FRANCISCANUM; revista de las ciencias del espiritur. see PHILOSOPHY

282 255   NE   ISSN 0015-9794
FRANCISKAANS LEVEN; tijdschrift tot verdieping en vernieuwing van de Franciskaanse beweging in Nederland en Vlaanderen. 1917. bi-m. fl.30. Franciskaanse Samenwerking in Nederland, Oude Gracht 23, 3511 AB Utrecht, Netherlands. TEL 31-30-319321. FAX 31-30-315998. Ed. G.P. Freeman. bk.rev.; bibl.; index, cum.index. circ. 1,000.

271   GW   ISSN 0016-0067
BX3601
FRANZISKANISCHE STUDIEN. (Text in various languages) 1918. q. DM.44. Dietrich Coelde Verlag GmbH, Walburgisstr. 41, 59457 Werl, Germany. TEL 02922-4011. Ed. P. Ildefons Vanderheyden. bk.rev. circ. 300. **Indexed:** CERDIC, M.L.A.
—BLDSC (4033.020000).

282   IT
FRATI MINORI CAPPUCCINI. ISTITUTO STORICO. VARIA. 1973. irreg., no.17, 1994. price varies. Frati Minori Cappuccini, Istituto Storico, Casella Postale 18283, Circonv. Occidentale 6850 (GRA km 65), 00163 Rome, Italy. TEL 39-6-66151958. FAX 39-6-66162401.

FREIBURGER ZEITSCHRIFT FUER PHILOSOPHIE UND THEOLOGIE. see PHILOSOPHY

282   NE   ISSN 0016-2175
FRONTLIJN; voor Katholieken en in buiten de kerk. 1953. m. fl.3.50. (Redemptorist Fathers) A. de Bot, Ed. & Pub., Sionsweg 2, 6525 EB Nijmegen, Netherlands. illus. circ. 8,000. (tabloid format)

282 301   US
FRONTLINE REPORT. bi-m. Society of African Missions, Inc., 23 Bliss Ave., Tenafly, NJ 07670. TEL 201-567-0450. FAX 201-567-7156. Ed. Sr. Betty Lamb; Pub. Rev. S. John Murray. circ. 50,000. **Document type:** newsletter.

282   IE   ISSN 0016-3120
THE FURROW. 1950. m. I£35($40) Furrow Trust, Maynooth, Co. Kildare, Ireland. TEL 01-6286215. FAX 01-7083908. Ed. Ronan Drury. adv.; bk.rev.; film rev.; play rev.; s-a. index. circ. 8,000. (also avail. in microform from UMI; reprint service avail. from UMI) **Indexed:** Canon Law Abstr., Cath.Ind., CERDIC, New Test.Abstr., Old Test.Abstr. **Document type:** academic/scholarly publication.
—BLDSC (4059.400000); UMI.

GARSAS. see ETHNIC INTERESTS

GAZETA NIEDZIELNA. see GENERAL INTEREST PERIODICALS — Poland

282   GW
GEIST UND AUFTRAG. (Text in German) 1921. q. Charitable Cooperation of the Missionary Holy Spirit Association Steyl e.V., Postfach 2308, 41310 Nettetal, Germany. TEL 077-734600. FAX 077-740224. Ed. Gabriele Hoelzer. bk.rev. circ. 45,000. **Document type:** newsletter.

282   US
GENERATION; the spiritual enrichment newsletter for mature Catholics. 1980. m. $12. Claretian Publications, 205 W. Monroe St., Chicago, IL 60606. TEL 312-236-7782. FAX 312-236-7230. Ed. Rev. Mark J. Brummel. circ. 25,366. (reprint service avail. from UMI) **Document type:** newsletter.
Description: Each newsletter examines one topic of special interest to older Catholics.

282   US
GEORGIA BULLETIN. 1962. w. $16. Catholic Archdiocese of Atlanta, 680 W. Peachtree St. N.W., Atlanta, GA 30308. Ed. Gretchen R. Keiser. adv. contact: Leonard Markun. bk.rev.; circ. 48,000 (paid). **Document type:** newspaper.

DE GIDS OP MAATSCHAPPELIJK GEBIED; tijdschrift voor syndicale, culturele en sociale problemen. see LABOR UNIONS

282   US
THE GLOBE (SIOUX CITY). 1953. w. $14. Catholic Diocese of Sioux City, 1825 Jackson St., Sioux City, IA 51105. TEL 712-255-2550. FAX 712-255-4901. (Subscr. to: Box 5079, Sioux City, IA 51102) Ed. Joe Maher. adv. circ. 34,250. **Document type:** newspaper.

282   CE
GNANARTHAPRADEEPAYA. (Text in Sinhala) 1866. w. Colombo Catholic Press, 2 Gnanarthapradeepaya Mawatha, Borella, Colombo 8, Sri Lanka. TEL 1-695984. Ed. Rev. Fr. Bertram Dabrera. circ. 26,000.

282   US   ISSN 0738-6419
THE GOOD NEWS LETTER (WASHINGTON, 1972). 1972. q. donation. National Institute for the Word of God, 487 Michigan Ave., N.E., Washington, DC 20017. TEL 202-529-0001. FAX 202-636-4460. Ed. Mary Ann C. McGuire. bk.rev.; circ. 2,500 (controlled). **Document type:** newsletter.
Description: Provide timely ideas on formation for everyone interested in preaching and bible sharing, including interviews and features on persons actively engaged in the church's ministry.

282 323.4   SA   ISSN 1012-5930
GRACE AND TRUTH. (Text in English) 1980. q. R.45 (foreign R.55 or £15($25). St. Joseph's Theological Institute, Private Bag 6004, Hilton 3245, South Africa. TEL 27-331-33293. FAX 27-331-431232. Ed. Paul Decock. bk.rev.; index. circ. 500. (back issues avail.) **Document type:** academic/scholarly publication.
Description: Concerned with the development of the Catholic church and society in Southern Africa.
Refereed Serial

GRADUATE SCHOOL GUIDE. see EDUCATION — Guides To Schools And Colleges

GRAIN DE SOLEIL; le journal des enfants curieux de Dieu. see CHILDREN AND YOUTH — For

282   US   ISSN 8755-9323
GREEN BAY CATHOLIC COMPASS. 1978. w. $25 (typically set in July). (Catholic Diocese of Green Bay) Green Bay Register, Inc., 1825 Riverside Dr., Box 23825, Green Bay, WI 54305-3825. TEL 414-437-7531. FAX 414-437-0694. Ed. Tony Staley. adv. circ. 14,500. (also avail. in microfiche) **Document type:** newspaper.

282   VC   ISSN 0017-4114
BX800.A1
GREGORIANUM. (Text in English, French, German, Italian, Latin or Spanish) 1920. q. L.80000($75) (effective 1995). (Pontificia Universita Gregoriana - Pontifical Gregorian University) Gregorian University Press, Piazza della Pilotta, 35, 00187 Rome, Italy. TEL 39-6-678-15-67. FAX 39-6-678-05-88. Ed. R.P. Dupuis. bk.rev.; bibl.; index, cum.index: vols.1-31 (1920-1950). circ. 1,200. (also avail. in microfiche from IDC) **Indexed:** Bull.Signal., Canon Law Abstr., Cath.Ind., CERDIC, New Test.Abstr., Old Test.Abstr., Phil.Ind., Rel.& Theol.Abstr. (1968-), Rel.Ind.One, Rel.Per.
—BLDSC (4215.300000); Faxon; SWETS; UnCover.
Description: A scientific review of theology and philosophy with occasional discussions problems in church history, canon law and social sciences.

RELIGIONS AND THEOLOGY — ROMAN CATHOLIC

282   GW
GUCKLOCH. 1973. q. free. Katholische Junge Gemeinde, Dioezesanverband Muenster, Rosenstr. 16, 48143 Muenster, Germany. TEL 0251-495500. Ed. Uta Forbrig. (back issues avail.) **Document type:** corporate report.

H L I CANADIAN REPORT. (Human Life International in Canada Inc.) see *POPULATION STUDIES*

H L I REPORTS. (Human Life International) see *POPULATION STUDIES*

H L I REPORTS. (Human Life International in Canada Inc.) see *POPULATION STUDIES*

282 940   BE
▼**HAGIOGRAPHICA;** rivista di agiografia e biografia. (Text in French, German, Italian) 1994. a. 1900 BEF (effective 1995). N.V. Brepols, Steenweg op Tielen 68, 2300 Turhout, Belgium. TEL 32-14-402500. FAX 32-14-428919. (back issues avail.) **Document type:** academic/scholarly publication.
    Description: Publishes articles relating to topics in hagiography and biography, with particular emphasis on medieval European history.
    Refereed Serial

260   US   ISSN 1045-3636
HAWAII CATHOLIC HERALD. 1936. fortn. $15. Roman Catholic Bishop of Honolulu, 1184 Bishop St., Honolulu, HI 96813. TEL 808-533-1791. FAX 808-521-8428. Ed. Patrick Downes. adv.; bk.rev. circ. 8,000.

282   US   ISSN 0893-536X
HEARTS AFLAME; Catholic youth magazine. 1987. q. $5 (foreign $7). (World Apostolate of Fatima) Blue Army of Our Lady of Fatima, U S A, Inc., Mountain View Rd., Box 976, Washington, NJ 07882-0976. TEL 908-689-1700. FAX 908-689-6279. Ed. Sr. Mary Celeste. illus. circ. 15,000. (back issues avail.)

282   PL   ISSN 0017-9914
HEJNAL MARIACKI; miesiecznik o tematyce religijno-kulturalno-spolecznej. 1956. m. $6. Chrzescijanskie Stowarzyszenie Spoleczne - Christian Social Association, Marszalkowska 4, 00-590 Warsaw, Poland. (Dist. by: RSW "Prasa-Ksiazka-Ruch" Centrala Kolportazu Prasy i Wyndawnictw, Ul. Towarowa 28, 00-958 Warsaw) Ed. Eugeniusz Zdanowicz. adv.; illus. circ. 5,000.

282   GW
HELIAND KORRESPONDENZ. 1969. q. DM.16. Kreis Katholischer Frauen im Heliandbund, Gabelsbergerstr. 19, 50674 Cologne, Germany. (Subscr. to: Lilienstr. 61, 67112 Mutterstadt, Germany) bk.rev. circ. 1,500. **Document type:** bulletin.

282   US   ISSN 0746-4185
EL HERALDO CATOLICO/CATHOLIC HERALD; el periodico digno de su familia. (Text in Spanish) 1979. fortn. $10. Roman Catholic Diocese of Sacramento, 5890 Newman Ct., Sacramento, CA 95819. TEL 916-452-3691. FAX 916-452-2945. Ed. Deacon Jose Ramirez. adv. contact: Ricardo A. Ramirez. bk.rev. circ. 6,500. (tabloid format; also avail. in microfilm) **Document type:** newspaper.

282   GW   ISSN 0018-0645
BX803
HERDER - KORRESPONDENZ; Monatshefte fuer Gesellschaft und Religion. 1946. m. DM.178.80. Verlag Herder GmbH und Co. KG, Hermann-Herder-Str. 4, 79104 Freiburg, Germany. TEL 0761-2717-388. FAX 0761-2717-407. Ed. Ulrich Ruh. adv.; bk.rev.; index. circ. 8,700. **Indexed:** Cath.Ind. **Document type:** newsletter.
—SWETS.

282   US   ISSN 1068-0330
HLAS NARODA/VOICE OF THE NATION. (Text in Czech, English, Slovak) w. $30. Czech-American Heritage Center, 2340 S. 61st Ave., Chicago, IL 60650-2608. TEL 312-656-1050. Ed. Vojtech Vit. (back issues avail.) **Document type:** newspaper.

282   SP
HOJA TRINITARIA. m. 800 ptas. Ediciones Secretariado Trinitario, Filiberto Villalobos, 82, 37003 Salamanca, Spain. TEL 235602.

282 956   IS   ISSN 0333-7189
HOLY LAND REVIEW; illustrated quarterly of the Franciscan custody of the holy land. (Text in English) 1975. q. $10. Franciscan Printing Press, P.O. Box 14064, Jerusalem 91140, Israel. TEL 972-2-286594. FAX 972-2-272274. (Subscr. in U.S. to: Holy Land Review, c/o Franciscan Monastery, 1400 Quincy St., N.E., Washington, DC 20017) Ed. William De Biase. adv.; bk.rev.; cum.index: 1975-1984. circ. 5,000. (back issues avail.)
    Description: Catholic voice on the troubled Middle East.

HOMELIFE; the Philippines' family magazine. see *GENERAL INTEREST PERIODICALS — Philippines*

250   US   ISSN 0018-4268
BX801
HOMILETIC AND PASTORAL REVIEW. 1900. m. (bi-m. Aug.-Sep.). $24. Catholic Polls, Inc., 86 Riverside Dr., New York, NY 10024. TEL 212-799-2600. FAX 212-787-0351. Ed. Rev. Kenneth Baker. adv. contact: Bernard Belson. bk.rev.; index; circ. 14,500 (paid). (also avail. in microform from UMI; reprint service avail. from UMI) **Indexed:** Canon Law Abstr., Cath.Ind., CERDIC, New Test.Abstr., Old Test.Abstr., Rel.& Theol.Abstr. **Document type:** academic/scholarly publication.
—UMI.

282   HK   ISSN 0073-3210
HONG KONG CATHOLIC CHURCH DIRECTORY/HSIANG-KANG T'IEN CHU CHIAO SHOU TS'E. (Text in Chinese, English) 1954. a. $5.20 (effective 1995). Catholic Truth Society, Catholic Centre, 16-Fl., Grand Bldg., 15-18 Connaught Road, Central, Hong Kong. TEL 2525-8021. FAX 2521-8700. Ed. Louis Lee. adv. contact: Rev. Edward Khong. circ. 2,600. **Document type:** directory.
    Description: Includes personnel of Curiae, churches, diocesan organizations, pious associations, Catholic schools, social services and religious congregations.

282   US   ISSN 0360-9669
BR1
HORIZONS (VILLANOVA). (Text in English) 1974. s-a. Can.$30($30) Villanova University, Villanova, PA 19085. TEL 215-645-4385. (Dist. by: Wilfrid Laurier University Press, Waterloo, Ont. N2L 3C5, Canada. TEL 519-884-1970) Ed. Walter E. Conn. adv.; bk.rev. circ. 1,500. (also avail. in microfilm from UMI; reprint service avail. from UMI) **Indexed:** Cath.Ind., INIS Atomind., New Test.Abstr., Old Test.Abstr., Rel.& Theol.Abstr., Rel.Ind.One, Rel.Per., SSCI. **Document type:** academic/scholarly publication. —BLDSC (4326.794400); Genuine Article; UMI.
    Description: Explores developments in Catholic theology, the total Christian tradition, human religious experience, and the concerns of creative teaching in the college and university environment.

282   US   ISSN 0018-6910
HRVATSKI KATOLICKI GLASNIK; mjesecnik za duhovnu izgradnju iseljenih Hrvata. 1942. m. $5. (Croatian Franciscan Fathers) Croatian Franciscan Press, 4851 Drexel Blvd., Chicago, IL 60615. TEL 312-268-2819. Ed. Fr. Harvoslav Ban, O.F.M. adv.; bk.rev.; illus. circ. 3,000. **Indexed:** CERDIC.

HUMAN LIFE INTERNATIONAL. SPECIAL REPORT. see *POPULATION STUDIES*

HYMNOLOGISKE MEDDELELSER; tidsskrift om salmer. see *RELIGIONS AND THEOLOGY — Protestant*

282 704.948   IT
ICONOGRAPHIA FRANCISCANA. 1973. irreg., no.8, 1995. price varies. Frati Minori Cappuccini, Istituto Storico, Casella Postale 18283, Circonv. Occidentale 6850 (GRA km 65), 00163 Rome, Italy. TEL 39-6-66151958. FAX 39-6-66162401.

282   US
IDAHO CATHOLIC REGISTER. 1958. 3/m. $16. Catholic Diocese of Idaho, 303 Federal Way, Boise, ID 83705. TEL 208-342-1311. FAX 208-342-0224. Ed. Colette Cowman. adv.: page $497. circ. 12,600. (tabloid format) **Document type:** newspaper.
    Formerly: Idaho Register (ISSN 0891-5792)

IDEENREICH. see *CHILDREN AND YOUTH — For*

282   SP
IGLESIA DE SEVILLA. s-a. 1100 ptas. Arzobispado de Sevilla, Oficina Diocesana de Informacion, Apdo. Postal 6, 41080 Sevilla, Spain. TEL 4220998. FAX 4214914. Ed. Angel G. Gomez Guillen. circ. 16,000.

282   GW   ISSN 0939-4656
IM DIENST DER KIRCHE; die groesste Fachzeitschrift fuer alle Kirchenangestellten. 1919. q. DM.50. (Zentralverband Katholischer Kirchenangestellter e.V.) Verlag Christoph Dohr, Kasselberger Weg 120, 50769 Cologne, Germany. TEL 0221-707002. FAX 0221-704395. Ed. Christoph Dohr. adv.: page DM.950. bk.rev.; bibl.; music rev. (back issues avail.) **Document type:** newsletter.

200   SP   ISSN 0211-5441
IMAGENES DE LA FE. 1963. m. 3400 ptas.($32) (Pontificial University of Salamanca) Promocion Popular Cristiana, E. Jardiel Poncela 4, E-28016 Madrid, Spain. Ed. Manuel Useros. circ. 10,000.

282   FR   ISSN 0750-3407
IMAGES DU MOIS. 1962. m. Vie Catholique Illustree, 163 bd. Malesherbes, 75849 Paris Cedex 17, France. Ed. Michel Houssin. circ. 600,000.

282   IT   ISSN 0019-3186
IN FAMIGLIA; rassegna mensile delle attivita spirituali, culturali e artistiche dell'angelicum-chiesa di S. Angelo. 1925. m. L.4000. Angelicum-Convento di S.Angelo, Piazza S. Angelo 2, 20121 Milan, Italy. Ed.Bd. adv.; bk.rev. (tabloid format)

282   US
IN THE MEANTIME; articulating a vision of Church. 1993. 10/yr. $27.95. Thomas More Association, 205 W. Monroe, 6th Fl., Chicago, IL 60606. TEL 312-609-8880. Ed. John Sprague. circ. 1,500 (paid). **Document type:** newsletter.
    Description: Contains interviews and discussions of the Catholic Church to affect and understand change.

282   VC
INCULTURATION. 1982. irreg., no.16, 1994. price varies. (Pontificia Universita Gregoriana, Centre "Culture e Religioni" - Pontifical Gregorian University, Center "Cultures and Religions") Gregorian University Press, Piazza della Pilotta, 35, 00187 Rome, Italy. TEL 39-6-687-15-67. FAX 39-6-687-05-88.
    Description: Working papers on living faith and cultures.

282   NR   ISSN 0331-7110
THE INDEPENDENT. (Text in English) 1960. w. Bodija Rd., PMB 5109, Ibadan, Nigeria. Ed. F.B. Cronin-Coltsman. circ. 13,000.
    Description: Independent Roman Catholic-based publication.

282   VC
INDEX ACTORUM ROMANORUM PONTIFICUM. 1975. irreg, no.5, 1990. price varies. Biblioteca Apostolica Vaticana, 00120 Vatican City (Rome), State of the Vatican City.

INFORMATION BULLETIN FOR CATHOLIC RURAL ORGANIZATIONS. see *AGRICULTURE*

282 374   IT
INFORMATORE DI URIO. 1973. bi-m. L.15000. Edizioni Ares, Via Stradivari 7, 20131 Milan, Italy. TEL 02-29526156. FAX 02-29514202. Ed. Giorgio Carimati. adv.; circ. 4,760 (controlled). (back issues avail.)

282   US   ISSN 0745-4252
INLAND CATHOLIC. (Text in English, occasionally Spanish) 1979. m. $12. Roman Catholic Bishop of San Bernardino, 1450 N. D St., San Bernardino, CA 92405. TEL 909-384-8240. FAX 909-384-8290. (Subscr. to: Box 2788, San Bernardino, CA 92406) Ed. Steven Barrie. adv. contact: Jimmy Ramirez. bk.rev.; circ. 24,000 (paid). (tabloid format) **Document type:** newspaper.

282   US   ISSN 0020-1510
INLAND REGISTER. 1942. 17/yr. $15. Catholic Diocese of Spokane, Box 48, Spokane, WA 99210-0048. TEL 509-456-7140. FAX 509-456-7108. Ed. Eric Meisfjord. adv.; bk.rev. circ. 8,500. **Document type:** newspaper.

RELIGIONS AND THEOLOGY — ROMAN CATHOLIC

282 UK ISSN 0020-157X
BX2597
INNES REVIEW. 1950. s-a. £14 (overseas £15). (Scottish Catholic Historical Association) John S. Burns & Sons, 25 Finlas St., Possilpark, Glasgow G22 5DS, Scotland. illus.; cum.index: 1950-1959. circ. 500. **Indexed:** Amer.Hist.& Life, Br.Archaeol.Abstr., Br.Hum.Ind., Hist.Abstr. —BLDSC (4515.460000).

282 375 IT ISSN 1121-1555
INSEGNARE RELIGIONE. 1988. bi-m. (5/yr.). L.26000 (foreign L.37000) (effective 1995). Editore Elle Di Ci, Corso Francia 214, 10096 Leumann (TO), Italy. TEL 39-11-9591091. FAX 39-11-9572900.
Description: For teachers of religion at all levels.

282 US ISSN 1068-8579
BX801
INSIDE THE VATICAN. 1993. 10/yr. Urbi et Orbi Communications, 3050 Gap Knob Rd., New Hope, KY 40052. TEL 502-325-3061. FAX 502-325-3091. (Alt. addr.: Inside the Vatican, Via delle Mura Aurelie 7c, 00165 Rome, Italy. TEL 39-6-39387471) Ed. Robert Moynihan. adv.
Document type: consumer publication.
Description: Covers news and activities of the Vatican.

200 230 FR ISSN 0752-9864
INSTITUT CATHOLIQUE DE PARIS. ANNUAIRE. a. Institut Catholique de Paris, 21 rue d'Assas, 75270 Paris Cedex 06, France. TEL 44-39-52-00. FAX 45-44-27-14. circ. controlled.
Description: Lists departments and teachers of the institut.

282 BE ISSN 0770-4720
INTERFACE; lettre d'information trimestrielle. 1981. q. 1300 BEF($38) (Centre Informatique et Bible) Promotion Biblique et Informatique a.s.b.l., CIB - Maredsous, B-5537 Denee, Belgium. TEL 32-82-699647. FAX 32-82-223269. Ed. R.F. Poswick. adv.; bk.rev. circ. 3,000. (back issues avail.) **Document type:** newsletter.

282 US ISSN 0273-6187
INTERMOUNTAIN CATHOLIC. (Text in English, Spanish) 1899. w. $13.50 (foreign $30). Catholic Diocese of Salt Lake City, 27 "C" St., Salt Lake City, UT 84103. TEL 801-328-8641. FAX 801-328-9680. (Subscr. to: Box 2489, Salt Lake City, UT 84110) Ed. Barbara S. Lee; Pub. Bishop George H. Niederauer. adv. contact: Ed. Anne M. Ibach. bk.rev.; film rev.; play rev.; index. circ. 13,700. (tabloid format; back issues avail.) **Document type:** newspaper.

282 VC ISSN 0074-5782
INTERNATIONAL EUCHARIST CONGRESS. PROCEEDINGS. irreg., 45th, 1993, Seville, Spain. Pontificio Comitato per i Congressi Eucaristici Internazionali, Palazzo S. Calisto, 00120 Vatican City (Rome), State of the Vatican City. Ed. H.E. Cardinal Edouard Gagnon. **Document type:** proceedings.

282 GW ISSN 0341-8693
BX803
INTERNATIONALE KATHOLISCHE ZEITSCHRIFT. 1972. s-m. DM.16 per no. Communio Verlagsgesellschaft mbH, Friesenstr. 50, 50670 Cologne, Germany. TEL 0221-123553. FAX 0221-123754. Ed. Maximilian Greiner. adv.; bk.rev. circ. 3,300. **Indexed:** CERDIC, New Test.Abstr., Old Test.Abstr., Rel.Ind.One. **Document type:** newsletter.

282 IE
IRISH CATHOLIC. 1888. w. I£45. Irish Catholic Ltd., 55 Lower Gardiner St., Dublin 1, Ireland. TEL 8747538. FAX 8364805. Ed. Bridget-Anne Ryan. adv. contact: Gerhard Crowley. bk.rev.; illus. circ. 39,000.
Document type: newspaper.

282 IE ISSN 0075-0735
BX1503.A3
IRISH CATHOLIC DIRECTORY. 1838. a. I£19.50. (Roman Catholic Church in All Ireland) Veritas Book Co. Ltd., Veritas House, 7-8 Lower Abbey St., Dublin, Ireland. Ed. Fiona Biggs. adv. contact: Brian Lynch. index. **Document type:** directory.
—BLDSC (4571.125000).
Refereed Serial

282 US
THE IRISH IN AMERICA. 1988. irreg. price varies. (Cushwa Center for the Study of American Catholicism) University of Notre Dame Press, Notre Dame, IN 46556. TEL 219-631-6346. FAX 219-631-8148. (Orders to: 11030 S. Langley Ave., Chicago, IL 60628. TEL 800-621-2736. FAX 800-621-8476; Overseas orders to: Eurospan University Press Group, Order Dept. 3 Henrietta St., London WC2E 8LU, England) **Document type:** academic/scholarly publication.

282 MG
ISIKA MIANAKAVY. (Text in Malagasy) 1958. m. Ambatomena, 301 Fianarantsoa, Madagascar. Ed. J. Ranaivomanana. circ. 21,000.

282 IT
ISTITUTO DI SCIENZE RELIGIOSE IN TRENTO. PUBBLICAZIONI. 1981. irreg. Centro Editoriale Dehoniano, Via Nosadella 6, 40123 Bologna, Italy. TEL 051-261254. FAX 051-341706. Ed.Bd.

ITALIA MISSIONARIA. see CHILDREN AND YOUTH — For

946 PO ISSN 0021-3209
ITINERARIUM; revista quadrimestral de cultura. 1955. 3/yr. Esc.2200($20) (effective 1995). (Portuguese Franciscans) Editorial Franciscana, Largo da Luz, 11, 1699 Lisbon Codex, Portugal. TEL 351-1-7142700. Ed. Jose Antonio da Silva Soares. bk.rev.; bibl.; index, cum.index: 1955-1970. circ. 400. (back issues avail.) **Indexed:** Amer.Hist.& Life, CERDIC, Hist.Abstr.
—BLDSC (4588.660000).

IT'S OUR WORLD; mission news from the Holy Childhood Association. see CHILDREN AND YOUTH — For

282 340 IT
IUS ECCLESIAE; rivista internazionale di diritto canonico. 1989. s-a. L.70000 (foreign L.90000). Casa Editrice Dott. A. Giuffre, Via Busto Arsizio 40, 20151 Milan, Italy. TEL 02-38000905. FAX 02-38009582.

IUSTITIA. see LAW

282 US
JACOB'S WELL. 1974. q. $10. North American Conference of Separated and Divorced Catholics, 80 St. Mary's Pl., Cranston, RI 02920. TEL 401-943-7903. FAX 401-943-0373. Ed. Dorothy J. Levesque. circ. 3,000. **Document type:** newsletter.
Description: Education resources pertinent to divorce recovery, remarriage and blended families.

282 AU
JAHRBUCH DER ERZDIOEZESE WIEN. 1950. a. S.60. Pastoralamt der Erxdioezese Wien, Stephansplatz 6, A-1010 Vienna, Austria. TEL 0222-51552399. FAX 0222-51552366. Eds. Alois Schwarz, Franz Ferstl. adv. contact: Walburga Barta. illus. **Document type:** bulletin.
Formerly: Jahrbuch fuer die Kirche von Wien.

282 GW ISSN 0075-2754
JAHRBUCH FUER SALESIANISCHE STUDIEN. 1963. a. price varies. (Arbeitsgemeinschaft fuer Salesianische Studien) Franz Sales Verlag, Postfach 1361, 85067 Eichstaett, Germany. TEL 08421-5379. FAX 08421-80805. Ed. Gottfried Prinz; Pub. Herbert Waldkirchner. adv. contact: Peter Keller. bk.rev. (back issues avail.) **Document type:** academic/scholarly publication.

282 GW ISSN 0934-8611
JAKOBUS-STUDIEN. irreg., no.7, 1994. price varies. Gunter Narr Verlag, Postfach 2567, 72015 Tuebingen, Germany. TEL 07071-9797-0. FAX 07071-75288. Eds. Klaus Herbers, Dieter Bauer. **Document type:** monographic series.

JEDNOTA/UNION. see ETHNIC INTERESTS

282 II ISSN 0970-1117
JEEVADHARA; an international theological journal. English edition (ISSN 0970-1125) 1971. m. (6/yr. in English, 6/yr. in Malayalam). Rs.48($18) Jeevadhara Theological Society, Kottayam 686 047, Kerala, India. TEL 091-481-597430. Ed. Joseph Constantine Manalel. adv.; bk.rev.; index. circ. 1,500. (back issues avail.) **Indexed:** New Test.Abstr. **Document type:** academic/scholarly publication, monographic series.
Description: Fights against all kinds of fundamentalism and conservatism.

271 US
JESUIT BULLETIN. 1922. 3/yr. Society of Jesus, Missouri Province Educational Institute, 4511 W. Pine Blvd., St. Louis, MO 63108. TEL 314-361-7765. FAX 314-758-7164. E-mail: misstudioj@aol.com. Ed. Mary Flick. adv. circ. 33,000. **Document type:** bulletin.

266 UK
JESUITS AND FRIENDS. 3/yr. free. Jesuit Missions, 11 Edge Hill, London SW19 4LR, England. TEL 0181-946-0466. FAX 0181-946-2292. Ed. Rev. D. Birchall. adv. contact: A.E. Montfort. circ. 24,000. (back issues avail.) **Document type:** bulletin.
Former titles (until 1985): Jesuit Missions; Missionary Magazine.

282 IT
JESUS CARITAS. 1961. q. L.20000($13) Communita Jesus Caritas, Abbazia di Sassovivo, 06034 Foligno - PG, Italy. TEL 0742 50620. adv.; bk.rev. circ. 2,500.

282 GW ISSN 0342-6386
JETZT; Frauen auf dem Weg des Evangeliums - Kirche - Ordensleben - Geistliche Gemeinschaften. 1969. q. DM.25. Verlag F. Schiwietz, Pappelstr. 22, 85579 Neubiberg, Germany. TEL 089-6519847. Ed. Hans Rotter. bk.rev. circ. 1,000.
Description: Articles discussing problems and questions about topics concerning women in the church.

282 BE
JEUNES EN MOUVEMENT. (Text in French) q. 250 BEF. Conseil de la Jeunesse Catholique, Rue Belliard 23A, 1040 Brussels, Belgium. TEL 32-2-2303283. FAX 32-2-2306811. Ed. Stephan Grawez. adv.; bk.rev. **Document type:** bulletin.
Description: Covers current topics of interest to young persons between the ages of 16 and 30.

282 US
JOSEPHINUM MAGAZINE. 1976. 2/yr. free. Pontifical College Josephinum, Columbus, OH 43235. TEL 614-885-5585. Ed. Lisa Komp. circ. 3,500. **Document type:** newsletter.
Formerly: Josephinum Newsletter (ISSN 0021-759X); Supersedes: Josephinum Review.
Description: For alumni of the Josephinum.

282 US
JUNIOR MESSENGER. m. Roman Catholic Diocese of Belleville, Chancery Office, 222 S. Third St., Belleville, IL 62220. TEL 618-235-9601. FAX 618-235-7416. (Subscr. to: 2620 Lebanon Ave., Belleville, IL 62221) Ed. Julie Wier. circ. 5,000.

JURIST; studies in church order and ministry. see LAW

282 GW ISSN 0175-5161
K A B; Katholische Arbeitnehmer-Zeitung. 1891. m. (11/yr.). (Katholische Arbeitnehmer-Bewegung Deutschlands) Ketteler Verlag GmbH, Pohlhausenstr. 17, 53332 Bornheim, Germany. TEL 02222-64083. FAX 02222-64085. (Co-sponsor: Katholische Arbeitnehmer-Bewegung Sueddeutschlands e.V.) bk.rev. circ. 260,000. **Document type:** newsletter.
Former titles: Westdeutsche Arbeiter-Zeitung; Kettelerwacht; Katholische Arbeiter-Bewegung. Gemeinsame Zeitung.

266 282 GW
K M - DIE KATHOLISCHEN MISSIONEN. 1873. 6/yr. DM.23.40. (Internationales Katholisches Missionswerk (MISSIO)) Verlag Herder GmbH und Co. KG, Hermann-Herder-Str. 4, 79104 Freiburg, Germany. FAX 0761-2717-407. adv.; bk.rev.; abstr.; bibl.; charts; illus.; index. circ. 51,000.
Formerly: Katholischen Missionen (ISSN 0022-9407)

RELIGIONS AND THEOLOGY — ROMAN CATHOLIC

282 PL ISSN 0860-410X
KALENDARZ SLOWA BOZEGO. 1979. a. 2.40 Zl. (Ksieza Werbisci) Wydawnictwo Ksiezy Werbistow Verbinum, Ostrobramska 98, 04-118 Warsaw, Poland. TEL 48-2-6107870. FAX 48-2-6102387. Ed. Marek Grzech. circ. 200,000. (back issues avail.)

KAPPA GAMMA PI NEWS. see EDUCATION — Higher Education

282 LI ISSN 0235-8050
KATALIKU PASAULIS. 1989. m. $45. (Lithuanian Catholic Church) Publishing House of the Episcopalian Conference, Pranciskonu 3-6, Vilnius 2001, Lithuania. TEL 0122-222263. FAX 0122-222122. Ed. Ausvydas Belickas. circ. 13,000.

282 GW ISSN 0341-0013
KATECHETISCHE BLAETTER; Zeitschrift fuer Religionsunterricht, Gemeindekatechese, Kirchliche Jugendarbeit. 1875. m. DM.94.80 (students DM.79.80). (Deutscher Katecheten-Verein e.V.) Koesel-Verlag GmbH und Co., Flueggenstr. 2, 80639 Munich, Germany. TEL 089-17801-0. FAX 089-17801111. (Co-sponsor: Arbeitstelle fuer Jugendseelsorge der Deutschen Bischofskonferenz) adv.; bk.rev.; film rev.; play rev.; illus.; index. circ. 10,000. (back issues avail.) **Document type:** academic/scholarly publication.
—CCC.

235 920 CN ISSN 0315-8020
KATERI; Lily of the Mohawks. (Editions in English, French) 1949. q. Can.$5. Cause for the Canonization of Blessed Kateri Tekakwitha, Box 70, Kahnawake, PQ J0L 1B0, Canada. TEL 514-638-1546. Ed. Rev. Jacques Bruyere, S.J. circ. 16,800. **Document type:** newsletter.
Description: News about Kateri Tekakwitha's life and virtues, and about native peoples of America.

282 NE ISSN 0924-0640
KATHOLIEK DOCUMENTATIE CENTRUM. BRONNEN & STUDIES. Key Title: Bronnen en Studies. 1971. irreg., vol.25, 1993. price varies. Katholiek Documentatie Centrum, Erasmuslaan 36, 6525 GG Nijmegen, Netherlands. TEL 31-80-612412. (back issues avail.) **Document type:** monographic series.
Formerly: Katholiek Documentatie Centrum. Publicaties (ISSN 0924-0772)

282 NE ISSN 0168-602X
KATHOLIEK DOCUMENTATIE CENTRUM. JAARBOEK. (Summaries in English) 1971. a. price varies. Katholiek Documentatie Centrum, Erasmuslaan 36, 6525 GG Nijmegen, Netherlands. TEL 31-80-612412. **Indexed:** CERDIC.

282 GW
KATHOLISCHE BILDUNG. m. DM.80. (Verein Katholischer Deutscher Lehrerinnen) Verlag Ferdinand Schoeningh GmbH, Postfach 2540, 33055 Paderborn, Germany. TEL 05251-127665. FAX 05251-127860. **Document type:** bulletin.

282 267.4 AU ISSN 0022-9377
KATHOLISCHE FRAUENBEWEGUNG OESTERREICHS. FUEHRUNGSBLATT. 1951. q. S.80. Katholisches Frauenwerk in Oesterreich, Spiegelgasse 3-II, A-1010 Vienna, Austria. Eds. Veronika Handschuh, Susanne Degenhart. bk.rev. circ. 2,500.

KATHOLISCHE OEFFENTLICHE BUECHEREI; Vierteljahreszeitschrift fuer Mitarbeiter der Katholischen Oeffentlichen Buechereien. see LIBRARY AND INFORMATION SCIENCES

282 GW
KATHOLISCHE SONNTAGSZEITUNG FUER DAS BISTUM AUGSBURG. 1946. w. DM.84. St. Ulrich Verlag GmbH, Postfach 111920, 86044 Augsburg, Germany. TEL 0821-50242-0. FAX 0821-5024280. Ed. Anton Fuchs; Pub. Dirk Voss. adv.; bk.rev. circ. 60,000. (back issues avail.) **Document type:** newsletter.
Formerly (until 1993): Kirchenzeitung fuer die Dioezese Augsburg.

282 GW
KATHOLISCHEN MILITAERBISCHOF FUER DIE DEUTSCHE BUNDESWEHR. VERORDNUNGSBLATT. (Text in German and Latin) 1965. 8/yr. Katholisches Militaerbischofsamt, Postfach 190199, 53037 Bonn, Germany. TEL 0228-9121-0. FAX 0228-9121-105. circ. 350. **Document type:** bulletin.

KATHOLISCHER BERUFSVERBAND FUER PFLEGEBERUFE. MITTEILUNGSBLATT. see MEDICAL SCIENCES

282 GW ISSN 0177-2872
KATHOLISCHER DIGEST; Europas grosse Kirchenzeitschrift. 1946. m. DM.97.20. Verlag Axel B. Trunkel, Landhausstr. 82, 70190 Stuttgart, Germany. TEL 0711-268630. Ed. Andrea Przyklenk. adv.; bk.rev.; film rev.; illus. circ. 38,900.

200 GW ISSN 0170-7302
KATHOLISCHES LEBEN UND KIRCHENREFORM IM ZEITALTER DER GLAUBENSSPALTUNG. 1927. irreg. price varies. Aschendorffsche Verlagsbuchhandlung, Soesterstr. 13, 48155 Muenster, Germany. TEL 0251-690-0. FAX 0251-690143. Ed. Klaus Ganzer. **Document type:** monographic series.

201 PL
KATOLICKI UNIWERSYTET LUBELSKI. WYDZIAL TEOLOGICZNO-KANONICZNY. ROZPRAWY. (Text in Polish; summaries in English or French) 1947. irreg. price varies. Katolicki Uniwersytet Lubelski, Towarzystwo Naukowe, Ul. Gliniana 21, 20-616 Lublin, Poland. index. circ. 3,150.

200 PL ISSN 0044-4405
AS262.L84
KATOLICKI UNIWERSYTET LUBELSKI. ZESZYTY NAUKOWE. (In four parts) (Text in Polish; summaries in English, French) 1958. q. price varies. Katolicki Uniwersytet Lubelski, Towarzystwo Naukowe, Ul. Gliniana 21, 20-616 Lublin, Poland. bk.rev.; illus.; index. circ. 1,125. **Document type:** academic/scholarly publication.

282 US
KATOLIKUS MAGYAROK VASARNAPJA/CATHOLIC HUNGARIANS' SUNDAY.* (Text in Hungarian) 1894. w. $25. (Custody of St. Stephen King, Franciscan Friars) Catholic Publishing Company, 8423 South St., Detroit, MI 48209-2709. Ed. Fr. Angelus A. Ligeti. adv.; bk.rev. circ. 3,100. (back issues avail.) **Document type:** newspaper.

282 SW ISSN 0345-6110
KATOLSK KYRKOTIDNING. 1926. 22/yr. SEK 225. Stiftelsen Katolsk Kyrkotidning, P.O. Box 4032, S-102 61 Stockholm, Sweden. TEL 46-8-643-80-70.
Former titles (until 1960): Hemmet och Helgedomen; (until 1959): Katolska Foersamlingsbladet Hemmet och Helgedomen; (until 1940): Hemmet och Helgedomen.

282 DK ISSN 0902-297X
KATOLSK ORIENTERING. 1975. 20/yr. DKK 230. Vesterbrogade 28, 4, DK-1620 Copenhagen V, Denmark. TEL 45-31-21-14-44. FAX 45-31-24-49-75. adv.; bk.rev. circ. 16,500.

282 GW ISSN 0138-2543
KATOLSKI POSOL. (Text in Upper Sorbian) 1863. w. DM.12. (Towarstwo Cyrila a Metoda) Domowina Verlag GmbH, Tuchmacherstr. 27, 02625 Bautzen, Germany. **Document type:** academic/scholarly publication.

282 JA ISSN 0387-3005
KATORIKKU KENKYU. (Text in Japanese; summaries in English) 1961. s-a. 2260 Yen. Sophia University, Theological Society - Jochi Daigaku, Kamishakujii 4-32-11, Nerima-ku, Tokyo 177, Japan. TEL 03-5991-0343. FAX 03-5991-6928. Ed. Tadahiko Iwashima. bk.rev.; circ. 1,000 (controlled). (back issues avail.) **Document type:** academic/scholarly publication.
Description: Contains articles in all fields of Christian theology and philosophy, past and present, written by scholars born or living in Japan.

282 283 SA ISSN 0022-9687
KEHILWENYANE; dikgang tsa bodumedi le morafe. (Text and summaries in English and Setswana) 1958. m. R.0.20 per no. (Roman Catholic Diocese of Kimberley) Kehilwenyane Publications, Box 309, Kimberley 8300, South Africa. Ed. Johannes Mogakwe. bk.rev.; abstr.; illus.; stat. circ. 4,500. **Indexed:** CERDIC.

282 BE
KERK EN LEVEN. (Text in Dutch) 1944. w. 600 BEF. N.V. Halewijn, Halewijnlaan 92, 2050 Antwerp, Belgium. TEL 32-3-2100940. FAX 32-3-2100936. Ed. Mark van de Voorde; Pub. Johan Cornille. adv. contact: Etienne Jacobin. bk.rev. circ. 740,000. (tabloid format; back issues avail.) **Document type:** newspaper.
Description: Covers all aspects of contemporary Catholic life, including education, social and community issues, and problems of Third World development, and related topics.

283 UK
KEYS OF PETER. 1969. bi-m. £4. Petrine Publications, 157 Vicarage Rd., London E10 5DU, England. TEL 0181-539-3876. Ed. Ronald King; Pub. Ronald King. bk.rev. **Document type:** newsletter.
Description: Catholic publication covering religious and world affairs in relation to the Christian social order and Papal teaching.

282 TZ ISSN 0856-2563
KIONGOZI/LEADER; gazeti la wananchi. (Text in Swahili) 1950. fortn. EAs.180. Catholic Publishers Ltd., Box 9400, Dar es Salaam, Tanzania. TEL 255-51-29505. Ed. Chrysostom C. Rweyemamu. adv. contact: Joseph Chonya. bk.rev. circ. 20,000. **Document type:** newsletter.
Incorporates: Ecclesia (ISSN 0012-9046)
Description: Roman Catholic publication.

282 AU ISSN 0023-1789
DIE KIRCHE; Dioezesanblatt fuer die Kirchenprovinz Mitteleuropa. 1954. q. S.80. Verein zur Foerderung der Liberalkatholischen Kirche, Erdenweg 21, A-1140 Vienna, Austria. TEL 01-9792211. Ed. Rt. Rev. Rudolf Hammer. bk.rev. circ. 600. **Document type:** bulletin.

282 GW
KIRCHE HEUTE. 11/yr. DM.48. Maria Aktuell Verlag GmbH, Postfach 25, 93322 Abensberg, Germany. TEL 09443-3433. FAX 09443-3960. Ed. J. Hans Benirschke. adv.; **B&W page** DM.2390. bk.rev. (back issues avail.) **Document type:** bulletin.
Formerly (until 1994): Offerten-Zeitung fuer die Katholische Geistlichkeit und Engagierte Glaeubige (ISSN 0946-5812)

284 GW
KIRCHE IN MARBURG; Mitteilungen der evangelischen und Katholischen Gemeinden. 1936. m. DM.11. Gesamtverband der Evangelischen Kirchengemeinden in Marburg, Leipzigerstr. 20, 35039 Marburg, Germany. (Co-sponsor: Katholische Pfarrgemeinde in Marburg-Stadt) Ed.Bd. adv.; bk.rev.; illus. circ. 4,000.
Formerly: Gemeindebote (ISSN 0016-6103)

282 GW
KIRCHE UND SCHULE. 1972. q. Bischoefliches Generalvikariat Muenster, Breul 23, 48143 Muenster, Germany. TEL 0251-495-415. FAX 0251-4956075. Ed. Edith Verweyen. circ. 5,000. **Document type:** newsletter.

KIRCHENMUSIKALISCHE MITTEILUNGEN. see MUSIC

KIRCHENMUSIKALISCHES JAHRBUCH. see MUSIC

282 GW
KIRCHENZEITUNG FUER DAS ERZBISTUM KOELN. 1946. w. DM.114.60 (foreign DM.129.40). J.P. Bachem Verlag GmbH, Ursulaplatz 1, 50668 Cologne, Germany. TEL 0221-16190. **Document type:** newspaper.

KOLPING BANNER. see CLUBS

282 GW
KONRADSBLATT. 1916. w. (Sun.). (Erbistum Freiburg) Badenia Verlag und Druckerei GmbH, Rudolf-Freytag-Str. 6, 76189 Karlsruhe, Germany. TEL 0721-578041. FAX 0721-579890. Ed. Josef Dewald. adv. contact: Hans-Dieter Zeiske. circ. 98,834. **Document type:** bulletin.
Description: Discusses current religious issues.

282 AU ISSN 0023-3676
KONTAKT DREI UND ZWANZIG.* 1954. bi-m. contribution. Roemisches Katholisches Pfarramt Atzgersdorf, Peter Kirchenplatz 1, A-1230 Vienna, Austria. Ed. Pfarrer Otto Novotny. bk.rev. circ. 2,100.
Formerly: Liesinger Pfarrblatt.

RELIGIONS AND THEOLOGY — ROMAN CATHOLIC

028.5   GW   ISSN 0942-136X
KONTRASTE. 1960. q. DM.22. Verlag Herder GmbH und Co. KG, Hermann-Herder-Str. 4, 79104 Freiburg, Germany. FAX 0761-2717-407. Ed. Christian Dau. adv.; bk.rev.; illus. circ. 20,000.
Formerly: Kontraste Impulse (ISSN 0344-5984)

282   HK
KUNG KAO PO/CATHOLIC CHINESE WEEKLY. (Text in Chinese) 1928. w. 16 Caine Rd., 11th Fl., Hong Kong. TEL 2522-0487. FAX 2521-3095. Ed. Fr. James Wan.

282   US
LA CROSSE TIMES - REVIEW. 1937. 40/yr. $22 (effective May 1993). Diocese of La Crosse, 3710 East Ave., S., Box 4004, La Crosse, WI 54602-4004. TEL 608-788-1524. FAX 608-788-8413. Ed. Jerry Ruff. adv. contact: Judith Tatarek. bk.rev. circ. 22,000. **Document type:** newspaper.

282   US
LAKE SHORE VISITOR. 1874. w. $28 to non-members; members $18. Erie Roman Catholic Diocese, 429 E. Grandview Blvd., Box 10668, Erie, PA 16514-0668. TEL 814-824-1160. FAX 814-824-1128. Ed. Gary C. Loncki. adv. contact: Thomas W. Brennan. bk.rev. circ. 19,300. (also avail. in microfilm) **Document type:** newspaper.

282   MG
LAKROAN'I MADAGASIKARA. (Text in French and Malagasy) 1927. w. Maison Jean XXIII, Mahamasina Sud, 101 Antananarivo, Madagascar. TEL 26141. Ed. Louis Rasolo. circ. 16,000.

282   UK
LANCASTER DIOCESAN DIRECTORY. 1925. a. £1.25. The Willows Church, Ribby Rd., Kirkham, Preston PR4 2BE, England. TEL 0772-683664. Ed. Rev. Dunstan Cooper. adv. circ. 4,500. **Document type:** directory.
Description: Covers all churches and Catholic organizations in the Lancaster Diocese.

LAND AKTUELL. see *POLITICAL SCIENCE*

282   PH   ISSN 0116-4856
BR1
LANDAS; journal of Loyola School of Theology. (Text in English) 1987. s-a. P.150($18) (effective 1991). Loyola School of Theology, Loyola Institute for Studies on Development of Man and Society, Ateneo de Manila University, P.O. Box 4082, Manila, Philippines. TEL 632-99-15-61. FAX 632-921-7311. Ed. Antonio B. Lambino. bk.rev. circ. 500.
Description: Features articles on scripture, theology, ethics and spirituality written from the perspective of authors, most of them Filipinos, working and teaching in the Philippines.

264.02 870   US
LATIN LITURGY ASSOCIATION NEWSLETTER. 1976. q. $10. Latin Liturgy Association, c/o Prof. Robert J. Edgeworth, 740 Carriage Way, Baton Rouge, LA 70808. TEL 504-769-4678. adv.; bk.rev. circ. 1,400. (back issues avail.) **Document type:** newsletter.
Description: Promotes the use of Latin in the rites of the Roman Catholic Church.

270   IT   ISSN 0023-902X
LAURENTIANUM. (Text in principal European languages) 1960. 3/yr. L.45000 (effective 1994). (International College of the Capuchin Order) Collegio Internazionale S. Lorenzo da Brindisi, Circonvallazione Occidentale 6850, 00163 Rome, Italy. TEL 39-6-66151949. FAX 39-6-66162401. Ed. Salvatore Vacca. bk.rev.; index. circ. 500. (back issues avail.) **Indexed:** Canon Law Abstr., CERDIC, M.L.A., New Test.Abstr., Old Test.Abstr. —BLDSC (5160.810000).

282   NR
THE LEADER. 1956. fortn. ₦N1000. Archdiocese of Owerri, PMB 1017, Owerri, Nigeria. TEL 230932. Ed. Kevin C. Akagha. circ. 27,000 (paid). **Document type:** newspaper.
Description: Informs and educates Nigerian Catholics on issues facing the country and the Church, so they can form their opinions and contribute meaningfully to these issues that affect their lives and faith.

282   US   ISSN 1072-7930
LEAFLET MISSAL. 1929. 8/yr. $18. American Catholic Press, 16565 S. Sate St., S. Holland, IL 60473. TEL 708-331-5485. Ed. Rev. Michael Gilligan. adv. contact: Joan Termini. circ. 125,000 (paid). (back issues avail.) **Document type:** consumer publication.
Description: Provides spiritual readings, prayer texts and hymns.

LEAPING; magazine of Christian dance fellowship of Australia. see *DANCE*

282   US
THE LEAVEN (KANSAS CITY).* 1939. w. $8. Catholic Archdiocese of Kansas City, 12615 Parallel Pkwy., Kansas City, KS 66109. TEL 913-721-1575. Ed. Rev. Mark Goldasich. adv.; bk.rev.; film rev. circ. 44,000. **Document type:** newspaper.
Formerly: Eastern Kansas Register (ISSN 0012-883X)
Description: Covers local news, national and international news on issues of concern and interest to Catholics.

282   GW   ISSN 0171-4171
LEBENDIGE KATECHESE. 1981. s-a. DM.19. Echter Wuerzburg, Juliuspromenade 64, 97070 Wuerzburg, Germany. Ed. Lothar Roos. adv.; bk.rev. (back issues avail.) **Document type:** bulletin. —BLDSC (5179.622800).

282   GW   ISSN 0931-8887
DIE LEBENDIGE ZELLE. 1957. 6/yr. DM.24. Landeskomitee der Katholiken in Bayern, Schaefflerstr. 9, 80333 Munich, Germany. TEL 089-21371228. Ed. Dr. Eder. circ. 5,400. **Document type:** newsletter.

282   GW   ISSN 0023-9941
LEBENDIGES ZEUGNIS. 1946. q. membership. Bonifatiuswerk der Deutschen Katholiken e.V., Postfach 1169, 33041 Paderborn, Germany. TEL 05251-29960. FAX 05251-299688. Ed. Guenter Risse. bk.rev. circ. 4,600. **Indexed:** CERDIC. **Document type:** newsletter.
Description: Examines topics in the fields of religion, philosophy and ethics.

282   MM
LEHEN IS-SEWWA. (Text in Maltese) 1928. w. (Sat.). £5($33) Malta Catholic Action, Catholic Institute, Floriana VLT 16, Malta. TEL 353-225847. Ed. Paul Sailba. adv.: B&W page £M110, color page £M296; adv. contact: Virgil Bugeja. cols./p.: 5. (standard format; back issues avail.) **Document type:** newspaper.
Description: Publishes news and commentary on events and issues of interest to Maltese Catholics.

282   LO
LESOTHO CATHOLIC DIRECTORY. 1977. irreg., latest 1988. $10. (Lesotho Catholic Bishops Conference) Mazenod Printing Works Pty. Ltd., Box 39, Mazenod 160, Lesotho. FAX 310131. TELEX 4271 LO. Ed. F. Mairot. circ. 500. **Document type:** directory.
Description: Contains statistics, personnel, addresses and services of the Catholic Church in Lesotho.

200   LU
LETZEBURGER SONNDESBLAD. 1867. 650 Fr. Editions Saint Paul, S.A., 2 rue Christophe Plantin, L-2339 Luxembourg, Luxembourg. TEL 4993-281. FAX 49-10-78. Ed. Andre Heiderscheid.

282   AU
LICHTENTALER PFARRNACHRICHTEN. 1978. 4/yr. free. Pfarre Lichtental, Marktgasse 40, A-1090 Vienna, Austria. adv. circ. 5,000.

282   IT
LIEB FRAUEN BOTE. (Text in German) 1950. bi-m. L.7000. Bertrand Vollmann, 39030 S. Lorenzo Sebato (BZ), Italy. circ. 4,000.

282   SY
LE LIEN; revue du patriarcat Grec-Melkite Catholique. 1936. bi-m. $25. P.O.B. 22249, Damascus, Syria. TEL 433129. FAX 963-11-5431266. TELEX 419413 SY CHAOUI. Ed. Patriarch Maximos V Hakim. adv.; bk.rev.; illus. circ. 2,500. (back issues avail.)
Description: Covers news of the Patriarchate, ecumenism, liturgy, and other religious topics.

282   FR   ISSN 0024-2926
LIEN ENTRE MERES ET PERES DE PRETRES.* q. 3 F. (Diocese de Paris) Imprimerie Dalex a Montrouge, 5 et 7 rue Victor-Basch, Montrouge, France.

282   US   ISSN 0024-3450
BX4020.A1
LIGUORIAN. 1913. m. $15. (Redemptorists, St. Louis Province) Liguori Publications, Liguori Dr., Liguori, MO 63057. TEL 314-464-2500. FAX 314-464-8449. Eds. Rev. Allen Weinert, Cheryl Plass. bk.rev.; illus. circ. 363,000. (also avail. in microfiche from UMI) **Indexed:** Cath.Ind., CERDIC. —UMI.
Description: Articles on spirituality and Catholic teaching for readers of all ages.

282   US
LILY OF THE MOHAWKS. 1936. q. $3. Tekakwitha League, Auriesville, NY 12016. TEL 518-853-3153. Ed. John J. Paret. bk.rev. circ. 6,000. (back issues avail.) **Document type:** newsletter.

282   AT   ISSN 0812-6240
THE LINK. 1979. q. free. Missionary Society of St. Paul, 477 Royal Parade, Parkville, Vic. 3052, Australia. TEL 03-801-1763. FAX 03-801-1802. Ed. Noel Bianco. circ. 20,000. (looseleaf format; back issues avail.) **Document type:** newsletter.
Formerly: Missionary Society of Saint Paul. Link (ISSN 0728-5493)
Description: Evangelical information from an international perspective.

282   VC
LITTERA ANTIQUA. 1980. irreg., no.8, 1991. price varies. Scuola Vaticana di Paleografia Diplomatica e Archivistica, 00120 Vatican City (Rome), State of the Vatican City.

282   CN
LITURGIE, FOI ET CULTURE. (Text in French) 1965. 4/yr. Can.$14($16) (outside US and Canada US$27). Canadian Conference of Catholic Bishops, Publications Service - Conference des Eveques Catholiques du Canada, 90 Ave. Parent, Ottawa, ON K1N 7B1, Canada. TEL 613-241-9461. FAX 613-241-5090. Ed. M. l'Abbe Paul Boily. bk.rev.; illus. circ. 1,400. **Document type:** bulletin.
Former titles: Conference des Eveques Catholiques du Canada. Bulletin National de Liturgie; Conference Catholique Canadienne. Bulletin National de Liturgie (ISSN 0384-5087)

264   US   ISSN 1046-9990
LITURGY 90. 1970. 8/yr. $18. (Archdiocese of Chicago) Liturgy Training Publications, 1800 N. Hermitage Ave., Chicago, IL 60622-1101. TEL 312-486-8970. FAX 800-933-7094. Ed. David Philippart. index. circ. 6,120. (back issues avail.) **Document type:** academic/scholarly publication.
Formerly: Liturgy 80 (ISSN 1040-6603)
Description: For those who prepare liturgy in Catholic parishes, including artists and musicians. Contains articles, lists of events, and a question and answer column.

282   UK
LIVERPOOL CATHOLIC DIRECTORY. 1828. a. £1.15. Catholic Pictorial Ltd., Media House, Mann Island, Pier Head, Liverpool L3 1DQ, England. TEL 051-236-2191. FAX 051-236-2216. Ed. P. Henegan. adv. circ. 9,000. **Document type:** directory.

282   US   ISSN 0884-1330
LIVING FAITH; daily Catholic devotions. 1985. q. $5.95 (large print ed. $7.95; cassette tape $29.95). Creative Communications for the Parish, 10300 Watson Rd., St. Louis, MO 63127. TEL 314-821-1363. FAX 314-821-9031. Ed. James E. Adams. circ. 450,000 (paid). (also avail. in audio cassette; large print edition in 14 pt.)
Formerly: Living Words.
Description: Provides daily reflection based on a Scripture passage from the daily Mass. Includes readings for daily Mass listed at the bottom of each devotion.

RELIGIONS AND THEOLOGY — ROMAN CATHOLIC

377.8 US ISSN 0024-5275
BX923
LIVING LIGHT; an interdisciplinary review of Catholic religious education, catechesis and pastoral ministry. 1964. q. $29.95. United States Catholic Conference, Office for Publishing and Promotion Services, 3211 Fourth St., N.E., Washington, DC 20017-1194. TEL 202-541-3098. FAX 202-541-3089. Ed. Berard L. Marthaler. adv.; bk.rev.; index; circ. 1,200 (controlled). (also avail. in microform from UMI) **Indexed:** Cath.Ind., CERDIC, Old.Test.Abstr.
—BLDSC (5282.700000); UMI.
  Description: Provides a forum for catechests and professional educators to identify problems and issues, report on research, encourage critical thinking, and to contribute to the decision-making in the field of religious educations and pastoral action.

282 US
▼**LIVING THE NEW CATECHISM**. 1995. m. $11. St. Anthony Messenger Press, 1615 Republic St., Cincinnati, OH 45210. TEL 513-241-5615. FAX 513-241-0399. Ed. John Bookser Feister. **Document type:** newsletter.
  Description: Offers commentary on Part III of the new Catechism of the Catholic Church.

282 CN ISSN 0703-6752
LIVING WITH CHRIST - COMPLETE EDITION. French edition: Prions en Eglise - Edition Complete. (French ed. also avail. in large print, 11 pt.) 1966. m. Can.$12.75($14.50) Novalis, St. Paul University, 233 Main St., Ottawa, ON K1S 1C4, Canada. TEL 613-236-1393. FAX 613-782-3004. (Subscr. to: 49 Front St., E., 2nd Fl., Toronto, ON M5E 1B3, Canada. TEL 416-363-3303) Ed. Louise Pambrun. circ. 107,000.
  Description: Liturgical texts of the Mass for Sundays and weekdays.

282 CN ISSN 0703-6760
LIVING WITH CHRIST - SUNDAY EDITION. French edition: Prions en Eglise - Edition Dominicale. 1936. bi-m., plus 2 special issues. Can.6$950($8.35) Novalis, St. Paul University, 223 Main St., Ottawa, ON K1S 1C4, Canada. TEL 613-236-1393. FAX 613-782-3004. (Subscr. to: 49 Front St., E., 2nd Fl., Toronto, ON M5E 1B3, Canada. TEL 416-827-1530) Ed. Louise Pambrun.
  Description: Liturgical texts for Sunday Mass.

282 SP
LLUVIA DE ROSAS. 1923. bi-m. 450 ptas.($4) c/o P. Eugenio Alsina Valls, Apdo. 112, 25080 Lerida, Spain. Eds. Pages, Virgili. circ. 20,000. (also avail. in microfilm)

282 US ISSN 0024-6255
LONG ISLAND CATHOLIC. 1962. w. $20. (Catholic Diocese of Rockville Centre) Catholic Press Association, 99 N. Village Ave., Rockville Centre, NY 11571-9009. TEL 516-594-1000. FAX 516-594-1092. (Subscr. to: Box 9009, Rockville Centre, NY 11571-9009) Ed. Elizabeth O'Connor; Pub. Rev. John R. McGann. adv. contact: William Hunt. bibl.; charts; illus.; tr.lit. circ. 118,388. (also avail. in microform) **Document type:** newspaper.

282 US
LOS ANGELES TIDINGS. 1895. w. $16.24. Roman Catholic Archbishop of Los Angeles, 1530 W. Ninth St., Los Angeles, CA 90015. TEL 213-251-3360. FAX 203-386-8667. Ed. Tod Tamberg. adv. contact: Ed Alvarez. bk.rev. circ. 50,000. (tabloid format) **Document type:** newspaper.

282 GW
LOURDES - ROSEN. 1880. q. membership. Deutscher Lourdes-Verein, Schwalbengasse 10, 50667 Cologne, Germany. TEL 0221-2576246. FAX 0221-2576189. circ. 25,000 (controlled). **Document type:** newsletter.

282 IT
LUISA LA SANTA TEREZIARIA DOMENICANA; periodico di spiritualita del divin volere. m. L.12000 (foreign L. 18000). Pia Associazione Luisa Piccarreta Piccoli Figli della Divina Volonta, Via N. Sauro, 25, 70033 Corato (Bari), Italy. TEL 080-898-2221. Ed. Suor. Assunta Marigliano.
  Description: Religious forum covering various religious topics, also includes calendar of events.

268 BE ISSN 0024-7324
BX800.A1
LUMEN VITAE; revue internationale de la formation religieuse. (Text in French) 1946. q. 1410 BEF. (International Centre for Religious Education) Lumen Vitae Press, 186 rue Washington, 1050 Brussels, Belgium. TEL 32-2-3490370. FAX 32-2-3465745. Ed. Stany Simon. bk.rev.; bibl.; index, circ. 1,800. (also avail. in microform from UMI) **Indexed:** Cath.Ind., CERDIC, Educ.Ind., New Test.Abstr., Rel.& Theol.Abstr. (1969-), Rural Recreat.Tour.Abstr., World Agri.Econ.& Rural Sociol.Abstr. **Document type:** academic/scholarly publication.
—SWETS.

200 378 PE
M I E C SERVICO DE DOCUMENTACION. 12/yr. $18 (includes subscr. to: SPES and America Latina Boletin). Movimiento Internacional de Estudiantes Catolicos, Centro de Documentacion, Apdo. 3564, Lima 100, Peru. bk.rev.; bibl.; illus.

282 GW
M S C KONTAKTE. 1980. q. (Missionaries of Sacred Heart) Birkenverlag der Herz-Jesu-Missionare, Postfach 1146, 83381 Freilassing, Germany. TEL 08654-9324. FAX 08654-67606. Ed. Alois Linder. circ. 8,000. **Document type:** bulletin.

282 IT ISSN 0391-7169
MADONNA. 1954. bi-m. L.50000. Opera Madonna del Divino Amore, Via Ardeatina, Km. 12, 00134 Rome, Italy. Dir. Don Pasquale Silla. circ. 1,500.

282 IT
LA MADONNA DEL DIVINO AMORE; bollettino mensile del santuario. 1932. m. Opera Madonna del Divino Amore, Via Ardeatina, Km. 12, 00134 Rome, Italy. Ed. Carlo Sabatini. illus. circ. 100,000.
  Description: Deals with religious events for young people and community affairs sponsored by local church organizations.

282 IT
MADRE DI DIO; mensile mariano fondato da don Giacomo Alberione. 1932. m. L.20000($15) (effective 1995). Societa S. Paolo (SSP), Via Alessandro Severo 56, 00145 Rome, Italy. TEL 39-6-5415501. FAX 39-6-5405290. Ed. Rev. Stefano Andreatta. adv.; bk.rev. circ. 11,000. (back issues avail.)
  Description: Religious publication covering religious news with special emphasis on the Virgin Mary.

266 SP
MADRE Y MAESTRA. 1871. m. (except July-Aug. combined). 1200 ptas.($20) Misioneros del Sagrado Corazon de Jesus, Avenida Pio XII, 31, 28016 Madrid, Spain. TEL 34-1-3599600. FAX 34-1-3459104. Ed. Angel Gonzalez. adv.; bk.rev.; illus. circ. 12,000.

282 IT ISSN 0024-9696
MAESTRO. 1944. m. L.35000 to non-members. Associazione Italiana Maestri Cattolici, Clivo di Monte del Gallo 50, 00165 Rome, Italy. TEL 634-651. FAX 06-6375903. Ed. Carlo Buzzi. adv.; bk.rev.; illus.; stat. circ. 60,000.
  Description: Presents articles from educators and others related to the field on the issues of school systems, the quality of education and the politics of schooling throughout Italy.

282 CN ISSN 0025-0007
MAGNIFICAT. English edition (ISSN 0381-0852) (Editions in English, French) 1965. m. Can.$10. Apostles of Infinite Love, Monastery of the Magnificat of the Mother of God, Box 308, St. Jovite, PQ J0T 2H0, Canada. TEL 819-688-5225. FAX 819-688-6548. illus.; circ. 4,000 (2,000 English edition; 2,000 French edition) (paid). (processed) **Indexed:** Eng.Ind.

282 AT
MAJELLAN; champion of the family. 1949. q. Aus.$12. Redemptorist Congregation, P.O. Box 43, Brighton, Vic. 3186, Australia. TEL 61-3-95922777. FAX 61-3-95931337. Ed. Rev. W.H. Stinson. circ. 56,000. (back issues avail.)

232 SZ ISSN 0025-2972
MARIA; marianischer digest. 1950. 6/yr. 13.50 SFr. Postfach 6407, CH-3001 Bern, Switzerland. TEL 031-221380. FAX 031-223071. Ed. Josef Gruebel. adv.; bk.rev.; illus. circ. 25,000.

282 SZ
MARIA HEUTE. 1969. m. 26 SFr. Parvis Verlag, CH-1648 Hauteville, Switzerland. TEL 029-51905. FAX 029-52793. **Document type:** newsletter.
  Formerly: Mater Nostra.

200 IT
MARIA NOSTRA LUCE. 1918. m. L.3000. Centro Nazionale Associazione Mariana, Via Francesco Albergotti 75, 00167 Rome, Italy. bk.rev. circ. 3,500.

282 US
MARIAN HELPERS BULLETIN. 1947. q. $2 membership. Association of Marian Helpers, Stockbridge, MA 01263. TEL 413-298-3691. FAX 413-298-3583. Ed. Vinnie Flynn. bk.rev. circ. 1,000,000.

200 020 US ISSN 0076-4434
BT595
MARIAN LIBRARY STUDIES. NEW SERIES. (Text in language of author) 1951; N.S. 1969. a. price varies. University of Dayton, Marian Library, Dayton, OH 45469-1390. TEL 513-229-4214. FAX 513-229-4590. Ed. Theodore Koehler. circ. 200. (also avail. in microform from UMI; reprint service avail. from UMI) **Indexed:** Cath.Ind., CERDIC. **Document type:** academic/scholarly publication.
  Description: Presents scholarly, historical and interdisciplinary studies related to Christology, Mariology and Ecclesiology.

282 US ISSN 0464-9680
BT596
MARIAN STUDIES. 1950. a. $12. Mariological Society of America, Marian Library, Box 1390, University of Dayton, Dayton, OH 45469-1390. TEL 513-229-4214. FAX 513-229-4590. Ed. Thomas A. Thompson. adv.; bibl.; cum.index. circ. 600. (also avail. in microform from UMI; reprint service avail. from UMI) **Indexed:** Cath.Ind.
—BLDSC (5373.555000); UMI.
  Description: Proceedings of society's annual convention.

232 AU ISSN 0025-3014
MARIANIST. 1956. q. S.80. Gesellschaft Mariae in Oesterreich und Deutschland - Marianist Catholic Order, Mistlberg 20, A-4284 Tragwein, Austria. FAX 07236-22523. illus. circ. 4,300. **Document type:** newsletter.

282 IT
MARIANUM. 1939. s-a. L.70000 (foreign L.80000($55)) (effective 1994). Pontificia Facolta Teologica Marianum, Viale Trenta Aprile 6, 00153 Rome, Italy. TEL 39-6-5890661. FAX 39-6-5880292. Ed. Ignazio M. Calabuig. adv.; bk.rev. circ. 800. **Indexed:** M.L.A., New Test.Abstr. **Document type:** academic/scholarly publication.
  Description: Offers to the Church a serious theological reflection on Mary the Mother of God.

282 CN
MARTYRS' SHRINE MESSAGE. 1937. s-a. Can.$5. Jesuit Fathers of Upper Canada, Martyrs' Shrine, Midland, ON L4R 4K5, Canada. TEL 705-526-3788. FAX 705-526-1546. Ed. Carl Matthews. circ. 12,000. (back issues avail.) **Document type:** bibliography.

266 US
MARYKNOLL MAGAZINE. 1907. m. $10. Maryknoll Fathers and Brothers, Box 301, Maryknoll, NY 10545-0301. TEL 914-941-7590. FAX 914-945-0670. (Co-sponsor: Catholic Foreign Mission Society of America) Ed. Joseph Veneroso. illus.; index; circ. 600,000. (paid). (also avail. in microform from UMI) **Indexed:** Cath.Ind., CERDIC. —UMI; UnCover.
  Former titles: Maryknoll (ISSN 0025-4142); (until 1938): Field Afar (ISSN 0271-7204); Supersedes (in 1907): Channel (ISSN 0009-1456)
  Description: Covers mission work in underdeveloped countries.

281.9 LE ISSN 0025-4975
MASSIS. 1947. w. Armenian Catholic Patriarchate, Rue de l'Hopital Grec Orthodoxe, Jeitawi 2400, Beirut, Lebanon. Ed. Fr. Antranik Granian. charts; illus. (tabloid format)

RELIGIONS AND THEOLOGY — ROMAN CATHOLIC

282   GW   ISSN 0934-8522
MATERIALDIENST DES KONFESSIONSKUNDLICHEN INSTITUTS. 1950. bi-m. DM.25. Evangelischer Bund, Konfessionskundliches Institut, Postfach 1255, 64602 Bensheim, Germany. TEL 06251-38000. FAX 06251-2045. Ed. Walter Fleischmann-Bisten. bk.rev. circ. 6,200. **Document type:** bulletin.
Formerly: Evangelischer Bund. Materialdienst.
Description: Ecumenical issues as they relate to the Roman Catholic Church.

282   PL   ISSN 0076-5244
MATERIALY ZRODLOWE DO DZIEJOW KOSCIOLA W POLSCE. 1965. irreg. price varies. Katolicki Uniwersytet Lubelski, Towarzystwo Naukowe, Ul. Gliniana 21, 20-616 Lublin, Poland. (Dist. by: Ars Polona-Ruch, Krakowskie Przedmiescie 7, Warsaw, Poland) (Co-sponsor: Instytut Geografii Historycznej Kosciola w Polsce przy K.U.L.) Ed. Jerzy Kloczowski. circ. 1,000.

MAVRICA/RAINBOW. see *CHILDREN AND YOUTH — For*

282   CK   ISSN 0121-4977
BX1751.2
MEDELLIN; teologia y pastoral para America Latina. 1975. q. Col.$10000 ($35 in U.S.; Europe $45). Consejo Episcopal Latinoamericano, Instituto Teologico Pastoral, Transversal 67, No. 173-71, Apdo. Aereo 253353, Bogota DE, Colombia. TEL 6776521. FAX 6714004. TELEX 41388 CELA CO. Dir. Alvaro Cadavid. bk.rev.; film rev. circ. 2,000. (back issues avail.)

282   US
MEDICAL MISSION NEWS. 1931. q. free. Catholic Medical Mission Board, Inc., 10 W. 17th St., New York, NY 10011. TEL 212-242-7757. FAX 212-807-9161. circ. 25,000.
Incorporates (1962-1992): Professional Placement Newsnotes.
Description: Distribution of medicines to 6,000 mission units in 60 countries, and placement of healthcare professionals and para-professionals in clinical facilities the world over.

200   FR   ISSN 0025-8911
BR3
MELANGES DE SCIENCE RELIGIEUSE. 1944. q. 150 F.($30) (effective Jan. 1991). Institut Catholique de Lille, 60 bd. Vauban, B.P. 109, 59016 Lille Cedex, France. TEL 20-30-88-27. Ed. Gerard-Henry Baudry. bk.rev.; cum.index: vols. 1-27, 1944-1970. circ. 500. (back issues avail.) **Indexed:** Bull.Signal., CERDIC, Int.Z.Bibelwiss, M.L.A., New Test.Abstr., Old Test.Abstr., Rel.& Theol.Abstr. (1968-), Rel.Ind.One, Rel.Per.
Description: Covers theology, philosophy, the histories of religions, institutions, law, anthropology, sociology, pedagogy, literature and art.

282   CL   ISSN 0716-0062
MENSAJE. 1951. m. Esc.10000($50) (Compania de Jesus, Provincia Chilena) Residencia San Roberto Bellarmino, Almirante Barroso 24, Casilla 10445, Santiago, Chile. TEL 2-696-0653. Ed. Fernando Montes. adv.; B&W page Esc.210000, color page Esc.380000; 152 x 211. bk.rev.; film rev.; play rev.; bibl.; illus.; stat.; cum.index. circ. 8,000. **Indexed:** Biol.Abstr., Hisp.Amer.Per.Ind. (1984-), HR Rep. (1986-1989).
Description: Church review that deals with theological, social, cultural, economic and political issues of Chile and South America.

282   US
THE MESSAGE (EVANSVILLE). 1970. w. $17.50. (Diocese of Evansville) Catholic Press of Evansville, 4200 N. Kentucky Ave., Box 4169, Evansville, IN 47724-0169. TEL 812-424-5536. FAX 812-421-1334. Ed. Paul R. Leingang. circ. 9,300. (tabloid format) **Document type:** newspaper.
Description: Catholic newspaper of Southwestern Indiana.

282   FR   ISSN 0026-0290
MESSAGES DU SECOURS CATHOLIQUE. 1945. m. 16 F. Editions S.O.S., 106 rue du Bac, 75341 Paris Cedex 07, France. Ed. Robert Prigent. adv.; bk.rev.; charts; illus.; stat. circ. 975,000. (tabloid format)

282   IT
MESSAGGERO CAPPUCCINO. 1957. bi-m. L.15000($20) Messaggero Cappuccino, Via Villa Clelia 10, 40026 Imola, Italy. TEL 0542-40265. FAX 0542-626940. Ed. Venanzio Reali. bk.rev. (back issues avail.)

282 255   IT   ISSN 0026-0312
MESSAGGERO DI S. ANTONIO. (Editions in English, French, German, Italian, Portuguese and Spanish) 1898. m. L.23000 (foreign L.35000) (effective 1995). (Provincia Padovana dei Frati Minori Conventuali) Editrice Grafiche Messaggero Sant' Antonio, Via Orto Botanico, 11, 35123 Padua, Italy. TEL 39-49-8225000. FAX 39-49-8225650. TELEX 430855 MSA PD I. (Subscr. to: Basilica del Santo, 35123 Padua, Italy) Ed. Giacomo Panteghini. adv.; bk.rev.; film rev. circ. 1,000,000. (back issues avail.) **Document type:** consumer publication.

282   US   ISSN 0279-3911
THE MESSENGER (BELLEVILLE). 1907. w. (48/yr.). $17 (effective 1992). Roman Catholic Diocese of Belleville, Chancery Office, 222 S. Third St., Belleville, IL 62220. TEL 618-235-9601. FAX 618-235-7416. (Subscr. to: 2620 Lebanon Ave., Belleville, IL 62221) Ed. Raphael H. Middeke. adv.; bk.rev.; film rev. circ. 15,000. (tabloid format; also avail. in microfilm) **Document type:** newspaper.

282   US
MICHIGAN CATHOLIC. 1872. w. $18. 305 Michigan Ave., Detroit, MI 48226. TEL 313-224-8000. FAX 313-224-8009. Ed. Jay McNally. adv. contact: Gerald Oscellet. bk.rev. circ. 30,000. **Document type:** newspaper.

268   US   ISSN 0300-6158
MIESIECZNIK FRANCISZKANSKI. (Text in Polish) 1907? m. $8. Catholic Order of the Franciscan Fathers, Layola University, 6525 N. Sheridan Rd., Chicago, IL 60626-5385. TEL 312-508-2350. Ed. David E. Aune. circ. 3,688.

MILITAERSEELSORGE. see *MILITARY*

282   GW
MINI; Taschenkalender fur Ministranten und junge Christen. 1949. a. DM.7.50. Franz Sales Verlag, Postfach 1361, 85067 Eichstaett, Germany. TEL 08421-5379. FAX 08421-80805. Pub. Herbert Winklehner. bk.rev. circ. 50,000. (back issues avail.) **Document type:** bulletin.

282   GW   ISSN 0947-9449
MINIBOERSE. 1960. q. DM.22. Verlag Haus Altenberg, Carl-Mosterts-Platz 1, 40477 Duesseldorf, Germany. TEL 0211-4693-173. FAX 0211-4693-143. E-mail: ab@project.fido.de. Ed. Andreas Buesch. adv.; bk.rev. circ. 3,000. (back issues avail.) **Document type:** newsletter.
Formerly: Im Heiligen Dienst (ISSN 0938-3190)
Description: Articles and information for people responsible for altar servants and youth choir members.

200   SZ
MIRJAM; Monatszeitschrift der weltoffenen Frau. 1934. m. 36 Fr. (Arbeitsstelle Bildungsdienst) Verlag U. Cavelti AG, CH-9202 Gossau, Switzerland. TEL 01-2521011. FAX 01-2611354. Ed. Annelies Schuepp. adv.; bk.rev.; film rev.; play rev.; illus.; index. circ. 16,000. (tabloid format)
Formerly: Ancilla (ISSN 0003-2867)

282   GW   ISSN 0252-2535
MIRROR. (Text in English) 1959. bi-m. $5. Kirche in Not - Ostpriesterhilfe e.V., Postfach 1209, 61452 Koenigstein, Germany. TEL 06174-291-0. FAX 06174-3423. Ed. Christine Decker. illus. (back issues avail.) **Document type:** newsletter.
Description: News about the persecuted Church and refugees in Eastern Europe and the Third World.

282   US
THE MIRROR (SPRINGFIELD). 1965. w. $10 (effective until Feb. 1996). Diocese of Springfield - Cape Girardeau, 601 S. Jefferson Ave., Springfield, MO 65806. TEL 417-866-0841. FAX 417-866-1140. Ed. Rev. Mark G. Boyer. adv.; bk.rev. circ. 16,900. (tabloid format) **Document type:** newspaper.

200   VC   ISSN 0026-587X
MISCELLANEA FRANCESCANA; rivista trimestrale di scienze teologiche e di studi francescani. (Text in English, French, Italian, Latin) 1886. q. L.40000($45) (Pontificia Facolta Teologica S. Bonaventura) Casa Editrice Miscellanea Francescana, Via del Serafico 1, 00142 Rome, Italy. Ed. Orlando Todisco. bk.rev.; illus.; index. circ. 600. **Indexed:** Amer.Hist.& Life, Hist.Abstr., M.L.A., RILA.

282   SP
MISIORAMA. (Supplement to: Comunidad) m. free. Semanario de la Iglesia Diocesana, Iscar Peyra, 26 Obispado, 37002 Salamanca, Spain.

282 325   AT
MISLI/THOUGHTS. (Text in Slovenian) m. Aus.$4. Franciscan Fathers, Slovenian Chaplaincy, Baraga House, 19 A'Beckett St., Kew, Vic. 3101, Australia. Ed. Basil A. Valentine. adv.; bk.rev. circ. 2,000.

262   GW   ISSN 0945-3407
MISSIO AKTUELL. 1969. bi-m. DM.15. Missio Internationales Katholisches Missionswerk e.V., Goethestr. 43, 52064 Aachen, Germany. TEL 0241-750700. FAX 0241-7507237. TELEX 832719-MIRAD. Ed. Toni Goertz. adv.; bk.rev. circ. 656,579. **Document type:** bulletin.
Former titles: Mission Aktuell; Weltmission.

266   FR   ISSN 0026-6035
MISSION DE L'EGLISE. 1925. q. 120 F. Union Pontificale Missionnaire, 5 rue Monsieur, 75007 Paris, France. FAX 47-34-26-63. Ed. Pere Michel Dujarier. adv.; bibl.; index. circ. 23,000. **Indexed:** CERDIC.

266   UK   ISSN 0962-8142
MISSION OUTLOOK. 1950. q. £5($12) Pontifical Mission Societies, 23 Eccleston Sq., London SW1V 1NU, England. Ed. F.J. McCarthy. circ. 2,000.
Formerly: Outlook (ISSN 0030-7211)

282   UK   ISSN 0967-8379
MISSION TODAY. 1937. q. free to members. Association for the Propagation of the Faith, 23 Eccleston Square, London SW1V 1NU, England. TEL 071-834-5680. Ed. John Corcoran. bk.rev. circ. 220,000.
Former titles: Missions, Missionaries and Young Churches & Missions and Missionaries.

266   US
MISSION UPDATE. 1971. bi-m. $30 (foreign $20). United States Catholic Mission Association, 3029 Fourth St., N.E., Washington, DC 20017. TEL 202-832-3112. Ed. Lucille Malaney. circ. 1,500. **Document type:** newsletter.
Formerly: Mission Intercom.

055.1   IT
MISSIONARI DEL P.I.M.E. 1914. m. (11/yr.). L.10000($16) Pontificio Istituto Missioni Estere, Via Mose Bianchi 94, 20149 Milan, Italy. TEL 39-2-48009191. FAX 39-2-4695193. Ed. P. Gianfranco Vianello. adv.; bk.rev. circ. 50,000.

248.83   AT
MISSIONARIES OF THE SACRED HEART. ANNALS AUSTRALIA; journal of Catholic culture. 1889. m. (10/yr.). Aus.$25 (effective 1995 & 1996). Chevalier Press, P.O. Box 13, Kensington, N.S.W. 2033, Australia. TEL 61-2-6627894. FAX 61-2-6621910. Ed. Paul Stenhouse. adv.; bk.rev.; bibl.; illus.; stat. circ. 14,000. **Indexed:** Gdlns.
Formerly: Our Lady of the Sacred Heart (ISSN 0030-6878)

266   US   ISSN 0026-6086
MISSIONHURST. 1948. 6/yr. free to qualified personnel. (Congregation of the Immaculate Heart of Mary) Missionhurst, Inc., 4651 N. 25th St., Arlington, VA 22207-3500. TEL 703-528-3800. FAX 703-522-7864. Ed. James P. Fischler. illus.; circ. 80,000 (controlled).

282   CN   ISSN 0700-4192
MISSIONS DES FRANCISCAINS. (Text in French) 1923. q. $10. Syndics Apostoliques des Freres Mineurs (Franciscains), 2080 Rene-Levesque Ouest, Montreal, Que. H3H 1R6, Canada. TEL 514-932-6094. FAX 514-259-7407. Ed. Raymond R. Lagace. circ. 6,000.

RELIGIONS AND THEOLOGY — ROMAN CATHOLIC

282 GW ISSN 0179-0102
MISSIONSBLAETTER. 1888. q. free. Erzabtei St. Ottilien, 86941 St. Ottilien, Germany. TEL 08193-710. Eds. Basilius Doppelfeld, Arnold Walloschek. bk.rev. circ. 23,000. (back issues avail.) **Document type:** bulletin.

282 GW
MISSIONSKALENDER. 1888. a. DM.3. Erzabtei St. Ottilien, 86941 St. Ottilien, Germany. TEL 08193-710. FAX 08193-6844. Eds. Arno Muenz, Bernhard Sirch. circ. 102,000. (back issues avail.) **Document type:** bulletin.

059 LO
MOELETSI OA BASOTHO/COUNSELLOR OF BASOTHO. (Text in Sesotho) 1933. w. R.40. Mazenod Institute, POB MZ 18, Mazenod, Lesotho. TEL 62224. TELEX 4271. Ed. William Lesenya. adv. circ. 12,000.
Description: Roman Catholic oriented publication.

282 US
EL MOMENTO CATOLICO. (Text in English, Spanish) 1991. 12/yr. $12. Claretian Publications, 205 W. Monroe St., Chicago, IL 60606. TEL 312-236-7782. FAX 312-236-7230. Ed. Rev. Mark J. Brummel.
Description: Focuses on specific topics of interest to the Hispanic community.

MOMENTUM (WASHINGTON). see *EDUCATION*

255 CN ISSN 0026-9190
BX2400
MONASTIC STUDIES. 1963. a. Can.$25($25) P.O. Box 52, Sta. Cote St. Luc, Montreal, PQ H4V 1H8, Canada. Ed. Laurence Freeman. bk.rev. circ. 2,500. (also avail. in microform from UMI) **Indexed:** Cath.Ind.

282 IT
MONASTICA. 1960. q. contribution. Monastero di Santa Scolastica, I-00060 Civitella San Paolo (Rome), Italy. circ. 850. (back issues avail.)

282 IT ISSN 1120-7353
MONDO DELLA BIBBIA. bi-m. (5/yr.) L.40000 (foreign L.48000) (effective 1996). Editore Elle Di Ci, Corso Francia 214, 10096 Leumann (TO), Italy. TEL 39-11-9591091. FAX 39-11-9572900.

282 266 IT ISSN 0026-6094
MONDO E MISSIONE. 1872. m. (10/yr.) L.30000. Pontificio Istituto Missioni Estere, Via Mose Bianchi 94, 20149 Milan, Italy. TEL 39-2-48009191. FAX 39-2-4695193. Ed. P. Giancarlo Politi. adv.; page L.1200000. bk.rev.; illus.; index. circ. 30,000. **Indexed:** CERDIC.
Formerly: Missioni Cattoliche.
Description: Covers missionary work in the country.

262.9 IT ISSN 0026-976X
MONITOR ECCLESIASTICUS; commentarius de re cannoica et pastorali post Vaticanum II. (Text in Latin and modern languages) 1876. q. L.5200($8.50) Agnesotti S.a.S., Piazza M. Fani 2, 01100 Viterbo, Italy. bk.rev. circ. 1,000. **Indexed:** Canon Law Abstr., CERDIC.
Description: Deals with canon law.

282 US ISSN 0883-7899
MONTANA CATHOLIC. 1932. 16/yr. $14. Roman Catholic Diocese of Helena, 515 N. Ewing, Box 1729, Helena, MT 59624. TEL 406-442-5820. FAX 406-442-5191. Ed. Gerald M. Korson. adv.; bk.rev. circ. 8,500. (tabloid format; back issues avail.) **Document type:** newspaper.
Formerly (until 1985): Westmont Word (ISSN 8750-4715)
Description: News of the church in Western Montana.

282 UK ISSN 0027-0172
MONTH. 1864. m. £15($37) (effective 1996). 114 Mount St., London W1Y 6AH, England. TEL 0171-491-7596. FAX 0171-495-1673. Ed. John McDade, S.J. adv. contact: M.T. Coleman. bk.rev.; film rev.; index. circ. 2,500. (also avail. in microform from UMI) **Indexed:** Br.Hum.Ind., Cath.Ind., CERDIC, Mid.East: Abstr.& Ind., New Test.Abstr.
Document type: academic/scholarly publication.
—BLDSC (5928.860000); Faxon; UMI.
Incorporates: Herder Correspondence.
Description: Review of Christian thought and world affairs.

200 IT ISSN 0077-1449
MONUMENTA HISTORICA ORDINIS MINORUM CAPUCCINORUM. (Text in Italian and Latin) 1937. irreg., no.23, 1995. price varies. Frati Minori Cappuccini, Istituto Storico, Cas. Post. 18283, Circonv. Occidentale 6850 (GRA km 65), 00163 Rome, Italy. TEL 39-6-66151958. FAX 39-6-66162401. index. circ. 500.

282 IT
MONUMENTA HISTORICA SOCIETATIS IESU. irreg., vol.143, 1992. Institutum Historicum Societatis Iesu - Jesuit Historical Institute, Via dei Penitenzieri 20, 00193 Rome, Italy. (also avail. in microfiche from IDC; back issues avail.)
Description: Editions of documents regarding early history of Jesuits and of Jesuit missions worldwide.

282 VC ISSN 0077-1457
MONUMENTA IURIS CANONICI. (In 3 series: A: Corpus Glossatorum; B: Corpus Collectionum; C: Subsidia) 1965. irreg. price varies. Biblioteca Apostolica Vaticana, 00120 Vatican City (Rome), State of the Vatican City.

266 SP ISSN 0210-0851
MORALIA; revista de ciencias morales. 1963. q. 3800 ptas. (Latin America $45; elsewhere $55) (effective 1993). Instituto Superior de Ciencias Morales, Felix Boix, 13, 28036 Madrid, Spain. TEL 345-36-00. FAX 345-86-79. Ed. Rev. Miguel Rubio. adv.; bk.rev. circ. 1,000. **Indexed:** CERDIC.
Document type: academic/scholarly publication.
Formerly (until vol.16, 1978): Pentecostes (ISSN 0479-9828)

282 UK ISSN 0307-5958
MOUNT CARMEL. 1953. 4/yr. £7.50. Teresian Carmelites, St. Ignatius', Meadow St., Preston, Lancs PR1 1TT, England. Ed. John McGowan. adv.; bk.rev. circ. 1,250. **Document type:** bulletin.
—BLDSC (5978.735000).
Description: Promotes personal growth in the Christian experience and practice of prayer.

282 GW ISSN 0580-1400
BR4
MUENCHENER THEOLOGISCHE ZEITSCHRIFT. 1950. q. DM.56. (Universitaet Muenchen, Katholisch-Theologische Fakultaet) E O S Verlag, Erzabtei St. Ottilien, 86941 St. Ottilien, Germany. TEL 08193-71261. FAX 08193-6844. bk.rev. circ. 350. (back issues avail.) **Document type:** bulletin.

282 SP ISSN 0027-3252
MUNDO CRISTIANO. 1963. m. $69. Ediciones Palabra, S.A., Castellana, 210, 28046 Madrid, Spain. TEL 34-1-3507720. FAX 34-1-359023030. (Dist. in U.S. by: DDL Books Inc., 6521 N.W. 87 Ave., Miami, FL 33166) Ed. Belen Martin G. Cabiedes. adv. contact: Arturo Hernansanz. film rev, bibl.; illus. circ. 45,000. (also avail. in record)

MUSICA SACRA. see *MUSIC*

266 CN ISSN 0316-8913
MY BROTHER AND I. 1968. q. Missionary Association of Mary Immaculate, Oblate Missionary Centre, Box 721, Winnipeg, Man. R3C 2K3, Canada. TEL 204-586-2906. illus. circ. 600.
Description: Highlights missionwork in the provinces.

282 US
MY DAILY VISITOR. 1955. bi-m. $9 (foreign $11). Our Sunday Visitor, Inc., 200 Noll Plaza, Huntington, IN 46750. TEL 219-356-8400. FAX 219-356-4872. Eds. William and Catherine Odell. circ. 30,000.
Description: Daily scripture readings and meditations for increasing personal spirituality.

282 028.5 US ISSN 0164-3568
MY FRIEND; a Catholic magazine for kids. 1979. m. (except summer). $18. Daughters of St. Paul, 50 St. Paul Ave., Boston, MA 02130. TEL 617-522-8911. Ed. Sister Anne Joan Flanagan. circ. 15,000. (back issues avail.)
Description: Entertainment, information and Christian formation for children from the ages of six to twelve.

N C E A NOTES. (National Catholic Educational Association) see *EDUCATION*

NAROD POLSKI. see *ETHNIC INTERESTS*

NASA NADA/OUR HOPE. see *ETHNIC INTERESTS*

282 XV
NASE OBCESTVO; glasilo zupnije Svete Trojice v Ljubljani. (Text in Slovenian) 1980. m. free. Zupnijski Urad Sveta Trojica, Trg Osvoboditve 17, p.p. 392, 61001 Ljubljana, Slovenia. TEL 061 224-864. circ. 1,000.

NASZA PRZESZLOSC. see *HISTORY — History Of Europe*

282 US ISSN 0027-8920
NATIONAL CATHOLIC REGISTER.* 1928. w. $49.95 (Canada $65). Twin Circle Publishing Co., 15760 Ventura Blvd., Ste. 1201, Encino, CA 91436-3002. TEL 800-421-3230. FAX 213-655-0344. Ed. Francis X. Maier. adv.; bk.rev.; film rev.; illus. circ. 35,000. **Indexed:** Cath.Ind.
Formerly: Denver Register.

282 US ISSN 0027-8939
NATIONAL CATHOLIC REPORTER. 1964. w. $32.95. National Catholic Reporter Publishing Company, Inc., 115 E. Armour Blvd., Box 419281, Kansas City, MO 64141. TEL 816-531-0538; 800-333-7373. FAX 816-931-5082. Ed. Thomas Fox. adv.; bk.rev.; illus. circ. 52,000. (tabloid format; also avail. in microform from UMI; reprint service avail. from UMI) **Indexed:** Access (1975-1987), Cath.Ind., CERDIC, Curr.Lit.Fam.Plan., Hlth.Ind., Mag.Ind.
—Genuine Article; UMI.
Description: Independent progressive views on religious, social and moral issues.

NATIONAL FEDERATION OF CATHOLIC PHYSICIANS' GUILDS. NEWSLETTER. see *MEDICAL SCIENCES*

282 US ISSN 1061-9615
NETWORK CONNECTION; national Catholic social justice lobby. 1971. bi-m. $35 (low-income $20). 801 Pennsylvania Ave., S.E., Ste. 460, Washington, DC 20003-2167. TEL 202-526-4070. FAX 202-832-4635. Ed. Beth Baker; Pub. Kathy Thornton. bk.rev.; charts; illus.; index. circ. 12,000. (back issues avail.)
Formerly: Network (Washington, 1971) (ISSN 0199-5723)

282 GW ISSN 0930-1143
NEUE GESPRAECHE; Handreichungen fuer Familien und Gruppen. bi-m. DM.12.80. (Arbeitsgemeinschaft fuer Katholische Familienbildung e.V.) Patmos Verlag GmbH, Am Wehrhahn 100, 40211 Duesseldorf, Germany. TEL 0211-16795-0. FAX 0211-16795-75. **Document type:** bulletin.

282 GW ISSN 0943-7584
NEUE MITTE; Stimme der Katholiken in Wirtschaft und Verwaltung. bi-m. DM.2. K K V - Bundesverwaltung der Katholiken in Wirtschaft und Verwaltung e.V., Bismarckstr. 61, 45128 Essen, Germany. TEL 0201-771024. adv.; bk.rev. circ. 12,000.

DIE NEUE ORDNUNG. see *SOCIOLOGY*

282 AU
NEUES ARCHIV FUER DIE GESCHICHTE DER DIOEZESE LINZ. 1983. irreg. Dioezesanarchiv Linz, Harrachstr. 7, A-4020 Linz, Austria. TEL 0732-771205-608. FAX 0732-771205100. Ed. Rudolf Zinnhobler. **Document type:** monographic series.

282 255 UK ISSN 0028-4289
NEW BLACKFRIARS. 1920; N.S. 1964. m. £15.50($40) (English Dominicans) Blackfriars, Oxford OX1 3LY, England. TEL 0865-278414. FAX 0865-278403. Ed. Allan White. adv.; bk.rev.; index. circ. 2,000. (also avail. in microfilm from UMI; reprint service avail. from UMI) **Indexed:** Br.Hum.Ind., Cath.Ind., CERDIC, Mid.East: Abstr.& Ind., New Test.Abstr., Old Test.Abstr. **Document type:** academic/scholarly publication.
—BLDSC (6082.270000); UMI.
Incorporates: Blackfriars; Life of the Spirit.
Description: Surveys theology, philosophy, sociology and the arts from the standpoint of Christian principles and their application to the modern world.

RELIGIONS AND THEOLOGY — ROMAN CATHOLIC

282 US ISSN 1044-8322
NEW CATHOLIC EXPLORER. 1960. w. $18 (typically set Jan.). Roman Catholic Diocese of Joliet, St. Charles Center, 402 S. Independence Blvd., Romeoville, IL 60441-2238. TEL 815-838-6475.
FAX 815-834-4067. Ed. Alfred Doblin; Pub. Rev. Joseph L. Imesch. adv.: B&W page $651; adv. contact: Chris Krainek. bk.rev.; circ. 28,000 (paid). **Document type:** newspaper.
Formerly (until Aug. 1988): Joliet Catholic Explorer.

282 US ISSN 1053-6558
THE NEW CATHOLIC MISCELLANY. 1822. w. $15. Roman Catholic Diocese of Charleston, 119 Broad St., Box 818, Charleston, SC 29402.
TEL 803-724-8375. FAX 803-724-8368. Ed. Philip M. Bowman. adv. circ. 22,000. (tabloid format) **Document type:** newspaper.

282 US
NEW CATHOLIC REVIEW; contemporary Catholic Christianity. 1982. m. $36. Dayspring Press, Inc., 18600 W. 58 Ave., Golden, CO 80403-1070. Ed. John C. Brainerd. (back issues avail.)

200 US ISSN 0744-8589
BX2350.57
NEW COVENANT. 1971. 11/yr. $18 (effective 1994). Our Sunday Visitor, Inc., 200 Noll Plaza, Huntington, IN 45750. TEL 219-356-8400.
FAX 219-356-8472. Ed. Jim Manney. adv.: B&W page $1455, color page $2555; trim 8 3/8 x 10 7/8. bk.rev.; illus. circ. 33,500. (back issues avail.) **Indexed:** Cath.Ind., CERDIC.
—UMI.
Formerly: Pastoral Newsletter.
Description: Articles on Catholic renewal.

282 US ISSN 1067-6406
NEW EARTH.* 1938. 12/yr. $5. (Catholic Diocese of Fargo, Media Office) Catholic Bulletin, c/o the Chancery, 1310 Broadway, Box 1750, Fargo, ND 58107. TEL 701-235-6429. FAX 701-235-0296. Ed. Joan A. Smithwick. adv.; bk.rev. circ. 31,000. (tabloid format)
Formerly (until May 1980): Catholic Action News (ISSN 0008-7890)

282 CN ISSN 0838-0341
NEW FREEMAN. 1900. w. Can.$20 (foreign Can.$30). New Freeman Ltd., One Bayard Dr., Saint John, NB E2L 3L5, Canada. TEL 506-653-6806.
FAX 506-653-6812. Ed. Theresa M. Nowlan; Pub. Rev. J. Edward Troy. adv.; bk.rev. circ. 6,950. (tabloid format; also avail. in microfilm) **Document type:** newspaper.

282 UK ISSN 0028-6079
NEW LIFE. 1947. q. £5. Young Christian Workers, 120A W. Heath Rd., London NW3 7TY, England. TEL 081-458-8416. FAX 081-458-7485. Ed. Michael Morton. bk.rev.; film rev.; play rev. circ. 500. (processed)

282 US ISSN 0149-4244
BR1
NEW OXFORD REVIEW. 1940. m. (10/yr.). $19. New Oxford Review, Inc., 1069 Kains Ave., Berkeley, CA 94706. TEL 510-526-5374. FAX 510-526-3492. Ed. Dale Vree. adv.; bk.rev.; illus.; circ. 14,825 (paid). (also avail. in microform from UMI; reprint service avail. from UMI) **Indexed:** Cath.Ind.
—BLDSC (6084.872000); UMI; UnCover.
Formerly (until Feb. 1977): American Church News (ISSN 0002-791X)
Description: Journal of ideas edited by lay Catholics interested in orthodoxy, evangelism, social justice, peace, and family life.

200 US ISSN 1043-3538
BX801
THE NEW WORLD. (Supplement avail. m.: Senior Lifestyles) 1892. w. $25. (Catholic Archdiocese of Chicago) New World Publications, 1144 W. Jackson Blvd., Chicago, IL 60607. TEL 312-243-1300.
FAX 312-243-1526. Ed. Rev. Thomas Widner. adv.; bk.rev. circ. 50,000. (also avail. in microform) **Indexed:** CERDIC. **Document type:** newspaper.
Former titles: Chicago Catholic (ISSN 0149-970X); New World (ISSN 0028-7016)

282 NZ ISSN 0028-8748
NEW ZEALAND TABLET; New Zealand's national Catholic weekly. 1873. w. NZ.$100. (Roman Catholic Church) New Zealand Tablet Co. Ltd., 39 Crawford St., Dunedin, New Zealand. FAX 03-477-8245. Ed. J.M. Hill. adv.; bk.rev.; film rev.; play rev. circ. 5,000. **Document type:** newspaper.
—CCC.

282 NZ ISSN 0114-5207
NEW ZEALANDIA. 1934. m. NZ.$39.60. Roman Catholic Bishop of Auckland, c/o Pompallier Diocesan Centre, 30 New Street, P.O. Box 845, Auckland, New Zealand. TEL 09-389-3380. FAX 039-360-3065. Ed. Paul F. Freedman. adv.; bk.rev.; film rev.; play rev.; bibl. circ. 14,000.
—CCC.
Supersedes (in 1989): Zealandia (ISSN 0044-202X)
Description: Covers Catholic faith and spirituality, news, features, short story, scripture, family life, ecumenical news, church history, poems, counseling.

282 US
NEWARK CATHOLIC ADVOCATE. (Supplements avail.) 1951. w. $20. Catholic Archdiocese of Newark, 31 Mulberry St., Newark, NJ 07102-5296.
TEL 201-678-0212. FAX 201-678-3489. Ed. S. Peter; Pub. Robert Dylak. adv.: B&W page $966; 9 3/4 x 14; adv. contact: A. Elbri. bk.rev. circ. 26,487. (tabloid format; also avail. in microfilm) **Document type:** newspaper.

282 VN
NGUOI CONG GIAO VIET-NAM/VIETNAMESE CATHOLIC. 1984. fortn. Committee for Solidarity of Patriotic Vietnamese Catholics, 59 Trang Thi, Hanoi, Socialist Republic of Vietnam. TEL 56242. Ed. Pham Van Kham.

282 281.9 IT ISSN 0390-2935
NICOLAUS. 1973. s-a. L.10000($14) Pontificia Universita S. Tommaso D'Aquino - Roma, Istituto di Teologia Ecumenica "S. Nicola", Via Bisanzio e Rainaldo 15, 70122 Bari, Italy. **Indexed:** CERDIC.
—BLDSC (6110.105000).

282 945 IT ISSN 1121-323X
NICOLAUS. STUDI STORICI. 1990. s-a. L.40000($45) Comunita dei Padri Domenicani della Basilica Pontificia di S. Nicola, Centro Studi Nicolaiani, Via Napoli 35, 70122 Bari, Italy. TEL 080-5237247. Ed. Gerardo Cioffari. bk.rev. **Document type:** academic/scholarly publication.

282 UG ISSN 0048-041X
NILE GAZETTE. (Text in English; supplements in Alur, Logbara and Madi) 1958. m. EAs.6. Diocese of Arua, Box 3230, Kampala, Uganda. Ed. Rev. A. Dalfovo. illus. circ. 7,000. (tabloid format)

282 US
NORTH CAROLINA CATHOLIC. 1946. w. $16. (Roman Catholic Diocese of Raleigh) North Carolina Catholic, 300 Cardinal Gibbons Dr., Raleigh, NC 27606. TEL 919-821-9730. FAX 919-821-9705. Ed. John Strange. adv.; bk.rev. circ. 36,600. (tabloid format; also avail. in microfilm; back issues avail.) **Document type:** newspaper.

282 US
NORTH COUNTY CATHOLIC. 1946. w. $15 (foreign $18). Diocese of Ogdensburg, Box 326, 308 Isabella St., Ogdensburg, NY 13669.
TEL 315-393-2540. FAX 315-393-5108. Ed. Mary Lou Kilian. adv. contact: Scott Wilson. bk.rev. circ. 10,000. (tabloid format) **Document type:** newspaper.

282 028.5 US ISSN 1074-2778
NORTHWEST INDIANA CATHOLIC. 1987. w. $16 (effective 1995) $17 (effective 1996). Catholic Diocese of Gary, 9292 Broadway, Merrillville, IN 46410. TEL 219-769-9292. FAX 219-738-9034. Ed. Brian T. Olszewski; Pub. Dale J. Melczek. adv. contact: Brian T. Olszewski. bk.rev.; circ. 21,000 (paid). (tabloid format) **Document type:** newspaper.

200 028.5 IT ISSN 0029-3903
NOTE DI PASTORALE GIOVANILE. 1967. m. (9/yr.). L.42000 (foreign L.50000) (effective 1996). (Centro Catechistico Salesiano) Editrice Elle Di Ci, Corso Francia 214, 10096 Leumann (TO), Italy. TEL 39-11-9591091. FAX 39-11-9572900. Ed. Riccardo Tonelli. bk.rev.; index. circ. 6,000. **Indexed:** CERDIC.

282 VC ISSN 0029-4306
NOTITIAE. (Text in English, French and Latin) 1965. m. L.40000 (foreign L.50000($45)) (effective 1996). Libreria Editrice Vaticana, 00120 Vatican City (Rome), State of the Vatican City. illus.; index. **Indexed:** Canon Law Abstr., Cath.Ind., CERDIC.
Description: Contains news of the Congregation for Divine Worship and information on liturgical matters.

282 CN
NOTRE DAME DE CAP. REVUE. (Text in French) 1892. 8/yr. $7. Notre Dame de Cap, 626 Notre Dame, Cap Madeleine, Que. G8T 3V4, Canada. Ed. Paul Arsenault. adv.: B&W page $950, color page $1650; trim 8 1/2 x 11. circ. 115,000.

282 US
NOTRE DAME STUDIES IN AMERICAN CATHOLICISM. 1979. irreg., vol.13, 1994. (Cushwa Center for the Study of American Catholicism) University of Notre Dame Press, Notre Dame, IN 46556.
TEL 219-631-6346. FAX 219-631-8148. (Orders to: 11030 S. Langley Ave., Chicago, IL 60628. TEL 800-621-2736. FAX 800-621-8476; Overseas orders to: Europspan University Press Group, Order Dept., 3 Henrietta St., London WC2E 8LU, England) bibl. **Document type:** academic/scholarly publication.

282 US
▼**NOTRE DAME STUDIES IN THEOLOGY.** 1994. irreg. price varies. University of Notre Dame Press, Notre Dame, IN 46556. TEL 219-631-6346.
FAX 219-631-8148. (Orders to: 11030 S. Langley Ave., Chicago, IL 60628. TEL 800-621-2736. FAX 800-621-5476; Overseas orders to: Europspan University Press Group, Order Dept., 3 Henrietta St., London WC2E 8LU, England) **Document type:** monographic series.

251 US ISSN 1047-2398
NOVA (NEW BERLIN). 1972. 6/yr. $56. Liturgical Publications Inc., 2875 South James Dr., New Berlin, WI 53151. TEL 414-785-1188.
FAX 414-785-9567. Ed. Rev. Albert Nevins. circ. 1,419. (looseleaf format) **Indexed:** Old Test.Abstr., Rel.& Theol.Abstr. **Document type:** trade publication.
Formerly: Nova et Vetera.
Description: Homily resource for ministers and priests.

282 SZ ISSN 0029-5027
AP24
NOVA ET VETERA. (Text in French) 1926. q. 50 SFr. Editions Saint-Augustin, CH-1890 Saint-Maurice, Switzerland. Ed. Georges Cottier. bk.rev.; index. **Indexed:** CERDIC, New Test.Abstr. **Document type:** bulletin.

282 IT ISSN 0078-253X
NOVARIEN. 1967. irreg. price varies. Associazione di Storia Ecclesiastica Novarese, Presso Archivio Storico Diocesano, Palazzo Vescovile, I-28100 Novara, Italy. Ed. Angelo L. Stoppa. bk.rev. circ. 1,000.
—BLDSC (6180.060000).

282 US
NUESTRA PARROQUIA. (Text in English, Spanish) 1991. m. $18. Claretian Publications, 205 W. Monroe St., Chicago, IL 60606. TEL 312-236-7782.
FAX 312-236-7230. Ed. Rev. Mark J. Brummel. circ. 1,200.

282 AG ISSN 0029-585X
NUEVA POMPEYA. 1924. m. Arg.$20000. (Santuario de la Virgen del Rosario) Orden de los Frailes Menores Capuchinos, Esquiu 974, C.C. 14-Suc.37, Buenos Aires, Argentina. Dir. R.P. Andres Guirao. index. circ. 18,000.

282 US ISSN 0278-288X
NUEVO AMANECER; the newspaper for the Catholic Hispanic community. (Text in Spanish) 1981. m. $10. Tablet, 653 Hicks St., Brooklyn, NY 11231-2695. TEL 718-858-3838.
FAX 718-858-2112. Ed. A. Romero. circ. 10,000. (tabloid format)

282 IT
NUOVA UMANITA. 1979. bi-m. L.25000 (foreign L.47000). Citta Nuova Editrice della PAMOM, Via degli Scipioni 265, 00192 Rome, Italy. Ed. Guglielmo Boselli.
Description: Features articles on justice, solidarity and other topics in the humanities.

RELIGIONS AND THEOLOGY — ROMAN CATHOLIC

282   DK   ISSN 0109-0518
NYT FRA D U K. 1978. bi-m. free. Danmarks Unge Katolikker, Bredgade 67, 2 t.h., DK-1260 Copenhagen K, Denmark. Ed.Bd. bk.rev.; illus. circ. 2,150. **Document type:** newsletter.

O E C T A REPORTER. (Ontario English Catholic Teachers Association) see *EDUCATION*

O I E C BULLETIN. (Office International de l'Enseignement Catholique) see *EDUCATION*

282   UK   ISSN 0144-9117
O R C NOTES. 1979. every 6 wks. free. Old Roman Catholic Church, Our Lady's Priory, 10 Barnmead Rd., Beckenham, Kent BR3 1JE, England. Ed. Archbishop-Primate F.G. Linale. bk.rev. circ. 2,000.

266   US
OBLATE WORLD AND VOICE OF HOPE; southern province edition. 1915. 5/yr. membership. Society of Oblate Fathers for Missions Among the Poor, Inc., Box 680, Tewksbury, MA 01876. (Subscr. to: Box 96, San Antonio, TX 78291) Ed. Thomas J. Reddy. illus. circ. 154,400.
Formerly: O M I Mission Magazine.
Description: Discusses mission work among the needy.

282   US   ISSN 0745-9491
THE OBSERVER (MONTEREY). 1967. m. $15. Diocese of Monterey, 500 Church St., Monterey, CA 93940. TEL 408-373-2919. (Subscr. to: Box 2079, Monterey, CA 93942) Ed. Pat Hillyer. adv. contact: Catherine Nolan. circ. 8,000. **Document type:** newspaper.

282   US   ISSN 0029-7739
OBSERVER (ROCKFORD). 1935. s-m. $18. Catholic Diocese of Rockford, 921 W. State St., Rockford, IL 61102. TEL 815-963-3471. FAX 815-968-2808. Ed. Owen Phelps, Jr. adv.; bk.rev.; film rev. circ. 33,000. (tabloid format; also avail. in microfilm) **Indexed:** High.Educ.Curr.Aware.Bull. **Document type:** newspaper.

282   MW   ISSN 0300-4651
ODINI/WELCOME. (Text in Chichewa, English) 1950. fortn. K.75 (foreign K.90). (Diocese of Lilongwe) Likuni Press and Publishing House, Box 133, Lilongwe, Malawi. TEL 265-721388. FAX 265-721141. Ed. Paul I. Akomenji. adv.; bk.rev.; illus.; circ. 12,000 (controlled). (tabloid format) **Document type:** newspaper.
Formerly (until 1984): African.

270 239   AU
OESTERREICHISCHE AKADEMIE DER WISSENSCHAFTEN. KOMMISSION ZUR HERAUSGABE DES CORPUS DER LATEINISCHEN KIRCHENVAETER. VEROEFFENTLICHUNGEN. irreg. Verlag der Oesterreichischen Akademie der Wissenschaften, Dr. Ignaz-Seipel-Platz 2, A-1010 Vienna, Austria. FAX 0222-5139541.

282   US   ISSN 0078-3854
BX845
OFFICIAL CATHOLIC DIRECTORY. 1817. a., 178th edition, 1995 (plus supplement). $190 to individuals; clergy $110. R.R. Bowker, A Reed Reference Publishing company, 121 Chanlon Rd., New Providence, NJ 07974. TEL 908-464-6800. FAX 908-665-6688. TELEX 138 755. (Subscr. to: Order Dept., Box 31, New Providence, NJ 07974-9903. TEL 800-521-8110) **Indexed:** SRI. **Document type:** directory.
Description: Lists 60,000 church leaders - from clergy to laity - in every Catholic institution in the United States, including all Catholic possessions, and a desription of the governing body of Rome.

282   US
OFFICIAL WISCONSIN PASTORAL HANDBOOK. 1962. a. $32. Milwaukee Catholic Press Apostolate, 3501 S. Lake Dr., Box 07913, Milwaukee, WI 53207-7913. TEL 414-769-3472. Ed. Maryangela Roman. adv.; circ. 2,300 (controlled).
Description: Directory for all five Catholic dioceses in Wisconsin.

282   SR
OMHOOG. 1953. w. $30. Gravenstraat 21, P.O. Box 1802, Paramaribo, Surinam. TEL 597-472521. Ed. S. Mulder. adv.; bk.rev. **Document type:** newsletter.

282   UK   ISSN 0030-252X
BX1781
ONE IN CHRIST; a Roman Catholic ecumenical review. 1936. q. £22($42) Vita et Pax-Foundation for Unity, Regina Pacis, Turvey Abbey, Turvey, Beds. MK43 8DE, England. TEL 01234-881432. FAX 01234-881538. Ed. Paschal A. Hardiment. adv.; bk.rev.; bibl.; index. circ. 800. (also avail. in microfilm from UMI; reprint service avail. from UMI) **Indexed:** Br.Hum.Ind., Cath.Ind., CERDIC, New Test.Abstr., Old Test.Abstr., Rel.Ind.One. **Document type:** directory.
—BLDSC (6260.230000); UMI.
Incorporates: Ecumenical Notes.
Description: Offers documentation and comment on current ecumenical initiatives, with items on the theology, history and spirituality of ecumenism.

282   US   ISSN 1059-3144
OPUS DEI AWARENESS NETWORK; providing support and education to those with serious questions about Opus Dei. Short title: O D A N. 1991. 8/yr. $15. Opus Dei Awareness Network, Inc., Box 4333, Pittsfield, MA 01202. TEL 413-499-7168. FAX 413-499-7860. Ed. Dianne Dinicola. circ. controlled. **Document type:** newsletter.

282 375   IT   ISSN 1121-1563
ORA DI RELIGIONE. m. (9/yr.). L.24000 (foreign L.38000) (effective 1996). Editore Elle Di Ci, Corso Francia 214, 10096 Leumann (TO), Italy. TEL 39-11-9591091. FAX 39-11-9572900.
Description: For use in teaching religion in elementary schools.

282   IT   ISSN 0030-4174
ORA ET LABORA; quaderni di interesse monastico. 1947. q. free. Monastero S. Benedetto, Via Bellotti 10, 20129 Milan, Italy. TEL 02-799495. Ed. Annamaria Valli. bk.rev.; bibl. circ. 600. **Indexed:** CERDIC.

282   CN   ISSN 0030-4344
ORATOIRE. (Editions in English and French) 1912. bi-m. Can.$8. Oratoire Saint-Joseph du Mont-Royal, 3800 Chemin Reine-Marie, Montreal, PQ H3V 1H6, Canada. TEL 514-733-8211. FAX 514-733-9735. illus. circ. 64,000 (55,000 Fr. ed.; 9,000 Eng. ed.). **Document type:** academic/scholarly publication.

282   CN   ISSN 0384-1871
THE ORATORY. 1927. bi-m. Can.$6($6) St. Joseph's Oratory, 3800 Queen Mary Rd., Montreal, PQ H3V 1H6, Canada. TEL 514-733-8211. FAX 514-733-9735. Ed. Therese Baron. circ. 8,500.

266   CN   ISSN 0472-0490
ORIENT. 1953. bi-m. Can.$2. Missions des Peres de Sainte-Croix, 4901 rue Piedmont, Montreal, PQ H3V 1E3, Canada. TEL 514-731-7820. Ed. Marcel Descheneaux. adv. contact: Marc Gagnon. illus. circ. 10,500.

282   ES
ORIENTACION. 1953. w. 1a Calle Poniente 3412, San Salvador, El Salvador. TEL 24-5166. FAX 26-4979. Dir. Fr. Jesus Delgado. circ. 8,000.

ORIENTALIA CHRISTIANA ANALECTA. see *ORIENTAL STUDIES*

282   SZ   ISSN 0030-5502
ORIENTIERUNG; katholische Blaetter fuer weltanschauliche Information. 1937. s-m. 51 SFr. (foreign 46 SFr.; students 35 SFr.). Institut fuer Weltanschauliche Fragen, Scheideggstr. 45, CH-8002 Zurich, Switzerland. TEL 01-2010760. FAX 01-2014983. Eds. Nikolaus Klein, Karl Weber. adv. contact: Karl Weber. bk.rev.; abstr.; bibl.; stat.; index, cum.index. circ. 10,000. (looseleaf format) **Indexed:** CERDIC, Old Test.Abstr., World Agri.Econ.& Rural Sociol.Abstr. **Document type:** bulletin.

282.73   US
BX801
ORIGINS, C N S DOCUMENTARY SERVICE. Key Title: Origins (Washington). 1971. 48/yr. $97. Catholic News Service, 3211 4th St., N.E., Washington, DC 20017. TEL 202-541-3290. FAX 202-541-3255. Ed. David Gibson. circ. 9,500. **Indexed:** Canon Law Abstr., Cath.Ind., CERDIC.
•Also available online. Vendor(s): NewsNet (CN03).
—BLDSC (6291.263900).
Formerly: Origins, N C Documentary Service (ISSN 0093-609X)

282   VC   ISSN 0391-688X
L'OSSERVATORE ROMANO. French edition (ISSN 1017-3862); German edition (ISSN 0179-7387) (Text in Italian; weekly editions avail. in English, French, German, Italian, Portuguese, Spanish; monthly edition in Polish) 1861. d. L.103000($80) for English ed. only. Via del Pellegrino, 00120 Vatican City (Rome), State of the Vatican City. TEL 06-6983461. FAX 06-6983675. Ed. Sergio Trasatti. circ. 70,000. (also avail. in microfilm from UMI) **Document type:** newspaper.

OTTAR; om sexualitet, samlevnad, samhaelle. see *SOCIOLOGY*

249   CN   ISSN 0030-6843
OUR FAMILY; Canada's Catholic family monthly magazine. 1949. m. Can.$15.98($21.98) Oblates of St. Mary's Province of Canada, Box 249, Battleford, SK S0M 0E0, Canada. TEL 306-937-7771. FAX 306-937-7644. Ed. Rev. Nestor Gregoire. adv.; illus. circ. 12,000.

200   ISSN 0030-6924
OUR NORTHLAND DIOCESE. 1946. 22/yr. $9.50 in diocese; outside diocese $11. Northland Diocese Association, Box 610, Crookston, MN 56716-0610. TEL 218-281-4050. FAX 218-281-3328. Ed. Carol J. Evenson. adv.; bk.rev. circ. 14,000. (tabloid format) **Document type:** newspaper.

282   US   ISSN 0030-6967
BX801
OUR SUNDAY VISITOR. 1912. w. $36 (foreign $48). Our Sunday Visitor, Inc., 200 Noll Plaza, Huntington, IN 46750. TEL 219-356-8400. FAX 219-356-8472. Ed. David Scott. adv.; bk.rev.; film rev.; play rev.; illus. circ. 118,000. **Indexed:** Cath.Ind.
Description: Catholic newsmagazine.

282   US   ISSN 0030-7564
OVERVIEW (CHICAGO); a continuing survey of issues affecting Catholics. 1968. m. (11/yr.). $15.95. Thomas More Association, 205 W. Monroe, 6th Fl., Chicago, IL 60606. TEL 312-609-8880. Ed. Sara Miller. circ. 4,000.
Description: Issues pertaining to the Catholic faith.

282   UK   ISSN 0266-6014
P A X; newsletter of the Benedictines of Prinknash. 1904. q. £2.50. Prinknash Abbey, Cranham, Gloucester GL4 8EX, England. FAX 0452-812529. bk.rev. circ. 300. (looseleaf format; back issues avail.)

266   US   ISSN 1066-5943
P I M E WORLD. 1954. m. (except Jul. & Aug.). $5. Pontifical Institute for Foreign Missionaries (PIME), 17330 Quincy St., Detroit, MI 48221-2765. TEL 313-342-6816. FAX 313-342-4066. Ed. Paul W. Witte. circ. 29,000. (also avail. in microfilm from UMI; reprint service avail. from UMI) **Indexed:** CERDIC.
—UMI.
Formerly (until 1991): Catholic Life (ISSN 0008-8218)

266   US   ISSN 0030-9222
PADRES' TRAIL; the mission newsletter for the Southwest Franciscans. 1938. q. free to qualified personnel. (Franciscan Friars, Our Lady of Guadalupe Province) Franciscan Mission Center, Box 645, St. Michaels, AZ 86511. TEL 520-871-4171. FAX 520-871-4172. illus. circ. 13,000. (also avail. in microfilm from UMI) **Document type:** newsletter.
Description: Focuses on the orders mission work.

PAEPSTE UND PAPSTTUM. see *HISTORY — History Of Europe*

282   SP   ISSN 1132-0591
PALABRA. 1965. m. $76. Ediciones Palabra, S.A., Castellana 210, 28046 Madrid, Spain. TEL 34-1-3501179. FAX 34-1-3590230. (Dist. in US by: DDL Books Inc., 6521 N.W. 87 Ave., Miami, FL 33166) Ed. Belen Martin G. Cabiedes. adv. contact: Arturo Hernansanz. circ. 18,000.

282   ISSN 0896-1727
LA PALABRA ENTRE NOSOTROS. (Text in Spanish) 1984. bi-m. $15 (foreign $20). Word Among Us, Box 6003, Gaithersburg, MD 20884-6003. TEL 301-990-2090. FAX 301-990-2087. bk.rev. circ. 35,000. (back issues avail.)

RELIGIONS AND THEOLOGY — ROMAN CATHOLIC

282 US ISSN 0274-9009
PAN Z WAMI. 6/yr. Polish American Liturgical Center, Box 240492, Orchard Lake, MI 48324. TEL 313-683-0409. **Document type:** newsletter.

282 248.83 FR ISSN 0031-1561
PARABOLES. 1949. 4/yr. 60 F. (foreign 70 F.). Communautes Chretiennes Universitaires, 5 rue de l'Abbaye, 75006 Paris, France. TEL 43-25-41-71. Ed. Paul Guiberteau. bk.rev. circ. 2,000. **Document type:** bulletin.

280 US ISSN 0279-7828
PARISH COMMUNICATION. 1981. q. $23 (foreign $28). Fred B. Estabrook Company, Inc., Rte.1, Box 142, New Hampton, NH 03256-9713. TEL 603-744-6316. FAX 603-744-6318. bk.rev.; abstr.; stat. circ. 1,100. **Document type:** newsletter.
  Description: Seasonal graphics, quotes from saints and modern leaders, weekly essays, puzzles, calendars, and sketches to be used in parish bulletins and newsletters.

PARISH COORDINATORS - DIRECTORS OF RELIGIOUS EDUCATION. see *EDUCATION*

282 US ISSN 0164-6443
PARISH LITURGY. 1978. q. $10. American Catholic Press, 16565 S. State St., S. Holland, IL 60473. TEL 708-331-5485. Ed. Michael Gilligan. adv. contact: Joan Termini. circ. 2,300 (paid). (back issues avail.) **Document type:** trade publication.
  Description: Serves the personnel of Roman Catholic parishes, especially concerning their preparation of the Sunday Eucharist celebration.

266 US ISSN 0271-728X
BX801
PARISH VISITOR. 1924. q. $2. Parish Visitors of Mary Immaculate, Box 658, Monroe, NY 10950. TEL 914-783-2251. Ed. George A. Morton. circ. 7,000.
  Description: Publishes articles about the life and work of the parish visitors. Includes articles of a general religious nature.

282 IT
PAROLA SPIRITO E VITA. 1979. s-a. L.33000 (foreign L.38000) (effective 1994). Centro Editoriale Dehoniano, Via Nosadella 6, 40123 Bologna, Italy. TEL 051-306811. FAX 051-341706. circ. 3,000. (back issues avail.)

220 IT ISSN 0031-2398
PAROLE DI VITA. 1956. bi-m. L.26000 (foreign L.30000) (effective 1996). (Centro Catechistico Salesiano) Editrice Elle Di Ci, Corso Francia 214, 10096 Leumann (Turin), Italy. TEL 39-11-9591091. FAX 39-11-9572900. Eds. Carlo Ghidelli, Francesco Mosetto. bk.rev.; index. circ. 3,000.

250 282 IT ISSN 0031-2428
PARROCCHIA. 1947. m. L.15000. Opera Madonna del Divino Amore, Via Ardeatina, Km 12, 00134 Rome, Italy. Dir. Pasquale Silla. bibl.; illus.; stat.; index, cum.index. circ. 8,000.

282 PE
PASTORAL ANDINA. 1974. bi-m. $30 (foreign $40). Instituto de Pastoral Andina, Apdo. 1018, Cusco, Peru. TEL 51-84-238068. FAX 51-84-225205. circ. 3,500. **Document type:** newspaper.
  Description: Current news on the Catholic Church and pastoral activities in the southern Andes of Peru.

282 GW
PASTORALBLATT. 1948. m. DM.61.64. J.P. Bachem Verlag GmbH, Ursulaplatz 1, 50668 Cologne, Germany. TEL 0221-16190. **Document type:** newsletter.

PATHWAYS (LAS VEGAS). see *RELIGIONS AND THEOLOGY — Protestant*

282 US ISSN 0897-9545
PAX CHRISTI U S A. 1975. 4/yr. $25 membership. Pax Christi U S A, National Catholic Peace Movement, c/o Anne McCarthy, OSB, National Coordinator, 348 E. Tenth St., Erie, PA 16503. TEL 814-453-4955. FAX 814-452-4784. E-mail: paxchristi@igc.apc.org. Ed. Michael Affleck. bk.rev. circ. 11,250.
  Description: Covers the world of Christianity and peace.

200 PO
PAZ E ALEGRIA. 1907. m. Esc.250($3) Familia Franciscana Portuguesa, R. Serpa Pinto, 7, P 1200 Lisbon, Portugal. bk.rev. circ. 3,000.
  Supersedes: Alma (ISSN 0002-6239)

282 FR ISSN 0031-4781
BX802
PENSEE CATHOLIQUE; cahiers de synthese. 1946. bi-m. 500 F. B.P. 39, 92370 Chaville, France. Ed. Yves Daoudal. bk.rev. **Indexed:** CERDIC.
—BLDSC (6422.040000).

282 IO ISSN 0553-6448
PERABA. (Text in Indonesian, Javanese) w. Bintaran Kidul 5, Yogyakarta, Indonesia. Ed. W. Kartosoeharsono.
  Formerly (until 1968): Praba.

262.9 VC
PERIODICA DE RE CANONICA. (Text in Latin) 1905. q. L.80000($75) (effective 1995). (Pontificia Universita Gregoriana - Pontifical Gregorian University) Gregorian University Press, Piazza della Pilotta, 35, 00187 Rome, Italy. TEL 39-6-678-15-67. FAX 39-6-678-05-88. Ed. Gianfranco Ghirlanda S.J. index. circ. 1,500. **Indexed:** Canon Law Abstr.
  Formerly: Periodica de Re Morali Canonica Liturgica (ISSN 0031-529X)
  Description: Offers research, articles and timely essays on the most recent church legislation regarding collegiality, marriage, consecrated life, and secularization.

PERLIN. see *CHILDREN AND YOUTH — About*

282 266 FR ISSN 0555-9952
PEUPLES DU MONDE. 1967. 10/yr. 295 F. S O C E N D I, 8 rue Francois Villon, 75015 Paris, France. adv.; bk.rev.; illus. **Indexed:** CERDIC. **Document type:** newspaper.

282 SZ
PFARRBLATT. 1911. w. Pfarrblattgemeinschaft Bern, Postfach 822, CH-3000 Bern 7, Switzerland. TEL 031-3110307. FAX 031-3125066. (Dist. by: Fischer Druck, CH-3110 Muensingen, Switzerland. TEL 031-7205111. FAX 031-7205112) **Document type:** newspaper.

282 US
PHILADELPHIA CATHOLIC STANDARD & TIMES. 1833. w. $18. Archdiocese of Philadelphia, 222 N. 17th St., Philadelphia, PA 19103. TEL 215-587-3660. FAX 215-587-3979. Ed. Rev. Paul S. Quinter. adv. contact: John Gallagher. bk.rev. circ. 60,000. (tabloid format) **Document type:** newspaper.

282 CN
PHILIPPINES. (Text in English and French) 1963. q. Can.$1. Centre cor Jesu (Philippines), 328, Rue Chapel, Ottawa, Ont. K1N 7Z3, Canada. Ed. Gerard Lefebvre. circ. 1,500.

255 IT ISSN 0392-1689
PICENUM SERAPHICUM. irreg. L.3500. Biblioteca Francescana, Conto Corrente Postale 15-27009, Falconara M. 60015, Italy.

282 US ISSN 0744-933X
PILOT. 1829. w. $20. (Roman Catholic Archdiocese of Boston) Pilot Publishing Co., 49 Franklin St., Boston, MA 02110. TEL 617-482-4316. FAX 617-482-5647. Ed. Rev. Peter V. Conley. adv. contact: Joan McAllister. bk.rev.; film rev.; play rev. circ. 34,000. (also avail. in microform) **Document type:** newspaper.

282 VC ISSN 0392-1492
PIO IX; studi e ricerche sulla vita della chiesa dal settecento ad oggi. 1972. 3/yr. L.30000($35) Editrice la Postulazione, Palazzo dei Canonici, 00129 Vatican City (Rome), State of the Vatican City. Ed. Mons. Antonio Piolanti.

282 US ISSN 0032-0323
PITTSBURGH CATHOLIC.* 1844. w. $11. (Catholic Diocese of Pittsburgh) Pittsburgh Catholic Publishing Associates, 135 First Ave., No. 200, Pittsburgh, PA 15222-1506. FAX 412-471-4228. Ed. William Fodiak. adv.; bk.rev.; film rev.; illus.; play rev. circ. 121,500. (also avail. in microform) **Document type:** newspaper.

266 FR ISSN 0032-2504
POLE ET TROPIQUES; revue apostolique des missionnaires oblats. 1920. bi-m. 75 F. Missionnaires Oblats de Marie Immaculee, 145 Montee de Choulans, 69322 Lyon Cedex 05, France. Ed. Noel Leca. abstr.; illus.; mkt.; stat.; index. circ. 21,000.

270 VC
PONTIFICIA UNIVERSITA GREGORIANA. DOCUMENTA MISSIONALIA. (Text in English, French, Italian or Spanish) 1964. irreg., no.22, 1992. price varies. (Pontificia Universita Gregoriana, Facolta di Missiologia - Pontifical Gregorian University, Faculty of Missiology) Gregorian University Press, Piazza della Pilotta, 35, 00187 Rome, Italy. TEL 39-6-678-15-67. FAX 39-6-678-05-88. Ed. Mariasusai Dhavamony.
  Description: Scholarly studies on missionary and cultural aspects of non-Christian peoples related to their religious, historical and ethnological contexts.

270 VC ISSN 0080-3979
PONTIFICIA UNIVERSITA GREGORIANA. MISCELLANEA HISTORIAE PONTIFICIAE. (Text in English, French, German, Italian, or Spanish) 1939. irreg., no.61, 1993. price varies. (Pontificia Universita Gregoriana, Facolta di Storia Ecclesiastica - Pontifical Gregorian University, Faculty of Church History) Gregorian University Press, Piazza della Pilotta, 35, 00187 Rome, Italy. TEL 39-6-678-15-67. FAX 39-6-678-05-88. Ed. Vincenzo Monachino.
  Description: Contains research studies on themes of the history of the Papacy.

266 VC ISSN 0080-3987
PONTIFICIA UNIVERSITA GREGORIANA. STUDIA MISSIONALIA. (Multi-language text) 1943. a. L.65000($60) (effective 1995). (Pontificia Universita Gregoriana, Facolta di Missiologia - Pontifical Gregorian University, Faculty of Missiology) Gregorian University Press, Piazza della Pilotta, 35, 00187 Rome, Italy. TEL 39-6-678-15-67. FAX 39-6-678-05-88. Ed. Mariasusai Dhavamony. index. circ. 600. (back issues avail.) **Indexed:** Cath.Ind., Rel.Ind.One.
—BLDSC (8483.060000).
  Description: Contains subjects such as: Islam, Buddhism, Hinduism, religious ethnology, revelation, worship and ritual, prayers, meditation, mystique, moral and religion, in Christianity and other religions.

POPE JOHN PAUL II CENTER NEWSLETTER. see *BIOGRAPHY*

282 262 US ISSN 0032-4353
BX850
POPE SPEAKS; the Church documents bi-monthly. 1954. bi-m. $18 (foreign $21). Our Sunday Visitor, Inc., 200 Noll Plaza, Huntington, IN 46750. TEL 219-356-8400. FAX 219-356-8472. Ed. Rev. Albert J. Nevins. adv.; bk.rev.; bibl.; illus.; index. circ. 6,000. (also avail. in microform from UMI) reprint service avail. from UMI) **Indexed:** Cath.Ind., CERDIC.
—Faxon; UMI; UnCover.
  Description: Publishes documents relating to the Pope's activities.

282 UK ISSN 0143-0149
POPE TEACHES; a monthly digest of the pastoral teaching of Pope John Paul II. 1978. m. £12($20) Incorporated Catholic Truth Society, 192 Vauxhall Bridge Rd., London SW1V 1PD, England. TEL 0171-834 4392. FAX 0171-630-1124. Ed. Sally Purcell.

282 CN ISSN 0032-664X
PRAIRIE MESSENGER. 1923. 46/yr. Can.$23($55.50) Order of St. Benedict, Inc., Muenster, SK S0K 2Y0, Canada. TEL 306-682-1772. FAX 306-682-5285. Ed. Andrew M. Britz. adv. contact: Rose Marie Streuby. bk.rev.; film rev.; illus. circ. 8,500. (tabloid format)

282 GW ISSN 0172-7478
PRAXIS IN DER GEMEINDE; Materialien und Erfahrungen. 1979. q. DM.27 (effective 1996). Matthias Gruenewald Verlag GmbH, Max-Hufschmidt-Str. 4a, 55130 Mainz, Germany. TEL 06131-839055. FAX 06131-834322. Ed. Anneliese Hueck. adv. contact: Andrea Buchauer. bk.rev.; cum.index. circ. 1,800. (back issues avail.) **Document type:** bulletin.

RELIGIONS AND THEOLOGY — ROMAN CATHOLIC

282   US   ISSN 0895-4968
PRAYING. 1983. bi-m. $18. National Catholic Reporter Publishing Company, Inc., 115 E. Armour Blvd., Box 419281, Kansas City, MO 64141. TEL 816-531-0538; 800-333-7373. FAX 816-931-5082. Ed. Art Winter. adv.; bk.rev.; illus. circ. 17,000.
  Description: Spiritual insight aimed at helping people find God in their daily lives.

282   GW   ISSN 0032-7212
DER PREDIGER UND KATECHET. 1850. 6/yr. DM.60. Erich Wewel Verlag, Anzingerstr. 15, 81671 Munich, Germany. TEL 089-41300138. adv.; index. circ. 15,000. **Document type:** bulletin.
  —CCC.

282 250   IT   ISSN 0032-7727
PRESENZA PASTORALE. 1931. 10/yr. L.35000. (Collegio Assistenti) Azione Cattolica Italiana, Via della Conciliazione 1, 00193 Rome, Italy. FAX 06-6620207. Ed. Fiorino Tagliaferri. bk.rev.; bibl. Indexed: CERDIC.
  Formerly: Assistente Ecclesiastico.

282   CN   ISSN 0383-8307
PRETRE ET PASTEUR; revue des agents de pastorale. 1897. m. (except Jul./Aug. combined). Can.$28.49. Blessed Sacrament Fathers, 4450 St-Hubert, Montreal, PQ H2J 2W9, Canada. TEL 514-525-6210. FAX 514-523-1693. Ed. Jean-Yves Garneau. bk.rev.; index; circ. 2,950 (paid). (back issues avail.) **Document type:** newspaper.
  Former titles (until 1970): Revue Eucharistique du Clerge (ISSN 0383-8293); (until 1936): Annales des Pretres - Adorateurs et de la Ligue Sacerdotale de la Communion (ISSN 0703-3567); Association des Pretres - Adorateurs et la Ligue Sacerdotale de la Communion. Annales (ISSN 0841-5404); Association des Pretres - Adorateurs. Annales (ISSN 0841-5390)
  Description: Provides priests and other ministers with up-to-date pastoral and liturgical theology.

282   FR   ISSN 0032-7956
PRETRES DIOCESAINS. 1862. m. 240 F. (Europe 300F.; elsewhere 350F.) (effective 1995). Union Apostolique du Clerge, 179 rue de Tolbiac, 75013 Paris, France. TEL 33-1-45893253. FAX 33-1-45899330. bk.rev.; abstr.; bibl.; index. (tabloid format)
  Description: Intended for those involved in the clergy. Addresses problems in the Catholic church as well as spiritual issues. Features Biblical studies and a bibliographic section.

282   US   ISSN 0032-8200
BX803
PRIEST. 1945. m. $30 (foreign $35). Our Sunday Visitor, Inc., 200 Noll Plaza, Huntington, IN 46750. TEL 219-356-8400. FAX 219-356-8472. Ed. Rev. Owen Campion. adv.; bk.rev.; tr.lit. circ. 9,000. (also avail. in microform from UMI; reprint service avail. from UMI) Indexed: Cath.Ind., CERDIC.
  —UMI.
  Description: Homily helps, commentary, and parish product showcase for Roman Catholic priests and deacons.

282   GW   ISSN 0172-0929
PRIESTERJAHRHEFT. 1926. a. free. Bonifatiuswerk der Deutschen Katholiken e.V., Postfach 1169, 33041 Paderborn, Germany. TEL 05251-29960. FAX 05251-299688. Ed. Georg Walf. circ. 20,000 (controlled). **Document type:** newsletter.
  Description: Sermon material for Catholic priests in Germany for the so-called "Diaspora-Sonntag".

250   UK   ISSN 0952-6390
BX801
PRIESTS AND PEOPLE. 1930. m. £21. (Catholic Church) Tablet Publishing Co. Ltd., 1 King St. Cloister, Clifton Walk, London W6 0QZ, England. TEL 0181-748-8484. FAX 0181-748-1550. Ed. David Sanders. adv. contact: Conor Taaffe. bk.rev.; index. circ. 3,450. (also avail. in microfilm from UMI; reprint service avail. from UMI) Indexed: Canon Law Abstr., Cath.Ind., CERDIC, New Test.Abstr., Old Test.Abstr., Rel.& Theol.Abstr. **Document type:** bulletin.
  —BLDSC (6612.900000); UMI.
  Formerly: Clergy Review (ISSN 0009-8736)
  Description: For those involved in active ministry, wether ordained or lay.

282   FR   ISSN 0982-4944
PRIONS EN EGLISE. 1987. m. 174 F. (outside EC 197 F.). Bayard Presse, 3 rue Bayard, 75393 Paris Cedex 08, France. TEL 44-35-60-60. FAX 44-35-60-91. TELEX 648 094 F. (Subscr. to: B.P. 12, 99505 Paris Entreprises, France. TEL 46-30-38-00. FAX 46-30-31-67)
  Description: Offers texts to Sunday as well as weekday masses.

282   CN   ISSN 0383-8277
PRIONS EN EGLISE - EDITION DOMINICALE. English edition: Living with Christ - Sunday Edition. w., plus 2 special issues. Can.$21.35. Novalis, St. Paul University, 223 Main St., Ottawa, ON K1S 1C4, Canada. TEL 613-236-1393. FAX 613-782-3004. (Subscr. to: 49 Front St., E., 2nd Fl., Toronto, ON M5E 1B3, Canada. TEL 416-363-3303) Ed. Pierre Dufresne; Pub. Michael O'Hearn.

282 028.5   FR   ISSN 1168-0024
PRIONS EN EGLISE JUNIOR. 1992. m. 194 F. (outside EC 234 F.). Bayard Presse, 3 rue Bayard, 75393 Paris Cedex 08, France. TEL 44-35-60-60. FAX 44-35-90-61. TELEX 648 094 F. (Subscr. to: B.P. 12, 99505 Paris Entreprises, France. TEL 46-30-38-00. FAX 46-30-31-67)
  Description: Helps children 8 to 12 years old to understand the Gospel.

282   US
PRO ECCLESIA MAGAZINE. 1965. q. $20. Pro Ecclesia Foundation, 350 Fifth Ave., Rm. 3304, New York, NY 10118-0110. TEL 212-673-7447. Ed. Timothy A. Mitchell. bk.rev.; illus.; circ. 5,000 (paid).
  Formerly (until 1990): Pro Ecclesia; Incorporates: Common Good; Talks of Pope John Paul II; Which was formerly: Talks of Pope Paul VI.
  Description: Examines attacks against the Catholic church and answers them with Catholic teachings.

282   US
PROBE (CHICAGO). feminist religious women. 1971. bi-m. $25. National Assembly of Religious Women (N.A.R.W.), 529 S. Wabash Ave., Ste. 404, Chicago, IL 60605-1608. TEL 312-663-1980. FAX 312-663-9161. Ed. Cecilia Lavan. bk.rev. circ. 2,500. Indexed: CERDIC, South.Bap.Per.Ind.
  Description: Includes includes theological reflection, social analysis and action suggestions.

282   BE   ISSN 0778-6735
PROBLEMES D'HISTOIRE DES RELIGIONS. (Text in French) 1971-1989; N.S. 1990. a. price varies. (Universite Libre de Bruxelles, Institut d'Histoire des Religions et de la Laicite) Editions de l'Universite de Bruxelles, Av. Paul Heger 26 - C.P. 163, B-1050 Brussels, Belgium. TEL 32-2-6503799. FAX 32-2-6503794. TELEX 23069 UNILIB BRUX. Ed. Alain Dierkens. Indexed: CERDIC. **Document type:** monographic series.
  —BLDSC (6617.871270).
  Formerly (until 1990): Problemes d'Histoire du Christianisme (ISSN 0778-6751)

282   US   ISSN 0739-6023
THE PROGRESS (SEATTLE). 1897. w. $25. Archdiocese of Seattle, 910 Marion St., Seattle, WA 98104. TEL 206-382-4850. FAX 206-382-3487. Ed. Kay Lagreid. adv. contact: Mary E. Molloy. circ. 18,365. (tabloid format) **Document type:** newspaper.

282   US   ISSN 8750-5452
PROVIDENCE VISITOR. 1875. w. (48/yr.). $15 (foreign $18). 184 Broad St., Providence, RI 02903. TEL 401-272-1010. FAX 401-421-8418. Ed. Michael K. Brown. adv. contact: Michael K. Brown. circ. 32,741. **Document type:** newspaper.

PUR-MAGAZIN. see *LITERARY AND POLITICAL REVIEWS*

QUE VOUS EN SEMBLE?. see *ANTHROPOLOGY*

282 947   US   ISSN 1044-0518
QUOTE...UNQUOTE; a public information service. 1980. m. free. (Catholic Traditionalist Movement, Inc.) C T M Publications, Inc., 210 Maple Ave., Westbury, NY 11590-3117. TEL 516-333-6470. FAX 516-333-7535. Ed. Gommar A. De Pauw. (looseleaf format; back issues avail.)
  Description: Comments from notable persons and publications about papal and Vatican affairs and activities within the context of traditional Catholicism.

282   AT   ISSN 1033-1050
R.C.I.A. RESOURCE. (Rite of Christian Initiation of Adults) 1986. 4/yr. Aus.$25 (effective Nov. 1994). (Melbourne Catechumenate Office) Resourceful Publishing Company, 406 Albert St., E. Melbourne, Vic. 3002, Australia. TEL 61-3-662-2637. FAX 61-3-639-1905. Ed. Margaret Mooney. bk.rev. circ. 1,000. **Document type:** academic/scholarly publication.
  Description: Resources for catechesis from the lectionary, commentary for local implementation of the R.C.I.A.

266 301   CN   ISSN 0035-3795
R N D. (Revue Notre-Dame) (Text in French) 1903. m. Can.$13 (foreign Can.$26) (effective 1995 & 1996). Missionnaires du Sacre-Coeur, 2215 rue Marie-Victorin, Sillery, Quebec, PQ G1T 1J6, Canada. TEL 418-681-3581. FAX 418-681-1139. Ed. Paul-Eugene Chabot; Pub. Yvon Labbe. adv. contact: Thomas Maurais. illus. circ. 140,000. Indexed: Pt.de Rep. (1979-).
  Description: Studies social and religious formation.

282   GW
R U. (Religionsunterricht); oekumenische Zeitschrift fuer die Praxis des Religionsunterrichts. q. DM.36.80 (students DM.33.60). Koesel-Verlag GmbH und Co., Flueggenstr. 2, 80639 Munich, Germany. TEL 089-17801-0. FAX 089-17801111. Ed. Horst Klaus Berg. **Document type:** academic/scholarly publication.

282   II   ISSN 0048-668X
RALLY. (Text in English) vol.50, 1973. m. $15. All India Catholic University Federation, 125 Sterling Rd., Madras 600 034, India. Ed. Michael Pinto. bk.rev. circ. 1,500.

282   UK   ISSN 0033-9245
RANSOMER. 1893. 3/yr. $12. Guild of Our Lady of Ransom, 31 Southdown Rd., Wimbledon, London SW20 8QJ, England. TEL 081-947-2598. FAX 081-944-6208. Ed. Msgr. Anthony George Stark. adv.; bk.rev.; circ. 2,000 (controlled).

282   IE   ISSN 0034-0960
REALITY. 1936. m. (11/yr.). I£14.40($30) Redemptorist Publications, 75 Orwell Rd., Rathgar, Dublin 6, Ireland. TEL 01-4922488. Ed. Gerard Moloney. adv. contact: Paul Soden. bk.rev.; illus. circ. 20,000. Indexed: CERDIC. **Document type:** bulletin.

200   AT   ISSN 1038-0493
THE RECORD (DARLINGHURST). 1917. q. Aus.$10. Saint Vincent de Paul Society, National Council of Australia, P.O. Box 740, Darlinghurst, N.S.W. 2010, Australia. TEL 02-332-4033. FAX 02-332-2305. Ed. John McNamara. bk.rev.; illus.; index. circ. 19,000.
  Formerly: Saint Vincent de Paul Record (ISSN 0036-3219)
  Description: Provides pictures and articles relating to society work of helping the needy in Australia or overseas.

282   AT
THE RECORD (NORTHBRIDGE). 1874. w. Aus.$60. P.O. Box 75, Leederville, W.A. 6902, Australia. TEL 61-9-2277080. FAX 61-9-2277087. Ed. David Kehoe. adv.; bk.rev. circ. 8,000. (tabloid format) **Document type:** newspaper.

RECUSANT HISTORY. see *HISTORY — History Of Europe*

282   US   ISSN 0745-3248
REDWOOD CROZIER. 1980. m. $12 donation. (Roman Catholic Diocese of Santa Rosa) Redwood Crozier, 547 B St., Santa Rosa, CA 95401. TEL 707-459-5710. Ed. Allan G. Bohner; Pub. Rev. G. Patrick Ziemann. adv.; illus. (tabloid format) **Document type:** newspaper.
  Description: Publishes local, regional, national and international news of interest to area Catholics.

282   IT
IL REGNO. (In 2 sections: Attualita and Documenti) 1956. s-m. L.56000 (foreign L.83000) (effective 1994). Centro Editoriale Dehoniano, Via Nosadella 6, 40123 Bologna, Italy. TEL 051-306811. FAX 051-341706. Ed. P. Alfio Filippi. circ. 13,500. Indexed: CERDIC.

RELIGIONS AND THEOLOGY — ROMAN CATHOLIC

282   IT   ISSN 0034-3498
REGNO - ATTUALITA. 1956. m. L.34000 (foreign L.48000) (effective 1994). Centro Editoriale Dehoniano, Via Nosadella 6, 40123 Bologna, Italy. TEL 051-306811. FAX 051-341706. adv.; bk.rev.; bibl.; index, cum.index. circ. 12,000.
  Description: Covers world events in church life. Features today's problem and discussions about recent events as well as original interviews.

282   GW   ISSN 0341-3322
REGNUM; internationale Vierteljahresschrift der Schoenstattbewegung. 1965. q. DM.28. Patris Verlag, Hoehrerstr. 109, 56171 Vallendar, Germany. TEL 0261-60409. Ed. Guenther Boll. bk.rev. circ. 1,700. (back issues avail.) **Document type:** bulletin.

266   US   ISSN 0048-7155
REIGN OF THE SACRED HEART. 1934. q. Priests of the Sacred Heart, 6889 S. Lovers Ln., Hales Corners, WI 53130. TEL 414-425-3383. FAX 414-425-5719. Ed. Father Brian. illus.; circ. 490,000 (controlled).

RELATIONS. see SOCIAL SERVICES AND WELFARE

282 370   IT
RELIGIONE E SCUOLA; mensile per l'animazione culturale e la ricerca religiosa. bi-m. L.42000 (foreign L.60000) (effective Sep. 1995). Editrice Queriniana, Via Piamarta 6, 25187 Brescia, Italy. TEL 39-30-294653. FAX 39-30-3756375. Ed. Roberto Laurita. adv. contact: Mario De Risio.

282   GW   ISSN 0173-0339
RELIGIONSPAEDAGOGISCHE BEITRAEGE. Short title: R p B. 1978. s-a. DM.30. Arbeitsgemeinschaft Katholischer Katechetikdozenten, c/o Prof. H.A. Zwergel, Wegmannstr. 1D, 34128 Kassel, Germany. TEL 0561-886207. Ed.Bd. bk.rev.; index. circ. 400. (back issues avail.)
  Description: Catholic publication concerned with the teaching of religion. Contains articles on the Church, Bible, Catholic doctrine, and social issues.

282   US
RELIGIOUS COMMUNITY PROFILES. (Published in 3 regional editions) 1979. a. $5. Catholic News Publishing Co., Inc., 210 North Ave., New Rochelle, NY 10801. TEL 914-632-1220; 800-433-7771. FAX 914-632-3412. Ed. Mari Castrovilla; Pub. Myles Ridder. adv.: B&W page $1210; trim 4 1/2 x 7; adv. contact: Tom White. tr.lit. circ. 45,000.
  Former titles: Guide to Religious Ministries for Catholic Men and Women; Guide to Religious Careers for Catholic Men and Women.

282   US   ISSN 0279-0459
RELIGIOUS LIFE. 1976. m. (10/yr.). $10. Institute on Religious Life, Box 41007, Chicago, IL 60641. TEL 312-267-1195. Ed. Fr. L. Dudley Day. adv.; bk.rev. circ. 5,500. (back issues avail.) **Document type:** newsletter.
  Description: Serves the Catholic religious communities by fostering a more effective understanding of the Church's teaching on religious life.

282   IE   ISSN 0332-4346
RELIGIOUS LIFE REVIEW. 1961. 6/yr. £17.58($28.48) Dominican Publications, 42 Parnell Sq., Upper Dorset, Dublin 1, Ireland. TEL 01-8721611. FAX 01-8731760. **Document type:** bulletin.
  Formerly (until 1980): Doctrine and Life. Supplement (ISSN 0419-5078)

REMNANT OF ISRAEL. see RELIGIONS AND THEOLOGY — Judaic

RENEWAL (CROWBOROUGH). see RELIGIONS AND THEOLOGY — Protestant

280   GW   ISSN 0340-8280
RENOVATIO; Zeitschrift fuer das interdisziplinaere Gespraech. 1945. 4/yr. DM.23.60. J.P. Bachem Verlag GmbH, Ursulaplatz 1, 50668 Cologne, Germany. TEL 0221-16190. (Co-sponsor: Katholische Aerztearbeit Deutschlands) Ed. Helmut-Josef Patt. bk.rev. circ. 6,500. **Indexed:** CERDIC, New Test.Abstr. **Document type:** bulletin.
  Formerly: Katholische Gedanke (ISSN 0022-9385)

266 282   US
REPORT ON U S CATHOLIC OVERSEAS MISSION. 1950. a. $20. United States Catholic Mission Association, 3029 Fourth St., N.E., Washington, DC 20017. TEL 202-832-3112. Ed. Lucille Malaney. circ. 1,500. **Indexed:** SRI. **Document type:** directory.
  Former titles: Mission Handbook; United States Catholic Mission Council. Handbook; United States Catholic Missionary Personnel Overseas (ISSN 0082-9560)

200   US   ISSN 0034-639X
BX2400
REVIEW FOR RELIGIOUS; Christian heritages and contemporary living. 1942. bi-m. $20. Jesuits of the Missouri Province, 3601 Lindell Blvd., St. Louis, MO 63108. TEL 314-977-7363. FAX 314-977-7362. (Subscr. to: P.O. Box 6070, Duluth, MN 55806) Ed. David L. Fleming, S.J. bk.rev.; index. circ. 10,500. (also avail. in microform from UMI; reprint service avail. from UMI) **Indexed:** Bk.Rev.Ind. (1965-), Cath.Ind., CERDIC, Child.Bk.Rev.Ind. (1965-), New Test.Abstr. **Document type:** academic/scholarly publication.
  —UMI.
  Description: Serves as a forum for shared reflection on the lived experience of those who find that the Church's heritage of spirituality supports their personal lives.
  Refereed Serial

282   CL   ISSN 0716-033X
REVISTA CATOLICA. 1843. q. $20. Seminario Pontificio Mayor de Santiago, Chile, Walker Martinez 2020, La Florida, Casilla 3-D, Santiago, Chile. TEL 2853119. FAX 2853679. Dir. P. Maximino Arias Reyero. adv.; bk.rev. circ. 1,200. **Document type:** academic/scholarly publication.

282 267   AG   ISSN 0034-9070
REVISTA DEL HOGAR.* s-m. Arg.$1.20. Jovenes de la Accion Catolica, Belgrand 239, Capillaudel Senor, Buenos Aires, Argentina. Ed. Reynaldo Dassat. (processed)

282   US   ISSN 0274-9092
REVISTA MARYKNOLL. (Text in Spanish) 1980. m. $3. Maryknoll Fathers, Pinesbridge Rd., Maryknoll, NY 19545-9999. TEL 914-941-7590. Ed. Moises Sandoval. adv. circ. 68,000.
  Description: Dedicated and directed toward Hispanics, their concerns and religiosity at home and abroad.

282   PE
REVISTA PERUANA DE HISTORIA ECLESIASTICA. s-a.? Instituto Peruano de Historia Eclesiastica, Calle Hatun-rumiyoc 414, Apdo. 148, Cuzco, Peru. TEL 225211.

282   PE
REVISTA TEOLOGICA LIMENSE. 1966. 3/yr. $20 (Latin America $35; elsewhere $45) (effective 1994). Facultad de Teologia Pontificia y Civil de Lima, Calle Carlos Bondy 700, Apdo. 21-0135, Lima 21, Peru. TEL 14-620732. FAX 14-610245. bk.rev. circ. 700.

282   ZR   ISSN 1016-2461
BR3
REVUE AFRICAINE DE THEOLOGIE. (Text in English, French; summaries in French) 1977. s-a. $70. Faculte de Theologie Catholique de Kinshasa, B.P. 1534, Kinshasa-Limite, Zaire. (back issues avail.) **Indexed:** CERDIC, New Test.Abstr., P.L.E.S.A. (1988-). **Document type:** academic/scholarly publication.

200   BE   ISSN 0035-0893
BX3001
REVUE BENEDICTINE; de critique, d'histoire et de litterature religieuses. (Text in English, French, German, Italian) 1884. 2/yr. 2500 BEF. Abbaye de Maredsous, B-5537 Denee, Belgium. TEL 32-82-69-91-55. FAX 32-82-69-96-25. Dir. Daniel Misonne. bk.rev.; abstr.; index. circ. 1,000. (also avail. in microfiche from IDC; back issues avail.) **Indexed:** Bull.Signal., M.L.A., New Test.Abstr., Old Test.Abstr.
  —Faxon; SWETS.
  Description: Studies occidental ecclesiastical history, with emphasis on biblical, patristic and monastic texts.

209   FR   ISSN 0035-2217
BX802
REVUE DES SCIENCES RELIGIEUSES. 1921. q. 190 F. (outside EC 200 F.). Universite de Strasbourg II, Faculte de Theologie Catholique, Palais Universitaire, 67084 Strasbourg, France. TEL 88-25-97-29. FAX 88-37-92-09. Ed. Dr. Marie-Anne Vannier. bk.rev.; index. circ. 700. (also avail. in microform from SWZ) **Indexed:** CERDIC, New Test.Abstr., Old Test.Abstr., Rel.Ind.One, Rel.Per. **Document type:** academic/scholarly publication, bulletin.
  —BLDSC (7948.500000); SWETS.
  Description: Aims to present all fields of theology through concise and scientific articles.

282   FR
REVUE DU ROSAIRE. 1927. 10/yr. 105 F. (foreign 140 F.). Editions du Cerf, 29 bd. Latour Maubourg, 75340 Paris Cedex 07, France. TEL 44-18-12-12. FAX 45-56-04-27. (Subscr. to: Service Abonnements, 3 chemin des Prunais, 94350 Villiers-sur-Marne, France)

248.894   BE   ISSN 0035-3620
BX2613
REVUE MABILLON. (Text in French, Latin; summaries in English, French) 1905; N.S. 1990. a. 1750 BEF (effective 1995). (Centre Nationale de Recherche Scientifique, Institut de Recherche et d'Histoire des Textes, FR) N.V. Brepols, Steenweg op Tielen 68, 2300 Turnhout, Belgium. TEL 32-14-402500. FAX 32-14-428919. Ed. Jean Becquet. adv.; abstr.; bibl.; charts; illus.; index. circ. 400. (also avail. in microform from JAI; back issues avail.) **Indexed:** Amer.Hist.& Life, Hist.Abstr. **Document type:** academic/scholarly publication.
  —BLDSC (7926.770000).
  Description: Studies the history of religious life and spirituality in the Middle Ages and modern times. Publishes previously unpublished texts and iconography.

200   BE   ISSN 0080-2654
REVUE THEOLOGIQUE DE LOUVAIN. (Supplement avail.: Revue Theologique de Louvain. Cahiers (ISSN 0771-601X)) 1970. 4/yr. 1600 BEF. Universite Catholique de Louvain, Faculte de Theologie et de Droit Canonique, Grand-Place 45, B-1348 Louvain-la-Neuve, Belgium. Ed. H. Bogaert. bk.rev.; cum.index: vols.1-10, 1970-1979; vols.11-20, 1980-1989. circ. 1,300. **Indexed:** Arts & Hum.Cit.Ind., Cath.Ind., New Test.Abstr. **Document type:** academic/scholarly publication.
  —BLDSC (7956.080000).

282   BE   ISSN 0771-601X
REVUE THEOLOGIQUE DE LOUVAIN. CAHIERS. Key Title: Cahiers de la Revue Theologique de Louvain. (Text in French) 1980. irreg. (approx. 2/yr.), vol.27, 1994. price varies. (Universite Catholique de Louvain, Facultes de Theologie et de Droit Canonique) Editions Peeters s.p.r.l., Bondgenotenlaan 153, 3000, Belgium. TEL 32-16-235170. FAX 32-16-228500. (back issues avail.) **Indexed:** CERDIC, Old Test.Abstr. **Document type:** monographic series.

282 100   IT   ISSN 0393-3830
RICERCHE STORICHE SALESIANE; rivista semestrale di storia religiosa e civile. 1982. s-a. L.30000 (foreign L.40000). (Istituto Storico Salesiano) Editrice Libreria Ateneo Salesiano, Piazza dell'Ateneo Salesiano, 1, 00139 Rome, Italy. TEL 39-6-872901. FAX 39-6-87290629. Ed. Francesco Motto. bk.rev. circ. 700. **Document type:** academic/scholarly publication.
  Description: Features study and research on the history of St. John Bosco and the Salesians. It also looks at religious history and civilization.

282   GW
RING DES WORTES; Seelsorgebrief fuer Hoergeschaedigte, Kranke und Senioren. 1958. bi-m. free. Erzbischoefliches Generalvikariat, Hauptabteilung Seelsorge, Marzellenstr. 32, 50668 Cologne, Germany. Ed. Karl-Heinz Stockhausen. circ. 10,500. **Document type:** newsletter.
  Description: Devotional material for hearing impaired and hospitalized people and seniors.

RELIGIONS AND THEOLOGY — ROMAN CATHOLIC

282   IT   ISSN 0042-7586
RIVISTA DEL CLERO ITALIANO. 1920. m. (11/yr.). L.39000 (foreign L.61000 ($47)) (effective 1996). (Universita Cattolica del Sacro Cuore) Vita e Pensiero, Largo Gemelli 1, 20123 Milan, Italy. TEL 39-2-72342310. FAX 39-2-72342260. TELEX 321033 UCATMI 1. Ed. Bruno Maggioni. adv: B&W page L.3000000. bk.rev.; bibl.; index. circ. 6,500. **Indexed:** CERDIC.
   Description: Looks at many different issues in theology and various religious cultures.

282   IT   ISSN 0394-0594
RIVISTA DI ASCETICA E MISTICA. 1929. q. L.25000 (foreign L.40000) (effective 1994). Via Cavour, 56, Florence, Italy. TEL 055-287628. Ed. F. Sbaffoni. bk.rev.
   Former titles (since 1978): Nuova Rivista di Ascetica e Mistica (ISSN 0394-0586); (until 1976): Rassegna di Ascetica e Mistica. S. Caterina da Siena (ISSN 0394-0578); Which was formed by the merger of (1950-1970): S. Caterina da Siena (ISSN 1120-0308); (1956-1970): Rivista di Ascetica e Mistica (ISSN 0485-232X); Which was formerly: Vita Cristiana (ISSN 1120-0316)

282   IT   ISSN 0391-0946
RIVISTA DI TEOLOGIA MORALE. 1969. q. L.43000 (foreign L.49000) (effective 1994). Centro Editoriale Dehoniano, Via Nosadella 6, 40123 Bologna, Italy. TEL 051-306811. FAX 051-341706. circ. 2,500.

282 248   IT   ISSN 0035-6638
RIVISTA DI VITA SPIRITUALE. 1947. bi-m. L.35000 (foreign L.42000) (effective 1995). (Centro Interprovinciale O.C.D.) Edizioni O.C.D., Via Anagnina 662-B, 00040 Morena (RM), Italy. TEL 39-6-7247482. FAX 39-6-7245387. Ed. R.P. Bruno Moriconi. bk.rev.; bibl.; index. circ. 2,000.
   Description: For priests, monks, nuns, and the laity.

282   IT   ISSN 0035-6654
RIVISTA DIOCESANA DEL PATRIARCATO DI VENEZIA. 1918. m. L.60000. Patriarcato di Venezia, Centro di Informazione e Documentazione, San Marco 333, 30124 Venice, Italy. TEL 39-41-2702411. FAX 39-41-2702420. Ed. Mons. Mario Ronzini; Pub. Mons. Valerio Comin. **Document type:** bulletin.

THE ROCK (EPPING). see RELIGIONS AND THEOLOGY — Protestant

262.9   PL   ISSN 0035-7723
BX806.P6
ROCZNIKI TEOLOGICZNO-KANONICZNE. (In six parts: 1. Holy Scripture; 2. Fundamental and Dogmatic Theology; 3. Moral Theology; 4. History of Church; 5. Canon Law; 6. Pastoral Theology) (Text in Polish; summaries in English, French, German, Italian and Latin) 1949. 6/yr. price varies. Katolicki Uniwersytet Lubelski, Towarzystwo Naukowe, Ul. Gliniana 21, 20-616 Lublin, Poland. Ed.Bd. bk.rev.; index. circ. 820. **Indexed:** CERDIC, New Test.Abstr., Old Test.Abstr.
—BLDSC (8522.250000).

282   US   ISSN 1046-5030
ROLA BOZA/GOD'S FIELD. (Text in English, Polish) 1923. bi-w. $8. (Polish National Catholic Church) Rola Boza Publishing Co., 5296 E. Locust St., Scranton, PA 18505. TEL 717-343-6017. Ed. Rev. Bishop Anthony M. Rysz. circ. 7,200 (paid). (tabloid format) **Document type:** newspaper.

282   US
ROMAN CATHOLIC STUDIES. irreg., latest no.7. $49.95 per no. Edwin Mellen Press, 415 Ridge St., Box 450, Lewiston, NY 14092. TEL 716-754-2788. FAX 716-754-4056.

282   PO   ISSN 0035-8274
ROSARIO DE MARIA; publicacao mensal de espiritualidade rosario mariana. 1944. m. Esc.50($4) Dominican Convent Friars-Fatima, Secretariado Nacional do Rosario, Fatima, Portugal. Ed. L. Cerdeira. bk.rev.; illus.; index. circ. 7,000.

282   US   ISSN 0035-8282
IL ROSARIO E LA NUOVA POMPEI. (English q. edition avail.) 1884. m. contribution. Pontificio Santuario di Pompei, 80045 Naples, Italy. TEL 081-863-83-44. FAX 081-850-33-57. Ed. Fr. Salvatore Parrone. bk.rev. circ. 320,000 (300,000 Italian ed.; 20,000 English ed.). **Document type:** newspaper.

282   US   ISSN 0745-3299
ROZE MARYI. (Text in Polish) 1944. m. $6. Association of Marian Helpers, Stockbridge, MA 01263. TEL 413-298-3691. Ed. Andrew Maczynski. bk.rev. circ. 9,500.

282   US
RURAL LANDSCAPES; a newsletter of faith, community and resources. 1981. 10/yr. $25 to individuals; institutions $100. National Catholic Rural Life Conference, 4625 Beaver Ave., Des Moines, IA 50310. TEL 515-270-2634. FAX 515-270-9447. Ed. Sandra A. LaBlanc. circ. 3,000. **Document type:** newsletter.
   Formerly (until 1993): Common Ground (Des Moines) (ISSN 0746-5114)

282   US
S C R C SPIRIT. 1973. bi-m. voluntary donation. Southern California Renewal Communities, 2810 Artesia Blvd., Redondo Beach, CA 90278. TEL 310-371-6433. FAX 310-371-8452. Eds. Fr. Bill Dalaney, Sandy Berardino. circ. 8,500. (looseleaf format) **Document type:** newsletter.
   Formerly (until 1994): S C R C Vision (ISSN 1041-4045)
   Description: Provides solid Catholic teaching articles and lists events for the Catholic charismatic renewal.

266   IE
S M A - THE AFRICAN MISSIONARY. (Text in English, Gaelic) 1914. 5/yr. I£3. S M A Fathers, Blackrock Rd., Cork, Ireland. TEL 021-292871. Ed. Fr. Peter McCawille. adv.; bk.rev. circ. 40,000. **Document type:** bulletin.
   Formerly: African Missionary (ISSN 0044-6580)

282   IE
SACRED HEART MESSENGER. 1888. m. I£10.50 (foreign I£16). (Jesuit Fathers) Messenger Publications, 37 Lower Leeson St., Dublin 2, Ireland. TEL 6767491. FAX 6611606. Ed. Father Brendan Murray, S.J. charts; illus.; pat.; tr.mk. circ. 196,000. **Document type:** bulletin.
   Formerly: Irish Messenger of the Sacred Heart (ISSN 0021-1303)
   Description: Publication of the Apostleship of prayer- practical spirituality, family appeal, modern and balanced.

282   US
SACRED SIGNS.* 1980. q. $10. Sacred Signs, 117 Washington St., Newport, RI 02848. TEL 401-847-5428. Ed. Helen Holland. adv.

282   CN   ISSN 0318-434X
ST. ANNE DE BEAUPRE. THE ANNALS. French edition: Revue Sainte Anne. (Editions in English, French) 1878. m. Can.$8.75. Redemptorist Fathers, Ste-Anne de Beaupre Province, Basilica of Ste. Anne, Quebec, PQ G0A 3C0, Canada. FAX 418-827-4530. Ed. Bernard Mercier. adv.; bk.rev. circ. 160,000 (50,000 English ed.; 110,000 French ed.).

282   US
ST. ANSGAR'S BULLETIN. 1914. a. $10. St. Ansgar's Scandinavian Catholic League, 40 W. 13th St., New York, NY 10011. TEL 212-675-0400. Ed. J.E. Halborg. illus.; stat. circ. 1,400. **Document type:** bulletin, newsletter.

282   US   ISSN 0036-276X
ST. ANTHONY MESSENGER. 1893. m. $19. (Franciscan Friars of St. John the Baptist Province) St. Anthony Messenger Press, 1615 Republic St., Cincinnati, OH 45210. TEL 513-241-5615. FAX 513-241-0399. Ed. Rev. Norman Perry. adv.: B&W page $2660, color page $4035. bk.rev.; film rev.; index. circ. 370,000. (also avail. in microform from UMI; reprint service avail. from UMI) **Indexed:** Cath.Ind., CERDIC. —UMI.
   Description: Contains news and features of interest to Catholic families.

215   US   ISSN 0080-5432
SAINT BONAVENTURE UNIVERSITY. FRANCISCAN INSTITUTE. PHILOSOPHY SERIES. 1944. irreg., no.16, 1972. price varies. Saint Bonaventure University, Franciscan Institute, St. Bonaventure, NY 14778. TEL 716-375-2105. Ed. Br. F. Edward Coughlin, O.F.M.

200   US   ISSN 0080-5440
SAINT BONAVENTURE UNIVERSITY. FRANCISCAN INSTITUTE. TEXT SERIES. 1951. irreg., no.16, 1972. price varies. Saint Bonaventure University, Franciscan Institute, St. Bonaventure, NY 14778. TEL 716-375-2105. Ed. Br. F. Edward Coughlin, O.F.M.

282   US   ISSN 0036-3022
ST. LOUIS REVIEW. 1941. w. $15 (effective 1995). Catholic Archdiocese of St. Louis, 462 N. Taylor Ave., St. Louis, MO 63108. TEL 314-531-9700. FAX 314-531-2269. Ed. Rev. Dennis M. Delaney. adv. contact: Harry Hinchey. bk.rev.; film rev.; illus.; circ. 100,000 (paid). (also avail. in microfilm) **Document type:** newspaper.
   Formerly: St. Louis Register.

SAINT PETER'S; the college magazine. see COLLEGE AND ALUMNI

284 282   IS
SALAM UAL KHEIR. (Text in Arabic) m. Franciscan Printing Press, P.O. Box 14064, Jerusalem 91140, Israel. TEL 972-2-286594. FAX 972-2-272274.

266   US   ISSN 0036-3480
SALESIAN. 1947. q. $4. Salesian Missions, Box 30, 2 Lefevre Ln., New Rochelle, NY 10802. TEL 914-633-8344. FAX 914-633-7404. Ed. Rev. E.J. Cappelletti. illus. circ. 1,000,000.
   Description: Describes the various educational and developmental programs for youth the Salesian Missions sponsors worldwide.

282   IE   ISSN 0790-1216
SALESIAN BULLETIN. (Text in English) 1939. q. I£5($10) Salesians of Don Bosco Media, Salesian House, St. Teresa's Rd., Dublin 12, Ireland. TEL 01-4555605. FAX 01-4558781. (Subscr. to: Salesian Missions, P.O. Box 50, Pallaskenry, Co. Limerick, Ireland) Ed. Eddie Fitzgerald. bk.rev. circ. 20,000. (back issues avail.) **Document type:** bulletin.

200   IT   ISSN 0036-3502
BX800.A1
SALESIANUM. (Text in English, French, German, Italian, Latin, Spanish) 1939. q. L.55000 (foreign L.65000). (Universita Pontificia Salesiana, VC) Editrice Libreria Ateneo Salesiano, Piazza Ateneo Salesiano 1, 00139 Rome, Italy. TEL 39-6-872901. FAX 39-6-87290629. Ed. Enrico dal Covolo. bk.rev. circ. 1,000. **Indexed:** Canon Law Abstr., CERDIC, M.L.A., New Test.Abstr., Rel.& Theol.Abstr. (1979-). **Document type:** academic/scholarly publication.
   Description: Features sections that deal with theology, philosophy, canon law, and religious research.

282 370   XV   ISSN 0353-0477
SALEZIJANSKI VESTNIK; glasilo salezijanske druzine. (Text in Slovenian) 1904. q. free. Salezijanski Inspektorat, Rakovniska ul. 6, 61108 Ljubljana, Slovenia. TEL 061 217-406. Ed. Tone Ciglar. circ. 7,500.
   Description: Information about the history of the Church, missions, mariology.

200 260   SP   ISSN 0036-3537
SALMANTICENSIS. 1954. 3/yr. 3600 ptas.($50) Universidad Pontificia, Departamento de Ediciones y Publicaciones, Apdo. de Correos 541, 37080 Salamanca, Spain. TEL 923-21-51-40. FAX 923-21-34-50. bk.rev.; bibl.; index; circ. 2,000 (controlled). (looseleaf format) **Indexed:** Amer.Hist.& Life, CERDIC, Hist.Abstr., Rel.Ind.One.
—BLDSC (8070.950000).

282   US
SAN FRANCISCO CATHOLIC. 1859. m. $15. Archdiocese of San Francisco, Catholic Communications Center, 441 Church St., San Francisco, CA 94114. TEL 415-565-3630. Ed. Charlotte Pace. adv.: B&W page $1100. film rev.; circ. 48,000 (controlled).
   Supersedes (in 1985): Monitor (ISSN 0026-9743)

200   IT
LA SAN VINCENZO IN ITALIA. 1856. bi-m. L.14000. Societa di San Vincenzo de Paoli, Consiglio Superiore Italiano, Via Pisacane 32, 20129 Milan, Italy. TEL 29526343. FAX 29526325. Ed. Antonio Strambi. bk.rev. circ. 4,000.
   Formerly: Samaritano (ISSN 0036-3723)

RELIGIONS AND THEOLOGY — ROMAN CATHOLIC

282   US
SANGRE DE CRISTO NEWSNOTES. 1973. s-a. $10. 210 S. Second St., Box 89, Westcliffe, CO 81252. TEL 719-783-2491. Ed. Fr. Dan Jones. bk.rev. circ. 950. (back issues avail.) **Document type:** newsletter.
Description: Deals with the Roman Catholic and Christian education, current Marian apparitions, and restoration of the true Catholic church.

282   US   ISSN 0036-116X
SANTA CASA DI LORETO. MESSAGGIO. English edition: Shrine of the Holy House. Loreto. 1881 (Eng. ed. 1968). m. (Eng. ed. 3/yr.). L.3000($10) for Italian ed. Congregazione Universale della Santa Casa, 60025 Loreto (Ancora), Italy. TEL 071-970104. Ed. Fr. Joseph Santarelli. bk.rev.; illus. circ. 36,000. **Document type:** bulletin.

SANTO; rivista antoniana di storia dottrina arte. see HISTORY — History Of Europe

282   255   IT   ISSN 0036-4606
SANTO DEI VOLI. 1946. bi-m. L.880($2) (Frati Minori Conventuali di Puglia, Provincia Religiosa) Santuario S. Giuseppe da Copertino, Via Piave 8, 73043 Copertino, Italy. TEL (0832) 947.011. Ed. Goffredo Giovanni Iasi. adv.; bk.rev.; film rev.; cum.index. circ. 4,500. (cards)

266   IT   ISSN 0036-4622
SANTUARIO DELLA MADONNA DELLE ROCCHE. 1920. bi-m. L.2000. Passionisti, 15074 Molare, Alessandria, Italy. bibl.; charts; illus.; stat.; index. circ. 1,000. (tabloid format)

SCHOOL EN GODSDIENST; catechetical periodical for elementary school teachers. see EDUCATION — Teaching Methods And Curriculum

SCHOOLBESTUUR. see EDUCATION — School Organization And Administration

282   NE   ISSN 0167-3114
SCHRIFT; populair bijbeltijdschrift. 1953. bi-m. fl.37.50. Gooi en Sticht, Postbus 133, 3700 AC Baarn, Netherlands. TEL 31-2154-15320. FAX 31-2154-20568. (Editorial addr.: Redactie Schrift, c/o R. Pirson, Postbus 10288, 5000 JG Tilburg, Netherlands) bk.rev. circ. 2,000. **Indexed:** CERDIC.
Formerly: Boek der Boeken (ISSN 0006-5544)
Description: Catholic publication devoted to Biblical studies.

282   GW
SCHULE UND MISSION; Hilfen fuer Religionsunterricht. 1950. q. DM.20. Kindermissionswerk, Stephanstr. 35, 52064 Aachen, Germany. TEL 0241-4461-0. FAX 0241-446140. Ed. Marlies Gahn. bk.rev. circ. 7,800. **Document type:** academic/scholarly publication.

282   US
SCRANTON CATHOLIC LIGHT. 1899. bi-w. $10. Scranton Catholic Light, 300 Wyoming Ave., Scranton, PA 18503. TEL 717-346-8915. FAX 717-346-8917. (Subscr. to: Box 708, Scranton, PA 18501) Ed. James B. Earley. **Document type:** newspaper.

SCRIBHINNI GAEILGENA NA BRATHAR MIONUR. see LITERATURE

220   282   UK   ISSN 0036-9780
BS410
SCRIPTURE BULLETIN. (DK) 1969. s-a. £4 (rest of Europe £5.50; elsewhere £7). Catholic Biblical Association of Great Britain, c/o Stephen Greenhalgh, Ed., LSU College of H.E., The Avenue, Southampton SO9 5HB, England. TEL 01703-228761. FAX 01703-230944. adv.; bk.rev. circ. 500. **Indexed:** Cath.Ind., Int.Z.Bibelwiss., New Test.Abstr., Old Test.Abstr. **Document type:** academic/scholarly publication, bulletin.
—BLDSC (8213.240000).
Description: Contains articles on Old and New Testament topics. Gives information on recent developments in area of biblical pastoral ministry.

282   US
▼**SCRIPTURE FROM SCRATCH**. 1994. m. $11. St. Anthony Messenger Pres, 1615 Republic St., Cincinnati, OH 45210. TEL 513-241-5616. FAX 513-241-0399. Ed. Diane Houdek. circ. 37,000. **Document type:** newsletter.
Description: Discusses Scripture-based topics for Catholics.

282   IE   ISSN 0332-1150
SCRIPTURE IN CHURCH. 1970. q. IE30.32($49.12) Dominican Publications, 42 Parnell Sq., Upper Dorset St., Dublin 1, Ireland. TEL 01-8721611. FAX 01-8731760. circ. 6,200. (back issues avail.) **Indexed:** New Test.Abstr., Old Test.Abstr. **Document type:** bulletin.

230   IT   ISSN 0036-9810
SCUOLA CATTOLICA. 1873. bi-m. L.50000($40) (foreign L.70000). Editrice Ancora Milano, Via G. B. Niccolini, 8, 20154 Milan, Italy. TEL 02-33608941. FAX 02-33608944. Ed. T. Citrini. bk.rev.; index. circ. 1,100. **Indexed:** CERDIC, New Test.Abstr., Rel.& Theol.Abstr.

282   CF   ISSN 0488-2024
SEMAINE AFRICAINE. 1952. w. B.P. 2080, Brazzaville, Congo. Ed. Bernard Mackiza. circ. 8,000.

200   VC   ISSN 0582-6314
SEMINARIUM; a review for seminaries, ecclesiastical vocations, universities. (Text in language of authors) 1950; N.S. 1961. q. L.50000 (foreign L.57000($42)) (effective 1996). (Pontifical Society for Priestly Vocations) Libreria Editrice Vaticana, 00120 Vatican City, Vatican City, Vatican City. bk.rev.; bibl.; index. circ. 2,500. **Indexed:** Cath.Ind., CERDIC.
Description: Commentaries for seminaries, ecclesiastical vocations and universities, edited by the Congregation for Catholic Education.

282   PY
SENDERO. 2/wk. Alberdi 874, Asuncion, Paraguay. TEL 21-95941. Ed. Ilde Silvero. circ. 15,000.

282   US   ISSN 0192-7418
SHARE. 1970. 3/yr. $4. Catholic Daughters of America, 10 W. 71st St., New York, NY 10023-4298. TEL 212-877-3041. FAX 301-816-8840. Ed. Peggy Eastman. adv. circ. 140,000.
Description: Contains news of the organization and topics of national current and moral interest.

282   US
SHRINE BULLETIN. 1978. 3/yr. $1. (World Apostolate of Fatima) Blue Army of Our Lady of Fatima, U S A, Inc., Mountain View Rd., Box 976, Washington, NJ 07882-0976. TEL 908-689-1700. FAX 908-689-6279. **Document type:** bulletin.
Description: Calendar of monthly and daily events and pilgrimage information for the Shrine of the Immaculate Heart of Mary.

282   FR   ISSN 0338-2052
SIGNES D'AUJOURD'HUI; la revue de l'animation liturgique. 1975? bi-m. 248 F. (outside EC 268 F.). Bayard Presse, 3 rue Bayard, 75393 Paris Cedex 08, France. TEL 44-35-60-60. FAX 44-35-60-91. TELEX 648 094 F. (Subscr. to: B.P. 12, 99505 Paris Entreprises, France. TEL 46-30-38-00. FAX 46-30-31-67)
Description: Shows how to make a liturgy more animated.

SIGNES MUSIQUES; la revue du chant liturgique. see MUSIC

282   SW   ISSN 0347-0423
SIGNUM. 1920. 10/yr. SEK 190 in the Nordic and Baltic countries; rest of Europe SEK 280; elsewhere SEK 310 (Swedish students SEK 120). Stiftelsen St. Lars, Sankt Johannesgatan 22 A, S-753 12 Uppsala, Sweden. TEL 46-18-12-51-15. FAX 46-18-12-71-25. Eds. Frans Josef Holin, Anna Maria Hodacs. adv.; bk.rev. circ. 2,300.
—BLDSC (8276.327000).
Formed by the merger of (1920-1975): Credo (ISSN 0011-1120); (1963-1975): K I T. Katolsk Informationstjenst (ISSN 0345-6102)
Description: Provides a Catholic orientation of the Church, culture and society. Publishes articles on social issues, religion, humanities, arts and sciences.

SINGENDE KIRCHE; Zeitschrift fuer katholische Kirchenmusik. see MUSIC

282   US
SISTER MIRIAM TERESA LEAGUE OF PRAYER BULLETIN. 1946. q. $5. Sisters of Charity, Box 476, Convent Station, NJ 07961-0476. TEL 201-292-6300. Ed. Sr. Marian Jose Smith. circ. 3,000. **Document type:** bulletin.
Description: Publicizes the life and mission of Sr. Miriam Teresa, a candidate for canonization.

248   US   ISSN 0037-590X
BX4200
SISTERS TODAY. 1929. bi-m. $19. Liturgical Press, Saint John's Abbey, Collegeville, MN 56321. TEL 612-363-2213. Ed. Sr. Mary Anthony Wagner. adv.; B&W page $295. bk.rev.; index. circ. 5,000. (also avail. in microform from UMI; reprint service avail. from UMI) **Indexed:** A.I.P.P., Cath.Ind., CERDIC. —BLDSC (8286.424000); UMI.
Formerly: Sponsa Regis.

SLOVAK CATHOLIC FALCON. see ETHNIC INTERESTS

282   PL   ISSN 1230-8668
SLOWO; dziennik katolicki. (Supplement avail.: Tygodnik Slowa (ISSN 0867-2792)) 1947. 5/w. Zespol Prasy PAX, I N C O - Veritas, Ul. Mokotowska 43, 00-551 Warsaw, Poland. TEL 48-22-297779. FAX 48-2-628-6739. Ed. Jerzy Marchlewski. adv.; illus. **Document type:** newspaper.
Formerly (until 1993): Slowo Powszechne (ISSN 0137-9283)

282   US   ISSN 0892-5100
SLOWO I LITURGIA. (Text in Polish) 1970. q. $25. Polish American Liturgical Center, Box 240492, Orchard Lake, MI 48324. TEL 313-683-0409. Ed. Rev. Eugene Edyk, S.T.D. circ. 130. (looseleaf format)

SOCIAL JUSTICE REVIEW; pioneer American journal of Catholic social action. see SOCIAL SCIENCES: COMPREHENSIVE WORKS

SOCIAL WORK AND CHRISTIANITY; an international journal. see SOCIAL SERVICES AND WELFARE

SOCIAL WORK PRACTICE MONOGRAPH SERIES. see SOCIAL SERVICES AND WELFARE

SOCIOLOGY OF RELIGION. see SOCIOLOGY

282   EC
SOLIDARIDAD. 1982. m. Confederation of Catholic Office Staff and Students, Calle Oriente 725, Quito, Ecuador. TEL 2-216-541. circ. 15,000.

282   GW   ISSN 0176-862X
SONNTAGSDIENSTE. 1972. m. DM.96. (Liturgische Arbeitsgruppe) Bergmoser und Hoeller Verlag GmbH, Karl-Friedrich-Str. 76, 52072 Aachen, Germany. TEL 0241-9388821. FAX 0241-9388834. circ. 2,400. (looseleaf format; back issues avail.) **Document type:** consumer publication.

282   US
SOONER CATHOLIC. 1974. fortn. $12 to non-members. Archdiocese of Oklahoma City, 7501 N.W. Expressway, Oklahoma City, OK 73132. TEL 405-721-1810. FAX 405-721-5210. (Subscr. to: Box 32180, Oklahoma City, OK 73123) Ed. David Monahan. bk.rev. circ. 29,000. (tabloid format; also avail. in microfilm) **Document type:** newspaper.

281.9   US   ISSN 0194-7958
SOPHIA; the review of the Melkite Church in America. 1971. q. $10 (typically set in June; effective Jan.). Melkite Diocese of Newton, Sophia Editorial Office, 11245 Rye St., N. Hollywood, CA 91602-2022. TEL 818-761-2034. FAX 818-761-2922. Ed. John Azar. bk.rev.; illus.; circ. 13,500 (controlled). **Indexed:** Cath.Ind. **Document type:** newspaper, academic/scholarly publication.

282   US   ISSN 0038-1756
SOUL; national Catholic magazine. 1950. bi-m. $5 (foreign $7). (World Apostolate of Fatima) Blue Army of Our Lady of Fatima, U S A, Inc., Mountain View Rd., Box 976, Washington, NJ 07882-0976. TEL 908-689-1700. FAX 908-689-6279. charts; illus. circ. 95,000.
Description: Roman Catholic Marian magazine promoting the message of Fatima and St. Louis de Montfort's total consecration to Jesus through Mary.

282   US   ISSN 0038-187X
BX1752
SOUNDS OF TRUTH AND TRADITION. 1965. irreg. free to qualified personnel. (Catholic Traditionalist Movement, Inc.) C T M Publications, Inc., 210 Maple Ave., Westbury, NY 11590-3117. TEL 516-333-6470. FAX 516-333-7535. Ed. Father Gommar A. De Pauw. bk.rev. **Indexed:** CERDIC.

RELIGIONS AND THEOLOGY — ROMAN CATHOLIC

282 US
SOUTH PLAINS CATHOLIC. 1984. s-m. $9. Diocese of Lubbock, Box 98700, Lubbock, TX 79499-8700. TEL 806-792-3643. Ed. Deacon Leray Behnke. adv. contact: Jacmar Graphics. circ. 8,250. (tabloid format) **Document type:** newspaper.
Description: Provides information, communication, and inspiration for the Catholic community on the Texas South Plains.

282 US ISSN 0745-9343
SOUTH TEXAS CATHOLIC. (Text in English, Spanish) w. $10. 1200 Lantana, Corpus Christi, TX 78407. TEL 512-289-1752. FAX 512-289-1783. Pub. Bishop Rene H. Gracida. adv. contact: Paula Espitia. bk.rev. circ. 17,000. **Document type:** newspaper.

282 SA ISSN 0038-4011
SOUTHERN CROSS. 1921. w. R.65 (foreign R.85). (Southern African Catholic Bishops' Conference) Catholic Newspaper and Publishing Co. Ltd., Box 2372, Cape Town 8000, South Africa. TEL 27-21-455007. FAX 27-21-453850. Ed. Rev. Father Bernard F. Connor, OP. adv. contact: Noel Bruyns. bk.rev.; film rev.; illus. circ. 11,000. (tabloid format) **Indexed:** CERDIC. **Document type:** newspaper.
Description: Publishes local and international Catholic church or church-related news and opinion.

282 US ISSN 0745-0257
SOUTHERN CROSS (SAN DIEGO). 1912. bi-w. $20. Roman Catholic Diocese of San Diego, Box 81869, San Diego, CA 92138. TEL 619-490-8266. FAX 619-490-8355. Ed. Lawrence R. Montali; Pub. Bishop Robert Brom. adv. contact: Lee Haralson. bk.rev.; film rev.; play rev.; illus.; tr.lit. circ. 50,714. (back issues avail.) **Document type:** newspaper.

282 US
SOUTHERN CROSS (SAVANNAH). 1920. w. (45/yr.). $15. Catholic Diocese - Savannah, 601 E. Liberty St., Savannah, GA 31401. TEL 912-238-2320. FAX 912-238-2335. Ed. John E. Markwalter. adv. circ. 10,200. **Document type:** newspaper.

282 US ISSN 0038-4690
SOUTHWEST KANSAS REGISTER. 1966. fortn. $22. Catholic Diocese of Dodge City, 910 Central, Box 137, Dodge City, KS 67801. FAX 316-227-1570. Ed. Timothy F. Wenzl; Pub. Bishop Stanley G. Schlarman. adv. contact: Timothy F. Wenzl. bk.rev.; illus. circ. 6,253. (tabloid format) **Document type:** newspaper.

282 UK ISSN 0269-8390
SOUTH WESTERN CATHOLIC HISTORY. 1983. a. £3. c/o Dominic Aidan Bellenger, Ed., Downside Abbey, Stratton-on-the-Fosse, Bath BA3 4RJ, England. TEL 01761-232206. FAX 01761-233575. bk.rev. circ. 250. **Document type:** academic/scholarly publication.
Description: Covers architectural, theological and biographical studies of the English Roman Catholic community (1558-1950).

282 331 GW ISSN 0584-5882
SOZIALES SEMINAR INFORMATIONEN; politisch-soziale Bildung in katholischer Traegerschaft. 1952. q. free. Akademie Franz-Hitze-Haus, Kardinal-von-Galen-Ring 50, 48149 Muenster, Germany. TEL 0251-9818-0. FAX 0251-9818480. Ed. Reinhard Max. circ. 6,000. **Document type:** academic/scholarly publication.

282 028.5 US ISSN 1068-8102
SPES NOSTRA - OUR HOPE; a marian missionary magazine for youth and families. 1993. bi-m. $8.95. (Missionaries of the Immaculata) Immaculata Press, 531 E. Merced Ave., West Covina, CA 91790. TEL 818-917-0040. FAX 818-917-0900. Ed. Antonella Di Piazza. adv. contact: Ann O'Donnell. bk.rev. circ. 7,000.

282 GW
SPEYER. DIOEZESE. DIREKTORIUM SPIRENSE - OFFIZIUM UND MESSFEIER. 1824. a. Bischoefliches Ordinariat Speyer, 67343 Speyer, Germany. Ed. Christian Huber. circ. 2,700. **Document type:** bulletin.

282 US
SPINNAKER. 1984. 5/yr. $4. I H M Sisters, 610 W. Elm Ave., Monroe, MI 48161. TEL 313-241-2628. FAX 313-457-1890. Ed. Ann Oestreich. bk.rev. circ. 1,300. (tabloid format; back issues avail.) **Document type:** newspaper.
Description: Catholic-oriented information regarding members and friends of the IHM Community.

282 255 US ISSN 0038-7592
SPIRIT & LIFE. 1905. 6/yr. $5. Benedictine Convent of Perpetual Adoration, 8300 Morganford Rd., St. Louis, MO 63123. TEL 314-638-6427. (Subscr. to: Benedictine Convent of Perpetual Adoration, Clyde, MO 64432) Ed. Sr. M. Romanus Penrose. bk.rev.; illus. circ. 4,700. (also avail. in microform from UMI; reprint service avail. from UMI) **Indexed:** CERDIC. —UMI.
Description: For readers who want short, pithy reading material which will inspire them and give them impetus to live out their Christ-life on a day-to-day basis. Aims to engender spirit and life in the Church from the stance of its Benedictine publishers.

SPIRIT OF BOOKS. see *PUBLISHING AND BOOK TRADE*

282 US ISSN 0038-7630
BX2350.A1
SPIRITUAL LIFE. 1955. q. $14. Washington Province of Discalced Carmelite Friars, Inc., 2131 Lincoln Rd., N.E., Washington, DC 20002. TEL 202-832-8489; 800-832-8489. FAX 202-832-8967. E-mail: EDODONNELL@AOL.COM. Ed. Rev. Edward O'Donnell; Pub. Rev. Phillip Thomas. bk.rev.; bibl. circ. 10,000. (also avail. in microform from UMI; reprint service avail. from UMI) **Indexed:** Cath.Ind.; CERDIC. **Document type:** consumer publication. —UMI.
Description: Discusses contemporary spirituality.

282 IT ISSN 0038-8750
SQUILLA. 1925. bi-m. L12000 (effective 1995 & 1996). Francescani di Recco, Via S. Francesco 4, 16036 Recco GE, Italy. TEL 39-185-74198. Ed. Ilario Rolandelli. adv.; bk.rev.; illus.; circ. 6,000 (controlled). (tabloid format)

282 255 NE ISSN 0038-8904
STAD GODS. 1932. m. fl.14.50. Zusters Augustinessen van Sint Monica, Klooster De Stad Gods, Soestdijkerstraatweg 151, 1213 VZ Hilversum, Netherlands. TEL 31-35-837528. bk.rev.; illus. circ. 50,000.

282 GH ISSN 0038-9374
STANDARD; national Catholic weekly. 1938. w. NC.7. (Ghana Catholic Hierarchy) Catholic Mission Press, Royal Lane, Box 60, Cape Coast, Ghana. Ed. Rev. Martin T. Peters. circ. 11,000. (processed)

282 IT
LA STELLA DEL MARE. 1908. m. L15000($10) Passionisti Scala Santa, 00048 Nettuno (Rome), Italy. TEL 06-9805011. circ. 4,000.
Formerly: Santuario di N.S.D. Grazie e di S. Maria Goretti (ISSN 0036-4630)

282 GW
STERNSINGER; diaspora. 1949. q. DM.2. Bonifatiuswerk der deutschen Katholiken Diaspora-Kinderhilfe, Kamp 22, 33098 Paderborn, Germany. TEL 05251-29960. FAX 05251-299688. Ed. Hans Dieter Huber. circ. 340,000. (back issues avail.) **Document type:** newsletter.
Description: Religious developments in Germany and the Scandinavian countries.

282 US ISSN 0744-771X
STEUBENVILLE REGISTER. 1945. fortn. $15. Diocese of Steubenville (Ohio), 422 Washington St., Box 160, Steubenville, OH 43952. TEL 614-282-6831. FAX 614-282-3327. Ed. James A. Boehm. adv.: page $540.27. circ. 17,900. (also avail. in microfiche) **Document type:** newspaper.

940 AU ISSN 0081-5594
STILLE SCHAR. 1953. a. S.55. (Emperor Charles League for Peace Among the Nations) Gebetsliga, Zisterzienserstift, A-3180 Lilienfeld, Austria. TEL 02762-2204-23. circ. 5,000.

250 IT ISSN 0039-2901
BX804
STUDI CATTOLICI; mensile di studi ed attualita. 1957. m. L.70000 (effective 1992). (Associazione Ricerche e Studi) Edizioni A.R.E.S., Via A. Stradivari 7, 20131 Milan, Italy. TEL 39-2-29526156. FAX 39-2-29514202. Ed. Cesare Cavalleri. adv.: B&W page L.3000000. bk.rev.; bibl.; charts; illus.; index. **Indexed:** CERDIC.

282 IT
STUDI E RICERCHE FRANCESCANE. 1972. q. L.45000. T D C Telediffusione Cattolica, Piazza S. Eframo Vecchio 21, 80137 Naples, Italy. TEL 081-751-94-03. FAX 081-751-93-74. Ed. Ferdinando Mastroianni. adv.; bk.rev.; index. circ. 400. **Indexed:** CERDIC.

271 IT ISSN 0039-3045
BX4055.A1
STUDI STORICI DELL'ORDINE DEI SERVI DI MARIA. (Text and summaries in English, French, German, Italian, Portuguese, Spanish) 1933. s-a. L.50000 (foreign L.60000) (effective 1994). Ordine dei Servi di Maria, Istituto Storico, Viale Trenta Aprile, 6, 00153 Rome, Italy. TEL 06-5814441, FAX 06-5880292. (Co-sponsor: Centro Edizioni Marianum) Ed. Davide M. Montagna. adv.; bk.rev.; bibl.; charts; illus.; pat.; stat.; index. circ. 300. **Document type:** academic/scholarly publication.

282 IT ISSN 0392-1719
STUDIA PICENA; rivista marchigiana di storia e cultura. 1925. a. L.25000. Istituto Teologico Marchigiano, Rivista "Studia Picena", Presso Istituto Teologico Marchigiano, Via Roma 118, 61032 Fano (Pesaro), Italy. TEL 0721-804042. circ. 300. (back issues avail.) **Indexed:** Numis.Lit.

282 GW ISSN 0303-4224
STUDIEN UND MITTEILUNGEN ZUR GESCHICHTE DES BENEDIKTINER. ORDENS UND SEINER ZWEIGE. 1880. 2/yr. price varies. (Bayerische Benediktinerakademie) E O S Verlag, Erzabtei St. Ottilien, 86941 St. Ottilien, Germany. TEL 08193-71261. FAX 08193-6844. Ed. Ulrich Faust. bk.rev.; illus.; cum.index. **Indexed:** RILM. **Document type:** academic/scholarly publication. —SWETS.

230 GW ISSN 0081-7295
STUDIEN ZUR GESCHICHTE DER KATHOLISCHEN MORALTHEOLOGIE. vol.3, 1955. irreg., vol.29, 1989. price varies. Verlag Friedrich Pustet, Gutenbergstr. 8, 93051 Regensburg, Germany. TEL 0941-92022-0. FAX 0941-948652. Ed. Johannes Gruendel. circ. 500. **Document type:** monographic series.

282 GW ISSN 0341-6909
STUDIEN ZUR PASTORALLITURGIE. irreg., vol.10. DM.68. Verlag Friedrich Pustet, Gutenbergstr. 8, 93051 Regensburg, Germany. TEL 0941-92022-0. FAX 0941-948652. **Document type:** academic/scholarly publication, monographic series.

235.2 BE ISSN 0777-8112
SUBSIDIA HAGIOGRAPHICA. 1886. irreg., no.78, 1994. price varies. Societe des Bollandistes, 24 bd. Saint-Michel, B-1040 Brussels, Belgium. TEL 32-2-7393338. **Document type:** monographic series.
Description: Critical studies about Saints' lives.

255 IT ISSN 0562-4649
SUBSIDIA SCIENTIFICA FRANCISCALIA. (Text in French, German, Italian and Latin) 1962. irreg., no.7, 1989. price varies. Frati Minori Cappuccini, Istituto Storico, Casella Postale 18283, Circonv. Occidentale 6850 (GRA km 65), 00163 Rome, Italy. TEL 39-6-66151958. FAX 39-6-66162401. index. circ. 500.

282 HK
SUNDAY EXAMINER. (Text in English) 1946. w. HK.$180 (foreign HK.$330). 11-F, Catholic Diocese Centre, 16 Caine Rd., Hong Kong. TEL 5220487. FAX 5213095. Ed. John J. Casey. adv. circ. 3,000. **Document type:** newspaper.

200 AT ISSN 0039-6184
SURSUM CORDA; lift up your hearts. 1955. bi-m. Aus.$6. Franciscan House of Formation of Australian - New Zealand Province, P.O. Box 79, Box Hill, Vic. 3128, Australia. Ed. Rev. Ralph Byrne. bk.rev.; index every 2 yrs. circ. 5,100.

RELIGIONS AND THEOLOGY — ROMAN CATHOLIC

282   IT
SUSSIDI PATRISTICI. 1981. irreg. Instituturn Patristicum Augustinianum, Via S. Uffizio, 25, 00193 Rome, Italy. (back issues avail.) **Document type:** academic/scholarly publication.

282   LI
SV. PRANCISKAUS VARPELIS/BELL OF ST. FRANCIS. (Text in Lithuanian) 1942. 6/yr. $5. Franciscan Fathers, Kretingos 77-13, Klaipeda 5818, Lithuania. Ed. Jeronimas Alvidas Remesa. bk.rev. circ. 1,400.

282   CN   ISSN 0039-7164
SVITLO/LIGHT. English edition: Beacon (ISSN 0382-6384) (Text in Ukrainian) 1939. m. $20. Basilian Fathers Press, 265 Bering Ave., Etobicoke, Ont. M8Z 3A5, Canada. TEL 416-234-1212. FAX 416-234-1213. Ed. N. Svirsky. circ. 2,250.

282   BN
SVJETLO RIJECI/LIGHT OF THE WORD; vjerski list/religious newspaper. (Text in Croatian) 1983. m. 3 din.($0.40) Franjevacki Provincijalati, Svjetlo Rijeci, N. Pozderca 6, 71000 Sarajevo, Bosnia Hercegovinia. TEL 071 535-407. Ed.Bd. circ. 10,000. (looseleaf format) **Document type:** newspaper.

282   US   ISSN 0039-8845
BX801
TABLET. 1908. w. $20. (Roman Catholic Diocese of Brooklyn) Tablet Publishing Co., Inc., 653 Hicks St., Brooklyn, NY 11231. TEL 718-858-3838. FAX 718-858-2112. Ed. Edward Wilkinson. adv.; bk.rev.; illus.; circ. 85,000. (paid). (also avail. in microform; microfilm from KTO) **Indexed:** Cath.Ind.
Formerly: Brooklyn Tablet.

282   GW   ISSN 0492-1283
TAG DES HERRN; katholisches Kirchenblatt. 1951. w. DM.1.50 per no. (Berliner Bischofskonferenz) St. Benno Verlag GmbH, Thueringerstr. 1-3, 04179 Leipzig, Germany. TEL 03741-474161. FAX 03741-470802. Ed. Gottfried Swoboda. adv. contact: Ingeborg Walzbuck. bk.rev. circ. 42,700. **Document type:** bulletin.
Description: Covers news of the Catholic Church, including events, issues and questions.

282   XV
TEDEN BOZJE BESEDE; redna stolniska oznanila. (Text in Slovenian) 1970. w. 6000 din.($7) Stolni Zupnijski Urad, Dolnicarjeva, 61000 Ljubljana, Slovenia. TEL 061 310-684. Ed. Vinko Vegelj. (looseleaf format; back issues avail.)

282   RE
TEMOIGNAGE CHRETIEN DE LA REUNION. w. 21 bis rue de l'Est, 97465 Saint-Denis, Reunion. Ed. Rene Payet. circ. 2,000.

282   US   ISSN 1041-1569
TENNESSEE REGISTER. 1937. fortn. $16 (effective Jan. 1995). Diocese of Nashville, 2400 21st Ave. S., Nashville, TN 37212-5302. TEL 615-783-0770. FAX 615-292-8411. E-mail: tnregister@aol.com. Ed. Anthony J. Spence. Pub. Edward U. Kuiec. adv. contact: Marilyn Rubin. circ. 15,000. (also avail. in microfilm) **Document type:** newspaper.
Description: News of social or religious significance to Catholics in Middle Tennessee.
Refereed Serial

301.5   BL   ISSN 0103-314X
BX805
TEOCOMUNICACAO. 1971. 4/yr. Cz.$15($9) (Pontificia Universidade Catolica do Rio Grande do Sul, Instituto de Teologia) Editora da P U C R S, c/o Antoninho M. Naime, Caixa Postal 12001, 90620 Porto Alegre RS, Brazil. Ed. Urbano Zilles. bk.rev. circ. 1,500.

282   HU   ISSN 0133-1779
TEOLOGIA. 1967. 4/yr. 60 Ft.($29.50) Teologia Kiadohivatale, Karoly Mihaly u. 4-8, 1053 Budapest 5, Hungary. FAX 36-1-117-3471. Ed. Szennay Andras. bk.rev. circ. 4,000. **Indexed:** CERDIC.

240   CL   ISSN 0049-3449
TEOLOGIA Y VIDA. 1960. q. $40. Universidad Catolica de Chile, Facultad de Teologia, Jaime Guzman Enazuriz 3300, Casilla 316, Santiago, 22, Chile. Eds. Marciano Barrios, Cecilia Coz Canas. adv. contact: Marciano Barrios Valdes. bk.rev.; abstr.; bibl.; cum.index: 1960-1979. circ. 700. **Indexed:** Bull.Signal., Canon Law Abstr., Cath.Ind., New Test.Abstr., Old Test.Abstr. **Document type:** academic/scholarly publication.
—UMI.

282   SP
TERESA DE JESUS. bi-m. 1100 ptas.($20) (foreign 1800 ptas.). Centro Teresianosanjuanista, Plaza de la Santa, 4, Apdo. 167, 05001 Avila, Spain. TEL 918-21-26-08. Dir. Francisco M. Tejedor.

282   VC   ISSN 0392-4556
TERESIANUM. (Text in several languages) 1947. s-a. L.60000 (effective 1996). (Pontificia Facolta Teresianum) Edizioni del Teresianum, Piazza S. Pancrazio 5-A, 00152 Rome, Italy. TEL 39-6-58540250. FAX 39-6-58540300. Ed. R.P. Virgilio Pasquetto. circ. 800. **Indexed:** CERDIC, New Test.Abstr., Old Test.Abstr. **Document type:** academic/scholarly publication.
—SWETS.
Formerly (until vol.33, 1982): Ephemerides Carmeliticae.

282   IS   ISSN 0040-3784
TERRA SANTA. English edition: Holy Land Review (ISSN 0333-7189); French edition: Terre Sainte (ISSN 0040-3873); Spanish edition: Tierra Santa (ISSN 0333-6212) (Text in Italian) bi-m. L.15000 (N. America $15). Franciscan Printing Press, P.O. Box 14064, Jerusalem 91140, Israel. TEL 972-2-286594. FAX 972-2-272274. (Subscr. to: Centro di Propaganda e Stampa di Terra Santa, Via Gherardini 5, 20145 Milan, Italy. TEL 39-2-311327) Ed.Bd. cum.index: 1921-1940, 1946-1970, 1971-1980. **Indexed:** Numis.Lit.

282   IT   ISSN 0040-3938
TESORO EUCARISTICO. 1917. bi-m. (except Jul.-Aug.) L.20000. Frati Minori Conventuali della Basilica di S. Francesco in Siena, Santuario delle Ss. Particole, 53100 Siena, Italy. TEL 0577-289081. Ed. P. Antonio Giannini. bk.rev. circ. 2,000.

282   IT
TESTIMONI; quindicinale di informazione e aggiornamento per istituti di vita consacrata. 1978. fortn. L.40000 (foreign L.55000) (effective 1994). Centro Editoriale Dehoniano, Via Nosadella, 6, 40123 Bologna, Italy. TEL 051-306811. FAX 051-341706. Ed.Bd. adv.; bk.rev. circ. 11,000.
Description: Informs consecrated men and women on psychology and spiritual life.

282   US   ISSN 0899-6296
TEXAS CATHOLIC. 1952. fortn. $15. Texas Catholic, Box 190347, Dallas, TX 75219. TEL 214-528-8792. FAX 214-528-3411. Ed. Bronson Havard. adv.; bk.rev.; circ. 12,600 (paid). (also avail. in microfilm) **Document type:** newspaper.
Description: Interprets secular and religious events from the Catholic viewpoint for Catholics in Dallas, Texas.

282   US
TEXAS CATHOLIC HERALD. 1964. fortn. $10 to individuals; institutions $15. (Diocese of Galveston - Houston) Texas Catholic Herald, 1700 San Jacinto, Houston, TX 77002. TEL 713-659-5461. FAX 713-659-3444. Ed. M.P. Zientek; Pub. Bishop Joseph A. Fiorenza. adv.: B&W page $1750; trim 10 1/2 x 13 1/2; adv. contact: Sam Listi. bk.rev.; film rev.; play rev.; charts; illus. circ. 180,500. (also avail. in microfilm) **Document type:** newspaper.
Description: Covers local, national and international church news.

900   IT   ISSN 0394-7793
TEXTUS ET STUDIA HISTORICA CARMELITANA. (Text in English, French, German, Italian, Latin and Spanish) 1954. irreg. price varies. (Order of Carmelites) Edizioni Carmelitane, Via Sforza Pallavicini 10, 00193 Rome, Italy. TEL 06-68803513. FAX 06-68307200. adv. circ. 500. **Document type:** monographic series.
Description: Forum covers a Carmelite history; critical editions.

200   CK   ISSN 0120-3649
THEOLOGICA XAVERIANA. 1950. q. Col.$16000($42) (effective 1995) Col.$18000($45) (effective 1996). Pontificia Universidad Javeriana, Facultad de Teologia, Apdo. Aereo 54953, Carrera 10, No. 65-48, Bogota 2 D.E., Colombia. FAX 571-2882335. Dir. Mario Gutierrez. adv.; bk.rev.; index; cum.index. (processed; back issues avail.) **Indexed:** Bull.Signal., Canon Law Abstr. —BLDSC (8814.518000).
Formerly (until 1975): Ecclesiastica Xaveriana (ISSN 0012-9054)

282   GW   ISSN 0049-366X
BR4
THEOLOGIE UND GLAUBE. 1908. q. DM.60. Verlag Ferdinand Schoeningh GmbH, Postfach 2540, 33055 Paderborn, Germany. TEL 05251-127665. FAX 05251-127860. Eds. Johannes Gamberoni, Winifred Schulz. adv.; bk.rev. **Indexed:** Canon Law Abstr., CERDIC, New Test.Abstr., Old Test.Abstr., Rel.& Theol.Abstr., Rel.Per. **Document type:** academic/scholarly publication.
—CCC.
Description: Covers a variety of theological issues, such as Church history, ethics, Bible, and liturgy.

282   GW   ISSN 0342-1430
BR4
THEOLOGISCHE QUARTALSCHRIFT. 1819. q. DM.64. Erich Wewel Verlag, Anzingerstr. 15, 81671 Munich, Germany. TEL 089-41300138. index. **Indexed:** Bibl.Ling., Rel.& Theol.Abstr. (1990-), Rel.Ind.One. **Document type:** bulletin.
—SWETS. **CCC.**

230   GW   ISSN 0040-568X
BR4
THEOLOGISCHE REVUE. 6/yr. DM.178. (Universitaet Muenster, Katholisch-Theologische Fakultaet) Aschendorffsche Verlagsbuchhandlung, Soesterstr. 13, 48155 Muenster, Germany. TEL 0251-690-0. FAX 0251-690143. Ed. Vinzenz Pfnuer. adv.; bk.rev.; bibl.; index. **Indexed:** Bibl.Ling., CERDIC, New Test.Abstr. **Document type:** academic/scholarly publication.
—SWETS. **CCC.**

200   FR   ISSN 1168-5638
THERESE DE LISIEUX. 1925. m. 170 F. Association Ste. Therese, 33 rue du Carmel, B.P. 95, 14102 Lisieux Cedex, France. TEL 31-48-55-00. FAX 31-48-55-25. Ed. Fr. Raymond Zambelli. bk.rev. circ. 35,000. **Document type:** bulletin.
Formerly: Sainte Therese de Lisieux. Annales (ISSN 0994-6373)

THOMAS BULLETIN. see *EDUCATION — Teaching Methods And Curriculum*

230 100   US   ISSN 0040-6325
BX801
THOMIST; a speculative quarterly review of theology and philosophy. 1939. q. $25 to individuals (foreign $35); all institutions $45. (Dominican Fathers, Province of St. Joseph) Thomist Press, 487 Michigan Ave., N.E., Washington, DC 20017. TEL 202-529-5300. FAX 202-636-4460. Ed. Rev. Joseph A. DiNoia. adv.; bk.rev.; bibl.; index, cum.index: vol.1-50, 1939-1986; circ. 1,000 (controlled). (also avail. in microfilm from UMI; reprint service avail. from KTO) **Indexed:** Arts & Hum.Cit.Ind., Cath.Ind., CERDIC, Curr.Cont., New Test.Abstr., Phil.Ind., Rel.& Theol.Abstr. (1969-). **Document type:** academic/scholarly publication.
—BLDSC (8820.234000); Faxon; Genuine Article; SWETS; UMI; UnCover.
Refereed Serial

282   US   ISSN 0040-6791
TIDINGS (LOS ANGELES); official Catholic weekly newspaper of Los Angeles. (Text mainly in English; occasionally in Spanish) 1895. w. $15. (Roman Catholic Archdiocese of Los Angeles) Tidings Corp., 1530 W. Ninth St., Los Angeles, CA 90015. TEL 213-251-3360. FAX 213-383-8667. Ed. Todd M. Tamberg. adv.: B&W page $2298. bk.rev.; film rev.; play rev.; illus. circ. 50,000. (also avail. in microform) **Document type:** newspaper.
Description: Publishes international, national and local Catholic news of interest to Catholic families.

RELIGIONS AND THEOLOGY — ROMAN CATHOLIC

282 284   NE   ISSN 0168-9959
TIJDSCHRIFT VOOR THEOLOGIE. (Text in Dutch; summaries in English) 1961. q. fl.69 (in Belgium 1280 BEF; elsewhere fl.89 (effective 1995). Theologisch Faculteit, Postbus 9103, 6500 HD Nijmegen, Netherlands. TEL 31-80-772077. Ed. T.M. Schoof. adv.; bk.rev.; index. circ. 1,600. (back issues avail.) Indexed: CERDIC, New Test.Abstr., Old Test.Abstr., Rel.& Theol.Abstr. (1968-1983,1990-). —SWETS.
Refereed Serial

282   US   ISSN 0746-0759
TIMES REVIEW. 1936. w. $18. Diocese of La Crosse, Box 4004, La Crosse, WI 54602-4004. TEL 608-788-1524. Ed. Rev. Bernard McGarty. adv.: B&W page $600. circ. 30,000. (also avail. in microfilm) **Document type:** newspaper.

282 052   IE
TIMIRE AN CHROI NAOFA; Iris Oifigiuil Aspalacht na hUrnai. (Text in Irish) 1911. q. I£3. Timire an Chroi Naofa, 16 Pairc Na Cabrai, Baile Atha Cliath 7, Ireland. TEL 8680449. Ed. Fr. D.O Laoghaire, S.J. adv.; bk.rev.; bibl. circ. 2,000. **Document type:** bulletin.

282   US   ISSN 0891-1533
TODAY'S CATHOLIC (FORT WAYNE). 1926. w. $15. Bishop John M. D'Arcy, Pub., Box 11169, Fort Wayne, IN 46856. TEL 219-456-2824. FAX 219-744-1473. (And: 150 E. Doan Dr., Fort Wayne, IN 46806) Ed. John Ankenbruck. adv.; bk.rev.; film rev.; charts; illus.; stat. circ. 12,700. (tabloid format; also avail. in talking book; back issues avail.)
Description: Roman Catholic diocesan newspaper.

282   US   ISSN 0745-3612
TODAY'S CATHOLIC (SAN ANTONIO). (Text in English, Spanish) 1892. fortn. $12. Box 28410, San Antonio, TX 78228. TEL 210-734-2620. FAX 210-734-2939. Ed. Martha Brinkmann. adv.; bk.rev.; circ. 24,000 (paid). **Document type:** newspaper.
Description: Covers family-oriented Catholic news.

TODAY'S CATHOLIC TEACHER. see *EDUCATION*

282   US   ISSN 0040-8549
TODAY'S PARISH. 1969. 7/yr. $22. Twenty-Third Publications, Box 180, Mystic, CT 06355. TEL 203-536-2611. FAX 203-572-0788. Ed. Dan Connors. adv.: B&W page $995, color page $1795; adv. contact: Julie McCabe. bk.rev.; abstr.; illus. circ. 14,000. Indexed: Cath.Ind., CERDIC. **Document type:** consumer publication.
Description: Practical assistance in parish affairs for clergy, staff and lay workers in liturgy, music, education, computers, finance, administration and ministry in Catholic churches.

282   US   ISSN 0897-327X
TOUCHSTONE (CHICAGO); the touchstone of the pilgrim Church's self-understanding is dialogue. 1985. q. $8. National Federation of Priests' Councils, 1337 W. Ohio, 3rd Fl., Chicago, IL 60622. TEL 312-226-3334. FAX 312-829-8915. Ed. Rev. Thomas G. Simons. bk.rev. circ. 27,000. (back issues avail.) **Document type:** newsletter.
Description: Contains information and news pertaining to priests, spirituality, and articles on various ministries.

282   FR   ISSN 0399-8185
TRADITION ET PROGRES. 1974. q. 30 Fr. Trois-Puits, 51500 F. Rilly, France.

282 949.2   NE   ISSN 0778-8304
BX1549.A1
TRAJECTA; tijdschrift voor de geshiedenis van het katholiek leven in de Nederlanden. 1959. 3/yr. fl.55. Postbus 9100, 6500 HA Nijmegen, Netherlands. Ed. Th. Clemens. adv.; bk.rev.; abstr.; bibl.; index, cum.index 1959-1991. circ. 800. (reprint service avail.) Indexed: Amer.Hist.& Life, Hist.Abstr. **Document type:** academic/scholarly publication.
—SWETS.
Formerly (until 1992): Archief voor de Geschiedenis van de Katholieke Kerk in Nederland (ISSN 0003-8326)
Description: Scholarly treatment of the history of Catholic life in the Low Countries.
Refereed Serial

282   FR   ISSN 1241-8986
TRAJETS. 1911. q. 160 F. (foreign 180 F.). Association Joseph Lotte, 170 bd. du Montparnasse, 75014 Paris, France. TEL 43-35-28-50.
—BLDSC (8883.889500).
Former titles (until 1992): Cahiers Universitaires Catholiques (ISSN 0223-5935); (until 1948): Cahiers de la Paroisse Universitaires (ISSN 1141-0299); (until 1946): Bulletin Joseph Lotte (ISSN 1141-0280); (until 1929): Bulletin des Professeurs Catholiques de l'Universite (ISSN 1141-0272)

384   US   ISSN 1063-4525
THE U.P. CATHOLIC. (Upper Peninsula) 1971. s-m. $18. Diocese of Marquette, Box 548, Marquette, MI 49855-0548. TEL 906-226-8821. FAX 906-226-6941. Ed. Joseph Zyble. adv.: page $352; adv. contact: Sandral L. Paull. bk.rev. circ. 5,000. **Document type:** newspaper.
Formerly: Upper Peninsula Catholic (ISSN 0747-1440)
Description: Covers local, national and international news both religious and other.

282   US   ISSN 0041-7548
BX801
U S CATHOLIC. 1963. m. $18. Claretian Publications, 205 W. Monroe St., Chicago, IL 60606. TEL 312-236-7782; 800-328-6515. FAX 312-236-7320. Ed. Rev. Mark J. Brummel. adv. contact: Diane Walde. bk.rev.; illus. circ. 50,000. (also avail. in microform from UMI; reprint service avail. from UMI) Indexed: Cath.Ind., CERDIC, G.Soc.Sci.& Rel.Per.Lit., Mag.Ind., PMR, R.G. —Faxon; UMI; UnCover.
Description: Provides informative articles on prayer, sacraments, marriage, work, parish, and society and interviews leading experts in theology, spirituality and parish life.

282 973   US   ISSN 0735-8318
BX1404
U S CATHOLIC HISTORIAN. 1980. q. $40 membership (foreign $50). (U S Catholic Historical Society) Our Sunday Visitor, Inc., 200 Noll Plaza, Huntington, IN 46750. TEL 800-348-2440. (Alt. addr.: P.O. Box 16229, Baltimore, MD 21210) Ed. Chris Kauffman; Pub. Robert P. Lockwood. adv. contact: Peter Schownir. illus.; circ. 1,200 (paid). (back issues avail.) Indexed: Amer.Hist.& Life.

282   US
U S PARISH; the newsletter that makes good parishes better. 1983. m. $24.95. Claretian Publications, 205 W. Monroe St., Chicago, IL 60606. TEL 312-236-7782. FAX 312-236-7230. Ed. Rev. Mark J. Brummel. circ. 1,800. **Document type:** newsletter.

282   IT
L'ULIVO. q. L.30000 (foreign L.50000). Congregazione Benedettina di Monte Oliveto, c/o Abbazia Monte Oliveta Maggiore, 53020 Chiusure (Siena), Italy. TEL 39-577-707017. Ed. D. Diego Donatelli.

282   US   ISSN 0041-6258
ULTREYA. 1959. bi-m. $10. U S Cusillo Movement, National Secretariat, Box 210226, 4500 W. Davis, Dallas, TX 75211. Ed. Thomas E. Sarg. bk.rev.; illus. circ. 4,000.

282   GW   ISSN 0724-2778
BX803
UNA VOCE KORRESPONDENZ. (Text in German, Latin) 1970. bi-m. DM.15. Una Voce Korrespondenz Schriftleitung, Geldorpstr. 4, 50733 Cologne, Germany. Ed. Rudolf Kaschewsky. bk.rev.; index. circ. 2,500. (back issues avail.) **Document type:** bulletin.

UNDA - U S A NEWSLETTER. see *COMMUNICATIONS — Television And Cable*

282 369.5   US
L'UNION. (Text in English and French) 1902. q. membership. Union Saint-Jean-Baptiste, P.O. Box F, 68 Cumberland St., Plaza Center, Woonsocket, RI 02895-0989. TEL 800-225-USJB. FAX 401-766-3014. (Co-sponsor: Catholic Family Life Insurance) Ed. Joseph E. Gadbois. bk.rev. circ. 14,000.

282   UK   ISSN 0041-8226
UNIVERSE. 1860. w. 40p. Gabriel Communications, St. James's Bldg., 1st Fl., Oxford St., Manchester M1 6FP, England. Ed. Ann Knowles. adv.; bk.rev.; illus. circ. 106,000. (tabloid format) **Document type:** newspaper.
Incorporates: Catholic Times.

200   CL   ISSN 0069-3596
UNIVERSIDAD CATOLICA DE CHILE. FACULTAD DE TEOLOGIA. ANALES. 1940. a. Universidad Catolica de Chile, Facultad de Teologia, Jaime Guzman Enazuriz 3300, Casilla 316, Santiago, 22, Chile. Eds. Juan Noemi Callejas, Cecilia Coz Canas. cum.index: 1940-1969. circ. 500. Indexed: Bull.Signal., Cath.Ind. **Document type:** academic/scholarly publication.

282   BE
UNIVERSITE CATHOLIQUE DE LOUVAIN. FACULTE DE THEOLOGIE ET DE DROIT CANONIQUE. COLLECTION DES DISSERTATIONS PRESENTEES POUR L'OBTENTION DU GRADE DE MAITRE A LA FACULTE DE THEOLOGIE OU A LA FACULTE DE DROIT CANONIQUE. 1841. irreg. (series quarto, vol.6, 1987). Universite Catholique de Louvain, Faculte de Theologie et de Droit Canonique, Grand-Place 45, B-1348 Louvain-la-Neuve, Belgium. **Document type:** academic/scholarly publication.
Formerly: Universite Catholique de Louvain. Facultes de Theologie et de Droit Canonique. Dissertationes ad Gradum Magistri in Facultate Theologica Vel in Facultate Iuris Canonici Consequendum Conscriptae.

200   BE   ISSN 0076-1230
UNIVERSITE CATHOLIQUE DE LOUVAIN. FACULTE DE THEOLOGIE ET DE DROIT CANONIQUE. TRAVAUX DE DOCTORAT EN THEOLOGIE ET EN DROIT CANONIQUE. NOUVELLE SERIE. 1969. irreg., vol.15, 1994. exchange basis. Universite Catholique de Louvain, Faculte de Theologie et de Droit Canonique, Grand-Place 45, B-1348 Louvain-la-Neuve, Belgium. circ. 120. **Document type:** academic/scholarly publication.

268   US   ISSN 0070-3052
UNIVERSITY OF DAYTON. SCHOOL OF EDUCATION. WORKSHOP PROCEEDINGS. 1970. irreg., latest 1971. $3.25. University of Dayton, School of Education, Dayton, OH 45469. TEL 513-229-3146. Ed. Louis J. Faerber. **Document type:** proceedings.
Description: Covers Catholic elementary and secondary education.

264   US   ISSN 0076-003X
UNIVERSITY OF NOTRE DAME. DEPARTMENT OF THEOLOGY. LITURGICAL STUDIES. 1955. irreg., no.11, 1977. price varies. University of Notre Dame Press, Notre Dame, IN 46556. TEL 219-631-6346. FAX 219-631-8148. (Orders to: 11030 S. Langley Ave., Chicago, IL 60628. TEL 800-621-2736. FAX 800-621-8476; Overseas orders to: Eurospan University Press Group, Order Dept., 3 Henrietta St., London WC2E 8LU, England) Indexed: Cath.Ind. **Document type:** academic/scholarly publication.

UPSOUTH; a newsletter for Catholic writers. see *LITERATURE*

280.4   NE
V U STUDIES ON PROTESTANT HISTORY. (Text in English) 1990. irreg. (Vrije Universiteit Amsterdam) V U Boekhandel-Uitgeverij B.V., De Boelelaan 1105, 1081 HV Amsterdam, Netherlands. TEL 31-20-6444355. FAX 31-20-6462719. **Document type:** monographic series, proceedings.

282 900   IT   ISSN 0394-7807
VACARE DEO. (Text in English, French, German, Italian, Latin and Spanish) 1956. irreg. price varies. (Order of Carmelites) Edizioni Carmelitane, Via Sforza Pallavicini 10, 00193 Rome, Italy. TEL 06-68803513. FAX 06-68307200. adv. circ. 500. **Document type:** monographic series.
Description: Forum includes Carmelite spirituality; critical editions.

282   IT   ISSN 0042-2304
VALLE SANTA DI RIETI;* periodico di cultura e propaganda Francescana. 1948. q. free. (Santuari Francescani Valle di Rieti) Convento S. Antonio al Monte, Rieti, Italy. Ed. Rev. Ettore Giustino Marini. adv.; bk.rev.; illus. circ. 5,000.

RELIGIONS AND THEOLOGY — ROMAN CATHOLIC

282 US ISSN 0889-0595
VATICAN VOICES AND NOTABLE PAPAL QUOTES. 1979. w. $20. Truth, Inc., 7346 W. Greenfield Ave., W. Allis, WI 53214. TEL 414-258-2665. Ed. Rev. Cletus Healy, S.J. index. circ. 100. (looseleaf format)

200 IT
VENGA IL TUO REGNO. 1945. m. (10/yr.). L.15000. Pontificio Istituto Missioni Estere (Naples), Viale Colli Aminei 36, 80131 Naples, Italy. TEL 39-81-7410296. Ed. P. Gaetano Maiello. adv.: half page L.35000; 80 x 132. bk.rev. circ. 10,000.
Description: Missionary magazine for families containing mainly correspondence from missionaries working in Asia, Africa, South America, and Oceania.

282 IT
VENITE ADOREMUS; mensile dello Studentato dei Padri Sacramentini. 1958. m. L.8000. Studentato dei Padri Sacramentini, Via Crispi 22, 63039 San Benedetto del Tronto (AP), Italy. index.

VERBUM; tijdschrift voor levensbeschouwelijke vorming van jongeren. see EDUCATION — Teaching Methods And Curriculum

282 CI ISSN 0352-5708
VERITAS; revija svetog Antuna. (Text in Croatian) 1962. m. $9. Hrvatska Provincija S. Jeronima Franjevaca Konventualaca, Miskinina 31, 41000 Zagreb, Croatia. TEL 041 579-645. Ed. Ferdinand Cavar. circ. 16,000. (back issues avail.)

282 362.6 FR ISSN 0293-5066
VERMEIL; la foi au fil des ans. m. 224 F. (outside EC 257 F.). Bayard Presse, 3 rue Bayard, 75393 Paris Cedex 08, France. TEL 44-35-60-60. FAX 44-35-60-91. TELEX 684 094 F. (Subscr. to: B.P. 12, 99505 Paris Entreprises, France. TEL 46-30-38-00. FAX 46-30-31-67)
Description: Puts a christian perspective on the changing world for those in their retirement years.

282 US ISSN 0042-4145
VERMONT CATHOLIC TRIBUNE. 1957. fortn. $10. Vermont Catholic Press Association, 351 North Ave., Burlington, VT 05401-2999. TEL 802-658-6110. Ed. John Jennings. adv.; bk.rev.; film rev.; illus. circ. 22,000. (tabloid format; also avail. in microfilm)
Document type: newspaper.

282 IT ISSN 0042-4242
VERONA FEDELE; settimanale cattolico della diocesi. 1946. w. L.60000. Editrice Verona Fedele, Via Pieta Vecchia 2, 37100 Verona, Italy. TEL 39-45-8000121. FAX 39-45-591745. Ed.Bd. adv.; bk.rev. circ. 30,000.

282 CN ISSN 0042-434X
VERS DEMAIN. 1939. 7/yr. Can.$10($14) for 2 yrs. (Institut Louis Even Pelerins de Saint Michel) Louis Even Institute, 1101 Principale St., Rougemont, Que. J0L 1M0, Canada. TEL 514-469-2209. (U.S. addr: Pilgrims of Saint Michael, Box 38, Richford, VT 05476-0038) Ed. Gilberte Cote-Mercier. charts; illus. circ. 35,000.
Description: Promotes the application of the teachings of the Roman Catholic Church in every aspect of social life, especially in economics with the social credit philosophy of Scottish engineer, Clifford Hugh Douglas.

255 IT ISSN 0042-4374
VERSO L'AZZURRO. 1963. m. free. Centro Nazionale Associazione Mariana, Via Francesco Albergotti 75, 00167 Rome, Italy. bk.rev. circ. 2,300.

282 SP ISSN 0505-4605
VIDA NUEVA. 1958. w. 7200 ptas.($120) (foreign $140). Promociones Populares Cristianas, Enrique Jardiel Poncela, 4, Apdo. 19049, 28016 Madrid, Spain. TEL 457-35-39. FAX 457-72-12. TELEX 45051 PPC E. Dir. Vicente Alejandro Guillamon. adv.; bk.rev.

266 SP ISSN 0211-9749
VIDA RELIGIOSA. 1944. s-m. (except July-Aug.). 5000 ptas.($50) for Europe and America; elsewhere $32 (effective 1992). Misioneros Hijos del Inmaculado Corazon de Maria (Claretianos), Buen Suceso, 22, 28008 Madrid, Spain. TEL 91-5482101. adv.; bk.rev.; bibl.; charts; stat.; tr.lit.; index; circ. 10,000 (controlled). (back issues avail.) **Indexed**: Canon Law Abstr., CERDIC. **Document type**: monographic series.

282 II ISSN 0970-1079
VIDYAJYOTI JOURNAL OF THEOLOGICAL REFLECTION. 1938. m. Rs.50($18) Vidyajyoti Educational and Welfare Society (VIEWS), 4A Raj Nivas Marg, Delhi 110 054, India. TEL 2524707. Ed. S. Arokiasamy. adv.; bk.rev. circ. 3,200. **Indexed**: Canon Law Abstr., New Test.Abstr., Old Test.Abstr.
—BLDSC (9234.501000).
Formerly: Clergy Monthly.
Description: Concerned with the life and thought of the church in India, inter-religious dialogue, theology and social concerns.

282 FR ISSN 0042-5362
VIE CATHOLIQUE DU BERRY. (Supplements avail.: Calendrier Litergique, Bourges (ISSN 0184-5713); Espoir de la Moisson (ISSN 0996-1445); Calendrier Litergique, Centre Bourges (ISSN 0181-1096)) 1865. w. 120 F. Association Diocesaine de Bourges, Archeveche de Bourges, 4 av. de 95e de Ligne, B.P. 95, 18002 Bourges (Cher), France. TEL 1-47-66-01-86. TELEX 649 333. Ed. Jose de Broucker. adv.; bk.rev. circ. 400,000.
Incorporates: Vocation (ISSN 1144-2549);
Formerly: Semaine Religiuese du Diocese de Bourges (ISSN 1141-1562)

282 CN ISSN 0318-9392
VIE OBLATE/OBLATE LIFE. (Text in English, French) 1942. 3/yr. Can.$20. 175 rue Main, Ottawa, ON K1S 1C3, Canada. TEL 613-237-0580. FAX 613-232-4064. Ed. Romuald Boucher. bk.rev.; cum.index: 1942-1961, 1962-1990. circ. 500. (back issues avail.)
Formerly: Etudes Oblates (ISSN 0318-9384)

248 FR ISSN 0042-5613
VIE SPIRITUELLE. 1919. 5/yr. 230 F. (foreign 280 F.). Editions du Cerf, 29 bd. Latour-Maubourg, 75340 Paris Cedex 07, France. TEL 45-50-34-07. FAX 45-56-04-27. (Subscr. to: Service Abonnement, 3 chemin des Prunais, 94350 Villiers-sur-Marne, France) bk.rev.; bibl. circ. 3,500. **Indexed**: Cath.Ind., CERDIC, Old Test.Abstr.
—BLDSC (9235.440000).

282 FR ISSN 0042-5621
VIE THERESIENNE. 1961. q. 170 F. Association Ste. Therese, 33 rue du Carmel, B.P. 95, 14102 Lisieux Cedex, France. TEL 31-48-55-00. FAX 31-48-55-00. Ed. Fr. Raymond Zambelli. bk.rev. circ. 2,500. **Document type**: bulletin.

282 800 HU ISSN 0042-6024
VIGILIA. (Text in Hungarian; summaries in English, French and German) 1935. m. 480 Ft.($35) Vigilia, Kossuth Lajos u. 1, P.Box 111, 1364 Budapest 5, Hungary. TEL 117-7246. FAX 117-4895. (Subscr. to: Kultura, Box 149, H-1389 Budapest, Hungary) Ed. Laszlo Lukacs. bk.rev. circ. 10,000. **Indexed**: CERDIC.

200 361 US
VISION (MILWAUKEE). 1968. 10/yr. $34 (includes Special Publications). National Association of Catholic Chaplains, 3501 S. Lake Dr., Box 07473, Milwaukee, WI 53207-0473. TEL 414-483-4898. Ed. Rev. Joseph J. Driscoll. bk.rev. circ. 3,700. **Indexed**: CERDIC.
Formerly (until 1991): Camillian.
Description: News and information about pastoral care and the activities of the association.

282 PR
EL VISITANTE DE PUERTO RICO. 1975. w. $20 in Puerto Rico; elsewhere $36. Puerto Rican Catholic Conference, Box 41305, Minillas Sta., San Juan, PR 00940-1305. TEL 809-728-3710. FAX 809-728-3656. Ed. Rev. Efrain Zabala. adv. contact: Carola Llompart. bk.rev.; circ. 59,500 (controlled). (tabloid format; also avail. in microfilm; back issues avail.)
Description: Follows Catholic church philosophy and applies it to social, moral, cultural and political issues.

282 US
VISITOR (ST. CLOUD). 1938. w. $17 (effective Jul. 1995). Diocese of St. Cloud, 305 N. Seventh Ave., St. Cloud, MN 56303. TEL 612-251-3022. FAX 612-251-0424. (Subscr. to: Box 1068, St. Cloud, MN 56301) Ed. Nancy Bauer. circ. 41,350. **Document type**: newspaper.

282 IT ISSN 0042-7233
VITA CATTOLICA. 1916. w. L.60000 (effective 1994). (Diocesi di Cremona) Nuova Editrece Cremonese S.r.l., Piazza S.A.M. Zaccaria 5, 26100 Cremona, Italy. TEL 0372-20666. FAX 0372-35721. Ed. Rini Vincenzo. adv.; illus. circ. 8,000. (tabloid format)

282 GW
VITA FRATRUM. 1964. 3/yr. Provinzialat der Franziskaner, St.-Anna-Str. 19, 80539 Munich, Germany. TEL 089-226601. Ed. Winthir Rauch. circ. 450.

282 IT ISSN 0042-7276
VITA GIUSEPPINA. 1895. m. L.20000($12) Congregazione di S. Giuseppe (Giuseppini del Murialdo), Via Belvedere Montello 77, 00166 Rome, Italy. TEL 39-6-6247144. FAX 39-6-6240846. Ed. Garuti Vittorio. adv.; bk.rev.; illus.; index, cum.index. circ. 16,000. (back issues avail.)

282 IT ISSN 0042-7365
VITA SOCIALE. 1944. bi-m. L.35000. Provincia Romana dei Frati Predicatori, Piazza S. Domenico 1, 51100 Pistoia, Italy. Ed. Marino Eugenio. bk.rev.; bibl.; illus.; stat.; index. circ. 1,000. (tabloid format) **Indexed**: CERDIC.

VIVRE ENSEMBLE; bulletin de liaison en pastorale interculturelle. see POPULATION STUDIES

282 IT
VOCE DEI BERICI; settimanale di informazione dell Diocesi di Vicenza. 1949. w. L.45000. Via Vescovado 1, 36100 Vicenza, Italy. TEL 0444 545855. FAX 0444-543783. Ed. Lucio Mozzo.

200 IT ISSN 0042-7845
VOCE DELLA MADONNA DELLE GRAZIE.* 1954. w. L.800($1.50) Opera Madonna delle Grazie, Via Andria, Corato, Bari 70033, Italy. Ed. Favia Ferrara Don Giuseppe. illus.

282 945 370 IT
VOCE SERAFICA DELLA SARDEGNA. (Text in Italian-Sardinian; summaries in Italian; 4-page section in French) 1921. m. L.25000 (effective Oct. 1994). Frati Minori Cappuccini di Sardegna, Via S. Ignazio da Laconi 94, 09123 Cagliari, Italy. TEL 39-70-660303. FAX 39-70-655583. Ed. P. Marco Tarcisio Mascia. adv.; bk.rev.; index; circ. 23,000 (paid); 3,000 (controlled). (also avail. in microfiche)
Description: Covers the Catholic religion and Capuchin information from Sardinia and Corsica.

282 IT
VOCI AMICHE; bollettino parrocchiale. 1951. bi-m. Tipografia Pistoiese, Corso Gramsci 49, 51100 Pistoia, Italy. TEL 0573 20764. Ed. D. Giuseppe Vignozzi. circ. 1,200.

282 JO
VOICE OF THE HOLY LAND/SAWT EL-ARD EL-MUKADDAS. (Text in Arabic) 1968. m. 10000 din. Catholic Bureau of Press and Publication, P.O. Box 5634, Amman, Jordan. TEL 694095. FAX 692502. Ed. Raouf Najjar. adv.; bk.rev. circ. 10,000.

282 US ISSN 8750-5975
VOICE OF THE SOUTHWEST; serving the Catholic Diocese of Gallup. m. $6. Diocese of Gallup, Box 1338, Gallup, NM 87305. TEL 505-863-4406. Ed. Tim Farrell. circ. 2,500. **Document type**: newspaper.

VOICES (AUSTIN). see SOCIAL SERVICES AND WELFARE

282 100 US ISSN 1068-168X
WANDERER. 1867. w. $35. Wanderer Printing Co., 201 Ohio St., St. Paul, MN 55107. TEL 612-224-5733. FAX 612-224-9666. Ed. A.J. Matt, Jr. adv.; B&W page $1988; adv. contact: Anne E. Matt. bk.rev. circ. 34,000. (also avail. in microfilm from UMI) **Document type**: newspaper.

282 US ISSN 0043-1583
BX806.R8
THE WAY/SHLIAKH; Ukrainian Catholic bi-weekly. (Text in English and Ukrainian) 1939. bi-w. $15 (foreign $20). (Ukrainian Catholic Archdiocese of Philadelphia) Apostolate, Inc., 827 N. Franklin St., Philadelphia, PA 19123-2004. TEL 215-922-5231. Eds. John M. Fields, Iwan Skoczylas. bk.rev.; illus. circ. 6,500. **Document type**: newspaper.

RELIGIONS AND THEOLOGY — ROMAN CATHOLIC

282 US ISSN 0273-8295
WAY OF ST. FRANCIS. 1948. 6/yr. $9. Franciscan Fathers of California, Inc., 1500 34th Ave., Oakland, CA 94601-3024. TEL 916-443-5717. Ed. Rev. Michael Harvey. adv. contact: Camille Franicevich. bk.rev.; illus.; circ. 5,000 (paid). **Indexed:** CERDIC. **Document type:** newsletter.
  Formerly: Way-Catholic Viewpoints (ISSN 0043-1591)
  Description: Franciscan life and spirituality.

282 US
WEEKDAY HOMILY HELPS. 1981. m. $55. St. Anthony Messenger Press, 1615 Republic St., Cincinnati, OH 45210. TEL 513-241-5615. FAX 513-241-0399. Ed. Diane Houdek. circ. 4,000. (looseleaf format)
  Description: Aid to Catholic clergy on preaching.

282 GW ISSN 0373-5885
WELT DES KINDES; Zeitschrift fuer Kleinkindpaedagogik und ausserschulische Erziehung. 1915. bi-m. DM.45 (students DM.36.60). (Verband Katholischer Tageseinrichtungen fuer Kinder Bundesverband e.V.) Koesel-Verlag GmbH und Co., Flueggenstr. 2, 80639 Munich, Germany. TEL 089-17801-0. FAX 089-17801111. Ed. Wolfgang Liegle. circ. 11,500. **Document type:** academic/scholarly publication.
  —CCC.

282 US
WEST NEBRASKA REGISTER. 1930. w. $13. Diocese of Grand Island, 311 W. 17th St., 804 W. Division, Grand Island, NE 68802. TEL 308-382-4660. Ed. Francis Curran. adv.: B&W page $200. circ. 16,842.

282 US
WEST RIVER CATHOLIC. 1973. m. $10.50. Diocese of Rapid City, Box 678, Rapid City, SD 57709. TEL 605-343-3541. FAX 605-348-7985. Ed. Eileen Sullivan; Pub. Charles J. Chaput. adv.: B&W page $207; adv. contact: Frank Pelkey. circ. 13,000. **Document type:** newspaper.

282 US ISSN 0273-7345
WEST TEXAS ANGELUS. (Text in English, Spanish) 1964. m. $10. Catholic Diocese of San Angelo, 804 Ford St., San Angelo, TX 76905. TEL 915-651-7500. FAX 915-651-6688. E-mail: WTAngelus@aol.com. (Subscr. to: Box 1829, San Angelo, TX 76902) Ed. Rev. Maurice J. Voity. adv.; bk.rev. circ. 19,400. (tabloid format) **Document type:** newspaper.
  Formerly: Texas Concho Register (ISSN 0040-425X)

282 US ISSN 0745-516X
WEST TEXAS CATHOLIC. 1936. w. $10. Roman Catholic Diocese of Amarillo, c/o Bishop L.T. Matthiesen, Box 5644, Amarillo, TX 79117-5644. FAX 806-383-8452. Ed. Chris Albrecht. adv. circ. 6,500.
  Formerly: West Texas Register (ISSN 0043-3187)

282 CN ISSN 0512-5235
WESTERN CATHOLIC REPORTER. 1965. w. Can.$22($50) Great Western Press Ltd., 8421-101 Ave., Edmonton, AB T6A 0L1, Canada. TEL 403-465-8030. FAX 403-465-8031. Ed. Glen Argan. adv.: B&W page $868; adv. contact: Linda Keer. circ. 37,000. (tabloid format) **Document type:** newspaper.

282 370 US
WESTERN NEW YORK CATHOLIC. 1873. m. $9 (foreign $10) (effective 1996). Diocese of Buffalo, 795 Main St., Buffalo, NY 14203. TEL 716-847-8719. FAX 716-847-8722. Ed. David M. Lee. adv. contact: Henry Falkowski. bk.rev. circ. 75,000. (tabloid format; back issues avail.) **Document type:** newspaper.
  Description: For Catholic community of the Diocese of Buffalo in the eight counties of Western New York, with a focus on sharing faith and service activities of a local nature.

282 UK ISSN 0262-1061
WHITE FATHERS - WHITE SISTERS. 1927. bi-m. free. Society of Missionaries of Africa, 129 Lichfield Rd., Sutton Coldfield, W. Midlands B74 2SA, England. TEL 0121-308-0226. FAX 0121-323-2476. E-mail: suttonlink@gn.apc.org. Ed. Rev. William Turnbull. bk.rev. circ. 37,500. (back issues avail.) **Document type:** bulletin.
  Description: Presents the missionary work of the Catholic Church in Africa.

282 333.7 US
WILDERNESS GAZETTE;* coverage of the apparitions and messages of the Blessed Virgin Mary in modern times. 1988. bi-m. $7.50 (foreign $10). Yellowstone Information Services, 605 Brady Ave., Steubenville, OH 43952-1459. TEL 304-965-5548. FAX 034-965-7785. Ed. Roger C. Thibault. bk.rev. circ. 1,000. (back issues avail.; reprint service avail.)
  Description: Covers the Church and the messages of the Mother of Jesus in her recent apparitions in various areas.

282 US
WINONA COURIER. 1910. m. $5. Diocese of Winona, Box 949, Winona, MN 55987. TEL 507-454-4643. Ed. Ivan J. Kubista. circ. 39,200. **Document type:** newspaper.

282 AU ISSN 1012-3067
WISSENSCHAFT UND GLAUBE. 1988. q. S.440. (Wiener Katholische Akademie) Verlag Herder und Co., Wollzeile 33, Postfach 248, A-1011 Vienna, Austria. TEL 0222-5121413.

282 US ISSN 0745-0427
THE WITNESS (DIOCESAN) NEWSPAPER. 1923. w. $12. (Archdiocese of Dubuque) Witness Publishing Company, 1229 Mt. Loretta Ave., P.O. Box 917, Dubuque, IA 52004-0917. TEL 319-588-0556. FAX 319-556-5464. (Subscr. to: Box 917, Dubuque, IA 52004-0917) Ed. Rev. Thomas J. Ralph. adv. contact: Judith Bandy. bk.rev. (back issues avail.) **Document type:** newspaper.
  Description: Provides national, international, and local news. Includes announcements, op-ed, entertainment, television reviews, and obituaries.

942 UK
WORCESTERSHIRE RECUSANT. 1963. s-a. membership. Worcestershire Catholic History Society, c/o Thomas Rock, More House, Haywood Drive, Tettenhall, Wolverhampton WV6 8RF, England. Ed. J.D. McEvilly. bibl. circ. 150.

282 US ISSN 0742-4639
THE WORD AMONG US. Spanish edition: Palabra Entre Nosotros (ISSN 0896-1727) (Editions also avail. in Japanese, Polish, Portuguese) 1981. m. (11/yr.). $18 for English ed. (overseas $28); Spanish ed. $15 (overseas $20). Word Among Us, Box 6003, Gaithersburg, MD 20884-6003. TEL 301-990-2090. FAX 301-990-2087. Ed. Anthony Bosnick. bk.rev. circ. 200,000. (back issues avail.)
  Description: Catholic Bible study and practical guide to Christian living.

282 US ISSN 0193-9211 BX801
WORD & SPIRIT. 1979. a. $8. (St. Scholastica Priory) St. Bede's Publications, Box 545, Rte. 32, Petersham, MA 01366. TEL 508-724-3407. FAX 508-724-3574. E-mail: stbedes@aol.com. Ed. Sr. Mary Joseph McManamon; Pub. Mother Mary Clare Vincent. circ. 300 (paid). (also avail. in microform from UMI; back issues avail.) **Indexed:** Cath.Ind., CERDIC, ERIC, Rel.& Theol.Abstr. (1979-). **Document type:** academic/scholarly publication.
  —BLDSC (9347.841000); UMI.
  Description: Focuses on scriptural, theological and spiritual themes, or commemorating the anniversary of a significant event in the history of Christianity.
  Refereed Serial

282 AT ISSN 0155-6894
WORD IN LIFE. 1953. q. Aus.$20. Australian Catholic University, 179 Albert Rd., Strathfield, N.S.W. 2135, Australia. FAX 02-955-8932. Ed. L. Woods. bk.rev. circ. 1,300. (back issues avail.) **Indexed:** CERDIC. **Document type:** academic/scholarly publication.
  Formerly (until 1977): Our Apostolate.
  Description: Covers religious education.

WORKERS' CHALLENGE; from the workers to the workers. see BUSINESS AND ECONOMICS — Labor And Industrial Relations

282.475 US
WORLD LITHUANIAN ROMAN CATHOLIC DIRECTORY. 1975. irreg., latest 1986. $10. Lithuanian R.C. Priests' League, 600 Liberty Hwy., Putnam, CT 06260-2503. TEL 203-928-9830. Ed. Rev. Valdemar M. Cukuras. adv.; stat. info. circ. 1,000. **Document type:** directory.

282 370 GW ISSN 0342-6378
WORT UND ANTWORT; Zeitschrift fuer Fragen des Glaubens. 1968. 4/yr. DM.37 (students DM.29) (effective 1996). Matthias Gruenewald Verlag GmbH, Max-Hufschmidt-Str. 4a, 55130 Mainz, Germany. TEL 06131-839055. FAX 06131-834322. Ed. Paulus Engelhardt. adv. contact: Andrea Buchauer. bk.rev.; index. circ. 1,100. (back issues avail.) **Document type:** academic/scholarly publication.

282 US ISSN 0746-5580
WYOMING CATHOLIC REGISTER. 1952. m. $4 inside diocese; outside diocese $7.50. Wyoming Catholic Register, 212 Capitol Ave., Cheyenne, WY 82001. TEL 307-638-1530. FAX 307-367-7936. (Subscr. to: Box 1308, Cheyenne, WY 82003. TEL 800-788-4606) Ed. Scott Farris; Pub. Bishop Joseph Hart. adv. contact: Scott Farris. bk.rev.; illus.; tr.lit. circ. 17,225. (tabloid format) **Document type:** newspaper.

266 US
XAVERIAN MISSIONS NEWSLETTER. 1951. bi-m. $5 donation. St. Francis Xavier Foreign Missionary Society, Inc., Box 5857, Holliston, MA 01746-5857. TEL 508-423-2144. FAX 508-423-4793. Ed. Rev. Dominic Calarco. bk.rev. circ. 30,000. (looseleaf format) **Document type:** newsletter.
  Description: Carries reports on Xaverian foreign missions and on related subjects involving the work of the Xaverian missionaries. Includes correspondence from missionaries, appeals for vocations, and news of activities on the home front.

YOU!. see CHILDREN AND YOUTH — For

282 US ISSN 0162-7031
YOUNGSTOWN CATHOLIC EXPONENT. (Supplements avail.) 1944. bi-w. $18. Catholic Exponent, Inc., Box 6787, Youngstown, OH 44501. TEL 216-744-5251. FAX 216-744-8451. Ed. Denny Finneran. adv. contact: Robert Berry. bk.rev. circ. 37,500. (tabloid format) **Document type:** newspaper.

282 US
YOUTH UPDATE. m. $12. (Franciscan Friars of St. John the Baptist Province) St. Anthony Messenger Press, 1615 Republic St., Cincinnati, OH 45210. TEL 513-241-5615. FAX 513-241-0399. Ed. Carol Ann Morrow. circ. 23,000. **Document type:** newsletter.
  Description: Addresses the concerns of teenagers promoting Christian values.

266 US ISSN 0514-2482
ZEAL. 1952. 3/yr. free. (St. Elizabeth Mission Society) Franciscan Sisters of Allegany, Allegany, NY 14706. TEL 716-373-0200. Ed. Sr. Marie Dolores Gionta. circ. 10,000.

282 AU ISSN 0044-2895 BX803
ZEITSCHRIFT FUER KATHOLISCHE THEOLOGIE. 1877. q. S.205. (Universitaet Innsbruck, Theologische Fakultaet) Verlag Herder, Wollzeile 33, A-1010 Vienna, Austria. TEL 01-5121413. Ed. P. Hans Bernh Meyer. adv.; bk.rev.; bibl.; index, cum.index. circ. 900. (reprint service avail. from SCH) **Indexed:** Canon Law Abstr., CERDIC, Old Test.Abstr. **Document type:** academic/scholarly publication.
  —SWETS.

280 GW
ZENTRALKOMITEE DER DEUTSCHEN KATHOLIKEN. MITTEILUNGEN. 1969. m. free. Zentralkomitee der deutschen Katholiken, Hochkreuzallee 246, 53175 Bonn, Germany. TEL 0228-382970. FAX 0228-3829744. TELEX 172283-748. Ed. Friedrich Kronenberg. circ. 2,000. **Document type:** newsletter.

282 GW ISSN 0179-6658
ZUR DEBATTE. 1970. bi-m. DM.21. Katholische Akademie in Bayern, Mandlstr. 23, Postfach 401008, 80802 Munich, Germany. TEL 089-381020. FAX 089-38102103.
  Description: Extracts of lectures given at the conferences at the academy.

282 GW ISSN 0342-6904
ZUR ZEIT; Zeitschrift der Redemptoristen. 1926. bi-m. DM.22.20 (foreign DM.28). Hofbauer-Verlag GmbH, Koelnstr. 415, 53177 Bonn, Germany. TEL 0228-670868. FAX 0228-672523. Ed.Bd. bk.rev. **Document type:** bulletin.

RELIGIONS AND THEOLOGY — OTHER DENOMINATIONS AND SECTS

282 323.4   US
10 THINGS JESUS WANTS YOU TO KNOW. 1992. q. newsstand price: $2. 1407 N.E. 45th St., Ste. 17, Seattle, WA 98105. TEL 206-547-9822. E-mail: ten@u.washington.edu. Ed. Dan Halligan. bk.rev.; film rev.; music rev.; illus. circ. 2,000.

282   ISSN 0897-2435
BX801
30 DAYS. 1991. m. (11/yr.). $35. Italcoser Corporation, 28 Trinity St., Newton, NJ 07860. TEL 201-383-0322. FAX 201-579-5541. Ed. Giulio Andreotti. adv.; index. circ. 10,000. (back issues avail.)

RELIGIONS AND THEOLOGY — Other Denominations And Sects

281.62   US
A M A A NEWS. (Text in Armenian and English) 1967. bi-m. contributions. Armenian Missionary Association of America, Inc., 140 Forest Ave., Paramus, NJ 07652. TEL 201-265-2607. FAX 201-265-6015. Ed. Moses B. Janbazian. adv.; bk.rev.; illus.; cum.index. circ. 13,000. **Document type:** newsletter.
Formerly (until 1976): A M A A Newsletter; **Incorporates:** Armenian-American Outlook (ISSN 0004-2307)

A R I E S. (Association pour la Recherche et l'Information sur l'Esoterisme) see *PARAPSYCHOLOGY AND OCCULTISM*

289   US
ACTS & FACTS. 1972. m. free. Institute for Creation Research, Box 2667, El Cajon, CA 92021. FAX 619-448-3469. Ed. Henry M. Morris. adv. contact: Donald Rohrer. circ. 120,000. **Indexed:** CERDIC. **Document type:** newsletter.
Description: Newsletter on the creation and evolution questions, including scientific articles.

289.9   DK   ISSN 0109-1743
ADVANCE. (Text in English, French, German, Italian) 1969. bi-m. membership. Church of Scientology, Advanced Organization Saint Hill Europe and Africa, Jernbanegade 6, DK-1608 Copenhagen V, Denmark. TEL 45-30-33-67-36. Eds. Alan Graham, Michael Garbe. adv.; bk.rev.; illus. circ. 70,000.

289.9 250   US   ISSN 0001-8589
ADVANCE (SPRINGFIELD); a magazine for Assemblies of God ministers and church leaders. 1965. m. $14.75. (General Council of the Assemblies of God) Gospel Publishing House, 1445 Boonville Ave., Springfield, MO 65802-9989. TEL 417-862-2781. Ed. Harris Jansen. adv.; bk.rev.; index, cum.index: 1965-1974, 1975-1979, 1980-1984. circ. 28,700.

289.9   US   ISSN 0741-4307
ADVENT CHRISTIAN WITNESS. 1952. m. $11. Advent Christian General Conference of America, Box 23152, Charlotte, NC 28212. TEL 704-545-6161. FAX 704-573-0712. Ed. Rev. Robert J. Mayer. bk.rev.; illus. circ. 4,000.
Formerly (until 1983): Advent Christian Witness to the World (ISSN 0274-9289)
Description: Promotes the gospel of Jesus Christ and the teaching of the Advent Christian Church.

286   US   ISSN 0360-389X
BX6101
ADVENTIST HERITAGE; a journal of Adventist history. 1974. q. $12 for 3 issues; Canada $18; elsewhere $22 for 4 issues. La Sierra University, Riverside, Box 1158, 4700 Pierce St., Riverside, CA 92515. TEL 909-785-2181. FAX 909-785-2901. Ed. Dorothy Minchin-Comm. adv.; bk.rev.; illus. circ. 2,000. (also avail. in microfilm from UMI; back issues avail.) **Indexed:** Amer.Hist.& Life, Hist.Abstr. —UMI.

AFFINITY. see *HOMOSEXUALITY*

200   II
AIM. (Text in English) 1970. m. Rs.50($20) Evangelical Fellowship of India, Publication Trust, 803 Deepali 92, Nehru Place, New Delhi 110, India. TEL 6431133. Ed. Rev. Francis Sunderaraj. adv.; bk.rev. circ. 3,300.
Supersedes: Evangelical Fellowship Quarterly.
Description: Promotes partnership, the defense and confirmation of the Christian Gospel, as well as increasing Christian evangelicalism.

200 940   UK
AISLING; the new voice of Druidry. q. £1.5. P.O. Box 196, London WC1A 2DY, England.

283   UK   ISSN 0002-5623
ALL THE WORLD. 1884. q. £3 (foreign £3.50). Salvation Army, International Headquarters, 101 Queen Victoria St., London EC4P 4EP, England. TEL 0171-236-5222. FAX 0171-329-3268. Ed. Connie Croly. circ. 18,000. **Document type:** newsletter.
Description: Reviews Salvation Army social services and Evangelism throughout the world.

284.8   AU   ISSN 0002-6514
ALTKATHOLISCHE KIRCHENZEITUNG. 1966. m. S.100($7) Altkatholische Kirche Oesterreichs, Schottenring 17-1-3-12, A-1010 Vienna, Austria. TEL 0222-3178394. FAX 0222-31783959. Ed. Rudolf Repits. adv.; bk.rev.; illus. circ. 2,700. (looseleaf format) **Document type:** bulletin.
Formerly: Alt-Katholik.

297.89   US   ISSN 1062-1113
AMERICAN BAHA'I. (Text in English, Persian, Spanish) 1969. 19/yr. National Spiritual Assembly of the Baha'is of the United States, 536 Sheridan Rd., Wilmette, IL 60091. TEL 708-869-9039. Ed. John Bowers. circ. 75,000. (tabloid format)
Description: Current events in the Baha'i community.

289.9   US
AMERICAN HORIZON. 1983. bi-m. (General Council of the Assemblies of God, Division of Home Missions) Gospel Publishing House, 1445 Boonville Ave., Springfield, MO 65802-1892. TEL 417-862-2781. Ed. Traci L. Countryman. circ. 30,000.
Formerly (until 1992): Mission America Newsletter.
Description: Covers DHM activities.

289.9   SA
AMKENI!. (Text in Swahili) 1993. s-m. R.19($5) Watch Tower Bible & Tract Society, Private Bag X2067, Krugersdorp 1740, South Africa. TEL 011-761-1000. FAX 011-764-4749. charts; illus.; index. circ. 6,100.

281.9   GR
ANALECTA VLATADON. irreg., latest no.50. price varies. Patriarchal Institute for Patristic Studies, Heptapyrgiou 64, 546 34 Thessaloniki, Greece.

ANGEL TIMES. see *NEW AGE PUBLICATIONS*

289.4   US   ISSN 1075-2897
▼**ARCANA;** inner dimensions of spirituality. 1994. q. $15 (foreign $20). Swedenborg Association, 1725 Huntingdon Rd., Box 533, Bryn Athyn, PA 19009. TEL 215-947-4243. FAX 215-947-2728. (Dist. by: Ubiquity Distributors, Inc., 607 Degraw St., Brooklyn, NY 11217. TEL 718-875-5491) Ed. Leonard Fox. adv. contact: Michelle Rose. bk.rev. (back issues avail.) **Document type:** academic/scholarly publication.
Description: Publishes articles on the universal truths of religion, especially from a Swedenborgian perspective. Seeks to give a new outlook for persons seeking spiritual growth and to affirm the unifying principles of various faiths.

281.62   US   ISSN 1075-7066
THE ARMENIAN CHURCH. 1980. bi-m. membership. Diocese of the Armenian Church of America, 630 Second Ave., New York, NY 10016. TEL 212-686-0710. Ed. Michael Zeytoonian. bk.rev.; illus. circ. 25,000. **Indexed:** CERDIC.
Former titles (until 1987): Bema (ISSN 0199-8765); Supersedes (in 1986): Armenian Church (ISSN 0004-2315); Hayastanyaitz Yegeghetzy (ISSN 0017-8667)

200   FR   ISSN 0083-6184
ASSEMBLEES DE DIEU DE FRANCE. ANNUAIRE.* 1958. a. 8 F. Viens et Vois, 10 rue de Sentier, 75002 Paris, France.

281.9   GR
ATHENISIN ETHNIKON KAI KAPODISTRIAKON PANEPISTEMION. THEOLOGIKE SCHOLE. EPISTEMONIKE EPETERIS. (Text in English, French and Greek) 1935. a. Athenisin Ethnikon kai Kapodistrakon, Theologike Schole, Odos Panepistimiou, Athens 143, Greece.

131.35   US   ISSN 0004-7651
AUDITOR; the monthly scientology journal. 1964. m. membership. Church of Scientology Western United States, American Saint Hill Organization, 1413 N. Berendo St., Los Angeles, CA 90027-0972. TEL 213-953-3250. FAX 213-953-3257. bk.rev.; bibl.; illus. circ. 600,000. **Document type:** bulletin.

289.9   DK
AUDITOR. (Editions for Africa, Europe, and U.S. avail.) 1969. m. membership. Church of Scientology, Advanced Organization Saint Hill Europe and Africa, Jernbanegade 6, DK-1608 Copenhagen V, Denmark. Ed. Michael Garbe. bk.rev. circ. 170,000.

282   US   ISSN 0005-237X
AWAKE. (Editions in 67 languages) 1919. s-m. (Jehovah's Witnesses, Governing Body) Watchtower Bible and Tract Society of New York, Inc., Writing Department, 25 Columbia Hts., Brooklyn, NY 11201. TEL 718-625-3600. FAX 718-625-3062. Ed.Bd. circ. 13,110,000.
Description: Discusses social issues from the perspective of the Jehovah's Witnesses

297.89   CN   ISSN 0708-5052
BAHA'I STUDIES. 1976. irreg. Can.$5 per no. Association for Baha'i Studies, 34 Copernicus St., Ottawa, ON K1N 7K4, Canada. TEL 613-233-1903. Ed.Bd. circ. 2,000. **Document type:** monographic series, academic/scholarly publication.
Refereed Serial

297.89   IS   ISSN 0045-1320
BAHA'I WORLD. (Text primarily in English; occasional articles in French, German and Persian) 1925. irreg., vol.19, 1991. price varies. Baha'i World Centre, P.O. Box 155, Haifa 31001, Israel. FAX 04-358280. TELEX 46626-BAYT IL. (Dist. in U.S. by: Baha'i Publishing Trust, 415 Linden Ave., Wilmette, IL 60091) Ed. Sherna Deamer. circ. 15,000.

THE BAHLASTI PAPERS. see *PARAPSYCHOLOGY AND OCCULTISM*

289.9   US
THE BANNER (ZANESVILLE); a newsletter for Christian Scientists. 1987. q. (plus special editions). free. 2040 Hazel Ave., Zanesville, OH 43701. Ed. Andrew W. Hartsook. bk.rev. **Document type:** newsletter.
Description: Focuses on items of current interest and concern.

268   US
BEADS OF TRUTH. 1972. s-a. $10. Three H O Foundation, 1620 Preuss Rd., Los Angeles, CA 90035. TEL 213-552-3416. Ed. S.S. Satsimran Kaur Khalsa. adv.; bk.rev.; illus. circ. 3,000.

BEFRIENDING CREATION. see *RELIGIONS AND THEOLOGY*

299.935   SZ
BEITRAEGE ZUR RUDOLF STEINER GESAMTAUSGABE. 1961. s-a. 24 Fr. Rudolf Steiner Verlag, Haus Duldeck, Postfach 135, CH-4143 Dornach, Switzerland. FAX 061-7012534. Ed. W. Kugler. circ. 2,000. (back issues avail.)
Description: Documents, notes, texts and other information from the Rudolf Steiner archives.

297.89 499.9   GW
BELMONDA LETERO. (Text in Esperanto) 1973. q. membership only. Bahaa Esperanto-Ligo, Postfach 500133, 60391 Frankfurt a.M., Germany. Ed. Bernhard Westerhoff. adv.; bk.rev. circ. 500. (looseleaf format) **Document type:** newsletter.
Description: News about the activities of Baha'i Esperantists around the world.

BHARATYA VIDYA. see *ORIENTAL STUDIES*

398.7   US
BIBLE TEACHER AND LEADER. q. $16.99. Standard Publishing, 8121 Hamilton Ave., Cincinnati, OH 45231. TEL 513-931-4050. FAX 513-931-0904. Ed. James I. Fehl.
Description: Sunday-school lesson manual for teachers of adults.

268.1   NE   ISSN 0006-2243
BIJBELLESSEN VOOR DE SABBATSCHOOL. 1897. q. fl.5.95. (Zevende-Dags Adventisten - Seventh-Day Adventists) Stichting Uitgeverij "Veritas", Biltseweg 14, 3735 ME Bosch en Duin, Netherlands. FAX 31-30-281084. illus.

RELIGIONS AND THEOLOGY — OTHER DENOMINATIONS AND SECTS

100 133 US
THE BLACK FLAME. 1989. s-a. $12 (foreign $16) for 2 nos. Box 499, Radio City Sta., New York, NY 10101-0499. TEL 212-245-2329. Ed. Peter H. Gilmore. adv.; bk.rev. circ. 2,000. **Document type:** newsletter.
Description: Discusses Satanism and the occult world.

377 CN ISSN 0006-4327
BLACKBOARD BULLETIN. 1957. m. (10/yr.). $6. (Amish Church) Pathway Publishing Corporation, Rte. 4, Aylmer, ON N5H 2R3, Canada. Ed. Delbert Farmwald. illus. circ. 16,200.

289 NE
BOODSCHAP. 1978. q. fl.20. Soefi-Orde Nederland, Hermelijnlaan 9, 1216 EB Hilversum, Netherlands. Ed. Akbar Helweg. adv.; bk.rev. circ. 350.

289.7 CN ISSN 0006-8209
BOTE; ein mennonitsches Familienblatt. (Text and summaries in German) 1924. w. Can.$27. General Conference Mennonite Church, 600 Shaftesburg Blvd., Winnipeg, MB R3P 0M4, Canada. TEL 204-888-6781. FAX 204-831-5675. (Co-sponsor: Conference of Mennonites in Canada) Ed. Erwin Strempler. adv.; bk.rev. circ. 4,500. (tabloid format; also avail. in diskette format) **Indexed:** CERDIC. **Document type:** newspaper.

299.934 II ISSN 0001-902X
BP500
BRAHMAVIDYA. Variant title: Adyar Library Bulletin. (Text in English and Sanskrit; occasionally French and German) 1937. a. Rs.115($20) (foreign $25). Adyar Library and Research Centre, Theosophical Society, Adyar, Madras 600 020, India. Ed.Bd. adv.; bk.rev.; cum.index: vols.1-51. (also avail. in microfiche from IDC; back issues avail.) **Indexed:** Bibl.Ling., M.L.A. **Document type:** academic/scholarly publication.

BRAILLE STAR THEOSOPHIST. see *HANDICAPPED — Visually Impaired*

289.9 US ISSN 0006-9663
BX7801
BRETHREN LIFE AND THOUGHT; a quarterly journal published in the interest of the Church of the Brethren. 1955. q. $15. Brethren Journal Association and Bethany Theological Seminary, c/o Christina Bucher, Ed., Elizabethtown College, One Alpha Dr., Elizabethtown, PA 17022-2298. bk.rev.; cum.index: vols.1-26. circ. 800. (also avail. in microfilm from UMI; reprint service avail. from UMI) **Indexed:** Rel.& Theol.Abstr. (1968-), Rel.Ind.One. **Document type:** academic/scholarly publication. —BLDSC (2279.732000); UMI.

266 US ISSN 0161-5238
BRETHREN MISSIONARY HERALD. 1940. m. $13.50. (Fellowship of Grace Brethren Churches) Brethren Missionary Herald, Inc., Box 544, Winona Lake, IN 46590. TEL 219-267-7158. FAX 219-267-4745. Ed. Jeff Carroll. adv.; bk.rev.; illus.; circ. 1,600. (controlled). (back issues avail.)

BRILLIANT STAR. see *CHILDREN AND YOUTH — For*

289.7 US ISSN 0090-242X
HJ9013
THE BUDGET. 1890. w. $28 (effective 1995). Sugarcreek Budget Publishers, Inc., 134 N. Factory St., Box 249, Sugarcreek, OH 44681-0249. TEL 216-852-4634. FAX 216-852-4421. Ed. George R. Smith; Pub. Albert Spector. adv. contact: Virginia Baab. circ. 20,000. (back issues avail.) **Document type:** newspaper.
Description: Serves the Amish and Mennonite communities across the Americas.

289 US ISSN 0745-1687
BUILDER (SCOTTDALE). 1950. m. $32. Mennonite Publishing House, 616 Walnut Ave., Scottdale, PA 15683. TEL 412-887-8500. FAX 412-887-3111. (Co-publisher: Faith and Life Press) Ed. David Hiebert. illus. circ. 5,300.
Description: Directed to Christian educators and congregational leaders. Includes Sunday school teaching guides for each Sunday, following the Uniform Series outline.

C H I L D NEWSLETTER. (Children's Healthcare Is a Legal Duty) see *CHILDREN AND YOUTH — About*

289.1 GW
C Z B REPORT. 1986. q. free. Christliches Zentrum Berlin e.V., Herwarthstr. 5, 12207 Berlin, Germany. TEL 030-768904-0. FAX 030-7736376. Eds. Peter Dippl, Peter Winkel. circ. 8,500. **Document type:** bulletin.

299.6 ZR ISSN 0008-0047
BL2400
CAHIERS DES RELIGIONS AFRICAINES. (Text in English, French) 1967. s-a. $35. Faculte de Theologie Catholique de Kinshasa, P.O. Box 712, Kinshasa - Limete, Zaire. TEL 78476. (Co-sponsor: Centre d'Etudes de Religions Africaines) Ed. Vincent Mulago. adv.; bk.rev.; bibl.; illus. circ. 1,000. **Indexed:** A.I.C.P., CERDIC, Curr.Cont.Africa, Documentatieblad. **Document type:** academic/scholarly publication.

284 327 US
CALL TO PEACEMAKING. 1983. q. free. New Call to Peacemaking, Box 500, Akron, PA 17501. TEL 717-859-1958. E-mail: johnstoner@aol.com. Ed. John K. Stoner. bk.rev. circ. 900. **Document type:** newsletter.
Description: Discusses nonviolence, alternatives to war and related issues for a church audience.

281.62 CN
CANADA ARMENIAN PRESS. NEWSLETTER. (Text in Armenian, English) 1963. q. contributions. Armenian Evangelical Church, 34 Glenforest Rd., Toronto, Ont. M4N 1Z8, Canada. TEL 416-489-3188. Ed. Rev. Yesai Sarmazian. adv.; bk.rev.; illus. circ. 450. **Document type:** newsletter.
Formerly: Canada Armenian Press (ISSN 0008-2562)

285 CN ISSN 0382-7658
CANADIAN FRIEND; Quaker news and thought. 1904. bi-m. Can.$15 (foreign Can.$23). Canadian Yearly of the Religious Society of Friends, 91A Fourth Ave., Ottawa, ON K1S 2L1, Canada. TEL 613-235-8553. E-mail: bs080@freenet.carleton.ca. Ed. Anne-Marie Zilliacus. bk.rev. circ. 1,200. (back issues avail.) **Document type:** newsletter.

289 CN ISSN 0820-554X
CANADIAN MESSENGER OF THE SACRED HEART. 1891. m. Can.$10. Apostleship of Prayer, 661 Greenwood Ave., Toronto, ON M4J 4B3, Canada. TEL 416-466-1195. Ed. Rev. F.J. Power, S.J. illus. circ. 17,000. (back issues avail.)
Former titles (until 1983): Messanger of the Sacred Heart (ISSN 0820-5531); (until 1982): Messenger (ISSN 0706-6619); (until 1980): Messenger of the Sacred Heart (ISSN 0708-3203); (until 1968): Messenger (ISSN 0708-3211); (until 1962): Canadian Messenger of the Sacred Heart (ISSN 0008-4425); (until 1899): Canadian Messenger (ISSN 0708-322X).

289.6 CN ISSN 1180-968X
CANADIAN QUAKER HISTORY JOURNAL. 1972. 2/yr. Can.$15 to individuals; libraries and institutions Can.$20. Canadian Friends Historical Association, 60 Lowther Ave., Toronto, Ont. M5R 1C7, Canada. TEL 416-839-4328. Ed.Bd. bk.rev.; bibl.; charts; illus.; stat.; index, cum.index. circ. 200. **Document type:** academic/scholarly publication, newsletter, proceedings.
Formerly: Canadian Quaker Historic Newsletter (ISSN 0319-3934)

CENTER FOR PROCESS STUDIES. NEWSLETTER. see *PHILOSOPHY*

289.9 US
CHILDREN OF THE EARTH;* for Pagan families with kids. 4/yr. $5. Cassidy, Box 1896, Elkins, WV 25341-1896. bk.rev.; illus.

200 UK ISSN 0009-5117
THE CHRISTADELPHIAN; dedicated wholly to the hope of Israel. 1864. m. £18 (U.S. $24.95; Canada Can.$48). Christadelphian Magazine and Publishing Association Ltd., 404 Shaftmoor Ln., Hall Green, Birmingham B28 8SZ, England. TEL 0121-777-6328. FAX 0121-778-5024. Ed. Michael J. Ashton. bk.rev.; illus.; index. circ. 6,700.
Description: Promotes Bible study and a better understanding of Christadelphian beliefs.

284 US ISSN 0893-8571
CHRISTIAN CONTENDER.* 1983. a. $1. Christian Chamber of Commerce, Box 267, Silver Springs, NV 89429-0267. TEL 713-855-3357. Ed. John P. Hansen. circ. 10,000. (tabloid format; back issues avail.)

268 289.1 US
CHRISTIAN EDUCATION COUNSELOR. 1939. m. $12. Assemblies of God, Sunday School Promotion and Training Department, 1445 Boonville, Springfield, MO 65802. TEL 417-862-2781. FAX 417-862-0503. Ed. Sylvia Lee. bk.rev.; cum.index: 1955-1988. circ. 30,000.
Formerly (until 1994): Sunday School Counselor (ISSN 0039-5285)
Description: Provides local Sunday school leaders and teachers with inspiration and practical helps.

267 UK
CHRISTIAN ENDEAVOUR PROGRAMME BOOK. 1896. a. £3. Christian Endeavour Union of Great Britain and Ireland, Wellesbourne House, Walton Rd., Wellesbourne, Warks. CV35 9JB, England. TEL 01789-470439. Ed. Keith Bernhardt. adv. contact: Goerge Campball. bk.rev. circ. 1,000. **Document type:** newsletter.
Former titles: Christian Endeavour Topic Book; Christian Endeavour Year Book (ISSN 0069-3863)
Description: Covers missions and missionary work in the U.K.

298.7 US ISSN 1080-8000
CHRISTIAN EXAMPLE. 1961. fortn. $7.50. Rod and Staff Publishers, Inc., State Rte. 172, Crockett, KY 41413. TEL 606-522-4348. FAX 606-522-4896. Ed. James L. Boll. circ. 4,800.

CHRISTIAN INSTITUTE FOR RELIGIOUS STUDIES. BULLETIN. see *RELIGIONS AND THEOLOGY*

289.7 US ISSN 0009-5419
CHRISTIAN LEADER. 1937. fortn. $19. U.S. Conference of Mennonite Brethren Churches, Box V, Hillsboro, KS 67063-0060. TEL 316-947-5543. Ed. Don Ratzlaff. adv. contact: Don Ratzlaff. bk.rev.; illus.; index. circ. 9,500.

281.9 GR
CHRISTIAN LITERATURE. irreg., latest vol.3. price varies. Patriarchal Institute for Patristic Studies, Heptapyrgiou 64, 546 34 Thessaloniki, Greece.

CHRISTIAN SCIENCE BIBLE LESSONS (BRAILLE EDITION). see *HANDICAPPED — Visually Impaired*

289.5 US ISSN 0009-5613
BX6901
CHRISTIAN SCIENCE JOURNAL. 1883. m. $35. Christian Science Publishing Society, Box 11341, Des Moines, IA 50340-1341. TEL 800-456-4851. Ed. William E. Moody. index. **Indexed:** CERDIC. —Faxon.

289.5 US ISSN 0009-563X
CHRISTIAN SCIENCE SENTINEL. 1898. w. $49. Christian Science Publishing Society, Box 11342, Des Moines, IA 50340-1342. TEL 800-456-4851. Ed. William B. Moody. adv.; index. **Indexed:** CERDIC.

289.3 US
CHURCH NEWS (SALT LAKE CITY). 1931. w. $17.50. Church of Jesus Christ of Latter-day Saints, Corporation of the President, 50 E. North Temple, Salt Lake City, UT 84150. TEL 801-240-2947. FAX 801-240-1727. Ed. Dell Van Orden. circ. 225.
Description: Contains news of the Church.

289.9 US ISSN 1047-4196
CIRCLE NETWORK NEWS; international nature spirituality networking newspaper - journal. 1980. 4/yr. $15 (foreign $24). Circle Sanctuary, Box 219, Mt. Horeb, WI 53572. TEL 608-924-2216. FAX 608-924-5961. Ed. Dennis Carpenter. adv.; bk.rev.; illus. (tabloid format; back issues avail.)
Description: Provides news, views, notices, rituals, and other information pertaining to Wiccan ways, Paganism, Shamanism, Goddess Worship, Positive Magik, and related Pantheistic ways.

289 US ISSN 0263-6743
CLARITY. 1968. bi-m. £3.50. Clarity Publications, 26 Valleyside, Hemel Hempstead, Herts, HP1 2LN, England. TEL 0442-252542. Ed. Jennifer Sprague. bk.rev.; index. circ. 165. (back issues avail.)
Description: Covers all aspects of Christianity.

RELIGIONS AND THEOLOGY — OTHER DENOMINATIONS AND SECTS

266 US
COLUMBIA UNION VISITOR. 1895. s-m. $7.50 to non-members. (Columbia Union Conference of Seventh-Day Adventists) Review and Herald Publishing Association, 55 W. Oak Ridge Dr., Hagerstown, MD 21740. TEL 301-791-7000. Ed. Richard Duerksen. adv.; bk.rev. circ. 35,000.

289 AT ISSN 0004-9662
COMMUNION. 1962. q. Aus.$13. Liberal Catholic Church in Australia, P.O. Box 220, Glebe, N.S.W. 2037, Australia. TEL 02-660-6242. FAX 02-692-8373. (Subscr. to: Communion, P.O. Box 1371, Lane Cove, N.S.W. 2066, Australia) Ed. Rev. Ronald Rivett. bk.rev.; illus. circ. 500. Indexed: CERDIC.
Formerly: Australian Liberal Catholic.
Description: Publishes articles on religious thought, poems, letters, church notices etc.

CONCORD. see *HOMOSEXUALITY*

299.51 CH
CONFUCIUS & MENCIUS SOCIETY OF THE REPUBLIC OF CHINA. JOURNAL. 1961. s-a. NT.$100($4) Confucius-Mencius Society of the Republic of China, 45, Nan Hai Rd., Taipei, Taiwan, Republic of China. Ed. Tung Chin-yue. bibl.; cum.index.

289.9 US
CONSCIOUS NEWSLETTER. (Former name of issuing body: World Consciousness Movement) m. $35 suggested donation. Consciousness Network, 464 N. 43rd St., Seattle, WA 98103. TEL 206-632-2018. Pub. Robert D. Wells. Document type: newsletter.
Formerly: Christian Science Open Forum.

281.7 NE ISSN 0167-5818
COPTIC STUDIES. 1978. irreg., vol.2, 1991. price varies. E.J. Brill, P.O. Box 9000, 2300 PA Leiden, Netherlands. TEL 31-71-5353500. FAX 31-71-5317532. TELEX 39296 BRILL NL. (In N. America: E.J. Brill, 24 Hudson St., Kinderhook, NY 12106. TEL 800-962-4406. FAX 518-758-1959) Ed. M. Krause. (back issues avail.) Document type: monographic series.
Description: Scholarly discussions of issues in early Egyptian Christianity and related disciplines.

281.7 CN ISSN 0229-1134
BX130
COPTOLOGIA; journal of Coptic thought and orthodox spirituality. 1981. a. Can.$10($8.50) P.O. Box 235, Don Mills Postal Station, Don Mills, ON M3C 2S2, Canada. TEL 416-391-1774. Ed. Fayek M. Ishak. bk.rev. circ. 450. Document type: academic/scholarly publication.
Description: Research publication which is mainly concerned with the Egyptological sources and multiple meaning of the Coptic tradition.

281.7 US ISSN 0360-649X
DT72.C7
COPTS; Christians of Egypt. 1974. 4/yr. American Coptic Association, Box 9119, Jersey City, NJ 07304. TEL 203-451-0972. Eds. Selim Naguib, Shawky F. Karas.
Description: Examines the problems facing the Christian Egyptians in Egypt (Copts), the history and culture of the Coptic people, and their contributions to civilization.

281.9 950 BE ISSN 0070-0398
CORPUS SCRIPTORUM CHRISTIANORUM ORIENTALIUM: AETHIOPICA. (Text in Amharic) 1904. irreg., no.100, 1994. price varies. (Universitatis Catholicae Lovaniensis) Editions Peeters s.p.r.l., Bondgenotenlaan 153, 3000 Leuven, Belgium. TEL 32-16-235170. FAX 32-16-228500. (Co-sponsor: Catholic University of America) bk.rev. (back issues avail.) Document type: monographic series.

281.9 950 BE ISSN 0070-0401
CORPUS SCRIPTORUM CHRISTIANORUM ORIENTALIUM: ARABICA. (Text in Arabic) 1903. irreg., no.47, 1987. price varies. (Universitatis Catholicae Lovaniensis) Editions Peeters s.p.r.l., Bondgenotenlaan 153, 3000 Leuven, Belgium. TEL 32-16-235170. FAX 32-16-228500. (Co-sponsor: Catholic University of America) bk.rev. (back issues avail.) Document type: monographic series.

281.9 950 BE ISSN 0070-041X
CORPUS SCRIPTORUM CHRISTIANORUM ORIENTALIUM: ARMENIACA. (Text in Armenian) 1953. irreg., no.22, 1993. price varies. (Universitatis Catholicae Lovaniensis) Editions Peeters s.p.r.l., Bondgenotenlaan 153, 3000 Leuven, Belgium. TEL 32-16-235170. FAX 32-16-228500. (Co-sponsor: Catholic University of America) bk.rev. (back issues avail.) Document type: monographic series.

281.9 950 BE ISSN 0070-0428
CORPUS SCRIPTORUM CHRISTIANORUM ORIENTALIUM: COPTICA. (Text in Coptic) 1906. irreg., no.48, 1993. price varies. (Universitatis Catholicae Lovaniensis) Editions Peeters s.p.r.l., Bondgenotenlaan 153, 3000 Leuven, Belgium. TEL 32-16-235170. FAX 32-16-228500. (Co-sponsor: Catholic University of America) bk.rev. (back issues avail.) Document type: monographic series.

281.9 950 BE ISSN 0070-0436
CORPUS SCRIPTORUM CHRISTIANORUM ORIENTALIUM: IBERICA. (Text in Georgian) 1950. irreg., no.24, 1992. price varies. (Universitatis Catholicae Lovaniensis) Editions Peeters s.p.r.l., Bondgenotenlaan 153, 3000 Leuven, Belgium. TEL 32-16-235170. FAX 32-16-228500. (Co-sponsor: Catholic University of America) bk.rev. (back issues avail.) Document type: monographic series.

281.9 950 BE ISSN 0070-0444
CORPUS SCRIPTORUM CHRISTIANORUM ORIENTALIUM: SUBSIDIA. (Text in English, French, German) 1950. irreg., no.87, 1995. price varies. (Universitatis Catholicae Lovaniensis) Editions Peeters s.p.r.l., Bondgenotenlaan 153, 3000 Leuven, Belgium. TEL 32-16-235170. FAX 32-16-228500. (Co-sponsor: Catholic University of America) Document type: monographic series.

281.9 950 BE ISSN 0070-0452
CORPUS SCRIPTORUM CHRISTIANORUM ORIENTALIUM: SYRIACA. (Text in Syriac) 1903. irreg., no.221, 1993. price varies. (Universitatis Catholicae Lovaniensis) Editions Peeters s.p.r.l., Bondgenotenlaan 153, 3000 Leuven, Belgium. TEL 32-16-235170. FAX 32-16-228500. (Co-sponsor: Catholic University of America) bk.rev. (back issues avail.) Document type: monographic series.

289.9 US
COUNCIL OF THE MYSTIC ARTS. NEWSLETTER. 12/yr. $24. Council of the Mystic Arts, Spectrum of the Seven Keys, 538 Hammond Ave., San Antonio, TX 78210. illus.

285.734 US ISSN 0011-0671
COVENANT COMPANION. 1926. m. $26. (Evangelical Covenant Church) Covenant Publications, 5101 N. Francisco Ave., Chicago, IL 60625. TEL 312-784-3000. FAX 312-784-1540. Ed. John E. Phelan, Jr. adv. contact: Steve Luce. bk.rev.; index. circ. 22,000.

289 UK
COVENANT VIEWPOINT. 1993. q. £6($12) to non-members (overseas £8). Covenant Peoples Fellowship, 36 Shaftesbury Ave., Worthing, W. Sussex BN12 4EQ, England. TEL 01093-505919. Ed. Kenneth Whittaker. charts; illus.; index.

289 UK
COVENANT VOICE. 1945. m. £6($12) to non-members (overseas £8). Covenant Peoples Fellowship, 36 Shaftesbury Ave., Worthing, W. Sussex BN12 4EQ, England. TEL 01093-505919. Ed. Rev. Kenneth Whittaker. charts; illus.; index. circ. 4,000.
Formerly (until June 1982): Brith (ISSN 0007-0211)

CRAFT - CRAFTS. see *ARTS AND HANDICRAFTS*

207 CI ISSN 0352-4000
CRKVA U SVIJETU. (Text in Croatian; summaries in English and French) 1966. q. $25. Nadbiskupija Splitsko-Makarska, Zrinjsko-Frankopanska 14, 58001 Split, Croatia. Ed. Drago Simundza. bk.rev. circ. 2,000.

266 US ISSN 0045-9119
CROSSROADS (MOOREHEAD). 1972. bi-m. £3($5) Middle East Christian Outreach Ltd., Box 1008, Moorehead, MN 56561-1008. TEL 218-236-5963. FAX 218-236-5963. (UK addr.: 22 Culverden Park Rd., Tunbridge Wells, Kent TN4 9RA, England) Ed. Peter D.L. Thomson. adv. circ. 5,000.
Description: Covers Christian Mission in the Middle East.

CULT AWARENESS NETWORK NEWS; alerting the world to the dangers of destructive cults. see *PSYCHOLOGY*

242.2 US ISSN 0092-7147
BV4810
DAILY BREAD; a devotional guide for every day of the year. 1969. a. $10.50. (Reorganized Church of Jesus Christ of Latter Day Saints) Herald Publishing House, 3225 S. Noland Rd., Box 1770, Independence, MO 64055. TEL 816-252-5010. FAX 816-252-3976. Ed. Richard Brown. circ. 10,000.

289.3 US ISSN 0745-4724
DESERET NEWS. w. Church of Jesus Christ of Latter-day Saints, Corporation of the President, 50 E. North Temple, Salt Lake City, UT 84150. TEL 801-240-2947. FAX 801-240-1727.

289.3 US ISSN 0093-786X
BX8606
DESERET NEWS CHURCH ALMANAC. 1974. biennial. $6.95 (effective 1996). Deseret News Publishing Co., Box 1257, Salt Lake City, UT 84110. TEL 801-237-2141. FAX 801-237-2121. E-mail: ab10sh4246.cin@desnews.com. Ed. Dell Van Orden; Pub. Wm. James Mortimer. circ. 25,000. Document type: consumer publication.
Description: Covers reference information, history of the Church by country and state, leadership biographies, review of church news, historical chronology, and current church membership statistics.

261 CE ISSN 0012-2181
DIALOGUE. 1963. 3/yr. $10. Ecumenical Institute for Study and Dialogue, 490-5 Havelock Rd., Colombo 6, Sri Lanka. Ed. Fr. Aloysius Pieris. adv.; bk.rev. circ. 1,000. Indexed: Rel.Ind.One.
—BLDSC (3579.753000).

289.3 US ISSN 0012-2157
BX8601
DIALOGUE: A JOURNAL OF MORMON THOUGHT. 1966. q. $25 to individuals; students and senior citizens $20. Dialogue Foundation, UMC 7805, University Sta., Logan, UT 84322-7805. TEL 801-750-1154. Eds. F. Ross Peterson, Mary Kay Peterson. bk.rev.; charts; illus.; index, cum.index: 1966-1987. circ. 4,000. (also avail. in microform from UMI; back issues avail.) Indexed: Amer.Hist.& Life, Hist.Abstr., Rel.Ind.One.
—UMI.
Description: Contains articles, essays, poetry, fiction and art.

299 II ISSN 0253-519X
DISCOURSE. (Text in English) 1972. m. Rs.10($10) Society of Servants of God, Yashwant Place, Satya Marg, Chanakyapuri, New Delhi 110021, India. Ed. Sundri P. Vaswani. bibl.; index. circ. 650.
—CCC.

299 GW ISSN 0012-6063
DIE DREI; Zeitschrift fuer Anthroposophie. 1921. m. DM.64. (Anthroposophische Gesellschaft in Deutschland) Verlag Freies Geistesleben GmbH, Haussmannstr. 76, 70188 Stuttgart, Germany. TEL 0711-283255. FAX 0711-2624606. Ed. Dietrich Rapp. adv.; bk.rev.; abstr.; illus.; index. circ. 5,000. Indexed: RILM.
—CCC.

DRUID HENGE. see *PARAPSYCHOLOGY AND OCCULTISM*

RELIGIONS AND THEOLOGY — OTHER DENOMINATIONS AND SECTS

200 333.7   US   ISSN 1050-0413
EARTHLIGHT; the magazine of spirituality and ecology. 1990. q. $19 (Canada & Mexico $25; elsewhere $29). (P Y M - C U N, Religious Society of Friends (Quakers)) Unity with Nature Committee of Pacific Yearly Meeting, 1558 Mercy St., Mountain View, CA 94041. TEL 415-960-1767. E-mail: paul.burks@aol.com. Ed. Paul Burks. adv.; bk.rev.; circ. 800. circ. 1,400 (paid).
   Description: Addresses the environmental crisis from the perspective that it has its roots in the crisis of the human spirit.

264.01   UK   ISSN 0012-8732
EASTERN CHURCHES NEWS LETTER. 1955. s-a. £3. Anglican & Eastern Churches Association, St. Dustan-in-the-West, 184 Fleet St., London EC4A 2EA, England. TEL 01-405 1929. Ed. N. Harrison. adv.; bk.rev.; rec.rev. circ. 850.
   Description: Includes news items, theological and historical articles, correspondence and announcements of events.

284.2 266   NE   ISSN 0012-9119
ECHO; hervormd blad. 1952. 12/yr. fl.10. Hervormde Bond voor Inwendige Zending - Reformed Alliance for Home Mission, Johan van Oldenbarneveltlaan 10, Amersfoort, Netherlands. FAX 033-637093. Ed. M.E. Brak. illus. circ. 20,000.

289.9
ECKANKAR JOURNAL. 1976. a. $4. Eckankar Publications, Box 27300, Minneapolis, MN 55427-0300. FAX 612-544-3754. Ed. Suzanne Alexander Ford. circ. 20,000.
   Former titles (until Oct. 1988): Eck Mata Journal; Eck News.
   Description: Contains personal spiritual experiences that have changed people's lives, as well as visualizations, exercises and approaches to experience the essence of God.

267.15   FR   ISSN 0013-6921
EN AVANT. 1882. w. 250 F. (foreign 280 F.). Armee du Salut, 60, rue des Freres Flavien, 75976 Paris Cedex 20, France. TEL 1-43-62-25-00. Ed. J.P. Thoeni; Pub. Emmanuel R. Niallia. bk.rev. circ. 10,000. **Document type:** newspaper.
   Description: Covers history related to the Salvation Army as well as current activities within the organization.

ENCHANTING NEWS. see *PARAPSYCHOLOGY AND OCCULTISM*

ENLIGHTENMENT BOOK CLUB. see *PHILOSOPHY*

289.3   US   ISSN 0884-1136
BX8601
ENSIGN. 1971. m. $10. Church of Jesus Christ of Latter-day Saints, Corporation of the President, 50 E. North Temple, Salt Lake City, UT 84150. TEL 801-240-2947. FAX 801-240-1727. Ed. Jay M. Todd. charts; illus. circ. 585.
   Formerly (until 1979): Ensign of the Church of Jesus Christ of Latter-day Saints (ISSN 0013-8606)
   Description: Contains news of the Church, "Message of the First Presidency," and articles pertaining to all adult church members worldwide.

ENSIGN TALKING BOOK. see *HANDICAPPED — Visually Impaired*

298.7   US
ESTRELLA DE ESPERANZA. (Text in Spanish) 1967. m. $3.75. Rod and Staff Publishers, Inc., State Rte. 172, Crockett, KY 41413. TEL 606-522-4348. FAX 606-522-4896. Ed. Eugene G. Cambell. circ. 6,800. (back issues avail.)

200   CN   ISSN 0014-3375
EVANGELICAL TRUTH. (Text in English, Ukrainian) 1939. bi-m. free. Rev. M. Fesenko, Ed. & Pub., 26 Robina Ave., Toronto, ON M6C 3Y6, Canada. TEL 416-654-4870. bk.rev.; illus. circ. 1,500.

DER EVANGELISCHE BUCHBERATER. see *LITERARY AND POLITICAL REVIEWS*

200   US   ISSN 0014-3626
EVANGELIST (PASADENA). (Editions in Arabic, Armenian, Dutch, English, German) 1960. q. £L5($2) Bible Land Mission, 814 E. Claremont St., Pasadena, CA 91104. TEL 818-798-7177. FAX 818-791-0036. Ed. Samuel Doctorian. bk.rev.; illus. circ. 20,000.

248.4   SA   ISSN 0014-7044
FAITH FOR DAILY LIVING; a guide to confident Christian living. (Text in English) 1960. bi-m. free. Faith for Daily Living Foundation, P.O. Box 3737, Durban, Natal, South Africa. Ed. Arnold J. Walker. circ. 120,000 (controlled).

289.73   CN   ISSN 0014-7303
FAMILY LIFE. 1968. m. (11/yr.) $9. (Amish Church) Pathway Publishing Corporation, Rte. 4, Aylmer, ON N5H 2R3, Canada. bk.rev.; illus. circ. 21,000. (also avail. in microform from UMI; reprint service avail. from UMI)
—UMI.

266   US
FAR EAST REPORTER (HOUSTON). vol.22, 1976. bi-m. $5. Church of Houston Baptist International, Inc., Box 3333, Houston, TX 77253-3333. TEL 713-820-9111. Ed. Deanza Brock. illus. circ. 200,000.

200   US   ISSN 0014-8830
FATIMA FINDINGS;* the smallest newspaper on earth for the greatest cause in heaven. 1946. m. $5 (foreign $5.50). Reparation Society of the Immaculate Heart of Mary, Inc., Fatima House, 8006 Caliburn Ct., Pasadena, MD 21122-6478. TEL 410-685-7403. Ed. Anna C. Pertsch. circ. 4,000 (controlled). (back issues avail.) **Document type:** newspaper.
   Description: Spreads knowledge of and devotion to Our Blessed Lady of Fatima and her message.

200   US   ISSN 0014-9837
FELLOWSHIP IN PRAYER. 1949. bi-m. $16. Fellowship in Prayer, Inc., 291 Witherspoon St., Princeton, NJ 08542-3269. TEL 609-924-6863. FAX 609-924-6910. Ed. Mary Ford-Grabowsky. bk.rev. circ. 10,000. (back issues avail.)

299 133.4   UK
FENRIR. q. Thormynd Press, P.O. Box 700, Shrewsbury, Shropshire, England.
   Description: Satanic magazine.

289.9   US
FIERY SYNTHESIS. 1965. 12/yr. donation. Aquarian Educational Group, Box 267, Sedona, AZ 86339. FAX 520-282-0514. Ed. Torkom Saraydarian. bk.rev. circ. 400.
   Formerly: Blue Aquarius.

FINDHORN FOUNDATION. GUEST PROGRAMME. see *NEW AGE PUBLICATIONS*

FISH DRUM. see *LITERATURE*

289   US   ISSN 0015-9182
FOURSQUARE WORLD ADVANCE. 1923. bi-m. free. International Church of the Foursquare Gospel, 1910 Sunset Blvd., Ste. 200, Los Angeles, CA 90026-3282. TEL 213-484-2400. FAX 213-413-3824. Ed. Ron Williams. bk.rev.; illus. circ. 95,000.
   Formerly: Foursquare Magazine.

200   US   ISSN 0016-0334
FREE CHURCH OF SCOTLAND. MONTHLY RECORD. (Text in English and Gaelic) 1843. m. £10 (typically set in Oct.). Free Church of Scotland Publications Committee, 15 N. Bank St., Edinburgh EH1 2LS, Scotland. TEL 0131-226-5286. FAX 0131-220-0597. Ed. Ronald C. Christie. bk.rev. circ. 6,500. (tabloid format; reprint service avail. from UMI)

FREEDOM MAGAZINE. see *JOURNALISM*

289.6   UK   ISSN 0016-1268
FRIEND; a Quaker weekly journal. 1843. w. £53. Friend Publications Ltd., Drayton House, 30 Gordon St., London WC1H 0BQ, England. TEL 0171-387-7549. FAX 0171-387-9382. Ed. Deborah Padfield. adv. contact: George Penaluna. bk.rev.; illus.; index; circ. 5,250 (paid). (also avail. in microform from WMP) **Document type:** newspaper.

289.6 248.82   US   ISSN 0009-4102
FRIEND. 1971. m. $8. Church of Jesus Christ of Latter-day Saints, Corporation of the President, 50 E. North Temple, Salt Lake City, UT 84150. TEL 801-240-2947. FAX 801-240-1727. Ed. Vivian Paulsen. bk.rev.; illus.; index. circ. 210,000. (also avail. in Braille) **Supersedes:** Children's Friend.
   Description: Contains stories and activities for children, or parents with children - ages 3 to 11.

267   UK   ISSN 0071-9587
BX7676.A1
FRIENDS HISTORICAL SOCIETY. JOURNAL. 1903. a. £5($10) to individuals; institutions £8 ($20). Friends Historical Society, c/o Friends House, Euston Rd., London NW1 2BJ, England. Ed. Gerald A.J. Hodgett. adv.; bk.rev. circ. 500. **Indexed:** Amer.Hist.& Life, Br.Hum.Ind., Hist.Abstr. **Document type:** academic/scholarly publication.
—BLDSC (4755.400000).

289.6   US   ISSN 0016-1322
BX7601
FRIENDS JOURNAL. m. $21. (Religious Society of Friends) Friends Publishing Corp., 1501 Cherry St., Philadelphia, PA 19102. TEL 215-241-7277. FAX 215-568-1377. Ed. Vinton Deming. adv.; bk.rev.; film rev.; illus.; index. circ. 9,500. (also avail. in microform from UMI; reprint service avail. from UMI)
—Faxon; UMI.
   Formed by the merger (1827-1955): Friend (ISSN 0362-8957); (1902-1955): Friends Intelligencer (ISSN 0362-8965)
   Description: Includes articles on peace, social concerns, Quaker history, and spirituality. Contains poetry, news, humor, reports and classified advertisements on schools, publications, services and employment opportunities.

200   UK   ISSN 0016-1357
FRIENDS' QUARTERLY. N.S 1946. q. £8. Headley Bros. Ltd., Ashford, Kent TN24 8HH, England. TEL 01233-623131. Ed. David Blamires. cum.index every 3 yrs. cert. 1,175. (also avail. in microform from WMP) **Indexed:** Bibl.Engl.Lang.& Lit., Br.Hum.Ind. **Document type:** academic/scholarly publication.
—BLDSC (4038.300000).

FRIENDS' QUARTERLY (ENFIELD). see *MUSEUMS AND ART GALLERIES*

289.6   UK   ISSN 0016-1365
FRIENDS WORLD NEWS. 1939. s-a. free to contributors. Friends World Committee for Consultation, 4 Byng Pl., London WC1E 7JH, England. TEL 0171-388-0497. FAX 0171-383-3722. Ed. Roger B. Sturge. bk.rev.; illus. circ. 9,100. **Indexed:** CERDIC. **Document type:** bulletin.
   Description: Presents articles from Quakers worldwide.

200   US   ISSN 0042-8264
FULL GOSPEL BUSINESS MEN'S VOICE. 1953. m. $7.95. Full Gospel Business Men's Fellowship International, 3150 Bear St., Box 5050, Costa Mesa, CA 92626. TEL 714-754-1400. FAX 714-557-9916. Ed. Jerry Jensen. bk.rev. circ. 500,000. (back issues avail.)
   Description: Designed to reach business men for Christ. Used by the organization's chapters and individuals as a witness tool.

289   SA   ISSN 0016-3988
GALAMUKANI!. (Text in Chichewa) 1957. m. R.9.50. Watch Tower Bible & Tract Society, Private Bag X2067, Krugersdorp 1740, South Africa. TEL 011-761-1000. FAX 011-764-4749. charts, illus.; index. circ. 3,500.

299.935   SZ   ISSN 0016-5867
GEGENWART. 1939. bi-m. 60 SFr. (foreign 65 SFr.). Baerenplatz 2, CH-3011 Bern, Switzerland. Ed. Gerold Aregger. adv.: B&W page 250 SFr. bk.rev.; index. circ. 1,800. **Document type:** academic/scholarly publication.

200   UK   ISSN 0072-0666
GENERAL CONFERENCE OF THE NEW CHURCH. YEARBOOK. 1789. a. £3 (typically set in Jan.). General Conference of the New Church, c/o G.S. Kuphal, Ed., 20 Red Barn Rd., Brightlingsea, Colchester, Essex CO7 0SH, England. TEL 01206-302932. circ. 500. **Document type:** corporate report.
   Description: Contains annual reports of the Church and directory information about congregations and members.

RELIGIONS AND THEOLOGY — OTHER DENOMINATIONS AND SECTS

289.9 362.7   US   ISSN 0885-7776
GENERAL COUNCIL OF THE ASSEMBLIES OF GOD. MEMOS; leadership magazine for Women's Ministries Auxiliary. 1956. q. $5.50. Gospel Publishing House, 1445 Boonville Ave., Springfield, MO 65802-1894. TEL 417-862-2781. Ed. Linda Upton. bk.rev. circ. 15,000.
   Formerly: Missionettes Memos.

289.9   US
GEORGIAN ANNUAL. 1989. a. $35. Georgian Church, 1908 Verde St., Bakersfield, CA 93304. TEL 805-323-3309. Eds. Dean & Lady Fauna. adv.; bk.rev.; illus. (back issues avail.)

289.9   US
GEORGIAN MONTHLY. 1976. 12/yr. $8. Georgian Church, 1908 Verde St., Bakersfield, CA 93304. TEL 805-323-3309. Eds. Dean & Lady Fauna. adv.; bk.rev.; illus. (back issues avail.)
   Formerly: Georgian Newsletter.

289   US   ISSN 0017-0739
GLAD TIDINGS OF GOOD THINGS. (Not avail. in printed format) 1953. q. free. Church of Christ, 12314 S.E. 104th Ct., Portland, OR 97266-7904. TEL 510-724-4152. Ed. John Bessire. circ. 270. (Braille)
   Description: Religious publication for the blind.

266   US   ISSN 0731-1125
GLOBAL CHURCH GROWTH; strategies for today's leader. 1964. q. $19.50 to individuals; students $18. Church Growth Center, 1230 US Hwy. 6, Box 145, Corunna, IN 46730. TEL 219-281-2452. FAX 219-281-2167. Ed. Kent Hunter. adv. contact: John Hinkley. bk.rev.; stat.; cum.index every 5 yrs. circ. 1,200. **Indexed:** CERDIC, Chr.Per.Ind. **Document type:** academic/scholarly publication.
   Former titles: Global Church Growth Bulletin (ISSN 0273-7183); Church Growth Bulletin (ISSN 0009-6385)
   Description: Focuses on world evangelization and missiology.

GNOSIS; a journal of the Western inner traditions. see *NEW AGE PUBLICATIONS*

291 299   SW   ISSN 0282-0889
GNOSIS. 1984. q. SEK 200. Bjoern Sahlin, Johannesberg, S-820 60 Delsbo, Sweden. TEL 46-43-04-29-1.

289.7   US   ISSN 0017-2340
BX8101
GOSPEL HERALD. 1908. w. $29.50. Mennonite Publishing House, 616 Walnut Ave., Scottdale, PA 15683-1999. TEL 412-887-8500. FAX 412-887-3111. Ed. J. Lorne Peachey. illus. circ. 18,500.
   Description: Covers weekly news and opinions of the Mennonite Church.

GREGORIOS O PALAMAS. see *HISTORY — History Of Europe*

248.83   US   ISSN 0017-5226
GUIDE (HAGERSTOWN). 1953. w. $35.97. (Seventh-day Adventist Church) Review and Herald Publishing Association, 55 W. Oak Ridge Dr., Hagerstown, MD 21740. TEL 301-791-7000. Ed. Carolyn Rathbun. adv.; illus.; index. circ. 38,000. (also avail. in microfilm from UMI; reprint service avail. from UMI)
   Description: Aimed at young readers, ages 10-16.

266   CN
HALLELUJAH! (VANCOUVER). 1949. bi-m. Can.$10. Bible Holiness Movement, Box 223, Sta. A, Vancouver, B.C. V6C 2M3, Canada. TEL 604-498-3895. Ed. Wesley H. Wakefield. bk.rev.; illus. circ. 5,000. (back issues avail.) **Document type:** consumer publication.
   Formerly (until 1990): Truth on Fire (ISSN 0821-6371)
   Description: Magazine of aggressive evangelical Christianity and social activism.

281   AG   ISSN 0017-8640
HAY GUETRON.* (Text in Armenian and Spanish) 1932. m. $3. Institucion Administrativa de la Iglesia Armenia, Acevedo 1353, Buenos Aires, Argentina. adv.; abstr.; bibl.; illus. circ. 1,300.

289.9   US
HEALING THOUGHTS. 6/yr. $18. Plainfield Christian Science Church (Independent), 905 Prospect Ave., Box 5619, Plainfield, NJ 07060. TEL 908-756-4669.

299   CN   ISSN 1188-5947
HECATE'S LOOM; Canada's national pagan magazine. (Text in English, French) 1986. q. Can.$11.15 (U.S. $13.18; elsewhere Can.$18.24). Hecate's Loom Publishing Collective, P.O. Box 5206, Sta. B, Victoria, BC V8R 6N4, Canada. TEL 604-477-8488. FAX 604-721-1029. E-mail: un837@freenet.victoria.bc.ca. Ed. Yvonne Owens. adv.: B&W page Can.$140; color ad; adv. contact: Patricia Van Nus. bk.rev.; illus. circ. 1,400. **Indexed:** Can.B.P.I. **Document type:** consumer publication.
   Description: Canada's national Pagan news and networking journal, providing an independent communications forum for Pagans and Witches across Canada and internationally.

281.5   CN   ISSN 0701-8290
HERALD (WINNIPEG)/VISNYK. (Text in English, Ukrainian) 1924. m. $15 (foreign $16). Ecclesia Publishing Co., Ltd., Nine St. Johns Ave., Winnineg, MB R2W 1G8, Canada. TEL 204-582-0996. Ed. Rev. S. Jarmus.

289.5   US   ISSN 0018-0475
HERALD OF CHRISTIAN SCIENCE. Swedish edition: Kristen Vetenskaps Herold (ISSN 0145-7543). Spanish edition: Heraldo de la Ciencia Cristiana (ISSN 0439-0148); Dutch edition: Heraut van de Christelijke Wetenschap (ISSN 0145-756X); German edition: Herold der Christlichen Wissenschaft (ISSN 0145-7578); Italian edition: Araldo della Scienza Cristiana (ISSN 0145-7519); Portuguese edition: Arauto da Ciencia Crista (ISSN 0145-7489); Danish edition: Kristen Videnskabs Herold (US ISSN 0145-7551) Greek edition (US ISSN 0145-9511) Indonesian edition: Bentara Ilmuipengetahuan Kristen (US ISSN 0409-0810) Japanese edition (US ISSN 0145-8019) Norwegian edition: Kristen Vitenskaps Herold (US ISSN 0145-7535) 1903. m. (French, German, Spanish and Portuguese eds.); q. (other eds. and English-Braille). $29 for monthly eds.; quarterly eds. $6; English-Braille ed. $1. Christian Science Publishing Society, Box 11390, Des Moines, IA 50340-1390. TEL 617-450-2000. Ed. William E. Moody.

289.73   US   ISSN 0300-8851
HEROLD DER WAHRHEIT. (Text in English and German) 1912. m. $6. Amish Mennonite Publishing Association, c/o Roy Beachy, Sec.-Treas., 2010 110th St., Kalona, IA 52247. Eds. Ben Raber, Cephos Kauffman. index. circ. 975.

266   GW
HERRNHUTER BOTE. 1949. m. DM.36. Evangelische Brueder-Unitaet, Postfach 21, 02745 Herrnhut, Germany. TEL 035873-48716. FAX 035873-48799. Ed. Martin Theile. adv.; bk.rev.; illus. circ. 1,650. **Document type:** newsletter.
   Formerly: Bruederbote (ISSN 0724-4533)

289.9   US   ISSN 0018-120X
HICALL. 1936. w. $5.20. (General Council of the Assemblies of God) Gospel Publishing House, 1445 Boonville, Springfield, MO 65802. TEL 417-862-2781. Ed. Deanna Harris. circ. 78,000.
   Description: Aimed at adolescents aged 12-17.

HIGH ADVENTURE; a Royal Rangers magazine for boys. see *CHILDREN AND YOUTH — For*

HUMANIST IN CANADA. see *PHILOSOPHY*

200   UK
I C F QUARTERLY PAPERS. 1963. q. £15 (foreign £23). Industrial Churches Forum, 86 Leadenhall St., London EC3A 3DH, England. TEL 0171-283-6120. FAX 0171-549-9161. Ed. D. Welbourn. bk.rev. circ. 2,000.
   Formerly: I C F Quarterly (ISSN 0018-8913)
   Description: Contains articles helping industry, commerce and finance to operate within a framework of Christian principles and values to the ultimate benefit of all employees, management, shareholders, customers and the whole community.

299.93   US
I G A S JOURNAL.* (International General Assembly of Spiritualists) 1931. bi-m. $15. Light of Divine Truth Foundation, c/o Rev. Betty Latham, 304 Boulevard, Florence, NJ 08518. TEL 609-499-0542. adv. circ. 1,000.

289.9   US   ISSN 0748-2280
I S K C O N WORLD REVIEW; newspaper of the Hare Krishna Movement. 1980. bi-m. $18 (foreign $20) (effective 1995). International Society for Krishna Consciousness, Box 238, Alachua, FL 32615. TEL 904-462-5054. FAX 904-462-5056. Ed. Mukunda Goswami. adv.: page $401; 10 x 15 1/2; adv. contact: Kunti Dasi. bk.rev.; circ. 10,000 (paid). (tabloid format; back issues avail.) **Document type:** newspaper.

ICONOGRAPHY OF RELIGIONS. SECTION 2, NEW ZEALAND. see *ART*

ICONOGRAPHY OF RELIGIONS. SECTION 5, AUSTRALIA. see *ART*

ICONOGRAPHY OF RELIGIONS. SECTION 7, AFRICA. see *ART*

ICONOGRAPHY OF RELIGIONS. SECTION 8, ARCTIC PEOPLES. see *ART*

ICONOGRAPHY OF RELIGIONS. SECTION 9, SOUTH AMERICA. see *ART*

ICONOGRAPHY OF RELIGIONS. SECTION 10, NORTH AMERICA. see *ART*

ICONOGRAPHY OF RELIGIONS. SECTION 11, ANCIENT AMERICA. see *ART*

ICONOGRAPHY OF RELIGIONS. SECTION 12, EAST AND CENTRAL ASIA. see *ART*

ICONOGRAPHY OF RELIGIONS. SECTION 13, INDIAN RELIGIONS. see *ART*

ICONOGRAPHY OF RELIGIONS. SECTION 14, IRAN. see *ART*

ICONOGRAPHY OF RELIGIONS. SECTION 15, MESOPOTAMIA AND THE NEAR EAST. see *ART*

ICONOGRAPHY OF RELIGIONS. SECTION 16, EGYPT. see *ART*

ICONOGRAPHY OF RELIGIONS. SECTION 17, GREECE AND ROME. see *ART*

ICONOGRAPHY OF RELIGIONS. SECTION 19, ANCIENT EUROPE. see *ART*

ICONOGRAPHY OF RELIGIONS. SECTION 20, MANICHAEISM. see *ART*

ICONOGRAPHY OF RELIGIONS. SECTION 21, MANDAEISM. see *ART*

220 289.9   SA   ISSN 0019-008X
IMBONISELO. (Text in Xhosa) 1955. s-m. R.19. Watch Tower Bible & Tract Society, Private Bag X2067, Krugersdorp 1740, South Africa. TEL 011-761-1000. FAX 011-764-4749. charts; illus.; index. circ. 16,200.

INDIAN LIFE. see *ETHNIC INTERESTS*

220 289.9   SA   ISSN 0019-0241
INQABAYOKULINDA. (Text in Zulu) 1950. s-m. R.19. Watch Tower Bible & Tract Society, Private Bag X2067, Krugersdorp 1740, South Africa. TEL 011-761-1000. FAX 011-764-4749. charts; illus.; index. circ. 36,500.

200   US
INSIGHT (LOVES PARK). 1971. m. Slavic Gospel Association, 6151 Commonwealth Dr., Loves Park, IL 61111. TEL 815-282-8900. FAX 815-282-8901. charts; illus. circ. 60,000. **Document type:** newsletter.
   Incorporates (1993-1994): Reflections (Loves Park); **Former titles (until 1993):** Breakthrough; Which incorporated (1927-1989): EuroVision Advance; Which was formerly: Slavic Gospel News (ISSN 0049-0709)

RELIGIONS AND THEOLOGY — OTHER DENOMINATIONS AND SECTS

261   US   ISSN 0073-9456
INSTITUTE OF MENNONITE STUDIES SERIES. 1961. irreg. price varies. (Associated Mennonite Biblical Seminaries) Faith & Life Press, 718 Main St., Box 347, Newton, KS 67114. TEL 316-283-5100. Ed. Susan Janzen. **Document type:** academic/scholarly publication.

289.9   US   ISSN 0161-1380
INTEGRAL YOGA. 1969. q. $15. Integral Yoga Publications, Satchidananda Ashram-Yogaville, Rt. 1, Box 1720, Buckingham, VA 23921. TEL 804-969-1200. FAX 804-969-1303. Ed. Kumari de Sachy. adv.; bk.rev.; circ. 800. **Document type:** newsletter.

INTERNATIONAL JOURNAL OF HUMANITIES AND PEACE; synergy, synthesis, transformation. see *HUMANITIES: COMPREHENSIVE WORKS*

289.9   US   ISSN 0031-4900
INTERNATIONAL PENTECOSTAL HOLINESS ADVOCATE. 1917. m. $9.75. International Pentecostal Holiness Church, Box 12609, Oklahoma City, OK 73157. TEL 405-787-7110. FAX 405-789-3957. (Subscr. to: Advocate Press, Box 98, Franklin Springs, GA 30639) Ed. Shirley Spencer. bk.rev.; bibl.; charts; illus. circ. 3,000. (also avail. in microform; back issues avail.) **Indexed:** CERDIC.

299   US   ISSN 0886-6910
ISKCON REVIEW; academic perspectives on the Hare Krishna movement. 1985. a. $6. Institute for Vaishnaya Studies, c/o Steven J. Gelberg, 41 West Allens Lane, Philadelphia, PA 19119. TEL 215-242-6578. bk.rev. circ. 1,200. (back issues avail.)

291 283   US   ISSN 0741-0352
ISSUES (SAN FRANCISCO). 1978. bi-m. free. (Jews for Jesus) A Messianic Jewish Perspective, Box 424885, San Francisco, CA 94142-4885. TEL 415-864-2600. FAX 415-552-8325. Ed. Susan Perlman. bk.rev./ circ. 40,000 (controlled). (back issues avail.) **Document type:** trade publication.

294.44   II   ISSN 0021-4043
B162.5
JAIN JOURNAL. (Text in English) 1966. q. Rs.70. Jain Bhawan, P-25 Kalakar St., Calcutta 700007, India. Ed. Ganesh Lalwani. adv.; bk.rev.; bibl.; illus.; index. circ. 1,000.
—UnCover.

299.56 952   JA   ISSN 0304-1042
BL2202
JAPANESE JOURNAL OF RELIGIOUS STUDIES. (Text in English) 1960. q. 3500 Yen($25) to individuals; institutions 5000 Yen ($35). Nanzan University, Nanzan Institute for Religion and Culture, 18 Yamazato-cho, Showa-ku, Nagoya 466, Japan. TEL 052-832-3111. FAX 052-833-6157. Ed. Paul L. Swanson. adv.; bk.rev.; illus.; stat.; index, cum.index. circ. 600. (reprint service avail. from UMI) **Indexed:** Arts & Hum.Cit.Ind., Curr.Cont., Rel.& Theol.Abstr. (1989-), Rel.Ind.One. **Document type:** academic/scholarly publication.
—BLDSC (4658.650000); Faxon; SWETS; UMI; UnCover.
Formerly: Contemporary Religions in Japan (ISSN 0010-7557)
Description: Presents academic studies of Japan's religions.

JAPANESE RELIGIONS. see *RELIGIONS AND THEOLOGY*

289.9   US   ISSN 0075-3602
JEHOVAH'S WITNESSES YEARBOOK. Variant title: Yearbook of Jehovah's Witnesses. (Text in 19 languages) 1927. a. (Jehovah's Witnesses, Governing Body) Watchtower Bible and Tract Society of New York, Inc., 25 Columbia Hts., Brooklyn, NY 11201. TEL 718-625-3600. (International Bible Students Association) charts; illus.; index. circ. 3,214,122. **Document type:** corporate report.
Description: Reports on Jehovah's Witnesses missionary and relief activities worldwide.

291   US   ISSN 0740-5901
JEWS FOR JESUS NEWSLETTER. 1973. m. free. Jews for Jesus, 60 Haight St., San Francisco, CA 94102. TEL 415-864-2600. FAX 415-552-8325. E-mail: Site addr.: http://jews.for.jesu.org Ed. Ceil Rosen. bk.rev.; illus.; circ. 135,000 (controlled). (also avail. in microfilm) **Document type:** newsletter.

JOTTINGS. see *HANDICAPPED — Visually Impaired*

299.935   US   ISSN 0021-8235
BP595.A1
JOURNAL FOR ANTHROPOSOPHY. 1965. s-a. $12 (foreign $15). Anthroposophical Society in America, 529 Grant Pl., Chicago, IL 60614-3705. TEL 512-858-1669. FAX 512-858-4080. (Subscr. to: 3700 S. Ranch Rd., Ste. 12, Dripping Springs, TX 78620) Ed. Hilmar Moore. adv.; bk.rev. circ. 1,800.
—UnCover.
Description: Contains articles by international contributors who directly or indirectly reflect the impact of the spiritual world on our physical world.

289   US   ISSN 1058-3084
BX6181
JOURNAL FROM THE RADICAL REFORMATION. 1991. q. $20. Church of God, General Conference, Box 100000, Morrow, GA 30260. TEL 800-347-4261. FAX 404-362-9307. Eds. Kent Ross, Anthony Buzzard. adv.; bk.rev. circ. 450. **Document type:** academic/scholarly publication.

377.8   US   ISSN 0021-8480
LC586.A3
JOURNAL OF ADVENTIST EDUCATION. 1939. bi-m. (except July-Sep.). $15.75. General Conference of Seventh-day Adventists, 12501 Old Columbia Pike, Silver Spring, MD 20904-6600. TEL 301-680-5075. FAX 301-622-9627. TELEX 440186. Ed. Beverly J. Rumble. adv.; bk.rev.; charts; illus.; index; circ. 9,000 (paid). (back issues avail.; reprint service avail. from UMI) **Document type:** academic/scholarly publication.
Formerly: Journal of True Education.

297.89   CN   ISSN 0838-0430
BP300
JOURNAL OF BAHA'I STUDIES. 1988. q. Can.$20 to individuals; institutions $30. Association for Baha'i Studies, 34 Copernicus St., Ottawa, ON K1N 7K4, Canada. TEL 613-233-1903. FAX 613-233-3644. Ed.Bd. bk.rev.; index. circ. 2,300. (also avail. in diskette format; avail. on diskette; back issues avail.) **Document type:** academic/scholarly publication.
Refereed Serial

299.51   CN   ISSN 0737-769X
BL1802
JOURNAL OF CHINESE RELIGIONS. 1975. a. $15 to individuals; institutions $25. Society for the Study of Chinese Religions, c/o Linda Penkwer, Treas., Department of Religious Studies, 2604 CL, University of Pittsburgh, Pittsburgh, PA 15260. TEL 412-624-2277. FAX 412-624-5994. Ed. Patricia E. Karetzky. bk.rev. circ. 300. **Document type:** academic/scholarly publication.
—UnCover.
Formerly (until 1982): Society for the Study of Chinese Religions. Bulletin.
Refereed Serial

JOURNAL OF EARLY CHRISTIAN STUDIES. see *RELIGIONS AND THEOLOGY*

289.3   US   ISSN 0094-7342
BX8601
JOURNAL OF MORMON HISTORY. 1974. a. $15 membership. Mormon History Association, Box 7010, University Sta., Provo, UT 84602. FAX 801-378-4048. Ed. Lavina Fielding Anderson. circ. 1,000. **Indexed:** Amer.Hist.& Life, CERDIC, Hist.Abstr.
●Also available online. Vendor(s): Knight-Ridder, Inc. (File nos.38,39).
—UnCover.
Description: Scholarly articles dealing with Mormon history.

294.6   II   ISSN 0379-8194
BL2017
JOURNAL OF SIKH STUDIES. (Text in English) 1974. s-a. $20. (Guru Nanak Dev University, Department of Guru Nanak Studies) Guru Nanak Dev University Press, Amritsar 143 005, India. TEL 62450. Ed. Jaswinder Kaur Dhillon. adv.; bk.rev. circ. 1,000.
—BLDSC (5064.470000).
Description: Aims to promote Sikh studies as a scientific discipline.

200   UK   ISSN 0022-5703
JOY & LIGHT. 1843. 3/yr. £5. Lord's Day Observance Society, 6 Sherman Rd., Bromley, Kent BR1 3JH, England. Ed. J.G. Roberts. bk.rev. circ. 13,000. **Document type:** bulletin.
Description: Describes the work and covers all matters of the society.

289.9   US   ISSN 0022-6718
JUNIOR TRAILS. 1926. w. $5.20. (General Council of the Assemblies of God) Gospel Publishing House, 1445 Boonville Ave., Springfield, MO 65802. TEL 417-862-2781. Ed. Sinda S. Zinn. circ. 65,000.
Description: Fictional, illustrated sketches, verse, and informational articles on Christian ethics as they pertain to the school, family, and social lives of fifth and sixth graders.

200   US
KEEP. 1993. q. Luna Ventures, Box 398, Suisun, CA 94585-0398. TEL 707-425-6657. **Document type:** newsletter.

291   II   ISSN 0047-3367
KERALA SABHA. (Text in Malayalam) 1970. m. Rs.12($0.75) Better Life Movement, Better Life Center, Aloor, Kallettumkara, Kerala 680 683, India. Ed. Fr. Thomas Vazhapilly. adv.; bk.rev.; film rev.; play rev.; abstr.; bibl.; charts; illus.; pat.; stat.; tr.lit.; cum.index; circ. 2,000 (controlled).

281.7 916.206   UA
AL-KERAZEH. English edition: El-Keraza English Magazine - Preaching. (Text in Arabic) w. Coptic Orthodox Church, St. Mark's Cathedral, Anba Ruess, 222 Sharia Ramses, P.O. Box 9035, Abbasiya, Cairo, Egypt. TEL 02-2825983. TELEX 23281.

281.9   GR   ISSN 1105-2139
KLERONOMIA. (Text in English, French, German, Greek, Italian) 1969. 2/yr. $32. Patriarchal Institute for Patristic Studies, Heptapyrgiou 64, 546 34 Thessaloniki, Greece. Ed. Panagiotis C. Christou. bk.rev.; bibl. circ. 2,400. **Indexed:** CERDIC. **Document type:** academic/scholarly publication.
—BLDSC (5099.245000); SWETS.

KOINONIA PARTNERS. NEWSLETTER. see *SOCIAL SERVICES AND WELFARE*

KONGZI YANJIU/STUDIES ON CONFUCIUS. see *PHILOSOPHY*

299   UK
KOSMON UNITY. 1946. s-a. £5 for 2 yrs. (Confraternity of Faithists) Kosmon Press, BM-KCKP, London WC1N 3XX, England. (Dist. in U.S. by: Kosmon Service Center, Box 664, Salt Lake City, UT 84110) Ed. Peter Andrews. bk.rev.

289.9   US   ISSN 0882-4606
KOSMON VOICE. 1977. bi-m. $13.75 (effecive 1995). Universal Faithists of Kosmon, Box 654, McCook, NE 69001. TEL 308-345-6369. Ed. Erma J. Lee. bk.rev. circ. 100. **Document type:** newsletter.
Formerly: Kosmon News.
Description: Covers self-mind and spiritual improvement, vegetarian diet, recipes, health, meditation, parenting, seeker discipline, letters, articles, meeting news, poetry, and science relating to the group's concerns.

299   II   ISSN 0047-3693
B5134.K754
KRISHNAMURTI FOUNDATION. BULLETIN. (Text in English) 1970. 3/yr. Rs.22($10) Krishnamurti Foundation (India), c/o Dr. Radhika Herzberger, 64-65 Greenways Rd., Madras 600028, India. TEL 4937803. Ed. Dr. Radhika Herzberger. bk.rev. circ. 1,300. **Document type:** bulletin.

289.6   SW   ISSN 0345-6005
KVAEKARTIDSKRIFT. (Text in Swedish) 1949. q. SEK 80 in Denmark, Finland, Norway, Sweden; elsewhere SEK 100. Vaennernas Samfund i Sverige - Society of Friends of Sweden (Quakers), P.O. Box 9166, S-102 72 Stockholm, Sweden. TEL 46-33-12-27-772. Ed. Ingmar Hollsing. bk.rev. circ. 700. (reprint service avail. from CAS)
Formerly (until 1974): Nordisk Kvaekartidskrift (ISSN 0029-1404)

RELIGIONS AND THEOLOGY — OTHER DENOMINATIONS AND SECTS

299.935   GW   ISSN 0174-6995
LAZARUS. 1983. q. DM.10. Lazarus Verlag und Buchhandel GmbH, Fridtjof-Nansen-Str. 7, 24223 Raisdorf, Germany. TEL 04307-6182. Ed. Monika Neve. adv.: page DM.400. bk.rev. **Document type:** bulletin.

255   FR   ISSN 0750-3695
LETTER FROM TAIZE. (Editions in Dutch, English, French, German, Italian and Spanish) 1970. bi-m. 30 F. (foreign 40 F.). Communaute de Taize, 71250 Cluny, France.

289.9   UK   ISSN 0024-1792
LIBERAL CATHOLIC; magazine of religious thought and practice in the world today. 1924. 3/yr. £7. Liberal Catholic Church, Hadleigh View, Kellington Rd., Canvey Island, Essex SS8 8EL, England. TEL 0268-685499. Ed. Rev. S. David Sandercock. adv.; bk.rev.; illus. circ. 450. **Document type:** bulletin.

289.7   CN   ISSN 0840-5972
LE LIEN DES FRERES MENNONITES. (Text in French) 1981. m. (11/yr.). Can.$8. Conference of Mennonite Brethren Churches of Canada, Board of Communications, 3-169 Riverton Ave., Winnipeg, MB R2L 2E5, Canada. TEL 204-669-6575. FAX 204-654-1865. Ed. Jim Coggins. adv. contact: Susan Brandt. bk.rev.; illus. circ. 700.

200   UK   ISSN 0308-3624
LIFELINE. 1976. m. £12.40 (rest of Europe £15.90; N. and S. America £22.30; Asia and Australia £23.60). General Conference of the New Church, c/o G.S. Kuphal, 20 Red Barn Rd., Brightlingsea, Colchester, Essex CO7 OSH, England. TEL 01206-302932. (Subscr. to: New Church House, 34 John Dalton St., Manchester M2 6LE, England. TEL 0161-834-4192) Ed. P.L. Johnson. circ. 600.
  Description: Deals with religious topics, news of the church and other matters of interest to members and friends.

299.93   US
THE LIVING LIGHT PHILOSOPHY. 1968. q. $5. Serenity Spiritualist Association, 322 Upper Rd., San Rafael, CA 94903. TEL 415-472-3633. Ed. Ronald C. Cavender. circ. 300.
  Formerly (until vol.1 no.1): Serenity Sentinel.

289.4   US
LOGOS (WEST CHESTER); the Swedenborg Foundation newsletter. 1968. 3/yr. membership only. Swedenborg Foundation, Inc., 320 N. Church St., West Chester, PA 19380. TEL 215-430-3222. FAX 215-430-7982. Ed. Daniel Eller. adv.; bk.rev.; circ. 5,000 (controlled). (reprint service avail. from SCH) **Indexed:** Met.Abstr., World Alum.Abstr. **Document type:** newsletter.

220   SA
LOLENI! (Text in Cibemba) 1981. m. R.9.50. Watch Tower Bible & Tract Society, Private Bag X2067, Krugersdorp 1740, South Africa. TEL 011-761-1000. FAX 011-764-4749. circ. 5,000.

281.62 914.706   US   ISSN 0024-6476
LOOYS. (Text in Armenian and English) 1953. m. (10/yr.). contributions. St. James Armenian Apostolic Church, 465 Mt. Auburn St, Watertown, MA 02172. TEL 617-923-8860. Eds. Rev. Dajad Davidian, Matilda Masrof. circ. 2,500. (looseleaf format) **Document type:** newsletter.

291   MY
MALAYSIA INTER-RELIGIOUS ORGANISATION. SUARA.* 1970. q. M.$3 (per issue). Malaysia Inter-Religious Organisation, 16 Road 49E, Petaling Jaya, Selangor, Malaysia. illus.

286   SA   ISSN 1019-5092
MARANATHA. (Text in English) 1940. bi-m. donation. South African Union Conference of Seventh-Day Adventists, P.O. Box 468, Bloemfontein 9300, South Africa. TEL 27-51-473871. FAX 27-51-488059. Ed. V.S. Wakaba. adv.; illus.; adv. circ. 13,592 (controlled). **Document type:** newsletter.
  Supersedes (in 1992): South African Union Lantern (ISSN 0038-2795) & Suid-Afrikaanse Unie-Lantern (ISSN 0377-0796)
  Description: Communicates news of church activities and provides devotional inspiration.

200   US   ISSN 0047-6064
MARTURION.* no.244, 1984. m. $1. People of the Living God, 2101 Prytania St., New Orleans, LA 70130. TEL 504-522-4821. Ed. H. Reigart Miller. bk.rev.; illus.

289.7   US   ISSN 0025-9330
THE MENNONITE. 1885. s-m. $25 in the U.S.; students $12.50; Canada $31; students $16. Mennonite Church, General Conference, 722 Main St., Box 347, Newton, KS 67114. TEL 316-283-5100. FAX 316-283-0454. Ed. Gordon Houser. adv.: page $575; trim 8 1/2 x 22. bk.rev.; illus.; index. circ. 8,500. (also avail. in microfilm from UMI) **Indexed:** G.Soc.Sci.& Rel.Per.Lit., Rel.Per.
  —UMI.
  Description: Devoted to informing and challenging the Christian fellowship.

289.7   CN   ISSN 0025-9349
MENNONITE BRETHREN HERALD. 1962. fortn. Can.$24. Conference of Mennonite Brethren Churches of Canada, Board of Communications, 3-169 Riverton Ave., Winnipeg, MB R2L 2E5, Canada. TEL 204-669-6575. FAX 204-654-1865. Ed. Jim Coggins. adv. contact: Susan Brandt. bk.rev.; illus.; index. circ. 14,500.

289.7 390   US   ISSN 0025-9357
BX8101
MENNONITE HISTORICAL BULLETIN. 1940. q. $20. Mennonite Church, Historical Committee, 1700 South Main St., Goshen, IN 46526. TEL 219-535-7477. Ed. John Sharp. bk.rev.; illus.; cum.index every 10 yrs. circ. 400. (also avail. in microfilm from UMI) **Indexed:** Amer.Hist.& Life, CERDIC, Hist.Abstr.
  —UMI.

289.7 209   US   ISSN 0025-9365
BX8101
MENNONITE LIFE. 1946. q. $15. Bethel College, 300 E. 27th St., N. Newton, KS 67117. TEL 316-283-2500. bk.rev.; bibl.; charts; illus.; cum.index every 5 yrs. circ. 650. (back issues avail.) **Indexed:** Amer.Bibl.Slavic & E.Eur.Stud., Amer.Hist.& Life, Hist.Abstr., Rel.& Theol.Abstr. (1989-), Rel.Ind.One.
  —UMI.
  Description: Articles related to Mennonite and Anabaptist history, faith, life and culture.

289.7   US   ISSN 0025-9373
BX8101
MENNONITE QUARTERLY REVIEW. (Text in English; occasionally in Dutch, German, and other languages.) 1927. q. $30. (Mennonite Historical Society) Goshen College, Goshen, IN 46526. TEL 219-535-7111. FAX 219-535-7438. (Co-sponsor: Associated Mennonite Biblical Seminary) Ed. John D. Roth. adv.; bk.rev.; bibl.; charts; illus.; index, cum.index every 10 yrs. circ. 1,000. **Indexed:** Amer.Bibl.Slavic & E.Eur.Stud., Amer.Hist.& Life, CERDIC, Hist.Abstr., Rel.& Theol.Abstr. (1989-), Rel.Ind.One, Rel.Per.
  —Faxon; SWETS; UnCover.
  Description: Scholarly journal covering Mennonite, Amish, Hutterian Brethren, Anabaptist, Radical Reformation, and related history and religious thought.

289.7   US   ISSN 0889-2156
MENNONITE WEEKLY REVIEW. 1923. w. $29. Herald Publishing Co., Inc., 129 W. Sixth St., Box 568, Newton, KS 67114. TEL 316-283-3670. FAX 316-283-6502. Ed. Robert M. Schrag. adv.; bk.rev.; circ. 10,400 (paid). (tabloid format) **Document type:** newspaper.

289.7   US   ISSN 0275-1178
BX8107
MENNONITE YEARBOOK AND DIRECTORY. 1905. a. $12.95. Mennonite Publishing House, 616 Walnut Ave., Scottdale, PA 15683-1999. TEL 412-887-8500. FAX 412-887-3111. Ed. James E. Horsch. **Document type:** directory.

289.7   CN   ISSN 0025-9314
MENNONITISCHE RUNDSCHAU/MENNONITE REVIEW. (Text in German) 1877. m. Can.$16. Conference of Mennonite Brethren Churches of Canada, Board of Communications, 3-169 Riverton Ave., Winnipeg, MB R2L 2E5, Canada. TEL 204-669-6575. FAX 204-654-1865. Ed. Lorina Marsch. adv.; bk.rev.; illus.; index. circ. 3,800.
  —UMI.

DER MERKURSTAB. see *MEDICAL SCIENCES*

286   SI   ISSN 0026-0371
MESSENGER. vol.18, 1968. bi-m. S.$3.50. Southeast Asia Union Mission of Seventh-Day Adventists, 251 Upper Serangoon Rd., Singapore, Singapore. Ed. Loralyn Horning. illus.; circ. 2,000 (controlled).

289.9   US
MESSENGER (DUNN). m. $6.50. Pentecostal Free Will Baptist Church, Inc., Box 1568, Dunn, NC 28335. TEL 910-892-4161. FAX 910-892-6876. Ed. George Thomas. bk.rev. circ. 4,500.

282   US   ISSN 0026-0355
BX7801
MESSENGER (ELGIN). 1851. m. $12.50. Church of the Brethren, General Services Commission, 1451 Dundee Ave., Elgin, IL 60120-1694. TEL 708-742-5100. FAX 708-742-6103. Ed. Kermon Thomasson; Pub. Dale E. Minnich. adv. contact: Nevin Dulabaum. bk.rev.; film rev.; index. circ. 23,000.

289.4   US
MESSENGER (JULIAN); official publication of the Swedenborgian Church. 1852. m. $12 (foreign $15). Swedenborgian Church, Department of Communications, Box 815, Julian, CA 92036. TEL 617-969-4240. FAX 617-964-3258. Ed. Patte Wheat Le Van. adv.; bk.rev.; charts; illus.; index. circ. 2,000.
  Formerly: New Church Messenger (ISSN 0028-4424)

281.1   US   ISSN 0893-0872
MESSENGER (WORCESTER). 1921? m. free. Armenian Church of Our Saviour, 87 Salisbury St., Worcester, MA 01609. TEL 508-756-2931. Ed. Harold A. Gregory. bk.rev. circ. 750. (back issues avail.) **Document type:** newsletter.

286.5   US
MESSENGER OF TRUTH. (Text in Ukrainian) 1927. bi-m $12. All-Ukrainian Evangelical Baptist Convention, 6751 Riverside Dr., Berwyn, IL 60402-2227. TEL 312-788-0999. Ed. O.R. Harbuziuk. bk.rev.; illus. circ. 5,000.

200   FR   ISSN 0026-0401
MESSIDOR; la tribune de Dieu-revue de la vie totale. 1951. q. 120 F.($25) Alliance Universelle, La Prefete, B.P. 27, 84140 Montfavet, France.

METROLINE. see *HOMOSEXUALITY*

289.9   SA
MIFOHAZA! (Text in Malagasy) 1992. q. R.4.25($5) Watch Tower Bible & Tract Society, Private Bag X2067, Krugersdorp 1740, South Africa. TEL 011-761-1000. FAX 011-764-4749. charts; illus.; index. circ. 12,400.

255   US   ISSN 0026-5802
MIRACULOUS MEDAL. 1928. q. free. Central Association of the Miraculous Medal, 475 E. Chelten Ave., Philadelphia, PA 19144. TEL 215-848-1010. Ed. Rev. John W. Gouldrick, C.M. illus.; circ. 340,000 (controlled).
  Description: Devotional magazine.

MIRROR (LANCASTER). see *HISTORY — History Of North And South America*

289.9   SA
MNARA WA MLINZI. (Text in Swahili) 1993. s-m. R.19($5) Watch Tower Bible & Tract Society, Private Bag X2067, Krugersdorp 1740, South Africa. TEL 011-761-1000. FAX 011-764-4749. charts; illus.; index. circ. 12,200.

200 289.9   SA   ISSN 0026-9093
MOLULA-QHOOA. (Text in Sesotho) 1954. s-m. R.19. Watch Tower Bible & Tract Society, Private Bag X2067, Krugersdorp 1740, South Africa. TEL 011-761-1000. FAX 011-764-4749. charts; illus.; index. circ. 14,500.

MOONCIRCLES. see *WOMEN'S INTERESTS*

RELIGIONS AND THEOLOGY — OTHER DENOMINATIONS AND SECTS

284.6 US ISSN 1041-0961
MORAVIAN (BETHLEHEM, 1856). 1856. m. (combined Jan.-Feb., July-Aug.). $9 to non-members (foreign $11). Moravian Church in America - North and South, Board of Publications, Box 1245, Bethlehem, PA 18016. TEL 610-867-0594. FAX 610-866-9223. Ed. Hermann I. Weinlick; Pub. Hermann I. Weinlick. adv. contact: Nena M. Asguith. bk.rev.; charts; illus.; maps; stat.; index. circ. 25,000. (also avail. in microfilm)
  Former titles: North American Moravian (ISSN 0027-1012); Moravian and Wachovia Moravian.

294.6 US
MORNINGLAND SPIRITUAL JOURNAL. 12/yr. $7. Morningland Publications, 2600 E. Seventh St., Long Beach, CA 90804. TEL 213-433-9906. Ed. Gopi Morningstar. adv.

200 289.9 SA ISSN 0027-1179
MOROKAMI. (Text in Sepedi) 1966. s-m. R.19. Watch Tower Bible & Tract Society, Private Bag X2067, Krugersdorp 1740, South Africa. TEL 011-761-1000. FAX 011-764-4749. charts; illus.; index. circ. 7,800.

289.9 US ISSN 0164-7253
MOUNTAIN MOVERS. 1959. m. $10 suggested contribution. Assemblies of God, Division of Foreign Missions, 1445 Boonville Ave., Springfield, MO 65802. TEL 417-862-2781. FAX 417-862-0085. Ed. Joyce Wells Booze. circ. 210,000.
 —BLDSC (4201.346000).
  Former titles: Good News Crusades (ISSN 0017-2162); Global Conquest.

289.9 SA
MUKAI!. (Text in Shona) 1982. m. R.9.50. Watch Tower Bible & Tract Society, Private Bag X2067, Krugersdorp 1740, South Africa. TEL 011-761-1000. FAX 011-764-4749. charts; illus. circ. 3,600.

158 US
MYSTIC MAGIC. m. Box 387, Springfield, OR 97477.
  Description: Covers the world of magical intrigue.

NAG HAMMADI AND MANICHAEAN STUDIES. see *RELIGIONS AND THEOLOGY*

200 BG
NATIONAL COUNCIL OF CHURCHES, BANGLADESH. ANNUAL REPORT. (Text in Bengali, English) a. National Council of Churches, Bangladesh, 395, New Eskaton Rd., Dhaka 2, Bangladesh. stat.

133 200 US ISSN 0882-1275
BF1001
NATIONAL SPIRITUALIST. 1919. m. $18. (National Spiritualist Association of Churches) Summit Publishing by Stow, Box 217, Lily Dale, NY 14752-0217. TEL 716-595-2020. (Subscr. to: 3521 W. Topeka Dr., Glendale, AZ 85301. TEL 602-581-6686. FAX 602-581-5544) Ed. Sandra Pfortmiller. bibl.; illus. circ. 2,000.
  Description: An inspirational, positive thought, spiritualist - religious magazine.

NEW AGE TEACHINGS. see *NEW AGE PUBLICATIONS*

200 UG
NEW CENTURY. 1959. m. $20. Church of Uganda, Box 14123, Mengo, Uganda. TEL 256-270218. FAX 256-250922. Ed. James E. Mutumba. adv.; bk.rev.; play rev. circ. 5,000. (tabloid format) **Document type:** newspaper.
  Formerly: New Day (ISSN 0028-4556)

289.9 US ISSN 0275-0805
BX8701
NEW CHURCH LIFE; a monthly magazine devoted to the teachings revealed through Emanuel Swedenborg. 1891. m. $16 (effective 1994). General Church of the New Jerusalem, Box 277, Bryn Athyn, PA 19009. TEL 215-947-4200. FAX 215-938-2616. Ed. Rev. Donald L. Rose. bk.rev./ circ. 1,900 (paid). **Document type:** academic/scholarly publication.
  Description: Contains sermons, religious articles and reviews, letters and church news.

200 UK
NEW CHURCH MAGAZINE. 1881. 3/yr. £3. General Conference of the New Church, c/o G.S. Kuphal, 20 Red Barn Rd., Brightlingsea, Colchester, Essex CO7 0SH, England. TEL 01206-302932. (Subscr. to: New Church College, 25 Radcliffe New Rd., Manchester M26 1LE, England. TEL 061-766-2521. FAX 0161-796-1142) Ed. B.M. Talbot. **Document type:** academic/scholarly publication.
  Description: Contains articles on religion and theology relating to the New Church.

289.33 US ISSN 0164-5285
NEW ERA (SALT LAKE CITY). 1971. m. $8. Church of Jesus Christ of Latter-day Saints, Corporation of the President, 50 E. North Temple, Salt Lake City, UT 84150. TEL 801-240-2947. Ed. Richard Romney. circ. 185. (also avail. in microform from UMI; back issues avail.; reprint service avail. from UMI) **Indexed:** A.I.P.P.
 —UnCover.
  Description: Written for those between the ages of 13 and 19.

289 US
▼**NEW HARMONY MAGAZINE**. 1994. q. $19.95. Divine Science Federation International, 1200 Lincoln St., Ste. 665, Denver, CO 80203. TEL 303-837-9680. Ed. Rev. Paul Schwegel.
  Description: Contains inspirational articles and stories.

150 US ISSN 0146-7832
NEW THOUGHT (MESA); a quarterly magazine dedicated to the spiritual enlightenment of the individual and of the world. 1916. q. $10. International New Thought Alliance, 5003 E. Broadway Rd., Mesa, AZ 85206. TEL 602-830-2461. Ed. Blaine C. Mays. adv.; bk.rev.; illus. circ. 5,000.
  Formerly (until 1950): New Thought Bulletin (ISSN 0146-8170)

299 322.4 US
NEWS FROM THE WHITE HOUSE. 1989? q. $8 (Canada and Mexico $10; elsewhere $12). (White House Network) White House Press, Box 6872, Harrisburg, PA 17112-0872. (Alt. addr.: W.H.N. Region III, Box 24322, Detroit, MI 48224-9998) Ed. Eric West. adv. contact: Eric West. bk.rev.; illus. circ. 3,000. (back issues avail.) **Document type:** newsletter.
  Description: Promotes the organization's philosophies through political action.

220 289.9 SA ISSN 0028-9639
NHARIREYOMURINDI. (Text in Shona) 1949. s-m. R.19. Watch Tower Bible & Tract Society, Private Bag X2067, Krugersdorp 1740, South Africa. TEL 011-761-1000. FAX 011-764-4749. charts; illus.; index. circ. 17,000.

NICOLAUS. see *RELIGIONS AND THEOLOGY — Roman Catholic*

289.9 PO ISSN 0029-5116
NOVAS DE ALEGRIA. Abbreviated title: N A. 1943. m. Esc.150($6) Casa Publicadora das Assembleias de Deus, Av. Alm. Gago Coutinho 158, 1700 Lisbon, Portugal. Ed. Fernando Martinez da Silva. adv.; bk.rev.; abstr.; illus.; circ. 10,400 (controlled).

220 289.9 SA ISSN 0029-5442
NSANJA YA OLONDA. (Text in Chichewa) 1948. s-m. R.19. Watch Tower Bible & Tract Society, Private Bag X2067, Krugersdorp 1740, South Africa. TEL 011-761-1000. FAX 011-764-4749. illus. circ. 16,700.

289.9 SA
NY TILIKAMBO FIAMBENANA. (Text in Malagasy) 1993. s-m. R.19($5) Watch Tower Bible and Tract Society, Private Bag X2067, Krugersdorp 1740, South Africa. TEL 011-761-1000. FAX 011-764-4749. charts; illus. circ. 12,500.

286.7 FI ISSN 0355-3280
NYKYAIKA; suomen adventti kirkon viikkolehti. 1897. w.(plus m. ed.). FIM 380; newsstand price: FIM 24. (Suomen Adventtikirkko - Seventh-Day Adventist Church in Finland) Kirjatoimi, P.O. Box 94, FIN-33101 Tempere, Finland.
TEL 358-31-3600-000. FAX 358-31-3600-454. Ed. Olavi Rouhe. circ. 2,800 (m. ed. 6,700). (back issues avail.)
  Description: Publishes a weekly journal for the Seventh-Day Adventist congregation and a monthly evangelistic journal for the general public.

OCCULT OBSERVER. see *PARAPSYCHOLOGY AND OCCULTISM*

299 322.4 US
▼**ODONIST PRISON PROJECT AND SECOND MOUNTAIN KINDRED. JOINT PUBLICATION**. 1994. irreg. free. White House Press, Box 6088, Harrisburg, PA 17112-0088. (Co-sponsor: Second Mountain Kindred) Ed. Eric West; Pub. Eric West. **Document type:** monographic series.
  Description: Discusses the organization's projects with prison inmates in several U.S. states.

299.9 US ISSN 0892-5984
OF A LIKE MIND. 1983. q. $15. Reformed Congregation of the Goddess, Box 6021, Madison, WI 53716. TEL 608-244-0072. Ed. Lynnie Levy. adv.; bk.rev. circ. 6,677. (tabloid format) **Document type:** newspaper.
  Description: International, feminist perspective on Goddess religions, women's spirituality, paganism and earth connections.

289.4 SZ ISSN 0030-0101
OFFENE TORE; Beitraege zu einem neuen christlichen Zeitalter. 1957. 6/yr. 25 SFr.($15) Swedenborg Verlag, Postfach 247, CH-8032 Zurich, Switzerland. TEL 01-3835944. FAX 01-3822944. Ed. Dr. Friedemann Horn. bk.rev. circ. 600. **Document type:** bulletin.
  Description: Covers new religious perspectives while providing contributions to a new Christian era.

OMEGA NEW AGE DIRECTORY. see *NEW AGE PUBLICATIONS*

299 CN
ON THE MARCH!. q. Bible Holiness Movement, Box 223, Sta. A, Vancouver, BC V6C 2M3, Canada. TEL 604-498-3895. **Document type:** newsletter.
  Description: Keeps friends and adherents informed of the new and prayer requests of the Movement.

ONE EARTH. see *NEW AGE PUBLICATIONS*

220 289.9 SA ISSN 0030-316X
ONTWAAK! (Text in Afrikaans) 1939. s-m. R.19. Watch Tower Bible & Tract Society, Private Bag X2067, Krugersdrop 1740, South Africa. TEL 011-761-1000. FAX 011-764-4749. charts; illus.; index. circ. 24,500.

200 JA ISSN 0030-3259
OOMOTO. (Text in English) 1956. bi-m. 1200 Yen($5) Oomoto International, Kameoka-shi, Kyoto-fu 621, Japan. TEL 07712-2-5561. bk.rev.; illus. circ. 5,000.

289.9 SA
OSHUNGONANGELO. (Text in Kwanyama) 1991. m. R.9.50($2.50) Watch Tower Bible & Tract Society, Private Bag X2067, Krugersdorp 1740, South Africa. TEL 011-761-1000. FAX 011-764-4749. charts; illus.; index. circ. 1,700.

281 GW ISSN 0030-6487
BX100
OSTKIRCHLICHE STUDIEN. (Text in English, French, German) 1952. q. DM.98. (Ostkirchliches Institut der Deutschen Augustiner) Augustinus Verlag, Grabenberg 2, 97070 Wuerzburg, Germany. TEL 0931-51157. Ed. H.M. Biedermann. adv.; bk.rev.; bibl.; index. circ. 500. **Indexed:** Amer.Hist.& Life, CERDIC, Hist.Abstr., New Test.Abstr., Rel.& Theol.Abstr. (1989-), Rel.Ind.One. **Document type:** academic/scholarly publication.
  Description: Studies the history and theology of the Eastern Orthodox Churches.

RELIGIONS AND THEOLOGY — OTHER DENOMINATIONS AND SECTS

289.9   GW   ISSN 0946-3933
OUR FAMILY; magazine of the New Apostolic Church. (Text in English) 1955. m. DM.42. Verlag Friedrich Bischoff GmbH, Postfach 110242, 60037 Frankfurt a.M., Germany. TEL 069-2696-0. FAX 069-252915. TELEX 416435-FBDV. Ed. Hellmut Wernher. circ. 70,000. **Document type:** bulletin.
  Description: Nondenominational publication devoted to evangelism, to the promotion of faith and to the belief in God through the use of real life stories.

289.4 110   UK   ISSN 0969-1049
OUTLOOK. 1992. q. free. General Conference of the New Church, c/o G.S. Kuphal, 20 Red Barn Rd., Brightlingsea, Colchester, Essex CO7 0SH, England. TEL 01206-302932. (Subscr. to: New Church House, 34 John Dalton St., Manchester M2 6LE, England. TEL 0161-834-4192; Alt. addr.: Swedenborg Movement, 98 Abbotts Dr., Wembley, Mddx. HA0 3SQ, England. TEL 01959-534220) (Co-sponsor: Swedenborg Movement) Ed. G. Roland Smith. bk.rev.; circ. 2,000 (controlled). (back issues avail.) **Document type:** newsletter.
  Description: Deals with religious and spiritual matters from a Swedenborgian point of view.

OUTREACH (NEW YORK). see *ETHNIC INTERESTS*

289   US   ISSN 0744-6381
PACIFIC UNION RECORDER. 1900. s-m. $10. Pacific Union Conference of Seventh Day Adventists, Box 5005, Westlake Village, CA 91359. TEL 805-497-9457. FAX 805-495-2644. Ed. C. Elwyn Platner.

299   UK   ISSN 1357-5147
PAGAN DAWN. 1968. q. £6 (Europe £8; overseas £10). Pagan Federation, BM Box 7097, London WC1N 3XX, England. TEL 0181-891-1302. Ed. Christina Oakley. adv.; circ. 3,000. **Document type:** newsletter.
  Formerly (until 1994): Wiccan.

200   UK
PAGAN NEWS. bi-m. £12. Phoenix Publications, P.O. Box 196, London WC1A 2DY, England.

289.9   US
PAGANA. 1980. 6/yr. $12. American Mensa Ltd., Pagan-Occult-Witchcraft Special Interest Group, Box 9336, San Jose, CA 95157-0336. TEL 415-856-6911. Ed. Valerie Voigt. adv.: B&W page $20; trim 5 1/2 x 8 1/2. bk.rev.; illus. circ. 400.

294.6 291   II   ISSN 0970-7689
PANCHBATI SANDESH. (Text in English, Hindi, Punjabi) 1978. q. free (foreign Rs.125). 20 Pritam Rd., Dehra Dun 248001, India. Pub. Balbir Singh Sahitya Kendra. **Document type:** bulletin.
  Description: Deals with the main tenets of Sikhism in particular and the traditional wisdom of all religions in general.

200   FR   ISSN 0031-0972
PANPERE. (Text in Armenian) 1925. m. 120 F.($25) Union of the Armenian Evangelical Churches in France, 13 rue des Allies, 69100 Villeurbanne, France. TEL 33-78-89-21-44. Ed. Ari Topouzkhanian. bk.rev. circ. 3,300. **Document type:** newspaper.

PANTHEIST VISION. see *PHILOSOPHY*

110   SA   ISSN 0031-2932
PATH OF TRUTH. Afrikaans edition: Huis van Geluk. 1937. m. free. School of Truth Ltd., Cape House, 5th Fl., Cnr. MacLaren & Fox Sts., Johannesburg 2001, South Africa. TEL 011-838-6954. FAX 011-833-1802. (Subscr. to: P.O. Box 6116, Johannesburg 2000, South Africa) Ed. Wille Martin. circ. 13,900 (3,450 Afrikaans ed.; 10,450 English ed.)
  Description: Contains daily reading, meditations, and metaphysics lectures.

294.3   US
PATHWAYS (WATSONVILLE). 1979. 9/yr. $12. Hanuman Fellowship, Mount Madonna Center, 445 Summit Rd., Watsonville, CA 95076-0759. TEL 408-847-0406. FAX 408-847-2876. Ed. Pratibha Sharan. adv.; bk.rev. circ. 600. **Document type:** newsletter.
  Formerly: Gateways.
  Description: Includes information on current events and perspectives on the spiritual pathways, including teachings of the Baba Hari Dass and others.

281.9   GR
PATRIARCHAL INSTITUTE FOR PATRISTIC STUDIES. THEOLOGICAL STUDIES. irreg., latest no.5. price varies. Patriarchal Institute for Patristic Studies, Heptapyrgiou 64, 546 34 Thessaloniki, Greece. Ed. P.C. Christou.

PEACEMAKER. see *POLITICAL SCIENCE*

PEARLS OF WISDOM. see *PHILOSOPHY*

200   US   ISSN 0031-4250
PENDLE HILL PAMPHLETS. 1934. 6/yr. $13. (Pendle Hill, a Quaker Center for Study and Contemplation) Pendle Hill Publications, 338 Plush Mill Road, Wallingford, PA 19086. TEL 215-566-4507. FAX 215-566-3679. Ed. Rebecca Kratz Mays. circ. 1,500. (also avail. in microfilm from UMI) **Indexed:** Vert.File Ind. **Document type:** monographic series.
  Description: Articles focus on spiritual formation and active social witness for peace and justice.

PENNSYLVANIA MENNONITE HERITAGE. see *GENEALOGY AND HERALDRY*

289.9   US   ISSN 0031-4897
BX6198.A7
PENTECOSTAL EVANGEL. 1913. w. $15.95. (General Council of the Assemblies of God) Gospel Publishing House, 1445 Boonville Ave., Springfield, MO 65802-1894. TEL 417-862-2781. FAX 417-862-0416. Ed. Richard G. Champion. bk.rev.; charts; illus.; index. circ. 260,000. (also avail. in microfilm) **Indexed:** A.I.P.P., G.Soc.Sci.& Rel.Per.Lit.

220   SA   ISSN 1018-3361
PHAFOGA! (Text in Sepedi) 1990. m. R.9.50. Watch Tower Bible & Tract Society, Private Bag X2067, Krugersdorp 1740, South Africa. TEL 011-761-1000. FAX 011-764-4749. charts; illus.; index. circ. 2,500.

220 289.9   SA   ISSN 0031-6806
PHAPHAMA!. (Text in Zulu) 1958. s-m. R.19. Watch Tower Bible & Tract Society, Private Bag X2067, Krugersdorp 1740, South Africa. TEL 011-761-1000. FAX 011-764-4749. charts; illus.; index. circ. 16,500.

289   US   ISSN 0032-0420
PLAIN TRUTH; proclaiming the Gospel of Jesus Christ. 1934. 10/yr. free. Worldwide Church of God, 300 W. Green St., Pasadena, CA 91129. TEL 818-304-6000. (Subscr. to: Pasadena, CA 91123-0428) Ed. Joseph W. Tkach; Pub. Joseph W. Tkach. circ. 1,300,000. (also avail. in audio cassette) **Document type:** consumer publication.
  Incorporates: Good News of Tomorrow's World (ISSN 0093-5026)

200   UK
PLOUGH. 1931. irreg. (2-3/yr.). £6.50. General Conference of the New Church, c/o G.S. Kuphal, 20 Red Barn Rd., Brightlingsea, Colchester, Essex CO7 0SH, England. TEL 01206-302932. (Subscr. to: New Church House, 34 John Dalton St., Manchester M2 6LE, England. TEL 0161-834-4192) (Co-sponsor: British New Church Federation) Ed. B. Johnson.
  Description: Deals with matters of interest to young people connected with the New Church.

268
PLUS: MAGAZINE OF POSITIVE THINKING. 1945. 10/yr. $10 contribution. Peale Center for Christian Living, Box 8000, Pawling, NY 12564. TEL 914-855-5000. Ed. Rick Cox. illus. circ. 650,000.
  Former titles: Magazine of Positive Thinking (ISSN 0747-217X); Creative Help for Daily Living.

PORTAL. see *PARAPSYCHOLOGY AND OCCULTISM*

294.4   II   ISSN 0554-9906
PRAKIT JAIN INSTITUTE RESEARCH PUBLICATION SERIES. (Text in English and Hindi) 1964. irreg. price varies. Bihar Research Institute of Prakit, Jainology, and Ahimsa, Vaishali, India. Ed. G.C. Choudhary.

259   US   ISSN 0032-7700
PRESENT TRUTH AND HERALD OF CHRIST'S EPIPHANY. (Editions in Danish, French, German, Norwegian and Polish) 1918. bi-m. $2. Laymen's Home Missionary Movement, Box 67, Chester Springs, PA 19425. TEL 610-827-7665. Ed. Bernard W. Hedman. circ. 1,100.

200   IT   ISSN 0033-0728
PROGRESSIO; Ignatian spirituality for laypeople. (Text in English, French and Spanish) 1924. 4/yr. (with s-a. supplements). $24 (effective 1995 & 1996). Christian Life Community, World Secretariat, Borgo Santo Spirito 8, Casella Postale 6139, 00195 Rome, Italy. Ed. Roswitha Cooper. illus.; index, cum.index every 10 yrs. circ. 3,500.

220   US   ISSN 0033-1341
PROPHETIC NEWSLETTER; the news in the light of the Bible. 1959. m. contributions. World Prophetic Ministry, Inc., P.O. Drawer 907, Colton, CA 92324. TEL 909-825-2767. Ed. David Breese. illus. circ. 25,000. **Document type:** newsletter.

200   US
PROPHETIC OBSERVER. 1938. m. $20 (and contributions). Southwest Radio Church, Box 1144, Oklahoma City, OK 73101. TEL 405-235-5396. FAX 405-236-4634. Ed. N.W. Hutchings. circ. 35,000. (also avail. in microform from UMI; reprint service avail. from UMI)
  Formerly (since 1993): Gospel Truths (ISSN 0017-2383); Supersedes (in 1990): Torch (Oklahoma City) (ISSN 0195-1823)

289.7   US   ISSN 0163-7274
PURPOSE. 1968. w. $14.45. Mennonite Publishing House, 616 Walnut Ave., Scottdale, PA 15683-1999. TEL 412-887-8500. FAX 412-887-3111. Ed. James E. Horsch. bk.rev.; illus. circ. 14,500.

QUAKER CONCERN. see *POLITICAL SCIENCE — Civil Rights*

289.6   US   ISSN 0033-5053
BX7635.A1
QUAKER HISTORY. 1902. s-a. $15. Friends Historical Association, Haverford College Library, Haverford, PA 19041. TEL 610-896-1161. Ed. Charles L. Cherry. bk.rev.; bibl.; cum.index every 5 yrs, vol.1-80; circ. 800 (paid). (also avail. in microform from UMI; reprint service avail. from UMI) **Indexed:** Amer.Hist.& Life, Bibl.Engl.Lang.& Lit., CERDIC, Hist.Abstr., Rel.Ind.One, Rel.Per. **Document type:** academic/scholarly publication.
  —Faxon; UnCover.
  Formerly: Friends' Historical Association. Bulletin (ISSN 0361-1957)
  Description: Consists of articles on Quaker contributions to issues such as social justice, education and literature.
  Refereed Serial

289.6   US   ISSN 0033-5061
BX7601
QUAKER LIFE. 1960. 10/yr. $19.95 (foreign $25). Friends United Meeting (Quakers), 101 Quaker Hill Dr., Richmond, IN 47374-1980. TEL 317-962-7573. FAX 317-966-1293. E-mail: 70524.1467@compuserve.com. Ed. Johan Maurer. adv.: B&W page $400, color page $900; adv. contact: Norma Cox. bk.rev.; illus.; index. circ. 7,700. **Indexed:** CERDIC.
  Formed by the merger of: American Friend; Quaker Action.
  Description: Publishes religious news, articles, and comments of special interest to Friends.

200   UK   ISSN 0033-507X
QUAKER MONTHLY. 1922. m. £11.75 (foreign £13.80) (effective 1996). Quaker Home Service, Friends House, Euston Rd, London NW1 2BJ, England. TEL 0171-387-3601. FAX 0171-388-1977. Ed. Elizabeth Cave. bk.rev.; illus. circ. 3,000. **Indexed:** CERDIC. **Document type:** bulletin.
  Formerly: Wayfarer.
  Description: Theologic articles on the relationship between Quaker tenets and human experience.

RELIGIONS AND THEOLOGY — OTHER DENOMINATIONS AND SECTS

289.6 US ISSN 0033-5088
BX7601
QUAKER RELIGIOUS THOUGHT. 1959. irreg. (approx. 2/yr.) $16 for 4 nos. Quaker Theological Discussion Group, 128 Tate St., Greensboro, NC 27403. TEL 919-274-8707. Ed. Arthur Roberts. bk.rev.; circ. 500 (paid). (also avail. in microform from UMI; back issues avail.) **Indexed:** CERDIC. **Document type:** academic/scholarly publication.
—BLDSC (7168.121000); UMI.

QUAKER YEOMEN. see *GENEALOGY AND HERALDRY*

289.9 US ISSN 0273-7159
BV3750
RAILROAD EVANGELIST. 1931. q. $6. (Railroad Evangelistic Association, Inc.) Bartel Printing Co., 502 E. Winona Ave., Warsaw, IN 46580. TEL 317-844-3176. (Subscr. to: c/o Ann Grissom. 5272 Longstone Rd., Carmel, IN 46032) Ed. Esther Peterson. circ. 2,500.
Description: Interdenominational patriotic Christian magazine for the railroad and allied transportation industries.

RAYS FROM THE ROSE CROSS. see *PHILOSOPHY*

248.48 US
REJOICE! (HILLSBORO). 1965. q. Kindred Productions, 4-169 Riverton Ave., Winnipeg, MB R2L 2E5, Canada. TEL 316-269-9185. (Co-sponsors: General Conference of Mennonite Brethren Churches; Mennonite Church; General Conference Mennonite Church) Ed. Katie Funk Wiebe. circ. 19,000. **Indexed:** RILM.
Description: Inter-Mennonite devotional ministry.

211.6 US ISSN 0034-4095
BL2747.6
RELIGIOUS HUMANISM;* a quarterly journal of religious and ethical humanism. 1967. q. $12. Fellowship of Religious Humanists, Box 597396, Chicago, IL 60659-7396. TEL 513-324-8130. Eds. Paul and Lucinda Beattie. adv.; bk.rev.; index, cum.index: vols.1-10. circ. 1,500. (also avail. in microform from UMI; reprint service avail. from UMI) **Indexed:** Arts & Hum.Cit.Ind., CERDIC, Curr.Cont., G.Soc.Sci.& Rel.Per.Lit., Phil.Ind., Phil.Ind., Rel.& Theol.Abstr. (1969-), Rel.Ind.One.
—BLDSC (7356.530000); Faxon; Genuine Article; UMI; UnCover.
Description: Presents scholarly articles and creative verse pertaining to the practice and philosophy of this liberal ministry that espouses the dignity and worth of man and his capacity for self-realization without devine intervention.

289.2 US ISSN 0191-0167
RESTORATION WITNESS; evangelistic magazine of the Reorganized Church of Jesus Christ of Latter-Day Saints. 1963. bi-m. $11.50 to individuals; groups $10.50 (foreign $13.75). (Reorganized Church of Jesus Christ of Latter Day Saints) Herald Publishing House, 3225 S. Noland Rd., Box 1770, Independence, MO 64055. TEL 816-252-5010. Ed. Barbara Howard. adv.; illus.; tr.lit. circ. 10,000.

289.9 US ISSN 1050-7930
BX8627
REVIEW OF BOOKS ON THE BOOK OF MORMON. 1989. a. $8.50 (typically set in Apr.). Foundation for Ancient Research and Mormon Studies, Box 7113, University Sta., Provo, UT 84602. TEL 801-378-3295. FAX 801-378-5254. Ed. Daniel C. Peterson. bk.rev. circ. 1,200.
Description: Review of books published in the past year on the Book of Mormon.

REVIEW OF INDIAN SPIRITUALISM. see *PARAPSYCHOLOGY AND OCCULTISM*

ROSICRUCIAN DIGEST. see *PHILOSOPHY*

291 US
ROYAL TETON RANCH NEWS. m. $8. Summit Lighthouse, Box 5000, Livingston, MT 59047-5000. TEL 406-848-7441. FAX 406-848-7441. Ed. Murray L. Steinman. (back issues avail.)
Description: Contains news and articles about Church Universal and Triumphant and the Royal Teton Ranch.

289.9 US
SABBATH SENTINEL; serving the Seventh-day Christian community. 1945. m. $12. Bible Sabbath Association, R.R. 1, Box 222, Fairview, OK 73737. TEL 405-227-3200. Ed. Richard Wiedenheft. adv.; bk.rev.; bibl.; illus. circ. 1,200. (back issues avail.)

200 US
SACRED NAME BROADCASTER. 1968. m. free. Assemblies of Yahweh, Box C, Bethel, PA 19507. TEL 717-933-4518. Ed. Jacob O. Meyer. illus. circ. 14,000.

289 133 CN ISSN 1198-9947
▼**SACRED SERPENT.** 1994. q. Can.$10 (U.S. $10; overseas $15). Iron Wolf Enterprises, P.O. Box 232, Sta. "D", Etobicoke, ON M9A 4X2, Canada. TEL 416-237-9831. Ed. Vilija Witte. adv.: page Can.$60. **Document type:** newsletter.
Description: Explores the culture of the Baltic region, including its old beliefs, indigenous spirituality, folklore and myths.

281.9 US
ST. MARY ARMENIAN CHURCH. BULLETIN. (Text in Armenian, English) 1965? m. St. Mary Armenian Church, Box 367, Yettem, CA 93670. Ed. Der Stepanos Dingilian. circ. 375. **Document type:** bulletin.

289.3 US ISSN 0036-3251
SAINTS' HERALD; family magazine of the Reorganized Church of Jesus Christ of Latter Day Saints. 1860. m. $21.80 to individuals; groups $18 (foreign $30.50). (Reorganized Church of Jesus Christ of Latter Day Saints) Herald Publishing House, 3225 S. Noland Rd., Box 1770, Independence, MO 64055. TEL 816-252-5010. Ed. Roger Yarrington. adv.; bk.rev.; illus.; tr.lit. circ. 39,000. (also avail. in microfilm)

SALLY ANN; a Christian magazine for women. see *WOMEN'S INTERESTS*

284 GR ISSN 0036-357X
SALPISMA.* 1945. m. Dr.40($3) Free Evangelical Churches of Greece, 3 Alkiviadou, Athens, Greece. bk.rev.; cum.index every 4 yrs. circ. 1,500. **Indexed:** CERDIC.

289 US ISSN 0586-7282
SALT LAKE CITY MESSENGER. 1964. irreg., no.87, 1994. free. Utah Lighthouse Ministry, 1350 S.W. Temple St., Box 1884, Salt Lake City, UT 84110. TEL 801-485-8894. Ed. Jerald Tanner. adv. circ. 18,000. (looseleaf format) **Document type:** newsletter.

287.9 UK ISSN 0080-567X
SALVATION ARMY YEAR BOOK. 1906. a. £5.50 paperback; £10.95 hardback. (Salvation Army) Salvationist Publishing and Supplies, Ltd., Judd St., Kings Cross, London WC1H 9NN, England. TEL 0171-387-1656. FAX 0171-387-3768. Ed. Karen Thompson. index. circ. 13,000. **Document type:** directory.

287.9 UK
SALVATIONIST. 1907. w. £35.10 (foreign £48.60). Salvation Army, 101 Queen Victoria St., London EC4P 4EP, England. TEL 0171-236-5222. FAX 0171-236-3491. Ed. Michael Marvell. circ. 24,000. **Document type:** bulletin.
Incorporates (in 1986): Musician.

289.9 US
SANCTUARY CIRCLES; events calendar newsletter. 1980. 8/yr. $10. Circle Sanctuary, Box 219, Mt. Horeb, WI 53572. TEL 608-924-2216. FAX 608-924-5961. **Document type:** newsletter.

SANT SIPAHI. see *POLITICAL SCIENCE*

362.8 KE
SAUTI YA VITA. (Text in English and Swahili) 1928. m. EAs.2. (Salvation Army) Slavation Army, P.O. Box 40575, Nairobi, Kenya. TEL 254-2-227541. FAX 254-2-335538. Ed. Capt. Julius Mukonga; Pub. Wycliffe Angoya. circ. 15,100. **Document type:** newsletter.

280 US ISSN 0036-8032
SCHWENKFELDIAN. 1903. 3/yr. $4 to non-members. (Schwenkfelder Church) Board of Publication of the Schwenkfelder General Conference, 105 Seminary St., Pennsburg, PA 18073-1898. TEL 215-679-3103. Ed. Andrew C. Anders. bk.rev.; illus. circ. 2,000. **Document type:** newsletter.

200 US ISSN 0036-8458
SCIENCE OF MIND MAGAZINE. 1927. m. $18 (foreign $25). United Church of Religious Science, Box 75127, Los Angeles, CA 90075. TEL 213-388-2181. FAX 213-388-1926. Ed. Sandra Sarr; Pub. Sandra Sarr. adv. contact: Kalpnaa Shah. bk.rev.; illus. circ. 100,000. **Indexed:** CERDIC. **Document type:** consumer publication.

299 SA ISSN 0036-8466
SCIENCE OF THE SOUL. 1963. q. R.28($20) Radha Soami Satsang Beas, P.O. Box 41355, Craighall 2024, South Africa. TEL 27-11-788-9152. FAX 27-11-6785782. Ed.Bd. adv. circ. 4,000. (back issues avail.)
Description: Concerns the practice of meditation taught by a living meditation master.

299.935 US ISSN 1063-2611
SECULAR HUMANIST BULLETIN. 1984. q. $18 (effective 1995). CODESH, Inc., Box 664, Amherst, NY 14226. TEL 716-636-7571. FAX 716-636-1733. E-mail: timmadigan@aol.com. Eds. Tim Madigan, Tom Flynn. circ. 5,000. (tabloid format; also avail. in microform from UMI) **Document type:** newsletter.
Description: Promotes the philosophy of Secular Humanism while critically examining supernatural claims. Contains news, opinions and humor items.

SELF-REALIZATION. see *RELIGIONS AND THEOLOGY*

289 US ISSN 0582-9348
SHAKER QUARTERLY. 1961. q. $15. United Society of Shakers, Sabbathday Lake, Poland Spring, ME 04274. TEL 207-926-4597. Ed.Bd. bk.rev.; bibl.illus. circ. 350. (back issues avail.)
—UnCover.
Description: Scholarly research and news from the last remaining active Shaker community.

SHARE IT; international journal for celebrating & sharing who we really are. see *NEW AGE PUBLICATIONS*

200 JA ISSN 0037-5055
SIGNS OF THE TIMES. (Text in Japanese) 1899. m. 5800 Yen($58) (Seventh-Day Adventist Church) Japan Publishing House, 1966 Kamikawai-cho, Asahi-ku, Yokohama 241, Japan. TEL 045-921-4349. FAX 045-921-4349. Ed. Yoshio Morakami. adv. contact: Soneda Kenji. circ. 50,000.
Description: Contains Bible stories and discusses health, education and family issues.

294.6 UK
SIKH COURIER INTERNATIONAL. 1960. q. £6. Sikh Cultural Society of Great Britain, 88 Mollison Way, Edgware, Middlesex HA8 5QW, England. TEL 0181-952-1215. Ed. A.S. Chhatwal. adv. contact: B.S. Grewal. bk.rev. circ. 3,000. **Indexed:** CERDIC. **Document type:** bulletin.
Formerly: Sikh Courier (ISSN 0037-511X)

294.6 UK ISSN 0266-9153
SIKH MESSENGER. 1984. 4/yr. Sikh Messenger Publications, 43 Dorset Rd., Merton Park, London SW19 3EZ, England. TEL 01-540-4148.

281.62 IS ISSN 0037-5810
BX120
SION. (Text in Armenian) 1866. bi-m. $108. Armenian Patriarchate, P.O. Box 14235, Jerusalem 91141, Israel. TEL 972-2-894866. FAX 972-2-894862. Ed. Patriarch Torkom Manoogian. bk.rev.; bibl.; illus.; index, cum.index. circ. 1,500.
Description: Official gazette of the Armenian Patriarchate of Jerusalem.

SKOOB ESOTERICA ANTHOLOGY. see *PARAPSYCHOLOGY AND OCCULTISM*

5830 RELIGIONS AND THEOLOGY — OTHER DENOMINATIONS AND SECTS

289.9   US   ISSN 1050-1940
SOCIETE. 1986. 3/yr. $15. Technicians of the Sacred, 1317 N. San Fernando Blvd., Ste. 310, Burbank, CA 91504. Ed. Courtney Willis. circ. 1,000. (back issues avail.)
Description: Covers voodoo and other neo-African religious belief systems, including magic and culture.

SOCIETE D'ARCHEOLOGIE COPTE. BIBLIOTHEQUE DE MANUSCRITS. see *ARCHAEOLOGY*

SOCIETE D'ARCHEOLOGIE COPTE. BULLETIN. see *ARCHAEOLOGY*

SOCIETE D'ARCHEOLOGIE COPTE. TEXTES ET DOCUMENTS. see *ARCHAEOLOGY*

240   US   ISSN 0364-2097
BR115.W6
SOJOURNERS. 1971. m. (except Feb.-Mar.; Sep.-Oct. combined). $30. 2401 15th St., N.W., Washington, DC 20009. TEL 202-328-8842. FAX 202-328-8757. Ed. Jim Wallis; Pub. Joe Roos. adv.: B&W page $1375; color page $1685; adv. contact: David Wade. bk.rev.; illus. circ. 23,000. (also avail. in microfiche) Indexed: Alt.Press Ind., CCR, CERDIC, Chr.Per.Ind., HR Rep. (1985-), Media Rev.Dig., Peace Res.Abstr., Rel.Ind.One, Rel.Per. —Faxon; UMI; UnCover.
Formerly: Post American (ISSN 0361-2422)
Description: Covers theological, social, cultural and political topics, and provides resources for spiritual discussion, study and renewal.

289.9   UK
SOUTH ENGLAND CONFERENCE COMMUNICATOR. 1987. q. free. South England Conference of Seventh-Day Adventists, Communication Department, 25 St. John's Rd., Watford, Herts. WD1 1PY, England. TEL 01923-232728. FAX 01923-250582. Ed. Keith Davidson. adv.; bk.rev. circ. 4,000. Document type: bulletin.
Description: Covers activities of the Seventh-Day Adventist Church and individual congregations.

250   II   ISSN 0038-3465
SOUTH INDIA CHURCHMAN. 1947. m. Rs.35. Church of South India, c/o Christian Literature Society, Box 501, Park Town, Madras 600003, India. TEL 044-852-1566. Ed. Rev. Dass Babu. adv.; bk.rev. circ. 2,000. Document type: academic/scholarly publication.
Refereed Serial

SOUTHERN FRIEND. see *HISTORY — History Of North And South America*

289.6   US   ISSN 0024-0591
SPARK (NEW YORK). 1970. 5/yr. membership only. New York Yearly Meeting of the Religious Society of Friends, 15 Rutherford Place, New York, NY 10003. TEL 212-673-5750. Ed. Joseph A. Vlaskamp. bk.rev.; bibl.; charts; illus. circ. 4,200. Indexed: Alt.Press Ind.

289.9   US
SPECTRUM (TAKOMA PARK). 1969. 5/yr. $25 (foreign $32). Association of Adventist Forums, Box 5330, Takoma Park, MD 20913. TEL 301-270-0423. FAX 301-270-2814. Ed. Roy Branson. bk.rev.; film rev.; bibl.; charts; illus.; cum.index every 5 yrs. circ. 5,400. (back issues avail.)
Description: Journal of opinion and scholarship for Seventh-Day Adventist readers.

THE SPIRITUAL HEALER; journal of spiritual healing and philosophy. see *NEW AGE PUBLICATIONS*

286   US   ISSN 0038-9447
STANDARD BEARER (SACRAMENTO). vol.11, 1973. q. $9. (Seventh-Day Adventist Reform Movement) Northwestern Publishing Association, Box 245360, Sacramento, CA 95824-5360. TEL 209-245-3131. Ed. Alfon Sas Balbachas. adv.; illus. circ. 2,000. Indexed: Rehabil.Lit.

269.2   US
STAR OF HOPE. 1967. m. $3.75. Rod and Staff Publishers, Inc., State Rte. 172, Crockett, KY 41413. TEL 606-522-4348. FAX 606-522-4896. Ed. Dallas Witmer. circ. 72,183.

289.9   UK   ISSN 0308-4531
STELLA POLARIS. (Supplement avail.) 1950. bi-m. £9 (foreign £10). White Eagle Publishing Trust, White Eagle Lodge, New Lands, Brewells Lane, Liss, Hants GU33 7HY, England. TEL 0730-893300. FAX 0730-892235. Ed. Ylana Hayward. bk.rev.; index. circ. 3,400. (back issues avail.) Document type: newsletter.
Description: Provides articles on healing, astrology, and other topics of interest to followers of the teaching, such as the ancient spiritual centers. Includes stories and articles for children.

STORY FRIENDS. see *CHILDREN AND YOUTH — For*

280   US   ISSN 0081-7538
STUDIES IN ANABAPTIST AND MENNONITE HISTORY. 1929. irreg., no.34, 1994. price varies. (Mennonite Historical Society) Mennonite Publishing House, Herald Press, 616 Walnut Ave., Scottdale, PA 15683. TEL 412-887-8500. FAX 412-887-3111.

STUDIES IN ASIAN THOUGHT AND RELIGION. see *PHILOSOPHY*

289   US   ISSN 1052-0503
STUDIES IN EVANGELICALISM. 1980. irreg., no.11, 1991. Scarecrow Press, Inc., 52 Liberty St., Box 4167, Metuchen, NJ 08840. TEL 800-537-7107. Eds. Kenneth E. Rowe, Donald W. Dayton. Document type: academic/scholarly publication.

291   GW   ISSN 0340-6792
STUDIES IN ORIENTAL RELIGIONS. (Text in English and German) 1976. irreg., vol.32, 1995. price varies. Harrassowitz Verlag, Taunusstr. 14, 65183 Wiesbaden, Germany. TEL 0611-530-0. FAX 0611-530570. TELEX 4186135. (Subscr. to: Postfach 2929, 65019 Wiesbaden, Germany) Eds. W. Heissig, H.J. Klimkeit. Document type: monographic series.

200   US   ISSN 0039-5161
SUNDAY; the magazine for the Lord's Day Alliance. 1913. 3/yr. $5 membership. Lord's Day Alliance of the U.S., 2930 Flowers Rd. S., Ste. 16, Atlanta, GA 30341. TEL 404-936-5376. Ed. Jack P. Lownoes. bk.rev.; charts; illus. circ. 12,000. (also avail. in microform) Indexed: CERDIC. Document type: academic/scholarly publication, bibliography, newsletter.
—UMI.

289.2   US   ISSN 0363-1370
AP2
SUNSTONE. 1975. 8/yr. $32. Sunstone Foundation, 331 S. Rio Grande, Ste. 206, Salt Lake City, UT 84101-1136. TEL 801-355-5926. FAX 801-355-4043. Ed. Elbert Peck; Pub. Elbert Peck. adv.: B&W page $700. bk.rev.; illus.; index; circ. 10,000 (paid). Document type: academic/scholarly publication.
—UnCover.
Description: Examines the Mormon experience with scholarship, issues, and art.

292   YU
SVETOSAVSKO ZVONCE. (Text in Serbian) 1968. bi-m. $10. Sveti Arhijerejski Sinod, Sedmog Jula 5, 11000 Belgrade, Yugoslavia. TEL 011 638-875. Ed. Rev. Sava Popovic. circ. 15,000.

SYNAPSE (BOSTON). see *LITERARY AND POLITICAL REVIEWS*

299.514   US   ISSN 1061-8805
BL1899
TAOIST RESOURCES. (Text in English, French) 1989. s-a. $20 to individuals; institutions $30. Indiana University, East Asian Studies Center, Memorial Hall W 207, Indiana University, Bloomington, IN 47405. TEL 812-855-3765. FAX 812-855-7762. TELEX 272279 INDIANA U BLOM. E-mail: easc@indiana.edu. Ed. Stephen Bokenkamp. adv. contact: Ai-hua Guo. bk.rev. circ. 75. (back issues avail.) Document type: academic/scholarly publication.
Refereed Serial

200   US   ISSN 1047-4250
TAWAGOTO. (Between 1988-1989 incorporated Divine Slave Gita (ISSN 0733-5369)) 1975. q. $30. (Hohm Community) Hohm Press, Box 4272, Prescott, AZ 86302. TEL 602-778-9189. FAX 602-717-1779. Eds. Angelon Young, Anthony Zuccarello. adv.; bk.rev.; film rev. circ. 500. (back issues avail.) Document type: newsletter.
Formerly: At Hohm Newsletter.
Description: Reflects the communication and teaching work of Lee Lozowick, and chronicles the process of spiritual growth of the members of Hohm.
Refereed Serial

281.62   LE   ISSN 0040-0297
TCHAHERT/TORCH. (Text in Armenian) 1966. s-a. $4. Armenian Evangelical Brotherhood Church, Box 4944, Beirut, Lebanon. Ed.Bd. bk.rev.; illus. circ. 1,500.

299   JA   ISSN 0040-3482
BL2222.T4
TENRIKYO. (Text in English) 1962-1970; resumed 1976. m. 1800 Yen in Asia; Europe, S. America & Africa 2280 Yen; elsewhere 2040 Yen. Tenrikyo Overseas Mission Department, Tenri, Nara, Japan. TEL 07436-3-1511. FAX 07436-2-0227. Ed. Y. Ueda. illus.; tr.lit. circ. 3,400. (tabloid format) Document type: newspaper.
Description: Contains news related to the Tenrikyo church, and doctrinal articles.

289.9   UK
TESTIMONY MAGAZINE. 1931. m. £9.75($20) Testimony Magazine Promoting Committee, 26 Tiercel Ave., Norwich NR7 8JN, England. TEL 01603-412978. Ed. R.A. Benson. bk.rev.; charts; illus.; index. circ. 2,300. (back issues avail.) Document type: academic/scholarly publication.
Description: For the study and defense of the Holy Scripture.

THEOSOFIA; brotherhood, problems of society, religion and occult research. see *PHILOSOPHY*

THEOSOPHICAL HISTORY; a quarterly journal of research. see *HISTORY*

THEOSOPHICAL JOURNAL. see *PHILOSOPHY*

299.934   GW   ISSN 0177-8005
THEOSOPHIE HEUTE. 1954. 3/yr. DM.15($10) Theosophische Gesellschaft in Deutschland, c/o Hans Beetz, Argentinische Allee 159, 14169 Berlin, Germany. TEL 030-8131680. circ. 1,200. (back issues avail.) Document type: academic/scholarly publication.

THEOSOPHIST. see *PHILOSOPHY*

299.934   AT   ISSN 1038-1139
THEOSOPHY IN AUSTRALIA. 1895. q. (plus special issue). Aus.$14 (effective 1993). Theosophical Society in Australia, 484 Kent St., Sydney, N.S.W. 2000, Australia. TEL 61-2-264-7056. FAX 61-2-264-5857. Ed. Linda Harris. bk.rev.; index. circ. 1,500.
Description: Publishes articles on theosophy, comparative religion, philosophy and science, written mainly by members.

289   NZ   ISSN 0049-3708
THEOSOPHY IN NEW ZEALAND. 1900. q. NZ.$7. Theosophical Society in New Zealand, 18 Belvedere St., Epsom, Auckland 3, New Zealand. TEL 64-4-523-1797. Ed. Pat Phillipps. bk.rev. circ. 2,400. Document type: academic/scholarly publication.
—CCC.
Description: Explores man's place in the universe through the study of religion, philosophy and science.

289.9 301.412   US
THESMOPHORIA; voice of the new women's religion. 1979. 8/yr. $10. Susan B. Anthony Coven No. 1, 5856 College Ave., Box 213, Oakland, CA 94618. TEL 415-444-7724. Ed. J. Roslund. adv.; bk.rev.; illus. circ. 2,000. (back issues avail.)
Formerly: Themis.

289.9   NE
THETA. 1972. m. membership. Scientology Kerk, N.Z. Voorburgwal 271, 1012 RS Amsterdam, Netherlands. Ed. L.A. Giacoppo. bk.rev. circ. 5,000.
Formerly: Nieuwe Theta.

RELIGIONS AND THEOLOGY — OTHER DENOMINATIONS AND SECTS

289.2 US ISSN 0273-6527
BX8601
THIS PEOPLE. 1979. q. $11.95. Utah Alliance Publishing Inc., Box 2250, Salt Lake City, UT 84110. TEL 801-581-0881. Eds. Scott & Maureen Proctor. adv.; bk.rev. circ. 20,000.
Description: A family-oriented magazine reflecting the Latter Day Saint lifestyle.

281.7 ET
TINSAE. (Text in English) 1979. 3/yr. Eth.$6.25($3) Ethiopian Orthodox Mission, P.O. Box 3137, Addis Ababa, Ethiopia. Ed. Haddis Terrefe. charts; illus.
Description: Covers activities of the Ethiopian Orthodox Church including latest news involving prominent figures of the church.

294 JA ISSN 0386-426X
TOHOKAI. 1973. m. 1200 Yen($6) Tohokai, Inc., 6-2-17 Nishitenma, Kita-ku, Osaka 530, Japan. Ed. Seigo Arashiba.

220 SA
TORA HA KU LIBELELA. (Text in Silozi) 1949. m. R.9.50. Watch Tower Bible & Tract Society, Private Bag X2067, Krugersdorp 1740, South Africa. TEL 011-761-1000. FAX 011-764-4749. charts; illus.; index. circ. 2,500.

220 289.9 SA ISSN 0040-9391
TORA YA TEBELO. (Text in Tswana) 1961. s-m. R.19. Watch Tower Bible & Tract Society, Private Bag X2067, Krugersdorp 1740, South Africa. TEL 011-761-1000. FAX 011-764-4749. charts; illus.; index. circ. 8,500.

289.6 UK
TOWARDS WHOLENESS. 3/yr. £3. Friends Fellowship of Healing, 20 Burnet Ave., Burpham, Guildford, Surrey GU1 1YD, England. TEL 01483-69257. Ed. Joanna Harris. bk.rev. circ. 1,250.
Description: Studies the practice of prayer and spiritual healing, alternative therapies, relaxation, and Quaker thought and practice.

299 II
TRIBAL RELIGIONS. 1982. q. Rs.430($63) (International Institute of Tribal Religions) K.K. Roy (Private) Ltd., 55 Gariahat Rd., P.O. Box 10210, Calcutta 700 019, India. Ed. Dr. K.K. Roy. adv.; bk.rev.; abstr.; bibl.; index. circ. 980.

100 US
TRIDENT. 1964. m. $49.95. Embassy of S.A.T.A.N., Box 666, Whitehall, PA 18052. Ed. Ted Storm. adv. contact: Bernie Attorney. **Document type:** newsletter.
Description: Discusses issues concerning the modern philosophy of Satanism.

281.9 RU
TSERKOV' I SPASENIE. 1991. w. 0.30 Rub. per issue. Pokrovskaya Tserkov', Ul. Sovetskaya 187, 652500 Leninsk-Kuznetsk, Kemerovskaya Oblast', Russia. Ed. S. Plaksin. circ. 5,000. **Document type:** newspaper.

289.9 SA ISSN 0258-9052
TSHIINGAMO. (Text in Venda) 1983. s-m. R.19. Watch Tower Bible & Tract Society, Private Bag X2067, Krugersdorp 1740, South Africa. TEL 011-761-1000. FAX 011-764-4749. charts; illus.; index. circ. 1,600.

220 SA
TSOGANG!. (Text in Tswana) 1990. m. R.9.50. Watch Tower Bible & Tract Society, Private Bag X2067, Krugersdorp 1740, South Africa. TEL 011-761-1000. FAX 011-764-4749. circ. 3,200.

220 289.9 SA
TSOHA! (Text in Sesotho) 1973. m. R.9.50. Watch Tower Bible & Tract Society, Private Bag X2067, Krugersdorp 1740, South Africa. TEL 011-761-1000. FAX 011-764-4749. charts; illus.; index. circ. 7,200.

289.9 US
U L C NEWS. vol.15, 1981. q. $5. Universal Life Church, 601 Third St., Modesto, CA 95351. TEL 209-527-8111. FAX 209-527-8116. Ed. Kirby J. Hensley. adv.; bk.rev. circ. 100,000. **Document type:** newsletter.
Formerly (until 1984): Universal Life.

220 SA
ULUPUNGU LWA KWA KALINDA. (Text in Cibemba) 1949. s-m. R.19. Watch Tower Bible & Tract Society, Private Bag X2067, Krugersdorp 1740, South Africa. TEL 011-761-1000. FAX 011-764-4749. circ. 21,000.

UNICORN (KIRKLAND). see *PARAPSYCHOLOGY AND OCCULTISM*

288.092 AT ISSN 0310-8384
UNITARIAN PIONEER. 1950. bi-m. Aus.$5. Sydney Unitarian Church, 15 Francis St., E. Sydney, N.S.W. 2010, Australia. TEL 02-360-2038. Ed. Geoffrey R. Usher. circ. 270. (back issues avail.) **Document type:** newsletter.
Description: Official newsletter of Sydney Unitarian Church.

288 US
UNITARIAN UNIVERSALIST SERVICE. SERVICE COMMITTEE NEWS. 3/yr. membership. Unitarian Universalist Service Committee, 130 Prospect St., Cambridge, MA 02139-1845. TEL 617-868-6600. FAX 617-868-7102. E-mail: postmaster@uusc.org. Ed. Denise Moorehead. circ. 25,000. (tabloid format; back issues avail.) **Document type:** newsletter.
Description: Discusses the human rights advocacy work of the organization, which supports programs for children in the U.S. and aids grassroots organizations overseas seeking social, political, cultural, and economic justice

658.32 US ISSN 0360-9782
BX7245.5
UNITED CHURCH OF CHRIST. PENSION BOARDS (ANNUAL REPORT). Key Title: Pension Boards. 1967. a. free. United Church of Christ, Pension Board, 475 Riverside Dr., 10th Fl., New York, NY 10115-1126. TEL 212-870-2790. FAX 212-870-2877. Ed. Edmund Tortora. circ. 22,681. **Document type:** corporate report.

289.9 US ISSN 0162-3567
UNITY MAGAZINE. 1889. m. $10.95 for inkprint edition; Braille edition free. Unity School of Christianity, 1901 N.W. Blue Pkwy, Unity Village, MO 64065. TEL 816-524-3550. Ed. Philip White. circ. 120,000. (also avail. in Braille)

289.6 UK ISSN 0267-6648
UNIVERSALIST. 1979. 3/yr. £5. Quaker Universalist Group, 25 Woodgrange Ave., Ealing Common, London W5 3NY, England. TEL 0181-992-4187. Ed. Chris Marsh. adv. contact: Jean Hardy. bk.rev. circ. 450. **Document type:** academic/scholarly publication.
Description: Theology and religious history, religious experience and mysticism. Specializes in the universalist aspects of Quakerism.

289.4 SW ISSN 1100-4681
VAERLDARNAS MOETE; Nya Kyrkans tidning. 1876-1984; resumed 1989. q. SEK 100. Nya Kyrkans Vaenner, Banergatan 4, S-114 56 Stockholm, Sweden. TEL 46-8-660-43-42. Ed. Olle Hjern. circ. 1,100. **Document type:** academic/scholarly publication.
Former titles (until 1984): Nya Kyrkans Tidning (ISSN 0345-8695); (until 1891): Skandinavisk Nykyrk-Tidning.

200 GW ISSN 0042-3696
VERBUM. (Text in English, French, German and Spanish) 1970. q. DM.48. (Missionswissenschaftliches Institut) Steyler Verlag, Bahnhofstr. 9, 41334 Nettetal, Germany. TEL 02157-1202-20. FAX 02157-1202-22. Ed. Rev. Karl Mueller. bk.rev.; abstr.; charts; pat.; tr.mk. circ. 1,400. **Document type:** bulletin.

VISVA - BHARATI JOURNAL OF PHILOSOPHY. see *PHILOSOPHY*

289.9 US ISSN 0042-7381
VITAL CHRISTIANITY. 1881. m. $19.95. (Church of God) Warner Press, Inc., Box 2499, Anderson, IN 46018. TEL 317-644-7721. FAX 317-622-9511. Ed. David C. Schultz. adv. contact: George Nalywaiko. illus. circ. 22,000. Indexed: G.Soc.Sci.& Rel.Per.Lit. **Document type:** consumer publication.
Description: Provides instruction for adults on how to live life as a Christian.

289 US ISSN 0049-6669
VOICE (GRANDVILLE). 1930. 6/yr. $7.50. Independent Fundamental Churches of America, Box 810, Grandville, MI 49468. TEL 616-457-5920. Ed. Paul J. Dollaske. adv.; bk.rev.; illus. circ. 11,500.
Description: Discusses personal growth, clergy development, biblical exegesis (texural and topical), and current themes.

294.44 II ISSN 0042-8086
VOICE OF AHINSA; magazine of the non-violence Ahinsa cult. (Text in English) 1951. m. Rs.25 (foreign $5). World Jain Mission - Virendra Prasad Jain, Jain Bhawan, Aliganj, Etah, Uttar Pradesh 207247, India. Ed. V.P. Jain. adv.; bk.rev.; illus. circ. 750.

299 323.4 CN
VOICE OF CHOICE. q. Bible Holiness Movement, Religious Freedom Council of Christian Minorities, Box 223, Sta. A, Vancouver, BC V6C 2M3, Canada. TEL 604-498-3895. **Document type:** newsletter.

294.6 II
VOICE OF SAMANVAYA. (Text in English) 1976. s-a. Rs.15. C.P. Ramaswami Aiyar Foundation, Centre for Studies in Tradition, Thought and Culture of India, The Grove, Eldams Rd, Madras 18, India. Ed. K. Seshadri.

289.9 US ISSN 0042-8213
VOICE OF THE NAZARENE. vol.19, 1970. m. free. God's Acres, Inc., Box 5175, Sun City, FL 33571-5175. FAX 813-634-6335. Ed. W.L. King. bk.rev.; illus. circ. 9,000. (processed)

289.9 US
VOR TRU/OUR FAITH. 1978. q. $12 (foreign $16). World Tree Publications, Box 961, Payson, AZ 85547. Ed. Thorsteinn Thorarinsson. bk.rev. circ. 500.
Description: Contains news of the Asatru faith (the ancient religion of the Northern European peoples) in North America and articles, poems and letters.

200 289.9 SA
VUKANI! (Text in Xhosa) 1973. m. R.9.50. Watch Tower Bible & Tract Society, Private Bag X2067, Krugersdorp 1740, South Africa. TEL 011-761-1000. FAX 011-764-4749. charts; illus.; index. circ. 9,000.

220 289.9 SA
DIE WAGTORING. (Text in Afrikaans) 1943. s-m. R.19.($5) Watch Tower Bible & Tract Society, Private Bag X2067, Krugersdorp 1740, South Africa. TEL 011-761-1000. FAX 011-764-4749. charts; illus.; index. circ. 28,500.

287.9 CN ISSN 0043-0218
WAR CRY. 1884. bi-w. Can.$17.50($25) Salvation Army, Canada Territorial Headquarters, Editorial Department, 455 N. Service Road E., Oakville, ON L6H 1A5, Canada. TEL 416-844-2561. Ed. Ed Forster. bk.rev.; illus.; circ. 60,000. (tabloid format) **Document type:** consumer publication, newspaper.

297.9 NR ISSN 0049-688X
WAR CRY. 1921. bi-m. £N10 (typically set in Mar.-Apr.). Salvation Army in Nigeria, Territorial Headquarters, Box 3025, Shomolu, Lagos State, Nigeria. TEL 234-1-4975481. FAX 234-1-821497. Ed. Capt. F.O. Oloruntoba. bk.rev. circ. 4,500.

287.9 NZ ISSN 0043-0242
WAR CRY. 1883. w. NZ.$52.60. Salvation Army, 204 Cuba Street, P.O. Box 6015, Wellington 2, New Zealand. TEL 04-384-5649. FAX 04-384-6277. Ed. Alan M. Robb. bk.rev. circ. 10,000. (also avail. in microfilm)
—CCC.

287.9 SA ISSN 0043-0250
WAR CRY/STRYDKREET. (Text in Afrikaans and English) 1884. fortn. R.20. Salvation Army, P.O. Box 1018, Johannesburg 2000, South Africa. TEL 27-11-403-3614. FAX 27-11-403-5638. Ed. Brian Tuck. bk.rev.; illus. circ. 6,500.

287.95 SI ISSN 0049-6898
WAR CRY. 1971. m. S.$5. Salvation Army in Malaysia and Singapore, 207 Clemenceau Ave., Singapore-9, Singapore. Ed. James R. Sloan. charts; illus.

287.9   UK   ISSN 0043-0226
WAR CRY. 1879. w. £23.54 (foreign £38.04. Salvation Army, 101 Queen Victoria St., London EC4P 4EP, England. TEL 0171-236-5222.
FAX 0171-236-3491. Ed. Charles King. adv. contact: Len Dormon. bk.rev.; illus. circ. 80,000. **Document type:** bulletin.

200   AT
WAR CRY. 1883. w. Aus.$44. John Clinch, 1-9 Drill St., Hawthorn, Melbourne, Vic. 3122, Australia.
TEL 61-3-98181438. FAX 61-3-98194864. Ed. Bradley Halse. bk.rev.; illus. circ. 55,000. **Document type:** newspaper.

287.9   US   ISSN 0043-0234
BX9701
THE WAR CRY. 1881. fortn. $7.50 canada $8; elsewhere $9. Salvation Army (Alexandria), 615 Slaters Ln., Alexandria, VA 22313.
TEL 703-684-5500. Ed. Col. Henry Gariepy. bk.rev. circ. 500,000. **Document type:** consumer publication.

289.9   US
WARM LINE. 10/yr. 9527 Bay Court, Carmel, CA 93923. TEL 408-625-0825.
Description: Discusses ideas of interest to Christian Scientists in and out of the church.

281.7 916.206   UA
WATANI. (Text in French) w. Coptic Orthodox Church, St. Mark's Cathedral, Anba Ruess, 222 Sharia Ramses, P.O. Box 9035, Abbasiya, Cairo, Egypt. TEL 02-2825983. TELEX 23281.

289.9   US   ISSN 0043-1087
WATCHTOWER; announcing Jehovah's kingdom. (Editions in 113 languages; also avail. in Braille) 1879. s-m. (Jehovah's Witnesses, Governing Body) Watchtower Bible and Tract Society of New York, Inc., 25 Columbia Hts., Brooklyn, NY 11201.
TEL 718-625-3600. circ. 16,100,000.

289.9   US
THE WAY FOURTH. 1979. q. $13. (Tayu Center) Tayu Press, Box 11554, Santa Rosa, CA 95406.
TEL 707-829-9579. Ed. Stuart E. Goodnick. bk.rev. circ. 200. **Document type:** newsletter.
Formerly: Ganymede.
Description: Dedicated to the teachings of this spiritual tradition, with emphasis on meditation.

200   UK   ISSN 0043-1605
WAY OF LIFE; the church's ministry of healing. 1911. q. £5. Guild of Health, 26 Queen Anne St., London W1M 9LB, England. Ed.Bd. bk.rev.; index. circ. 1,900. **Indexed:** CERDIC.
Former titles: For Health; Healing.

294.37   US
WHEEL SERIES. 1973. irreg., no.3, 1982. Four Seasons Foundation, Box 31190, San Francisco, CA 94131. (Subscr. to: Subco, Box 160, Monroe, OR 97456) Ed. Donald Allen. circ. 3,000. **Document type:** monographic series.

WHICH WAY? - WITCH WAY? see *PARAPSYCHOLOGY AND OCCULTISM*

289   US   ISSN 0043-5007
WHITE WING MESSENGER. 1923. bi-w. $10. (Church of God of Prophecy) White Wing Publishing House, Box 3000, Cleveland, TN 37311. TEL 615-476-8536. FAX 615-559-5133. Ed. Billy D. Murray. bk.rev.; illus. circ. 16,000.

299   NE
WICCAN REDE. (Text in Dutch and English) 1980. q. fl.25($15) Silver Circle, P.O. Box 473, 3700 AL Zeist, Netherlands. Eds. Merlin and Morgana. adv.; bk.rev. circ. 250. **Document type:** newsletter.
Description: Discusses the heritage, symbolism, archetypes, natural magic, elements and seasonal tides of witchcraft.

281.62 917.306   US
WINDOW (RESEDA);* view of the Armenian Church. 1989. q. $18. Armenian Church Research & Analysis Group, c/o Armenian National Commission, 104 N. Belmont St., Ste. 208, Glendale, CA 91206-4492. TEL 818-881-5734. Ed. Rev. Vazken Movsesian. bk.rev. circ. 3,000.
●Also available online.
Description: Serves as a forum to address contemporary issues facing the Armenian Church and people; publishes scholarly articles, comments, reflections, viewpoints, translations.

289.9   US   ISSN 0190-4620
WOMAN'S TOUCH; an inspirational magazine for women. 1977. bi-m. $6. (General Council of the Assemblies of God) Gospel Publishing House, 1445 Boonville Ave., Springfield, MO 65802-1894. TEL 417-862-2781. FAX 417-862-8558. Ed. Sandra G. Clopine. circ. 20,000.
Description: Inspirational, general readership magazine for women with articles that are compatible with Christian teachings.

289   AT   ISSN 0158-6262
WORLD MISSIONS UPDATE. 1971. bi-m. Aus.$5 (effective 1993). Assemblies of God World Missions, P.O. Box 254, Mitcham, Vic. 3132, Australia. TEL 613-872-4566. FAX 613-872-3220. Ed. W. Robert McQuillan. bk.rev. circ. 14,500. **Document type:** bulletin.
Formerly: Garamut (ISSN 0311-0362)
Description: Publishes information regarding AGWM's activities.

297.89   US   ISSN 0043-8804
BP300
WORLD ORDER; a Baha'i magazine. 1966. q. $10. National Spiritual Assembly of the Baha'is of the United States, 536 Sheridan Rd., Wilmette, IL 60091. TEL 708-869-9039. FAX 708-251-3652. (Subscr. to: World Order Subscr. Service, 112 Linden Ave., Wilmette, IL 60091) Ed. Betty J. Fisher. bk.rev.; cum.index: vols.1-12. circ. 1,000. (also avail. in microform from UMI; reprint service avail. from UMI) **Indexed:** Ind.Amer.Per.Verse, Rel.Ind.One. —UMI; UnCover.
Description: Articles intended to show the relationship between contemporary life and the teachings and philosophy of contemporary religions.

289.9   SA
XALAMUKA!. (Text in Tsonga) 1993. m. R.9.50($2.50) Watch Tower Bible & Tract Society, Private Bag X2067, Krugersdorp 1740, South Africa.
TEL 011-761-1000. FAX 011-764-4749. charts; illus.; index. circ. 2,000.

200 289.9   SA   ISSN 0258-9079
XIHONDZO XO RINDZA. (Text in Tsonga) 1974. s-m. R.19. Watch Tower Bible & Tract Society, Private Bag X2067, Krugersdorp 1740, South Africa.
TEL 011-761-1000. FAX 011-764-4749. charts; illus.; index. circ. 6,300.

299   US
YGGDRASIL/FREYA'S FOLK. 1984. q. $6 (foreign $8). 537 Jones St., Ste. 165, San Francisco, CA 94102-2007. Ed. Prudence Priest. adv.: page $20; trim 4 1/2 x 7 1/2. film rev.; video rev.; music rev.; circ. 300 (paid). (back issues avail.) **Document type:** newsletter.

YOGA; tidsskrift for universel religion. see *PHILOSOPHY*

289 341.1   CN
YOUNG COMPANION. 1966. 11/yr. $6. (Amish Church) Pathway Publishing Corporation, Rte. 4, Aylmer, ON N5H 2R3, Canada. Ed. Joseph Stoll. bk.rev.; bibl.; illus. circ. 20,700.
Formerly: Ambassador of Peace.

287.9   AT   ISSN 0300-3264
YOUNG SOLDIER. 1890. w. Aus.$33. (Salvation Army) John Clinch, 1-9 Drill St., Hawthorn, Melbourne, Vic. 3122, Australia. TEL 61-3-98181438. FAX 61-3-9819-4864. Ed. Cilla Bone. illus. circ. 16,000. **Document type:** newspaper.

200   UK
YOUR TOMORROW. 1918. m. £8.50($12) Prophetic Witness Movement International, 59 Baldwin Avenue, Eastbourne, E. Sussex NB21 1U1, England. Ed. Rev. Glyn L. Taylor. adv.; bk.rev.; illus. circ. 4,500.
Indexed: CERDIC.
Formerly: Prophetic Witness (ISSN 0033-135X); Incorporates: Prophetic News and Israel's Watchman (ISSN 0033-1333)

248.48   US
YOUTHGUIDE. 1989. q. $15. Mennonite Publishing House, 616 Walnut Ave., Scottdale, PA 15683-1999. TEL 412-887-8500.
FAX 412-887-3111. Eds. Carol Duerksen, Eddy Hall. circ. 340.
Description: For Mennonite youth teachers and leaders.

299.935   GW   ISSN 0936-546X
ZEITSCHRIFT INFO3; die etwas andere Zeitschrift zum Thema Anthroposophie. 1976. m. DM.52 (foreign DM.68). Info3 Verlag, Kirchgartenstr. 1, 60439 Frankfurt a.M., Germany. TEL 069-584645.
FAX 069-584616. Ed. Ramon Bruell. bk.rev.; illus. circ. 12,000. (back issues avail.) **Document type:** academic/scholarly publication.
Formerly (until 1983): Info3 (ISSN 0721-5347)

299.514   CC
ZHONGGUO DAOJIAO/CHINESE TAOISM. (Text in Chinese) q. Zhongguo Daojiao Xiehui - Chinese Taoism Association, Baiyunguan Nei, Xibianmen Wai, Beijing 100045, People's Republic of China.
TEL 363531. Ed. Li Yangzheng.

RESPIRATORY DISEASES

see *Medical Sciences–Respiratory Diseases*

RHEUMATOLOGY

see *Medical Sciences–Rheumatology*

ROADS AND TRAFFIC

see *Transportation–Roads and Traffic*

ROBOTICS

see *Computers–Robotics*

ROMAN CATHOLICISM

see *Religions and Theology–Roman Catholic*

RUBBER

678.2 668.4   US
ADHESIVE TRENDS. Variant title: Indicators. bi-m. free. Adhesive Manufacturers Association, 401 N. Michigan Ave., Chicago, IL 60611-4267.
TEL 312-644-6610. FAX 312-321-6869. circ. 300 (controlled). **Document type:** newsletter.

ANNUAL BOOK OF A S T M STANDARDS. VOLUME 09.01. RUBBER, NATURAL AND SYNTHETIC - GENERAL TEST METHODS; CARBON BLACK. see *ENGINEERING — Engineering Mechanics And Materials*

ANNUAL BOOK OF A S T M STANDARDS. VOLUME 09.02. RUBBER PRODUCTS, INDUSTRIAL - SPECIFICATIONS AND RELATED TEST METHODS; GASKETS; TIRES. see *ENGINEERING — Engineering Mechanics And Materials*

678 668   FR
ASSOCIATION FRANCAISE DES INGENIEURS ET CADRES DU CAOUTCHOUC ET DES PLASTIQUES. ANNUAIRE. 1956. biennial. membership. Association Francaise des Ingenieurs et Cadres du Caoutchouc et des Plastiques, 60 rue Auber, 94408 Vitry-Seine, France. FAX 45-21-03-50. TELEX 202963. adv.; bk.rev.
Formerly: Association Francaise des Ingenieurs du Caoutchouc et des Plastiques. Annuaire (ISSN 0066-9229)

678.2   IT
ASSOGOMMA NOTIZIE. 1980. w. L.500000 to non-members. Associazione Nazionale fra le Industrie della Gomma, Cavi Elettrici ed Affini - Italian Rubber and Manufacturers Association, Via S. Vittore 36, 20123 Milan, Italy. TEL 39-2-466020. FAX 39-2-435432. Ed. Mario Saltalamacchia. **Document type:** bulletin.

BAUEN MIT KUNSTSTOFFEN. see *BUILDING AND CONSTRUCTION*

BRITISH PLASTICS AND RUBBER MAGAZINE. see *PLASTICS*

BUSINESS TIMES. see *BUSINESS AND ECONOMICS*

678 668.4   FR   ISSN 0035-3175
TS1870   CODEN: RCPLA5
CAOUTCHOUCS ET PLASTIQUES; l'information economique et technique de la profession. (Summaries in English, French) 1924. m. 787 F. (foreign 900 F.). Societe d'Expansion Technique et Economique (SETE), 5, rue Jules Lefebvre, 75009 Paris, France. TEL 48-74-53-70. FAX 48-74-30-28. TELEX EDISETE 650896 F. Ed. Marc Bohy. adv.; bk.rev.; abstr.; bibl.; charts; illus.; stat.; index. circ. 7,000. (back issues avail.) Indexed: C.I.S. Abstr., Chem.Abstr., Excerp.Med., Hort.Abstr., PROMT, Soils & Fert., Weed Abstr., World Agri.Econ.& Rural Sociol.Abstr.
—CASDDS; SWETS. **CCC**.
   Formerly (until 1990): Revue Generale des Caoutchoucs Plastiques.
   Description: Provides information for the plastics manufacturing and processing industries, as well as for machine builders.

CHINA PLASTIC AND RUBBER JOURNAL/ZHONGGUO CUOLIAO XIANGJIAO; a plastic and rubber journal for P.R. China. see *PLASTICS*

COMMUNICATION PNEU. see *TRANSPORTATION — Automobiles*

COMPOSITES. see *PLASTICS*

678.2   UK   ISSN 0262-1584
TS1870   CODEN: DERTD4
DEVELOPMENTS IN RUBBER TECHNOLOGY. 1979. irreg., vol.4, 1987. Elsevier Science Ltd., Books Division, P.O. Box 800, Kidlington, Oxford OX5 1DX, England. TEL 44-1865-843000. FAX 44-1865-843010.
E-mail: nlinfo-f@elsevier.nl; usinfo-f@elsevier.com; forinfo-kyf04035@niftyserve.or.jp; Site addr.: http://www.elsevier.nl/. (Subscr. in U.S. and Canada to: Elsevier Science, 660 White Plains Rd., Tarrytown, NY 10591-5153. TEL 914-524-9200) (back issues avail.) Indexed: Chem.Abstr. **Document type:** monographic series.
—CASDDS.
   Refereed Serial

ENVIRONEWS. see *ENVIRONMENTAL STUDIES*

EPIC INNOVATOR. see *PLASTICS*

678   UK   ISSN 0266-4151
TS1870   CODEN: ERJODH
EUROPEAN RUBBER JOURNAL. 1882. m. (except Aug.) £60($99) (effective 1995). Crain Communications Inc., Cowcross Ct., 2nd Fl., 75-77 Cowcross St., London EC1M 6BP. TEL 0171-608-1116. FAX 0171-608-1173. (Subscr. to: Reader Service Dept., 120-126 Lavender Ave., Mitcham, Surrey CR4 34P, England) Ed. David Shaw. adv.; illus. circ. 6,739. (also avail. in microform from UMI; back issues avail.) Indexed: Anal.Abstr., Br.Tech.Ind., Fluidex, Intl.Polym.Sci.& Tech., Key to Econ.Sci., PROMT, RAPRA. **Document type:** trade publication.
—BLDSC (3829.960000); CASDDS; Ei; SWETS; UMI. **CCC**.
   Former titles (until 1982): European Rubber Journal and Urethanes Today (ISSN 0260-5317); (until 1980): European Rubber Journal (ISSN 0305-2222); (until 1975): Rubber Journal (ISSN 0035-9505); India Rubber Journal.
   Description: Covers commercial and technical developments pertinent to the rubber processing and manufacturing industries.

FIRE & FLAMMABILITY BULLETIN; an international newsletter. see *FIRE PREVENTION*

338.476   AG   ISSN 0533-4500
GUIA DE LA INDUSTRIA DEL CAUCHO. 1970. biennial. Arg.$50($50) or exchange basis. Federacion Argentina de la Industria del Caucho, Av. Leandro N. Alem 1067, Piso 16, 1001 Buenos Aires, Argentina. TEL 54-1-313-2009. FAX 54-1-312-9892. Ed. Antonio C. Castro. adv. contact: A. Cortez Ruiz. circ. 3,000. **Document type:** directory.

678   IT
GUIDA ALL'INDUSTRIA ITALIANA DELLA GOMMA/GUIDE TO THE ITALIAN RUBBER INDUSTRY. (Text in English, French, German and Spanish) 1962. a. L.90000. (Associazione Nazionale fra le Industrie della Gomma) Gesto s.r.l., Via C. Battisti, 21, 20122 Milan, Italy. TEL 39-2-55187581. FAX 39-2-5465310. Ed. Enzo Belli-Nicoletti. adv.: color page L.3500000. **Document type:** directory.
   Formerly: Annuario dell'Industria Italiana della Gomma (ISSN 0066-4499)
   Description: Directory of Italian rubber manufacturers and their suppliers.

678   GW   ISSN 0176-1625
TS1870   CODEN: GFKUED
GUMMI, FASERN, KUNSTSTOFFE; internationale Fachzeitschrift. 1947. m. DM.294.50 (foreign DM.312.70). Dr. Gupta Verlag, Postfach 104125, 40852 Ratingen, Germany. Ed. Heinz Gupta. adv. contact: H. Schuveling. bk.rev.; bibl.; charts; illus.; pat.; stat.; index. circ. 2,500. Indexed: ASCA, Chem.Abstr., Curr.Cont., Dok.Arbeitsmed., Eng.Ind., Excerp.Med., Fluidex, INIS Atomind., Intl.Polym.Sci.& Tech., Packag.Sci.Tech., PROMT, RAPRA, Sh.& Vib.Dig. **Document type:** trade publication.
—BLDSC (4230.950000); CASDDS; Ei; SWETS. **CCC**.
   Formerly (until 1984): Gummi, Asbest, Kunststoffe (ISSN 0017-5595)

678   GW   ISSN 0017-5609
GUMMIBEREIFUNG; Fachzeitschrift fuer Vulkanisation, Runderneuerung, Reifenhandel und Zubehoer. 1924. m. DM.165.60. Bielefelder Verlagsanstalt GmbH & Co. KG, Niederwall 53, 33602 Bielefeld, Germany. TEL 0521-595-520. adv.; bk.rev.; bibl.; charts; illus.; mkt.; pat.; index. circ. 6,000. Indexed: C.I.S. Abstr., Chem.Abstr., Intl.Polym.Sci.& Tech., RAPRA, RAPRA. **Document type:** trade publication.
   Description: For the tire trade industry. Information on tire technology, retreading, marketing, and recycling.

678   SZ   ISSN 0073-0076
HANDBUCH DER INTERNATIONALEN KAUTSCHUKINDUSTRIE/INTERNATIONAL RUBBER DIRECTORY/MANUEL INTERNATIONAL DE CAOUTCHOUC. (Text in English, French, German) 1955. every 10 yrs. 300 SFr. Verlag fuer Internationale Wirtschaftsliteratur GmbH, Postfach 30, CH-8047 Zurich, Switzerland. FAX 01-4010545. Ed. Walter Hirt. **Document type:** directory.

668.4   MX   ISSN 0018-7127
                            CODEN: HMPLAX
HULE MEXICANO Y PLASTICOS; revista tecnica industrial. 1944. m. Mex.$20000($60) Juan Solorzano Gomez, Ed. & Pub., Filomeno Mata 13-11, Colonia Centro, Delegacion Cuauhtemoc, 06000 Mexico, D.F., Mexico. TEL 5-21-57-51. adv.; bk.rev.; abstr.; bibl.; charts; illus.; mkt.; stat. circ. 3,500. Indexed: Chem.Abstr., Intl.Polym.Sci.& Tech., RAPRA, RAPRA.
—CASDDS.

678.2   MX
HULEQUIPO. 1978. m. Queretaro No. 229-402, Mexico 06700 DF, Mexico. Dir. Carlos Villagran Arevalo. adv. circ. 5,000.

678 668.4   US   ISSN 0272-4685
TK5   CODEN: ICEPD2
I E E E CONFERENCE OF ELECTRICAL ENGINEERING PROBLEMS IN THE RUBBER AND PLASTICS INDUSTRIES. CONFERENCE RECORD. a. (I E E E, Industry Applications Society) Institute of Electrical and Electronics Engineers, Inc., 345 E. 47th St., New York, NY 10017-2394. TEL 212-705-7900. FAX 212-705-7682. (Subscr. to: IEEE Service Center, Box 1331, 445 Hoes Lane, Piscataway, NJ 08855-1331) **Document type:** proceedings.
—BLDSC (4362.841500); Ei; UMI. **CCC**.
   Former titles: Electrical Engineering Problems in the Rubber and Plastics Industry Technical Conference. Record (ISSN 0732-295X); Rubber and Plastics Industry Technical Conference. Record (ISSN 0080-4762)

678.2   II   ISSN 0970-2431
SB291.H4   CODEN: IJNREZ
INDIAN JOURNAL OF NATURAL RUBBER RESEARCH. (Text and abstracts in English) 1988. s-a. Rs.200($50) Rubber Research Institute of India, Kottayam 686 009, Kerala, India. TEL 91-481-578316. FAX 91-481-578317. TELEX 888 285 RRII IN. Ed. M.R. Sethuraj. bibl.; charts. Indexed: Abstr.Trop.Agri., Agrindex, Chem.Abstr., Curr.Adv.Plant Sci., Indian Sci.Abstr., Intl.Polym.Sci.& Tech., RAPRA. **Document type:** academic/scholarly publication.
—BLDSC (4417.436000); CASDDS.
   Description: Features biological and technological aspects of natural rubber, including propagation techniques and planting methods, morphology and anatomy, growth and productivity and many other disciplines.
   Refereed Serial

678 668.4   II   ISSN 0019-6312
INDIAN RUBBER & PLASTICS AGE. (Text in English) 1966. m. $24. Wadhera Publications, General Assurance Bldg., 232 Dr. D.N. Rd., Bombay 400 001, India. Ed. Roshanlal Wadhera. adv.; bk.rev. circ. 12,000.

INDIAN RUBBER STATISTICS. see *RUBBER — Abstracting, Bibliographies, Statistics*

678   IT
                            CODEN: INGOAF
INDUSTRIA DELLA GOMMA - ELASTICA. 1957. m. L.135000. (Associazione Nazionale fra le Industrie della Gomma Cavi Elettrici ed Affini) Gesto s.r.l., Via Cesare Battisti 21, 20122 Milan, Italy. TEL 39-2-55187581. FAX 39-2-5465310. Ed. Dr. Enzo Belli-Nicoletti. adv.: color page L.2700000. bk.rev.; abstr.; charts; illus.; mkt.; pat.; stat.; tr.lit.; index. Indexed: Chem.Abstr., Intl.Polym.Sci.& Tech., PROMT, RAPRA, RAPRA. **Document type:** trade publication.
—BLDSC (4438.650000); CASDDS.
   Formerly: Industria della Gomma (ISSN 0019-7556)
   Description: Technical and economic news for the rubber industry.

678 668.4   FR   ISSN 0247-3518
INFORMATIONS DU CAOUTCHOUC ET DES PLASTIQUES. 1949. m. 1500 F. Union des Industries et de la Distribution des Plastiques et du Caoutchouc, 1 Square la Bruyere, 75009 Paris, France. Ed. M. Mercier. adv.; charts; illus.; mkt. circ. 2,000. Indexed: RAPRA.
   Formerly: Informations du Caoutchouc (ISSN 0020-0468)
   Description: Periodical of economic research on plastics.

INFORMATIONS OFFICIELLE DES PLASTIQUES ET DU CAOUTCHOUC. see *PLASTICS*

678   US   ISSN 0146-3977
TS1871   CODEN: APIPDP
INTERNATIONAL INSTITUTE OF SYNTHETIC RUBBER PRODUCERS. ANNUAL MEETING PROCEEDINGS. 1961. a. $135 in N. America; elsewhere $161. International Institute of Synthetic Rubber Producers, 2077 S. Gessner Rd., Ste. 133, Houston, TX 77063-1121. TEL 713-783-7511. FAX 713-783-7253. TELEX 791062. Ed. P. Ballinger. circ. 350. Indexed: Chem.Abstr. **Document type:** proceedings.
—BLDSC (1085.725000); CASDDS.
   Description: Contains scientific papers on industrial hygiene, polymer development, raw material and product situations, and information on the business outlook.

678   II   ISSN 0047-1062
INTERNATIONAL PRESS CUTTING SERVICE: RUBBER AND RUBBER TECHNOLOGY. 1967. w. $65. International Press Cutting Service, Box 63, Allahabad 211001, India. Ed. N. Khanna. bk.rev.; index. circ. 1,200. (processed)

RUBBER

678   UK   ISSN 0020-8655
INTERNATIONAL RUBBER DIGEST. m. £80 (overseas £90) (effective 1996). International Rubber Study Group, 8th Fl., York House, Empire Way, Wembley, Mddx. HA9 0PA, England. TEL 0181-903 7727. FAX 0181-903-2848. TELEX 895 1293 RUBBER G. circ. 600. (also avail. in microfiche from CIS) **Indexed:** IIS, Intl.Polym.Sci.& Tech., RAPRA. **Document type:** bulletin.
—BLDSC (4548.700000).
Description: Reports on the natural rubber market. Covers topical items drawn from many sources on all matters affecting the rubber industry.

678   UK
INTERNATIONAL RUBBER FORUM. a. £45 (overseas £50) (effective 1996). International Rubber Study Group, 8th Fl., York House, Empire Way, Wembley, Mddx. HA9 0PA. TEL 0181-903-7727. FAX 0181-903-2848. TELEX 895 1293 RUBBER G. (also avail. in microfiche from CIS) **Indexed:** IIS. **Document type:** proceedings.
Description: Disseminates research presented at the international conference.

678   UK
INTERNATIONAL RUBBER STUDY GROUP. SECRETARIAT PAPERS. irreg., no.101. price varies. International Rubber Study Group, Secretariat, 8th Fl., York House, Empire Way, Wembley, Mddx. HA9 0PA, England. TEL 0181-903-7727. FAX 0181-903-2848. TELEX 895 1293 RUBBER G. (back issues avail.) **Document type:** proceedings.
Description: Presents statistical, economic, and techno-economic papers on a wide range of topics relating to rubber.

678   UK   ISSN 0074-7823
INTERNATIONAL RUBBER STUDY GROUP. SUMMARY OF PROCEEDINGS OF THE GROUP MEETINGS AND ASSEMBLIES. a. price varies. International Rubber Study Group, 8th Fl., York House, Empire Way, Wembley, Mddx. HA9 0PA. TEL 0181-903-7727. FAX 0181-903-2848. TELEX 895 1293 RUBBER G. (also avail. in microfiche from CIS) **Indexed:** IIS. **Document type:** proceedings.

JOURNAL OF ADHESION SCIENCE AND TECHNOLOGY. see *PLASTICS*

678   MY   ISSN 0127-7065
SB290   CODEN: JNRREQ
JOURNAL OF NATURAL RUBBER RESEARCH. Cover title: J N R R. (Text in English) 1928. q. M.$100($50) Rubber Research Institute of Malaysia, Publications, Library & Information Division, P.O. Box 10150, 50908 Kuala Lumpur, Malaysia. TEL 4567033. FAX 6-03-4573512. bibl.; charts; index, cum.index. circ. 1,000. **Indexed:** Agroforest.Abstr., Biol.Abstr., Chem.Abstr., Curr.Adv.Ecol.Sci., Curr.Cont., Excerp.Med., Hort.Abstr., Intl.Polym.Sci.& Tech., Plant Breed.Abstr., RAPRA, Rev.Appl.Entomol., Rev.Plant Path., Rural Recreat.Tour.Abstr., Soils & Fert., Weed Abstr., World Agri.Econ.& Rural Sociol.Abstr. **Document type:** academic/scholarly publication.
—BLDSC (5021.230000); CASDDS; Faxon; SWETS.
Former titles (until 1986): Rubber Research Institute of Malaysia. Journal (ISSN 0035-953X); (until 1973): Kuala Lumpur. Rubber Research Institute of Malaya. Journal.
Description: Covers all aspects of natural rubber research.

678   GW   ISSN 0022-9520
TS1870   CODEN: KGUKAC
K G K - KAUTSCHUK GUMMI KUNSTSTOFFE. (Text in English, German) 1947. 11/yr. DM.439 (foreign DM.457). (Verband der Deutschen Kautschukgesellschaften) Huethig GmbH, Postfach 102869, 69018 Heidelberg, Germany. TEL 06221-489281. FAX 06221-489205. TELEX 461727-HUEHDD. Eds. Hans Schnecko, Martina Bechstedt. adv.; B&W page DM.2890; trim 210 x 297; adv. contact: Ludger Aulich. bk.rev.; abstr.; bibl.; charts; illus.; pat.; index. circ. 3,265. (also avail. in microfilm from PMC) **Indexed:** Anal.Abstr., Chem.Abstr., Curr.Cont., Excerp.Med., INIS Atomind., Intl.Polym.Sci.& Tech., PROMT, RAPRA, RAPRA, Risk Abstr. **Document type:** trade publication.
—BLDSC (5088.050000); CASDDS; Ei; Genuine Article; SWETS. **CCC.**
Description: Trade journal for high polymeric materials, auxiliary materials and additives, as well as machines and testing equipment for the caoutchouc and rubber industries.

678   RU   ISSN 0022-9466
TS1870   CODEN: KCRZAE
KAUCHUK I REZINA. 1927. bi-m. $87 (effective 1996). Izdatel'stvo Nauka, 90 Pforsoyuznaya ul., 117864 Moscow, Russia. (Dist. by: Mezhdunarodnaya Kniga, ul. Dimitrova D.39, 113095 Moscow, Russia) bk.rev.; bibl.; index. (tabloid format) **Indexed:** Biol.Abstr., Chem.Abstr., Intl.Polym.Sci.& Tech., RAPRA.
—BLDSC (0088.500000); CASDDS. **CCC.**

678.2   UK
KEY NOTE REPORT: RUBBER MANUFACTURERS & PROCESSORS. Variant title: Rubber Manufacturers & Processors. irreg. £185. Key Note Publications Ltd., Field House, 72 Oldfield Rd., Hampton, Middlesex TW12 2HQ, England. TEL 0181-783-0755. FAX 0181-783-1720. **Document type:** trade publication.
●Also available online.
Also available on CD-ROM.

378   UK
KEY RUBBER INDICATORS. 1993. biennial. £120 (overseas £125); with diskette £150 (overseas £155) (effective 1996). International Rubber Study Group, 8th Fl., York House, Empire Way, Wembley, Mddx. HA9 0PA, England. TEL 0181-903-2848. FAX 0181-903-2848. TELEX 895 1293 RUBBER G. stat. (also avail. in diskette format) **Document type:** trade publication.
Description: Provides data on rubber trade, consumption and production; supplies statistics on the production, sales, and use of motor vehicles.

KOMPASS PROFESSIONNEL. CHIMIE, PLASTIQUES, CAOUTCHOUC, PRODUITS MINERAUX. see *BUSINESS AND ECONOMICS — Trade And Industrial Directories*

668.4025489   DK   ISSN 0106-1216
KOMPASS SELECT EXPORT. RUBBER INDUSTRY, PLASTICS INDUSTRY. Cover title: Euro Kompass Denmark. Plastics and Rubber. (Text in Danish, English, French, German and Spanish) 1980. a. DKK 300 (listed companies DKK 100). Forlaget Kompass Danmark, Oeveroedvej 5, DK-2840 Holte, Denmark. TEL 45-45-41-21-00. FAX 45-45-41-06-65. illus. **Document type:** directory.
●Also available on CD-ROM.
Formerly: Kompass Select Denmark. Plastics and Rubber.

KOVACH TIRE REPORT. see *TRANSPORTATION — Automobiles*

678.2   MY   ISSN 0126-8309
HD9161.M32
MALAYSIAN RUBBER PRODUCERS' COUNCIL. ANNUAL REPORT/MAJLIS PENGELUAR-PENGELUAR GETAH MALAYSIA. LAPURAN TAHUNAN. (Text in English, Malay) 1951. a. M.$12. Malaysian Rubber Producers' Council - Majlis Pengeluar-Pengeluar Getah Malaysia, P.O. Box 12688, 50786 Kuala Lumpur, Malaysia. TEL 2482677. stat. circ. 600. **Document type:** corporate report.
Formerly: Rubber Producers' Council of Malaysia. Annual Report.

633.895   MY
MALAYSIAN RUBBER PRODUCERS' COUNCIL. MONTHLY BULLETIN. (Text in English) 1957. m. M.$166. Malaysian Rubber Producers' Council - Majlis Pengeluar-Pengeluar Getah Malaysia, P.O. Box 12688, 50786 Kuala Lumpur, Malaysia. Ed.Bd. charts; stat. **Document type:** bulletin.
Former titles (until 1973): Malaysian Rubber Producers' Council. Monthly Statistical Bulletin (ISSN 0303-1640); (until 1966): Rubber Producers' Council of Malaysia. Monthly Statistical Bulletin (ISSN 0126-5865)

678.32   US   ISSN 0026-8496
MODERN TIRE DEALER; covering tire sales and car service. 1919. 13/yr. $60 (foreign $90) includes Facts Directory. Bill Communications, Inc. (Akron), 341 White Pond Dr., Box 3599, Akron, OH 44309-3599. TEL 216-867-4401. FAX 216-867-0019. E-mail: 753.0308@MCIMAIL.COM. Ed. Lloyd Stoyer. adv.; illus.; tr.lit. circ. 33,000. (reprint service avail. from UMI) **Indexed:** Bus.Ind., Intl.Polym.Sci.& Tech., PROMT, RAPRA, Tr.& Indus.Ind. **Document type:** trade publication.
●Also available online. Vendor(s): Knight-Ridder, Inc.
—SWETS; UMI. **CCC.**
Description: Serves owners and managers of retail tire stores primarily in North America.

MUANYAG ES GUMI/PLASTICS AND RUBBER. see *PLASTICS*

678.32   US   ISSN 0027-7045
N T D R A DEALER NEWS. 1942. m. $13. National Tire Dealers and Retreaders Association, Inc., 1250 I St., N.W., Ste. 400, Washington, DC 20005. TEL 202-789-2300. Ed. C.D. Hylton, III. adv. circ. 6,331. **Indexed:** RAPRA. **Document type:** trade publication.
Incorporates: Tire Dealers Survey (ISSN 0077-5886)

N V R - INFORMATIEF. (Nederlandse Vereniging van Rubber- en Kunststoffabrikanten) see *PLASTICS*

678   JA   ISSN 0029-022X
   CODEN: NGOKAF
NIHON GOMU KYOKAISHI/SOCIETY OF RUBBER INDUSTRY. JOURNAL. (Text in Japanese; summaries in English and Japanese) 1929. m. 6000 Yen. Nihon Gomu Kyokai - Society of Rubber Industry, 1-5-26 Moto-Akasaka, Minato-ku, Tokyo 107, Japan. Ed. Tutomu Furuyama. adv.; bk.rev.; abstr.; bibl.; charts; pat.; cum.index. circ. 4,000. **Indexed:** Intl.Polym.Sci.& Tech., RAPRA. **Document type:** academic/scholarly publication.
—BLDSC (4897.000000); CASDDS. **CCC.**

NOTICIERO DEL PLASTICO - ELASTOMEROS. see *PLASTICS*

OIL CHEMICAL RUBBER WORKERS TRADE UNION OF TURKEY. YEARBOOK. see *LABOR UNIONS*

678   UK
▼**OUTLOOK FOR ELASTOMERS (YEAR).** 1994. a. £20 (overseas £25) (effective 1996). International Rubber Study Group, Secretariat, 8th Fl., York House, Empire Way, Wembley, Mddx. HA9 0PA, England. TEL 0181-903-7727. FAX 0181-903-2848. TELEX 895 1293 RUBBER G. stat. **Document type:** trade publication.
Description: Summarizes data of the rubber economy in each member nation and forecasts the market for the coming year.

PANORAMA PLASTICO; la revista mexicana del plastico. see *PLASTICS*

678 630   MY   ISSN 0032-096X
SB290   CODEN: RRMPA5
PLANTERS BULLETIN. 1952. q. M.$12($24) Rubber Research Institute of Malaysia, Publications, Library & Information Division, P.O. Box 10150, 50908 Kuala Lumpur, Malaysia. TEL 6-3-4567033. FAX 6-3-4573512. bk.rev.; charts; illus.; mkt.; pat.; tr.mk.; index, cum.index every 4 and 8 yrs. circ. 6,000. **Indexed:** Biol.Abstr., Chem.Abstr., Curr.Adv.Ecol.Sci., Intl.Polym.Sci.& Tech., RAPRA, Rev.Appl.Entomol. **Document type:** bulletin.

PLASTFORUM SCANDINAVIA. see *PLASTICS*

PLASTICS AND RUBBER WEEKLY. see *PLASTICS*

PLASTICS NEWS. see *PLASTICS*

PLASTICS, RUBBER & COMPOSITES PROCESSING AND APPLICATIONS. see *PLASTICS*

PLASTIKA I GUMA. see *PLASTICS*

PLASTINDUSTRIEN. see *PLASTICS*

678   FR   ISSN 0296-9386
PNEUMATIQUE; industrie - distribution - rechapage. 1929. 5/yr. 300 F. (foreign 350 F.). (Chambre Nationale du Commerce du Pneumatique et de l'Industrie du Rechapage) V B Promotion, 15 rue du 19 janvier, 92380 Garches, France. TEL 47-01-44-74. FAX 47-01-48-25. TELEX 631 191 F. Ed. Jean-Pierre Gosselin. adv. contact: Helene Hernandez. circ. 2,500.

678.32   IT
PNEURAMA. 1970. 6/yr. free. Promotec s.r.l., Via A.G. Ragazzi 9, 40011 Anzola dell'Emilia (BO), Italy. TEL 39-51-733000. FAX 39-51731886. Ed. Renzo Servadei. adv. contact: Paola Macchiavelli. circ. 15,000 (controlled). **Document type:** trade publication.

POLIMERI; Jugoslavenski casopis za plastiku i gumu. see *PLASTICS*

678.2   US
POLY TOPICS. q. Polyurethane Manufacturers Association, Bldg. C, Ste. 20, 800 Roosevelt Rd., Glen Ellyn, IL 60137. TEL 708-858-2670.

678.4 668.4   JA   ISSN 0032-4779
POLYMER FRIENDS FOR RUBBER, PLASTICS AND FIBER/PORIMA NO TOMO. (Text in Japanese) 1964. m. 2400 Yen($6.66) Taiseisha Ltd., Publishing Division, 1-5 Kyobashi, Chuo-ku, Tokyo 104, Japan. Ed. Sadanori Itonori. adv.; charts; illus.; index. circ. 3,000.

POLYMER RECYCLING. see *ENVIRONMENTAL STUDIES — Waste Management*

POLYMERS AND POLYMER COMPOSITES. see *PLASTICS*

POLYMERS AND RUBBER ASIA. see *PLASTICS*

PREVISIONS GLISSANTES DETAILLEES EN PERSPECTIVES SECTORIELLES (VOL.23): TRANSFORMATION DU CAOUTCHOUC ET DES MATIERES PLASTIQUES. see *BUSINESS AND ECONOMICS — Economic Situation And Conditions*

678.2 668.4   UK   ISSN 0266-7320
TS1870   CODEN: PRPTEE
PROGRESS IN RUBBER AND PLASTICS TECHNOLOGY. q. £185 (foreign £205). (Institute of Materials) R A P R A Technology Ltd., Shawbury, Shrewsbury, Shrops. SY4 4NR, England. TEL 01939-250383. FAX 01939-251118. TELEX 35134. Ed. Jack Buist. adv.; bk.rev.; abstr.; bibl.; charts; illus.; stat. (back issues avail.) Indexed: Intl.Polym.Sci.& Tech., RAPRA. **Document type:** academic/scholarly publication.
—BLDSC (6924.526700); CASDDS; Ei; Faxon; SWETS. **CCC.**
     Supersedes: Progress of Rubber Technology (ISSN 0306-3542)
     Description: Contains in-depth reviews on topics important to the rubber and plastics industries. *Refereed Serial*

678 668.4   UK   ISSN 0747-4954
HD9161.A1
R A P R A NEW TRADE NAMES IN THE RUBBER AND PLASTICS INDUSTRIES. 1926. a. £130 (foreign £140). (Rubber and Plastics Research Association of Great Britain) R A P R A Technology Ltd., Shawbury, Shrewsbury, Shrops. SY4 4NR, England. TEL 01939-250383. FAX 01939-251118. TELEX 35134. circ. 500. **Document type:** directory.
●Also available online. Vendor(s): Data-Star, Knight-Ridder, Inc., European Space Agency, Orbit Search Service (RAPRA), STN International.
—UMI. **CCC.**
     Formerly: New Trade Names in the Rubber and Plastics Industries (ISSN 0077-8869)
     Description: Lists more than 5,000 new trade names introduced by the plastics and rubber industries worldwide.

R A P R A NEWS. see *PLASTICS*

678   CE   ISSN 1391-0051
R R I S L BULLETIN. (Text in English) a. Rs.25 (foreign Rs.160). Rubber Research Institute of Sri Lanka, Dartonfield, Agalawatta, Sri Lanka. **Indexed:** Biol.Abstr., Hort.Abstr., Plant Breed Abstr., Rev.Plant Path., Sri Lanka Sci.Ind. **Document type:** bulletin.
     Supersedes: R R I C Bulletin.

RADNEWS. see *PLASTICS*

RECENT ADVANCES IN CROSSLINKING & CURING. see *PLASTICS*

678.2   AG   ISSN 0528-3280
TS1870   CODEN: CAUCDV
REVISTA CAUCHO. 1958. 4/yr. $10 per no. or exchange basis. Federacion Argentina de la Industria del Caucho, Av. Leandro N. Alem 1067, Piso 16, 1001 Buenos Aires, Argentina. TEL 54-1-313-2009. FAX 54-1-312-9892. Ed. Antonio C. Castro. adv. contact: A. Cortez Ruiz. bk.rev.; charts; illus.; stat. circ. 1,000. **Document type:** trade publication.

338.476   SP   ISSN 0212-2138
REVISTA DEL CAUCHO. 1958. bi-m. 7200 ptas. (foreign 10500 ptas.). (Consorcio Nacional de Industriales del Caucho) Reclamo Tecnico, S.A., Casanovas, 212, 08036 Barcelona, Spain. TEL 4104372. FAX 3223812. Ed. Jorge Foix Cusco. adv.: B&W page 83200 ptas., color page 120500 ptas.; 190 x 270. circ. 1,500. **Indexed:** Ind.SST.
—BLDSC (7847.650000).
     Formerly (until 1979): Caucho (ISSN 0210-0991)

678 668   II
RUBBER AND PLASTICS DIGEST. (Text in English) vol.7, 1972. q. 640 Double Storey, New Rajinder Nagar, New Delhi 60, India. Ed. S.K. Bhanot. adv.; charts; illus.

678   US   ISSN 0300-6123
RUBBER & PLASTICS NEWS; the rubber industry's international newspaper. 1971. fortn. $62. Crain Communications Inc. (Akron), 1725 Merriman Rd., Ste. 300, Akron, OH 44313-5251. TEL 216-836-9180. FAX 216-836-1005. (Subscr. to: 965 E. Jefferson Ave., Detroit, MI 48207-3185. TEL 800-678-9595. FAX 313-446-6777) Ed. Edward Noga. adv.; bk.rev.; charts; illus.; stat.; cum.index; circ. 15,837 (controlled). (tabloid format; also avail. in microfiche from UMI; reprint service avail. from UMI) **Indexed:** Intl.Polym.Sci.& Tech., PROMT, RAPRA. **Document type:** newspaper, trade publication.
—BLDSC (8040.030000); SWETS; UMI. **CCC.**
     Description: Newspaper for rubber industry. Contains commentary, editorials, news items, and technical notes on legislative, technological, financial, and corporate issues that affect the rubber industry worldwide.

678   US   ISSN 0197-2219
RUBBER & PLASTICS NEWS II. (Supplement to Rubber & Plastics News) 1979. fortn. $62. Crain Communications Inc. (Akron), 1725 Merriman Rd., Ste. 300, Akron, OH 44313-5251. TEL 216-836-9180. FAX 216-836-1005. (Subscr. to: 965 E. Jefferson Ave., Detroit MI 48207-3185. TEL 800-678-9595. FAX 313-446-6777) Ed. Edward Noga. (reprint service avail. from UMI) **Indexed:** Intl.Polym.Sci.& Tech., PROMT, RAPRA. **Document type:** trade publication.
—BLDSC (8040.034000); SWETS; UMI. **CCC.**

RUBBER AND PLASTICS NEWSLETTER. see *OCCUPATIONAL HEALTH AND SAFETY*

678.2   UK   ISSN 0955-8772
RUBBER AND POLYURETHANE DIRECTORY B.R.M.A. 1967. biennial. £38 (effective 1995-1997). British Rubber Manufacturers' Association Ltd., 90 Tottenham Court Rd., London W1P 0BR, England. TEL 0171-580-2794. FAX 0171-631-5471. Ed. R.J. German. circ. 1,000. **Document type:** directory.
     Formerly: British Rubber Industry Directory (ISSN 0266-397X)

678   II   ISSN 0970-4124
RUBBER BOARD BULLETIN. (Text in English) 1951. q. Rs.20 (foreign Rs.70). Rubber Board, Box 280, Kottayam 686001, Kerala, India. Ed. P.N. Narayanan Nair. **Indexed:** Agroforest.Abstr., Biol.Abstr., Chem.Abstr., Excerpt.Med., Hort.Abstr., Indian Sci.Abstr., Plant Breed Abstr., RAPRA, Rev.Appl.Entomol., Soils & Fert., Trop.Abstr., Weed Abstr., World Agri.Econ.& Rural Sociol.Abstr. **Document type:** bulletin.
—BLDSC (8040.700000).

678   US   ISSN 0035-9475
TS1870   CODEN: RCTEA4
RUBBER CHEMISTRY AND TECHNOLOGY. 1928. 5/yr. $95. American Chemical Society, Inc., Rubber Division, University of Akron, Akron, OH 44309-0499. TEL 216-972-7814. FAX 216-972-5269. Ed. C.M. Roland. adv.; bk.rev.; abstr.; charts; illus.; index. circ. 6,000. (also avail. in microform from UMI) **Indexed:** A.S.& T.Ind., Chem.Abstr., Curr.Cont., Eng.Ind., Fluidex, Intl.Polym.Sci.& Tech., RAPRA, Text.Tech.Dig. **Document type:** academic/scholarly publication.
—BLDSC (8041.000000); CASDDS; Ei; Faxon; Genuine Article; SWETS; UMI; UnCover.
     Description: Provides papers on fundamental research, technical development, and chemical engineering relating to rubber and its allied substances.

678   UK   ISSN 0035-9483
TS1870   CODEN: RUDVAX
RUBBER DEVELOPMENTS. 1947. q. free. Malaysian Rubber Producers' Research Association, Tun Abdul Razak Laboratory, Brickendonbury, Hertford SG13 8NL, England. TEL 01992-584966. FAX 01992-554837. Ed. G.M. Reader. bk.rev.; bibl.; charts; illus.; index. circ. 14,000. **Indexed:** Abstr.Bull.Inst.Pap.Chem., Br.Tech.Ind., Cadscan, Chem.Abstr., Eng.Ind., Fluidex, Hort.Abstr., Intl.Polym.Sci.& Tech., Lead Abstr., RAPRA, World Surf.Coat., World Text.Abstr., Zincscan. **Document type:** academic/scholarly publication, trade publication.
—BLDSC (8042.000000); CASDDS; Ei; UMI.
     Incorporates (1970-1990): N R Technology (ISSN 0307-9007)
     Description: A review of developments in natural rubber research, technology and use.

678   II   ISSN 0035-9491
TS1885.I5   CODEN: RUIDA4
RUBBER INDIA. (Text in English) 1949. m. Rs.300 (foreign $50). All India Rubber Industries Association, Navjivan Society, Bldg. No. 3, 8th Fl., Lamington Rd., Bombay 400 008, India. TEL 022-3062174. FAX 022-3073702. TELEX 011-75033. Ed. Manu M. Patel. adv.: B&W page Rs.2000; 175 x 235. bk.rev. circ. 1,300. **Indexed:** Chem.Abstr.
—BLDSC (8043.800000); CASDDS.
     Description: Devoted to the dissemination of information within the rubber industry.

338   US
RUBBER: LATIN AMERICAN INDUSTRIAL REPORT. (Avail. for each of 22 Latin American countries) 1985. a. $435 per country report. Aquino Productions, Box 15760, Stamford, CT 06901. TEL 203-325-3138. Ed. Andres C. Aquino.

678   II   ISSN 0035-9513
     CODEN: RUBNAX
RUBBER NEWS. 1961. m. Rs.250($20) Polymer Publications, 41-1191, Adarsh Nagar, Prabhadevi, Bombay 400023, India. TEL 4373813. Ed. D.S. Kulkarni. adv.: B&W page Rs.3000. bk.rev.; charts; illus.; mkt.; index. circ. 1,000. **Indexed:** Chem.Abstr., Intl.Polym.Sci.& Tech., RAPRA. **Document type:** trade publication.
—CASDDS.
     Description: Covers the manufacture of rubber and like materials.

678   US   ISSN 0361-0640
TS1877
RUBBER RED BOOK; directory of the rubber industry. 1936. a. $89.95. Argus Inc., 6151 Powers Ferry Rd., N.W., Atlanta, GA 30339-2941. TEL 404-955-2500. FAX 404-955-0400. Ed. Barbara Katinsky. circ. 4,400. **Document type:** directory, trade publication.
     Formerly: Elastomerics Rubber Red Book.

338.476 678.2   II   ISSN 0257-859X
RUBBER REPORTER. (Text in English) 1975. bi-m. Rs.125($20) 332, Hind Rajasthan Bldg., D.S. Phalke Road, Dadar, Bombay-400014, India. TEL 4110364. Ed. K.S. Mathew. adv.; bk.rev. circ. 4,016. (Reprint service avail.)

5836 RUBBER

633.895   MY   ISSN 0126-8279
SB290
RUBBER RESEARCH INSTITUTE OF MALAYSIA. ANNUAL REPORT. a. M.$25($30) Rubber Research Institute of Malaysia, Publications, Library & Information Division, 260 Jalan Ampang, 50450 Kuala Lumpur, Malaysia. circ. 1,700. **Indexed**: Biol.Abstr., Hort.Abstr., Rev.Plant Path.
    Formerly (until 1973): Kuala Lumpur. Rubber Research Institute of Malaya. Annual Report.

633.895   MY   ISSN 0127-9785
RUBBER RESEARCH INSTITUTE OF MALAYSIA. RUBBER GROWERS' CONFERENCE - PROCEEDINGS. biennial. $150. Rubber Research Institute of Malaysia, P.O. Box 10150, 50908 Kuala Lumpur, Malaysia. TEL 6-3-4567022. FAX 6-3-4573512. TELEX MA 30369. charts; illus. circ. 1,000. **Indexed**: Chem.Abstr., Seed Abstr. **Document type**: proceedings.
    Formerly: Rubber Research Institute of Malaysia. Planters Conference Proceedings (ISSN 0126-5849)

633.895   MY   ISSN 0126-9410
RUBBER RESEARCH INSTITUTE OF MALAYSIA. TECHNOLOGY BULLETIN. s-a. M.$3($2) Rubber Research Institute of Malaysia, Publications, Library & Information Division, P.O. Box 10150, 50908 Kuala Lumpur, Malaysia. TEL 6-3-4567033. FAX 6-3-4573512. circ. 1,500. **Document type**: bulletin.

678   CE   ISSN 1391-0043
RUBBER RESEARCH INSTITUTE OF SRI LANKA. ANNUAL REVIEW. (Text in English) a. Rs.50 (foreign Rs.320). Rubber Research Institute of Sri Lanka, Dartonfield, Agalawatta, Sri Lanka. **Indexed**: Biol.Abstr., Hort.Abstr., Rev.Plant Path, Weed Abstr.
    Supersedes: Rubber Research Institute of Ceylon. Annual Review.

678 668.4   CE   ISSN 0379-1130
TS1870   CODEN: JRRLDZ
RUBBER RESEARCH INSTITUTE OF SRI LANKA. JOURNAL. (Text in English) vol.53, 1976. a. Rs.50 (foreign Rs.320). Rubber Research Institute of Sri Lanka, Dartonfield, Agalawatta, Sri Lanka. Ed. Dr. L.M.K. Tillekerathe. adv.; bk.rev.; charts; illus. circ. 1,000. **Indexed**: Abstr.Trop.Agri., Biol.Abstr., Chem.Abstr., Hort.Abstr., Plant Breed.Abstr., RAPRA, Rev.Plant Path., Rural Recreat.Tour.Abstr., Soils & Fert., Sri Lanka Sci.Ind., Trop.Abstr., World Agri.Econ.& Rural Sociol.Abstr.
—CASDDS.
    Formerly (until 1976): Rubber Research Institute of Sri Lanka. Quarterly Journal (ISSN 0035-9521)

678.2 668.4   SA   ISSN 0258-9737
RUBBER SOUTHERN AFRICA. 1985. bi-m. R.92. George Warman Publications (Pty.) Ltd., P.O. Box 3847, Cape Town 8000, South Africa. TEL 27-21-245320. FAX 27-21-261332. Ed. Martin Wells. circ. 1,700. **Indexed**: Intl.Polym.Sci.& Tech., RAPRA. **Document type**: trade publication.
—BLDSC (8045.300000).
    Description: Contains information on rubber compounding, moulding, tire manufacturing, repair and marketing.

678   UK   ISSN 0035-9548
HD9161.A1
RUBBER STATISTICAL BULLETIN. m. £135 (overseas £150) (effective 1994-1995). International Rubber Study Group, 8th Fl., York House, Empire Way, Wembley HA9 0PA, England. TEL 081-903-7727. FAX 081-903-2848. TELEX 895 1293 RUBBER G. mkt.; stat. circ. 1,000. (also avail. in microfiche from CIS; back issues avail.) **Indexed**: IIS, PROMT. **Document type**: bulletin.
    Formerly (until 1946): International Rubber Regulatory Commission. Statistical Bulletin.
    Description: Provides statistics on the production, consumption, import and export of natural and synthetic rubbers for many countries for the current and preceding year. Includes annual data for the previous five years.

678   US   ISSN 0035-9564
HD9161.A1
RUBBER TRENDS; a quarterly review of production, markets, prices, etc. q. £360($685) Economist Intelligence Unit, 111 W. 57th St., New York, NY 10019. TEL 212-554-0600; 800-938-4685. FAX 212-586-1182. TELEX 175567. (U.K. addr.: Economist Intelligence Unit Ltd., Subscriptions Dept., P.O. Box 154, Dartford, Kent DA1 1QB, England. TEL 01322-289194) charts; stat.; cum.index. (also avail. in microform from UMI) **Indexed**: Asian-Pac.Econ.Lit., Intl.Polym.Sci.& Tech., Key to Econ.Sci., PROMT, RAPRA. **Document type**: trade publication.
—BLDSC (8046.300000); UMI. **CCC**.
    Description: Analyzes the consumer outlook, as well as trends in rubber-using industries and countries.

678   US   ISSN 0035-9572
TS1870   CODEN: RUBWAQ
RUBBER WORLD. 1889. 16/yr. $29. Lippincott & Peto, Inc., 1867 W. Market St., Akron, OH 44313. TEL 216-864-2122. Ed. Don R. Smith. adv.; bk.rev.; bibl.; charts; illus.; mkt.; stat.; tr.lit.; index. circ. 11,400. (also avail. in microform from UMI,PMC; reprint service avail. from UMI) **Indexed**: Anal.Abstr., Bus.Ind., Chem.Abstr., Eng.Ind., Fluidex, Intl.Polym.Sci.& Tech., Key to Econ.Sci., PROMT, RAPRA, Rural Recreat.Tour.Abstr., SRI (until 1991), Tr.& Indus.Ind., World Agri.Econ.& Rural Sociol.Abstr. **Document type**: trade publication.
—BLDSC (8047.000000); CASDDS; Ei; Faxon; Genuine Article; SWETS; UMI; UnCover. **CCC**.

678   US
RUBBER WORLD BLUE BOOK OF MATERIALS, COMPOUNDING INGREDIENTS AND MACHINERY FOR RUBBER. 1916. a. $107 (foreign $135). Lippincott & Peto, Inc., 1867 W. Market St., Akron, OH 44313. TEL 216-864-2122. Ed. Don R. Smith. **Document type**: directory.

678.2   UK
RUBBICANA-EUROPE (YEAR). (Text in English, French and German) a. £75 (foreign £80). R A P R A Technology Ltd., Shawbury, Shrewsbury, Shrops. SY4 4NR, England. TEL 01939-250383. FAX 01939-251118. Ed. Kate Evans. **Document type**: directory.
    Description: Provides comprehensive company listings of all sectors of the European rubber and polyurethane industries. Includes suppliers, manufacturers and associations.

338.476   US   ISSN 1076-710X
RUBBICANA: RUBBER DIRECTORY AND BUYERS GUIDE (YEAR); a directory of rubber product manufacturers and rubber industry suppliers in North America. Variant title: Rubber Directory and Buyers Guide. 1978. a. $80. (Rubber and Plastic News) Crain Communications Inc. (Akron), 1725 Merriman Rd., Ste. 300, Akron, OH 44313-5251. TEL 216-836-9180. FAX 216-836-1005. TELEX 241 634. (Subscr. to: 965 E. Jefferson Ave., Detroit, MI 48207-3185. TEL 800-678-9595) adv. circ. 15,057. (back issues avail.) **Document type**: directory, trade publication.

678.32   IT   ISSN 0393-7526
RUOTASPRING; tyre-rubber fortnightly journal. (Text in English, French, Italian) 1970. bi-m. L.72000. Minuti Luisa, Via Alatri 30, 00171 Rome, Italy. TEL 25 83 389. Ed. Riccardo Borasi. adv.; bk.rev.; bibl.; charts; illus.; stat. circ. 9,780. (back issues avail.)

678.2 668.4   US
SEALANTS; the professional's guide. a. $16.45. Sealant, Waterproofing and Restoration Institute, 3101 Broadway, Ste. 585, Kansas City, MO 64111. TEL 816-561-8230. FAX 816-561-7765. Ed. Michelle Groner; Pub. Ken Bowman. charts; illus.; stat.
    Description: Covers joints, sealants, and specifications for the industry.

678   GW
SERVICE - JAHRBUCH. 1952. a. DM.34.80. Bielefelder Verlagsanstalt GmbH & Co. KG, Niederwall 53, 33602 Bielefeld, Germany. TEL 0521-595-520. adv. circ. 2,000. **Document type**: trade publication.
    Formerly: Vulkaniseur - Jahrbuch (ISSN 0083-694X)

678.32   MY   ISSN 0126-5806
SIARAN PEKEBUN. q. M.$12($24) Rubber Research Institute of Malaysia, Publications, Library & Information Division, P.O. Box 10510, 50908 Kuala Lumpur, Malaysia. TEL 6-3-4567033. FAX 6-3-4573512.

678   US
SYNTHETIC RUBBER END-USE SURVEY. triennial, latest 1990. $305 in N. America; elsewhere $315. International Institute of Synthetic Rubber Producers, 2077 S. Gessner Rd., Ste. 133, Houston, TX 77063-1123. TEL 713-783-7511. FAX 713-783-7253. TELEX 791062. Ed. B. Theismann.
    Description: Defines how major synthetic elastomers are used. Divided in geographical sections, by elastomer and by end-use category.

678   US
SYNTHETIC RUBBER MANUAL. triennial, latest, 12th ed. $55 in N. America; elsewhere $65. International Institute of Synthetic Rubber Producers, 2077 S. Gessner Rd., Ste. 133, Houston, TX 77063-1123. TEL 713-783-7511. FAX 713-783-7253. TELEX 791062. Ed. R. Killian.
    Description: Lists over 2000 individual polymers and elastomers with technical and quality criteria.

678.32   US
TIRE AND RIM ASSOCIATION YEAR BOOK. 1927. a. $32. Tire and Rim Association, Inc., Crown Pointe, 175 Montrose Ave. W., No. 150, Copley, OH 44321. TEL 216-666-8121. Ed. J.F. Pacuit. circ. 4,500. **Document type**: trade publication.
    formerly: Tire and Rim Association. Standards Year Book (ISSN 0082-4496)

338.476 388.3   US   ISSN 0746-9071
TIRE BUSINESS. 1983. fortn. $50. Crain Communications Inc. (Akron), 1725 Merriman Rd., Ste. 300, Akron, OH 44313-5251. TEL 216-836-9180; 800-678-9595. FAX 216-836-1005. (Subscr. to: 965 E. Jefferson Ave., Detroit, MI 48207-3185. FAX 313-446-6777) Ed. David Zielasko. circ. 21,000. (tabloid format; back issues avail.) **Indexed**: Intl.Polym.Sci.& Tech., RAPRA. **Document type**: newspaper, trade publication.
—UMI. **CCC**.
    Description: For independent tire dealers and others involved in automotive service.

678.32   US   ISSN 1046-7157
TIRE RETREADING - REPAIR JOURNAL; a technical digest for tire retreaders. 1956. m. $50 (foreign $60). (American Retreaders Association) Tire Industry Publication Service, Inc., Box 37203, Louisville, KY 40233-7203. TEL 502-968-8900; 800-426-8835. FAX 502-964-7859. Ed. Marvin Bozarth. adv.: B&W page $550; adv. contact: Bunny McDermott. index; circ. 2,550. (controlled). (back issues avail.) **Document type**: trade publication.
    Formed by the merger of (1982-1989): Tire Repair Journal (ISSN 0731-7298) & Retreader's Journal (ISSN 0482-430X)
    Description: Discusses matters of interest to tire retread production employees, retread and repair material sales personnel, equipment sales people, and other professionals in the tire and transportation industries.

TIRE REVIEW; the authority on tire dealer profitability. see *TRANSPORTATION — Automobiles*

678.32   US   ISSN 0090-8657
TL270   CODEN: TSTCAU
TIRE SCIENCE AND TECHNOLOGY. 1973. q. $18. Tire Society Inc., Box 1502, Akron, OH 44309-1502. Ed. Daniel I. Livingston. bibl.; charts; illus. circ. 600. **Indexed**: Agri.Eng.Abstr., Appl.Mech.Rev., Eng.Ind, Intl.Polym.Sci.& Tech., ISMEC, RAPRA.
—BLDSC (8858.403000); Ei; Faxon; SWETS; UMI. **CCC**.

331.8   TU
TURKIYE PETROL KIMYA, LASTIK ISCILEERI SENDIKASI. MAGAZINE. m. Turkiye Petrol, Kimya, Lastik Iscileeri Sendikasi - Oil Chemical Rubber Workers Trade Union of Turkey, Yildiz, Posta Cad P.O. Box 284, Evren Sitesi Gayrettepe, Istanbul 80280, Turkey. TEL 1748896. FAX 1747446.

SCIENCES: COMPREHENSIVE WORKS

678.2 629.286 AT
TYRE AND RIM ASSOCIATION OF AUSTRALIA STANDARDS MANUAL. 1958. a. Aus.$22.50 (effective 1996). Tyre and Rim Association of Australia, c/o F.A. & W.A. Coghlan, 795 Glenferrie Rd., Hawthorn, Vic. 3122, Australia. TEL 61-3-98180759. FAX 61-3-98180750. circ. 1,700. **Document type:** trade publication.

678.32 UK ISSN 0041-4859
TYRES AND ACCESSORIES. 1946. m. £12. Tyre Industry Publications Ltd., 136 Valley Rd., Clacton-on-Sea, Essex CO15 6LX, England. Ed. George Marshall. adv.; bk.rev.; illus. circ. 6,100. **Indexed:** Chem.Abstr., Intl.Polym.Sci.& Tech., RAPRA. **Document type:** trade publication.
—SWETS.

UNION DES INDUSTRIES ET DE LA DISTRIBUTION DES PLASTIQUES ET DU CAOUTCHOUC. GUIDE. see BUSINESS AND ECONOMICS — Trade And Industrial Directories

UNITED RUBBER WORKER. see LABOR UNIONS

678.2 UK ISSN 0265-637X
URETHANES TECHNOLOGY. 1984. bi-m. £46($98) Crain Communications Ltd., Cowcross Ct., 2nd Fl., 75-77 Cowcross St., London EC1M 6BP, England. TEL 0171-608-1116. FAX 0171-608-1173. TELEX 28544. Ed. David R. Reed; Pub. Paul Mitchell. adv.: B&W page $936, color page $1596; adv. contact: Paul Mitchell. circ. 3,523. **Indexed:** Intl.Polym.Sci.& Tech., RAPRA. **Document type:** trade publication.
—BLDSC (9124.148700); Ei; SWETS.
Description: Reports commercial and technical developments in the polyurethane industry worldwide.

678.2 US ISSN 0083-5218
TS1890
VANDERBILT RUBBER HANDBOOK. 1926. irreg. $100 (effective 1995). R.T. Vanderbilt Co., Inc., 30 Winfield St., Norwalk, CT 06855. TEL 203-853-1400. FAX 203-853-1452. TELEX 221125. Ed. Robert F. Ohm. index. **Document type:** trade publication.
Description: Contains technical information for those directly connected with the compounding and processing of rubber and synthetic elastomers in their dry form.

678.2 CC ISSN 1000-890X
CODEN: XIGOED
XIANGJIAO GONGYE/CHINA RUBBER INDUSTRY. (Text in Chinese; table of contents in Chinese, English) m. Beijing Xiangjiao Gongye Yanjiu Shejiyuan - Beijing Research and Design Institute of Rubber Industry, Banbidian, Xijiao (West Surburb), Beijing 100039, People's Republic of China. TEL 815831. **Indexed:** Intl.Polym.Sci.& Tech., RAPRA. **Document type:** academic/scholarly publication.
—BLDSC (3180.234280); CASDDS.

RUBBER — Abstracting, Bibliographies, Statistics

678.2 CN ISSN 0835-0027
HD9161.C2
CANADA. STATISTICS CANADA. RUBBER AND PLASTIC PRODUCTS INDUSTRIES. (Catalogue 33-250) (Text in English and French) 1919. a. Can.$35($42) (foreign $49). Statistics Canada, Publications Sales and Services, Ottawa, Ont. K1A 0T6, Canada. TEL 613-951-7277. FAX 613-951-1584.
Formerly (until 1985): Canada. Statistics Canada. Rubber Products Industries (ISSN 0300-0214)
Description: Annual census of manufactures.

678 FR
FRANCE. SERVICE D'ETUDE DES STRATEGIES ET DES STATISTIQUES INDUSTRIELLES. RESULTATS MENSUELS DES ENQUETES DE BRANCHE. INDUSTRIE DU CAOUTCHOUC. m. 260 F. (foreign 310 F.)(effective 1991). Service d'Etude des Strategies et des Statistiques Industrielles (SESSI), 85 bd. du Montparnasse, 75270 Paris Cedex 06, France. TEL 45-56-42-34. FAX 45-56-40-71. stat.
Description: Follows developments in the rubber industry through the performance of selected indicators.

678 FR
FRANCE. SERVICE D'ETUDE DES STRATEGIES ET DES STATISTIQUES INDUSTRIELLES. RESULTATS TRIMESTRIELS DES ENQUETES DE BRANCHE. INDUSTRIE DE CAOUTCHOUC. q. 180 F. (foreign 210 F.)(effective 1991). Service d'Etude des Strategies et des Statistiques Industrielles (SESSI), 85 bd. du Montparnasse, 75270 Paris Cedex 06, France. TEL 45-56-42-34. FAX 45-56-40-71. stat.
Description: Provides detailed industry-wide performance statistics for comparative evaluations.

678 II ISSN 0073-6651
INDIAN RUBBER STATISTICS. (Text in English) 1958. a. price varies. Rubber Board, Box 280, Kottayam 686001, Kerala, India. TEL 91-0481-563231. FAX 91-0481-564639. TELEX 0888-205 RUBR IN.

633.895 310 MY ISSN 0127-6778
HD9161.M32
MALAYSIA. DEPARTMENT OF STATISTICS. MONTHLY RUBBER STATISTICS OF MALAYSIA. (Text in English) m. M.$5 per no. Department of Statistics, Wisma Statistik, Jalan Cenderasari, 50514 Kuala Lumpur, Malaysia. TEL 03-2922133. **Document type:** government publication.

633.895 310 MY ISSN 0127-8509
MALAYSIA. DEPARTMENT OF STATISTICS. RUBBER STATISTICS HANDBOOK, MALAYSIA. (Text in English) 1988. irreg., latest 1990. M.$8. Department of Statistics, Wisma Statistik, Jalan Cenderasari, 50514 Kuala Lumpur, Malaysia. TEL 03-2922133. FAX 03-2937018. **Document type:** government publication.

MARO POLYMER NOTES. see PLASTICS — Abstracting, Bibliographies, Statistics

678 BL ISSN 0025-9748
MERCADO DA BORRACHA NO BRASIL. BOLETIM MENSUAL. 1967. m. Superintendencia da Borracha, Ministerio de Industria e do Comercio, SAS QD 05-LT 05-BL. H, CEP 70070 Brasilia, DF, Brazil, Brazil. charts; mkt.; stat. circ. 1,000. (processed)

678 668.4 016 UK ISSN 0033-6750
TS1870
R A P R A ABSTRACTS. 1923. m. £1050 (foreign £1150). (Rubber and Plastics Research Association of Great Britain) R A P R A Technology Ltd., Shawbury, Shrewsbury, Shrops. SY4 4NR, England. TEL 01939-250383. FAX 01939-251118. TELEX 35134. Ed. C. Wright. adv.; bk.rev.; stat.; index. circ. 700. (back issues avail.) **Indexed:** Art & Archaeol.Tech.Abstr., World Surf.Coat., World Text.Abstr. **Document type:** abstracting/indexing.
●Also available online. Vendor(s): Data-Star, Knight-Ridder, Inc., European Space Agency, Orbit Search Service (RAPRA), Telesystemes - Questel. Also available on CD-ROM.
—BLDSC (7289.500000); UMI. **CCC.**
Description: Provides a comprehensive up-to-date survey of current information from all around the globe, relevant to the rubber, plastics, composites and associated industries. Material is selected from more than 450 journals, conference proceedings, books, trade and technical literature, standards and government publications.
Refereed Serial

678 668.4 UK
R A P R A ABSTRACTS - C D - R O M. 1991. bi-m. £3250. (Rubber and Plastics Research Association of Great Britain) R A P R A Technology Ltd., Shawbury, Shrewsbury, Shrops. SY4 4NR, England. TEL 01939-250383. FAX 01939-251118. TELEX 35134. **Document type:** abstracting/indexing.
●Available only on CD-ROM.
—**CCC.**
Formerly (until 1993): Plastics and Rubbers Materials Disk (ISSN 0961-9305)
Description: CD-ROM version of R A P R A Abstracts.

R A P R A REVIEW REPORTS; current developments in polymeric materials technology and engineering. see PLASTICS — Abstracting, Bibliographies, Statistics

678.2 US
RUBBER MANUFACTURERS ASSOCIATION. MONTHLY RUBBER REPORT. m. $1500. Rubber Manufacturers Association, 1400 K St., 9th Fl., Washington, DC 20005. TEL 202-682-4860.
Description: Covers shipment, inventories, consumption and trade of natural and synthetic rubber (by type).

338.476 310 US
RUBBER MANUFACTURERS ASSOCIATION. NATURAL AND SYNTHETIC RUBBER IMPORT AND EXPORT REPORT. m. $500. Rubber Manufacturers Association, 1400 K St., N.W., 9th Fl., Washington, DC 20005. TEL 202-682-4860. charts; stat.

338.476 310 US
RUBBER MANUFACTURERS ASSOCIATION. STATISTICAL REPORT. MONTHLY TIRE REPORT. 1974. m. $1000. Rubber Manufacturers Association, 1400 K St., N.W., 9th Fl., Washington, DC 20005. TEL 202-682-4860. charts; stat. **Indexed:** SRI.
Description: Shows import-export activity of passenger car, light and heavy truck, and bus tires. Includes statistics on tire shipments.

338.476 310 US
RUBBER MANUFACTURERS ASSOCIATION. TIRE AND TUBE IMPORT AND EXPORT REPORT. m. $500. Rubber Manufacturers Association, 1400 K St., 9th Fl., Washington, DC 20005. TEL 202-682-4860. charts; stat.

678 UK
WORLD RUBBER STATISTICS HANDBOOK. quinquennial. £99($100) (overseas £105); with diskette £149 (overseas £155) (effective 1996). International Rubber Study Group, 8th Fl., York House, Empire Way, Wembley, Mddx. HA9 0PA. TEL 0181-903-7727. FAX 0181-903-2848. TELEX 895 1293 RUBBER G. (also avail. in microfiche from CIS; diskette format) **Indexed:** IIS. **Document type:** trade publication.
Description: Covers all aspects of the world elastomer rubber economy and associated products. Provides statistics on natural and synthetic rubber production and statistics on the production and use of cars.

338.476 US
WORLDWIDE RUBBER STATISTICS. a. $205 in N.A.; elsewhere $215. International Institute of Synthetic Rubber Producers, 2077 S. Gessner Rd., Ste. 133, Houston, TX 77063-1123. TEL 713-783-7511. FAX 713-783-7253. TELEX 791062. Ed. B. Theismann.
Description: Covers synthetic and natural rubber industry. Lists producers, tabulates plant production, provides forecasts and gives statistical histories.

SCHOOL ORGANIZATION AND ADMINISTRATION

see Education–School Organization and Administration

SCIENCE FICTION, FANTASY, HORROR

see Literature–Science Fiction, Fantasy, Horror

SCIENCES: COMPREHENSIVE WORKS

500 US ISSN 1062-2195
Q11
A A A S HANDBOOK. a. $7.50. American Association for the Advancement of Science, 1333 H St., N.W., Washington, DC 20005. TEL 202-326-6446.
Document type: directory.
Formerly (until 1991): American Association for the Advancement of Science. Handbook (ISSN 0361-7874)
Description: Lists AAAS section officers, council and committee members, and institutional affiliates. Includes information on association activities, policies and history.

508.1 US ISSN 0271-2229
Q181.A1 CODEN: AAAPEH
A A A S PUBLICATION. a. free. American Association for the Advancement of Science, 1333 H St., N.W., Washington, DC 20005. TEL 202-326-6446. bk.rev. **Indexed:** Deep Sea Res.& Oceanogr.Abstr., GeoRef.
Formerly: A A A S Miscellaneous Publication (ISSN 0569-2342)
Description: Lists current AAAS titles on AIDS, arms control, astronomy, biotechnology, chemistry, neuroscience, science education, and science policy.

5838 SCIENCES: COMPREHENSIVE WORKS

500 US ISSN 1041-8857
A A A S REPORT: RESEARCH AND DEVELOPMENT. 1976. a. $16.95 to non-members; members $13.50. American Association for the Advancement of Science, 1333 H St., N.W., Washington, DC 20005. TEL 202-326-6600. circ. 2,500. (back issues avail.) **Indexed:** SRI. **Document type:** monographic series.
   Description: Details information on the President's proposed federal research and development budget.

A F P SCIENCES; bulletin information scientifique, technique, medicale. (Agence France-Presse) see *MEDICAL SCIENCES*

500 919.8 AT ISSN 0728-6414
A N A R E NEWS. 1981. q. free. Australian National Antarctic Research Expeditions, Australian Antarctic Division, Channel Highway, Kingston, Tas. 7050, Australia. Ed.Bd. bk.rev.; abstr.; illus. circ. 2,000. (tabloid format) **Document type:** government publication, newsletter.

500 919.8 550 AT ISSN 1038-2135
G845 CODEN: ANRPEN
A N A R E REPORTS. (Australian National Antarctic Research Expeditions) 1950. irreg. free. Department of Environment, Sport and Territories, Antarctic Division, Channel Highway, Kingston, Tas. 7050, Australia. circ. 400. (back issues avail.) **Indexed:** AESIS, GeoRef.
   —BLDSC (7030.400000).
   Formerly (until 1984): A N A R E Scientific Report (ISSN 0572-127X)

500 AT ISSN 0729-6533
CODEN: ANRNDG
A N A R E RESEARCH NOTES. (Australian National Antarctic Research Expeditions) 1982. irreg. free. Department of Environment, Sport and Territories, Antarctic Division, Channel Highway, Kingston, Tas. 7050, Australia. circ. 400. (back issues avail.) **Indexed:** AESIS.
   —BLDSC (0897.730000).

A N U REPORTER. (Australian National University) see *COLLEGE AND ALUMNI*

500 AT ISSN 0312-8059
CODEN: PANSDH
A N Z A A S CONGRESS PAPERS. 1970. a. price varies. (Australian and New Zealand Association for the Advancement of Science) University of New South Wales Library, P.O. Box 1, Kensington, N.S.W. 2033, Australia. FAX 02-663-4097. (microfiche) **Indexed:** Aus. P.A.I.S., Aus.Sci.Ind., Chem.Abstr. **Document type:** proceedings.
   —BLDSC (3415.150000); CASDDS.

A S T C NEWSLETTER. (Association of Science-Technology Centers) see *MUSEUMS AND ART GALLERIES*

910.0911 CN ISSN 0225-5170
A S T I S OCCASIONAL PUBLICATIONS. 1979. irreg. price varies. Arctic Science & Technology Information System, Arctic Institute of North America, University of Calgary, Calgary, AB T2N 1N4, Canada. TEL 403-220-4036. FAX 403-282-4609. Ed. C. Ross Goodwin. (also avail. in microfiche; back issues avail.) **Document type:** bulletin.
   ●Also available online. Vendor(s): QL Systems Ltd. Also available on CD-ROM.

A W I S MAGAZINE. (Association for Women in Science) see *WOMEN'S INTERESTS*

500 GW ISSN 0943-366X
ABENTEUER NATUR. 1992. bi-m. W D V Wirtschaftsdienst, Lange Str. 13, 60311 Frankfurt a.M., Germany. TEL 069-29907-0. FAX 069-29907499. Ed. Wolfgang Ehrnsperger. adv. contact: Thomas Bock. circ. 120,000. **Document type:** consumer publication.

500 BL ISSN 0001-3765
Q33 CODEN: AABCAD
ACADEMIA BRASILEIRA DE CIENCIAS. ANAIS. (Text in English, French and Portuguese) 1929. q. $50. Academia Brasileira de Ciencias, Rua Anfilofio de Carvalho 29, Caixa Postal 229, 20000 Rio de Janeiro, Brazil. bibl.; charts; illus.; index. **Indexed:** Abstr.Hyg., Biol.Abstr., Chem.Abstr., Curr.Adv.Ecol.Sci., Geo.Abstr., Helminthol.Abstr., Ind.Med, INIS Atomind., INSPEC (1968-), Math.R., Met.Abstr., Sci.Cit.Ind., Trop.Dis.Bull.
   —BLDSC (0860.000000); CASDDS; Faxon; SWETS; UnCover.

500 SP ISSN 1130-4723
ACADEMIA CANARIA DE CIENCIAS. REVISTA. 1990. a. 2000 ptas. Academia Canaria de Ciencias, Santiago Cuadrado 2, 38006 Santa Cruz de Tenerife, Islas Canarias, Spain.

500 PO ISSN 0001-3781
ACADEMIA DAS CIENCIAS DE LISBOA. BOLETIM. 1929. q. Esc.2000. Academia das Ciencias de Lisboa, Rua D. Francisco Manuel de Melo 5, Lisbon 1, Portugal. (also avail. in microfiche from BHP) **Indexed:** GeoRef.

500 DR
ACADEMIA DE CIENCIAS DE LA REPUBLICA DOMINICANA. ANUARIO. (Text in English, French and Spanish; summaries in Spanish) 1975. a. $15. Academia de Ciencias de la Republica Dominicana, Calle las Damas 112, Esquina el Conde, Apdo. 932, Santo Domingo, Dominican Republic.

500 SP
ACADEMIA DE CIENCIAS EXACTAS, FISICAS, QUIMICAS Y NATURALES DE ZARAGOZA. MONOGRAFIAS. 1988. irreg. Academia de Ciencias Exactas, Fisicas, Quimicas y Naturales de Zaragoza, c/o Fac. de Ciencias, Univ. de Zaragoza, Pza. de San Francisco, s-n, 50009 Zaragoza, Spain. **Document type:** monographic series, academic/scholarly publication.

500 SP ISSN 0370-3207
Q65 CODEN: RACZA2
ACADEMIA DE CIENCIAS EXACTAS, FISICO-QUIMICAS Y NATURALES. REVISTA. (Text in English, French, German and Spanish) 1916. irreg. price varies. Academia de Ciencias Exactas, Fisico-Quimicas y Naturales, Facultad de Ciencias, Plaza de San Francisco, s-n, 50009 Zaragoza, Spain. Ed. J. Casas. **Indexed:** Biol.Abstr., Chem.Abstr., Math.R.
   —BLDSC (7801.000000); CASDDS.

500 510 VE
ACADEMIA DE CIENCIAS FISICAS MATEMATICAS Y NATURALES. BOLETIN. 1934. q. exchange basis to qualified personnel. Ministerio de Educacion de Venezuela, Academia de Ciencias Fisicas Matematicas y Naturales, Apdo. 1421, Palacio de las Academias, Caracas 101, Venezuela. TEL 58-2-4834133. FAX 58-2-416611. Ed. Eugenio de Bellaro. bibl.; charts; illus. circ. 1,500. **Indexed:** Biol.Abstr., Chem.Abstr., Math.R. **Document type:** bulletin.

500 FI ISSN 0356-6927
ACADEMIA SCIENTIARUM FENNICA. YEARBOOK/SUOMALAINEN TIEDEAKATEMIA. VUOSIKIRJA. (Text in Finnish or English; summaries in English) 1977. a. FIM 120. Suomalainen Tiedeakatemia - Academia Scientiarum Fennica, Mariankatu 5, FIN-00170 Helsinki 1, Finland. FAX 358-0-660-117. (Orders to: The Bookstore Tiedekirja, Kirkkokatu 14, SF-00170 Helsinki, Finland) Ed. Pentti Kauranen. index. circ. 1,000. (back issues avail.; reprint service avail. from UMI) **Indexed:** Bibl.Ling., Biol.Abstr., Ref.Zh.
   —BLDSC (9371.637000).
   Supersedes (in 1977): Academia Scientiarum Fennica. Proceedings - Sitzungsberichte (ISSN 0065-0501)

500 BE
CODEN: MKAWAW
ACADEMIAE ANALECTA. KLASSE DER WETENSCHAPPEN. (Text in Dutch and English; summaries in English) 1938. irreg., vol.56, no.1, 1994. price varies. Koninklijke Academie voor Wetenschappen, Letteren en Schone Kunsten van Belgie, 1 Hertogsstraat, B-1000 Brussels, Belgium. FAX 32-2-5110143. (Dist. by: N.V. Brepols, Steenweg op Tielen 68, 2300 Turnhout, Belgium. TEL 32-14-402500. FAX 32-14-428919) Ed. G. Verbeke. circ. 600. (back issues avail.) **Indexed:** Zoo.Rec. **Document type:** academic/scholarly publication.
   —CASDDS.
   Former titles: Koninklijke Academie voor Wetenschappen, Letteren en Schone Kunsten van Belgie. Mededelingen. Klasse der Wetenschappen (ISSN 0770-1098); (until 1972): Koninklijke Vlaamse Academie voor Wetenschappen, Letteren en Schone Kunsten van Belgie. Mededelingen. Klasse der Wetenschappen (ISSN 0369-285X)

500 BU ISSN 0366-8681
Q69 CODEN: DBANAD
ACADEMIE BULGARE DES SCIENCES. COMPTES RENDUS. (Text in English, French, German and Russian) 1948. m. 2.70 lv. per no. (Bulgarska Akademiia na Naukite) Publishing House of the Bulgarian Academy of Sciences, Akad. G. Bonchev St., Bldg. 6, 1113 Sofia, Bulgaria. (Dist. by: Hemus, 6, Rouski Blvd., 1000 Sofia, Bulgaria) illus.; index. (reprint service avail. from IRC) **Indexed:** Abstr.Bulg.Sci.Med.Lit., Biol.Abstr., BSL Biol., BSL Geo., BSL Math., Chem.Abstr., Curr.Adv.Biochem., Curr.Adv.Genetics & Molec.Biol., Curr.Cont., Dairy Sci.Abstr., Excerp.Med., Geo.Abstr., Hort.Abstr., Ind.Med., INIS Atomind., INSPEC (1968-), Math.R., Met.Abstr., Plant Grow.Reg.Abstr., Seed Abstr., Soils & Fert., Triticale Abstr., World Alum.Abstr.
   —BLDSC (3369.050000); CASDDS; Ei. **CCC**.

500 FR ISSN 0065-0552
Q46
ACADEMIE DES SCIENCES. ANNUAIRE. 1917. a. Academie des Sciences, 23 Quai Conti, 75006 Paris, France.
   Description: Informs reader of the present state of l'Academie des Sciences, list of prizes and grants available at the university, member addresses.

500 FR ISSN 1251-8069
CODEN: CMCAEK
ACADEMIE DES SCIENCES. COMPTES RENDUS. SERIE 2. MECANIQUE, PHYSIQUE, CHIMIE, ASTRONOMIE. (Text and summaries in English or French) 1835. 26/yr. 4000 F. Gauthier-Villars, 15 rue Gossin, 92543 Montrouge Cedex, France. TEL 33-1-40-92-65-00. FAX 33-1-40-92-65-97. TELEX 634 916 F. (Subscr. to: Centrale des Revues, 11 rue Gossin, 92543 Montrouge Cedex, France) Eds. P. Germain, F. Gros. **Indexed:** INSPEC (1968-). **Document type:** academic/scholarly publication.
   —BLDSC (3370.042105); CASDDS; Faxon; Genuine Article; PADDS; SWETS. **CCC**.
   Supersedes in part (in 1994): Academie des Sciences. Comptes Rendus. Serie 2. Mecanique, Physique, Chimie, Sciences de la Terre, Sciences de l'Univers (ISSN 0764-4450); Which was formerly (until 1984): Academie des Sciences. Comptes Rendus des Seances. Serie 2: Mecanique - Physique, Chimie, Sciences de l'Univers, Sciences de la Terre (ISSN 0750-7623); (until 1981): Academie des Sciences. Comptes Rendus des Seances. Serie 2: Mecanique, Physique, Chimie, Sciences de la Terre, Sciences de l'Univers (ISSN 0249-6305); Which was formed by the 1981 merger of: Academie des Sciences. Comptes Rendus Hebdomadaires des Seances. Serie B: Sciences Physiques (ISSN 0335-5993) & Academie des Sciences. Comptes Rendus Hebdomadaire des Seances. Serie C: Sciences Chimiques (ISSN 0567-6541).

SCIENCES: COMPREHENSIVE WORKS

500   **QD1**   **FR**   **ISSN 1251-8050**
CODEN: CRSPEA
ACADEMIE DES SCIENCES. COMPTES RENDUS. SERIE 2. SCIENCES DE LA TERRE ET DES PLANETES. (Text and summaries in English or French) 1835. 26/yr. 4000 F. Gauthier-Villars, 15 rue Gossin, 92543 Montrouge Cedex, France. TEL 33-1-40-92-65-00. FAX 33-1-40-92-65-97. TELEX 634 916 F. (Subscr. to: Centrale des Revues, 11 rue Gossin, 92543 Montrouge Cedex, France. TEL 33-1-46-56-52-66) Eds. P. Germain, F. Gros. charts; illus.; index. circ. 3,200. (also avail. in microform from PMC) **Indexed:** Appl.Mech.Rev., Astron.& Astrophys.Abstr., Biol.Abstr., Biotech.Abstr., Chem.Abstr., Curr.Chem.React., Curr.Cont., Deep Sea Res.& Oceanogr.Abstr., Ecol.Abstr., Ecol.Abstr., Eng.Ind., Excerp.Med., Geo.Abstr., Geol.Abstr., Geotech.Abstr., Ind.Chem., Ind.Med., INIS Atomind., INSPEC, Int.Aerosp.Abstr., Mass Spectr.Bull., Math.R., Met.Abstr., Meteor.& Geoastrophys.Abstr., Nutr.Abstr., Phys.Ber., Sel.Water Res.Abstr., World Alum.Abstr., Zent.Math. **Document type:** academic/scholarly publication.
—BLDSC (3370.042108); CASDDS; Faxon; SWETS. CCC.
Supersedes in part (in 1994): Academie des Sciences. Comptes Rendus. Serie 2. Mecanique, Physique, Chimie, Sciences de la Terre, Sciences de l'Univers (ISSN 0764-4450); Which was formerly (until 1984): Academie des Sciences. Comptes Rendus des Seances. Serie 2: Mecanique - Physique, Chimie, Sciences de l'Univers, Sciences de la Terre (ISSN 0750-7623); (until 1981): Academie des Sciences. Comptes Rendus des Seances. Serie 2: Mecanique, Physique, Chimie, Sciences de la Terre, Sciences de l'Univers (ISSN 0249-6305); Which was formed by the 1981 merger of: Academie des Sciences. Comptes Rendus Hebdomadaires des Seances. Serie B: Sciences Physiques (ISSN 0335-5993) & Academie des Sciences. Comptes Rendus Hebdomadaires des Seances. Serie C: Sciences Chimiques (ISSN 0567-6541).

ACADEMIE DES SCIENCES. COMPTES RENDUS. SERIE 3: SCIENCES DE LA VIE. see *BIOLOGY*

500   **FR**   **ISSN 0065-0560**
ACADEMIE DES SCIENCES. INDEX BIOGRAPHIQUE DES MEMBRES ET CORRESPONDANTS. 1931. irreg. Academie des Sciences, 23 Quai Conti, 75006 Paris, France.

500   **Q46**   **FR**   **ISSN 0567-6576**
ACADEMIE ET SOCIETE LORRAINES DE SCIENCES. BULLETIN. (Former name of issuing body: Academie et Societe Lorraines des Sciences) 1961. q. 110 F. (effective 1995 & 1996). Academie et Societe Lorraines des Sciences, Biologie Vegetales, B.P. 239, 54506 Vandoeuvre, France. TEL 83-91-22-53. FAX 83-91-22-53. Ed. J.F. Pierre. advt. contact: P.L. Maubeuge. bk.rev. circ. 600. (also avail. in microfilm) **Indexed:** Biol.Abstr., Bull.Signal., Chem.Abstr., Curr.Adv.Ecol.Sci., VITIS. **Document type:** bulletin.
Refereed Serial

500   **NE**   **ISSN 0169-7897**
ACADEMIE INTERNATIONALE D'HISTOIRE DES SCIENCES. COLLECTION DES TRAVAUX. irreg., no.37, 1995. price varies. E.J. Brill, P.O. Box 9000, 2300 PA Leiden, Netherlands. TEL 31-71-5353500. FAX 31-71-5317532. TELEX 39296 BRILL NL. (In N. America: E.J. Brill, 24 Hudson St., Kinderhook, NY 12106. TEL 800-962-4406. FAX 518-758-1959) **Document type:** monograph series, proceedings.

500 001.3   **MG**   **ISSN 1021-0474**
ACADEMIE MALGACHE. BULLETIN D'INFORMATION ET DE LIAISON. (Text in French) 1902. 2/yr. Academie Malgache, B.P. 6217, Tsimbazaza, Antananarivo, Madagascar. **Indexed:** P.L.E.S.A. (1986-1987). **Document type:** bulletin.
Formerly (until 1988): Academie Malgache. Bulletin (ISSN 0366-4473).

500   **DT469.M21**   **MG**   **ISSN 0374-9002**
CODEN: MEACAW
ACADEMIE MALGACHE. MEMOIRES. (Text in French) 1926. irreg. Academie Malgache, B.P. 6217, Tsimbazaza, Antananarivo, Madagascar. **Document type:** monograph series.

500 940   **BE**   **ISSN 0001-4176**
CODEN: AOBSAN
ACADEMIE ROYALE DES SCIENCES D'OUTRE-MER. BULLETIN DES SEANCES/KONINKLIJKE ACADEMIE VOOR OVERZEESE WETENSCHAPPEN. MEDEDELINGEN DER ZITTINGEN. (Text in Dutch, French) 1929. 4/yr. 2650 BEF (effective 1994). Academie Royale des Sciences d'Outre-Mer - Koninklijke Academie voor Overzeese Wetenschappen, B.P. 3, 1 rue Defacqz, B-1050 Brussels, Belgium. TEL 32-2-5380211. FAX 32-2-5392353. Ed. J.J. Symoens. bk.rev.; charts; illus.; index. cum.index every 10 yrs. **Indexed:** A.I.C.P., Abstr.Hyg., Amer.Hist.& Life, Bibl.Ling., Chem.Abstr., Curr.Cont.Africa, Documentatieblad, GeoRef., Hist.Abstr., Trop.Dis.Bull. **Document type:** academic/scholarly publication, proceedings.
—BLDSC (2895.015000); CASDDS.
Former titles: Academie Royale des Sciences Coloniales. Bulletin des Seances; Koninklijke Academie voor Koloniale Wetenschapen. Mededelingen der Zittingen.

500   **BE**   **ISSN 0770-1896**
ACADEMIE ROYALE DES SCIENCES D'OUTRE-MER. CLASSE DES SCIENCES NATURELLES ET MEDICALES. COLLECTION IN 8/KONINKLIJKE ACADEMIE VOOR OVERZEESE WETENSCHAPPEN. KLASSE DER NATUUR- EN GENEESKUNDIGE WETENSCHAPPEN. VERZAMELING IN 8. (Text in Dutch, English, French) 1932; N.S. 1955. irreg., vol.23, no.1, 1990. price varies. Academie Royale des Sciences d'Outre-Mer - Koninklijke Academie voor Overzeese Wetenschappen, B.P. 3, 1 rue Defacqz, 1050 Brussels, Belgium. TEL 32-2-5384772. FAX 32-2-5392353. (back issues avail.) **Document type:** monographic series.
Former titles (until 1964): Academie Royale des Sciences d'Outre-Mer. Classe des Sciences Naturelles et Medicales. Memoires - Collection in 8 (ISSN 0567-6606); (until 1960): Academie Royale des Sciences Coloniales. Classe des Sciences Naturelles et Medicales. Memoires - Collection in 8 (ISSN 0770-6766); (until 1954): Institut Royal Colonial Belge. Section des Sciences Naturelles et Medicales. Memoires - Collection in 8 (ISSN 0367-6994).

500   **BE**   **ISSN 0777-1525**
ACADEMIE ROYALE DES SCIENCES D'OUTRE-MER. CLASSE DES SCIENCES TECHNIQUES. COLLECTION IN 8/KONINKLIJKE ACADEMIE VOOR OVERZEESE WETENSCHAPPEN. KLASSE VOOR TECHNISCHE WETENSCHAPPEN. VERZAMELING IN 8. (Text in Dutch, English, French) 1929; N.S. 1955. irreg., vol.19, no.1, 1994. price varies. Academie Royale des Sciences d'Outre-Mer - Koninklijke Academie voor Overzeese Wetenschappen, B.P. 3, 1 rue Defacqz, 1050 Brussels, Belgium. TEL 32-2-5380211. FAX 32-2-5392353. (back issues avail.) **Document type:** monographic series.
Former titles (until 1964): Academie Royale des Sciences d'Outre-Mer, Classe des Sciences techniques. Memoires in 8 (ISSN 0777-1517); (until 1960): Academie Royales des Sciences Coloniales. Classe des Sciences Techniques. Memoires in 8 (ISSN 0777-1509); (until 1955): Institut Royal Colonial Belge. Section des Sciences Techniques. Memoires - Collection in 8 (ISSN 0777-1487).

ACADEMIE ROYALE DES SCIENCES, DES LETTRES ET DES BEAUX-ARTS DE BELGIQUE. ANNUAIRE. see *HUMANITIES: COMPREHENSIVE WORKS*

500   **AS242**   **BE**   **ISSN 0001-4141**
CODEN: BCSAAF
ACADEMIE ROYALE DES SCIENCES DES LETTRES ET DES BEAUX-ARTS DE BELGIQUE. CLASSE DES SCIENCES. BULLETIN. 1899. m. 1800 BEF. Academie Royale des Sciences des Lettres et des Beaux-Arts de Belgique, Classe des Sciences, Palais des Academies, 1 rue Ducale, B-1000 Brussels, Belgium. charts; illus.; stat.; index. circ. 1,500. **Indexed:** Anim.Breed.Abstr., Biol.Abstr., Chem.Abstr., Deep Sea Res.& Oceanogr.Abstr., Eng.Ind., INSPEC (1968-1969; 1983-). **Document type:** academic/scholarly publication, bulletin.
—CASDDS.

500   **BE**   **ISSN 0365-0936**
CODEN: ABSCA3
ACADEMIE ROYALE DES SCIENCES, DES LETTRES ET DES BEAUX-ARTS DE BELGIQUE. CLASSE DES SCIENCES. MEMOIRES. 1904. irreg. price varies. Academie Royale des Sciences, des Lettres et des Beaux-Arts de Belgique, Classe des Sciences, Palais des Academies, 1 rue Ducale, B-1000 Brussels, Belgium. (Dist. by: Librairie Alain Ferraton, 162 Ch. de Charleroi, B-1060 Brussels, Belgium) Ed.Bd. circ. 500. **Indexed:** Deep Sea Res.& Oceanogr.Abstr., INSPEC (1968-). **Document type:** monographic series.
—CASDDS.

ACADEMIE SERBE DES SCIENCES ET DES ARTS. CLASSE DES SCIENCES MATHEMATIQUES ET NATURELLES. BULLETIN. SCIENCES MATHÉMATIQUES. see *MATHEMATICS*

500 574   **YU**   **ISSN 0352-5740**
CODEN: BASNA6
ACADEMIE SERBE DES SCIENCES ET DES ARTS. CLASSE DES SCIENCES MATHEMATIQUES ET NATURELLES. BULLETIN. SCIENCES NATURELLES. (Text in English, French, Russian) 1952. s-a. price varies. Srpska Akademija Nauka i Umetnosti, Odeljenje Prirodno-Matematickih Nauka - Serbian Academy of Sciences and Arts, Knez Mihailova 35, 11001 Belgrade, Serbia, Yugoslavia. TEL 011-187-144. FAX 182-825. TELEX 72593 SANU. (Dist. by: Prosveta, Terazije 16, Belgrade, Serbia, Yugoslavia) Ed. Vladimir Pantic. circ. 1,000. **Indexed:** Biol.Abstr., Chem.Abstr., Deep Sea Res.& Oceanogr.Abstr.
—CASDDS.
Supersedes in part: Academie Serbe des Sciences et des Arts. Classe des Sciences Mathematiques et Naturelles. Bulletin. Nouvelle Serie (ISSN 0001-4184).

500   **US**   **ISSN 0096-7750**
ACADEMY OF NATURAL SCIENCES OF PHILADELPHIA. MONOGRAPHS. 1935. irreg., no.22, 1983. price varies. Academy of Natural Sciences of Philadelphia, 1900 Benjamin Franklin Pkwy., Philadelphia, PA 19103-1195. TEL 215-299-1050. FAX 215-299-1028. Ed. Alfred E. Schuyler. bibl.; charts; illus.; stat. (back issues avail.) **Indexed:** Biol.Abstr., GeoRef. **Document type:** academic/scholarly publication, monograph series.

500   **QH1**   **US**   **ISSN 0097-3157**
CODEN: PANPA5
ACADEMY OF NATURAL SCIENCES OF PHILADELPHIA. PROCEEDINGS; original research in systematics, evolution & ecology. 1842. a. $30. Academy of Natural Sciences of Philadelphia, 1900 Benjamin Franklin Pkwy., Philadelphia, PA 19103-1195. TEL 215-299-1050. FAX 215-299-1028. Ed. Alfred E. Schuyler. bibl.; charts; illus.; stat. (back issues avail.; reprint service avail. from KTO) **Indexed:** Biol.Abstr., Curr.Adv.Ecol.Sci., Curr.Cont., Deep Sea Res.& Oceanogr.Abstr., Excerp.Med., Geo.Abstr., GeoRef., Sport Fish.Abstr., Wild.Rev., Zoo.Rec. **Document type:** academic/scholarly publication, proceedings.
—BLDSC (6618.000000); Faxon; UnCover.

500   **US**   **ISSN 0097-3254**
CODEN: AYSPAX
ACADEMY OF NATURAL SCIENCES OF PHILADELPHIA. SPECIAL PUBLICATIONS. 1922. irreg., no.15, 1985. price varies. Academy of Natural Sciences of Philadelphia, 1900 Benjamin Franklin Pkwy., Philadelphia, PA 19103-1195. TEL 215-299-1050. FAX 215-299-1028. Ed. Alfred E. Schuyler. bibl.; charts; illus.; stat. (back issues avail.) **Indexed:** Biol.Abstr., GeoRef. **Document type:** academic/scholarly publication.

500.2 510   **IT**   **ISSN 0001-4419**
CODEN: AATFAA
ACCADEMIA DELLE SCIENZE DI TORINO. ATTI. PART 1. CLASSE DI SCIENZE FISICHE, MATEMATICHE E NATURALI. 1865. 6/yr. price varies. Accademia delle Scienze di Torino, Via Maria Vittoria 3, 10123 Turin, Italy. (Subscr. to: Bottega d'Erasmo, via G. Ferrari 9, 10124 Turin, Italy) Ed. Vittorio Cirilli. charts; illus.; cum.index: vols. 50-100. circ. 500. **Indexed:** Appl.Mech.Rev., Chem.Abstr., Chem.Abstr., INIS Atomind., INSPEC, Math.R.
—CASDDS.
Formerly (1928-1946): Reale Accademia delle Scienze di Torino. Atti. Part 1. Classe di Scienze Fisiche, Matematiche e Naturali; Which supersedes in part (1865-1927): Reale Accademia delle Scienze di Torino. (ISSN 1122-1364)

SCIENCES: COMPREHENSIVE WORKS

500.2 510   IT   ISSN 1120-1630
ACCADEMIA DELLE SCIENZE DI TORINO. MEMORIE. PART 1. CLASSE DI SCIENZE FISICHE, MATEMATICHE E NATURALI. 1759. irreg. (1-4/yr.). price varies. Accademia delle Scienze di Torino, Via Maria Vittoria 3, 10123 Turin, Italy. (Subscr. to: Bottega d'Erasmus, via G. Ferrari 9, 10124 Turin, Italy) Ed. Vittorio Cirilli. charts; illus. circ. 500. **Indexed:** Biol.Abstr.
   Former titles (until 1951): Reale Accademia delle Scienze di Torino. Memorie. Part 1. Classe di Scienze Fisiche, Matematiche e Naturali (ISSN 1120-1614); Which supersedes in part (in 1915): Reale Accademia delle Scienze di Torino. Memorie (ISSN 1120-1592); Which was formerly (until 1818): Academie Royale des Sciences de Turin (ISSN 1120-1576), which was formed by the 1813 merger of: Academie Impriale des Sciences Littrature et Beaux-Arts de Turin. Memoires. Sciences Physiques et Mathmatiques (ISSN 1120-1568) and Academie Impriale des Sciences Littrature et Beaux-Arts de Turin. Memoires. Littrature et Beaux-Arts (ISSN 1120-1584).

500   IT   ISSN 1122-651X
CODEN: AALGA7
ACCADEMIA LIGURE DI SCIENZE E LETTERE. ATTI. (Text in English, French and Italian) 1890. a. L.60000. Accademia Ligure di Scienze e Lettere, Palazzo Ducale, Piazza G. Matteotti, 5, 16123 Genoa GE, Italy. Ed. Luigi Brian. circ. 800. **Indexed:** Biol.Abstr., Chem.Abstr., Deep Sea Res.& Oceanogr.Abstr., GeoRef, INSPEC (1969-), Math.R. **Document type:** academic/scholarly publication.

500   IT   ISSN 1120-6349
QC1   CODEN: ANLNEL
ACCADEMIA NAZIONALE DEI LINCEI. ATTI. RENDICONTI LINCEI. SCIENZE FISICHE E NATURALI. (Text in English, French, Italian; summaries in English, Italian) 1847. 4/yr. L.70000 (foreign L.90000). Accademia Nazionale dei Lincei, Via della Lungara 10, 00165 Rome, Italy. TEL 39-6-6838831. Ed. Cesare Franco Golisano. bibl.; charts; illus.; index. circ. 1,200. **Indexed:** Appl.Mech.Rev., Biol.Abstr., Chem.Abstr., INIS Atomind., INSPEC (1990-), Math.R.
—CASDDS; Ei; UnCover.
   Supersedes in part (in 1989): Accademia Nazionale dei Lincei. Atti. Classe di Scienze Fisiche Matematiche e Naturali. Rendiconti (ISSN 0392-7881); Which was formerly (until 1944): Reale Accademia d'Italia. Atti. Classe di Scienze Fisiche, Matematiche e Naturali. Rendiconti (ISSN 0365-5946); (until 1939): Reale Accademia dei Lincei. Atti. Classe di Scienze Fisiche, Matematiche e Naturali. Rendiconti (ISSN 0001-4435)
   Description: Includes articles by academy fellows or by scholars presented by fellows.

500   IT   ISSN 0392-0836
ACCADEMIA TOSCANA DI SCIENZE E LETTERE LA COLOMBARIA. ATTI E MEMORIE. 1947. a. price varies. Casa Editrice Leo S. Olschki, Casella Postale 66, 50100 Florence, Italy. TEL 39-55-6530684. FAX 39-55-6530214. **Indexed:** Bibl.Ling. **Document type:** academic/scholarly publication.

500 060   IT   ISSN 0065-0781
ACCADEMIA TOSCANA DI SCIENZE E LETTERE LA COLOMBARIA. STUDI. 1953. irreg. vol.144, 1995. price varies. Casa Editrice Leo S. Olschki, Casella Postale 66, 50100 Florence, Italy. TEL 39-55-6530684. FAX 39-55-6530214. circ. 1,000. **Indexed:** Avery Ind.Archit.Per. **Document type:** academic/scholarly publication.

500 370   CN   ISSN 1193-7114
ACCELERATOR. 1964. irreg. (4-5/yr.). Can.$20 for 2 yrs. (Saskatchewan Science Teachers' Society) Saskatchewan Teachers' Federation, Box 1108, Saskatoon, SK S7K 3N3, Canada. TEL 306-525-0368. Ed. Sharon Bender. adv.; bk.rev.; illus.; stat. circ. 300. (processed) **Indexed:** Can.Educ.Ind. **Document type:** newsletter.
   Former titles (until 1988): Accelerator Newsletter (ISSN 0712-1377); (until 1980): Saskatchewan Science Teachers' Society. Newsletter (ISSN 0712-1369); (until 1976): Saskatchewan Science Teachers' Society (ISSN 0316-2893)

500   US   ISSN 0898-9621
Q180.55.E9   CODEN: ARQAEZ
ACCOUNTABILITY IN RESEARCH; policies and quality assurance. 1989. 4/yr. (in 1 vol, 4 nos./vol.). 91 ECU (effective 1996). Gordon & Breach Science Publishers, c/o International Publishers Distributor, 820 Town Center Dr., Langhorne, PA 19047. TEL 215-750-2642. FAX 215-750-6343. (Subscr. to: International Publishers Distributor, P.O. Box 90, Reading, Berkshire RG1 8JL, England. TEL 44-173-456-8316) Ed. Adil Shamoo. (also avail. in microfilm; microfiche) **Indexed:** Soc.Work Res.& Abstr. **Document type:** academic/scholarly publication.
—BLDSC (0573.539500). CCC.
   Description: Covers historical perspectives, data auditing, research policies, ethical issues, legal issues and standards for data analysis.
   Refereed Serial

ACTA ACADEMIAE ABOENSIS, SERIES B: MATHEMATICA ET PHYSICA. see *MATHEMATICS*

500   BL   ISSN 0044-5967
CODEN: AAMZAZ
ACTA AMAZONICA. (Text in English, Portuguese and Spanish) 1971. irreg. (1-3/yr.). $100. Instituto Nacional de Pesquisas da Amazonia, Alameda Cosme Ferreira 1756, P.O. Box 478, 69083-000 Manaus, Amazonas, Brazil. TEL 55-92-6423220. FAX 55-92-643-3030. TELEX 0922269. E-mail: biblio@cr.am.rnp.br. Ed. Jose Seixas Lourenco. bk.rev. circ. 1,500. (also avail. in microfilm from OMN) **Indexed:** Abstr.Hyg., Agroforest.Abstr., Apic.Abstr., Biol.Abstr., Chem.Abstr., Curr.Adv.Ecol.Sci., Deep Sea Res.& Oceanogr.Abstr., Forest.Abstr., Forest Prod.Abstr., GeoRef., INIS Atomind., Rev.Appl.Entomol., Rev.Med.& Vet.Mycol., Rural Devel.Abstr., Sel.Water Res.Abstr., Soils & Fert., Sport Fish.Abstr., Vet.Bull., Wild.Rev., Zoo.Rec. **Document type:** academic/scholarly publication.
—BLDSC (0593.100000); CASDDS; UMI.
   Description: Publication in pure and applied sciences including botany, agronomy, aquatic biology, tropical pathology, forest research, zoology and wood technology.
   Refereed Serial

500 919 998   DK   ISSN 0065-1028
G601
ACTA ARCTICA. (Text in English, French and German) 1943. irreg. (every 3-5 yrs.). price varies. (Arktisk Institut) C.A. Reitzels Forlag, Norregade 20, DK-1165 Copenhagen K, Denmark. Ed. Helge Larsen. (back issues avail.) **Indexed:** Biol.Abstr.

500   VE   ISSN 0001-5504
Q22   CODEN: ACVEAU
ACTA CIENTIFICA VENEZOLANA. (Text in Spanish; summaries in English and Spanish) 1950. 6/yr. Bs.600 to individuals ($55); institutions Bs.1200 ($150). Asociacion Venezolana para el Avance de la Ciencia, Av. Neveri, Colinas de Bello Monte, Apdo. 47286, Caracas, Venezuela. TEL 752-1002. FAX 751-1420. Ed. Vidal Rodriguez Lemoine. adv.; bk.rev.; abstr.; bibl.; charts; illus.; stat.; index, cum.index. circ. 4,000. (reprint service avail. from ISI) **Indexed:** ASCA, Biol.Abstr., Biotech.Abstr., Chem.Abstr., Curr.Adv.Biochem., Curr.Adv.Cell & Devel.Biol., Curr.Adv.Ecol.Sci., Curr.Adv.Genetics & Molec.Biol., Curr.Cont., Curr.Tit.Ocean, Dairy Sci.Abstr., Dent.Ind., Excerpt.Med., Field Crop Abstr., GeoRef., Helminthol.Abstr., Herb.Abstr., Ind.Med., Ind.Vet., Math.R., Nutr.Abstr., Sci.Cit.Ind., Soils & Fert., Vet.Bull, Zent.Math.
—BLDSC (0611.500000); CASDDS; Ei; Faxon; UMI.
   Description: Research papers and essays discussing general scientific problems, not exclusively based on original experimental results.
   Refereed Serial

500 600   LV
ACTA HISTORIAE SCIENTIARUM BALTICA/BALTIJAS ZINATNU VESTURES APCERĒJUMI. (Text in Russian; contents in English) 1968. irreg. approx. a. 1.60 Ls. Rigas Tehniskas Universitates, Kalku str.1, 1658 Riga, Latvia. TEL 0132-212797. Ed. Andris Kreslins. bk.rev. circ. 1,000. **Indexed:** Bull.Signal., Chem.Abstr., Ref.Zh.
   Formerly (until vol.9): Iz Istorii Estestvoznaniya i Tekhniki Pribaltiki (ISSN 0130-3252)

500.9 610   GW   ISSN 0001-5857
CODEN: ACHLAG
ACTA HISTORICA LEOPOLDINA. (Supplements avail.) 1963. irreg., vol.22, 1993. price varies. (Deutsche Akademie der Naturforscher Leopoldina, Archiv fuer Geschichte der Naturforschung und Medizin) Johann Ambrosius Barth, Postfach 102869, 69018 Heidelberg, Germany. TEL 06221-489281. FAX 06221-489205. bibl.; charts; illus. circ. 1,200. **Indexed:** Biol.Abstr., Math.R. **Document type:** academic/scholarly publication.

509 610.9   DK   ISSN 0065-1311
CODEN: AHSMA7
ACTA HISTORICA SCIENTIARUM NATURALIUM ET MEDICINALIUM. (Text in English, German) 1942. irreg. price varies. (Danish National Library of Science and Medicine) Munksgaard International Publishers Ltd., Book Division, Noerre Soegade 35, DK-1016 Copenhagen K, Denmark. TEL 45-33-12-70-30. FAX 45-33-12-93-87. E-mail: fsub@mail.munksfaard.dk. Poul Aagaard Christiansen. (back issues avail.) **Indexed:** GeoRef, Ind.Med. **Document type:** monographic series.
—CCC.

505   DK   ISSN 0105-6824
ACTA JUTLANDICA. NATURVIDENSKABELIG SERIE/ACTA JUTLANDICA. NATURAL SCIENCE SERIES. Variant title: Naturvidenskabelig Serie. (Subseries of: Acta Jutlandica) (Text in various languages) 1939. s-a. (Laerde Selskab i Aarhus) Aarhus University Press, Aarhus University, Building 170, DK-8000 Aarhus, Denmark. TEL 45-86-19-70-33. FAX 45-86-19-84-33.

500 616.99   PH   ISSN 0065-1370
CODEN: ACTMEF
ACTA MANILANA. (Text and summaries in English) 1965. a. P.80($15) (University of Santo Tomas, Research Center for the Natural Sciences) Santo Tomas University Press, Espana St., Manila 1008, Philippines. TEL 010-632-731-4031. FAX 010-632-732-7486. Ed. Fortunato Sevilla III. circ. 500. (back issues avail.) **Indexed:** Biol.Abstr., Curr.Adv.Ecol.Sci., Ind.Phil.Per., INSPEC (1985-), Nutr.Abstr. **Document type:** academic/scholarly publication.
—BLDSC (0629.750000); UnCover.
   Description: Papers dealing with all aspects of the natural sciences.

500 600   MX   ISSN 0567-7785
CODEN: AMXCB4
ACTA MEXICANA DE CIENCIA Y TECNOLOGIA. (Text in English or Spanish) 1967. irreg., vol.14, 1980. Instituto Politecnico Nacional, Comision de Operacion y Fomento de Actividades Academicas, Apdo. Postal 42-161, Mexico 17, D.F., Mexico. bibl.; charts; illus.; index. circ. 1,000. **Indexed:** Biol.Abstr., INSPEC (1968-), Math.R.
—BLDSC (0637.800000); CASDDS.

ACTA REGIAE SOCIETATIS SCIENTIARUM ET LITTERARUM GOTHOBURGENSIS. INTERDISCIPLINARIA. see *HUMANITIES: COMPREHENSIVE WORKS*

500   SP   ISSN 0365-6446
CODEN: ASALAP
ACTA SALMANTICENSIA. CIENCIAS. 1954. irreg. Ediciones Universidad de Salamanca, Apdo. 325, 37080 Salamanca, Spain. TEL 34-23-294598.
—CASDDS.

500 610   SW   ISSN 0282-8928
ACTA UNIVERSITATIS UPSALIENSIS. (Text in various European languages) 1773. irreg. price varies. (Kungliga Vetenskaps-Societeten - Royal Society of Sciences of Uppsala) A W I International AB, P.O. Box 4627, S-116 91 Stockholm, Sweden. TEL 468-640-8800. FAX 468-641-1180. bibl.; charts; illus.; index. **Indexed:** Bibl.Ling., GeoRef., M.L.A.
   Formerly (until 1968): Nova Acta Regiae Societatis Scientiarum Upsaliensis (ISSN 0029-5000)

500   SP   ISSN 0212-8608
ACTAS CLINICAS DELFOS. 2/yr. Avda. Hospital Militar 149-161, 08023 Barcelona, Spain. TEL 3-211-31-00. Ed. J.A. Ginesta Armengol.

AEON; a journal of interdisciplinary science. see *SOCIAL SCIENCES: COMPREHENSIVE WORKS*

SCIENCES: COMPREHENSIVE WORKS

500   UN   ISSN 1010-5271
CODEN: ASTSE9
AFRICAN JOURNAL OF SCIENCE AND TECHNOLOGY. SERIES B. BASIC SCIENCES. 1982. 2/yr. African Network of Scientific and Technical Institutions - Reseau Africain d'Instituts Scientifiques et Techniques, ANSTI-RAIST Secretariat, UNESCO ROSTA, P.O. Box 30592, Nairobi, Kenya. **Indexed:** P.L.E.S.A. **Document type:** academic/scholarly publication.
—CASDDS.
    Supersedes in part (in 1986): African Journal of Science and Technology.

500   UN
AFRICAN JOURNAL OF SCIENCE AND TECHNOLOGY. SERIES C. GENERAL. 1990. 2/yr. African Network of Scientific and Technical Institutions - Reseau Africain d'Instituts Scientifiques et Techniques, ANSTI-RAIST Secretariat, UNESCO ROSTA, P.O. Box 30592, Nairobi, Kenya. **Indexed:** P.L.E.S.A. **Document type:** academic/scholarly publication.

500   PH   ISSN 0115-5679
CODEN: AGHADE
AGHAM; D L S U Journal of Science. (Text in English) 1975. s-a. P.60($4.40) (De La Salle University, College of Science) De La Salle University Press, 2401 Taft Ave., Manila, Philippines. TEL 2-59-48-32. FAX 632-521-9094. adv.; bk.rev. circ. 300. **Indexed:** Ind.Phil.Per. **Document type:** academic/scholarly publication.
—CASDDS.
    Description: Presents scientific research and reports. Contains articles, notes, communications, and reviews concerning all areas of biology, chemistry, physics, mathematics, and engineering.

500   II   ISSN 0002-1032
Q73   CODEN: AURSA9
AGRA UNIVERSITY JOURNAL OF RESEARCH (SCIENCE). (Text in English) 1952. 3/yr. Rs.20. Agra University, Agra 282004, Uttar Pradesh, India. Ed. Dr. M. Ray. charts; illus. **Indexed:** Anim.Breed.Abstr., Biol.Abstr., Chem.Abstr., Field Crop Abstr., GeoRef., Herb.Abstr., Ind.Vet., Plant Breed.Abstr., Rev.Appl.Entomol., Rev.Plant Path, Vet.Bull.
—CASDDS.

700   JA   ISSN 0388-7367
AS552.K343
AICHI KYOIKU DAIGAKU KENKYU HOKOKU. GEIJUTSU, HOKEN TAIIKU, KASEI, GIJUTSU KAGAKU. 1975. a. exchange basis. Aichi University of Education - Aichi Kyoiku Daigaku, 1, Hirosawa, Igaya-cho, Kariya-shi, Aichi-ken 448, Japan. circ. 600. **Indexed:** INIS Atomind.

510 500   JA   ISSN 0365-3722
Q4   CODEN: AKDSA5
AICHI KYOIKU DAIGAKU KENKYU HOKOKU. SHIZEN KAGAKU/AICHI UNIVERSITY OF EDUCATION. NATURAL SCIENCE BULLETIN. (Text and summaries in Japanese) 1952. a. Aichi University of Education - Aichi Kyoiku Daigaku, 1, Hirosawa, Igaya-cho, Kariya-shi, Aichi-ken 448, Japan. **Document type:** bulletin.
    Formerly (until 1967): Aichi Gakugei Daigaku Kenkyu Hokoku. Shizen Kagaku (ISSN 0515-779X)

AKADEMIA ROLNICZO-TECHNICZNA IM. M. OCZAPOWSKIEGO. HUMANISTYKA I PRZYRODOZNAWSTWO. see *HUMANITIES: COMPREHENSIVE WORKS*

500   GW   ISSN 0084-6082
AKADEMIE DER WISSENSCHAFTEN IN GOETTINGEN. JAHRBUCH. 1939. a. price varies. Vandenhoeck und Ruprecht, Robert-Bosch-Breite 6, 37079 Goettingen, Germany. TEL 0551-6959-0. FAX 0551-695917. (Subscr. to: 37070 Goettingen, Germany) **Indexed:** Bibl.Ling., GeoRef. **Document type:** academic/scholarly publication.

001.3 500   GW   ISSN 0084-6104
AS182   CODEN: AWLJAY
AKADEMIE DER WISSENSCHAFTEN UND DER LITERATUR, MAINZ. JAHRBUCH. a. price varies. Franz Steiner Verlag Wiesbaden GmbH, Birkenwaldstr. 44, 70191 Stuttgart, Germany. TEL 0711-2582-0. FAX 0711-2582390. (Subscr. to: Postfach 101061, 70009 Stuttgart, Germany) **Indexed:** Bibl.Ling., GeoRef. **Document type:** academic/scholarly publication.

510 500   GW   ISSN 0002-2993
Q49   CODEN: AWLMA9
AKADEMIE DER WISSENSCHAFTEN UND DER LITERATUR, MAINZ. MATHEMATISCH - NATURWISSENSCHAFTLICHE KLASSE. ABHANDLUNGEN. (Text in English, French and German) 1950. irreg. price varies. (Mathematisch - Naturwissenschaftliche Klasse) Franz Steiner Verlag Wiesbaden GmbH, Birkenwaldstr. 44, 70191 Stuttgart, Germany. TEL 0711-2582-0. FAX 0711-2582390. (Subscr. to: Postfach 101061, 70009 Stuttgart, Germany) abstr.; charts; illus.; index. **Indexed:** Biol.Abstr., Chem.Abstr., GeoRef. **Document type:** monographic series.

500   GW   ISSN 0065-5538
AKADEMISCHE VORTRAEGE UND ABHANDLUNGEN. 1946. irreg., no.72, 1992. price varies. Bouvier Verlag Herbert Grundmann, Am Hof 28, 53113 Bonn, Germany. TEL 0228-7290124. FAX 0228-7290179. **Document type:** monographic series.

500 060   AI
CODEN: DANAAW
AKADEMIYA NAUK ARMENII. DOKLADY/HAYASTANI HANRAPETUTIAN GITUTSUNNERI AZGAIN ACADEMIAY ZEKUITSNER. (Text in Armenian and Russian) 1944. 10/yr. 400 dram. Akademiya Nauk Armenii, Pr. Marshala Bagramayana, 24, 375019 Erevan, Armenia. TEL 52-45-80. TELEX 243344. Ed. D.M. Sedrakian. **Indexed:** Anal.Abstr., Biol.Abstr., Chem.Abstr., GeoRef., INIS Atomind., Math.R. **Document type:** academic/scholarly publication.
—CASDDS. **CCC.**
    Formerly (until 1991): Akademiya Nauk Armyanskoi S.S.R. Doklady (ISSN 0321-1339)

AKADEMIYA NAUK ARMENII. IZVESTIYA. SERIYA TEKHNICHESKIKH NAUK/HAYASTANI HANRAPETUTIAN GITUTSUNNERY AZGAIN ACADEMIAY TEKHNIKAKAN GITUTSUNNERY HANDES. see *TECHNOLOGY: COMPREHENSIVE WORKS*

500   GS
AS262
AKADEMIYA NAUK GRUZII. SOOBSHCHENIYA. (Text in Georgian and Russian; summaries in English) 1940. m. 51.60 Rub. Akademiya Nauk Gruzii, Ul. Kutuzova 19, 380060 Tbilisi, Georgia. TEL 7-8832-372297. Ed. E.K. Kharadze. bibl.; index. circ. 1,400. **Indexed:** Biol.Abstr., Field Crop Abstr., Forest.Abstr., Helminthol.Abstr., Herb.Abstr., Hort.Abstr., Ind.Vet., Irr.& Drain.Abstr., Numis.Lit., Rev.Plant Path., Sel.Water Res.Abstr., Soils & Fert., Vet.Bull.
—CCC.
    Formerly (until 1991): Akademiya Nauk Gruzinskoi S.S.R. Soobshcheniya (ISSN 0132-1447)

500   KZ
AS262   CODEN: VANKAM
AKADEMIYA NAUK KAZAKHSTANA. VESTNIK. 1944. m. 29 Rub. Gylym, Ul. Pushkina 111-113, 480100 Alma-Ata, Kazakhstan. TEL 3272-611877. Ed. Sh.E. Esenov. adv.; bk.rev.; abstr.; bibl.; charts; illus.; stat. **Indexed:** Biol.Abstr., Chem.Abstr., Crop Physiol.Abstr., Field Crop Abstr., Math.R., Triticale Abstr.
—CASDDS.
    Formerly (until 1992): Akademiya Nauk Kazakhskoi S.S.R. Vestnik (ISSN 0002-3213)

500   KR
AS262   CODEN: VNUKAC
AKADEMIYA NAUK UKRAINY. VISNYK. (Text in Ukrainian) 1928. m. $170. (Akademiya Nauk Ukrainy, Prezidium) Vidavnitstvo Naukova Dumka, Vul. Tereshchenkivska 3, 252601 Kiev, Ukraine. TEL 228-81-39. (Dist. by: Mezhdunarodnaya Kniga, B. Yakimanka 39, 117049 Moscow, Russia; Dist. by: Victor Kamkin Inc., 4956 Boiling Brook Pkwy., Rockville, MD 20852. TEL 301-881-5973. FAX 301-881-1637) Ed. B.E. Paton. (also avail. in microfiche from IDC)
—CASDDS.
    Formerly: Akademiya Nauk Ukrainskoi S.S.R. Visnyk (ISSN 0372-6436)

500   UZ   ISSN 1019-8954
CODEN: DANUAO
AKADEMIYA NAUK UZBEKISTANA. MATEMATIKA, TEKHNICHESKIE NAUKI, ESTESTVOZNANIE. 1944. m. Izdatel'stvo Fan, Ul. Gogolya 70, k. 105, 700000 Tashkent, Uzbekistan. TEL 3712-336961.
—BLDSC (0053.850000); CASDDS. **CCC.**
    Formerly (until 1992): Akademiya Nauk Uzbekskoi S.S.R. Doklady (ISSN 0134-4307)

500   BW
Q60   CODEN: DBLRAC
AKADEMIYA NAVUK BELARUSI. DOKLADY. (Text in Russian; contents page and summaries in English) 1957. m. 24.60 Rub. Vydavetstvo Navuka i Tekhnika, Zhodzinskaya, 18, 220067 Minsk 67, Belarus. TEL 39-55-17. FAX 252494. TELEX 252277 NAUKA. Ed. V.P. Platonov. bibl.; charts; illus.; index. circ. 900. **Indexed:** Biol.Abstr., Crop Physiol.Abstr., Deep Sea Res.& Oceanogr.Abstr., Field Crop Abstr., Helminthol.Abstr., INIS Atomind., Met.Abstr., Triticale Abstr.
—CASDDS; Genuine Article. **CCC.**
    Formerly: Akademiya Navuk Belarusskai S.S.R. Doklady (ISSN 0002-354X)
    Description: Publishes scientific results in mathematics, natural sciences and engineering.

AKITA-KENRITSU HAKUBUTSUKAN KENKYU HOKOKU/AKITA PREFECTURAL MUSEUM. ANNUAL REPORT. see *MUSEUMS AND ART GALLERIES*

500   JA   ISSN 0285-0257
AKITA SHIZENSHI KENKYU/AKITA NATURAL HISTORY ASSOCIATION. (Text in Japanese) 1973. a. Akita Natural History Association - Akita Shizenshi Gakkai, c/o Mr. Jun Takado, 6-36 Yabasedagoro, 2-chome, Akita-shi, Akita-ken 010, Japan.

500   US   ISSN 0002-4112
CODEN: JAASAJ
ALABAMA ACADEMY OF SCIENCE. JOURNAL. 1924. q. $20 to non-members. Auburn University Press (Auburn), Ralph Brown Draughon Library, Auburn University, Auburn, AL 36849. TEL 205-844-9262. FAX 205-844-9234. Ed. James T. Bradley. adv.; bk.rev.; abstr.; illus. circ. 1,100. (also avail. in microform from UMI; reprint service avail. from UMI) **Indexed:** Amer.Hist.& Life, Biol.Abstr., Chem.Abstr., Excerp.Med., GeoRef., Hist.Abstr., Sci.Cit.Ind., Sel.Water Res.Abstr., Sport Fish.Abstr., Wild.Rev., Zoo.Rec. **Document type:** academic/scholarly publication.
—CASDDS; Faxon; UMI; UnCover.

ALBERTA GEOLOGICAL SURVEY. REPORTS. see *TECHNOLOGY: COMPREHENSIVE WORKS*

500   UA   ISSN 1110-0176
ALEXANDRIA SCIENCE EXCHANGE. (Text in English; summaries in Arabic, English) 1980. 4/yr. $40. Prof. Dr. A.M. Balba Group for Soil and Water Research, College of Agriculture, University of Alexandria, El-Shatby, Alexandria 21545. TEL 03-5975405. FAX 03-5954684. Ed. A.M. Balba. abstr. **Document type:** academic/scholarly publication.
—BLDSC (0786.945000).
    Description: Publishes original research in various disciplines of science.
    Refereed Serial

500.9   GW
ALPENINSTITUT. SCHRIFTENREIHE. (Text in French, German and Italian) 1974. irreg. price varies. (Alpeninstitut fuer Umweltforschung and Entwicklungsplanung in der GFL) Nelles Verlag, Schleissheimer Str. 371 b, 80935 Munich, Germany. Ed. Walter Danz.
    Description: Focuses on natural history.

500   NZ   ISSN 0111-1957
ALPHA. 1980. s-m. NZ.$3 per no. (Royal Society of New Zealand) S I R Publishing, P.O. Box 399, Wellington, New Zealand. TEL 64-4-472-7421. FAX 64-4-473-1841. Ed. G.P. Sutherland. circ. 2,000.
—CCC.

AMBIO; a journal of the human environment. see *ENVIRONMENTAL STUDIES*

AMERICAN ACADEMY OF ARTS AND SCIENCES. BULLETIN. see *HUMANITIES: COMPREHENSIVE WORKS*

AMERICAN HERITAGE OF INVENTION & TECHNOLOGY. see *TECHNOLOGY: COMPREHENSIVE WORKS*

AMERICAN MEN AND WOMEN OF SCIENCE; a biographical directory of today's leaders in physical, biological and related sciences. see *BIOGRAPHY*

SCIENCES: COMPREHENSIVE WORKS

500.9   US   ISSN 0003-0031
QH1   CODEN: AMNAAF
AMERICAN MIDLAND NATURALIST. 1909. q. $75 (foreign $80) (effective 1996). University of Notre Dame, Room 285 GLSC, Notre Dame, IN 46556. TEL 219-239-7481. Ed. Robert P. McIntosh. bibl.; charts; illus.; index. circ. 1,400. (also avail. in microform from UMI,JSC,PMC; microfiche from IDC) Indexed: Bio-Contr.News & Info., Biol.Abstr., Biol.& Agr.Ind., Chem.Abstr., Crop Physiol.Abstr., Curr.Adv.Ecol.Sci., Curr.Cont., Deep Sea Res.& Oceanogr.Abstr., Environ.Per.Bibl., Field Crop Abstr., Forest.Abstr., Forest Prod.Abstr., Gen.Sci.Ind., Geo.Abstr., Helminthol.Abstr., Herb.Abstr., Ind.Sci.Rev., INIS Atomind., Irr.& Drain.Abstr., Key Word Ind.Wildl.Res., Plant Breed.Abstr., Sci.Cit.Ind., Sel.Water Res.Abstr., Soils & Fert., Sport Fish.Abstr., Weed Abstr., Wild.Rev., Zoo.Rec. **Document type:** academic/scholarly publication.
—BLDSC (0843.000000); CASDDS; Faxon; Genuine Article; SWETS; UMI; UnCover.
   Description: Covers the spectrum of laboratory and field studies in biology, ecology, life histories, evolution and physiology.
   Refereed Serial

AMERICAN MUSEUM NOVITATES. see *BIOLOGY — Zoology*

AMERICAN MUSEUM OF NATURAL HISTORY. ANNUAL REPORT. see *MUSEUMS AND ART GALLERIES*

AMERICAN MUSEUM OF NATURAL HISTORY. BULLETIN. see *BIOLOGY — Zoology*

900 500 100   US   ISSN 0065-9738
   CODEN: MAPSAP
AMERICAN PHILOSOPHICAL SOCIETY. MEMOIRS. 1935. irreg., vol.202, 1992. price varies. American Philosophical Society, 104 S. Fifth St., Philadelphia, PA 19106. TEL 215-440-3400. FAX 215-440-3450. Ed. Herman H. Goldstine. index. (reprint service avail. from UMI, ISI) Indexed: Biol.Abstr., GeoRef., Math.R. **Document type:** academic/scholarly publication.
—BLDSC (5577.100000); Faxon.
   Description: Titles in separate volumes cover various fields of learning.

900 500 100   US   ISSN 0065-9746
Q11   CODEN: TAPSAY
AMERICAN PHILOSOPHICAL SOCIETY. TRANSACTIONS. 1771. 1 vol./yr. (containing 1-7 parts published irregularly). $90. American Philosophical Society, 104 S. Fifth St., Philadelphia, PA 19106. TEL 215-440-3400. Ed. Herman H. Goldstine. index, cum.index: 1771-1960. (reprint service avail. from ISI,KTO,UMI) Indexed: Deep Sea Res.& Oceanogr.Abstr., GeoRef., Math.R., SSCI. **Document type:** academic/scholarly publication.
—BLDSC (8894.000000); Genuine Article; UMI.

500   US   ISSN 0003-0996
LJ85   CODEN: AMSCAC
AMERICAN SCIENTIST; published in the interest of scientific research. 1913. bi-m. $28 to individuals; institutions $45 (includes Sigma Xi Newsletter). Sigma Xi, Scientific Research Society, Box 13975, 99 Alexander Dr., Research Triangle Park, NC 27709. TEL 919-549-0097. FAX 919-549-0090. Ed. Rosalind Reid. adv.; bk.rev.; bibl.; illus.; index, cum.index: vols.34-61 (1946-1973). circ. 103,000. (also avail. in microform from UMI,PMC; reprint service avail. from UMI,ISI) Indexed: A.S.& T.Ind., Abstr.Anthropol., Acad.Ind., Anthropol.Lit., Biog.Ind., Biol.Abstr., Biol.Dig., Bk.Rev.Ind. (1989-), Br.Archaeol.Abstr., CAD CAM Abstr., Cadscan, Chem.Abstr., Child.Bk.Rev.Ind. (1989-), Child Devel.Abstr., Comput. Rev., Curr.Adv.Ecol.Sci., Curr.Cont., Curr.Pack.Abstr., Deep Sea Res.& Oceanogr.Abstr., Ecol.Abstr., Energy Rev., Eng.Ind., Environ.Abstr., Environ.Per.Bibl. (1986-), Excerp.Med., Field Crop Abstr., Fut.Surv., Gen.Sci.Ind., Geo.Abstr., Geol.Abstr., Helminthol.Abstr., Herb.Abstr., HRIS, Ind.Med., Ind.Sci.Rev., INIS Atomind., INSPEC (1970-), Key Word Ind.Wildl.Res., Lang.& Lang.Behav.Abstr., Lead Abstr., Math.R., Met.Abstr., Mid.East: Abstr.& Ind., NRN, Nucl.Sci.Abstr., Nutr.Abstr., Ocean.Abstr., PMR, Psychol.Abstr., Ref.Sour., Sci.Cit.Ind., Sel.Water Res.Abstr., So.Pac.Per.Ind., Sport Fish.Abstr., Wild.Rev., World Alum.Abstr., Zincscan, Zoo.Rec. **Document type:** academic/scholarly publication.
—BLDSC (0857.000000); CASDDS; CIS; Ei; Faxon; Genuine Article; SWETS; UMI; UnCover. CCC.

AMERICANS FOR THE UNIVERSALITY OF UNESCO NEWSLETTER. see *POLITICAL SCIENCE — International Relations*

500   IR   ISSN 1015-0951
   CODEN: AMIREB
AMIRKABIR; journal of science & technology. Key Title: Amir Kabir. 1985. s-a. Amirkabir University, Office of Vice Chancellor in Research Affairs, Hafez Ave., Tehran 15, Iran. TEL 98-21-6406591. FAX 98-21-6419728. Ed. M. Sohrabi. **Indexed:** Chem.Abstr.
—BLDSC (0859.192000).

500 630   PE   ISSN 0003-2484
   CODEN: ANCNA6
ANALES CIENTIFICOS. (Text in Spanish; summaries in English) 1963. q. S/10($6) Universidad Nacional Agraria La Molina, Av. La Universidad s-n, Apdo. 456, La Molina, Lima, Peru. TEL 35-2035. FAX 35-2473. Dir. Antonio Bacigalupo. adv.; index. circ. 1,000. Indexed: Biol.Abstr., Chem.Abstr., Nutr.Abstr. **Document type:** academic/scholarly publication.
—CASDDS.

ANALOG SCIENCE FICTION & FACT. see *LITERATURE — Science Fiction, Fantasy, Horror*

500   CC   ISSN 1000-2162
ANHUI DAXUE XUEBAO (ZIRAN KEXUE BAN)/ANHUI UNIVERSITY. JOURNAL (NATURAL SCIENCE EDITION). (Text in Chinese) 1960. q. $11.10. Anhui Daxue, Xuebao Bianjibu, No. 3, Feixi Lu, Hefei, Anhui 230039, People's Republic of China. TEL 0551-5112632. (Dist. overseas by: China International Book Trading Corp., P.O. Box 399, Beijing, P.R. China) Ed. Zheng Zuxiu. circ. 2,000. **Document type:** academic/scholarly publication.
   Description: Contains scientific papers on mathematics, physics, chemistry, biology and engineering.

500   CC   ISSN 1001-2443
ANHUI SHIDA XUEBAO/ANHUI NORMAL UNIVERSITY. JOURNAL.* (Text in Chinese) q. Anhui Shifan Daxue - Anhui Normal University, Xuebao Bianjibu, 1 Renmin Rd., Wuhu, Anhui 241000, People's Republic of China. TEL 35966. Ed. Ni Guangming.

500 001   US   ISSN 1079-5146
▼**THE ANNALS OF IMPROBABLE RESEARCH.** 1995. bi-m. $17.95 (Canada & Mexico $27; elsewhere $40). Annals of Improbable Research, Box 380853, Cambridge, MA 02238. TEL 617-491-4437. FAX 617-661-0927. E-mail: air@improb.com; Site addr.: http://www.improb.com. Ed. Marc Abrahams.
   Description: Humorous articles about science and scientists.

509   UK   ISSN 0003-3790
Q1   CODEN: ANNSA8
ANNALS OF SCIENCE; a review of the history of science since the thirteenth century. 1936. bi-m. £303($500) (effective 1996). Taylor & Francis Ltd., Rankine Rd., Basingstoke, Hants. RG24 8PR, England. TEL 44-1256-840366. FAX 44-1256-479438. TELEX 858540. E-mail: info@tandf.co.uk. (Subscr. in N. America to: Taylor & Francis Inc., 1900 Frost Rd., Ste. 101, Bristol, PA 19007-1598. TEL 800-821-8312. FAX 215-785-5515) Ed. G.L.E. Turner. adv.; bk.rev.; bibl.; illus.; index. (also avail. in microfiche from KTO) Indexed: Amer.Hist.& Life, Arts & Hum.Cit.Ind., Biol.Abstr., Br.Geol.Lit. (1972-), Br.Hum.Ind., Cadscan, Chem.Abstr., CLOSS, Curr.Adv.Ecol.Sci., Curr.Cont., Deep Sea Res.& Oceanogr.Abstr., Helminthol.Abstr., Hist.Abstr., Ind.Sci.Rev., INSPEC (1972-), Lead Abstr., Math.R., Sci.Cit.Ind., SSCI, Zincscan. **Document type:** academic/scholarly publication.
—BLDSC (1044.000000); CASDDS; Ei; Faxon; Genuine Article; SWETS; UnCover. CCC.
   Description: Directed to all who are interested in the evolution of science and its impact on the development of related arts and industries.

ANNALS OF THE CAPE PROVINCIAL MUSEUMS: HUMAN SCIENCES. see *ANTHROPOLOGY*

508 069   SA   ISSN 0570-1880
QH194   CODEN: ACPVAI
ANNALS OF THE CAPE PROVINCIAL MUSEUMS: NATURAL HISTORY. (Text in English) 1961. irreg. price varies. Albany Museum, Somerset St., Grahamstown 6140, South Africa. TEL 27-461-22397. FAX 27-461-22398. (Co-sponsors: East London Museum; Kaffrarian Museum, King William's Town; McGregor Museum, Kimberley; Port Elizabeth Museum) (back issues avail.) Indexed: Sport Fish.Abstr., Wild.Rev., Zoo.Rec. **Document type:** monographic series.
—BLDSC (1021.700000).

509   US   ISSN 0003-5335
G845   CODEN: AJUSAF
ANTARCTIC JOURNAL OF THE UNITED STATES. 1966. q., plus a. review. $14 (foreign $17.50); Annual Review issue $22 (foreign $27.50). U.S. National Science Foundation, Office of Polar Programs, 4201 Wilson Blvd., Arlington, VA 22230. (Subscr. to: Superintendent of Documents, U.S. Government Printing Office, Box 371954, Pittsburgh, PA 15250-7954. TEL 202-512-1800. FAX 202-512-2250) Ed. Winifred Reuning. charts; illus.; maps. circ. 4,500. (also avail. in microform from MIM,UMI; back issues avail.) Indexed: Biol.Abstr., Curr.Adv.Ecol.Sci., Deep Sea Res.& Oceanogr.Abstr., Geo.Abstr., GeoRef., Ind.U.S.Gov.Per., INIS Atomind., Meteor.& Geoastrophys.Abstr., Ocean.Abstr., Ref.Zh., Sci.Cit.Ind., Soils & Fert. **Document type:** academic/scholarly publication, government publication.
—BLDSC (1542.107000); Faxon; SWETS; UMI; UnCover.
   Description: Provides a common outlet for all information on the National United States Antarctic Program to a broad audience of participants and interested general public.

ANUARIO DE DERECHO PENAL Y CIENCIAS PENALES. see *LAW*

500   US   ISSN 0882-4347
APPLIED ORGONOMETRY; notes from the workshop of applied orgonometry. 1986. 3/yr. $25. R R P Publishers, Box 8, Easton, PA 18044-0008. TEL 215-252-1199. Ed. Jacob Meyerowitz. (looseleaf format)

500   NE   ISSN 0929-0702
APPLIED RESEARCH. 1983. bi-m. free. Nederlandse Organisatie voor Toegepast Natuurwetenschappelijk Onderzoek (TNO) - Netherlands Organization for Applied Scientific Research, Postbus 6050, 2600 JA Delft, Netherlands. TEL 31-15-2696900. FAX 31-15-2612403. E-mail: PB@mp.tno.nl. Ed. Peter M. Baven. illus. circ. 4,000. **Document type:** newsletter.
   Description: Covers applied scientific research in the Netherlands.

500   US   ISSN 0885-1549
APPLIED SCIENCE. (Subseries of: S I R S Science (ISSN 0885-1530)) 1985. a. $80. Social Issues Resources Series, Box 2348, Boca Raton, FL 33427-2348. TEL 407-994-0079; 800-232-7477. FAX 407-994-4704. (looseleaf format; also avail. in microfiche)
   Description: Reprints 70 articles that explore the social dimensions of developments in computer science, engineering, and medicine.

SCIENCES: COMPREHENSIVE WORKS

500   **NE**   ISSN 0003-6994
TA349   CODEN: ASRHAU
APPLIED SCIENTIFIC RESEARCH; an international journal on the applications of fluid dynamics. (Text in English) 1947. 8/yr. fl.1052 to institutions; $642 to institutions in U.S. (effective 1996). Kluwer Academic Publishers, Postbus 17, 3300 AA Dordrecht, Netherlands. TEL 31-78-392392. FAX 31-78-392254. TELEX 29245 KAPG NL. E-mail: SERVICES@WKAP.NL. (Dist. by: Kluwer Academic Publishers Group, P.O. Box 322, 3300 AH Dordrecht. TEL 31-78-392392. FAX 31-78-546474; N. America dist. addr.: Box 358, Accord Sta., Hingham, MA 02018-0358. TEL 617-871-6600. FAX 617-871-6528) Ed. F.T.M. Nieuwstadt. (also avail. in microform from UMI) Indexed: Appl.Mech.Rev., Bull.Signal., Chem.Abstr., Chem.Eng.Abstr., Curr.Adv.Ecol.Sci., Curr.Cont., Eng.Ind., Fluidex, Ind.Sci.Rev., INSPEC (1968-), Math.R., Met.Abstr., Petrol.Abstr., Sci.Cit.Ind., T.C.E.A., World Alum.Abstr., Zent.Math. **Document type:** academic/scholarly publication.
—BLDSC (1576.900000); CASDDS; Ei; Faxon; Genuine Article; SWETS; UMI; UnCover. **CCC.**
   Description: Publishes original theoretical and experimental contributions and research reports relating to fluid dynamics and heat and mass transfer, with an emphasis on applied research.
   Refereed Serial

APPRAISAL; science books for young people. see PUBLISHING AND BOOK TRADE

500 510   **SU**   ISSN 1015-4442
   CODEN: AGSREJ
ARAB GULF JOURNAL OF SCIENTIFIC RESEARCH. (Text in Arabic, English) 1983. 3/yr. SRI.100($25) to individuals; institutions $50. Arab Bureau of Education for the Gulf States, P.O. Box 3908, Riyadh 11481, Saudi Arabia. TEL 966-1-4774644. FAX 966-1-4783165. TELEX 401441 TARBIA SJ. Ed. Daham Alani. circ. 2,000. (back issues avail.) Indexed: Anim.Breed.Abstr., Biodet.Abstr., Cott.& Trop.Fibr.Abstr., Curr.Adv.Ecol.Sci., Curr.Ref.Fish Res., Ecol.Abstr., Environ.Per.Bibl. (1989-), Excerp.Med., Geo.Abstr., Geol.Abstr., Herb.Abstr., IDA, INSPEC (1983-), Math.R., Poult.Abstr., Rev.Med.& Vet.Mycol., Sorghum & Millets Abstr., Vet.Bull., Zoo.Rec. **Document type:** academic/scholarly publication.
—BLDSC (1583.226630); CASDDS; Genuine Article.
   Formed by the 1989 merger of: Arab Gulf Journal of Scientific Research. Section A: Mathematical and Physical Sciences (ISSN 0259-8930); Arab Gulf Journal of Scientific Research. Section B: Agricultural and Biological Sciences (ISSN 0259-8949); Which superseded was: Arab Gulf Journal of Scientific Research (ISSN 0256-4548)

ARAB LEAGUE EDUCATIONAL, SCIENTIFIC, AND CULTURAL ORGANIZATION. INFORMATION NEWSLETTER. see EDUCATION

ARABIAN JOURNAL FOR SCIENCE AND ENGINEERING. see ENGINEERING

500 297   **UK**   ISSN 0957-4239
DS36.8
ARABIC SCIENCES AND PHILOSOPHY; a historical journal. 1991. s-a. £59($92) (effective 1996). Cambridge University Press, Edinburgh Bldg., Shaftesbury Rd., Cambridge CB2 2RU, England. TEL 01223-312393. FAX 01223-315052. TELEX 851817256. (N. American addr.: Cambridge University Press, Journals Dept., 40 W. 20th St., New York, NY 10011. TEL 212-924-3900. FAX 212-691-3239) Ed.Bd. adv. (back issues avail.) Indexed: Amer.Hist.& Life (until 1992), Hist.Abstr. (until 1992). **Document type:** academic/scholarly publication.
—BLDSC (1583.329400); UMI; UnCover. **CCC.**
   Description: Covers the history of the Arabic sciences, mathematics and philosophy in the world of Islam between the eighth and eigtheenth centuries.

500   **SP**   ISSN 1132-2292
ARANZADIANA; aranzadiko berriak. 1953. a. 4000 ptas. includes Munibe. Sociedad de Ciencias Aranzadi, Plaza I. Zuloaga (Museo), 20003 Donostia-San Sebastian, Spain. TEL 943-42-29-45. FAX 943-42-13-16. **Document type:** bulletin.
   Description: Reviews the association's activities.

ARCHAEOLOGY AND NATURAL SCIENCE. see ARCHAEOLOGY

ARCHIMEDES; natural science magazine for the whole family. see CHILDREN AND YOUTH — For

509   **GW**   ISSN 0003-9519
Q125   CODEN: AHESAN
ARCHIVE FOR HISTORY OF EXACT SCIENCES. (Text in English; occasionally in French, German, Italian, Latin, Spanish) 1960. 8/yr. (in 2 vols., 4 nos./vol.). DM.590($428) (effective 1996). Springer-Verlag, Heidelberger Platz 3, 14197 Berlin, Germany. TEL 030-8207-0. FAX 030-8214091. E-mail: orders@springer.de. (Subscr. in N. America to: Springer-Verlag New York, Inc., 44 Hartz Way, Secaucus, NJ 07096-2491. TEL 201-348-4033. FAX 201-348-4505) Ed. C. Truesdell. adv.; bibl.; charts; index. (also avail. in microform from UMI; reprint service avail. from ISI) Indexed: Br.Archaeol.Abstr., Compumath, Curr.Cont., Ind.Sci.Rev., Math.R., Sci.Cit.Ind., SSCI, Zent.Math. **Document type:** academic/scholarly publication.
—BLDSC (1634.430000); Faxon; Genuine Article; SWETS; UMI; UnCover. **CCC.**
   Description: Focuses on mathematics and natural philosophy. Includes examination of the physical sciences.

509   **SZ**   ISSN 0252-9289
Q67   CODEN: ASGVAH
ARCHIVES DES SCIENCES ET COMPTE RENDU DES SEANCES DE LA SOCIETE DE PHYSIQUE ET D'HISTOIRE NATURELLE DE GENEVE. (Text in English, French, German, Italian) 1846. 3/yr. 120 SFr. Societe de Physique et d'Histoire Naturelle de Geneve, Museum d'Histoire Naturelle de Geneve, Case Postale 6434, CH-1211 Geneva 6, Switzerland. TEL 022-7359130. FAX 022-7353445. adv. (also avail. in microform from PMC) Indexed: Appl.Mech.Rev., Biol.Abstr., Chem.Abstr., Curr.Adv.Ecol.Sci., Helminthol.Abstr., INSPEC (1968-), Math.R. **Document type:** academic/scholarly publication.
—BLDSC (1642.000000); CASDDS; Ei; Faxon; UMI; UnCover.
   Formed by 1980 merger of: Compte Rendu des Seances de la Societe de Physique et d'Histoire Naturelle de Geneve (ISSN 0583-8401); Archives des Sciences (ISSN 0003-9705); (until 1947: Archives des Sciences Physiques et Naturelles (ISSN 0365-7116)

500.9   **IT**   ISSN 0003-9810
   CODEN: AIHSAB
ARCHIVES INTERNATIONALES D'HISTOIRE DES SCIENCES. (Text in English, French, German, Italian, Russian, Spanish) 1919; N.S. 1972. 2/yr. L.90000. Istituto della Enciclopedia Italiana, Piazza della Enciclopedia Italiana 4, 00186 Rome, Italy. TEL 39-6-68981. FAX 39-6-68982175. Ed. R. Halleux. adv.; bk.rev.; bibl.; charts; illus.; index. circ. 1,200. (back issues avail.) Indexed: Amer.Hist.& Life, Chem.Abstr., Hist.Abstr., Math.R., Per.Islam. (1991-). **Document type:** academic/scholarly publication.
—BLDSC (1635.000000); SWETS.

508.09   **UK**   ISSN 0260-9541
Z7403
ARCHIVES OF NATURAL HISTORY. 1936. 3/yr. £90($160) Society for the History of Natural History, c/o The Natural History Museum, Cromwell Rd., London SW7 5BD, England. bk.rev.; bibl.; index. circ. 850. Indexed: Amer.Hist.& Life, Biol.Abstr., Br.Geol.Lit. (1972-), Deep Sea Res.& Oceanogr.Abstr., Geo.Abstr., GeoRef., Hist.Abstr., So.Pac.Per.Ind., Sport Fish.Abstr., Wild.Rev., Zoo.Rec. **Document type:** academic/scholarly publication.
—BLDSC (1637.947000); Faxon; UnCover.
   Formerly: Society for the Bibliography of Natural History. Journal (ISSN 0037-9778)

500   **IT**   ISSN 1122-0929
ARCHIVIO DELLA CORRISPONDENZA DEGLI SCIENZIATI ITALIANI. 1985. irreg., no.11, 1994. price varies. Casa Editrice Leo S. Olschki, Casella Postale 66, 50100 Florence, Italy. TEL 39-55-6530684. FAX 39-55-6530214. **Document type:** academic/scholarly publication.

ARCHIWUM ENERGETYKI. see ENGINEERING

919 551   **CN**   ISSN 0004-0843
G600   CODEN: ATICAB
ARCTIC. (Text and summaries in English, French, Russian) 1947. q. $95 (effective 1996). Arctic Institute of North America, MLT 11th Fl., University of Calgary, 2500 University Dr. N.W., Calgary, AB T2N 1N4, Canada. TEL 403-220-7515. FAX 403-282-4609. Ed. Karen McCullough. bk.rev.; abstr.; bibl.; charts; illus.; maps; index. circ. 2,200. (also avail. in microform from UMI; reprint service avail. from UMI; back issues avail.) Indexed: Abstr.Anthropol., Amer.Hist.& Life, Anthropol.Lit., Arct.Bibl., ASTIS, Biol.Abstr., Can.B.P.I., Can.Per.Ind., Chem.Abstr., CMI, Curr.Adv.Ecol.Sci., Curr.Cont., Deep Sea Res.& Oceanogr.Abstr., E&P Hlth. (1993-), Ecol.Abstr., Environ.Abstr., Environ.Per.Bibl., Excerp.Med., Field Crop Abstr., Forest.Abstr., Forest Prod.Abstr., Gas Process.& Ppl. (1993-), Geo.Abstr., Geol.Abstr., GeoRef., Herb.Abstr., Hist.Abstr., IDA, Ind.Sci.Rev., Key Word Ind.Wildl.Res., Meteor.& Geoastrophys.Abstr., Ocean.Abstr., Off.Tech. (1993-), Petrol.Abstr. (1972-), Pollut.Abstr., Sci.Cit.Ind., Sel.Water Res.Abstr., Soils & Fert., Sport Fish.Abstr., Wild.Rev., Zoo.Rec. **Document type:** academic/scholarly publication.
—BLDSC (1663.000000); CIS; Faxon; Genuine Article; PADDS; UMI; UnCover. **CCC.**
   Description: Multi-disciplinary journal presents papers from circumpolar scientists.
   Refereed Serial

550   **US**   ISSN 0004-0851
GB395   CODEN: ATLPAV
ARCTIC AND ALPINE RESEARCH. 1969. q. $80 (foreign $86) (effective 1996). University of Colorado, Institute of Arctic and Alpine Research, Campus Box 450, Boulder, CO 80309-0450. TEL 303-492-3765. FAX 303-492-6388. Ed. Kathleen Salzberg. bk.rev.; bibl.; charts; illus.; stat.; index. circ. 850. (also avail. in microform from UMI; back issues avail.) Indexed: Abstr.Anthropol., Acid Rain Abstr., Acid Rain Ind., Biol.Abstr., Bull.Signal., Chem.Abstr., Curr.Adv.Ecol.Sci., Curr.Adv.Genetics & Molec.Biol., Curr.Cont., Deep Sea Res.& Oceanogr.Abstr., Ecol.Abstr., Environ.Per.Bibl. (1989-), Field Crop Abstr., Forest.Abstr., Forest Prod.Abstr., Geo.Abstr., Geol.Abstr., GeoRef., Herb.Abstr., IDA, INIS Atomind., Irr.& Drain.Abstr., Key Word Ind.Wildl.Res., Meteor.& Geoastrophys.Abstr, Ref.Zh., Sci.Cit.Ind., Sel.Water Res.Abstr., Soils & Fert., Sport Fish.Abstr., Weed Abstr., Wild.Rev., World Agri.Econ.& Rural Sociol.Abstr., Zoo.Rec. **Document type:** academic/scholarly publication.
—BLDSC (1663.060000); CASDDS; Faxon; Genuine Article; SWETS; UMI; UnCover. **CCC.**
   Description: Presents original research pertaining to cold environments, both past and present.
   Refereed Serial

508.311 910   **US**   ISSN 1045-4764
G615
ARCTIC RESEARCH OF THE UNITED STATES. 1987. s-a. free. National Science Foundation, Office of Polar Programs, 4201 Wilson Blvd., Arlington, VA 22230. TEL 703-306-1031. FAX 703-306-0139. E-mail: cmyers@nsf.gov. Ed. Charles E. Myers. circ. 2,000. **Document type:** government publication.
—Faxon.

509.798   **US**
ARCTIC SCIENCE CONFERENCE. PROCEEDINGS. 1950. a. $15. American Association for the Advancement of Science, Arctic Division, Box 80271, Fairbanks, AK 99708. TEL 907-474-7371. FAX 907-474-7290. circ. 600. Indexed: Biol.Abstr., GeoRef, Sport Fish.Abstr., Wild.Rev., Zoo.Rec. **Document type:** proceedings.
   Former titles: Alaska Science Conference. Proceedings (ISSN 0084-6120); (until 1969): Science in Alaska (ISSN 0191-2151)

SCIENCES: COMPREHENSIVE WORKS

500   US   ISSN 0193-8509
Q11.A72   CODEN: JNASDB
ARIZONA-NEVADA ACADEMY OF SCIENCE. JOURNAL. 1959. 2/yr. $25. Arizona-Nevada Academy of Science, Office of Climatology, Arizona State University, Box 871508, Tempe, AZ 85287-1508. TEL 602-965-6265. FAX 602-965-1473. Eds. Leslie R. Landrum, Donald J. Pinkava. adv.; bk.rev.; charts; illus. **Indexed:** Biol.Abstr., Chem.Abstr., Energy Info.Abstr., Excerp.Med., Field Crop Abstr., Geo.Abstr., GeoRef., Herb.Abstr., Sel.Water Res.Abstr., Soils & Fert., World Agri.Econ.& Rural Sociol.Abstr. **Document type:** academic/scholarly publication.
—BLDSC (4700.800000); CASDDS; CIS; UnCover.
   Formerly: Arizona Academy of Science Journal (ISSN 0004-1378)
   Refereed Serial

500 061.67   US   ISSN 0097-4374
AS36   CODEN: AKASAO
ARKANSAS ACADEMY OF SCIENCE. PROCEEDINGS. 1941. a. $45. Arkansas Academy of Science, Dept. of Math & Sciences, Univ. of Arkansas at Monticello, Monticello, AR 71656. TEL 501-460-1265. FAX 501-460-1316. E-mail: wileyr@uamont.edu. Ed. Stan Tranth. circ. 450. **Indexed:** Bibl.Agri., Biol.Abstr., Chem.Abstr., Excerp.Med., Geo.Ref., Sport Fish.Abstr., Wild.Rev., Zoo.Rec. **Document type:** proceedings.
—BLDSC (6649.000000); CASDDS.

500 600   US
ARTS AND SCIENCES NEWSLETTER. 1984. s-a. membership. Vermont Academy of Arts and Sciences, 2 Buxton Ave., Middletown Springs, VT 05757. TEL 802-235-2302. Ed. Frances B. Krouse. circ. 500. **Document type:** newsletter.

ASCENT TECHNOLOGY MAGAZINE. see *TECHNOLOGY: COMPREHENSIVE WORKS*

500   BG   ISSN 1016-6947
ASIATIC SOCIETY OF BANGLADESH. JOURNAL: SCIENCE. (Text in English) 1956. s-a. Tk.100($20) per no. Asiatic Society of Bangladesh, 5 Old Secretariat Rd. (Nimtali), Ramna, Dhaka 2, Bangladesh. TEL 2-866582. **Document type:** academic/scholarly publication.
   Supersedes in part (in 1975): Asiatic Society of Bangladesh. Journal (ISSN 0377-0540); Which was formerly (until 1972): Asiatic Society of Pakistan. Journal (ISSN 0571-317X)

500   AG   ISSN 0325-2809
ASOCIACION DE CIENCIAS NATURALES DEL LITORAL. REVISTA. (Text in Spanish; summaries in English) 1970. s-a. $30. Asociacion de Ciencias Naturales del Litoral, J. Macia 1933, 3016 Santo Tome (S.Fe), Argentina. Ed. Federico Emiliani. adv.; bk.rev.; index, cum.index: 1970-1976; 1977-1981; 1982-1986. circ. 1,000. (back issues avail.) **Indexed:** Curr.Adv.Ecol.Sci., Sel.Water Res.Abstr.
—CCC.

500   SP
ASOCIACION ESPANOLA DE ENSAYOS NON-DESTRUCTIVOS. BOLETIN INFORMATIVO. 4/yr. Asociacion Espanola de Ensayos Non-Destructivos, Isal de Saipan 47, 28035 Madrid, Spain. TEL 1-373-47-50. FAX 1-316-91-77. Ed. M. Pelegri Torres.

500 600   SA   ISSN 0373-4250
   CODEN: ATSAAL
ASSOCIATED SCIENTIFIC AND TECHNICAL SOCIETIES OF SOUTH AFRICA. ANNUAL PROCEEDINGS. (Text in English) 1921. a. free. Associated Scientific and Technical Societies of South Africa, P.O. Box 93480, Yeoville 2143, South Africa. TEL 27-11-487-1512. FAX 27-11-648-1876. circ. controlled. (back issues avail.) **Indexed:** Biol.Abstr., INSPEC (1968-). **Document type:** proceedings.

500   CN   ISSN 0066-8842
ASSOCIATION CANADIENNE - FRANCAISE POUR L'AVANCEMENT DES SCIENCES. ANNALES. 1935. a. Can.$12. Association Canadienne - Francaise pour l'Avancement des Sciences, 425 rue de la Gauchetiere E., Montreal, PQ H2L 2M7, Canada. TEL 514-849-0045. FAX 514-849-5558. circ. 4,000. **Indexed:** Arct.Bibl., Biol.Abstr., GeoRef.
   Description: Summaries of all the communications presented at the association's congress.

500   CN
ASSOCIATION CANADIENNE - FRANCAISE POUR L'AVANCEMENT DES SCIENCES. CAHIERS SCIENTIFIQUES. irreg. price varies. Association Canadienne - Francaise Pour l'Avancement des Sciences, 2730 Cote Ste. Catherine, Montreal, PQ H3T 1B7, Canada. TEL 514-342-1411. FAX 514-342-9552. **Document type:** monographic series.
   Formerly: Cahiers de l'A C F A S.

500   CN   ISSN 0826-4864
QC21
ASSOCIATION CANADIENNE - FRANCAISE POUR L'AVANCEMENT DES SCIENCES. INTERFACE. (Text in French) 1984. 5/yr. Can.$41.60 to individuals; institutions Can.$90.14; students Can.$20.80 (foreign Can.$78). Association Canadienne - Francaise pour l'Avancement des Sciences, 425 rue de la Gauchetiere E., Montreal, PQ H2L 2M7, Canada. TEL 514-849-0045. FAX 514-849-5558. Ed. Sophie Malavoy. adv.: B&W page Can.$1000, color page Can.$1545; trim 7 11/16 x 10 1/4; adv. contact: Pierette Lefrancois. circ. 8,000. (back issues avail.) **Indexed:** Pt.de Rep. (1988-).
   Formerly: Association Canadienne - Francaise pour l'Avancement des Sciences. Bulletin (ISSN 0066-8850)
   Description: A multi-disciplinary magazine addressed to members of the scientific community in the university, public, parapublic and private sectors.

500.9   FR   ISSN 1167-9786
ASSOCIATION DES NATURALISTES DES YVELINES. BULLETIN. serie 4, 1974. q. 170 F. Association des Naturalistes des Yvelines, E.N.S.H, 4 rue Hardy, R.P. no.914, 78009 Versailles Cedex, France. TEL 39-55-56-06. illus. circ. 500. **Indexed:** Bibl.& Ind.Geol. **Document type:** bulletin.
   Former titles (until 1992): Societe Versaillaise des Sciences Naturelles. Bulletin (ISSN 0336-8300); Federation Francaise des Societes de Sciences Naturelles. Revue (ISSN 0014-9365)

500.9   ML
ASSOCIATION DES NATURALISTES DU MALI. BULLETIN. a. Association des Naturalistes du Mali, B.P. 1746, Bamako, Mali. **Document type:** bulletin.

ASTER; recherches en Didactique des Sciences Experimentales. see *EDUCATION*

500   IT   ISSN 0392-419X
   CODEN: ANPMD3
ATENEO PARMENSE. ACTA NATURALIA. (Text and summaries in English, Italian) 1965. q. L.20000 (foreign L.25000). (Societa di Medicina e Scienze Naturali di Parma) Ateneo Parmense, Via Gramsci 14 (Ospedale Maggiore), 43100 Parma, Italy. TEL 39-521-983364. Ed. Paolo Bobbio. charts; illus.4. stat. circ. 550. **Indexed:** Biol.Abstr., Chem.Abstr., Excerp.Med., Ind.Med., Nutr.Abstr. **Document type:** academic/scholarly publication, proceedings.
—CASDDS.
   Supersedes: Ateneo Parmense. Sezione 2: Acta Naturalia (ISSN 0004-654X)
   Description: Presents research papers and articles on sciences. Includes various articles on oceanography, geology, and topology.

500 700   IT   ISSN 0004-6558
ATENEO VENETO; rivista di scienze, lettere ed arti. 1812. a. exchange basis. Ateneo Veneto, Campo S. Fantin 1897, Venice, Italy. TEL 39-41-5224459. Ed. Marino Zorzi. bk.rev.; bibl.; charts; illus.; index, cum.index. circ. 1,000. **Indexed:** Amer.Hist.& Life, Hist.Abstr., M.L.A. **Document type:** academic/scholarly publication.
   Description: Covers Venetian history and culture, humanities in general.

ATLANTE. see *GEOGRAPHY*

500   CN
ATLANTIC SCIENCE. 1975. 3/yr. free. Atlantic Provinces Council on the Sciences, Memorial University of Newfoundland, P.O. Box 4200, St. John's, NF A1C 5S7, Canada. TEL 709-737-8918. FAX 709-737-4569. E-mail: jatkinson@kean.ucs.mun.ca. Ed. Joan Atkinson. circ. 3,000.
   Formerly: A P I C S News.
   Description: News about members of the council and research conducted by scientists in the Atlantic provinces.

574.966   DK   ISSN 0067-0227
   CODEN: ATREAS
ATLANTIDE REPORT. SCIENTIFIC RESULTS OF THE DANISH EXPEDITION TO THE COASTS OF TROPICAL WEST AFRICA. (Text in English and French) 1950. irreg., vol.14, 1988. price varies. (University of Copenhagen) Apollo Books, Kirkeby Sand 19, DK-5771 Stenstrup, Denmark. TEL 45-62-26-37-37. FAX 45-62-26-37-80. (Co-sponsor: British Museum) Eds. Joergen Knudsen, Torben Wolff. (back issues avail.) **Indexed:** Biol.Abstr., Deep Sea Res.& Oceanogr.Abstr., Zoo.Rec. **Document type:** monographic series, academic/scholarly publication.
   Refereed Serial

AULA. see *EDUCATION*

500 600 614.7   AT   ISSN 1036-0875
AUSTRALASIAN SCIENCE. 1980. q. Aus.$30 (foreign Aus.$40) (effective 1996). (University of Southern Queensland) U S Q Press, P.O. Box 58, Darling Heights, Toowoomba, Qld. 4350, Australia. TEL 61-76-31-2768. FAX 61-76-311758. TELEX 40010. E-mail: usqpress@usq.edu.au. Ed. Jennifer Wright. adv.; illus. circ. 5,000. (back issues avail.)
—UnCover. **CCC.**
   Former titles: Australian Science Magazine (ISSN 0729-6924); Science Magazine (ISSN 0159-9062)
   Description: Current scientific issues for students, teachers and the public.

501   NE   ISSN 0929-6425
AUSTRALASIAN STUDIES IN HISTORY AND PHILOSOPHY OF SCIENCE. 1982. irreg. price varies. Kluwer Academic Publishers, Postbus 17, 3300 AA Dordrecht, Netherlands. TEL 31-78-392392. FAX 31-78-392254. TELEX 29245 KAPG NL. (Dist. by: Kluwer Academic Publishers Group, P.O. Box 322, 3300 AH Dordrecht, Netherlands. TEL 31-78-392392. FAX 31-78-546474; N. America dist. addr.: Box 358, Accord Sta., Hingham, MA 02018-0358. TEL 617-871-6600) Ed. R.W. Home. **Document type:** monographic series.
—BLDSC (1796.370000).
   Formerly: Australasian Studies in History and Philosophy.
   Refereed Serial

500   AT
AUSTRALIAN ACADEMY OF SCIENCE. YEAR BOOK. 1956. a. Aus.$30. Australian Academy of Science, G.P.O. Box 783, Canberra, A.C.T. 2601, Australia. index. circ. 1,500. **Indexed:** AESIS.
   Formerly: Australian Academy of Science. Handbook (ISSN 0811-9635)

508 069   AT   ISSN 0067-1975
QH1   CODEN: RAUMAJ
AUSTRALIAN MUSEUM, SYDNEY. RECORDS. (Supplement avail.) 1890. 3/yr. Aus.$100. Australian Museum, P.O. Box A285, Sydney, N.S.W. 2000, Australia. FAX 02-339-8313. Ed. J.K. Lowry. **Indexed:** AESIS, Biol.Abstr., Deep Sea Res.& Oceanogr.Abstr., GeoRef., Sport Fish.Abstr., Wild.Rev., Zoo.Rec. **Document type:** academic/scholarly publication.
—BLDSC (7315.000000); UnCover.
   Description: Original research in zoology, geology and anthropology in Australia, Southwest Pacific and Indian Ocean areas.

508 069   AT   ISSN 0812-7387
   CODEN: RAMSEZ
AUSTRALIAN MUSEUM, SYDNEY. RECORDS SUPPLEMENTS. (Supplement to: Australian Museum, Sydney. Records) 1890. irreg. price varies. Australian Museum, P.O. Box A285, Sydney, N.S.W. 2000, Australia. Ed. Jim Lowry. **Indexed:** Biol.Abstr., GeoRef., Sport Fish.Abstr., Wild.Rev., Zoo.Rec. **Document type:** monographic series.
—BLDSC (7315.100000); UnCover.
   Formerly (until 1983): Australian Museum, Sydney. Memoirs (ISSN 0067-1967)
   Description: Monographs in zoology, geology and anthropology in Australia, Southwest Pacific and the Indian Ocean.

500.9   AT   ISSN 0004-9840
QH1   CODEN: AUNHAO
AUSTRALIAN NATURAL HISTORY. 1921. q. Aus.$30 (foreign Aus.$42). Australian Museum, 6-8 College St., Sydney, N.S.W. 2000, Australia. Ed. Jennifer Saunders. adv. contact: Sari Jarvenpaa. bk.rev.; cum.index every 3 yrs. circ. 20,000. **Indexed:** AESIS, Biol.Abstr., Environ.Per.Bibl. (1977-), Gdlns, GeoRef. **Document type:** consumer publication.
—BLDSC (1815.500000); UnCover.
    Formerly: Australian Museum Magazine.
    Description: Popular science magazine with feature articles on nature, culture and environmental issues.

500 600   AT   ISSN 1032-2167
AUSTRALIAN SCIENCE AND TECHNOLOGY NEWSLETTER. m. free. Department of Foreign Affairs and Trade, Overseas Information Branch, G.P.O. Box 12, Canberra, A.C.T. 2601, Australia. TEL 06-261-3983. FAX 06-2613900. Ed. Barry Bretland. circ. 2,900. **Document type:** newsletter, government publication.
    Former titles (until 1988): Science and Energy Newsletter (ISSN 0815-4171); (until 1985): Australian Overseas Information Service. Science Newsletter (ISSN 0815-4163)

500   AU
AUSTRIA. BUNDESMINISTERIUM FUER WISSENSCHAFT, FORSCHUNG UND KUNST. FORSCHUNGSBERICHT. 1968. triennial. free. Bundesministerium fuer Wissenschaft, Forschung und Kunst, Minoritenplatz 5, A-1014 Vienna, Austria. TEL 0222-53120-0. FAX 0222-53120-6480. TELEX 111157. stat. **Document type:** government publication.
    Formerly: Austria. Bundesministerium fuer Wissenschaft und Forschung. Bericht der Bundesregierung an den Nationalrat (ISSN 0300-2772)
    Description: Report to the Austrian Parliament on the current situation of scientific research.

AUTOMATIC DOCUMENTATION AND MATHEMATICAL LINGUISTICS. see LIBRARY AND INFORMATION SCIENCES

600   II   ISSN 0970-6607
AWISHKARA. (Text in Hindi) 1971. m. Rs.30. National Research Development Corporation, 20-22 Zamroodpur Community Centre, Kailash Colony Extension, New Delhi 110 048, India. TEL 11-6418615. TELEX 031-71358. Ed. D.N. Bhatnagar. adv.; bk.rev.; abstr.; charts; illus. circ. 30,000. **Indexed:** Indian Sci.Abstr.

500   US   ISSN 0141-6413
B A S R A JOURNAL. 1962. q. $25. British-American Scientific Research Association, UK , 614 1/2 N. Emerson Ave., Indianapolis, IN 46219. TEL 317-356-2170. Ed. D.E. Thurlow. bk.rev.; charts; illus. circ. 50. (processed) **Document type:** academic/scholarly publication.
—BLDSC (1865.290000).
    Formerly: British Amateur Scientific Research Association (ISSN 0005-2671)
    Description: Publishes scientific papers from members and others. Its purpose is an exchange of scientific ideas, many of which are unorthodox.

500   CN   ISSN 0228-8842
B.C. NATURALIST. 1969. 6/yr. Can.$15 (effective 1996). Federation of British Columbia Naturalists, 321-1367 West Broadway, Vancouver, BC V6H 4A9, Canada. TEL 604-737-3057. Ed. Clare M. Murphy. adv. contact: Germain Marc'Hadour. bk.rev. circ. 6,000. **Indexed:** Sport Fish.Abstr., Wild.Rev. **Document type:** newsletter.
    Former titles: Federation of British Columbia Naturalists. Newsletter (ISSN 0046-3566); B.C. Nature Council.
    Refereed Serial

B L A S T. see LAW

007   GW
B M F T FORKAT. 1971. a. DM.30. (Bundesministerium fuer Forschung und Technologie, Referat 022) Verlag T Ue V Rheinland GmbH, Victoriastr. 26, 51149 Cologne, Germany. TEL 02203-170902. FAX 02203-15411. circ. 3,000. **Document type:** catalog.
    ●Also available online. Vendor(s): STN International.
    Formerly (until 1984): Germany (Federal Republic, 1949-). Bundesministerium fuer Forschung und Technologie. B M F T Foerderungskatalog.

B M F T JOURNAL. (Bundesministerium fuer Forschung und Technologie) see TECHNOLOGY: COMPREHENSIVE WORKS

509   UK   ISSN 0144-6347
B S H S NEWSLETTER. 1980. 3/yr. £6($12) to non-members. British Society for the History of Science, 31 High St., Stanford in the Vale, Faringdon, Oxon. SN7 8LH, England. TEL 01367-710223. FAX 01367-718963. Ed. F.A.J.L. James. bk.rev. circ. 850. **Document type:** newsletter.
    Description: Reports on developments in history of science, reports of meetings, and forthcoming meetings.

BAHIA, BRAZIL (STATE). CENTRO DE PESQUISAS E DESENVOLVIMENTO. BOLETIM TECNICO. see TECHNOLOGY: COMPREHENSIVE WORKS

001.3   CC
BAIKE ZHISHI/ENCYCLOPEDIC KNOWLEDGE. (Text in Chinese) m. Y11.04($43.10) Zhongguo Dabaike Quanshu Chubanshe - China Encyclopaedia Publishing House, 17 Fuchengmen Beidajie, Beijing 100037, People's Republic of China. TEL 8317319. (Dist. outside China by: China International Book Trading Corp., P.O. Box 2820, Beijing, P.R.C.; Dist. in US by: China Books & Periodicals, Inc., 2929 24th St., San Francisco, CA 94110) Ed. Mei Yi. adv.
    Description: Popular science periodical.

500   BG   ISSN 0378-8121
Q80.B3   CODEN: JBACDF
BANGLADESH ACADEMY OF SCIENCES. JOURNAL. 1977. 2/yr. Tk.200($40) Bangladesh Academy of Sciences, c/o Department of Chemistry, Dhaka University, Dhaka 1000, Bangladesh. FAX 880-2-865583. Ed. S.Z. Haider. bk.rev. circ. 500. **Indexed:** Biol.Abstr., Chem.Abstr., Forest Prod.Abstr., INSPEC. **Document type:** academic/scholarly publication.
—BLDSC (4707.662000); CASDDS; Ei.

500   BG   ISSN 0304-9809
Q1   CODEN: BJSIBL
BANGLADESH JOURNAL OF SCIENTIFIC AND INDUSTRIAL RESEARCH. (Text in English) 1964. q. Tk.100 (foreign $24). Bangladesh Council of Scientific and Industrial Research (BCSIR), Mirpur Road, Dhanmondi, Dhaka 1205, Bangladesh. FAX 880-2-863022. Ed. F.Z. Majid. **Indexed:** Biol.Abstr., Chem.Abstr., Crop Physiol.Abstr., Dairy Sci.Abstr., Field Crop Abstr., Food Sci.& Tech.Abstr., Herb.Abstr., Hort.Abstr., INSPEC (1973-), Nutr.Abstr., Rice Abstr., Seed Abstr., Soils & Fert., Sport Fish.Abstr., Triticale Abstr., Weed Abstr., Wild.Rev., Zoo.Rec. **Document type:** academic/scholarly publication.
—BLDSC (1861.680000); CASDDS; UnCover.
    Formerly (until Jan. 1973): Scientific Researches (ISSN 0036-8830)
    Description: Reports the findings of scientific and industrial research conducted in Bangladesh, India, Pakistan and Africa.

574.192   BG   ISSN 0253-5432
    CODEN: BJSRDG
BANGLADESH JOURNAL OF SCIENTIFIC RESEARCH. (Text in English) 1978. 2/yr. Tk.80($10) Bangladesh Association for the Advancement of Science, Department of Biochemistry, University of Dhaka, Ramna, Dhaka 2, Bangladesh. Ed. Abdul Mannan. adv.; bk.rev. circ. 2,500. **Indexed:** Biol.Abstr., Chem.Abstr., Diar.Dis.Res., Field Crop Abstr., Herb.Abstr., Plant Grow.Reg.Abstr.
—CASDDS.

BANGLADESH JOURNAL OF SOIL SCIENCE. see AGRICULTURE — Crop Production And Soil

500   BG
BANGLADESH SCIENCE CONFERENCE. PROCEEDINGS. a. (Bangladesh Association for the Advancement of Science) University of Dhaka, Ramna, Dhaka 1000, Bangladesh. **Document type:** proceedings.

500.9   IQ
BASRAH NATURAL HISTORY MUSEUM. BULLETIN. (Text in English; summaries in Arabic and English) 1974. irreg. exchange basis. Basrah Natural History Museum, University of Basrah, Basrah, Iraq. Ed. Khalaf al-Robaae. abstr.; bibl.; index. **Indexed:** Biol.Abstr. **Document type:** bulletin.

500.9   IQ
BASRAH NATURAL HISTORY MUSEUM. PUBLICATION. 1976. irreg. exchange basis. Basrah Natural History Museum, University of Basrah, Basrah, Iraq. Ed. Khalaf al Robaae. **Indexed:** Biol.Abstr.

500   GW   ISSN 0084-6090
AS182   CODEN: BAWJAE
BAYERISCHE AKADEMIE DER WISSENSCHAFTEN. JAHRBUCH. 1912. a. price varies. C.H. Beck'sche Verlagsbuchhandlung, Wilhelmstr. 9, 80801 Munich, Germany. TEL 089-38189-338. FAX 089-38189-398. index. (back issues avail.) **Indexed:** Bibl.Ling., Biol.Abstr., GeoRef. **Document type:** academic/scholarly publication.

500.9   GW   ISSN 0005-6995
AS182   CODEN: ABWMAJ
BAYERISCHE AKADEMIE DER WISSENSCHAFTEN. MATHEMATISCH-NATURWISSENSCHAFTLICHE KLASSE. ABHANDLUNGEN. 1929. irreg. Bayerische Akademie der Wissenschaften, Marstallplatz 8, 80539 Munich, Germany. FAX 089-23031100. **Indexed:** Appl.Mech.Rev., Biol.Abstr., Chem.Abstr., GeoRef., Math.R. **Document type:** academic/scholarly publication.

500 510   GW   ISSN 0340-7586
    CODEN: AMNSB2
BAYERISCHE AKADEMIE DER WISSENSCHAFTEN. MATHEMATISCH-NATURWISSENSCHAFTLICHE KLASSE. SITZUNGSBERICHTE. 1871. a. (plus offprints). price varies. Bayerische Akademie der Wissenschaften, Marstallplatz 8, 80539 Munich, Germany. FAX 089-23031100. **Indexed:** Biol.Abstr., GeoRef., Math.R. **Document type:** academic/scholarly publication.
—BLDSC (8292.000000).

BAYERISCHE AKADEMIE DER WISSENSCHAFTEN. PHILOSOPHISCH-HISTORISCHE KLASSE. ABHANDLUNGEN, N.F. see HUMANITIES: COMPREHENSIVE WORKS

BAYERISCHE AKADEMIE DER WISSENSCHAFTEN. PHILOSOPHISCH-HISTORISCHE KLASSE. SITZUNGSBERICHTE. see HUMANITIES: COMPREHENSIVE WORKS

500   CC   ISSN 0479-8023
    CODEN: PCTHAP
BEIJING DAXUE XUEBAO (ZIRAN KEXUE BAN)/BEIJING UNIVERSITY. JOURNAL (NATURAL SCIENCE EDITION). (Text in Chinese) 1955-1966; resumed 1977. bi-m. Y5.90. (Beijing University) Beijing University Press, Honglou (Red Building), No. 205, Beijing University, Beijing 100871, People's Republic of China. TEL 86-01-2501216. Ed. Gao Congshou. circ. 5,500. **Document type:** academic/scholarly publication.
—BLDSC (0663.190000); CASDDS.
    Description: Publishes research papers and dissertations on various fields of natural sciences.

600   CC   ISSN 1004-0579
    CODEN: JBITE5
BEIJING INSTITUTE OF TECHNOLOGY. JOURNAL. Chinese edition: Beijing Ligong Daxue Xuebao (ISSN 1001-0645) (Text in English; summaries in Chinese) 1992. s-a. Beijing Ligong Daxue, 7, Baishiqiao Lu, Beijing 100081, People's Republic of China. TEL 8416688. (Dist. outside China by: China National Publications Import and Export Corp., Box 88, Beijing 100704, P.R. China) Ed. Peiran Yan. **Document type:** academic/scholarly publication.
—CASDDS.

500   CC   ISSN 1001-053X
TS300   CODEN: BKDXEZ
BEIJING KEJI DAXUE XUEBAO/BEIJING UNIVERSITY OF SCIENCE AND TECHNOLOGY. JOURNAL. (Text in Chinese) 1960. bi-m. Beijing Keji Daxue, Xuebao Bianjibu, Beijing 100083, People's Republic of China. TEL 2019944. Ed. Zhang Wenqi.
—BLDSC (4912.120000); CASDDS.
    Formerly (until 1988): Beijing Gangtie Xueyuan (ISSN 1000-5609)

SCIENCES: COMPREHENSIVE WORKS

500 CC ISSN 1001-0645
CODEN: BLXUEV
BEIJING LIGONG DAXUE XUEBAO. English edition: Beijing Institute of Technology. Journal (ISSN 1004-0579) (Text in Chinese) q. Beijing Ligong Daxue - Beijing Institute of Technology, 7, Baishiqiao Lu, Beijing 100081, People's Republic of China. TEL 8416688. Ed. Mei Fengxiang. **Document type:** academic/scholarly publication.
—BLDSC (4707.889500); CASDDS.

500 CC ISSN 0476-0301
CODEN: BSDKDH
BEIJING SHIFAN DAXUE XUEBAO (ZIRAN KEXUE BAN)/BEIJING NORMAL UNIVERSITY. JOURNAL (NATURAL SCIENCE EDITION). (Text in Chinese) bi-m. Y40. Beijing Shifan Daxue, Xinwai Dajie, Beitaipingzhuang, Beijing 100875, People's Republic of China. TEL 2012288. Ed. Fang Fukang. **Document type:** academic/scholarly publication.
—BLDSC (4707.890900); CASDDS.

500 CC ISSN 1000-5366
BEIJING SHIFAN XUEYUAN XUEBAO (ZIRAN KEXUE BAN)/BEIJING NORMAL INSTITUTE. JOURNAL (NATURAL SCIENCE EDITION). (Text in Chinese) 1980. q. Beijing Shifan Xueyuan, Huayuancun, Fuchengmenwai, Beijing 100037, People's Republic of China. TEL 8414411. Ed. Mei Xiangming.

500 GW ISSN 0232-1556
BEITRAEGE ZUR ALEXANDER-VON-HUMBOLDT-FORSCHUNG. 1968. irreg., vol.18, 1994. Akademie Verlag GmbH, Muehlenstr. 33-34, 13187 Berlin, Germany. TEL 030-47889348. FAX 030-47889357. **Document type:** monographic series.
Description: Studies various aspects of Humboldt's life.

500 GW ISSN 0522-6570
BEITRAEGE ZUR GESCHICHTE DER WISSENSCHAFT UND DER TECHNIK. 1961. irreg., vol.21, 1990. price varies. (Deutsche Gesellschaft fuer Geschichte der Medizin, Naturwissenschaft und Technik e.V.) Franz Steiner Verlag Wiesbaden GmbH, Birkenwaldstr. 44, 70191 Stuttgart, Germany. TEL 0711-2582-0. FAX 0711-2582390. (Subscr. to: Postfach 101061, 70009 Stuttgart, Germany) illus. **Document type:** monographic series.

500 BE ISSN 0067-5407
BELGIUM. NATIONAAL FONDS VOOR WETENSCHAPPELIJK ONDERZOEK. JAARVERSLAG. (Text in Dutch, summaries in English) 1928. a. Nationaal Fonds voor Wetenschappelijk Onderzoek, Egmontstraat 5, B-1050 Brussels, Belgium. TEL 32-2-5129110. FAX 32-2-5125890. TELEX 25498 BEREFO B. (back issues avail.)
Supersedes (in 1989): Belgium Fonds National de la Recherche Scientifique. Rapport Annuel.
Description: Report of activities of the Flemish Board of Trustees of the National Fund for Scientific Research of Belgium and its associated funds.

507 BE
BELGIUM. NATIONAAL FONDS VOOR WETENSCHAPPELIJK ONDERZOEK. LIJST DER KREDIETGENIETERS. (Text in Dutch, summaries in English) 1928. a. Nationaal Fonds voor Wetenschappelijk Onderzoek, Egmontstraat 5, B-1050 Brussels, Belgium. TEL 32-2-5129110. FAX 32-2-5125890. TELEX 25498 BEREFO B. circ. 2,100. **Document type:** government publication.
Supersedes (in 1989): Belgium. Fonds National de la Recherche Scientifique. Liste des Beneficiaires d'une Subvention.
Description: Scientific projects supported by the Flemish Board of Trustees of the National Fund for Scientific Research of Belgium and its associated funds.

500.9 II ISSN 0409-0756
BENGAL NATURAL HISTORY SOCIETY. JOURNAL. (Text in English) 1926. s-a. $5. B. Dasgupta, Ed. & Pub., Darjeeling Government College, Darjeeling (West Bengal) 734 101, India. TEL 91-354-54316. circ. 150.
—BLDSC (4707.900000).
Formerly (until 1940): Darjeeling Natural History Society. Journal (ISSN 0970-2350)

500.9 GW ISSN 0067-5806
BERICHTE DES VEREINS NATUR UND HEIMAT UND DES NATURHISTORISCHEN MUSEUMS ZU LUEBECK. 1959. irreg. (every 2-3 yrs.). DM.30. Naturhistorisches Museum zu Luebeck, Muehlendamm 1-3, 23539 Luebeck, Germany. Eds. M. Diehl, G. Studnitz. circ. 800. **Document type:** monographic series.

500 GW ISSN 0170-6233
Q124.6 CODEN: BEWID8
BERICHTE ZUR WISSENSCHAFTSGESCHICHTE. (Text in German; summaries in English) 1978. q. DM.165($124) (effective 1996). V C H Verlagsgesellschaft mbH, Postfach 101161, 69451 Weinheim, Germany. TEL 06201-606-147. FAX 06201-606117. TELEX 465516-VCHWH-D. (U.S. addr.: V C H Publishers Inc., 220 E. 23rd St., New York, NY 10010-4606. TEL 212-683-8333) Ed. Fritz Krafft. adv. contact: R. Roth. bk.rev.; illus. circ. 750. **Document type:** academic/scholarly publication.
—BLDSC (1938.400000). **CCC.**

500 IO ISSN 0125-9156
BERITA ILMU PENGETAHUAN DAN TEKNOLOGI. Cover title: Berita I P T E K. (Text in English and Indonesian) 1957. q. $10. Indonesian Institute of Sciences - Lembaga Ilmu Pengetahuan Indonesia, Jalan Jenderal Gatot Subroto 10, P.O. Box 250, Jakarta 10002, Indonesia. TEL 021-525-1542. (Subscr. to: Yayasan Memajukan Jasa Informasi, Jln. Widya Chandra IX/3, Kompleks LIPI, P.O. Box 4509, Jakarta 12045, Indonesia) Ed. Didin Sastrapradja. bk.rev.; bibl. (microform)
Formerly: Berita L.I.P.I. (ISSN 0005-9137)

500 GW ISSN 0171-3302
BERLINER WISSENSCHAFTLICHER GESELLSCHAFT. JAHRBUCH. 1978. a. DM.50. Berliner Wissenschaftlicher Gesellschaft e.V., Malteserstr. 74-100, 12249 Berlin, Germany. TEL 030-7792448. FAX 030-7762213. Ed. Bernd Soesemann. circ. 500. **Document type:** academic/scholarly publication.

500.9 572 US ISSN 0067-6160
CODEN: OPBMAU
BERNICE PAUAHI BISHOP MUSEUM, HONOLULU. OCCASIONAL PAPERS. 1898. a. $35. Bishop Museum Press, 1525 Bernice St., Box 19000-A, Honolulu, HI 96817. TEL 808-848-4135. (reprint service avail. from UMI) Indexed: Biol.Abstr., Deep Sea Res.& Oceanogr.Abstr., GeoRef.
Description: Contains original contributions in anthropology, history, and the natural sciences of Hawaii and the Pacific.

500.9 572 US ISSN 0067-6179
GN670
BERNICE PAUAHI BISHOP MUSEUM, HONOLULU. SPECIAL PUBLICATIONS. 1892. irreg. price varies. Bishop Museum Press, 1525 Bernice St., Box 19000-A, Honolulu, HI 96817. TEL 808-848-4135. (reprint service avail. from UMI) Indexed: Biol.Abstr., Deep Sea Res.& Oceanogr.Abstr.
—BLDSC (2094.263050).
Description: Popular and scholarly books on Hawaii and the Pacific Basin.

500 600 JA ISSN 0285-1008
BESSATSU SAIENSU. 8/yr. price varies. Nikkei Science, Inc. (Subsidiary of: Nihon Keizai Shimbun, Inc.), 2-2-1 Uchisaiwai-cho, Chiyoda-ku, Tokyo 100, Japan. TEL 03-5255-2125. FAX 03-3293-2759. TELEX J22308-NIHONKEIZAI. Eds. K. Ohtake, S. Katayose. circ. 28,751.
Description: Covers current topics in science with photographs and easy-to-understand explanations.

BHAGALPUR UNIVERSITY JOURNAL. see SOCIAL SCIENCES: COMPREHENSIVE WORKS

500 IT ISSN 0394-5065
BIBLIOTECA DI STORIA DELLA SCIENZA. 1947. irreg., no.36, 1994. price varies. Casa Editrice Leo S. Olschki, Casella Postale 66, 50100 Florence, Italy. TEL 39-55-6530684. FAX 39-55-6530214. **Document type:** monographic series.
Formerly (until 1987): Rivista di Storia delle Scienze Mediche e Naturali. Biblioteca (ISSN 0080-326X)
Description: Examines the history of science.

500 CK ISSN 0120-484X
BIBLIOTECA JOSE JERONIMO TRIANA (SERIAL). (Text in English and Spanish) 1983. irreg. $30 or exchange basis. Universidad Nacional de Colombia, Instituto de Ciencias Naturales, Apdo. 7495, Bogota, D.E., Colombia. Ed. Polidoro Pinto-E. circ. 1,000. **Document type:** academic/scholarly publication, monographic series.

500.9 GW ISSN 0006-2375
Q3 CODEN: BIWIAX
BILD DER WISSENSCHAFT; das Magazin fuer Wissenschaft und Technik. 1964. m. DM.124.80 (students DM.103.80). Deutsche Verlags-Anstalt GmbH, Postfach 106012, 70049 Stuttgart, Germany. TEL 0711-2631-0. FAX 0711-2631-292. Ed. Reiner Korbmann. adv.; bk.rev.; bibl.; charts; illus.; index. circ. 133,350. Indexed: Biol.Abstr., Chem.Abstr., Excerp.Med., INIS Atomind., Key word Ind.Wildl.Res., Numis.Lit. **Document type:** academic/scholarly publication.
—BLDSC (2058.950000); CASDDS; SWETS. **CCC.**

500 NE ISSN 0929-1016
QH527 CODEN: BRHREI
BIOLOGICAL RHYTHM RESEARCH. (Text in English, French and German) 1970. 4/yr. $299. Swets & Zeitlinger bv, Heereweg 347, 2161 CA Lisse, Netherlands. TEL 31-2521-35111. FAX 31-2521-15888. TELEX 41325. (Dist. in N. America by: Swets & Zeitlinger, 440 Creamery Way, Ste. A, Exton, PA 19341. TEL 800-447-9387. FAX 610-524-5366) Ed. W.J. Rietveld. adv.; bk.rev.; charts; illus. circ. 600. (also avail. in microform from SWZ; reprint service avail. from SWZ) Indexed: Biol.Abstr., Chem.Abstr., Curr.Adv.Ecol.Sci., Curr.Cont., Dairy Sci.Abstr., Deep Sea Res.& Oceanogr.Abstr., Ecol.Abstr., Excerp.Med., GeoRef., Helminthol.Abstr., Ind.Sci.Rev., Ind.Vet., Sci.Cit.Ind., Small Anim.Abstr., Sport Fish.Abstr., Vet.Bull., Wild.Rev., Zoo.Rec. **Document type:** academic/scholarly publication.
—BLDSC (2079.590000); CASDDS; Faxon; Genuine Article; SWETS; UnCover. **CCC.**
Formerly: Journal of Interdisciplinary Cycle Research (ISSN 0022-1945)

BIOLOGIE, CHEMIE, ZEMEPIS. see EDUCATION

508 971 CN ISSN 0006-5099
CODEN: BLJYA3
BLUE JAY. 1942. 4/yr. Can.$25 (foreign Can.$30). Nature Saskatchewan, 1860 Lorne St., Rm. 206, Regina, SK S4P 2L7, Canada. TEL 306-780-9273. FAX 306-781-6021. adv.; B&W page Can.$800. bk.rev.; charts; illus. circ. 2,000. Indexed: Biol.Abstr., Sport Fish.Abstr., Wild Life Rev., Wild.Rev., Zoo.Rec. **Document type:** academic/scholarly publication.
—BLDSC (2114.150000); UnCover.
Description: General interest scientific information dealing with the natural history of Saskatchewan.

501 CN ISSN 0822-9988
BLUE JAY NEWS. 1963. 4/yr. Can.$25 (free with subscr. to Blue Jay). Nature Saskatchewan, 1860 Lorne St., Rm. 206, Regina, SK S4P 2L7, Canada. TEL 306-780-9273. FAX 306-781-6021. Ed. John Pollock. adv.; B&W page Can.$400. circ. 2,000. **Document type:** academic/scholarly publication.
Formerly (until 1983): Saskatchewan Natural History Society Newsletter (ISSN 0581-8443)
Description: Concerns society activities and current environmental and conservation issues in Saskatchewan.

500 GW ISSN 0523-8226
BOETHIUS; Texte und Abhandlungen zur Geschichte der Mathematik und der Naturwissenschaften. 1962. irreg., vol.36, 1994. price varies. Franz Steiner Verlag Wiesbaden GmbH, Birkenwaldstr. 44, 70191 Stuttgart, Germany. TEL 0711-2582-0. FAX 0711-2582390. (Subscr. to: Postfach 101061, 70009 Stuttgart, Germany) Ed.Bd. illus. **Document type:** monographic series.

500 CU
BOLETIN DE EVENTOS CIENTIFICO-TECNICOS. w. Academia de Ciencias, Instituto de Documentacion e Informacion Cientifico-Tecnica (I D I C T), Capitolio Nacional, Padro y San Jose, Havana, 2, Cuba.

SCIENCES: COMPREHENSIVE WORKS

500   EC   ISSN 0366-1830
CODEN: BOICAL
BOLETIN DE INFORMACIONES CIENTIFICAS NACIONALES. 1947. irreg., no.124, 1993. Casa de Cultura Ecuatoriana, Av. 6 de Diciembre 794, Casilla 67, Quito, Ecuador. Dir. Celin Astudillo Espinosa. bibl. **Document type**: academic/scholarly publication.

500 600   EC   ISSN 0253-5033
Q224.3.E2
BOLETIN S I N I C Y T. (Sistema Nacional de Informacion Cientifica y Tecnologia) 1982. s-a. free. Fundacion para la Ciencia y la Tecnologia, Edificio Banco de Prestamos, Av. Patria 850 y 10 de Agosto, piso 9, Casilla 17-12-00404, Quito, Ecuador. TEL 593-2-509027. FAX 593-2-509054. TELEX 22027 FUNCYT DE. (Co-sponsor: Programa Regional de Desarrollo Cientifico y Tecnologico de la Organizacion de los Estados Americanos) bk.rev.; charts; illus. circ. 1,200. **Document type**: bulletin. **Description**: Covers themes related to the development of scientific and technological information in Ecuador and Latin America.

500.9   II   ISSN 0006-6982
QH1   CODEN: JBOMAA
BOMBAY NATURAL HISTORY SOCIETY. JOURNAL. 1886. 3/yr. £40($80) Bombay Natural History Society, Hornbill House, Shahid Bhagat Singh Rd., Bombay 400023, India. TEL 244085. Ed.Bd. bk.rev.; charts; illus. circ. 3,000. (also avail. in microfiche from IDC) **Indexed**: Bio-Contr.News & Info., Biol.Abstr., Curr.Adv.Ecol.Sci., Deep Sea Res.& Oceanogr.Abstr., Excerp.Med., Field Crop Abstr., Forest.Abstr., Forest Prod.Abstr., Geo.Abstr, Helminthol.Abstr., Herb.Abstr., Ind.Vet., Key Word Ind.Wildl.Res., Nutr.Abstr., Ornam.Hort., Rev.Appl.Entomol., Sel.Water Res.Abstr., Sport Fish.Abstr., Wild.Rev., Zoo.Rec. **Document type**: academic/scholarly publication.
—BLDSC (4709.900000); UnCover.

500   II   ISSN 0006-7903
CODEN: TBICAQ
BOSE INSTITUTE. TRANSACTIONS.* (Text in English) 1918. q. Rs.32($7.50) Bose Institute, 93-1 Acharya Prafulla Chandra Rd., Calcutta 700009, India. Ed. Dr. D.M. Bose. (back issues avail.) **Indexed**: Biol.Abstr., Chem.Abstr., Field Crop Abstr., Herb.Abstr., INSPEC (1968-), Nucl.Sci.Abstr.
—BLDSC (8905.000000); CASDDS.

501   NE   ISSN 0068-0346
Q174   CODEN: BPSCDD
BOSTON STUDIES IN THE PHILOSOPHY OF SCIENCE; Boston colloquium for the philosophy of science. (Text in English) 1963. irreg., vol.149, 1993. price varies. Kluwer Academic Publishers, Postbus 17, 3300 AA Dordrecht, Netherlands. TEL 31-78-392392. FAX 31-78-392254. TELEX 29245 KAPG NL. (Dist. by: Kluwer Academic Publishers Group, P.O. Box 322, 3300 AH Dordrecht, Netherlands. TEL 31-78-392392. FAX 31-78-546474; N. America dist. addr.: Box 358, Accord Sta., Hingham, MA 02018-0358. TEL 617-871-6600. FAX 617-871-6528) Eds. Robert S. Cohen, Marx W. Wartofsky. **Indexed**: Biol.Abstr., Math.R. **Document type**: monograph series.
—BLDSC (2251.830000). **CCC**.
Refereed Serial

500   GW
BRAUNSCHWEIGISCHE WISSENSCHAFTLICHE GESELLSCHAFT. ABHANDLUNGEN. 1949. irreg. price varies. Verlag Erich Goltze GmbH und Co. KG, Hans-Boeckler-Str. 7, 37079 Goettingen, Germany. TEL 0551-506760. FAX 0551-5067622. Ed. K.H. Olsen. **Indexed**: Biol.Abstr., GeoRef, Math.R. **Document type**: academic/scholarly publication, monograph series.

500   BL
BRAZIL. CONSELHO NACIONAL DE DESENVOLVIMENTO CIENTIFICO E TECNOLOGICO. PROGRAMA DO TROPICA SEMI-ARIDO (PUBLICACION). irreg. Conselho Nacional de Desenvolvimento Cientifico e Tecnologico, Programa do Tropico Semi-Arido, Av. W-3 Norte Q-507-B, 11-1142 Brasilia, Brazil. Ed. Domingos Carvalho da Silva. charts; stat.

500   BL
BRAZIL. CONSELHO NACIONAL DE DESENVOLVIMENTO CIENTIFICO E TECNOLOGICO. RELATORIO DE ATIVIDADES. 1975. irreg. Conselho Nacional de Desenvolvimento Cientifico e Tecnologico, Edificio CNPQ, SEPN 507 Norte, Bloco B, 70740-901 Brasilia DF, Brazil. FAX 061-274-1950.

500   CR   ISSN 0304-3711
QH7   CODEN: BRNSBE
BRENESIA. (Text in various languages; summaries in Spanish; abstracts in English, Spanish) 1972. 2/yr. $22 or exchange basis. Museo Nacional de Costa Rica, Departamento de Historia Natural, Box 749-1000, San Jose, Costa Rica. TEL 57-1433. FAX 506-33-74-27. illus. circ. 1,000. (tabloid format) **Indexed**: Apic.Abstr., Biol.Abstr., Curr.Adv.Ecol.Sci., GeoRef., Protozool.Abstr., Rev.Appl.Entomol., Rev.Plant Path., Sport Fish.Abstr., Wild.Rev., Zoo.Rec., Zoo.Rec.
—BLDSC (2277.960000).
Supersedes: Revista Historia Natural de Costa Rica.

BRILL'S STUDIES IN INTELLECTUAL HISTORY. see *HUMANITIES: COMPREHENSIVE WORKS*

509   UK   ISSN 0141-3325
QH84.2
BRITISH ANTARCTIC SURVEY. ANNUAL REPORT. 1970. a. £6. (British Antarctic Survey) Turpin Transactions, Blackhorse Rd., Letchworth, Herts SG6 1HN, England. TEL 04626-72555. FAX 0223-62616. TELEX 825372-TURPIN-G. circ. 700.
—BLDSC (7383.680000).

509   UK   ISSN 0007-0874
Q125   CODEN: BJHSAT
BRITISH JOURNAL FOR THE HISTORY OF SCIENCE. 1962. q. £83($144) (effective 1996). (British Society for the History of Science) Cambridge University Press, Edinburgh Bldg., Shaftesbury Rd., Cambridge CB2 2RU, England. TEL 01223-312393. FAX 01223-315052. TELEX 851817256. (N. American addr.: Cambridge University Press, Journals Dept., 40 W. 20th St., New York, NY 10011. TEL 212-924-3900. FAX 212-691-3239) Ed. Janet Browne. adv.; bk.rev.; charts; illus.; index. circ. 1,300. (also avail. in microform from UMI; back issues avail.; reprint service avail. from UMI) **Indexed**: Amer.Hist. & Life, Arts & Hum.Cit.Ind., Br.Geol.Lit. (1972-), Br.Hum.Ind., Bull.Signal., Chem.Abstr., CLOSS, Curr.Cont., GeoRef., Hum.Ind., Ind.Sci.Rev., INSPEC (1973-1993), Math.R., Mid.East: Abstr.& Ind., Sci.Cit.Ind., SSCI. **Document type**: academic/scholarly publication.
—BLDSC (2309.400000); Faxon; Genuine Article; SWETS; UMI; UnCover. **CCC**.
Description: Covers all aspects of the history of science.
Refereed Serial

501   UK   ISSN 0007-0882
Q175   CODEN: BJPIA5
THE BRITISH JOURNAL FOR THE PHILOSOPHY OF SCIENCE. 1951. q. £40($76) (effective 1996). (British Society for the Philosophy of Science) Oxford University Press, Oxford Journals, Walton St., Oxford OX2 6DP, England. TEL 01865-267907. FAX 01865-267773. TELEX 837330-OXPRES-G. E-mail: jnlorders@oup.co.uk. (U.S. subscr. to: Oxford University Press Inc., 2001 Evans Rd., Cary, NC 27513. TEL 919-677-0977. FAX 919-677-1714) Ed. D. Papineau. adv. contact: Jane Parker. bk.rev.; bibl.; index. circ. 1,650. (also avail. in microfiche; back issues avail.) **Indexed**: Arts & Hum.Cit.Ind., Br.Hum.Ind., Cont.Pg.Manage., Curr.Cont., Hum.Ind., Ind.Bk.Rev.Hum., Ind.Sci.Rev., INSPEC (1973-1993), Math.R., Psychol.Abstr., Sci.Cit.Ind., SSCI. **Document type**: academic/scholarly publication.
—BLDSC (2316.000000); Faxon; Genuine Article; SWETS; UMI; UnCover. **CCC**.
Description: Addresses the study of the logic, the method, and the philosophy of science, including the social sciences.

800 700 500   US   ISSN 0007-2869
AP2
BUCKNELL REVIEW; a scholarly journal of letters, arts and science. 1941. s-a. $32. Bucknell University Press, c/o Associated University Presses, 440 Forsgate Dr., Cranbury, NJ 08512. TEL 609-655-4770. FAX 609-655-8366. Ed. Pauline Fletcher. illus.; index. circ. 500. (also avail. in microform from UMI; back issues avail.; reprint service avail. from UMI) **Indexed**: Amer.Hist.& Life, Hist.Abstr., LCR, M.L.A., Sociol.Abstr. **Document type**: academic/scholarly publication.
—BLDSC (2355.850000); UMI.

550   US   ISSN 0096-4131
QH1   CODEN: BBNSA3
BUFFALO SOCIETY OF NATURAL SCIENCES. BULLETIN. 1873. irreg., vol.33, 1988. price varies. Buffalo Society of Natural Sciences, 1020 Humboldt Pkwy., Buffalo, NY 14211. TEL 716-896-5200. FAX 716-897-6723. charts; illus. circ. 500. (back issues avail.) **Indexed**: Biol.Abstr., GeoRef. **Document type**: bulletin.

500   US
BUFFALO SOCIETY OF NATURAL SCIENCES. OCCASIONAL PAPERS. 1976. irreg., no.4, 1990. price varies. Buffalo Society of Natural Sciences, 1020 Humboldt Pkwy., Buffalo, NY 14211. TEL 716-896-5200. FAX 716-897-6723.

500   AA
BULETINI I SHKENCAVE TEKNIKE/BULLETIN DES SCIENCES TECHNIQUES. (Text in Albanian; summaries in French) q. $7.20. Enver Hoxha Universitet, Tirana, Albania.

500   BU   ISSN 0007-3989
AS343
BULGARSKA AKADEMIIA NA NAUKITE. SPISANIE. 1956. bi-m. 7.80 lv. Publishing House of the Bulgarian Academy of Sciences, Acad. G. Bonchev St., Bldg. 6, 1113 Sofia, Bulgaria. (Dist. by: Hemus, 6, Rouski Blvd., 1000 Sofia, Bulgaria) Ed. G. Brankov. illus. circ. 800. (reprint service avail. from IRC) **Indexed**: Biol.Abstr., BSL Biol., BSL Econ., BSL Math., Met.Abstr., World Alum.Abstr.
—BLDSC (0166.360000). **CCC**.

BULLETIN HISTORIQUE ET SCIENTIFIQUE DE L'AUVERGNE. see *HISTORY — History Of Europe*

500 300   US   ISSN 0270-4676
Q175.4   CODEN: BSTSDJ
THE BULLETIN OF SCIENCE, TECHNOLOGY & SOCIETY. 1981. bi-m. $30 to individuals; institutions $95. S T S Press, 102 Materials Research Laboratory, Pennsylvania State University, University Park, PA 16802. TEL 814-865-1137. FAX 814-863-7040. Eds. Rustum Roy, Kathleen Mourant. bk.rev. circ. 300. (also avail. in microform from MIM,UMI; back issues avail.) **Indexed**: Curr.Adv.Ecol.Sci., Curr.Cont., Energy Rev., Eng.Ind., Risk Abstr., Sociol.Abstr., SSCI. **Document type**: academic/scholarly publication.
—BLDSC (2887.760000); Ei; Faxon; Genuine Article; SWETS; UnCover. **CCC**.
Description: Brings together and edits material to serve the broad range of S.T.S. teachers, social scientists, and international planners concerned with the effects of science and technology on society.
Refereed Serial

500   II   ISSN 0970-0145
BULLETIN OF SCIENCES. (Text in English) 1983. q. Rs.140($55) (Indian Institute of Science) New Age International Pvt. Ltd., Journals Division, 4835-24 Ansari Rd., Daryaganj, New Delhi 110 002, India. TEL 91-11-3267996. FAX 91-11-3267437. TELEX 031-66507-WELIN. circ. 800. **Document type**: academic/scholarly publication.
—BLDSC (2887.790000).

500.1 560   FR   ISSN 0373-2061
Q2   CODEN: BSBNAD
BULLETIN SCIENTIFIQUE DE BOURGOGNE. 1931. biennial. 100 F. Societe des Sciences Naturelles de Bourgogne, Faculte de Sciences, Departement de Biologie, 6 bd. Gabriel, F 21100-Dijon, France. (Subscr. to: Librairie de l'Universite, 17 rue de la Liberte, 21014 Dijon, France) (Co-sponsor: Universite de Dijon) Dir. J.P. Henry. bk.rev. circ. 400. **Indexed**: Bull.Signal, GeoRef.

500   US
BUSINESS - SCIENCE - TECHNOLOGY DEVELOPMENTS AND NEWS. 1964. m. $96. Government Data Publications, Inc., 1155 Connecticut Ave., N.W., Washington, DC 20036. Ed. Siegfried Lobel. s-a. index.
Formerly: U S - R and D (ISSN 0436-2225)

500   SA
C A S M E NEWSLETTER. 1993. q. Centre for the Advancement of Science & Mathematics, P.O. Box 17112, Congela 4013, South Africa. **Document type**: newsletter.

SCIENCES: COMPREHENSIVE WORKS

500   BL   ISSN 0034-7361
C E C REVISTA.* 1963. m. Cr.$2000($2) Centro de Estudos Cientificos, Caixa Postal 11585, Sao Paulo - SP, Brazil. Ed. Geraldo Lino de Campos. adv.; bk.rev.; charts; illus.; tr.lit. circ. 1,000.

500   GW   ISSN 0341-4116
CODEN: CFSEDS
C F S. (Courier Forschunginstitut Senckenberg) 1972. irreg., no.177, 1995. Senckenbergische Naturforschende Gesellschaft, Abt. Schriftentausch, Senckenberganlage 25, 60325 Frankfurt, Germany. TEL 069-7542-1. FAX 069-746238. **Indexed:** Sport Fish.Abstr., Wild.Rev., Zoo.Rec. **Document type:** academic/scholarly publication.
—BLDSC (3482.569000). **CCC.**

C I R A S NEWS. (Center for Industrial Research and Service) see *TECHNOLOGY: COMPREHENSIVE WORKS*

500   FR   ISSN 0538-6918
Q10
C O D A T A NEWSLETTER. (Text in English) 1968. q. free. International Council of Scientific Unions, Committee on Data for Science and Technology, CODATA Secretariat, 51 bd. de Montmorency, 75016 Paris, France. FAX 42-88-14-66. TELEX 630553. Ed. Edgar F. Westrum, Jr. adv.; bk.rev.; bibl. circ. 6,500. **Indexed:** Br.Ceram.Abstr. **Document type:** newsletter.

500 600   II
C O S T E D NEWSLETTER. (Text in English) 1976. q. free. (Committee on Science and Technology in Developing Countries) Association for the Application of Science to Human Affairs (ASHA), c/o Indian Institute of Science, Bangalore 560012, India. Ed.Bd. bk.rev. circ. 10,000. **Document type:** newsletter.

500 600   US
C P S T OCCASIONAL PAPERS. 1989. irreg., latest 1992. (Commission on Professionals in Science & Technology) C P S T Publications, 1500 Massachusetts Ave., N.W., Ste. 831, Washington, DC 20005. TEL 202-223-6995. FAX 202-223-6444.
Description: Covers topics of special interest to producers and users of scientists and engineers.

500 600   BE   ISSN 0770-0725
C R I C RAPPORT DE RECHERCHE. (Text in Dutch, English, French) 1962. irreg. 500 BEF. Centre National de Recherches Scientifiques et Techniques pour l'Industrie Cimentiere, 46 rue Cesar Franck, B-1050 Brussels, Belgium. FAX 32-2-640-0670. **Indexed:** Concr.Abstr. **Document type:** monographic series.
Formerly: Centre National de Recherches Scientifiques et Techniques pour l'Industrie Cimentiere. Brussels. C R I C Rapport de Recherche (ISSN 0069-2026)

500 600   SA
C S I R ANNUAL REPORT - TECHNOLOGY IMPACT. (Text in English) 1945. a. free. C S I R Marketing Services, P.O. Box 395, Pretoria 0001, South Africa. TEL 27-12-841-4302. FAX 27-12-841-3789. circ. 10,000. **Document type:** corporate report.
Incorporates: W N N R Tegnologie Inslag; **Formerly:** C S I R Annual Report (ISSN 0370-8454)
Description: Features the year's research, development and implementation successes, division reports, executive overviews, and financial statements.

500   GH
C S I R HANDBOOK. 1970. irreg. Council for Scientific and Industrial Research, Box M32, Accra, Ghana. (back issues avail.)

500 370   US
C S S P NEWS. 1986. q. Council of Scientific Society Presidents, 1155 16th St., N.W., Washington, DC 20036. TEL 202-872-4452. FAX 202-872-4079. E-mail: cssp@acs.org. Ed. Martin Apple. bk.rev.; circ. 1,000 (controlled). (back issues avail.) **Document type:** newsletter.
Description: A forum for exchange of ideas on science policy, education, ethics, and scientific research.

500 600   FR
CAHIERS DE LA RECHERCHE SCIENTIFIQUE ET TECHNIQUE. 1993. 4/yr. 400 F. (foreign 500 F.). Editions Hermes, 14 rue Lantiez, 75017 Paris, France. TEL 42-29-44-66. FAX 42-29-15-56. Ed. Edwige Pissaloux.

508   FR   ISSN 0008-0039
CODEN: CNBNAN
CAHIERS DES NATURALISTES. 1946. q. 260 F. Naturalistes Parisiens, 45 rue de Buffon, 75005 Paris, France. Ed. Claude Dupuis. bk.rev.; bibl.; charts; illus.; index. circ. 500. **Indexed:** Bio-Contr.News & Info., Biol.Abstr., Bull.Signal, Chem.Abstr., Field Crop Abstr., GeoRef., Herb.Abstr., Zoo.Rec.
—BLDSC (2949.850000).

500   FR   ISSN 0008-0462
CAHIERS RATIONALISTES. 1931. 10/yr. 385 F. Union Rationaliste, 14 rue de l'Ecole Polytechnique, 75005 Paris, France. bk.rev.; index.

500   CK   ISSN 0366-5232
QH7   CODEN: CALDAK
CALDASIA. (Text in English, French, Portuguese and Spanish) 1942. s-a. $20 or exchange basis. Universidad Nacional de Colombia, Instituto de Ciencias Naturales, Apdo. 7495, Bogota, Colombia. Ed. Polidoro Pinto-E. bibl.; illus. circ. 1,200. **Indexed:** Biol.Abstr., Bull.Signal, Deep Sea Res.& Oceanogr.Abstr., Excerp.Bot., Field Crop Abstr., Forest.Abstr., Geo.Abstr., GeoRef., Herb.Abstr., Potato Abstr., Ref.Zh., Seed Abstr., Sport Fish.Abstr., VITIS, Wild.Rev., Zoo.Rec. **Document type:** academic/scholarly publication.
—BLDSC (2955.500000).

CALENDARIO DE EVENTOS EM CIENCIA E TECNOLOGIA. see *TECHNOLOGY: COMPREHENSIVE WORKS*

CALIFORNIA ACADEMY OF SCIENCES. ACADEMY NEWSLETTER. see *MUSEUMS AND ART GALLERIES*

509   US
CALIFORNIA STUDIES IN THE HISTORY OF SCIENCE. 1989. irreg., vol.12, 1993. price varies. University of California Press, 2120 Berkeley Way, Berkeley, CA 94720. TEL 510-642-4247. FAX 510-643-7127. (Orders to: California-Princeton Fulfillment Services, 1445 Lower Ferry Rd., Ewing, NJ 08618. TEL 800-777-4726. FAX 800-999-1958) (back issues avail.) **Document type:** monographic series.
Description: Publishes research on various phases of the history of science.
Refereed Serial

500   GW   ISSN 0945-0041
CAMPUS. 1977. q. free. Universitaet - Gesamthochschule Essen, Universitaetsstr. 2, 45141 Essen, Germany. TEL 0201-1832085. FAX 0201-1832151. adv. circ. 8,400. **Document type:** bulletin.
Former titles (until 1993): Essener Universitaetsberichte (ISSN 0935-3658); (until 1987): Hochschuljournal Essen.
Description: General information on scientific research at Essen University.

500.9   CN   ISSN 0008-3550
CODEN: CAFNAK
CANADIAN FIELD-NATURALIST. 1879. q. Can.$38 to non-members (foreign Can.$43) (effective 1996). Ottawa Field-Naturalists' Club, Box 35069, Westgate P.O., Ottawa, ON K1Z 1A2, Canada. TEL 613-722-3050. Ed. F.R. Cook. bk.rev.; bibl.; charts; illus.; maps; index. circ. 2,200. (back issues avail.) **Indexed:** Acid Rain Abstr., Acid Rain Ind., Biol.Abstr., Curr.Adv.Ecol.Sci., Curr.Cont., Curr.Ref.Fish Res., Deep Sea Res.& Oceanogr.Abstr., Environ.Abstr., Environ.Per.Bibl. (1973-), Field Crop Abstr., Forest.Abstr., Geo.Abstr., GeoRef., Herb.Abstr., Ind.Sci.Rev., Ind.Vet., INIS Atomind., Key Word Ind.Wildl.Res., Sci.Cit.Ind., Sel.Water Res.Abstr., Soils & Fert., Sport Fish.Abstr., Sport Fish.Abstr., Vet.Bull., Wild.Rev.
—BLDSC (3023.000000); Faxon; Genuine Article; SWETS; UnCover. **CCC.**

500.9   CN   ISSN 0846-2054
CODEN: SYLGBY
CANADIAN MUSEUM OF NATURE. SYLLOGEUS. (Text in English, French) 1972. irreg., latest no.73, 1995. price varies. Canadian Museum of Nature, Publishing Division, P.O. Box 3443, Stn. D, Ottawa, ON K1P 6P4, Canada. TEL 613-990-6594. FAX 613-990-0318. Ed. Cathy Ripley; Pub. Don McAllister. adv. contact: Dawn Arnold. circ. 1,000. (back issues avail.) **Indexed:** Biol.Abstr. **Document type:** academic/scholarly publication.
—BLDSC (8580.200000).
Formerly: National Museum of Natural Sciences. Syllogeus (ISSN 0704-576X)

500.9   CN   ISSN 0316-0343
CANADIAN PLAINS BULLETIN. 1970. s-a. Can.$5. Canadian Plains Research Center, University of Regina, Regina, SK S4S 0A2, Canada. TEL 306-585-4758. FAX 306-585-4699. Ed. Brian Mlazgar. bk.rev.; bibl. circ. 1,850. (back issues avail.) **Document type:** bulletin, newsletter.

500.9   CN   ISSN 0317-6401
CODEN: CPLPDS
CANADIAN PLAINS PROCEEDINGS. 197? irreg., no.26, 1993. price varies. Canadian Plains Research Center, University of Regina, Regina, SK S4S 0A2, Canada. TEL 306-585-5056. FAX 306-585-4699. **Indexed:** Geo.Abstr., Geol.Abstr. **Document type:** monographic series.
—BLDSC (3043.870000); CASDDS.

500.9 920   CN
CANADIAN PLAINS REFERENCE WORKS. 1988. irreg. price varies. Canadian Plains Research Center, University of Regina, Regina, SK S4S 0A2, Canada. TEL 306-585-5056. FAX 306-585-4699. **Document type:** monographic series.
Formerly: Canadian Plains Biographies (ISSN 1192-8999)

500.9   CN   ISSN 0384-8930
CANADIAN PLAINS REPORTS. 1977. irreg., no.9, 1992. price varies. Canadian Plains Research Center, University of Regina, Regina, SK S4S 0A2, Canada. TEL 306-585-5056. FAX 306-585-4699. **Document type:** monographic series.
—BLDSC (3043.875000).

500.9   CN   ISSN 0317-6290
CANADIAN PLAINS STUDIES. 1973. irreg., no.28, 1994. price varies. Canadian Plains Research Center, University of Regina, Regina, SK S4S 0A2, Canada. TEL 306-585-5056. FAX 306-585-4699. **Document type:** monographic series.

CARIBBEAN JOURNAL OF SCIENCE. see *BIOLOGY*

508 574 572 560   US   ISSN 0097-4463
AS36   CODEN: CIMUAU
CARNEGIE MUSEUM OF NATURAL HISTORY. ANNALS. Key Title: Annals of Carnegie Museum. 1901. q. $25 to individuals; institutions and foreign $65. Carnegie Museum of Natural History, Office of Scientific Publications, 4400 Forbes Ave., Pittsburgh, PA 15213-4080. TEL 412-622-3287. FAX 412-622-8837. Ed.Bd. charts; illus.; index. circ. 900. (back issues avail.) **Indexed:** Anthropol.Lit., Biol.Abstr., Deep Sea Res.& Oceanogr.Abstr., Ecol.Abstr., Geo.Abstr., Geol.Abstr., GeoRef., Sport Fish.Abstr., Wild.Rev., Zoo.Rec. **Document type:** academic/scholarly publication.
—BLDSC (1022.000000); UnCover.
Description: Contributions in organismal biology, earth sciences and anthropology.

500 574 508 560   US   ISSN 0145-9058
CODEN: BCMHD9
CARNEGIE MUSEUM OF NATURAL HISTORY. BULLETIN. 1976. irreg., no.30, 1994. price varies. Carnegie Museum of Natural History, Office of Scientific Publications, 4400 Forbes Ave., Pittsburgh, PA 15213-4080. TEL 412-622-3287. FAX 412-622-8837. Ed.Bd. bibl.; charts; illus.; index; circ. controlled. (back issues avail.) **Indexed:** Biol.Abstr., GeoRef., Sport Fish.Abstr., Wild.Rev., Zoo.Rec. **Document type:** academic/scholarly publication.
—BLDSC (2434.550000).
Description: Monographs in organismal biology, earth sciences and anthropology.

SCIENCES: COMPREHENSIVE WORKS

500.9 US ISSN 0145-9031
CODEN: SPCHDX
CARNEGIE MUSEUM OF NATURAL HISTORY. SPECIAL PUBLICATIONS. 1975. irreg., no.19, 1994. price varies. Carnegie Museum of Natural History, Office of Scientific Publications, 4400 Forbes Ave., Pittsburgh, PA 15213-4080. TEL 412-622-3287. FAX 412-622-8837. Ed.Bd. (back issues avail.) Indexed: Biol.Abstr. Document type: academic/scholarly publication.
—BLDSC (8373.850000).
Description: Variety of monographs in natural history.

500 CK ISSN 0120-5986
CARTA DE COLCIENCIAS. 1970. m. Colciencias, Transversal 9A, No.133-28, Bogota, Colombia. TEL 2169800. FAX 6251788. TELEX 44305. Ed. Magola Delgado.

500 UK ISSN 0069-0945
CASS LIBRARY OF SCIENCE CLASSICS. 1967. irreg., no.23, 1971. price varies. Frank Cass, Newbury House, 890-900 Eastern Ave., Newbury Park, Ilford, Essex 1G2 7HH, England. TEL 44-181-599-8866. FAX 44-181-599-0984. E-mail: 100067,1576@compuserve.com. (Dist. in the U.S. by: I.S.B.S., 5804 N.E. Hassalo St., Portland, OR 97213-3644) Document type: academic/scholarly publication.

CATALYST (VANCOUVER). see EDUCATION — Teaching Methods And Curriculum

500 UK ISSN 0958-3629
CATALYST G C S E SCIENCE REVIEW. 1989. 4/yr. (Sept.-Apr.). £14.95 (outside Europe £23; elsewhere £28.50) (effective 1996). Philip Allan Publishers Ltd., Market Pl., Deddington, Oxon. OX15 0SE, England. TEL 01869-338652. FAX 01869-338803. Ed. Liz Sheffield. adv. contact: Ceri Jenkins. Document type: academic/scholarly publication.

500 CN ISSN 0835-5932
CATALYST: RESEARCH AT THE UNIVERSITY OF CALGARY. 1986. 8/yr. free. University of Calgary, Research Services, Public Affairs, 2500 University Drive N.W., Calgary, AB T2N 1N4, Canada. TEL 403-220-3783. FAX 403-282-8413. Ed. Scott MacArthur. adv. contact: Kevin Pennoch. circ. 3,000 (controlled). (tabloid format) Document type: newspaper.

500 300 NQ
CATEDRA; revista de ciencia, cultura y educacion. 1991. q. Universidad Nacional Autonoma de Nicaragua, Facultad de Ciencias de la Educacion, Recinto Universitario Ruben Dario, Managua, Nicaragua. Document type: academic/scholarly publication.

500.9 SP
CAZA FOTOGRAFICA. (Text in English and Spanish) 1973. bi-m. 1500 ptas. Instituto de la Caza Fotografica y Ciencias de la Naturaleza., Castello, 59, Madrid, Spain. illus.

509 DK ISSN 0008-8994
CODEN: CENTA4
CENTAURUS; international magazine of the history of mathematics, science and technology. (Text in English, French, German) 1950. 4/yr. DKK 1200 (effective 1996). Munksgaard International Publishers Ltd., 35 Noerre Soegade, P.O. Box 2148, DK-1016 Copenhagen K, Denmark. TEL 33-12-70-30. FAX 33-12-93-87. Ed. Kurt Moeller Pedersen. adv.; bk.rev.; bibl.; illus.; cum.index: vols.1-30, 1950-1984 in vol.32. circ. 500. Indexed: Amer.Hist.& Life, Arts & Hum.Cit.Ind., Chem.Abstr., Curr.Cont., Hist.Abstr., Ind.Med., Math.R., Mid.East: Abstr.& Ind., SSCI.
—BLDSC (3104.000000); Faxon; Genuine Article; SWETS; UnCover. CCC.
Refereed Serial

CENTRALE VIDENSKABETISKE KOMITE. BERETNING/CENTRAL SCIENTIFIC - ETHICAL COMMITTEE OF DENMARK. REPORT. see PHILOSOPHY

CENTRE FOR THE STUDY OF THE CIVILIZATIONS OF CENTRAL ASIA. PUBLICATIONS. see HISTORY — History Of Asia

CENTRE NATIONAL DE DOCUMENTATION SCIENTIFIQUE ET TECHNIQUE. RAPPORT D'ACTIVITE. see TECHNOLOGY: COMPREHENSIVE WORKS

500 IT ISSN 0394-0705
CODEN: CCLADS
CENTRO LINCEO INTERDISCIPLINARE BENIAMINO SEGRE. CONTRIBUTI. 1974. irreg. Accademia Nazionale dei Lincei, Via della Lungara 10, 00165 Rome, Italy. TEL 39-6-6838831.
—CASDDS.
Formerly (until 1987): Centro Linceo Interdisciplinare di Scienze Matematiche e Loro Applicazioni. Contributi (ISSN 0391-8041)

CENTRO UNIVERSITARIO DE ESTUDIOS GENERALES. REVISTA. see SOCIAL SCIENCES: COMPREHENSIVE WORKS

500 XR
QH1 CODEN: PPUCA4
CESKOSLOVENSKA ACEDEMIE VED. USTAV V BRNE. PRIRODOVEDNE PRACE/ACTA SCIENTIARUM NATURALIUM ACADEMIAE SCIENTIARUM BOHEMOSLOVACAE BRNO. (Text in English, French or German; summaries in English and Russian) 1967. m. price varies. Academia, Publishing House of the Czechoslovak Academy of Sciences, Vodickova str. 40, 112 29 Prague, Czech Republic. TEL 23-63-065. (Subscr. to: Artia, Ve Smeckach 30, P.O. Box 790, 111 27 Prague 1, Czech Republic) adv. Indexed: Anim.Breed.Abstr., Biol.Abstr., Bull.Signal., Chem.Abstr., Curr.Adv.Ecol.Sci., Ecol.Abstr., Field Crop Abstr., Geo.Abstr., GeoRef., Herb.Abstr., Key Word Ind.Wildl.Res., Math.R., Plant Breed.Abstr., Ref.Zh., Sport Fish.Abstr., Wild.Rev., Zoo.Rec.
Formerly: Ceskoslovenska Akademie Ved. Brnenska Zakladna. Prace (ISSN 0032-6758)

500 600 CE
CEYLON INSTITUTE OF SCIENTIFIC & INDUSTRIAL RESEARCH. ANNUAL REPORT. 1956. a. $25. Ceylon Institute of Scientific & Industrial Research, 363 Bauddhaloka Mawatha, Box 787, Colombo 07, Sri Lanka. adv. contact: P.M. Jayatissa. circ. 300. Document type: corporate report.

500 600 CE
CEYLON INSTITUTE OF SCIENTIFIC AND INDUSTRIAL RESEARCH. NEWS BULLETIN. 1992. q. Ceylon Institute of Scientific and Industrial Research, 363, Bauddhaloka Mawatha, Box 787, Colombo 07, Sri Lanka. circ. 500. Document type: bulletin.

001.9 CN ISSN 0706-5337
CHAOS. 1978. 8/yr. Can.$16. Res Bureaux, Box 1598, Kingston, Ont. K7L 5C8, Canada. TEL 613-542-7277.

CHAOS NETWORK. see BUSINESS AND ECONOMICS

500 CC
CHENGDU DAXUE XUEBAO (ZIRAN KEXUE BAN)/CHENGDU UNIVERSITY. JOURNAL (NATURAL SCIENCE EDITION). (Text in Chinese) q. Y4.80. Chengdu Daxue - Chengdu University, Xiaojia Cun, Renmin Beilu, Chengdu, Sichuan 610081, People's Republic of China. TEL 337939. Ed. Yang Qiwei. Document type: academic/scholarly publication.
Description: Publishes scientific research results and technology news in the natural sciences, including food processing and industrial management.

500 CC ISSN 0253-2263
Q4 CODEN: CKDXDB
CHENGDU KEJI DAXUE XUEBAO/CHENGDU UNIVERSITY OF SCIENCE AND TECHNOLOGY. JOURNAL. (Text in Chinese) bi-m. Chengdu Keji Daxue, Xuebao Bianjibu, Chengdu, Sichuan 610065, People's Republic of China. TEL 581554. Ed. Xu Xi. Document type: academic/scholarly publication.
—CASDDS.

500 US ISSN 0009-3491
Q11
CHICAGO ACADEMY OF SCIENCES. BULLETIN. 1883. irreg., vol.15, 1992. price varies. Chicago Academy of Sciences, 2001 N. Clark St., Chicago, IL 60614. TEL 312-549-0606. FAX 312-549-5199. Ed. Paul G. Heltne. charts; illus.; bibl. circ. 1,019. (also avail. in microform from UMI; reprint service avail. from UMI) Indexed: Biol.Abstr. Document type: academic/scholarly publication.
—UMI.
Description: Booklets on natural history subjects.

CHICKADEE. see CHILDREN AND YOUTH — For

500 IR ISSN 1022-7806
CHIKIDAH-I TAZAHHA-YI TAHQIQ DAR DANISHGAHHA VA MARAKIZ-I TAHQIQATI IRAN/CURRENT RESEARCH IN IRANIAN UNIVERSITIES AND RESEARCH CENTERS. (Text in Persian) 1993. q. $30 or exchange basis. Iranian Information & Documentation Center (IRANDOC), 1188 Enqelab Ave., P.O. Box 13185-1371, Tehran, Iran. TEL 98-21-6462548. FAX 98-21-6462254. (back issues avail.) Document type: academic/scholarly publication, abstracting/indexing.

500 JA ISSN 0912-3318
CHIKUHO HAKUBUTSU/NATURHISTORICA CHIKUHOANA. (Text in Japanese) a. Society of Natural History of Chikuho - Chikuho Hakubutsu Kenkyukai, Iizuka-shiritsu Toshokan, 2-58 Nishi-machi, Iizuka-shi, Fukuoka-ken 820, Japan.
Formerly (until 1971): Chikuho Seibutsu Kenkyukai Kaishi (ISSN 0912-330X)

500 600 US ISSN 0894-2536
CODEN: CCTPEC
CHINA CENTER OF ADVANCED SCIENCE AND TECHNOLOGY SERIES. 1987. irreg., latest vol.10. Gordon & Breach Science Publishers, c/o International Publishers Distributor, 820 Town Center Dr., Langhorne, PA 19047. TEL 215-750-2642. FAX 215-750-6343. (Subscr. to: International Publishers Distributor, P.O. Box 90, Reading, Berkshire RG1 8JL, England. TEL 44-173-456-8316) Ed.Bd. (also avail. in microfilm; microfiche) Document type: monographic series.
—BLDSC (6842.817800); CASDDS.
Refereed Serial

500 600 US ISSN 0272-0086
E183.8.C5
CHINA EXCHANGE NEWS; a review of science, education, and academic relations with the PRC. 1973. q. free. Committee on Scholarly Communication with China, 1055 Thomas Jefferson St., N.W., Ste. 2013, Washington, DC 20007. TEL 202-337-1250. FAX 202-337-3109. Ed. Kathlin Smith. bk.rev.; abstr.; bibl.; stat.; circ. 2,500 (controlled). (also avail. in microfiche) Document type: academic/scholarly publication.
—BLDSC (3180.144000); Faxon; UnCover.
Formerly: China Exchange Newsletter (ISSN 0145-6318); Supersedes: China Science Notes.

500 600 US ISSN 0271-0099
CHINA REPORT: SCIENCE AND TECHNOLOGY. irreg. (approx. 50/yr.) $7 per no. (foreign $14 per no.). U.S. Joint Publications Research Service, Box 12507, Arlington, VA 22209. TEL 703-487-4630. (Orders to: NTIS, Springfield, VA 22161)

500 CC
CHINESE ACADEMY OF SCIENCES. BULLETIN. Chinese edition: Zhongguo Kexueyuan Yuankan (ISSN 1000-3045) (Text in English) s-a. $52. Science Press, Marketing and Sales Department, 16 Donghuangchenggen North St., Beijing 100717, People's Republic of China. TEL 4010642. FAX 4019810. Document type: academic/scholarly publication.
Description: Publishes research results, science and technology development trends. Some of the articles are original, not translations.

951 500 US ISSN 0361-9001
Q145
CHINESE SCIENCE. 1975. a. $45 (F.250) for 3 nos. to individuals; institutions $60 (F.330). Center for Chinese Studies, University of California, Los Angeles, Los Angeles, CA 90024-1487. TEL 310-825-3078. FAX 310-206-3555. E-mail: elman@histr.sscnet.ucla.edu. (Subscr. to: Catherine Jami, Treasurer, 35 rue Geoffroy Saint Hilaire, 75005 Paris, France. TEL 33-1-47078922. FAX 33-1-45807847) Ed. Benjamin A. Elman. adv. contact: Richard Gunde. bk.rev. circ. 350. Document type: academic/scholarly publication.
—BLDSC (3181.079000); UnCover.
Description: Dedicated to the study of traditional and modern East Asian science, technology and medicine in the Chinese tradition.

5850 SCIENCES: COMPREHENSIVE WORKS

500   CC   ISSN 1001-6538
Q4   CODEN: CSBUEF
CHINESE SCIENCE BULLETIN. Chinese edition: Kexue Tongbao (ISSN 0023-074X) (Text in English) 1980. 24/yr. fl.1444($802) (effective 1995). (Chinese Academy of Sciences) Science Press, Marketing and Sales Department, 16 Donghuangchenggen Beijie, Beijing, People's Republic of China. TEL 4010642. FAX 4019810. (Dist. outside China by: I O S Press, Van Diemenstraat 94, 1013 CN Amsterdam, Netherlands. TEL 31-20-638-2189. FAX 31-20-6203419; Subscr. in U.S. and Canada to: I O S Press, Box 10558, Burke, VA 22009-0558. TEL 703-323-5554. FAX 703-250-4705) Ed. Dong-Sheng Yan. adv.; index. circ. 5,000. (back issues avail.) **Indexed:** INSPEC (1989-), Meteor.& Geoastrophys.Abstr., Sugar Ind.Abstr. **Document type:** academic/scholarly publication.
—BLDSC (3181.086000); CASDDS; Ei; SWETS; UMI. **CCC.**
   Formerly (until 1988): Kexue Tongbao (Foreign Language Edition) (ISSN 0250-7862)
   Description: Presents concise reports on important recent results in basic and applied sciences. Reflects the current level of development of science and technology in China.
   Refereed Serial

500   CC   ISSN 1000-582X
CODEN: CPAOD4
CHONGQING DAXUE XUEBAO/CHONGQING UNIVERSITY. JOURNAL. (Text in Chinese) 1978. bi-m. $1.50 per no. Chongqing Daxue - Chongqing University, 74, Zhengjie, Shapingba, Chongqing, Sichuan 660044, People's Republic of China. (Dist. overseas by: China International Book Trading Corp., P.O. Box 399, Beijing, P.R.C.) **Indexed:** Art & Archaeol.Tech.Abstr., Cyb.Abstr. **Document type:** academic/scholarly publication.
—CASDDS.

500 600   CC
CHONGQING KEJI/CHONGQING SCIENCE AND TECHNOLOGY. (Text in Chinese) m. Chongqing Shi Kexue Jishu Weiyuanhui - Chongqing Science and Technology Commission, 236, Renmin Lu, Chongqing, Sichuan 630015, People's Republic of China. TEL 352263. Ed. Zhou Yongxin.

500   ZR   ISSN 0009-6040
CHRONIQUE DE L'I R S A C. (Text in English and French) 1966. 3/yr. $2. Institut pour la Recherche Scientifique en Afrique Centrale, Lwiro- Bukavu, Zaire. abstr.; illus.

500 600   JA   ISSN 0578-2228
CODEN: CDSEAB
CHUO DAIGAKU RIKOGAKUBU KIYO/CHUO UNIVERSITY. FACULTY OF SCIENCE AND ENGINEERING. BULLETIN. (Text in Japanese; summaries and some articles in English) 1957. a. free. Chuo Daigaku, Rikogakubu - Chuo University, Faculty of Science and Engineering, 1-13-27 Kasuga, Bunkyo-ku, Tokyo 112, Japan. FAX 03-814-0955. illus. **Indexed:** INIS Atomind.
—BLDSC (2508.900000); CASDDS.
   Description: Contains articles as well as full length studies, statistics, charts, graphs, tables and photographs from the faculty.

500   DR
CIENCIA. 1972. q. RD.$8($11) Universidad Autonoma de Santo Domingo, Direccion de Investigaciones Cientificas, Santo Domingo, Dominican Republic. Ed. Jose del Castillo. bibl.; charts; illus. **Indexed:** Biol.Abstr.

500 600   BL   ISSN 0084-8794
CIENCIA. (Text in Portuguese; summaries in English) vol.1, no.2, 1980. irreg. avail. on exchange. Centro Academico Piraja da Silva, Faculdade de Ciencias Medicas e Biologicas de Botucatu, C.P. 102, Rubiao-Junior, Botucatu, S.P., Brazil.

500 300   MX   ISSN 0185-075X
Q4   CODEN: CIENA3
CIENCIA. (Text in Spanish; summaries in English and Spanish) 1940. q. $78 to individuals; institutions $158 (effective 1993). Academia de la Investigacion Cientifica, A.C., Av. San Jeronimo 260, Col. Jardines del Pedregal, Mexico, D.F. 04500, Mexico. TEL 550-6278. FAX 550-1143. (Subscr. to: Apartado Postal 69-692, 04460 Mexico D.F., Mexico) Ed. Julio Rubio. adv.; bk.rev.; index. circ. 3,000. (back issues avail.) **Indexed:** Biol.Abstr., Chem.Abstr., Deep Sea Res.& Oceanogr.Abstr., Helminthol.Abstr., INIS Atomind., INSPEC (1968-).

500   CU
CIENCIA. s-a. $15 in N. and S. America; Europe $16. (Academia de Ciencias Instituto de Documentacion e Informacion Cientifico- Tecnica (Havana)) Ediciones Cubanas, Obispo No. 527, Apdo. 605, Havana, Cuba.

500   BL   ISSN 0009-6725
Q4   CODEN: CCUPAD
CIENCIA E CULTURA. (Text in English; summaries in English and Portuguese) 1949. bi-m. Cr.$33($80) (effective 1995). Sociedade Brasileira para o Progresso da Ciencia, Rua Maria Antonia 294, 4o andar, 01222-010 Sao Paulo, SP, Brazil. TEL 55-11-2592766. FAX 55-11-6061002. Ed. Luiz Rodolpho Travassos. adv.; bk.rev.; bibl.; charts; illus.; cum.index: 1948-1993. circ. 2,000. (tabloid format; also avail. in microform; reprint service avail.) **Indexed:** Apic.Abstr., Biodet.Abstr., Biol.Abstr., Chem.Abstr., Curr.Cont., Deep Sea Res.& Oceanogr.Abstr., Excerp.Med., Field Crop Abstr., Helminthol.Abstr., INIS Atomind., Plant Breed.Abstr. **Document type:** academic/scholarly publication.
—BLDSC (3195.900000); CASDDS; Ei.
   Description: Includes reviews, reports, research articles, news and comments.

500   AG   ISSN 0009-6733
Q4   CODEN: CIBAAH
CIENCIA E INVESTIGACION.* 1945. m. $15. Asociacion Argentina para el Progreso de las Ciencias, Avda. Alvear 1711, Piso 4, 1014 Buenos Aires, Argentina. Ed.Bd. adv.; bk.rev.; bibl.; charts; illus.; index. circ. 2,000. **Indexed:** Biol.Abstr., Chem.Abstr.
—CASDDS.

500   CU
CIENCIA, INNOVACION Y DESARROLLO. Short title: Cinde. q. $30. Ministerio de la Ciencia, la Tecnologia y el Medio Ambiente, Instituto de Documentacion e Information Cientifica y Tecnologica, Apdo. Postal 2213, 10200 Havana, Cuba. TEL 62-6501. FAX 62-6501. Ed. Andres Castillo Bernal.

500   US   ISSN 0009-675X
Q4.C43   CODEN: CIIABJ
CIENCIA INTERAMERICANA. (Text in English, Spanish, Portuguese) 1960. 2/yr. $1 per no. Organization of American States, General Secretariat, 1889 F St. N.W., Washington, DC 20006. TEL 202-789-3386. Ed. Gelmi Arrieta. bk.rev.; charts; illus.; tr.lit.; index. circ. 5,000. (back issues avail.) **Indexed:** Deep Sea Res.& Oceanogr.Abstr., GeoRef.

500 600   MX
CIENCIA PARA TODOS. 1974. m. Mex.$130($14) Publicaciones Herrerias, S.A., Morelos, 16-3er Piso, Mexico 1, D.F., Mexico. Ed. Jose Pichel. adv.; bk.rev. circ. 15,000.
   Formerly: Ciencia Popular.

500 790.1   SP
CIENCIA Y DEPORTE. 6/yr. Comercio 4, bajo C, 1a escalera, 28007 Madrid, Spain. TEL 1-433-45-23. Ed. Alberto Munoz Soler.

500 600   MX   ISSN 0185-0008
Q4   CODEN: CIDED8
CIENCIA Y DESARROLLO. 1975. bi-m. Mex.$60($36) (Europe $44) (effective 1995). Consejo Nacional de Ciencia y Tecnologia, Av. Constituyentes 1046, Col. Lomas Altas, 11950 Mexico, D.F., Mexico. TEL 525-573-0364. FAX 525-626-0370. TELEX 017-74521. Ed. Alfredo Gomez. adv. contact: Jose Luis Miranda Salgado. bk.rev.; bibl.; index. circ. 8,000. **Indexed:** Chem.Abstr. **Document type:** academic/scholarly publication.
—BLDSC (3196.570000); CASDDS.

500.1   EC   ISSN 0009-6768
CODEN: CINQAN
CIENCIA Y NATURALEZA. (Text and summaries in English or Spanish) 1957. s-a. exchange basis. Universidad Central del Ecuador, Instituto de Ciencias Naturales, Casilla 633, Quito, Ecuador. Dir. Francisco Latorre. bibl.; charts; illus.; index. circ. 2,500. **Indexed:** Biol.Abstr., Chem.Abstr., Field Crop Abstr., GeoRef., Herb.Abstr.

500   DR   ISSN 0378-7680
HC157.D6
CIENCIA Y SOCIEDAD. (Text in Spanish; summaries in English) 1975. q. RD.$60($30) Instituto Tecnologico de Santo Domingo, Apdo. Postal 342-9, Santo Domingo, Dominican Republic. Ed. Jose Marmol. adv.; bk.rev.; bibl.; charts. circ. 1,000. **Document type:** academic/scholarly publication.

500   CR   ISSN 0378-052X
CODEN: CITEDK
CIENCIA Y TECNOLOGIA. 1976. s-a. $20. Editorial de la Universidad de Costa Rica, Apartado 75-2060, Ciudad Universitaria Rodrigo Facio, 2050 San Pedro de Montes de Oca, San Jose, Costa Rica. TEL 506-25-3133. FAX 506-24-9367. TELEX UNICORI 2544. Dir. Jorge Paez P. (also avail. in microfilm from OMN) **Indexed:** Math.R. **Document type:** academic/scholarly publication.
—CASDDS.

500   SP   ISSN 0009-6776
Q65   CODEN: CINSAT
CIENCIAS. 1934. q. 1500 ptas. Asociacion Espanola para el Progreso de las Ciencias, Valverde 22, Madrid (13), Spain. adv. circ. 1,500. **Indexed:** Biol.Abstr.
—CASDDS.

CIENCIAS TECNICAS FISICAS Y MATEMATICAS. see *TECHNOLOGY: COMPREHENSIVE WORKS*

508 001.3   SX   ISSN 1012-4926
Q85.8   CODEN: CIMBEB
CIMBEBASIA. (Text in English; summaries in French or German) 1962. irreg., approx a. price varies. State Museum of Namibia, P.O. Box 1203, Windhoek, Namibia. TEL 061-2934360. Ed. John Kinahan. charts; illus. circ. 400. (back issues avail.) **Indexed:** Anthropol.Lit., Biol.Abstr., Deep Sea Res.& Oceanogr.Abstr., Ind.S.A.Per., Nutr.Abstr., Zoo.Rec. **Document type:** academic/scholarly publication.
—UnCover.
   Formed by the 1988 merger of: Cimbebasia. Series A, Natural History (ISSN 0590-6342) & Cimbebasia. Series B, Cultural History (ISSN 0253-2522); Which superseded (in 1967): Cimbebasia (ISSN 0578-2732)

508   SX   ISSN 0578-2724
CIMBEBASIA. MEMOIR. (Text mainly in English; summaries in French or German) 1967. irreg., vol.6, 1985. price varies. State Museum of Namibia, P.O. Box 1203, Windhoek, Namibia. TEL 061-2934360. Ed. J. Kinahan. index. circ. 400. (back issues avail.) **Document type:** monographic series.

500   SP
CINCO. 3/yr. Eugenio Salazar 27, 2o, 28002 Madrid, Spain.

500 100   US   ISSN 1042-4628
CLASSICS IN THE HISTORY AND PHILOSOPHY OF SCIENCE. irreg., latest vol.13. price varies. Gordon and Breach Science Publishers, c/o International Publishers Distributor, 820 Town Center Dr., Langhorne, PA 19047. TEL 215-750-2642. FAX 215-750-6343. (Subscr. to: International Publishers Distributor, P.O. Box 90, Reading, Berkshire RG1 8JL, England. TEL 44-173-456-8316) Ed. Roger Hahn. **Document type:** monographic series.
   Refereed Serial

500   SP
COLECCION CIENCIAS, HUMANIDADES E INGENIERIA. irreg. (approx. 4/yr.). price varies. Colegio de Ingenieros de Caminos, Canales y Puertos, Almagro, 42, 28010 Madrid, Spain. TEL 1-308-19-88. FAX 1-308-39-32.

500   NZ   ISSN 0112-2479
COLLECTED PAPERS FROM THE JOURNAL OF THE ROYAL SOCIETY OF NEW ZEALAND. 1984. irreg. price varies. (Royal Society of New Zealand) S I R Publishing, 11 P.O. Box 399, Wellington, New Zealand. TEL 64-4-472-7421. FAX 64-4-473-1841. Ed. Carolyn M. King. **Document type:** academic/scholarly publication.

500   US   ISSN 0160-0664
QH1
COLLECTIONS (BUFFALO). 1920. q. $5. Buffalo Society of Natural Sciences, 1020 Humboldt Pkwy., Buffalo, NY 14211. TEL 716-896-5200. FAX 716-897-6723. Ed. Barbara Park Leggett. illus. circ. 8,000. **Indexed:** Biol.Abstr., GeoRef.
   Formerly (until vol.56): Science on the March (ISSN 0036-8474)

SCIENCES: COMPREHENSIVE WORKS

500   CK   ISSN 0120-5595
COLOMBIA: CIENCIA Y TECNOLOGIA. 1983. q. Col.$8000($20) Colciencias, Transversal 9a No. 133-28, P.O. Box 051580, Bogota, Colombia. TEL 2169800. FAX 6251788. TELEX 44305. Ed. Magola Delgado. adv.; charts; illus.; stat. circ. 3,000.
    Formerly: Ciencia y Tecnologia.
    Description: Presents studies in science and technology.

500   US   ISSN 0096-2279
AS36   CODEN: JCOQAT
COLORADO-WYOMING ACADEMY OF SCIENCES. JOURNAL. 1929. a. $5. Colorado-Wyoming Academy of Science, c/o Clait E. Braun, Wildlife Research Center, 317 W. Prospect Rd., Ft. Collins, CO 80526. FAX 970-490-6066. abstr. circ. 300. **Indexed:** Biol.Abstr., GeoRef., Sport Fish.Abstr., Wild.Rev., Zoo.Rec. **Document type:** academic/scholarly publication.

500   FR
COMITE DES TRAVAUX HISTORIQUES ET SCIENTIFIQUES. SECTION DES SCIENCES. ACTES DU CONGRES NATIONAL DES SOCIETES HISTORIQUES ET SCIENTIFIQUES. 1961. a. price varies. Comite des Travaux Historiques et Scientifiques, 173 blvd St Germain, 75006 Paris, France. TEL 40-65-75-32.
    Former titles: Comite des Travaux Historiques et Scientifiques. Section des Sciences. Actes du Congres National des Societes Savantes; Comite des Travaux Historiques et Scientifiques. Section des Sciences. Comptes Rendus du Congres National des Societes Savantes.

500   UA
COMMUNICATIONS IN SCIENCE AND DEVELOPMENT RESEARCH. (Text and summaries in Arabic, English) 1982. 4/yr. $40. Prof. Dr. A.M. Balba Group for Soil and Water Research, College of Agriculture, University of Alexandria, El-Shatby, Alexandria 21545. TEL 03-5975405. FAX 03-5954684. Ed. A.M. Balba. abstr. **Document type:** academic/scholarly publication, bulletin.
    Description: Publishes original research work in various disciplines of science.
    Refereed Serial

500   US
CONDUCT OF SCIENCE SERIES. irreg. (approx. 1/yr.). Guilford Publications, Inc., 72 Spring St., New York, NY 10012. TEL 212-431-9800; 800-365-7006. FAX 212-966-6708. Ed. Steve Fuller. **Document type:** monographic series.
    Description: Presents works from a variety of disciplines concerned with how science is practiced. Topics such as peer review, scientific discovery, fraud - deception - self-deception, and policy are considered.

CONFIGURATIONS; a journal of literature, science and technology. see *LITERATURE*

500 600   SW   ISSN 0074-9540
CONGRES INTERNATIONAL D'HISTOIRE DES SCIENCES. ACTES. 1947. quadrennial. International Union of the History & Philosophy of Science, c/o Tore Frangsmyr, Office of History of Science, Uppsala University, Box 256, S-75105 Uppsala, Sweden.

CONGRESSIONAL REPORT: SCIENCE, ENERGY & ENVIRONMENT. see *PUBLIC ADMINISTRATION*

CONNECT (BRATTLEBORO); the newsletter of practical science and math for K-8 teachers. see *EDUCATION — Teaching Methods And Curriculum*

001.3 500   US   ISSN 0069-8970
CONNECTICUT ACADEMY OF ARTS AND SCIENCES. MEMOIRS. 1801. irreg., vol.23, 1992. Connecticut Academy of Arts and Sciences, Box 208211, New Haven, CT 06520-8211. TEL 203-432-3113. FAX 203-432-5712. Ed. Catherine Skinner. illus. **Indexed:** Biol.Abstr.

CONNECTICUT ACADEMY OF ARTS AND SCIENCES. TRANSACTIONS. see *HUMANITIES: COMPREHENSIVE WORKS*

CONNECTICUT GEOLOGIC AND NATURAL HISTORY BULLETINS. see *EARTH SCIENCES — Geology*

500   SP
CONOCER LA VIDA Y EL UNIVERSO. m. Ediciones Mensuales, O'Donnell 12, 28009 Madrid, Spain. TEL 34-1-5863300. circ. 900,000.

550   US   ISSN 0459-8113
Q11   CODEN: LAMSAX
CONTRIBUTIONS IN SCIENCE. (Text in English; occasional summaries in Spanish) 1957. irreg., no.449, 1995. Natural History Museum of Los Angeles County, 900 Exposition Blvd., Los Angeles, CA 90007. TEL 213-744-3330. FAX 213-742-0730. circ. 2,000. **Indexed:** Biol.Abstr., Deep Sea Res.& Oceanogr.Abstr., GeoRef., Ocean.Abstr., Sport Fish.Abstr., Wild.Rev., Zoo.Rec. **Document type:** monographic series.
—UnCover.
    Formerly: Natural History Museum of Los Angeles County. Contributions in Science (ISSN 0076-0900); Incorporates (in 1978): Science Bulletin (ISSN 0076-0935)
    Refereed Serial

CORRIERE DEL MEZZOGIORNO; il tridente. see *POLITICAL SCIENCE*

500.9   UK   ISSN 0011-023X
COUNTRY-SIDE; a wildlife magazine. 1905. bi-m. £12 (overseas £18). British Naturalists' Association, c/o Mrs. J. Pearton, 48 Russell Way, Higham Ferrers, Northants. NN10 8EJ, England. FAX 01933-314672. (Subscr. to: Mrs. Y. Griffiths, 1 Bracken Mews, Chingford, London E1X 7HE, England) Ed. David Applin. adv. contact: Jon Montgomery. bk.rev.; illus.; stat. circ. 14,000. **Indexed:** Farm & Garden Ind., Key Word Ind.Wildl.Res. **Document type:** consumer publication.
—BLDSC (3482.000000).

COURIER (PARIS). see *POLITICAL SCIENCE — International Relations*

500   US   ISSN 0070-1416
Q11
CRANBROOK INSTITUTE OF SCIENCE, BLOOMFIELD HILLS, MICHIGAN. BULLETIN. (Each bulletin has a distinctive title) 1931. irreg., no.48, 1987. price varies. Cranbrook Institute of Science, Box 801, Bloomfield Hills, MI 48303-0801. TEL 313-645-3203. FAX 313-645-3050. Dir. Daniel E. Appleman. adv.; bk.rev. (reprint service avail. from UMI) **Indexed:** Biol.Abstr. **Document type:** bulletin.
    Description: Disseminates scientific information concerning Michigan and the Great Lakes region. Aimed at practicing scientists, serious students and informed laypeople.

CREATION. see *RELIGIONS AND THEOLOGY*

500.9   US   ISSN 0738-6001
QH359   CODEN: CREVEQ
CREATION - EVOLUTION; the journal of evolution and science education which explores aspects of evolution and antievolutionism. 1980. 2/yr. $25 (foreign $32) includes: N C S E Reports. National Center for Science Education, Box 9477, Berkeley, CA 94709-0477. TEL 510-526-1674; 800-290-6006. FAX 510-526-1675. E-mail: ncse@crl.com. Ed. John R. Cole. bk.rev.; bibl.; cum.index: nos.1-31 on diskette. circ. 3,000. (back issues avail.) **Indexed:** Zoo.Rec. **Document type:** academic/scholarly publication.
—BLDSC (3487.234000); Faxon; UnCover.
    Description: Promotes the understanding of evolutionary science, with articles addressing creationist claims about dinosaurs and other anti-evolutionist arguments and analyzing the creationist phenomenon.
    Refereed Serial

CREATION EX NIHILO. see *RELIGIONS AND THEOLOGY*

CREATION EX NIHILO TECHNICAL JOURNAL. see *RELIGIONS AND THEOLOGY*

500 200   US   ISSN 0092-9166
BS651
CREATION RESEARCH SOCIETY QUARTERLY. 1964. q. $24 (foreign $29). Creation Research Society, Box 969, Ashland, OH 44805. Ed. Eugene Chaffin. adv.; bk.rev.; index. circ. 1,800. (also avail. in microfilm from UMI; back issues avail.; reprint service avail. from UMI) **Indexed:** Biol.Abstr., Chr.Per.Ind., Zoo.Rec. **Document type:** academic/scholarly publication.
—BLDSC (3487.235000); UMI.
    Description: Presents original research and reviews pertinent to the study of origins science, creation and evolution. Provides a creationist perspective.
    Refereed Serial

500   CL   ISSN 0716-0313
CRECES. 1979. m. $70. Bustos 2030, Providencia, Santiago, Chile. TEL 2-496692. TELEX 341011. Dir. Fernando Monckeberg. adv.; bk.rev. circ. 12,000.

500 600   US   ISSN 1065-2388
CRITICAL REVIEWS IN MULTIPHASE SCIENCE & TECHNOLOGY. vol.9, 1995. bi-m. $175 (effective 1996). Begell House Inc., 79 Madison Ave., Ste. 1201, New York, NY 10016-7892. TEL 212-725-1999. FAX 212-213-8368. E-mail: 74353.2052@compuserve.com. Eds. G.F. Hewitt, J.M. Delahaye. **Document type:** academic/scholarly publication.
    Description: Covers all aspects of multiphase, multi-component systems, including mehcanical, fluid dynamics, thermal, hydraulic and property behavior of systems.

500 300
CROSS-THINKING FOR DISCOVERY AND CREATIVITY. 1992. q. $12. Cross-Thinking, Box 449, Reese, MI 48757. TEL 517-662-4169. Eds. Deborah Italvorson, Kermit Kranz. (looseleaf format; back issues avail.)

500   UK   ISSN 0309-6149
CROYDON NATURAL HISTORY & SCIENTIFIC SOCIETY. BULLETIN. 1967. irreg. (approx. 3-4/yr). (subscr. includes Proceedings of the Croydon Natural History & Scientific Society). Croydon Natural History & Scientific Society Ltd., 96a Brighton Rd., South Croydon, Surrey CR2 6AD, England. Ed. J. Greig. bk.rev.; bibl. circ. 850. **Document type:** bulletin.

500.9   UK   ISSN 0309-8656
CROYDON NATURAL HISTORY & SCIENTIFIC SOCIETY. PROCEEDINGS AND TRANSACTIONS. 1871. irreg. (approx. 3-4/yr.). £8 (subscr. includes Bulletin). Croydon Natural History and Scientific Society Ltd., 96a Brighton Rd., South Croydon, Surrey CR2 6AD, England. Ed. B. Lancanster. charts; illus.; cum.index. circ. 1,000. **Indexed:** Br.Archaeol.Abstr., Br.Geol.Lit. **Document type:** proceedings.
—BLDSC (6688.000000).

CRYPTOLOGIA; a quarterly journal devoted to all aspects of cryptology. see *MATHEMATICS*

CUADERNOS VALENCIANOS DE HISTORIA DE LA MEDICINA Y DE LA CIENCIA. see *MEDICAL SCIENCES*

500   CU   ISSN 0138-7049
CUBA. MINISTERIO DE LA INDUSTRIA LIGERA. REVISTA CIENCIA Y TECNICA. (Text in Spanish; summaries in English, Spanish) 1983. 3/yr. $16 in N. America; S. America $17; elsewhere $22. Ministerio de la Industria Ligera, Empedrado 302, esq. a Aguiar, Havana 10100, Cuba. TEL 60-3111. TELEX 051-1141. E-mail: minilict@ceniai.cu. Ed. Ausberto Bianchi Diaz. adv. contact: Hector de la Torre. circ. 1,000. **Indexed:** Ref.Zh. **Document type:** government publication.
    Description: Examines research work on light industries production branches: textiles, ready-made garments, leather and shoes, perfumery and soaps, plastics and woodworking (furniture).

SCIENCES: COMPREHENSIVE WORKS

500   II   ISSN 0011-3891
Q1   CODEN: CUSCAM
CURRENT SCIENCE. (Text in English) 1932. 24/yr. Rs.350($200) (effective 1996). Indian Academy of Sciences, C.V. Raman Avenue, P.B. No. 8005, Bangalore 560 080, India. TEL 91-080-3342310. FAX 91-080-2346094. TELEX 0845-2178-ACAD-IN. (Co-sponsor: Current Science Association) Eds. S. Ramaseshan, P. Balaram. adv.; bk.rev.; illus.; index. circ. 3,500. (also avail. in microfilm from UMI; reprint service avail. from ISI and UMI) **Indexed:** Agroforest.Abstr., Anim.Breed.Abstr., Apic.Abstr., Bio-Contr.News & Info., Biol.Abstr., Chem.Abstr., Cott.& Trop.Fibr.Abstr., Crop Physiol.Abstr., Curr.Cont., Curr.Leather Lit., Dairy Sci.Abstr., Excerp.Med., Fababean Abstr., Field Crop Abstr., Food Sci.& Tech.Abstr., Forest.Abstr., Forest Prod.Abstr., GeoRef., Helminthol.Abstr., Herb.Abstr., Hort.Abstr., Ind.Sci.Rev., Ind.Vet., INIS Atomind., INSPEC, Irr.& Drain.Abstr., Maize Abstr., Met.Abstr., Meteor.& Geoastrophys.Abstr., Numis.Lit., Ocean.Abstr., Ornam.Hort., Plant Grow.Reg.Abstr., Pollut.Abstr., Potato Abstr., Poult.Abstr., Protozool.Abstr., Rev.Appl.Entomol., Rev.Med.& Vet.Mycol., Rev.Plant Path., Rice Abstr., Seed Abstr., Sel.Water Res.Abstr., Soils & Fert., Sorghum & Millets Abstr., Soyabean Abstr., Triticale Abstr., Trop.Oil Seeds Abstr., Vet.Bull., Weed Abstr. **Document type:** academic/scholarly publication.
— BLDSC (3504.000000); CASDDS; Ei; Faxon; Genuine Article; SWETS; UMI.

CURRENT SCIENCE. see *CHILDREN AND YOUTH — For*

500 200   US
CURRENTS IN SCIENCE, TECHNOLOGY AND SOCIETY. 1991. q. $25 to individuals; educators $15 (students free). Access Research Network, Box 38069, Colorado Springs, CO 80937-8069. **Document type:** newspaper.

DAEDALUS. see *HUMANITIES: COMPREHENSIVE WORKS*

DAEDALUS. see *MUSEUMS AND ART GALLERIES*

500   JA   ISSN 0912-2346
DAITO BUNKA DAIGAKU KIYO. SHIZEN KAGAKU/DAITO BUNKA UNIVERSITY. BULLETIN. NATURAL SCIENCES. (Text and summaries in English and Japanese) a. Daito Bunka University - Daito Bunka Daigaku, 9-1, Takashimadaira, 1-chome, Itabashi-ku, Tokyo 175, Japan.

500 378   US
DAKOTA SCIENTIST. 1921. m. free. North Dakota State College of Science, Information Publications, Wahpeton, ND 58076-0002. TEL 701-671-2248. FAX 701-671-2587. circ. 4,500. **Document type:** newspaper.
Description: News of issues and trends in science education and college activities.

500   CC   ISSN 1000-8608
CODEN: DLXUEJ
DALIAN LIGONG DAXUE XUEBAO/DALIAN UNIVERSITY OF TECHNOLOGY. JOURNAL. (Text in Chinese; abstracts in English) 1950. bi-m. $4 per no. Dalian Ligong Daxue - Dalian University of Technology, c/o Library, Dalian, Liaoning 116024, People's Republic of China. TEL 0411-4708608. FAX 0411-4671009. TELEX 86231 DUT CN. (Dist. overseas by: China International Book Trading Corp., P.O. Box 399, Beijing, P.R. China) Ed. Zhu Cheng. circ. 1,500. **Indexed:** INSPEC (1989-). **Document type:** academic/scholarly publication.
— BLDSC (4732.666000); CASDDS; Ei.
Description: Covers the latest developments of theoretical and applied researches in the fields of engineering, electronics, computer science, applied mathematics and physics.

001 500   DK   ISSN 0108-7606
DANDOKNOTATER. (Text in Danish, English) 1982. irreg. free. Forsknings- og Teknologiministeriet, Statens Udvalg for Videnskabelig og Teknisk Information og Dokumentation - Ministry of Research and Technology, Bredgade 43, DK-1260 Copenhagen K, Denmark. TEL 45-33-92-97-00. FAX 45-33-32-35-01. E-mail: DANDOK@fsk.dk. circ. 650. **Document type:** bibliography, monographic series.

500 600   IR   ISSN 1011-3495
DANESHMAND. 1963. m. $120. P.O. Box 15875-3649, Teheran, Iran. TEL 98-21-8751323. E-mail: ctmseai@attmail.com. Ed. Dr. A. Farmad.

919.82072   DK   ISSN 0905-8915
DANISH POLAR CENTER. NEWSLETTER. (Text in English) 1979. s-a. free. Danish Polar Center, Strandgade 100 H, DK-1401 Copenhagen K, Denmark. TEL 45-32-88-01-00. FAX 45-32-88-01-01. bibl. circ. 2,000. (back issues avail.) **Document type:** newsletter.
Formerly (until 1990): Commission for Scientific Research in Greenland. Newsletter (ISSN 0106-1372)
Description: Provides information on current and planned scientific research activities in Greenland.

DANYAG; journal of studies in the humanities, education and the sciences, basic and applied. see *HUMANITIES: COMPREHENSIVE WORKS*

500   CC   ISSN 0255-7800
QH7
DAZIRAN/NATURE. (Text in Chinese) q. $1 per no. (Beijing Ziran Bowuguan - Beijing Natural History Museum) Daziran Zazhishe, 126 Tianqiao Nandajie, Beijing 100050, People's Republic of China. TEL 754431. Ed. Jin Jianming.

500   CC   ISSN 1000-4041
DAZIRAN TANSUO/EXPLORATION OF NATURE. (Text in Chinese) 1982. q. Y11.80. Sichuan Kexue Jishu Chubanshe, 3, Yandao Jie, Chengdu, Sichuan 610012, People's Republic of China. TEL 6664688. Ed. Chen Dunhe. circ. 4,000. **Document type:** academic/scholarly publication.
Description: Covers new theories of natural science, interdisciplinary programs, scientific studies, and history of science and technology.

LES DEBROUILLARDS. see *CHILDREN AND YOUTH — For*

DEFENCE SCIENCE JOURNAL. see *MILITARY*

DELFIN; eine deutsche Zeitschrift fuer Konstruktion, Analyse und Kritik. see *ART*

500   CN   ISSN 1180-1859
DELTA. (Text in English, French) 1990. q. free. Royal Society of Canada, Canadian Global Change Program - Societe Royale du Canada, Programme Canadien des Changements a l'Echelle du Globe, Box 9734, Ottawa, ON K1G 5J4, Canada. TEL 613-991-6990. FAX 613-991-6996. E-mail: admin@resudox.net. **Document type:** newsletter.
— Faxon.

500   US
DENVER MUSEUM OF NATURAL HISTORY. PROCEEDINGS. irreg. Denver Museum of Natural History, 2001 Colorado Blvd., Denver, CO 80205-5798.

500   GW   ISSN 0933-1271
Q180.G3
DEUTSCHE FORSCHUNGSGEMEINSCHAFT. AUFGABEN UND FINANZIERUNG. 1983. irreg. V C H Verlagsgesellschaft mbH, Postfach 101161, 69451 Weinheim, Germany. TEL 06201-606-0. FAX 06201-606328. **Document type:** monographic series.

500   GW   ISSN 0070-3974
DEUTSCHE FORSCHUNGSGEMEINSCHAFT. DENKSCHRIFTEN ZUR LAGE DER DEUTSCHEN WISSENSCHAFT. 1957. irreg. price varies. V C H Verlagsgesellschaft mbH, Postfach 101161, 69451 Weinheim, Germany. TEL 06201-606-0. FAX 06201-606328. TELEX 465516-VCHWH-D. (U.S. addr.: V C H Publishers Inc., 220 E. 23rd. St., New York, NY 10010-4606. TEL 212-683-8333) bk.rev. **Document type:** monographic series.

500   GW   ISSN 0070-3982
DEUTSCHE FORSCHUNGSGEMEINSCHAFT. FORSCHUNGSBERICHTE. 1957. irreg. price varies. V C H Verlagsgesellschaft mbH, Postfach 101163, 69451 Weinheim, Germany. TEL 06201-606-0. FAX 06201-606328. TELEX 465516-VCHWH-D. (U.S. addr.: V C H Publishers Inc., 220 E. 23rd. St., New York, NY 10010-4606. TEL 212-683-8333) **Document type:** monographic series.

500   GW   ISSN 0070-3990
DEUTSCHE FORSCHUNGSGEMEINSCHAFT. KOMMISSIONENMITTEILUNGEN. 1964. irreg. price varies. V C H Verlagsgesellschaft mbH, Postfach 101163, 69451 Weinheim, Germany. TEL 06201-606-147. FAX 06201-606117. TELEX 465516-VCHWH-D. (U.S. addr.: V C H Publishers, Inc., 220 E. 23rd St., New York, NY 10010-4606. TEL 212-683-8333) bk.rev. **Indexed:** Chem.Abstr., GeoRef. **Document type:** monographic series.

500   GW   ISSN 0418-842X
DEUTSCHE FORSCHUNGSGEMEINSCHAFT. MEXIKO-PROJEKT; eine deutsch-mexikanische interdisziplinaere Regionalforschung im Becken von Puebla-Tlaxcala. (Text in German and Spanish) irreg., vol.21, 1991. price varies. Franz Steiner Verlag Wiesbaden GmbH, Birkenwaldstr. 44, 70191 Stuttgart, Germany. TEL 0711-2582-0. FAX 0711-2582390. (Subscr. to: Postfach 101061, 70009 Stuttgart, Germany) Ed. Wilhelm Lauer. **Indexed:** GeoRef. **Document type:** monographic series.

DIE DEUTSCHE VOLKSHOCHSCHULE; allgemeinverstaendliche Beitraege aus Wissenschaft, Kunst und Philosophie. see *PHILOSOPHY*

500   GW   ISSN 0722-0847
DEUTSCHER FORSCHUNGSDIENST. APPLIED SCIENCE. (Text in English) m. DM.60. Deutscher Forschungsdienst, Ahrstr. 45, 53175 Bonn, Germany. TEL 0228-302210. FAX 0228-302270. **Document type:** academic/scholarly publication.

500   GW   ISSN 0722-5318
DEUTSCHER FORSCHUNGSDIENST. BERICHTE AUS DER WISSENSCHAFT. 51/yr. DM.200. Deutscher Forschungsdienst, Ahrstr. 45, 53175 Bonn, Germany. TEL 0228-302210. FAX 0228-302270. **Document type:** academic/scholarly publication.

500   GW   ISSN 0722-0812
DEUTSCHER FORSCHUNGSDIENST. BERICHTE AUS DER WISSENSCHAFT (AUSLANDAUSGABE). m. DM.96. Deutscher Forschungsdienst, Ahrstr. 45, 53175 Bonn, Germany. TEL 0228-302210. FAX 0228-302270. **Document type:** academic/scholarly publication.

500   GW   ISSN 0722-5229
DEUTSCHER FORSCHUNGSDIENST. SONDERDIENST ANGEWANDTE WISSENSCHAFT. 25/yr. DM.120. Deutscher Forschungsdienst, Ahrstr. 45, 53175 Bonn, Germany. TEL 0228-302210. FAX 0228-302270. **Document type:** academic/scholarly publication.

500   GW   ISSN 0722-0820
DEUTSCHER FORSCHUNGSDIENST. SONDERDIENST ANGEWANDTE WISSENSCHAFT (AUSLANDAUSGABE). m. DM.60. Deutscher Forschungsdienst, Ahrstr. 45, 53175 Bonn, Germany. TEL 0228-302210. FAX 0228-302270. **Document type:** academic/scholarly publication.

500   GW   ISSN 0933-7814
DEUTSCHER FORSCHUNGSDIENST. SPECIAL SCIENCE REPORTS. (Text in English) m. DM.96. Deutscher Forschungsdienst, Ahrstr. 45, 53175 Bonn, Germany. TEL 0228-302210. FAX 0228-302270. **Indexed:** Meteor.& Geoastrophys.Abstr. **Document type:** academic/scholarly publication.
— BLDSC (8401.730000).

500   GW   ISSN 0178-8965
DEUTSCHER FORSCHUNGSDIENST MAGAZIN. m. DM.78. Deutscher Forschungsdienst, Ahrstr. 45, 53175 Bonn, Germany. TEL 0228-302210. FAX 0228-302270. **Document type:** academic/scholarly publication.

DEVONSHIRE ASSOCIATION FOR THE ADVANCEMENT OF SCIENCE, LITERATURE AND ART. REPORT AND TRANSACTIONS. see *ART*

500 BG
AS472.D3 CODEN: DUSBAU
DHAKA UNIVERSITY STUDIES. PART B: SCIENCE. (Text in English) vol.18, 1970. irreg.? University of Dhaka, Department of Physics, Ramna, Dhaka 1000, Bangladesh. bibl.; charts. **Indexed:** Amer.Hist.& Life, Biol.Abstr., ExtraMED, Hist.Abstr. **Document type:** academic/scholarly publication.
●Also available on CD-ROM.
—CASDDS.
Formerly: Dacca University Studies. Part B: Science (ISSN 0253-5467)

DIALEKTIK; enzyklopaedische Zeitschrift fuer Philosophie und Wissenschaften. see PHILOSOPHY

DIALOGO; quaderni europei di dialogica. see PHILOSOPHY

DIDASKALIA; recherches sur la communication et l'apprentissage des sciences et des techniques. see EDUCATION

DIDATTICA DELLE SCIENZE E INFORMATICA NELLA SCUOLA. see EDUCATION — Teaching Methods And Curriculum

501 149 YU ISSN 0350-1272
DIJALEKTIKA/DIALECTICS; casopis za metodolosko filozofske probleme matematickih, prirodnih i tehnickih nauka. 1966. q. 40 din. Univerzitet u Beogradu, Studentski trg 16, Belgrade, Serbia, Yugoslavia. Eds. Milorad Bertolino, Andrija Stojkovic.
—BLDSC (3588.397800).

DIRASAT. SERIES A: HUMANITIES. see HUMANITIES: COMPREHENSIVE WORKS

500 JO ISSN 0253-424X
QH1 CODEN: DJSSE8
DIRASAT. SERIES B: PURE AND APPLIED SCIENCES. (Consists of Series A: Humanities (ISSN 0255-8033), Series B: Pure and Applied Sciences) (Text in Arabic, English) 1974. 6/yr. $90 (Series A&B $180). University of Jordan, Deanship of Academic Research, Amman, Jordan. FAX 962-6-832318. TELEX UNVJ JO 21629. Ed. Anwar M. Battikki. index; circ. 1,000 (controlled). (back issues avail.) **Indexed:** Sport Fish.Abstr., Wild.Rev., Zoo.Rec. **Document type:** academic/scholarly publication.
—CASDDS.
Description: Publishes original research contributions in the pure and applied sciences.
Refereed Serial

500 UK ISSN 0957-0748
DIRECTORY OF EUROPEAN PROFESSIONAL & LEARNED SOCIETIES. 1975. irreg., no. 5, 1995. £125($262.50) C.B.D. Research Ltd., 15 Wickham Rd., Beckenham, Kent BR2 2JS, England. TEL 0181-650-7745. FAX 0181-650-0768. (Dist. in the U.S. by: Gale Research Co., Penobscot Bldg., Detroit, MI 48226) Ed. S. Greenslade. circ. 4,000. **Document type:** directory.
—BLDSC (3593.521000).
Formerly: Directory of European Associations. Part 2: National Learned, Scientific and Technical Societies (ISSN 0309-5339)
Description: Lists 6,000 European national professional and learned societies outside Ireland and the UK.

500 RH
DIRECTORY OF ORGANIZATIONS CONCERNED WITH SCIENTIFIC RESEARCH AND TECHNICAL SERVICES IN ZIMBABWE. 1959. triennial. $20. Scientific Liaison Office, P.O. Box CY 294, Causeway, Harare, Zimbabwe. TEL 700573. TELEX 22141. **Document type:** directory.
Formerly: Directory of Organizations Concerned with Scientific Research and Technical Services in Rhodesia.

DIRECTORY OF PERSECUTED SCIENTISTS, ENGINEERS AND HEALTH PROFESSIONALS. see POLITICAL SCIENCE — Civil Rights

500 NR ISSN 0070-6280
DIRECTORY OF SCIENTIFIC RESEARCH IN NIGERIA. 1968. a. Science Association of Nigeria, Box 4039, Ibadan, Nigeria. Ed. Sunday O. Ajayi. **Document type:** directory.

500 600 PK
DIRECTORY OF THE SCIENTISTS, TECHNOLOGISTS, AND ENGINEERS OF THE P C S I R. (Text in English) 1972. irreg. Pakistan Council of Scientific and Industrial Research, Scientific Information Centre, 39 Garden Rd., Karachi 74400, Pakistan. TEL 92-21-7725943. FAX 92-21-2636704. circ. controlled. **Document type:** directory.

500 600 US ISSN 0274-7529
Q1 CODEN: DISCEL
DISCOVER (BURBANK). 1980. m. $19.97 (foreign $39.95). Walt Disney Magazine Publishing Group, 500 S. Buena Vista, Burbank, CA 91521-6012. TEL 818-973-4320. (Subscr. to: Subscription Department, Box 420235, Palm Coast, FL 32142-0235. TEL 800-829-9132) Ed. Paul Hoffman. adv.; bk.rev.; film rev.; play rev.; charts; illus.; pat.; tr.lit. circ. 1,031,496. (also avail. in Braille; talking book; record; microform from UMI,MCR; back issues avail.; reprint service avail. from UMI) **Indexed:** A.I.Abstr., Acad.Ind., Access, Acid Rain Abstr., Acid Rain Ind., Biol.Dig., CAD CAM Abstr., Comput.Lit.Ind., Deep Sea Res.& Oceanogr.Abstr., GdIns., Gen.Sci.Ind., GeoRef., Hlth.Ind., Ind.Sci.Rev., Mag.Ind., PMR, PROMT, Rehabil.Lit., Robomat, TOM.
●Also available online. Vendor(s): Knight-Ridder, Inc., Lexis-Nexis, VU/TEXT Information Services, Inc.
—BLDSC (3595.870000); CASDDS; Faxon; Genuine Article; SWETS; UMI; UnCover. **CCC.**
Description: Provides extensive coverage of science and technology in nontechnical language.

500.9 574 333.7 CN ISSN 0319-8480
DISCOVERY. N.S. 1972. q. Can.$35 to non-members. Vancouver Natural History Society, Box 3021, Vancouver, BC V6B 3X5, Canada. TEL 604-737-3057. FAX 604-738-7175. Ed.Bd. adv.: page Can.$150; adv. contact: Iva Clark. bk.rev. circ. 1,500. **Indexed:** Can.B.P.I., Can.Per.Ind., CMI, Sport Fish.Abstr., Wild.Rev. **Document type:** academic/scholarly publication.
Description: Covers natural history topics such as herpetology, mycology, entomology, botany, mammalogy, ornithology, marine biology and conservation issues.
Refereed Serial

500.9 US ISSN 0012-3625
QH1 CODEN: DISCAH
DISCOVERY (NEW HAVEN). 1965. s-a. $12 (foreign $16) (effective 1993). Peabody Museum of Natural History, Yale University, 170 Whitney Ave., Box 208118, New Haven, CT 06520-8118. TEL 203-432-3786. FAX 203-432-9816. Ed. Zelda Edelson. charts; illus. circ. 700. (back issues avail.) **Indexed:** Biol.Abstr., Biol.Dig., GeoRef., Sport Fish.Abstr., Wild.Rev., Zoo.Rec. **Document type:** consumer publication.
—BLDSC (3596.100000); UnCover.
Description: Research and scientific activities in the area of natural history written for the general reader.
Refereed Serial

DISCOVERY CREW SCIENCE CLUB NEWS. see CHILDREN AND YOUTH — For

500 510 591 IS
DIVREI HA-AKADEMIA HA-LEUMIT HA-YISRAELIT LEMADAIM-HA-HATIVA LE-MADAEI HA-TEVA. (Text in Hebrew) 1966. irreg. price varies. Israel Academy of Sciences and Humanities, 43 Jabotinski St., P.O. Box 4040, Jerusalem 91040, Israel. TEL 02-636211. FAX 02-666059. Ed. S. Re'em. circ. 900. **Indexed:** Ind.Heb.Per.
Description: Reprints of scientific papers read at meetings of the Academy.

500 VE
DIVULGA. q. Universidad Nacional Experimental del Tachira, Comision de Cultura, Av. Universidad-Paramillo, Apdo. 436, San Cristobaol, Venezuela. Ed. Gilberto A. Labrador.

500 SW ISSN 0347-5719
DOCUMENTA. 1972. irreg. (1-5/yr.). Kungliga Vetenskapsakademien - Royal Swedish Academy of Sciences, P.O. Box 50005, S-104 05 Stockholm, Sweden. FAX 46-8-155670. bibl.; illus.

500 FR ISSN 0046-0478
DOCUMENTATION PAR L'IMAGE; revue des activites d'eveil. 1936. 9/yr. 284 F. (effective 1995-96). Librairie Fernand Nathan, 9 rue Mechain, 75680 Paris Cedex 14, France. illus.
—CCC.

DOCUMENTS HISTORIQUES DES SCIENCES. see HISTORY — History Of Europe

DOGAR'S GENERAL KNOWLEDGE DIGEST. see POLITICAL SCIENCE

DONGBEI GONGXUEYUAN XUEBAO/NORTHEAST INSTITUTE OF TECHNOLOGY. JOURNAL. see TECHNOLOGY: COMPREHENSIVE WORKS

500 CC ISSN 1000-1832
DONGBEI SHIDA XUEBAO (ZIRAN KEXUE BAN)/NORTHEAST NORMAL UNIVERSITY. JOURNAL (NATURAL SCIENCE EDITION). (Text in Chinese) q. Dongbei Shifan Daxue, Xuebao Bianjibu, 110, Stalin Street, Changchun, Jilin 130024, People's Republic of China. TEL 885085. Ed. Chen Ripeng. **Document type:** academic/scholarly publication.

500 620 CC ISSN 1001-0505
CODEN: DDXUEV
DONGNAN DAXUE XUEBAO/SOUTHEAST UNIVERSITY. JOURNAL. (Text in Chinese; abstracts in Chinese, English) 1955. bi-m. $120 (effective till 1995). Dongnan Daxue - Southeast University, Sibai Lou, Nanjing, Jiangsu 210018, People's Republic of China. TEL 025-6631700. FAX 025-721714. TELEX 34137 SEULBCN. Ed. Chen Shunsheng. **Document type:** academic/scholarly publication.
—CASDDS.
Description: Covers various branches of science and engineering.

500.9 IT ISSN 0417-9927
CODEN: DRNAAF
DORIANA. (Supplement to its Annali) (Text and summaries in English, French, German, Italian and Spanish) 1949. irreg., no.281, 1993. exchange basis only. Museo Civico di Storia Naturale "Giacomo Doria", Via Brigata Liguria 9, 16121 Genoa, Italy. **Indexed:** Biol.Abstr., Bull.Signal., Curr.Adv.Ecol.Sci., Entomol.Abstr., Rev.Appl.Entomol., Zoo.Rec.
Description: Discusses natural history of the area.

500.9 913 UK ISSN 0070-7112
DORSET NATURAL HISTORY AND ARCHAEOLOGICAL SOCIETY. PROCEEDINGS. 1877. a. £12 (effective 1995). Dorset County Museum, Dorchester, Dorset, England. TEL 01305-202735. Ed. Jo Draper. circ. 2,100. **Indexed:** Br.Archaeol.Abstr., Br.Geol.Lit., Br.Hum.Ind., Numis.Lit. **Document type:** proceedings.
—BLDSC (6691.000000).
Description: Covers all aspects of natural history, geology, archaeology, local history, biography in Dorset.

500 US
DREXEL FACULTY PUBLICATION. 1978. a. free. Drexel University, Office of Sponsored Projects, 32nd & Market Sts., Philadelphia, PA 19104. TEL 215-895-2499. FAX 215-895-1619. E-mail: gellerkn@duvm.ocs.drexel.edu. Ed. Dr. Kenneth N. Geller. circ. 200. **Document type:** bibliography.
Supersedes (1971-1978): Drexel Research Conference. Summary Report (ISSN 0085-0071)

DYNAMICS AND STABILITY OF SYSTEMS. see COMPUTERS

600 MP
DZALUU DZOHION BUTEEGCH/YOUNG INVENTOR. (Text in Mongolian) 1981. q. $1. Editorial Office for Mongolian Youth, P.O. Box 1053, Ulan Bator 210613, Mongolia. TEL 29651. Ed. S. Batmonh. adv.; bk.rev. circ. 21,000.

EARLY SCIENCE AND MEDICINE; a journal for the study of science, medicine and technology in the pre-modern period. see MEDICAL SCIENCES

500 US
EARTH CORPS: THE DAILY PLANET. 1971. bi-m. $25. Earthwatch Expeditions, Inc., 680 Mount Auburn St., P.O. Box 403, Watertown, MA 02272. TEL 617-926-8200. FAX 617-926-8532. Ed. Peter Tyson.

SCIENCES: COMPREHENSIVE WORKS

500 300 US ISSN 8750-0183
EARTHWATCH. 1980. 6/yr. $25 (foreign $35). Earthwatch Expeditions, Inc., 680 Mount Auburn St., Box 403N, Watertown, MA 02272. TEL 617-926-8200. FAX 617-926-8532. TELEX 5106006452. Ed. Mark Cherrington. illus. circ. 50,000. **Indexed:** Energy Rev., Environ.Per.Bibl. (1989-).
—CIS.
Description: Includes compendium of scientific research expeditions, feature stories on leading researchers, cultural heritage quesitons, and environmental and science-related topics.

EDUCATION IN SCIENCE. see EDUCATION

500.9 ER ISSN 0131-5862
EESTI LOODUS/ESTONIAN NATURE. (Text in Estonian; summaries in English) 1958. m. $58 (effective 1993). (Estonian Academy of Sciences) Kirjastus Perioodika, Parnu mnt. 8, 0090 Tallinn, Estonia. TEL 0142-441-262. FAX 0142-442-484. (Co-sponsor: Ministry of Environment) Ed. Ain Raitviir. bk.rev.; abstr.; charts; illus.; maps. circ. 5,000. **Indexed:** Biol.Abstr.

500 XO ISSN 0323-2778
ELEKTRON. 1973. m. $0.50. (Socialisticky Svaz Mladeze C.S.S.R. - Socialist Union of Youth) Smena Publishing House, Prazska 11, 812 84 Bratislava, Slovakia. TEL 406-06. Ed. Eduard Drobny. adv.; bk.rev. circ. 55,000.
●Also available online.

507 SW ISSN 0013-5933
Q4 CODEN: EMNTAE
ELEMENTA; matematik, fysik och kemi. (Text in Danish, Norwegian and Swedish) 1917. 5/yr. SEK 260 (typically set in Jan.). Stiftelsen Elementa, Stabby Alle 13, S-752 29 Uppsala, Sweden. TEL 018-512065. E-mail: gunnar.welin@astro.uu.se. Ed. Gunnar Welin. adv.; bk.rev.; film rev.; bibl.; illus.; stat.; index. circ. 1,700. **Indexed:** Chem.Abstr. **Document type:** academic/scholarly publication.
—CASDDS.
Formerly (until 1938): Tidskrift foer Elementaer Matematik, Fysik och Kemi.
Description: Presents history of science, study and teaching methods.

500 HU ISSN 0013-6077
ELET ES TUDOMANY. 1946. w. $82. (Tudomanyos Ismeretterjeszto Tarsulat) Hirlapkiado Vallalat, Blaha Lujza ter 3, 1959 Budapest 8, Hungary. TEL 1-382-399. TELEX 22-5554. (Subscr. to: Kultura, Box 149, H-1389 Budapest, Hungary) Ed. Andras Wolfner. circ. 30,000. **Indexed:** Hung.Build.Bull.

500 US ISSN 0013-6220
 CODEN: JEMSA5
ELISHA MITCHELL SCIENTIFIC SOCIETY. JOURNAL. 1883. q. $45. North Carolina Academy of Science, NCSSM, Box 2418, Durham, NC 27715. TEL 919-286-3366. Ed. Robert R. Bryden. bibl.; charts; illus.; index. circ. 800. (also avail. in microform from UMI; reprint service avail. from UMI) **Indexed:** Anim.Breed.Abstr., Biol.Abstr., Chem.Abstr., Curr.Adv.Ecol.Sci., Deep Sea Res.& Oceanogr.Abstr., Field Crop Abstr., GeoRef., Helminthol.Abstr., Herb.Abstr., Math.R., Ocean.Abstr., Rev.Plant Path., Soils & Fert., VITIS.
—BLDSC (4739.000000); CASDDS; Faxon; UMI; UnCover.
Description: Publishes papers in all scientific disciplines as related to North Carolina and the Southeast.

500 UA
EL-ELM/SCIENCES MONTHLY MAGAZINE. 1976. m. Dar al-Tahrir, 24 Sharia Zakaria Ahmed, Cairo, Egypt. TEL 02-741611. FAX 02-749949. TELEX 92475 TAHRIR UN. adv.; illus. circ. 25,000.

070.5 NE
ELSEVIER SCIENCE. CATALOGUE - BOOKS. (Supplement avail.: New and Forthcoming Publications) (Text in English) a. Elsevier Science B.V., P.O. Box 211, 1000 AE Amsterdam, Netherlands. TEL 31-20-4853911. FAX 31-20-4853598. TELEX 18582 ESPA NL. E-mail: nlinfo-f@elsevier.nl; usinfo-f@elsevier.com; forinfo-kyf04035@niftyserve.or.jp; Site addr.: http://www.elsevier.nl/. (Subscr. in U.S. and Canada to: Elsevier Science Inc., Box 882, Madison Sq. Sta., New York, NY 10159. TEL 212-989-5800. FAX 212-633-3990) **Document type:** catalog.
●Also available online.
Also available on CD-ROM.
Formerly (until 1994): Elsevier Science Publishers. Catalogue - Books.
Description: Complete listing of all Elsevier scientific books and book series published throughout the world, including the Excerpta Medica, North-Holland and Pergamon imprints.

070.5 NE
ELSEVIER SCIENCE. CATALOGUE - JOURNALS. (Supplement avail.: New and Forthcoming Publications) (Text in English) a. Elsevier Science B.V., P.O. Box 211, 1000 AE Amsterdam, Netherlands. TEL 31-20-4853911. FAX 31-20-4853598. TELEX 18582 ESPA NL. E-mail: nlinfo-f@elsevier.nl; usinfo-f@elsevier.com forinfo-kyf04035@niftyserve.or.jp; Site addr.: http://www.elsevier.nl/. (Subscr. in U.S. and Canada to: Elsevier Science Inc., Box 882, Madison Sq. Sta., New York, NY 10159. TEL 212-989-5800. FAX 212-633-3990) **Document type:** catalog.
●Also available online.
Also available on CD-ROM.
Formerly (until 1994): Elsevier Science Publishers. Catalogue - Journals.
Description: Complete listing, ordered by subject areas, of all scientific, technical and academic journals, newsletters and abstracting journals published worldwide under the Elsevier name, including the North-Holland, Pergamon and Excerpta Medica imprints, and affiliated publishing companies in 7 countries.

070.5 NE
ELSEVIER SCIENCE. CATALOGUE ON C D - R O M. (Text in English) 1993. a. Elsevier Science B.V., P.O. Box 211, 1000 AE Amsterdam, Netherlands. TEL 31-20-4853911. FAX 31-20-4853598. TELEX 18582 ESPA NL. E-mail: nlinfo-f@elsevier.nl; usinfo-f@elsevier.com; forinfo-kyf04035@niftyserve.or.jp; Site addr.: http://www.elsevier.nl/. (Subscr. in U.S. and Canada to: Elsevier Science Inc., Box 882, Madison Sq. Sta., New York, NY 10159. TEL 212-989-5800. FAX 212-633-3990) **Document type:** catalog.
●Available only on CD-ROM.
Formerly (until 1994): Elsevier Science Publishers. Catalogue on C D - R O M.
Description: Complete, fully searchable listing of all Elsevier scientific book and journal publications, including book series, software and other products. Provides complete descriptions and contents lists, independent reviews of published books, and forthcoming title information. Also lists journal editors and editorial boards, recently published papers, and coverage by abstracting services.

070.5 NE
ELSEVIER SCIENCE. DISPATCH LIST FOR JOURNALS, BOOK SERIES AND PROCEEDINGS. (Text in English) m. Elsevier Science B.V., P.O. Box 211, 1000 AE Amsterdam, Netherlands. TEL 31-20-4853911. FAX 31-20-4853598. TELEX 18582 ESPA NL. E-mail: nlinfo-f@elsevier.nl; usinfo-f@elsevier.com; forinfo-kyf04035@niftyserve.or.jp; Site addr.: http://www.elsevier.nl/. (Subscr. in U.S. and Canada to: Elsevier Science Inc., Box 882, Madison Sq. Sta., New York, NY 10159. TEL 212-989-5800. FAX 212-633-3990) **Document type:** catalog.
Formerly (until Nov. 1993): Elsevier Science Publishers. Dispatch List for Journals, Book Series and Proceedings.
Description: Provides news of most recent publications, including volume, number and date, for all Elsevier book series, journals, and proceedings worldwide.

070.5 NE
ELSEVIER SCIENCE. NEW AND FORTHCOMING PUBLICATIONS. (Supplement to: Elsevier Science Publishers. Catalogue) (Text in English) no.283, 1992. m. Elsevier Science B.V., P.O. Box 211, 1000 AE Amsterdam, Netherlands. TEL 31-20-4853911. FAX 31-20-4853598. TELEX 18582 ESPA NL. E-mail: nlinfo-f@elsevier.nl; usinfo-f@elsevier.com; forinfo-kyf04035@niftyserve.or.jp; Site addr.: http://www.elsevier.nl/. (Subscr. in U.S. and Canada to: Elsevier Science Inc., Box 882, Madison Sq. Sta., New York, NY 10159. TEL 212-989-5800. FAX 212-633-3990) **Document type:** catalog.
Former titles (until 1994): Elsevier Science Publishers. New and Forthcoming Publications; (until July 1993): Elsevier Science Publishers. New and Forthcoming Books and Journals; Supersedes: Pergamon New Publications Booklet.
Description: Contains all new and forthcoming book and journal publications worldwide from Elsevier and its imprints and affiliated companies in 7 countries, including Pergamon, Excerpta Medica and North-Holland.

949.4 US ISSN 0046-1865
DQ1
EMBASSY OF SWITZERLAND BULLETIN. (Text in English, French and German) 1960. 3/yr. free to qualified personnel. Embassy of Switzerland, Science and Technology Section, 2900 Cathedral Ave., N.W., Washington, DC 20008. TEL 202-745-7900. FAX 202-387-2564. Ed. Cheryl Fairi. adv.; bk.rev.; bibl.; circ. 2,500 (controlled). **Document type:** government publication, bulletin.
Description: Contains news articles from Swiss sources covering science and technology for swiss scientists and engineers working in North America.

500 060 US ISSN 0196-9110
Q11 CODEN: ENCYDI
ENCYCLIA. 1924. a. $12. Utah Academy of Sciences, Arts, and Letters, c/o Thomas F. Rogers, Ed., 4089A JKHB, Brigham Young University, Provo, UT 84602. TEL 801-378-3385. FAX 802-378-4649. circ. 1,000. **Indexed:** Arts & Hum.Cit.Ind., Chem.Abstr., Excerp.Bot., Field Crop Abstr., GeoRef., Herb.Abstr., Hort.Abstr., Lang.& Lang.Behav.Abstr., M.L.A., Math R., Rev.Plant Path., Sociol.Abstr., Sport Fish.Abstr., Wild.Rev., Zoo.Rec. **Document type:** proceedings.
—BLDSC (3738.556000); CASDDS.
Formerly (until vol.54, 1977): Utah Academy of Sciences, Arts, and Letters. Proceedings (ISSN 0083-4823)
Description: Resolutions, citations, titles, abstracts, and selected papers presented at the meeting of the Utah Academy.
Refereed Serial

500 530.4 621.366
030 US ISSN 0898-9842
Q123
ENCYCLOPEDIA OF PHYSICAL SCIENCE & TECHNOLOGY YEARBOOK. irreg. Academic Press, Inc., 525 B St., Ste. 1900, San Diego, CA 92101-4495. TEL 619-230-1840. FAX 619-699-6715. (Subscr. to: Order Dept., 6277 Sea Harbor Dr., 4th Fl., Orlando, FL 32887. TEL 800-321-5068)

500 FR ISSN 0396-4957
ENCYCLOPEDIE D'UTOVIE; revue mensuelle de science populaire. 1976. m. 30 F. Editions d' Utovie, Bats, 40320 Geaune, France. Dir. Jean-Marc Carite.

SCIENCES: COMPREHENSIVE WORKS

500 UK ISSN 0160-9327
Q1 CODEN: ENDEAS
ENDEAVOUR; a review of the progress of science and technology in the service of mankind. 1942; N.S. 1977. 4/yr. £97($145) (effective 1995). Elsevier Science Ltd., Pergamon, P.O. Box 800, Kidlington, Oxford OX5 1DX, England. TEL 44-1865-843000. FAX 44-1865-843010.
E-mail: nlinfo-f@elsevier.nl; usinfo-f@elsevier.com; forinfo-kyf04035@niftyserve.or.jp; Site addr.: http://www.elsevier.nl/. (Subscr. in U.S. and Canada to: Elsevier Science, 660 White Plains Rd., Tarrytown, NY 10591-5153. TEL 914-524-9200. FAX 914-333-2444) Ed. Trevor I. Williams. adv.; bk.rev.; charts; illus.; index, cum.index: 1942-1961 (in 2 vols.). circ. 10,000. (also avail. in microfiche from MIM; microfilm from UMI; back issues avail.) **Indexed:** Anim.Breed.Abstr., Appl.Mech.Rev., Art & Archaeol.Tech.Abstr., Biodet.Abstr., Biol.Abstr., Br.Tech.Ind., C.I.S. Abstr., Cadscan, Chem.Abstr., Curr.Adv.Ecol.Sci., Curr.Biotech.Abstr., Deep Sea Res.& Oceanogr.Abstr., Ecol.Abstr., Eng.Ind., Excerp.Med., Fuel & Energy Abstr., Gen.Sci.Ind., Geo.Abstr., Geol.Abstr., HRIS, Ind.Med., Ind.Sci.Rev., INSPEC (1977-), Lead Abstr., Met.Abstr., Meteor.& Geoastrophys.Abstr., Psychol.Abstr., RAPRA, Sci.Cit.Ind., Sport Fish.Abstr., Wild.Rev., Zincscan, Zoo.Rec. **Document type:** academic/scholarly publication.
—BLDSC (3740.000000); CASDDS; Ei; Faxon; Genuine Article; SWETS; UMI; UnCover. **CCC.**
Description: Publishes articles discussing current advances in science and technology, as well as examinations of issues in the history and philosophy of science of enduring interest to practicing scientists, engineers and general readers.
Refereed Serial

ENGINEERING & SCIENCE. see *ENGINEERING*

500.9 JA ISSN 0386-5037
ENSHU NO SHIZEN/NATURE OF ENSHU. (Text in Japanese) 1978. a. 1,000 Yen. Enshu Shizen Kenkyukai - Society for the Study of Nature, Enshu, c/o Mr. Hideo Toda, 895-3 Kanasashi, Inasa-cho, Shizuoka-ken 431-22, Japan.
Description: Contains original papers, reviews, and commentary.

500 600 NE ISSN 0165-0904
CODEN: episda
EPISTEME; a series in the foundational methodological, philosophical, psychological, sociological and political aspects of the sciences, pure and applied. (Text in English) 1975. irreg., vol.20, 1993. price varies. Kluwer Academic Publishers, Postbus 17, 3300 AA Dordrecht, Netherlands. TEL 31-78-392392. FAX 31-78-392254. TELEX 29245 KAPG NL. (Dist. by: Kluwer Academic Publishers Group, P.O. Box 322, 3300 AH Dordrecht, Netherlands. TEL 31-78-392392. FAX 31-78-546474; N. America dist. addr.: Box 358, Accord Sta., Hingham, MA 02018-0358. TEL 617-871-6600. FAX 617-871-6528) Ed. Mario Bunge. **Indexed:** Math.R. **Document type:** monographic series.
—BLDSC (3793.845000); CASDDS.
Refereed Serial

EPISTEMOLOGIA; an Italian journal for the philosophy of science. see *PHILOSOPHY*

500 US ISSN 1069-6490
EQUIPMENT AND MATERIALS UPDATE. m. $269 (Canada $309; elsewhere $339). Merton Allen Associates, InfoTeam Inc., Box 15640, Plantation, FL 33318-5640. TEL 305-473-9560.
FAX 305-473-0544. Ed. Walter Treff. **Document type:** newsletter.
—**CCC.**
Description: Covers all areas and subjects related to materials development and process equipment design, operation, maintenance, and integrity.

500 PL ISSN 0137-4990
ERGONOMIA. (Text in Polish; summaries in English) 1978. s-a. price varies. Polska Akademia Nauk, Komitet Ergonomii - Polish Academy of Sciences, Committee of Ergonomics, Ul. Sw. Jana 28, 31-018 Krakow, Poland. FAX 48-12-222791. (Dist. by: ORWN-PAN, Export Department, Palac Kultury i Nauki, 00-901 Warsaw, Poland) Ed. Andrzej Jozefik. bk.rev. **Indexed:** Ergon.Abstr. **Document type:** newsletter.
—BLDSC (3808.450000).

500 GW ISSN 0340-8833
ERNST-MACH-INSTITUT, FREIBURG. BERICHT. irreg. Ernst-Mach Institut, Eckerstr. 4, 79104 Freiburg, Germany.
Formerly: Ernst-Mach-Institut, Freiburg. Wissenschaftlicher Bericht (ISSN 0071-1217)

040 400 US ISSN 0361-5634
AS36
ESSAYS IN ARTS AND SCIENCES. 1971. a. $10 to individuals; libraries $8 (typically set in Oct.). University of New Haven, School of Arts and Sciences, West Haven, CT 06516.
TEL 203-932-7371. FAX 203-932-1469. Ed. David E. E. Sloane. adv.; bk.rev.; circ. 250 (paid). **Indexed:** Abstr.Engl.Stud., M.L.A., Mid.East: Abstr.& Ind. **Document type:** academic/scholarly publication.
—BLDSC (3811.675500); UnCover.
Description: Features scholarly articles in the arts and sciences.

500 SP ISSN 1133-5777
ESTRATOS. 1986. 4/yr. 600 ptas. Empresa Nacional de Residuos Radioactivos, Emilio Vargus 7, 28043 Madrid, Spain. TEL 1-402-92-42. Ed. Valentin Gonzalez. adv.; bk.rev. circ. 4,000.

500 PO ISSN 0870-001X
CODEN: EEDUDG
ESTUDOS ENSAIOS E DOCUMENTOS. 1950. irreg. price varies. Instituto de Investigacao Cientifica Tropical, Rua da Junqueira 30, 1300 Lisbon, Portugal. TEL 3622621. FAX 363-1460. (Subscr. to: Centro de Documentacao e Informacao, Rua Jua 47, 1300 Lisbon, Portugal) circ. 1,000. **Document type:** monographic series.
—BLDSC (3812.990000).

720 620 551 BL ISSN 0101-5303
CODEN: ESTTEM
ESTUDOS TECNOLOGICOS. (In three series: Geologia, Engenharia, Arquitetura) (Text in Portuguese; summaries in English) 1976. 5/yr. $24 for series; or exchange basis. (Universidade do Vale do Rio dos Sinos) Unisinos, Av. Unisinos, 950, 93022-000 Sao Leopoldo RS, Brazil. TEL 55-51-5920333 ext. 1951. FAX 55-51-5921035. bibl.; charts; illus. **Indexed:** Old Test.Abstr. **Document type:** academic/scholarly publication.

200 AU ISSN 1021-8122
ETHICA - WISSENSCHAFT UND VERANTWORTUNG. 1986. q. S.486. Resch Verlag, Maximilianstr. 8, A-6010 Innsbruck, Austria. TEL 0512-574772. FAX 0512-586463. Ed.Bd. circ. 700. **Document type:** academic/scholarly publication.
Formerly (until 1992): Impulse aus Wissenschaft und Forschung.

500 AG ISSN 0326-9442
ETICA & CIENCIA. (Text in English, Spanish) 1987. 2/yr. $4 per no. (effective 1995). Zagier & Urruty Publicaciones, P.O. Box 94, Sucursal 19, 1419 Buenos Aires, Argentina. TEL 541-572-1050. FAX 541-572-5766. (U.S. addr.: Box 526806, Miami, FL 33152-6806) Ed. Patricia Morales. circ. 1,500. (back issues avail.) **Document type:** academic/scholarly publication.
Description: Includes articles on scientific ethics and moral questions of scientists.

500 IR ISSN 1022-7822
ETTELA' RESANI. (Text in Persian) 1993. q. $30 or exchange basis. Iranian Information & Documentation Center (IRANDOC), 1188 Enqelab Ave., P.O. Box 13185-1371, Tehran, Iran. TEL 98-21-6462548. FAX 98-21-6462254. Ed. H. Gharibi. (back issues avail.) **Document type:** bulletin.
Description: Contains technical items and information.

500 IR
ETTELA'AT-E ELMI. (Text in Persian) 1987. m. IRl.6800 (N. America $95) (effective 1994). Ettela'at Publications, P.O. Box 11365-9365, Khayyam Ave., Tehran 11144, Iran. TEL 98-21-328516. FAX 98-21-3111223. TELEX 212336. Ed. Mrs. Sayyedeh Tahereh Ghassemi. adv. circ. 50,000. **Document type:** consumer publication.
Description: Covers developments and advances in all fields of science and technology, including relevant medical and health related issues.

500 US ISSN 0270-188X
CODEN: EISSDB
ETTORE MAJORANA INTERNATIONAL SCIENCE SERIES. PHYSICAL SCIENCES. 1979. irreg., vol.60, 1992. price varies. Plenum Publishing Corp., 233 Spring St., New York, NY 10013-1578.
TEL 212-620-8000. FAX 212-463-0742. TELEX 23-421139. Ed. Antonino Zichichi. (back issues avail.) **Document type:** proceedings.
—BLDSC (3816.506000); CASDDS. **CCC.**
Refereed Serial

ETUDES SCIENTIFIQUES. see *SOCIAL SCIENCES: COMPREHENSIVE WORKS*

500 600 US
EUROPE - LATIN AMERICA REPORT: SCIENCE AND TECHNOLOGY. irreg. (approx. 40/yr.). $7 per no. (foreign $14 per no.). U.S. Joint Publications Research Service, Box 12507, Arlington, VA 22209. TEL 703-487-4630. (Orders to: NTIS, Springfield, VA 22161)

500 600 UK
EUROPEAN RESEARCH CENTRES; a directory of organizations in science, technology, agriculture and medicine. triennial, 9th ed., 1992. £340. Longman Group UK Ltd., Westgate House, 6th Fl., The High, Harlow, Essex CM20 1YR, England.
TEL 0279-442601. FAX 0279-444501. (Dist. in U.S. & Canada by: Gale Research Inc., 835 Penobscot Bldg., Detroit, MI 48226) **Document type:** directory.

500 UK ISSN 1062-7987
AS9 CODEN: EURREK
EUROPEAN REVIEW. 1993. q. $295 (foreign $295) (effective 1996). (Academia Europaea) John Wiley & Sons Ltd., Journals, Baffins Ln., Chichester, W. Sussex PO19 1UD, England. TEL 01243-779777. FAX 01243-766128. TELEX 86290 WIBOOK G. (Subscr. in the Americas to: John Wiley & Sons, Inc., 605 Third Ave., New York, NY 10158. TEL 212-850-6645. FAX 212-850-6021) Ed. A. Burgen. circ. 213. (also avail. in microform from UMI; back issues avail.) **Indexed:** Geo.Abstr., Geol.Abstr. **Document type:** academic/scholarly publication.
—BLDSC (3829.935100).
Description: Promotes intra-European studies relating to society, education, and research from an interdisciplinary approach including the humanities, law, economics, social sciences, cognitive science, mathematics, medicine, natural sciences, and technological sciences.
Refereed Serial

500 600 UK
EUROPEAN SOURCES OF SCIENTIFIC AND TECHNICAL INFORMATION. triennial, 10th ed., 1992. £165. Longman Group UK Ltd., Westgate House, 6th Fl., The High, Harlow, Essex CM20 1YR, England.
TEL 0279-442601. FAX 0279-444501. (Dist. in U.S. & Canada by: Gale Research Inc., 835 Penobscot Bldg., Detroit, MI 48226) **Document type:** directory.

600 500 II ISSN 0531-495X
EVERYMAN'S SCIENCE. (Text in English) 1966. bi-m. Rs.36. Indian Science Congress Association, 14 Dr. Biresh Guha St., Calcutta 700017, India.
TEL 033-247-4530. FAX 033-402-511. circ. 100,000. **Indexed:** INIS Atomind.
Description: Contains popular science articles.

500 US
EXCITEMENT AND FASCINATION OF SCIENCE; reflections by eminent scientists. 1965. irreg., vol.4, 1995. price varies. Annual Reviews Inc., 4139 El Camino Way, Box 10139, Palo Alto, CA 94303-0139. TEL 415-493-4400; 800-523-8635.
FAX 415-855-9815. E-mail: annrevu@class.org. **Document type:** academic/scholarly publication.
Description: Publishes auto-biographical essays by prominent scientists.

EXPERIENTIA; interdisciplinary journal for life sciences. see *BIOLOGY*

EXPERIENTIA. SUPPLEMENTUM. see *BIOLOGY*

EXPLORATIONS IN KNOWLEDGE; an international journal in the philosophy of science. see *PHILOSOPHY*

SCIENCES: COMPREHENSIVE WORKS

500.9   US   ISSN 0014-5009
QH1   CODEN: EXPOAI
EXPLORER (CLEVELAND). 1938. q. membership or exchange basis. Cleveland Museum of Natural History, One Wade Oval Dr., University Circle, Cleveland, OH 44106. TEL 216-231-4600. Ed. Megan Harding. bk.rev.; charts; illus.; index. circ. 10,300. (talking book; back issues avail.) **Indexed:** Biol.Abstr., Biol.Dig., GeoRef.
—UnCover.
    Description: Addresses natural history, environmental, conservation and general science topics for members of natural history museums, science centers, and schools.

500 700 028.5   US
EXPLORING (SAN FRANCISCO). 1977. q. $18 to individuals; institutions, libraries $24; foreign $36. Exploratorium, 3601 Lyon St., San Francisco, CA 94123. TEL 415-561-0395. FAX 415-561-0307. E-mail: exploring@exploratorium.edu. Ed. Pat Murphy. adv. contact: Kurt Feichtmein. bk.rev. circ. 11,000. (back issues avail.) **Indexed:** Vert.File Ind. **Document type:** academic/scholarly publication.
    Former titles: Exploratorium Quarterly (ISSN 0889-8197); (until 1985): Exploratorium.
    Description: Magazine of science, art, and human perception reflecting the philosophy of the Exploratorium, a museum where people learn by doing.

500   US   ISSN 0092-9824
Q11
F A S PUBLIC INTEREST REPORT. 1946. bi-m. $25. Federation of American Scientists, 307 Massachusetts Ave., N.E., Washington, DC 20002. TEL 202-546-3300. FAX 202-675-1010. TELEX 9102509251 FAS DC UQ. E-mail: JSTONE@IGC.APC.ORG. circ. 4,000. **Indexed:** HR Rep.
—BLDSC (3896.527000).
    Formerly: F A S Newsletter.

500 058.81   DK   ISSN 0906-4370
FACTS & FAENOMENER. Variant title: Lexikon. 1991. m. DKK 38.50 per no. Bonniers Specialmagasiner A-S, Strandboulevarden 130, DK-2100 Copenhagen Oe, Denmark. TEL 45-39-29-55-00. FAX 45-39-29-01-99. TELEX 60211. Ed. Anker Tiedemann; Pub. Lars Engstroem. adv.: color page DKK 11500; 182 x 245. circ. 24,579. **Document type:** consumer publication.
    Formerly: Lexikon.

500   SW   ISSN 0014-8903
    CODEN: FUOFAA
FAUNA OCH FLORA. 1906. bi-m. SEK 185 in Sweden; other Scandinavian countries SEK 260; elsewhere SEK 315. Naturhistoriska Riksmuseet - Swedish Museum of Natural History, P.O. Box 50007, S-104 05 Stockholm, Sweden. TEL 46-8-666-40-14. FAX 46-8-666-40-85. E-mail: fauna-flora@nrm.se. Ed. Goeran Molin. adv.: B&W page SEK 4000. bk.rev.; charts; illus. circ. 7,000. **Indexed:** Biol.Abstr., Deep Sea Res.& Oceanogr.Abstr., GeoRef.
    Description: Articles on biology, zoology, botany, ecology, geology, astronomy, fossils, natural history and nature in general.

FERTILISER TECHNOLOGY. see *TECHNOLOGY: COMPREHENSIVE WORKS*

FEUILLETS DU NATURALISTE. see *CHILDREN AND YOUTH — For*

FIBEROPTIC PRODUCT NEWS. see *COMMUNICATIONS — Telephone And Telegraph*

FILOSOFI OG VIDENSKABSTEORI PAA ROSKILDE UNIVERSITETSCENTER. see *PHILOSOPHY*

FILOSOFSKIE NAUKI (MOSCOW). see *PHILOSOPHY*

500   UN   ISSN 1014-2800
FLORA, FAUNA Y AREAS SILVESTRES. 1986. q. Food and Agriculture Organization of the United Nations (Rome), Via delle Terme di Caracalla, 00100 Rome, Italy. TEL 57974350. FAX 57974608.

574.9489   DK   ISSN 0015-3818
    CODEN: FLFAAN
FLORA OG FAUNA. (Text in Danish; summaries in English) 1894. q. DKK 125($18) Naturhistorisk Forening for Jylland, Natural History Museum, DK-8000 Aarhus C, Denmark. TEL 45-89-42-27-58. FAX 45-86-12-51-75. Ed. Henrik A. Pedersen. bk.rev.; illus.; index. circ. 1,000. **Indexed:** Biol.Abstr., Deep Sea Res.& Oceanogr.Abstr., Zoo.Rec. **Document type:** academic/scholarly publication.
—BLDSC (3954.900000).
    Description: Original papers on taxonomy, distribution, biology, ecology and conservation of Danish plants and animals.
    Refereed Serial

500   US   ISSN 0098-4590
Q11   CODEN: FLSCAQ
FLORIDA SCIENTIST. 1936. q. $40 to libraries ($25 membership) (effective 1995). Florida Academy of Sciences, Inc., Box 33012, Indialantic, FL 32903-0012. TEL 407-723-6835. Eds. Dean F. and Barbara B. Martin. adv.; bk.rev.; charts; illus.; stat.; index. circ. 900. (also avail. in microform from UMI; back issues avail.; reprint service avail. from UMI) **Indexed:** Abstr.N.Amer.Geol., Biol.Abstr., Chem.Abstr., Deep Sea Res.& Oceanogr.Abstr., Excerp.Med., Geo.Abstr., GeoRef., Ocean.Abstr., Pollut.Abstr., Sel.Water Res.Abstr., Sport Fish.Abstr., Wild.Rev., Zoo.Rec. **Document type:** academic/scholarly publication.
—BLDSC (3956.130000); CASDDS; Faxon; UMI; UnCover.
    Formerly (until 1973): Florida Academy of Sciences. Quarterly Journal (ISSN 0015-3850)
    Description: Scientific and educational material in many categories of science for professionals, non-professionals, students and laypersons.
    Refereed Serial

500   US   ISSN 1043-4275
FLORIDA STATE UNIVERSITY RESEARCH IN REVIEW. 1969. q. free. Florida State University, Office of Graduate Studies and Research, 109 HMB R-23, Tallahassee, FL 32306. TEL 904-644-8634. Ed. Frank H. Stephenson. bk.rev.; charts; illus. circ. 9,500. **Indexed:** Ind.Free Per.
—UnCover.
    Formerly (until 1989): Florida State University Bulletin: Research in Review (ISSN 0885-2073)
    Refereed Serial

500   FR   ISSN 1154-2721
T57.85
FLUX. (Text in English or French; summaries in English, French) 4/yr. 430 F. (Europe 490 F., elsewhere 570 F.). Centre National de la Recherche Scientifique, Groupement de Recherche "Reseaux" C N R S Editions, 20-22 rue St. Amand, 75015 Paris. TEL 45-33-16-00. FAX 45-33-91-13. (also avail. in microfiche from DFR) **Document type:** government publication.
    Formerly (until 1989): Groupement de Recherch "Reseaux". Cahier (ISSN 1162-9630)

FOCUS ON SCIENCE EDUCATION. see *EDUCATION — Teaching Methods And Curriculum*

910   XR
FOLIA FACULTATIS SCIENTIARUM NATURALIUM UNIVERSITATIS MASARYKIANAE BRUNENSIS: GEOGRAPHIA. a. price varies. Masarykova Universita, Prirodovedecka Fakulta - Masaryk University, Faculty of Sciences, Kotlarska 2, 611 37 Brno, Czech Republic. **Document type:** monographic series.
    Formerly: Folia Facultatis Scientiarum Naturalium Universitatis Purkynianae Brunensis: Geographia (ISSN 0323-018X)

500 700 800   SP   ISSN 0015-5594
AS301
FOLIA HUMANISTICA; ciencias, artes, letras. (Monographic supplement avail.) 1963. 6/yr. 4800 ptas.($65) (effective 1995). Fundacion Letamendi Forns, Muntaner 303, 1o 2a, 08021 Barcelona, Spain. TEL 34-3-2094929. FAX 34-3-2018684. Ed. Fransisco Arasa. bk.rev. circ. 5,000. **Indexed:** Amer.Hist.& Life, Arts & Hum.Cit.Ind., Curr.Cont., Hist.Abstr., SSCI. **Document type:** academic/scholarly publication.
—BLDSC (3970.500000); Faxon; Genuine Article.
    Description: Interdisciplinary works by university professors.

500   GW   ISSN 0172-1518
Q180.G4
FORSCHUNG. 1983. q. DM.66($45) (effective 1996). (Deutsche Forschungsgemeinschaft) V C H Verlagsgesellschaft mbH, Postfach 101161, 69451 Weinheim, Germany. TEL 06201-606-147. FAX 06201-606117. TELEX 465516-VCHWH-D. (U.S. addr.: V C H Publishers Inc., 220 E. 23rd St., New York, NY 10010-4606. TEL 212-683-8333) Ed. E. Streier. adv. contact: R. Roth. bk.rev. circ. 15,000. (back issues avail.) **Indexed:** Lang.& Lang.Behav.Abstr. **Document type:** academic/scholarly publication.
—BLDSC (4008.993000). **CCC.**

500   GW   ISSN 0176-263X
FORSCHUNG AKTUELL; Wissenschaft fuer die Praxis. 1984. 3/yr. free. Technische Universitaet Berlin, Presse- und Informationsreferat, Str. des 17. Juni 135, 10623 Berlin, Germany. TEL 030-31423922. FAX 030-31423909. TELEX 184262-TUBLN-D. E-mail: pressestelle@tu-berlin.de. index. circ. 12,500. (back issues avail.) **Document type:** academic/scholarly publication.

500 378   GW   ISSN 0937-2873
FORSCHUNG AN DER UNIVERSITAET BIELEFELD. 1990. 2/yr. DM.10. Universitaet Bielefeld, Informations- und Pressestelle, Postfach 100131, 33501 Bielefeld, Germany. TEL 0521-1064146. FAX 0521-1062964. TELEX 932362-UNIBI. Ed. Veronika Reiss. adv. circ. 4,000. **Document type:** academic/scholarly publication.

500   GW   ISSN 0175-0992
FORSCHUNG FRANKFURT. 1984. q. DM.20. Johann Wolfgang Goethe-Universitaet, Senckenberganlage 31, 60054 Frankfurt a.M., Germany. TEL 069-79823266. FAX 069-79828530. Ed. Ulrike Jaspers. adv. circ. 5,000. (back issues avail.) **Document type:** academic/scholarly publication.

500   SW   ISSN 0015-7937
    CODEN: FSFMA6
FORSKNING OCH FRAMSTEG. 1966. 8/yr. SEK 373 (effective 1995). Stiftelsen Forskning och Framsteg, P.O. Box 1191, S-111 91 Stockholm, Sweden. FAX 46-8-21-81-89. E-mail: es@fof.se. Ed. Bjoern Fjaestad. charts; illus.; index. circ. 50,000. **Indexed:** NAA. **Document type:** consumer publication.
—CASDDS.
    Description: A general interest popular science magazine.

052   SA   ISSN 0015-8054
AS611   CODEN: FHPADE
FORT HARE PAPERS. (Text and summaries in English) 1945. irreg. R.5 per no. Fort Hare University Press, Private Bag X1314, Alice 5700, South Africa. TEL 27-404-22011. FAX 27-404-31255. TELEX 250863. Ed. M.J. Prins. charts; illus. circ. 200. (tabloid format) **Indexed:** A.I.C.P., Biol.Abstr., Chem.Abstr., Curr.Cont., Field Crop Abstr., Herb.Abstr., IDA, Ind.S.A.Per., M.L.A., Maize Abstr., Weed Abstr., World Agri.Econ.& Rural Sociol.Abstr. **Document type:** academic/scholarly publication.
—BLDSC (4014.845000); CASDDS; UMI.
    Description: Covers natural sciences, humanities, arts, education, and economics from a South African perspective.
    Refereed Serial

FORTEAN TIMES; the journal of strange phenomena. see *PARAPSYCHOLOGY AND OCCULTISM*

500 333.78 639.9   UK   ISSN 0309-7560
FORTH NATURALIST AND HISTORIAN SERIES. 1976. a. £5($15) Forth Naturalist and Historian Editorial Board, University of Stirling, Stirling FK9 4LA, Scotland. TEL 01259-215091.
FAX 01786-464994. TELEX 777557 SUNIV G. E-mail: dsm2@stirling.ac.uk. Ed. Lindsay Corbett. adv.; bk.rev.; cum.index (vols.1-5, 6-10); circ. 400 (paid). (back issues avail.) **Indexed:** Aqua.Sci.& Fish.Abstr., Biol.Abstr., Zoo.Rec. **Document type:** academic/scholarly publication.
—BLDSC (4017.700000).
    Description: Promotes research in the natural history, environment and heritage of central Scotland.

FORTHCOMING INTERNATIONAL SCIENTIFIC AND TECHNICAL CONFERENCES. see *MEETINGS AND CONGRESSES*

SCIENCES: COMPREHENSIVE WORKS

500 GW ISSN 0937-8316
FORUM (ESSEN). 1976. bi-m. free. Gemeinnuetzige Verwaltungsgesellschaft fuer Wissenschaftspflege mbH, Postfach 230360, 45071 Essen, Germany. TEL 0201-7221-0. FAX 0201-714968. Ed. Norbert Schuergers. circ. 7,000.

500 GW ISSN 0178-6563
FORUM WISSENSCHAFT; das kritische Wissenschaftsmagazine. 1984. q. DM.35 (foreign DM.40). Bund Demokratischer Wissenschaftlerinnen und Wissenschaftler e.V., Gisselbergerstr. 7, 35037 Marburg, Germany. TEL 06421-21395. FAX 06421-24654. adv.; bk.rev.; bibl.; illus. circ. 4,500. **Document type:** academic/scholarly publication.
  Description: Deals with science and research policy, and the social responsibility of scientists.

500 US
FOUNDATIONS FOR ORGANIZATIONAL SCIENCE SERIES. irreg., latest 1995. price varies. Sage Publications, Inc., 2455 Teller Rd., Thousand Oaks, CA 91320. TEL 805-499-0721. FAX 805-499-0871. (Orders outside N. America to: Sage Publications Ltd., 6 Bonhill St., London EC2A 4PU, England; or: Sage Publications India (Pvt.) Ltd., M-32 Greater Kailash Market-1, New Delhi 110 048, India) **Document type:** monographic series, academic/scholarly publication.

500 028.5 UK ISSN 0967-9928
THE FOUNTAIN; popular, educational and scientific magazine. 1993. q. £10($16) Truestar Ltd., 49 Mountfield Rd., Finchley, London N3 3NR, England. TEL 0181-343-3928. FAX 0181-346-8170. E-mail: fountain@truestar.demon.co.uk. Ed. Isa Sarac. adv. contact: S. Eyles. bk.rev. **Document type:** academic/scholarly publication.
  Description: Informs readers about current issues related to science and technology, history, and social and environmental issues.

FRANCIS BACON RESEARCH TRUST JOURNAL; studies in ancient wisdom. see PHILOSOPHY

500 CC ISSN 0427-7104
Q4 CODEN: FHPTAY
FUDAN XUEBAO (ZIRAN KEXUE BAN)/FUDAN JOURNAL (NATURAL SCIENCE EDITION). (Text in Chinese) 1955. bi-m. $4 per no. (Fudan Daxue - Fudan University) Shanghai Kexue Jishu Chubanshe - Shanghai Science and Technical Publishers, 450 Ruijin Rd., Shanghai 200020, People's Republic of China. TEL 5484906. (Dist. outside China by: China International Book Trading Corp., P.O. Box 2820, Beijing, P.R. China) Ed. Zhou Xiuling. **Indexed:** Chem.Abstr., INIS Atomind., INSPEC, Math.R. **Document type:** academic/scholarly publication.
  —BLDSC (4755.440000); CASDDS.

500 CC ISSN 1000-5277
Q4 CODEN: FSDKES
FUJIAN SHIFAN DAXUE XUEBAO. (ZIRAN KEXUE BAN)/FUJIAN NORMAL UNIVERSITY. JOURNAL (NATURAL SCIENCE EDITION). (Text in Chinese) 1985. q. Fujian Shifan Daxue, 137 Shangsan Lu, Cangshan Qu, Fuzhou, Fujian 350007, People's Republic of China. (Dist. overseas by: Jiangsu Publications Import & Export Corp., 56 Gao Yun Ling, Nanjing, Jiangsu, P.R.C.) **Document type:** academic/scholarly publication.
  —BLDSC (4755.512200); CASDDS.

500 JA ISSN 0071-9781
FUKUI DAIGAKU KYOIKUGAKUBU KIYO. DAI 2-BU. SHIZEN KAGAKU/FUKUI UNIVERSITY. FACULTY OF EDUCATION. MEMOIRS. SERIES 2: NATURAL SCIENCE. (Text and summaries in English and Japanese) 1961. a. free. Fukui University, Faculty of Education - Fukui Daigaku Kyoikugakubu, 9-1 Bunkyo, 3-chome, Fukui-shi, Fukui-ken 910, Japan. Ed. Terutsugu Ando. **Document type:** academic/scholarly publication.
  Description: Contains original papers.

510 JA ISSN 0532-811X
Q4 CODEN: FKDRAN
FUKUOKA KYOIKU DAIGAKU KIYO. DAI-3-BUNSATSU. SUGAKU, RIKA, GIJUTSUKA HEN/FUKUOKA UNIVERSITY OF EDUCATION. BULLETIN. PART 3: MATHEMATICS, NATURAL SCIENCES AND TECHNOLOGY. (Text in English and Japanese; summaries in English) 1951. a. Fukuoka University of Education - Fukuoka Kyoiku Daigaku, Akama, Munakata-shi, Fukuoka-ken 811-41, Japan. **Indexed:** Biol.Abstr., Chem.Abstr., INIS Atomind. **Document type:** academic/scholarly publication.
  —CASDDS.

500 JA ISSN 0387-0855
Q4 CODEN: FDKRA9
FUKUSHIMA DAIGAKU KYOIKUGAKUBU RONSHU. RIKA HOKOKU/FUKUSHIMA UNIVERSITY. FACULTY OF EDUCATION. SCIENCE REPORTS. (Text in English and Japanese; summaries in English) 1951. s-a. Fukushima University, Faculty of Education - Fukushima Daigaku Kyoikugakubu, 2 Sugumichi, Asakawa, Matsukawa-machi, Fukushima-shi, Fukushima-ken 960-12, Japan. Ed. Yosio Watanabe. **Indexed:** Chem.Abstr., INIS Atomind. **Document type:** academic/scholarly publication, bulletin.
  —BLDSC (8152.450000).

060 AG
FUNDACION BARILOCHE. MEMORIA ANUAL. a. Fundacion Bariloche, Casilla de Correo 138, San Carlos de Bariloche - Rio Negro, Argentina.

FUNDACION LA CAIXA. PANORAMA. see MUSEUMS AND ART GALLERIES

FUSION; Wissenschaft - Technik fuer das 21. Jahrhundert. see ENERGY

500 SZ
FUTURA; Ergebnisse der Forschungspolitischen Frueherkennung des Schweizerischen Wissenschaftsrates. (Text in English, French, German, Italian) 1989. 4/yr. 28 SFr. Schweizerischer Wissenschaftsrat, Inselgasse 1, CH-3003 Bern, Switzerland. FAX 031-3228070. **Document type:** government publication.
  Description: Findings of the early warning system within the science policy of the Swiss Science Council.

FUTURE SEX. see SINGLES' INTERESTS AND LIFESTYLES

500 016 US ISSN 8755-3317
CB158
FUTURES RESEARCH QUARTERLY. 1985. q. $90. World Future Society, 7910 Woodmont Ave., Ste. 450, Bethesda, MD 20814. TEL 301-656-8274. FAX 301-951-0394. bk.rev.; bibl. circ. 1,700. (also avail. in microform from UMI; back issues avail.) **Indexed:** C.I.J.E., Fut.Surv. **Document type:** academic/scholarly publication.
  —BLDSC (4060.653600); Faxon; SWETS; UMI; UnCover.
  Formerly (1967-1984): World Future Society Bulletin (ISSN 0049-8092)

500 US ISSN 0016-3317
CB158 CODEN: FUTUAC
THE FUTURIST; a journal of forecasts, trends, and ideas about the future. 1967. bi-m. $42. World Future Society, 7910 Woodmont Ave., Ste. 450, Bethesda, MD 20814. TEL 301-656-8274. Ed. Edward S. Cornish. adv.; bk.rev.; charts; illus.; cum.index: 1967-1975, 1976-1980, 1981-1983, 1984-1988, 1987-1991. circ. 30,000. (also avail. in microform from UMI; back issues avail.; reprint service avail. from UMI) **Indexed:** A.I.Abstr., ABI Inform., Acad.Ind., Bk.Rev.Ind. (1978-), BPIA, Bus.Ind., C.I.J.E., Child.Bk.Rev.Ind. (1978-), Comput.Bus., Curr.Cont., Educ.Admin.Abstr., Energy Info.Abstr., Energy Rev., Environ.Abstr., Environ.Per.Bibl., Fut.Surv., INIS Atomind., INSPEC, Int.Lab.Doc., Lang.& Lang.Behav.Abstr., Mag.Ind., Manage.Cont., Mid East: Abstr.& Ind., Oper.Res.Manage.Sci., Pers.Lit., PMR, Qual.Contr.Appl.Stat., R.G., Soc.Sci.Ind., SSCI, Telegen, Tr.& Indus.Ind.
  ●Also available online. Vendor(s): Knight-Ridder, Inc., University Microfilms International.
  —BLDSC (4060.700000); Faxon; Genuine Article; SWETS; UMI; UnCover. **CCC**.

500 IT ISSN 0390-217X
IL FUTURO DELL'UOMO. 1974. 2/yr. L.30000 (effective 1995 & 1996). Istituto Niels Stensen, Viale Don Minzoni 25-a, 50129 Florence, Italy. TEL 39-55-576551. (And: c/o Fabio Mantovani, Dpty. Ed., Casella Postale 8, 37024 Negrar (VR), Italy) Ed. Lorenzo del Zanna. adv. contact: Fabio Mantovani. bk.rev. circ. 500. (back issues avail.) **Document type:** academic/scholarly publication.

FUTUROLOGY. see TECHNOLOGY: COMPREHENSIVE WORKS

500 CC ISSN 1000-2243
CODEN: FDXKEN
FUZHOU DAXUE XUEBAO (ZIRAN KEXUE BAN)/FUZHOU UNIVERSITY. JOURNAL (NATURAL SCIENCE EDITION). (Text in Chinese) 1961. bi-m. Y12. Fuzhou Daxue - Fuzhou University, Gongye Lu, Fuzhou, Fujian 350002, People's Republic of China. TEL 710845. (Dist. overseas by: Chinese Publications Import and Export Corp., book and Journal Department, Journal Section, P.O. Box 782, Beijing 100011, P.R.C.) Ed. Qian Kuangwu. **Document type:** academic/scholarly publication.
  —CASDDS.
  Description: Covers mathematics, computer science, physics, electrical engineering, civil engineering, chemistry and other fields of science.

G S F MENSCH UND UMWELT. see ENVIRONMENTAL STUDIES

GAIA; oekologische Perspektiven in Natur-, Geistes- und Wirtschaftswissenschaften. see HUMANITIES: COMPREHENSIVE WORKS

500 JA ISSN 0387-2440
GAKUJUTSU GEPPO/JAPANESE SCIENTIFIC MONTHLY. (Text in Japanese; summaries in English) 1948. m. 800 Yen. Japan Society for the Promotion of Science - Nihon Gakujutsu Shikokai, 3-1 Koji-machi, 5-chome, Chiyoda-ku, Tokyo 102, Japan. abstr. **Indexed:** INIS Atomind., Jap.Per.Ind.
  —UnCover.
  Description: Contains reviews, commentary, and news.

500 YU ISSN 0350-123X
Q4
GALAKSIJA; casopis za popularizaciju nauke. 1972. m. $55. B I G Z, Bulevar vojvode Misica 17, Belgrade, Yugoslavia. Ed. Stanko Stojiljkovic. illus.

500 US
GENERAL SYSTEMS BULLETIN. 1956. 4/yr. $15 per no. International Society for the Systems Sciences, Box 6808, Louisville, KY 40206-0808. TEL 502-899-3332. FAX 502-899-3332. **Document type:** academic/scholarly publication, bulletin.

500 001.4 US ISSN 0072-0798
H9
GENERAL SYSTEMS YEARBOOK. 1956. a. $35 to non-members. International Society for the Systems Sciences, Box 6808, Louisville, KY 40206-0808. TEL 502-899-3332. FAX 502-899-3332. bk.rev. circ. 2,000. (back issues avail.) **Document type:** academic/scholarly publication.
  —SWETS.

500 GW ISSN 0945-3512
GEORG-AUGUST-UNIVERSITAET GOETTINGEN. SPEKTRUM. 1971. q. Georg-August-Universitaet Goettingen, Wilhelmsplatz 1, 37073 Goettingen, Germany. TEL 0551-394341. FAX 0551-394251. E-mail: hsuesse1@gwdgv1.dnet.gwdg.de. Ed. Frank Woesthoff. adv.; bk.rev. circ. 10,000. **Document type:** academic/scholarly publication.
  Formerly (until 1993): Georg-August-Universitaet Goettingen. Informationen.

SCIENCES: COMPREHENSIVE WORKS

500 US ISSN 0147-9369
Q11 CODEN: GJSCDQ
GEORGIA JOURNAL OF SCIENCE. 1943. q. $25 membership. Georgia Academy of Science, c/o Norris O'Dell, Ed., Medical College of Georgia, Augusta, GA 30912. TEL 706-731-2526. FAX 706-721-6276. adv.; abstr.; bibl.; charts; illus.; stat.; cum.index: 1943-1967. circ. 500. (also avail. in microform from UMI) **Indexed:** Biol.Abstr., Field Crop Abstr., Herb.Abstr., Ind.Vet., INIS Atomind., Soils & Fert., Sport Fish.Abstr., Vet.Bull., Wild.Rev., Zoo.Rec. **Document type:** academic/scholarly publication.
—CASDDS; Faxon; UMI; UnCover.
Formerly (until vol.34, no.4, Sep. 1976): Georgia Academy of Science. Bulletin (ISSN 0016-8114)
Refereed Serial

500 GW ISSN 0172-1526
GERMAN RESEARCH. (Text in English) 1983. 3/yr. DM.68($49) (effective 1996). (Deutsche Forschungsgemeinschaft) V C H Verlagsgesellschaft mbH, Postfach 101161, 69451 Weinheim, Germany. TEL 06201-606-147. FAX 06201-606117. TELEX 465516-VCHWH-D. (U.S. addr.: V C H Publishers Inc., 220 E. 23rd St., New York, NY 10010-4606. TEL 212-683-8333) adv. contact: R. Roth. circ. 8,000. **Document type:** academic/scholarly publication.
—UnCover. **CCC.**

500 007 GW ISSN 0072-1476
GERMAN RESEARCH SERVICE. (Text in English) 1962. m. DM.96. Deutscher Forschungsdienst, Ahrstr. 45, 53175 Bonn, Germany. TEL 0228-302210. FAX 0228-302270. Ed. Karl-Heinz Preuss. circ. 2,200. **Document type:** academic/scholarly publication.
—Faxon.

500.9 GW ISSN 0037-5942
GESELLSCHAFT NATURFORSCHENDER FREUNDE ZU BERLIN. SITZUNGSBERICHTE. NEUE FOLGE. 1961. a. price varies. Duncker und Humblot GmbH, Postfach 410329, 12113 Berlin, Germany. TEL 030-7900060. FAX 030-79000631. Ed. W. Sudhaus. **Document type:** proceedings.
—CCC.

GESNERUS; Swiss journal of the history of medicine and sciences. see *MEDICAL SCIENCES*

GETTING STARTED IN SCIENCE. see *CHILDREN AND YOUTH — For*

500 NE ISSN 0928-303X
GEWINA; tijdschrift voor de geschiedenis der geneeskunde, natuurwetenschappen, wiskunde en techniek. 1978. 4/yr. fl.95 to non-members; members fl.50. Erasmus Publishing B.V., Mathenesserlaan 332, 3021 HZ Rotterdam, Netherlands. TEL 31-10-4777277. FAX 31-10-4779580. Ed.Bd. adv.; bk.rev. circ. 1,000. **Document type:** academic/scholarly publication.
Former titles (until 1992): Tijdschrift voor de Geschiedenis der Geneeskunde, Natuurwetenschappen, Wiskunde en Techniek (ISSN 0167-2088); (until 1978): GeWina (Leiden) (ISSN 0928-382X)
Description: Covers the history of mathematics, physics, engineering, medical and other sciences.

500 GH ISSN 0016-9544
Q1 CODEN: GHJSAC
GHANA JOURNAL OF SCIENCE. 1961. s-a. 15 s. per no. ($.60). (Council for Scientific and Industrial Research) National Science and Technology Press, Box M.32, Accra, Ghana. TEL 233-21-777651. FAX 223-21-777355. (Alt. addr.: Ghana Science Association, Box 7, Legon, Ghana) (Co-sponsor: Ghana Science Association) Ed. Dr. A.K. Ahafia. adv.; bk.rev.; charts; illus.; maps. circ. 1,000. (also avail. in microfilm from UMI) **Indexed:** Biol.Abstr., Chem.Abstr., INIS Atomind. **Document type:** academic/scholarly publication.
—CASDDS.
Description: Publishes papers of a scientific and technical nature from Ghana and elsewhere.
Refereed Serial

500 GH
GHANA UNIVERSITY PRESS. INAUGURAL LECTURE SERIES. irreg. Ghana University Press, Legon, Nr. Accra, Ghana. (Dist. outside Africa by: African Books Collective Ltd., The Jam Factory, 27 Park End St., Oxford OX1 1HU, England. TEL 0865-726686. FAX 0865-793298) **Document type:** monographic series.

500 JA ISSN 0533-9529
Q4 CODEN: GDGKAD
GIFU DAIGAKU KYOIKUGAKUBU KENKYU HOKOKU. SHIZEN KAGAKU/GIFU UNIVERSITY. FACULTY OF EDUCATION. SCIENCE REPORT. NATURAL SCIENCE. (Text in Japanese and English; summaries in English) 1953. a. Gifu University, Faculty of Education - Gifu Daigaku Kyoikugakubu, 1-1 Yanagido, Gifu-shi, Gifu-ken 501-11, Japan. **Indexed:** Chem.Abstr., Jap.Per.Ind. **Document type:** academic/scholarly publication.

500 JA ISSN 0388-550X
GIFU-KEN HAKUBUTSUKAN CHOSA KENKYU HOKOKU/GIFU PREFECTURAL MUSEUM. BULLETIN. (Text and summaries in Japanese and English) 1980. a. free. Gifu Prefectural Museum - Gifu-ken Hakubutsukan, Hakunen Koen, Oyana, Seki-shi, Gifu-ken 501-32, Japan. TEL 0575-28-3111. FAX 0575-28-3110. **Document type:** bulletin.
Description: Contains research reports from the museum.

GLASGOW NATURALIST. see *BIOLOGY*

500 600 US ISSN 0886-6236
QH344 CODEN: GBCYEP
GLOBAL BIOGEOCHEMICAL CYCLES. 1987. q. $250 to non-members (foreign $260); members $56 (foreign $66); students $25 (foreign $35). American Geophysical Union, 2000 Florida Ave., N.W., Washington, DC 20009. TEL 202-462-6900. FAX 202-328-0566. TELEX 710-822-9300. Ed. Karl K. Turekian. (also avail. in microform from AGU) **Indexed:** Ecol.Abstr., Geo.Abstr., Geol.Abstr., Meteor.& Geoastrophys.Abstr., Sel.Water Res.Abstr. **Document type:** academic/scholarly publication.
—BLDSC (4195.352000); CASDDS; Faxon; Genuine Article; SWETS; UnCover. **CCC.**
Description: Publishes papers in the broad areas of global change involving the geosphere and biosphere. Previews marine, hydrologic, atmospheric, extraterrestrial, geologic, biologic, and human causes of and response to environmental change on time scales of tens, thousands, and millions of years.
Refereed Serial

500 NR ISSN 0795-6770
GLOBAL SCIENCE JOURNAL; an international journal of science. (Text and summaries in English) 1988. m. Global Science Union, P.O. Box 10123, Ugbowo, Benin City, Nigeria. Ed. O.S.A. Aromose.

500 BL
GLOBO CIENCIA. m. Editora Globo S.A., Rua do Curtume 665, 05065-001 Sao Paulo SP, Brazil. TEL 55-11-8746000. FAX 55-11-8612042. adv.; illus.; circ. 147,092 (paid). **Document type:** consumer publication.
Description: Covers technology, research, environment, health and culture. Includes informatics, genetics, and energy.

500 300 GW
GLOBULUS. 1993. a. DM.19.80. (Natur- und Kulturwissenschaftliche Gesellschaft) Polygon Verlag, Am Aschweg 57, 85114 Buxheim, Germany. TEL 08458-8281. FAX 08458-4746. Ed. Karl Roettel. circ. 500 (paid). (back issues avail.) **Document type:** academic/scholarly publication.
Refereed Serial

500 JA ISSN 0385-7433
GOCHO/OKOCHI MEMORIAL FOUNDATION. JOURNAL. (Text in Japanese) irreg. 600 Yen. Okochi Kinenkai - Okochi Memorial Foundation, 17-1 Toranomon 1-chome, Minato-ku, Tokyo 105, Japan.
Description: Contains reviews, commentary, and news of the foundation.

500 SW ISSN 0348-6788
GOTHENBURG STUDIES IN THE HISTORY OF SCIENCE AND IDEAS. (Subseries of Acta Universitatis Gothoburgensis) 1979. irreg., vol.12, 1991. price varies; also exchange basis. Acta Universitatis Gothoburgensis, P.O. Box 5096, S-402 22 Goeteborg, Sweden. Ed. Sven-Eric Liedman. **Document type:** monographic series.

500 II ISSN 0970-6925
GRAM SHILP. Key Title: Grama Silpa. (Text in Hindi) 1980. q. Rs.3. National Research Development Corporation, 20-22 Zamroopur Community Centre, Kailash Colony Extension, New Delhi 110 048, India. TEL 11-6418615. TELEX 031-71358. Ed. D.N. Bhatnagar. adv.; bk.rev.; abstr.; charts; illus. circ. 3,000.
Description: Concerns technology.

500 600 US
GRANTS FOR SCIENCE AND TECHNOLOGY PROGRAMS. (Subseries of: Grant Guides) a. $70 (effective Oct. 1994). Foundation Center, 79 Fifth Ave., New York, NY 10003. TEL 212-620-4230.
Description: Lists grants of $10,000 or more, given to educational and research institutions, scientific societies, associations and institutes, science museums, planetariums and libraries.

500 100 200 GW ISSN 0933-5366
GRENZFRAGEN. 1972. irreg., vol.7, 1978. (Goerres-Gesellschaft) Karl Alber GmbH, Hermann Herder Str. 4, 79104 Freiburg, Germany. Ed. Norbert A. Luyten. **Document type:** monographic series.
Supersedes (1957-1970): Naturwissenschaft und Theologie (ISSN 0547-9762)

500 AU ISSN 1021-8130
GRENZGEBIETE DER WISSENSCHAFT. 1951. q. S.450. Resch Verlag, Maximilianstr. 8, A-6010 Innsbruck, Austria. TEL 0512-574772. FAX 0512-586463. Ed. Andreas Resch. adv.; bk.rev. circ. 700. **Document type:** academic/scholarly publication.

500 GW
GRUNDLAGEN DER EXAKTEN NATURWISSENSCHAFTEN. (Text in English, German) 1980. irreg., vol.9, 1994. DM.48. Bibliographisches Institut und F.A. Brockhaus AG, Dudenstr. 6, Postfach 100311, 68003 Mannheim, Germany. TEL 0621-3901-01. FAX 0621-3901-389. Ed. Peter Mittelstaedt. **Document type:** academic/scholarly publication.

GRUNDLAGEN UND PERSPEKTIVEN FUER BILDUNG UND WISSENSCHAFT. BERUFSBILDUNGSBERICHT. see *EDUCATION*

GRUNDLAGENSTUDIEN AUS KYBERNETIK UND GEISTESWISSENSCHAFT; Humankybernetik. see *COMPUTERS — Cybernetics*

GUANGDONG MINZU XUEYUAN XUEBAO/GUANGDONG INSTITUTE OF NATIONALITIES. JOURNAL. see *SOCIAL SCIENCES: COMPREHENSIVE WORKS*

500 II
GUJARAT RESEARCH SOCIETY. JOURNAL. (Text in English, Gujarati) 1939. q. Rs.25. Gujarat Research Society, Samshodhan Sadan, Ramkrishna Mission Rd., Khar (West), Bombay 400 052, India. Ed. Dr. M.R. Shah. adv.; bk.rev. circ. 400. **Indexed:** Biol.Abstr.

500.9 JA ISSN 0017-5668
Q4 CODEN: GDSHAU
GUNMA DAIGAKU KYOIKUGAKUBU KIYO. SHIZEN KAGAKU HEN/GUNMA UNIVERSITY. FACULTY OF EDUCATION. SCIENCE REPORTS. (Text in English and Japanese; summaries in English) 1950. a. exchange basis. Gunma University, Faculty of Education - Gunma Daigaku Kyoikugakubu, Library, 4-2 Aramaki-cho, Maebashi-shi, Gunma-ken 371, Japan. Ed.Bd. **Indexed:** Biol.Abstr., Chem.Abstr., Jap.Per.Ind.
—BLDSC (8152.470000).

500 600 CC
GUOJI KEJI JIAOLIU/INTERNATIONAL SCIENCE AND TECHNOLOGY EXCHANGE. (Text in Chinese) m. Zhongguo Kexue Jishu Qingbao Yanjiusuo - Chinese Institute of Science and Technology Information, 15 Fuxing Lu, Beijing 100038, People's Republic of China. TEL 8015544. Ed. Hu Quanming.

500 600 CC ISSN 1002-7092
GUOWAI KEJI DONGTAI/FOREIGN SCIENCE AND TECHNOLOGY DEVELOPMENT. (Text in Chinese) 1962. m. Zhongguo Kexue Jishu Qingbao Yanjiusuo - Chinese Institute of Science and Technology Information, 15 Fuxing Lu, Beijing 100038, People's Republic of China. TEL 8015544. Ed. Bai Yiran.

SCIENCES: COMPREHENSIVE WORKS

500   GY
GUYANA SCIENCE TEACHERS' ASSOCIATION. NEWSLETTER. 3/yr. membership. Guyana Science Teachers' Association, c/o Honorary Secretary, Mr. B.N. Kumar, Unity Village, East Coast Demerara, Guyana.

500   UK   ISSN 0017-5897
Y GWYDDONYDD. (Text in Welsh) 1965. a. £2. University of Wales Press, 6 Gwennyth St., Cathays, Cardiff CF2 4YD, Wales. TEL 01222-231919. FAX 01222-230908. Ed. Iolo Gwynn. illus. circ. 250. **Document type:** academic/scholarly publication.
    Description: Contains science articles for the general reader.

500.9   UK   ISSN 0028-9043
HABITAT (LONDON). 1959. 10/yr. £13.50 (foreign £17.50). Environment Council, 21 Elizabeth St., London SW1W 9RP, England. TEL 071-824-8411. FAX 071-730-9941. Ed. S.M. Joy. adv.; bk.rev. circ. 3,200. **Indexed:** AESIS, Avery Ind.Archit.Per., Excerp.Med., Mid.East: Abstr.& Ind. **Document type:** academic/scholarly publication.
—BLDSC (4237.350000).
    Formerly: News for Naturalists.
    Description: Contains short articles on a variety of environmental topics, including wildlife protection, habitat encroachment, environmental policy, and ecological research.

510 620   TU   ISSN 0379-5918
                 CODEN: HBNSAZ
HACETTEPE BULLETIN OF NATURAL SCIENCES AND ENGINEERING. (Series A: Biology; Series B: Mathematics and Statistics; Series C: Chemistry, Physics, and Engineering) (Text in English, summaries in Turkish) 1972. a. TL.20000($10) Hacettepe Universitesi, Fen Fakultesi - Hacettepe University, Faculty of Science, 06532 Beytepe, Ankara, Turkey. FAX 90-4-2352531. Ed. Hulya Cingi. adv.; bk.rev. **Indexed:** Zoo.Rec. **Document type:** academic/scholarly publication.
—BLDSC (4237.436000); CASDDS.
    Description: Publishes short to medium length original research papers.
    Refereed Serial

HACETTEPE FEN VE MUHENDISLIK BILIMLERI DERGISI. SERI A: BIYOLOJI/HACETTEPE BULLETIN OF NATURAL SCIENCES AND ENGINEERING. SERIES A: BIOLOGY. see *BIOLOGY*

HACETTEPE FEN VE MUHENDISLIK BILIMLERI DERGISI. SERI B: MATEMATIK VE ISTATISTIK/HACETTEPE BULLETIN OF NATURAL SCIENCES AND ENGINEERING. SERIES B: MATHEMATICS AND STATISTICS. see *MATHEMATICS*

530 540   TU   ISSN 1300-4271
HACETTEPE FEN VE MUHENDISLIK BILIMLERI DERGISI. SERI C: KIMYA, FIZIK VE MUHENDISLIK/HACETTEPE BULLETIN OF NATURAL SCIENCES AND ENGINEERING. SERIES C: CHEMISTRY, PHYSICS AND ENGINEERING. (Text in English, Turkish) 1971. a. Hacetteppe Universitesi, Fen Fakultesi, 06532 Beytepe, Ankara, Turkey. TEL 90-212-2352531. Ed. Hulya Cingi. **Document type:** academic/scholarly publication.

500   JA   ISSN 0289-4092
HAKUBUTSUKAN DAYORI/SAITO HO-ON KAI MUSEUM OF NATURAL HISTORY. NEWS. (Text in Japanese) 1981. q. free. Saito Ho-on Kai - Saito Gratitude Foundation, 20-2, Hon-cho 2-chome, Aoba-ku, Sendai 980, Japan. TEL 022-262-5506. FAX 22-262-5508. Ed. Sadako Takeuti. **Document type:** newsletter.

500   GW   ISSN 0072-9566
HD72
HAMBURGER JAHRBUCH FUER WIRTSCHAFTS- UND GESELLSCHAFTSPOLITIK. 1956. a. price varies. (HWWA-Institut fuer Wirtschaftsforschung Hamburg) Verlag J.C.B. Mohr (Paul Siebeck), Wilhelmstr. 18, 72074 Tuebingen, Germany. TEL 07071-923-0. FAX 07071-51104. TELEX 7262872-MOHR-D. Ed.Bd. **Document type:** bulletin.
    Description: Studies the political, economic and social dilemmas created by new scientific developments.

HANDBUCH DER DATENBANKEN FUER NATURWISSENSCHAFT, TECHNIK, PATENTE. see *COMPUTERS — Data Base Management*

500   CC   ISSN 0253-3618
Q4   CODEN: HHHPD7
HANGZHOU DAXUE XUEBAO (ZIRAN KEXUE BAN)/HANGZHOU UNIVERSITY. JOURNAL (NATURAL SCIENCE EDITION). (Text in Chinese) 1956. q. $1.50 per no. Hangzhou Daxue - Hangzhou University, 34 Tianmushan Lu, Hangzhou, Zhejiang 310028, People's Republic of China. (Dist. by: Guoji Shudian - China International Book Trading Corporation, P.O. Box 399, Beijing, P.R.C.) circ. 2,000. **Indexed:** Chem.Abstr., Curr.Adv.Ecol.Sci., Math.R. **Document type:** academic/scholarly publication.
● Also available online. Vendor(s): Knight-Ridder, Inc.
—BLDSC (4757.876000); CASDDS.

500   CC   ISSN 1000-5897
                 CODEN: HKJXET
HARBIN KEXUE JISHU DAXUE XUEBAO/HARBIN UNIVERSITY OF SCIENCE AND TECHNOLOGY. JOURNAL. (Text in Chinese) q. Harbin Kexue Jishu Daxue, Xuebao Bianjibu, 22, Xuefu Lu, Nangang-qu, Harbin, Heilongjiang 150080, People's Republic of China. TEL 61081. Ed. Ren Shanzhi. **Document type:** academic/scholarly publication.
—CASDDS.

500   CC   ISSN 1000-5617
HARBIN SHIFAN DAXUE ZIRAN KEXUE XUEBAO/HARBIN NORMAL UNIVERSITY. JOURNAL OF NATURAL SCIENCES. (Text in Chinese) q. Harbin Shifan Daxue, Xuebao Bianjibu, 24, Hexing Lu, Nangang-qu, Harbin, Heilongjiang 150080, People's Republic of China. TEL 62912. Ed. Han Junjie. **Document type:** academic/scholarly publication.

HARWELL INFORMATION BULLETIN. see *BIBLIOGRAPHIES*

THE HASTINGS & EAST SUSSEX NATURALIST. see *CONSERVATION*

500   US
HAWKHILL SCIENCE NEWSLETTER; a newsletter of scientific literacy. irreg. (3-7/yr.). Hawkhill Science Associates, Inc., 125 E. Gilman St., Box 1029, Madison, WI 53701-1029. TEL 800-422-4295. Ed. Bill Stonebarger. **Document type:** newsletter, consumer publication.
    Description: Explores the philosophic and social aspects of a variety of scientific issues, many of them controversial, and presents them to the general reader. Informs teachers in the sciences where they can obtain free or low-cost materials.

500   CC   ISSN 1000-1565
                 CODEN: HDXKEB
HEBEI DAXUE XUEBAO (ZIRAN KEXUE BAN)/HEBEI UNIVERSITY. JOURNAL (NATURAL SCIENCES). (Text in Chinese) 1975. q. Y12 (foreign $12). Hebei Daxue - Hebei University, No. 1 Hezuolu Rd., Baoding, Hebei 071002, People's Republic of China. TEL 0312-5022929. FAX 0312-5022648. Ed.Bd. **Document type:** academic/scholarly publication.
—CASDDS.

500   CC   ISSN 1000-5854
                 CODEN: HSDKEG
HEBEI SHIFAN DAXUE XUEBAO (ZIRAN KEXUE BAN)/HEBEI NORMAL UNIVERSITY. JOURNAL (NATURAL SCIENCE EDITION). (Text in Chinese) q. Hebei Shifan Daxue - Hebei Normal University, Yuhua Lu, Shijiazhuang, Hebei 050016, People's Republic of China. TEL 49941. Ed. Jin Shixun. **Document type:** academic/scholarly publication.
—CASDDS.

500   US   ISSN 0073-1595
                 CODEN: HSCLAA
HEIDELBERG SCIENCE LIBRARY. 1967. irreg.; unnumbered after vol.22. price varies. Springer-Verlag, 175 Fifth Ave., New York, NY 10010. TEL 212-460-1500. FAX 212-473-6272. (Also: Berlin, Heidelberg, Tokyo and Vienna) (reprint service avail. from ISI) **Indexed:** Biol.Abstr. **Document type:** academic/scholarly publication.

500   US   ISSN 0371-0165
AS182   CODEN: SHWMAL
HEIDELBERGER AKADEMIE DER WISSENSCHAFTEN. MATHEMATISCH - NATURWISSENSCHAFTLICHE KLASSE. SITZUNGSBERICHTE. 1948. irreg. price varies. Springer-Verlag, 175 Fifth Ave., New York, NY 10010. TEL 212-460-1500. FAX 212-473-6272. (Also: Berlin, Heidelberg, Tokyo and Vienna) (reprint service avail. from ISI) **Indexed:** Nutr.Abstr. **Document type:** academic/scholarly publication.
—BLDSC (8288.500000); CASDDS.

500   US   ISSN 0073-1633
HEIDELBERGER ARBEITSBUECHER. 1971. irreg. price varies. Springer-Verlag, 175 Fifth Ave., New York, NY 10010. TEL 212-460-1500. FAX 212-473-6272. (Also: Berlin, Heidelberg, Tokyo and Vienna) (reprint service avail. from ISI) **Document type:** monographic series.

500   US   ISSN 0073-1641
AS181   CODEN: HDJBAC
HEIDELBERGER JAHRBUECHER. 1957. a. price varies. (Universitaets-Gesellschaft Heidelberg, GW) Springer-Verlag, 175 Fifth Ave., New York, NY 10010. TEL 212-460-1500. FAX 212-473-6292. (Also: Berlin, Heidelberg, Tokyo and Vienna) Ed. H. Schipperges. (reprint service avail. from ISI) **Indexed:** Amer.Hist.& Life, Biol.Abstr., Hist.Abstr. **Document type:** monographic series.
—CCC.

500   GW   ISSN 0935-6576
HEIDELBERGER STUDIEN ZUR NATURKUNDE DER FRUEHEN NEUZEIT. irreg., vol.4, 1994. price varies. Franz Steiner Verlag Wiesbaden GmbH, Birkenwaldstr. 44, 70191 Stuttgart, Germany. TEL 0711-2582-0. FAX 0711-2582390. (Subscr. to: Postfach 101061, 70009 Stuttgart, Germany) Eds. Wolf-Dieter Mueller-Jahncke, Joachim Telle. **Document type:** monographic series.

500   US   ISSN 0073-1684
                 CODEN: HDTSAB
HEIDELBERGER TASCHENBUECHER. 1964. irreg. price varies. Springer-Verlag, 175 Fifth Ave., New York, NY 10010. TEL 212-460-1500. FAX 212-473-6272. (Also: Berlin, Heidelberg, Tokyo and Vienna) (reprint service avail. from ISI) **Indexed:** Biol.Abstr. **Document type:** monographic series.

500   CC   ISSN 1001-7011
HEILONGJIANG DAXUE ZIRAN KEXUE XUEBAO/HEILONGJIANG UNIVERSITY. JOURNAL OF NATURAL SCIENCES. (Text in Chinese) q. Heilongjiang Daxue, Xuebao Bianjibu, Xuefu Lu, Nangang-qu, Harbin, Heilongjiang 150083, People's Republic of China. TEL 64941. **Document type:** academic/scholarly publication.

500   CC   ISSN 1000-2472
                 CODEN: HDAXE3
HENAN DAXUE XUEBAO (ZIRAN KEXUE BAN)/HENAN UNIVERSITY. JOURNAL (NATURAL SCIENCE EDITION). (Text in Chinese) 1989. q. $40. Henan Daxue, Xuebao Bianjibu, Kaifeng, Henan 475001, People's Republic of China. TEL 0378-5950394. Ed. Si Ximing. bk.rev. circ. 1,500. **Document type:** academic/scholarly publication.
—CASDDS; Ei.
    Description: Covers geography, mathematics, physics, chemistry and biology.

500   CC   ISSN 1000-2367
                 CODEN: HESKER
HENAN SHIFAN DAXUE XUEBAO (ZIRAN KEXUE BAN)/HENAN NORMAL UNIVERSITY. JOURNAL (NATURAL SCIENCE EDITION). (Text in Chinese) 1960. q. $7.20. Henan Shifan Daxue, Xuebao Bianjibu, Xinxiang, Henan 453002, People's Republic of China. TEL 0373-3054921. Ed. Ding Chengjie. **Document type:** academic/scholarly publication.

341   NE
HENRY DUNANT INSTITUTE. SCIENTIFIC COLLECTION. 1970. irreg. (approx a.). (Henry Dunant Institute) Kluwer Academic Publishers, Postbus 17, 3300 AA Dordrecht, Netherlands. TEL 31-78-392392. FAX 31-78-392254. TELEX 29245 KAPG NL. (Dist. by: Kluwer Academic Publishers Group, P.O. Box 322, 3300 AH Dordrecht, Netherlands. TEL 31-78-392392. FAX 31-78-546474; N. America dist. addr.: Box 358, Accord Sta., Hingham, MA 02018-0358. TEL 617-871-6600. FAX 617-871-6528) (Affiliate: International Red Cross)

SCIENCES: COMPREHENSIVE WORKS

500.9 GW ISSN 0018-0637
CODEN: HERCAS
HERCYNIA;* Beitraege zur Erforschung und Pflege der Natuerlichen Ressourcen. N.S. 1963. 4/yr. DM.60 per no. Martin-Luther-Universitaet Halle-Wittenberg, Mathematisch-Naturwissenschaftliche Fakultaet, Institut fuer Zoologie, PF Universitaet, 06099 Halle, Germany. TEL 0345-2028182.
FAX 0345-2029515. Ed. D. Heideckei. bk.rev.; bibl.; charts; illus.; maps. Indexed: Agri.Eng.Abstr., Biol.Abstr., Chem.Abstr., Excerp.Med., Forest.Abstr., Herb.Abstr., Irr.& Drain.Abstr., Key Word Ind.Wildl.Res., Maize Abstr., Triticale Abstr., Weed Abstr.
—BLDSC (4298.310000); CASDDS.
Description: Covers biosciences, geography, plant life, and ecology.

500.9 JA ISSN 0389-5491
HIBA KAGAKU/HIBA SOCIETY OF NATURAL HISTORY. JOURNAL. (Text in Japanese) 1947. 3/yr. $30. Hiba Science Educational Foundation - Hiba Kagaku Kyoiku Shinkokai, 1-1-7 Nishihon-machi, Shobara-shi, Hiroshima-ken 727, Japan.
TEL 08247-2-3234. adv.; bk.rev. **Document type:** bulletin.
Description: Contains original articles as well as reviews and commentary.

500 JA ISSN 0917-0502
Q179.9
HIMEIJI KOGYO DAIGAKU RIGAKUBU KENKYU HOKOKU/HIMEIJI INSTITUTE OF TECHNOLOGY. FACULTY OF SCIENCE. REPORTS. (Text in English, Japanese) 1990. a. Himeji Kogyo Daigaku, Rigakubu, 2167 Shosha, Himeji-shi, Japan.

500 JA ISSN 0367-6439
Q4 CODEN: HUSRAK
HIROSAKI UNIVERSITY. FACULTY OF SCIENCE. SCIENCE REPORTS/HIROSAKI DAIGAKU RIKA HOKOKU. (Text in English, Japanese) 1954. 2/yr. free. Hirosaki Daigaku, Rigakubu, - Hirosaki University, Faculty of Science, 3 Bunkyo-cho, Hirosaki-shi, Aomori-ken 036, Japan. FAX 0172-33-2524. Ed.Bd. circ. 500. Indexed: Biol.Abstr., Deep Sea Res.& Oceanogr.Abstr., Math.R.
—BLDSC (8153.300000); CASDDS.
Formerly: Hirosaki University. Faculty of Literature and Science. Science Reports (ISSN 0439-1705)
Description: Contains research reports written by members of the Faculty of Science and College of General Arts, Hirosaki University.

500 FR ISSN 0073-2362
HISTOIRE DE LA PENSEE. 1960. irreg. price varies. Editions Hermann, 293 rue Lecourbe, 75015 Paris, France. TEL 45-57-45-40.

500.9 FR ISSN 1141-4588
HISTOIRE DES SCIENCES ET DES TECHNIQUES. 1969. irreg., no.5, 1991. price varies. Editions de l' Ecole des Hautes Etudes en Sciences Sociales, 131 bd. St-Michel, 75005 Paris, France. TEL 46-33-51-46. FAX 44-07-08-89. (Dist. by: Centre Interinstitutionnel pour la Diffusion de Publications en Sciences Humaines, 131 bd St-Michel, 75005 Paris, France. TEL 43-54-47-15. FAX 43-54-80-73)

500 US ISSN 0761-1102
HISTOIRE DES SCIENCES ET DES TECHNIQUES. irreg., latest vol.2. Gordon and Breach Science Publishers, c/o International Publishers Distributor, 820 Town Center Dr., Langhorne, PA 19047.
TEL 215-750-2642; 800-545-8398.
FAX 215-750-6343. (Subscr. to: International Publishers Distributor, P.O. Box 90, Reading, Berkshire RG1 8JL, England. TEL 44-173-456-8316) Eds. R. Hahn, M. Levy.
Document type: monographic series.
Refereed Serial

500.9 FR ISSN 0396-9681
HISTOIRE ET NATURE. (Text in French; summaries in English and French) 1968. s-a. 300 F. per no. Association pour l'Histoire des Sciences de la Nature, 24 bis, rue Tournefort, 75005 Paris, France.
TEL 44-37-82-25. Ed. F. Paillart. bibl.; illus. circ. 350. (also avail. in microform; microfiche; back issues avail.) **Indexed:** Bull.Signal.
Formerly (until 1969): Histoire et Biologie (ISSN 0441-6732)

508 AG ISSN 0326-1778
CODEN: HINAEY
HISTORIA NATURAL. 1979. irreg. Casilla Correo 26, 3400 Corrientes, Argentina. **Indexed:** Sport Fish.Abstr., Wild.Rev., Zoo.Rec.

509 JA ISSN 0285-4821
Q124.6
HISTORIA SCIENTIARUM. (Text in English, French, German) 1962. 3/yr. 10000 Yen. Nihon Kagakushi Gakkai - History of Science Society of Japan, West Pine Bldg., 2-15-19 Hirakawa-cho, Chiyoda-ku, Tokyo 102, Japan. Ed. Mikara Sasaki. **Indexed:** Amer.Hist.& Life, Hist.Abstr., Math.R. **Document type:** academic/scholarly publication.
—Faxon; UnCover.
Formerly (until 1980): Japanese Studies in the History of Science (ISSN 0090-0176)

500 GW ISSN 0073-2532
HISTORIAE SCIENTIARUM ELEMENTA. (Text in English, German and Latin) 1962. irreg., vol.5, 1973. price varies. (Werner Fritsch Verlag) Theodor Ackermann, Ludwigstr. 7, 80539 Munich, Germany.
TEL 284787. Ed. Werner Fritsch.

500 AT ISSN 0727-3061
Q93
HISTORICAL RECORDS OF AUSTRALIAN SCIENCE. 1966. s-a. Aus.$32.95 per issue. Australian Academy of Science, G.P.O. Box 783, Canberra, A.C.T. 2601, Australia. index. circ. 1,000. **Indexed:** AESIS, Deep Sea Res.& Oceanogr.Abstr., INIS Atomind.
—UnCover.
Formerly (until 1980): Australian Academy of Science. Records (ISSN 0067-155X)

500 600 900 IE
HISTORICAL STUDIES IN IRISH SCIENCE AND TECHNOLOGY. (Text in English) 1980. irreg., approx. a. price varies. Royal Dublin Society, Science and Arts Dept., Ballsbridge, Dublin 4, Ireland.
TEL 680645. FAX 604014. Ed. R. Charles Mollan. (back issues avail.)

500 US ISSN 0890-9997
QC7 CODEN: HSPSEW
HISTORICAL STUDIES IN THE PHYSICAL AND BIOLOGICAL SCIENCES. 1970. s-a. $25 to individuals (foreign $29); institutions $49 (foreign $53) (effective 1996). University of California Press, Journals Division, 2120 Berkeley Way, Berkeley, CA 94720. TEL 510-643-7154.
FAX 510-642-9917. Ed. J.L. Heilbron. adv. circ. 800. (also avail. in microform from UMI; back issues avail.) **Indexed:** Amer.Hist.& Life, Chem.Abstr., Hist.Abstr. **Document type:** academic/scholarly publication.
—BLDSC (4317.069800); CASDDS; Faxon; Genuine Article; SWETS; UMI; UnCover. CCC.
Formerly: Historical Studies in the Physical Sciences (ISSN 0073-2672)
Description: Covers the history of physics, biology, and other sciences.
Refereed Serial

500 US
HISTORICAL STUDIES IN THE PHYSICAL SCIENCES. 1977. irreg. price varies. Johns Hopkins University Press, 701 W. 40th St., Ste. 275, Baltimore, MD 21211. TEL 401-516-6987. FAX 410-516-6998. (reprint service avail. from UMI)

500 BE
HISTORISCHE DOCUMENTEN VAN DE WETENSCHAPPEN. (Editions in Dutch and French) 1966. irreg. price varies. Belgisch Komitee voor de Geschiedenis der Wetenschappen, Koninklyke Bibliotheek, Keizerslaan 4, B-1000 Brussels, Belgium.

500 507 UK ISSN 0073-2753
Q125 CODEN: HISCAR
HISTORY OF SCIENCE; review of literature and research. 1962. 4/yr. £68($136) Science History Publications Ltd., 16 Rutherford Rd., Cambridge CB2 2HH, England. TEL 01223-565532. Ed. R.S. Porter. adv.; bk.rev.; illus.; index. circ. 800. (back issues avail.) **Indexed:** Amer.Hist.& Life, Hist.Abstr., Math.R. **Document type:** academic/scholarly publication.
—BLDSC (4318.460000); Faxon; Genuine Article; SWETS; UnCover. CCC.
Description: Review of literature and research on the history of science, medicine and technology in its intellectual and social context.
Refereed Serial

500 US ISSN 0739-4934
HISTORY OF SCIENCE SOCIETY NEWSLETTER. q. $41.65 membership. University of Chicago Press, 5720 Woodlawn Ave., Chicago, IL 60637.
TEL 312-753-4243. Ed. Amy L. Lanfear. adv.: page $300; adv. contact: Amy Lanfear. bibl. circ. 4,000.
Document type: newsletter.
Description: Reports on news of the society and contains notices of job openings, forthcoming meetings, awards, fellowships, and grants available.

700 500 JA ISSN 0073-2788
AS551
HITOTSUBASHI JOURNAL OF ARTS AND SCIENCES. (Text in English, French or German) 1960. a. Hitotsubashi Daigaku, Hitotsubashi Gakkai - Hitotsubashi University, Hitotsubashi Academy, 2-1 Naka, Kunitachi-shi, Tokyo 186, Japan. Ed. H. Arai. cum.index. circ. 900. **Indexed:** M.L.A., Math.R.
Document type: academic/scholarly publication.
—UnCover.

500.9 JA ISSN 0285-5615
HIWA KAGAKU HAKUBUTSUKAN KENKYU HOKOKU/HIWA MUSEUM FOR NATURAL HISTORY. MISCELLANEOUS REPORTS. (Text and summaries in Japanese and English) 1958. a. $20. Hiwa Museum for Natural History - Hiwa Kagaku Hakubutsukan, Hiwa, Hiwa-cho, Hiba-gun, Hiroshima-ken 727-03, Japan. TEL 082485-2111. FAX 082485-2421.
Document type: bulletin.

HOBSONS SCIENCE CASEBOOK. see *OCCUPATIONS AND CAREERS*

500 JA ISSN 0386-4464
HOKKAIDO KYOIKU DAIGAKU TAISETSUZAN SHIZEN KYOIKU KENKYU SHISETSU KENKYU HOKOKU/HOKKAIDO UNIVERSITY OF EDUCATION. TAISETSUZAN INSTITUTE OF SCIENCE. REPORTS. (Text in Japanese; summaries in English and Japanese) a. Hokkaido University of Education, Taisetsuzan Institute of Science - Hokkaido Kyoiku Daigaku Taisetsuzan Shizen Kyoiku Kenkyu Shisetsu, 9 Kitakado-cho, Asahikawa-shi, Hokkaido 070, Japan. **Indexed:** Jap.Per.Ind.

500 028.5 AA
HORIZONTI. 1979. m. Bashkimi i Rinise se Punes te Shqiperise - Union of Working Youth of Albania, c/o Prane Ministrise se Arsimit, Tirana, Albania.
TEL 42-29204. Ed. Thanas Qerama. circ. 18,850.

500 CC ISSN 1000-5641
HUADONG SHIFAN DAXUE XUEBAO (ZIRAN KEXUE BAN)/EAST CHINA NORMAL UNIVERSITY. JOURNAL (NATURAL SCIENCE EDITION). (Text in Chinese) q. Huadong Shifan Daxue - East China Normal University, 3663 Zhongshan Beilu, Shanghai 200062, People's Republic of China. TEL 2577577.
Document type: academic/scholarly publication.

500 600 CC ISSN 1000-565X
CODEN: HLDKEZ
HUANAN LIGONG DAXUE XUEBAO (ZIRAN KEXUE BAN)/SOUTH-CHINA UNIVERSITY OF SCIENCE AND ENGINEERING. JOURNAL (NATURAL SCIENCE EDITION). (Text in Chinese) Huanan Ligong Daxue, Xuebao Bianjibu, Wushan, Guangzhou, Guangdong 510641, People's Republic of China. TEL 511311. Ed. Xu Bingzheng. **Document type:** academic/scholarly publication.
—CASDDS; Ei.

500 CC ISSN 1000-5463
CODEN: HSDZER
HUANAN SHIFAN DAXUE XUEBAO (ZIRAN KEXUE BAN)/SOUTH CHINA NORMAL UNIVERSITY. JOURNAL (NATURAL SCIENCE EDITION). (Text in Chinese, abstracts in Chinese, English) 1956. q. $8. Huanan Shifan Daxue, Xuebao Bianjibu, Shipai, Guangzhou, Guangdong 510631, People's Republic of China.
TEL 5516911. FAX 5516011. TELEX 6754. (Dist. overseas by: China International Book Trading Corp., P.O. Box 399, Beijing, P.R. China) Ed. Zhao Duancheng. bk.rev. circ. 1,500. **Document type:** academic/scholarly publication.
Description: Reports the university's current achievements in scientific and educational researches.

SCIENCES: COMPREHENSIVE WORKS

500   CC   ISSN 1000-5013
CODEN: HDZIEF
HUAQIAO DAXUE XUEBAO (ZIRAN KEXUE BAN)/HUAQIAO UNIVERSITY. JOURNAL (NATURAL SCIENCE EDITION). (Text in Chinese) 1980. q. Y8. Huaqiao Daxue - Huaqiao University, c/o Huaqiao Daxue Tushuguan, Quanzhou, Fujian 362011, People's Republic of China. TEL 224921. FAX 0595-226969. TELEX 5478. (Dist. overseas by: Jiangsu Publications Import & Export Corp., 56 Gao Yun Ling, Nanjing, Jiangsu, P.R.C.) Ed. Shi Yushan. **Document type**: academic/scholarly publication.
—CASDDS.
Description: Carries scientific essays on theories of basic and applied sciences, new technologies, designs and products. Includes foreign news.

500 600   CC   ISSN 1000-8616
Q4   CODEN: HLDXE6
HUAZHONG LIGONG DAXUE XUEBAO/CENTRAL-CHINA UNIVERSITY OF SCIENCE AND ENGINEERING. JOURNAL. (Text in Chinese) bi-m. Huazhong Ligong Daxue, Xuebao Bianjibu, Yujiashan, Wuchang-qu, Wuhan, Hubei 430074, People's Republic of China. TEL 701154. Ed. Kang Huaguang. **Document type**: academic/scholarly publication.
—BLDSC (4758.967800); CASDDS; Ei.

500   CC   ISSN 1000-1190
CODEN: HDZKEL
HUAZHONG SHIFAN DAXUE XUEBAO (ZIRAN KEXUE BAN)/CENTRAL-CHINA NORMAL UNIVERSITY. JOURNAL (NATURAL SCIENCE EDITION). (Text in Chinese) q. Huazhong Shifan Daxue, Xuebao Bianjibu, Guizishan, Wuchang-qu, Wuhan, Hubei 430070, People's Republic of China. TEL 715601. Ed. Deng Zongqi. **Document type**: academic/scholarly publication.

500   CC   ISSN 1000-2537
CODEN: HSDXEL
HUNAN SHIFAN DAXUE XUEBAO (ZIRAN KEXUE BAN)/HUNAN NORMAL UNIVERSITY. JOURNAL (NATURAL SCIENCE EDITION). (Text in Chinese; summaries in English) 1956. q. Y14. Hunan Shifan Daxue, Xuebao Bianjibu, Yuelushan, Changsha, Hunan 410081, People's Republic of China. TEL 8883131. (Dist. outside China by: China International Book Trading Corporation, P.O. Box 399, Beijing, People's Republic of China) Ed. Ren Chuwei. index. circ. 3,500. (back issues avail.; reprint service avail. from UMI) **Indexed**: Chem.Abstr. **Document type**: academic/scholarly publication.
—BLDSC (0663.188000); CASDDS; Ei.
Description: Academic journal of scientific research in the natural sciences.

500 374.1   JA   ISSN 0911-6230
CODEN: HKDKES
HYOGO KYOIKU DAIGAKU KENKYU KIYO. DAI-3-BUNSATSU. SHIZENKEI KYOIKU, SEIKATSU KENKOKEI KYOIKU/HYOGO UNIVERSITY OF TEACHER EDUCATION JOURNAL. SERIES 3: NATURAL SCIENCE, PRACTICAL LIFE STUDIES. (Text in English and Japanese; summaries in English) a. Hyogo University of Teacher Education - Hyogo Kyoiku Daigaku, 942-1 Shimokume, Yashiro-cho, Kato-gun, Hyogo-ken 673-14, Japan. abstr.

500.9   US   ISSN 0264-5092
HYPOTENUSE. 1980. q. Research Triangle Institute, Box 12194, Research Triangle Park, NC 27709-2194. **Indexed**: Environ.Abstr. **Document type**: newsletter.

500   II   ISSN 0970-0102
I A P Q R TRANSACTIONS. (Text in English) 1976. 2/yr. Rs.100($15) per vol. (effective 1993). Indian Association for Productivity, Quality and Reliability, c/o Dept. of Statistics, Calcutta University, 35 Ballygunge Circular Rd., Calcutta 700 019, India. TEL 475-3680. FAX 91-33-943333. Ed. S.P. Mukherjee. adv.; bk.rev.; cum.index: 1976-1989. circ. 350. (back issues avail.) **Indexed**: Math.R., Qual.Contr.Appl.Stat., Stat.Theor.Meth.Abstr., Zent.Math. **Document type**: academic/scholarly publication.
—BLDSC (4359.536100).
Description: Covers theories and applications of productivity enhancing and regulatory techniques, with special reference to statistical quality control, reliability and life testing and production management.

500   US   ISSN 0075-0344
I A S BULLETIN. 1967. irreg. Iowa Academy of Science, Sci. 3538, University of Northern Iowa, Cedar Falls, IA 50614. TEL 319-273-2021. **Document type**: academic/scholarly publication.

I A T U L QUARTERLY. (International Association of Technological Universities Libraries) see LIBRARY AND INFORMATION SCIENCES

I C A C H; organo de divulgacion cultural. (Instituto de Ciencias y Artes de Chiapas) see ART

I C A S E - L A R C INTERDISCIPLINARY SERIES IN SCIENCE. (International Council of Associations for Science Education) see EDUCATION

500   FR
I C S U NEWSLETTER; science international. (Text in English) 1964. q. International Council of Scientific Unions, 51 bd. de Montmorency, 75016 Paris, France. TEL 45-25-03-29. FAX 42-88-94-31. TELEX ICSU 645554 F. Ed. J. Marton-Lefevre. circ. 5,000.
Former titles: I C S U AB News (ISSN 0253-5572); (until 1980): I C S U Bulletin (ISSN 0536-132X)

500.1   SG   ISSN 0018-9634
QH3   CODEN: BASNB7
I F A N BULLETIN. SERIE A: SCIENCES NATURELLES. (Text in French; occasionally in English or other languages) 1954. q. 190 F. Institut Fondamental d'Afrique Noire - Cheikh Anta Diop, B.P. 206, Dakar, Senegal. Ed. Abdoulaye Bara Diop. bk.rev.; charts; illus. **Indexed**: Anthropol.Lit., Biol.Abstr., Deep Sea Res.& Oceanogr.Abstr., Field Crop Abstr., Geo.Abstr., Helminthol.Abstr., Herb.Abstr., Rev.Appl.Entomol.

500   US   ISSN 0019-0144
I N F O JOURNAL; science and the unknown. 1966. 3/yr. $15 (foreign $20). International Fortean Organization, Box 367, Arlington, VA 22210-0367. Ed. Michael T. Shoemaker. adv.; bk.rev.; illus.; cum.index: 1966-1985; circ. 600 (paid). (also avail. in microfilm from UMI; back issues avail.; reprint service avail. from UMI) **Indexed**: Abstr.Folk.Stud., Biol.Dig. **Document type**: academic/scholarly publication.
—UMI.
Description: Study of anomalies and unexplainable happenings in science and related areas.

500   BL   ISSN 0019-0233
CODEN: ININDP
I N T INFORMATIVO. (Abstract in English and Portuguese) 1968. 3/yr. free. Instituto Nacional de Tecnologia, Av. Venezuela 82, 20081 Cais do Porto, Rio de Janeiro RJ, Brazil. TEL 021-263-9390. TELEX 21-30056 FINT BR. (Co-sponsor: Secretariat of Science and Technology) Ed. Gilda Massari Coelho. bk.rev. circ. 3,000. **Indexed**: Chem.Abstr., INIS Atomind., Met.Abstr.
—CASDDS.

500   GW   ISSN 0179-5775
I P N - BLAETTER. 1984. q. Institut fuer die Paedagogik der Naturwissenschaften, Olshausenstr. 62, 24098 Kiel, Germany. TEL 0431-8803123. FAX 0431-880-1521. Ed. Peter Nentwig. bk.rev. circ. 7,500. (back issues avail.) **Document type**: academic/scholarly publication.

500   JA   ISSN 0386-7668
IBARAKI DAIGAKU KYOIKUGAKUBU KIYO. SHIZEN KAGAKU/IBARAKI UNIVERSITY. FACULTY OF EDUCATION. BULLETIN. NATURAL SCIENCES. (Text in English, Japanese; summaries in English) 1952. a. free. Ibaraki Daigaku, Kyoikugakubu - Ibaraki University, Faculty of Education, 1-1, Bunkyo 2-chome, Mito-shi, Ibaraki-ken 310, Japan. TEL 0292-28-8282. FAX 0292-29-8329. Ed. Noriyoshi Takahashi. circ. 300. **Indexed**: Jap.Per.Ind. **Document type**: bulletin.
Refereed Serial

IBYKUS; Zeitschrift fuer Poesie, Wissenschaft und Staatskunst. see LITERATURE — Poetry

IDAHO MUSEUM OF NATURAL HISTORY. OCCASIONAL PAPERS. see MUSEUMS AND ART GALLERIES

ILLINOIS. NATURAL HISTORY SURVEY. REPORTS. see CONSERVATION

ILLINOIS. STATE MUSEUM. INVENTORY OF THE COLLECTIONS. see MUSEUMS AND ART GALLERIES

500   US   ISSN 0360-0297
ILLINOIS. STATE MUSEUM. POPULAR SCIENCE SERIES. Key Title: Popular Science Series. 1939. irreg., vol.10, 1992. price varies. Illinois State Museum, Springfield, IL 62706. TEL 217-782-7386. FAX 217-782-1254. illus. **Indexed**: GeoRef. **Document type**: monographic series.
Refereed Serial

500   US   ISSN 0360-0270
CODEN: ISRIB
ILLINOIS. STATE MUSEUM. REPORTS OF INVESTIGATIONS. Key Title: Reports of Investigations - Illinois State Museum. 1948. irreg., no.47, 1992. price varies. Illinois State Museum, Springfield, IL 62706. TEL 217-782-7386. FAX 217-782-1254. bibl.; charts; illus. **Indexed**: Biol.Abstr. **Document type**: monographic series.

557 970 570   US   ISSN 0445-3395
ILLINOIS. STATE MUSEUM. SCIENTIFIC PAPERS SERIES. 1940. irreg., vol.23, 1991. price varies. Illinois State Museum, Springfield, IL 62706. TEL 217-782-7386. FAX 217-782-1254. illus. **Document type**: monographic series.
Refereed Serial

500   US   ISSN 0360-0289
ILLINOIS. STATE MUSEUM. STORY OF ILLINOIS SERIES. 1943. irreg., no.14, 1982. Illinois State Museum, Springfield, IL 62706. TEL 217-782-7386. FAX 217-782-1254. **Document type**: monographic series.

500   US   ISSN 0019-2252
Q11   CODEN: TISAAH
ILLINOIS STATE ACADEMY OF SCIENCE. TRANSACTIONS. 1908. q. membership. Illinois State Academy of Sciences, Illinois State Museum, Springfield, IL 62706. TEL 217-782-6436. FAX 217-782-1254. Ed. Teresa L. North. charts; illus. circ. 1,100. (also avail. in microform from UMI) **Indexed**: Biol.Abstr., Chem.Abstr., Excerp.Med., Field Crop Abstr., Herb.Abstr., Ind.Vet., Key Word Ind.Wildl.Res., Math.R., Plant Breed.Abstr., Protoz.Abstr., Rev.Med.& Vet.Mycol., Rev.Plant Path., Sel.Water Res.Abstr., Soils & Fert., Sport Fish.Abstr., Wild.Rev., World Agri.Econ.& Rural Sociol.Abstr., Zoo.Rec. **Document type**: proceedings.
—BLDSC (8935.000000); CASDDS; UMI; UnCover.
Refereed Serial

500 600 610   DK   ISSN 0281-9341
ILLUSTRERAD VETENSKAP. (Text in Swedish) 1984. m. SEK 38.50 per no.; newsstand price: SEK 39.50. Bonniers Specialmagasiner A-S, Strandboulevarden 130, DK-2100 Copenhagen Oe, Denmark. TEL 45-39-29-55-00. FAX 45-39-29-01-99. Eds. Birgitte Engen, Sture Axelsson; Pub. Michael Cordsen. adv.: B&W page SEK 31200, color page 31200; trim 182 x 245. illus. circ. 149,900. cols./p.: 4; pp./issue: 84.

500   DK   ISSN 0109-2456
ILLUSTRERET VIDENSKAB. (Editions in Danish, German, Finnish, French, Norwegian, Swedish) 1984. m. Bonniers Specialmagasiner A-S, Strandboulevarden 130, 2100 Copenhagen OE, Denmark. Ed. Birgitte Engen. illus.
Description: Examines the natural sciences and social sciences: psychology, biology, astronomy, geography, medicine, anthropology, geology and archaeology; also deals with new technology.

500   UK   ISSN 1352-3368
IMPERIAL COLLEGE OF SCIENCE, TECHNOLOGY AND MEDICINE. CALENDAR. 1908. a. Imperial College of Science, Technology and Medicine, University of London, London SW7 2AZ, England. TEL 0171-589-5111. FAX 0171-584-7596. TELEX 929484 IMPCOL G.
—BLDSC (2966.100000).
Formerly (until 1989): Imperial College of Science and Technology. Calendar (ISSN 0305-4578)
Description: Provides information on the governing body and staff, introductions to departments and centers, and general information about the college.

SCIENCES: COMPREHENSIVE WORKS

500.9 US ISSN 1051-4546
AM101.C58
IN THE FIELD. 1930. bi-m. $6. (Field Museum of Natural History) Field Museum Press, Roosevelt Rd. at Lake Shore Dr., Chicago, IL 60605-2498. TEL 312-922-9410. FAX 312-427-7269. Ed. Ron Dorfman. illus.; index. circ. 24,000. (also avail. in microfiche from BHP; reprint service avail. from UMI) **Indexed:** So.Pac.Per.Ind.
—UnCover.
Formerly (until June 1990): Field Museum of Natural History Bulletin (ISSN 0015-0703); Chicago Natural History Museum. Bulletin.

500 BL
INCRIVEL. 1992. m. $33. Bloch Editores S.A., Rua do Russel 766-804, 22210-000 Rio de Janeiro, RJ, Brazil. TEL 021-5554000. FAX 021-2059998. TELEX 2121525 BLOC. Ed. Janir Hollanda. circ. 80,000. **Document type:** consumer publication.

500 600 II ISSN 0085-1779
INDIA. DEPARTMENT OF SCIENCE & TECHNOLOGY. ANNUAL REPORT. (Text in English) 1969. a. Ministry of Science and Technology, Department of Science & Technology, New Delhi 110 016, India. FAX 0091-652731. TELEX 3166096 DST IN. charts; stat. circ. 5,000.
Formerly: India. Committee on Science and Technology. Annual Report.

500 II ISSN 0019-4964
Q1 CODEN: JIISAD
INDIAN INSTITUTE OF SCIENCE. JOURNAL. (Text in English) 1914. 12/yr. Rs.120($40) Indian Institute of Science, Bangalore 560 012, India. TEL 812-344411.2256. FAX 812-341683. TELEX 0845-8349. Ed. M. Vijayan. adv.; bk.rev.; abstr.; bibl.; charts; illus.; index. circ. 500. (also avail. in microfilm from UMI; reprint service avail. from UMI) **Indexed:** Abstr.Hyg., Apic.Abstr., Appl.Mech.Rev., Biol.Abstr., Biotech.Abstr., Chem.Abstr., Curr.Adv.Ecol.Sci., Curr.Cont, Deep Sea Res.& Oceanogr.Abstr., Eng.Ind., Excerp.Med., Forest.Abstr., Helminthol.Abstr., INIS Atomind., INSPEC (1968-), Int.Aerosp.Abstr., Math.R., Met.Abstr., Nutr.Abstr., Rev.Med.& Vet.Mycol., Soils & Fert., Trop.Dis.Bull. **Document type:** academic/scholarly publication.
—CASDDS; UMI. **CCC.**

509 II ISSN 0019-5235
Q125 CODEN: IJHSA4
INDIAN JOURNAL OF HISTORY OF SCIENCE. 1966. q. Rs.200 (foreign 344.50 Fr.) Indian National Science Academy, Bahadur Shah Zafar Marg, New Delhi 110 002, India. TEL 91-11-3313153. FAX 91-11-3716648. TELEX 31-61835 INSA IN. (Dist. by: UBS Publishers' Distributors Ltd., 5 Ansari Rd., Darya Ganj, New Delhi 110 003, India) Ed. S. Sriramachari. bk.rev.; illus.; index. circ. 300. **Indexed:** Art & Archaeol.Tech.Abstr., Math.R. **Document type:** academic/scholarly publication.
—BLDSC (4414.700000).

INDIAN JOURNAL OF PHYSICS AND PROCEEDINGS OF THE INDIAN ASSOCIATION FOR THE CULTIVATION OF SCIENCE. see PHYSICS

INDIAN NATIONAL SCIENCE ACADEMY. BIOGRAPHICAL MEMOIRS OF FELLOWS. see BIOGRAPHY

500 II ISSN 0378-6242
CODEN: BIDNAL
INDIAN NATIONAL SCIENCE ACADEMY. BULLETIN. 1952. irreg. price varies per issue. Indian National Science Academy, Bahadur Shah Zafar Marg, New Delhi 110002, India. TEL 91-11-3313153. FAX 91-11-3716648. TELEX 31-61835 INSA IN. abstr.; charts; illus. circ. 600. **Indexed:** GeoRef., INSPEC (1973-). **Document type:** bulletin.
Formerly: National Institute of Sciences of India. Bulletin (ISSN 0027-9528).

500 II ISSN 0073-6600
QH301 CODEN: PIBSBB
INDIAN NATIONAL SCIENCE ACADEMY. PROCEEDINGS. (Text in English) 1935; in separate pts. since 1955. Parts A (Physical Sciences) and B (Biological Sciences) published in alternate months. Rs.600 (foreign $240). Indian National Science Academy, Bahadur Shah Zafar Marg, New Delhi 110 002, India. TEL 91-11-3313153. FAX 91-11-3716648. TELEX 31-61835 INSA IN. (Dist. by: UBS Publishers' Distributors Ltd., 5 Ansari Rd., Darya Ganj, New Delhi 110 002, India) Eds. B.L.S. Prakasa Rao, T.J. Pandian. index. circ. 1,000. **Indexed:** Biol.Abstr., C.R.I.Abstr., C.R.I.Curr.Cont., Chem.Abstr., Cott.& Trop.Fibr.Abstr., Deep Sea Res.& Oceanogr.Abstr., Excerp.Med., Field Crop Abstr., GeoRef., INSPEC, Irr.& Drain.Abstr., Maize Abstr., Math.R., Met.Abstr., Nutr.Abstr., Rural Devel.Abstr., Soils & Fert., Sugar Ind.Abstr. **Document type:** proceedings.
—BLDSC (6711.800000); CASDDS; Faxon.
Formerly: National Institute of Sciences of India. Proceedings.

500 II ISSN 0073-6619
Q73
INDIAN NATIONAL SCIENCE ACADEMY. YEAR BOOK. (Text in English) 1960. a. Rs.80($27) Indian National Science Academy, Bahadur Shah Zafar Marg, New Delhi 110002, India. TEL 91-11-3313153. FAX 91-11-3716648. TELEX 31-61835 INSA IN. Eds. B.L.S. Prakasa Rao, T.J. Pandian. circ. 1,000. **Indexed:** Biol.Abstr.
Former titles: National Institute of Sciences of India. Yearbook (ISSN 0547-7573); National Institute of Sciences of India, Calcutta. Year Book.

500 600 II ISSN 0085-1817
INDIAN SCIENCE CONGRESS ASSOCIATION. PROCEEDINGS. (Text in English) 1914. a. Rs.200. Indian Science Congress Association, 14 Dr. Biresh Guha St., Calcutta 700017, India. TEL 033-247-4530. FAX 033-40-2551. index. circ. 5,000. **Indexed:** Biol.Abstr. **Document type:** proceedings.

500 II ISSN 0970-4256
INDIAN SCIENCE CRUISER. 1987. 3/yr. Rs.40($40) to individuals; institutions Rs.80 ($80) (effective 1996). Institute of Science, Education and Culture, 42-B Syed Amir Ali Avenue, Calcutta 700 017, India. TEL 247-7985. Ed. Murali Mohan Biswas. adv. contact: D.P. Bhattacharyya. bk.rev. circ. 450. **Document type:** academic/scholarly publication.
Description: Disseminates knowledge of science and scientific information.

500 US ISSN 0073-6767
Q11 CODEN: PIACAP
INDIANA ACADEMY OF SCIENCE. PROCEEDINGS. 1891. s-a. $12 per no. Indiana Academy of Science, 140 N. Senate Ave., Indianapolis, IN 46204. TEL 317-232-3686. Ed. Gary Dolph. cum.index: 1891-1980, vols.1-90. **Indexed:** Biol.Abstr., Chem.Abstr., Crop Physiol.Abstr., Field Crop Abstr., GeoRef., Herb.Abstr., Maize Abstr., Seed Abstr., Sel.Water Res.Abstr., Soils & Fert., Soyabean Abstr., Sport Fish.Abstr., Triticale Abstr., Vet.Bull., Weed Abstr., Wild.Rev., Zoo.Rec. **Document type:** proceedings.
—BLDSC (6713.000000); CASDDS; UnCover.
Refereed Serial

500 CN ISSN 1192-3385
T177.C2
INDUSTRIAL RESEARCH AND DEVELOPMENT (YEAR) INTENTIONS/RECHERCHE ET DEVELOPPEMENT INDUSTRIELS PERSPECTIVE (YEAR). 1983. a. Can.$44 (US $53, elsewhere $62). Statistics Canada, Publication Sales and Research, Ottawa, ON K1A 0V7, Canada.
Formerly (until 1992): Industrial Research and Development Statistics (ISSN 0824-8133)

500 MX ISSN 0185-0261
Q23 CODEN: ICTEEB
INFORMACION CIENTIFICA Y TECNOLOGICA. 1979. m. Mex.$84($48) (Europe $57; Africa $70; Asia $77) (effective 1995). Consejo Nacional de Ciencia y Tecnologia, Patricio Sanz 1317, Col. del Valle, Mexico 03100, D.F., Mexico. TEL 525-5591944 ext. 325. FAX 5255754081. TELEX 017-74521. Ed. Clairette Ranc. adv. contact: Jose Luis Miranda Salgado. illus. circ. 39,000.

500 CU
INFORMACIONES ESPECIALES. fortn. Academia de Ciencias, Instituto de Documentacion e Informacion Cientifico-Tecnica (I D I C T), Capitolio Nacional, Prado y San Jose, Habana 2, Havana, Cuba.

INFORMATIKA ES TUDOMANYELEMZES. see LIBRARY AND INFORMATION SCIENCES

917 500 CN ISSN 0315-2561
CODEN: IFNRE7
INFORMATION NORTH. 1968. 4/yr. included with subscr. to "Arctic". Arctic Institute of North America, University of Calgary, 2500 University Dr. N.W., Calgary, AB T2N 1N4, Canada. TEL 403-220-7515. FAX 403-282-4609. Ed. Karen M. McCullough. bk.rev. circ. 2,400. (also avail. in microfilm from UMI; back issues avail.) **Indexed:** Anthropol.Lit., Can.B.P.I., Can.Per.Ind., Curr.Adv.Ecol.Sci. **Document type:** academic/scholarly publication.
—UMI.
Formerly: Arctic Institute of North America. Newsletter (ISSN 0066-6963)
Description: Presents theamtic essays on topics of northern interest.
Refereed Serial

605 IR
INFORMATIONS ET NOUVEAUTES TECHNIQUES/ETTELA'AT VA TAZEHA-YE FANNI. (Text in French, Persian) 1961. irrege. free. Centre Francais d'Information Technique et Industrielle, 62 Forsat Ave., Shahreza Ave., Box 11-1555, Teheran, Iran. Eds. Aleksandr Gerigoriyans, Bahman Shahparast. circ. 800.

500 600 BL ISSN 0104-3595
INFORMATIVO I B I C T. 1981. bi-m. free. Instituto Brasileiro de Informacao em Ciencia e Tecnologia, SAS Quadro 5, Lote 6, Bloco H, 70070-000 Brasilia, D.F., Brazil. TEL 217-6161. FAX 226-2677. **Document type:** bulletin.

060 PL ISSN 0537-667X
INFORMATOR NAUKI POLSKIEJ. 1958. a. $50 in Europe; elsewhere $70. Osrodek Przetwarzania Informacji - Information Processing Centre, Redakcja Wydawnictw, P.O.Box 355, 00-950 Warsaw, Poland. FAX 25-33-19. TELEX 813716 CINT PL. (Co-sponsor: Komitet Badan Naukowych) Ed. Mieczyslaw Stanczak. adv. circ. 7,200.

658.4 US
HD29 CODEN: TIMBD
INFORMS. 1976. s-a. $25. Informs, 290 Westminster St., Providence, RI 02903. TEL 401-274-2525. adv. contact: Sandra S. Owens. abstr. circ. 3,000. (back issues avail.) **Indexed:** Appl.Mech.Rev., INSPEC (1976-). **Document type:** bulletin.
—BLDSC (6293.835000); UnCover.
Formerly: T I M S - O R S A Meeting Bulletin (ISSN 0161-0295); Which superseded (1957-1975): Operations Research Society of America. Meeting Bulletin (ISSN 0030-3666)

500 CK ISSN 0121-5140
T4
INNOVACION Y CIENCIA. 1992. q. $40. Asociacion Colombiana para el Avance de la Ciencia, Carrera 50 No. 27-70, Edif. C. Torres, Apdo. Aereo 92581, Santafe de Bogota, Colombia. TEL 57-1-2217348. FAX 57-1-2216950. E-mail: acac1@colciencias.gov.co. Dir. Nohora Elizabeth Hoyos. biennial index. **Document type:** academic/scholarly publication.

500 UK ISSN 0264-9861
INNOVATION. 1982. s-a. £187. Longman Cartermill Ltd., Technology Centre, St. Andrews, Fife KY16 9EA, Scotland. TEL 0334-77660. Ed. A.R. Butler. **Document type:** consumer publication.
●Also available online.

500 600 US
INNOVATIONEWS; an advanced technical materials fact sheet. 1987. a. free. Aremco Products, Inc., 23 Snowden Ave., Box 429, Ossining, NY 19562. TEL 914-762-0685. FAX 914-762-1663. Ed. Brenda T. Lyons. circ. 20,000. **Document type:** newsletter.

SCIENCES: COMPREHENSIVE WORKS

500 — **US**
INNOVATIONS (KANSAS CITY). 1992. q. free. Midwest Research Institute, 425 Volker Blvd., Kansas City, MO 64110. TEL 816-753-7600. FAX 816-753-8420. Ed. Karen Alexander. circ. 10,000.
Description: Covers research and development in the areas of environment, health, renewable energy, engineering, and social and management sciences.

500 600 — **US** — **ISSN 1059-2091**
INNOVATIONS & IDEAS.* (Supplement avail.) 1991. q. $29.99. Publishing & Business Consultants, 101 W. 64th St., Unit 3, Inglewood, CA 90302-1255. TEL 213-732-3477. FAX 213-732-9123. (Subscr. to: Box 75392, Los Angeles, CA 90075) Ed. Andeson Napoleon Atia. adv. circ. 120,000.
Document type: consumer publication.
Previously announced as: American Innovation.
Description: Covers breakthroughs in scientific research and high technology fields, with emphasis on human applications.

INNOVATIONS-NACHRICHTEN. see *TECHNOLOGY: COMPREHENSIVE WORKS*

500 — **US** — **ISSN 0890-300X**
INNOVATOR'S DIGEST. 1979. bi-w. $319 (Canada $359; elsewhere $419). Merton Allen Associates, InfoTeam Inc., Box 15640, Plantation, FL 33318-5640. TEL 305-473-9560. FAX 305-473-0544. *Document type:* newsletter.
●*Also available online. Vendor(s):* Data-Star, Knight-Ridder, Inc., NewsNet (RD09).
—BLDSC (4515.491000). **CCC.**
Description: Covers worldwide innovative activities, accomplishments, and happenings in science, engineering, technology, manufacture, finance, management, marketing, and regulation.

500 — **FR** — **ISSN 1250-5943**
INSTITUT DE L'INFORMATION SCIENTIFIQUE ET TECHNIQUE. LETTRE. Key Title: Lettre de l'I N I S T. (Text in English, French) q. Institut de l'Information Scientifique et Technique, INIST - CNRS, 2 allee du Parc de Brabois, 54514 Vandoeuvre-les-Nancy Cedex, France. TEL 83-50-46-00. FAX 83-50-46-50. Ed. Catherine Come. *Document type:* newsletter.
—BLDSC (5185.206840).
Formerly (until 1994): I N I S T - Info (ISSN 0992-0692)
Description: Information on activities, products, services of I N I S T and new technologies used for information processing.

500 — **II** — **ISSN 0971-3107**
CODEN: TSSTA8
INSTITUT FRANCAIS DE PONDICHERY. PUBLICATIONS DU DEPARTEMENT D'ECOLOGIE. (Text and summaries in English, French) 1957. irreg. (approx. 3/yr.). price varies. Institut Francais de Pondichery, Departement d'Ecologie - French Institute of Pondicherry, P.O. Box 33, Pondichery 605 001, India. TEL 91-413-34170. FAX 91-413-29534. TELEX 469224 FRAN IN. Ed. J.P. Pascal. index. circ. 500. *Indexed:* Biol.Abstr., Bull.Signal., Forest.Abstr., Forest Prod.Abstr.
Formed by the merger of: Institut Francais de Pondichery. Section Scientifique et Technique. Travaux. (ISSN 0073-8336) & Institut Francais de Pondichery. Section Scientifique et Technique. Travaux. Hors Serie (ISSN 0073-8344)

500 — **US** — **ISSN 0897-1013**
INSTITUTE OF NOETIC SCIENCES. QUARTERLY BULLETIN. 1973. q. $35 membership. Institute of Noetic Sciences, 475 Gate 5 Rd., Ste. 300, Sausalito, CA 94965. TEL 415-563-5650. FAX 415-331-5673. Ed. Carol Guion. illus. circ. 25,000. (back issues avail.) *Indexed:* PROMT. *Document type:* bulletin.
Former titles: Institute of Noetic Sciences. Newsletter (ISSN 0888-3432); Institute of Noetic Sciences Investigations.
Description: Helps members to network through local study groups.

500 — **AO** — **ISSN 0020-3912**
CODEN: IANBBN
INSTITUTO DE INVESTIGACAO CIENTIFICA DE ANGOLA. BOLETIM. (Text in Portuguese; summaries in English, French and German) 1962. s-a. Instituto de Investigacao Cientifica de Angola, Departamento de Documentacao e Informacao, Caixa Postal 3244, Luanda, Angola. bibl.; charts. *Indexed:* Biol.Abstr.

500 600 — **AO** — **ISSN 0074-0098**
INSTITUTO DE INVESTIGACAO CIENTIFICA DE ANGOLA. MEMORIAS E TRABALHOS. (Text in Portuguese; summaries in English, French, German) 1960. irreg., no.8, 1971. price varies. Instituto de Investigacao Cientifica de Angola, Departamento de Documentacao e Informacao, Box 3244, Luanda, Angola. abstr. (also avail. in microform)

500 600 — **AO** — **ISSN 0003-343X**
Q180.A58 — **CODEN: RCIAA5**
INSTITUTO DE INVESTIGACAO CIENTIFICA DE ANGOLA. RELATORIOS E COMMUNICACOES. 1962. irreg., no.25, 1973. Instituto de Investigacao Cientifica de Angola, Departamento de Documentacao e Informacao, Box 3244, Luanda, Angola.

500 — **PO**
INSTITUTO DE INVESTIGACAO CIENTIFICA TROPICAL. ANUARIO DE ACTIVIDADES. 1986. a. Instituto de Investigacao Cientifica Tropical, Rua da Junqueira 30, 1300 Lisbon, Portugal. TEL 3622621. FAX 363-1460. (Subscr. to: Centro de Documentacao e Informacao, Rua Jau 47, 1300 Lisbon, Portugal) *Document type:* directory.

500 — **PO** — **ISSN 0870-0036**
CODEN: MIITEJ
INSTITUTO DE INVESTIGACAO CIENTIFICA TROPICAL. MEMORIAS. 1943, N.S. irreg. Instituto de Investigacao Cientifica Tropical, Rua da Junqueira 30, 1300 Lisbon, Portugal. TEL 3622621. FAX 363-1460. (Subscr. to: Centro de Documentacao e Informacao, Rua Jau 47, 1300 Lisbon) circ. 1,000. *Document type:* monographic series.
Formerly: Junta de Investigacoes Cientificas do Ultramar. Memorias.

500 — **PO**
INSTITUTO DE INVESTIGACAO CIENTIFICA TROPICAL. PLANO DE ACTIVIDADES. 1988. a. Instituto de Investigacao Cientifica Tropical, Rua da Junqueira 30, 1300 Lisbon, Portugal. TEL 362-2621. FAX 363-1460. (Subscr. to: Centro de Documentacao e Informacao, Rua Jau 47, 1300 Lisbon, Portugal) *Document type:* corporate report.

500 — **PO**
INSTITUTO DE INVESTIGACAO CIENTIFICA TROPICAL. RELATORIO DE ACTIVIDADES. 1987. a. Instituto de Investigacao Cientifica Tropical, Rua da Junqueira 30, 1300 Lisbon, Portugal. TEL 362-2621. FAX 363-1460. (Subscr. to: Centro de Documentacao e Informacao, Rua Jau 47, 1300 Lisbon, Portugal) *Document type:* corporate report.

500 — **EC** — **ISSN 0010-7972**
INSTITUTO ECUATORIANO DE CIENCIAS NATURALES. CONTRIBUCIONES. (Text in English and Spanish) 1937. s-a. exchange basis. Instituto Ecuatoriano de Ciencias Naturales - Ecuadorian Institute of Natural Sciences, P.O. Box 408, Center, Quito, Ecuador. Ed. Dr. M. Acosta-Solis. circ. 2,500. *Indexed:* Biol.Abstr.

500 — **DR** — **ISSN 0378-956X**
T173.S2497
INSTITUTO TECNOLOGICO DE SANTO DOMINGO. DOCUMENTOS. 1976. irreg., no.6, 1981. free. Instituto Tecnologico de Santo Domingo, Apdo. Postal 249-2, Santo Domingo, Dominican Republic.

INTEGRATION. see *POLITICAL SCIENCE — International Relations*

INTER-AMERICAN COUNCIL FOR EDUCATION, SCIENCE, AND CULTURE. FINAL REPORT. see *EDUCATION*

500 — **VE** — **ISSN 0378-1844**
Q4 — **CODEN: ITRCDB**
INTERCIENCIA. (Text and summaries in English, Portuguese and Spanish) 1976. bi-m. $45 to institutions in Latin America; N. America $60; Europe $63; Asia $65; individuals $25. Interciencia Association, Apdo. 51842, Caracas 1050 A, Venezuela. TEL 582-92-32-24. FAX 582-92-32-24. Ed. Dr. Marcel Roche. adv.; bk.rev. circ. 3,000. (back issues avail.) *Indexed:* Biol.Abstr., Chic.Per.Ind., Crop Physiol.Abstr., Curr.Adv.Ecol.Sci., Curr.Cont., Deep Sea Res.& Oceanogr.Abstr., Energy Ind., Energy Info.Abstr., Environ.Abstr., Geo.Abstr., Helminthol.Abstr., Herb.Abstr., Hisp.Amer.Per.Ind. (1981-), Ind.Sci.Rev., Ind.Vet., Plant Grow.Reg.Abstr., Repindex, Sci.Cit.Ind, Sport Fish.Abstr., Vet.Bull., Wild.Rev., World Agri.Econ.& Rural Sociol.Abstr. *Document type:* academic/scholarly publication.
—BLDSC (4533.080000); CASDDS; Ei; Faxon; Genuine Article; SWETS; UnCover. **CCC.**
Description: Interdisciplinary approach to the study of science and technology.

INTERCOM (NEW YORK, 1960?). see *RELIGIONS AND THEOLOGY — Judaic*

500 — **UK** — **ISSN 0308-0188**
Q1 — **CODEN: ISCRD8**
INTERDISCIPLINARY SCIENCE REVIEWS. Abbreviated title: I S R. 1976. q. £150($296) to non-members and institutions; members £50 ($120). Institute of Materials, 1 Carlton House Terrace, London SW1Y 5DB, England. TEL 071-839-4071. FAX 071-839-2078. TELEX 8814813-METSOC-G. Ed. Anthony Michaelis. adv.; bk.rev. *Indexed:* Chem.Abstr., CLOSS, Curr.Cont., Field Crop Abstr., INSPEC. *Document type:* academic/scholarly publication.
—BLDSC (4533.357000); CASDDS; Ei; Faxon; Genuine Article; SWETS; UMI. **CCC.**
Description: Covers global warming, molecular electronics, languages and the search for extraterrestrial intelligence, as well as the potential and limits of socially organized humankind for specialists and students of all scientific disciplines worldwide.

500 — **IS** — **ISSN 0334-1100**
INTERFACE. (Text in English) 1975. s-a. free. Weizmann Institute of Science, Public Affairs Department, Rehovot, Israel. TEL 972-8-343852. FAX 972-8-344104. circ. 25,000. (looseleaf format)

500 — **NE** — **ISSN 0531-5131**
CODEN: EXMDA4
INTERNATIONAL CONGRESS SERIES. Variant title: Excerpta Medica International Congress Series. irreg., (approx. 40/yr.), vol.1065, 1994. price varies. Elsevier Science B.V., Books Division, P.O. Box 211, 1000 AE Amsterdam, Netherlands. TEL 31-20-4853911. FAX 31-20-4853705. TELEX 18582 ESPA NL.
E-mail: nlinfo-f@elsevier.nl; usinfo-f@elsevier.com; forinfo-kyf04035@niftyserve.or.jp; Site addr.: http://www.elsevier.nl/. (Subscr. in U.S. and Canada to: Elsevier Science Inc., Box 882, Madison Sq. Sta., New York, NY 10159. TEL 212-989-5800) (back issues avail.) *Indexed:* Anim.Breed.Abstr., Biol.Abstr., Chem.Abstr., Zoo.Rec. *Document type:* monographic series, proceedings.
—BLDSC (3835.850000); CASDDS; Genuine Article. **CCC.**
Refereed Serial

500 — **FR** — **ISSN 0074-4387**
Q10 — **CODEN: YBIUE3**
INTERNATIONAL COUNCIL OF SCIENTIFIC UNIONS. YEAR BOOK. 1954. a. £40($65) International Council of Scientific Unions - Conseil International des Unions Scientifiques, 51 bd. de Montmorency, Paris 75016, France. TEL 45-25-03-29. FAX 42-88-94-31. TELEX ICSU 645554 F. (Dist. by: Portland Press Limited, 59 Portland Pl., London W1N 3AJ, England. TEL 071-580-5530) index. circ. 4,750.
—CASDDS.
Description: Provides historical information and a short description of every ICSU body, as well as the names and addresses of the 1800 individuals who serve as officers for the various groups and committees.

5864 SCIENCES: COMPREHENSIVE WORKS

500 II
INTERNATIONAL JOURNAL OF LIFE SCIENCES. (Text in English) 1993. s-a. Muslim Association for the Advancement of Science, 44, Ahmad Nagar, Dodhpur, Aligarh 202 001, India. TEL 0571-401209. Ed. M. Kaleemur Rahman. abstr.

INTERNATIONAL JOURNAL OF POWER AND ENERGY SYSTEMS. see *ENERGY*

INTERNATIONAL JOURNAL OF RADIATION BIOLOGY. see *MEDICAL SCIENCES — Oncology*

620 II ISSN 0257-7828
CODEN: ISENE7
INTERNATIONAL JOURNAL OF SCIENCE & ENGINEERING. (Text in English) 1984. q. Rs.300($50) 416, Mumfordganj, Allahabad 211 002, India. Ed. L.M. Srivastava. adv. (reprint service avail.)
—BLDSC (4542.544500); CASDDS.

500 US ISSN 0891-5083
Q1 CODEN: IJSTEW
INTERNATIONAL JOURNAL OF SCIENCE AND TECHNOLOGY. 1971. s-a. $30 to individuals; institutions $45; students $15. Foundation for International Development, Box 38, Plainfield, IN 46168. TEL 317-839-8157. FAX 317-839-1840. TELEX 650 288 4110. Ed. Syed Imtiaz Ahmad. adv.; bk.rev.; abstr.; index. circ. 1,000. **Indexed:** Abstr.Musl.Rel.
—CASDDS.
Formerly (until 1987): Muslin Scientist (ISSN 0743-085X)

INTERNATIONAL JOURNAL OF SCIENCE EDUCATION. see *EDUCATION*

500 US ISSN 0896-2294
BD255 CODEN: IJUSE5
INTERNATIONAL JOURNAL ON THE UNITY OF THE SCIENCES. 1988. q. $25. I C F, 147 Goodrich Ave., Lexington, KY 40503-1911. Ed. Gregory Breland. adv.; bk.rev. circ. 500. **Indexed:** Int.Polit.Sci.Abstr. **Document type:** academic/scholarly publication.
Description: Devoted to the study of values and their relationship to the sciences and the unity of knowledge.
Refereed Serial

500 US
INTERNATIONAL SOCIETY FOR THE SYSTEMS SCIENCES. PROCEEDINGS. 1956. a. $65. International Society for the Systems Sciences, Box 6808, Louisville, KY 40206-0808. TEL 502-899-3332. FAX 502-899-3332. **Document type:** proceedings.
Formerly: Society for General Systems Research. Proceedings.

INTERNATIONAL SOROPTIMIST. see *CLUBS*

INTERNATIONAL STUDIES IN GLOBAL CHANGE. see *BUSINESS AND ECONOMICS — Management*

500 GW ISSN 0374-3365
INTERNATIONALES WISSENSCHAFTLICHES KOLLOQUIUM. a. Technische Universitaet Ilmenau, Prof.-Schmidt-Str. 21, 98693 Ilmenau, Germany. Ed. Andrea Schneider. **Document type:** monographic series.
—BLDSC (4557.190100).

500 IT ISSN 0393-2451
INTERSEZIONI; rivista di storia delle idee. 1981. 3/yr. L.68000 (foreign L.120000). Societa Editrice Il Mulino, Strada Maggiore, 37, 40125 Bologna, Italy. TEL 39-51-256011. FAX 39-51-256034. Ed.Bd. adv.: B&W page L.1800000. index. circ. 1,300. (back issues avail.)
—BLDSC (4557.444540).

500 608.7 II ISSN 0970-0056
INVENTION INTELLIGENCE. (Text in English) 1965. m. Rs.40. National Research Development Corporation, 20-22 Zamroodpur Community Centre, Kailash Colony Extension, New Delhi 110 048, India. TEL 6420336. FAX 11-6449401. TELEX 031-71358. Ed. B. Khan. adv.; bk.rev.; abstr.; charts; illus.; tr.lit. circ. 6,000. **Indexed:** Agri.Eng.Abstr., Food Sci.& Tech.Abstr., Indian Sci Abstr., PROMT.

INVENTIVA; periodico tecnico - scientifico - sociale. see *TECHNOLOGY: COMPREHENSIVE WORKS*

500 US
INVENTORS CLUBS OF AMERICA. NEWS. 1935. bi-m. membership only. Inventors Clubs of America, Box 450261, Atlanta, GA 30345. TEL 404-938-5089. Ed. Alexander T. Marinaccio. adv. contact: Frank Davis. bk.rev. circ. 6,000. (back issues avail.) **Document type:** newsletter.
Description: Introduces new inventions, and presents articles to help inventors.

500 600 SP ISSN 0210-136X
INVESTIGACION Y CIENCIA. Spanish translation of: Scientific American (US ISSN 0036-8733) 1976. m. 7700 ptas. (foreign 8400 ptas.). Prensa Cientifica, S.A., Muntaner 339, pral. 1a, 08021 Barcelona, Spain. TEL 414-33-44. FAX 414-54-13. Eds. Francisco Gracia, Jose Maria Valderas. adv. contact: Gustavo Martinez. bk.rev.; bibl.; charts; illus.; index; circ. 29,222 (paid). (back issues avail.)
—SWETS.

500 US ISSN 0896-8381
Q11 CODEN: JIASEB
IOWA ACADEMY OF SCIENCE. JOURNAL. q. $20. Iowa Academy of Science, 175 Baker Hall, University of Northern Iowa, Cedar Falls, IA 50614. TEL 319-273-2021. Ed. Kenneth E. Windom. charts; illus.; circ. 2,100 (controlled). (also avail. in microform from UMI; reprint service avail. from UMI) **Indexed:** Biol.Abstr., Curr.Adv.Ecol.Sci., Excerp.Med., Field Crop Abstr., GeoRef., Herb.Abstr., INSPEC, Rev.Plant Path., Seed Abstr., Soils & Fert., Sport Fish.Abstr., Wild.Rev., Zoo.Rec. **Document type:** academic/scholarly publication.
—BLDSC (4802.529000); CASDDS; UMI; UnCover.
Formerly: Iowa Academy of Science. Proceedings (ISSN 0085-2236)
Refereed Serial

500 600 IR ISSN 0360-1307
T1 CODEN: IJSTBT
IRANIAN JOURNAL OF SCIENCE AND TECHNOLOGY. (Text in English) 1971. 3/yr. $200. Shiraz University, School of Engineering, Shiraz, Iran. TEL 98-71-672060. FAX 98-71-52725. TELEX 332169 SHU-IR. E-mail: SHIRAZ@IREARN.BITNET. Ed. M. Moshfeghian. adv.; bk.rev.; bibl.; charts. circ. 1,000. (also avail. in microform from UMI) **Indexed:** Appl.Mech.Rev., Biol.Abstr., Eng.Ind., INSPEC (1977-). **Document type:** academic/scholarly publication.
—BLDSC (4567.529500); Ei.
Description: Publishes theoretical, fundamental and experimental research papers from the engineering disciplines and all areas of basic science.
Refereed Serial

500.9 IQ
IRAQ NATURAL HISTORY MUSEUM. BULLETIN. (Text in English; summaries in Arabic and English) 1961. irreg. ID.2500 per no. Iraq Natural History Museum, University of Baghdad, Bab al-Muadham, Baghdad, Iraq. Ed. Munir K. Bunni. (back issues avail.) **Indexed:** Biodet.Abstr., Biol.Abstr., Zoo.Rec.
Former titles: Iraq Natural History Research Center and Museum. Bulletin; Iraq Natural History Museum. Bulletin (ISSN 0021-0897)

500 IQ ISSN 0067-2904
Q80.I68 CODEN: IRJSD5
IRAQI JOURNAL OF SCIENCE. (Text and summaries in Arabic and English) 1956. a. exchange basis. University of Baghdad, College of Science, Adamiya Jadiriyah, Baghdad, Iraq. TEL 7760730. Ed. Muthana A. Shanshal. bk.rev.; charts. circ. 1,000. **Indexed:** Apic.Abstr., Biol.Abstr., Chem.Abstr., Geo.Abstr., INSPEC, Math.R. **Document type:** academic/scholarly publication.
—CASDDS.
Formerly (until vol.18, no.2, 1977): University of Baghdad. College of Science. Bulletin (ISSN 0304-9531)

500.9 UK ISSN 0021-1311
CODEN: INAJA4
THE IRISH NATURALISTS' JOURNAL. 1925. q. £14($25) (Ireland I£15). Irish Naturalists' Journal Ltd., School of Biology and Biochemistry, Queen's University, Belfast BT7 1NN, N. Ireland. TEL 01232-335793. FAX 01232-236505. E-mail: r.govier@v2.qub.ac.uk. Ed. Robin N. Govier. adv.; bk.rev.; bibl.; illus.; cum.index every 3 yrs. circ. 500. **Indexed:** Biol.Abstr., Br.Geol.Lit., Deep Sea Res.& Oceanogr.Abstr., Ecol.Abstr., Field Crop Abstr., Geo.Abstr., Geol.Abstr., Herb.Abstr. **Document type:** academic/scholarly publication.
—BLDSC (4574.000000).
Refereed Serial

509 US ISSN 0021-1753
Q1 CODEN: ISISA4
ISIS; international review devoted to the history of science and its cultural influences. 1912. q. (plus a. Current Bibliography). $49 to individuals; institutions $125; students $26. (History of Science Society, Inc.) University of Chicago Press, Journals Division, 5720 S. Woodlawn Ave., Chicago, IL 60637. TEL 312-753-3347. FAX 312-753-0811. (Subscr. to: Box 37005, Chicago, IL 60637) Ed. Margaret Rossiter. adv.; bk.rev.; bibl.; charts; illus.; index. circ. 4,400. (also avail. in microfilm from UMI,PMC; microfiche from JAI,KTO; reprint service avail. from ISI,SCH,UMI) **Indexed:** Acad.Ind., Alt.Press Ind., Amer.Hist.& Life, Arts & Hum.Cit.Ind., Biol.Abstr., Bk.Rev.Ind. (1989-), Bull.Signal., Chem.Abstr., Child.Bk.Rev.Ind. (1989-), Curr.Cont., Deep Sea Res.& Oceanogr.Abstr., Eng.Ind., Gen.Sci.Ind., Hist.Abstr., Hum.Ind., Ind.Med., Ind.Sci.Rev., INSPEC (1990-), Math.R., Ref.Sour., SSCI. **Document type:** academic/scholarly publication.
—BLDSC (4583.000000); CASDDS; Faxon; Genuine Article; SWETS; UMI; UnCover. **CCC**.
Refereed Serial

500 PK ISSN 0304-5218
Q1 CODEN: IJSCDE
ISLAMABAD JOURNAL OF SCIENCES. (Text in English) 1974. irreg. Quaid-i-Azam University, Department of Physics, c/o Bookshop, Bookbank and Publication Cell, Islamabad, Pakistan. TEL 812563. Ed. Dr. Kamaluddin Ahmed. **Indexed:** Biol.Abstr., INSPEC (1974-), Math.R. (until 19??). **Document type:** academic/scholarly publication.
—CASDDS.
Formerly (until1975): University of Islamabad. Journal of Mathematics and Sciences (ISSN 0304-9906)

500 610 TU ISSN 1016-3360
Q80.T8
ISLAMIC ACADEMY OF SCIENCES. JOURNAL. Key Title: Journal of the Islamic Academy of Sciences. (Text in English) 1988. bi-m. $40. (Islamic Academy of Sciences, JO) Anadolu Health and Research Foundation, Mithatpasa Caddesi 66-5, Kizilay, 06420 Ankara, Turkey. TEL 90-312-4250319. FAX 90-312-4259487. (Co-sponsor: Organization of Islamic Conference, Standing Committee on Scientific Cooperation) Ed. Naci M. Bor. adv.; bk.rev.; abstr.; charts; illus.; stat.; circ. 2,000 (paid). (also avail. in microfilm; diskette format) **Indexed:** Per.Islam. (1992-). **Document type:** academic/scholarly publication.
—BLDSC (4803.102000).
Description: Presents results of original research in different scientific disciplines.
Refereed Serial

ISLAMIC THOUGHT AND SCIENTIFIC CREATIVITY. see *RELIGIONS AND THEOLOGY — Islamic*

ISLE OF MAN NATURAL HISTORY AND ANTIQUARIAN SOCIETY. PROCEEDINGS. see *HISTORY*

500 IS ISSN 0333-6190
ISRAEL ACADEMY OF SCIENCES AND HUMANITIES. SECTION OF SCIENCES. PROCEEDINGS. (Text in English) 1963. irreg. Israel Academy of Sciences and Humanities, 43 Jabotinski St., P.O. Box 4040, Jerusalem 91040, Israel. TEL 02-636211. FAX 02-666059. circ. 900. (back issues avail.) **Indexed:** Ind.Heb.Per. **Document type:** proceedings.
Description: Reprints of scientific papers read at meetings of the academy.

500 600   US   ISSN 0748-5492
Q124.6
ISSUES IN SCIENCE AND TECHNOLOGY. 1984. q. $75 to institutions (effective 1995). (University of Texas at Dallas) John Wiley & Sons, Inc., Journals, 605 Third Ave., New York, NY 10158. TEL 212-850-6645. FAX 212-850-6021. (Subscr. to: Box 661, Holmes, PA 19043. TEL 214-705-6325; Subscr. outside the Americas to: John Wiley & Sons Ltd., Rolling Renewal Division, Baffins Ln., Chichester, W. Sussex PO19 1UD, England. TEL 44-1243-779777. FAX 44-1243-776128) (Co-sponsors: Institute of Medicine; National Academy of Engineering; National Academy of Sciences) Ed. Kevin Finneran. adv.; bk.rev.; index. circ. 18,500. (also avail. in microform from UMI) **Indexed:** Acad.Ind., Access (1985-1991), CAD CAM Abstr., Energy Ind., Energy Info.Abstr., Environ.Abstr., Ind.Sci.Rev., INIS Atomind., Med.Care Rev., Oper.Res.Manage.Sci., Qual.Contr.Appl.Stat., R.G., R.G., Risk Abstr., Tel.Abstr., Telegen. **Document type:** academic/scholarly publication.
●Also available online. Vendor(s): University Microfilms International.
—BLDSC (4584.325500); CIS; Ei; Faxon; Genuine Article; SWETS; UMI; UnCover.
Description: A journal of ideas and opinions, exploring the policy implications of developments in science, technology and health.

500   IT
ISTITUTO COMELIANA DI LUGANO. COLLECTIO MONOGRAPHICA MINOR. 1976. irregr., vol.4, 1978. L.25000. Giardini Editori e Stampatori, Via Santa Bibbiana 28, 56100 Pisa, Italy. TEL 050 502531.

500   IT   ISSN 0075-1499
ISTITUTO E MUSEO DI STORIA DELLA SCIENZA. BIBLIOTECA. 1957. irregr., no.8; 1970. price varies. Casa Editrice Leo S. Olschki, Casella Postale 66, 50100 Florence, Italy. TEL 39-55-6530684. FAX 39-55-6530214. Ed. Paolo Galluzzi. circ. 1,000. **Document type:** monographic series.

500   IT   ISSN 0021-2504
Q54   CODEN: RLMAAK
ISTITUTO LOMBARDO ACCADEMIA DI SCIENZE E LETTERE. RENDICONTI. A. vol.107, 1973. a. price varies. Istituto Lombardo Accademia di Scienze e Lettere, Via Borgonuovo 25, 20121 Milan, Italy. **Indexed:** Appl.Mech.Rev., Bibl.Ling., GeoRef., M.L.A., Math.R. (until 19??).
—CASDDS.

500   JA   ISSN 0287-3532
IWATANI NAOJI KINEN ZAIDAN KENKYU HOKOKUSHO/IWATANI NAOJI FOUNDATION. RESEARCH REPORT. (Text in Japanese; summaries in English and Japanese) 1977. a. Iwatani Naoji Kinen Zaidan - Iwatani Naoji Foundation, TBR Bldg., 10-2 Nagata-cho 2-chome, Chiyoda-ku, Tokyo 100, Japan.

500 300   JA   ISSN 0385-4132
   CODEN: KKNDDL
IWATE MEDICAL UNIVERSITY SCHOOL OF LIBERAL ARTS & SCIENCES. ANNUAL REPORT/IWATE IKA DAIGAKU KYOYOBU NENPO. (Text in English, German, Japanese) 1966. a. free. Iwate Ika Daigaku Kyoyobu - Iwate Medical University School of Liberal Arts & Sciences, 16-1, 3-chome, Honcho-dori, Morioka-shi, Iwate-ken 020, Japan. TEL 0196-51-5111. FAX 0196-25-5816. circ. 330 (controlled). (back issues avail.) **Document type:** academic/scholarly publication.
●Also available online. Vendor(s): JICST (JOIS-III).
—CASDDS.
Description: Reports of studies by faculty staff.

IWATE UNIVERSITY. FACULTY OF EDUCATION. ANNUAL REPORT/IWATE DAIGAKU KYOIKUGAKUBU KENKYU NENPO. see *SOCIAL SCIENCES: COMPREHENSIVE WORKS*

500   GW
J.C. POGGENDORFF: BIOGRAPHISCH-LITERARISCHES HANDWOERTERBUCH DER EXAKTEN NATURWISSENSCHAFTEN. vol.7, 1955. irregr., latest 1995. (Saechsische Akademie der Wissenschaften zu Leipzig) Akademie Verlag GmbH, Muehlenstr. 33-34, 13187 Berlin, Germany. TEL 030-47889348. FAX 030-47889357. **Document type:** bibliography.

500   PK   ISSN 0021-3888
JADEED SCIENCE. (Text in Urdu; summaries in English and German) 1956. bi-m. Rs.15($3.00) Scientific Society of Pakistan, University of Karachi, Dept. of Zoology, Karachi 32, Pakistan. Ed. Aftab Hassan. adv.; bk.rev.; illus. circ. 2,000.

500 600   GW   ISSN 0938-152X
HD6331.2.G282
JAHRBUCH ARBEIT UND TECHNIK. 1985. a. DM.35. J.H.W. Dietz Nachf. GmbH, In der Raste 2, 53129 Bonn, Germany. TEL 0228-238083. FAX 0228-234104. Ed. Fricke Werner. **Document type:** academic/scholarly publication.

500   GW   ISSN 0173-7600
JAHRBUCH FUER REGIONALWISSENSCHAFT. 1980. a. price varies. Vandenhoeck und Ruprecht, Robert-Bosch-Breite 6, 37079 Goettingen, Germany. TEL 0551-6959-26. FAX 0551-695917. (Subscr. to: 37070 Goettingen, Germany) Ed.Bd. circ. 350. **Document type:** academic/scholarly publication.
—CCC.

500   GW
Q49   CODEN: LEOPAS
JAHRBUCH LEOPOLDINA (REIHE 3). (Reihe 1: 1859-1923; Reihe 2: 1926-1930) 1955. a. DM.20. Deutsche Akademie der Naturforscher Leopoldina, August-Bebel-Str. 50a, 06108 Halle, Germany. TEL 0345-2024723. FAX 0345-2021727. Ed. Benno Parthier. bk.rev. circ. 1,500. **Indexed:** GeoRef. **Document type:** academic/scholarly publication.
—BLDSC (5182.800000).
Formerly: Leopoldina (ISSN 0323-4444)

500   JM   ISSN 1016-2054
Q29
JAMAICAN JOURNAL OF SCIENCE AND TECHNOLOGY. 1970. s-a. J.$100($20) to individuals; institutions J.$150($25). Scientific Research Council, P.O. Box 350, Kingston 6, Jamaica, W.I. TEL 809-927-1771. FAX 809-927-5347. TELEX 3631 SRCSTIN JA. Ed. Tara P. Dasgupta. adv.: B&W page J.$3000. illus. circ. 2,500. **Indexed:** Chem.Abstr., GeoRef., Nutr.Abstr. **Document type:** academic/scholarly publication.
—BLDSC (4645.120000).
Formerly (until 1989): Scientific Research Council of Jamaica. Journal (ISSN 0036-8822); **Supersedes:** Scientific Research Council. Information.
Description: Publishes scientific research papers based on original data on research of interest and relevance to Jamaica.
Refereed Serial

500   JA   ISSN 0386-2208
QH301   CODEN: PJABDW
JAPAN ACADEMY. PROCEEDINGS. SERIES B: PHYSICAL AND BIOLOGICAL SCIENCES/NIPPON GAKUSHIIN KIYO B. (Text in English) 1945. 10/yr. Nippon Gakushiin - Japan Academy, 7-32 Ueno Koen, Taito-ku, Tokyo 110, Japan. (Order from: Maruzen Co., Ltd., 3-10 Nihonbashi 2-chome, Chuo-ku, Tokyo 103, Japan; or Import and Export Dept., Box 5050, Tokyo International, Tokyo 100-31, Japan) (also avail. in microform from PMC) **Indexed:** Anim.Breed.Abstr., Biol.Abstr., Chem.Abstr., Curr.Adv.Biochem., Curr.Adv.Cell & Devel.Biol., Curr.Adv.Ecol.Sci., Curr.Adv.Genetics & Molec.Biol., Curr.Cont., Deep Sea Res.& Oceanogr.Abstr., GeoRef., INIS Atomind., INSPEC, Math.R., Met.Abstr., Sci.Cit.Ind., Sport Fish.Abstr., Wild.Rev., Zoo.Rec. **Document type:** academic/scholarly publication, proceedings.
—BLDSC (6742.100000); CASDDS; Faxon.
Supersedes in part and continues numbering of (vol.53): Japan Academy. Proceedings (ISSN 0021-4280)

501   JA   ISSN 0453-0691
Q174
JAPAN ASSOCIATION FOR PHILOSOPHY OF SCIENCE. ANNALS. (Text in English) 1954. a. 2400 Yen. Japan Association for Philosophy of Science - Kagaku Kisoron Gakkai, c/o Dept. of Philosophy, Otyanomizu University, 2-1-1 Ootuka, Bunkyo-ku, Tokyo 112, Japan. TEL 03-3943-3151. FAX 03-3943-9637. **Indexed:** Biol.Abstr., INSPEC, Math.R., Psychol.Abstr. **Document type:** academic/scholarly publication.
—UnCover.

JAPAN INSTITUTE OF NAVIGATION. JOURNAL/NIHON KOKAI GAKKAI RONBUNSHU. see *TRANSPORTATION — Ships And Shipping*

500 600   US
JAPAN REPORT: SCIENCE AND TECHNOLOGY. irregr. (approx. 40/yr.). $7 per no. (foreign $14 per no.). U.S. Joint Publications Research Service, Box 12507, Arlington, VA 22209. TEL 703-487-4630. (Subscr. to: NTIS, Springfield, VA 22161)

508   US   ISSN 1061-1878
JEFFERSONIANA. 1992. irregr. price varies. Virginia Museum of Natural History, 1001 Douglas Ave., Martinsville, VA 24112. TEL 703-666-8631. FAX 703-632-6487. E-mail: rboland@leo.vsla.edu. Ed. Rick Boland; Pub. Rick Boland. **Document type:** academic/scholarly publication.
Refereed Serial

500   CC   ISSN 1001-3679
JIANGXI KEXUE/JIANGXI SCIENCE. (Text in Chinese; abstracts in English) 1983. q. $40. Jiangxi Sheng Kexueyuan - Jiangxi Academy of Sciences, Pengjia Qiao, Beijing Donglu, Nanchang, Jiangxi 330029, People's Republic of China. TEL 0791-8331714. FAX 0791-8333149. Ed. Liao Yanxiong. index. circ. 3,000. **Document type:** academic/scholarly publication.
Description: Covers various fields of natural sciences such as agriculture, biology, chemistry, engineering, environmental sciences, mathematics, physics, and veterinary microbiology.

500   CC   ISSN 1000-5862
JIANGXI SHIFAN DAXUE XUEBAO (ZIRAN KEXUE BAN)/JIANGXI NORMAL UNIVERSITY. JOURNAL (NATURAL SCIENCE EDITION). (Text in Chinese) q. $20. Jiangxi Shifan Daxue, Xuebao Bianjibu - Jiangxi Normal University, Journal Editorial Department, Beijing Xilu, Nanchang, Jiangxi 330027, People's Republic of China. TEL 333993. Ed. Chen Dingru. adv. contact: Xiaoyan Guan. **Document type:** academic/scholarly publication.

500   CC   ISSN 0529-0279
Q4   CODEN: CLTPD6
JILIN DAXUE ZIRAN KEXUE XUEBAO/JILIN UNIVERSITY. JOURNAL OF NATURAL SCIENCE. (Text in Chinese) q. $4.40 per no. Jilin Daxue Chubanshe - Jilin University Press, Changchun, Jilin, People's Republic of China. TEL 23189. (Dist. overseas by: China International Book Trading Corp., P.O. Box 399, Beijing, P.R.C.) **Indexed:** Chem.Abstr. **Document type:** academic/scholarly publication.
—BLDSC (0663.180000); CASDDS.

500 610   CC   ISSN 1000-9965
   CODEN: JDXUET
JINAN DAXUE XUEBAO/JINAN UNIVERSITY. JOURNAL. (First and third issues cover natural science; second and fourth issues cover medical science.) (Text in Chinese; table of contents in English) 1979. q. Y8. Jinan Daxue, Xuebao Bianjibu - Jinan University, Journal Editorial Department, Rm. 217, 2nd Fl., Bldg. 75, Shipai, Guangzhou, Guangdong 510632, People's Republic of China. TEL 5516511. (Dist. outside China by: Guoji Shudian - China International Book Trading Corp., P.O. Box 399, Beijing, P.R.C.) Ed. Wang Weiliang. **Document type:** academic/scholarly publication.
—BLDSC (4809.599000); CASDDS.
Formerly (until 1989): Jinan Li-yi Xuebao - Jinan University. Journal of Science and Medicine (ISSN 1000-5064)

500 600   CC
JINRI KEJI/SCIENCE AND TECHNOLOGY TODAY. (Text in Chinese) m. Zhejiang Sheng Keji Qingbao Yanjiusuo - Zhejiang Provincial Institute of Science and Technology Information, 91 Huancheng Xilu, Hangzhou, Zhejiang 310006, People's Republic of China. TEL 754087. Ed. Chen Guangzhong.

500   GW
JOACHIM-JUNGLUS-GESELLSCHAFT DER WISSENSCHAFTEN, HAMBURG. VEROEFFENTLICHUNGEN. 1957. irregr. Vandenhoeck und Ruprecht, Robert-Bosch-Breite 6, 37079 Goettingen, Germany. TEL 0551-6959-0. FAX 0551-695917. (Subscr. to: 37070 Goettingen, Germany) **Document type:** monographic series.

SCIENCES: COMPREHENSIVE WORKS

500　　　　　　JA　　ISSN 0911-9639
JOETSU KYOIKU DAIGAKU KENKYU KIYO. DAI-3-BUNSATSU. SHIZENKEI KYOIKU, SEIKATSU KENKOKEI KYOIKU/JOETSU UNIVERSITY OF EDUCATION. BULLETIN. 3. NATURAL SCIENCES AND HUMAN LIVING. (Text and summaries in English and Japanese) a. Joetsu University of Education - Joetsu Kyoiku Daigaku, 1 Yamayashiki-machi, Joetsu-shi, Niigata-ken 943, Japan.

500　　　　　　GW　　ISSN 0178-4757
JOHANNES GUTENBERG-UNIVERSITAET MAINZ. FORSCHUNGSMAGAZIN. 1985. s-a. DM.8. Johannes Gutenberg-Universitaet Mainz, Postfach 39 80, 55020 Mainz, Germany. FAX 06131-393382. TELEX 4187-476-UNI-D. Ed. J. Zoellner. adv. circ. 7,000. (back issues avail.)
Description: Report on current research at the university.

500　　　　　　AU　　ISSN 0259-0689
JOHANNES-KEPLER-UNIVERSITAET LINZ. DISSERTATIONEN. 1974. irreg., no.100, 1992. price varies. (Johannes-Kepler-Universitaet Linz) Verband der Wissenschaftlichen Gesellschaften Oesterreichs, Lindengasse 37, A-1070 Vienna, Austria. TEL 932166.
Formerly: Johannes-Kepler-Hochschule Linz. Dissertationen.

JOSAI DAIGAKU KENKYU NENPO. SHIZEN KAGAKU HEN/JOSAI UNIVERSITY BULLETIN OF LIBERAL ARTS. NATURAL SCIENCE, HEALTH AND PHYSICAL EDUCATION. see HUMANITIES: COMPREHENSIVE WORKS

501　　　　　　NE　　ISSN 0925-4560
Q3　　　　　　　　　　CODEN: JGPSE4
JOURNAL FOR GENERAL PHILOSOPHY OF SCIENCE/ZEITSCHRIFT FUER ALLGEMEINE WISSENSCHAFTSTHEORIE. (Text in English and German) 1969. s-a. fl.307 to institutions; $197 to institutions in U.S. (effective 1996). Kluwer Academic Publishers, Postbus 17, 3300 AA Dordrecht, Netherlands. TEL 31-78-392392. FAX 31-78-392254. TELEX 29245 KAPG NL. E-mail: SERVICES@WKAP.NL. (Dist by: Kluwer Academic Publishers Group, P.O. Box 322, 3300 AH Dordrecht, Netherlands. TEL 31-78-392392. FAX 31-78-546474; N. America dist. addr.: Box 358, Accord Station, Hingham, MA 02018-0358. TEL 617-871-6600. FAX 617-871-6528) Eds. L. Geldsetzer, G. Koenig. adv.; bk.rev.; bibl.; index. (also avail. in microform from UMI; back issues avail.; reprint service avail. from SWZ) **Indexed:** Ind.Bk.Rev.Hum., INSPEC (1970-), Math.R., Phil.Ind. **Document type:** academic/scholarly publication.
—BLDSC (4988.600000); Faxon; SWETS; UMI; UnCover. **CCC.**
Formerly (until vol.21, 1990): Zeitschrift fuer Allgemeine Wissenschaftstheorie (ISSN 0044-2216)
Description: Discusses issues relating to the philosophical, methodological, epistemological and ethical foundations of the sciences.
Refereed Serial

500　　　　　　SY　　ISSN 0379-2927
Q127.A5
JOURNAL FOR THE HISTORY OF ARABIC SCIENCE. (Text in Arabic, English, French, German) 1977. s-a. £S15($15) University of Aleppo, Institute for the History of Arabic Science, Aleppo, Syria. TEL 963-21-236130. FAX 963-21-229184. TELEX 331018 SY ALUNIV. Dir. Dr. Khaled Maghout. adv.; bk.rev.; illus.; index, cum.index: 1977-1981 (vols.1-5). circ. 1,500. (back issues avail.) **Indexed:** Bull.Signal., Ind.Islam., Math.R., Mid.East: Abstr.& Ind. **Document type:** academic/scholarly publication.
—BLDSC (5000.575000).

JOURNAL FUER U F O - FORSCHUNG. see AERONAUTICS AND SPACE FLIGHT

500　　　　　　RH　　ISSN 1019-7788
▼**JOURNAL OF APPLIED SCIENCE IN SOUTHERN AFRICA.** Short title: J A S S A. 1994. s-a. Z.$54. University of Zimbabwe Publications, P.O. Box MP 203, Mt.Pleasant, Harare, Zimbabwe. TEL 263-4-303211. FAX 263-4-333407. bk.rev. **Document type:** academic/scholarly publication.
Description: Multidisciplinary science journal specializing in applied research that is important to or deals with matters specific to the southern African region.

133　　　　　　US
JOURNAL OF BORDERLAND RESEARCH. 1945. q. $25. Borderland Sciences Research Foundation, P.O. Box 220, Bayside, CA 95524-0220. TEL 707-825-7733. FAX 707-825-7779. Ed. Michael Theroux. bk.rev.; charts; illus. circ. 2,000. (back issues avail.)

JOURNAL OF COLLEGE SCIENCE TEACHING. see EDUCATION — Higher Education

JOURNAL OF CONSCIOUSNESS STUDIES; controversies in science & the humanities. see PSYCHOLOGY

JOURNAL OF EAST AFRICAN NATURAL HISTORY. see BIOLOGY

500　　　　　　US　　ISSN 1069-5869
▼**JOURNAL OF FOURIER ANALYSIS AND APPLICATIONS.** 1994. 4/yr. $80 to individuals (foreign $87.95); institutions $195 (foreign $202.95). C R C Press, Inc., 2000 Corporate Blvd., N.W., Boca Raton, FL 33431. TEL 407-994-0555; 800-272-7737. FAX 407-997-0949. TELEX 568689-CRC PRESS. Ed. John J. Benedetto. **Document type:** academic/scholarly publication.
—BLDSC (4986.050000).

500　　　　　　US　　ISSN 1045-389X
TA418.9.S62　　　　　　CODEN: JMSSER
JOURNAL OF INTELLIGENT MATERIAL SYSTEMS AND STUCTURES. 1990. bi-m. $425. Technomic Publishing Co., Inc., 851 New Holland Ave., Box 3535, Lancaster, PA 17604. TEL 717-291-5609. FAX 717-295-4538. TELEX 230 753565 (TECHNOMIC UD). Ed. Craig A. Rogers. circ. 310. **Indexed:** INSPEC (1990-). **Document type:** academic/scholarly publication.
—BLDSC (5007.538550); CASDDS; Ei; Faxon; Genuine Article; SWETS; UMI; UnCover. **CCC.**
Description: Publishes papers related to the science and engineering of diverse intelligent systems.
Refereed Serial

500　　　　　　US　　ISSN 0022-2038
Q167
JOURNAL OF IRREPRODUCIBLE RESULTS. 1955. bi-m. $21 to individuals; institutions $45. Blackwell Scientific Publications, Inc., 238 Main St., Ste. 501, Cambridge, MA 02142-1413. TEL 617-876-7000. FAX 617-876-7022. Ed. Marc Abrahams. adv.; bk.rev.; illus. circ. 9,000. (back issues avail.) **Indexed:** Biol.Abstr., Curr.Cont., Mid.East: Abstr.& Ind., PROMT.
—BLDSC (5008.400000); Faxon; Genuine Article; SWETS; UMI; UnCover.
Description: Contains humorous articles of interest to scientists, doctors and the general public.

574 530　　　　II　　ISSN 0970-3799
JOURNAL OF NATURAL & PHYSICAL SCIENCES. 1987. s-a. Rs.100($50) Gurukul Kangri University, Department of Mathematics, Hardwar 249 404, India. Ed. S.L. Singh. bk.rev. circ. 200.
Description: Covers biology, chemistry, physics, and mathematics.

500　　　　　　JA　　ISSN 0075-4307
JOURNAL OF NATURAL SCIENCE. (Text in English and Japanese) vol.2, 1952. a. avail. on exchange basis. Tokushima Daigaku, Kyoikugakubu - Tokushima University, Faculty of Education, Tokushima-shi, Tokushima-ken 770, Japan.

500.1 510　　　　PK　　ISSN 0022-2941
Q1　　　　　　　　　　CODEN: JNSMAC
JOURNAL OF NATURAL SCIENCES AND MATHEMATICS. (Text in English) 1961. s-a. Rs.150($15) Government College, Research Council, P.O. Box 1750, Lahore 54000, Pakistan. Ed. M. Zakria Butt. bk.rev.; index. circ. 250. **Indexed:** Chem.Abstr., INIS Atomind., INSPEC, Math.R., Poult.Abstr.
—BLDSC (5021.300000); CASDDS; UnCover.

500　　　　　　TU　　ISSN 0022-4057
Q80.T8　　　　　　　　CODEN: JPASBN
JOURNAL OF PURE AND APPLIED SCIENCES/TEMEL VE UYGULAMALI BILMLER DERGISI. Title varies: M E T U Journal of Pure and Applied Sciences. (Text in English and Turkish) 1968. irreg. (approx. 3/yr.). TL.60($5) (Turk Tarih Kurumu Basimevi) Middle East Technical University, Public Relations and Publications Office, Ismet Inonu Bulvari, Ankara, Turkey. Ed. Dogan Altinbilek. bk.rev.; abstr.; bibl.; charts; illus.; index. circ. 500. **Indexed:** Appl.Mech.Rev., Chem.Abstr., Curr.Cont., GeoRef., Math.R., Sci.Cit.Ind.
—BLDSC (5761.402500); CASDDS.

507　　　　　　US　　ISSN 0022-4308
Q181.A1　　　　　　　CODEN: JRSTAR
JOURNAL OF RESEARCH IN SCIENCE TEACHING. 1963. 10/yr. $39 (foreign $545) (effective 1996). (National Association for Research in Science Teaching) John Wiley & Sons, Inc., Journals, 605 Third Ave., New York, NY 10158. TEL 212-850-6645. FAX 212-850-6021. TELEX 12-7063. E-mail: SUBINFO@JWILEY.COM. (Subscr. outside the Americas to: John Wiley & Sons Ltd., Baffins Ln., Chichester, W. Sussex PO19 1UD, England. TEL 44-1243-779777. FAX 44-1243-776128) Ed. Ronald Good. adv.; bibl.; charts; index. circ. 2,000. (also avail. in microform from UMI; back issues avail.; reprint service avail. from UMI) **Indexed:** C.I.J.E., Cont.Pg.Educ., Educ.Ind., Educ.Tech.Abstr., Energy Ind., Energy Info.Abstr., Mid.East: Abstr.& Ind., Mult.Ed.Abstr., Psychol.Abstr. (1981-), Res.High.Educ.Abstr., Sociol.Educ.Abstr., SSCI, Stud.Wom.Abstr., Tech.Educ.Abstr. **Document type:** academic/scholarly publication.
—BLDSC (5052.030000); Ei; Faxon; Genuine Article; SWETS; UMI; UnCover. **CCC.**
Description: Publishes research articles related to the philosophy, historical perspective, teaching strategies, curriculum development and other topics relevant to science education.
Refereed Serial

JOURNAL OF SCIENCE AND MATHEMATICS EDUCATION IN SOUTHEAST ASIA. see EDUCATION — Teaching Methods And Curriculum

500 600　　　　　PK　　ISSN 0250-5339
Q80.P3　　　　　　　　CODEN: JSTPDU
JOURNAL OF SCIENCE AND TECHNOLOGY. 1977. s-a. Rs.50($10) University of Peshawar, Department of Zoology, Peshawar, Pakistan. Ed. M. Nasim Siddiqi. circ. 500. **Indexed:** Biol.Abstr., INIS Atomind., Soils & Fert.
—CASDDS.

JOURNAL OF SCIENCE EDUCATION AND TECHNOLOGY. see EDUCATION

500　　　　　　IR　　ISSN 1016-1104
　　　　　　　　　　　CODEN: JSIIEN
JOURNAL OF SCIENCES, ISLAMIC REPUBLIC OF IRAN. (Text in English) 1989. q. $60 to individuals; institutions $80. National Center for Scientific Research, 1188 Enghelab Ave., P.O. Box 13145-478, Tehran, Iran. TEL 98-21-6462707. FAX 98-21-6462254. Ed. M.R. Noori-Daloii. circ. 1,500. **Document type:** academic/scholarly publication.
—BLDSC (5056.750000); CASDDS.
Description: Promotes the exchange of knowledge between scientific centers and scientists, researchers and international experts.

SCIENCES: COMPREHENSIVE WORKS

500   II   ISSN 0022-4456
T1   CODEN: JSIRAC
JOURNAL OF SCIENTIFIC AND INDUSTRIAL RESEARCH. (Text in English) 1942. m. Rs.400($200) (Council of Scientific and Industrial Research, Publications & Information Directorate) Scientific Publishers, P.O. Box 91, 5A, New Pali Rd., Jodhpur 342 001, India. TEL 0291-33323. Ed. S.S. Nathan. bk.rev. (also avail. in microform from UMI; back issues avail.; reprint service avail. from UMI) Indexed: A.I.Abstr. (until 1992), Anal.Abstr., Appl.Mech.Rev., Biol.Abstr., CAD CAM Abstr. (until 1992), Cadscan, Ceram.Abstr., Chem.Abstr., Chem.Eng.Abstr., CLOSS, Crop Physiol.Abstr., Curr.Biotech.Abstr., Dairy Sci.Abstr., Energy Ind., Energy Info.Abstr., Environ.Abstr., Excerpt.Med., Field Crop Abstr., Food Sci.& Tech.Abstr., GeoRef., Herb.Abstr., Hort.Abstr., Ind.Sci.Rev., INIS Atomind., INSPEC, Irr.& Drain.Abstr., Lead Abstr., Nutr.Abstr., Plant Grow.Reg.Abstr., Protozool.Abstr., Rev.Med.& Vet.Mycol., Rice Abstr., Risk Abstr., Robomat. (until 1992), T.C.E.A., Text.Tech.Dig., Trop.Oil Seeds Abstr., Weed Abstr., World Text.Abstr., Zincscan. **Document type:** academic/scholarly publication.
—BLDSC (5057.000000); CASDDS; CIS; Ei; Faxon; Genuine Article; SWETS; UMI; UnCover.

500 133   US   ISSN 0892-3310
Q180.55.M4
JOURNAL OF SCIENTIFIC EXPLORATION. Abbreviated title: J S E. 1987. q. $45 to individuals (foreign $50); institutions $100 (effective 1994). Society for Scientific Exploration, ERL 306, Stanford University, Stanford, CA 94305-4055. TEL 415-593-8581. FAX 415-595-4466. E-mail: sims@flare.stanford.edu. Ed. Dr. Bernhard Haisch. adv. contact: Marsha Sims. bk.rev. circ. 1,500. (back issues avail.) Indexed: Sociol.Abstr. **Document type:** academic/scholarly publication.
—Ei; Faxon; UnCover.
Description: Publishes original research papers in areas falling outside the established scientific arena. Attempts to provide an unbiased, professional forum for discussion and debate about anomalous phenomena.
Refereed Serial

JOURNAL OF SCIENTIFIC RESEARCH IN PLANTS & MEDICINES. see PHARMACY AND PHARMACOLOGY

JOURNAL OF WOMEN AND MINORITIES IN SCIENCE AND ENGINEERING. see ENGINEERING

500   GW   ISSN 0179-8529
JUNGE WISSENSCHAFT. 1986. q. DM.44 (foreign DM.48). Erhard Friedrich Verlag GmbH, Im Brande 17, 30926 Seelze, Germany. TEL 0511-40004-0. FAX 0511-4000444. (Subscr. to: Postfach 100150, 30917 Seelze, Germany) **Document type:** academic/scholarly publication.

JUNIOR SCIENCE/KODOMO NO KAGAKU. see CHILDREN AND YOUTH — For

JUNIOR SCIENTIST. see EDUCATION — Teaching Methods And Curriculum

500   GW   ISSN 0722-0456
K F A INTERN. (Kernforschungsanlage); Nachrichten und Berichte. 1970. q. free. Forschungszentrum Juelich GmbH, 52425 Juelich, Germany. TEL 02461-614662. FAX 02461-614666. E-mail: p.schaefer@kfa-juelich.de. Ed. Peter Schaefer. bk.rev. circ. 7,500. (back issues avail.) **Document type:** academic/scholarly publication.

500   JA   ISSN 0022-7625
Q4   CODEN: KAGTAT
KAGAKU/SCIENCE JOURNAL KAGAKU. (Text and summaries in Japanese) 1931. m. 10100 Yen. Iwanami Shoten Publishers, 5-5 Hitotsubashi 2-chome, Chiyoda-ku, Tokyo 101-02, Japan. FAX 03-239-9618. (Dist. overseas by: Japan Publications Trading Co., Ltd., Box 5030, Tokyo International, Tokyo 100-31, Japan; Or: 1255 Howard St., San Francisco, CA 94103) Ed. Shigeki Kobayashi. adv.; bk.rev.; charts; illus.; index. circ. 20,000. Indexed: Chem.Abstr., INIS Atomind., Jap.Per.Ind.
—CASDDS.

500   JA   ISSN 0368-4741
Q4   CODEN: KAASAU
KAGAKU ASAHI/SCIENTIFIC ASAHI. (Text in Japanese) 1941. m. $119. Asahi Shimbun Publishing Co., 3-2, Tsukiji 5-chome, Chuo-ku, Tokyo 104-11, Japan. TEL 03-3545-0131. (Subscr. to: Japan Publications Trading Co., Ltd., Box 5030, Tokyo International, Tokyo, Japan) Ed. Takashi Iida. Indexed: Biol.Abstr., Jap.Per.Ind.

500   JA   ISSN 0022-7633
KAGAKU GIJUTSU BUNKEN SABISU/SCIENCE AND TECHNOLOGY INFORMATION SERVICE. (Text in Japanese; table of contents in English) 1962. q. 824 Yen per no. National Diet Library - Kokuritsu Kokkai Toshokan Senmon Shiryobu, 1-10-1 Nagata-cho, Chiyoda-ku, Tokyo 100, Japan. TEL 03-3581-2331. FAX 03-3597-9104. bk.rev.; bibl.; charts; illus.; cum.index. circ. 1,225. Indexed: INIS Atomind., Jap.Per.Ind.
—BLDSC (8134.257000).

KAGAKU GIJUTSU HAKUSHO/WHITE PAPER OF SCIENCE AND TECHNOLOGY IN JAPAN. see TECHNOLOGY: COMPREHENSIVE WORKS

KAGAKU GIJUTSU HAKUSHO NO ARAMASHI. see TECHNOLOGY: COMPREHENSIVE WORKS

KAGAKU GIJUTSU SHINKO CHOSEIHI NYUSU. see TECHNOLOGY: COMPREHENSIVE WORKS

KAGAKU GIJUTSU SHINKO CHOSEIHI SHIKEN KENKYU JISSHI KEIKAKU. see TECHNOLOGY: COMPREHENSIVE WORKS

KAGAKU GIJUTSUCHO NENPO. see TECHNOLOGY: COMPREHENSIVE WORKS

500   JA   ISSN 0022-7668
KAGAKU KISORON KENKYU/JAPAN ASSOCIATION FOR PHILOSOPHY OF SCIENCE. JOURNAL. 1954. s-a. 800 Yen. Japan Association for Philosophy of Science - Kagaku Kisoron Gakkai, c/o Dept. of Philosophy, Otyanomizu University, 2-1-1 Ootuka, Bunkyo-bu, Tokyo 112, Japan. TEL 03-3943-3151. FAX 03-3943-9637. Ed. Yoichiro Murakami. bk.rev. circ. 700. Indexed: Psychol.Abstr. **Document type:** academic/scholarly publication.
—BLDSC (4804.600000).

500 370   JA   ISSN 0386-4553
KAGAKU KYOIKU KENKYU/JOURNAL OF SCIENCE EDUCATION IN JAPAN. (Text in English and Japanese; summaries in English) 1977. q. 8000 Yen membership. Nihon Kagaku Kyoiku Gakkai - Japan Society for Science Education, 5-22 Shimomeguro 6-chome, Meguro-ku, Tokyo 153, Japan. TEL 81-886-87-1311. FAX 81-886-87-2180. E-mail: yhonda@naruto-u.ac.jp. bk.rev. circ. 1,200. **Document type:** academic/scholarly publication.
Description: Covers disciplinary areas of science education including theory, methods and instructions.

500   JA   ISSN 0289-3428
KAGAKU TETSUGAKU/PHILOSOPHY OF SCIENCE. (Text in Japanese) 1968. a. 2000 Yen. (Nihon Kagaku Tetsugakkai - Philosophy of Science Society, Japan) Waseda Daigaku Shuppanbu - Waseda University Press, 1-103 Totsuka-machi, Shinjuku-ku, Tokyo 169, Japan. TEL 03-3203-1551. FAX 03-3207-0406. bk.rev. Indexed: Jap.Per.Ind.

KAGAKU TO KOGYO (OSAKA)/SCIENCE AND INDUSTRY. see TECHNOLOGY: COMPREHENSIVE WORKS

509   JA   ISSN 0022-7692
   CODEN: KAGKA2
KAGAKUSHI KENKYU/JOURNAL OF HISTORY OF SCIENCE. (Text in Japanese; summaries in European languages) 1941. q. 10000 Yen. Nihon Kagakushi Gakkai - History of Science Society of Japan, West Pine Bldg., 2-15-19 Hirakawa-cho, Chiyoda-ku, Tokyo 102, Japan. Ed. Masanori Onuma. Indexed: Chem.Abstr.
—BLDSC (5002.000000); CASDDS.

500 370   JA   ISSN 0389-3057
AS552.K24   CODEN: KDKDAM
KAGAWA DAIGAKU KYOIKUGAKUBU KENKYU HOKOKU. DAI-2-BU/KAGAWA UNIVERSITY. FACULTY OF EDUCATION. MEMOIRS. PART 2. (Text in English and Japanese; summaries in English) 1950. s-a. Kagawa Daigaku, Kyoikugakubu - Kagawa University, Faculty of Education, 1-1 Saiwai-cho, Takamatsu-shi, Kagawa-ken 760, Japan. Indexed: Jap.Per.Ind.
—CASDDS.

500   JA   ISSN 0389-6692
   CODEN: KDSHA6
KAGOSHIMA DAIGAKU KYOIKUGAKUBU KENKYU KIYO. SHIZEN KAGAKU HEN/KAGOSHIMA UNIVERSITY. FACULTY OF EDUCATION. BULLETIN. NATURAL SCIENCE. (Text and summaries in English and Japanese) 1949. a. Kagoshima Daigaku, Kyoikugakubu - Kagoshima University, Faculty of Education, 20-6 Koorimoto 1-chome, Kagoshima-shi, Kagoshima-ken 890, Japan. Indexed: Chem.Abstr., Jap.Per.Ind.
—CASDDS.

510 530 540   JA   ISSN 0385-4027
   CODEN: KSBKB2
KAGOSHIMA DAIGAKU RIGAKUBU KIYO. SUGAKU, BUTSURIGAKU, KAGAKU/KAGOSHIMA UNIVERSITY. FACULTY OF SCIENCE. REPORTS. MATHEMATICS, PHYSICS, CHEMISTRY. (Text in English and Japanese; summaries in English) 1968. a. Kagoshima Daigaku, Rigakubu - Kagoshima University, Faculty of Science, 21-35 Koorimoto 1-chome, Kagoshima-shi, Kagoshima-ken 890, Japan. Indexed: Biol.Abstr., Chem.Abstr., Jap.Per.Ind.
—BLDSC (7467.170000).

500   JA   ISSN 0286-1208
   CODEN: KTDHDC
KAGOSHIMA-KENRITSU TANKI DAIGAKU KIYO. SHIZEN KAGAKU HEN/KAGOSHIMA PREFECTURAL JUNIOR COLLEGE. BULLETIN. NATURAL SCIENCES. (Text in Japanese and English; summaries in English) 1950. a. Kagoshima Prefectural Junior College - Kagoshima-kenritsu Tanki Daigaku, 44 Shimoishiki-cho, Kagoshima-shi, Kagoshima-ken 870, Japan. Indexed: Jap.Per.Ind.
—CASDDS.

500   II   ISSN 0022-7870
KALAIKATHIR. (Text in Tamil) 1948. m. Rs.30. G R D Trust, Foundation Avanashi Rd., Coimbatore 641 037, India. Ed. Dr. D. Padmanaban. adv.; bk.rev.; charts; illus.; index.

500.9 069   JA   ISSN 0915-5074
KAMISHIHORO-CHO HIGASHI TAISETSU HAKUBUTSUKAN KENKYU HOKOKU/HIGASHI TAISETSU MUSEUM OF NATURAL HISTORY. BULLETIN. (Text in Japanese; summaries in English) 1975. irreg. Higashi Taisetsu Museum of Natural History - Kamishihoro-cho Higashi Taisetsu Hakubutsukan, Nukabira, Kamishihoro-cho, Kato-gun, Hokkaido 080-15, Japan.
Description: Contains original research papers.

500   JA   ISSN 0453-1906
QH188
KANAGAWA-KENRITSU HAKUBUTSUKAN KENKYU HOKOKU. SHIZEN KAGAKU/KANAGAWA PREFECTURAL MUSEUM. BULLETIN. NATURAL SCIENCE. (Text and summaries in English and Japanese) 1968. a. Kanagawa-kenritsu Hakubutsukan - Kanagawa Prefectural Museum, 5-60 Minami-nakadoori, Naka-ku, Yokohama-shi, Kanagawa-ken 231, Japan. Indexed: Biol.Abstr., Geo.Abstr., Geol.Abstr., Jap.Per.Ind.
—BLDSC (2597.965000).

KANAGAWA KOKA DAIGAKU KENKYU HOKOKU. B RIKOGAKU HEN/KANAGAWA INSTITUTE OF TECHNOLOGY. RESEARCH REPORTS. PART B. SCIENCE AND TECHNOLOGY. see TECHNOLOGY: COMPREHENSIVE WORKS

500.9   JA   ISSN 0388-9009
KANAGAWA SHIZENSHI SHIRYO/NATURAL HISTORY REPORT OF KANAGAWA. (Text in Japanese; summaries in English and Japanese) 1980. a. Kanagawa-kenritsu Hakubutsukan - Kanagawa Prefectural Museum, 5-60 Minami-nakadoori, Naka-ku, Yokohama-shi, Kanagawa-ken 231, Japan.

SCIENCES: COMPREHENSIVE WORKS

500 JA ISSN 0387-0995
Q4 CODEN: KADSAB
KANAZAWA DAIGAKU KYOIKUGAKUBU KIYO. SHIZEN KAGAKU HEN/KANAZAWA UNIVERSITY. FACULTY OF EDUCATION. BULLETIN. NATURAL SCIENCES. (Text in Japanese; summaries and some articles in English) 1952. a. Kanazawa Daigaku, Kyoikugakubu - Kanazawa University, Faculty of Education, 1-1 Marunouchi, Kanazawa-shi, Ishikawa-ken 920, Japan. **Indexed:** Biol.Abstr., GeoRef., Jap.Per.Ind.

500 JA ISSN 0302-0479
Q4
KANAZAWA DAIGAKU KYOYOBU RONSHU. SHIZEN KAGAKU HEN/KANAZAWA UNIVERSITY. COLLEGE OF LIBERAL ARTS. ANNALS OF SCIENCE. (Text in English and Japanese; summaries in English) 1965. a. Kanazawa Daigaku, Kyoyobu - Kanazawa University, College of Liberal Arts, 1-1 Marunouchi, Kanazawa-shi, Ishikawa-ken 920, Japan. illus. **Indexed:** Biol.Abstr., INIS Atomind., Jap.Per.Ind., Math.R.
—BLDSC (1043.990000).

500 JA ISSN 0022-8338
Q4 CODEN: SRKAAT
KANAZAWA UNIVERSITY. SCIENCE REPORTS/KANAZAWA DAIGAKU RIKA HOKOKU. (Text in English and French) 1951. s-a. exchange basis. Kanazawa Daigaku, Rigakubu - Kanazawa University, Faculty of Science, Kakuma-machi, Kanazawa-shi, Ishikawa-ken 920-11, Japan. TEL 0762-64-5620. FAX 0762-64-5737. Ed. Y. Furuta. bibl.; charts; illus.; index. circ. 500. **Indexed:** Biol.Abstr., Chem.Abstr., INIS Atomind., INSPEC, JTA, Math.R.
—BLDSC (8155.000000); CASDDS.

500 JA ISSN 0285-3205
KANSAI SHIZEN KAGAKU. (Text in Japanese) 1944. a. 1500 Yen (typically set in Apr.). Kansai Natural Science Research Society - Kansai Shizen Kagaku Kenkyukai, Kinki Nihon Tetsudo K.K., 1-55 Uehon-machi 6-chome, Tennoji-ku, Osaka-shi, Osaka-fu 543, Japan.
Description: Contains reviews, commentary, and news.

500 PK ISSN 0250-5363
Q80.P3 CODEN: KUJSDE
KARACHI JOURNAL OF SCIENCE. (Text in English) 1972. s-a. Rs.100($50) University of Karachi, Department of Physics, Karachi 75270, Pakistan. FAX 92-21-473-226. Eds. S.A. Husain, S.N. Hasnain. adv.; bk.rev.; abstr.; bibl.; charts. circ. 500. **Indexed:** Biol.Abstr., Chem.Abstr., INSPEC (1981-), Math.R. **Document type:** academic/scholarly publication.
—BLDSC (5085.698300); CASDDS.

500 II ISSN 0075-5168
Q1 CODEN: KUJSAB
KARNATAK UNIVERSITY, DHARWAD, INDIA. JOURNAL. SCIENCE. Key Title: Journal of the Karnatak University. Science. (Text in English) 1956. a. Rs.8($4) Karnatak University, Director, Prasaranga, Dharwad 580003, Karnataka, India. Ed. M.I. Savadatti. circ. 250. **Indexed:** Biol.Abstr., Chem.Abstr., Entomol.Abstr., GeoRef. **Document type:** academic/scholarly publication.
—CASDDS.

500 GW ISSN 0941-8482
KAUPIA; Darmstaedter Beitraege zur Naturgeschichte. irreg., no.5, 1995. Hessisches Landesmuseum Darmstadt, Friedensplatz 1, 64283 Darmstadt, Germany. (Co-sponsor: Technische Hochschule Darmstadt) Ed.Bd. **Document type:** academic/scholarly publication.
—BLDSC (5087.793000).

500 IR
KAYHAN ELMI. (Text in Persian) 1989. m. $222 to N. America (effective 1994). Kayhan Publications, Ferdowsi Ave., P.O. Box 113365-9361, Tehran, Iran. TEL 98-21-3110251. FAX 98-21-3114228. TELEX 212467. illus. **Document type:** consumer publication.

KE XUE. Chinese translation of: Scientific American (US ISSN 0036-8733) 1978. m. Y96($50) (effective 1992). I S T I C Chongqing, P.O. Box 2104, Chongqing, Sichuan, People's Republic of China. TEL 0811-3863170. FAX 0811-3852473. TELEX 62128 CBIST CN. Ed. Zeng Xiaodong; Pub. Chen Yuanshu. adv. contact: Wang Shide. bk.rev. circ. 20,000. (back issues avail.) **Document type:** academic/scholarly publication.

500 JA ISSN 0911-7237
KEIO GIJUKU DAIGAKU HIYOSHI KIYO. SHIZEN KAGAKU/HIYOSHI REVIEW OF NATURAL SCIENCE. (Text in English and Japanese; summaries in English) 1985. a. Keio Gijuku Daigaku, Hiyoshi Kiyo Kanko Iinkai, 1-1, Hiyoshi 4-chome, Kohoku-ku, Yokohama-shi, Kanagawa-ken 223, Japan.
—BLDSC (4319.084000).

KEIO GIJUKU DAIGAKU RIKOGAKUBUHO. see TECHNOLOGY: COMPREHENSIVE WORKS

620 JA ISSN 0286-4215
CODEN: KSTREE
KEIO SCIENCE AND TECHNOLOGY REPORTS. (Text in English, French and German) 1948. irreg. exchange basis only. Keio Gijuku Daigaku, Rikogakubu - Keio University, Faculty of Science and Technology, Matsushita Memorial Library, 14-1, Hiyoshi 3-chome, Kohoku-ku, Yokohama-shi, Kanagawa-ken 223, Japan. Ed. Yasuji Ohtsuka. charts; illus.; stat. circ. 1,000. **Indexed:** Chem.Abstr., Eng.Ind., INSPEC (1984-), JCT, JTA, Math.R. **Document type:** academic/scholarly publication.
—BLDSC (5089.010000); CASDDS.
Former titles: Keio Engineering Reports; Keio University. Fujihara Memorial Faculty of Engineering. Proceedings. (ISSN 0016-2507)

500 600 CC ISSN 1000-7857
KEJI DAOBAO/SCIENCE AND TECHNOLOGY HERALD. (Text in Chinese, English) bi-m. (New York Educational Foundation of Science and Technology, US) Zhongguo Keji Daobaoshe, 19 Dahuisi, Haidianqu, Beijing 100081, People's Republic of China. TEL 8313553. Ed. Meng Zhaoying.

500 CC ISSN 1000-7695
KEJI GUANLI YANJIU. (Text in Chinese) 1981. bi-m. Y15 (Asia $60; elsewhere $66). Zhongguo Kexueyuan, Guangzhou Fenyuan - Chinese Academy of Sciences, Guangzhou Branch, No. 100, Xianlie Zhonglu, Guangzhou, Guangdong 510070, People's Republic of China. TEL 86-20-7668145. (Co-sponsors: Guangdong Association of Science and Technology Management Research; Guangdong Province Science and Technology Commission; Guangzhou City S & T Commission.) Ed. Xu Huizhong. adv. contact: Liao Shengchu. software rev. **Document type:** academic/scholarly publication, proceedings.
Description: Covers management theories, management practices, science and technology development strategies, and personnel management.

500 600 CC ISSN 1001-7348
KEJI JINBU YU DUICE. (Text in Chinese) bi-m. Hubei Sheng Kexue Jishu Weiyuanhui, Xiaohongshan, Wuchang-qu, Wuhan, Hubei 430071, People's Republic of China. TEL 813110. Ed. Chen Hongyu.

500 600 CC ISSN 1003-014X
KEJI KAIFA DONGTAI/R & D INFORMATION. (Text in Chinese) 1988. bi-m. $24. Zhongguo Kexueyuan, Wenxian Qingbao Zhongxin - Chinese Academy of Sciences, Documentation Information Center, 8 Kexueyuan Nanlu, Zhongguancun, Beijing 100080, People's Republic of China. TEL 2566850. FAX 2566846. Ed. Chen Xueliang. **Document type:** academic/scholarly publication.
Description: Reports on the new products and technologies developed by the 123 institutes of the Chinese Academy of Sciences.

500 600 US
KEJI RIBAO/SCIENCE & TECHNOLOGY DAILY. (Text in Chinese) d. $329.40. China Books & Periodicals, Inc., 2929 24th St., San Francisco, CA 94110. TEL 415-282-2994. FAX 415-282-0994. **Document type:** newspaper.

KEJI YINGYU XUEXI/LEARNING ENGLISH FOR SCIENCE & TECHNOLOGY. see LINGUISTICS

KEJI YU FALU/SCIENCE, TECHNOLOGY AND LAW. see LAW

500 600 CC ISSN 1002-7084
KEJI YU FAZHAN/SCIENCE, TECHNOLOGY AND DEVELOPMENT. (Text in Chinese) q. Y2.10 per no. (Zhongguo Kexue Jishu Qingbao Yanjiusuo - Chinese Institute of Science and Technology Information) Kexue Jishu Wenxian Chubanshe, 15 Fuxing Lu, Beijing 100038, People's Republic of China. TEL 8015544. (Scientific and Technical Document Publishing House) Ed. Su Zhongjie.
—BLDSC (8164.831000).

KENKYU GIJUTSU KEIKAKU/JOURNAL OF SCIENCE POLICY AND RESEARCH MANAGEMENT. see BUSINESS AND ECONOMICS — Management

550
KENKYU JOSEIKIN JUKYUSHA KENKYU HOKOKUSHU. (Text in Japanese) 1984. a. Saneyoshi Shogakkai - Saneyoshi Scholarship Foundation, Nihon Bldg. 433, 6-2 Ote-machi 2-chome, Chiyoda-ku, Tokyo 100, Japan. abstr.
Description: Research reports of the foundation.

500 100 NE ISSN 0165-1773
KENNIS EN METHODE; tijdschrift voor wetenschapsfilosofie en methodologie. (Text in Dutch; summaries in English) 1977. 6/yr. fl.91.50 to individuals (foreign fl.141.50); institutions fl.162 (foreign fl.172) (effective 1994). Uitgeverij Boom, P.O. Box 400, 7940 AK Meppel, Netherlands. TEL 31-5220-57012. FAX 31-5220-53864. Ed.Bd. adv. circ. 675. **Indexed:** Phil.Ind.
—SWETS.

500 US ISSN 0023-0081
Q11 CODEN: TKASAT
KENTUCKY ACADEMY OF SCIENCE. TRANSACTIONS. 1939. s-a. $15 (foreign $30). Kentucky Academy of Science, c/o Vardley Wiedeman, University of Louisville, Louisville, KY 40292. TEL 502-588-5943. Ed. Branley A. Branson. charts; illus.; index. circ. 840. **Indexed:** Bibl.Agri., Biol.Abstr., Chem.Abstr., Excerp.Med., GeoRef., Helminthol.Abstr., Sci.Cit.Ind., Sel.Water Res.Abstr., Sport Fish.Abstr., Wild.Rev., Zoo.Rec. **Document type:** academic/scholarly publication.
—BLDSC (8977.000000); CASDDS; UnCover. *Refereed Serial*

500 600 KE
QH301 CODEN: KSTSDG
KENYA JOURNAL OF SCIENCES. SERIES A: PHYSICAL AND CHEMICAL SCIENCES. 1979. s-a. EAs.145($29) Kenya National Academy of Sciences, Box 39450, Nairobi, Kenya. Ed. J.O. Malo. (back issues avail.) **Indexed:** Chem.Abstr., Curr.Cont., Sci.Cit.Ind. **Document type:** academic/scholarly publication.
—CASDDS.
Former titles: Kenya Journal of Science and Technology. Series A: Physical and Chemical Sciences (ISSN 0250-8257); Kenya Science and Technology Journal.

500 600 KE
KENYA NATIONAL ACADEMY FOR ADVANCEMENT OF ARTS AND SCIENCES. NEWSLETTER. Short title: K N A A S News. 1977. a. Kenya National Academy for Advancement of Arts and Sciences, Box 47288, Nairobi, Kenya. Ed. Francis Inganji.

500 700 KE
KENYA NATIONAL ACADEMY OF SCIENCES. ANNUAL REPORT. (Text in English) a. Kenya National Academy of Science, Box 47288, Nairobi, Kenya.
Formerly: Kenya National Academy for Advancement of Arts and Sciences. Annual Report.

KENYA PAST AND PRESENT. see HISTORY — History Of Africa

500 CC ISSN 0368-6396
CODEN: KEZAEV
KEXUE (SHANGHAI)/SCIENCE. (Text in Chinese; abstract in English) 1915. bi-m. Y10.80 (foreign $10.80). Shanghai Scientific and Technical Publishers, Journal Department, 450 Ruijin 2 Lu, Shanghai 200020, People's Republic of China. Ed.Bd. adv. circ. 4,000.
●Also available online. Vendor(s): University Microfilms International.
—CASDDS.
Description: Introduces the frontiers of science and technology in the world and achievements by Chinese scientists.

SCIENCES: COMPREHENSIVE WORKS

500   CC
KEXUE DAGUANYUAN/GRAND VIEW GARDEN OF SCIENCE. JOURNAL. (Text in Chinese) bi-m. $0.40 per no. (Kexue Daguanyuan - Grand View Garden of Science) Guoji Shudian, Qikan Bu - China International Book Trading Corp., Chegongzhuang Xilu 21, P.O. Box 399, Beijing 100044, People's Republic of China.

KEXUE DUI SHEHUI DE YINGXIANG/SCIENCE IMPACT ON SOCIETY. see *SOCIAL SCIENCES: COMPREHENSIVE WORKS*

500   CC   ISSN 0454-0905
KEXUE HUABAO/SCIENCE PICTORIAL. (Text in Chinese) 1926. m. $5 per no. Shanghai Scientific and Technical Publishers, Journal Department, 450 Ruijin 2 Lu, Shanghai 200020, People's Republic of China. TEL 4370160. Ed. Xu Fusheng.

500 600   CC   ISSN 1002-7076
KEXUE JISHU YANJIU CHENGGUO GONGBAO/BULLETIN OF SCIENTIFIC AND TECHNOLOGICAL ACHIEVEMENTS. (Text in Chinese) m. Guojia Kewei, Chengguo Guanli Bangongshi - National Science Commission, Achievements Management Office, No. 15, Fuxing Lu, Beijing 100038, People's Republic of China. TEL 8015544. Ed. Wang Hongji.

500 600   CC   ISSN 1003-5680
KEXUE JISHU YU BIANZHENGFA/SCIENCE, TECHNOLOGY, AND DIALECTICS. (Text in Chinese) 1984. bi-m. Y6 (effective 1994). Shanxi Sheng Ziran Bianzhengfa Yanjiuhui - Shanxi Institute of Dialectics of Nature, Bldg. 128, Shanxi University, 36 Wucheng Rd., Taiyuan, Shanxi 030006, People's Republic of China. TEL 0351-7074871. (Co-sponsors: Shanxi University; Taiyuan University of Engineering and Technology) Ed. Zhang Jiazhi. adv. contact: Wang Hongqi. bk.rev. circ. 2,500.
Document type: academic/scholarly publication.
Description: Covers the philosophy of science, theory of technology, science and society, and the history of scientific development.

500   CC   ISSN 1003-1162
KEXUE SHIJIE/SCIENTIFIC WORLD. (Text in Chinese) m. $11.50. Science Press, Marketing and Sales Department, 16 Donghuangchenggen North St., Beijing 100707, People's Republic of China. TEL 4010642. FAX 4012180. TELEX 210247 SPBJ CN. **Document type:** academic/scholarly publication.
Description: Popular science magazine.

500   CC   ISSN 0379-4156
                   CODEN: KHSYAH
KEXUE SHIYAN/SCIENTIFIC EXPERIMENTS. (Text in Chinese) m. $0.40 per no. Shanghai Shudian, Qikan Bu - China International Book Trading Corp., Chegongzhuang Xilu 21, P.O. Box 399, Beijing 100044, People's Republic of China.
—CASDDS.

500   CC   ISSN 0023-074X
Q4   CODEN: KHTPAT
KEXUE TONGBAO. English edition: Chinese Science Bulletin (ISSN 1001-6538) (Text in Chinese, summaries in English) 1950. s-m. $298. (Chinese Academy of Sciences) Science Press, Marketing and Sales Department, 16 Donghuangchenggen North St., Beijing 100717, People's Republic of China. TEL 4010642. FAX 4019810. adv. circ. 15,000.
Indexed: Biol.Abstr., Chem.Abstr., Geo.Abstr., GeoRef., Helminthol.Abstr., Ind.Sci.Rev., INSPEC, Mass Spectr.Bull., Math.R., Sugar Ind.Abstr.
Document type: academic/scholarly publication.
—BLDSC (5091.500000); CASDDS.
Description: Presents concise reports on important recent results of scientific research in basic and applied sciences, reflecting the current level of development of science and technology in mainland China. Includes a letters column.
Refereed Serial

500   CC
KEXUE YU SHENGHUO/SCIENCE AND LIFE. (Text in Chinese) bi-m. Tianjin Kexue Jishu Chubanshe - Tianjin Science and Technology Press, 130 Shifeng Dao, Tianjin 300041, People's Republic of China. TEL 706821. Ed. Dou Xiurong.

500   CC   ISSN 1000-3398
KEXUE YU WENHUA/SCIENCE & CULTURE. (Text in Chinese) 1980. bi-m. $16.20. (Fujian Sheng Kexue Jishu Xiehui) Fujian Kexue Jishu Chubanshe - Fujian Science & Technology Publishers, 51 Hudong Lu, Fuzhou, Fujian 350003. TEL 550151. (Dist. in US by: China Books & Periodicals, Inc., 2929 24th St., San Francisco, CA 94110. TEL 415-282-2994) Ed. Zheng Qiguang.

500 630   CC   ISSN 1001-4284
KEXUE ZHIFU YU SHENGHUO/SCIENCE PROSPERITY AND LIFE. (Text in Chinese) 1978. m. Y1.00 per no. Science Press, Marketing and Sales Department, 16 Donghuangchenggen North St., Beijing 100717, People's Republic of China. TEL 4010642. FAX 4012180. TELEX 210247-SPBJ-CN. (US office: Science Press New York, Ltd., 8311 Alderton St., Rego Park, NY 11374. TEL 718-459-4638) Ed. Xu Tianxing. adv. circ. 100,000.
Former titles: Nongcun Kexue - Science in Countryside (ISSN 1000-307X); Nongcun Kexue Shiyan.
Description: Comprehensive popular science publication for rural areas of China. Covers agricultural techniques, rural architecture, energy resources, environmental protection, life and hygiene.

500 658   CC   ISSN 1000-2995
Q180.55.M3
KEYAN GUANLI/SCIENCE RESEARCH MANAGEMENT. (Text in Chinese) 1980. bi-m. $50.80. (Chinese Academy of Sciences, Institute of Science and Technology Policy Management) Science Press, Marketing and Sales Department, 16 Donghuangchenggen North St., Beijing 100717, People's Republic of China. TEL 4010642. FAX 4019810. Ed. Luo Wei. adv. circ. 21,000.
Document type: academic/scholarly publication.
—BLDSC (8164.191700).
Description: Explores the characteristics and laws of modern scientific development, theories and methods of science research management, scientific and technological policies, research systems, personnel training, and trends in newly emerging areas of research.

500 600   VN
KHOA HOC KY THUAT KINH TE THE GIOI/WORLD SCIENCE, TECHNOLOGY AND ECONOMY. 1982. w. 5 Ly Thuong Kiet, Hanoi, Socialist Republic of Vietnam. TEL 52931.

500   VN   ISSN 0866-7942
KHOA HOC VA DOI SONG/SCIENCE AND LIFE. 1959. fortn. 70 Tran Hung Dao St., Hanoi, Socialist Republic of Vietnam. TEL 53427. (Dist. abroad by: Xunhasaba - Export and Import Revue Company, 32, Hai Ba Trung St., Hanoi, Vietnam. TEL 252313) Ed. Duong Hong Dat. circ. 25,000.

500   SU   ISSN 1018-3647
Q80.S2   CODEN: JKSSED
KING SAUD UNIVERSITY. JOURNAL. SCIENCE. Key Title: Magallat Gami'at al-Malik Sa'ud, al-'Ulum. (Other sections avail.: Administrative Sciences, Agricultural Sciences, Architecture and Planning, Arts, Computer and Information Sciences, Educational Sciences and Islamic Studies, Engineering Sciences) (Text in Arabic, English) 1969. s-a. $10. King Saud University, University Libraries, P.O Box 22480, Riyadh 11495, Saudi Arabia. TEL 966-1-4676148. FAX 966-1-4676162. TELEX 401019 KSU SJ. Ed. Mohammed I. Al-Hassan. charts; illus. circ. 2,000.
Indexed: Curr.Adv.Ecol.Sci., Herb.Abstr., INSPEC (1991-), Seed Abstr. **Document type:** academic/scholarly publication.
—CASDDS; UMI.
Former titles (until 1989): King Saud University. College of Science. Journal (ISSN 0735-9799); University of Riyadh. Faculty of Sciences. Bulletin.
Refereed Serial

500 600   JA   ISSN 0386-4928
Q77   CODEN: KDRKBB
KINKI DAIGAKU RIKOGAKUBU KENKYU HOKOKU/KINKI UNIVERSITY. FACULTY OF SCIENCE AND TECHNOLOGY. JOURNAL. (Text in English and Japanese; summaries in English) 1966. a. Kinki Daigaku, Rikogakubu - Kinki University, Faculty of Science and Technology, 4-1 Kowakae 3-chome, Higashi-Osaka-shi, Osaka-fu 577, Japan. **Indexed:** Chem.Abstr., INIS Atomind., Jap.Per.Ind.
—BLDSC (4747.400000).

500.9 913   US   ISSN 0075-6245
QH1   CODEN: KIRTA4
KIRTLANDIA. 1967. irreg., no.47, 1985. price varies. Cleveland Museum of Natural History, One Wade Oval Dr., University Circle, Cleveland, OH 44106. TEL 216-231-4600. Ed. Joseph Hannibal. circ. 850.
Indexed: Biol.Abstr., GeoRef., Zoo.Rec.
—BLDSC (5097.590000).

KISO, KANKYO KAGAKU KENKYU/HIROSHIMA UNIVERSITY. FACULTY OF INTEGRATED ARTS AND SCIENCES. SCIENCE REPORTS. see *ENVIRONMENTAL STUDIES*

500   JA   ISSN 0386-0655
KITAKAMI-SHIRITSU HAKUBUTSUKAN KENKYU HOKOKU/KITAKAMI CITY MUSEUM. BULLETIN. (Text in Japanese) 1975. irreg. 1500 Yen. Kitakami-shiritsu Hakubutsukan - Kitakami City Museum, 14-59 Tachibana, Kitakami-shi, Iwate-ken 024, Japan. TEL 0197-64-1756. Dir. Yoshikazu Takata. **Document type:** bulletin.
Description: Features comprehensive coverage on the humanities and natural sciences.

500.9   JA   ISSN 0387-964X
                   CODEN: KHKHEW
KITAKYUSHU SHIRITSU SHIZENSHI HAKUBUTSUKAN KENKYU HOKOKU/KITAKYUSHU MUSEUM OF NATURAL HISTORY. BULLETIN. (Text in English and Japanese) 1979. a. universities and libraries on exchange basis. Kitakyushu Shiritsu Shizenshi Hakubutsukan - Kitakyushu Museum and Institute of Natural History, 3-6 Nishihon-machi, Yahatahigashi-ku, Kitakyushu-shi, Fukuoka-ken, Japan. TEL 093-661-7308. FAX 093-661-7503. Ed. Masamichi Ota. circ. 1,200. **Indexed:** Sport Fish.Abstr., Wild.Rev., Zoo.Rec. **Document type:** bulletin.
Description: Covers original articles and short notes on natural history

KNOWLEDGE; dedicated to the dissemination of knowledge for the happiness, health, security, and survival of humankind. see *LITERARY AND POLITICAL REVIEWS*

500   JA   ISSN 0287-6515
KOBE DAIGAKU DAIGAKUIN SHIZEN KAGAKU KENKYUKA KIYO B/KOBE UNIVERSITY. GRADUATE SCHOOL OF SCIENCE AND TECHNOLOGY. MEMOIRS. SERIES B. (Text in Japanese; summaries in English and Japanese) 1983. a. Kobe Daigaku, Daigakuin Shizen Kagaku Kenkyuka - Kobe University, Graduate School of Science and Technology, 1-1, Rokkodai-cho, Nada-ku, Kobe-shi, Hyogo-ken 657, Japan. abstr.

500   JA   ISSN 0389-9578
KOBE TOKIWA TANKI DAIGAKU KIYO/KOBE TOKIWA COLLEGE. BULLETIN. (Text in English and Japanese) 1971. a. free. Kobe Tokiwa Tanki Daigaku - Kobe Tokiwa College, 2-6-2 Otani-cho, Nagata-ku, Kobe-shi 653, Japan. TEL 078-611-1821. FAX 078-643-4361. Ed. Reiko Shimomura. circ. 650. (back issues avail.)
Description: Covers topics in the fields of liberal arts, pedagogy, medical science and technology.

500   JA   ISSN 0450-609X
VK4   CODEN: KDKRDX
KOBE UNIVERSITY OF MERCANTILE MARINE. REVIEW. PART 2. MARITIME STUDIES, AND SCIENCE AND ENGINEERING. (Text in Japanese; abstracts in English) 1953. a. Kobe University of Mercantile Marine - Kobe Shosen Daigaku, 1-1, Fukaeminami-cho 5-chome, Higashinada-ku, Kobe-shi, Hyogo-ken 658, Japan. **Indexed:** INIS Atomind.
—BLDSC (7786.250000); CASDDS.
Formerly (until 1980): Kobe University of Mercantile Marine. Review. Part 2. Navigation, Marine Engineering, Nuclear Engineering and Scientific Section.

551.44   SP   ISSN 0214-6967
KOBIE, REVISTA DE BELLAS ARTES Y CIENCIAS: SERIE CIENCIAS NATURALES. (Text in Basque, English and Spanish; summaries in English and French) 1969. a. 2000 ptas. Diputacion Foral de Bizkaia, Departamento de Cultura, P.O. Box 97, Bilbao, Spain. TEL 34-4-415-7217. FAX 34-4-416-2981. (back issues avail.)
Supersedes in part (in 1985): Kobie. Paleoantropologia y Ciencias Naturales (ISSN 0214-7963); Which supersedes in part (in 1984): Kobie (ISSN 0211-1942)

5870 SCIENCES: COMPREHENSIVE WORKS

500   JA   ISSN 0389-0244
CODEN: KDGAAR
KOCHI DAIGAKU GAKUJUTSU KENKYU HOKOKU. SHIZEN KAGAKU/KOCHI UNIVERSITY. RESEARCH REPORTS. NATURAL SCIENCE. (Text in English and Japanese; summaries in English) 1951. a. Kochi Daigaku - Kochi University, 5-1 Akebono-cho 2-chome, Kochi-shi, Kochi-ken 780, Japan. **Indexed:** Chem.Abstr., Jap.Per.Ind.
—CASDDS.

KOCHI DAIGAKU KYOIKUGAKUBU KENKYU HOKOKU. DAI-3-BU/KOCHI UNIVERSITY. FACULTY OF EDUCATION. BULLETIN. SERIES 3. see *EDUCATION*

500   JA   ISSN 0452-2486
CODEN: KJDSA6
KOCHI JOSHI DAIGAKU KIYO. SHIZEN KAGAKU HEN/KOCHI WOMEN'S UNIVERSITY. BULLETIN. SERIES OF NATURAL SCIENCES. (Text and summaries in English and Japanese) 1952. a. Kochi Joshi Daigaku - Kochi Women's University, 5-15 Eikokuji-cho, Kochi-shi, Kochi-ken 780, Japan. Dir. Katsuhiko Ikuta. **Indexed:** Chem.Abstr., Jap.Per.Ind. **Document type:** bulletin.
—BLDSC (2600.135000).

KOKURITSU KAGAKU HAKUBUTSUKAN NENPO. see *MUSEUMS AND ART GALLERIES*

500   JA   ISSN 0082-4755
KOKURITSU KAGAKU HAKUBUTSUKAN SENPO/NATIONAL SCIENCE MUSEUM. MEMOIRS. (Text in English and Japanese; summaries in English) 1968. a. exchange basis. Monbusho, Kokuritsu Kagaku Hakubutsukan - Ministry of Education, National Science Museum, 7-20 Ueno Koen, Taito-ku, Tokyo 110, Japan. Ed.Bd. circ. 1,000 (controlled). **Indexed:** Biol.Abstr., Curr.Adv.Ecol.Sci., GeoRef., Jap.Per.Ind.
—BLDSC (5627.700000).

069   JA   ISSN 0288-7975
KOMATSU-SHIRITSU HAKUBUTSUKAN KENKYU KIYO/KOMATSU CITY MUSEUM. MEMOIRS. (Text in Japanese) 1965. a. price varies. Komatsu-shiritsu Hakubutsukan - Komatsu City Museum, Rojo Koen, Marunouchi Koen-machi, Komatsu-shi, Ishikawa-ken 923, Japan. circ. 500.

500   JA   ISSN 0452-4160
Q1   CODEN: MKOUAS
KONAN DAIGAKU KIYO. RIGAKU HEN/KONAN UNIVERSITY. SCIENCE SERIES. (Text and summaries in English and Japanese) 1955. a. Konan Daigaku - Konan University, 9-1 Okamoto 8-chome, Higashi-nada-ku, Kobe-shi, Hyogo-ken 658, Japan. **Indexed:** Biol.Abstr., Chem.Abstr., INIS Atomind, Jap.Per.Ind.
—BLDSC (5623.200000); CASDDS.

068.489   DK   ISSN 0368-7201
KONGELIGE DANSKE VIDENSKABERNES SELSKAB. OVERSIGT OVER SELSKABETS VIRKSOMHED. (Text in Danish; summary in English) 1814. a. Kongelige Danske Videnskabernes Selskab - Royal Danish Academy of Sciences and Letters, H.C. Andersens Blvd. 35, DK-1553 Copenhagen V, Denmark. TEL 45-33-12-85-70. FAX 45-33-12-93-87. (Orders to: Munksgaard Export and Subscription Service, P.O. Box 2148, Noerre Soegade 35, DK-1060 Copenhagen K, Denmark) illus. **Indexed:** Biol.Abstr., Chem.Abstr. **Document type:** monographic series.
—BLDSC (6317.790000).
Formerly (until 1932): Oversigt over det Kongelige Danske Videnskabernes Selskabs Forhandlinger (ISSN 0369-7169)

068 500   NO   ISSN 0368-6302
AS283   CODEN: KNSFA2
KONGELIGE NORSKE VIDENSKABERS SELSKAB. FORHANDLINGER. 1926. a. Erling Skakkes gt. 47 b, N-7013 Trondheim, Norway. TEL 47-73-59-21-57. FAX 47-73-59-58-95. (U.S. addr.: Publications Expediting Inc., 200 Meacham Ave., Elmont, NY 11003) Ed. Nils Soevik. **Indexed:** A.I.C.E., Anthropol.Lit., Biol.Abstr., INSPEC, Math.R. **Document type:** corporate report.
—BLDSC (5107.000000).
Formerly: Kongelige Norske Videnskabers Selskab. Aarsberetning.
Description: Includes reports of meetings, selected lectures, and list of members.

001.3 500   NO   ISSN 0368-6310
CODEN: KNSSA7
KONGELIGE NORSKE VIDENSKABERS SELSKAB. SKRIFTER/ROYAL NORWEGIAN SOCIETY OF SCIENCES AND LETTERS. PUBLICATIONS. (Text in English) 1761. irreg. price varies. Erling Skakkes gt. 47 b, N-7013 Trondheim, Norway. TEL 47-73-59-21-57. FAX 47-73-59-58-95. (U.S. addr.: Publications Expediting Inc., 200 Meacham Ave., Elmont, NY 11003) Ed. Nils Soevik. charts; illus.; stat. **Indexed:** Biol.Abstr., Chem.Abstr., Deep Sea Res.& Oceanogr.Abstr., INSPEC, Math.R. **Document type:** monographic series, academic/scholarly publication.
—BLDSC (5109.000000); CASDDS.
Refereed Serial

500   BE   ISSN 0770-7665
CODEN: VKKWAB
KONINKLIJKE ACADEMIE VOOR WETENSCHAPPEN, LETTEREN EN SCHONE KUNSTEN VAN BELGIE. VERHANDELINGEN. KLASSE DER WETENSCHAPPEN. 1941. irreg. Koninklijke Academie voor Wetenschappen, Letteren en Schone Kunsten van Belgie, 1 Hertogsstraat, B-1000 Brussels, Belgium. **Document type:** monographic series.
—CASDDS.
Formerly (until 1972): Koninklijke Vlaamse Academie voor Wetenschappen, Letteren en Schone Kunsten. Verhandeling. Klasse der Wetenschappen (ISSN 0372-6916)

500   NE   ISSN 0065-552X
KONINKLIJKE NEDERLANDSE AKADEMIE VAN WETENSCHAPPEN. AFDELING NATUURKUNDE. VERHANDELINGEN. TWEEDE REEKS. (Text in English, French, German and Dutch) 1893. irreg., vol.87, 1989. price varies. Elsevier Science B.V., Books Division, P.O. Box 211, 1000 AE Amsterdam, Netherlands. TEL 31-20-4853911. FAX 31-20-4853705. TELEX 18582 ESPA NL. E-mail: nlinfo-f@elsevier.nl; usinfo-f@elsevier.com; forinfo-kyf04035@niftyserve.or.jp; Site addr.: http://www.elsevier.nl/. (Subscr. in U.S. and Canada to: Elsevier Science Inc., Box 882, Madison Sq. Sta., New York, NY 10159. TEL 212-989-5800) Ed. A.M. Verheggen. adv.; bk.rev. circ. 1,000. **Document type:** monographic series.
Refereed Serial

500   GW   ISSN 0023-4230
Q3   CODEN: KSMSAC
KOSMOS. 1904. m. DM.104.40 (student DM.93). (Kosmos Gesellschaft der Naturfreunde) Deutsche Verlags-Anstalt GmbH, Postfach 106012, 70094 Stuttgart, Germany. TEL 0711-2631-0. FAX 0711-2631292. Ed. R. Koethe. adv.; bk.rev.; charts; illus.; index; circ. 71,201 (controlled). **Indexed:** GeoRef., INIS Atomind., Protozool.Abstr. **Document type:** consumer publication.
—BLDSC (5114.010000). CCC.
Description: Non-technical and popular magazine covering natural science subjects such as plants, animals, environmental protection, geology, astronomy, physics, technology, and medicine. Includes readers' comments, questions and answers.

KOTONOURA. see *MUSEUMS AND ART GALLERIES*

KULTURBERICHTE AUS NIEDEROESTERREICH. see *ART*

500   JA   ISSN 0454-6148
KUMAMOTO DAIGAKU KYOIKUGAKUBU KIYO. SHIZEN KAGAKU/KUMAMOTO UNIVERSITY. FACULTY OF EDUCATION. MEMOIRS. NATURAL SCIENCE. (Text and summaries in English and Japanese) 1953. a. Kumamoto Daigaku, Kyoikugakubu - Kumamoto University, Faculty of Education, 40-1, Kurokami 2-chome, Kumamoto-shi, Kumamoto-ken 860, Japan. TEL 096-343-1800. circ. 300. **Indexed:** Biol.Abstr., Chem.Abstr., INIS Atomind., Jap.Per.Ind.
—BLDSC (5593.310000).

500   JA   ISSN 0286-5769
Q4
KUMAMOTO DAIGAKU KYOYOBU KIYO. SHIZEN KAGAKU HEN/KUMAMOTO UNIVERSITY. FACULTY OF GENERAL EDUCATION. MEMOIRS. NATURAL SCIENCES. (Text and summaries in English and Japanese) 1966. a. Kumamoto Daigaku, Kyoyobu - Kumamoto University, Faculty of General Education, 40-1, Kurokami 2-chome, Kumamoto-shi, Kumamoto-ken 860, Japan. **Indexed:** Jap.Per.Ind.

500 060   SW   ISSN 0081-9956
KUNGLIGA VETENSKAPSAKADEMIEN. BIDRAG TILL KUNGLIGA VETENSKAPSAKADEMIENS HISTORIA. 1963. irreg., vol.24, 1991. Kungliga Vetenskapsakademien - Royal Swedish Academy of Sciences, P.O. Box 50005, S-104 05 Stockholm, Sweden. FAX 46-8-155670.

500 700   NE   ISSN 0927-3506
KUNST EN WETENSCHAP. 1992. 4/yr. fl.18. De Studenten Uitgeverij, Smidstraat 12, 8746 NG Schraard, Netherlands. TEL 31-5175-31583. FAX 31-5175-32042. Ed. J. Willems. adv.; bk.rev. circ. 12,500.

500   JA   ISSN 0286-9500
KUOKU/QUARK. (Text in Japanese) 1982. m. Kodansha Ltd., 12-21 Otowa 2-chome, Bunkyo-ku, Tokyo 112, Japan. TEL 03-5395-3519. FAX 03-3942-7203. TELEX J34509 KODANSHA. Ed. Kazuya Yanagida. adv.; bk.rev. circ. 90,000.

500.9   JA   ISSN 0913-1566
KURASHIKI-SHIRITSU SHIZENSHI HAKUBUTSUKAN KENKYU HOKOKU/KURASHIKI MUSEUM OF NATURAL HISTORY. BULLETIN. (Text in Japanese; summaries in English and Japanese) 1986. a. 430 Yen. Kurashiki-shiritsu Shizenshi Hakubutsukan - Kurashiki Museum of Natural History, 6-1 Chuo 2-chome, Kurashiki, Okayama 710, Japan. TEL 0864-25-6037. FAX 0864-25-6038. abstr. (back issues avail.)
Description: Contains mainly original papers.

KURASHIKI-SHIRITSU SHIZENSHI HAKUBUTSUKANPO. see *MUSEUMS AND ART GALLERIES*

500 069   JA   ISSN 0912-1897
KUSHIRO-SHIRITSU HAKUBUTSUKAN KIYO/KUSHIRO CITY MUSEUM. MEMOIRS. (Text in Japanese; summaries in English and Japanese) 1972. a. Kushiro-shiritsu Hakubutsukan - Kushiro City Museum, 1-7 Shunkodai, Kushiro-shi, Hokkaido 085, Japan. FAX 0154-41-5809. **Document type:** bulletin.

500   KU   ISSN 0250-4065
T1   CODEN: ARKRDL
KUWAIT INSTITUTE FOR SCIENTIFIC RESEARCH. ANNUAL RESEARCH REPORT. (Text in English) 1977. a. free. Kuwait Institute for Scientific Research, P.O. Box 24885, 13109 Safat, Kuwait. TEL 965-4836100. FAX 965-4846891. TELEX 22299 KISR KT. Ed.Bd. circ. 2,000. (back issues avail.) **Indexed:** Chem.Abstr. **Document type:** corporate report, newsletter.
—CASDDS.
Description: Contains articles meant to promote scientific and applied research in relation to industry, energy, environment, natural resources, food resources and economics.

500 510   RU   ISSN 0130-2221
QA1
KVANT. English translation: Quantum (New York) (US ISSN 1048-8820) (Text in Russian) 1970. bi-m. $60 (effective 1996). (Rossiyskaya Akademiya Nauk, Quantum Bureau - Russian Academy of Sciences, Quantum Bureau) Kvant Magazine, K-6 1st Tverskaya-Yamskaya 2-1, 103006 Moscow, Russia.
Description: Science and math magazine for children.

500   KO
KWAHAK DONG-A. 1986. m. Dong-A Ilbo, 139 Sejongno, Chongno-gu, Seoul, S. Korea. TEL 02-721-7114. Ed. Kwon O-Kie. circ. 52,000.

500   KN   ISSN 1019-4223
KWAHAKWON TONGBO/BULLETIN OF THE ACADEMY OF SCIENCES. (Text in Korean) bi-m. Korean Academy of Sciences, Pyongyang, N. Korea.

KWANSEI GAKUIN DAIGAKU RIGAKUBU TSUSHIN. see *COLLEGE AND ALUMNI*

SCIENCES: COMPREHENSIVE WORKS

607   PL   ISSN 0023-589X
Q4
KWARTALNIK HISTORII NAUKI I TECHNIKI/QUARTERLY JOURNAL OF THE HISTORY OF SCIENCE AND TECHNOLOGY. 1956. q. $38. Polska Akademia Nauk, Instytut Historii Nauki, Ul. Nowy Swiat 72, Palac Staszica, 00-330 Warsaw, Poland. TEL 48-22-268754. FAX 48-22-266137. (Dist. by: Ars Polona, Krakowskie Przedmiescie 7, 00-068 Warsaw, Poland) bk.rev.; abstr.; charts; illus.; index, cum.index every 10 yrs. circ. 740. (tabloid format) **Indexed:** Amer.Hist.& Life, Chem.Abstr., Hist.Abstr., Math.R.

500   JA   ISSN 0912-6449
KYODO TO KAGAKU/NATURE AND SCIENCE. (Text in Japanese) 1954. s-a. 1000 Yen. Hokkaido Kyoiku Daigaku, Sapporo Ko Chigaku Kyoshitsu, 1-5, 5-jo 3-chome, Ainosato, Kita-ku, Sapporo, Hokkaido 002, Japan. FAX 011-778-8822. Ed. Masaichi Kimura. **Document type:** academic/scholarly publication. **Description:** Contains original papers, reviews, commentary, and news on nature and science.

509   JA   ISSN 0023-6004
KYOKUCHI/POLAR NEWS. (Text in Japanese) 1965. s-a. 6000 Yen (effective May 1991). Japan Polar Research Association - Nihon Kyokuchi Kenkyu Shinkokai, 2-3-4 Hirakawacho, Chiyoda-ku, Tokyo 102, Japan. TEL 81-3-3239-7615. FAX 81-3-3239-7617. Ed. Yoshimichi Harada. adv.; bk.rev.; charts; illus.; stat. circ. 3,000. **Indexed:** Geo.Abstr., Meteor.& Geoastrophys.Abstr. **Document type:** newsletter. **Description:** Contains Antarctic and Arctic information and relevant news on geoscience and polar-science.

500   JA
KYOTO-FURITSU DAIGAKU GAKUJUTSU HOKOKU: RIGAKU SEIKATSU KAGAKU/KYOTO PREFECTURAL UNIVERSITY. SCIENTIFIC REPORTS: NATURAL SCIENCE AND LIVING SCIENCE. (Text in Japanese) 1952. irreg. exchange basis only. Kyoto Prefectural University - Kyoto-furitsu Daigaku, Shimogamo Hangi-cho, Sakyo-ku, Kyoto 606, Japan. TEL 075-781-3131. FAX 075-723-2670. **Indexed:** C.I.S.Abstr., Food Sci.& Tech.Abstr., INIS Atomind., Math.R. **Document type:** academic/scholarly publication.
—BLDSC (8198.450000).
Formerly: Kyoto Prefectural University. Scientific Reports: Natural Science, Domestic Science and Social Welfare (ISSN 0075-739X)

505 605   JA   ISSN 0911-0305
Q77.K74   CODEN: MFETEC
KYOTO INSTITUTE OF TECHNOLOGY. FACULTY OF ENGINEERING AND DESIGN. MEMOIRS. (Text in English and European languages) 1952. a. exchange basis. Kyoto Institute of Technology, Faculty of Engineering and Design - Kyoto Kogei Sen'i Daigaku Kogeigakubu, Matsugasaki, Sakyo-ku, Kyoto 606, Japan. circ. 790. **Indexed:** Chem.Abstr., Energy Info.Abstr., INSPEC, Math.R.
—BLDSC (5593.345000); CASDDS.
Formerly: Kyoto Technical University. Faculty of Industrial Arts. Memoirs: Science and Technology (ISSN 0453-0047)

KYOTO KYOIKU DAIGAKU KIYO. B. SHIZEN KAGAKU/KYOTO UNIVERSITY OF EDUCATION. BULLETIN. SERIES B: MATHEMATICS AND NATURAL SCIENCE. see MATHEMATICS

500   JA   ISSN 0287-7902
CODEN: KSRODS
KYOTO SANGYO DAIGAKU RONSHU. SHIZEN KAGAKU KEIRETSU/ACTA HUMANISTICA ET SCIENTIFICA UNIVERSITATIS SANGIO KYOTIENSIS. NATURAL SCIENCE SERIES. (Text and summaries in English and Japanese) 1972. a. Kyoto Sangyo Daigaku - Kyoto Sangyo University, Motoyama, Kamigamo, Kita-ku, Kyoto-shi, Kyoto-fu 603, Japan. **Indexed:** Chem.Abstr.
—CASDDS.

500.2   JA   ISSN 0368-9689
Q77   CODEN: MFKPAQ
KYOTO UNIVERSITY. FACULTY OF SCIENCE. MEMOIRS. SERIES OF PHYSICS, ASTROPHYSICS, GEOPHYSICS AND CHEMISTRY. (Text in English) 1914. s-a. exchange basis. Kyoto University, Faculty of Science - Kyoto Daigaku Rigakubu, Kitashirakawa Oiwake-cho, Sakyo-ku, Kyoto 606, Japan. illus. **Indexed:** Chem.Abstr., Deep Sea Res.& Oceanogr.Abstr., INSPEC, JTA.
—BLDSC (5597.900000); CASDDS; UnCover.

KYUSHU INSTITUTE OF TECHNOLOGY. BULLETIN: MATHEMATICS, NATURAL SCIENCE/KYUSHU KOGYO DAIGAKU KENKYU HOKOKU: SHIZEN KAGAKU. see MATHEMATICS

KYUSHU INSTITUTE OF TECHNOLOGY. BULLETIN: SCIENCE AND TECHNOLOGY/KYUSHU KOGYO DAIGAKU KENKYU HOKOKU: KOGAKU. see TECHNOLOGY: COMPREHENSIVE WORKS

500   US   ISSN 0882-1305
QC789.U62
L B L RESEARCH REVIEW. 1985. 3/yr. free to qualified personnel. University of California at Berkeley, Lawrence Berkeley Laboratory, Public Information Department, 1 Cyclotron Rd., Berkeley, CA 94720. TEL 510-486-6598. FAX 510-486-6641. Ed. Adrienne Kopa. bk.rev. circ. 8,000. (back issues avail.) **Indexed:** Energy Rev., Environ.Per.Bibl. (1990-), INIS Atomind. **Document type:** academic/scholarly publication.
—BLDSC (5162.213600); UnCover.
Formerly (until 1985): L B L News Magazine.
Description: Reviews important research accomplishments at the laboratory.

LAB TALK. see EDUCATION — Teaching Methods And Curriculum

500   SP   ISSN 0213-7275
LAB 2000. 1985. 6/yr. 3000 ptas. (effective 1995). Ediciones Mayo, S.A., Muntaner 374, 4o, 08006 Barcelona, Spain. TEL 34-3-2090255. FAX 34-3-2020643. Ed. J.L. Marin Soria. adv. contact: Ferran Montoliu. circ. 5,000 (controlled). **Document type:** academic/scholarly publication.
Description: Covers microbiology, analytical chemistry, laboratory techniques, parasitology, immunology and hematology.

500 619   IT
LABNEWS. 12/yr. Gruppo Editoriale Jackson S.p.A., Via Rosellini 12, 20124 Milan. TEL 02-680-368. circ. 10,000.

500   IE
LABORATORY. 9/yr. 128 Lower Baggot St., Dublin, Ireland. TEL 619236. FAX 612417. Ed. John Low.

500 658   US   ISSN 1060-5118
LABORATORY INDUSTRY REPORT; the bi-monthly on lab management and marketing intelligence. 1992. bi-m. $192. Washington G-2 Reports, 1111 14th St., N.W., Ste. 500, Washington, DC 20005. TEL 202-789-1034; 800-LAB-REGS. FAX 202-289-4062. Ed. Jim Curren; Pub. Dennis Weismann. circ. 1,000. (looseleaf format; back issues avail.) **Document type:** trade publication.
Description: Offers a wealth of analysis of market trends, industry developments, and insights on evolving business arrangements. Aimed at lab industry executives, lab marketers, and lab directors.

LABORATORY PRACTICE; research techniques and equipment. see MEDICAL SCIENCES — Experimental Medicine, Laboratory Technique

LANTERN; cultural journal. see EDUCATION

LASER. see TECHNOLOGY: COMPREHENSIVE WORKS

500   LV   ISSN 0868-6556
AS262   CODEN: LZAVEP
LATVIJAS ZINATNU AKADEMIJAS VESTIS. (In 2 parts) (Text in English, German, Latvian; summaries in English, German) 1947. m. $18020. Latvijas Zinatny Akademijas - Latvian Academy of Sciences, Turgeneva iela, 19, Riga LV-1524, Latvia. TEL 371-2-223732. Ed. Inta Rozenvalde. bk.rev.; abstr.; bibl.; charts; illus.; index. circ. 800 (Part A); 600 (Part B). **Indexed:** Abstr.Bull.Inst.Pap.Chem., Amer.Hist.& Life, Biol.Abstr., Chem.Abstr., Crop Physiol.Abstr., Field Crop Abstr., Forest.Abstr., Forest Prod.Abstr., Hist.Abstr., Hort.Abstr., INIS Atomind., INSPEC (1992-), M.L.A., Mass Spectr.Bull., Math.R., Numis.Lit., Plant Breed.Abstr., Plant Grow.Reg.Abstr., Soils & Fert., World Agri.Econ.& Rural Sociol.Abstr.
—BLDSC (5160.558100); CASDDS.
Formerly (until 1990): Latvijas P.S.R. Zinatnu Akademijas Vestis (ISSN 0132-6422)

500 539   US
QC789.U62
LAWRENCE BERKELEY LABORATORY. CATALOG OF RESEARCH PROJECTS. 1967. a. free. Lawrence Berkeley Laboratory, Technology Transfer Office, Bldg. 71F, Berkeley, CA 94720. TEL 415-486-6502. FAX 415-486-5401. circ. 12,500. (back issues avail.)
Formerly: Lawrence Berkeley Laboratory. Research Highlights (ISSN 0091-9489)

500.2   UK   ISSN 0260-1036
LEEDS NATURALISTS' CLUB AND SCIENTIFIC ASSOCIATION. NEWSLETTER. 1976. s-a. £3 membership. Leeds Naturalists' Club and Scientific Association, c/o Mrs. P.P. Abbott, 73 Ridgeway, Leeds LS8 4DD, England. Ed. A. Hawkswell. bk.rev. circ. 200.

500   UK
LEEDS PHILOSOPHICAL AND LITERARY SOCIETY. PROCEEDINGS. SCIENTIFIC. 1925. a. price varies. Leeds Philosophical and Literary Society, Central Museum, Calverley St., Leeds 2, England. Ed. H. Pantin. charts; index. circ. 650. **Indexed:** Biol.Abstr., Br.Hum.Ind., Curr.Adv.Ecol.Sci., GeoRef., INSPEC. **Document type:** proceedings.
Description: Presents articles on any area of scientific investigation.

500 300   GW   ISSN 0947-5850
▼**LEIBNIZ-SOZIETAET. SITZUNGSBERICHTE.** 1994. 10/yr. DM.290. Reinhardt Becker Verlag, Postfach 53, 16721 Velten, Germany. TEL 03304-397430. FAX 03304-397432. Ed. Herbert Woeltge. **Document type:** academic/scholarly publication.
Description: Publishes scientific lectures given during sessions of the Leibniz Society as well as announcements and information from this association of academics.

LEONARDO: ART SCIENCE AND TECHNOLOGY; oriented towards readers interested in the application of contemporary science and technology to music and the arts. see ART

LEVENDE NATUUR; tijdschrift voor natuurbehoud en natuurbeheer. see CONSERVATION

500   CC   ISSN 1000-1735
Q4   CODEN: LSDKEQ
LIAONING SHIFAN DAXUE XUEBAO (ZIRAN KEXUE BAN)/LIAONING NORMAL UNIVERSITY. JOURNAL (NATURAL SCIENCE EDITION). (Text in Chinese) 1984. q. Liaoning Shifan Daxue - Liaoning Normal University, 850 Huanghe Lu, Dalian, Liaoning 116022, People's Republic of China. TEL 401181. Ed. Zheng Yingshun.
—CASDDS.

500   US   ISSN 0075-9104
LIBRARY OF EXACT PHILOSOPHY. Short title: L E P. (Text in English and German) 1970. irreg. price varies. Springer-Verlag, 175 Fifth Ave., New York, NY 10010. TEL 212-460-1500. FAX 212-473-6272. (Also: Berlin, Heidelberg, Tokyo and Vienna) Ed. M. Bunge. (reprint service avail. from ISI) **Document type:** academic/scholarly publication.

SCIENCES: COMPREHENSIVE WORKS

500   LY   ISSN 0368-7481
Q1   CODEN: LBJSAP
LIBYAN JOURNAL OF SCIENCES; an international journal. (Text in English; summaries in Arabic) 1971. s-a. $3.50 to individuals; institutions $5.25. Al-Fateh University, Faculty of Science, P.O. Box 13040, Tripoli, Libya. Ed. M. J. Salem. adv. circ. 400. **Indexed:** Amer.Abstr., Chem.Abstr., GeoRef., Math.R., Petrol.Abstr.
— CASDDS.

LIFE IN ACTION MAGAZINE. see *PHILOSOPHY*

500   UK   ISSN 0024-3205
QH301   CODEN: LIFSAK
LIFE SCIENCES. (Text in English, French and German) 1962. 52/yr. $2750 to institutions (effective 1996). Elsevier Science Ltd., Pergamon, P.O. Box 800, Kidlington, Oxford OX5 1DX, England. TEL 44-1865-843000. FAX 44-1865-843010. E-mail: nlinfo-f@elsevier.nl; usinfo-f@elsevier.com; forinfo-kyf04035@niftyserve.or.jp; Site addr.: http://www.elsevier.nl/. (Subscr. in U.S. and Canada to: Elsevier Science, 660 White Plains Rd., Tarrytown, NY 10591-5153. TEL 914-524-9200. FAX 914-333-2444) Eds. Rubin Bressler, Thomas F. Burks. adv.; charts; illus.; index. circ. 2,200. (also avail. in microfiche from MIM; microfilm from UMI; back issues avail.) **Indexed:** Anim.Breed.Abstr., Biol.Abstr., Chem.Abstr., Curr.Cont., Dent.Ind., Excerp.Med., Geo.Abstr., Ind.Med., Kidney, Med.& Surg.Dermat., Nutr.Abstr., Protozool.Abstr., Psychol.Abstr. (1984-), Rev.Med.& Vet.Mycol., Sport Fish.Abstr., Wild.Rev., Zoo.Rec. **Document type:** academic/scholarly publication.
— BLDSC (5208.930000); ADONIS; CASDDS; EMDOCS; Faxon; Genuine Article; SWETS; UMI; UnCover. **CCC.**
    Formed by the 1973 merger of: Life Sciences. Part 1: Physiology and Pharmacology (ISSN 0300-9653); Life Sciences. Part 2: Biochemistry, General and Molecular (ISSN 0300-9637); Which superseded: Life Sciences.
    Refereed Serial

THE LIGHTBULB; for the professional inventor. see *TECHNOLOGY: COMPREHENSIVE WORKS*

500   GW   ISSN 0024-3728
TP242   CODEN: LIBEAQ
LINDE BERICHTE AUS TECHNIK UND WISSENSCHAFT. English edition: Linde Reports on Science and Technology (ISSN 0024-3736) 1957. s-a. free. Linde AG, Abraham-Lincoln-Str. 21, 65189 Wiesbaden, Germany. TEL 0611-770309. FAX 0611-770455. Ed. Volker R. Leski. **Indexed:** INIS Atomind., INSPEC (1974-). **Document type:** trade publication.
— BLDSC (5220.800000); CASDDS.

LIPPISCHE MITTEILUNGEN AUS GESCHICHTE UND LANDESKUNDE. see *HISTORY — History Of Europe*

500.9   US   ISSN 0024-5283
QH1   CODEN: LIMUAR
THE LIVING MUSEUM. (Braille and Inkprint Editions) 1939. q. free. Illinois State Museum, Springfield, IL 62706. TEL 217-782-7386. FAX 217-782-1254. illus.; index, cum.index: 1939-1955. circ. 18,000. **Indexed:** Biol.Abstr., Biol.Dig., Sport Fish.Abstr., Wild.Rev. **Document type:** academic/scholarly publication.
— Faxon; UnCover.
    Description: Describes Illinois' natural history, art, and anthropology.

LODZKIE TOWARZYSTWO NAUKOWE. SPRAWOZDANIA Z CZYNNOSCI I POSIEDZEN NAUKOWYCH. see *HUMANITIES: COMPREHENSIVE WORKS*

500   US
LOS ALAMOS SERIES IN BASIC AND APPLIED SCIENCES. 1979. irreg., no.12, 1992. price varies. (Los Alamos National Laboratory) University of California Press, 2120 Berkeley Way, Berkeley, CA 94720. TEL 510-642-4247. FAX 510-643-7127. (Orders to: California-Princeton Fulfillment Services, 1445 Lower Ferry Rd., Ewing, NJ 08618. TEL 800-777-4726. FAX 800-999-1958) (back issues avail.) **Document type:** monographic series.
    Description: Explores various physical and mathematical principles and phenomena.
    Refereed Serial

500   US   ISSN 0096-9192
Q11   CODEN: PLAAA6
LOUISIANA ACADEMY OF SCIENCES. PROCEEDINGS. 1932. a. $20. Louisiana Academy of Sciences, c/o Dr. Brad Mc Pherson, Department of Biology, Centenary College, Shreveport, LA 71104. Ed. Paul R. Ramsey. circ. 400. (back issues avail.) **Indexed:** Biol.Abstr., Chem.Abstr., Deep Sea Res.& Oceanogr.Abstr., Sport Fish.Abstr., Wild.Rev., Zoo.Rec. **Document type:** proceedings.
— BLDSC (6753.000000); CASDDS.

LRABER HASARAKAKAN GITUT'YUNNERI/VESTNIK OBSHCHESTVENNYKH NAUK/HERALD OF SOCIAL SCIENCES. see *HUMANITIES: COMPREHENSIVE WORKS*

509 016   SW   ISSN 0076-163X
LYCHNOS-BIBLIOTEK. STUDIES OCH KAELLSKRIFTER UDGIVNA AV LAERDOMSHISTORISKA SAMFUNDET. STUDIES AND SOURCES PUBLISHED BY THE SWEDISH HISTORY OF SCIENCE SOCIETY. 1936. irreg. price varies. (Laerdomshistoriska Samfundet - Swedish History of Science Society) A W I International AB, P.O. Box 4627, S-116 91 Stockholm, Sweden. TEL 468-640-8800. FAX 468-641-1180. Ed. Gunnar Erikson. index. **Indexed:** Amer.Hist.& Life, Hist.Abstr.

509   SW   ISSN 0076-1648
Q64
LYCHNOS-LAERDOMSHISTORISKA SAMFUNDETS AARSBOK. ANNUAL OF THE SWEDISH HISTORY OF SCIENCE SOCIETY. 1936. a. price varies. (Laerdomshistoriska Samfundet) A W I International AB, P.O. Box 4627, S-116 91 Stockholm, Sweden. Ed. Gunnar Erikson. bk.rev.; index.

500 600   GW   ISSN 0341-7727
Q49
M P G SPIEGEL. 1972. bi-m. Max-Planck-Gesellschaft zur Foerderung der Wissenschaften, Hofgartenstr. 2, 80539 Munich, Germany. TEL 089-2108-1275. FAX 089-2108-1111. Ed.Bd. charts; illus. circ. 22,000. **Document type:** academic/scholarly publication.
    Description: News for members of the Max-Planck Society.

505.8   US   ISSN 0076-2016
Q121
MCGRAW-HILL YEARBOOK OF SCIENCE AND TECHNOLOGY. 1962. a. $125. McGraw-Hill, Inc., Professional & Reference Division, Engineering and Science Group, 11 W. 19th St., New York, NY 10011. TEL 212-337-5904. FAX 212-337-5999. TELEX 12-7960 MCGRAWH NYK. Ed. Sybil Parker.
— BLDSC (5413.482000).
    Description: Provides summaries of some of the most significant developments in science, technology, and engineering during the past year.

500   II   ISSN 0085-2945
MADRAS. GOVERNMENT MUSEUM. BULLETIN. NEW SERIES. (Text in English) 1931. irreg. price varies. Government Museum, Madras, Director of Museums, Pantheon Road, Egmore, Madras 600008, India.

500   II
MADRAS UNIVERSITY. JOURNAL. SECTION B: SCIENCES. (Text in English) 1978. irreg. (1-3/yr.). University of Madras, c/o Director, Publications Division, Madras 600 005, India. TEL 91-44-568778. FAX 91-44-566693. **Document type:** academic/scholarly publication.

500   RM
MAGAZIN. 1957. w. Piata Presei Libere 1, 71341 Bucharest, Rumania. Ed. Maria Costache. circ. 520,000.

500   HU   ISSN 0025-0325
MAGYAR TUDOMANY/HUNGARIAN SCIENCE. (Text in Hungarian, contents page in English, French, German and Russian) 1890. m. 960 Ft. (Magyar Tudomanyos Akademia) Akademiai Kiado, Publishing House of the Hungarian Academy of Sciences, P.O. Box 245, 1519 Budapest, Hungary. TEL 181-2134. FAX 166-6466. TELEX 22-6228 AKNYO H. Ed. Bela Koepeczi. adv.; bk.rev.; illus.; index. **Indexed:** Amer.Hist.& Life, Forest.Abstr., Geo.Abstr., Hist.Abstr., Hung.Lib.& Info.Sci.Abstr. (1990), INIS Atomind., Rural Recreat.Tour.Abstr., World Agri.Econ.& Rural Sociol.Abstr.

500   II   ISSN 0025-0422
AS472.M23   CODEN: JMAHA2
MAHARAJA SAYAJIRAO UNIVERSITY OF BARODA. JOURNAL. (In 3 parts: Humanities, Social Science, Science.) (Text in English) 1952. 3/yr. (in 1 vol.). exchange basis. Maharaja Sayajirao University of Baroda, Baroda 390002, Gujarat, India. Ed. K.T.M. Hedge. adv.; bk.rev.; bibl.; charts; illus. circ. 500. **Indexed:** Amer.Hist.& Life, Biol.Abstr., Chem.Abstr., Hist.Abstr., Int.Polit.Sci.Abstr., Nutr.Abstr., VITIS.
— CASDDS.

500 600   KU
MAJALLAT AL-ULUM. Arabic translation of: Scientific American (US ISSN 0036-8733) (Text in Arabic) m. $40 (effective 1992). P.O. Box 20856, Safat, Kuwait. adv.

500 001.3   XN   ISSN 0580-4981
MAKEDONSKA AKADEMIJA NA NAUKITE I UMETNOSTITE. LETOPIS. 1969. a. Makedonska Akademija na Naukite i Umetnostite, Bulevar Krste Misrkov bb, P.O. Box 428, Skopje, Macedonia. TEL 235-506. Ed. Krum Tomovski.
    Description: Report of activities in symposia and congresses with information on scientific projects, exhibitions, publications, and membership listings.

510 570   XN   ISSN 0351-3246
QA1   CODEN: PMANDL
MAKEDONSKA AKADEMIJA NA NAUKITE I UMETNOSTITE. ODDELENIE ZA MATEMATICKI I TEHNICKI NAUKI. PRILOZI/MACEDONIAN ACADEMY OF SCIENCES AND ARTS. SECTION OF MATHEMATICAL AND TECHNICAL SCIENCES. CONTRIBUTIONS. 1969. s-a. Makedonska Akademija na Naukite i Umetnostite, Oddelenie za matematicki i Tehnicki Nauki, Bulevar Krste Misirkov bb, P.O.Box 428, Skopje, Macedonia. TEL 235-506. Ed. Krum Tomovski. **Indexed:** Chem.Abstr., Math.R.
— CASDDS.
    Supersedes (in 1980): Makedonska Akademija na Naukite i Umetnostite. Oddelenie za Prirodno-Matematicki Nauki. Prilozi. (ISSN 0581-0833)
    Description: Research in mathematics, physics, chemistry and earth sciences.

507   UG
MAKERERE UNIVERSITY. SCIENCE FACULTY. HANDBOOK. irreg. Makerere University, Science Faculty, Box 7062, Kampala, Uganda. Ed. A.J. Lutalo. circ. 1,000.

500   MW
MALAWI JOURNAL OF SCIENCE. 1972. a. 25p. Association for the Advancement of Science of Malawi, Box 280, Zomba, Malawi. adv.; bk.rev. circ. 1,000.

MALAYAN NATURALIST. see *CONSERVATION*

508   MY   ISSN 0025-1291
QH1   CODEN: MANJAM
MALAYAN NATURE JOURNAL. (Supplement avail.: Malayan Naturalist (ISSN 0127-0206)) 1940. q. M.$50 to individuals; institutions M.$100. Malayan Nature Society, 485 Jalan 5-53, Petaling Jaya 46000, Selangor, Malaysia. Ed. Geoffrey Davison. adv.; bk.rev.; charts; illus.; maps; index. circ. 2,500. **Indexed:** Apic.Abstr., Bio-Contr.News & Info., Biol.Abstr., Curr.Adv.Ecol.Sci., Forest.Abstr., Hort.Abstr., Soils & Fert., Sport Fish.Abstr., Weed Abstr., Wild.Rev., Zoo.Rec.
— BLDSC (5356.007000); UnCover. **CCC.**
    Description: Discusses natural history.

500   MY   ISSN 0126-7906
Q1   CODEN: MLJSA4
MALAYSIAN JOURNAL OF SCIENCE/JERNAL SAINS MALAYSIA.* (Text in English) 1971. a. (University of Malaya, Faculty of Science) University of Malaya Co-operative Bookshop Ltd., Lembah Pantai, 59100 Kuala Lumpur, Malaysia. TEL 565000. TELEX UNIMAL-MA-37453. Ed. Dr. Yong Hoi-Sen. adv.; bk.rev. circ. 1,000. **Indexed:** Biol.Abstr., Chem.Abstr., Deep Sea Res.& Oceanogr.Abstr.
— BLDSC (5356.069000).
    Refereed Serial

MANITOBA SCIENCE TEACHER. see *EDUCATION*

MARATHWADA UNIVERSITY JOURNAL. see *EDUCATION — Higher Education*

500.9   JA
MARINE PARK RESEARCH STATIONS. BULLETIN/KAICHU KOEN KENKYUJO KENKYU HOKOKU. (Text in English or Japanese) 1975. s-a. exchange basis. Marine Parks Center of Japan, 1157 Kushimotocho Arita, Nishi-Muro-Gun, Kushimoto, Wakayama, Japan. Ed. Michitaka Uda. illus. circ. 600.

500 913 581 551   GW
MARSCHENRAT ZUR FOERDERUNG DER FORSCHUNG IM KUESTENGEBIET DER NORDSEE. NACHRICHTEN. 1962. a. free. Marschenrat zur Foerderung der Forschung im Kuestengebiet der Nordsee, Viktoriastr. 26, 26382 Wilhelmshaven, Germany. Ed.Bd. circ. 1,200. **Document type:** academic/scholarly publication.

910   XR
MASARYK UNIVERSITY. FACULTY OF SCIENCES. SCRIPTA GEOGRAPHIA/SCRIPTA FACULTATIS SCIENTIARUM NATURALIUM UNIVERSITATIS MASARYKIANAE BRUNENSIS: GEOGRAPHIA. (Text in English, French, German and Russian) 1971. a. price varies. Masarykova Universita, Prirodovedecka Fakulta - Masaryk University, Faculty of Sciences, Kotlarska 2, 611 37 Brno, Czech Republic. Ed. Rudolf Brazdil. charts; illus.; maps. **Document type:** academic/scholarly publication.
Former titles: Scripta Gacultatis Scientiarum Naturalium Universitatis Purkynianae Brunensis: Geographia (ISSN 0231-5874); Supersedes in part (in 1970): Universita J.E. Purkyne. Prirodovedecka Fakulta. Spisy.

500 600   US   ISSN 1053-2110
Z7401
MASTER'S THESES IN THE NATURAL AND TECHNICAL SCIENCES. 1990. a. $40. Master's Theses Directories, Box 92, Cedar Falls, IA 50613. TEL 319-273-6412. FAX 319-273-2742. Ed. H.M. Silvey.

MASTER'S THESES IN THE PURE AND APPLIED SCIENCES; accepted by colleges and universities in the United States and Canada. see SCIENCES: COMPREHENSIVE WORKS — Abstracting, Bibliographies, Statistics

MATHEMATICAL CONCEPTS AND METHODS IN SCIENCE AND ENGINEERING. see MATHEMATICS

MATHEMATICAL METHODS IN THE APPLIED SCIENCES. see MATHEMATICS

500   GW   ISSN 0233-173X
QH149   CODEN: MAUREH
MAURITIANA (ALTENBURG). 1958. a. price varies. Naturkundliches Museum Mauritianum, Postfach 1644, 04590 Altenburg, Germany. TEL 03447-2589. Ed. Norbert Hoeser. circ. 1,000. **Document type:** academic/scholarly publication.
Formerly (until 1986): Naturkundliches Museum "Mauritianum" Altenburg. Abhandlungen und Berichte (ISSN 0065-6631)

500   MF   ISSN 0373-3890
QH1   CODEN: MAUBA
MAURITIUS INSTITUTE BULLETIN. 1937. a? Mauritius Institute, P.O. Box 54, Port Louis, Mauritius. **Indexed:** P.L.E.S.A.

500   GW   ISSN 0341-0218
Q3   CODEN: MPJADF
MAX-PLANCK-GESELLSCHAFT. JAHRBUCH. 1951. a. price varies. Vandenhoeck und Ruprecht, Robert-Bosch-Breite 6, 37079 Goettingen, Germany. TEL 0551-695926. FAX 0551-695917. Eds. Ulrike Emrich, Robert Gerwin. bk.rev.; index. circ. 4,000. (back issues avail.) **Indexed:** Biol.Abstr. **Document type:** academic/scholarly publication.
—BLDSC (4624.800000).

500   GW   ISSN 0076-5635
MAX-PLANCK-GESELLSCHAFT ZUR FOERDERUNG DER WISSENSCHAFTEN. JAHRBUCH. 1951. a. DM.110. Max-Planck-Gesellschaft zur Foerderung der Wissenschaften, Hofgartenstr. 2, 80539 Munich, Germany. TEL 089-2108-1275. FAX 089-2108-1111. Ed. S. Deutschmann. **Document type:** academic/scholarly publication.
Description: Official report of the Max-Planck Society, with information on its 68 research institutes.

500   GW   ISSN 0341-7778
MAX-PLANCK-GESELLSCHAFT ZUR FOERDERUNG DER WISSENSCHAFTEN BERICHTE UND MITTEILUNGEN. 1952. 5/yr. Max-Planck-Gesellschaft zur Foerderung der Wissenschaften, Hofgartenstr. 2, 80539 Munich, Germany. TEL 089-2108-1275. FAX 089-2108-1111. Ed. S. Deutschmann. bibl.; charts; illus. circ. 6,000. **Document type:** academic/scholarly publication.
—BLDSC (1937.348000).
Formerly: Max-Planck-Gesellschaft zur Foerderung der Wissenschaften Mitteilungen (ISSN 0025-6102)
Description: Information on selected Max-Plank institutes.

MECANICA POPULAR. see TECHNOLOGY: COMPREHENSIVE WORKS

MEIJI DAIGAKU KAGAKU GIJUTSU KENKYUJO HOKOKU. SOGO KENKYU/MEIJI UNIVERSITY. INSTITUTE OF SCIENCE AND TECHNOLOGY. REPORT. SPECIAL PROJECT. see TECHNOLOGY: COMPREHENSIVE WORKS

MEIJI DAIGAKU KAGAKU GIJUTSU KENKYUJO KIYO/MEIJI UNIVERSITY. INSTITUTE OF SCIENCE AND TECHNOLOGY. MEMOIRS. see TECHNOLOGY: COMPREHENSIVE WORKS

MEIJI DAIGAKU KAGAKU GIJUTSU KENKYUJO NENPO/MEIJI UNIVERSITY. INSTITUTE OF SCIENCE AND TECHNOLOGY. ANNUAL REPORT. see TECHNOLOGY: COMPREHENSIVE WORKS

500   NE   ISSN 0921-559X
Q4
MENS & WETENSCHAP; magazine over mens, natuur, wetenschap en techniek. 1974. 8/yr. fl.69.50 (effective 1995-1996); newsstand price: fl.8.95. Stichting Educatief Centrum, Postbus 386, 1270 AJ Huizen, Netherlands. TEL 31-2152-58388. FAX 31-2152-69928. Ed.Bd. adv.: B&W page fl.2300, color page fl.3450; trim 215 x 285. bk.rev.; index; circ. 14,000 (paid). **Indexed:** Excerp.Med., Geo.Abstr. **Document type:** academic/scholarly publication, consumer publication.
—SWETS.
Incorporates: Technovisie; **Former titles** (until 1987): Aarde en Kosmos - D J O (ISSN 0921-769X); Which was formed by the 1985 merger of: D J O - De Jonge Onderzoeker (ISSN 0166-4697); Aarde en Kosmos (ISSN 0166-4786)
Description: Publishes articles on topics relating to the physical and biological sciences, new technologies, anthropology and the natural world.

500   NE   ISSN 0543-6095
METHODOLOGY AND SCIENCE; interdisciplinary journal for the empirical study of the foundations of science and their methodology. 1968. q. fl.100 (foreign fl.125) (effective 1994). Esser Scientific Press, Beelslaan 20, 2012 PK Haarlem, Netherlands. TEL 31-23-280290. Ed. Dr. P.H. Esser. adv.; bk.rev. circ. 200. **Indexed:** Math.R., Phil.Ind. **Document type:** academic/scholarly publication.
—BLDSC (5746.450000); Faxon; UnCover.

500   NE   ISSN 0377-9025
                    CODEN: MPTTDK
METHODS AND PHENOMENA; their applications in science and technology. (Text in English) 1975. irreg., vol.7, 1984. price varies. Elsevier Science B.V., Books Division, P.O. Box 211, 1000 AE Amsterdam, Netherlands. TEL 31-20-4853911. FAX 31-20-4853705. TELEX 18582 ESPA NL. E-mail: nlinfo-f@elsevier.nl; usinfo-f@elsevier.com; forinfo-kyf04035@niftyserve.or.jp; Site addr.: http://www.elsevier.nl/. (Subscr. in U.S. and Canada to: Elsevier Science Inc., Box 882, Madison Sq. Sta., New York, NY 10159. TEL 212-989-5800) Eds. S.P. Wolsky, A.W. Czanderna. **Indexed:** Chem.Abstr. **Document type:** monographic series.
—CASDDS.
Refereed Serial

500   US   ISSN 0026-2005
AS30   CODEN: MACDAH
MICHIGAN ACADEMICIAN. 1969. q. $40 (foreign $45). Michigan Academy of Science, Arts and Letters, 400 Fourth St., Ann Arbor, MI 48109-4816. TEL 313-936-2938. Ed. Kathleen F. Duke. bk.rev.; illus. circ. 1,100. (back issues avail.) **Indexed:** Abstr.Anthropol., Abstr.Engl.Stud., Amer.Bibl.Slavic & E.Eur.Stud., Amer.Hist.& Life, Bibl.Engl.Lang.& Lit., Biol.Abstr., Chem.Abstr., Film Lit.Ind. (1989-), GeoRef., Hist.Abstr., J.of Econ.Lit., Lang.& Lang.Behav.Abstr., M.L.A., Mich.Mag.Ind., Psychol.Abstr., Sociol.Abstr. **Document type:** academic/scholarly publication.
—Faxon; UnCover.
Supersedes: Michigan Academy of Science, Arts and Letters. Papers.
Description: Forum for scholars across the state and region. Presents papers of the academy derived from its meetings.
Refereed Serial

MICROLOGUS; natura, scienza e societa medievali - nature, science and medieval societies. see HISTORY — History Of Europe

500   US
MIDWEST RESEARCH INSTITUTE. ANNUAL REPORT. 1945. a. free. Midwest Research Institute, 425 Volker Blvd., Kansas City, MO 64110. TEL 816-753-7600. FAX 816-753-8420. TELEX 910-771-2128. Ed. Lola Butcher. circ. 13,000.
Description: Reports on research performed at MRI in a varied spectrum, including chemical and biological sciences, engineering, economics, social and management sciences, and solar energy.

500   JA   ISSN 0389-9225
MIE DAIGAKU KYOIKUGAKUBU KENKYU KIYO. SHIZEN KAGAKU/MIE UNIVERSITY. FACULTY OF EDUCATION. BULLETIN. NATURAL SCIENCE. (Text and summaries in English and Japanese) a. Mie Daigaku, Kyoikugakubu - Mie University, Faculty of Education, 1515 Kamihama-cho, Tsu-shi, Mie-ken 514, Japan. **Indexed:** Jap.Per.Ind.

MILLENNIUM WHOLE EARTH CATALOG; access to tools & ideas for the twenty-first century. see NEW AGE PUBLICATIONS

MINAMI-KYUSHU DAIGAKU ENGEIGAKUBU KENKYU HOKOKU. SHIZEN KAGAKU, JINBUN SHAKAI KAGAKU/MINAMI KYUSHU UNIVERSITY. FACULTY OF HORTICULTURE. BULLETIN. NATURAL SCIENCE, CULTURAL SCIENCE, AND SOCIAL SCIENCE. see GARDENING AND HORTICULTURE

500 300   JA   ISSN 0916-0752
MINAMI TAIHEIYO KENKYU/SOUTH PACIFIC STUDY. (Text in English, Japanese) 1980. s-a. exchange basis. Kagoshima University, Research Center for the South Pacific, 1-21-24, Korimoto, Kagoshima 890, Japan. TEL 0992-85-7394. FAX 0992-56-9358. E-mail: PXW10307@niftyserve.or.jp. Ed. Munemoto Nedachi. circ. 700 (controlled). **Document type:** academic/scholarly publication.
—BLDSC (8352.127000).
Formerly (until 1987): Nankaiken Kiyo (ISSN 0389-5351)
Description: Dedicated to the multi-disciplinary studies on the South Pacific region. Covers a comprehensive range of fields from agriculture to zoology.
Refereed Serial

959 398   PH   ISSN 0115-7329
MINDANAO STATE UNIVERSITY. U R C PROFESSIONAL PAPERS. 1981. irreg. $5. Mindanao State University, Mamitua Saber Research Center, P.O. Box 5594, Iligan City 9200, Philippines. Ed. Raymond Llorca. **Document type:** academic/scholarly publication.

MINERVA; a review of science, learning and policy. see EDUCATION — Higher Education

500 001   US   ISSN 1076-500X
▼**THE MINI-ANNALS OF IMPROBABLE RESEARCH.** 1994. m. free. Annals of Improbable Research, Box 380853, Cambridge, MA 02238. TEL 617-491-4437. FAX 617-661-0927. E-mail: air@improb.com; Site addr.: http://www.improb.com/. Ed. Marc Abrahams. **Document type:** newsletter.
●Available only online.
Description: Short humorous pieces about science and scientists.

5874 SCIENCES: COMPREHENSIVE WORKS

500 US ISSN 0026-539X
Q11 CODEN: JMNAAC
MINNESOTA ACADEMY OF SCIENCE. JOURNAL. 1932. s-a. $20. Minnesota Academy of Science, 350 Robert St. N., Ste. 583, St. Paul, MN 55101-1502. TEL 612-227-6361. Ed. Dr. Alan Olness. bk.rev.; charts; illus.; stat. circ. 1,600. (also avail. in microform from UMI; reprint service avail. from UMI) **Indexed:** Biol.Abstr., Chem.Abstr., Excerp.Med., GeoRef., Sel.Water Res.Abstr., Sport Fish.Abstr., Wild.Rev., Zoo.Rec. **Document type:** academic/scholarly publication.
—UMI; UnCover.
  Formerly (until 1964): Minnesota Academy of Science. Proceedings (ISSN 0096-9397)
  Refereed Serial

500 US ISSN 0026-5675
 CODEN: MINSB4
MINNESOTA SCIENCE. 1943. 3/yr. free. University of Minnesota, Agricultural Experiment Station, 405 Coffey Hall, St. Paul, MN 55108. TEL 612-625-7290. Ed. David L. Hansen. index; circ. 24,000 (controlled). (processed) **Indexed:** Biol.Abstr., Sport Fish.Abstr., Wild.Rev.
  Description: Presents results of university research projects related to agriculture, forestry, human ecology, natural resources and the environment.

MINNESOTA STUDIES IN THE PHILOSOPHY OF SCIENCE. see *PHILOSOPHY*

574 US ISSN 0076-9436
Q11 CODEN: JMSSAN
MISSISSIPPI ACADEMY OF SCIENCE. JOURNAL. 1940. 3/yr. $25. Mississippi Academy of Sciences, Inc., 405 Briarwood Dr., Ste. 107E, Jackson, MS 39206-3032. TEL 601-977-0627. Ed. John D. Tiftickjian. circ. 1,000. (also avail. in microform from UMI) **Indexed:** Biol.Abstr., Chem.Abstr., GeoRef., Hort.Abstr., Sport Fish.Abstr., Wild.Rev., Zoo.Rec. **Document type:** academic/scholarly publication.
—BLDSC (4828.200000); CASDDS; UMI; UnCover.

500 JA ISSN 0285-8576
Q4 CODEN: MDKSAL
MIYAZAKI DAIGAKU KYOIKUGAKUBU KIYO. SHIZEN KAGAKU/MIYAZAKI UNIVERSITY. FACULTY OF EDUCATION. MEMOIRS. NATURAL SCIENCE. (Text in Japanese; summaries in English and Japanese) 1955. s-a. Miyazaki Daigaku, Kyoikugakubu - Miyazaki University, Faculty of Education, 1-1 Funatsuka, Miyazaki-shi, Miyazaki-ken 880, Japan. **Indexed:** Chem.Abstr., Jap.Per.Ind.
—BLDSC (5593.322000).

MOKHTAREIN VA MOBTAKERIN. see *TECHNOLOGY: COMPREHENSIVE WORKS*

500 SP
MOLL MONOGRAFIES CIENTIFIQUES. (Text in Catalan) irreg., latest no.4. 3850 ptas. Editorial Moll, Apdo. 142, 07080 Palma de Mallorca, Spain. TEL 971-72-41-76. FAX 971-72-62-52. **Document type:** monographic series.

500 FR ISSN 0221-0436
JV1802
MONDES ET CULTURES; comptes-rendus trimestriels de l'Academie des Sciences d'Outre-Mer. 1941. q. 300 F. Academie des Sciences d'Outre-Mer, Paris, 15 rue La Perouse, 75116 Paris, France. TEL 47-20-87-93. FAX 47-20-89-72. Dir. Gilbert Mangin. adv.; bk.rev.; bibl.; charts; index. **Indexed:** Bibl.Ling., Curr.Cont.Africa, Documentatieblad. **Document type:** academic/scholarly publication.
  Formerly: Academie des Sciences d'Outre-Mer, Paris. Comptes Rendus des Seances (ISSN 0001-4044)

500 600 PL ISSN 0077-054X
MONOGRAFIE Z DZIEJOW NAUKI I TECHNIKI. (Text in Polish; summaries in English, French, German, Russian) 1957. irreg., vol.151, 1995. price varies. Polska Akademia Nauk, Instytut Historii Nauki, Ul. Nowy Swiat 72, 00-330 Warsaw, Poland. TEL 48-22-267853. FAX 48-22-296302. Ed. Jerzy Roziewicz. adv. contact: Jerzy Dobrzycki. **Indexed:** Math.R. **Document type:** monographic series.

MONOGRAPHS ON SCIENCE, TECHNOLOGY, AND SOCIETY. see *TECHNOLOGY: COMPREHENSIVE WORKS*

500 SP ISSN 0211-3058
MUNDO CIENTIFICO. 1981. 11/yr. $64. Editorial Fontalba, S.A., Valencia 359, 6o 1a, 08009 Barcelona, Spain. TEL 93-458-5508. FAX 93-458-6602. TELEX 97835 FON E. Ed. Jose Gili Casals. circ. 31,000.
—SWETS.

508 SP ISSN 0214-7688
QH7
MUNIBE CIENCIAS NATURALES. (Monographic supplements avail.) (Text mainly in Spanish; occasionally in English & French) 1949. a. 4000 ptas. (foreign 5000 ptas.). Sociedad de Ciencias Aranzadi, Plaza de I. Zuloaga (Museo), 20003 Donostia-San Sebastian, Spain. TEL 943-42-29-45. FAX 943-42-13-16. Ed.Bd. circ. 2,500. **Indexed:** A.I.C.P., Amer.Hist.& Life, Biol.Abstr., Chem.Abstr., GeoRef., Hist.Abstr., Ind.SST.
—BLDSC (5983.915010).
  Supersedes in part (in 1984): Munibe (ISSN 0027-3414)

500 IT ISSN 0392-0062
QH7 CODEN: BMCVD3
MUSEO CIVICO DI STORIA NATURALE DI VERONA. BOLLETTINO. (Text in English, French, German, Italian and Spanish; summaries in English) 1974. a., vol.18, 1991. L.35000 per no. Museo Civico di Storia Naturale di Verona, Lungadige Porta Vittoria Nr. 9, 37129 Verona, Italy. TEL 39-45-8001987. Ed.Bd. circ. 600. (back issues avail.) **Indexed:** A.I.C.P., Biol.Abstr., Deep Sea Res.& Oceanogr.Abstr., GeoRef., Zoo.Rec. **Document type:** bulletin.

500.9 IT
MUSEO CIVICO DI STORIA NATURALE DI VERONA. MEMORIE. SERIE 2, SEZIONE C: SCIENZE DELL'UOMO. 1976. irreg., vol.4, 1994. price varies. Museo Civico di Storia Naturale di Verona, Lungadige Porta Vittoria, 9, 37129 Verona, Italy. TEL 39-45-8001987. **Document type:** monographic series.
  Formerly: Museo Civico di Storia Naturale di Verona. Memorie. Serie 2, Part 3: Preistorica.

500.9 IT ISSN 0365-4389
 CODEN: AMGDAN
MUSEO CIVICO DI STORIA NATURALE "GIACOMO DORIA", GENOA. ANNALI. (Text in English, French, German, Italian and Spanish) 1870. biennial. exchange basis only. Museo Civico di Storia Naturale "Giacomo Doria", Via Brigata Liguria 9, 16121 Genoa, Italy. **Indexed:** Biol.Abstr., Bull.Signal., Entomol.Abstr., Rev.Appl.Entomol., Zoo.Rec.
—BLDSC (1008.400000).

508 CL ISSN 0716-0178
 CODEN: AMHVEI
MUSEO DE HISTORIA NATURAL DE VALPARAISO. ANALES. 1968. a. Museo de Historia Natural de Valparaiso, Condell 1546, Casilla 3208 Correo 3, Valparaiso, Chile. **Indexed:** Sport Fish.Abstr., Wild.Rev., Zoo.Rec. **Document type:** academic/scholarly publication.

MUSEO MUNICIPAL DE HISTORIA NATURAL DE SAN RAFAEL. INSTITUTO DE CIENCIAS NATURALES. NOTAS. see *EARTH SCIENCES — Geology*

500.9 AG ISSN 0375-1155
MUSEO MUNICIPAL DE HISTORIA NATURAL DE SAN RAFAEL. REVISTA. 1956. irreg. exchange basis. Museo Municipal de Historia Natural de San Rafael, Parque Mariano Moreno, 5600 San Rafael, Mendoza, Argentina. FAX 54-0627-21244. Ed. Humberto A. Lagiglia. bk.rev.; charts; illus.; index. circ. 1,500. **Indexed:** Anthropol.Lit., Biol.Abstr.
  Former titles: Museo de Historia Natural de San Rafael. Revista; Museo de Historia Natural de San Rafael. Revista Cientifica de Investigaciones (ISSN 0027-3902)

500.9 CL ISSN 0027-3910
QH7
MUSEO NACIONAL DE HISTORIA NATURAL. BOLETIN. 1908. irreg., no.42, 1991. $12. Museo Nacional de Historia Natural, Casilla 787, Santiago, Chile. Ed. Daniel Frassinetti C. **Indexed:** Biol.Abstr.
—BLDSC (2182.000000).

500.9 CL ISSN 0027-3945
MUSEO NACIONAL DE HISTORIA NATURAL. NOTICIARIO MENSUAL. 1956. m. $4. Museo Nacional de Historia Natural, Casilla 787, Santiago, Chile. Ed. Herman Nunez. circ. 800. **Indexed:** Biol.Abstr., GeoRef.

MUSEOSCIENZA. see *MUSEUMS AND ART GALLERIES*

500.9 FR
MUSEUM NATIONAL D'HISTOIRE NATURELLE, PARIS. GRANDS NATURALISTES FRANCAIS. 1952. irreg. price varies. Museum National d'Histoire Naturelle, 38 rue Geoffroy Saint-Hillaire, 75005 Paris, France. illus.

500.9 FR ISSN 1243-4442
QH3 CODEN: MMNNEK
MUSEUM NATIONAL D'HISTOIRE NATURELLE, PARIS. MEMOIRES. (Text in French, summaries in English, French) 1936; N.S. 1950. irreg., vol.159, 1994. price varies. Museum National d'Histoire Naturelle, 57 rue Cuvier, 75005 Paris, France. TEL 40-79-30-00. FAX 40-79-34-84. TELEX MUSNAHN 202641F. (Dist. by: Backhuys Publishers - Universal Book Services, P.O. Box 321, 2300 AH Leiden, Netherlands. TEL 31-71-170208. FAX 31-71-171856) Ed. Jean-Lou Justine. adv. circ. 600. (back issues avail.) **Indexed:** Biol.Abstr., Curr.Adv.Ecol.Sci., Deep Sea Res.& Oceanogr.Abstr., Forest.Abstr., Forest.Prod.Abstr., GeoRef., Helminthol.Abstr., Ocean.Abstr., Pollut.Abstr., Protozool.Abstr., Zoo.Rec. **Document type:** monographic series.
—BLDSC (5558.950000); UnCover.
  Formed by the 1993 merger of: Museum National d'Histoire Naturelle, Paris. Memoires. Nouvelle Serie. Serie A, Zoologie (ISSN 0078-9747) & Museum National d'Histoire Naturelle, Paris. Memoires. Nouvelle Serie. Serie B, Botanique (ISSN 0078-9755) & Museum National d'Histoire Naturelle, Paris. Memoires. Nouvelle Serie. Serie C, Sciences de la Terre (ISSN 0246-1196) & Museum National d'Histoire Naturelle, Paris. Memoires. Nouvelle Serie. Serie D, Sciences Physico-Chimiques (ISSN 0078-9771); Which supersedes (in 1950): Museum National d'Histoire Naturelle, Paris. Memoires (ISSN 0246-0254)
  Description: Covers zoology and animal taxonomy, biology and ecology, including entomology and ornithology.

MUSEUMSNYTT. see *MUSEUMS AND ART GALLERIES*

500 JO ISSN 1021-6812
MU'TAH LIL-BUHUTH WAL-DIRASAT. AL-SILSILAH B: AL-'ULUM AL-TABI'IYYAH WAL-TATBIQIYYAH/MU'TAH LIL-BUHUTH WAL-DIRASAT. SERIES B: NATURAL AND APPLIED SCIENCES. Spine title: Mu'tah Journal for Research and Studies. (Text in Arabic, English) 1986. 6/yr. 5 din. to individuals (foreign 10 din.); institutions 10 din. (foreign 15 din.). Mu'tah University, Deanship of Scientific Research and Graduate Studies - Jami'at Mu'tah, 'Imadat al-Bahth al-'Ilmi wal-Dirasat al-'Ulya, P.O. Box 7, Mu'tah, Jordan. FAX 962-2-654061. Eds. Abdulrahman Attiyat, Abdelrahim Hunaiti. abstr.; bibl.; illus.; stat. **Document type:** academic/scholarly publication.
  Description: Publishes original research papers and articles on topics in agricultural sciences, engineering and technology, medical and biological sciences, and basic science.
  Refereed Serial

500 SP ISSN 1130-4081
MUY INTERESANTE. 1981. m. 3100 ptas. (Europe 7200 ptas.; elsewhere 10800 ptas.). G y J Espana Ediciones, S.L. (Subsidiary of: Gruner & Jahr USA Publishing), Marques de Villamagna 4, 28001 Madrid, Spain. TEL 341-435-8100. FAX 341-576-7781. TELEX 43419. Dir. Jose Pardina. adv. contact: Elena Sanchez Fabres. circ. 290,000. **Document type:** consumer publication.
  Description: Covers scientific subjects, putting all the latest discoveries and new technologies within the reader's reach.

500 US
N A S A FORMAL SERIES REPORTS. irreg. (approx. 415/yr.). $15 per no. in U.S. only. (U.S. National Aeronautics and Space Administration) U.S. National Technical Information Service, 5825 Port Royal Rd., Springfield, VA 22161. TEL 703-487-4630. **Document type:** government publication.
  Description: Reports available in the following selections: aeronautics, astronautics, chemistry and mechanics, engineering, geosciences, life sciences, mathematical and computer sciences, physics, social sciences, and space sciences.

SCIENCES: COMPREHENSIVE WORKS

500 600 AT ISSN 0311-662X
N A T A NEWS. 1974. q. National Association of Testing Authorities, 7 Leeds St., Rhodes, N.S.W. 2138, Australia. TEL 61-2-736-8222. Ed. P.H. Davies. circ. 6,200.

N A T O ADVANCED SCIENCE INSTITUTES SERIES C: MATHEMATICAL AND PHYSICAL SCIENCES. (North Atlantic Treaty Organization) see MATHEMATICS

N A T O CHALLENGES OF MODERN SOCIETY. see ENVIRONMENTAL STUDIES

500 300 BE
N A T O SCIENCE AND SOCIETY NEWSLETTER. q. North Atlantic Treaty Organization, Scientific Affairs Division, B-1110 Brussels, Belgium. (Co-sponsors: NATO Science Committee; NATO Committee on the Challenges of Modern Society) Ed. Jacques Ducuing. Document type: newsletter, bulletin.

500 BE ISSN 0255-7134
N A T O SCIENTIFIC PUBLICATIONS. NEWSLETTER. 1980. q. free. (North Atlantic Treaty Organization, Scientific Affairs Division) N A T O Publication Coordination Office, Elcerlyclaan 2, B-3090 Overijse, Belgium. TEL 32-2-6876636. Ed. Mrs. B. Kester. adv.; bk.rev. circ. 25,000. Document type: newsletter.

500 CN ISSN 0047-9551
N.B. NATURALIST/NATURALISTE DU N.B. (Text in English, French) 1970. 4/yr. Can.$15 (foreign Can.$20). New Brunswick Federation of Naturalists, 277 Douglas Ave., Saint John, N.B. E2K 1E5, Canada. TEL 506-882-2100. E-mail: marysp1@nbnet.nb.ca. Eds. D.S. Christie, M. Majka. adv.; bk.rev. circ. 350. (processed) Document type: academic/scholarly publication.
Description: Covers natural history of New Brunswick.

500 370 US ISSN 1064-2358
N C S E REPORTS. 1981. 4/yr. National Center for Science Education, Box 9477, Berkeley, CA 94709-0477. TEL 510-526-1674; 800-290-6006. FAX 510-526-1675. E-mail: ncse@crl.com. Ed. John Cole. bk.rev.; cum.index: vols.1-13 on diskette. (back issues avail.) Document type: newsletter.
—BLDSC (7560.199000).
Description: Discusses issues and current events in science education, particularly evolutionary science. Opposes the teaching of creationism as science in schools.

500 NO ISSN 0800-4412
N D R E PUBLICATIONS. (Text and summaries in English) 1953. irreg., no.84, 1987. Norwegian Defence Research Establishment - Forsvarets Forskningsintitutt, Box 25, N-2007 Kjeller, Norway. FAX 63-807159. circ. controlled. Document type: academic/scholarly publication, corporate report.
—BLDSC (6067.854000).
Formerly: Norway. Forsvaret Forskningsinstitutt. N D R E Report (ISSN 0085-4301)

500 II ISSN 0970-0188
N I S S A T NEWSLETTER. (Text in English) 1978. q. free. National Information System for Science and Technology, Society for Information Science, Technology Bhavan, New Mehrauli Rd., New Delhi 110 016, India. TEL 641-2916. FAX 641-4339. TELEX 31-66096 DST IN. Ed. Ram D. Taneja. bk.rev. circ. 4,000. Indexed: C.R.I.Abstr., C.R.I.Curr.Cont., Ind.Sci.Rev.
—BLDSC (6113.623000).
Description: Reports news about the development of information systems, centers, and networks in science and technology in India and abroad.

N J AUDUBON. see BIOLOGY — Ornithology

N K H NAGAOKA-SHIRITSU KAGAKU HAKUBUTSUKANPO. see MUSEUMS AND ART GALLERIES

500 CH ISSN 0255-4399
Q72.5
N S C REVIEW. (Text in English) 1965. a. free. National Science Council, No. 106, Ho-Ping E. Rd., Sec. 2, Taipei, Taiwan 106, Republic of China. Document type: government publication.
—BLDSC (6180.567000).

500 CH ISSN 0252-9947
CODEN: HCYKD8
N S C SPECIAL PUBLICATION. 1978. irreg., no.6, 1989. National Science Council, No. 106, Ho-Ping E.Rd., Sec. 2, Taipei, Taiwan 106, Republic of China. Document type: monographic series.

500 CH ISSN 0252-8177
CODEN: NSYSD6
N S C SYMPOSIUM SERIES. 1979. irreg., no.14, 1988. National Science Council, 106 Ho-ping E. Rd. Sec. 2, Taipei, Taiwan 106, Republic of China. Indexed: Biol.Abstr. Document type: proceedings.
—CASDDS.

500 350 US ISSN 0145-0670
CODEN: BNSFD8
N S F BULLETIN. Key Title: Bulletin - National Science Foundation. 1974. m. (except Jul. & Aug.) free. U.S. National Science Foundation, 4201 Wilson Blvd., Ste. 245, Arlington, VA 22230. Ed. Mary Wilson. Document type: bulletin, government publication.
●Also available online.

500 375 US
N S S A NEWSLETTER. 1969. q. $20. National Science Supervisors Association, 82 Deepwood Dr., E. Hartford, CT 06118-2411. TEL 203-633-5231. FAX 203-659-3366. Ed. Carol Mitch. adv. circ. 1,000. (tabloid format; back issues avail.) Document type: newsletter.

N S T A REPORTS. (National Science Teachers Association) see EDUCATION

500.9 SZ
N T M; internationale Zeitschrift fuer Geschichte und Ethik der Naturwissenschaften, Technik und Medizin. 1960. 4/yr. 111.20 SFr. (foreign 118.50 SFr.). Birkhaeuser Verlag, P.O. Box 133, CH-4010 Basel, Switzerland. TEL 061-2717400. FAX 061-2717666. (Dist. in N. America by: Springer-Verlag, Mercedes Distribution Center, 160 Imlay St., Brooklyn, NY 11231, USA) Ed. H.R. Tobies. adv.; bk.rev.; bibl.; charts; illus.; index. Document type: academic/scholarly publication.
—BLDSC (6180.606000).
Former titles: N T M Geschichte der Naturwissenschaften, Technik und Medizin. Schriftenreihe (ISSN 0036-6978); Geschichte der Naturwissenschaften, Technik und Medizin. Schriftenreihe; Zeitschrift fuer Geschichte der Naturwissenschaften, der Technik und der Medizin.

500.9 NE ISSN 0921-1713
N V O N MAANDBLAD. 1930. m. (Nederlandse Vereniging voor het Onderwijs in de Natuurwetenschappen) Ten Brink Meppel B.V., Postbus 1064, 7940 KB Meppel, Netherlands. TEL 31-5220-54646. FAX 31-5220-55517. adv.; bk.rev.; charts; illus.; index. circ. 2,100.
—SWETS.
Formed by the 1984 merger of: Nederlandse Vereniging voor het Onderwijs in de Natuurwetenschappen. Mededelingenblad (ISSN 0166-6126); Faraday (ISSN 0014-7656)

NAGAOKA COLLEGE OF TECHNOLOGY. RESEARCH REPORTS/NAGAOKA KOGYO KOTO SENMON GAKKO KENKYU KIYO. see ENGINEERING

500 JA ISSN 0285-6085
NAGAOKA-SHIRITSU KAGAKU HAKUBUTSUKAN KENKYU HOKOKU/NAGAOKA MUNICIPAL SCIENCE MUSEUM. BULLETIN. (Text and summaries in Japanese) 1973. a. Nagaoka-shiritsu Kagaku Hakubutsukan - Nagaoka Municipal Science Museum, 2-1 Yanagihara, Nagaoka-shi, Niigata-ken 940, Japan. Ed. Hisashi Watanabe. Indexed: Jap.Per.Ind.
Description: Contains research reports from the museum.

500 JA ISSN 0386-443X
CODEN: NADKBL
NAGASAKI DAIGAKU KYOIKUGAKUBU SHIZEN KAGAKU KENKYU HOKOKU/NAGASAKI UNIVERSITY. FACULTY OF EDUCATION. SCIENCE BULLETIN. (Text and summaries in English and Japanese) 1951. s-a. exchange basis. Nagasaki Daigaku, Kyoikugakubu - Nagasaki University, Faculty of Education, 1-14 Bunkyo-machi, Nagasaki-shi, Nagasaki-ken 852, Japan. TEL 0958-47-111. FAX 0958-44-0401. Ed. Hiroshi Kondo. Indexed: Chem.Abstr., INIS Atomind., Jap.Per.Ind. Document type: academic/scholarly publication, bulletin.
—BLDSC (8137.200000).

500 JA ISSN 0287-1319
Q4
NAGASAKI DAIGAKU KYOYOBU KIYO. SHIZEN KAGAKU HEN/NAGASAKI UNIVERSITY. FACULTY OF LIBERAL ARTS. BULLETIN. (Text in English, German, Japanese; summaries in English and German) 1960. s-a. free. Nagasaki Daigaku, Kyoyobu - Nagasaki University, Faculty of Liberal Arts, 1-14 Bunkyo-machi, Nagasaki-shi, Nagasaki-ken 852, Japan. circ. 200. Indexed: Jap.Per.Ind.

NAGOYA DAIGAKU FURUKAWA SOGO KENKYU SHIRYOKAN HOKOKU/NAGOYA UNIVERSITY FURUKAWA MUSEUM. BULLETIN. see MUSEUMS AND ART GALLERIES

500 JA ISSN 0387-4532
CODEN: NDKBDI
NAGOYA DAIGAKU KYOYOBU KIYO B. SHIZEN KAGAKU, SHINRIGAKU/NAGOYA UNIVERSITY. COLLEGE OF GENERAL EDUCATION. RESEARCH BULLETIN B. NATURAL SCIENCE AND PSYCHOLOGY. (Text in English and Japanese; summaries in English) a. Nagoya Daigaku, Kyoyobu - Nagoya University, College of General Education, Furo-cho, Chikusa-ku, Nagoya-shi, Aichi-ken 464, Japan. Indexed: Chem.Abstr., Jap.Per.Ind.
—CASDDS.

500 JA
NAGOYA KAGAKUKAN NYUSU/SCIENCE MUSEUM NEWS. (Text in Japanese) 1966. m. free. Nagoyashi Kagakukan - Nagoya City Science Museum, 17-22 Sakae 2-chome, Naka-ku, Nagoya-shi, Aichi-ken 460, Japan. TEL 052-201-4486. FAX 052-203-0988. circ. 9,000.
Description: Contains news of the museum.

500 JA ISSN 0285-4538
CODEN: IGDKEB
NAGOYA KEIZAI DAIGAKU, ICHIMURA GAKUEN TANKI DAIGAKU SHIZEN KAGAKU KENKYUKAI KAISHI/NAGOYA ECONOMICS UNIVERSITY AND ICHIMURA GAKUEN JUNIOR COLLEGE. NATURAL SCIENTIFIC SOCIETY. JOURNAL. (Text and summaries in English and Japanese) 1966. a. Shizen Kagaku Kenkyukai - Natural Scientific Society, Ichimura Gakuen Tanki Daigaku, Inoya-shi, Aichi-ken 484, Japan. (Co-sponsors: Nagoya Keizai Daigaku - Nagoya Economics University)
—CASDDS.

500 JA ISSN 0465-7772
CODEN: NSKKAB
NAGOYA-SHIRITSU DAIGAKU KYOYOBU KIYO. SHIZEN KAGAKU HEN/NAGOYA CITY UNIVERSITY. COLLEGE OF GENERAL EDUCATION. BULLETIN. NATURAL SCIENCE SECTION. (Text in English and Japanese; summaries in English) 1955. a. free. Nagoya-shiritsu Daigaku, Kyoyobu - Nagoya City University, College of General Education, 1-1 Yamanohata, Mizuho-cho, Mizuho-ku, Nagoya-shi, Aichi-ken 467, Japan. TEL 52-872-5801. FAX 052-882-3075. Ed. Akihiko Moriyama. circ. 300. Indexed: Chem.Abstr., Jap.Per.Ind. Document type: bulletin.

500 JA ISSN 0911-971X
NAITO ZAIDAN JIHO. (Text in Japanese) 1969. a. free. Naito Kinen Kagaku Shinko Zaidan - Naito Foundation, 42-6 Hongo 3, Bunkyo-ku, Tokyo 113, Japan. TEL 03-3813-3005. FAX 03-3811-2917.
Description: Contains reviews, commentary, and news of the foundation.

500 SX ISSN 1018-7685
CODEN: MNWGEH
NAMIBIA SCIENTIFIC SOCIETY. NEWSLETTER/NAMIBIA WISSENSCHAFTLICHE GESELLSCHAFT. MITTEILUNGEN. (Text in Afrikaans, English and German) 1959. m. membership. Namibia Scientific Society, 110 Leutwein St., P.O. Box 67, Windhoek 9000, Namibia. TEL 061-225372. Ed. A. Henrichsen. Indexed: Zoo.Rec. Document type: newsletter, academic/scholarly publication.
Formerly: South West Africa Scientific Society. Newsletter - S W A Wetenskaplike Vereniging. Nuusbrief - S W A Wissenschaftliche Gesellschaft. Mitteilungen (ISSN 0036-2069); Incorporates (in 1983): Botanische Mitteilungen.

SCIENCES: COMPREHENSIVE WORKS

500 600   CC   ISSN 0469-5097
Q111   CODEN: NCHPAZ
NANJING DAXUE XUEBAO (ZIRAN KEXUE BAN)/NANJING UNIVERSITY. JOURNAL (NATURAL SCIENCE EDITION). (Text in Chinese) 1955. q. $20 (effective 1996). (Nanjing Daxue - Nanjing University) Nanjing Daxue Chubanshe - Nanjing University Press, Nanjing, Jiangsu 210008, People's Republic of China. TEL 86-25-6634651. FAX 86-25-3302728. (Subscr. to: Tianjin Publishing Trading Corp., 130 Chifong Dao, Tianjin 300041, P.R. China) Ed. Cao Zhengzhong.
—BLDSC (4828.680000); CASDDS.
Refereed Serial

500   JA   ISSN 0547-2407
    CODEN: NKDSAC
NARA KYOIKU DAIGAKU KIYO. SHIZEN KAGAKU/NARA UNIVERSITY OF EDUCATION. BULLETIN. NATURAL SCIENCE. (Text and summaries in English and Japanese) 1951. a. Nara Kyoiku Daigaku - Nara University of Education, Takabatake-cho, Nara-shi, Nara-ken 630, Japan. **Indexed:** Biol.Abstr., Chem.Abstr., Jap.Per.Ind.

500   XR   ISSN 0036-5343
QH7   CODEN: SNMPAM
NARODNI MUZEUM V PRAZE. SBORNIK. RADA B: PRIRODNI VEDY/ACTA MUSEI NATIONALIS PRAGAE. SERIES B: HISTORIA NATURALIS. (Text in Czech, English, French, German) 1937. a. 20 Kc.($21.07) Narodni Muzeum, Prirodovedecke Muzeum, Vaclavske nam. 68, 115 79 Prague 1, Czech Republic. FAX 42-2-24226488. (Subscr. to: P N S - Ustredni Expedice a Dovoz Tisku Prague, Zavod 01, Administrace Vyvozu Tisku, Hvozdanska 5-7, 149 00 Prague 4 - Roztyly, Czech Republic) Ed. Jiri Cejka. charts; illus.; index. **Indexed:** Biol.Abstr., Chem.Abstr. **Document type:** academic/scholarly publication.
—BLDSC (8083.000000).
Formerly: Narodni Muzeum v Praze. Sbornik: Prirodni Vedy.

500   SA   ISSN 0067-9208
GN656   CODEN: NVNMAJ
NASIONALE MUSEUM, BLOEMFONTEIN. NAVORSINGE/NATIONAL MUSEUM, BLOEMFONTEIN. RESEARCHES. Key Title: Navorsinge van die Nasionale Museum. (Text and summaries in Afrikaans, English) 1952. irreg. (1 vol./yr. in 10-14 parts), vol.10, pt.10, 1994. price varies. Nasionale Museum, Bloemfontein - National Museum, Bloemfontein, P.O. Box 266, Bloemfontein 9300, South Africa. TEL 27-51-479609. FAX 27-51-479681. Ed. J. Haasbroek. abstr.; bibl.; charts; illus.; stat.; index. circ. 850. (back issues avail.) **Indexed:** Biol.Abstr., Ecol.Abstr., Entomol.Abstr., Sport Fish.Abstr., Wild.Rev., Zoo.Rec. **Document type:** academic/scholarly publication, monographic series.
Incorporates (after vol.25, 1989): National Museum, Bloemfontein. Memoirs (ISSN 0374-9665)
Description: Publishes original research papers in natural science and the human sciences, with particular emphasis on the research disciplines of the National Museum, studies relating to collections of the Museum, local ecology, fauna and history.
Refereed Serial

NATIONAL ACADEMY OF SCIENCES. BIOGRAPHICAL MEMOIRS. see *BIOGRAPHY*

500 530   II   ISSN 0369-8203
Q73   CODEN: PAIAA3
NATIONAL ACADEMY OF SCIENCES, INDIA. PROCEEDINGS. SECTION A. PHYSICAL SCIENCES. (Text in English) 1931. q. Rs.150($50) National Academy of Sciences, 5 Lajpatra Rd., Allahabad 211002, Uttar Pradesh, India. Ed. H.C. Khare. adv.; bibl.; charts; illus. circ. 500. **Indexed:** Biol.Abstr., Chem.Abstr., Curr.Cont., INSPEC, Mass Spectr.Bull., Math.R. **Document type:** proceedings.
—BLDSC (6761.900000); CASDDS.

NATIONAL ACADEMY OF SCIENCES, INDIA. PROCEEDINGS. SECTION B. BIOLOGICAL SCIENCES. see *BIOLOGY*

500   II   ISSN 0250-541X
Q73   CODEN: NASLDX
NATIONAL ACADEMY OF SCIENCES, INDIA. SCIENCE LETTERS. (Text in English) 1978. m. Rs.150($50) National Academy of Sciences, 5 Lajpatra Rd., Allahabad 211002, Uttar Pradesh, India. Ed. H.C. Khare. **Indexed:** Bio-Contr.News & Info., Biol.Abstr., Curr.Cont., Field Crop Abstr., Forest.Abstr., Forest Prod.Abstr., Hort.Abstr., Ind.Vet., INSPEC, Maize Abstr., Plant Grow.Reg.Abstr., Potato Abstr., Rev.Med.& Vet.Mycol., Rev.Plant Path., Seed Abstr., Soils & Fert., Soyabean Abstr., Triticale Abstr., Trop.Oil Seeds Abstr., Weed Abstr.
—BLDSC (6015.756000); CASDDS; Ei; Genuine Article.

505   US   ISSN 0027-8424
Q11   CODEN: PNASA6
NATIONAL ACADEMY OF SCIENCES OF THE UNITED STATES OF AMERICA. PROCEEDINGS. Key Title: Proceedings of the National Academy of Sciences of the United States of America. 1915. bi-w. $230 to individuals (foreign $325); institutions $420 (foreign $515) (effective 1995). National Academy of Sciences, Proceedings Office, 2101 Constitution Ave., N.W., Washington, DC 20418. TEL 202-625-4725. FAX 202-625-4747. Ed. Lawrence Bogorad. bibl.; charts; illus.; index, cum.index: vol.1-50. circ. 9,500. (also avail. in microfilm from UMI,PMC) **Indexed:** Abstr.Hyg., Anim.Breed.Abstr., Bio-Contr.News & Info., Biol.Abstr., Chem.Abstr., Crop Physiol.Abstr., Curr.Adv.Biochem., Curr.Adv.Cancer Res., Curr.Adv.Cell & Devel.Biol., Curr.Adv.Ecol.Sci., Curr.Adv.Genetics & Molec.Biol., Curr.Biotech.Abstr., Curr.Ref.Fish Res., Dairy Sci.Abstr., Deep Sea Res.& Oceanogr.Abstr., Excerp.Med., Food Sci.& Tech.Abstr., Forest.Abstr., Geo.Abstr., Helminthol.Abstr., Hort.Abstr., Ind.Med., Ind.Vet., INSPEC, Kidney, Maize Abstr., Mass Spectr.Bull., Math.R., Med.& Surg.Dermat., Nutr.Abstr., Plant Breed.Abstr., Plant Grow.Reg.Abstr., Potato Abstr., Poult.Abstr., Rev.Med.& Vet.Mycol., Rice Abstr., Seed Abstr., Soils & Fert., Sorghum & Millets Abstr., Soyabean Abstr., Sport Fish.Abstr., Telegen, Triticale Abstr., Trop.Dis.Bull., Vet.Bull., Weed.Abstr., Wild.Rev., Zoo.Rec. **Document type:** academic/scholarly publication, proceedings.
—BLDSC (6762.000000); CASDDS; Ei; EMDOCS; Faxon; Genuine Article; SWETS; UnCover. **CCC.**
Former titles (until 1985): National Academy of Sciences of the United States of America. Proceedings. Physical Sciences (ISSN 0273-1142); National Academy of Sciences of the United States of America. Proceedings. Biological Sciences (ISSN 0273-1134); Which superseded in part: National Academy of Sciences. Proceedings.
Description: Publishes reports that describe the results of original theoretical or experimental research of exceptional importance.
Refereed Serial

500   US   ISSN 1071-8966
Q11
NATIONAL ASSOCIATION OF ACADEMIES OF SCIENCE. DIRECTORY, PROCEEDINGS AND HANDBOOK. 1977. a. $15. National Association of Academies of Science, Science Division, Northeast Missouri State University, Kirksville, MO 63501. TEL 816-785-4618. FAX 816-785-4045. (Affiliate: American Association for the Advancement of Science) Ed. James H. Shaddy. circ. 500. (back issues avail.) **Indexed:** ERIC.
Former titles: National Association of Academies of Science. Proceedings, Directory and Handbook (ISSN 0739-361X); Association of Academies of Science. Directory and Proceedings.

623   JA   ISSN 0388-4112
Q1   CODEN: MNDEDH
NATIONAL DEFENSE ACADEMY. MEMOIRS. MATHEMATICS, PHYSICS, CHEMISTRY AND ENGINEERING/BOEI DAIGAKKO KIYO RIKOGAKU-HEN. (Text in English) 1956. 4/yr. free. National Defense Academy, 10-20, Hashirimizu 1-chome, Yokosuka-shi, Kanagawa-ken 239, Japan. Ed. Otohiko Nomoto. abstr.; charts; illus.; index. circ. 700. **Indexed:** Chem.Abstr., INIS Atomind., Math.R., Sci.Abstr.
—BLDSC (5626.650000); CASDDS.
Formerly (until 1980): Defense Academu. Memoirs (ISSN 0025-9136)

500   JA   ISSN 0386-555X
NATIONAL INSTITUTE OF POLAR RESEARCH. MEMOIRS. SERIES F: LOGISTICS. (Text and summaries in English) 1964. irreg., no.4, 1982. exchange basis. National Institute of Polar Research - Kokuritsu Kyokuchi Kenkyujo, Library, 9-10, Kaga 1-chome, Itabashi-ku, Tokyo 173, Japan. TEL 03-3962-2214. FAX 03-3962-2225. TELEX 272-3515 POLRSCJ. Ed. Takeo Hirasawa. circ. 1,000. **Document type:** monographic series.
—BLDSC (5626.820000).
Supersedes: Japanese Antarctic Research Expedition, 1956-1962. Scientific Reports. Series F: Logistics (ISSN 0075-3408)

500 301   US   ISSN 1059-4566
NATIONAL MUSEUM OF NATURAL HISTORY QUEST. 1991. q. free to qualified members. Smithsonian Institution, 900 Jefferson Dr., Washington, DC 20560. TEL 202-357-2627. Ed. Laura A. Kennedy. **Document type:** academic/scholarly publication.
Description: Disseminates research in anthropology, zoology, botany, and mineralogy at the Museum.

507   US   ISSN 1057-6886
Q180.U5
NATIONAL PATTERNS OF R & D RESOURCES. 1968. a. U.S. National Science Foundation, 4201 Wilson Blvd., Ste. 245, Arlington, VA 22230. (Also avail. from: Bernan, 4611-F Assembly Dr., Lanham, MD 20706. TEL 800-274-4447. FAX 301-459-0056) **Document type:** government publication.
Former titles (until 1989): National Patterns of Science and Technology Resources (ISSN 1049-3069); National Patterns of R and D Resources: Funds and Manpower in the United States (ISSN 0093-8572)

500 600   UA   ISSN 1110-0591
NATIONAL RESEARCH CENTRE. BULLETIN. (Text in English; summaries in Arabic, English) 1976. 4/yr. $107 (effective 1996). National Information and Documentation Centre (NIDOC), Tahrir St., Dokki, Awqaf P.O., Cairo, Egypt. TEL 20-2-701696. Ed. Salah M. Zayed. (reprint service avail. from IRC) **Document type:** academic/scholarly publication, bulletin.
Description: Original papers in chemistry and the physical and biological sciences.

500 620   US   ISSN 0027-8432
Q11   CODEN: NERPAV
NATIONAL RESEARCH COUNCIL. NEWS REPORT. Key Title: NewsReport. 1951. 4/yr. $10 (foreign $12). National Research Council, 2101 Constitution Ave., N.W., Washington, DC 20418. TEL 202-334-2138. (Subscr. to: NewsReport, Box 665, Holmes, PA 19043) (Co-sponsors: National Academy of Engineering; National Academy of Sciences; Institute of Medicine) Ed. Patricia Worns. bk.rev.; bibl.; charts; illus.; index. circ. 18,000. (also avail. in microfilm from UMI; back issues avail.; reprint service avail. from UMI) **Indexed:** Ind.Hyg.Dig.
—BLDSC (6105.900000); CASDDS; Faxon; UMI; UnCover.

500   CN   ISSN 0842-6066
NATIONAL RESEARCH COUNCIL OF CANADA. N R C ANNUAL REPORT - RAPPORT ANNUEL DU C N R C. (Text in English & French) 1916. a. free. National Research Council of Canada, Corporate Services, M-58, Ottawa, ON K1A 0R6, Canada. TEL 613-993-9101. FAX 613-952-9696. Ed. Huguette Brunet. circ. 6,000. **Document type:** corporate report.
Former titles (until 1984): National Research Council. Annual Report (ISSN 0823-5759); (until 1980): National Research Council of Canada. Report of the President - Rapport du President (ISSN 0373-904X); (until 1968): National Research Council of Canada. Annual Report (ISSN 0369-5484); (until 1967): National Research Council of Canada. Report (ISSN 0228-6300); (until 1965): National Research Council of Canada. Annual Report (ISSN 0228-6319); (until 1930): National Research Council of Canada. Report of the President and Financial Statement; (until 1924): Honourary Advisory Council for Science and Industrial Research of Canada. Report.

SCIENCES: COMPREHENSIVE WORKS

500   TH   ISSN 0028-0011
CODEN: JRCTAF
NATIONAL RESEARCH COUNCIL OF THAILAND. JOURNAL. (Text in English or Thai) 1960. s-a. B.100 (foreign $10). National Research Council of Thailand, 196 Phahonyothin Rd., Chatuchak, Bangkok 10900, Thailand. FAX 66-2-5613049. TELEX 82213-NARECOU-TH. Ed. Aphirat Arunin. charts; illus.; stat. circ. 1,000. **Indexed:** Abstr.Hyg., Biol.Abstr., Chem.Abstr., Curr.Adv.Ecol.Sci., Excerp.Med., Field Crop Abstr., Food Sci.& Tech.Abstr., Herb.Abstr., INSPEC (1968-), Met.Abstr., Plant Breed.Abstr., Soils & Fert., Trop.Dis.Bull. **Document type:** academic/scholarly publication.
—BLDSC (4831.150000); CASDDS.

500   CE   ISSN 0300-9254
Q4   CODEN: JNSCBH
NATIONAL SCIENCE COUNCIL OF SRI LANKA. JOURNAL. (Text in English) 1973. q. $80. Natural Resources, Energy and Science Authority, 47-5 Maitland Place, Colombo 7, Sri Lanka. Ed. R. Ramasamy. (reprint service avail.) **Indexed:** Biol.Abstr., Chem.Abstr., Curr.Cont., Dairy Sci.Abstr., Field Crop Abstr., Food Sci.& Tech.Abstr., Herb.Abstr., Irr.& Drain.Abstr., Packag.Sci.Tech., Poult.Abstr., Ref.Zh., Soils & Fert., Sri Lanka Sci.Ind., Sugar Ind.Abstr., Weed Abstr.
—BLDSC (4831.170000); CASDDS. **CCC.**

NATIONAL TECHNICAL ASSOCIATION. JOURNAL. see *ETHNIC INTERESTS*

500.9   IC   ISSN 0028-0550
NATTURUFRAEDINGURINN. (Text in Icelandic; summaries in English) 1930. q. ISK 2900($50) (effective 1992). Hid Islenska Natturufraedifelag - Icelandic Natural History Society, Hlemmur 3, IS-105 Reykjavik, Iceland. TEL 354-567-6731. Ed. Sigmundur Einarsson. bk.rev.; charts; illus.; index. circ. 1,900. (back issues avail.) **Indexed:** Biol.Abstr., Chem.Abstr., Geo.Abstr., GeoRef., Ocean.Abstr., Pollut.Abstr.
—BLDSC (6033.730000).
Description: Research papers and reviews on the natural history of Iceland. Includes articles of more general interest.

505   DK   ISSN 0028-0585
NATUR OG MUSEUM. (Text in Danish) 1951. q. DKK 118($15) Naturhistorisk Museum, Bygning 210, Universitetsparken, DK-8000 Aarhus C, Denmark. TEL 45-86-12-97-77. FAX 45-86-13-08-82. Ed. Anders Holm Joensen. charts; illus. circ. 9,000.

500.9   GW   ISSN 0028-0593
QH5   CODEN: NTRHAA
NATUR UND HEIMAT. 1934. 4/yr. DM.26. Westfaelisches Museum fuer Naturkunde, Sentruperstr. 285, 48161 Muenster, Germany. TEL 0251-59105. FAX 0251-5916098. bibl.; charts; illus.; maps. **Indexed:** Biol.Abstr. **Document type:** academic/scholarly publication.

500.9   AU   ISSN 0028-0607
NATUR UND LAND. vol.56, 1970. irreg. (4-6/yr.). S.180 (foreign S.230). Oesterreichischer Naturschutzbund, Arenbergstr. 10, A-5020 Salzburg, Austria. TEL 0662-642909. FAX 0662-6437344. (Co-sponsor: Oesterreichische Gesellschaft fuer Natur- und Umweltschutz) Eds. Hannes Augustin, Ingrid Hagenstein. adv.; bk.rev.; charts; illus.; stat.; index. circ. 10,000. (also avail. in microform) **Indexed:** Biol.Abstr., Ecol.Abstr., Environ.Abstr. **Document type:** academic/scholarly publication.

500.9   GW   ISSN 0722-7795
NATUR- UND LANDSCHAFTKUNDE. 1965. q. DM.36. Bergmann-Verlag, Werlerstr. 269, 59063 Hamm, Germany. TEL 02381-51144. Ed.Bd. adv.; bk.rev. circ. 2,900. **Indexed:** Agroforest.Abstr.
Former titles: Natur- und Landschaftkunde in Westfalen; Naturkunde in Westfalen (ISSN 0028-0992)
Description: Devoted to the protection of nature and environment in the Northrhein-Westphalia region. Articles on research and conservation of trees, forests and land. Includes magazine reviews.

500.9   GW   ISSN 0028-1301
QH5   CODEN: NAMUAR
NATUR UND MUSEUM. 1867. m. DM.60. Senckenbergische Naturforschende Gesellschaft, Abt. Schriftentausch, Senckenberganlage 25, 60325 Frankfurt a.M., Germany. TEL 069-7542-1. FAX 069-746238. TELEX 413129. Ed. Willi Ziegler. adv.; bk.rev.; charts; illus.; index. circ. 6,000. **Indexed:** Biol.Abstr., Chem.Abstr., Deep Sea Res.& Oceanogr.Abstr., GeoRef., Ocean.Abstr., Pollut.Abstr., Sport Fish.Abstr., Wild.Rev., Zoo.Rec. **Document type:** academic/scholarly publication.
—UMI. **CCC.**

508   NE   ISSN 0028-0631
NATURA. 1906. 10/yr. fl.45. Koninklijke Nederlandse Natuurhistorische Vereniging, Oude Gracht 237, 3511 NK Utrecht, Netherlands. TEL 31-30-314797. FAX 31-30-368907. Ed. G. Hooymans. adv.; bk.rev.; charts; illus.; index. circ. 9,000. **Indexed:** Biol.Abstr.
—SWETS.
Description: Covers all aspects of natural history.

500.9   VE   ISSN 0028-064X
CODEN: NTRCBU
NATURA; revista trimestral de divulgacion cientifica, tecnica y cultural. 1958. q. Bs.2000($25) Fundacion La Salle de Ciencias Naturales, Edificio Fundacion La Salle, Av. Boyaca-Mariperez, Apdo. 1930, Caracas 1010A, Venezuela. Ed. Jose A. Monente. adv. circ. 1,200. **Indexed:** GeoRef.
—BLDSC (6035.200000).

500   IT   ISSN 0369-6243
QH7   CODEN: NTRMAP
NATURA; rivista di scienze naturali. (Text in Italian) 1909. s-a. L.45000 membership (effective 1995). Societa Italiana di Scienze Naturali, Corso Venezia, 55, 20121 Milan, Italy. TEL 39-2-62085405. (Co-sponsor: Museo Civico di Storia Naturale di Milano) Ed. Giovani Pinna. bk.rev.; index. circ. 2,000. (back issues avail.) **Indexed:** Biol.Abstr., Chem.Abstr., Deep Sea Res.& Oceanogr.Abstr., GeoRef., Mineral.Abstr., Sport Fish.Abstr., Wild.Rev., Zoo.Rec. **Document type:** monographic series.

500   US   ISSN 0193-8355
CODEN: NSOBD7
NATURAL HAZARDS OBSERVER. 1976. bi-m. free in N. America; elsewhere $15. University of Colorado, Institute of Behavioral Science, Natural Hazards Research & Applications Information Center, Campus Box 482, Boulder, CO 80309. TEL 303-492-6818. FAX 303-492-2151. Eds. David L. Butler, Sylvia C. Dane. bk.rev.; abstr.; bibl.; illus. circ. 13,000. (also avail. in tabloid format; back issues avail.) **Indexed:** Environ.Abstr., GeoRef., Meteor.& Geoastrophys.Abstr. **Document type:** newsletter.
Description: Reports on new research and findings from completed projects, pertinent legislation, applications of research at federal, state, and local levels and by private agencies. Includes announcements of recent publications and future conferences.

500.9   US   ISSN 0028-0712
QH1   CODEN: NAHIAX
NATURAL HISTORY. 1900. m. $28. American Museum of Natural History, Central Park W. at 79th St., New York, NY 10024-5192. TEL 212-769-5500. FAX 212-769-5511. E-mail: scipubs@amnh.org. Ed. Alan Ternes. adv.; bk.rev.; bibl.; illus.; index. circ. 510,000. (also avail. in microform from UMI; reprint service avail. from UMI) **Indexed:** A.I.C.P., Abr.R.G., Abstr.Anthropol., Acad.Ind., Acid Pre.Dig., Amer.Bibl.Slavic & E.Eur.Stud., Anthropol.Lit., Biol.Abstr., Biol.Dig., Bk.Rev.Dig., Bk.Rev.Ind. (1965-), Child.Bk.Rev.Ind., Child.Lit.Abstr., Curr.Adv.Ecol.Sci., Curr.Cont., Curr.Ref.Fish Res., Deep Sea Res.& Oceanogr.Abstr., Energy Ind., Energy Info.Abstr., Energy Rev., Environ.Abstr., Environ.Per.Bibl., Gard.Lit. (1992-), Gen.Sci.Ind., Helminthol.Abstr., Ind.Sci.Rev., Jun.High.Mag.Abstr., Key Word Ind.Wildl.Res., Mag.Ind., Mid.East: Abstr.& Ind., Peace Res.Abstr., R.G., So.Pac.Per.Ind., Sport Fish.Abstr., TOM, Wild.Rev., Zoo.Rec. (until 19??). **Document type:** academic/scholarly publication, consumer publication.
●Also available online. Vendor(s): Knight-Ridder, Inc., University Microfilms International.
Also available on CD-ROM. Producer(s): University Microfilms International.
—BLDSC (6038.000000); Faxon; Genuine Article; SWETS; UMI; UnCover.
Incorporates: Nature Magazine.
Description: Articles written by professional scientists and scholars on the biological sciences, ecology, anthropology, archeology, earth science and astronomy.
Refereed Serial

500 069   UK   ISSN 1360-0745
NATURAL HISTORY MUSEUM. BIENNIAL REPORT FOR SCIENCE. biennial, latest 1996. free. Natural History Museum, Science Directorate, Cromwell Rd., London SW7 5BD, England. TEL 0171-938-9399. FAX 0171-938-9506. **Document type:** government publication.

500   UK   ISSN 1360-0761
QH70.G72
NATURAL HISTORY MUSEUM. TRIENNIAL REPORT. 1966. triennial, latest 1996. price varies. Natural History Museum, Cromwell Rd., London SW7 5BD, England. TEL 0171-938-8761. FAX 0171-938-8709. bibl.; illus.; stat. **Indexed:** Br.Archaeol.Abstr., Deep Sea Res.& Oceanogr.Abstr. **Document type:** government publication.
Former titles: British Museum (Natural History). Triennial Report (ISSN 1359-0766); British Museum (Natural History). Report (ISSN 0524-6474)

505   US   ISSN 0076-0943
NATURAL HISTORY MUSEUM OF LOS ANGELES COUNTY. SCIENCE SERIES. 1930. irreg., no.38, 1993. Natural History Museum of Los Angeles County, 900 Exposition Blvd., Los Angeles, CA 90007. TEL 213-744-3330. FAX 213-742-0730. bk.rev.; illus.; index. circ. 1,000. **Indexed:** Biol.Abstr., Deep Sea Res.& Oceanogr.Abstr. **Document type:** monographic series, proceedings.
Refereed Serial

NATURAL HISTORY MUSEUM OF LOS ANGELES REPORT. see *MUSEUMS AND ART GALLERIES*

574   IQ   ISSN 1012-3571
NATURAL HISTORY RESEARCH CENTER. PUBLICATION. (Text in English; summaries in English and Arabic) 1950. irreg. ID.2000 per no. Natural History Research Center - Markaz Buhuth al-Tarikh al-Tabi'i, University of Baghdad, Bab al-Muadham, Baghdad, Iraq. Ed. Munir K. Bunni. **Indexed:** Biol.Abstr., Zoo.Rec. **Document type:** academic/scholarly publication.
Former titles: Iraq Natural History Research Center and Museum. Publication; (until 1972): Iraq Natural History Museum. Publication (ISSN 0375-0477)

SCIENCES: COMPREHENSIVE WORKS

500.9 UK ISSN 0144-221X
QH1 CODEN: TNHND5
NATURAL HISTORY SOCIETY OF NORTHUMBRIA. TRANSACTIONS. 1831. a. membership. Natural History Society of Northumbria, Hancock Museum, Newcastle upon Tyne NE2 4PT, England. TEL 0191-232-6386. Ed. R.B. Clark. charts; illus.; cum.index. circ. 650. **Indexed:** Biol.Abstr., Geo.Abstr. **Document type:** academic/scholarly publication, proceedings.
   Formerly: Natural History Society of Northumberland Durham and Newcastle upon Tyne. Transactions (ISSN 0028-0720)
   Description: Covers all aspects of natural history of northern England.
   Refereed Serial

NATURAL SCIENCES AND ENGINEERING RESEARCH COUNCIL OF CANADA. HIGHLIGHTS. see *EDUCATION — Higher Education*

NATURAL SCIENCES AND ENGINEERING RESEARCH COUNCIL OF CANADA. LIST OF SCHOLARSHIPS AND GRANTS IN AID OF RESEARCH/CONSEIL DE RECHERCHES EN SCIENCES NATURELLES ET EN GENIE DU CANADA. LISTE DES BOURSES ET SUBVENTIONS DE RECHERCHE. see *EDUCATION — Higher Education*

500.9 TR
NATURALIST. 1975. bi-m. $35. (Field Naturalists Club of Trinidad & Tobago) S.M. Publications Publishing House, 20 Collens Rd., Maraval, Port-of-Spain, Trinidad & Tobago, W.I. TEL 809 622-6625. Ed. Stephen Mohammed. adv.; bk.rev.; illus.; stat.; index. circ. 20,000. (back issues avail.)
   Formerly: Trinidad Naturalist (ISSN 0379-4016)

500 AT
THE NATURALIST NEWS. 11/yr. Aus.$38 membership. Western Australian Naturalists' Club Inc., P.O. Box 156, Nedlands, W.A. 6009, Australia. FAX 610-272-8688. **Document type:** newsletter.

500 JA ISSN 0914-028X
NATURALISTS. (Text in Japanese) 1987. irreg. Shizen Kagaku Kenkyukai, Shikoku Joshi Daigaku Seibutsugaku Kyoshitsu, 123-1 Ebisuno, Furukawa, Ojin-cho, Tokushima 771-11, Japan.

500 UK ISSN 0028-0836
Q1 CODEN: NATUAS
NATURE; international weekly journal of science. 1869. w. £86 to individuals in Europe ($145 in U.S.; elsewhere £105); institutions in Europe £200 ($425 in U.S.; elsewhere £280). Macmillan Magazines Ltd., 4 Little Essex St., London WC2R 3LF, England. TEL 44-171-836-6633. (Subscr. to: Brunel Rd., Basingstoke, Hants. RG21 2XS, England. TEL 44-1256-29242. FAX 44-1256-842084; In U.S.: Box 1733, Riverton, NJ 08077-7333. TEL 800-524-0384) Ed. John Maddox. adv.; bk.rev.; abstr.; bibl.; charts; illus.; tr.lit.; index. circ. 30,821. (also avail. in microform from UMI,PMC; Braille; talking book) **Indexed:** A.I.Abstr., A.I.C.P., ABC, Abstr.Bull.Inst.Pap.Chem., Acad.Ind., Acid Pre.Dig., Acid Rain Abstr., Acid Rain Ind., AESIS, Anal.Abstr., Anthropol.Lit., Appl.Mech.Rev., Art & Archaeol.Tech.Abstr., Bibl.Dev.Med.& Child Neur., Biol.Abstr., Biol.Dig., Biostat., Biotech.Abstr., Biwk.Pap.Rad.Chem.& Photochem., Bk.Rev.Ind. (1982-), Br.Archaeol.Abstr., Br.Ceram.Abstr., Br.Educ.Ind., Br.Geol.Lit., Br.Tech.Ind., C.I.S. Abstr., Cadscan, Chem.Abstr., Child.Bk.Rev.Ind. (1982-), Curr.Adv.Biochem., Curr.Adv.Ecol.Sci., Curr.Biotech.Abstr., Curr.Cont., Curr.Ref.Fish Res., Curr.Tit.Dent., Dairy Sci.Abstr., Deep Sea Res.& Oceanogr.Abstr., Dent.Ind., Diab.Cont., Diar.Dis.Res., Ecol.Abstr., Energy Info.Abstr., Eng.Ind., Environ.Abstr., Excerp.Med., Field Crop Abstr., Fluidex, Food Sci.& Tech.Abstr., Forest.Abstr., Forest Prod.Abstr., Fut.Surv., Gen.Sci.Ind., Geo.Abstr., Geol.Abstr., GeoRef., Helminthol.Abstr., High.Educ.Curr.Aware.Bull., Hort.Abstr., I.P.A., IDA, Ind.Chem., Ind.Med., Ind.Sci.Rev., INSPEC (1968-), Int.Aerosp.Abstr., Int.Nurs.Ind., Kidney, Lab.Haz.Bull., Lead Abstr., Mass Spectr.Bull., Math.R., Med.& Surg.Dermat., Met.Abstr., Meteor.& Geostrophys.Abstr., Mid.East: Abstr.& Ind., Nutr.Abstr., Psychol.Abstr. (1928-), Peace Res.Abstr., Petrol.Abstr., Plant Breed.Abstr., PMR, Pollut.Abstr., Protozool.Abstr., RAPRA, Res.High.Educ.Abstr., Rev.Appl.Entomol., Rev.Med.& Vet.Mycol., Rev.Plant Path., Rice Abstr., Risk.Abstr., Sel.Water Res.Abstr., So.Pac.Per.Ind., Sport Fish.Abstr., Telegen, Trop.Dis.Bull., Vet.Bull., VITIS, W.R.C.Inf., Wild.Rev., World Alum.Abstr., World Text.Abstr., Zincscan, Zoo.Rec. **Document type:** academic/scholarly publication.
   —BLDSC (6045.000000); CASDDS; CIS; Ei; EMDOCS; Faxon; Genuine Article; PADDS; SWETS; UMI; UnCover. **CCC.**
   Description: Publishes original scientific research reports, review articles surveying recent developments in specific disciplines, short contributions, letters, and commentary.
   Refereed Serial

NATURE AND RESOURCES (ENGLISH EDITION); international news about research on environment, resources, and conservation of nature. see *CONSERVATION*

502 UK
NATURE IN AVON: PROCEEDINGS OF THE BRISTOL NATURALISTS' SOCIETY. 1862. a. £4.50. Bristol Naturalists' Society, City Museum, Bristol BS8 1RL, England. (Ed. addr.: 81 Cranbrook Rd., Redland, Bristol GS6 7B2, England) Ed. Mrs. A.F. Hollowell. adv. circ. 600. **Indexed:** Br.Hum.Ind., GeoRef. **Document type:** academic/scholarly publication, proceedings.
   —BLDSC (6665.000000).
   Former titles (until 1994): Bristol Naturalists' Society. Proceedings (ISSN 0068-1040); (until 1935): Bristol Naturalists' Society. Annual Report and Proceedings.
   Description: Studies the natural history and geology of the Bristol area.
   Refereed Serial

NATURE STRUCTURAL BIOLOGY. see *BIOLOGY*

500.9 NO ISSN 0028-0887
  CODEN: NTUNA9
NATUREN; populaervitenskapelig tidsskrift. 1877. bi-m. NOK 285 in Nordic countries; elsewhere $55 320 (effective 1996). (University of Bergen) Scandinavian University Press, P.O. Box 2959 Toeyen, N-0608 Oslo, Norway. TEL 47-22-57-54-00. FAX 47-22-57-53-53. (U.S. addr.: Scandinavian University Press, 200 Meacham Ave., Elmont, NY 11003. TEL 516035207300) Ed. Per M. Joergensen. adv.; bk.rev.; charts; illus.; index. circ. 2,200. (back issues avail.) **Indexed:** Chem.Abstr., Curr.Adv.Ecol.Sci., Energy Res.Abstr., GeoRef.
   —BLDSC (6047.800000); CASDDS.
   Description: Covers all fields of natural sciences

508 DK ISSN 0028-0895
Q4 CODEN: NAVDAL
NATURENS VERDEN. 1917. m. DKK 298. Rhodos, International Science and Art Publishers, Strandgade 36 D, DK-1401 Copenhagen K, Denmark. TEL 45-31-543080. FAX 45-31-954742. TELEX 31502. Niels Blaedel. adv.; bk.rev.; illus.; maps; index. circ. 8,000. **Indexed:** Biol.Abstr., Chem.Abstr., NAA, Zoo.Rec.
   —BLDSC (6048.000000); CASDDS; UMI.
   Description: Publishes articles on the high school level.

NATURESOUTH. see *BIOLOGY*

500 BL ISSN 0100-4700
NATUREZA EM REVISTA. 1976. s-a. price varies. Fundacao Zoobotanica do Rio Grande do Sul, Caixa Postal 1188, 90000 Porto Alegre, Rio Grande do sul, Brazil. Ed. Elisabete Monlleo Martins da Silva. adv.; bk.rev.; bibl.; illus. circ. 10,000. **Indexed:** Biol.Abstr.

500 SZ
NATURFORSCHENDE GESELLSCHAFT DES KANTONS SOLOTHURN. irreg. Naturforschende Gesellschaft Solothurn, Zentralbibliothek, Bielstr. 39, CH-4500 Solothurn, Switzerland. **Document type:** monographic series.

500 SZ ISSN 0077-6130
Q67 CODEN: MNGBAK
NATURFORSCHENDE GESELLSCHAFT IN BERN. MITTEILUNGEN. (Text in German; summaries in English and French) 1843. a. 30 SFr. Naturforschende Gesellschaft in Bern, Stadt- und Universitaetsbibliothek, Muenstergasse 61, CH-3000 Bern 7, Switzerland. TEL 031-3203211. FAX 031-3203299. Ed. H. Hutzli. adv.; cum,index: 1944-1968 in no.26 (1969). circ. 1,400. **Indexed:** Biol.Abstr., GeoRef, VITIS. **Document type:** academic/scholarly publication, bulletin.

500.9 SZ ISSN 0042-5672
Q67 CODEN: VNGZAL
NATURFORSCHENDE GESELLSCHAFT IN ZUERICH. VIERTELJAHRESSCHRIFT. 1855. q. 90 SFr. Ehrli Druck AG, Dorfplatz 3, CH-6060 Sarnen, Switzerland. Ed. H.H. Bosshard. adv.; bk.rev.; bibl.; charts; illus.; index. **Indexed:** Biol.Abstr., Chem.Abstr., GeoRef.
   —BLDSC (9235.903000); CASDDS. **CCC.**

500 GW ISSN 0028-0917
Q49 CODEN: BEFBAZ
NATURFORSCHENDE GESELLSCHAFT ZU FREIBURG. BERICHTE. 1855. s-a. DM.30. Naturforschende Gesellschaft Freiburg, Albertstr. 23b, 79104 Freiburg, Germany. FAX 0761-2036483. bk.rev.; charts; illus.; index, cum.index: 1855-1955. circ. 1,300. **Indexed:** Biol.Abstr., GeoRef., VITIS. **Document type:** academic/scholarly publication.
   —BLDSC (1923.040000).

500 551 560 SZ
NATURHISTORISCHES MUSEUM BASEL. VEROEFFENTLICHUNGEN. 1960. irreg. Naturhistorisches Museum Basel, Augustinergasse 2, CH-4001 Basel, Switzerland. FAX 061-2665546. Ed.Bd. circ. 2,500. (back issues avail.) **Indexed:** Biol.Abstr. **Document type:** monographic series.

SCIENCES: COMPREHENSIVE WORKS

500.9 SZ ISSN 0253-4401
CODEN: JNMBEL
NATURHISTORISCHES MUSEUM BERN. JAHRBUCH. (Text in English, French or German.) 1960. triennial. 75 SFr. Naturhistorisches Museum, Bernastr. 15, CH-3005 Bern, Switzerland. TEL 031-3507111. FAX 031-3507499. Ed.Bd. illus. circ. 250. (back issues avail.) Indexed: Key Word Ind.Wildl.Res., Sport Fish.Abstr., Wild.Rev., Zoo.Rec. **Document type:** corporate report.
Description: Contains activity reports and miscellaneous articles (original papers and reports on collections) in the fields of mineralogy, palaeontology, invertebrate and vertebrate zoology and anthropology.

500.9 AU ISSN 0255-0091
QE1 CODEN: ANAPE6
NATURHISTORISCHES MUSEUM IN WIEN. ANNALEN. SERIE A, MINERALOGIE UND PETROGRAPHIE, GEOLOGIE UND PALEONTOLOGIE, ANTHROPOLOGIE UND PRAEHISTORIE. (Text in English, French and German; summaries in English, French, German, Italian and Spanish) 1886. irreg. price varies. Naturhistorisches Museum in Wien, Burgring 7, Postfach 417, A-1014 Vienna, Austria. FAX 0222-935254. bk.review; index. circ. 1,200. (back issues avail.) Indexed: Bibl.& Ind.Geol., Bio-Contr.News & Info., Biol.Abstr., Curr.Adv.Ecol.Sci., Deep Sea Res.& Oceanogr.Abstr., GeoRef, Rev.Appl.Entomol., So.Pac.Per.Ind., Zoo.Rec. **Document type:** academic/scholarly publication.
—BLDSC (0907.010000).
Supersedes in part (in 1980): Naturhistorisches Museum in Wien. Annalen (ISSN 0083-6133)

581 591.1 AU ISSN 0255-0105
QL1 CODEN: ANMBEO
NATURHISTORISCHES MUSEUM IN WIEN. ANNALEN. SERIE B: BOTANIK UND ZOOLOGIE. (Text in English, French, German) 1886. irreg. price varies. Naturhistorisches Museum in Wien, Burgring 7, Postfach 417, A-1014 Vienna, Austria. TEL 0222-935254. (back issues avail.) Indexed: Bibl.& Ind.Geol., Bio-Contr.News& Info., Biol.Abstr., Curr.Adv.Ecol.Sci., Deep Sea Res.& Oceanogr.Abstr., GeoRef, Rev.Appl.Entomol., So.Pac.Per.Ind., Sport Fish.Abstr., Wild.Rev., Zoo.Rec. **Document type:** academic/scholarly publication.
—BLDSC (0907.020000).
Supersedes in part (in 1980): Naturhistorisches Museum in Wien. Annalen (ISSN 0083-6133)

500.9 AU ISSN 0255-0113
QH70.A92 CODEN: ANMCER
NATURHISTORISCHES MUSEUM IN WIEN. ANNALEN. SERIE C: JAHRESBERICHT. 1886. a. Naturhistorisches Museum in Wien, Burgring 7, Postfach 417, A-1014 Vienna, Austria. TEL 0222-935254.
Supersedes in part (in 1980): Naturhistorisches Museum in Wien. Annalen (ISSN 0083-6133)

500.9 AU ISSN 0505-5164
NATURHISTORISCHES MUSEUM IN WIEN. VEROEFFENTLICHUNGEN. NEUE FOLGE. 1958. irreg. price varies. Naturhistorisches Museum in Wien, Burgring 7, Postfach 417, A-1014 Vienna, Austria. FAX 0222-935254. Indexed: Bibl.& Ind.Geol. **Document type:** proceedings.

500 AU ISSN 0470-3901
NATURKUNDLICHES JAHRBUCH DER STADT LINZ. 1955. a. S.350. Naturkundliche Station der Stadt Linz, Roseggerstr. 22, A-4020 Linz, Austria. Ed. Gerhard Pfitzner. illus. circ. 500. Indexed: Key Word Ind.Wildl.Res. **Document type:** government publication.

500 DK ISSN 0109-2995
NATURLIGVIS; fra data til viden, forskningshistorier. 1983. a. free. Koebenhavns Universitet, Informationsudvalget ved det Naturvidenskabelige Fakultet, Blegdamsvej 3, 2200 Copenhagen N, Denmark. illus.

500 SW ISSN 0345-8296
NATURVETAREN. 1975. 18/yr. SEK 400. Sveriges Naturvetareforbund, P.O. Box 760, S-131 24 Nacka, Sweden. TEL 46-8-466-24-80. FAX 46-8-716-52-91. Ed. Harry Raagvik; Pub. Goeran Bengtsson. illus.; B&W page SEK 8400, color page SEK 12400; trim 188 x 260. circ. 9,000. cols./p.: 3; pp./issue: 32.

500.9 GW ISSN 0028-1042
Q3 CODEN: NATWAY
NATURWISSENSCHAFTEN. 1913. 12/yr. DM.398($289) (effective 1996). (Max-Planck-Gesellschaft zur Foerderung der Wissenschaften) Springer-Verlag, Heidelberger Platz 3, 14197 Berlin, Germany. TEL 030-8207-0. FAX 030-8214091. E-mail: orders@springer.de. (Subscr. in N. America to: Springer-Verlag New York, Inc., 44 Hartz Way, Secaucus, NJ 07096-2491. TEL 201-348-4033. FAX 201-348-4505) (Co-sponsor: Gesellschaft Deutscher Naturforscher und Aertze) Ed. H. Autrum. (also avail. in microform from UMI,PMC; reprint service avail. from ISI) Indexed: Anim.Breed.Abstr., Apic.Abstr., Appl.Mech.Rev., Art & Archaeol.Tech.Abstr., Bio-Contr.News & Info., Biol.Abstr., Biotech.Abstr., Chem.Abstr., Chem.Infd., Curr.Adv.Ecol.Sci., Curr.Ref.Fish Res., Dairy Sci.Abstr., Deep Sea Res.& Oceanogr.Abstr., Excerp.Med., Field Crop Abstr., Forest.Abstr., Forest Prod.Abstr., Geo.Abstr., Helminthol.Abstr., Herb.Abstr., Hort.Abstr., Ind.Chem., Ind.Med., Ind.Vet., INSPEC, Mass Spectr.Bull., Nutr.Abstr., Plant Breed.Abstr., Rev.Appl.Entomol., Rev.Med.& Vet.Mycol., Rev.Plant Path., Sel.Water Res.Abstr., Soils & Fert., Sport Fish.Abstr., Vet.Bull., Weed Abstr., Wild.Rev., Zoo.Rec. **Document type:** academic/scholarly publication.
—BLDSC (6049.000000); ADONIS; CASDDS; Ei; EMDOCS; Faxon; Genuine Article; SWETS; UMI; UnCover. CCC.

500 370 GW ISSN 0342-5487
NATURWISSENSCHAFTEN IM UNTERRICHT. BIOLOGIE. 1952. 10/yr. DM.103.50. Erhard Friedrich Verlag GmbH, Im Brande 15, 30926 Seelze, Germany. (Subcr. to: Postfach 100150, 30917 Seelze, Germany) Ed.Bd. Indexed: W.R.C.Inf.
—BLDSC (6049.050000). CCC.
Supersedes in part: Naturwissenschaften im Unterricht.

500.9 GW ISSN 0028-1050
Q3 CODEN: NARSAC
NATURWISSENSCHAFTLICHE RUNDSCHAU. 1948. m. DM.145 (students DM.64.80). Wissenschaftliche Verlagsgesellschaft mbH, Postfach 101061, 70009 Stuttgart, Germany. TEL 0711-2582-0. FAX 0711-2582-290. TELEX 723636-DAZ-D. Eds. Hans Rotta, Roswitha Schmid. adv.; bk.rev.; bibl.; charts; illus.; index. circ. 7,880. Indexed: Bibl.& Ind.Geol., Biol.Abstr., Biotech.Abstr., Chem.Abstr., Excerp.Med., Meteor.& Geoastrophys.Abstr., VITIS. **Document type:** academic/scholarly publication.
—BLDSC (6049.275000); CASDDS; SWETS. CCC.
Description: Covers all fields of science: biology, medicine, pharmacy, chemistry, physics, astronomy and geography.

500 GW ISSN 0077-6157
NATURWISSENSCHAFTLICHE RUNDSCHAU. BUECHER DER ZEITSCHRIFT. 1966. irreg. price varies; special rate for subscribers of "Naturwissenschaftliche Rundschau". Wissenschaftliche Verlagsgesellschaft mbH, Postfach 101061, 70009 Stuttgart, Germany. TEL 0711-2582-0. FAX 0711-2582-290. TELEX 723636-DAZ-D. **Document type:** monographic series.
Description: Covers all fields of science: biology, medicine, pharmacy, chemistry, physics, astronomy and geography.

500 GW ISSN 0077-6165
Q49 CODEN: SNSHAS
NATURWISSENSCHAFTLICHER VEREIN FUER SCHLESWIG-HOLSTEIN. SCHRIFTEN. 1870. a. DM.35. Lipsius & Tischer, Holstenstr. 40, 24103 Kiel, Germany. TEL 0431-8802944. FAX 0431-8804658. Ed. Heinz Klug. bk.rev. circ. 150. Indexed: Bibl.& Ind.Geol., Biol.Abstr., Deep Sea Res.& Oceanogr.Abstr. **Document type:** academic/scholarly publication.
—BLDSC (8094.810000).

500.9 AU ISSN 0369-1136
CODEN: MNVSAA
NATURWISSENSCHAFTLICHER VEREIN FUER STEIERMARK. MITTEILUNGEN. 1863. a. S.250. Naturwissenschaftlicher Verein fuer Steiermark, Universitaetsbibliothek, Universitaetsplatz 3, A-8010 Graz, Austria. TEL 0316-3805649. FAX 0316-381221. E-mail: anton.drescher@kfunigraz.ac.at. Eds. A. Drescher, H.L. Holzer. bk.rev.; charts; illus.; index, cum.index. circ. 200. (back issues avail.) Indexed: Bibl.& Ind.Geol., Biol.Abstr., Sport Fish.Abstr., VITIS, Wild.Rev., Zoo.Rec. **Document type:** academic/scholarly publication.
—BLDSC (5861.760000).
Description: Covers such subjects as mineralogy, petrology, geology, paleontology, geography, climatology, biology, botany and zoology.

500.9 NE ISSN 0028-1085
NATUUR EN MUSEUM. 1957. q. fl.7.50. Natuurhistorisch Museum, van Sambeekstichting, M. H. Tromplaan 19, 7511 JJ Enschede, Netherlands. FAX 31-53-323409. Ed. P. Venema. bk.rev. circ. 2,800. **Document type:** bulletin.

500.9 NE ISSN 0028-1093
Q4 CODEN: NATTAP
NATUUR EN TECHNIEK/NATURE AND TECHNOLOGY; natuurwetenschappelijk en technisch maandblad/scientific and technical monthly. 1932. m. fl.130 (effective 1994). Centrale Uitgeverij en Adviesbureau B.V., Postbus 415, 6200 AK Maastricht, Netherlands. TEL 31-43-254044. FAX 31-43-216124. TELEX 56642 NATU NL. Eds. Th. J.M. Martens, G.M.N. Verschuuren. adv.; bk.rev.; illus.; index. circ. 45,000. Indexed: C.I.S. Abstr., Chem.Abstr., Excerp.Med. **Document type:** consumer publication.
—BLDSC (6051.000000); CASDDS; SWETS.

508 NE ISSN 0028-1107
NATUURHISTORISCH MAANDBLAD. (Text mainly in Dutch; contributions in English, French and German; summaries in English) 1911. m. fl.128($64) (Natuurhistorisch Genootschap in Limburg) Publicatie bureau N H G, Groenstraat 106, 6074 EL Melick, Netherlands. TEL 31-4752-2351. Ed. Jo van der Coelen. bk.rev. circ. 1,200. Indexed: Biol.Abstr., Rev.Appl.Entomol. **Document type:** academic/scholarly publication.
Description: Covers research in the biology and the geology of Limburg. Includes association news, reports, lists of events.

508 BE ISSN 0770-1748
CODEN: NATGAK
NATUURWETENSCHAPPELIJK TIJDSCHRIFT. 1919. q. 1000 BEF. Natuur- en Geneeskundige Vennootschap, Krijgslaan 281 S.8, B-9000 Ghent, Belgium. Ed. Dr. L. Walschot. bk.rev.; charts; illus.; index. circ. 400. Indexed: Bibl.& Ind.Geol., Biol.Abstr., Bull.Signal., Chem.Abstr., Geo.Abstr. **Document type:** academic/scholarly publication.
—BLDSC (6053.000000).

NAUCNI I STRUCNI SKUPOVI U JUGOSLAVII I U INOSTRANSTVU/SCIENTIFIC AND PROFESSIONAL MEETINGS IN YUGOSLAVIA AND FOREIGN COUNTRIES. see *MEETINGS AND CONGRESSES*

500 PL ISSN 1231-8515
AS261
NAUKA; czasopismo poswiecone rozwojowi nauki w Polsce. 1953. q. $90. (Polska Akademia Nauk) Ossolineum, Publishing House of the Polish Academy of Sciences, Rynek 9, 50-106 Wroclaw, Poland. TEL 48-71-386-25. FAX 48-71-448-103. TELEX 0712771 OSS PL. Ed. Leszek Kuznicki. bk.rev.; charts; illus.; index. circ. 1,400. Indexed: Amer.Hist.& Life, Biol.Abstr., Hist.Abstr. **Document type:** academic/scholarly publication.
—BLDSC (6058.780000).
Formerly (until 1994): Nauka Polska (ISSN 0028-1271)
Description: Development and achievements of Polish science.

SCIENCES: COMPREHENSIVE WORKS

500　　　　　　　PL　　ISSN 0077-6181
　　　　　　　　　　　CODEN: NAWSD6
NAUKA DLA WSZYSTKICH/SCIENCE FOR EVERYONE. 1966. irreg., vol.473, 1995. price varies. (Polska Akademia Nauk, Oddzial w Krakowie) Secesja, Ul. Sw. Jana 28, 31-018 Krakow, Poland. TEL 48-12-227066. FAX 48-12-335654. E-mail: wwalecki@filon.filg.uj.edu.pl. Ed. Waclaw Walecki. **Document type:** academic/scholarly publication.
—CASDDS.
　　Description: Popular-science publication. Presents the latest achievements of all domains of science.

500　　　　　　　RU　　ISSN 0130-7037
NAUKA I SUSPIL'STVO. (Text in Ukrainian) 1951. m. $98 (effective 1996). Stroiizdat, Shchosseva, rm. 60, Moscow, Russia. index.

500　　　　　　　RU　　ISSN 0028-1263
Q4
NAUKA I ZHIZN'; nauchno-populyarnyi zhurnal. 1934. m. $120 (effective 1996). Izdatel'stvo Pressa, Nauka i Zhizn, Ul. Myasnitskaya 24, 101877 Moscow, Russia. TEL 095-923-2122. FAX 095-200-2259. Ed. Igor K. Lagovsky. adv. contact: Rudolf A. Svoren. bk.rev.; bibl.; charts; illus.; maps; index. circ. 65,000. **Indexed:** Biol.Abstr., Curr.Dig.Sov.Press, Int.Aerosp.Abstr.
—BLDSC (0119.300000).
　　Description: Presents information on domestic and world science and technology, including humanities, natural and health sciences. Provides materials for self-education.

500　　　　　　　RU　　ISSN 0869-706X
Q60　　　　　　　　　　CODEN: NASRDH
NAUKA V ROSSII. (Editions in English, German, Russian and Spanish) 1981. bi-m. $62. (Rossiiskaya Akademiya Nauk) Izdatel'stvo Nauka, 90, Profsoyuznaya ul., 117864 Moscow, Russia. TEL 234-3506. (Dist. by: Mezhdunarodnaya Kniga, ul. B. Yakimanka 39, 117049 Moscow, Russia; Dist. in the U.S. by: Victor Kamkin Inc., 4956 Boiling Brook Pkwy, Rockville, MD 20852. TEL 301-881-5973) Ed. Rem V. Petrov. adv.; bk.rev. circ. 110,000. **Indexed:** Chem.Abstr., Int.Aerosp.Abstr.
—CASDDS.
　　Formerly: Nauka v S.S.S.R. (ISSN 0203-4425)
　　Description: Topics covered include: ecology, discoveries and inventions, human environment, museums, astronomy, agronomy, medical research, geochemistry, space technology and more.

500　　　　　　　US
NAUKOVE TOVARYSTVO IMENI SHEVCHENKA. PROCEEDINGS OF THE SECTION OF MATHEMATICS AND PHYSICS. (Text in English and Ukrainian) vol.6, 1964. irreg. price varies. Shevchenko Scientific Society, 63 Fourth Ave., New York, NY 10003. TEL 212-254-5130. circ. 500. **Document type:** proceedings.
　　Supersedes in part: Naukove Tovarystvo Imeni Shevchenka. Proceedings of the Section of Mathematics, Natural Science and Medicine (ISSN 0470-5017)

NAUKOVE TOVARYSTVO IMENI SHEVCHENKA. ZAPYSKY/SHEVCHENKO SCIENTIFIC SOCIETY. MEMOIRS/MITTEILUNGEN. see *ETHNIC INTERESTS*

500　　　　　　　US　　ISSN 0077-6343
Q11　　　　　　　　　　CODEN: PNBAAP
NEBRASKA ACADEMY OF SCIENCES. PROCEEDINGS. a. $2. Nebraska Academy of Sciences, 302 Morrill Hall, 14th & U Sts., Lincoln, NE 68588-0339. FAX 402-472-8899. Ed. A.W. Zechmann. circ. 2,000. **Indexed:** Bibl.& Ind.Geol., Biol.Abstr., VITIS. **Document type:** academic/scholarly publication, proceedings.

500　　　　　　　US　　ISSN 0077-6351
　　　　　　　　　　　CODEN: TNASBH
NEBRASKA ACADEMY OF SCIENCES. TRANSACTIONS. 1970. a. price varies. Nebraska Academy of Sciences, 302 Morrill Hall, 14th & U Sts., Lincoln, NE 68588-0339. FAX 402-472-8899. Ed. Robert B. Kaul. circ. 1,800. **Indexed:** Bibl.& Ind.Geol., Biol.Abstr., Sel.Water Res.Abstr., Sport Fish.Abstr., VITIS, Wild.Rev., Zoo.Rec. **Document type:** academic/scholarly publication.
　　Refereed Serial

508　　　　　　　NE　　ISSN 0926-4264
　　　　　　　　　　　CODEN: NTINEL
NEDERLANDS TIJDSCHRIFT VOOR NATUURKUNDE. 20/yr. fl.145. Nederlandse Natuurkundige Vereniging, P.O. Box 302, 1170 AH Badhoevedorp, Netherlands. TEL 31-20-6580228. FAX 31-20-6592477. Ed.Bd. adv.; bk.rev.; charts; illus. circ. 3,500. **Indexed:** Bibl.& Ind.Geol., Chem.Abstr., INSPEC (1968-), Zoo.Rec. **Document type:** newsletter.
—BLDSC (6072.000000); CASDDS.
　　Formed by the 1991 merger of: Nederlands Tijdschrrift voor Natuurkunde. Part A (ISSN 0378-6374); Nederlands Tijdschrift voor Natuurkunde. Part B (ISSN 0166-5987); Which supersedes (in 1977): Nederlands Tijdschrift voor Natuurkunde (ISSN 0028-2189)

500　　　　　　　NE　　ISSN 0925-5621
NEDERLANDSE ORGANISATIE VOOR TOEGEPAST NATUURWETENSCHAPPELIJK ONDERZOEK. JAARVERSLAG. Short title: T N O Jaarverslag. English edition: Netherlands Organization for Applied Scientific Research. Annual Report (ISSN 0924-591X) (Text in Dutch) a. Nederlandse Organisatie voor Toegepast Natuurwetenschappelijk Onderzoek (TNO), Postbus 6050, 2600 JA Delft, Netherlands. TEL 31-15-2696900. FAX 31-15-627335. **Indexed:** Biol.Abstr. **Document type:** corporate report.

500　　　　　　　JA　　ISSN 0287-3052
NEEDS. (Text in Japanese) 1975. a. Iwatani Naoji Kinen Zaidan - Iwatani Naoji Foundation, TBR Bldg., 10-2 Nagata-cho 2-chome, Chiyoda-ku, Tokyo 100, Japan.
　　Description: News of the foundation.

500　　　　　　　CC　　ISSN 1000-1638
　　　　　　　　　　　CODEN: NDZKEJ
NEI MENGGU DAXUE XUEBAO (ZIRAN KEXUE BAN)/ACTA SCIENTIARUM NATURALIUM UNIVERSITATIS INTRAMONGOLICAE. (Text in Chinese or English) 1959. q. $20 per no. Nei Menggu Daxue - Inner Mongolian University, No. 1 West University Rd., Huhhot, Nei Menggu 010021, People's Republic of China. TEL 0471-43156. FAX 0471-611761. (Subscr. to: China International Book Trading Corp., P.O. Box 399, Beijing, P.R. China) Ed. Fang Tianqi. (back issues avail.) **Document type:** academic/scholarly publication.
—CASDDS.
　　Description: Covers mathematics, physics, chemistry, biology, electronics and computer science.

500　　　　　　　CC　　ISSN 1001-8735
　　　　　　　　　　　CODEN: NSXKEC
NEI MENGGU SHIFAN DAXUE XUEBAO (ZIRAN KEXUE BAN)/INNER MONGOLIAN TEACHERS UNIVERSITY. JOURNAL (NATURAL SCIENCE EDITION). (Editions in Chinese, English) 1958. q. Y1.40 per no. Nei Menggu Shifan Daxue, Huhhot, Nei Menggu 010022, People's Republic of China. TEL 464444. circ. 1,000. **Document type:** academic/scholarly publication.

500　　　　　　　JA　　ISSN 0466-6089
NEICHA SUTADI/NATURE STUDY. (Text in Japanese) 1955. m. 3000 Yen (effective 1995). (Osaka-shiritsu Shizenshi Hakubutsukan - Osaka Museum of Natural History) Osaka-shiritsu Shizenshi Hakubutsukan Tomo no Kai, 1-23 Nagai Koen, Higashi-sumiyoshi-ku, Osaka-shi, Osaka-fu 546, Japan. FAX 06-697-6225. Ed. M. Okamoto. bk.rev. circ. 2,000.
　　Description: Contains reviews, commentary, and news of the museum.

NEKOTORYE FILOSOFSKIE VOPROSY SOVREMENNOGO ESTESTVOZNANIYA. see *PHILOSOPHY*

053.1 500　　　　　GW　　ISSN 0028-3169
DAS NEUE ERLANGEN; Zeitschrift fuer Wissenschaft, Wirtschaft und kulturelles Leben. 1965. 2/yr. DM.10. Universitaetsbuchhandlung Rudolf Merkel, Untere Karlstr. 9-11, 91054 Erlangen, Germany. FAX 09131-862995. Ed. H. Lerche. adv.; charts; illus.; stat. circ. 5,000. **Document type:** newsletter.

500　　　　　　　GW
NEUE MUENCHNER BEITRAEGE ZUR GESCHICHTE DER MEDIZIN UND NATURWISSENSCHAFTEN. NATURWISSENSCHAFTSHISTORISCHE REIHE. 1969. irreg., vol.6, 1979. price varies. (Werner Fritsch Verlag) Theodor Ackermann, Ludwigstr. 7, 80539 Munich, Germany. TEL 284787. Eds. Friedrich Klemm, Christa Habrich. index.

500.9　　　　　　US　　ISSN 0077-7900
NEVADA. STATE MUSEUM, CARSON CITY. NATURAL HISTORY PUBLICATIONS. 1962. irreg., no.4, 1980. price varies. Nevada State Museum, Capitol Complex, Carson City, NV 89710. TEL 702-687-4810. Ed. J. Scott Miller. circ. 1,000.

500　　　　　　　US　　ISSN 0742-7514
Q162
NEW BOOK OF POPULAR SCIENCE ANNUAL; a science anthology with reviews of the year highlighting science news. 1964. a. $21.75. Grolier Incorporated, Sherman Turnpike, Danbury, CT 06816. TEL 203-797-3500. Ed. Joseph M. Castagno. charts; illus.; stat.; index.
　　Description: Contains special reports and summaries of the year's major events and trends in modern science.

500　　　　　　　US　　ISSN 0028-5455
Q11　　　　　　　　　　CODEN: BJASAS
NEW JERSEY ACADEMY OF SCIENCE. BULLETIN. 1955. s-a. $30. New Jersey Academy of Science, Beck Hall, Rm. 216, Livingston Campus, Rutgers University, Piscataway, NJ 08854. TEL 908-463-0511. (Affiliate: American Association for the Advancement of Science) Ed. Robert Evans. charts; illus.; stat. circ. 800. (also avail. in microform from UMI; reprint service avail. from UMI) **Indexed:** Bibl.& Ind.Geol., Biol.Abstr., Chem.Abstr., Excerp.Med. **Document type:** bulletin.
—BLDSC (2646.800000); UMI.

500　　　　　　　US　　ISSN 0028-5463
　　　　　　　　　　　CODEN: BJASAS
NEW JERSEY ACADEMY OF SCIENCE. NEWSLETTER. 1966. irreg. membership. New Jersey Academy of Science, Beck Hall, Rm. 216, Livingston Campus, Rutgers University, Piscataway, NJ 08854. TEL 908-463-0511. Ed. Eugene Varney. bk.rev. circ. 700. **Document type:** newsletter.
—CASDDS.

500　　　　　　　UK　　ISSN 0951-6026
NEW PARADIGMS NEWSLETTER. 1986. irreg. £12 (foreign £15). New Paradigms Publications, 29 Fairford Crescent, Downhead Park, Milton Keynes MK15 9AF, England. TEL 0908-607022. Ed. Alan Mayne. bk.rev. **Document type:** newsletter.
　　Description: Covers science, philosophy, religion, parascience, human affairs, and technology.

500　　　　　　　US　　ISSN 0028-6591
AS25
NEW RESEARCH CENTERS. (Supplement to: Research Centers Directory) 1965. s-a. $300 (effective Nov. 1993). Gale Research Inc., 835 Penobscot Bldg., Detroit, MI 48226. TEL 313-961-2242; 800-877-4253. FAX 313-961-6083. TELEX 810-221-7086. Ed. Karen Hill. cum.index in each issue.
—UnCover.
　　Description: Provides entries on newly formed and newly established research centers in the U.S. and Canada.

SCIENCES: COMPREHENSIVE WORKS

500　　　　　UK　　ISSN 0262-4079
Q1　　　　　　　　CODEN: NWSCAL
NEW SCIENTIST. 1956. w. £67($130) I P C Magazines, Specialist Magazine Group (Subsidiary of: Reed Elsevier group), King's Reach Tower, Stamford St., London SE1 9LS, England. TEL 0171-261-7301. FAX 0171-261-6464. (Subscr. to: Oakfield House, 35 Perrymount Rd., Haywards Heath, W. Sussex RH16 3DH, England. TEL 01444-445511) Ed. Alun Anderson. adv.; bk.rev.; charts; illus.; pat.; q. index. circ. 100,923. (back issues avail.) **Indexed:** A.I.Abstr. (until 1992), A.S.& T.Ind., ABC, Abstr.Bull.Inst.Pap.Chem., Abstr.Hum.Comp.Inter., Acad.Ind., Acid Pre.Dig., Acid Rain Abstr., Acid Rain Ind., Anim.Breed.Abstr., Appl.Mech.Rev., Art & Archaeol.Tech.Abstr., Art.Hosp.& Tour., Biodet.Abstr., Biol.Abstr., Biol.Dig., Bk.Rev.Ind. (1990-), BMT, Br.Archaeol.Abstr., Br.Ceram.Abstr., Br.Tech.Ind., Build.Manage.Abstr., C.I.S. Abstr., CAD CAM Abstr., Cadscan, Chem.Eng.Abstr., Child.Bk.Rev.Ind. (1990-), Copper Abstr., Curr.Adv.Biochem., Curr.Adv.Ecol.Sci., Curr.Biotech.Abstr., Curr.Cont., Dairy Sci.Abstr., Deep Sea Res.& Oceanogr.Abstr., Diar.Dis.Res., Energy Info.Abstr., Energy Rev., Environ.Abstr., Fluidex, Forest.Abstr., Fuel & Energy Abstr., Fut.Surv., Gdlns., Gen.Sci.Ind., Geo.Abstr., Geol.Abstr., Helminthol.Abstr., Herb.Abstr., High.Educ.Curr.Aware.Bull., Hort.Abstr, IDA, Ind.Sci.Rev., INSPEC, Int.Aerosp.Abstr., Int.Packag.Abstr., Intl.Polym.Sci.& Tech., J.of Ferroc., Key to Econ.Sci., Lab.Haz.Bull., Lead Abstr., Met.Abstr., Meteor.& Geoastrophys.Abstr., Mid.East: Abstr.& Ind., Ocean.Abstr., Paper & Bd.Abstr., Peace Res.Abstr., Pollut.Abstr., Print.Abstr., PROMT, Protozool.Abstr., RAPRA, Res.High.Educ.Abstr., Rev.Appl.Entomol., RICS, Risk Abstr., Robomat. (until 1992), Rural Devel.Abstr., Rural Recreat.Tour.Abstr., Sel.Water Res.Abstr., So.Pac.Per.Ind., Sport Fish.Abstr., Stud.Wom.Abstr., Telegen, Trop.Dis.Bull, W.R.C.Inf., Weed.Abstr., Wild.Rev., World.Alum.Abstr., World Text.Abstr., Zincscan, Zoo.Rec. **Document type:** academic/scholarly publication, consumer publication.
●Also available online. Vendor(s): VU/TEXT Information Services, Inc.
Also available on CD-ROM. Producer(s): Bowker - Saur Ltd.
—BLDSC (6087.800000); CASDDS; CIS; Faxon; Genuine Article; SWETS; UnCover. **CCC.**
Former titles (until 1971): New Scientist and Science Journal (ISSN 0369-5808); Formed by the merger of: New Scientist (ISSN 0028-6664); (1965-1971): Science Journal (ISSN 0582-2092)
Description: Offers comprehensive coverage of a wide range of science-related fields and topics. Subjects of articles include botany, physics, evolution, nuclear power, mathematics and environmental studies.

500　　　　　US　　ISSN 0077-8923
Q11　　　　　　　CODEN: ANYAA9
NEW YORK ACADEMY OF SCIENCES. ANNALS. 1823. irreg. price varies. New York Academy of Sciences, 2 E. 63rd St., New York, NY 10021. TEL 212-838-0230. Ed. Bill Boland. bibl.; charts; illus.; index, cum.index: 1960-1974. circ. 1,000. (also avail. in microfilm from PMC; back issues avail.; reprint service avail. from UMI) **Indexed:** Abstr.Health Care Manage.Stud., Anim.Breed.Abstr., Bibl.& Ind.Geol., Biodet.Abstr., Biol.Abstr., Biotech.Abstr., C.I.S. Abstr., Cadscan, Chem.Abstr., Curr.Adv.Cell & Devel.Biol., Curr.Adv.Ecol.Sci., Dairy Sci.Abstr., Deep Sea Res.& Oceanogr.Abstr., Dent.Ind., Excerp.Med., Field Crop Abstr., Helminthol.Abstr., Herb.Abstr., Hort.Abstr., Ind.Med., Ind.Vet., INIS Atomind., INSPEC, Int.Aerosp.Abstr., Lead Abstr., M.L.A., Math.R., Nutr.Abstr., Psychol.Abstr., Rev.Med.& Vet.Mycol., Sci.Cit.Ind., Soils & Fert., Sport Fish.Abstr., Sugar Ind.Abstr., Telegen, Vet.Bull., Wild.Rev., Zincscan, Zoo.Rec. **Document type:** academic/scholarly publication.
—BLDSC (1031.000000); ADONIS; CASDDS; EMDOCS; Faxon; Genuine Article; SWETS; UMI; UnCover. **CCC.**
Refereed Serial

500　　　　　US　　ISSN 0028-7113
Q11　　　　　　　CODEN: TNYAAE
NEW YORK ACADEMY OF SCIENCES. TRANSACTIONS. 1881. irreg. New York Academy of Sciences, 2 E. 63rd St., New York, NY 10021. Ed. Bill Boland. (also avail. in microform from UMI; back issues avail.; reprint service avail. from UMI) **Indexed:** Biol.Abstr., CAD CAM Abstr., Chem.Abstr., Curr.Adv.Ecol.Sci., Deep Sea Res.& Oceanogr.Abstr., Helminthol.Abstr., Ind.Vet., Math.R., Vet.Bull.
—CASDDS; UMI. **CCC.**
Refereed Serial

500　　　　　US　　ISSN 0278-3355
　　　　　　　　　　CODEN: NYMBA2
NEW YORK STATE MUSEUM. BULLETIN. 1887. irreg., no.477, 1990. price varies. New York State Museum, 3140 Cultural Education Center, Albany, NY 12230. TEL 518-474-3505. illus. **Indexed:** Bibl.& Ind.Geol., Biol.Abstr., Rev.Appl.Entomol., Sport Fish.Abstr., Wild.Rev., Zoo.Rec. **Document type:** government publication, bulletin.
—UnCover.
Description: Reports current research in the natural history of New York State.

500　　　　　US　　ISSN 1052-2018
Q11
NEW YORK STATE MUSEUM. CIRCULAR. 1928. irreg., no.54, 1990. price varies. New York State Museum, 3140 Cultural Education Center, Albany, NY 12230. charts; illus. **Indexed:** Bibl.& Ind.Geol., Biol.Abstr., Deep Sea Res.& Oceanogr.Abstr. **Document type:** government publication.
Formerly: New York State Museum and Science Service. Circular.
Description: Research updates, short scientific reports and indices.

500　　　　　US
NEW YORK STATE MUSEUM. LEAFLET. Variant title: Educational Leaflet. 1949. irreg., no.33, 1990. price varies. New York State Museum, 3140 Cultural Education Center, Albany, NY 12230. charts; illus. **Indexed:** Biol.Abstr. **Document type:** government publication.
Description: Popular and educational booklets covering topics in anthropology, biology, geology and history.

500　　　　　US　　ISSN 0749-1158
　　　　　　　　　　CODEN: NYSMEZ
NEW YORK STATE MUSEUM. MEMOIR. 1889. irreg., no.23, 1983. New York State Museum, 3140 Cultural Education Center, Albany, NY 12230. charts; illus. **Indexed:** Bibl.& Ind.Geol., Biol.Abstr. **Document type:** government publication, monographic series.
—CASDDS.
Formerly: New York State Museum and Science Service. Memoir.
Description: Works on New York's natural history and prehistory.

500　　　　　NZ　　ISSN 0028-8667
NEW ZEALAND SCIENCE REVIEW. vol.15, 1957. bi-m. NZ.$40. New Zealand Association of Scientists, P.O. Box 1874, Wellington, New Zealand. FAX 64-4-712070. Ed. F. Brian Shorland. adv.; bk.rev.; charts; illus.; stat.; cum.index. circ. 1,000. **Indexed:** Biol.Abstr., Chem.Abstr.
—Faxon; UnCover. **CCC.**
Description: Reviews on science and science policy.

NEWSCOPE - SCIENCE EDITION; a weekly science news summary and teaching quiz. see EDUCATION — Teaching Methods And Curriculum

500 600　　　JA　　ISSN 0286-0651
NEWTON/NYUTON. 1981. m. 9720 Yen. Kyoikusha Co. Ltd., 1-20, Nishi Shinjuku, Shinjuku-ku, Tokyo 160, Japan. TEL 03-344-4841. Ed. Hitoshi Takeuchi. adv. circ. 400,000.

500 600　　　JA　　ISSN 0285-3922
　　　　　　　　　　CODEN: BSFADV
NICHI-FUTSU RIKOKA KAISHI/SOCIETE FRANCO-JAPONAISE DES SCIENCES PURES ET APPLIQUEES. BULLETIN. (Text in French and Japanese) 1960. a. Nichi-Futsu Rikokakai - Societe Franco-Japonaise des Sciences Pures et Appliquees, Nichi-Futsu Kaikan, 2-3 Kanda Surugadai, Chiyoda-ku, Tokyo 101, Japan.
—CASDDS.

500.9　　　　　NR　　ISSN 0029-0076
QH195.N5　　　　　CODEN: NIFIAC
NIGERIAN FIELD. 1931. q. £10 to individuals; institutions £20 (effective 1996). Nigerian Field Society, P.O. Box 30385, Secretariat Post Office, Ibadan, Nigeria. TEL 234-2-8102138. (Subscr. to: Chief Roy Carrington, Treasurer, Nigerian Field Society, c/o Nigerian Gas Cylinders, Km. 22 Iwo Rd., Ibadan, Nigeria; Foreign subscr. to: Dr. Joyce Lowe, 464A, Bradgate Rd., Newton-Linford, Leicester LE6 0AHA, England. TEL 01530-242126) Ed. Pat Oyelola. adv. contact: E. Odu. bk.rev.; illus. circ. 1,000. **Indexed:** Apic.Abstr., Biol.Abstr., Chem.Abstr., Curr.Adv.Ecol.Sci., Curr.Cont.Africa, Forest.Abstr., Forest.Prod.Abstr., GeoRef., M.L.A., Sport Fish.Abstr., Wild.Rev., Zoo.Rec. **Document type:** academic/scholarly publication.
Description: Provides a forum for academics to exchange information on all aspects of science and culture in Nigeria. Contains society news.
Refereed Serial

500　　　　　NR　　ISSN 0029-0114
Q1　　　　　　　　CODEN: NJSCAW
NIGERIAN JOURNAL OF SCIENCE. 1966. s-a. $35. Science Association of Nigeria, P.O. Box 4039, University of Ibadan, Ibadan, Nigeria. Ed. Sunday O. Ajayi. adv.; bk.rev.; abstr.; charts; illus.; index. circ. 2,000. (back issues avail) **Indexed:** Biol.Abstr., Chem.Abstr., Field Crop Abstr., Herb.Abstr., Hort.Abstr., Math.R., Nutr.Abstr., Rural Recreat.Tour.Abstr., Soils & Fert., World Agri.Econ.& Rural Sociol.Abstr.

500　　　　　JA　　ISSN 0369-3562
G1　　　　　　　　CODEN: NDBSAL
NIHON DAIGAKU BUNRIGAKUBU SHIZEN KAGAKU KENKYUJO KENKYU KIYO/NIHON UNIVERSITY. INSTITUTE OF NATURAL SCIENCES. PROCEEDINGS. (Text in English and Japanese; summaries in English) 1965. a. Nihon Daigaku, Bunrigakubu Shizen Kagaku Kenkyujo - Nihon University, College of Humanities and Sciences, Institute of Natural Sciences, 25-40 Sakurajosui 3-chome, Setagaya-ku, Tokyo 156, Japan. **Indexed:** Chem.Abstr., Jap.Per.Ind. **Document type:** proceedings.

NIHON DAIGAKU RIKOGAKU KENKYUJO SHOHO/NIHON UNIVERSITY. RESEARCH INSTITUTE OF SCIENCE AND TECHNOLOGY. JOURNAL. see TECHNOLOGY: COMPREHENSIVE WORKS

NIHON FUJIN KAGAKUSHA NO KAI NYUSU/SOCIETY OF JAPANESE WOMEN SCIENTISTS. NEWS. see WOMEN'S INTERESTS

500　　　　　JA　　ISSN 0029-019X
NIHON GAKUJUTSU KAIGI GEPPO/SCIENCE COUNCIL OF JAPAN. MONTHLY REPORT. (Text in Japanese) 1960. m. free. Nihon Gakujutsu Kaigi - Science Council of Japan, 22-34 Roppongi 7-chome, Minato-ku, Tokyo 106, Japan. TEL 03-3403-6291. FAX 03-3403-6224. circ. 5,300. (looseleaf format) **Document type:** bulletin.

500　　　　　JA
NIHON KAGAKUSHI GAKKAI NENKAI KENKYU HAPPYO KOEN YOSHISHU. (Text in Japanese) a. 1000 Yen. Nihon Kagakushi Gakkai - History of Science Society of Japan, West Pine Bldg., 2-15-19 Hirakawa-cho, Chiyoda-ku, Tokyo 102, Japan. abstr. **Document type:** proceedings.
Description: Contains abstracts of the annual meeting of the society.

509.2　　　　　JA　　ISSN 0029-0335
NIHON NO KAGAKUSHA/JOURNAL OF JAPANESE SCIENTISTS. (Text in Japanese) 1966. m. 600 Yen per no. Nihon Kagakusha Kaigi - Japan Scientists Association, 9-16 Yushima 1-chome, Bunkyo-ku, Tokyo 113, Japan. Ed. Harumi Kohara. adv.; bk.rev.; index. circ. 12,000.

500 600　　　JA　　ISSN 0549-2998
NIHON UNIVERSITY. RESEARCH INSTITUTE OF SCIENCE AND TECHNOLOGY. REPORT. (Text in English) 1952. s-a. exchange basis. Nihon Daigaku, Rikogaku Kenkyujo - Nihon University, Research Institute of Science and Technology, 1-8 Kanda Surugadai, Chiyoda-ku, Tokyo 101, Japan. **Indexed:** INSPEC, JCT, JTA.

SCIENCES: COMPREHENSIVE WORKS

500   JA   ISSN 0288-3422
CODEN: NDSKBF
NIIGATA DAIGAKU KYOIKUGAKUBU KIYO. SHIZEN KAGAKU HEN/NIIGATA UNIVERSITY. FACULTY OF EDUCATION. MEMOIRS. NATURAL SCIENCES. (Text and summaries in English and Japanese) 1960. a. Niigata Daigaku, Kyoikugakubu - Niigata University, Faculty of Education, 8050 Igarashi Nino-cho, Niigata-shi, Niigata-ken 950-11, Japan. **Indexed:** Biol.Abstr., Chem.Abstr., Jap.Per.Ind.
—BLDSC (5593.323000); CASDDS.

NIIHAMA KOGYO KOTO SENMON GAKKO KIYO. RIKOGAKU HEN/NIIHAMA NATIONAL COLLEGE OF TECHNOLOGY. MEMOIRS. SCIENCE AND ENGINEERING. see *TECHNOLOGY: COMPREHENSIVE WORKS*

500 600   JA   ISSN 0917-009X
NIKKEI SAIENSU. Japanese translation of: Scientific American (US ISSN 0036-8733) (Supplement avail.: Bessatsu Saiensu (ISSN 0258-1008)) (Text and summaries in Japanese) 1971. m. 10753 Yen (foreign 13393 Yen). Nikkei Science, Inc. (Subsidiary of: Nihon Keizai Shimbun, Inc.), 2-2-1 Uchisaiwai-cho, Chiyoda-ku, Tokyo 100, Japan. TEL 03-5255-2125. TELEX J22308-NIHONKEIZAI. adv.
Formerly (until 1990): Saiensu (ISSN 0386-4324)

500   CC   ISSN 1001-5132
CODEN: NDXLEC
NINGBO DAXUE XUEBAO (LIGONG BAN)/NINGBO UNIVERSITY. JOURNAL (NATURAL SCIENCE AND ENGINEERING EDITION). (Text in Chinese) q. Ningbo Daxue - Ningbo University, Ningbo, Zhejiang 315211, People's Republic of China. TEL 0574-6694294. FAX 0574-6694161. Ed. Wang Lili. **Document type:** academic/scholarly publication.

500   JA   ISSN 0914-1340
NISSAN KAGAKU SHINKO ZAIDAN JIGYO HOKOKUSHO/NISSAN SCIENCE FOUNDATION. ANNUAL REPORT. (Text in Japanese) 1975. a. Nissan Kagaku Shinko Zaidan - Nissan Science Foundation, 17-2 Ginza 6-chome, Chuo-ku, Tokyo 104, Japan. FAX 03-3543-5598. **Document type:** academic/scholarly publication.

500   JA   ISSN 0911-4572
NISSAN KAGAKU SHINKO ZAIDAN KENKYU HOKOKUSHO/NISSAN SCIENCE FOUNDATION. RESEARCH PROJECTS IN REVIEW. (Text in Japanese; summaries in English and Japanese) 1979. a. Nissan Kagaku Shinko Zaidan - Nissan Science Foundation, 17-2 Ginza 6-chome, Chuo-ku, Tokyo 104, Japan. TEL 03-3543-5597. FAX 03-3543-5598. **Document type:** academic/scholarly publication.

NO D E A - NONLINEAR DIFFERENTIAL EQUATIONS AND APPLICATIONS. see *MATHEMATICS*

500   JA   ISSN 0078-0944
QR1   CODEN: RNIRAV
NODA INSTITUTE FOR SCIENTIFIC RESEARCH. REPORT/NODA SANGYO KAGAKU KENKYUJO KENKYU HOKOKU. (Text in English) 1957. a. free or exchange. Noda Sangyo Kagaku Kenkyujo - Noda Institute for Scientific Research, 399 Noda, Noda-shi, Chiba-ken 278, Japan. TEL 0471-23-5585. FAX 0471-23-5550. Ed. Hiroshi Sekine. bk.rev. circ. 1,000. **Indexed:** Biol.Abstr., Chem.Abstr., Rev.Plant Path., VITIS. **Document type:** academic/scholarly publication.
Description: Technical journal specializing in microbiology and related fields.

500   US   ISSN 0897-1005
NOETIC SCIENCES REVIEW. 1986. 4/yr. $35 membership. Institute of Noetic Sciences, 475 Gate Five Rd., Ste. 300, Sausalito, CA 94965. TEL 415-331-5650. FAX 415-331-5673. Ed. Barbara McNeill. bk.rev.; illus. **Document type:** newsletter.
—UnCover.
Description: Contains articles, interviews, research updates, and review essays on the people and ideas in the forefront of consciousness research.

NORDICANA. see *ANTHROPOLOGY*

001.3 500 600   GW   ISSN 0944-8799
CODEN: RWAVAW
NORDRHEIN-WESTFAELISCHE AKADEMIE DER WISSENSCHAFTEN. VORTRAEGE NATUR-INGENIEUR-UND WIRTSCHAFTSWISSENSCHAFTEN. 1950. irreg. Westdeutscher Verlag GmbH (Leverkusen), Postfach 300944, 51338 Leverkusen, Germany. TEL 02171-44741. FAX 02171-48308. **Indexed:** Bibl.& Ind.Geol., Biol.Abstr., Chem.Abstr. **Document type:** monographic series.
—BLDSC (9258.040200); CASDDS.
Former titles: Rheinisch-Westfaelische Akademie der Wissenschaften. Vortraege Natur-, Ingenieur- und Wirtschaftswissenschaften; Rheinisch-Westfaelische Akademie der Wissenschaften. Veroeffentlichungen (ISSN 0066-5754); (until 1970): Arbeitsgemeinschaft fuer Forschung des Landes Nordrhein-Westfalen. Veroeffentlichungen.

500   NO   ISSN 0078-1231
NORGES TEKNISK-NATURVITENSKAPELIGE FORSKNINGSRAAD. AARSBERETNING/ROYAL NORWEGIAN COUNCIL FOR SCIENTIFIC AND INDUSTRIAL RESEARCH. ANNUAL REPORT. 1947. a. free. Norges Teknisk-Naturvitenskapelige Forskningsraad - Royal Norwegian Council for Scientific and Industrial Research, Sognsveien 72, Taasen, 0801 Oslo, Norway. TEL 47-2-237685. FAX 47-2-181139. circ. 5,000.

500   US   ISSN 1056-8360
QH1
NORTH COUNTRY NATURALIST. 1987. irreg., vol.2, 1990. $10 to individuals; institutions $35. North County Institute for Natural Philosophy, Inc., RD No. 3, Emery Rd. Box 53, Mexico, NY 13114. TEL 315-963-4854. E-mail: 76436.257@compuserve.com. Ed. Donald Stone Sade. **Document type:** academic/scholarly publication.
Description: Publishes original articles, reviews and reprints on topics in natural history, the history and philosophy of science of interest to members.
Refereed Serial

506.2784   US   ISSN 0096-9214
Q11   CODEN: PNDAAZ
NORTH DAKOTA ACADEMY OF SCIENCE. PROCEEDINGS. 1947. a. $7.50 per no. North Dakota Academy of Science, Box 5567, University Sta., Fargo, ND 58105. TEL 701-231-8697. Ed. Roy Garvey. circ. 750 (paid). **Indexed:** Bibl.& Ind.Geol., Biol.Abstr., Chem.Abstr., Sport Fish.Abstr., Wild.Rev., Zoo.Rec. **Document type:** proceedings.
—UnCover.

500   UK   ISSN 0144-0586
QH1   CODEN: NNHJAQ
NORTHAMPTONSHIRE NATURAL HISTORY SOCIETY AND FIELD CLUB JOURNAL. 1880. a. £2. Northamptonshire Natural History Society and Field Club, c/o S.V.F. Leleux, Treas., 34 Broadway, Northampton NN1 4SF, England. Ed. C.A. Robinson. charts; illus. circ. 500. (back issues avail.). **Indexed:** Bibl.& Ind.Geol., Br.Archaeol.Abstr., Geo.Abstr.

500   US   ISSN 0029-344X
Q1   CODEN: NOSCAX
NORTHWEST SCIENCE. 1927. q. $20 to individuals; institutions $40 (overseas $47.50) (effective 1996). (Northwest Scientific Association) Washington State University Press, Pullman, WA 99164-5910. TEL 509-335-3518; 800-354-7360. FAX 509-335-8568. Ed. David L. Peterson. charts; illus.; cum.index: vols. 21-46. circ. 800. (also avail. in microfilm from UMI; reprint service avail. from UMI) **Indexed:** Abstr.Anthropol., Bibl.Agri., Bibl.& Ind.Geol., Biol.Abstr., Chem.Abstr., Curr.Adv.Ecol.Sci., Curr.Ref.Fish Res., Ecol.Abstr., Excerp.Med., Forest Abstr., Forest Prod.Abstr., Geo.Abstr., Herb.Abstr., Ind.Sci.Rev., Irr.& Drain.Abstr., Ornam.Hort., Sci.Cit.Ind., Seed Abstr., Sel.Water Res.Abstr., Soils & Fert., Sport Fish.Abstr., W.R.C.Inf., Weed Abstr., Wild.Rev., Zoo.Rec. **Document type:** academic/scholarly publication.
—BLDSC (6152.000000); CASDDS; Faxon; Genuine Article; UMI; UnCover.
Refereed Serial

500   US   ISSN 0550-1067
CODEN: NOGAB2
NOTICIAS DE GALAPAGOS. (Text in English, French, and Spanish) 1963. s-a. $25 contribution (effective 1995 & 1996). Charles Darwin Foundation for the Galapagos Isles, 100 N. Washington St., Ste. 311, Falls Church, VA 22046. FAX 703-538-6835. Ed. Howard L. Snell. adv. contact: Johanna Barry. bk.rev. circ. 6,000. **Indexed:** Biol.Abstr., Curr.Tit.Ocean., Deep Sea Res.& Oceanogr.Abstr., Sport Fish.Abstr., Wild.Rev., Zoo.Rec. **Document type:** academic/scholarly publication.
Description: Covers science and conservation in Galapagos, the Galapagos National Park Service, and the Charles Darwin Research Station.

500   CU
NOTICIERO DEL SISTEMA - INTERNACIONAL DE INFORMACION CIENTIFICO-TECNICA. 3/yr. $14 in N. America; S. America $16; Europe $20. (Academia de Ciencias, Instituto de Documentacion e Informacion Cientifico-Tecnica (I D I C T)) Ediciones Cubanas, Obispo No. 527, Apdo. 605, Havana, Cuba.

500.9   US   ISSN 0029-4608
Q111   CODEN: NONAA2
NOTULAE NATURAE. Key Title: Notulae Naturae of the Academy of Natural Sciences of Philadelphia. 1939. irreg., no. 469, 1988. $1. Academy of Natural Sciences of Philadelphia, 1900 Benjamin Franklin Pkwy., Philadelphia, PA 19103-1195. TEL 215-299-1050. FAX 215-299-1028. Ed. Alfred E. Schuyler. abstr.; bibl.; charts; illus.; stat. (back issues avail.) **Indexed:** Biol.Abstr., Chem.Abstr., Deep Sea Res.& Oceanogr.Abstr. **Document type:** academic/scholarly publication.

510   GW   ISSN 0369-5034
Q49   CODEN: NOALA4
NOVA ACTA LEOPOLDINA; Abhandlungen der Deutschen Akademie der Naturforscher Leopoldina. (Text in English and German) 1932. irreg. price varies. Deutsche Akademie der Naturforscher Leopoldina, August-Bebel-Str. 50a, 06108 Halle, Germany. TEL 0345-2024723. FAX 0345-2021727. Ed. Werner Koehler. charts; illus.; stat. (back issues avail.) **Indexed:** Bibl.& Ind.Geol., Biol.Abstr., Chem.Abstr., Deep Sea Res.& Oceanogr.Abstr., Math.R. **Document type:** academic/scholarly publication.
—CASDDS.

NOVA SCOTIA RESEARCH FOUNDATION CORPORATION. ANNUAL REPORT. see *TECHNOLOGY: COMPREHENSIVE WORKS*

500   CN   ISSN 0078-2521
Q21   CODEN: PNSIAW
NOVA SCOTIAN INSTITUTE OF SCIENCE. PROCEEDINGS. 1862. irreg. Can.$15 (diskette Can.$25) (effective 1996). Nova Scotian Institute of Science, Science Services, Killam Library, Dalhousie University, Halifax, NS B3H 4H8, Canada. TEL 902-494-2384. FAX 902-494-2062. Ed. Derek S. Davis. bk.rev. circ. 600. (also avail. in microfilm; diskette format) **Indexed:** Bibl.& Ind.Geol., Biol.Abstr., Deep Sea Res.& Oceanogr.Abstr., Sport Fish.Abstr., Wild.Rev., Zoo.Rec. **Document type:** academic/scholarly publication, proceedings.
—BLDSC (6779.000000); CASDDS; UnCover. **CCC.**
Description: Reports of original scientific work and reviews of scientific topics with special reference to the natural history of the Atlantic Provinces of Canada and the Northeastern US.
Refereed Serial

500   GW   ISSN 0722-0855
NOVEDADES CIENTIFICAS ALEMANAS. (Text in Spanish) m. DM.80. Deutscher Forschungsdienst, Ahrstr. 45, 53175 Bonn, Germany. TEL 0228-302210. FAX 0228-302270. **Document type:** academic/scholarly publication.

500 600   GW   ISSN 0722-0863
NOVEDADES CIENTIFICAS ALEMANAS - CIENCIA APLICADA. (Text in Spanish) m. DM.60. Deutscher Forschungsdienst, Ahrstr. 45, 53175 Bonn, Germany. TEL 0228-302210. FAX 0228-302270. **Document type:** academic/scholarly publication.

500 600   SP   ISSN 1133-0597
NUEVO DE LA CIENCIA Y LA TECNICA. 1989. w. Pl. de Espana 18, Torres de Madrid 7o, 28008 Madrid, Spain. TEL 1-247-31-01. FAX 1-248-04-06. Ed. J. Garcia Abad. circ. 211,530.

500   IT   ISSN 0394-7394
NUNCIUS; annali di storia della scienza. 1976. s-a. L.90000 (foreign L.115000) (effective 1995) US $77 (effective 1996). (Istituto e Museo di Storia della Scienza Firenze) Casa Editrice Leo S. Olschki, Casella Postale 66, 50100 Florence, Italy. TEL 39-55-6530684. FAX 39-55-6530214. Ed. Paolo Galluzzi. **Document type:** academic/scholarly publication.
—BLDSC (6184.790000).

500   IT   ISSN 1122-0910
NUNCIUS. BIBLIOTECA. 1989. irreg., no.16, 1995. price varies. Casa Editrice Leo S. Olschki, Casella Postale 66, 50100 Florence, Italy. TEL 39-55-6530684. FAX 39-55-6530214. **Document type:** monographic series.

500   IT   ISSN 0393-9332
NUOVA SCIENZA. 10/yr. Lungo Tevere dei Sangallo 1, Rome, Italy. adv. circ. 46,000.

507 373   US
O A S NEWSLETTER. 1948. irreg. membership. Ohio Academy of Science, 1500 W. Third Ave., Ste. 223, Columbus, OH 43212. TEL 614-488-2228. adv.; bk.rev.; charts; illus.; stat. circ. 2,500. **Document type:** newsletter.
Formerly: Ohio Academy of Science News (ISSN 0030-0764)
Description: News for academy membership.

003 658.4   US
O R - M S TODAY. (Operations Research - Management Science) 1971. bi-m. $30 to individuals (foreign $44); institutions $50 (foreign $64) (effective 1995). Institute for Operations Research and the Management Sciences, 940-A Elkridge Landing Rd., Linthicum, MD 21090-2909. TEL 410-850-0300. FAX 410-684-2963. (Subscr. to: Box 64794, Baltimnore, MD 21264-4794) Ed. John Llewellyn. adv. **Indexed:** Oper.Res.Manage.Sci., Qual.Contr.Appl.Stat. **Document type:** newsletter.
Description: Reports on the most recent developments in the field of operations research and management science, and covers applications to problems in all areas, including manufacturing, telecommunications, health care and defence.

500 600   FR   ISSN 0071-9013
Q180.F7
O R S T O M INSTITUT FRANCAIS DE RECHERCHE POUR LE DEVELOPEMENT EN COOPERATION. RAPPORT D'ACTIVITE. irreg. (Institut Francais de Recherche Scientifique pour le Developpement en Cooperation) O R S T O M Editions - Diffusion, 72 Route d'Aulnay, 93143 Bondy Cedex, France. TEL 48-02-55-00. FAX 48-47-30-88.

500 350   US
O T A BROCHURE. (Office of Technology Assessment) irreg. free. U.S. Office of Technology Assessment, Publication Distribution, U.S. Congress, 600 Pennsylvania Ave., S.E., Washington, DC 20510-8025. TEL 202-224-8996. FAX 202-228-6098. E-mail: PUBREQUEST@OTA.GOV. **Document type:** bulletin, government publication.
Description: Defines the purpose of O.T.A. and lists recently completed projects.

500   NE   ISSN 0928-2211
O T B WORKING PAPER. 1992. irreg. (Onderzoeksinstituut Technische Bestuurskunde, Research Institute Policy Sciences and Information Systems) Delft University Press, Stevinweg 1, 2628 CN Delft, Netherlands. TEL 31-15-2783254. FAX 31-15-2781661. **Document type:** monographic series.

500   NG
OBAFEMI AWOLOWO UNIVERSITY. INAUGURAL LECTURE SERIES. irreg., latest no.95. Obafemi Awolowo University Press, Periodicals Department, P.O. Box 1044, Ife-Ife, Osun State, Nigeria. TEL 234-36-231780. (Dist. outside Africa by: African Books Collective Ltd., The Jam Factory, 27 Park End St., Oxford OX1 1HU, England. TEL 0865-726686. FAX 0865-793298) **Document type:** monographic series.
Description: Each monograph covers a scientific, environmental, technological, political, or economic topic.

500   GW   ISSN 0078-2920
OBERHESSISCHE GESELLSCHAFT FUER NATUR- UND HEILKUNDE, GIESSEN. BERICHTE. a. Wilhelm Schmitz Verlag, Staufenbergerweg 22, 35457 Lollar, Germany. TEL 06406-2324. Ed. Ruediger Knapp. circ. 600. **Indexed:** Deep Sea Res.& Oceanogr.Abstr., GeoRef, VITIS.

500.1   JA   ISSN 0029-8190
Q77   **CODEN:** NASOA5
OCHANOMIZU JOSHI DAIGAKU SHIZEN KAGAKU HOKOKU/OCHANOMIZU UNIVERSITY. NATURAL SCIENCE REPORT. (Text in English, French, German, Japanese) 1951. s-a. exchange basis only. Ochanomizu Joshi Daigaku - Ochanomizu University, 1-1 Otsuka 2-chome, Bunkyo-ku, Tokyo 112, Japan. TEL 03-3943-3151. Ed. Yosuke Ogawa. charts; illus.; index. circ. 800. **Indexed:** Appl.Mech.Rev., Bibl.& Ind.Geol., Biol.Abstr., Chem.Abstr., Deep Sea Res.& Oceanogr.Abstr., Math.R. **Document type:** bulletin.
—BLDSC (6041.300000); Faxon; UnCover.
Formerly: Ochanomizu Women's University. Natural Science Report.

500   RM   ISSN 0029-8263
   CODEN: OCRNAM
OCROTIREA NATURII SI A MEDIULUI INCONJURATOR. (Text in Rumanian; summaries in English, French, German, and Russian) 1955. s-a. 60 lei($34) (Academia Romana) Editura Academiei Romane, Calea Victoriei 125, 79717 Bucharest, Rumania. (Dist. by: Rompresfilatelia, Export-Import Presa, Calea Grivitei 64-66, P.O. Box 12-201, 78104 Bucharest, Rumania) Ed. N. Botnariuc. bk.rev.; charts; illus.; bibl.; index, cum.index. **Indexed:** Biol.Abstr., Sport Fish.Abstr., Wild.Rev., Zoo.Rec.
—BLDSC (6235.143000).

500.9   AU
OEKO.L. 1979. q. S.130 (foreign S.150). Naturkundliche Station der Stadt Linz, Roseggerstr. 22, A-4020 Linz, Austria. Ed. Gerhard Pfitzner. adv.; bk.rev.; charts; illus.; stat. circ. 6,000. **Indexed:** Bk.Rev.Ind., Ind.Bk.Rev.Hum., Key Word Ind.Wildl.Res., RILA. **Document type:** government publication.
Formerly: Apollo (ISSN 0003-6528)

001.3 500   AU   ISSN 0378-8644
AS142   **CODEN:** OAWABT
OESTERREICHISCHE AKADEMIE DER WISSENSCHAFTEN. ALMANACH. 1851. a. price varies. Verlag der Oesterreichischen Akademie der Wissenschaften, Dr. Ignaz-Seipel-Platz 2, A-1010 Vienna, Austria. FAX 0222-5139541. **Indexed:** Bibl.Ling., GeoRef.

OESTERREICHISCHE AKADEMIE DER WISSENSCHAFTEN, VIENNA. MATHEMATISCH - NATURWISSENSCHAFTLICHE KLASSE. DENKSCHRIFTEN. see *MATHEMATICS*

500   AU
OESTERREICHISCHE HOCHSCHULZEITUNG. 1949. m. $50. Verband der Wissenschaftlichen Gesellschaften Oesterreichs, Lindengasse 37, A-1070 Vienna, Austria. TEL 932166.

500   JA   ISSN 0386-8176
OGASAWARA KENKYU/OGASAWARA RESEARCH. (Text in English; summaries in Japanese) 1978. a. free. Tokyo-toritsu Daigaku, Ogasawara Kenkyu Iinkai - Tokyo Metropolitan University, Ogasawara Research Committee, Minami-Ohsawa 1-1, Hachioji-shi, Tokyo 192-03, Japan. TEL 0426-77-1111. FAX 0426-77-1222. Ed. Nobuyuki Hori. circ. 800. (back issues avail.) **Document type:** academic/scholarly publication.
Formerly: Ogasawara Research Committee. Publications.

500   JA   ISSN 0387-9844
OGASAWARA KENKYU NENPO/TOKYO METROPOLITAN UNIVERSITY. ANNUAL REPORT OF RESEARCH ON THE OGASAWARA (BONIN) ISLANDS. (Text in Japanese) 1977. a. free. Tokyo-toritsu Daigaku, Ogasawara Kenkyu Iinkai - Tokyo Metropolitan University, Ogasawara Research Committee, Minami-Ohsawa 1-1, Hachioji-shi, Tokyo 192-03, Japan. TEL 0426-77-1111. FAX 0426-77-1222. Ed. Nobuyuki Hori. circ. 800. (back issues avail.) **Document type:** bulletin.

500   US   ISSN 0030-0950
   CODEN: OJSCA9
OHIO JOURNAL OF SCIENCE. 1901. 5/yr. $50 (foreign $55) (effective 1996). Ohio Academy of Science, 1500 W. Third Ave., Ste. 223, Columbus, OH 43212. TEL 614-488-2228. Ed. Lee Meserve. bk.rev.; abstr.; charts; illus.; index. circ. 2,500. (also avail. in microfilm from PMC; back issues avail.) **Indexed:** Bibl.& Ind.Geol., Biol.Abstr., Chem.Abstr., Curr.Adv.Ecol.Sci., Curr.Cont., Deep Sea Res.& Oceanogr.Abstr., Ecol.Abstr., Environ.Abstr., Forest.Abstr., Forest Prod.Abstr., Geo.Abstr., Geol.Abstr., Helminthol.Abstr., Hort.Abstr., Rev.Plant Path., Sel.Water Res.Abstr., Sport Fish.Abstr., Wild.Rev., World Agri.Econ.& Rural Sociol.Abstr., Zoo.Rec. **Document type:** academic/scholarly publication.
—BLDSC (6247.000000); CASDDS; CIS; Ei; Faxon; Genuine Article; UMI; UnCover. CCC.
Description: Multi-disciplinary scientific journal.
Refereed Serial

500 551 551.5   US
OHIO STATE UNIVERSITY. BYRD POLAR RESEARCH CENTER. CONTRIBUTION SERIES. 1961. irreg., no. 733, 1990. free or exchange basis. Ohio State University, Byrd Polar Research Center, 125 S. Oval Mall, Columbus, OH 43210-1308. TEL 614-292-6531.
Formerly: Ohio State University. Institute of Polar Studies. Contribution Series (ISSN 0472-6979)
Description: Scientific studies by the research staff of the center.
Refereed Serial

500 551 551.5   US
OHIO STATE UNIVERSITY. BYRD POLAR RESEARCH CENTER. MISCELLANEOUS SERIES. 1958. irreg., no. 292, 1990. free or exchange basis. Ohio State University, Byrd Polar Research Center, 125 S. Oval Mall, Columbus, OH 43210-1308. TEL 614-292-6531.
Formerly: Ohio State University. Institute of Polar Studies. Miscellaneous Series.
Description: Articles not appropriate to the Contribution Series (i.e. abstracts, letters to the editor, non-technical articles), published by members.

500 551   US   ISSN 0896-2472
OHIO STATE UNIVERSITY. BYRD POLAR RESEARCH CENTER. REPORT SERIES. 1962. irreg., no.87, 1984. price varies. Ohio State University, Byrd Polar Research Center, 103 Mendenhall, 125 S. Oval Mall, Columbus, OH 43210-1308. TEL 614-292-6531. circ. 250. **Indexed:** Bibl.& Ind.Geol., Geo.Abstr.
Formerly: Ohio State University. Institute of Polar Studies. Report Series (ISSN 0078-415X)
Description: Scientific investigations that are too lengthy for regular journal articles.

500   JA   ISSN 0914-580X
OITA DAIGAKU KYOIKUGAKUBU KENKYU KIYO/OITA UNIVERSITY. FACULTY OF EDUCATION. RESEARCH BULLETIN. (Text in English and Japanese; summaries in English) 1952. s-a. Oita Daigaku, Kyoikugakubu - Oita University, Faculty of Education, 700 Dannohara, Oita-shi, Oita-ken 870-11, Japan. **Indexed:** Jap.Per.Ind.
—BLDSC (7722.120000).

500   JA   ISSN 0385-2776
   CODEN: KHHDD4
OKAYAMA RIKA DAIGAKU. HIRUZEN KENKYUJO KENKYU HOKOKU/OKAYAMA UNIVERSITY OF SCIENCE. HIRUZEN RESEARCH INSTITUTE. BULLETIN. (Text and summaries in English and Japanese) 1975. a. Okayama Rika Daigaku, Hiruzen Kenkyujo - Okayama University of Science, Hiruzen Research Institute, Kamifukuda, Kawakamimura, Maniwa-gun, Okayama-ken 717-06, Japan.
—CASDDS.
Description: Contains original papers.

500   JA   ISSN 0285-7685
   CODEN: ORDKDH
OKAYAMA RIKA DAIGAKU KIYO A. SHIZEN KAGAKU/OKAYAMA UNIVERSITY OF SCIENCE. BULLETIN A. NATURAL SCIENCE. (Text and summaries in English and Japanese) 1965. a. Okayama Rika Daigaku - Okayama University of Science, 1-1 Ridai-machi, Okayama-shi, Okayama-ken 700, Japan. **Indexed:** Chem.Abstr., INSPEC (1983-), Jap.Per.Ind. **Document type:** academic/scholarly publication.
—CASDDS.

SCIENCES: COMPREHENSIVE WORKS

OKINAWA KENRITSU HAKUBUTSUKAN KIYO/OKINAWA PREFECTURAL MUSEUM. BULLETIN. see *MUSEUMS AND ART GALLERIES*

500   US   ISSN 0078-4303
Q11   CODEN: POASAD
OKLAHOMA ACADEMY OF SCIENCE. PROCEEDINGS. 1920. a. $25 (effective 1995 & 1996). Oklahoma Academy of Science, c/o Edward N. Nelson, Exec. Sec.-Treas., Box 70195, Tulsa, OK 74170-1915. E-mail: firefly@bbm-fs1.biochem.okstate.edu. Ed. Franklin R. Leach. cum.index every 10 yrs. circ. 800. **Indexed:** Biol.Abstr., Chem.Abstr., Deep Sea Res.& Oceanogr.Abstr., Field Crop Abstr., Helminthol.Abstr., Herb.Abstr., Plant Breed.Abstr., Rev.Plant Path., Soils & Fert., Sport Fish.Abstr., Wild.Rev., Zoo.Rec. **Document type:** proceedings.
—BLDSC (6781.000000); CASDDS; Faxon.
Refereed Serial

OMETECA. see *HUMANITIES: COMPREHENSIVE WORKS*

500 600   US   ISSN 0149-8711
AP2
OMNI. 1978. q. Omni International, Ltd. (Subsidiary of: General Media Publishing Group), 277 Park Ave., 4th Fl., New York, NY 10172. TEL 212-702-6000. FAX 212-702-6282. Ed. Keith Ferrell. adv.; bk.rev.; illus. circ. 702,843. (also avail. in microfiche from UMI; reprint service avail. from UMI) **Indexed:** A.I.Abstr., Acad.Ind., Access, CAD CAM Abstr., Can.B.P.I., Deep Sea Res.& Oceanogr.Abstr., Environ.Abstr., Gdlns., Hlth.Ind., Info.Media & Tech., Jun.High.Mag.Abstr., Mag.Ind., PMR, Robomat., Tel.Abstr., TOM. **Document type:** consumer publication.
●Also available online. Vendor(s): University Microfilms International.
Also available on CD-ROM. Producer(s): University Microfilms International.
—BLDSC (6256.470000); Faxon; Genuine Article; SWETS; UMI; UnCover.
Description: Covers science and technology for readers interested in their universe, past, present and future. Also publishes original science fiction stories.
Refereed Serial

003   NE   ISSN 0167-6377
T57.6.A1   CODEN: ORLED5
OPERATIONS RESEARCH LETTERS. (Text in English) 1981. 10/yr. fl.878($535) (effective 1996). (Operations Research Society of America, US) North-Holland (Subsidiary of: Elsevier Science B.V.), P.O. Box 211, 1000 AE Amsterdam, Netherlands. TEL 31-20-4853911. FAX 31-20-4853598. TELEX 18582 ESPA NL. (Subscr. in U.S. and Canada to: Elsevier Science Inc., Box 882, Madison Sq. Sta., New York, NY 10159. TEL 212-989-5800. FAX 212-633-3990) Ed. G.L. Nemhauser. (also avail. in microform from UMI; back issues avail.; reprint service avail. from SWZ) **Indexed:** ASCA, Biostat., Compumath, Comput.Abstr., Cont.Pg.Manage., Eng.Ind., INSPEC (1981-), Int.Abstr.Oper.Res., J.Cont.Quant.Meth., Math.R., Oper.Res.Manage.Sci., Qual.Contr.Appl.Stat., Risk Abstr. **Document type:** academic/scholarly publication.
—BLDSC (6269.363800); Ei; Faxon; Genuine Article; SWETS; UnCover. **CCC.**
Description: Covers all aspects of operations research and the management and decision sciences.
Refereed Serial

500   FR   ISSN 0078-5601
ORDRE DES GEOMETRES-EXPERTS. ANNUAIRE. 1956. a. 1600 F. Publi-Topex, 13 rue Leon Cogniet, 75017 Paris, France. Ed. Helene Alvares-Correa. adv. circ. 3,000.

300   US   ISSN 0370-1093
Q11   CODEN: PORSAU
OREGON ACADEMY OF SCIENCE. PROCEEDINGS. 1943. a. $12. Oregon Academy of Science, c/o Richard W. Thies, College of Science, Oregon State University, Corvallis, OR 97331-4608. TEL 503-737-3879. FAX 503-737-1009. E-mail: thiesr@ccmail.orst.edu. Ed. Bill Keith. circ. 200. (reprint service avail.) **Indexed:** Biol.Abstr., Chem.Abstr. **Document type:** proceedings.

507 370   US   ISSN 0030-4794
OREGON SCIENCE TEACHER.* 1959. m. (Sep.-May). $8. Oregon Science Teachers Association, c/o Bill Marker, Ed., 700 Pringle Pkwy, S.E., Salem, OR 97310. TEL 503-667-5489. adv.; bk.rev.; illus. circ. 600.

500 600   NR   ISSN 0474-6171
ORGANIZATION OF AFRICAN UNITY. SCIENTIFIC TECHNICAL AND RESEARCH COMMISSION. PUBLICATION. 1951. irreg. Organization of African Unity, Scientific Technical and Research Commission, P.M.B. 2359, Lagos, Nigeria.

500   US
ORGANIZATION OF AMERICAN STATES. DEPARTMENT OF SCIENTIFIC AFFAIRS. REPORT OF ACTIVITIES. 1963. irreg. Organization of American States, 1889 F St., N.W., Washington, DC 20006. TEL 703-941-1617.
Formerly: Pan American Union. Department of Scientific Affairs. Report of Activities. (ISSN 0553-0334)

500 574   US
ORGANIZATION OF AMERICAN STATES. GENERAL SECRETARIAT. PROGRAM OF SCIENTIFIC MONOGRAPHS. (Text in Spanish and Portuguese) 1965. irreg. (5-7/yr.). $3.50 per no. Organization of American States, General Secretariat, Office of Sales & Promotion, 1889 F St., N.W., Washington, DC 20006. TEL 202-789-3338. Ed. Eva V. Chesneau. circ. 10,000. (back issues avail.) **Indexed:** Biol.Abstr., Chem.Abstr. **Document type:** monographic series.

500   IT
ORGANIZZAZIONE SCIENTIFICA. 1973. m. Comitato Nazionale per l'Organizzazione Scientifica, Viale dell'Astronomia 30, 00144 Rome, Italy. Ed.Bd. bibl.

500   PL   ISSN 0078-6500
Q9
ORGANON. (Text in English, French, German and Russian) 1963. irreg., vol. 25, 1995. price varies. Polska Akademia Nauk, Instytut Historii Nauki - Polish Academy of Sciences, Institute of History of Science, Ul. Nowy Swiat 72, 00-330 Warsaw, Poland. TEL 48-22-268754. FAX 48-22-266137. (Co-sponsor: Division d'Histoire des Sciences de l'Union Internationale d'Histoire et de Philosophie des Sciences) bibl.; illus. circ. 660. **Document type:** academic/scholarly publication.
—BLDSC (6291.105000).
Description: Devoted to international research on the history of science, culture and human civilization.

500   US   ISSN 0748-9919
ORIGINS RESEARCH. 2/yr. free to students and educators. Access Research Network, Box 38069, Colorado Springs, CO 80937-8069. **Document type:** newspaper.
Description: Considers aspects of the creation-evolution debate from a creationist viewpoint.

OSAKA DENKI TSUSHIN DAIGAKU KENKYU RONSHU. SHIZEN KAGAKU HEN/OSAKA ELECTRO-COMMUNICATION UNIVERSITY. MEMOIRS. NATURAL SCIENCE. see *COMMUNICATIONS*

500 613.7   JA   ISSN 0289-8888
OSAKA JOSHI DAIGAKU KIYO. KISO RIGAKU HEN, TAIIKUGAKU HEN/OSAKA WOMEN'S UNIVERSITY. BULLETIN. SERIES OF NATURAL SCIENCE, PHYSICAL EDUCATION. (Text and summaries in English and Japanese) a. Osaka Joshi Daigaku, Kiso Rigakka - Osaka Women's University, 2-1 Daisen-cho, Sakai-shi, Osaka-fu 590, Japan. abstr.

OSAKA KOGYO DAIGAKU KIYO. RIKO HEN/OSAKA INSTITUTE OF TECHNOLOGY. MEMOIRS. SERIES A. SCIENCE AND TECHNOLOGY. see *TECHNOLOGY: COMPREHENSIVE WORKS*

500   JA   ISSN 0373-7411
CODEN: OKDSBO
OSAKA KYOIKU DAIGAKU KIYO. DAI-3-BUMON. SHIZEN KAGAKU/OSAKA KYOIKU UNIVERSITY. MEMOIRS. SERIES 3: NATURAL SCIENCE AND APPLIED SCIENCE. (Text and summaries in English and Japanese) 1952. s-a. Osaka Kyoiku Daigaku - Osaka Kyoiku University, 4-88 Minami-Kawahori-cho, Tennoji-ku, Osaka-shi, Osaka-fu 543, Japan. **Indexed:** Biol.Abstr., Chem.Abstr., INIS Atomind., Jap.Per.Ind.
—BLDSC (5629.540000); CASDDS.

509.2   JA   ISSN 0911-209X
OSAKA NO KAGAKUSHA. (Text in Japanese) a. Nihon Kagakusha Kaigi, Osaka Shibu - Japan Scientists Association, Osaka Branch, Rm.7, 45 Bldg., 4-5 Ohmichi, Ten-nohji, Osaka 543, Japan.

500   JA   ISSN 0287-1394
OSAKA SANGYO DAIGAKU RONSHU. SHIZEN KAGAKU HEN/OSAKA SANGYO UNIVERSITY. JOURNAL. NATURAL SCIENCES. (Text in English, French, Japanese; summaries in English) 1956. q. free. Osaka Sangyo Daigaku Gakkai - Society of Osaka Sangyo University, 1-1 Nakagaito 3-chome, Daito-shi, Osaka-fu 574, Japan. TEL 0720-75-3001. FAX 0720-75-6551. circ. 3,300. **Indexed:** Jap.Per.Ind.

500.9   JA   ISSN 0078-6675
CODEN: OSSKAS
OSAKA SHIRITSU SHIZENSHI HAKUBUTSUKAN KENKYU HOKOKU/OSAKA MUSEUM OF NATURAL HISTORY. BULLETIN. (Text in English or Japanese) 1954. a. 1200 Yen exchange basis. Osaka shiritsu Shizenshi Hakubutsukan - Osaka Museum of Natural History, 1-23 Nagai Koen, Higashi-Sumiyoshi-ku, Osaka-shi, Osaka-fu 546, Japan. Ed. Ryohei Yamanishi. circ. 1,000. **Indexed:** Bibl.& Ind.Geol., Biol.Abstr., Curr.Adv.Ecol.Sci., Deep Sea Res.& Oceanogr.Abstr., Jap.Per.Ind. **Document type:** bulletin.
—UnCover.

505   JA   ISSN 0474-781X
Q1.A1   CODEN: SREOA7
OSAKA UNIVERSITY. COLLEGE OF GENERAL EDUCATION. SCIENCE REPORTS.* (Text in English, French, or German) 1953. s-a. Osaka Daigaku, Kyoyobu - Osaka University, College of General Education, 1-1 Machikaneyama-cho, Toyonaka-shi, Osaka-fu 560, Japan. Ed. Kozo Imahori. charts; illus. circ. 1,000. **Indexed:** Biol.Abstr., INIS Atomind., INSPEC (1968-), JTA, Math.R.
—BLDSC (8156.300000); CASDDS; UnCover.

OSAKA UNIVERSITY. FACULTY OF ENGINEERING. TECHNOLOGY REPORTS/OSAKA DAIGAKU KOGAKU HOKOKU. see *TECHNOLOGY: COMPREHENSIVE WORKS*

500 900   US   ISSN 0369-7827
Q1   CODEN: OSIRE3
OSIRIS (CHICAGO); a research journal devoted to the history of science and its cultural influences. 1936. a. $25 for paper; cloth $39. (History of Science Society) University of Chicago Press, Journals Division, 5720 S. Woodlawn Ave., Chicago, IL 60637. TEL 312-753-3347. FAX 312-753-0811. (Subscr. to: Box 37005, Chicago, IL 60637) Ed. Margaret Rossiter. bibl.; charts; illus. circ. 1,000. (back issues avail.; reprint service avail. from SWZ) **Document type:** academic/scholarly publication.
—BLDSC (6301.020000); SWETS; UMI. **CCC.**
Refereed Serial

500   GW   ISSN 0340-4781
QH5   CODEN: ONMIDS
OSNABRUECKER NATURWISSENSCHAFTLICHE MITTEILUNGEN. (Text in German; summaries in English and German) 1873. a. DM.50. Naturwissenschaftlicher Verein Osnabrueck, Am Schoelerberg 8, 49082 Osnabrueck, Germany. TEL 0541-5600332. FAX 0541-5600337. (Co-sponsor: Museum am Schoelerberg, Natur und Umwelt) Ed.Bd. bk.rev.; illus.; maps. circ. 820. **Indexed:** Bibl.& Ind.Geol., Numis.Lit. **Document type:** academic/scholarly publication, proceedings.
Refereed Serial

500 350   UK   ISSN 0165-0262
OUTLOOK ON SCIENCE POLICY. 1978. m. (except Aug.). £34($61) to individuals; institutions £110 ($195) (effective 1996). (International Science Policy Foundation) Beech Tree Publishing, 10 Watford Close, Guildford, Surrey GU1 2EP, England. TEL 01483-67497. FAX 01483-67497. (Subscr. to: Turpin Distribution Services Ltd., Blackhorse Rd., Letchworth, Herts. SG6 1HN, England. TEL 01462-672555. FAX 01462-480947) Ed.Bd. adv.; bk.rev. (back issues avail.) **Document type:** newsletter.
Description: International news on public science and technology policy.

OWL. see *CHILDREN AND YOUTH* — For

500   CN   ISSN 1180-1867
OYEZ 3; news notes on scientific societies and the public. (Text in English, French) 1989. s-a. free. Royal Society of Canada - Societe Royale du Canada, Box 9734, Ottawa, ON K1G 5J4, Canada. TEL 613-991-6990. FAX 613-991-6996. E-mail: admin@resudox.net. **Document type:** newsletter.

SCIENCES: COMPREHENSIVE WORKS

500   GW   ISSN 0935-9400
P.M. PERSPEKTIVE. 1986. 4/yr. DM.39.20. Gruner und Jahr AG & Co. (Munich), Neherstr. 9, 81675 Munich, Germany. TEL 089-4152-0. FAX 089-4152665. Eds. G.P. Moosleitner, Hans-Hermann Sprado. adv. circ. 170,000. (back issues avail.) **Document type:** consumer publication.

P S L S. (Publication of the Society for Literature and Science) see LITERATURE

P T B BERICHTE. (Physikalisch-Technische Bundesanstalt) see TECHNOLOGY: COMPREHENSIVE WORKS

500.9   US   ISSN 0030-8641
Q1   CODEN: PADIAZ
PACIFIC DISCOVERY; exploring a world worth saving. 1948. q. $12.95 (foreign $22). California Academy of Sciences, Golden Gate Park, San Francisco, CA 94118. TEL 415-750-7116. Ed. Keith Howell. adv. contact: Doug Corwin. bk.rev.; illus.; cum.index: vols.1-34 (1948-1981). circ. 30,000. (also avail. in microfilm from UMI; microfiche; back issues avail.) **Indexed:** Bibl.& Ind.Geol., Biol.Abstr., Cal.Per.Ind. (1984-), Deep Sea Res.& Oceanogr.Abstr., So.Pac.Per.Ind., Sport Fish.Abstr., Wild.Rev., Zoo.Rec. **Document type:** bulletin.
—BLDSC (6329.100000); UMI.

570   US   ISSN 0030-8870
QH1   CODEN: PASCAP
PACIFIC SCIENCE; a quarterly devoted to the biological and physical sciences of the Pacific Region. 1947. q. $33 to individuals (foreign $39); institutions $50 (foreign $55). University of Hawaii Press, Journals Department, 2840 Kolowalu St., Honolulu, HI 96822. TEL 808-956-8833. FAX 808-988-6052. E-mail: eakay@zoogate.zoo.hawaii.edu. Ed. E. Alison Kay. adv.; bibl.; charts; illus.; index. circ. 650. (also avail. in microform from UMI,PMC; back issues avail.; reprint service avail. from UMI,ISI) **Indexed:** Bibl.& Ind.Geol., Biol.Abstr., Chem.Abstr., Curr.Adv.Ecol.Sci., Curr.Cont., Deep Sea Res.& Oceanogr.Abstr., Ecol.Abstr., Environ.Per.Bibl (1990-), Field Crop Abstr., Forest.Abstr., Forest Prod.Abstr., Geo.Abstr., Geol.Abstr., Herb.Abstr., Hort.Abstr., Mineral.Abstr., Ocean.Abstr., Plant Breed.Abstr., Rev.Appl.Entomol., Rev.Plant Path., Sel.Water Res.Abstr., So.Pac.Per.Ind., Sport Fish.Abstr., Wild.Rev., Zoo.Rec. **Document type:** academic/scholarly publication.
—BLDSC (6331.000000); CASDDS; Faxon; SWETS; UMI; UnCover.
Description: Presents international and multidisciplinary reports on biological and physical sciences of the Pacific region.
Refereed Serial

500   US
PACIFIC SCIENCE ASSOCIATION. CONGRESS AND INTER-CONGRESS PROCEEDINGS. (Proceedings published by host country.) 1920. biennial. Pacific Science Association, Box 17801, Honolulu, HI 96817. TEL 808-848-4139. FAX 808-841-8968. E-mail: psa@bishop.bishop.hawaii.org. **Indexed:** Deep Sea Res.& Oceanogr.Abstr. **Document type:** proceedings.
Formerly: Pacific Science Association. Congress Proceedings (ISSN 0078-7647)

500   US   ISSN 0030-8889
PACIFIC SCIENCE ASSOCIATION. INFORMATION BULLETIN. (Supplement avail.: Pacific Research Titles) 1949. 4/yr. membership. Pacific Science Association, Box 17801, Honolulu, HI 96817. TEL 808-848-4139. FAX 808-841-8968. E-mail: psa@bishop.bishop.hawaii.org. Ed. L.G. Eldredge. bk.rev.; bibl. circ. 2,000. **Document type:** newsletter.
Description: Publishes news, information and original research articles.
Refereed Serial

PACT. see ARCHAEOLOGY

505   PK   ISSN 0377-2969
Q1   CODEN: PKSPAW
PAKISTAN ACADEMY OF SCIENCES. PROCEEDINGS. (Text in English) 1964. q. Rs.160($12) Pakistan Academy of Sciences, Constitution Avenue, G-5, Islamabad, Pakistan. TELEX 54349 COMST PK. Ed. M.M. Qurashi. bk.rev.; bibl.; charts; illus. circ. 350. **Indexed:** Biol.Abstr., Chem.Abstr., INSPEC (1982-), Math.R. **Document type:** academic/scholarly publication, proceedings.
—BLDSC (6784.000000); CASDDS.

500   PK
PAKISTAN ASSOCIATION FOR THE ADVANCEMENT OF SCIENCE. ANNUAL REPORT. (Text in English) a. Rs.36($2) Pakistan Association for the Advancement of Science, 273 N Model Town, Lahore, Pakistan.

500 607   PK   ISSN 0078-804X
PAKISTAN COUNCIL OF SCIENTIFIC AND INDUSTRIAL RESEARCH. ANNUAL REPORT. Abbreviated title: P C S I R Annual Report. (Text in English) 1953. a. price varies. Pakistan Council of Scientific and Industrial Research, Scientific Information Centre, 39 Garden Rd., Karachi 74400, Pakistan. TEL 92-21-7725943. FAX 92-21-2636704. Ed. J.N. Usmani. circ. 1,000. **Document type:** corporate report.
—BLDSC (1392.330000).

500   PK   ISSN 0030-9877
Q73   CODEN: PAJSAS
PAKISTAN JOURNAL OF SCIENCE. 1949. q. Rs.100($30) Pakistan Association for the Advancement of Science, 6-B Gulberg II, Lahore 11, Pakistan. Ed. Ghulam Rasool Chaudhry. decennial index. **Indexed:** Bibl.& Ind.Geol., Biol.Abstr., Chem.Abstr., Dairy Sci.Abstr., Food Sci.& Tech.Abstr., Herb.Abstr., Hort.Abstr., Ind.Vet., INSPEC (1968-), Packag.Sci.Tech., Plant Breed.Abstr., Soils & Fert., Vet.Bull. **Document type:** academic/scholarly publication.
—BLDSC (6342.000000); CASDDS.

500   PK   ISSN 0030-9885
Q180.A1   CODEN: PSIRAA
PAKISTAN JOURNAL OF SCIENTIFIC AND INDUSTRIAL RESEARCH. (Text in English) 1958. m. Rs.800($108) Pakistan Council of Scientific and Industrial Research, 39 Garden Rd., Karachi 74400, Pakistan. TEL 92-21-7725943. FAX 92-21-2636704. Ed. J.N. Usmani. adv.; bk.rev.; charts; illus.; index. circ. 800. (also avail. in microfilm from UMI; reprint service avail. from UMI) **Indexed:** Agri.Eng.Abstr., Bio-Contr.News & Info., Biol.Abstr., Chem.Abstr., Cott.& Trop.Fibr.Abstr., Crop Physiol.Abstr., Dairy Sci.Abstr., Deep Sea Res.& Oceanogr.Abstr., Ecol.Abstr., Excerp.Med., Field Crop Abstr., Food Sci.& Tech.Abstr., Forest.Abstr., Forest Prod.Abstr., Geo.Abstr., Helminthol.Abstr., Herb.Abstr., Hort.Abstr., Ind.Chem., INSPEC (1968-1982), Irr.& Drain.Abstr., Mass Spectr.Bull., Nutr.Abstr., Poult.Abstr., Rev.Med.& Vet.Mycol., Rev.Plant Path., Rice Abstr., Sci.Cit.Ind., Seed Abstr., Soils & Fert., Sorghum & Millets Abstr., Soyabean Abstr., Sport Fish.Abstr., Sugar Ind.Abstr., Triticale Abstr., Trop.Oil Seeds Abstr., Weed Abstr., Wild.Rev., Zoo.Rec. **Document type:** academic/scholarly publication.
—BLDSC (6342.700000); CASDDS; Ei; UMI; UnCover.

500   PK   ISSN 0552-9050
Q180.P25   CODEN: PJSRAV
PAKISTAN JOURNAL OF SCIENTIFIC RESEARCH. (Text in English) 1949. q. Rs.100($30) Pakistan Association for the Advancement of Science, 6-B Gulberg II, Lahore 11, Pakistan. Ed. Ghulam Rasool Chaudhry. cum.index every 10 yrs. **Indexed:** Bibl.& Ind.Geol., Biol.Abstr., Chem.Abstr., Dairy Sci.Abstr., Food Sci.& Tech.Abstr., Herb.Abstr., Ind.Vet., INSPEC (1968-), Mass Spectr.Bull., Plant Breed.Abstr., Plant Grow.Reg.Abstr., Soils & Fert., Vet.Bull. **Document type:** academic/scholarly publication.
—BLDSC (6343.000000); CASDDS.

500   PK   ISSN 0078-8430
PAKISTAN SCIENCE CONFERENCE. PROCEEDINGS. (Text in English) a. Rs.100($30) Pakistan Association for the Advancement of Science, 273 N Model Town, Lahore, Pakistan. Ed. Ghulam Rasool Chaudry. index. **Indexed:** Bibl.& Ind.Geol., Biol.Abstr. **Document type:** proceedings.

505   FR   ISSN 0180-3344
PALAIS DE LA DECOUVERTE. REVUE. 1972. m. (10/yr.). 160 F. (foreign 190 F.) (effective 1995). Palais de la Decouverte, Av. Franklin D. Roosevelt, 75008 Paris, France. FAX 40-74-81-81. Ed. Michel Demazure; Pub. Michel Demazure. adv.; bk.rev.; illus. circ. 4,000. (back issues avail.)

500 600   US   ISSN 0883-8305
QE39.5.P25   CODEN: POCGEP
PALEOCEANOGRAPHY. 1986. bi-m. $270 to non-members (foreign $280); members $58 (foreign $68); students $27 (foreign $37). American Geophysical Union, 2000 Florida Ave., N.W., Washington, DC 20009. TEL 202-462-6900. FAX 202-328-0566. TELEX 710-822-9300. Ed. Ken Miller. abstr. (also avail. in microform from AGU; back issues avail.) **Indexed:** Geo.Abstr., Geol.Abstr., Meteor.& Geoastrophys.Abstr.
—BLDSC (6345.295000); Ei; Faxon; Genuine Article; PADDS; SWETS; UnCover. CCC.
Description: Deals with the history of the ocean system and its plants and animal life. Studies based on marine sedimentary sections from the ocean basin and margins and from those ancient sediments exposed on the continents.
Refereed Serial

508   II   ISSN 0555-7631
Q180.I5   CODEN: RBJUAT
PANJAB UNIVERSITY RESEARCH BULLETIN (SCIENCES). (Text in English) 1950. s-a. Rs.250($25) Panjab University, Publication Bureau, Chandigarh 160 014, Union Territory, India. Ed. S. Khera. **Indexed:** Bio-Contr.News & Info., Soyabean Abstr., Sport Fish.Abstr., Triticale Abstr., Trop.Oil Seeds Abstr., Wild.Rev., Zoo.Rec. **Document type:** academic/scholarly publication.
—BLDSC (7731.200000); CASDDS; UnCover.
Description: Multi-disciplinary studies of sciences, on both pre-doctoral and post-doctoral levels.

500.9   FR   ISSN 0180-961X
QH147
PARC NATIONAL DE LA VANOISE. TRAVAUX SCIENTIFIQUES. (Text in French; summaries in English, German and Italian) 1970. irreg. 45 F. per vol. Ministere de l'Environnement, Direction de la Nature et des Paysages, Parc National de la Vanoise, B.P. 705, 73007 Chambery Cedex, France. TEL 79-62-30-54. FAX 79-96-37-18. bk.rev. circ. 600. **Document type:** monographic series.
Description: Works covering the history, geography, geology, biology, botany, zoology, ornithology, culture, people, economy of the Vanoise region of the French Alps.

PATTERN RECOGNITION. see COMPUTERS — Computer Graphics

500.9   US   ISSN 0079-032X
QH1   CODEN: YUPBA8
PEABODY MUSEUM OF NATURAL HISTORY. BULLETIN. Key Title: Bulletin - Peabody Museum of Natural History. 1926. irreg., no.44, 1991. price varies. Peabody Museum of Natural History, Yale University, 170 Whitney Ave., Box 208118, New Haven, CT 06520-8118. TEL 203-432-3786. FAX 203-432-9816. Eds. John Ostrom, Zelda Edelson. circ. 500. (back issues avail.) **Indexed:** Biol.Abstr., GeoRef. **Document type:** monographic series.
Supersedes (in 1967): Bulletin of Bingham Oceanographic Collection.
Description: Consists of research in the fields of study encompassed by the Museum.

500   US   ISSN 1044-6753
Q11   CODEN: JPSCEY
PENNSYLVANIA ACADEMY OF SCIENCE. JOURNAL. 1924. 3/yr. $35. Pennsylvania Academy of Science, c/o Dr. S.K. Majumdar, Ed., Dept. of Biology, Lafayette College, Easton, PA 18042. TEL 610-250-5464. FAX 610-250-6557. bk.rev.; abstr. circ. 700. (back issues avail.) **Indexed:** Biol.Abstr., Chem.Abstr., Sel.Water Res.Abstr., Sport Fish.Abstr., Wild.Rev., Zoo.Rec. **Document type:** academic/scholarly publication.
●Also available online.
—BLDSC (4839.645000); CASDDS; Faxon; UnCover.
Formerly: Pennsylvania Academy of Science. Proceedings (ISSN 0096-9222)
Description: Presents papers from the natural, engineering and social sciences.
Refereed Serial

500   CK   ISSN 0031-4765
HN110.5.Z9
PENSAMIENTO Y ACCION. 1968. bi-m. Universidad Pedagogica y Tecnologica de Colombia, Fundo Especial de Publicaciones y Ayudas Educativas, Apdo. Nacional 34, Tunja, Boyaco, Colombia. Ed. E.S. Celis. adv.; bk.rev.; play rev.; charts; illus.

5886 SCIENCES: COMPREHENSIVE WORKS

PERSPECTIVES ON SCIENCE AND CHRISTIAN FAITH. see RELIGIONS AND THEOLOGY

500　　　　　　　US　　ISSN 1063-6145
Q124.6　　　　　　　CODEN: PRSIEU
PERSPECTIVES ON SCIENCE: HISTORICAL, PHILOSOPHICAL, SOCIAL. 1993. q. $35 to individuals; institutions $70; students $25. University of Chicago Press, Journals Division, 5720 S. Woodlawn Ave., Chicago, IL 60637. TEL 312-702-7600. FAX 312-753-0811. TELEX 25-4603. (Subscr. to: Box 37005, Chicago, IL 60637) Ed. Joseph C. Pitt. (also avail. in microfilm from UMI) **Indexed:** Amer.Hist.& Life (1993-), Hist.Abstr. (1993-). **Document type:** academic/scholarly publication.
—BLDSC (6428.163680); UMI; UnCover. **CCC.**
Description: Devoted to the studies of the sciences that integrate historical, philosophical, and sociological perspectives.
Refereed Serial

500 600　　　　MY　　ISSN 0128-7680
　　　　　　　　CODEN: PERTDY
PERTANIKA JOURNAL OF SCIENCE AND TECHNOLOGY. (Text in English, Malay) 2/yr. $60 (effective 1996). (Agricultural University of Malaysia) Universiti Pertanian Malaysia Press, Serdang, Selangor, Malaysia. TEL 03-9486101. FAX 03-9483745. TELEX UNIPER-37454. Ed. Mohamed Suleiman. circ. 300. **Document type:** academic/scholarly publication.
—BLDSC (6428.183000); CASDDS.
Superseded in part (in 1993): Pertanika (ISSN 0126-6128)
Refereed Serial

PETERSON'S GUIDE TO GRADUATE PROGRAMS IN THE PHYSICAL SCIENCES AND MATHEMATICS (YEAR) (BOOK 4). see EDUCATION — Guides To Schools And Colleges

500　　　　　　　PH　　ISSN 0031-7683
Q75　　　　　　　　CODEN: PJSCAK
PHILIPPINE JOURNAL OF SCIENCE. (Text in English) 1906. q. P.260($80) Industrial Technology Development Institute, P. Gil, Taft Ave., Manila, P.O. Box 744, Philippines. FAX 632-592275. (Subscr. to: Science and Technology Information Institute, Dept. of Science and Technology, P.O.Box 3596, Manila, Philippines) Ed. Quintin L. Kintanar. bk.rev.; abstr.; bibl.; charts; index, cum.index: 1951-1970 (vols. 80-99), 1971-1975 (vols. 100-104). circ. 1,300. (also avail. in microform from PMC) **Indexed:** Appl.Mech.Rev., Bibl.& Ind.Geol., Biol.Abstr., Chem.Abstr., Curr.Adv.Ecol.Sci., Deep Sea Res.& Oceanogr.Abstr., Excerp.Med., Field Crop Abstr., Food Sci.& Tech.Abstr., Herb.Abstr., Hort.Abstr., Ind.Phil.Per., Plant Breed.Abstr., Rev.Appl.Entomol., Sport Fish.Abstr., Wild.Rev., Zoo.Rec.
—BLDSC (6456.000000); CASDDS; Faxon.

500　　　　　　　PH　　ISSN 0031-7799
PHILIPPINE SCIENTIFIC JOURNAL. 1947. q. P.5($5) Manila Central University, Caloocan Campus, Caloocan City, Philippines. Ed. Walfrido W. Sumpaido. adv.; bk.rev.; abstr.; charts; index. circ. 2,500.

500　　　　　　　PH　　ISSN 0079-1466
Q76　　　　　　　　CODEN: PHISB5
PHILIPPINE SCIENTIST. (Text in English) 1964. a. P.300($12) (University of San Carlos) San Carlos Publications, P.O. Box 182, 6000 Cebu City, Philippines. Ed. Joseph Baumgartner. circ. 80. (back issues avail.) **Indexed:** Biol.Abstr., Deep Sea Res.& Oceanogr.Abstr., Ind.Phil.Per. **Document type:** academic/scholarly publication.
—BLDSC (6456.170000); CASDDS.
Description: Deals with research in various natural science fields, emphasizing marine biology and entomology.

500　　　　　　　PH
PHILIPPINE TECHNICAL INFORMATION SHEETS. irreg.? P.75 per no. (foreign $10 per no.). Science and Technology Information Institute, Department of Science and Technology, P.O. Box 3596, Manila, Philippines. TEL 822-0954. (Subscr. to: Dept. of Science and Technology, Bicutan, Taguig, P.O. Box 2131, Manila, Philippines) **Document type:** monographic series.
Description: Provides comprehensive information on the 15 Philippine S & T leading edges in the Science and Technology Master Plan (STMP).

PHILIPS JOURNAL OF RESEARCH. see ENGINEERING

PHILOSOPHY IN SCIENCE. see PHILOSOPHY

501　　　　　　　US　　ISSN 0031-8248
Q1　　　　　　　　CODEN: PHSCA6
PHILOSOPHY OF SCIENCE. 1934. q. $60 per vol. ($65 outside U.S.) Philosophy of Science Association, 503 S. Kedzie Hall, Dept. of Philosophy, Michigan State Univ., East Lansing, MI 48824-1032. TEL 517-353-9392. Ed. Merrilee Salmon. adv.; bk.rev.; bibl.; index. circ. 2,200. (also avail. in microform from UMI,PMC) **Indexed:** Arts & Hum.Cit.Ind., Biol.Abstr., Bull.Signal., CLOSS, Curr.Cont., Curr.Ind.Stat., Deep Sea Res.& Oceanogr.Abstr., Hum.Ind., Ind.Bk.Rev.Hum., INSPEC, Lang.& Lang.Behav.Abstr., Math.R., Phil.Ind., Psychol.Abstr., Sci.Cit.Ind., Sociol.Abstr., SSCI. **Document type:** academic/scholarly publication.
—BLDSC (6465.000000); Faxon; Genuine Article; SWETS; UMI; UnCover. **CCC.**
Refereed Serial

500　　　　　　　US　　ISSN 0885-1581
PHYSICAL SCIENCE. (Subseries of: S I R S Science (ISSN 0885-1530)) 1985. a. $80. Social Issues Resources Series, Box 2348, Boca Raton, FL 33427-2348. TEL 407-994-0079; 800-232-7477. FAX 407-994-4704. (looseleaf format; also avail. in microfiche)
Description: Reprints 70 articles that explore the social dimensions of thories of the size, nature, and origin of the universe.

PHYSIKALISCH-TECHNISCHE BUNDESANSTALT. JAHRESBERICHT. see TECHNOLOGY: COMPREHENSIVE WORKS

PHYSIKALISCH-TECHNISCHE BUNDESANSTALT. PRUEFREGELN. see TECHNOLOGY: COMPREHENSIVE WORKS

530　　　　　　　IT　　ISSN 0031-9414
Q54　　　　　　　　CODEN: PYSSA3
PHYSIS; rivista internazionale di storia della scienza. (Text in English, French, German, Italian and Spanish) 1959. 3/yr. L.90000 (foreign L.115000) (effective 1995) US $77 (effective 1996). Casa Editrice Leo S. Olschki, Casella Postale 66, 50100 Florence, Italy. TEL 39-55-6530684. FAX 39-55-6530214. Ed.Bd. adv.; bk.rev.; illus. circ. 1,000. **Indexed:** Amer.Hist.& Life, Biol.Abstr., Chem.Abstr., Helminthol.Abstr., Hist.Abstr., Numis.Lit., Ocean.Abstr., Pollut.Abstr. **Document type:** academic/scholarly publication.
—Faxon; SWETS.

PITTSBURGH SERIES IN PHILOSOPHY & HISTORY OF SCIENCE. see PHILOSOPHY

500　　　　　　　XR　　ISSN 0032-2423
Q44.J3　　　　　　　CODEN: PMFAA4
POKROKY MATEMATIKY, FYZIKY A ASTRONOMIE/PROGRESS IN MATHEMATICS, PHYSICS AND ASTRONOMY. 1956. bi-m. DM.152. Jednota Ceskych Matematiku a Fyziku, Zitna 25, 117 10 Prague 1, Czech Republic. (Dist. in Western countries by: Kubon & Sagner, P.O. Box 34 01 08, 8000 Munich 34, Germany) (Co-sponsor: Jednota Slovenskych Matematikov a Fyzikov (XO)) Eds. Oldrich Kowalski, Miroslav Rozsival. bk.rev.; illus.; stat.; index. circ. 4,600. **Indexed:** Chem.Abstr., Math.R.
—CASDDS.
Description: Publishes articles concerning mathematics, physics and astronomy (expository papers, history, philosophy, science and society, modern trends in education) news and activities of the association.

919.8 500　　　　　NO　　ISSN 0800-0395
　　　　　　　　CODEN: POREEQ
POLAR RESEARCH. (Text in English) 1982. s-a. NOK 100 per no. Norwegian Polar Institute - Norsk Polarinstitutt, Middelthuns gate 29, P.O. Box 5072 Majorstua, N-0301 Oslo, Norway. TEL 47-22-95-95-00. FAX 47-22-95-95-01. TELEX 74745 POLAR. E-mail: mcberge@npolar.no. Ed. Paal Prestrud. circ. 300. **Indexed:** Curr.Cont., Deep Sea Res.& Oceanogr.Abstr., Ecol.Abstr., Geo.Abstr., Geol.Abstr., INSPEC (1985-), Key Word Ind.Wildl.Res., Meteor.& Geoastrophys.Abstr., Sport Fish.Abstr., Wild.Rev., Zoo.Rec. **Document type:** proceedings.
●Also available online.
—BLDSC (6542.300000); Genuine Article; UnCover. **CCC.**
Description: Treats various subjects within the field of polar research.
Refereed Serial

500　　　　　　　PL　　ISSN 0860-097X
　　　　　　　　CODEN: MPKKEH
POLITECHNIKA KRAKOWSKA. MONOGRAFIE. (In 9 series: Architectura; Ekonomia, Socjologia, Filozofia; Inzynieria i Techologia Chemiczna; Inzynieria Ladowa; Inzynieria Sanitarna i Wodna; Inzynieria Elektryczna; Mechanika; Podstawowe Nauki Techniczne; Seria Historyczno-Techniczna) (Text in Polish; summaries in English, French, German, Russian) 1985. irreg. price varies. Politechnika Krakowska, Ul. Warszawska 24, 31-155 Krakow, Poland. TEL 48-12-37-42-89. FAX 48-12-335-773. TELEX 322468 PK PL. bibl.; charts; illus. circ. 200. **Document type:** academic/scholarly publication, monographic series.
—BLDSC (5912.290000); CASDDS.

500　　　　　　　PL　　ISSN 1230-1868
POLITECHNIKA WROCLAWSKA. BADANIA OPERACYJNE I DECYZJE. (Text in English, Polish or Russian; summaries in English and Russian) 1969. q. price varies. Wydawnictwo Politechniki Wroclawskiej, Wybrzeze Wyspianskiego 27, 50-370 Wroclaw, Poland. FAX 22-36-64. TELEX 712559 PWRPL. (Dist. by: Ars Polona-Ruch, Krakowskie Przedmiescie 7, Warsaw, Poland) Ed. J. Galanc. circ. 450. **Document type:** academic/scholarly publication.
—BLDSC (1856.225000).
Former titles (until 1991): Politechnika Wroclawska. Prace Naukoznawcze i Prognostyczne (ISSN 0137-1215); (until 1972): Politechnika Wroclawska. Prace Naukoznawcze Politechniki (ISSN 0137-1207)

500　　　　　　　PL　　ISSN 0137-6225
POLITECHNIKA WROCLAWSKA. BIBLIOTEKA GLOWNA I OSRODEK INFORMACJI NAUKOWO-TECHNICZNEJ. PRACE NAUKOWE. STUDIA I MATERIALY. (Text in Polish; summaries in English and Russian) 1974. irreg., no.2, 1977. price varies. Wydawnictwo Politechniki Wroclawskiej, Wybrzeze Wyspianskiego 27, 50-370 Wroclaw, Poland. FAX 22-36-64. TELEX 712254 PWRPL. (Dist. by: Ars Polona-Ruch, Krakowskie Przedmiescie 7, Warsaw, Poland) circ. 965. **Document type:** academic/scholarly publication.

POLITECNICA; revista de informacion tecnico-cientifica. see ENGINEERING

500 060　　　　PL　　ISSN 0079-354X
POLSKA AKADEMIA NAUK. ODDZIAL W KRAKOWIE. KOMISJE NAUKOWE. SPRAWOZDANIA Z POSIEDZEN. (Text in Polish; summaries in English and Polish) 1957. s-a. price varies. Polska Akademia Nauk, Oddzial w Krakowie, Ul. Slawkowska 17, 31-016 Krakow, Poland. TEL 48-12-224853. FAX 48-12-222791. Ed. Jozef Duzyk. **Indexed:** Bibl.Ling., Numis.Lit. **Document type:** proceedings.
Description: Contains summaries of papers presented and discussed at meetings of Scientific Commissions.

500　　　　　　　VC
PONTIFICIA ACADEMIA SCIENTIARUM. COMMENTARII. irreg. Pontificia Academia Scientiarum, Casina Pio IV, 00120 Vatican City (Rome), State of the Vatican City. TEL 39-0-6-69883195. FAX 39-0-6-69885218. TELEX 2024 DIRGENTEL VA.

SCIENCES: COMPREHENSIVE WORKS

500 574   VC
PONTIFICIA ACADEMIA SCIENTIARUM. DOCUMENTA. (Text in English, French) irreg. Pontificia Academia Scientiarum, Casina Pio IV, 00120 Vatican City (Rome), State of the Vatican City.
TEL 39-0-6-69883195. FAX 39-0-6-69885218. TELEX 2040 DIRIGENTEL VA. **Indexed:** Biol.Abstr.

500 574   VC   ISSN 0377-9971
CODEN: PASVAE
PONTIFICIA ACADEMIA SCIENTIARUM. SCRIPTA VARIA. (Text in English, French) irreg. Pontificia Academia Scientiarum, Casina Pio IV, 00120 Vatican City (Rome), State of the Vatican City.
TEL 39-0-6-69883195. FAX 39-0-6-69885218. TELEX 2024 DIRGENTEL VA. **Indexed:** Biol.Abstr.
—CASDDS.

500 600   KE   ISSN 0253-5963
Q225   CODEN: POKEDO
POST; a magazine for the promotion of science and technology. 3/yr.? Kenya National Academy for Advancement of Arts and Sciences, Box 47288, Nairobi, Kenya.

500.9   US   ISSN 0079-4295
QH1   CODEN: PSTLAD
POSTILLA. 1950. irreg., no.208, 1991. price varies. Peabody Museum of Natural History, Yale University, 170 Whitney Ave., Box 208118, New Haven, CT 06520-8118. TEL 203-432-3786. FAX 203-432-9816. Eds. John Ostrom, Zelda Edelson. circ. 500. (back issues avail.) **Indexed:** Biol.Abstr., Deep Sea Res.& Oceanogr.Abstr. **Document type:** monographic series.
—BLDSC (6563.930000).
 Description: Research in the fields of study encompassed by the museum.

500 600   FR   ISSN 0153-4092
POUR LA SCIENCE. French translation of: Scientific American (US ISSN 0036-8733) 1977. m. 340 F. (foreign 417 F.) (effective 1995). Societe pour la Science, 8 rue Ferou, 75006 Paris, France. FAX 43-25-18-29. TELEX LIBELIN 202978F. Ed. Philippe Boulanger; Pub. Olivier Brossollet. adv. contact: Susan Mackie. bk.rev. circ. 52,000. **Indexed:** Pt.de Rep. (1979-), RILM. **Document type:** newspaper.
—SWETS.

PRAIRIE FORUM. see *ENVIRONMENTAL STUDIES*

574.52643   US   ISSN 0091-0376
QH540   CODEN: PRNTBZ
PRAIRIE NATURALIST. 1968. q. $10 to individuals (foreign $15); institutions $20 (foreign $25) (effective 1992). Box 4050, Emporia, KS 66801-5087. TEL 701-328-5368. FAX 701-328-5363. Ed. Elmer J. Finck. bk.rev.; circ. 500 (paid). **Indexed:** Biol.Abstr., Key Word Ind.Wildl.Res., Sport Fish.Abstr., Wild Life Rev., Wild.Rev., Zoo.Rec. **Document type:** academic/scholarly publication.
—BLDSC (6598.551000); Faxon; UnCover.
 Description: Presents research on the North American grasslands and their biota.
 Refereed Serial

500   XV   ISSN 0351-6652
PRESEK; list za mlade matematike, fizike, astronome in racunalnikarje. (Text in Slovenian) 1971. bi-m. $10. Drustvo Matematikov, Fizikov in Astronomov Slovenije, Podruznica Ljubljana, Jadranska 19, p.p. 64, 61111 Ljubljana, Slovenia. TEL 061-265-061. Ed. Marija Vencelj. adv.; bk.rev. circ. 20,000.

507 370   UK   ISSN 0269-2465
PRIMARY SCIENCE REVIEW. 1986. 5/yr. £36 (overseas £48) (effective 1995). Association for Science Education., College Ln., Hatfield, Herts. AL10 9AA, England. TEL 01707-267411. FAX 01707-266532. Ed. Peter Ovens. adv. contact: Brenda Dearing. bk.rev. circ. 7,000. (back issues avail.) **Document type:** academic/scholarly publication.
—BLDSC (6612.912900).
 Description: Contains reference material and practical ideas for science primary teachers.
 Refereed Serial

PRIMI PIANI; mensile d'arte, costume, cultura, scienza, spettacolo e turismo. see *MUSIC*

PRINCETON UNIVERSITY LIBRARY CHRONICLE. see *HUMANITIES: COMPREHENSIVE WORKS*

500   BU   ISSN 0032-8731
CODEN: PRIRB4
PRIRODA. 1952. 6/yr. 6.80 lv.($10) (Bulgarska Akademiia na Naukite) Publishing House of the Bulgarian Academy of Sciences, Acad. G. Bonchev St., Bldg. 6, 1113 Sofia, Bulgaria. (Dist. by: Hemus, 6, Rouski Blvd., 1000 Sofia, Bulgaria) adv.; bk.rev.; abstr.; illus.; index. circ. 2,200. (reprint service avail. from IRC) **Indexed:** Anim.Breed.Abstr., Biol.Abstr., BSL Biol., Chem.Abstr., Curr.Dig.Sov.Press.
—BLDSC (0133.020000); CASDDS.

500   RU   ISSN 0032-874X
Q4   CODEN: PRIRA3
PRIRODA; populyarnyi estestvenno nauchnyi zhurnal. 1912. m. 27.60 Rub.($93) (Rossiiskaya Akademiya Nauk) Izdatel'stvo Nauka, 90 Profsoyuznaya ul., 117864 Moscow, Russia. TEL 095-336-0266. FAX 095-420-2220. (Dist. in U.S. by: Victor Kamkin Inc., 4956 Boiling Brook Pkwy., Rocville, MD 20852. TEL 301-881-5973. FAX 301-881-1637) Ed. N.G. Basov. bk.rev.; bibl.; illus.; maps; index. circ. 62,000. **Indexed:** Anim.Breed.Abstr., Art & Archaeol.Tech.Abstr., Bibl.& Ind.Geol., Biol.Abstr., Chem.Abstr., Curr.Dig.Sov.Press, INSPEC, Int.Aerosp.Abstr.
—BLDSC (0133.000000); CASDDS. **CCC.**

500 300   XO   ISSN 0322-7707
PRIRODA A SPOLOCNOST. 1947. fortn. $70. (Socialisticka Akademia Slovenskej Socialistickej Republiky - Socialist Academy of the Slovak Socialist Republic) Obzor, Spitalska 35, 815 85 Bratislava, Slovakia. (Dist. by: Slovart, Gottwaldovo nam. 48, 805 32 Bratislava, Slovakia) Ed. Pavel Berta. adv.; bk.rev.; illus. circ. 22,000.

500 370 600 700   GW   ISSN 0171-3604
PRISMA (KASSEL) 1973. s-a. DM.10. Universitaet Gesamthochschule Kassel, Moenchebergstr. 19, 34109 Kassel, Germany. TEL 0561-8042216. FAX 0561-8042330. adv. circ. 5,500. (back issues avail.) **Document type:** academic/scholarly publication.

PROBABLE LEVELS OF R & D EXPENDITURES: FORECAST AND ANALYSIS. see *TECHNOLOGY: COMPREHENSIVE WORKS*

500   GW   ISSN 0343-7965
GB457.5
PROBLEME DER KUESTENFORSCHUNG IM SUEDLICHEN NORDSEEGEBIET. 1940. irreg., vol.16, 1986. (Niedersechsisches Landesinstitut fuer Marschen und Kuestenforschung) Verlag Isensee, Haarenstr. 20, 26122 Oldenburg, Germany. **Document type:** monographic series.
 Formerly (until 1964): Probleme der Kuestenforschung im Gebiet der Suedlichen Nordsee (ISSN 0343-7973)

500   PL   ISSN 0032-9487
PROBLEMY; miesiecznik popularno-naukowy. 1945. m. $6.60. Towarzystwo Wiedzy Powszechnej, Palac Kultury i Nauki, XII Fl., 00-901 Warsaw, Poland. TEL 48-22-266404. (Dist. by: Ars Polona-Ruch, Krakowskie Przedmiescie 7, Warsaw, Poland) bk.rev.; bibl.; charts; illus.; index. circ. 30,000.

PROFESSIONAL ETHICS REPORT. see *PHILOSOPHY*

500   CN   ISSN 1183-5001
PROFILE/PROFIL. (Text in English, French) 1991. s-a. free. Royal Society of Canada - Societe Royale du Canada, Box 9734, Ottawa, ON K1G 5J4, Canada. TEL 613-991-6990. FAX 613-991-6996. E-mail: admin@resudox.net. **Document type:** newsletter.

PROGRES TECHNIQUE. see *TECHNOLOGY: COMPREHENSIVE WORKS*

500   US   ISSN 1002-0071
Q72   CODEN: PNASEA
PROGRESS IN NATURAL SCIENCE; communication of state key laboratories of China. Chinese edition: Ziran Kexue Jinzhan (ISSN 1002-008X) (Text in English) 1991. bi-m. £115($190) (effective 1996). (National Natural Science Foundation of China, CC) Taylor & Francis, 1900 Frost Rd., Ste. 101, Bristol, PA 19007-1598. TEL 215-785-5800; 800-821-8312. FAX 215-785-5515. (Subscr. in Europe to: Taylor & Francis Ltd., Rankine Rd., Basingstoke, Hants. RG24 8PR, England. TEL 44-1256-840366. FAX 44-1256-479438) **Document type:** academic/scholarly publication.
—BLDSC (6870.260000); CASDDS; Ei.
 Description: Covers reviews of specialized subjects, theses, research news, and academic activities of State Key Laboratories in China.

500   BE   ISSN 0033-1082
PROMETHEE. 1950. q. 80 Fr.($2) Universite Libre de Bruxelles, Cercle des Sciences, 22 av. Heger, Brussels 5, Belgium. Dir. David Pierre. adv.; charts; illus. circ. 2,000.

500   XV   ISSN 0033-1805
PROTEUS; ilustriran casopis za poljudno prirodoznanstvo. (Text in Slovenian) 1939. 10/yr. 80 din. Prirodoslovno Drustvo Slovenije, Novi trg 4, Ljubljana, Slovenia. Ed. France Adamic.
—BLDSC (6936.200000).

500   UK   ISSN 0963-6625
Q225   CODEN: PUNSEM
PUBLIC UNDERSTANDING OF SCIENCE. 1992. q. £102($167) (effective 1996). (Institute of Physics) I O P Publishing Ltd., Techno House, Redcliffe Way, Bristol, Avon BS1 6NX, England. TEL 0117-929-7481. FAX 0117-929-4318. TELEX 449149 INSTP G. (U.S. subscr. to: American Institute of Physics, Subscriber Services, 500 Sunnyside Blvd., Woodbury, NY 11797-2900. TEL 516-349-7800) (Co-sponsor: London Science Museum) Ed. John Durant. index. (also avail. in microfiche) **Document type:** academic/scholarly publication.
—BLDSC (6969.550000); SWETS. **CCC.**
 Description: Provides a forum for the emerging interdisciplinary field of public understanding of science.

500 300   AO
PUBLICACOES CULTURAIS DA COMPANHIA. (Alternating series: biology, geology, climatology, history, archaeology and ethnology) (Text in English, French and Portuguese) irreg. Museu de Dundo, Dundo, Luanda, Angola.

500 940   US   ISSN 0079-7685
PUBLICATIONS IN MEDIEVAL SCIENCE. 1952. irreg. price varies. (University of Wisconsin at Madison) University of Wisconsin Press, 114 N. Murray St., Madison, WI 53715. TEL 608-262-4952. (reprint service avail. from UMI) **Document type:** monographic series.

500   KN   ISSN 0555-781X
QD71   CODEN: PUHWAY
PUNSOK HWAHAK. (Text in Korean) 1962. q. Korean Academy of Sciences, Central Analytical Institute, Pyongyang, N. Korea.
—CASDDS.

500 600   JA   ISSN 0386-2828
PUROMETEUSU. (Text in Japanese) 1977. bi-m. (Kagaku Gijutsu-cho - Science and Technology Agency) Sozo Co., Ltd., Torii Bldg., 6-12 Shinkawa 2-chome, Chuo-ku, Tokyo 104, Japan. **Indexed:** Jap.Per.Ind.

PURSUIT - S I T U. see *PARAPSYCHOLOGY AND OCCULTISM*

500   CC   ISSN 1000-0054
CODEN: QDXKE8
QINGHUA DAXUE XUEBAO/QINGHUA UNIVERSITY. JOURNAL. (Text in Chinese) bi-m. Qinghua Daxue, Xuebao Bianjibu, Beijing 100084, People's Republic of China. TEL 282451. Ed. Wu Youshou.
—BLDSC (4910.507000); CASDDS.

500   IT
QUADERNI DI SCIENZA. 1959. irreg., no.5, 1976. price varies. Giardini Editori e Stampatori, Via Santa Bibbiana 28, 56100 Pisa, Italy. TEL 050 502531.

SCIENCES: COMPREHENSIVE WORKS

500 510 028.5   US   ISSN 1048-8820
QC30
QUANTUM (NEW YORK); the magazine of math and science. Key Title: Quantum (Washington, DC). English translation of: Kvant (RU ISSN 0130-2221) 1990. bi-m. $45 (effective 1996). (National Science Teachers Association) Springer-Verlag, Journals, 175 Fifth Ave., New York, NY 10010. TEL 212-460-1500. FAX 212-473-6272. (N. America subscr. to: Journal Fulfillment Services, Box 2485, Secaucus, NJ 07096-2491. TEL 800-777-4643. FAX 201-348-4505; Elsewhere: Heidelberger Platz 3, 1000 Berlin 33, Germany. TEL 030-8207-1. FAX 030-821-4091) (Co-sponsors: American Association of Physics Teachers; National Council of Teachers of Mathematics; Russian Academy of Sciences, Quantum Bureau) Pub. B.G. Alridge. adv.; illus.; circ. 40,000 (controlled). (also avail. in microform from UMI; reprint service avail.) **Document type**: academic/scholarly publication.
—SWETS; UnCover. CCC.
   Description: Contains challenging and entertaining articles on physics and mathematics designed to inspire children and encourage thinking in math and science.
   Refereed Serial

QUATERNARY SCIENCE REVIEWS; international multidisciplinary review and research journal. see *EARTH SCIENCES — Geology*

500   CN   ISSN 0021-6127
QUEBEC SCIENCE. (Text in French) 1969. m. Can.$25($35) Presses de l'Universite du Quebec, 2875 blvd Laurier, Ste-Foy, Que, G1V 2M3, Canada. TEL 418-657-3551. FAX 418-657-2096. TELEX 051-31623. Ed. Jacki Dallaire. adv.; bk.rev.; bibl.; charts; illus.; index. circ. 20,000. (also avail. in microform from UMI; reprint service avail. from UMI) **Indexed**: Acid Pre.Dig., Can.B.P.I., Can.Per.Ind., Chem.Abstr., Pt.de Rep. (1979-).
—BLDSC (7210.700000); Faxon; UMI.
   Supersedes: Jeune Scientifique.
   Description: News and features on science and technology.

QUEEN VICTORIA MUSEUM AND ART GALLERY. LAUNCESTON, TASMANIA. RECORDS. see *MUSEUMS AND ART GALLERIES*

QUESTIONS. see *EDUCATION — Teaching Methods And Curriculum*

500 600   MX   ISSN 0185-5093
QUIPU; revista latinoamericana de historia de las ciencias y la tecnologia. (Text in English, French, Portuguese, Spanish; summaries in English) 1984. 3/yr. $25 to individuals; institutions $100 (effective 1993). Sociedad Latinoamericana de Historia de las Ciencias y la Tecnologia, Apdo. Postal 21-873, CP 04000 Mexico, DF, Mexico. TEL 622-18-64. FAX 525-659-64-06. Ed. Juan Jose Saldana. adv.; bk.rev.; bibl.; charts; illus.; index. circ. 2,500. (back issues avail.) **Indexed**: Amer.Hist.& Life, Bull.Signal., Hist.Abstr.
   Description: Covers the history of science and technology in Latin America.

500   US   ISSN 0033-6793
R & D CONTRACTS MONTHLY. (Research & Development); a continuously up-dated sales and R & D tool for all research organizations and manufacturers. (Annual Directory) 1962. m. $96. Government Data Publications, Inc., 1155 Connecticut Ave., N.W., Washington DC 20036. Ed. Siegfried Lobel. **Indexed**: DM&T, PROMT.
   Description: Coverage of sales as well as research and development intelligence. Lists recently awarded government contracts.

500   SI   ISSN 0217-6440
R & D SURVEY. (Text in English) 1983. a. free. National Science and Technology Board, 16 Science Park Drive, 01-03 The Pasteur, Singapore Science Park, Singapore 0511, Singapore. TEL 65-779-7066. FAX 65-777-1711. **Document type**: government publication.

R E C S A M NEWS. (Regional Centre for Education in Science and Mathematics) see *EDUCATION — Teaching Methods And Curriculum*

500 600   KO
R I S T JOURNAL OF R & D. (Text in English, Korean) q. Research Institute of Industrial Science & Technology, Central Laboratories, P.O. Box 35, Pohang, Kyoungbuk 790 600, S. Korea. TEL 0562-75-0900. FAX 0562-79-6099. TELEX RISTROK K 54494.

R N I B SCIENTIFIC ENQUIRY. see *HANDICAPPED — Visually Impaired*

500   UK   ISSN 1352-3325
R S E NEWS. 1993. q. free. Royal Society of Edinburgh, 22 George St., Edinburgh EH2 2PQ, Scotland. TEL 0131-225-6057. FAX 0131-220-6889. E-mail: rse@festival.ed.ac.uk. Ed. V.B. Proudfoot. circ. 1,200. **Document type**: newsletter.

500   UK   ISSN 1358-1627
▼ **R S E OCCASIONAL PAPERS**. 1995. irreg. £2.50 per no. Royal Society of Edinburgh, 22 George St., Edinburgh EH2 2PQ, Scotland. TEL 0131-225-6057. FAX 0131-220-6889. E-mail: rse@festival.ed.ac.uk. Ed. F. Selkirk. **Document type**: academic/scholarly publication.
   Description: Series of short publications which address topics of current concern or public interest, and have been written for the non-specialist reader.

500   US
R T P VIEWPOINTS. 1990. q. free. Research Triangle Park, 2 Hanes Dr., Box 12255, Research Triangle Park, NC 27709. TEL 919-549-8181. FAX 919-549-8246. Ed. Jeanne P. Brewer. circ. 3,500 (controlled). (looseleaf format) **Document type**: newsletter.
   Description: Reports events, new products and ongoing research projects in the research facilities and universities of Research Triangle Park.

500   US   ISSN 0033-8222
QC798.D3   CODEN: RACAAT
RADIOCARBON; an international journal of cosmogenic isotopic research. 1959. 3/yr. $85 to individuals; institutions $115; students $42.50 (effective Jan. 1995). University of Arizona, Department of Geosciences, 4717 E. Ft. Lowell Rd., Tucson, AZ 85712. TEL 602-881-0857. FAX 602-881-0554. E-mail: rkra@packrat.aml.arizona.edu. Eds. Rene Kia, Austin Long. adv.; bk.rev.; bibl.; charts; illus.; cum.index: 1950-1965. circ. 600. (back issues avail.) **Indexed**: A.I.C.P., Anthropol.Lit., Art & Archaeol.Tech.Abstr., Bibl.& Ind.Geol., Biol.Abstr., Br.Archaeol.Abstr., Chem.Abstr., Curr.Adv.Ecol.Sci., Deep Sea Res.& Oceanogr.Abstr., Geo.Abstr., Geol.Abstr. **Document type**: academic/scholarly publication, proceedings.
—BLDSC (7234.460000); CASDDS; Faxon; Genuine Article; SWETS; UnCover.
   Description: Covers radiocarbon dating applications atmospheric sciences, archaeology, palynology, geophysics, geochemistry, oceanography, soil sciences, hydrology, and paleoclimatology.
   Refereed Serial

500 016   IR   ISSN 1022-7792
RAHNAMA-YI SIMINARHA-YI IRAN/DIRECTORY OF SCIENTIFIC MEETINGS HELD IN IRAN. (Text in Persian) 1993. q. $30 or exchange basis. Iranian Information & Documentation Center (IRANDOC), 1188 Enqelab Ave., P.O. Box 13185-1371, Tehran, Iran. TEL 98-21-6462548. FAX 98-21-6462254. (back issues avail.) **Document type**: directory.

RAKUNO GAKUEN DAIGAKU KIYO. SHIZEN KAGAKU HEN/RAKUNO GAKUEN UNIVERSITY. JOURNAL: NATURAL SCIENCE. see *AGRICULTURE — Dairying And Dairy Products*

081 500 600   US
RAND RESEARCH PUBLICATIONS. irreg. $595 (foreign $795). Rand Corporation, Publications Department, 1700 Main St., Box 2138, Santa Monica, CA 90407-2138. TEL 310-451-7002. FAX 310-451-6915. E-mail: order@rand.org. **Indexed**: Geo.Abstr., IDA, Med.Care Rev., Popul.Ind.
   Former titles: Rand Corporation's Research Publications; Rand Report Series; Rand Paper Series (ISSN 0092-2803); Rand Corporation. Paper.

500   SP   ISSN 0210-3648
REAL ACADEMIA DE CIENCIAS EXACTAS, FISICAS Y NATURALES. MEMORIA. SERIE DE CIENCIAS FISICAS Y QUIMICAS. 1974. irreg. price varies. Real Academia de Ciencias Exactas, Fisicas y Naturales, Valverde 22, 28004 Madrid, Spain.
—BLDSC (5668.310000).

500   SP   ISSN 0034-0596
Q65   CODEN: RCFNAT
REAL ACADEMIA DE CIENCIAS EXACTAS, FISICAS Y NATURALES. REVISTA. (Text in English, French, German and Spanish) 1904. q. 5000 ptas. (effective 1992). Real Academia de Ciencias Exactas, Fisicas y Naturales, Valverde 22, 28004 Madrid, Spain. adv.; bk.rev. circ. 800. **Indexed**: Biol.Abstr., Chem.Abstr., Deep Sea Res.& Oceanogr.Abstr., Math.R.
—CASDDS; UnCover.

500   SP   ISSN 1132-6247
CODEN: RAGCEP
REAL ACADEMIA GALEGA DE CIENCIAS. REVISTA. (Text in English, Spanish; abstracts in English) 1982. a. 2000 ptas. Real Academia Galega de Ciencias, Rua do Franco 2, 15702 Santiago de Compostela, Spain. TEL 91-582049. FAX 91-582049. Ed. L. Cordero. adv. contact: Ernesto Vieitez. bk.rev. circ. 250. **Document type**: bulletin.
—BLDSC (7802.140000); CASDDS. CCC.
   Formerly (until 1991): Academia Galega de Ciencias. Boletin (ISSN 0212-9051)
   Refereed Serial

500   FR   ISSN 0029-5671
Q2   CODEN: RCCHBV
RECHERCHE. (Text in French; summaries in English) 1960. m. 325 F. Societe d'Editions Scientifiques, 57 rue de Seine, 75006 Paris, France. TEL 43-54-32-84. FAX 46-34-75-08. Ed. Olivier Postel-Vinay; Pub. Stephane Khemis. adv. contact: Simone Sicsic. bk.rev.; charts; illus.; index. circ. 92,000. (reprint service avail. from ISI) **Indexed**: Appl.Mech.Rev., Bio-Contr.News & Info., Biol.Abstr., Chem.Abstr., Curr.Adv.Ecol.Sci., Curr.Biotech.Abstr., Curr.Cont., Dairy Sci.Abstr., Deep Sea Res.& Oceanogr.Abstr., Energy Ind., Energy Info.Abstr., Excerp.Med., Geo.Abstr., Helminthol.Abstr., INSPEC, Int.Lab.Doc., Key to Econ.Sci., Lang.& Lang.Behav.Abstr., Met.Abstr., Pt.de Rep. (1979-), Risk Abstr., World Alum.Abstr. **Document type**: newspaper.
—BLDSC (7305.380000); CASDDS; Ei; Faxon; Genuine Article; SWETS; UMI. CCC.
   Incorporates: Atomes & Nucleus.

REDSTART. see *BIOLOGY — Ornithology*

REGENSBURGER UNIVERSITAETSZEITUNG. see *COLLEGE AND ALUMNI*

500   UK   ISSN 0961-5334
THE REGIONAL REVIEW. 1991. q. £55. Yorkshire and Humberside Regional Research Observatory, University of Leeds, School of Geography, Leeds LS2 9JT, England. TEL 0113-233-3336. FAX 0113-233-3308. E-mail: chris@goeg.leeds.ac.uk. Ed. Christine Leigh. circ. 110.
—BLDSC (7336.711500).
   Description: Designed to offer expert and objective commentary on all important social, economic, political and environmental trends within the region.
   Refereed Serial

500   CR   ISSN 1021-6294
REPERTORIO CIENTIFICO. 1993. 3/yr. Universidad Estatal a Distancia, Escuela de Ciencias Exactas y Naturales, Apdo. 474-2020, San Pedro de Montes de Oca, Costa Rica. TEL 506-53-8978. FAX 506-53-4990. Ed. Marvin Calvo Montoya. **Document type**: academic/scholarly publication.

500 323.4 327   US   ISSN 0895-5999
REPORT ON SCIENCE AND HUMAN RIGHTS. 1978. irreg. free. American Association for the Advancement of Science, Science and Human Rights Program, 1333 H St., N.W., Washington, DC 20005. TEL 202-326-6787. FAX 202-289-4950. Ed. Alexander Allen. bk.rev. circ. 3,000. **Indexed**: HR Rep. **Document type**: newsletter.
   Formerly (until 1987): Clearinghouse Report on Science and Human Rights (ISSN 0734-4171)

500   CH
REPUBLIC OF CHINA. NATIONAL SCIENCE COUNCIL. ANNUAL REPORT. (Text in Chinese) 1963. a. free. National Science Council, 106 Ho-Ping E. Rd. Sec.2, Taipei, Taiwan 106, Republic of China. **Document type**: government publication.

SCIENCES: COMPREHENSIVE WORKS

500　　　　　　CH　ISSN 0250-1651
Q4　　　　　　　　CODEN: KHFKDF
REPUBLIC OF CHINA. NATIONAL SCIENCE COUNCIL MONTHLY. Key Title: Kexue Fazhan. (Text in Chinese) 1973. m. NT.$600($24) National Science Council, 106 Ho-ping E. Rd. Sec. 2, Taipei, Taiwan 106, Republic of China. Indexed: Biol.Abstr., Crop Physiol.Abstr., Field Crop Abstr., Herb.Abstr., Plant Grow.Reg.Abstr. Document type: government publication.
—BLDSC (6033.044000); CASDDS.

500 600　　　　　CH　ISSN 1017-7124
REPUBLIC OF CHINA. NATIONAL SCIENCE COUNCIL. PROCEEDINGS. PART D: MATHEMATICS, SCIENCE, AND TECHNOLOGY EDUCATION. (Text in English) 1991. s-a. NT.$120($8) National Science Council, 106 Ho-ping E. Rd. Sec.2, Taipei, Taiwan 106, Republic of China. TEL 2-737-7294. FAX 2-737-7548. Ed. Chi-Lin Yen. (also avail. in microfiche) Document type: proceedings.
—BLDSC (6769.886000); UnCover.

500　　　　　　US　ISSN 0080-1461
Q180.U5
RESEARCH AND DEVELOPMENT DIRECTORY. (Title varies: Unique 3-in-1 Research & Development Directory) 1959. a. $15. Government Data Publications, Inc., 1155 Connecticut Ave., N.W., Washington, DC 20036. Ed. Siegfried Lobel. Document type: directory.

RESEARCH AND DEVELOPMENT IN JAPAN AWARDED THE OKOCHI MEMORIAL PRIZE. see TECHNOLOGY: COMPREHENSIVE WORKS

500 007　　　　　US　ISSN 0080-1518
AS25
RESEARCH CENTERS DIRECTORY; a guide to approximately 13,000 university-related & other non-profit research organizations. 1962. a. (plus suppl.). $455 (effective July 1993). Gale Research Inc., 835 Penobscot Bldg., Detroit, MI 48226. TEL 313-961-2242; 800-877-4253. FAX 313-961-6083. TELEX 810-221-7086. Ed. Annette Piccirelli. index. circ. 2,500.
●Also available online. Vendor(s): Knight-Ridder, Inc..
—BLDSC (7734.700000).
Description: Lists research centers in the U.S.

500　　　　　　UK　ISSN 0958-2029
　　　　　　　　　CODEN: REEVW
RESEARCH EVALUATION. 1991. 3/yr. £34($61) to individuals; institutions £71 ($126) (effective 1996). Beech Tree Publishing, 10 Watford Close, Guildford, Surrey GU1 2EP, England. TEL 01483-67497. FAX 01483-67497. (Subscr. to: Turpin Distribution Services Ltd., Blackhorse Rd., Letchworth, Herts. SG6 1HN, England. TEL 01462-672555. FAX 01462-480947) Eds. Tony van Raan, Carlos Kruytbosch. bk.rev.; bibl.; index. Document type: academic/scholarly publication.
—BLDSC (7739.920000).
Description: Publishes original research in various sciences.
Refereed Serial

500　　　　　　II　ISSN 0253-9306
　　　　　　　　　CODEN: UIRJAG
RESEARCH JOURNAL: SCIENCE. (Text in English) 1972. q. University of Indore, University House, Indore 452001, Madhya Pradesh, India.
—BLDSC (7741.646000); CASDDS.

600 658　　　　　NE　ISSN 0048-7333
　　　　　　　　　CODEN: REPYBP
RESEARCH POLICY; a journal devoted to research policy, research management and planning. 1972. 8/yr. fl.1525($930) (effective 1996). North-Holland (Subsidiary of: Elsevier Science B.V.), P.O. Box 211, 1000 AE Amsterdam, Netherlands. TEL 31-20-4853911. FAX 31-20-4853598. TELEX 18582 ESPA NL. (Subscr. in N. America to: Elsevier Science Inc., Box 882, Madison Sq. Sta., New York, NY 10159. TEL 212-989-5800. FAX 212-633-3990) Ed.Bd. adv.; bk.rev.; charts; illus.; index. (also avail. in microform from UMI; back issues avail.; reprint service avail. from SWZ) Indexed: ABI Inform., Asian-Pac.Econ.Lit., BPIA, Cont.Pg.Manage., Curr.Cont., Energy Ind., Energy Info.Abstr., Excerpt.Med., High.Educ.Curr.Aware.Bull., Int.Polit.Sci.Abstr., Key to Econ.Sci., SSCI, World Agri.Econ.& Rural Sociol.Abstr. Document type: academic/scholarly publication.
—BLDSC (7755.076000); Ei; Faxon; Genuine Article; SWETS; UMI; UnCover. CCC.
Description: Multidisciplinary journal examining policy problems posed by research and development activities.
Refereed Serial

RESOURCE DIRECTORY OF SCIENTISTS AND ENGINEERS WITH DISABILITIES. see BIOGRAPHY

REVIEWS OF NATIONAL SCIENCE AND TECHNOLOGY POLICY. see TECHNOLOGY: COMPREHENSIVE WORKS

500　　　　　　CL　ISSN 0716-0127
QE1　　　　　　　CODEN: CCTEDC
REVISTA CONTRIBUCIONES CIENTIFICAS Y TECNOLOGICAS. (Text in Spanish; summaries in English) 1971. irreg. $5. Universidad de Santiago de Chile, Departamento de Investigaciones Cientificas y Tecnologicas, Alameda 3363, Casilla 442, Correo 2, Santiago, Chile. FAX 56-2-6813083. illus. circ. 1,000. Indexed: Chem.Abstr.
—BLDSC (3429.017000); CASDDS.

500　　　　　　CU
REVISTA DOCUMENTOS DE CIENCIA Y TECNICA. irreg. exchange basis. Instituto Superior Ciencias Agropecuarias de la Habana (ISCAH), Direccion de Informacion Cientifico-Tecnica, Apdo. Postal 18-19, San Jose de las Lajas, Havana, Cuba.

REVISTA ESPANOLA DE DOCUMENTACION CIENTIFICA. see LIBRARY AND INFORMATION SCIENCES

500 600　　　　　FR　ISSN 0151-4105
Q2
REVUE D'HISTOIRE DES SCIENCES. 1972. q. 440 F. (foreign 520 F.) (effective 1996). (Centre International de Synthese) Presses Universitaires de France, Departement des Revues, 14 av. du Bois-de-l'Epine, B.P.90, 91003 Evry Cedex, France. TEL 1-60-77-82-05. FAX 1-60-79-20-45. TELEX PUF 600 474 F. Ed. Michel Blay. bk.rev.; illus.; index, cum.index. circ. 800. (reprint service avail. from KTO) Indexed: Math.R.
—BLDSC (7919.998000); SWETS. CCC.
Formed by the merger of (1947-1972): Revue d'Histoire des Sciences et de Leurs Applications (ISSN 0048-7996); (1947-1972): Thales (ISSN 0398-7817)
Description: For those interested in the evolution of scientific ideas and the history of scientific techniques.

509　　　　　　BE　ISSN 0035-2160
Q2　　　　　　　　CODEN: RQSCAN
REVUE DES QUESTIONS SCIENTIFIQUES. (Text in French; summaries in English) 1877. 4/yr. 2000 BEF (effective 1995). Societe Scientifique de Bruxelles, Rue de Bruxelles 61, B-5000 Namur, Belgium. TEL 32-81-724464. FAX 32-81-724502. E-mail: dominique.lambert@fundp.ac.be. Ed. C. Courtoy; Pub. D. Lambert. adv.; bk.rev.; abstr.; charts; illus.; index. circ. 700. Indexed: Bibl.& Ind.Geol., Biol.Abstr., Bull.Signal., Chem.Abstr., Excerpt.Med., Math.R., Zoo.Rec., Zoo.Rec. Document type: academic/scholarly publication.
—BLDSC (7945.000000); CASDDS; Faxon.
Description: Covers general scientific topics, with historical and philosophical concerns.
Refereed Serial

378 500　　　　　FR　ISSN 0035-2241
REVUE DES SOCIETES SAVANTES DE HAUTE NORMANDIE. 1956. q. 25 F. J. Liger, Ed. & Pub., 190 rue Beauvoisine, Rouen, France. charts; illus.

REVUE IMPREVUE. see SOCIOLOGY

RIJKSUNIVERSITEIT UTRECHT. WETENSCHAPPELIJK JAAVERSLAG. see EDUCATION — Higher Education

530 540 550　　　JA　ISSN 0287-718X
　　　　　　　　　CODEN: RIGAD6
RIKAGAKKAISHI/JOURNAL OF PHYSICS, CHEMISTRY AND EARTH SCIENCE. (Text in Japanese) 1958. a. 500 Yen for members. Toyama-ken Rikagakkai, Toyama-ken Sogo Kyoiku Senta, Shotakata Toyama-shi, Toyama-ken 930, Japan.
—CASDDS.

500　　　　　　JA　ISSN 0387-6837
Q77　　　　　　　CODEN: RDKSA8
RIKKYO DAIGAKU KENKYU HOKOKU. SHIZEN KAGAKU/ST. PAUL'S REVIEW OF SCIENCE. (Text in English) 1956. a. free. Rikkyo Daigaku, Ippan Kyoikubu - Rikkyo University, Faculty of General Education, 34-1 Nishi-Ikebukuro 3-chome, Toshima-ku, Tokyo 171, Japan.
FAX 03-3986-8784. Indexed: Jap.Per.Ind.

500　　　　　　IT
RIZA SCIENZA; scienza del'uomo. m. L.80000. Edizioni Riza, Via Luigi Anelli, 1, 20122 Milan, Italy. TEL 39-2-58301022. FAX 39-2-58318162. adv.: B&W page L.4500000. circ. 18,000.

ROCKEFELLER FOUNDATION. ANNUAL REPORT. see SOCIAL SERVICES AND WELFARE

500　　　　　　RU　ISSN 0869-5652
AS262　　　　　　CODEN: DANKAS
ROSSIISKAYA AKADEMIYA NAUK. DOKLADY; svodnyi vypusk. Partial English translation: Russian Academy of Sciences. Transactions (Doklady). Earth Science Sections; Russian Academy of Sciences. Doklady. Mathematics. (Text in Russian; contents page in English) 1933. 36/yr. 191.40 Rub. Interperiodica, Ul. Profsoyuznaya 90, 117864 Moscow, Russia. TEL 7-095-3360066. FAX 7-095-3360066. (Dist. by: Mezhdunarodnaya Kniga, ul. Dimitrova D.39, 113095 Moscow, Russia) Ed. V.A. Kabanov. charts; illus.; index. circ. 5,250. (also avail. in microform from BHP; reprint service avail. from KTO) Indexed: Anal.Abstr., Art & Archaeol.Tech.Abstr., Biol.Abstr., Chem.Abstr., Comput.Rev., Cott.& Trop.Fibr.Abstr., Crop Physiol.Abstr., Cyb.Abstr., Deep Sea Res.& Oceanogr.Abstr., Dent.Ind., Field Crop Abstr., Geo.Abstr., GeoRef., Geotech.Abstr., Helminthol.Abstr., Hort.Abstr., INIS Atomind., INSPEC (1968-1992), Maize Abstr., Math.R., Met.Abstr., Meteor.& Geoastrophys.Abstr., Nutr.Abstr., Psychol.Abstr., Soyabean Abstr., Triticale Abstr., Vet.Bull., World Alum.Abstr. Document type: academic/scholarly publication.
—BLDSC (0053.900000); CASDDS; Genuine Article; PADDS. CCC.
Formerly (until no.4, 1992): Akademiya Nauk S.S.S.R. Doklady (ISSN 0002-3264)

500　　　　　　RU　ISSN 0869-5873
AS262　　　　　　CODEN: VANSAC
ROSSIISKAYA AKADEMIYA NAUK. VESTNIK. English edition: Russian Academy of Sciences. Herald (ISSN 1019-3316) 1931. m. $173 (effective 1996). (Rossiskaya Akademiya Nauk, Vestnik) Interperiodica, Ul. Profsoyuznaya 90, Moscow 117864, Russia. TEL 7-095-3360066. FAX 7-095-3360066. (Dist. by: Mezhdunarodnaya Kniga, B. Yakimanka 39, 117049 Moscow, Russia) Ed. I.M. Makarov. bk.rev.; bibl.; charts; illus.; index. circ. 5,125. Indexed: Biol.Abstr., Chem.Abstr., GeoRef., Lang.& Lang.Behav.Abstr., Math.R., Psychol.Abstr.
—BLDSC (0032.754000); CASDDS; Genuine Article. CCC.
Formerly: Akademiya Nauk S.S.S.R. Vestnik (ISSN 0002-3442)

ROYAL BRITISH COLUMBIA MUSEUM MEMOIRS. see MUSEUMS AND ART GALLERIES

SCIENCES: COMPREHENSIVE WORKS

500   **UK**   ISSN 0035-8959
Q41   CODEN: PIGBAI
ROYAL INSTITUTION OF GREAT BRITAIN. PROCEEDINGS. 1851. a. (Royal Institution of Great Britain) Oxford University Press, Walton St., Oxford OX2 6DP, England. TEL 01865-267907. FAX 01865-267773. TELEX 837330-OXPRES-G. E-mail: jnlorders@oup.co.uk. (US subscr. to: Oxford University Press Inc., 2001 Evans Rd., Cary, NC 27513. TEL 919-677-0977. FAX 919-677-1714) **Indexed:** Amer.Hist.& Life, Br.Archaeol.Abstr., Br.Ceram.Abstr., Br.Hum.Ind., Chem.Abstr., Deep Sea Res.& Oceanogr.Abstr., Hist.Abstr., INSPEC. **Document type:** proceedings.
—BLDSC (6798.000000); CASDDS; Faxon; UMI.

500   **UK**
ROYAL INSTITUTION OF GREAT BRITAIN. RECORD. 1799. a. Royal Institution of Great Britain, 21 Albemarle St., London W1X 4BS, England. TEL 01-409-2992. circ. 3,000 (controlled). **Document type:** corporate report.
Formerly: Royal Institution of Great Britain. Annual Report.

500   **UK**
ROYAL INSTITUTION OF GREAT BRITAIN. ROYAL INSTITUTION LECTURES. 1853. 3/yr. Royal Institution of Great Britain, 21 Albemarle St., London W1X 4BS, England. TEL 01-409-2992. circ. 4,000 (controlled). **Document type:** academic/scholarly publication.

500   **NE**   ISSN 0924-8323
Q57   CODEN: PKNSEK
ROYAL NETHERLANDS ACADEMY OF SCIENCES. PROCEEDINGS; biological, chemical, geological, physical and medical sciences. Key Title: Proceedings of the Koninklijke Nederlandse Akademie van Wetenschappen. (Text in English) 1937. 4/yr. fl.370($226) (effective 1996). (Royal Netherlands Academy of Sciences - Koninklijke Nederlandse Akademie van Wetenschappen) North-Holland (Subsidiary of: Elsevier Science B.V.), P.O. Box 211, 1000 AE Amsterdam, Netherlands. TEL 31-20-4853911. FAX 31-20-4853598. TELEX 18582 ESPA NL. (Subscr. in U.S. and Canada to: Elsevier Science Inc., Box 882, Madison Sq. Sta., New York, NY 10159. TEL 212-989-5800. FAX 212-633-3990) charts; illus.; index. circ. 850. (also avail. in microform from PMC; back issues avail.) **Indexed:** Anal.Abstr., Anim.Breed.Abstr., Apic.Abstr., Cadscan, Chem.Abstr., Crop Physiol.Abstr., Curr.Cont., E.I., Excerp.Med., Field Crop Abstr., Forest.Abstr., Forest Prod.Abstr., Helminthol.Abstr., Herb.Abstr., Ind.Vet., INSPEC, Lead Abstr., Math.R., Nutr.Abstr., Rev.Plant Path., Vet.Bull., Weed Abstr., Zincscan. **Document type:** academic/scholarly publication, proceedings.
—BLDSC (6743.950000); CASDDS; Faxon; Genuine Article; SWETS; UnCover. **CCC.**
Formed by the 1990 merger of: Koninklijke Nederlandse Akademie van Wetenschappen. Series C: Biological and Medical Sciences. Proceedings (ISSN 0023-3374); Koninklijke Nederlandse Akademie van Wetenschappen. Series B: Palaeontology, Geology, Physics, and Chemistry. Proceedings (ISSN 0920-2250); Which was formerly (until 1983): Koninklijke Nederlandse Akademie van Wetenschappen. Series B: Physical Sciences. Proceedings (ISSN 0023-3366); Incorporates: Koninklijke Nederlandse Akademie van Wetenschappen. Afdeling Natuurkunde, Verhandelingen. Eerste Reeks (ISSN 0065-5503).
Refereed Serial

500 600   **UK**   ISSN 0260-2725
ROYAL SOCIETY NEWS. 1980. bi-m. Royal Society of London, 6 Carlton House Terrace, London SW1Y 5AG, England. TEL 0171-839-5561. FAX 0171-976-1837. Ed. Sally Nutman. adv. contact: Peter Cooper. circ. 4,000 (controlled). **Document type:** newsletter.

500   **CN**   ISSN 0080-4517
AS42   CODEN: PRYCA4
ROYAL SOCIETY OF CANADA. PROCEEDINGS. (Text in English, French) 1882. a. Can.$15. Royal Society of Canada, P.O. Box 9734, Ottawa, ON K1G 5J4, Canada. TEL 613-991-6990. FAX 613-991-6996. E-mail: admin@resudox.net. Ed. Gerard Hebert. (also avail. in microform from UMI,BHP; microfilm from BHP; reprint service avail. from UMI) **Indexed:** Bibl.& Ind.Geol., Can.Per.Ind., Math.R. **Document type:** proceedings.
—BLDSC (6802.700000); UMI. **CCC.**
Incorporates: Royal Society of Canada. Report of Council (ISSN 1180-4130); **Supersedes in part:** Royal Society of Canada. Proceedings and Transactions (ISSN 0316-4616)

500   **CN**   ISSN 0035-9122
     CODEN: TRSCAI
ROYAL SOCIETY OF CANADA. TRANSACTIONS. (Text and summaries in English, French) 1882. a. Can.$20. Royal Society of Canada, P.O. Box 9734, Ottawa, ON K1G 5J4, Canada. TEL 613-991-6990. FAX 613-991-6996. E-mail: admin@resudox.net. Ed. Gerard Hebert. bibl.; charts; illus.; cum.index: 1882-1957 (in several vols.). circ. 1,800. (also avail. in microform from MML,PMC; reprint service avail. from UMI) **Indexed:** Amer.Hist.& Life, Bibl.& Ind.Geol., Biol.Abstr., Can.B.P.I., Chem.Abstr., Deep Sea Res.& Oceanogr.Abstr., Eng.Ind., Hist.Abstr., Hort.Abstr., INSPEC (1970-), Math.R., Met.Abstr., Petrol.Abstr., Rev.Plant Path. **Document type:** academic/scholarly publication.
—BLDSC (8999.000000); UMI. **CCC.**
Supersedes in part: Royal Society of Canada. Proceedings and Transactions (ISSN 0316-4616)
Refereed Serial

500   **UK**   ISSN 0080-4576
Q41   CODEN: RSEYAX
ROYAL SOCIETY OF EDINBURGH. YEAR BOOK. 1941. a. £10($25) Royal Society of Edinburgh, 22 George St., Edinburgh EH2 2PQ, Scotland. TEL 0131-225-6057. FAX 0131-220-6889. E-mail: rse@festival.ed.ac.uk. Ed. J.H. Knox. circ. 1,500. **Document type:** academic/scholarly publication.

500   **UK**   ISSN 0268-2206
ROYAL SOCIETY OF LONDON. ANNUAL REPORT. 1979. a. Royal Society of London, 6 Carlton House Terrace, London SW1Y 5AG, England. TEL 0171-839-5561. FAX 0171-976-1837. **Document type:** bulletin.

500   **UK**   ISSN 0035-9149
Q41   CODEN: NOREAY
ROYAL SOCIETY OF LONDON. NOTES AND RECORDS. 1938. s-a. £31 in Europe; U.S. and Canada £33. Royal Society of London, 6 Carlton House Terrace, London SW1Y 5AG, England. TEL 0171-839-5561. FAX 0171-976-1837. Ed. D.G. King-Hele. adv. contact: Peter Cooper. bk.rev.; bibl.; illus.; index, cum.index: vols.1-20 (1938-1965). circ. 1,434. (reprint service avail. from ISI) **Indexed:** Amer.Hist.& Life, Arts & Hum.Cit.Ind., Biol.Abstr., Br.Archaeol.Abstr., Curr.Cont., Hist.Abstr., Math.R. **Document type:** academic/scholarly publication.
—BLDSC (6165.075000); Faxon; Genuine Article; UnCover.
Description: Original papers on the history of science, medicine and technology as related to the Royal Society.
Refereed Serial

ROYAL SOCIETY OF LONDON. PROCEEDINGS. SERIES A. MATHEMATICAL AND PHYSICAL SCIENCES. see MATHEMATICS

506   **UK**   ISSN 0080-4673
ROYAL SOCIETY OF LONDON. YEAR BOOK. 1898. a. £17 in Europe; U.S. and Canada £18. Royal Society of London, 6 Carlton House Terrace, London SW1Y 5AG, England. TEL 0171-839-5561. FAX 0171-976-1837. adv. contact: Peter Cooper. circ. 1,521. (reprint service avail. from ISI) **Document type:** directory.
—**CCC.**

500   **AT**   ISSN 0035-9173
     CODEN: JPRSA5
ROYAL SOCIETY OF NEW SOUTH WALES. JOURNAL AND PROCEEDINGS. 1867. q. Aus.$53 (effective 1996). Royal Society of New South Wales, P.O. Box 1525, Macquarie Centre, N.S.W. 2113, Australia. TEL 02-887-4448. Ed. Mrs. M. Krysko. bk.rev.; bibl.charts; illus.; cum.index: 1862-1865, 1867-1916. circ. 900. (also avail. in microform from PMC) **Indexed:** AESIS, Bibl.& Ind.Geol., Biol.Abstr., Chem.Abstr., Deep Sea Res.& Oceanogr.Abstr., Geol.Abstr., INSPEC, Math.R., Rev.Plant Path. **Document type:** academic/scholarly publication, proceedings, monographic series.
—CASDDS; UnCover. **CCC.**
Refereed Serial

500 500   **NZ**   ISSN 0370-6559
     CODEN: RNZBAY
ROYAL SOCIETY OF NEW ZEALAND. BULLETIN SERIES. 1910. irreg. (Royal Society of New Zealand) S I R Publishing, P.O. Box 399, Wellington, New Zealand. TEL 64-4-472-7421. FAX 64-4-473-1841. **Indexed:** Deep Sea Res.& Oceanogr.Abstr. **Document type:** academic/scholarly publication.
—BLDSC (2701.000000); CASDDS. **CCC.**
Formerly: Royal Society of New Zealand. Bulletin.

500   **NZ**   ISSN 0303-6758
Q1   CODEN: JRNZAK
ROYAL SOCIETY OF NEW ZEALAND. JOURNAL. 1971. q. NZ.$170($140) (Royal Society of New Zealand) S I R Publishing, 11 Turnbull St., P.O. Box 399, Wellington, New Zealand. TEL 64-4-472-7421. FAX 64-4-473-1841. Ed. Carolyn M. King. bibl.; charts; illus.; maps, cum.index: 1869-1971, 1976, 1981. circ. 300. **Indexed:** Bibl.& Ind.Geol., Biol.Abstr., Chem.Abstr., Curr.Adv.Ecol.Sci., Curr.Cont., Deep Sea Res.& Oceanogr.Abstr., Environ.Abstr., Field Crop Abstr., Forest.Abstr., Forest Prod.Abstr., Geo.Abstr., Geol.Abstr., Helminthol.Abstr., INIS Atomind., Nutr.Abstr., Petrol.Abstr., Rev.Appl.Entomol., Rev.Plant Path., Risk Abstr., So.Pac.Per.Ind., Soils & Fert., SSCI, Zoo.Rec.
—BLDSC (4864.630000); CASDDS; Faxon; Genuine Article; UnCover. **CCC.**
Supersedes: Royal Society of New Zealand. Transactions (ISSN 0035-9181)

500   **NZ**   ISSN 0111-3895
     CODEN: MSRZEG
ROYAL SOCIETY OF NEW ZEALAND. MISCELLANEOUS SERIES. irreg. (Royal Society of New Zealand) S I R Publishing, 11 Turnbull St., P.O. Box 399, Wellington, New Zealand. TEL 64-4-472-7421. FAX 64-4-473-1841. **Document type:** monographic series.
—BLDSC (5827.500000).

506   **AT**   ISSN 0080-469X
Q93   CODEN: PRSQAG
ROYAL SOCIETY OF QUEENSLAND. PROCEEDINGS. 1884. s-a. Aus.$25 (effective 1993). Royal Society of Queensland, P.O. Box 21, St. Lucia, Queensland 4067, Australia. TEL 07-870-1697. E-mail: c.king@qut.edu.au. Ed. C.R. King. circ. 640. **Indexed:** AESIS, Bibl.& Ind.Geol., Curr.Adv.Ecol.Sci., Deep Sea Res.& Oceanogr.Abstr., Field Crop Abstr., Forest.Abstr., Forest Prod.Abstr., Herb.Abstr., Hort.Abstr., Nutr.Abstr., Rev.Appl.Entomol., Rev.Plant Path., Sel.Water Res.Abstr., Soils & Fert., Sport Fish.Abstr., Wild.Rev., Zoo.Rec. **Document type:** academic/scholarly publication, proceedings.
—BLDSC (6806.000000); UnCover.
Description: Publishes papers in the natural sciences with reference to Australia, and Queensland in particular.
Refereed Serial

500   SA   ISSN 0035-919X
Q85   CODEN: TRSAAC
ROYAL SOCIETY OF SOUTH AFRICA. TRANSACTIONS. (Text in English) 1877. irreg., approx. 2/yr. R.100($42.50) per no. (effective 1993). Royal Society of South Africa, P.D. Hahn Building, P.O. Box 594, Cape Town 8000, South Africa. TEL 27-21-650-2543. FAX 27-21-650-3726. TELEX 521439 SA. E-mail: roysoc@psipsy.uct.ac.za. Ed. J.R.E. Lutjeharms. bibl.; charts; illus.; cum.index: 1878-1909, 1909-1955, 1956-1985. circ. 800. (also avail. in microfilm from UMI) **Indexed:** Biol.Abstr., Chem.Abstr., Curr.Adv.Ecol.Sci., Curr.Cont., Deep Sea Res.& Oceanogr.Abstr., Excerp.Med., Geo.Abstr., Ind.S.A.Per., INSPEC, Math.R., S.A.Waterabstr., Sel.Water Res.Abstr., W.R.C.Inf. **Document type:** academic/scholarly publication.
—BLDSC (9001.000000); Faxon; Genuine Article; UMI; UnCover.
Refereed Serial

500   AT   ISSN 0085-5812
ROYAL SOCIETY OF SOUTH AUSTRALIA. TRANSACTIONS. 1878. a. Aus.$40. Royal Society of South Australia Inc., S.A. Museum, North Terrace, Adelaide, S.A. 5000, Australia. TEL 61-8-223-5360. Ed. J. Bird. index. circ. 800. **Indexed:** Abstr.Anthropol., AESIS, Anim.Behav.Abstr., Aqua.Sci.& Fish.Abstr., Biol.Abstr., Curr.Adv.Ecol.Sci., Deep Sea Res.& Oceanogr.Abstr., Ecol.Abstr., Entomol.Abstr., Field Crop Abstr., GeoRef., Herb.Abstr., Microbiol.Abstr., Mineral.Abstr., Rev.Plant Path., Soils & Fert., Zoo.Rec. **Document type:** academic/scholarly publication.
—UnCover.
Description: Publishes original papers in natural sciences.

506   AT   ISSN 0080-4703
Q93   CODEN: PPRTA6
ROYAL SOCIETY OF TASMANIA, HOBART. PAPERS AND PROCEEDINGS. 1848. a. price varies. Royal Society of Tasmania, Box 1166M, Hobart, Tas. 7001, Australia. TEL 61-02-350777. FAX 61-02-347139. Ed. M.R. Banks. circ. 700 (paid). **Indexed:** AESIS, Bibl.& Ind.Geol., Biol.Abstr., Curr.Adv.Ecol.Sci., Deep Sea Res.& Oceanogr.Abstr., Geol.Abstr., Math.R., VITIS. **Document type:** academic/scholarly publication.
—BLDSC (6396.000000); UnCover.
Refereed Serial

500   AT   ISSN 0035-9211
Q93   CODEN: PRSVAV
ROYAL SOCIETY OF VICTORIA. PROCEEDINGS. 1860. s-a. Aus.$65. Royal Society of Victoria, 8 La Trobe St., Melbourne, Vic. 3000, Australia. TEL 61-3-663-5259. FAX 61-3-663-2301. Ed. R. Baird. charts; illus.; index. circ. 1,000. **Indexed:** AESIS, Agroforest.Abstr., Bibl.& Ind.Geol., Biol.Abstr., Chem.Abstr., Curr.Adv.Ecol.Sci., Deep Sea Res.& Oceanogr.Abstr., Field Crop Abstr., Forest.Abstr., Forest Prod.Abstr., Geo.Abstr., Geol.Abstr., Herb.Abstr., INSPEC, Rev.Appl.Entomol., Rev.Plant Path., Soils & Fert. **Document type:** academic/scholarly publication.
—BLDSC (6807.000000); UnCover. CCC.

500   AT   ISSN 0035-922X
Q93   CODEN: JRSUAU
ROYAL SOCIETY OF WESTERN AUSTRALIA. JOURNAL. 1914. q. Aus.$60 (effective 1995). Royal Society of Western Australia, Inc., c/o Western Australian Museum, Perth, W.A. 6000, Australia. TEL 61-9-3802235. FAX 61-9-3801029. E-mail: pwithers@uniwa.uwa.edu.au. Ed. P.C. Withers. charts; illus.; index. circ. 700. **Indexed:** AESIS, Aus.Sci.Ind., Bibl.& Ind.Geol., Biol.Abstr., Chem.Abstr., Curr.Adv.Ecol.Sci., Deep Sea Res.& Oceanogr.Abstr., Field Crop Abstr., Geo.Abstr., Geol.Abstr., Herb.Abstr., Rev.Plant Path., Sport Fish.Abstr., Wild.Rev., Zoo.Rec. **Document type:** academic/scholarly publication.
—BLDSC (4865.000000); CASDDS; Faxon; UnCover.
Description: Promotes science in Western Australia and counteracts the effects of specialization.
Refereed Serial

500   CC   ISSN 1001-8409
RUAN KEXUE/SOFT SCIENCE. (Text in Chinese; summaries in Chinese, English) 1987. q. Y10. Sichuan Keji Cujin Fazhan Yanjiu Zhongxin - Sichuan Provincial Research Center of Science and Technology Promoting Development, 11, 4th Section Renmin Nanlu, 7th Fl., Chengdu, Sichuan 610041, People's Republic of China. TEL 581835. FAX 028-582972. Ed. Xu Wenbin. adv. contact: Jinghui Zhang. circ. 3,500. **Document type:** academic/scholarly publication.
Description: Covers the applications of science and technology to Chinese economics and agriculture.

500   RU   ISSN 1019-3316
Q60   CODEN: HRUSEG
RUSSIAN ACADEMY OF SCIENCES. HERALD. Russian edition: Rossiiskaya Akademiya Nauk. Vestnik (ISSN 0869-5873) bi-m. $712 in U.S. & Canada (elsewhere $890). Interperiodica, Ul. Profsoyuznaya 90, Moscow 117864, Russia. TEL 7-095-3360066. FAX 7-095-23360666. (Subscr. to: Interperiodica, Box 1831, Birmingham, AL 35201-1831. TEL 205-995-1567. FAX 205-995-1588) **Document type:** academic/scholarly publication.
—BLDSC (0412.076000).

500 600   PH
S & T POST. (Science and Technology) m. free. Science and Technology Information Institute, Department of Science and Technology, P.O. Box 3596, Manila, Philippines. TEL 822-0954.
Description: Official publication of the Department of Science and Technology.

500   AG   ISSN 0325-6146
S C A R BOLETIN. English edition: S C A R Bulletin (ISSN 0036-1097) 1959. 3/yr. (Scientific Committee on Antarctic Research) Direccion Nacional del Antartico, Instituto Antartico Argentino, Cerrito 1248, 1010 Buenos Aires, Argentina. TEL 541-812-1689. FAX 541-812-2039. (Published in English by: Scott Polar Research Institute, Lensfield Rd., Cambridge, England) (Co-sponsor: International Council of Scientific Unions) abstr.; bibl.; charts; illus.; stat.; index. circ. 750. **Document type:** bulletin.

S I I A S NEWS. (Staten Island Institute of Arts and Sciences) see HUMANITIES: COMPREHENSIVE WORKS

500 610   US   ISSN 0885-1530
S I R S SCIENCE. (Consists of: Applied Science (ISSN 0885-1549); Earth Science (ISSN 0885-1565); Life Science (ISSN 0885-1573); Medical Science (ISSN 0085-1557); Physical Science (ISSN 0085-1581)) 1985. a. $350 for 5-vol. set. Social Issues Resources Series, Box 2348, Boca Raton, FL 33427-2348. TEL 407-994-0079; 800-232-7477. FAX 407-994-4704. (looseleaf format; also avail. in microfiche)
Description: Reprints articles on topics in the physical and medical sciences dealing with important social issues.

S S M A CLASSROOM ACTIVITIES MONOGRAPH SERIES. (School Science and Mathematics Association) see EDUCATION — Teaching Methods And Curriculum

S S M A TOPICS FOR TEACHERS MONOGRAPH SERIES. (School Science and Mathematics Association) see EDUCATION — Teaching Methods And Curriculum

S S M ARRT. (School Science and Mathematics Association) see EDUCATION — Teaching Methods And Curriculum

S T A: ITS ROLES AND ACTIVITIES. (Science and Technology Agency) see TECHNOLOGY: COMPREHENSIVE WORKS

S U T BULLETIN. (Science University of Tokyo) see TECHNOLOGY: COMPREHENSIVE WORKS

991.1 570   MY   ISSN 0036-2131
DS646.33
SABAH SOCIETY. JOURNAL. 1961. irreg., vol.8, no.4, 1988. M.$20 per no. Sabah Society - Pertubuhan Sabah, P.O. Box 10547, 88806 Kota Kinabalu, Sabah, Malaysia. Ed. Patricia Regis. bk.rev. circ. 500. (tabloid format) **Indexed:** Anthropol.Lit., Bibl.Ling., E.I.

500   II   ISSN 0256-2499
Q73   CODEN: SAPSER
SADHANA; academy proceedings in engineering sciences. (Text in English) 1978. 6/yr. Rs.75($100) (effective 1995). Indian Academy of Sciences, C.V. Raman Avenue, P.B. No. 8005, Bangalore 560 080, India. TEL 91-80-3342546. FAX 91-80-3346094. TELEX 0845-2178-ACAD-IN. Ed. N. Viswanadham. circ. 800. (also avail. in microform from UMI; reprint service avail. from ISI, UMI) **Indexed:** Chem.Abstr., Curr.Cont., Energy Ind., Energy Info.Abstr., Fluidex, INSPEC, Int.Aerosp.Abstr. **Document type:** academic/scholarly publication.
—BLDSC (8062.798000); CASDDS; Ei.
Former titles (until 1984): Indian Academy of Sciences. Proceedings. Engineering Sciences (ISSN 0253-4096); And (until 1979): Indian Academy of Sciences. Proceedings. Section C. Engineering Sciences (ISSN 0250-5444).
Description: Wide-ranging, original papers and reviews of interest to engineering scientists.

500 069   JA
SADO HAKUBUTSUKAN KENKYU HOKOKU/PUBLICATIONS FROM THE SADO MUSEUM. (Text in English and Japanese; summaries in English) 1957. irreg. Sado Hakubutsukan - Sado Museum, Nakae, Yawata, Sawada-cho, Sado-gun, Niigata-ken 952-13, Japan.
Description: Contains research reports.

500   GW   ISSN 0080-5262
AS182
SAECHSISCHE AKADEMIE DER WISSENSCHAFTEN, LEIPZIG. JAHRBUCH. 1955 (covering 1949-53). irreg., latest 1992 (covering 1989-90). price varies. Akademie Verlag GmbH, Muehlenstr. 33-34, 13187 Berlin, Germany. TEL 030-47889348. FAX 030-47889357. Ed. Gerald Wiemers. **Indexed:** Amer.Hist.& Life, Hist.Abstr. **Document type:** bulletin.

500 510   GW   ISSN 0365-6470
                    CODEN: ASAWAO
SAECHSISCHE AKADEMIE DER WISSENSCHAFTEN, LEIPZIG. MATHEMATISCH-NATURWISSENSCHAFTLICHE KLASSE. ABHANDLUNGEN. 1896. irreg., vol.58, no.4, 1995. price varies. Akademie Verlag GmbH, Muehlenstr. 33-34, 13187 Berlin, Germany. TEL 030-47889348. FAX 030-47889357. **Indexed:** Math.R. **Document type:** monographic series.
—CASDDS.

510 500   GW   ISSN 0371-327X
AS182   CODEN: SSWMAU
SAECHSISCHE AKADEMIE DER WISSENSCHAFTEN, LEIPZIG. MATHEMATISCH-NATURWISSENSCHAFTLICHE KLASSE. SITZUNGSBERICHTE. 1896. irreg., vol.125, no.5, 1995. price varies. Akademie Verlag GmbH, Muehlenstr. 33-34, 13187 Berlin, Germany. TEL 030-47889348. FAX 030-47889357. **Indexed:** Bibl.& Ind.Geol. **Document type:** proceedings.
—CASDDS.

SAFETY IS ELEMENTARY. see PUBLIC HEALTH AND SAFETY

500   MY   ISSN 0126-6039
Q1   CODEN: SAMADP
SAINS MALAYSIANA: JERNAL SAINS ALAM SEMULA; jadi. (Text in English, Malay) 1972. q. $60. Penerbit Universiti Kebangsaan Malaysia, 43600 UKM Bangi Selangor, Malaysia. TEL 8250001. Ed. H.D. Tjia. charts; index. circ. 5,000. **Indexed:** Chem.Abstr., GeoRef.
—BLDSC (5021.247000); CASDDS.
Description: Explores earth sciences, physical and applied sciences and quantitative studies.

500 600   PK
SA'INSU. Back cover title: Monthly Science Magazine. (Text in Sindhi) 1971. m. Rs.8. University of Sind, Institute of Sindhology, Jamshoro, Hyderabad 6, Pakistan.

SAINT LOUIS UNIVERSITY RESEARCH JOURNAL; an interdisciplinary journal in the sciences and the humanities. see HUMANITIES: COMPREHENSIVE WORKS

SCIENCES: COMPREHENSIVE WORKS

500   JA   ISSN 0581-3662
SAITAMA DAIGAKU KIYO. SHIZEN KAGAKU HEN/SAITAMA UNIVERSITY. JOURNAL. NATURAL SCIENCE. (Text in Japanese; summaries in English) 1965. a. Saitama Daigaku, Kyoyobu - Saitama University, College of Liberal Arts, 255 Shimo-Okubo, Urawa-shi, Saitama-ken 338, Japan. **Indexed:** INIS Atomind., Jap.Per.Ind.
—BLDSC (4869.050000).

500.9 069   JA   ISSN 0288-5611
SAITAMA-KENRITSU SHIZENSHI HAKUBUTSUKAN KENKYU HOKOKU/SAITAMA MUSEUM OF NATURAL HISTORY. BULLETIN. (Text and summaries in English, Japanese) 1983. a. Saitama-kenritsu Shizenshi Hakubutsukan - Saitama Museum of Natural History, 1417-1 Nagatoro, Nagatoro-machi, Chichibu-gun, Saitama-ken 369-13, Japan.
TEL 81-0494-66-0404. FAX 81-0494-69-1002.

500.9   JA   ISSN 0375-1821
                CODEN: SHMRBL
SAITO HO-ON KAI MUSEUM OF NATURAL HISTORY. RESEARCH BULLETIN. (Text in English) 1934. a. free. Saito Ho-on Kai - Saito Gratitude Foundation, 20-2, Hon-cho 2-chome, Aoba-ku, Sendai 980, Japan. TEL 022-262-5506. FAX 022-262-5508. **Document type:** academic/scholarly publication.

SALARIES OF SCIENTISTS, ENGINEERS AND TECHNICIANS; a summary of salary surveys. see *OCCUPATIONS AND CAREERS*

500   IS   ISSN 0792-1896
SAMUEL NEAMAN INSTITUTE FOR ADVANCED STUDIES IN SCIENCE AND TECHNOLOGY. ANNUAL REPORT. (Text in English) 1978. a. free. Technion - Israel Institute of Technology, Samuel Neaman Institute for Advanced Studies in Science and Technology, Technion City, Haifa 32000, Israel.
TEL 972-4-292329. FAX 972-4-231889. Ed. David Kohn. bk.rev. circ. 2,000. **Document type:** bulletin.
Description: Includes the director's report, current projects, publications, staff and workshops.

508   US   ISSN 1059-8707
QH1   CODEN: PSDHER
SAN DIEGO SOCIETY OF NATURAL HISTORY. PROCEEDINGS. 1990. irreg. price varies. San Diego Society of Natural History, San Diego Natural History Museum Library, Box 1390, San Diego, CA 92112. TEL 619-232-3821. FAX 619-232-0248. E-mail: libsdnhm@class.org. Ed. Philip A. Unitt. index.
Indexed: Biol.Abstr., Deep Sea Res.& Oceanogr.Abstr., Ecol.Abstr., Geo.Abstr., GeoRef., Sel.Water Res.Abstr., Sport Fish.Abstr., Wild.Rev., Zoo.Rec. **Document type:** academic/scholarly publication, proceedings.
—UnCover.
Formed by the merger of (1931-1990): San Diego Society of Natural History. Memoirs (ISSN 0080-5920); (1905-1989): San Diego Society of Natural History. Transactions (ISSN 0080-5947); Which incorporates: San Diego Society of Natural History. Occasional Papers (ISSN 0080-5939)
Description: Publishes papers in the biological and geological sciences.
Refereed Serial

SAN JOSE STUDIES. see *HUMANITIES: COMPREHENSIVE WORKS*

500   SZ
SANKT GALLISCHE NATURWISSENSCHAFTLICHE GESELLSCHAFT. BERICHTE. 1860. irreg., vol.87, 1994. $30. Sankt Gallische Naturwissenschaftliche Gesellschaft, Myrtenstr. 9, CH-9010 St. Gallen, Switzerland. TEL 071-253470. Ed. Oskar Keller. circ. 1,000. **Document type:** academic/scholarly publication.
Formerly: Sankt Gallische Naturwissenschaftliche Gesellschaft. Bericht ueber die Taetigkeit (ISSN 0080-6056)

SANTA BARBARA MUSEUM OF NATURAL HISTORY. MUSEUM BULLETIN. see *MUSEUMS AND ART GALLERIES*

500   IT   ISSN 0036-4681
SAPERE. 1935; N.S. 1974; N.S. 1983. m. L.60000 (foreign L.90000) (effective 1994). Edizioni Dedalo s.r.l., Casella Postale 362, 70100 Bari, Italy.
TEL 080-5311413. FAX 080-5311414. (Edit. addr.: Corso Trieste 95, 00188 Rome, Italy. TEL 06-8840586) Dir. Carlo Bernardini. adv.: page L.2200000. bk.rev.; bibl.; charts; illus.; tr.lit. circ. 48,000.
Description: Deals with everything the public should know: energy, armaments, nutrition, medicine, didactics, environment, etc.

SAPPORO IKA DAIGAKU JINBUN SHIZEN KAGAKU KIYO/SAPPORO MEDICAL COLLEGE. JOURNAL OF LIBERAL ARTS AND SCIENCES. see *HUMANITIES: COMPREHENSIVE WORKS*

500   JA   ISSN 0914-2401
SAPPORO-SHI SEISHONEN KAGAKUKAN KIYO. 1984. a. free. Sapporo-shi Seishonen Kagakukan - Sapporo Science Center, 2-20 Atsubetsu chuo 1-jo 5-chome, Atsubetsu-ku, Sapporo-shi, Hokkaido 004, Japan. FAX 011-894-5445. circ. 1,000.

500   CN   ISSN 0080-6587
T177.C2
SASKATCHEWAN RESEARCH COUNCIL. ANNUAL REPORT. 1947. a. free. Saskatchewan Research Council, 15 Innovation Blvd., Saskatoon, Sask. S7N 2X8, Canada. TEL 306-933-6670.
FAX 306-933-7896. TELEX SARECO-074-2484. Ed. Rick Tofani. circ. 200,000 (controlled). **Indexed:** Bibl.& Ind.Geol. **Document type:** corporate report, newsletter.

SCANDINAVIAN JOURNAL OF MEDICINE & SCIENCE IN SPORTS. see *MEDICAL SCIENCES — Sports Medicine*

700 500 390   GW   ISSN 0036-6153
DD491.S4
SCHLESIEN; arts, science, folklore. 1956. q. DM.30. (Verein der Freunde und Foerderer der Stiftung Kulturwerk Schlesien e.V.) Verlag Nuernberger Presse, Marienplatz 1, 90402 Nuernberg, Germany. TEL 0931-53696. Ed. Eberhard Guenter Schulz. bk.rev.; bibl.; illus. circ. 1,100. **Indexed:** RILM.
—BLDSC (8090.620000).

507   II   ISSN 0036-679X
SCHOOL SCIENCE; quarterly journal for secondary schools. (Text in English) 1962. q. Rs.12($11.60) National Council of Educational Research and Training, Department of Education in Science and Mathematics, Publication Department, Sri Aurbindo Marg, New Delhi 110016, India. Ed. R.P. Singhami. adv.; bk.rev.; illus.; index. circ. 1,000.

SCHOOL SCIENCE AND MATHEMATICS; journal for all science and mathematical teachers. see *EDUCATION*

507 370   UK   ISSN 0036-6811
Q1   CODEN: SSCRAD
SCHOOL SCIENCE REVIEW. 1919. q. £54 (overseas £76) (effective 1995). Association for Science Education, College Ln., Hatfield, Herts. AL10 9AA, England. TEL 01707-237411.
FAX 01707-266532. Ed. Andrew Bishop. adv. contact: Brenda Dearing. bk.rev.; charts; illus.; cum.index: vols.48-57 (1967-1977). circ. 19,000. (also avail. in microform from UMI; reprint service avail. from UMI) **Indexed:** C.I.J.E., Chem.Abstr., Cont.Pg.Educ., Dairy Sci.Abstr., Educ.Tech.Abstr., Environ.Abstr., Excerp.Med., High.Educ.Curr.Aware.Bull., Stud.Wom.Abstr., Tech.Educ.Abstr. **Document type:** academic/scholarly publication.
—BLDSC (8093.000000); CASDDS; CIS; Faxon; SWETS; UMI; UnCover.

500.9   SZ   ISSN 0036-7427
SCHWEIZER NATURSCHUTZ/PROTECTION DE LA NATURE. (Text in French and German) 1935. 8/yr. membership. Schweizerischer Bund fuer Naturschutz, Postfach, CH-4020 Basel, Switzerland. TEL 061-3179191. FAX 061-3179266. Ed. Juerg Kaenzig. adv.: B&W page 3090 SFr., color page 4620 SFr.; trim 148 x 219; adv. contact: Markus Degen. bk.rev.; illus.; index. circ. 104,950. **Indexed:** Biol.Abstr., Key Word Ind.Wildl.Res. **Document type:** newsletter.

500   SZ   ISSN 1022-3495
SCHWEIZERISCHE AKADEMIE DER NATURWISSENSCHAFTEN. DENKSCHRIFTEN. (Text in English, French and German) 1829. irreg. price varies. (Schweizerische Akademie der Naturwissenschaften) Birkhaeuser Verlag, P.O. Box 133, CH-4010 Basel, Switzerland.
TEL 061-2717400. FAX 061-2717666. (Dist. in N. America by: Springer-Verlag, Mercedes Distribution Center, 160 Imlay St., Brrooklyn, NY 11231, USA) **Indexed:** Bibl.& Ind.Geol., Biol.Abstr., Deep Sea Res.& Oceanogr.Abstr. **Document type:** academic/scholarly publication.
Formerly: Schweizerische Naturforschende Gesellschaft. Denkschriften.

500   SZ
SCHWEIZERISCHER WISSENSCHAFTSRAT. JAHRESBERICHT/CONSEIL SUISSE DE LA SCIENCE. RAPPORT ANNUEL. (Text in French, German) 1965. a. free. Schweizerischer Wissenschaftsrat, Inselgasse 1, CH-3003 Bern, Switzerland. TEL 031-3229666. FAX 031-3228070. **Document type:** government publication.

500   US   ISSN 0036-8075
Q1   CODEN: SCIEAS
SCIENCE. 1880. w. (4 vols./yr.) $228 to institutions; members $97. American Association for the Advancement of Science, 1333 H St., N.W., Washington, DC 20005. TEL 202-326-6417. (Subscr. to: Box 2033, Marion, OH 43305-2033) Ed. Daniel Koshland. adv.: B&W page $6190, color page $7590. bk.rev.; abstr.; bibl.; illus.; tr.lit. circ. 165,000. (also avail. in microform from UMI; PMC; reprint service avail. from UMI) **Indexed:** A.I.Abstr., A.S.& T.Ind., ABC, Abstr.Anthropol., Abstr.Bull.Inst.Pap.Chem., Abstr.J.Earthq.Eng., Acad.Ind., Acid Pre.Dig., AESIS, Anal.Abstr., Anim.Breed.Abstr., Anthropol.Lit., API Abstr., Art & Archaeol.Tech.Abstr., Biol.Abstr., Biol.Dig., Biostat., Biotech.Abstr., Bk.Rev.Dig., Bk.Rev.Ind. (1965-), Br.Archaeol.Abstr., C.I.J.E., Ceram.Abstr., Chem.Abstr., Chem.Infd., Child.Bk.Rev.Ind. (1965-), Child Devel.Abstr., Comput.Rev., Curr.Adv.Ecol.Sci., Curr.Biotech.Abstr., Curr.Cont., Curr.Lit.Fam.Plan., Cyb.Abstr., Dairy Sci.Abstr., Dent.Ind., Diar.Dis.Res., Ecol.Abstr., Energy Rev., Environ.Abstr., Excerp.Med., Field Crop Abstr., Food Sci.& Tech.Abstr., Forest.Abstr., Forest Prod.Abstr., Fut.Surv., Gen.Sci.Ind., Geo.Abstr., Geol.Abstr., Geotech.Abstr., Helminthol Abstr., High.Educ.Curr.Aware.Bull., Hort.Abstr., IDA, Ind.Chem., Ind.Med., Ind.Sci.Rev., Ind.Vet., INSPEC (1968-), Int.Aerosp.Abstr., Lab.Haz.Bull., Lang.& Lang.Behav.Abstr., M.L.A., Mag.Ind., Mass Spectr.Bull., Math.R., Med.Care Rev., Met.Abstr., Meteor.& Geoastrophys.Abstr., Mid.East: Abstr.& Ind., Nutr.Abstr., Ocean.Abstr., Peace Res.Abstr., Plant Grow.Reg.Abstr., PMR, Pollut.Abstr., Popul.Ind., Poult.Abstr., Protozool.Abstr., Psychol.Abstr. (1925-), R.G., Repindex, Rev.Med.& Vet.Mycol., Rev.Plant Path., Risk Abstr., Rural Recreat.Tour.Abstr., Sci.Abstr., Sci.Cit.Ind., Sel.Water Res.Abstr., So.Pac.Per.Ind., Sociol.Abstr., Soils & Fert., Sport Fish.Abstr., Sugar Ind.Abstr., Tel.Abstr., Telegen, Trop.Dis.Bull.,Bull., Vet.Bull., W.R.C.Inf., Weed Abstr., Wild.Rev., World Alum.Abstr., Zoo.Rec. **Document type:** academic/scholarly publication.
●Also available online. Vendor(s): Ovid Technologies (SCIE), University Microfilms International.
—BLDSC (8130.000000); CASDDS; Ei; EMDOCS; Faxon; Genuine Article; PADDS; SWETS; UMI; UnCover. **CCC.**
Description: News of recent international developments and research in all fields of science. Publishes original research results, reviews and short features.
Refereed Serial

500 001.3   UA
SCIENCE AND ARTS - RESEARCH STUDIES/ULUM WA FUNUN - DIRASAT WA BUHUTH. 1989. q. Helwan University, 95 Sharia Ahmed Ouraby, Mohandiseen, Cairo, Egypt. TEL 02-344055.

SCIENCES: COMPREHENSIVE WORKS

507 372   US   ISSN 0036-8148
LB1585
SCIENCE AND CHILDREN. 1963. 8/yr. $52. National Science Teachers Association, 1840 Wilson Blvd., Arlington, VA 22201. Ed. Lolie Gwynn. adv.; bk.rev.; film rev.; charts; illus.; index. circ. 24,000. (also avail. in microfilm from UMI; reprint service avail.) **Indexed:** C.I.J.E., Cont.Pg.Educ., Educ.Ind., Except.Child Educ.Abstr., Media Rev.Dig., Wom.Stud.Abstr. **Document type:** academic/scholarly publication.
—BLDSC (8131.800000); Faxon; SWETS; UMI; UnCover.
 Description: Presents ideas and activities for science educators from preschool through middle school level.

500   II   ISSN 0036-8156
QH1   CODEN: SCINAL
SCIENCE AND CULTURE; a monthly journal of natural and cultural sciences. (Text in English) 1935. m. Rs.100($30) (foreign Rs.100). Indian Science News Association, 92 Acharya Prafulla Chandra Rd., Calcutta 700 009, India. TEL 35-2224. Ed.Bd. adv.; bk.rev.; charts; illus. circ. 2,000. **Indexed:** Bibl.& Ind.Geol., Biol.Abstr., Chem.Abstr., Excerp.Med., Field Crop Abstr., Food Sci.& Tech.Abstr., Herb.Abstr., Hort.Abstr., Ind.Vet., INSPEC, Plant Breed.Abstr., Rev.Plant Path., Rice Abstr., Soils & Fert., Vet.Bull., Weed Abstr.
—BLDSC (8132.000000); CASDDS; Faxon; UnCover.

501   NE   ISSN 0926-7220
Q181.A1
SCIENCE & EDUCATION; contributions from history, philosophy & sociology of science and mathematics. (Text in English) 1992. q. fl.368 to institutions; $236 to institutions in U.S. (effective 1996). (International History, Philosophy and Science Teaching Group) Kluwer Academic Publishers, Postbus 17, 3300 AA Dordrecht, Netherlands. TEL 31-78-392392. FAX 31-78-392254. TELEX 29245 KAPG NL. E-mail: SERVICES@WKAP.NL. (Dist. by: Kluwer Academic Publishers Group, P.O. Box 322, 3300 AH Dordrecht, Netherlands. TEL 31-78-392392. FAX 31-78-546474; N. America dist. addr.: Box 358, Accord Sta., Hingham, MA 02018-0358. TEL 617-871-6600. FAX 617-871-6528) Ed. Michael R. Matthews. (also avail. in microform from UMI; back issues avail.; reprint service avail. from SWZ) **Indexed:** C.I.J.E., Zent.Math. **Document type:** academic/scholarly publication.
—BLDSC (8132.140000); SWETS; UMI. **CCC.**
 Description: Promotes research seeking to improve teaching, learning and curricula in science and mathematics.
 Refereed Serial

500 174   UK   ISSN 1353-3452
▼**SCIENCE AND ENGINEERING ETHICS.** 1995. q. £42($66) to individuals; institutions £77($130). Opragen Publications, P.O. Box 54, Guildford, Surrey GU2 2YF, England. TEL 01483-560074. Eds. Stephanie Bird, Raymond Spier. adv.: page $300; adv. contact: Merilyn Spier. **Document type:** academic/scholarly publication.
—BLDSC (8133.023800).
 Description: Explores ethical issues of direct concern to scientists and engineers concerning professional education, research, practice and the effect of innovations on society.
 Refereed Serial

500   US   ISSN 0892-9882
UA12.5   CODEN: SGSEE8
SCIENCE AND GLOBAL SECURITY; the technical basis for arms control and environmental policy initiatives. 1989. 3/yr. 54 ECU (effective 1996). Gordon & Breach Science Publishers, c/o International Publishers Distributor, 820 Town Center Dr., Langhorne, PA 19047. TEL 215-750-2642. FAX 215-750-6343. (Subscr. to: International Publishers Distributor, P.O. Box 90, Reading, Berkshire RG1 8JL, England. TEL 44-173-456-8316) (also avail. in microform)
—BLDSC (8134.055000); UnCover. **CCC.**
 Refereed Serial

SCIENCE AND GLOBAL SECURITY MONOGRAPH SERIES.
 see *POLITICAL SCIENCE — International Relations*

500   US
SCIENCE AND ITS CONCEPTUAL FOUNDATIONS. 1985. irreg., latest 1986. price varies. University of Chicago Press, 5801 S. Ellis Ave., Chicago, IL 60637. TEL 312-702-7899. (Subscr. to: 11030 Langley Ave., Chicago, IL 60628) Ed. David L. Hull.
 Refereed Serial

501   NE   ISSN 0924-4697
SCIENCE AND PHILOSOPHY. 1984. irreg., vol.5, 1990. price varies. Kluwer Academic Publishers, Postbus 17, 3300 AA Dordrecht, Netherlands. TEL 31-78-392392. FAX 31-78-392254. TELEX 29245 KAPG NL. (Dist. by: Kluwer Academic Publishers Group, P.O. Box 322, 3300 AH Dordrecht, Netherlands. TEL 31-78-392392. FAX 31-78-546474; N. America dist. addr.: Box 358, Accord Sta., Hingham, MA 02018-0358. TEL 617-871-6600. FAX 617-871-6528) Ed. Nancy J. Nersessian. **Document type:** monographic series.
 Description: Forum for contemporary analysis of philosophical problems arising in connection with the construction of theories in the physical and biological sciences, reflecting the belief that the philosophy of science must be firmly rooted in an examination of actual scientific practice.
 Refereed Serial

500   UK   ISSN 0268-490X
Q175.4
SCIENCE AND PUBLIC AFFAIRS. 1986. q. £10 in Europe; U.S. and Canada £11. Royal Society of London, 6 Carlton House Terrace, London SW1Y 5AG, England. TEL 0171-839-5561. FAX 0171-976-1837. Ed. Walter Bodmer. circ. 3,407. **Document type:** academic/scholarly publication.
—BLDSC (8134.178100).
 Description: Articles on science and technology policies and their implications.

500   UK   ISSN 0302-3427
Q179.9
SCIENCE AND PUBLIC POLICY. 1973. bi-m. £34($61) to individuals; institutions £118 ($199) (effective 1996). (International Science Policy Foundation) Beech Tree Publishing, 10 Watford Close, Guildford, Surrey GU1 2EP, England. TEL 01483-67497. FAX 01483-67497. (Subscr. to: Turpin Distribution Services Ltd., Blackhorse Rd., Letchworth, Herts. SG6 1HN, England. TEL 01462-372555. FAX 01462-4830111) Eds. Phil Gummett, John de la Mothe. adv.; bk.rev.; bibl.; charts; illus.; index. (back issues avail.) **Indexed:** Asian-Pac.Econ.Lit., Bibl.& Ind.Geol., CLOSS, Curr.Cont., Energy Ind., Energy Info.Abstr., Energy Rev., Environ.Abstr., Excerp.Med., Fuel & Energy Abstr., Geo.Abstr., High.Educ.Curr.Aware.Bull., IDA, Lang.& Lang.Behav.Abstr., World Agri.Econ.& Rural Sociol.Abstr. **Document type:** academic/scholarly publication.
—BLDSC (8134.179000); Faxon; Genuine Article; SWETS; UnCover. **CCC.**
 Former titles: Science Policy (ISSN 0048-9700) & 2Science Policy News.
 Description: Reports on how science and technology affect public policy.
 Refereed Serial

500 600   KO
SCIENCE AND TECHNOLOGY.* (Text in English, Korean; summaries in English) 1955. irreg. exchange basis. Korea University, College of Science and Engineering, 1 Anam-Dong, Seoul 132, S. Korea.
 Formerly: Goryo Daehakgyo Nonmunjip Science.

500 600   US
SCIENCE AND TECHNOLOGY DESK REFERENCE. 1992. triennial. $39.95. (Carnegie Library of Pittsburgh) Gale Research Inc., 835 Penobscot Bldg., Detroit, MI 48226. TEL 313-961-2242. FAX 313-961-6083. charts; illus.; maps.
 Description: Subject-arranged compendium of 1500 inquiries in science and technology. Includes citations for locating further information.

500 600   UK
SCIENCE AND TECHNOLOGY IN CHINA. 1984. triennial. £95. Longman Group UK Ltd., Westgate House, 6th Fl., The High, Harlow, Essex CM20 1YR, England. TEL 0279-442601. FAX 0279-444501. Ed. Alan M. Anderson. **Document type:** academic/scholarly publication.

500 600   JA   ISSN 0286-0406
Q127.J3   CODEN: STJAE8
SCIENCE AND TECHNOLOGY IN JAPAN. (Text in English) 1982. q. 4720 Yen($60) Three 'I' Publications Ltd., Kamakara-cho Parking Bldg., 5-16 Uchi-Kanda 1-chome, Chiyoda-ku, Tokyo 101, Japan. TEL 03-3291-3761. FAX 03-3291-3764. (Subscr. to: Maruzen Co. Ltd., Box 5050, Tokyo International 100-31, Japan) Ed. Miyakawa Yasuhiro. adv. circ. 10,320. (back issues avail.) **Indexed:** CAD CAM Abstr., Energy Info.Abstr., JTA, Telegen.
—BLDSC (8134.260000); Faxon; SWETS; UnCover.

500 600   UK
SCIENCE AND TECHNOLOGY IN JAPAN. 1984. triennial. £95. Longman Group UK Ltd., Westgate House, 6th Fl., The High, Harlow, Essex CM20 1YR, England. TEL 0279-442601. FAX 0279-444501. Ed. Alan M. Anderson. **Document type:** academic/scholarly publication.

500   PH
SCIENCE AND TECHNOLOGY INFORMATION INSTITUTE. DEPARTMENT OF SCIENCE AND TECHNOLOGY. ANNUAL REPORT. Short title: D O S T Annual Report. a. Science and Technology Information Institute, Department of Science and Technology, P.O. Box 3596, Manila, Philippines. charts; illus.
 Former titles: Philippines. National Science and Technology Authority. Annual Report; Philippines. National Science Development Board. Annual Report.

500 320   UK   ISSN 0950-5431
SCIENCE AS CULTURE. 1974. q. £25 to individuals (U.S. $30; Canada and Mexico $45; elsewhere £35); institutions £50 (U.S. $65; Canada and Mexico $80; elsewhere £60) (effective 1995). Free Association Books, 26 Freegrove Rd., London N7, England. TEL 0171-609-0507. FAX 0171-609-4837. E-mail: pp@rmy1.demon.co.uk. (Subscr. to: Worldwide Subscription Service Ltd., Ticehurst TN5 7HE, England. TEL 01580-200657. FAX 01580-200616; Co-publisher: Guilford Publications, Inc., 72 Spring St., 4th Fl., New York, NY 10012. TEL 800-365-7006. FAX 212-966-6708) Ed. Robert M. Young. adv. contact: Jody Falco. bk.rev.; abstr.; bibl.; index. circ. 750. (also avail. in microform from UMI; back issues avail.; reprint service avail. from UMI) **Indexed:** Alt.Press Ind., Curr.Cont., Lang.& Lang.Behav.Abstr., Left Ind. (1987-), Sociol.Abstr. **Document type:** academic/scholarly publication.
—BLDSC (8142.250000); Genuine Article; SWETS; UMI; UnCover. **CCC.**
 Former titles (until 1987): Radical Science Series; (until 1974): Radical Science Journal (ISSN 0305-0963)
 Description: Explores all the ways in which science, technology and medicine are involved in shaping society's values and priorities.
 Refereed Serial

500   CH   ISSN 0250-4189
SCIENCE BULLETIN. 1969. m. free. National Science Council of the Republic of China, 106 Ho-ping E. Rd. Sec. 2, Taipei, Taiwan 106, Republic of China.
 Indexed: Bibl.& Ind.Geol. **Document type:** bulletin.

500   UK   ISSN 0300-3361
SCIENCE CHELSEA. 1965. irreg., vol.8, 1979. £0.50($1.50) Chelsea College, Students Union, Manresa Rd., London SW3 6LX, England. Ed. P. Ansell. adv.; bk.rev.; bibl.; charts; illus.; index. circ. 1,000.

500   PR   ISSN 0164-7741
SCIENCE - CIENCIA;* boletin cientifico del Sur. (Text in English, Spanish) 1973. q. free to qualified personnel. Fundacion Sala, Inc., P.O. Box 7004, Ponce, PR 00731. TEL 848-4191. Ed. Luis F. Sala. bk.rev.; charts; illus.; stat. circ. 1,000. **Indexed:** Sport Fish.Abstr., Wild.Rev.

SCIENCES: COMPREHENSIVE WORKS

500 US ISSN 0161-3170
CODEN: SJCREM
SCIENCE CITATION INDEX JOURNAL CITATION REPORT. Short title: S C I - J C R. (Not avail. in printed format. Includes Journal Ranking, Reference Data, and Source Data Packages) 1975. a. $290. Institute for Scientific Information, 3501 Market St., Philadelphia, PA 19104. TEL 215-386-0100. FAX 215-386-2991. (Add: Brunel Science Park, Brunel University, Uxbridge UB8 3PQ, England) (microfiche) **Document type:** academic/scholarly publication, bibliography.
—BLDSC (8141.802500).
Formerly: I S I Journal Citation Reports.
Description: Provides citation data to reveal the relationship between journals in the sciences.

SCIENCE COMMUNICATION. see *COMMUNICATIONS*

500 300 PH ISSN 0115-7809
CODEN: SCDIEJ
SCIENCE DILIMAN. (Text in English and Filipino) 1980. a. P.45($10) University of the Philippines, Office of Research Coordination, Rm. 309 Malcolm Hall, Diliman, Quezon City, Philippines. Ed. Bienvenido T. Miranda. circ. 750. (back issues avail.) **Indexed:** Ind.Phil.Per.
—CASDDS.

507 US ISSN 0036-8326
CODEN: SEDUAV
SCIENCE EDUCATION. 1916. bi-m. $324 (foreign $417) (effective 1996). John Wiley & Sons, Inc., Journals, 605 Third Ave., New York, NY 10158. TEL 212-850-6645. FAX 212-850-6021. TELEX 12-7063. E-mail: SUBINFO@JWILEY.COM. (Subscr. outside the Americas to: John Wiley & Sons Ltd., Baffins Ln., Chichester, W. Sussex PO19 1UD, England. TEL 44-1243-779777. FAX 44-1243-776128) Ed. Leopold E. Klopfer. adv.; charts; illus.; stat.; index. circ. 2,045. (also avail. in microform from UMI; back issues avail.; reprint service avail. from UMI) **Indexed:** C.I.J.E., Cont.Pg.Educ., Curr.Cont., Educ.Ind., Psychol.Abstr. (1989-), Res.High.Educ.Abstr., SSCI, Tech.Educ.Abstr.
—BLDSC (8142.800000); Faxon; Genuine Article; SWETS; UMI; UnCover. **CCC.**
Description: Examines the latest practices, issues and trends occurring in the U.S. and abroad in science instruction, learning, and preparation of science teachers.
Refereed Serial

500 BE ISSN 0773-3429
SCIENCE ET CULTURE. 1954. bi-m. 500 BEF. Institut de Physique, B-5 Sart Tilman, 4000 Liege, Belgium. TEL 32-41-663858. FAX 32-41-662355. Ed. Roger Moreau; Pub. F.X. Neve de Mevergnies. adv. **Indexed:** Chem.Abstr. **Document type:** bulletin.
Formerly: T.V. (ISSN 0041-4476)

500 FR ISSN 0036-8369
SCIENCE ET VIE; magazine of popular science. 1913. m. 242 F. (foreign 303 F.) Excelsior Publications, 1 rue du Colonel Pierre Avia, 75503 Paris Cedex 15, France. TEL 46-48-48-00. FAX 46-48-47-58. TELEX 641 886 F. Ed. Philippe Cousin. adv. contact: Gilles de Keranflech. bk.rev.; illus. circ. 364,855. (back issues avail.) **Indexed:** Biol.Abstr., Pt.de Rep. (1979-).
—Faxon; SWETS.

500 028.5 FR ISSN 0992-5899
SCIENCE ET VIE JUNIOR. 1989. 11/yr. 223 F. (foreign 279 F.) (effective 1992). Excelsior Publications, 1 rue du Colonel Pierre Avia, 75503 Paris Cedex 15, France. TEL 46-48-48-48. FAX 46-48-48-09. TELEX 631 994 F. Ed. Sven Ortoli. adv. contact: Gilles de Keranflech. circ. 183,012. **Indexed:** Pt.de Rep. (1991-).
Description: Explores scientific and technical progress.

SCIENCE EXPERIMENTS FOR YOUNG PEOPLE. see *CHILDREN AND YOUTH — For*

500 US ISSN 0048-9662
Q175.52.U5
SCIENCE FOR THE PEOPLE. 1968. bi-m. $15 to individuals; institutions $24. Science Resource Center, Inc., Box 364, Somerville, MA 02143-0005. TEL 617-547-3580. Ed. Seth Shulman. adv.; bk.rev.; bibl.; illus. circ. 5,000. (also avail. in microfilm; back issues avail.; reprint service avail. from UMI) **Indexed:** Alt.Press Ind., CAD CAM Abstr., Energy Info.Abstr., Environ.Abstr., Environ.Ind., Left Ind. (1982-1989), Telegen. **Document type:** academic/scholarly publication, consumer publication.
—UMI; UnCover.
Description: Contains articles concerned with the effects of scientific innovations on humans. Features topics such as nutrition, health, nuclear technology and workplace safety.

500 US
SCIENCE FRONTIERS. 1976. bi-m. $7. Sourcebook Project, Box 107, Glen Arm, MD 21057. TEL 410-668-6047. Ed. William R. Corliss. adv.; bk.rev. circ. 1,200. (back issues avail.) **Document type:** newsletter.
Description: Digests articles dealing with scientific anomalies and appearing in the current literature.

500 610 US ISSN 0897-8581
Q162
SCIENCE ILLUSTRATED. 1987. bi-m. $15. Science Illustrated, L.P., 8428 Holly Leaf Dr., McLean, VA 22102. TEL 703-356-1688. FAX 703-356-1688. Ed. Jane Alexander; Pub. Tod Herbers. adv. contact: Tod Herbers. bk.rev. circ. 103,000. (back issues avail.) **Document type:** trade publication.

500 CC ISSN 1001-6511
QA1 CODEN: SCASEY
SCIENCE IN CHINA. SERIES A: MATHEMATICS, PHYSICS, ASTRONOMY & TECHNOLOGICAL SCIENCES. Chinese edition: Zhongguo Kexue A (ISSN 1000-3126) (Text in English) 1952. 12/yr. £415($619) (£625($932) with Series B) (effective 1995). Science Press, Marketing and Sales Department, 16 Donghuangchenggen North St., Beijing 100717, People's Republic of China. TEL 4010642. FAX 4019810. (Dist. overseas by: Elsevier Science Ltd., Pergamon, P.O. Box 800, Kidlington, Oxford OX5 1DX, England. TEL 44-865-843000. FAX 44-865-843010; Subscr. in U.S. and Canada to: Elsevier Science, 660 White Plains Rd., Tarrytown, NY 10591-5153. TEL 914-524-9200. FAX 914-333-2444) Ed.Bd. adv.; index. circ. 10,000. (back issues avail.) **Indexed:** INSPEC (1989-), Lead Abstr., Meteor.& Geoastrophys.Abstr., Zincscan. **Document type:** academic/scholarly publication.
—BLDSC (8141.659000); CASDDS; Ei; Faxon; Genuine Article; SWETS; UMI; UnCover.
Formerly (until 1989): Scientia Sinica. Series A: Mathematics, Physics, Astronomy and Technological Sciences (ISSN 0253-5831)
Description: Covers mathematics, physics, astronomy, and technology. Contains mainly academic papers on scientific work.
Refereed Serial

500 CC ISSN 1001-652X
QD1 CODEN: SCBSE5
SCIENCE IN CHINA. SERIES B: CHEMISTRY, LIFE SCIENCES & EARTH SCIENCES. Chinese edition: Zhongguo Kexue B (ISSN 1000-3134) (Text in English) 1952. 12/yr. £415($619) (£625($932) with Series A) (effective 1995). Science Press, Marketing and Sales Department, 16 Donghuangchenggen North St., Beijing 100717, People's Republic of China. TEL 4010642. FAX 4019810. (Dist. overseas by: Elsevier Science Ltd., Pergamon, P.O. Box 800, Kidlington, Oxford OX5 1DX, England. TEL 44-865-843000. FAX 44-865-843010; Subscr. in U.S. and Canada to: Elsevier Science, 660 White Plains Rd., Tarrytown, NY 10591-5153. TEL 914-524-9200. FAX 914-333-2444) Ed.Bd. adv.; index. circ. 10,000. (also avail. in microform; back issues avail.; reprint service avail. from KTO) **Indexed:** Cadscan, Curr.Ref.Fish Res., Ecol.Abstr., Geo.Abstr., Geol.Abstr., Lead Abstr., Meteor.& Geoastrophys.Abstr., Triticale Abstr., Zincscan. **Document type:** academic/scholarly publication.
—BLDSC (8141.669000); CASDDS; Ei; Faxon; Genuine Article; SWETS; UMI; UnCover. **CCC.**
Formerly (until 1989): Scientia Sinica. Series B: Chemistry, Life Sciences and Earth Sciences (ISSN 0253-5823); Supersedes in part: Scientia Sinica.
Description: Covers chemistry, biology, earth science, medical science, and agronomy. Contains mainly academic papers on scientific work.
Refereed Serial

500 UK ISSN 0269-8897
Q175.4 CODEN: SCCOEW
SCIENCE IN CONTEXT. 1987. q. £62($112) (effective 1996). Cambridge University Press, Edinburgh Bldg., Shaftesbury Rd., Cambridge CB2 2RU, England. TEL 01223-312393. FAX 01223-315052. TELEX 851817256. (N. American addr.: Cambridge University Press, Journals Dept., 40 W. 20th St., New York, NY 10011. TEL 212-924-3900. FAX 212-691-3239) Ed. Yehuda Elkana. adv.; bk.rev. (back issues avail.) **Document type:** academic/scholarly publication.
—BLDSC (8141.820000); Faxon; SWETS; UMI; UnCover. **CCC.**
Description: Studies the history, philosophy, sociology and epistemology of science.

500 PP ISSN 0310-4303
SCIENCE IN NEW GUINEA. 1949. 3/yr. K.20 to individuals and schools; institutions K.30. University of Papua New Guinea, Faculty of Science, P.O. Box 320, University, Papua New Guinea. FAX 267-187. TELEX NE 22366. Ed. K. Singh. bk.rev. circ. 400. **Indexed:** Bibl.& Ind.Geol., Biol.Abstr., Chem.Abstr., Ecol.Abstr., Food Sci.& Tech.Abstr., Geo.Abstr., Mineral.Abstr., Nutr.Abstr., Soils & Fert. **Document type:** academic/scholarly publication.
—BLDSC (8149.900000); UnCover.
Supersedes (in 1972): Papua New Guinea Scientific Society. Annual Report and Proceedings (ISSN 0085-4697)
Description: Covers scientific research, the teaching of science and the social implications of science in New Guinea.

500 II ISSN 0036-8407
SCIENCE IN PARLIAMENT. (Text in English) 1965. q. Rs.5. Indian Parliamentary and Scientific Committee, 2 Telegraph Lane, New Delhi 1, India. Ed. Krishan Kant. adv.; bk.rev.

500 UK ISSN 0263-6271
SCIENCE IN PARLIAMENT. 1982. 6/yr. £74.50. (Parliamentary and Scientific Committee) Westminster Publishing Ltd., 28 Ponsonby Terrace, London SW1P 4QA, England. TEL 0171-821-6772. FAX 0171-834-6694. Ed. M. Goldsmith. adv.: B&W page £750, color page £1300; trim 259 x 180; adv. contact: Andrew Loudon. **Indexed:** Cadscan, Intl.Polym.Sci.& Tech., Lead Abstr., RAPRA, Zincscan. **Document type:** academic/scholarly publication.
—BLDSC (8150.600000); SWETS. **CCC.**

500 US
SCIENCE LEADERSHIP TREND NOTES. 1990. 6/yr. (Sep.-May). $12. National Science Supervisors Association, 82 Deepwood Dr., E. Hartford, CT 06118-2411. TEL 203-633-5231. FAX 203-659-3366. Ed. Jim Banks. adv. circ. 1,000. (tabloid format; back issues avail.) **Document type:** newsletter.

SCIENCES: COMPREHENSIVE WORKS

500 UK ISSN 0968-2031
SCIENCE MATTERS. 1989. s-a. £6. Associated Examining Board, Stag Hill House, Guildford, Surrey GU2 5XJ, England. TEL 01483-506506. FAX 01483-300152. Ed. George Turnbull. circ. 13,000. **Document type:** newsletter.

500 US
SCIENCE MUSEUM OF MINNESOTA. MONOGRAPH. 1972. irreg. Science Museum of Minnesota, 30 E. 10th St., St. Paul, MN 55101. TEL 612-221-9488. Ed. Bruce R. Erickson. **Indexed:** Bibl.& Ind.Geol., Biol.Abstr. **Document type:** monographic series.

500 US ISSN 0161-4452
Q11 CODEN: SCSPBA
SCIENCE MUSEUM OF MINNESOTA. SCIENTIFIC PUBLICATIONS, NEW SERIES. Key Title: Scientific Publications of the Science Museum of Minnesota. 1966. irreg. $0.55. Science Museum of Minnesota, 30 E. 10th St., St. Paul, MN 55101. TEL 612-221-9488. Ed. Bruce R. Erickson. **Indexed:** Bibl.& Ind.Geol., Biol.Abstr.
Supersedes: Science Museum of Minnesota. Scientific Bulletin; Formerly: Science Museum of Minnesota. Scientific Publications (ISSN 0080-5521)

500 SZ
SCIENCE NETWORKS HISTORICAL STUDIES. irreg. Birkhaeuser Verlag, P.O. Box 133, CH-4010 Basel, Switzerland. TEL 061-227400. FAX 061-227666. **Document type:** academic/scholarly publication.

500 US ISSN 0036-8423
Q1 CODEN: SCNEBK
SCIENCE NEWS; the weekly newsmagazine of science. 1921. w. $49.50 (effective July 1995). Science Service, Inc., 1719 N St., N.W., Washington, DC 20036. TEL 202-785-2255. FAX 202-659-0365. (Subscr. to: 231 W. Center St., Box 1925, Marion, OH 43306-4025. TEL 800-347-6969) Ed. Patrick Young; Pub. Alfred S. McLaren. adv. contact: Donald R. Harless. bk.rev.; illus.; index; circ. 235,000 (paid). (also avail. in microfilm from UMI; reprint service avail. from UMI) **Indexed:** A.I.Abstr., Abr.R.G., Acad.Ind., Acid Rain Abstr., Acid Rain Ind., ASCA, Bibl.& Ind.Geol., Biol.Dig., BPIA, C.I.J.E., CAD CAM Abstr., Can.B.P.I., Chem.Abstr., Deep Sea Res.& Oceanogr.Abstr., Energy Rev., Eng.Ind., Environ.Abstr., Environ.Ind., Gard.Lit. (1992-), Gen.Sci.Ind., Hlth.Ind., Jun.High.Mag.Abstr., Mag.Ind., Ocean.Abstr., Pollut.Abstr., PROMT, R.G., Telegen, TOM. **Document type:** trade publication.
●Also available online. Vendor(s): University Microfilms International.
Also available on CD-ROM. Producer(s): University Microfilms International.
—BLDSC (8150.010000); CASDDS; CIS; Ei; Faxon; SWETS; UMI; UnCover.
Former titles (until 1966): Science News Letter; Science News Bulletin.
Description: Publishes reports on new research findings, developments and issues in all disciplines of science, for a non-specialist audience. Includes short reports from major conferences and congresses, reviews of results published in scientific journals and coverage of legislative and political events relevant to scientific policy.

371.3 500 JM
SCIENCE NOTES AND NEWS. irreg. Association of Science Teachers of Jamaica, c/o Honorary Secretary, Olive Baxter, 46 Paddington Terrace, Kingston 6, Jamaica, WI.

500 FR ISSN 0080-7540
SCIENCE NOUVELLE.* No.8, 1970. irreg. price varies. Editions R. Laffont, 6 Place Saint-Sulpice, 75006 Paris, France.
Formerly (until 1970): Jeune Science.

500 100 PL ISSN 0138-0532
Q180.A1
SCIENCE OF SCIENCE; an international journal of studies on scientific reasoning and scientific enterprise. (Text in English; summaries in French, German and Russian) 1980. q. $48. (Polish Academy of Science, Committee of the Science of Science) Ossolineum, Publishing House of the Polish Academy of Sciences, Rynek 9, 50-106 Wroclaw, Poland. TEL 48-71-386-25. FAX 48-71-448-103. TELEX 0712771 OSS PL. Ed. I. Malecki. adv.; bk.rev.; index. **Indexed:** Lang.& Lang.Behav.Abstr. **Document type:** academic/scholarly publication.
Formerly: Problems of the Science of Science.

500 NE ISSN 0167-191X
SCIENCE POLICY IN THE NETHERLANDS. Cover title: Science Policy. Dutch edition: Wetenschapsbeleid (ISSN 0166-8471) (Text in English) 1978. q. free. Ministerie van Onderwijs, Cultuur en Wetenschappen, Voorlichtingsdienst - Ministry of Education, Culture and Science, International Relations Division, Postbus 25000, 2700 LZ Zoetermeer, Netherlands. TEL 31-79-532825. FAX 31-79-512089. Ed. M. Verzantvoort. illus. (back issues avail.) **Document type:** government publication.
Description: Covers current topics relating to Dutch governmental policy on the sciences, including news and information of noteworthy research projects and initiatives.

500 UN ISSN 0080-7591
SCIENCE POLICY STUDIES AND DOCUMENTS. French edition: Etudes et Documents de Politique Scientifique (ISSN 0251-5695) 1965. irreg., latest no.72, 1991. price varies. Unesco, 7-9 Place de Fontenoy, 75700 Paris, France. TEL 45-77-16-10. (Dist. in U.S. by: Unipub, 4611-F Assembly Dr., Lanham, MD 20706-4391) (also avail. in microform)
—BLDSC (8150.770000).

500 UK ISSN 0036-8504
Q1 CODEN: SCPRAY
SCIENCE PROGRESS; a review journal of current scientific advance. 1894. q. £86.50 (foreign £95) (effective 1996). Science Reviews Ltd., P.O. Box 81, Northwood, Middlesex HA6 3DY, England. TEL 01923-823586. FAX 01923-825066. E-mail: stl@scitech.demon.co.uk. Ed.Bd. adv.; bk.rev.; index. circ. 900. (also avail. in microform from UMI; back issues avail.; reprint service avail. from ISI) **Indexed:** Agri.Eng.Abstr., Anim.Breed.Abstr., ASCA, Bibl.& Ind.Geol., Biol.Abstr., Br.Tech.Ind., Chem.Abstr., Curr.Adv.Ecol.Sci., Curr.Cont., Ecol.Abstr., Field Crop Abstr., Geol.Abstr., Herb.Abstr., Ind.Med., Ind.Vet., INSPEC, Plant Breed.Abstr., Rev.Plant Path., Sci.Cit.Ind., Vet.Bull. **Document type:** academic/scholarly publication.
—BLDSC (8151.000000); CASDDS; Ei; Faxon; Genuine Article; SWETS; UMI; UnCover.
Refereed Serial

SCIENCE PROJECTS. see *CHILDREN AND YOUTH* — For

500 370 US ISSN 0887-2376
LB1585.3
SCIENCE SCOPE; a journal for middle-junior high science teachers. 1978. 8/yr. $52. National Science Teachers Association, 1840 Wilson Blvd., Arlington, VA 22201. Ed. Kenneth L. Roberts. adv.; bk.rev.; charts; illus.; tr.lit.; index. circ. 12,000. (also avail. in microform; back issues avail.) **Document type:** academic/scholarly publication.
—BLDSC (8164.237000); Faxon; SWETS; UMI; UnCover.
Description: Covers teacher-developed science activities (all disciplines) for use in the science classroom.

500 TH ISSN 0303-8122
Q80.T5 CODEN: VKSTDB
SCIENCE SOCIETY OF THAILAND. JOURNAL. 1975. q. $30. Science Society of Thailand, Faculty of Science, Chulalongkorn University, Bangkok 5, Thailand. Ed. I-Ming Tang. index. circ. 1,000. (back issues avail.) **Indexed:** AIT Reports, Biol.Abstr., Chem.Abstr., Curr.Adv.Ecol.Sci., Dairy Sci.Abstr., INSPEC (1975-), J.of Ferroc., Rice Abstr., Sci.Cit.Ind., Soils & Fert. **Document type:** academic/scholarly publication.
—CASDDS; Genuine Article.

500 US ISSN 1323-1413
▼**SCIENCE SPECTRA.** 1995. 4/yr. Gordon and Breach Science Publishers, c/o International Publishers Distributor, 820 Town Centre Dr., Langhorne, PA 19047. TEL 215-750-2642; 800-545-8398. FAX 215-750-6343. (Subscr. to: International Publishers Distributor, P.O. Box 90, Reading, Berkshire RG1 8JL, England. TEL 44-173-456-8316) **Document type:** academic/scholarly publication.

500 600 FI ISSN 0786-3012
SCIENCE STUDIES; a Scandinavian journal. (Text in English) 1988. 2/yr. FIM 150 to individuals; institutions FIM 190. Finnish Society for Science Studies, c/o Petri Ylikoski, P.O. Box 117, FIN-00171 Helsinki, Finland. TEL 358-0-77267730. FAX 358-0-77267715. Ed. Marja Alestalo. bk.rev. circ. 300. **Document type:** academic/scholarly publication.
Description: Presents a forum for international, particularly Scandinavian contributors in the field of science and technology studies. The subject area ranges from history and philosophy of science to social studies of science and technology.

507 370 US ISSN 0036-8555
Q181
THE SCIENCE TEACHER. 1934. 9/yr. $52. National Science Teachers Association, 1840 Wilson Blvd., Arlington, VA 22201. Ed. Shelley Carey. adv.; bk.rev.; film rev.; charts; illus.; index. circ. 23,000. (also avail. in microfilm from UMI; reprint service avail. from UMI) **Indexed:** Acad.Ind., Biol.Dig., C.I.J.E., Cont.Pg.Educ., Educ.Ind., Media Rev.Dig. **Document type:** academic/scholarly publication.
—BLDSC (8164.750000); Faxon; SWETS; UMI; UnCover.
Description: For science teachers of grades 7-12.

500 II ISSN 0378-8717
CODEN: VISHDT
SCIENCE TEACHER/VIGYAN SHIKSHAK. 1950. q. $25. All India Science Teachers' Association, Sardar Patel Vidyalaya, Lodi Estate, Road No. 3, New Delhi 110003, India. TEL 4615768. Ed. R.K. Mohta. adv.; bk.rev. circ. 1,000.
—CASDDS.

500 AT
SCIENCE TEACHERS ASSOCIATION OF QUEENSLAND. NEWSLETTER. 1961. 6/yr. Aus.$3 per no. Science Teachers Association of Queensland, Care Dept. of Mathematics, Science & Technology Education, QUT - Kelvin Grove Campus, Locked Bag No. 2, Red Hill, Qld. 4059, Australia. TEL 61-7-8643314. Ed. John Hunt. adv.: Cath/Nimmo. bk.rev. circ. 500. **Document type:** newsletter.

SCIENCE, TECHNOLOGY & DEVELOPMENT; journal of the Third World Science, Technology & Development Forum. see *BUSINESS AND ECONOMICS — International Development And Assistance*

170 600 US ISSN 0162-2439
Q175.4
SCIENCE, TECHNOLOGY & HUMAN VALUES. 1972. q. $61 to individuals; institutions $162 (effective Sep. 1995). (Society for Social Studies of Science) Sage Publications, Inc., 2455 Teller Rd., Thousand Oaks, CA 91320. TEL 805-499-0721. FAX 805-499-0871. E-mail: libraries@sagepub.com. (Overseas subscr. to: Sage Publications Ltd., 6 Bonhill St., London EC2A 4PU, England; Sage Publications India Pvt. Ltd., P.O. Box 4215, New Delhi 110 048, India) Ed. Olga Amsterdamska. bibl.; index. circ. 1,900. (also avail. in microform; back issues avail.; reprint service avail.) **Indexed:** ASCA, Curr.Cont., Int.Polit.Sci.Abstr., Lang.& Lang.Behav.Abstr., P.A.I.S., Phil.Ind., SSCI, Telegen. **Document type:** academic/scholarly publication.
—BLDSC (8164.850000); CIS; Faxon; Genuine Article; SWETS; UMI; UnCover. **CCC.**
Former titles (until 1978): Newsletter on Science, Technology, and Human Values; (until 1976): Harvard University. Program of Public Conceptions of Science. Newsletter.
Description: Takes an international and multidisciplinary approach to the study of science and technology, including their involvement in politics, society, and culture.

500 UK
SCIENCE, TECHNOLOGY AND INNOVATION. 1988. bi-m. £105 (foreign £115) (effective 1996). Science Reference & Information Service, 25 Southampton Bldgs., London WC2A 1AW, England. TEL 0171-323-7959. FAX 0171-323-7947. (Dist. by: Turpin Distribution Services Ltd., Blackhorse Rd., Letchworth, Herts SG6 1HN, England. TEL 01462-672555. FAX 01462-480947) Ed. Lesley Grayson. adv. contact: V. McBurney. bk.rev. **Document type:** academic/scholarly publication.
—BLDSC (8134.280820).
Formerly: Science and Technology Policy (ISSN 0952-9616)
Description: Monitors the happenings in UK science policy.

SCIENCES: COMPREHENSIVE WORKS

500 300 II
▼SCIENCE, TECHNOLOGY & SOCIETY. (Text in English) Announced for publication in 1996. 2/yr. $35 to individuals; institutions $75 (effective 1996). Sage Publications India Pvt. Ltd., P.O. Box 4215, New Delhi 110 048, India. TEL 91-11-6444958. FAX 91-11-6472426. (Overseas subscr. to: Sage Publications Ltd., 6 Bonhill St., London EC2A 4PU, England; Subscr. in N. America to: Sage Publications, Inc., 2455 Teller Rd., Thousand Oaks, CA 91320. TEL 805-499-0721. FAX 805-499-0871)
Document type: academic/scholarly publication.

500 II **ISSN 0036-858X**
Q1 **CODEN: SCTYB8**
SCIENCE TODAY; presenting the future perfect. (Text in English) 1966. m. Rs.120($25) Bennett, Coleman & Co. Ltd. (Bombay), Times Bldg., Dr. D.N. Rd., P.O. Box 213, Bombay 400 001, India. TEL 4150271. (U.S. subscr. addr.: c/o Ms. Kalpana, 42-75 Main St., Flushing, NY 11355) Ed. Mukul Sharma. adv.; bk.rev.; charts; illus.; index. circ. 78,586. (also avail. in microform)

650 US **ISSN 0043-0749**
SCIENCE TRENDS. 1958. s-m. $650. Trends Publishing Inc., National Press Bldg., Washington, DC 20045. TEL 202-393-0031. FAX 202-392-1732. Ed. Arthur Kranish. bk.rev.; abstr.; charts; pat.; stat.; tr.lit. (looseleaf format; also avail. in microform from UMI; reprint service avail. from UMI)
—UMI.
Formerly: Washington Science Trends.
Description: Reports on developments in general science, education and research, and development.

500 US **ISSN 1047-8043**
CODEN: SCWAEM
SCIENCE WATCH. 1990. m. $345. Institute for Scientific Information, 3501 Market St., Philadelphia, PA 19104. TEL 215-386-0100. FAX 215-386-2991. (And: Brunel Science Park, Brunel University, Uxbridge UB8 3PQ, England) Ed. David A. Pendlebury. **Document type:** academic/scholarly publication, bibliography.
—BLDSC (8165.079000); CASDDS; SWETS.
Description: Tracks trends and developments in scientific research. Evaluates the research activities and performance of countries, universities, industrial firms, private and government labs, and other organizations.

SCIENCE WEEKLY. see CHILDREN AND YOUTH — For

500 US **ISSN 0036-8601**
SCIENCE WORLD. 1959. m. $12 to students; teachers $24. Scholastic Inc., 555 Broadway, New York, NY 10012-3999. TEL 212-343-6100. (Subscr. to: Box 3710, Jefferson City, MO 65102. TEL 800-325-6149) Ed. Bonnie Price. adv.; bk.rev.; charts; illus.; tr.lit.; index. circ. 550,000. (also avail. in microform from UMI; reprint service avail. from UMI) **Indexed:** Ind.Child.Mag.
Formerly: Senior Science and Science World.
Description: Covers recent developments in science and technology, as well as science experiments and current events. Aimed at children ages 12-15.

SCIENCE YEAR. see ENCYCLOPEDIAS AND GENERAL ALMANACS

SCIENCELAND; to nurture scientific thinking. see CHILDREN AND YOUTH — For

500 JA
SCIENCEPEDIA/SAIENSUPEDIA. (Text in Japanese) 1982. 2/yr. Obunsha Publishing Co., Ltd., 55 Yokodera-cho, Shinjuku-ku, Tokyo 162, Japan.

500 US **ISSN 0036-861X**
Q1 **CODEN: SCNCAD**
SCIENCES. 1961. 6/yr. $14.50. New York Academy of Sciences, 2 E. 63rd St., New York, NY 10021. Ed. Peter Brown. adv.; bk.rev.; illus.; index. circ. 75,000. (also avail. in microform from UMI,MIM; reprint service avail. from UMI) **Indexed:** Abstr.Anthropol., Access (1976-), Bibl.Agri., Biol.Abstr., Biol.Dig., Curr.Adv.Ecol.Sci., Curr.Pack.Abstr., Deep Sea Res.& Oceanogr.Abstr., Fut.Surv., Gard.Lit. (1992-), Gen.Sci.Ind., Helminthol.Abstr., Lang.& Lang.Behav.Abstr., Risk Abstr.
●Also available online. Vendor(s): University Microfilms International.
—BLDSC (8165.550000); CASDDS; Ei; Faxon; Genuine Article; SWETS; UMI; UnCover.
Description: Contains a wide selection of articles on scientific subjects. Topics covered include space technology, environmental science, agriculture, electronics and computer sciences.
Refereed Serial

500 FR **ISSN 0036-8636**
Q2
SCIENCES ET AVENIR; revue de grande information scientifique. 1947. m. 375 F. (foreign 448 F.). 9 rue Saint Florentin, 75008 Paris, France. TEL 42-60-56-30. FAX 1-42-60-36-25. Ed. Paul Ceuzin. adv. contact: Cahterine Gardin. bk.rev.; illus. circ. 189,000. **Indexed:** Curr.Adv.Ecol.Sci., Excerp.Med., Geo.Abstr., Pt.de Rep. (1979-).
—BLDSC (8165.850000); Faxon; SWETS. **CCC**.
Description: Articles covering all areas of science in a general sense: Environmental issues, technology, space explorations, medicine, etc. with an insight into future implications.

500 FT
SCIENCES & TECHNIQUES. (Text in French) 1989. 2/yr. $30. Institut Superieur d'Etudes et de Recherches Scientifiques et Techniques, B.P. 486, Djibouti, Djibouti. TEL 253-35-27-95. FAX 253-35-48-12. **Indexed:** P.L.E.S.A. (1989-).

500 LS **ISSN 1021-2442**
SCIENCES & TECHNIQUES. (Text in Lao) 1991. q. $35. C N D I S T - Science, Technology and Environment Organization, P.O. Box 2279, Vientiane, Laos. TEL 213470. Ed. Sisavanh Boupha. adv. contact: Viengsavanh Dounagsavanh.

500 CL **ISSN 0036-8679**
Q4 **CODEN: SCNTAU**
SCIENTIA; revista cientifica y tecnologica. (Text in Spanish; summaries in English) 1934. 2/yr. $10. Universidad Tecnica Federico Santa Maria, Casilla 110-V, Valparaiso, Chile. TEL 0056-32-626364. FAX 0056-32-660504. TELEX 330622 UTFSM CK. E-mail: scientia@utfsm.bitnet. Ed. Carlos Gonzalez. charts; illus.; cum.index: 1934-1958, 1959-1968. circ. 2,000. **Indexed:** ASCA, Bibl.& Ind.Geol., Chem.Abstr., INSPEC, Math.R., Repindex.
—CASDDS.

500 BL **ISSN 0104-1770**
SCIENTIA. 1990. s-a. $20 or exchange basis. (Universidade do Vale do Rio dos Sinos) Unisinos, Av. Unisinos, 950, 93022-000 Sao Leopoldo RS, Brazil. TEL 55-51-5920333 ext. 1951. FAX 55-51-5921035. Ed. Carlos Gianotti. bibl.; index, cum.index. circ. 250. (back issues avail.) **Document type:** academic/scholarly publication.

500 SP **ISSN 0213-5930**
CODEN: ASCGDN
SCIENTIA GERUNDENSIS; annals de la seccio de ciencies. 1976. a. 1200 ptas. Universidad de Gerona, Estudio de Ciencias, Pza. Hospital 6, 17071 Gerona, Spain.
—CASDDS.
Former titles (until 1985): Collegi Universitari de Girona. Seccio de Ciencies. Annals (ISSN 0213-5922); (until 1983): Colegio Universitario de Gerona. Seccion de Ciencias. Anales (ISSN 0378-9543)

500 US **ISSN 0036-8733**
T1 **CODEN: SCAMAC**
SCIENTIFIC AMERICAN. Arabic translation: Majallat al-Ulum. Chinese translation: Ke Xue (ISSN 1002-1299); French translation: Pour la Science (ISSN 0153-4092); German translation: Spektrum der Wissenschaft (ISSN 0170-2971); Hungarian translation: Tudomany (ISSN 0237-322X); Italian translation: Le Scienze (ISSN 0036-8083) Japanese translation: Nikkei Saiensu (JA ISSN 0917-009X) Polish translation: Swiat Nauki (PL ISSN 0867-6380) Spanish translation: Investigacion y Ciencia (SP ISSN 0210-136X) Turkish translation: Bilim. (European and International editions also avail.) 1845. m. $36 (effective 1994). Scientific American, Inc., 415 Madison Ave., New York, NY 10017. TEL 212-754-0550. FAX 212-754-1138. (Subscr. to: Box 3187, Harlan, IA 51537. TEL 800-333-1199. FAX 515-246-1020) Ed. John Rennie; Pub. John Moeling. adv.: B&W page $22950, color page $34400; trim 8 1/8 x 10 3/4; adv. contact: Kate Dobson. bk.rev.; charts; illus.; index, cum.index: 1948-1992 on diskette; circ. 637,528 (paid). (also avail. in microform from UMI,KTO,PMC; back issues avail.; reprint service avail.) **Indexed:** A.I.Abstr., A.S.& T.Ind., Abstr.Anthropol., Abstr.Bull.Inst.Pap.Chem., Acad.Ind., Acid Pre.Dig., Amer.Bibl.Slavic & E.Eur.Stud., Anthropol.Lit., Appl.Mech.Rev., ASCA, Bibl.Dev.Med.& Child Neur., Biol.Abstr., Biol.Dig., Biostat., Bk.Rev.Dig., Bk.Rev.Ind. (1965-), BMT, Br.Archaeol.Abstr., Br.Rail.Bd., C.I.J.E., CAD CAM Abstr. (until 1992), Cadscan, Chem.Abstr., Child.Bk.Rev.Ind. (1965-), CINAHL, CMI, Comput.Lit.Ind., Curr.Adv.Ecol.Sci., Curr.Biotech.Abstr., Curr.Cont., Curr.Lit.Fam.Plan., Deep Sea Res.& Oceanogr.Abstr., Dent.Abstr., Diar.Dis.Res., Energy Info.Abstr., Environ.Abstr., Environ.Ind., Excerp.Med. (until 1994), Field Crop Abstr., Fluidex, Fut.Surv., Gard.Lit. (1992-), Gas Abstr., Gdlns., Gen.Sci.Ind., Geo.Abstr., Graph.Arts Lit.Abstr., Helminthol.Abstr., Herb.Abstr., High.Educ.Curr.Aware.Bull., Ind.How To Do It (1963-), Ind.Med., INSPEC (1968-), Int.Aerosp.Abstr., Int.Packag.Abstr., J.of Ferroc., Key Word Ind.Wildl.Res., Lang.& Lang.Behav.Abstr., Lead Abstr., Mag.Ind., Mass Spectr.Bull., Math.R., Med.& Surg.Dermat., Med.Care Rev., Met.Abstr., Meteor.& Geoastrophys.Abstr., Mgmt.& Market.Abstr., Mid.East: Abstr.& Ind., NAA, Numis.Lit., Ocean.Abstr., Oper.Res.Manage.Sci., Peace Res.Abstr., Pers.Lit., Petrol.Abstr., Plant.Breed.Abstr., PMR, Pollut.Abstr., PROMT, Psychol.Abstr., Qual.Contr.Appl.Stat., Rat., R.G., Robomat. (until 1992), Rural Recreat.Tour.Abstr., Sage Urb.Stud.Abstr., Sh.& Vib.Dig., So.Pac.Per.Ind., Sport Fish.Abstr., Telegen (until 1989), Trop.Dis.Bull., Weed Abstr., Wild.Rev., World Alum.Abstr., Zincscan, Zoo.Rec. **Document type:** academic/scholarly publication, consumer publication.
●Also available online. Vendor(s): Ovid Technologies (SAMM).
—BLDSC (8175.000000); CASDDS; CIS; Ei; EMDOCS; Faxon; Genuine Article; SWETS; UMI; UnCover. **CCC**.
Description: Contains a variety of original articles on topics relating to the impact of science on life and society, including current research, new trends and historical issues.
Refereed Serial

600 US **ISSN 1048-0943**
SCIENTIFIC AMERICAN. SPECIAL ISSUE. (Supplement to: Scientific American (ISSN 0036-8733)) 1988. a. $8.95 per issue. Scientific American, Inc., 415 Madison Ave., New York, NY 10017-1111. TEL 212-754-0550. FAX 212-355-0408. (Subscr. to: Box 11314, Des Moines, IA 50340-1314. TEL 800-777-0444) adv.; bk.rev.; illus. (back issues avail.) **Document type:** academic/scholarly publication, consumer publication.
Description: In-depth examination of a single topic or trend in contemporary science.

SCIENCES: COMPREHENSIVE WORKS

500 — US — ISSN 1040-3213
SCIENTIFIC AMERICAN LIBRARY. m. Scientific American, Inc., 415 Madison Ave., New York, NY 10017-1111. TEL 212-754-0550. FAX 212-754-1138. (Orders to: Scientific American Library, Box 646, Holmes, PA 19043. TEL 800-345-8112) (back issues avail.) **Document type:** monographic series.
—BLDSC (8175.050000).
Description: Publishes studies of current topics in modern science.

500 600 — JA
SCIENTIFIC AND TECHNICAL INFORMATION IN FOREIGN COUNTRIES/KAIGAKI KAGAKU GIJUTSU JOHO SHIRYO. (Text in Japanese) irreg. Kagaku Gijutsucho, Keikaku-kyoku - Science and Technology Agency, Planning Bureau, 2-1 Kasumigaseki 2-chome, Chiyoda-ku, Tokyo 100, Japan. **Document type:** government publication.

500 — LY
SCIENTIFIC BULLETIN. m. Jamahiriya News Agency, Sharia al-Fateh, P.O. Box 2303, Tripoli, Libya. TEL 37106. TELEX 20841.

SCIENTIFIC, ENGINEERING, TECHNICAL MANPOWER COMMENTS. see *OCCUPATIONS AND CAREERS*

500 — SJ
SCIENTIFIC INFORMATION BULLETIN. (Text in English) 1977. m. Industrial Research and Consultancy Institute, Department of Documentation and Technical Information, Box 268, Khartoum, Sudan.

SCIENTIFIC MEETINGS. see *MEETINGS AND CONGRESSES*

500 Q1 — US — ISSN 0890-3670 — CODEN: SCIEEW
THE SCIENTIST; the newspaper for science professionals. 1986. 24/yr. $58 (foreign $79). The Scientist, Inc., 3600 Market St., Philadelphia, PA 19104. TEL 215-386-9601. FAX 215-387-7542. E-mail: garfield@aurora.cis.upenn.edu. (Subscr. to: The Scientist, 5615 W. Cermak Rd., Cicero, IL 60650) Ed. Eugene Garfield. adv.; bk.rev. circ. 50,000. (also avail. in microfilm from UMI) **Indexed:** Curr.Cont., Environ.Abstr., Tel.Abstr., Telegen. **Document type:** newspaper.
●Also available online. Vendor(s): CompuServe, Inc. (71764.2561).
—BLDSC (8205.010000); CASDDS; Faxon; Genuine Article; SWETS; UMI. **CCC.**
Description: News and commentary on business, policy and politics of science.

500 Q1 — NE — ISSN 0138-9130 — CODEN: SCNTDX
SCIENTOMETRICS; an international journal for all quantitative aspects of the science of science, communication in science and science policy. (Text in English) 1978. 9/yr. fl.1185($723) (effective 1996). Elsevier Science B.V., P.O. Box 211, 1000 AE Amsterdam, Netherlands. TEL 31-20-4853911. FAX 31-20-4853598. TELEX 18582 ESPA NL. E-mail: nlinfo-f@elsevier.nl; usinfo-f@elsevier.com; forinfo-kyf04035@niftyserve.or.jp; Site addr.: http://www.elsevier.nl/. (Subscr. in U.S. and Canada to: Elsevier Science Inc., Box 882, Madison Sq. Sta., New York, NY 10159. TEL 212-989-5800. FAX 212-633-3990) (Co-publisher: Akademiai Kiado, HU) Ed. T. Braun. adv.; bk.rev.; bibl. (also avail. in microform from UMI; back issues avail.) **Indexed:** ASCA, Biol.Abstr., CLOSS, Compumath, Curr.Adv.Ecol.Sci., Curr.Cont., INSPEC (1978-1991), Lang.& Lang.Behav.Abstr., Lang.Teach.& Ling.Abstr., LISA, Sociol.Abstr., SSCI. **Document type:** academic/scholarly publication.
—BLDSC (8205.080000); CASDDS; Ei; Faxon; Genuine Article; SWETS; UnCover. **CCC.**
Incorporates (in 1982): Journal of Research Communication Studies (ISSN 0378-5939)
Description: Publishes original studies, short communications, preliminary reports, review papers on scientometrics.
Refereed Serial

790.13 — IT
SCIENZA DUEMILA. 1979. m. Perodici Tattilo s.r.l., Via del Casale Piombino 30, 00135 Rome, Italy. TEL 06-305-26-41. FAX 06-30-52-506. Ed. Sebastiano Fusco. adv. circ. 200,000.
Formerly: Test.

500 — IT — ISSN 0394-0195
SCIENZA E DOSSIER. 1985. m. (11/yr.). L.62000 (foreign L.83000). Giunti Gruppo Editoriale S.p.A., Via Vincenzo Gioberto, 34, 50121 Florence, Italy. TEL 055-66791. FAX 055-268312. TELEX 571438. Ed. Massimo Casini.

500 — IT — ISSN 0582-2580
SCIENZA E TECNICA. 1937-1951; N.S. 1957-1963; N.S. 1970. m. Societa Italiana per il Progresso delle Scienze, 202 Viale Reg. Margherita, 00198 Rome, Italy. TEL 8554156. Dir. Rocco Capasso.

500 — IT — ISSN 0036-8083
LE SCIENZE. Italian translation of: Scientific American (US ISSN 0036-8733) 1968. m. L.55000 (foreign L.75000) (effective 1994). Le Scienze S.p.A., Piazza della Repubblica 8, 20121 Milan, Italy. TEL 39-2-290017535. FAX 39-2-6552908. Eds. Felice Ippolito, Jonathan Piel. adv.: color page L.13365000. bk.rev.; bibl.; charts; illus.; index. circ. 67,704. (back issues avail.)

500 — IT — ISSN 0392-8810
SCIENZE, LA MATEMATICA E IL LORO INSEGNAMENTO. 1964. bi-m. L.34500 (foreign L.56000($44)) (effective 1994). Editoriale e Finanziaria Le Monnier, S.p.a., Via A. Meucci 2, Casella Postale 202, 50100 Florence, Italy. TEL 39-55-6813801. FAX 39-55-643983. bk.rev.
Former titles (until 1976): Scienze ed il Loro Insegnamento (ISSN 0036-8903); Scienze e i Giovani.
Description: Covers the scientific and didactic aspects of mathematics and the techniques behind the science of instruction.

500 Q1 — AT — ISSN 0004-9549 — CODEN: SRCHAA
SEARCH; science and technology in Australia and New Zealand. 1970. m. Aus.$59 to individuals in Australia & New Zealand (elsewhere Aus.$70); institutions Aus.$180 (elsewhere Aus.$245). (Australian and New Zealand Association for the Advancement of Science) Control Publications, 14 Acheron St., Doncater, Vic. 3108, Australia. TEL 61-3-8489041. FAX 61-3-8482626. E-mail: search@control.com.au. Ed. Guy Nolch. adv.: B&W page Aus.$495, color page Aus.$990; trim 280 x 210; adv. contact: Jennifer Kempson. bk.rev. circ. 3,000. (also avail. in microform from UMI; reprint service avail. from UMI) **Indexed:** ASCA, Aus.Educ.Ind., Aus.Rd.Ind., Bibl.& Ind.Geol., Biol.Abstr., Curr.Adv.Ecol.Sci., Dairy Sci.Abstr., Deep Sea Res.& Oceanogr.Abstr., Field Crop Abstr., Forest.Abstr., Forest Prod.Abstr., Geo.Abstr., Geol.Abstr., Herb.Abstr., Ind.Vet., Plant Breed.Abstr., Rural Recreat.Tour.Abstr., Sci.Cit.Ind., Soils & Fert., Sport Fish.Abstr., Wild.Rev., World Agri.Econ.& Rural Sociol.Abstr., Zoo.Rec. **Document type:** academic/scholarly publication.
—BLDSC (8214.300000); CASDDS; Ei; Faxon; Genuine Article; UMI; UnCover. **CCC.**
Formerly: Australian Journal of Science.
Description: Provides a forum for news, discussion and debate of recent scientific and technological developments in the Asia Pacific region.

SEASONS; the nature & outdoors magazine. see *CONSERVATION*

SECRECY & GOVERNMENT BULLETIN. see *PUBLIC ADMINISTRATION*

500 — US
SELECTED RESEARCH IN MICROFICHE. Short title: S R I M. 1975. s-m. $1.25 per no. U.S. Department of Commerce, National Technical Information Service, 5285 Port Royal Rd., Springfield, VA 22161. TEL 703-487-4650. FAX 703-321-8547. cum.index. (back issues avail.) **Document type:** government publication, bibliography.

500 600 — II — ISSN 0970-6755
SEMINAR REPORTEUR; journal of science and technology. (Text in English) 1961. m. Rs.50($30) De Indiana Overseas Publications, 1424 Chandni Chowk, Delhi 6, India. Ed. I.D. Gupta.

500 — JA — ISSN 0386-5827
SENSHU SHIZEN KAGAKU KIYO/SENSHU UNIVERSITY. ASSOCIATION OF NATURAL SCIENCE. BULLETIN. (Text in English and Japanese; summaries in English) 1969. a. 3000 Yen (effective till 1995). Senshu Daigaku, Shizen Kagaku Kenkyukai - Senshu University, Association of Natural Science, 1-1 Higashi-Mita 2-chome, Tama-ku, Kawasaki-shi, Kanagawa-ken 214, Japan. TEL 81-44-911-0588. FAX 81-44-911-1243. Ed. Masakatsu Hirose. circ. 350 (controlled). **Document type:** bulletin.

500 — JA — ISSN 0287-4466
SETSUNAN UNIVERSITY. SCIENTIFIC REVIEW. SERIES A, NATURAL SCIENCES/SETSUDAI GAKUJUTSU. SHIZEN KAGAKU HEN. (Text and summaries in English and Japanese) 1980. a. Setsunan Daigaku, 17-8 Ikedanaka-machi, Neyagawa-shi, Osaka-fu 572, Japan.

500 — CC — ISSN 0559-7234 — CODEN: SDXKEU
SHANDONG DAXUE XUEBAO (ZIRAN KEXUE BAN)/SHANDONG UNIVERSITY. JOURNAL (NATURAL SCIENCE EDITION). (Text in Chinese) q. Shandong Daxue, Xuebao Bianjibu, No. 27, Shanda Nanlu, Jinan, Shandong 250100, People's Republic of China. TEL 643861. Ed. Wang Chengrui. **Document type:** academic/scholarly publication.
—CASDDS.

SHANGHAI JIAOTONG DAXUE XUEBAO/SHANGHAI JIAOTONG UNIVERSITY. BULLETIN. see *TECHNOLOGY: COMPREHENSIVE WORKS*

500 — CC — ISSN 1001-4217
SHANXI DAXUE XUEBAO (ZIRAN KEXUE BAN)/SHANXI UNIVERSITY. JOURNAL (NATURAL SCIENCE EDITION). (Text in Chinese) q. Shanxi Daxue, Xuebao Bianjibu, Wucheng Lu, Taiyuan, Shanxi 030006, People's Republic of China. TEL 773441. Ed. Liu Po. **Document type:** academic/scholarly publication.

SHAONIAN KEXUE/JUVENILE SCIENCE. see *CHILDREN AND YOUTH — For*

SHAONIAN KEXUE HUABAO/JUVENILE SCIENTIFIC PICTORIAL. see *CHILDREN AND YOUTH — For*

500 600 Q4 — CC — ISSN 1000-2618 — CODEN: SDXLEX
SHENZHEN DAXUE XUEBAO (LIGONG BAN)/SHENZHEN UNIVERSITY. JOURNAL (SCIENCE, ENGINEERING EDITION). (Text in Chinese) 1984. 2/yr. (2 nos. per issue). Y6. Shenzhen Daxue, Xuebao Bianjibu, Shenzhen, Guangdong 518060, People's Republic of China. TEL 6660277. Ed. Liao Keren. **Document type:** academic/scholarly publication.
Description: Contains academic papers. Aims to reflect research results and promote academic exchange.

500.9 — UK — ISSN 0080-9241
SHERBORN FUND FACSIMILES. (Text mainly in English; occasionally in other European languages) 1959. irreg., no.4, 1973. price varies. Society for the History of Natural History, c/o The Natural History Museum, Cromwell Rd., London SW7 5BD, England. **Document type:** monographic series.

500 — JA — ISSN 0488-6291 — CODEN: SDKGAH
SHIGA DAIGAKU KYOIKUGAKUBU KIYO. SHIZEN KAGAKU/SHIGA UNIVERSITY. FACULTY OF EDUCATION. MEMOIRS. NATURAL SCIENCE. (Text and summaries in English, French, and Japanese) 1952. a. free. Shiga Daigaku, Kyoikugakubu - Shiga University, Faculty of Education, 5-1 Hiratsu 2-chome, Otsu-shi, Shiga-ken 520, Japan. **Indexed:** Biol.Abstr., Chem.Abstr., Jap.Per.Ind. **Document type:** academic/scholarly publication.
—BLDSC (5593.327100).

500 600 — CC — ISSN 1003-1049
SHIJIE FAMING/REVIEW OF WORLD INVENTIONS. (Text in Chinese) 1978. m. Y12. China Patent News, Xueyuan Lukou, Beisanhuan Xilu, Beijing 100088, People's Republic of China. TEL 2021177. FAX 2019516. Ed. Wang Zhifu.

SCIENCES: COMPREHENSIVE WORKS

500 600   CC   ISSN 1003-1898
SHIJIE KEXUE JISHU/WORLD SCIENCE AND TECHNOLOGY. (Text in Chinese, Esperanto) 1985. q. $12. Zhongguo Kexueyuan, Keji Gongzuoze Shijieyu Xiehui - Chinese Academy of Sciences, Esperanto Association of Scientists and Technicians, 52 Sanlihe, Beijing 100864, People's Republic of China. TEL 861-2561724. Ed. Shen Chengru. adv. contact: Wang Yuchun. **Document type:** academic/scholarly publication.

500   JA   ISSN 0586-9943
SHIMANE DAIGAKU KYOIKUGAKUBU KIYO. SHIZEN KAGAKU/SHIMANE UNIVERSITY. FACULTY OF EDUCATION. MEMOIRS. NATURAL SCIENCE. (Text in English and Japanese; summaries in English) 1972. a. Shimane Daigaku, Kyoikugakubu - Shimane University, Faculty of Education, 1060 Nishi-Kawatsu-cho, Matsue-shi, Shimane-ken 690, Japan. **Indexed:** Jap.Per.Ind.

500   JA   ISSN 0387-9925
Q1   CODEN: SDRKDX
SHIMANE DAIGAKU RIGAKUBU KIYO/SHIMANE UNIVERSITY. FACULTY OF SCIENCE. MEMOIRS. (Text in English and Japanese) 1966. a. free. Shimane Daigaku, Rigakubu - Shimane University, Faculty of Science, 1060 Nishi-Kawatsu-cho, Matsue-shi, Shimane-ken 690, Japan. TEL 0852-32-6100. FAX 0852-32-6126. Ed. Jiro Sakamoto. circ. 600. **Indexed:** Biol.Abstr., Chem.Abstr., INIS Atomind., Jap.Per.Ind., Math.R. **Document type:** academic/scholarly publication.
    Description: Covers mathematics, physics, chemistry, biology, geology, and computer science.

SHIMANE IKA DAIGAKU KIYO/SHIMANE MEDICAL UNIVERSITY. BULLETIN. see *MEDICAL SCIENCES*

500.9   JA
SHIMANE NO SHIZEN. (Text in Japanese) 1976. irreg. Shimane-ken Shizen Koen Kyokai, Shimane-ken Kankyo Hokenbu Kankyo Hozenka, 1 Tono-machi, Matsue-shi, Shimane-ken 690, Japan.
    Description: Contains news about the association, and about natural parks in Shimane Prefecture.

500   MP
SHINJLEH UHAAN AM'DRAL/SCIENCE AND LIFE. (Text in Mongolian) 1935. m. Academy of Sciences, P.O. Box 48-17, Ulan Bator, Mongolia. TEL 21794. (Co-sponsor: Society for Dissemination of Scientific Knowledge) Ed. L. Jambaldorj. circ. 20,000.

500   MP
SHINJLEH UHAANY AKADEMIYN MEDEE/ACADEMY OF SCIENCES NEWS. (Text in Mongolian) 1961. q. Academy of Sciences, P.O. Box 48-17, Ulan Bator, Mongolia. Ed. S. Norovsambuu.

505   JA   ISSN 0583-063X
    CODEN: JFSSB9
SHINSHU UNIVERSITY. FACULTY OF SCIENCE. JOURNAL/SHINSHU DAIGAKU RIGAKUBU KIYO. (Text in Japanese and European languages) 1966. s-a. exchange basis. Shinshu University, Faculty of Science - Shinshu Daigaku Rigakubu, 1-1 Asahi 3-chome, Matsumoto-shi, Nagano-ken 390, Japan. Ed. Kiyoshi Mochizuki. **Indexed:** Bibl.& Ind.Geol., Biol.Abstr., Chem.Abstr., Text.Tech.Dig.
—BLDSC (4749.800000); CASDDS.

500 069   JA   ISSN 0387-8716
SHIRETOKO HAKUBUTSUKAN KENKYU HOKOKU/SHIRETOKO MUSEUM. BULLETIN. (Text in Japanese; summaries in English and Japanese) 1979. a. Shari-choritsu Shiretoko Hakubutsukan - Shiretoko Museum, 4-1 Moto-machi, Shari-cho, Shari-gun, Hokkaido 099-41, Japan.

SHIVAJI UNIVERSITY. JOURNAL (HUMANITIES). see *HUMANITIES: COMPREHENSIVE WORKS*

500   II   ISSN 0250-5347
    CODEN: JSUSDA
SHIVAJI UNIVERSITY. JOURNAL (SCIENCE). (Text in English) 1975. a. Rs.100. Shivaji University, Registrar, Shivaji University, Vidyangsar, Kolhapur (Maharashtra) 415 004, India. TEL 0231-25068. FAX 0231-24033. Ed. A.T. Varute. **Document type:** academic/scholarly publication.
—BLDSC (4876.184000); CASDDS.
    Formerly (until 1976): Shivaji University. Science Journal (ISSN 0379-0541)

SHIYOU DAXUE XUEBAO (ZIRAN KEXUE BAN)/UNIVERSITY OF PETROLEUM, CHINA. JOURNAL (NATURAL SCIENCE EDITION). see *PETROLEUM AND GAS*

500   JA   ISSN 0914-6385
Q77
SHIZEN KAGAKU KENKYU (TOKUSHIMA)/UNIVERSITY OF TOKUSHIMA. FACULTY OF INTEGRATED ARTS AND SCIENCES. NATURAL SCIENCE RESEARCH. (Text in Japanese; summaries in English) 1988. a. Tokushima Daigaku, Sogo Kagakubu - University of Tokushima, Faculty of Integrated Arts and Sciences, 1-1 Minami-Josanjima-cho, Tokushima-shi, Tokushima-ken 770, Japan.

500   JA   ISSN 0441-0017
Q4   CODEN: SZKKAD
SHIZEN KAGAKU KENKYU (TOKYO)/HITOTSUBASHI UNIVERSITY RESEARCH SERIES. SCIENCES. (Text in Japanese) 1959. a. Hitotsubashi Daigaku - Hitotsubashi University, 2-1 Naka, Kunitachi-shi, Tokyo 186, Japan. **Indexed:** Jap.Per.Ind.
—BLDSC (4318.988000).

500   JA   ISSN 0285-8150
SHIZEN KAGAKU RONSO. (Text in Japanese) 1969. a. Kyoto Joshi Daigaku, Shizen Kagaku Hoken Taiiku Kenkyushitsu - Kyoto Women's University, Society of Natural Science and Physical Education, 35 Kita-Hiyoshi-machi, Imagumano, Higashiyama-ku, Kyoto-shi, Kyoto-fu 605, Japan. **Indexed:** Jap.Per.Ind.

SHIZEN KANSATSUKAI KAIHO. see *ENVIRONMENTAL STUDIES*

500   JA   ISSN 0385-759X
SHIZEN KYOIKUEN HOKOKU/MINISTRY OF EDUCATION. NATIONAL SCIENCE MUSEUM. INSTITUTE FOR NATURE STUDY. MISCELLANEOUS REPORTS. (Text and summaries in English and Japanese) 1969. a. Monbusho, Kokuritsu Kagaku Hakubutsukan, Fuzoku Shizen Kyoikuen - Ministry of Education, National Science Museum, Institute for Nature Study, 21-5 Shiroganedai 5-chome, Minato-ku, Tokyo 108, Japan. TEL 03-3441-7176. FAX 03-3441-7012. **Document type:** government publication.

500.9   JA   ISSN 0078-6683
SHIZENSHI KENKYU/OSAKA MUSEUM OF NATURAL HISTORY. OCCASIONAL PAPERS. (Text in English or Japanese; summaries in English) 1968. irreg. (1-3/yr.). price varies; also avail. on exchange basis. Osaka-shiritsu Shizenshi Hakubutsukan - Osaka Museum of Natural History, 1-23 Nagai Koen, Higashi-Sumiyoshi-ku, Osaka-shi, Osaka-fu 546, Japan. Ed. Ryohei Yamanishi. circ. 1,000. **Indexed:** Bibl.& Ind.Geol., Biol.Abstr., Rev.Appl.Entomol.

500   JA   ISSN 0286-7311
SHIZUOKA DAIGAKU KYOIKUGAKUBU KENKYU HOKOKU. SHIZEN KAGAKU HEN/SHIZUOKA UNIVERSITY. FACULTY OF EDUCATION. BULLETIN. NATURAL SCIENCES SERIES. (Text and summaries in English and Japanese) 1950. a. not commercially avail. Shizuoka Daigaku, Kyoikugakubu, 836 Oya, Shizuoka-shi, Shizuoka-ken 422, Japan. TEL 054-237-1170. FAX 054-237-9376. **Indexed:** Jap.Per.Ind. **Document type:** academic/scholarly publication.
—BLDSC (2507.630000).

500   JA   ISSN 0285-0435
SHIZUOKA DAIGAKU KYOYOBU KENKYU HOKOKU. SHIZEN KAGAKU HEN/SHIZUOKA UNIVERSITY. FACULTY OF LIBERAL ARTS. REPORTS. SCIENCES. (Text in English and Japanese; summaries in English) 1965. a. Shizuoka Daigaku, Kyoyobu - Shizuoka University, Faculty of Liberal Arts, 836 Oya, Shizuoka-shi, Shizuoka-ken 422, Japan. **Indexed:** Jap.Per.Ind.

505   JA   ISSN 0583-0923
Q77   CODEN: RFSSBT
SHIZUOKA UNIVERSITY. FACULTY OF SCIENCE. REPORTS/SHIZUOKA DAIGAKU RIGAKUBU KENKYU HOKOKU. (Text in European languages) 1965. a. exchange basis. Shizuoka Daigaku, Rigakubu - Shizuoka University, Faculty of Science, 836 Oya, Shizuoka-shi, Shizuoka-ken 422, Japan. TEL 054-237-111. FAX 054-237-9895. Ed.Bd. circ. 500. **Indexed:** Bibl.& Ind.Geol., Biol.Abstr., Chem.Abstr., INIS Atomind., INSPEC, Math.R.
—BLDSC (7467.180000); CASDDS.
    Description: Contains original papers on mathematics, physics, chemistry, radiochemistry, biology, and geoscience.

500   AA
SHKENCA DHE JETA/SCIENCE ET VIE; reviste tekniko shkencore. 1969. bi-m. $10. Bashkimi i Rinise se Punes te Shqunerise - Union de la Jeunesse du Travail d'Albanie, Rruga "Punetoret e Rilindjes", Tirana, Albania. TEL 42-27818. Ed. Kudret Isai. bk.rev.; illus. circ. 17,500.

500   CC   ISSN 0253-2743
    CODEN: CHIKDA
SHULI KEXUE YU HUAXUE. (Text in Chinese) 1975. bi-m. Chongqing Shi Guangxue Jixie Yanjiusuo, 13, Changshicun, Shiqiaopu, Chongqing, Sichuan 630041, People's Republic of China. TEL 811450. Ed. Yang Keda. adv.; bk.rev. circ. 2,000. **Document type:** academic/scholarly publication.
—CASDDS.

500.9   TH   ISSN 0080-9462
QH1   CODEN: NHSAAC
SIAM SOCIETY. NATURAL HISTORY BULLETIN. 1913. a. $15 to non-members. Siam Society, 131 Soi Asoke Lane, Sukhumvit 21, Bangkok 10110, Thailand. TEL 662-259-4999. FAX 662-258-3491. E-mail: kanitk@nwg.nectec.or.th. Ed.Bd. bk.rev. (back issues avail.) **Indexed:** Amer.Hist.& Life, Biol.Abstr., Curr.Adv.Ecol.Sci., Hist.Abstr., Sport Fish.Abstr., Wild.Rev., Zoo.Rec. **Document type:** bulletin.
—BLDSC (6039.000000).

500   CC   ISSN 0490-6756
QH7   CODEN: SCTHAO
SICHUAN DAXUE XUEBAO (ZIRAN KEXUE BAN)/SICHUAN UNIVERSITY. JOURNAL (NATURAL SCIENCE EDITION). (Text in Chinese, English) 1955. q. Y6.40($4) Sichuan Daxue, Xuebao Bianjibu, Jiuyanqiao, Chengdu, Sichuan 610064, People's Republic of China. TEL 583875. Ed. Liu Yingming. circ. 2,000.
—BLDSC (4876.275000); CASDDS.

500   CC   ISSN 1001-8220
SICHUAN SHIFAN XUEYUAN XUEBAO (ZIRAN KEXUE BAN)/SICHUAN NORMAL COLLEGE. JOURNAL (NATURAL SCIENCE EDITION). (Text in Chinese) q. Sichuan Shifan Xueyuan, Xuebao Bianjibu, 10, Renmin Xilu, Nanchong, Sichuan 637002, People's Republic of China. TEL 22244. Ed. Tang Zesheng.

500   CL   ISSN 0716-8136
SIGLO XXI CIENCIA AND TECNOLOGIA. 1990. w. $360. El Mercurio S.A.P., Av. Santa Maria 5542, Apdo. Postal 13 D, Las Condes, Chile. TEL 562-3301461. FAX 562-2421128. TELEX 341635. E-mail: sigloxxi@reuna.cl; Site addr.: http://www.reuna.cl. Ed. Nicolas Luco. adv. contact: Alesandro Arze. circ. 60,000. (tabloid format)
●Also available online.
    Description: Covers computers, info-sciences, and technology for youth and young adults.

500   US
SIGMA XI NEWSLETTER. Issued with: American Scientist (ISSN 0003-0996) 1991. m. membership. Sigma Xi, Scientific Research Society, Box 13975, Research Triangle Park, NC 27709. TEL 919-549-4691. **Document type:** newsletter.
    Description: Contains society news and announcements.

500   PH   ISSN 0037-5284
AS540
SILLIMAN JOURNAL; a quarterly of investigation and discussion in the humanities and in the sciences. 1954. q. P.50($25) Silliman University, Dumaguete City 6200, Philippines. TEL 2252516. FAX 2254776. E-mail: succfred@durian.usc.edu.ph. Eds. Rose Baseleres, Ceres Pioquinto. bk.rev.; charts; illus.; index. circ. 500. (also avail. in microform from UMI; reprint service avail. from UMI) **Indexed:** Biol.Abstr., Chem.Abstr., Ind.Phil.Per., M.L.A. **Document type:** academic/scholarly publication.
—UMI; UnCover.
    Description: Covers humanities and sciences with an emphasis on Negros, Cebu, and the Visayan region.

500 ET ISSN 0379-2897
CODEN: SINTD7
SINET; Ethiopian journal of science. (Text in English) 1978. s-a. $12 to individuals; institutions $30. Addis Ababa University, Faculty of Science, P.O. Box 31226, Addis Ababa, Ethiopia. TEL 251-1-553177. FAX 251-1-552112. TELEX 21205. Ed. Legesse Negash. **Indexed:** Bibl.& Ind.Geol., Biol.Abstr., Excerp.Med., Field Crop Abstr., Seed Abstr., Sorghum & Millets Abstr., Zoo.Rec. **Document type:** academic/scholarly publication.
—BLDSC (8285.410000); CASDDS.
  Description: Features review articles, research papers or short notes in science and technology and related disciplines.
  Refereed Serial

500 ET ISSN 1011-9507
CODEN: SINNEO
SINET NEWSLETTER. (Text in English) 1978. m. Addis Ababa University, Faculty of Science, P.O. Box 31226, Addis Ababa, Ethiopia. TEL 251-1-553177. FAX 251-1-552112. TELEX 21205. **Indexed:** Zoo.Rec. **Document type:** newsletter.

500 ET
SINET: PROCEEDINGS OF ANNUAL PROGRAMMES REVIEW CONFERENCE. (Text in English) 1978. a. Addis Ababa University, Faculty of Science, P.O. Box 31226, Addis Ababa, Ethiopia. TEL 251-553177. FAX 251-1-552112. TELEX 21205. **Document type:** proceedings.

500 SI
SINGAPORE. NATIONAL SCIENCE AND TECHNOLOGY BOARD. ANNUAL REPORTS. 1972. a. free. National Science and Technology Board, 16 Science Park Drive, 01-03 The Pasteur, Singapore Science Park, Singapore 0511, Singapore. TEL 7797066. FAX 7771711. charts; illus.; stat.
  Formerly: Singapore. Science Council. Annual Reports.

SIPISCOPE. see *JOURNALISM*

SMITHSONIAN. see *SOCIAL SCIENCES: COMPREHENSIVE WORKS*

500 US ISSN 0364-0175
Q179.9 CODEN: SIRRDL
SMITHSONIAN INSTITUTION RESEARCH REPORTS. 1972. 4/yr. free. Smithsonian Institution, Office of Public Affairs, 900 Jefferson Dr., Rm. 2410, Washington, DC 20560. TEL 202-357-1300. Ed. Jo Ann Webb. illus. circ. 30,000. **Indexed:** Bibl.& Ind.Geol., Environ.Abstr., Ind.U.S.Gov.Per.
  Formerly: Smithsonian Research Reports.
  Description: Smithsonian programs and research.

500 US ISSN 0081-0339
SMITHSONIAN OPPORTUNITIES FOR RESEARCH AND STUDY IN HISTORY ART SCIENCE. Title varies: Smithsonian Research Opportunities. 1964. a. free. Smithsonian Institution, Office of Fellowships and Grants, 955 L'Enfant Plaza, Ste. 7000, Washington, DC 20560. TEL 202-287-3271. E-mail: siofg@sivm.si.edu. index. **Document type:** academic/scholarly publication.
  Formerly: Smithsonian Institution Opportunities for Research and Advanced Study.

500 300 UK ISSN 0306-3127
Q1
SOCIAL STUDIES OF SCIENCE; an international review of research in the social dimensions of science and technology. q. £38 to individuals; institutions £140. Sage Publications Ltd., 6 Bonhill St., London EC2A 4PU, England. TEL 0171-374-0645. FAX 0171-374-8741. E-mail: market@sageltd.co.uk. Ed. David Edge. adv.: B&W page £200; trim 170 x 100; adv. contact: Bernie Folan. bk.rev.; index. (back issues avail.) **Indexed:** Amer.Hist.& Life, Arts & Hum.Cit.Ind., ASCA, ASSIA, CIJE, Curr.Cont., Deep Sea Res.& Oceanogr.Abstr., Excerp.Med., High.Educ.Curr.Aware.Bull., Hist.Abstr., IBZ, Int.Polit.Sci.Abstr., Lang.& Lang.Behav.Abstr., Mid.East: Abstr.& Ind., Res.High.Educ.Abstr., Sage Pub.Admin.Abstr., Sci.Cit.Ind., Sociol.Abstr. (1971-), SSCI, Stud.Wom.Abstr. **Document type:** academic/scholarly publication.
  —BLDSC (8318.214100); Faxon; SWETS; UnCover.
  Description: Serves the growing community of historians, philosophers, sociologists, political scientists and economists who are contributing research on the study of science in its social dimension.
  Refereed Serial

500 AG ISSN 0037-8437
Q33 CODEN: ASCAA2
SOCIEDAD CIENTIFICA ARGENTINA. ANALES. (Text in English, Spanish; summaries in English) 1876. a. $50. Sociedad Cientifica Argentina, Avda. Santa Fe 1145, 1059 Buenos Aires, Argentina. Ed. Eduardo A. Castro. adv.; bk.rev.; bibl.; charts; illus.; index. circ. 3,000. **Indexed:** Biol.Abstr., Chem.Abstr., Deep Sea Res.& Oceanogr.Abstr., Field Crop Abstr., Geo.Abstr., Herb.Abstr., Rev.Appl.Entomol., Rev.Plant Path. **Document type:** academic/scholarly publication.
  —CASDDS.

500 AG
SOCIEDAD CIENTIFICA ARGENTINA. CICLO DE CONFERENCIAS. irreg. (2-3/yr.). Sociedad Cientifica Argentina, Comision de Cursos y Conferencias, Av. Santa Fe 1145, Buenos Aires, Argentina. illus.

500.9 VE ISSN 0037-8518
Q4 CODEN: SCNSAR
SOCIEDAD DE CIENCIAS NATURALES LA SALLE. MEMORIA. 1940. s-a. Bs.300($25) Fundacion La Salle de Ciencias Naturales, Av. Boyaca-Maripez, Apdo. 1930, Caracas 1010A, Venezuela. adv.; charts; illus.; index, cum.index: 1940-1990. circ. 1,300. (also avail. in microfilm from UMI; reprint service avail. from KTO,UMI) **Indexed:** Bibl.& Ind.Geol., Biol.Abstr., Chem.Abstr., Deep Sea Res.& Oceanogr.Abstr., Int.Abstr.Biol.Sci.
  Incorporates: Novedades Cientificas Serie Zoologia.

509 600 CK ISSN 0185-5107
SOCIEDAD LATINOAMERICANA DE HISTORIA DE LA CIENCIA Y LA TECNOLOGIA. BOLETIN INFORMATIVO. (Text in English, Spanish) 1983. 3/yr. $5. Sociedad Latinoamericana de Historia de la Ciencia y la Tecnologia, c/o Colciencias, Tranversal 9a, 133-28, Bogota D.E., Colombia. Ed. Luis Carlos Arboleda. bk.rev.

500 BL ISSN 0103-1899
SOCIEDADE BRASILEIRA DE HISTORIA DA CIENCIA. BOLETIM. s-a.? Sociedade Brasileira de Historia da Ciencia, Pont. Univ. Catolica de Sao Paulo, Rua Monte Alegre, 984, 4o andar, Predio Novo, Sala 427, 05014 Sao Paulo SP, Brazil. FAX 55-11-872-2413. Ed. Ana Maria Goldfarb. bibl. **Document type:** bulletin.

508 IT ISSN 0037-8844
Q54 CODEN: ASIMAY
SOCIETA ITALIANA DI SCIENZE NATURALI E DEL MUSEO CIVICO DI STORIA NATURALE. ATTI. (Text in Italian; summaries in English, French, German) 1856. s-a. L.45000 (effective 1995). Societa Italiana di Scienze Naturali, Corso Venezia 55, 20121 Milan, Italy. TEL 39-2-62085405. (Co-sponsor: Museo Civico di Storia Naturale) Ed. Giovanni Pinna. bk.rev.; charts; illus.; index. circ. 1,500. (back issues avail.) **Indexed:** Bibl.& Ind.Geol., Biol.Abstr., Chem.Abstr., Deep Sea Res.& Oceanogr.Abstr., Sport Fish.Abstr., Wild.Rev., Zoo.Rec. **Document type:** academic/scholarly publication.
  —CASDDS.

500.9 IT ISSN 0376-2726
Q54 CODEN: MINSA3
SOCIETA ITALIANA DI SCIENZE NATURALI E DEL MUSEO CIVICO DI STORIA NATURALE. MEMORIE. 1865. irreg. price varies. Societa Italiana di Scienze Naturali, Corso Venezia, 55, 20121 Milan, Italy. TEL 39-2-62085405. (Co-sponsor: Museo Civico di Storia Naturale) Ed. Giovanni Pinna. circ. 1,000. (back issues avail.) **Document type:** monographic series.

500 IT
SOCIETA ITALIANA PER IL PROGRESSO DELLE SCIENZE. ATTI DELLA RIUNIONE. 1907. biennial. L.30000 to non-members. Societa Italiana per il Progresso delle Scienze, 202 Viale Reg. Margherita, 00198 Rome, Italy. TEL 8554156.

500 IT ISSN 0365-7655
CODEN: ATVAA2
SOCIETA TOSCANA DI SCIENZA NATURALI. ATTI. SERIE A. (Supplement avail.: Societa Toscana di Scienza Naturali. Processi Verbali (ISSN 0365-7477)) 1875. a. L.50000 (effective 1995). Pacini Editore s.r.l., Via A. Gherardesca 1, 56121 Ospedaletto (Pisa), Italy. TEL 39-50-982439. FAX 39-50-983906. Ed. L. Trevisan. **Document type:** academic/scholarly publication.
  —BLDSC (1783.500000); CASDDS.
  Supersedes in part (in 1948): Societa Toscana di Scienze Naturali Residente in Pisa. Atti e Memorie (ISSN 0365-7108); Which was formerly (until 1880): Societa Toscana di Scienze Naturali Residente in Pisa. Atti (ISSN 0394-7165)

500 IT ISSN 0365-7450
CODEN: ATMBAS
SOCIETA TOSCANA DI SCIENZA NATURALI. ATTI. SERIE B. (Supplement avail.: Societa Toscana di Scienza Naturali. Processi Verbali (ISSN 0365-7477)) 1875. a. L.65000 (effective 1995). Pacini Editore s.r.l., Via A. Gherardesca 1, 56121 Ospedaletto (Pisa), Italy. TEL 050-982439. FAX 050-983906. Ed. L. Trevisan. **Document type:** academic/scholarly publication.
  —BLDSC (1783.600000).
  Supersedes in part (in 1948): Societa Toscana di Scienze Naturali Residente in Pisa. Atti e Memorie (ISSN 0365-7108); Which was formerly (until 1880): Societa Toscana di Scienze Naturali Residente in Pisa. Atti (ISSN 0394-7165)

500 SP ISSN 1130-4758
Q65 CODEN: BSCMDI
SOCIETATS CATALANES DE FISICA, QUIMICA, MATEMATIQUES I TECNOLOGIA. BUTLLETI. 1934. s-a. 3000 ptas. Sociedades Catalanes de Fisica, Quimica, Matematicas y Tecnologia, Carrer del Carme 47, 08001 Barcelona, Spain.
  —CASDDS.
  Formerly (until 1991): Societat Catalana de Ciencies Fisiques Quimiques i Matematiques. Butlleti (ISSN 0211-4305)

500.9 FR ISSN 0753-4655
SOCIETE D'HISTOIRE NATURELLE DU DOUBS. BULLETIN. (Text in French; summaries occasionally in English) 1899; N.S. 1968. a. membership. Societe d'Histoire Naturelle du Doubs, Institut des Sciences Naturelles, Place Leclerc, 25030 Besancon Cedex, France. Ed. Bernard Bonnet. adv.; bk.rev.; bibl.; charts; cum.index. circ. 500. **Indexed:** Biol.Abstr., VITIS.
  —BLDSC (2742.950000).
  Former titles (1968-78): Federation des Societes d'Histoire Naturelle de Franche-Comte. Bulletin (ISSN 0014-9357); Societe d'Histoire Naturelle du Doubs. Bulletin.

500 800 PL ISSN 0459-6854
AS262.L6 CODEN: BSSEA3
SOCIETE DES SCIENCES ET DES LETTRES DE LODZ. BULLETIN. (Text in English, French, German, Russian) 1950. a. $29 (effective 1996). Lodzkie Towarzystwo Naukowe - Lodz Scientific Society, Piotrkowska 179, 90-447 Lodz, Poland. TEL 48-42-361026. FAX 48-42-361995. (Dist. by: Ars Polona-Ruch, Krakowskie Przedmiescie 7, 00-068 Warsaw, Poland) Ed. Julian Lawrynowicz. bibl.; illus. circ. 500. **Indexed:** Bibl.& Ind.Geol., Biol.Abstr., Math.R.

500 MR ISSN 0037-9255
CODEN: BSMAAT
SOCIETE DES SCIENCES NATURELLES ET PHYSIQUES DU MAROC. BULLETIN. (Text in French; summaries in English and French) 1920. s-a. DH.45($9) Societe des Sciences Naturelles et Physiques du Maroc, Institut Scientifique Cherifiens, Ave. Moulay Cherif, Rabat, Morocco. **Indexed:** Bibl.& Ind.Geol., Biol.Abstr., Bull.Signal.

500.1 510 FR ISSN 0374-9231
SOCIETE NATIONALE DES SCIENCES NATURELLES ET MATHEMATIQUES DE CHERBOURG. MEMOIRES. 1852. a. Societe Nationale des Sciences Naturelles et Mathematiques de Cherbourg, 21 rue Bonhomme, 50100 Cherbourg, France.
  —BLDSC (5569.550000).
  Formerly (until 1879): Societe des Sciences Naturelles de Cherbourg. Memoires (ISSN 0373-4781)

5900 SCIENCES: COMPREHENSIVE WORKS

500   BE   ISSN 0037-9565
Q56   CODEN: BSRSA6
SOCIETE ROYALE DES SCIENCES DE LIEGE. BULLETIN. (Text in English, French) 1843. 6/yr. 2500 Fr. (Societe Royale des Sciences de Liege) Editions Derouaux, 15 av. des Tilleuls, B-4000 Liege, Belgium. FAX 041-522169. Ed. J. Godeaux. charts. **Indexed:** Appl.Mech.Rev., Bibl.& Ind.Geol., Biol.Abstr., Chem.Abstr., Deep Sea Res.& Oceanogr.Abstr., Geo.Abstr., INIS Atomind., INSPEC (1968-), Math.R.
—BLDSC (2751.000000); CASDDS; Ei; Faxon; SWETS; UnCover.

500   FR   ISSN 0037-9581
Q46   CODEN: BSSBAS
SOCIETE SCIENTIFIQUE DE BRETAGNE. BULLETIN. 1924. q. price varies. Societe Scientifique de Bretagne, Faculte des Sciences, 35000 Rennes, France. Ed. Leon Grillet. bibl.; charts; illus.; cum.index: 1924-1973. **Indexed:** Bibl.& Ind.Geol., Biol.Abstr., Bull.Signal., Chem.Abstr., Deep Sea Res.& Oceanogr.Abstr., INSPEC (1977-1980).
—CASDDS.

500.1   SZ   ISSN 0037-9603
                   CODEN: BSVAA6
SOCIETE VAUDOISE DES SCIENCES NATURELLES. BULLETIN. (Text in French; summaries in English, German and Italian) 1844. s-a. 50 SFr.($32) Societe Vaudoise des Sciences Naturelles, Palais de Rumine, CH-1005 Lausanne, Switzerland. TEL 021-312-4334. Ed. Jean-Louis Moret. adv.; bk.rev.; bibl.; charts; illus.; index, cum.index: vols.1-50, 51-60. (Reprint service avail. from UMI.) **Indexed:** Biol.Abstr., Chem.Abstr., Field Crop Abstr., Geo.Abstr., Geol.Abstr., Herb.Abstr. **Document type:** academic/scholarly publication, bulletin.
—UMI.

500.1   SZ   ISSN 0037-9611
Q67   CODEN: MSVNAU
SOCIETE VAUDOISE DES SCIENCES NATURELLES. MEMOIRES. (Text in French; summaries in English, German and Italian) 1922. irreg. price varies. Societe Vaudoise des Sciences Naturelles, CH-1005 Lausanne, Switzerland. TEL 021-3124334. adv.; bibl.; charts; illus.; maps; index, cum.index: vols.1-17. (reprint service avail. from UMI) **Indexed:** Bibl.& Ind.Geol., Biol.Abstr., Chem.Abstr. **Document type:** academic/scholarly publication.
—BLDSC (5573.000000); UMI.
Description: Scientific studies in geology, paleontology, botany, zoology, physiology, agronomy, chemistry, ecology, ethnology, mathematics, medicine, meteorology, and physics.

SOCIETY FOR COMMON INSIGHTS. JOURNAL. see *RELIGIONS AND THEOLOGY*

500   MW   ISSN 0037-993X
DT858   CODEN: SMJODY
SOCIETY OF MALAWI JOURNAL. vol.23, 1970. s-a. $20 (effective 1992). Society of Malawi, P.O. Box 125, Blantyre, Malawi. Ed. T. Hopper. bk.rev.; charts; illus.; stat.; index. circ. 500. **Indexed:** A.I.C.P., Amer.Hist.& Life, Biol.Abstr., Documentatieblad, Hist.Abstr., P.L.E.S.A.
—BLDSC (8319.800000).
Formerly (until 1965): Nyasaland Journal.

301 500   NE   ISSN 0167-2320
SOCIOLOGY OF THE SCIENCES. YEARBOOK. Key Title: Sociology of the Sciences. (Text in English) 1977. a., vol.17, 1994. fl.170 (effective 1994). Kluwer Academic Publishers, Postbus 17, 3300 AA Dordrecht, Netherlands. TEL 31-78-392392. FAX 31-78-392254. TELEX 29245 KAPG NL. (Dist. by: Kluwer Academic Publishers Group, P.O. Box 322, 3300 AH Dordrecht. TEL 31-78-392392. FAX 31-78-546474; N. America dist. addr.: Box 358, Accord Sta., Hingham, MA 02018-0358. TEL 617-871-6600. FAX 617-871-6528) Ed. R.D. Whitley. **Document type:** monographic series.
—BLDSC (8319.696700); Faxon.
Refereed Serial

SOCIOLOGY OF THE SCIENCES MONOGRAPHS. see *SOCIOLOGY*

500 600   JA   ISSN 0913-6584
SOGO GAKUJUTSU KENKYU SHUKAI. (Text in Japanese) 1976. irreg. Nihon Kagakusha Kaigi - Japan Scientists Association, 9-16 Yushima 1-chome, Bunkyo-ku, Tokyo 113, Japan.
Description: Contains research reports of the association.

SOGO KENKYUJO HOKOKU. see *TECHNOLOGY: COMPREHENSIVE WORKS*

SOMERSET ARCHAEOLOGY AND NATURAL HISTORY. see *ARCHAEOLOGY*

500.9   US
SONORENSIS. 1972. q. membership. Arizona-Sonora Desert Museum, Inc., 2021 N. Kinney Rd., Tucson, AZ 85743. TEL 602-833-1380. FAX 602-883-2500. bibl.; illus. **Indexed:** Sport Fish.Abstr., Wild.Rev. **Document type:** newsletter.
Formerly: A S D M Newsletter (ISSN 0044-8850)

SOOCHOW JOURNAL OF MATHEMATICS. see *MATHEMATICS*

500.9   UK   ISSN 0038-1551
SORBY NATURAL HISTORY SOCIETY NEWSLETTER. 1964. 12/yr. membership. Sorby Natural History Society, 9 Rosslyn Ave., Aston, Sheffield, Yorkshire, England. TEL 0742-879622. Ed. L. Storer. bk.rev.; bibl. circ. 500. (processed) **Document type:** newsletter.
Description: Details of society meetings and local natural history news.

500.9   UK   ISSN 0260-2245
SORBY RECORD; a journal of natural history for the Sheffield area. 1958. irreg. membership. Sorby Natural History Society, 9 Rosslyn Ave., Aston, Sheffield, Yorkshire, England. TEL 0742-879622. Ed. D. Whiteley. circ. 1,000. **Document type:** academic/scholarly publication.
Description: Articles on all aspects of natural history in the Sheffield area.

509   II
SOURCE MATERIALS ON THE HISTORY OF SCIENCE IN INDIA. irreg. price varies. Indian National Science Academy, Bahadur Zafar Marg, New Delhi 110002, India. TEL 91-11-3313153. FAX 91-11-3716648. TELEX 31-61835 INSA IN.

500 600   SA   ISSN 0081-2455
Q845   CODEN: SAARCF
SOUTH AFRICAN JOURNAL OF ANTARCTIC RESEARCH. 1971. a. free. Department of Environment Affairs and Tourism, Sub-directorate: Antarctica and Islands, Private Bag X447, Pretoria 0001, South Africa. TEL 27-12-310-3548. FAX 27-12-322682. TELEX 321914. Ed. Mrs. A van Deventer. circ. 500. **Indexed:** Bibl.& Ind.Geol., Biol.Abstr., Chem.Abstr., Deep Sea Res.& Oceanogr.Abstr., Geo.Abstr., Ind.S.A.Per., INSPEC (1972-). **Document type:** academic/scholarly publication, government publication.
—BLDSC (8338.700000); CASDDS; Faxon.

500   SA   ISSN 0038-2353
Q85   CODEN: SAJSAR
SOUTH AFRICAN JOURNAL OF SCIENCE/SUID-AFRIKAANSE TYDSKRIF VIR WETENSKAP. (Text mainly in English, occasionally in Afrikaans) 1903. 11/yr. R.160 to individuals; institutions R.250 (effective 1994). Foundation for Research Development - Stigting vir Navorsingsontwikkeling, P.O. Box 2600, Pretoria 0001, South Africa. TEL 27-12-8414076. FAX 27-12-8042679. (Subscr. to: Foundation for Education, Science and Technology, P.O. Box 1758, Pretoria 0001, South Africa. TEL 27-12-322-644) (Co-sponsor: Department of National Education) Ed. Graham S. Baker. adv.: B&W page R.1320, color page R.1980; trim 210 x 297; adv. contact: Robyn Arnold. bk.rev.; bibl.; charts; illus.; stat.; index. circ. 1,000. (also avail. in microform from UMI; reprint service avail. from ISI,UMI) **Indexed:** A.I.C.P., Agroforest.Abstr., Anim.Breed.Abstr., Anthropol.Lit., Bio-Contr.News & Info., Biol.Abstr., Chem.Abstr., Curr.Adv.Ecol.Sci., Curr.Cont., Curr.Ref.Fish Res., Dairy Sci.Abstr., Deep Sea Res.& Oceanogr.Abstr., Ecol.Abstr., Energy Ind., Energy Info.Abstr., Eng.Ind., Excerp.Med., Field Crop Abstr., Forest.Abstr., Forest Prod.Abstr., Geo.Abstr., Geol.Abstr., Geotech.Abstr., Helminthol.Abstr., Herb.Abstr., Hort.Abstr., IDA, Ind.S.A.Per., Ind.Vet., INSPEC (1968-1977), Met.Abstr., Meteor.& Geoastrophys.Abstr., Nutr.Abstr., Ocean.Abstr., Ornam.Hort., Plant Breed.Abstr., Plant Grow.Reg.Abstr., Pollut.Abstr., Protozool.Abstr., Res.High.Educ.Abstr., Rev.Plant Path., Rural Devel.Abstr., Rural Ext.Educ.& Tr.Abstr., Seed Abstr., Sel.Water Res.Abstr., Soils & Fert., Trop.Oil Seeds Abstr., Vet.Bull., Weed Abstr., World Agri.Econ.& Rural Sociol.Abstr. **Document type:** academic/scholarly publication.
—BLDSC (8340.000000); CASDDS; Ei; Faxon; Genuine Article; SWETS; UMI; UnCover.
Incorporates (in 1984): Scientific Progress - Wetenskaplike Vordering (ISSN 0036-8814)
Description: Publishes original research results, and short communications, in all fields of scientific endeavor. Also discusses science policy issues relevant to the South African and international scientific communities.
Refereed Serial

500 600   SA
Q180.A6
SOUTH AFRICAN NATIONAL ANTARCTIC PROGRAMME. ANNUAL REPORT TO S C A R. (Scientific Committee for Antarctic Research) 1963. a. free. c/o D.J. van Schalkwyk, Dept. of Environment Affairs, Private Bag X447, Pretoria 0001, South Africa. TEL 27-12-310-3911. FAX 27-12-322-2682. TELEX 321914. (Affiliate: South African National Committee for Antarctic Research) bibl. circ. 300. **Document type:** government publication.
Supersedes: Report to S C A R on South African Antarctic Research (ISSN 0081-2412)
Description: Provides a record of activities in all scientific disciplines conducted at the 4 South African research stations in Antarctica and on Gough and Marion Islands, and discusses planned activities.

500.9   AT   ISSN 0376-2750
QL1   CODEN: RAMUA3
SOUTH AUSTRALIAN MUSEUM. RECORDS. 1918. s-a. Aus.$35. South Australian Museum, N. Terrace, Adelaide, S.A. 5000, Australia. TEL 08-207-7500. FAX 08-207-7222. bk.rev. circ. 450. (back issues avail.) **Indexed:** Aus.Sci.Ind., Biol.Abstr., Deep Sea Res.& Oceanogr.Abstr., So.Pac.Per.Ind., Zoo.Rec. **Document type:** academic/scholarly publication.
—BLDSC (7325.180000).

508   AT   ISSN 0038-2965
QH1   CODEN: SANAAR
SOUTH AUSTRALIAN NATURALIST; a quarterly journal of natural history. 1919. q. Aus.$25 to non-members. Field Naturalists' Society of South Australia, Inc., G.P.O. Box 1594, Adelaide, S.A. 5001, Australia. Ed. R. Cook. bk.rev.; charts; illus.; maps. circ. 600. **Indexed:** AESIS, Aus.Sci.Ind., Biol.Abstr., Sport Fish.Abstr., Wild.Rev., Zoo.Rec.

SCIENCES: COMPREHENSIVE WORKS

500 US ISSN 0096-414X
Q11 CODEN: BSCAAD
SOUTH CAROLINA ACADEMY OF SCIENCE. BULLETIN. 1935. a. $25. South Carolina Academy of Science, c/o John L. Safko, Treas., Dept. of Physics & Astronomy, University of South Carolina, Columbia, SC 29208. TEL 803-777-6466. FAX 803-777-3065. E-mail: cowley@brol.scarolina.edu. Ed. G.T. Cowley. index; circ. 750 (paid). (back issues avail.) **Indexed:** Biol.Abstr., Sport Fish.Abstr., Wild.Rev. **Document type:** bulletin.

500 US ISSN 0096-378X
Q11 CODEN: PSDAA2
SOUTH DAKOTA ACADEMY OF SCIENCE. PROCEEDINGS. 1916. a. $12. South Dakota Academy of Science, University of South Dakota, 414 E. Clark St., Vermillion, SD 57069. TEL 605-677-6176. Ed. Emil Knapp. abstr.; charts; illus.; stat.; circ. 350 (controlled). **Indexed:** Bibl.& Ind.Geol., Chem.Abstr., Field Crop Abstr., Geo.Abstr., Irr.& Drain.Abstr., Maize Abstr., Sel.Water Res.Abstr., Soils & Fert., Soyabean Abstr., Sport Fish.Abstr., Wild.Rev., Zoo.Rec. **Document type:** proceedings.
—BLDSC (6821.000000); CASDDS; UnCover.
Description: Presents lectures and papers submitted at the proceedings.

500 US ISSN 0038-3872
Q11 CODEN: BCASAD
SOUTHERN CALIFORNIA ACADEMY OF SCIENCES. BULLETIN. 1902. 3/yr. $30 (foreign $35) (effective 1995). Southern California Academy of Sciences, 1041 New Hampshire Ave., Box 1897, Lawrence, KS 66044-8897. TEL 800-627-0629. FAX 913-843-1274. (Alt. addr.: Southern California Academy of Sciences, 900 Exposition Blvd., Los Angeles, CA 90007. TEL 213-744-3384. FAX 213-746-2999) Ed. Daniel A. Guthrie. bibl.; charts; illus.; index. circ. 500. **Indexed:** Bibl.& Ind.Geol., Biol.Abstr., Deep Sea Res.& Oceanogr.Abstr., Ocean.Abstr., Pollut.Abstr. **Document type:** academic/scholarly publication.
—BLDSC (2763.000000); Faxon.
Refereed Serial

500 US
SOUTHERN RESEARCH INSTITUTE. ANNUAL REPORT. 1945. a. free. Southern Research Institute, Box 55305, Birmingham, AL 35255. TEL 205-581-2000. FAX 205-581-2726. Ed. Barbara F. Caspar. **Document type:** corporate report.

508 US ISSN 0038-4909
QH1 CODEN: SWNAAB
SOUTHWESTERN NATURALIST. (Text in English and Spanish) 1953. q. $25 to individuals; institutions $35; students $15 (effective 1996). Southwestern Association of Naturalists, c/o Dr. Paula Williamson, Treas., Biology Department, Southwest Texas State University, 601 University Dr., San Marcos, TX 78666. TEL 512-245-2171. FAX 512-245-8095. Ed. Edie Marsh. adv.; bk.rev.; bibl.; charts; illus.; Bibl.& Ind.Geol. circ. 1,400. (also avail. in microform from UMI; reprint service avail. from UMI) **Indexed:** ASCA, Biol.Abstr., Curr.Adv.Ecol.Sci., Curr.Cont., Field Crop Abstr., Forest.Abstr., Forest Prod.Abstr., Geo.Abstr., Helminthol.Abstr., Herb.Abstr., Key Word Ind.Wildl.Res., Ornam.Hort., Sel.Water Res.Abstr., Soils & Fert., Sport Fish.Abstr., Wild.Rev., Zoo.Rec. **Document type:** academic/scholarly publication.
—BLDSC (8357.280000); Faxon; Genuine Article; UMI; UnCover.
Description: Contains articles on scientific investigations on plants and animals (living and fossil) endemic to the southwestern U.S., Mexico, and Central America.
Refereed Serial

500.5 NO ISSN 0801-9517
SPACE RESEARCH IN NORWAY. (Text in English) 1963. a. free. Norwegian Space Centre, P.O. Box 85, Smestad, N-0309 Oslo, Norway. TEL 47-22-523800. FAX 47-22-522397. E-mail: bo@admin.nsc.no. Ed. Bo N. Andersen. bk.rev.; bibl.; illus. circ. 1,500.
Former titles: Space Activity in Norway (ISSN 0801-9525); Norway. Komite for Romforskning. N.S.C. Report (ISSN 0452-3687)
Description: Presents an overview of all space science projects in Norway, with description of infrastructure and organizations.

508 SA ISSN 0257-005X
SPECTRUM; natural science journal for teachers and lecturers. 1963. q. R.24 (effective 1995). Foundation for Education, Science and Technology, P.O. Box 1758, Pretoria 0001, South Africa. TEL 27-12-322-6404. FAX 27-12-320-7803. bk.rev. circ. 2,500. **Indexed:** Chem.Abstr., Ind.S.A.Per. **Document type:** academic/scholarly publication.
—BLDSC (8411.174500).

SPECTRUM; jornal brasileiro ciencias. see
TECHNOLOGY: COMPREHENSIVE WORKS

500 UK ISSN 0155-7785
Q1 CODEN: SPSTDD
SPECULATIONS IN SCIENCE AND TECHNOLOGY; an international journal devoted to speculative papers in the physical, mathematical, biological and engineering sciences. (Text and summaries in English) 1977. q. £66($131) to individuals; institutions £121 (N. America $242). Chapman & Hall, Journals Department (Subsidiary of: International Thomson Publishing Group), 2-6 Boundary Row, London SE1 8HN, England. TEL 0171-856-0066. FAX 0171-522-9623. TELEX 290164 CHAPMA G. E-mail: journal@chall.mhs.compuserve.com. (Subscr. to: International Thomson Publishing Services Ltd., Cheriton House, N. Way, Andover, Hants. SP10 5BE, England. TEL 01264-342713. FAX 01264-342807; N. American subscr. to: Chapman & Hall, Journals Promotion Department, One Penn Plaza, 41st Fl., New York, NY 10119. TEL 212-564-1060. FAX 212-564-1505) Ed. Akhlesh Lakhtekia. adv.; charts; illus. (reprint service avail.) **Indexed:** Bibl.& Ind.Geol., Biol.Abstr., Chem.Abstr., Comput.Abstr., Curr.Cont., Deep Sea Res.& Oceanogr.Abstr., Energy Ind., Energy Info.Abstr., Eng.Ind., Environ.Abstr., Excerp.Med., Field Crop Abstr., INSPEC, Lang.& Lang.Behav.Abstr., Met.Abstr., Sci.Cit.Ind., Sci.Res.Abstr., So.Pac.Per.Ind., Solid St.Abstr. **Document type:** academic/scholarly publication.
—BLDSC (8411.176000); CASDDS; Ei; Faxon; Genuine Article; SWETS; UnCover. **CCC.**
Refereed Serial

500 GW ISSN 0170-2971
CODEN: SPEKDI
SPEKTRUM DER WISSENSCHAFT. German translation of: Scientific American (US ISSN 0036-8733) 1978. m. DM.125.40 (foreign DM.135.20). Spektrum der Wissenschaft Verlagsgesellschaft mbH, Vangerowstr. 20, 69115 Heidelberg, Germany. TEL 06221-50460. FAX 06221-504751. E-mail: redaktion@spektrum.com. Ed. Albrecht Kunkel; Pub. Claus-G. Firchow. adv.; bk.rev.; index; circ. 118,000 (paid). (back issues avail.) **Document type:** academic/scholarly publication.
—CASDDS; Faxon; SWETS.
Incorporates: Academie Spectrum (ISSN 0940-225X); Spektrum (ISSN 0049-1861)

500 GW ISSN 0176-3008
CODEN: SPFOE2
SPIEGEL DER FORSCHUNG. 1983. s-a. free. Justus Liebig Universitaet, Ludwigstr. 23, 35390 Giessen, Germany. TEL 0641-7022035. FAX 0641-7022039. Ed. Christel Lauterbach. adv. circ. 10,000. **Document type:** academic/scholarly publication.

500 639.9 CN ISSN 0381-4459
TD427.P4
SPILL TECHNOLOGY NEWSLETTER/BULLETIN DE LA LUTTE CONTRE LES DEVERSEMENTS. 1976. q. Environment Canada, Technology Development and Technical Services Branch, Ottawa, ON K1A 0H3, Canada. TEL 819-953-9370. Ed. Merv Fingas. circ. 1,700. **Indexed:** Energy Info.Abstr., Environ.Abstr., INSPEC, Pollut.Abstr. **Document type:** academic/scholarly publication, newsletter.
—BLDSC (8413.840000).
Description: A forum for the exchange of information on spill counter measures and related matters.

500 CE ISSN 0081-3745
CODEN: SPZEAY
SPOLIA ZEYLANICA/NATIONAL MUSEUMS OF SRI LANKA. BULLETIN. (Text in English) 1904. a. price varies. Department of National Museums, Box 854, Sir Marcus Fernando Mawatha, Colombo 7, Sri Lanka. **Indexed:** Bibl.& Ind.Geol., Biol.Abstr., Deep Sea Res.& Oceanogr.Abstr.

500 US ISSN 0172-7389
CODEN: SSSYDF
SPRINGER SERIES IN SYNERGETICS. vol.32, 1986. irreg. price varies. Springer-Verlag, 175 Fifth Ave., New York, NY 10010. TEL 212-460-1500. FAX 212-473-6272. (Also: Berlin, Heidelberg, Vienna and Tokyo) Ed. H. Haken. **Indexed:** Chem.Abstr, INSPEC. **Document type:** monographic series.
—BLDSC (8424.778000); CASDDS.

500 US ISSN 0081-3877
SPRINGER TRACTS IN NATURAL PHILOSOPHY. 1964. irreg. price varies. Springer-Verlag, 175 Fifth Ave., New York, NY 10010. TEL 212-460-1500. FAX 212-473-6272. (Also: Berlin, Heidelberg, Tokyo and Vienna) Ed. B.D. Coleman. circ. 2,000. (reprint service avail. from ISI) **Indexed:** Math.R. **Document type:** monographic series.
—BLDSC (8424.900000). **CCC.**
Continues: Ergebnisse der Angewandten Mathematik.

500 CE ISSN 1391-023X
SRI LANKA ASSOCIATION FOR THE ADVANCEMENT OF SCIENCE. PROCEEDINGS. PART 1: ABSTRACTS. (Text in English) 1945. a. Sri Lanka Association for the Advancement of Science, Vidya Mawatha, Colombo 7, Sri Lanka. Ed. C.L.M. Nethsingha. circ. 2,000. **Indexed:** Bibl.& Ind.Geol., Biol.Abstr., Sri Lanka Sci.Ind. **Document type:** proceedings.

500 CE ISSN 1391-0248
SRI LANKA ASSOCIATION FOR THE ADVANCEMENT OF SCIENCE. PROCEEDINGS. PART 2: PRESIDENTIAL ADDRESSES, GUEST LECTURES. (Text in English) 1945. a. Sri Lanka Association for the Advancement of Science, Vidya Mawatha, Colombo 7, Sri Lanka. TEL 691681. Ed. C.L.M. Nethsingha. circ. 2,000. **Indexed:** Bibl.& Ind.Geol., Biol.Abstr., Sri Lanka Sci.Ind. **Document type:** proceedings.

500 YU ISSN 0081-4024
SRPSKA AKADEMIJA NAUKA I UMETNOSTI. ODELJENJE PRIRODNO-MATEMATICKIH NAUKA. POSEBNA IZDANJA. (Text in Serbo-Croatian; summaries in English, French, German or Russian) 1950. irreg., no.39, 1972. price varies. Srpska Akademija Nauka i Umetnosti, Knez Mihailova 35, 11001 Belgrade, Serbia, Yugoslavia. FAX 38-11-182-825. TELEX 72593 SANU YU. (Dist. by: Prosveta, Terazije 16, Belgrade, Serbia, Yugoslavia) circ. 500. **Indexed:** Bibl.& Ind.Geol., Biol.Abstr., Chem.Abstr., Ref.Zh.

060 500 YU
SRPSKA AKADEMIJA NAUKA I UMETNOSTI. POVREMENA IZDANJA. irreg. Srpska Akademija Nauka i Umetnosti, Knez Mihailova 35, 11001 Belgrade, Serbia, Yugoslavia. FAX 38-11-182-825. TELEX 72593 SANU YU.

SRPSKA AKADEMIJA NAUKA I UMETNOSTI SPOMENICA. see *HUMANITIES: COMPREHENSIVE WORKS*

STEVENS INDICATOR. see *COLLEGE AND ALUMNI*

500 600 GW
STIFTERVERBAND FUER DIE DEUTSCHE WISSENSCHAFT. TAETIGKEITSBERICHT. 1950. a. membership. Stifterverband fuer die Deutsche Wissenschaft, Brucker Holt 56-60, 45133 Essen, Germany. circ. 10,000.
Supersedes: Stifterverband fuer die Deutsche Wissenschaft. Jahrbuch (ISSN 0081-5551)

500 RM ISSN 0039-1417
STIINTA SI TEHNICA. 1949. m. 36 lei($20) (Comitetul Central al Uniunii Tineretului Comunist) Editura Scinteia, Piata Presei Libere 1, 79781 Bucharest, Rumania. (Subscr. to: ILEXIM, Str. 13 Decembrie Nr. 3, P.O. Box 136-137, Bucharest, Rumania) Ed. Ioan Eremia Albescu. bk.rev. circ. 75,000.

STRANGE MAGAZINE. see *PARAPSYCHOLOGY AND OCCULTISM*

501 215 VC
STUDI CRITICI SULLE SCIENZE. 1961. irreg., no.6, 1993. price varies. (Pontificia Universita Gregoriana, Facolta di Filosofia) Gregorian University Press, Piazza della Pilotta 35, 00187 Rome, Italy. TEL 39-6-678-15-67. FAX 39-6-678-05-88.

STUDIA LEIBNITIANA; Zeitschrift fuer Geschichte der Philosophie und der Wissenschaften. see *PHILOSOPHY*

SCIENCES: COMPREHENSIVE WORKS

STUDIA SPINOZANA; an international & interdisciplinary series. see *PHILOSOPHY*

500   GW   ISSN 0081-7384
STUDIENBUECHEREI. 1970. irreg. price varies. Deutscher Verlag der Wissenschaften, Postfach 1216, 1080 Berlin, Germany.

800 500 100   IE   ISSN 0039-3495
AP4
STUDIES; an Irish quarterly review. 1912. q. I£14($30) to individuals; institutions I£16($35). 35 Lower Leeson St., Dublin 2, Ireland. TEL 01-6766785. FAX 01-6762984. Ed. Noel Barber. adv.; bk.rev.; cum.index: vols.1-50. circ. 1,300. (also avail. in microform from UMI; reprint service avail. from UMI) **Indexed:** Abstr.Engl.Stud., Amer.Hist.& Life, Bibl.Engl.Lang.& Lit., Br.Hum.Ind., Cath.Ind., CERDIC, Hist.Abstr., Mid.East: Abstr.& Ind., P.A.I.S. **Document type:** academic/scholarly publication.
—BLDSC (8484.250000); Faxon; UMI; UnCover.

509   UK   ISSN 0039-3681
Q125   CODEN: SHPSB5
STUDIES IN HISTORY AND PHILOSOPHY OF SCIENCE. 1970. q. £170($271) (effective 1996). Elsevier Science Ltd., Pergamon, P.O. Box 800, Kidlington, Oxford OX5 1DX, England. TEL 44-1865-843000. FAX 44-1865-843010.
E-mail: nlinfo-f@elsevier.nl; usinfo-f@elsevier.com; forinfo-kyf04035@niftyserve.or.jp; Site addr.: http://www.elsevier.nl/. (Subscr. in U.S. and Canada to: Elsevier Science, 660 White Plains Rd., Tarrytown, NY 10591-5153. TEL 914-524-9200. FAX 914-333-2444) Ed. Nicholas Jardine. adv.: B&W page $550, color page $1350. bk.rev.; charts. circ. 1,100. (also avail. in microfilm from UMI; back issues avail.) **Indexed:** Amer.Hist.& Life, Arts & Hum.Cit.Ind., ASCA, ASSIA, Biol.Abstr., Br.Hum.Ind., GeoRef., Hist.Abstr., Hum.Ind., INSPEC, Math.R., Phil.Ind., SSCI. **Document type:** academic/scholarly publication.
—BLDSC (8490.651900); Faxon; Genuine Article; SWETS; UMI; UnCover. **CCC**.
Description: Concerned with the historical, social and intellectual contexts of the sciences and with their methodology and epistemology.
Refereed Serial

STUDIES IN HISTORY AND PHILOSOPHY OF SCIENCE PART B: STUDIES IN HISTORY AND PHILOSOPHY OF MODERN PHYSICS. see *PHYSICS*

STUDIES IN LOCATIONAL ANALYSIS. see *HOUSING AND URBAN PLANNING*

STUDIES IN REGIONAL AND URBAN PLANNING. see *HOUSING AND URBAN PLANNING*

STUDIES IN SCIENCE AND THE HUMANITIES. see *HUMANITIES: COMPREHENSIVE WORKS*

354   SJ
SUDAN. NATIONAL COUNCIL FOR RESEARCH. SCIENCE POLICY AND ANNUAL REPORT. (Text in English) a. exchange basis. National Council for Research, Box 2404, Khartoum, Sudan.

SUDAN RESEARCH INFORMATION BULLETIN. see *HUMANITIES: COMPREHENSIVE WORKS*

SUDHOFFS ARCHIV; Zeitschrift fuer Wissenschaftsgeschichte. see *MEDICAL SCIENCES*

SUDHOFFS ARCHIV. BEIHEFTE. see *MEDICAL SCIENCES*

500   SA   ISSN 0039-4807
SUID-AFRIKAANSE AKADEMIE VIR WETENSKAP EN KUNS. NUUSBRIEF. 1961. q. R.13 (effective 1995). Suid Afrikaanse Akademie vir Wetenskap en Kuns, P.O. Box 538, Pretoria 0001, South Africa. TEL 27-12-3285082. FAX 27-12-3285091. Ed. D.J.C. Geldenhuys. adv.; bibl.; illus. circ. 2,000. (looseleaf format) **Document type:** newsletter.

500   SA   ISSN 0254-3486
CODEN: SATTDF
SUID AFRIKAANSE TYDSKRIF VIR NATUURWETENSKAP EN TEGNOLOGIE. (Text in Afrikaans; summaries in Afrikaans and English) 1982. q. R.48 (effective 1995). Suid Afrikaanse Akademie vir Wetenskap en Kuns, P.O. Box 538, Pretoria 0001, South Africa. TEL 27-12-3285082. FAX 27-12-3285091. Ed. A. Strasheim. adv.; bk.rev.; charts; illus.; stat.; index. circ. 1,500. (back issues avail.) **Indexed:** INSPEC (1983-). **Document type:** academic/scholarly publication.
—CASDDS.

SUMMARY OF WHITE PAPER ON SCIENCE AND TECHNOLOGY. see *TECHNOLOGY: COMPREHENSIVE WORKS*

SUPER SCIENCE BLUE. see *CHILDREN AND YOUTH — For*

SUPER SCIENCE RED. see *CHILDREN AND YOUTH — For*

500   JA   ISSN 0389-5025
QH188   CODEN: SJTKBF
SUZUGAMINE JOSHI TANDAI KENKYU SHUHO. SHIZEN KAGAKU/SUZUGAMINE WOMEN'S COLLEGE. BULLETIN. NATURAL SCIENCE. (Text in English or Japanese) 1954. a., vol.33, 1992. Suzugamine Joshi Tanki Daigaku - Suzugamine Women's College, 6-8 Inokuchi 4-chome, Nishi-ku, Hiroshima-shi, Hiroshima-ken 733, Japan. TEL 082-278-1103. FAX 082-277-0301. Ed. Hisako Kawakami. circ. 300. **Indexed:** Biol.Abstr., Jap.Per.Ind. **Document type:** academic/scholarly publication.
—CASDDS.
Description: Contains original researches in the broad field of natural science.
Refereed Serial

500 600   SQ   ISSN 1012-5957
SWAZILAND JOURNAL OF SCIENCE AND TECHNOLOGY. (Text in English) 1982. 2/yr. Royal Swaziland Society for Science and Technology, c/o University of Swaziland, Private Bag, Kwaluseni, Swaziland. **Indexed:** P.L.E.S.A. (1989-). **Document type:** academic/scholarly publication.
Formerly (until 1988): Royal Swaziland Society for Science and Technology. Journal.

500 600   PL   ISSN 0867-6380
SWIAT NAUKI. Polish translation of: Scientific American (US ISSN 0036-8733) 1991. m. 22000 Zl. per no. (effective 1992). Science Press, Sp. z o.o., Ul. Sloneczna 35, 00-789 Warsaw, Poland. TEL 48-22-499261. FAX 48-22-489227. Ed. Andrzej Gorzym. adv. circ. 20,000.

500   US
SYMMETRIES IN SCIENCE. vol.4, 1990. irreg., vol.7, 1993. Plenum Publishing Corp., 233 Spring St., New York, NY 10013-1578. TEL 212-620-8000. FAX 212-463-0742. TELEX 23-421139. (back issues avail.) **Document type:** proceedings.

SYMMETRY: CULTURE AND SCIENCE. see *SOCIAL SCIENCES: COMPREHENSIVE WORKS*

500   RH
SYMPOSIUM ON SCIENCE AND TECHNOLOGY. PROCEEDINGS. 1992. biennial. $40. Scientific Liaison Office, P.O. Box CY 294, Causeway, Harare, Zimbabwe. TEL 700573. TELEX 22141. **Document type:** proceedings.

500   SI   ISSN 0218-3188
SYNERGY. (Text in English) bi-m. free. National Science and Technology Board, 16 Science Park Dr., 01-03 The Pasteur, Singapore Science Park, Singapore 0511, Singapore. TEL 65-779-7066. FAX 65-777-1711. **Document type:** newsletter.
Description: Covers national science and technology policies and news of research and development projects.

SYNTHESE; an international journal for epistemology, methodology and philosophy of science. see *PHILOSOPHY*

500 600   PL   ISSN 0082-1241
SZCZECINSKIE TOWARZYSTWO NAUKOWE. SPRAWOZDANIA. 1960. irreg. price varies. Szczecinskie Towarzystwo Naukowe, Ul. Wojska Polskiego 96, 70-481 Szczecin, Poland. TEL 23-18-62.

500   PL   ISSN 0137-5326
DK4600.L43
SZKICE LEGNICKIE. 1962. irreg., vol.13, 1987. price varies. Legnickie Towarzystwo Przyjaciol Nauk, Ul. Zamkowa 2, 59-920 Legnica, Poland. (Dist. by: Ars Polona-Ruch, Krakowskie Przedmiescie 7, Warsaw, Poland) Ed. Tadeusz Guminski.
Description: Studies in the history, culture and social life of Legnica region.

500   TH
T I S T R RESEARCH NEWS. m. Thailand Institute of Scientific and Technological Research, 196 Phahonyothin Rd., Chatuchak, Bangkok 10900, Thailand. TEL 579-8594. FAX 662-5798594. circ. 1,000. **Document type:** newsletter.
Formerly: A S R C T Research News.

T N C - AKTUELLT; information fraan Tekniska Nomenklaturcentralen. (Tekniska Nomenklaturcentralen) see *LINGUISTICS*

500   JA   ISSN 0386-6890
TAKAYAMA TANKI DAIGAKU KENKYU KIYO/TAKAYAMA JUNIOR COLLEGE. MEMOIRS. (Text in Japanese; summaries in English) 1978. a. Takayama Tanki Daigaku - Takayama Junior College, 1155 Shimobayashi-machi, Takayama-shi, Gifu-ken 506, Japan.

508   NZ   ISSN 0496-8026
QH197.5   CODEN: TJACA8
TANE. 1948. a. NZ.$16 for institutions. Offshore Islands Research Group, c/o Auckland Museum, Private Bag 921018, Auckland, New Zealand. TEL 09-3090443. FAX 09-3799956. Ed. Anthony Wright. illus. circ. 300. **Indexed:** Biol.Abstr., Curr.Adv.Ecol.Sci., Sport Fish.Abstr., Wild.Rev., Zoo.Rec.
—BLDSC (8601.900000).
Description: Covers natural history of northern New Zealand, particularly its offshore islands.

500   TZ   ISSN 0856-1761
CODEN: TJSCEY
TANZANIA JOURNAL OF SCIENCE. (Text in English) 1975. a. $30. University of Dar es Salaam, Faculty of Science, Box 35065, Dar es Salaam, Tanzania. TELEX 41327 UNISCIE TZ. Ed. E.C. NJau. bk.rev. **Indexed:** Chem.Abstr., Deep Sea Res.& Oceanogr.Abstr. **Document type:** academic/scholarly publication.
—CASDDS.
Formerly: University of Dar es Salaam. University Science Journal (ISSN 0250-5592)

500.9 370   UK   ISSN 0263-6107
TEACHING SCIENCE. 1903. 3/yr. £6. School Natural Science Society, c/o J. Williams, The Surgery, St. Christopher School, Letchworth, Hertfordshire SG6 3JZ, England. (Subscr. to: Association for Science Education, College Lane, Hatfield, Hertfordshire AL10 9AA, England) adv.; bk.rev.; charts; illus.; index. circ. 1,500. (also avail. in microform from UMI) **Document type:** academic/scholarly publication.
—UMI.
Formerly (until 1982): Natural Science in Schools (ISSN 0028-0763)
Description: For science and technology teachers of children ages 5 to 13. Articles, reviews, lesson ideas.

500   HU   ISSN 0133-2929
TECHNICAL UNIVERSITY FOR HEAVY INDUSTRY. PUBLICATIONS. SERIES D, NATURAL SCIENCES. (Text in English, German, Russian) irreg., vol.35, no.3, 1986. Nehezipari Muszaki Egyetem, Miskolc, Hungary. TEL 46-65111. FAX 46-69554. TELEX 62223-NMEMIS. bibl.; index. circ. 400. **Indexed:** C.R.I.Abstr., C.R.I.Curr.Cont.
—BLDSC (7113.414000).

500   GR   ISSN 0040-4764
TECHNIKA CHRONIKA/ANNALES TECHNIQUES. (Text in Greek; summaries in English) 1932. q. $100 per no. Technical Chamber of Greece, 4 Karageorgi Servias, 125 62 Athens, Greece. TEL 3222-466. FAX 3221772. TELEX 218374. Ed. D. Rokos. bk.rev.; charts; illus.; index. circ. 12,000. **Indexed:** INSPEC.

SCIENCES: COMPREHENSIVE WORKS

500 FR ISSN 0248-6016
TECHNIQUES & CULTURE. (Text in English or French, summaries in English, French, Spanish) 1976. s-a. 150 F. to individuals; institutions 165 F. (foreign 180 F.). Maison des Sciences de l'Homme, 54 bd Raspail, 75270 Paris Cedex 06, France. TEL 49-54-20-30. FAX 45-48-83-53. (Dist. by: C.I.D., 131 bd. Saint Michel, 75005 Paris, France. TEL 43-54-47-15) (Co-sponsor: Centre National de la Recherche Scientifique) Ed.Bd. bk.rev. **Indexed:** Bibl.Ling.

500 SA ISSN 1017-4966
Q1
TECHNOBRIEF. (Text in English) 1991. m. free. C S I R Marketing Services, P.O. Box 395, Pretoria 0001, South Africa. TEL 27-12-8414304. FAX 27-12-8413789. Ed. Hoepel Scheepers. circ. 12,000. **Indexed:** Fuel & Energy Abstr., Ind.S.A.Per., Met.Abstr., World Alum.Abstr., World Text.Abstr. **Document type:** newsletter.
Supersedes (1959-1991): Scientiae (ISSN 0036-8717)
Description: Highlights CSIR's achievements in scientific and technological research, development and implementation, focusing on technology transfer partnership with industry, and environmental impact issues.

600 US
TECHNOCRACY INFORMATION BRIEFS. irreg. Technocracy Inc., 2475 Harksell Rd., Ferndale, WA 98248. TEL 360-366-1012.

TECHNOLOGIA; historical and social studies in science, technology and industry. see TECHNOLOGY: COMPREHENSIVE WORKS

500 US ISSN 0040-1692
T171 CODEN: TEREAU
TECHNOLOGY REVIEW. 1899. 8/yr. $32. Massachusetts Institute of Technology, Association of Alumni and Alumnae, W59-200, Cambridge, MA 02139. TEL 617-253-8250. Ed. Steven Marcus. adv.; bk.rev.; illus. circ. 92,000. (also avail. in microform from UMI; reprint service avail. from UMI) **Indexed:** A.I.Abstr., A.S.& T.Ind., ABI Inform, Acad.Ind., Acid Pre.Dig., Amer.Bibl.Slavic & E.Eur.Stud., ASCA, B.P.I., Biol.Abstr., Biol.Dig., Bk.Rev.Ind. (1978-), BPIA, Bus.Ind., CAD CAM Abstr., Chem.Abstr., Child.Bk.Rev.Ind. (1978-), Comput.Bus., Comput.Lit.Ind., Curr.Cont., Energy Info.Abstr., Energy Rev., Eng.Ind., Environ.Abstr., Environ.Per.Bibl. (1972-), Excerp.Med., G.Soc.Sci.& Rel.Per.Lit., Geo.Abstr., High.Educ.Curr.Aware.Bull., Hlth.Ind., IDA, Int.Aerosp.Abstr., Key to Econ.Sci., Mag.Ind., Ocean.Abstr., P.A.I.S., Polit.Sci.Abstr., Pollut.Abstr., PROMT, Risk Abstr., Robomat., Sage Urb.Stud.Abstr., Tel.Abstr., Telegen, Text.Tech.Dig., Tr.& Indus.Ind.
●Also available online. Vendor(s): Knight-Ridder, Inc., University Microfilms International.
—BLDSC (8761.000000); CASDDS; Ei; Faxon; Genuine Article; SWETS; UMI; UnCover.

500 US
TECHNOLOGY TODAY. 1949. 3/yr. free to qualified personnel. Southwest Research Institute, Drawer 28510, San Antonio, TX 78228-0510. TEL 210-522-2289. FAX 210-522-3547. Ed. Elizabeth Douglas. illus. circ. 10,740. **Indexed:** Br.Ceram.Abstr.
Formerly (until 1978): Tomorrow Through Research (ISSN 0040-9146)

500 790.13 RM
TEHNIUM. 1970. m. 500 lei. Piata Presei Libere 1, 79784 Bucharest, Rumania. TEL 40-0-2223374. Ed. Ilie Mihaescu. adv.; bk.rev. circ. 50,000.

500 KR ISSN 0235-3474
TEKHNICHESKAYA DIAGNOSTIKA I NERAZRUSHAYUSHCHII KONTROL'; vsesoyuznyi nauchno-teoreticheskii zhurnal. (Text and summaries in Russian; contents page in English, Russian) 1989. q. $61 (effective 1996). (Akademiya Nauk Ukrainy, Otdelenie Fiziko-Tekhnicheskikh Problem Materialovedeniya) Vidavnitstvo Naukova Dumka, Vul. Tereshchenkivska 3, 252601 Kiev, Ukraine. (Dist. by: Mezhdunarodnaya Kniga, B. Yakimanka 39, 117049 Moscow, Russia; Dist. in U.S. by: Victor Kamkin Inc., 4956 Boiling Brook Pkwy., Rockville, MD 20852. TEL 301-881-5973. FAX 044-224-7060) Ed. B.E. Paton.
—BLDSC (0180.352800).

500 SW ISSN 0282-9274
TEKNIK & VETENSKAP. 1985. 5/yr. SEK 360 (students SEK 200); newsstand price: SEK 75. Aktuell Forskning Foerlags AB, Oestra Hamngatan 41-43, S-411 10 Goeteborg, Sweden. TEL 46-31-11-61-66. FAX 46-31-13-48-44. Ed. Lars Alvegaard. adv.: B&W page SEK 13000, color page SEK 16500; trim 186 x 270. circ. 10,800. pp./issue: 56.

500 613.1 IT
TEKNOS. 1990. m. L.60000 (foreign L.120000). Via Achile Loria 7, 00191 Rome, Italy. TEL 39-6-36300568. FAX 39-6-36300579. Ed. Giuseppe Meneguzzi. adv.: color page L.8000000. circ. 15,000. **Document type:** consumer publication.

TEKSTILEC; glasilo slovenskih tekstilcev. see TEXTILE INDUSTRIES AND FABRICS

500 FR ISSN 0040-2419
AP20
TEL QUEL; litterature - philosophie - science - politique. 1960. q. 130 F. Editions du Seuil, 27 rue Jacob, 75261 Paris Cedex 06, France. Ed. Marcelin Pleynet. bk.rev. **Indexed:** Curr.Cont.
—CCC.

500 US ISSN 0040-313X
Q11 CODEN: JTASAG
TENNESSEE ACADEMY OF SCIENCE. JOURNAL. 1926. q. $15 to non-members. Tennessee Academy of Science, 2001 Craven Ln., Prairie Peninsula, Hixson, TN 37343. TEL 615-251-1573. Ed. Libby Workman. adv.; bk.rev.; abstr.; charts; illus.; index. circ. 1,200. **Indexed:** Biol.Abstr., Chem.Abstr., Excerp.Med., Geo.Abstr., GeoRef., Helminthol.Abstr., INIS Atomind., Sel.Water Res.Abstr., Sport Fish.Abstr., Wild.Rev., Zoo.Rec.
—CASDDS; Faxon; UMI; UnCover.
Refereed Serial

500 HU ISSN 0040-3717
Q44 CODEN: TEVIAS
TERMESZET VILAGA. 1869. m. $38. (Tudomanyos Ismeretterjeszto Tarsulat) Hirlapkiado Vallalat, Biaha Lujza ter 3, 1959 Budapest 8, Hungary. TEL 1-382-399. TELEX 22-5554. (Subscr. to: Kultura, Box 149, H-1389 Budapest, Hungary) Ed. Gyula Staar. bk.rev.; charts; illus.; index. circ. 17,500. **Indexed:** Chem.Abstr.
—BLDSC (8792.800000); CASDDS.
Formerly: Termeszettudomanyi Kozlony.

500 US ISSN 0040-4403
Q1 CODEN: TJSCAU
TEXAS JOURNAL OF SCIENCE. 1949. q. $45. Texas Academy of Science, c/o Texas Tech University, The Museum, Box 4499, Lubbock, TX 79409. TEL 806-742-2487. Ed. J. Knox Jones, Jr. charts; illus.; index. circ. 1,000. (also avail. in microform from UMI; reprint service avail. from ISI) **Indexed:** Abstr.Anthropol., Anal.Abstr., ASCA, Bio-Contr.News & Info., Biol.Abstr., Biol.Dig., Chem.Abstr., Curr.Adv.Ecol.Sci., Curr.Cont., Curr.Ref.Fish Res., Deep Sea Res.& Oceanogr.Abstr., GeoRef., Helminthol.Abstr., INSPEC, Math.R., Nutr.Abstr., Rev.Appl.Entomol., Soils & Fert., Sport Fish.Abstr., Wild.Rev., Zoo.Rec. **Document type:** academic/scholarly publication.
—BLDSC (8799.000000); CASDDS; Ei; Faxon; Genuine Article; SWETS; UMI; UnCover.
Refereed Serial

500 JA ISSN 0286-5092
TEZUKAYAMA TANKI DAIGAKU KIYO. SHIZEN KAGAKU HEN/TEZUKAYAMA COLLEGE. JOURNAL. NATURAL SCIENCE. (Text and summaries in English and Japanese) 1963. a. Tezukayama Tanki Daigaku - Tezukayama Junior College, 3-1 Gakuen minami, Nara-shi, Nara-ken 631, Japan. FAX 0742-41-2941.

500 PL ISSN 0867-4159
Q174
THEORIA ET HISTORIA SCIENTIARUM. 1991. irreg. price varies. Uniwersytet Mikolaja Kopernika, Biblioteka Uniwersytecka, Ul. Gagarina 13, 87-100 Torun, Poland. TEL 233-52. TELEX 552382. Ed. Wieslaw Mincer.
—BLDSC (8814.587000).

500 CC ISSN 0493-2137
Q4 CODEN: TCHHA9
TIANJIN DAXUE XUEBAO/TIANJIN UNIVERSITY. JOURNAL. (Text in Chinese) 1955. bi-m. $10. Tianjin Daxue - Tianjin University, Qilitai, Nankai Qu, Tianjin 300072, People's Republic of China. TEL 022-3359116. FAX 022-3358706. (Dist. overseas by: China International Book Trading Corporation, P.O. Box 399, Beijing, P.R. China) Eds. Li Guangquan, Zhang Runsheng. circ. 2,000. **Document type:** academic/scholarly publication.
—CASDDS.
Refereed Serial

500 CC ISSN 1006-4982
▼**TIANJIN UNIVERSITY. TRANSACTIONS.** (Text in English) 1995. 2/yr. $20. Tianjin Daxue - Tianjin University, Qilitai, Nankai Qu, Tianjin 300072, People's Republic of China. TEL 022-3359116. FAX 022-3358706. (Dist. overseas by: China International Book Trading Corporation, P.O. Box 399, Beijing, P.R. China) Eds. Li Guangquan, Zhang Runsheng. circ. 1,000. **Document type:** academic/scholarly publication.
Refereed Serial

509 RM
TIBISCUS. SERIA STIINTELE NATURII. (Text in Rumanian; summaries in German) a. Muzeul Banatului, Piata Huniade Nr.1, Timisoara, Rumania.

500 FI ISSN 0358-1039
TIEDE 2000. 1980. 8/yr. FIM 295. Sanomaprint, PL 113, SF-00381 Helsinki, Finland. FAX 358-0-120-5456. TELEX 125848-SACOM. Ed. Tuule Koullee. adv.; bk.rev. circ. 38,000.
Description: Contains articles and news relating to science in general.

500 MX ISSN 0186-5730
Q23
TIEMPOS DE CIENCIA; revista de difusion cientifica. 1985. q. $20. Universidad de Guadalajara, Coordinacion de Difusion Cientifica, Av. Juarez y Enrique Diaz de Leon, 8 piso, C.P. 44170 Guadalajara, Jalisco, Mexico. Ed. Javier Garcia de Alba Garcia. adv.; bk.rev.

051 US ISSN 0748-9579
F491
TIMELINE. 1984. bi-m. $22.50. Ohio Historical Society, 1982 Velma Ave., Columbus, OH 43211-2497. TEL 614-297-2332. Ed. Christopher S. Duckworth. circ. 15,300. **Document type:** consumer publication.
—BLDSC (8852.630000); UnCover.
Description: Articles cover the fields of history, prehistory and the natural sciences for a general audience.

500 069 JA ISSN 0910-4100
TOCHIGI-KENRITSU HAKUBUTSUKAN KENKYU HOKOKUSHO/TOCHIGI PREFECTURAL MUSEUM. MEMOIRS. (Text in Japanese; summaries in English and Japanese) 1983. a. Tochigi-kenritsu Hakubutsukan - Tochigi Prefectural Museum, 2-2 Mutsumi-cho, Utsunomiya-shi, Tochigi-ken 320, Japan. TEL 0286-34-1314. FAX 0286-34-1310. **Document type:** academic/scholarly publication.
Description: Covers zoology, botany, geology, and related subjects.

500 AT ISSN 1033-6893
CODEN: TOLSEE
TODAY'S LIFE SCIENCES. 1989. m. Aus.$75. Thomson Business Publishing, 47 Chippen St., Chippendale, N.S.W. 2008, Australia. TEL 02-699-2411. FAX 02-698-3920. Ed. Ray Welling. circ. 7,229.
—BLDSC (8859.761000); UnCover.

500 NE ISSN 0920-4571
TOEGEPASTE WETENSCHAP. 1971; N.S. 1985. bi-m. free. Nederlandse Organisatie voor Toegepast Natuurwetenschappelijk Onderzoek (TNO) - Netherlands Organization for Applied Scientific Research, Postbus 6050, 2600 JA Delft, Netherlands. TEL 31-15-2696900. FAX 31-15-2627335. E-mail: JBR@mp.tno.nl. Ed. W.J. van den Brink. adv.; bk.rev.; illus.; index. circ. 10,000. **Indexed:** C.I.S. Abstr., Excerp.Med., Food Sci.& Tech.Abstr., HRIS, Key to Econ.Sci., Met.Abstr., World Alum.Abstr. **Document type:** newsletter.
Formed by the 1985 merger of: Innovatie (ISSN 0167-3475) & T N O Project (ISSN 0376-6993); Which was formerly titled (until 1973): T N O Nieuws (ISSN 0039-8446)
Description: Covers topics relating to applied scientific research.

SCIENCES: COMPREHENSIVE WORKS

500   JA   ISSN 0910-7177
TOHOKU NO SHIZEN/NATURE OF TOHOKU. (Text in Japanese) 1985. m. Tohoku no Shizensha, Bunanoki Shuppan, 5-11 Tori-machi 5-chome, Yonezawa-shi, Yamagata-ken 992, Japan.

500   JA   ISSN 0919-5025
Q77   CODEN: TUFPBE1
TOKAI UNIVERSITY. SCHOOL OF SCIENCE. PROCEEDINGS.* (Text in English and German; summaries in English) 1966. a. (Tokai Daigaku, Rigakubu - Tokai University, School of Science) Tokai Daigaku Shuppankai - Tokai University Press, 2-28-4 Tomigaya, Shibuya-ku, Tokyo 151, Japan. **Indexed:** Chem.Abstr., INIS Atomind., Math.R. —CASDDS.
    Formerly (until 1993): Tokai University. Faculty of Science. Proceedings (ISSN 0563-6795)

509   JA   ISSN 0912-0599
TOKUSHIMA KAGAKUSHI ZASSHI/TOKUSHIMA SOCIETY FOR THE HISTORY OF SCIENCE. JOURNAL. (Text in Japanese) 1982. a. 200 Yen. Tokushima Kagakushi Kenkyukai, c/o Mr. Toshimi Saijo, 651-4, Kamiura, Urasho, Ishiicho, Myozai-gun, Tokushima-ken 779-32, Japan. Ed. Toshimi Saijo. bk.rev.

500   574.192   JA   ISSN 0371-6813
                        CODEN: TGDSBH
TOKYO GAKUGEI DAIGAKU KIYO/TOKYO GAKUGEI UNIVERSITY. BULLETIN. (Consists of 6 sections) (Text and summaries in English and Japanese) 1949. a. free. Tokyo Gakugei Daigaku, Shuppan linkai - Tokyo Gakugei University, Publication Committee, 1-1 Nukui Kita-machi 4-chome, Koganei-shi, Tokyo 184, Japan. Ed. Tosuke Nomura. circ. 600. **Indexed:** Chem.Abstr., INIS Atomind., INSPEC (1969-), Jap.Per.Ind.

500   ISSN 0386-4006
                      CODEN: SRTUDZ
TOKYO JOSHI DAIGAKU KIYO. RONSHU. KAGAKU BUMON HOKOKU/TOKYO WOMAN'S CHRISTIAN UNIVERSITY. SCIENCE REPORTS. (Text and summaries in English and Japanese) 1950. a. Tokyo Joshi Daigaku Gakkai - Tokyo Woman's Christian University, Academic Society, 2 Zenpukuji, Suginami-ku, Tokyo 167, Japan.
—CASDDS.

508   JA   ISSN 0918-3760
QL468
TOKYO METROPOLITAN UNIVERSITY. BULLETIN OF NATURAL HISTORY. (Text in English) 1992. irreg. donation or exchange. Tokyo Toritsu Daigaku, Rigakubu, Shizenshi Koza - Tokyo Metropolitan University, Faculty of Science, Department of Natural History, 1-1, Minamiosawa, Hachioji-shi, Tokyo 192-03, Japan. Ed. Tsukane Yamasaki. **Document type:** academic/scholarly publication, bulletin.
    Refereed Serial

500   JA   ISSN 0918-0753
TOKYO RIKA DAIGAKU KENKYU RONBUNSHU/SCIENCE UNIVERSITY OF TOKYO. COLLECTED PAPERS. (Text and summaries in English, German, and Japanese) 1958. a. exchange basis only. Tokyo Rika Daigaku - Science University of Tokyo, 1-3 Kagurazaka, Shinjuku-ku, Tokyo 162, Japan. circ. 200. **Document type:** academic/scholarly publication.

500   387.5   JA   ISSN 0493-4474
TOKYO SHOSEN DAIGAKU KENKYU HOKOKU. SHIZEN KAGAKU/TOKYO UNIVERSITY OF MERCANTILE MARINE. JOURNAL. NATURAL SCIENCES. (Text and summaries in English and Japanese) 1951. a. Tokyo Shosen Daigaku - Tokyo University of Mercantile Marine, 1-6 Etchujima 2-chome, Koto-ku, Tokyo 135, Japan. **Indexed:** Jap.Per.Ind.
—BLDSC (4909.030000).

500   JA   ISSN 0288-2329
TOKYO-TO NO SHIZEN. (Text in Japanese) 1973. a. Tokyo-to Takao Shizen Kagaku Hakubutsukan - Takao Museum of Natural History, 2436 Takao-machi, Hachioji-shi, Tokyo 193, Japan.

TOKYO-TO SHIKEN KENKYU KIKAN NO KENKYU KEIKAKU. see *PUBLIC ADMINISTRATION — Municipal Government*

500   JA   ISSN 0286-8768
TOKYO-TO TAKAO SHIZEN KAGAKU HAKUBUTSUKAN KENKYU HOKOKU/TAKAO MUSEUM OF NATURAL HISTORY. SCIENCE REPORT. (Text in Japanese; summaries in English and Japanese) 1970. irreg. Tokyo-to Takao Shizen Kagaku Hakubutsukan - Takao Museum of Natural History, 2436 Takao-machi, Hachioji-shi, Tokyo 193, Japan.

500   JA
TORAY KAGAKU SHINKOKAI JIGYO HOKOKUSHO/TORAY SCIENCE FOUNDATION. ANNUAL REPORT. (Text mainly in Japanese, partly in English) 1960. a. free. Toray Science Foundation, Toray Bldg., 8-1, Mihama 1-chome, Urayasu, Chiba 279, Japan. FAX 0473-50-6082. abstr. circ. 700.

500   JA
TORAY KAGAKU SHINKOKAI KAGAKU KOENKAI KIROKU. (Text in Japanese) 1963. a. free. Toray Science Foundation, Toray Bldg., 8-1, Mihama 1-chome, Urayasu, Chiba 279, Japan. FAX 0473-50-6082. circ. 2,400. **Document type:** proceedings.
    Description: Contains proceedings from the lecture meetings sponsored by the foundation.

500   JA
TORAY RIKA KYOIKUSHO JUSHO SAKUHINSHU. (Text in Japanese) 1969. a. free. Toray Science Foundation, Toray Bldg., 8-1, Mihama 1-chome, Urayasu, Chiba 279, Japan. FAX 0473-50-6082. circ. 14,000. **Indexed:** Chem.Abstr.
    Description: Publishes works which have received the Toray Science Education Prize.

500.9   UK   ISSN 0082-5344
TORQUAY NATURAL HISTORY SOCIETY. TRANSACTIONS AND PROCEEDINGS. 1909. a. £3. Torquay Natural History Society, The Museum, Babbacombe Rd., Torquay TQ1 1HG, England. TEL 01803-293975. Ed. M.S. Ackland. circ. 600. **Indexed:** Br.Archaeol.Abstr. **Document type:** proceedings.
    Refereed Serial

500   JA   ISSN 0371-5965
TOTTORI DAIGAKU KYOIKUGAKUBU KENKYU HOKOKU. SHIZEN KAGAKU/TOTTORI UNIVERSITY. FACULTY OF EDUCATION. JOURNAL: NATURAL SCIENCE. (Text in English and Japanese; summaries in English) 1950. s-a. Tottori Daigaku, Kyoikugakubu - Tottori University, Faculty of Education, 4-101 Minami, Koyama-cho, Tottori-shi, Tottori-ken 680, Japan. **Indexed:** Biol.Abstr., INIS Atomind., Jap.Per.Ind.
—BLDSC (4743.700000).

500   JA   ISSN 0287-1688
TOTTORI-KENRITSU HAKUBUTSUKAN KENKYU HOKOKU/TOTTORI PREFECTURAL MUSEUM. BULLETIN. (Text in Japanese; summaries in English and Japanese) 1962. a. Tottori-kenritsu Hakubutsukan - Tottori Prefectural Museum, 2-124 Higashi-machi, Tottori-shi, Tottori-ken 680, Japan. FAX 0857-26-8041. circ. 1,000.

500   PL   ISSN 0079-4805
TOWARZYSTWO NAUKOWE W TORUNIU. PRACE POPULARNONAUKOWE. (Text in Polish; summaries in English, German) 1961. irreg., no.55, 1992. price varies. Towarzystwo Naukowe w Toruniu, Ul. Wysoka 16, 87-100 Torun, Poland. TEL 48-56-23941. TELEX 552388 FSBH PL. Ed. Cecylia Iwaniszewska. circ. 6,500. **Document type:** monographic series.

500   PL   ISSN 0371-375X
TOWARZYSTWO NAUKOWE W TORUNIU. SPRAWOZDANIA. 1949. a. price varies. Towarzystwo Naukowe w Toruniu - Torun Scientific Society, Ul. Wysoka 16, 87-100 Torun, Poland. TEL 48-56-23941. TELEX 552388 FSBH PL. Ed. Janusz Kryszak. circ. 700.

500   JA   ISSN 0285-9610
Q4   CODEN: TDKBDG
TOYAMA DAIGAKU KYOIKUGAKUBU KIYO, B. RIKAKEI/TOYAMA UNIVERSITY. FACULTY OF EDUCATION. MEMOIRS, B. NATURAL SCIENCE. (Text in English and Japanese; summaries in English) 1953. irreg. (1-2/yr.), no.44, 1993. Toyama Daigaku, Kyoikugakubu - Toyama University, Faculty of Education, 3190 Gofuku, Toyama-shi, Toyama-ken 930, Japan. TEL 0764-41-1271. FAX 0764-32-4212. Ed. Tsutomu Anayama. **Indexed:** Chem.Abstr., Jap.Per.Ind. **Document type:** academic/scholarly publication.
—BLDSC (5593.332000).

500   JA   ISSN 0387-9089
Q4
TOYAMA-SHI KAGAKU BUNKA SENTA KENKYU HOKOKU/TOYAMA SCIENCE MUSEUM. BULLETIN. (Text and summaries in English and Japanese) 1979. a. Toyama-shi Kagaku Bunka Senta - Toyama Science Museum, 1-8-31 Nishi-nakano-machi, Toyama-shi, Toyama-ken 939, Japan. TEL 0764-91-2123. FAX 0764-21-5950. Ed. Hisao Nanbu. **Document type:** bulletin.
    Description: Contains research papers.

TOYAMA TO SHIZEN. see *MUSEUMS AND ART GALLERIES*

500   JA   ISSN 0372-0330
Q4   CODEN: TODKBF
TOYO DAIGAKU KIYO. KYOYO KATEI HEN. SHIZEN KAGAKU/TOYO UNIVERSITY. JOURNAL. GENERAL EDUCATION. NATURAL SCIENCE. (Text in Japanese; summaries in English) a. Toyo Daigaku - Toyo University, 28-20, Hakusan 5-chome, Bunkyo-ku, Tokyo 112, Japan. **Indexed:** Jap.Per.Ind.
—CASDDS.

509   NE   ISSN 0924-0829
Q127.N4
TRACTRIX; yearbook for the history of science, medicine, technology, and mathematics. (Text mainly in English; occasionally in French, German) 1989. a. fl.47($27.50) to individuals; institutions fl.87($51) (effective 1994). (Dutch Society for the History of Medicine, Mathematics, Science, and Technology) Editions Rodopi B.V., Keizersgracht 302-304, 1016 EX Amsterdam, Netherlands. TEL 31-20-6227507. FAX 31-20-6380948. E-mail: F.van.der.Zee@Rodopi.nl. (In N. America: 233 Peachtree St., N.E., Ste. 404, Atlanta, GA 30303-1504. TEL 800-225-3998) Ed. C.F. Cohen. **Document type:** academic/scholarly publication.
—UnCover.
    Description: Promotes international information for historians of science, medicine, and technology.

500   600   UK
TRAFODION Y GYMDEITHAS WYDDONOL GENEDLAETHOL. (Text in Welsh) 1978. a. £2. Y Gymdeithas Wyddonol Genedlaethol, Talafon, Golan, Garndolbenmaen, Gwynedd LL51 9YU, Wales. TEL 01766-75224. Ed. J.S. Davies. circ. 300. (back issues avail.)

508   SA   ISSN 0041-1752
QH1   CODEN: ATVMA4
TRANSVAAL MUSEUM. ANNALS/TRANSVAAL MUSEUM. ANNALE. (Text in English) 1908. irreg., vol.35, 1989. price varies. Transvaal Museum, P.O. Box 413, Pretoria 0001, South Africa. TEL 27-12-322-7632. FAX 27-12-322-7939. Ed. A. Dreyer. illus.; index. circ. 350. (tabloid format; back issues avail.; reprint service avail. from SWZ). **Indexed:** Biol.Abstr., GeoRef., Ind.S.A.Per., Sport Fish.Abstr., Wild.Rev., Zoo.Rec. **Document type:** academic/scholarly publication.
—BLDSC (1034.000000).
    Description: Original research articles in the field of zoology. Includes information on systematics and taxonomy.

500   TS   ISSN 1019-6919
TRIBULUS. (Text in Arabic, English) 1977. q. Cultural Foundation, Emirates Natural History Group - Jami'iyyat al-Imarat lil-Ta'rikh al-Tabi'i, P.O. Box 2380, Abu Dhabi, United Arab Emirates. TEL 212900. FAX 336059. TELEX 2214 CULCEN EM. Ed. Ian Hammer. bk.rev.; circ. 500 (controlled). **Indexed:** Sport Fish.Abstr., Wild.Rev. **Document type:** academic/scholarly publication.
    Formerly (until 1991): Jam'iyyat al-Tarikh al-Tabi'i. Nashrat - Emirates Natural History Group Bulletin.
    Description: Publishes original research in archaeology and natural history in the United Arab Emirates.

500   CR   ISSN 0069-2107
TROPICAL SCIENCE CENTER, COSTA RICA. OCCASIONAL PAPER. 1963. irreg., vol.16, 1987. price varies. Tropical Science Center, Calle 1, No. 442, Apdo. 8-3840, San Jose, Costa Rica. FAX 506-57-04-04. TELEX 506 35 53 90. Ed. Joseph A. Tosi, Jr. circ. 250. **Indexed:** Chem.Abstr.

SCIENCES: COMPREHENSIVE WORKS

500   US   ISSN 0259-3637
TSUNAMI NEWSLETTER. 1968. 2/yr. free. International Tsunami Information Center, Box 50027, Honolulu, HI 96850-4993. TEL 808-541-1658. FAX 808-541-1678. Ed. Dennis J. Sigrist. bk.rev. circ. 1,000. (back issues avail.) **Document type:** newsletter.
    Description: Providing news and information for scientists, engineers, educators, community protection agencies and government throughout the world.

500 600   HU   ISSN 0237-322X
TUDOMANY. Hungarian translation of: Scientific American (US ISSN 0036-8733) 1985. m. 1176 Ft.($40) Tudomany, P.O. Box 338, H-1536 Budapest, Hungary. (Subscr. to: Kultura, P.O. Box 149, H-1389 Budapest, Hungary) Eds. Jonathan Piel, Futasz Dezso. adv.; bk.rev.; bibl.; charts; illus. circ. 25,000. (back issues avail.)

501   HU   ISSN 0082-6707
TUDOMANYSZERVEZESI FUZETEK. 1965. irreg., latest 1991. price varies. (Magyar Tudomanyos Akademia) Akademiai Kiado, Publishing House of the Hungarian Academy of Sciences, P.O. Box 245, 1519 Budapest, Hungary. TEL 181-2134.

500   FI   ISSN 0082-7002
                 CODEN: AUTUAP
TURUN YLIOPISTO. JULKAISUJA. SARJA A. I. ASTRONOMICA - CHEMICA - PHYSICA - MATHEMATICA. (Latin title: Annales Universitatis Turkuensis) (Text in English, Finnish, French and German) 1922. irreg. price varies. Turun Yliopisto - University of Turku, SF-20500 Turku 50, Finland. FAX 358-21-6335050. TELEX 62123 TYK SF. **Indexed:** INIS Atomind., INSPEC (1968-). **Document type:** monographic series.
    —BLDSC (0963.345000).
    Description: Studies astronomy, chemistry, physical sciences and mathematics.

505   LB
U L SCIENCE AND TECHNOLOGY MAGAZINE.* 1972. s-a. $2. University of Liberia, Division of Science and Technology, Monrovia, Liberia. Ed. Kabineh Koroma. adv.; illus. **Indexed:** Biol.Abstr.
    Former titles: U L Science Magazine & Liberian Naturalist (ISSN 0459-2298)

300 500   GT   ISSN 1015-339X
U S A C. 1983. q. Q.825($10.20) Universidad de San Carlos de Guatemala, Direccion General de Extension Universitaria, Edif. de Rectoria, 3er Nivel, Of. 307, Ciudad Universitaria, Zona 12, Guatemala City, Guatemala. Ed. Eduardo Meyer Maldonado. bk.rev.; bibl.; charts; stat. **Indexed:** Hisp.Amer.Per.Ind. (1989-).
    Formerly (until 1987): Perspectiva (ISSN 0257-7356)

500.9   GW   ISSN 0944-4602
UEBERSEE-MUSEUM BREMEN. VEROEFFENTLICHUNGEN. NATURWISSENSCHAFTEN. 1949. irreg., vol.12, 1993. price varies. Uebersee-Museum Bremen, Bahnhofsplatz 13, 28195 Bremen, Germany. Ed. Herbert Hohmann. **Document type:** monographic series.
    —BLDSC (9190.900000).
    Formerly: Uebersee-Museum Bremen. Veroeffentlichungen. Reihe A: Naturwissenschaften (ISSN 0068-0885)

600 500   UN   ISSN 0503-4434
UNESCO. REGIONAL OFFICE FOR SCIENCE AND TECHNOLOGY FOR AFRICA. BULLETIN. (Editions in English and French) 1966. 2/yr. free to qualified institutions or on exchange basis. Unesco, Regional Office for Science and Technology for Africa (R.O.S.T.A.), P.O. Box 30592, Nairobi, Kenya. FAX 254-2521045. TELEX 22275 NAIROBI. bk.rev.; bibl. circ. 1,500. **Document type:** academic/scholarly publication.

500 600   GW   ISSN 0179-7182
UNI REPORT. 1985. s-a. DM.15. Universitaet Dortmund, August-Schmitt-Str., 44227 Dortmund, Germany. TEL 0231-7552222. FAX 0231-7554819. TELEX 822465-UNIDO-D. (Subscr. to: Rhein Ruhr Druck Sander, Hengsener Str. 8a, 44309 Dortmund, Germany) Ed. Kurt Jauslin. adv.; bibl.; illus. circ. 5,000. (back issues avail.) **Document type:** academic/scholarly publication.
    Description: News and essays concerning scientific and technological research.

500   CR   ISSN 1011-0275
UNICIENCIA. (Text in English, Spanish) 1984. s-a. Col.700($40) (effective Jan. 1995). Universidad Nacional, Facultad de Ciencias Exactas y Naturales, Apdo. 86, 3000 Heredia, Costa Rica. TEL 506-2376363. FAX 506-2376427. Ed. Jorge Gunther. bk.rev.; bibl.; charts; illus.; stat. circ. 300. (back issues avail.) **Document type:** academic/scholarly publication.
    Description: Covers basic and applied research in biology, chemistry, physics and mathematics, with emphasis on natural bioresources.
    Refereed Serial

UNION LIST OF SCIENTIFIC AND TECHNICAL PERIODICALS IN ZAMBIA. see *BIBLIOGRAPHIES*

500   TS   ISSN 1021-0806
UNITED ARAB EMIRATES UNIVERSITY. FACULTY OF SCIENCE. JOURNAL/JAMI'AT AL-IMARAT AL-ARABIYYAH AL-MUTTAHIDAH. KULLIYYAT AL-ULUM. MAJALLAH. (Text in Arabic, English) 1988. a. exchange basis. United Arab Emirates University, Faculty of Science, P.O. Box 17551, Al-Ain, United Arab Emirates. TEL 677280. TELEX 33521 JAMEAH EM. Ed. Saleh El-Nahwy. circ. 500. **Document type:** academic/scholarly publication.
    Description: Publishes papers in mathematics, computer science, physics, chemistry, geology and the life sciences.

UNITED ARAB EMIRATES UNIVERSITY. JOURNAL/JAMI'AT AL-IMARAT AL-ARABIYYAH AL-MUTTAHIDAH. MAJALLAH. see *HUMANITIES: COMPREHENSIVE WORKS*

U.S. NATIONAL COMMITTEE FOR MAN AND THE BIOSPHERE PROGRAM. BULLETIN. see *CONSERVATION*

338.973   US
U.S. NATIONAL SCIENCE FOUNDATION. FEDERAL FUNDS FOR RESEARCH DEVELOPMENT. (Subseries of: U.S. National Science Foundation. Surveys of Science Resource Series) a. U.S. National Science Foundation, 4201 Wilson Blvd., Ste. 245, Arlington, VA 22230. (Also avail. through: Bernan, 4611-F Assembly Dr., Lanham, MD 20706. TEL 800-274-4447. FAX 301-459-0056) **Document type:** government publication.
    Former titles: U.S. National Science Foundation. Federal Funds for Research, Development, and other Scientific Activities (ISSN 0198-8700); U.S. National Science Foundation. Federal Funds for Science (ISSN 0083-2359)

U.S. NATIONAL SCIENCE FOUNDATION. GUIDE TO PROGRAMS. see *EDUCATION — School Organization And Administration*

500 507.2   US
Q180.U5   CODEN: NSFAAO
U.S. NATIONAL SCIENCE FOUNDATION. STATE AWARD SUMMARY, FISCAL YEAR (YEAR). 1951. a. free. U.S. National Science Foundation, Budget, Finance & Awards Office, 4201 Wilson Blvd., Ste. 245, Arlington, VA 22230. **Indexed:** Biol.Abstr. **Document type:** government publication.
    —CASDDS.
    Former titles: U.S. National Science Foundation. Fiscal Year Awards; U.S. National Science Foundation. Grants and Awards (ISSN 0565-825X); U.S. National Science Foundation. Annual Report (ISSN 0083-2332)
    Description: Provides information on recent NSF grants.

500   US
U.S. OFFICE OF TECHNOLOGY ASSESSMENT. ASSESSMENT ACTIVITIES. irreg. free. U.S. Office of Technology Assessment, Publication Distribution, U.S. Congress, 600 Pennsylvania Ave., S.E., Washington, DC 20510-8025. TEL 202-224-8996. FAX 202-228-6098. E-mail: PUBREQUEST@OTA.GOV. (Dist. by: Superintendent of Documents, U.S. Government Printing Office, Box 371954, Pittsburgh, PA 15250-7954. TEL 202-783-3238. FAX 202-512-2250; And: National Technical Information Service, 5285 Port Royal Rd., Springfield, VA 22161. TEL 703-487-4650. FAX 703-321-8547) **Document type:** government publication.
    Description: Summarizes ongoing O.T.A. activities and projects and lists publications in press.

U.S. OFFICE OF TECHNOLOGY ASSESSMENT. REPORTS. SCIENCE, EDUCATION, AND TRANSPORTATION PROGRAM. see *EDUCATION*

500   IS
UNITED STATES - ISRAEL BINATIONAL SCIENCE FOUNDATION. BIENNIAL REPORT. (Text in English) 1974. biennial. free. United States - Israel Binational Science Foundation, P.O. Box 7677, Jerusalem 91076, Israel. FAX 972-2-633287. circ. 4,000. **Document type:** corporate report.
    Formerly: United States - Israel Binational Science Foundation. Annual Report.

500   FR   ISSN 0083-3673
UNIVERS HISTORIQUE. 1970. irreg. price varies. Editions du Seuil, 27 rue Jacob, 75261 Paris Cedex 06, France. Eds. Jacques Julliard, Michel Winock.
    —CCC.

502   DR
UNIVERSIDAD AUTONOMA DE SANTO DOMINGO. DIRECCION DE INVESTIGACIONES. D I C BOLETIN. Cover title: D I C Boletin. vol.2, 1974. m. (Direccion de Investigaciones) Imprenta de Universidad Autonoma de Santo Domingo, Edificio Dr. Defillo, Ciudad Universitaria, Dominican Republic.

500   SP   ISSN 0075-7721
Q65
UNIVERSIDAD DE LA LAGUNA. FACULTAD DE CIENCIAS. ANALES. 1962. irreg. $15 to individuals; institutions $20. Universidad de la Laguna, Secretariado de Publicaciones, San Agustin, 30, 38201 La Laguna-Tenerife, Canary Islands, Spain. TEL 922-28-81-27. adv.; bk.rev.

500   SP   ISSN 0559-6645
                 CODEN: AUHCAD
UNIVERSIDAD DE SEVILLA. SERIE: CIENCIAS. 1967. irreg., latest no.29. Universidad de Sevilla, Servicio de Publicaciones, Valparaiso 5, 41013 Seville, Spain. TEL 954-231958. FAX 954-232245. charts; illus.
    —CASDDS.
    Formerly: Universidad Hispalense. Anales. Serie: Ciencias (ISSN 0374-5880)

500   PY
UNIVERSIDAD NACIONAL DE ASUNCION. FACULTAD DE CIENCIAS EXACTAS Y NATURALES. MEMORIA. 1966. irreg. exchange basis. Universidad Nacional de Asuncion, Casilla de Correo 1039, Asuncion, Paraguay. TEL 595-21-585601. FAX 595-21-585600. Ed. Oscar Esquivel. circ. 300. **Document type:** academic/scholarly publication.
    Formerly: Universidad Nacional de Asuncion. Instituto de Ciencias. Memoria.
    Refereed Serial

500   SP
UNIVERSIDADE DE SANTIAGO DE COMPOSTELA. MONOGRAFIAS. 1971. irreg. price varies. Universidade de Santiago de Compostela, Servicio de Publicacions e Intercambio Cientifico, Campus Universitario, 15703 Santiago de Compostela (La Coruna), Spain. **Document type:** monographic series.

500   IT   ISSN 0041-8951
UNIVERSITA DEGLI STUDI DI CAGLIARI. SEMINARIO DELLA FACOLTA DI SCIENZA. RENDICONTI. (Text in English and Italian) 1931. s-a. exchange basis. Universita degli Studi di Cagliari, Seminario della Faculta di Scienze, Via Canelles, 15, 09124 Cagliari, Italy. Ed.Bd. bibl.; charts; illus. **Indexed:** Chem.Abstr. **Document type:** proceedings.

001.3 500   GW   ISSN 0512-1523
UNIVERSITAET FRANKFURT. WISSENSCHAFTLICHE GESELLSCHAFT. SITZUNGSBERICHTE. 1962. irreg., vol.33, no.1, 1995. price varies. (Wissenschaftliche Gesellschaft) Franz Steiner Verlag Wiesbaden GmbH, Birkenwaldstr. 44, 70191 Stuttgart, Germany. TEL 0711-2582-0. FAX 0711-2582390. (Subscr. to: Postfach 101061, 70009 Stuttgart, Germany) **Document type:** monographic series.

500   AU   ISSN 0259-0700
UNIVERSITAET SALZBURG. DISSERTATIONEN. 1970. irreg., no.33, 1992. price varies. (Universitaet Salzburg) Oesterreichischer Kunst- und Kulturverlag, Postfach 17, A-1016 Vienna, Austria. **Document type:** academic/scholarly publication.

5906 SCIENCES: COMPREHENSIVE WORKS

500   AU   ISSN 0379-1424
UNIVERSITAET WIEN. DISSERTATIONEN. 1967. irreg., no.234, 1992. price varies. Universitaet Wien, Institut fuer Orientalistik, Universitaetsstr. 7-V, A-1010 Vienna, Austria. Ed. Hermann Hunger. **Document type:** monographic series.

500   BL   ISSN 0102-6054
UNIVERSITAS. CIENCIA. 1968. q. Universidade Federal da Bahia, Centro Editorial e Didatico, Rua Augusto Viana s-n, Canela, 40000 Salvador, Bahia, Brazil. TEL 071-245-2811. bk.rev.; illus.; cum.index; circ. 500 (controlled).
Supersedes in part (in 1985): Universitas (ISSN 0041-9052)

500 700 800   GW   ISSN 0341-0129
AP4
UNIVERSITAS (ENGLISH EDITION); interdisciplinary journal for the sciences and humanities. German edition (ISSN 0041-9079) 1956. q. DM.48. Wissenschaftliche Verlagsgesellschaft mbH, Postfach 101061, 70009 Stuttgart, Germany. TEL 0711-2582-0. FAX 0711-2582-290. TELEX 723636-DAZ-D. Ed. Christian Rotta. circ. 7,000. **Document type:** academic/scholarly publication.
—BLDSC (9101.344000); Faxon.

500 700 800   GW   ISSN 0041-9079
AP30   CODEN: UNIVA8
UNIVERSITAS (GERMAN EDITION); Zeitschrift fuer interdisziplinaere Wissenschaft. English edition (ISSN 0341-0129) 1946. m. DM.97.80 (students DM.72.60). Wissenschaftliche Verlagsgesellschaft mbH, Postfach 101061, 70009 Stuttgart, Germany. TEL 0711-2582-0. FAX 0711-2582-290. TELEX 723636-DAZ-D. Ed. Christian Rotta. adv.; bk.rev.; film rev.; play rev.; abstr.; bibl.; index. circ. 6,300. Indexed: Chem.Abstr., Curr.Cont., Phil.Ind. **Document type:** academic/scholarly publication.
—Faxon; SWETS; UnCover. **CCC.**

500   RM
UNIVERSITATEA BUCURESTI. ANALELE. STIINTELE NATURII. (Text in English, French, or Rumanian) a. $10. Universitatea Bucuresti, Bd. 6h. Gheorghi-Dej Nr. 64, Bucharest, Rumania. Indexed: Biol.Abstr.

500.2   AE   ISSN 0002-533X
UNIVERSITE D'ALGER. PUBLICATIONS SCIENTIFIQUES. SERIE B: SCIENCES PHYSIQUES.* 1954. irreg. 15 F. per no. Universite d'Alger, 2 rue Didouche-Mourad, Algiers, Algeria. charts.

500 510   MG   ISSN 0374-549X
Q91.M27
UNIVERSITE DE MADAGASCAR. ETABLISSEMENT D'ENSEIGNEMENT SUPERIEUR DES SCIENCES. ANNALES: SERIE SCIENCES DE LA NATURE ET MATHEMATIQUES. (Text in French) no.4, 1966. a. Universite de Madagascar, Etablissement d'Enseignement Superieur des Sciences, B.P. 138, Antananarivo, Madagascar.
Formerly (until 1966): Universite de Madagascar. Annales: Serie Sciences et Techniques (ISSN 1011-0542)

505   CM   ISSN 0566-201X
UNIVERSITE DE YAOUNDE. FACULTE DES SCIENCES. ANNALES. 1968. irreg. $50 for 3 vols. Universite de Yaounde, Faculte des Sciences, Box 337, Yaounde, Cameroon. FAX 237-23-53-88. TELEX 8384 KN. (Dist. by: Service Central des Bibliotheques, Services des Publications, B.P. 1312, Yaounde, Cameroon) illus.
Continues: Universite Federale du Cameroun. Faculte des Sciences. Annales.

500 300   SA   ISSN 1018-0761
UNIVERSITEIT VAN STELLENBOSCH. ANNALE. (Text in English) 1989. a. Universiteit van Stellenbosch, Stellenbosch 7600, South Africa. **Document type:** academic/scholarly publication.
Formed by the 1989 merger of (1923-1988): Universiteit van Stellenbosch. Annale. Serie B (ISSN 0365-8058); (1979-1980): Universiteit van Stellenbosch. Annale. Serie A4, Bosbou (ISSN 0254-1882); (1979-1988): Universiteit van Stellenbosch. Annale. Serie A3, Landbou (ISSN 1012-0653); (1978-1984): Universiteit van Stellenbosch. Annale. Serie A2, Sologie (ISSN 1012-0645); (1975-1988): Universiteit van Stellenbosch. Annale. Serie A1, Geologie (ISSN 1013-218X)

UNIVERSITY OF CAPE TOWN. COMMITTEE FOR UNDERGRADUATE EDUCATION IN SCIENCE. COLLOQUIUM SERIES. see *EDUCATION — Higher Education*

550 919.8   US   ISSN 0069-6145
                               CODEN: CAAOA
UNIVERSITY OF COLORADO. INSTITUTE OF ARCTIC AND ALPINE RESEARCH. OCCASIONAL PAPERS. 1971. irreg., no.49, 1992. price varies. University of Colorado, Institute of Arctic and Alpine Research, Campus Box 450, Boulder, CO 80309-0450. TEL 303-492-3765. FAX 303-492-6388. Ed. Kathleen A. Salzberg. circ. 200. (also avail. in microfiche from NTI) **Indexed:** Biol.Abstr., Geo.Abstr., Geol.Abstr. **Document type:** monographic series.
—BLDSC (6217.436000).
Description: Contains miscellaneous work performed by institute personnel and associates.
Refereed Serial

UNIVERSITY OF KANSAS. MUSEUM OF NATURAL HISTORY. MISCELLANEOUS PUBLICATIONS. see *BIOLOGY*

UNIVERSITY OF KANSAS. MUSEUM OF NATURAL HISTORY. MONOGRAPHS. see *BIOLOGY*

574 500.9   US   ISSN 0091-7958
QH1   CODEN: OPMNAK
UNIVERSITY OF KANSAS. MUSEUM OF NATURAL HISTORY. OCCASIONAL PAPERS. 1971. irreg., no.164, 1994. University of Kansas, Museum of Natural History, 602 Dyche Hall, Lawrence, KS 66045-2454. Ed. Joseph T. Collins. circ. 1,500. **Indexed:** Biol.Abstr., Deep Sea Res.& Oceanogr.Abstr., GeoRef., Sport Fish.Abstr., Wild.Rev., Zoo.Rec. **Document type:** academic/scholarly publication.
Refereed Serial

UNIVERSITY OF KANSAS. MUSEUM OF NATURAL HISTORY. PUBLIC EDUCATION SERIES. see *BIOLOGY*

UNIVERSITY OF KANSAS. MUSEUM OF NATURAL HISTORY. SPECIAL PUBLICATIONS. see *BIOLOGY*

500   KU   ISSN 0376-4818
Q80.K9   CODEN: JUKSD8
UNIVERSITY OF KUWAIT. JOURNAL (SCIENCE). (Text in English; summaries in Arabic) 1974. s-a. free. University of Kuwait, Faculty of Science, P.O. Box 5969, Kuwait. Ed. Riad Halwagy. circ. 1,000. **Indexed:** Anal.Abstr., Appl.Ecol.Abstr., Aqua.Sci.& Fish.Abstr., Biol.Abstr., Chem.Abstr., Chem.Titles, Crop Physiol.Abstr., Dairy Sci.Abstr., Excerp.Med. (until 19??), ExtraMED, Field Crop Abstr., Hort.Abstr., I.M.M.Abstr., Ind.Vet., INIS Atomind., INSPEC, Math.R., Microbiol.Abstr., Plant Breed.Abstr., Rev.Appl.Entomol., Rev.Med.& Vet.Mycol., Triticale Abstr., Vet.Bull. **Document type:** academic/scholarly publication.
●Also available on CD-ROM.
—BLDSC (4911.550000); CASDDS; Ei; Genuine Article; PADDS; UnCover.

500   NR   ISSN 0075-7713
UNIVERSITY OF LAGOS. SCIENTIFIC MONOGRAPH SERIES.* 1971. irreg. price varies. University of Lagos, Centre for Cultural Studies, Akoba, Yaba, Hiseha, Nigeria. **Document type:** monographic series.

UNIVERSITY OF MICHIGAN. DIVISION OF RESEARCH DEVELOPMENT AND ADMINISTRATION. RESEARCH NEWS. see *EDUCATION — Higher Education*

500   US   ISSN 0897-6376
UNIVERSITY OF NEVADA. DESERT RESEARCH INSTITUTE. TECHNICAL REPORT. 1966. irreg. price varies. University of Nevada, Desert Research Institute, Social Sciences Center, Box 60220, Reno, NV 89506. TEL 702-673-7303. circ. 750. **Indexed:** Abstr.Anthropol.
Refereed Serial

500   AT   ISSN 0811-7640
UNIVERSITY OF NEW SOUTH WALES. FACULTY HANDBOOKS: SCIENCES. a. Aus.$5. University of New South Wales, Kensington, N.S.W. 2052, Australia. TEL 02-697-2840. FAX 02-662-2163.

UNIVERSITY OF OSAKA PREFECTURE. BULLETIN. SERIES A: ENGINEERING AND NATURAL SCIENCES/OSAKA-FURITSU DAIGAKU KIYO, A. KOGAKU, SHIZEN KAGAKU. see *ENGINEERING*

500   PK   ISSN 0080-9624
Q1.A1   CODEN: SURJAA
UNIVERSITY OF SIND. RESEARCH JOURNAL. SCIENCE SERIES. (Text in English) 1965. a. Rs.25($4) University of Sind, Faculty of Science, Jamshoro, Hyderabad 6, Pakistan. Ed. M. Rais Ahmed.
—CASDDS.

500 375   AT   ISSN 1036-0719
UNIVERSITY OF TECHNOLOGY, SYDNEY. FACULTY OF SCIENCE HANDBOOK. 1990. a. Aus.$5 (foreign Aus.$10). University of Technology, Sydney, P.O. Box 123, City Campus, Broadway, N.S.W. 2007, Australia. TEL 02-330-1990. FAX 02-330-1551. circ. 3,000.
Description: Contains detailed information on the faculty, schools, staff, courses, subject synopses, and general information on the university.

UNIVERSITY OF TECHNOLOGY, SYDNEY. RESEARCH REPORT. see *TECHNOLOGY: COMPREHENSIVE WORKS*

500   IR   ISSN 0042-0131
                               CODEN: TUSQAD
UNIVERSITY OF TEHERAN. FACULTY OF SCIENCE. QUARTERLY BULLETIN. (Text in English, French or Persian) 1968. q. Rs.350($10) (University of Teheran, Faculty of Science) University of Teheran Press Co., Enghelab Ave., Teheran, Iran. Ed.Bd. circ. 1,000. **Indexed:** Biol.Abstr., Chem.Abstr. **Document type:** bulletin.
—CASDDS.

500   JA   ISSN 0289-7520
Q1   CODEN: SPCTDZ
UNIVERSITY OF TOKYO. COLLEGE OF ARTS AND SCIENCES. SCIENTIFIC PAPERS/TOKYO DAIGAKU KYOYOGAKUBU SHIZEN KAGAKU KIYO. (Text in European languages) 1951. s-a. exchange basis. University of Tokyo, College of Arts and Sciences - Tokyo Daigaku Kyoyogakubu, 8-1 Komaba 3-chome, Meguro-ku, Tokyo 153, Japan.
FAX 81-3-3485-2904. TELEX 2426728 TODAIK J. Ed. Tadao Matsumoto. charts; illus.; index. circ. 460. **Indexed:** Appl.Mech.Rev., Biol.Abstr., Chem.Abstr., Curr.Adv.Ecol.Sci., Deep Sea Res.& Oceanogr.Abstr., GeoRef., INIS Atomind., INSPEC (1983-), Math.R., Plant Breed.Abstr.
—CASDDS; UnCover.
Formerly: University of Tokyo. College of General Education. Scientific Papers (ISSN 0040-8964)

500   JA   ISSN 0910-481X
                               CODEN: BUTMDF
UNIVERSITY OF TOKYO. UNIVERSITY MUSEUM. BULLETIN/TOKYO DAIGAKU SOGO KENKYU SHIRYOKAN KENKYU HOKOKU. (Text in English) 1970. irreg. Tokyo Daigaku, Sogo Kenkyu Shiryokan, 3-1, Hongo 7-chome, Bunkyo-ku, Tokyo 113, Japan. **Indexed:** Anthropol.Lit. **Document type:** bulletin.
—BLDSC (2796.850000).
Description: Contains original research papers.

UNIVERSITY OF WESTERN ONTARIO SERIES IN PHILOSOPHY OF SCIENCE. see *PHILOSOPHY*

500   YU   ISSN 0351-6962
UNIVERZITET SVETOZAR MARKOVIC U KRAGUJEVCU. PRIRODNO-MATEMATICKI FAKULTET. ZBORNIK RADOVA/FACULTY OF SCIENCE, KRAGUJEVAC. COLLECTION OF SCIENTIFIC PAPERS. (Text in English and Serbo-Croatian; summaries in English) 1980. a. $100. Univerzitet Svetozar Markovic, Prirodno-Matemeticki Fakultet, Box 60, 34000 Kragujevac, Yugoslavia. TEL 69120.
FAX 38-34-60252. circ. 100. (back issues avail.) **Indexed:** Math.R.
Description: Original scientific papers in the natural sciences and mathematics.

500   PL   ISSN 0239-5894
UNIWERSYTET GDANSKI. ZESZYTY NAUKOWE. ROZPRAWY I MONOGRAFIE. 1978. irreg. price varies. Uniwersytet Gdanski, c/o Biblioteka Glowna, Ul. Armii Krajowej 110, 81-824 Sopot, Poland. TEL 51-0061. TELEX 051 2247 BMOR PL. (Dist. by: Ars Polona-Ruch, Krakowskie Przedmiescie 7, 00-680 Warsaw, Poland) **Document type:** academic/scholarly publication, monographic series.
Description: Dissertations and monographs of the University of Gdansk.

SCIENCES: COMPREHENSIVE WORKS

500 600   SW   ISSN 0284-9682
UPPFINNAREN & KONSTRUKTOEREN. 1985. 5/yr. SEK 180. Teknikfoerlaget T F AB, P.O. Box 104, S-301 04 Halmstad, Sweden. TEL 46-35-10-41-50. FAX 46-35-18-65-09. Ed. K-V. Bengtsson. adv.: B&W page SEK 9500, color page SEK 12300; trim 186 x 265; adv. contact: Ronald Carlsson. circ. 6,400. cols./p.: 4; pp./issue: 56.
Formerly (until 1987): Uppfinnaren (ISSN 0283-0809)

500   JA   ISSN 0287-2900
UTAN. (Text in Japanese) 1982. m. 5400 Yen. Gakken Co. Ltd. - Gakushu Kenkyusha, 40-5, Kamiikedai 4-chome, Ota-ku, Tokyo 145, Japan. Ed. Nobuhiro Masuda.

500   JA   ISSN 0385-2415
AS552.U86   CODEN: UDKKBI
UTSUNOMIYA DAIGAKU KYOIKUGAKUBU KIYO. DAI-2-BU/UTSUNOMIYA UNIVERSITY. FACULTY OF EDUCATION. BULLETIN. SECTION 2. (Text and summaries in English and Japanese) 1950. a. Utsunomiya Daigaku, Kyoikugakubu - Utsunomiya University, Faculty of Education, 350, Mine-machi, Utsunomiya-shi, Tochigi-ken 321, Japan. **Indexed:** INIS Atomind., Jap.Per.Ind. **Document type:** bulletin.
—BLDSC (2507.670000); CASDDS; UnCover.

500   JA   ISSN 0286-6293
AS552.U86   CODEN: UDKKAH
UTSUNOMIYA DAIGAKU KYOYOBU KENKYU HOKOKU. DAI-2-BU/UTSUNOMIYA UNIVERSITY. FACULTY OF GENERAL EDUCATION. BULLETIN. SECTION 2. (Text and summaries in English and Japanese) 1968. a. Utsunomiya Daigaku, Kyoyobu - Utsunomiya University, Faculty of General Education, 350, Mine-machi, Utsunomiya-shi, Tochigi-ken 320, Japan. **Indexed:** Biol.Abstr., Chem.Abstr., Jap.Per.Ind. **Document type:** bulletin.
—CASDDS.

500   II   ISSN 0083-5013
UTTAR PRADESH, INDIA. SCIENTIFIC RESEARCH COMMITTEE MONOGRAPH SERIES. (Text in English) irreg. price varies. Scientific Research Committee, Uttar Pradesh, Chhattar Manzil Palace, Lucknow, Uttar Pradesh, India. **Document type:** monographic series, government publication.

V R B - INFORMATIE. (Vereniging van Religieus - Wetenschappelijke Bibliothecarissen) see *LIBRARY AND INFORMATION SCIENCES*

500 600   FI   ISSN 1235-0621
    CODEN: VTTPEY
V T T PUBLICATIONS. (Text in English) 1981. irreg. Valtion Teknillinen Tutkimuskeskus, Information Service - Technical Research Centre of Finland, P.O. Box 2000, FIN-02044 VTT, Finland. FAX 358-0-4564374. (reprint service avail. from NTI) **Indexed:** Biol.Abstr., Chem.Abstr., INSPEC. **Document type:** monographic series.
—BLDSC (9258.906930); CASDDS; Ei.
Formerly (until 1992): Technical Research Centre of Finland. Publications (ISSN 0358-5069)

500 600   GW   ISSN 0083-5080
VADEMECUM DEUTSCHER LEHR- UND FORSCHUNGSSTAETTEN. STAETTEN DER FORSCHUNG. 1954. irreg., vol.11, 1994. DM.590. Raabe Fachverlag fuer Wissenschaftsinformation, Koenigswintererstr. 418, 53227 Bonn, Germany. TEL 0228-970200. FAX 0228-9702036. adv. circ. 5,000. **Document type:** monographic series.
● Also available online. Vendor(s): STN International.

500.1   UK   ISSN 0049-5891
VASCULUM. 1915. q. £6. Northern Naturalists Union, Sunderland Museum & Art Gallery, Borough Rd., Sunderland, Tyne and Wear SR1 1PP, England. TEL 0191-565-0723. FAX 0191-565-0713. Ed. L. Jessop. bk.rev. circ. 250. **Indexed:** Curr.Adv.Ecol.Sci., GeoRef. **Document type:** academic/scholarly publication.
—BLDSC (9149.000000).

VEDA, TECHNIKA A MY/SCIENCE, TECHNOLOGY AND WE. see *CHILDREN AND YOUTH — For*

500   US   ISSN 0083-5846
    CODEN: VEWIAL
VERSTAENDLICHE WISSENSCHAFT. (Issues not numbered consecutively) (Text in German) 1952. irreg. price varies. Springer-Verlag, 175 Fifth Ave., New York, NY 10010. TEL 212-460-1500. FAX 212-473-6272. (Also: Berlin, Heidelberg, Tokyo and Vienna) (reprint service avail. from ISI) **Indexed:** Biol.Abstr. **Document type:** monographic series.

500   XR   ISSN 0042-4544
    CODEN: VESMAD
VESMIR/UNIVERSE; prirodovedecky casopis. (Text in Czech and Slovak) 1871. m. DM.87. (Ceska Akademie Ved) Vesmir, spol. s r.o., Narodni tr. 3, 111 42 Prague 1, Czech Republic. TEL 236-74-70. (Subscr. to: Artia, Ve Smeckach 30, 111 27 Prague 1, Czech Republic) Ed. Ivan M. Havel. bk.rev.; illus.; index. circ. 31,000. **Indexed:** Biol.Abstr., Chem.Abstr., GeoRef, Helminthol.Abstr.
—BLDSC (9218.500000); CASDDS.
Description: Covers general issues of scientific information and discoveries in science, medicine and technology.

500.9   AT   ISSN 0042-5184
QH1   CODEN: VICNAW
VICTORIAN NATURALIST. 1884. bi-m. Aus.$50. Field Naturalists Club of Victoria, c/o National Herbarium, Birdwood Avenue, South Yarra, Vic. 3141, Australia. TEL 03-650-8661. Ed. Robyn Watson. adv.; bk.rev.; charts; illus.; index. circ. 1,500. **Indexed:** Biol.Abstr., Forest.Abstr., Forest Prod.Abstr., Geo.Abstr., GeoRef., M.L.A., Sport Fish.Abstr., Wild.Rev., Zoo.Rec.
—BLDSC (9232.650000); UnCover. CCC.
Description: Publishes articles on all facts of natural history, primarily in Australia.

500   CE   ISSN 1391-0302
VIDURAVA. (Text in English, Sinhala) 1976. q. $8. Natural Resources, Energy & Science Authority, 47-5 Maitland Place, Colombo 7, Sri Lanka. Ed. K. Ramasamy. (reprint service avail.)

500   II   ISSN 0505-4753
    CODEN: VIBBDS
VIDYA. vol.16, 1973. s-a. Rs.5. Gujarat University, P.O. Box 4010, Ahmedabad 380009, India. Ed.Bd. bibl.; charts; illus. **Indexed:** Chem.Abstr.
—CASDDS.

500   FR   ISSN 0762-0969
Q46   CODEN: CRAGET
LA VIE DES SCIENCE; comptes rendus de l'Academie des Sciences - serie generale. 1984. 5/yr. 320 F. to individuals; institutions 530 F. Gauthier-Villars, 15 rue Gossin, 92543 Montrouge Cedex, France. TEL 33-1-40-92-65-00. FAX 33-1-40-92-65-97. TELEX 634 916 F. (Subscr. to: Centrale des Revues, 11 rue Gossin, 92543 Montrouge Cedex, France. TEL 33-1-46-56-52-66) Eds. Paul Germain, Francois Gros. index. circ. 3,200. **Indexed:** INIS Atomind., INSPEC (1984-).
—CASDDS; SWETS. CCC.

500 600   II   ISSN 0377-8487
Q73   CODEN: VBHAD6
VIGNANA BHARATHI. * (Text in English) 1975. s-a. Rs.10. Bangalore University, Department of Publications and Extension Lectures, Bangalore 560056, India. **Indexed:** GeoRef, INSPEC, Math.R.
Description: Contains research articles on science and technology.

500   II   ISSN 0042-6075
VIGYAN PRAGATI. (Text in Hindi; titles in English) 1952. m. Rs.50($15) Council of Scientific and Industrial Research, Publications and Information Directorate Bldg., Dr. K.S. Krishnan Marg, New Delhi 110 012, India. TEL 5786301. FAX 5731353. TELEX 031-7741 PID IN. Ed. G.P. Phondke. adv.; bk.rev. circ. 76,000. (reprint service avail.) **Indexed:** Chem.Abstr. **Document type:** government publication.
Description: Presents the popularization of science in simple terms.

500   II   ISSN 0042-6121
VIKRAM.* (Text in English, Hindi and Sanskrit) 1957. 4/yr. (nos. 1 & 3 devoted to Physical and Biological Sciences, Agriculture, Medicine; nos. 2 & 4 devoted to Arts & Indology). Rs.10. Vikram University, Registrar, Ujain, Madhya Pradesh, India. Eds. Dr. Har Swarup (Science Issue), Shri V. Venkatachalam (Arts Issue). charts; illus. **Indexed:** Abstr.Mil.Bibl., Biol.Abstr., Chem.Abstr., Math.R.

500   US   ISSN 0042-658X
Q1   CODEN: VJSCAI
VIRGINIA JOURNAL OF SCIENCE. (Including Proceedings) 1950. q. Virginia Academy of Science, c/o J.H. Martin, J.S. Reynolds Community College, Box 85622, Richmond, VA 23285-5622. TEL 804-371-3064. adv.; bk.rev.; charts; illus.; index. circ. 2,000. (also avail. in microform from UMI) **Indexed:** Biol.Abstr., Chem.Abstr., Deep Sea Res.& Oceanogr.Abstr., Geo.Abstr., GeoRef., Math.R., Sel.Water Res.Abstr., Sport Fish.Abstr., Wild.Rev., Zoo.Rec. **Document type:** academic/scholarly publication.
—BLDSC (9239.000000); CASDDS; Faxon; UnCover.

500   IC   ISSN 0376-2599
    CODEN: VIISA9
VISINDAFELAG ISLENDINGA. RIT/ICELANDIC SCIENTIFIC SOCIETY. OCCASIONAL PAPERS. (Text in English) 1923. irreg., no.45, 1988. price varies. Visindafelag Islendinga - Societas Scientiarum Islandica (Icelandic Scientific Society), University of Iceland, Haskolabokasafn - University Library, 101 Reykjavik, Iceland. TEL 354-569-4326. (Subscr. to: Bokaverslun Sigfusar Eymundssonar, Austurstraeti 18, 101 Reykjavik, Iceland; or: Bokabud Mals og Menningar, Laugavegi 18, 101 Reykjavik, Iceland) circ. 1,000. **Indexed:** Biol.Abstr.

500   IC   ISSN 1010-7193
VISINDAFELAG ISLENDINGA - RADSTEFNURIT. 1987. irreg. Visindafelag Islendinga - Societas Scientiarum Islandica, University of Iceland, Haskolabokasafn - University Library, 101 Reykjavik, Iceland. TEL 354-569-4326. **Document type:** proceedings.

500   SZ
VISION. 1972. 4/yr. plus 2 to 5 special thematic nos. 32 SFr. (free to qualified individuals). Office Federal de l'Education et de la Science - Bundesamt fuer Bildung und Wissenschaft - Ufficio Federale dell'Educazione e della Scienza - Federal Office for Science and Education, Wildhainweg 9, Case Postale 5675, CH-3001 Bern, Switzerland. TEL 031-3229691. FAX 031-3227854. Ed. Peter Bucher. adv. contact: Urs Aeberhard. bibl.; index. circ. 2,000. **Document type:** academic/scholarly publication.
—CCC.
Formerly (until 1993): Politique de la Science (ISSN 0085-4980)
Description: Publishes information on Swiss science policy and national and international higher education policy activities.

500 947   RU   ISSN 0205-9606
VOPROSY ISTORII ESTESTVOZNANYA I TEKHNIKI. 1956. q. $151 (effective 1996). (Institut Istorii Estestvoznaniya i Tekhniki) Izdatel'stvo Nauka, 90 Profsoyuznaya ul., 117864 Moscow, Russia. TEL 234-05-84. (Subscr. addr.: Staropanskii Per. 1-5, 103012 Moscow, Russia) bk.rev.; illus.; bibl. **Indexed:** Amer.Hist.& Life, Hist.Abstr., Math.R.
—BLDSC (0042.750400). CCC.

500   JA   ISSN 0511-0831
    CODEN: WDKSAT
WAKAYAMA DAIGAKU KYOIKUGAKUBU KIYO. SHIZEN KAGAKU/WAKAYAMA UNIVERSITY. FACULTY OF EDUCATION. BULLETIN: NATURAL SCIENCE. (Text in English and Japanese; summaries in English) 1950. a. Wakayama Daigaku, Kyoikugakubu - Wakayama University, Faculty of Education, 930, Sakaedani, Wakayama-shi, Wakayama-ken 640, Japan. (Co-sponsor: Wakayama Daigaku Gakugei Gakkai - Wakayama University, Liberal Arts Society) **Indexed:** Biol.Abstr., Chem.Abstr., Jap.Per.Ind.

500   US
WAKE-ROBIN. 1970. a. free. John Burroughs Association, 15 W. 77th St., New York, NY 10024. TEL 212-769-5169. FAX 212-769-5233. Ed. Dr. Alfred Marks. bk.rev. circ. 480. (back issues avail.)
Description: Focuses on nature-oriented and conservation essays, as well as news of the association.

SCIENCES: COMPREHENSIVE WORKS

500 620   JA   ISSN 0372-7181
CODEN: WDRKA6
WASEDA DAIGAKU RIKOGAKU KENKYUJO HOKOKU/WASEDA UNIVERSITY. SCIENCE AND ENGINEERING RESEARCH LABORATORY. BULLETIN. (Text in Japanese and European languages) 1944. q. Waseda Daigaku, Rikogaku Kenkyujo - Waseda University, Science and Engineering Research Laboratory, 17 Kikui-cho, Shinjuku-ku, Tokyo 162, Japan. FAX 03-203-3231. charts; illus. circ. 1,000. **Indexed:** Chem.Abstr., Eng.Ind., INIS Atomind., Jap.Per.Ind., Math.R. **Document type:** bulletin.
—BLDSC (2702.700000); CASDDS; UnCover.

500 620   JA   ISSN 0369-1950
T4   CODEN: MSEWA6
WASEDA UNIVERSITY. SCHOOL OF SCIENCE AND ENGINEERING. MEMOIRS/WASEDA DAIGAKU RIKOGAKUBU KIYO. (Text in English) 1922. a. free. Waseda Daigaku, Rikogakubu - Waseda University, School of Science and Engineering, 4-1 Okubo 3-chome, Shinjuku-ku, Tokyo 169, Japan. Ed. Fusao Hayama. **Indexed:** Chem.Abstr., INIS Atomind., INSPEC, JCT, JTA, Math.R., Met.Abstr., World Alum.Abstr.
—BLDSC (5634.500000); CASDDS; UnCover.
Formerly (until 1954): Waseda University. Faculty of Science and Engineering. Memoirs (ISSN 0368-9735)

500 620   JA   ISSN 0285-4333
WASEDA UNIVERSITY. SCIENCE AND ENGINEERING RESEARCH LABORATORY. REPORT. (Text in English) 1973. irreg. Waseda Daigaku, Rikogaku Kenkyujo - Waseda University, Science and Engineering Research Laboratory, 17 Kikui-cho, Shinjuku-ku, Tokyo 162, Japan. FAX 03-203-3231.

500   US   ISSN 0043-0439
Q11   CODEN: JWASA3
WASHINGTON ACADEMY OF SCIENCES. JOURNAL.* Key Title: Journal of the Washington Academy of Sciences. 1899. q. $25 (foreign $35). Washington Academy of Sciences, 2100 Foxhall Rd., N.W., No.COLE, Washington, DC 20007-1199. FAX 703-524-1457. Ed. Bruce Hill. bk.rev.; bibl.; charts; illus. circ. 1,000. (also avail. in microform from UMI,PMC) **Indexed:** Bibl.Ling., Biol.Abstr., Biol.Dig., Chem.Abstr., Deep Sea Res.& Oceanogr.Abstr., Eng.Ind., GeoRef., INSPEC, Leg.Per., Math.R., Met.Abstr., Rev.Plant Path., RILM, Sport Fish.Abstr., Wild.Rev., Zoo.Rec. **Document type:** academic/scholarly publication.
—BLDSC (4913.000000); CASDDS; Faxon; SWETS; UMI; UnCover.
Supersedes (in 1911): Washington Academy of Sciences. Proceedings (ISSN 0363-1095)

500   US   ISSN 0740-0535
WASHINGTON FEDERAL SCIENCE NEWSLETTER. 1989. s-m. (m. Jan. and Aug.). $410 in N. America; elsewhere $500. Washington Federal Science Newsletter, Inc., 1057-B National Press Bldg., Washington, DC 20045. TEL 202-393-3640. FAX 301-428-0557. (Subscr. to: Box 2075, Washington, DC 20013) Ed. Murray Felsher; Pub. Murray Felsher. bk.rev.; bibl.; stat.; tr.lit. (tabloid format; back issues avail.) **Document type:** newsletter.
Description: Covers science and technology research being undertaken by all U.S. agencies. Includes programs, budgets, and personnel.

500.9   JA   ISSN 0389-6951
WATASHITACHI NO SHIZENSHI/NATURAL HISTORY. (Text in Japanese) 1979. 4/yr. 3000 Yen. Kitakyushu Shizenshi Tomo no Kai, Kitakyushu Shizenshi Hakubutsukan, Yahataeki Bldg., 3-6, Nishi-Hon-machi, Yahatahigashi-ku, Kitakyushu-shi, Fukuoka-ken 805, Japan. FAX 093-661-7503. circ. 2,000. **Document type:** bulletin.

WECHSELWIRKUNG; Technik Naturwissenschaft Gesellschaft. see TECHNOLOGY: COMPREHENSIVE WORKS

500   IS   ISSN 0334-1151
WEIZMANN INSTITUTE OF SCIENCE. RESEARCH. (Text in English) 1977. s-a. free. Weizmann Institute of Science, Public Affairs Department, Rehovot, Israel. TEL 972-8-343852. FAX 972-8-344104. abstr. circ. 6,000. (looseleaf format)

500   IS
WEIZMANN INSTITUTE OF SCIENCE, REHOVOT, ISRAEL. ANNUAL REPORT. (Text in English) 1989. a. free. Weizmann Institute of Science, Office of the Special Assistant to the President, Rehovot, Israel. TEL 972-8-343888. FAX 972-8-344104. illus. circ. 17,000. **Document type:** corporate report.

500 600   IS   ISSN 0083-7849
Q80.I78
WEIZMANN INSTITUTE OF SCIENCE, REHOVOT, ISRAEL. SCIENTIFIC ACTIVITIES. (Text in English) 1953. a. Weizmann Institute of Science, Office of the Academic Secretary, Rehovot, Israel. TEL 972-8-343859. FAX 972-8-471667. circ. 3,000.

500   UK   ISSN 0083-7989
CODEN: WGCSA
WENNER GREN CENTER INTERNATIONAL SYMPOSIUM SERIES. Variant title: Wenner-Gren International Series. 1962. irreg. price varies. Elsevier Science Ltd., Pergamon, P.O. Box 800, Kidlington, Oxford OX5 1DX, England. TEL 44-1865-843000. FAX 44-1865-843010. E-mail: nlinfo-f@elsevier.nl; usinfo-f@elsevier.com; forinfo-kyf04035@niftyserve.or.jp; Site addr.: http://www.elsevier.nl/. **Indexed:** Biol.Abstr., Chem.Abstr. **Document type:** monographic series, proceedings.
—CASDDS.

500   NR   ISSN 0043-3020
WEST AFRICAN SCIENCE ASSOCIATION. JOURNAL. irreg. West African Science Association, P.O. Box 4039, University of Ibadan, Ibadan, Nigeria. TEL 400-550.

500   US   ISSN 0096-4263
Q11   CODEN: PWVAAI
WEST VIRGINIA ACADEMY OF SCIENCE. PROCEEDINGS. 1925. s-a. $20 to non-members; members $15. West Virginia Academy of Science, Marshall University, College of Science, 400 Hal Greer Blvd., Huntington, WV 25755. TEL 304-696-2338. FAX 304-696-3243. Ed. Ralph W.Taylor. adv.; abstr.; cum.index: 1925-1975; circ. 425 (paid). (back issues avail.) **Indexed:** Bio-Contr.News & Info., Biol.Abstr., Field Crop Abstr., Geo.Abstr., Herb.Abstr., Math.R., Plant Breed.Abstr., Plant Grow.Reg.Abstr., Rev.Plant Path., Sport Fish.Abstr., Weed Abstr., Wild.Rev., Zoo.Rec. **Document type:** proceedings.
—BLDSC (6833.000000).
Description: Publishes papers primarily dealing with regional ecological or biological issues.

500   AT   ISSN 0508-4865
CODEN: WAUNA9
WESTERN AUSTRALIAN NATURALIST. 1947. 2/yr. Aus.$40 (effective 1994). Western Australian Naturalists' Club Inc., P.O. Box 156, Nedlands, W.A. 6009, Australia. FAX 610-272-8688. Ed. John Dell. adv. circ. 550. **Indexed:** Biol.Abstr., Sport Fish.Abstr., Wild.Rev., Zoo.Rec. **Document type:** academic/scholarly publication.

500.9   GW   ISSN 0175-3495
WESTFAELISCHEN MUSEUM FUER NATURKUNDE. ABHANDLUNGEN. 1930. 4/yr. price varies. Westfaelisches Museum fuer Naturkunde, Sentruperstr. 285, 48161 Muenster, Germany. TEL 0251-59105. FAX 0251-5916098. charts; illus.; index. **Indexed:** Biol.Abstr. **Document type:** academic/scholarly publication.
Formerly: Landesmuseum fuer Naturkunde zu Muenster in Westfalen. Abhandlungen (ISSN 0023-7906)

500   NE   ISSN 0166-8471
WETENSCHAPSBELEID. English edition: Science Policy in the Netherlands (ISSN 0167-191X) 1978. bi-m. free. Ministrie van Onderwijs, Cultuur en Wetenschappen, Voorlichtingsdienst, Postbus 25000, 2700 LZ Zoetermeer, Netherlands. TEL 31-79-532832. FAX 31-79-512089. Ed. M. Verzantvoort. illus. (back issues avail.) **Indexed:** ELLIS. **Document type:** government publication.
Description: Covers issues relating to the Dutch governmental policy on the sciences, including news and information on noteworthy research projects and initiatives.

500 610 510 378 UK
WHICH DEGREE. SCIENCES, MEDICINE, MATHEMATICS. 1968? a. £16.99 (5 vol. set £75. (Careers Research and Advisory Centre) Hobsons Publishing plc., Bateman St., Cambridge CB2 1LZ, England. TEL 01223-354551. FAX 01223-323154. TELEX 81546 HOBCAM G. (Orders to: Biblios Publishers' Distribution Services Ltd., Star Rd., Partridge Green, W. Sussex RH13 8LD, England. TEL 01403-710851. FAX 01403-711143) **Document type:** directory.
Description: Guides students and career counselors to degree programs in the natural sciences, along with medicine and mathematics, with concise course descriptions.

590 580 579   AT   ISSN 0812-423X
WHIRRAKEE. 1967. m. (except Jan.). Aus.$30. Bendigo Field Naturalist Club, P.O. Box 396, Bendigo, Vic. 3550, Australia. Ed. T. Burton. circ. 170. (back issues avail.)
Supersedes (in 1980): Bendigo Naturalist.

WHITE PAPER ON SCIENCE AND TECHNOLOGY (YEAR). see TECHNOLOGY: COMPREHENSIVE WORKS

500   SA
WHO-DOES-WHAT: REGISTER OF GRANT HOLDERS. 1992. a. free. Foundation for Research Development, Communications - Stigting vir Navorsingsontwikkeling, Kommunikasie, P.O. Box 2600, Pretoria 0001, South Africa.

500 600 020   US
JK6
WHO KNOWS WHAT: A GUIDE TO EXPERTS. (Subseries of: Business Research Series (ISSN 0894-881X)) 1978. irreg. (approx. every 18 mos.). $195 (effective 1995). Washington Researchers Publishing (Subsidiary of: Washington Researchers, Ltd.), Box 19005, 20th St. Sta., Washington, DC 20036-9005. TEL 202-333-3499. FAX 202-625-0656. Ed. Walt Seager. **Document type:** directory.
Former titles (until 1995): Who Knows: A Guide to Washington Experts (ISSN 0894-8801); (until 1986): Researcher's Guide to Washington Experts (ISSN 0740-087X)
Description: Lists 15,000 experts in 14,000 areas and subareas.

WHO'S WHO IN INDIAN SCIENCE. see BIOGRAPHY

WHO'S WHO IN SCIENCE AND ENGINEERING. see BIOGRAPHY

WHO'S WHO IN SCIENCE IN EUROPE. see BIOGRAPHY

500   KE   ISSN 1015-4957
WHYDAH. 1987. q. KShs.50 (foreign $10) (effective 1995). (African Academy of Sciences) Academy Science Publishers, P.O. Box 14798, Nairobi, Kenya. TEL 254-2-884401. FAX 254-2-884406. TELEX 25446 AFACS. E-mail: aas@kaact.kenya-net.org. Ed. Maggie Anaminyi. **Document type:** newsletter.
Description: Provides a forum for scientists and policy makers throughout Africa.

WILEY LIBRARIANS' NEWSLETTER. see PUBLISHING AND BOOK TRADE

WILTSHIRE ARCHAEOLOGICAL AND NATURAL HISTORY MAGAZINE. see ARCHAEOLOGY

WILTSHIRE ARCHAEOLOGICAL AND NATURAL HISTORY SOCIETY. ANNUAL REPORT (YEAR). see ARCHAEOLOGY

500   US   ISSN 0084-0505
AS36   CODEN: TWASAB
WISCONSIN ACADEMY OF SCIENCES, ARTS AND LETTERS. TRANSACTIONS. 1870. a. Wisconsin Academy of Sciences, Arts and Letters, 1922 University Ave., Madison, WI 53705. Ed. Bill Urblock. bk.rev. circ. 1,550. **Indexed:** Biol.Abstr., Deep Sea Res.& Oceanogr.Abstr., Field Crop Abstr., GeoRef, Herb.Abstr., Rev.Plant Path., Sel.Water Res.Abstr., Sport Fish.Abstr., Wild.Rev., Zoo.Rec. **Document type:** academic/scholarly publication.
—UnCover.

SCIENCES: COMPREHENSIVE WORKS

500   GW
WISSENSCHAFT UND FRIEDEN. 1983. q. DM.48. Informationsdienst Wissenschaft und Frieden e.V., Reuterstr. 44, 53115 Bonn, Germany. TEL 06421-21395. FAX 0228-214924. (Co-sponsor: Bund Demokratischer Wissenschaftlerinnen und Wissenschaftler e.V.) Ed. Caroline Thomas.
  Formed by merger of: Informationsdienst Wissenschaft und Frieden (ISSN 0177-1213) & Frieden.

500 370   GW   ISSN 0947-9546
▼**WISSENSCHAFTSMANAGEMENT.** 1995. bi-m. DM.198. C.H. Beck'sche Verlagsbuchhandlung, Wilhelmstr. 9, 80801 Munich, Germany. TEL 089-38189338. FAX 089-38189398. Ed.Bd. adv. **Document type:** academic/scholarly publication.

WOMEN AI KEXUE/WE LOVE SCIENCE. see *CHILDREN AND YOUTH — For*

500 600   US   ISSN 1057-2821
WONDER: OBSERVING & CONFRONTING THE ENIGMAS THAT SURROUND US. 1991. a. $5. Ziggurat Press, Box 394, Sound Beach, NY 11789. Ed. Norman Weisberg.
  Description: For students of all ages; explores the interconnections and machineries of the universe.

500   CN   ISSN 0049-7886
WOOD DUCK. 1947. 9/yr. membership. Hamilton Naturalists' Club, c/o Federation of Ontario Naturalists, 355 Lesmill Rd., Don Mills, ON M3B 2W8, Canada. TEL 905-634-3538. FAX 905-634-3538. Ed. Jean Stollard. bk.rev. circ. 600. **Document type:** newsletter.

500 600   US   ISSN 0897-926X
WORCESTER POLYTECHNIC INSTITUTE - STUDIES IN SCIENCE, TECHNOLOGY AND CULTURE. (Text in English and other West European languages) 1988. irreg. Peter Lang Publishing, Inc., 62 W. 45th St., 4th Fl., New York, NY 10036. TEL 212-302-6740. Eds. Lance Schachterle, Francis C. Lutz. **Document type:** academic/scholarly publication, monographic series.
—BLDSC (9347.625000).

500   US   ISSN 1059-1931
WORLD & SCIENCE.* 1991. q. $29.99. Publishing & Business Consultants, 101 W. 64th St., Unit 3, Inglewood, CA 90302-1255. TEL 213-732-3477. FAX 213-732-9123. (Subscr. to: Box 75932, Los Angeles, CA 90075) Ed. Andeson Napoleon Atia. **Document type:** consumer publication.

500 011   GW
WORLD GUIDE TO SCIENTIFIC ASSOCIATIONS AND LEARNED SOCIETIES. irreg., 6th ed., 1994. $245. K.G. Saur Verlag KG, A part of Reed Reference Publishing, Ortlerstr. 8, 81373 Munich, Germany. TEL 089-769020. FAX 089-76902150. (Subscr. to: Postfach 701620, 81316 Munich, Germany; N. America subscr. to: K.G. Saur, 121 Chanlon Rd., New Providence, NJ 07974-9903, USA. TEL 908-665-3576) **Document type:** directory.
  Description: Provides descriptions of more than 17,000 national and international societies involved in science, culture and technology. Includes a subject index arranged by country, name index, and publication index cross-referenced to the main section entries.

500 600   UK
WORLD TECHNOLOGY POLICIES. 1992. a. £145. Longman Group UK Ltd., Westgate House, 6th Fl., The High, Harlow, Essex CM20 1YR, England. TEL 0279-442601. FAX 0279-444501. (Dist. in US & Canada by: Gale Research, Inc., 835 Penobscot Bldg., Detroit, MI 48226. TEL 800-877-4253) Ed.Bd. **Document type:** trade publication.

500   PL   ISSN 0371-4756
WROCLAWSKIE TOWARZYSTWO NAUKOWE. SPRAWOZDANIA. SERIA A. irreg., vol.39, 1986. price varies. Wroclawskie Towarzystwo Naukowe, Ul. Parkowa 13, 50-616 Wroclaw, Poland. TEL 48-71-484061. Ed. A. Galos. **Indexed:** Bibl.Ling. **Document type:** proceedings.
  Description: Reports of activities and sessions of the Humanistic Section of the Wroclaw Scientific Society. Summaries of dissertations.

500.9   PL   ISSN 0043-9592
WSZECHSWIAT/UNIVERSE. (Text in Polish) 1882. m. 240000 Zl.($21) (Polskie Towarzystwo Przyrodnikow im. Kopernika) Platam, Ul. Krypinow 189, 32-068 Liszki, Poland. TEL 48-12-222924. (Dist. by: Ars Polona, Krakowskie Przedmiescie 7, 00-068 Warsaw, Poland) Ed. J. Vetulani; Pub. Z. Jurkowski. bk.rev.; charts; illus.; index. circ. 1,200. **Indexed:** Biol.Abstr. **Document type:** academic/scholarly publication.

500   CC   ISSN 0253-9888
                              CODEN: WTHPDI
WUHAN DAXUE XUEBAO (ZIRAN KEXUE BAN)/WUHAN UNIVERSITY. JOURNAL (NATURAL SCIENCE EDITION). (Text in Chinese) bi-m. Y24. Wuhan Daxue, Xuebao Bianjibu, Luo Jia Shan, Wuchang-qu, Wuhan, Hubei 430072, People's Republic of China. TEL 027-7882712. FAX 027-7882661. (Dist. outside China by: China International Book Trading Corp., P.O. Box 399, Beijing, P.R. China) Eds. Li Weihua, Yang Yugao. **Indexed:** Chem.Abstr., Math.R. **Document type:** academic/scholarly publication.
—BLDSC (4917.469300); CASDDS.
  Formerly: Wuhan Daxue Ziran Kexue Xuebao (ISSN 0509-397X)

500   CC   ISSN 0438-0479
Q4   CODEN: HMHHAF
XIAMEN DAXUE XUEBAO (ZIRAN KEXUE BAN)/XIAMEN UNIVERSITY. JOURNAL (NATURAL SCIENCE EDITION)/ACTA SCIENTIARUM UNIVERSITATIS AMOIENSIS. (Text in Chinese; abstracts in English) 1952. q. $1.50 per no. Xiamen Daxue - Xiamen University, c/o Xiamen Daxue Tushuguan, Xiamen, Fujian 361005, People's Republic of China. TEL 592-2086255. (Dist. outside China by: China International Book Trading Corp., P.O. Box 399, Beijing, P.R.C.) Ed. Zhang Hongbin. **Document type:** academic/scholarly publication.
—BLDSC (4917.469600); CASDDS.

XIANDAIHUA/MODERNIZATION. see *TECHNOLOGY: COMPREHENSIVE WORKS*

500 028.5   CC
XIAOXUE KEJI/ELEMENTARY SCHOOL SCIENCE AND TECHNOLOGY. (Text in Chinese) m. Shanghai Keji Jiaoyu Chubanshe - Shanghai Science and Technology Education Publishers, 393, Guanshengyuan Lu, Shanghai 200233, People's Republic of China. TEL 86-21-4367970. FAX 86-21-4702835. Ed. Gu Fangben. **Document type:** academic/scholarly publication.

500   CC   ISSN 1001-988X
                            CODEN: XDXKEH
XIBEI SHIFAN DAXUE XUEBAO (ZIRAN KEXUE BAN)/NORTHWEST NORMAL UNIVERSITY. JOURNAL (NATURAL SCIENCES EDITION). (Text in Chinese) 1942. q. Y1.20 per no. Northwest Normal University, Department of the University Journal, Lanzhou, Gansu Province 730070, People's Republic of China. TEL 0931-7666821. FAX 0931-7668159. (Dist. by: China International Book Trading Corporation, P.O. Box 399, Beijing, People's Republic of China) Ed. Zhao Gengji. circ. 1,500. **Document type:** academic/scholarly publication.
—BLDSC (4834.407500); CASDDS.

500   CC   ISSN 1000-5471
                            CODEN: XSDKEM
XINAN SHIFAN DAXUE XUEBAO (ZIRAN KEXUE BAN)/SOUTHWEST NORMAL UNIVERSITY. JOURNAL (NATURAL SCIENCE EDITION). (Text in Chinese) 1957. bi-m. Xinan Shifan Daxue, Xuebao Bianjibu, Beipei, Chongqing, Sichuan 630715, People's Republic of China. TEL 863901. Ed. Qiu Yuhui. circ. 700. **Document type:** academic/scholarly publication.
—BLDSC (4902.255000).

500 001.3   CQ   ISSN 1019-9039
YA MKOBE. (Text in French, occasionally in Arabic, Comorian) 1984. irreg., no.3, 1987. Centre National de Documentation et de Recherche Scientifique, B.P. 169, Moroni, Comoros. (Co-sponsors: Archives Nationales; Bibliotheque National; Musee National des Sciences de l'Homme et des Sciences de la Nature) **Indexed:** P.L.E.S.A. **Document type:** academic/scholarly publication.

500   US   ISSN 0091-0287
YALE SCIENTIFIC. 1894. q. $10. Yale University Press, Box 209117, Yale Sta., New Haven, CT 06520. TEL 203-432-0940. Ed. Bret Ancowite; Pub. J. Michael Collaco. adv. contact: Amer B. Khan. bk.rev.; charts; illus.; stat.; index. circ. 7,000. (also avail. in microform from UMI; back issues avail.; reprint service avail. from UMI) **Indexed:** Biol.Abstr., Biol.Dig., Chem.Abstr., Deep Sea Res.& Oceanogr.Abstr., Educ.Ind., Eng.Ind., P.A.I.S., R.G. **Document type:** academic/scholarly publication.
—Faxon; UMI; UnCover.
  Formerly: Yale Scientific Magazine (ISSN 0044-0140)
  Description: Articles on every scientific topics such as engineering, natural sciences, and computer sciences.
Refereed Serial

YAMA TO HAKUBUTSUKAN/MOUNTAIN AND MUSEUM. see *MUSEUMS AND ART GALLERIES*

500   JA
YAMADA CONFERENCE. PROCEEDINGS. (Text and summaries in English) 1979. irreg. Yamada Kagaku Shinko Zaidan - Yamada Science Foundation, Roto Seiyaku, 8-1 Tatsumi Nishi 1-chome, Ikuno-ku, Osaka-shi, Osaka-fu 544, Japan. **Document type:** proceedings.

500   JA
YAMADA KAGAKU SHINKO ZAIDAN JIGYO HOKOKUSHO/YAMADA SCIENCE FOUNDATION ANNUAL REPORT. (Text in English and Japanese; summaries in English) 1977. a. Yamada Kagaku Shinko Zaidan - Yamada Science Foundation, Roto Seiyaku, 8-1, Tatsumi-Nishi 1-chome, Ikuno-ku, Osaka-shi, Osaka-fu 544, Japan.

500   JA   ISSN 0912-2354
YAMADA KAGAKU SHINKO ZAIDAN NYUSU/YAMADA SCIENCE FOUNDATION NEWS. (Text in English and Japanese) 1974. s-a. Yamada Kagaku Shinko Zaidan - Yamada Science Foundation, 8-1, Tatsumi Nishi 1-chome, Ikuno-ku, Osaka-shi, Osaka 544, Japan.

500   JA   ISSN 0513-1693
YAMAGUCHI DAIGAKU KYOIKUGAKUBU KENKYU RONSO. DAI-2-BU. SHIZEN KAGAKU/YAMAGUCHI UNIVERSITY. FACULTY OF EDUCATION. BULLETIN, PART 2. (Text and summaries in English and Japanese) 1951. a. free. Yamaguchi Daigaku, Kyoikugakubu - Yamaguchi University, Faculty of Education, 1677-1, Yoshida, Yamaguchi-shi, Yamaguchi-ken 753, Japan. FAX 81-839-23-8612. circ. 300. **Indexed:** Biol.Abstr., INIS Atomind., Jap.Per.Ind. **Document type:** bulletin.
—BLDSC (2507.700000).

500   JA   ISSN 0387-4087
YAMAGUCHI DAIGAKU KYOYOBU KIYO. SHIZEN KAGAKU HEN/YAMAGUCHI UNIVERSITY. FACULTY OF LIBERAL ARTS. JOURNAL: NATURAL SCIENCE. (Text and summaries in English and Japanese) 1967. a. Yamaguchi Daigaku, Kyoyobu - Yamaguchi University, Faculty of Liberal Arts, 1677-1, Yoshida, Yamaguchi-shi, Yamaguchi-ken 753, Japan. **Indexed:** Jap.Per.Ind.

500   JA   ISSN 0385-2946
YAMAGUCHI JOSHI DAIGAKU KENKYU HOKOKU. DAI-2-BU. SHIZEN KAGAKU/YAMAGUCHI WOMEN'S UNIVERSITY. BULLETIN. SECTION 2, NATURAL SCIENCE. (Text and summaries in English and Japanese) 1975. 2/yr. Yamaguchi Joshi Daigaku - Yamaguchi Women's University, 2-1, Sakurabatake 3-chome, Yamaguchi-shi, Yamaguchi-ken 753, Japan. **Indexed:** Jap.Per.Ind. **Document type:** bulletin.

500   JA   ISSN 0288-4232
AM101.Y2858
YAMAGUCHI KENRITSU YAMAGUCHI HAKUBUTSUKAN KENKYU HOKOKU/YAMAGUCHI MUSEUM. BULLETIN. (Text in Japanese; abstracts in English) 1970. a. Yamaguchi Kenritsu Yamaguchi Hakubutsukan - Yamaguchi Museum, 8-2, Kasuga-cho, Yamaguchi-shi, Yamaguchi-ken 753, Japan. TEL 0839-22-0294. FAX 0839-22-0353. **Document type:** bulletin.
  Description: Contains research reports from the museum.

SCIENCES: COMPREHENSIVE WORKS

500   JA   ISSN 0288-4240
YAMAGUCHIKEN NO SHIZEN. (Text in Japanese) 1959. a. Yamaguchi Kenritsu Yamaguchi Hakubutsukan - Yamaguchi Museum, 8-2, Kasuga-cho, Yamaguchi-shi, Yamaguchi-ken 753, Japan. TEL 0839-22-0294. FAX 0839-22-0353. **Document type:** academic/scholarly publication.
    Description: Publishes articles on the natural history of Yamaguchi Prefecture.

500   JA   ISSN 0385-8766
Q4   CODEN: MLMSDM
YAMANASHI DAIGAKU KYOIKUGAKUBU KENKYU HOKOKU. DAI-2-BUNSATSU, SHIZEN KAGAKUKEI/YAMANASHI UNIVERSITY. FACULTY OF LIBERAL ARTS & EDUCATION. MEMOIRS. PART 2: MATHEMATICS & NATURAL SCIENCES. (Text and summaries in English and Japanese) 1950. a. Yamanashi Daigaku, Kyoikugakubu - Yamanashi University, Faculty of Liberal Arts & Education, 4-37, Takeda 4-chome, Kofu-shi, Yamanashi-ken 400, Japan. **Indexed:** Chem.Abstr., INIS Atomind., Jap.Per.Ind. **Document type:** academic/scholarly publication.
—BLDSC (5597.234000); CASDDS.

YANTAI DAXUE XUEBAO/YANTAI UNIVERSITY. JOURNAL. see *HUMANITIES: COMPREHENSIVE WORKS*

500   US   ISSN 0096-3291
Q9
YEARBOOK OF SCIENCE AND THE FUTURE. 1969. a. $36.95. Encyclopaedia Britannica, Inc., 310 S. Michigan Ave., Chicago, IL 60604. TEL 312-347-7000. FAX 312-347-7914. Ed. David Calhoun. index.
    Formerly: Britannica Yearbook of Science and the Future (ISSN 0068-1199)

500   CC   ISSN 0255-8297
T4   CODEN: YKXUD4
YINGYONG KEXUE XUEBAO/JOURNAL OF APPLIED SCIENCES. (Text mostly in Chinese; partly in English; abstracts in English) 1983. q. $60. (Shanghai Kexue Jishu Daxue - Shanghai University of Science and Technology) Shanghai Scientific and Technical Publishers, Journal Department, 450 Ruijin 2 Lu, Shanghai 200020, People's Republic of China. TEL 4310310. Ed. Huang Hongjia.
—BLDSC (4947.075000); CASDDS.

YOGA AND TOTAL HEALTH. see *PHILOSOPHY*

500   JA   ISSN 0085-8366
Q77   CODEN: SYUMAS
YOKOHAMA NATIONAL UNIVERSITY. SCIENCE REPORTS. SECTION 1: MATHEMATICS, PHYSICS, CHEMISTRY/YOKOHAMA KOKURITSU DAIGAKU RIKA KIYO. DAI-1-RUI, SUGAKU, BUTSURIGAKU, KAGAKU. (Text in European languages and Japanese) 1952. a. exchange basis only. Yokohama Kokuritsu Daigaku, Kyoikugakubu - Yokohama National University, Faculty of Education, 156 Tokiwadai, Hodogaya-ku, Yokohama-shi, Kanagawa-ken 240, Japan. **Indexed:** INSPEC, Jap.Per.Ind., JCT, JTA, Math.R., Met.Abstr.
—BLDSC (8162.000000); UnCover.

500   JA   ISSN 0913-9664
YOKOHAMA-SHIRITSU DAIGAKU KIYO. SHIZEN KAGAKU HEN/YOKOHAMA CITY UNIVERSITY. JOURNAL. SERIES OF NATURAL SCIENCE. (Text and summaries in English and Japanese) 1986. a. Yokohama-shiritsu Daigaku - Yokohama City University, 4646, Mutsuura-machi, Kanazawa-ku, Yokohama-shi, Kanagawa-ken 236, Japan.

500   JA   ISSN 0911-7733
YOKOHAMA-SHIRITSU DAIGAKU RONSO. SHIZEN KAGAKU KEIRETSU/YOKOHAMA CITY UNIVERSITY. BULLETIN: NATURAL SCIENCE. (Text in Japanese) 1949. s-a. Yokohama-shiritsu Daigaku, Gakujutsu Kenkyukai - Yokohama City University, Arts and Science Society, 22-2, Seto, Kanazawa-ku, Yokohama-shi, Kanagawa-ken 236, Japan. **Indexed:** Chem.Abstr., Jap.Per.Ind. **Document type:** bulletin.

500   JA   ISSN 0513-2622
                 CODEN: SRYMAX
YOKOSUKA-SHI HAKUBUTSUKAN KENKYU HOKOKU. SHIZEN KAGAKU/YOKOSUKA CITY MUSEUM. SCIENCE REPORT. (Text and summaries in English and Japanese) 1956. irreg. $5. Yokosuka-shi Shizen Hakubutsukan - Yokosuka City Museum, 95 Fukadadai, Yokosuka-shi, Kanagawa-ken 238, Japan. Ed. N. Onba. circ. 1,000. (back issues avail.) **Indexed:** Biol.Abstr., Jap.Per.Ind., Sel.Water Res.Abstr.
—BLDSC (8163.500000).

500   JA   ISSN 0386-4286
AM101.Y58
YOKOSUKA-SHI HAKUBUTSUKAN SHIRYOSHU/YOKOSUKA CITY MUSEUM. MISCELLANEOUS REPORT. (Text in Japanese; summaries in English) 1978. a. Yokosuka-shi Shizen Hakubutsukan - Yokosuka City Museum, 95, Fukadadai, Yokosuka-shi, Kanagawa-ken 238, Japan.

YOKOSUKA-SHI HAKUBUTSUKANPO/YOKOSUKA CITY MUSEUM. ANNUAL REPORT. see *MUSEUMS AND ART GALLERIES*

YOSHIDA KAGAKU GIJUTSU ZAIDAN NYUSU/YOSHIDA FOUNDATION FOR SCIENCE AND TECHNOLOGY. NEWS. see *TECHNOLOGY: COMPREHENSIVE WORKS*

YOUR BIG BACKYARD. see *ENVIRONMENTAL STUDIES*

ZAGADNIENIA INFORMACJI NAUKOWEJ. see *LIBRARY AND INFORMATION SCIENCES*

500   PL   ISSN 0044-1619
ZAGADNIENIA NAUKOZNAWSTWA. (Text in Polish; summaries in English and Russian) 1965. q. $56. (Polska Akademia Nauk, Komitet Naukoznawstwa) Ossolineum, Publishing House of the Polish Academy of Sciences, Rynek 9, 50-106 Wroclaw, Poland. TEL 48-71-386-25. FAX 48-71-448-103. TELEX 0712771 OSS PL. Ed. T. Pszczolowski. bk.rev.; index. circ. 1,000. **Document type:** academic/scholarly publication.
    Description: Modern achievements in science.

500   ZA   ISSN 0084-4950
ZAMBIA. NATIONAL COUNCIL FOR SCIENTIFIC RESEARCH. ANNUAL REPORT. 1968. a. National Council for Scientific Research, Box CH 158, Chelston, Lusaka, Zambia. **Document type:** government publication.

500 600   ZA   ISSN 0378-8857
Q91.Z33   CODEN: ZJSTDE
ZAMBIA JOURNAL OF SCIENCE AND TECHNOLOGY. (Text in English) 1976. q. $12.50 per no. National Council for Scientific Research, P.O. Box 310158, Chelston, 15302 Lusaka, Zambia. TEL 260-1-281081. TELEX ZA 40005. Ed.Bd. adv.; charts; stat. circ. 2,500. **Indexed:** Biol.Abstr., Chem.Abstr., Curr.Cont., Dairy Sci.Abstr., Field Crop Abstr., Food Sci.& Tech.Abstr., GeoRef, Herb.Abstr., Ind.Vet., Protozool.Abstr., Vet.Bull. **Document type:** academic/scholarly publication.
—CASDDS.

ZEITSCHRIFT FUER GESCHICHTE DER ARABISCH-ISLAMISCHEN WISSENSCHAFTEN. see *ORIENTAL STUDIES*

500 600   XO   ISSN 0862-1845
ZENIT. 1986. fortn. Smena Publishing House, Prazska 11, 812 84 Bratislava, Slovakia. (Subscr. to: P N S, Gottwaldovo nam 6, 813 81 Bratislava, Slovakia) Ed. Ladislav Gyorffy. circ. 45,000.
    Formerly: Zenit Pionierov.

500   NE   ISSN 0928-978X
Q4
ZENO OVER WETENSCHAP, TECHNOLOGIE EN SAMENLEVING. Cover title: Zeno. 1947. bi-m. fl.87.50 to individuals; institutions fl.125; students fl.45 (effective 1995). (Vereniging voor Wetenschap en Samenleving) Van Gorcum en Co. B.V., P.O. Box 43, 9400 AA Assen, Netherlands. TEL 31-5920-46846. FAX 31-5920-72064. (Editorial addr.: Ondegracht 42, 3511 AR Utrecht, Netherlands. TEL 31-20-322180) Ed. Frank Biesboer; Pub. Jaap Hagedoorn. adv. contact: Jaap Hagedoorn. bk.rev.; abstr.; illus. circ. 1,200. **Indexed:** Chem.Abstr., Excerpt.Med. **Document type:** academic/scholarly publication.
—BLDSC (9500.487000); SWETS.
    Formerly (until 1993): Wetenschap en Samenleving (ISSN 0043-4442)
    Description: Discusses technology, science and the impact on society and life.

500   CC   ISSN 0253-9861
               CODEN: CHHPDK
ZHEJIANG DAXUE XUEBAO (ZIRAN KEXUE BAN)/ZHEJIANG UNIVERSITY. JOURNAL (NATURAL SCIENCE EDITION). (Text in Chinese; abstracts in English) 1956. bi-m. $30. Zhejiang Daxue, Yu Quan (Jade Spring), Hangzhou, Zhejiang 310027, People's Republic of China. TEL 0571-5172242. FAX 0571-7951358. TELEX 35040 ZUFAO CN. (Dist. by: China International Book Trading Corp., P.O. Box 399, Beijing, P.R. China) Ed. Jiang Jingping. **Indexed:** Chem.Abstr., Math.R. **Document type:** academic/scholarly publication.
—BLDSC (4918.150500).

500   CC   ISSN 1001-8212
ZHENGZHOU DAXUE XUEBAO (ZIRAN KEXUE BAN)/ZHENGZHOU UNIVERSITY. JOURNAL (NATURAL SCIENCE EDITION). (Text in Chinese) q. Zhengzhou Daxue, Xuebao Bianjibu, No. 75, Daxue Lu, Zhengzhou, Henan 450052, People's Republic of China. TEL 446455. Ed. Li Min. **Document type:** academic/scholarly publication.

500   CC
ZHISHI CHUANG/WINDOW OF KNOWLEDGE. (Text in Chinese) bi-m. Jiangxi Kexue Jishu Chubanshe - Jiangxi Science and Technology Publishers, No.5, Xinwei Lu, Nanchang, Jiangxi 330002, People's Republic of China. TEL 332459. Ed. Tang Yulong.

500   CC
ZHISHI JIUSHI LILIANG/KNOWLEDGE IS POWER. (Text in Chinese) m. $0.60 per no. Guoji Shudian, Qikan Bu - China International Book Trading Corp., Chegongzhuang Xilu 21, P.O. Box 399, Beijing 100044, People's Republic of China.

500 600   CC
ZHONGGUO KEJI SHILIAO/CHINA HISTORICAL MATERIALS OF SCIENCE AND TECHNOLOGY. (Text in Chinese; summaries and table of contents in English) q. 4 Yen per no. (Zhongguo Kexue Jishu Xiehui - China Association for Science and Technology) Zhongguo Kexue Jishu Chubanshe, 32, Baishiqiao Lu, Wei Gong Cun, Haidian Qu, Beijing, People's Republic of China. (Dist. outside China by: China International Book Trading Corp., P.O. Box 339, Beijing, P.R.C.; Editorial addr.: 137, Chaoyang Mennei Dajie, Beijing 100010, P.R.C.) bibl.; illus. **Document type:** academic/scholarly publication.

500 600   CC   ISSN 1000-0798
ZHONGGUO KEJI SHILIAO/HISTORICAL MATERIAL OF CHINESE SCIENCE AND TECHNOLOGY. (Text in Chinese) q. Zhongguo Kexue Jishu Xuehui - Chinese Association of Science and Technology, 137 Chaoyangmennei Dajie, Beijing 100010, People's Republic of China. TEL 896731. Ed. Wang Dezhao.

SCIENCES: COMPREHENSIVE WORKS — ABSTRACTING, BIBLIOGRAPHIES, STATISTICS

500   CC   ISSN 1000-3126
ZHONGGUO KEXUE A. English edition: Science in China. Series A: Mathematics, Physics, Astronomy & Technological Sciences (ISSN 1001-6511) (Text in Chinese; summaries in English) 1950. m. $210. (Zhongguo Kexueyuan - Academia Sinica) Science Press, Marketing and Sales Department, 16 Donghuangchenggen North St., Beijing 100717, People's Republic of China. TEL 4010642. FAX 4109810. (Co-sponsor: Chinese Medical Association) adv. circ. 10,000. (reprint service avail. from KTO) **Indexed:** AESIS, BMT, Chem.Abstr., Curr.Cont., Deep Sea Res.& Oceanogr.Abstr., Helminthol.Abstr., INSPEC, Int.Aerosp.Abstr., Math.R., Met.Abstr., Plant Breed.Abstr., Soils & Fert., World Alum.Abstr., World Surf.Coat., World Text.Abstr. **Document type:** academic/scholarly publication.
  Supersedes in part: Scientia Sinica.
  Description: Covers mathematics, physics, astronomy, and technology. Contains mainly academic papers on scientific work.
  Refereed Serial

500   CC   ISSN 1000-3134
ZHONGGUO KEXUE B. English edition: Science in China. Series B: Chemistry, Life Sciences & Earth Sciences (ISSN 1001-652X) (Text in Chinese; summaries in English) 1950. m. $210. (Chinese Academy of Sciences) Science Press, Marketing and Sales Department, 16 Donghuangchenggen North St., Beijing 100717, People's Republic of China. TEL 4010642. FAX 4019810. (Co-sponsor: Chinese Medical Association) adv. (reprint service avail. from KTO) **Indexed:** AESIS, Biol.Abstr., BMT, Chem.Abstr., Curr.Adv.Biochem., Curr.Adv.Cell & Devel.Biol., Curr.Adv.Ecol.Sci., Curr.Adv.Genetics & Molec.Biol., Curr.Cont., Deep Sea Res.& Oceanogr.Abstr., Helminthol.Abstr., Ind.Med., Math.R., Met.Abstr., Seed Abstr., Soyabean Abstr., World Surf.Coat., World Text.Abstr. **Document type:** academic/scholarly publication.
  Supersedes in part: Scientia Sinica.
  Description: Covers chemistry, biology, earth science, medical science, and agronomy. Contains mainly academic papers on scientific work.
  Refereed Serial

500   US
ZHONGGUO KEXUE BAO/CHINA'S SCIENCE. (Text in Chinese) 3/w. $91.10. China Books & Periodicals, Inc., 2929 24th St., San Francisco, CA 94110. TEL 415-282-2994. FAX 415-282-0994. **Document type:** newspaper.

500   CC   ISSN 1000-8217
ZHONGGUO KEXUE JIJIN/NATIONAL NATURAL SCIENCE FOUNDATION OF CHINA. BULLETIN. (Text in Chinese; summaries in English) 1987. q. $30. (Zhongguo Kexue Jijinhui - National Natural Science Foundation of China) Science Press, Marketing and Sales Department, 16 Donghuangchenggen North St., Beijing 100717, People's Republic of China. TEL 4010642. FAX 4019810. Ed. Shi Changxu. adv. circ. 5,000. **Document type:** bulletin.
—BLDSC (2641.172000).
  Description: Publishes academic papers, science foundation policies, and technology trends and developments.

500 600   CC   ISSN 0253-2778
Q4   CODEN: CKHPD7
ZHONGGUO KEXUE JISHU DAXUE XUEBAO/CHINA UNIVERSITY OF SCIENCE AND TECHNOLOGY. JOURNAL. (Text in Chinese) q. $2 per no. Zhongguo Kexue Jishu Daxue - China University of Science and Technology, 96 Jinzhai Lu, Hefei, Anhui 230026, People's Republic of China. (Dist. by: Guoji Shudian (China Publications Centre), Chegongzhuang Xilu 21, P.O. Box 399, Beijing, P.R.C.) **Indexed:** Cyb.Abstr., Math.R. **Document type:** academic/scholarly publication.
—BLDSC (4729.219400); CASDDS.

500   CC   ISSN 1000-3045
ZHONGGUO KEXUEYUAN YUANKAN. English edition: Chinese Academy of Sciences. Bulletin. (Issuing body also known as Academia Sinica.) (Text in Chinese; table of contents and summaries in English) 1985. q. $52. Science Press, Marketing and Sales Department, 16 Donghuangchenggen North St., Beijing 100717, People's Republic of China. TEL 4010642. FAX 4019810. Ed. Yu Zhihua. adv. circ. 7,000. **Document type:** bulletin.
—BLDSC (2444.496000).
  Description: Publicizes mainland China's policies on science and technology, and shows trends and directions in the development of science in China. Also introduces the work and achievements of the Academia Sinica and its scientists.

500   CC   ISSN 0253-4088
                 CODEN: CHTHAJ
ZHONGSHAN DAXUE XUEBAO (ZIRAN KEXUE BAN)/ACTA SCIENTIARUM NATURALIUM UNIVERSITATIS SUNYATSENI. (Text in Chinese) q. $1.30 per no. Zhongshan Daxue, Xuebao Bianjibu, 135 Xingang Xilu, Guangzhou, Guangdong 510275, People's Republic of China. TEL 020-4186300. TELEX 44604-ZSUFO-CN. (Dist. outside China by: China International Book Trading Corp., P.O. Box 399, Beijing, P.R.C.) **Indexed:** Bio-Contr.News & Info., Chem.Abstr., Crop Physiol.Abstr., Curr.Adv.Ecol.Sci., Field Crop Abstr., Herb.Abstr., Hort.Abstr., Ind.Vet., INSPEC (1978-), Math.R., Ornam.Hort., Plant Grow.Reg.Abstr., Seed Abstr., Trop.Oil Seeds Abstr., Weed Abstr. **Document type:** academic/scholarly publication.
—BLDSC (0663.200000); CASDDS; Ei.
  Supersedes in part: Zhongshan Daxue Xuebao (ISSN 0529-6579)

500 600   CC
ZHONGWAI JISHU QINGBAO/CHINESE AND FOREIGN TECHNOLOGY INFORMATION. (Text in Chinese) m. Anhui Sheng Keji Qingbao Yanjiusuo - Anhui Provincial Institute of Science and Technology Information, Shengkewei, Building No.3, 145 Caohu Lu, Hefei, Anhui 230001, People's Republic of China. TEL 278453. Ed. Yang Qinghua.

ZHONGXUE KEJI/MIDDLE SCHOOL SCIENCE & TECHNOLOGY. see EDUCATION

500   RH   ISSN 1016-1503
Q1   CODEN: ZSNED7
ZIMBABWE SCIENCE NEWS. 1967. 4/yr. Zimbabwe Scientific Association, P.O. Box CY 124, Causeway, Harare, Zimbabwe. Ed. P. Taylor. adv.; bk.rev.; abstr.; bibl.; charts; illus.; index. circ. 1,500. **Indexed:** Biol.Abstr., Field Crop Abstr., Geo.Abstr., GeoRef., Herb.Abstr., Ind.S.A.Per., Key Word Ind.Wildl.Res., P.L.E.S.A., W.R.C.Inf., Zoo.Rec. **Document type:** academic/scholarly publication.
—BLDSC (9513.282000).
  Former titles (until 1980): Zimbabwe Rhodesia Science News (ISSN 0253-049X); (until 1979): Rhodesia Science News (ISSN 0035-4732)

500   RH   ISSN 0254-2765
Q180.55.M4   CODEN: TZASDZ
ZIMBABWE SCIENTIFIC ASSOCIATION. TRANSACTIONS. (Text in English) 1901. irreg. $10. Zimbabwe Scientific Association, P.O. Box CY 124, Causeway, Harare, Zimbabwe. Ed. Brian Marshall. circ. 550. (back issues avail.) **Indexed:** A.I.C.P., Biol.Abstr., GeoRef., Ind.S.A.Per., INSPEC (1970-), Soils & Fert., Zoo.Rec. **Document type:** proceedings.
—BLDSC (9013.950000).
  Former titles (until vol.60, no.1, 1980): Rhodesia Scientific Association. Transactions (ISSN 0379-9638); (until vol.56, 1974): Rhodesia Scientific Association. Proceedings and Transactions (ISSN 0370-2294)

500 600   CC
ZIRAN BIANZHENGFA TONGXUN/JOURNAL OF DIALECTICS OF NATURE. (Text in Chinese) bi-m. $1 per no. Guoji Shudian, Qikan Bu - China International Book Trading Corp., Chegongzhuang Xilu 21, P.O. Box 399, Beijing 100044, People's Republic of China.

500.9   CC   ISSN 1000-0224
ZIRAN KEXUE SHI YANJIU/STUDIES IN THE HISTORY OF NATURAL SCIENCES. (Text in Chinese; summaries in English) 1982. q. $51.20. Science Press, Marketing and Sales Department, 16 Donghuangchenggen North St., Beijing 100717, People's Republic of China. TEL 4010642. FAX 4019810. adv.; bk.rev. circ. 6,000. **Document type:** academic/scholarly publication.
  Description: Contains articles on theories of the history of science, biographies of scientists, and historical records of important scientific events in China and the world.

500   CC   ISSN 0253-9608
Q4   CODEN: TJTCD4
ZIRAN ZAZHI/NATURE JOURNAL. (Text in Chinese) m. $2.30 per no. Ziran Zazhishe, P.O. Box 040-056, Shanghai 200040, People's Republic of China. TEL 4336850. Ed. He Zongying. **Indexed:** Art & Archaeol.Tech.Abstr., Chem.Abstr.
—CASDDS.

500   SP   ISSN 0213-4306
ZUBIA. (Monographic supplements avail. (ISSN 1131-5423)) 1983. a. 1200 ptas. (foreign 1500 ptas.) (effective 1995 & 1996). Instituto de Estudios Riojanos, C. Calvo Sotelo 15, 26071 Logrono, Spain. TEL 34-41-291305. FAX 34-41-291307. Dir. Felix Perez-Lorente. illus.
—BLDSC (9534.850000).
  Formerly (until 1985): Berceo. Ciencias (ISSN 0213-4292)
  Description: Presents research in natural sciences, experimental science, and mathematics, especially dealing with local themes.

500   SP   ISSN 1131-5423
ZUBIA. MONOGRAFICO. 1989. a. 700 ptas. (effective 1995 & 1996). Instituto de Estudios Riojanos, Calvo Sotelo 15, 26003 Logrono, Spain. TEL 34-41-291305. FAX 34-41-291307. **Document type:** monographic series.

500.9   NE
ZUIDHOLLANDS LANDSCHAP. 1972. q. fl.30. Stichting Het Zuidhollands Landschap, Schiedamsesingel 181, 3012 BB Rotterdam, Netherlands. FAX 010-4331570. Ed.Bd. adv.; bk.rev. circ. 45,000.

3-2-1 CONTACT. see CHILDREN AND YOUTH — For

SCIENCES: COMPREHENSIVE WORKS — Abstracting, Bibliographies, Statistics

016.500   US
A A A S ANNUAL MEETING PROGRAM - ABSTRACTS OF PAPERS. 1982. a. $25. American Association for the Advancement of Science, 1333 H St., N.W., Washington, DC 20005. TEL 202-326-6450. Ed. Sue O'Connell. adv.; index. circ. 8,000. (reprint service avail. from UMI) **Indexed:** GeoRef. **Document type:** abstracting/indexing.
—BLDSC (1087.640000).
  Formed by the merger of (1978-1982): American Association for the Advancement of Science. Abstracts of Papers of the National Meeting (ISSN 0196-2922); (1976-1982): American Association for the Advancement of Science. Program of the National Meeting (ISSN 0272-4189); Which was formerly (1972-1976): American Association for the Advancement of Science. Annual Meeting (ISSN 0361-1833)

500 600   RM   ISSN 0365-6330
T4   CODEN: ARSTCW
ABSTRACTS OF ROMANIAN SCIENTIFIC AND TECHNICAL LITERATURE. French edition: Bulletin Analytique de la Litterature Scientifique et Technique Roumaine. (Text in English) 1965. s-a. $121 or exchange basis. Institutul National de Informare si Documentare, Str. George Enescu 27-29, 70141 Bucharest, Rumania. TEL 6134010. FAX 3126734. Ed. Melania Ghitescu. adv. contact: Florentina Mazurchevici. abstr. **Indexed:** Anal.Abstr., Corros.Abstr., Hort.Abstr., Plant Breed.Abstr., World Surf.Coat., World Text.Abstr. **Document type:** abstracting/indexing.
  Formerly (until 1971): Abstracts of Romanian Technical Literature (ISSN 0001-365X)
  Description: Contains abstracts of articles published in Rumanian periodicals concerning different fields of pure and applied sciences.

5912 SCIENCES: COMPREHENSIVE WORKS — ABSTRACTING, BIBLIOGRAPHIES, STATISTICS

ABSTRACTS OF SCIENTIFIC AND TECHNOLOGICAL PUBLICATIONS. see TECHNOLOGY: COMPREHENSIVE WORKS — Abstracting, Bibliographies, Statistics

500 016   SW   ISSN 0001-3676
ABSTRACTS OF UPPSALA DISSERTATIONS IN SCIENCE. 1961. 20/yr. price varies. A W I International AB, P.O. Box 4627, S-116-91 Stockholm, Sweden. TEL 468-640-8800. FAX 468-641-1180. index. **Indexed:** Biol.Abstr., Chem.Abstr., INSPEC. **Document type:** abstracting/indexing.

ALTERNATIVE ALTERNATIVE. see SOCIOLOGY — Abstracting, Bibliographies, Statistics

919.8 011   US   ISSN 0066-4626
Z6005.P7
ANTARCTIC BIBLIOGRAPHY. (Cumulates: Current Antarctic Literature (ISSN 0096-879X)) 1965. a. price varies. U.S. Library of Congress, Washington, DC 20540. TEL 202-707-1181. (Avail. from: Superintendent of Documents, U.S. Government Printing Office, Box 317954, Pittsburgh, PA 15250-7954. TEL 202-783-3238. FAX 202-512-2233) Ed. Stuart Hibben. circ. 1,500. **Document type:** bibliography, government publication. ●Also available online. Vendor(s): Orbit Search Service (COLD).
Also available on CD-ROM. Producer(s): NISC (Arctic & Antarctic Regions).
Description: Comprehensive bibliography of the world's antarctic literature, covering the biological, geological, medical and physical sciences, as well as meteorology, oceanography, and discussions of law or political issues relating to Antarctica.

APPLIED SCIENCE & TECHNOLOGY INDEX; a cumulative subject index to English language periodicals in the fields of aeronautics and space science, computer technology and applications, chemistry, construction industry, energy resources and research, engineering, etc. see ENGINEERING — Abstracting, Bibliographies, Statistics

500 700 011   UK
Z7403
ASLIB BOOK GUIDE; a monthly list of recommended scientific and technical books. 1935. m. £80($180) to non-members; members £70. Aslib, Association for Information Management, Publications Department, Information House, 20-24 Old St., London EC1V 9AP, England. TEL 071-253-4488. FAX 071-430-0514. (Dist. in N. America by: Learned Information, Inc., 143 Old Marlton Pike, Medford, NJ 08055-8750. TEL 609-654-6266) Ed. L.J. Anthony. bibl. circ. 600.
—BLDSC (1742.998000). CCC.
Formerly: Aslib Book List (ISSN 0001-2521)
Description: Reviews new books in English on all scientific, medical and technical subjects.

500   US   ISSN 0145-0379
BERKELEY PAPERS IN HISTORY OF SCIENCE. 1977. irreg., no.17, 1994. price varies. University of California at Berkeley, Office for History of Science and Technology, 543 Stephens Hall, No. 2350, Berkeley, CA 94720-2350. TEL 510-642-4581. FAX 510-643-5321. E-mail: diana@garnet.berkeley.edu. Ed. J.L. Heilbron. bk.rev. circ. 1,000. (back issues avail.) **Indexed:** Math.R. **Document type:** bibliography.
—BLDSC (1940.615000).
Description: Bibliographies of works by and about scientists, and of inventories of their published and unpublished correspondence.

500 016   YU   ISSN 0352-5945
Z7409
BIBLIOGRAFIJA JUGOSLAVIJE. CLANCI I PRILOZI U SERIJSKIM PUBLIKACIJAMA. SERIJA B: PRIRODNE, PRIMENJENE, MEDICINSKE I TEHNICKE NAUKE. 1950. m. $662 or exchange basis. Jugoslovenski Bibliografsko-Informacijski Institut (YUBIN) - Yugoslav Institute for Bibliography and Information, Terazije 26, Belgrade, Yugoslavia. FAX 11-687-760. Ed. Radomir Glavicki.
●Also available online.
Former titles (until 1985): Bibliografija Jugoslavije. Naucni i Strucni Radovi u Serijskim Publikacijama. Serija B: Prirodne, Primenjene, Medicinske i Tehnicke Nauke (ISSN 0352-2393); Bibliografija Jugoslavije. Serija B: Prirodne i Primenjene Nauke. Clanci i Prilozi u Casopisima, Listovima i Zbornicima (ISSN 0523-218X)

500 015   SZ   ISSN 0067-6829
BIBLIOGRAPHIA SCIENTIAE NATURALIS HELVETICA. (Text in French, German) 1927. a. 35 SFr. Bibliotheque Nationale Suisse - Schweizerische Landesbibliothek, Hallwylstr. 15, CH-3003 Bern, Switzerland. Ed. Anton Caflisch. circ. 700 (controlled). (back issues avail.) **Indexed:** GeoRef. **Document type:** bibliography.

500 011   US   ISSN 0888-7551
CODEN: BSTEEC
BIBLIOGRAPHIES AND INDEXES IN SCIENCE AND TECHNOLOGY. 1987. irreg. price varies. Greenwood Press, Inc. (Subsidiary of: Greenwood Publishing Group Inc.), 88 Post Rd. W., Box 5007, Westport, CT 06881-5007. TEL 203-226-3571. FAX 203-222-1502. **Document type:** abstracting/indexing, bibliography.
—BLDSC (1993.097520).

500 600   US
BIBLIOGRAPHIES ON THE HISTORY OF SCIENCE AND TECHNOLOGY. 1982. irreg. price varies. Garland Publishing, Inc., 1000A Sherman Ave., Hamden, CT 06514. TEL 800-627-6273. (And: 717 Fifth Ave., New York, NY 10022-8101. TEL 212-751-7447) Eds. Robert Multhauf, Ellen Wells. circ. 375. **Document type:** monographic series.

500 016   II
BIBLIOGRAPHY OF DOCTORAL DISSERTATIONS: NATURAL AND APPLIED SCIENCES. (Text in English) irreg., latest 1990. price varies. Association of Indian Universities, A.I.U. House, 16 Kotla Marg., New Delhi 110 002, India. TEL 11-3310059. FAX 11-3315105. TELEX 31-66180-AIU-IN. circ. 500. **Document type:** bibliography.

500 011   SP   ISSN 0211-4046
BOLETIN DE TRADUCCIONES. 1966. s-m. 1300 ptas. (effective 1995). Centro de Informacion y Documentacion Cientifica (Cindoc), Joaquin Costa 22, 28002 Madrid, Spain. TEL 34-1-5635482. FAX 34-1-5642644. TELEX 22628 CIDMD E. E-mail: bib__icyt@bib.csic.es.
●Also available online.
Also available on CD-ROM.

500 016 600   UK   ISSN 0959-4922
Z7403
BRITISH REPORTS, TRANSLATIONS AND THESES. 1971. m. £93 (overseas £98) (effective 1996). British Library, Document Supply Centre, Publishing Section, Boston Spa, Wetherby, W. Yorks. LS23 7BQ, England. TEL 01937-546077.
FAX 01937-546333. TELEX 557381. (Subscr. to: Turpin Distribution Services Ltd., Blackhorse Rd., Letchworth, Herts. SG6 1HN, England. TEL 01462-672555. FAX 01462-480947) bibl. circ. 900. (back issues avail.) **Indexed:** Agri.Eng.Abstr., Bio-Contr.News & Info., Br.Ceram.Abstr., Dairy Sci.Abstr., Field Crop Abstr., Fluidex, Forest.Abstr., Herb.Abstr., Int.Packag.Abstr., Mgmt.& Market.Abstr., Nutr.Abstr., Paper & Bd.Abstr., Print.Abstr., Rev.Appl.Entomol., World.Text.Abstr. **Document type:** academic/scholarly publication.
—BLDSC (2342.160000).
Former titles: B L L D Announcement Bulletin (ISSN 0308-4094); N L L Announcement Bulletin (ISSN 0007-1749)

500   GW
BUECHER FUER DAS STUDIUM - NATURWISSENSCHAFTEN; Mathematik, Physik, Chemie, Biologie, Botanik, Zoologie, Geowissenschaften. a. Dr. Lothar Rossipaul Verlagsgesellschaft mbH, Menzingerstr. 37, 80638 Munich, Germany. TEL 089-179106-0. FAX 089-179106-22. Ed. Rainer Rossipaul. circ. 25,000. **Document type:** bibliography.
Description: Bibliography of available books in the natural sciences for students.

500 600   RM   ISSN 0374-1834
BULLETIN ANALYTIQUE DE LA LITTERATURE SCIENTIFIQUE ET TECHNIQUE ROUMAINE. English edition: Abstracts of Romanian Scientific and Technical Literature. (Text in French) 1965. s-a. $121 or exchange basis. Institutul National de Informare si Documentare, Str. George Enescu 27-29, 70141 Bucharest, Rumania. TEL 6134010. FAX 3126734. Ed. Sanda Popescu. adv. contact: Florentina Mazurchevici. abstr. **Document type:** abstracting/indexing.
Formerly: Bulletin Analytique de la Litterature Technique Roumaine.
Description: Contains abstracts of articles published in Rumanian periodicals in the fields of pure and applied science.

500.9 016.971   CN   ISSN 0823-8936
CANADIAN PLAINS BIBLIOGRAPHIES. 1985. irreg. price varies. Canadian Plains Research Center, University of Regina, Regina, SK S4S 0A2, Canada. TEL 306-585-5056. FAX 306-585-4699. **Document type:** monographic series, bibliography.

500 600   TR   ISSN 1011-4866
CARINDEX: SCIENCE & TECHNOLOGY. 1987. s-a. T.T.$45. University of the West Indies, Main Library, St. Augustine, Trinidad & Tobago, W.I. TEL 809-662-2002. FAX 809-662-9238. TELEX 24-520 UWI-WG. Eds. Sharida Hosein, Hannah Francis. **Document type:** abstracting/indexing.
Description: Guide to science and technology literature (excluding medicine) published in the English-speaking Caribbean.

500 600   BL
CATALOGO COLETIVO DE ANAIS DE EVENTOS. 1983. a. $60. Comissao Nacional de Energia Nuclear, Centro de Informacoes Nucleares, Rua General Severiano, 90 Botafogo, 22294-900 Rio de Janeiro RJ, Brazil. TEL 55-21-546-2467. FAX 55-21-546-2447. TELEX 21280 CNEN BR. E-mail: diprom@sin.cnen.br. (microfiche) **Document type:** catalog.
●Also available online.
Also available on CD-ROM.
Formerly: Catalogo Coletivo de Conferencias em Ciencia e Tecnologia.
Description: Includes information on conference proceedings available in Brazilian libraries.

500 378   IR   ISSN 1022-7814
CHIKIDAH-I PAYAN'NAMAHHA-YI IRAN/IRANIAN DISSERTATION ABSTRACTS. (Text in Persian) 1993. q. $30 or exchange basis. Iranian Information & Documentation Center (IRANDOC), 1188 Enqelab Ave., P.O. Box 13185-1371, Tehran, Iran. TEL 98-21-6462548. FAX 98-21-6462254. (back issues avail.) **Document type:** abstracting/indexing.

016   CC   ISSN 0254-5179
QA1
CHINESE SCIENCE ABSTRACTS. PART A; mathematics, mechanics, astronomy and space science, physics, technical sciences. Chinese edition: Zhongguo Kexue Wenzhai A. (Text in English) 1982. 6/yr. £315($470) (effective 1995). Science Press, Marketing and Sales Department, 16 Donghuangchenggen North St., Beijing 100717, People's Republic of China. TEL 4010642. FAX 4019810. (Dist. outside China by: Elsevier Science Ltd., Pergamon, P.O. Box 800, Kidlington, Oxford OX5 1DX, England. TEL 44-865-843000. FAX 44-865-843010; Subscr. in U.S. and Canada to: Elsevier Science, 660 White Plains Rd., Tarrytown, NY 10591-5153. TEL 914-524-9200. FAX 914-333-2444) Ed.Bd. adv. circ. 5,000. **Document type:** abstracting/indexing.
—UMI.
Description: Publishes abstracts from more than 120 of China's leading scientific journals.

SCIENCES: COMPREHENSIVE WORKS — ABSTRACTING, BIBLIOGRAPHIES, STATISTICS

016   CC   ISSN 0254-4903
QD1
CHINESE SCIENCE ABSTRACTS. PART B; chemistry, life sciences, earth sciences. Chinese edition: Zhongguo Kexue Wenzhai B. (Text in English) 1982. 6/yr. £315($470) (effective 1995). Science Press, Marketing and Sales Department, 16 Donghuangchenggen North St., Beijing 100717, People's Republic of China. TEL 4010642. FAX 4019810. (Dist. outside China by: Elsevier Science Ltd., Pergamon, P.O. Box 800, Kidlington, Oxford OX5 1DX, England. TEL 44-865-843000. FAX 44-865-843010; Subscr. in U.S. and Canada to: Elsevier Science, 660 White Plains Rd., Tarrytown, NY 10591-5153. TEL 914-524-9200. FAX 914-333-2444) adv. circ. 5,000. (also avail. in microfilm from UMI) Document type: abstracting/indexing.
—UMI.
    Description: Publishes abstracts from more than 120 of China's leading scientific journals.

500 011   US
CHINESE SCIENCE AND TECHNOLOGY ABSTRACTS. 1993. irreg. price varies. Nova Science Publishers, Inc., 6080 Jericho Tpke., Ste. 207, Commack, NY 11725-2808. TEL 516-499-3103. **Document type:** abstracting/indexing.

500 015   BU   ISSN 0861-9700
CHUZHDESTRANNI PERIODICHNI IZDANIA V PO-GOLEMITE NAUCHNI BIBLIOTEKI. 1966. a. price varies. Narodna Biblioteka Sv.sv. Kiril i Metodii, 88, V. Levski Blvd., 1504 Sofia, Bulgaria. TEL 359-2-882811. FAX 359-2-881600. **Document type:** bibliography.
    Description: Lists foreign-language periodicals in the larger scientific libraries.

500 600 016   SP
CIENCIA Y TECNICA; boletin bibliografico nacional y extranjero. 1960. q. free. Diaz de Santos, S.A., Libreria Cientifico-Tecnica, Lagasca 95, 28006 Madrid, Spain. TEL 431-24-82. adv. bk.rev. circ. 25,000.

CONFERENCE PAPERS ANNUAL INDEX. see *MEETINGS AND CONGRESSES — Abstracting, Bibliographies, Statistics*

CONFERENCE PAPERS INDEX. see *MEETINGS AND CONGRESSES — Abstracting, Bibliographies, Statistics*

011   II   ISSN 0304-5358
CONTENTS LIST OF SOVIET SCIENTIFIC PERIODICALS. 1971. m. free. Indian National Scientific Documentation Centre, 14 Satsang Vihar Marg, New Delhi 110 067, India. Ed. B.K. Sen.

500 016   UK   ISSN 0309-8591
CROYDON BIBLIOGRAPHIES FOR REGIONAL SURVEY. 1968. irreg. included in subscription to the Proceedings of the Croydon Natural History & Scientific Society. Croydon Natural History & Scientific Society Ltd., 96a Brighton Rd., South Croydon, Surrey CR2 6AD, England. Ed. P.W. Sowan. bibl. circ. 850. **Document type:** bibliography.

919.8 500   US   ISSN 0096-879X
Z6005.P7   CODEN: CAALAX
CURRENT ANTARCTIC LITERATURE. (Cumulated annually in: Antarctic Bibliography (ISSN 0066-4626)) 1966. m. free to qualified personnel. U.S. National Science Foundation, Office of Polar Programs, 4201WBilson Blvd., Arlington, VA 22230. Ed. Stuart Hibben. bk.rev. circ. 700. **Indexed:** GeoRef. **Document type:** abstracting/indexing.
    Description: Provides citations and abstracts of the world's antarctic literature, including the biological sciences, cartography, geological and medical sciences, meteorology, oceanography, terrestrial and atmospheric physics, ice and snow, logistics and equipment, as well as law and political aspects of Antarctica.

CURRENT BIOTECHNOLOGY. see *BIOLOGY — Abstracting, Bibliographies, Statistics*

500 016   II   ISSN 0379-4504
CURRENT LITERATURE ON SCIENCE OF SCIENCE. (Text in English) 1972. m. National Institute of Science, Technology and Development Studies, Dr. K.S. Krishnan Marg, New Delhi 110 012, India. Ed. Ashok Jain. bk.rev.; charts; stat. circ. 500. (back issues avail.) **Document type:** abstracting/indexing.
—CCC.
    Formerly: Index to Literature on Science of Science.
    Description: Reports contributions and developments in science and technology studies, with reference to dilemmas of developing nations.

500 020 015   UK   ISSN 0267-1948
Z7403
CURRENT RESEARCH IN BRITAIN. PHYSICAL SCIENCES. (Other vols. avail.: Biological Sciences, Humanities, Social Sciences) 1980. a. £90 (foreign £95). Longman Cartermill Ltd., Technology Centre, St. Andrews, Fife KY16 9EA, Scotland. TEL 44-1937-843434. FAX 44-1937-546333. TELEX 557381. Ed. Mike Bate. **Document type:** abstracting/indexing.
    ● Also available online. Vendor(s): Orbit Search Service (CRIB).
    Formerly (until 1985): Research in British Universities Polytechnics and Colleges. Vol.1: Physical Sciences (ISSN 0142-2472)

500   JA   ISSN 0288-6022
Q77
CURRENT SCIENCE AND TECHNOLOGY RESEARCH IN JAPAN. (Text in English) 1980. biennial. $385. Japan Information Center of Science and Technology - Nihon Kagaku Gijutsu Joho Senta, 5-3, Yonbancho, Chiyoda-ku, Tokyo 102, Japan. TEL 03-5214-8413. FAX 03-5214-8410. abstr.; index. circ. 600.
    ● Also available online. Vendor(s): JICST.

500 600   SP   ISSN 1132-6654
DIRECTORIO DE REVISTAS ESPANOLAS DE CIENCIA Y TECNOLOGIA. 1990. a. 3800 ptas. (effective 1995). Centro de Informacion y Documentacion Cientifica (Cindoc), C. Joaquin Costa 22, 28002 Madrid, Spain. TEL 34-91-563-54-82. FAX 34-91-564-26-44. **Document type:** bibliography, directory.
    Description: Lists over 500 scientific and technical magazines and journals from Spain. In 3 sections: I. Complete active listings alphabetically by title; II. Indexes by subject, publisher, ISSN, & geographical region; III. Complete listings of cessations and former titles.

500 600 016   US   ISSN 0012-3293
Z7409   CODEN: DPPSAV
DIRECTORY OF PUBLISHED PROCEEDINGS. SERIES S E M T - SCIENCE, ENGINEERING, MEDICINE AND TECHNOLOGY. 1965. 10/yr. $545. InterDok Corp., 173 Halstead Ave., Box 326, Harrison, NY 10528. TEL 914-835-3506. FAX 914-835-6757. bibl.; index, cum.index. **Document type:** abstracting/indexing, directory.
—BLDSC (3594.930000); CASDDS.
    Description: Index of conferences and the published proceedings in the fields of science, engineering, medicine and technology. Domestic and foreign conferences are cited.

016   PK
DIRECTORY OF SCIENTIFIC PERIODICALS OF PAKISTAN. irreg. Rs.5($1) Pakistan Scientific and Technological Information Centre, Quaid-i-Azam University Campus, Box 1217, Islamabad, Pakistan. Dir. Aejaz Ahmed Malik. circ. 500. (also avail. in microfilm)

500 016   II   ISSN 0376-8554
Z7401
DIRECTORY OF SCIENTIFIC RESEARCH IN INDIAN UNIVERSITIES. a. Rs.35. (University Grants Commission) Indian National Scientific Documentation Centre, Hillside Rd., New Delhi 110012, India. (Co-sponsor: Council of Scientific and Industrial Research)

500 300 016   US   ISSN 0419-4217
Z5053   CODEN: DABBBA
DISSERTATION ABSTRACTS INTERNATIONAL. SECTION B: PHYSICAL SCIENCES AND ENGINEERING. 1938. m. $575. U M I Company, 300 N. Zeeb Rd., Ann Arbor, MI 48106. TEL 313-761-4700; 800-521-0600. FAX 313-761-1203. index. (also avail. in microfiche from UMI; magnetic tape; reprint service avail. from UMI) **Indexed:** Abstr.Bull.Inst.Pap.Chem., Agroforest.Abstr., Anim.Breed.Abstr., API Abstr., API Catal., API Hlth.& Environ., API Oil., API Pet.Ref., API Pet.Subst., API Transport., Art.Int.Abstr., Bio-Contr.News & Info., Biol.Abstr., Chem.Abstr., Crop Physiol.Abstr., Dairy Sci.Abstr., E&P Hlth. (1993-), Eng.Ind., Fababean Abstr., Field Crop Abstr., Food Sci.& Tech.Abstr., Forest.Abstr., Forest Prod.Abstr., Gas Process.& Ppl. (1993-), Geotech.Abstr., Helminthol.Abstr., Herb.Abstr., Hort.Abstr., Ind.Vet., Irr.& Drain.Abstr., Key Word Ind.Wildl.Res., Maize Abstr., Mass Spectr.Bull., Music Ind., Nutr.Abstr., Off.Tech. (1993-), Ornam.Hort., Packag.Sci.Tech., Petrol.Abstr. (1961-), Pig News & Info., Plant Grow.Reg.Abstr., Potato Abstr., Poult.Abstr., Protozool.Abstr., Psychol.Abstr., RAPRA, Rev.Med.& Vet.Mycol., Rice Abstr., Seed Abstr., Sh.& Vib.Dig., Sorghum & Millets Abstr., Soyabean Abstr., Sport Fish.Abstr., Sugar Ind.Abstr., Triticale Abstr., Trop.Oil Seeds Abstr., Vet.Bull., Weed Abstr., Wild.Rev., Zoo.Rec. (until 19??). **Document type:** abstracting/indexing.
    ● Also available online. Vendor(s): Data-Star, Knight-Ridder, Inc. (File no.35), Ovid Technologies (DISS), STN International.
    Also available on CD-ROM. Producer(s): University Microfilms International.
    —BLDSC (3599.040000); CASDDS; PADDS; UMI.
    Formerly (until 1969): Dissertation Abstracts. Section B: the Sciences and Engineering (ISSN 0420-073X); Supersedes in part (in 1966): Dissertation Abstracts (ISSN 0099-3123).

DISSERTATION ABSTRACTS INTERNATIONAL. SECTION C: WORLDWIDE. see *HUMANITIES: COMPREHENSIVE WORKS — Abstracting, Bibliographies, Statistics*

DISSERTATION ABSTRACTS ON DISC. see *HUMANITIES: COMPREHENSIVE WORKS — Abstracting, Bibliographies, Statistics*

600 016   FR   ISSN 0012-4583
DOCUMENTATION - TECHNIQUE, SCIENTIFIQUE ET COMMERCIALE; revue d'information de l'edition francaise et etrangere. (Text and summaries in English, French) 1947. 7/yr. free. Librairie Lavoisier, 11 rue Lavoisier, 75008 Paris, France. FAX 47-40-67-02. TELEX TDL632020F. E-mail: group@lavoisier.fr; Site addr.: http://www.lavoisier.fr/. Ed. Patrick Fenouil. adv.; bk.rev. circ. 20,000. (preprod)

500   SZ
DOKUMENTATIONSSTELLE FUER WISSENSCHAFTSPOLITIK. NEUANSCHAFFUNGEN/CENTRE DE DOCUMENTATION DE POLITIQUE DE LA SCIENCE. NOUVELLES ACQUISITIONS. (Text in English, French, German, Italian) 1992. 4/yr. free. Schweizerischer Wissenschaftsrat, Dokumentationsstelle fuer Wissenschaftspolitik, Inselgasse 1, CH-3003 Bern, Switzerland. TEL 031-3229655. FAX 031-3228070. **Document type:** bibliography.

500 011   HU   ISSN 0238-5562
EOTVOS LORAND TUDOMANYEGYETEM. TUDOMANYOS TAJEKOZTATO. English edition: Lorand Eotvos University. Scientific Guide (ISSN 0238-5910) 1982. irreg. Eotvos Lorand Tudomanyegyetem, Egyetem ter. 1-3, 1364 Budapest, Hungary. Ed. Janos Almasi. circ. 500.
    Description: Lists university staff and Hungarian science publications.

500 011   US   ISSN 0190-3241
HM24
FUTURE SURVEY; a monthly abstract of books, articles, and reports concerning trends, forecasts, and ideas about the future. (Supplement avail.: Future Survey Annual) 1979. m. $79 to individuals; libraries $119. World Future Society, 7910 Woodmont Ave., Ste. 450, Bethesda, MD 20814. TEL 301-656-8274. FAX 301-951-0394. Ed. Michael Marien. index. circ. 2,300. (back issues avail.; reprint service avail. from UMI) **Indexed:** Pers.Lit. **Document type:** abstracting/indexing.
    —BLDSC (4060.637000).
    Formerly: Public Policy Book Forecast (ISSN 0197-9035)

SCIENCES: COMPREHENSIVE WORKS — ABSTRACTING, BIBLIOGRAPHIES, STATISTICS

GENERAL INDEX TO IRAQI PERIODICAL LITERATURE. PART A: SCIENCES AND ENGINEERING. see ENGINEERING — Abstracting, Bibliographies, Statistics

016 500   US   ISSN 0162-1963
Z7401
GENERAL SCIENCE INDEX. 1978. m. (except Jun. & Dec.), plus q. and a. cumulations. service basis. H.W. Wilson Co., 950 University Ave., Bronx, NY 10452. TEL 718-588-8400; 800-367-6770. FAX 718-590-1617. TELEX 4990003HWILSON. Ed. James Kochones. (also avail. in magnetic tape) **Document type:** abstracting/indexing.
●Also available online. Vendor(s): Wilsonline (File GSI).
Also available on CD-ROM. Producer(s): H.W. Wilson (WILSONDISC).
—BLDSC (4111.196000).
Description: Cumulative subject index to English-language periodicals covering the essential science periodicals.

011   GW   ISSN 0931-8593
GERMANY. DEUTSCHER BUNDESTAG. WISSENSCHAFTLICHE DIENSTE. NEUE AUFSAETZE IN DER BIBLIOTHEK. 1962. 6/yr. Deutscher Bundestag, Abteilung Wissenschaftliche Dienste, Bundeshaus, 53113 Bonn, Germany. TEL 0228-1622967. index. **Document type:** government publication.
Formerly: Germany (Federal Republic, 1949-). Deutscher Bundestag. Wissenschaftliche Dienste. Aufsaetze aus Zeitschriften und Sammelwerken (ISSN 0931-3400)

016 500   GH   ISSN 0855-0115
GHANA SCIENCE ABSTRACTS. (Text in English). q. Council for Scientific and Industrial Research, Box M32, Accra, Ghana. Ed. J.A. Villars. abstr.; bibl. **Indexed:** Field Crop Abstr., Herb.Abstr., Nutr.Abstr. **Document type:** abstracting/indexing.

GUIDE TO AMERICAN SCIENTIFIC AND TECHNICAL DIRECTORIES. see TECHNOLOGY: COMPREHENSIVE WORKS — Abstracting, Bibliographies, Statistics

500 600   HU   ISSN 0237-0808
HUNGARIAN R AND D ABSTRACTS. SCIENCE AND TECHNOLOGY. 1985. q. $80. Orszagos Muszaki Informacios Kozpont es Konyvtar (O.M.I.K.K.) - National Technical Information Centre and Library, Muzeum u. 17, Box 12, 1428 Budapest, Hungary. TEL 36-1-1185852. Ed. Zsuzsanna Bana. index. **Indexed:** C.R.I.Abstr., C.R.I.Curr.Cont., Corros.Abstr., World Surf.Coat., World Text.Abstr. **Document type:** abstracting/indexing.
Supersedes: Hungarian Technical Abstracts (ISSN 0018-7771)
Description: Covers all fields of science and technology, excluding humanities. Includes author and subject index.

500   HU
HUNGARY. KOZPONTI STATISZTIKAI HIVATAL. TUDOMANYOS KUTATAS ES FEJLESZTES. a. 230 Ft. Statisztikai Kiado Vallalat, Kazasdulo u. 2, Box 99, 1033 Budapest 3, Hungary. TEL 688-635. TELEX 22-6699. (Subscr. to: Kultura, Box 149, H-1389 Budapest, Hungary) circ. 1,000.

500 011   AO   ISSN 0018-9863
I I C A. DOCUMENTACAO; boletim bibliografico. 1969. s-m. free to qualified personnel. Instituto de Investigacao Cientifica de Angola, Departamento de Documentacao e Informacao, C. P. 3244, Luanda, Angola.

500 600 016   II   ISSN 0304-534X
I N S D O C. RUSSIAN SCIENTIFIC AND TECHNICAL PUBLICATIONS. ACCESSIONS LIST. bi-m. free. Indian National Scientific Documentation Centre, 14 Satsang Vihar Marg, New Delhi 110 067, India.

INDEX DOCUMENTATION - ECONOMIE - SCIENCE - TECHNIQUE. see BUSINESS AND ECONOMICS — Abstracting, Bibliographies, Statistics

500 016   US   ISSN 0149-8088
Z7403   CODEN: ISTPDJ
INDEX TO SCIENTIFIC & TECHNICAL PROCEEDINGS. Short title: I S T P. (Includes Author/Editor Index, Permuterm Subject Index, Sponsor Index, Meeting Location Index, Category Index, Contents of Proceedings Index, and Corporate Index) 1978. m. (with a. cumulation). $1570. Institute for Scientific Information, 3501 Market St., Philadelphia, PA 19104. TEL 215-386-0100. FAX 215-386-2991. (And: Brunel Science Park, Brunel University, Uxbridge UB8 3PQ, England. TEL 44-1895-70016. FAX 44-1895-256710) (also avail. in magnetic tape) **Document type:** academic/scholarly publication, bibliography.
●Also available online. Vendor(s): Orbit Search Service.
Also available on CD-ROM. Producer(s): Institute for Scientific Information.
—BLDSC (4385.660000); CASDDS.
Description: Indexes bibliographic information from scientific and technical conference proceedings.

010   US   ISSN 0884-8440
Z7401
INDEX TO SCIENTIFIC BOOK CONTENTS. Short title: I S B C. (Includes Contents of Books Index, Author - Editor Index, Corporate Index, Category Index, and Permuterm Subject Index) 1985. q. (with a. cumulation). $1340. Institute for Scientific Information, 3501 Market St., Philadelphia, PA 19104. TEL 215-386-0100. FAX 215-386-2291. (And: Brunel Science Park, Brunel University, Uxbridge UB8 3PQ, England. TEL 0895-70016) (also avail. in magnetic tape) **Document type:** academic/scholarly publication, bibliography.
●Also available online. Vendor(s): DIMDI (ISTP&B Search).
—BLDSC (4385.663000).
Description: Indexes published scientific books, book series, and proceedings.

011   US   ISSN 0360-0661
Z7403
INDEX TO SCIENTIFIC REVIEWS. Short title: I S R. (Permuterm Subject Index, Source Index, Corporate Index, and Research-Front Specialty Index) 1974. s-a.(annual cumulation). $960. Institute for Scientific Information, 3501 Market St., Philadelphia, PA 19104. TEL 215-386-0100. FAX 215-386-2291. (And: Brunel Science Park, Brunel University, Uxbridge UB8 3PQ, England. TEL 0895-70016) (also avail. in magnetic tape) **Document type:** abstracting/indexing.
—BLDSC (4385.670000).
Description: Indexes review articles and surveys of scientific literature internationally.

500 600   II
INDIA. DEPARTMENT OF SCIENCE AND TECHNOLOGY. RESEARCH AND DEVELOPMENT STATISTICS. 1973. biennial. Rs.80. Department of Science and Technology, New Mehrauli Rd., New Delhi 110016, India. TEL 0091-651912. FAX 0091-6862418. TELEX 73381 DST IN. Ed. A.R. Rajeswari. charts; stat. circ. 2,000. **Document type:** government publication.
Formerly: National Committee on Science and Technology. Research and Development Statistics.

500 016   II   ISSN 0019-6339
Q1   CODEN: IDSAAV
INDIAN SCIENCE ABSTRACTS. 1965. fortn. Rs.1500($600) Indian National Scientific Documentation Centre, 14 Satsang Vihar Marg, New Delhi 110 067, India. Ed. J.M. Bharadwaj. abstr.; index. circ. 800. **Indexed:** Anim.Breed.Abstr., C.R.I.Abstr., C.R.I.Curr.Cont., Chem.Abstr., Field Crop Abstr., Herb.Abstr., Hort.Abstr., Nutr.Abstr., Plant Breed.Abstr., World Surf.Coat. **Document type:** abstracting/indexing.

INDIAN SCIENCE INDEX. SER. B: PRE-MODERN PERIOD. see TECHNOLOGY: COMPREHENSIVE WORKS — Abstracting, Bibliographies, Statistics

500 011   SP   ISSN 0210-9409
Z7401
INDICE ESPANOL DE CIENCIA Y TECNOLOGIA. 1980. q. 8800 ptas. (effective 1995). (Consejo Superior de Investigaciones Cientificas (C.S.I.C.)) Centro de Informacion y Documentacion Cientifica (Cindoc), Joaquin Costa 22, 28002 Madrid, Spain. TEL 34-1-5635482. FAX 34-1-5642644. TELEX 22628 CIDMD E. E-mail: bib_icyt@bib.csic.es. adv. contact: Godofredo Aguado. circ. 600. (also avail. in diskette format)
●Also available online.
Also available on CD-ROM.

500 020   SP   ISSN 0214-1086
INDICE ESPANOL DE CIENCIAS SOCIALES. SERIES D: SCIENCE AND SCIENTIFIC INFORMATION. 1979. a. 8800 ptas. or exchange basis (effective 1995). Centro de Documentacion y Documentacion Cientifica (Cindoc), Pinar, 25, 3, 28006 Madrid, Spain. TEL 34-1-4112220. FAX 34-1-5645069. E-mail: bib_isoc@bib.csic.es. adv. contact: Angela Sorli. (also avail. in diskette format)
●Also available online.
Also available on CD-ROM.
Supersedes in part (in 1982): Indice Espanol de Ciencias Sociales (ISSN 0211-1373)

500 010   AO   ISSN 0074-008X
INSTITUTO DE INVESTIGACAO CIENTIFICA DE ANGOLA. BIBLIOGRAFICAS TEMATICAS. 1969. irreg., 1973, no.19. free to qualified personnel. Instituto de Investigacao Cientifica de Angola, Departamento de Documentacao e Informacao, Box 3244, Luanda, Angola. **Indexed:** Trop.Abstr.

INTERNATIONAL RARE BOOK PRICES - SCIENCES & MEDICINE. see PUBLISHING AND BOOK TRADE — Abstracting, Bibliographies, Statistics

500 016   GW   ISSN 0020-918X
Z5051
INTERNATIONALE BIBLIOGRAPHIE DER REZENSIONEN WISSENSCHAFTLICHER LITERATUR/INTERNATIONAL BIBLIOGRAPHY OF BOOK REVIEWS OF SCHOLARLY LITERATURE. Short title: I B R. (Text in English, French, German) 1971. 6/yr. (in 2 vols., 3 nos./vol.). DM.2900 (CD-ROM DM.1200 with printed edition). Zeller Verlag GmbH, Postfach 1949, 49009 Osnabrueck, Germany. TEL 0541-4045914. FAX 0541-41255. Eds. Otto Zeller, Wolfram Zeller. **Document type:** bibliography.
●Also available online.
Also available on CD-ROM.
—BLDSC (4554.090000).
Description: Universal bibliography of book reviews with German and English keywords.

500   SZ
INTERNATIONALE WISSENSCHAFTSPOLITIK: PRESSESCHAU/POLITIQUE SCIENTIFIQUE INTERNATIONALE: REVUE DE PRESSE/INTERNATIONAL SCIENCE POLICY: PRESS REVIEW. (Text in English, French, German) 1991. 5/yr. free. Schweizerischer Wissenschaftsrat, Dokumentationsstelle fuer Wissenschaftspolitik, Inselgasse 1, CH-3003 Bern, Switzerland. TEL 031-3229655. FAX 031-3228070. **Document type:** abstracting/indexing.

500   JA   ISSN 0514-2253
JAPANESE PERIODICALS INDEX. SCIENCE AND TECHNOLOGY/ZASSHI KIJI SAKUIN. KAGAKU GIJUTSU HEN. (Text in Japanese and European languages) 1950. q. 20600 Yen. National Diet Library - Kokuritsu Kokkai Toshokan, 1-10-1 Nagata-cho, Chiyoda-ku, Tokyo 100, Japan. TEL 03-3581-2331. FAX 03-3597-9104. abstr. circ. 805. **Document type:** abstracting/indexing.
●Also available on CD-ROM.

KAGAKU GIJUTSU BUNKEN TOYAMA/TOYAMA SCIENCE AND TECHNICAL DOCUMENTS. see TECHNOLOGY: COMPREHENSIVE WORKS — Abstracting, Bibliographies, Statistics

KAGAKU GIJUTSU FORAMU HOKOKUSHO. see TECHNOLOGY: COMPREHENSIVE WORKS — Abstracting, Bibliographies, Statistics

SCIENCES: COMPREHENSIVE WORKS — ABSTRACTING, BIBLIOGRAPHIES, STATISTICS

500 JA
KANAZAWA DAIGAKU RIGAKUBU RONBUN OYOBI CHOSHO MOKUROKU/KANAZAWA UNIVERSITY. FACULTY OF SCIENCE. LIST OF PUBLICATIONS. (Text in English, German, French, Japanese) 1961. quinquennial. Kanazawa Daigaku, Rigakubu - Kanazawa University, Faculty of Science, Kakuma-machi, Kanazawa-shi, Ishikawa-ken 920-11, Japan. TEL 0762-64-5620. FAX 0762-64-5737. bibl.

500.9 016 SZ ISSN 0250-3859
KEY WORD INDEX OF WILDLIFE RESEARCH. (Text in English or German) 1974. a. 70 SFr. Swiss Wildlife Information Service, University of Zurich, Strickhofstr. 39, CH-8057 Zurich, Switzerland. TEL 01-3627728. FAX 01-3627117. Ed. Christa Mosler-Berger. **Document type:** abstracting/indexing.

500 016 KO ISSN 0023-4052
Q1
KOREAN SCIENTIFIC ABSTRACTS. 1969. bi-m. $30. Korea Institute for Economics and Technology, P.O.B. 205, 206-9 Cheongryangri-Dong, Dongdaimun-Ku, S. Korea. abstr.; index. circ. 700. (reprint service avail. from UMI) **Indexed:** AESIS, Anim.Breed.Abstr., BMT, Br.Ceram.Abstr., Forest.Abstr., Forest Prod.Abstr., Graph.Arts Lit.Abstr., Nutr.Abstr., Plant Breed.Abstr., Sport Fish.Abstr., Wild.Rev. **Document type:** abstracting/indexing.

KUNI NO SHIKEN KENKYU GYOMU KEIKAKU. see TECHNOLOGY: COMPREHENSIVE WORKS — Abstracting, Bibliographies, Statistics

500 US ISSN 0090-5232
Z7401
L C SCIENCE TRACER BULLET. 1972. irreg. free. U.S. Library of Congress, Science and Technology Division, Washington, DC 20540. TEL 202-707-5664. (Avail. from: Superintendent of Documents, U.S. Government Printing Office, Box 317954, Pittsburgh, PA 15250-7954. TEL 202-783-3238. FAX 202-512-2233) **Document type:** government publication.

500 011 PL
LIBREX AGRO; bibliographic database. (Text in English, Polish) 1992. q. $350. Madex, Ul. Grounwaldzka 11, 60-782 Poznanan, Poland. TEL 48-61-666066. FAX 48-61-659-643. TELEX 413374. Ed. Wlodzimierz Golab. adv. contact: Marek Marcinowski. (also avail. in diskette format) **Document type:** abstracting/indexing.
  Description: Indexes the contents of Polish journals and series covering biology, agriculture, forestry, horticulture, animal science, wood, food, nutrition, environmental and veterinary scienes.

500 015 TH ISSN 0125-4537
LIST OF SCIENTIFIC AND TECHNICAL LITERATURE RELATING TO THAILAND. (Text in English) 1964. irreg. $5 per no. (Thai National Documentation Centre) Thailand Institute of Scientific and Technological Research, 196 Phahonyothin Rd., Chatuchak, Bangkok 10900, Thailand. TEL 579-8594. FAX 662-579-8594. circ. 500. **Document type:** bibliography.
  ●Also available online.

500 015 HU
MAGYAR TUDOMANYOS AKADEMIA KONVYTARANAK KOZLEMENYEI/PUBLICATIONES BIBLIOTHECAE ACADEMIAE SCIENTIARUM HUNGARICAE. (Text in Hungarian; summaries in English, French, German) 1956. irreg. price varies or exchange basis. Magyar Tudomanyos Akademia Konyvtara, Arany Janos u.1, P.O. Box 7, 1361 Budapest 5, Hungary. Eds. G. Fekete, L. Vekerdi. **Document type:** monographic series.
  Formerly: Magyar Tudomanyos Akademia Konvytaranak Kiadvanyai (ISSN 0133-8862)
  Description: Monographs dealing with the history of the academy and the library. Colletions of data and general studies on the history of science and library science.

500 600 MW ISSN 1019-7079
Q91.M3 CODEN: RBBADY
MALAWI JOURNAL OF SCIENCE AND TECHNOLOGY. (Text in English) s-a. $20. University of Malawi, Faculty of Science, Research and Publication Committee, Box 278, Zomba, Malawi. TEL 265-50-522222. Ed.Bd. adv.; bk.rev.; bibl.; charts; illus. circ. 500. (back issues avail.) **Indexed:** Anim.Breed.Abstr., Biol.Abstr., Chem.Abstr., Dairy Sci.Abstr., Ecol.Abstr., Field Crop.Abstr., Geo.Abstr., Hort.Abstr., Maize Abstr., Poult.Abstr., Seed Abstr. **Document type:** academic/scholarly publication.
—BLDSC (5354.924700); CASDDS.
  Formed by the merger of (1980-1992): Luso (ISSN 0251-0154); (1970-1992): Bunda Journal of Agricultural Research (ISSN 1011-7830); Which was formerly (until 1989): Bunda College of Agriculture. Research Bulletin (ISSN 0253-827X)

500 011 IR
MARKAZ-I NASHARIYAT-I 'ILMI VA FARHANGI. FIHRIST-I MUNDARIJAT-I MAJALLAH-HA-YI JARI-I/CENTER FOR SCIENTIFIC AND CULTURAL PERIODICALS. TABLE OF CONTENTS OF CURRENT JOURNALS. (Text in English, Persian) 1991. m. IRI.250 per no. Markaz-i Nahsariyat-i 'Ilmi va Farhangi - Center for Scientific and Cultural Periodicals, Irshad Islami int., Bldg. 1, Vali Asr Ave., Tehran, Iran. (Co-sponsor: Vizarat-i Farhang va Irshad-i Islami - Ministry of Culture and Islamic Guidance)

500 600 US
MASTER'S THESES IN THE PURE AND APPLIED SCIENCES; accepted by colleges and universities in the United States and Canada. 1955. a., vol.37, 1993. price varies. Plenum Publishing Corp., 233 Spring St., New York, NY 10013-1578. TEL 212-620-8000. FAX 212-463-0742. TELEX 23-421139. Ed. W.H. Shafer. (back issues avail.) **Document type:** bibliography.
  Refereed Serial

NATIONAL DIET LIBRARY. ANNUAL LIST OF FOREIGN SCIENTIFIC AND TECHNICAL PUBLICATIONS/KAIGAI KAGAKU GIJUTSU SHIRYO UKEIRE MOKUROKU. see TECHNOLOGY: COMPREHENSIVE WORKS — Abstracting, Bibliographies, Statistics

500 US
NATIONAL TECHNICAL INFORMATION SERVICE. PUBLISHED SEARCH MASTER CATALOG. a. free. U.S. National Technical Information Service, 5285 Port Royal Rd., Springfield, VA 22161. TEL 703-487-4650. FAX 703-321-8547. **Document type:** catalog, bibliography, government publication.
  Description: Lists more than 2,000 searches available through NTIS databases.

500 SZ
NATIONALE WISSENSCHAFTSPOLITIK: PRESSESCHAU/POLITIQUE SCIENTIFIQUE NATIONALE: REVUE DE PRESSE/POLITICA SCIENTIFICA NAZIONALE: RASSEGNA STAMPA. (Text in French, German, Italian) 1991. 10/yr. free. Schweizerischer Wissenschaftsrat, Dokumentationsstelle fuer Wissenschaftspolitik, Inselgasse 1, CH-3003 Bern, Switzerland. TEL 031-3229655. FAX 031-3228070. **Document type:** abstracting/indexing.

500 RU
NAUKOVEDENIE: OTECHESTVENNAYA I ZARUBEZHNAYA LITERATURA; referativnyi zhurnal. 1973. q. $64. Rossiiskaya Akademiya Nauk, Institut Nauchnoi Informatsii po Obshchestvennym Naukam, Ul. Krasikova 28-21, 117418 Moscow V-418, Russia. Ed. A.M. Kul'kin. **Document type:** abstracting/indexing.
  Formerly: Obshchestvennye Nauki za Rubezhom. Naukovedenie (ISSN 0202-2141)

600 016 US ISSN 0028-6869
Z5854 CODEN: NTBOAJ
NEW TECHNICAL BOOKS; a selective list with descriptive annotations. 1915. bi-m. $30 (foreign $35). New York Public Library, Science and Technology Research Center, Rm. 120, Fifth Ave. and 42nd St., New York, NY 10018. TEL 212-930-0920. FAX 212-869-7824. Ed. Gloria Rohmann. bk.rev.; index. circ. 1,700. **Indexed:** Abstr.Bull.Inst.Pap.Chem., Bk.Rev.Ind. (1985-), Child.Bk.Rev.Ind. (1985-). **Document type:** bibliography.
—CASDDS.
  Description: Provdes an annotated listing of recently published science and technology monographs, monographic series and conference proceedings, predominantly at the undergraduate major, graduate and research level.

500 016 JA ISSN 0916-1198
NIHON KAGAKU GIJUTSU KANKEI CHIKUJI KANKOBUTSU SORAN/DIRECTORY OF JAPANESE SCIENTIFIC PERIODICALS. (Text in English and Japanese) quinquennial, latest 1992. 23000 Yen. National Diet Library - Kokuritsu Kokkai Toshokan, 1-10-1 Nagata-cho, Chiyoda-ku, Tokyo 100, Japan. TEL 03-3581-2331. FAX 03-3597-9104. **Document type:** directory.
  Formerly (until 1988): Nihon Kagaku Gijutsu Kankei Chikuji Kankobutsu Mokuroku (ISSN 0911-0151)

NIJHOFF INFORMATION, NEW PUBLICATIONS FROM GERMANY, AUSTRIA AND SWITZERLAND. see PUBLISHING AND BOOK TRADE — Abstracting, Bibliographies, Statistics

500 UK ISSN 1351-525X
▼**NITRIC OXIDE.** 1994. s-m. (diskette m.) £105 (diskette £115; both £175) (effective 1995). S U B I S, Mansion House, 19 Kingfield Rd., Sheffield S11 9AS, England. TEL 0114-2554433. FAX 0114-2554626. E-mail: admin@sheffac.demon.co.uk. (also avail. in diskette format) **Document type:** abstracting/indexing.
  Description: Current awareness service for researchers in clinical and life sciences.

OUTSTANDING SCIENCE TRADE BOOKS FOR CHILDREN. see CHILDREN AND YOUTH — Abstracting, Bibliographies, Statistics

500 016 PK ISSN 0031-0085
PAKISTAN SCIENCE ABSTRACTS. (Text in English) 1961. q. Rps.35($14) Pakistan Scientific and Technological Information Centre, Quaid-i-Azam University Campus, Box 1217, Islamabad, Pakistan. Ed. Ghulam Hamid Khan. abstr.; pat.; index. circ. 500. (also avail. in microfilm) **Document type:** abstracting/indexing.

016 500 MX ISSN 0185-1004
Z7403
PERIODICA. INDICE DE REVISTAS LATINOAMERICANAS EN CIENCIAS. (Text in Spanish; key words in English, Spanish) 1978. q. $190. Universidad Nacional Autonoma de Mexico, Centro de Informacion Cientifica y Humanistica, Apdo. Postal 70-392, C.P. 04510 Mexico, D.F., Mexico. TEL 525-6223958. FAX 525-6162557. E-mail: biblat@selene.cichcu.unam.mx. Ed. Antonio Llorens-Cruset. **Document type:** abstracting/indexing.
  ●Also available online.
  Also available on CD-ROM.
  Formerly (until 1979): Periodica. Indice de Revistas Mexicanas en Ciencias.

500 PH ISSN 0116-3582
PHILIPPINE MEN OF SCIENCE. 1967. a. P.250 (foreign $45). Science and Technology Information Institute, Department of Science and Technology, P.O. Box 3596, Taguig, Metro Manila, Philippines. TEL 822-0954.
  Description: Contains bio-bibliographic information of outstanding living Filipino scientists and technologists.

SCIENCES: COMPREHENSIVE WORKS — ABSTRACTING, BIBLIOGRAPHIES, STATISTICS

500 016   PH
PHILIPPINE SCIENCE AND TECHNOLOGY ABSTRACTS.
1960. q. P.200($65) Science and Technology Information Institute, Scientific Library and Documentation Division, P.O. Box 3596, Manila, Philippines. FAX 822-05-64. abstr.; index. circ. 500. **Indexed:** Biol.Abstr., J.of Ferroc. **Document type:** abstracting/indexing.
Formerly: Philippine Science and Technology Abstracts Bibliography (ISSN 0115-8724); Formed by the merger of: Philippine Abstracts (ISSN 0031-7438); Philippine Science Index.

PROCEEDINGS IN PRINT. see *MEETINGS AND CONGRESSES — Abstracting, Bibliographies, Statistics*

500   US   ISSN 0743-6955
Z7403
PUBLISHED SEARCHES. (Supplement avail.) a. $65 in U.S., Canada, Mexico; elsewhere $85. U.S. National Technical Information Service, 5285 Port Royal Rd., Springfield, VA 22161. TEL 703-487-4630. (also avail. in microfiche)
Description: Includes scientific information from over 23 other international sources as well as NTIS.

500   IQ   ISSN 1012-3458
RESEARCH ABSTRACTS IN SCIENTIFIC RESEARCH COUNCIL. (Text in Arabic) 1984. irreg. free. Scientific Research Council, Jadiriyah P.O. Box 2441, Baghdad, Iraq. TELEX 213976 SR IK. Ed. Radhwan K. Abdul-Halim. circ. 500. **Document type:** abstracting/indexing.

RESEARCH AND STUDIES. see *EDUCATION — Abstracting, Bibliographies, Statistics*

500   JA
RIKA NENPYO/SCIENCE ALMANAC. (Text in Japanese) 1924. a. (University of Tokyo, Tokyo Astronomical Observatory - Tokyo Daigaku Tokyo Tenmondai) Maruzen Co., Ltd., 3-10, Nihonbashi 2-chome, Chuo-ku, Tokyo 103, Japan. stat.

500 016   RM   ISSN 0035-8096
RUMANIAN SCIENTIFIC ABSTRACTS.* 1973. s-a. (Academia de Stiinte Sociale si Politice, Office of Information and Documentation in Social and Political Sciences - Academy of Social and Political Sciences of the S.R.R) Editura Academiei Romane, Calea Victoriei 125, 79717 Bucharest, Rumania. (Subscr. to: ILEXIM, P.O. Box 136-137, 13 Decembrie St., no. 3, 11226 Bucharest, Rumania) Ed. Mircea Ioanid. bk.rev.; abstr.; index. circ. 1,000. **Indexed:** Appl.Mech.Rev., Bull.Signal, Field Crop Abstr., Herb.Abstr., Ref.Zh.

500 600   PH
S E A ABSTRACTS. q. P.200 (foreign $45). Science and Technology Information Institute, Department of Science and Technology, P.O. Box 3596, Manila, Philippines. TEL 822-0954. (Subscr. to: Dept. of Science and Technology, Bicutan, Taguig, P.O. Box 2131, Manila, Philippines) **Document type:** abstracting/indexing.
Description: Abstracts and summarizes the latest scientific and technical studies in Asia, excluding the Philippines.

505   US   ISSN 1065-1381
SCIDEX CUMULATIVE INDEX. a. Scientific American, Inc., 415 Madison Ave., New York, NY 10017-1111. TEL 212-754-0550. FAX 212-754-1138. (diskette format) **Document type:** abstracting/indexing.
Description: Cumulative index to Scientific American magazine, 1948 to the present.

500   US   ISSN 1048-6313
Q172.5.S34   CODEN: SENIEF
SCIENCE & ENGINEERING INDICATORS. 1973. biennial. U.S. Government Printing Office, Superintendent of Documents, Washington, DC 20402. TEL 202-634-4634. FAX 202-634-4683. bibl.; charts; stat.; index. circ. 10,000.
—BLDSC (8133.025000); CASDDS.
Formerly (until 1986): Science Indicators (ISSN 0092-315X).

500 600   US
SCIENCE AND TECHNOLOGY (PITTSBURGH); a purchase guide for libraries. 1960. a. $12 (effective 1994). Carnegie Library of Pittsburgh, Science and Technology Department, 4400 Forbes Ave., Pittsburgh, PA 15213-4080. TEL 412-622-3141. FAX 412-621-1267. circ. 500. (also avail. in microform from CMC) **Document type:** bibliography.
Formerly (until 1963): Basic Collection of Science and Technology Books.
Description: Lists new books in science and technology of general interest to the nonspecialist.

500 016   US   ISSN 0098-342X
Z7403
SCIENCE BOOKS & FILMS. 1965. 9/yr. $40. American Association for the Advancement of Science, 1333 H St., N.W., Washington, DC 20005. TEL 202-326-6454. (Subscr. to: Dept. SBF, Box 3000, Denville, NJ 07834) Ed. Maria Sosa. adv.; bk.rev.; index. circ. 4,500. (also avail. in microform from UMI; reprint service avail. from UMI) **Indexed:** Bk.Rev.Ind. (1966-), Child.Bk.Rev.Ind. (1966-), Child.Lit.Abstr. **Document type:** bibliography, newsletter.
—Faxon; UMI.
Formerly: Science Books (ISSN 0036-8253)
Description: Reviews of print, film, and software materials in all sciences for all age levels, for librarians and educators.

500 016   US   ISSN 0036-827X
Z7401   CODEN: SCIXAH
SCIENCE CITATION INDEX. Short title: S C I. (Includes Source Index, Citation Index, Permuterm Subject Index, and Corporate Index) 1961. 6/yr. (plus annual cum.). $11650. Institute for Scientific Information, 3501 Market St., Philadelphia, PA 19104. TEL 215-386-0100. FAX 215-386-2991. (And: Brunel Science Park, Brunel University, Uxbridge UB8 3PQ, England) 10 yr. cum.index: 1955-1964, 1945-1954; 5 yr. cum.index: 1965-1969, 1970-1974, 1975-1979, 1980-1984, 1985-1989. (also avail. in magnetic tape) **Document type:** academic/scholarly publication, bibliography.
●Also available online. Vendor(s): DIMDI, Data-Star, Knight-Ridder, Inc. (Files nos.34,432,433,434/SCISEARCH), Orbit Search Service.
Also available on CD-ROM. Producer(s): Institute for Scientific Information (SCI CDE).
—BLDSC (8141.802000).
Description: Indexes the world's science and technology literature. Provides cited reference searching and related records.

500   FR   ISSN 1162-7387
SCIENCE CULTURE; la revue des sommaires de revues. m. 380 F.($90) to individuals; institutions 1000 F. ($180). Science Culture SARL, 19 rue des Cordelieres, 75013 Paris, France. TEL 33-1-47-26-46-58. FAX 33-1-46-77-97-18. Ed. Jean-Claude Salomon.

500 600   BU
SCIENTIFIC AND TECHNICAL PUBLICATIONS IN BULGARIA. (Text in English) q. $33. National Centre for Information and Documentation, 52-A, Dr. G.M. Dimitrov Blvd., 1125 Sofia, Bulgaria. Ed. Kamen Markov.
Description: Contains abstracts of selected articles, published in prestigious Bulgarian journals, proceedings of scientific institutes and universities.

500 016   TH   ISSN 0125-4529
SCIENTIFIC SERIALS IN THAI LIBRARIES. (Text in English) 1968. a. B.2000($80) Thailand Institute of Scientific and Technological Research, 196 Phahonyothin Rd., Chatuchak, Bangkok 10900, Thailand. TEL 579-8594. FAX 662-579-8594. **Indexed:** Biol.Abstr. **Document type:** bibliography.
●Also available online.
Description: Lists over 13,800 journals and report series on science, technology, and socio-economic aspects of the sciences received by 148 libraries in Bangkok.

500 600   US   ISSN 1063-8717
Z403
SCITECH REFERENCE PLUS; complete bibliographic information on SciTech books and serials, bibliographical data on science professionals, and corporate profiles of research and business facilities. 1989. a. $995. R.R. Bowker, A Reed Reference Publishing company, 121 Chanlon Rd., New Providence, NJ 07974. TEL 908-665-2866. FAX 908-665-3528. TELEX 138 755. (avail. for MS-DOS version)
●Available only on CD-ROM. Producer(s): Bowker - Reed Reference Electronic Publishing.
Description: Merges six definitive databases to provide access to the most current information.

016   US   ISSN 0037-1343
AS36   CODEN: SRABAG
SELECTED RAND ABSTRACTS; a biannual guide to publications of the Rand Corporation. 1946. 2/yr. free to institutions. Rand Corporation, Publications Department, 1700 Main St., Box 2138, Santa Monica, CA 90407-2138. TEL 310-451-7002. FAX 310-451-6915. TELEX 9103436878. E-mail: order@rand.org; Site addr.: http://www.rand.org/. abstr.; index. circ. 1,000. **Indexed:** Abstr.Mil.Bibl., Fluidex, Rehabil.Lit. **Document type:** abstracting/indexing.
—BLDSC (8234.700000); CASDDS.
Formerly (until 1962): Rand Corporation. Index of Selected Publications (ISSN 0485-9790)

500 600   JA   ISSN 0917-7574
SHINKU TANKU NENPO/ABSTRACTS OF THINK TANK REPORTS. (Text in Japanese) 1976. a. 6000 Yen. Sogo Kenkyu Kaihatsu Kiko - National Institute for Research Advancement, P.O. Box 5004, 34F Yebisu Garden Place Tower, 4-20-3 Ebisu, Shibuya-ku, Tokyo 150, Japan. TEL 03-5448-1735. FAX 03-5448-1745. E-mail: tigarashi@niral.nira.go.jp. abstr. circ. 1,400.
—BLDSC (8256.806200).
Description: Introduces the results of research conducted at Japanese think tanks and research institutes.

016 500   CE
SRI LANKA SCIENCE INDEX. (Text in English) 1977. q. $7 (or exchange basis). (Sri Lanka Scientific and Technical Information Centre) Natural Resources, Energy and Science Authority, 47-5 Maitland Place, Colombo 7, Sri Lanka. (reprint service avail.)

500 338   KU
STATISTICS ON SCIENTIFIC AND TECHNOLOGICAL ACTIVITIES/IHSA'AT AL-ANSHITAH AL-'ILMIYYAH WAL-TEKNOLOJIYYAH FI DAWLAT AL-KUWAYT. (Text in Arabic, English) 1977. irreg., latest 1984. Central Statistical Office - Al-Idarah al-Markaziyyah lil-Ihsa', P.O. Box 26188, Safat 13122, Kuwait. TEL 965-2428200. FAX 965-2430464. TELEX 22468 TAKHTET KT. **Document type:** government publication.
Description: Provides statistical data on economic input (labor force and expenditures) deriving from scientific and technical activity in Kuwait.

500 016   SJ   ISSN 0255-4054
SUDAN SCIENCE ABSTRACTS. 1980. a., vol.17, 1993. National Centre for Research, Documentation and Information Centre, P.O. Box 2404, Khartoum, Sudan. **Document type:** abstracting/indexing.

016   TH   ISSN 0125-0000
THAI ABSTRACTS, SERIES A. SCIENCE AND TECHNOLOGY. (Text in English) 1974. s-a. B.100($5) per no. Thailand Institute of Scientific and Technological Research, 196 Phahonyothin Road, Bang Khen, Bangkok 10900, Thailand. TEL 579-8594. FAX 662-579-8594. Ed.Bd. author and subject indexes. circ. 500. **Document type:** abstracting/indexing.
●Also available online.
—BLDSC (8813.889000).

500 300 001.3   PH
U P RESEARCH MONITOR. 1978. a. University of the Philippines, Office of Research Coordination, Rm. 309 Malcolm Hall, Diliman, Quezon City, Philippines. Ed. Bienvenido T. Miranda. circ. 750. (back issues avail.)

U P THESIS AND DISSERTATION ABSTRACTS. (University of the Philippines) see *EDUCATION — Abstracting, Bibliographies, Statistics*

SCIENCES: COMPREHENSIVE WORKS — COMPUTER APPLICATIONS

310 500   UN
UNESCO STATISTICAL YEARBOOK. (Text in English, French and Spanish) 1964. a. 375 F. Unesco, Division of Statistics on Science and Technology, Office of Statistics, 7-9 Place de Fontenoy, 75700 Paris, France. TEL 33 1 568-10-00. **Document type:** academic/scholarly publication.
    Formerly: Unesco. Statistics on Science and Technology.

500 016   CN   ISSN 0082-7657
Z7403
UNION LIST OF SCIENTIFIC SERIALS IN CANADIAN LIBRARIES/CATALOGUE COLLECTIF DES PUBLICATIONS SCIENTIFIQUES EN SERIE DANS LES BIBLIOTHEQUES CANADIENNES. 1957. a., 18th, 1994. Can.$350. (National Research Council of Canada) Canada Institute for Scientific and Technical Information, Cataloguing Section, Ottawa, ON K1A 0S2, Canada. TEL 613-993-3449. circ. 300.
●Also available online. Vendor(s): CISTI.
Also available on CD-ROM.

500 011   GW   ISSN 0344-0915
UNIVERSITAET HOHENHEIM FORSCHUNGSBERICHT. 1976. triennial. free. Universitaet Hohenheim, Presse und Forschungsinformation, 70593 Stuttgart, Germany. TEL 0711-459-2001. FAX 0711-4593289. Ed. Klaus H. Grabowski. abstr. circ. 1,800. **Document type:** bulletin.

500 600   RU   ISSN 0135-0617
Z7409
VSESOYUZNYI INSTITUT NAUCHNO-TEKHNICHESKOI INFORMATSII. DEPONIROVANNYE NAUCHNYE RABOTY. 1963. m. 35 Rub. Vsesoyuznyi Institut Nauchno-Tekhnicheskoi Informatsii (VINITI), Baltiiskaya ul. 14, Moscow A-219, Russia. (Subscr. to: Mezhdunarodnaya Kniga, Moscow 121200, Russia)
    Formerly: Vsesoyuznyi Institut Nauchno-Tekhnicheskoi Informatsii. Deponirovannye Rukopisi.

VYBER NOVINEK BRNENSKYCH KNIHOVEN. SERIE A: PRIRODDNI VEDY, ZEMEDELSTVI. see *AGRICULTURE — Abstracting, Bibliographies, Statistics*

500   GW   ISSN 0177-5928
W L A SELECTA. (Wissenschaftlicher Literatur Anzeiger) 1985. s-a. Verlag M. Veit M.A., Erlenweg 10, 33428 Harsewinkel, Germany. TEL 05247-5466. adv. circ. 4,000. (back issues avail.) **Document type:** abstracting/indexing.

WASEDA DAIGAKU DAIGAKUIN RIKOGAKU KENKYU IHO/WASEDA UNIVERSITY. GRADUATE SCHOOL OF SCIENCE AND ENGINEERING. SYNOPSES OF SCIENCE AND ENGINEERING PAPERS. see *ENGINEERING — Abstracting, Bibliographies, Statistics*

WISSENSCHAFTLICHER LITERATURANZEIGER. see *PUBLISHING AND BOOK TRADE — Abstracting, Bibliographies, Statistics*

500 016   NE   ISSN 0259-8264
Z7403
WORLD TRANSLATIONS INDEX. Abbreviated title: W T I. (Text in English, French, German) 1978. 10/yr. (plus a. cumulation). fl.1500 in ITC member countries; elsewhere fl.1600 (effective 1995). International Translations Centre (ITC), Schuttersveld 2, 2611 WE Delft, Netherlands. TEL 31-15-142242. FAX 31-15-158535. E-mail: ITC@library.tudelft.nl. (Co-sponsor: Centre National de la Recherche Scientifique, Institut de l'Information Scientifique et Technique (INIST-CNRS), Vandoeuvre-les-Nancy, France) adv.; cum.index 1967-1989. circ. 500. (back issues avail.) **Indexed:** GeoRef. **Document type:** abstracting/indexing.
●Also available online. Vendor(s): Knight-Ridder, Inc. (File no.295), European Space Agency (File no.33/WTI).
—BLDSC (9360.154130).
    Formerly (until 1987): World Transindex (ISSN 0378-6803); Formed by the merger of: Bulletin Signaletique. Part 900. Bulletin des Traductions (ISSN 0007-571X); Transatom Bulletin (ISSN 0041-1086); World Index of Scientific Translations and List of Translations Notified to the International Translation Centre (ISSN 0376-6381); Which was formerly: World Index of Scientific Translations and List of Translations Notified to E T C (ISSN 0304-0755); Which was formed by the merger of: World Index of Scientific Translations (ISSN 0043-8553); List of Translations Notified to the E T C (ISSN 0046-2829).
    Description: Gives bibliographic data of existing translations of scientific and technical literature from any language. Includes author and source index.

500   ZA
ZAMBIA. NATIONAL COUNCIL FOR SCIENTIFIC RESEARCH. N C S R BIBLIOGRAPHY. Short title: N C S R Bibliography. 1976. irreg., latest 1979. K.1.50. National Council for Scientific Research, Box CH 158, Chelston, Lusaka, Zambia. **Document type:** bibliography, government publication.

500 016   ZA
ZAMBIA SCIENCE ABSTRACTS. 1977. a. K.5. National Council for Scientific Research, Box CH 158, Chelston, Lusaka, Zambia. Ed. W.C. Mushipi. **Document type:** abstracting/indexing.

500 016   RH
ZIMBABWE RESEARCH INDEX; register of current research in Zimbabwe. 1971. a. $40. Scientific Liaison Office, P.O. Box CY 294, Causeway, Harare, Zimbabwe. TEL 700573. TELEX 22141. (Subscr. to: Government Printer, P.O. Box CY 341, Causeway, Harare, Zimbabwe) index; circ. 500 (controlled). (processed) **Indexed:** Anim.Breed.Abstr. **Document type:** abstracting/indexing.
    Formerly: Rhodesia Research Index.

SCIENCES: COMPREHENSIVE WORKS — Computer Applications

600 621.381   US   ISSN 0733-8074
QA76.5   CODEN: ACCSEG
ACCESS (RESEARCH TRIANGLE PARK).* 1982. 6/yr. $21. L E D S Publishing Co. Inc., 1014 Evergreen Dr., Durham, NC 27712-2214. TEL 919-477-3690. Ed. Leslie E. Sparks. adv.; bk.rev. circ. 4,000. **Indexed:** Oper.Res.Manage.Sci., Qual.Contr.Appl.Stat.
—UnCover.
    Description: Features technical articles on applications to engineering and science. Regular columns include statistics column, numerical analysis, scientific use of Amiga and Macintosh.

500   US   ISSN 0888-2231
APPLICATIONS OF COMPUTER SCIENCE SERIES. 1986. irreg. Computer Science Press, Inc., 41 Madison Ave., 37th Fl., New York, NY 10010-3546. TEL 212-576-9400. Ed. Arthur D. Friedman. (back issues avail.)

500 301.1 016   US   ISSN 0005-7940
BF1   CODEN: BEHSAS
BEHAVIORAL SCIENCE. 1956. q. $41 to individuals; institutions $76; foreign $81.50 (effective 1995). General Systems Science Foundation, Box 8369, La Jolla, CA 92038-8369. Ed. Warren Froelich; Pub. Dr. James G. Miller. adv.; bk.rev.; abstr.; charts; illus.; index. circ. 1,600. (also avail. in microform from UMI; reprint service avail. from UMI) **Indexed:** A.B.C.Pol.Sci., A.I.C.P., Adol.Ment.Hlth.Abstr., Amer.Hist.& Life, ASSIA, Biol.Abstr., Comput.Rev., Cont.Pg.Manage., Curr.Adv.Ecol.Sci., Curr.Cont., Educ.Admin.Abstr., Ergon.Abstr., Excerp.Med., Geo.Abstr., Hist.Abstr., Ind.Med., INIS Atomind., INSPEC (1972-), Int.Polit.Sci.Abstr., J.Cont.Quant.Meth., Lang.& Lang.Behav.Abstr., M.L.A., Mark.Res.Abstr. (1964-), Math.R., Mid.East Abstr.& Ind., Oper.Res.Manage.Sci., Pers.Lit., Psychol.Abstr. (1986-), Qual.Contr.Appl.Stat., Soc.Sci.Ind., Sociol.Abstr., SSCI. **Document type:** academic/scholarly publication.
—BLDSC (1877.850000); Faxon; Genuine Article; SWETS; UMI; UnCover. CCC.

001.6 539.7   SZ   ISSN 0304-2898
C E R N SCHOOL OF COMPUTING. PROCEEDINGS. (Former name of issuing body: Conseil Europeen pour la Recherche Nucleaire) 1970. a. C E R N - European Laboratory for Particle Physics, CH-1211 Geneva 23, Switzerland. **Indexed:** INIS Atomind. **Document type:** academic/scholarly publication.

500 600   CN
    CODEN: CSTNDF
C I S T I NEWS INTERNATIONAL. 4/yr. (Canadian Institute for Scientific and Technical Information - Institut Canadien de l'Information Scientifique et Technique) National Research Council Canada, Ottawa, ON K1A 0S2, Canada. TEL 613-993-3854. FAX 613-952-9112. Ed. Elizabeth Katz. **Document type:** newsletter.
—CASDDS.
    Former titles (until 1994): C I S T I News (ISSN 0715-8661); (until 1983): Infoscope (ISSN 0382-2400)
    Description: Information on developments and initiatives at CISTI and serves as a reminder of its products and services.

621.381 500   AT   ISSN 0816-6013
COMMONWEALTH SCIENTIFIC AND INDUSTRIAL RESEARCH ORGANIZATION. DIVISION OF GEOMECHANICS. GEOMECHANICS COMPUTER PROGRAMS. 1972. irreg. Aus.$10 per no. C.S.I.R.O. Division of Geomechanics, Box 54, Mount Waverley, Vic. 3149, Australia.
    Description: Documentation of computer programs for the solution of practical problems in geomechanics.

COMPUTERS IN EDUCATION: ENGINEERING, SCIENCE, AND MATHEMATICS. see *EDUCATION — Computer Applications*

DATA HANDLING IN SCIENCE AND TECHNOLOGY. see *COMPUTERS — Data Base Management*

HUANJING YAOGAN/REMOTE SENSING OF ENVIRONMENT. see *GEOGRAPHY*

621.3   UK   ISSN 0266-1616
    CODEN: IMTTAK
INSPEC MATTERS. 1974. q. free. INSPEC, I.E.E., Michael Faraday House, Six Hills Way, Stevenage, Herts. SG1 2AY, England. TEL 01438-313311. FAX 01438-742840. TELEX 825578 IEESTV G. E-mail: inspec@iee.org.uk. (Avail. from: Publication Sales Dept., P.O. Box 96, Stevenage, Herts SG1 2SD, England; U.S. addr.: INSPEC/IEEE, P.O. Box 1331, 445 Hoes Ln., Piscataway, NJ 08855-1331. TEL 908-562-5549. FAX 908-562-8737) Ed. Geoff Jones. (tabloid format; back issues avail.) **Indexed:** Br.Ceram.Abstr., Graph.Arts Lit.Abstr. **Document type:** trade publication.
—BLDSC (4518.380000); CASDDS.
    Description: Keeps researchers up to date with changes, improvements, and events of interest.

SECURITY

621.3   UK
INSPEC THESAURUS. biennial. £50($95) INSPEC, I.E.E., Michael Faraday House, Six Hills Way, Stevenage, Herts. SG1 2AY, England. TEL 01438-313311. FAX 01438-742840. TELEX 825578 IEESTV G. E-mail: inspec@iee.org.uk. (Subscr. to: Publication Sales Dept., P.O. Box 96, Stevenage, Herts. SG1 2SD, England; U.S. addr.: INSPEC/IEEE, Box 1331, 445 Hoes Ln., Piscataway, NJ 08855-1331. TEL 908-562-5549. FAX 908-562-8737) **Document type:** trade publication.

INTERNATIONAL JOURNAL OF MODERN PHYSICS C: PHYSICS AND COMPUTERS. see *PHYSICS*

500 350   US
J I C S T ONLINE INFORMATION SYSTEM. Short title: J O I S. (Text in English, Japanese) s-m. (Japanese Information Center of Science and Technology) U.S. National Technical Information Service, 5285 Port Royal Rd., Springfield, VA 22161. TEL 703-487-4630. (avail. in US only) ●Available only online. Vendor(s): JICST. **Description:** Provides access to many monographs, journal articles and technical reports from Japan.

JAPAN SOCIETY FOR SIMULATION TECHNOLOGY. JOURNAL. see *COMPUTERS — Computer Simulation*

543 001.6   UK   ISSN 0142-0453
QD75.4.A8   CODEN: JAUCD6
JOURNAL OF AUTOMATIC CHEMISTRY. (Text in English; summaries in French and German) 1978. bi-m. £155($255) (effective 1996). Taylor & Francis Ltd., Rankine Rd., Basingstoke, Hants. RG24 8PR, England. TEL 44-1256-840366. FAX 44-1256-479438. TELEX 858540. E-mail: info@tandf.co.uk. (Subscr. in N. America to: Taylor & Francis Inc., 1900 Frost Rd., Bristol, PA 19007-1598. TEL 800-821-8312. FAX 215-7855-5515) Ed. P.B. Stockwell. **Indexed:** AESIS, Anal.Abstr.; Br.Rail.Bd., Chem.Abstr., Dairy Sci.Abstr., Excerp.Med., Food Sci.& Tech.Abstr., Ind.Sci.Rev., INSPEC, Sci.Cit.Ind., W.R.C.Inf. **Document type:** academic/scholarly publication.
—BLDSC (4949.560000); ADONIS; CASDDS; Ei; Faxon; Genuine Article; SWETS; UnCover. **CCC.**
Description: Covers all aspects of automation and mechanization in analytical, clinical and industrial environments. Contains articles on instrumentation, management economics and the philosophy of automation.
Refereed Serial

JOURNAL OF COMPUTERS IN MATHEMATICS AND SCIENCE TEACHING. see *MATHEMATICS — Computer Applications*

500 620   NE   ISSN 0925-5001
QA402.5   CODEN: JGOPEO
JOURNAL OF GLOBAL OPTIMIZATION. 1991. 8/yr. fl.862 to institutions; $553 to institutions in U.S. (effective 1996). Kluwer Academic Publishers, Postbus 17, 3300 AA Dordrecht, Netherlands. TEL 31-78-392392. FAX 31-78-392254. TELEX 29245 KAPG NL. E-mail: SERVICES@WKAP.NL. (Dist. by: Kluwer Academic Publishers, P.O. Box 322, 3300 AH Dordrecht, Netherlands. TEL 31-78-392392. FAX 31-78-546474; N. America dist. addr.: Box 358, Accord Sta., Hingham, MA 02018-0358. TEL 617-871-6600. FAX 617-871-6528) Ed. R. Horst. (also avail. in microform from UMI; back issues avail.; reprint service avail. from SWZ) **Indexed:** ASCA, Compumath, Eng.Ind., Math.R., Stat.Theor.Meth.Abstr., Zent.Math. **Document type:** academic/scholarly publication.
—BLDSC (4996.302000); Ei; Genuine Article; SWETS; UMI. **CCC.**
Description: International journal dealing with theoretical and computational aspects of seeking global optima and their applications in science, management, and engineering.
Refereed Serial

500   US   ISSN 0885-7474
Q183.9   CODEN: JSCOEB
JOURNAL OF SCIENTIFIC COMPUTING. 1986. q. $265 (foreign $310) (effective 1996). Plenum Publishing Corp., 233 Spring St., New York, NY 10013-1578. TEL 212-620-8000. FAX 212-463-0742. TELEX 23-421139. Ed. Steven A. Orzag. adv. (also avail. in microfilm from JSC; back issues avail.) **Indexed:** Comput.Abstr., Curr.Cont., INIS Atomind. **Document type:** academic/scholarly publication.
—BLDSC (5057.250000); Ei; Faxon; SWETS; UMI; UnCover. **CCC.**
Refereed Serial

003   NE   ISSN 1381-141X
QC53   CODEN: CALAEF
LABORATORY AUTOMATION AND INFORMATION MANAGEMENT. 1991. 3/yr. fl.556($339) (effective 1996). Elsevier Science B.V., P.O. Box 211, 1000 AE Amsterdam. TEL 31-20-4853911. FAX 31-20-4853598. TELEX 18582 ESPA NL. E-mail: nlinfo-f@elsevier.nl; usinfo-f@elsevier.com; forinfo-kyf04035@niftyserve.or.jp; Site addr.: http://www.elsevier.nl/. (Subscr. in U.S. and Canada to: Elsevier Science Inc., Box 882, Madison Sq. Sta., New York, NY 10159-0882. TEL 212-989-5800. FAX 212-633-3990) Ed. R.D. McDowell. adv.; bk.rev.; charts; illus.; stat.; index. circ. 2,500. (also avail. in microform from UMI; back issues avail.) **Indexed:** INSPEC (1991-). **Document type:** academic/scholarly publication.
—CASDDS; Faxon; SWETS. **CCC.**
Formerly (until 1995): Chemometrics and Intelligent Laboratory Systems: Laboratory Information Management (ISSN 0925-5281); Incorporates (in 1994): Intelligent Instruments and Computers (ISSN 0889-8308); Which was formerly: C A L: Computer Applications in the Laboratory (ISSN 0724-0031)
Description: Covers all aspects of information management in a laboratory environment, such as information technology, storage, processing and flow of data.
Refereed Serial

500   UK   ISSN 0954-898X
QA76.87   CODEN: NEWKEB
NETWORK - COMPUTATION IN NEURAL SYSTEMS. 1990. q. £225($420) (effective 1996). (Institute of Physics) I O P Publishing Ltd., Techno House, Redcliffe Way, Bristol BS1 6NX, England. TEL 0117-929-7481. FAX 0117-929-4318. TELEX 449149 INSTP G. (U.S. subsr. to: American Institute of Physics, Member and Subscription Services, 500 Sunnyside Blvd., Woodbury, NY 11797-2900. TEL 516-349-7800) Ed. D.J. Amit. index. circ. 247. (also avail. in microfiche; microform; back issues avail.) **Indexed:** INSPEC (1990-). **Document type:** academic/scholarly publication.
—BLDSC (6077.203020); Faxon; Genuine Article; SWETS; UnCover. **CCC.**
Description: Subject coverage includes experimental neuroscience; physics; computer science; applied mathematics and engineering proposing, analyzing, simulating and designing models with the aim of synthesizing the biological results.

913   UK   ISSN 0586-9668
CC1
SCIENCE AND ARCHAEOLOGY. 1970. a. £6. Research Centre for Computer Archaeology, Computer Centre, Blackheath Lane, Stafford ST18 0AD, England. TEL 0785-53511. FAX 0785-51058. (Subscr. to: 88 Caverswall Rd., Weston Coyney, Stoke-on-Trent, Staffordshire ST3 6PL, England) (Co-sponsor: Staffordshire Polytechnic) Ed. J.D. Wilcock. adv.; bk.rev.; bibl.; charts; illus. circ. 250. (also avail. in microfiche) **Indexed:** Anthropol.Lit., Art & Archaeol.Tech.Abstr., Br.Archaeol.Abstr.

500   US   ISSN 0891-9003
Q180.55.E4   CODEN: SCOAEG
SCIENTIFIC COMPUTING & AUTOMATION. 1984. 12/yr. $60 (Canada $64.20; Mexico $60; elsewhere $90) (effective 1996). Gordon Publications, Inc., Part of Cahners Publishing Company, Division of Reed Elsevier Inc., Box 650, Morris Plains, NJ 07950-0650. TEL 201-292-5100. FAX 201-898-9281. Ed. Dan Breeman. adv.; tr.lit. circ. 70,000. (tabloid format; reprint service avail.) **Indexed:** Comput.Lit.Ind., INSPEC (1991-).
—BLDSC (8177.902300); CASDDS. **CCC.**
Description: For scientists who work in industrial and analytical, clinical, life science research and electronics laboratories. Provides information on the latest technology available.

500 510   CC   ISSN 1000-3266
SHUZHI JISUAN YU JISUANJI YINGYONG/JOURNAL ON NUMERICAL METHODS AND COMPUTER APPLICATIONS. (Text in Chinese) 1979. q. $60.80. (Chinese Academy of Sciences, Computer Centre) Science Press, Marketing and Sales Department, 16 Donghuangchenggen North St., Beijing 100717, People's Republic of China. TEL 4010642. FAX 4019810. adv. circ. 12,000. **Document type:** academic/scholarly publication.
Description: Contains articles on mathematic modules and calculation methods in the solution of problems through the use of the computer in various scientific and technical spheres.
Refereed Serial

SECURITY

see *Criminology and Law Enforcement–Security*

SHIPS AND SHIPPING

see *Transportation–Ships and Shipping*

SHOES AND BOOTS

see also *Leather and Fur Industries*

685.3   US   ISSN 0003-1038
AMERICAN SHOEMAKING. 1896. m. $49. Shoe Trades Publishing Co., Box 198, Cambridge, MA 02140. TEL 617-648-8160. Ed. James D. Sutton; Pub. John Moynihan. adv. contact: Nancy Robinson. charts; illus.; mkt.; stat. circ. 3,500. **Document type:** trade publication.

338.4 685.31   US   ISSN 0146-6437
TS945
AMERICAN SHOEMAKING DIRECTORY OF SHOE MANUFACTURERS. 1901. a. $49. Shoe Trades Publishing Co., Box 198, Cambridge, MA 02140. TEL 617-648-8160. James Sutton; John Moynihan. circ. 2,000. (back issues avail.) **Document type:** directory.

APPAREL INTERNATIONAL. see *CLOTHING TRADE*

685.5   IT   ISSN 0004-265X
ARS SUTORIA; cultural fashion review on Italian and international footwear. (Text in English, French, German, Italian, Spanish) 1947. 8/yr. $474. Editrice Ars s.r.l., Via Ippolito Nievo 33, 20145 Milan, Italy. TEL 39-2-315951. FAX 39-2-3491097. TELEX 330555 ARSMIL I. Ed. Laura Muggiani. adv.: B&W page L.3200000, color page L.3800000. circ. 50,000.

ARS WEEK; fashion and economy news on footwear and leather field. see *LEATHER AND FUR INDUSTRIES*

685.31   IT
AZETA CALZATURE. 1980. bi-m. L.10000. C.E.G., Via del Bosco 125, 56029 S. Croce s-Arno, Italy. Ed. Luca Tafi. adv. circ. 25,000.

BOR- ES CIPOTECHNIKA. see *LEATHER AND FUR INDUSTRIES*

685.31 658.8   UK   ISSN 0261-8133
BUSINESS RATIO REPORT: FOOTWEAR DISTRIBUTORS; an industry sector analysis. 1979. a. I C C Business Ratios Ltd., Freepost, Field House, Hampton, Mddx. TW12 1BR, England. TEL 081-783-0977. FAX 081-783-1940. charts; stat. **Document type:** trade publication.

685.31 658.8   UK   ISSN 0261-8141
BUSINESS RATIO REPORT: FOOTWEAR MANUFACTURERS; an industry sector analysis. 1974. a. I C C Business Ratios Ltd., Freepost, Field House, Hampton, Middx. TW12 1BR, England. TEL 081-783-0977. FAX 081-783-1940. charts; stat. **Document type:** trade publication.
—BLDSC (3985.128500).

C F I INTERNATIONAL DIRECTORY. see *CLOTHING TRADE*

SHOES AND BOOTS

CANADIAN FOOTWEAR & LEATHER DIRECTORY. see BUSINESS AND ECONOMICS — Trade And Industrial Directories

685.31 675   CN   ISSN 0705-1433
CANADIAN FOOTWEAR JOURNAL. (Annual Directory Number) 1888. 8/yr. $50 (foreign $70). McLeish Communications, Inc., 1 rue Pacifique, Ste. Anne de Bellevue, PQ H9X 1C5, Canada. TEL 514-457-2423. FAX 514-457-2577. Ed. Barbara McLeish; Pub. Brian Murphy. adv. contact: Brian Murphy. illus.; stat.; index. circ. 9,000. (also avail. in microfiche from MML; reprint service avail. from MML) Indexed: Can.B.P.I.
  Formerly: Shoe and Leather Journal (ISSN 0037-4032)
  Description: Edited to meet the specialized needs of those engaged in all aspects of the footwear business and its allied trades. Features on fashion, business management, efficient buying and stock control, store design and new developments in technology, materials and manufacturing processes.

685.31   FR   ISSN 0151-4040
CHAUSSER MAGAZINE. 1946. m. (10/yr.). 460 F. (foreign 665 F.). Societe des Publications le Cuir, 1 rue Garnier, 92200 Neuilly Seine, France. TEL 47-38-11-07. FAX 46-24-99-24. Ed. Stephanie Moge. adv. contact: M. Chantelat. illus. **Document type:** trade publication.
  Former titles (until 1968): Nouveau Chausser (ISSN 0151-4032); (until 1967): Chausser (ISSN 0151-4024)

685.31   UK
CLARKS COURIER. 10/yr. Clarks Ltd., P.O. Box 100, 40 High St., Somerset BA16 OYA, England. TEL 0458-43131. FAX 0458-47547. TELEX 44102-CLKS-G. Ed. M. Lazidou. circ. 7,500.

CLEO EN LA MODA. see LEATHER AND FUR INDUSTRIES

CLOTHING, TEXTILES, AND FOOTWEAR (YEAR). see CLOTHING TRADE

CUOIO PELLI MATERIE CONCIANTI. see LEATHER AND FUR INDUSTRIES

685.31   SP
FICE - PRESS. 12/yr. Pedeca Sociedad Cooperativa, Ltda., Maria Auxiliadora 5, Madrid, Spain. TEL 1-450-88-37. FAX 1-450-94-29. Ed. Carlos Miguel Sanz. circ. 7,500.

685.31   UK   ISSN 0966-7466
FOOTWEAR BUSINESS INTERNATIONAL. 1971. m. membership. S A T R A Footwear Technology Centre, SATRA House, Rockingham Rd., Kettering, Northants NN16 9JH, England. TEL 01536-410000. FAX 01536-410626. TELEX 34232. Ed. Mark Holmes. adv. contact: Kathleen Whittaker. bk.rev.; circ. 1,500 (controlled). **Document type:** trade publication.
  Former titles: Footwear Digest International; Footwear Digest; Shoemaking Progress.
  Description: Reviews world's footwear industries, materials, machines, technology and fashion.

685.31   CN   ISSN 0706-7534
FOOTWEAR FORUM. 1978. 7/yr. Can.$25 (foreign Can.$35). Style Communications Inc., 1448 Lawrence Ave. E., Ste. 302, Toronto, ON M4A 2V6, Canada. TEL 416-775-6191. FAX 416-955-9123. Ed. Victoria Curran. adv.: B&W page Can.$2868, color page Can.$3768; trim 10 7/8 x 14 5/8; adv. contact: John Peters. circ. 7,325. **Document type:** trade publication.

685.31 675   US
FOOTWEAR INDUSTRIES OF AMERICA. EXECUTIVE DIGEST. m. $60 to non-members. Footwear Industries of America, 1420 K St., N.W., Ste. 600, Washington, DC 20005. TEL 202-789-1420. FAX 202-789-4058. Ed. Barbara Singer. circ. 900. (back issues avail.) **Document type:** trade publication.
  Description: Covers the technology, marketing, statistics and legislation of the footwear industry.

685.31   US   ISSN 0742-2555
FOOTWEAR INDUSTRIES OF AMERICA. QUARTERLY REPORT. q. $100. Footwear Industries of America, 1420 K St., N.W., Ste. 600, Washington, DC 20005. TEL 202-789-1420. FAX 202-789-4058. (also avail. in microfiche from CIS) Indexed: SRI. **Document type:** trade publication, newsletter.
  Description: Provides data on production, foreign trade, marketing, labor, prices, consumer expenditures and quarterly trends in the footwear industry.

685.31   US   ISSN 0162-914X
FOOTWEAR NEWS. 1945. w. $51 to retailers; manufacturers and others $62 (effective 1992). Fairchild Fashion & Merchandising Group (Subsidiary of: Capital Cities - A B C, Inc.), 7 W. 34th St., New York, NY 10001. TEL 212-630-4199. FAX 212-630-4201. Ed. Dick Silverman. adv.; bk.rev.; illus.; mkt. circ. 23,000. (also avail. in microfilm from FCM) Indexed: Bus.Ind., Key to Econ.Sci., PROMT, Tr.& Indus.Ind. **Document type:** trade publication.
  ●Also available online. Vendor(s): Knight-Ridder, Inc., Lexis-Nexis.
  Description: Covers new developments, fashion trends, retailing, design and business news of the international footwear industry.

338.4   US   ISSN 0429-0208
HD9787.U4
FOOTWEAR NEWS FACT BOOK. 1954. a. $15. Fairchild Fashion & Merchandising Group, 7 W. 34th St., New York, NY 10001. TEL 212-630-4199. FAX 212-630-4201. illus.

685.31   US   ISSN 1054-898X
FOOTWEAR PLUS. 1990. s-a. Earnshaw Publications, Inc., 225 W. 34th St., Ste. 1212, New York, NY 10001. TEL 212-563-2742. Ed. Christina Gruber. circ. 18,000 (controlled).
  Description: For footwear retailers; covers the entire footwear market: dress, casual and athletic footwear, as well as hosiery and accessories.

685   IT
FOTO SHOE 15; il nuovo corriere della calzatura. 1963. m. $165 (effective 1992). Editoriale di Foto Shoe s.r.l., Via Leonardo Da Vinci, 43, 20090 Trezzano S-N (MI), Italy. TEL 4459091. FAX 48402959. TELEX 320606 FOSHOE I. adv.; charts; illus. circ. 14,000. (tabloid format)
  Former titles: Foto Shoe 15-3 Nuovo Corriere della Calzatura; Nuovo Corriere della Calzatura.
  Description: Covers technical information about footwear production: materials, technologies, accessories and component parts.

685   IT
FOTO SHOE 15 INTERNATIONAL. (Text in English) 1963. m. $165. Editoriale di Foto Shoe s.r.l., Via Leonardo da Vinci, 43, 20090 Trezzano S-N (MI), Italy. TEL 4459091. FAX 48402959. TELEX 320606 FOSHOE I. Ed. G. Fossati. adv.: B&W page L.3400000. illus. circ. 18,200.
  Supersedes in part: Foto Shoe.
  Description: Deals with the allied footwear industries, materials, machines, technology and components and accessories. Also covers previews on fashion trends and writes about leading shoe fairs in Italy and abroad.

685   IT
FOTO SHOE 30. (Text in English and Italian; occasionally in French, German, or Spanish) 1969. m. L.125000($165) Editoriale di Foto Shoe s.r.l., Via Leonardo da Vinci, 43, 20090 Trezzano S-N (MI), Italy. TEL 4459091. FAX 48402959. TELEX 320606 FOSHOE I. Ed. Adriano Pizzocaro. adv.; bk.rev.; illus. circ. 20,000.
  Supersedes in part: Foto Shoe.
  Description: Covers the shoe fashion industry, distribution and commercialization of footwear, and trade fairs held worldwide.

685.31   SZ
FUSS UND SCHUH. m. SSOMV Schweiz, Haenibuel 18, CH-6300 Zug, Switzerland. TEL 042-210521. Ed. Peter Wolf. circ. 1,460.

FUTURA. see LEATHER AND FUR INDUSTRIES

685.31   SP
GUIA DE LA MODA DEL CALZADO. s-a. 2800 ptas. Prensa Tecnica, S.A., Caspe, 118-20, Barcelona 13, Spain.

HIDE AND LEATHER BULLETIN; for the tanning and shoe manufacturing industry. see LEATHER AND FUR INDUSTRIES

688.76   IT
JOGGING; photographic collection on Italian and international leisure shoes. 2/yr. $191. Editrice Ars s.r.l., Via Ippolito Nievo 33, 20145 Milan, Italy. TEL 2-315-951. FAX 2-349-10-97. TELEX 330555 ARSMIL I.

685.31   IT
JOLLY; photographic collection on Italian and international man footwear models. 2/yr. $191. Editrice Ars s.r.l., Via Ippolito Nievo 33, 20145 Milan, Italy. TEL 2-315-951. FAX 2-349-10-97.
  Formerly: Professional.

685.31   IT
JULIA; photographic collection on Italian and international woman footwear models. 4/yr. $342. Editrice Ars s.r.l., Via Ippolito Nievo 33, 20145 Milan, Italy. TEL 2-315-951. FAX 2-349-10-97.

685.31   IT
JUNIOR; photographic collection on Italian and international children footwear models. 2/yr. $191. Editrice Ars s.r.l., Via Ippolito Nievo 33, 20145 Milan, Italy. TEL 2-315-951. FAX 2-349-10-97.

KAWA TO HAKIMONO/LEATHER & FOOTWEARS. see LEATHER AND FUR INDUSTRIES

685.31   FI   ISSN 0355-6999
KENKALUSIKKA. 1962. 6/yr. FIM 400. Suomen Kenkakauppiaiden Liitto r.y. - Finnish Shoe Retailers' Association, Fredrikinkatu 67 E 42, FIN-00100 Helsinki 10, Finland. TEL 358-0-409-932. FAX 358-0-409-563. Ed. Sinikka Nieminen. adv.: B&W page FIM 5700, color page FIM 8300; trim 210 x 297; adv. contact: Aija Lindfors. circ. 1,427 (controlled). **Document type:** trade publication.
  Description: Aimed at shoe manufacturers, importers, exporters, wholesalers and retailers.

685.31   UK   ISSN 0954-5190
KEY NOTE REPORT: FOOTWEAR. Variant title: Footwear. irreg. £185. Key Note Publications Ltd., Field House, 72 Oldfield Rd., Hampton, Middlesex TW12 2HQ, England. TEL 0181-783-0755. FAX 0181-783-1720. **Document type:** trade publication.
  ●Also available online.
  Also available on CD-ROM.
  —BLDSC (3985.138000).

KOZARSTVI/LEATHER INDUSTRY; odborny casopis pro prumysl kozedelny, obuvnicky a gumove obuvi. see LEATHER AND FUR INDUSTRIES

KOZHARSKA I OBUVNA PROMISHLENOST. see LEATHER AND FUR INDUSTRIES

685.31   RU   ISSN 0023-4354
                              CODEN: KOOPAJ
KOZHEVENNO-OBUVNAYA PROMYSHLENNOST. 1959. m. $118 (effective 1996). Izdatel'stvo Kniga, 50, Gorky St., 125047 Moscow, Russia. adv.; bibl.; illus. Indexed: C.I.S. Abstr., Chem.Abstr.
  —BLDSC (0089.500000); CASDDS.

685.31   IT
MICRONOTIZIA. 2/yr. Via Modigliani 25, 20090 Segrate (MI), Italy. TEL 2-21-30-381. FAX 2-213-79-57. Ed. Vittorio Valente. circ. 12,000.

685.31   SP   ISSN 0211-7827
MODAPIEL. (Text in English and Spanish) 1969. s-a. 3400 ptas. Prensa Tecnica, S.A., Caspe 118-120, 6o, 08013 Barcelona, Spain. TEL 3-245-51-90. FAX 3-232-27-73. TELEX 93457 PRTC E. Ed. F. Canet Tomas. adv.; illus. circ. 5,000.

685.31   IT
MONDO DELLA CALZATURA: DESIGN E PRODUZIONE/SHOE WORLD: DESIGN AND PRODUCTION. m. L.100000 (foreign L.130000) (effective 1995). Servizi Editoriali Riuniti S.p.A., Via M.M. Taddei 3, 20146 Milan, Italy. TEL 39-2-4815566. FAX 39-2-4816148. TELEX 318517 MONSER I. Ed. Nella Zanotti; Pub. Odoacre Mercatanti. adv.: B&W page L.3100000, color page L.3900000; trim 220 x 304. circ. 14,715. **Document type:** trade publication.

5919

S

SHOES AND BOOTS

685.31   IT
MONDO DELLA CALZATURA: TECNOLOGIE E MATERIE. 1983. m. Servizi Editoriali Riuniti S.p.A., Via M.M. Taddei 3, 20146 Milan, Italy. TEL 39-2-4815566. FAX 39-2-4816148. TELEX 318517 MONSER I. Pub. Odoacre Mercatanti. adv.: B&W page L.2700000, color page L.3550000; trim 220 x 304. circ. 8,370. **Document type:** trade publication.

685.31   UK
NATIONAL UNION OF THE FOOTWEAR, LEATHER AND ALLIED TRADES JOURNAL AND REPORT. vol.9, 1970. bi-m. £3 (foreign £4). National Union of the Footwear Leather and Allied Trades, The Grange, Earls Barton, Northampton NN6 OJH, England. FAX 0604-812496. adv.; bk.rev.; charts; illus.; stat. circ. 5,000.
   Former titles: National Union of the Footwear, Leather and Allied Trades Monthly Journal and Report (ISSN 0028-0356); National Union of Boot and Shoe Operatives Monthly Report.

685.31   IT
NEW SKIN ITALIA. 2/yr. Compagnia Italiana Editoriale, Via Donizetti 16 E, 51016 Montecatini Terme, Italy. TEL 572-766-385. FAX 572-76-63-85. TELEX 573612 MARIEL I. Ed. Sergio Garzotto. circ. 20,000.

685.31   IT
NOTIZIA DELLA CALZATURA. 1979. m. Vallardi & C. s.a.s., Piazza Repubblica 9, 20121 Milan, Italy. Ed. Roberto Vallardi. adv. circ. 15,000.

685.31   GW   ISSN 0344-6026
ORTHOPAEDIE-SCHUHTECHNIK. 1949. 11/yr. DM.179.50 (foreign DM.196.50). (Bundesinnungsverband fuer Orthopaedieschuhtechnik) C. Maurer Druck und Verlag, Schubartstr. 21, 73312 Geislingen, Germany. TEL 07331-930156. FAX 07331-930191. Ed. Wilfried Menzel. adv. contact: Sybille Lutz. bk.rev.; illus.; index. **Document type:** trade publication.
   Formerly: Orthopaedieschuhmachermeister (ISSN 0030-5871)

ORTHOPEDISCHE SCHOENTECHNIEK. see *MEDICAL SCIENCES — Orthopedics And Traumatology*

685.31   US
ROUNDUP (CLARKSVILLE). 1967. bi-m. Acme Boot Co., Inc., 1002 Stafford St., Box 749, Clarksville, TN 37040. TEL 615-552-2000. Ed. Pam McCaslin. illus.; circ. 2,500 (controlled).

685.31   NE   ISSN 0036-6269
SCHOEN - VISIE; vakblad voor schoenhandel en schoenindustrie. Short title: S V. 1959. 11/yr. fl.121.50. Misset (Subsidiary of: Reed Elsevier plc), Postbus 4, 7000 BA Doetinchem, Netherlands. TEL 31-8340-49911. FAX 31-8340-63638. Ed. Ellis Faber, Alida Dijk. adv.: B&W page fl.2377, color page fl.4772; trim 210 x 297; adv. contact: Cor van Nek. charts; illus.; stat.; tr.lit circ. 2,530. **Indexed:** Key to Econ.Sci. **Document type:** trade publication.
   Description: Covers all aspects of shoes: manufacture, import, sales and repair.

685.31   NE   ISSN 0036-6307
SCHOENWERELD. 1922. 4/yr. fl.60 to non-members. Verenigde Organisatie van Schoenmakers, Havenstraat 41A, 1736 KD Zijdewind, Netherlands. TEL 31-2262-3149. FAX 31-2262-1637. Ed. P.A. Idema. adv.: B&W page fl.605, color page fl.2000; trim 195 x 270; adv. contact: M.G. Hoehenga-Idema. illus. circ. 2,600. (reprint service avail.) **Document type:** trade publication.
   Description: Covers national and international news of interest to members of the shoe manufacturing, sales and repair industries.

685.31   SZ
SCHUH-GAZETTE.* 1919. m. Schweizerisches Schuhhaendlerverband, Altmarktstr. 96, CH-4410 Liestal, Switzerland. **Document type:** trade publication.
   Formerly (until 1994): Schuhhandel.

685.31   GW   ISSN 0036-7044
HD9787.G3
SCHUH-KURIER. 1946. w. DM.401. Verlag Otto Sternefeld GmbH, Postfach 111249, 40512 Duesseldorf, Germany. TEL 0211-577080. FAX 0211-5770890. Ed. F.G. Heide. adv.; bibl.; mkt.; pat.; tr.mk.; index. circ. 9,300. **Indexed:** Key to Econ.Sci. **Document type:** trade publication.

685.31   AU
SCHUH-REVUE UND LEDERWAREN. 1946. s-m. S.520. Johann L. Bondi und Sohn, Industriestr. 2, A-2380 Perchtoldsdorf, Austria. TEL 01-864921. FAX 01-86492144. Ed. Franz Bondi. circ. 4,000. **Document type:** trade publication.
   Former titles: Schuh-Revue; Oesterreichische Schuhhaendler (ISSN 0029-9456)

685.31   GW
SCHUH - SERVICE - POST. 1972. 3/yr. free. C. Maurer Druck und Verlag, Schubartstr. 21, 73312 Geislingen, Germany. TEL 07331-930-0. FAX 07331-930191. Ed. Wolfgang Best. adv. contact: Sybille Lutz. bk.rev.; illus. circ. 20,000. **Document type:** bulletin.

685.31   AU   ISSN 0036-7060
SCHUH-ZEITUNG. 1903. 24/yr. S.300. (Verband der Schuhindustrie und dem Schuhhandel) Verlag Michael Fischer, Neulerchenfelderstr. 8, 1160 Vienna, Austria. Ed. Michael Fischer. adv.; bk.rev.; abstr.; illus.; stat.; tr.lit. circ. 4,500.

685.31   GW   ISSN 0936-6121
DER SCHUHMACHER. 1947. 6/yr. DM.59. Ingo Geisler Verlag, Am Brueckfeld 10, 93497 Willmering, Germany. TEL 09971-40506. FAX 09971-40504. Ed. Ingo Geisler. adv.; bk.rev.; illus.; mkt.; pat.; tr.mk.; tr.lit.; index. circ. 5,900. **Document type:** trade publication.
   Formerly: Deutsche Schuhmacherhandwerk (ISSN 0012-0723)

685.31   GW
SCHUHMACHER FACHREPORT. 4/yr. free. Ingo Geisler Verlag, Am Brueckfeld 10, 93497 Willmering, Germany. TEL 09971-40506. FAX 09971-40504. circ. 21,400. **Document type:** trade publication.

685.31   GW   ISSN 0036-7079
DER SCHUHMARKT. 1857. w. DM.209.50. (Bundesverband des Deutschen Schuheinzelhandels) Umschau Zeitschriftenverlag Breidenstein GmbH, Stuttgarter Str. 18-24, 60329 Frankfurt a.M., Germany. TEL 069-2600-0. FAX 069-2600-666. Ed. Manfred Willsch. adv.: B&W page DM.3789, color page DM.7089; trim 270 x 190; adv. contact: Thomas Mueller-Eggersgluess. bk.rev.; charts; illus.; stat.; tr.lit.; tr.mk.; index. circ. 11,000. **Document type:** trade publication.
   —CCC.

685.31   GW   ISSN 0933-808X
SCHUHTECHNIK INTERNATIONAL; Fachzeitschrift fuer die Schuhindustrie. 1906. 8/yr. DM.174 (foreign DM.198). (Deutsche Schuhfachschule Pirmasens) Huethig GmbH, Postfach 102869, 69018 Heidelberg, Germany. TEL 06221-489281. FAX 06221-489481. TELEX 461727-HUEHDD. Ed. Albert Wilhelm. adv.: B&W page DM.3260; trim 210 x 297; adv. contact: G. Merkel. bk.rev.; abstr.; charts; illus.; tr.lit.; index. circ. 4,000. **Document type:** trade publication.
   —SWETS.
   Formerly: Schuhtechnik A B C (ISSN 0001-0405)

685.31 675   UK   ISSN 0037-4040
SHOE AND LEATHER NEWS. 1916. w. £30. E M A P Maclaren Ltd., Maclaren House, 19 Scarbrook Rd., Croydon, Surrey CR9 1QH, England. TEL 0181-688-7788. FAX 0181-688-9300. Ed. Alan Cork; Pub. Paul Keenan. adv.: B&W page £700, color page £1300; trim 297 x 230; adv. contact: Tim Whitehouse. bk.rev.; charts; illus.; mkt.; pat.; stat. circ. 5,000. **Indexed:** PROMT. **Document type:** trade publication.
   —BLDSC (8267.521000).

SHOE FACTORY BUYER'S GUIDE; directory of suppliers to the shoe manufacturing industry. a. $41. Shoe Trades Publishing Co., Box 198, Cambridge, MA 02140. TEL 617-648-8160. Ed. James Sutton; Pub. John Moynihan. adv. circ. 2,000. (back issues avail.) **Document type:** directory.

685.31   US   ISSN 0886-0963
SHOE RETAILING TODAY. m. $25 to non-members; members free. National Shoe Retailers Association, 9861 Broken Land Pkwy., Ste. 255, Columbia, MD 21046-1151. TEL 410-381-8282. FAX 410-381-1167. Ed. Cynthia Mullaly. **Document type:** trade publication.
   Formerly: N S R A News.
   Description: Covers trends in the shoe retailing industry.

685.31   US   ISSN 0193-256X
SHOE SERVICE. 1920. m. $18. Shoe Service Institute of America, 5024-R Campbell Blvd., Baltimore, MD 21236. TEL 410-931-8100. FAX 410-931-8111. Ed. Mitchell Lebovic. adv. circ. 17,500. **Document type:** trade publication.

685.31   UK
SHOE SERVICE JOURNAL. 1963. m. £15. 21 Station Rd., Desborough, Northants NN14 2SA, England. TEL 01536-760374. FAX 01536-762348. Ed. A. Turner. adv.: B&W page £82. circ. 800 (paid). **Document type:** trade publication.

338   US
HD9787.U4
SHOE STATS. 1975. a. (plus Quarterly Report). $295 to non-members; libraries $200; members $130. Footwear Industries of America, 1420 K St., N.W., Ste. 600, Washington, DC 20005. TEL 202-789-1420. FAX 202-789-4058. Ed. John Stebbins. stat. circ. 300. (also avail. in microfiche from CIS) **Indexed:** SRI. **Document type:** trade publication.
   Formerly: Footwear Manual (ISSN 0095-1048); **Supersedes:** Facts and Figures on Footwear (ISSN 0362-3890)
   Description: Analysis of today's industry including marketing, manufacturing, international trade, finance and raw materials.

684.3   UK   ISSN 0080-9349
SHOE TRADES DIRECTORY. 1948. a. £50. E M A P Maclaren Ltd., Maclaren House, 19 Scarbrook Rd., Croydon, Surrey CR9 1QH, England. TEL 0181-688-7788. FAX 0181-688-9300. Ed. Alan Cork; Pub. Paul Keenan. adv. contact: Tim Whitehouse. circ. 1,000. **Document type:** directory.
   Incorporates: Shoe Retailers Manual (ISSN 0140-5578)

685.31   SA
SHOES & VIEWS. 1935. 9/yr. R.165.98 includes Directory (foreign R.190.95). Shoes & Views, P.O. Box 47197, Greyville 4023, South Africa. Ed. Tony Dickson. adv. contact: Chantal Catlin. circ. 2,500. **Document type:** trade publication.

685.31   SA
SHOES & VIEWS TRADE DIRECTORY. 1977. a. Shoes & Views, P.O. Box 47197, Greyville 4023, South Africa. Ed. Tony Dickson. adv. **Document type:** trade publication, directory.
   Former titles: Shoes and Views Telephone and Telex Directory; (until 1983): Shoes and Leather Trades Directory of Southern Africa.
   Description: Lists manufacturers, wholesalers, suppliers, institutions, retailers, agents and brand names throughout southern Africa.

658.42   US
SHOW REPORTER. 1968. 6/yr. free. Show Reporter Publishing Co., Inc., 335 Boylston St., Newton Center, MA 02159. TEL 617-965-4577. Ed. Irving B. Roberts. adv.; bk.rev. circ. 10,000.

685.31 746.92   IT
SIMAC - PRESELEZIONE ITALIANA MODA.* s-a. Vallardi & C. s.a.s., Piazza Repubblica 9, 20121 Milan, Italy. Ed. Roberto Vallardi. adv. circ. 22,000.

685.31   SW   ISSN 0346-1300
SKOHANDLAREN. 1942. 12/yr. SEK 420. Skohandlarens Foerlags AB, Surbrunnsgatan 12, S-114 21 Stockholm, Sweden. TEL 46-8-791-53-00. FAX 46-8-213-690. Ed. Mariette Baecklund. adv.; bk.rev.; circ. 1,900 (controlled).

SOLE SOURCE; the footwear industry resource directory. see *BUSINESS AND ECONOMICS — Trade And Industrial Directories*

685 SA ISSN 0250-1333
SOUTH AFRICAN SHOEMAKER AND LEATHER REVIEW.
Variant title: S.A. Shoemaker and Leather Review. (Text in English) 1973. bi-m. R.92. George Warman Publications (Pty.) Ltd., P.O. Box 3847, Cape Town 8000, South Africa. TEL 27-21-245320. FAX 27-21-26-1332. Ed. Colleen Jacka. adv. circ. 1,650. **Document type:** trade publication.
Description: Covers shoe, leather, handbag, luggage and saddlery industries.

685.31 GW
SUEDWESTDEUTSCHER EINZELHANDEL (STUTTGART). m. Verband des Schuh-Einzelhandels Baden-Wuerttemberg e.V., Neue Weinsteige 44, 70180 Stuttgart, Germany. TEL 603025.

TANNER. see *LEATHER AND FUR INDUSTRIES*

685.31 FR ISSN 0040-1196
TECHNIQUE CHAUSSURE. 1955. m. 428 F. (foreign 535 F.). P P I Promotion Presse Internationale, 7 ter, Cour des Petites-Ecuries, 75010 Paris, France. Ed. H. Thiron. adv. circ. 3,000.
—CCC.

685.31 IT ISSN 0394-9796
TECNICA CALZATURIERA. (Text in English, Italian) 1964. m. L.110000 (foreign L.235000) (effective 1995). Tecniche Nuove s.p.a., Via C. Menotti, 14, 20129 Milan, Italy. TEL 02-75701. FAX 02-7610351. TELEX 334647 TECHS I. Ed. Giuseppe Nardella. adv. page L.1770000, color page L.2700000; trim 185 x 266. abstr.; illus.
Description: Features articles on manufacturing in the shoe industry. Covers machinery, fashion and materials.

685.31 SP
TECNICA DEL CALZADO. 1968. bi-m. 2000 ptas. Prensa Tecnica, S.A., Caspe, 118-120, 6o, 08013 Barcelona, Spain. TEL 3-245-51-90. FAX 3-232-27-73. TELEX 93457 PRTC E. Ed. F. Canet Tomas. adv.; abstr.; bibl.; charts; illus.; pat.; stat.; tr.lit. circ. 2,500.

685.31
TOP STYLE. 2/yr. Prensa Tecnica, S.A., Caspe 118, 120 6o, 08013 Barcelona, Spain. TEL 3-245-51-90. FAX 3-332-27-73. TELEX 93457 PRTC E.

685.37 US
TWO - TEN TODAY. q. 56 Main St., Waterdown, MA 02172. TEL 617-923-4500. FAX 617-926-6037. Ed. Carol Kennedy. circ. 12,000 (controlled).
Formerly: Two - Ten Foundation Update.
Description: Written for members of this charitable organization that provides human services to members of the footwear industry. Highlights programs and member news.

685.31 US ISSN 0894-3079
WORLD FOOTWEAR. 1987. bi-m. $60. Shoe Trades Publishing Co., Inc., Box 198, Cambridge, MA 02140. TEL 617-648-8160. FAX 617-492-0126. Iain Howie. adv.: B&W page $2,995; adv. contact: Nancy Robinson. circ. 15,000. **Document type:** trade publication.
—SWETS.
Description: Directed to shoe manufacturers worldwide.

SHOES AND BOOTS — Abstracting, Bibliographies, Statistics

685.31 310 UK
BRITISH FOOTWEAR MANUFACTURERS FEDERATION. STATISTICS. m. £110. British Footwear Manufacturers Federation, 5 Portland Pl., London W1N 3AA, England. TEL 0171-580-8687. FAX 0171-580-8696. **Document type:** trade publication.

310 685 UK ISSN 0308-9398
FOOTWEAR INDUSTRY STATISTICAL REVIEW. 1972. a. £55. British Footwear Manufacturers Federation, 5 Portland Pl., London W1N 3AA, England. TEL 0171-580-8687. FAX 0171-580-8696. circ. 400. **Document type:** trade publication.
—BLDSC (3985.130000).

SINGLES' INTERESTS AND LIFESTYLES

051 US
ACTIVE SINGLES LIFE. 1973. m. $15 (typically set in Jan.). Voice Publishing, 15830 Ambaum Blvd., S.W., Burien, WA 98166. TEL 206-243-8536. FAX 206-243-1956. Ed. Walt Briem. adv. contact: Bob Beasley. bk.rev.; film rev. circ. 10,000.
Document type: consumer publication, newspaper.
Description: Deals with the life-styles of single adults in the Northwest. Includes self-help articles, personal ads, and features on local well-known singles.

051 917.93 US ISSN 1041-4002
ALASKAMEN U S A. vol.3, no.2, 1990. q. $24.95 in US; Canada $34.95; elsewhere $37.95. Alaska Quest Publisher, 205 E. Dimond Blvd., No. 522, Anchorage, AK 99515-2099. TEL 907-522-1492. FAX 907-344-1493. Ed. Susie Carter. adv.; illus. **Document type:** consumer publication.
Formerly: AlaskaMen.
Description: Introduces single men in Alaska for interested single women.

051 US ISSN 0897-4608
ATLANTA SINGLES MAGAZINE.* 1977. bi-m. $19. Hudson Brooke Publishing, 180 Allen Rd., N.E., Ste. 304-N, Atlanta, GA 30328. TEL 404-636-2260. FAX 404-636-2366. Ed. Shannon V. McClintock; Pub. Graham Anthony. adv. contact: Judy Williams. **Document type:** newsletter.
Formerly (until 1988): Atlanta Singles Magazine and Date Book (ISSN 8750-8435)

051 US ISSN 0882-4460
B B W EXPRESS. (Big Beautiful Woman) m. $19.95 (foreign $29.95). Larry Flynt Publications, Inc., 9171 Wilshire Blvd., Ste. 300, Beverly Hills, CA 90210. TEL 310-858-7100. FAX 310-274-7985. adv. (back issues avail.) **Document type:** consumer publication.
Formerly: B B W Friendship Express.
Description: Provides current news and information.

051 US
BACHELOR BOOK MAGAZINE; magazine for today's woman. 1991. q. $31.25. Bachelor International Enterprises, Inc., 8222 Wiles Rd., Ste. 111, Coral Springs, FL 33067-1937. TEL 305-341-8801. FAX 305-341-8982. Ed. Lisa Hall. adv.: B&W page $2380, color page $3095; adv. contact: Hank Rudan. bk.rev.; circ. 90,000 (paid). **Document type:** consumer publication.
Description: Lifestyle magazine with travel, health and other information for single women. Features 75-100 single, eligible men seeking relationships via a 500 word profile, photograph, and contact information.

051 US
▼**BACHELORETTE BOOK MAGAZINE.** 1994. q. $31.25. Bachelor International Enterprises, Inc., 8222 Wiles Rd., Ste. 111, Coral Springs, FL 33067-1937. TEL 305-341-8801. FAX 305-341-8982. Ed. Paul Gallotta. circ. 32,000. **Document type:** consumer publication.
Description: Lifestyle magazine with travel, health and other features for single men. Profiles 75-100 single, eligible women seeking relationships via a 500 word profile, photograph and contact information.

051 910.03 US ISSN 0882-4460
CHOCOLATE SINGLES. m. $15. Priorities Publications Inc., Box 333, Jamaica, NY 11413. adv.

268 US ISSN 0191-4294
BV4596.S5
CHRISTIAN SINGLE. m. $19.95. Southern Baptist Convention, Sunday School Board, 127 Ninth Ave., N., Nashville, TN 37234. TEL 800-458-2772. **Document type:** consumer publication.
Description: Provides articles and features on life-style topics for Christian singles.

051 US
CHRISTIAN SINGLES NEWS. 1987. m. $29. Christian Singles International, Box 100, Harrison, OH 45030. TEL 513-598-8900. Ed. James Lloyd Sloan. adv. contact: Carol Neal. bk.rev. circ. 100,000. **Document type:** newspaper.
Formerly: U S A Singles News.
Description: For Christian singles and churches. Contains articles on establishing and cultivating relationships, plus 500-600 Christian personal ads per issue.

051 US
CONCERNED SINGLES NEWSLETTER.* 1984. m. membership. Concerned Singles, Box 555-1, Stockbridge, MA 01262. adv. **Document type:** newsletter.
Description: Covers political, social and civic interests of the liberal community.

051 US
CONTINENTAL SPECTATOR. q. $45. Continental Spectator, Box 278, Canal St. Sta., New York, NY 10013. TEL 800-325-4122. Ed. Linda Lee.
Description: Worldwide listings of personal contact ads with photos; includes stories, and articles of interest to swingers. Catering to all fetishes and sexual fantasies.

051 US
DATE BOOK; articles, personals, classified and daily listing of events for New Haven, Westchester, Fairfield counties and New York City singles. 1978. m. $21. Dateline Inc., 257 Ely Ave., Norwalk, CT 06854-4205. Ed. David Faulknor. adv. circ. 80,000. (back issues avail.) **Document type:** consumer publication.

052 UK
DATELINE MAGAZINE. 1977. 12/yr. £24. Singles Scene Ltd., c/o John Patterson, 23 Abingdon Rd., Kensington, London W8 6AH, England. TEL 071-938-1011. FAX 071-937-3146. **Document type:** consumer publication.
Former titles: Singles; (1982-1984): Select; Singles.
Description: Articles of interest to single people. Includes activities, meeting places, plus personal classified ads.

051 US
DOMINANTLY YOURS. a. $14. Continental Spectator, Box 278, Canal St. Sta., New York, NY 10013. TEL 800-325-4122. Ed. Linda Lee.
Description: Dedicated to interest of dominants and submissives. Includes personal ads with photos of advertisers.

052 SA
EXCLUSIVELY SINGLE. 1993. m. R.84; newsstand price: R.9.30. P.O. Box 59502, Kengray 2100, South Africa. Ed. Roderick C. Knight. adv. contact: Glenn Reinecke. illus. **Document type:** consumer publication.

051 600 US ISSN 1061-6977
FUTURE SEX.* 1992. q. $18 (effective Nov. 1992). Kundalini Publishing, Inc., P.O. Box 31129, San Francisco, CA 94131-0129. TEL 415-621-5496. FAX 415-621-4946. Ed. Lisa Palac. adv. contact: Brett Beutel. bk.rev.; illus. **Document type:** consumer publication.
Description: Covers the evolution of eroticism in the 90s, including cybersex and the impact of computer and information technology on sex.

GET KINKY. see *MEN'S INTERESTS*

051 US ISSN 0882-8598
GET - TWO - GETHER. 1981. m. $15. Get - Two - Gether Inc., Box 1413, Ft. Collins, CO 80522. TEL 303-221-4544. FAX 303-221-0234. Ed. Gary F. Hirt. adv. circ. 4,500.

051 US
HERE'S TO FRIENDS; articles, personals, classified and daily listing of events for central and eastern Connecticut and Rhode Island singles. 1987. m. $15. Dateline Inc., 257 Ely Ave., Norwalk, CT 06854-4205. TEL 203-866-6617. FAX 203-838-1313. Ed. David Faulknor. adv.; circ. 30,000 (paid). **Document type:** consumer publication.

SINGLES' INTERESTS AND LIFESTYLES

296 051 US
INTERNATIONAL CONNECTOR FOR JEWISH SINGLES.* 1986. 4/yr. $14. Midwest Jewish Singles Network, 9205 Western Ave., Ste. 316, Omaha, NE 68114-2295. Ed. Mary Fellman. adv.
Formerly: Connector.

296 051 US
JEWISH SINGLES MAGAZINE (BLOOMFIELD). irreg. Box 728, Bloomfield, CT 06002. TEL 203-243-1514. adv.

296 051 US
JEWISH SINGLES MAGAZINE (NEWTON). 1983. m. $20. Mark B. Golden, Ed. & Pub., Box 247, Newton, MA 02159-0002. TEL 617-278-4330. adv.; bk.rev. circ. 50,000.
Formerly: Jewish Singles.

LIFE AND WORK PURSUITS: BIBLE STUDIES FOR SINGLE ADULTS. see RELIGIONS AND THEOLOGY — Protestant

051 US
LIFESTYLE. NORTHERN CALIFORNIA. bi-m. $7. 419 W. MacArthur Blvd., Oakland, CA 94609. TEL 415-420-1381. adv.

051 US
LIFESTYLE SOUTHERN CALIFORNIA; single adults news & events. 1967. bi-m. $7. Gladys Smith & Associates, Box 5062, Sherman Oaks, CA 91413-5062. TEL 818-980-4786. Ed. R.H. Smith, Jr. adv.; bk.rev.; film rev.; play rev. circ. 40,000. (back issues avail.)
Formerly: Singles Critique.
Description: Discusses relationships, medical issues, theater, wine and travel. Includes calendar of events, astrological forecasts and personals.

051 US
LIFESTYLES MAGAZINE. Variant titles: Pittsburgh Singles Lifestyles. Quality Singles Lifestyles. 1981. m. $12.99. Su-Bre Enterprises, 300 Mt. Lebanon Blvd., 210-B, Pittsburgh, PA 15234. TEL 412-561-2277. FAX 412-561-3960. Ed. Sue Lauer. adv.; bk.rev. circ. 5,000. Document type: consumer publication.
Former titles (until 1993): Pittsburgh Singles Connections; (until 1992): Pittsburgh Singles' Lifestyles (ISSN 1048-5554); Lifestyles Pittsburgh.
Description: Publishes articles geared to single adults ages 30-50. Contains a guide to local singles' events and quality personal ads.

051 US
LONG ISLAND SWINGERS MAGAZINE. 1981. q. $12 per no. Bizzare Publishing Co., Box 25, Islip Terrace, NY 11752-0025. Ed. John Jay. adv.: B&W page $650. circ. 10,000.

051 US ISSN 1067-2079
LONG ISLAND UPDATE. 1991. m. $20. M M B Publishers, 990 Motor Pkwy., Central Islip, NY 11722-1001. TEL 516-435-8890. Ed. Cheryl Meglio. Document type: consumer publication.
Formerly: Long Island Nightlife.

051 US
M W PENPAL WORLD. 1990. q. $8 for 10 issues. Big Chief International, 15 N. Plum, Ste. B, Hutchinson, KS 67501. TEL 316-665-3614. Ed. M.L. Webben. circ. 5,000.

306.77 US
THE MASTER'S WAY. 1993. m. $40. Church of Epiphany, 4533 MacArthur Blvd., Ste. 339, Newport Beach, CA 92660. TEL 714-833-3979. Ed. Bruce Hoyt; Pub. Donna Wood. adv. contact: Bruce Hoyt. bk.rev.; film rev. Document type: newsletter.

051 US
MEET PEOPLE. 1986. m. $14.95. Box 247, Osseo, MN 55369. TEL 612-424-4266. FAX 612-425-6117. Ed. Ken Christianson. adv.: Gerry/Knodson. circ. 60,000. (tabloid format) Document type: newspaper.
Formerly: Di's Meet People.
Description: For singles who want to meet other singles. Carries personal ads, calendar of events and directories of clubs.

051 US
METRO SINGLES LIFESTYLES; an upbeat publication for single women & single men of all ages. 1984. q. $15 for 12 nos. Box 28203, Kansas City, MO 64118. TEL 816-436-8424. Ed. Robert Huffstutter. adv.; bk.rev.; illus. circ. 25,000. (tabloid format) Document type: newspaper.
Description: Includes 12 pages of personal ads in each issue, as well as interviews with singles, poetry and fiction.

051 US
METROLINA SINGLES MAGAZINE & DATEBOOK. 1982. m. $16. Creative Communications, Box 11627, Charlotte, NC 28220. TEL 704-542-4747. Ed. Thomas W. Nunnenkamp. adv. circ. 10,000. Document type: consumer publication.
Formerly: Metrolina Singles Datebook.
Description: Serves the unmarried adults of the Carolinas. Provides information on local singles group; articles on relationships and other topics of interest to the unmarried.

MINI EXAMINER. see ASTROLOGY

051 US
NATIONAL SINGLES REGISTER. bi-m. $11. Box 509, Norwalk, CA 90650. TEL 310-864-2741. adv.

051 US
OHIO'S FINEST SINGLES; news, views, personals, travel. 1982. m. $13. Box 770610, Cleveland, OH 44107-0030. TEL 216-521-1111. FAX 216-226-3283. Ed. Joyce N. Krost. adv. circ. 50,000. (tabloid format) Document type: consumer publication.
Formerly (until 1990): Cleveland's Finest Singles.

ON THE SCENE; Albuquerque's entertainment & lifestyles magazine. see LEISURE AND RECREATION

796 US
OUTDOOR SINGLES NETWORK. 1989. bi-m. $35. O S N - U, Box 2031, McCall, ID 83638. TEL 208-634-3909. Pub. Kathleen Menke. Document type: newsletter.
Description: Brings together outdoor-loving singles ages 19-90.

PARTNERS-IN-TRAVEL. see TRAVEL AND TOURISM

SCARLET LETTER. see WOMEN'S INTERESTS

051 US
SINCERE SINGLES. 1982. m. $15. Andy Schiff, Ed. & Pub., Box 1719, Ann Arbor, MI 48106-1719. TEL 810-476-6110. FAX 810-476-6110. adv. contact: Andy Schiff. circ. 15,000. Document type: consumer publication.
●Also available online.
Description: Provides personal ads for educated singles with 900 voice mail system.

051 202 US
SINGLE ADULT MINISTRIES JOURNAL; ideas, resources and guidance for ministry with single adults. 1982. 6/yr. $24. David C. Cook Publishing Co., 850 N. Grove Ave., Elgin, IL 60120-0430. TEL 312-741-2400. (Subscr. to: Box 62056, Colorado Springs, CO 80962-2056) Ed. Jerry D. Jones. adv.; bk.rev. circ. 5,000. Document type: trade publication.
Description: Provides ideas and encouragement for those involved in ministry with single adults from a transdenominational perspective.

301.412 305.3 US
SINGLE AGAIN. 1976. 6/yr. $15. Box 384, Union City, CA 94587. TEL 510-793-6315. Ed. Len Harris. adv.; illus. circ. 10,000. Document type: consumer publication.
Description: Directed to people who are divorced, separated, or widowed.

051 US
SINGLE CONNECTIONS (FULLERTON). m. $24. Box 2527, Fullerton, CA 92633. TEL 714-773-5405. adv.

051 US
SINGLE FILE MAGAZINE;* the lifestyle guide. 1982. 12/yr. $15. Single Association, Inc., 250 Pearl St., Grand Rapids, MI 49503-2624. TEL 616-774-8100. FAX 616-459-5943. Ed. Penelope J. Barrett. adv.; circ. 15,000 (controlled).
Description: Attempts to help singles of all ages meet through personalized ads. Includes an advice column, articles and a calendar of events.

051 US
SINGLE LIFE (LINCOLN). m. $12. Box 83289, Lincoln, NE 68501. TEL 402-466-8521. adv.

SINGLE MAGAZINE AND ENTERTAINMENT GUIDE. 1965. bi-m. $6. Box 420966, San Diego, CA 92142-0966. TEL 619-296-6948. adv. Document type: consumer publication.

SINGLE PARENT. see SOCIAL SERVICES AND WELFARE

051 US
SINGLE SCENE - ARIZONA. 1972. m. $9.50 (effective 1995). Box 10159, Scottsdale, AZ 85271. TEL 602-945-6746. FAX 602-945-3766. E-mail: singles@primenet.com. (Alt. addr.: 7432 E, Diamond, Scottsdale, AZ 85257) Ed. Janet L. Jacobsen; Pub. Harlan L. Jacobsen. adv. contact: Janet L. Jacobsen. bk.rev.; stat. circ. 10,000. (tabloid format; back issues avail.) Document type: newspaper.
●Also available online.
Formerly: Single Scene (ISSN 0747-4350)
Description: Presents a forum for single adults through news, self-help advice, and a calendar of events.

301.412 US ISSN 0738-8578
SINGLE SOURCE NEWSLETTER. 1987. a. $5. Bibliotheca Press, c/o Prosperity & Profits Unlimited, Distribution Services, Box 416, Denver, CO 80201-0416. TEL 303-575-5676. Ed. A. Doyle. circ. 1,500. (looseleaf format; back issues avail.) Document type: newsletter.

051 US ISSN 1050-2998
SINGLE TODAY. 1987. bi-m. $25. Septo Enterprises, Inc., 5830 Mt. Moriah Rd., Ste. 17, Memphis, TN 38115-1628. TEL 901-365-3988. FAX 901-365-0699. Ed. September Young; Pub. September Young. adv.; bk.rev. circ. 30,000. Document type: consumer publication.
Formerly (until 1989): Memphis Singles.
Description: Allows singles in the Memphis area to meet other singles through an introduction service.

051 US ISSN 8756-0380
SINGLELIFE MAGAZINE; the interactive magazine for Wisconsin and Illinois. 1982. bi-m. $12. SingleLife Enterprises, Inc., 606 W. Wisconsin Ave., Ste. 1800, Milwaukee, WI 53203. TEL 414-271-9700. Ed. Gail Levine. adv.; film rev.; illus. circ. 17,000. (back issues avail.) Document type: consumer publication.

052 AT
SINGLES. m. Aus.$18. Associated Communications, 272 Rosslyn St., W. Melbourne, Vic. 3001, Australia. TEL 03 329 0277. (Subscr. to: P.O. Box 4516, World Trade Centre, Vic. 3005, Australia) Ed. Geoff Hawthorne. circ. 30,000.
Description: Editorial stories on Australian singles, promoting being single.

051 US
SINGLES ALMANAC (JERSEY CITY); activities in NYC, the boros, NJ, Westchester & LI. 1968. w. $24. Almanac Publications, 38 Kellogg St., Jersey City, NJ 07355. TEL 201-433-8644. FAX 201-433-0847. Ed. Michael Brandon. adv.; bk.rev. circ. 28,500. (back issues avail.) Document type: consumer publication.
Former titles: Metropolitan Almanac (ISSN 1045-5108); Singles Almanac of New York; New York Almanac (ISSN 0745-8940); Metropolitan Almanac; Manhattan Almanac (ISSN 0025-2085)

051 US ISSN 1044-6184
SINGLES ALMANAC (MONROE);* New England's leading singles magazine. 1981. m. $12. Bailey Inc., 51 Shelton Rd., Monroe, CT 06478. TEL 203-261-2908. adv.; illus. circ. 100,000. (back issues avail.) Document type: consumer publication.
Description: Contains personal ads interspersed with editorial content relevant to singles. Includes a calendar of events.

SOCIAL SCIENCES: COMPREHENSIVE WORKS

051 US ISSN 1077-0887
SINGLES & LEADERS NEWSLETTER. 1973. m. $15. Singles Support Services, Box 842, Norman, OK 73070-0842. TEL 405-364-4733. FAX 405-321-2087. (Alt. addr.: 425 Castro, Norman, OK 73069) Ed. Hazel R. Bell. bk.rev.; circ. 700 (paid). pp./issue: 8. (tabloid format; back issues avail.) **Document type:** newsletter.
  Former titles (until 1993): Single Adult Ministry Information (ISSN 0887-1167); Single i.
  Description: Provides Christian, motivational and current information for singles and leaders.

051 US ISSN 1058-0638
SINGLES CHOICE. 1988. m. $14. Singles Choice, Inc., Box 454, Milwaukee, WI 53201-0454. TEL 414-272-8700. FAX 414-272-8711. Ed. Debra Schreibman; Pub. Bob Grossman. adv. contact: Bob Grossman. bk.rev.; circ. 45,000 (paid). (back issues avail.) **Document type:** consumer publication.
  Description: Provides forum for Milwaukee-area singles to meet other single adults. Contains articles on dating, relationships, money, sex, and single life.

051 US
SINGLES JOURNAL. bi-m. $10. 103 Cobblestone Ln., Cherry Hill, NJ 08003. TEL 609-424-3080. adv. (tabloid format)

301.435 US
SINGLE'S LIFE. 1967. m. $15. Voice Publishing, 15830 Ambaum Blvd., S.W., Burien, WA 98166. TEL 206-243-8536. FAX 206-243-1956. Ed. Walt Briem. adv. contact: Bob Beasley. illus. circ. 10,000. **Document type:** consumer publication.
  Description: Directed to singles of all ages looking for companionship.

051 US
SINGLES LIFELINE. 1983. bi-m. $7. Singles Lifeline Co., Box 639, Randolph, MA 02368. TEL 617-341-8332. FAX 617-344-7207. Ed. Mark Snyder. adv.; bk.rev.; film rev. circ. 60,000.

051 US
SINGLES NEWS MAGAZINE (SACRAMENTO). 1975. m. $10. Box 601061, Sacramento, CA 95860. TEL 916-486-1414. adv. circ. 22,000. **Document type:** newspaper.

051 US
SINGLES OUTREACH SERVICES NEWSLETTER. (Former name of issuing body: Singles Outreach Support) 1985. m. $15. Singles Outreach Services, Box 12511, Albany, NY 12212. TEL 518-785-9438. Ed. Gregg Millett. adv. circ. 5,500. **Document type:** newsletter.
  Formerly: S O S Newsletter.
  Description: Covers educational and social activities for adult singles.

051 202 US
SINGLES SCENE - SPIRIT & LIFE. 1981. m. $25. Sandra S. Turner, Ed. & Pub., Box 310, Allardt, TN 38504. TEL 615-879-4625. adv. contact: Sandra S. Turner. bk.rev. circ. 5,500. **Document type:** consumer publication.
  Formerly: Singles Scene (Allardt) (ISSN 0746-7982)
  Description: Geared to Christian singles or those with traditional Judeo-Christian values.

051 US
SINGLES' SERENDIPITY. 1985. bi-m. $11. Box 5794, Jacksonville, FL 32247. TEL 904-731-7111. Ed. Judy Lanier. adv. circ. 55,000. **Document type:** consumer publication.
  Description: Lists activities and other single organizations. Includes articles and personal ads.

051 US
SINGLES TIMES. m. $24. Box 1015, Valley Stream, NY 11582. TEL 516-565-9100. Pub. Greg Pelini. adv. **Document type:** newspaper.

051 US
SINGLES TRUMPET. s-m. $25. Box 460303, Aurora, CO 80015. TEL 303-745-0818. adv.

051 US
SINGLES VOICE. m. $20. 4818 Rosemar Rd., Parkersburg, WV 26101. TEL 304-428-3283. FAX 304-428-8090. Ed. Louise Chambers. adv. contact: Roger Stoll. **Document type:** directory.
  Former titles: National Singles Directory; S C A N (Singles Connection and Network).

051 US
SOUTH FLORIDA SINGLE LIVING. 1982. bi-w. $25. Single Living, Inc., Box 22421, Ft. Lauderdale, FL 33335-2421. TEL 305-845-9537. Ed. Harry Baun. adv.: page $960. circ. 48,000. (tabloid format) **Document type:** consumer publication.

070.48346 301.412 US
SOUTHEAST SINGLES ASSOCIATION MONTHLY PUBLICATION. 1987. $20 to non-members (membership including subscr. $49). Southeast Singles Association, Inc., Box 267, Biloxi, MS 39533. TEL 601-872-1717. Ed. Patricia A. Stephens; Pub. Hugh B. Jones. bk.rev. circ. 3,000. (tabloid format; back issues avail.) **Document type:** directory.
  Formerly (until 1991): Gulf Coast Singles Association Monthly Book.
  Description: Offers advice and guidance for single adults and serves as a forum for their communications worldwide.

155.642 US
SWEETHEART MAGAZINE. 1988. m. $23 (effective 1996). Sweetheart Magazine, 12944 Old Freight Rd., P.O. Box 514, St. Ignatius, MT 59865. TEL 406-745-4209. Ed. Katie James; Pub. Charlie James. adv. contact: Lise James. circ. 40,000. (back issues avail.) **Document type:** consumer publication.
  Formerly: Sweetheart Connection.
  Description: Promotes healthy singles life and singles activities.

SWINGER'S TODAY. see *MEN'S INTERESTS*

SWINGING TIMES. see *MEN'S INTERESTS*

051 US
T M'S SINGLES R S V P. (True Match); America's connection for the discriminating professional. m. $18. T M Publishing, Inc., 26009 S. Highland, Box 18000-5, Las Vegas, NV 89109. TEL 702-796-9966. FAX 702-796-5655. Ed. M.S. Bram.

051 US
TENNESSEE SINGLE LIFE.* 1987. 11/yr. $16. 3156 Lake Brook Blvd., Knoxville, TN 37909-1170. adv. circ. 15,000.

367 US ISSN 0748-7355
TODAY'S SINGLE; serving the singles of America. 1980. q. $10. National Association of Christian Singles, 1933 W. Wisconsin Ave., Milwaukee, WI 53233. TEL 414-344-7300. Ed. John M. Fisco, Jr. adv.; bk.rev. circ. 12,000. **Document type:** consumer publication.

306.8 US
TOUCHPOINT; network for the nonmonogamous. 1988. $14. Major Publications, Box 408-UD, Chloride, AZ 86431. Ed. Stanfield Major. circ. 350 (paid). **Document type:** newsletter.
  Description: Lists people, groups, organizations and publications exploring alternatives to monogamy. Seeks to create a network of these persons and entities.

TRAVEL COMPANIONS; North America's foremost newsletter for solo travelers. see *TRAVEL AND TOURISM*

051 US
TRELLIS SINGLES MAGAZINE. 1975. bi-m. $8. Paul S. Reese, Ed. & Pub., 4400 Horner St., Ste. 36, Union City, CA 94587-2552. TEL 510-489-8888. FAX 510-489-8877. adv. circ. 55,000. **Document type:** consumer publication.
  Description: Reviews singles clubs and activities, special events, and many other resources. Offers guidance and advice, along with many personal advertisements.

THE VEGAS CONNECTION. see *MEN'S INTERESTS*

296 US
WASHINGTON JEWISH SINGLES NEWSLETTER. 1988. m. $21. 444 N. Frederick Ave., Ste. L, Gaithersburg, MD 20877. TEL 301-990-0210. FAX 301-330-3671. Ed. Ben Levitan. adv.; bk.rev. circ. 1,000. **Document type:** newsletter.

051 US
YELLOW PAGE MODEL DIRECTORY. a. $12. Continental Spectator, Box 278, Canal St. Sta., New York, NY 10013. TEL 800-325-4122. Ed. Linda Lee. **Document type:** directory.
  Description: Photo lay-outs and personal ads of nude female models nationwide.

SMALL BUSINESS

see *Business and Economics–Small Business*

SOCIAL SCIENCES: COMPREHENSIVE WORKS

A C S BULLETIN. (Association for Canadian Studies) see *HUMANITIES: COMPREHENSIVE WORKS*

A F B INFO. (Arbeitsstelle Friedensforschung Bonn) see *POLITICAL SCIENCE*

300 GW ISSN 0934-8417
A F E T - MITGLIEDER - RUNDBRIEF. 1948. q. DM.32. Arbeitsgemeinschaft fuer Erziehungshilfe (AFET) e.V., Gandhistr. 2, 30559 Hannover, Germany. TEL 0511-511212. FAX 0511-5179007. Ed. Cornelie Bauer. bk.rev. circ. 1,200. (looseleaf format; also avail. in diskette format) **Document type:** newsletter.

305 US ISSN 1062-5968
E184.E2
A I M. 1987. q. Association of Indian Muslims of America, Box 10654, Silver Spring, MD 20914. TEL 410-730-5456. FAX 410-922-0665. Ed. Kaleem Kawaja. circ. 800. **Document type:** newsletter.

300 370 US ISSN 0044-9687
A T S S BULLETIN. vol.39, 1971. irreg. (5-6/yr.). membership. Association of Teachers of Social Studies in the City of New York, c/o Bell Sigelalis Pres., John Dewey High School, 50 Avenue X, Brooklyn, NY 11223. Ed. William McGinn. adv.; bk.rev.; bibl. circ. 1,200. **Document type:** bulletin.

300 US
A W A I R'S MIDDLE EAST RESOURCES; a quarterly newsletter for social studies educators. (Text in English and Spanish) q. $18. Arab World and Islamic Resources and School Services, 2095 Rose St., Ste. 4, Berkeley, CA 94709. TEL 510-704-0517. **Document type:** newsletter.

300 FI ISSN 0358-5654
AABO AKADEMI. EKONOMISK-STATSVETENSKAPLIGA FAKULTETEN. MEDDELANDEN. (Text in English, Finnish, Swedish) 1956. irreg. price varies. Aabo Akademi, Statsvetenskapliga Institutionen - Aabo Akademi, Department of Political Science, Biskopsgatan 15, FIN-20500 Aabo 50, Finland. TEL 921-2654-830. FAX 921-2654-585. Ed. Marina Hamberg. circ. 200.
  Formerly: Aabo Akademi. Statsvetenskapliga Fakulteten. Meddelanden; Which was formed by the Jan. 1979 merger of: Aabo Akademi. Statsvetenskapliga Fakulteten. Meddelanden. Serie A (ISSN 0355-4031); Aabo Akademi. Statsvetenskapliga Fakulteten. Meddelanden. Serie B (ISSN 0355-4465)

001.3 II ISSN 0970-2385
HD70.I4
ABHIGYAN; the journal of foundation for organization research and education. (Text in English) 1983. q. Rs.150($20) (effective Jan. 1993). Foundation for Organisational Research and Education, Adhitam Kendra, B-18, Qutab Institutional Area, New Delhi 110 016, India. TEL 6866305. FAX 6856294. TELEX 031-73215 FORE IN. Ed. N.K. Singh. adv.: B&W page Rs.7000; adv. contact: Mereeda Mathew. bk.rev. circ. 500. (back issues avail.) Indexed: Psychol.Abstr. (1983-). **Document type:** academic/scholarly publication.
  Description: Original work in organizational and social research and public systems.

ACADEMIA. JINBUN, SHAKAI KAGAKU HEN/ACADEMIA. HUMANITIES, SOCIAL SCIENCES. see *HUMANITIES: COMPREHENSIVE WORKS*

SOCIAL SCIENCES: COMPREHENSIVE WORKS

ACADEMIA DE CIENCIAS POLITICAS Y SOCIALES. BOLETIN. see *POLITICAL SCIENCE*

ACADEMIA NACIONAL DE DERECHO Y CIENCIAS SOCIALES DE CORDOBA. ANALES. see *LAW*

300   AT
ACADEMY OF THE SOCIAL SCIENCES IN AUSTRALIA. ANNUAL REPORT. 1971. a. membership. Academy of the Social Sciences in Australia, G.P.O. Box 1956, Canberra, A.C.T. 2601, Australia. TEL 062-491788. FAX 062-486287. circ. 600.

056.1   PY   ISSN 0001-4605
HC222
ACCION; revista Paraguaya de reflexion y dialogo. N.S. 1969. 10/yr. 40000 g.($35) Centro de Estudios Paraguayos "Antonio Guasch", Calle Guarani 2256, Casilla 1072, Asuncion, Paraguay. TEL 595-21-333962. FAX 595-21-211549. (Co-sponsor: Society of Jesus) Ed. Bartolmeu Melia, S.J; Pub. Jose Luis Caravias S.J. adv. contact: Andres Martin. bk.rev.; illus. circ. 2,000. **Document type:** academic/scholarly publication.
     Incorporates: Dimension.

300   FR   ISSN 0335-5322
H3
ACTES DE LA RECHERCHE EN SCIENCES SOCIALES. (Quarterly supplement avail.: Liber: Revue Europeenne des Livres) (Text in French; summaries in English, German, Spanish) 1975. q. 185 F. (foreign 270 F.). (Maison des Sciences de l'Homme) Editions de Seuil, 27 rue Jacob, 75261 Paris Cedex 06, France. TEL 42-22-37-94. (Subscr. to: Altek Data, 49 rue de la Vanne, 92126 Montrouge Cedex, France. TEL 41-17-14-00) Ed. Pierre Bourdieu. bibl.; illus. **Indexed:** Amer.Hist.& Life, Hist.Abstr., Int.Polit.Sci.Abstr., Lang.& Lang.Behav.Abstr., Mult.Ed. Abstr., Sociol.Educ.Abstr., SSCI. **Document type:** academic/scholarly publication.
—BLDSC (0675.315000); Faxon; SWETS.
     Description: Discusses leading research in the social sciences - sociology, ethnology, social psychology, psychology, social history, sociolinguistics, the economics of consumption and symbolic goods, etc.

300 610   US   ISSN 0275-5742
ADVANCES IN MEDICAL SOCIAL SCIENCE; health and illness as view by anthropology, geography, history, psychology and sociology. 1983. irreg., vol.2, 1984. price varies. Gordon & Breach Science Publishers, c/o International Publishers Distributor, 820 Town Center Dr., Langhorne, PA 19047. TEL 215-750-2642. FAX 215-750-6343. (Subscr. to: International Publishers Distributor, P.O. Box 90, Reading, Berkshire, RG1 8JL, England. TEL 44-173-456-8316) Ed. Julio L. Ruffini. **Indexed:** Anthropol.Lit. **Document type:** monographic series.
—CCC.
     Refereed Serial

300   UK   ISSN 0968-2473
ADVANCES IN PERSONAL RELATIONSHIPS. 1987. irreg., vol.5, 1993. $75. Jessica Kingsley Publishers, 116 Pentonville Rd., London N1 9JB, England. TEL 071-833-2307. FAX 071-837-2917. (Dist. by: Kogan Page Ltd., 120 Pentonville Rd., London N1 9JN, England. TEL 071-278-0433. FAX 071-837-6348; U.S. subscr. to: Taylor & Francis, 1900 Frost Rd., Ste. 101, Bristol, PA 19007-1598. TEL 800-821-8312. FAX 215-785-5515) Ed. Kim Bartholomew. **Document type:** monographic series.
—BLDSC (0709.598800).

300   US   ISSN 1047-2002
H1
ADVANCES IN SOCIAL SCIENCE METHODOLOGY. 1989. irreg., no.2, 1992. J A I Press Inc., 55 Old Post Rd., No. 2, Greenwich, CT 06830. TEL 203-661-7602. FAX 203-661-0792. Ed. Bruce Thompson. **Document type:** monographic series.

300 500   US   ISSN 1066-5145
AEON; a journal of interdisciplinary science. 1988. 4/yr. $40 (foreign $55) (effective 1995 & 1996). c/o Ev Cochrane, Ed., 601 Hayward Ave., Ames, IA 50014-7366. TEL 515-292-6565. FAX 515-292-2603. E-mail: ecochrane@delphi.com. adv.; bk.rev. circ. 1,000. **Document type:** academic/scholarly publication.
     Description: Explores the relationship between myth and science, particularly as it applies to the possibility of a synthesis between ancient myth and history.

300   IT   ISSN 1121-8495
AFRICA E MEDITERRANEO; trimestrale ISCOS di cultura, politica, economia, societa. 1992. q. L.50000 (foreign L.80000) (effective 1992-93). Istituto Sindacale per la Cooperazione allo Sviluppo, Via S. Mamolo 24, 40136 Bologna, Italy. TEL 39-51-6448707. Ed. Nino Sergi.

300 001.3   SA   ISSN 1019-2182
HN800.S59
AFRICA 2001; dialogue with the future. (Text in Afrikaans, English) 1974. 2/yr. R.20. Human Sciences Research Council, Centre for Science Development - Raad vir Geesteswetenskaplike Navorsing, Sentrum vir Wetenskapontwikkeling, Private Bag X41, Pretoria 0001, South Africa. TEL 27-12-321710. FAX 27-12-265362. Ed. Marilyn Farquharson. circ. 4,000. **Indexed:** Documentatieblad, Ind.S.A.Per. **Document type:** academic/scholarly publication.
—BLDSC (0732.195200).
     Former titles (until 1993): R S A 2000 (ISSN 1011-1913); R S A: Dialogue with the Future.
     Description: Publishes conference papers and academic articles on topics relating to development issues in Africa.

300   US
AFRICAN-AMERICAN ISSUES CENTER DISCUSSION PAPERS. 1984. irreg., no.16, 1986. $4 per no. Boston University, African Studies Center, 270 Bay State Rd., Boston, MA 02215. TEL 617-353-7306. FAX 617-353-4975. **Indexed:** IDA.

300 960   US
AFRICAN RESEARCH STUDIES. 1958. irreg., no.16, 1989. price varies. Boston University, African Studies Center, 270 Bay State Rd., Boston, MA 02215. TEL 617-353-7306. FAX 617-353-4975. (back issues avail.)

300   PL   ISSN 0002-029X
DT19.9.P6
AFRICANA BULLETIN. (Text in English and French) 1962. irreg., vol.42, 1994. price varies. (Uniwersytet Warszawski, Instytut Krajow Rozwijajacych Sie) Wydawnictwa Uniwersytetu Warszawskiego, Ul. Nowy Swiat 4, 00-497 Warsaw, Poland. TEL 48-22-625-3044. bk.rev.; abstr.; charts; illus.; stat. circ. 1,000. **Indexed:** A.I.C.P., Abstr.Hyg., Amer.Hist.& Life, Bibl.Ling., Curr.Cont.Africa, Documentatieblad, Geo.Abstr., Hist.Abstr., IDA, M.L.A., Rural Recreat.Tour.Abstr., Soils & Fert., Trop.Dis.Bull., World Agri.Econ.& Rural Sociol.Abstr.
—BLDSC (0735.150000).

960   SL   ISSN 0259-9651
DT470
AFRICANA RESEARCH BULLETIN. (Text in English) 1971. 2/yr. $20. University of Sierra Leone, Fourah Bay College, Institute of African Studies, Freetown, Sierra Leone. Ed. Arthur Abraham. bk.rev.; bibl. circ. 250. **Indexed:** Bibl.Ling., Documentatieblad, M.L.A. **Document type:** bulletin.

300 910.03   US   ISSN 0882-5297
AFRO-AMERICAN CULTURE AND SOCIETY MONOGRAPH SERIES. Variant title: C A A S Monograph Series. 1980. irreg. price varies. University of California at Los Angeles, Center for Afro-American Studies, 160 Haines Hall, 405 Hilgard Ave., Los Angeles, CA 90024-1545. TEL 310-825-3528. FAX 310-206-3421. **Document type:** monographic series.

AGEING AND SOCIETY. see *GERONTOLOGY AND GERIATRICS*

300   IT   ISSN 0002-094X
AGGIORNAMENTI SOCIALI. 1950. m. L.35000 (foreign L.50000) (effective 1995 & 1996). Istituto Aggiornamenti Sociali, Piazza S. Fedele 4, 20121 Milan, Italy. TEL 39-2-86352212. FAX 39-2-86352582. Ed. Mario Reguzzoni. adv.: B&W page L.500000; adv. contact: A. Garavaglia. bk.rev.; bibl.; charts; stat.; index, cum.index: 1950-1979, 1980-1989. circ. 25,000. **Indexed:** ELLIS, Int.Lab.Doc., Int.Polit.Sci.Abstr. **Document type:** academic/scholarly publication.
—BLDSC (0736.275000).

AJKAL. see *LITERATURE*

300 330.1   PL   ISSN 0208-7669
H8.P6
AKADEMIA ROLNICZA W SZCZECINIE. ZESZYTY NAUKOWE. NAUKI SPOLECZNE I EKONOMICZNE. (Text in Polish; abstract in English) 1976. irreg. price varies. Akademia Rolnicza w Szczecinie, Dzial Wydawnictw, Ul. Doktora Judyma 22, 71-460 Szczecin, Poland. TEL 48-91-541639. FAX 48-91-541642. TELEX 0425494 AR. Ed. Antoni Furowicz. bk.rev. **Indexed:** Chem.Abstr., Dairy Sci.Abstr., Field Crop Abstr., Nutr.Abstr., Potato Abstr., Rural Ext.Educ.& Tr.Abstr. **Document type:** academic/scholarly publication.
     Refereed Serial

301.18   PL   ISSN 0209-0538
AKADEMIA ROLNICZA WE WROCLAWIU. ZESZYTY NAUKOWE. NAUKI SPOLECZNE. (Subseries of: Akademia Rolnicza we Wroclawiu. Zeszyty Naukowe (ISSN 0867-7964)) 1983. irreg. price varies. Akademia Rolnicza we Wroclawiu, Ul. Norwida 25, 50-375 Wroclaw, Poland. FAX 48-71-229576. (Subscr. to: Dzial Wydawnictw i Poligrafii Akademii Rolniczej, ul. Sopocka 23, 50-344 Wroclaw, Poland. TEL 48-71-211277) circ. 270. **Document type:** academic/scholarly publication.

300   KZ
AKADEMIYA NAUK KAZAKHSTANA. IZVESTIYA. SERIYA OBSHCHESTVENNYKH NAUK. 1963. 6/yr. Gylym, Ul. Pushkina 111-113, 480100 Alma-Ata, Kazakhstan. TEL 3272-611877. Ed. R.B. Suleimenov. **Indexed:** Int.Bibl.Soc.Sci., Met.Abstr.
     Formerly (until 1993): Akademiya Nauk Kazakhskoi S.S.R. Izvestiya. Seriya Obshchestvennykh Nauk (ISSN 0132-6163)

300   KG   ISSN 1023-4845
Q60   CODEN: INKSAD
AKADEMIYA NAUK RESPUBLIKI KYRGYZSTAN. IZVESTIYA. OBSHCHESTVENNYE NAUKI. (Text in Russian) 1955. bi-m. $8.40. Izdatel'stvo Ilim, Leninsky pr. 265 A, 720071 Bishkek, Kyrgyzstan. Ed. T.K. Koichuev. **Indexed:** Biol.Abstr., Chem.Abstr., GeoRef., INIS Atomind.
—BLDSC (0073.777010); CASDDS.
     Formerly (until 1991): Akademiya Nauk Kirgizkoi S.S.R. Izvestiya. Obshchestvennye Nauki (ISSN 0235-0068); Which supersedes in part (in 1985): Akademiya Nauk Kirgizskoi S.S.R. Izvestiya (ISSN 0002-3221)

300   TA
AKADEMIYA NAUK TAJIKISTANA. IZVESTIYA. OTDELENIE OBSHCHESTVENNYKH NAUK. (Text in Russian and Tadzhik) 1952. 4/yr. 12.40 Rub. Akademiya Nauk Tajikistana, Pr. Rudaki 33, 734025 Dushanbe, Tajikistan. **Indexed:** A.I.C.P. **Document type:** academic/scholarly publication.
     Formerly (until 1992): Akademiya Nauk Tadzhikskoi S.S.R. Izvestiya. Otdelenie Obshchestvennykh Nauk (ISSN 0321-1738)

300   TK
AKADEMIYA NAUK TURKMENISTANA. IZVESTIYA. SERIYA OBSHCHESTVENNYKH NAUK. bi-m. 13.50 Rub. (effective Jan. 1992). Akademiya Nauk Turkmenistana, Ul. Gogolya, 15, 744000 Ashkhabad, Turkmenistan. circ. 500.
     Formerly (until 1992): Akademiya Nauk Turkmenskoi S.S.R. Izvestiya. Seriya Obshchestvennykh Nauk.

300   BW
AKADEMIA NAVUK BELARUSI. VESTSI. SERIYA GRAMADSKIKH NAVUK. (Text in Byelorussian; contents in Byelorussian, English) 1956. bi-m. 19.80 Rub. Vydavetstvo Navuka i Tekhnika, Zhodzinskaya, 18, 220067 Minsk 67, Belarus. TEL 39-55-17. FAX 252494. TELEX 252277 NAUKA. Ed. N.V. Birillo. charts; illus.; index. circ. 610.
     Formerly (until 1992): Akademiya Navuk Belarusskai S.S.R. Vestsi. Seriya Gramadskikh Navuk (ISSN 0321-1649)
     Description: Presents papers on problems of philosophy and law, sociology, economics, Byelorussian history, art, folklore, literature and linguistics.

SOCIAL SCIENCES: COMPREHENSIVE WORKS

300   CN
F1075
ALBERTA COMMUNITY DEVELOPMENT. ANNUAL REPORT. 1975. a. free. Alberta Community Development, Communications Branch, Standard Life Centre, 7th Fl., 10405 Jasper Ave., Edmonton, AB T5J 3N4, Canada. TEL 403-427-6530. FAX 403-427-1496. circ. 500. **Document type:** government publication.
    Former titles: Alberta Culture and Multiculturalism. Annual Report (ISSN 0848-2128); (until 1983): Alberta Culture. Annual Report (ISSN 0702-9659)

300   MX   ISSN 0187-5973
ALEGATOS. no.22, 1992. 3/yr. Mex.$25. Universidad Autonoma Metropolitana, Departamento de Derecho, Division de Ciencias Sociales y Humanidades, Av. San Pablo 180, 02200 Mexico DF, Mexico. bk.rev. circ. 1,000. **Document type:** academic/scholarly publication.

ALERO. see LITERATURE

300   SP   ISSN 0212-5064
DP302.M1
ALFOZ. 1983. m. 3500 ptas. (Europe 4000 ptas.; elsewhere 4500 ptas.). Centro de Investigacion y Documentacion Urbana y Rural, Infantas 13, 1o Izqda., 28004 Madrid, Spain. TEL 91-532-70-03. FAX 91-532-64-48. Dir. Javier Erchenagusia. circ. 5,000.
    Description: Debates current questions in the social sciences.

300   GW   ISSN 0176-9251
ALLENSBACHER BERICHTE. 1949. irreg. (2-3/mo.). DM.70. (Institut fuer Demoskopie Allensbach) Verlag fuer Demoskopie, Radolfzeller Str. 8, 78472 Allensbach, Germany. TEL 07533-8050. FAX 07533-3048. Eds. Elisabeth Noelle-Neumann, Edgar Piel. circ. 500. (back issues avail.) **Document type:** academic/scholarly publication.

980.1   PE   ISSN 0252-8835
F3429
ALLPANCHIS. Variant title: Allpanchis Phuturinga. 1969. s-a. $60. Instituto de Pastoral Andina, Area de Cultura Andina y Sociedad, Apdo. Aereo 1018, Cusco, Peru. TEL 51-84-238068. FAX 51-84-225205. Ed.Bd. adv.; bk.rev.; bibl.; charts. circ. 2,500. **Indexed:** A.I.C.P., Anthropol.Lit., Hisp.Amer.Per.Ind. (1991-). **Document type:** academic/scholarly publication.

300 572   CN   ISSN 0702-8865
ALTERNATE ROUTES; a journal of critical social research. 1977. a. Can.$12 to individuals; institutions $18. c/o Department of Sociology-Anthropology, Carleton University, Ottawa, ON K1S 5B6, Canada. TEL 613-788-7400. FAX 613-788-4062. Ed. David Robinson. adv. contact: Leopard St.Marie. bk.rev. circ. 250. **Indexed:** Lang.& Lang.Behav.Abstr., Left Ind. (1983-1988), Sociol.Abstr. (1980-). **Document type:** newspaper.
    Description: Multidisciplinary journal of the social sciences; focuses on contemporary theoretical issues within sociology.
    Refereed Serial

ALTERNATIVES; perspectives on society technology and environment. see ENVIRONMENTAL STUDIES

AMERICAN ACADEMY OF POLITICAL AND SOCIAL SCIENCE. ANNALS. see POLITICAL SCIENCE

320 300   US   ISSN 0002-7642
H1
AMERICAN BEHAVIORAL SCIENTIST. 1957. 8/yr. $70 to individuals; institutions $248 (effective Sep. 1995). Sage Publications, Inc., 2455 Teller Rd., Thousand Oaks, CA 91320. TEL 805-499-0721. FAX 805-499-0871. E-mail: libaries@sagepub.com. (Overseas subscr. to: Sage Publications Ltd., 6 Bonhill St., London EC2A 8PU, England; Sage Publications India Pvt. Ltd., Box 4215, New Delhi 110 048, India) Ed.Bd. adv.; index. circ. 1,750. (also avail. in microform from UMI; back issues avail.; reprint service avail.) **Indexed:** A.B.C.Pol.Sci., Abstr.Crim.& Pen., Acad.Ind., Adol.Ment.Hlth.Abstr., Amer.Hist.& Life, ASSIA, Bibl.Engl.Lang.& Lit., Bibl.Ind., Bk.Rev.Ind., C.I.J.E., Chic.Per.Ind., Commun.Abstr., Cont.Pg.Manage., Crim.Just.Abstr., Curr.Cont., Educ.Admin.Abstr., Fut.Surv., Geo.Abstr., Hist.Abstr., IDA, IMFL, Int.Polit.Sci.Abstr., Mid.East: Abstr.& Ind., P.A.I.S., Pers.Lit., Psychol.Abstr. (1962-), Sage Pub.Admin.Abstr., Sage Urb.Stud.Abstr., Soc.Sci.Ind., Sociol.Abstr., SSCI, Urb.Aff.Abstr. **Document type:** academic/scholarly publication.
—BLDSC (0810.780000); Faxon; Genuine Article; SWETS; UMI; UnCover. **CCC.**
    Description: Focuses, in theme-organized issues prepared under guest editors, on emerging cross-disciplinary interests, research, and problems in the social and bahavioral sciences.

AMERICAN BENEDICTINE REVIEW. see RELIGIONS AND THEOLOGY — Roman Catholic

AMERICAN ENTERPRISE. see POLITICAL SCIENCE

AMERICAN JOURNAL OF ECONOMICS AND SOCIOLOGY. see BUSINESS AND ECONOMICS

AMERICAN JOURNAL OF ISLAMIC SOCIAL SCIENCES. see RELIGIONS AND THEOLOGY — Islamic

AMERICAN JOURNAL OF SEMIOTICS. see HUMANITIES: COMPREHENSIVE WORKS

970 300   US   ISSN 0026-3079
E169.1
AMERICAN STUDIES. 1960. s-a. $15 to individuals (foreign $23); institutions $25 (foreign $33) (includes M A A S A Newsletter). (Mid-America American Studies Association) University of Kansas at Lawrence, American Studies Department, 2120 Wescoe Hall, Lawrence, KS 66045-2117. TEL 913-864-4878. FAX 913-864-4120. Eds. David Katzman, Norman Yetman. adv.; bk.rev.; charts; illus.; cum.index every 3 yrs. circ. 1,500. (also avail. in microform from UMI) **Indexed:** Abstr.Engl.Stud., Amer.Hist.& Life, Amer.Hum.Ind., Child.Lit.Abstr., Hist.Abstr., Hum.Ind., LCR, M.L.A., P.A.I.S., Soc.Sci.Ind. **Document type:** academic/scholarly publication.
—BLDSC (0857.657600); Faxon; SWETS; UMI; UnCover. **CCC.**
    Former titles (until 1970): Midcontinent American Studies Association. Journal; (until 1961): Central Mississippi Valley American Studies Association. Journal.
    Description: Crosses academic disciplines to explore issues that have something to tell about the society or culture of the United States.
    Refereed Serial

800   PL   ISSN 0209-1232
AMERICAN STUDIES. (Text in English) 1981. irreg., vol.13, 1994. price varies. (Uniwersytet Warszawski, Osrodek Studiow Amerykanskich) Wydawnictwa Uniwersytetu Warszawskiego, Ul. Nowy Swiat 4, 00-497 Warsaw, Poland. TEL 48-22-6253044. (Dist. by: Ars Polona, Krakowskie Przedmiescie 7, 00-068 Warsaw, Poland) Ed. Michal Rozbicki. circ. 800.

306   US   ISSN 0740-0489
AMERICAN UNIVERSITY STUDIES. SERIES 11. ANTHROPOLOGY AND SOCIOLOGY. 1984. irreg. Peter Lang Publishing, Inc., 62 W. 45th St., 4th Fl., New York, NY 10036. TEL 212-302-6740. Ed. Christopher Myers. **Document type:** academic/scholarly publication, monographic series.
—BLDSC (0858.078500).

300 943.8   PL   ISSN 1230-1159
H8
ANALECTA. (Text in Polish; summaries in English) 1992. s-a. price varies. Polska Akademia Nauk, Instytut Historii Nauki, Nowy Swiat 72, Palac Staszica, 00-330 Warsaw, Poland. TEL 48-22-268754. FAX 48-22-266137. (Dist. by: Ars Polona, Krakowskie Przedmiescie 7, 00-068 Warsaw, Poland) Ed. H. Lichocka. illus. circ. 320.
    Formed by the merger of (1986-1992): Studia i Materialy z Dziejow Nauki Polskiej. Seria 1. Historia Nauk Spolecznych (ISSN 0860-1011); (1988-1992): Studia i Materialy z Dziejow Nauki Polskiej. Seria 2. Historia Nauk Scislych, Przyrodniczych i Technicznych (ISSN 0860-102X)

ANALES DE CIENCIAS POLITICAS Y SOCIALES. see POLITICAL SCIENCE

300   UY
ANALISIS Y DESAFIOS. 1991. m.? 6000 N$ per no. (Instituto "Liberalis" Centro de Investigacion y Analisis de la Sociedad) Laster S.A., Ciudadela 1432, piso 2o, Of. 202, Montevideo, Uruguay. TEL 98-56-69. Ed. Jorge O. Casella. **Document type:** consumer publication.

300   GW   ISSN 0171-5860
H1
ANALYSE & KRITIK; Zeitschrift fuer Sozialwissenschaften. (Text in English and German) 1979. s-a. DM.76 (students DM.57) (effective 1996). Westdeutscher Verlag GmbH, Postfach 1546, 65005 Wiesbaden, Germany. TEL 0611-534389. FAX 0611-534430. Ed.Bd. **Document type:** academic/scholarly publication.
—BLDSC (0890.880000); SWETS. **CCC.**

ANGELAKI. see PHILOSOPHY

300   CC   ISSN 1001-5019
ANHUI DAXUE XUEBAO (SHEHUI KEXUE BAN)/ANHUI UNIVERSITY. JOURNAL (SOCIAL SCIENCE EDITION). (Text in Chinese) 1960. bi-m. $11.10. Anhui Daxue, Xuebao Bianjibu, No. 3, Feixi Lu, Hefei, Anhui 230039, People's Republic of China. TEL 0551-5115180. (Dist. overseas by: China International Book Trading Corp., P.O. Box 399, Beijing, P.R. China) Ed. Chen Wentong. circ. 3,000. **Document type:** academic/scholarly publication.
    Description: Covers philosophy and other aspects of social sciences.

300 100   CC   ISSN 1001-2435
ANHUI SHIDA XUEBAO (SHEHUI KEXUE BAN)/ANHUI NORMAL UNIVERSITY. JOURNAL (SOCIAL SCIENCE EDITION).* (Text in Chinese) 1957. q. Y1.2 (foreign $2). Anhui Shifan Daxue - Anhui Normal University, Xuebao Bianjibu, 1 Renmin Rd., Wuhu, Anhui 241000, People's Republic of China. TEL 0553-35966. FAX 33730. TELEX 91125 ANU CN. Ed. Wen Bingmo. adv.; index. circ. 3,500. (back issues avail.)

300   IT   ISSN 0394-1736
ANNALI ACCADEMICI CANADESI. 1985. a. membership. Centro Accademico Canadese in Italia - Centre Academique Canadien en Italie - Canadian Academic Centre in Italy, Via Tacito 50, 00193 Rome, Italy. TEL 39-6-6873677. FAX 39-6-6873693. Ed. Egmont Lee. bk.rev. circ. 200. **Document type:** academic/scholarly publication.
    Description: Covers Canadian studies.

300   FR   ISSN 0066-2607
ANNUAIRE DE L'AFRIQUE DU NORD. 1962. a. price varies. (Centre National de la Recherche Scientifique) C N R S Editions, 20-22 rue St. Amand, 75015 Paris, France. TEL 45-33-16-00. FAX 45-33-92-13. TELEX 200 356 F. adv.; bk.rev.; index; circ. 1,500 (controlled). **Indexed:** Bibl.Ling., Curr.Cont.Africa, Documentatieblad, Int.Polit.Sci.Abstr.
—BLDSC (1066.650000).

969.005 910   FR   ISSN 0247-400X
DT468
ANNUAIRE DES PAYS DE L'OCEAN INDIEN. (Text in French; summaries in English) 1974. a. price varies. (Centre National de la Recherche Scientifique, Centre d'Etudes et de Recherches sur les Societes de l'Ocean Indien) C N R S Editions, 20-22 rue St. Amand, 75015 Paris, France. TEL 45-33-16-00. FAX 45-33-92-13. TELEX 200 356 F. (Co-sponsor: Universite d'Aix-Marseille III (Universite de Droit d'Economie et des Sciences)) Eds. L. Favoreu, J. Benoit. adv.; bk.rev.; illus.; index. circ. 1,500. **Indexed:** Curr.Cont.Africa, Documentatieblad.

SOCIAL SCIENCES: COMPREHENSIVE WORKS

ANNUAL EDITIONS: HUMAN RESOURCES. see *SOCIOLOGY*

300   986.1   CK   ISSN 0066-5045
ANUARIO COLOMBIANO DE HISTORIA SOCIAL Y DE LA CULTURA. 1963. irreg. exchange basis. Universidad Nacional de Colombia, Facultad de Ciencias Humanas, Departamento de Historia, Apdo. Aereo 14490, Ciudad Universitaria, Bogota, D.E., Colombia. Dir. Bernardo Tovar Zambrano. circ. 5,000. **Indexed:** Amer.Hist.& Life, Hisp.Amer.Per.Ind. (1970-), Hist.Abstr.

300   CR   ISSN 0377-7316
F1421
ANUARIO DE ESTUDIOS CENTROAMERICANOS. 1974. 2/yr. $20. Editorial de la Universidad de Costa Rica, Apartado 75-2060, Ciudad Universitario Rodrigo Facio, 2050 San Pedro de Montes de Oca, San Jose, Costa Rica. TEL 506-25-3133. FAX 506-24-9367. TELEX UNICORI 2544. Dir. Oscar Fernandez. bk.rev. circ. 1,000. (also avail. in microfilm from OMN) **Indexed:** Amer.Hist.& Life, Curr.Adv.Ecol.Sci., Hisp.Amer.Per.Ind. (1974-), Hist.Abstr., P.A.I.S.For.Lang.Ind. **Document type:** academic/scholarly publication.

300   JA   ISSN 0286-3901
AOYAMA JOURNAL OF SOCIAL SCIENCES/AOYAMA SHAKAI KAGAKU KIYO. 1973. s-a. Aoyama-Gakuin University - Aoyama Gakuin Daigaku, 4-4-25 Shibuya, Shibuya-ku, Tokyo 150, Japan.
—BLDSC (1567.732000).

300   UK   ISSN 0954-4232
APPLIED COMMUNITY STUDIES. 1991. q. £45 (N. America $90; rest of world £55) (effective 1996). Whiting & Birch Ltd., P.O. Box 872, Forest Hill, London SE23 3HL, England. TEL 0181-244-2421. FAX 0181-244-2448. Ed. Malcolm Payne. **Document type:** academic/scholarly publication.
—BLDSC (1571.936800). **CCC.**

300   PE   ISSN 0252-1865
H8
APUNTES; revista semestral de ciencias sociales. 1973. s-a. $21. Universidad del Pacifico, Centro de Investigacion, Av. Salaverry 2020, Jesus Maria Lima 11, Peru. TEL 51-14-4712277. FAX 51-14-4709747. TELEX 25650 PE CP SHERA. (Subscr. to: Libreria de la Universidad del Pacifico, Apdo. 4683, Lima 100, Peru) Ed. Jose Luis Sardon. adv.; bk.rev. circ. 1,000. (back issues avail.) **Indexed:** Hisp.Amer.Per.Ind. (1973-), P.A.I.S.For.Lang.Ind. **Document type:** academic/scholarly publication.

ARANZADI SOCIAL. see *LAW*

300   GW   ISSN 0941-5025
ARBEIT; Zeitschrift fuer Arbeitsforschung, Arbeitsgestaltung und Arbeitspolitik. 1992. q. DM.88 (students DM.66) (effective 1996). Westdeutscher Verlag GmbH, Postfach 1546, 65005 Wiesbaden, Germany. TEL 0611-534389. FAX 0611-534430. Ed.Bd. circ. 1,000. **Document type:** academic/scholarly publication.

300   SP   ISSN 0210-1963
AP60
ARBOR; revista general de investigacion y cultura. 1944. m. 6000 ptas. (foreign 9500 ptas.). Consejo Superior de Investigaciones Cientificas (C.S.I.C.), Vitruvio, 8, 28006 Madrid, Spain. Dir. Miguel Angel Quintanilla. **Indexed:** Amer.Hist.& Life, Arts & Hum.Cit.Ind., Bibl.Engl.Lang.& Lit., CERDIC, Forest.Abstr., Forest Prod.Abstr., Hist.Abstr., M.L.A.
—Faxon; SWETS.
Description: Expresses the view that scientific and technological industries must be sensitive and responsible to the needs of the society that supports them.

ARCHAEOLOGY IN MONTANA. see *ARCHAEOLOGY*

ARCHIV FUER WISSENSCHAFT UND PRAXIS DER SOZIALEN ARBEIT. see *SOCIAL SERVICES AND WELFARE*

ARCHIVAL ISSUES. see *HISTORY*

ARCHIWUM HISTORII FILOZOFII I MYSLI SPOLECZNEJ. see *PHILOSOPHY*

053.1   GW   ISSN 0004-1157
DAS ARGUMENT; Zeitschrift fuer Philosophie und Sozialwissenschaften. 1959. bi-m. DM.72 (students DM.57). Argument-Verlag GmbH, Rentzelstr. 1, 20146 Hamburg, Germany. TEL 040-456018. FAX 040-445189. Ed. Wolfgang Fritz Haug. adv.; bk.rev.; index. circ. 10,000. **Indexed:** Lang.& Lang.Behav.Abstr., RILM, SSCI. **Document type:** academic/scholarly publication.
—BLDSC (1664.355000); Genuine Article; SWETS.

300   BL
ARGUMENTO; uma publicacao interdisciplinar. 1992. s-a. Faculdades Integradas Candido Mendes, Rua Joana Angelica 63, 22420 Ipanema, Rio de Janeiro RJ, Brazil. TEL 021-267-7141. FAX 021-267-7495. Ed. Monica Grin. adv. **Document type:** academic/scholarly publication.

ARHIV ZA PRAVNE I DRUSTVENE NAUKE. see *LAW*

300   BL
ARQUIVO EDGARD LEUENROTH. GUIA. a. Instituto de Filosofia e Ciencias Humanas, Centro de Pesquisa e Documentacao Social, Cidade Universitaria Zeferino Vaz, Caixa Postal 6110, 13081 Campinas SP, Brazil. (Co-sponsor: Associacao Cultural do Arquivo Edgard Leuenroth)

300   GT
ASI ES. no.5, 1991. irreg. Asociacion de Investigacion y Estudios Sociales, Apdo. Postal 1005 A, Guatemala, Guatemala. Ed. Raquel Zelaya. **Document type:** bulletin, academic/scholarly publication.

300   II   ISSN 0970-6305
ASIAN ECONOMIC AND SOCIAL REVIEW; techno-economic quarterly of Asian co-operation. (Text in English) 1976; N.S. 1984. q. Rs.250($75) (Indian Institute of Asian Studies) Asian Studies Press, 23-354 Azadnagar, Jaiprakash Rd., Andheri, Bombay 400 058, India. TEL 22-6263974. Ed. M.R. Sinha. adv.; bk.rev.; charts; index. circ. 3,500. (reprint service avail.) **Indexed:** Rural Recreat.Tour.Abstr., World Agri.Econ.& Rural Sociol.Abstr.
Incorporates: I F C E P Journal & Quarterly Journal of Indian Studies in Social Sciences (ISSN 0033-5584)

ASIAN PROFILE. see *ORIENTAL STUDIES*

300   001.3   US   ISSN 0361-3968
DS1
ASIAN THOUGHT AND SOCIETY: AN INTERNATIONAL REVIEW. 1976. 3/yr. $40. (State University of New York at Oneonta) East-West Publishing Co., 1 Bugbee Rd., Oneonta, NY 13820. TEL 607-431-3553. (Co-sponsors: Boston College; University of Hong Kong) Ed. Ignatius J.H. Ts'ao. adv.; bk.rev.; index. (back issues avail.) **Indexed:** A.B.C.Pol.Sci., Amer.Hist.& Life, E.I., Hist.Abstr., Int.Polit.Sci.Abstr.
—BLDSC (1742.752500); Faxon; UMI; UnCover.

300   UK   ISSN 0265-2587
ASSIGNATION. 1983. q. £30 (typically set in July). Aslib, Association for Information Management, Social Sciences Information Group, c/o Mrs. Hogan, Ed., National Institute of Social Work, 5 Tavistock Pl., London WC1H 9S, England. TEL 0171-387-9681. FAX 0171-387-7968. Ed. Margaret Hogan. adv.; bk.rev.; circ. 350 (paid). (back issues avail.) **Indexed:** LISA. **Document type:** academic/scholarly publication.
—BLDSC (1746.654000).
Description: Provides information on activities, sources, and resources in the social sciences information field.

ASSOCIATION FOR THE STUDY OF PLAY NEWSLETTER. see *PSYCHOLOGY*

300   VE
ATLANTIDA. 1974. irreg. free to qualified personnel. Universidad Simon Bolivar, Division de Sociales y Humanidades, Valle de Sartenejas, Caracas, Venezuela. circ. 1,000.

300 800   DR   ISSN 0254-7597
AULA. 1972. q. RD.$6. Universidad Nacional "Pedro Henriquez Urena", Apdo. 1423, Santo Domingo, Dominican Republic. Ed. Carlos Esteban Deive. bk.rev.; bibl. circ. 1,000. **Indexed:** Hisp.Amer.Per.Ind. (1978-1985).

300   AT   ISSN 1035-1132
AUSTRALIAN NATIONAL UNIVERSITY. AUSTRALIAN DEVELOPMENT STUDIES NETWORK. DEVELOPMENT BULLETIN. q. Aus.$25 (students Aus.$15). Australian National University, Australian Development Studies Network, G.P.O. Box 4, Canberra, A.C.T. 2601, Australia. TEL 61-6-249-4705. FAX 61-6-257-2886. TELEX 61364. E-mail: helen.skeat@anu.edu.au. Ed. Pamela Thomas. bk.rev. **Document type:** academic/scholarly publication.
—UnCover.
Formerly: Australian National University. National Centre for Development Studies. Newsletter (ISSN 0313-9980)
Description: Provides information on development issues, development research, and development-related courses, summaries of national and international conferences, information on development-related organizations and recent publications and other resources.

300   AT   ISSN 0157-6232
AUSTRALIAN NATIONAL UNIVERSITY. NATIONAL CENTRE FOR DEVELOPMENT STUDIES. DEMOGRAPHY TEACHING NOTES. Key Title: Demography Teaching Notes. 1979. irreg. price varies. Australian National University, National Centre for Development Studies, Canberra, A.C.T. 0200, Australia. TEL 616-249-4705. FAX 616-257-2886. Ed. Maree Tait.

300   FR
AUTREMENT. 1975. 14/yr. Editions Autrement, 4 rue d'Enghien, 75010 Paris, France. TEL 47-70-12-50. adv. circ. 20,000.

AZTLAN; a journal of Chicano studies. see *ETHNIC INTERESTS*

300   CN   ISSN 0005-2949
F1086
B C STUDIES. 1969. q. Can.$40 (U.S. Can.$45; elsewhere Can.$50). University of British Columbia, 2029 West Mall, Vancouver, BC V6T 1Z2, Canada. TEL 604-822-3727. FAX 604-822-9452. bk.rev.; bibl.; charts; illus. circ. 1,000. (tabloid format; also avail. in microform from UMI,MML; microfilm; back issues avail.) **Indexed:** Abstr.Anthropol., Amer.Hist.& Life, Can.B.P.I., Can.Per.Ind., CMI, Hist.Abstr. **Document type:** academic/scholarly publication.
—Faxon; UMI; UnCover.
Description: Focuses on all aspects of human history in British Columbia.

BALKAN STUDIES. see *HISTORY* — *History Of Europe*

BASIC AND APPLIED SOCIAL PSYCHOLOGY. see *PSYCHOLOGY*

300   GW
BASIS-INFO. (Editions in English, French, German and Spanish) 9/yr. Inter Nationes e.V., Kennedyallee 91-103, 53175 Bonn, Germany. TEL 0228-880-0. FAX 0228-880457. TELEX 17228308-IND-D. **Document type:** newsletter.
Formed by the merger of: Sozial Report (ISSN 0171-8738) & Sonderthema; **Formerly:** Sonderdienst.
Description: Background information on German politics, economics and social welfare.

300   II   ISSN 0304-9078
BF1
BEHAVIOROMETRIC. (Text in English) 1970. s-a. $7 to individuals; academic institutions $10. Council of Behavioral Research, Maharani Rd., Gaya 823002, Bihar, India. Ed. C.N. Daftuar. adv.; bk.rev.; charts. circ. 1,000. **Indexed:** Indian Psychol.Abstr., Psychol.Abstr.

300   CC   ISSN 1002-3054
BEIJING SHEHUI KEXUE/BEIJING SOCIAL SCIENCES. (Text in Chinese) 1986. q. Beijing Shehui Kexueyuan - Beijing Academy of Social Sciences, No.6, Chegongzhuang Dajie, Fuchengmenwai, Beijing 100044, People's Republic of China. TEL 8311675. Ed. Zhou Yixing.

SOCIAL SCIENCES: COMPREHENSIVE WORKS

300   CC   ISSN 1002-0209
BEIJING SHIFAN DAXUE XUEBAO (SHEHUI KEXUE BAN)/BEIJING NORMAL UNIVERSITY. JOURNAL (SOCIAL SCIENCE EDITION). (Text in Chinese; table of contents in English) 1975. bi-m. Y17. Beijing Shifan Daxue - Beijing Normal University, Beitaipingzhuang, Beijing 100875, People's Republic of China. TEL 2012288. (Dist. overseas by: China Publications Foreign Trade Corp., P.O. Box 782, Beijing, P.R.C.) Ed. Bai Shouyi.
—BLDSC (4707.891000); UnCover.

300   CC
BEIJING SHIFAN XUEYUAN XUEBAO (SHEHUI KEXUE BAN)/BEIJING NORMAL INSTITUTE. JOURNAL (SOCIAL SCIENCE EDITION). (Text in Chinese) bi-m. Beijing Shifan Xueyuan, Huayuancun, Fuchengmenwai, Beijing 100037, People's Republic of China. TEL 8414411. Ed. Zhang Shoukang.

300   GW
BEITRAEGE ZUR GESCHICHTE THUERINGENS. 1968. irreg. DM.4.80. (Museen der Stadt Erfurt) S E D Bezirksleitung Erfurt, Eislebenerstr. 1, 99086 Erfurt, Germany. Ed. Wolfgang Geist. illus.

300   GW   ISSN 0724-1097
BEITRAEGE ZUR GESELLSCHAFTS- UND BILDUNGSPOLITIK. 1976. 10/yr. DM.109.10. Deutscher Instituts Verlag GmbH, Postfach 510670, 50942 Cologne, Germany. TEL 0221-3708341. FAX 0221-3708191. Ed. W. Schlaffke. bk.rev.; abstr.; bibl.; charts; illus.; stat.; index. circ. 2,000. (back issues avail.) Document type: academic/scholarly publication.

BEITRAEGE ZUR SOZIALGESCHICHTE BREMEN. see HISTORY — History Of Europe

300 500   II
BHAGALPUR UNIVERSITY JOURNAL.* (Text in English and Hindi) vol.4, 1971. q. Rs.12. Bhagalpur University, Bhagalpur 7, India. Ed.Bd.

300   AG
BIBLIOTECA DE CIENCIAS SOCIALES. irreg., no.2, 1982. Consejo Latinoamericano de Ciencias Sociales, Centro Internacional de Formacion de Ciencias Ambientales, Av. Callao 873, Buenos Aires, Argentina. Ed. Mario R. dos Santos.

BIBLIOTECA DE ECONOMIA, POLITICA, SOCIEDAD. SERIE MAYOR.* irreg. Editorial Paidos, Defensa 599, Buenos Aires, 1065, Argentina.

300   AG
BIBLIOTECA DE ECONOMIA, POLITICA, SOCIEDAD. SERIE MENOR.* irreg., vol.6, 1976. Editorial Paidos, Defensa 599, Buenos Aires, 1065, Argentina.

300   PY
BIBLIOTECA DE ESTUDIOS PARAGUAYOS. 1981. irreg., vol.41, 1992. price varies. Universidad Catolica Nuestra Senora de la Asuncion, Centro de Estudios Antropologicos, Casilla de Correo 1718, Asuncion, Paraguay. TEL 595-21-446251. FAX 595-21-445245. Ed. Adriano Irala-Burgos. adv. circ. 1,000. (back issues avail.)

300   IT
BIBLIOTECA DI STORIA SOCIALE. 1973. irreg., no.27, 1990. price varies. Edizioni di Storia e Letteratura s.r.l., Via Lancellotti, 18, 00186 Rome, Italy. TEL 6540-556. FAX 06-6872567.

500 001.3   FI   ISSN 0067-8481
BIDRAG TILL KAENNEDOM AV FINLANDS NATUR OCH FOLK. (Text in Finnish or Swedish) 1857. irreg. price varies. Societas Scientiarum Fennica - Finnish Society of Sciences and Letters, Marieg 5, FIN-00170 Helsinki 17, Finland. TEL 358-0-633-005. FAX 358-0-661-065. Ed. Paul Fogelberg. circ. 500.

BLACK SCHOLAR; journal of Black studies and research. see ETHNIC INTERESTS

BLUEPRINT FOR SOCIAL JUSTICE. see POLITICAL SCIENCE — Civil Rights

300   UK   ISSN 1357-034X
▼**BODY & SOCIETY.** 1995. q. £30 to individuals; institutions £95 (effective 1996). Sage Publications Ltd., 6 Bonhill St., London EC2A 4PU, England. TEL 0171-374-0645. FAX 0171-374-8741. E-mail: market@sageltd.co.uk. Eds. Mike Featherstone, Bryan Turner. adv.: B&W page £180; trim 190 x 114; adv. contact: Bernie Folan. Indexed: ASSIA, Sociol.Abstr. Document type: academic/scholarly publication.
Description: Caters for the upsurge of interest in the social and cultural analysis of the human body. Includes work from anthropology, art history, cultural history, feminism, film studies and other related areas.

300   TU
BOGAZICI UNIVERSITY JOURNAL: MANAGEMENT, ECONOMIC AND SOCIAL SCIENCES/BOGAZICI UNIVERSITESI DERGISI: EY ONETICILIK, EKONOMI, VE SOSYAL BILIMLER. (Text in English or Turkish) 1973. irreg. $10. Bogazici Universitesi, Bebek, 80815 Istanbul, Turkey. TEL 90-1-2631500. FAX 90-1-2656357. TELEX 26411 BOUN TR. bibl.; stat. Document type: academic/scholarly publication.
Formerly: Bogazici University Journal: Social Sciences.

300   AG   ISSN 0497-0292
HC171
BOLETIN INFORMATIVO TECHINT. 1959. q. free. Organizacion Techint, Cordoba 320, 3er piso, 1054 Buenos Aires, Argentina. TEL 54-1-3185660. FAX 54-1-3110888. Ed. Jorge Lattes. circ. 4,000.
Formerly: Organizacion Techint. Boletin Informativo.

300 960   US   ISSN 0524-1332
BOSTON UNIVERSITY PAPERS ON AFRICA. 1964. irreg., no.8, 1987. Boston University, African Studies Center, 270 Bay State Rd., Boston, MA 02215. TEL 617-353-7306. FAX 617-353-4975. Indexed: Anthropol.Lit.

BRAZIL. SERVICO NACIONAL DE APRENDIZAGEM COMERCIAL. BOLETIM TECNICO. see EDUCATION

300   UK   ISSN 0958-6229
BRISTOL PAPERS. Variant title: Bristol Papers in Applied Social Studies. 1988. 2/yr. varies. University of Bristol, School of Applied Social Studies, 40 Berkeley Sq., Bristol BS8 1HY, England. TEL 0272-303030. circ. 500. Document type: academic/scholarly publication.
—BLDSC (2284.885000).

301   UK   ISSN 1351-5667
BRITISH ASSOCIATION FOR CANADIAN STUDIES. NEWSLETTER. (Text in English) 3/yr. £25 (foreign Can.$55) (includes British Journal of Canadian Studies (ISSN 0269-9222)) (effective 1996). British Association for Canadian Studies, 21 George Sq., Edinburgh EH8 9LD, Scotland. TEL 0131-662-1117. FAX 0131-662-1118. E-mail: jrobson@afbl.ssc.ed.ac.uk. Ed. Leon Litvack. Document type: newsletter.
Description: Covers various facets of Canadian studies: literature, history, geography, and political science.

301   UK   ISSN 0269-9222
F1021
BRITISH JOURNAL OF CANADIAN STUDIES. (Text in English, French) 1977. s-a. £25 (foreign Can.$55) (includes British Association for Canadian Studies. Newsletter (ISSN 1351-5667)) (effective 1996). British Association for Canadian Studies, 21 George Sq., Edinburgh EH8 9LD, Scotland. TEL 0131-662-1117. FAX 0131-662-1118. E-mail: jrobson@afbl.ssc.ed.ac.uk. Ed. Colin Nicholson. bk.rev.; index. Indexed: Bibl.Engl.Lang.& Lit., Can.B.P.I. Document type: academic/scholarly publication.
—BLDSC (2306.900000).
Formerly (until 1986): Bulletin of Canadian Studies.
Description: Covers Canadian literature, history, geography, and political science.
Refereed Serial

300   UK   ISSN 0265-6175
BRITISH PUBLIC OPINION. 10/yr. £75($150) Market & Opinion Research International, 32 Old Queen St., London SW1H 9HP, England. TEL 071-222-0232. FAX 071-222-1653. index. (back issues avail.) Document type: consumer publication.

300   US
BROOKINGS REPRINT SERIES. 1954? irreg. $20. Brookings Institution, 1775 Massachusetts Ave., N.W., Washington, DC 20036-2188. TEL 202-797-6255. FAX 202-797-6195. (Subscr. to: Box 037, Washington, DC 20042-0037. TEL 202-797-6255) Document type: academic/scholarly publication.
Former titles: Brookings Pamphlet Series; Brookings Institution. Reprint (ISSN 0068-2810); Brookings Research Report Series (ISSN 0068-2829)

300   SJ   ISSN 0304-2561
BUHUTH. (Publication suspended Aug.-Dec. 1973 and Aug. 1974-Oct. 1977) 1972. m. National Council for Research, Box 2404, Khartoum, Sudan.

300 920   II
BUILDERS OF INDIAN ANTHROPOLOGY. (Text in English) 1978. irreg. Rs.12. N.K. Bose Memorial Foundation, B-8-9 Bara Gambhir Singh, Gauriganj, Varanasi 221001, India. Ed. Surajit Sinha. circ. 500.

BULLETIN ANALYTIQUE DE DOCUMENTATION POLITIQUE, ECONOMIQUE ET SOCIALE CONTEMPORAINE. see POLITICAL SCIENCE

980   UK   ISSN 0261-3050
F1401   CODEN: BLARE9
BULLETIN OF LATIN AMERICAN RESEARCH. 1981. 3/yr. £116($185) (effective 1996). (Society for Latin American Studies) Elsevier Science Ltd., Pergamon, P.O. Box 800, Kidlington, Oxford OX5 1DX, England. TEL 44-1865-843000. FAX 44-1865-843010. E-mail: nlinfo-f@elsevier.nl; usinfo-f@elsevier.com; forinfo-kyf04035@niftyserve.or.jp; Site addr.: http://www.elsevier.nl/. (Subscr. in U.S. and Canada to: Elsevier Science, 660 White Plains Rd., Tarrytown, NY 10591-5153. TEL 914-524-9200. FAX 914-333-2444) Ed.Bd. adv.; bk.rev. circ. 800. (also avail. in microform from UMI) Indexed: A.B.C.Pol.Sci., Amer.Hist.& Life, Curr.Cont., Geo.Abstr., Hisp.Amer.Per.Ind. (1981-), Hist.Abstr., IDA. Document type: academic/scholarly publication, bulletin.
—BLDSC (2865.440000); Faxon; SWETS; UMI; UnCover. CCC.
Supersedes (in Oct. 1981): Society for Latin America Studies. Bulletin.
Description: Publishes original research papers on topics of current interest on Latin America from all academic disciplines of the social sciences and humanities.
Refereed Serial

THE BULLETIN OF SCIENCE, TECHNOLOGY & SOCIETY. see SCIENCES: COMPREHENSIVE WORKS

300   BR
BURMA RESEARCH SOCIETY. JOURNAL/MYANMA NAING NGAN THUTEITHANA ATHIN.* (Text in Burmese or English) 1911. s-a. Burma Research Society, University Library, University Estate, Yangon, Union of Myanmar. bk.rev.; charts; illus. (also avail. in microfiche from IDC; reprint service avail. from KTO) Indexed: Amer.Hist.& Life, Hist.Abstr.

300   BO
BUSQUEDA; revista semestral de ciencias sociales. 1959. s-a. exchange basis. Universidad Mayor de "San Simon", Facultad de Ciencias Economicas y Sociologia, Instituto de Estudios Sociales y Economicos, Casilla 992, Cochabamba, Bolivia. TEL 32540 ext. 314. TELEX 6363 UMSS BV. circ. 1,000.
Supersedes (in 1990): Universidad Boliviana Mayor de San Simon. Instituto de Estudios Sociales y Economicos. Revista (ISSN 0041-8617)

300   US   ISSN 1051-4589
E185.5   CODEN: CRPOEQ
C A A S REPORT. 1977. a. free. University of California at Los Angeles, Center for Afro-American Studies, 160 Haines Hall, 405 Hilgard Ave., Los Angeles, CA 90024-1545. TEL 310-825-3528. FAX 310-206-3421. Ed.Bd. bk. rev. circ. 5,500. (back issues avail.) Indexed: ERIC. Document type: academic/scholarly publication.
Formerly: C A A S Newsletter (ISSN 0197-5579)

SOCIAL SCIENCES: COMPREHENSIVE WORKS

300 910.03   US   ISSN 0882-5300
C A A S SPECIAL PUBLICATION SERIES. 1977. irreg. price varies. University of California at Los Angeles, Center for Afro-American Studies, 160 Haines Hall, 405 Hilgard Ave., Los Angeles, CA 90024-1545. TEL 310-825-3528. FAX 310-206-3421. **Document type:** academic/scholarly publication.
—BLDSC (2943.771000).

C D R RESEARCH REPORTS. (Centre for Development Research) see BUSINESS AND ECONOMICS — *International Development And Assistance*

301 410   UK   ISSN 0309-9229
C E C T A L BIBLIOGRAPHICAL AND SPECIAL SERIES. irreg., no.6, 1991. price varies. University of Sheffield, Centre for English Cultural Tradition and Language, Sheffield S10 2TN, England. TEL 0114-2826296. FAX 0114-2768251. **Document type:** monographic series.

301 410   UK   ISSN 0263-4805
C E C T A L OCCASIONAL PUBLICATIONS. irreg., no.5, 1991. price varies. University of Sheffield, Centre for English Cultural Tradition and Language, Sheffield S10 2TN, England. TEL 0114-2826296. FAX 0114-2768251. **Document type:** monographic series.

C E D E J EGYPTE - MONDE ARABE; droit, economie, societe. (Centre d'Etudes et de Documentation Economique, Juridique et Sociale) see *POLITICAL SCIENCE*

980 300   NE
C E D L A LATIN AMERICA STUDIES. Abbreviated title: C L A S. (Text in English, Spanish) irreg., no.71, 1993. price varies. Centrum voor Studie en Documentatie van Latijns Amerika - Center for Latin America Research and Documentation - Centro de Estudios y Documentacion Latinoamericanos, Keizersgracht 395-397, 1016 EK Amsterdam, Netherlands. TEL 31-205253498. FAX 31-206255127. (back issues avail.) **Document type:** monographic series.

300   FR   ISSN 0395-5621
C F D T MAGAZINE. (Includes weekly: Syndicalisme) 1976. m. (11/yr.) 162 F. (foreign 246 F.) (effective Jan. 1992). Confederation Francaise Democratique du Travail, 4 bd. de la Villette, 75955 Paris Cedex 19, France. TEL 42-03-81-40. Dir. Pierre Hureau. bk.rev.; film rev.; illus.
Formerly: Syndicalisme Magazine.

C Q RESEARCHER. see *POLITICAL SCIENCE*

C R: CENTENNIAL REVIEW. see *HUMANITIES: COMPREHENSIVE WORKS*

C R E S R RESEARCH PAPER. (Centre for Regional Economic and Social Research) see BUSINESS AND ECONOMICS — *Economic Situation And Conditions*

300 001.3   SA
C S D - S W O BULLETIN. (Centre for Science Development - Sentrum vir Wetenskapontwikkeling) (Text in Afrikaans, English) 1971. 10/yr. R.15. Human Sciences Research Council, Centre for Science Development - Raad vir Geesteswetenskaplike Navorsing. Sentrum vir Wetenskapontwikkeling, Private Bag X41, Pretoria 0001, South Africa. Ed. Marilyn Farquharson. index. circ. 3,500. **Document type:** academic/scholarly publication, bulletin.
Former titles: Human Sciences Research Council. Bulletin - News for the Human Sciences; Human Sciences Research Council. Institute for Development. Bulletin (ISSN 1017-6136); Human Sciences Research Council. Research Bulletin - Raad vir Geesteswetenskaplike Navorsing. Navorsingsbulletin (ISSN 1011-1816); **Supersedes:** Register of Research in the Human Sciences in South Africa - Register van Navorsing in die Geesteswetenskappe in Suid-Afrika.
Description: Covers newsworthy developments in the human sciences for an academic audience.

C U F NOTAT. see BUSINESS AND ECONOMICS — *International Development And Assistance*

300   PO
CADERNOS DE CIENCIAS SOCIAIS. 1984. irreg., no.14, 1994. Esc.4000 (Europe Esc.8000) for 2 nos. Edicoes Afrontamento, Lda., Rua de Costa Cabral, 859, Apdo. 2009, 4201 Porto Codex, Portugal. TEL 351-2-529271. FAX 351-2-591777. Ed. Jose Madureira Pinto.

360   BL
CADERNOS DE ESTUDOS SOCIAIS. (Text in Portuguese; summaries in English) 1985. s-a. (Fundacao Joaquim Nabuco) Editora Massangana, Rua Dois Irmaos, 15, Apipucos, 52071 Recife, Brazil. TEL 55-81-268-4611. FAX 55-81-268-9600. bibl. circ. 1,000.

300   BL
CADERNOS DO PATRIMONIO CULTURAL. 1991. 3/yr. Secretaria Municipal de Cultura, Turismo e Esportes, Departamento Geral do Patrimonio Cultural, Rua Alfonso Cavalcanti, 455, sala 207, Cidade Nova, Rio de Janeiro RJ, Brazil. Ed.Bd.

300   FR   ISSN 0068-4953
CAHIERS BRETONS/AR GWYR. 1958-61; 1970 N.S. m. 150 F. (foreign 175 F.). Grand College Celtique, 7 Residence du Lac, 35380 Paimpont, France. TEL 99-07-87-37. Ed. Jean Thos. bk.rev. circ. 300.

CAHIERS D'ECONOMIE ET SOCIOLOGIE RURALES. see AGRICULTURE — *Agricultural Economics*

980 300   FR   ISSN 1141-7161
CAHIERS DES AMERIQUES LATINES. 1968. 2/yr. 200 F. Institut des Hautes Etudes de l'Amerique Latine, 28 rue Saint-Guillaume, 75007 Paris, France. Ed.Bd. abstr.; bibl. **Indexed:** Amer.Hist.& Life, Hisp.Amer.Per.Ind. (1968-), Hist.Abstr., Int.Polit.Sci.Abstr.
—BLDSC (2948.616400); Faxon.
Formerly (until 1984): Cahiers des Ameriques Latines. Serie - Sciences de l'Homme (ISSN 0008-0020)

500   FR   ISSN 0768-9829
DT521
CAHIERS DES SCIENCES HUMAINES. (Text in French; summaries in English) 1963. q. 420 F. (Institut Francais de Recherche Scientifique pour le Developpement en Cooperation) O R S T O M Editions - Diffusion, 72 Route d'Aulnay, 93143 Bondy Cedex, France. TEL 48-02-55-00. FAX 48-47-30-88. circ. 1,000. (back issues avail.) **Indexed:** Bibl.Ling., Curr.Cont.Africa, Documentatieblad, Geo.Abstr., IDA, Int.Lab.Doc., Rice Abstr., Rural Recreat.Tour.Abstr., World Agri.Econ.& Rural Sociol.Abstr. **Document type:** academic/scholarly publication.
—BLDSC (2952.195680).
Formerly: Cahiers O R S T O M Serie Sciences Humaines (ISSN 0008-0403)

300   SZ   ISSN 0008-0497
CAHIERS VILFREDO PARETO; revue europeenne des sciences sociales. Variant title: R E S S. (Text in English, French, German and Italian) 1963. irreg., no.100, 1995. Librairie Droz S.A., 11, rue Massot, CH-1211 Geneva 12, Switzerland. TEL 022-3466666. FAX 022-3472391. Ed. Giovanni Busino. bk.rev. circ. 2,000. **Indexed:** SSCI. **Document type:** academic/scholarly publication.
—BLDSC (7900.180000); SWETS. **CCC**.
Description: European studies of social sciences.

CAHIERS ZAIROIS D'ETUDES POLITIQUES ET SOCIALES. see *POLITICAL SCIENCE*

300   UA
CAIRO PAPERS IN SOCIAL SCIENCES. (Text in English) 1977. 4/yr. £E8($15) to individuals; institutions £E10($25). American University in Cairo, Social Research Center, Box 2511, Cairo, Egypt. (Subscr. to: American University Cairo Library, c/o Unsworth & Co., 1831 Pennsylvania Ave., Linden, NJ 07036, U.S.A.) Ed.Bd.

306   US   ISSN 1053-2285
CAKELELE: MALUKU RESEARCH JOURNAL. 1990. s-a. $25 to individuals; institutions $40; students $15. University of Hawaii, Center for Southeast Asian Studies, 1890 East-West Rd., Moore 416, Honolulu, HI 96822. Eds. James T. Collins, Susan McKinnon.
—UnCover.
Description: Publishes the results of research in and about Maluku, as well as the Maluku communities scattered through Indonesia and the Netherlands.

300   IT   ISSN 0393-3741
CALENDARIO DEL POPOLO.* 1945. m. L.40000. Nicola Teti e C., Via Rezia 4, 20135 Milan, Italy. TEL 39-2-55015575. FAX 39-2-55015575. Ed. Franco Della Peruta. adv.: B&W page L.3700000; 169 x 234. circ. 25,000.

971 300 900   CN   ISSN 0043-8170
D839
CANADA & THE WORLD; the magazine for students of current events. 1934. 9/yr. (Sep.-May). Can.$20. P.O. Box 7004, Oakville, Ont. L6J 6L5, Canada. TEL 416-338-3394. Ed. Rupert J. Taylor. adv.; illus. circ. 20,000. (also avail. in microform from UMI) **Indexed:** Can.B.P.I., Can.Per.Ind., CMI.
—UMI.
Formerly: World Affairs.
Description: Current events for high school students.

CANADIAN ASSOCIATION OF SLAVISTS NEWSLETTER. see *HUMANITIES: COMPREHENSIVE WORKS*

CANADIAN ISSUES/THEMES CANADIENS. see *HUMANITIES: COMPREHENSIVE WORKS*

960   CN   ISSN 0008-3968
DT19.9.C3
CANADIAN JOURNAL OF AFRICAN STUDIES/REVUE CANADIENNE DES ETUDES AFRICAINES. (Text in English, French) 1967. 3/yr. Can.$70 to individuals; students Can.$35. Canadian Association of African Studies, Centre for Urban and Community Studies, University of Toronto, 455 Spadina Ave., Ste. 426, Toronto, Ont. M5S 2G8, Canada. TEL 613-237-6885. FAX 613-237-2105. Ed.Bd. adv.; bk.rev.; bibl. circ. 1,000. **Indexed:** A.B.C.Pol.Sci., A.I.C.P., Abstr.Anthropol., Abstr.Rural Dev.Trop., Amer.Hist.& Life, Bibl.Ling., CERDIC, Curr.Cont., Documentatieblad, Hist.Abstr., HR Rep., IDA, Int.Lab.Doc., Int.Polit.Sci.Abstr., Lang.& Lang.Behav.Abstr., M.L.A., Mid.East: Abstr.& Ind., Periodex, RADAR, Rural Devel.Abstr., Rural Recreat.Tour.Abstr., Sociol.Abstr., SSCI, World Agri.Econ.& Rural Sociol.Abstr. **Document type:** academic/scholarly publication.
—BLDSC (3027.900000); Faxon; Genuine Article; UnCover. **CCC**.
Supersedes: Bulletin of African Studies in Canada.
Description: Covers African political economy, history, development, and literature. Includes papers on agriculture, rural economy and medicine.

300   CN   ISSN 0225-5189
HC59
CANADIAN JOURNAL OF DEVELOPMENT STUDIES/REVUE CANADIENNE D'ETUDES DU DEVELOPPEMENT. (Text in English, French, Spanish) 1980. 3/yr. Can.$30 to individuals; institutions Can.$50. Institute for International Development and Cooperation - Institut de Developpement International et de Cooperation, University of Ottawa, 550 Cumberland, Rm. 160B, Ottawa, ON K1A 6N5, Canada. TEL 613-564-5459. FAX 613-564-9518. Ed. Jose Havet. adv.; bk.rev. circ. 1,000. (back issues avail.) **Indexed:** A.B.C.Pol.Sci., Abstr.Rural Dev.Trop., Abstr.Rural Dev.Trop., Amer.Hist.& Life, Asian-Pac.Econ.Lit., Can.B.P.I., Curr.Cont., Geo.Abstr., Hist.Abstr., IDA, Int.Lab.Doc., Int.Polit.Sci.Abstr., J.of Econ.Lit., P.A.I.S.For.Lang.Ind., P.A.I.S., Per.Islam. (1991-), Rural Devel.Abstr., Rural Ext.Educ.& Tr.Abstr., SSCI, World Agri.Econ.& Rural Sociol.Abstr. **Document type:** academic/scholarly publication.
—BLDSC (3031.135000); Genuine Article; UnCover. **CCC**.
Description: Provides an interdisciplinary forum for the discussion of a wide range of development issues. Open to all theoretical and development strategy orientations and publishes contributions dealing with all regions and countries of the developing world.

CANADIAN NOTES & QUERIES/QUESTIONS & REPONSES CANADIENNES. see *HUMANITIES: COMPREHENSIVE WORKS*

CANADIAN REVIEW OF STUDIES IN NATIONALISM. see *HISTORY*

CANADIAN SLAVONIC PAPERS/REVUE CANADIENNE DES SLAVISTES. see *HUMANITIES: COMPREHENSIVE WORKS*

CANADIAN SOCIAL STUDIES. see EDUCATION — *Teaching Methods And Curriculum*

300   SA
CAPE NEWSLETTER/KAAPSE NUUSBRIEF. (Text in Afrikaans, English) 2/yr. free. Human Sciences Research Council, Cape Regional Office, Private Bag X41, Pretoria 0001, South Africa. **Document type:** newsletter.
Description: Details the activities and services of the HSRC Cape Regional Office.

300   UK   ISSN 0969-2304
RA421   CODEN: CAPLFZ
▼**CARE IN PLACE: THE INTERNATIONAL JOURNAL OF NETWORKS AND COMMUNITY**. 1994. 3/yr. £28 to individuals (U.S. and Canada $46; elsewhere £32); institutions £55 (U.S. and Canada $90; elsewhere £60). Routledge, 11 New Fetter Ln., London EC4P 4EE, England. TEL 0171-583-9855. FAX 0171-842-2298. E-mail: sample.journals@routledge.com. (Subscr. to: ITPS Ltd., Cheriton House, N. Way, Andover, Hants. SP10 5BE, England. TEL 01264-332424. FAX 01264-342807) **Document type:** academic/scholarly publication.
—BLDSC (3051.585000).

972.9 300   PR   ISSN 0008-6533
F2161
CARIBBEAN STUDIES/ESTUDIOS DEL CARIBE/ESTUDES DES CARAIBES. (Text in English, French or Spanish) 1961. s-a. $25 to individuals; institutions $50. Universidad de Puerto Rico, Institute of Caribbean Studies, P.O. Box 23361, UPR Sta., San Juan, PR 00931-3361. bk.rev.; bibl.; index. circ. 1,500. **Indexed:** Amer.Hist.& Life, ASSIA, Curr.Cont., Geo.Abstr., Hisp.Amer.Per.Ind. (1970-), Hist.Abstr., Int.Polit.Sci.Abstr., PROMT, Soc.Sci.Ind., SSCI.
—BLDSC (3053.130000); Faxon; UnCover.

300   US   ISSN 0008-7661
CATALYST (AMHERST). 1965-1985; resumed 1993. irreg. Can.$10. State University of New York at Buffalo, Department of Sociology, Amherst, NY 14260. TEL 716-645-2417. Ed. E. Powell. adv.; bk.rev. circ. 2,000. (also avail. in microfilm from UMI; reprint service avail. from UMI) **Indexed:** Amer.Hist.& Life, Hist.Abstr., Int.Bibl.Soc.Sci., Sociol.Abstr. **Document type:** academic/scholarly publication.
—UMI.

CATEDRA; revista de ciencia, cultura y educacion. see SCIENCES: COMPREHENSIVE WORKS

CATHOLIC INSIGHT; a magazine for Canada in the universal Church. see RELIGIONS AND THEOLOGY — Roman Catholic

CEIBA. see LITERATURE

CENTER FOR MIGRATION STUDIES. BIBLIOGRAPHIES AND DOCUMENTATION SERIES. see POPULATION STUDIES

CENTER FOR MIGRATION STUDIES. GIOVANNI SCHIAVO COLLECTION. see POPULATION STUDIES

CENTER FOR MIGRATION STUDIES. OCCASIONAL PAPERS AND DOCUMENTATION SERIES. see POPULATION STUDIES

CENTER FOR MIGRATION STUDIES. PASTORAL SERIES. see POPULATION STUDIES

CENTRE PIERRE LEON D'HISTOIRE ECONOMIQUE ET SOCIALE. BULLETIN. see HISTORY — History Of Europe

300   AG   ISSN 0328-185X
CENTRO DE ESTUDIOS AVANZADOS. ESTUDIOS. 1993. s-a. $24 (foreign $40). Universidad Nacional de Cordoba, Centro de Estudios Avanzados, Ave. Velez Sarsfield 153, 5000 Cordoba, Argentina. TEL 54-51-215750. FAX 54-51-239731. (Foreign dist.: Fernando Garcia Cambeiro, Box 014 Skyway USA, 2886 N.W. 79th Ave., Miami, FL 33122) Dir. Hector Schmucler. bk.rev. **Document type:** academic/scholarly publication.
Description: Presents intellectual works of the university on contemporary civilization issues.

300   UY
CENTRO DE INFORMACIONES Y ESTUDIOS DEL URUGUAY. SERIE DOCUMENTOS DE TRABAJO. irreg., no.177, 1991. Centro de Informaciones y Estudios del Uruguay, Casilla 10587, 11100 Montevideo, Uruguay. TEL 48-3205. FAX 5982-48-0762.

300   UY
CENTRO DE INFORMACIONES Y ESTUDIOS DEL URUGUAY. SERIE ESTUDIOS. irreg., no.12, 1989. Centro de Informaciones y Estudios del Uruguay, Casilla 10587, 11100 Montevideo, Uruguay. TEL 48-3205. FAX 5982-48-0762.

300   UY
CENTRO DE INFORMACIONES Y ESTUDIOS DEL URUGUAY. SERIE INFORMES. irreg., no.47, 1991. Centro de Informaciones y Estudios del Uruguay, Casilla 10587, 11100 Montevideo, Uruguay. TEL 48-3205. FAX 5982-48-0762.

322.4   AG   ISSN 0325-1306
H8.S7
CENTRO DE INVESTIGACION Y ACCION SOCIAL. REVISTA. 1961. m. Arg.$45($50) Centro de Investigacion y Accion Social (CIAS), O'Higgins 1331, 1426 Buenos Aires, Argentina. TEL 01-783-8300. Ed. Fernando Storni. adv.; bk.rev. circ. 2,000.
Former titles (until 1969): C I A S Centro de Investigacion y Accion Social (ISSN 0007-8387); (until 1965): Centro de Investigacion y Accion Social. Boletin Mensual.

300   US   ISSN 0252-9971
CENTRO DE INVESTIGACIONES REGIONALES DE MESOAMERICA. SERIE MONOGRAFICA. 1981. s-a. price varies. Centro de Investigaciones Regionales de Mesoamerica (CIRMA), Plumsock Mesoamerican Studies, Rt. 106, Box 38, S. Woodstock, VT 05071. TEL 802-457-1199. Eds. Christopher H. Lutz, Cherri M. Pancake. **Indexed:** A.I.C.P., Abstr.Anthropol., Int.Bibl.Soc.Sci. **Document type:** monographic series.

300   UY   ISSN 0797-6062
HC121
CENTRO LATINOAMERICANO DE ECONOMIA HUMANA. CUADERNOS. 1958; N.S. 1976. 4/yr. Urg.$55000($19) (typically set in Mar.). Centro Latinoamericano de Economia Humana, Zelmar Michelini 1220, Casilla de Correo 5021, 11100 Montevideo, Uruguay. FAX 598-2-921127. adv.; bk.rev.; charts; tr.lit.; index, cum.index. circ. 2,000. **Indexed:** Hisp.Amer.Per.Ind. (1991-).
Former titles (until 1984): Centro Latinoamericano de Economia Humana. Publicaciones (ISSN 0797-6070); (until 1967): Cuadernos Latinoamericanos de Economia Humana (ISSN 0797-6089)

300 500   HO
CENTRO UNIVERSITARIO DE ESTUDIOS GENERALES. REVISTA. 1991. s-a.? exchange basis. Universidad Nacional Autonoma de Honduras, Centro Universitario de Estudios Generales, Blvd. Morazan, Tegucigalpa, Honduras. **Document type:** academic/scholarly publication.
Description: Presents research work from the university in the areas of social sciences, natural sciences and physical-mathematical sciences.

300   US   ISSN 1015-082X
CHEIRON NEWSLETTER. 1973. s-a. $20 to individuals; institutions $30. International Society for History of the Behavioral and Social Sciences, c/o Psychology Office, Bulfinch 501, Massachusetts General Hospital, Boston, MA 02114. TEL 617-492-1130. (Co-sponsor: Cheiron Society) Ed. Eugene Taylor. adv.; bk.rev.; bibl. circ. 500. (back issues avail.) **Document type:** newsletter.
Description: Summarizes on-going research of historians in psychology and the behavioral and social sciences who are largely members of the Cheiron Society.

300 614.7   UK   ISSN 0144-9877
CHELMER WORKING PAPERS IN ENVIRONMENTAL PLANNING. 1979. irreg. Chelmer Institute of Higher Education, Faculty of Social Sciences, Department of Planning, Victoria Rd. S., Chelmsford, Essex CM1 1LL, England. Ed. David Crouch. **Indexed:** Geo.Abstr.

300   CC
CHENGDU DAXUE XUEBAO (SHEHUI KEXUE BAN)/CHENGDU UNIVERSITY. JOURNAL (SOCIAL SCIENCE EDITION). (Text in Chinese) q. Y4.80. Chengdu Daxue - Chengdu University, Renmin Beilu, Chengdu, Sichuan 610081, People's Republic of China. (Dist. overseas by: China Publications Foreign Trade Corp., P.O. Box 782, Beijing, P.R.C.)
Description: Publishes research papers. Includes regular columns on Song dynasty literature, Sichuanese humanities, local literature and history, the Three Kingdoms and Zhuge Liang, political theses, economic and social development, library and information science, and Sichuan writers and their works.

300   CC   ISSN 1002-2031
CHENGSHI WENTI/URBAN ISSUES. (Text in Chinese) bi-m. Beijing Shehui Kexueyuan - Beijing Academy of Social Sciences, No.6, Chegongzhuang Dajie, Fuwai, Beijing 100044, People's Republic of China. TEL 890551.

300   CC
CHENGSHI YANJIU/URBAN STUDIES. (Text in Chinese) bi-m. Taiyuan Shi Shehui Yanjiusuo, 20, Hanxiguan, Taiyuan, Shanxi 030002, People's Republic of China. TEL 345483. Ed. Yang Guangliang.

THE CHINA JOURNAL. see ORIENTAL STUDIES

CHINA REPORT; a journal of East Asian studies. see POLITICAL SCIENCE — International Relations

CHRISTIAN STATESMAN. see RELIGIONS AND THEOLOGY

CHRONIQUES DE LA S.E.D.E.I.S. see BUSINESS AND ECONOMICS — Economic Situation And Conditions

CIENCIA. see SCIENCES: COMPREHENSIVE WORKS

300   BL   ISSN 0304-2685
HN281
CIENCIA & TROPICO. (Text in Portuguese; abstracts in English and French) 1952. s-a. R.2.92 per no. (Fundacao Joaquim Nabuco) Editora Massangana, Rua Dois Irmaos, 15, Apipucos, 52071 Recife, Brazil. TEL 55-81-268-4611. FAX 55-81-268-9600. bk.rev.; abstr.; bibl.; charts; illus.; stat. circ. 2,000. (also avail. in microfilm from OMN)
Formerly (until 1971): Instituto Joaquim Nabuco de Pesquisas Sociais. Boletim.

300   CK   ISSN 0134-5494
CIENCIAS SOCIALES. 1976. q. (Akademiya Nauk S.S.R., Social Sciences Section, UR) Centro de Estudios e Investigaciones Sociales, Calle 21 no. 17-42, Apdo. Aereo 11968, Bogota, Colombia. Ed. Alvaro Delgado Guzman.

300   PE
CIENCIAS SOCIALES; revista de investigacion analisis y debate. 1993. irreg.? Universidad Nacional del Altiplano, Facultad de Ciencias Sociales, Av. El Ejercito 329, Puno, Peru. Ed. Jorge Adan Villegas Montoya.

300   BL
CIENCIAS SOCIAS HOJE (YEAR). irreg. Associacao Nacional de Pos-Graduacao e Pesquisa em Ciencias Sociais, Largo de Sao Francisco 1, 4o andar, sala 408, 20051 Rio de Janeiro RJ, Brazil. Ed.Bd.

CIMARRON REVIEW. see LITERATURE

300   CE
CINTANA DHARA. (Text in Sinhalese) 1977. q. Rs.3.50. Pushparama Institute, Delkanda, Nugegoda, Sri Lanka.

CIRCOLO CULTURALE B.G. DUNS SCOTO DI ROCCARAINOLA. ATTI. see ARCHAEOLOGY

CIVILISATIONS ET SOCIETES. see HISTORY — History Of Europe

CIVILIZATION AND SOCIETY: STUDIES IN SOCIAL, ECONOMIC AND CULTURAL HISTORY. see HISTORY

300   IT   ISSN 1120-9860
CIVILTA DEL MEDITERRANEO. s-a. L.25000($40) Editoriale Scientifica s.r.l., Via Gen. V. Giordano Orsini 42, 80132 Naples, Italy. TEL 081-7646084. Ed. Gino Cavallo.

SOCIAL SCIENCES: COMPREHENSIVE WORKS

300   NE   ISSN 0587-5994
H1   CODEN: COEXEB
COEXISTENCE; a review of East-West and development issues. (Text and summaries in English) 1963. q. fl.380 to institutions; $243 to institutions in U.S. (effective 1996). Kluwer Law International (Subsidiary of: Wolters Kluwer N.V.), Postbus 85889, 2508 CN The Hague, Netherlands. TEL 31-70-3081500. FAX 31-70-3081515. E-mail: SERVICES@WKAP.NL. (Dist. by: Kluwer Academic Publishers Group, P.O. Box 322, 3300 AH Dordrecht, Netherlands. TEL 31-78-546392. FAX 31-78-546477; N. America dist. addr.: Box 358, Accord Sta., Hingham, MA 02018-0358. TEL 617-871-6600. FAX 617-871-6528) Eds. S. White, R. Beerman. adv.; bk.rev.; index. (also avail. in microform from UMI; microfiche from WSH; back issues avail.) **Indexed**: A.B.C.Pol.Sci., Amer.Hist.& Life, Curr.Cont., Hist.Abstr., IBZ, Int.Polit.Sci.Abstr., Mid.East: Abstr.& Ind., Polit.Sci.Abstr., Sociol.Abstr., SSCI. **Document type**: academic/scholarly publication.
—BLDSC (3292.830000); Faxon; SWETS; UMI; UnCover. **CCC**.
    Description: Publishes original and substantive contributions on East-West relations, on comparative studies of East and West, and on issues of socioeconomic development.
    Refereed Serial

300   CL
COLECCION FE E HISTORIA. 1977. irreg. Instituto Latinoamericano de Doctrina y Estudios Sociales, Departamento de Publicaciones, Almirante Barroso 6, Casilla 14446, Correo 21, Santiago, Chile.

300   BL
COLLOR. 1991. a. Instituto Brasileiro de Analises Sociais e Economicas, Rua Vincente de Souza 29, 22251 Botafogo, Rio de Janiero RJ, Brazil. TEL 021-286-0348.

COLOQUIO DE ESTUDOS LUSO BRASILEIROS. ANAIS. see *LINGUISTICS*

300   FI   ISSN 0355-256X
COMMENTATIONES SCIENTIARUM SOCIALIUM. (Text in English, Finnish) 1972. irreg. price varies. Societas Scientiarum Fennica - Finnish Society of Sciences and Letters, Marieg 5, SF-000170 Helsinki 17, Finland. TEL 63-30-05. Ed. Leif Nordberg. circ. 600. **Indexed**: Refug.Abstr. **Document type**: academic/scholarly publication.

300   EI
COMMISSION OF THE EUROPEAN COMMUNITIES. REPORT ON THE SOCIAL DEVELOPMENTS. (Published with its General Report on the Activities of the Communities) (Editions in Dutch, English, French, German) 1968. a. $25. Office for Official Publications of the European Communities, L-2985 Luxembourg, Luxembourg. (Dist. in U.S. by: Unipub, 4611-F Assembly Dr., Lanham, MD 20706-4391. TEL 800-274-4888. FAX 301-459-0056)
    Former titles: Commission of the European Communities. Report on the Social Situation; Commission of the European Communities. Expose sur l'Evolution Sociale dans la Communaute (ISSN 0531-3724)

300   US   ISSN 0147-4642
P87
COMMUNICATION YEARBOOK. 1977. a. $44.95. International Communication Association, Box 9589, Austin, TX 78766. TEL 512-454-8299. FAX 512-454-4221. Dir. Robert L. Cox.
—BLDSC (3363.470000); UnCover.

300   US   ISSN 1052-7656
HV697   CODEN: CALTE4
COMMUNITY ALTERNATIVES. 1989. s-a. $30. Human Service Associates, Inc., 336 N. Robert St., Ste. 1520, St. Paul, MN 55101. TEL 612-224-8967. FAX 612-224-6057. Ed. Curt Anderson. bk.rev. circ. 400. **Indexed**: Psychol.Abstr. (1989-). **Document type**: academic/scholarly publication.
—BLDSC (3363.586000); UnCover.
    Description: An international journal of family care.
    Refereed Serial

300   US
COMMUNITY COLLEGE SOCIAL SCIENCE NEWSLETTER. 1976. 5/yr. $25 to individuals; libraries $35; foreign $40. Community College Social Science Association, Grossmont College, Box 191303, San Diego, CA 92119. TEL 619-465-1700. Ed. Dr. Gerald Baydo. adv.; bk.rev.; film rev.; bibl.; charts; illus.; stat.; index. circ. 2,000. (tabloid format; also avail. in microform; reprint service avail. from UMI) **Indexed**: C.I.J.E.
    Formerly (until vol.3): Community College Social Science Journal; Supersedes (in Oct. 1976): Community College Social Science Quarterly (ISSN 0045-7728)

301 410   UK   ISSN 0143-7704
COMMUNITY STUDIES SERIES. 1980. irreg. price varies. University of Sheffield, Centre for English Cultural Tradition and Language, Sheffield S10 2TN, England. TEL 0114-2826296. FAX 0114-2768251. Ed. J.D.A. Widdowson. bk.rev. circ. 1,000. **Document type**: academic/scholarly publication.

300   IT
COMO; cultura, turismo, commercio, industria. 1955. q. L.15000. Domenico Discacciati, Via Carloni 8, 22100 Como, Italy. Ed. Alberto Longatti. adv. circ. 3,200.

301 572   US   ISSN 0733-4540
CB3
COMPARATIVE CIVILIZATIONS REVIEW. 1973. 2/yr. $15 to individuals; institutions $20. International Society for the Comparative Study of Civilizations, Dept. of History & Political Science, University of Missouri - Rolla, Rolla, MO 65401. TEL 314-341-4815. FAX 314-341-6127. (Subscr. to: Midori Rynn, Dept. of Sociology, Univ. of Scranton, Scranton, PA 18510-4605) adv.; bk.rev. circ. 700. **Indexed**: Abstr.Engl.Stud.; Arts & Hum.Cit.Ind., Curr.Cont., M.L.A., Per.Islam. (1991-), Sociol.Abstr. **Document type**: academic/scholarly publication.
—BLDSC (3363.752700).
    Formerly (until 1979): Comparative Civilization Bulletin (ISSN 0734-0621)
    Description: Provides a forum for humanists, social scientists and natural scientists to present scholarly ideas that cast new light on the processes and structures of civilizations or that reconsider the problems of interpreting civilizations.
    Refereed Serial

300.285   NE   ISSN 0925-9724
    CODEN: CSCWEQ
COMPUTER SUPPORTED COOPERATIVE WORK; an international journal. Short title: C S C W. (Text in English) 1992. q. fl.438 to institutions; $280 to institutions in U.S. (effective 1996). Kluwer Academic Publishers, Postbus 17, 3300 AA Dordrecht, Netherlands. TEL 31-78-392392. FAX 31-78-392254. TELEX 29245 KAPG NL. E-mail: SERVICES@WKAP.NL. (Dist. by: Kluwer Academic Publishers Group, P.O. Box 322, 3300 AH Dordrecht, Netherlands. TEL 31-78-392392. FAX 31-78-546474; N. American dist. addr.: Box 358, Accord Sta., Hingham, MA 02018-0358. TEL 617-871-6600. FAX 617-871-6528) Ed. Kjeld Schmidt. (also avail. in microform from UMI; back issues avail.; reprint service avail. from SWZ) **Indexed**: Ergon.Abstr., INSPEC (1992-). **Document type**: academic/scholarly publication.
—BLDSC (3394.285000); Ei; UMI. **CCC**.
    Description: Interdisciplinary forum for papers on theoretical, practical, technical and social issues in computer supported cooperative work.
    Refereed Serial

CONCEPTOS BOLETIN. see *SOCIOLOGY*

CONCEPTS AND TRANSFORMATION; international journal of action research and organizational renewal. see *BUSINESS AND ECONOMICS — Management*

055.1   IT   ISSN 0010-5228
CONCILIATORE. 1952. q. L.7000. Corso di Porta Vittoria 32, 20122 Milan, Italy. Ed. Jose Franchini. adv.; bk.rev.; play rev.; bibl.; illus.; stat.

301   US
CONFERENCE GROUP FOR SOCIAL AND ADMINISTRATIVE HISTORY. TRANSACTIONS.* 1971. s-a. $5. Conference Group for Social and Administrative History, 639 Wisconsin St., Oshkosh, WI 54901. Ed. Werner Braatz. circ. 200. **Indexed**: Amer.Hist.& Life, Hist.Abstr.

300
CONFLICT AND SOCIAL CHANGE SERIES. 1990. irreg. (approx. biennial); vol. 3, 1993. price varies. Athelone Press Ltd., 1 Park Dr., London NW11 7SG, England. TEL 0181-458-0888. FAX 0181-201-8115. (Dist. in U.S. by: Athlone Press, 165 First Ave., Atlantic Highlands, NJ 07781. TEL 908-872-1441) **Document type**: monographic series.
    Description: Contains assessments of areas of British life involving conflict and change.

CONFUCIUS & MENCIUS SOCIETY OF THE REPUBLIC OF CHINA. JOURNAL. see *RELIGIONS AND THEOLOGY — Other Denominations And Sects*

300   CK
CONGRESO INTERNACIONAL DE VIVIENDA POPULAR. irreg.?, no.3, 1974. Col.$90. (Servicio Latino-Americano y Asiatico de Vivienda Popular) Centro de Investigacion y Educacion Popular, Carrera 5 No.33A-08, Apdo. Aereo 25916, Bogota, Colombia. TEL 2858977.

300   CN   ISSN 0827-5548
JL241.A1
CONJONCTURES. 1982. s-a. Can.$30($33) 4076 St. Hubert, Montreal, Que. H2L 4A8, Canada. TEL 514-523-4724. FAX 514-525-0967. bk.rev. (back issues avail.)

CONNEXIONS DIGEST; a social change sourcebook. see *POLITICAL SCIENCE*

300   AG
CONSEJO LATINOAMERICANO DE CIENCIAS SOCIALES. CARTA. m. Consejo Latinoamericano de Ciencias Sociales, Callao 875, piso 3, 1023 Buenos Aires, Argentina. TEL 54-1-811-7313. FAX 54-1-812-8459. E-mail: rvclacso@arcriba.edu.ar. Ed. Jorge Fraga. **Document type**: newsletter.
    Description: Informs of activities, trends, accomplishments and opportunities in the social sciences.

CONSORTIUM ON REVOLUTIONARY EUROPE. SELECTED PAPERS. see *HISTORY — History Of Europe*

300 600   UK
▼**CONTEMPORARY TRENDS IN EUROPEAN SOCIAL SCIENCES**. 1994. irreg., no.3, 1994. £38.50. (Interdisciplinary Centre for Comparative Research in the Social Sciences (ICCR), AU) Ashgate Publishing Group, Gower House, Croft Rd., Aldershot, Hants. GU11 3HR, England. TEL 01252-331551. FAX 01252-344405. Ed.Bd. **Document type**: monographic series.

300 350   UK   ISSN 0951-4937
HN398.W26
CONTEMPORARY WALES; an annual review of economic and social research. 1987. a. £7.50($14) (Board of Celtic Studies) University of Wales Press, 6 Gwennyth St., Cathay, Cardiff CF2 4YD, Wales. TEL 01222-231919. FAX 01222-230908. (Subscr. in U.S.: Books International Inc., P.O. Box 605, Herndon, VA 22070) Eds. Graham Day, Dennis Thomas. adv.; stat.; circ. 300 (paid). (back issues avail.) **Document type**: academic/scholarly publication.
—BLDSC (3425.315000).
    Description: Contains an authoritative analysis of economic and social development in Wales.
    Refereed Serial

CONTINUUM (NEW YORK). see *HUMANITIES: COMPREHENSIVE WORKS*

300   BL
CONTRIBUICOES EM CIENCIAS SOCIAIS. irreg. Editora Campus Ltda. (Subsidiary of: Elsevier Science B.V.), Rua Sete de Setembro 111-16 andar, 20159-900 Centro, Rio de Janeiro RJ, Brazil. TEL 021-221-5340. FAX 021-252-2904. **Document type**: monographic series.

SOCIAL SCIENCES: COMPREHENSIVE WORKS

305.8 — US — ISSN 0196-7088
CONTRIBUTIONS IN ETHNIC STUDIES. 1980. irreg., no.30, 1992. price varies. Greenwood Press, Inc. (Subsidiary of: Greenwood Publishing Group Inc.), 88 Post Rd. W., Box 5007, Westport, CT 06881-5007. TEL 203-226-3571. FAX 203-222-1502. Ed. Leonard W. Doob. **Document type:** monographic series.
—BLDSC (3458.415000).

CONTRIBUTIONS IN LATIN AMERICAN STUDIES. see HISTORY — History Of North And South America

300 — US — ISSN 1058-2029
AP2
COSMOS; a journal of emerging issues. 1991. a. $4. Cosmos Club, 2121 Massachusetts Ave., N.W., Washington, DC 20008. TEL 202-387-7783. FAX 202-234-6817. Ed. Murray J. Gart. circ. 4,000. **Document type:** academic/scholarly publication.

300 — TZ
COUNCIL FOR THE SOCIAL SCIENCES IN EAST AFRICA. SOCIAL SCIENCE CONFERENCE. PROCEEDINGS. a. EAs.200($29) c/o University of Dar-es-Salaam, Faculty of Arts and Social Science, Box 35091, Dar-es-Salaam, Tanzania. charts; stat.

CRIME, LAW, AND DEVIANCE SERIES. see CRIMINOLOGY AND LAW ENFORCEMENT

300 — PE
CRITICA ANDINA. 1978. irreg. $12 to individuals; institutions $18. Instituto de Estudios Sociales, Director de Publicaciones, Casilla Postal 790, Cusco, Peru. Dir. Marco Villasante. adv.; bk.rev. circ. 2,000.

300 — AG
CRITICA DE NUESTRO TIEMPO; revista internacional de teoria y politica. 1991. 3/yr. $30 to individuals; institutions $50 (effective 1995). (Centro de Estudios Marxistas Pedro Milesi) Busqueda de Nuestro Tiempo Editorial, Casilla de Correo 3509, 1000 Buenos Aires, Argentina. TEL 54-1-3252723. Ed. Luis Bilbao; Pub. Carlos Beacon. adv. contact: Juan Gandolfo. bk.rev. circ. 2,000. **Document type:** academic/scholarly publication.

330 — US
CRITICAL PERSPECTIVES IN SOCIAL THEORY. 1983. irreg. price varies. Praeger Publishers (Subsidiary of: Greenwood Publishing Group Inc.), 88 Post Rd. W., Box 5007, Westport, CT 06881-5007. TEL 203-226-3571. FAX 203-222-1502. **Document type:** monographic series.

300 — US — ISSN 1069-3971
H1 — CODEN: CRCRE4
CROSS-CULTURAL RESEARCH; the journal of comparative social science. 1966. q. $51 to individuals; institutions $112 (effective Sep. 1995). (Society for Cross-Cultural Research) Sage Publications, Inc., 2455 Teller Rd., Thousand Oaks, CA 91320. TEL 805-499-0721. FAX 805-499-0871. E-mail: libraries@sagepub.com. (Overseas subscr. to: Sage Publications Ltd., 6 Bonhill St., London EC2A 4PU, England; Sage Publications India Pvt. Ltd., P.O. Box 4125, New Delhi 110 048, India) (Co-sponsor: Human Relations Area Files, Inc.) Ed. Melvin Ember. bk.rev.; bibl.; charts; index. circ. 500. (processed; also avail. in microform from UMI; back issues avail.; reprint service avail. from UMI) **Indexed:** A.I.C.P., Abstr.Anthropol., Anthropol.Lit., ASSIA, E.I., IMFL, Psychol.Abstr. (1974-), SSCI. **Document type:** academic/scholarly publication.
—BLDSC (3488.825000); Faxon; UMI; UnCover. **CCC.**
Former titles (until 1993): Behavior Science Research (ISSN 0094-3673); Behavior Science Notes (ISSN 0005-7886)
Description: Studies cross-cultural or comparative issues in the social and behavioral sciences.
Refereed Serial

CROSS-THINKING FOR DISCOVERY AND CREATIVITY. see SCIENCES: COMPREHENSIVE WORKS

300 — PE
CUADERNOS DE CAPACITACION CAMPESINA. 1975. irreg., latest no.5040. price varies. Centro de Estudios Regionales Andinos "Bartolome de Las Casas", Apdo. 4779, Cusco, Peru. TEL 084-236494. FAX 084-238255.
Formerly: Cuadernos de Capacitacion Popular.

300 — SP — ISSN 0210-847X
DP302.G11
CUADERNOS DE ESTUDIOS GALLEGOS. a. 3000 ptas. (foreign 4500 ptas.). Consejo Superior de Investigaciones Cientificas (C.S.I.C.), C. Vitruvio 8, 28006 Madrid, Spain. TEL 261-28-33. FAX 262-96-34.

300 — AG — ISSN 0326-6060
CUADERNOS DE HISTORIA REGIONAL. 1984. 4/yr. price varies or exchange basis. (Universidad Nacional de Lujan, Departamento de Ciencias Sociales) Editorial Universitaria de Buenos Aires, Casilla de Correo 221, 6700 Lujan, Argentina. bk.rev.

300 — US — ISSN 0893-7494
F1788
CUBA ANNUAL REPORT. 1986. irreg., latest 1989. $79.95. (Voice of America Radio Programming) Transaction Publishers, Transaction Periodicals Consortium, Department 3901, Rutgers University, New Brunswick, NJ 08803. TEL 908-445-2280. FAX 908-445-3138. (back issues avail.)
Description: A series of statistical and empirical reports that provide basic data on the structure and function of life in Cuba.

CULTURA NACIONAL; revista bimestrale de politica y ciencias sociales. see POLITICAL SCIENCE

300 — II — ISSN 0011-2895
CULTURAL RESEARCH INSTITUTE. BULLETIN. (Text in Bengali or English) 1962. q. Rs.50. Cultural Research Institute, P1-4, C.I.T. Scheme, VIIM, V.I.P. Road, P.O. Kankurgachi, Calcutta 700054, India. (Affiliate: West Bengal. Sch. Castes & Tribal Welfare Department) Ed.Bd. bk.rev.; bibl.; charts; illus.; stat. circ. 1,000. **Indexed:** A.I.C.P., Anthropol.Lit. **Document type:** bulletin.

960 800 301 410 — ZR — ISSN 0302-5640
DT641
CULTURES AU ZAIRE ET EN AFRIQUE. Abbreviated title: Cultures. (Text in English, French) 1973. q. $16. Office National de la Recherche et du Developpement, Section des Sciences de l'Homme, B.P. 16706, Kinshasa 1, Zaire. bk.rev.; bibl.
Supersedes: Dombi.

CURRENT ISSUES IN LANGUAGE AND SOCIETY. see LINGUISTICS

CYCLES (WAYNE). see BUSINESS AND ECONOMICS — Economic Systems And Theories, Economic History

300 — CY — ISSN 1015-2881
DS54.A2 — CODEN: CYREEL
THE CYPRUS REVIEW; a journal of social, economic and political issues. (Text in English) 1989. s-a. $40 to individuals; institutions $60 (effective 1996). Intercollege - Research and Development Center, P.O. Box 4005, 1700 Nicosia, Cyprus. TEL 357-2-456892. FAX 357-2-357964. TELEX 4969 INTERCOL CY. (Co-sponsor: University of Indianapolis (US)) Ed. Nicos Peristianis. adv.; B&W page $200; adv. contact: Andreas Antoniades. bk.rev. circ. 150. **Indexed:** Int.Bibl.Soc.Sci., Int.Polit.Sci.Abstr., P.A.I.S., Peace Res.Abstr., Polit.Sci.Abstr., Sociol.Abstr. **Document type:** academic/scholarly publication.
● Also available online. Vendor(s): Data-Star, Knight-Ridder, Inc., Ovid Technologies.
Description: Deals exclusively with issues concerning social, economic, and political issues of Cyprus life.

D L S U DIALOGUE. (De La Salle University) see HUMANITIES: COMPREHENSIVE WORKS

300 — BL — ISSN 0011-5258
DADOS; revista de ciencias sociais. (Text in Portuguese; summaries in English, French) 1966. 3/yr. Instituto Universitario de Pesquisas do Rio de Janeiro, Rua do Matriz No. 82, Botafogo, 22260-100 Rio de Janeiro RJ, Brazil. Eds. Charles Pessanha, Amaury de Souza. bk.rev.; bibl.; charts; index, cum.index: 1966-1972. circ. 4,000. (back issues avail.; reprint service avail. from ISI) **Indexed:** Curr.Cont., Hisp.Amer.Per.Ind. (1978-), Int.Polit.Sci.Abstr., Sociol.Abstr.
—Genuine Article.

300 — PE
DEBATES ANDINOS. irreg., latest no.3018. Centro de Estudios Regionales Andinos "Bartolome de Las Casas", Apdo. 477, Cusco, Peru. TEL 084-236494. FAX 084-238255.

300 900 400 — II — ISSN 0045-9801
DECCAN COLLEGE. POSTGRADUATE & RESEARCH INSTITUTE. BULLETIN. (Text in English) 1939. a. $30. Deccan College, Postgraduate & Research Institute, Poona 411006, India. bk.rev. circ. 500. (also avail. in microfiche from IDC; back issues avail.) **Indexed:** Bibl.Ling., GeoRef. **Document type:** bulletin.

DELFIN; eine deutsche Zeitschrift fuer Konstruktion, Analyse und Kritik. see ART

300 — AG — ISSN 0328-0101
DELITO Y SOCIEDAD; revista de ciencias sociales. 1992. s-a. Universidad de Buenos Aires, Facultad de Ciencias Sociales, Talcahuano 256, 1o piso, Buenos Aires, Argentina. TEL 541-476-0570. (Co-sponsor: Centro de Informatica Aplicada) Ed. Juan S. Pegoraro. **Document type:** academic/scholarly publication.

DERECHO Y CIENCIAS SOCIALES. see LAW

300 — GW — ISSN 0341-7239
DEUTSCH-BRASILIANISCHE HEFTE. (Text and summaries in German, Portuguese) 1960. bi-m. DM.48. Lateinamerika-Zentrum e.V., Schumannstr. 2b, 53113 Bonn, Germany. TEL 0228-210788. Ed. Hermann M. Goergen. adv.; bk.rev. circ. 8,000. **Indexed:** Maize Abstr., Soyabean Abstr., World Agri.Econ.& Rural Sociol.Abstr.

300 338 — UK — ISSN 0012-155X
HD82
DEVELOPMENT AND CHANGE. 1969. q. £119($192) (foreign £119) (effective 1996). (Institute of Social Studies, The Hague, NE) Basil Blackwell Ltd., 108 Cowley Rd., Oxford OX4 1JF, England. TEL 44-865-791100. FAX 44-865-791347. (Subscr. to: P.O. Box 87, Oxford OX2 0DT, England. TEL 44-865-791155. FAX 44-865-791927; in N. America: Blackwell Publishers, 238 Main St., Cambridge, MA 02142. TEL 617-547-7110. FAX 617-547-0789) Ed.Bd. bk.rev.; charts. (also avail. in microform from UMI) **Indexed:** A.B.C.Pol.Sci., Abstr.Rural Dev.Trop., Amer.Hist.& Life, Asian-Pac.Econ.Lit., ASSIA, Commun.Abstr., Curr.Cont., Documentatieblad, E.I., Energy Ind., Energy Info.Abstr., Geo.Abstr., Hist.Abstr., HR Rep., IDA, Int.Lab.Doc., Int.Polit.Sci.Abstr., J.of Econ.Lit., Key to Econ.Sci., Mid.East: Abstr.& Ind., Rice Abstr., Rural Devel.Abstr., Rural Ext.Educ.& Tr.Abstr., Rural Recreat.Tour.Abstr., Sage Fam.Stud.Abstr., Sage Urb.Stud.Abstr., SSCI. **Document type:** academic/scholarly publication.
—BLDSC (3578.750000); Faxon; Genuine Article; SWETS; UMI; UnCover. **CCC.**
Description: Contributes to the understanding of Third World problems. Publishes critical analysis and articles from all disciplines of the social sciences discussing current development issues.

DHAKA UNIVERSITY STUDIES. PART A: ARTS, HUMANITIES, AND SOCIAL SCIENCE. see HUMANITIES: COMPREHENSIVE WORKS

300 — MX — ISSN 0185-7770
DIALECTICA. 1976-1986; resumed 1987. 4/yr. Mex.$75($40) Universidad Autonoma de Puebla, Escuela de Filosofia y Letras, Reforma 913, Altos, 7200 Puebla, Pue., Mexico. TEL 32-70-88. Ed.Bd. bk.rev. circ. 3,000. (back issues avail.)
Description: Covers philosophy, social sciences, literature, culture and politics.

300 — AU
DIALOG. BEITRAEGE ZUR FRIEDENSFORSCHUNG. q. $51.50. Oesterreichisches Studienzentrum fuer Frieden und Konflikt loesung, Burg, A-7461 Stadtschlaining, Austria. **Document type:** academic/scholarly publication.

DIALOGUE. see LITERATURE

SOCIAL SCIENCES: COMPREHENSIVE WORKS

300 325   US   ISSN 1044-2057
JV6001.A1
DIASPORA: A JOURNAL OF TRANSNATIONAL STUDIES. 1991. 3/yr. $25.50 to individuals (foreign $35.50); institutions $51 (foreign $61) (effective 1995). (Zoryan Institute) Oxford University Press, Journals, 2001 Evans Rd., Cary, NC 27513. TEL 919-677-0977; 800-852-7323. FAX 919-677-1714. E-mail: jnlorders@oup-usa.org. (Subscr. outside N. America to: Oxford University Press, Journals, Walton St., Oxford OX2 6DP, England. TEL 44-1865-56767. FAX 44-1865-267773) Ed. Khachig Tololyan. adv.: B&W page $200. circ. 820. **Document type:** academic/scholarly publication.
—BLDSC (3580.230000); SWETS; UMI; UnCover. CCC.
Description: Publishes essays on diasporas and other transnational and infranational phenomena that challenge the homogeneity of the nation-state. Includes specific accounts of ancient and contemporary diasporal communities, of their relations with real and imagined homelands, as well as their literatures, cultural productions, social structures, politics, and history.
Refereed Serial

300   UK
DISCUSSION PAPERS IN SOCIOLOGY. irreg. University of Leicester, Department of Sociology, University Rd., Leicester LE1 7RH, England. TEL 01533-522738. FAX 01533-522746. **Document type:** monographic series.

300   UK   ISSN 0263-3221
DITCHLEY CONFERENCE REPORTS. 1981. 15/yr. free. Ditchley Foundation, Enstone, Chipping Norton, Oxon. OX7 4ER, England. TEL 01608-677346. FAX 01608-677399. (U.S. subscr. to: American Ditchley Foundation, 477 Madison Ave., 6th Fl., New York, NY 10022) Ed. Heather Weeks.
—BLDSC (3604.255900).

300 340   UK   ISSN 0262-8015
HN1
DITCHLEY NEWSLETTER. 1981. 3/yr. free. Ditchley Foundation, Enstone, Chipping Norton, Oxon. OX7 4ER, England. TEL 01608-677346. FAX 01608-677399. (U.S. subscr. to: American Ditchley Foundation, 477 Madison Ave., 6th Fl., New York, NY 10022) Ed. Heather Weeks. adv.; bibl.; index. circ. 1,000. **Document type:** newsletter.
Supersedes: Ditchley Journal (ISSN 0305-4322)

300   SP   ISSN 0417-8106
DOCUMENTACION SOCIAL; revista de estudios sociales y de sociologia aplicada. 1958. 4/yr. 3400 ptas. (Europe 8400 ptas.; America $93) (effective 1995). Caritas Espanola, San Bernardo, 99 bis, 7a, 28015 Madrid, Spain. TEL 34-91-4455300. FAX 34-91-5934882. **Indexed:** SCIMP (1989-), World Agri.Econ.& Rural Sociol.Abstr.

300 100   CC
DONGBEI SHIDA XUEBAO (ZHEXUE SHEHUI KEXUE BAN)/NORTHEAST NORMAL UNIVERSITY. JOURNAL (PHILOSOPHY, SOCIAL SCIENCE EDITION). (Text in Chinese) 1951. bi-m. Y9. Dongbei Shifan Daxue, Xuebao Bianjibu, 110, Stalin Street, Changchun, Jilin 130024, People's Republic of China.
Description: Publishes research results in philosophy, political science, economics, history, education, linguistics, and literature.

300   CC
DONGNAN YA ZONGHENG. (Text in Chinese) q. Guangxi Shehui Kexueyuan, Dongnan Ya Yanjiusuo - Guangxi Academy of Social Sciences, Southeast Asian Studies Institute, No. 30, Xinzhu Lu, Nanning, Guangxi 530022, People's Republic of China. TEL 20584. Ed. Zhao Heman.

300   CC
DONG'OU/EASTERN EUROPE. (Text in Chinese) q. Beijing Waiyu Xueyuan - Beijing Foreign Language Institute, No.2, Xisanhuan Beilu, Beijing 100081, People's Republic of China. TEL 890351. Ed. Yang Yanjie.

300   CC
DONGYUE LUNCONG/DONGYUE TRIBUNE. (Text in Chinese) bi-m. $35.60. Shandong Sheng Shehui Kexueyuan - Shandong Academy of Social Sciences, No. 28, Yuhan Lu, Jinan, Shandong 250002, People's Republic of China. TEL 615540. (Dist. in US by: China Books & Periodicals, Inc., 2929 24th St., San Francisco, CA 94110. TEL 415-282-2994) Ed. Guo Molan.

DIE DREI; Zeitschrift fuer Anthroposophie. see RELIGIONS AND THEOLOGY — Other Denominations And Sects

DROIT SOCIAL. see LAW

300   CI   ISSN 1330-0288
DRUSTVENA ISTRAZIVANJA; casopis za opca drustvan pitanja. bi-m. $50. Institut za Primijenjena Drustvena Istrazivanja - Institute for Applied Social Research, Marulicev trg 19-I, 41000 Zagreb, Croatia. TEL 385-41-445068. FAX 385-41-448566. Ed. Sinisa Zrinscak. **Indexed:** Sociol.Abstr.
—BLDSC (3630.145500).
Description: Publishes works in different social disciplines sociology, philosophy, psychology, political sciences, psychiarty, history, law, economics, demography, linguistics etc.

300   MX
DUDA; lo increible es la verdad. w. Editorial Posada, S.A., Oculistas No. 43, Col. El Sifon, 09400 Mexico, D.F., Mexico.

300   UK   ISSN 0732-5819
E F L GAZETTE. (English Foreign Language) 1978. m. $65. E F L (Gazette) Ltd., 10 Wrights Ln., Kensington, London W8 6TA, England. TEL 0171-938-1818. FAX 0171-937-7534. E-mail: 100130,20370@compuserve.com. Ed. Dan Ward. adv.; bk.rev.; circ. 5,000 (paid). (also avail. in microform from UMI,MIM) **Indexed:** Lang.Teach.& Ling.Abstr. **Document type:** academic/scholarly publication, newspaper.
—UMI. CCC.
Description: Contains news related to teaching English as a foreign language.

300   EI   ISSN 0258-1965
E F NEWS. Variant title: News from the Foundation. 1986. 5/yr. free. European Foundation for the Improvement of Living and Working Conditions, Loughlinstown House, Shankill, Co. Dublin, Ireland. TEL 01-2826888. FAX 01-2826456. Ed. Brid Nolan. **Document type:** newsletter.

300   UK   ISSN 0736-2048
E L T DOCUMENTS. (English Language Teacher) 3/yr. £10.95. MacMillan Press Ltd., Houndsmills, Basingstoke, Hants RG21 2XS, England. TEL 0256-29242. FAX 0256-28339. Ed. C.J. Brumfit. (also avail. in microform from UMI,MIM) **Indexed:** Lang.& Lang.Behav.Abstr., Lang.Teach.& Ling.Abstr. **Document type:** academic/scholarly publication.
—CCC.

300 001.3   UK
E S R C DATA ARCHIVE BULLETIN. 1975. 3/yr. free. University of Essex, Economic and Social Research Council Data Archive, Colchester CO4 3SQ, England. TEL 01206-872001. FAX 01206-872003. E-mail: archive@essex.ac.uk. Ed. Bridget Winstanley. adv. contact: Rowan Currie. bk.rev. circ. 5,000. **Document type:** bulletin.
Former titles: S S R C Data Archive Bulletin; S S R C Survey Archive Bulletin (ISSN 0307-1391)
Description: News, articles and book reviews on data analysis and management in the humanities and social sciences.

300   UK   ISSN 0962-7782
E S R C RESEARCH CENTRE ON MICRO-SOCIAL CHANGE IN BRITAIN. TECHNICAL PAPERS. 1991. irreg., no.6, 1993. University of Essex, Economic and Social Research Council, Research Centre on Micro-social Change in Britain, Colchester, Essex CO4 3SQ, England. TEL 01206-872938. FAX 01206-873151. TELEX 98440 UNILIB G. (back issues avail.) **Document type:** monographic series.
—BLDSC (9349.227000).

300   UK   ISSN 0962-1318
E S R C RESEARCH CENTRE ON MICRO-SOCIAL CHANGE IN BRITAIN. WORKING PAPERS. 1991. irreg., no.11. University of Essex, Economic & Social Research Council, Research Centre on Micro-social Change in Britain, Colchester, Essex CO4 3SQ, England. TEL 01206-872938. FAX 01206-873151. TELEX 98440 UNILIB G. (back issues avail.) **Document type:** monographic series.
—BLDSC (9349.200000).

E S R C STUDENTSHIP HANDBOOK; postgraduate studentships in the social sciences. (Economic and Social Research Council) see EDUCATION — Guides To Schools And Colleges

300   US
EARTH: WHERE DO WE GO FROM HERE?. 1993. bi-m. $3 (effective 1993). 2802 Shelley Rd., Philadelphia, PA 19152. TEL 215-677-8146. Ed. Joseph Olszewski, Jr. adv.; bk.rev. circ. 53. (looseleaf format) **Document type:** newsletter.
Description: Attempts to change-stimulate the reader's mind with information about the world we live in today. Challenges modern theories, tries to establish new, more effective ones.

EARTHWATCH. see SCIENCES: COMPREHENSIVE WORKS

300   TZ   ISSN 0424-0928
EAST AFRICAN STUDIES.* 1953. irreg. (Makerere University, Makerere Institute of Social Research, UG) East African Publishing House, POB 3209, Dar es Salaam, Tanzania. charts. **Document type:** monographic series.

EAST ASIAN SOCIAL SCIENCE MONOGRAPHS. see HISTORY — History Of Asia

940 947   US   ISSN 0012-8449
DR1
EAST EUROPEAN QUARTERLY. (Text in English, French, German) 1967. q. $20. East European Quarterly, University of Colorado, Box 29, Regent Hall, Boulder, CO 80309. TEL 941-753-4782. Ed. Stephen Fischer-Galati. adv.; bk.rev. circ. 950. (also avail. in microform from UMI; reprint service avail. from SCH,UMI) **Indexed:** Amer.Bibl.Slavic & E.Eur.Stud., Amer.Hist.& Life, Curr.Cont., Hist.Abstr., Int.Polit.Sci.Abstr., Mid.East: Abstr.& Ind., P.A.I.S., Polit.Sci.Abstr., RILA, Soc.Sci.Ind., SSCI. **Document type:** academic/scholarly publication.
●Also available online. Vendor(s): University Microfilms International.
—BLDSC (3646.320000); Faxon; SWETS; UMI; UnCover.

EASTERN AFRICA SOCIAL SCIENCE RESEARCH REVIEW. 1985. 2/yr. $18 in Africa; elsewhere $25. Organization for Social Science Research in Eastern Africa, P.O. Box 31971, Addis Ababa, Ethiopia. TEL 251-1-119505. FAX 251-1-551399. TELEX 21646. E-mail: OSSREA@PADIS.GN.APC.ORG. Eds. Ali Abdel Gadir Ali, Wilfred Mlay. bk.rev. circ. 500. (back issues avail.) **Indexed:** P.L.E.S.A. **Document type:** academic/scholarly publication.
Refereed Serial

300   US
ECOJUSTICE QUARTERLY. 1981. q. $10. Center for Religion, Ethics, and Social Policy, Anabel Taylor Hall, Cornell University, Ithaca, NY 14853. TEL 607-255-4225. FAX 607-255-2920. Ed. Dana Horrell. bk.rev. circ. 4,000.
Formerly (until vol.13, no.4, 1993): Egg (Ithaca) (ISSN 1059-5821)
Description: Promotes understanding and action on issues of ecology and social justice understood as inseparable.

ECONOMIC AND SOCIAL RESEARCH INSTITUTE. BROADSHEET SERIES. see BUSINESS AND ECONOMICS

ECONOMIC AND SOCIAL RESEARCH INSTITUTE. MEMORANDUM SERIES. see BUSINESS AND ECONOMICS

ECONOMIC AND SOCIAL RESEARCH INSTITUTE. TECHNICAL SERIES. see BUSINESS AND ECONOMICS

ECONOMIC AND SOCIAL REVIEW. see BUSINESS AND ECONOMICS

SOCIAL SCIENCES: COMPREHENSIVE WORKS

300 330   FR   ISSN 0245-9132
HB3
ECONOMIE ET HUMANISME. 1942. q. 270 F. (foreign 350 F.) (effective 1995). Economie et Humanisme, 14 rue Antoine Dumont, 69372 Lyon Cedex 08, France. TEL 78-61-32-23. FAX 78-69-86-96. Ed. Vincent Berthe. adv. contact: Philippe Blancher. bk.rev.; bibl.; charts; illus.; index. circ. 5,000. (reprint service avail. from SCH) **Indexed:** C.I.S. Abstr., Geo.Abstr., Int.Lab.Doc., Key to Econ.Sci., P.A.I.S.For.Lang.Ind., Pt.de Rep. (1979-), World Agri.Econ.& Rural Sociol.Abstr.
—BLDSC (3657.510000); SWETS.
 Description: Aims at providing information and reflexion to nonspecialists about major socioeconomic world issues.

320.351   UK   ISSN 0308-5147
ECONOMY AND SOCIETY. 1972. q. £36 (U.S. and Canada $66; rest of world £40) to individuals; institutions £68 (U.S. and Canada $115; rest of world £74). Routledge, 11 New Fetter Ln., London EC4P 4EE, England. TEL 0171-583-9855. FAX 0171-842-2298. TELEX 263398-ROUT-G. E-mail: sample.journals@routledge.com. (Subscr. to: ITPS Ltd., Cheriton House, Andover, Hants SP10 5BE, England. TEL 01264-342919. FAX 01264-342807) Ed. Grahame Thompson. adv.: page £200; trim 115 x 190. bk.rev.; index. circ. 1,300. (also avail. in microform from UMI; reprint service avail. from UMI) **Indexed:** Asian-Pac.Econ.Lit., ASSIA, E.I., Geo.Abstr., IDA, Int.Polit.Sci.Abstr., Lang.& Lang.Behav.Abstr., Mid.East: Abstr.& Ind., Sociol.Abstr. (1972-), SSCI, World Bank.Abstr. **Document type:** academic/scholarly publication.
—BLDSC (3659.520000); Faxon; Genuine Article; SWETS; UnCover. **CCC.**
 Description: Interdisciplinary journal that covers the social sciences, history and philosophy with an emphasis on theoretical perspectives.

300   SP
EDICIONES PENINSULA. SERIE UNIVERSITARIA. HISTORIA, CIENCIA, SOCIEDAD. 1966. irreg. Ediciones 62, S.A., Provenca 278, 08008 Barcelona, Spain. TEL 487-00-62.

EDUCATIONAL BOOK REVIEW. see *HUMANITIES: COMPREHENSIVE WORKS*

300   ER
EESTI TEADUSTE AKADEEMIA. TOIMETISED. HUMANITAAR JA SOTSIAALTEADUSED/ESTONIAN ACADEMY OF SCIENCES. PROCEEDINGS. HUMANITIES AND SOCIAL SCIENCES. (Text and summaries in English, Estonian, French, Russian) 1956. q. $60 (effective 1995). Teaduste Akadeemia Kirjastus, Estonia pst.7, EE-0100 Tallinn, Estonia. TEL 7-3722-454156. (Subscr. to: Akateeminen Kirjakauppa 128 SF, 00101 Helsinki, Finland; or to: Bibliotekstajanst AB 200, S22100 Lund, Sweden) index. circ. 700. **Document type:** academic/scholarly publication.
 Formerly: Eesti Teaduste Akadeemia. Toimetised. Uhiskonnateadused (ISSN 0373-6431)

ELDERS; een kroniek van zaken buiten de grenzen. see *POPULATION STUDIES*

300   ZR
ELIMU;* revue des sciences humaines. 1973. q. Universite Nationale du Zaire, Lubumbashi, B.P. 945, Lubumbashi, Zaire.
 Supersedes: Syntheses.

300   US
ELMWOOD NEWSLETTER. irreg. Elmwood Institute, Box 5805, Berkeley, CA 94705. TEL 415-845-4595. Ed. Shana Penn. **Document type:** newsletter.

300   GW   ISSN 0341-7832
EMPIRISCHE SOZIALFORSCHUNG. (Text in English, German) 1983. a. DM.80. (Zentralarchiv fuer Empirische Sozialforschung) Campus Verlag GmbH, Heerstr. 149, 60488 Frankfurt a.M., Germany. TEL 069-9765160. FAX 069-97651678. Ed. Harald Rohlinger. circ. 800. (back issues avail.) **Document type:** academic/scholarly publication.

344 347   US   ISSN 1044-3541
KF3002
EMPLOYEE RELATIONS UPDATE.* m. Industrial Relations, Inc., Heritage Bank Bldg., Box 3703, Troy, MI 48007-3703.

300   NQ   ISSN 0424-9674
ENCUENTRO. Variant title: Revista Encuentro. 1968. 3/yr. $30. Universidad Centroamericana, Apdo. 69, 70352 Managua, Nicaragua. TEL 505-2-670352. FAX 505-2-670106. Ed. Nelly Miranda Miranda; Pub. Alejandro Brovo. bk.rev.; illus. circ. 1,500. **Indexed:** Hisp.Amer.Per.Ind. (1970-), Int.Lab.Doc. **Document type:** academic/scholarly publication.
 Description: Covers the natural and social sciences in Nicaragua.
 Refereed Serial

ENCYCLOPAEDIA AFRICANA. INFORMATION REPORT. see *HISTORY — History Of Africa*

ENTOURAGE. see *HANDICAPPED*

ENVIRONMENTAL VALUES. see *ENVIRONMENTAL STUDIES*

ESSAYS ON THE ECONOMY AND SOCIETY OF THE SUDAN. see *BUSINESS AND ECONOMICS — Economic Situation And Conditions*

300   HO
ESTIQUIRIN; arte-ciencia-literatura. bi-m. Editorial Guaymuras, Apdo. Postal 1843, Tegucigalpa, Honduras. Ed.Bd.

300   PE
ESTUDIOS ANDINOS. 1990. irreg., no. 3101, 1990. price varies. Centro de Estudios Regionales Andinos "Bartolome de las Casas", Apdo. 477, Cusco, Peru. TEL 084-236494. FAX 084-238255.

972.8 300   ES   ISSN 0014-1445
AP63   CODEN: ESCEES
ESTUDIOS CENTRO AMERICANOS. 1946. m. Col.50($60) (effective 1992). Universidad Centroamericana "Jose Simeon Canas", Apdo. Postal (01) 575, San Salvador, El Salvador. FAX 503-24-0288. Ed. Rodolfo Cardenal. adv.; bk.rev.; charts; illus.; index. circ. 3,000. **Indexed:** Amer.Hist.& Life (until 1991), Hisp.Amer.Per.Ind. (1970-), Hist.Abstr. (until 1991).

300   SP   ISSN 0423-4847
ESTUDIOS DE DEUSTO. 1953. s-a. 3500 ptas.($45) Universidad de Deusto, Departamento de Publicaciones, Apdo. 1, 48080 Bilbao, Spain. Ed. Ignacio Beobide. bk.rev.; index. circ. 400. (back issues avail.) **Indexed:** Amer.Hist.& Life, CERDIC, Hist.Abstr.

300   PY   ISSN 0251-2483
F2661
ESTUDIOS PARAGUAYOS. 1973. s-a. (in 1 vol.). 18000 g.($30) (effective 1995). Universidad Catolica Nuestra Senora de la Asuncion, Centro de Estudios Antropologicos, Casilla de Correo 1718, Asuncion, Paraguay. TEL 595-21-446251. FAX 595-21-445245. Ed. Adriano Irala-Burgos. adv.; bk.rev.; cum.index. circ. 1,000. (back issues avail.) **Indexed:** Amer.Hist.& Life, Hisp.Amer.Per.Ind. (1973-), Hist.Abstr.

330   CL   ISSN 0716-1115
ESTUDIOS PUBLICOS. (Text in Spanish) 1980. q. Esc.6000 (foreign $44) (effective 1995). Centro de Estudios Publicos, Monsenor Sotero Sanz No. 175, Providencia, Santiago 9, Chile. TEL 56-2-2315324. FAX 56-2-2335253. Ed. Arturo Fontaine Talavera. adv. contact: Maria Teresa Miranda. bk.rev. circ. 2,500. **Indexed:** Hisp.Amer.Per.Ind. (1986-), Int.Polit.Sci.Abstr., P.A.I.S., Sociol.Abstr., World Agri.Econ.& Rural Sociol.Abstr. **Document type:** academic/scholarly publication.
●Also available online.
 Description: Journal covering interdisciplinary issues.

378   CL   ISSN 0716-0321
HC191
ESTUDIOS SOCIALES. (Text in Spanish; abstracts in English) 1973. q. Esc.2500($60) (effective 1995). Corporacion de Promocion Universitaria, Avda. Miguel Claro 1460, Casilla 42, Correo 22, Santiago, Chile. TEL 562-2043418. FAX 562-2741828. (Co-sponsor: Fundacion Konrad Adenauer) Ed. Antonio Cruz. bk.rev.; abstr.; charts; stat. circ. 1,500. **Indexed:** Amer.Hist.& Life, Hisp.Amer.Per.Ind. (1973-), Hist.Abstr., Rural Devel.Abstr. **Document type:** academic/scholarly publication.
—Faxon.
 Description: Scholarly articles on employment, education, politics and social sciences.

300   AG   ISSN 0327-4934
ESTUDIOS SOCIALES; revista universitaria semestral. 1991. s-a. c/o Universidad Nacional del Litoral, Blvd. Pellegrini 2750, 3000 Santa Fe, Argentina. Ed. Dario Macor. **Document type:** academic/scholarly publication.

300   CR   ISSN 0303-9676
ESTUDIOS SOCIALES CENTROAMERICANOS. 1972. 3/yr. Cr.$250($8) (or exchange basis). Confederacion Universitaria Centro-Americana, Apdo. 37, 2060 Ciudad "Rodrigo Facio", San Jose, Costa Rica. TEL 252744. FAX 220478. TELEX 3011 COSUCA. Ed. Mario Lungo Ucleslo S. adv.; bk.rev.; bibl.; charts; stat.; cum.index every 4 yrs. circ. 2,000. (also avail. in microfiche) **Indexed:** Amer.Hist.& Life, Hisp.Amer.Per.Ind. (1972-1993), Hist.Abstr., Int.Lab.Doc., SSCI.

300   BL   ISSN 0101-546X
ESTUDOS AFRO-ASIATICOS. (Text in Portuguese; abstracts in English and French) 1978. 2/yr. $30 (foreign $40) or exchange basis (effective 1995 & 1996). Sociedade Brasileira de Instrucao, Centro de Estudos Afro-Asiaticos, Rua da Assembleia, 10 Conj. 501, 20011-000 Rio de Janeiro, Brazil. TEL 55-21-221-3536. FAX 55-21-5312155. E-mail: ceaa@ax.apc.org. Ed. Carlos Hasenbalg. adv. contact: Candido Mendes. bk.rev.; circ. 2,000. circ. 1,000 (controlled). **Document type:** academic/scholarly publication.
 Description: Publishes relevant articles in the field of African and Asian studies. Specializes in race relations and Afro-Brazilian studies.
 Refereed Serial

300   BL
ESTUDOS BRASILEIROS. 1990? m. Universidade de Sao Paulo, Instituto de Estudos Brasileiros, Av. Prof. Mello Moraes, 140, Travessa 8, 05508-900 Sao Paulo, Brazil. TEL 55-11-210-2429. FAX 55-11-818-3143. Ed. Neuma Cavalcante. adv. contact: Marta Rossetti Batista. **Document type:** newsletter.

300 869   BL   ISSN 0103-1821
PQ9000
ESTUDOS PORTUGUESES E AFRICANOS. 1983. s-a. exchange basis. Universidade Estadual de Campinas, Instituto de Estudos da Linguagem, Caixa Postal 6045, 13081-970 Campinas SP, Brazil. FAX 55-192-391501. **Document type:** academic/scholarly publication.
 Description: Presents studies in Portuguese culture and literature and Portuguese culture and literature in African countries.

300   GW   ISSN 0937-938X
                                  CODEN: ETSOE9
ETHIK UND SOZIALWISSENSCHAFTEN; Streitforum fuer Erwaegungskultur. (Text in German; summaries in English) 1990. q. DM.112 (students DM.84) (effective 1996). Westdeutscher Verlag GmbH, Postfach 1546, 65005 Wiesbaden, Germany. TEL 0611-534389. FAX 0611-534430. Ed.Bd. index. circ. 600. (back issues avail.) **Document type:** academic/scholarly publication.

305   US   ISSN 1056-2354
DT371
ETHIOPIAN REVIEW. 1991. m. $26 to individuals; institutions $60. Box 191220, Los Angeles, CA 90019. TEL 310-670-8513. FAX 310-678-3824. Ed. Elias Kifle. adv.: page $1200. bk.rev.

SOCIAL SCIENCES: COMPREHENSIVE WORKS

305.8   UK   ISSN 0141-9870
HT1501
ETHNIC AND RACIAL STUDIES. 1978. q. £30 (U.S. and Canada $60; rest of world £37) to individuals; institutions £77 (U.S. and Canada $115; rest of world £82). Routledge, 11 New Fetter Ln., London EC4P 4EE, England. TEL 0171-583-9855. FAX 0171-842-2298. TELEX 263398-ROUT-G. E-mail: sample.journals@routledege.com. (Subscr. to: ITPS Ltd., Cheriton House, Andover, Hants SP10 5BE, England. TEL 01264-342919. FAX 01264-342807) Ed. Martin Bulmer. adv.: page £225; trim 115 x 190. bk.rev.; index. circ. 1,550. (back issues avail.) **Indexed:** A.B.C.Pol.Sci., Adol.Ment.Hlth.Abstr., Amer.Hist.& Life, Asian-Pac.Econ.Lit., ASSIA, Curr.Cont., Documentatieblad, E.I., Hist.Abstr., HR Rep. (1991-), Int.Polit.Sci.Abstr., Lang.& Lang.Behav.Abstr., Mult.Ed.Abstr., Per.Islam. (1991-), Soc.Sci.Ind., Soc.Work Res.& Abstr., Sociol.Educ.Abstr., SSCI. **Document type:** academic/scholarly publication.
—BLDSC (3814.834000); Faxon; Genuine Article; SWETS; UnCover. **CCC.**
    Description: Provides an interdisciplinary academic forum for the presentation of research and theoretical analysis, drawing on sociology, social policy, anthropology, political science, economics, international relations, history and social psychology.

304.2   US   ISSN 0162-3095
BF1   CODEN: ETSOD8
ETHOLOGY AND SOCIOBIOLOGY. 1979. bi-m. $393 to institutions (effective 1996). Elsevier Science Inc., 655 Ave. of the Americas, New York, NY 10010. TEL 212-989-5800. FAX 212-633-3990. TELEX 420643 AEP UI. (Subscr. to: Box 882, Madison Sq. Sta., New York, NY 10159-0882) Ed.Bd. (also avail. in microform from UMI; reprint service avail. from SWZ) **Indexed:** Anthropol.Lit., ASSIA, Curr.Adv.Ecol.Sci., Curr.Cont., Excerp.Med., Geo.Abstr., Lang.& Lang.Behav.Abstr., Psychol.Abstr. (1980-), Risk Abstr., S.S.C.I., Sociol.Abstr., Sport Fish.Abstr., Wild.Rev., Zoo.Rec. **Document type:** academic/scholarly publication.
—BLDSC (3815.250000); Faxon; Genuine Article; SWETS; UnCover. **CCC.**
    Description: Publishes new studies on ethological and sociobiological theories using comparative data, experimental results and literature reviews.

300   AT
ETHOS ANNUAL. 1971. a. Aus.$50 to individuals; institutions Aus.$90; students Aus.$30. Victorian Association of Social Studies Teachers Inc., 217-225 Church St., Richmond, Vic. 3121, Australia. TEL 61-3-94287400. FAX 61-3-94280313. adv. circ. 1,500.
    Supersedes in part: Ethos.

ETHOS P - 6; ideas for the classroom, discussions & reviews for primary teachers of social education. see EDUCATION — Teaching Methods And Curriculum

ETHOS 7-12; ideas for the classroom discussions & reviews. see EDUCATION — Teaching Methods And Curriculum

300 500   FR
ETUDES SCIENTIFIQUES. bi-m. Peres Jesuites, c/o Mme Irene Kher, 8 av. Cesar-Caire, 75008 Paris, France.

300   IT
EUROPA EUROPE. 1992. q. L.60000 (foreign L.90000) (effective 1994). (Istituto Gramsci Roma) Edizioni Dedalo s.r.l., Casella Postale 362, 70100 Bari, Italy. TEL 080-5311413. FAX 080-5311414. (Edit. addr.: Istituto Gramsci, Via del Conservatorio 55, 00186 Rome, Italy. TEL 06-6833756. FAX 06-6877736) Dir. Giuseppe Vacca. bk.rev.; bibl. circ. 14,000.
    Description: Covers the political, economical and social problems of Europe.

300   EI   ISSN 1017-6713
HD5660.E86
EUROPEAN PARTICIPATION MONITOR. 1992. 2/yr. free. European Foundation for the Improvement of Living and Working Conditions, Loughlinstown House, Shankill, Co. Dublin, Ireland. TEL 02-2826888. FAX 01-2826456. TELEX 30726-EURF-EI. Ed. Michael Gold. **Document type:** newsletter.
—BLDSC (6327.231000).

980 300   NE   ISSN 0924-0608
F1401   CODEN: RELCEA
EUROPEAN REVIEW OF LATIN AMERICAN AND CARIBBEAN STUDIES/REVISTA EUROPEA DE ESTUDIOS LATINOAMERICANOS Y DEL CARIBE. (Text in English and Spanish) 1965. s-a. fl.40($30) to individuals; institutions fl.90($55). Centrum voor Studie en Documentatie van Latijns Amerika - Center for Latin American Research and Documentation - Centro de Estudios y Documentacion Latinoamericanos, Keizersgracht 395-397, 1016 EK Amsterdam, Netherlands. TEL 31-205253498. FAX 31-206255127. Ed. K. Willingham. adv.; bk.rev.; bibl.; charts. circ. 1,000. (also avail. in microfiche from IDC; back issues avail.) **Indexed:** Amer.Hist.& Life, Hisp.Amer.Per.Ind. (1970-1974; 1991-), Hist.Abstr., Int.Lab.Doc., Key to Econ.Sci., P.A.I.S.For.Lang.Ind., P.A.I.S. **Document type:** academic/scholarly publication.
—BLDSC (3829.951000); Faxon; SWETS; UnCover.
    Former titles (until 1989): Boletin de Estudios Latinoamericanos y del Caribe (ISSN 0304-2634); Boletin de Estudios Latinoamericanos; Boletin Informativo sobre Estudios Latinoamericanos en Europa (ISSN 0006-6397)
    Description: Addresses major debates and problems of historical interpretations in social science research of the Caribbean and Latin America.

EUROPEAN STUDIES. see HISTORY — History Of Europe

943   US   ISSN 0046-2802
D1050.82.U6
EUROPEAN STUDIES NEWSLETTER. 1972. bi-m. $40 to institutions (effective 1995 & 1996). Council for European Studies, Columbia University, Box 44, Schermerhorn, New York, NY 10027. TEL 212-854-4172. FAX 212-749-0397. Ed. Marion A. Kaplan. adv.; bk.rev.; bibl.; circ. 1,500 (paid). **Document type:** newsletter.
    Description: Carries notices of the council's programs as well as announcements of conferences; grants and fellowships; organizations and institutes; publications; drawn from a wide range of sources in Europe and North America.

300   UK   ISSN 0969-7764
▼**EUROPEAN URBAN AND REGIONAL STUDIES.** 1994. 4/yr. £58 (Europe £60; rest of world £64($109)) to individuals; institutions £97(Europe £99; rest of world £107($182)). Longman Group UK Ltd., Longman House, Burnt Mill, Harlow, Essex CM20 2JE, England. TEL 01279-426721. FAX 01279-431059. Ed.Bd. adv.; bk.rev. **Document type:** academic/scholarly publication.
—BLDSC (3830.370440).
    Description: Covers academic and policy debate related to processes of urban and regional development in Europe.

300   UK
▼**EVALUATION;** international journal of theory, research and practice. 1995. q. £36 to individuals; institutions £120 (effective 1996). Sage Publications Ltd., 6 Bonhill St., London EC2A 4PU, England. TEL 0171-374-0645. FAX 0171-374-8741. E-mail: market@sageltd.co.uk. Ed. Elliot Stern. adv.: B&W page £180; trim 190 x 120; adv. contact: Bernie Folan. **Indexed:** ASSIA, Sociol.Abstr. **Document type:** academic/scholarly publication.
    Description: Seeks to advance theoretical and methodological understandings of evaluation in the context of evaluation policy and practice, and to locate evaluation policy and practice within wider theoretical and methodological debates.

300   UK   ISSN 0149-7189
H62.A1
EVALUATION AND PROGRAM PLANNING; an international journal. 1978. q. £249($396) (effective 1996). Elsevier Science Ltd., Pergamon, P.O. Box 800, Kidlington, Oxford OX5 1DX, England. TEL 44-1865-843000. FAX 44-1865-843010. E-mail: nlinfo-f@elsevier.nl; usinfo-f@elsevier.com; forinfo-kyf04035@niftyserve.or.jp; Site addr.: http://www.elsevier.nl/. (Subscr. in U.S. and Canada to: Elsevier Science, 660 White Plains Rd., Tarrytown, NY 10591-5153. TEL 914-524-9200. FAX 914-333-2444) Ed. Jonathan A. Morell. adv. circ. 650. (also avail. in microfilm from UMI) **Indexed:** Abstr.Health Care Manage.Stud., C.I.J.E., CINAHL, Curr.Cont., E.I., Excerp.Med., Med.Care Rev., Psychol.Abstr. (1978-), Rural Ext.Educ.& Tr.Abstr., Sociol.Abstr. **Document type:** academic/scholarly publication.
—BLDSC (3830.565000); Faxon; Genuine Article; SWETS; UMI; UnCover. **CCC.**
    Description: Assists evaluators and planners to better practice their professions.
    Refereed Serial

300   US   ISSN 0886-1633
H1
EVALUATION PRACTICE. 1980. 3/yr. $70 to individuals (foreign $90); institutions $155 (foreign $180) (effective 1996). (American Evaluation Association) J A I Press Inc., Box 1678, 55 Old Post Rd., No. 2, Greenwich, CT 06836. TEL 203-661-7602. FAX 203-661-0792. (Addr. in Europe: J A I Press Ltd., The Courtyard, 28 High St., Hampton Hill, Mddx. TW12 1PD, England. TEL 44-81-943-9296. FAX 44-81-943-9317) Ed. M.F. Midge Smith. adv.; bk.rev. (back issues avail.) **Indexed:** Educ.Admin.Abstr., Sage Pub.Admin.Abstr., Sociol.Abstr. **Document type:** academic/scholarly publication.
—BLDSC (3830.614000); Faxon; UMI; UnCover. **CCC.**
    Former titles (until 1986): Evaluation News; E N. Evaluation News (ISSN 0191-8036)

300   US   ISSN 0193-841X
HM1
EVALUATION REVIEW; a journal of applied social research. 1977. bi-m. $76 to individuals; institutions $231 (effective Sep. 1995). Sage Publications, Inc., 2455 Teller Rd., Thousand Oaks, CA 91320. TEL 805-499-0721. FAX 805-499-0871. E-mail: libraries@sagepub.com. (Overseas subscr. to: Sage Publications Ltd., 6 Bonhill St., London EC2A 4PU, England; Sage Publications India Pvt. Ltd., P.O. Box 4215, New Delhi 110 048, India) Ed. Richard A. Berk. adv.; bk.rev.; abstr.; index. circ. 1,600. (also avail. in microform from UMI; back issues avail.; reprint service avail.) **Indexed:** Abstr.Health Care Manage.Stud., Adol.Ment.Hlth.Abstr., C.I.J.E., C.L.I., Crim.Just.Abstr., Curr.Cont., Curr.Lit.Fam.Plan., HRIS, L.R.I., Mid.East: Abstr.& Ind., P.A.I.S., Psychol.Abstr. (1977-), Risk Abstr., Sage Fam.Stud.Abstr., Sage Pub.Admin.Abstr., Soc.Sci.Ind., Soc.Work Res.& Abstr., Sociol.Abstr., SSCI, World Agri.Econ.& Rural Sociol.Abstr. **Document type:** academic/scholarly publication.
—BLDSC (3830.618500); Faxon; Genuine Article; SWETS; UMI; UnCover. **CCC.**
    Formerly (until vol.4, Feb. 1980): Evaluation Quarterly (ISSN 0145-4692)
    Description: Provides a forum for researchers, planners, and policymakers engaged in the development, implementation, and utilization of evaluation studies.

300   VE
F A C E S. 1976. bi-m. Universidad Central de Venezuela, Facultad de Ciencias Economicas y Sociales, Caracas, Venezuela. Ed. Jose Eliseo Lopez.

300 914.4   CC   ISSN 1002-0888
FAGUO YANJIU/ETUDES FRANCAISES. (Text in Chinese and French) 1983. irreg. (2-4/yr.) $12. (Wuhan Daxue, Faguo Wenti Yanjiusuo) Wuhan Daxue Chubanshe - Wuhan University Press, Luo Jia Shan, Wuchang, Hubei 430072, People's Republic of China. TEL 812723-840. (Dist. in US by: China Books & Periodicals, Inc., 2929 24th St., San Francisco, CA 94110) bk.rev. circ. 2,000.
    Description: Covers French social sciences. Contains articles, translations, and original records on French language, literature, history, philosophy, politics, and economics. Includes columns on academic activities and personal profiles.

SOCIAL SCIENCES: COMPREHENSIVE WORKS

300   IT
LA FAMIGLIA. 1965. bi-m. L.60000. Editrice la Scuola S.p.A., Via Cadorna 11, 25186 Brescia, Italy. TEL 39-30-29931. FAX 39-30-2993299. Ed. Mario Cattaneo.

300   US
FERNAND BRAUDEL CENTER. NEWSLETTER. 1977. a. Fernand Braudel Center, Binghamton University, Box 6000, Binghamton, NY 13902-6000. TEL 607-777-4924. FAX 607-777-4315. Ed. Immanuel Wallerstein. (back issues avail.) **Document type:** newsletter.

368.4   FI   ISSN 0430-5205
FINLAND. KANSANELAKELAITOS. JULKAISUJA. SARJA A. (Text in Finnish and English; summaries in English) 1967. irreg., no.A25, 1990. Kansanelakelaitos - Social Insurance Institution of Finland, Research and Development Centre, P.O. Box 78, FIN-00381 Helsinki 38, Finland. Ed. Kaino Laaksonen. bibl.

610 368.4   FI   ISSN 0355-4821
FINLAND. KANSANELAKELAITOS. JULKAISUJA. SARJA M. (Text in Finnish, summaries in English) 1967. irreg., no.M89, 1994. Kansanelakelaitos - Social Insurance Institution of Finland, Research and Development Centre, P.O. Box 78, FIN-00381 Helsinki 38, Finland. **Document type:** monographic series.

THE FLAG & BANNER. see *GENEALOGY AND HERALDRY*

300   GW   ISSN 0932-5859
FLENSBURGER HEFTE. 1987. q. DM.56 (foreign DM.60). Flensburger Hefte Verlag GmbH, Holm 64, 24937 Flensburg, Germany. TEL 0461-26363. FAX 0461-26912. Eds. Wolfgang Weirauch, Klaus-Dieter Neumann. adv.: page DM.740; trim 115 x 165. bk.rev.; illus.; circ. 7,000 (paid). (back issues avail.) **Document type:** academic/scholarly publication.

300   GW   ISSN 0943-5549
FLENSBURGER HEFTE. SONDERHEFT. 1987. irreg. Flensburger Hefte Verlag GmbH, Holm 64, 24937 Flensburg, Germany. TEL 0461-26363. FAX 0461-26912. **Document type:** monographic series.

300   CE
FOCUS. (Text in English) 1977. m. Rs.36. Collective, 26 Clifford Ave., Colombo 3, Sri Lanka.

300 338.91   FR   ISSN 0339-0462
FOI ET DEVELOPPEMENT. (Includes special nos.) 1973. m. (10/yr.) 140 F. (foreign 160 F.). Centre Lebret, 43 ter, rue de la Glaciere, 75013 Paris, France. TEL 43-54-57-58. FAX 47-07-68-66. Ed. Fred Martinache. bk.rev.; bibl. circ. 2,000. (back issues avail.) **Indexed:** CERDIC.

301 945   IT   ISSN 0544-1374
HX15
FONDAZIONE GIANGIACOMO FELTRINELLI. ANNALI. 1958. a. price varies. Fondazione Giangiacomo Feltrinelli, Via Romagnosi 3, 20121 Milan, Italy. TEL 39-2-874175. FAX 39-2-86461855. bk.rev. circ. 3,000. **Indexed:** Amer.Hist.& Life (until 1993); Hist.Abstr. (until 1993). **Document type:** academic/scholarly publication.

300 320 100   UK   ISSN 0959-311X
FOR A CHANGE; for moral re-armament. (Former name of issuing body: Grosvenor Productions Ltd.) 1952. m. £16($25) M R A Productions Fund, 12 Palace St., London SW1E 5JF, England. TEL 0171-828-6591. FAX 0171-828-7609. (Subscr. to: Tirley Garth, Tarporley, Cheshire CW6 0LZ, England; Dist. in US by: MRA Inc., 1156 15th St., N.W., Ste. 910, Washington, DC 20005-1704) Ed.Bd. bk.rev.; play rev.; illus.; index. circ. 8,500. (tabloid format) **Document type:** consumer publication.
Former titles (until 1987): New World News; M R A Information Service (ISSN 0024-3289).
Description: Concerns the factor of faith in human and international relations.

300 060 370   US   ISSN 0071-7274
AS911.F6
FORD FOUNDATION ANNUAL REPORT. a. free. Ford Foundation, Office of Communications, c/o Carolee Iltis, 320 E. 43rd St., New York, NY 10017. TEL 212-573-5000. Ed. Lloyd Garrison. (also avail. in microfiche from BHP) **Document type:** corporate report.
Description: Lists foundation grants and other financial data for the fiscal year. Includes information on grant applications.

300 378.3 658.15   US   ISSN 1063-7281
AS911.F6
FORD FOUNDATION REPORT. 1970. 4/yr. free. Ford Foundation, Office of Communications, c/o Carolee Iltis, 320 E. 43rd St., New York, NY 10017. TEL 212-573-5000. Ed. Lloyd Garrison. bibl.; illus.; index. circ. 35,000. (also avail. in microform from UMI; back issues avail.; reprint service avail. from UMI) **Indexed:** HR Rep. **Document type:** newsletter. —UMI.
Formerly: Ford Foundation Letter (ISSN 0015-699X)
Description: Contains articles and reports on subjects related to the foundation's interests in the U.S. and abroad. Includes brief announcements of recent grants, publications and appointments.

300   IT
FORMAZIONE E SOCIETA. 1981. 3/yr. L.58000 (foreign L.80000) (effective 1993). Franco Angeli Editore, Viale Monza 106, 20127 Milan, Italy. TEL 02-2827651. Eds. G.P. Catelli, P. Guidicini.

FORSCHUNGSJOURNAL NEUE SOZIALE BEWEGUNGEN. see *POLITICAL SCIENCE*

300   GW   ISSN 0341-1508
FORTSCHRITTE DER SOZIALPAEDIATRIE. 1973. irreg., vol.13, 1990. DM.56. Schmidt-Roemhild Verlag, Mengstr. 16, 23552 Luebeck, Germany. TEL 0451-1605-0. FAX 0451-1605253. Ed. Dr. Theodor Hellbruegge. **Document type:** monographic series.

300 320   GW   ISSN 0943-7088
FORUM DER AG SPAK. 1970. 4/yr. DM.20. AG Spak, Adlzreiterstr. 23, 80337 Munich, Germany. TEL 089-774078. FAX 089-774077. Ed. Dieter Koschek. bk.rev. **Document type:** newsletter.
Formerly: Spak-Forum (ISSN 0171-3159)

300   GW   ISSN 0942-0045
FORUM SUPERVISION. 1993. s-a. DM.28. Edition Diskord, Schwaerzlocherstr. 104-b, 72070 Tuebingen, Germany. TEL 07071-40102. FAX 07071-44710. Eds. Gerhard Leuschner, Gerhard Wittenberger. adv.; bk.rev. circ. 2,000. **Document type:** academic/scholarly publication.

300 800   ZR
FORUM UNIVERSITAIRE.* 1973. q. K.150. Universite Nationale du Zaire, Junction des Etudiants, Bloc VIII No 1109, B.P. 945, Lubumbashi, Zaire. Ed. Eloko a Nongo Obhudiema. bibl.; illus.

300 323.4   UG
FORWARD. 1979-1985; resumed 1986. q. EAs.400($10) Forward Publications Ltd., Box 5160, Kampala, Uganda. Ed.Bd. adv.; bk.rev.; play rev. circ. 3,000.

FOUND OBJECT. see *LITERARY AND POLITICAL REVIEWS*

300   US
FOUNDATIONS OF POPULAR CULTURE. irreg., vol.3, 1992. Sage Publications, Inc., 2455 Teller Rd., Thousand Oaks, CA 91320. TEL 805-499-0721. FAX 805-499-0871. E-mail: libraries@sagepub.com. (Overseas orders to: Sage Publications Ltd., 6 Bonhill St., London EC2A 4PU, England; Sage Publications India Pvt. Ltd., P.O. Box 4215, New Delhi 110 048, India) **Document type:** monographic series.

300   US
FRATERNA COMPANION. irreg. $3 per no. Hoya Society International, Inc., Box 1043, Porterdale, GA 30270-1043.

FREE ASSOCIATIONS; psychoanalysis, groups, politics, culture. see *PSYCHOLOGY*

300   II
FRENCH INSTITUTE, PONDICHERRY. PONDY PAPERS IN SOCIAL SCIENCES. (Text in English; summaries in French) 1989. irreg., approx. 3/yr. price varies. Institut Francais de Pondichery, Departement de Sciences Sociales, Box 33, Pondichery 605 001, India. TEL 91-413-34170. FAX 91-413-29534. TELEX 569335 FRAN IN. Ed. J. Pouchepadass. circ. 250.

300   CC   ISSN 0257-0289
FUDAN XUEBAO (SHEHUI KEXUE BAN)/FUDAN JOURNAL (SOCIAL SCIENCES EDITION). (Text in Chinese; table of contents in English) bi-m. Y3.20 per no. (Fudan Daxue - Fudan University) Fudan Daxue Chubanshe - Fudan University Press, 222 Handan Lu, Shanghai 200433, People's Republic of China. TEL 5492222. TELEX 33317-HUAFU-CN. (Dist. outside China by: China International Book Trading Corp., P.O. Box 399, Beijing, P.R. China) Yin Xiaorong. **Document type:** academic/scholarly publication.

300   SP   ISSN 1020-1327
FUENTES UNESCO. Catalan edition: Fonts Unesco (ISSN 1020-153X) m. 2000 ptas.($16) (effective 1995). Centre Unesco de Catalunya, Mallorca 285, 08037 Barcelona, Spain. TEL 34-3-2075805. FAX 34-3-4575851. E-mail: ecuco@cc.uab.es. Ed. Rene Lefort. circ. 8,200 (2,200 Catalan ed.; 6,000 Spanish ed.).
Description: Presents the activities of the organization in education, science, social science, culture and communication.

300   CC   ISSN 1000-5285
FUJIAN SHIFAN DAXUE XUEBAO (SHEHUI KEXUE BAN)/FUJIAN NORMAL UNIVERSITY. JOURNAL (SOCIAL SCIENCE EDITION). (Text in Chinese) q. Y2.40. Fujian Shifan Daxue - Fujian Normal University, 137 Shangsan Lu, Cangshan Qu, Fuzhou, Fujian 350007, People's Republic of China. TEL 541616. (Dist. overseas by: Jiangsu Publications Import & Export Corp., 56 Gao Yun Ling, Nanjing, Jiangsu, P.R.C.) Ed. Chen Zheng.
Description: Covers research results in different fields of the social sciences, including philosophy, economics, linguistics, literature, history, education and the arts.

300   CC   ISSN 1003-370X
FUJIAN XUEKAN. (Text in Chinese) 1978. bi-m. $24. Fujian Sheng Shehui Kexue Lianhehui, No. 18, Liuhe Rd., Fuzhou, Fujian 350001, People's Republic of China. TEL 0591-7535984. Ed. Jian Yimu. adv.: page $1000; adv. contact: Wang Bixiu. **Document type:** academic/scholarly publication.
Description: Covers all aspects of social sciences such as politics, economy, philosophy, law, literature, history and education.

300   BL
FUNDACAO JOAQUIM NABUCO. SERIE MONOGRAFIAS. 1975. irreg., no.31a, 1989. $2.50 per no. Editora Massangana, Rua Dois Irmaos, 15, Apipucos, 52071-440 Recife, Brazil. TEL 081-268-4611. FAX 081-268-9600. **Document type:** monographic series.
Formerly: Instituto Joaquim Nabuco de Pesquisas Sociais. Serie Monografias.

300   CK   ISSN 0120-7075
FUNDACION ANTIOQUENA PARA LOS ESTUDIOS SOCIALES. ESTUDIOS SOCIALES. 1986. s-a. Col.$7000($50) Fundacion Antioquena para los Estudios Sociales, Carrera 45 N. 5977, Apdo. Aereo 8650, Medellin, Colombia. TEL 2541792. FAX 2544953. Ed. Hector Abad Faciolince; Pub. Juan Manuel Ospina Restrepo. adv. contact: Juan Manuel Ospina Restrepo. bk.rev./ circ. 1,000 (paid). **Indexed:** Amer.Hist.& Life (1993-), Hist.Abstr. (1993-). **Document type:** academic/scholarly publication.
Description: Presents research and studies in the social sciences.

300   EC
FUNDACION LOS ANDES DE ESTUDIOS SOCIALES. ANUARIO. a. Fundacion Los Andes de Estudios Sociales, Casilla 2, surcursal 12, Quito, Ecuador.

FUTURESCAN. see *BUSINESS AND ECONOMICS — Economic Situation And Conditions*

FUTUROLOGY. see *TECHNOLOGY: COMPREHENSIVE WORKS*

SOCIAL SCIENCES: COMPREHENSIVE WORKS

300   CC
FUZHOU DAXUE XUEBAO (SHEHUI KEXUE BAN)/FUZHOU UNIVERSITY. JOURNAL (SOCIAL SCIENCE EDITION). (Text in Chinese) 1981-1984; resumed 1987. s-a. Y2 per no. Fuzhou Daxue - Fuzhou University, Gongye Lu, Fuzhou, Fujian 350002, People's Republic of China. TEL 710845. Ed. Huang Zheng. **Document type:** academic/scholarly publication.

300   CC
GAIGE/REFORM. (Text in Chinese) bi-m. Chongqing Shehui Kexueyuan - Chongqing Academy of Social Sciences, 83 Zhongshan Silu, Congqing, Sichuan 630020, People's Republic of China. TEL 352445. Ed. Jiang Yiwei.

333.3   US   ISSN 0195-962X
HN90.P8
GALLUP POLL. 1971. a. $65. (Gallup Poll News Service) Scholarly Resources, Inc., 104 Greenhill Ave., Wilmington, DE 19805. TEL 302-654-7713. FAX 302-654-3871. stat.
—BLDSC (4067.549400); SWETS.

300   II
GANDHIAN PERSPECTIVES. (Text in English) 1978-19??; resumed 1991. s-a. Rs.120($24) to individuals; institutions Rs.150 ($30). (Gandhian Institute of Studies) Tara Book Agency, Kamacha, Varanasi 221010 (U.P.), India. Ed. Ali Ashraf.

300   CC   ISSN 1003-3637
GANSU SHEHUI KEXUE/GANSU SOCIAL SCIENCE. (Text in Chinese) 1979. bi-m. $24. Gansu Sheng Shehui Kexueyuan - Gansu Academy of Social Sciences, Shi Li Dian, Lanzhou, Gansu 730070, People's Republic of China. TEL 86-931-7668021. (Dist. overseas by: China International Book Trading Corporation, P.O. Box 399, Beijing, P.R. China) Ed. Wang Bugui. adv.; bk.rev.; circ. 3,500 (paid). **Document type:** academic/scholarly publication.
Formerly (until 1990): Shehui Kexue (Lanzhou). Refereed Serial

300   CC
GAOXIAO SHEHUI KEXUE/SOCIAL SCIENCES IN HIGHER EDUCATION. (Text in Chinese) bi-m. Zhongguo Jiaoyu Zazhishe - China Education Journal Publishing, 35, Damucang Hutong, Xidan, Beijing 100816, People's Republic of China. TEL 654921. Ed. Li Changzheng.

GAVEA - BROWN; revista bilingue de letras e estudos Luso-Americanos - a bilingual journal of Portuguese-American letters and studies. see *LITERATURE*

GEARY LECTURE SERIES. see *BUSINESS AND ECONOMICS*

300 900   GW   ISSN 0340-613X
H5
GESCHICHTE UND GESELLSCHAFT; Zeitschrift fuer Historische Sozialwissenschaft. 1975. q. DM.96. Vandenhoeck und Ruprecht, Robert-Bosch-Breite 6, 37079 Goettingen, Germany. TEL 0551-6959-26. FAX 0551-695917. (Subscr. to: 37070 Goettingen, Germany) Ed. Hans-Ulrich Wehler. adv.; index. **Indexed:** Amer.Hist.& Life, Arts & Hum.Cit.Ind., Curr.Cont., E.I., Hist.Abstr., INIS Atomind., SSCI. **Document type:** academic/scholarly publication.
—BLDSC (4162.521000); Faxon; Genuine Article; SWETS. **CCC.**

300   GW   ISSN 0933-5706
CODEN: GESCEQ
GESCHICHTSWERKSTATT. 1985. 3/yr. DM.36. (Geschichtswerkstatt e.V.) Calenberg Press Weigang, Auf der Horst 40, 30823 Garbsen, Germany. TEL 05137-121139. Ed. Dirk Schindelbeck. adv. contact: Stefan Weigang. circ. 2,500. **Indexed:** Amer.Hist.& Life (1992-), Hist.Abstr. (1992-). **Document type:** academic/scholarly publication.

300   GW   ISSN 0179-1605
GESELLSCHAFT, RECHT, WIRTSCHAFT. 1978. irreg., vol.18, 1994. DM.24.80. Bibliographisches Institut und F.A. Brockhaus AG, Postfach 100311, 68003 Mannheim, Germany. TEL 0621-3901-01. FAX 0621-3901-389. Ed.Bd. **Indexed:** Math.R. **Document type:** academic/scholarly publication.

GLEDISTA. see *HUMANITIES: COMPREHENSIVE WORKS*

GLOBULUS. see *SCIENCES: COMPREHENSIVE WORKS*

GOOD GOVERNMENT; a journal of political, social & economic comment. see *BUSINESS AND ECONOMICS — Economic Systems And Theories, Economic History*

300   UK   ISSN 0266-2043
H11
GREAT BRITAIN. ECONOMIC AND SOCIAL RESEARCH COUNCIL. ANNUAL REPORT. 1966. a. £10. Economic and Social Research Council, Polaris House, N. Star Ave., Swindon, Wilts. SN2 1UJ, England. TEL 01793-413000. FAX 01793-413001. **Document type:** corporate report.
—BLDSC (1241.048000).
Former titles: Great Britain. Economic and Social Research Council. Report; (until Jan. 1984): Great Britain. Social Science Research Council. Report (ISSN 0081-0444)

300   UK
GREAT BRITAIN. ECONOMIC & SOCIAL RESEARCH COUNCIL. STUDENTSHIP HANDBOOK. 1966. a. free. Economic and Social Research Council, Training Division, Polaris House, N. Star Ave., Swindon, Wilts. SN2 1UJ, England. TEL 01793-413000. FAX 01793-413001.
Formerly: Great Britain. Social Science Research Council. Studentship Handbook.

300   GR   ISSN 0013-9696
H8
GREEK REVIEW OF SOCIAL RESEARCH/EPITHEORISIS KOINONIKON EREVNON. (Text in Greek) 1969. q. $30. National Center of Social Research, 1 Sophocleou, 105 59 Athens, Greece. FAX 30-1-3216471. Ed. K. Tsoukalas. adv.; bk.rev.; bibl.; charts; stat. circ. 2,000. **Indexed:** Lang.& Lang.Behav.Abstr. **Document type:** academic/scholarly publication.

300   GW
GRUNDRISS DER SOZIALWISSENSCHAFT. 1953. irreg. Vandenhoeck und Ruprecht, Robert-Bosch-Breite 6, 37079 Goettingen, Germany. TEL 0551-6959-0. FAX 0551-695917. (Subscr. to: 37070 Goettingen, Germany) **Document type:** monographic series.

300 500   CC
GUANGDONG MINZU XUEYUAN XUEBAO/GUANGDONG INSTITUTE OF NATIONALITIES. JOURNAL. (In 2 vols.: Parts 1-3 Social Sciences; Part 4: Natural Sciences) (Text in Chinese) 1980. q. Y8 (effective 1996). Guangdong Minzu Xueyuan - Guangdong Institute of Nationalities, Shipai, Guangzhou, Guangdong 510633, People's Republic of China. (Dist. overseas by: China Publications Foreign Trade Corp., P.O. Box 782, Beijing, P.R.C.) Ed. Cai Zhongsu. adv. contact: Li Shichen. bk.rev. circ. 1,200. **Document type:** academic/scholarly publication.
Description: Publishes papers on the natural and social sciences, emphasizing minority issues in South China and the history and current conditions in Guangdong Province. The 4th issue covers natural sciences.

300   CC   ISSN 1000-114X
GUANGDONG SHEHUI KEXUE/GUANGDONG SOCIAL SCIENCE. (Text in Chinese) 1984. q. Guangdong Sheng Shehui Kexueyuan - Guangdong Academy of Social Sciences, No.222, Yuexiu Beilu, Guangzhou, Guangdong 510050, People's Republic of China. TEL 334820. Ed. Zhang Lei.

300   CC   ISSN 1000-4777
GUOWAI SHEHUI KEXUE/SOCIAL SCIENCE ABROAD. (Text in Chinese) 1980. m. Zhongguo Shehui Kexueyuan, Wenxian Qingbao Zhongxin - Chinese Academy of Social Sciences, Documentation Information Center, 5, Jianguomennei Dajie, Beijing 100732, People's Republic of China. TEL 5137744. Ed. Wu Andi.

300   CC   ISSN 1000-4785
GUOWAI SHEHUI KEXUE KUAIBAO/FOREIGN SOCIAL SCIENCE BULLETIN. (Text in Chinese) m. Zhongguo Shehui Kexueyuan, Wenxian Qingbao Zhongxin - Chinese Academy of Social Sciences, Documentation Information Center, 5, Jianguomennei Dajie, Beijing 100732, People's Republic of China. TEL 5137744. Ed. Qu Hanzhang.

GYPSY LORE SOCIETY. NEWSLETTER. see *ANTHROPOLOGY*

300 001.3   SA   ISSN 1018-726X
HF5549.5.M3
H S R C - R G N IN FOCUS. (Text in Afrikaans, English) 1969. m. free. Human Sciences Research Council, Group: Corporate Communications, Private Bag X41, Pretoria 0001, South Africa. Ed. Maryna Swarts. circ. 4,000 (controlled). **Document type:** newsletter.
Supersedes: Human Sciences Research Council. Newsletter - Raad vir Geesteswetenskaplike Navorsing. Nuusbrief (ISSN 0256-6796)
Description: Discusses HSRC services, products, expertise and other activities.

H W W A - REPORT. see *BUSINESS AND ECONOMICS*

300   CC
HANGZHOU DAXUE XUEBAO (SHEHUI KEXUE BAN)/HANGZHOU UNIVERSITY. JOURNAL (SOCIAL SCIENCE EDITION). (Text in Chinese) q. Hangzhou Daxue - Hangzhou University, 34 Tianmushan Lu, Hangzhou, Zhejiang 310028, People's Republic of China. TEL 881224. Ed. Jin Jiang.

300   CC   ISSN 1000-2146
AS452.H29
HANGZHOU SHIFAN XUEYUAN XUEBAO (SHEHUI KEXUE BAN)/HANGZHOU NORMAL COLLEGE. JOURNAL (SOCIAL SCIENCE EDITION). (Text in Chinese) 1979. 6/yr. Y6. Hangzhou Shifan Xueyuan - Hangzhou Teachers College, Hangzhou, Zhejiang 310012, People's Republic of China. TEL 86-571-8078124. FAX 86-571-8081082. Ed. Yu Xiuyuan. adv.; bk.rev. circ. 2,000. **Document type:** academic/scholarly publication.

HARRY S. TRUMAN RESEARCH INSTITUTE FOR THE ADVANCEMENT OF PEACE. REPRINT SERIES. see *BIBLIOGRAPHIES*

HARYANA AGRICULTURAL UNIVERSITY. JOURNAL OF RESEARCH. see *AGRICULTURE*

300 100   CC   ISSN 1005-6378
HEBEI DAXUE XUEBAO (SHEHUI ZHEXUE BAN)/HEBEI UNIVERSITY. JOURNAL (PHILOSOPHY & SOCIAL SCIENCES). (Text in Chinese) q. Y12 (foreign $12). Hebei Daxue, No. 1, Hezuolu Rd., Baoding, Hebei 071002, People's Republic of China. TEL 0312-5022929. FAX 0312-5022648. Ed.Bd. circ. 2,000. **Document type:** academic/scholarly publication.

300   CC   ISSN 1000-5587
HEBEI SHIFAN DAXUE XUEBAO (SHEHUI KEXUE BAN)/HEBEI NORMAL UNIVERSITY. JOURNAL (SOCIAL SCIENCE EDITION). (Text in Chinese) q. Hebei Shifan Daxue - Hebei Normal University, Yuhua Lu, Shijiazhuang, Hebei 050016, People's Republic of China. TEL 49941. Ed. Jin Shixun.

300   CC   ISSN 1003-7071
HEBEI XUEKAN/HEBEI ACADEMIC JOURNAL. (Text in Chinese; table of contents in English) 1981. bi-m. Y9. Hebei Sheng Shehui Kexueyuan - Hebei Provincial Academy of Social Sciences, 9 Shiyi Lu, Shijianzhuang, Hebei 050051, People's Republic of China. TEL 335767. Ed. Chen Yaobin. adv. contact: Chen Yaobin. circ. 3,000. (reprint service avail.)

300   IS   ISSN 0333-6964
Q180.I78
HEBREW UNIVERSITY OF JERUSALEM. AUTHORITY FOR RESEARCH AND DEVELOPMENT. CURRENT RESEARCH. (Vol. 1: Research; Vol. 2: Publications) (Text in English) 1964. a. Hebrew University of Jerusalem, Mount Scopus, Jerusalem 91905, Israel. TEL 972-2-630241. FAX 972-2-664740. Ed. S. Glatzer. author index; circ. controlled.
—BLDSC (7714.120000).
Formed by the merger of: Hebrew University of Jerusalem. Authority for Research and Development. Research Report: Humanities, Social Sciences, Law, Education, Social Work, Library (ISSN 0075-3645); Hebrew University of Jerusalem. Authority for Research and Development. Research Report. Science and Agriculture (ISSN 0075-3653); Hebrew University of Jerusalem. Authority for Research Report. Medicine, Pharmacy, Dental Medicine (ISSN 0075-3637)

300   CC   ISSN 1000-2359
HENAN SHIFAN DAXUE XUEBAO (SHEHUI KEXUE BAN)/HENAN NORMAL UNIVERSITY. JOURNAL (SOCIAL SCIENCE EDITION). (Text in Chinese) bi-m. $9. Henan Shifan Daxue, Xuebao Bianjibu, Xinxiang, Henan 453002, People's Republic of China. TEL 0373-3054921. Ed. Zeng Xiangqin. **Document type:** academic/scholarly publication.

300   GW
HILDESHEIMER SCHRIFTEN ZUR SOZIALPAEDAGOGIK UND SOZIALARBEIT. 1992. irreg., vol.4, 1994. price varies. Georg Olms Verlag, Hagentorwall 7, 31134 Hildesheim, Germany. TEL 05121-1501-0. FAX 05121-150150. (U.S. subscr. to: 111 W. 57th St., New York, NY 10019. TEL 212-757-5237) Eds. Udo Wilken, F. Vahsen. **Document type:** monographic series.

HISTORICAL METHODS. see *HISTORY*

HISTORISCHE ANTHROPOLOGIE; Kultur - Gesellschaft - Alltag. see *HISTORY*

306.8   US   ISSN 1081-602X
▼**HISTORY OF THE FAMILY;** an international quarterly. Announced for publication in 1996. q. $60 to individuals (foreign $80); institutions $150 (foreign $170) (effective 1996). J A I Press Inc., 55 Old Post Rd., No. 2, Box 1678, Greenwich, CT 06836-1678. TEL 203-661-7602. FAX 203-661-0792. (In Europe: J A I Press Ltd., The Courtyard, 28 High St., Hampton Hill, Mddx TW12 1PD, England. TEL 44-181-943-9296. FAX 44-181-943-9317) Eds. Tamara K. Hareven, Andrejs Plakans. **Document type:** academic/scholarly publication.

300 301   UK   ISSN 0952-6951
H1
HISTORY OF THE HUMAN SCIENCES. 1988. q. £35 to individuals; institutions £120 (effective 1996). Sage Publications Ltd., 6 Bonhill St., London EC2A 4PU, England. TEL 0171-374-0645. FAX 0171-374-8741. E-mail: market@sageltd.co.uk. Eds. Arthur Still, Irving Velody. adv.: B&W page £180; trim 180 x 114; adv. contact: Bernie Folan. bk.rev.; illus.; index. (back issues avail.) **Indexed:** Amer.Hist.& Life, ASCA, Br.Hum.Ind., Curr.Cont., Hist.Abstr., IBZ, Int.Polit.Sci.Abstr., Intl.Bibl.S.S.Soc.Cult.Anthro., Phil.Ind., Soc.Sci.Ind. (1994-), Sociol.Abstr., SSCI. **Document type:** academic/scholarly publication.
—BLDSC (4318.143000); Faxon; Genuine Article; SWETS; UnCover. **CCC.**
  Description: Provides a forum for contemporary social science research that examines its own historical origins and interdisciplinary influences in an effort to review current practice.
  Refereed Serial

300   JA   ISSN 0073-280X
H1
HITOTSUBASHI JOURNAL OF SOCIAL STUDIES. 1960. s-a. Hitotsubashi Daigaku, Hitotsubashi Gakkai - Hitotsubashi University, Hitotsubashi Academy, 2-1 Naka, Kunitachi-shi, Tokyo 186, Japan. Ed. Takashi Machimura. circ. 900. **Indexed:** P.A.I.S., SSCI. **Document type:** academic/scholarly publication.
—Faxon; UnCover.

HITOTSUBASHI REVIEW/HITOTSUBASHI RONSO. see *BUSINESS AND ECONOMICS*

300   JA   ISSN 0386-4480
HOKKAIDO KYOIKU DAIGAKU KIYO. DAI-1-BU, B. SHAKAI KAGAKU HEN/HOKKAIDO UNIVERSITY OF EDUCATION. JOURNAL. SECTION 1 B. SOCIAL SCIENCE. vol.32, 1982. s-a. exchange basis. Hokkaido University of Education - Hokkaido Kyoiku Daigaku, Ainosoto 5-jo, 3-chome, Kita-ku, Sapporo 002, Hokkaido, Japan.

300   PR   ISSN 0252-8908
H8.S7   CODEN: HOMIER
HOMINES; revista latinoamericana de ciencias sociales. 1977. s-a. $15 (N. America $22; elsewhere $25). (Universidad Interamericana, Departamento de Ciencias Sociales) Editorial Homines, Apdo. 191293, Hato Rey, PR 00919. TEL 809-250-1912. FAX 809-250-0782. Ed. Aline Frambes-Buxeda. bk.rev.; cum.index: 1977-1992. circ. 7,000. (back issues avail.) **Indexed:** Hisp.Amer.Per.Ind. (1987-), Int.Bibl.Soc.Sci., Sociol.Abstr. **Document type:** academic/scholarly publication.

HOW INSTITUTIONS VOTED ON SOCIAL RESPONSIBILITY SHAREHOLDER RESOLUTIONS. see *BUSINESS AND ECONOMICS — Investments*

300   US   ISSN 0270-3602
HOYAN. 1979. q. $25. Hoya Society International, Inc., Box 1043, Porterdale, GA 30270-1043. Ed. Christine M. Burton. adv.; bk.rev.; charts; illus.; index. circ. 500. (looseleaf format)
  Description: Presents nomenclatural and taxonomical research, republication of original descriptions with translation, cultural articles and society news.

300 100   CC   ISSN 1000-5579
HUADONG SHIFAN DAXUE XUEBAO (ZHEXUE SHEHUI KEXUE BAN)/EAST CHINA NORMAL UNIVERSITY. JOURNAL. (SOCIAL SCIENCE EDITION). (Text in Chinese; table of contents in English) bi-m. Y12.72. Huadong Shifan Daxue - East China Normal University, 3663 Zhongshan Beilu, Shanghai 200062, People's Republic of China. (Dist. outside China by: China International Book Trading Corp., P.O. Box 399, Beijing, P.R.C.) Ed. Guo Yushi.

300   CC   ISSN 1000-5455
HUANAN SHIFAN DAXUE XUEBAO (SHEHUI KEXUE BAN)/SOUTH CHINA NORMAL UNIVERSITY. JOURNAL (SOCIAL SCIENCE EDITION). (Text in Chinese) 1956. q. $8. Huanan Shifan Daxue, Xuebao Bianjibu, Shipai, Guangzhou, Guangdong 510631, People's Republic of China. TEL 5516911. FAX 5516011. TELEX 6754. (Dist. overseas by: China International Book Trading Corp., P.O. Box 399, Beijing, P.R. China) Ed. Liu Weiling. bk.rev. circ. 1,500. **Document type:** academic/scholarly publication.
  Description: Covers the scientific and educational researches in the areas of history, philosophy, education, economy, Chinese language and literature.

300   CC
HUAQIAO DAXUE XUEBAO (SHEHUI KEXUE BAN)/HUAQIAO UNIVERSITY. JOURNAL (SOCIAL SCIENCE EDITION). (Text in Chinese) s-a. Huaqiao Daxue - Huaqiao University, c/o Huaqiao Daxue Tushuguan, Quanzhou, Fujian 362011, People's Republic of China. TEL 224921. Ed. Chen Juewan.

300   CC   ISSN 1000-2456
AS452.W54
HUAZHONG SHIFAN DAXUE XUEBAO (SHEHUI KEXUE BAN)/CENTRAL-CHINA NORMAL UNIVERSITY. JOURNAL (SOCIAL SCIENCE EDITION). (Text in Chinese) bi-m. Huazhong Shifan Daxue, Xuebao Bianjibu, Guizishan, Wuchang-qu, Wuhan, Hubei 430070, People's Republic of China. TEL 715601. Ed. Deng Zongqi.
—UnCover.

001.3 613.7   US
HUMAN ECOLOGY. ANNUAL REPORT. a. New York State College of Human Ecology, 1150 Comstock Hall, Cornell University, Ithaca, NY 14853. TEL 607-255-2216. FAX 607-255-3794. E-mail: jcs@cornell.edu.

301.3   US   ISSN 0018-7178
HM206
HUMAN ECOLOGY FORUM. 1970. q. $25 (Canada $30; elsewhere $33). New York State College of Human Ecology, 1150 Comstock Hall, Cornell University, Ithaca, NY 14850-0998. E-mail: jcs@cornell.edu. Ed. Judy Stewart. bibl.; charts; illus.; index. circ. 5,000. (back issues avail.) **Indexed:** Energy Rev., Environ.Per.Bibl. (1972-), P.A.I.S., Soc.Sci.Ind. (until 1994).
—BLDSC (4336.063000); CIS; Faxon; UMI; UnCover.
  Description: Intended to inform alumni, legislators, and other key audiences about the activities, programs, and research of the college.

300 301.1   GW   ISSN 1045-6767
GN365.9   CODEN: HNATER
HUMAN NATURE; an interdisciplinary biosocial perspective. 1990. q. DM.130 to individuals; institutions DM.249. Walter de Gruyter und Co., Genthiner Str. 13, 10785 Berlin, Germany. TEL 030-26005-0. FAX 030-26005251. (US addr.: Walter de Gruyter, Inc., 200 Saw Mill River Rd., Hawthorne, NY 10532. TEL 914-747-0110. FAX 914-747-1326) Ed. Jane B. Lancaster. circ. 250. (back issues avail.) **Indexed:** Psychol.Abstr. (1990-). **Document type:** academic/scholarly publication.
—BLDSC (4336.223500); Faxon; Genuine Article; UnCover. **CCC.**
  Description: Dedicated to advancing the interdisciplinary investigation of the biological, social, and environmental factors which underline human behavior.

HUMAN ORGANIZATION. see *ANTHROPOLOGY*

300   US   ISSN 0018-7267
H1   CODEN: HUREAA
HUMAN RELATIONS; towards the integration of the social sciences. 1947. m. $415 (foreign $485) (effective 1996). (Tavistock Institute of Human Relations, UK) Plenum Publishing Corp., 233 Spring St., New York, NY 10013-1578. TEL 212-260-8000. FAX 212-463-0742. TELEX 23-421139. Ed. Ray Loveridge. adv.; bk.rev.; bibl.; charts; index. (also avail. in microfilm from JSC) **Indexed:** A.I.C.P., ABI Inform., Abstr.Anthropol., Abstr.Crim.& Pen., ASSIA, BPIA, Br.Hum.Ind., Bus.Ind., Commun.Abstr., Cont.Pg.Manage., Curr.Cont., Educ.Admin.Abstr., IMFL, Int.Lab.Doc., Lang.& Lang.Behav.Abstr., Manage.Cont., Mark.Res.Abstr. (1964-), Mid.East: Abstr.& Ind., P.A.I.S., Peace Res.Abstr., Pers.Lit., Psychol.Abstr. (1949-), Psycscan, SCIMP (1978-), Soc.Sci.Ind., SOMA, SSCI, Stud.Wom.Abstr. **Document type:** academic/scholarly publication.
●Also available online. Vendor(s): University Microfilms International.
—BLDSC (4336.400000); Faxon; Genuine Article; SWETS; UMI; UnCover. **CCC.**
  Refereed Serial

HUMAN SCIENCES RESEARCH COUNCIL. ANNUAL REPORT. see *HUMANITIES: COMPREHENSIVE WORKS*

HUMANE STUDIES REVIEW. see *PHILOSOPHY*

300 600   GW   ISSN 0439-884X
CB478
HUMANISMUS UND TECHNIK. a. DM.18. Technische Universitaet Berlin, Universitaetsbibliothek, Str. des 17. Juni 135, 10623 Berlin, Germany. TEL 030-31423980. FAX 030-31424743. Ed. Rudolf Trostel. **Document type:** academic/scholarly publication.

300   YU   ISSN 0354-1991
HUMANITAS; strucni casopis studenata Univerziteta u Nisu. (Text in Serbo-Croatian; summaries in English) 1969. q. 2500 din. Univerzitet u Nisu, Trg Pratislava i Jedinstva 2, 1800 Nis, Serbia, Yugoslavia. Ed. Miroslav Pavlovic. adv. circ. 500.
  Former titles (until 1991): Naucni Podmladak. Sveska za Drustvene Nauke i Filozofiju (ISSN 0352-5821); (until 1985): Naucni Podmladak. Sveska za Drustvene Nauke, Filozofiju i Kulturu (ISSN 0351-5699); (until 1981): Humanitas (ISSN 0351-1790); Supersedes in part (in 1971): Naucni Podmladak: Tehnicke Nauki. Drustvene Nauki.

301   US   ISSN 0160-4341
HN65   CODEN: HJSRAB
HUMBOLDT JOURNAL OF SOCIAL RELATIONS. 1973. s-a. $16 to individuals; institutions $26; Humboldt State University, College of Behavioral & Social Science, Arcata, CA 95521. TEL 707-826-3716. adv.; bk.rev.; index. circ. 400. **Indexed:** Abstr.Soc.Work, Chic.Per.Ind., Lang.& Lang.Behav.Abstr., Mid.East: Abstr.& Ind., Psychol.Abstr. (1973-), Sociol.Abstr. (1973-).
—BLDSC (4336.595000); Faxon; UnCover.

SOCIAL SCIENCES: COMPREHENSIVE WORKS

300   GW   ISSN 0933-1719
PN6149.P5   CODEN: HUMRES
HUMOR; international journal of humor research. 1988. q. DM.243. Walter de Gruyter und Co., Mouton de Gruyter, Genthiner Str. 13, 10785 Berlin, Germany. TEL 030-26005-0. FAX 030-26005251. TELEX 184027. (U.S. subscr. to: Walter de Gruyter Inc., 200 Saw Mill River Rd., Hawthorne, NY 10532. TEL 914-747-0110) Ed. Victor Raskin. bk.rev. (back issues avail.) **Indexed:** Bibl.Ling., Lang.& Lang.Behav.Abstr., Psychol.Abstr. (1988-), Sociol.Abstr. **Document type:** academic/scholarly publication.
—BLDSC (4336.730500); Genuine Article; SWETS; UnCover. **CCC**.
Former titles: World Humor and Irony Movement Serials Yearbook; World Humor and Irony Membership Serial Yearbook; Western Humor and Irony Membership Serial Yearbook (ISSN 0737-0342)
Description: Scholarly journal for the publication of research papers on humor as an important and universal human faculty.

300   CC   ISSN 1000-2529
HUNAN SHIFAN DAXUE XUEBAO (SHEHUI KEXUE BAN)/HUNAN NORMAL UNIVERSITY. JOURNAL (SOCIAL SCIENCE EDITION). (Text in Chinese) bi-m. Y14. Hunan Shifan Daxue, Xuebao Bianjibu, Yuelushan, Changsha, Hunan 410081, People's Republic of China. TEL 8883131. **Document type:** academic/scholarly publication.
—UnCover.

HUNGARIAN STUDIES. see *HUMANITIES: COMPREHENSIVE WORKS*

300   IT   ISSN 0393-9367
HYRIA; cultura e societa della nuova Europa. 1972. q. L.10000. Via Tanzillo, 4, 80035 Nola (Naples), Italy. Ed. Aristide LaRocca. bk.rev.; charts; illus.
Description: Forum covering new social, cultural and educational ideas relating to the southern region of Italy.

320   US
I C P S R BULLETIN. 4/yr. $15. (Inter-University Consortium for Political and Social Research) Institute for Social Research, University of Michigan, Box 1248, Ann Arbor, MI 48106. TEL 313-764-2570. FAX 313-764-8041. Ed. Mary B. Vardigan. **Document type:** bulletin.

I C S A NEWSLETTER. (International Christian Studies Association) see *RELIGIONS AND THEOLOGY*

300   II   ISSN 0018-9049
H62.5.I5
I C S S R NEWSLETTER. (Text in English) 1969. q. free. Indian Council of Social Science Research, 35 Ferozshah Rd., New Delhi 110 001, India. TEL 91-11-388342. FAX 91-11-388037. TELEX 31-61083-ISSR-IN. Ed. R.C. Bindra. abstr.; stat. circ. 5,500. (back issues avail.) **Indexed:** A.I.C.P., Rural Devel.Abstr., World Agri.Econ.& Rural Sociol.Abstr., World Bibl.Soc.Sec. **Document type:** newsletter.
Description: Lists all projects, fellowships, contingency and other grants given to social scientists. Includes other news of relevance to social scientists in India, featuring political implications of research.

I F E P P INFORMATIONS. (Institut de Formation et d'Etudes Psycho-Sociologiques et Pedagogiques) see *PSYCHOLOGY*

I N R A SCIENCES SOCIALES. (Institut National de la Recherche Agronomique) see *AGRICULTURE — Agricultural Economics*

I P S S BULLETIN. (Institute of Political and Social Studies) see *POLITICAL SCIENCE*

I S E A S SERIES ON JAPAN AND THE ASIA - PACIFIC. (Institute of Southeast Asian Studies) see *HISTORY — History Of Asia*

300   SA
I S E R FACT PAPER. (Text in English) 1983. irreg., no.6, 1986. University of Durban-Westville, Institute for Social and Economic Research, Private Bag X54001, Durban 4000, South Africa. TEL 27-31-820-2298. FAX 27-31-820-2834. Dir. J.J. McCarthy. (back issues avail.) **Document type:** academic/scholarly publication.

300   SA
I S E R OCCASIONAL PAPER. (Text in English) 1981. irreg., vol.24, 1989. exchange basis. University of Durban-Westville, Institute for Social and Economic Research, Private Bag X54001, Durban 4000, South Africa. TEL 27-31-820-2298. FAX 27-31-820-2834. Dir. J.J. McCarthy. (back issues avail.) **Document type:** academic/scholarly publication.

300   US
I S E R OCCASIONAL PAPERS. 1970. irreg., no.22, 1994. $4 per no. University of Alaska, Institute of Social and Economic Research, 3211 Providence Dr., Anchorage, AK 99508-4614. TEL 907-786-7710. FAX 907-786-7739. Ed. Linda Leask. bibl. **Document type:** monographic series.
Formerly: I S E G R Occasional Papers.

300   SA
I S E R REPORT. (Text in English) 1976. irreg., vol.25, 1988. exchange basis. University of Durban-Westville, Institute for Social and Economic Research, Private Bag X54001, Durban 4000, South Africa. TEL 27-31-820-2298. FAX 27-31-820-2834. Dir. J.J. McCarthy. (back issues avail.) **Document type:** academic/scholarly publication.

300   SA
I S E R SPECIAL PUBLICATION. 1985. irreg., no.5, 1988. University of Durban-Westville, Institute for Social and Economic Research, Private Bag X54001, Durban 4000, South Africa. TEL 27-31-820-2298. FAX 27-31-820-2834. Dir. J.J. McCarthy. (back issues avail.) **Document type:** academic/scholarly publication.

946 300   UK   ISSN 0307-3262
DP233
IBERIAN STUDIES. 1972. s-a. £12 in the U.K.; elsewhere £20. University of Keele, Centre for Iberian Studies, Keele, Staffs. ST5 5BG, England. TEL 01782-621111. FAX 01782-613847. TELEX 36113-UNKLIB-G. Ed. Dr. J. Naylon. bk.rev.; bibl.; illus.; stat.; circ. 300. **Indexed:** Amer.Hist.& Life, Hist.Abstr. **Document type:** academic/scholarly publication.
—BLDSC (4359.790000).
Description: English language journal devoted to the study of Spanish and Portuguese society. Articles written by Iberian specialists from all over the world in the areas of history, politics, economics, geography, education, sociology and social anthropology.
Refereed Serial

300   AG   ISSN 0326-386X
H8.S7
IDEAS EN CIENCIAS SOCIALES. 1984. 3/yr. $30 (foreign $48). Universidad de Belgrano, Teodoro Gracia 2090, 1426 Buenos Aires, Argentina. TEL 774-2133. Ed. Avelino J. Porto. adv.; bk.rev.; bibl.; charts; stat. circ. 1,000. (back issues avail.)
Description: Covers politics, law and sociology in Latin America.

IMMIGRATION THEORY AND POLICY SERIES. see *POPULATION STUDIES*

300   PH   ISSN 0300-4155
DS1
IMPACT; Asian magazine for human transformation. (Text in English) 1967. m. P.175 (Asia & Pacific Isles $9; Europe & N. America $30). Social Impact Foundation Inc., Noel St. 2948, United Paranaque III M.M., P.O. Box 2950, Metro Manila, Philippines. TEL 827-65-81. FAX 827-65-81. Ed. Cornelius G. Breed. adv.: page P.3000; trim 8 1/4 x 10 3/4. bk.rev.; illus.; index; circ. 1,400 (paid); 300 (controlled). (also avail. in microform from UMI; microfiche from IDC; reprint service avail. from UMI) **Indexed:** Abstr.Rural Dev.Trop., HR Rep., I.C.U.I.S.Abstr., Ind.Phil.Per., Lang.& Lang.Behav.Abstr., Sociol.Abstr.
—UMI.
Description: Covers social development issues in Asia.

300   US   ISSN 0741-6180
IN CONTEXT; a journal of hope, sustainability and change. 1980. q. $24 (foreign $31). Context Institute, Box 11470, Bainbridge Island, WA 98110. TEL 206-842-0216. FAX 206-842-5208. E-mail: ci@context.org. Ed. Sarah VanGelder; Pub. Robert Gilman. bk.rev.; illus.; circ. 11,000 (paid). **Indexed:** Alt.Press Ind. **Document type:** academic/scholarly publication.
Description: Provides a balanced perspective on social and environmental issues, concentrating on creative solutions. Encourages direct participation in development of sustainable culture.

300 301   CN   ISSN 0228-2518
IN SUMMARY. 1979. 3/yr. free. University of Alberta, Department of Sociology, Population Research Laboratory, Edmonton, AB T6G 2H4, Canada. TEL 403-492-4659. FAX 403-492-2589. Ed. Fran Russell. circ. 650.
Description: Newsletter of the Population Research Laboratory, with information on its research activities, publications, seminars and conferences.

960   II   ISSN 0971-5312
IND-AFRICANA: COLLECTED RESEARCH PAPERS ON AFRICA. (Text in English) 1988. s-a. University of Delhi, Department of African Studies, Delhi 100 007, India. TEL 7257725. Ed. K.K. Virmani. circ. 400. **Indexed:** Documentatieblad.

INDEX TO INTERNATIONAL PUBLIC OPINION. see *POLITICAL SCIENCE — International Relations*

300   II   ISSN 0256-4491
INDIAN COUNCIL OF SOCIAL RESEARCH. ANNUAL REPORT. (Editions in English and Hindi) 1970. a. free. Indian Council of Social Science Research, National Social Science Documentation Centre, 35 Ferozshah Rd., New Delhi 110 001, India. TEL 91-11-385959. FAX 91-11-388037. TELEX 31-61083-ISSR-IN. circ. 1,200 (both eds.). (back issues avail.)
Description: Bulletin of the Indian Council of Social Science Research.

330 300   II   ISSN 0019-4646
HC431
INDIAN ECONOMIC AND SOCIAL HISTORY REVIEW. (Text in English) 1963. q. Rs.250($36) to individuals; institutions Rs.525($83). (Indian Economic and Social History Association) Sage Publications India Pvt. Ltd., P.O. Box 4215, New Delhi 110 048, India. TEL 91-11-644-4958. FAX 91-11-647-2426. (Overseas subscr. to: Sage Publications Ltd., 6 Bonhill St., London EC2A 4PU, England. TEL 44-071-374-0645. FAX 44-071-374-8741; Subscr. in N. America: Sage Publications, Inc., 2455 Teller Rd., Thousand Oaks, CA 91320. TEL 805-499-0721. FAX 805-499-0871) Ed. Dr. Dharma Kumar; Pub. Tejeshwar Singh. adv.: page Rs.1000; adv. contact: Sunanda Ghosh. bk.rev.; cum.index: 1963-1969. circ. 900. (also avail. in microform from UMI; back issues avail.; reprint service avail. from UMI) **Indexed:** Amer.Hist.& Life, Hist.Abstr., J.of Econ.Lit., Numis.Lit. **Document type:** academic/scholarly publication.
—BLDSC (4396.320000); Faxon; Genuine Article; SWETS; UMI; UnCover.
Description: Covers the histories, economies, and societies of India and Southeast Asia and includes comparative studies of world development.
Refereed Serial

INDIAN INSTITUTE OF PUBLIC OPINION. MONTHLY PUBLIC OPINION SURVEYS. see *POLITICAL SCIENCE*

300   II   ISSN 0046-9017
HT395.I5
INDIAN JOURNAL OF REGIONAL SCIENCE. (Text and summaries in English) 1968. s-a. Rs.125($20) (typically out in Jan.). (Regional Science Association, India) Indian Institute of Technology, Kharagpur, Dept. of Arch. & Regional Planning, Kharagpur 721302, West Bengal, India. TEL 03222-2221. FAX 03222-2303. TELEX 06401-201 IT KGIN. Eds. A.N. Bose, C.R. Pathak. adv. contact: C.R. Pathak. bk.rev.; index. circ. 525. (tabloid format) **Indexed:** ASSIA. **Document type:** academic/scholarly publication.
—BLDSC (4421.030000); Faxon.

SOCIAL SCIENCES: COMPREHENSIVE WORKS

300   II   ISSN 0971-0817
INDIAN JOURNAL OF SOCIAL SCIENCE. 1988. q. Rs.250($45) to individuals; institutions Rs.495($80). (Indian Council of Social Science Research) Sage Publications India Pvt. Ltd., P.O. Box 4215, New Delhi 110 048. TEL 91-11-644-4958. FAX 91-11-647-2426. (Overseas subscr. to: Sage Publications Ltd., 6 Bonhill St., London EC2A 4PU, England. TEL 44-071-374-0645. FAX 44-071-374-8741; Subscr. in N. America to: Sage Publications, Inc., 2455 Teller Rd., Thousand Oaks, CA 91320. TEL 805-499-0721. FAX 805-499-0871) Ed. G. Ram Reddy; Pub. Tejeshwar Singh. adv.: page Rs.1000; adv. contact: Sunanda Ghosh. circ. 600. (also avail. in microform from UMI; back issues avail.; reprint service avail.) Indexed: Geo.Abstr., IDA, Int.Polit.Sci.Abstr. **Document type:** academic/scholarly publication.
—BLDSC (4421.180000).
   Formerly: Indian Journal of Social Science Research.
   Description: Promotes scientific discussion on the diverse concerns of social science research from comparative research, innovative approaches and the analysis and implications of accepted paradigms and their alternatives to the understanding of the diverse and and complex social and economic issues facing developing countries.
   Refereed Serial

300   II   ISSN 0376-9879
H1
INDIAN JOURNAL OF SOCIAL SCIENCES. (Text in English) 1971. 3/yr. $5. Society for the Study of Social Sciences, c/o Treasurer, Dept. of Sociology, Osmania University, Hyderabad 7, India.

INDIAN JOURNAL OF SOCIAL WORK. see *SOCIAL SERVICES AND WELFARE*

300   II   ISSN 0073-6694
INDIAN STATISTICAL INSTITUTE. ECONOMETRIC AND SOCIAL SCIENCES SERIES. RESEARCH MONOGRAPHS. irreg. Indian Statistical Institute, 203 Barrackpore Trunk Rd., Calcutta 700035, India. Ed. C.R. Rao.

300   SA
INDICATOR S A REPORT. Variant series title: Indicator S A Issue Focus. (Text in English) 1983. s-a. R.34.20($20) (University of Natal, Centre for Social and Development Studies) Indicator Project S A, Centre for Social and Development Studies, King George V Ave., Durban 4001, South Africa. TEL 27-31-260-2525. FAX 27-31-260-2359. Ed. Graham W. Howe. (back issues avail.) **Document type:** monographic series.
   Description: In-depth analyses of specific topics in contemporary South African political, social and economic affairs.

300   SA   ISSN 0259-188X
INDICATOR SOUTH AFRICA; the barometer of social trends. 1983. q. R.171($150) includes s-a. Indicator S A Report. (University of Natal, Centre for Social and Development Studies) Indicator Project S A, Centre for Social and Development Studies, King George V Ave., Durban 4001, South Africa. TEL 27-31-260-2525. FAX 27-31-260-2359. Ed. Graham W. Howe. adv.; bk.rev.; stat.; index. circ. 1,000. (back issues avail.) Indexed: Ind.S.A.Per. **Document type:** academic/scholarly publication.
—BLDSC (4432.460000).
   Description: Monitors socio-political and economic trends in South Africa. Contributes to informed debate and regional scholarship, with data analyses, diagnosis of trends, and a policy prognosis service. Publishes objective and original research using primary statistics, investigative fieldwork, attitude surveys and documentary research.

INDOCHINA UNIT SERIES. see *HISTORY — History Of Asia*

INDUSTRIAL AND SOCIAL RELATIONS. see *BUSINESS AND ECONOMICS — Labor And Industrial Relations*

300   SA   ISSN 1017-7485
HN801.Z9
INFORMATION UPDATE - HUMAN SCIENCES RESEARCH COUNCIL. 1991. q. R.660. Human Sciences Research Council, Research Division, P.O. Box 9086, Pretoria 0001, South Africa. TEL 27-12-2022673. FAX 27-12-2022671. Ed. Cynthia Marais. circ. 250. **Document type:** newsletter.
—BLDSC (4496.387400).
   Description: Discusses the results of opinion survey on topical issues, and provides a review of the year's trends.

301 058.7   SW   ISSN 1101-4431
INFORMATIONSBULLETINEN; tidskrift foer sjaelvfoersoerjning, miljoe, energi, odling. kultur, politik, solidaritet och fred. Key Title: Informationsbulletinen (Helsingborg). 1986. bi-m. SEK 120 (effective 1995). Circulus, P.O. Box 15057, S-750 15 Uppsala, Sweden. TEL 46-295-43034. FAX 46-295-43018. E-mail: Guy.Madison@psyk.uu.se. Ed. Guy Madison. adv. circ. 2,000. **Document type:** bulletin.

300   AG
INICIATIVAS PARA EL DESARROLLO DE ESPACIOS SOLIDARIOS. 1992. q. $12. Fundacion Generacion 2000, Agrelo 3356, 1o piso, 1224 Buenos Aires, Argentina. TEL 54-01-93-8842. Ed. Roderto Di Lorenzo.

INIZIATIVA ISONTINA. see *BUSINESS AND ECONOMICS — Economic Situation And Conditions*

300 600   UK
H1
INNOVATION: THE EUROPEAN JOURNAL OF SOCIAL SCIENCES. 1988. q. £40 to individuals; institutions £192 (effective 1996). (Interdisciplinary Centre for Comparative Research in the Social Sciences (ICCR), AU) Carfax Publishing Co., P.O. Box 25, Abingdon, Oxon. OX14 3UE, England. TEL 01235-555335. FAX 01235-553559. (Editorial addr.: Hamburgerstr. 14-20, A-1050 Vienna, Austria; N. American subscr. to: Carfax Publishing Co., 875-81 Massachusetts Ave., Cambridge, MA 02139) Ed. Ronald Pohoryles. adv.; bk.rev.; index. (back issues avail.) Indexed: Geo.Abstr., Int.Polit.Sci.Abstr. **Document type:** academic/scholarly publication.
—UMI. CCC.
   Formerly (until 1994): Innovation in Social Sciences Research (ISSN 1012-8050)
   Refereed Serial

INQUIRY; an interdisciplinary journal of philosophy. see *PHILOSOPHY*

300   CN   ISSN 1188-746X
F1001
INROADS; a journal of opinion. 1992. s-a. $60. P.O. Box 77042, Ottawa, ON K1S 5N2, Canada. TEL 613-730-5835. Eds. Henry Milner, John Richards. Indexed: Amer.Hist.& Life, Hist.Abstr.

INSTITUT DES HAUTES ETUDES DE L'AMERIQUE LATINE. COLLECTION DES TRAVAUX ET MEMOIRES. see *HUMANITIES: COMPREHENSIVE WORKS*

300 550   PE   ISSN 0303-7495
F2212   CODEN: BIFEB5
INSTITUT FRANCAIS D'ETUDES ANDINES. BULLETIN/INSTITUTO FRANCES DE ESTUDIOS ANDINOS. BOLETIN. (Text in English, French, Spanish) 1972. 3/yr. $30 to individuals; institutions $45 (effective 1995). Institut Francais d'Etudes Andines, Casilla 18-1217, Lima 18, Peru. TEL 5114-476070. FAX 5114-457650. E-mail: postmaster@ifea.org.pe. Ed. Anne-Marie Brougere. adv.; illus. circ. 850. Indexed: A.I.C.P., Anthropol.Lit., Geo.Abstr., Hisp.Amer.Per.Ind. (1975-), Hisp.Amer.Per.Ind. **Document type:** bulletin.
   Description: Covers many areas in earth and social sciences, including anthropology, agriculture, archaeology, ethnic history, sociology, biology, linguistics, geology and paleontology.

300 550   PE   ISSN 0768-424X
INSTITUT FRANCAIS D'ETUDES ANDINES. TRAVAUX. (Text in French and Spanish) 1949. irreg. price varies. Institut Francais d'Etudes Andines, Casilla 18-1217, Lima 18, Peru. TEL 5114-476070. FAX 5114-457650. E-mail: postmaster@ifea.org.pe. Ed. Anne-Marie Brougere. Indexed: A.I.C.P. **Document type:** monographic series.

300   II   ISSN 0971-3085
INSTITUT FRANCAIS DE PONDICHERY. DEPARTEMENT DE SCIENCES SOCIALES. PUBLICATIONS. (Text and summaries in English, French) 1991. irreg. price varies. Institut Francais de Pondichery, Departement de Sciences Sociales, Box 33, Pondichery 605 001, India. TEL 91-413-34170. FAX 91-413-29534. TELEX 469224 FRAN IN. Ed. J. Pouchepadass. index. circ. 500.

300   JA   ISSN 0563-8186
INSTITUTE FOR COMPARATIVE STUDIES OF CULTURE. ANNALS. (Text in Japanese) 1955. a. 1500 Yen. Institute for Comparative Studies of Culture, c/o Tokyo Woman's Christian University, 2-6-1 Zempukuji, Suginami-ku, Tokyo 167, Japan. title index. circ. 600.
   Formerly: Institute for Comparative Studies of Culture. Publications.

300   US
INSTITUTE FOR SOCIAL ECOLOGY NEWSLETTER. 1989. s-a. donation. Institute for Social Ecology, Box 89, Plainfield, VT 05667. TEL 802-454-8493. bk.rev. circ. 4,000. (back issues avail.) **Document type:** newsletter.
   Description: Covers anarchism, community development, political and social change, ecological design, ecological technology, and biological agriculture.

300   US   ISSN 0020-2622
INSTITUTE FOR SOCIAL RESEARCH. NEWSLETTER. Abbreviated title: I S R Newsletter. 1969. 3/yr. free. University of Michigan, Institute for Social Research, I.S.R. Administration, Box 1248, Ann Arbor, MI 48106. TEL 313-763-8363. FAX 313-747-4575. bk.rev.; charts; illus. circ. 18,000. (also avail. in microform from UMI; back issues avail.; reprint service avail. from UMI) **Document type:** newsletter.
—UMI.

INSTITUTE OF SOCIAL AND ECONOMIC RESEARCH. REPORTS. see *BUSINESS AND ECONOMICS*

300   SI   ISSN 0217-7099
INSTITUTE OF SOUTHEAST ASIAN STUDIES. FIELD REPORTS SERIES. (Text in English) 1973. irreg., no.28, 1994. price varies. Institute of Southeast Asian Studies, Heng Mui Keng Terrace, Pasir Panjang, Singapore 0511, Singapore. TEL 7780955. FAX 7781735. TELEX RS 37068 ISEAS. E-mail: pubsunit@merlion.iseas.ac.sg. (Subscr. in U.S. to: Ashgate, Old Post Rd., Brookfield, VT 05036. TEL 802-276-3162)
   Description: Field reports of research on southeast Asian economics, politics and social issues.

300   SI
INSTITUTE OF SOUTHEAST ASIAN STUDIES. MONOGRAPHS SERIES. (Text in English) 1973. irreg., no.145, 1995. price varies. Institute of Southeast Asian Studies, Heng Mui Keng Terrace, Pasir Panjang, Singapore 0511, Singapore. TEL 7780955. FAX 7781735. TELEX RS 37068 ISEAS. E-mail: pubsunit@merlion.iseas.ac.sg. **Document type:** monographic series, academic/scholarly publication.
   Description: Major works on Southeast Asia, particularly current economics, political and social issues.

300   SI   ISSN 0073-9731
INSTITUTE OF SOUTHEAST ASIAN STUDIES. OCCASIONAL PAPER. (Text in English) 1970. irreg., no.90, 1994. price varies. Institute of Southeast Asian Studies, Heng Mui Keng Terrace, Pasir Panjang, Singapore 0511, Singapore. TEL 7780955. FAX 7781735. TELEX RS 37068 ISEAS. E-mail: pubsunit@merlion.iseas.ac.sg. (Subscr. in U.S. to: Ashgate, Old Post Rd., Brookfield, VT 05036. TEL 802-276-3162) bibl. (back issues avail.) Indexed: Geo.Abstr.
—BLDSC (4582.832500).
   Description: Studies on Southeast Asia, particularly current economic, political and social issues.

SOCIAL SCIENCES: COMPREHENSIVE WORKS

300   SI   ISSN 0129-8828
INSTITUTE OF SOUTHEAST ASIAN STUDIES. RESEARCH NOTES AND DISCUSSION SERIES. (Text in English) 1976. irreg., no.75, 1992. price varies. Institute of Southeast Asian Studies, Heng Mui Keng Terrace, Pasir Panjang, Singapore 0511, Singapore. TEL 7780955. FAX 7781735. TELEX RS 37068 ISEAS. E-mail: pubsunit@merlion.iseas.ac.sg. (Subscr. in U.S. to: Ashgate, Old Post Rd., Brookfield, VT 05036. TEL 802-276-3162) bibl.; charts; stat. (back issues avail.) Document type: academic/scholarly publication.
—BLDSC (7749.741000).
Description: Short papers on current research on Southeast Asia, particularly economic, political and social issues.

300   CK   ISSN 0121-7194
INSTITUTO COLOMBIANO DE CULTURA. GACETA; revista internacional de cultura. 1975. bi-m. $60. Instituto Colombiano de Cultura, Calle 11, no. 5-16, Apdo. Aereo 43617, Santafe de Bogota, DC, Colombia. TEL 57-1-3410675. FAX 57-1-2820854. Ed. Ruben Sierra Mejia. adv.: B&W page $62.50, color page $87.50; 240 x 340; adv. contact: Martha Traslavina. bk.rev.; film rev. circ. 5,000. Document type: government publication.
Description: Contains literary essays and contemporary poetry.

918.503   PE   ISSN 0258-8536
INSTITUTO DE ESTUDIOS AYMARAS. BOLETIN. 1978. 3/yr. $6 to individuals; institutions $9. Instituto de Estudios Aymaras, Apdo. 295, Puno, Peru. Ed. Diego Irarrazaval. (back issues avail.) **Indexed:** Anthropol.Lit.

300   PE   ISSN 1021-2760
INSTITUTO DE ESTUDIOS PERUANOS. BOLETIN ARGUMENTOS. 1992. m. $70. I E P Ediciones, Horacio Urteaga 694, Lima 11, Peru. TEL 51-14-323070. FAX 51-14-32-4981. E-mail: postmaster@iep.org.pe. Document type: bulletin.

300   PE   ISSN 1019-4479
INSTITUTO DE ESTUDIOS PERUANOS. COLECCION MINIMA. 1973. irreg., no.30, 1994. price varies. I E P Ediciones, Horacio Urteaga 694, Lima 11, Peru. TEL 54-14-323070. FAX 54-14-324981. E-mail: postmaster@iep.org.pe.

300   PE   ISSN 1022-0356
INSTITUTO DE ESTUDIOS PERUANOS. DOCUMENTOS DE TRABAJO. (In 8 series: Linguistica, Antropologia, Sociologia-Politica, Economia, Historia, Etnohistoria, Talleres, Documentos de Politica) 1986. irreg., no.69, 1994. price varies. I E P Ediciones, Horacio Urteaga 694, Lima 11, Peru. TEL 51-14-323070. FAX 51-14-324981. E-mail: postmaster@iep.org.pe. (back issues avail.)

INSTITUTO DE INVESTIGACAO CIENTIFICA TROPICAL. COMUNICACOES. SERIE DE CIENCIAS HISTORICAS, ECONOMICAS E SOCIOLOGICAS. see HISTORY

300   RM
INSTITUTUL DE SUBINGINERI ORADEA. LUCRARI STIINTIFICE: SERIA STIINTE SOCIALE. (Text in Rumanian, occasionally in English or French; summaries in English, French, German or Rumanian) 1973. a. Institutul de Subingineri Oradea, Calea Armatei Roseii Nr. 5, 3700 Oradea, Rumania.
Formerly: Institutul Pedagogica Oradea. Lucrari Stiintifice: Seria Stiinte Sociale; Which continues in part (in 1973): Institutul Pedagogica Oradea. Lucrari Stiintifice: Seria Istorie, Stiinte Sociale, Pedagogie; Which superseded in part (in 1971): Institutul Pedagogic Oradea. Lucrari Stiintifice: Seria A and Seria B; Which was formerly (until 1969): Institutul Pedagogic Oradea. Lucrari Stiintifice.

INSTRUCTIONAL SCIENCE; an international journal of learning and cognition. see EDUCATION

300   NG   ISSN 0534-4751
INTER-AFRICAN CONFERENCE ON SOCIAL SCIENCE MEETING.* 1955. irreg. (Commission for Technical Co-Operation in Africa South of the Sahara) Maison de l'Afrique, B.P. 878, Niamey, Niger.

INTER-AMERICAN ECONOMIC AND SOCIAL COUNCIL. FINAL REPORT OF THE ANNUAL MEETING AT THE MINISTERIAL LEVEL. see HISTORY — History Of North And South America

INTERCOLLEGIATE REVIEW; a journal of scholarship and opinion. see LITERARY AND POLITICAL REVIEWS

INTERDISCIPLINARIA; revista de psicologia y ciencias afines/journal of psychology and related sciences. see PSYCHOLOGY

INTERFACES: LINGUISTICS, PSYCHOLOGY AND HEALTH THERAPEUTICS; an international journal of research, notes and commentary. see LINGUISTICS

INTERNATIONAL CULTURAL SOCIETY OF KOREA. NEWSLETTER. see HUMANITIES: COMPREHENSIVE WORKS

INTERNATIONAL JOURNAL OF ENVIRONMENTAL STUDIES. SECTIONS A & B. see ENVIRONMENTAL STUDIES

INTERNATIONAL JOURNAL OF INFORMATION MANAGEMENT. see COMPUTERS — Information Science And Information Theory

300   UK   ISSN 0954-2892
HM261   CODEN: IJPOE2
INTERNATIONAL JOURNAL OF PUBLIC OPINION RESEARCH. 1989. q. £70($125) (effective 1996). (World Association for Public Opinion Research) Oxford University Press, Oxford Journals, Walton St., Oxford OX2 6DP, England. TEL 01865-267907. FAX 01865-267773. TELEX 837330-OXPRES-G. E-mail: jnlorders@oup.co.uk. (U.S. subscr. to: Oxford University Press Inc., 2001 Evans Rd., Cary, NC 27513. TEL 919-677-0977. FAX 919-677-1714) Ed.Bd. adv. contact: Jane Parker. bk.rev. circ. 1,000. **Indexed:** Int.Polit.Sci.Abstr., Mark.Res.Abstr. (1989-). Document type: academic/scholarly publication.
—BLDSC (4542.509100); Genuine Article; UMI; UnCover. CCC.
Description: Provides a source of informed analysis and comment in the field of public opinion research. Covers matters of interest to both the professional and academic community.

954.5   II   ISSN 0971-5223
DS485.P88
INTERNATIONAL JOURNAL OF PUNJAB STUDIES. (Text in English) s-a. $34 to individuals; institutions $75 (effective Sep. 1995). (Association for Punjab Studies) Sage Publications India Pvt. Ltd., Box 4215, New Delhi 110 048, India. TEL 91-11-644-4958. FAX 91-11-647-2426. (Subscr. overseas to: Sage Publications Ltd., 6 Bonhill St., London EC2A 4PU, England. TEL 44-171-374-0645. FAX 44-171-374-8741; Subscr. in. N. America to: Sage Publications, Inc., 2455 Teller Rd., Thousand Oaks, CA 91320. TEL 805-499-0721. FAX 805-499-0871) Ed.Bd. adv.: page Rs.1000; adv. contact: Sunanda Ghosh. circ. 500. (back issues avail.; reprint service avail.) Document type: academic/scholarly publication.
●Also available online.
Also available on CD-ROM. Producer(s): SilverPlatter Information, Inc.
Description: Provides a forum for an authoritative analysis on the Punjab region with contributions from a wide range of disciplines, including history, political science, economics, sociology, anthropology, geography, theology, literature, and linguistics.
Refereed Serial

300   US   ISSN 0889-0293
H1
INTERNATIONAL JOURNAL OF SOCIAL EDUCATION. 1945. 2/yr. $10 (foreign $13). (Indiana Council for the Social Studies) Ball State University, Department of History, Muncie, IN 47306-0480. TEL 317-285-8704. Ed. John E. Weakland. adv. circ. 1,100. (also avail. in microform from UMI; reprint service avail. from UMI) **Indexed:** Amer.Hist.& Life, C.I.J.E., ERIC, Hist.Abstr. Document type: academic/scholarly publication.
—BLDSC (4542.556000); Faxon; UMI; UnCover.
Formerly (until 1986): Indiana Social Studies Quarterly (ISSN 0019-6746)

300   CN   ISSN 1192-2664
INTERNATIONAL JOURNAL OF SOCIAL SCIENCES. (Text in Arabic, English) 1993. 4/yr. Can.$400 (free to qualified personnel). Box 98029, S. Common Post, 2150 Burnhamthorpe Rd., Mississauga, ON L5L 3A0, Canada. FAX 516-277-2875. (And: Box 38552, Abdulla Al-Salem, Kuwait City 72256, Kuwait. FAX 965-489-1179) Ed M.I. Ismail.
Description: Designed for concise, cooperative publication of simple and creative ideas.
Refereed Serial

INTERNATIONAL JOURNAL OF SOCIOLOGY AND SOCIAL POLICY. see SOCIOLOGY

INTERNATIONAL MIGRATION REVIEW; a quarterly studying sociological, demographic, economic, historical, and legislative aspects of human migration movements and ethnic group relations. see POPULATION STUDIES

300   US   ISSN 0160-0176
HT390
INTERNATIONAL REGIONAL SCIENCE REVIEW. 1975. 3/yr. $18 to individuals; institutions $35; students $8 (effective 1995 & 1996). West Virginaia University, Regional Research Institute, Morgantown, WV 26506-6825. TEL 304-293-2896. FAX 304-293-6699. E-mail: irsrB@wvnvm.wvnet.edu. Ed. Andrew Isserman. bibl.; charts; circ. 2,500 (paid). **Indexed:** A.B.C.Pol.Sci., ASSIA, Avery Ind.Archit.Per., Curr.Cont., Energy Ind., Energy Info.Abstr., Geo.Abstr., IDA, J.of Econ.Lit., Popul.Ind., Rural Recreat.Tour.Abstr., Sage Urb.Stud.Abstr., SSCI, World Agri.Econ.& Rural Sociol.Abstr. Document type: academic/scholarly publication.
—BLDSC (4545.785000); Faxon; Genuine Article; SWETS; UnCover.
Description: Multidisciplinary journal designed to strengthen the regional and spatial aspects of quantitative research in existing social science disciplines, particularly economics and geography.
Refereed Serial

300   UK   ISSN 0020-8701
H1
INTERNATIONAL SOCIAL SCIENCE JOURNAL. Revue Internationale des Sciences Sociales. 1949. q. £56($116) (foreign £72) (effective 1996). (Unesco) Basil Blackwell Ltd., 108 Cowley Road, Oxford OX4 1JF, England. TEL 01865-791100. FAX 01865-791347. TELEX 837022 OXBOOK G. (Dist. in U.S. by: Bernan-Unipub, 4611-F Assembly Dr., Lanham, MD 20706-4391) Ed. A. Kazancigil. bibl.; charts; index. circ. 4,500. (also avail. in microform from MIM,UMI; reprint service avail. from UMI) **Indexed:** A.B.C.Pol.Sci., A.I.C.P., Abstr.Anthropol., Abstr.Rural Dev.Trop., Amer.Hist.& Life, Asian-Pac.Econ.Lit., ASSIA, Bibl.Ling., C.I.J.E., Cont.Pg.Manage., Curr.Cont., E.I., Excerp.Med., Fut.Surv., Geo.Abstr., High.Educ.Curr.Aware.Bull., Hist.Abstr., IDA, Int.Lab.Doc., Int.Polit.Sci.Abstr., Lang.& Lang.Behav.Abstr., M.L.A., Mid.East: Abstr.& Ind., Mult.Ed.Abstr., P.A.I.S., Polit.Sci.Abstr., Psychol.Abstr., Rural Recreat.Tour.Abstr., Sage Fam.Stud.Abstr., Sage Pub.Admin.Abstr., Soc.Sci.Ind., Sociol.Abstr. (1952-), SOMA, SSCI, World Agri.Econ.& Rural Sociol.Abstr. Document type: academic/scholarly publication.
—BLDSC (4549.450000); Faxon; Genuine Article; SWETS; UMI; UnCover.

300   US   ISSN 0278-2308
H1
INTERNATIONAL SOCIAL SCIENCE REVIEW. 1925. q. $10. Pi Gamma Mu, University of Toledo, Toledo, OH 43606. TEL 419-537-4395. (Subscr. to: 1717 Ames, Winfield, KS 67156) Ed. Panos D. Bardis. bk.rev.; index. cum.index: vols.21-25 (1946-1950). circ. 10,000. **Indexed:** Abstr.Soc.Work., Amer.Bibl.Slavic & E.Eur.Stud., Amer.Hist.& Life, ASSIA, Curr.Cont., Econ.Abstr., Geo.Abstr., Hist.Abstr., Int.Bibl.Soc.Sci., Int.Polit.Sci.Abstr., Int.Polit.Sci.Abstr., Key to Econ.Sci., Lang.& Lang.Behav.Abstr., Mid.East: Abstr.& Ind., Mult.Ed.Abstr., P.A.I.S., Peace Res.Abstr., Polit.Sci.Abstr., Sociol.Abstr., Sociol.Educ.Abstr., SSCI, Stud.Wom.Abstr., World Bibl.Soc.Sec. Document type: academic/scholarly publication.
—BLDSC (4549.459000); Faxon; UnCover. CCC.
Formerly (until Jan. 1982): Social Science (ISSN 0037-7848)
Description: Publishes historical and modern, quantitative and qualitative studies in all social sciences, humanities, and related fields.

INTERNATIONAL STUDIES IN SOCIOLOGY AND SOCIAL ANTHROPOLOGY. see SOCIOLOGY

300   UY
INTERSTICIOS; de la socio-cultura. 1990. m.? Ituzaingo 1522, Apto. 103, 11000 Montevideo, Uruguay. TEL 95-81-70. Eds. Gabriela DelSignore, Basilio Munoz. Document type: consumer publication.

SOCIAL SCIENCES: COMPREHENSIVE WORKS

300 US ISSN 0362-8736
H61.3
INTER-UNIVERSITY CONSORTIUM FOR POLITICAL AND SOCIAL RESEARCH. GUIDE TO RESOURCES AND SERVICES. 1962. a. free. Inter-University Consortium for Political and Social Research, Box 1248, Ann Arbor, MI 48106. TEL 313-764-2570. FAX 313-764-8041. **Document type:** directory.
●Also available online.
Description: Detailed descriptions of the 3000 data collections available from computerized social science data archive. Lists services offered, membership information, and computer access procedures.

300 IS ISSN 0334-133X
ISRAEL SOCIAL SCIENCE RESEARCH; a multidisciplinary journal. (Text in English) 1983. s-a. $15 to individuals; institutions $25. Hubert H. Humphrey Institute for Social Ecology, Ben-Gurion University of the Negev, P.O. Box 653, Beersheva 84105, Israel. TEL 972-7-461112. FAX 972-7-271536. E-mail: logan@bgumail.bgu.ac.il. (Co-sponsor: Israel Sociological Society) Ed. Stephen Sharot. bk.rev. circ. 750. **Indexed:** Psychol.Abstr. (1983-), Sociol.Abstr. (1983-). **Document type:** academic/scholarly publication.
—BLDSC (4583.914700).
Description: A forum for analytical and comparative studies on issues related to social behavior in Israel.
Refereed Serial

300 IS
HA4560.Z9
ISRAEL STUDIES. 1981. s-a. free. Jerusalem Institute for Israel Studies, 20A Radak St., Jerusalem 92186, Israel. TEL 972-2-630175. FAX 972-2-639814. Ed. Ora Ahimeir. bk.rev. circ. 1,000. **Indexed:** Ind.Jew.Per. **Document type:** academic/scholarly publication.
Formerly (until 1988): Jerusalem Institute for Israel Studies. Discussion Papers - Research Series (ISSN 0333-9831)

ISSUES IN NIGERIAN DEVELOPMENT SERIES. see *GENERAL INTEREST PERIODICALS — Nigeria*

ISTITUTO GIAPPONESE DI CULTURA IN ROMA. ANNUARIO. see *HISTORY — History Of Europe*

300 IT
ISTITUTO UNIVERSITARIO ORIENTALE. DIPARTIMENTO DI SCIENZE SOCIALI. QUADERNI. 1988. irreg., no.5, 1992. price varies. Liguori Editore s.r.l., Via Mezzocannone, 19, 80134 Naples, Italy. TEL 081-5527139. **Document type:** monographic series.

300 US ISSN 0049-0903
H62
ITEMS. 1947. q. free. Social Science Research Council, 605 Third Ave., 17th Fl., New York, NY 10158. TEL 212-661-0280. FAX 212-370-7896. Ed. Gloria Kirchheimer. bk.rev. circ. 8,000. (also avail. in microform; back issues avail.) **Indexed:** A.I.C.P., Amer.Hist.& Life (until 1990), Anthropol.Lit., Hist.Abstr. (until 1990), Mid.East: Abstr.& Ind. **Document type:** academic/scholarly publication.
—BLDSC (4588.600000); UMI; UnCover.

IWATE MEDICAL UNIVERSITY SCHOOL OF LIBERAL ARTS & SCIENCES. ANNUAL REPORT/IWATE IKA DAIGAKU KYOYOBU NENPO. see *SCIENCES: COMPREHENSIVE WORKS*

300 800 500 375 JA ISSN 0367-7370
AS552.I9 CODEN: IDKKBM
IWATE UNIVERSITY. FACULTY OF EDUCATION. ANNUAL REPORT/IWATE DAIGAKU KYOIKUGAKUBU KENKYU NENPO. 1950. a. Iwate University, Faculty of Education - Iwate Daigaku Ku, 3-18-8 Ueda, Morioka, Iwate 020, Japan. Ed. Y. Saito. index. circ. 450. (back issues avail.) **Indexed:** Biol.Abstr., INIS Atomind.
—BLDSC (1248.553500).

J A S T. (Journal of American Studies of Turkey) see *HISTORY — History Of North And South America*

300 GW ISSN 0931-4938
JAHRBUCH DER BUNDESREPUBLIK DEUTSCHLAND. 1984. a. DM.19.90. C.H. Beck'sche Verlagsbuchhandlung, Wilhelmstr. 9, 80801 Munich, Germany. TEL 089-38189-338. FAX 089-38189-398. Eds. Horst-Hennek Rohlfs, Ursel Schaefer. index. **Document type:** bulletin.

300 GW ISSN 0941-8563
DS145
JAHRBUCH FUER ANTISEMITISMUSFORSCHUNG. 1992. a. (Technische Universitaet Berlin, Zentrum fuer Antisemitismusforschung) Campus Verlag GmbH, Heerstr. 149, 60488 Frankfurt a.M., Germany. TEL 069-97651610. FAX 069-97651678. Ed. Juliane Wetzel. bk.rev. circ. 2,000. **Document type:** academic/scholarly publication.
Refereed Serial

300 GW ISSN 0940-9378
JAHRBUCH FUER SOZIAL-OEKOLOGISCHE FORSCHUNG. 1991. a. (Institut fuer Sozial-Oekologische Forschung) Verlag fuer Interkulturelle Kommunikation, Postfach 900965, 60449 Frankfurt a.M., Germany. Ed. Egon Becker. **Document type:** academic/scholarly publication.

300 943 GW ISSN 0936-465X
JAHRBUCH FUER SOZIOLOGIEGESCHICHTE. 1989. a. DM.58. Verlag Leske und Budrich GmbH, Postfach 300551, 51334 Leverkusen, Germany. TEL 02171-2079. FAX 02171-41209. Ed. Carsten Klingemann. bk.rev. **Document type:** academic/scholarly publication.

300 II ISSN 0075-3548
JAWAHARLAL NEHRU UNIVERSITY. SCHOOL OF INTERNATIONAL STUDIES SERIES.* (Text in English) 1961. q. price varies. (Jawaharlal Nehru University, School of International Studies) Vikas Publishing House Pvt. Ltd., 576 Masjid Rd., Jangpura, New Delhi 110 014, India. TEL 11-624605. TELEX 31592252.
Vols. for 1972 issued by the school under its earlier name: Indian School of International Studies (ISSN 0073-666X).

296 US ISSN 0021-6704
DS101
JEWISH SOCIAL STUDIES; history, culture and society. 1939. 3/yr. $45 (foreign $55). Indiana University Press, 601 N. Morton St., Bloomington, IN 47404. TEL 812-855-9449. FAX 812-855-7953. E-mail: Journals@Indinna.edu. Eds. Steven J. Zipperstein, Aron Rodrigue. bk.rev.; index, cum.index every 25 yrs. circ. 1,300. (also avail. in microform; reprint service avail. from KTO) **Indexed:** Abstr.Anthropol., Amer.Bibl.Slavic & E.Eur.Stud., Amer.Hist.& Life, Arts & Hum.Cit.Ind., ASSIA, Bk.Rev.Ind. (1965-), Child.Bk.Rev.Ind. (1965-), Curr.Cont., Hist.Abstr., Ind.Jew.Per., Int.Polit.Sci.Abstr., Lang.& Lang.Behav.Abstr., Mid.East: Abstr.& Ind., P.A.I.S., Soc.Sci.Ind., SSCI.
—Faxon; UnCover.

300 CC ISSN 1000-856X
AS452.N35924
JIANGHAI XUEKAN/JIANGHAI ACADEMIC JOURNAL. (Text in Chinese; table of contents in English) 1958. bi-m. Y20.40($53.40) Jiangsu Sheng Shehui Kexueyuan, Jianghai Xuekan Bianjibu - Jiangsu Academy of Social Sciences, 70-1, Beijing Xilu, Nanjing, Jiangsu 210024, People's Republic of China. TEL 025-6635429. (Dist. outside China by: China International Book Trade Corp., P.O. Box 2820, Beijing, P.R.C.; Dist. in US by: China Books & Periodicals, Inc., 2929 24th St., San Francisco, CA 94110. TEL 415-282-2994) (Co-sponsor: Jiangsu Sheng Zhexue Shehui Kexue Lianhehui) Ed. Wu Gongzheng. adv.; bk.rev. circ. 3,200. **Document type:** academic/scholarly publication.
—UnCover.
Formed by the 1988 merger of: Jianghai Xuekan (Wen-Shi-Zhe Ban) (ISSN 1000-601X); Jianghai Xuekan (Jingji Shehui Ban) (ISSN 1000-6001)
Description: Contains high quality academic papers in the fields of philosophy, economics, political science, law, sociology, history and literature.

300 CC ISSN 1003-854X
JIANGHAN LUNTAN/JIANGHAN FORUM. (Text in Chinese) 1959. m. Y14.40($54) Hubei Sheng Shehui Kexueyuan - Hubei Academy of Social Sciences, 81, Donghu Lu, Wuchang, Hubei 430077, People's Republic of China. TEL 613507. (Dist. outside China by: China International Book Trading Corp., P.O. Box 399, Beijing, P.R.C.; Dist. in US by: China Books & Periodicals, Inc., 2929 24th St., San Francisco, CA 94110. TEL 415-282-2994) Ed. Rong Kaiming.
—UnCover.

300 CC ISSN 1001-862X
JIANGHUAI LUNTAN/JIANGHUAI FORUM. (Text in Chinese) 1979. bi-m. $32.90. Anhui Sheng Shehui Kexueyuan - Anhui Provincial Academy of Social Sciences, Weigang, Hefei, Anhui 230053, People's Republic of China. TEL 331171. (Dist. in US by: China Books & Periodicals, Inc., 2929 24th St., San Francisco, CA 94110. TEL 415-282-2994)

300 CC ISSN 1000-579X
AS452.N352
JIANGXI SHIFAN DAXUE XUEBAO (SHEHUI KEXUE BAN)/JIANGXI NORMAL UNIVERSITY. JOURNAL (SOCIAL SCIENCE EDITION). (Text in Chinese) 1957. q. $20. Jiangxi Shifan Daxue, Xuebao Bianjibu - Jiangxi Normal University, Journal Editorial Department, Beijing Xilu, Nanchang, Jiangxi 330027, People's Republic of China. TEL 333993. Ed. Chen Dingru. adv. contact: Xiaoyan Guan. **Document type:** academic/scholarly publication.

300 CC
JIATING - YU'ER. (Text in Chinese) m. Tianjin Shi Kexue Jishu Xiehui, 287, Heping Lu, Tianjin 300041, People's Republic of China. TEL 311552. Ed. Zhou Xiuping.

JINAN XUEBAO (ZHEXUE SHEHUI KEXUE BAN)/JINAN UNIVERSITY. JOURNAL (PHILOSOPHY & SOCIAL SCIENCES EDITION). see *PHILOSOPHY*

JINBUN SHIZEN KAGAKU RONSHU/JOURNAL OF HUMANITIES AND NATURAL SCIENCES. see *HUMANITIES: COMPREHENSIVE WORKS*

300 CC ISSN 1000-2987
AS452.T379
JINYANG XUEKAN/JINYANG JOURNAL. (Text in Chinese) 1980. bi-m. Y1.50($30.60) (effective 1989). Shanxi Sheng Shehui Kexueyuan - Shanxi Academy of Social Sciences, 38 Bingzhou Lu, Taiyuan, Shanxi 030006, People's Republic of China. TEL 775843. (Dist. outside China by: China International Book Trading Corp., P.O. Box 399, Beijing, P.R.C.; Dist. in US by: China Books & Periodicals, Inc., 2929 24th St., San Francisco, CA 94110. TEL 415-282-2994) Ed. Kang Wenbin. adv.; bk.rev. circ. 2,000. (back issues avail.)

JOURNAL FOR THE STUDY OF BRITISH CULTURES. see *HUMANITIES: COMPREHENSIVE WORKS*

JOURNAL FOR THE THEORY OF SOCIAL BEHAVIOUR. see *PSYCHOLOGY*

JOURNAL OF APPLIED SOCIAL PSYCHOLOGY. see *PSYCHOLOGY*

JOURNAL OF ASIAN BUSINESS. see *BUSINESS AND ECONOMICS — Economic Situation And Conditions*

300 US ISSN 0148-611X
H1
JOURNAL OF ASIAN-PACIFIC & WORLD PERSPECTIVES;* an international journal of the social sciences. 1977. s-a. $7. Asian-Pacific Services Institute, c/o Twork, 4526 Brookridge Dr., Kingsport, TN 37660. Ed. Dorothy Dye Lee. adv.; bk.rev.; charts. circ. 2,000. (also avail. in Braille; back issues avail.)

SOCIAL SCIENCES: COMPREHENSIVE WORKS

910.03 — US — ISSN 0021-9347
E185.5
JOURNAL OF BLACK STUDIES. 1970. bi-m. $67 to individuals; institutions $211 (effective Sep. 1995). (Association of Black Psychologists) Sage Publications, Inc., 2455 Teller Rd., Thousand Oaks, CA 91320. TEL 805-499-0721. FAX 805-499-0871. E-mail: libraries@sagepub.com. (Overseas subscr. to: Sage Publications Ltd., 6 Bonhill St., London EC2A 4PU, England; Sage Publications India Pvt. Ltd., P.O. Box 4215, New Delhi 110 048, India) Eds. Molefi Kete Asante, Terry Kershaw. adv.; bk.rev.; index. circ. 1,750. (also avail. in microform from UMI; back issues avail.; reprint service avail. from UMI) Indexed: Abstr.Soc.Work., Amer.Hist.& Life., ASSIA, Bk.Rev.Ind. (1984-), C.I.J.E., Child.Bk.Rev.Ind. (1984-), Curr.Cont.Africa, Curr.Cont., Hist.Abstr., IMFL, Ind.Per.Negroes, Int.Polit.Sci.Abstr., Lang.& Lang.Behav.Abstr., Mult.Ed.Abstr., P.A.I.S., PHRA, Polit.Sci.Abstr., Psychol.Abstr. (1991-), Sage Fam.Stud.Abstr., Sage Pub.Admin.Abstr., Soc.Sci.Ind. (1994-), Soc.Work Res.& Abstr., Sociol.Abstr., SSCI. **Document type:** academic/scholarly publication.
—BLDSC (4954.200000); Faxon; Genuine Article; SWETS; UMI; UnCover. **CCC.**
Description: Sustains full analytical discussion of economic, political, sociological, historical, literary, and philosophical issues related to African-Americans.

JOURNAL OF CANADIAN STUDIES/REVUE D'ETUDES CANADIENNES. see HUMANITIES: COMPREHENSIVE WORKS

301.2 — US — ISSN 0022-0027
JX1901 — CODEN: JCFRAL
JOURNAL OF CONFLICT RESOLUTION; research on war and peace between and within nations. 1957. q. $66 to individuals; institutions $216 (effective Sep. 1995). (Peace Science Society) Sage Publications, Inc., 2455 Teller Rd., Thousand Oaks, CA 91320. TEL 805-499-0721. FAX 805-499-0871. E-mail: libraries@sagepub.com. (Overseas subscr. to: Sage Publications Ltd., 6 Bonhill St., London EC2A 4PU, England; Sage Publications India Pvt. Ltd., P.O. Box 4215, New Delhi 110 048, India) Ed. Bruce M. Russett. adv.; bk.rev.; charts. circ. 2,200. (also avail. in microfilm from UMI; back issues avail.; reprint service avail. from UMI) Indexed: A.B.C.Pol.Sci., Abstr.Mil.Bibl., Abstr.Soc.Work., Acad.Ind., Amer.Bibl.Slavic & E.Eur.Stud., Amer.Hist.& Life (until 1993), Curr.Cont., E.I., Educ.Admin.Abstr., Hist.Abstr. (until 1993), Int.Polit.Sci.Abstr., J.of Econ.Lit., Mid.East: Abstr.& Ind., P.A.I.S., Peace Res.Abstr., Polit.Sci.Abstr., PROMT, Psychol.Abstr. (1959-), Psyscan, Soc.Sci.Ind., Soc.Work Res.& Abstr., Sociol.Abstr., Sociol.Educ.Abstr., SSCI. **Document type:** academic/scholarly publication.
—BLDSC (4965.130000); Faxon; Genuine Article; SWETS; UMI; UnCover. **CCC.**
Formerly: Conflict Resolution (ISSN 0731-4086)
Description: Takes an interdisciplinary approach in analyzing the causes, prevention, and solution of international, domestic, and interpersonal conflicts.

300 — UK — ISSN 0258-9001
DT1 — CODEN: JCASF4
JOURNAL OF CONTEMPORARY AFRICAN STUDIES. 1981-199?; resumed 1995. s-a. £24 to individuals; institutions £94 (effective 1996). Africa Institute of South Africa, SA , P.O. Box 25, Abingdon, Oxon. OX14 3UE, England. TEL 01235-555335. FAX 01235-553559. (Subscr. in N. America to: 875-81 Massachusetts Ave., Cambridge, MA 02139) Ed.Bd. bk.rev.; index. circ. 2,000. (reprint service avail. from UMI) Indexed: Documentatieblad, Ind.S.A.Per. **Document type:** academic/scholarly publication.
—BLDSC (4965.221000); Faxon. **CCC.**
Description: Takes an interdisciplinary approach to foster a better understanding of African politics, sociology, geography, and literature.

300 — US — ISSN 1074-6897
CODEN: JCPOEW
▼**JOURNAL OF CULTURAL POLICY.** Variant title: Cultural Policy. 1994. 2/yr. 35 ECU (effective 1996). Harwood Academic Publishers, c/o International Publishers Distributor, 820 Town Center Dr., Langhorne, PA 19047. TEL 215-750-2642; 800-545-8398. FAX 215-750-6343. (Subscr. to: International Publishers Distributor, P.O. Box 90, Reading, Berkshire RG1 8JL, England. TEL 44-173-456-8316) (back issues avail.) **Document type:** academic/scholarly publication.

300 001.3 — NE — ISSN 0169-796X
DS1 — CODEN: JDSOEK
JOURNAL OF DEVELOPING SOCIETIES; a forum for developmental issues in developing and developed societies. 1971. 2/yr. fl.106($68) to individuals; institutions fl.195($126) (effective 1996). E.J. Brill, P.O. Box 9000, 2300 PA Leiden, Netherlands. TEL 31-71-5353500. FAX 31-71-5317532. TELEX 39296 BRILL NL. E-mail: ejborders@ejbrill.com. (In N. America to: E.J. Brill, 24 Hudson St., Kinderhook, NY 12106. TEL 800-962-4406. FAX 518-758-1959) Ed. K. Ishwaran. (back issues avail) Indexed: Anthropol.Lit., Asian-Pac.Econ.Lit., ASSIA, E.I., Geo.Abstr., IDA, Int.Polit.Sci.Abstr., Rel.Ind.One, Rural Devel.Abstr., World Agri.Econ.& Rural Sociol.Abstr. **Document type:** academic/scholarly publication.
—BLDSC (4969.202000); Faxon; SWETS; UnCover. **CCC.**
Formerly (until 1985): Contributions to Asian Studies (ISSN 0304-2693)
Description: Interdisciplinary, international analysis of all aspects of the processes of development and change in all times and places, including research in contemporary societies as well as historical, theoretical and applied studies.
Refereed Serial

JOURNAL OF ETHIOPIAN STUDIES. see HISTORY — History Of Africa

JOURNAL OF GENDER, CULTURE AND HEALTH. see MEDICAL SCIENCES

300 — US — ISSN 0092-2323
CB201
JOURNAL OF INDO-EUROPEAN STUDIES. 1973. q. $45 to individuals; institutions and libraries $100. Institute for the Study of Man, Box 34070, N.W., Washington, DC 20043. TEL 202-371-2700. FAX 202-371-1523. Ed.Bd. adv.; bk.rev.; circ. 350 (paid); 80 (controlled). Indexed: A.I.C.P., Abstr.Anthropol., Amer.Bibl.Slavic & E.Eur.Stud., Anthropol.Lit., Arts & Hum.Cit.Ind., Bibl.Engl.Lang.& Lit., Bibl.Ling., Br.Archaeol.Abstr., Curr.Cont., Lang.& Lang.Behav.Abstr., M.L.A., Mid.East: Abstr.& Ind., Soc.Sci.Ind., Sociol.Abstr. **Document type:** academic/scholarly publication.
—BLDSC (5005.380000); Faxon; Genuine Article; SWETS; UMI; UnCover.

300 — US — ISSN 0895-7258
JOURNAL OF INDO-EUROPEAN STUDIES MONOGRAPH SERIES. irreg., latest no.14. price varies. Institute for the Study of Man, Box 34070, N.W., Washington, DC 20043. TEL 202-371-2700. FAX 202-371-1523. **Document type:** monographic series, academic/scholarly publication.
Description: Monographs of interest to Indo-Europeanists in the areas of historical linguistics, mythology, archeology, and anthropology.

JOURNAL OF INTERDISCIPLINARY STUDIES; an international journal of interdisciplinary and interfaith dialogue. see HUMANITIES: COMPREHENSIVE WORKS

301 320 — UK — ISSN 0954-1748
HC59.72.E44 — CODEN: JINDEV
JOURNAL OF INTERNATIONAL DEVELOPMENT: POLICY, ECONOMICS, & INTERNATIONAL RELATIONS. 1981. 8/yr. $345 (foreign $345) (effective 1996). (University of Manchester, Institute for Development Policy and Management) John Wiley & Sons Ltd., Journals, Baffins Ln., Chichester, W. Sussex PO19 1UD, England. TEL 01243-779777. FAX 01243-776128. TELEX 86290 WIBOOK G. (Subscr. in the Americas to: John Wiley & Sons, Inc., 605 Third Ave., New York, NY 10158. TEL 212-850-6645. FAX 212-850-6021) Eds. Paul Mosley, John Harriss. adv.; bk.rev. circ. 347. (also avail. in microform from UMI; back issues avail.) Indexed: Abstr.Rural Dev.Trop., Asian-Pac.Econ.Lit., Geo.Abstr., IDA, Int.Lab.Doc., Rural Devel.Abstr. **Document type:** academic/scholarly publication.
—BLDSC (5007.635000); UMI. **CCC.**
Formerly (until 1989): Manchester Papers on Development (ISSN 0260-8235)
Description: Presents scholarly research articles on the broad field of economic, political, and social development.

JOURNAL OF LATIN AMERICAN CULTURAL STUDIES. see HISTORY — History Of North And South America

300 — US — ISSN 0363-2873
JC571
JOURNAL OF LIBERTARIAN STUDIES. 1976. a. $24 to individuals; institutions $32. Center for Libertarian Studies, Box 4091, Burlingame, CA 94011-4091. FAX 415-342-9164. Ed. Murray N. Rothbard. adv. circ. 1,000. (also avail. in microform from MIM,UMI; reprint service avail. from UMI) Indexed: Amer.Hist.& Life, Hist.Abstr., Int.Polit.Sci.Abstr., Phil.Ind.
—BLDSC (5010.320000); Faxon; UMI; UnCover. **CCC.**

300 — FJ — ISSN 1011-3029
DU1
JOURNAL OF PACIFIC STUDIES. (Text in English) 1975. a. $6.50. University of the South Pacific, School of Social and Economic Development, P.O. Box 1168, Suva, Fiji. TEL 313-900. Ed. Nii K. Plange. bk.rev. circ. 250. (back issues avail.) Indexed: Asian-Pac.Econ.Lit.
—UnCover.

300 — UK — ISSN 0143-814X
H96
JOURNAL OF PUBLIC POLICY. 1981. 1/yr. £67($114) (effective 1996). Cambridge University Press, Edinburgh Bldg., Shaftesbury Rd., Cambridge CB2 2RU, England. TEL 01223-312393. FAX 01223-315052. TELEX 851817256. (N. American addr.: Cambridge University Press, Journals Dept., 40 W. 20th St., New York, NY 10011. TEL 212-924-3900. FAX 212-691-3239) Ed. Richard Rose. adv.; bk.rev. (also avail. in microform from UMI; back issues avail.; reprint service avail. from SWZ) Indexed: A.B.C.Pol.Sci., ASSIA, Geo.Abstr., IDA, Int.Polit.Sci.Abstr., Lang.& Lang.Behav.Abstr., Mid.East: Abstr.& Ind., P.A.I.S., Polit.Sci.Abstr., Res.High.Educ.Abstr., Sage Pub.Admin.Abstr., Sage Urb.Stud.Abstr., Soc.Sci.Ind. (1994-), Sociol.Educ.Abstr. **Document type:** academic/scholarly publication.
—BLDSC (5043.640000); Faxon; SWETS; UMI; UnCover. **CCC.**
Description: Social scientists and policymakers analyze the problems facing contemporary governments in their social, economic and political contexts.

JOURNAL OF REGIONAL AND LOCAL STUDIES. see HISTORY — History Of Europe

JOURNAL OF SOCIAL BEHAVIOR AND PERSONALITY. see PSYCHOLOGY

300 — JA — ISSN 0454-2134
JOURNAL OF SOCIAL SCIENCE. (Text in English, Japanese) 1960. 3/yr. 1000 Yen per no. (typically set in Apr.). International Christian University, Social Science Research Institute - Kokusai Kiristokyo Daigaku, 3-10-2 Osawa, Mitaka, Tokyo 181, Japan. FAX 0422-33-9887. Eds. Koya Azumi, Shin Chiba. bk.rev. circ. 650.
—BLDSC (5064.911000).

300 — II — ISSN 0449-3168
JOURNAL OF SOCIAL SCIENCES. 1958. s-a. Agra University, Institute of Social Sciences, Agra 282004, Uttar Pradesh, India.

JOURNAL OF SOCIAL SCIENCES AND HUMANITIES/JINBUN GAKUHO. see HUMANITIES: COMPREHENSIVE WORKS

300 — BG — ISSN 1012-7844
JOURNAL OF SOCIAL STUDIES. Bengali edition: Samaj Nirikkhon. (Text in English) 1978. q. Tk.152($40) to individuals; institutions Tk.172($48) (effective 1996). Centre for Social Studies - Samaj Nirikkhon Kendro, Dhaka University, Arts Bldg., Rm. 1107, Dhaka 1000, Bangladesh. Ed. B.K. Jahangir. adv.; bk.rev.; cum.index: vols.1-58 (1978-1992). circ. 500. Indexed: Rice Abstr., Rural Devel.Abstr., Rural Recreat.Tour.Abstr., World Agri.Econ.& Rural Sociol.Abstr. **Document type:** academic/scholarly publication.
—BLDSC (5064.913700).
Description: Covers the socio-economic problems of the world in general, focusing on Bangaladesh.

JOURNAL OF SOCIAL THEORY IN ART EDUCATION. see ART

SOCIAL SCIENCES: COMPREHENSIVE WORKS

300   UK   ISSN 0305-7070
DT727
JOURNAL OF SOUTHERN AFRICAN STUDIES. 1975. q. £32 to individuals; institutions £98 (effective 1996). Carfax Publishing Co., P.O. Box 25, Abingdon, Oxon. OX14 3UE, England. TEL 01235-555335. FAX 01235-553559. (Subscr. in N. America to: Carfax Publishing Co., 875-81 Massachusetts Ave., Cambridge, MA 02139) Ed.Bd. adv.; bk.rev.; index. circ. 900. (also avail. in microform from UMI; back issues avail.) **Indexed:** A.B.C.Pol.Sci., Abstr.Rural Dev.Trop., Amer.Hist.& Life, ASSIA, Br.Hum.Ind., Curr.Cont.Africa, Curr.Cont., Documentatieblad, Geo.Abstr., Hist.Abstr., IDA, Int.Lab.Doc., Int.Polit.Sci.Abstr., Mult.Ed.Abstr., Polit.Sci.Abstr., Rural Devel.Abstr., Rural Recreat.Tour.Abstr., Sociol.Educ.Abstr., SSCI, Stud.Wom.Abstr., World Agri.Econ.& Rural Sociol.Abstr. **Document type:** academic/scholarly publication.
—BLDSC (5066.030000); Faxon; Genuine Article; SWETS; UMI; UnCover. **CCC.**
   Description: Provides a scholarly inquiry and exposition in the fields of economics, sociology, geography, demography, social anthropology, administration, law, political science, international relations, history, and natural sciences, as they relate to the human condition.
   Refereed Serial

300   KU   ISSN 0253-1097
H1
JOURNAL OF THE SOCIAL SCIENCES/MAJALLAT AL-ULUM AL-IJTIMA'IYYAH. (Text in Arabic, English) 1973. q. Kuwait University, Faculty of Commerce, Economics and Political Science, P.O. Box 5969, 13060 Safat, Kuwait. **Document type:** academic/scholarly publication.

153.4   US   ISSN 0022-5231
L11
JOURNAL OF THOUGHT. 1965. 4/yr. $40 to individuals; institutions $50. (Northern Illinois University) Caddo Gap Press, 3145 Geary Blvd., Ste. 275, San Francisco, CA 94118. TEL 415-750-9978. FAX 415-668-5450. Ed.Bd. adv.; bk.rev.; index. circ. 500. (also avail. in microform from UMI; reprint service avail. from UMI) **Indexed:** C.I.J.E., Curr.Cont., Lang.& Lang.Behav.Abstr., Phil.Ind., Soc.Sci.Ind., Sociol.Abstr., SSCI. **Document type:** academic/scholarly publication.
—BLDSC (5069.300000); Faxon; UMI; UnCover.
   Description: Features interdisciplinary articles with a focus on philosophy of education.

JOURNAL OF UKRAINIAN STUDIES. see *LITERATURE*

JUDICATURE. see *LAW — Judicial Systems*

KALYANI; journal of humanities and social sciences of the University of Kelaniya. see *HUMANITIES: COMPREHENSIVE WORKS*

300   II   ISSN 0075-5176
KARNATAK UNIVERSITY, DHARWAD, INDIA. JOURNAL. SOCIAL SCIENCES. (Text in English) 1965. a. Rs.8($4) Karnatak University, Director, Prasaranga, Dharwad 580003, Karnataka, India. Ed. K. Chandrasekharaiah. circ. 500.

300   PL
KATOLICKI UNIWERSYTET LUBELSKI. WYDZIAL NAUK SPOLECZNYCH. ROZPRAWY. (Text in Polish; summaries in English or French) 1947. irreg. price varies. Katolicki Uniwersytet Lubelski, Towarzystwo Naukowe, Ul. Gliniana 21, 20-616 Lublin, Poland. index. circ. 1,025.

300   US   ISSN 0748-8815
JK1
KETTERING REVIEW; a journal of ideas and activities dedicated to improving the quality of public life in the American democracy. 1983. 4/yr. $9. Charles F. Kettering Foundation, 200 Commons Rd., Dayton, OH 45459-2799. TEL 513-434-7300. Ed. Robert J. Kingston. circ. 8,000. **Document type:** academic/scholarly publication.

300   CC   ISSN 0254-8763
KEXUE DUI SHEHUI DE YINGXIANG/SCIENCE IMPACT ON SOCIETY. (Text in Chinese) q. Zhongguo Kexueyuan, Keji Zhengce yu Guanli Kexue Yanjiusuo - Chinese Academy of Sciences, Research Institute of Science and Technology Policy and Management, P.O. Box 8712, Beijing 100080, People's Republic of China. TEL 289831. Ed. Shen Chenru.

300   CC   ISSN 1001-3210
KEXUE SHEHUI ZHUYI/SCIENTIFIC SOCIALISM. (Text in Chinese) bi-m. Zhongguo Gongyun Xueyuan, 2, Huayuancun, Haidian-qu, Beijing 100037, People's Republic of China. TEL 8314477. Ed. An Naizhang.

300   US   ISSN 0897-1986
T10.5
KNOWLEDGE AND POLICY; the international journal of knowledge transfer. 1988. q. $66 to individuals (foreign $98); institutions $132 (foreign $164) (effective Aug. 1995). Transaction Publishers, Transaction Periodicals Consortium, Department 3092, Rutgers University, New Brunswick, NJ 08903. TEL 908-445-2280. FAX 908-445-3138. Ed. Esther Hicks. adv.; bk.rev. circ. 500. **Indexed:** Int.Polit.Sci.Abstr. **Document type:** academic/scholarly publication.
—Faxon; UMI; UnCover. **CCC.**
   Formerly (until 1991): Knowledge in Society.
   Description: Devoted to the development of an interdisciplinary science of knowledge transfer.

KOBE UNIVERSITY OF MERCANTILE MARINE. REVIEW. PART 1. STUDIES IN HUMANITIES AND SOCIAL SCIENCE. see *HUMANITIES: COMPREHENSIVE WORKS*

300   NE   ISSN 0923-5418
KONINKLIJK INSTITUUT VOOR TAAL-, LAND- EN VOLKENKUNDE. WORKING PAPERS SERIES. (Text in Dutch or English) 1988. irreg., no.13, 1995. price varies. K I T L V Press, P.O. Box 9515, 2300 RA Leiden, Netherlands. TEL 31-71-272372. FAX 31-71-272638. (back issues avail.) **Document type:** monographic series.
   Description: Scholarly monographs on topics in the social, cultural and legal history of Southeast Asia, with particular emphasis on Indonesia.

300 327   DK   ISSN 0105-0982
KONTAKT (COPENHAGEN, 1948). 1946. 8/yr. DKK 199. Mellemfolkeligt Samvirke - Danish Association for International Co-operation, Borgergade 14, DK-1300 Copenhagen K, Denmark. TEL 45-33-32-62-44. FAX 45-33-15-62-43. Ed. Alex Frank Larsen. circ. 7,000.
   Formerly (until 1948): Fredsvenners Hjaelpearbejde (ISSN 0903-0239)
   Description: Third World magazine which presents an introduction to development questions.

309.1   KO   ISSN 1225-0368
KOREAN SOCIAL SCIENCE JOURNAL. (Text in English) 1973. a. $10. Korean National Commission for UNESCO, Box Central 64, Seoul, S. Korea. FAX 82-2-774-3956. TELEX MOCNDM-K23231-2 EXT.6364. (Co-sponsor: Korean Social Science Research Council) bibl.; stat. **Indexed:** Asian-Pac.Econ.Lit., Int.Polit.Sci.Abstr., Mid.East: Abstr.& Ind., Polit.Sci.Abstr., Psychol.Abstr. **Document type:** academic/scholarly publication.
   Formerly: Social Science Journal.

KULTUR UND GESELLSCHAFT; Neue historische Forschungen. see *HISTORY*

KULTURGEOGRAFISKE HAEFTER. see *GEOGRAPHY*

KYUSHU INSTITUTE OF TECHNOLOGY. BULLETIN: HUMANITIES, SOCIAL SCIENCES/KYUSHU KOGYO DAIGAKU KENKYU HOKOKU: JINBUN-SHAKAI-KAGAKU. see *HUMANITIES: COMPREHENSIVE WORKS*

980   US   ISSN 0890-7218
F1401
L A S A FORUM. 1969. q. $30 to non-members (effective 1993). Latin American Studies Association, William Pitt Union, 9th Fl., University of Pittsburgh, Pittsburgh, PA 15260. TEL 412-648-7929. FAX 412-624-7145. Ed. Reid Reading. adv. contact: Glenn Sheldon. circ. 3,350. **Document type:** newsletter.
   Formerly: Latin American Studies Association Newsletter (ISSN 0023-8805)
   Description: Contains brief, research-based articles, letters and announcements, employment, research, and study opportunities, opinion pieces, and other information of interest to members.

331 960   CN   ISSN 0706-1706
LABOUR, CAPITAL AND SOCIETY/TRAVAIL, CAPITAL ET SOCIETE; a journal on the Third World. (Text in English, French) 1968. s-a. Can.$18 to individuals; institutions Can.$27; Third World countries Can.$12. McGill University, Centre for Developing Area Studies, 3715 Peel St., Montreal, PQ H3A 1X1, Canada. TEL 514-398-3508. FAX 514-398-8432. Ed. Rosalind E. Boyd. adv.; bk.rev. circ. 800. **Indexed:** Abstr.Rural Dev.Trop., Alt.Press Ind., ASSIA, Documentatieblad, E.I., Geo.Abstr., Human Resour.Abstr., IDA, Int.Lab.Doc., P.A.I.S., Rural Devel.Abstr., Rural Ext.Educ.& Tr.Abstr., Rural Recreat.Tour.Abstr., Soc.Sci.Ind., SSCI, World Agri.Econ.& Rural Sociol.Abstr. **Document type:** academic/scholarly publication.
—BLDSC (5142.065000); UnCover.
   Former titles (until vol.12, 1979): Manpower and Unemployment Research; Manpower and Unemployment Research in Africa. Newsletter.

918 980   CC   ISSN 1002-6649
LADING MEIZHOU YANJIU/LATIN AMERICAN STUDIES. (Text in Chinese) 1979. bi-m. Y13.80($17.60) Zhongguo Shehui Kexueyuan, Lading Meizhou Yanjiusuo - Chinese Academy of Social Sciences, Institute on Latin America, P.O. Box 1113, No.3, Zhangzizhong Lu, Beijing 100007, People's Republic of China. TEL 4014009. (Dist. overseas by: China International Book Trading Corp., P.O. Box 399, Beijing, P.R. China) Ed. Zhou Junnan. circ. 1,000. **Document type:** academic/scholarly publication.

LANTERNINO; trimestrale di storia della medicina e studi sociali. see *MEDICAL SCIENCES*

300 001.3   US
LATIN AMERICAN MONOGRAPH AND DOCUMENT SERIES. irreg., latest 1995. $10 (effective 1995) (free to students at the Center for Latin American Studies). University of Pittsburgh, Center for Latin American Studies, 4E04 Forbes Quad., University Center for International Studies, Pittsburgh, PA 15260. TEL 412-648-7392. FAX 412-648-2199. **Document type:** monographic series.

970   US   ISSN 0075-8108
LATIN AMERICAN MONOGRAPHS. 1965. irreg., no.26, 1984. price varies. (University of Florida, Center for Latin American Studies) University Press of Florida, 15 N.W. 15 St., Gainesville, FL 32611. TEL 904-392-1351. FAX 904-392-7302. Ed.Bd. (reprint service avail. from KTO) **Indexed:** SSCI. **Document type:** monographic series.

300 320.531   US   ISSN 0094-582X
F1401
LATIN AMERICAN PERSPECTIVES; a journal on capitalism and socialism. 1974. q. $49 to individuals; institutions $171 (effective Sep. 1995). (Latin American Perspective Collective) Sage Publications, Inc., 2455 Teller Rd., Thousand Oaks, CA 91320. TEL 805-499-0721. FAX 805-499-0871. E-mail: libraries@sagepub.com. (Overseas subscr. to: Sage Publications Ltd., 6 Bonhill St., London EC2A 4PU, England; Sage Publications India Pvt. Ltd., P.O. Box 4215, New Delhi 110 048, India) Ed. Ronald H. Chilcote. adv.; bk.rev. circ. 1,500. (also avail. in microfiche; microform from UMI; back issues avail.; reprint service avail.) **Indexed:** A.B.C.Pol.Sci., Alt.Press Ind., Amer.Hist.& Life, Bibl.Ind., Chic.Per.Ind., Curr.Cont., Geo.Abstr., Hisp.Amer.Per.Ind. (1974-), Hist.Abstr., IDA, Int.Lab.Doc., Left Ind. (1982-), P.A.I.S., Peace Res.Abstr., Polit.Sci.Abstr., Sage Fam.Stud.Abstr., Sociol.Abstr., SSCI. **Document type:** academic/scholarly publication.
—BLDSC (5160.085000); Faxon; Genuine Article; SWETS; UMI; UnCover. **CCC.**
   Description: Discusses critical issues relating to capitalism, imperialism, and socialism as they affect individuals, societies, and nations.

SOCIAL SCIENCES: COMPREHENSIVE WORKS

980 300   US   ISSN 0023-8791
F1401
LATIN AMERICAN RESEARCH REVIEW; a journal to achieve greater and more systematic communication among individuals and institutions concerned with scholarly studies of Latin America. (Text in English and Spanish) 1965. 3/yr. $27 to non-members (Latin America $20); institutions $42 (Latin America $27); students $20 (Latin America $18). Latin American Studies Association (Albuquerque), c/o University of New Mexico, 801 Yale N.E., Albuquerque, NM 87131-1016. TEL 505-277-5985. FAX 505-277-5989. E-mail: larr@unm.edu. Ed. Gilbert W. Merkx. adv. contact: Nita Daily. bk.rev.; bibl.; charts; index, cum.index. circ. 4,500. (also avail. in microfilm from UMI; microfiche from JAI; back issues avail.; reprint service avail. from KTO) **Indexed**: A.B.C.Pol.Sci., Acad.Ind., Amer.Hist.& Life, Anthropol.Lit., Chic.Per.Ind., Curr.Cont., Film Lit.Ind. (1989-), Geo.Abstr., Hisp.Amer.Per.Ind. (1970-), Hist.Abstr., IDA, Int.Lab.Doc., Int.Polit.Sci.Abstr., P.A.I.S., Polit.Sci.Abstr., Soc.Sci.Ind., SSCI. **Document type**: academic/scholarly publication.
● Also available online. Vendor(s): University Microfilms International.
Also available on CD-ROM.
—BLDSC (5160.120000); Faxon; SWETS; UMI; UnCover.
   Description: Scholarly articles, research reports and notes, and review essays to promote and expound studies of Latin American culture, politics, and economics.

300 016
LATIN AMERICAN STUDIES WORKING PAPERS. (Text in English and Spanish) 1972. irreg., no.8, 1980. price varies. Indiana University, Center for Latin American & Caribbean Studies, 313 N. Jordan, Bloomington, IN 47405. (back issues avail.)

300   US
LATINOAMERICA. 1968. a. $15. Universidad Nacional Autonoma de Mexico, Centro Coordinador y Difusor de Estudios Latinoamericanos, Torre I de Humanidades, 2o piso, Ciudad Universitaria, 04510 Mexico, D.F., Mexico. TEL 52-6221901. FAX 52-6221910. Ed. Patricia Escandon. bk.rev. circ. 1,000. **Indexed**: Amer.Hist.& Life, Hisp.Amer.Per.Ind. (1970-), Hist.Abstr. **Document type**: academic/scholarly publication.
   Description: Contains studies on South and Central America: politics, history, culture, education, biography, art, literature, geography, philosophy.

LAW AND SOCIAL INQUIRY. see *LAW*

LAW & SOCIETY REVIEW. see *LAW*

LEIBNIZ-SOZIETAET. SITZUNGSBERICHTE. see *SCIENCES: COMPREHENSIVE WORKS*

LER HISTORIA. see *HISTORY — History Of Europe*

300   GW   ISSN 0340-0425
H5
LEVIATHAN; Zeitschrift fuer Sozialwissenschaft. 1973. q. DM.94 (students DM.70.50) (effective 1996). Westdeutscher Verlag GmbH, Postfach 1546, 65005 Wiesbaden, Germany. TEL 0611-534389. FAX 0611-534430. Ed. B.v Greiff. adv.; bk.rev. (reprint service avail. from SCH) **Indexed**: Int.Polit.Sci.Abstr., P.A.I.S.For.Lang.Ind. **Document type**: academic/scholarly publication.
—BLDSC (5185.590000); SWETS. CCC.

966.6 300   US   ISSN 0024-1989
DT621
LIBERIAN STUDIES JOURNAL.* 1968. s-a. $25. Liberian Studies Association, c/o Dr. Arnold Odio, Albany State College, 504 College Dr., P.O. Box 9220, Albany, GA 31705-2791. TEL 708-848-2202. Ed. D. Elwood Dunn. bk.rev.; bibl. (back issues avail.) **Indexed**: Amer.Hist.& Life, Bibl.Ling., Curr.Cont.Africa, Documentatieblad, Hist.Abstr., Int.Polit.Sci.Abstr., M.L.A. **Document type**: academic/scholarly publication.
—BLDSC (5186.740000); Faxon.

966.6 300   US
LIBERIAN STUDIES MONOGRAPH SERIES. 1972. irreg., no.8, 1985. price varies. Arden Associates, Corp., Box 232, Lansdowne, PA 19050. charts; illus. **Document type**: monographic series.

966.6 300   US
LIBERIAN STUDIES RESEARCH WORKING PAPERS. 1971. irreg., no.7, 1980. price varies. Arden Associates, Corp., Box 232, Lansdowne, PA 19050. bibl. **Document type**: monographic series.

LIBERTARIAN ALLIANCE. SCIENTIFIC NOTES. see *POLITICAL SCIENCE*

300   CC
LILUN YU XIANDAIHUI/THEORY AND MODERNIZATION. (Text in Chinese) m. Tianjin Shi Shehui Kexuejie Lianhehui, 4, Machang Dao, Heping-qu, Tianjin 300050, People's Republic of China. TEL 398649. Ed. Yu Zonghao. **Document type**: academic/scholarly publication.

LOCATION SCIENCE. see *PSYCHOLOGY*

300   US
LONG WAVES NEWSLETTER. irreg. Fernand Braudel Center, Binghamton University, Box 6000, Binghamton, NY 13902-6000. TEL 607-777-4924. FAX 607-777-4315. Ed. Immanuel Wallerstein. circ. 300. (back issues avail.) **Document type**: newsletter.

300   NE   ISSN 0924-4905
LONGITUDINAL RESEARCH IN THE BEHAVIORAL, SOCIAL AND MEDICAL SCIENCES. (Text in English) 1981. irreg. price varies. Kluwer Academic Publishers, Postbus 17, 3300 AA Dordrecht, Netherlands. TEL 31-78-392392. FAX 31-78-392254. TELEX 29245 KAPG NL. (Dist. by: Kluwer Academic Publishers Group, P.O. Box 322, 3300 AH Dordrecht, Netherlands. TEL 31-78-392392. FAX 31-78-546474; N. America dist. addr.: Box 358, Accord Sta., Hingham, MA 02018-0358. TEL 617-871-6600. FAX 617-871-6528) **Document type**: monographic series.
Refereed Serial

300   US
▼**LONGITUDINAL RESEARCH IN THE SOCIAL AND BEHAVIORAL SCIENCES**; an interdisciplinary series. 1995. irreg. price varies. Plenum Publishing Corp., 233 Spring St., New York, NY 10013-1578. TEL 212-620-8035. FAX 212-463-0742. TELEX 23-421139. Ed.Bd. **Document type**: monographic series.
   Description: Focuses on key topics in the growing field of research methodology.

306   SW   ISSN 1101-9948
LUND MONOGRAPHS IN SOCIAL ANTHROPOLOGY. (Text in English, Swedish) 1991. irreg. price varies. Lund University Press, P.O. Box 141, S-221 00, Lund, Sweden. TEL 46-46-30-55-38. FAX 46-46-30-53-38. E-mail: Order@Studli.se. Eds. K. Ekholm-Friedman, J. Friedman. **Document type**: academic/scholarly publication, monographic series.

300   MY
M C D S OCCASIONAL PAPER SERIES. (Former issuer of the publication: Malaysian Centre for Development Studies) (Text in English) 1974. irreg., latest no.6. exchange basis. Socio-Economic Research Unit, Prime Minister's Department, Level 2, Block K, Pusat Bandar Damansara, 50529 Kuala Lumpur, Malaysia. **Document type**: monographic series.

M I. (Mladi Istrazivaci Srbije) see *EDUCATION*

300   HU   ISSN 1216-6235
DB901
MAGYAR SZEMLE. 1992. m. $50. Hirlapkiado Vallalat, Blaha Lujza ter 3, 1959 Budapest 8, Hungary. TEL 1-382-399. TELEX 22-5554. (Subscr. to: Kultura, Box 149, 1389 Budapest, Hungary) Ed. Gyula Kodolanyi. circ. 10,000.
   Supersedes (1927-1944): Magyar Szemle (ISSN 0200-8858)

MAISON FRANCO-JAPONAISE. BULLETIN. see *ORIENTAL STUDIES*

300   UK   ISSN 0959-7646
MAJORITY MINORITY REVIEW. 1989. irreg. University of Ulster, Centre for the Study of Conflict, Coleraine BT52 1SA, N. Ireland. TEL 0265-44141. FAX 0265-40917. E-mail: csc@ulst.ac.uk. **Document type**: academic/scholarly publication.
—BLDSC (5353.694520).

300   XN   ISSN 0350-1698
MAKEDONSKA AKADEMIJA NA NAUKITE I UMETNOSTITE. ODDELENIE ZA OPSTESTVENI NAUKI. PRILOZI/MACEDONIAN ACADEMY OF SCIENCES AND ARTS. SECTION OF SOCIAL SCIENCES. CONTRIBUTIONS. 1970. s-a. Makedonska Akademija na Naukite i Umetnostite, Oddelenie za Opstestveni Nauki, Bulevar Krste Misirkov bb, Box 428, Skopje, Macedonia. TEL 235-506. Ed. Ksente Bogoev.
—BLDSC (0132.072000).
   Description: Research in economy, law, education, history, sociology and philosophy.

300   MW
MALAWI JOURNAL OF SOCIAL SCIENCE. 1972. a. $7. University of Malawi, Faculty of Social Science, Box 280, Zomba, Malawi. Ed.Bd. bk.rev. circ. 500. (back issues avail.) **Indexed**: Anthropol.Lit., Hist.Abstr. (until 1986).
   Formerly: Chancellor College. Journal of Social Science (ISSN 0302-3060)

MANAB MON; a journal depicting the modern trends in psychology, biology, and sociology. see *PSYCHOLOGY*

MANCHESTER SCHOOL OF ECONOMIC AND SOCIAL STUDIES. see *BUSINESS AND ECONOMICS — Economic Systems And Theories, Economic History*

300   II
MANTHAN. (Text in English and Hindi) 1978. m. Rs.80($25) Deendayal Research Institute, 7E, Swami Ramtirath Nagar, New Delhi 110055, India. TEL 526735. FAX 526792. Ed. Devendra Swarup. adv. contact: B.D. Kapoor. bk.rev. circ. 10,000. **Indexed**: G.Indian Per.Lit. **Document type**: academic/scholarly publication.

MARE BALTICUM. see *POLITICAL SCIENCE — International Relations*

954.93 300   CE   ISSN 0047-5912
HC424.A1
MARGA. (Text in English) 1972. q. $30. Marga Institute, Sri Landa Centre for Development Studies, P.O. Box 601, 61 Isipathana Mawatha, Colombo 5, Sri Lanka. TEL 941-585186. FAX 941-580585. TELEX 21642-MARGA-CE. Ed. Godfrey Gunatilleke. adv.; bk.rev. circ. 2,000. **Indexed**: HR Rep., Int.Lab.Doc., Rural Devel.Abstr., Rural Recreat.Tour.Abstr., Sri Lanka Sci.Ind., World Agri.Econ.& Rural Sociol.Abstr. **Document type**: bulletin.
—BLDSC (5373.503000).
   Description: Touches on social and economic problems.

300   CE   ISSN 0304-7709
H62.5.C4
MARGA INSTITUTE. ANNUAL REPORT. (Text in English) 1973. a. Marga Institute, P.O. Box 601, 61 Isipathana Mawatha, Colombo 5, Sri Lanka. TEL 941-585186. FAX 941-580585. TELEX 21643-MARGA-CE.

300   BL   ISSN 0103-8915
H8.P8
MARGEM. 1992. s-a. Pontificia Universidade Catolica de Sao Paulo, Faculdade de Ciencias Sociais, Rua Monte Alegre 984, sala S-21, 05014 Sao Paulo SP, Brazil. TEL 263-0211 ext. 337. Ed. Jose Mario Ortiz Ramos. **Document type**: academic/scholarly publication.

MARXIST VEEKSHANAM; theoretical discussion forum. see *POLITICAL SCIENCE*

300 320.531   GW   ISSN 0171-3698
MARXISTISCHE STUDIEN.* 1978. biennial. DM.32($11) Institut fuer Marxistische Studien und Forschungen, Koelnerstr. 66, 6000 Frankfurt a.M. 1, Germany. Ed.Bd. circ. 3,000. (back issues avail.)

MASTER'S THESES IN THE ARTS AND SOCIAL SCIENCES. see *HUMANITIES: COMPREHENSIVE WORKS*

SOCIAL SCIENCES: COMPREHENSIVE WORKS

300   IO   ISSN 0125-9989
MASYARAKAT INDONESIA: MAJALAH ILMU - ILMU SOSIAL INDONESIA. (Text in English, Indonesian) 1974. s-a. Rps.10000($25) Indonesian Institute of Sciences - Lembaga Ilmu Pengetahuan Indonesia, Jalan Jenderal Gatot Subroto 10, P.O. Box 250, Jakarta 10002, Indonesia. TEL 021-525-1542. (Subscr. to: Yayasan Memajukan Jasa Informasi, JLN. Widya Chandra IX/3, Kompleks LIPI, P.O. Box 4509, Jakarta 12045, Indonesia) Ed. Hilman Adil. index. circ. 1,500. **Indexed:** Asian-Pac.Econ.Lit.

MATHEMATICAL SOCIAL SCIENCES. see *MATHEMATICS*

300   UG   ISSN 0047-6293
DT1
MAWAZO; the Makerere journal of the arts and social sciences. (Text in English) 1968. s-a. $6 per no. Makerere University, Faculty of Arts & Social Sciences, P.O. Box 7062, Kampala, Uganda. Ed. Mahmood Mamdani. adv.; bk.rev. circ. 2,500. **Indexed:** Amer.Hist.& Life (until 1985), Documentatieblad, Hist.Abstr. (until 1985), M.L.A.

MAX-PLANCK-GESELLSCHAFT. JAHRBUCH. see *SCIENCES: COMPREHENSIVE WORKS*

059.96   TZ   ISSN 0025-6234
MBIONI. (Text in English) 1964. m. 10s.($4.20) Kivukoni College, POB 9193, Dar es Salaam, Tanzania. bk.rev.; index. circ. 4,000.

MEASUREMENT METHODS FOR THE SOCIAL SCIENCES SERIES. see *METROLOGY AND STANDARDIZATION*

MEDDELELSER OM GROENLAND, MAN & SOCIETY. see *ANTHROPOLOGY*

MEDIA MONITOR (WASHINGTON). see *COMMUNICATIONS*

300 610   GW
MEDIZINSOZIOLOGIE. irreg., vol.3, 1993. Lit Verlag, Dieckstr. 56, 48145 Muenster, Germany. TEL 0251-235091. Ed.Bd. **Document type:** monographic series.

390   II
MEERUT UNIVERSITY SANSKRIT RESEARCH JOURNAL. (Text in English, Hindi or Sanskrit) 1976. s-a. Rs.60($10) c/o R.K. Lowe, Ed. & Dir., Department of Sanskrit, S.D. College, Muzaffar Nagar (U.P.) 251001, India. adv.; bk.rev. circ. 200.
Formerly: Meerut University Sanskrit Research.

300   CC   ISSN 1002-8986
E151
MEIGUO YANJIU/AMERICAN STUDIES. (Text in Chinese) 1987. q. $17. Zhongguo Shehui Kexueyuan, Meiguo Yanjiusuo - Chinese Academy of Social Sciences, Institute of American Studies, No.5, Jianguomennei Dajie, Beijing 100732, People's Republic of China. TEL 5137559. Ed. Zi Zhongyun. bk.rev. circ. 1,600. **Document type:** academic/scholarly publication.
Description: Contains articles on American political, economic, diplomatic and military affairs and policies, sciences and technology, literature and arts.
Refereed Serial

300   US   ISSN 0252-9963
F1421
MESOAMERICA. 1980. a. $20. Centro de Investigaciones Regionales de Mesoamerica (CIRMA), Plumsock Mesoamerican Studies, Box 38, S. Woodstock, VT 05071. TEL 802-457-1199. Eds. Christopher H. Lutz, Cherri M. Pancake. adv.; bk.rev.; cum.index. (back issues avail.) **Indexed:** A.I.C.P., Abstr.Anthropol., Hisp.Amer.Per.Ind. (1980-), Int.Bibl.Soc.Sci., M.L.A., Popul.Ind., SSCI. **Document type:** academic/scholarly publication.
—Faxon.

300   IT
MEZZOCIELO. m. L.20000 (effective 1992). c/o Rosanna Pirjano, Via Giusti 44, 90144 Palermo, Italy. Ed. Simona Mafai.

300   VI   ISSN 0147-7935
JC365
MICROSTATE STUDIES. 1977. a. College of the Virgin Islands, Caribbean Research Institute, St. Thomas, VI 00801. Ed. Norwell Harrigan. circ. 200.

956 300   US   ISSN 0026-3184
DS41   CODEN: MESBEL
MIDDLE EAST STUDIES ASSOCIATION BULLETIN. 1967. 2/yr. $60 membership. Middle East Studies Association of North America, Inc., 1232 N. Cherry Ave., University of Arizona, Tucson, AZ 85721. TEL 602-621-5850. FAX 602-321-7752. Ed. Jon W. Anderson. adv.; bk.rev.; abstr.; bibl. circ. 2,200. **Indexed:** Amer.Bibl.Slavic & E.Eur.Stud., Amer.Hist.& Life, Bibl.Ling., Hist.Abstr., Int.Polit.Sci.Abstr., Mid.East: Abstr.& Ind.
—Faxon; SWETS; UnCover.

300   US   ISSN 0739-8069
H62.5.U5
MIDDLE STATES COUNCIL FOR THE SOCIAL STUDIES. JOURNAL. 1978. a. $10. Middle States Council for the Social Studies, Rider College, 2083 Lawrenceville Rd., Lawrenceville, NJ 08648-3099. TEL 609-896-5068. Eds. David Pierfy, David W. Saxe. adv.; bk.rev. circ. 1,100. (back issues avail.; reprint service avail. from UMI) **Document type:** academic/scholarly publication.
Supersedes (1903-1978): Middle States Council for the Social Studies. Proceedings.
Refereed Serial

MIGRATION AND ETHNICITY SERIES. see *POPULATION STUDIES*

MIGRATION WORLD; a bi-monthly magazine focusing on the newest immigrant and refugee groups; policy and legislation; resources. see *POPULATION STUDIES*

THE MILBANK QUARTERLY. see *POLITICAL SCIENCE*

MINAMI TAIHEIYO KENKYU/SOUTH PACIFIC STUDY. see *SCIENCES: COMPREHENSIVE WORKS*

300   CC   ISSN 1002-4360
MINSU YANJIU/FOLKLORE STUDIES. (Text in Chinese) 1985. q. $32. Shandong Daxue - Shandong University, Shandong Daxue Laoxiao, Jinan, Shandong 250100, People's Republic of China. TEL 86-531-8906961. FAX 86-531-8902167. Ed. Li Wanpeng; Pub. Xu Jingze. adv.: page $500. circ. 3,018. **Document type:** academic/scholarly publication.

MINZU TUANJIE/UNITY OF NATIONALITIES. see *ETHNIC INTERESTS*

MODERN CHINA; an international quarterly of history and social science. see *HISTORY — History Of Asia*

300   CE
MODERN SRI LANKA STUDIES; journal of the social sciences. (Text in English) 1970. s-a. Rs.120($20) University of Peradeniya, P.O. Box 35, Peradeniya, Sri Lanka. Eds. Rarijith Amarasinghe, W.M. Sirisena. bk.rev. circ. 500.
Formerly: Modern Ceylon Studies.

MONDE ARABE MAGHREB, MACHREK. see *POLITICAL SCIENCE*

MONOGRAPHS IN ECONOMIC AND SOCIAL HISTORY. see *BUSINESS AND ECONOMICS — Economic Systems And Theories, Economic History*

301.15 331.1   US
MONOGRAPHS IN ORGANIZATIONAL BEHAVIOUR AND INDUSTRIAL RELATIONS. 1983. irreg., vol.10, 1989. $58.50 to institutions. J A I Press Inc., 55 Old Post Rd., No. 2, Box 1678, Greenwich, CT 06836-1678. TEL 203-661-7602. Ed. Samuel B. Bacharach. bibl.; index.

MONOGRAPHS ON SCIENCE, TECHNOLOGY, AND SOCIETY. see *TECHNOLOGY: COMPREHENSIVE WORKS*

MUSEE ROYAL DE L'AFRIQUE CENTRALE. ANNALES - SCIENCES HUMAINES. SERIE IN 8/KONINKLIJK MUSEUM VOOR MIDDEN-AFRIKA. ANNALEN - MENSELIJKE WETENSCHAPPEN. SERIE IN 8. see *HUMANITIES: COMPREHENSIVE WORKS*

300   LE
AL-MUSTAQBAL AL-ARABI/ARAB FUTURE. 1978. m. $60 to individuals in Arab countries ($80 in Europe; $90 in U.S.); institutions in Arab countries $100 (elsewhere $120). Centre for Arab Unity Studies - Markaz Dirasat al-Wahdah al-Arabiyyah, P.O. Box 113-6001, Beirut, Lebanon. TEL 961-1-801582. FAX 961-1-865548. adv.; bk.rev. circ. 8,000.

312 614 301   NE   ISSN 0258-123X
                       CODEN: NADSDD
N A T O ADVANCED SCIENCE INSTITUTES SERIES D: BEHAVIOURAL AND SOCIAL SCIENCES. (Text in English) 1974. s-a. (North Atlantic Treaty Organization, Scientific Affairs Division) Kluwer Academic Publishers, Postbus 17, 3300 AA Dordrecht, Netherlands. TEL 31-78-392392. FAX 31-78-392254. TELEX 29245 KAPG NL. (Dist. by: Kluwer Academic Publishers Group, P.O. Box 322, 3300 AH, Dordrecht, Netherlands. TEL 31-78-392392. FAX 31-78-546474; N. America dist. addr.: Box 358, Accord Sta., Hingham, MA 02018-0358. TEL 617-871-6600) **Indexed:** Math.R. **Document type:** monographic series.
•Also available online. Vendor(s): European Space Agency (File no.128).
—BLDSC (6033.648750); CASDDS. **CCC.**
Formerly: N A T O Advanced Study Institutes Series D: Behavioural and Social Sciences.
Refereed Serial

N A T O SCIENCE AND SOCIETY NEWSLETTER. (North Atlantic Treaty Organization) see *SCIENCES: COMPREHENSIVE WORKS*

N F E - W I D EXCHANGE - ASIA. NEWSLETTER. see *EDUCATION*

300   JA   ISSN 0289-7725
N I R A REPORT (TOKYO, 1984). (Text in English) 1982. s-a. National Institute for Research Advancement - Sogo Kenkyu Kaihatsu Kiko, P.O. Box 5004, 34F Yebisu Garden Place Tower, 4-20-3 Ebisu, Shibuya-ku, Tokyo 150, Japan. TEL 03-5448-1735. FAX 03-5448-1745. E-mail: tigarashi@niral.nira.go.jp.
Formerly (until 1984): N I R A Profile (ISSN 0289-7717)

300   JA   ISSN 0914-6172
HD87
N I R A SEISAKU KENKYU. (Text in Japanese) 1979. m. National Institute for Research Advancement - Sogo Kenkyu Kaihatsu Kiko, P.O. Box 5004, 34F Yebisu Garden Place Tower, 4-20-3 Ebisu, Shibuya-ku, Tokyo 150, Japan. TEL 03-5448-1735. FAX 03-5448-1745. E-mail: tigarashi@niral.nira.go.jp.
—BLDSC (6113.568800).
Formerly (until 1988): Gekkan N I R A (ISSN 0387-9054); Which was formed by the merger of: Kiho N I R A (ISSN 0387-995X); N I R A Report (ISSN 0386-1937)

300   SX
N I S E R DISCUSSION PAPERS. 1990. irreg. (3-5/yr.). price varies. University of Namibia, Namibian Institute for Social and Economic Research, P.O. Box 13301, Windhoek 9000, Namibia. **Document type:** academic/scholarly publication.
Description: Covers legal, social, economic and development related issues affecting present-day Namibia.

300 330   NR
N I S E R OCCASIONAL PAPERS. irreg. price varies. Nigerian Institute of Social and Economic Research, P.M.B. 5, University of Ibadan, Ibadan, Nigeria. TEL 234-22-400501-5. TELEX 31119 NISER G. Ed. Remi Lawal.

300   SX
N I S E R RESEARCH REPORTS. 1990. irreg., no.9, 1992. price varies. University of Namibia, Namibian Institute for Social and Economic Research, P.O. Box 13301, Windhoek 9000, Namibia. **Document type:** academic/scholarly publication.
Description: Presents research in social and economic conditions affecting specific regions or population groups in present-day Namibia.

300   II
N.K. BOSE MEMORIAL FOUNDATION. NEWSLETTER. (Text in English) 1978. q. Rs.15. N.K. Bose Memorial Foundation, B-8-9 Bara Gambhir Singh, Gauriganj, Varanasi 221001, India. Ed. Baidyanath Saraswati. bk.rev. circ. 300.

300   US   ISSN 0147-0124
HM261.A1
N O R C REPORT. 1941. biennial. National Opinion Research Center, 1155 E. 60th St., Chicago, IL 60637. TEL 312-702-1200. Ed. Jeff Hackett.
Formerly (until 1981): National Opinion Research Center. Report (ISSN 0077-5274)

SOCIAL SCIENCES: COMPREHENSIVE WORKS

300   PP
N R I DISCUSSION PAPERS. 1976. irreg. price varies. National Research Institute, P.O. Box 5854, Boroko, NCD, Papua New Guinea. TEL 675-26-0300. FAX 675-26-0213. **Indexed:** IDA, Rural Devel.Abstr., Rural Recreat.Tour.Abstr., World Agri.Econ. & Rural Sociol.Abstr.
    Formerly: I A S E R Discussion Papers.

300   PP
N R I MONOGRAPHS. 1976. irreg. price varies. National Research Institute, P.O. Box 5854, Boroko, NCD, Papua New Guinea. TEL 675-26-0300. FAX 674-26-0213. **Indexed:** Geo.Abstr.
    Formerly: I A S E R Monographs.

300   PP
N R I SPECIAL PUBLICATIONS. 1981. irreg. price varies. National Research Institute, P.O. Box 5854, Boroko, NCD, Papua New Guinea. TEL 675-26-0300. FAX 675-26-0312. Ed. Jim Robbins. circ. 350. **Indexed:** Rural Devel.Abstr., World Agri.Econ.& Rural Sociol.Abstr.
    Formerly (until 1989): I A S E R Special Publications.

300   SX   ISSN 1018-7677
NAMIBIA SCIENTIFIC SOCIETY. JOURNAL. (Text in Afrikaans, English and German) 1925. a. membership. Namibia Scientific Society, 110 Leutwein St., P.O. Box 67, Windhoek 9000, Namibia. TEL 061-225372. Ed. A. Henrichsen. adv.; bk.rev.; illus. **Indexed:** Anthropol.Lit.
    Formerly: South West Africa Scientific Society. Journal (ISSN 0379-6051)

378 371   CC   ISSN 0257-5892
NANJING DAXUE XUEBAO (ZHEXUE SHEHUI KEXUE BAN)/NANJING UNIVERSITY. JOURNAL (SOCIAL SCIENCE EDITION). (Text in Chinese; table of contents in English) bi-m. Nanjing Daxue Chubanshe - Nanjing University Press, Nanjing, Jiangsu 210008, People's Republic of China. index.
—BLDSC (4828.682500); UnCover.
    Description: Each issue is devoted to a specific topic.

300   CC   ISSN 1001-8263
NANJING SHEHUI KEXUE/NANJING SOCIAL SCIENCES. (Text in Chinese) 1990. m. Y30($20) (effective 1994). Nanjing Zhexue Shehui Kexue Lianhehui, 257 Baixia Lu, Nanjing, Jiangsu 210001, People's Republic of China. TEL 025-4412647. Ed. Lu Jianjie. adv.: color page $2000; adv. contact: Gu Zhaolu. bk.rev.; index; circ. 2,000 (paid). **Document type:** academic/scholarly publication.
    Description: Covers literature, history, philosophy, economics, law, sociology and other aspects of social sciences.

300   CC   ISSN 1001-4608
AS452.N34
NANJING SHIFAN DAXUE XUEBAO (SHEHUI KEXUE BAN)/NANJING NORMAL UNIVERSTIY. JOURNAL (SOCIAL SCIENCE EDITION). (Text in Chinese) 1955. q. $10. Nanjing Shifan Daxue - Nanjing Normal Universtiy, 122 Ninghai Rd., Nanjing, Jiangsu 210024, People's Republic of China. TEL 025-3303666. Ed. Zhang Chunyi. bk.rev. circ. 3,100. **Document type:** academic/scholarly publication.
—UnCover.
    Formerly (until 1984): Nanjing Normal College. Academic Journal.
    Description: Publishes academic articles on philosophy, economics, education, literature, linguistics, and history.

300 100   CC   ISSN 1001-4667
NANKAI XUEBAO. ZHEXUE SHEHUI KEXUE BAN/NANKAI UNIVERSITY. JOURNAL. PHILOSOPHY AND SOCIAL SCIENCES EDITION. (Text in Chinese; table of contents in English) m. Y2 per no. (Nankai Daxue - Nankai University) Nankai Xuebao Bianjibu, Balitai, Nankai-qu, Tianjin 300071, People's Republic of China. TEL 34412-538. (Dist. outside China by: China International Book Trading Corp., P.O. Box 2820, Beijing, P.R.C.) Ed. Zhu Guanghua. charts.
—UnCover.

300   GW   ISSN 0176-6023
NASSAUER GESPRAECHE DER FREIHERR-VOM-STEIN-GESELLSCHAFT. 1985. irreg., vol.4, 1991. price varies. Franz Steiner Verlag Wiesbaden GmbH, Birkenwaldstr. 44, 70191 Stuttgart, Germany. TEL 0711-2582-0. FAX 0711-2582390. (Subscr. to: Postfach 101061, 70009 Stuttgart, Germany) **Document type:** proceedings.

300   US   ISSN 0077-4049
H62
NATIONAL COUNCIL FOR THE SOCIAL STUDIES. BULLETINS. 1964. irreg. price varies. National Council for the Social Studies, 3501 Newark St., N.W., Washington, DC 20016. TEL 202-966-7840. adv. **Indexed:** Curr.Cont., SSCI. **Document type:** bulletin.

300   UK   ISSN 0077-491X
H11
NATIONAL INSTITUTE OF ECONOMIC AND SOCIAL RESEARCH. ANNUAL REPORT. 1941. a. free. National Institute of Economic and Social Research, 2 Dean Trench St., Smith Sq., London SW1P 3HE, England. TEL 071-222-7665. FAX 071-222-1435. circ. 2,000. **Indexed:** A.I.C.P. **Document type:** corporate report.

NATIONAL INSTITUTE OF ECONOMIC AND SOCIAL RESEARCH. REPORT SERIES. see *BUSINESS AND ECONOMICS*

NATIONAL INSTITUTE OF ECONOMIC AND SOCIAL RESEARCH, LONDON. ECONOMIC AND SOCIAL STUDIES. see *BUSINESS AND ECONOMICS*

NATIONAL RESEARCH COUNCIL OF THAILAND. JOURNAL. see *SCIENCES: COMPREHENSIVE WORKS*

300 364   UA   ISSN 0028-0062
NATIONAL REVIEW OF SOCIAL SCIENCES. (Text in Arabic and English) 1964. 3/yr. 150. National Center for Social and Criminological Research, Zamalek P.O., Cairo, Egypt. Ed. Dr. Ahmed M. Khalifa. bk.rev.; charts; illus.

300   CH   ISSN 0077-5835
H8.C47
NATIONAL TAIWAN UNIVERSITY. COLLEGE OF LAW. JOURNAL OF SOCIAL SCIENCE. (Text in Chinese or English) 1950. irreg., no.41, 1993. National Taiwan University, College of Law, Taipei, Taiwan, Republic of China. FAX 02-3948914.
—BLDSC (5064.890000).

300 320   UK   ISSN 0090-5992
DR24
NATIONALITIES PAPERS. 1972. q. £25 to individuals; institutions £25 (effective 1996). (Association for the Study of Nationalities (Ex-U.S.S.R. and East Europe), Inc.) Carfax Publishing Co., P.O. Box 25, Agingdon, Oxon. OX14 3UE, England. TEL 01235-521154. FAX 01235-553559. (Subscr. in N. America to: Carfax Publishing Co., 875-81 Massachusetts Ave., Cambridge, MA 02139) Ed. Henry R. Huttenbach. adv.; bk.rev.; bibl.; index. circ. 1,200. (also avail. in microfiche; back issues avail.; reprint service avail. from ISI,UMI) **Indexed:** Amer.Bibl.Slavic & E.Eur.Stud., Amer.Hist.& Life, Hist.Abstr., HR Rep. (1987-), Int.Polit.Sci.Abstr., Lang.& Lang.Behav.Abstr., M.L.A., Polit.Sci.Abstr. **Document type:** academic/scholarly publication.
—BLDSC (6033.449000); Faxon; UMI; UnCover. CCC.
    Description: Focuses on nationality and minority questions in Eastern Europe and former U.S.S.R.
    Refereed Serial

330   DK   ISSN 0028-0453
HB9
NATIONALOEKONOMISK TIDSSKRIFT. (Text in Danish; occasionally in other Scandinavian languages or English; summaries in English) 1873. 3/yr. DKK 312.50. Nationaloekonomisk Forening, Danmarks Nationalbank, Havnegade 5, DK-1093 Copenhagen K, Denmark. TEL 45-33-14-14-11. FAX 45-33-91-30-41. Ed. Thorkild Davidsen. adv.; bk.rev.; bibl.; index, cum.index every 25 yrs. circ. 2,200. (also avail. in microfilm from UMI; reprint service avail. from ISI,UMI) **Indexed:** Amer.Hist.& Life, Hist.Abstr., J.of Econ.Lit., SSCI.
—Genuine Article; UMI.

300   US   ISSN 0082-5166
NATURAL HAZARD RESEARCH WORKING PAPERS. 1968. irreg., latest no.85. $4.50. University of Colorado, Institute of Behavioral Science, Natural Hazards Research & Applications Center, Campus Box 542, Boulder, CO 80309. TEL 303-492-6818. FAX 303-492-2151. Eds. Sylvia Dane, David Butler. circ. 130. **Indexed:** Geo.Abstr. **Document type:** academic/scholarly publication.
—BLDSC (6037.700000).

146.3205 321   US   ISSN 0890-6130
B809.8
NATURE, SOCIETY, AND THOUGHT; a journal of dialectical and historical materialism. 1987. q. $15 to individuals; institutions $28. (Marxist Educational Press) M E P Publications, University of Minnesota, 116 Church St., S.E., Minneapolis, MN 55455. TEL 612-922-7993. (Orders to: Nature, Society, and Thought, University of Minnesota, 116 Church St., S.E., Minneapolis, MN 55455) Ed. Erwin Marquit. adv.; bk.rev. **Indexed:** Alt.Press Ind, Left Ind. (1987-). **Document type:** academic/scholarly publication.
—BLDSC (6047.357000). **CCC.**
    Description: Devoted to applications of Marxist methods to various fields of study.

NATURES - SCIENCES - SOCIETES. see *EARTH SCIENCES*

300   CC   ISSN 1000-5218
NEI MENGGU DAXUE XUEBAO (SHEHUI KEXUE BAN)/INNER MONGOLIAN UNIVERSITY. JOURNAL (SOCIAL SCIENCE EDITION). (Text in Chinese) 1959. q. $20 per no. Nei Menggu Daxue - Inner Mongolian University, No. 1 West University Rd., Huhhot, Nei Menggu 010021, People's Republic of China. TEL 0471-43156. FAX 0471-611761. (Subscr. to: China International Book Trading Corp., P.O. Box 399, Beijing, P.R. China) Ed. Xu Bonian. index. **Document type:** academic/scholarly publication.
    Description: Covers linguistics, literature, philosophy, Mongolian studies, religion, history, politics, economics and law.

300   CC
NEI MENGGU SHEHUI KEXUE/INNER MONGOLIAN SOCIAL SCIENCES. (Editions in Chinese and Mongolian) bi-m. $22.50 for Chinese ed.; Mongolian ed. $23.90. Nei Menggu Shehui Kexueyuan - Inner Mongolian Academy of Social Sciences, Daxue Donglu, Huhhot, Nei Menggu 010010, People's Republic of China. (Dist. outside China by: China International Book Trading Corp., P.O. Box 399, P.R.C.; Dist. in US by: China Books & Periodicals, Inc., 2929 24th St., San Francisco, CA 94119. TEL 415-282-2994)

NEI MENGGU SHIFAN DAXUE XUEBAO (ZHEXUE SHEHUI KEXUE HANWEN BAN)/INNER MONGOLIAN TEACHERS UNIVERSITY. JOURNAL (PHILOSOPHY & SOCIAL SCIENCE CHINESE EDITION). see *PHILOSOPHY*

300   GW
NEUES SCHRIFTTUM ZUR DEUTSCHEN LANDESKUNDE. 1941. a. price varies. Zentralausschuss fuer Deutsche Landeskunde e.V., Universitaet Trier, 54286 Trier, Germany. TEL 0651-2014526. FAX 0651-2013975. Ed. Walter Sperling. index. **Document type:** academic/scholarly publication, bibliography.

NEW AMERICAN (APPLETON). see *POLITICAL SCIENCE*

NEW ENGLAND JOURNAL OF HISTORY. see *HISTORY — History Of North And South America*

300   UK   ISSN 0953-1432
NEW EUROPEAN. 1988. q. (Centre for European Studies) M C B University Press Ltd., 60-62 Toller Ln., Bradford, W. Yorks BD8 9BY, England. TEL 0274-499821. FAX 0274-547143. Ed. John Coleman. (reprint service avail. from SWZ) **Indexed:** ELLIS. **Document type:** academic/scholarly publication.
—UMI.

341.24 940.559 UK
NEW EUROPEAN SEMINAR PAPERS. 1993. irreg. University of Huddersfield, Department of Humanities, Queensgate, Huddersfield HD1 3DH, England. TEL 01484-422288. FAX 01484-516151. Ed. Graham Timmins. **Document type:** academic/scholarly publication.
Description: Facilitates academic debate on contemporary issues in the political and socio-economic development of the New Europe.

NEW HUMANIST. see *PHILOSOPHY*

NEW ZEALAND SLAVONIC JOURNAL. see *HUMANITIES: COMPREHENSIVE WORKS*

300 056.1 MX ISSN 0185-1535
F1201
NEXOS; SOCIEDAD, CIENCIA, LITERATURA. 1978. m. Mazatlan 119, Col. Condesa, 06140 Mexico DF, Mexico. **Indexed:** Hisp.Amer.Per.Ind. (1992-).
—BLDSC (6109.056000).

NEXUS: CHINA IN FOCUS. see *GENERAL INTEREST PERIODICALS — China*

301 NE ISSN 0028-9930
NIEUWE WEST INDISCHE GIDS/NEW WEST INDIAN GUIDE. Short title: N W I G. (Text in English) 1919. 2/yr. fl.135 includes Caribbean Abstracts (effective 1996). (Koninklijk Instituut voor Taal-, Land- en Volkenkunde) K I T L V Press, P.O. Box 9515, 2500 RA Leiden, Netherlands. TEL 31-71-272372. FAX 31-71-272638. Ed: Gert Oostindie. adv.; bk.rev.; bibl.; illus.; index, cum.index. circ. 600. **Indexed:** Amer.Hist.& Life, Hisp.Amer.Per.Ind. (1994-), Hist.Abstr., Key to Econ.Sci. **Document type:** academic/scholarly publication.
Formerly: West Indische Gids.
Description: Publishes articles in the social sciences and the humanities pertaining to the Caribbean, with an extensive review section on Caribbean books.

300 330 NR ISSN 0078-074X
NIGERIAN INSTITUTE OF SOCIAL AND ECONOMIC RESEARCH. ANNUAL REPORT. 1954. a. free. Nigerian Institute of Social and Economic Research, Private Mail Bag 5, University of Ibadan, Ibadan, Nigeria. TEL 01-410935.
Formerly: West African Institute of Social and Economic Research. Annual Report.

300 NR ISSN 0189-0085
HC1055.A1
NIGERIAN INSTITUTE OF SOCIAL AND ECONOMIC RESEARCH. RESEARCH FOR DEVELOPMENT. 1981. s-a. Nigerian Institute of Social and Economic Research, Private Mail Bag 5, University of Ibadan, Ibadan, Nigeria.

300 CC ISSN 1001-5124
AS452.H314
NINGBO DAXUE XUEBAO (RENWEN KEXUE BAN)/NINGBO UNIVERSITY. JOURNAL (LIBERAL ARTS EDITION). (Text in Chinese) q. Ningbo Daxue - Ningbo University, Ningbo, Zhejiang 315211, People's Republic of China. TEL 0574-6694294. FAX 0574-6694161. Ed. Jin Tao. **Document type:** academic/scholarly publication.

300 CC ISSN 1002-0292
NINGXIA SHEHUI KEXUE/SOCIAL SCIENCE IN NINGXIA. (Text in Chinese) 1982. bi-m. $15 (effective 1994). Ningxia Shehui Kexueyuan - Ningxia Academy of Social Sciences, Yinchuan, Ningxia 750021, People's Republic of China. (Dist. in US by: China Books & Periodicals, Inc., 2929 24th St., San Francisco, CA 94110. TEL 415-282-2994) Ed. Tongming Chen. adv.; B&W page $500, color page $1000; adv. contact: Ding Jun. bk.rev. **Document type:** academic/scholarly publication.

300 CC ISSN 0546-9503
NONGCUN GONGZUO TONGXUN/RURAL AFFAIRS BULLETIN. (Text in Chinese) m. Zhongguo Nongcun Zazhishe, No. 61, Fuxing Lu, Beijing 100036, People's Republic of China. TEL 8215244. Ed. Zhou Hongfei. circ. 400,000.
Description: Offers a comprehensive guidance on Chinese policies on rural work.

300 910 FI ISSN 0345-8326
NORD REFO. (Text in Danish, Norwegian and Swedish) 1969. q. free. Nordiska Institutet foer Regionalpolitisk Forskning, PO Box 257, 001 71 Helsinki, Finland. FAX 01-602927. Ed. Goesta Oscarsson. circ. 1,500. (back issues avail.)
Description: Deals with regional questions and regional policies in the Nordic countries.

300 SW ISSN 0029-1234
NORDENS TIDNING. 1943-1969; resumed 1982. q. SEK 95 (effective 1995). Svenska Foreningen Norden, P.O. Box 12707, 112 94 Stockholm, Sweden. Eds. Mats Jonsson, Eriq Agelii. adv. contact: Jan Linden. illus.

NORTH DAKOTA QUARTERLY. see *HUMANITIES: COMPREHENSIVE WORKS*

NORTHERN REVIEW. see *HUMANITIES: COMPREHENSIVE WORKS*

300 US ISSN 0029-3474
HB1
NORTHWEST TECHNOCRAT. 1939. q. $12. Technocracy Inc., 2475 Harksell Rd., Ferndale, WA 98248. TEL 360-366-1012. Ed. John Berge. (back issues avail.)

NOTEBOOKS FOR STUDY AND RESEARCH. see *POLITICAL SCIENCE*

300 UV ISSN 0550-0923
DT553.U7
NOTES ET DOCUMENTS VOLTAIQUES; bulletin trimestriel d'information scientifique. 1950. q. 3000 Fr.CFA. Centre National de la Recherche Scientifique et Technique, B.P. 7047, Ouagadougou, Burkina Faso. circ. 350. **Indexed:** A.I.C.P., M.L.A., P.A.I.S.For.Lang.Ind.
Formerly (until 1963): Etudes Voltaiques.

300 BL ISSN 0101-3300
F2501
NOVOS ESTUDOS C E B R A P. 1971. 3/yr. $40 (foreign $60) (effective 1995). (Centro Brasileiro de Analise e Planejamento) Editora Brasileira de Ciencias, Ltda., Rua Morgado de Mateus 615, 04015-1902 Sao Paulo, SP, Brazil. TEL 55-11-574-0399. FAX 55-11-574-5928. Ed. Rodrigo Naves; Pub. Francisco de Oliveira. bk.rev. circ. 2,500. **Indexed:** Curr.Cont., Sociol.Abstr., SSCI. **Document type:** academic/scholarly publication.
Supersedes (in 1981): Estudos C E B R A P (ISSN 0100-7025)

NUEVA CACERES REVIEW. see *ANTHROPOLOGY*

300 AG ISSN 0327-7437
NUEVAS PROPUESTAS. 3/yr. $16. Universidad Catolica de Santiago del Estero, Avda. Alsina, Casilla de Correo 285, 4200 Santiago del Estero, Argentina. TEL 21-3820.
Formerly (until 1986): Propuestas.

NURSING RESEARCH. see *MEDICAL SCIENCES — Nurses And Nursing*

300 RU ISSN 0869-0499
OBSHCHESTVENNYE NAUKI I SOVREMENNOST. (Editions in English, French, German, Portuguese, Spanish) 1970. bi-m. $60 (effective 1996). (Rossiiskaya Akademiya Nauk) Izdatel'stvo Nauka, 90 Profzoyuznaya ul., 117864 Moscow, Russia. TEL 095-336-0266. FAX 095-420-2220. (Dist. by: Mezhdunarodnaya Kniga, B. Yakimanka 39, 117049 Moscow, Russia; Dist. in U.S. by: Victor Kamkin Inc., 4956 Boiling Brook Pkwy., Rockville, MD 20852. TEL 301-881-5973. FAX 301-881-1637) Ed. I. Grigulevich. bk.rev.; bibl. **Indexed:** Amer.Hist.& Life, Hist.Abstr., Int.Lab.Doc. —CCC.
Formerly (until 1991): Akademiya Nauk S.S.S.R. Obshchestvennye Nauki (ISSN 0132-3458)

300 UZ ISSN 0029-7763
OBSHCHESTVENNYE NAUKI V UZBEKISTANE. (Text in Russian and Uzbek) 1956. m. 21 Rub. Akademiya Nauk Uzbekistana, Ul. Gogolya 70, k. 105, 700000 Tashkent, Uzbekistan. Ed. P.M. Krumov. bk.rev.; bibl.; charts; illus.; stat. circ. 1,420.

OFAKIM. see *POLITICAL SCIENCE*

OFFSHOOTS OF ORGONOMY. see *HUMANITIES: COMPREHENSIVE WORKS*

300 VE ISSN 1012-1587
OPCION/OPTION; revista de ciencias humanas y sociales. (Text and abstracts in English, Spanish) 1984. 3/yr. $25 in Latin America; Europe and US $42. Universidad del Zulia, Facultad Experimental de Ciencias, Departamento de Ciencias Humanas, Apdo. 526, Edif. Grano de Oro, 4001A Maracaibo, Venezuela. TEL 58-61-529432. FAX 58-061-524310. E-mail: serbiluz@dino.conicit.ve. Ed. Lourdes Molero de Cabeza. bk.rev.; circ. 1,000 (paid). **Document type:** academic/scholarly publication.
Description: Publishes results of fundamental research in the human and social sciences areas.

300 GW ISSN 0170-8406
HM131
ORGANIZATION STUDIES. bi-m. DM.146 to individuals; institutions DM.401. (European Group for Organizational Studies) Walter de Gruyter und Co., Genthiner Str. 13, 10785 Berlin, Germany. TEL 030-26005-0. FAX 030-26005251. TELEX 184027. (U.S. addr.: Walter de Gruyter, Inc., 200 Saw Mill River Rd., Hawthorne, NY 10532. TEL 914-747-0110) **Indexed:** ABI Inform., BPIA, Bus.Ind., CINAHL, CLOSS, Cont.Pg.Manage., Curr.Cont., E.I., Int.Polit.Sci.Abstr., Lang.& Lang.Behav.Abstr., Polit.Sci.Abstr., PSI, Psychol.Abstr. (1982-), SCIMP (1981-), SSCI. **Document type:** academic/scholarly publication.
●Also available online. Vendor(s): University Microfilms International.
—BLDSC (6290.730000); Faxon; Genuine Article; SWETS; UMI; UnCover. **CCC.**

300 GW ISSN 0724-5246
ORIENTIERUNGEN ZUR GESELLSCHAFTS- UND WIRTSCHAFTSPOLITIK. q. DM.80 (foreign DM.88). Gustav Fischer Verlag, Wollgrasweg 49, 70599 Stuttgart, Germany. TEL 0711-458030. FAX 0711-4580334. TELEX 7111488-FIBUCH-D. (Subscr. to: Postfach 720143, 70577 Stuttgart, Germany) **Document type:** academic/scholarly publication.

300 UK ISSN 0963-8504
OUTLOOK (DEDDINGTON). 1992. 3/yr. (Sep.-Apr.). £11.85 (rest of Europe £17.85; elsewhere £20.85) (effective 1996). Philip Allan Publishers Ltd., Market Pl., Deddington, Oxon. OX15 OSE, England. TEL 01869-338652. FAX 01869-338803. adv. contact: Ceri Jenkins.

320 338 UK ISSN 0954-3694
P S I DISCUSSION PAPERS. 1980. irreg. £55 (subscription also includes Report Series; Studies in European Politics; Policy Studies) Policy Studies Institute, 100 Park Village East, London NW1 3SR, England. TEL 071-387-2171. FAX 071-388-0914.

P S I: REPORT SERIES. (Policy Studies Institute) see *POLITICAL SCIENCE*

300 AT ISSN 0155-9060
PACIFIC RESEARCH MONOGRAPHS. irreg. price varies. Australian National University, National Centre for Development Studies, Canberra, A.C.T. 0200, Australia. TEL 616-249-4705. FAX 616-257-2886. **Indexed:** Rural Devel.Abstr., Trop.Oil Seeds Abstr., World Agri.Econ.& Rural Sociol.Abstr. **Document type:** monographic series.
—BLDSC (6330.875000).
Description: Economic development, Pacific history, politics and policy issues.

572 US ISSN 0275-3596
DU1
PACIFIC STUDIES; an interdisciplinary journal devoted to the study of the Pacific--its islands and adjacent countries. 1977. 4/yr. $30. (Institute for Polynesian Studies) Brigham Young University, Hawaii Campus, Box 1829, Laie, HI 96762. TEL 808-293-3667. FAX 808-293-3645. TELEX 6502972475 MCIUW. E-mail: robertsd@byuh.edu. Ed. Dale B. Robertson. adv.; bk.rev. circ. 500. (back issues avail.) **Indexed:** Abstr.Anthropol., Amer.Hist.& Life, Anthropol.Lit., Asian-Pac.Econ.Lit., Bk.Rev.Ind. (1989-), Child.Bk.Rev.Ind. (1989-), Hist.Abstr., Int.Polit.Sci.Abstr., P.A.I.S., Sociol.Abstr. **Document type:** academic/scholarly publication.
—BLDSC (6331.520000); Faxon.
Refereed Serial

SOCIAL SCIENCES: COMPREHENSIVE WORKS

300 IT
PADANIA (MILAN); societa ambiente economia tradizioni. 1992. m. (11/yr.) L.50000. Editoriale Padania s.r.l., Viale Elvezia 12, 20154 Milan, Italy. TEL 02-33607240. FAX 02-33607616. Ed. Pier Maria Paoletti. **Document type:** consumer publication.

PANJAB UNIVERSITY RESEARCH BULLETIN (ARTS). see *HUMANITIES: COMPREHENSIVE WORKS*

300 900 500 US ISSN 1056-8190
HT390
PAPERS IN REGIONAL SCIENCE. 1955. q. $45 to individuals; institutions $120 (effective 1993). Regional Science Association International, 1-3 Observatory, 901 S. Mathews, Univ. of Illinois, Urbana, IL 61801-3681. TEL 217-333-8904. FAX 217-244-1785. Ed.Bd. circ. 3,000. **Indexed:** ASCA, C.R.E.J., Geo.Abstr., IDA, Rural Recreat.Tour.Abstr., SSCI, World Agri.Econ.& Rural Sociol.Abstr. **Document type:** academic/scholarly publication.
—BLDSC (6400.035000); Faxon; SWETS; UnCover.
Formerly (until vol.70, 1991): Regional Science Association. Papers (ISSN 0486-2902)
Refereed Serial

300 CH
PAPERS IN SOCIAL SCIENCES. no.80, 1980. irreg. Academia Sinica, Sun Yat-Sen Institute for Social Sciences and Philosophy - Chung Yang Yen Chiu Yuan Chung Shan Ren Wen Sheh Hui Ko Sheyue Yen Chiu So, Nankang, Taipei 11529, Taiwan, Republic of China. TEL 886-2-782-1693. FAX 886-2-785-4160. **Indexed:** Psychol.Abstr.

300 NQ ISSN 1016-9628
PENSAMIENTO PROPIO. 1982. m. C.$20000($27) in Latin America and North America; Europe $32. Coordinadora Regional de Investigaciones Economicas y Sociales, Apdo. 3516, Managua, Nicaragua. FAX 26218. FAX 26180. (Co-sponsor: Novib de Holanda) Ed. Sanda Garcia. adv.; bk.rev. circ. 5,000. (back issues avail.)

PENSAMIENTO Y ACCION. see *SCIENCES: COMPREHENSIVE WORKS*

300 IT
PENSIERO E SOCIETA; rivista semestrale di cultura filosofica e scienze sociali. s-a. Bulzoni Editore, Via dei Liburni 14, 00185 Rome, Italy. TEL 06-4455207. FAX 06-4450355.

PERIODICA POLYTECHNICA. HUMANITIES AND SOCIAL SCIENCES. see *HUMANITIES: COMPREHENSIVE WORKS*

300 200 CL ISSN 0716-730X
PERSONA Y SOCIEDAD. 1987. 3/yr. Esc.4500($30) to individuals; institutions Esc.5000($38). Instituto Latinoamericano de Doctrina y Estudios Sociales, Departamento de Publicaciones, Almirante Barroso 6, Casilla 14446, Correo 21, Santiago, Chile. TEL 02-717499. FAX 02-6986873. Ed. Francisco Lopez F.
Description: Analyzes and discusses the problems of the relationship between faith and culture in Latin America.

300 BL ISSN 0101-3459
AS80.A1 CODEN: PRSVDY
PERSPECTIVAS; revista de ciencias sociais. (Text in Portuguese; summaries in English and Portuguese) 1976-1977; resumed 1980. a. $30 or exchange basis. Universidade Estadual Paulista, Av. Vicente Ferreira 1278, Caixa Postal 603, 17515-901 Marilia SP, Brazil. TEL 0144-33-1844. FAX 0144-22-2504. TELEX 111-9016-UJME-BR. bk.rev.; abstr.; charts. circ. 1,000. **Indexed:** Abstr.Anthropol., Bull.Signal., Int.Polit.Sci.Abstr., Sociol.Abstr. **Document type:** academic/scholarly publication.
—BLDSC (6428.107700).
Description: Covers original articles and research in the social sciences.

PERSPECTIVES ON CULTURE AND MEDICINE. see *MEDICAL SCIENCES*

300 001.3 MY ISSN 0128-7702
  CODEN: PERTDY
PERTANIKA JOURNAL OF SOCIAL SCIENCE AND HUMANITIES. (Text in English, Malay) 2/yr. $50 to individuals; institutions $60. (Agricultural University of Malaysia) Universiti Pertanian Malaysia Press, Serdang, Selangor, Malaysia. TEL 03-9486101. FAX 03-9483745. TELEX UNIPER-37454. circ. 200.
—BLDSC (6428.183000); CASDDS.
Superseded in part (in 1993): Pertanika (ISSN 0126-6128)
Refereed Serial

300 FR ISSN 0399-1253
DE1
PEUPLES MEDITERRANEENS - MEDITERRANEAN PEOPLES. (Text and summaries in English or French) 1977. q. 230 F. to individuals; institutions 380 F. Institut d'Etudes Mediterraneennes, B.P. 18807, 75326 Paris Cedex 07, France. TEL 45-67-01-41. Ed. Paul Vieille. abstr. circ. 2,000. **Indexed:** Amer.Hist.& Life, Curr.Cont.Africa, Geo.Abstr., Hist.Abstr., IDA, Int.Polit.Sci.Abstr., Lang.& Lang.Behav.Abstr. **Document type:** academic/scholarly publication.
—BLDSC (5534.742000); SWETS.

300 PH ISSN 0116-7081
PHILIPPINE-AMERICAN STUDIES JOURNAL. (Text in English) 1987. a. P.30($3.20) (De La Salle University, Dept. of History and Area Studies, American Studies Program) De La Salle University Press, 2401 Taft Ave., Manila, Philippines. TEL 2-59-48-32. FAX 632-521-9094. adv.; bk.rev. circ. 300. **Indexed:** Ind.Phil.Per. **Document type:** academic/scholarly publication.
Description: Publishes scholarly articles reflecting significant quantitative or qualitative research. Includes speeches, research reports, and "state of the art" papers.

PHILOSOPHICAL STUDIES IN CONTEMPORARY CULTURE. see *PHILOSOPHY*

300 II ISSN 0377-2772
HN681
PHILOSOPHY & SOCIAL ACTION. (Text in English and Hindi) 1975. q. Rs.50 to individuals (foreign $40); institutions Rs.150 (foreign $60) (effective 1994). Committee of Concerned Indian Philosophers for Social Action, M-120 Greater Kailash 1, New Delhi 110 048, India. TEL 091-11-641-5365. FAX 091-11-647-4646. Ed. Dhirendra Sharma. adv.; bk.rev. circ. 1,000. **Indexed:** HR Rep., Lang.& Lang.Behav.Abstr., Phil.Ind., Sociol.Abstr. **Document type:** academic/scholarly publication.
—BLDSC (6464.805000).
Description: Discusses substantive socio-economic, political, legal and science and public policy issues that concern the people of India and the Third World in particular.
Refereed Serial

300 US ISSN 0048-3931
H1
PHILOSOPHY OF THE SOCIAL SCIENCES. 1971. q. $55 to individuals; institutions $142 (effective Sep. 1995). Sage Publications, Inc., 2455 Teller Rd., Thousand Oaks, CA 91320. TEL 805-499-0721. FAX 805-499-0871. E-mail: libraries@sagepub.com. (Overseas subscr. to: Sage Publications Ltd., 6 Bonhill St., London EC2A 4PU, England; Sage Publications India Pvt. Ltd., P.O. Box 4215, New Delhi 110 048, India) Eds. J.N Hattiangadi, John O'Neill. adv.; bk.rev.; index. circ. 1,300. (also avail. in microform from UMI; back issues avail.; reprint service avail. from UMI) **Indexed:** Abstr.Crim.& Pen., Arts & Hum.Cit.Ind., ASSIA, Can.B.P.I., Can.Per.Ind., Curr.Cont., Ind.Bk.Rev.Hum., Int.Polit.Sci.Abstr., Lang.& Lang.Behav.Abstr., Mid.East: Abstr.& Ind., Phil.Ind., Soc.Sci.Ind. (1994-), SSCI. **Document type:** academic/scholarly publication.
—BLDSC (6465.080000); Faxon; Genuine Article; SWETS; UMI; UnCover. **CCC.**
Description: Publishes articles, discussions, symposia, literature surveys, translations, and reviews of interest to both philosophers concerned with the social sciences and social scientists concerned with the philosophical foundations of their subject.

300 327 US
PITT LATIN AMERICAN SERIES. (Includes as of 1986 subseries: Cuban Studies (ISSN 0361-4441)) 1965. irreg. price varies. University of Pittsburgh Press, 127 N. Bellefield Ave., Pittsburgh, PA 15260. TEL 800-666-2211. FAX 412-624-7380. Ed. James Malloy. **Document type:** monographic series.

300 US ISSN 0192-5059
HN50
PLANTATION SOCIETY IN THE AMERICAS; an interdisciplinary journal of tropical and subtropical history and culture. 1979. 3/yr. $20 to individuals; libraries $40. Plantation Society, c/o Prof. Edward Lazzerini, Man. Ed., Department of History, University of New Orleans, New Orleans, LA 70148. TEL 504-286-6886. Ed. Thomas Fiehrer. adv.; bk.rev. circ. 800. **Indexed:** Amer.Hist.& Life, Hist.Abstr., M.L.A.

THE PLOUGH (FARMINGTON). see *RELIGIONS AND THEOLOGY — Protestant*

300 FR ISSN 0336-1721
HT1501
PLURIEL. 1975. q. 60 F. Editions Pluriel, Mantilly, 61350 Passais-La-Conception, France. TEL 33-38-77-23. Ed. Jean Foucher. bk.rev. **Indexed:** Anthropol.Lit.

POLICY BITES. see *BUSINESS AND ECONOMICS*

POLICY STUDIES. see *POLITICAL SCIENCE*

300 330.1 PL
POLITECHNIKA KRAKOWSKA. MONOGRAFIE. SERIA: EKONOMIA, SOCJOLOGIA, FILOZOFIA. (Subseries of: Politechnika Krakowska. Monografie (ISSN 0860-097X)) (Text in Polish; summaries in English, French, German, Russian) 1985. irreg. price varies. Politechnika Krakowska, Ul. Warszawska 24, 31-155 Krakow, Poland. TEL 48-12-374289. FAX 48-12-335773. TELEX 322468 PK PL. bibl.; charts; illus. circ. 200. **Document type:** academic/scholarly publication, monographic series.
Formerly: Politechnika Krakowska. Monografie. Seria: Nauki Spoleczne i Ekonomiczne.

300 330 PL ISSN 0137-2599
POLITECHNIKA LODZKA. ZESZYTY NAUKOWE. ORGANIZACJA I ZARZADZANIE. (Text in Polish; summaries in English and Russian) 1975. irreg. price varies. Wydawnictwo Politechniki Lodzkiej, Ul. Wolczanska 223, 93-005 Lodz, Poland. (Krakowkie Przedmiescie 7, Warsaw, Poland) Ed. Jerzy Lewandowski. circ. 226. **Document type:** academic/scholarly publication.
Description: Industrial arrangement of textile institutions.

300 PL ISSN 0072-4718
POLITECHNIKA SLASKA. ZESZYTY NAUKOWE. NAUKI SPOLECZNE. (Text in Polish; summaries in English, German, Russian) 1964. irreg. price varies. Politechnika Slaska, Katowicka 7, 44-100 Gliwice, Poland. FAX 371655. TELEX 036304. (Dist by: Ars Polona, Krakowskie Przedmiescie 7, 00-068 Warsaw, Poland) Ed. Jozef Haber. circ. 205.
—BLDSC (9512.329100).

300 PL ISSN 0860-3200
POLITECHNIKA WROCLAWSKA. INSTYTUT NAUK EKONOMICZNO-SPOLECZNYCH. PRACE NAUKOWE. KONFERENCJE. 1986. irreg., no.2, 1989. price varies. Wydawnictwo Politechniki Wroclawskiej, Wybrzeze Wyspianskiego 27, 50-370 Wroclaw, Poland. FAX 22-36-64. TELEX 712559 PWRPL. **Document type:** proceedings.

300 PL ISSN 0239-3204
POLITECHNIKA WROCLAWSKA. INSTYTUT NAUK EKONOMICZNO-SPOLECZNYCH. PRACE NAUKOWE. MONOGRAFIE. (Text in Polish; summaries in English and Russian) 1971. irreg., no.31, 1991. price varies. Wydawnictwo Politechniki Wroclawskiej, Wybrzeze Wyspianskiego 27, 50-370 Wroclaw, Poland. FAX 22-36-64. TELEX 712559 PWRPL. (Dist. by: Ars Polona-Ruch, Krakowskie Przedmiescie 7, Warsaw, Poland) **Document type:** monographic series.
Formerly: Politechnika Wroclawska. Instytut Nauk Spolecznych. Prace Naukowe. Monografie (ISSN 0324-9506)

SOCIAL SCIENCES: COMPREHENSIVE WORKS

300   PL   ISSN 0239-3212
H31
POLITECHNIKA WROCLAWSKA. INSTYTUT NAUK EKONOMICZNO-SPOLECZNYCH. PRACE NAUKOWE. STUDIA I MATERIALY. (Text in Polish; summaries in English and Russian) 1969. irreg., no.13, 1992. price varies. Wydawnictwo Politechniki Wroclawskiej, Wybrzeze Wyspianskiego 27, 50-370 Wroclaw, Poland. FAX 22-36-64. TELEX 712559 PWRPL. (Dist. by: Ars Polona-Ruch, Krakowskie Przedmiescie 7, Warsaw, Poland) Document type: academic/scholarly publication.
    Formerly: Politechnika Wroclawska. Instytut Nauk Spolecznych. Prace Naukowe. Studia i Materialy (ISSN 0324-9514)

POLSKA AKADEMIA NAUK. ODDZIAL W KRAKOWIE. KOMISJE NAUKOWE. SPRAWOZDANIA Z POSIEDZEN. see *SCIENCES: COMPREHENSIVE WORKS*

300   UK   ISSN 0140-5918
POLYTECHNIC OF CENTRAL LONDON. FACULTY OF BUSINESS, MANAGEMENT AND SOCIAL STUDIES. RESEARCH WORKING PAPER. 1976. irreg., no.43, 1992. Polytechnic of Central London, Faculty of Business, Management and Social Studies, 32-38 Wells St., London W1P 3FG, England. Document type: monographic series.

300   PE
PONTIFICIA UNIVERSIDAD CATOLICA. REVISTA. N.S. 1977. irreg., approx. a. $8. Pontificia Universidad Catolica del Peru, Fondo Editorial, Apdo. 1761, Lima 100, Peru. TEL 626390. FAX 5114-611785. Ed. Gerardo Alarco. bk.rev.

300   AG
PONTIFICIA UNIVERSIDAD CATOLICA ARGENTINA. FACULTAD DE CIENCIAS SOCIALES Y ECONOMICAS. CUADERNOS. 1976. Ediciones Macchi, Alsina 1535-37, 1088 Buenos Aires, Argentina. TEL 46-2506. FAX 46-0594.

300   PE
PONTIFICIA UNIVERSIDAD CATOLICA DEL PERU. DEPARTAMENTO DE CIENCIAS SOCIALES. SERIE: EDICIONES PREVIAS. no.5, 1975. irreg. Pontificia Universidad Catolica del Peru, Departamento de Ciencias Sociales, Fondo Editorial, Apdo. 1761, Lima 100, Peru. FAX 51-14-611785. Ed. Enrique Carrion.

300   VC   ISSN 0080-3960
PONTIFICIA UNIVERSITA GREGORIANA. ISTITUTO DI SCIENZE SOCIALI STUDIA SOCIALIA. (Text in English, French, Italian or Spanish) 1957; N.S. 1985. irreg., N.S. no.4, 1990. price varies. (Pontificia Universita Gregoriana, Facolta de Scienze Sociali - Pontifical Gregorian University, Faculty of Social Sciences) Gregorian University Press, Piazza della Pilotta, 35, 00187 Rome, Italy. TEL 39-6-678-15-67. FAX 39-6-678-05-88. Ed. Sergio Bernal Restrepo, SJ. circ. 200.
    Description: Covers contemporary religious sociology: family, population, religious belonging, theology and progress, church teaching on social problems and more.

POPULATION ET SOCIETES. see *POPULATION STUDIES*

PRINCETON UNIVERSITY LIBRARY CHRONICLE. see *HUMANITIES: COMPREHENSIVE WORKS*

PRIRODA A SPOLOCNOST. see *SCIENCES: COMPREHENSIVE WORKS*

300   IT
PROBLEMI DI CIVILTA. 1978. bi-m. L.30000. Societa Editrice Napoletana s.r.l., Corso Umberto I 34, 80138 Naples, Italy. Ed. D. Migliucci.

300   RU   ISSN 0079-5763
PROBLEMS OF THE CONTEMPORARY WORLD/PROBLEMES DU MONDE CONTEMPORAIN/PROBLEMAS DEL MUNDO CONTEMPORANEO. (Text in English, French, Spanish) 1969. irreg. available on exchange. (Akademiya Nauk S.S.S.R.) Izdatel'stvo Nauka, 90 Profsoyuznaya ul., 117864 Moscow, Russia. TEL 234-05-84. Ed. I. Grigulevich. circ. 750. Indexed: Math.R.

225   FR   ISSN 0033-0884
AP20
PROJET. 1946. q. 230 F. (foreign 260 F.). Assas Editions, 14 rue d'Assas, 75006 Paris, France. TEL 44-39-48-48. FAX 40-49-01-92. Ed. Christian Mellon. adv.; bk.rev.; bibl.; charts; index. circ. 5,200. Indexed: C.I.S. Abstr., Int.Lab.Doc., Int.Polit.Sci.Abstr., Pt.de Rep. (1979-), World Bibl.Soc.Sec.
    —BLDSC (6924.930000).
    Formerly: Revue de l'Action Populaire.

PROSPECT. see *HOUSING AND URBAN PLANNING*

303.49   NO
PROSUS 21. 1989. q. NOK 170 in Nordic countries; elsewhere $40 (effective 1996); newsstand price: NOK 40. (Alternativ Framtid) Scandinavian University Press, P.O. Box 2959 Toeyen, N-0608 Oslo, Norway. TEL 47-22-57-53-00. FAX 47-22-57-53-53. E-mail: tidskrift@af.nfr.no. Ed. Paal Mugaas. adv.; B&W page NOK 3000; trim 25 x 17. bk.rev.; index. circ. 1,000. (back issues avail.) Document type: academic/scholarly publication.
● Also available online.
    Former titles: Tidsskriftet Alternativ Framtid (ISSN 0803-7655); (until 1993): I Praksis (ISSN 0803-2246); (until 1991): Alternativer i Praksis (ISSN 0802-4200)

PSYCHOLOGY TODAY. see *PSYCHOLOGY*

320.9   US   ISSN 0033-3395
JK4801
PUBLIC AFFAIRS COMMENT. 1955. q. free. University of Texas at Austin, Lyndon B. Johnson School of Public Affairs, Austin, TX 78713-7450. TEL 512-471-4962. Ed. David C. Warner. circ. 3,500. Indexed: P.A.I.S. Document type: academic/scholarly publication.
    —BLDSC (6962.700000).
    Description: Contains articles of current interest in the field of public affairs.

320   US   ISSN 0033-3557
H1   CODEN: PUBIBV
PUBLIC INTEREST. 1965. q. $25. National Affairs, Inc., 1112 16th St., N.W., Ste. 530, Washington, DC 20036. TEL 202-785-8555. FAX 202-467-0006. Eds. Irving Kristol, Nathan Glazer. bk.rev.; charts. circ. 6,000. (also avail. in microform from UMI; back issues avail., reprint service avail. from ISI,UMI) Indexed: A.B.C.Pol.Sci., ABI Inform., Acad.Ind., Amer.Hist.& Life, Avery Ind.Archit.Per., B.P.I., BPIA, C.I.J.E., Curr.Cont., Curr.Lit.Fam.Plan., Energy Ind., Energy Info.Abstr., Fut.Surv., Hist.Abstr., Int.Polit.Sci.Abstr., Lang.& Lang.Behav.Abstr., Med.Care Rev., Mid.East: Abstr.& Ind., Mult.Ed.Abstr., P.A.I.S., Pers.Manage.Abstr., Polit.Sci.Abstr., Soc.Sci.Ind., Soc.Work Res.& Abstr., Sociol.Educ.Abstr., SSCI. Document type: academic/scholarly publication.
● Also available online. Vendor(s): University Microfilms International.
    —BLDSC (6967.100000); Faxon; Genuine Article; SWETS; UMI; UnCover.
    Description: Addresses domestic policy issues including education, welfare, housing and poverty.

PUBLIC OPINION QUARTERLY. see *POLITICAL SCIENCE*

300   US
PUBLIC POLICY STUDIES IN THE SOUTH; a selected research guide. 1975. irreg. $6. Southern Center for Studies in Public Policy, Clark Atlanta University, Atlanta, GA 30314. TEL 404-880-8085.

PUBLICACOES CULTURAIS DA COMPANHIA. see *SCIENCES: COMPREHENSIVE WORKS*

PUBLICAR EN ANTROPOLOGIA Y CIENCIAS SOCIALES. see *ANTHROPOLOGY*

300 954 572   FR   ISSN 0339-1744
PURUSHARTHA. 1975. irreg., no.17, 1995. price varies. (Centre d'Etudes de l'Inde et de l'Asie du Sud) Editions de l' Ecole des Hautes Etudes en Sciences Sociales, 131 bd. St-Michel, 75005 Paris, France. TEL 46-33-51-46. FAX 44-07-08-89. (Dist. by: Centre Interinstitutionnel pour la Diffusion de Publications en Sciences Humaines, 131 bd. St-Michel, 75005 Paris, France. TEL 43-54-47-15. FAX 43-54-80-73) adv. circ. 500. Indexed: Anthropol.Lit.

300   CC   ISSN 1001-022X
QILU XUEKAN. (Text in Chinese) 1974. bi-m. Y18. Qufu Shifan Daxue - Qufu Normal University, Qufu, Shandong 273165, People's Republic of China. TEL 411831. Ed. Liu Shouan. Document type: academic/scholarly publication.
    Formerly (until 1980): Po yu Li.
    Description: Covers philosophy, literature, history, educational and social sciences.

QINGHAI MINZU XUEYUAN XUEBAO/QINGHAI INSTITUTE OF NATIONALITIES. JOURNAL. see *ORIENTAL STUDIES*

300   CC   ISSN 1000-5102
QINGHAI SHIFAN DAXUE XUEBAO (SHEHUI KEXUE BAN)/QINGHAI NORMAL UNIVERSITY. JOURNAL (SOCIAL SCIENCE EDITION). (Text in Chinese) 1960. q. Y10 (effective 1993-1995). Qinghai Shifan Daxue - Qinghai Normal University, 36 West Wusi Road, Xining, Qinghai 810008, People's Republic of China. TEL 0971-36201. (Dist. overseas by: China Publications Foreign Trade Corp., P.O. Box 782, Beijing, P.R.C.) Ed. Guo Hongji. bk.rev. circ. 2,500. Document type: academic/scholarly publication.
    Description: Contains research papers on political science, economics, philosophy, literature, history, education, psychology, and art.

300   CC   ISSN 0529-3766
QIU SHI/SEEKING TRUTH. (Text in Chinese) s-m. $64.60. Qiu Shi Zazhishe, 2 Shatan Beijie, Beijing 100727, People's Republic of China. TEL 01-4011155. TELEX 1219. (Dist. in US by: China Books & Periodicals, Inc., 2929 24th St., San Francisco, CA 94110. TEL 415-282-2994) circ. 1,830,000.
    Formerly (until 1988): Hong Qi - Red Flag.
    Description: Theoretical journal of the Chinese Communist Party.

300   CC   ISSN 1000-7504
QIU SHI WENXUAN/SEEKING TRUTH - SELECT ARTICLES. Select translation of: Qiu Shi. (Editions in Kazakh, Korean, Mongolian, Tibetan, Uighur) m. $27.80. Heilongjiang Daxue - Heilongjiang University, 24, Xuefu Lu, Harbin, Heilongjiang 1500880, People's Republic of China. TEL 64941. (Dist. in US by: China Books & Periodicals, Inc., 2929 24th St., San Francisco, CA 94110. TEL 415-282-2994) Ed. Yu Shihui.

QUADERNI SARDI DI FILOSOFIA E SCIENZE UMANE. see *PHILOSOPHY*

301   US   ISSN 1077-8004
▼**QUALITATIVE INQUIRY.** 1995. q. $54 to individuals; institutions $144 (effective Sep. 1995). Sage Publications, Inc., 2455 Teller Rd., Thousand Oaks, CA 91320. TEL 805-499-0721. FAX 805-499-0871. E-mail: libraries@sagepub.com. (Overseas subscr. to: Sage Publications Ltd., 6 Bonhill St., London EC2A 4PU, England; Sage Publications India Pvt. Ltd., P.O. Box 4215, New Delhi 110 048, India) Eds. Norman K. Denzin, Yvonna S. Lincoln. adv.; bk.rev. (back issues avail.; reprint service avail.) Document type: academic/scholarly publication.
    Description: Takes an interdisciplinary approach to examine qualitative methodology and related issues in the human sciences.

300   US   ISSN 0888-5397
QUALITATIVE RESEARCH METHODS SERIES. (Subseries of: Sage University Paper Series) 1986. irreg., no.32, 1993. Sage Publications, Inc., 2455 Teller Rd., Thousand Oaks, CA 91320. TEL 805-499-0721. FAX 805-499-0871. (Overseas orders to: Sage Publications Ltd., 6 Bonhill Rd., London EC2A 4PU, England; Sage Publications India Pvt. Ltd., P.O. Box 4215, New Delhi 110 048, India) (back issues avail.) Document type: monographic series.
    —BLDSC (7168.124400).
    Description: Covers various aspects of the use of qualitative research methods in social sciences research.

SOCIAL SCIENCES: COMPREHENSIVE WORKS

300   US   ISSN 0149-192X
QUANTITATIVE APPLICATIONS IN THE SOCIAL SCIENCES SERIES. (Subseries of: Sage University Paper Series) 1976. irreg., no.105, 1995. $9.50 per no. (effective 1995). Sage Publications, Inc., 2455 Teller Rd., Thousand Oaks, CA 91320. TEL 805-499-0721. FAX 805-499-0871. E-mail: libraries@sagepub.com. (Overseas orders to: Sage Publications Ltd., 6 Bonhill St., London EC2A 4PU, England; Sage Publications India Pvt. Ltd., P.O. Box 4215, New Delhi 110 048, India) Eds. John L. Sullivan, Richard G. Niemi. bk.rev. (back issues avail.) **Document type:** monographic series.
—BLDSC (8069.271900).

QUERSCHNITTE. see *RELIGIONS AND THEOLOGY — Protestant*

300   CC   ISSN 1001-5337
Q4   CODEN: QSDXEI
QUFU SHIFAN DAXUE XUEBAO/QUFU NORMAL UNIVERSITY. JOURNAL. (Text in Chinese) 1964. q. Y8 (foreign $40) (effective 1995). Qufu Shifan Daxue, Xuebao Bianjibu, Qufu, Shandong 273165, People's Republic of China. TEL 0537-4411831. Ed. Li Zhengyin. bk.rev. **Document type:** academic/scholarly publication.
●Also available on CD-ROM.
Description: Contains research papers on mathematics, physics, chemistry, biology, geography, philosophy and history.

RADICAL PHILOSOPHY REVIEW OF BOOKS. see *PHILOSOPHY*

300   FR   ISSN 1150-1367
RAISONS PRATIQUES; epistemologie, sociologie, theorie sociale. 1990. a. price varies. Editions de l' Ecole des Hautes Etudes en Sciences Sociales, 131 bd. St-Michel, 75005 Paris, France. TEL 46-33-51-46. FAX 44-07-08-89. (Dist. by: Centre Interinstitutionnel pour la Diffusion de Publications en Sciences Humaines, 131 bd. St-Michel, 75005 Paris, France. TEL 43-54-47-15. FAX 43-54-80-73)

300   RE   ISSN 0243-0150
RASSEMBLEMENT POUR LA REPUBLIQUE;* organe trimestriel d'informations politiques, economiques et sociales. q. 123, rue de Lille, 75007 Paris, France.

300   UK   ISSN 1043-4631
H62.A1   CODEN: RTSOEG
RATIONALITY AND SOCIETY. 1989. q. £39 to individuals; institutions £107 (effective 1996). Sage Publications Ltd., 6 Bonhill St., London EC2A 4PU, England. FAX 0171-374-8741. E-mail: market@sageltd.co.uk. Ed. Mary Brinton. adv.: B&W page £180; trim 170 x 100; adv. contact: Bernie Folan. circ. 750. (back issues avail.; reprint service avail.) Indexed: Int.Polit.Sci.Abstr., PSI. **Document type:** academic/scholarly publication.
—BLDSC (7295.473000); Faxon; Genuine Article; SWETS; UMI; UnCover. CCC.
Description: Focuses on the growing contributions of rational-action based theory, and the questions and controversies surrounding this growth.

300   UK   ISSN 1353-1190
REACTION!. 1993. 3/yr. (Sep.-Apr.). £11.85 (rest of Europe £17.85; elsewhere £20.85) (effective 1996). Philip Allan Publishers Ltd., Market Pl., Deddington, Oxon. OX15 0SE, England. TEL 01869-338652. FAX 01869-338803. adv. contact: Ceri Jenkins.

300   IT
REALTA SOCIALE D'OGGI; rivista mensile di sintesi e documentazione sociale. 1946. m. Istituto Sociale Ambrosiano, Via della Signora 3, Milan, Italy. abstr.

300   II
RECENT TRENDS IN SOCIAL SCIENCES. 1975. irreg. Rs.24 (foreign $10). Anu Books, Shivaji Rd., Meerut 25001, India. Ed. Dr. Ram Nath Sharma. adv.; bk.rev.

300   MG
RECHERCHE ET CULTURE. 1985. s-a. University of Antananarivo, French Department, B.P. 907, 101 Antananarivo, Madagascar. TEL 26660. Ed. Ginette Ramaroson. circ. 1,000.

300   FR   ISSN 0034-124X
HM3
RECHERCHE SOCIALE. 1965. q. 245 F. (foreign 275 F.) (effective 1996). Fondation pour la Recherche Sociale (FORS), 28 rue Godefroy Cavaignee, 75011 Paris, France. TEL 40-09-15-12. FAX 40-09-15-32. Ed. Roger Benjamin. bk.rev.; bibl.; charts; tr.lit. circ. 1,600. (reprint service avail. from SCH) **Indexed:** Amer.Hist.& Life, Curr.Cont.Africa, Hist.Abstr., P.A.I.S.For.Lang.Ind.
—BLDSC (7307.500000).
Formerly: Etudes et Documents.

RECHERCHES D'HISTOIRE ET DE SCIENCES SOCIALES/STUDIES IN HISTORY AND THE SOCIAL SCIENCES. see *HISTORY*

300   UY   ISSN 0797-0005
REFLEXIONES DEL BATALLISMO. irreg. Revista Reflexiones, Casa del Partido Colorado, Andres Martinez Trueba 1271, Montevideo, Uruguay.

300   RU   ISSN 0135-5538
REGION: EKONOMIKA I SOTSIOLOGIYA; vserosiiskii nauchnyi zhurnal. 1963. q. $44 (effective 1996). Rossiiskaya Akademiya Nauk, Sibirskoe Otdelenie, Institut Ekonomiki, Pr. Akademika Lavrenteva 17, 630090 Novosibirsk, Russia. TEL 3832-353954. (Subscr. to: Rossiiskaya Akademiya Nauk, Sibirskoe Otdelenie, Morskoy pr. 2, 630090 Novosibirsk, Russia. TEL 3832-350570. FAX 3832-356002) Ed. V.E. Seliverstov. bk.rev.; illus. circ. 500. **Indexed:** Amer.Hist.& Life, Hist.Abstr. **Document type:** academic/scholarly publication.
—BLDSC (0140.585840).
Former titles (until 1994): Rossiiskaya Akademiya Nauk. Sibirskoe Otdelenie. Izvestiya. Region: Ekonomika i Sotsiologiya; Akademiya Nauk S.S.S.R. Sibirskoe Otdelenie. Izvestiya. Seriya Region: Ekonomika i Sotsiologiya (ISSN 0868-5169); (until 1989): Akademiya Nauk S.S.S.R. Sibirskoe Otdelenie. Izvestiya. Seriya Ekonomiki i Prikladnoi Sotsiologii (ISSN 0233-7606); (until 1984): Akademiya Nauk S.S.S.R. Sibirskoe Otdelenie. Izvestiya. Seriya Obshchestvennykh Nauk (ISSN 0130-1748)

300   AT   ISSN 0158-7102
REGIONAL JOURNAL OF SOCIAL ISSUES. 1979. a. Aus.$10. Deakin University, Warrnambool, P.O. Box 423, Warrnambool, Vic. 3280, Australia. TEL 055-633-314. FAX 055-633-534. bk.rev. circ. 200. (back issues avail.) **Indexed:** Aus.P.A.I.S.
—UnCover.

300 352.7   US
REGIONAL SCIENCE ASSOCIATION NEWSLETTER. irreg. Regional Science Association International, 1 Observatory, 901 S. Matthews, Urbana, IL 61801. TEL 217-333-8904. **Document type:** newsletter.
Description: Aimed at those interested in the advancement of urban and regional analysis.

RELIGION AND SOCIETY. see *RELIGIONS AND THEOLOGY*

300   BL   ISSN 0103-183X
REMATE DE MALES. 1980. a. exchange basis. Universidade Estadual de Campinas, Instituto de Estudos da Linguagem, Caixa Postal 6045, 13081-970 Campinas SP, Brazil. FAX 55-192-391501. **Document type:** academic/scholarly publication.
Description: Presents studies in Brazilian and Latin American culture and literature.

300 100   SZ
RENCONTRES INTERNATIONALES DE GENEVE. 1947. biennial. 42 SFr. Editions de la Baconniere S.A., P.O. Box 185, CH-2017 Boudry, Switzerland. TEL 038-421004. (reprint service avail. from UMI) **Document type:** proceedings.

RENOVACION. see *POLITICAL SCIENCE*

300   CC   ISSN 1003-5001
RENSHENG YU BANLU/LIFE AND COMPANIONS. (Text in Chinese) 1985. m. Y36. Henan Sheng Shehui Kexue Lianhehui - Henan Society of Social Sciences, No. 9, Fengchan Lu, Zhengzhou, Henan 450002, People's Republic of China. TEL 0371-3933739. FAX 0371-3933739. (Dist. overseas by: China International Book Trading Corp., P.O. Box 2820, Beijing, P.R. China) Ed. Ren Shoushun. circ. 500,000. **Document type:** consumer publication.
Description: Discusses family, marriage, love and related issues.

RENWEN JI SHEHUI KEXUE JIKAN/JOURNAL OF SOCIAL SCIENCES AND PHILOSOPHY. see *PHILOSOPHY*

300   UN   ISSN 0080-1348
REPORTS AND PAPERS IN THE SOCIAL SCIENCES. French edition: Rapports et Documents de Sciences Sociales (ISSN 0251-544X); Spanish edition: Informes y Documentos de Ciencias Sociales (ISSN 0251-4559) 1955. irreg., no.58, 1988. price varies. Unesco, 7-9 Place de Fontenoy, 75700 Paris, France. TEL 45-77-16-10. (Dist. in U.S. by: Unipub, 4611-F Assembly Dr., Lanham, MD 20706-4391)

300 001.3   CH   ISSN 1018-4473
AS455.T259
REPUBLIC OF CHINA. NATIONAL SCIENCE COUNCIL. PROCEEDINGS. PART C: HUMANITIES AND SOCIAL SCIENCES. (Editions in Chinese, English) 1991. s-a. NT.$120($8) National Science Council, 106 Ho-ping E. Rd. Sec.2, Taipei, Taiwan 106, Republic of China. TEL 2-737-7594. FAX 2-737-7248. Ed. Kuo-Shu Yang. (also avail. in microform) **Document type:** proceedings.

RESEARCH IN THE SOCIAL SCIENTIFIC STUDY OF RELIGION. see *RELIGIONS AND THEOLOGY*

RESEARCH JOURNAL: HUMANITIES AND SOCIAL SCIENCES. see *HUMANITIES: COMPREHENSIVE WORKS*

RESEARCH NOTES. see *LAW*

RESOURCES FOR FEMINIST RESEARCH/DOCUMENTATION SUR LA RECHERCHE FEMINISTE. see *WOMEN'S STUDIES*

300   US
RESOURCES ON CONTEMPORARY ISSUES. irreg., no.7, 1995. $40. Pierian Press, Box 1808, Ann Arbor, MI 48106. TEL 313-434-5530; 800-678-2435. FAX 313-434-6409. Ed. Newell Stultz. **Document type:** monographic series.

REVIEW JOURNAL OF PHILOSOPHY AND SOCIAL SCIENCE. see *PHILOSOPHY*

918.503   PE   ISSN 0259-9600
REVISTA ANDINA. 1983. s-a. $50 to individuals (foreign $60); institutions $60 (foreign $75) (effective 1995). Centro de Estudios Regionales Andinos "Bartolome de las Casas", Apdo. 14-0087, Lima 14, Peru. TEL 51-14-223703. FAX 51-14-427894. E-mail: postmaster@cbclim.inv.pe. adv.; bk.rev.; cum.index: 1983-1995. circ. 1,000. (back issues avail.) **Indexed:** Anthropol.Lit., Hisp.Amer.Per.Ind. (1991-).

300   BO
REVISTA BOLIVIANA DE INVESTIGACION. 4/yr. Universidad Autonoma "Gabriel Rene Moreno", Direccion Universitaria de Investigacion, Sta. Cruz, Bolivia.

300   BL   ISSN 0102-6909
H8.P8   CODEN: RBCSEQ
REVISTA BRASILEIRA DE CIENCIAS SOCIAIS. 1986. 3/yr. Associacao Nacional de Pos-Graduacao e Pesquisa em Ciencias Sociais, Avda. Prof. L. Gualberto 315, Sala 116, 05508-900 Sao Paulo, SP, Brazil. **Indexed:** Hisp.Amer.Per.Ind. (1992-).

REVISTA CANARIA DE FILOSOFIA Y CIENCIA SOCIAL. see *PHILOSOPHY*

300   EC   ISSN 0252-8681
REVISTA CIENCIAS SOCIALES. 1977. q. S/250($20) Universidad Central del Ecuador, Escuela de Sociologia, Biblioteca, Ciudad Universitaria, Quito, Ecuador.

300   PO   ISSN 0254-1106
REVISTA CRITICA DE CIENCIAS SOCIAIS. 1978. 3/yr. Esc.3000($35) to individuals; institutions Esc.4500($50). Centro de Estudos Sociais, Faculdade de Economia, Apdo. 3087, 3000 Coimbra, Portugal. TEL 351-39-29076. Ed. Boaventura de Sousa Santos. adv.; bk.rev. circ. 1,500. **Indexed:** Int.Polit.Sci.Abstr., Sociol.Educ.Abstr. **Document type:** academic/scholarly publication.
—BLDSC (7852.095500).

SOCIAL SCIENCES: COMPREHENSIVE WORKS

300   CU
REVISTA CUBANA DE CIENCIAS SOCIALES. 1983. s-a. $12 in S. America; N. America $14; elsewhere $16. (Academia de Ciencias de Cuba, Instituto de Filosofia) Ediciones Cubanas, Obispo No. 527, Apdo. 605, Havana, Cuba. (Alt. addr.: Industria No. 2, Apdo. 2291, Zona 2, Havana, Cuba) Ed. Thalia Fung. circ. 6,000.

300   DR
REVISTA DE CIENCIAS ECONOMICAS Y SOCIALES.* 1972. q. Universidad Autonoma de Santo Domingo, Facultad de Ciencias Economicas y Sociales, Santo Domingo, Dominican Republic. stat.

300   BL   ISSN 0104-0111
AS80.C932
REVISTA DE CIENCIAS HUMANAS. 1992. a. exchange basis. Universidade Federal do Parana, Sector de Ciencias Humanas, Letras e Artes, Travessa Alfredo Bufren, 140, 80020-240 Curitiba, Parana, Brazil. TEL 041-224-6623. Ed. Roberto Gomes. **Document type:** academic/scholarly publication.

300 100   BL   ISSN 0303-9862
H8
REVISTA DE CIENCIAS SOCIAIS. (Text in Portuguese; summaries in English and French) 1970. s-a. Cr.$400($12) or exchange basis. Universidade Federal do Ceara, Departamento de Ciencias Sociais e Filosofia, C.P. 1257, Fortaleza, Ceara, Brazil. Ed. Paulo Elpidio De Menezes Neto. adv.; bk.rev.; bibl.; charts; index, cum.index. circ. 3,000. **Indexed:** Hisp.Amer.Per.Ind. (1970-1982), Lang.& Lang.Behav.Abstr., Psychol.Abstr.

300   PR   ISSN 0034-7817
REVISTA DE CIENCIAS SOCIALES. (Text in Spanish) 1957. s-a. $15 to individuals; institutions $20. Universidad de Puerto Rico, Centro de Investigaciones Sociales, Recinto de Rio Piedras, Apdo. 23345, Estacion UPR, San Juan, PR 00391-3345. Ed.Bd. adv.; bk.rev.; bibl.; charts; illus.; cum.index: 1957-1991. circ. 1,000. **Indexed:** Hisp.Amer.Per.Ind. (1970-), Int.Polit.Sci.Abstr.

300   CR   ISSN 0482-5276
K19
REVISTA DE CIENCIAS SOCIALES. (Title varies each issue) 1956. 4/yr. $40. Editorial de la Universidad de Costa Rica, Apdo. 75-2060, Ciudad Universitaria Rodrigo Facio, San Jose, Costa Rica. TEL 506-25-3133. FAX 506-24-9367. TELEX UNICORI 2544. Dir. Daniel Camacho. **Indexed:** Hisp.Amer.Per.Ind. (1972-), P.A.I.S.For.Lang.Ind. **Document type:** academic/scholarly publication.
—BLDSC (7851.048000).

300   VE
REVISTA DE CIENCIAS SOCIALES. N.S. 1974. irreg. exchange basis. Universidad del Zulia, Facultad de Ciencias Economicas y Sociales, Apdo. 526, Maracaibo 4001A, Venezuela. FAX 061-416025. Ed. N. Urdaneta de Barroso. circ. 1,000. **Indexed:** Amer.Hist.& Life, Hist.Abstr.

300   BL   ISSN 0100-7076
REVISTA DE CULTURA VOZES. Cover title: Vozes Cultura. 1907. 6/yr. $65. Editora Vozes Ltda, Rua Frei Luis 100, Caixa Postal 90023, 25689-900 Petropolis, RJ, Brazil. TEL 0242-43-5112. FAX 0242-42-0692. Ed. Leonardo Boff. adv.; bk.rev.; bibl. **Indexed:** Hisp.Amer.Per.Ind. (1975-).

REVISTA DE DERECHO (CONCEPCION). see *LAW*

REVISTA DE ESTUDIOS DE EGIPTOLOGIA. see *HISTORY* — History Of Africa

300   AG   ISSN 0327-3032
F2911
REVISTA DE ESTUDIOS REGIONALES. 1988. s-a. Arg.$40($40) (effective 1995 & 1996). Universidad Nacional de Cuyo, Facultad de Filosofia y Letras, Centro Universitario, Parque Gral. San Martin, CC 345, 5500 Mendoza, Argentina. TEL 54-61-253010. FAX 54-61-380457. E-mail: gabrielg@logos.edu.ar. Dir. Adolfo Omar Cueto. circ. 500. (diskette format; back issues avail.) **Document type:** academic/scholarly publication.
Description: Presents works in the human and social sciences related to the region of Cuyo.
Refereed Serial

300   BO
REVISTA DE HUMANIDADES, CIENCIAS SOCIALES Y RELACIONES INTERNACIONALES. 2/yr. Universidad Autonoma "Gabriel Rene Moreno", Dirrecion Universitaria de Investigacion, Sta. Cruz, Bolivia.

REVISTA DE INDIAS. see *HISTORY* — History Of North And South America

REVISTA DE LEGISLACION Y DOCUMENTACION EN DERECHO Y CIENCIAS SOCIALES. see *LAW*

300   UY   ISSN 0797-4892
D880
REVISTA DEL SUR. English edition: Third World Resurgence. 1990. m. 2500 N$ per no. (Red del Tercer Mundo) Instituto del Tercer Mundo, Miguel del Corro 1461, 11200 Montevideo, Uruguay. TEL 598-2-49-61-92. TELEX 0402-6105926 GMA LU. Ed. S.M. Mohamed Idris. **Document type:** consumer publication.

300 917.1   SP   ISSN 1132-7839
REVISTA ESPANOLA DE ESTUDIOS CANADIENSES. 1990. irreg. Asociacion de Estudios Canadienses en Espana, Lucano 8, 2o, 4a, 08022 Barcelona, Spain. Ed. Kathleen Firth. **Indexed:** Amer.Hist.& Life (1994-), Hist.Abstr. (1994-).

306   CK   ISSN 0121-2559
REVISTA FORO. 1986. q. $40 (effective 1995). Fundacion Foro Nacional por Colombia, Carrera 3A No. 26-52, A.A. 10141, Bogota, D.E., Colombia. TEL 57-1-2433464. FAX 57-1-2861299. Dir. Pedro Santana. circ. 5,000 (paid). **Document type:** academic/scholarly publication.
Description: Reflects on contemporary ideas in the field of social science.

300   SP   ISSN 0379-0762
REVISTA INTERNACIONAL DE CIENCIAS SOCIALES. 1987. q. 5000 ptas.($45) (developing countries 3000 ptas($27)) (effective 1995 & 1996). Center Unesco de Catalunya, Mallorca, 285, 08037 Barcelona, Spain. TEL 34-3-2075805. FAX 34-3-4575851. E-mail: ecuco@cc.uab.es. Ed. Ali Kazancigil. adv.; bk.rev.; index. circ. 1,300.

REVISTA LATINOAMERICANA DE ESTUDIOS EDUCATIVOS. see *EDUCATION*

REVISTA PASOS. see *RELIGIONS AND THEOLOGY*

300   BL   ISSN 0102-8839
HC188.S3
REVISTA SAO PAULO EM PERSPECTIVA. 1985. 4/yr. $76.10. Fundacao Sistema Estadual de Analise de Dados, Av. Casper Libero 464, 01033 Sao Paulo, Brazil. FAX 011-229-5259. TELEX 011-31390. circ. 2,000.
Formerly (until vol.5, no.2): Fundacao S E A D E. Revista.

300   BO
REVISTA TEMAS ECONOMICOS Y SOCIALES. a. Universidad Autonoma "Gabriel Rene Moreno", Direccion Universitaria de Investigacion, Sta. Cruz, Bolivia.

300   MQ   ISSN 0990-7866
REVUE CARBET; cheminement et destins dans l'oever d'Edouard Glissant. triennial, no.10, 1990. Editions Desormeaux, B.P. 145, Fort de France, Cedex, Martinique. Dir. Alain Anselin.

300   FR   ISSN 1249-7207
REVUE D'EUROPE CENTRALE. 1993. s-a. Centre d'Etudes Germaniques, 8 rue des Ecrivains, 67081 Strasbourg Cedex, France. TEL 88-36-45-14. FAX 88-52-92-28. **Indexed:** Amer.Hist.& Life (1993-), Hist.Abstr. (1993-).

REVUE DE COREE. see *ORIENTAL STUDIES*

300   FR   ISSN 0336-1578
                                     CODEN: RSSEED
REVUE DES SCIENCES SOCIALES DE LA FRANCE DE L'EST. 1972. a. 130 F. Universite de Strasbourg II, 22 rue Descartes, 67084 Strasbourg, France. TEL 88-41-73-17. Ed. Freddy Raphael. bk.rev. **Document type:** academic/scholarly publication.
Description: Covers research in methodology and cultural anthropology and in demographic, economical, and social problems of the eastern region of France and of neighboring Europe.

REVUE INFORMATIQUE ET STATISTIQUE DANS LES SCIENCES HUMAINES. see *COMPUTERS*

300   UN   ISSN 0304-3037
REVUE INTERNATIONALE DES SCIENCES SOCIALES. English edition: International Social Science Journal (ISSN 0020-8701); Spanish edition: Revista Internacional de Ciencias Sociales (ISSN 0379-0762) (Editions also in Arabic, Chinese, Russian) 1949. q. 385 F. (Unesco) Editions Eres, 19, rue Gustave-Courbet, 31400 Toulouse, France. TEL 61-75-15-76. FAX 61-73-52-89. (Subscr. in UK to: Basil Blackwell, 108 Cowley Rd., Oxford OX4 1JF, England; Subscr. in US to: 238 Main St., Cambridge, MA 02142) Ed. A. Kazancigil. adv.; bibl.; charts; index. circ. 1,800. (also avail. in microfilm from UMI) **Indexed:** Abstr.Rural Dev.Trop., CERDIC, Int.Lab.Doc., Int.Polit.Sci.Abstr. **Document type:** academic/scholarly publication.
—SWETS.
Description: Reflects broadly the diversity of theoretical approaches in all subject fields with contributions by leading scholars from various regions of the world.

300   MG
REVUE ITA. 1985. m. Ministry of Social Welfare, B.P. 681, 101 Antananarivo, Madagascar. TEL 23630. Ed. Paulin Rakotoarivony. circ. 500.

300   TI   ISSN 0035-4333
H3
REVUE TUNISIENNE DES SCIENCES SOCIALES. (Text in Arabic and French) q. 2000 din. Universite de Tunis, Centre d'Etudes et de Recherches Economiques et Sociales, 23 rue d'Espagne, Tunis, Tunisia. bk.rev.; charts; stat.; cum.index: 1964-1968. **Indexed:** Curr.Cont.Africa, Int.Lab.Doc., Int.Polit.Sci.Abstr., Lang.& Lang.Behav.Abstr., M.L.A., Popul.Ind.

300   IT   ISSN 0392-1131
RICERCA SOCIALE; quadrimestrale di sociologia urbana, rurale e cooperazione. 1972. 3/yr. L.75000 (foreign L.90000) (effective 1993). (Universita degli Studi di Bologna, Dipartimento di Sociologia) Franco Angeli Editore, Viale Monza 106, 20127 Milan, Italy. TEL 02-2827651. Ed. Achille Ardigo. bibl.

300   IT   ISSN 0035-5623
RISVEGLIO DEL MOLISE E DEL MEZZOGIORNO; di attualita, cultura, economia, politica e problemi meridionali. 1961. m. L.30000($40) Editrice Rismol s.r.l., Via Luigi Arati 25, 00151 Rome, Italy. TEL 06-58-26790. Ed. Franco Romagnuolo. adv.; B&W page L.1500000. illus. circ. 15,000. (back issues avail.)
Description: Deals with current events and problems facing southern Italy.

300   FR
RIVAROL AND POLITICAL. 1951. w. 650 Fr. Editions des Tuileries, 9 Passage des Marais, 75010 Paris, France. TEL 42-06-40-50. FAX 42-38-03-08. Ed. Camille Galic. adv.; bk.rev. circ. 18,000. (also avail. in microfiche) **Document type:** newspaper.
Formerly: Rivarol (ISSN 0035-5666)

300   IT   ISSN 0035-676X
RIVISTA INTERNAZIONALE DI SCIENZE SOCIALI. (Text in English, French, Italian) 1893. q. L.107000 (foreign L.160000 ($120)) (effective 1996). (Universita Cattolica del Sacro Cuore, Istituto di Economia) Vita e Pensiero, Largo Gemelli 1, 20123 Milan, Italy. TEL 39-2-72342310. FAX 39-2-72342260. TELEX 321033-UCATHI-1. Dir. Giancarlo Mazzocchi. adv.; B&W page L.2500000. bk.rev.; bibl.; charts; illus.; stat.; index. circ. 1,050. **Indexed:** Amer.Hist.& Life (until 1985), Hist.Abstr. (until 1985), Int.Polit.Sci.Abstr., Lang.& Lang.Behav.Abstr. **Document type:** academic/scholarly publication.
—SWETS.
Description: Covers various areas in social sciences, with emphasis on economics.

300   US   ISSN 0886-9154
F1405.9
ROCKY MOUNTAIN COUNCIL ON LATIN AMERICAN STUDIES. PROCEEDINGS.* (36th annual meeting: Fort Collins, CO) a. (University of New Mexico, Latin America Institute) Center for Latin American Studies, c/o Theo Crevanna, Albuquerque, NM 87131. Ed. Patricia A. Sullivan. **Document type:** proceedings.

SOCIAL SCIENCES: COMPREHENSIVE WORKS

300   PL   ISSN 0137-4176
ROCZNIKI NAUK SPOLECZNYCH. (Text in Polish; summaries in English) 1949. a. price varies. Katolicki Uniwersytet Lubelski, Towarzystwo Naukowe, Ul. Gliniana 21, 20-616 Lublin, Poland. circ. 820. **Document type:** academic/scholarly publication.

RUSSIAN SOCIAL SCIENCE REVIEW; a journal of translations. see *POLITICAL SCIENCE*

300   UK   ISSN 1350-4649
S E I WORKING PAPERS. 1993. irreg., no.5, 1994. £5. University of Sussex, Sussex European Institute, Arts Bldg., Falmer, Brighton BN1 9QN, England. TEL 01273-678578. FAX 01273-678571. E-mail: sei@sussex.ac.uk. **Document type:** monographic series.
—BLDSC (8218.795200).
Description: Aims to make research results, accounts of work-in-progress and background information available to those concerned with contemporary European issues.

300   US   ISSN 0893-7605
S I R S CRITICAL ISSUES. (Consists of: The AIDS Crisis (ISSN 0893-7613); The Atmosphere Crisis (ISSN 1043-5972)) 1976. a. $85 price varies; each a. supplement $17. Social Issues Resources Series, Box 2348, Boca Raton, FL 33427-2348. TEL 407-994-0079; 800-232-7477. FAX 407-994-4704. (looseleaf format; also avail. in microfiche)
Description: Reprints articles that deal with critical issues from more than 800 U.S. and international periodicals.

300   US   ISSN 1058-1731
S I R S GLOBAL PERSPECTIVES. (Consists of: Economics (ISSN 1058-1758); History (ISSN 1058-174X); Government (ISSN 1058-1774), World Affairs (ISSN 1058-1766)) 1991. a. $280 for 4-vol. set. Social Issues Resources Series, Box 2348, Boca Raton, FL 33427-2348. TEL 407-994-0079; 800-232-7477. FAX 407-994-4704. (looseleaf format; also avail. in microfiche)
Description: Reprints articles from more than 100 international publications; topics explore social issues in current affairs, economics, history, and political science.

300   US   ISSN 0740-3127
S I R S SOCIAL ISSUES. (Consists of 30 vols.) a. price varies; each a. supplement $17. Social Issues Resources Series, Box 2348, Boca Raton, FL 33427-2348. TEL 407-994-0079; 800-232-7477. FAX 407-994-4704. (looseleaf format; also avail. in microfiche)
Description: Reprints articles that explore a wide variety of social issues from more than 800 U.S. and international periodicals.

300   IS   ISSN 0334-5971
S S D A YEDION - NEWSLETTER. (Social Science Data Archives) (Text in Hebrew) 1983. s-a. free. Hebrew University, Faculty of Social Sciences, Mount Scopus, Jerusalem 91905, Israel. TEL 972-2-883007. FAX 972-2-883004. Ed. Michal Peleg. bk.rev. circ. 800. **Document type:** newsletter.
●Also available online.

300   FI   ISSN 0358-7088
S S I D LIAISON BULLETIN. (Social Science Information and Documentation) (Text in English) 1981. irreg. (2-3/yr.) free. Helsinki School of Economics, Runeberginkatu 22-24, 00100 Helsinki, Finland. Ed.Bd. circ. 450. **Indexed:** Int.Polit.Sci.Abstr., LISA.
—BLDSC (5186.210000).

300   301   AU
S W S - RUNDSCHAU. 1961. q. S.290 to individuals; institutions S.490; students S.150. Sozialwissenschaftliche Studiengesellschaft, Maria-Theresien-Str. 9, A-1090 Vienna, Austria. TEL 0222-3173127. FAX 0222-3102238. Ed. C. Haerpfer. adv. contact: Heinz Kienzl. bk.rev.; charts; illus.; stat.; index. circ. 2,500. (back issues avail.) **Indexed:** Lang.& Lang.Behav.Abstr. **Document type:** academic/scholarly publication.
Formerly: Journal fuer Sozialforschung.
Description: Quantative and empirical research in political science, sociology and survey research.

300   US
SAGE LIBRARY OF SOCIAL RESEARCH. 1973. irreg., Dec. 1993. $22.95 (hardcover edition $46) (effective 1994). Sage Publications, Inc., 2455 Teller Rd., Thousand Oaks, CA 91320. TEL 805-499-0721. FAX 805-499-0871. E-mail: libraries@sagepub.com. (Overseas subscr. to: Sage Publications Ltd., 6 Bonhill St., London EC2A 4PU, England; Sage Publications India Pvt. Ltd., P.O. Box 4215, New Delhi, India) (back issues avail.)
Document type: monographic series.

300   US
SAGE UNIVERSITY PAPERS SERIES. (Includes subseries: Quantitative Applications in the Social Sciences (ISSN 0149-192X); Qualitative Research Methods Series (ISSN 0888-5397)) 1976? irreg. Sage Publications, Inc., 2455 Teller Rd., Thousand Oaks, CA 91320. TEL 805-499-0721. FAX 805-499-0871. (Overseas orders to: Sage Publications Ltd., 6 Bonhill St., London EC2A 4PU, England; Sage Publications India Pvt. Ltd., P.O. Box 4215, New Delhi 110 048, India) (back issues avail.) **Document type:** monographic series.
Description: Discusses various aspects of research in the social sciences.

300   KN
SAHOEKWAHAK/SOCIAL SCIENCES. (Text in Korean) bi-m. Academy of Social Sciences, Pyongyang, N. Korea.

SALMAGUNDI; a quarterly of the humanities & social sciences. see *HUMANITIES: COMPREHENSIVE WORKS*

300   BG
SAMAJ NIRIKKHON. English edition: Journal of Social Studies. (Text in Bengali) 1978. q. Tk.152($40) to individuals; institutions Tk.172($48). Centre for Social Studies - Samaj Nirikkhon Kendro, Rm. 1107, Arts Bldg., Dhaka University, Dhaka 1000, Bangladesh. TEL 500016. FAX 880-2-865583. Ed. B.K. Jahangir. cum.index: vols.1-58 (1978-1992). (reprint service avail.) **Document type:** academic/scholarly publication.

300   297   TU   ISSN 1300-2511
SAMANYOLU; uc aylik egitim dergisi - quarterly magazine of the social sciences. (Text and summaries in English, Turkish) 1990. q. TL.40000($15) to individuals; institutions $25. Ozel Samanyolu Erkek Lisesi, 06383 Yenimahalle, Ankara, Turkey. TEL 90-312-3359292. FAX 90-312-3451020. E-mail: ED-ALAN@TRHUN.BITNET. Ed. Atilla Alan. adv.; abstr.; bibl.; illus. **Indexed:** Per.Islam. (1991-). **Document type:** academic/scholarly publication.
Description: Publishes articles in all disciplines of the social sciences, including historiography, education and sociology. Also addresses issues related to the role of religion in modern society.

SAN JOSE STUDIES. see *HUMANITIES: COMPREHENSIVE WORKS*

966.9   NR   ISSN 0331-0523
HC517.N48
SAVANNA; a journal of the environmental & social sciences. (Text and summaries in English) 1972-1979 (vol.8, no.2); resumed 1988. s-a. £N15($18) to individuals; institutions £N25($28). Ahmadu Bello University Press, Private Mail Bag 1094, Zaria, Nigeria. TELEX 75241-ZARABU-NIG. Ed. Audee T. Giwa. adv.; bk.rev.; bibl.; charts; illus.; index. circ. 1,000. **Indexed:** A.I.C.P., Abstr.Rural Dev.Trop., Biol.Abstr., Documentatieblad, Field Crop Abstr., Geo.Abstr., Herb.Abstr., Rural Recreat.Tour.Abstr., Soils & Fert., World Agri.Econ.& Rural Sociol.Abstr. **Document type:** academic/scholarly publication.
—BLDSC (8077.235000); UnCover. **CCC.**
Description: Multidisciplinary journal including bibliographies and articles focusing on the savanna.

300   SW   ISSN 0280-2791
HC59.69
SCANDINAVIAN JOURNAL OF DEVELOPMENT ALTERNATIVES. Variant title: Scandinavian Journal of Developing Countries. 1982. q. $40 to individuals; institutions $75; outside Europe $100. Bethany Books, Sweden, P.O. Box 7444, S-103 91 Stockholm, Sweden. Ed. Franklin Vivekananda. adv.; bk.rev. circ. 2,000. (back issues avail.) **Indexed:** Geo.Abstr., IDA, Int.Lab.Doc., Int.Polit.Sci.Abstr., P.A.I.S., Polit.Sci.Abstr., Rural Devel.Abstr., Sociol.Abstr. **Document type:** academic/scholarly publication.
—BLDSC (8087.505650); Faxon; UnCover.
Description: Devoted to the studies of genuine development related to basic human needs satisfaction such as socio-economic problems, conflict and peace, human rights, migration, environment, North-South relations and anthropological views.
Refereed Serial

SCANDINAVIAN JOURNAL OF SOCIAL MEDICINE. see *MEDICAL SCIENCES*

SCANDINAVIAN JOURNAL OF SOCIAL MEDICINE. SUPPLEMENT. see *MEDICAL SCIENCES*

300   AU
SCHRIFTEN ZUR FRIEDENS- UND KONFLIKTFORSCHUNG. irreg., no.3, 1991. varies. Universitaet Graz, Institut fuer Ethik und Sozialwissenschaft, Halbaerthgasse 2, A-8010 Graz, Austria. **Document type:** monographic series.

SCIENCE DILIMAN. see *SCIENCES: COMPREHENSIVE WORKS*

SCIENCE, TECHNOLOGY & SOCIETY. see *SCIENCES: COMPREHENSIVE WORKS*

300   FR   ISSN 1168-1446
SCIENCES DE LA SOCIETE. 1983. 3/yr. 320 F. in Europe; elsewhere 360 F. (effective 1995-96). Presses Universitaires du Mirail, 56, rue du Taur, 31000 Toulouse, France. TEL 33-61-22-58-31. FAX 33-61-21-84-20. (Co-sponsor: Laboratoire d'Etudes et de Recherches Appliquees en Sciences Sociales) Ed. Robert Boure. adv. contact: Marc Vitse. circ. 1,100. **Document type:** academic/scholarly publication.
Formerly (until 1992): Cahiers du L E R A S S (ISSN 0998-8262)
Description: Thematic issues deal with transformations of society and those of public and private organizations, which is then analysed with interdisciplinary approaches.
Refereed Serial

300   PE   ISSN 0559-1414
H8
SCIENTIA ET PRAXIS.* 1964. Universidad Nacional Mayor de San Marcos, Av. Republica de Chile 295, Lima, Peru.

SCOTTISH CHILD. see *CHILDREN AND YOUTH — About*

300   330   UK   ISSN 0269-5030
HC257.S4
SCOTTISH ECONOMIC AND SOCIAL HISTORY. 1981. a. £15 to individuals (outside the E.U. £16.25 ($27.50)); institutions £30 (outside the E.U. £32.50 ($55)) (effective 1996). 22 George Sq., Edinburgh EH8 9LF, Scotland. TEL 44-131-650-4223. FAX 44-131-662-0053. Eds. A. Durie, C. Whatley. adv. contact: Kathryn MacLean. bk.rev. circ. 400. **Document type:** academic/scholarly publication.
—BLDSC (8206.825000).
Description: Disseminates articls, essays, and reviews on issues relating to Scottish economic and social history.
Refereed Serial

SCRIPTA HIEROSOLYMITANA. see *HUMANITIES: COMPREHENSIVE WORKS*

300   IT
SECONDO RINASCIMENTO; logica e industria della parola. 1992. bi-m. (5/yr.) L.40000 (effective 1992). Editore Spirali-Vel s.r.l., Via Fratelli Gabba 3, 20121 Milan, Italy. TEL 02-805-4417. FAX 02-869-2631. (Subscr. to: Via Bellezza, 11, 20136 Milan, Italy. TEL 02-5831-5871) Ed. Armando Verdiglione. **Document type:** consumer publication.

SOCIAL SCIENCES: COMPREHENSIVE WORKS

300 UN
SELECTIVE INVENTORY OF SOCIAL SCIENCE INFORMATION AND DOCUMENTATION SERVICES. (Text in English, French, Spanish) irreg., 3rd ed., 1988. Unesco, 7 Place de Fontenoy, 75700 Paris, France. TEL 45-77-16-10.

SEMIOTIC REVIEW OF BOOKS. see *HUMANITIES: COMPREHENSIVE WORKS*

300 620 JA ISSN 0386-4243
SENDAI DENPA KOGYO KOTO SENMON GAKKO KENKYU KIYO/SENDAI NATIONAL COLLEGE OF TECHNOLOGY. RESEARCH REPORT. (Text in Japanese; summaries in English, French, Japanese) 1972. a. free. Sendai Denpa Kogyo Koto Senmon Gakko, 1, Kitahara, Kamiayashi, Aoba-ku, Sendai-shi, Miyagi-ken 989-21, Japan. TEL 03-581-6411. charts; index. circ. 270.

300 BL
SERIE NOVAS PERSPECTIVAS. 1982? irreg., latest no.41. price varies. Editora Mercado Aberto Ltda., Rua da Conceicao 165, 90030-030 Porto Alegre RS, Brazil. TEL 55-51-2218595. FAX 55-51-2272829. **Document type:** monographic series.

300 CC
SHANDONG DAXUE XUEBAO (SHEHUI KEXUE BAN)/SHANDONG UNIVERSITY. JOURNAL (SOCIAL SCIENCE EDITION). (Text in Chinese) q. Shandong Daxue, Xuebao Bianjibu, No. 27, Shanda Nanlu, Jinan, Shandong 250100, People's Republic of China. TEL 643861. Ed. Yuan Shishuo. **Document type:** academic/scholarly publication.

300 CC ISSN 1000-5323
SHANDONG GONGYE DAXUE XUEBAO (SHEHUI KEXUE BAN)/SHANDONG INDUSTRIAL UNIVERSITY. JOURNAL (SOCIAL SCIENCE EDITION). (Text in Chinese) q. Shandong Gongye Daxue, Xuebao Bianjibu, No. 33, Jing 10 Lu, Jinan, Shandong, People's Republic of China. TEL 615081. Ed. Wei Bingquan. **Document type:** academic/scholarly publication.

300 CC ISSN 1003-4145
SHANDONG SHEHUI KEXUE/SHANDONG SOCIAL SCIENCES. (Text in Chinese) 1987. bi-m. newsstand price: Y3. Shandong Sheng Shehui Kexue Lianhehui, No. 10, Yuhan Lu, Jinan, Shandong 250002, People's Republic of China. TEL 0531-6915174. Ed. Tao Zi Nian. adv. contact: Luan Xiaoping. bk.rev.; circ. 8,000 (paid). **Document type:** academic/scholarly publication. **Description:** Deals with current research on literature, history, philosophy, econnomics, politics and law.

300 CC ISSN 1001-5973
SHANDONG SHIDA XUEBAO (SHEHUI KEXUE BAN)/SHANDONG NORMAL UNIVERSITY. JOURNAL (SOCIAL SCIENCE EDITION). (Text in Chinese) 1981? bi-m. Y7.20. Shandong Shifan Daxue, Xuebao Bianjibu, Wenhua Donglu, Jinan, Shandong 250014, People's Republic of China. TEL 643711. (Dist. overseas by: China Publications Foreign Trade Corp., P.O. Box 782, Beijing, P.R.C.) **Document type:** academic/scholarly publication. **Description:** Contains research papers on literature, history, philosophy, economics, education, and middle school teaching.

300 CC ISSN 1000-5595
SHANDONG YIKE DAXUE XUEBAO (SHEHUI KEXUE BAN)/SHANDONG UNIVERSITY OF MEDICAL SCIENCES. JOURNAL (SOCIAL SCIENCES EDITION). (Text in Chinese) 1987. q. Shandong Yike Daxue, Xuebao Bianjibu, No. 44, Wenhua Xilu, Jinan, Shandong 250012, People's Republic of China. TEL 0531-2952424. FAX 0531-2953813. TELEX 390007 MED JN CN. (Dist. overseas by: China International Book Trading Corp., P.O. Box 399, Beijing, P.R. China) Ed. Wu Xianglian. circ. 8,000. **Document type:** academic/scholarly publication. **Description:** Covers philosophy, political economy, history, social medicine, medical ethics, medical philosophy, health law, health economics, traditional Chinese medical science.

300 CC
SHANGHAI SHEHUI KEXUEYUAN XUESHU JIKAN/SHANGHAI ACADEMY OF SOCIAL SCIENCES. QUARTERLY JOURNAL. (Text in Chinese) q. $43.10. (Shanghai Shehui Kexueyuan - Shanghai Academy of Social Sciences) Shanghai Shehui Kexueyuan Chubanshe, No. 7, Alley 622, Huaihai Zhonglu, Shanghai 200020, People's Republic of China. (Dist. in US by: China Books & Periodicals, Inc., 2929 24th St., San Francisco, CA 94110. TEL 415-282-2994) **Document type:** academic/scholarly publication.

300 CC
SHANGHAI SHIFAN DAXUE XUEBAO (SHEHUI KEXUE BAN)/SHANGHAI NORMAL UNIVERSITY. JOURNAL (SOCIAL SCIENCE EDITION). (Text in Chinese) 1959. q. Y2 per no. Shanghai Shifan Daxue, Xuebao Bianjibu, 10, Guilin Lu, Shanghai 200234, People's Republic of China. TEL 4700700. (Dist. overseas by: China International Book Trade Corp., Box 399, Beijing, P.R. China) Ed. Wang Bangzuo. circ. 6,000. **Document type:** academic/scholarly publication.

300 100 CC ISSN 1000-5935
SHANXI DAXUE XUEBAO (SHEHUI KEXUE BAN)/SHANXI UNIVERSITY. JOURNAL (SOCIAL SCIENCE EDITION). (Text in Chinese; table of contents in English) q. Y0.80 per no. Shanxi Daxue, Xuebao Bianjibu, Wucheng Lu, Taiyuan, Shanxi 030006, People's Republic of China. Eds. Meng Weizhi, Xu Jiugang. **Document type:** academic/scholarly publication.

301 US ISSN 1054-0695
SHAREDEBATE INTERNATIONAL; a ShareWare diskette magazine. 1990. q. $60 (diskette $20). Applied Foresight, Inc., Box 20607, Bloomington, MN 55420. FAX 612-933-3092. Ed. R.H. Martin. adv.; bk.rev. (also avail. in diskette format)
●Also available online.
Also available on CD-ROM.
Description: Debate forum for PC users by PC users who are concerned about the present and the future.

300 CC ISSN 1004-8804
SHEHUI/SOCIETY. (Text in Chinese; summaries in Chinese, English) m. Y24. Shanghai Daxue, Wenxueyuan - Shanghai University, Liberal Arts College, 574 Xijiangwan Lu, Shanghai 200083, People's Republic of China. TEL 021-6664074. (Subscr. to: 661 Sanmen Rd., Shanghai 200434, P.R. China. TEL 021-5443149) Ed. Wu Shenlin. adv.: page Y4000; adv. contact: Zhang Guibin. index. **Document type:** academic/scholarly publication. **Description:** Covers social theories, cultural and social changes, social psychology and behaviors.

300 CC
SHEHUI GONGZUO YANJIU/SOCIAL AFFAIRS STUDY. (Text in Chinese) q. Zhongguo Minzheng Lilun he Shehui Fuli Yanjiuhui - China Civil Administration Theory and Social Welfare Research Society, 7, Baiguang Lu, Xuanwu-qu, Beijing 100053, People's Republic of China. TEL 365331. Ed. Peng Chuanrong.

300 CC ISSN 0257-5833
SHEHUI KEXUE (SHANGHAI)/SOCIAL SCIENCES. (Text in Chinese) 1980. m. $61.20. (Shanghai Shehui Kexueyuan - Shanghai Academy of Social Sciences) Shanghai Shehui Kexueyuan Chubanshe, No. 7, Alley 622, Huaihai Zhonglu, Shanghai 200020, People's Republic of China. (Dist. in US by: China Books & Periodicals, Inc., 2929 24th St., San Francisco, CA 94110. TEL 415-282-2994) **Document type:** academic/scholarly publication.

300 CC ISSN 1001-6198
SHEHUI KEXUE JIKAN/SOCIAL SCIENCE JOURNAL. (Text in Chinese, English) 1979. bi-m. Y16.80. Liaoning Shehui Kexueyuan - Liaoning Academy of Social Sciences, 86, Taishan Lu, Huanggu Qu, Shenyang, Liaoning 110031, People's Republic of China. TEL 86-24-6807511. FAX 86-24-601899. (Dist. outside China by: China International Book Trading Corp., P.O. Box 399, Beijing, P.R.C.; Dist. in US by: China Books & Periodicals, Inc., 2929 24th St., San Francisco, CA 94110) Ed. Gao Lisheng. bk.rev. circ. 8,000. **Document type:** academic/scholarly publication.
—UnCover.
Description: Publishes academic papers on literature, history, philosophy, sociology and economics pertaining to Northeast China.

300 CC ISSN 1000-4769
SHEHUI KEXUE YANJIU/SOCIAL SCIENCE RESEARCH. (Text in Chinese) 1979. bi-m. Y12. Sichuan Sheng Shehui Kexueyuan - Sichuan Academy of Social Sciences, Qingyang Gong, Chengdu, Sichuan 610072, People's Republic of China. TEL 769347-124. (Dist. outside China by: Guoji Shudian - China International Book Trading Corp., P.O. Box 399, Beijing, P.R.C.) Ed. Liu Changguo. adv.; bk.rev. circ. 3,600. **Document type:** academic/scholarly publication.

300 CC ISSN 0257-0246
SHEHUI KEXUE ZHANXIAN/SOCIAL SCIENCE FRONT. (Text in Chinese) 1978. bi-m. Y27. Jilin Sheng Shehui Kexueyuan - Jilin Academy of Social Sciences, 2-1 Fujin Rd., Changchun, Jilin 130021, People's Republic of China. TEL 0431-652589. (Dist. in U.S. by: China Books & Periodicals, Inc., 2929 24th St., San Francisco, CA 94110. TEL 415-282-2994) Ed. Wang Shenrong. adv.: page $1000; adv. contact: Wang Yuhua. bk.rev.; circ. 5,000 (paid). **Document type:** academic/scholarly publication.

300 CC ISSN 1000-5226
SHENYANG SHIFAN XUEYUAN XUEBAO. SHEHUI KEXUE BAN/SHENYANG TEACHERS COLLEGE. JOURNAL. SOCIAL SCIENCE EDITION. (Text in Chinese; table of contents in English) 1977. q. Y12 (effective 1995 & 1996). Shenyang Shifan Xueyuan, Xuebao Bianjibu - Shenyang Teachers College, Editorial Department, 95, Huanghe Nandajie, Huanggu Qu, Shenyang, Liaoning 110031, People's Republic of China. TEL 6840501. (Dist. outside China by: China Publications Foreign Trade Corp., P.O. Box 782, Beijing, P.R.C.) Ed. Sun Jiguo. adv.; bk.rev. **Document type:** academic/scholarly publication. **Description:** Reflects the scientific researches conducted by the faculties and students of the college.

300 JA ISSN 0388-6859
SHIMANE DAIGAKU HOBUNGAKUBU KIYO. BUNGAKUKA HEN/SHIMANE UNIVERSITY. FACULTY OF LAW AND LITERATURE. MEMOIRS. (Text in English, Japanese) 1973. a. Shimane Daigaku, Hobungakubu - Shimane University, Faculty of Law and Literature, 1060 Nishi-Kawazu-machi, Matsue-shi, Shimane-ken 690, Japan. Ed.Bd. circ. 400. **Document type:** academic/scholarly publication.

SHISO/THOUGHT. see *HUMANITIES: COMPREHENSIVE WORKS*

SHIZUOKA DAIGAKU KYOIKUGAKUBU KENKYU HOKOKU. JINBUN, SHAKAI KAGAKU HEN/SHIZUOKA UNIVERSITY. FACULTY OF EDUCATION. BULLETIN. LIBERAL ARTS AND SOCIAL SCIENCES SERIES. see *HUMANITIES: COMPREHENSIVE WORKS*

300 TH ISSN 0304-226X
DS561
SIAM SOCIETY. JOURNAL. 1904. s-a. $32 to non-member individuals; institutions $80. Siam Society, 131 Asoke Lane, Sukhumvit 21, Bangkok 10110, Thailand. TEL 662-259-4999. FAX 662-258-3491. E-mail: kanitk@nwg.nectec.or.th. adv.; bk.rev.; bibl.; charts; illus.; cum.index: vols. 1-50. circ. 1,500. (reprint service avail. from KTO) Indexed: Amer.Hist.& Life, Bibl.Ling., E.I., Hist.Abstr.
—BLDSC (4876.250000); UnCover.

300 VE ISSN 0254-1645
SIC. 1938. 10/yr. Bs.900($26) (foreign Bs.1000) (effective Jan. 1993). Fundacion Centro Gumilla, Edificio Centro Valores, Local 2, Esq. Luneta, Apdo. 4838, Caracas 1010-A, Venezuela. TEL 582-564-7557. FAX 582-5618205. Ed. Arturo Sosa S.J. adv.; bk.rev.; film rev.; abstr.; bibl.; charts; illus.; stat.; index. circ. 6,500.

300 CC ISSN 0490-6748
SICHUAN DAXUE XUEBAO (SHEHUI KEXUE BAN)/SICHUAN UNIVERSITY. JOURNAL (SOCIAL SCIENCES EDITION). (Text in Chinese; table of contents in English) 1955. q. Y7.20. Sichuan Daxue, Xuebao Bianjibu, Jiuyanqiao, Chengdu, Sichuan 610064, People's Republic of China. (Dist. outside China by: China International Book Trading Corp., P.O. Box 399, Beijing, P.R.C.) Ed. Tian Zuwu. bibl. **Document type:** academic/scholarly publication.

SOCIAL SCIENCES: COMPREHENSIVE WORKS

300 CC ISSN 1000-5315
SICHUAN SHIFAN DAXUE XUEBAO (SHEHUI KEXUE BAN)/SICHUAN NORMAL UNIVERSITY. JOURNAL. (SOCIAL SCIENCE EDITION) 1974. q. Y2 per no. Sichuan Shifan Daxue, Xuebao Bianjibu, Shizishan, Chengdu Shiwai, Chengdu, Sichuan 610068. TEL 028-442612. Ed. Zhu Wenxian. **Document type:** academic/scholarly publication.
  Formerly (until Oct. 1985): Sichuan Teacher's College. Journal.
  Description: Covers philosophy, political science, economics, literature, linguistics, history and law.

300 CC
SICHUAN SHIFAN XUEYUAN XUEBAO (ZHEXUE SHEHUI KEXUE BAN)/SICHUAN NORMAL COLLEGE. JOURNAL. (SOCIAL SCIENCE EDITION). (Text in Chinese) q. Sichuan Shifan Xueyuan, Xuebao Bianjibu, 10, Renmin Xilu, Nanchong, Sichuan 637000, People's Republic of China. TEL 2244-338. (Dist. overseas by: Jiangsu Publications Import & Export Corp., 56 Gao Yun Ling, Nanjing, Jiangsu, P.R.C.) Ed. Yan Zengye. **Document type:** academic/scholarly publication.

SIGNES DU PRESENT. see **BUSINESS AND ECONOMICS**

300 954.9 PK
SINDH QUARTERLY. (Text in English) 1973. q. £35($45) (effective 1994). Sayid Ghulam Mustafa Shah, Ed. & Pub., 36-D Karachi Administration Co-operative Housing Society, Off Shahid Millat Rd., Karachi 8, Pakistan. TEL 43-19-83. adv. contact: M. Ashgar. bk.rev. circ. 1,750. (back issues avail.) **Document type:** academic/scholarly publication.
  Description: Covers the socio-political and economic history of Sindh, Pakistan, and India.

SINTESE. see **PHILOSOPHY**

300 SP ISSN 0213-7577
SINTESIS; revista documental de ciencias sociales iberoamericanas. 1987. 3/yr. 4500 ptas. (Europe 6500 ptas.; elsewhere $70). Asociacion de Investigacion y Especializacion sobre Temas Iberoamericanas, Claudio Coello, 86 4o Dcha., 28006 Madrid, Spain. TEL 91-577-06-40. FAX 91-576-30-70. TELEX 27944 AIETI. Dir. Guadalupe Ruiz-Gimenez. adv.; bk.rev.; bibl. circ. 1,000. **Indexed:** Int.Polit.Sci.Abstr.
  Description: Presents articles and documents on social issues in Latin America. Each issue focuses on a single topic such as European-Latin American relations, economics, the environment, and democracy in Latin America.

SIR ROBERT MADGWICK LECTURE SERIES (NO.). see **HUMANITIES: COMPREHENSIVE WORKS**

300 SP ISSN 0210-0223
H8
SISTEMA. 1973. bi-m. 4300 ptas. (foreign 5200 ptas.). (Instituto de Tecnicas Sociales de la Fundacion Fondo Social Universitario) Fundacion Sistema, Fuencarral, 127, 1o, 28010 Madrid, Spain. TEL 91-448-73-19. FAX 91-448-73-39. Dir. Elias Diaz. adv.; bk.rev.; index. cum.index every 20 nos. circ. 8,000. **Indexed:** Int.Polit.Sci.Abstr., P.A.I.S.For.Lang.Ind.
  —SWETS.
  Description: Covers sociology, political science, philosophy, methodology, and social history.

300 370 SP ISSN 1010-2965
SISTEMA DE INDICADORES SOCIO-ECONOMICOS Y EDUCATIVOS DE LA O E I. 1980. a. 50000 ptas.($500) Organizacion de Estados Iberoamericanos para la Educacion, la Ciencia y la Cultura (OEI), C. Bravo Murillo 38, 28015 Madrid, Spain. TEL 594-43-82. FAX 594-32-86. circ. 1,000. (also avail. in diskette format) **Document type:** directory.
  Formerly: Educacion en Iberoamerica: Sistema de Indicadores Socio-Economicos y Educativos.

300 CC ISSN 0561-7650
SIXIANG ZHANXIAN/IDEOLOGY FRONT. Variant title: Yunnan Daxue Xuebao (Shehui Kexue Ban) - Yunnan University. Journal (Social Sciences). (Text in Chinese; table of contents in English) bi-m. Y0.80 per no. (Yunnan Daxue - Yunnan University) Yunnan Renmin Chubanshe, Qikan Bu - Yunnan People's Publishing House, 100, Shulin Jie, Kunming, Yunnan 650091, People's Republic of China. (Dist. outside China by: China International Book Trading Corp., P.O. Box 399, Beijing, P.R.C.; Editorial addr.: 52, Cuihu Beilu, Kunming, Yunnan 650091, P.R.C.) Ed. Zhou Gengxin. **Document type:** academic/scholarly publication.

300 947 US ISSN 0037-6779
D377.A1
SLAVIC REVIEW. 1941. q. $50 to non-members. American Association for the Advancement of Slavic Studies, Jordan Quad - Acacia Bldg., Stanford University, Stanford, CA 94305-4130. TEL 415-723-9668. FAX 415-725-7737. (Alt. addr.: University of Pennsylvania, Center for Soviet and Eastern European Studies, 636 Williams Hall, Philadelphia, PA 19104-6305) Ed. Elliott Mossman. adv. contact: Richard Frost. bk.rev.; film rev.; bibl.; charts; illus.; index, cum.index: 1941-1964, 1965-1979. circ. 4,500. (also avail. in microform from UMI; reprint service avail. from UMI; back issues avail.) **Indexed:** A.B.C.Pol.Sci., Acad.Ind., Amer.Bibl.Slavic & E.Eur.Stud., Amer.Hist.& Life, Arts & Hum.Cit.Ind., Bibl.Ling., Bk.Rev.Ind. (1990-), Child.Bk.Rev.Ind. (1990-), Hist.Abstr., Hum.Ind., M.L.A., P.A.I.S., Ref.Sour., RILM, Soc.Sci.Ind. (1994-). **Document type:** academic/scholarly publication.
  —BLDSC (8309.385000); Faxon; Genuine Article; SWETS; UMI; UnCover.
  Formerly: American Slavic and East European Review.
  Description: Publishes scholarly articles and essays on all areas of Russian, Eurasian and East European studies.

001.4 US ISSN 0037-7333
AS30 CODEN: SMSNA5
SMITHSONIAN. 1970. m. $22. Smithsonian Institution, Arts & Industries Bldg., 900 Jefferson Dr. S.W., Washington, DC 20560. TEL 202-357-2888. FAX 202-786-2564. Ed. Don Moser. adv.; bk.rev.; illus.; index. circ. 2,100,000. (also avail. in microform from UMI; back issues avail.) **Indexed:** Abr.R.G., Abstr.Anthropol., Acad.Ind., Acid Rain Abstr., Acid Rain Ind., Amer.Hist.& Life, Anthropol.Lit., Arts & Hum.Cit.Ind., Bibl.Engl.Lang.& Lit., Biol.Dig., Bk.Rev.Ind. (1988-), CAD CAM Abstr., Can.B.P.I., Child.Bk.Rev.Ind. (1988-), Child.Lit.Abstr., Curr.Cont., Curr.Lit.Fam.Plan., Deep Sea Res.& Oceanogr.Abstr., Environ.Abstr., Environ.Per.Bibl., Gard.Lit. (1992-), Hist.Abstr., Jun.High.Mag.Abstr., Mag.Ind., Ocean.Abstr., PMR, Pollut.Abstr., R.G., SSCI, Telegen.
  ●Also available online. Vendor(s): Knight-Ridder, Inc.
  —BLDSC (8311.450000); CIS; Faxon; Genuine Article; SWETS; UMI; UnCover.
  Description: Disseminates all aspects of sciences as well as history and the arts.

300 NE ISSN 0928-5083
SOCIAAL WETENSCHAPPELIJKE STUDIES. 1992. irreg. Amsterdam University Press, Prinsengracht 747-751, 1017 JX Amsterdam, Netherlands. TEL 31-20-4200050. FAX 31-20-4203214. **Document type:** monographic series.

370 II ISSN 0037-7627
HN681 CODEN: SOACE2
SOCIAL ACTION. (Text in English) 1951. q. Rs.125($50) Social Action Trust, Lodi Rd., New Delhi 110 003, India. Ed. Sebasti L. Ray. adv.; bk.rev.; index. circ. 2,000. (also avail. in microform from UMI; reprint service avail. from UMI) **Indexed:** Agroforest.Abstr., Bk.Rev.Ind., Forest.Abstr., Int.Lab.Doc., Mult.Ed.Abstr., Rel.Ind.One, Rural Devel.Abstr., Rural Ext.Educ.& Tr.Abstr., Sociol.Educ.Abstr., Stud.Wom.Abstr., World Agri.Econ.& Rural Sociol.Abstr.
  —BLDSC (8318.040000); UMI; UnCover.

301 330 JM ISSN 0037-7651
HN244
SOCIAL AND ECONOMIC STUDIES. 1953. 4/yr. $35 to individuals; sinstitutions & libraries $55. University of the West Indies, Institute of Social and Economic Research, Mona Campus, Kingston 7, Jamaica, W.I. TEL 809-927-1020. FAX 809-927-2409. TELEX 2123 JA. Eds. Elsie Le Franc, Annie Paul. adv.: page $250. bk.rev.; charts; stat.; index. circ. 2,000. (also avail. in microform from UMI; reprint service avail. from ISI,UMI) **Indexed:** A.I.C.P., Amer.Hist.& Life, ASCA, ASSIA, C.R.E.J., Curr.Cont., Geo.Abstr., Hisp.Amer.Per.Ind. (1970-), Hist.Abstr., Hort.Abstr., IDA, Int.Lab.Doc., J.of Econ.Lit., Lang.& Lang.Behav.Abstr., Mult.Ed.Abstr., P.A.I.S., Popul.Ind., Psychol.Abstr., Rural Devel.Abstr., Rural Recreat.Tour.Abstr., Soc.Sci.Ind., Sociol.Abstr., SSCI, Stud.Wom.Abstr., World Agri.Econ.& Rural Sociol.Abstr.
  —BLDSC (8318.045000); Faxon; SWETS; UMI; UnCover.
  Description: Brings information on the current social and economic thinking in the West Indies, Latin America and the rest of the Third World.
  Refereed Serial

SOCIAL CHANGE. see **SOCIOLOGY**

300 960 SA ISSN 0253-3952
HM1
SOCIAL DYNAMICS. 1975. 2/yr. R.45.06 to individuals (foreign R.100); institutions R.85 (foreign R.160) (effective 1994). University of Cape Town, Centre for African Studies, Rondebosch 7700, South Africa. TEL 27-21-6502338. FAX 27-21-650-3724. TELEX 521439. Eds. Jane Taylor, David Bunn. adv.; bk.rev. circ. 300. **Indexed:** Documentatieblad, Geo.Abstr., Ind.S.A.Per., Lang.& Lang.Behav.Abstr., Rural Devel.Abstr., Sociol.Abstr. (1976-), World Agri.Econ.& Rural Sociol.Abstr. **Document type:** academic/scholarly publication.
  —BLDSC (8318.081000); Genuine Article.
  Description: Publishes original multidisciplinary works on topics in African studies, with an emphasis on contemporary theoretical debate.

300 370 US ISSN 0037-7724
H62.A1
SOCIAL EDUCATION. 1937. 7/yr. $55 to non-members. National Council for the Social Studies, 3501 Newark St., N.W., Washington, DC 20016. TEL 202-966-7840. Ed. Salvatore J. Natoli. adv. contact: Peter Stavros. bk.rev.; illus.; index. circ. 24,000. (also avail. in microform from UMI; reprint service avail. from UMI) **Indexed:** Acad.Ind., Adol.Ment.Hlth.Abstr., Amer.Bibl.Slavic & E.Eur.Stud., Amer.Hist.& Life (until 1990), ASSIA, Bk.Rev.Ind. (1965-), C.I.J.E., Child.Bk.Rev.Ind. (1965-), Cont.Pg.Educ., Curr.Cont., Educ.Ind., Educ.Tech.Abstr., Hist.Abstr. (until 1990), HR Rep., Mid.East: Abstr.& Ind., SSCI. **Document type:** academic/scholarly publication.
  —BLDSC (8318.087000); Faxon; SWETS; UMI; UnCover.

SOCIAL EPISTEMOLOGY; a journal of knowledge, culture and policy. see **PHILOSOPHY**

300 UK ISSN 0307-1022
HN1 CODEN: SOHSEH
SOCIAL HISTORY. 1976. 3/yr. £30 (U.S. and Canada $58; rest of world £32) to individuals; institutions £75 (U.S. and Canada $115; rest of world £80). Routledge, 11 New Fetter Ln., London EC4P 4EE, England. TEL 0171-583-9855. FAX 0171-842-2298. TELEX 263398-ROUT-G. E-mail: sample.journals@routledge.com. (Subscr. to: ITPS Ltd., Cheriton House, Andover, Hants SP10 5BE, England. TEL 01264-342919. FAX 01264-342807) Eds. Janet Blackman, Keith Nield. adv.: page £200; trim 135 x 205. bk.rev.; index. circ. 1,000. (reprint service avail. from KTO) **Indexed:** Amer.Hist.& Life, Arts & Hum.Cit.Ind., Hist.Abstr., Soc.Sci.Ind. **Document type:** academic/scholarly publication.
  —BLDSC (8318.092900); Faxon; Genuine Article; SWETS; UnCover. **CCC.**
  Description: Presents articles, reviews and debates of high quality historical analysis without restrictions on place, period or viewpoint.

SOCIAL SCIENCES: COMPREHENSIVE WORKS

361 US ISSN 0037-7767
SOCIAL JUSTICE REVIEW; pioneer American journal of Catholic social action. 1908. bi-m. $15 (foreign $18). Catholic Central Union of America, 3835 Westminster Pl., St. Louis, MO 63108-3409. TEL 314-371-1653. Ed. Rev. John H. Miller. bk.rev.; circ. 4,500 (paid). (also avail. in microfilm) Indexed: ASSIA, Cath.Ind., CERDIC. **Document type:** academic/scholarly publication.
—UMI; UnCover.

300 NE ISSN 0378-8733
HM73
SOCIAL NETWORKS; an international journal of structural analysis. (Text and summaries in English) 1979. q. fl.424($259) (effective 1996). (International Network for Social Network Analysis) North-Holland (Subsidiary of: Elsevier Science B.V.), P.O. Box 211, 1000 AE Amsterdam, Netherlands. TEL 31-20-4853911. FAX 31-20-4853598. TELEX 18582 ESPA NL. (Subscr. in U.S. and Canada to: Elsevier Science Inc., Box 882, Madison Sq. Sta., New York, NY 10159. TEL 212-989-5800. FAX 212-633-3990) Ed. Linton C. Freeman. adv.; bk.rev. (also avail. in microform from UMI; back issues avail.; reprint service avail. from SWZ) Indexed: Anthropol.Lit., ASCA, ASSIA, Curr.Cont., J.Cont.Quant.Meth., Lang.& Lang.Behav.Abstr., Math.R., Mid.East: Abstr.& Ind., Psychol.Abstr. (1982-), Sage Urb.Stud.Abstr., Sci.Cit.Ind., Sociol.Abstr., SSCI. **Document type:** academic/scholarly publication.
—BLDSC (8318.125300); Faxon; Genuine Article; SWETS; UnCover. **CCC.**
Description: Provides a common forum for representatives of anthropology, sociology, history, social psychology, political science, human geography, biology, economics, communications science.
Refereed Serial

300 US ISSN 0192-8686
HN1
SOCIAL PRACTICE. 1978. q. $6. Inter-University Consortium for Ethics and Aesthetics, Box 211, Winfield, IL 60190. Ed. D.A. Strickland.

300 320 US ISSN 0037-783X
H1
SOCIAL RESEARCH; an international journal of political and social science. 1934. q. $24 (foreign $28) to individuals; libraries and institutions $70 (foreign $74). New School for Social Research, 66 W. Twelfth St., New York, NY 10003. TEL 212-229-5776. FAX 212-229-5476. Ed. Arien Mack. adv.; index. circ. 3,000. (also avail. in microform from JAI,UMI,PMC; reprint service avail. from KTO,UMI) Indexed: A.B.C.Pol.Sci., Amer.Bibl.Slavic & E.Eur.Stud., Amer.Hist.& Life, ASCA, ASSIA, Bk.Rev.Ind. (1965-1977), Child.Bk.Rev.Ind. (1965-1977), Commun.Abstr., Curr.Cont., E.I., Hist.Abstr., Int.Polit.Sci.Abstr., Lang.& Lang.Behav.Abstr., Mid.East: Abstr.& Ind., P.A.I.S., Peace Res.Abstr., Polit.Sci.Abstr., Soc.Sci.Ind., Sociol.Abstr., SSCI. **Document type:** academic/scholarly publication.
●Also available online. Vendor(s): University Microfilms International.
—BLDSC (8318.150000); Faxon; SWETS; UMI; UnCover.

300 UK
SOCIAL RESEARCH TODAY. irreg., no.7, 1995. £35. University College London Press Ltd., Gower St., London WC1E 6BT, England. TEL 0171-380-7707. FAX 0171-413-8392. (Dist. in US by: Taylor & Francis Inc., 1900 Frost Rd., Ste. 101, Bristol, PA 19007. TEL 215-785-5800) Ed. Martin Bulmer. adv. contact: Jon Millington. **Document type:** monographic series.

SOCIAL SCIENCE COMPUTER REVIEW. see *EDUCATION — Computer Applications*

300 CN ISSN 0709-7824
SOCIAL SCIENCE FEDERATION OF CANADA. ANNUAL REPORT. (Text in English, French) 1940. a. free. Social Science Federation of Canada, 151 Slater St., Ste. 415, Ottawa, ON K1P 5H3, Canada. TEL 613-238-6112. FAX 613-238-6114. circ. 600. **Document type:** corporate report.
Formerly: Social Science Research Council of Canada. Report (ISSN 0081-0452)

300 US ISSN 0145-5532
H1
SOCIAL SCIENCE HISTORY. 1976. q. $50 to individuals (foreign $62); institutions $75 (foreign $87) (effective 1996). (Social Science History Association) Duke University Press, Box 90660, Durham, NC 27708-0660. TEL 919-687-3600. FAX 919-688-4574. Ed.Bd. adv.; bk.rev. circ. 1,000. (also avail. in microform; reprint service avail. from SCH) Indexed: Amer.Bibl.Slavic & E.Eur.Stud., Amer.Hist.& Life, ASCA, ASSIA, Hist.Abstr., Int.Polit.Sci.Abstr., Lang.& Lang.Behav.Abstr., Sage Pub.Admin.Abstr., Sage Urb.Stud.Abstr., SSCI, Stud.Wom.Abstr. **Document type:** academic/scholarly publication.
—BLDSC (8318.160500); Faxon; Genuine Article; SWETS; UMI; UnCover. **CCC.**
Refereed Serial

300 UK ISSN 0539-0184
H1
SOCIAL SCIENCE INFORMATION. (Text in English, French) 1954; N.S. 1961. q. £42 to individuals; institutions £136 (effective 1996). Sage Publications Ltd., 6 Bonhill St., London EC2A 4PU, England. TEL 0171-374-0645. FAX 0171-374-8741. E-mail: market@sageltd.co.uk. Eds. E. Almasy, A. Rocha-Perazzo. adv.: B&W page £180; trim 170 x 100; adv. contact: Bernie Folan. Indexed: A.B.C.Pol.Sci., Abstr.Rural Dev.Trop., Amer.Hist.& Life, ASSIA, Cont.Pg.Manage., Curr.Cont., Hist.Abstr. (until 1991), Human.Resour.Abstr., IBZ, Int.Polit.Sci.Abstr., Intl.Bibl.S.S.Soc.Cult.Anthro., Lang.& Lang.Behav.Abstr., Psychol.Abstr., Sage Fam.Stud.Abstr., Sage Pub.Admin.Abstr., Sociol.Abstr., SSCI, World Agri.Econ.& Rural Sociol.Abstr. **Document type:** academic/scholarly publication.
—BLDSC (8318.161000); Faxon; SWETS; UnCover.
Formerly: Social Sciences Information - Information sur les Sciences Sociales (ISSN 0037-7864)
Description: Provides a forum for research in social anthropology, sociology of science, social psychology and sociological theory.
Refereed Serial

300 US ISSN 0362-3319
H1
SOCIAL SCIENCE JOURNAL. 1963. q. $70 to individuals (foreign $90); institutions $170 (foreign $190) (effective 1996). J A I Press Inc., 55 Old Post Rd., No. 2, Box 1678, Greenwich, CT 06836-1678. TEL 203-661-7602. FAX 203-661-0792. (Addr. in Europe: J A I Press Ltd., The Courtyard, 28 High St., Hampton Hill, Mddx. TW12 1PD, England. TEL 44-81-943-9296. FAX 44-81-943-9317) Ed. Michael Katovitch. adv.; bk.rev.; bibl.; charts; illus.; stat.; index, cum.index: 1963-68, 1969-72. circ. 2,000. (also avail. in microform from JAI; back issues avail.) Indexed: A.B.C.Pol.Sci. (1994-), Abstr.Soc.Work, Amer.Bibl.Slavic & E.Eur.Stud., Amer.Hist.& Life, ASCA, Chic.Per.Ind., Commun.Abstr., Curr.Cont., Econ.Abstr., Hist.Abstr., Int.Polit.Sci.Abstr., Lang.& Lang.Behav.Abstr., Mult.Ed.Abstr., P.A.I.S., Peace Res.Abstr., Psychol.Abstr. (1984-), Risk Abstr., Sage Pub.Admin.Abstr., Soc.Sci.Ind., Sociol.Abstr., Sociol.Educ.Abstr., SSCI, Stud.Wom.Abstr. **Document type:** academic/scholarly publication.
—BLDSC (8318.162000); Faxon; Genuine Article; SWETS; UMI; UnCover. **CCC.**
Formerly (until 1976): Rocky Mountain Social Science Journal (ISSN 0035-7634)
Description: Includes articles from persons in all fields who have comments to make about the social sciences. Articles may be theoretical, speculative, or heavily armed with statistical data or mathematical models.

300 UK ISSN 0307-0042
SOCIAL SCIENCE MONOGRAPHS. 1975. irreg. price varies. (Board of Celtic Studies) University of Wales Press, 6 Gwennyth St., Cathays, Cardiff CF2 4YD, Wales. TEL 01222-231919. FAX 01222-230908. Ed. Harold Carter. **Document type:** monographic series.

SOCIAL SCIENCE PROBINGS. see *POLITICAL SCIENCE*

300 US ISSN 0038-4941
H1
SOCIAL SCIENCE QUARTERLY. 1920. q. $25 to individuals; institutions $54. (Southwestern Social Science Association) University of Texas Press, Box 7819, Austin, TX 78713. TEL 512-471-4531. FAX 512-320-0668. TELEX 776453 UTEXPRES AUS. E-mail: leah@utpress.ppb.utexas.edu. Ed. Robert Lineberry. adv. contact: Leah Dixon. bk.rev.; abstr.; bibl.; index. circ. 2,900. (also avail. in microform from KTO,UMI; reprint service avail. from SCH,UMI) Indexed: A.B.C.Pol.Sci., Amer.Bibl.Slavic & E.Eur.Stud., Amer.Hist.& Life, ASCA, Asian-Pac.Econ.Lit., ASSIA, Bk.Rev.Ind. (1975-), C.I.J.E., Chic.Per.Ind., Child.Bk.Rev.Ind. (1975-), Commun.Abstr., Crim.Just.Abstr., Curr.Cont., Educ.Admin.Abstr., Energy Ind., Energy Info.Abstr., ERIC, Hist.Abstr., IMFL, Int.Polit.Sci.Abstr., J.of Econ.Abstr., J.of Econ.Lit., Lang.& Lang.Behav.Abstr., Leg.Per., Mid.East: Abstr.& Ind., Mult.Ed.Abstr., P.A.I.S., Polit.Sci.Abstr., Popul.Ind., Psychol.Abstr. (1991-), Res.High.Educ.Abstr., Sage Fam.Stud.Abstr., Sage Pub.Admin.Abstr., Sage Urb.Stud.Abstr., Soc.Sci.Ind., Sociol.Abstr., Sociol.Educ.Abstr., SSCI, Stud.Wom.Abstr., World Agri.Econ.& Rural Sociol.Abstr. **Document type:** academic/scholarly publication.
—BLDSC (8318.167000); Faxon; Genuine Article; SWETS; UMI; UnCover. **CCC.**
Formerly: Southwestern Social Science Quarterly.
Description: Dedicated to developing communication across traditional disciplinary boundaries.

300 US ISSN 0049-089X
H1 CODEN: SSREBG
SOCIAL SCIENCE RESEARCH; a quarterly journal of social science methodology and quantitative research. 1972. q. $210 (foreign $270) (effective 1996). Academic Press, Inc., Journal Division, 525 B St., Ste. 1900, San Diego, CA 92101-4495. TEL 619-230-1840. FAX 619-699-6800. (Subscr. to: Box 620000, Orlando, FL 32891-8340. TEL 800-543-9534) Ed. James D. Wright. adv.; charts; stat.; index. (back issues avail.) Indexed: A.B.C.Pol.Sci., Abstr.Crim.& Pen., Adol.Ment.Hlth.Abstr., Amer.Hist.& Life, ASCA, ASSIA, Crim.Just.Abstr., Curr.Cont., Hist.Abstr., Lang.& Lang.Behav.Abstr., Mid.East: Abstr.& Ind., Mult.Ed.Abstr., Psychol.Abstr. (1972-), Soc.Sci.Ind., Sociol.Educ.Abstr., Sp.Ed.Needs Abstr., SSCI, Stud.Wom.Abstr. **Document type:** academic/scholarly publication.
—BLDSC (8318.170100); Faxon; Genuine Article; SWETS; UnCover. **CCC.**
Description: Illustrates the use of quantitative methods in the empirical solution of substantive problems, and emphasizes those concerned with issues or methods that cut across traditional disciplinary lines.

300 CE
SOCIAL SCIENCE REVIEW. (Text in English) 1979. q. $10 to individuals; institutions $15. Social Science Association of Sri Lanka, 120-10 Wijerama Mawatha, Colombo, Sri Lanka. Indexed: Crim.Just.Abstr., Sri Lanka Sci.Ind.

300 CC ISSN 0252-9203
HC426
SOCIAL SCIENCES IN CHINA. Chinese edition: Zhongguo Shehui Kexue (ISSN 1002-4921) (Text in English) 1980. q. $60. (Zhongguo Shehui Kexueyuan - Chinese Academy of Social Sciences) Shehui Kexue Zazhishe, A-158 Gulou Xidajie, Beijing 100720, People's Republic of China. (Dist. overseas by: China International Book Trading Corp., P.O. Box 399, Beijing, P.R.C.; Dist. in US by: China Books & Periodicals, Inc., 2929 24th St., San Francisco, CA 94110. TEL 415-282-2994) Indexed: ASSIA, Geo.Abstr., Int.Lab.Doc., P.A.I.S., Polit.Sci.Abstr. **Document type:** academic/scholarly publication.
—BLDSC (8318.187400); Faxon; UnCover.
Description: Academic journal on China's history, economics, anthropology and sociology.

SOCIAL SCIENCES IN HEALTH. see *PUBLIC HEALTH AND SAFETY*

SOCIAL SCIENCES: COMPREHENSIVE WORKS

300   UK   ISSN 0957-4026
SOCIAL SCIENCES - NEWS FROM THE E S R C. 1989. bi-m. free. Economic and Social Research Council, Polaris House, North Star Ave., Swindon, Wilts. SN2 1UJ, England. TEL 01973-413122. FAX 01793-413120. Ed. Amy Cavanagh. bk.rev. circ. 12,000. (back issues avail.) **Document type:** newsletter.
—BLDSC (8318.183400).
    Description: Covers all social science topics for professionals in higher-education institutions and in business.

300   II   ISSN 0251-348X
SOCIAL SCIENCES RESEARCH JOURNAL. (Text in English) 1976. 3/yr. Rs.30($6) Panjab University, Arts Block No. 3, Panjab University Campus, Chandigarh 160014, India.

300   II   ISSN 0970-0293
HN681
SOCIAL SCIENTIST. (Text in English) 1972. m. Rs.100 to individuals; institutions Rs.150; students Rs.75 (foreign $50). Tulika Print Communication (P) Ltd., C-20 Qutab Institutional Area (Behind Gutab Hotel), New Delhi 110 016, India. TEL 6862924. FAX 651442. Ed. Prabhat Patnaik. adv.: B&W page Rs.2000. bk.rev.; play rev.; bibl.; charts; illus.; stat.; index. circ. 2,000. (back issues avail.) **Indexed:** Geo.Abstr., Rural Recreat.Tour.Abstr., World Agri.Econ.& Rural Sociol.Abstr.
—UnCover.
    Description: Deals with a variety of current problems: economic policy, educational reform, social change, as well as problems in history, methodology, and social theory.

300   NR   ISSN 0081-0487
SOCIAL SCIENTIST.* 1965. a. University of Ife, Economics Society, Ile-Ife, Nigeria. **Indexed:** Geo.Abstr.

SOCIAL STUDIES OF SCIENCE; an international review of research in the social dimensions of science and technology. see *SCIENCES: COMPREHENSIVE WORKS*

300   375   US   ISSN 0586-6235
THE SOCIAL STUDIES PROFESSIONAL. 1969. 5/yr. membership. National Council for the Social Studies, 3501 Newark St., N.W., Washington, DC 20016. TEL 202-966-7840. bibl. (also avail. in microform from UMI; reprint service avail. from UMI) **Document type:** academic/scholarly publication, newsletter.
—UMI.
    Description: Covers news developments and issues of interest to social studies teachers. Includes calendar of conferences and programs for professional development.

300   US   ISSN 1056-6325
LB1584
SOCIAL STUDIES REVIEW. 1973. 3/yr. $25. California Council for Social Studies, 1255 Vista Grande, Millbrae, CA 94030-2213. TEL 415-692-4830. Ed. Bill Hanna. adv. circ. 2,600. (also avail. in microform from UMI; back issues avail.; reprint service avail. from UMI) **Indexed:** C.I.J.E., Chic.Per.Ind. **Document type:** academic/scholarly publication.
—UMI.
    Description: Thematic bases with relevance to K-12 and college - university education professors of history - social science.

300   NE   ISSN 0037-8097
SOCIALE WETENSCHAPPEN. vol.13, 1970. q. fl.35 (students fl.25). Tilburg University, Faculty of Social Sciences, Postbus 90153, 5000 LE Tilburg, Netherlands. FAX 31-13-66270. E-mail: Mel.vanElteren@hub.nl. Ed. Mel van Elteren. adv.; bk.rev.; charts; stat.; index. circ. 600. **Indexed:** E.I., Key to Econ.Sci. **Document type:** academic/scholarly publication.
—SWETS.
    Refereed Serial

300   UK   ISSN 0966-7040
SOCIALISM OF THE FUTURE. 1992. s-a. £25 to individuals; institutions £50. Pluto Publishing Ltd., 345 Archway Rd., London N6 5AA, England. TEL 081-348-2724. FAX 081-348-9133. Ed. Tom Bottomore. **Document type:** academic/scholarly publication.
—BLDSC (8318.243760).

SOCIALIST PERSPECTIVE; a quarterly journal of social sciences. see *POLITICAL SCIENCE*

300   XO
SOCIALNA POLITIKA. m. Obzor, Spitalska ul. 35, 815 85 Bratislava, Slovakia.

300   AG   ISSN 0327-7712
H8.S7
SOCIEDAD. 1992. s-a. $20 to individuals; institutions $30. Universidad de Buenos Aires, Facultad de Ciencias Sociales, Marcelo T. de Alvear 2230, 1122 Buenos Aires, Argentina. TEL 961-2015. FAX 541-9622531. bk.rev. **Document type:** academic/scholarly publication.

300   CL
SOCIETAS. 1991. s-a.? Academia Chilena de Ciencias Sociales, Politicas y Morales, Clasificador 1349, Correo Central, Santiago, Chile. TEL 331902. Ed. Cristian Zegers Ariztia. circ. 1,000. **Document type:** academic/scholarly publication.

300   913   FR   ISSN 0300-953X
DU1
SOCIETE DES OCEANISTES. JOURNAL. (Text in English and French) 1945. s-a. 300 F. (typically set in Feb. or Mar.). Societe des Oceanistes, Musee de l'Homme, 75116 Paris, France. bk.rev.; bibl.; illus.; cum.index: 1945-1960 in vol.16, 1960-1970 in vol.26. circ. 1,100. (reprint service avail. from SCH) **Indexed:** A.I.C.P., Anthropol.Lit., Bibl.Ling., E.I., So.Pac.Per.Ind.
—Faxon.

300   FR   ISSN 0081-0894
SOCIETE DES OCEANISTES. PUBLICATIONS. 1951. irreg. (typically set in Feb. or Mar.). Societe des Oceanistes, Musee de l'Homme, 75116 Paris, France. bk.rev. 1,100.

300   US   ISSN 0147-2011
H1
SOCIETY; social science & modern society. 1963. bi-m. $48 to individuals (foreign $80); institutions $108 (foreign $140) (effective Aug. 1995). Transaction Publishers, Transaction Periodicals Consortium, Department 3092, Rutgers University, New Brunswick, NJ 08903. TEL 908-445-2280. FAX 908-445-3138. E-mail: ihorowit@gandalf.rutgers.edu. (Dist. addr.: 140 W. Ethel Rd., Units K,L,M, Piscataway, NJ 08854. TEL 908-777-0600. FAX 908-777-0999) Ed. Irving Louis Horowitz. adv. contact: Alicja Garbie. bk.rev.; abstr.; bibl.; charts; illus.; stat.; index, cum.index: vols.1-5. circ. 15,000. (also avail. in microform from UMI,JAI,MIM; back issues avail.; reprint service avail. from UMI) **Indexed:** A.B.C.Pol.Sci., Abstr.Crim.& Pen., Acad.Ind., Amer.Hist.& Life, ASCA, Bk.Rev.Ind. (1976-), C.I.J.E., Child.Bk.Rev.Ind. (1976-), Commun.Abstr., Curr.Cont., Educ.Admin.Abstr., ERIC, Film Lit.Ind. (1973-), Fut.Surv., Hist.Abstr., Lang.& Lang.Behav.Abstr., Mag.Ind., Med.Care Rev., MEDSOC, Mid.East: Abstr.& Ind., P.A.I.S., Peace Res.Abstr., PMR, Polit.Sci.Abstr., PSI, R.G., Sage Pub.Admin.Abstr., Sage Urb.Stud.Abstr., Soc.Work Res.& Abstr., Sociol.Abstr., SSCI, Urb.Aff.Abstr. **Document type:** academic/scholarly publication.
—BLDSC (8319.183000); Faxon; Genuine Article; SWETS; UMI; UnCover. **CCC**.
    Formerly: Trans-Action-Social Science and Modern Society (ISSN 0041-1035)
    Description: Explores and analyzes issues in the social sciences and public policy. Presents new ideas and research findings from all the social sciences for decision-makers and others concerned with trends in modern society.

300   II   ISSN 0970-5279
SOCIETY AND CHANGE. (Text in English) 1980. q. $16. 8B Madhu Gupta Ln., Calcutta 700 012, India. Ed. Buddhadeva Bhattacharyya. **Document type:** academic/scholarly publication.

300.2   II   ISSN 0037-9662
HN681
SOCIETY AND CULTURE.* (Text in English) 1970. s-a. Rs.20($10) Institute of Social Studies, 179 Bipin Behari Ganguly St., Calcutta 12, India. Ed. K.L. Bhowmik. adv.; bk.rev.; bibl.; charts. **Indexed:** Amer.Hist.& Life, Hist.Abstr., Lang.& Lang.Behav.Abstr., Psychol.Abstr.

SOCIETY AND NATURAL RESOURCES. see *ENVIRONMENTAL STUDIES*

SOCIETY & NATURE/KOINONIA KAI PHYSI; the international journal of political ecology. see *ENVIRONMENTAL STUDIES*

300   800   US   ISSN 0891-7477
SOCIETY FOR THE ADVANCEMENT OF SCANDINAVIAN STUDY. NEWS AND NOTES. 1973. q. Ohio State University, Department of German, 314 Cunz Hall, 1841 Millikin Rd., Columbus, OH 43210. TEL 614-292-8687. Ed. Marilyn Johns Blackwell. circ. 700 (controlled).

SOCIO-LEGAL NEWSLETTER. see *LAW*

SOCIOLOGIA (ROME); rivista di scienze storiche e sociali. see *SOCIOLOGY*

300   IT   ISSN 0392-5048
HD6951
SOCIOLOGIA DEL LAVORO. q. L.95000 (foreign L.130000) (effective 1993). (Universita degli Studi di Bologna, Centro Internazionale di Documentazione e Studi sui Problemi del Lavoro) Franco Angeli Editore, Viale Monza 106, 20127 Milan, Italy. TEL 02-2827651. Ed.Bd. **Indexed:** Int.Lab.Doc., Lang.& Lang.Behav.Abstr., Sociol.Abstr. (1981-). **Document type:** academic/scholarly publication.
    Formerly (until 1978): Analisi e Documenti.

300   CH   ISSN 1019-0449
HM7
SOOCHOW JOURNAL OF SOCIOLOGY/DONGWU SHEHUI XUEBAO. 1977. a. $15 per no. Soochow University, Wai Shuang Hsi, Shih Lin, Taipei, Taiwan, Republic of China. FAX 886-02-8812317. (reprint service avail.) **Document type:** academic/scholarly publication.
    Supersedes in part (in 1992): Soochow Journal of Political Science and Sociology (ISSN 0259-3785); Which was formerly: Soochow Journal of Social and Political Sciences.

SOUNDINGS (KNOXVILLE); an interdisciplinary journal. see *HUMANITIES: COMPREHENSIVE WORKS*

300   CE
SOUTH ASIAN REVIEWS AND ABSTRACTS. (Text in English) 1987. 12/yr. $45 in S. Asia; other developing countries $75; elsewhere $150. Marga Institute, Committee on Studies for Cooperation in Development in South Asia, P.O. Box 601, 61 Isipathana Mawatha, Colombo 5, Sri Lanka. TEL 941-585186. FAX 941-580585. TELEX 21642-MARGA-CE. Ed. Godfrey Gunatilleke. **Document type:** abstracting/indexing.
    Formerly: D E V I N S A Abstracts (ISSN 1391-0035)

SOUTH ASIAN SOCIAL SCIENTIST. see *ORIENTAL STUDIES*

SOUTH ASIAN STUDIES. see *ORIENTAL STUDIES*

300   SI   ISSN 0303-8246
SOUTHEAST ASIAN JOURNAL OF SOCIAL SCIENCES. 1968. s-a. S.$48($30) (National University of Singapore, Department of Sociology) Chopmen Publishers, Katong Shopping Centre, Mountbatten Rd., No. 05-28, Singapore 1543, Singapore. TEL 3441495. FAX 3440180. Ed. Peter S.J. Chen. adv.; bk.rev.; illus. circ. 500. **Indexed:** Asian-Pac.Econ.Lit., ASSIA, Bibl.Ling. **Document type:** academic/scholarly publication.
—SWETS; UnCover.
    Incorporates: Southeast Asia Ethnicity and Development Newsletter; **Formerly:** South-East Asian Journal of Sociology.

300   US   ISSN 1047-7942
LB1585
SOUTHERN SOCIAL STUDIES JOURNAL. 1975. s-a. $10. Kentucky Council for the Social Studies, Morehead State University, U.P.O 738, Morehead, KY 40351. TEL 606-783-2765. FAX 606-783-2678. Ed. Kent Freeland. adv.; bk.rev. circ. 500. (back issues avail.) **Indexed:** C.I.J.E. **Document type:** academic/scholarly publication.
    ●Also available online. Vendor(s): Knight-Ridder, Inc., Ovid Technologies.
—BLDSC (8355.644000).
    Formerly (until 1990): Southern Social Studies Quarterly (ISSN 0741-143X)
    Description: Articles of interest to social studies educators of all levels.

300 976.3   US   ISSN 0735-8342
F366
SOUTHERN STUDIES; an interdisciplinary journal of the South. 1961; N.S. 1990. q. $20 (foreign $35). Northwestern State University of Louisiana, Southern Studies Institute, Natchitoches, LA 71497. TEL 318-357-5507. FAX 318-357-6153. Ed. Maxine Taylor. adv.; bk.rev.; bibl.; charts; illus.; index, cum.index: 1962-1966. circ. 400. (also avail. in microform from UMI; reprint service avail. from UMI) **Indexed:** Abstr.Engl.Stud., Amer.Hist.& Life, Hist.Abstr., M.L.A. **Document type:** academic/scholarly publication.
—BLDSC (8356.030000); Faxon; UMI; UnCover.
Formerly (until 1977): Louisiana Studies (ISSN 0024-693X)
Description: Publishes original research in various fields contributing to greater knowledge and understanding of the south.
Refereed Serial

SOZIAL- UND WIRTSCHAFTSHISTORISCHE STUDIEN. see *BUSINESS AND ECONOMICS — Economic Systems And Theories, Economic History*

360   GW   ISSN 0038-609X
HN441
SOZIALER FORTSCHRITT; unabhaengige Zeitschrift fuer Sozialpolitik. 1952. m. DM.158. (Gesellschaft fuer Sozialen Fortschritt E.V., Bonn) Duncker und Humblot GmbH, Postfach 410329, 12113 Berlin, Germany. TEL 030-7900060. FAX 030-79000631. Ed. Eve-Elisabeth Schewe. adv.; bk.rev.; index. **Indexed:** Int.Lab.Doc., P.A.I.S.For.Lang.Ind., World Bibl.Soc.Sec. **Document type:** academic/scholarly publication.
—BLDSC (8361.080000); SWETS. CCC.

300   GW   ISSN 0490-1657
SOZIALGERICHTSBARKEIT. 1953. m. DM.644. Verlag Chmielorz GmbH und Co., Marktplatz 13, 65183 Wiesbaden, Germany. TEL 0611-36098-0. FAX 0611-301303. circ. 966. (back issues avail.) **Indexed:** ELLIS. **Document type:** academic/scholarly publication.
—CCC.

SOZIALPOLITISCHE INFORMATIONEN. see *POLITICAL SCIENCE*

300   GW   ISSN 0175-6559
SOZIALWISSENSCHAFTLICHE LITERATUR RUNDSCHAU; Sozialarbeit-Sozialpaedagogik-Sozialpolitik-soziale Probleme. 1978. s-a. DM.45. Karin Boellert K T-Verlag, Postfach 1406, 4800 Bielefeld, Germany. TEL 0521-885890. Ed.Bd. adv.; bk.rev. circ. 900. **Document type:** academic/scholarly publication, bibliography.

300   SZ
SOZIOOEKONOMISCHE FORSCHUNGEN. 1974. irreg., no.28, 1993. price varies. Paul Haupt AG, Falkenplatz 14, CH-3001 Bern, Switzerland. TEL 031-3012345. FAX 031-3014669. **Document type:** monographic series.

300   PL   ISSN 0867-0412
LA840
SPOLECZENSTWO OTWARTE. 1969. 11/yr. $22. (Ministerstwo Edukacji Narodowej) Centralny Osrodek Doskonalenia Nauczycieli, Al. Ujazdowskie 28, pok. 204, 00-478 Warsaw, Poland. TEL 48-22-213031. (Dist. by: Ars Polona-Ruch, Krakowskie Przedmiescie 7, Warsaw, Poland) Ed. Edward Wieczorek. circ. 10,000. (back issues avail.)
Supersedes: Wychowanie Obywatelskie (ISSN 0512-4263)
Description: Searches for new ideas, democratic ideas as a base of educational reform.

SPORT, EDUCATION AND SOCIETY. see *SPORTS AND GAMES*

SRI LANKA JOURNAL OF HISTORICAL AND SOCIAL STUDIES. see *HISTORY*

954   NE
SRI LANKA STUDIES IN THE HUMANITIES AND THE SOCIAL STUDIES. (Text in English) 1993. irreg. price varies. V U Boekhandel-Uitgeverij B.V., De Boelelaan 1105, 1081 HV Amsterdam, Netherlands. TEL 31-20-6444355. FAX 31-20-6462719. **Document type:** monographic series.

300   II
SRIMANTA SANKARADEVA RESEARCH INSTITUTE JOURNAL. (Text in English) 1990. a. Rs.60. Srimanta Sankaradeva Research Institute, Batadrawa, Nagaon, Assam, India. Ed. Bhaba Prasad Chaliha.

300   YU   ISSN 0081-394X
SRPSKA AKADEMIJA NAUKA I UMETNOSTI. ODELJENJE DRUSTVENIH NAUKA. GLAS. (Text in Serbo-Croatian; summaries in English, French, German or Russian) 1951. irreg. price varies. Srpska Akademija Nauka i Umetnosti, Knez Mihailova 35, 11001 Belgrade, Serbia, Yugoslavia. FAX 38-11-182-825. TELEX 72593 SANU YU. (Dist. by: Prosveta, Terzije 16, Belgrade, Serbia, Yugoslavia) circ. 1,000. **Indexed:** Amer.Hist.& Life, Art & Archaeol.Tech.Abstr., Hist.Abstr., Int.Aerosp.Abstr.

300   YU   ISSN 0081-3982
SRPSKA AKADEMIJA NAUKA I UMETNOSTI. ODELJENJE DRUSTVENIH NAUKA. POSEBNA IZDANJA. (Text in Serbo-Croatian; summaries in English, French, German or Russian) N.S. 1949. irreg. price varies. Srpska Akademija Nauka i Umetnosti, Knez Mihailova 35, 11001 Belgrade, Serbia, Yugoslavia. FAX 38-11-182-825. TELEX 72593 SANU YU. (Dist. by: Prosveta, Terazije 16, Belgrade, Serbia, Yugoslavia) circ. 1,000. **Indexed:** Amer.Hist.& Life, Hist.Abstr.

300 913 720   YU   ISSN 0081-4059
SRPSKA AKADEMIJA NAUKA I UMETNOSTI. ODELJENJE DRUSTVENIH NAUKA. SPOMENIK. (Text in Serbo-Croatian; summaries in English, French, German or Russian) N.S. 1950. irreg. price varies. Srpska Akademija Nauka i Umetnosti, Knez Mihailova 35, 11001 Belgrade, Serbia, Yugoslavia. FAX 38-11-182-825. TELEX 72593 SANU YU. (Dist. by: Prosveta, Terazije 16, Belgrade, Serbia, Yugoslavia) circ. 1,000.

SRPSKA AKADEMIJA NAUKA I UMETNOSTI SPOMENICA. see *HUMANITIES: COMPREHENSIVE WORKS*

SSU YU YEN/THOUGHT AND WORDS; journal of the humanities and social sciences. see *HUMANITIES: COMPREHENSIVE WORKS*

300   US   ISSN 1053-7740
HA203
STATES IN PROFILE. 1990. a. Brizius & Foster, Rd. 1, Box 445D, McConnellsburg, PA 17233. **Indexed:** SRI.

300   IT   ISSN 0392-1735
STUDI GORIZIANI. 1923. s-a. L.12000 per no. Biblioteca Statale Isontina di Gorizia, Via Mameli 12, 34170 Gorizia, Italy. TEL 0481-531802. FAX 0481-531802. Ed. Otello Silvestri. bk.rev.; bibl.; illus. circ. 800.

300   IT
AS221
STUDI URBINATI. SERIE B: SCIENZE UMANE E SOCIALI. N.S. 1950. a. L.95000. (Universita degli Studi di Urbino) Edizioni Quattroventi, Casella Postale 156, 61029 Urbino, Italy. Ed. Carlo Bo. bk.rev.; charts; illus.; index. **Indexed:** Arts & Hum.Cit.Ind., Curr.Cont.
Former titles (until 1988): Studi Urbinati. Serie B: Letteratura, Storia, Filosofia (ISSN 0039-3088); Studi Urbinati. Serie B: Letteratura.

300   US   ISSN 0039-3606
H31
STUDIES IN COMPARATIVE INTERNATIONAL DEVELOPMENT. 1964. q. $62 to individuals (foreign $94); institutions $124 (foreign $156) (effective Aug. 1995). Transaction Publishers, Transaction Periodicals Consortium, Department 3092, Rutgers University, New Brunswick, NJ 08903. TEL 908-445-2280. FAX 908-445-3138. Ed. John D. Martz. circ. 800. (also avail. in microform from MIM,UMI; reprint service avail. from UMI) **Indexed:** A.B.C.Pol.Sci., Amer.Hist.& Life, ASCA, Asian-Pac.Econ.Lit., ASSIA, Curr.Cont., Geo.Abstr., Hisp.Amer.Per.Ind. (1977-), Hist.Abstr., IDA, Int.Lab.Doc., Int.Polit.Sci.Abstr., Lang.& Lang.Behav.Abstr., Mid.East: Abstr.& Ind., Polit.Sci.Abstr., Rural Devel.Abstr., SSCI, World Agri.Econ.& Rural Sociol.Abstr. **Document type:** academic/scholarly publication.
—BLDSC (8490.250000); Faxon; Genuine Article; SWETS; UMI; UnCover. **CCC.**
Description: Performs an interdisciplinary exploration of current issues in development theory and practice.

300   US   ISSN 1024-5286
▼**STUDIES IN CULTURES ORGANIZATIONS & SOCIETIES.** 1995. 2/yr. 46 ECU (effective 1996). Harwood Academic Publishers, c/o International Publishers Distributor, 820 Town Center Dr., Langhorne, PA 19047. TEL 215-750-2642; 800-545-8398. FAX 215-750-6343. (Subscr. to: International Publishers Distributor, P.O. Box 90, Reading, Berkshire RG1 8JL, England. TEL 44-173-456-8316) **Document type:** academic/scholarly publication.

STUDIES IN SOCIAL CHANGE AND DEVELOPMENT. see *SOCIOLOGY*

300   NE   ISSN 0924-428X
STUDIES IN SOCIAL HISTORY. (Text in English) 1976. irreg., vol.14, 1993. price varies. (International Institute for Social History) Kluwer Academic Publishers, Postbus 17, 3300 AA Dordrecht, Netherlands. TEL 31-78-392392. FAX 31-78-392254. TELEX 29245 KAPG NL. (Dist. by: Kluwer Academic Publishers Group, P.O. Box 322, 3300 AH Dordrecht, Netherlands. TEL 31-78-392392. FAX 31-78-546474; N. America dist. addr.: Box 358, Accord Sta., Hingham, MA 02018-0358. TEL 617-871-6600. FAX 617-871-6528) **Document type:** monographic series.
Refereed Serial

300   SJ
SUDAN. ECONOMIC AND SOCIAL RESEARCH COUNCIL OCCASIONAL PAPER. irreg., no.7, 1976. Economic and Social Research Council, P.O. Box 1166, Khartoum, Sudan. bibl.

300   SJ
SUDAN. NATIONAL COUNCIL FOR RESEARCH. ECONOMIC AND SOCIAL RESEARCH COUNCIL BULLETIN. (Text in Arabic, English) 1974. irreg., no.152, 1990. National Council for Research, Economic and Social Research Council, P.O. Box 1166, Khartoum, Sudan. TEL 78805. TELEX 22342 ILIMI. **Indexed:** Rural Devel.Abstr.
Description: Presents papers on specific topics relating to agricultural, industrial, social and theoretical economics issues in the Sudan.

300 338.91   SJ
SUDAN. NATIONAL COUNCIL FOR RESEARCH. ECONOMIC AND SOCIAL RESEARCH COUNCIL RESEARCH METHODS. (Text in Arabic, English) 1983. irreg., no.3, 1989. National Council for Research, Economic and Social Research Council, P.O. Box 1166, Khartoum, Sudan. TEL 78805. TELEX 22342 ILIMI.

300   SJ
SUDAN. NATIONAL COUNCIL FOR RESEARCH. ECONOMIC AND SOCIAL RESEARCH COUNCIL RESEARCH REPORT. (Text in Arabic, English) 1976. irreg., no.42, 1989. National Council for Research, Economic and Social Research Council, P.O. Box 1166, Khartoum, Sudan. TEL 78805. TELEX 22342 ILIMI.
Description: Presents reports on social and economic issues in the Sudan, with emphasis on the impact of modernization programs.

330.9   SJ   ISSN 0377-5828
HC591.S8
SUDAN JOURNAL OF ECONOMIC AND SOCIAL STUDIES. (Text in English) 1974. s-a. $5. (University of Khartoum, Faculty of Economic and Social Studies) Khartoum University Press, PO Box 321, Khartoum, Sudan. Ed. Ahmed A. Ahmed. **Indexed:** Rural Recreat.Tour.Abstr., Soils & Fert., World Agri.Econ.& Rural Sociol.Abstr.

SUDAN RESEARCH INFORMATION BULLETIN. see *HUMANITIES: COMPREHENSIVE WORKS*

300   CH   ISSN 0300-3302
SUN YAT-SEN CULTURAL FOUNDATION BULLETIN/CHUNG SHAN HSUEH SHU WEN HUA CH'I K'AN. (Text in Chinese and English) 1968. s-a. NT.$250($16) per no. Sun Yat-sen Cultural Foundation, No. 23, Lane 13, Yung Kang St., Taipei, Taiwan, Republic of China. charts.

310 300.723   UK
SURVEY METHODS CENTRE. WORKING PAPERS. irreg., no.6. Survey Methods Centre, Social and Community Planning Research, 35 Northampton Sq., London EV1V OAX, England. TEL 0171-250-1866. **Document type:** monographic series.

SOCIAL SCIENCES: COMPREHENSIVE WORKS

300.723   UK
SURVEY METHODS CENTRE NEWSLETTER. 1980. 3/yr. Survey Methods Centre, Social and Community Planning Research, 35 Northampton Sq., London EV1V 0AX, England. TEL 0171-250-1866. **Document type:** newsletter.

300 100   CC   ISSN 1001-4403
SUZHOU DAXUE XUEBAO (ZHEXUE SHEHUI KEXUE BAN)/SUZHOU UNIVERSITY. JOURNAL (PHILOSOPHY AND SOCIAL SCIENCES). (Text in Chinese) 1906. q. Y8($40) Suzhou Daxue - Suzhou University, 1 Shizi Jie, Suzhou, Jiangsu 215006, People's Republic of China. TEL 0512-5223614. FAX 0512-5231918. (Dist. overseas by: China Publications Foreign Trade Corp., P.O. Box 782, Beijing, P.R.C.) Ed. Chen Shaoying. adv.; bk.rev. circ. 2,500. **Document type:** academic/scholarly publication.
    Formerly: Dongwu Daxue. Xuebao.
    Description: Covers the studies of the Chinese language, Chinese and foreign literature, history, law, economics, philosophy, and psychology with special columns featuring the studies of poetry and prose of the Ming and Qing dynasties, Wu culture, and local history of Suzhou.
Refereed Serial

300   US   ISSN 0195-6086
HM1
SYMBOLIC INTERACTION. 1977. q. $70 to individuals (foreign $90); institutions $170 (foreign $190) (effective 1996). (Society for the Study of Symbolic Interaction) J A I Press Inc., 55 Old Post Rd., No. 2, Box 1678, Greenwich, CT 06836-1678. TEL 203-661-7602. FAX 203-661-0792. (Addr. in Europe: J A I Press Ltd., The Courtyard, 28 High St., Hampton Hill, Mddx. TW12 1PD, England. TEL 44-181-943-9296. FAX 44-181-943-9317) Ed. David Maines. (also avail. in microform from UMI; back issues avail.) **Indexed:** ASCA, IMFL, Lang.& Lang.Behav.Abstr., Mid.East: Abstr.& Ind., Psychol.Abstr., Sociol.Abstr. (1977-). **Document type:** academic/scholarly publication.
—BLDSC (8582.080000); Faxon; Genuine Article; SWETS; UnCover. **CCC.**

300 500   HU   ISSN 0865-4824
Q172.5.S95
SYMMETRY: CULTURE AND SCIENCE. 1990. q. $96 to non-members. International Society for the Interdisciplinary Study of Symmetry, c/o Institute for Research Org., P.O. Box 4, 1361 Budapest, Hungary. TEL 361-131-8326. FAX 361-131-3161. Eds. Gyorgy Darvas, Denes Nagy.
—BLDSC (8582.390000).

SYNTHESE LIBRARY; monographs on epistemology, logic, methodology, philosophy of science and of knowledge, and the mathematical methods of social and behavioral sciences. see *PHILOSOPHY*

SYSTEM DYNAMICS REVIEW. see *BUSINESS AND ECONOMICS — Management*

300   PL   ISSN 0860-2212
SZCZECINSKIE ROCZNIKI NAUKOWE, NAUKI SPOLECZNE. Variant title: Annales Scientairum Stetinenses, Nauki Spoleczne. (Text in Polish; summaries in English, Russian) 1986. a. price varies. (Szczecinskie Towarzystwo Naukowe - Szczecin Scientific Society) Ossolineum, Publishing House of the Polish Academy of Sciences, Rynek 9, 50-106 Wroclaw, Poland. TEL 48-71-386-25. FAX 48-71-448-103. TELEX 0712771 OSS PL. Ed. Eugeniusz Mietkiewski. **Document type:** academic/scholarly publication.
    Description: Papers on different research fields by scientists from the region of Szczecin Pomerania.

300   PL   ISSN 0082-1292
SZCZECINSKIE TOWARZYSTWO NAUKOWE. WYDZIAL NAUK SPOLECZNYCH. PRACE. (Text in Polish; summaries in English, German or Russian) 1959. irreg. price varies. (Szczecinskie Towarzystwo Naukowe, Wydzial Nauk Spolecznych) Ossolineum, Publishing House of the Polish Academy of Sciences, Rynek 9, 50-106 Wroclaw, Poland. TEL 48-71-386-25. FAX 48-71-448-103. TELEX 0712771 OSS PL. (Dist. by: Ars Polona, Krakowskie Przedmiescie 7, 00-068 Warsaw, Poland) Ed. E. Mietkiewski. circ. 400.

300   US
TAIWAN YANJIU/TAIWAN STUDY. (Text in Chinese) q. $22.25. China Books & Periodicals, Inc., 2929 24th St., San Francisco, CA 94110. TEL 415-282-2994. FAX 415-282-0994.
    Description: Contains mainland Chinese studies of Taiwan's society.

300 972   PN   ISSN 0494-7061
F1561
TAREAS. 1960. q. $15. Centro de Estudios Latinoamericanos "Justo Arosemena", Apdo. 87-1918, Panama 7, Panama. TEL 507-230028. FAX 507-692032. E-mail: cela@nicarao.apc.org. Ed. Ricaurte Soler. bk.rev. circ. 1,500. (back issues avail.) **Document type:** academic/scholarly publication.

300   HU   ISSN 0133-0381
TARSADALOMTUDOMANYI KOZLEMENYEK. 1974. q. 100 Ft.($29) (Magyar Szocialista Munkaspart (MSZMP), Tarsadalomtudomanyi Intezet) Kossuth Konyvkiado, Steindl Imre u. 6, 1366 Budapest 5, Hungary. bk.rev. **Indexed:** World Agri.Econ.& Rural Sociol.Abstr.

329   US   ISSN 0040-1587
TECHNOCRACY DIGEST. 1934. q. $12. Technocracy Inc., 2475 Harksell Rd., Ferndale, WA 98248. TEL 360-366-1012. (Alt. addr.: Section 1, R.D. 12349, 2946 272nd St., Aldergrove, BC, Canada. TEL 604-856-1535) Ed. Elizabeth Hiebert.
—UnCover.

300   GW   ISSN 0940-9467
▼**TECHNOLOGY STUDIES.** (Text in English) 1994. 2/yr. DM.70 to individuals; institutions DM.140. Walter de Gruyter und Co., Genthiner Str. 13, 10785 Berlin, Germany. TEL 030-26005-0. FAX 030-26005251. TELEX 184027. (U.S. addr.: 200 Saw Mill River Rd., Hawthorne, NY 10532. TEL 914-747-0110) Ed. Urs Gattiker. **Document type:** academic/scholarly publication.

300   SA
TEMPO. m. free to qualified personnel. Human Sciences Research Council, Group: Corporate Communications, Private Bag X41, Pretoria 0001, South Africa. **Document type:** newsletter.
    Description: Discusses official corporate decisions and announces forthcoming activities in and around the different branches of the HSRC.

300   SZ   ISSN 1010-1691
LE TEMPS STRATEGIQUE. (Text in French) 1982. bi-m. 128 SFr. Edipresse SA, 10 rue de l'Arguebuse, CH-1204 Geneva, Switzerland. TEL 022-3282448. (Subscr. to: 33 rue de la Gase, C.P. 930, CH-1001 Lausanne, Switzerland. TEL 021-3493233. FAX 021-3493229) Ed. Claude Monnier. adv.; bk.rev.; bibl.; charts; illus. circ. 6,000. (back issues avail.) **Document type:** academic/scholarly publication.

300   IT   ISSN 0040-392X
D848
TERZO MONDO/THIRD WORLD; rivista trimestrale di studi, ricerche e documentazione sui paesi afro-asiatici e latino-americani. (Text mainly in English, Italian; occasionally in French, Portuguese, Spanish) 1968. q. L.60000($60) (effective 1995 & 1996). Centro Studi Terzo Mondo, Via G. B. Morgagni 39, 20129 Milan, Italy. TEL 39-2-29409041. Ed. Dr. Umberto Melotti. adv. contact: Elena Sala. bk.rev.; abstr.; bibl.; index. circ. 3,500. **Indexed:** Curr.Cont.Africa, Int.Polit.Sci.Abstr. **Document type:** academic/scholarly publication.
—BLDSC (8796.198000).
    Description: Covers the problems of the Third World, with contributions from various social disciplines.

TEXTUAL STUDIES IN CANADA; Canada's journal of cultural literacy. see *LITERARY AND POLITICAL REVIEWS*

THEORIA; a journal of studies in the arts, humanities and social sciences. see *HUMANITIES: COMPREHENSIVE WORKS*

300 100   NE   ISSN 0040-5833
H61   CODEN: THDCBA
THEORY AND DECISION; an international journal for methods and models in the social and decision sciences. 1970. bi-m. fl.713 to institutions; $457 to institutions in U.S. (effective 1996). Kluwer Academic Publishers, Postbus 17, 3300 AA Dordrecht, Netherlands. TEL 31-78-392392. FAX 31-78-392254. TELEX 29245 KAPG NL. E-mail: SERVICES@WKAP.NL. (Dist. by: Kluwer Academic Publishers Group, P.O. Box 322, 3300 AH Dordrecht, Netherlands. TEL 31-78-392392. FAX 31-78-546474; N. America dist. addr.: Box 358, Accord Sta., Hingham, MA 02018-0358. TEL 617-871-6600. FAX 617-871-6528) Ed. Bertrand Munier. adv.; bk.rev. (also avail. in microform from UMI; reprint service avail. from SWZ) **Indexed:** ASCA, Bull.Signal., Commun.Abstr., Curr.Cont., IBR, IBZ, Int.Polit.Sci.Abstr., J.Cont.Quant.Meth., Lang.& Lang.Behav.Abstr., Math.R., Phil.Ind., Psychol.Abstr. (1973-), Ref.Zh., Risk Abstr., Sage Pub.Admin.Abstr., Sociol.Abstr., SSCI, Zent.Math. **Document type:** academic/scholarly publication.
—BLDSC (8814.627000); Ei; Faxon; Genuine Article; SWETS; UMI; UnCover. **CCC.**
    Description: Publishes papers discussing issues related to the engineering of decision making, including intelligence, choice, uncertainty and conflict resolution.
Refereed Serial

300 100   NE   ISSN 0921-3384
THEORY AND DECISION LIBRARY. SERIES A: PHILOSOPHY AND METHODOLOGY OF THE SOCIAL SCIENCES. (Text in English) 1973; N.S. 1987. irreg., vol.18, 1993. price varies. Kluwer Academic Publishers, Postbus 17, 3300 AA Dordrecht, Netherlands. TEL 31-78-392392. FAX 31-78-392254. TELEX 29245 KAPG NL. (Dist. by: Kluwer Academic Publishers Group, P.O. Box 322, 3300 AH Dordrecht, Netherlands. TEL 31-78-392392. FAX 31-78-546474; N. America dist. addr.: Box 358, Accord Sta., Hingham, MA 02018-0358. TEL 617-871-6600. FAX 617-871-6528) (back issues avail.) **Document type:** monographic series.
—BLDSC (8814.628020).
    Supersedes in part (in 1987): Theory and Decision Library (ISSN 0921-3376)
Refereed Serial

THEORY AND DECISION LIBRARY. SERIES B: MATHEMATICAL AND STATISTICAL METHODS. see *MATHEMATICS*

THEORY AND DECISION LIBRARY. SERIES C: GAME THEORY, MATHEMATICAL PROGRAMMING AND OPERATIONS RESEARCH. see *MATHEMATICS — Computer Applications*

THEORY AND DECISION LIBRARY. SERIES D: SYSTEM THEORY, KNOWLEDGE ENGINEERING AND PROBLEM SOLVING. see *COMPUTERS — Cybernetics*

371.3   US   ISSN 0093-3104
H1
THEORY AND RESEARCH IN SOCIAL EDUCATION. Variant title: Theory and Research. 1972. q. $35. National Council for the Social Studies, 3501 Newark St., N.W., Washington, DC 20016-3167. TEL 202-966-7840. FAX 202-966-2061. Ed. Jack R. Fraenkel. adv. contact: Peter Stavros. bk.rev. circ. 900. (also avail. in microform from UMI) **Indexed:** C.I.J.E., Cont.Pg.Educ., Educ.Tech.Abstr., Mult.Ed.Abstr., Psychol.Abstr. (1973-), Sociol.Abstr., Sociol.Educ.Abstr. **Document type:** academic/scholarly publication.
—BLDSC (8814.629000); Faxon; SWETS; UMI; UnCover.
    Description: Covers all aspects of social studies research, including teacher training, instructional strategies, curriculum development, student involvement and social action.

300   US
▼**THEORYSLUT.** 1994. irreg. $3. Box 426965, San Francisco, CA 94142. **Document type:** bulletin.

SOCIAL SCIENCES: COMPREHENSIVE WORKS 5959

300 US ISSN 0273-2599
HC57.7
THIRD WORLD. (Subseries of: S I R S Social Issues (ISSN 0740-3127) 1978. a. price varies; a. supplement $17. Social Issues Resources Series, Box 2348, Boca Raton, FL 33427-2348. TEL 407-994-0079; 800-232-7477. FAX 407-994-4704. (looseleaf format; also avail. in microfiche; back issues avail.)
Description: Reprints articles that explore social, political, and economic conditions in developing nations.

300 CC
TIANFU XINLUN. (Text in Chinese) bi-m. Sichuan Sheng Zhexue Shehui Kexue Lianhehui, 30, Shiye Jie, Building No. 1, Chengdu, Sichuan 610031, People's Republic of China. TEL 661619. Ed. Fu Jiangzhong.

300 NO ISSN 0040-716X
TIDSSKRIFT FOR SAMFUNNSFORSKNING; Norwegian journal of social research. (Text in Scandinavian languages; summaries in English) 1960. bi-m. NOK 565 in Nordic countries; elsewhere $107 (effective 1996). Scandinavian University Press, P.O. Box 2959 Tøyen, N-0608 Oslo, Norway. TEL 47-22-57-54-00. FAX 47-22-57-53-53. (U.S. addr.: Scandinavian University Press, 200 Meacham Ave., Elmont, NY 11003) Ed.Bd. adv.; bk.rev.; bibl.; charts; stat.; index. circ. 1,700. (back issues avail.; reprint service avail. from ISI) **Indexed:** Amer.Hist.& Life, ASCA, Commun.Abstr., Curr.Cont., Hist.Abstr. (until 1991), Lang.& Lang.Behav.Abstr., Sociol.Abstr., Sociol.Educ.Abstr., SSCI, Stud.Wom.Abstr., Tech.Educ.Abstr.
—Genuine Article.
Description: Discusses social issues.

TIJDSCHRIFT GEZONDHEIDSBEVORDERING. see
MEDICAL SCIENCES

TIJDSCHRIFT VOOR ECONOMISCHE EN SOCIALE GEOGRAFIE/NETHERLANDS JOURNAL OF ECONOMIC AND SOCIAL GEOGRAPHY. see GEOGRAPHY

TIJDSCHRIFT VOOR SOCIAAL WETENSCHAPPELIJK ONDERZOEK VAN DE LANDBOUW. see
AGRICULTURE — Agricultural Economics

301 658 NE
TINBERGEN INSTITUTE RESEARCH SERIES. (Text in English) 1991. irreg., vol.62, 1994. price varies. Thesis Publishers, P.O. Box 14791, 1001 LG Amsterdam, Netherlands. TEL 31-20-6255429. FAX 31-20-6203395. E-mail: thesis@thesis.aps.nl. (back issues avail.) **Document type:** monographic series.

TOKAI DAIGAKU KIYO. BUNGAKUBU/TOKAI UNIVERSITY. FACULTY OF LETTERS. BULLETIN. see LITERATURE

300 CC ISSN 1003-0484
TONGYI LUNTAN/UNITED TRIBUNE. (Text in Chinese) 1989. bi-m. $29.10. Tongyi Luntan Zazhishe, 74, Xichen-qu Xishiku Daijie, Beijing 100034, People's Republic of China. TEL 606-3321. (Dist. in US by: China Books & Periodicals, Inc. 2929 24th St., San Francisco, CA 94110. TEL 415-282-2994) Ed. Miu Qun. circ. 10,000.
Description: Covers politics, current affairs, and social and cultural events.

TOPIC (WASHINGTON); a journal of the liberal arts. see
HUMANITIES: COMPREHENSIVE WORKS

300 GY ISSN 1012-8263
TRANSITION. 1978. a. $10. University of Guyana, Faculty of Social Sciences and the Institute of Development Studies, Georgetown, Guyana. TEL 592-22-5409. adv. circ. 500. **Indexed:** IDA.
Document type: academic/scholarly publication.
Description: Progressive multidisciplinary journal of Third World scholarship.

TRANSITIONS; ex-revue des pays de l'est. see
POLITICAL SCIENCE — International Relations

300 SZ ISSN 0082-6022
TRAVAUX DE DROIT, D'ECONOMIQUE DE SOCIOLOGIE ET DE SCIENCES POLITIQUES. (Text in English and French) 1963. irreg., no.170, 1994. price varies. Librairie Droz S.A., 11, rue Massot, CH-1211 Geneva 12, Switzerland. TEL 022-3466666. FAX 022-3472391. Ed. G. Busino. circ. 800.
Document type: monographic series.
—CCC.
Description: Covers research on law, economics, political science and sociology.

300 GW
TUDUV-STUDIEN. REIHE SOZIALWISSENSCHAFTEN. 1976. irreg. price varies. Tuduv Verlagsgesellschaft mbH, Gabelsbergerstr. 15, 8000 Munich 2, Germany. adv.

TURNING POINT 2000. see CONSERVATION

300 US ISSN 0743-748X
THE TWINS LETTER. 1984. q. $25 membership (foreign $30). Twins Foundation, Box 6043, Providence, RI 02940-6043. TEL 401-729-1000. Ed. Kay Cassill. bk.rev.; charts; illus.; cum. index (1984-1992). circ. 2,500. **Document type:** newsletter.
Description: Serves twins, their family, the media, medical and social scientists, and the general public with articles on multiple births.

300 UN ISSN 1012-6511
HC59.69
U N R I S D DISCUSSION PAPER SERIES. (Text in English, ocassionally French, Spanish) 1987. bi-m. $3.50 per no. United Nations Research Institute for Social Development, Reference Centre, Palais des Nations, 1211 Geneva 10, Switzerland. TEL 41-22-798-8400. FAX 41-22-740-0791. TELEX 41 29 62 UNO CH. (back issues avail.) **Indexed:** Geo.Abstr., IDA.
Description: Preliminary documents circulated in a limited number to stimulate discussion and critical comment on topical and pressing social issues such as sustainable development, gender issues, ethnic conflict, political conflict, illicit drugs, crisis-adjustment and social change.
Refereed Serial

300 UN ISSN 1020-0754
HN978
U N R I S D SOCIAL DEVELOPMENT NEWS. (Editions in English, French, Spanish) 1963. biennial. free. United Nations Research Institute for Social Development, Reference Centre, Palais des Nations, CH-1211 Geneva 10, Switzerland. TEL 798-8400. FAX 740-0791. TELEX 412962 UNO CH. circ. 5,500 (3,000 English edition; 1,000 French edition; 1,500 Spanish edition). **Indexed:** Geo.Abstr., IDA, Rural Devel.Abstr. **Document type:** newsletter.
Former titles (until 1994): U N R I S D News (ISSN 1014-8361); (until 1989): United Nations Research Institute for Social Development. Research Notes (ISSN 0258-9834); United Nations Research Institute for Social Development. Report.
Description: Provides updated information on U.N.R.I.S.D. research work.

U S A C. (Universidad de San Carlos de Guatemala) see
SCIENCES: COMPREHENSIVE WORKS

300 800 AT ISSN 1323-1677
▼**U T S REVIEW;** cultural studies and new writing. 1995. 3/yr. Aus.$45 to individuals (Europe & U.S. Aus.$56); institutions Aus.$60 (Europe & U.S. Aus.$72) (effective 1995 & 1996). University of Technology, Sydney, Faculty of Humanities and Social Sciences, P.O. Box 123, Broadway, N.S.W. 2007, Australia. TEL 61-2-3301960. FAX 31-2-3302296. E-mail: s.muecke@uts.edu.au. Eds. Meaghan Morris, Stephen Muecke. (back issues avail.) **Document type:** academic/scholarly publication.
Description: Forum for the critical discussion of academic and creative writing on cultural studies, with a regionalist perspective.
Refereed Serial

300 GW ISSN 0178-1405
UEBERGAENGE. 1983. irreg., vol.29. DM.78. Wilhelm Fink Verlag, Ohmstr. 5, 80802 Munich, Germany. TEL 089-348017. FAX 089-341378. **Document type:** monographic series.

UNDUGU BULLETIN. see EDUCATION

UNITED NATIONS. ECONOMIC AND SOCIAL COUNCIL. ANNEXES. see BUSINESS AND ECONOMICS

UNITED NATIONS ECONOMIC AND SOCIAL COUNCIL. OFFICIAL RECORDS. SUPPLEMENTS AND SPECIAL SUPPLEMENTS. see BUSINESS AND ECONOMICS

UNITED NATIONS ECONOMIC AND SOCIAL COUNCIL. RESOLUTIONS AND DECISIONS. see BUSINESS AND ECONOMICS

UNITED NATIONS ECONOMIC AND SOCIAL COUNCIL. SUMMARY RECORDS OF PLENARY MEETINGS. see BUSINESS AND ECONOMICS

309.2 US ISSN 0091-6234
HC125
U.S. GENERAL ACCOUNTING OFFICE. SOCIAL DEVELOPMENT ACTIVITIES IN LATIN AMERICA PROMOTED BY THE INTER-AMERICAN FOUNDATION: REPORT TO THE CONGRESS BY THE COMPTROLLER GENERAL OF THE UNITED STATES. Key Title: Social Development Activities in Latin America Promoted by the Inter-American Foundation. no longer available. a. U.S. General Accounting Office, Office of Public Affairs, Box 6015, Gaithersburg, MD 20877. TEL 202-275-6241. **Document type:** government publication.

UNIVERSIDAD DE SAN CARLOS. REVISTA; artes - literatura - ciencias humanas. see ART

300 PR
UNIVERSIDAD INTERAMERICANA DE PUERTO RICO. DEPARTAMENTO DE CIENCIAS SOCIALES. REVISTA ANALES.* 1980. a. $6. (Universidad Interamericana, Departamento de Ciencias Sociales) Antillian College Press, P.O. Box 118, Mayaguez, PR 00708. TEL 809-832-3490. Ed. Hector Feliciano. bk.rev. circ. 2,000. **Indexed:** Sociol.Abstr.

300 900 PR
UNIVERSIDAD INTERAMERICANA DE PUERTO RICO. RECINTO DE SAN GERMAN. REVISTA DE CIENCIAS SOCIALES E HISTORIA. ANALES. 1984. a. $6. (Universidad Interamericana de Puerto Rico, Recinto de San German, Revista de Ciencias Sociales e Historia) Antillian College Press, P.O. Box 118, Mayaguez, PR 00708. TEL 809-832-3490. Ed. Gilberto Arroyo.

300 HO ISSN 0252-8770
UNIVERSIDAD NACIONAL AUTONOMA DE HONDURAS. INSTITUTO DE INVESTIGACIONES ECONOMICAS Y SOCIALES. BOLETIN. 1971. m. Universidad Nacional Autonoma de Honduras, Instituto de Investigaciones Economicas y Sociales, Tegucigalpa, Honduras. Ed. Victor Meza. bibl.

300 CL
UNIVERSIDAD TECNICA DEL ESTADO. REVISTA. 1970. irreg. $4. Universidad Tecnica del Estado, Avda. Ecuador 3469, Correo 2, Santiago, Chile. illus.

300 BL ISSN 0020-3874
F2501
UNIVERSIDADE DE SAO PAULO. INSTITUTO DE ESTUDOS BRASILEIROS. REVISTA. 1966. s-a. R.8 per no. or exchange basis. Universidade de Sao Paulo, Instituto de Estudos Brasileiros, Av. Prof. Mello Moraes, Travessa 8, No. 140, 05508-900 Sao Paulo SP, Brazil. TEL 55-11-210-2429. FAX 55-11-818-3143. TELEX 011-36950 USPO BR. Ed. Yedda Dias Lima. bk.rev.; bibl.; charts; illus. circ. 2,000. **Indexed:** Amer.Hist.& Life, Bull.Signal., Hisp.Amer.Per.Ind. (1970-), Hist.Abstr. **Document type:** academic/scholarly publication.
Description: Publishes original articles related to Brazilian studies.

500 BL
UNIVERSIDADE DO AMAZONAS. CENTRO DE PESQUISAS SOCIO-ECONOMICAS. BOLETIM TECNICO INFORMATIVO.* irreg. Universidade do Amazonas, Centro de Pesquisas Socio-Economicas, Rua Jose Paranagua 200, C.P. 348, 69000 Manaus, AM, Brazil.

300 BL ISSN 0103-9024
AS80.U53
UNIVERSIDADE DO AMAZONAS. REVISTA. SERIE: CIENCIAS HUMANAS. 1991. s-a. Cr.$10000($50) or on exchange basis. Universidade do Amazonas, Instituto de Ciencias Humanas e Letras, Estrada do Contorno, 3000, Campus Universitario, 69068 Manaus, Amazonas, Brazil. **Document type:** academic/scholarly publication.

SOCIAL SCIENCES: COMPREHENSIVE WORKS

300 100   BL   ISSN 0041-8870
UNIVERSIDADE FEDERAL DO CEARA. DEPARTAMENTO DE CIENCIAS SOCIAIS E FILOSOFIA. DOCUMENTOS. (Text in English, Portuguese; summaries in English) 1967. irreg., vol.8, no.2, 1977. Cr.$5($6) (Universidade Federal do Ceara, Departamento de Ciencias Sociais e Filosofia) Imprensa Universitaria do Ceara, 2762 Avda. da Universidade, C.P. 1257, Fortaleza BR Ceara, Brazil. Ed. Paulo Elpidio De Menezes Neto. adv.; bk.rev. circ. 2,000.

300   BE   ISSN 0076-1214
UNIVERSITE CATHOLIQUE DE LOUVAIN. ECOLE DES SCIENCES POLITIQUES ET SOCIALES. COLLECTION. * (Text in Flemish, French) 1894. irreg. price varies. 1348 Louvain-la-Neuve, Belgium.

301.3   FR   ISSN 0065-4949
UNIVERSITE D'AIX-MARSEILLE I. CENTRE D'ETUDES DES SOCIETES MEDITERRANEENNES. CAHIERS. 1966. a. Universite d'Aix-Marseille I (Universite de Provence), Centre d'Etudes des Societes Mediterraneennes, Service des Publications, 13621 Aix en Provence, France.

UNIVERSITE DE DROIT, ECONOMIE ET DE SCIENCES SOCIALES DE PARIS. TRAVAUX DU SEMINAIRE DE RECHERCHES SUR LES FAITS ELECTORAUX DE MONSIEUR LE PROFESSEUR ROBERT VILLERS. see LAW

300   FR   ISSN 0563-9727
UNIVERSITE DES SCIENCES SOCIALES DE TOULOUSE. ANNALES. 1953. a. 170 F. Universite de Toulouse I (Sciences Sociales), Bibliotheque Droit, 2 rue Lautman, 31042 Toulouse, France. **Indexed:** Int.Polit.Sci.Abstr.

UNIVERSITEIT VAN STELLENBOSCH. ANNALE. see SCIENCES: COMPREHENSIVE WORKS

300   II   ISSN 0304-2286
UNIVERSITY OF BOMBAY. JOURNAL. (Arts section in Oct.; Science section in Nov.) vol.41, 1972. s-a. Rs.12. University of Bombay, Registrar, Bombay 400032, India. Ed. V. G. Moghe. adv.; bk.rev.; abstr. circ. 400. (back issues avail.) **Indexed:** Amer.Hist.& Life, Hist.Abstr., Math.R.

300   SA   ISSN 0377-8533
UNIVERSITY OF DURBAN-WESTVILLE. INSTITUTE FOR SOCIAL AND ECONOMIC RESEARCH. ANNUAL REPORT. 1973. a. free. University of Durban-Westville, Institute for Social and Economic Research, Private Bag X54001, Durban 4000, South Africa. TEL 27-31-820-2298. FAX 27-31-820-2834. Dir. J.J. McCarthy. circ. 250. **Document type:** corporate report.
—BLDSC (1480.350000).

300 900   US   ISSN 0071-6197
UNIVERSITY OF FLORIDA MONOGRAPHS. SOCIAL SCIENCES. 1959. irreg., no.80, 1983. price varies. University Press of Florida, 15 N.W. 15th St., Gainesville, FL 32611. TEL 904-392-1351. FAX 904-392-7302. Ed.Bd. **Document type:** monographic series.

300   GH
UNIVERSITY OF GHANA. INSTITUTE OF STATISTICAL, SOCIAL AND ECONOMIC RESEARCH. DISCUSSION PAPERS. (Text in English) 1977. irreg., no.26, 1986. University of Ghana, Institute of Statistical, Social and Economic Research, P.O. Box 74, Legon, Ghana.
Description: Examines the dimensions of the problems of childhood survival.

UNIVERSITY OF HONG KONG. CENTRE OF ASIAN STUDIES. OCCASIONAL PAPERS AND MONOGRAPHS. see ORIENTAL STUDIES

UNIVERSITY OF KHARTOUM. DEVELOPMENT STUDIES AND RESEARCH CENTRE. DISCUSSION PAPERS. see BUSINESS AND ECONOMICS — International Development And Assistance

UNIVERSITY OF LONDON. CONTEMPORARY CHINA INSTITUTE. RESEARCH NOTES AND STUDIES. see ORIENTAL STUDIES

325.3   UK   ISSN 0076-0781
UNIVERSITY OF LONDON. INSTITUTE OF COMMONWEALTH STUDIES. ANNUAL REPORT. 1949. a. free. University of London, Institute of Commonwealth Studies, 28 Russell Sq., London WC1B 5DS, England. TEL 0171-580-5876. FAX 0171-255-2160. **Document type:** bulletin.

300   UK   ISSN 0076-0773
UNIVERSITY OF LONDON. INSTITUTE OF COMMONWEALTH STUDIES. COLLECTED SEMINAR PAPERS. 1967. irreg., no.48, 1994. price varies. University of London, Institute of Commonwealth Studies, 28 Russell Sq., London WC1B 5DS, England. TEL 0171-580-5876. FAX 0171-255-2160. circ. 400. **Document type:** monographic series.
—BLDSC (3310.250000).
Description: Papers presented to research seminars.

300   UK
UNIVERSITY OF LONDON. SIR ROBERT MENZIES CENTRE FOR AUSTRALIAN STUDIES. WORKING PAPER. irreg. £15. University of London, Sir Robert Menzies Centre for Australian Studies, 28 Russell Sq., London WC1B 5DS, England. TEL 0171-580-5876. FAX 0171-255-2160. Ed. Tom Griffiths. adv. contact: Brian Matthews. **Document type:** monographic series.

300   SA
UNIVERSITY OF NATAL. CENTRE FOR SOCIAL AND DEVELOPMENT STUDIES. ANNUAL REPORT AND CATALOGUE OF PUBLICATIONS. 1959. a. free. University of Natal, Centre for Social and Development Studies, King George V Ave., Durban 4001, South Africa. TEL 27-31-2602361. FAX 27-31-2602359. TELEX 6-21231 SA. Ed. S. Bekker. circ. 150. **Document type:** corporate report.
Former titles: University of Natal. Centre for Social and Development Studies. Annual Report; University of Natal. Centre for Applied Social Research. Annual Report; University of Natal. Institute for Social Research. Annual Report (ISSN 0070-7759)

300   US   ISSN 0734-5976
UNIVERSITY OF NEW MEXICO. LATIN AMERICAN INSTITUTE. RESEARCH PAPER SERIES. 1979. irreg., no.19, 1987. University of New Mexico, Latin American Institute, 801 Yale N.E., Albuquerque, NM 87131. TEL 505-277-6839. FAX 505-277-5989. bibl.; charts; stat.; index. circ. 800. **Document type:** academic/scholarly publication.
Formerly (until 1981): University of New Mexico. Latin American Institute. Working Paper (ISSN 0737-2019)

UNIVERSITY OF NEW SOUTH WALES. FACULTY HANDBOOKS: ARTS AND SOCIAL SCIENCES. see ART

300   US
UNIVERSITY OF NORTH CAROLINA, CHAPEL HILL. INSTITUTE FOR RESEARCH IN SOCIAL SCIENCE. TECHNICAL PAPERS. 1977. irreg., no.7, 1983. I R S S Publications, Manning Hall 026A, Chapel Hill, NC 27514. TEL 919-962-2211. Ed. Angell Beza.

300   US
UNIVERSITY OF NORTH CAROLINA, CHAPEL HILL. INSTITUTE FOR RESEARCH IN SOCIAL SCIENCE. WORKING PAPERS IN METHODOLOGY. 1967. irreg., no.10, 1978. I R S S Publications, Manning Hall 026A, Chapel Hill, NC 27514. Ed. Angell Beza.

300 001.3   PH   ISSN 0047-5742
AS539.5
UNIVERSITY OF SANTO TOMAS. GRADUATE SCHOOL. JOURNAL OF GRADUATE RESEARCH. Variant title: University of Santo Tomas Journal of Graduate Research. (Text in English) 1971. s-a. $10 to individuals; free to students. (University of Santo Tomas, Graduate School) Santo Tomas University Press, Espana St., Manila 1008, Philippines. TEL 632-731-3101. FAX 632-732-7486. Ed. Elena P. Polo. bk.rev.; bibl.; illus.; charts. circ. 1,500.
—UnCover.

300 375   AT   ISSN 1036-0727
UNIVERSITY OF TECHNOLOGY, SYDNEY. FACULTY OF SOCIAL SCIENCES HANDBOOK. 1990. a. Aus.$5 (foreign Aus.$10). University of Technology, Sydney, P.O. Box 123, City Campus, Broadway, N.S.W. 2007, Australia. TEL 02-330-1990. FAX 02-330-1551. circ. 3,000.
Description: Contains detailed information on the faculty, schools staff, courses, the media center, centers for information studies, publications, and information management.

300   TR
UNIVERSITY OF THE WEST INDIES, TRINIDAD. INSTITUTE OF SOCIAL & ECONOMIC RESEARCH. OCCASIONAL PAPERS: GENERAL SERIES. 1977. irreg. price varies. University of the West Indies, Institute of Social & Economic Research, St. Augustine, Trinidad & Tobago, W.I. Ed. Jack Harewood. charts; stat. circ. 220. (back issues avail.)

300   JA   ISSN 0563-8054
UNIVERSITY OF TOKYO. INSTITUTE OF SOCIAL SCIENCE. ANNALS. * (Text in English) 1953. a. free to research and educational institutions. University of Tokyo, Institute of Social Science - Tokyo Daigaku Shakai Kagaku Kenkyujo, 7-3-1 Hongo, Bunkyo-ku, Tokyo 113, Japan. circ. 200.
—BLDSC (1027.900000); UnCover.
Formerly: Social Science Abstracts.

301.4   US
UNIVERSITY OF WISCONSIN AT MADISON. INSTITUTE FOR RESEARCH ON POVERTY. MONOGRAPH SERIES. 1970. irreg., no.32, 1986. (University of Wisconsin at Madison, Institute for Research on Poverty) Academic Press, Inc., 525 B St., Ste. 1900, San Diego, CA 92101-4495. TEL 619-231-0973. FAX 619-699-6715. (Subscr. to: Order Dept., 6277 Sea Harbor Dr., 4th Fl., Orlando, FL 32887. TEL 800-321-5068) (reprint service avail. from ISI) **Document type:** monographic series.

301.45   US   ISSN 0084-0769
UNIVERSITY OF WISCONSIN AT MADISON. INSTITUTE FOR RESEARCH ON POVERTY. REPRINT SERIES. 1966. irreg. $25. University of Wisconsin at Madison, Institute for Research on Poverty, 3412 Social Sciences Bldg., 1180 Observatory Dr., Madison, WI 53706. TEL 608-262-6358. (reprint service avail.) **Document type:** monographic series, academic/scholarly publication.

301.4   US   ISSN 0275-2980
UNIVERSITY OF WISCONSIN AT MADISON. INSTITUTE FOR RESEARCH ON POVERTY. SPECIAL REPORT SERIES. 1966. irreg. price varies. University of Wisconsin at Madison, Institute for Research on Poverty, 3412 Social Science Bldg., 1180 Observatory Dr., Madison, WI 53706. TEL 608-262-6358. **Document type:** monographic series.
Description: Summarizes Institute projects, prepared for government agencies, committees or commissions.

301.4   US
UNIVERSITY OF WISCONSIN, MADISON. INSTITUTE FOR RESEARCH ON POVERTY. DISCUSSION PAPER SERIES. 1967. irreg. $40. University of Wisconsin at Madison, Institute for Research on Poverty, 3412 Social Science Bldg., 1180 Observatory Dr., Madison, WI 53706. TEL 608-262-6358. **Document type:** monographic series.

300   XO
UNIVERZITA KOMENSKEHO. USTAV MARXIZMU-LENINIZMU. ZBORNIK: VEDECKY KOMUNIZMUS. (Text in Slovak; summaries in German, Russian) 1978. a. exchange basis. Univerzita Komenskeho, Ustav Marxizmu-Leninizmu, c/o Study and Information Center, Safarikovo nam. 6, 818 06 Bratislava, Slovakia. Ed. Peter Kulasik. circ. 450.

URBAN AFFAIRS. see HOUSING AND URBAN PLANNING

URBAN AFFAIRS REVIEW. see HOUSING AND URBAN PLANNING

URBAN HISTORY. see HISTORY — History Of Europe

URBAN INSTITUTE. ANNUAL REPORT. see BUSINESS AND ECONOMICS

URBAN INSTITUTE. POLICY AND RESEARCH REPORT. see BUSINESS AND ECONOMICS

SOCIAL SCIENCES: COMPREHENSIVE WORKS

300   US   ISSN 0732-7277
URBAN RESEARCH REVIEW. 1974. s-a. free. Howard University, Institute for Urban Affairs and Research, 2900 Van Ness St., N.W., Washington, DC 20008. TEL 202-806-8770. Ed. Lula A. Beatty. bk.rev. circ. 3,000. (back issues avail.) **Indexed:** Urb.Aff.Abstr., Vert.File Ind.
   Description: Social science newsletter for the dissemination of research findings.

UTAFITI; journal of the faculty of arts and social science. see LITERATURE

300   AT
V C E POLITICAL AND INTERNATIONAL STUDIES PAPERS. s-a. Aus.$40 to non-members; members Aus.$30. Victorian Association of Social Studies Teachers Inc., 217-225 Church St., Richmond, Vic. 3121, Australia. TEL 61-3-94287400. FAX 61-3-94280313.
   Former titles: Journal for Students of V C E Political and International Studies & Journal for Students of Year 12 Politics.

300   NP   ISSN 0887-2023
VEDIC GLOBE. (Text in English) 1982. q. $120. Siveast Consultants, Inc., USA, P.O. Box 8510, Kathmandu, Nepal. Ed. C.V. Ramasastry. circ. 500. (looseleaf format)
   Description: Features socio-economic aspects including folklore stories of the Southeastern countries.

VERHALTENSTHERAPIE UND PSYCHOSOZIALE PRAXIS. see PSYCHOLOGY

300   US
VERITAS; The world's best kept secrets. 1988. q. free. Box 10041, Silver Spring, MD 20914. TEL 301-593-1686. Ed. Abraham H. Kalish. circ. 1,000. **Document type:** newsletter.
   Description: Provides a forum for specific solutions to economic and social problems.

VICTORIAN STUDIES; a journal of the humanities, arts and sciences. see HUMANITIES: COMPREHENSIVE WORKS

VIDYA BHARATHI. see HUMANITIES: COMPREHENSIVE WORKS

300   CE
VIDYODAYA JOURNAL OF SOCIAL SCIENCE. (Text in English, Sinhalese and Tamil) 1968. s-a. Rs.100($10) University of Sri Jayewardenepura, Nugegoda, Sri Lanka. TEL 55-2695. FAX 55-2604. Ed.Bd. bk.rev.; bibl.; charts; illus.; stat.; index, cum.index. circ. 1,000. **Indexed:** Sci.Cit.Ind., Sri Lanka Sci.Ind.
   Supersedes in part (in Jul. 1987): Vidyodaya (ISSN 0042-532X)

330 300   GW   ISSN 0340-8728
VIERTELJAHRSCHRIFT FUER SOZIAL- UND WIRTSCHAFTSGESCHICHTE. (Text in English, German) 1903. 4/yr. DM.148 (supplements priced individually). Franz Steiner Verlag Wiesbaden GmbH, Birkenwaldstr. 44, 70191 Stuttgart, Germany. TEL 0711-2582-0. FAX 0711-2582390. (Subscr. to: Postfach 101061, 70009 Stuttgart, Germany) Ed.Bd. adv.; bk.rev.; cum.index: vols.21-50 (1928-1963). circ. 1,100. (back issues avail.; reprint service avail. from SCH) **Indexed:** Amer.Hist.& Life, Hist.Abstr., P.A.I.S.For.Lang.Ind. **Document type:** academic/scholarly publication.
   —BLDSC (9235.910150); SWETS.

330 300   GW   ISSN 0341-0846
VIERTELJAHRSCHRIFT FUER SOZIAL- UND WIRTSCHAFTSGESCHICHTE. BEIHEFTE. irreg., vol.121, 1995. price varies. Franz Steiner Verlag Wiesbaden GmbH, Birkenwaldstr. 44, 70191 Stuttgart, Germany. TEL 0711-2582-0. FAX 0711-2582390. (Subscr. to: Postfach 101061, 70009 Stuttgart, Germany) Ed.Bd. **Document type:** monographic series.

300   VN   ISSN 1013-4328
VIETNAM SOCIAL SCIENCES. French edition: Viet Nam Sciences Sociales (ISSN 1017-5423) (Text in English) 1984. q. Viet-Nam Institute of Social Science, 27 Tran Xuan Soan, Hanoi, Socialist Republic of Vietnam. TEL 52031. Ed. Nguyen Huu Thanh.

VIETNAMESE STUDIES. see HISTORY — History Of Asia

300   US   ISSN 0507-1305
H1   CODEN: VSSJF5
VIRGINIA SOCIAL SCIENCE JOURNAL. 1966. a. $15 to individuals; institution price varies. Virginia Social Science Association, c/o Thomas Bertsch, Man. Ed., Marketing Department, James Madison University, Harrisonburg, VA 22807. FAX 703-568-2754. Eds. Greg Weiss, Daniel Larsen. circ. 300 (paid). (back issues avail.) **Document type:** academic/scholarly publication.
   Description: Provides original research articles on social science issues.

300 060   FR   ISSN 0083-6672
VISTI IZ SARSELIU. (Text in Ukrainian) 1963. irreg., no.31-32, 1988. $5. Societe Scientifique Sevcenko, 29, rue des Bauves, 95200 Sarcelles, France. Ed. Athanas Figol. bk.rev. circ. 1,000.

VITA SOCIALE. see RELIGIONS AND THEOLOGY — Roman Catholic

VITAL ISSUES; the journal of African American speeches. see POLITICAL SCIENCE

VIVANT UNIVERS; revue de la promotion humaine et chretienne en Afrique et dans le monde. see POLITICAL SCIENCE — International Relations

300   GW   ISSN 0173-1955
VON DEUTSCHLAND NACH AMERIKA. irreg., vol.8, 1994. price varies. Franz Steiner Verlag Wiesbaden GmbH, Birkenwaldstr. 44, 70191 Stuttgart, Germany. TEL 0711-2582-0. FAX 0711-2582390. (Subscr. to: Postfach 101061, 70009 Stuttgart, Germany) Ed. Guenter Moltmann. **Document type:** monographic series.

VYBER NOVINEK BRNENSKYCH KNIHOVEN. SERIE C: CLOVEK A SPOLECNOST. see BIBLIOGRAPHIES

330 331.8 300   GW   ISSN 0342-300X
HC281
W S I MITTEILUNGEN. 1948. m. DM.144. (Deutscher Gewerkschaftsbund, Wirtschafts- und Sozialwissenschaftliches Institut) Bund-Verlag GmbH, Postfach 900840, 51118 Cologne, Germany. Ed. Mario Helfert. adv.; bk.rev.; charts; stat.; index. circ. 6,500. **Indexed:** ELLIS, P.A.I.S.For.Lang.Ind., World Bibl.Soc.Sec. **Document type:** bulletin.
   —BLDSC (9364.930000); SWETS. **CCC.**
   Formerly: W W I Mitteilungen (ISSN 0042-9872)

300   GW   ISSN 0174-3120
W Z B - MITTEILUNGEN. 1978. q. free. Wissenschaftszentrum Berlin fuer Sozialforschung, Reichpietschufer 50, 10785 Berlin, Germany. TEL 030-25491509. FAX 030-25491684. TELEX 308897-WZB-D. Ed. Burckhard Wiebe. circ. 11,000. (back issues avail.) **Document type:** newsletter.

300 600   GW
W Z B PAPERS. irreg. (approx. 100/yr.). Wissenschaftszentrum Berlin fuer Sozialforschung, Reichpietschufer 50, 10785 Berlin, Germany. TEL 030-25491-0. FAX 030-25491684. TELEX 308897-WZB-D. **Document type:** academic/scholarly publication, monographic series.
   Refereed Serial

300   CC
WAIGUO WENTI YANJIU. (Text in Chinese) 1980. q. Y2 per no. Dongbei Shifan Daxue, Riben Yanjiusuo - Northeast Normal University, Institute of Japanese Studies, 110, Stalin St., Changchun, Jilin 130024, People's Republic of China. TEL 0431-685085. (Dist. overseas by: China International Book Trading Corp., P.O. Box 399, Beijing, P.R. China) Ed. Song Shaoying. bk.rev. **Document type:** academic/scholarly publication.
   Description: Covers economics, politics, history, philosophy, education, and international relations in Northeast Asia.

300   US   ISSN 1069-8043
WAR AND SOCIETY SERIES. 1993. irreg., latest vol.2. Gordon and Breach Science Publishers, c/o International Publishers Distributor, 820 Town Center Dr., Langhorne, PA 19047. TEL 215-750-2642; 800-545-8398. FAX 215-750-6343. (Subscr. to: International Publishers Distributor, P.o. Box 90, Reading, Berkshire RG1 8JL, England. TEL 44-173-456-8316) Eds. S. Reyna, R. Downs. (reprint service avail. from SCH) **Document type:** monographic series.

300 895.1   CC   ISSN 1002-9869
WENSHI ZHISHI/KNOWLEDGE OF LITERATURE AND HISTORY. (Text in Chinese) 1981. m. Y24($63) Zhonghua Shuju - Zhonghua Book Company, 36 Wangfujing Jie, Beijing 100710, People's Republic of China. TEL 513-4923. FAX 513-4902. (Dist. in US by: China Books & Periodicals, Inc., 2929 24th St., San Francisco, CA 94110. TEL 415-282-2994) Eds. Li Kan, Chai Jianhong. bk.rev.; abstr.; bibl.; charts; illus.; index. circ. 70,000. (also avail. in microfiche)
   Description: Concerns Chinese literature and history.

300   US   ISSN 0081-8682
WEST GEORGIA COLLEGE STUDIES IN THE SOCIAL SCIENCES. 1962. a. $5. West Georgia College, School of Arts and Sciences, Carrollton, GA 30118-0001. TEL 404-836-6505. FAX 404-836-6717. Ed. Francis Conner. adv.; bk.rev.; bibl. circ. 500. (back issues avail.) **Indexed:** Amer.Hist.& Life, Hist.Abstr. **Document type:** academic/scholarly publication.
   —BLDSC (9298.940900).
   Description: Provides a forum to discuss ideas of noted scholars in the social sciences.

320 378 371.42   UK
WHICH DEGREE. SOCIAL SCIENCES, BUSINESS, EDUCATION. 1968? a. £16.99 (5 vol. set £75). (Careers Research and Advisory Centre) Hobsons Publishing plc., Bateman St., Cambridge CB2 1LZ, England. TEL 01223-354551. FAX 01223-323154. TELEX 81546 HOBCAM G. (Orders to: Biblios Publishers' Distribution Services Ltd., Star Rd., Partridge Green, W. Sussex RH13 8LD, England. TEL 01403-710851. FAX 01403-711143) **Document type:** directory.
   Description: Guides students and career counselors to degree programs in business, education, and the social sciences, with concise course descriptions.

300   GW
WISSENSCHAFT VOM MENSCHEN; Jahrbuch der internationalen Erich-Fromm-Gesellschaft. 1990. a. (Internationale Erich-Fromm-Gesellschaft) Lit Verlag, Dieckstr. 56, 48145 Muenster, Germany. TEL 0251-231972. **Document type:** academic/scholarly publication.

300   GW   ISSN 0342-8990
WOCHENSCHAU FUER POLITISCHE ERZIEHUNG, SOZIAL- UND GEMEINSCHAFTSKUNDE. AUSGABE FUER SEKUNDARSTUFE I. 1949. 7/yr. DM.80.30. Wochenschau Verlag GmbH, Adolf-Damaschke-Str. 103-105, 65824 Schwalbach, Germany. TEL 06196-84010. FAX 06196-86060. Ed. Bernward Debus. bk.rev.; index. **Document type:** academic/scholarly publication.

300   GW   ISSN 0342-8974
WOCHENSCHAU FUER POLITISCHE ERZIEHUNG, SOZIAL- UND GEMEINSCHAFTSKUNDE. AUSGABE FUER SEKUNDARSTUFE II. 1949. 7/yr. DM.80.30. Wochenschau Verlag GmbH, Adolf-Damaschke-Str. 103-105, 65824 Schwalbach, Germany. TEL 06196-84010. FAX 06196-86060. Ed. Ursula Buch. adv.; bk.rev.; charts; illus.; stat.; index. (back issues avail.) **Document type:** academic/scholarly publication.

320.5   AT   ISSN 0311-5801
WOMEN'S ELECTORAL LOBBY (W.A.) BROADSHEET. 1975. 11/yr. Aus.$30. Women's Electoral Lobby (W.A.), P.O. Box 8215, Perth Business Centre, W.A. 6849, Australia. TEL 61-9-328-2407. Ed.Bd. bk.rev.; bibl.; circ. 300 (paid). **Document type:** newsletter.

300 960   US   ISSN 0281-6814
GN643
WORKING PAPERS IN AFRICAN STUDIES. 1976. irreg., no.193, 1995. $4 per no. Boston University, African Studies Center, 270 Bay State Rd., Boston, MA 02215. TEL 617-353-7306. FAX 617-353-4975.

300 371.3 900   US   ISSN 0193-7871
WORLD EAGLE; the monthly social studies resource. 1977. 10/yr. $59.95. World Eagle, Inc., 111 King St., Littleton, MA 01460-1527. TEL 508-486-9180. FAX 508-486-9652. Ed. Martine L. Crandall-Hollick. illus.; maps; stat.; index.
   Description: Presents comparative information for use as a resource and reference tool for social studies teachers, libraries and medical centers.

SOCIAL SCIENCES: COMPREHENSIVE WORKS

116 303.4   US   ISSN 1043-9331
WORLD FUTURES GENERAL EVOLUTION STUDIES. 1990. irreg., latest vol.15. (General Evolution Research Group) Gordon & Breach Science Publishers, c/o International Publishers Distributor, 820 Town Center Dr., Langhorne, PA 19047. TEL 215-750-2642. FAX 215-750-6343. (Subscr. to: International Publishers Distributor, P.O. Box 90, Reading, Berkshire RG1 8JL, England. TEL 44-173-456-8316) Ed. Ervin Laszlo. Document type: monographic series.

WORLD MEETINGS: SOCIAL & BEHAVIORAL SCIENCES, HUMAN SERVICES AND MANAGEMENT. see *MEETINGS AND CONGRESSES*

300   CC   ISSN 1000-5374
WUHAN DAXUE XUEBAO (ZHEXUE SHEHUI KEXUE BAN)/WUHAN UNIVERSITY. JOURNAL (PHILOSOPHY AND SOCIAL SCIENCE EDITION). (Text in Chinese; table of contents in English) bi-m. Y24. Wuhan Daxue, Xuebao Bianjibu, Luo Jia Shan, Wuchang, Hubei 430072, People's Republic of China. TEL 027-7882712. FAX 027-7882661. (Dist. outside China by: China International Book Trading Corp., P.O.Box 399, Beijing, P.R.China) Ed. Tao Delin. bk.rev. Document type: academic/scholarly publication.
—UnCover.

300   PL   ISSN 0239-670X
WYZSZA SZKOLA PEDAGOGICZNA, OPOLE. ZESZYTY NAUKOWE. SERIA A. NAUKI SPOLECZNO-POLITYCZNE. (Text in Polish; summaries in English) 1985. irreg., vol.8, 1993. price varies, avail. on exchange basis. Wyzsza Szkola Pedagogiczna, Opole, Oleska 48, 45-951 Opole, Poland. TEL 48-77-383-87. (Dist. by: Ars Polona-Ruch, Krakowskie Przedmiescie 7, Warsaw, Poland) Ed. Jozef Jagas. Document type: academic/scholarly publication.

300   CC   ISSN 0438-0460
XIAMEN DAXUE XUEBAO (ZHEXUE SHEHUI KEXUE BAN)/XIAMEN UNIVERSITY. JOURNAL (PHILOSOPHY AND SOCIAL SCIENCES EDITION). (Text in Chinese; table of contents in English) q. Y1.20 per no. Xiamen Daxue - Xiamen University, c/o Xiamen Daxue Tushuguan, Xiamen, Fujian 361005, People's Republic of China. TEL 592-2086255. (Dist. outside China by: China International Book Trading Corp., P.O. Box 399, Beijing, P.R.C.) Ed. Luo Yucong. Document type: academic/scholarly publication.
—UnCover.

300   CC   ISSN 1000-2731
XIBEI DAXUE XUEBAO. SHEHUI KEXUE BAN/NORTHWEST UNIVERSITY. JOURNAL SOCIAL SCIENCES EDITION. (Text in Chinese; table of contents in English) 1957. q. Y0.60 per no. Xibei Daxue - Northwest University, Xiao Nan Menwai, Xi'an, Shaanxi 710069, People's Republic of China. (Dist. outside China by: China International Book Trading Corp., P.O. Box 2820, Beijing, P.R.C.) Eds. Xu Huaidong, Zhang Tianjie. Document type: academic/scholarly publication.
—UnCover.

300   CC   ISSN 1004-3926
XINAN MINZU XUEYUAN XUEBAO (ZHEXUE SHEHUI KEXUE BAN)/SOUTHWEST INSTITUTE OF NATIONALITIES. JOURNAL (PHILOSOPHY, SOCIAL SCIENCE EDITION). (Text in Chinese) 1979. q. Y9. Xinan Minzu Xueyuan, Xuebao Bianjibu, Nanjiao (Southern Suburb), Chengdu, Sichuan 610041, People's Republic of China. TEL 553811. (Dist. overseas by: China Publishing Corporation of Foreign Trade, P.O. Box 782, Beijing, P.R. China) Ed. Xu Qichao. adv.; bk.rev. Document type: academic/scholarly publication.
Description: Contains academic papers mainly focusing on minority nationalities of southwestern China. Covers politics, philosophy, economics, education, linguistics, and literature.

300   CC   ISSN 1000-2677
AS452.C48
XINAN SHIFAN DAXUE XUEBAO (SHEHUI KEXUE BAN)/SOUTHWEST NORMAL UNIVERSITY. JOURNAL (SOCIAL SCIENCE EDITION). (Text in Chinese) q. Xinan Shifan Daxue, Xuebao Bianjibu, Beipei Qu, Chongqing, Sichuan 630715, People's Republic of China. TEL 3901. Ed. Ji Ping. Document type: academic/scholarly publication.

300   CC   ISSN 1000-4262
AP95.C4
XINJIANG SHEHUI KEXUE/SOCIAL SCIENCE IN XINJIANG. (Text in Chinese) 1981. q. $20.40. Xinjiang Weiwuer Zizhiqu Shehui Kexueyuan - Xinjiang Uighur Autonomous Region Academy of Social Sciences, Beijing Lu, Wulumuqi (Urumqi), Xijiang 830011, People's Republic of China. TEL 37942. (Dist. in US by: China Books & Periodicals, Inc., 2929 24th St., San Francisco, CA 94110. TEL 415-282-2994) bibl. Document type: academic/scholarly publication.

940 339   CC   ISSN 1000-3576
XI'OU YANJIU/WESTERN EUROPEAN STUDIES. Variant English title: Studies in Western Europe. (Text in Chinese) 1984. bi-m. $18. Zhongguo Shehui Kexueyuan, Xi'ou Yanjiusuo - Chinese Academy of Social Sciences, Institute on Western Europe, No.5, Jianguomennei Dajie, Beijing 100732, People's Republic of China. TEL 861-513-7744. FAX 861-512-5818. (Dist. in US by: China Books & Periodicals, Inc., 2929 24th St., San Francisco, CA 94110. TEL 415-282-2994) Ed. Liu Fei. Document type: academic/scholarly publication.

300   CC
XIWANG/HOPE. (Text in Chinese) bi-m. Xin Shiji Chubanshe, No. 10, 4 Malu, Dashatou, Guangzhou, Guangdong 510102, People's Republic of China. TEL 335210. Ed. Chen Sang.

300   CC   ISSN 1002-7122
XIYA FEIZHOU/WEST ASIA AND AFRICA. (Text in Chinese; summaries in English) 1980. bi-m. Y10.20. Zhongguo Shehui Kexueyuan, Xiya Feizhou Yanjiusuo - Chinese Academy of Social Sciences, Institute of West-Asia and African Studies, No.3, Zhangzizhong Lu, Dongcheng-qu, Beijing 100007, People's Republic of China. TEL 4035718. Ed. Chen Gongyuan. adv.; bk.rev. Document type: academic/scholarly publication.

300   CC   ISSN 1001-9790
XUE HAI. (Text in Chinese) 1990. bi-m. Y20. Jiangsu Sheng Shehui Kexueyuan - Jiangsu Academy of Social Sciences, 12 Huju Beilu, Nanjing, Jiangsu 210013, People's Republic of China. TEL 025-637995. FAX 025-3312385. Ed. Chen Ling. adv. contact: Dun Yulin. bk.rev. circ. 1,500.

300   CC   ISSN 0438-1033
XUESHU LUNTAN. (Text in Chinese) bi-m. Guangxi Shehui Kexueyuan - Guangxi Academy of Social Sciences, No. 30, Xinzhu Lu, Nanning, Guangxi 530022, People's Republic of China. TEL 20201. Ed. Chen Xian'an. Document type: academic/scholarly publication.

300   CC   ISSN 1000-7326
XUESHU YANJIU/ACADEMIC RESEARCH. (Text in Chinese) 1962. bi-m. $30.60. (Guangdong Sheng Shehui Kexue Xuehui Lianhehui) Guangdong Renmin Chubanshe, Qikan Bu - Guangdong People's Publishing House, Dashatou Si Ma Lu 10, Guangzhou, Guangdong, People's Republic of China. (Dist. in US by: China Books & Periodicals, Inc., 2929 24th St., San Francisco, CA 94110. TEL 415-282-2994)

300   CC   ISSN 0439-8041
XUESHU YUEKAN/ACADEMIC MONTHLY. (Text in Chinese) 1957. m. Y14.40($54) (Shanghai Shehui Kexue Xuehui Lianhehui - Shanghai Federation of Social Sciences Societies) Shanghai Renmin Chubanshe, No. 54 Shaoxin Road, Shanghai 200020, People's Republic of China. TEL 86-21-3279173. FAX 86-21-3272894. (Dist. overseas by: China International Book Trading Corp., P.O. Box 399, Beijing, P.R. China; Dist. in US by: China Books & Periodicals, Inc., 2929 24th St., San Francisco, CA 94110. TEL 415-282-2994) Ed. Zhang Lingyun. circ. 6,500. Document type: academic/scholarly publication.
Description: Covers philosophy, political science, ethics, literature, history, economics, culture, aesthetics, important issues in China.

300   CC   ISSN 1002-462X
XUEXI YU TANSUO/STUDY & EXPLORATION. (Text and summaries in Chinese; table of contents in English) bi-m. Y11.40($35.10) (Heilongjiang Sheng Shehui Kexueyuan - Heilongjiang Provincial Academy of Social Sciences) Xuexi yu Tansuo Zazhishe, 124 Huayuan Jie, Nangang Qu, Harbin, Heilongjiang 150006, People's Republic of China. (Dist. outside China by: China International Book Trading Corp., P.O. Box 339, Beijing, P.R.C.; Dist. in US by: China Books & Periodicals, Inc., 2929 24th St., San Francisco, CA 94110. TEL 415-282-2994) Eds. Sun Qinglin, Ji Kefei.

300 001.3   PP   ISSN 0254-0681
YAGL-AMBU; Papua New Guinea journal of the social sciences and humanities. vol.6, 1979. q. K.10. University of Papua New Guinea, PO Box 320, University P.O., Papua New Guinea. Ed.Bd. Indexed: So.Pac.Per.Ind.
—BLDSC (9369.420000).

300   US   ISSN 0084-3326
YALE FASTBACKS. 1970. irreg. price varies. Yale University Press, Box 209040, New Haven, CT 06520. TEL 203-432-0940.

YALE SOUTHEAST ASIA STUDIES. MONOGRAPH SERIES. see *ORIENTAL STUDIES*

300   CC   ISSN 1002-4077
YAN DU/CAPITAL OF YAN. (Text in Chinese) bi-m. Yanshan Chubanshe, No. 36, Fuxue Hutong, Dongcheng-qu, Beijing 100007, People's Republic of China. TEL 4014694. Ed. Song Tishui.

300   CC
YANTAI DAXUE XUEBAO (SHEHUI KEXUE BAN)/YANTAI UNIVERSITY. JOURNAL (SOCIAL SCIENCE EDITION). (Text in Chinese) q. Yantai Daxue, Xuebao Bianjibu, Yantai, Shandong 264005, People's Republic of China. TEL 248995. Ed. Yang Chunxian. Document type: academic/scholarly publication.

300 296.7   US   ISSN 1050-8864
DS101
YIVO ANNUAL. 1946-1983; resumed vol.19, 1990. a. $45.95 (effective 1994). (Y I V O Institute for Jewish Research) Northwestern University Press, 625 Colfax Ave., Evanston, IL 60208-4210. TEL 708-491-5313. Ed.Bd. index. circ. 2,500. (back issues avail.) Indexed: Amer.Hist.& Life, Hist.Abstr., Lang.& Lang.Behav.Abstr., SSCI. Document type: academic/scholarly publication.
Formerly: Yivo Annual of Jewish Social Science (ISSN 0084-4209)

296.7   US   ISSN 0084-4217
PJ5120
YIVO BLETER/YIVO PAGES. (Text in Yiddish; summaries in English) 1931; N.S. 1991. irreg. $25. Y I V O Institute for Jewish Research, 1048 Fifth Ave., New York, NY 10028. TEL 212-535-6700. Ed.Bd. bk.rev. circ. 1,500. Indexed: Amer.Hist.& Life (until 1980), Hist.Abstr. (until 1980).

YIVO NEWS/YEDIES FUN YIVO. see *HUMANITIES: COMPREHENSIVE WORKS*

100 300   JA   ISSN 0513-5621
YOKOHAMA KOKURITSU DAIGAKU JINBUN KIYO DAI-1-RUI, TETSUGAKU, SHAKAI KAGAKU/YOKOHAMA NATIONAL UNIVERSITY. HUMANITIES. SECTION 1: PHILOSOPHY AND SOCIAL SCIENCES. (Text in Japanese; summaries in English) 1953. a. Yokohama Kokuritsu Daigaku, Shakaigaku Kyoshitsu - Yokohama National University, Department of Sociology, 156 Tokiwadai, Hodogaya-ku, Yokohama-shi, Kanagawa-ken 240, Japan. Document type: academic/scholarly publication.

300   CN   ISSN 1196-6459
YOUTH ACTION FORUM/FORUM ACTION JEUNESSE. (Text in English, French) 1992. q. free. Youth Action Network - Action Jeunesse, 100 Adelaide St., W., Ste. 906, Toronto, ON M5H 1S3, Canada. TEL 416-368-2277; 800-618-LINK. FAX 416-368-8354. Ed. Raymond Fung. circ. 5,000. (back issues avail.)
Formerly (until 1994): World Affairs Canada Quarterly (ISSN 1188-6870)
Description: Educates youth on current issues and encourages them to act upon national and international concerns. Provides a listing of Action projects and activities across Canada.

SOCIAL SCIENCES: COMPREHENSIVE WORKS — ABSTRACTING, BIBLIOGRAPHIES, STATISTICS

300   CC   ISSN 1000-8691
YUNNAN SHEHUI KEXUE/SOCIAL SCIENCE IN YUNNAN. (Text in Chinese; table of contents in English) bi-m. Y3.60($27) Yunnan Shehui Kexueyuan - Yunnan Academy of Social Sciences, 45, Qixiang Lu, Kunming, Yunnan 650032, People's Republic of China. (Dist. outside China by: China International Book Trading Corp., P.O. Box 339, Beijing, P.R.C.; Dist. in US by: China Books & Periodicals, Inc., 2929 24th St., San Francisco, CA 94110) Eds. He Yaohua, Fan Zuqi.

300   RH   ISSN 0379-0622
H1
ZAMBEZIA: THE JOURNAL OF THE UNIVERSITY OF ZIMBABWE. (Supplements avail.) 1969. s-a. $20 (effective 1995). University of Zimbabwe, Publications Office, P.O. Box MP 203, Mt. Pleasant, Harare, Zimbabwe. TEL 263-4-303211. FAX 263-4-333407. TELEX 26580 ZW. E-mail: uzpub@mango.apc.org. Ed. M.F.C. Bourdillon. adv.; bk.rev.; illus. circ. 400. **Indexed:** Amer.Hist.& Life, Bibl.Ling., Documentatieblad, Hist.Abstr., Ind.S.A.Per., M.L.A., P.L.E.S.A. **Document type:** academic/scholarly publication.
—BLDSC (9426.150000).
    Formerly: Zambezia: A Journal of Social Studies in Southern and Central Africa (ISSN 0514-5236); Which incorporated: University of Rhodesia. Series in Education. Occasional Paper; University of Rhodesia. Series in Humanities. Occasional Paper; University of Rhodesia. Series in Science. Occasional Paper; University of Rhodesia. Series in Social Studies. Occasional Paper.
    Description: Multidisciplinary journal with a particular focus on southern Africa.
    Refereed Serial

300   YU   ISSN 0044-1937
AS346
ZBORNIK ZA DRUSTVENE NAUKE. (Text in Serbo-Croatian, written in Cyrillic alphabet) 1915. a. Matica Srpska, Matice Srpske 1, Novi Sad, Vojvodina, Yugoslavia. Ed. Miladen Stojanov. **Indexed:** A.I.C.P., Amer.Hist.& Life, Hist.Abstr., IDA.

300   GW   ISSN 0044-2429
HD2951
ZEITSCHRIFT FUER DAS GESAMTE GENOSSENSCHAFTSWESEN. 1950. 4/yr. DM.112. Vandenhoeck und Ruprecht, Robert-Bosch-Breite 6, 37079 Goettingen, Germany. TEL 0551-6959-26. FAX 0551-695917. (Subscr. to: 37070 Goettingen, Germany) Ed. Oswald Hahn. adv.; bk.rev.; bibl.; charts; index. circ. 840. **Indexed:** Key to Econ.Sci., P.A.I.S.For.Lang.Ind. **Document type:** academic/scholarly publication.
—CCC.

300   GW   ISSN 0175-0488
ZEITSCHRIFT FUER ENTWICKLUNGSPAEDAGOGIK. 1978. q. DM.46. Verlag Schoeppe und Schwarzenbart, Nonnengasse 1, 72070 Tuebingen, Germany. TEL 07071-22801. Ed. Alfred K. Treml. adv.; bk.rev.; illus. (back issues avail.)

300   GW   ISSN 0930-9381
ZEITSCHRIFT FUER INTERNATIONALE ERZIEHUNGS- UND SOZIALWISSENSCHAFTLICHE FORSCHUNG. 2/yr. DM.24. Boehlau Verlag GmbH, Theodor-Heuss-Str. 76, 51149 Cologne, Germany. TEL 02203-307021. FAX 02203-307349. **Document type:** academic/scholarly publication.

ZEITSCHRIFT FUER OSTMITTELEUROPA-FORSCHUNG. see HISTORY — History Of Europe

ZEITSCHRIFT FUER UMWELTPOLITIK UND UMWELTRECHT. see ENVIRONMENTAL STUDIES

ZENO OVER WETENSCHAP, TECHNOLOGIE EN SAMENLEVING. see SCIENCES: COMPREHENSIVE WORKS

300   ISSN 1003-8612
ZHEJIANG DAXUE XUEBAO (SHEHUI KEXUE BAN)/ZHEJIANG UNIVERSITY. JOURNAL (SOCIAL SCIENCES EDITION). (Text in Chinese) 1987. q. $25.6. Zhejiang Daxue, Zheda Lu, Hangzhou, Zhejiang 310027, People's Republic of China. TEL 0571-7981153. FAX 0571-7951358. TELEX 35040 ZUFAO CN. Ed. Zhang Naida. **Document type:** academic/scholarly publication.

300   CC   ISSN 1001-5035
AS452.C4753
ZHEJIANG SHIFAN DAXUE XUEBAO (SHEHUI KEXUE BAN)/ZHEJIANG NORMAL UNIVERSITY. JOURNAL (SOCIAL SCIENCE EDITION). (Text in Chinese) q. Zhejiang Shifan Daxue - Zhejiang Normal University, Jinhua Shi Beijiao (Northern Suburb), Zhejiang 321004, People's Republic of China. Ed. Luo Xiangfa. **Document type:** academic/scholarly publication.

300   CC   ISSN 1004-5902
ZHENGMING. (In 2 editions: Learning and Theory; Society and Culture) (Text in Chinese) 1961-1964; resumed 19?? m. Y2.50 per no. for Learning and Theory Edition; Y2.80 per no. for Society and Culture Edition. Jiangxi Sheng Shehui Kexue Xuehui Lianhehui, 19 Fuzhou Lu, Nanchang, Jiangxi 330006, People's Republic of China. TEL 69402. Ed. Zheng Keqiang. adv.: page Y10000. bk.rev. circ. 60,000 (combined eds.). **Document type:** academic/scholarly publication.

300   CC
ZHENGZHOU DAXUE XUEBAO (SHEHUI KEXUE BAN)/ZHENGZHOU UNIVERSITY. JOURNAL (SOCIAL SCIENCE EDITION). (Text in Chinese) bi-m. Zhengzhou Daxue, Xuebao Bianjibu, No. 75, Daxue Lu, Zhengzhou, Henan 450052, People's Republic of China. TEL 446455. Ed. Li Min. **Document type:** academic/scholarly publication.

300   CC   ISSN 1004-8111
HD2096
ZHONGGUO NONGCUN/CHINA RURAL. (Text in Chinese) bi-m. newsstand price: Y4.20. Zhongguo Nongcun Zazhishe, No. 61 Fuxing Lu, Beijing 100036, People's Republic of China. TEL 8235515. Ed. Sun Hongzhi. circ. 50,000.
    Description: Covers new strategies and thoughts on China's rural reform, and trends in export-oriented development of Chinese rural economy.

ZHONGGUO QINGNIAN YANJIU/CHINA YOUTH STUDY. see CHILDREN AND YOUTH — About

300   CC   ISSN 1000-5420
ZHONGGUO RENMIN DAXUE XUEBAO/CHINA PEOPLE'S UNIVERSITY. JOURNAL. (Text in Chinese) bi-m. Zhongguo Renmin Daxue, Xuebao Bianjibu, Haidian Qu, Beijing 100872, People's Republic of China. TEL 2563399. Ed. Wei Xinghua. **Document type:** academic/scholarly publication.
—UnCover.

ZHONGGUO SHAOSHU MINZU. see ORIENTAL STUDIES

ZHONGGUO SHEHUI JINGJISHI YANJIU/JOURNAL OF CHINESE SOCIAL AND ECONOMIC HISTORY. see HISTORY — History Of Asia

300   CC   ISSN 1002-4921
ZHONGGUO SHEHUI KEXUE/SOCIAL SCIENCES IN CHINA. English edition: Social Sciences in China (ISSN 0252-9203) 1980. q. $60 (effective 1994). Shegui Kexue Zazhishe, A-158 Gulou Xidajie, Beijing 100720, People's Republic of China. TEL 441531. bk.rev. **Indexed:** Asian-Pac.Econ.Lit. **Document type:** academic/scholarly publication.
—UnCover.
    Description: Reflects the highest level of current academic research in the social sciences in China. Includes articles on law, economy, demography, sociology, politics, philosophy and history.

300   CC   ISSN 1000-2952
ZHONGGUO SHEHUI KEXUEYUAN YANJIUSHENGYUAN XUEBAO/CHINESE ACADEMY OF SOCIAL SCIENCES. GRADUATE SCHOOL JOURNAL. (Text in Chinese) 1985. bi-m. $30.60. Zhongguo Shehui Kexueyuan, Yanjiushengyuan, No. 131, Xibajianfang, Dongzhimenwai, Beijing 100015, People's Republic of China. TEL 472019. (Dist. in US by: China Books & Periodicals, Inc 2929 24th St., San Francisco, CA 94110. TEL 415-282-2994) Ed. Wang Haibo. **Document type:** academic/scholarly publication.
—UnCover.

ZHONGGUO XIZANG. see GENERAL INTEREST PERIODICALS — China

300 951   CC   ISSN 1000-5439
DS730
ZHONGNAN MINZU XUEYUAN XUEBAO (SHEHUI KEXUE BAN)/SOUTH-CENTRAL COLLEGE FOR NATIONALITIES. JOURNAL (SOCIAL SCIENCE EDITION). (Text in Chinese; table of contents in English) 1960. bi-m. Y2.50 per no. Zhongnan Minzu Xueyuan, Xuebao Bianjibu - South-Central College for Nationalities, Journal Editorial Department, No. 5, Minyuan Lu, Wuhan, Hubei 430074, People's Republic of China. TEL 851-27-7801426. FAX 851-27-701223. (Dist. outside China by: China International Book Trading Corp., P.O. Box 399, Beijing, P.R.C.) Ed. Tang Qitian; Pub. Zhou Xiufang. adv.; bk.rev. circ. 2,000. **Document type:** academic/scholarly publication.
—UnCover.
    Description: Contains theses on all areas of social science and philosophy. Emphasizes papers on issues in Chinese minority history, development of minority areas in South China, and aid to the poor.

300   CC   ISSN 1000-9639
AS451   CODEN: CHTHAJ
ZHONGSHAN DAXUE XUEBAO (ZHEXUE SHEHUI KEXUE BAN)/SUN YAT-SEN UNIVERSITY. JOURNAL (SOCIAL SCIENCE EDITION). (Text in Chinese; table of contents in English) 1955. 4/yr. Y4 per no. Zhongshan Daxue, Xuebao Bianjibu, 135 Xingang Xilu, Guangzhou, Guangdong 510275, People's Republic of China. TEL 020-4186300. TELEX 44604-ZSUFO-CN. (Dist. outside China by: China International Book Trading Corp., P.O. Box 399, Beijing, P.R.C.) Eds. Liao Wenhui, He Zhiping. bk.rev.; bibl.; index. **Document type:** academic/scholarly publication.
—BLDSC (4904.470000); CASDDS; Ei.
    Formerly: Zhongshan Daxue Shehui Kexue Xuebao (ISSN 0412-443X); Supersedes in part: Zhongshan Daxue Xuebao (ISSN 0529-6579)

300   CC
ZHONGZHOU XUEKAN. (Text in Chinese) bi-m. $24.80. Henan Sheng Shehui Kexueyuan - Henan Academy of Social Science, 50, Wenhua Lu, Zhengzhou, Henan 450002, People's Republic of China. TEL 336507. (Dist. in US by: China Books & Periodicals, Inc., 2929 24th St., San Francisco, CA 94110. TEL 415-282-2994) Ed. Hu Siyong. **Document type:** academic/scholarly publication.

300   SP   ISSN 0210-2692
ZONA ABIERTA. 1974. q. 3200 ptas. (Europe 4000 ptas.; elsewhere 6200 ptas.) Editorial Pablo Iglesias, Monte Esquinza 30, 2o, 28010 Madrid, Spain. TEL 91-310-43-13. Dir. Ludolfo Paramio. adv. contact: Mercedes Garcia Lenberg. bibl.; illus. circ. 2,000.
    Description: Focuses on the problems of the theory of social science. Covers post-Marxism.

300   CC   ISSN 1001-2370
ZOUXIANG SHIJIE. (Text in Chinese) bi-m. Shandong Shengwei Xuanchuanbu, No. 484, Wei 1 Lu, Jinan, Shandong 250001, People's Republic of China. TEL 615823. Ed. Jiang Jinde.

ZUKUENFTE. see TECHNOLOGY: COMPREHENSIVE WORKS

300   SZ
ZUKUNFTSFORSCHUNG. (Text in English, French, German) 1972. 4/yr. 85 SFr.($70) Schweizerische Vereinigung fuer Zukunftsforschung - Swiss Association for Futures Research, Haldenweg 10A, CH-3074 Muri, Switzerland. TEL 031-952-6655. FAX 031-952-6800. Ed. Gerhard Kocher. bk.rev.; abstr.; bibl.; charts; stat. circ. 1,020. (back issues avail.) **Document type:** bulletin.
    Formerly: S Z F-Bulletin.
    Description: Focuses on long-range planning, forecasts, strategic management and futures research.

ZWISCHENSCHRITTE; Beitraege zu einer morphologischen Psychologie. see PSYCHOLOGY

21ST CENTURY AFRO REVIEW; a jounral of issues in the Afro-community. see ETHNIC INTERESTS

SOCIAL SCIENCES: COMPREHENSIVE WORKS — Abstracting, Bibliographies, Statistics

A P T FOR LIBRARIES (YEAR); alternative press titles for the general reader. see BIBLIOGRAPHIES

SOCIAL SCIENCES: COMPREHENSIVE WORKS — ABSTRACTING, BIBLIOGRAPHIES, STATISTICS

300   UK   ISSN 0950-2238
Z7163
A S S I A: APPLIED SOCIAL SCIENCES INDEX & ABSTRACTS. 1987. bi-m. (plus a. cum.). £700($1285) (foreign £765) (effective 1995). Bowker - Saur Ltd., A part of Reed Reference Publishing, Part of the Reed Elsevier group, Maypole House, Maypole Rd., E. Grinstead, W. Sussex RH19 1HH, England. TEL 44-1342-330100. FAX 44-1342-330191. E-mail: custserv@bowker-saur.co.uk. Ed. Peter F. Broxis. (back issues avail.) **Document type:** abstracting/indexing.
●Also available online. Vendor(s): Data-Star (ASSI). Also available on CD-ROM. Producer(s): Bowker - Saur Ltd.
—BLDSC (1746.648800).
    Description: Studies of social sciences, with emphasis on the needs of people and social work.

300   UK   ISSN 0966-8764
Z7163
A S S I A PLUS. (Applied Social Science Index & Abstracts). q. £1175($1895) (effective 1995). Bowker - Saur Ltd., A part of Reed Reference Publishing, Maypole House, Maypole Rd., E. Grinstead, W. Sussex RH19 1HH, England. TEL 44-1342-330100. FAX 44-1342-330191. E-mail: custserv@bowker-saur.co.uk. (avail. for MS-DOS version) **Document type:** abstracting/indexing.
●Available only on CD-ROM. Producer(s): Bowker - Saur Ltd..

300   DK   ISSN 0106-0937
ACTA JUTLANDICA. SAMFUNDSVIDENSKABELIG SERIE/ACTA JUTLANDICA. SOCIAL SCIENCES SERIES. Variant title: Samfundsvidenskabelig Serie. (Subseries of: Acta Jutlandica) (Text in various languages) s-a. (Laerde Selskab i Aarhus) Aarhus University Press, Building 170, DK-8000 Aarhus, Denmark. TEL 45-86-19-70-33. FAX 45-86-19-84-33.

360   UK   ISSN 0262-5261
ACTIVITIES OF SOCIAL SERVICES DEPARTMENTS. 1975. a. Welsh Office, Statistical Directorate, New Crown Bldg., Cathays Park, Cardiff CF1 3NQ, Wales. TEL 01222-825054. FAX 01222-825350. **Document type:** government publication.
—BLDSC (0676.625000).

960 300   UK   ISSN 1352-2175
Z3501
AFRICAN STUDIES ABSTRACTS. (Text in Dutch, English, French, German) 1968. q. £40($67.50) to individuals; institutions £80($135) (effective 1995). (Afrika-Studiecentrum, NE - African Studies Centre) Hans Zell Publishers (Subsidiary of: Bowker-Saur Ltd.), P.O. Box 56, Oxford OX1 25J, England. TEL 01865-511428. FAX 01865-311534. (Subscr. to: World Wide Subscription Services Ltd., Unit 4, Gibbs Reed Farm, Ticehurst, E. Sussex TN5 7HE, England. TEL 01580-200657. FAX 01580-200616; Editorial addr.: Postbus 9555, 2300 RB Leiden, Netherlands. TEL 31-71-273372. FAX 31-71-273344) Ed.Bd. circ. 500. **Indexed:** World Agri.Econ.& Rural Sociol.Abstr. **Document type:** abstracting/indexing.
    Former titles (until vol.25, 1994): Documentatieblad: The Abstracts Journal of the African Studies Centre Leiden (ISSN 0166-2694); Supersedes (in 1980): Afrika Studiecentrum. Documentatieblad (ISSN 0002-0419)
    Description: Provides up-to-date coverage of recent periodicals and edited works on Africa in the field of the social sciences and the humanities, compiled from the leading journals in the field of African studies, as well as journals dealing with Third World countries and development studies in general.

200 300 016   FR   ISSN 0335-5985
BL60
ARCHIVES DE SCIENCES SOCIALES DES RELIGIONS. (Text in English and French; occasionally in German) 1956. s-a. (Groupe de Sociologie des Religions) C N R S Editions, 20-22 rue St. Amand, 75015 Paris, France. TEL 45-33-16-00. FAX 45-33-92-13. TELEX 200 356 F. Ed. J. Seguy. bk.rev.; abstr.; bibl.; charts; illus.; stat. circ. 1,200. **Indexed:** A.I.C.P., Amer.Hist.& Life, Arts & Hum.Cit.Ind., Bull.Signal., Curr.Cont., Hist.Abstr., Int.Polit.Sci.Abstr., Lang.& Lang.Behav.Abstr., Rel.& Theol.Abstr. (1989-), Rel.Ind.One, Rel.Per., Sociol.Abstr. (1956-), SSCI.
—BLDSC (1643.110000); SWETS.
    Formerly: Archives de Sociologie des Religions (ISSN 0003-9659)
    Description: Articles can be grouped under various headings- methodology, epistemology, status of scientific approaches to religions, classics of the sociology of religions, new religious movements.

300   II   ISSN 0066-8478
Z7165.A74
ASIAN SOCIAL SCIENCE BIBLIOGRAPHY WITH ANNOTATIONS AND ABSTRACTS. (Text in English) 1966. a. Institute of Economic Growth, University Enclave, New Delhi 110007, India. TEL 7257101. **Document type:** bibliography.

306 310   AT
AUSTRALIA. BUREAU OF STATISTICS. ATTENDANCE AT SELECTED CULTURAL VENUES, AUSTRALIA. 1991. irreg., latest 1995. Aus.$19.50. Australian Bureau of Statistics, P.O. Box 10, Belconnen, A.C.T. 2616, Australia. **Document type:** government publication.
    Description: Contains details on characteristics of people who attend, and frequency of visits, a range of cultural venues including libraries, museums, various categories of music and performing arts, cinemas, botanic gardens and animal parks.

300 310   AT   ISSN 1321-1781
HN844
▼**AUSTRALIA. BUREAU OF STATISTICS. AUSTRALIAN SOCIAL TRENDS.** 1994. a. Aus.$39. Australian Bureau of Statistics, P.O. Box 10, Belconnen, A.C.T. 2616, Australia. **Document type:** government publication.
    Description: Presents statistical analysis and commentary on a wide range of current social issues within the following broad areas of interest: population, families, health, education and training, work, income and housing.

300 314   BE   ISSN 0067-5563
BELGIUM. INSTITUT NATIONAL DE STATISTIQUE. STATISTIQUES SOCIALES. Key Title: Statistiques Sociales (Brussels). (Editions in Dutch, French) 1970. irreg. (approx 3/yr.). 460 BEF for 3 nos. (foreign 575 BEF) (effective 1993). Institut National de Statistique, 44 rue de Louvain, B-1000 Brussels, Belgium. TEL 32-2-5486211. FAX 32-2-5486367. **Indexed:** P.A.I.S.For.Lang.Ind. **Document type:** government publication.

300   NE   ISSN 0928-5121
Z7164.S68
BIBLIOGRAFIE NEDERLANDSE SOCIALE WETENSCHAPPEN; vakbibliografie voor nederland en Nederlandstalig Belgie. 1972. a. fl.125. Universiteit Utrecht, Bureau Bibliografie Nederlandse Sociale Wetenschappen, Plompetorengracht 11, 3512 CA Utrecht, Netherlands. TEL 31-30-537272. FAX 31-30-536560. E-mail: BNSW@ubu.ruu.nl. Ed.Bd. bk.rev. circ. 200. **Document type:** bibliography.
●Also available online.
    Formerly (until 1992): Bibliografie Nederlandse Sociologie (ISSN 0167-8272)

300   NE   ISSN 0168-5988
Z7165.N4
BIBLIOGRAFIE VAN REGIONALE ONDERZOEKINGEN OP SOCIAAL-WETENSCHAPPELIJK TERREIN/BIBLIOGRAPHY OF REGIONAL STUDIES IN THE SOCIAL SCIENCES. (Text in Dutch and English) 1945. a. Centraal Bureau voor de Statistiek, Prinses Beatrixlaan 428, Voorburg, Netherlands. (Orders to: SDU - Publishers, Christoffel Plantijnstraat, The Hague) **Document type:** government publication, bibliography.

300 015   YU   ISSN 0352-5899
BIBLIOGRAFIJA JUGOSLAVIJE. CLANCI I PRILOZI U SERIJSKIM PUBLIKACIJAMA. SERIJA A: DRUSTVENE NAUKE. 1950. m. $662 or exchange basis. Jugoslovenski Bibliografsko-Informacijski Institut (YUBIN) - Yogoslav Institute for Bibliography and Information, Terazije 26, Belgrade, Yugoslavia. FAX 11-687-760. Ed. Radomir Glavicki. **Document type:** bibliography.
●Also available online.
    Formerly (until 1985): Bibliografija Jugoslavije. Serija A: Drustvene Nauke. Clanci i Prilozi u Casopisima, Listovima i Zbornicima (ISSN 0373-6369)

BIBLIOGRAPHIC GUIDE TO EAST ASIAN STUDIES. see ORIENTAL STUDIES — Abstracting, Bibliographies, Statistics

BIBLIOGRAPHIC GUIDE TO LATIN AMERICAN STUDIES. see BIBLIOGRAPHIES

300   BE   ISSN 0773-3933
BIBLIOGRAPHIE DE L'AFRIQUE SUD-SAHARIENNE; sciences humaines et sociales. 1932. biennial, latest 1992 (for the years 1988-1989). 2440 BEF. Musee Royal de l'Afrique Centrale - Koninklijk Museum voor Midden-Afrika, 13 Steenweg op Leuven, B-3080 Tervuren, Belgium. TEL 32-2-7675401. FAX 32-2-7670242. Eds. M. d'Hertefelt, A.M. Bottiaux. (back issues avail.) **Indexed:** A.I.C.P. **Document type:** bibliography.
    Former titles (until 1982): Bibliographie Ethnographique de l'Afrique Sud-Saharienne (ISSN 0772-3741); (until 1962): Bibliographie Ethnographique du Congo Belge et des Regions Avoisinantes (ISSN 0772-3725)

BIBLIOGRAPHIES AND INDEXES IN LATIN AMERICAN AND CARIBBEAN STUDIES. see HISTORY — Abstracting, Bibliographies, Statistics

BIBLIOGRAPHIES COMMENTEES. see BUSINESS AND ECONOMICS — Abstracting, Bibliographies, Statistics

300 016   II
BIBLIOGRAPHY OF DOCTORAL DISSERTATIONS: SOCIAL SCIENCES AND HUMANITIES. (Text in English) 1974. irreg., latest 1991. price varies. Association of Indian Universities, A.I.U. House, 16 Kotla Marg, New Delhi 110 002, India. TEL 11-3310059. FAX 11-3315105. TELEX 31-66180-AIU-IN. circ. 500. **Document type:** bibliography.

BIBLIOGRAPHY OF EDUCATION THESES IN AUSTRALIA. see EDUCATION — Abstracting, Bibliographies, Statistics

015   BU   ISSN 0861-5683
BIULETIN ZA NOVONABAVENI KNIGI NA CHUZHDI EZTIZI. SERIIA A: OBSHTESTVENI I HUMANITARNI NAUKI. 1960. m. 240 lv.($40) Narodna Biblioteka Sv.sv. Kiril i Metodii, 88, V. Levski Blvd., 1504 Sofia, Bulgaria. TEL 389-20882811. FAX 359-2-882811.
    Description: Lists newly acquired foreign-language books in the social sciences.

300   II
BOOK REVIEW INDEX: AFRICA. (Text in English, French) 1971. a. $30. University of Delhi, Department of African Studies, Delhi 110 007, India. TEL 7257725. Ed. R.P. Sood. index. circ. 300. **Document type:** abstracting/indexing.

300 016   MX
Z7163
C L A S E. (Citas Latinoamericanas en Ciencias Sociales y Humanidades) 1976. q. $190. Universidad Nacional Autonoma de Mexico, Centro de Informacion Cientifica y Humanistica, Ciudad Universitaria, Apdo. Postal 70-392, C.P. 04510 Mexico, D.F., Mexico. TEL 525-6223958. FAX 525-6162557. E-mail: biblat@selene.cichcu.unam.mx. Ed. Antonia Llorens-Cruset. **Indexed:** P.A.I.S.For.Lang.Ind. **Document type:** abstracting/indexing.
●Also available online.
Also available on CD-ROM.
    Formerly (until 1986): C L A S E. Citas Latinoamericanas en Sociologia, Economia, y Humanidades (ISSN 0185-0903)

SOCIAL SCIENCES: COMPREHENSIVE WORKS — ABSTRACTING, BIBLIOGRAPHIES, STATISTICS

300 350   US   ISSN 0749-4394
C O S S A WASHINGTON UPDATE. 1981. s-w. $65 to individuals; institutions $130. Consortium of Social Science Associations, 1522 K St., N.W., Ste. 836, Washington, DC 20005. TEL 202-842-3525. FAX 202-842-2788. Ed. Michael Buckley. index. (looseleaf format; back issues avail.) **Document type:** newsletter.
   Formerly: C O S S A Legislative Report.
   Description: Discusses latest developments in congress that affect funding for social and behavioral science research. Reports on current issues of federal policy such as regualtions affecting research.

300 001.3   TR   ISSN 0250-7617
CARINDEX: SOCIAL SCIENCES AND HUMANITIES. 1977. s-a. T.T.$45. University of the West Indies, Main Library, St. Augustine, Trinidad & Tobago, W.I. TEL 809-662-2002. FAX 809-662-9238. TELEX 24-520-UWI-WG. Ed. Sandra Barnes. bk.rev. circ. 100. (back issues avail.) **Document type:** abstracting/indexing.
   Formerly (until 1982): Carindex: Social Sciences.
   Description: Guide to the social sciences and humanities literature published in the English-speaking Caribbean. Covers periodical articles, as well as conference proceedings, reports, and theses presented to the university.

CURRENT DIGEST OF THE POST-SOVIET PRESS. see *POLITICAL SCIENCE — Abstracting, Bibliographies, Statistics*

300 020 015   UK   ISSN 0267-1964
H62.5.G7
CURRENT RESEARCH IN BRITAIN. SOCIAL SCIENCES. (Other vols. avail.: Biological Sciences, Humanities, Physical Sciences) 1980. a. £70 (foreign £75). Longman Cartermill Ltd., Technology Centre, St. Andrews, Fife KY16 9EA, Scotland. TEL 44-1937-843434. FAX 44-1937-546333. TELEX 557381. Ed. Mike Bate. **Document type:** abstracting/indexing.
   Formerly (until 1985): Research in British Universities Polytechnics and Colleges. Vol.3: Social Sciences (ISSN 0143-0742)

312   CY   ISSN 0253-875X
CYPRUS. DEPARTMENT OF STATISTICS AND RESEARCH. STATISTICAL ABSTRACT. (Text in English) 1955. a. £C10 (effective 1995). Department of Statistics and Research, Ministry of Finance, Nicosia, Cyprus. TEL 357-2-303286. FAX 357-2-456712. bk.rev. circ. 420. **Document type:** government publication.
   Description: Summarizes statistics concerning the economic and social conditions in Cyprus on a time-series basis.

DIRECTORY OF PUBLISHED PROCEEDINGS. SERIES S S H - SOCIAL SCIENCES - HUMANITIES. see *HUMANITIES: COMPREHENSIVE WORKS — Abstracting, Bibliographies, Statistics*

DISSERTATION ABSTRACTS INTERNATIONAL. SECTION A: HUMANITIES AND SOCIAL SCIENCES. see *HUMANITIES: COMPREHENSIVE WORKS — Abstracting, Bibliographies, Statistics*

300 016   BO
EXTENSION BIBLIOGRAFICA. 1974. irreg., no.10, 1984. price varies. Centro de Investigaciones Sociales, Casilla 6931 - C.C., La Paz, Bolivia.

FICHIER AFRIQUE. see *BUSINESS AND ECONOMICS — Abstracting, Bibliographies, Statistics*

314   FI
FINLAND. TILASTOKESKUS. TILASTOLLISIA TIEDONANTOJA. KULTTUURITILASTO/FINLAND. STATISTIKCENTRALEN. STATISTISKA MEDDELANDEN. KULTURSTATISTIK/FINLAND. CENTRAL STATISTICAL OFFICE. STATISTICAL SURVEYS. CULTURAL STATISTICS. (Text in English, Finnish and Swedish) 1978. irreg., latest 1981. FIM 150. Tilastokeskus, Annankatu 44, SF-00100 Helsinki 10, Finland.

300   IQ   ISSN 1012-3415
GENERAL INDEX TO IRAQI PERIODICAL LITERATURE. PART B: HUMANITIES AND SOCIAL SCIENCES. (Text in Arabic, English) 1986. irreg. free. Scientific Research Council, Jadiriyah P.O. Box 2441, Baghdad, Iraq. TELEX 213976 SR IK. Ed. Radhwan K. ABdul-Halim. circ. 500. **Document type:** abstracting/indexing.

300 016   US
GUIDE TO ALTERNATIVE PERIODICALS. 1980. a. price varies. New Pages Press, Box 438, Grand Blanc, MI 48439. TEL 313-743-8055. FAX 313-743-2730. Ed. Casey Hill. adv.; illus. **Document type:** bibliography.

300 200 016   US   ISSN 0017-5307
Z7753
GUIDE TO SOCIAL SCIENCE AND RELIGION IN PERIODICAL LITERATURE. 1964. s-a. (triennal cumulation). $88. National Periodical Library, Box 3278, Clearwater, FL 34630. Ed. Albert M. Wells. index. circ. 500. **Document type:** abstracting/indexing.

300   US   ISSN 1058-4862
GUIDES TO MAJOR SOCIAL SCIENCE DATA BASES. 1992. 3/yr. Sage Publications, Inc., 2455 Teller Rd., Thousand Oaks, CA 91320. TEL 805-499-0721. FAX 805-499-0871. E-mail: libraries@sagepub.com. (Overseas subscr. to: Sage Publications Ltd., 6 Bonhill St., London EC2A 4PU, England; Sage Publications India Pvt. Ltd., P.O. Box 4125, New Delhi 110 048, India) **Document type:** monographic series.
   —BLDSC (4229.570930).

300   CC   ISSN 1002-8676
GUOWAI SHEHUI KEXUE LUNWEN SUOYIN/FOREIGN SOCIAL SCIENCE DISSERTATION INDEX. (Text in Chinese) 1979. bi-m. Zhongguo Shehui Kexueyuan, Wenxian Qingbao Zhongxin - Chinese Academy of Social Sciences, Documentation Information Center, 5, Jianguomennei Dajie, Beijing 100732, People's Republic of China. TEL 5137744. Ed. Zhu Tiesheng. **Document type:** abstracting/indexing.

I A S S I S T QUARTERLY. (International Association for Social Science Information Services and Technology) see *LIBRARY AND INFORMATION SCIENCES*

300 016   II   ISSN 0376-4206
I C S S R RESEARCH ABSTRACTS QUARTERLY. (Text in English) 1971. q. Rs.30 to individuals; institutions Rs.50. Indian Council of Social Science Research, 35 Ferozshah Rd., New Delhi 110 001, India. TEL 91-11-388342. FAX 91-11-338037. TELEX 31-61083-ISSR-IN. Ed. S. Saraswathi. adv.; bk.rev.; abstr.; bibl.; charts; cum. index: vols. 1-11. circ. 550. (back issues avail.) **Document type:** abstracting/indexing.
   Description: Abstracts reports of research projects funded by the ICSSR. Covers objectives, methodology, and major findings.

011   II
I C S S R UNION CATALOGUE OF SOCIAL SCIENCE PERIODICALS. (Text in English) 1973. irreg. Rs.1530($460) Indian Council of Social Science Research, National Social Science Documentation Centre, 35 Ferozshah Rd., New Delhi 110 001, India. TEL 91-11-388342. FAX 91-11-388037. TELEX 31-61083-ISSR-IN. Ed. K.G. Tyagi. bibl.; index. circ. 1,000. **Document type:** catalog.
   Formerly: I C S S R Union Catalogue of Social Science Periodicals - Serials.

300   IT   ISSN 0250-7641
I D O C INTERNAZIONALE. (Text in English) 1970. 4/yr. L.25000($30) International Documentation and Communication Center, Via S. Maria dell'Anima 30, 00186 Rome, Italy. FAX 0039-6-6832766. Ed. Gabriela Fabiani. adv.; bk.rev.; bibl. circ. 1,500. (back issues avail.) **Indexed:** HR Rep. (1985-).
   —BLDSC (4362.509500).

IBERO-AMERICANA; Nordic journal of Latin American studies/revista nordica de estudios latinoamericanos. see *HISTORY — Abstracting, Bibliographies, Statistics*

960 016   SG
INDEX OF AFRICAN SOCIAL SCIENCE PERIODICAL ARTICLES. 1993. irreg. £19.95($35) outside Africa. Council for the Development of Economic and Social Research in Africa (CODESRIA), B.P. 3304, Dakar, Senegal. TEL 221-230211. FAX 221-241289. TELEX 61339 CODES SG24. (Dist. outside Africa by: African Books Collective Ltd., The Jam Factory, 27 Park End St., Oxford OX1 1HU, England. TEL 0865-726686. FAX 0865-793298) **Document type:** abstracting/indexing.

300 001.3   US   ISSN 0191-0574
Z7163
INDEX TO SOCIAL SCIENCES & HUMANITIES PROCEEDINGS. Short title: I S S H P. (Includes Author-Editor Index, Permuterm Subject Index, Sponsor Index, Meeting Location Index, Category Index, Contents of Proceedings, and Corporate Index.) 1979. q. (plus a. cumulation). $1025. Institute for Scientific Information, 3501 Market St., Philadelphia, PA 19104. TEL 215-386-0100. FAX 215-386-2991. (And: Brunel Science Park, Brunel University, Uxbridge UB8 3PQ, England. TEL 44-1895-270016. FAX 44-1895-256710) **Document type:** proceedings.
   ●Also available on CD-ROM. Producer(s): Institute for Scientific Information.
   —BLDSC (4386.400000).
   Description: International multidisciplinary index of papers presented at social sciences and humanities professional meetings.

300 011   TH   ISSN 0125-5827
AI19.T47
INDEX TO THAI PERIODICAL LITERATURE. (Text in Thai) 1964. a. $30. National Institute of Development Administration, Library and Information Center, Publication and Dissemination of Information Division, Klongjan, Bangkapi, Bangkok 10240, Thailand. circ. 200. **Document type:** abstracting/indexing.

016.3091   II
INDIA. MINISTRY OF EDUCATION AND SOCIAL WELFARE. DEPARTMENT OF SOCIAL WELFARE. DOCUMENTATION SERVICE BULLETIN. 1968. a. free. Ministry of Education and Social Welfare, Department of Social Welfare, Shastri Bhavan, New Delhi 110001, India. circ. controlled. **Document type:** government publication.

300 016   II   ISSN 0250-9709
INDIAN DISSERTATION ABSTRACTS. (Text in English) 1973. q. Rs.30 to individuals; institutions Rs.50. Indian Council of Social Science Research, 35, Ferozshah Rd., New Delhi 110 001, India. TEL 91-11-388342. FAX 91-11-388037. TELEX 31-61083-ISSR-IN. (Co-sponsor: Association of Indian Universities) Ed. Dinesh C. Sharma. adv.; abstr.; index. circ. 550. (back issues avail.) **Document type:** abstracting/indexing, academic/scholarly publication.
   Description: Abstracts of research theses in social sciences on which Ph.D. degrees were awarded by Indian universities. Features topic, methodology, and results of each project.

INTERNATIONAL AFRICAN BIBLIOGRAPHY; current books, articles and papers in African studies. see *BIBLIOGRAPHIES*

951   RU
KITAEVEDENIE: ZARUBEZHNAYA LITERATURA; referativnyi zhurnal. 1973. q. $62. Rossiiskaya Akademiya Nauk, Institut Nauchnoi Informatsii po Obshchestvennym Naukam, Ul. Krasikova 28-21, 117418 Moscow V-418, Russia. Ed. S.L. Tikhvinskii. **Document type:** abstracting/indexing.
   Formerly: Obshchestvennye Nauki za Rubezhom. Kitaevedenie (ISSN 0235-6821)

300   HU   ISSN 0133-6894
AI19.H8
MAGYAR NEMZETI BIBLIOGRAFIA. IDOSZAKI KIADVANYOK REPERTORIUMA; tarsadalomtudomanyok, termeszettudomanyok. 1946. m. 2400 Ft.($33) Orszagos Szechenyi Konyvtar - National Szechenyi Library, Budavari Palota F epulet, 1827 Budapest, Hungary. TEL 36-1-156-9378. FAX 36-1-202-0804. TELEX 224226 BIBLN H. (Subscr. to: Kultura Kulkereskedelmi Vallalat, Pf. 149, 1389 Budapest, Hungary) Ed. Domotor Lajosne. bibl.; index, cum.index. circ. 800. **Document type:** bibliography.
   Formerly: Magyar Folyoiratok Repertoriuma (ISSN 0025-0112); Which supersedes in part (in 1977): Magyar Nemzeti Bibliografia (ISSN 0373-1766)
   Description: Contains articles in the fields of social and exact sciences from scientific, literary and art periodicals, leading newspapers, and yearbooks published in Hungary.

MARKAZ-I NASHARIYAT-I 'ILMI VA FARHANGI. FIHRIST-I MUNDARIJAT-I MAJALLAH-HA-YI JARI-I/CENTER FOR SCIENTIFIC AND CULTURAL PERIODICALS. TABLE OF CONTENTS OF CURRENT JOURNALS. see *SCIENCES: COMPREHENSIVE WORKS — Abstracting, Bibliographies, Statistics*

SOCIAL SERVICES AND WELFARE

300 310 NR ISSN 0189-6067
NIGERIA. FEDERAL OFFICE OF STATISTICS. SOCIAL STATISTICS IN NIGERIA. a. $10. Federal Office of Statistics, P.M.B. 12528, Lagos, Nigeria.

300 NR ISSN 0078-0766
NIGERIAN INSTITUTE OF SOCIAL AND ECONOMIC RESEARCH. LIBRARY. LIST OF ACCESSIONS. 1963. q. exchange basis. Nigerian Institute of Social and Economic Research, Private Mail Bag 5, University of Ibadan, Ibadan, Nigeria.

300 011 NR ISSN 0189-8671
NIGERIAN JOURNAL OF SOCIAL SCIENCE RESEARCH ABSTRACTS. 1982. s-a. Nigerian Institute of Social and Economic Research, Private Mail Bag 5, University of Ibadan, Ibadan, Nigeria. **Document type:** abstracting/indexing.

300 011 028.5 US
NOTABLE CHILDREN'S TRADE BOOKS IN THE FIELD OF SOCIAL STUDIES. 1971. a. (National Council for the Social Studies, Joint Committee Project) Children's Book Council, Inc., 568 Broadway, New York, NY 10012-3225. TEL 212-966-1990. Ed. David Riederman. **Document type:** bibliography.
  Description: Annotated bibliography of books for kindergarten to eighth grade in American and world history and culture. Includes biographies, folktales, myths and legends.

P A I S INTERNATIONAL IN PRINT. (Public Affairs Information Service, Inc.) see BUSINESS AND ECONOMICS — Abstracting, Bibliographies, Statistics

300 US ISSN 0730-3335
REFERENCE SOURCES FOR THE SOCIAL SCIENCES AND HUMANITIES. 1982. irreg. price varies. Greenwood Press, Inc. (Subsidiary of: Greenwood Publishing Group Inc.), 88 Post Rd. W., Box 5007, Westport, CT 06881-5007. TEL 203-226-3571. FAX 203-222-1502. Ed. Raymond G. McInnis. —BLDSC (7331.927500).

300 016 FR ISSN 0080-2484
REVUE BIBLIOGRAPHIQUE DE SINOLOGIE. (Text in French, English) 1955; N.S. 1984. a. price varies. Editions de l' Ecole des Hautes Etudes en Sciences Sociales, 131 bd. St-Michel, 75005 Paris, France. TEL 46-33-51-46. FAX 44-07-08-89. (Dist. by: Centre Interinstitutionnel pour la Diffusion de Publications en Sciences Humaines, 131 bd. St-Michel, 75005 Paris, France. TEL 43-54-47-15. FAX 43-54-80-73) Eds. Michel Cartier, Danielle Elliseeff. adv.; bk.rev. circ. 400. **Document type:** abstracting/indexing.
  —BLDSC (7892.750000).
  Description: Aims at providing a quick survey of the most recent trends in Chinese studies. Each volume offers a number of abstracts of books and articles selected from various periodicals in different fields, from archaeology to history of science and technology.

SCITECH BOOK NEWS; an annotated bibliography of new books in science, technology, & medicine. see BIBLIOGRAPHIES

016 300 US ISSN 0091-3707
Z7161
SOCIAL SCIENCES CITATION INDEX. Short title: S S C I. (Includes Source Index, Citation Index, Permuterm Subject Index, and Corporate Index) 1969. 3/yr. (plus a. cum.). $5920. Institute for Scientific Information, 3501 Market St., Philadelphia, PA 19104. TEL 215-386-0100. FAX 215-386-2991. (And: Brunel Science Park, Brunel University, Uxbridge UB8 3PQ, England) cum.index: 1956-1965, 1966-1970, 1971-1975, 1976-1980, 1981-1985, 1986-1990. (also avail. in magnetic tape) **Document type:** academic/scholarly publication, bibliography.
  ●Also available online. Vendor(s): DIMDI, Data-Star, Knight-Ridder, Inc. (File no.7/SOCIAL SCISEARCH), Ovid Technologies (SSCI).
  Also available on CD-ROM. Producer(s): Institute for Scientific Information (SSCI).
  —BLDSC (8318.188200).
  Description: Multidisciplinary indexing of research in all fields of social sciences.

300 US ISSN 0161-3162
Z7161
SOCIAL SCIENCES CITATION INDEX JOURNAL CITATION REPORTS; a bibliometric analysis of social science journals in the ISI database. Short title: S S C I - J C R. (Not avail. in printed format. Includes Journal Ranking, Reference Data, and Source Data Packages) 1977. a. $290. Institute for Scientific Information, 3501 Market St., Philadelphia, PA 19104. TEL 215-386-0100. FAX 215-386-2991. (And: Brunel Science Park, Brunel University, Uxbridge UB8 3PQ, England) (microfiche) **Document type:** academic/scholarly publication, bibliography.
  Formerly: I S I Journal Citation Reports.
  Description: Provides citation data of journals in the social sciences.

300 016 US ISSN 0094-4920
AI3
SOCIAL SCIENCES INDEX. 1974. q. (plus a. cum.). service basis. H.W. Wilson Co., 950 University Ave., Bronx, NY 10452. TEL 718-588-8400; 800-367-6770. FAX 718-590-1617. TELEX 4990003 HWILSON. Ed. Cheryl Ehrens. (also avail. in magnetic tape) **Document type:** abstracting/indexing.
  ●Also available online. Vendor(s): Wilsonline (File SSI).
  Also available on CD-ROM. Producer(s): H.W. Wilson.
  —BLDSC (8318.191000). CCC.
  Supersedes in part: Social Sciences and Humanities Index (ISSN 0037-7899)
  Description: Author and subject index to periodicals in the fields of anthropology, community health and medicine, economics, geography, international relations, law, criminology and police science, political science, psychology and psychiatry, public administration, sociology, social work, and related subjects.

300 GW
STUDIENKATALOG-GRUNDKATALOG. WIRTSCHAFTS- UND SOZIALWISSENSCHAFTEN. 1954. s-a. DM.4.30. Buchwerbung in Berlin GmbH, Luetzowstr. 105-106, 10785 Berlin, Germany. **Document type:** bibliography.
  Formerly: Wirtschafts- und Sozialwissenschaften.
  Description: A learner's bibliography of social sciences.

SUDAN. NATIONAL COUNCIL FOR RESEARCH. ECONOMIC AND SOCIAL RESEARCH COUNCIL. BIBLIOGRAPHIES. see BUSINESS AND ECONOMICS — Abstracting, Bibliographies, Statistics

U P RESEARCH MONITOR. (University of the Philippines) see SCIENCES: COMPREHENSIVE WORKS — Abstracting, Bibliographies, Statistics

300 015 JM
UNIVERSITY OF THE WEST INDIES. INSTITUTE OF SOCIAL AND ECONOMIC RESEARCH. OCCASIONAL BIBLIOGRAPHY SERIES. 1974. irreg., no.9, 1987? University of the West Indies, Institute of Social and Economic Research, Mona Campus, Kingston 7, Jamaica, W.I. TEL 809-927-1020. FAX 809-927-2409. TELEX 2123 JA.

011 II
VIKRAM RESEARCH GUIDE.* (Text in English) 1971. q. Rs.21. Vikram University, Maharaja Jiwajirao Library, P.O. 12, Ujjain, Madhya Pradesh, India. Ed. N.K. Trivedi. abstr.

300 GW ISSN 0932-3481
W Z B FORSCHUNG; Hinweise auf neue Arbeiten. 1978. 3/yr. Wissenschaftszentrum Berlin fuer Sozialforschung, Reichpietschufer 50, 10785 Berlin, Germany. TEL 030-25491-0. FAX 030-25491684. TELEX 308897-WZB-D. Ed. Heidi Hilzinger. abstr. circ. 4,800. **Document type:** bulletin.

300 US ISSN 0734-9033
HM206
WHOLE AGAIN RESOURCE GUIDE; periodical and resource directory. 1982. irreg., 2nd ed. 1987. $26.95. SourceNet, Box 6767, Santa Barbara, CA 93160. TEL 805-373-7123. Ed. Tim Ryan. bk.rev.; bibl.; illus.; index. circ. 5,000. (back issues avail.) **Document type:** directory.
  —CCC.
  Incorporates: International Guide to Psi-Periodicals (ISSN 0277-9870).

300 UN ISSN 0084-1870
WORLD LIST OF SOCIAL SCIENCE PERIODICALS. (Text in English and French) irreg., 8th ed., 1991. $40. Unesco, 7-9 Place de Fontenoy, 75700 Paris, France.

ZASSHI KIJI SAKUIN. JINBUN SHAKAI HEN/JAPANESE PERIODICALS INDEX. HUMANITIES AND SOCIAL SCIENCE SECTION. see HUMANITIES: COMPREHENSIVE WORKS — Abstracting, Bibliographies, Statistics

300 011 CC
ZHONGGUO SHEHUI KEXUE WENXIAN TILU/CHINESE SOCIAL SCIENCE DOCUMENTATIONS INDEX. (Text in Chinese) bi-m. Zhongguo Shehui Kexueyuan, Wenxian Qingbao Zhongxin - Chinese Academy of Social Sciences, Documentation Information Center, No.5, Jianguomennei Dajie, Beijing 100732, People's Republic of China. TEL 5137144. Ed. Mo Zuoqin. **Document type:** abstracting/indexing.

SOCIAL SERVICES AND WELFARE

see also Drug Abuse and Alcoholism; Handicapped; Public Health and Safety

A A - B A NEWSLETTER. (American Anorexia - Bulimia Association, Inc.) see PSYCHOLOGY

A A R P HIGHLIGHTS. (American Association of Retired Persons) see GERONTOLOGY AND GERIATRICS

A B P CONTACT/B V V CONTACT. (Association Belge des Paralyses) see HANDICAPPED

A C A NEWS; the provincial newsletter for seniors. (Alberta Council on Aging) see GERONTOLOGY AND GERIATRICS

A C A R T S O D NEWSLETTER. (African Centre for Applied Research and Training in Social Development) see BUSINESS AND ECONOMICS — International Development And Assistance

A C R O D NEWSLETTER. (Australian Council for Rehabilitation of Disabled) see HANDICAPPED

614 US ISSN 0279-1692
A H C A NOTES. 1972. m. $150 to non-members; members $15. American Health Care Association, 1201 L St., N.W., Washington, DC 20005. TEL 202-842-4444. FAX 202-842-3860. Ed. Marla Gold. illus. circ. 10,000.
  —UnCover.
  Formerly: A H C A Weekly Notes (ISSN 0146-6321)

A H R C CHRONICLE. (Association for the Help of Retarded Children) see MEDICAL SCIENCES — Psychiatry And Neurology

360 US
A L M A SEARCHLIGHT. 1974. q. membership. Adoptees' Liberty Movement Association, Box 727, Radio City Sta., New York, NY 10101-0727. TEL 212-581-1568. Ed. Florence Fisher.

A M S STUDIES IN MODERN SOCIETY. see PUBLIC HEALTH AND SAFETY

A P I ACCOUNT. (Accountants for the Public Interest) see BUSINESS AND ECONOMICS — Accounting

360 US
A P W A NEWS. 1986. q. membership only. American Public Welfare Association, c/o Publication Services, 810 First St., N.E., Ste. 500, Washington, DC 20002-4267. TEL 202-682-0100. FAX 202-289-6555. illus. circ. 8,000. (tabloid format)
  Description: Contains articles on APWA events and projects; includes calendar, conference reports, and interviews.

360 PK ISSN 0001-2262
A P W A NEWSLETTER. 1967. 3/yr. free. All Pakistan Women's Association, Information and Research Bureau, 67-B Garden Rd., Karachi 3, Pakistan. Ed. Ishrat Aftab. charts; illus. **Document type:** newsletter.

SOCIAL SERVICES AND WELFARE

361.73 US
A R N O V A NEWS. q. Association for Research on Nonprofit Organizations and Voluntary Action, c/o Anita H. Plotinsky, Exec. Officer, Indiana Univ., Center on Philanthropy, 550 W. North St., Ste. 301, Indianapolis, IN 46202. TEL 317-684-2120. FAX 317-684-8900. E-mail: aplotin@indyvaz.iupui.edu.
Description: Promotes multi-disciplinary, scholarly research on voluntary - non-profit organizations, volunteering and voluntary action, including philanthropy, charity and the common good.

360 US ISSN 0001-2335
A R S HAI SIRD. 1939. a. $10. Armenian Relief Society, Inc., 80 Bigelow Ave., Watertown, MA 02172-2021. TEL 617-926-5892. FAX 617-926-4855. Ed. Arpie Balian. adv.; bk.rev. circ. 1,000.

361.8 UK ISSN 0263-1873
A R V A C BULLETIN. (Former name of issuing body: Association of Research in Voluntary Action and Community Involvement - Unit 29) 1978. q. £24 to individuals (overseas £32); institutions £62 (effective April 1995). Association for Research in the Voluntary and Community Sector - Unit 29, Wivenhoe Business Centre, Brook St., Wivenhoe, Essex CO7 9DP, England. TEL 01206-824281. FAX 01206-824287. Ed. Pat Marsden. adv.: quarter page £50. bk.rev.; bibl. circ. 300. (looseleaf format; back issues avail.) **Document type:** bulletin.
Description: Contains articles, research news and reports, and conference reports.

361.8 UK
A R V A C OCCASIONAL PAPERS. no.5, 1983. irreg., no.12, 1992. price varies. Association for Research in the Voluntary and Community Sector, Wivenhoe Business Centre, Brook St., Wivenhoe, Essex CO7 9DP, England. TEL 01206-824281. FAX 01206-824287. (back issues avail.) **Document type:** monographic series.
Description: Discusses various issues and topics in providing social services.

613 NE ISSN 0168-2857
A S. (Aktiviteitensektor); maandblad voor de actezigheidstherapie - aktiviteitenbegeleiding. Key Title: AS. Maandblad Aktiviteitensektor. 1956. m. (11/yr.). fl.103 (students fl.78). Uitgeverij De Tijdstroom b.v., P.O. Box 19135, 3501 DC Utrecht, Netherlands. TEL 31-30-586900. FAX 31-30-586950. Ed.Bd. adv.; bk.rev. circ. 6,000. **Document type:** trade publication. —SWETS.
Incorporates (in 1982): Ligament (ISSN 0024-3264)
Description: Covers recreational therapy.

649 178 IT ISSN 0394-6479
A S P E. (Agenzia di Stampa sui Problemi dell'Emarginazione) 1983. m. L.60000 to individuals; institutions L.80000; foreign L.110000 (effective 1995). Edizioni Gruppo Abele, Via Giolitti 21, 10123 Turin, Italy. TEL 39-11-8142745. FAX 39-11-8395577. Ed. Mirta Da Pza. Pocchiesa. adv.; cum.index: 1983-1986. circ. 7,500. (back issues avail.)
Description: Features news, surveys and documents concerning social issues, peace and environment. Reports on national and international meetings on conventions, seminars and training courses.

360 ET
A S W E A JOURNAL FOR SOCIAL WORK EDUCATION IN AFRICA. (Editions in English and French) 1974. s-a. Association for Social Work Education in Africa, c/o College of Social Sciences, Addis Ababa University, PO Box 1176, Addis Ababa, Ethiopia.
Supersedes: Association for Social Work Education in Africa. Bulletin.

361.3 929 US
A T M REUNION REGISTRY.* 1985. q. $50. Adoption Triangle Ministries, c/o Adoption Reunion Center, Box 1860, Cape Coral, FL 33910-1860. TEL 813-542-1342. FAX 813-549-9393. (Subscr. to: Musser Foundation, Box 1860, Cape Coral, FL 33910) Ed. Sandy Musser. **Document type:** directory.
Description: Adopted persons seeking birth parents and other family members.

360 GW
A W O MITTEILUNGEN; Kreisverband Karlsruhe-Stadt e.V. 1969. q. DM.1.60. Kreisverband Karlsruhe-Stadt e.V., Kronenstr. 15, 76133 Karlsruhe, Germany. TEL 0721-69070. FAX 0721-690770. bk.rev.; bibl.; stat. circ. 4,500. (back issues avail.) **Document type:** newsletter.
Formerly: A W Mitteilungen.

ABILITIES. see HANDICAPPED — Hearing Impaired

361 PE ISSN 0258-2678
HV110.5
ACCION CRITICA. 1976. s-a. $6. Asociacion Latinoamericana de Escuelas de Servicio Social, Centro Latinoamericano de Trabajo Social, Jr. Jorge Vanderghen No. 351, Apdo. 348, Lima, Peru. Dir. Maria Cecilia Tobon. bk.rev.

362.8 FR ISSN 0223-5420
ACCUEILLIR. 1972. bi-m. 120 F. (foreign 180 F.). Service Social d'Aide aux Emigrants, 72 rue Regnault, 75640 Paris Cedex 13, France. TEL 40-77-94-47. FAX 45-84-43-05. Ed. Monique Moreira. adv.; bk.rev. circ. 2,000. **Indexed:** Refug.Abstr. **Document type:** bulletin.

323.4 US
ACTING OUT. 1979? q. $4. Mental Patients Liberation Front, Box 514, Cambridge, MA 02138.

360 AT ISSN 0300-4678
ACTION (FITZROY). 1969. q. Aus.$5. Brotherhood of St. Laurence, 67 Brunswick St., Fitzroy, Vic. 3065, Australia. TEL 61-3-419-7055. FAX 61-3-417-2691. bk.rev. circ. 42,000. **Document type:** newsletter.
Description: For donors and supporters of the brotherhood on its services and advocacy for the disadvantaged.

360 US
ACTION (WASHINGTON). irreg. (4-8/yr.). $40 membership. Interfaith Impact for Justice and Peace, 110 Maryland Ave., N.E., Washington, DC 20002. TEL 202-543-2800.
Formerly: Action Alert.
Description: Each issue covers a different topic in areas such as civil rights, world peace, poverty, environment and economics.

360 AT ISSN 1030-7451
ACTIVNEWS. 1953. m. Aus.$12.50 includes membership. Activ Foundation Inc., P.O. Box 446, Jolimont, W.A. 6014, Australia. TEL 09-387-0555. FAX 09-387-0599. Ed. Lindy Markes. adv.; bk.rev. circ. 2,700. (back issues avail.) **Document type:** newsletter.
Formerly: Our Children (ISSN 0048-2382)
Description: Promotes the wide range of services for adults and children with developmental disabilities in Western Australia.

360 FR ISSN 1145-8690
ACTUALITES SOCIALES HEBDOMADAIRES. 1955. w. 340 F. (foreign 740 F.)(typically set in Sep.). Actualites Sociales Hebdomadaires, s.a.r.l., 14 bd. Montmartre, 75009 Paris, France. TEL 47-70-84-59. FAX 48-00-06-74. Ed. Cecile Tresarieux. adv.: B&W page 6250 F., color page 7140 F. bk.rev. circ. 43,500. (looseleaf format)

361 BG ISSN 0042-1057
ADHUNA. (Text in Bengali) 1974. m. $10. Association of Development Agencies in Bangladesh, 1-3 Block F, Lalmatia, Dhaka 1207, Bangladesh. Ed. Minar Monsur. adv.; bk.rev. circ. 7,000.
Former titles (until 1991): A D A B Sangbad; Adab Sangbad; Adab.
Description: For grassroots organization of Bangladesh's NGO workers.

360 US ISSN 0364-3107
HV1 CODEN: ASWODB
ADMINISTRATION IN SOCIAL WORK; the quarterly journal of human services management. 1977. q. $235 (foreing $329) (effective 1996). Haworth Press, Inc., 10 Alice St., Binghamton, NY 13904. TEL 607-722-5857; 800-342-9678. FAX 607-722-1424. Ed. Rino J. Patti. adv.; bk.rev. circ. 794. (also avail. in microfiche from HAW; back issues avail.; reprint service avail. from HAW)
Indexed: ABI Inform., Abstr.Health Care Manage.Stud., ASSIA, BPIA, Bull.Signal., Curr.Cont., Hosp.Lit.Ind., Human Resour.Abstr., IMFL, Manage.Abstr., Manage.Cont., Mid.East: Abstr.& Ind., PSI, Psychol.Abstr., Ref.Zh., Sage Fam.Stud.Abstr., Soc.Sci.Ind. (1994-), Soc.Work Res.& Abstr., Sociol.Abstr., SSCI. **Document type:** academic/scholarly publication.
—BLDSC (0696.270000); Faxon; Genuine Article; Haworth; SWETS; UnCover.
Description: Provides current information to administrators, supervisors, managers and sub-executives in social work and related human services fields.
Refereed Serial

362.7 US ISSN 0273-6497
ADOPTALK. 1976. q. $30 (effective 1992). North American Council on Adoptable Children (NACAC), 970 Raymond Ave., No. 106, St. Paul, MN 55114-1149. TEL 612-644-3036. FAX 612-644-9848. Ed. Diane Riggs. adv.; bk.rev. circ. 8,000. (processed) **Document type:** newsletter.
Supersedes (1965-1976): National Adoptalk (ISSN 0027-8459)
Description: Information and articles about special needs adoption, foster care, adoptive family support, resources, and federal legislation.

ADOPTED CHILD. see CHILDREN AND YOUTH — About

362.7 US ISSN 1046-3569
HV875.55
ADOPTION.* 1989. bi-m. $30. Ulick Publishing Co., 150 Houston St., Ste. 308, Batavia, IL 60510-1953. TEL 708-406-8330. Ed. Geoffrey Golson.
Description: For people exploring the various options of adopting children.

362.7 UK ISSN 0308-5759
HV875
ADOPTION AND FOSTERING. 1976. q. £25 (foreign £30) (typically set in Apr.). British Agencies for Adoption & Fostering, Skyline House, 200 Union St., London SE1 0L4, England. TEL 0171-593-2000. Ed. Shaila Shah. adv.; bk.rev.; stat.; cum.index. circ. 5,000. (back issues avail.) **Indexed:** ASSIA, Euro.LJI, LJI, Psychol.Abstr., Soc.Work Res.& Abstr. **Document type:** academic/scholarly publication.
—BLDSC (0696.592000).
Formerly: Child Adoption.
Description: Multi-disciplinary professional look at children in danger of separation from their families or needing foster care or adoption.

362.7 UK ISSN 0966-2103
ADOPTION & FOSTERING NEWS. 1979. m. British Agencies for Adoption & Fostering, Skyline House, Union St., London SE1 0L4, England. TEL 0171-593-2000. **Document type:** newsletter.
Former titles (until 199?): B A A F News (ISSN 0260-3888); (until 1981): A B A F A News (ISSN 0143-2591)
Description: Includes news and information on publications, practice, policy, legislation, training events and seminars.

362.7 US
ADOPTION FACTBOOK; United States data, issues, regulations and resources. 1985. irreg., 2nd ed., 1989. $39.95. National Council for Adoption, Inc., 1930 17th St., N.W., Washington, DC 20009-6207. TEL 202-328-1200.
Description: Comprehensive U.S. statistics on adoption. Information sources for adoption and related services, especially services to young, single or troubled parents. Includes a hotline.

ADOPTION HELPER; devoted to helping people adopt. see CHILDREN AND YOUTH — About

ADOPTION NEWSLETTER DIRECTORY. see CHILDREN AND YOUTH — Abstracting, Bibliographies, Statistics

SOCIAL SERVICES AND WELFARE

361 929   US
ADOPTION REFORM ORGANIZATIONS.* 1985. s-a. $35. Adoption Triangle Ministries, c/o Adoption Reunion Center, Box 1860, Cape Coral, FL 33910-1860. TEL 813-542-1342. FAX 813-549-9393. (Subscr. to: Musser Foundation, Box 1860, Cape Coral, FL 33910) Ed. Sandy Musser. circ. 350. (looseleaf format) **Document type:** directory.
Description: A mailing list of active networking organizations working for adoption reform.

362   US
ADULT AND FAMILY SERVICES IN OREGON. m. Department of Human Resources, Public Welfare Division, 304 Public Service Bldg., Salem, OR 97310. TEL 503-378-2720. illus.
Formerly: Public Welfare in Oregon (ISSN 0474-4039)

360   US   ISSN 0899-1995
HV85
ADULT RESIDENTIAL CARE JOURNAL. 1987-1991; resumed 1992. s-a. $20 to individuals; institutions $30 (effective 1995). John M. McCoin, Ed. & Pub., 4913 W. Colonial Way, Lawrence, KS 66049. TEL 913-842-1386. bk.rev. (back issues avail.; reprint service avail. from UMI) **Indexed:** Abstr.Soc.Geront., Psychol.Abstr. (1987-), Soc.Work Res.& Abstr., Sp.Ed.Needs Abstr. **Document type:** academic/scholarly publication.
—BLDSC (0696.684700); UMI. **CCC.**
Formerly (until 1988): Adult Foster Care Journal (ISSN 8756-6559)
Description: Publishes empirical research communications and discussions of practical and policy issues in the field of non-institutional community-based residential care for adults with histories of mental illness, mental illness or frailties of aging.
Refereed Serial

361 309.2   GH   ISSN 0515-4510
ADVANCE. 1954. q. Ministry of Social Welfare and Community Development, P.O. Box 778, Accra, Ghana. (processed)

360   US
ADVANCES (PRINCETON). 1988. q. Robert Wood Johnson Foundation, Box 2316, Princeton, NJ 08543-2316. TEL 609-452-8701. Ed. Paul Tarini. **Document type:** newsletter.
Description: Grants, programs sponsored by the Robert Wood Johnson Foundation.

ADVANCES IN CLINICAL REHABILITATION. see *MEDICAL SCIENCES — Physical Medicine And Rehabilitation*

362.1   US   ISSN 1053-0606
RA644.5
ADVANCES IN LONG-TERM CARE. 1991. biennial. Springer Publishing Company, 536 Broadway, New York, NY 10012-3955. TEL 212-431-4370. FAX 212-941-7842. **Document type:** academic/scholarly publication.

361.73   US
HG177
ADVANCING PHILANTHROPY. q. $50 to non-members. National Society of Fund Raising Executives, 1101 King St., Ste. 700, Alexandria, VA 22314. TEL 703-684-0410. FAX 703-684-0540. Ed. Donald Levy. adv.; bk.rev. circ. 16,000. (back issues avail.) **Document type:** academic/scholarly publication.
Formerly: N S F R E Journal (ISSN 0196-3295)
Description: Provides a forum for research and the presentation of practical new ideas in the fund-raising profession.

360 352.7   UK   ISSN 0950-5458
ADVISER. 1979. bi-m. £20. Shelter National Housing Aid Trust, 63 Waterloo Rd., Wolverhampton, West Midlands WV1 4QU, England. TEL 0902-310568. FAX 0902-710068. (Co-sponsor: National Association of Citizens Advice Bureau) Eds. Roman Leszczyszyn, Carolan Davidge. adv.; bk.rev.; index. circ. 3,500. **Indexed:** Euro.LJI, LJI.
—BLDSC (0712.289400).
Former titles: Housing Aid; S N H A T News Bulletin (ISSN 0262-4885)
Description: Guide to social security, housing, employment. Includes consumer and money advice.

362.4   US
THE ADVOCATE (ALBANY). 1980. 4/yr. free. Office of Advocate for Persons with Disabilities, 1 Empire State Plaza, Ste. 1001, Albany, NY 12223. FAX 518-473-6005. Ed. Alan J. Sangiacomo. **Document type:** government publication, newsletter.

360   CN   ISSN 0847-2890
ADVOCATE (EDMONTON). 1975. q. Can.$20. Alberta Association of Social Workers, 9912 - 106 St., No. 52, Edmonton, AB T5K 1C5, Canada. TEL 403-421-1167. FAX 403-421-1168. Ed. Margaret Duncan. adv. contact: Gladys Smecko. circ. 1,600. **Document type:** newsletter.
Description: Advocates for the profession of social work and its clients; ensures that quality services are provided in fully-funded, effective organizations.

THE ADVOCATE (INDIANAPOLIS). see *POLITICAL SCIENCE — Civil Rights*

360 305.4   US   ISSN 0886-1099
HV1442
AFFILIA; journal of women and social work. 1986. q. $50 to individuals; institutions $145 (effective Sep. 1995). Sage Publications, Inc., 2455 Teller Rd., Thousand Oaks, CA 91320. TEL 805-499-7021. FAX 805-499-0871. E-mail: libraries@sagepub.com. (Overseas subscr. to: Sage Publications Ltd., 6 Bonhill St., London EC2A 4PU, England; Sage Publications India Pvt. Ltd., P.O. Box 4025, New Delhi 110 048, India) Ed. Carol H. Meyer. adv.; bk.rev. circ. 1,150. (back issues avail.; reprint service avail.) **Indexed:** IMFL, Mult.Ed.Abstr., PSI, Sage Fam.Stud.Abstr., Soc.Work Res.& Abstr., Sociol.Abstr., Viol.& Abuse Abstr., Wom.Stud.Abstr. (1986-). **Document type:** academic/scholarly publication.
—BLDSC (0731.720700); Faxon; UMI; UnCover. **CCC.**
Description: Brings insight and knowledge to the field of social work from a feminist perspective and provides research and tools necessary to make large changes and improvements in the delivery of social services.

360   SA
AFFORDABILITY. 2/yr. free. Human Sciences Research Council, Co-operative Programme: Affordable Social Security, Private Bag X41, Pretoria 0001, South Africa. Ed. Ina Snyman. circ. 1,200. **Document type:** newsletter.
Description: Covers initiatives and studies on subjects relating to affordable material provision, personal safety and social provision.

361   US
▼**AID TO LITHUANIA;** keeping the lifeline of hope flowing. 1994. q. Aid to Lithuania, Inc., 4557 Fairway Ct., Wasterford, MI 48328-3483. TEL 810-682-0098. **Document type:** newsletter.
Description: Covers the organization's and the U.S. Lithuanian community's efforts to provide medical and financial assistance to the needy in their homeland.

362.1 616.9   US   ISSN 1055-0380
RA644.A25
AIDS & SOCIETY. 1989. biennial. $20 to individuals; institutions $30. African - Caribbean Institute, 4 W. Wheelock St., Hanover, NH 03755. TEL 802-649-5296. FAX 802-649-2331. TELEX 4930372 RPC UI. Ed. Richard Fredland. (back issues avail.) **Document type:** academic/scholarly publication, bulletin.

THE AIDS CRISIS. see *MEDICAL SCIENCES — Communicable Diseases*

AKRON JEWISH NEWS. see *ETHNIC INTERESTS*

360   GW
AKTUELL JOSEFS - GESELLSCHAFT. 1986. q. Josefs - Gesellschaft e.V., Alarichstr. 40, 50679 Cologne, Germany. TEL 0221-88998-0. FAX 0221-8899860. circ. 50,000.
Formerly (until 1990): Dankbrief.

ALERT; maandblad voor rampenbestrijding en crisisbeheersing. see *CIVIL DEFENSE*

360   AT   ISSN 0706-1870
ALERT (ADELAIDE). 1980. q. Aus.$20 membership. Diabetic Association of South Australia, Unit 4 159 Burbridge Rd., Hilton, S.A. 5033, Australia. TEL 08-234-1977. FAX 08-234-2013. Ed. J. Barber. circ. 10,000. **Document type:** newsletter.

360 616.9   US
ALERT (LOS ANGELES). 1987. q. $10 (free to qualified personnel). Universal Fellowship of Metropolitan Community Churches, c/o Rev. Steve Pieters Ed., 5300 Santa Monica Blvd., Ste. 304, Los Angeles, CA 90029. TEL 213-464-5100. FAX 213-464-2123. bk.rev. circ. 1,600. **Document type:** newsletter.
Description: Covers AIDS related legislation, education, research and treatment.

368.4   NE   ISSN 0401-331X
ALGEMEEN WERKLOOSHEIDSFONDS. JAARVERSLAG. 1949. a. Tijdelike Instituut voor Coordinatie en Afstemming (TICA), Sectorbureau Fondsen en Indelingen, Postbus 429, 2700 AK Zoetermeer, Netherlands. TEL 31-20-5047621. FAX 31-20-5047666. **Document type:** corporate report.

ALL THE WORLD. see *RELIGIONS AND THEOLOGY — Other Denominations And Sects*

360   UK
ALMSHOUSE ASSOCIATION. ANNUAL REPORT AND STATEMENT OF ACCOUNTS. a. £1. Almshouse Association, Billingbear Lodge, Wokingham, Berks. RG40 5RU, England. TEL 01344-52922. Ed.Bd. stat. **Document type:** corporate report.
Formerly: National Association of Almshouses. Yearbook and Statement of Accounts.

362.6   UK
ALMSHOUSES GAZETTE. 1950. q. 50p. Almshouse Association, Billingbear Lodge, Wokingham, Berks. RG40 5RU, England. TEL 01344-52922. **Document type:** bulletin.

ALTENHILFE; Beispiele, Informationen, Meinungen. see *GERONTOLOGY AND GERIATRICS*

ALZHEIMER'S RESEARCH REVIEW. see *MEDICAL SCIENCES — Psychiatry And Neurology*

AMENTIA; la voix des parents. see *HANDICAPPED*

AMERICAN FOUNDATION FOR THE BLIND. ANNUAL REPORT. see *HANDICAPPED — Visually Impaired*

361.7   US   ISSN 0071-9617
AMERICAN FRIENDS SERVICE COMMITTEE. ANNUAL REPORT. 1917. a. free to contributors. American Friends Service Committee, Inc., 1501 Cherry St., Philadelphia, PA 19102. TEL 215-241-7000. FAX 215-241-7275. TELEX 247559 AFSC UR.

362.1 614   US   ISSN 0888-0352
RA973.5
AMERICAN HEALTH CARE ASSOCIATION. PROVIDER. 1975. m. $48. American Health Care Association, 1201 L St., N.W., Washington, DC 20005. TEL 202-842-4444. FAX 202-842-3860. Ed. Marla Gold. adv.; illus. circ. 36,000. **Indexed:** Abstr.Soc.Geront., CLOA, I.P.A., Med.Care Rev.
●Also available online.
—BLDSC (6937.687000); Faxon; UMI; UnCover.
Formerly: American Health Care Association. Journal (ISSN 0360-4969)

AMERICAN JOURNAL OF ORTHOPSYCHIATRY. see *PSYCHOLOGY*

362.6   US
AMERICAN PARKINSON DISEASE ASSOCIATION. NEWSLETTER. q. donation. American Parkinson Disease Association, 60 Bay St., Staten Island, NY 10301. TEL 800-223-2372. Dr. Paul Maestrone. **Document type:** newsletter.
Description: Informs donors of A.P.D.A. activities, how to cope with their disorder, and of developments in medical research.

361.6   US   ISSN 0163-8300
AMERICAN PUBLIC WELFARE ASSOCIATION. W - MEMO. 1961. irreg. (10/yr.) $75 to non-members; members $65; foreign $85. American Public Welfare Association, c/o Publication Services, 810 First St., N.E., Ste. 500, Washington, DC 20002-4267. TEL 202-682-0100. FAX 202-289-6555. (looseleaf format)
Description: Covers national human service issues and policies aimed principally at state administrators.

SOCIAL SERVICES AND WELFARE

361 US ISSN 0894-5454
HV575
AMERICAN RED CROSS. ANNUAL REPORT. 1901. a. free. American National Red Cross, Communications, 8111 Gatehouse Rd., Falls Church, VA 22042. TEL 703-206-7542. FAX 703-206-7578. E-mail: davisj@usa.red-cross.org. circ. 25,000. (also avail. in microfilm from BHP) **Document type:** corporate report.
Formerly: American National Red Cross. Annual Report (ISSN 0080-0384)

362 610 US ISSN 0362-4048
HD7255.A2
AMERICAN REHABILITATION. 1975. q. $9 (foreign $11.25) (effective 1995). (U.S. Rehabilitation Services Administration) U.S. Department of Education, Mary E. Switzer Bldg., Rm. 3127, 330 C St., S.W., Washington, DC 20202. TEL 202-732-1296. (Subscr. to: Superintendent of Documents, U.S. Government Printing Office, Box 371954, Pittsburgh, PA 15250-7954. TEL 202-512-1800. FAX 202-512-2250) Ed. Frank Romano. bk.rev. circ. 8,000. (also avail. in microfilm from UMI; back issues avail.) **Indexed:** Hlth.Ind., Ind.U.S.Gov.Per., Med.Care Rev., MEDOC, Rehabil.Lit. **Document type:** academic/scholarly publication, government publication.
●Also available online. Vendor(s): University Microfilms International.
—BLDSC (0853.541000); Faxon; UMI.
  Description: Comments on all aspects of life affecting handicapped persons, bringing program, treatment, news, and legislative affairs to interested professional and consumer groups.

360 323.4 362.4 US
AMERICANS WITH DISABILITIES ACT TECHNICAL ASSISTANCE MANUAL: TITLE I. base vol. (plus irreg. updates). $25 (foreign $31.25). U.S. Equal Employment Opportunity Commission (EEOC), Office of Communications, 1801 L St., N.W., Washington, DC 20507. (Subscr. to: Superintendent of Documents, U.S. Government Printing Office, Box 371954, Pittsburgh, PA 15250-7954. TEL 202-512-1800. FAX 202-512-2250) (looseleaf format) **Document type:** government publication.
  Description: Provides guidance on the practical application of legal requirements of the Americans with Disabilities Act of 1990, as established by the E.E.O.C.

360 323.4 362.4 US
AMERICANS WITH DISABILITIES ACT TECHNICAL ASSISTANCE MANUAL: TITLE II. base vol. (plus irreg. updates). $24 (foreign $30). U.S. Department of Justice, 10th St. & Constitution Ave., N.W., Washington, DC 20530. (Subscr. to: Superintendent of Documents, U.S. Government Printing Office, Box 371954, Pittsburgh, PA 15250-7954. TEL 202-512-1800. FAX 202-512-2250) (looseleaf format) **Document type:** government publication.
  Description: Shows how discrimination on the basis of disability in state and local governments is prohibited by the Americans with Disabilities Act of 1990.

360 323.4 362.4 US
AMERICANS WITH DISABILITIES ACT TECHNICAL ASSISTANCE MANUAL: TITLE III. base vol. (plus irreg. updates). $25 (foreign $31.25). U.S. Department of Justice, 10th St. & Constitution Ave., N.W., Washington, DC 20530. (Subscr. to: Superintendent of Documents, U.S. Government Printing Office, Box 371954, Pittsburgh, PA 15250-7954. TEL 202-512-1800. FAX 202-512-2250) (looseleaf format) **Document type:** government publication.
  Description: Shows how discrimination against persons with disabilities in commercial facilities and places of public accommodation is prohibited by the Americans with Disabilities Act of 1990.

361.73 US ISSN 1048-4965
HV87
AMERICA'S NEW FOUNDATIONS. a. $195. Taft Group, 12300 Twinbrook Pwky., Ste. 520, Rockville, MD 20852. TEL 301-816-0210. FAX 301-816-0811. (Subscr. to: Taft Group, Box 33477, Detroit, MI 48232-5477. TEL 800-877-TAFT. FAX 313-961-6083) Ed. Mark Scott; Pub. Dennis Poupard. **Document type:** directory.
  Description: Lists more than 3,400 new private and corporate foundations.

360 US ISSN 0886-1196
AMERICA'S SPIRIT. 1941. q. free to qualified personnel. United Service Organizations, Inc., U S O World Headquarters, Washington Navy Yard, 901 M St., S.E., Bldg. 198, Washington, DC 20374-5096. TEL 202-610-5700. FAX 202-610-5701. Ed. Jennifer L. Blanck. illus. circ. 10,000. (tabloid format; also avail. in microform from UMI) **Document type:** newsletter.
  Formerly: Wherever They Go.

AMTLICHES MITTEILUNGSBLATT DER MARKTGEMEINDE LEOBERSDORF. see *PUBLIC ADMINISTRATION — Municipal Government*

362.8 UK ISSN 0003-2840
ANCHOR.* 1947. q. $60. Apostleship of the Sea, National Board for England and Wales, Anchor House, Anlaby Rd., Hull, Yorks., England. Ed. Rev. M.F. Hardy. adv.; bk.rev.; abstr.; illus.; index. circ. 6,000.

360 IT ISSN 0003-4568
ANNALI DELLA CARITA. 1930. m. L.20000. (Vincentian Fathers) Centro Liturgico Vincenziano, Via Pompeo Magno 21, 00192 Rome, Italy. circ. 3,000.

ANNUAIRE H L M. (Habitations a Loyer Modere) see *HOUSING AND URBAN PLANNING*

ANNUAL EDITIONS: HUMAN RESOURCES. see *SOCIOLOGY*

309.1 US ISSN 0272-4464
HN51
ANNUAL EDITIONS: SOCIAL PROBLEMS. 1973. a. $12.95. Dushkin Publishing Group, Sluice Dock, Guilford, CT 06437-9989. TEL 203-453-4351. FAX 203-453-6000. Ed. Harold Widdison; Pub. Ian Nielsen. illus. **Indexed:** Lang.& Lang.Behav.Abstr., Soc.Sci.Ind. **Document type:** academic/scholarly publication.
  Formerly: Annual Editions: Readings in Social Problems (ISSN 0094-9183)
  Refereed Serial

ANNUAL REPORT ON PRIVATIZATION. see *PUBLIC ADMINISTRATION*

ANTI-CENSORSHIP NEWSLETTER. see *SOCIOLOGY*

APPAREL GUILD. JOURNAL. see *CLOTHING TRADE*

366 FR ISSN 0991-7357
ARC-BOUTANT;* organe d'information des questions scolaires et familiales. 1952. m. 15 F. U.R.O.G, 28 rue de l'Ande, 31500 Toulouse, France. charts; stat.
  Formed by the 1952 merger of: Midi-Occident (ISSN 0991-7365); Bulletin Regional de Liaison de L'A.P.E.L. (ISSN 0991-7381)

362.3 US
THE ARC TODAY. 1952. q. $15. Arc, National Headquarters, 500 E. Border St., Ste. 300, Arlington, TX 76010. TEL 817-261-6003. FAX 817-277-3491. Eds. Jim Humphrey, Liz Moore. adv.; bk.rev.; illus. circ. 140,000. (tabloid format; also avail. in microform from UMI; reprint service avail. from UMI) **Document type:** newspaper.
—UMI.
  Former titles: A R C (ISSN 0199-9435); Mental Retardation News (ISSN 0009-4072); Children Limited.

360 300 GW ISSN 0340-3564
ARCHIV FUER WISSENSCHAFT UND PRAXIS DER SOZIALEN ARBEIT. 1970. q. DM.60. (Deutscher Verein fuer Offentliche und Private Fuersorge) W. Kohlhammer GmbH, Hessbruehlstr. 69, 70565 Stuttgart, Germany. TEL 0711-7863-1. FAX 0711-7863263. Ed. Teresa Bock. bk.rev. circ. 800. **Document type:** bulletin.

300 US ISSN 0363-2903
PN6099.6
ARETE. 1970. s-w. $15. University of South Carolina, College of Social Work, Columbia, SC 29208. TEL 803-777-5291. Ed. Terry Tirrito. abstr. circ. 900. **Indexed:** Abstr.Soc.Work, Lang.& Lang.Behav.Abstr., Mid.East: Abstr.& Ind., Phys.Ed.Ind., Soc.Work Res.& Abstr., Sociol.Abstr.
  Description: Focuses on problems, issues and new developments in social work practice, social work education and social welfare.

ARIZONA MEDICINE. see *PUBLIC HEALTH AND SAFETY*

ARKANSAS. DIVISION OF REHABILITATION SERVICES. ANNUAL REPORT. see *EDUCATION — Special Education And Rehabilitation*

ASAHIGAWASO KENKYU NENPO/ASAHIGAWASO INSTITUTE OF MEDICAL WELFARE. ANNUAL REPORT. see *MEDICAL SCIENCES*

ASIAN AMERICAN POLICY REVIEW. see *ETHNIC INTERESTS*

ASSOCIATION FRANCAISE DES AMIS D'ALBERT SCHWEITZER. CAHIERS. see *PHILOSOPHY*

ASSOCIATION OF GAY AND LESBIAN PSYCHIATRISTS. NEWSLETTER. see *HOMOSEXUALITY*

ASSOCIATION OF MENTAL HEALTH ADMINISTRATORS. NEWSLETTER. see *PUBLIC HEALTH AND SAFETY*

ASSOCIAZIONE NAZIONALE MUTILATI E INVALIDI DI GUERRA. SEZIONE DI ROMA. NOTIZIARIO. see *MILITARY*

360 362 FR
ATELIERS PROTEGES. 1960. q. 30 F. 7 bd. Chastenet-de-Gery, 96270 le Kremlin-Bicetre, France.

362.7 346.1 649 SW ISSN 0347-6324
ATT ADOPTERA. 1970. bi-m. SEK 225 (effective 1994). Adoptionscentrum (AC), P.O. Box 1520, S-172 29 Sundbyberg, Sweden. TEL 46-8-627-44-00. Ed. Ingert Nilsson. adv.; bk.rev. circ. 10,500. **Document type:** bulletin.
  Formerly (until 1975): Adoptionscentrum. Rapport.

AUF - EINE FRAUENZEITSCHRIFT. see *WOMEN'S INTERESTS*

361 US
AUGUSTUS. 1978. m. $22 to individuals; institutions $45; students $17. National Center on Institutions and Alternatives, 635 Slaters Ln., Ste. G100, Alexandria, VA 22314. TEL 703-684-0373. Ed. Jerome G. Miller. bk.rev.; illus.; index. circ. 3,000. (back issues avail.)
  Formerly: Institutions, Etc. (ISSN 0276-8836)

AUSTRALIAN AND NEW ZEALAND JOURNAL OF FAMILY THERAPY. see *SOCIOLOGY*

360 AT ISSN 0004-9557
HN841
AUSTRALIAN JOURNAL OF SOCIAL ISSUES. 1961. q. $50 to individuals; institutions $75 (effective 1993). Australian Council of Social Service, Inc. (ACOSS), Lacked Bag 11, Darlinghurst, Sydney, N.S.W. 2010, Australia. TEL 61-2-3324355. FAX 61-2-3321515. Ed. Gisela Kaplan. adv.; bk.rev.; abstr.; bibl.; index, cum.index. circ. 1,000. (also avail. in microfilm from UMI) **Indexed:** Abstr.Soc.Work, ASSIA, Aus.P.A.I.S., Curr.Cont., Gdlns., Geo.Abstr., Int.Lab.Doc., Lang.& Lang.Behav.Abstr., Soc.Work Res.& Abstr., SSCI, World Bibl.Soc.Sec.
—UMI. CCC.
  Supersedes in part: A C O S S Quarterly (ISSN 0045-0391)
  Description: Articles discuss particular social issues, review conceptual problems, present empirical reports and debate policy alternatives.

360 340 AT
AUSTRALIAN SOCIAL SECURITY GUIDE. (In 2 vols.) 1984. 8/yr. C C H Australia Ltd., P.O. Box 230, North Ryde, N.S.W. 2113, Australia. TEL 61-2-8571555. FAX 61-2-8571601. (looseleaf format)
  Description: Contains full legislation of the Social Security Act with up-to-date commentary, notes and tables.

SOCIAL SERVICES AND WELFARE

360   AT   ISSN 0312-407X
AUSTRALIAN SOCIAL WORK. 1947. q. Aus.$90 (effective 1995). Australian Association of Social Workers, P.O. Box 84, Hawker, Canberra, A.C.T. 2614, Australia. TEL 61-6-255-1626. FAX 61-6-255-2225. Ed. Anne Roughley. adv. contact: Anne Raghley. bk.rev.; charts; index; circ. 4,300 (paid). (tabloid format; reprint service avail.) **Indexed:** ASSIA, Aus.P.A.I.S., Soc.Work Res.& Abstr., Sp.Ed.Needs Abstr., Stud.Wom.Abstr. **Document type:** academic/scholarly publication.
—BLDSC (1820.600000); UnCover.
     Formerly: Australian Journal of Social Work (ISSN 0004-9565)
     Description: Provides access to informed opinion on current social, political, economic and human relations, trends and issues.

362.7   AU
AUSTRIA. STATISTISCHES ZENTRALAMT. STATISTIK DER JUGENDWOHLFAHRT. (Subseries of its: Beitraege zur Oesterreichischen Statistik) 1965. a. S.300. Oesterreichisches Statistisches Zentralamt, Hintere Zollamtsstr. 2b, A-1033 Vienna, Austria. TEL 0222-71128-0. FAX 0222-7156828. **Document type:** government publication.
     Formerly: Austria. Statistisches Zentralamt. Jugendwohlfahrtspflege.
     Description: Activity of tribunals and administrative authorities, with information on education assistance and child welfare work.

360   IT   ISSN 0392-2278
AUTONOMIE LOCALI E SERVIZI SOCIALI; vademecum a schede. 1978. 3/yr. L.120000. Societa Editrice Il Mulino, Strada Maggiore, 37, 40125 Bologna, Italy. TEL 39-51-256011. FAX 39-51-256034. Ed.Bd. adv.; index. circ. 4,000. (back issues avail.)

AUTUMN SCHOOL OF STUDIES ON ALCOHOL & DRUGS. PROCEEDINGS OF SEMINARS. see *DRUG ABUSE AND ALCOHOLISM*

360   IS   ISSN 0334-4525
AVAREYANUT VESTIYA CHEURATI/CRIME AND SOCIAL DEVIANCE. (Text in Hebrew; summaries in English) 1972. q. $14. (Bar-Ilan University, Department of Criminology) Bar-Ilan University Press, Ramat Gan 52900, Israel. Ed. Israel Nachshon. adv.; bk.rev.; abstr.; bibl.; charts; illus.; stat.; index. circ. 500. (back issues avail.) **Indexed:** Ind.Heb.Per., Sociol.Abstr. **Document type:** academic/scholarly publication.

360   IT   ISSN 0005-2566
AZIONE COOPERATIVA. 1911. 11/yr. membership. Comitato Regionale Lombardo delle Cooperative, Via Palmanova 22, 20132 Milan, Italy. TEL 2845-6208. Ed. Roberta Meneghini. adv.; B&W page L.2000000. bk.rev.; circ. 10,000 (controlled).

361   UK   ISSN 0260-082X
B A A F DISCUSSION SERIES. irreg. British Agencies for Adoption & Fostering, Skyline House, 200 Union St., London SE1 0L4, England. TEL 0171-593-2000. **Document type:** academic/scholarly publication, monographic series.
     Description: Presents current issues of interest to workers in the area of social service and welfare.

361   UK   ISSN 0260-0803
B A A F PRACTICE SERIES. irreg. British Agencies for Adoption & Fostering, Skyline House, 200 Union St., London SE1 0L4, England. TEL 0171-593-2000. **Document type:** trade publication, monographic series.
     Description: Covers the major practice needs of workers in adoption, fostering and child care.

361   UK   ISSN 0260-0811
B A A F RESEARCH SERIES. irreg. British Agencies for Adoption & Fostering, Skyline House, 200 Union St., London SE1 0L4, England. TEL 0171-593-2000. **Document type:** academic/scholarly publication, monographic series.
     Description: Covers recent research on adoption, fostering, and child care.

B D K J JOURNAL. (Bund der Deutschen Katholischen Jugend) see *CHILDREN AND YOUTH — For*

361 362.7   UN
B F H I NEWS. (Baby-Friendly Hospital Initiative) (Editions in Portuguese and Spanish) 1992. m. free. United Nations Children's Fund (UNICEF), UNICEF House, 3 United Nations Plaza, New York, NY 10017. TEL 212-326-7000. FAX 212-888-7465. TELEX 7607848. Ed. Martha Thomas. **Document type:** newsletter.
     Description: Promotes breastfeeding of infants and dispels the myths of the advantages of formulas.

352.4 362.6   UK
B L E S M A G. 1947. 3/yr. £1. (British Limbless Ex-Servicemen's Association) M & B (Felstead) Ltd., 185-187 High Rd., Chadwell Heath, Essex RM6 6NA, England. TEL 0181-590-1124. FAX 0181-599-2932. Ed. R.R. Holland. adv. contact: H.R. Twitchett. bk.rev.; circ. 10,000 (controlled). (back issues avail.) **Document type:** consumer publication.
     Description: Promotes the welfare of those of either sex who have lost a limb or limbs, or one or both eyes as a result of service in any branch of Her Majesty's Forces.

362.7   SW   ISSN 1101-9417
B U D - INFORMATION. 1989. irreg. Civildepartmentet, Barn- och Ungdomsdelegationen, S-103 33 Stockholm, Sweden.

361.77   GW
BAFF. 1970. q. Bayerisches Jugendrotkreuz, Holbeinstr. 11, 81679 Munich, Germany. TEL 089-9241341. FAX 089-9241210. bk.rev. circ. 10,500. **Document type:** newspaper.
     Description: Information about Red Cross youth and youth activities for readers between the ages of 8 and 25.

362   JA   ISSN 0912-8662
BANBU/BAMBOO. (Text in Japanese) m. 900 Yen per no. Nihon Iryo Kikaku, 16-1, Kanda Sudacho 1-chome, Chiyoda-ku, Tokyo 101, Japan.

360   AU   ISSN 0005-5999
BARMHERZIGKEIT; Blaetter fuer die Freunde des Hauses der Barmherzigkeit. 1959. q. free. Institut Haus der Barmherzigkeit, Vinzenzgasse 2-6, A-1180 Vienna, Austria. TEL 0222-40199. FAX 0222-40199222. Ed. Karl Pilnacek. abstr. circ. 800,000. **Document type:** newsletter.

360   UK
BARNARDO NEWS. bi-m. free. Barnardo's, Tanners Ln., Barkingside, Ilford, Essex IG6 1QG, England. TEL 0181-550-5522. FAX 0181-550-0429. Ed. Dorothy Howes. circ. 7,000 (controlled). **Document type:** newspaper.
     Description: Contains news about child care and appeals work.

362.7 346.1   SW   ISSN 0282-454X
BARNEN FRAMFOER ALLT/CHILDREN ABOVE ALL. 1980. q. SEK 50 (effective 1990). Barnen Framfoer Allt (BFA), P.O. Box 3006, S-400 10 Goeteborg, Sweden.

360   GW   ISSN 0171-9319
BEGEGNEN UND HELFEN. 1912. q. DM.16. Verband der Caritas-Konferenzen Deutschlands, Postfach 420, 79004 Freiburg, Germany. TEL 0761-2001. (Co-sponsor: Gemeinschaft der Vinzenzkonferenzen Deutschlands) Ed. Elisabeth Goetz. bk.rev.; index. circ. 11,000. **Document type:** bulletin.

362.6 363.6   BE   ISSN 0067-558X
BELGIUM. MINISTERE DE LA PREVOYANCE SOCIALE. RAPPORT GENERAL SUR LA SECURITE SOCIALE. (Text in Flemish or French) 1962. a. 900 BEF. Ministere de la Prevoyance Sociale, Rue de la Vierge Noire 3C, 1000 Brussels, Belgium. Ed.Bd. **Document type:** government publication.

360 614   BE   ISSN 0771-792X
BELGIUM. MINISTERE DE LA SANTE PUBLIQUE ET DE LA FAMILLE. RAPPORT ANNUEL. Dutch edition (ISSN 0771-7946) (Text in French) 1954. a. Ministere de la Sante Publique et de la Famille, Cite Administrative de l'Etat, Bibliotheque, Quartier Vesale, 1010 Brussels, Belgium. charts; stat. **Document type:** government publication.

361.3 158   UK   ISSN 0268-2621
BEREAVEMENT CARE; an international journal for those who help bereaved people. 1982. 3/yr. £11 to individuals (rest of Europe £13; U.S. $30; Canada $40; Australia $38; elsewhere £20); institutions £20 (rest of Europe £23; U.S. $45; Canada $60; Austrlia £57; elsewhere £30) (effective 1995). Cruse - Bereavement Care, 126 Sheen Rd., Richmond, Surrey TW9 1UR, England. TEL 0181-940-4818. FAX 0181-940-7638. Ed. Patricia Scowen. adv. contact: Rosie Dalzell. bk.rev.; abstr.; charts; illus.; index. circ. 2,000. (back issues avail.) **Document type:** academic/scholarly publication.
—BLDSC (1893.880000).
     Description: Contains articles of importance to those who help bereaved persons, including counsellors, psychotherapists, social workers, the clergy, funeral directors, doctors, and nurses.
     Refereed Serial

362.7 370   GW
BERUFSAUSBILDUNG JUGENDARBEITSLOSIGKEIT. 1976. m. DM.350. U. Kurz Verlag, Korallenweg 10, 70619 Stuttgart, Germany. TEL 0711-442076. FAX 0711-445644. Ed. Heinz Kurz. circ. 450. **Document type:** bulletin.

BETHPHAGE MESSENGER. see *EDUCATION — Special Education And Rehabilitation*

360   NE
DE BIJSTAANDER; personeelsblad. 1952. 11/yr. free. Sociale Dienst, Vlaardingenlaan 15, 1062 HM Amsterdam, Netherlands. TEL 31-20-5160800. FAX 31-20-6690151. Ed.Bd. adv.; B&W page fl.800; adv. contact: Dick Weeda. bk.rev.; illus.; circ. 2,900 (controlled). **Document type:** newspaper.
     Formerly: Socioscoop (ISSN 0038-0458)
     Description: For staff members of Sociale Dienst and persons interested in the organization's activities.

360   NE
▼**BIJSTAND.** (Supplement to: Sociaal Bestek (ISSN 0921-5344)) 1994. m. free. (Landelijke Veranderingsorganisatie (LVO)) Stichting L V O, Postbus 85932, 2508 CP The Hague, Netherlands. TEL 31-70-3469300. FAX 31-70-3617372. **Document type:** bulletin.
     Description: Information bulletin concerning the new Algemene Bijstandswet (public assistance law) in the Netherlands.

BLACK CHILD ADVOCATE. see *CHILDREN AND YOUTH — About*

360   GW   ISSN 0340-8574
BLAETTER DER WOHLFAHRTSPFLEGE; Deutsche Zeitschrift fuer Sozialarbeit. 1848. m. DM.79. Wohlfahrtswerk fuer Baden-Wuerttemberg, Falkertstr. 29, 70176 Stuttgart, Germany. Ed. Gerhard Pfannendoerfer. adv.; bk.rev.; bibl.; index. circ. 10,500. **Document type:** government publication.

360
BLAULICHT. q. Pillergasse 24, A-1150 Vienna, Austria. TEL 01-89145. circ. 52,000.

BOARD MEMBER. see *BUSINESS AND ECONOMICS — Management*

362   JA   ISSN 0915-8634
BOBASU JANARU/JAPAN BOBATH ASSOCIATION. JOURNAL. (Text in Japanese) s-a. 4000 Yen. Nihon Bobasu Kenkyukai - Japan Bobath Association, 6-5, Higashinakahama 1-chome, Joto-ku, Osaka 536, Japan. TEL 06-962-3131. FAX 06-963-2233. Ed. Masamichi Furusawa. **Document type:** academic/scholarly publication.
     Formerly (until 1988): Nihon Bobath Kenkyukai Nyusu.

362.7   US   ISSN 0889-6828
BOYS TOWN QUARTERLY. 1976. q. $10 donation. Father Flanagan's Boys Home, Boys Town, NE 68010. TEL 402-498-1300. FAX 402-498-1348. E-mail: melingaJ@boystown.org. Ed. Randal R. Blauvelt. illus. circ. 600,000. (also avail. in microform from UMI) **Document type:** newsletter.
     Supersedes: Boys Town Times.
     Description: Provides news of the programs and of the people from around the world who visit the world-famous Boys Town campus.

SOCIAL SERVICES AND WELFARE

BRAILLE MONITOR (INKPRINT EDITION). see
HANDICAPPED — Visually Impaired

BRAILLE SPORTING RECORD. see HANDICAPPED —
Visually Impaired

361.6   BL
BRASILIA. FUNDACAO DO SERVICO SOCIAL DO DISTRITO FEDERAL. RELATORIO ANUAL DAS ATIVIDADES. a. Fundacao do Servico Social do Distrito Federal, Brasilia, Brazil.

360   BL
BRAZIL. SERVICO SOCIAL DO COMERCIO. ADMINISTRACAO REGIONAL NO ESTADO DE SAO PAULO. RELATORIO ANUAL. 1946. a. free. Servico Social do Comercio, Administracao Regional no Estado de Sao Paulo, Caixa Postal 6643, Av. Paulista, 119, 01311-903 Sao Paulo, Brazil. TEL 284-2111. FAX 288-6206. TELEX 1123423. charts. circ. 2,000. **Document type:** corporate report.

362.8   US   ISSN 1045-1005
BREAD FOR THE WORLD NEWSLETTER. 1974. 9/yr. $25. Bread for the World, 1100 Wayne Ave., Ste. 1000, Silver Spring, MD 20910. TEL 301-608-2400. FAX 301-608-2401. Ed. Carole Zimmerman. circ. 40,000. (back issues avail.) **Document type:** newsletter.
    Incorporates (1980-1989): Leaven (Washington); (1986-1989): Action Alert (Washington, 1986); (1974-1989): Bread; Which was formerly (until 1986): Bread for the World (ISSN 0198-6511)
    Description: News of the movement; progress of hunger legislation; and background articles on issues relevant to worship and world hunger.

BRIEF AUS WAHLWIES; Mitteilungen aus dem Pestalozzi Kinder- und Jugenddorf. see CHILDREN AND YOUTH — About

361   BS   ISSN 1017-6233
BRIGADES BOPANG BOTSWANA. 1978. q. free. Department of Vocational Education and Training, Ministry of Education, Private Bag 0062, Gaborone, Botswana. TEL 267-352589. FAX 267-313191. Ed. Angela Schaeken. circ. 4,000. **Document type:** newsletter, government publication.
    Description: Covers news of the brigades, Vocational Training Centres, and organizations involved in training for production and commercial services, community development, and extension work primarily in rural areas.

361   UK
BRITISH ASSOCIATION OF SOCIAL WORKERS. ANNUAL REPORT. 1970. a. free. British Association of Social Workers, 16 Kent St., Birmingham B5 6RD, England. adv.; bk.rev.; bibl.; tr.lit. circ. 14,000. **Document type:** corporate report.

361   CN
BRITISH COLUMBIA. MINISTRY OF SOCIAL SERVICES. SERVICES FOR PEOPLE. ANNUAL REPORT (YEAR). 1945. a. free. Ministry of Social Services, Communications Division, Parliament Buildings, Victoria, BC V8V 1X4, Canada. TEL 604-387-6485. FAX 604-356-7801. circ. 5,000. **Document type:** government publication.
    Former titles: British Columbia. Ministry of Social Services and Housing. Services for People. Annual Report (Year); British Columbia. Ministry of Human Resources. Services for People (ISSN 0317-4670); British Columbia. Department of Human Resources. Annual Report (ISSN 0068-1466)

361   UK   ISSN 0045-3102
HV1   CODEN: BJSWAS
THE BRITISH JOURNAL OF SOCIAL WORK. 1971. bi-m. £95($175) (effective 1996). Oxford University Press, Oxford Journals, Walton St., Oxford OX2 6DP, England. TEL 01865-267907. FAX 01865-267773. TELEX 837330-OXPRES-G. E-mail: jnlorders@oup.co.uk. (U.S. subscr. to: Oxford University Press Inc., 2001 Evans Rd., Cary, NC 27513. TEL 919-677-0977. FAX 919-677-1714) Eds. Richard Hugman, David Smith. adv. contact: Jane Parker. bk.rev.; abstr. circ. 1,700. (also avail. in microform from UMI) **Indexed:** Abstr.Health Care Manage.Stud., Adol.Ment.Hlth.Abstr., ASSIA, Br.Hum.Ind., Curr.Cont., Mid.East: Abstr.& Ind., Mult.Ed.Abstr., Psychol.Abstr. (1971-), Sage Fam.Stud.Abstr., Sage Urb.Stud.Abstr., Soc.Work Res.& Abstr., Sociol.Educ.Abstr., SSCI, Stud.Wom.Abstr., Tech.Educ.Abstr. **Document type:** academic/scholarly publication.
    —BLDSC (2324.790000); Faxon; Genuine Article; SWETS; UMI. **CCC.**
    Description: Publishes papers on the research and practice of every aspect of social work. Examines its principles and theories.

BRITISH POLIO FELLOWSHIP. BULLETIN. see MEDICAL SCIENCES — Psychiatry And Neurology

360   AT   ISSN 1320-8632
BROTHERHOOD COMMENT; a newsletter of social policy and research. 3/yr. Aus.$20 to individuals; institutions Aus.$30. Brotherhood of St. Laurence, 67 Brunswick St., Fitzroy, Vic. 3065, Australia. TEL 61-3-419-7055. FAX 61-3-417-2691. **Document type:** newsletter.

BROWN UNIVERSITY CHILD AND ADOLESCENT BEHAVIOR LETTER; monthly reports on the problems of children and adolescents growing up. see CHILDREN AND YOUTH — About

361.73   US
▼ **BY THE WAY.** 1994. q. free. United Way of Morris County, Box 1948, Morristown, NJ 07962-1948. TEL 201-993-1160. Ed. Tiffany Haworth; Pub. Tiffany Haworth. **Document type:** newsletter.
    Description: Reports on the social welfare agencies funded by this United Way chapter. Also contains Morris County, NJ, news about health and welfare.

360   FR
C A F REVUE. 1948. 8/yr. 120 F. Caisse Nationale des Allocations Familiales, 23 rue Daviel, 75634 Paris Cedex 13, France. Ed. Daniel Bequignon. bk.rev.; bibl.; charts; illus. circ. 7,500.
    Formerly: C A F Bulletin Mensuel (ISSN 0409-6568)

360 374   UK   ISSN 0306-4956
C C E T S W ANNUAL REPORT. 1973. a. £9. Central Council for Education and Testing in Social Work, Derbyshire House, St. Chad's St., London WC1H 8AD, England. TEL 0171-278-2455. FAX 0171-278-2934. **Document type:** corporate report.

360 374   UK
C C E T S W INFORMATION SHEETS. (Supplement to: C C E T S W Leaflet (ISSN 0306-4425)) irreg., latest Feb. 1994. free. Central Council for Education and Training in Social Work, Derbyshire House, St. Chad's St., London WC1H 8HD, England. TEL 0171-278-2455. FAX 0171-278-2934. (back issues avail.) **Document type:** trade publication.
    Description: Answers the questions most often asked concerning social work training and careers.

360 374   UK   ISSN 0306-4425
C C E T S W LEAFLET. (Supplement avail.: C C E T S W Information Sheets) 1973. irreg., latest 1994. free. Central Council for Education and Training in Social Work, Derbyshire House, St. Chad's St., London WC1H 8AD, England. TEL 0171-278-2455. FAX 0171-278-2934. (back issues avail.) **Document type:** monographic series.
    —BLDSC (3095.865000).
    Description: Covers career opportunities and vocational requirements in social work.

360 374   UK
C C E T S W NEWS. 1991. q. free. Central Council for Education and Training in Social Work, Derbyshire House, St. Chad's St., London WC1H 8AD, England. FAX 071-278-2934. **Document type:** newsletter.

360 374   UK   ISSN 0306-4433
C C E T S W PAPER. 1973. irreg., vol.19, no.29, 1994. price varies. Central Council for Education and Training in Social Work, Derbyshire House, St. Chad's St., London WC1H 8AD, England. TEL 0171-278-2455. FAX 0171-278-2934. (back issues avail.) **Document type:** monographic series.
    —BLDSC (3095.870000).
    Description: Covers professional standards and developments in the field of social work.

360 374   UK   ISSN 0140-9573
C C E T S W STUDY. 1978. irreg., latest 1993. price varies. Central Council for Education and Training in Social Work, Derbyshire House, St. Chad's St., London WC1H 8AD, England. TEL 0171-278-2455. FAX 0171-278-2934. bibl. (back issues avail.) **Document type:** monographic series, trade publication.
    Description: Discusses theory and research in social work training and practice.

060   UN
C C I V S NEWS; newsletter on current initiatives and programmes of youth voluntary service. (Text in English and French) 1959. 3/yr. $6. Unesco, Coordinating Committee for International Voluntary Service, 1 rue Miollis, 75015 Paris, France. TEL 1-45-68-27-31. FAX 1-42-73-05-21. TELEX 204461-F-UNESCO. Ed. Andre Neumann. bk.rev.; illus. circ. 2,000.
    Former titles: News from C C I V S; C C I V S News; Volunteer Service Bulletin (ISSN 0007-4942); Volunteer World (ISSN 0042-8698)
    Description: Publicizes the activities and ideas of CCIVS and its member organizations, as well as UNESCO and other United Nations agencies, and announcements concerning voluntary service or youth.

C E N S I S NOTE E COMMENTI. (Centro Studi Investimenti Sociali) see SOCIOLOGY

360   NQ
C E P A D. INFORME ANUAL. a. Comite Evangelico Pro-Ayuda al Desarrollo, Departamento de Documentacion y Comunicacion Popular, Managua, Nicaragua.

360   US   ISSN 1054-4445
C J F ANNUAL REPORT. a. Council of Jewish Federations, Inc., 730 Broadway, 2nd Fl., New York, NY 10003. TEL 212-474-5000.
    Formerly: C J F Annual Review.

360 296   US
C J F ENDOWMENT REVIEW. 1983. q. $8. Council of Jewish Federations, Inc., Endowment Development Department, 730 Broadway, New York, NY 10003. TEL 212-475-5000. Ed. Donald Kent. bk.rev. circ. 27,000.
    Description: Focuses on charitable giving.

C N S W NEWSLETTER. (Council of Nephrology Social Workers) see MEDICAL SCIENCES — Urology And Nephrology

C N S W PERSPECTIVES. (Council of Nephrology Social Workers) see MEDICAL SCIENCES — Urology And Nephrology

360 320   UK   ISSN 0261-0183
C S P: CRITICAL SOCIAL POLICY; a journal of socialist theory and practice in social welfare. 1981. q. £28 to individuals; institutions £78 (effective 1996). (Critical Social Policy) Sage Publications Ltd., 6 Bonhill St., London EC2A 4PU, England. TEL 0171-374-0645. FAX 0171-374-8741. E-mail: market@sageltd.co.uk. Ed.Bd. adv.: B&W page £180; trim 185 x 114; adv. contact: Bernie Folan. bk.rev.; illus. circ. 800. **Indexed:** ASSIA, Geo.Abstr., Lang.& Lang.Behav.Abstr., Mult.Ed.Abstr., Sociol.Educ.Abstr., SOMA. **Document type:** academic/scholarly publication.
    —BLDSC (3487.485500); UMI. **CCC.**
    Description: Provides a forum to develop an understanding of welfare from socialist, feminist, anti-racist and radical perspectives within the British and international context for teachers, practitioners, and welfare activists.

C U B COMMUNICATOR. ADOPTION NEWSLETTER. (Concerned United Birthparents, Inc.) see SOCIOLOGY

C U S A N. (Catholics United for Spiritual Action) see RELIGIONS AND THEOLOGY — Roman Catholic

SOCIAL SERVICES AND WELFARE

CALIFORNIA FAMILY LAW MONTHLY. see *LAW — Family And Matrimonial Law*

360　　　　　　US
CALIFORNIA STATE PLAN FOR REHABILITATION FACILITIES. a. free. Health and Welfare Agency, Department of Rehabilitation, 830 K St. Mall, Sacramento, CA 95814. TEL 916-323-0390. FAX 916-322-0503. **Document type:** government publication.

360　　　　CN　　ISSN 0848-2691
HV101
CANADA. STANDING COMMITTEE ON HEALTH AND WELFARE, SOCIAL AFFAIRS, SENIORS AND THE STATUS OF WOMEN. MINUTES OF THE PROCEEDINGS AND EVIDENCE. 1989. irreg. Canadian Government Publishing Center, Supply and Services Canada, Ottawa, Ont. K1A 0S9, Canada. **Document type:** proceedings.

300　　　　CN　　ISSN 0068-8584
CANADIAN COUNCIL ON SOCIAL DEVELOPMENT. ANNUAL REPORT - RAPPORT ANNUEL. (Text in English and French) 1920. a. Can.$50 membership. Canadian Council on Social Development, 55 Parkdale Ave., Box 3505, Sta. C, Ottawa, ON K1Y 4G1, Canada. TEL 613-728-1865. FAX 613-728-9387. Ed. Nancy Perkins. circ. 5,000.

361.73　　CN
CANADIAN DIRECTORY TO FOUNDATIONS. 1986. biennial. Can.$250. Canadian Center for Philanthropy, 1329 Bay St., Ste. 200, Toronto, ON M5R 2C4, Canada. TEL 416-515-0764. Ed. Norah McClintock. circ. 4,000. (also avail. in magnetic tape) **Document type:** directory.
　Formerly: Canadian Index to Foundation Grants.
　Description: Lists addresses and contact persons of Canadian foundations, a description of what the foundation supports, its current officers and directors, names and addresses of recipients, the dollar amount of grant and how-to information on researching and writing proposals.

360　　　　CN
CANADIAN FACT BOOK ON POVERTY/DONNEES DE BASE SUR LA PAUVRETE AU CANADA. 1975. irreg. price varies. Canadian Council on Social Development, 55 Parkdale Ave., Box 3505, Sta. C, Ottawa, ON K1Y 4G1, Canada. TEL 613-728-1865. FAX 613-728-9387. **Document type:** trade publication.

361.7　　CN　　ISSN 1183-8957
CANADIAN FUNDRAISER. 1990. 30/yr. Can.$187($187) Hilborn: The Newsletter Group Inc., 109 Vanderhoof Ave., Ste. 205, Toronto, ON M4G 2H7, Canada. TEL 416-696-8816. FAX 416-424-3016. Ed. Peter Madely. adv. contact: Bonnie Bird. bk.rev.; charts; stat.; tr.lit. (back issues avail.) **Document type:** newsletter.
　Description: News, legislation, tips, advice, trends and economic development affecting professional fund raisers in Canada.

CANADIAN NATIONAL INSTITUTE FOR THE BLIND. NATIONAL ANNUAL REVIEW. see *HANDICAPPED — Visually Impaired*

361.5　　CN　　ISSN 0068-9572
CANADIAN RED CROSS SOCIETY. ANNUAL REPORT. (Text in English and French) 1914. a. free. Canadian Red Cross Society, National Headquarters, 5700 Cancross Court, Mississauga, Ont. L5R 3E9, Canada. TEL 416-890-1000. circ. 60,000. **Document type:** corporate report.

361.77　　CN　　ISSN 0700-9828
CANADIAN RED CROSS SOCIETY. MANITOBA DIVISION. NEWS AND VIEWS. 1971. q. free. Canadian Red Cross Society, Manitoba Division, 200 - 360 Broadway, Winnipeg, MB R3C 0T6, Canada. TEL 204-982-7300. FAX 204-942-8367. Ed.Bd. circ. 4,500. (back issues avail.)
　Description: Includes information of Red Cross activities in Manitoba and around the world.

360　　　　CN　　ISSN 0820-909X
HV105　　　　CODEN: CSWRE9
CANADIAN SOCIAL WORK REVIEW/REVUE CANADIENNE DE SERVICE SOCIAL. (Text in English and French) 1974. s-a. Can.$22 to individuals (foreign Can.$27); institutions Can.$34 (foreign Can.$39). Canadian Association of Schools of Social Work - Association Canadienne des Ecoles de Service Social, 30 Rosemount Ave., Ste. 100-B, Ottawa, ON K1Y 1P4, Canada. TEL 613-722-2974. FAX 613-722-5661. (Subscr. to: Wilfrid Laurier University Press, Waterloo, ON N2L 3C5, Canada. TEL 519-884-1970. FAX 519-725-1399) Eds. Roland Lecomte, Marilyn Callahan. adv.; bk.rev. circ. 450. Indexed: ASSIA, Can.Wom.Per.Ind., Child Devel.Abstr., Crim.Just.Abstr., Soc.Work Res.& Abstr., Sociol.Abstr. **Document type:** academic/scholarly publication.
　—BLDSC (3044.741000).
　Supersedes (in 1983): Canadian Journal of Social Work Education (ISSN 0316-8565)
　Description: Focuses a national perspective on Canadian social work.
　Refereed Serial

362.6 610.736　　UK　　ISSN 0959-5066
CARE HOME PROPRIETOR. 1986. q. £15 to non-members; free with membership. (British Federation of Care Home Proprietors) Newton Mann Ltd., Stretton Rd., Tansley, Matlock, Derbys. DE4 5GE, England. TEL 0116-264-0095. Ed. Colin Grimes. adv. contact: Peter Mann. bk.rev. circ. 10,000.
　Description: Covers all issues affecting the business and professional interests of persons involved in providing residential and nursing care in the private and voluntary sectors.

360　　　　UK　　ISSN 0952-8636
CARE WEEKLY; the newsmagazine for all social care professionals. 1987. w. £48 (rest of Europe £53; elsewhere £53-£68) (effective 1995). Inside Communications, 9 White Lion St., Islington, London N1 9XJ, England. TEL 0171-837-8727. FAX 0171-278-1889. adv.; bk.rev. circ. 29,000.
　—BLDSC (3051.620000).

361.5　　　　US
CARE WORLD REPORT. 1972. q. free. CARE, Inc., 151 Ellis St., N.E., Atlanta, GA 30303-2426. Ed. Erin M. Blair. circ. 400,000. **Document type:** newsletter.
　Description: Covers the relief work of CARE worldwide and provides information on world hunger and infant mortality.

360　　　　UK　　ISSN 1354-2311
CAREDATA ABSTRACTS. 1989. m. £25 to individuals; institutions £35; overseas £45. National Institute for Social Work, 5 Tavistock Pl., London WC1H 9SN, England. TEL 0171-387-9681. **Document type:** bulletin.
　Formerly (until 1994): Social Care Update (ISSN 0955-7156)

CAREER PLANNING & ADULT DEVELOPMENT JOURNAL. see *EDUCATION — Adult Education*

CAREER PLANNING AND ADULT DEVELOPMENT NETWORK NEWSLETTER; a newsletter for career counselors, educators, and human resource specialists. see *EDUCATION — Adult Education*

253.5 268　　US　　ISSN 1070-9681
CAREGIVING; a resource for Christian ministry. 1993. q. $26.95. Southern Baptist Convention, Sunday School Board, 127 Ninth Ave., N., Nashville, TN 37234. TEL 800-458-2772.

362.4 362.6　　UK　　ISSN 0968-8838
CARERS WORLD. 1982. 6/yr. £9 (foreign £12). A.E. Morgan Publications Ltd., Stanley House, 9 West St., Epsom, Surrey KT18 7RL, England. TEL 01372-741411. FAX 01372-744493. Ed. Jennie Davidson; Pub. Terence Morgan. adv. contact: Julia Dempster. circ. 3,300. **Document type:** consumer publication.
　—BLDSC (3051.854000).
　Former titles (until 1993): Practical Caring (ISSN 0964-864X); (until 1991): Caring (ISSN 0955-8020); Handicapped Living.
　Description: Provides information and encouragement for caretakers of the disabled and elderly.

CARING (WASHINGTON). see *MEDICAL SCIENCES — Nurses And Nursing*

360　　　　UK　　ISSN 0953-4873
CARING TIMES. 1988. m. £22.50 (effective Mar. 1994). Hawker Publications, 13 Park House, 140 Battersea Park Rd., London SW11 4NB, England. TEL 0171-720-2108. FAX 0171-498-3023. Ed. R. Hawkins. adv.; bk.rev.; circ. 300 (paid); 16,500 (controlled). **Document type:** academic/scholarly publication.
　Incorporates (in Mar. 1993): Care Concern (ISSN 0266-4933)
　Description: Contains information about residential, nursing home, and sheltered housing management.

360　　　　UK　　ISSN 0265-7821
CARING TODAY. 1983. bi-m. £12. 1 Ewood Ct., Hebden Bridge, W. Yorks. HX7 5QX, England. TEL 01422-882467. FAX 01422-885160. Ed. Vivien Shepard. adv. contact: Vivien Shepherd. bk.rev.; circ. 12,500. **Document type:** trade publication.
　Description: Provides information for an audience of owners and managers of private and voluntary residential and nursing homes.

360　　　　GW　　ISSN 0008-6614
CARITAS; Zeitschrift fuer Caritasarbeit und Caritaswissenschaft. 1896. m. DM.72 (foreign DM.90). (Deutscher Caritasverband) Lambertus-Verlag GmbH, Woelflinstr. 4, 79104 Freiburg, Germany. TEL 0761-36825-25. FAX 0761-37064. Ed. Thomas Becker. adv.; bk.rev.; bibl.; charts; index. circ. 2,500. Indexed: CERDIC, SSCI. **Document type:** bulletin.

360　　　　GW
CARITAS AKTUELL. q. membership. Deutscher Caritasverband, Karlstr. 40, 79104 Freiburg, Germany. TEL 0761-200-0. FAX 0761-200509. (back issues avail.) **Document type:** bulletin.

361　　　　GW　　ISSN 0069-0570
CARITAS; JAHRBUCH DES DEUTSCHEN CARITASVERBANDES. 1968. a. DM.21($10) Deutscher Caritasverband e.V., Karlstr. 40, 79104 Freiburg, Germany. FAX 0761-200572. Ed. Thomas Becker. **Document type:** corporate report.

361　　　　GW　　ISSN 0008-6622
CARITAS-KORRESPONDENZ; Informationsblaetter fuer die Caritaspraxis. 1929. m. DM.62 (foreign DM.80). (Deutscher Caritasverband) Lambertus-Verlag GmbH, Woelflinstr. 4, 79104 Freiburg, Germany. TEL 0761-36825-25. FAX 0761-37064. Ed. Hans Harro Buehler. adv. circ. 5,500. (processed) **Document type:** bulletin.

360　　　　AU
CARITAS-ZEITSCHRIFT. 1947. 6/yr. Caritas, Trauttmansdorffg. 15, A-1130 Vienna, Austria. FAX 01-8767538. Ed. Wolfgang Bergmann; Pub. Wolfgang Bergmann. adv.; bk.rev.; abstr.; bibl. circ. 12,000. **Document type:** bulletin.
　Former titles: Caritas; Oesterreichische Caritas Zeitschrift (ISSN 0029-8980)

361.73　　US　　ISSN 0069-0635
HV97.C3
CARNEGIE CORPORATION OF NEW YORK ANNUAL REPORT. 1921. a. free. Carnegie Corporation of New York, 437 Madison Ave., New York, NY 10022. TEL 212-371-3200. FAX 212-754-4073. TELEX US166776. Ed. Avery Russell. circ. 10,000. (also avail. in microfiche from BHP) **Document type:** corporate report.
　—BLDSC (1137.600000).
　Formerly (until 1971): Carnegie Corporation of New York. Reports of the Officers.
　Description: Promotes the advancement and diffusion of knowledge and understanding; and the use of funds for the same purpose among the people of the United States and certain countries that are or have been members of the British overseas Commonwealth.

SOCIAL SERVICES AND WELFARE

361.73 US ISSN 0576-7954
LB2336
CARNEGIE QUARTERLY. 1953. q. free. Carnegie Corporation of New York, 437 Madison Ave., New York, NY 10022. TEL 212-371-3200. FAX 212-754-4073. TELEX US166776. Ed. Avery Russell. illus. circ. 38,500. (also avail. in microfilm; reprint service avail. from UMI) **Indexed:** Ind.Free Per. —BLDSC (3055.070000); Faxon; UMI.
  Former titles (until 1966): Carnegie Corporation of New York Quarterly (ISSN 0146-1613); Carnegie Corporation of New York. Quarterly Report (ISSN 0146-1605)
  Description: Promotes the advancement and diffusion of knowledge and understanding; and the use of funds for the same purpose among the people of the United States and in certain countries that are or have been members of the British overseas Commonwealth.

301.4 IT ISSN 0008-7122
CASA; rivista della famiglia - studi, esperienze, documentazioni e pagine varie per la famiglia e la casa. (Supplements avail.) 1943. m. L.35000. Istituto "la Casa", Via Lattuada 14, 20135 Milan, Italy. Ed. Paolo Liggeri. adv.; bk.rev.; illus.

360 UK ISSN 0955-7989
CASE STUDIES FOR PRACTICE. 1989. irreg., vol.7, 1994. $19.50. Jessica Kingsley Publishers, 116 Pentonville Rd., London N1 9JB, England. TEL 071-833-2307. FAX 071-837-2917. (U.S. subscr. to: Taylor & Francis, 1900 Frost Rd., Ste. 101, Bristol, PA 19007-1598. TEL 800-821-8312. FAX 215-785-5515) Ed. Philip Seed. **Document type:** monographic series.
  —BLDSC (3058.215250).

360 282 US
CATALYST (ST. DAVIDS). bi-m. membership. North American Association of Christians in Social Work, Box 7090, St. Davids, PA 19087-7090. TEL 610-687-5777.

361 US
CATHOLIC RELIEF SERVICES. ANNUAL REPORT. a. Catholic Relief Services, 209 W. Fayette St., Baltimore, MD 21201-3443. TEL 410-625-2220. FAX 410-234-2983. **Document type:** corporate report.
  Description: Covers various types of information including financial statements, country updates, and headquarters information.

360 US ISSN 0886-1811
CATHOLIC WAR VETERAN. 1935. bi-m. Catholic War Veterans, U.S.A., 441 N. Lee St., Alexandria, VA 22314. TEL 216-333-2951. Ed. William J. Gill. circ. 36,000.
  Description: Covers veteran news, legislation and veteran administration policies.

360 374 UK
CENTRAL COUNCIL FOR EDUCATION AND TRAINING IN SOCIAL WORK. DISCUSSION PAPER. irreg., latest 1993. price varies. Central Council for Education and Training in Social Work, Derbyshire House, St. Chad's St., London WC1H 8AD, England. TEL 071-278-2455. FAX 071-278-2934. (back issues avail.) **Document type:** monographic series.
  Description: Discusses various aspects of the training needs of professional social workers.

360 374 UK
CENTRAL COUNCIL FOR EDUCATION AND TRAINING IN SOCIAL WORK. IN EUROPE SERIES. 1990. irreg., latest 1993. price varies. Central Council for Education and Training in Social Work, Derbyshire House, St. Chad's St., London WC1H 8AD, England. TEL 071-278-2455. FAX 071-278-2934. (back issues avail.) **Document type:** monographic series, trade publication.
  Description: Confronts social work training issues in the E.C.

360 374 UK
CENTRAL COUNCIL FOR EDUCATION AND TRAINING IN SOCIAL WORK. REPORT OF COUNCIL MEETING. 1978. irreg. free. Central Council for Education and Training in Social Work, Derbyshire House, St. Chad's St., London WC1H 8AD, England. TEL 071-278-2455. FAX 071-278-2934. Ed. George Smith. circ. controlled. **Document type:** newsletter.
  —BLDSC (3095.867000).
  Supersedes (in 1988): C C E T S W Reporting (ISSN 0269-0462); Which superseded (with no.3, 1979): C C E T S W News (ISSN 0142-2693); Which was formerly (until 1978): C C E T S W Bulletin (ISSN 0306-4247)

CENTREPIECES. see *WOMEN'S INTERESTS*

360 BG
CHAKRA. (Text in Bengali) w. 242A Nakhalpara, P.O. Box 2682, Dhaka 1215, Bangladesh. TEL 2-604568. Ed. Husneara Aziz.

362.7 AT
CHALLENGE ADVOCATE. 1956; N.S. q. free. Challenge Foundation of New South Wales, 8 Junction St., P.O. Box 229, Ryde, N.S.W. 2112, Australia. TEL 02-807-2822. FAX 02-809-5327. adv. circ. 4,500.
  Formerly (until 1984): Sub-Normal Children's Welfare Association. Welfare News (ISSN 0049-2418)

CHALLENGING TIMES; educating children and youth at risk. see *EDUCATION*

360 UK ISSN 0263-8371
RC475 CODEN: CNGEEP
CHANGES; an international journal of psychology and psychotherapy. 1983. q. $125 (foreign $125) (effective 1996). (Psychology and Psychotherapy Association) John Wiley & Sons Ltd., Journals, Baffins Ln., Chichester, W. Sussex PO19 1UD, England. TEL 01243-779777. FAX 01243-776128. TELEX 86290 WIBOOK G. (Subscr. in the Americas to: John Wiley & Sons, Inc., Journals Administration Dept., 605 Third Ave., New York, NY 10158. TEL 212-850-6645. FAX 212-850-6021) Ed.Bd. adv.; bk.rev. circ. 515. (also avail. in microform from UMI) **Indexed:** ASSIA. **Document type:** academic/scholarly publication.
  —BLDSC (3129.656500).
  Description: Provides a forum for ideas, experiences, and views of people working in psychology, nursing, education, medicine, and social work.
  Refereed Serial

CHANNELS (EXETER); communications and management ideas for non-profit organizations. see *ADVERTISING AND PUBLIC RELATIONS*

361.73 US ISSN 1052-3979
HV89
CHARITABLE ORGANIZATIONS OF THE U S. 1990. biennial. $139.50. Gale Research Inc., 835 Penobscot Bldg., Detroit, MI 48226. TEL 800-877-4253. FAX 313-961-6083. TELEX 810-221-7086. Ed. Doris Morris Maxfield.

360 UK ISSN 0590-9783
CHARITIES DIGEST (YEAR). 1882. a. £16.95. Family Welfare Association, 501-505 Kingsland Rd., London E8 4AU, England. TEL 0171-254-6251. FAX 0171-249-5443. Ed. Chris Hollins. adv. circ. 5,000. **Document type:** directory.
  —BLDSC (3129.918000).
  Description: Lists major U.K. charities with contact addresses and other details. Covers the histories of key local voluntary organizations.

361.7 US ISSN 0364-0760
HV530
CHARITIES U S A. 1974. q. $25 (foreign $33). Catholic Charities U S A, 1731 King St., Ste. 200, Alexandria, VA 22314. TEL 703-549-1390. FAX 703-549-1656. Ed. Alexandra Peeler. illus. circ. 3,000.
  Description: Focuses on social justice and social service issues of interest to Catholic Charities USA members, such as poverty, family counseling, aging issues, low-income housing, emergency service, teen pregnancy, and adoption.

361.73 UK ISSN 0265-5209
CHARITY. 1983. m. £30. Charities Aid Foundation, 48 Pembury Rd., Tonbridge, Kent TN9 2JD, England. TEL 0732-771-333. Ed. Stewart Lawrie. bk.rev. circ. 2,500. (back issues avail.)
  Description: For people giving, receiving and managing charitable money.

361.73 UK ISSN 1350-7311
CHARITY WORLD. 1993. bi-m. £75 (£65 for charities) (foreign £96). Tolley Publishing Co. Ltd., Tolley House, 2 Addiscombe Rd., Croyden, Surrey CR9 5AF, England. TEL 0181-686-9141. FAX 0181-760-0588. Ed. Jennie Hawthorne. adv. contact: David Jeffries. circ. 5,000. (back issues avail.) **Document type:** bulletin.
  Description: Contains practical advice on fundraising, investments, trusteeship, accountancy and law.

CHARLOTTE JEWISH NEWS. see *ETHNIC INTERESTS*

361 UK ISSN 0968-7807
CHART AND COMPASS INTERNATIONAL. 1818. s-a. free. British Sailors' Society, Orchard Pl., Southampton, Hants. SO14 3AT, England. TEL 01703-337333. FAX 01703-338333. TELEX 477986 SAILOR G. Ed. Karen Watts. bk.rev.; illus. circ. 55,000.
  Formerly: Chart and Compass (ISSN 0262-5059)

CHECKLISTS AND ILLUSTRATIVE FINANCIAL STATEMENTS FOR NONPROFIT ORGANIZATIONS. see *BUSINESS AND ECONOMICS — Accounting*

362.7 970.1 US ISSN 0890-5185
CHEROKEE VOICE. 1981. q. Cherokee Center for Family Services, Box 507, Cherokee, NC 28719. TEL 704-497-5001. FAX 704-497-5818. Ed. Joy Evans-Widenhouse. circ. 5,000. **Document type:** newsletter.
  Description: Contains items of interest to the American Indian community.

361.8 296.7 US
CHICAGO J U F NEWS. 1972. m. $10 donations. Jewish United Fund - Jewish Federation of Metropolitan Chicago, One S. Franklin St., Rm. 706, Chicago, IL 60606. TEL 312-444-2853. FAX 312-855-2470. E-mail: aharon@interaccess.com. Ed. Aaron B. Cohen. adv. contact: Janet Buzil. bk.rev. circ. 55,000. **Document type:** newsletter.
  Description: Covers news of community service programs and events in the greater Chicago area.

362.7 155.4 UK ISSN 0952-9136
  CODEN: CABEEB
CHILD ABUSE REVIEW. 1992. 5/yr. $115 (foreign $115) (effective 1996). John Wiley & Sons Ltd., Journals, Baffins Ln., Chichester, Sussex PO19 1UD, England. TEL 01243-779777. FAX 01243-776128. TELEX 86290 WIBOOK G. (Subscr. in the Americas to: John Wiley & Sons, Inc., 605 Third Ave., New York, NY 10158. TEL 212-850-6645. FAX 212-850-6021) Eds. Kevin Browne, Margaret Lynch. circ. 2,265. **Indexed:** Viol.& Abuse Abstr. **Document type:** academic/scholarly publication.
  —BLDSC (3172.912700); UMI. **CCC.**
  Description: Reflects current child welfare issues and concerns.

360 UK ISSN 1356-7500
▼**CHILD & FAMILY SOCIAL WORK.** Announced for publication in 1996. q. £90 in Europe; elsewhere £99($153.50) (effective 1996). Blackwell Science Ltd., Osney Mead, Oxford OX2 0EL, England. TEL 44-1865-206206. FAX 44-1865-206219. Ed. David Howe. **Document type:** academic/scholarly publication.

SOCIAL SERVICES AND WELFARE

362.7   **US**   **ISSN 0145-935X**
HV701   **CODEN: CYSEDP**
CHILD & YOUTH SERVICES. 1977. s-a. $48 to individuals; institutions $140; libraries $175. Haworth Press, Inc., 10 Alice St., Binghamton, NY 13904. TEL 607-722-5857; 800-342-9678. FAX 607-722-1424. Ed. Jerome Beker. adv.; bk.rev.; abstr.; bibl. circ. 262. (also avail. in microfiche from HAW; back issues avail.; reprint service avail. from HAW) **Indexed:** Abstr.Crim.& Pen., Adol.Ment.Hlth.Abstr., Behav.Abstr., Biol.Abstr., Bull.Signal., C.I.J.E., Chicago Psychoanal.Lit.Ind., Child Devel.Abstr., CJPI, Crim.Just.Abstr., Educ.Ind., Except.Child Educ.Abstr., Human Resour.Abstr., IMFL, Lang.& Lang.Behav.Abstr., Mult.Ed.Abstr., Past.Care & Couns.Abstr., PSI, Psychol.Abstr. (1977-), Ref.Zh., Rehabil.Lit., Sage Fam.Stud.Abstr., Soc.Work Res.& Abstr., Sociol.Abstr., Sp.Ed.Needs Abstr., Stud.Wom.Abstr.
—BLDSC (3172.916000); Faxon; Haworth; SWETS; UnCover.
Description: Each issue covers one particular topic regarding conditions of young people in our society.
Refereed Serial

CHILD CARE FOCUS. see *CHILDREN AND YOUTH — About*

CHILD HEALTH TALK. see *CHILDREN AND YOUTH — About*

360   **US**   **ISSN 0884-8076**
HV741
CHILD SUPPORT REPORT. 1979. irreg. U.S. Dept. of Health & Human Services, Office of Child Support Enforcement, National Child Support Enforcement Center, 370 L'Enfant Promenade, S.W., Mail Stop OCSE-RC, Washington, DC 20447. **Document type:** government publication.

362.7   **US**   **ISSN 0009-4021**
   CODEN: CHWFA
CHILD WELFARE; journal of policy, practice and program. 1920. bi-m. $77 (effective 1996). (Child Welfare League of America), Transaction Publishers, Transaction Periodicals Consortium, Department 3092, Rutgers University, New Brunswick, NJ 08903. TEL 908-445-2280. FAX 908-445-3138. Ed. Carl Schoenberg. adv.; bk.rev.; charts; index. circ. 12,100. (also avail. in microform from UMI; reprint service avail. from KTO,UMI) **Indexed:** Abstr.Crim.& Pen., Acad.Ind., Adol.Ment.Hlth.Abstr., ASSIA, C.I.J.E., Child Devel.Abstr., CINAHL, Crim.Just.Abstr., Curr.Cont., Curr.Lit.Fam.Plan., Educ.Ind., Except.Child Educ.Abstr., Hlth Ind., Ind.Med., Lang & Lang.Behav.Abstr., Mult.Ed.Abstr., P.A.I.S., PHRA, PSI, Psychol.Abstr. (1973-), Sage Fam.Stud.Abstr., Soc.Sci.Ind., Soc.Work Res.& Abstr., Sp.Ed.Needs Abstr., SSCI, Viol.& Abuse Abstr. **Document type:** academic/scholarly publication.
—BLDSC (3172.950000); Faxon; Genuine Article; SWETS; UMI; UnCover. **CCC.**
Formerly: Child Welfare League of America. Bulletin.
Description: Presents special problems facing millions of children who are homeless, abused, new to this country, or severely disabled.

362.7   **JA**   **ISSN 0289-6842**
CHILD WELFARE; quarterly news from Japan. q. $66. Intercontinental Marketing Corp., P.O. Box 5056, Tokyo 100-31, Japan. TEL 81-3-3661-7458. FAX 81-3-3667-9646.
Formerly: Child Welfare Quarterly.

362.7   **US**   **ISSN 1042-9042**
HV741
CHILD WELFARE LEAGUE OF AMERICA. DIRECTORY OF MEMBER AGENCIES. 1968. a. $14. Child Welfare League of America, Inc., 440 First St., Ste. 310, Washington, DC 20001-2085. TEL 202-638-2952. FAX 202-638-4004. **Document type:** directory.
Former titles (until 1987): C W L A Directory of Member and Associate Agencies (ISSN 0737-786X); Which was formed by the 1982 merger of: C W L A Directory of Member Agencies (ISSN 0147-9180); Which superseded in part (in 1976): C W L A Directory of Member Agencies and Associates (ISSN 0361-767X); Child Welfare League of America. Directory of Associate Agencies (ISSN 0277-7177); Which was formerly (until 1981): C W L A Associate Agencies (ISSN 0163-3694); (until 1978): C W L A Directory of Associate Agencies (ISSN 0147-9172); Which superseded in part (in 1976): C W L A Directory of Member Agencies and Associates (ISSN 0361-767X).

CHILDREN AND YOUTH SERVICES REVIEW; an international multidisciplinary review of the welfare of young people. see *CHILDREN AND YOUTH — About*

562.7   **FI**   **ISSN 0783-6244**
CHILDREN IN FINLAND. irreg. FIM 10. Lastensuojelun Keskusliitto - Central Union for Child Welfare in Finland, Armfeltintie 1, 00150 Helsinki 15, Finland. FAX 0-627990. Ed. M. Launis.

362.7   **UK**
CHILDREN IN FOCUS. 1881. 3/yr. free. Children's Society, Edward Rudolf House, Margery St., London WC1X 0JL, England. TEL 0171-837-4299. FAX 0171-837-0211. E-mail: childsoc.demon.co.uk. Ed. Rachel O'Brien. adv.; bk.rev. circ. 380,000. **Document type:** consumer publication.
Former titles: Children in Form; (until Summer 1993): Gateway.
Description: Discusses child welfare issues.

CHILDREN TODAY; an interdisciplinary journal for the professions serving children. see *CHILDREN AND YOUTH — About*

CHILDREN U K. see *CHILDREN AND YOUTH — About*

362.7   **US**
CHILDREN'S AID SOCIETY. ANNUAL REPORT. 1854. a. free. Children's Aid Society, 105 East 22 St., New York, NY 10010. TEL 212-949-4933. FAX 212-477-3705. Ed. Truda C. Jewett. circ. 35,000. **Document type:** corporate report.

362.7   **US**
CHILDREN'S AID SOCIETY NEWS. 1971. s-a. free. Children's Aid Society, 105 East 22 St., New York, NY 10010. TEL 212-949-4933. FAX 212-477-3705. Ed. Truda C. Jewett. charts; illus. circ. 35,000. **Document type:** newsletter.
Former titles: Children's Aid Society Newsletter; Children's Aid Society News (ISSN 0045-6667)

362.7   **US**   **ISSN 0273-9615**
RJ242
CHILDREN'S HEALTH CARE. 1973. q. $30 to individuals (foreign $55); institutions $100 (foreign $125). (Association for the Care of Children's Health) Lawrence Erlbaum Associates, Inc., 10 Industrial Dr., Mahwah, NJ 07430-2262. TEL 201-236-9500. FAX 201-236-0072. Eds. Kenneth Tarnowski, Richard Thompson. adv.: page $275; 5 x 8. circ. 4,000. (controlled). (also avail. in microform from UMI; reprint service avail. from UMI) **Indexed:** CINAHL, Psychol.Abstr. (1978-). **Document type:** academic/scholarly publication.
—BLDSC (3172.990200); Faxon; UMI; UnCover.
Former titles: Association for the Care of Children's Health. Journal (ISSN 0274-8916); Association for the Care of Children in Hospitals. Journal (ISSN 0145-3351)
Description: Publishes empirically-based articles addressing the theoretical, clinical, programmatic, training and professional practice issues relevant to the family-centered, developmental and psychosocial aspects of children's health care.

362.7   **US**   **ISSN 1057-736X**
HV741
CHILDREN'S VOICE. 1985. q. $50 to individuals; institutions $50. Child Welfare League of America, Inc., 440 First St., N.W., Ste. 310, Washington, DC 20001-2085. TEL 202-638-2952. FAX 202-638-4004. Ed. Mary L. Liepold.
—UnCover.
Formed by the merger of (1976-1984): Child Welfare Planning Notes; (1971-1984): Child Welfare League Newsletter (ISSN 0045-6659); (1979-1984): C W L A - Crittenton Reporter on School-Age Parenting.
Description: Reports current program and policy developments in child welfare services.

361.73   **US**   **ISSN 1040-676X**
CHRONICLE OF PHILANTHROPY; the newspaper of the non-profit world. 1988. bi-w. $67.50 (foreign $95) (effective 1996). Chronicle of Higher Education, Inc., 1255 23rd St., N.W., Ste. 700, Washington, DC 20037. TEL 202-466-1200. FAX 202-296-2691. TELEX 892505. (Subscr. to: Box 1989, Marion, OH 43306-2089) Ed. Philip Semas. circ. 30,066. (tabloid format; reprint service avail. from UMI) **Indexed: PSI. Document type:** newspaper.
—UMI.
Description: Provides news and information for fund raisers, professional employees of foundations, corporate grant makers, and people who work for non-profit, tax-exempt organizations in health, education, religion, the arts, and social services.

362.4   **AT**
CITIZEN ADVOCACY NEWS. 1983. bi-m. Aus.$5. Citizen Advocacy Perth West, Inc., Suite 3, 266 Hay St., Subiaco, W.A. 6008, Australia. TEL 61-9-382-4833. FAX 61-9-382-4360. Carolyn Comman. circ. 220. **Document type:** newsletter.

361.8   **US**
CITIZEN NEWS. 6/yr. $5. Long Beach Area Citizens Involved, 56 Park Ave., Long Beach, CA 90803. TEL 213-433-1974. Ed. Chris Conrad. adv. (tabloid format)

CIVIL AND MILITARY REVIEW. see *MILITARY*

CIVIL SERVICE PENSIONER. see *GERONTOLOGY AND GERIATRICS*

361.73 362.5   **NE**   **ISSN 0166-3488**
CLAMAVI. bi-m. contribution. Stichting Mensen in Nood - Caritas Neerlandica, Hekellaan 6, 5211 LX 's-Hertogenbosch, Netherlands. TEL 31-73-144544. FAX 31-73-132115. TELEX 50090 CARIT NL. Ed. I de Haes. bk.rev.; circ. 250,000 (controlled).
Description: Covers Dutch aid to Third World countries and Eastern Europe. Includes lists of projects and expenditures in different countries.

360 614.8   **US**   **ISSN 0898-6339**
CLEVELAND FOUNDATION. ANNUAL REPORT. a. Cleveland Foundation, 1422 Euclid Ave., Ste. 1400, Cleveland, OH 44115-2001. TEL 216-861-3810. FAX 216-861-1729. Ed. Lynne E. Woodman. **Document type:** corporate report.
Description: The foundation exists to enhance the quality of life for all residents of Greater Cleveland. Using funds entrusted to its stewardship by thousands of people of various means, the foundation makes grants to non-profit organizations and governmental agencies to address the community's needs and opportunities.

CLINICAL CHILD PSYCHOLOGY & PSYCHIATRY. see *CHILDREN AND YOUTH — About*

CLINICAL GERONTOLOGIST; the journal of aging and mental health. see *GERONTOLOGY AND GERIATRICS*

361.3   **US**   **ISSN 0091-1674**
HV1   **CODEN: CSWJBG**
CLINICAL SOCIAL WORK JOURNAL. 1973. q. $245 (foreign $285) (effective 1996). (National Federation of Societies for Clinical Social Work) Human Sciences Press, Inc. (Subsidiary of: Plenum Publishing Corp.), 233 Spring St., New York, NY 10013-1578. TEL 212-620-8000. FAX 212-463-0742. TELEX 23-421139. Ed. Carolyn Saari. adv.; bk.rev.; index. (also avail. in microform from ISI,UMI) **Indexed:** Abstr.Crim.& Pen., Abstr.Soc.Work., Adol.Ment.Hlth.Abstr., ASCA, ASSIA, Child.Devel.Abstr., Curr.Cont., IMFL, Mid.East: Abstr.& Ind., Psychol.Abstr. (1973-), Sage Fam.Stud.Abstr., Sage Pub.Admin.Abstr., Soc.Work Res.& Abstr., Sociol.Abstr., Sp.Ed.Needs Abstr., SSCI, Viol.& Abuse Abstr. **Document type:** academic/scholarly publication.
—BLDSC (3286.381000); Faxon; Genuine Article; SWETS; UMI; UnCover. **CCC.**
Description: Devoted to clinical social work theory and practice, and provides a cross-fertilization of ideas and concepts.
Refereed Serial

SOCIAL SERVICES AND WELFARE

361 US ISSN 0732-5223
RC336 CODEN: CLSUEH
CLINICAL SUPERVISOR; the journal of supervision in psychotherapy and mental health. 1982. s-a. $225 (foreign $315) (effective 1996). Haworth Press, Inc., 10 Alice St., Binghamton, NY 13904. TEL 607-722-5857; 800-342-9678. FAX 607-722-1424. Ed. Carlton E. Munson. adv.; bk.rev. circ. 448. (also avail. in microfiche from HAW; reprint service avail. from HAW) **Indexed:** Bull.Signal., Chicago Psychoanal.Lit.Ind., CINAHL, IMFL, Past.Care & Couns.Abstr., Psychol.Abstr. (1983-), Rehabil.Lit., Soc.Work Res.& Abstr. —BLDSC (3286.387000); Haworth; UnCover.
Formerly (until 1983): Journal of Social Work Supervision.
Description: Reflects the concerns, needs, and interests of supervisors in a variety of professional settings. Highlights current supervisory techniques and methods.
Refereed Serial

360 SP
COLECCION CUADERNOS DE TRABAJO SOCIAL. 1973. irreg., no.4, 1974. price varies. (Universidad de Navarra, Escuela de Asistentes Sociales) Ediciones Universidad de Navarra, S.A., Apdo. 396, 31080 Pamplona, Spain. TEL 94 825 6850.

360 IE
COMBAT POVERTY AGENCY. RESOURCE SERIES. irreg., no.8. £4. Combat Poverty Agency, 8 Charlemont St., Dublin 2, Ireland. TEL 01-783355. **Document type:** bulletin.

COMENIUS; wetenschappelijk forum voor opvoeding, onderwijs en cultuur. see EDUCATION

COMMON CAUSE; open the window on the developing world. see BUSINESS AND ECONOMICS — *International Development And Assistance*

362.8 US
COMMON GROUND (AKRON). 1992. q. free. United Way of Summit County, 90 Prospect St., Box 1260, Akron, OH 44309-1260. TEL 216-762-7601. FAX 216-762-0317. Ed. Kay Hehr Smith. **Document type:** newsletter.
Description: Contains United Way and affiliated agency-related news including volunteer profiles, social services, and human care issues.

361 UK ISSN 1352-0040
COMMUNICARE. s-m.? Department of Health, National Users and Carers Group, Social Services Inspectorate, Rm. 602, Wellington House, 135-155 Waterloo Rd., London SE1 8UG, England. TEL 0171-972-4047. (Subscr. to: Health Publications Unit, Department of Health, Manchester Rd., Heywood, Lancs. OL10 2PZ, England) Eds. Chris Heppenstall, Nigel Jones. **Document type:** government publication, newsletter.
Incorporates (in Aug. 1993): Caring for People (ISSN 0968-4786)

COMMUNICATION (LONDON, 1967). see EDUCATION — *Special Education And Rehabilitation*

362.7 CN ISSN 0319-7468
COMMUNIQUE (OTTAWA). 1965. q. free. Children's Aid Society of Ottawa-Carleton, 1602 Telesar Ct., Gloucester, ON K1B 1B1, Canada. TEL 613-748-0670. FAX 613-747-4456. Pub. Karen McCarthy. bk.rev. circ. 1,500. **Document type:** newsletter.
Formerly: C.A.S. Record (ISSN 0045-6675)

361.8 UK
COMMUNITY. 1980. q. £6. Community Matters, 8-9 Upper St., London N1 0PQ, England. TEL 0171-226-0189. FAX 0171-354-9570. Ed. Charles Woodd. adv.; bk.rev. circ. 3,000. **Document type:** newsletter.
Description: For volunteers involved in community groups.

360 US ISSN 0736-2099
HV88
COMMUNITY (ALEXANDRIA). 1977. q. $10. United Way of America, 701 N. Fairfax St., Alexandria, VA 22314. TEL 703-836-7100. Ed. Roberta A. Lewis. charts; illus. circ. 9,000.
Former titles (until 1982): Community Focus; Community (ISSN 0045-771X)
Description: Covers issues that affect the U.S. social service system. Includes welfare reform, computer networking, marketing research data on giving, and community problem solving.

COMMUNITY (CHICAGO). see SOCIOLOGY

COMMUNITY (LOUISVILLE). see ETHNIC INTERESTS

361.8 CN ISSN 0833-0816
COMMUNITY ACTION. 1985. 22/yr. Can.$29.95($39.95) (foreign $48.95). Community Action Publishers, Box 448, Don Mills, ON M3C 2T2, Canada. TEL 416-449-6766. FAX 416-444-5850. Ed. Leon Kumove; Pub. Leon Kumove. adv.: B&W page Can.$1828, color page Can.$2228; trim 11 3/8 x 17. bk.rev.; circ. 6,514 (paid). (tabloid format)
Description: Provides news and information on health and social services in Canada.

360 350 UK
COMMUNITY CARE (EDINBURGH). 1991. a. price varies. Social Work Services Group, 43 Jeffrey St., Rm. 24, Edinburgh EH1 1DN, Scotland. (Subscr. to: Scottish Office Library, Publication Sales, Rm. 1-44, New St. Andrew's House, Edinburgh EH1 3TG, Scotland. FAX 0131-244-4785) **Document type:** government publication.

361 UK ISSN 0307-5508
HV241
COMMUNITY CARE (SUTTON); for everyone in good care. 1974. w. £66 (foreign £82.50). Reed Business Publishing Group, Quadrant House (Subsidiary of: Reed Elsevier plc), The Quadrant, Sutton, Surrey SM2 5AS, England. TEL 0181-652-4861. FAX 0181-652-4739. (Subscr. to: Oakfield House, Perrymount Rd., Haywards Heath, West Sussex RH16 3DH, England) Ed. Terry Philpot. adv.; bk.rev.; s-a. index. circ. 28,303. **Indexed:** ASSIA. —BLDSC (3363.598000); UMI; UnCover.
Incorporates (1970-1993): Social Work Today (ISSN 0037-8070); Which was formerly: Residential Social Work (ISSN 0308-7816)
Description: For social workers in the United Kingdom.

360 UK
COMMUNITY CARE IN SCOTLAND DISCUSSION PAPER. irreg., no.5, 1995. £5. University of Stirling, Social Work Research Centre, Stirling FK9 4LA, Scotland. TEL 01786-67724. FAX 01786-63000. **Document type:** monographic series.

360 UK ISSN 0968-9249
COMMUNITY CARE MANAGEMENT & PLANNING. 1993. bi-m. £115 (Europe £118; rest of world £122). Pitman Publishing, 128 Long Acre, London WC2E 9AN, England. TEL 0171-379-7383. FAX 0171-240-5771. Ed. Peter Thistlethwaite. **Document type:** bulletin.
—BLDSC (3363.600500).

COMMUNITY CHANGE. see BUSINESS AND ECONOMICS — *Economic Situation And Conditions*

360 350 UK ISSN 0010-3802
HN1
COMMUNITY DEVELOPMENT JOURNAL. 1966. q. £50($90) (effective 1996). Oxford University Press, Oxford Journals, Walton St., Oxford OX2 6DP, England. TEL 01865-267907. FAX 01865-267773. TELEX 837330-OXPRES-G. E-mail: jnlorders@oup.co.uk. (U.S. subscr. to: Oxford University Press Inc., 2001 Evans Rd., Cary, NC 27513. TEL 919-677-0977. FAX 919-677-1714) Ed. Gary Craig. adv. contact: Jane Parker. bk.rev.; index, cum.index. circ. 1,400. (also avail. in microform from UMI) **Indexed:** Abstr.Rural Dev.Trop., Agri.Eng.Abstr., Asian-Pac.Econ.Lit., ASSIA, Br.Hum.Ind., C.I.J.E., Curr.Cont.Africa, Curr.Cont., Documentatieblad, E.I., Geo.Abstr., IDA, Int.Lab.Doc., Int.Polit.Sci.Abstr., J.of Ferroc., Lang.& Lang.Behav.Abstr., Mid.East: Abstr.& Ind., Mult.Ed.Abstr., P.A.I.S., PSI, Rural Ext.Educ.& Tr.Abstr., Rural Recreat.Tour.Abstr., Sage Pub.Admin.Abstr., Soc.Sci.Ind., Soc.Work Res.& Abstr., Sociol.Abstr., SSCI, Stud.Wom.Abstr., World Agri.Econ.& Rural Sociol.Abstr. **Document type:** academic/scholarly publication.
—BLDSC (3363.621000); Faxon; Genuine Article; SWETS; UMI; UnCover. CCC.
Formerly: Community Development Bulletin.
Description: Covers community work and development in industrial and developing nations.

352 301 US ISSN 0010-3829
HN1
COMMUNITY DEVELOPMENT SOCIETY. JOURNAL. 1970. s-a. $55 includes Vanguard (foreign $65). Community Development Society, 1123 North Water St., Milwaukee, WI 53202. TEL 414-276-7106. FAX 414-276-7704. Ed. Robert Blair. adv.; bk.rev.; abstr.; bibl.; charts. circ. 1,000. (also avail. in microfilm; reprint service avail. from UMI) **Indexed:** C.I.J.E., ERIC, P.A.I.S., Soc.Work Res.& Abstr., Sociol.Abstr., SOPODA. **Document type:** academic/scholarly publication.
—Faxon; UMI; UnCover.
Description: Devoted to improving knowledge and practice in the field of purposive community change by disseminating information on theory, research and practice.

COMMUNITY FOCUS. see ADVERTISING AND PUBLIC RELATIONS

360 UK ISSN 0951-9815
COMMUNITY LIVING. 1987. q. £21 to individuals (rest of Europe £27; elsewhere £36); institutions £27 (outside Europe £36) (effective 1995). Hexagon Publishing, Airport House, Ste. 152, Purley Way, Croydon, Surrey CR0 0X2. TEL 0181-781-6924. FAX 0181-781-1824. Ed. Elinor Harbridge; Pub. Elinor Harbridge. adv. contact: Vincent de Souza. bk.rev. circ. 3,000. **Document type:** academic/scholarly publication.
—BLDSC (3363.635300).

301.1 362 US ISSN 0010-3853
RA790.A1 CODEN: CMHJAY
COMMUNITY MENTAL HEALTH JOURNAL. 1965. bi-m. $285 (foreign $335) (effective 1996). (National Council of Community Mental Health Centers, Inc.) Human Sciences Press, Inc. (Subsidiary of: Plenum Publishing Corp.), 233 Spring St., New York, NY 10013-1578. TEL 212-620-8000. FAX 212-463-0742. TELEX 23-421139. Ed. David Cutler. adv.; bk.rev.; film rev.; abstr.; bibl.; charts; illus.; index. (also avail. in microform from UMI; back issues avail.; reprint service avail. from ISI,UMI) **Indexed:** Abstr.Health Care Manage.Stud., Abstr.Soc.Work., Adol.Ment.Hlth.Abstr., ASSIA, Biol.Abstr., CERDIC, CINAHL, Coll.Stud.Pers.Abstr., Crime Delinq.Abstr., Curr.Adv.Ecol.Sci., Curr.Cont., Excerp.Med., Hosp.Lit.Ind., Human Resour.Abstr., Ind.Med., Media Rev.Dig., Ment.Retard.Abstr., Mid.East: Abstr.& Ind., Mult.Ed.Abstr., P.H.R.A., Psychol.Abstr. (1973-), Saf.Sci.Abstr., Sci.Cit.Ind., Soc.Sci.Ind., Soc.Work Res.& Abstr., Sociol.Abstr., Sp.Ed.Needs Abstr., SSCI. **Document type:** academic/scholarly publication.
—BLDSC (3363.643000); Faxon; Genuine Article; SWETS; UMI; UnCover. CCC.
Description: Coordinates emergent approaches to mental health and social well-being, covering crisis intervention, suicide prevention, family therapy, social welfare, etc.
Refereed Serial

SOCIAL SERVICES AND WELFARE

360 US
COMMUNITY RIGHT-TO-KNOW NEWS. 1986. s-m. $379. Thompson Publishing Group, 1725 K St. N.W., Ste. 200, Washington, DC 20006. TEL 202-872-4000. FAX 301-543-2921. Ed. Nancy Nickell. (looseleaf format; back issues avail.) Document type: newsletter.
— Formerly: Toxic Exposure Bulletin.

360 UK ISSN 0264-2719
COMMUNITY SERVICE BY OFFENDERS. 1981. a. price varies. Social Work Services Group, 43 Jeffrey St., Rm. 24, Edinburgh EH1 1DN, Scotland. (Subscr. to: Scottish Office Library, Publication Sales, Rm. 1-44, New St. Andrew's House, Edinburgh EH1 3TG, Scotland. FAX 0131-244-4785) Document type: government publication.
—BLDSC (7674.191200).

COMMUNITY TRANSPORT MAGAZINE; the journal for minibus & non-profit transport operators. see TRANSPORTATION

COMPENDIUM OF RESOURCES FOR TEACHING ABOUT THE NONPROFIT SECTOR, VOLUNTARISM AND PHILANTHROPY. see EDUCATION — Teaching Methods And Curriculum

361 610 US
CONCERN NEWS. 1961. 4/yr. free. Project Concern International, 3550 Afton Rd., San Diego, CA 92123. TEL 619-279-9690. FAX 619-694-0294. Ed. Charles Goldberg. illus. circ. 5,000. (tabloid format) Document type: newsletter.
— Former titles: Project Concern News (ISSN 0033-0906); Project Concern Newsletter.
  Description: News of projects and people working to ensure the survival of children whose lives are at risk and the access to health care for those in need, reporting on medical assistance & malnutrition issues, and efforts to build self-reliant health care systems in countries throughout the world.

CONFLICT RESOLUTION NOTES. see LAW

CONNECTIONS (DAYTON). see POLITICAL SCIENCE

CONNECTOR (ST. PAUL). see HANDICAPPED

362.6 IT
CONQUISTE DEI PENSIONATI. 1953. m. L.10000. Federazione Nazionale Pensionati, Via Alessandria, 26, 00198 Rome, Italy. TEL 06-84-15-670. FAX 06-84-17-565. Ed. Carlo Candida. adv.: B&W page L.25000000, color page L.32000000. circ. 1,300,000.

CONSUMERS AFFAIRS COUNCIL OF TASMANIA. ANNUAL REPORT. see CONSUMER EDUCATION AND PROTECTION

CONTACT; voice of the Irish deaf. see HANDICAPPED — Hearing Impaired

CONTINUING CARE; supporting the transition into post hospital care. see HOSPITALS

CONTINUUM (CHICAGO); an interdisciplinary journal on continuity of care. see HOSPITALS

COPE. see DRUG ABUSE AND ALCOHOLISM

360 US ISSN 1061-1274
HG4028.C6
CORPORATE AND FOUNDATION GRANTS. 1992. a. $195. Taft Group, 12300 Twinbrook Pkwy., Ste. 520, Rockville, MD 20852. TEL 301-816-0210. FAX 301-816-0811. (Subscr. to: Taft Group, Box 33477, Detroit, MI 4832-5477. TEL 800-777-TAFT. FAX 313-961-6083) Ed. Mark Scott; Pub. Dennis Poupard. Document type: directory.
  Description: Lists grants and donations made by corporations and organizations.

365 US ISSN 1055-0623
HV97.A3
CORPORATE GIVING DIRECTORY. (Section of: Taft Corporate Information System) 1981. a. $350. Taft Group, 12300 Twinbrook Pkwy., Ste. 520, Rockville, MD 20852. TEL 301-816-0210. FAX 301-816-0811. (Subscr. to: Taft Group, Box 33477, Detroit, MI 48232-5477. TEL 800-877-TAFT. FAX 313-961-6083) Ed. Mark Scott; Pub. Dennis Poupard. Document type: directory.
— Former titles: Taft Corporate Giving Directory (ISSN 0882-7176); (until 1984): Taft Corporate Directory (ISSN 0732-8958)
  Description: Features in-depth profiles of the top 1,000 corporate foundations and corporate direct-giving programs in the U.S.

360 US ISSN 0747-8003
HV97.A3
CORPORATE GIVING WATCH; news and ideas for nonprofit organizations seeking corporate funds. 1981. m. $149 includes Corporate Updates. Taft Group, 12300 Twinbrook Pkwy., Ste. 520, Rockville, MD 20852. TEL 301-816-0210. FAX 301-816-0811. (Subscr. to: Taft Group, Box 33477, Detroit, MI 48232-5477. TEL 800-877-TAFT. FAX 313-961-6083) Ed. Mark Scott; Pub. Dennis Poupard. Document type: directory.
● Also available online. Vendor(s): NewsNet (GB49).

361.73 US ISSN 1058-689X
CORPORATE GIVING YELLOW PAGES; guide to corporate giving contacts. 1983. a. $88. Taft Group, 12300 Twinbrook Pkwy., Ste. 520, Rockville, MD 20852. TEL 301-816-0210. FAX 301-816-0811. (Subscr. to: Gale Research Inc., Box 33477, Detroit, MI 48232-5477. TEL 800-877-GALE. FAX 313-961-6083) Ed. Bohdan Romaniuk. index. Document type: directory.
  Description: Provides contact names and addresses for more than 3,600 corporate philanthropic programs throughout the United States. Includes an index to companies, their headquarters, and their major products or industries.

361.73 US ISSN 0885-8365
CORPORATE PHILANTHROPY REPORT. m. (except Jan. & Sep.). $200 (non-profit $165). Capitol Publications Inc., 1101 King St., Ste. 444, Alexandria, VA 22314. TEL 703-683-4100; 800-655-5597. FAX 703-739-6501. Ed. Craig Smith; Pub. Cindy Carter. adv. contact: Mary Lou Probka.
—CCC.
  Description: Explores why companies give, where and what they give, and which ones are setting the corporate giving pace.

361.7 380 US ISSN 0197-937X
HV97.A3
CORPORATE 500: THE DIRECTORY OF CORPORATE PHILANTHROPY. 1980. a. $375. Public Management Institute, 358 Brannan St., San Francisco, CA 94107. TEL 415-896-1900. FAX 415-896-0321. Ed. Kenneth Gilman. circ. 2,000. Document type: directory.
  Description: Directory of corporate philanthropic programs, with profiles and indices.

CORRECTIONAL INDUSTRIES ASSOCIATION NEWSLETTER. see PUBLIC ADMINISTRATION

362 616.21 IT
CORRIERE DEI LARINGECTOMIZZATI. 1957. q. Associazione Italiana Laringectomizzati, Via Friuli 28, 20135 Milan, Italy. TEL 02-5510819. Ed. Dr. Giuseppe Sapa. adv.; illus. (tabloid format)
  Description: Organizational news for laryngectomees and users of artificial speaking devices.

360 UN ISSN 0538-8295
THE COST OF SOCIAL SECURITY. irreg. price varies. (International Labour Office) I L O Publications, CH-1211 Geneva 22, Switzerland. TEL 022-799-6111. FAX 022-798-6358. TELEX 415647-ILO-CH. (U.S. distributor: I L O Publications Center, 49 Sheridan Ave., Albany, NY 12210. TEL 518-436-9686. FAX 518-436-7433) (also avail. in microform from ILO,CIS) Indexed: IIS. Document type: bulletin.

361.74 US
COUNCIL COLUMNS. 1980. s-m. $60. Council on Foundations, Inc., 1828 L St., N.W., Ste. 300, Washington, DC 20036. TEL 202-466-6512. FAX 202-785-3926. Ed. Robin Hettleman. circ. 8,000. (back issues avail.) Document type: newsletter.

360 327 EI
COUNCIL OF EUROPE. COMMITTEE OF INDEPENDENT EXPERTS ON THE EUROPEAN SOCIAL CHARTER. CONCLUSIONS. (Text in English; French edition also available) 1970. biennial. price varies. Council of Europe, Publishing and Documentation Service, 67075 Strasbourg Cedex, France. (Dist. in U.S. by: Manhattan Publishing Co., Box 650, Croton-on-Hudson, N.Y. 10520)

360 US ISSN 0277-4259
COUNCIL ON FOUNDATIONS. ANNUAL REPORT. 1964. a. Council on Foundations, Inc., 1828 L St., N.W., Ste. 300, Washington, DC 20036. TEL 202-466-6512. FAX 202-785-3926. Document type: corporate report.

COUNSELING AND VALUES. see RELIGIONS AND THEOLOGY — Roman Catholic

COURIER (BOSTON). see PHILOSOPHY

CRIME, LAW AND SOCIAL CHANGE; an international journal. see CRIMINOLOGY AND LAW ENFORCEMENT

360 BL
CRITICA SOCIAL. 1974. irreg. Universidade Catolica de Minas Gerais, Escola de Servico Social, Av. Dom Jose Gaspar 500, Belo Horizonte 30000, Minas Gerais, Brazil.

360 UK
CRONER'S CARE HOME MANAGEMENT. 1986. q. £82.10 (subscr. includes m. newsletter) (effective 1993). Croner Publications Ltd. (Subsidiary of: Wolters Kluwer N.V.), Croner House, London Rd., Kingston-upon-Thames, Surrey KT2 6SR, England. TEL 081-547-3333. FAX 081-547-2637. Ed. Nick O'Connor. (looseleaf format)
  Description: For residential care home or nursing home owners and managers.

361 SP ISSN 0210-4482
CRUZ ROJA ESPANOLA. 1942. 12/yr. Asociacion Cruz Roja Espanola, Eduardo Data 16, 28010 Madrid, Spain. TEL 1-537-07-07. FAX 1-319-09-99. TELEX 23853 ASCR E. Ed. Jose Carlos Clemente. circ. 6,500,000.
— Supersedes (1899-1936): Cruz Roja (ISSN 0210-4474).

300 VE ISSN 0798-0841
CUADERNOS DE ACTUALIDAD INTERNACIONAL. 1990. s-a. Bs.1200($34) (foreign $42) to individuals; institutions Bs.2400($58) (foreign $74) (effective 1993). Universidad Central de Venezuela, Centro de Estudios del Desarrollo, Apdo. Postal 6622, Caracas 1010-A, Venezuela. TEL 4523266. FAX 7512691. (U.S. subscr. addr.: Poba International, No. 151, 02-5255, Miami, FL 33102-5255) (Co-sponsor: Editorial Trilce de Uruguay) Eds. Nelme Preto B., Pablo Harari. adv. circ. 1,000. (back issues avail.)
  Description: Selection of articles published by Documentation Francaise about different topics of the current world in an international perspective.

CULTURAL RESEARCH INSTITUTE. BULLETIN. see SOCIAL SCIENCES: COMPREHENSIVE WORKS

300 360 US
D S S NEWSLETTER. 1960. m. free. Department of Social Services, Public Information Office, 1510 Guilford Ave., Baltimore, MD 21202. TEL 301-361-2002. FAX 301-361-3150. Ed. Sue Fitzsimmons. circ. 4,000 (controlled). Document type: newsletter.

362.4 US
D V R NEWS. 1979. 2/yr. free. Department of Health and Social Services, Division of Vocational Rehabilitation, 1 W. Wilson St., Rm. 830, Box 7852, Madison, WI 53707. TEL 608-266-3956. Ed. Karen Eckland. bk.rev.; stat. circ. 3,200. (tabloid format)
— Former titles: D V R Newsletter & Our News.

SOCIAL SERVICES AND WELFARE

362.7 US ISSN 0092-4199
HV854
DAY CARE AND EARLY EDUCATION. 1973. q. $125 (foreign $145) (effective 1995). Human Sciences Press, Inc. (Subsidiary of: Plenum Publishing Corp.), 233 Spring St., New York, NY 10013-1578. TEL 212-620-8000. FAX 212-463-0742. TELEX 23-421139. Ed. Randa Roen Nachbar, Mary Renck Jalongo. adv.; bk.rev.; illus. (also avail. in microform from UMI; back issues avail.; reprint service avail. from ISI,UMI) Indexed: C.I.J.E., Cont.Pg.Educ., Educ.Ind., Except.Child Educ.Abstr., Soc.Work Res.& Abstr., Sp.Ed.Needs Abstr. **Document type:** academic/scholarly publication.
—BLDSC (3535.866100); Faxon; UMI; UnCover. CCC.
Description: Provides a practical and lively forum for early childhood teachers, program administrators, day care workers, and other professionals concerned with the education of young children.
Refereed Serial

362.7 US
DAY CARE U S A; the independent biweekly for day care professionals. (Supplement avail.: Day Care Information Service Special Reports) 1971. fortn. $239. United Communications Group, 5225 Pooks Hill Rd., Bethesda, MD 20814-2044. TEL 301-493-6296. FAX 301-816-8945. (Subscr. to: 11300 Rockville Pike, Ste. 1100, Rockville, MD 20852-3030. TEL 301-816-8950) Ed. Charles Pekow. bk.rev. (back issues avail.) **Document type:** newsletter.
Description: Covers new programs, funding and challenges facing day care.

DEAF SAN DIEGO. see *HANDICAPPED — Hearing Impaired*

360 BL ISSN 0011-7242
DEBATES SOCIAIS. 1965. s-a. membership or exchange basis. Centro Brasileiro de Cooperacao e Intercambio de Servicos Sociais, Rua Santa Luzia 685, 2 andar, 20030 Rio de Janeiro R.J., Brazil. Ed. Moacyr Velloso Cardoso de Oliveira. bk.rev. circ. 5,000.
Description: Examines community development.

300.720489 DK ISSN 0907-6514
H62.5.D4
DENMARK. SOCIALFORSKNINGSINSTITUTTET. AARSBERETNING (YEAR). 1960. a. free. Socialforskningsinstituttet - Danish National Institute of Social Research, Borgergade 28, DK-1300 Copenhagen K, Denmark. TEL 33-139811. FAX 33-138992. **Document type:** government publication, corporate report.
Formerly: Denmark. Socialforskningsinstituttet. Beretning om Socialforskningsinstituttets Virksomhed (ISSN 0107-4377)

300 DK ISSN 0904-9398
DENMARK. SOCIALFORSKNINGSINSTITUTTET. ARBEJDSNOTATER. 1987. irreg. free. Socialforskningsinstituttet - Danish National Institute of Social Research, Borgergade 28, DK-1300 Copenhagen K, Denmark. TEL 33-13-98-11. FAX 33-138992. **Document type:** monographic series, government publication.

948.9057 DK ISSN 0905-0957
DENMARK. SOCIALFORSKNINGSINSTITUTTET. PJECER. 1978. irreg., no.41, 1992. price varies. Socialforskningsinstituttet - Danish National Institute of Social Research, 28 Borgergade, DK-1300 Copenhagen K, Denmark. TEL 45-33-13-98-11. FAX 45-33-13-89-92. **Document type:** monographic series, government publication.

300 DK ISSN 0903-6814
DENMARK. SOCIALFORSKNINGSINSTITUTTET. RAPPORTER. 1988. irreg., no.95,1993. price varies. Socialforskningsinstituttet - Danish National Institute of Social Research, 28 Borgergade, DK-1300 Copenhagen K, Denmark. TEL 45-33-13-98-11. FAX 45-33-13-89-92. **Document type:** monographic series, government publication.

948.9057 DK ISSN 0903-7535
HN541
DENMARK. SOCIALFORSKNINGSINSTITUTTET. SOCIAL FORSKNING (YEAR). 1977. 4/yr. free. Socialforskningsinstituttet - Danish National Institute of Social Research, 28 Borgergade, DK-1300 Copenhagen K, Denmark. TEL 33-13-98-11. FAX 33-13-89-92. **Document type:** newsletter, government publication.

360 GW ISSN 0012-1185
DEUTSCHER VEREIN FUER OEFFENTLICHE UND PRIVATE FUERSORGE. NACHRICHTENDIENST. vol.50, 1970. m. DM.30. Deutscher Verein fuer Oeffentliche und Private Fuersorge, Am Stockborn 1-3, 60439 Frankfurt a.M., Germany. FAX 069-5803381. Ed. Prof. Dr. Teresa Bock. adv.; bk.rev.; index. (tabloid format)
—BLDSC (6010.700000); SWETS.

360 US
DEVELOPMENT RESEARCH DIGEST. 1986. q. free. State Developmental Research Institutes, Department of Developmental Services, 2501 Harbour Blvd., Costa Mesa, CA 92626. Ed.Bd. bk.rev. circ. 650.

360 SZ
DEZIBEL; fuer Schwerhoerige und Spaetertaubte. m. 25 SFr. (foreign 45 SFr.). Bruhin AG, Pfarrmatte 6, CH-8807 Freienbach, Switzerland. TEL 055-483366. Ed. Richard Wurz. circ. 8,500. **Document type:** bulletin.
Former titles: B S S V Monatsblatt; Monatsblatt der Hoerbehinderten.

362.3 CN ISSN 0383-8528
DIALECT. 1977. bi-m. free. Saskatchewan Association for Community Living, 3031 Louise St., Saskatoon, SK S7J 3L1, Canada. TEL 306-955-3344. FAX 306-373-3070. Ed. Karin Melberg Schwier. bk.rev.; film rev. circ. 5,600. (back issues avail.) **Document type:** newsletter.

DIARY OF SOCIAL LEGISLATION AND POLICY. see *PUBLIC ADMINISTRATION*

360 FR ISSN 1161-2428
DICTIONNAIRE PERMANENT: ACTION SOCIALE. base vol. plus m. updates. 1380 F. for base vol. (updates 400 F.) (effective 1995). Editions Legislatives et Administratives, 80 av. de la Marne, 92546 Montrouge Cedex, France. TEL 40-92-68-68. FAX 46-56-00-15. TELEX 632 855 F. Ed. Michel Vaillant. (looseleaf format)

362 GW ISSN 0722-0014
DIGEST FUER JUGEND UND BILDUNGEINRICHTUNGEN. 8/yr. DM.54. Deutscher Forschungsdienst, Ahrstr. 45, 53175 Bonn, Germany. TEL 0228-302210. FAX 0228-302270. **Document type:** academic/scholarly publication.

DIRECTORIO DE OBRAS SOCIALES. see *BUSINESS AND ECONOMICS — Trade And Industrial Directories*

261.7 US ISSN 1062-6492
HG4027.65
DIRECTORY OF BUILDING AND EQUIPMENT GRANTS. 1992. biennial. $49.50 for 2nd ed. Research Grant Guides, Box 1214, Loxahatchee, FL 33470. TEL 407-795-6129. **Document type:** directory.
Description: Lists more than 900 funding sources for equipment, building, and renovation grants. Profiles foundations, corporations, federal programs, and associations.

361.7 US
DIRECTORY OF CATHOLIC CHARITIES DIOCESAN AGENCIES AND ORGANIZATIONS (YEAR). biennial. $35 non-members; members $20. Catholic Charities U S A, 1731 King St., Ste. 200, Alexandria, VA 22314. TEL 703-549-1390. FAX 703-549-1656. **Document type:** directory.
Former titles: Directory of Catholic Charities, Diocesan Agencies and Organizations. United States, Puerto Rico and Canada (Year); Directory. Diocesan Agencies of Catholic Charities and Catholic Charities U S A Member Institutions. United States, Puerto Rico and Canada; Directory. Diocesan Agencies of Catholic Charities and N C C C Member Institutions. United States, Puerto Rico and Canada; Directory. Diocesan Agencies of Catholic Charities. United States, Puerto Rico and Canada (ISSN 0091-1003)

DIRECTORY OF COLLEGES AND UNIVERSITIES WITH ACCREDITED SOCIAL WORK DEGREE PROGRAMS. see *EDUCATION — Guides To Schools And Colleges*

360 US
DIRECTORY OF COMMUNITY RESOURCES AND SERVICES. 1943. a. $40 for paperback edition. United Way of the Texas Gulf Coast, Information and Referral Department, 2200 North Loop West, Houston, TX 77018. TEL 713-685-2300; 800-833-5948. FAX 713-956-2868. (Orders to: Box 924507, Houston, TX 77292) Isabel Wanza. index. circ. 1,800. (also avail. in diskette format) **Document type:** directory.
Description: Lists nonprofit health and human services in the Greater Houston area and the surrounding counties.

361.6 CN ISSN 0315-0631
DIRECTORY OF COMMUNITY SERVICES IN METROPOLITAN TORONTO. 1938. a. Can.$50. Community Information Centre of Metropolitan Toronto, 590 Jarvis St., 5th Fl., Toronto, ON M4Y 2J4, Canada. TEL 416-392-4575. FAX 416-392-4404. Ed. Beth White; Pub. Allyson Hewitt. adv. circ. 5,500. **Document type:** directory.

361.6 CN ISSN 0319-258X
HV110.M6
DIRECTORY OF COMMUNITY SERVICES OF GREATER MONTREAL/REPERTOIRE DES SERVICES COMMUNAUTAIRES DU GRAND MONTREAL; welfare-health-recreation. (Text in English and French) 1956. biennial. Can.$45. Information and Referral Centre of Greater Montreal - Centre de Reference du Grand Montreal, 881 de Maisonneuve E., Montreal, PQ H2L 1Y8, Canada. TEL 514-527-1375. FAX 514-527-9712. Ed. Laurent L'Ecuyer. adv. circ. 3,000. **Document type:** directory.
Formerly: Directory of Health, Welfare and Recreation Services of Greater Montreal (ISSN 0070-5640)

360 US ISSN 1070-3950
HG177.5.U6
DIRECTORY OF COMPUTER AND HIGH TECHNOLOGY GRANTS. 1991. biennial. $52.50 (effective 1994). Research Grant Guides, Box 1214, Loxahatchee, FL 33740. TEL 407-765-6129. Ed. Andrew J. Grant. **Document type:** directory.
Description: Contains information for nonprofit organizations seeking funding or donations to purchase or upgrade computers, software and high-tech office equipment.

361.73 US
DIRECTORY OF CORPORATE AND FOUNDATION GIVERS. 1992. a. (in 2 vols.). $225. Taft Group, 12300 Twinbrook Pkwy., Ste. 520, Rockville, MD 20852. TEL 301-813-0210. FAX 301-816-0811. (Subscr. to: Taft Group, Box 33477, Detroit, MI 48232-5477. TEL 800-877-TAFT. FAX 313-961-6083) Ed. Mark Scott; Pub. Dennis Poupard. **Document type:** directory.
Description: Provides a guide on corporate and foundation funding.

360 US
DIRECTORY OF FEDERAL AID FOR HEALTH AND ALLIED FIELDS. irreg. Ready Reference Press, Box 5879, Santa Monica, CA 90405. **Document type:** directory.

362.6 US
DIRECTORY OF FEDERAL AID FOR THE AGING. irreg. Ready Reference Press, Box 5879, Santa Monica, CA 90405. **Document type:** directory.

362.4 371 US
DIRECTORY OF FEDERAL AID FOR THE HANDICAPPED. irreg. Ready Reference Press, Box 5879, Santa Monica, CA 90405. **Document type:** directory.

360 UK ISSN 0070-5624
DIRECTORY OF GRANT-MAKING TRUSTS. 1968. biennial. £49. Charities Aid Foundation, 48 Pembury Rd., Tonbridge, Kent TN9 2JD, England. Ed. Anne Villemur. circ. 7,000. **Document type:** directory.
—BLDSC (3593.840000).
Description: Lists 2,500 grant-making bodies to whom charitable organizations may apply for funds.

DIRECTORY OF GRANTS FOR ORGANIZATIONS SERVING PEOPLE WITH DISABILITIES; a guide to sources of funding in the United States for handicapped programs & services. see *HANDICAPPED*

SOCIAL SERVICES AND WELFARE

360   HK
DIRECTORY OF HONG KONG SERVICES.* a. HK.$200. Hong Kong Trade and Industry Promotion Centre, c/o Hong Kong Trade Development Council, 36th-39th Fl., Office Tower, Conventional Plaza, 1 Harbor Rd., Wanchai, Hong Kong. TEL 3-882708. FAX 3-7716438. **Document type:** directory.

640.73   US   ISSN 0749-050X
HV89
DIRECTORY OF INFORMATION AND REFERRAL AGENCIES IN THE UNITED STATES AND CANADA. 1975. biennial. $30 to non-members; members $25 (foreign $37). Alliance of Information and Referral Systems, Box 3546, Joliet, IL 60434-3546. TEL 815-744-6922. **Document type:** academic/scholarly publication, directory.

DIRECTORY OF INTERNATIONAL CORPORATE GIVING IN AMERICA AND ABROAD. see BUSINESS AND ECONOMICS — Trade And Industrial Directories

361.7   US   ISSN 0161-2638
HV3191
DIRECTORY OF JEWISH FEDERATIONS, WELFARE FUNDS AND COMMUNITY COUNCILS. 1936. a. $10. Council of Jewish Federations, Inc., 730 Broadway, 2nd Fl., New York, NY 10003. index. circ. 1,000. **Document type:** directory.
    Formerly: Jewish Federations, Welfare Funds and Community Councils Directory (ISSN 0075-3734)
    Description: Lists all member agencies geographically; includes names of executive directors and presidents.

DIRECTORY OF NEBRASKA SERVICES. see PUBLIC ADMINISTRATION

360   US
RA997.A2
DIRECTORY OF NURSING HOMES. 1982. a. $249. H C I A Inc., 300 E. Lombard St., Baltimore, MD 21202. TEL 800-568-3280. FAX 410-539-5220. **Document type:** directory.
    Formerly: Directory of Nursing Home Facilities (ISSN 0888-7624)
    Description: Covers nearly 16,300 state licensed long-term care facilities, with complete profiles of each facility.

360   US   ISSN 1071-6726
HV97.A3
DIRECTORY OF OPERATING GRANTS. 1992. biennial. $42.50. Research Grant Guides, Box 1214, Loxahatchee, FL 33470. **Document type:** directory.
    Description: Profiles more than 640 foundations providing operating grants for nonprofit organizations.

364   CN   ISSN 0847-3668
HV6250.3.C2
DIRECTORY OF SERVICES FOR VICTIMS OF CRIME/REPERTOIRE DES SERVICES AUX VICTIMES D'ACTES CRIMINELS. 1988. s-a. Can.$17.25. Canadian Criminal Justice Association - Association Canadienne de Justice Penale, 383 Parkdale Ave., Ste. 304, Ottawa, ON K1Y 4R4, Canada. TEL 613-725-3715. FAX 613-725-3720. circ. 320. **Document type:** directory.
    Description: Lists services for victims of crime in Canada, with addresses and phone numbers.

DISABILITY ISSUES. see HANDICAPPED

362.4   UK   ISSN 1351-6191
THE DISABLEMENT INCOME GROUP. JOURNAL. 1993. q. £5 to individuals; institutions £35. Disablement Income Group, Unit 5, Archway Business Centre, 19-23 Wedmore St., London N19 4RZ, England. TEL 0171-263-3981. Eds. Pauline Thompson, Jean MacQueen. circ. 5,000 (paid). **Document type:** academic/scholarly publication.

360 267 796.3   US   ISSN 8755-965X
DISCOVERY Y M C A. (Young Men's Christian Association) 1982. q. $8 (free to qualified personnel). Y M C A of the U S A, 101 N. Wacker Dr., Chicago, IL 60606. TEL 312-977-0031. FAX 312-977-9063. Ed. Mary Pyke. adv. circ. 105,000.
    Description: Concentrates on challenges and accomplishments of the 2060 YMCAs in the U.S.A. and on issues facing the movement as a whole.

362.7   GW   ISSN 0937-9614
HQ799.G5
DISKURS; Studien zu Kindheit, Jugend, Familie und Gesellschaft. (Text in German; summaries in English, French) s-a. DM.74 (foreign DM.84). Deutsches Jugendinstitut e.V. - German Youth Institute, Freibadstr. 30, 81543 Munich, Germany. TEL 089-623060. FAX 089-62306162. (Subscr. to: Juventa Verlag, Ehretstr. 3, 69469 Weinheim, Germany. TEL 06201-61035) Ed. Wolfgang Gaiser. **Document type:** academic/scholarly publication.

360   US
DOMESTIC HUMAN NEEDS NETWORKER. 10/yr. $25 contribution. Interfaith Action for Economic Justice, 110 Maryland Ave., N.E., Washington, DC 20002. TEL 202-543-2800.

360   FR   ISSN 0758-6531
HN421
DONNEES SOCIALES; la societe francaise. 1973. triennial. 285 F. Institut National de la Statistique et des Etudes Economiques, 18 bd. Adolphe Pinard, 75675 Paris Cedex 14, France. TEL 33-1-41-17-60-54. FAX 41-17-66-66.
—BLDSC (3619.237000).
    Description: Information on French society such as population, employee salaries, working conditions, lifestyles, health conditions, education, welfare, and social justice.

361.73   US   ISSN 0886-9359
DONOR BRIEFING; a biweekly digest for the nonprofit fundraising community. 1986. bi-w. $167. Business Publishers, Inc., 951 Pershing Dr., Silver Spring, MD 20910-4464. TEL 301-587-6300. FAX 301-587-1081. Eds. Albert Copland, Amy Jo Mendelson. **Document type:** newsletter.
    Description: Provides both donors and candidates with a timely forum for news of donor activity.

E C H O NEWS. (European Community Humanitarian Office) see BUSINESS AND ECONOMICS — International Development And Assistance

E S S EMPLOYMENT OPPORTUNITIES. (Executive Search Service) see OCCUPATIONS AND CAREERS

ECHO DE L'UNION. see GERONTOLOGY AND GERIATRICS

971   CN   ISSN 0012-9321
ECHOES. 1902. 3/yr. Can.$3. I O D E, 40 Orchard View Blvd., Toronto, Ont. M4R 1B9, Canada. TEL 416-487-4416. FAX 416-487-4417. Ed. Winifred Anderson. adv.; bk.rev.; illus.; tr.lit.; index. circ. 10,000.

330   US   ISSN 0013-0206
ECONOMIC OPPORTUNITY REPORT; the independent weekly source for news of all economic opportunity programs. 1965. w. $330. Business Publishers, Inc., 951 Pershing Dr., Silver Spring, MD 20910-4464. TEL 301-587-6300. FAX 301-585-9075. Ed. Jay Fletcher. (looseleaf format; back issues avail.) **Document type:** newsletter.
    ●Also available online. Vendor(s): NewsNet.
    —CCC.
    Description: Provides inside news from Washington on money, trends, innovations, and research results for antipoverty administrators.

360   VE   ISSN 0013-0680
ECOS. 1945. bi-m. free. (Asociacion Benefico - Social Hogar Virgen de los Dolores) Editorial Sucre, Monzon a Barcenas No. 135, Caracas, Venezuela. Ed. Hermann Gonzalez-Oropeza. bk.rev./ circ. 18,000 (controlled). (looseleaf format; also avail. in record) **Document type:** bulletin.

EDUCATION PERMANENTE. see EDUCATION

360   ES
EL SALVADOR BOLETIN DE ANALISIS E INFORMACION. bi-m. Col.10 ($8 in C. America, $10 in S. America; $12 in US; $15 in Europe). Centro de Investigacion y Accion Social, Av. Washington 402, Col. Libertad, Apdo. 3371, San Salvador, El Salvador.

EMPATHY; an interdisciplinary journal for persons working to end oppression on the basis of sexual identities. see HOMOSEXUALITY

EN AVANT. see RELIGIONS AND THEOLOGY — Other Denominations And Sects

361   US   ISSN 0071-0237
HV35
ENCYCLOPEDIA OF SOCIAL WORK. 1929. irreg. (approx. every 10 yrs.), 19th ed., 1995. $120 softcover; casebound $150; CD-ROM $225. (National Association of Social Workers) N A S W Press, 750 First St., N.E., Ste. 700, Washington, DC 20002-4241. TEL 202-408-8600. FAX 202-336-8312. Ed. Richard L. Edwards. circ. 25,000. Indexed: Abstr.Soc.Work. **Document type:** academic/scholarly publication.
    ●Also available on CD-ROM.
    Formerly: Social Work Year Book.
    Description: Accesses data on the entire range of activities in social work and social welfare.

362.7   UN   ISSN 0013-757X
ENFANTS DU MONDE. 1965. q. 90 F. Fonds des Nations Unies pour l'Enfance (UNICEF), Comite Francais, 3 rue Duguay-Trouin, 75006 Paris, France. TEL 44-39-77-77. FAX 44-39-77-78. Ed. Josette Tagher Roche. bk.rev.; charts; illus. circ. 80,000. **Document type:** newspaper.
    Description: Aim is to promote assistance to deprived children worldwide, by exposing their unsatisfactory living conditions.

360   SZ
ENTRAIDE FAMILIALE. (Text in French) m. Case Postale 3007, CH-1002 Lausanne, Switzerland. TEL 021-6524032. Ed. Renee Hermenjat. circ. 11,000.

360   GW   ISSN 0343-656X
ENTSCHEIDUNGEN DER SPRUCHSTELLEN FUER FUERSORGESTREITIGKEITEN. 1947. m. DM.139. Deutscher Gemeindeverlag GmbH, Postfach 400263, 50832 Cologne, Germany. TEL 02234-1060. FAX 02234-106284. circ. 970. **Document type:** bulletin.
    —CCC.

EPILEPSIA-LEHTI. see MEDICAL SCIENCES — Psychiatry And Neurology

360 616.8   AT   ISSN 0729-7823
EPILETTER. 1967. q. Aus.$10. Epilepsy Foundation of Victoria, 818 Burke Rd., Camberwell, Vic. 3124, Australia. TEL 61-3-813-2866. FAX 61-3-882-7159. Ed. Gail Chrisfield. bk.rev. circ. 2,500. (back issues avail.) **Document type:** consumer publication, newsletter.
    Description: Covers all aspects of epilepsy, including research, human interest, medicine, fundraising and welfare.

267   FR   ISSN 0763-5184
EQUIPES ST. VINCENT. 3/yr. 55 F. Federation Francaise des Equipes Saint-Vincent, 67 rue de Sevres, 75006 Paris, France. Ed. Mauricette Borloo. bk.rev. circ. 4,000.
    Formerly: Echos des Charites de St. Vincent de Paul (ISSN 0070-8305)

364.77   IT
ERASMO. 1989. bi-m. L.50000. (Croce Rossa Italiana) Emmeffe s.r.l., Via della Cavona 2, C.P. 3, 00040 Morena (RM), Italy. TEL 06-79840020. FAX 06-79840024. Ed. Dr. G.B. Conforti. adv.: color page L.14000000. circ. 200,000.

368 658.3   GW   ISSN 0014-0279
DIE ERSATZKASSE. 1916. m. DM.5. Verband der Angestellten-Krankenkassen e.V., Frankfurter Str. 84, 53721 Siegburg, Germany. Ed. Rainer Josteu. adv.; bk.rev.; illus.; stat. circ. 7,000. Indexed: Excerp.Med., World Bibl.Soc.Sec. **Document type:** bulletin.

360   FR   ISSN 0338-4330
ESCLAVAGE; document social. 1974. q. 5 F. Equipes d'Action Contre la Traite des Femmes et des Enfants, 21, rue Sainte Croix de la Bretonnerie, 75004 Paris, France.

ESCOGE LA VIDA! see POPULATION STUDIES

362.82   FR   ISSN 0994-219X
ESPACES ET FAMILLES. 1988. bi-m. Caisse Nationale des Allocations Familiales, Direction de la Recherche, des Previsions et des Statistiques, 23 rue Daviel, 75634 Paris Cedex 13, France. Ed. Catherine Blanc.

SOCIAL SERVICES AND WELFARE 5979

360   IT   ISSN 0014-0678
ESPERIENZA; mensile di attualita, cultura e informazione. 1951. m. membership. (Associazione Nazionale Lavoratori Anziani di Azienda) Editoriale Esperienza s.r.l., Largo Teatro Valle, 6, 00186 Rome, Italy. FAX 39-6-6877019. Ed. Renzo Radice. adv.; B&W page L.5000000, color page L.5500000. bk.rev. circ. 247,165. **Document type:** newspaper.

360   917.306   US   ISSN 0737-1411
ETHNIC AMERICAN VOLUNTARY ORGANIZATIONS. 1983. irreg. price varies. Greenwood Press, Inc. (Subsidiary of: Greenwood Publishing Group Inc.), 88 Post Rd. W., Box 5007, Westport, CT 06881-5007. TEL 203-226-3571. FAX 203-222-1502.

EUROPEAN COMMUNITY HUMANITARIAN OFFICE. ANNUAL REPORT. see *BUSINESS AND ECONOMICS* — *International Development And Assistance*

360   AU   ISSN 0253-7427
EUROSOCIAL NEWSLETTER/EUROSOCIAL BULLETIN D'INFORMATION/EUROSOCIAL NACHRICHTEN. (Text in English, French and German) 1974. 2/yr. free. European Centre for Social Welfare Policy and Research, Berggasse 17, A-1090 Vienna, Austria. TEL 0222-3194505-0. FAX 0222-319450519. Ed. Bernd Marin. adv. contact: Willem Stamatiou. bk.rev. circ. 5,000. (back issues avail.) **Document type:** newsletter.
—BLDSC (3830.429300).
Description: Reports on activities of the European Centre in the areas of social welfare policy and research.

330.9   SP
EVOLUCION SOCIOECONOMICA DE ESPANA. Organizacion Sindical Espanola, Secretariado Central de Asuntos Economicos, Casa Sindical, Paseo del Prado 18, Madrid, Spain. illus.; stat.

361.73   US
EXCHANGE (NEW YORK). 1985. 3/yr. Funding Exchange, 666 Broadway, Ste. 500, New York, NY 10012. TEL 212-529-5300. Ed. Nan Robin. circ. 4,000. (back issues avail.)
Formerly: Donor Update.
Description: Covers organizational activities, social exchange issues, philanthropy, and donors.

EXCHANGE PROJECT. see *POLITICAL SCIENCE*

362.87   341.4   325   DK
EXIL. 1992. q. DKK 150. Dansk Flygtninghjaelp - Danish Refugee Council, P.O. Box 53, DK-1002 Copenhagen K, Denmark. FAX 45-33-32-84-48. Ed. Klaus Rothstein. illus. circ. 1,200. **Document type:** bulletin.

361   US
EYE ON L S S I. 1988. 3/yr. free. Lutheran Social Services of Illinois, 1001 E. Touhy Ave., Des Plaines, IL 60018. TEL 708-635-4600. (Affiliate: Evangelical Lutheran Church in America) Ed. Sherie L. Beirne. illus. circ. 82,000. (tabloid format) **Document type:** newsletter.
Description: Introduces programs and achievements of the organization.

F C L ACTION ALERTS. (Friends Committee on Legislation of California) see *POLITICAL SCIENCE*

362.4   US
F.H.I. CHALLENGER.* 1978? m. $2. (Federation of Handicapped Individuals) Handicapped Industries, 1120 Cummins Rd., Ste. 113, Des Moines, IA 50315-5964. Ed. Ray Benson.

360   US   ISSN 0014-6137
F R I MONTHLY PORTFOLIO. 1962. m. $75. Fund Raising Institute, Div. of the Taft Group, 12300 Twinbrook Pkwy., Ste. 520, Rockville, MD 20852. TEL 301-816-0210. FAX 301-816-0811. Ed. Jill Johnson. adv. contact: Cheryl Slobodian. bk.rev.; index. circ. 3,500. **Document type:** newsletter.
Description: Contains articles on sources for and examples of philanthropic fund-raising ideas and techniques. For individuals and nonprofit organizations.

362.8   US
F S C MONTHLY BULLETIN. m. free. Federation of Southern Cooperatives, Box 95, Epes, AL 35460. TEL 202-652-9676. **Document type:** bulletin.

360   NE   ISSN 0920-6469
FACT SHEET ON THE NETHERLANDS. (Text in Dutch, English, French, German and Spanish) irreg. Ministerie van Welzijn Volksgezondheid en Sport, Publieksvoorlichting - Ministry of Health, Welfare and Sport, Public Information Office, Postbus 5406, 2280 HK Rijswijk, Netherlands. TEL 31-70-3406015. **Document type:** government publication.

338.1   360   FR   ISSN 0014-6889
FAIMS ET SOIFS DES HOMMES. 1969. 4/yr. 200 F. (effective 1995). Mouvement Emmaus, 179 bis, quai de Valmy, 75010 Paris, France. TEL 46-07-51-51. FAX 46-07-69-10. Ed. Abbe Pierre. adv.; bk.rev.; film rev.; play rev.; illus. circ. 5,000.
Supersedes: Faim et Soif.

FAIRE FACE. see *MEDICAL SCIENCES*

FAMILIA Y SOCIEDAD. see *SOCIOLOGY*

361.3   US   ISSN 1044-3894
HV1   CODEN: FASOEN
FAMILIES IN SOCIETY; the journal of contemporary human services. 1920. m. (10/yr.) $42 to individuals (foreign $59); institutions $79 (foreign $89). Families International, Inc., 11700 W. Lake Park Dr., Milwaukee, WI 53224. TEL 414-359-1040; 800-852-1944. FAX 414-359-1074. (Subscr. to: Subscription Department, Box 6649, Syracuse, NY 13217) Ed. Ralph J. Burant. adv.; bk.rev.; index; circ. 5,000 (paid). (also avail. in microform from JAI,UMI; back issues avail.; reprint service avail. from KTO,UMI) **Indexed:** Abstr.Crim.& Pen., Abstr.Health Care Manage.Stud., Abstr.Soc.Geront., Acad.Ind., ASSIA, Behav.Abstr., Bk.Rev.Ind. (1965-), Chicago Psychoanal.Lit.Ind., Child.Bk.Rev.Ind. (1965-), CLOA, Crim.Just.Abstr., Curr.Cont., Except.Child.Educ.Abstr., Hosp.Lit.Ind., IMFL, Lang.& Lang.Behav.Abstr., Mid.East: Abstr.& Ind., Mult.Ed.Abstr., PSI, Psychol.Abstr. (1946-), Soc.Sci.Ind., Soc.Work Res.& Abstr., Sociol.Abstr., SSCI, Stud.Wom.Abstr. **Document type:** academic/scholarly publication.
●Also available online. Vendor(s): University Microfilms International.
—BLDSC (3865.553973); Faxon; Genuine Article; SWETS; UMI; UnCover. **CCC.**
Formerly (until Jan. 1990): Social Casework (ISSN 0037-7678)
Description: Directed to human service professionals. Deals with the theory, practice, and management of family, individual and group counseling and therapy.
Refereed Serial

362.7   346.01   SW   ISSN 1102-2353
FAMILJEFOERENINGEN FOER INTERNATIONELL ADOPTION. 1980. 3/yr. SEK 290 membership (effective 1991). Familjefoereningen foer Intenationell Adoption (FFIA), P.O. Box 12027, S-402 41 Goeteborg, Sweden.
Former titles (until vol.2, 1988): Familjenytt; (until vol.1, 1982): Information fraan Familjefoereningen foer Adoption.

FAMILLE ET DEVELOPPEMENT. see *PUBLIC HEALTH AND SAFETY*

361.3   301.42   US
FAMILY CAREGIVER APPLICATIONS SERIES. irreg., no.4, 1994. price varies. (Center for Practice Innovations, Case Western University Mandel School of Applied Social Sciences) Sage Publications, Inc., 2455 Teller Rd., Thousand Oaks, CA 91320. TEL 805-499-0721. FAX 805-499-0871. E-mail: libraries@sagepub.com. (Overseas orders to: Sage Publications Ltd., 6 Bonhill St., London EC2A, England; Sage Publications India Pvt. Ltd., P.O. Box 4215, New Delhi 110 048, India) **Document type:** monographic series.

FAMILY MATTERS. see *SOCIOLOGY*

346   362.82   UK   ISSN 1350-9756
FAMILY MEDIATION. 1991. 3/yr. £10. National Family Mediation, 9 Tavistock Pl., London WC1H 9SN, England. TEL 0171-383-5993. FAX 0171-383-5994. Ed. Arthur Robinson. adv.; bk.rev. **Document type:** bulletin.
—BLDSC (3865.567440).
Formerly (until 1994): Family Conciliation.
Description: Provides information and commentary on the work of National Family Mediation, its affiliated services in the UK, and similar agencies elsewhere.

FAMILY NOTES. see *SOCIOLOGY*

FAMILY PLANNING ASSOCIATION OF NEPAL. ANNUAL REPORT. see *BIRTH CONTROL*

362.7   US   ISSN 1041-8660
HV699
FAMILY RESOURCE COALITION REPORT. 1981. 4/yr. $50 to individuals; institutions $90 (includes membership). Family Resource Coalition, 200 S. Michigan Ave., 16th Fl., Chicago, IL 60604-2404. TEL 312-341-0900. FAX 312-341-9361. Ed. Kathy Goetz. bk.rev.; bibl. circ. 5,000. (also avail. in microfiche; back issues avail.) **Indexed:** ERIC. **Document type:** academic/scholarly publication, consumer publication, trade publication.
Description: For professionals in family support and related fields.

360   US   ISSN 1045-1684
HV89
FAMILY SERVICE AMERICA DIRECTORY OF MEMBER AGENCIES; in the United States and Canada. 1987. a. Family Service America, Inc., 11700 W. Lake Park Dr., Milwaukee, WI 53224. TEL 414-359-1040. FAX 414-359-1074. circ. 700.
Description: Contains addresses, telephone numbers, chief executives and areas served for all members of F.S.A.

FAMILY SUPPORT BULLETIN. see *HANDICAPPED* — *Physically Impaired*

FAMILY THERAPY. see *MEDICAL SCIENCES* — *Psychiatry And Neurology*

FAMILY THERAPY NETWORKER. see *PSYCHOLOGY*

FAMILY THERAPY NEWS. see *PSYCHOLOGY*

362.82   364   US   ISSN 1067-7283
HV6626.2   CODEN: FVSBET
FAMILY VIOLENCE & SEXUAL ASSAULT BULLETIN. 1985. s-a. $25 to individuals; institutions $40. Family Violence & Sexual Assualt Institute, 1310 Clinic Dr., Tyler, TX 75701. TEL 903-595-6600. FAX 903-595-6799. Ed. Robert Geffner. adv. contact: Mary Sals-Lewis. bk.rev. circ. 3,000. **Document type:** bulletin.
Formerly (until 1991): Family Violence Bulletin (ISSN 1055-7938)
Refereed Serial

THE FAR EAST; mission magazine of the Columban fathers. see *RELIGIONS AND THEOLOGY* — *Roman Catholic*

FAST FACTS AND FIGURES ABOUT SOCIAL SECURITY (YEAR). see *INSURANCE*

FEDERAL BENEFITS FOR VETERANS AND DEPENDENTS. see *INSURANCE*

FEDERAL BENEFITS FOR VETERANS AND DEPENDENTS, IS-1 FACT SHEET. see *MILITARY*

360   FR   ISSN 0248-3165
FEUILLE DE ROUTE. m. 50 F. (A.T.D. Fourthworld) Editions Quart Monde, 107 av. du General Leclerc, 95480 Pierrelaye, France. circ. 100,000.

FILM AUSTRALIA HEALTH & WELFARE CATALOGUE. see *MOTION PICTURES*

SOCIAL SERVICES AND WELFARE

360 FI ISSN 0355-4759
HA1448
FINLAND. SOSIAALIHALLITUS. HUOLTOAPU/FINLAND. NATIONAL BOARD OF SOCIAL WELFARE. HOMEHELP/FINLAND. SOCIALSTYRELSEN. SOCIALHJAELP. (Text in English, Finnish and Swedish) 1969. biennial. FIM 25. Sosiaalihallitus, Siltaarenkatu 18 C, SF-00530 Helsinki, Finland. (Dist. by: Government Printing Center, Box 516, SF-00101 Helsinki, Finland) Ed. Kyllikki Korpi. circ. 1,000. **Document type:** government publication.

360 FI ISSN 0355-4767
FINLAND. SOSIAALIHALLITUS. KODINHOITOAPU/FINLAND. NATIONAL BOARD OF SOCIAL WELFARE. SOCIAL ASSISTANCE/FINLAND. SOCIALSTYRELSEN. HEMVAARDSHJAELP. (Text in English, Finnish and Swedish) 1971. biennial. FIM 21. Sosiaalihallitus, Siltaarenkatu 18 C, SF-00530 Helsinki, Finland. (Dist. by: Government Printing Center, Box 516, SF-00101 Helsinki, Finland) Ed. Kyllikki Korpi. circ. 1,200. **Document type:** government publication.

360 FI ISSN 0071-5328
FINLAND. SOSIAALIHALLITUS. SOSIAALIHUOLTOTILASTON VUOSIKIRJA/FINLAND. NATIONAL BOARD OF SOCIAL WELFARE. YEARBOOK OF SOCIAL WELFARE STATISTICS/FINLAND. SOCIALSTYRELSEN. SOCIALVAARDSSTATISTISK AARSBOK. (Section XXV B of Official Statistics of Finland) (Text in English, Finnish and Swedish) 1959. a. Sosiaalihallitus, Siltaarenkatu 18 C, Helsinki, Finland. Ed. Kyllikki Korpi. circ. 1,100. **Document type:** government publication.

361 362.7 UN ISSN 1014-9023
FIRST CALL FOR CHILDREN. French ed.: Enfants d'Abord (ISSN 1014-9457); Spanish ed.: Ninos Primero (ISSN 1014-9465) 1988. bi-m. free. United Nations Children's Fund (UNICEF), UNICEF House, 3 United Nations Plaza, New York, NY 10017. TEL 212-326-7787. FAX 212-326-7768. TELEX 76077848. bk.rev.; film rev.; circ. 65,000 (controlled). (tabloid format; also avail. in diskette format) Indexed: HR Rep. (1986-1988). **Document type:** newsletter.
Formed by the 1991 merger of: African Kora (ISSN 1014-9449) & Kora Africaine (ISSN 1014-9430) & Unicef Intercom (ISSN 0259-8167) & Action for Children (ISSN 1010-3384)
Description: Discusses social, political, and economic problems and what can be and what is being done to solve them.

THE FITZHUGH DIRECTORY OF INDEPENDENT HEALTHCARE. FINANCIAL INFORMATION. ACUTE SECTOR. see MEDICAL SCIENCES

THE FITZHUGH DIRECTORY OF N H S TRUSTS. FINANCIAL INFORMATION. see MEDICAL SCIENCES — Abstracting, Bibliographies, Statistics

FIVE-YEAR INFORMATION RESOURCES MANAGEMENT PROGRAM. see LIBRARY AND INFORMATION SCIENCES

353.9 US
FLORIDA. DEPARTMENT OF CORRECTIONS. ANNUAL REPORT. 1973. a. free. Department of Corrections, 2601 Blair Stone Rd., Tallahassee, FL 32399-2500. TEL 904-488-1776. FAX 904-488-4602. Ed.Bd. stat. circ. 4,000. (also avail. in microfiche from CIS) Indexed: SRI. **Document type:** government publication.
Formerly: Florida. Division of Corrections. Financial Report (ISSN 0094-6435)

362.87 DK ISSN 0900-2537
FLYGTNINGE NYT. 1982. 8/yr. free. Dansk Flygtningehjaelp, P.O. Box 53, 1002 Copenhagen K, Denmark. FAX 45-33-32-84-48. Ed. Klaus Rothstein. illus. circ. 22,000. **Document type:** newsletter.
Formerly: Nyt om Flygtninge (ISSN 0108-1845)

362.5 US ISSN 0195-5705
HC79.P6
FOCUS (MADISON). 1976. q. free. University of Wisconsin at Madison, Institute for Research on Poverty, 3412 Social Science Bldg., 1180 Observatory Dr., Madison, WI 53706. TEL 608-262-6358. cum.index: 1976-1993. circ. 6,000. (back issues avail.) **Document type:** academic/scholarly publication.
—BLDSC (3964.194940).
Formerly: Focus on Poverty Research (ISSN 0191-2186)
Description: Provides coverage of poverty-related research, events, and issues in essay form and acquaints others with the institute's work.

FOCUS (WASHINGTON, 1978). see HANDICAPPED

FOKUS PAA FAMILIEN; tidsskrift for familiebehandling. see MEDICAL SCIENCES — Psychiatry And Neurology

616.99 362.1 FR ISSN 0180-9792
FONDAMENTAL. 1978. q. 40 F. Association pour la Recherche sur le Cancer (ARC), B.P. 3, 7, rue Guy Moquet, 94801 Villejuif Cedex, France. TEL 45-59-59-59. FAX 47-26-04-75. Ed. J. Crozemarie. adv.; bk.rev.
Description: French cancer information on research and prevention for the public.

360 US
FOOD & POVERTY NOTES. 1976. bi-m. $10. Maryland Food Committee, 2521 N. Charles St., Baltimore, MD 21218. TEL 410-366-0600. FAX 410-366-3963. Ed. Peter Rolph. circ. 37,000. **Document type:** newsletter.
Description: Covers various issues dealing with food assistance, advocacy and the hunger problem nationwide.

362.8 US ISSN 0736-0010
FOODLINES. 1982. bi-m. $25. Food Research & Action Center, 1875 Connecticut Ave., N.W., Ste. 540, Washington, DC 20009. TEL 202-986-2200. FAX 202-986-2525. Ed. Christin M. Driscoll. circ. 2,000. **Document type:** newsletter.

FOR THOSE WHO GIVE AND GRIEVE; a quarterly newsletter for donor families. see MEDICAL SCIENCES — Urology And Nephrology

360 GW ISSN 0071-7835
FORTBILDUNG UND PRAXIS. (Supplement to: Wege zur Sozialversicherung) 1949. irreg. price varies. Asgard-Verlag Dr. Werner Hippe KG, Einsteinstr. 10, 53757 St. Augustin, Germany. TEL 02241-3164-0.

FORTUNE NEWS. see CRIMINOLOGY AND LAW ENFORCEMENT

360 GW ISSN 0947-8957
FORUM ERZIEHUNGSHILFEN. 1972. 5/yr. DM.48. (Internationale Gesellschaft fuer erzieherische Hilfen) Votum Verlag GmbH, Studtstr. 20, 48149 Muenster, Germany. Ed. Wolfgang Trede. index. circ. 2,500. (back issues avail.) **Document type:** bulletin.
Formerly (until 1994): Materialien zur Heimerziehung (ISSN 0723-2047)

362.7 364 GW ISSN 0171-7669
FORUM JUGENDHILFE. 1950. 4/yr. DM.12. Arbeitsgemeinschaft fuer Jugendhilfe, Haager Weg 44, 53127 Bonn, Germany. TEL 0225-910240. FAX 0225-9102466. Eds. P. Marguard, Peter Klausch. adv.; bk.rev. circ. 1,500. **Document type:** bulletin.
Former titles: Arbeitsgemeinschaft fuer Jugendhilfe. Mitteilungen; Arbeitsgemeinschaft fuer Jugendpflege und Jugendfuersorge. Mitteilungen (ISSN 0003-7710)

360 UK
FORWARD. 1889. q. Sandes Soldiers' & Airmen's Centres, 30-A Belmont Rd., Belfast BT4 2AN, N. Ireland. TEL 01232-472717. Ed. Hazel Knox. adv. contact: Hazel Knox. circ. 3,000. **Document type:** newsletter.

FOSTER CARE. see CHILDREN AND YOUTH — About

361.73 US
AS911.A2
FOUNDATION DIRECTORY PART 2: A GUIDE TO GRANT PROGRAMS FIFTY THOUSAND DOLLARS TO TWO HUNDRED THOUSAND DOLLARS. 1990. a. $175 (effective 1995). Foundation Center, 79 Fifth Ave., New York, NY 10003. TEL 212-620-4230. FAX 212-807-3677. Ed. Margaret Feczko. **Document type:** directory.
Formerly: Foundation Directory Part 2: A Guide to Grant Programs Twenty Five Thousand Dollars to One Hundred Thousand Dollars (ISSN 1058-6210)
Description: Provides current information on over 4,200 foundations that maintain mid-sized grant programs.

360 US ISSN 0741-7004
FOUNDATION GIVING WATCH; the monthly report to non-profit organizations seeking foundation support. 1981. m. $149 includes Foundation Updates. Taft Group, 12300 Twinbrook Pkwy., Ste. 520, Rockville, MD 20852. TEL 301-816-0210. FAX 301-816-0811. (Subscr. to: Taft Group, Box 33477, Detroit, MI 48232-5477. TEL 800-877-TAFT. FAX 313-961-6083) index. **Document type:** bulletin.
●Also available online. Vendor(s): NewsNet (GB50).

361.7 US ISSN 0015-8976
AS911.A2
FOUNDATION NEWS; philanthropy and the nonprofit sector. 1960. bi-m. $35. Council on Foundations, Inc., 1828 L St., N.W., Ste. 300, Washington, DC 20036. TEL 202-466-6512. FAX 202-785-3926. Ed. Leslie Howell. adv. contact: Patrick Gough. bk.rev.; illus.; stat. circ. 15,000. Indexed: Rehabil.Lit.
●Also available online. Vendor(s): University Microfilms International.
—Faxon; UMI; UnCover.
Description: Information exchange between grantmakers and grantseekers.

360 US ISSN 1055-4998
HV97.A3
FOUNDATION REPORTER. 1971. a. $365. Taft Group, 12300 Twinbrook Pkwy., Ste. 520, Rockville, MD 20852. TEL 301-816-0210. FAX 301-816-0811. (Subscr. to: Taft Group, Box 33477, Detroit, MI 48232-5477. TEL 800-877-TAFT. FAX 313-961-6083) **Document type:** directory.
Former titles (until 1990): Taft Foundation Reporter (ISSN 0730-6237); (until 1978): Taft Foundation Reporter. National Edition (ISSN 0197-0240)
Description: Provides in-depth profiles of the top 1,000 private foundations in the U.S.

FOURTH WORLD JOURNAL. see POLITICAL SCIENCE — Civil Rights

FRAENKISCHER HAUSKALENDER UND CARITASKALENDER. see BIOGRAPHY

360 FR ISSN 0184-6469
FRANCE. CAISSE NATIONALE DES ALLOCATIONS FAMILIALES. STATISTIQUES PRESTATIONS DE LOGEMENT. a. free. Caisse Nationale des Allocations Familiales, 23 rue Daviel, 75634 Paris Cedex 13, France.

361 614 350.6 US ISSN 0734-1601
FROM THE STATE CAPITALS. PUBLIC ASSISTANCE AND WELFARE TRENDS. Variant title: Public Assistance and Welfare Trends - From the State Capitals. 1946. w. $235 (effective 1994). Wakeman-Walworth, Inc., 300 N. Washington St., Alexandria, VA 22314. TEL 703-549-8606. FAX 703-549-1372. (processed; back issues avail.) **Document type:** newsletter.
—CCC.
Former titles (until 1983): From the State Capitals. Public Assistance (ISSN 1062-6689); (until 1982): From the State Capitals. Public Assistance and Welfare Trends (ISSN 0016-1861)
Description: Summarizes of developments in state welfare.

360 GW ISSN 0945-3253
FUERSORGERECHTLICHE ENTSCHEIDUNGEN DER VERWALTUNGS- UND SOZIALGERICHTE. 1951. m. DM.105. Richard Boorberg Verlag GmbH und Co., Kestnerstr. 44, 30159 Hannover, Germany. TEL 0511-810592. FAX 0511-810575. Ed. J. Basse. circ. 1,850. **Document type:** bulletin.
Formerly: Fuersorgerechtliche Entscheidungen.

SOCIAL SERVICES AND WELFARE

360 JA ISSN 0285-712X
FUKUSHI KIKI JOHO/INFORMATION OF WELFARE EQUIPMENT. (Text in Japanese) 1978. a. Fukushi Kiki Kaihatsu Senta - Welfare Equipment Development Center of Japan, 2-8, Nishiwaseda 2-chome, Shinjuku-ku, Tokyo 162, Japan.

361.73 US ISSN 1077-2405
FUND RAISING REGULATION REPORT. bi-m. $96 to institutions worldwide (effective 1995). John Wiley & Sons, Inc., Journals, 605 Third Ave., New York, NY 10158. TEL 212-850-6645. FAX 212-850-6021. TELEX 12-7063. (Subscr. to: Box 2575, Secaucus, NJ 07096-2575) **Document type:** newsletter.

352 BL
FUNDACAO DE ASSISTENCIA AOS MUNICIPIOS DO ESTADO DO PARANA. BOLETIM DOS MUNICIPIOS. 1972. irreg. free. Fundacao de Assistencia aos Municipios, Rua Mariano Torres 135, 8000 Curitiba, Parana, Brazil.

362.7 US ISSN 1073-0966
FUNDING ALERT. 1972. w. $60. Community Congress of San Diego, 3255 Wing St., Ste. 109, San Diego, CA 92110-4639. TEL 619-223-7101. FAX 619-221-8611. Ed. Barbara Karlin. bk.rev. circ. 80. (back issues avail.) **Document type:** newsletter.
Description: Overview of funding available to nonprofits from the Federal Register, nationwide foundations and others.

361.73 US ISSN 1045-1951
HV89
FUNDRAISER'S GUIDE TO HUMAN SERVICE FUNDING. 1989. a. $130. Taft Group, 12300 Twinbrook Pkwy., Ste. 520, Rockville, MD 20852. TEL 301-816-0210. FAX 301-816-0811. (Subscr. to: Gale Research Inc., Box 33477, Detroit, MI 48232-5477. TEL 800-877-GALE. FAX 313-961-6083) **Document type:** directory.
Description: Profiles more than 1,000 of the largest corporate and foundation supporters of human service organizations

THE FUTURE OF CHILDREN. see *CHILDREN AND YOUTH — About*

362.7 PO ISSN 0016-3910
GAIATO; obra de rapazes, para rapazes, pelos rapazes. 1944. s-m. Esc.750. Casa do Gaiato, Paco de Sousa, 4560 Penafiel, Portugal. TEL 351-55-752285. FAX 351-55-753799. Ed. Julio Mendes. adv. contact: Carlos Galamba. circ. 73,500. (tabloid format; also avail. in microform) **Document type:** newspaper.

362.8 GW ISSN 0016-5794
GEFAEHRDETENHILFE; Aktuelles aus Theorie und Praxis. 1959. q. DM.35. Bundesarbeitsgemeinschaft Wohnungslosenhilfe e.V., Postfach 130148, 33544 Bielefeld, Germany. TEL 0521-1443613. FAX 0521-1442818. Ed. Heinrich Holtmannspoetter. adv.; bk.rev.; index. circ. 2,000. **Document type:** bulletin.
Description: Covers the topic of homelessness of single persons in Germany.

GEISTIGE BEHINDERUNG; Fachzeitschrift der Lebenshilfe fuer geistig Behinderte. see *EDUCATION — Special Education And Rehabilitation*

368 NE ISSN 0929-7936
GEREGELD. 1977. q. (Voorlichtingscentrum Sociale Verzekering) Uitegeverij Kluwer B.V., Postbus 23, 7400 GA Deventer, Netherlands. TEL 31-5700-47111. FAX 31-5700-37533.
Formerly (until 1994): Vast en Zeker (ISSN 1381-0960)

GERONTOLOSKO DRUSTVO S R SRBIJE. see *GERONTOLOGY AND GERIATRICS*

360 GW ISSN 0016-9153
GESICHERTES LEBEN. 1954. bi-m. DM.7.80. Wirtschaftsdienst Gesellschaft fuer Medien & Kommunikation mbH & Co. OHG, Lange Str. 13, 60311 Frankfurt a.M., Germany. Ed. M. Stuetzel. adv. circ. 1,900,000. **Document type:** bulletin.

360 610 JA ISSN 0388-743X
GIFUKEN KOSEIREN IGAKU ZASSHI/GIFU WELFARE FEDERATION. JOURNAL. (Text in Japanese) 1980. a. Gifuken Koseiren Igaku Zasshi Henshushitsu, 13-1, Usa Minami 4-chome, Gifu-shi, Gifu-ken 500, Japan.

360 UK ISSN 0956-3229
GINGER. 1973. 6/yr. £12 to individuals; institutions £15. Gingerbread, Association for One Parent Families, 35 Wellington St., London WC2 7BN, England. TEL 071-240-0953. FAX 071-836-4500. Ed. Doug Bollen. adv.; bk.rev.; illus. circ. 10,000. **Document type:** newspaper.
Description: Contains self-help information for single-parent families in England and Wales.

361.73 US ISSN 0436-0257
HV89
GIVING U S A; the annual compilation of total philanthropic giving estimates. 1956. a. $45. (American Association of Fund-Raising Counsel) A A F R C Trust for Philanthropy, 25 W. 43rd St., New York, NY 10036. TEL 212-354-5799. FAX 212-768-1795. Ed. Ann E. Kaplan. circ. 9,000. (also avail. in microfiche from CIS) **Indexed:** SRI. **Document type:** academic/scholarly publication.
Formerly: Giving U S A Annual Report.

361.73 US ISSN 0899-3793
HV41
GIVING U S A UPDATE. 1955. q. $35. (American Association of Fund-Raising Counsel) A A F R C Trust for Philanthropy, 25 W. 43rd St., Ste. 820, New York, NY 10036. TEL 212-354-5799. FAX 212-768-1795. Ed. Ann E. Kaplan. bk.rev. circ. 9,000. **Document type:** newsletter.
Former titles: Fund-Raising Review (ISSN 0735-8873); Giving U S A Bulletin (ISSN 0731-5678); American Association of Fund-Raising Counsel. Bulletin (ISSN 0002-743X)

361 UK ISSN 0143-7429
GLASGOW DIRECTORY OF VOLUNTARY ORGANIZATIONS. 1980. biennial. £5. Glasgow Council for Voluntary Service, 11 Queens Crescent, Glasgow G4 9AS, Scotland. TEL 041-332-2444. FAX 041-332-0175. adv.; illus. circ. 2,000. **Document type:** directory.

THE GLEANER (MADISON). see *HOMOSEXUALITY*

360 SW ISSN 1101-8550
GLOED. 1990. bi-a. Socialstyrelsen, Folkhaelsoenheten, S-106 30 Stockholm, Sweden. (Dist. by: Skoloeverstyrelsen, S-106 42 Stockholm, Sweden) **Document type:** government publication.

610.734 US
GOOD NEIGHBOR. 1952. bi-m. free. American Red Cross, 17th and D Sts. N.W., Washington, DC 20006. Ed. Sally Ann Stewart. circ. 80,000.
Formerly: Red Cross Newsletter (ISSN 0034-1983)
Description: Discusses services provided by the Red Cross.

362.1 US
GOOD NEWS LETTER (NEW YORK). vol.5, 1993. q. God's Love We Deliver, 895 Amsterdam Ave., New York, NY 10025.
Description: News of the organization, which sends meals to homebound people with AIDS & HIV in the NYC area.

360 614 UK
GOOD PRACTICE SERIES. irreg., latest vol.2. Jessica Kingsley Publishers, 116 Pentonville Rd., London N1 9JB, England. TEL 071-833-2307. FAX 071-837-2917. (Dist. in US by: Taylor & Francis, 1900 Frost Rd., Ste. 101, Bristol, PA 19007-1598. TEL 215-785-5800. FAX 215-785-5515) Ed. Jacki Pritchard. **Document type:** monographic series.
Description: Explores topics of current concern to professionals working in social work, health care and the probation service.

360 370 338 US ISSN 1055-825X
GOVERNMENT PROGRAMS. (Supplement avail.) 1991. q. $29.99. Publishing & Business Consultants, 101 W. 64th St. Unit 3, Inglewood, CA 90302-1255. TEL 213-732-3477. FAX 213-732-9123. (Subscr. to: Box 75392, Los Angeles, CA 90075) Ed. Andeson Napoleon Atia. adv. circ. 120,000. **Document type:** consumer publication.
Previously announced as: Subsidized Government Programs.
Description: Lists government programs covering education, employment, housing, families, and business.

360 JM
GRACE, KENNEDY FOUNDATION. ANNUAL REPORT. 1984. a. free. Grace, Kennedy Foundation, 64 Harbour St., P.O. Box 86, Kingston, Jamaica, W.I. TEL 809-922-3440. FAX 809-922-7567. TELEX 2290. (Subscr. to: One St. Lucia Cres., Kingston 5, Jamaica, W.I.) Ed. Marjorie Humphreys. circ. 500. (back issues avail.) **Document type:** corporate report.

GRANTS, FELLOWSHIPS, AND PRIZES OF INTEREST TO HISTORIANS (YEAR). see *HISTORY*

360 US ISSN 1076-1500
▼**GRANTSEEKER.** 1994. m. $98. Government Information Services, 4301 Fairfax Dr., Ste. 875, Arlington, VA 22203-1627. TEL 703-528-1000. FAX 703-528-6060. Ed. Patricia Reed; Pub. James J. Marshall. **Document type:** newsletter.
Description: Helps grantseekers and proposal writers improve their grant-getting and proposal writing skills.

360 US
GRANTSMANSHIP CENTER MAGAZINE; a compendium of resources for nonprofit organizations. 1984. irreg. free to qualified personnel. Grantsmanship Center, Box 17220, Los Angeles, CA 90017. TEL 213-482-9860. FAX 213-482-9863. Ed. Marc Green; Pub. Norton J. Kiritz. adv. circ. 175,000. **Document type:** trade publication.
Formerly: Whole Nonprofit Catalog.

361 BG
GRASSROOTS. (Text in English) 1974. q. Tk.50($25) Association of Development Agencies in Bangladesh, 1-3 Block F, Lalmatia, Dhaka 1207, Bangladesh. TEL 2-327424. TELEX 642940. Ed. Rasheda K. Choudhury. bk.rev. circ. 10,000. **Indexed:** Irr.& Drain.Abstr., Rural Devel.Abstr., World Agri.Econ.& Rural Sociol.Abstr.
Former titles (until 1991): A D A B News; Association of Department Agencies of Bangladesh. Newsletter.
Description: Articles on contemporary developmental issues and problems affecting Bangladesh.

361.8 US ISSN 0740-4832
GRASSROOTS FUNDRAISING JOURNAL. 1981. bi-m. $25. Kim Klein, Ed. & Pub., Box 11607, Berkeley, CA 94712. TEL 510-704-8714. FAX 510-649-7913. adv. contact: Stephanie Roth. bk.rev. circ. 1,500. (back issues avail.) **Indexed:** Alt.Press Ind. **Document type:** newsletter.
—UnCover.
Description: Teaches small to mid-sized nonprofit organizations how to raise money in their communities.

GREAT BRITAIN. CONTRIBUTIONS AGENCY. FRAMEWORK DOCUMENT (YEAR). see *INSURANCE*

GREAT BRITAIN. DEPARTMENT OF HEALTH AND SOCIAL SECURITY. HEALTH BUILDING NOTES. see *HOSPITALS*

GREAT BRITAIN. DEPARTMENT OF HEALTH AND SOCIAL SECURITY. HEALTH EQUIPMENT NOTES. see *HOSPITALS*

GREAT BRITAIN. DEPARTMENT OF HEALTH AND SOCIAL SECURITY. HOSPITAL IN-PATIENT INQUIRY. see *PUBLIC HEALTH AND SAFETY*

362.82 US
GREATER NORTHERN NEWS. 1990. q. free to donors. Planned Parenthood of Greater Northern New Jersey, Inc., 196 Speedwell Ave., Morristown, NJ 07960. TEL 201-539-9580. Ed. Loretta Ernst. **Document type:** newsletter.
Description: Informs donors and others interested in the family-planning services this organization provides; urges readers to take action on specific issues.

SOCIAL SERVICES AND WELFARE

360 UK ISSN 0951-824X
GROUPWORK. (Text in English; summaries in French, German, Spanish) 1988. 3/yr. £37.50 (N. America $85; rest of world £47.50) (effective 1996). Whiting & Birch Ltd., P.O. Box 872, Forest Hill, London SE23 3HL, England. TEL 0181-244-2421. FAX 0181-244-2448. Eds. Allan Brown, Nano McCoughan. index. circ. 750. (back issues avail.) Indexed: ASSIA, Mult.Ed.Abstr., Soc.Work Res.& Abstr., Sociol.Abstr. **Document type:** academic/scholarly publication.
—BLDSC (4220.460000). **CCC.**
Description: Covers social work with groups of all types.

GUIDE TO ARKANSAS FUNDING SOURCES. see *BUSINESS AND ECONOMICS — Management*

GUIDE TO FEDERAL FUNDING FOR GOVERNMENTS AND NONPROFITS. see *PUBLIC ADMINISTRATION — Municipal Government*

360 352.7 US
GUIDE TO FEDERAL FUNDING FOR HOUSING & HOMELESS PROGRAMS. 1992. irreg. Government Information Services, 4301 N. Fairfax Dr., Ste. 875, Arlington, VA 22203-1627. TEL 703-528-1000. FAX 703-528-6060. Eds. Charles Edwards, Jeanne Williams.
Description: Describes 54 housing programs and 31 programs for the homeless.

360 US
GUIDE TO FEDERAL FUNDING FOR VOLUNTEER PROGRAMS & COMMUNITY SERVICE. 1991. biennial (plus q. updates). $89.50 (updates $49.95). Government Information Services, 4301 N. Fairfax Dr., Ste. 875, Arlington, VA 22203-1627. TEL 703-528-1000. FAX 703-528-6060. Eds. Amy McAuliffe, Heather C. Bodell. (looseleaf format)
Formerly (until Jun. 1993): Guide to Federal Funding for Volunteer Programs.
Description: Describes in detail about 60 federal programs that provide aid to establish and operate volunteer programs.

GUIDE TO HEALTH SERVICES OF THE WORLD. see *HOSPITALS*

361.73 US ISSN 1045-2133
HV27
GUIDE TO PRIVATE FORTUNES. Key Title: Fund Raiser's Guide to Private Fortunes. 1991. a. $225. Taft Group, 12300 Twinbrook Pkwy., Ste. 520, Rockville, MD 20852. TEL 301-816-0210. FAX 301-816-0210. (Subscr. to: Taft Group, Box 33477, Detroit, MI 48232-5477. TEL 800-877-TAFT. FAX 313-961-6083) **Document type:** directory.
Description: Lists philanthropic wealthy Americans.

GUIDE TO THE NURSING HOME INDUSTRY. see *HOSPITALS*

362 UK ISSN 0072-8756
GUIDE TO THE SOCIAL SERVICES. 1882. a. £13.95. Family Welfare Association, 501-505 Kingsland Rd., London E8 4AU, England. TEL 0171-254-6251. FAX 0171-249-5443. Ed. Chris Hollins. circ. 3,000.
—CCC.
Description: Reference book on the structure and organization of the public social services in the U.K.

361.77 GW ISSN 0017-5803
DIE GUTE TAT. 1954. 4/yr. membership. (Deutsches Rotes Kreuz - German Red Cross) Sueddeutscher Verlag GmbH, Unternehmensbereich Zeitschriften, Karlstr. 35-37, 80333 Munich, Germany. TEL 089-54852-0. FAX 089-54852192. Ed.Bd. adv.: B&W page DM.21010, color page DM.33620; trim 185 x 250. illus. circ. 1,363,500. **Document type:** bulletin.

362.4 GW
DER GUTE WILLE; zur Sicherung der eingliederung Schwerbehinderter. 1967. bi-m. free. Arbeitsgemeinschaft der Deutschen Hauptfuersorgestellen, Mindenerstr. 2, Postfach 210720, 50679 Cologne, Germany. bk.rev. circ. 217,600. (looseleaf format)

H L I CANADIAN REPORT. (Human Life International in Canada Inc.) see *POPULATION STUDIES*

H L I REPORTS. (Human Life International) see *POPULATION STUDIES*

H L I REPORTS. (Human Life International in Canada Inc.) see *POPULATION STUDIES*

360 DK ISSN 0901-2389
HAANDBOG FOR SOCIAL- OG SUNDHEDSSEKTOR. 1982. a. (in 2 vols.). DKK 750 per vol. Forlag for Social- og Sundhedssektor, Vibeholms Alle 11-15, 2605 Bronoby, Denmark. TEL 43-43-43-80. FAX 43-43-60-29.
Formerly (until 1985): Plejehjemsshaandbogen (ISSN 0108-0857); Incorporates: Bistandshaandbogen (ISSN 0108-8351)

362.7 DK ISSN 0907-8770
HAANDBOGEN DAG- OG DOEGNINSTITUTIONER. Key Title: Dag- og Doeginstitutioner. 1984. triennial. DKK 240. Kroghs Forlag A-S, Chr. Hansensvej 3, 7100 Vejle, Denmark. TEL 75 82 3900. adv. circ. 3,000.
Former titles (until 1992): Haandbogen Daginstitutioner (ISSN 0904-5902); Haandbog for Boerne- og Ungdominstitutioner. Daginstitutioner (ISSN 0109-4181); Haandbog for Boerne- og Ungdominstitutioner.

HABITAT WORLD. see *HOUSING AND URBAN PLANNING*

361.8 US
HAIGHT ASHBURY NEWSPAPER. 1977. q. free. Newspaper Collective, 409 Clayton St., San Francisco, CA 94117. TEL 415-863-5498. Ed.Bd. adv.; bk.rev. circ. 6,500. **Document type:** newspaper.

362.409 263 DK
HANDICAP - JUL. 1958. a. DKK 20. Dansk Handicap Forbund, Hans Knudsen Plads 1A, 2100 Copenhagen OE, Denmark. TEL 45-39-29-35-55. FAX 45-31-29-39-48. Ed. Keld Soegaar. adv.; bk.rev.; illus.
Former titles: Julehaeftet, Vanfoeres Jul; Vanfoeres Jul (ISSN 0900-2863)

HANDICAP NEWS. see *HANDICAPPED*

HANDISCOOP. see *HANDICAPPED*

360 US
HAPPENINGS. m. free. International Union of Gospel Missions, 1045 Swift Ave., N. Kansas City, MO 64116. TEL 816-471-8020. E-mail: iugm@fileshop.com. Ed. Stephen E. Burger. circ. 1,500. **Document type:** newsletter.
Description: Relates the events and interests of those involved in Rescue Mission and other Rescue ministries.

HARICOT; newsletter for the renal patients of Australia. see *MEDICAL SCIENCES — Urology And Nephrology*

HARTMANNBUND IN BADEN - WUERTTEMBERG. see *PUBLIC HEALTH AND SAFETY*

362.7 US ISSN 0362-6296
RJ501.H3
HAWAII. DEPARTMENT OF HEALTH. MENTAL HEALTH SERVICES FOR CHILDREN AND YOUTH; children's MH services branch. Key Title: Mental Health Services for Children and Youth. 1970. a. Department of Health, Child and Adolescent Mental Health Division, 3627 Kilauea Ave., Rm. 101, Honolulu, HI 96816. TEL 808-548-6335. stat. circ. 300. **Document type:** government publication.

HAWAII'S NATIONAL GAY COMMUNITY NEWS; Hawaii and Western States. see *HOMOSEXUALITY*

325 US
HEADLINES & HIGHLIGHTS. 1983. bi-m. free. H I A S Inc., 333 Seventh Ave., New York, NY 10001-5004. Ed. Marcia Tabenken. bk.rev.; illus. circ. 10,000. **Document type:** newsletter.
Former titles (until 1992): H I A S Reporter; H I A S Bulletin (ISSN 0097-0263); U H S Bulletin (ISSN 0041-509X)

360 US
HEALTH & HUMAN SERVICES DIRECTORY; health and social agencies in Greater Cleveland. 1946. biennial. $18. Federation for Community Planning, 614 W. Superior Ave., Ste. 300, Cleveland, OH 44113-1306. TEL 216-781-2944. FAX 216-781-2988. circ. 5,000. **Document type:** directory.
Former titles: Human Services Directory; Health and Welfare Directory.

HEALTH AND SOCIAL SERVICE WORKFORCE IN ALBERTA. see *PUBLIC HEALTH AND SAFETY*

360 US ISSN 0360-7283
HV687.5.U5 CODEN: HSWODK
HEALTH & SOCIAL WORK. 1976. q. $85 (foreign $100) (effective 1996). (National Association of Social Workers) N A S W Press, 750 First St., N.E., Ste. 700, Washington, DC 20002-4241. TEL 202-408-8600. FAX 202-336-8312. (Subscr. to: NASW Distribution Center, Box 431, Annapolis Jct., MD 20701) Ed. Dennis L. Poole. adv.; bk.rev.; index. circ. 6,500. (also avail. in microfiche from UMI; back issues avail.; reprint service avail. from UMI) Indexed: Abstr.Crim.& Pen., Abstr.Health Care Manage.Stud., Adol.Ment.Hlth.Abstr., ASSIA, Behav.Med.Abstr., Biol.Abstr., CINAHL, Dent.Ind., DSH Abstr., Except.Child Educ.Abstr., Excerp.Med., IMFL, Ind.Med., Mult.Ed.Abstr., Psychol.Abstr. (1976-), Rehabil.Lit., Soc.Work Res.& Abstr., Soc.Work Res.& Abstr., Sociol.Abstr., Sp.Ed.Needs Abstr., World Bibl.Soc.Sec. **Document type:** academic/scholarly publication.
●Also available online. Vendor(s): University Microfilms International.
—BLDSC (4274.884000); Faxon; Genuine Article; SWETS; UMI; UnCover. **CCC.**
Description: Examines health-related social problems and issues dealing with the client and the community.

HEALTH CARE FACILITY MANAGEMENT. see *HOSPITALS*

HEALTH CARE FINANCING REVIEW. see *MEDICAL SCIENCES*

HEALTH CARE FINANCING REVIEW. SUPPLEMENT. see *PUBLIC HEALTH AND SAFETY*

HEALTH DIRECTOR. see *PUBLIC HEALTH AND SAFETY*

361 610 UK ISSN 0268-1153
CODEN: HRTPE2
HEALTH EDUCATION RESEARCH; theory and practice. 1986. q. £125($195) (effective 1996). Oxford University Press, Oxford Journals, Walton St., Oxford OX2 6DP, England. TEL 01865-267907. FAX 01865-267773. TELEX 837330-OXPRES-G. E-mail: jnlorders@oup.co.uk. (U.S. subscr. to: Oxford University Press Inc., 2001 Evans Rd., Cary, NC 27513. TEL 919-677-0977. FAX 919-677-1714) Eds. Keith Tones, K.R. McLeroy. adv.; bk.rev.; index. circ. 700. (back issues avail.; reprint service avail. from SWZ) Indexed: ASSIA, Biol.Abstr., CINAHL, Cont.Pg.Educ., Curr.Cont., Curr.Tit.Dent., Excerp.Med., Ind.Med., Psychol.Abstr. (1986-), Sci.Cit.Ind., Stud.Wom.Abstr., Tech.Educ.Abstr. **Document type:** academic/scholarly publication.
—BLDSC (4275.011440); Faxon; Genuine Article; SWETS; UMI; UnCover. **CCC.**
Description: Promotes understanding of the processes, rationale and philosophy underlying the work of practicing health educators in an international forum.
Refereed Serial

362.1 US ISSN 0361-2929
RA981.C3
HEALTH FACILITIES DIRECTORY. Spine title: Directory of Health Facilities. 1975. q. free. Department of Health Services, Licensing and Certification Division, 714-744 P St., Box 942732, Sacramento, CA 94234-7320. TEL 916-322-2810. **Document type:** government publication.

HEALTH SERVICE JOURNAL; for people involved in management. see *HOSPITALS*

HEALTH WORKFORCE IN ALBERTA. ANNUAL REPORT. see *PUBLIC HEALTH AND SAFETY*

360 GW
HELFENDE HAENDE; Zeitschrift des diakonischen Werkes Westfalen. 1950. q. free. Diakonisches Werk der Evangelischen Kirche von Westfalen, Friesenring 32-34, 48147 Muenster, Germany. TEL 0251-2709-790. FAX 0251-2709-573. Ed. Achim Kuhlmann. bk.rev.; bibl.; charts; illus.; stat. circ. 10,000. (back issues avail.) **Document type:** bulletin.

360 AU
HELFT UNS HELFEN. 6/yr. Wiener Hilfswerk, Falkestr. 3, A-1010 Vienna, Austria. TEL 01-5123661. circ. 5,000. **Document type:** newsletter.

SOCIAL SERVICES AND WELFARE

HEM OCH SAMHAELLE; Husmoderfoerbundets tidskrift. see *HOME ECONOMICS*

HEMLOCK TIMELINES. see *MEDICAL SCIENCES*

HIDDEN CHILD. see *HISTORY — History Of Europe*

360 649   JA   ISSN 0018-327X
HOIKU NO TOMO. 1952. m. 6360 Yen. National Council of Social Welfare - Zenkoku Shakai Fukushi Kyogikai, 3-3-2 Kasumigaseki, Chiyoda-ku, Tokyo, Japan. Ed. Takao Kawajiri. adv.; bk.rev. circ. 35,000.

360   UK
▼**HOMECARE PROFESSIONAL**. 1995. 10/yr. £40 (overseas £72. Hawker Publications, 12 Park House, 140 Battersea Park Rd., London SW11 4NB, England. TEL 0171-720-2108. FAX 0171-498-3023. Ed. Alison Docherty. circ. 4,000. **Document type:** academic/scholarly publication.
Description: Provides news information, expert advice, and reviews for professionals providing care for people in their own homes.

361.6   HO
HONDURAS. SECRETARIA DE TRABAJO Y PREVISION SOCIAL. BOLETIN DE ESTADISTICAS LABORALES. 1973. a. free. Ministerio de Trabajo y Prevision Social, Planificacion Sectorial y Estadistica Laboreal, Tegucigalpa, Honduras. TEL 22-15-58. FAX 22-32-20. circ. 500. **Document type:** government publication.
Description: Provides labor statistics.

360   US   ISSN 0275-3065
HOOSHARAR - MIOUTUNE. (Text in Armenian) 1914. m. (except Jul. & Aug.) $10 to non-members. Armenian General Benevolent Union, 585 Saddle River Rd., Saddle Brook, NJ 07662. TEL 201-797-7600. Ed. Antranig Poladian. circ. 2,000.

HOSPICE. see *ALTERNATIVE MEDICINE*

362   US
HOSPICE TODAY. 1981. q. free. Hospice of the Florida Suncoast, 300 E. Bay Dr., Largo, FL 34640. TEL 813-586-4432. FAX 813-586-5213. Ed. Kimberly Walter. bk.rev.; circ. 65,000 (controlled). **Document type:** newsletter.
Formerly (until 1987): Hospice Care Newsletter.
Description: Informs friends, volunteers, and financial supporters about the activities and programs of the agency, its services to the community, and its role as a resource and an advocate on issues related to death, grief and terminal illness.

362.7   CN   ISSN 0845-9568
HV1441.C3
HOT 100; a quick guide to federal programs and services for youth. (Text in English, French) 1986. a. free. Public Enquiries Centre, Employment and Immigration Canada, Ottawa, ON K1A 0J9, Canada. TEL 819-994-6313. FAX 819-953-7260. **Document type:** government publication.

THE HOUSING ADVOCATE. see *HOUSING AND URBAN PLANNING*

HOUSING THE ELDERLY REPORT. see *HOUSING AND URBAN PLANNING*

360   UK
HOW TO LIVE IN BRITAIN. 1952. a. price varies. British Council, 10 Spring Gardens, London, England. TEL 071-930-8466. FAX 071-493-5035.

HUMAN RIGHTS RESOURCES. see *POLITICAL SCIENCE — Civil Rights*

361.6 323.4   US
HUMAN SERVE CAMPAIGN NEWSLETTER. irreg. (3-4/yr.) free. Human Serve Campaign, c/o Columbia University, 622 W. 113th St., Rm. 410, New York, NY 10025. TEL 212-854-4053.

360   US   ISSN 0193-9009
HV85
HUMAN SERVICES IN THE RURAL ENVIRONMENT. 1974. q. $25 to individuals (foreign $35); institutions and libraries $35 (foreign $45). Eastern Washington University, Inland Empire School of Social Work and Human Services, Cheney, WA 99004. TEL 509-359-6474. Ed. Lynne Clemmons Morris. adv.; bk.rev. circ. 1,000. (also avail. in microform) **Indexed:** Abstr.Soc.Geront., C.I.J.E., Soc.Work Res.& Abstr.
—Faxon; UMI; UnCover.
Description: Dedicated to the concerns of people living in rural areas. Serves as an information exchange and communication forum among those interested in rural service settings, by focusing on policy and legislative developments, program models, research and evaluation projects, and innovative efforts to document aspects of rural life.

301.4   US   ISSN 0164-6079
HUMAN SERVICES REPORTER. 1978. 6/yr. free. Department of Human Services, CN 700, Trenton, NJ 08625. TEL 609-292-3703. FAX 609-393-4846. Eds. Ed Rogan, Margaret Bergmann. circ. 33,500. (tabloid format)
Incorporates (in 1978): Family.

HUNGER NOTES. see *SOCIOLOGY*

360   US   ISSN 1040-3604
HD9000.1
HUNGER REPORT. 1988. a. Alan Shawn Feinstein World Hunger Program, Box 1831, Brown University, Providence, RI 02912.

I B I S REVIEW. (International Benefits Information Service) see *INSURANCE*

362.7   II
I C C W JOURNAL. (Text in English) 1954. q. Rs.35. Indian Council for Child Welfare, 4 Deen Dayal Upadhayaya Marg, New Delhi 110 002, India. TEL 11-331-9539. Ed. Smt. Kusum Kapur. adv.; bibl.; charts; illus. circ. 1,000. **Document type:** bulletin.
Formerly: I C C W News Bulletin (ISSN 0018-8867)
Description: Covers nutrition, education, labor, health and allied disciplines relevant to the welfare of children.

360   US   ISSN 1065-1675
I F C O NEWS. 1970. q. $15 to individuals; $20 libraries and institutions. Interreligious Foundation for Community Organization, 402 W. 145th St., New York, NY 10031. TEL 212-926-5757. FAX 212-926-5842. Ed.Bd. adv.; bk.rev.; bibl.; illus. circ. 113,000.
Description: Focuses on local, national and international community organizing efforts.

I P C POVERTY RESEARCH SERIES. (Institute of Philippine Culture) see *SOCIOLOGY*

362.4   FI   ISSN 0356-7249
I T - INVALIDITYOE. 1941. m. FIM 150. Invalidiliitto r.y., Kumpulantie 1, 00520 Helsinki, Finland. FAX 358-0-146-1443. Ed. Voitto Korhonen. adv.; bk.rev.; illus. circ. 53,114.
Formerly: Suomen Invalidi (ISSN 0049-2566)

ICARUS FILE. see *MEDICAL SCIENCES*

ILCO-PRAXIS. see *MEDICAL SCIENCES — Oncology*

360   UK
IMPACT (LONDON). bi-m. £24. National Council for Voluntary Organisations, Community Care Information Service, Regent's Wharf, 8 All Saints St., London N1 9RL, England. TEL 0171-713-6161. FAX 0171-713-6300. Ed. David Glasman. **Document type:** newsletter.

360   AT   ISSN 0706-5914
IMPACT (NORTH FITZROY). 1979. q. $5. Melbourne Citymission, 472 Nicholson St., North Fitzroy, Vic. 3068, Australia. TEL 03-489-9666. Ed. Peter Philp. circ. 7,000. (back issues avail.)
Description: Report on Melbourne Citymission's services for families, children, homeless, young people and adults, aged persons, the terminally ill and the intellectually disabled.

360   AT   ISSN 1032-4321
IMPACT (SYDNEY). 1971. 11/yr. $39. Australian Council of Social Service, Inc. (ACOSS), Locked Bag 11, Darlinghurst, Sydney, N.S.W. 2010, Australia. TEL 61-2-3324355. FAX 61-2-3321515. Ed. Jane Inglis. adv.; bk.rev. circ. 1,300. **Indexed:** ASSIA, Aus.P.A.I.S., World Bibl.Soc.Sec.
—BLDSC (1812.550000); Genuine Article; UnCover. CCC.
Former titles (until 1988): Australian Social Welfare: Impact (ISSN 0157-6321); Australian Social Welfare; Supersedes in part: A C O S S Quarterly (ISSN 0045-0391)

362.7   US
IMPACT (WESTPORT). 1982. q. free. Save the Children, Public Affairs and Communication, 54 Wilton Rd., Box 950, Westport, CT 06881. TEL 203-221-4000. FAX 203-222-1067. Ed. Lee Mullane. illus. circ. 150,000. **Document type:** newsletter.
Formerly (until vol.6, no.4): Lifeline (Westport).

360 374   UK
IMPROVING SOCIAL WORK EDUCATION AND TRAINING SERIES. 1989. irreg. (1-3/yr.). price varies. Central Council for Education and Training in Social Work, Derbyshire House, St. Chad's St., London WC1H 8AD, England. TEL 071-278-2455. FAX 071-278-2934. (back issues avail.) **Document type:** monographic series, trade publication.
Description: Presents effective models of social work training and learning.

361.77   UK
IN CONTACT. 1975. q. membership. British Red Cross Society, 9 Grosvenor Crescent, London SW1X 7EJ, England. TEL 0171-235-5454. FAX 0171-245-6315. Ed. Andrew Glen. adv. circ. 41,000.
Formerly: Red Cross News.

IN TOUCH (AUSTIN). see *HANDICAPPED — Visually Impaired*

360   AT   ISSN 0728-6503
IN UNITY. 1949. q. Australian Council of Churches, P.O. Box C199, Clarence St., Sydney, N.S.W. 2000, Australia. FAX 02-262-4514. bk.rev. circ. 6,500.
Incorporates (in Jan. 1978): Christian Action News.

360   IT   ISSN 0046-8819
INCHIESTA. 1971. q. L.35000 (foreign L.52500) (effective 1994). Edizioni Dedalo s.r.l., Casella Postale 362, 70100 Bari, Italy. TEL 080-5311413. FAX 080-5311414. (Edit. addr.: Casella Postale 752, 40100 Bologna, Italy) Dir. Vittorio Capecchi. bk.rev.; charts. circ. 12,000.
—BLDSC (4374.960000).
Description: Includes research on social issues in Italy. For students, researchers, social and political workers.

INCLUSION TIMES. see *EDUCATION — Special Education And Rehabilitation*

362.6   US   ISSN 1073-1393
INCOME OF THE AGED CHARTBOOK. 1976. biennial. U.S. Social Security Administration, O.R.S. - Publications Staff, Van Ness Center, 4301 Connecticut Ave., N.W., Rm. 209, Washington, DC 20008. TEL 202-282-7161. FAX 202-282-7219. (Subscr. to: Superintendent of Documents, U.S. Government Printing Office, Box 371954, Pittsburgh, PA 15250-7954. TEL 202-783-3238. FAX 202-512-2233) Ed. Marilyn R. Thomas. **Document type:** government publication.
Description: Reports the income of senior citizens, using data collected by the U.S. Bureau of the Census.

INCOME OF THE POPULATION 55 OR OLDER. see *INSURANCE*

362.4 616.836   US   ISSN 1048-3772
RA645.35
INDEPENDENT LIVING. 1983. 7/yr. $18. Equal Opportunity Publications, Inc., 150 Motor Pkwy. No. 420, Hauppauge, NY 11788-5108. TEL 516-261-8899. FAX 516-261-8935. Ed. Anne Kelly. bk.rev. circ. 35,000. **Indexed:** Hlth.Ind.
Former titles: Independent Living and Health Care Today; Independent Living; S H R (Social Health Review).

SOCIAL SERVICES AND WELFARE

360 US ISSN 0743-1236
HV97.I57
INDEPENDENT SECTOR. ANNUAL REPORT. 1980. a. free. Independent Sector, 1828 L St., N.W., Ste. 1200, Washington, DC 20036. TEL 202-223-8100. Ed. Sharon Fitzgerald Noga. circ. 10,000.
 Description: Overview of the independent sector's activities: communications, research, government relations.

362.7 II
INDIAN COUNCIL FOR CHILD WELFARE. ANNUAL REPORT. (Text in English) a. Indian Council for Child Welfare, 4 Deen Dayal Upadhyaya Marg, New Delhi 110 002, India. TEL 11-331-9539. **Document type:** corporate report.

360 II ISSN 0019-5634
HV1 CODEN: IJSWA3
INDIAN JOURNAL OF SOCIAL WORK. (Text in English) 1940. q. Rs.120($33) to individuals; institutions Rs.200($35). Tata Institute of Social Sciences, Sion-Trombay Rd., Deonar, Bombay 400 088, India. TEL 556-3290. FAX 556-2912. (Subscr. to: Tata Institute of Social Sciences, P.O. Box 8313, Bombay 400 088, India) Ed. Armaity S. Desai. adv.; bk.rev.; index. circ. 1,200. (also avail. in microfilm from UMI; back issues avail.; reprint service avail. from UMI) Indexed: Adol.Ment.Hlth.Abstr., ASSIA, Curr.Cont., IMFL, Lang.& Lang.Behav.Abstr., Mult.Ed.Abstr., Psychol.Abstr., Rehabil.Lit., Rural Ext.Educ.& Tr.Abstr., Rural Recreat.Tour.Abstr., Soc.Work Res.& Abstr., Sociol.Abstr., SSCI, Stud.Wom.Abstr., World Agri.Econ.& Rural Sociol.Abstr. **Document type:** academic/scholarly publication.
—BLDSC (4421.200000); Genuine Article; SWETS; UMI; UnCover.
 Description: Takes an interdisciplinary approach to the study of social work and the social sciences; devoted to the scientific interpretation of social problems.

INDIAN YOUTH OF AMERICA NEWSLETTER. see CHILDREN AND YOUTH — About

INFANCIA E JUVENTUDE. see LAW — Family And Matrimonial Law

INFOCUS NEWS MAGAZINE. see ETHNIC INTERESTS

361 US ISSN 0278-2383
HV85 CODEN: IREFD9
INFORMATION AND REFERRAL. Variant title: Alliance of Information and Referral Systems. Journal. 1979. s-a. $26 to individuals; institutions $30; members $20. Alliance of Information and Referral Systems, Box 3546, Joliet, IL 60434. TEL 815-744-6922. adv.; bk.rev. circ. 400. Indexed: INSPEC, Lang.& Lang.Behav.Abstr., LISA. **Document type:** academic/scholarly publication, newsletter.
—BLDSC (4481.853000); UnCover.

INFORMATION JUIVE. see ETHNIC INTERESTS

360 GW ISSN 0179-8863
INFORMATIONEN ZUM ARBEITSLOSENRECHT UND SOZIALHILFERECHT. q. DM.58. Nomos Verlagsgesellschaft mbH und Co. KG, Waldseestr. 3-5, 76530 Baden-Baden, Germany. TEL 07221-21040. FAX 07221-210427. (Subscr. to: Postfach 610, 76484 Baden-Baden, Germany) **Document type:** bulletin.

360 FR ISSN 0046-9459
HN421
INFORMATIONS SOCIALES. 8/yr. 200 F. Caisse Nationale des Allocations Familiales, 23 rue Daviel, 75634 Paris Cedex 13, France. TEL 45-65-54-32. Ed. Daniel Bequignon. adv.; bk.rev. circ. 12,000. (back issues avail.) Indexed: World Bibl.Soc.Sec.

360 GW ISSN 0721-1295
INFORMATIONSDIENST ZUR AUSLAENDERARBEIT. 1979. q. DM.60. Institut fuer Sozialarbeit und Sozialpaedagogik e.V., Am Stockborn 5-7, 60439 Frankfurt a.M., Germany. TEL 069-582025. FAX 069-582029. Ed. Hermann Scheib. adv.; bk.rev.; film rev.; abstr.; bibl. circ. 2,500. (back issues avail.) **Document type:** newsletter.

360 SZ
INFORMATIONSZEITSCHRIFT FUER A H V UND KRANKENKASSEN. (Text in French, German) m. Via Dufour 4, Case Postale 3365, CH-6901 Lugano, Switzerland. TEL 091-227518. FAX 091-238171. Ed. G. Santoro. circ. 30,000.

301 IT ISSN 0020-0816
INFORMAZIONI SOCIALI. 1946. bi-m. free. Patronato A C L I, Via G. Marcora 18-20, 00153 Rome, Italy. Dir. Domenico Rosati. adv.; illus.

INNOVATING. see BUSINESS AND ECONOMICS — Management

INSIGHTS (BELLE MEAD). see HOSPITALS

360 US
INSIGHTS (WASHINGTON, 1977). 1977. q. free. American Association of Retired Persons, Social Outreach and Support, 601 E St., N.W., Washington, DC 20049. TEL 202-434-2260. (Co-sponsors: Widowed Persons Service; Social Outreach and Support) Ed. Marjory Marvel. **Document type:** newsletter.
 Description: Serves Widowed Persons Service volunteers and other volunteers, professionals, and groups serving the newly widowed.

INSTITUT DE READAPTATION DE MONTREAL. BULLETIN. see MEDICAL SCIENCES

360 301 CN ISSN 0834-1729
H62.A1
INSTITUTE FOR SOCIAL RESEARCH NEWSLETTER. 1985. 3/yr. free. Institute for Social Research, York University, 4700 Keele St., North York, ON M3J 1P3, Canada. TEL 416-736-5061. FAX 416-736-5749. E-mail: isrnews@vm1.uorku.ca. Ed. John Pollard. circ. 2,600. **Document type:** newsletter.
 Description: Presents articles on findings of research studies of interest to academics and government agencies - housing, health, gender issues, politics, education, ethnocultural studies, law, policy, evaluation, quality of life, research methodology.
 Refereed Serial

362.7 371.9 UY
INSTITUTO INTERAMERICANO DEL NINO. EDUCACION ESPECIAL. INFORMES TECNICOS. irreg. Instituto Interamericano del Nino, Avda. 8 de Octubre No. 2904, Montevideo, Uruguay.

362.7 310 UY
INSTITUTO INTERAMERICANO DEL NINO. ESTADISTICA E INFORMATICA. INFORMES TECNICOS. irreg. Instituto Interamericano del Nino, Avda. 8 de Octubre No. 2904, Montevideo, Uruguay.

362.7 UY
INSTITUTO INTERAMERICANO DEL NINO. REGISTRO CIVIL. INFORMES TECNICOS. irreg. Instituto Interamericano del Nino, Avda. 8 de Octubre No. 2904, Montevideo, Urugay.

362.7 UY
INSTITUTO INTERAMERICANO DEL NINO. SERVICIO SOCIAL. INFORMES TECNICOS. irreg. Instituto Interamericano del Nino, Avda. 8 de Octubre no. 2904, Montevideo, Uruguay. circ. 600.
 Formerly: Instituto Interamericano del Nino. Publicaciones sobre Servicio Social.

360 SZ ISSN 1012-6848
INTEGRO; Gesundheits- und Sozialmagazin des V.P.O.D. m. (10/yr.). 60 SFr. Postfach, CH-8030 Zurich, Switzerland. TEL 01-2519935. FAX 01-2514316. **Document type:** bulletin.
 Formerly (until 1983): Praktische Psychiatrie (ISSN 0257-7704)

362.7 UY
INTERAMERICAN CHILDREN'S INSTITUTE. REPORT OF THE GENERAL DIRECTOR. a. Instituto Interamericano del Nino, Avda. 8 de Octubre no. 2904, Montevideo, Uruguay. illus.

360 BL
INTERCAMBIO; revista quadrimestral de informacao e cultura. 1965-1976; N.S. 1980; N.S. 1988. 3/yr. free. Servico Social do Comercio, Assessoria de Divulgacao e Promocao Institucional, Rua Voluntarios da Patria 169, 11o andar, 22270 Rio de Janeiro, Brazil. bibl. circ. 2,500.
 Formerly (until 1987): Brazil. Servico Social do Comercio. Boletim de Intercambio.

361 UK ISSN 0144-3488
INTERCHANGE. 1980. m. £12 to non-members. Glasgow Council for Voluntary Service, 11 Queen's Crescent, Glasgow G4 9AS, Scotland. TEL 041-332-2444. FAX 041-332-0175. adv.; bk.rev. circ. 1,500. **Document type:** newsletter.
 Description: Covers news of voluntary groups and contains listings on events, publications, and training for voluntary sector groups.

300 320 AU ISSN 0020-5362
INTERESSE; soziale Information. 1963. q. contribution. Pastoralamt der Dioezese Linz, Referat fuer soziale und politische Erwachsenenbildung, Kapuzinerstr. 84, A-4020 Linz, Austria. TEL 0732-761062. Ed. Alfred Koller. bk.rev. circ. 4,900. **Document type:** bulletin.

INTERNATIONAL ASSOCIATION OF WORKERS FOR TROUBLED CHILDREN AND YOUTH. CONGRESS REPORTS. see EDUCATION — Special Education And Rehabilitation

361.77 SZ
INTERNATIONAL COMMITTEE OF THE RED CROSS. ANNUAL REPORT - RAPPORT D'ACTIVITE - INFORME DE ACTIVIDAD. (Text in English, French, and Spanish) a. 12 SFr. International Committee of the Red Cross, 19 Avenue de la Paix, CH-1202 Geneva, Switzerland. TEL 022-7346001. FAX 022-7348280. **Document type:** corporate report.

361.77 SZ
INTERNATIONAL COMMITTEE OF THE RED CROSS. PANORAMA. (Text in Arabic, English, French, German, Japanese, Russian, Spanish) a. 3.50 SFr. International Committee of the Red Cross, 19 Avenue de la Paix, CH-1202 Geneva, Switzerland. TEL 022-7346001. FAX 022-7348280. **Document type:** corporate report.
 Formerly: International Committee of the Red Cross. Reference Report.
 Description: Contains a summary of the ICRC's activities during the year, including its field operations to protect and assist civilian and military victims of armed conflicts and internal disturbances; its work in the area of principles and law, and the activities of its administrative support staff and Central Tracing Agency at headquarters.

361 CN ISSN 0074-2961
INTERNATIONAL CONFERENCE OF SOCIAL WORK. CONFERENCE PROCEEDINGS. 1928. biennial, 26th, 1994, Helsinki. International Council on Social Welfare - Conseil International de l'Action Sociale, c/o Sirpa Utriainen, Sec.-Gen., 380 St. Antoine St. W., Ste. 3200, Montreal, PQ H2Y 3X7, Canada. TEL 514-287-3280. FAX 514-987-1567. E-mail: icswintl@web.apc.org. **Document type:** proceedings.

INTERNATIONAL DIRECTORY OF PRISONERS AID AGENCIES. see CRIMINOLOGY AND LAW ENFORCEMENT

INTERNATIONAL ENCYCLOPAEDIA OF LAWS. SOCIAL SECURITY LAW. see INSURANCE

361 MY ISSN 0020-6784
INTERNATIONAL FORUM.* (Summaries in French) 1960. q. Aus.$0.08($1.20) World Council of Young Men's Service Clubs, KTM Godown No. 2A, Jalan Tun Sambanthan, 50470 Kuala Lumpur, Malaysia. Ed. John Bremner. adv.; illus. circ. 25,000.

362.7 US
INTERNATIONAL FRIENDSHIP AND GOOD WILL BULLETIN.* 1978. q. $10 to non-members; free to members. International Society of Friendship and Good Will, 9538 Summerfield St., Spring Valley, CA 91977-2852. TEL 704-864-7906. Ed. S.J. Drake. adv.; bk.rev. circ. 1,000. (back issues avail.) **Document type:** bulletin.

SOCIAL SERVICES AND WELFARE

360   UK   ISSN 0749-6753
                        CODEN: IJHMEO
INTERNATIONAL JOURNAL OF HEALTH PLANNING AND MANAGEMENT. 1986. q. $525 (foreign $525) (effective 1996). John Wiley & Sons Ltd., Journals, Baffins Ln., Chichester, W. Sussex PO19 1UD, England. TEL 01243-779777. FAX 01243-776128. TELEX 86290 WIBOOK G. (Subscr. in the Americas to: John Wiley & Sons, Inc., 605 Third Ave., New York, NY 10158. TEL 212-850-6645. FAX 212-850-6021) Ed. K. Lee. adv. circ. 273. (back issues avail.; reprint service avail. from SWZ) **Indexed:** Abstr.Health Care Manage.Stud., Curr.Cont., Excerp.Med., Geo.Abstr., IDA, Sociol.Abstr. **Document type:** academic/scholarly publication.
—BLDSC (4542.277600); Faxon; SWETS; UMI; UnCover. **CCC.**
    Description: Discusses major issues in health planning, management systems, and practices; maintains a balance between practice and theory from a variety of schools of thought.
    Refereed Serial

360   364   US   ISSN 0020-8396
INTERNATIONAL PRISONERS AID ASSOCIATION. NEWSLETTER.* 1950. 3/yr. $5. International Prisoners Aid Association, U. of Louisville, Dept. of Sociology, Louisville, KY 40292. bk.rev. circ. 500. (processed) **Document type:** newsletter.

360   325   US
INTERNATIONAL RESCUE COMMITTEE. FIELD REPORTS. 3/yr. free. International Rescue Committee, 122 E 42nd St., 12th Fl., New York, NY 10168-0002. TEL 212-551-3000. FAX 212-551-3180. circ. 65,000.
    Description: Studies refugee issues.

361   US   ISSN 0538-9461
INTERNATIONAL RESCUE COMMITTEE ANNUAL REPORT. a. free. International Rescue Committee, 122 E. 42nd St., 12th Fl., New York, NY 10168-0002. TEL 212-679-0010.

INTERNATIONAL REVIEW OF THE RED CROSS. see *LAW — International Law*

INTERNATIONAL REVIEW OF VICTIMOLOGY. see *CRIMINOLOGY AND LAW ENFORCEMENT*

360   NE   ISSN 0924-4859
INTERNATIONAL SERIES IN SOCIAL WELFARE. (Text in English) 1982. irreg. price varies. Kluwer Academic Publishers, Postbus 17, 3300 AA Dordrecht, Netherlands. TEL 31-78-392392. FAX 31-78-392254. TELEX 29245 KAPG NL. (Dist. by: Kluwer Academic Publishers Group, P.O. Box 322, 3300 AH Dordrecht, Netherlands. TEL 31-78-392392. FAX 31-78-546474; N. America dist. addr.: Box 358, Accord Sta., Hingham, MA 02018-0358. TEL 617-871-6600. FAX 617-871-6528) **Document type:** monographic series.
    Refereed Serial

360   UK   ISSN 0020-8728
HV1
INTERNATIONAL SOCIAL WORK. 1958. q. £36 to individuals; institutions £110 (effective 1996). (International Council on Social Welfare) Sage Publications Ltd., 6 Bonhill St., London EC2A 4PU, England. TEL 0171-374-0645. FAX 0171-374-8741. E-mail: market@sageltd.co.uk. (Co-sponsors: International Association of Schools of Social Work; International Federation of Social Workers) Ed. Francis J. Turner. adv.: B&W page £180; trim 170 x 100; adv. contact: Bernie Folan. bk.rev.; index, cum.index: 1958-1977. (also avail. in microform from UMI; reprint service avail. from UMI) **Indexed:** Abstr.Soc.Work., ASSIA, IBZ, IDA, Mid.East: Abstr.& Ind., PSI, Psychol.Abstr. (1984-), Soc.Sci.Ind. (1994-), Soc.Work Res.& Abstr., Sociol.Abstr., World Bibl.Soc.Sec. **Document type:** academic/scholarly publication.
—BLDSC (4549.500000); Faxon; SWETS; UMI.
    Description: Designed to promote communication and extend knowledge in the fields of social development, social welfare and human services.
    Refereed Serial

360   US
INTERNATIONAL UNION OF GOSPEL MISSIONS MEMBERSHIP DIRECTORY & RESOURCE GUIDE. biennial. $10. International Union of Gospel Missions, 1045 Swift Ave., N. Kansas City, MO 64116-4127. TEL 816-471-8020. FAX 816-471-3718. E-mail: iuhm@fileshop.com. Ed. Madeleine Wooley. **Document type:** directory, abstracting/indexing.
    Description: Lists member organizations in I.U.G.M. with a breakdown of services provided.

INTERNATIONAL WORKCAMP LISTING (YEAR). see *BUSINESS AND ECONOMICS — International Development And Assistance*

361   CN   ISSN 0047-1321
INTERVENTION. (Text in English and French) 1969. 3/yr. Can.$30 to institutions (foreign Can.$35); individuals Can.$40 (foreign Can.$45). Corporation Professionnelle des Travailleurs Sociaux du Quebec - Professional Corporation of Social Workers of Quebec, 5757 Decelles Ave., Ste. 335, Montreal, PQ H3S 2C3, Canada. TEL 514-731-2749. FAX 514-731-6785. Ed. Rene Page. adv.; bk.rev.; bibl. circ. 2,000. (also avail. in audio cassette) **Indexed:** Pt.de Rep. (1983-), RADAR.
    Description: Provides opportunities for members of the Corporation to publish and share the results of their research and professional experience, stimulates new ideas and serves as a source of information and continuing education.

INVENTORY OF HEALTH WORKFORCE IN ALBERTA. see *PUBLIC HEALTH AND SAFETY*

360   IE
IRELAND. DEPARTMENT OF SOCIAL WELFARE. STATISTICAL INFORMATION ON SOCIAL WELFARE. 1983. a. I£7. Department of Social Welfare, Statistics Unit, Store St., 4th Fl., Dublin 1, Ireland. TEL 01-8748444. FAX 01-87043868. Ed. Paul Lynch. circ. 1,300 (controlled). **Document type:** government publication.

IRYO TO FUKUSHI/JAPANESE JOURNAL OF MEDICAL SOCIAL WORK. see *MEDICAL SCIENCES*

362   IS   ISSN 0075-1014
HA1931
ISRAEL. CENTRAL BUREAU OF STATISTICS. DIAGNOSTIC STATISTICS OF HOSPITALIZED PATIENTS. (Subseries of its Special Series) (Text in English and Hebrew) 1950. irreg. price varies. Central Bureau of Statistics, Box 13015, Jerusalem 91 130, Israel. TEL 02-21 12 11. **Document type:** government publication.

361   IS
ISRAEL. MINISTRY OF LABOUR AND SOCIAL AFFAIRS. DEPARTMENT OF INTERNATIONAL RELATIONS. THE PRESS ON WELFARE; a selection of articles on welfare from the Israeli press. (Text in English) 1970. s-a. $35. Ministry of Labour and Social Affairs, Department of International Relations, 10 Yad Harutzim St., Talpiot, P.O. Box 1260, Jerusalem, Israel. **Document type:** government publication.
    Formerly: Israel. Ministry of Social Welfare. Department of International Relations. The Press on Welfare.

ISSUES IN CHILD ABUSE ACCUSATIONS. see *CHILDREN AND YOUTH — About*

360   378   UK   ISSN 0261-4154
ISSUES IN SOCIAL WORK EDUCATION. 1970. s-a. £25 (overseas £40) (effective 1995-1996). Association of Teachers in Social Work Education, Department of Sociological Studies, University of Sheffield, Sheffield S10 2TN, England. TEL 0114-276-8555. FAX 0114-276-8125. E-mail: sociological.studies@sheffield.ac.uk. (Co-sponsor: University of Sheffield) Ed. Steven Shardlow. adv.; bk.rev.; index. circ. 350. (back issues avail.) **Document type:** academic/scholarly publication.
—BLDSC (4584.327000).
    Description: Concentrates on theory, research, practice and policy.
    Refereed Serial

J A C S VOLUNTEER. (Joint Action in Community Service, Inc.) see *OCCUPATIONS AND CAREERS*

J A O G NEWS. (Japan Association of Obstetricians & Gynecologists) see *MEDICAL SCIENCES — Obstetrics And Gynecology*

J C C CIRCLE. (Jewish Community Centers Association of North America) see *ETHNIC INTERESTS*

J K - BESLUT; beslut och yttranden af Justiekanslern vilka har bedoemts vara af allmaent intresse. see *LAW*

360   GW   ISSN 0173-6515
JAHRBUCH DES SOZIALRECHTS DER GEGENWART. 1979. a. price varies. Erich Schmidt Verlag GmbH & Co. (Bielefeld), Viktoriastr. 44a, 33602 Bielefeld, Germany. TEL 0521-5830855. (Subscr. to: Postfach 102451, 33524 Bielefeld, Germany) Eds. G. Wannagat, W. Gitter. (back issues avail.) **Document type:** academic/scholarly publication.
    Supersedes (1969-1973): Sozialordnung der Gegenwart (ISSN 0561-290X)

JAHRBUCH KRITISCHE MEDIZIN. see *MEDICAL SCIENCES*

JANUS. see *BUSINESS AND ECONOMICS — Labor And Industrial Relations*

JEWISH COMMUNITY NEWS. see *ETHNIC INTERESTS*

362.5   296.7   US   ISSN 0021-6437
JEWISH EXPONENT. 1887. w. $30. Federation of Jewish Agencies of Greater Philadelphia, 226 S. 16th St., Philadelphia, PA 19102. TEL 215-893-5700. FAX 215-790-0087. Ed. Albert Erlick. adv.; bk.rev.; illus. circ. 80,000. (tabloid format; also avail. in microfilm from AJP) **Document type:** newspaper.
    Description: Contains items of interest to the Jewish community.

JEWISH JOURNAL (YOUNGSTOWN). see *ETHNIC INTERESTS*

JEWISH JOURNAL OF SAN ANTONIO. see *ETHNIC INTERESTS*

JEWISH OBSERVER (DEWITT). see *ETHNIC INTERESTS*

JEWISH POPULATION SERIES. see *POPULATION STUDIES*

360   296   US   ISSN 0021-6712
HV3190
JEWISH SOCIAL WORK FORUM. 1964. a. $10 (effective 1993). Yeshiva University, Wurzweiler School of Social Work, Alumni Association, 2495 Amsterdam Ave., New York, NY 10033. TEL 212-960-0841. FAX 212-960-0822. Ed. Edwin Simon. adv. contact: Norman Linzer. bk.rev.; charts. circ. 950. **Indexed:** Abstr.Soc.Geront., Lang.& Lang.Behav.Abstr., Mid.East: Abstr.& Ind., Soc.Work Res.& Abstr., Sociol.Abstr. **Document type:** academic/scholarly publication.

JEWISH STAR. see *ETHNIC INTERESTS*

JEWISH TIMES (HUNTINGDON VALLEY). see *ETHNIC INTERESTS*

THE JEWISH VOICE. see *ETHNIC INTERESTS*

JEWISH VOICE (DEAL PARK). see *ETHNIC INTERESTS*

JEWISH VOICE (NEW ORLEANS). see *ETHNIC INTERESTS*

THE JEWISH VOICE (WILMINGTON). see *ETHNIC INTERESTS*

360   GW
DIE JOHANNITER. 4/yr. (Johanniter-Unfall-Hilfe e.V.) Beta Verlag GmbH, Postfach 140121, 53056 Bonn, Germany. TEL 0228-252061. FAX 0228-252067. Ed. Joerg Hengster. circ. 910,000. **Document type:** bulletin.

JONQUIL. see *CLUBS*

360   SZ
JOURNAL DES CAISSES MALADIE SUISSES. 1986. m. 30 SFr. Concordat des Caisses Maladie Suisses, CH-4502 Soleure, Switzerland. TEL 065-204218. FAX 065-226246. Ed. G.D. Giffieron. circ. 2,100.

361   FR
JOURNAL DES ORPHELINS DE GUERRE. 1930. bi-m. 100 F. Federation Nationale "les Fils des Tues", 25, rue Lavoisier, 75008 Paris, France.

S

SOCIAL SERVICES AND WELFARE

JOURNAL OF ADDICTIONS & OFFENDER COUNSELING.
see *PSYCHOLOGY*

360 616.89 US ISSN 1052-9950
HV40 CODEN: JASWEN
JOURNAL OF ANALYTIC SOCIAL WORK. 1987. q. $60 (foreign $84) (effective 1996). Haworth Press, Inc., 10 Alice St., Binghamton, NY 13904. TEL 607-722-5857; 800-342-9678. FAX 607-722-1424. Ed. Jerrold R. Brandell. adv.: page $300. bk.rev. circ. 119. (also avail. in microfiche from UMI; back issues avail.) **Indexed:** Abstr.Anthropol., Crim.Just.Abstr., Human Resour.Abstr., IMFL, Psychol.Abstr., Sage Fam.Stud.Abstr., Soc.Work Res.& Abstr., Sociol.Abstr., Stud.Wom.Abstr., Viol.& Abuse Abstr.
—BLDSC (4928.080000); Haworth; UnCover.
Formerly (until Fall, 1992): Journal of Independent Social Work (ISSN 0883-7562)
Description: Provides social work clinicians and clinical educators with highly informative and stimulating articles relevant to the practice of psychoanalytic social work with the individual client.
Refereed Serial

362.4 US ISSN 0047-2220
CODEN: JRCOD3
JOURNAL OF APPLIED REHABILITATION COUNSELING. 1970. q. $15 to individuals; institutions $30. National Rehabilitation Counseling Association, 8807 Sudley Rd., Ste. 102, Manassas, VA 22110-4719. Ed. Arnold Wolf. adv.; bk.rev. circ. 6,500. (also avail. in microfilm from UMI; back issues avail. from UMI) **Indexed:** Except.Child.Educ.Abstr., Psychol.Abstr. (1971-), Rehabil.Lit. **Document type:** academic/scholarly publication.
—BLDSC (4947.030000); UMI; UnCover.

JOURNAL OF CASE MANAGEMENT. see *MEDICAL SCIENCES*

JOURNAL OF CHILD AND YOUTH CARE. see *CHILDREN AND YOUTH — About*

362.7 US ISSN 1053-8712
HV6570 CODEN: JCABEK
JOURNAL OF CHILD SEXUAL ABUSE; research, treatment & program innovations for victims, survivors & offenders. 1992. q. $85 (foreign $119) (effective 1996). Haworth Press, Inc., 10 Alice St., Binghamton, NY 13904-1580. TEL 607-722-5857; 800-342-9678. FAX 607-722-1424. Ed. Robert A. Geffner. adv.: page $300. bk.rev. (also avail. in microfiche from HAW) **Indexed:** Behav.Med.Abstr., Crim.Just.Abstr., DNP, Educ.Admin.Abstr., Except.Child Educ.Abstr., Excerp.Med. (1993-), G.Soc.Sci.& Rel.Per.Lit., IMFL, Ind.Per.Art.Relat.Law, Psychol.Abstr. (1992-), Ref.Zh., Sage Fam.Stud.Abstr., Sage Urb.Stud.Abstr., Soc.Work Res.& Abstr., Sociol.Abstr., SOPODA, Stud.Wom.Abstr., Viol.& Abuse Abstr. **Document type:** academic/scholarly publication.
—BLDSC (4957.905000); Haworth.
Description: Covers research issues, clinical issues, case studies and brief reports on young victims, adult survivors and the offenders.
Refereed Serial

360 US ISSN 1070-5422
HN1 CODEN: JOPREN
▼**JOURNAL OF COMMUNITY PRACTICE.** 1994. q. $75 (foreign $105) (effective 1996). (Association for Community Organization and Social Administration) Haworth Press, Inc., 10 Alice St., Binghamton, NY 13904-1580. TEL 607-722-5857; 800-342-9678. FAX 607-722-1424. Ed. Marie Weil. (also avail. in microform from UMI) **Indexed:** G.Soc.Sci.& Rel.Per.Lit., Ind.Per.Art.Relat.Law, Oper.Res.Manage.Sci., P.A.I.S., Sociol.Abstr., Trans.Res.Abstr. **Document type:** academic/scholarly publication.
—BLDSC (4961.745000); Haworth.
Description: Forum for the development, debate and exchange of ideas on community practice in research, theory development, intervention models, curriculum development, and teaching.

361.3 US ISSN 1052-2158
HV697 CODEN: JFSWEO
JOURNAL OF FAMILY SOCIAL WORK. 1981. q. $60 (foreign $84) (effective 1996). Haworth Press, Inc., 10 Alice St., Binghamton, NY 13904. TEL 607-722-5857; 800-342-9678. FAX 607-722-1424. Ed. Donald Ray Bardill. adv.; bk.rev. circ. 207. (also avail. in microfiche from UMI; back issues avail.) **Indexed:** Abstr.Anthropol., Abstr.Crim.& Pen., Abstr.Soc.Geront., ASSIA, Behav.Abstr., Biol.Abstr., Bull.Signal., Chicago Psychoanal.Lit.Ind., Child Devel.Abstr., Crim.Just.Abstr., Educ.Admin.Abstr., Human Resour.Abstr., IMFL, Ind.Per.Art.Relat.Law, Past.Care & Couns.Abstr., Per.Islam., Psychol.Abstr., Risk Abstr., Sage Fam.Stud.Abstr., Soc.Work Res.& Abstr., Sociol.Abstr., SOPODA, Stud.Wom.Abstr.
—BLDSC (4983.737000); Haworth.
Formerly (until 1992): Journal of Social Work and Human Sexuality (ISSN 0276-3850)
Description: Dedicated to the study of couples and families. Serves as a forum for family practitioners, scholars, and educators in the social work profession.
Refereed Serial

JOURNAL OF GAY & LESBIAN PSYCHOTHERAPY. see *HOMOSEXUALITY*

362.8 301.415 US ISSN 1053-8720
HV1449 CODEN: JGLSEI
▼**JOURNAL OF GAY & LESBIAN SOCIAL SERVICES;** issues in practice, policy & research. 1994. q. $60 (foreign $84) (effective 1996). Haworth Press, Inc., 10 Alice St., Binghamton, NY 13904-1580. TEL 607-722-5857; 800-342-9678. FAX 607-722-1424. Eds. James J. Kelley, Raymond M. Berger. (also avail. in microform from UMI; reprint service avail. from HAW) **Indexed:** DNP, IMFL, Ind.Per.Art.Relat.Law, Risk Abstr., Soc.Work Res.& Abstr., Stud.Wom.Abstr.
—BLDSC (4987.643000); Haworth.
Description: Focuses on policy, program and practice issues aiming to promote the well-being of homosexuals and bisexuals in contemporary society.
Refereed Serial

360 614.8 US ISSN 0897-7186
RA418 CODEN: JHSPEH
JOURNAL OF HEALTH & SOCIAL POLICY. 1989. q. $145 (foreign 203) (effective Mar. 1995). Haworth Press, Inc., 10 Alice St., Binghamton, NY 13904. TEL 607-722-5857; 800-342-9678. FAX 607-722-1424. Ed. Marvin D. Feit. adv.; bk.rev. (also avail. in microfiche from UMI; reprint service avail. from HAW) **Indexed:** Geo.Abstr. (1989-), IDA, IMFL, Int.Polit.Sci.Abstr., Psychol.Abstr.
—BLDSC (4996.731000); Haworth.
Description: Addresses health and social policy issues, concerns, and questions.
Refereed Serial

JOURNAL OF HEALTH CARE FOR THE POOR AND UNDERSERVED. see *MEDICAL SCIENCES*

JOURNAL OF INTELLECTUAL DISABILITY RESEARCH. see *MEDICAL SCIENCES — Psychiatry And Neurology*

362.5 296.7 US ISSN 0022-2089
HV1
JOURNAL OF JEWISH COMMUNAL SERVICE. 1899. q. $30 (foreign $36). Jewish Communal Service Association, 3084 State Hwy. 27, Ste. 9, Kendall Park, NJ 08824-1657. TEL 908-821-1871. FAX 908-821-5335. E-mail: JCSANA@AOL.COM. Ed. Gail Naron Chalew. adv.; bk.rev.; charts; index, cum.index every 10 yrs. circ. 2,800. (also avail. in microform from UMI; reprint service avail. from UMI) **Indexed:** ASSIA, Ind.Jew.Per., Mid.East: Abstr.& Ind., P.A.I.S., Psychol.Abstr., Soc.Work Res.& Abstr. **Document type:** academic/scholarly publication.
—BLDSC (5009.500000); UMI.
Refereed Serial

JOURNAL OF MARITAL AND FAMILY THERAPY. see *PSYCHOLOGY*

JOURNAL OF MENTAL HEALTH ADMINISTRATION. see *PUBLIC HEALTH AND SAFETY*

JOURNAL OF MULTICULTURAL SOCIAL WORK. see *SOCIOLOGY*

JOURNAL OF OFFENDER REHABILITATION; a multidisciplinary journal of innovation in research, services, and programs in corrections and criminal justice. see *CRIMINOLOGY AND LAW ENFORCEMENT*

360 312 KO
JOURNAL OF POPULATION, HEALTH AND SOCIAL WELFARE. (Text in English, Korean) 1981. s-a. free. Korea Institute for Health and Social Affairs, San 42-14, Bulgwang-Dong, Eunpyung-Ku, Seoul 122 040, S. Korea. TEL 02-355-8003. FAX 02-352-9129. circ. 500. **Indexed:** ExtraMED. **Document type:** academic/scholarly publication.
●Also available on CD-ROM.

360 320.531 US ISSN 1042-8232
HV85 CODEN: JPHSER
JOURNAL OF PROGRESSIVE HUMAN SERVICES. 1978. s-a. $60 (foreign $84) (effective 1996). (Institute for Social Services Alternatives, Inc.) Haworth Press, Inc., 10 Alice St., Binghamton, New York, NY 13904. TEL 607-722-5857; 800-342-9678. FAX 607-722-1424. TELEX 4932599. Ed. Cheryl Hyde. adv.; bk.rev.; film rev. circ. 579. (also avail. in microfiche from UMI; back issues avail.; reprint service avail. from HAW) **Indexed:** Alt.Press Ind., IMFL, Left Ind. (1982-), Mult.Ed.Abstr., Soc.Work Res.& Abstr., Sociol.Abstr.
—BLDSC (5042.745000); Haworth; UnCover.
Formerly (until 1990): Catalyst (New York, 1978) (ISSN 0191-040X)
Description: Deals with social problems and human services from the progressive perspective.
Refereed Serial

JOURNAL OF PSYCHOSOCIAL NURSING AND MENTAL HEALTH SERVICES. see *MEDICAL SCIENCES — Nurses And Nursing*

360 614 UK ISSN 0957-4832
CODEN: JPHME9
JOURNAL OF PUBLIC HEALTH MEDICINE. 1979. q. £98($180) (effective 1996). Oxford University Press, Oxford Journals, Walton Rd., Oxford OX2 6DP, England. TEL 01865-267907. FAX 01865-267773. TELEX 8373300-OXPRES-G. E-mail: jnlorders@oup.co.uk. (U.S. subscr. to: Oxford University Press Inc., 2001 Evans Rd., Cary, NC 27513. TEL 919-677-0977. FAX 919-677-1714) Eds. R. Madeley, P.C. Milner. adv.; bk.rev.; index. circ. 2,750. **Indexed:** Abstr.Hyg., ASSIA, Bibl.Dev.Med.& Child Neur., Curr.Adv.Ecol.Sci., Excerp.Med., Med.Care Rev., Protozool.Abstr., Rev.Plant Path., Risk Abstr., Trop.Dis.Bull. **Document type:** academic/scholarly publication.
—BLDSC (5043.560000); Genuine Article; SWETS; UMI; UnCover. CCC.
Formerly: Community Medicine (ISSN 0142-2456)
Description: Addresses the practice of community medicine.

362 615.8 US ISSN 0022-4154
HD7255.A2 CODEN: JOREA
JOURNAL OF REHABILITATION. 1935. q. $50. National Rehabilitation Association, 633 S. Washington St., Alexandria, VA 22314-4109. TEL 703-836-0850. FAX 703-836-0848. Ed. Paul Leung. adv.; bk.rev.; illus.; pat.; index. circ. 24,000. (also avail. in Braille; audio cassette; microfilm from KTO) **Indexed:** Adol.Ment.Hlth.Abstr., ASSIA, C.I.J.E., C.I.S. Abstr., CINAHL, Curr.Cont., Except.Child.Educ.Abstr., Excerp.Med., Hlth.Ind., Hosp.Lit.Ind., Ind.Med., Psychol.Abstr., Rehabil.Lit., Soc.Sci.Ind., SSCI. **Document type:** academic/scholarly publication.
●Also available online. Vendor(s): University Microfilms International.
—BLDSC (5048.850000); Faxon; Genuine Article; SWETS; UMI; UnCover.

360 BG
JOURNAL OF SOCIAL DEVELOPMENT. (June issue is in English; Dec. issue is in Bengali.) 1966-1969; resumed in 1984. s-a. Tk.25($3) per no. University of Dhaka, Institute of Social Welfare and Research, Ramna, Dhaka 1000, Bangladesh. bk.rev. circ. 200.
Formerly (until 1984): Social Horizon (ISSN 0037-7759)

SOCIAL SERVICES AND WELFARE

360 RH ISSN 1012-1080
JOURNAL OF SOCIAL DEVELOPMENT IN AFRICA. 1986. 2/yr. $15 to individuals (in Third World $10); institutions $30 (in Third World $20) (effective 1995 & 1996). School of Social Work, Private Bag 66022, Kopje, Harare, Zimbabwe. TEL 263-4-707414. FAX 263-4-751903. Ed. Nigel Hall. adv.; bk.rev.; index. circ. 350. (back issues avail.) **Indexed:** Abstr.Rural Dev.Trop., Abstr.Trop.Agri., ASSIA, Documentatieblad, Geo.Abstr., Hum.Ind., IDA, Per.Islam., Rural Devel.Abstr., Soc.Sci.Ind., Soc.Work Res.& Abstr., Sociol.Abstr. **Document type:** academic/scholarly publication.
—BLDSC (5064.752700).
 Description: Specializes in social development. Publishes critical analyses of issues affecting development and poverty, popular participation, equality and productivity. Aimed at practitioners, academics and policy makers.
 Refereed Serial

360 US ISSN 1053-0789
HN1 CODEN: JSDHET
JOURNAL OF SOCIAL DISTRESS AND THE HOMELESS. 1992. q. $135 (foreign $160) (effective 1996). Human Sciences Press, Inc. (Subsidiary of: Plenum Publishing Corp.), 233 Spring St., New York, NY 10013. TEL 212-620-8000. FAX 212-463-0742. TELEX 23-421139. Ed. R. W. Rieber. adv. **Indexed:** IMFL, Psychol.Abstr. (1992-). **Document type:** academic/scholarly publication.
—BLDSC (5064.753000); Faxon; UnCover. **CCC.**
 Description: Explores the link between social distress and issues such as homelessness, violence, and racial tension and its institutionalization in modern society.
 Refereed Serial

JOURNAL OF SOCIAL SECURITY LAW. see *LAW*

360 US ISSN 0148-8376
HV1 CODEN: JSSRDV
JOURNAL OF SOCIAL SERVICE RESEARCH. 1977. q. $225 (foreign $335) (effective Mar. 1995). Haworth Press, Inc., 10 Alice St., Binghamton, NY 13904. TEL 607-722-5857; 800-342-9678. FAX 607-722-1424. TELEX 4932599. Ed. David F. Gillespie. adv.; bk.rev. circ. 432. (also avail. in microfiche from UMI; back issues avail.; reprint service avail. from HAW) **Indexed:** Abstr.Crim.& Pen., Adol.Ment.Hlth.Abstr., ASSIA, Behav.Abstr., Bull.Signal., Chicago Psychoanal.Lit.Ind., CJPI, Crim.Just.Abstr., Curr.Cont., Human Resour.Abstr., IMFL, Lang.& Lang.Behav.Abstr., Left Ind., Past.Care & Couns.Abstr., Psychol.Abstr. (1977-), Sage Pub.Admin.Abstr., Soc.Work Res.& Abstr., Sociol.Abstr., SSCI, Viol.& Abuse Abstr.
—BLDSC (5064.913000); Faxon; Haworth; SWETS; UnCover.
 Description: Devoted to empirical research and its application to the design, delivery, and management of social services.
 Refereed Serial

JOURNAL OF SOCIAL WELFARE AND FAMILY LAW. see *LAW — Family And Matrimonial Law*

360 IS ISSN 0334-9977
HV378.5
JOURNAL OF SOCIAL WORK AND POLICY IN ISRAEL. (Text in English; summaries in Hebrew) a. $17 per no. (effective 1993). Bar-Ilan University Press, Ramat Gan 52900, Israel. TEL 972-3-5318401. Eds. F.M. Loewenberg, M.H. Spero. (back issues avail.) **Document type:** academic/scholarly publication.
—BLDSC (5064.918930).

361 US ISSN 1043-7797
HV11
JOURNAL OF SOCIAL WORK EDUCATION. 1965. 3/yr. membership. Council on Social Work Education, 1600 Duke St., Alexandria, VA 22314-3421. TEL 703-683-8080. FAX 703-683-8099. Ed. J. Longres. bk.rev.; charts; cum.index. circ. 3,800. (also avail. in microform from UMI; back issues avail.; reprint service avail. from UMI) **Indexed:** Abstr.Soc.Work., C.I.J.E., Cont.Pg.Educ., Curr.Cont., Educ.Ind., Lang.& Lang.Behav.Abstr., Mid.East: Abstr.& Ind., Mult.Ed.Abstr., Res.High.Educ.Abstr., Soc.Sci.Ind., Soc.Work Res.& Abstr., Sociol.Abstr., Sociol.Educ.Abstr., SSCI, Stud.Wom.Abstr., Tech.Educ.Abstr. **Document type:** academic/scholarly publication.
—BLDSC (5064.918950); Faxon; Genuine Article; SWETS; UMI; UnCover.
 Formerly: Journal of Education for Social Work (ISSN 0022-0612)
 Description: Contains research articles on education in the fields of social work knowledge and social welfare, focusing on developments, innovations, and problems pertaining to social work education at the undergraduate, master's, and postgraduate levels.
 Refereed Serial

360 369.4 UK ISSN 0265-0533
 CODEN: JSWPEC
JOURNAL OF SOCIAL WORK PRACTICE. 1983. s-a. £40 to individuals; institutions £104 (effective 1996). Carfax Publishing Co., P.O. Box 25, Abingdon, Oxon. OX14 3UE, England. TEL 01235-555335. FAX 01235-553559. (Subscr. in N. America to: Carfax Publishing Co., 875-81 Massachusetts Ave., Cambridge, MA 02139) Ed.Bd. adv.; bk.rev.; index. (also avail. in microfiche; back issues avail.) **Indexed:** ASSIA, Psychol.Abstr. **Document type:** academic/scholarly publication.
—BLDSC (5064.919000); UMI. **CCC.**
 Refereed Serial

JOURNAL OF SOCIOLOGY AND SOCIAL WELFARE. see *SOCIOLOGY*

JOURNAL OF TEACHING IN SOCIAL WORK. see *EDUCATION — Teaching Methods And Curriculum*

360 UK ISSN 0959-7670
JOURNAL OF TRAINING AND DEVELOPMENT. 1990. q. Pepar Publications Ltd., 249 Ladypool Rd., Sparkbrook, Birmingham B12 8LF, England. **Document type:** bulletin.
—BLDSC (5069.780000).

360 US ISSN 0733-6535
HV91
JOURNAL OF VOLUNTEER ADMINISTRATION. 1968. q. $29 in U.S.: Canada and Mexico $32; elsewhere $40. Association for Volunteer Administration, Box 4584, Boulder, CO 80306. TEL 303-541-0238. FAX 303-541-0277. Ed. Connie Baird. adv. contact: Martha Martin. bk.rev.; abstr.; bibl.; charts; illus.; cum.index: 1982-1992. circ. 2,000. (back issues avail.) **Indexed:** BPIA, Sage Pub.Admin.Abstr. **Document type:** academic/scholarly publication, trade publication.
—BLDSC (5072.517500); Faxon; UnCover.
 Supersedes (in 1982): Volunteer Administration.
 Description: Contains articles on program management, model projects and tested techniques for successful volunteer involvement.

JUGEND BERUF GESELLSCHAFT; Journal for professionals in youth social service. see *CHILDREN AND YOUTH — About*

362.7 GW ISSN 0022-5940
JUGENDHILFE. 1963. 6/yr. DM.61.20. Luchterhand Verlag, Heddesdorferstr. 31, 56564 Neuwied, Germany. TEL 02631-801-00. FAX 02631-801210. Ed. Christiane Jaeger. adv. contact: Gabriele Pannwitz. charts; illus.; stat.; index. **Document type:** bulletin.

JUGENDROTKREUZ. see *CHILDREN AND YOUTH — For*

362.7 GW ISSN 0022-5975
JUGENDWOHL; Zeitschrift fuer Kinder- und Jugendhilfe. 1912. m. DM.62 (foreign DM.80). (Deutscher Caritasverband) Lambertus-Verlag GmbH, Woelflinstr. 4, 79104 Freiburg, Germany. TEL 0761-36825-25. FAX 0761-37064. Ed. Heribert Moersberger. adv.; bk.rev.; charts; index. circ. 2,000. (processed) **Indexed:** Abstr.Crim.& Pen. **Document type:** bulletin.

360 364 CN ISSN 0225-4115
HV9308
JUSTICE - DIRECTORY OF SERVICES/JUSTICE - REPERTOIRE DES SERVICES. (Text in English, French) 1980. a. Can.$25. Canadian Criminal Justice Association - Association Canadienne de Justice Penale, 383 Parkdale Ave., Ste. 304, Ottawa, ON K1Y 4R4, Canada. TEL 613-725-3715. FAX 613-725-3720. circ. 700. **Document type:** directory.
 Formerly: Directory of Correctional Services in Canada - Repertoire des Services de Correction du Canada (ISSN 0070-5381)
 Description: Addresses, phone numbers and names of persons responsible for criminal justice and related services in Canada.

JUSTICE REPORT/ACTUALITES JUSTICE. see *CRIMINOLOGY AND LAW ENFORCEMENT*

331.137 360 NE
K A B A M. (Krant voor Aktieve Baanlozen in Amsterdam) 1987. m. Werklozen Belangen Vereniging Amsterdam (WBVA), Postbus 2419, 100 CK Amsterdam, Netherlands. TEL 31-20-6834423. bk.rev. **Document type:** bulletin, newspaper.
 Formerly: Baanbreker (ISSN 0925-6075)
 Description: For unemployed people in the Netherlands.

360 613.7 KO
K I H A S A BULLETIN. (Former name of issuing body: Korean Institute for Population and Health) (Text in English) 1981-1993 (vol.25). s-a. free. Korean Institute for Health and Social Affairs, SAN 42-14 Bulgwang-dong, Eunpyung-ku, Seoul, 122, S. Korea. TEL 02-355-8003. FAX 02-352-9129. (Co-sponsor: Ministry of Health and Social Affairs) **Document type:** bulletin.
 Formerly: K I P H Bulletin.

362.7 GW
K J R BURG INFO; Jugendpolitik und Jugendarbeit im Landkreis Muenchen. 1972. m. Kreisjugendring Muenchen-Land, Burg Schwaneck, 82049 Pullach im Isartal, Germany. TEL 089-7441400. FAX 089-74414033. Eds. Marlis Kuepper, Christoph Poschenrieder. bk.rev. circ. 2,000. **Document type:** newsletter.
 Formerly (until 1992): Informationen ueber Jugendarbeit und Jugendpolitik in Landkreis Muenchen.

360 IR
KAR VA TAWSI'AH/LABOUR AND DEVELOPMENT. (Text in English, Farsi) 1990. m. Rs.350 per no. Mu'assasah-i Kar va Ta'min-i Ijtima'i, 80 Khalid Islamboli Ave., Teheran, Iran.

360 614.8 US
KEEPING THE TRUST. 1987. q. free. Cleveland Foundation, 1422 Euclid Ave., Ste. 1400, Cleveland, OH 44115-2001. TEL 216-861-3810. Ed. Lynne E. Woodman. illus. circ. 5,000. **Document type:** newsletter.

362.7 US
KENTUCKY. DEPARTMENT OF HUMAN RESOURCES. ANNUAL REPORT. a. Department for Human Resources, Frankfort, KY 40601. TEL 502-564-2336. **Document type:** government publication.
 Incorporates: Kentucky. Department of Child Welfare. Annual Report.

KENYA. MINISTRY OF COOPERATIVES AND SOCIAL SERVICES. SESSIONAL PAPERS. see *PUBLIC ADMINISTRATION*

360 KE ISSN 0075-594X
KENYA. PUBLIC SERVICE COMMISSION. ANNUAL REPORT. a. EAs.3. Government Printing and Stationery Department, Box 30128, Nairobi, Kenya. **Document type:** government publication.

360 KE
KENYA NATIONAL COUNCIL OF SOCIAL SERVICES. ANNUAL REPORT. (Text in English) a. Kenya National Council of Social Services, Box 47628, Nairobi, Kenya. **Document type:** corporate report.

KENYA SOCIETY FOR THE BLIND. ANNUAL REPORT AND ACCOUNTS. see *HANDICAPPED — Visually Impaired*

SOCIAL SERVICES AND WELFARE

360   UK   ISSN 0963-4436
KEY NOTE REPORT: CHARITIES. Variant title: Charities. irreg. £185. Key Note Publications Ltd., Field House, 72 Oldfield Rd., Hampton, Middlesex TW12 2HQ, England. TEL 0181-783-0755.
FAX 0181-783-1720. **Document type:** trade publication.
●Also available online.
Also available on CD-ROM.
—BLDSC (3129.918100).

360 301   GW   ISSN 0930-0775
KINDERSCHUTZ AKTUELL. 1974. q. DM.16. Deutscher Kinderschutzbund e.V., Bundesgeschaeftsstelle, Schiffgraben 29, 30159 Hannover, Germany. TEL 0511-30485-0. FAX 0511-3048549. adv.; bk.rev. circ. 47,000. (back issues avail.) **Document type:** bulletin.

360 266   US   ISSN 0023-1703
KINSHIP. 1961. q. $7. Glenmary Home Mission Sisters of America, 405 W. Parrish Ave., Box 22264, Owensboro, KY 42304-2264. TEL 502-686-8401. Ed. Sr. Christine Beckett. illus. circ. 11,000. **Document type:** newsletter.

362.7   GW
KLINGE. 1954. q. DM.15($3) Kinder- und Jugenddorf Klinge e.V., Klingerstr. 30, 74743 Seckach, Germany. FAX 06292-78200. Ed. Norbert Georg Mueller. bk.rev.; bibl.; illus. circ. 9,000.
Formerly: Jugenddorf-Zeitung (ISSN 0022-5924).
Description: Focuses on child welfare.

361.8 289.9   US
KOINONIA PARTNERS. NEWSLETTER. q. free. Koinonia Partners, 1324 Georgia State Hwy. 49 S., Americus, GA 31709. **Document type:** newsletter.
Description: Discusses this Christian organization's community outreach programs.

362.4   IS
KOL NECEI MILCHAMA. s-a. 8 Haarbaa St., Tel Aviv, Israel. **Document type:** bulletin.

301.4   GW   ISSN 0023-2947
KOLPINGBLATT. 1900. m. DM.24. Deutsche Kolpingsfamilie e.V., Kolpingplatz 5-11, 50667 Cologne, Germany. TEL 0221-20701173. FAX 0221-20701186. Ed. Martin Gruenewald. adv.; bk.rev.; film rev.; abstr.; illus.; stat. circ. 208,000. **Document type:** newsletter.

361.8   GW
KOMBA RUNDSCHAU. bi-m. Komba Gewerkschaft Schleswig-Holstein, Lerchenstr. 17, 24103 Kiel, Germany. TEL 0431-673318. FAX 0431-673000. Ed. Horst Bendixen. **Document type:** bulletin.

KRANKENDIENST; Zeitschrift fuer kath. Krankenhaeuser, Sozialstationen und Pflegeberufe. see *HOSPITALS*

KUULOVIESTI/HEARING NEWS. see *HANDICAPPED — Hearing Impaired*

362.8   US
L A CO-OPS AND THE SHARED HOUSING NETWORKER. 6/yr. $10. Cooperative Resources & Services Project, Box 27731, Los Angeles, CA 90027. TEL 213-738-1254. Ed. Lois Arkin. adv.; illus.
Formerly: C R S Networking Newsletter.

L A S NEWS. (London Ambulance Service) see *MEDICAL SCIENCES — Orthopedics And Traumatology*

360   GW
L W V INFO; Bericht Nachricht. 1989. q. free. Landeswohlfahrtsverband Hessen, Staendeplatz 6-10, 34117 Kassel, Germany. TEL 0561-1004-0. circ. 8,800. **Document type:** newsletter.
Formerly: L W V-Nachrichten.

LAND AND LIFE. see *ETHNIC INTERESTS*

260   GW   ISSN 0340-3270
LANDESVERSICHERUNGSANSTALT WUERTTEMBERG. MITTEILUNGEN. 1908. m. DM.126. W. Kohlhammer GmbH, Hessbruehlstr. 69, 70565 Stuttgart, Germany. TEL 0711-7863-1. FAX 0711-7863263. Ed. L. Fichtner. stat.; index; circ. controlled. **Document type:** government publication.

362.7   GW   ISSN 0937-7123
LANDSCHAFTSVERBAND WESTFALEN-LIPPE. MITTEILUNGEN DES LANDESJUGENDAMTES; Beitraege, Entscheidungen und Informationen zur Jugendhilfe. 1969. q. DM.40. Landschaftsverband Westfalen-Lippe, Landesjugendamt, 48133 Muenster, Germany. TEL 0251-591-3641. FAX 0251-591-275. TELEX 892835-LAWEL-D. Ed. Hans Joachim Stahl. bk.rev. circ. 1,200. (back issues avail.) **Document type:** academic/scholarly publication.
Refereed Serial

362.7   FI   ISSN 0786-0188
LAPSEN MAILMA/CHILD'S WORLD. 1938. m. FIM 160($40) Lastensuojelun Keskusliitto - Central Union for Child Welfare in Finland, Armfeltintie 1, 00150 Helsinki 15, Finland. TEL 90-625901. FAX 90-627990. Ed. Soila Niklander. adv.; bk.rev.; bibl.; illus.; index. circ. 6,000.
Former titles: Lapset Ja Yhteiskunta (ISSN 0355-3736); Lapsi Ja Nuoriso (ISSN 0047-407X)

360 179   US   ISSN 0740-5820
LATHAM LETTER. 1980. q. $12. Latham Foundation, Latham Plaza Bldg., Clement & Schiller Sts., Alameda, CA 94501. TEL 510-521-0920. FAX 510-521-9861. Ed. Judy Johns. bk.rev. (back issues avail.) *Indexed:* InterActions Bibl. (1989-).
Description: Promotes respect for all life through humane education. Features balanced information on debatable topics.

IL LAVORATORE ELETTRICO. see *ENERGY*

LAW ENFORCEMENT VOLUNTEERS. see *CRIMINOLOGY AND LAW ENFORCEMENT*

LAW OF ASSOCIATIONS: AN OPERATING LEGAL MANUAL FOR EXECUTIVES AND COUNSEL. see *LAW*

371.9 344.73   US
LAWS AFFECTING CHILDREN WITH SPECIAL NEEDS; federal statutes and regulations. 1991. q. $125. L R P Publications, 747 Dresher Rd., Box 980, Horsham, PA 19044-0980. TEL 215-784-0941. FAX 215-784-9639. (looseleaf format)
●Also available on CD-ROM.
Description: Compiles the laws and regulations needed to provide services to children with disabilities.

360   US
HV91
LEADERSHIP (WASHINGTON, 1992). 1992. q. $25. Points of Light Foundation, 1737 H St., N.W., Washington, DC 20006. TEL 202-223-9186. Ed. Jane Harvey. adv.; bk.rev. circ. 5,000.
—BLDSC (9254.572000); UnCover. **CCC.**
Supersedes (1975-1992): Voluntary Action Leadership (ISSN 0149-6492); *Incorporates* (in 1976): Voluntary Action News (ISSN 0300-6638)

LEADERSHIP TIMES FOR SPECIAL SERVICES PERSONNEL. see *EDUCATION — Special Education And Rehabilitation*

360   GW   ISSN 0724-3820
LEBEN UND WEG; Magazin fuer Koerperbehinderte. 1960. bi-m. DM.30. Bundesverband Selbsthilfe Koerperbehinderter e.V., Altkrautheimerstr. 17, 74238 Krautheim, Germany. TEL 06294-68109. FAX 06294-95383. Ed. Ulrich Mannsbart. circ. 15,000. **Document type:** newsletter.

360   GW
LEBENSABEND. m. Zentralverband der Sozialversicherten- der Rentner- und deren Hinterbliebenen Deutschland e.V., Bruckenweg 30, 42929 Wermelskirchen, Germany. TEL 02196-2760. adv.; bk.rev. circ. 10,000. (looseleaf format)
Description: Information on social insurances for insured people and pensioners.

360   AU   ISSN 1023-8220
DIE LEBENSHILFE. q. S.130. Lebenshilfe Oesterreich, Schoenbrunnerstr. 179-2, A-1120 Vienna, Austria. TEL 01-8122642. FAX 01-812264285. Ed. Irmgard Bauer. adv.; B&W page S.13000, color page S.15190; trim 189 x 270; adv. contact: Christa Ortner. circ. 14,500. **Document type:** bulletin.

362.7 369.4   SW   ISSN 0345-7060
LEDARTIPS; Oe M Us tidskrift foer foeraeldrar, barn- och ungdomsledare. 1956. bi-m. SEK 50 (effective 1991). Oerebromissionens Ungdom, P.O. Box 1623, S-701 16 Oerebro, Sweden.

360   DK   ISSN 0906-8147
LEDERFORUM.* s-m. Landsforeningen af Forsorgsledere, Vejle, Denmark. Ed. Preben Danglev. adv. circ. 3,658.
Former titles (until 1991): Plejehjemslederen (ISSN 0108-6693); (until 1981): Forsorgslederen (ISSN 0106-2824); And (until 1977): Centralorgan (ISSN 0903-3564); (until 1975): Centralorgan for Ledere ved Forsorgsinstitutioner.

LESBIAN AND GAY COUNSELLING NEWS. see *HOMOSEXUALITY*

362.82   CN
LET'S TALK FAMILIES! (Editions in English, French) 1984. 3/yr. Can.$45($44) Family Service Canada - Services a la Famille-Canada, 600-220 Laurier Ave., W., Ottawa, ON K1P 5Z9, Canada. TEL 613-230-9960. FAX 613-230-5884. Ed. Margaret Fietz. adv. contact: Kim Tytler. circ. 4,000 (controlled). (back issues avail.) **Document type:** newsletter.
Description: Publicizes activities of FSC, addresses issues affecting families in Canada, major issues faced by organizations providing services to families and provides a forum for information exchange on resources and national events related to family life.

362.5   FR
LETTER TO FRIENDS AROUND THE WORLD. (Editions in English, French, Spanish) 1981. q. 20 F.($4) (Fourth World Movement) Editions Quart Monde, 107 av. General Leclerc, 95480 Pierrelaye, France. TEL 34-21-69-69. Ed. Ms. Alwine de Vos van Steenwijk. index. circ. 3,500. (back issues avail.)

LIAISONS SOCIALES. see *BUSINESS AND ECONOMICS — Labor And Industrial Relations*

354   LB
LIBERIA. GENERAL SERVICES AGENCY. ANNUAL REPORT.* a. General Services Agency, Box 9027, Monrovia, Liberia. stat.

354   LB
LIBERIA. MINISTRY OF LABOUR, YOUTH & SPORTS. ANNUAL REPORT.* (Text in English) a. Ministry of Labour, Youth & Sports, Camp Johnson Rd., Monrovia, Liberia. stat. **Document type:** government publication.

LIBRARY BULLETIN. see *LAW — Abstracting, Bibliographies, Statistics*

613.082   CN
LIFE GUARDIAN. 1971. bi-m. Can.$10. Birthright, 777 Coxwell Ave., Toronto, ON M4C 3C6, Canada. TEL 416-469-4789. FAX 416-469-1772. Eds. Mary Berney, Elizabeth Burman. circ. 1,600. (tabloid format; back issues avail.) **Document type:** newsletter.
Description: Articles on counselling, human interest, information on running a crisis pregnancy center.

LIGHT (WHEATON). see *HANDICAPPED — Visually Impaired*

THE LINK (ALBUQUERQUE). see *ETHNIC INTERESTS*

360   UK   ISSN 0266-8750
LIVERPOOL LINK; Liverpool's voluntary sector news magazine. 1966. m. (10/yr.). £6.95. (Liverpool Council of Social Service) Liverpool Council for Voluntary Service, 14 Castle St., Liverpool L2 0NJ, England. TEL 0151-236-7728.
FAX 0151-258-1153. Ed. Deirdre Morley. adv.; bk.rev. circ. 1,200. **Document type:** newsletter.
Supersedes (in 1984): Castle Street Circular (ISSN 0045-592X)

360   US   ISSN 0896-2154
LIVING WORLD. 1985. q. $15. International Life Services, Inc., 2606 1-2 W. 8th St., Los Angeles, CA 90057. TEL 213-382-2156. FAX 213-382-4203. Ed. Sister Paula Vandegaer. adv. contact: Ruth Phillips. bk.rev. circ. 9,000. **Document type:** consumer publication.
Description: Contains information on sexuality, counseling techniques, euthanasia, teenage life styles and other issues concerning family life.

SOCIAL SERVICES AND WELFARE

360   UK
LOCAL ECONOMIC DEVELOPMENT INFORMATION SERVICE. m. £110 to non-members; members £80. Planning Exchange, Tontine House, 8 Gordon St., Glasgow G1 3PL, Scotland. TEL 0141-248-8541. FAX 0141-248-8277. **Document type:** bulletin.

LOCAL - STATE FUNDING REPORT. see BUSINESS AND ECONOMICS — Public Finance, Taxation

HALOCHAME. see MILITARY

360   GW   ISSN 0724-1829
LOCKE; fuer Auszubildende im Friseurhandwerk. 1982. q. Berufsgenossenschaft fuer Gesundheitsdienst und Wohlfahrtspflege, Pappelallee 35-37, 22089 Hamburg, Germany. TEL 040-202070. FAX 040-20207525. Ed. Eckart Wiedemann. film rev. circ. 70,000. (back issues avail.) **Document type:** trade publication.

LONDON DISABILITY NEWS. see HANDICAPPED

362.82 361.73 200   US   ISSN 0024-6425
LOOKOUT (NEW YORK). 1909. 3/yr. $5. Seamen's Church Institute of New York and New Jersey, 241 Water St., New York, NY 10038. TEL 212-349-9090. FAX 212-349-8342. Ed. Andrea Laine. bk.rev.; illus.; circ. 10,000 (controlled). **Document type:** newsletter.
Description: Informs and educates the public about the institute's activities on behalf of merchant seafarers and the maritime issues that affect them and the institute's work. Also includes personal profiles, maritime art, articles on maritime history, and fundraising reports.

360 610   CN
M A P NEWS. French edition: Info A M P. 1989. q. free. Medical Aid for Palestine - Aide Medicale pour la Palestine, 356 Sherbrooke E., Montreal, PQ H2X 1E6, Canada. TEL 514-843-7875. FAX 514-843-3061. bk.rev.; illus. circ. 2,000. **Document type:** newsletter.
Description: Reports on the events and medical conditions in the Occupied Territories.

M G Z. (Maatschappelijke Gezondheidszorg) see MEDICAL SCIENCES — Nurses And Nursing

350   AT
M I M S ASSIST. a. Aus.$30. M I M S Australia, 48 Albany St., Crows Nest, N.S.W. 2065, Australia. **Document type:** directory.
Formerly: M I M S Services Directory (ISSN 1035-5707)
Description: Comprehensive listing of health, welfare, patient advisory and self-help services nationwide.

360   US
M M I BULLETIN. q. membership. Medicaid Management Institute, c/o American Public Welfare Association, 810 First St., N.E., Ste. 500, Washington, DC 20002-4205. TEL 202-682-0100. FAX 202-289-6555. Ed. Lee Partridge. **Document type:** bulletin.
Formerly: M I A P Bulletin.

360   PH
M S D.D DIGEST. 1978. q. Department of Social Welfare and Development, Public Information Division, 389 San Rafael St., Manila, Philippines. Ed. Susan Argel.

361   NE
MAATSCHAPPELIJK WERK MAGAZINE. (Text in Dutch) 1989. q. fl.35 for non-members. Nederlandse Vereniging van Maatschappelijk Werkers - Dutch Association of Social Workers, Leidseweg 80, 3531 BE Utrecht, Netherlands. TEL 31-30-948603. Ed.Bd. adv.; bk.rev. circ. 2,500.
Formerly: L V M W Nieuws (ISSN 0926-0161)

360   AU
MAGAZIN MOBIL. m. Verein Aktion Mobil, Laxenburgerstr. 90a-10, A-1100 Vienna. TEL 01-626393. Ed. Peter Schumann. circ. 25,000.

MAGIC CARPET. see HANDICAPPED

360   US
MAIN STREET MEMORANDUM. vol.8, 1989. q. $25 donation. Rockford Institute, 934 N. Main St., Rockford, IL 61103. TEL 815-964-5813. FAX 815-965-1826. Ed. Michael Warder. **Document type:** newsletter.
Description: Interprets the principles of a free society for modern America.

361.73   US   ISSN 1061-1266
HV91
MAJOR DONORS. 1992. a. $185. Taft Group, 12300 Twinbrook Pkwy., Ste. 520, Rockville, MD 20852. TEL 301-813-0210. FAX 301-816-0811. (Subscr. to: Taft Group, Box 33477, Detroit, MI 48232-5477. TEL 800-877-TAFT. FAX 313-961-6083) **Document type:** directory.
Description: Helps fundraisers seek donors who give to organizations similar to their own.

MALAWI. NATIONAL STATISTICAL OFFICE. SURVEY OF HANDICAPPED PERSONS. see HANDICAPPED — Abstracting, Bibliographies, Statistics

MALAY; dyornal ng humanidades at agham panlipunan - journal of humanities and social sciences. see HUMANITIES: COMPREHENSIVE WORKS

360   CN   ISSN 0715-3481
MANITOBA SOCIAL WORKER. 1971. 6/yr. Can.$20. Manitoba Association of Social Workers, 103-2015 Portage Ave., Winnipeg, MB R3J OK3, Canada. TEL 204-888-9477. FAX 204-889-0021. Ed.Bd. adv. contact: Diane Cullen. bk.rev. circ. 650. (looseleaf format; back issues avail.) **Document type:** newsletter.

361.73 361.8   SP   ISSN 0214-5979
MANOS UNIDAS. (Includes special nos.) no.44, July 1978. q. 1000 ptas. (foreign $15). Campana Contra el Hambre en el Mundo, Barquillo 38-2, 28004 Madrid, Spain. TEL 91-308-2020. FAX 91-308-4208. Ed. Ana de Felipe; Pub. Javier Marmol. bk.rev.; charts; illus.; bibl. circ. 60,000. **Document type:** bulletin.

360 362.5   IT
MARGINALITA E SOCIETA. q. L.50000 (foreign L.75000) (effective 1993). Franco Angeli Editore, Viale Monza, 106, Casella Postale 17175, 20100 Milan, Italy. TEL 02-2895762. Ed. G. Pietropolli Charmet.
Formerly: Devianza ed Emarginazione.

368.4   MF
MAURITIUS. MINISTRY OF SOCIAL SECURITY. NATIONAL SOLIDARITY AND REFORM INSTITUTIONS. 1962. a. Rs.25. Ministry of Social Security, National Solidarity and Reform Institution, Astor Court, Lislet Geoffroy St., Port Louis, Mauritius. (Orders to: Government Printing Office, Elizabeth II Ave., Port Louis, Mauritius) Ed.Bd. circ. 300. **Document type:** government publication.
Former titles: Mauritius. Ministry for Employment and of Social Security and National Solidarite; (until 1982): Mauritius. Ministry of Social Security. Annual Report (ISSN 0076-5538)
Description: Information on various branches of the ministry.

360   US
MEDICAID DIRECTORS' NETWORK. membership. m. State Medicaid Directors' Association, c/o American Public Welfare Association, 810 First St., N.E., Ste. 500, Washington, DC 20002-4205. TEL 202-682-0100. FAX 202-289-6555.

360 610   US   ISSN 0098-3616
HD7106.U5
MEDICAID RECIPIENT CHARACTERISTICS AND UNITS OF SELECTED MEDICAL SERVICES. (NCSS Report B-4 Supplement) a. U.S. National Center for Social Statistics, U.S. Dept. of Health and Human Services, 330 Independence Ave., S.W., Washington, DC 20201. TEL 301-436-7900.

361.73   US
MEDICAL RESEARCH FUNDING BULLETIN. 1972. 3/m. $68. Science Support Center, Box 7507, New York, NY 10150. TEL 212-371-3398. Ed. Carroll Jordon. bk.rev.; tr.lit.; circ. 2,500 (controlled). **Document type:** bulletin.

MEDICINE NORTHWEST. see MEDICAL SCIENCES

MELBOURNE. PORT COUNCIL NEWS. see PUBLIC ADMINISTRATION — Municipal Government

360   AT   ISSN 0728-1897
MELBOURNE CITYMISSION. ANNUAL REPORT. 1855. a. Melbourne Citymission, 472 Nicholson St., North Fitzroy, Vic. 3068, Australia. TEL 03-489-9666. Ed. Peter Philp. circ. 5,000. (back issues avail.) **Document type:** corporate report.

MENTAL HEALTH IN CHILDREN. see PSYCHOLOGY

362.2   US   ISSN 0191-6750
MENTAL HEALTH REPORT. 1976. bi-w. $312. Business Publishers, Inc., 951 Pershing Dr., Silver Spring, MD 20910-4464. TEL 301-587-6300. FAX 301-585-9075. Ed. Lisa Rabasca. (looseleaf format; back issues avail.) **Document type:** newsletter. •Also available online. Vendor(s): NewsNet. —CCC.
Description: Provides funding and operational tips for managers of mental health programs in public and private sectors.

362   US   ISSN 0076-6453
MENTAL HEALTH STATISTICS FOR ILLINOIS. 1930. a. free. Department of Mental Health and Developmental Disabilities, 100 N. Ninth St., Rm. 204, Springfield, IL 62765. TEL 217-785-9404. Ed. John Brunk. circ. 950. **Indexed:** SRI. **Document type:** government publication.
Formerly: Illinois. Department of Mental Health. Administrator's Data Manual.

362 368   CN   ISSN 0026-1556
METROPOLITAN PENSIONER. 1966. m. $3. Metropolitan Pensioners Welfare Association, Box 2929, Vancouver 3, B.C., Canada. Ed. George S. Hobson. adv.; bk.rev.; abstr.; illus.; stat. circ. 4,800.

METROWEST JEWISH NEWS. see ETHNIC INTERESTS

362.5 286.7   US
METROWEST JEWISH REPORTER. 1970. m. Combined Jewish Philanthropies of Greater Boston, 76 Salem End Rd., Framingham, MA 01701. TEL 508-879-5856. FAX 508-879-5856. Ed. Marcia T. Rivin. **Document type:** newsletter.

MICHAEL SIEFF FOUNDATION. CONFERENCE REPORT. see CHILDREN AND YOUTH — About

360   US
MICHIGAN. DEPARTMENT OF SOCIAL SERVICES. ASSISTANCE PAYMENTS STATISTICS. m. Department of Social Services, Box 30037, 300 S. Capitol Ave., Lansing, MI 48909. TEL 517-373-2005. (also avail. in microfiche from CIS) **Indexed:** SRI. **Document type:** government publication.

MIETERZEITUNG. see HOUSING AND URBAN PLANNING

MIEUX-VIVRE CHEZ LES AVEUGLES ET LES GRANDS INFIRMES. see HANDICAPPED

MIGRATION ACTION. see SOCIOLOGY

353.9   US
MISSOURI. DIVISION OF YOUTH SERVICES. ANNUAL REPORT. 1949. a. Department of Social Services, Division of Youth Services, Broadway State Office Bldg., Box 447, Jefferson City, MO 65101. TEL 314-751-3324. Ed. Mark Steward. illus.; stat. circ. 500. **Document type:** government publication, corporate report.
Formerly: Missouri. State Board of Training Schools. Annual Report (ISSN 0098-0110)

MITEINANDER. see MEDICAL SCIENCES

361 338.91   US   ISSN 1043-8157
MONDAY DEVELOPMENTS. 1983. bi-w. $65 to individuals; institutions $275. (American Council for Voluntary International Action) InterAction, 1717 Massachusettes Ave., N.W., 8th Fl., Washington, DC 20036. TEL 202-667-8227. FAX 202-667-8236. E-mail: tgeoghegan@interactions.org; Site addr.: http://www.vita.org/iaction/iaction.html. Ed. Tracy Geoghegan. adv.; bk.rev. circ. 2,500. **Document type:** newsletter.
Description: Contains news and commenatry on international humanitarian activities, including crisis situations abroad, sustainable development work, policy changes, newly available resources, coming events and employment opportunities.

MOSAIKK. see ETHNIC INTERESTS

SOCIAL SERVICES AND WELFARE

MOTHER AND CHILD. see *WOMEN'S INTERESTS*

362.7   US
MOUNTAIN SPIRIT. 1982. bi-m. $6. Christian Appalachian Project, 322 Crab Orchard Rd., Lancaster, KY 40446. TEL 606-792-3051. FAX 606-792-6560. Ed. Margaret Gabriel. cum.index: 1982-1992. circ. 30,000. (back issues avail.)
    Description: Describes the problems of people who live in Appalachia and how CAP attempts to resolve the issues in question.

N A A C P ANNUAL REPORT. (National Association for the Advancement of Colored People) see *SOCIOLOGY*

300   UK
N A C A B OCCASIONAL PAPERS. irreg. National Association of Citizens Advice Bureaux, Research and Development Unit, Myddleton House, 115-123 Pentonville Rd., London N1 9LZ, England. **Document type:** bulletin.

368.4   US
N A D E ADVOCATE. 1978. bi-m. $40. National Association of Disability Examiners, Box 4188, Frankfort, KY 40603. TEL 502-875-8388. Ed. Lavonne Hoglund. adv.; stat.; tr.lit. circ. 2,500. (back issues avail.)

361.7   US
N A E I R ADVANTAGE. 1982. bi-m. free. National Association for the Exchange of Industrial Resources, 560 McClure St., Box 8076, Galesburg, IL 61402. TEL 309-343-0704; 800-562-0955. FAX 309-343-0862. Ed. Jack Zavada. circ. 40,000 (controlled). **Document type:** newsletter.
    Formerly: N A E I R News.
    Description: Discusses corporate donations of excess inventory for use by schools and charities, and the subsequent tax benefits for the donors.

360   UK
N A H A T RESEARCH PAPER. irreg. National Association of Health Authorities and Trusts, Birmingham Research Park, Vincent Dr., Birmingham B15 2SQ, England. TEL 0121-471-4444. FAX 0121-414-1120. **Document type:** monographic series.

360   US
N A P C W A NETWORK. 1983. q. $75 membership. National Association of Public Child Welfare Administrators, c/o American Public Welfare Association, 810 First St., N.E., Ste. 500, Washington, DC 20002-4205. TEL 202-682-0100. FAX 202-289-6555. Ed. Elizabeth Thielman. bk.rev. circ. 500. **Document type:** newsletter.

360   CN   ISSN 0820-7364
N A P O NEWS/ECHO DE L'O N A P. (Text in English and French) 1983. q. membership. National Anti-Poverty Organization, 316 - 256 King Edward Ave., Ottawa, Ont. K1N 7M1, Canada. TEL 613-789-0096. FAX 613-789-0141. bk.rev. circ. 1,000. (back issues avail.)
    Description: News on poverty, anti-poverty organizations and issues of importance to low-income Canadians.

360   UK   ISSN 0142-1328
N A P O PROBATION DIRECTORY. 1974. a. £7.50. (National Association of Probation Officers) Owen Wells Publishing Company, 23 Eaton Rd., Ilkley, W. Yorks LS29 9PU, England. TEL 01943-602270. FAX 01943-816732. Ed. Owen Wells. circ. 10,500. **Document type:** directory.

360 371.9   UK
N A P S A C BULLETIN. 1992. q. £10 membership. National Association for the Protection from Sexual Abuse of Adults and Children with Learning Disabilities, Department of Learning Disabilities, University Hospital, Floor E, South Block, Nottingham NG7 2UH, England. TEL 0115-970-9987. FAX 0115-978-1598. E-mail: pamela__cook@vme.ccc.nottingham.ac.uk. Ed. Pam Cooke. **Document type:** bulletin.

360   US
N A R C E A CONFERENCE PROCEEDINGS. irreg. price varies. National Aging Resource Center on Elder Abuse, c/o American Public Welfare Association, 810 First St., N.E., Ste. 500, Washington, DC 20002-4205. TEL 202-682-0100. FAX 202-289-6555. **Document type:** proceedings.

360   US
N A R C E A PROJECT REPORTS. 1986. irreg. price varies. National Aging Resource Center on Elder Abuse, c/o American Public Welfare Association, 810 First Ave., N.E., Ste. 500, Washington, DC 20002-4205. TEL 202-682-0100. FAX 202-289-6555.

360   US
N A R C E A SELECTED PUBLICATIONS. irreg. price varies. National Aging Resource Center on Elder Abuse, c/o American Public Welfare Association, 810 First St., N.E., Ste. 500, Washington, DC 20002-4205. TEL 202-682-0100. FAX 202-289-6555.

360   US   ISSN 0027-6022
HV1
N A S W NEWS. 1956. m. (except Aug. & Dec.). $25 to non-members. National Association of Social Workers, 750 First St., N.E., Ste. 700, Washington, DC 20002. TEL 202-408-8600; 800-638-8799. FAX 202-336-8312. Ed. Scott Moss. adv. contact: Lyn Carter. illus. circ. 155,000. (tabloid format; also avail. in microform from UMI; reprint service avail. from UMI) **Document type:** newspaper.
—UMI.
    Formerly: Personnel Information; Incorporates: American Association of Psychiatric Services for Children. Newsletter (ISSN 0093-0237); Which was formerly: American Association of Psychiatric Clinics for Children. Newsletter (ISSN 0569-2733)

N C H ACTION FOR CHILDREN FACTFILE. see *CHILDREN AND YOUTH* — About

360   UK   ISSN 0955-2170
N C V O NEWS. 1979. 10/yr. £25 to individuals and voluntary organizations; others £50. National Council for Voluntary Organisations, Regent's Wharf, 8 All Saints St., London N1 9RL, England. TEL 0171-713-6161. FAX 0171-713-6300. (back issues avail.) **Document type:** newsletter.
—BLDSC (6067.841520). **CCC.**
    Formerly (until 1989): Voluntary Action (ISSN 0143-5744)
    Description: Information and ideas about ways in which voluntary agencies can improve their effectiveness.

360   UK
N C V O TRUSTEE BRIEFING. 1993. irreg., no.3, 1994. £3. National Council for Voluntary Organisations, Regent's Wharf, 8 All Saints St., London N1 9RL, England. TEL 0171-713-6161. FAX 0171-713-6300. **Document type:** monographic series.

N H O NEWSLINE. (National Hospice Organization) see *ALTERNATIVE MEDICINE*

346.01   SW   ISSN 0282-8731
N I A INFORMERAR. 1976. q. Statens Naemnd foer Internationella Adoptionsfraagor, P.O. Box 22086, S-104 22 Stockholm, Sweden. TEL 46-8-651-92-92. FAX 46-8-650-41-10. circ. 2,000. **Document type:** bulletin.
    Description: Contains information on law, practice, psychology, research and other topics related to international child adoptions.

360   II   ISSN 0253-6757
N I H F W TECHNICAL REPORTS. 1978. irreg. free. National Institute of Health and Family Welfare, New Mehrauli Rd., Munirka, New Delhi 110 067, India. circ. 3,000.

360   UK
N I S W DISCUSSION PAPER. irreg., no.2, 1994. National Institute for Social Work, 5 Tavistock Pl., London WC1H 9SN, England. TEL 0171-387-9681. Eds. Dave Pottage, Mike Evans. **Document type:** monographic series.

361.73   US   ISSN 0890-2828
N S F R E NEWS. 1963. 6/yr. $25 to non-members. National Society of Fund Raising Executives, 1101 King St., Ste. 700, Alexandria, VA 22314. TEL 703-684-0410. FAX 703-684-0540. Ed. Stacey Todd. adv.; bk.rev. circ. 16,000. (back issues avail.) **Document type:** newsletter.
    Description: Current events in the nonprofit fund-raising field.

362.7   UK   ISSN 1351-864X
N S P C C NEWS. 1887. 4/yr. free. National Society for the Prevention of Cruelty to Children, 67 Saffron Hill, London EC1N 8RS, England. TEL 071-242-1626. FAX 071-831-9562. bk.rev.; illus. circ. 20,000. **Document type:** newsletter.
    Formerly: Child's Guardian (ISSN 0009-4218)

360   GW   ISSN 0937-7425
NACHRICHTEN - PARITAET. 1950. bi-m. DM.18. Deutscher Paritaetischer Wohlfahrtsverband e.V., Heinrich-Hoffmann-Str. 3, 60528 Frankfurt a.M., Germany. Eds. Gerlinde Geffers, Martin Wisskirchen. bk.rev.; index. circ. 12,500. (tabloid format) **Document type:** bulletin.
    Formerly (until 1990): D P W V - Nachrichten (ISSN 0011-510X)

NAMIBIA DEVELOPMENT BRIEFING; the voice of the Namibian non-governmental forum. see *BUSINESS AND ECONOMICS* — International Development And Assistance

362.7   US   ISSN 1046-5103
NATIONAL ADOPTION REPORTS. 1979. q. $50. National Council for Adoption, Inc., 1930 17th St. N.W., Washington, DC 20009-6207. TEL 202-328-1200. **Document type:** newsletter.
    Description: Newsletter and bulletin service on adoption matters.

362.7   US
NATIONAL ADVOCATE. 1981. q. $10. National Foster Parent Association, Inc., 3 Key Ct., Newport, RI 02840. TEL 401-846-8064. FAX 401-842-0355. Ed. Elaine Reidy. bk.rev. circ. 3,500. (back issues avail.)
    Description: Contains information for foster parents and other child advocates.

360   UK
NATIONAL CARER. 10/yr. National Confederation of Registered Residential Care-Home Associations, Publishing House, 33 Sewardstone Rd., London E4 7PU, England. TEL 081-524-6464. FAX 081-524-5866. Ed. P. Warwick. bk.rev. circ. 160,000.

361.6   US
NATIONAL CONFERENCE OF STATE SOCIAL SECURITY ADMINISTRATORS. PROCEEDINGS. 1952. a. membership only. National Conference of State Social Security Administrators, c/o Social Security Division, c/o Jim Larche, Deputy Dir., Employee Retirement System of Georgia, Two Northside 75, Ste. 300, Atlanta, GA 30318. TEL 404-352-6400. circ. controlled. **Document type:** proceedings.

362.7   US
NATIONAL COUNCIL FOR ADOPTION. LEGAL NOTES. bi-m. $200. National Council for Adoption, Inc., 1930 17th St., N.W., Washington, DC 20009-6207. TEL 202-328-1200.
    Formerly: National Committee for Adoption. Legal Notes.
    Description: Features reports on legal issues, court cases and rulings on adoption.

362.7   US
NATIONAL COUNCIL FOR ADOPTION. MEMO. bi-w. $1000 membership. National Council for Adoption, Inc., 1930 17th St., N.W., Washington, DC 20009-6207. TEL 202-328-1200. **Document type:** newsletter.
    Formerly: National Committee for Adoption. Memo.
    Description: Covers fast-breaking news on adoption and related topics.

NATIONAL COUNCIL FOR THE ELDERLY. PUBLICATION. see *GERONTOLOGY AND GERIATRICS*

360   UK
NATIONAL COUNCIL FOR VOLUNTARY ORGANIZATIONS. ANNUAL REPORT. a. free. National Council for Voluntary Organisations, Regent's Wharf, 8 All Saints St., London N1 9RL, England. TEL 0171-713-6161. FAX 0171-713-6300. circ. 6,000. **Document type:** proceedings.
    Formerly: National Council of Social Service. Annual Report (ISSN 0077-409X)

NATIONAL COUNCIL NEWS. see *MEDICAL SCIENCES* — Psychiatry And Neurology

NATIONAL COUNCIL OF LA RAZA. AIDS NEWSLETTER. see *MEDICAL SCIENCES* — Communicable Diseases

SOCIAL SERVICES AND WELFARE

362.5 US
NATIONAL COUNCIL OF LA RAZA. POVERTY PROJECT NEWSLETTER.* q. free. National Council of La Raza, 1111 19th St., N.W., Washington, DC 20036-3603. TEL 202-289-1380. FAX 202-289-8173. Ed. Sonia Perez. **Document type:** newsletter.
Description: Covers legislative and social welfare issues affecting the Hispanic community.

361.73 378.002 069 AS29.5 US ISSN 1048-8154
NATIONAL DIRECTORY OF NONPROFIT ORGANIZATIONS. (In 2 vols.) a. (in 2 vols.). $450 for both vols. Taft Group, 12300 Twinbrook Pkwy., Ste. 520, Rockville, MD 20852. TEL 301-816-0210. FAX 301-816-0811. (Subscr. to: Taft Group, Box 33477, Detroit, MI 48232-5477. TEL 800-877-TAFT. FAX 313-961-6083) **Document type:** directory.
Description: Covers more than 265,000 organizations such as hospitals, universitites, museums, and health clinics.

360 US
NATIONAL DIRECTORY OF PRIVATE SOCIAL AGENCIES.* 1964. base vol. (plus m. supplements). $79.90. (Social Service Publications) Croner Publications, Inc., 5 Longmeadow Ln., Cleveland, OH 44122-7518. TEL 800-441-4033. FAX 516-338-4986. Ed. Carol Sixt. adv. circ. 1,000. (looseleaf format) **Document type:** directory.
Description: Lists by field of service and geographical location. Includes addresses, telephone numbers and description of services.

360 US
NATIONAL EASTER SEAL COMMUNICATOR. vol.32, 1972. 3/yr. free. National Easter Seal Society, 230 W. Monroe St., 18th Fl., Chicago, IL 60606-4703. TEL 312-726-6200. FAX 312-726-1494. Ed. Jay Becker. bk.rev. circ. 10,000. **Document type:** newsletter.
Former titles: Easter Seal Communicator; Easter Seal Bulletin (ISSN 0012-8651)
Description: Highlights news of the society.

361.73 658 US ISSN 0272-0825
NATIONAL FUND RAISER. 1974. m. $95 (foreign $111). Barnes Associates, Inc., 603 Douglas Blvd., Roseville, CA 95678-3244. TEL 800-231-4157. FAX 916-782-2145. Ed. W. David Barnes. bk.rev. circ. 2,200. (back issues avail.) **Document type:** newsletter.
Description: For the nonprofit fund raising professional. Contains specific, "how-to" fund raising information in an easy to read format.

NATIONAL HOMECARE AND HOSPICE DIRECTORY. see HOSPITALS

360 UK
NATIONAL INSTITUTE FOR SOCIAL WORK. INTERNATIONAL CENTRE PAPER. 1993. irreg., no.3, 1994. £5. National Institute for Social Work, 5 Tavistock Pl., London WC1H 9SN, England. TEL 0171-387-9681. **Document type:** monographic series.

360 UK ISSN 0959-0781
NATIONAL INSTITUTE FOR SOCIAL WORK INFORMATION SERVICE. BRIEFING PAPERS. 1988. irreg., no.7, 1994. £5.95. National Institute for Social Work, 5 Tavistock Pl., London WC1H 9SN, England. TEL 0171-387-9681. **Document type:** monographic series.

361 US
NATIONAL LEAGUE OF FAMILIES OF AMERICAN PRISONERS AND MISSING IN ACTION IN SOUTHEAST ASIA NEWSLETTER. 1974. bi-m. $10. National League of Families of American Prisoners and Missing in Action in Southeast Asia, 1001 Connecticut Ave. N.W., Ste. 219, Washington, DC 20036-5504. TEL 202-223-6846. FAX 202-785-9410. Dir. Ann Mills Griffiths. circ. 15,000. **Document type:** newsletter.
Description: Purpose is the return of all prisoners, the fullest possible accounting for the missing and the repatriation of remains of those who died while serving in Southeast Asia.

NATIONAL LIBRARY FOR THE HANDICAPPED CHILD. NEWSLETTER. see EDUCATION — Special Education And Rehabilitation

360 US
NATIONAL ORGANIZATION FOR VICTIM ASSISTANCE NEWSLETTER. 1977. a. $30 individual membership; institutions $100. National Organization for Victim Assistance, 1757 Park Rd., N.W., Washington, DC 20010. TEL 202-232-6682. FAX 202-462-2255. Ed. John H. Stein. circ. 3,500. (looseleaf format; back issues avail.) **Document type:** newsletter.
Description: Covers victim rights and services in the U.S. and abroad.

360 US ISSN 0164-7415
HQ767.15
NATIONAL RIGHT TO LIFE NEWS. 1973. s-m. $16 (foreign $28). National Right to Life Committee, Inc., 419 Seventh St., N.W., Ste.500, Washington, DC 20004. TEL 202-626-8824. FAX 202-737-9189. Ed. Dave Andrusko. adv. contact: Dave Andrusko. bk.rev.; film rev.; play rev.; charts; illus.; pat.; stat.; index. circ. 225,000. (tabloid format; back issues avail.) **Document type:** newspaper.
Description: Covers issues of abortion, infanticide, and euthanasia from medical, ethical, social and public policy perspectives.

362.7 UK ISSN 0077-5754
NATIONAL SOCIETY FOR PREVENTION OF CRUELTY TO CHILDREN. ANNUAL REPORT. 1885. a. National Society for the Prevention of Cruelty to Children, 67 Saffron Hill, London EC1N 8RS, England. TEL 071-242-1626. FAX 071-831-9562. circ. 90,000. **Document type:** corporate report.

NEBELHORN; Regionalmagazin fuer Politik und Kultur. see BUSINESS AND ECONOMICS — Labor And Industrial Relations

360 US
NEBRASKA. DEPARTMENT OF SOCIAL SERVICES. ANNUAL REPORT. no.38, 1974. a. Department of Social Services, Research and Finance Division, Box 95026, 301 Centennial Mall So., Lincoln, NE 68509. FAX 402-471-9455. Ed. Marvin E. Kanne. charts; stat.; circ. 500 (controlled). (also avail. in microfiche from CIS) **Indexed:** SRI. **Document type:** government publication.
Formerly: Nebraska. Department of Public Welfare. Annual Report.

361.8 US
NEIGHBORLINE. 1974. q. $15. University of Dayton, Dayton, OH 45469. TEL 513-229-4639. bk.rev.; circ. 900 (controlled).
Formerly: R & D for Justice Sake.
Description: Examines community and neighborhood development, as well as housing.

360 UK ISSN 0265-783X
NETWORK WALES. 1982. 11/yr. membership. Wales Council for Voluntary Action - Cyngor Gweithredu Gwirfoddol Cymru, Crescent Rd., Caerphilly, Mid Glamorgan CF8 1XL, Wales. TEL 01222-869224. FAX 01222-860627. Ed. Penny Taylor. bk.rev. circ. 900. **Document type:** newsletter.

360 GW
NETZ. 1979. q. DM.30($20) (Entwicklung und Gerechtigkeit e.V.) Netz, c/o Elisabeth Dissinger, Van Wingenastr. 5, 26736 Groothusen, Germany. (Subscr. to: Ringstr. 14, 35641 Laufdorf, Germany. TEL 06445-7779. FAX 06445-5165) Ed. Peter Dietzel. bk.rev. circ. 1,300. (back issues avail.) **Document type:** newsletter.

360 GW ISSN 0342-9857
HV275
NEUE PRAXIS; Zeitschrift fuer Sozialarbeit, Sozialpaedagogik und Sozialpolitik. 1970. bi-m. DM.114. Luchterhand Verlag, Heddesdorferstr. 31, 56564 Neuwied, Germany. TEL 02631-801-0. FAX 02631-801210. TELEX 867853-HLVN-D. Ed. Karin Boellert. adv. contact: Gabriele Pannwitz. **Indexed:** Abstr.Crim.& Pen., Excerp.Med. **Document type:** bulletin.
—CCC.

301 US
NEW AMERICAN FAMILY. 1978. q. $20. Stepfamily Foundation, Inc., 333 West End Ave., New York, NY 10023. TEL 212-877-3244. FAX 212-362-7030. Pub. Jeannette Lofas. adv. contact: Michael Weston. bk.rev. circ. 2,750. (looseleaf format; back issues avail.) **Document type:** newsletter.
Formerly: Stepnews - Stepfamily Foundation Newsletter.
Description: Provides educational information about structuring the household, as well as making other relationships.

NEW CHOICES FOR RETIREMENT LIVING. see GERONTOLOGY AND GERIATRICS

381 US
NEW DETROIT, INC. ANNUAL REPORT. (Not published for year 1991.) 1968. a. New Detroit, Inc., 2900 Penobscot Bldg., 645 Griswold St., Detroit, MI 48226-4206. TEL 313-496-2000. FAX 313-496-2071. Ed. John R. Huls. circ. 10,000. **Document type:** corporate report.
Former titles: New Detroit Annual Report; New Detroit Progress Report; New Detroit Incorporated.
Description: Covers projects of nation's oldest urban coalition.

NEW DIRECTIONS FOR PROGRAM EVALUATION. see EDUCATION

361.706 658 US ISSN 1072-172X
HV41.9
NEW DIRECTIONS IN PHILANTROPIC FUND RAISING. 1993. q. $59 to individuals; institutions $79. (Indiana University, Fund Raising School) Jossey-Bass Inc., Publishers, 350 Sansome St., 5th Fl., San Francisco, CA 94104. TEL 415-433-1767. FAX 415-433-0499. Ed. Robert E. Fogal. bk.rev. circ. 500. **Document type:** academic/scholarly publication.
Description: Aims to strengthen voluntary giving and build professionalism in fundraising by addressing how the concepts and traditions of philantrophy pertain to fundraising practice.

353.9 US ISSN 0090-077X
RJ506.M4
NEW JERSEY. DEVELOPMENTAL DISABILITIES COUNCIL. ANNUAL REPORT. 1971. a. free. New Jersey Developmental Disabilities Council, 20 W. State St., CN 700, Trenton, NJ 08625. TEL 609-292-3745. FAX 609-292-7114. Ed. Rachel Hickson. circ. 3,000. **Document type:** government publication.
Supersedes: New Jersey Mental Retardation Planning Board. Annual Report.

NEW MEXICO. VETERANS' SERVICE COMMISSION. REPORT. see MILITARY

NEW REVIEW. see SOCIOLOGY

NEW TECHNOLOGY IN THE HUMAN SERVICES. see SOCIOLOGY — Computer Applications

361 US
NEW YORK (STATE). ASSEMBLY. STANDING COMMITTEE ON CHILDREN AND FAMILIES. ANNUAL REPORT. a. State Assembly, Standing Committee on Children and Families, Legislative Office Bldg. Rm. 422, Albany, NY 12248. TEL 518-455-5474. FAX 518-455-5857. **Document type:** government publication, corporate report.
Description: Highlights the year's legislation concerning foster care and adoption, youth services, child care and other related human services areas.

NEW YORK (STATE). ASSEMBLY. STANDING COMMITTEE ON VETERANS' AFFAIRS. ANNUAL REPORT. see MILITARY

NEW YORK (STATE). COMMISSION ON QUALITY OF CARE FOR THE MENTALLY DISABLED. ANNUAL REPORT. see HOSPITALS

361 US ISSN 0363-9835
HV98.N7
NEW YORK (STATE). DEPARTMENT OF SOCIAL SERVICES. ANNUAL REPORT. 1974. a. free. Department of Social Services, 40 N. Pearl St., Albany, NY 12243. TEL 518-473-8207. FAX 518-474-7688. **Indexed:** SRI. **Document type:** government publication.
Formerly: New York (State). Board of Social Welfare. Annual Report (ISSN 0363-9843)

SOCIAL SERVICES AND WELFARE

NEW YORK (STATE). DEPARTMENT OF SOCIAL SERVICES. ANNUAL REPORT. STATISTICAL SUPPLEMENT. see SOCIAL SERVICES AND WELFARE — Abstracting, Bibliographies, Statistics

362.974   US   ISSN 0090-4716
HV86
NEW YORK (STATE). DEPARTMENT OF SOCIAL SERVICES. BUREAU OF DATA MANAGEMENT AND ANALYSIS. PROGRAM ANALYSIS REPORT. 1954. irreg., no.65, 1980. free. Department of Social Services, 40 N. Pearl St., Albany, NY 12243. **Document type:** government publication.
    Formerly: New York (State). Department of Social Services. Bureau of Research. Program Analysis Report.

362.974   US   ISSN 0162-6302
NEW YORK (STATE). DEPARTMENT OF SOCIAL SERVICES. BUREAU OF DATA MANAGEMENT AND ANALYSIS. PROGRAM BRIEF. 1961. irreg. free. Department of Social Services, 40 N. Pearl St., Albany, NY 12243. illus. **Document type:** government publication.
    Formerly: New York (State). Department of Social Services. Bureau of Research. Program Brief (ISSN 0361-6436)

362.4   US
NEW YORK (STATE). OFFICE OF ADVOCATE FOR PERSONS WITH DISABILITIES. ANNUAL REPORT. 1980. a. free. Office of Advocate for Persons with Disabilities, 1 Empire State Plaza, Ste. 1001, Albany, NY 12223. FAX 518-473-6005. Ed. Alan J. Sangiacomo. circ. 3,000. **Document type:** government publication.
    Formerly: New York (State). Office of Advocate for the Disabled. Annual Report.

051   US
NEW YORK HABITAT TIMES. 1984. irreg. (approx. 4/yr.). free. Habitat New York City, 7 W. 11th St., New York, NY 10011-8601. TEL 212-691-5080. FAX 212-691-4935. (Co-sponsor: Habitat for Humanity, Inc.) circ. 12,000.
    Description: Covers the work of the organizations to build affordable housing and support efforts to remove urban poverty.

361.8   US
NEW YORK URBAN LEAGUE. ANNUAL REPORT.* a. New York Urban League, Inc., 204 W 136th St., New York, NY 10030-2696. TEL 212-730-5200. **Document type:** corporate report.
    Formerly: Urban League of Greater New York. Annual Report.

362.7 355.133   NZ
NEW ZEALAND R S A REVIEW. 1921. bi-m. NZ.$13.50. New Zealand Returned Services Association, 181-183 Willis St., P.O. Box 27248, Wellington, New Zealand. TEL 04-384-7994. FAX 04-385-3325. Ed. J.E. Cummings. adv. contact: J.E. Mandahl. circ. 86,005 (controlled). **Document type:** newspaper.

361   CN   ISSN 0078-0294
NEWFOUNDLAND. DEPARTMENT OF SOCIAL SERVICES. ANNUAL REPORT. 1950. a. free. Department of Social Services, P.O. Box 8700, Confederation Bldg., W. Block, St. John's, Nfld. A1B 4J6, Canada. TEL 709-576-3607. FAX 709-576-6996. TELEX 016-4197. circ. 500.

NEWORLD; the multicultural magazine of the arts. see ART

360   AT   ISSN 1038-5509
NEWSBEAT AUSTRALIA. 1977. q. free. Sydney City Mission, 28 Regent St., Chippendale, N.S.W. 2008, Australia. TEL 02-212-6277. FAX 02-281-3854. Ed. Kenneth B. Harrison. circ. 30,000. (back issues avail.)
    Former titles (until 1991): Newsbeat (ISSN 1030-794X); (until 1988): Mission Beat (ISSN 0157-8057)
    Description: Examines poverty and programs to deal with it: welfare, youth work programs and employment training.

NEWSLETTER OF THE INTERNATIONAL STUDY OF ORGANIZED PERSECUTION OF CHILDREN. see CHILDREN AND YOUTH — About

360   NE   ISSN 0928-8090
NIEUWSBRIEF SOCIALE VERNIEUWING. 1991. bi-m. Samsom H.D. Tjeenk Willink B.V. (Subsidiary of: Wolters Kluwer N.V.), Postbus 316, 2400 AH Alphen aan den Rijn, Netherlands. TEL 31-1720-66822. FAX 31-1720-66639. **Document type:** newsletter.

361   JA   ISSN 0916-765X
NIHON SHAKAI JIGYO DAIGAKU KENKYU KIYO/JAPAN COLLEGE OF SOCIAL WORK. STUDY REPORT. 1953. a. Nihon Shakai Jigyo Daigaku, 3-1-30 Takeoka, Kiyose-shi, Tokyo 204, Japan. bk.rev.
    Formerly (until 1988): Shakai Jigyo no Shomondai - Issues in Social Work (ISSN 0546-1324)

NO. see WOMEN'S INTERESTS

NONPRIVATE FOUNDATIONS: A TAX GUIDE FOR CHARITABLE ORGANIZATIONS. see BUSINESS AND ECONOMICS — Public Finance, Taxation

361.73   US   ISSN 0899-7640
HV1   CODEN: NVSQEQ
NONPROFIT AND VOLUNTARY SECTOR QUARTERLY. 1971. q. $56 to individuals; institutions $86. (Association of Voluntary Action Scholars) Jossey-Bass Inc., Publishers, 350 Sansome St., 5th Fl., San Francisco, CA 94104. TEL 415-433-1767. FAX 415-433-0499. Ed. Peter R. Maida. bk.rev. circ. 800. (back issues avail.; reprint service avail. from UMI) **Indexed:** Int.Polit.Sci.Abstr. **Document type:** academic/scholarly publication.
    —BLDSC (6117.340100); Faxon; UMI.
    Description: Explores the unique dynamics, needs, and concerns of today's nonprofit and voluntary organizations.
    Refereed Serial

361.73   US
HD62.6
NONPROFIT WORLD. 1983. bi-m. $79. Society for Nonprofit Organizations, 6314 Odana Rd., Ste. One, Madison, WI 53719. TEL 608-274-9777. FAX 608-274-9978. Ed. Jill Muehrcke. adv. contact: Jeff Ferguson. bk.rev. circ. 15,000. (back issues avail.) **Indexed:** ABI Inform., PSI. **Document type:** academic/scholarly publication.
    •Also available online. Vendor(s): University Microfilms International.
    —BLDSC (6117.340200); UMI; UnCover.
    Formerly: Nonprofit World Report (ISSN 8755-7614)
    Description: Focuses on all aspects of running an effective nonprofit organization, including fundraising, income generation, and legal advice.

NORCAL CENTER ON DEAFNESS NEWSLINE. see HANDICAPPED — Hearing Impaired

360   NO   ISSN 0333-1342
HV333
NORDISK SOSIALT ARBEID; tidsskrift for sosialarbeidere i Norden. (Text in Danish, Norwegian, Swedish; summaries in English, Finnish) 1981. q. NOK 480 in Nordic countries; elsewhere $87 (effective 1996). Scandinavian University Press, P.O.Box 2959 Toeyen, N-0608 Oslo, Norway. TEL 47-22-57-54-00. FAX 47-22-57-53-53. (U.S. addr.: Scandinavian University Press, 200 Meacham Ave., Elmont, NY 11003. TEL 516-352-7300) Ed. Anna Meeuwisse. circ. 2,000. **Document type:** trade publication.
    Description: Covers research, theoretical and practical questions, and debate in relation to social work

360   UK
NORTHERN CARING HOMES. m. Wharncliffe House, Church St., Barnsley, S. Yorks S70 2AS, England. TEL 0226-734239. FAX 0226-734444. Ed. K. Dixon. circ. 5,500.
    Description: Addresses industry information for rest homes, nursing homes and hospices in the region.

360 374   UK
NORTHERN DEVELOPMENT CURRICULUM PROJECT. 1991. irreg., no.7, 1993. price varies. Central Council for Education and Training in Social Work, Derbyshire House, St. Chad's St., London WC1H 8HD, England. TEL 071-278-2455. FAX 071-278-2934. (back issues avail.) **Document type:** monographic series, trade publication.
    Description: Discusses issues in social work that can be incorporated into training curricula.

NORWEGIAN REFUGEE COUNCIL. REPORTS. see POLITICAL SCIENCE — International Relations

360   SZ
NOUS, SAMARITAINS. (Text in French) 23/yr. 25 SFr. 195, route de St. Maurice, CH-1814 La Tour-de-Peilz, Switzerland. TEL 021-9443562. FAX 021-9442806. Ed. Willy Bietry. circ. 7,000. **Document type:** newsletter.

360 301   CN   ISSN 0762-0810
NOUVELLES PRATIQUES SOCIALES. 1989. s-a. Can.$20 (effective 1991). Presses de l'Universite du Quebec, C.P. 250, Sillery, PQ G1T 2R1, Canada. TEL 418-657-3551. FAX 418-657-2096. (back issues avail.) **Indexed:** Pt.de Rep. (1991-).

361.6   CN   ISSN 0844-7535
NOVA SCOTIA DEPARTMENT OF COMMUNITY SERVICES (YEAR). 1964. a. Can.$12. Department of Community Services, P.O. Box 696, Halifax, NS B3J 2T7, Canada. TEL 902-424-4455. FAX 902-424-0502. illus.; stat. circ. 1,000. **Document type:** government publication.
    Former titles (until 1988): Social Services for Nova Scotians (ISSN 0833-3491); (until 1982): Social Services in Nova Scotia (ISSN 0317-4336); (until 1973): Welfare Services in Nova Scotia (ISSN 0550-8665); Which incorporates (in 1975): Nova Scotia. Department of Social Services. Annual Report (ISSN 0383-4808); Which was formerly (until 1974): Nova Scotia. Department of Public Welfare. Annual Report (ISSN 0550-1776)

O A S D I BENEFICIARIES BY STATE AND COUNTY. (Old Age, Survivors, Disability Insurance) see INSURANCE

300   FR   ISSN 0154-8530
OBJECTIF ET ACTION MUTUALISTES. 1972. bi-m. 45 F. Cooperative d'Information et d'Edition Mutualiste (C.I.E.M.), 67 rue Blomet, 75015 Paris, France. TEL 40-43-30-10. FAX 40-43-30-06. Ed. Philippe Marchal. adv.; film rev.; illus.

OBSERVER (NASHVILLE). see ETHNIC INTERESTS

OCCUPATIONAL PENSIONS. see INSURANCE

OCCUPATIONAL THERAPY IN MENTAL HEALTH; a journal of psychosocial practice and research. see MEDICAL SCIENCES — Psychiatry And Neurology

360   CN   ISSN 1195-9975
ODDYSEY: THE NATIONAL MENTOR PROGRAM NEWSLETTER. 1993. 4/yr. free. Peer Resources, 1052 Davie St., Victoria, BC V8S 4E3, Canada. TEL 604-595-3503. FAX 604-595-3504. E-mail: rcarr@islandnet.com. Ed. Rey A. Carr. circ. 1,500. **Document type:** newsletter.
    Description: Reports on research, program ideas, practical tips and suggestions on the use of mentors in business, industry, and education.

614   AU   ISSN 0029-9901
OESTERREICHISCHES JUGENDROTKREUZ. ARBEITSBLAETTER. 1947. q. free. Oesterreichisches Jugendrotkreuz, Wiedner Hauptstr. 32, A-1041 Vienna 4, Austria. FAX 0222-58900179. adv.; bk.rev.; illus.; index; circ. 10,000 (controlled). **Document type:** newsletter.
    Description: News and information of the Austrian Youth Red Cross.

OEVERGREPP. see LAW

362.6 612.67   IT
OGGI DOMANI ANZIANI. 1988. q. L.40000 (foreign L.60000) (effective 1993). (Federazione Nazionale Pensionati Cisl) Franco Angeli Editore, Viale Monza, 106, Casella Postale 17175, 20100 Milan, Italy. TEL 02-2895762. circ. 1,500,000.

360 350   US
OHIO UNITED WAY. ADMINISTRATIVE REPORT. 1976. 24/yr. $44 to non-members; members $22. Ohio United Way, 16 E. Broad St., 8th Fl., Columbus, OH 43215. TEL 614-224-8146. FAX 614-224-6597. Ed. Linda Danter. s-a. index. circ. 500. (looseleaf format; back issues avail.) **Document type:** newsletter.

SOCIAL SERVICES AND WELFARE 5993

360 US ISSN 0277-8289
HV86
OKLAHOMA. DEPARTMENT OF HUMAN SERVICES. ANNUAL REPORT. 1936. a. free (includes Statistical Report). Department of Human Services, Research, Evaluation and Statistics Unit, Box 25352, Oklahoma City, OK 73125. TEL 405-521-3551. FAX 405-521-6684. charts; stat. (also avail. in microfiche from CIS) **Indexed:** SRI. **Document type:** government publication.
 Formerly (until 1979): Oklahoma. Department of Institutions, Social and Rehabilitative Services. Annual Report (ISSN 0078-4362)

OLD AGE: A REGISTER OF SOCIAL RESEARCH. see GERONTOLOGY AND GERIATRICS

301.435 362.6 US ISSN 0146-3640
OLDER AMERICANS REPORT. 1976. w. $320 (effective Sep. 1992). Business Publishers, Inc., 951 Pershing Dr., Silver Spring, MD 20910-4464. TEL 301-587-6300. FAX 301-585-9075. Ed. Nancy Aldrich. (looseleaf format; back issues avail.) **Document type:** newsletter.
 ●Also available online. Vendor(s): NewsNet.
 —CCC.
 Incorporates: Aging Service News (ISSN 0197-4025)
 Description: News for directors of senior citizens programs; includes funding, nutrition and social security news.

362 610.7 649 SW ISSN 0280-4123
OMVAARDAREN. 1953. 5/yr. SEK 150. Laerarfoerbundet, P.O. Box 12239, S-102 26 Stockholm, Sweden. TEL 46-8-737-65-00. FAX 46-8-657-97-48. Ed. Britta Morberger. adv.: B&W page SEK 4400, color page SEK 6600; trim 182 x 266. circ. 4,500. cols./p.: 3; pp./issue: 24.
 Former titles (until 1974): Svensk Sjuksoeterskefoerening - Pedagogiska Sektionens Medlemsblad; (until 9182): Tidskrift foer Sjuksvaardspedagoger.

361.763 338.025 UK ISSN 1356-6385
▼**THE ONE MILLION PLUS CHARITIES DIRECTORY.** 1995. biennial. Rowland Lybrand of London, 28 Wheatley Ct., Mixenden, Halifax, W. Yorks HX2 8QL, England. TEL 01422-241197. **Document type:** directory.

362 CN
ONTARIO. MINISTRY OF COMMUNITY AND SOCIAL SERVICES. SOCIAL ASSISTANCE REVIEW BOARD. ANNUAL REPORT OF THE BOARD. (Report year ends Mar. 31.) a. Ministry of Community and Social Services, Social Assistance Review Board, Toronto, Ont. M7A 1E9, Canada. TEL 416-326-5104. FAX 416-326-5135. (Subscr. to: Social Assistance Review Board, 1075 Bay St., 7th Fl., Toronto, Ont. M5S 2B1, Canada)
 Formerly: Ontario. Ministry of Community and Social Services. Social Assistance Review Board. Annual Report of the Chairman.

362.7 CN ISSN 0030-283X
ONTARIO ASSOCIATION OF CHILDREN'S AID SOCIETIES. JOURNAL. 1952. 4/yr. Can.$26.50. Ontario Association of Children's Aid Societies, 75 Front Street E., Ste. 203, Toronto, ON M5E 1V9, Canada. TEL 416-366-8115. FAX 416-366-8137. Ed. Diane Cresswell. adv. contact: Siobhan Devine. bk.rev. circ. 8,000. (back issues avail.)
 Description: Tackles child welfare issues.

OPEN ADOPTION BIRTHPARENT. see CHILDREN AND YOUTH — About

OPEN HOUSE. see CHILDREN AND YOUTH — About

OPEN MIND; the mental health magazine. see MEDICAL SCIENCES — Psychiatry And Neurology

307 320 US ISSN 1063-9403
ORGANIZING. 1989. q. $25 to individuals; institutions $40. (Regional Council of Neighborhood Organizations) St. Joseph's University Press, 5600 City Ave., Philadelphia, PA 19131. TEL 215-878-4253. FAX 215-879-3148. Ed. John Vanover. adv.; bk.rev.; circ. 1,000 (paid). **Indexed:** Alt.Press Ind. **Document type:** academic/scholarly publication.
 Description: For and about community organizing. Refereed Serial

362.7 FR ISSN 1148-621X
ORPHELINAT. m. 5 F. Orphelinat Mutualiste de la Police Nationale, 19 rue du Renard, 75004 Paris, France. Ed. Paul Bareaud. adv. circ. 66,235.

360 IS
OSIM INYAN. 1989. bi-m. (General Labor Federation of Israel) Union of Social Workers - Israel, P.O. Box 303, Tel Aviv, Israel. TEL 03-431644. Ed. Neomi Sagee.

OUR REVIEW/MABAT SHELANV. see HANDICAPPED — Hearing Impaired

360 614 US
OVERVIEW (OLYMPIA). 1973. m. free. Department of Social and Health Services, MS. OB-44Q, Olympia, WA 98504. TEL 206-753-7039. Ed. Mary Vaughn. illus.

P B O BLAD. (Publiek Rechtelijke Organisaties) see PUBLIC ADMINISTRATION

P C C SOUND CONSUMER. (Puget Consumers Co-op) see NUTRITION AND DIETETICS

360 SW ISSN 0345-9225
P R O PENSIONAEREN. Variant title: Pensionaeren. (Text in Finnish, Swedish) 1942. 10/yr. SEK 90. Pensionaerarnas Riksorganisation (PRO), P.O. Box 3274, 103 65 Stockholm, Sweden. TEL 08-701-6700. FAX 08-203-358. Ed. Monica Swaerd. adv.; bk.rev. circ. 292,500. (also avail. in audio cassette)
 Formerly (until 1972): Folkpensionaeren.

360 UK ISSN 1350-4703
P S S R U BULLETIN. irreg. free. Personal Social Services Research Unit, Cornwallis Bldg., The University, Canterbury, Kent CT2 7NF, England. TEL 0227-764000. FAX 0227-764327. **Document type:** bulletin.
 —BLDSC (6945.964000).

P T A COMMUNICATOR. see CHILDREN AND YOUTH — About

P W A COALITION NEWSLINE. (People with AIDS) see MEDICAL SCIENCES — Communicable Diseases

P W ALIVE. see MEDICAL SCIENCES — Communicable Diseases

PAA FLUKT - NYHETER. see POLITICAL SCIENCE — International Relations

PAA FLUKT - TEMA. see POLITICAL SCIENCE — International Relations

362.7 US ISSN 0737-5131
PAEDOVITA;* an international journal of child-life. (Text in English, French, German, and Spanish) 1984. q. Eterna International, Inc., Box 6558, Flushing, NY 11365-6558. Ed. Stephen B. Parrish. adv.; bk.rev.; abstr.; illus.; pat.; index. **Indexed:** Int.Nurs.Ind., Psychol.Abstr.

362.8 325 UN ISSN 0031-0336
HV640.5.A6
PALESTINE REFUGEES TODAY. French edition: Refugies de Palestine Aujourd'hui (ISSN 0250-894X); Arabic edition (ISSN 0250-8931) 1960. s.a. free. United Nations Relief and Works Agency, Vienna International Centre, P.O. Box 700, A-1400 Vienna, Austria. TEL 01-213454530. FAX 01-213455877. TELEX 135310 UNRA A. Ed. Lynn Failing. bk.rev.; charts; illus.; stat. circ. 12,500. (tabloid format) **Indexed:** Refug.Abstr. **Document type:** bulletin.
 —BLDSC (6345.325500).

PALLIATIVE CARE TODAY; the journal for today's palliative care team. see MEDICAL SCIENCES — Oncology

362.7 346.01 UK ISSN 0961-222X
PANEL NEWS; a quarterly journal for guardians ad litem, reporting officers and other child care law professionals. 1988. q. Independent Representation for Children in Need (IRCHIN), 23A Hawthorne Dr., Heswall, Wirral, Merseyside L61 6UP, England. TEL 051-342-7852. Ed. Guy Mitchell.

362.7 II ISSN 0031-2096
PARIYAL KALYAN. (Text in Assamese) 1965. m. free. Assam State Social Welfare Advisory Board, Uzanbazar, Gauhati 1, Assam, India. Ed. Sri R. K. Gautam. circ. 500.
 Formerly: Bala-Sevika.
 Description: Covers child welfare.

PATEN; Mitteilung der Vereinigung der Pflege- und Adoptiveltern im Lande Nordrhein-Westfalen. see SOCIOLOGY

PATIENTENPOST. see CHILDREN AND YOUTH — For

PAX CONNECTION. see BUSINESS AND ECONOMICS — Investments

PEACE NEWSLETTER; central New York's voice for peace and social justice. see POLITICAL SCIENCE

362.7 US ISSN 0195-5926
PEDIATRIC SOCIAL WORK;* an international journal. 1980. q. Eterna International, Inc., Box 6558, Flushing, NY 11365-6558. Ed. Allen F. Johnson. adv. circ. 5,000. **Indexed:** Psychol.Abstr.

360 301.1 CN ISSN 1194-8167
PEER COUNSELLOR JOURNAL. 1983. s-a. free. Peer Resources, 1052 Davie St., Victoria, BC V8S 4E3, Canada. TEL 604-595-3503. FAX 604-595-3504. E-mail: rcarr@islandnet.com. Ed. Rey A. Carr. bk.rev. circ. 5,000. (back issues avail.) **Document type:** academic/scholarly publication.
 Formerly: Peer Counsellor Newsletter (ISSN 1180-470X)
 Description: Studies peer helping in education, business and community agencies at all levels from children to senior citizens. Provides news, program ideas and resources.

PENSION AND BENEFITS UPDATE. see BUSINESS AND ECONOMICS — Public Finance, Taxation

PENSION FUNDS & THEIR ADVISERS. see INSURANCE

PENSION MANAGEMENT. see BUSINESS AND ECONOMICS — Banking And Finance

368.43 UK ISSN 0048-3281
PENSIONERS VOICE. 1940. m. £6. National Federation of Retirement Pensions Associations, Melling House, 14 St. Peter St., Blackburn, Lancs. BB2 2HD, England. TEL 01254-52606. Ed. Robert Stansfield. adv. circ. 7,000. **Document type:** newsletter.

360 640.73 AT ISSN 1035-3615
PENSIONERS VOICE. 1956. 11/yr. Aus.$9($34) Combined Pensioners and Superannuants Association of N.S.W. Inc., Level 5, 405 Sussex St., Haumarket, N.S.W. 2000, Australia. TEL 02-281-1811. FAX 02-281-5958. Ed. Eric Cameran. adv.; bk.rev.; film rev.; play rev.; stat. circ. 20,000. (tabloid format)
 Description: Covers social services and welfare, consumer education and protection and taxation information, social security entitlements.

PENSIONS WORLD. see INSURANCE

362.734 US ISSN 1047-6598
PEOPLE SEARCHING NEWS. 1986. q. $18 (Canada $27; elsewhere $32). Adoption Education Resources, Box 100444, Palm Bay, FL 32910-0444. TEL 305-370-7100. FAX 305-370-7100. Ed. Lynn-Claire Davis. adv. contact: Joyce Barstow. bk.rev. circ. 25,000. (reprint service avail.)

PEOPLENET. see EDUCATION — Special Education And Rehabilitation

PEOPLE'S MEDICAL SOCIETY NEWSLETTER. see CONSUMER EDUCATION AND PROTECTION

SOCIAL SERVICES AND WELFARE

360   CN   ISSN 0704-5263
HV1
PERCEPTION. 1977. 4/yr. Can.$20($23) Canadian Council on Social Development, 55 Parkdale Ave., P.O. Box 3505, Sta. C, Ottawa, ON K1Y 4G1, Canada. TEL 613-728-1865. FAX 613-728-9387. adv.; bk.rev.; illus. circ. 4,500. (also avail. in microform from MIM,UMI; reprint service avail. from UMI) **Indexed:** Abstr.Soc.Work., Can.B.P.I., Can.Per.Ind., CMI, P.A.I.S, Sp.Ed.Needs Abstr., SSCI, World Bibl.Soc.Sec. **Document type:** newsletter.
—BLDSC (6423.160000); UMI.
    Formerly: Canadian Welfare (ISSN 0008-5332)
    Description: Journal of social comment.

360   MY   ISSN 0552-6426
PERSATUAN PURE LIFE. ANNUAL REPORT. (Text in English) 1953. a. membership. Pure Life Society, Batu 6, Jalan Puchong, Jalan Kelang Lama P.O., 58200 Kuala Lumpur, Malaysia. TEL 03-792-9391. FAX 03-792-8303. Ed.Bd. circ. 2,000. **Document type:** corporate report.
    Description: Aims to establish spiritual and educational institutions, orphanages, workshops and dispensaries.

PERSIAN GULF REVIEW; information for veterans who served in Desert Storm. see *MILITARY*

361   US   ISSN 1059-6097
PERSPECTIVE (CLEVELAND). 1975. irreg. free. Cleveland Foundation, 1422 Euclid Ave., Ste. 1400, Cleveland, OH 44115. TEL 216-861-3810. Ed. Lynne E. Woodman. charts; illus. circ. 5,000.
    Former titles: Cleveland Foundation Perspective; Cleveland Foundation Quarterly.

360   US   ISSN 0480-2853
PHILANTHROPIC DIGEST. 1955. m. $79.50. Philanthropic Digest, Inc., Box 380252, Cambridge, MA 02238-0252. TEL 617-661-8146. Eds. Richard Seager, Ann Castle. circ. 600 (paid). **Document type:** newsletter.
    Description: Discusses gifts and grants from corporations, foundations and individuals to non-profit organizations, and reports recent news and publications of interest.

361   US   ISSN 1065-1659
PHILANTHROPIC TRENDS DIGEST. 1983. bi-m. $48. Douglas M. Lawson Associates, Inc., 545 Madison Ave., New York, NY 10022. TEL 212-759-5660. FAX 212-759-1893. Ed. Douglass E. Ray. bk.rev. circ. 4,000. **Document type:** newsletter.
    Description: News of issues, events, legislation and trends in philanthropy of interest to non-profit organizations.

PHILIPPINE STUDIES; quarterly publication of Philippine thought and culture. see *HUMANITIES: COMPREHENSIVE WORKS*

361.73 362.5
338.91   NE   ISSN 0167-6172
PLAN AND ACTION. (Text in English, French and Spanish) s-a. free. Stichting Mensen in Nood - Caritas Neerlandica, Postbus 1041, 5200 BA Hertogenbosch, Netherlands. TEL 31-73-144544. FAX 31-73-132115. TELEX 50090 CARIT NL. Ed. W. Hooglugt. circ. 2,000 (controlled).
    Description: News about the possibilities of co-sponsoring development projects in third world countries by Stichting Mensen in Nood - Caritas Neerlandica.

PLANETE JEUNES. see *CHILDREN AND YOUTH — For*

361.73 332.04   US   ISSN 0891-4443
PLANNED GIFTS COUNSELOR. m. $150. Taft Group, 12300 Twinbrook Pkwy., Ste. 520, Rockville, MD 20852. TEL 301-816-0210. FAX 301-813-0811. (Subscr. to: Taft Group, Box 33477, Detroit, MI 48232-5477. TEL 800-877-TAFT. FAX 313-961-6083) Ed. Alden Tueller. bk.rev. **Document type:** newsletter.
    Description: Advises managers of nonprofit organizations on how to operate and market a planned-giving program.

361.8   US
PLANNING AND ACTION NEWSLETTER. 1948. 4/yr. free. Federation for Community Planning, 614 W. Superior Ave., Ste. 300, Cleveland, OH 44113-1306. TEL 216-781-2944. FAX 216-781-2988. illus. circ. 4,000. **Document type:** newsletter.
    Former titles: Federation Forum (ISSN 0300-6999); Welfare Talks.
    Description: Covers the organization's current activities.

PLAY AND PARENTING CONNECTIONS. see *CHILDREN AND YOUTH — About*

POLICY ANALYSIS RESEARCH UNIT. DISCUSSION PAPER. see *PUBLIC ADMINISTRATION*

360   US
POLICY STUDIES IN EMPLOYMENT AND WELFARE. 1969. irreg., no.39, 1983. price varies. Johns Hopkins University Press, 701 W. 40th St., Ste. 275, Baltimore, MD 21211. TEL 410-516-6900. FAX 410-516-6998. (reprint service avail. from UMI)

360   BE
LES POLITIQUES SOCIALES. (Text in French; summaries in English, Spanish) 1935. 2/yr. 800 BEF (foreign 950 BEF) (effective 1995). Service Social dans le Monde, Rue du Gouvernement 50, 7000 Mons, Belgium. TEL 32-65-335686. FAX 32-65-351177. Ed. Marie-Anne Beauduin. adv. contact: F. Goffinet. bk.rev.; abstr.; cum.index (5/yr.). circ. 1,250. **Indexed:** Cath.Ind. **Document type:** academic/scholarly publication.
    Formerly: Service Social dans le Monde (ISSN 0037-2641)

POPOLO. see *RELIGIONS AND THEOLOGY*

PORTLAND JEWISH REVIEW. see *ETHNIC INTERESTS*

362.7   UK   ISSN 0032-5856
HC260.P63
POVERTY. 1966. 3/yr. £12 membership. C P A G Ltd. (Child Poverty Action Group), 1-5 Bath St., London EC1V 9PY, England. Ed. Julia Lewis. adv.; bk.rev. circ. 7,000. **Indexed:** ASSIA, World Bibl.Soc.Sec.
—BLDSC (6571.450000).

362.7   UK
POVERTY PUBLICATIONS SERIES. 3/yr. £18. C P A G Ltd. (Child Poverty Action Group), 1-5 Bath St., London EC1V 9PY, England.
    Formerly: Poverty Pamphlets.

360   UK   ISSN 0950-3153
PRACTICE (BIRMINGHAM). 1987. q. £29.50 to non-member individuals (outside Europe £35 ($75)); institutions £45 (outside Europe £52 ($104)); members £20 (outside Europe £30 ($67)). British Association of Social Workers, 16 Kent St., Birmingham B5 6RD, England. Ed. Laura Middleton. adv.; bk.rev.; index. circ. 2,000. (back issues avail.) **Indexed:** ASSIA, Soc.Work Res.& Abstr., Sociol.Abstr. **Document type:** academic/scholarly publication.
—BLDSC (6597.117000). CCC.
    Description: Covers issues in analytical and clinical social work practice.

360   GW
DIE PRAXIS; sozialpolitische Vierteljahresschrift. 1948. q. DM.10. Reichsbund der Kriegs- und Wehrdienstopfer, Behinderten, Sozialrentner und Hinterbliebenen e.V. - German Association of Victims of War and Military Service, Handicapped, Social Insurance, Pensioners and Dependents, Beethovenallee 56-58, 53173 Bonn, Germany. TEL 0228-363071. FAX 0228-361550. Ed. Wolfgang Falk. circ. 8,000. (also avail. in microform from PMC) **Document type:** bulletin.

361.77   FR   ISSN 0301-0260
PRESENCE CROIX-ROUGE. 1865. 6/yr. 30 F.($5) Croix-Rouge Francaise, 17 rue Quentin Bauchart, 75384 Paris Cedex 08, France. Ed. J. Boulet. adv.; bk.rev.; charts; illus.; stat.; index. circ. 30,000. (also avail. in microform; micropaque)
    Formerly: Vie et Bonte (ISSN 0042-5486)

360 001.3   CN   ISSN 0317-0179
AS42
PRESENTATIONS. (Text in French) 1943. a. Can.$10. Royal Society of Canada - Societe Royale du Canada, P.O. Box 9734, Ottawa, ON K1G 5J4, Canada. TEL 613-991-6990. FAX 613-991-6996. E-mail: admin@resudox.net. Ed. Gerard Hebert. **Document type:** academic/scholarly publication.

362 355.115   IT
PRESENZA: IL BOLLETTINO. 1918. m. membership. Associazione fra Mutilati e Invalidi di Guerra, Piazza Adriana 3, 00193 Rome, Italy. TEL 06-6875352. FAX 06-6877165. Ed. Gerardo Agostini.
    Formerly: Associazione fra Mutilati e Invalidi di Guerra. Bollettino.

360   UK   ISSN 0264-5033
PRIMARY HEALTH CARE. 10/yr. £30 (overseas £60). R C N Publishing Co., Viking House, 17-19 Peterborough Rd., Harrow-on-the-Hill, Middlesex HA1 2AX, England. TEL 0181-423-1066. FAX 0181-423-3867. (Subscr. to: Nursing Standard, Glynteg House, Station Terrace, Ely, Cardiff CF5 4XG, Wales. TEL 01222-553411. FAX 01222-576208) Ed. J. Sylvester. circ. 13,000. **Document type:** academic/scholarly publication.
—BLDSC (6612.908900).
    Description: Directed to members of staff in health centers, health clinics, and major group practices in the United Kingdom.

PRIME OF LIFE. see *SOCIOLOGY*

360   SZ   ISSN 1022-4424
PRO INFIRMIS. (Text in French, German, Italian) 1942. 6/yr. Postfach 129, CH-8032 Zurich, Switzerland. TEL 01-9285631. FAX 01-9285630. Ed. Tony Holenstein. circ. 3,000.

360   UK   ISSN 1352-3112
▼**PROFESSIONAL SOCIAL WORK.** 1994. m. £28. British Association of Social Workers, 16 Kent St., Birmingham B5 6RD, England. Ed. Simon Crompton. adv. contact: Mark Pearson. bk.rev.; circ. 10,000 (paid). **Document type:** trade publication.
—BLDSC (6864.220350).

360   IT   ISSN 1122-6307
PROFESSIONE SOCIALE; rivista di studio analisi e ricerca. 1991. s-a. L.35000 (foreign L.60000) (effective 1994). (Centro Studi di Servizio Sociale) Cooperativa Libraria Universitaria Editrice Bologna, Via Marsala 24, 40126 Bologna, Italy. TEL 39-51-220736. FAX 39-51-237758. Ed. Edda Samory. **Document type:** monographic series.

361 362.7   UN
THE PROGRESS OF NATIONS; the nations of the world ranked according to their achievements in health, nutrition, education, family planning, and progress for women. (Editions in English, French, Spanish) 1993. a. United Nations Children's Fund (UNICEF), UNICEF House, 3 United Nations Plaza, New York, NY 10017. TEL 212-326-7000. FAX 212-888-7465. TELEX 7607848. Ed. Peter Adamson. charts; stat.; circ. 71,500 (controlled).
    Description: Monitors the social and economic conditions of nations and how they affect the well-being of children living there.

362.7 364   US   ISSN 0893-4231
PROTECTING CHILDREN. 1984. q. $35 in US & Canada to libraries and resource centers (foreign $39). American Humane Association, Children's Division, 63 Inverness Dr. E., Englewood, CO 80112-5117. TEL 303-792-9900. FAX 303-792-5333. Ed. Robyn Alsop. adv.; bk.rev.; biennial index. circ. 1,500. **Indexed:** Adol.Ment.Hlth.Abstr. **Document type:** academic/scholarly publication.
—BLDSC (6935.762300).
    Formerly (until 1984): National Child Protective Services Newsletter.
    Description: Focuses on child abuse, child neglect; child protection and child welfare systems; research; training and education for child welfare professionals; advocacy and public information; and association membership information.

PSYCHIATRIC REHABILITATION JOURNAL. see *PSYCHOLOGY*

PSYCHOSOZIALE UMSCHAU. see *MEDICAL SCIENCES — Psychiatry And Neurology*

PUBLIC AUTHORITIES DIRECTORY. see *PUBLIC ADMINISTRATION — Municipal Government*

SOCIAL SERVICES AND WELFARE

361.6   AU
PUBLIC POLICY AND SOCIAL WELFARE. irreg., vol.17, 1994. price varies. European Centre for Social Welfare Policy and Research, Berggasse 17, A-1090 Vienna, Austria. TEL 01-3194505-0. FAX 01-319450519. (Subscr. to: Avebury Publishing Ltd., Gower House, Croft Rd., Aldershot, Hants. GU11 3HR, England; U.S. subscr. to: Ashgate Publishing Company, Old Post Rd., Brookfield, VT 05036) Ed. Bernd Marin. **Document type:** monographic series.

360   UK
PUBLIC SERVICES INFORMATION BULLETIN. 1977. m. N I Education Board Library Service, 1 Spillars Pl., Omagh, Co. Tyrone BT78 1HL, N. Ireland. TEL 0662-244821. FAX 0662-246716.

360   ISSN 0033-3816
HV1
PUBLIC WELFARE. 1943. q. $30 (foreign $40). American Public Welfare Association, c/o Publication Services, 810 First St., N.E., Ste. 500, Washington, DC 20002-4267. TEL 202-682-0100. FAX 202-289-6555. Ed. Steve Boehm. adv.; bk.rev.; abstr.; charts; illus.; index. circ. 4,000. (also avail. in microform from UMI; reprint service avail. from ISI, UMI) **Indexed:** Adol.Ment.Hlth.Abstr., Curr.Cont., Curr.Lit.Fam.Plan., Lang.& Lang.Behav.Abstr., Med. Care Rev., P.A.I.S., Soc.Sci.Ind., Soc.Work Res.& Abstr., SSCI.
● Also available online. Vendor(s): University Microfilms International.
—BLDSC (6969.750000); Faxon; Genuine Article; SWETS; UMI; UnCover. **CCC.**
   Description: Contains articles ranging from commentary by national leaders to practical features by administrators and direct service practitioners.

360   US   ISSN 0163-8297
HV89
PUBLIC WELFARE DIRECTORY. 1940. a. $75 to non-members; members $70; foreign $85. American Public Welfare Association, 810 First St., N.E., Ste. 500, Washington, DC 20002-4267. TEL 202-682-0100. FAX 202-289-6555. Ed. Amy Weinstein. circ. 5,500. **Document type:** directory.
   Description: Describes welfare programs and agencies in the US and Canada. Tells where to write and lists personnel contacts and phone numbers for records and administrative information, what programs are offered in each state and locality, and how federal and state programs are administered.

PUERTO RICO. DEPARTMENT OF HEALTH. BOLETIN ESTADISTICO. see *PUBLIC HEALTH AND SAFETY — Abstracting, Bibliographies, Statistics*

PUERTO RICO. DEPARTMENT OF HEALTH. INFORME DE RECURSOS HUMANOS DE LA SALUD. see *MEDICAL SCIENCES*

PUERTO RICO. DEPARTMENT OF HEALTH. INFORME ESTADISTICO DE FACILIDADES DE SALUD. see *HOSPITALS*

361.8   US
PUGET SOUND CO-OP FEDERATION NEWSLETTER. 4/yr. $15. Puget Sound Co-op Federation, 4201 Roosevelt Way, N.E., Seattle, WA 98105-6092. TEL 206-632-4559. FAX 206-545-7131. adv. contact: Audrey Malan. **Document type:** newsletter.
   Description: For and about the cooperative community in the Pacific Northwest.

360   US
Q C REVIEW. (Quality Control) q. membership. National Association of Human Service Quality Control Directors, c/o American Public Welfare Association, 810 First St. N.E., Ste. 500, Washington, DC 20002-4205. TEL 202-682-0100. FAX 202-289-6555.

RAAKPUNT. see *MEDICAL SCIENCES*

362.7   UK
RAPPORT. 1970. m. £15. Community and Youth Workers' Union, Unit 202A, The Argent Center, 60 Frederick St., Hockley, Birmingham B1 3HS, England. FAX 021-236-7842. Ed. Doug Nicholls. adv.; bk.rev. circ. 3,000.

360   IT   ISSN 0033-9601
RASSEGNA DI SERVIZIO SOCIALE. 1962. q. L.40000 (foreign L.45000). Ente Italiano di Servizio Sociale, Via Ferdinando Baldelli 41, 00146 Rome, Italy. Ed. Giuseppe Rizzo. adv.; bk.rev.; abstr.; charts; stat.; index. circ. 1,500.
—BLDSC (7294.740000).

360   GW
RAUTE; Magazin fuer Hilfesuchende und Helfer. 1973. q. DM.10. Bundesverband der Allgemeinen Rettungsverbaende Deutschlands e.V., Postfach 1166, 92601 Weiden, Germany. Ed.Bd. circ. 3,000.

360   FR   ISSN 0220-9926
REALITES FAMILIALES. 1946. 4/yr. 110 F. Union Nationale des Associations Familiales, 28 place St. Georges, 75009 Paris, France. adv.; bk.rev.; film rev.; illus.; index. circ. 10,000.
   Formerly: U N A F. Bulletin de Liaison (ISSN 0041-5219)

360   GW   ISSN 0944-5579
RECHTSDIENST DER LEBENSHILFE. 1993. q. Bundesvereinigung Lebenshilfe fuer geistig Behinderte e.V., Raiffeisenstr. 18, 35043 Marburg, Germany. TEL 06421-491-0. FAX 06421-491167. Ed. Klaus Lachwitz. circ. 9,000. **Document type:** bulletin.

360   US   ISSN 0360-4608
HV86
RECORD (NASHVILLE). 1938. s-a. free. Department of Human Services, 400 Deaderick St., Citizens Plaza, Nashville, TN 37219. FAX 615-741-3241. Ed. Patricia Harris-Moorehead. illus. circ. 9,800.
   Formerly (until 1975): Tennessee Public Welfare Record (ISSN 0040-3377)

361.77   NP   ISSN 0048-7023
RED CROSS QUARTERLY/REDA KRASA TRAIMASIKA.* (Text in English and Nepali) 1969. q. Nepal Red Cross Society, P.O. 217, Kathmandu, Nepal. adv.; illus.

360   SZ   ISSN 1019-9349
RED CROSS, RED CRESCENT. French edition: Croix-Rouge, Croissant-Rouge (ISSN 1019-9330); Spanish edition: Cruz Roja, Media Luna Roja (ISSN 1019-9357) (Text in English) 1985. 3/yr. free. International Federation of Red Cross and Red Crescent Societies, P.O. Box 372, CH-1211 Geneva 19, Switzerland. TEL 022-7304222. FAX 022-7530395. TELEX 412133. Eds. Barbara Geary, Christina Grisewood. bk.rev. circ. 60,000. **Document type:** bulletin.
   Refereed Serial

360 371.9   US   ISSN 1080-0220
▼**REFLECTIONS: NARATIVES OF PROFESSIONAL HELPING.** 1995. q. $35 to individuals (foreign $35); libraries $35 (foreign $48). University Press, California State University at Long Beach, Long Beach, CA 90840-9002. TEL 310-985-4626. FAX 310-985-5514. Ed. Sonia Lieb Abels. adv.; film rev.; index. (back issues avail.) **Document type:** academic/scholarly publication.
   Description: Publishes personal narratives by and for persons in the helping and academic professions - anyone engaged in bringing about social change.
   Refereed Serial

360 350   IT
REGIONE ABRUZZO. 1972. m. free. Servizio Informazione Stampa e Pubbliche Relazioni, Via Michele Jacobucci, 4, 67100 L'Aquila, Italy. circ. 8,500. (back issues avail.)

360   UK   ISSN 0954-3406
RELATE NEWS. q. Relate, Herbert Gray College, Rugby, Warks. CV21 3AP, England. TEL 01788-573241. FAX 01788-535007. Ed. Suzy Powling. bk.rev. circ. 6,000. **Document type:** newsletter.

362.5   CN   ISSN 0034-3781
BX802
RELATIONS. 1941. m. Can.$25 (foreign $27)(effective Jan. 1994). (Peres de la Compagnie de Jesus) Revue Relations, 25 Jarry Ouest, Montreal, PQ H2P 1S6, Canada. TEL 514-387-2541. FAX 514-387-0206. Ed. Carolyn Sharp. adv.; bk.rev.; bibl.; index. circ. 8,108. (also avail. in microform from UMI; reprint service avail. from UMI) **Indexed:** Can.B.P.I., Can.Per.Ind., Cath.Ind., CERDIC, Pt.de Rep. (1979-).
—UMI.
   Description: Concerned with social welfare and economic justice for the poor.

360   US
RELIGIOUS FUNDING RESOURCE GUIDE. 11th ed., 1994. a. $75 to individuals; institutions $90. ResourceWomen, 4527 S. Dakota Ave., N.E., Washington, DC 20017. TEL 202-832-8071. **Document type:** directory.
   Formerly: Church Funding Resource Guide.
   Description: Provides information about religious funders who support national and local organizations working for change in their communities.

RENEWAL MAGAZINE. see *ETHNIC INTERESTS*

362.4   US   ISSN 1043-1209
KF480.A15
REPORT ON DISABILITY PROGRAMS. 1978. bi-w. $273. Business Publishers, Inc., 951 Pershing Dr., Silver Spring, MD 20910-4464. TEL 301-587-6300. FAX 301-585-9075. Ed. Lisa Rabasca. (looseleaf format; back issues avail.) **Indexed:** Rehabil.Lit. **Document type:** newsletter.
● Also available online. Vendor(s): NewsNet.
—CCC.
   Former titles: Handicapped Americans Report (ISSN 0276-2889); (until 1985): Handicapped Rights and Regulations (ISSN 0191-6734)
   Description: Covers funding advice, new programs for managers of disabled programs; especially for occupational development of disabled.

REPORT ON EDUCATION OF THE DISADVANTAGED; the biweekly newsletter on Title I and other federal programs for disadvantaged children. see *EDUCATION — Special Education And Rehabilitation*

362.5 371.4 296.7   US   ISSN 1053-2676
THE REPORTER (NEW YORK, 1966). 1966. q. $5 to non-members; members $1. Women's America O R T, Inc., 315 Park Ave. S., New York, NY 10010. TEL 212-505-7700. FAX 212-674-3057. Ed. Dana B. Asher. adv.; bk.rev.; film rev.; play rev.; illus. circ. 100,000. (also avail. in microform from AJP.) **Document type:** trade publication.
   Formerly: Women's American O R T Reporter (ISSN 0043-7514)
   Description: National publication for Jewish-American women.

THE REPORTER (NEW YORK, 1972). see *ETHNIC INTERESTS*

REPORTS MAGAZINE. see *EDUCATION*

RESEARCH COMMUNICATIONS IN PSYCHOLOGY, PSYCHIATRY AND BEHAVIOR. see *PSYCHOLOGY*

360   UK   ISSN 0955-7970
RESEARCH HIGHLIGHTS IN SOCIAL WORK. 1981. irreg., vol.24, 1993. $45. Jessica Kingsley Publishers, 116 Pentonville Rd., London N1 9JB, England. TEL 0171-833-2307. FAX 0171-837-2917. (U.S. subscr. to: Taylor & Francis, 1900 Frost Rd., Ste. 101, Bristol, PA 19007-1598. TEL 800-821-8312. FAX 215-785-5515) Ed. Lorraine Waterhouse. **Document type:** monographic series.
—BLDSC (7741.304500).
   Formerly: Research Highlights.

RESEARCH ON SOCIAL WORK PRACTICE. see *SOCIOLOGY*

5996 SOCIAL SERVICES AND WELFARE

360   UK   ISSN 0264-519X
RESEARCH, POLICY AND PLANNING. 1977. s-a. £27 to non-members. Social Services Research Group, c/o Roger Lightup, Ed., Manchester SSD, P.O. Box 536, Manchester M60 2AF, England.
TEL 0161-234-3880. (Subscr. addr.: c/o Brian McClay, Bradford SSD, Olicana House, Chapel St., Bradford BD1 5RE, England) adv.; bk.rev. circ. 1,000. **Document type:** academic/scholarly publication.
—BLDSC (7755.076200).
   Supersedes (in 1983): Social Services Research Group. Journal (ISSN 0144-0640).
   Description: Concentrates on publishing research on social welfare services carried out by practitioners working in local and central government, other statutory authorities and voluntary agencies.

RESPONSE TO THE VICTIMIZATION OF WOMEN AND CHILDREN. see WOMEN'S INTERESTS

361.73   US   ISSN 1065-0008
RESPONSIVE PHILANTHROPY. 1979. q. $25 (effective 1994). National Committee for Responsive Philanthropy, 2001 S St., N.W., Ste. 620, Washington, DC 20009. TEL 202-387-9177. FAX 202-332-5084. Ed. Beth Baker. bk.rev. circ. 5,000. (back issues avail.) **Document type:** newsletter.
   Description: Covers changes and trends in philanthropy and fund raising, with emphasis on "social justice" and non-traditional non-profit organizations.

360   US
REUNIONS - THE MAGAZINE.* 1990. q. $24. Adoption Awareness Press, Box 1860, Cape Coral, FL 33910-1860. TEL 813-542-1342. FAX 813-549-9393. (Subscr to: Musser Foundation, Box 1860, Cape Coral, FL 33910) Ed. Mary Thiele Fobian.
   Description: Covers all types of reunion stories, as well as a classified section for locating missing persons.

360   SP   ISSN 0211-4364
HQ799.S7
REVISTA DE ESTUDIOS DE JUVENTUD. 1980. q. 1700 ptas. (foreign 2800 ptas.). Instituto de la Juventud, Jose Ortega y Gaset, 71, 28006 Madrid, Spain. TEL 347-76-90. FAX 402-21-94. Ed. Magdy Martinez Soliman. bk.rev.; cum.index: 1980-1986. circ. 3,000. (back issues avail.) **Indexed:** Psychol.Abstr.
   Formerly: De Juventud: Revista de Estudios e Investigaciones.

360   CL   ISSN 0716-2642
REVISTA TRABAJO SOCIAL. 1970. 3/yr. $20. Pontificia Universidad Catolica de Chile, Escuela de Trabajo Social, Vicuna Mackena 4860, Casilla 114-D, Santiago, Chile. Ed. Maria Ignacia Jimenez Suarez. bk.rev. circ. 700.
   Formerly: Trabajo Social.

REVISTA VENEZOLANA DE SANIDAD Y ASISTENCIA SOCIAL. see PUBLIC HEALTH AND SAFETY

362.6 363.6   BE   ISSN 0035-0834
REVUE BELGE DE SECURITE SOCIALE. Dutch edition: Belgisch Tijdschrift voor Sociale Zekerheid (ISSN 0775-0234) (Text in Flemish or French) 1959. 4/yr. 900 BEF (effective 1996). Ministere de la Prevoyance Sociale, Rue de la Vierge Noire 3C, 1000 Brussels, Belgium. **Indexed:** Int.Lab.Doc., P.A.I.S.For.Lang.Ind., World Bibl.Soc.Sec. **Document type:** government publication.
—BLDSC (7892.500000).

REVUE DU TRAVAIL. see BUSINESS AND ECONOMICS — Labor And Industrial Relations

360   FR   ISSN 0297-0376
BX1751.2
REVUE FRANCAISE DE SERVICE SOCIAL. 1945. q. 270 F. (foreign 300 F.) (effective 1996). Association Nationale des Assistants de Service Social, 15 rue de Bruxelles, 75009 Paris, France. TEL 45-26-33-79. FAX 42-80-07-03. Ed. Lucette Mallet. adv.; bk.rev.; illus.; circ. 2,700 (controlled).
   Formerly (until 1971): Feuillets de l'A N A S (ISSN 0004-5586).

REVUE INTERNATIONALE D'ACTION COMMUNAUTAIRE; international review of community development. see SOCIOLOGY

360   FR   ISSN 0980-7764
REVUE QUART MONDE. q. 160 F. (A.T.D. Fourthworld) Editions Quart Monde, 107 av. du General-Leclerc, 95480 Pierrelaye, France. Ed. Louis J. Lambert. illus.
   Former titles (until 1986): Igloos (ISSN 0766-3811); (until 1984): Quart Monde Igloos (ISSN 0290-6686); (until 1976): Igloos le 4e Monde (ISSN 0290-6678); (until 1969): Igloos (ISSN 0290-666X)

360   US
RIGHT-TO-KNOW PLANNING GUIDE (SERIES). 1987. m. $567 (effective July 1995). The Bureau of National Affairs, Inc., 1231 25th St., N.W., Washington, DC 20037. TEL 202-452-4200. FAX 202-822-8092. TELEX 285656 BNAI WSH. (Subscr. to: 9435 Key West Ave., Rockville, MD 20850. TEL 800-372-1033) Ed. Karen Walker. (looseleaf format; back issues avail.) **Document type:** newsletter.
●Also available online. Vendor(s): Human Resources Information Network (File DD).
   Description: Reference service providing information on new community right-to-know and community emergency response program.

360   US   ISSN 1074-8652
RIGHT-TO-KNOW PLANNING GUIDE NEWSLETTER. (Subseries of: Right-to-Know Planning Guide) 1987. bi-w. $320 (effective July 1995). The Bureau of National Affairs, Inc., 1231 25th St., N.W., Washington, DC 20037. TEL 202-452-4200. FAX 202-822-8092. TELEX 285656 BNAI WSH. (Subscr. to: 9435 Key West Ave., Rockville, MD 20850. TEL 800-372-1033) Ed. Karen Walker. (back issues avail.) **Document type:** newsletter.
●Also available online. Vendor(s): Human Resources Information Network (File DD).
—CCC.
   Formerly (until 1992): Right-to-Know Planning Report.
   Description: Provides information on new community right-to-know and community emergency response programs.

362.4   JA   ISSN 0035-5305
RIHABIRITESHON/REHABILITATION (TOKYO, 1953). (Text in Japanese) 1953. 10/yr. 260 Yen per no. Handicapped Persons Association of Japan Railways - Tetsudo Shinshosha Kyokai, 5-1 Koji-machi, Chiyoda-ku, Tokyo 102, Japan. Ed. Takeo Oshida. adv.; bk.rev.; charts; illus. circ. 8,000.

360   IT   ISSN 0035-6522
RIVISTA DI SERVIZIO SOCIALE. 1961. q. L.60000. Istituto per gli Studi Sui Servizi Sociali, Via di Villa Pamphili 84, 00152 Rome, Italy. TEL 06-5897179. Ed. Aurelia Florea. adv.; bk.rev.; abstr.; bibl.; tr.lit.; index. circ. 2,000. **Indexed:** P.A.I.S.For.Lang.Ind., Sociol.Abstr.

361.7   US   ISSN 1052-8881
HV97.R6
ROCKEFELLER FOUNDATION. ANNUAL REPORT. 1914. a. Rockefeller Foundation, 420 Fifth Ave., New York, NY 10018. TEL 212-869-8500. FAX 212-398-1858. circ. 18,000 (controlled). **Document type:** corporate report.
   Former titles (until 1986): Rockefeller Foundation. President's Review and Annual Report (ISSN 0557-885X); Which was formed by the 1966 merger of: Rockefeller Foundation. President's Review from the Annual Report (ISSN 0145-0808); Rockefeller Foundation. Annual Report (ISSN 0080-3391)

361.77   SW   ISSN 1101-413X
ROEDA KORSET. Variant title: Roeda Korsets Tidning. 1909. 6/yr. SEK 90. Svenska Roeda Korset - Swedish Red Cross, P.O. Box 27316, S-102 54 Stockholm, Sweden. Ed. Marianne Roennberg. adv.; bk.rev.; illus. circ. 420,000. (tabloid format; also avail. in audio cassette)
   Formerly (until 1990): Apropaa Roeda Korset; Supersedes in part: Vaart Roeda Kors; Reflex - Socialt Apropaa.

360   RU   ISSN 0869-7698
QH540
ROSSIISKAYA AKADEMIYA NAUK. DAL'NEVOSTOCHNOE OTDELENIE. VESTNIK/RUSSIAN ACADEMY OF SCIENCES. FAR EASTERN BRANCH. BULLETIN. (Text in Russian; table of contents in English) 1990. bi-m. $141 (effective 1996). Rossiiskya Akademiya Nauk, Dal'nevostochnoe Otdelenie - Russian Academy of Sciences, Far Eastern Branch, Ul. Svetlanskaya 50, Vladivostok 690600, Russia. TEL 22-25-88. (Dist. by: Mezhdunarodnaya Kniga, B. Yakimanka 39, 117049 Moscow, Russia) Ed. Alexey V. Zhirmunsky. adv.; bk.rev. circ. 1,000. **Document type:** academic/scholarly publication, bulletin.
—BLDSC (0027.745000).
   Formerly: Akademiya Nauk S.S.S.R. Dal'nevostochnoe Otdelenie. Vestnik (ISSN 0235-8611)
   Description: Contains research papers and reviews of recent developments in all areas of science.

ROSTER OF AFRICA SOCIAL SCIENTISTS. see BUSINESS AND ECONOMICS — International Development And Assistance

360   AU
DAS ROTE KREUZ. 1929. q. S.10. Oesterreichisches Rotes Kreuz, Gusshausstr. 3, A-1041 Vienna, Austria. Ed. Walter Vilt. adv.; bk.rev.; illus. circ. 40,000.

361.77   GW   ISSN 0938-9687
ROTES KREUZ. 1953. bi-m. membership. (Deutsches Rotes Kreuz) Sueddeutscher Verlag GmbH, Unternehmensbereich Zeitschriften, Karlstr. 35-37, 80333 Munich, Germany. TEL 089-54852-0. FAX 089-54852192. adv.; B&W page DM.5860, color page DM.9376; trim 185 x 275. bk.rev.; index. circ. 41,000. **Document type:** bulletin.
   Formed by the 1991 merger of: Rotkreuz-Zeitung (ISSN 0722-3897) & Rotkreuz (ISSN 0863-5455); Which was formerly (until 1990): Detusches Rotes Kreuz der Deutschen Demokratischen Republik (ISSN 0323-567X); (until 1964): D K R in der Deutschen Demokratischen Republik (ISSN 0323-729X); Rotkreuz-Zeitung was formerly (until 1982): Deutsches Rotes Kreuz (ISSN 0415-746X)

361.77   GW
DIE ROTKREUZ-SCHWESTER. q. membership. (Verband der Schwesternschaften von Deutschen Roten Kreuz e.V.) Sueddeutscher Verlag GmbH, Unternehmensbereich Zeitschriften, Karlstr. 35-37, 80333 Munich, Germany. TEL 089-54852130. FAX 089-54852192. adv.; B&W page DM.2780, color page DM.3770; trim 185 x 275. circ. 25,000. **Document type:** bulletin.

362.7   US
THE ROUNDTABLE (SOUTHFIELD). 1986. q. free. Spaulding for Children, National Resource Center for Special Needs Adoption, 16250 Northland Dr., Ste. 120, Southfield, MI 48075-4325. TEL 313-443-7080. FAX 313-443-7099. Ed. Nancy Burkhalter. bk.rev. circ. 12,000. **Document type:** newsletter.
   Description: Informs adoption practitioners, administrators and advocates of the center's activities and of new developments in the field of special needs adoption. Shares ideas, problems and successes.

179.3   UK
ROYAL HUMANE SOCIETY. ANNUAL REPORT. 1774. a. free. (Royal Humane Society) Blackfords Truro Cornwall, Brettenham House, Lancaster Pl., London WC2E 7EP, England. TEL 0171-836-8155. Ed. Maj. A.J. Dickinson. circ. 800. **Document type:** corporate report.

SOCIAL SERVICES AND WELFARE

360 613 UK ISSN 0264-0325
ROYAL SOCIETY OF HEALTH JOURNAL. 1876. bi-m. $135. Royal Society of Health, R S H House, 38A St., George's Dr., London SW1V 4BH, England. TEL 0171-630-0121. FAX 0171-976-6847. Ed. Iris Murphy. adv.; bk.rev.; bibl.; charts; illus.; index. circ. 9,600. (also avail. in microform from UMI) **Indexed:** Abstr.Hyg.; Art.Hosp.& Tour., ASSIA, Biol.Abstr., Br.Tech.Ind., Chem.Abstr., Curr.Adv.Ecol.Sci., Curr.Cont., Dairy Sci.Abstr., Dent.Ind., Excerp.Med., Food Sci.& Tech.Abstr., Geo.Abstr., Helminthol.Abstr., HRIS, I.P.A, Ind.Med., Ind.Vet., Nutr.Abstr., Rev.Med.& Vet.Mycol., Risk Abstr., Sel.Water Res.Abstr., Soc.Work Res.& Abstr., SSCI, Trop.Dis.Bull., Vet.Bull., W.R.C.Inf. **Document type:** academic/scholarly publication.
—BLDSC (4864.500000); Faxon; Genuine Article; SWETS; UMI.
Description: Devoted to all aspects of health care, nutrition, and social services.
Refereed Serial

S C I PSYCHOSOCIAL PROCESS. (Spinal Cord Injury) see *PSYCHOLOGY*

S E T FREE; the newsletter against television. (Society for the Eradication of Television) see *COMMUNICATIONS — Television And Cable*

361 647.9 SZ
S K A V - FACHBLATT; Zeitschrift fuer stationaere Betreuung. (Text in French, German and Italian) 1939. bi-m. 60 Fr.($45) Schweizerischer Verband Christlicher Institutionen, Zaehringerstr. 19, 6000 Lucerne 7, Switzerland. Ed. Xaver Schorno. adv.; bk.rev.; play rev.; illus.; cum.index; circ. 1,500 (controlled). (tabloid format) **Indexed:** Excerp.Med.
Formerly: Heim und Anstalt (ISSN 0017-9671)

361.1 SZ ISSN 0253-0414
S K Z. 1925. 24/yr. Roemerstr. 20, CH-4502 Solothurn, Switzerland. TEL 065-204204. FAX 065-226246. Ed. W. Frei. circ. 11,000.
Formerly (until 1952): Schweizerische Krankenkassen Zeitung (ISSN 0253-0422)

360 FR ISSN 0003-1887
S O S AMITIE FRANCE. BULLETIN NATIONAL. 1961. q. 120 F. (foreign 150 F.) S.O.S. Amitie France, 11 rue des Immeubles Industriels, 75011 Paris, France. TEL 40-09-15-22. FAX 40-09-74-35. Ed. Marie-Fernande Cabannes. adv.; bk. rev. circ. 2,000. **Document type:** bulletin.

362.7 AU
S O S KINDERDORF INTERNATIONAL. (Text in English and German) 1962. q. S O S Kinderdorf Verlag, International Office, Stafflerstr. 10a, A-6020 Innsbruck, Austria. TEL 05918-308. illus. **Document type:** newsletter.
Formerly: S O S Messenger (ISSN 0036-178X)

362.7 AU ISSN 0023-1509
S O S KINDERDORFBOTE. 1950. q. S O S Kinderdorf Verlag, Stafflerstr. 10a, A-6020 Innsbruck, Austria. TEL 05918-308. Ed. Herbert Genser. illus. circ. 1,000,000. **Document type:** newsletter.

360 301 AT
S P R C NEWSLETTER. 1980. q. free. Social Policy Research Centre, c/o University of New South Wales, Sydney, N.S.W. 2052, Australia. Ed. Julia Martin. bk.rev.; stat.; tr.lit. circ. 2,500. (back issues avail.) **Document type:** newsletter.
Formerly: S W R C Newsletter (ISSN 0159-9615)

360 301 AT ISSN 1036-2835
S P R C REPORTS AND PROCEEDINGS. 1980. irreg. Aus.$120 for 15 issues. Social Policy Research Centre, c/o University of New South Wales, Sydney, N.S.W. 2052, Australia. TEL 61-2-3853857. FAX 61-2-3851049. Ed. Diana Encel. stat. (back issues avail.) **Document type:** monographic series.
—UnCover.
Formerly: S W R C Reports and Proceedings (ISSN 0159-9607)

S S I RECIPIENTS BY STATE AND COUNTY (YEAR). (Social Security Insurance) see *INSURANCE*

360 SW ISSN 0283-1910
S S R - TIDNINGEN. 1958. 41/yr; w. (Oct.-Apr.); fortn. (May-Sep.). SEK 265 to individuals; institutions Kr.385. Sveriges Socionomers Riksfoerbund - Swedish Union of Social Workers and Public Administrators, Mariedalsvaegen 4, S-112 51 Stockholm, Sweden. FAX 08-6174465. Ed. Anders Ljungberg. adv.; illus. circ. 29,000. **Document type:** trade publication.
Former titles: S S R - Tidningen Socionomen (ISSN 0282-1001); Socionomen (ISSN 0038-044X)

309.26 US
SAFETY NETWORK. 6/yr. donation. National Coalition for the Homeless, 1612 K St., N.W., 10th Fl., No. 1004, Washington, DC 20006. TEL 202-775-1322. FAX 202-775-1316. bk.rev. circ. 15,000. **Document type:** newsletter.

SAGE CRIMINAL JUSTICE SYSTEMS SERIES. see *CRIMINOLOGY AND LAW ENFORCEMENT*

360 370 UK ISSN 0955-3517
ST. CATHERINE'S CONFERENCE REPORT. 1988. irreg., no.41, 1994. £2. King George VI and Queen Elizabeth Foundation of St. Catharine's, Cumberland Lodge, The Great Park, Windsor, Berkshire SL4 2HP, England. TEL 01784-432316. FAX 01784-438507. **Document type:** bulletin.
—BLDSC (8070.152450).

361.8 US
ST. PAUL URBAN LEAGUE. ANNUAL REPORT. 1924. a. free. St. Paul Urban League, 401 Selby Ave., St. Paul, MN 55102. TEL 612-224-5771. Ed. Willie Mac Wilson. circ. 3,000. (tabloid format) **Document type:** corporate report.

360 IT ISSN 0392-4505
SALUTE E TERRITORIO.* bi-m. L.45000. Regione Toscana, Via dei Servi 51, 50122 Florence, Italy. Ed. Mariella Crocella.

360 CU
SALVACION. s-m. Ejercito de Salvacion, 96 No. 5513rd, 55 y 57 Marianao 14, Havana, Cuba.

SALVATIONIST. see *RELIGIONS AND THEOLOGY — Other Denominations And Sects*

360 II ISSN 0036-3693
SAMAJ KALYAN. (Text in Assamese) 1956. m. Rs.12 (foreign $20). Assam State Social Welfare Advisory Board, Uzanbazar, Gauhati 1, Assam, India. Ed. Sri R.K. Gautam. adv.; abstr.; bibl.; illus.; stat. circ. 1,100. (tabloid format)

SAMANTHA SMITH FOUNDATION NEWSLETTER. see *CHILDREN AND YOUTH — For*

SANTA CRUZ ACTION NETWORK. NEWSLETTER. see *HOUSING AND URBAN PLANNING*

059.91 II ISSN 0036-4835
SARVODAYA. (Text in English) 1951. m. Rs.24($8) Tamilnadu Sarvodaya Sangh, Gandhinagar, Tirupur 638603, India. Ed. Sri S. Sivan Pillay. adv.; bk.rev.; illus.; index. circ. 1,500.
Description: Presents Gandhi's ideal of social service.

360 CN
SASKATCHEWAN. DEPARTMENT OF SOCIAL SERVICES. ANNUAL REPORT. 1915. a. free. Department of Social Services, 1920 Broad St., Regina, SK S4P 3V6, Canada. TEL 306-787-3494. illus. **Document type:** government publication.
Formerly: Saskatchewan. Department of Social Welfare. Annual Report (ISSN 0708-3882)

362.7 US
SAVE THE CHILDREN. ANNUAL REPORT. a. Save the Children, Public Affairs and Communication, 54 Wilton Rd., Box 950, Westport, CT 06881. TEL 203-221-4000. FAX 203-222-1067. **Document type:** corporate report.

360 DK ISSN 0907-2055
HV316
SCANDINAVIAN JOURNAL OF SOCIAL WELFARE. (Text in English) 1992. q. DKK 325 to individuals; institutions DKK 600 (effective 1996). (University of Stockholm, School of Social Work) Munksgaard International Publishers Ltd., 35 Noerre Soegade, P.O. Box 2148, DK-1016 Copenhagen K, Denmark. TEL 45-33-12-70-30. FAX 45-33-12-93-87. Ed. Sven Hessle. adv.; bk.rev.; illus. (reprint service avail.) **Document type:** academic/scholarly publication.
—BLDSC (8087.548500); Genuine Article; SWETS. CCC.
Refereed Serial

SCARLET LETTER. see *WOMEN'S INTERESTS*

SCHOOL LEAVER. see *EDUCATION*

SCHOOL SOCIAL WORK JOURNAL. see *EDUCATION — Special Education And Rehabilitation*

SCHOOL VOLUNTEERING; linking school volunteers nationwide. see *EDUCATION*

301.3 GW ISSN 0080-7133
SCHRIFTENREIHE FUER LAENDLICHE SOZIALFRAGEN. 1951. irreg., no.117, 1993. price varies. Agrarsoziale Gesellschaft e.V., Kurze Geismarstr. 33, 37073 Goettingen, Germany. TEL 0551-497090. FAX 0551-4970916. index. **Document type:** monographic series.
—BLDSC (8104.346000).

360 SZ
SCHWEIZER HEIMWESEN. m. Seegartenstr. 2, CH-8008 Zurich, Switzerland. TEL 01-7103560. FAX 01-7104073. Ed. Erika Ritter. circ. 4,050.

360 UK ISSN 0144-0462
SCOPE (BELFAST); a review of social policy & voluntary action in Northern Ireland. 1975. m. 50p. Northern Ireland Council for Voluntary Action, 127-131 Ormeau Rd., Belfast BT7 1SH, N. Ireland. TEL 0232-321224. FAX 0232-438350. Ed. Liz Law. adv. contact: Mary O'Neill. bk.rev.; illus.; index. circ. 2,000. **Document type:** bulletin.
—BLDSC (8205.700000).
Formerly: Voluntary Organisations News.

360 UK ISSN 0144-5081
HV249.S5
SCOTTISH EDUCATION DEPARTMENT. SOCIAL WORK SERVICES GROUP. STATISTICAL BULLETIN. m. Scottish Education Department, Social Work Services Group, New St. Andrew's House, Rm. 5-52, Edinburgh EH1 3TG, Scotland. TEL 031-244-4991. **Document type:** government publication.

SCUGNIZZO. see *CHILDREN AND YOUTH — About*

362 UK ISSN 0958-3467
SEARCH (YORK). 1989. q. free. Joseph Rowntree Foundation, The Homestead, 40 Water End, York YO3 6LP, England. TEL 01904-629241. FAX 01904-620072. Ed. Sharon Telfer. bk.rev.; circ. 8,500 (controlled). (back issues avail.) **Document type:** academic/scholarly publication.
—BLDSC (8214.370000).
Description: Research and development work supported by the foundation in housing, social policy, social care, disability, local and central government relations.

SEE HEAR!. see *HANDICAPPED — Hearing Impaired*

338.1 360 US ISSN 0194-4495
SEEDS; hope for the healing and hunger of poverty. 1977. q. $20 libraries $40; foreign $34 (subscr. includes Sprouts Newsletter). Box 6170, Waco, TX 76706-0170. TEL 817-755-7745. FAX 817-755-3740. Ed. Katie Cook. adv. contact: Kelley Hogewood. bk.rev. circ. 3,000. **Document type:** academic/scholarly publication.
Description: Offers analysis and information to understand US and world hunger and poverty issues. Provides practical information for direct involvement.

THE SEEING EYE ANNUAL REPORT. see *HANDICAPPED — Visually Impaired*

THE SEEING EYE GUIDE. see *HANDICAPPED — Visually Impaired*

SOCIAL SERVICES AND WELFARE

360 614.8   MX   ISSN 0582-4001
SEGURIDAD SOCIAL. 1958. q. $50. Conferencia Interamericana de Seguridad Social, Calle San Ramon, Unidad Independencia, Apto. 99089, 10100 Mexico, D.F., Mexico. TEL 5950011. FAX 6838524. (Co-sponsor: Instituto Mexicano del Seguro Social) Ed.Bd. film rev.; charts; illus.; stat. circ. 700. **Indexed:** World Bibl.Soc.Sec.

360   GW   ISSN 0724-5572
SELBSTHILFE; Zeitschrift der Bundesarbeitsgemeinschaft Hilfe fuer Behinderte. 1926. 4/yr. DM.36 (students DM.30). Verlag fuer Medizin Dr. Ewald Fischer GmbH, Fritz-Frey-Str. 21, 69121 Heidelberg, Germany. TEL 06221-4062-0. Ed. Dr. Rolf Bieker. bk.rev.; illus. **Document type:** bulletin.
—CCC.

360   GW
SELBSTHILFE SPEKTRUM RHEIN - MAIN. 1984. a. Koordination und Entwicklung von Selbsthilfe e.V. (KES), Theodor-Stern-Kai 7, 60596 Frankfurt a.M., Germany. TEL 069-63017603. FAX 069-63016301. circ. 2,000. (back issues avail.)

SELF HELP REPORTER NEWSLETTER. see *PSYCHOLOGY*

361.8 614.58   US   ISSN 8756-1425
HV547
SELF-HELP SOURCEBOOK; finding and forming mutual aid self-help groups. 1986. biennial. $10. New Jersey Self-Help Clearinghouse, St. Clares-Riverside Medical Center, 25 Pocono Rd., Denville, NJ 07834. TEL 201-625-7101. Eds. E. Madara, B. White. circ. 5,000. **Document type:** directory.
    Former titles (until 1986): Self-Help Group Directory (ISSN 0740-7548); Self-Help Group Sourcebook.
    Description: Lists national groups, toll-free helplines and clearinghouses around the world for professionals working in the health, mental health, and social service fields. Also contains a how-to section for starting up groups and accessing them via personal computer.

SENIOR BULLETIN. see *GERONTOLOGY AND GERIATRICS*

362.6   US   ISSN 0199-7947
SENIOR CITIZEN SENTINEL.* 1942. q. $5. California League of Senior Citizens, 1917 S. Chestnut Ave., Apt. 16E, Fresno, CA 93702-5552. TEL 213-386-7771. Ed. Kay Corbutt. adv.; bk.rev. circ. 1,000. (tabloid format; back issues avail.)

SENIOR CITIZENS SERVICES. see *GERONTOLOGY AND GERIATRICS*

SENIOR NEWS. see *GERONTOLOGY AND GERIATRICS*

SENIOREN ZEITSCHRIFT. see *PUBLIC ADMINISTRATION*

360   AF
SERAMIASHT. (Text in English, Persian or Pushto) 1977. q. Afghan Red Crescent Society, Pul-i Hartan, P.O. Box 3066, Kabul, Afghanistan. TEL 30969. TELEX 318 ARC AF.

361.5   CN   ISSN 0227-034X
SERVICE. (Text in English and French) 1940. q. free. Canadian Red Cross Society, National Headquarters, 5700 Cancross Court, Mississauga, Ont. L5R 3E9, Canada. TEL 416-890-1000. Ed.Bd. circ. 60,000.
    Formerly (until 1977): Despatch (ISSN 0046-0087)

360   CN   ISSN 0037-2633
HV2
SERVICE SOCIAL. (Text in French) 1951. 3/yr. Can.$28 to individuals; institutions Can.$40; students Can.$23. Universite Laval, Cite Universitaire, Quebec, PQ G1K 7P4, Canada. TEL 418-656-3288. FAX 418-656-3567. Ed. Rene Auclair. adv.; bk.rev.; bibl.; charts; cum.index. circ. 800. (also avail. in microform from BNQ,UMI; back issues avail.; reprint service avail. from UMI) **Indexed:** P.A.I.S.For.Lang.Ind., Pt.de Rep. (1979-). **Document type:** academic/scholarly publication.
—UMI.

360 362.7   UK
SERVICES FOR CHILDREN. 1992. a. price varies. Social Work Services Group, 43 Jeffrey St., Rm. 24, Edinburgh EH1 1DN, Scotland. (Subscr. to: Scottish Office Library, Publication Sales, Rm. 1-44, New St. Andrew's House, Edinburgh EH1 3TG, Scotland. FAX 0131-244-4785) **Document type:** government publication.

361   BL   ISSN 0101-6628
HV193
SERVICO SOCIALE E SOCIEDADE. 1979. 3/yr. Cr.$20 (effective 1994). Cortez Editora, Rua Bartira 387, 05009 Sao Paulo SP, Brazil. TEL 55-11-8640111. FAX 55-11-8644290.
    Description: Provides professionals in social service and related areas with the latest news regarding themes dealing with social reality. Introduces theoretical and practical proposals within the new concept of citizenship for all people.

SETTIMANA DEL SORDO; organo di informazione dei minorati dell'udito e della parola. see *HANDICAPPED — Hearing Impaired*

SETTLEMENTS INFORMATION NETWORK AFRICA NEWSLETTER. see *HOUSING AND URBAN PLANNING*

360   UK
SHAFTESBURY PEOPLE. 1848. s.a. membership. Shaftesbury Society, 18-20 Kingston Rd., South Wimbledon, London SW19 1JZ, England. TEL 081-542-5550. FAX 081-545-0605. Ed. Gill Faragher. illus. circ. 10,000. **Document type:** newsletter.
    Former titles: Shaftesbury Review (ISSN 0037-3168); Shaftesbury Newsletter.

360   JA
SHAKAI FUKUSHI NO DOKO. 1957. a. 2200 Yen. National Council of Social Welfare - Zenkoku Shakai Fukushi Kyogikai, 3-3-2 Kasumigaseki, Chiyoda-ku, Tokyo, Japan. Ed. Takao Kawajiri. circ. 7,000.

360   UK   ISSN 1355-5731
SHARE (LONDON); health and race - creating social change. 1991. m. King's Fund Centre, 126 Albert St., London NW1 7NF, England. TEL 0171-267-6111. **Document type:** bulletin.
—BLDSC (8254.608300).

362.8   US
SHARED HOUSING QUARTERLY.* 1982. q. $20. Shared Housing Resource Center, 1221 Fairmoint Ave., Philadelphia, PA 19123-2412. TEL 215-848-1220. Ed. Milton Marks. bk.rev. circ. 500. (back issues avail.)
    Description: Features articles on programs, legislation, research, financing, marketing and fund raising. Includes listings of conference and workshop dates.

SHOFAR (CHATTANOOGA). see *ETHNIC INTERESTS*

360   GW
SICHER SCHAFFEN - LAENGER LEBEN. 1963. q. free. Landwirtschaftliche Sozialversicherung, Postfach 310110, 86062 Augsburg, Germany. TEL 0821-4081-0. FAX 0821-4081115. adv.: page DM.2000. circ. 55,000. (back issues avail.) **Document type:** government publication.

SILENT NEWS JOB BULLETIN; career opportunities working with deaf and hard-of-hearing people. see *HANDICAPPED — Hearing Impaired*

301.4   US   ISSN 0037-5748
HQ1
SINGLE PARENT. 1958. bi-m. $15 to non-members. Parents Without Partners Inc., 401 N. Michigan Ave., Chicago, IL 60611. TEL 312-644-6610. FAX 312-245-1083. Ed. Ms. Mercedes Vance. adv. contact: Mercedes Vance. bk.rev.; charts; illus.; tr.lit.; circ. 110,000 (controlled). **Indexed:** PMR.
—UnCover.
    Description: Covers all aspects of single parenting. Includes stories for children of single parents.

360 305.4   US
SINGLE PARENT NEWS. 1985. 9/yr. free. Utah Issues, 1385 W. Indiana Ave., Salt Lake City, UT 84104-2754. TEL 801-521-2035; 800-351-5627. FAX 801-355-7540. Ed. Evelyn W. Johnson. adv. circ. 3,500. **Document type:** newsletter.
    Description: Resource and information newsletter for low-income single parents working toward self-support.

SJOMANNADAGSBLADID. see *TRANSPORTATION — Ships And Shipping*

SMALL TOWN. see *HOUSING AND URBAN PLANNING*

360   US   ISSN 0037-7317
HV1   CODEN: SMSWAW
SMITH COLLEGE STUDIES IN SOCIAL WORK. 1930. 3/yr. $16 (foreign $19) (effective 1995). Smith College, School for Social Work, Lilly Hall, Northampton, MA 01063. TEL 413-585-7950. FAX 413-585-7994. Ed. Gerry Shamess. bk.rev.; abstr.; index. circ. 2,000. (back issues avail.) **Indexed:** ASCA, ASSIA, IMFL, Lang.& Lang.Behav.Abstr., Mid.East: Abstr.& Ind., P.A.I.S., Psychol.Abstr. (1930-), Sage Fam.Stud.Abstr., Soc.Work Res.& Abstr., SSCI.
—BLDSC (8311.200000); Faxon; Genuine Article; SWETS; UnCover.

361.73 362   US   ISSN 1074-4398
SMITH MEDICAL FUNDING REPORT; the quarterly guide to research - project grant opportunities for hospitals & medical centers. 1983. q. $195 (outside N. America $205); with Smith University Funding Report $297 (outside N. America $307) (effective 1996). S F R, Inc., 76 O'Neil Cir., Monroe, NY 10950-3210. TEL 914-774-4449. Ed. Melanie Smith; Pub. Melanie Smith. abstr.; index. (looseleaf format; back issues avail.) **Document type:** bulletin, newsletter.
    Supersedes in part (in 1994): Smith Funding Report (ISSN 0739-2184)
    Description: Provides up-to-date information on private foundation research and project grant opportunities in the biological and medical sciences.

SMITH UNIVERSITY FUNDING REPORT; the quarterly guide to private foundation research - project grant opportunities for colleges and universities. see *EDUCATION — Higher Education*

360   NE   ISSN 0921-5344
SOCIAAL BESTEK; tijdschrift voor lokaal beleid en management. (Supplement avail.: Bijstand) 1938. 11/yr. fl.125. Vuga Uitgeverij B.V., P.O. Box 16400, 2500 BK The Hague, Netherlands. TEL 31-70-3614011. FAX 31-70-3625468. Ed. E.S.M. van der Loo. adv.: B&W page fl.2315, color page fl.4420; trim 215 x 285. **Document type:** trade publication.
—SWETS.
    Former titles (until 1986): Sociaal Bestek en Lektuurkeuze Welzijnsterrein (ISSN 0921-5352); (until 1982): Sociaal Bestek (ISSN 0165-8344); (until 1969): Sociale Zorg.
    Description: Covers issues relating to the provision of social services, including social security, care of the elderly, unemployment assistance, and related topics, with emphasis on the local level.

360   UK   ISSN 0968-0985
SOCIAL ACTION. 1992. q. £37.50 (N. America $85; rest of world £47.50) (effective 1996). (Centre for Social Action) Whiting & Birch Ltd., P.O. Box 872, Forest Hill, London SE23 3HL, England. TEL 0181-244-2421. FAX 0181-244-2448. Eds. Mark Harrison, David Ward. **Document type:** bulletin.

360 331.8   FR   ISSN 0758-0959
SOCIAL ACTUALITE; bulletin de la protection sociale. 1984. 10/yr. 305 F. (foreign 363 F.) (effective 1995). (Confederation Francaise Democratique du Travail) C F D T Presse, 4 bd. de la Villette, 75955 Paris Cedex 19, France. TEL 42-03-81-40. FAX 42-03-81-48. Ed. Jean Marie Syacth. adv. contact: Valeugene Salmon. bk.rev.; index. circ. 3,600. (back issues avail.)

360   UK   ISSN 0958-3815
SOCIAL CARE RESEARCH FINDINGS. 1989. irreg., no.63, 1995. Joseph Rowntree Foundation, The Homestead, 40 Water End, York YO3 6LP, England. TEL 01904-629241. FAX 01904-620072. **Document type:** bulletin.
—BLDSC (8318.058500).

SOCIAL SERVICES AND WELFARE

360   GW   ISSN 0176-1714
SOCIAL CHOICE AND WELFARE. (Text in English) 1984. 4/yr. DM.420($305) (effective 1996). Springer-Verlag, Heidelberger Platz 3, 14197 Berlin, Germany. TEL 030-8207-0. FAX 030-8214091. E-mail: orders@springer.de. (Subscr. in N. America to: Springer-Verlag New York, Inc., 44 Hartz Way, Secaucus, NJ 07096-2491. TEL 201-348-4033. FAX 201-348-4505) Ed. W. Gaertner. Indexed: J.of Econ.Lit. Document type: academic/scholarly publication.
—BLDSC (8318.072000); Faxon; Genuine Article; SWETS; UMI; UnCover. **CCC**.
    Description: Covers the ethical and positive aspects of welfare economics and collective theory, with topics including social choice and voting theory, as well as all aspects of welfare theory.

360   US   ISSN 0147-1473
HV1
SOCIAL DEVELOPMENT ISSUES; alternative approaches to global human needs. 1977. 3/yr. $20 to individuals; institutions $30 (foreign $35); students $15 (foreign $18). Southern Illinois University, School of Social Work, Carbondale, IL 62901. TEL 618-458-2243. FAX 618-453-1219. (Subscr. to: Social Development Issues, The University of Iowa Publications Services, Grahpic Services Building, Iowa City, IA 52242) Eds. Martin Tracy, Roland Meinert. bk.rev.; bibl.; circ. 500 (paid). Indexed: Geo.Abstr., IDA, Lang.& Lang.Behav.Abstr., Soc.Work Res.& Abstr., Sociol.Abstr. Document type: academic/scholarly publication.
—BLDSC (8318.079400); Faxon; UnCover.
    Supersedes: Iowa Journal of Social Work (ISSN 0021-0536).
    Description: Serves as a forum for achieving linkages between multiple disciplines, nations, and cultures. Attempts to advance social, cultural, political, and economic theory, policy, and practice (and their interrelationship) in a global framework.

360   370   EI   ISSN 0255-0776
HD5764.5.A6
SOCIAL EUROPE. French edition: Europe Sociale (ISSN 0255-0792); German edition (ISSN 0255-0784) (Editions in English, French and German) 1983. 3/yr., plus 4-5 supplements/yr.). 50 ECU($145) (Commission of the European Communities, Directorate-General for Employment, Social Affairs and Education) Office for Official Publications of the European Communities, L-2985 Luxembourg, Luxembourg. (Dist. in the U.S. by: Unipub, 4611-F Assembly Dr., Lanham, MD 20706-4391. TEL 800-274-4888. FAX 301-459-0056) circ. 7,000. (back issues avail.) Indexed: IIS, Int.Lab.Doc., World Bibl.Soc.Sec.
—BLDSC (8318.088000); SWETS.
    Description: Presents an overview of developments and current events in the fields of employment, education, vocational training, industrial relations and social measures; covers international conferences, research, studies and other activities stimulating debate on these issues; reports on the latest developments in national employment policies, and on the introduction of new technologies.

362.4   362.6   SW   ISSN 0280-848X
SOCIAL OMSORG. 1950. s-m. SEK 140. Foereningen Social Omsorg, Solnaegangsvaegen 9, S-172 37 Sundbyberg, Sweden. TEL 46-8-29-40-65. Eds. Ulla Lena Larsson, Aasa Vidman; Pub. Bo Sjoeberg. adv.: B&W page SEK 3600; trim 185 x 270. cols./p.: 3; pp./issue: 16. Document type: trade publication.

360   UK
SOCIAL POLICY RESEARCH FINDINGS. irreg., no.72, 1995. Joseph Rowntree Foundation, The Homestead, 40 Water End, York YO3 6LP, England. TEL 01904-629241. FAX 01904-620072. Document type: bulletin.

362   UK
SOCIAL RESPONSIBILITY; a directory of resources in the Church of England. 1950. biennial. £4.50. Board for Social Responsibility, General Synod of the Church of England, Church House, Great Smith St., London, SW1P 3NZ, England. TEL 01-222 9011. Ed. Alison Webster. circ. 1,000. Document type: directory.
    Former titles: Directory of Church of England Social Services (ISSN 0070-5268); Directory of Church of England Moral and Social Welfare Work.

SOCIAL SECURITY BULLETIN. see *INSURANCE*

360   AT   ISSN 0726-1195
HD7250
SOCIAL SECURITY JOURNAL. 1973. s-m. Aus.$40 (Asia Aus.$61; N. America Aus.$71; Europe Aus.$78.50) for 4 issues. (Australian Department of Social Security) Australian Government Publishing Service, G.P.O. Box 84, Canberra, A.C.T. 2601, Australia. TEL 61-6-295-4411. FAX 61-6-295-4455. TELEX AA62013. Ed. Rosemary Lynch. bk.rev. circ. 10,000. Document type: government publication.
—UnCover. **CCC**.
    Former titles (until 1981): Australian Department of Social Security. Social Security (ISSN 0159-6349); (until 1979): Australian Department of Social Security. Social Security Quarterly (ISSN 0310-544X).

SOCIAL SECURITY LAW & PRACTICE. see *INSURANCE*

SOCIAL SECURITY LAW & PRACTICE NEWSLETTER. see *INSURANCE*

SOCIAL SECURITY PRACTICE GUIDE. see *INSURANCE*

362.6   US   ISSN 1073-1415
SOCIAL SECURITY PROGRAMS IN THE UNITED STATES. biennial. U.S. Social Security Administration, O.R.S. - Publications Staff, Van Ness Center, 4301 Connecticut Ave., N.W., Rm. 209, Washington, DC 20008. TEL 202-282-7161. FAX 202-282-7219. (Subscr. to: Superintendent of Documents, U.S. Government Printing Office, Box 371954, Pittsburgh, PA 15250-7954. TEL 202-783-3238. FAX 202-512-2233) Ed. Marilyn R. Thomas. charts. Document type: government publication.
    Description: Provides a lay guide to public cash and in-kind income-maintenance programs and the health insurance and medical-assistance programs under the Social Security Act.

SOCIAL SECURITY RULINGS, ACQUIESCENCE RULINGS ON FEDERAL OLD-AGE, SURVIVORS, DISABILITY, SUPPLEMENTAL SECURITY INCOME AND BLACK LUNG BENEFITS. see *INSURANCE*

SOCIAL SERVICE JOBS. see *OCCUPATIONS AND CAREERS*

360   US   ISSN 0737-3627
HV89
SOCIAL SERVICE ORGANIZATIONS AND AGENCIES DIRECTORY. 1982. irreg. $140. Gale Research Inc., 835 Penobscot Bldg., Detroit, MI 48226. TEL 313-961-2242. FAX 3130961-6083. TELEX 810-221-7086. Ed. Anthony T. Kruzas.
    Description: Guide to social service organizations and agencies.

360   US   ISSN 0037-7961
HV1   CODEN: SSRVA
SOCIAL SERVICE REVIEW; devoted to the scientific and professional interests of social work. 1927. q. $31 to individuals; institutions $58; students $22. University of Chicago Press, Journals Division, 5720 S. Woodlawn Ave., Chicago, IL 60637. TEL 312-753-3347. FAX 312-753-0811. TELEX 25-4603. (Subscr. to: Box 37005, Chicago, IL 60637) Ed. John R. Schuerman. adv.; bk.rev.; bibl.; index. circ. 3,000. (also avail. in microform from MIM,UMI,PMC; reprint service avail. from UMI,ISI,SCH,) Indexed: Abstr.Crim.& Pen., Adol.Ment.Hlth.Abstr., Amer.Hist.& Life, ASCA, ASSIA, Bk.Rev.Ind. (1984-), Child.Bk.Rev.Ind. (1984-), CLOA, Curr.Cont., Excerp.Med., Hist.Abstr., IMFL, Irrit.Polit.Sci.Abstr., Lang.& Lang.Behav.Abstr., Med.Care Rev., Mid.East: Abstr.& Ind., Mult.Ed.Abstr., P.A.I.S., Polit.Sci.Abstr., PSI, Sage Fam.Stud.Abstr., Sage Urb.Stud.Abstr., Soc.Sci.Ind., Soc.Work Res.& Abstr., Sociol.Abstr., Sp.Ed.Needs Abstr., SSCI. Document type: academic/scholarly publication.
—BLDSC (8318.203000); Faxon; Genuine Article; SWETS; UMI. **CCC**.
    Refereed Serial

360   362.7   UK   ISSN 0265-6957
SOCIAL SERVICES RESEARCH. 1972. q. £55 (foreign £60). University of Birmingham, Department of Social Policy and Social Work, Edgbaston, Birmingham B15 2TT, England. TEL 0121-414-5733. FAX 0121-414-5726. E-mail: h.m.harris@bham.ac.uk. Eds. Martin Willis, Nicholas Deakin. bk.rev. circ. 249. (back issues avail.) Indexed: ASSIA. Document type: academic/scholarly publication.
—BLDSC (8318.204830).
    Formerly: Clearing House for Local Authority Social Services Research.
    Description: Applied research concerned with all aspects of personal social services: articles, notes and summaries of reports.

360   UK   ISSN 0961-3137
SOCIAL SERVICES RESEARCH & INFORMATION UNIT. OCCASIONAL PAPER. Abbreviated title: S S R I U Occasional Paper. irreg., no.30, 1993. £5. Social Services Research & Information Unit, School of Social and Historical Studies, Kings Rooms, Bellevue Terrace, Portsmouth, Hants. PO1 3AS, England. TEL 01705-811504. (Co-sponsors: Hampshire Social Services Department; University of Portsmouth) Document type: academic/scholarly publication.
—BLDSC (8425.256100).

360   UK   ISSN 0952-9772
SOCIAL SERVICES RESEARCH & INFORMATION UNIT. REPORT (NO.). Abbreviated title: S S R I U Report. irreg., no.28, 1994. £6.50. Social Services Research & Information Unit, School of Social and Historical Studies, Kings Rooms, Bellevue Terrace, Portsmouth, Hants. PO1 3AS, England. TEL 01705-811504. (Co-sponsors: Hampshire Social Services Department; University of Portsmouth) Document type: academic/scholarly publication.

360   UK   ISSN 0307-093X
SOCIAL SERVICES YEARBOOK. 1972. a. Pitman Publishing, 128 Long Acre, London WC2E 9AN, England. TEL 0171-379-7383. FAX 0171-240-5771. Ed. Rachel Vermont. adv.: B&W page £572; 203 x 128; adv. contact: Alan Burfoot. Document type: bulletin.
—BLDSC (8318.206000).

300   AT   ISSN 0037-8011
SOCIAL SURVEY.* 1951. m. Aus.$8($1.92) Institute of Social Order, P.O. Box 66A, Malbourne, Vic. 3001, Australia. Ed. Rev. W.G. Smith. adv.; bk.rev.; abstr.; charts; illus.; stat.; index. circ. 4,000. (tabloid format) Indexed: Aus.P.A.I.S., Gdlns.

361   200   US   ISSN 0099-183X
HN30
SOCIAL THOUGHT; journal of religion in the social services. 1974. q. $75 (foreign $105) (effective Mar. 1995). Haworth Press, Inc., 10 Alice St., Binghamton, NY 13904. TEL 607-722-5857; 800-342-9678. FAX 607-722-1424. adv.; bk.rev.; charts; illus.; index. circ. 1,000. (also avail. in microform from UMI; back issues avail.; reprint service avail. from UMI) Indexed: Adol.Ment.Hlth.Abstr., ASSIA, Cath.Ind., CERDIC, G.Soc.Sci.& Rel.Per.Lit., Lang.& Lang.Behav.Abstr., Soc.Work Res.& Abstr. Document type: academic/scholarly publication.
—Haworth. **CCC**.

360   II   ISSN 0037-8038
SOCIAL WELFARE. (Text in English) 1954. m. Rs.12 (foreign $20). Central Social Welfare Board, B-12, Tara Crescent, Institutional Area, New Delhi 110 016, India. TEL 6960059. Ed. Poonam Sharma. adv.; bk.rev.; charts; illus. circ. 3,000. Indexed: World Bibl.Soc.Sec. Document type: government publication.
—BLDSC (8318.219800); UnCover.

SOCIAL WELFARE LAW. see *LAW*

SOCIAL SERVICES AND WELFARE

360 SA ISSN 0037-8054
SOCIAL WORK/MAATSKAPLIKE WERK. (Text in Afrikaans and English; summaries in English) 1965. q. R.55($80) (effective 1995). University of Stellenbosch, Department of Social Work, B.J. Vorster Building, Stellenbosch 7600, South Africa. TEL 27-21-8082439. FAX 27-21-8084336. E-mail: jic@maties.sun.ac.za. (Subscr. to: P.O. Box 223, Stellenbosch 7600, South Africa) Ed. Johan Cronje. adv.; bk.rev.; abstr.; bibl.; index. circ. 2,000. (back issues avail.) **Indexed:** Chic.Per.Ind., Ind.S.A.Per. **Document type:** academic/scholarly publication.
—BLDSC (8318.223100).
  Description: A professional journal for social workers.
  Refereed Serial

360 US ISSN 0037-8046
HV1 CODEN: SOWOA
SOCIAL WORK. 1956. 6/yr. $96 (Canada $102; elsewhere $111) (effective 1996). (National Association of Social Workers) N A S W Press, 750 First St., N.E., Ste. 700, Washington, DC 20002-4241. TEL 202-408-8600. FAX 202-336-8312. (Subscr. to: NASW Distribution Center, Box 431, Annapolis Jct., MS 20701) Ed. Patricia L. Ewalt. adv.; bk.rev.; index. circ. 160,000. (also avail. in microform from UMI; back issues avail.; reprint service avail. from UMI) **Indexed:** Abstr.Health Care Manage.Stud., Acad.Ind., ASCA, Bk.Rev.Ind. (1980-), C.I.J.E., Child.Bk.Rev.Ind. (1980-), Crim.Just.Abstr., Curr.Cont., Except.Child.Educ.Abstr., Excerp.Med., Hosp.Lit.Ind., Lang.& Lang.Behav.Abstr., Mid.East: Abstr.& Ind., Mult.Ed.Abstr., P.A.I.S., PSI, Psychol.Abstr. (1956-), Rehabil.Lit., Sage Pub.Admin.Abstr., Soc.Sci.Ind., Soc.Work Res.& Abstr., Soc.Work Res.& Abstr., Sp.Ed.Needs Abstr., SSCI, Stud.Wom.Abstr., Viol.& Abuse Abstr., World Bibl.Soc.Sec. **Document type:** academic/scholarly publication.
●Also available online. Vendor(s): University Microfilms International.
—BLDSC (8318.221100); Faxon; Genuine Article; SWETS; UMI; UnCover. **CCC.**
  Description: Includes scholarly research, critical analyses of the profession and current information on social issues.

360 282 US ISSN 0737-5778
HV530
SOCIAL WORK AND CHRISTIANITY; an international journal. 1974. s-a. $10. North American Association of Christians in Social Work, Box 7090, St. Davids, PA 19087-7090. TEL 610-687-5777. Ed. David A. Sherwood. adv.; bk.rev. circ. 1,200. (back issues avail.) **Indexed:** Chr.Per.Ind., Soc.Work Res.& Abstr.

360 US ISSN 0081-055X
SOCIAL WORK AND SOCIAL ISSUES. 1969. irreg., no.5, 1977. Columbia University Press, 562 W. 113th St., New York, NY 10025. TEL 212-666-1000. **Document type:** monographic series.

360 UK ISSN 0953-5225
CODEN: SWSREN
SOCIAL WORK AND SOCIAL SCIENCES REVIEW. 1989. 3/yr. £49.50 (N. America $90; rest of world £60) (effective 1996). Whiting & Birch Ltd., P.O. Box 872, Forest Hill, London SE23 3HZ, England. TEL 0181-244-2421. FAX 0181-244-2448. Ed. Joseph Oliver. adv.; bk.rev. (back issues avail.) **Indexed:** Psychol.Abstr. (1989-). **Document type:** academic/scholarly publication.
—BLDSC (8318.223400). **CCC.**

360 UK ISSN 0261-5479
SOCIAL WORK EDUCATION. 1980. 4/yr. £47.50 (N. America $95; rest of world £62.50) (effective 1996). Whiting & Birch Ltd., P.O. Box 872, Forest Hill, London SE23 3HL, England. TEL 0181-244-2421. FAX 0181-244-2448. Ed. Michael Preston-Shoot. index. circ. 800. (back issues avail.) **Indexed:** ASSIA, Sociol.Abstr., Tech.Educ.Abstr. **Document type:** academic/scholarly publication.
—BLDSC (8318.223700); UnCover. **CCC.**
  Description: Covers social work education and training.

SOCIAL WORK EDUCATION REPORTER. see
EDUCATION — Higher Education

361 II ISSN 0583-7065
HV1
SOCIAL WORK FORUM. 1963. q. Indian Association of Trained Social Workers, 3 University Rd., Delhi 110007, India.

360 US ISSN 0162-7961
LB3013.4
SOCIAL WORK IN EDUCATION. 1978. q. $83 (Canada $89; elsewhere $98) (effective 1996). (National Association of Social Workers) N A S W Press, 750 First St., N.E., Ste. 700, Washington, DC 20002-4241. TEL 202-408-8600. FAX 202-336-8312. (Subscr. to: N A S W Distribution Center, Box 431, Annapolis Jct., MD 20701) Ed. Edith M. Freeman. adv.; bk.rev. circ. 3,700. (also avail. in microform from UMI; reprint service avail. from UMI) **Indexed:** Adol.Ment.Hlth.Abstr., Cont.Pg.Educ., IMFL, Mult.Ed.Abstr., PSI, Psychol.Abstr., Soc.Work Res.& Abstr., Sociol.Abstr., SOMA, Sp.Ed.Needs.Abstr. **Document type:** academic/scholarly publication.
—BLDSC (8318.223720); Faxon; UMI; UnCover. **CCC.**
  Description: Publishes articles for school social workers and their colleagues on problems they encounter in daily work.

360 UK ISSN 1353-1670
▼**SOCIAL WORK IN EUROPE.** 1994. 3/yr. £20 (EC £24.50; elsewhere £30) to individuals; institutions £50 (EC £54.50; elsewhere £60). Russell House Publishing Ltd., 38 Silver St., Lyme Regis, Dorset DT7 3HS, England. TEL 01297-443948. Ed. John Pitts. **Document type:** academic/scholarly publication.
—BLDSC (8318.224700).

360 362 US ISSN 0098-1389
HV687.A2 CODEN: SWHCDO
SOCIAL WORK IN HEALTH CARE; quarterly journal of medical & psychiatric social work. 1975. q. (2 vols./yr.). $280 (foreign $392) (effective Mar. 1995). Haworth Press, Inc., 10 Alice St., Binghamton, NY 13904. TEL 607-722-5857; 800-342-9678. FAX 607-722-1424. TELEX 4932599 HAWORTH. Ed. Gary Rosenburg. adv.; bk.rev.; abstr.; charts. circ. 1,373. (also avail. in microfiche from UMI; back issues avail.; reprint service avail. from HAW) **Indexed:** Abstr.Health Care Manage.Stud., Abstr.Hosp.Manage.Stud., Abstr.Soc.Geront., Adol.Ment.Hlth.Abstr., ASCA, ASSIA, Behav.Abstr., Behav.Med.Abstr., Biol.Abstr., Bull.Signal., Chicago Psychoanal.Lit.Ind., CINAHL, CLOA, Curr.Cont., Excerp.Med., Hosp.Lit.Ind., IMFL, Ind.Med., Int.Nurs.Ind., Med.Care Rev., PSI, Psychol.Abstr. (1975-), Rehabil.Lit., Sage Fam.Stud.Abstr., Sage Pub.Admin.Abstr., Soc.Work Res.& Abstr., Sociol.Abstr., Sp.Ed.Needs Abstr., SSCI, Viol.& Abuse Abstr.
—BLDSC (8318.225600); EMDOCS; Faxon; Genuine Article; Haworth; SWETS; UnCover.
  Description: Devoted to social work, theory, practice, and administration in a wide variety of health care settings.
  Refereed Serial

360 SA
SOCIAL WORK PRACTICE. (Text and summaries in English) 1983. 3/yr. free. Department of Welfare, Subdirectorate Information Education and Communication - Departement van Welsyn, Subdirektoraat Inligting, Opvoeding en Kommunikasie, Private Bag X901, Pretoria 0001, South Africa. TEL 27-12-3127648. FAX 27-12-3242647. TELEX 321366. Ed. Mariette van der Merwe. bk.rev.; cum.index: 1983-1994. circ. 4,500. **Document type:** government publication.
  Description: Devoted to enhancing the professionalism of social workers.

360 282 US ISSN 8756-5013
SOCIAL WORK PRACTICE MONOGRAPH SERIES. Key Title: Practice Monograph Series. 1985. irreg. $6 per no. North American Association of Christians in Social Work, Box 7090, St. Davids, PA 19087-7090. TEL 610-687-5777. Ed. Alan Keith-Lucas. **Document type:** monographic series.
  Formerly: North American Association of Christians in Social Work. Practice Monograph Series.

360 US ISSN 1070-5309
HV1
SOCIAL WORK RESEARCH. 1965. q. $86 (Canada $92; elsewhere $101) (effective 1996). (National Association of Social Workers) N A S W Press, 750 First St., N.E., Ste. 700, Washington, DC 20002-4241. TEL 202-408-8600. FAX 202-336-8312. (Subscr. to: NASW Distribution Center, Box 431, Annapolis Jct., MD 20701. TEL 800-227-3590. FAX 301-206-7989) Ed. Stuart A. Kirk. adv.; index. circ. 3,000. (also avail. in microform from UMI) **Indexed:** Psychol.Abstr. (1994-), Soc.Work Res.& Abstr. **Document type:** academic/scholarly publication.
—Genuine Article; SWETS; UMI; UnCover. **CCC.**
  Supersedes in part (in 1994): Social Work Research and Abstracts (ISSN 0148-0847); Which was formerly (until 1977): Abstracts for Social Workers (ISSN 0001-3412)
  Description: Covers new technology, strategies and methods, and results of research and evaluation.

360 UK
SOCIAL WORK RESEARCH CENTRE. RESEARCH REPORTS. irreg., no.33, 1994. £3. University of Stirling, Social Work Research Centre, Stirling FK9 4LA, Scotland. TEL 01786-67724. FAX 01786-63000. **Document type:** monographic series.

360 UK
SOCIAL WORK RESEARCH CENTRE. WORKING PAPERS. 1986. irreg., no.21, 1990. £2. University of Stirling, Social Work Research Centre, Stirling FK9 4LA, Scotland. TEL 01786-67724. FAX 01786-63000. **Document type:** monographic series.

362.8 US ISSN 0160-9513
HV45 CODEN: SWGRDU
SOCIAL WORK WITH GROUPS; a journal of community and clinical practice. 1978. q. $225 (foreign $315) (effective 1996). Haworth Press, Inc., 10 Alice St., Binghamton, NY 13904. TEL 607-722-5857; 800-342-9678. FAX 607-722-1424. TELEX 4932599. Ed. Roselle Kurland. adv.; bk.rev. circ. 634. (also avail. in microfiche from UMI; reprint service avail. from HAW,ISI; back issues avail.) **Indexed:** Adol.Ment.Hlth.Abstr., ASCA, ASSIA, Chic.Per.Ind., Curr.Cont., IMFL, Lang.& Lang.Behav.Abstr., Psychol.Abstr. (1979-), Soc.Sci.Ind. (1994-), Soc.Work Res.& Abstr., Sociol.Abstr., Sp.Ed.Needs Abstr., SSCI, Viol.& Abuse Abstr.
—BLDSC (8318.225000); Faxon; Genuine Article; Haworth; SWETS; UnCover.
  Description: Covers the areas of groupwork in psychiatric, rehabilitative, and multipurpose social work and social services agencies.
  Refereed Serial

360 CN ISSN 0037-8089
SOCIAL WORKER/TRAVAILLEUR SOCIAL. (Text in English and French) 1932. q. Can.$37($40) (Canadian Association of Social Workers) Myropen Publications Ltd., 383 Parkdale Ave., Ste. 402, Ottawa, ON K1Y 4R4, Canada. TEL 613-729-6668. FAX 613-729-9608. Ed. Penny Sipkes. adv.; bk.rev.; index. circ. 14,000. (also avail. in microform from MML) **Indexed:** Can.B.P.I., Soc.Work Res.& Abstr. **Document type:** academic/scholarly publication, newsletter.
—BLDSC (8318.235000); UnCover.
  Description: Information about social work groups in Canada and current social welfare policy. Examines regional, national and international social issues.
  Refereed Serial

360 NE
SOCIALE DIENST POST. 1988. 12/yr. free. Sociale Dienst, Vlaardingenlaan 15, 1062 HM Amsterdam, Netherlands. TEL 31-20-5160801. FAX 31-20-6690151. adv.; B&W page fl.10000; adv. contact: L.A. Renardel de Lavalette. circ. 75,000 (controlled). **Document type:** government publication, newsletter.
  Description: Answers questions about services provided by Sociale Dienst and other organizations.

360 SW ISSN 0037-8100
SOCIALFOERFATTNINGAR. 1957. 20/yr. SEK 1495. Foerlagshuset Gothia AB, P.O. Box 15169, S-104 65 Stockholm, Sweden. TEL 46-08-743-6500. FAX 46-08-641-4585. Eds. Gunnar Gaardhagen, Karl-Aake Claesson. adv.; charts; index. circ. 1,460.

SOCIALISM AND HEALTH. see *PUBLIC HEALTH AND SAFETY*

SOCIAL SERVICES AND WELFARE

360   GW
SOCIALMANAGEMENT; Magazin fuer Organisation und Innovation. 1991. q. DM.118. Nomos Verlagsgesellschaft mbH und Co. KG, Waldseestr. 3-5, 76530 Baden-Baden, Germany. TEL 07221-2104-0. FAX 07221-210427. TELEX 781201. (Subscr. to: Postfach 610, 76484 Baden-Baden, Germany) **Document type:** bulletin.

SOCIALNI POLITIKA. see *POLITICAL SCIENCE*

360   DK   ISSN 0105-5399
SOCIALPAEDAGOGEN. vol.24, 1967. 26/yr. DKK 482. Socialpaedagogernes Landsforbund, Brolaeggerstraede 9 St., DK-1211 Copenhagen K, Denmark. adv. circ. 28,000.
     Formerly: Boernesagspaedagogen.

361   DK   ISSN 0108-6103
SOCIALRAADGIVEREN. 1938. s-m. DKK 480. Dansk Socialraadgiverforening - Danish Association of Social Workers, Toldbodgade 19 A, 1253 Copenhagen K, Denmark. FAX 33-913019. Eds. Rie Graesberg, Wittus Nielsen. adv.; bk.rev. circ. 9,000.

360   AG   ISSN 0037-8569
SOCIEDAD ESPANOLA DE SOCORROS MUTUOS Y BENEFICENCIA. BOLETIN.* 1968. irreg. (4-5/yr.). free. Sociedad Espanola de Socorros Mutuos y Beneficencia, Rodriquez No. 545, Tandil, Buenos Aires, Argentina. Ed. Ernesto Enrique Reclusa. circ. 2,000. (looseleaf format)

SOCIEDADE E ESTADO. see *SOCIOLOGY*

360   IS   ISSN 0334-4029
SOCIETY AND WELFARE/HEVRA U-REVAHA; quarterly for social work. (Text in Hebrew and English) 1978. irreg. IS.20($15) Ministry of Labour and Social Affairs, P.O. Box 1260, Jerusalem, Israel. TEL 02-719081. Ed. Dr. Shimon Spiro. bk.rev.

301   CI   ISSN 0038-0105
SOCIJALNI RAD/SOCIAL WORK; teorija i praksa. (Text in Serbo-Croatian; abstracts in English) 1961. s-a. Republicki Zavod za Socijalni Rad, c/o Visnja Gracin, Ul. 8 Maja 1945, br. 42, 41000 Zagreb, Croatia. TEL 431-555. Ed. Bozo Zaja. bk.rev.

301   GW   ISSN 0038-0164
HM1.A1
SOCIOLOGIA INTERNATIONALIS; internationale Zeitschrift fuer Soziologie, Kommunikations- und Kulturforschung. (Supplements avail.) (Text in English, French, German and Spanish; summaries in English) 1963. s-a. DM.128. Duncker und Humblot GmbH, Postfach 410329, 12113 Berlin, Germany. TEL 030-7900060. FAX 030-79000631. Ed.Bd. adv.; bk.rev. **Indexed:** Int.Polit.Sci.Abstr., Lang.& Lang.Behav.Abstr., Sociol.Abstr. (1963-). **Document type:** academic/scholarly publication.
—BLDSC (8319.605000); SWETS. **CCC.**

301.4   FR   ISSN 0338-1757
SOLIDAIRES (PARIS). 1956. q. 75 F. (foreign 80 F.) (Federation des Associations de Veuves Civiles Chefs de Famille) Association d'Edition Solidaires, 28 place St. Georges, 75009 Paris, France. TEL 42-85-18-30. FAX 45-96-01-06. Ed. Christiane Sonet. adv.; bk.rev.; illus. circ. 70,000. (back issues avail.)
     Formerly: Survivre.

360   AT   ISSN 0813-4650
SOLO; Victorian newsletter for parents without partners. 1967. m. Aus.$15. (Parents Without Partners (Vic) Inc.) New Lithographics Ltd., Sunbury Cres., Surrey Hills, Vic. 3126, Australia. (Subscr. to: Parents Without Partners (Vic) Inc., 220 Canterbury Rd., Canterbury, Vic. 3156, Australia. TEL 836-3211) Ed. Anne Matthies. adv.; bk.rev. circ. 5,000. (back issues avail.) **Document type:** newsletter.

360   US   ISSN 0097-9562
HD6050
SOROPTIMIST; of the Americas. 1932. 7/yr. $8. Soroptimist International of the Americas, Inc., 1616 Walnut St., Ste. 700, Philadelphia, PA 19082. TEL 215-732-0512. FAX 215-732-7508. Ed. Darlene Friedman. adv.; bk.rev.; illus.; index. circ. 35,000.
     Description: Covers organization news, as well as issues of interest to women.

360   FI   ISSN 0038-1594
SOSIAALINEN AIKAKAUSKIRJA/SOCIAL REVIEW. (Text in Finnish; summaries in English and Swedish) 1907. 6/yr. FIM 165. Sosiaali- ja Terveysministerio - Ministry of Social Affairs and Health, Snellmaninkatu 4-6, P.O. Box 267, SF-00170 Helsinki, Finland. TEL 358-0-1601. FAX 358-0-650-442. TELEX 125073 SFM SF. Ed. Heikki S. von Hertzen. circ. 3,993. **Document type:** government publication.
     Description: Problems of public health, social welfare, social security and occupational health.

360   368   NO   ISSN 0038-1608
SOSIAL TRYGD. 1937. m. NOK 335 in Nordic countries; elsewhere $74 (effective 1996). (Trygdekontorenes Landsforening) Scandinavian University Press, P.O. Box 2959 Toeyen, N-0608 Oslo, Norway. TEL 47-22-57-54-00. FAX 47-22-57-53-53. Ed. Barth Tholens. adv.; bk.rev.; bibl.; charts; illus. circ. 7,000.
     Formerly (until 1937): Sykeforsikringsbladet (ISSN 0332-9526)
     Description: Covers social security policies in Norway.

362.4   FI   ISSN 0049-1349
SOTAINVALIDI. (Text in Finnish and Swedish) 1940. m. FIM 60($2) membership. Sotainvalidien Veljesliitto - Disabled War Veterans Association of Finland, Kasarmikatu 34 A, FIN-00130 Helsinki, Finland. TEL 358-90-478-500. FAX 358-90-4785-0100. Ed. Juhani Saari. adv.; bk.rev. circ. 52,500. **Document type:** newspaper.

361   US   ISSN 0740-4549
HV99.N59
SOURCE BOOK: SOCIAL AND HEALTH SERVICES IN THE GREATER NEW YORK AREA. 1984. irreg., latest 1993. $52.50 (effective 1995). (Department of Social Services, Human Resources Administration) Oryx Press, 4041 N. Central Ave., No. 700, Phoenix, AZ 85012-3397. TEL 602-265-2651. FAX 602-265-6250. (Co-sponsor: United Way of New York City) Pub. Phyllis Steckler. **Document type:** directory.
     Description: Information on more than 2,000 non-profit, voluntary, public and private agencies and their 5,000 individual program sites in greater New York, with community or district location, names of directors and chairpersons.

SOUTH AFRICAN MEDICAL AND DENTAL COUNCIL. REGISTER OF SUPPLEMENTARY HEALTH SERVICES PROFESSIONS. see *MEDICAL SCIENCES*

360   AT   ISSN 0816-9594
SOUTH AUSTRALIAN VOLUNTEERING. 1984. q. Aus.$40. Volunteer Centre of South Australia Inc., 155 Pirie St., Adelaide, S.A. 5000, Australia. TEL 61-8-232-0199. FAX 61-8-232-5161. Ed. Georgia Koronis. bk.rev. circ. 750. **Document type:** newsletter.
     Description: A statewide newsletter focusing on volunteering issues and policy and practice matters.

SOWER. see *RELIGIONS AND THEOLOGY*

360   AU   ISSN 1019-7729
SOZIALARBEIT IN OESTERREICH. 1965. 4/yr. S.200. Oesterreichischer Berufsverband Diplomierter Sozialarbeiterinnen, Mariahilferstr. 81, A-1060 Vienna, Austria. TEL 0222-5874656. Eds. Peter Sitte, Ursula Nader. adv.; bk.rev.; index. circ. 3,000.

360   GW   ISSN 0490-1606
HV3
SOZIALE ARBEIT; deutsche Zeitschrift fuer soziale und sozialverwandte Gebiete. 1951. m. DM.82. Deutsches Zentralinstitut fuer Soziale Fragen, Bernadottestr. 94, 14195 Berlin, Germany. TEL 030-839001-0. FAX 030-8314750. adv.; bk.rev.; abstr.; bibl. circ. 1,200. **Indexed:** Excerp.Med., P.A.I.S.For.Lang.Ind. **Document type:** newsletter.
—BLDSC (8361.030000).

SOZIALE MEDIZIN. see *MEDICAL SCIENCES*

360   GW   ISSN 0340-8469
SOZIALMAGAZIN; die Zeitschrift fuer soziale Arbeit. 1976. m. (11/yr.) DM.92 (foreign DM.102). Juventa Verlag GmbH, Ehretstr. 3, 69469 Weinheim, Germany. TEL 06201-61035. FAX 06201-13135. adv.; bk.rev.; index. circ. 7,000. **Document type:** trade publication.
—**CCC.**

SOZIALPSYCHIATRISCHE INFORMATIONEN. see *PSYCHOLOGY*

362   GW   ISSN 0939-401X
SOZIALRECHT & PRAXIS; Fachzeitschrift des VdK Deutschland fuer Vertrauensleute der Behinderten und fuer Sozialpolitiker. 1950. m. DM.43.50. Verband der Kriegs- und Wehrdienstopfer, Behinderten und Rentner Deutschlands e.V. (VdK), Wurzerstr. 4a, 53175 Bonn, Germany. TEL 0228-82093-0. FAX 0228-8209343. Ed. Guenter Neuberger. circ. 15,000. **Document type:** bulletin.
     Former titles: V D K - Mitteilungen Sozialpolitische Fachzeitschrift; V D K - Mitteilungen (ISSN 0042-1774)
     Description: Covers social politics, social law, laws covering pensions, health & accident insurance and other aspects of international social welfare laws.

360   AU
SOZIALVERSICHERUNG AKTUELL. 6/yr. Oesterreichischer Wirtschaftsverlag GmbH, Nikolsdorfergasse 7-11, A-1051 Vienna, Austria. TEL 01-555585. FAX 01-555585295. circ. 347,000. **Document type:** bulletin.

SOZIALWISSENSCHAFTEN UND BERUFSPRAXIS. see *SOCIOLOGY*

SOZIALWISSENSCHAFTLICHE LITERATUR RUNDSCHAU; Sozialarbeit-Sozialpaedagogik-Sozialpolitik-soziale Probleme. see *SOCIAL SCIENCES: COMPREHENSIVE WORKS*

361.77   CN   ISSN 0847-3390
SPIRIT. 1970. q. Canadian Red Cross Society, Alberta - Northwest Territories Division, 9931-106th St., Edmonton, Alta. T5K 1E2, Canada. TEL 403-423-2680. FAX 403-428-7092. Ed. Kathy Krug. illus. circ. 2,000.
     Former titles: Action (ISSN 0382-4527); Supersedes in part: Volunteer (ISSN 0382-4551); Swim Signals (ISSN 0382-4535); Red Cross Youth (ISSN 0382-4543)

360   SZ
SPITAELER ALTERS PFLEGEHEIME. q. Masanserstr. 124, Postfach 92, CH-7005 Chur 5, Switzerland. TEL 081-225252. FAX 081-274939. Ed. Giovanni Viecelli. circ. 8,600.

SPRINGER SERIES ON REHABILITATION. see *MEDICAL SCIENCES — Physical Medicine And Rehabilitation*

360   US   ISSN 0891-9720
SPRINGER SERIES ON SOCIAL WORK. irreg., vol.25, 1994. price varies. Springer Publishing Company, 536 Broadway, New York, NY 10012-3955. TEL 212-431-4370. FAX 212-941-7842. Ed. Albert Roberts. **Document type:** monographic series, academic/scholarly publication.
     Description: Covers various aspects of social work practice and resarch.

361.8   UK   ISSN 0260-5457
STAFF OF SCOTTISH SOCIAL WORK DEPARTMENTS. 1979. a. £1.50. Social Work Services Group, 43 Jeffrey St., Rm. 424, Edinburgh EH1 1DN, Scotland. (Subscr. to: Scottish Office Library, Publication Sales, Rm. 1-44, New St. Andrew's House, Edinburgh EH1 3TG, Scotland. FAX 0131-244-4785) **Document type:** government publication.
     Formerly: Staff of Scottish Work Departments.

STAR AND GARTER MAGAZINE. see *HOSPITALS*

STARK JEWISH NEWS. see *ETHNIC INTERESTS*

360   350   US   ISSN 1070-7719
STATE HOUSE WATCH. 1982. 20/yr. $75 to individuals; institutions $125. Massachusetts Human Service Coalition, Inc., 37 Temple Pl., 3rd Fl., Boston, MA 02111. TEL 617-482-6119. FAX 617-695-1295. Ed. Donna Southwell. circ. 700.
     Description: Covers Massachusetts human service legislation and budgets, including housing, health care, children and families, senior citizens, disabilities and mental health.

SOCIAL SERVICES AND WELFARE

362.7 US
HV741
STATE OF AMERICA'S CHILDREN YEARBOOK; an analysis of our nation's investment in children. 1981. a. $14.95. Children's Defense Fund, 25 E St., N.W., Washington, DC 20001. TEL 202-628-8787. FAX 202-662-3530. charts; stat. circ. 18,000. Indexed: SRI.
 Former titles (until 1992): State of America's Children (ISSN 1055-9213); (until 1991): Vision for America's Future; (until 1989): Children's Defense Budget (ISSN 0736-6701)
 Description: Presents an analysis of federal programs affecting children and families. Includes recommendations for positive investments in children.

361 362.7 UK ISSN 0265-718X
HQ792.2
THE STATE OF THE WORLD'S CHILDREN. (Text in Arabic, Chinese, English, French, Portugese, Spanish; summaries in more than 40 languages) 1980. a. £4($7.50) (United Nations Children's Fund (UNICEF)) Oxford University Press, Walton St., Oxford OX2 6DP, England. TEL 01865-56767. FAX 01865-56646. Ed. Peter Adamson. charts; stat. circ. 70,000. (back issues avail.)
 —BLDSC (8438.335600); Faxon. **CCC**.
 Description: Discusses worldwide events that pertain to the work of UNICEF.

361.6 153.1 US ISSN 0743-5916
HV3006.P4
STATE PLAN FOR DEVELOPMENTAL DISABILITIES. 1977. a. Developmental Disabilities Planning Council, Health & Welfare Bldg., Harrisburg, PA 17120. circ. 2,000. Document type: government publication.
 Formerly: Pennsylvania. Development Disabilities Planning Council. Pennsylvania State Plan (ISSN 0193-1423)

STATISTICS ON SOCIAL WORK EDUCATION IN THE UNITED STATES. see EDUCATION — Abstracting, Bibliographies, Statistics

361 IT
LA STILLA; organo di stampa dell'A.V.I.S. provinciale di Montova. 1965. m. Associazione Volontari Italiani Sangue (A.V.I.S.), c/o Ospedale "C. Poma", Via Albertoni 1, 46100 Mantova, Italy.

360 SW ISSN 0281-2851
STOCKHOLM STUDIES IN SOCIAL WORK. (Text in English) 1983. irreg. price varies. A W I International AB, P.O. Box 4627, S-116 91 Stockholm, Sweden. TEL 468-640-8800. FAX 468-641-1180. Ed. Hans Berglind. circ. 500.
 —BLDSC (8465.741000).

STRATHCLYDE PAPERS ON SOCIOLOGY AND SOCIAL POLICY. see SOCIOLOGY

STREETWIZE COMICS; youth rights comics. see CHILDREN AND YOUTH — For

362.8 UK
STUDENT WELFARE MANUAL. 1970. a. £15. National Union of Students, 461 Holloway Rd., London N7 6LJ, England. circ. 3,000.

STUDIENSTIFTUNG. JAHRESBERICHT. see EDUCATION — Special Education And Rehabilitation

STUDIES IN HEALTH AND HUMAN SERVICES. see PHYSICAL FITNESS AND HYGIENE

360 US
STUDIES IN SOCIAL POLICY AND WELFARE.* no.6, 1978. irreg. £8. Gower Publishing Co. Ltd., Gower Hse., Croft Rd., Aldershot, Hants GU11 3HR, England. TEL 052-331551. Ed. Robert Pinker. bibl.

360 US ISSN 8755-5360
STUDIES IN SOCIAL WELFARE POLICIES AND PROGRAMS. 1985. irreg. price varies. Greenwood Press, Inc. (Subsidiary of: Greenwood Publishing Group Inc.), 88 Post Rd. W., Box 5007, Westport, CT 06881-5007. TEL 203-226-3571. FAX 203-222-1502.
 —BLDSC (8491.626000).

SUIZIDPROPHYLAXE. see MEDICAL SCIENCES — Psychiatry And Neurology

SUMMARY INFORMATION ON MASTER OF SOCIAL WORK PROGRAMS. see EDUCATION — Higher Education

362.4 US ISSN 1047-952X
SUPPORTED EMPLOYMENT INFOLINES. 1990. m. $89 (outside N. America $129). Training Resource Network, Inc., Box 439, St. Augustine, FL 32085-0439. TEL 904-823-9800. Ed. Dawn Langton. Pub. Dale DiLeo. adv. contact: Dawn Langton. bk.rev. circ. 5,000. (back issues avail.) Document type: newsletter.
 Description: Contains news, trends, hands-on tips and strategies, and research for professionals who support people with all types of disabilities in jobs in the community. Provides career and vocational guidance.

360 UK
SURREY COMMUNITY CARE PLAN. a. Social Services Department, Planning & Performance Section, High St., Thames Ditton, Surrey KT7 0QA, England. TEL 0181-541-9672. Document type: government publication.
 —BLDSC (8548.341500).
 Formerly: Community Care Plan.

SURVEY; a quarterly journal. see BUSINESS AND ECONOMICS — Management

362 SW ISSN 0346-2129
SVENSK HANDIKAPPTIDSKRIFT. 1923. 10/yr. SEK 190. Handikappades Riksfoerbund, S-117 43 Stockholm, Sweden. TEL 46-8-18-91-00. FAX 46-8-645-65-41. Ed. Elisabet Geite; Pub. Kerstin Denkert. adv.: B&W page SEK 8900, color page SEK 13500; trim 190 x 270; adv. contact: Lars Goeran Andersson. circ. 31,600. cols./p.: 3; pp./issue: 32.
 Formerly (until 1966): Svensk Vanfoeretidskrift.

360 SW ISSN 0346-6019
SWEDEN. SOCIALSTYRELSEN. FOERFATTNINGSSAMLING: SOCIAL. Alternate title: S O S F S (S). 1976. irreg. (approx. 4/yr.). SEK 152. Socialstyrelsen - National Board of Health and Welfare, 106 30 Stockholm, Sweden. (Subscr. to: Fritzes Subscription Department, S-106 47 Stockholm, Sweden. TEL 46-8-690-90-90. FAX 46-8-205021) Ed. Gunnar Fahlberg. index. circ. 6,000. (looseleaf format) Document type: directory.
 •Also available online.
 Supersedes in part (1883-1976): Sweden. Medicinalvaesendet. Foerfattningssamling (ISSN 0346-5837).
 Description: Directory and general advice in the field of social welfare.

360 SW ISSN 1100-2808
SWEDEN. SOCIALSTYRELSEN. S O S - RAPPORT. irreg. (7-25)/yr. price varies. Fritzes AB, S-106 47 Stockholm, Sweden. TEL 46-8-690-9090. FAX 46-8-205021. charts. circ. 2,500. Document type: government publication.
 Formerly: Sweden. Socialstyrelsen. Redovisar (ISSN 0346-5799)

362.4 UK
TALKING SENSE. 1956. 4/yr. £10. Sense - National Deaf-Blind and Rubella Association, 11-13 Clifton Terrace, Finsbury Park, London N4 3SR, England. TEL 0171-272-7774. FAX 0171-272-6012. Ed. Helen Matson. adv.; bk.rev.; bibl. circ. 4,000. (processed) Document type: bulletin.
 Former titles: National Association for Deaf - Blind and Rubella Handicapped. Newsletter; National Association for Deaf - Blind and Rubella Children. Newsletter.
 Description: Covers the entire spectrum of topics relevant to deafblind people, their families and professionals in the field.

361.77 NO ISSN 0804-9807
TANKEKORS. 1921. 6/yr. NOK 100. Norges Roede Kors - Norwegian Red Cross, P.O. Box 6875, St. Olavs Plass, 0130 Oslo 1, Norway. TEL 47-02-94-30-30. FAX 47-02-20-68-40. TELEX 76011-NORCR-N. Ed. Liv Ranglan. adv. contact: Bent Westlie. bk.rev.; illus. circ. 200,000.
 —CCC.
 Former titles (until 1992): Roede Kors (ISSN 0333-2985); (until 1981): Over Alle Graenser (ISSN 0030-7335); (until 1955): Norges Roede Kors (ISSN 0332-5326)

TAX TREATMENT OF CROSS-BORDER DONATIONS; including the tax status of charities and foundations. see BUSINESS AND ECONOMICS — Public Finance, Taxation

TEL AVIV UNIVERSITY. FACULTY OF THE HUMANITIES AND SOCIAL SCIENCES. YEDION. see HUMANITIES: COMPREHENSIVE WORKS

TELEPHONE PIONEER. see CLUBS

361.6 CR ISSN 0492-6471
TEMAS SOCIALES. 1954. q. Ministerio de Trabajo y Prevision Social, Apartado 2041, San Jose, Costa Rica.

362 US
TEXAS. DEPARTMENT ON AGING. ANNUAL REPORT. 1982. a. free. (Department on Aging) S, Box 12786, Austin, TX 78711. TEL 512-444-2727. Ed. James Grabbs. Document type: government publication.
 Former titles: Texas Department on Aging. Biennial Report; Texas. Department on Aging. Annual Report; Texas. Governor's Committee on Aging. Biennial Report (ISSN 0082-3058)

360 SZ
THEMA. (Text in German) 1919. q. 36.80 SFr. Verlag Pro Juventute, Seehofstr. 15, CH-8022 Zurich, Switzerland. TEL 01-2520719. FAX 01-2522824. Ed. Christian Urech. adv. contact: Christian Urech. bk.rev. circ. 3,300. Document type: bulletin.
 Formerly: Team (ISSN 1012-7895)

360 GW ISSN 0342-2275
THEORIE UND PRAXIS DER SOZIALEN ARBEIT. 1947. m. DM.60. Arbeiterwohlfahrt Bundesverband e.V., Oppelner Str. 130, 53119 Bonn, Germany. TEL 0228-6685148. FAX 0228-6685209. Ed. Heinz Niedrig. adv.; bk.rev. circ. 3,000. Document type: bulletin.
 Formerly (until 1972): Neues Beginnen (ISSN 0028-3592)
 Description: News about social work and social politics.

THERAPY WEEKLY; the newspaper for the remedial professions. see HOSPITALS

360 UK
THIRD FORCE NEWS AND INFORM. 1985. fortn. £36. Scottish Council for Voluntary Organisations, 18-19 Claremont Crescent, Edinburgh EH7 4QD, Scotland. TEL 0131-556-3882. FAX 0131-556-0279. Eds. Sarah Nelson, Ulla Hipkin. adv. contact: Sarah Nelson. circ. 1,300. Document type: newsletter.
 Former titles: Third Sector Fortnight and Inform; Third Sector (ISSN 0267-3053)
 Description: News and information for voluntary and community organizations in Scotland.

360 UK ISSN 0268-4047
THIS CARING BUSINESS. 1985. 10/yr. £50 (rest of Europe £75; elsewhere £80). Careworld Publishing House Ltd., 1 St. Thomas's Rd., Hastings, E. Sussex TN34 3LG, England. TEL 01424-718406. FAX 01424-718460. Ed. Mary Glossup. adv.; bk.rev.; charts; stat.; tr.lit. circ. 18,366. (tabloid format; back issues avail.) Document type: trade publication.
 Description: Covers commercially oriented matters relating to long-stay health and residential care.

360 US ISSN 0743-2437
THIS WEEK IN WASHINGTON. 1980. w. (50/yr.). $105 to non-members; members $95; foreign $115. American Public Welfare Association, 810 First St., N.E., Ste. 500, Washington, DC 20002-4267. TEL 202-682-0100. Ed. Susan Kellam. circ. 800.
 Description: Updates on legislative action, federal legislation, and personnel changes.

TIJDSCHRIFT VOOR BEDRIJFS- EN VERZEKERINGSGENEESKUNDE. see MEDICAL SCIENCES

TINNITUS TODAY. see MEDICAL SCIENCES — Otorhinolaryngology

TOLEDO JEWISH NEWS; the monthly newspaper for the Jewish community of greater Toledo. see ETHNIC INTERESTS

361.7 US
TOLSTOY FOUNDATION NEWS. (Text in English and Russian) 1978. s-a. free. Tolstoy Foundation, Inc., 200 Park Ave. S., Rm. 1612, New York, NY 10003-1522. TEL 212-677-7770. FAX 212-674-0519. TELEX 66366. circ. 4,000 (controlled).

SOCIAL SERVICES AND WELFARE

300   MX   ISSN 0187-7542
F1234
TOPODRILO; sociedad, ciencia y arte. 1988. bi-m. $45. Universidad Autonoma Metropolitana, Iztapalapa, Division de Ciencias Sociales y Humanidades, Av. Michoacan y la Purisima, Col. Vicentina, 09340 Mexico DF, Mexico. TEL 525-77244760. FAX 6125682. E-mail: asga@xanum.uam.mx. Ed. Antulio Sanchez Garcia.
    Description: Presents the new cultural, political, artistic, scientific and social trends in Mexico. Reflects Mexico's current problems and worries.

TRANSIZIONE. see *POLITICAL SCIENCE*

360   FR   ISSN 0753-9711
TRAVAIL SOCIAL ACTUALITES. 1983. w. 555 F. (Europe 690 F.; America 840 F.) (effective Sep. 1995). Droit et Societe, 67 rue de l'Aqueduc, 75010 Paris, France. TEL 40-35-95-40. FAX 40-35-17-11. Ed. Pierre Bance. adv. circ. 13,000.

TREATING ABUSE TODAY; an international magazine of abuse survivorship and therapy. see *PSYCHOLOGY*

362   NE
TREFPUNT. 1965. 52/yr. fl.62.50. Ministerie van Welzijn, Volksgezondheid en Sport, Publieksvoorlichting - Ministry of Health, Welfare and Sport, Public Information Office, Postbus 5406, 2280 HK Rijswijk, Netherlands. TEL 31-70-3406015. Ed. G. Zandbergen. bk.rev.; abstr.; film rev.; play rev.; index. circ. 8,000. **Indexed**: Key to Econ.Sci. **Document type**: government publication.

360 340   US
TRIUMPH OF HOPE. 1986. a. $5. National Right to Life Committee, Inc., 419 Seventh St., N.W., Ste. 500, Washington, DC 20004. TEL 202-626-8800. FAX 202-737-9189. Ed. David Andrusko.
    Description: Covers recent developments, legislation, education and political activities regarding abortion, infanticide and euthanasia.

TRUDOV INVALID. see *INSURANCE*

TULSA JEWISH REVIEW. see *ETHNIC INTERESTS*

TWIN SERVICES REPORTER. see *CHILDREN AND YOUTH — About*

U C S F MAGAZINE. (University of California at San Francisco) see *MEDICAL SCIENCES*

362.5 296.7   US
U J F VIRGINIA NEWS. (United Jewish Federation) 1959. 21/yr. free. United Jewish Federation of Tidewater, 7300 Newport Ave., Norfolk, VA 23505. TEL 804-489-8040. FAX 804-489-8230. Ed. Reba Karp. **Document type**: newspaper.
    Description: Discusses local community-service projects and programs.

361 362.7   UN   ISSN 1013-3194
U N I C E F POLICY REVIEW SERIES. (Text in English; occasionally Arabic, French, Spanish) 1988. irreg. price varies. United Nations Children's Fund (UNICEF), 3 United Nations Plaza, Rm.H-12G, New York, NY 10017. TEL 212-702-7279. FAX 212-755-1449. TELEX 175989TRT. Ed. Dr. Pierre-Emeric Mandl. circ. 12,000. (also avail. in microform from CMC) **Indexed**: IDA. **Document type**: monographic series.

360   US   ISSN 0082-8556
U S O ANNUAL REPORT. a. free. United Service Organizations, Inc., U S O World Headquarters, Washington Navy Yard, 901 M St., S.E., Bldg. 198, Washington, DC 20374-5096. TEL 202-610-5700. FAX 202-610-5701. Ed. Miguel Monteverde. circ. 5,000. **Document type**: corporate report.

UNDERVISNING OG VELFERD/EDUCATION AND WELFARE. see *MILITARY*

360   FR   ISSN 0041-7041
UNION SOCIALE.* 1947. m. 75 F. Union Nationale Interfederale des Oeuvres Privees Sanitaires et Sociales, c/o Federation Nationale des Syndicats Autonomes, 19 bvd. Sebastopol, 75001 Paris, France. TEL 42-25-16-76. FAX 42-56-42-15. Ed. Jean Vellard. adv.; illus.; index. circ. 8,000.

UNIONIST. see *LABOR UNIONS*

361.8   US
UNITED COMMUNITY PLANNING CORPORATION. REPORT.* irreg., no.161, 1979. United Community Planning Corporation, c/o Boston Foundation, 1 Boston Pl., no.2400, Boston, MA 02103-4402.

361   US
UNITED FOR SERVICE.* 1977. q. free. United Way International, 701 N. Fairfax St., Alexandria, VA 22314. TEL 703-519-0092. Ed. Margaret McLaughlin. circ. 300. (looseleaf format) **Document type**: newsletter.
    Description: Covers international philanthropic activities of United Way.

361 362.7   UN   ISSN 0254-2447
UNITED NATIONS CHILDREN'S FUND. ANNUAL REPORT. Cover title: UNICEF Annual Report. (Text in English, French, Spanish) 1977. a. free. United Nations Children's Fund (UNICEF), UNICEF House, 3 United Nations, New York, NY 10017. TEL 212-326-7000. FAX 212-888-7465. TELEX 7607848. Ed.Bd. circ. 66,650 (controlled). (also avail. in diskette format; back issues avail.) **Document type**: corporate report.
    Description: Discusses the work that UNICEF has done over the past year to improve the condition of children worldwide.

361 362.7   UN   ISSN 1013-3178
UNITED NATIONS CHILDREN'S FUND. PROGRAMME DIVISION. STAFF WORKING PAPERS SERIES. 1988. irreg. (2-4/yr). price varies. United Nations Children's Fund (UNICEF), Programme Division, 3 United Nations Plaza, Rm. DH-49B, New York, NY 10017. TEL 212-702-7279. FAX 212-755-1449. TELEX 175989TRT. Ed. Dr. Pierre-Emeric Mandl. circ. 4,000. (also avail. in microform from CMC)

360   UN   ISSN 0252-452X
UNITED NATIONS ECONOMIC AND SOCIAL COMMISSION FOR ASIA AND THE PACIFIC. SOCIAL DEVELOPMENT DIVISION. SOCIAL WORK EDUCATION AND DEVELOPMENT. 1966. irreg. United Nations Economic and Social Commission for Asia and the Pacific (ESCAP), Social Development Division, United Nations Bldg., Rajadamnern Ave., Bangkok 10200, Thailand.
    Formerly: United Nations Economic and Social Commission for Asia and the Pacific. Social Development Division. Social Work Training and Teaching Materials Newsletter (ISSN 0085-7513)

361.6   US   ISSN 0190-373X
HC110.P63
U.S. COMMUNITY SERVICES ADMINISTRATION. ANNUAL REPORT.* Key Title: Annual Report of Community Services Administration. 1976. a. U.S. Community Services Administration, 1200 19th St., N.W., Washington, DC 20506. TEL 202-655-4000.
    Formerly: U.S. Office of Economic Opportunity. Annual Report.

U.S. DEPARTMENT OF VETERANS AFFAIRS. ANNUAL REPORT. see *INSURANCE*

U.S. DEPARTMENT OF VETERANS AFFAIRS. SUMMARY OF MEDICAL PROGRAMS. see *MEDICAL SCIENCES*

353.007   US   ISSN 0091-6242
JK1672
U.S. GENERAL SERVICES ADMINISTRATION. MANAGEMENT REPORT. Key Title: Management Report - General Services Administration. a. U.S. General Services Administration, Office of Public Affairs, 18th and F Sts., N.W., Washington, DC 20405. TEL 202-501-1794. FAX 202-501-4281. (Avail. from: Supt. of Documents, U.S. Government Printing Office, Washington, DC 20402. TEL 202-783-3238) stat. **Document type**: government publication.

362   US   ISSN 0161-2417
HV91.N25b
U.S. NATIONAL CENTER FOR SOCIAL STATISTICS. HEARINGS IN PUBLIC ASSISTANCE. (NCSS E-8) 1970. s-a. free. U.S. National Center for Social Statistics, U.S. Department of Health, Education and Welfare, 330 Independence Ave., S.W., Washington, DC 20201. TEL 301-436-7900. stat.
    Formerly (until 1976): U.S. National Center for Social Statistics. Fair Hearings in Public Assistance (ISSN 0145-9422)

362   CN   ISSN 0841-9698
UNITED WAY CANADA. DIRECTORY. (Text in English and French) 1963. a. membership. United Way of Canada, 56 Sparks St., Ste. 404, Ottawa, ON K1P 5A9, Canada. TEL 613-236-7041. index, cum.index; circ. controlled. (processed) **Document type**: directory.
    Former titles (until 1988): United Way of Canada. Directory of Members (ISSN 0705-1107); (until 1977): United Way Canada. Directory (ISSN 0319-7182); Directory of Canadian Community Funds and Councils (ISSN 0084-9863)

360   UK
UNIVERSITY OF BIRMINGHAM. DEPARTMENT OF SOCIAL POLICY AND SOCIAL WORK. WORKING WITH POVERTY SERIES. irreg., no.5, 1993. £3.50. University of Birmingham, Department of Social Policy and Social Work, Edgbaston, Birmingham B15 2TT, England. TEL 0121-414-5733. FAX 0121-414-5726. **Document type**: monographic series.

362.7 340   US
UNMARRIED PARENTS TODAY. 1981. bi-m. $200 membership. National Council for Adoption, Inc., 1930 17th St., N.W., Washington, DC 20009-2607. TEL 202-328-1200. Ed. Mary Beth Seader. (back issues avail.)
    Description: For social workers and other professionals providing services to pregnant and parenting teens.

360   II   ISSN 0377-6352
HN681
UPLIFT. (Text in English and Hindi) 1973. q. Rs.20($10) Low Income Family Emancipation (Life) Society, 69, Sector XII, R.K. Puram, New Delhi 110 022, India. TEL 11-600-410. Ed. T.J. Abraham. adv. contact: Kishore Kumar. illus. circ. 2,500.

360 352.7   US   ISSN 0042-0832
HT101
URBAN AND SOCIAL CHANGE REVIEW. 1967. s-a. $8. Boston College, Graduate School of Social Work, McGuinn Hall, Rm. 109, Chestnut Hill, MA 02167. TEL 617-552-4038. Ed. Robert M. Moroney. adv.; bk.rev.; film rev. circ. 2,500. (also avail. in microform from UMI; reprint service avail. from UMI) **Indexed**: A.B.C.Pol.Sci. (until 1989), Abstr.Soc.Work, Adol.Ment.Hlth.Abstr., Amer.Hist.& Life, Curr.Cont., Econ.Abstr., Geo.Abstr., Hist.Abstr., Human Resour.Abstr., Int.Polit.Sci.Abstr., Lang.& Lang.Behav.Abstr., Med.Care Rev., Pers.Manage.Abstr., Sage Fam.Stud.Abstr., Sage Pub.Admin.Abstr., Sage Urb.Stud.Abstr., Sociol.Abstr., SSCI, Trans.Res.Abstr. —UMI. CCC.
    Formerly: Institute of Human Sciences. Review.

360   SW   ISSN 0042-1553
UTE OCH HEMMA; tidning for svenskt sjoefolk och turister. 1928. 8/yr. SEK 80 (effective 1991). Naemnden foer Svenska Kyrkan i Utlandet, P.O. Box 205, S-751 04 Uppsala, Sweden. FAX 18-124568. Ed. Lena Sjoestroem. adv.; bk.rev.; illus.; indes. circ. 12,500.
    Description: Church of Sweden, seamen's and tourist's mission abroad.

V A C R O REPORTER. (Victorian Association for the Care and Resettlement of Offenders) see *CRIMINOLOGY AND LAW ENFORCEMENT*

355   GW
V D K ZEITUNG. 1946. m. DM.18. Verband der Kriegs- und Wehrdienstopfer, Behinderten und Rentner Deutschlands e.V. (VdK), Wurzerstr. 4a, 53175 Bonn, Germany. TEL 0228-820930. FAX 0228-8209343. Ed. Joachim Faustmann. circ. 1,000,000. **Document type**: bulletin.
    Formerly: Fackel (ISSN 0014-6447)
    Description: Covers social politics, social law, laws covering pensions, health and accident insurance and other aspects of international social welfare laws.

VAEL & VE. see *PUBLIC HEALTH AND SAFETY*

VALUES. see *RELIGIONS AND THEOLOGY — Protestant*

711.4   US   ISSN 0892-6433
VANGUARD (MILWAUKEE, 1970). 1970. q. $55 includes the Journal (foreign $65). Community Development Society, 1123 N. Water St., Milwaukee, WI 53202. TEL 414-276-7106. FAX 414-276-7704. Ed. Linda Sunde. (reprint service avail. from UMI) **Document type**: newsletter.

SOCIAL SERVICES AND WELFARE

VANISHED CHILDREN'S ALLIANCE NEWSLETTER; news and views from the Vanished Children's Alliance. see *CHILDREN AND YOUTH — About*

361.6   VE   ISSN 0798-9474
VENEZUELA. MINISTERIO DE SANIDAD Y ASISTENCIA SOCIAL. MEMORIA Y CUENTA. 1936. a. Ministerio de Sanidad y Asistencia Social, Oficina de Publicaciones, Biblioteca y Archivo, Centro Simon Bolivar, Edificio Sur, Caracas, Venezuela. Ed. Manuel Boet. circ. 3,000. **Document type:** government publication.

368   AU
VERBAND DER VERSICHERUNGSUNTERNEHMEN OESTERREICHS. GESCHAEFTSBERICHT. 1956. a. S.296. Verband der Versicherungsunternehmen Oesterreichs, Schwarzenbergplatz 7, A-1030 Vienna, Austria. Ed. Gregor Kozak. circ. 1,000. **Document type:** corporate report.
    Formerly: Verband der Versicherungsunternehmungen Oesterreichs. Bericht ueber das Geschaeftsjahr (ISSN 0083-5501)

360   GW   ISSN 0935-1558
DIE VERSORGUNGSVERWALTUNG. 1949. bi-m. DM.94. (Gewerkschaft der Versorgungsverwaltung) W. Kohlhammer GmbH, Hessbruehlstr. 69, 70565 Stuttgart, Germany. TEL 0711-7863-1. FAX 0711-7863263. Ed. G. Geist. **Document type:** bulletin.
  —CCC.
    Formerly: Versorgungsbeamte (ISSN 0340-3289)

360   UK   ISSN 0083-601X
VICTORIA LEAGUE FOR COMMONWEALTH FRIENDSHIP. ANNUAL REPORT. 1901. a. membership. Victoria League, 18 Northumberland Ave., London WC2N 5BJ, England. **Document type:** corporate report.

VIEWPOINT (LONDON, 1995). see *MEDICAL SCIENCES — Psychiatry And Neurology*

362.7   SA
VILLAGE NEWS. 1993. q. donation. S O S Children's Village Association of South Africa, P.O. Box 22, Randburg 2125, South Africa. (Affiliate: S O S Kinderdorf International) illus. **Document type:** newsletter.

360   CN   ISSN 0823-0404
VIS-A-VIS; a national newsletter on family violence. (Text in English, French) 1986. q. free. Canadian Council on Social Development, 55 Parkdale Ave., Box 3505, Sta. C, Ottawa, ON K1Y 4G1, Canada. TEL 613-728-1865. FAX 613-728-9387. film rev. circ. 10,000. (back issues avail.) **Document type:** newsletter.
    Description: Covers family violence, abuse, alcoholism, addiction, violence in the workplace, elder abuse, disabled victims.

VISION (MILWAUKEE). see *RELIGIONS AND THEOLOGY — Roman Catholic*

VIVRE ENSEMBLE. see *EDUCATION — Special Education And Rehabilitation*

VOCE DELL'EMIGRANTE. see *ETHNIC INTERESTS*

VOICE OF SILENCE NEWSLETTER. see *HANDICAPPED — Hearing Impaired*

VOICE OF THE DUTCHESS JEWISH COMMUNITY. see *ETHNIC INTERESTS*

361.8 382   US
VOICES (AUSTIN). 1972. m. free. Texas Conference, Volunteers for Educational and Social Services, 3001 S. Congress Ave., Austin, TX 78704-6489. Colleen Pritchard. **Document type:** newsletter.
    Description: Describes the organization's community-service volunteer programs and participants to serve God by helping the poor.

VOICES OF THAI WOMEN. see *WOMEN'S INTERESTS*

360   FR
VOIX DE FRANCE. 1927. m. 150 F. Union des Francais de l'Etranger, 146 bd. Haussmann, 75008 Paris, France. FAX 42-56-34-56. Ed. Bruno de Leusse. adv.; illus.

360   UK   ISSN 0951-4481
VOLUNTARY AGENCIES DIRECTORY. 1928. biennial. £15.95. National Council for Voluntary Organisations, Regent's Wharf, 8 All Saints St., London N1 9RL. TEL 0171-713-6161. FAX 0171-713-6300. adv. **Document type:** directory.
  —BLDSC (9254.573300).
    Former titles: Voluntary Organisations; Voluntary Social Services (ISSN 0083-6907)
    Description: Lists over 2,000 leading national agencies, ranging from small, specialist, self-help groups to long-established charities.

360   UK   ISSN 0268-4543
VOLUNTARY VOICE. 1985. 10/yr. 68 Chalton St., London NW1 1JR, England. TEL 0171-388-0241. FAX 0171-387-2191. Ed. C. Mercer. bk.rev. circ. 1,600.
  —BLDSC (9254.577600).
    Formed by the merger of (1980-1985): London Community Work Service Newsletter (ISSN 0264-0015); (1979-1985): London Voluntary News (ISSN 0263-9386); Which was formerly (until 1978): London Council of Social Services. Information Bulletin (ISSN 0143-9936)

360   US
HV89
VOLUNTEER! (NEW YORK, 1944); the comprehensive guide to voluntary service in the US and abroad. 1944. s-a. Council on International Educational Exchange, 205 E. 42nd St., New York, NY 10017. TEL 212-661-1414. Ed. Richard Christiano. adv. contact: Stephanie Orange. circ. 8,000. **Document type:** directory, trade publication.
    Formerly (until 1985): Invest Yourself (ISSN 0148-6802)
    Description: Directory of voluntary service and work camp opportunities in the US and abroad for all ages.

VOLUNTEER LEADER. see *HOSPITALS*

361.8   US   ISSN 0000-1325
HN90.V64
VOLUNTEERISM; the directory of organizations, training, programs and publications. 1984. irreg., 3rd edition, 1991. $119. R.R. Bowker, A Reed Reference Publishing company, 121 Chanlon Rd., New Providence, NJ 07974. TEL 908-464-6800. FAX 908-665-6688. TELEX 138 755. (Subscr. to: Order Dept., Box 31, New Providence, NJ 07974-9903. TEL 800-521-8110) Ed. Harriet Clyde Kipps. **Document type:** bibliography, directory.
    Formerly (until 1990): Community Resources Directory (ISSN 1042-2315)
    Description: Covers volunteer organizations, services and training programs that provide human services in many areas.

360   US
VOLUNTEER'S GAZETTE.* q. free. Volunteers of America, 3939 N. Causeway, Ste. 400, Metairie, LA 70002. Ed. Denise Chetta. circ. 32,000. (controlled). (tabloid format; back issues avail.)
    Description: Describes the mission and work of Volunteers of America across the nation.

VOLUNTEERS IN DIRECT ACTION. see *GERONTOLOGY AND GERIATRICS*

VOTE AND SURVEY; magazine of political, social and economic issues. see *POLITICAL SCIENCE*

360   SZ
VOTRE CROIX ROUGE.* 1974. q. Section Genevoise de la Croix-Rouge Suisse, 9 route des Acacias, CH-1211 Geneva 24, Switzerland. circ. 500.

362.5   US   ISSN 1046-7548
HC79.P6
W H Y; challenging hunger and poverty. Variant title: Why. 1976. q. $18 (foreign $25). World Hunger Year, 505 Eigth Ave., 21st Fl., New York, NY 10018-6582. TEL 212-629-8850. FAX 212-465-9274. E-mail: why ria@aol.com; 43140,3153@compuserve.com. Ed. Peter Mann. adv.; bk.rev. circ. 3,000. (also avail. in microfilm from UMI) **Indexed:** Alt.Press Ind., HR Rep., P.A.I.S. **Document type:** academic/scholarly publication.
  —BLDSC (9312.565500); UMI.
    Former titles (until no.46, 1989): Food Monitor (ISSN 0162-0045); (until 1985): Mini-Monitor.
    Description: Provides information to the general public, the media and policymakers on the extent and causes of hunger and poverty in the United States and abroad. Deals with poverty-related issues such as environment and development, food and agriculture, and self-reliance.
  Refereed Serial

362.7   UK
WAKE UP (LONDON). 2/yr. membership. National Society for the Prevention of Cruelty to Children, 67 Saffron Hill, London EC1N 8RS, England. TEL 071-242-1626. FAX 071-831-9562. illus. circ. 10,000. **Document type:** bulletin.
    Former titles: Wings; Young N S P C C News; League of Pity Paper (ISSN 0047-4258)

360   UK
WALES COUNCIL FOR VOLUNTARY ACTION. BRIEFING PAPER. irreg., no.4, 1995. £2.50. Wales Council for Voluntary Action - Cyngor Gweithredu Gwirfoddol Cymru, Crescent Rd., Caerphilly, Mid Glamorgan CF8 1XL, Wales. TEL 01222-869224. FAX 01222-860627. **Document type:** monographic series.

360   UK
▼**WALES COUNCIL FOR VOLUNTARY ACTION. REPORT SERIES/CYNGOR GWEITHREDU GWIRFODDOL CYMRU CYFRES ADRODDIAD.** (Text in English, Welsh) 1994. irreg., no.3, 1994. £3. Wales Council for Voluntary Action - Cyngor Gweithredu Gwirfoddol Cymru, Crescent Rd., Caerphilly, Mid Glamorgan CF8 1XL, Wales. TEL 01222-869224. FAX 01222-860627. **Document type:** monographic series.

361.7   US   ISSN 0148-3188
HV98.W3
WASHINGTON (STATE). ATTORNEY GENERAL'S OFFICE. CHARITABLE TRUST DIRECTORY. 1967. a. 20 (effective 1994). Attorney General's Office, Charitable Trust Division, c/o Sandy Stenberg, 1110 Capitol Way S., Box 40106, Olympia, WA 98504-0106. TEL 206-753-0863. FAX 206-586-8772. Ed. Jeanette Dieckman. circ. 1,000. **Document type:** directory, government publication.
    Formerly: Washington (State). Attorney General's Office. Directory of Charitable Organizations and Trusts Registered with the Office of Attorney General (ISSN 0093-6693)
    Description: Consists of organizations and trusts registered with the Attorney General's Office.

360 610   US   ISSN 0095-1609
HV86
WASHINGTON (STATE) DEPARTMENT OF SOCIAL AND HEALTH SERVICES. INCOME MAINTENANCE, COMMUNITY SOCIAL SERVICES AND MEDICAL ASSISTANCE. vol.27, 1974. m. free. Department of Social and Health Services, Office of Program Analysis, MS. OB-34F, Olympia, WA 98504. TEL 206-753-7039. charts; stat. **Document type:** government publication.

WASHINGTON DIOCESE. see *RELIGIONS AND THEOLOGY — Protestant*

SOCIAL SERVICES AND WELFARE

328 353.84   US   ISSN 0149-2578
WASHINGTON SOCIAL LEGISLATION BULLETIN. 1944. s-m. $65. Child Welfare League of America, Inc., Social Legislation Information Service, 440 First St., N.W., Ste. 310, Washington, DC 20001-2085. TEL 202-638-2952. FAX 202-638-4004. Ed. Marjorie Kopp. index every 2 yrs. circ. 2,300. (also avail. in microfiche from UMI; reprint service avail. from UMI) **Document type:** newsletter.
—UMI.
    Formerly: Washington Bulletin (ISSN 0037-7775)
    Description: Reports on federal social legislation and the activities of federal agencies in health, education, welfare, housing, employment, and other social welfare affecting children, the elderly, the handicapped, and juvenile delinquents.

361.3   US
WASHINGTON STATE CASE MANAGEMENT RESOURCE DIRECTORY. Variant title: Case Management Resource Directory. a. a. $10. Employment Security Department, Labor Market and Economic Analysis Branch, Box 9046, Olympia, WA 98507-9046. TEL 800-235-7761. FAX 360-438-3216. **Document type:** directory, government publication.
    Description: Lists mental health services for each of the 39 counties and explains services offered by statewide organizations.

360   GW   ISSN 0043-2059
WEGE ZUR SOZIALVERSICHERUNG. 1947. m. DM.66. Asgard-Verlag Dr. Werner Hippe KG, Einsteinstr. 10, 53757 St. Augustin, Germany. TEL 02241-3164-0. Eds. W. Hippe, A. Guenther. adv.; bk.rev.; abstr.; bibl. circ. 4,500. (tabloid format) **Indexed:** World Bibl.Soc.Sec.

360   AT   ISSN 0310-6969
WELCARE. 1973. q. Aus.$1 per no. Jewish Welfare Society Inc., 466 Punt Rd., South Yarra, Vic. 3141, Australia. Ed. Laurence A. Joseph. adv. circ. 17,000.

360   UK   ISSN 0269-879X
WELFARE. 1980. 3/yr. £15. Institute of Welfare Officers, 254 The Corn Exchange, Hanging Ditch, Manchester M4 3ES, England. TEL 061-832-1374. Ed. Lisa Davies. adv.; bk.rev.; illus. circ. 2,000.
—BLDSC (9293.499500).
    Former titles (until 1990): Welfare Journal; Welfare and Social Services Journal (ISSN 0261-4049); Welfare Officer.

WELFARE BENEFITS GUIDE. see *BUSINESS AND ECONOMICS — Labor And Industrial Relations*

360   SA   ISSN 0250-3468
WELFARE FOCUS/WELSYNSFOKUS. (Text in Afrikaans and English) 1971. s-a. free. Department of Welfare and Population Development, Private Bag X 828, Pretoria 0001, South Africa. TEL 27-12-3120000. FAX 27-12-3242647. bk.rev. circ. 2,000. (back issues avail.) **Document type:** government publication.

360   UK   ISSN 0263-2098
WELFARE RIGHTS BULLETIN. 1974. 6/yr. £12($20) C P A G Ltd. (Child Poverty Action Group), 1-5 Bath St., London EC1V 9PY, England. TEL 071-253-3406. **Indexed:** Euro.LJI, LJI.
    Description: Includes information about the rights information, practice, law, news, and reviews for the UK welfare adviser. Complements and updates the CPAG Benefit Guides to provide the fullest coverage of the workings of the UK social security system.

361 331.1   US   ISSN 1060-5622
WELFARE TO WORK; a review of developments in the welfare job training and placement field. 1992. bi-w. $267. M I I Publications, Inc., 1211 Connecticut Ave. N.W., Ste. 705, Washington, DC 20036. TEL 202-293-1740. FAX 202-293-0377. Ed. D. Lucas Graves; Pub. Cecilio Morales. bk.rev. (back issues avail.) **Document type:** newsletter.

WELFARER. see *ETHNIC INTERESTS*

360   UK   ISSN 0043-2407
WELLDOER. 1956. q. 50p. League of Welldoers, 119-133 Limekiln Lane, Liverpool 5, England. Ed. W.J. Horn. bk.rev. circ. 5,000.

360   UK
WELSH OFFICE. SOCIAL SERVICES INSPECTORATE. TRAINING SUPPORT PROGRAMME FOR THE PERSONAL SOCIAL SERVICES. PROGRESS REPORT. a. Welsh Office, Social Services Inspectorate, New Crown Bldg., Cathays Park, Cardiff CF1 3NQ, Wales. **Document type:** government publication.
—BLDSC (6922.866000).

360   GW   ISSN 0043-2644
WELTWEITE HILFE. 1951. 4/yr. free. Diakonisches Werk in Hessen und Nassau, Ederstr. 12, 6000 Frankfurt a.M. 90, Germany. FAX 069-7947-310. Ed. Juergen Albert. bk.rev.; illus. circ. 7,000.

354   AT   ISSN 1320-0666
WESTERN AUSTRALIA. DEPARTMENT FOR COMMUNITY DEVELOPMENT. ANNUAL REPORT. 1973. a. free. Department for Community Development, 189 Royal St., E. Perth, W.A. 6004, Australia. TEL 61-9-222-2555. FAX 61-9-222-2776. stat.; circ. 2,000 (controlled). **Document type:** government publication.
    Former titles (until 1992): Western Australia. Department for Community Services. Annual Report (ISSN 0817-1327); (until 1985): Western Australia. Department for Community Welfare. Annual Report.
    Description: A report on the operations of the government department responsible for areas such as support of disadvantaged communities (eg Aboriginal communities), facilitating the development of self supporting communities, early childhood services, parent-child conflict, families and individuals facing financial crises, child protection, homeless youth, young offenders, foster care, and adoptions.

WHAT'S HAPPENING IN WASHINGTON. see *EDUCATION*

362.4   UK
WHEELS. 1986. q. £4. Wheels Club, Queen Elizabeth Military Hospital, Stadium Rd., Woolwich SE18 4QH, England. TEL 0322-347651. (Subscr. to: 45 Castleton Ave., Bexleyheath, Kent DA7 6QT, England) Ed. Major B.H. Tinton. adv.; bk.rev. circ. 10,000. (reprint service avail. from KTO) **Document type:** newsletter.

WHO CARES; a journal of service and action. see *CHILDREN AND YOUTH — For*

360   UK   ISSN 0141-7126
WHO MINDS? 1977. q. membership. (National Childminding Association) Nexus Media Ltd., Warwick House, Azalea Dr., Swanley, Kent BR8 8HY, England. TEL 01322-660070. FAX 01322-667633. adv.: B&W page £892, color page £1260; trim 187 x 268. circ. 63,000 (controlled). **Document type:** consumer publication.

363   US   ISSN 1072-2513
GE60
WHOLE TERRAIN. 1992. a. Antioch New England Graduate School, 40 Avon St., Keene, NH 03431-3516. TEL 603-357-3122. FAX 603-357-0718.

361.73   US   ISSN 1048-809X
E154.7
WHO'S WEALTHY IN AMERICA; a prospecting list & directory of 102,000 affluent Americans. 1991. a. (in 2 vols.). $415. Taft Group, 12300 Twinbrook Pkwy., Ste. 520, Rockville, MD 20852. TEL 301-816-0210. FAX 301-816-0210. (Subscr. to: Taft Group, Box 33477, Detroit, MI 48232-5477. TEL 800-877-TAFT. FAX 313-961-60833) (also avail. in diskette format)
    Description: Lists wealthy Americans, along with their political contributions, major stockholdings, education and alma mater, and important life-style indicators.

360   GW   ISSN 0721-8834
WIDERSPRUECHE. 1981. q. DM.63. Verlag 2000 GmbH, Bleichstr. 5-7, 63065 Offenbach, Germany. TEL 069-821116. circ. 4,500. **Document type:** bulletin.

361.7   UK
WILL TO CHARITY GROUP: CHARITIES BY COUNTIES AND REGIONS. 1978. a. free. Will to Charity Ltd., Equus House, Rear of 48 High St., Walton-on-Thames, Surrey KT12 1BY, England. TEL 0932-227711. FAX 0932-253988.

361.7   UK
WILL TO CHARITY GROUP: CHARITIES' STORY BOOK. no.4, 1974. a. free. Will to Charity Ltd., Equus House, Rear of 48 High St., Walton-on-Thames, Surrey KT12 1BY, England. TEL 0932-227711. FAX 0932-253988. Ed. Anne Frazer Simpson. adv.; illus. circ. 20,000.
    Formerly: Will to Charity: Charities' Story Book.

361.7   UK
WILL TO CHARITY GROUP: HANDBOOK OF CHARITIES. 1984. a. free. Will to Charity ltd., Equus House, Rear of 48 High St., Walton-on-Thames, Surrey KT12 1BY, England. TEL 0932-227711. FAX 0932-253988.

360   UK
WILLIAM TEMPLE FOUNDATION. OCCASIONAL PAPER. irreg., no.23, 1993. £3. William Temple Foundation, Manchester Business School, Manchester M15 6PB, England. Ed. Malcolm Brown. **Document type:** monographic series.

WINDSOR JEWISH FEDERATION. see *ETHNIC INTERESTS*

WOMEN AGAINST RAPE NEWSLETTER. see *WOMEN'S INTERESTS*

WOMEN'S DIARY (YEAR). see *WOMEN'S INTERESTS*

360   AT   ISSN 0310-9062
WOMEN'S ELECTORAL LOBBY (SOUTH AUSTRALIAN) NEWSLETTER. 1972. b-m. Aus.$30. Women's Electoral Lobby (S.A.), 155 Pirie St., Rm. 2, Adelaide, S.A. 5000, Australia. TEL 08-232-2245. FAX 08-232-0675. (Subscr. to.: G.P.O. Box 2026, Adeleide, S.A. 5001, Australia) Ed. Denise Tzumli. bk.rev. (looseleaf format; back issues avail.) **Document type:** newsletter.

361   US
WOODEN BELL. 5/yr. Catholic Relief Services, 209 W. Fayette St., Baltimore, MD 21201-3443. TEL 410-625-2220. FAX 410-234-2983. Ed. Carol Caldwell.
    Formerly: Spectrum (New York).
    Description: Informs donors of what's happening in the world of CRS. Highlights various development programs and disaster relief efforts in different countries.

WORD FROM WASHINGTON. see *HANDICAPPED*

360   US
WORKPLACE IN THE COMMUNITY.* 1985. q. membership. Points of Light Foundation, 1737 H St. N.W., Washington, DC 20006. TEL 202-223-9186. Ed. Brenda Hanlon. circ. 3,500. **Document type:** newsletter.
    Description: Provides information on corporate volunteerism and corporate social responsibility.

369.4   NZ
WORLD COUNCIL OF SERVICE CLUBS. MINUTES OF THE GENERAL MEETING. 1962. a. free. World Council of Service Clubs, P.O. Box 240, Blenheim 7301, New Zealand. FAX 57-88968. circ. 500. (processed)
    Formerly: World Council of Young Men's Service Clubs. Minutes of the General Meeting (ISSN 0052-2678)

361.7   US   ISSN 0818-4984
WORLD GOODWILL NEWSLETTER. 1955. q. donation. Lucis Publishing Co., 113 University Place, 11th fl., Box 722, Cooper Sta., New York, NY 10276. TEL 212-982-8770. (In Europe: Case Postale 31, 1 Rue de Varembe (3e), 1211 Geneva 20, Switzerland; In U.K.: 3 Whitehall Court, Ste. 54, London SW1A 2EF, England) Ed. Jan Nation. bk.rev. circ. 30,000. **Document type:** newsletter.
    Description: Provides current information on constructive current action in world affairs as well as details on the work and program of World Goodwill.

360 028.5   UK
WORLD ISSUES. irreg., no.2, 1992. World Association of Girl Guides and Girl Scouts, 12c Lyndhurst Rd., London NW3 5PQ, England. TEL 0171-794-1181. FAX 0171-431-3764. **Document type:** bulletin.

362   FR   ISSN 0084-2044
WORLD MOVEMENT OF MOTHERS. REPORTS OF MEETINGS. 1949. a. 50 F. World Movement of Mothers - Mouvement Mondial des Meres, c/o M. de Vaublanc, Secretaire Generale, 56 rue de Passy, 75016 Paris, France. TEL 45-20-55-80. circ. 500.

362.8 US ISSN 0197-5439
HV640
WORLD REFUGEE SURVEY. 1958. a. $13. U.S. Committee for Refugees, American Council for Nationalities Service, 1717 Massachusetts Ave., N.W., Ste. 701, Washington, DC 20036. TEL 202-347-3507. Ed. Virginia Hamilton. bk.rev.; charts; illus.; stat. circ. 20,000. (also avail. in microfiche from CIS) **Indexed:** HR Rep. (1992-), Refug.Abstr., SRI.
   Formerly (until **1980**): World Refugee Survey Report (ISSN 0162-9832)
   Description: Provides a unique source of information on refugee situations around the world. Contains the year's research and on-site documentation by the staff of U.S. Committee for Refugees.

WORLD VISION. see *RELIGIONS AND THEOLOGY — Protestant*

WORLD VISION PARTNERS. see *RELIGIONS AND THEOLOGY — Protestant*

WORLD'S WOMAN'S CHRISTIAN TEMPERANCE UNION. TRIENNIAL REPORT. see *DRUG ABUSE AND ALCOHOLISM*

360 US ISSN 1069-2266
WYOMING. DEPARTMENT OF FAMILY SERVICES. ANNUAL STATISTICAL BULLETIN. 1960. q. $25. Department of Family Services, Administrative Services Division, Hathaway Bldg., 3rd Fl., 2300 Capitol Ave., Cheyenne, WY 82002. TEL 307-777-5366. FAX 307-777-7747. Ed. Joseph Golden. charts; stat. circ. 100. **Document type:** government publication, bulletin.
   Formerly: Wyoming. Division of Public Assistance and Social Services. Quarterly Statistical Bulletin.

360 FR ISSN 1256-9941
▼**XOANA**; images et sciences sociales. 1994. s-a. 380 F. (foreign 500 F.) (effective 1996). Editions Jean Michel Place, 12 rue Pierre et Marie Curie, 75005 Paris, France. TEL 46-33-05-11. FAX 46-34-52-65.

267.3 US ISSN 0084-4292
Y M C A DIRECTORY. (Young Men's Christian Association) 1877. a. Y M C A of the U S A, 101 N. Wacker Dr., Chicago, IL 60606-1718. TEL 312-977-0031. FAX 312-977-9063. adv. contact: Wendi Wyatt. circ. 2,000. **Document type:** directory.
   Formerly: Y M C A Yearbook and Official Roster.

362.7 UK ISSN 0956-2842
YOUNG PEOPLE NOW. 1973. m. £22.80. National Youth Agency, 17-23 Albion St., Leicester LE1 6GD, England. TEL 0116-285-6789. FAX 0116-247-1043. Ed. Mary Durkin. adv.; bk.rev.; circ. 5,000 (paid); 5,000. **Indexed:** ASSIA, High.Educ.Curr.Aware.Bull., Mult.Ed.Abstr., SOMA. **Document type:** bulletin.
   —BLDSC (9421.451554).
   Formerly (until **1989**): Youth in Society (ISSN 0307-1790); Incorporates: Youth Social Work Bulletin (ISSN 0307-3513)
   Description: Focuses on issues that affect young people and those who work with them.

360 US
YOUR (YEAR) GUIDE TO SOCIAL SECURITY BENEFITS. 1982. a. $19.95 hardbound; paperbound $10.95. Facts on File, Inc., 460 Park Ave. S., New York, NY 10016. TEL 212-683-2244. Ed. Leona G. Rubin.

YOUTH AND POLICY. see *CHILDREN AND YOUTH — About*

YOUTH LAW NEWS. see *LAW*

362.7 US ISSN 0196-9668
YOUTH - SERVING ORGANIZATIONS DIRECTORY. 1978. irreg., 2nd ed., 1980. $85. Gale Research Inc., 835 Penobscot Bldg., Detroit, MI 48226. TEL 313-961-2242. FAX 313-961-6083. TELEX 810-221-7086. **Document type:** directory.
   Description: Guide to youth service organizations.

360 SZ
Z O K U INFO. q. Schweizerische Kranken und Unfallkasse Z O K U, Schwamendingerstr. 44, CH-8050 Zurich, Switzerland. TEL 01-3118081. FAX 01-3111803. Ed. H.-U. Regius. circ. 45,000.

ZAGADNIENIA WYCHOWAWCZE A ZDROWIE PSYCHICZNE. see *MEDICAL SCIENCES — Psychiatry And Neurology*

360 309.1 ZA
ZAMBIA. DEPARTMENT OF SOCIAL DEVELOPMENT. REPORT. 1964. irreg. (approx. a.). Zambia Government Printing Department, P.O. Box 30136, Lusaka, Zambia. **Document type:** government publication.
   Formed by the merger of: Zambia. Department of Social Welfare. Report (ISSN 0084-4667) & Zambia. Department of Community Development. Report (ISSN 0084-4608)

360 ZA ISSN 0084-5035
ZAMBIA. PUBLIC SERVICE COMMISSION. REPORT. 1964. a. Zambia Government Printing Department, P.O. Box 30136, Lusaka, Zambia. **Document type:** government publication.

360 GW ISSN 0342-3379
ZEITSCHRIFT FUER DAS FUERSORGEWESEN. 1948. m. DM.111.80. (Stadt Hannover, Sozialamt) Richard Boorberg Verlag GmbH und Co., Kestnerstr. 44, 30159 Hannover, Germany. TEL 0511-810592. FAX 0511-810575. Ed. U. Harmening. circ. 2,400. **Document type:** government publication.

360 SZ ISSN 0044-3204
ZEITSCHRIFT FUER OEFFENTLICHE FUERSORGE; Monatsschrift fuer oeffentliche Fuersorge und Jugendhilfe. bi-m. 67 SFr. (foreign 87 SFr.). (Schweizerische Konferenz fuer Oeffentliche Fuersorge) Schulthess Polygraphischer Verlag AG, Zwingliplatz 2, CH-8022 Zurich, Switzerland. TEL 01-2519336. FAX 01-2616394. **Document type:** bulletin.
   Formerly: Armenpfleger.

ZEITSCHRIFT FUER SOZIALREFORM. see *POLITICAL SCIENCE*

360 SZ
ZENTRAL BLATT. 11/yr. Fronalpstr. 5, CH-8753 Mollis, Switzerland. TEL 01-2426868. FAX 01-2423489. Ed. Karin Faelkner. circ. 9,900.

360 GW ISSN 0177-3836
ZENTRALER BEWERBERANZEIGER MARKT UND CHANCE. 1955. w. Zentralstelle fuer Arbeitsvermittlung, Postfach 170545, 60079 Frankfurt a.M, Germany. TEL 069-71110. FAX 069-7111-555. (looseleaf format) **Document type:** government publication, consumer publication.

ZERO TO THREE. see *CHILDREN AND YOUTH — About*

ZHONGNAN MINZU XUEYUAN XUEBAO (SHEHUI KEXUE BAN)/SOUTH-CENTRAL COLLEGE FOR NATIONALITIES. JOURNAL (SOCIAL SCIENCE EDITION). see *SOCIAL SCIENCES: COMPREHENSIVE WORKS*

361.73 US ISSN 0897-5736
501 (C) (3) MONTHLY LETTER. 1980. m. $46. Great Oaks Communication Services, 400 Chestnut St., Box 192, Atlantic, IA 50322. TEL 712-243-5257. E-mail: marilyn.miller@iowa.com. Ed. Marilyn Miller. bk.rev.; charts; stat.; circ. 5,000 (paid) **Document type:** newsletter.
   Description: For nonprofit organizations. Emphasizes fundraising, communication and management.

SOCIAL SERVICES AND WELFARE — Abstracting, Bibliographies, Statistics

361 314 AU
AUSTRIA. STATISTISCHES ZENTRALAMT. SOZIALHILFE. vol.360, 1974. a. S.50. Oesterreichisches Statistisches Zentralamt, Hintere Zollamtsstr. 2b, A-1033 Vienna, Austria. TEL 0222-71128-0. FAX 0222-7156828. circ. 330. **Document type:** government publication.
   Formerly: Austria. Statistisches Zentralamt. Oeffentliche Fuersorge.
   Description: Data on the extent and output of social assistance in Austria.

362.7 GW
BERLIN. SENATSVERWALTUNG FUER FRAUEN, JUGEND UND FAMILIE. STATISTISCHER DIENST. 1980. s-a. free. Senatsverwaltung fuer Frauen, Jugend und Familie, Am Karlsbad 8, 10785 Berlin, Germany. TEL 030-26041. FAX 030-2628864. circ. 400. (back issues avail.)
   Description: Annotated statistics on children's and youth services and welfare, and the situation of women in West Berlin.

360 US ISSN 0361-9214
BIBLIOGRAPHY ON HEALTH INDEXES. q. $7 (foreign $8.75). U.S. Centers for Disease Control and Prevention, National Center for Health Statistics, Data Dissemination Branch, 6525 Belcrest Rd., Rm. 1064, Hyattsville, MD 20782. TEL 301-436-8500. E-mail: http://www.cdc.gov/nchswww/nchshome.htim. (Subscr. to: Superintendent of Documents, U.S. Government Printing Office, Box 371954, Pittsburgh, PA 15250-7954. TEL 202-512-1800. FAX 202-512-2250) (back issues avail.) **Document type:** bibliography, government publication.

360 016 BL
BRAZIL. DEPARTAMENTO NACIONAL DO SERVICO SOCIAL DO COMERCIO. BOLETIM BIBLIOGRAFICO. 1969. s-a. free. Departamento Nacional do Servico Social do Comercio, Divisao Administrativo, Rua Voluntarios da Patria 169, 22270-000 Rio de Janeiro, Brazil. TEL 286-5152. FAX 286-2638. TELEX 021-22782. charts; stat. **Document type:** bibliography.
   Description: Social services bibliography.

CANADA. STATISTICS CANADA. HEALTH REPORTS. SUPPLEMENT. see *HOSPITALS — Abstracting, Bibliographies, Statistics*

360 UK ISSN 0969-1707
CHARITY TRENDS. (In 2 parts) 1978. a. £28.95. Charities Aid Foundation, 48 Pembury Rd., Tonbridge, Kent TN9 2JD, England. Ed. J. McQuillan. circ. 2,000.
   Formerly (until **1992**): Charity Statistics (ISSN 0142-0216)

310 360 UK ISSN 0309-653X
CHARTERED INSTITUTE OF PUBLIC FINANCE AND ACCOUNTANCY. PERSONAL SOCIAL SERVICES STATISTICS. ACTUALS. 1949. a. £63. Chartered Institute of Public Finance and Accountancy, Statistical Information Service, 3 Robert St., London WC2N 6BH, England. TEL 0171-895-8823. FAX 0171-895-8825. (back issues avail.)
   —BLDSC (6427.890000).
   Formerly: Chartered Institute of Public Finance and Accountancy. Local Health and Social Services Statistics (ISSN 0307-0506)

360 UK ISSN 0144-610X
CHARTERED INSTITUTE OF PUBLIC FINANCE AND ACCOUNTANCY. PERSONAL SOCIAL SERVICES STATISTICS. ESTIMATES. 1974. a. £63. Chartered Institute of Public Finance and Accountancy, Statistical Information Service, 3 Robert St., London WC2N 6BH, England. TEL 0171-895-8823. FAX 0171-895-8825. (back issues avail.)

364 UK ISSN 0967-5140
HV9346.A5
CHARTERED INSTITUTE OF PUBLIC FINANCE AND ACCOUNTANCY. PROBATION. ESTIMATES & ACTUALS. 1983. a. £47. Chartered Institute of Public Finance and Accountancy, Statistical Information Service, 3 Robert St., London WC2N 6BH, England. TEL 0171-895-8823. FAX 0171-895-8825. (back issues avail.)
   Formed by the merger of: Chartered Institute of Public Finance and Accountancy. Probation. Estimates (ISSN 0264-6544) & Chartered Institute of Public Finance and Accountancy. Probation Statistics. Actuals (ISSN 0140-8291)

CHILDREN LOOKED AFTER BY LOCAL AUTHORITIES IN WALES. see *CHILDREN AND YOUTH — Abstracting, Bibliographies, Statistics*

SOCIAL SERVICES AND WELFARE — ABSTRACTING, BIBLIOGRAPHIES, STATISTICS

360 011   UK   ISSN 0264-4088
COMMUNITY CURRENTS; the community development information digest. 1982. bi-m. £19.25. Community Development Foundation, 60 Highbury Grove, London N5 2AG, England. TEL 0171-226-5375. FAX 0171-704-0313. Ed. Kevin Harris. bk.rev. circ. 450. **Document type:** abstracting/indexing.
● Also available on CD-ROM.
— BLDSC (3363.608700).
   Description: Covers the entire spectrum of community development literature

361.73   US
CORPORATE FOUNDATION PROFILES. biennial. $145. Foundation Center, 79 Fifth Ave., New York, NY 10003. TEL 212-620-4230. FAX 212-807-3677. Ed. Francine Jones. **Document type:** directory.
   Description: Lists current information on over 228 of America's top corporate foundations. Examines corporate grantmakers with annual giving of $1.25 million or more.

361.6 318   DR
DOMINICAN REPUBLIC. SECRETARIA DE SANIDAD Y ASISTENCIA PUBLICA. CUADROS ESTADISTICOS. irreg. Secretaria de Sanidad y Asistencia Publica, Ciudad Trujillo, Dominican Republic.

360   GR   ISSN 0256-3630
HD7181
ENQUETE ANNUELLE SUR L'ACTIVITE DES ORGANISMES DE SECURITE SOCIALE. (Text in Greek; summaries in French) 1962. a. $8. National Statistical Service of Greece, Statistical Information and Publications Division - Ethniki Statistiki Yperesia tes Ellados, 14-16 Lykourgou, 101 66 Athens, Greece. TEL 30-1-3244-748. FAX 30-1-3222-205. TELEX 216734 ESYE GR. (back issues avail.) **Document type:** government publication.

360   PN   ISSN 1023-330X
ESTADISTICA PANAMENA. INDICADORES SOCIALES. SECCION 012. 1965. biennial. Bl..50 (foreign Bl.1.50) (effective 1995). Direccion de Estadistica y Censo, Contraloria General de la Republica, Apdo. 5213, Panama 5, Panama. FAX 507-69-7294. circ. 1,000. **Document type:** government publication, bulletin.
   Supersedes in part (in 1994): Estadistica Panamena. Indicadores Economicos y Sociales. Seccion 011 (ISSN 0378-4940)
   Description: Presents data on population, housing, education, health, services, social security, justice, and public safety.

318   PN
ESTADISTICA PANAMENA. SITUACION SOCIAL. SECCION 431. SERVICIOS DE SALUD. 1957. a. Bl.0.50 (foreign Bl.1.50) (effective 1995). Direccion de Estadistica y Censo, Contraloria General, Apdo. 5213, Panama 5, Panama. FAX 507-69-7294. circ. 1,100. **Document type:** government publication, bulletin.
   Formerly: Estadistica Panamena. Situacion Social. Seccion 431. Asistencia Social (ISSN 0378-262X)
   Description: Presents numerical information on health institutions, beds, doctors, dentists, nurses, pharmacists, laboratory technicians, x-ray technicians, and auxiliary health personnel.

010 060   US   ISSN 0190-3357
Z733
FOUNDATION CENTER. ANNUAL REPORT. 1956. a. free. Foundation Center, 79 Fifth Ave., New York, NY 10003. TEL 212-620-4230. FAX 212-807-3677. **Document type:** corporate report.
   Formerly: Foundation Center. Report (ISSN 0548-7269)
   Description: Describes how network of cooperating libraries works to provide free, convenient access to accurate information on private funding sources to nonprofit groups and other interested individuals and organizations throughout the country.

010 060   US   ISSN 0071-8092
AS911.A2
FOUNDATION DIRECTORY. (Supplement avail.) 1960. a. $195 hardcover; softcover $175 (effective 1995). Foundation Center, 79 Fifth Ave., New York, NY 10003. TEL 212-620-4230. FAX 212-807-3677. Ed. Margaret Feczko. charts; stat.; index. circ. 8,000. **Indexed:** ERIC. **Document type:** directory.
● Also available online. Vendor(s): Knight-Ridder, Inc.
— BLDSC (4024.923000).
   Supersedes: American Foundation and Their Fields.
   Description: Contains current information on the nation's largest grantmakers.

361.73   US   ISSN 1066-0445
HV85
FOUNDATION GIVING (YEAR). a. $24.95 (effective 1994). Foundation Center, 79 Fifth Ave., New York, NY 10003. TEL 212-620-4230. FAX 212-807-3677. **Indexed:** SRI.
   Formerly (until 1991): Foundations Today: Current Facts and Figures on Private Foundations.
   Description: Provides a summary of current facts and figures on private foundations drawn from the Center's exclusive databases of foundation information.

060   US   ISSN 0090-1601
AS911.A2
FOUNDATION GRANTS INDEX. 1970. irreg., 23rd ed., 1994. $150 (effective 1994). Foundation Center, 79 Fifth Ave., New York, NY 10003. TEL 212-620-4230. FAX 212-807-3677. Ed. Ruth Kovacs. **Document type:** abstracting/indexing.
● Also available online. Vendor(s): Knight-Ridder, Inc.
   Description: Offers comprehensive coverage of over 68,000 grants of $10,000 or more.

361.73   US
FOUNDATION GRANTS INDEX QUARTERLY. 1983. q. $95. Foundation Center, 79 Fifth Ave., New York, NY 10003. TEL 212-620-4230. FAX 212-807-3677. **Document type:** abstracting/indexing.
● Also available online. Vendor(s): Knight-Ridder, Inc.
   Former titles (until 1989): Foundation Grants Index Bimonthly (ISSN 0735-2522); Foundation Grants Index Bibliography.
   Description: Presents information on over 5000 recently awarded grants, updated information on foundations, and listings of new foundation publications.

361.73   US
FOUNDATION GRANTS TO INDIVIDUALS. 1977. biennial. $65 (effective 1995). Foundation Center, 79 Fifth Ave., New York, NY 10003. TEL 212-620-4230. FAX 212-807-3677. **Document type:** directory.
   Description: Contains information on over 2,600 independent and corporate foundations which award grants to individuals.

010 060   US   ISSN 1067-7828
HV97.F65
FOUNDATION 1000. 1977. a. $265 (effective 1994). Foundation Center, 79 Fifth Ave., New York, NY 10003. TEL 212-620-4230. FAX 212-807-3677. Ed. Francine Jones. **Document type:** directory.
   Former titles (until 1993): Source Book Profiles (ISSN 1067-7925); (until 1989): Foundation Center Source Book Profiles (ISSN 0741-2002); (until 1976): Foundation Center Source Book (ISSN 0362-1170)
   Description: Lists the nation's 1,000 largest foundations which hold over $100 billion in assets and award nearly $6 billion in grants annually.

362.8   FR   ISSN 0181-0804
FRANCE. CAISSE NATIONALE DES ALLOCATIONS FAMILIALES. STATISTIQUES ACTION SOCIALE. a. free. Caisse Nationale des Allocations Familiales, 23 rue Daviel, 75634 Paris Cedex 13, France. charts; stat.
   Formerly: France. Caisse Nationale des Allocations Familiales. Action Sociale.

362.5   FR   ISSN 0182-1598
FRANCE. CAISSE NATIONALE DES ALLOCATIONS FAMILIALES. STATISTIQUES PRESTATIONS FAMILIALES. RESULTATS GENERAUX: RECETTES, DEPENSES, BENEFICIAIRES. a. free. Caisse Nationale des Allocations Familiales, 23 rue Daviel, 75634 Paris Cedex 13, France. charts; stat.
   Formerly: France. Caisse Nationale des Allocations Familiales. Prestations Familiales. Resultats Generaux: Recettes, Depenses, Beneficiaires.

362 314   GW   ISSN 0072-3754
GERMANY. STATISTISCHES BUNDESAMT. FACHSERIE 13, REIHE 2: SOZIALHILFE; REIHE 3: KRIEGSOPFERFUERSORGE. a. DM.10.80. 65180 Wiesbaden, Germany. TEL 0611-75-1. FAX 0611-724000. TELEX 61186-STBA-D. **Document type:** government publication.

362 314   GW   ISSN 0072-3762
GERMANY. STATISTISCHES BUNDESAMT. FACHSERIE 13, SOZIALLEISTUNGEN, REIHE 6: JUGENDHILFE. (Consists of several subseries) a. price varies. 65180 Wiesbaden, Germany. TEL 0611-75-1. FAX 0611-724000. TELEX 61186-STBA-D. **Document type:** government publication.

010 060   US
GRANT GUIDES. 1972. a. $70 per vol. (effective Oct. 1994). Foundation Center, 79 Fifth Ave., New York, NY 10003. TEL 212-620-4230. FAX 212-807-3677. (also avail. in microfiche)
   Formed by the merger of (1972-1991): Comsearch: Broad Topics; (1980-1991): Comsearch: Geographics; (1982-1991): Comsearch: Subjects; Which was formerly: Comsearch Printouts: Subjects; Supersedes in part: Comsearch Printouts; Supersedes (in 1977): Foundation Grants Index: Subjects on Microfiche (ISSN 0090-1601); Broad Topics incorporated International Philanthropy.
   Description: Lists actual foundation grants categorized into 30 key areas of grantmaking.

368.4   UK
GREAT BRITAIN. DEPARTMENT OF HEALTH AND SOCIAL SECURITY. SOCIAL SECURITY STATISTICS. 1973. a. price varies. H.M.S.O., P.O. Box 276, London SW8 5DT, England. illus.; stat. (reprint service avail. from UMI) **Document type:** government publication.

360   GR   ISSN 0253-9454
RA407.5.G73
GREECE. NATIONAL STATISTICAL SERVICE. SOCIAL WELFARE AND HEALTH STATISTICS. (Text in English, Greek) 1967. a. $12. National Statistical Service of Greece, Statistical Information and Publications Division - Ethniki Statistiki Yperesia tes Ellados, 14-16 Lykourgou, 101 66 Athens, Greece. TEL 30-1-3244-748. FAX 30-1-3222-205. TELEX 216734 ESYE GR. (back issues avail.) **Document type:** government publication.

010 060   US   ISSN 1071-202X
HV97.A3
GUIDE TO U.S. FOUNDATIONS, THEIR TRUSTEES, OFFICERS & DONORS; a comprehensive guide to grantmaking foundations. 1975. a. $225 (effective Apr. 1995). Foundation Center, 79 Fifth Ave., New York, NY 10003. TEL 212-620-4230. FAX 212-807-3677. circ. 26,000.
   Former titles (until 1993): National Data Book of Foundations (ISSN 1045-151X); (until 1989): National Data Book (ISSN 0732-8788); (until 1980): Foundation Center National Data Book (ISSN 0730-1677)
   Description: Provides information on over 37,500 active grantmaking foundations.

360 614   UK   ISSN 0307-0840
HV249
HEALTH AND PERSONAL SOCIAL SERVICES STATISTICS FOR WALES. a. Welsh Office, Statistical Directorate, New Crown Bldg., Cathays Park, Cardiff CF1 3NQ, Wales. TEL 01222-825054. FAX 01222-825350. **Document type:** government publication.
— BLDSC (4274.830000).

IDAHO. DEPARTMENT OF HEALTH AND WELFARE. ANNUAL SUMMARY OF VITAL STATISTICS. see *PUBLIC HEALTH AND SAFETY — Abstracting, Bibliographies, Statistics*

361.6   US
IDAHO. DEPARTMENT OF HEALTH AND WELFARE. RESEARCH AND STATISTICS SECTION. QUARTERLY WELFARE STATISTICAL BULLETIN. q. Department of Health and Welfare, Research and Statistics Section, Statehouse, Boise, ID 83720. TEL 208-334-5685. Ed. R.V. Atwood. circ. 180. **Document type:** government publication, bulletin.
   Former titles: Idaho. Department of Health and Welfare. Bureau of Research and Statistics. Quarterly Welfare Statistical Bulletin; Idaho. Department of Health and Welfare. Bureau of Research and Statistics. Research Report (ISSN 0098-8561)

360 314   IT
ITALY. ISTITUTO NAZIONALE DI STATISTICA. STATISTICHE DELLA PREVIDENZA, DELLA SANITA E DELL'ASSISTENZA SOCIALE. 1953. a. L.18000 (effective 1993). Istituto Nazionale di Statistica, Via Cesare Balbo 16, 00184 Rome, Italy. TEL 06-4673-2380. FAX 06-46735198. circ. 1,200. **Document type:** government publication.
   Former titles: Italy. Istituto Centrale di Statistica. Statistiche dell'Assistenza e della Previdenza Sociale; Italy. Istituto Centrale di Statistica. Annuario Statistico dell'Assistenza e della Previdenza Sociale (ISSN 0075-1790)

SOCIAL SERVICES AND WELFARE — ABSTRACTING, BIBLIOGRAPHIES, STATISTICS

JAPAN. MINISTRY OF HEALTH AND WELFARE. STATISTICS AND INFORMATION DEPARTMENT. HANDBOOK OF HEALTH AND WELFARE STATISTICS. see PUBLIC HEALTH AND SAFETY — Abstracting, Bibliographies, Statistics

362 315 JA ISSN 0448-4002
JAPAN. MINISTRY OF HEALTH AND WELFARE. STATISTICS AND INFORMATION DEPARTMENT. REPORT ON SURVEY OF PUBLIC ASSISTANCE. Key Title: Seikatsu Hogo Dotai Chosa Hokoku. (Text in Japanese) 1960. a. 4429 Yen. Ministry of Health and Welfare, Statistics and Information Department - Koseisho Daijin Kanbo Tokei Johobu, 7-3 Ichigaya-Honmura-cho, Shinjuku-ku, Tokyo 162, Japan. TEL 03-3260-3181. FAX 03-3269-8824. (Subscr. to: Health & Welfare Statistics Association, 5-13-14 Roppongi, Minato-ku, Tokyo, Japan. TEL 03-3586-3361. FAX 03-3584-4710) **Document type:** government publication.

362 315 JA ISSN 0448-4029
JAPAN. MINISTRY OF HEALTH AND WELFARE. STATISTICS AND INFORMATION DEPARTMENT. REPORT ON SURVEY OF SOCIAL WELFARE INSTITUTIONS. Key Title: Shakai Fukushi Shisetsu Chosa Hokoku. 1960. a. (in 2 vols.). 6500 Yen for vol.1; vol.2 6000 Yen. Ministry of Health and Welfare, Statistics and Information Department - Koseisho Daijin Kanbo Tokei Johobu, 7-3 Ichigaya-Honmura-cho, Shinjuku-ku, Tokyo 162, Japan. TEL 03-3260-3181. FAX 03-3269-8824. (Subscr. to: Health & Welfare Statistics Association, 5-13-14 Roppongi, Minato-ku, Tokyo, Japan. TEL 03-3586-3361. FAX 03-3584-4710) **Document type:** government publication.

362 315 JA ISSN 0448-4010
JAPAN. MINISTRY OF HEALTH AND WELFARE. STATISTICS AND INFORMATION DEPARTMENT. STATISTICAL REPORT ON SOCIAL WELFARE ADMINISTRATION AND SERVICES. Key Title: Shakai Fukushi Gyosei Gyomu Hokoku. 1960. a. 5253 Yen. Ministry of Health and Welfare, Statistics and Information Department - Koseisho Daijin Kanbo Tokei Johobu, 7-3 Ichigaya Honmura-cho, Shinjuku-ku, Tokyo 162, Japan. TEL 03-3260-3181. FAX 03-3269-8829. (Subscr. to: Health & Welfare Statistics Association, 5-13-14 Roppongi, Minato-ku, Tokyo, Japan. TEL 03-3586-3361. FAX 03-3584-4710) **Document type:** government publication.

360 KU
KUWAIT. CENTRAL STATISTICAL OFFICE. SOCIAL STATISTICS BULLETIN/KUWAIT. AL-IDARAH AL-MARKAZIYYAH LIL-IHSA'. NASHRAT AL-IHSA'AT AL-IJTIMA'IYYAH. (Text in Arabic, English) 1972. a., latest for year 1992. Central Statistical Office - Al-Idarah al-Markaziyyah lil-Ihsa', P.O. Box 26188, Safat 13122, Kuwait. TEL 965-2428200. FAX 965-2430464. TELEX 22468 TAKHTET KT. **Document type:** government publication.
Supersedes in part (in 1981): Kuwait. Al-Idarah al-Markaziyyah lil-Ihsa'. Nashrah Sanawiyyah li-Ihsa'at al-Khadamat al-Aamah.
Description: Provides statistical data on public health, education, security and justice, cultural, social and religious services.

362.1 616.891 US ISSN 0361-9311
RC443
MENTAL HEALTH STATISTICAL NOTES. 1969. irreg. free. U.S. Center for Mental Health Services, Division of State and Community Systems Development, Survey and Analysis Branch, Rm. 15C-04, 5600 Fishers Ln., Rockville, MD 20857. TEL 301-443-3344. FAX 301-443-7926. E-mail: msonnews@aoachms1.ssw.dhhs.gov. Ed. Mary Anne Sonnenschein. circ. 6,000. (back issues avail.) **Document type:** government publication.
—BLDSC (5678.585750).
Description: Provides statistical information on mental health services in the U.S. for selected organizations, years, and patient populations.

361 US ISSN 0093-7835
HV86
MICHIGAN. DEPARTMENT OF SOCIAL SERVICES. PROGRAM STATISTICS. Key Title: Program Statistics - Michigan Department of Social Services. (Report year ends Sept. 30) a. Department of Social Services, Box 30037, 300 S. Capitol Ave., Lansing, MI 48909. TEL 517-373-2005. **Document type:** government publication.
Supersedes: Michigan. Department of Social Services. Public Assistance Statistics (ISSN 0093-6774).

360 317 US ISSN 0091-1143
HV86
MONTANA. DEPARTMENT OF SOCIAL AND REHABILITATION SERVICES. STATISTICAL REPORT. vol.36, 1974. m. free. Department of Social and Rehabilitation Services, 111 Sanders St., Helena, MT 59601. TEL 406-449-3860. charts; stat. circ. 400. (also avail. in microfiche from CIS) **Indexed:** SRI. **Document type:** government publication.

361.73 US ISSN 1050-9852
HV89
NATIONAL DIRECTORY OF CORPORATE GIVING. 1989. biennial. $195 (effective Oct. 1993). Foundation Center, 79 Fifth Ave., New York, NY 10003. TEL 212-620-4230. FAX 212-807-3677. Ed. Suzanne W. Haile. **Document type:** directory.
Description: Offers information on over 2300 corporate philanthropic programs.

360 314.9 NE ISSN 0168-549X
HC321
NETHERLANDS. CENTRAAL BUREAU VOOR DE STATISTIEK. SOCIAAL-ECONOMISCHE MAANDSTATISTIEK. 1953. m. Centraal Bureau voor de Statistiek, Prinses Beatrixlaan 428, Voorburg, Netherlands. (Dist. by: SDU - Publishers, Christoffel Plantijnstraat, The Hague, Netherlands) circ. 1,250. **Document type:** government publication.
Formerly: Netherlands. Centraal Bureau voor de Statistiek. Sociale Maandstatistiek (ISSN 0470-6978).

360 336 NE ISSN 0168-4086
NETHERLANDS. CENTRAAL BUREAU VOOR DE STATISTIEK. STATISTIEK VAN DE ALGEMENE BIJSTAND/NETHERLANDS. CENTRAL BUREAU OF STATISTICS. STATISTICS OF PUBLIC ASSISTANCE. (Text in Dutch and English) 1965. a. Centraal Bureau voor de Statistiek, Prinses Beatrixlaan 428, Voorburg, Netherlands. (Dist. by: SDU - Publishers, Christoffel Plantijnstraat 2, Postbus 20014, 2500 EA The Hague, Netherlands) **Document type:** government publication.

362 NE ISSN 0077-7099
HV1481.N4
NETHERLANDS. CENTRAAL BUREAU VOOR DE STATISTIEK. STATISTIEK VAN DE BEJAARDENOORDEN/NETHERLANDS. CENTRAL BUREAU OF STATISTICS. STATISTICS OF HOMES FOR THE AGED. (Text in Dutch and English) 1950. a. Centraal Bureau voor de Statistiek, Prinses Beatrixlaan 428, Voorburg, Netherlands. (Dist. by: SDU - Publishers, Christoffel Plantijnstraat 2, Postbus 20014, 2500 EA The Hague, Netherlands) **Document type:** government publication.

360 US
NEW YORK (STATE). DEPARTMENT OF SOCIAL SERVICES. ANNUAL REPORT. STATISTICAL SUPPLEMENT. a. free. Department of Social Services, 40 N. Pearl St., Albany, NY 12243. TEL 518-473-8207. FAX 518-474-7688. Ed. George Cusack. **Document type:** government publication.

360 US
NEW YORK (STATE). DEPARTMENT OF SOCIAL SERVICES. SOCIAL STATISTICS. a. free. Department of Social Services, 40 N. Pearl St., Albany, NY 12243. TEL 518-473-8207. FAX 518-474-7688. Ed. George Cusack. **Document type:** government publication.
Description: Contains statistical data relating to NY State social services programs, including public assistance, Medicaid and Food Stamps.

362 US ISSN 0098-051X
HV86
NORTH CAROLINA. DIVISION OF SOCIAL SERVICES. STATISTICAL JOURNAL. Key Title: Statistical Journal - State Department of Human Resources, Division of Social Services. 1970-1980; resumed. q. free. Department of Human Resources, Division of Social Services, 325 N. Salisbury St., Raleigh, NC 27611. Ed. Susan Shaw. charts; illus.; stat.; index. circ. 1,000. **Indexed:** SRI.

362.7 US
OHIO. DEPARTMENT OF HUMAN SERVICES. CHILD WELFARE STATISTICS. q. free. Department of Human Services, 30 E. Broad St., 30th Fl., Columbus, OH 43215. TEL 614-466-3366. FAX 614-466-3863. Ed. Florence C. Odita. circ. 500. (looseleaf format; back issues avail.) **Document type:** government publication.

360.016 US ISSN 1058-6946
HV85
PHILANTHROPIC STUDIES INDEX. 1991. 3/yr. (plus a. cumulation). $75 (foreign $87.50). (Indiana University Center on Philanthropy) Indiana University Press, Journals Division, 601 N. Morton St., Bloomington, IN 47404. TEL 812-855-9449. FAX 812-855-7931. Ed. Dwight F. Burlingame. **Document type:** abstracting/indexing.
Description: Indexes relevant books, periodical articles, dissertations and other information sources that cover philanthropy, including nonprofit management, voluntarism and fund raising.

REFUGEE SURVEY QUARTERLY. see POPULATION STUDIES — Abstracting, Bibliographies, Statistics

360 315 CH
SOCIAL AFFAIRS STATISTICS OF TAIWAN/CHUNG HUA MIN KUO T'AI-WAN SHENG SHE HUI SHIH YEH T'UNG CHI. (Text in Chinese and English) a. Department of Social Affairs, Nantou Hsien, Taiwan, Republic of China. stat.

360 315 JA
SOCIAL INDICATORS BY PREFECTURE (YEAR). 1989. a. 6800 Yen. Nihon Tokei Kyokai - Japan Statistical Association, Crest 21, 6-21, Yocho-machi, Shinjuku-ku, Tokyo 162, Japan. TEL 03-5269-3051. FAX 03-5269-3058.

360 016 US ISSN 0195-7988
HV1 CODEN: SOPODA
SOCIAL PLANNING - POLICY & DEVELOPMENT ABSTRACTS. Short title: SOPODA. 1979. s-a. $165. Sociological Abstracts, Inc., Box 22206, San Diego, CA 92192. TEL 619-695-8803. FAX 619-695-0416. Ed. Miriam Chall. **Document type:** abstracting/indexing.
●Also available online. Vendor(s): Ovid Technologies (SOCA), DIMDI (SA63), Data-Star (SOCA), Knight-Ridder, Inc. (File No.37).
Also available on CD-ROM. Producer(s): SilverPlatter Information, Inc. (SocioFile).
—CCC.
Formerly: Social Welfare, Social Planning, Policy and Social Development.

360 UK ISSN 0309-4693
HV1
SOCIAL SERVICE ABSTRACTS. 1977. m. £44.10 (effective 1994). (Departments of Health and Social Security) H.M.S.O., 51 Nine Elms Ln., London SW8 5DR, England. TEL 071-873-0011. FAX 071-873-8463. (Subscr. to: H.M.S.O. Publications Centre, P.O. Box 276, London SW8 5DT, England. TEL 071-873-9090. FAX 071-873-8200) Ed. Janet Cockayne. (reprint service avail. from UMI) **Indexed:** CERDIC. **Document type:** abstracting/indexing, government publication.
—BLDSC (8318.198100). **CCC.**

362 016   US   ISSN 1070-5317
HV1
SOCIAL WORK ABSTRACTS. 1965. q. $97 canada $103; (foreign $112) (effective 1996). (National Association of Social Workers) N A S W Press, 750 First St., N.E., Ste. 700, Washington, DC 20002-4241. TEL 202-408-8500. FAX 202-336-8312. (Subscr. to: NASW Distribution Center, Box 431, Annapolis Jct., MD 20701. TEL 800-227-3590. FAX 301-206-7989) adv.; index. circ. 2,500. (also avail. in microform from UMI; back issues avail.; reprint service avail. from UMI) **Indexed:** Abstr.Crim.& Pen., Abstr.Health Care Manage.Stud., Adol.Ment.Hlth.Abstr., ASCA, ASSIA, CLOA, Crim.Just.Abstr., Hosp.Lit.Ind., Lang.& Lang.Behav.Abstr., Med.Care Rev., Psychol.Abstr., Rehabil.Lit., Sage Pub.Admin.Abstr., Sociol.Abstr., SSCI. **Document type:** academic/scholarly publication, abstracting/indexing.
•Also available online. Vendor(s): Ovid Technologies (SWAB).
Also available on CD-ROM. Producer(s): SilverPlatter Information, Inc. (SWAB-PLUS).
—BLDSC (8318.223180); Genuine Article; UMI; UnCover. **CCC.**
Supersedes in part (in 1994): Social Work Research and Abstracts (ISSN 0148-0847); Which was formerly (until 1977): Abstracts for Social Workers (ISSN 0001-3412)
Description: Provides abstracts of articles appearing in major social work and human services journals.

360 316.8   SA   ISSN 0258-7777
SOUTH AFRICA. CENTRAL STATISTICAL SERVICE. CENSUS OF SOCIAL, RECREATIONAL AND PERSONAL SERVICES - WELFARE ORGANISATIONS. (Report No. 93-07-01) irreg., latest 1988. R.4.40 (foreign R.5.50). Central Statistical Service - Sentrale Statistiekdiens, Private Bag X44, Pretoria 0001, South Africa. TEL 27-12-310-8911. FAX 27-12-310-8500. (Orders to: Government Printing Works, Private Bag X85, Pretoria 0001, South Africa) **Document type:** government publication.

360 316.8   SA
SOUTH AFRICA. CENTRAL STATISTICAL SERVICE. STATISTICAL RELEASE. CENSUS OF SOCIAL, RECREATIONAL AND PERSONAL SERVICES (YEAR). (No. P9307) irreg., latest 1988. free. Central Statistical Service - Sentrale Statistiekdiens, Private Bag X44, Pretoria 0001, South Africa. TEL 27-12-310-8911. FAX 27-12-310-8500. **Document type:** government publication.

360 310   US
SOUTH DAKOTA. STATE DEPARTMENT OF SOCIAL SERVICES. ANNUAL STATISTICAL REPORT. 1971. a. State Department of Social Services, Division of Management Information, Statistical Analysis and Reports, Richard F. Kneip Bldg., 700 Governors Dr., Pierre, SD 57501. TEL 605-773-3226. FAX 605-773-4855. Ed. Richard Jensen. stat. circ. 300. **Indexed:** SRI. **Document type:** government publication.
Formerly: South Dakota. State Department of Public Welfare. Research and Statistical Annual Report (ISSN 0099-2305)

STAFF OF SOCIAL SERVICES DEPARTMENTS. see BUSINESS AND ECONOMICS — Labor And Industrial Relations

SWEDEN. SJUKVAARDENS OCH SOCIALVAARDENS PLANERINGS- OCH RATIONALISERINGSINSTITUT. S P R I LITTERATURTJAENST. (Sjukvaardens och Socialvaardens Planerings- och Rationaliseringsinstitut) see PUBLIC HEALTH AND SAFETY — Abstracting, Bibliographies, Statistics

360 314   SW   ISSN 0283-8605
SWEDEN. STATISTISKA CENTRALBYRAAN. STATISTISKA MEDDELANDEN. SERIE S, SOCIALTJAENST OCH SOCIALFOERSAEKRING. (Text in Swedish; table heads and summaries in English) 1963. irreg. SEK 1000. Statistiska Centralbyraan, Publishing Unit, S-701 89 Oerebro, Sweden. circ. 1,300.
Former titles (until vol.26, 1982): Sweden. Statistiska Centralbyraan. Statistiska Meddelanden. Serie S, Socialtjaenst och Socialfoersaekring; (until 1977): Sweden. Statistiska Centralbyraan. Statistiska Meddelanden. Serie S, Socialvaard, Haelso- och Sjukvaard; (until 1976): Sweden. Statistiska Centralbyraan. Statistiska Meddelanden. Serie S, (until 1969): Sweden. Statistiska Centralbyraan. Statistiska Meddelanden. Serie S, Social-, Haelso- och Sjukvaard

---

361 016   US
UNITED WAY OF AMERICA. INFORMATION CENTER. DIGEST OF SELECTED REPORTS. 1947. 2/yr. $10. United Way of America, 701 N. Fairfax St., Alexandria, VA 22314. TEL 703-836-7100. abstr.; circ. controlled.
Supersedes: United Way of America. Information Center. Bibliography of Reports and Manuals; Which was formerly: United Way of America. Information Center. Digest of Current Reports (ISSN 0090-3191)

WASHINGTON (STATE). EMPLOYMENT SECURITY DEPARTMENT. MONTHLY JOB SERVICE STATISTICS. see OCCUPATIONS AND CAREERS — Abstracting, Bibliographies, Statistics

ZEITSCHRIFTENBIBLIOGRAPHIE GERONTOLOGIE. see GERONTOLOGY AND GERIATRICS — Abstracting, Bibliographies, Statistics

SOCIOLOGY

see also Folklore; Social Sciences: Comprehensive Works; Social Services and Welfare

301   US
A A P O R NEWS. q. membership. American Association for Public Opinion Research, Box 1248, Ann Arbor, MI 48106. Ed. Murray Edelamn. circ. 1,579. **Document type:** newsletter.

A B Q CORRESPONDENT. see TECHNOLOGY: COMPREHENSIVE WORKS

A I L A MONTHLY MAILING. (American Immigration Lawyers Association) see LAW

A R T I NEWS LETTER. (Agrarian Research and Training Institute) see AGRICULTURE

301   US   ISSN 0749-6931
HM1
A S A FOOTNOTES. 9/yr. $25 (foreign $35). American Sociological Association, 1722 N St., N.W., Washington, DC 20036. TEL 202-833-3410. FAX 202-785-0146. (reprint service avail from UMI) **Document type:** bulletin.
Description: Contains departmental news, activities of the ASA and the Executive Office; developments on the Washington scene; and the ASA official reports and proceedings.

ACADEMIA; Zeitschrift fuer Politik und Kultur. see LITERARY AND POLITICAL REVIEWS

ACADEMIA DE STIINTE A REPUBLICA MOLDOVA. BULETINUL. ECONOMIE SI SOCIOLOGIE/AKADEMIYA NAUK MOLDAVSKOI RESPUBLIKI. IZVESTIYA. EKONOMIKA I SOTSIOLOGIYA. see BUSINESS AND ECONOMICS — Economic Situation And Conditions

614   BU   ISSN 0515-2925
ACTA MEDICA ET SOCIOLOGICA. 1962. irreg., 6th, 1972, Varna; latest 9th, 1983, Barcelona, Spain. International Medical Association for the Study of Living Conditions and Health, c/o T. Tashev, Bd. D. Nestorov 15, BG-1431 Sofia, Bulgaria.

---

301   NO   ISSN 0001-6993
HM1.A1
ACTA SOCIOLOGICA; journal of the Scandinavian Sociological Association. (Text in English) 1955. q. NOK 695 in Nordic countries; elsewhere $124 (effective 1996). (Scandinavian Sociological Association) Scandinavian University Press, P.O. Box 2959 Toeyen, N-0608 Oslo, Norway. TEL 47-22-57-54-00. FAX 47-22-57-53-53. (U.S. addr.: Scandinavian University Press, 200 Meacham Ave., Elmont, NY 11003. TEL 516-352-7300) Ed. Peter Hedstroem. adv.; bk.rev.; charts; index. circ. 3,200. (also avail. in microform from SWZ,UMI; back issues avail.; reprint service avail. from ISI,SWZ) **Indexed:** A.B.C.Pol.Sci., Adol.Ment.Hlth Abstr., Amer.Hist.& Life (until 1992), ASCA, ASSIA, Bibl.Ind., Curr.Cont., E.I., Hist.Abstr. (until 1992), Human Resour.Abstr., Int.Polit.Sci.Abstr., Lang.& Lang.Behav.Abstr., Mid.East: Abstr.& Ind., Mult.Ed.Abstr., P.A.I.S, Polit.Sci.Abstr., Sage Fam.Stud.Abstr., Sage Pub.Admin.Abstr., Sage Urb.Stud.Abstr., Soc.Sci.Ind., Sociol.Abstr. (1955-), Sociol.Educ.Abstr., Sp.Ed.Needs Abstr., Stud.Wom.Abstr., Tech.Educ.Abstr.
—BLDSC (0663.350000); Faxon; Genuine Article; SWETS; UMI; UnCover. **CCC.**
Description: Publishes innovative sociological research written from different theoretical and methodological starting points written by both Scandinavian and non-Scandinavian sociologists, presenting alternative ways of understanding and conceptualizing social life.

301   MX   ISSN 0186-6028
HM7   CODEN: ACSOFH
ACTA SOCIOLOGICA. 1969. 3/yr. $70. Universidad Nacional Autonoma de Mexico, Facultad de Ciencias Politicas y Sociales, Coordinacion de Sociologia, Ciudad Universitaria, 04510 Mexico D.F., Mexico. Ed. Enrique Nieto. bibl.; illus.

301 370   PL   ISSN 0208-600X
HM7
ACTA UNIVERSITATIS LODZIENSIS: FOLIA SOCIOLOGICA. (Text in Polish; summaries in various languages) 1975. irreg. Wydawnictwo Uniwersytetu Lodzkiego, Ul. Jaracza 34, Lodz, Poland. TEL 331671. (Dist. by: Ars Polona-Ruch, Krakowskie Przedmiescie 7, Warsaw, Poland) **Document type:** academic/scholarly publication.
—BLDSC (0585.208750).
Supersedes in part (in 1980): Uniwersytet Lodzki. Zeszyty Naukowe. Seria 3: Nauki Ekonomiczne i Socjologiczne (ISSN 0076-0374)
Description: Covers studies on culture, sociology of art, industry and occupations, basic theory of interactions and methodology.

301   PL
ACTA UNIVERSITATIS WRATISLAVIENSIS. SOCJOLOGIA. (Text in Polish; summaries in English or German) 1992. irreg. price varies. (Uniwersytet Wroclawski) Wydawnictwo Uniwersytetu Wroclawskiego, Pl. Uniwersytecki 9-13, 50-137 Wroclaw, Poland. TEL 44-10-06. (Dist. by: Ksiegarnia Uniwersytetu Wroclawskiego, Pl. Uniwersytecki 9-13, 50-137 Wroclaw, Poland) Ed. Zbigniew Kurcz. **Document type:** academic/scholarly publication.

ACTA WASAENSIA. see BUSINESS AND ECONOMICS — Economic Systems And Theories, Economic History

AD MARGINEM; Randbemerkungen zur musikalischen Volkskunde. see MUSIC

ADMINISTRATION & SOCIETY. see PUBLIC ADMINISTRATION

ADMINISTRATIVE SCIENCE QUARTERLY. see PUBLIC ADMINISTRATION

362.7   US
ADOPTOLOGIST. 1979. q. $15. Kansas City Adult Adoptees Organization, Box 11828, Kansas City, MO 64138. TEL 816-229-4075. Dir. Sandy Hassler. circ. 250. **Document type:** newsletter.
Description: Education regarding adoption and its life-long effects.

ADVANCES IN APPLIED SOCIAL PSYCHOLOGY. see PSYCHOLOGY

6010 SOCIOLOGY

301.15 US ISSN 0065-2601
HM251 CODEN: AXSPAQ
ADVANCES IN EXPERIMENTAL SOCIAL PSYCHOLOGY.
1964. irreg., vol.25, 1993. Academic Press, Inc.,
525 B St., Ste. 1900, San Diego, CA 92101-4495.
TEL 619-231-0926. FAX 619-699-6715. (Subscr.
to: Order Dept., 6277 Sea Harbor Dr., 4th Fl.,
Orlando, FL 32887. TEL 800-321-5068) Ed.
Leonard Berkowitz. index. (reprint service avail. from
ISI) **Indexed:** Biol.Abstr., SSCI.
—BLDSC (0706.100000); Faxon; SWETS; UnCover.
CCC.

ADVANCES IN FAMILY INTERVENTION, ASSESSMENT AND THEORY. see *PSYCHOLOGY*

301 US ISSN 0882-6145
HM131
ADVANCES IN GROUP PROCESSES. 1984. a. $63.50 to
institutions. J A I Press Inc., 36 Sherwood Pl.,
Greenwich, CT 06836-1678. TEL 203-661-7602.
Ed. Edward J. Lawler.
—BLDSC (0709.007500). **CCC.**

301 610 US ISSN 1057-6290
RA418 CODEN: AMSOEI
ADVANCES IN MEDICAL SOCIOLOGY. 1990. a. J A I
Press Inc., 55 Old Post Rd., No. 2, Box 1678,
Greenwich, CT 06836-1678. TEL 203-661-7602.
—BLDSC (0709.376200).

ADVANCES IN SUICIDOLOGY. see *MEDICAL SCIENCES — Psychiatry And Neurology*

ADVANCES IN THE STUDY OF COMMUNICATION AND AFFECT. see *PSYCHOLOGY*

301 327 IT ISSN 0390-1181
H7
AFFARI SOCIALI INTERNAZIONALI. 1973. q. L.90000
(foreign L.130000) (effective 1993). Franco Angeli
Editore, Viale Monza 106, 20127 Milan, Italy.
TEL 02-28-97-651. Ed. Pier Marcello Masotti.
bk.rev.; bibl. circ. 5,000. **Indexed:** ELLIS, Int.Lab.Doc.
—BLDSC (0731.400000).

AFRICA. see *HISTORY — History Of Africa*

301 KE ISSN 1010-4127
HM22.A4
AFRICAN JOURNAL OF SOCIOLOGY. 1981. s-a.
University of Nairobi, Department of Sociology, P.O.
Box 30022, Nairobi, Kenya. **Indexed:**
Documentatieblad, Lang.& Lang.Behav.Abstr.,
Sociol.Abstr. (1981-).

AFRICAN LANGUAGES AND CULTURES. see *LINGUISTICS*

301 960 ZA ISSN 0002-0168
HN771 CODEN: ASREDO
AFRICAN SOCIAL RESEARCH. 1944. s-a. University of
Zambia, P.O. Box 32379, Lusaka, Zambia. Ed.Bd.
adv.; bk.rev.; charts; cum.index. circ. 1,000. **Indexed:**
A.I.C.P., Amer.Hist.& Life, ASSIA, Curr.Cont.,
Curr.Cont.Africa, Documentatieblad, Geo.Abstr.,
Hist.Abstr., Lang.& Lang.Behav.Abstr., Mid.East:
Abstr.& Ind., Psychol.Abstr., Rural
Recreat.Tour.Abstr., SSCI, World Agri.Econ.& Rural
Sociol.Abstr. **Document type:** academic/scholarly
publication.
 Supersedes: Rhodes-Livingstone Journal.
 Description: Articles in social research, with
emphasis on sociology, economics, history and
related disciplines.

AFRIKA SPEKTRUM; Zeitschrift fuer
gegenwartsbezogene Afrikaforschung. see *POLITICAL SCIENCE*

AFRIQUE MON PAYS. see *POLITICAL SCIENCE*

AFTERLOSS; the monthly newsletter to comfort and
care for those who mourn. see *MEDICAL SCIENCES — Psychiatry And Neurology*

301 321 FR ISSN 1245-3749
AGIR. 1993. q. Harmattan, B.P. 7, 91301 Massy
Cedex, France. Dir. Francis Lara.

AGORA (RAVENNA). see *PHILOSOPHY*

301.4 338.1 GW ISSN 0944-4165
AGRARSOZIALE GESELLSCHAFT. ARBEITSBERICHT.
1950. a. free. Agrarsoziale Gesellschaft e.V., Kurze
Geismarstr. 33, 37073 Goettingen, Germany.
TEL 0551-497090. FAX 0551-4970916. **Document type:** academic/scholarly publication.
 Former titles: Agrarsoziale Gesellschaft.
Geschaefts- und Arbeitsbericht (ISSN 0065-437X);
(until 1968): Agrarsoziale Gesellschaft.
Arbeitsbericht.

301.4 GW ISSN 0170-7671
AGRARSOZIALE GESELLSCHAFT. KLEINE REIHE. 1970.
irreg., no.49, 1992. price varies. Agrarsoziale
Gesellschaft e.V., Kurze Geismarstr. 33, 37073
Goettingen, Germany. TEL 0551-497090.
FAX 0551-4970916. **Indexed:** Rural
Recreat.Tour.Abstr., World Agri.Econ.& Rural
Sociol.Abstr. **Document type:** monographic series.

338.1 301.4 GW ISSN 0179-7603
AGRARSOZIALE GESELLSCHAFT. LAENDLICHER RAUM. RUNDBRIEF. 1950. bi-m. DM.70. Agrarsoziale
Gesellschaft e.V., Kurze Geismarstr. 33, 37073
Goettingen, Germany. TEL 0551-497090.
FAX 0551-4970916. index. **Document type:**
academic/scholarly publication.
 Formerly: Agrarsoziale Gesellschaft. Rundbriefe
(ISSN 0065-4388)

301.4 GW ISSN 0344-5712
AGRARSOZIALE GESELLSCHAFT. MATERIALSAMMLUNG.
1953. irreg., no.189, 1993. price varies.
Agrarsoziale Gesellschaft e.V., Kurze Geismarstr. 33,
37073 Goettingen, Germany. TEL 0551-497090.
FAX 0551-4970916. **Indexed:** Geo.Abstr. **Document type:** monographic series.

AGRO SUR. see *AGRICULTURE*

AGROEKONOMIKA. see *AGRICULTURE — Agricultural Economics*

AGROTROPICA. see *AGRICULTURE*

ALBATROZ; literatura de aguarras. see *LITERATURE*

ALBERTA - EDMONTON SERIES REPORT. see *POPULATION STUDIES*

301.15 GW ISSN 0175-9191
ALLENSBACHER JAHRBUCH DER DEMOSKOPIE. 1947.
irreg., vol.8, 1983. price varies. (Institut fuer
Demoskopie, Allensbach) K.G. Saur Verlag KG, A
part of Reed Reference Publishing, Ortlerstr. 8,
81373 Munich, Germany. TEL 089-76902-0.
FAX 089-76902150. (Subscr. to: Postfach
701620, 81316 Munich, Germany) adv.; bk.rev.
circ. 3,000. **Document type:** monographic series.
 Formerly: Jahrbuch der Oeffentlichen Meinung
(ISSN 0075-2347)

ALTERNATIVE RESEARCH NEWSLETTER. see *LITERARY AND POLITICAL REVIEWS*

ALZHEIMER'S ASSOCIATION NEWSLETTER. see *GERONTOLOGY AND GERIATRICS*

301.4 973 US ISSN 0044-7471
E184.O6 CODEN: AMEJEZ
AMERASIA JOURNAL. 1971. 3/yr. $24 to individuals;
institutions $36 (includes subscr. to: Cross
Currents). University of California at Los Angeles,
Asian American Studies Center, 3230 Campbell
Hall, Los Angeles, CA 90095-1546.
TEL 310-825-2968. FAX 310-206-9844. Ed.
Russell C. Leong. adv.; bk.rev.; bibl.; charts; circ.
1,500 (paid). (also avail. in microform from UMI)
Indexed: Amer.Hist.& Life, Arts & Hum.Cit.Ind.,
C.I.J.E., Curr.Cont., ERIC, Hist.Abstr. **Document type:** academic/scholarly publication, bibliography.
—BLDSC (0809.655000); Faxon; Genuine Article;
SWETS; UMI; UnCover.
 Description: Contains information about
Asian-American history and life. Includes
bibliography of Asian-American studies.
 Refereed Serial

301 PE ISSN 1019-4460
AMERICA - PROBLEMA. 1968. irreg., no.16, 1993.
price varies. (Instituto de Estudios Peruanos) I E P
Ediciones, Horacio Urteaga 694, Lima 11, Peru.
TEL 51-14-323070. FAX 51-14-324981. E-mail:
postmaster@iep.org.pe.

AMERICAN CROSSDRESSER. see *PSYCHOLOGY*

AMERICAN FAMILY THERAPY ACADEMY NEWSLETTER. see *PSYCHOLOGY*

AMERICAN INDIAN AND ALASKA NATIVE MENTAL HEALTH RESEARCH. see *ETHNIC INTERESTS*

301.1 US ISSN 0091-0562
RA790.A1 CODEN: AJCPCK
AMERICAN JOURNAL OF COMMUNITY PSYCHOLOGY.
1973. bi-m. $395 (foreign $460) (effective 1996).
Plenum Publishing Corp., 233 Spring St., New York,
NY 10013-1578. TEL 212-620-8000.
FAX 212-463-0742. TELEX 23-421139. Ed. Julian
Rappaport. adv. (also avail. in microfilm from JSC;
back issues avail.) **Indexed:** Abstr.Crim.& Pen.,
Adol.Ment.Hlth.Abstr., ASSIA, CINAHL, Curr.Cont.,
Except.Child.Educ.Abstr., Excerp.Med., IMFL,
Ind.Med., INIS Atomind., Mid.East: Abstr.& Ind.,
Mult.Ed.Abstr., PSI, Psychol.Abstr. (1974-), Sage
Fam.Stud.Abstr., Sage Pub.Admin.Abstr.,
Sp.Ed.Needs Abstr., SSCI. **Document type:**
academic/scholarly publication.
—BLDSC (0824.070000); Faxon; Genuine Article;
SWETS; UMI; UnCover. **CCC.**
 Refereed Serial

AMERICAN JOURNAL OF FAMILY THERAPY. see *PSYCHOLOGY*

301 US ISSN 0002-9602
HM1
AMERICAN JOURNAL OF SOCIOLOGY. 1895. bi-m. $39
to individuals; institutions $87; students $27.
University of Chicago Press, Journals Division, 5720
S. Woodlawn Ave., Chicago, IL 60637.
TEL 312-753-3347. FAX 312-753-0811. TELEX
25-4603. (Subscr. to: Box 37005, Chicago, IL
60637) Ed. Marta Tienda. adv.; bk.rev.; abstr.; bibl.;
charts; index, cum.index: vols.1-70 (1895-1965),
vols.71-75 (1965-1970), vols.76-80
(1971-1980). circ. 6,700. (also avail. in microform
from UMI; reprint service avail. from UMI,ISI,SCH)
Indexed: A.B.C.Pol.Sci., A.I.C.P., Abstr.Anthropol.,
Abstr.Crim.& Pen., Abstr.Crim.& Pen., Acad.Ind.,
Amer.Bibl.Slavic & E.Eur.Stud., Amer.Hist.& Life,
Asian-Pac.Econ.Lit., ASSIA, Bk.Rev.Ind. (1965-),
C.I.J.E., Chic.Per.Ind., Child.Bk.Rev.Ind. (1965-),
CLOA, Cont.Pg.Manage., Crim.Just.Abstr., Curr.Cont.,
G.Soc.Sci.& Rel.Per.Lit., Geo.Abstr., Hist.Abstr., IDA,
IMFL, Int.Lab.Doc., Int.Polit.Sci.Abstr., Lang.&
Lang.Behav.Abstr., Mark.Res.Abstr. (1964-), P.A.I.S.,
Polit.Sci.Abstr., Popul.Ind., Psychol.Abstr. (1950-),
Res.High.Educ.Abstr., Rural Ext.Educ.& Tr.Abstr.,
Rural Recreat.Tour.Abstr., Sage Fam.Stud.Abstr.,
Sage Urb.Stud.Abstr., Soc.Sci.Ind., Soc.Work Res.&
Abstr., Sociol.Abstr. (1952-59), Sociol.Educ.Abstr.,
Sociol.Educ.Abstr., SOMA, Sp.Ed.Needs Abstr., SSCI,
Stud.Wom.Abstr., Trop.Dis.Bull., World Agri.Econ.&
Rural Sociol.Abstr. **Document type:**
academic/scholarly publication.
—BLDSC (0838.300000); Faxon; Genuine Article;
SWETS; UMI; UnCover. **CCC.**
 Description: Publishes articles and review essays
on the theory, methods, and practice of sociology.
 Refereed Serial

301 US ISSN 1052-7184
HM9
AMERICAN SOCIOLOGICAL ASSOCIATION. BIOGRAPHICAL DIRECTORY OF MEMBERS. 1990. biennial. American
Sociological Association, 1722 N St., N.W.,
Washington, DC 20036-2981. TEL 202-833-3410.
FAX 202-785-0146. **Document type:** directory.
 Formerly: American Sociological Association.
Directory of Members (ISSN 0093-898X)

301 US
AMERICAN SOCIOLOGICAL ASSOCIATION. PROCEEDINGS OF ANNUAL MEETING. a. $6 (foreign $12) (effective
1993). American Sociological Association, 1722 N
St., N.W., Washington, DC 20036.
TEL 202-833-3410. FAX 202-785-0146. (reprint
service avail. from UMI) **Document type:** proceedings.

301 US ISSN 0003-1224
HM1   CODEN: ASRRB
AMERICAN SOCIOLOGICAL REVIEW. 1936. bi-m. $50 to individuals (foreign $60); institutions $105 (foreign $115). American Sociological Association, 1722 N St., N.W., Washington, DC 20036.
TEL 202-833-3410. FAX 202-785-0146. Ed. Paula England. adv.; bk.rev.; charts. circ. 15,000. (also avail. in microform from MIM,UMI; reprint service avail. from UMI,SCH) **Indexed:** A.B.C.Pol.Sci., Abstr.Anthropol., Abstr.Crim.& Pen., Acad.Ind., Adol.Ment.Hlth.Abstr., Amer.Bibl.Slavic & E.Eur.Stud., ASSIA, Bibl.Engl.Lang.& Lit., C.I.J.E., Child.Bk.Rev.Ind. (1965-), Commun.Abstr., Cont.Pg.Manage., Crim.Just.Abstr., Curr.Cont., Deep Sea Res.& Oceanogr.Abstr., E.I., Educ.Admin.Abstr., G.Soc.Sci.& Rel.Per.Lit., Geo.Abstr., Hist.Abstr., IDA, Int.Lab.Doc., Int.Polit.Sci.Abstr., Lang.& Lang.Behav.Abstr., Mid.East: Abstr.& Ind., Mult.Ed.Abstr., P.A.I.S., Polit.Sci.Abstr., Popul.Ind., Psychol.Abstr. (1936-), Rural Recreat.Tour.Abstr., Sage Fam.Stud.Abstr., Sage Urb.Stud.Abstr., SCIMP, Soc.Sci.Ind., Soc.Work Res.& Abstr., Sociol.Abstr. (1952-), Sociol.Educ.Abstr., SOMA, SSCI, Stud.Wom.Abstr., World Agri.Econ.& Rural Sociol.Abstr. **Document type:** academic/scholarly publication.
• Also available online. Vendor(s): University Microfilms International.
—BLDSC (0857.500000); Faxon; Genuine Article; SWETS; UMI; UnCover.
Description: Publishes work of interest to the discipline in general: new theoretical developments, results of research advancing understanding of fundamental social processes, and methodological innovations.

301 US ISSN 0003-1232
HM9
AMERICAN SOCIOLOGIST. 1969. q. $50 to individuals (foreign $82); institutions $116 (foreign $148) (effective Aug. 1995). (American Sociological Association) Transaction Publishers, Transaction Periodicals Consortium, Department 3092, Rutgers University, New Brunswick, NJ 08903.
TEL 908-445-2280. FAX 908-445-3138. Ed. Jonathan Imber. adv. circ. 500. (also avail. in microform from MIM,UMI; reprint service avail. from SWZ,UMI) **Indexed:** Curr.Cont., E.I., Int.Polit.Sci.Abstr., Lang.& Lang.Behav.Abstr., Mid.East: Abstr.& Ind., Res.High.Educ.Abstr., Soc.Sci.Ind., Sociol.Abstr. (1966-), SSCI, Stud.Wom.Abstr. **Document type:** academic/scholarly publication.
—BLDSC (0857.503000); Faxon; SWETS; UMI; UnCover. **CCC.**
Description: Examines the history, status, and prospects of sociology as a profession and a discipline. Emphasizes new trends in the profession and focuses on how sociologists have shaped or influenced social policy and the intellectual issues of the age.
Refereed Serial

AMERICAN UNIVERSITY STUDIES. SERIES 16. ECONOMICS. see *POPULATION STUDIES*

301 NE ISSN 0921-4933
AMSTERDAMS SOCIOLOGISCH TIJDSCHRIFT. 1974. 4/yr. fl.99.75 to individuals; institutions fl.155; students fl.67.50. WoltersgroepGroningen b.v. (Subsidiary of: Wolters Kluwer N.V.), Postbus 58, 9700 MB Groningen, Netherlands.
TEL 31-50-226922. **Indexed:** Sociol.Abstr. (1987-). **Document type:** academic/scholarly publication.
—BLDSC (0859.610000); SWETS.
Former titles (until **1988**): Sociologisch Tijdschrift (ISSN 0168-731X); (until 1982): Amsterdams Sociologisch Tijdschrift (ISSN 0165-0297)

301 SP ISSN 0066-1473
ANALES DE MORAL SOCIAL Y ECONOMICA. 1962. irreg. 125 ptas. Centro de Estudios Sociales de la Santa Cruz del Valle de los Caidos, Madrid, Spain. (Dist. by: Aguilar, S.A. de Publicaciones, Juan Bravo 38, Madrid 6, Spain)

300 PO ISSN 0003-2573
HM7
ANALISE SOCIAL. (Summaries in English and French) 1963. 5/yr. Esc.1300($45) Universidade de Lisboa, Instituto de Ciencias Sociais, Av. das Forcas Armadas, Edif. I.S.C.T.E., Ala Sul, 1 Andar, 1600 Lisbon, Portugal. Ed.Bd. bk.rev.; charts. circ. 3,000. (back issues avail.) **Indexed:** Int.Polit.Sci.Abstr., Lang.& Lang.Behav.Abstr., Sociol.Abstr. **Document type:** academic/scholarly publication.

ANARCHIST STUDIES. see *POLITICAL SCIENCE*

ANCIENT GREEK CITIES REPORT. see *HOUSING AND URBAN PLANNING*

301 AU ISSN 0587-5234
ANGEWANDTE SOZIALFORSCHUNG. 1972. q. S.370. Institut fuer Angewandte Soziologie, Lerchenfelderstr. 36, A-1080 Vienna, Austria. Ed. Henrik Kreutz. adv.; bk.rev.

301 IT ISSN 0392-5870
ANIMAZIONE SOCIALE; mensile per gli operatori sociali. 1970. m. L.65000 to individuals; institutions L.80000; foreign L.105000 (effective 1995). Edizioni Gruppo Abele, Via Giolitti 21, 10123 Turin, Italy. TEL 39-11-8142745. FAX 39-11-8395577. Ed. G.A. Ellena.
Description: Deals with social issues, as they relate to political and cultural institutions.

301 FR ISSN 0395-2649
AP20
ANNALES; histoire, sciences sociales. 1929. bi-m. 70 ECU($87) (typically set in Jan.). Armand Colin (Subsidiary of: Masson), 103 bd. Saint Michel, 75005 Paris, France. TEL 46-34-12-19. FAX 43-26-96-38. (Subscr. to: BP 22, 41353 Vineuil, France. TEL 54-43-89-94. FAX 54-26-96-38) Ed. Jean-Yves Grenier. adv. circ. 5,000. (also avail. in microform from UMI; reprint service avail. from KTO) **Indexed:** Amer.Hist.& Life, Arts & Hum.Cit.Ind., Br.Archaeol.Abstr., C.I.S. Abstr., Curr.Cont., Geo.Abstr., Hist.Abstr., IDA, Int.Polit.Sci.Abstr., Lang.& Lang.Behav.Abstr., Popul.Ind., SSCI.
—Faxon. **CCC.**
Former titles (until **1946**): Annales d'Histoire Sociale (ISSN 1243-258X); (until 1945): Melanges d'Histoire Sociale (ISSN 1243-2571); (until 1942): Annales d'Histoire Sociale (ISSN 1243-2563); (until 1939): Annales d'Histoire (ISSN 0003-441X)

ANNALES DE L'EST. see *HISTORY — History Of Europe*

ANNALES UNIVERSITATIS MARIAE CURIE-SKLODOWSKA. SECTIO I. PHILOSOPHIA - SOCIOLOGIA. see *PHILOSOPHY*

301 GW ISSN 0066-2275
ANNALI DI SOCIOLOGIA/SOZIOLOGISCHES JAHRBUCH. (Text in German, Italian) 1964. s-a. DM.120. Duncker und Humblot GmbH, Postfach 410329, 12113 Berlin, Germany. TEL 030-7900060. FAX 030-79000631. Ed. A. Zingerle. adv.; bk.rev. **Indexed:** Lang.& Lang.Behav.Abstr., Sociol.Abstr. (1985-). **Document type:** academic/scholarly publication.

301 FR ISSN 0066-2399
ANNEE SOCIOLOGIQUE. 1896. s-a. 380 F. (foreign 430 F.) (effective 1996). Presses Universitaires de France, Departement des Revues, 14 av. du Bois-de-l'Epine, B.P.90, 91003 Evry Cedex, France. TEL 1-60-77-82-05. FAX 1-60-79-20-45. TELEX PUF 600 474 F. (reprint service avail. from KTO) **Indexed:** A.I.C.P., CERDIC, Int.Polit.Sci.Abstr., Lang.& Lang.Behav.Abstr., P.A.I.S.For.Lang.Ind., Sociol.Abstr. (1960-).
—**CCC.**
Description: Covers general, political, and theoretical sociology, methodology, social and cultural anthropology, religious, demographic and family sociology, criminology.

301 309 157.63 US
ANNUAL EDITIONS: DRUGS, SOCIETY & BEHAVIOR. 1986. a. $12.95. Dushkin Publishing Group, Sluice Dock, Guilford, CT 06437-9989.
TEL 203-453-4351. FAX 203-453-6000. Ed. Erich Goode; Pub. Ian Nielsen. illus. **Document type:** academic/scholarly publication.

ANNUAL EDITIONS: DYING, DEATH, AND BEREAVEMENT. see *PSYCHOLOGY*

300 360 US
ANNUAL EDITIONS: HUMAN RESOURCES. 1989. a. $12.95. Dushkin Publishing Group, Sluice Dock, Guilford, CT 06437-9989. TEL 203-453-4351. FAX 203-453-6000. Ed. Fred H. Maidment; Pub. Ian Nielsen. illus. **Document type:** academic/scholarly publication.
Refereed Serial

ANNUAL EDITIONS: HUMAN SEXUALITY. see *BIOLOGY*

ANNUAL EDITIONS: MARRIAGE AND FAMILY. see *MATRIMONY*

305.8 US ISSN 1075-5195
E184.A1
ANNUAL EDITIONS: RACE & ETHNIC RELATIONS. 1991. a. $12.95. Dushkin Publishing Group, Sluice Dock, Guilford, CT 06437-9989. TEL 203-453-4351. FAX 203-453-6000. Ed. John A. Kromkowski; Pub. Ian Nielsen. illus. **Document type:** academic/scholarly publication.
Refereed Serial

301 US ISSN 0277-9315
HM1
ANNUAL EDITIONS: SOCIOLOGY. 1972. a. $12.95. Dushkin Publishing Group, Sluice Dock, Guilford, CT 06437-9989. TEL 203-453-4351. FAX 203-453-6000. Ed. Kurt Finsterbusch; Pub. Ian Nielsen. illus.; index. (back issues avail.) **Indexed:** Soc.Sci.Ind. **Document type:** academic/scholarly publication.
Formerly: Annual Editions: Readings in Sociology (ISSN 0090-4236)
Refereed Serial

301.364 US ISSN 0160-9815
HT101
ANNUAL EDITIONS: URBAN SOCIETY. 1978. biennial. $12.95. Dushkin Publishing Group, Sluice Dock, Guilford, CT 06437-9989. TEL 203-453-4351. FAX 203-453-6000. Ed. Fred Siegel; Pub. Ian Nielsen. illus.; index. (back issues avail.) **Document type:** academic/scholarly publication.
Formerly: Focus: Urban Society.
Refereed Serial

ANNUAL REVIEW OF SEX RESEARCH. see *PSYCHOLOGY*

301 US ISSN 0360-0572
HM1   CODEN: ARVSDB
ANNUAL REVIEW OF SOCIOLOGY. 1975. a. $52 (foreign $57) (effective Jan. 1995). Annual Reviews Inc., 4139 El Camino Way, Box 10139, Palo Alto, CA 94303-0139. TEL 415-493-4400; 800-523-8635. TELEX 910-290-0275. E-mail: annrevu@class.org. Ed. John Hagan. bibl.; cum.index. (also avail. in microform from UMI; back issues avail.; reprint service avail.) **Indexed:** Amer.Bibl.Slavic & E.Eur.Stud., Biol.Abstr., Curr.Cont., Int.Polit.Sci.Abstr., Lang.& Lang.Behav.Abstr., PSI, Psychol.Abstr. (1975-), Soc.Sci.Ind., Sociol.Abstr. (1974-), SSCI. **Document type:** academic/scholarly publication.
• Also available online. Vendor(s): University Microfilms International.
—BLDSC (1529.100000); Faxon; Genuine Article; SWETS; UMI; UnCover. **CCC.**
Description: Original critical reviews of the significant primary literature and current developments in sociology.

301 GW
ANSTOESSE ZUR FRIEDENSARBEIT. 1990. irreg., vol.11, 1992. price varies. Georg Olms Verlag, Hagentorwall 7, 31134 Hildesheim, Germany.
TEL 05121-1501-0. FAX 05121-150150. (U.S. subscr. to: 111 W. 57th St., New York, NY 10019. TEL 212-757-5237) **Document type:** monographic series.

301.4 360 362.7 US
ANTI-CENSORSHIP NEWSLETTER.* m. $15 (foreign $40). The Parent S I G, 1640 Via Pacifica, Ste.F-105, Corona, CA 91720. Ed. Lawrence A. Stanley. bk.rev.
• Also available online.
Formerly (until **1980**): Parent S I G NewsFliers.
Description: Covers anti-censorship and pro-censorship in reference to child pornography; includes sex education, childhood sexuality and sex exploitation of children.

ANVESAK. see *BUSINESS AND ECONOMICS*

301 PY ISSN 0044-8524
AQUI. 1971. w. $50. Editorial Emegebe S.A., Alberdi 1393, Asuncion, Paraguay. TEL 448-688-443-536. FAX 448-271-495-901.
Description: Treats themes in the political and judicial atmospheres and covers social and economic issues.

ARBEITEN ZUR SOZIALWISSENSCHAFTLICHEN PSYCHOLOGIE. see *PSYCHOLOGY*

SOCIOLOGY

ARMED FORCES AND SOCIETY; an interdisciplinary journal on military institutions, civil-military relations, arms control and peacekeeping, and conflict management. see MILITARY

301   SI   ISSN 0217-6742
ASIAN CULTURE. Key Title: Ya Zhou Wen Hua. 1983. 2/yr. $10. Singapore Society of Asian Studies, No. 10-319, Blk 72 Telok Blangah Height, Singapore 0410, Singapore. TEL 271-3652.

ASPECTS OF FRANCE. see ETHNIC INTERESTS

301   US
ASSOCIATION FOR THE SOCIOLOGY OF RELIGION. NEWS AND ANNOUNCEMENTS. 1965. q. $25. Association for the Sociology of Religion (Lancaster), Lebanon Valley College, 931 Harrisburg Ave., Lancaster, PA 17603. TEL 717-867-6336. FAX 717-399-4464. (Subscr. to: Marist Hall, Rm. 108, Catholic University, Washington, DC 20064) Ed. Barbara J. Denison. bk.rev. circ. 738.
Description: Social commentary on religion.

ASSOCIATION INTERNATIONALE D'ETUDES DU SUD-EST EUROPEEN. BULLETIN. see HISTORY — History Of Europe

360   FR   ISSN 0587-3746
ASSURE SOCIAL. 1964. bi-m. 100 F. (Union Nationale pour l'Avenir de la Medecine) B.C. Savy, 18 av. de la Marne, 92600 Asnieres, France. adv.; bk.rev. circ. 15,000.

ATMA JAYA RESEARCH CENTRE. SOCIO-MEDICAL RESEARCH REPORT/PUSAT PENELITIAN ATMA JAYA. PENELITIAN TENTANG KEBUTUHAN KESEHATAN MASYARAKAT DAN SISTEM PELEYANAN KESEHATAN DI KECAMATAN PENJARINGAN. see MEDICAL SCIENCES

ATMA JAYA RESEARCH CENTRE. SOCIO-RELIGIOUS RESEARCH REPORT/PUSAT PENELITIAN ATMA JAYA. LAPORAN PENELITIAN KEAGAMAAN. see RELIGIONS AND THEOLOGY

301.4 360 150   AT   ISSN 0814-723X
CODEN: ANZTE7
AUSTRALIAN AND NEW ZEALAND JOURNAL OF FAMILY THERAPY. 1979. q. Aus.$65($70) to individuals (foreign $67); institutions Aus.$90 (foreign $79) (effective 1995). Australian and New Zealand Journal of Family Therapy Inc., P.O. Box 633, Lane Cove, N.S.W. 2066, Australia. TEL 61-2-8796144. FAX 61-2-879-6440. Ed. Max Cornwell. adv.; bk.rev.; circ. 1,500 (paid). (back issues avail.) **Indexed:** IMFL, Psychol.Abstr. (1983-), Sage Fam.Stud.Abstr., Soc.Work Res.& Abstr. **Document type:** academic/scholarly publication.
—BLDSC (1796.886500).
Formerly: Australian Journal of Family Therapy.
Description: Promotes theory and practice of family therapy.

301   AT   ISSN 0004-8690
HM1
AUSTRALIAN & NEW ZEALAND JOURNAL OF SOCIOLOGY. 1965. 3/yr. Aus.$60 to individuals; institutions Aus.$75. (Sociological Association of Australia and New Zealand) Longman Australia, 95 Coventry St., S. Melbourne, Vic. 3205, Australia. TEL 61-3-6970666. FAX 61-3-6992041. Ed. Pamela Lewis. adv.; bk.rev.; abstr.; index, cum.index every 2 yrs. circ. 1,200. (also avail. in microfilm from UMI) **Indexed:** Amer.Hist.& Life, ASSIA, Aus.Educ.Ind., Aus.P.A.I.S., Curr.Cont., Geo.Abstr., Hist.Abstr., Lang.& Lang.Behav.Abstr., Mid.East: Abstr.& Ind., Mult.Ed.Abstr., Psychol.Abstr. (1982-), Res.High.Educ.Abstr., So.Pac.Per.Ind., Sociol.Abstr. (1965-), SSCI, Stud.Wom.Abstr. **Document type:** academic/scholarly publication.
●Also available on CD-ROM.
—BLDSC (1796.897000); Faxon; Genuine Article; SWETS; UMI; UnCover.

AUSTRALIAN FAMILY BRIEFINGS. see LAW — Family And Matrimonial Law

AUSTRALIAN FOLKLORE. see FOLKLORE

AUTO-BIOGRAPHY. see BIOGRAPHY

AZAD MAZDUR; Hindi weekly. see POLITICAL SCIENCE

301 338.91   BG
B I D S. MONOGRAPH. 1949. irreg., latest no.9. price varies. Bangladesh Unnayan Gobeshona Protishthan - Bangladesh Institute of Development Studies, G.P.O. Box 3854, E - 17 Agargoan, Sher-e-Banglanagar, Dhaka 1207, Bangladesh. TEL 325041. Ed.Bd. **Document type:** monographic series.

B I D S. NEWSLETTER. see BUSINESS AND ECONOMICS — International Development And Assistance

301 338.91   BG
B I D S. RESEARCH REPORTS. (Text in English) irreg., latest no.72. Bangladesh Unnayan Gobeshona Protishthan - Bangladesh Institute of Development Studies, G.P.O. Box 3854, E - 17 Agargoan, Sher-e-Banglanagar, Dhaka, Bangladesh. TEL 325041. Ed.Bd.

301 338.91   BG
B I D S. WORKING PAPER. irreg., no.4, 1987. price varies. Bangladesh Unnayan Gobeshona Protishthan - Bangladesh Institute of Development Studies, G.P.O. Box 3854, E - 17 Agargoan, Sher-e-Banglanagar, Dhaka 1207, Bangladesh. TEL 325041. Ed.Bd.

301.16   US   ISSN 1059-8235
BAD SEED. 1983. q. $15. Kicks, Box 646, Cooper Sta., NY 10003. TEL 718-789-4438. FAX 718-398-9215. Ed. Miriam Linna. bk.rev.; film rev. circ. 2,000. (back issues avail.)
Description: Contains studies, discussions, and research on juvenile delinquency in popular culture; film, literature, media.

300   IS   ISSN 0005-4542
BAMA'ARAKHA. 1961. m. Council of the Sephardi and Oriental Communities, P.O. Box 10, 12A Haavatzelet St., Jerusalem 91000, Israel. Ed. Yehezkel Soffer. adv.; bk.rev.; bibl. circ. 4,000. **Indexed:** Ind.Heb.Per.

301   GW   ISSN 0931-2110
BAUSTEINE.* 1977. irreg. DM.46.80. Institut fuer Soziale Gegenwartsfrage, Prinz-Eugen-Str., 7800 Freiburg, Germany. circ. 300.
Formerly (until 1986): Bausteine fuer eine Geisteswissenschaftliche Wirtschafts- und Sozialwissenschaft (ISSN 0176-7607); (until 1983): Bausteine fuer eine Soziale Zukunft (ISSN 0344-1717)

BEHAVIOR AND SOCIAL ISSUES. see PSYCHOLOGY

BEITRAEGE ZUR NATIONALSOZIALISTISCHEN GESUNDHEITS- UND SOZIALPOLITIK. see MEDICAL SCIENCES

BEITRAEGE ZUR PSYCHOLOGIE UND SOZIOLOGIE DES KRANKEN MENSCHEN. see PSYCHOLOGY

301   GW   ISSN 0522-7119
BEITRAEGE ZUR SOZIOLOGIE UND SOZIALKUNDE LATEINAMERIKAS. 1967. irreg., vol.43. DM.38. Wilhelm Fink Verlag, Ohmstr. 5, 80802 Munich, Germany. TEL 089-348017. FAX 089-341378. **Document type:** monographic series.

BELARUSKAYA CARKVA. see RELIGIONS AND THEOLOGY — Eastern Orthodox

BELGIUM. MINISTERE DE L'EDUCATION NATIONALE. REVUE. see EDUCATION

BERITA I D S DEVELOPMENT REVIEW. see BUSINESS AND ECONOMICS

301   US   ISSN 0067-5830
HM1
BERKELEY JOURNAL OF SOCIOLOGY; critical review. 1955. a. $8 to individuals; institutions $15 (foreign $21.13); students $6. University of California at Berkeley, Sociology Department, 410 Barrows Hall, Berkeley, CA 94720. TEL 510-642-2771. FAX 510-642-0659. E-mail: bjs@violet.berkeley.edu. (Subscr. to: 458 A Barrows Hall, Berkeley, CA 94720) Ed.Bd. adv.; bk.rev.; index. circ. 1,500. (back issues avail.) **Indexed:** Alt.Press Ind., Amer.Bibl.Slavic & E.Eur.Stud., Int.Polit.Sci.Abstr., Lang.& Lang.Behav.Abstr., Mid.East: Abstr.& Ind., Sociol.Abstr. (1955-), Stud.Wom.Abstr. **Document type:** academic/scholarly publication.
—BLDSC (1940.350000); SWETS; UnCover.
Formerly (until vol. 4, 1958): Berkeley Publications in Society and Institutions.

301   GW   ISSN 0863-1808
HM5   CODEN: BJSOE8
BERLINER JOURNAL FUER SOZIOLOGIE. 1991. 4/yr. DM.154 (foreign DM.161) (students DM.72). (Humboldt Universitaet zu Berlin, Fachbereich Sozialwissenschaften) Verlag Leske und Budrich GmbH, Postfach 300551, 51334 Leverkusen, Germany. TEL 02171-2079. FAX 02171-41209. **Document type:** academic/scholarly publication.

301.2   PL   ISSN 0067-7655
BIBLIOTEKA ETNOGRAFII POLSKIEJ. (Text in English or Polish; summaries in English, French or German) 1958. a. price varies. Polska Akademia Nauk, Instytut Historii Kultury Materialnej, Al. Solidarnosci 105, 00-140 Warsaw, Poland. Ed. Maria Frankowska.

THE BLACKCOUNTRYMAN. see HISTORY — History Of Europe

300   GW
BLAUE FEDER; alle "Thema Null"-Beitraege. 1965. m. DM.160. OHO-Verlag, Schlagwew 5, Postfach 30, 3501 Zierenberg 1, Germany. Ed. Horst Brede. adv.; bk.rev.; film rev.; play rev.; illus.; pat.; tr.lit. circ. 200-2,000.
Former titles: Thema Null (ISSN 0023-9968); Arbeitsmethodik Briefe.

BLAUWE WEGWIJZER. see DRUG ABUSE AND ALCOHOLISM

301   UY   ISSN 0006-6508
BOLETIN URUGUAYO DE SOCIOLOGIA. (Text in Spanish; summaries in English, French, Portuguese and Spanish) 1961. q. $6. Mario Bon Espasandin, Ed. & Pub., Calle Juncal 1395, Piso 2, Escritorio 5, Montevideo, Uruguay. adv.; bk.rev.; abstr.; bibl.; charts; stat.; index. circ. 1,500. **Indexed:** Lang.& Lang.Behav.Abstr.

BOULITE. see FOLKLORE

301   UK   ISSN 0007-1315
HM1
BRITISH JOURNAL OF SOCIOLOGY. 1950. q. £44 (rest of world £46) to individuals; institutions £78 (rest of world £84). (London School of Economics) Routledge, 11 New Fetter Ln., London EC4P 4EE, England. TEL 0171-583-9855. FAX 0171-842-2298. TELEX 263398-ROUT-G. E-mail: sample.journals@routledge.com. (Subscr. to: ITPS Ltd., Cheriton House, Andover, Hants SP10 5BE, England. TEL 01264-342919. FAX 01264-342807) Ed. Paul Rock. adv.: page £225; trim 115 x 190. bk.rev.; index, cum.index every 10 yrs. circ. 2,700. (also avail. in microform from WMP) **Indexed:** A.I.C.P., Abstr.Crim.& Pen., Adol.Ment.Hlth.Abstr., Amer.Hist.& Life, ASSIA, Br.Hum.Ind., C.I.J.E., Commun.Abstr., Cont.Pg.Manage., Curr.Cont., E.I., Geo.Abstr., High.Educ.Curr.Aware.Bull., Hist.Abstr., Ind.Med., Int.Lab.Doc., Int.Polit.Sci.Abstr., Lang.& Lang.Behav.Abstr., Mark.Res.Abstr. (1964-), Mid.East: Abstr.& Ind., P.A.I.S., Psychol.Abstr. (1950-), Res.High.Educ.Abstr., SCIMP (1979-), Soc.Sci.Ind., Sociol.Abstr. (1952-), Sociol.Educ.Abstr., SOMA, Sp.Ed.Needs Abstr., SSCI, Trop.Dis.Bull. **Document type:** academic/scholarly publication.
—BLDSC (2324.800000); Faxon; Genuine Article; SWETS; UnCover. **CCC.**
Description: Publishes research projects and discussion notes as well as articles and papers in sociology and other related fields.

SOCIOLOGY

BRITISH JOURNAL OF SOCIOLOGY OF EDUCATION. see *EDUCATION*

301   EI   ISSN 1017-4877
BULLETIN OF EUROPEAN STUDIES ON TIME. French edition: Bulletin Europeen d'Etudes Europeennes sur le Temps. German edition: Bulletin fuer Europaeische Zeitstudien. 2/yr. free. European Foundation for the Improvement of Living and Working Conditions, Loughlinstown House, Shankill, Co. Dublin, Ireland. TEL 353-1-28-26-888. FAX 353-1-28-26-456. TELEX 30726 EURF EI. E-mail: postmaster@eurofound.ie. Ed. Alexander Wedderburn. **Document type:** academic/scholarly publication.

BULLETIN OF TIBETOLOGY. see *HISTORY — History Of Asia*

C A P SULE (LEVITTOWN). (Children of Aging Parents) see *GERONTOLOGY AND GERIATRICS*

301 360   IT
C E N S I S NOTE E COMMENTI. 1965. 12/yr. L.70000 (foreign L.150000) (effective Jan. 1992). Centro Studi Investimenti Sociali, Piazza di Novella, 2-00, 00199 Rome, Italy. TEL 39-6-860911. FAX 39-6-8315200. Dir. Nadio Delai. stat.; index. circ. 4,500. (processed) **Document type:** bulletin.
    Formerly: C E N S I S Quindicinale di Note e Commenti (ISSN 0007-8271)
    Description: Investigates and interprets the most significant events in the Italian socio-economic and cultural phenomenology and in the sectors of social policy.

C I R E S CAHIERS. (Centre Ivoirien de Recherches Economiques et Sociales) see *BUSINESS AND ECONOMICS*

C M J S CENTERPIECES. (Cohen Center for Modern Jewish Studies) see *ETHNIC INTERESTS*

C S E MONOGRAPH SERIES IN EVALUATION. (Center for the Study of Evaluation) see *EDUCATION — Teaching Methods And Curriculum*

C S S S DIGEST. (Center for the Study of Sport in Society) see *SPORTS AND GAMES*

301   US   ISSN 0749-8799
C U B COMMUNICATOR. 1976. m. $50. Concerned United Birthparents, Inc., 2000 Walker St., Des Moines, IA 50317-5255. TEL 800-822-2777. Ed. Carole Anderson. adv.; bk.rev. circ. 2,500. **Document type:** newspaper.

301 362.734   US
C U B COMMUNICATOR. ADOPTION NEWSLETTER. 1978. m. $50 includes membership. Concerned United Birthparents, Inc., 2000 Walker St., Des Moines, IA 50317-5255. TEL 800-822-2777. Ed. Carole Anderson. **Document type:** newsletter.
    Description: Contains news and articles about adoption and letters and articles by or about birthparents.

301 320   BL   ISSN 0102-9711
HN281
CADERNOS DO C.E.A.S. 1969. bi-m. $20. Centro de Estudos e Acao Social, Rua Aristides Novis 101, Salvador, Bahia, Brazil. Ed. Claudio Perani. adv.; bk.rev.; bibl.; charts; stat. circ. 2,000. **Indexed:** HR Rep., Int.Lab.Doc., Rural Devel.Abstr.

301   BL   ISSN 0102-6518
CADERNOS RIOARTE. 1985. 2/yr. Instituto Municipal de Arte e Cultura, Rua Rumania 20, Laranjeiras, CEP 22240 Rio de Janeiro, Brazil.

CAHIERS CRITIQUES DE THERAPIE FAMILIALE ET DE PRATIQUES DE RESEAUX. see *PSYCHOLOGY*

CAHIERS DE PRAXEMATIQUE. see *LINGUISTICS*

301   CN   ISSN 0831-1048
    CODEN: CARSEV
CAHIERS DE RECHERCHE SOCIOLOGIQUE. 1983. s-a. Universite du Quebec a Montreal, Departement de Sociologie, C.P. 8888, Succ. A, Montreal, PQ H3C 3P8, Canada. TEL 514-987-4380. Ed. Jean-Guy Lacroix.

301 331   FR   ISSN 0761-9871
GN502
CAHIERS DE SOCIOLOGIE ECONOMIQUE ET CULTURELLE. 1959; N.S. 1979. s-a. 140 F. (foreign 160 F.). Institut Havrais de Sociologie Economique et de Psychologie des Peuples, 56 rue Anatole France, 76600 Le Havre, France. TEL 35-46-69-55. Ed. Albert Nicollet. (also avail. in microform from SWZ) **Indexed:** Documentatieblad, Lang.& Lang.Behav.Abstr., Psychol.Abstr., Sociol.Abstr. (1984-).
    Formerly (until 1984): Cahiers de Sociologie Economique (ISSN 0007-9987); Incorporating: Ethnopsychologie (ISSN 0046-2608)

CAHIERS DES RELIGIONS AFRICAINES. see *RELIGIONS AND THEOLOGY — Other Denominations And Sects*

301   FR   ISSN 0008-0276
HM3
CAHIERS INTERNATIONAUX DE SOCIOLOGIE. 1946. s-a. 270 F. (foreign 340 F.) (effective 1996). (Ecole des Hautes Etudes en Sciences Sociales) Presses Universitaires de France, Departement des Revues, 14 av. du Bois-de-l'Epine, B.P.90, 91003 Evry Cedex, France. TEL 1-60-77-82-05. FAX 1-60-79-20-45. TELEX PUF 600 474 F. Dir. G. Balandier. bk.rev.; bibl.; index. circ. 3,500. (reprint service avail. from KTO,SCH) **Indexed:** E.I., Int.Polit.Sci.Abstr., Lang.& Lang.Behav.Abstr., Pt.de Rep. (1979-), Sociol.Abstr. (1952-), SSCI.
    —Genuine Article; SWETS. **CCC.**
    Description: Covers the new work on sociological theory and practice.

CAHIERS POUR CROIRE AUJOURD'HUI. see *RELIGIONS AND THEOLOGY*

CALIFORNIA FAMILY LAW: PRACTICE AND PROCEDURE. see *LAW — Family And Matrimonial Law*

301.05   US   ISSN 0162-8712
HM1
CALIFORNIA SOCIOLOGIST; a journal of sociology and social work. 1978. s-a. $10 to individuals; institutions $18. California State University, Los Angeles, Department of Sociology, 5151 State University Dr., Los Angeles, CA 90032. TEL 213-343-2200. FAX 213-343-5155. Ed. Terry R. Kandal. adv. circ. 200. **Indexed:** Adol.Ment.Hlth.Abstr., Lang.& Lang.Behav.Abstr., Soc.Work Res.& Abstr., Sociol.Abstr. **Document type:** academic/scholarly publication.
    —BLDSC (3015.332000).
    Description: Publishes theoretical and empirical articles and articles on practice and social policy issues.

301   UK   ISSN 0068-6727
CAMBRIDGE PAPERS IN SOCIOLOGY. 1970. irreg., no.5, 1975. $32.50 for latest vol. Cambridge University Press, Edinburgh Bldg., Shaftesbury Rd., Cambridge CB2 2RU, England. TEL 01223-312393. FAX 01223-315052. TELEX 851817256. (N. American addr.: Cambridge University Press, Journals Dept., 40 W. 20th St., New York, NY 10011. TEL 212-924-3900. FAX 212-691-3239) Eds. R.M. Blackburn, J.H. Goldthorpe. index. **Document type:** monographic series.

301   UK   ISSN 0068-6808
CAMBRIDGE STUDIES IN SOCIOLOGY. 1968. irreg., no.10, 1978. price varies. Cambridge University Press, Edinburgh Bldg., Shaftesbury Rd., Cambridge CB2 2RU, England. TEL 01223-312393. FAX 01223-315052. TELEX 851817256. (N. American addr.: Cambridge University Press, Journals Dept., 40 W. 20th St., New York, NY 10011. TEL 212-924-3900. FAX 212-691-3239) Eds. R.M. Blackburn, J.H. Goldthorpe. **Document type:** monographic series.

CAMBRIDGE STUDIES IN WORK AND SOCIAL INEQUALITY. see *BUSINESS AND ECONOMICS — Labor And Industrial Relations*

CAMPUS REVIEW. see *LITERARY AND POLITICAL REVIEWS*

CANADIAN JOURNAL OF BEHAVIOURAL SCIENCE/REVUE CANADIENNE DES SCIENCES DU COMPORTEMENT. see *PSYCHOLOGY*

CANADIAN JOURNAL OF POLITICAL & SOCIAL THEORY/REVUE CANADIENNE DE THEORIE POLITIQUE ET SOCIALE. see *POLITICAL SCIENCE*

301   CN   ISSN 0318-6431
HM1
CANADIAN JOURNAL OF SOCIOLOGY/CAHIERS CANADIENS DE SOCIOLOGIE. (Text in English or French) q. Can.$50 to individuals; institutions Can.$85; students Can.$25 (effective 1996). University of Alberta, Department of Sociology, Edmonton, AB T6G 2H4, Canada. Ed. Susan A. McDaniel. adv. contact: Joanne Milson. bk.rev.; index. **Indexed:** Can.B.P.I., Can.Per.Ind., Can.Wom.Per.Ind., IMFL, Lang.& Lang.Behav.Abstr., Mult.Ed.Abstr., Sociol.Abstr. (1975-), SOPODA, SSCI. **Document type:** academic/scholarly publication.
    —BLDSC (3035.630000); Genuine Article; UnCover. **CCC.**
    Description: Covers all aspects of sociology, with particular emphasis on politics and history.
    Refereed Serial

301 572   CN   ISSN 0008-4948
CANADIAN REVIEW OF SOCIOLOGY AND ANTHROPOLOGY/REVUE CANADIENNE DE SOCIOLOGIE ET D'ANTHROPOLOGIE. (Text in English, French) 1964. q. Can.$88 membership. Canadian Sociology and Anthropology Association, Concordia University, 1455 bd. de Maisonneuve W., Montreal, PQ H3G 1M8, Canada. TEL 514-848-8780. FAX 514-848-4539. Ed. Rosalind Sydie. adv.; bk.rev.; charts; index, cum.index 1964-1984. circ. 1,800. (also avail. in microform from MIM,KTO,UMI) **Indexed:** A.I.C.P., Abstr.Anthropol., Amer.Bibl.Slavic & E.Eur.Stud., Amer.Hist.& Life, Anthropol.Lit., ASSIA, Can.B.P.I., Can.Per.Ind., CMI, Commun.Abstr., Curr.Cont., Educ.Admin.Abstr., Hist.Abstr., Int.Polit.Sci.Abstr., Lang.& Lang.Behav.Abstr., Mid.East: Abstr.& Ind., Mult.Ed.Abstr., Polit.Sci.Abstr., Psychol.Abstr. (1984-), Rural Recreat.Tour.Abstr., Soc.Sci.Ind., Sociol.Abstr. (1964-), SSCI, Stud.Wom.Abstr., World Agri.Econ.& Rural Sociol.Abstr. **Document type:** academic/scholarly publication.
    —BLDSC (3044.650000); Faxon; Genuine Article; SWETS; UMI; UnCover.
    Description: Carries articles, commentaries and book reviews on key research findings and the current theoretical debates in the social sciences.
    Refereed Serial

CARAVELLE; cahiers du monde hispanique et luso-bresilien. see *HISTORY — History Of North And South America*

CATALYST (TORONTO). see *POLITICAL SCIENCE — Civil Rights*

301.15   US   ISSN 0889-0765
CENTER FOCUS. 1971. bi-m. $25. Center of Concern, 3700 13th St., N.E., Washington, DC 20017. TEL 202-635-2757. FAX 202-832-9494. Ed. John Predergast. adv.; bk.rev. circ. 21,000. **Indexed:** CERDIC, HR Rep. **Document type:** newsletter.

CENTRE D'ETUDES ETHNOLOGIQUES. PUBLICATIONS. SERIE 2: MEMOIRES ET MONOGRAPHIES. see *ANTHROPOLOGY*

CENTRE D'ETUDES ETHNOLOGIQUES BANDUNDU. PUBLICATIONS. see *ANTHROPOLOGY*

301.45   SA
CENTRE FOR CONFLICT RESOLUTION. ANNUAL REPORT. (Former name of issuing body: Centre for Intergroup Studies) (Text in English) 1968. a. free. Centre for Conflict Resolution, c/o University of Cape Town, Rondebosch 7700, South Africa. TEL 27-21-6502503. FAX 27-21-6852142. TELEX 5-21439. E-mail: mailbox@ccr.uct.ac.za. Ed. Laurie Nathan. bibl.; circ. 2,200 (controlled). **Document type:** corporate report.
    Former titles (until 1994): Centre for Intergroup Studies. Annual Report; Abe Bailey Institute of Inter-Racial Studies. Annual Report.
    Description: Reports on the centre's activities in promoting constructive, creative and cooperative approaches to the resolution of conflict and the reduction of violence in South Africa.

CENTRE FOR URBAN AND COMMUNITY STUDIES. BIBLIOGRAPHIC SERIES. see *HOUSING AND URBAN PLANNING*

CENTRE FOR URBAN AND COMMUNITY STUDIES. MAJOR REPORT SERIES. see *HOUSING AND URBAN PLANNING*

SOCIOLOGY

CENTRE FOR URBAN AND COMMUNITY STUDIES. RESEARCH PAPERS. see *HOUSING AND URBAN PLANNING*

616.8 362   FR   ISSN 0534-8021
CENTRE INTERNATIONAL DE L'ENFANCE. PARIS. TRAVAUX ET DOCUMENTS.* 1950. irreg. Centre International de l'Enfance - International Children's Center, Chateau de Longchamp, Bois de Boulogne, 75016 Paris, France. TEL 1-45-20-79-92. FAX 1-45-25-73-67.

301.364   AG   ISSN 0326-8470
CENTRO DE ESTUDIOS URBANOS Y REGIONALES. BOLETIN. 1986. 2/yr. $4. Ediciones C E U R, Av. Corrientes 2835, Cuerpo A, Piso 7-A, 1193 Buenos Aires, Argentina. TEL 961-8593. circ. 500.
   Description: Articles and research news on urban and regional development.

301.364   AG   ISSN 0326-1417
HT395.A7
CENTRO DE ESTUDIOS URBANOS Y REGIONALES. CUADERNOS. 1982. irreg. Ediciones C E U R, Av. Corrientes 2835, Piso 7 A, 1193 Buenos Aires, Argentina. TEL 961-8593. circ. 500.
   Description: Monographs and short research reports on urban and regional social problems.

301.364   AG
CENTRO DE ESTUDIOS URBANOS Y REGIONALES. INFORMES DE INVESTIGACION. 1985. irreg. Ediciones C E U R, Av. Corrientes 2835, Piso 7 A, 1193 Buenos Aires, Argentina. TEL 961-8593. circ. 500.
   Description: Research reports on Argentine and Latin American development process on urban and regional problems.

CETERIS PARIBUS; revista de investigaciones socio-economicas. see *BUSINESS AND ECONOMICS*

301.4   US
CHANGING ISSUES IN THE FAMILY. 1981. irreg. price varies. Praeger Publishers (Subsidiary of: Greenwood Publishing Group Inc.), 88 Post Rd. W., Box 5007, Westport, CT 06881-5007. TEL 203-226-3571. FAX 203-222-1502. **Document type:** monographic series.

301   US   ISSN 0300-6921
F548.9.N3
CHICAGO REPORTER; a monthly investigative news magazine focusing on issues of race and poverty in metropolitan Chicago. 1972. 11/yr. $38. Community Renewal Society, 332 S. Michigan, Chicago, IL 60604-4301. TEL 312-427-4830. FAX 312-427-6130. Ed. Laura Washington. bk.rev.; illus.; index. circ. 3,100. **Document type:** newsletter.
   Description: Reports and comments on the social, economic and political issues of metropolitan Chicago, with a special focus on race and poverty.

CHILD ABUSE & NEGLECT; the international journal. see *CHILDREN AND YOUTH — About*

150 301   US   ISSN 0738-0151
HV701   CODEN: CASWDD
CHILD AND ADOLESCENT SOCIAL WORK JOURNAL. 1983. bi-m. $275 (foreign $320) (effective 1996). Human Sciences Press, Inc. (Subsidiary of: Plenum Publishing Corp.), 233 Spring St., New York, NY 10013-1578. TEL 212-620-8000. FAX 212-463-0742. TELEX 23-421139. Ed. Florence Lieberman. adv.; bibl. (reprint service avail. UMI) **Indexed:** Adol.Ment.Hlth.Abstr., ASSIA, Child Devel.Abstr., IMFL, Lang.& Lang.Behav.Abstr., Psychol.Abstr. (1984-), Soc.Sci.Ind. (1994-), Soc.Work Res.& Abstr. **Document type:** academic/scholarly publication.
  —BLDSC (3172.914000); Faxon; UMI; UnCover. CCC.
   Supersedes (1972?-1981): Family and Child Mental Health Journal (ISSN 0190-230X); Which was formerly: Issues in Child Mental Health (ISSN 0362-403X); (until vol.5, 1977): Psychosocial Process (ISSN 0556-431X)
   Description: Focuses on clinical social work practice with children, adolescents, and their families.
   Refereed Serial

CHINA REPORT: POLITICAL, SOCIOLOGICAL, AND MILITARY AFFAIRS. see *POLITICAL SCIENCE*

301   US   ISSN 0895-4690
E184.C5
CHINESE AMERICAN FORUM; a cultural bridge and nationwide communication. 1984. q. $14 to individuals; institutions $20 (effective 1995-96). Chinese American Forum, Inc., 606 Brantford Ave., Silver Spring, MD 20904. TEL 301-622-3053. (Subscr. to: Box 4487, Silver Spring, MD 20904) Ed. S. Yen Lee. adv.; bk.rev. circ. 500. (back issues avail.) **Document type:** academic/scholarly publication.
  —UnCover.

301 572   US   ISSN 0009-4625
HM1
CHINESE SOCIOLOGY AND ANTHROPOLOGY; a journal of translations. 1968. q. $419 to institutions (foreign $472) (effective Jul. 1995). M.E. Sharpe, Inc., 80 Business Park Dr., Armonk, NY 10504. TEL 914-273-1800; 800-541-6563. FAX 914-273-2106. Ed. Anita Chan. adv.; index. (back issues avail.) **Indexed:** Asian-Pac.Econ.Lit., Curr.Cont., Hist.Abstr. (until 1994), Lang.& Lang.Behav.Abstr., SSCI, Stud.Wom.Abstr. **Document type:** academic/scholarly publication.
  —BLDSC (3181.100000); Faxon; Genuine Article; SWETS; UMI; UnCover. CCC.
   Refereed Serial

200 917.306   US   ISSN 1040-8622
CHRISTIAN IRELAND TODAY. 1987. m. free. Christian Ireland Ministries Inc., Box 11057, Albany, NY 12211. TEL 518-329-3003. Ed. Rev Francis G. McCloskey. circ. 763. (back issues avail.) **Document type:** newsletter.
   Description: Deals with issues of reconciliation, violence and non-violence, and cross-cultural cooperation.

CHRISTIAN SOCIAL ACTION. see *RELIGIONS AND THEOLOGY — Protestant*

CHRISTLICHE DEMOKRATIE; Vierteljahresschrift fuer Zeitgeschichte, Sozial-, Kultur- und Wirtschaftsgeschichte. see *HISTORY — History Of Europe*

300   FR   ISSN 1249-2701
CHRONIQUE ECONOMIQUE SYNDICALE & SOCIALE. 1955. bi-m. 260 F. (foreign 360 F.). Association d'Etudes Economiques, Sociales et Syndicales, 53 rue Sainte-Anne, 75002 Paris, France. TEL 46-14-09-29. FAX 46-14-09-25. Ed. Morvan Duhamel. bk.rev.; index. circ. 3,500.
  —BLDSC (3186.927500).
   Former titles (until 1994): Etudes Economiques, Sociales et Syndicales (ISSN 1165-3876); (until 1993): Etudes Sociales et Syndicales (ISSN 0014-2212)

CHURCH & SOCIETY. see *RELIGIONS AND THEOLOGY — Protestant*

301 340   II
CITIZEN ACTION. 1981. q. Rs.480($77) K.K. Roy (Private) Ltd., 55 Geriahat Rd., P.O. Box 10210, Calcutta 700 019, India. Ed. Dr. K.K. Roy. **Indexed:** HR Rep.

CIVILIAN CONGRESS; includes a directory of persons holding executive branch-military office in Congress contrary to constitutional prohibition (Art.1, Sec.6, Cl.2) of concurrent office-holding. see *LAW*

301   BE   ISSN 0009-8140
AP1
CIVILISATIONS; revue international de sciences humaines et des civilisation differentes. (Text in English, French) 1951. s-a. 1300 BEF (foreign 1430 BEF) (effective 1994). (Universite Libre de Bruxelles, Institut de Sociologie) Revue Civilisations, 44 Av. Jeanne, 1050 Brussels, Belgium. TEL 32-2-6503359. FAX 32-2-6503521. TELEX 23069 UNILIB B. Ed. Jacqueline Gilissen. bk.rev.; bibl.; index. circ. 1,000. (reprint service avail. from SWZ) **Indexed:** A.B.C.Pol.Sci., A.I.C.P., Amer.Hist.& Life, Bull.Signal., Documentatieblad, E.I., Hist.Abstr., Int.Polit.Sci.Abstr., Mid.East: Abstr.& Ind., Rural Recreat.Tour.Abstr., Sociol.Abstr., World Agri.Econ.& Rural Sociol.Abstr. **Document type:** academic/scholarly publication.
  —Faxon; UnCover.

301   FR   ISSN 0760-7202
DJK24
CIVILISATIONS DE L'EUROPE CENTRALE ET DU SUD-EST. irreg., latest no.9. price varies. Institut National des Langues et Civilisations Orientales, 2 rue de Lille, 75343 Paris Cedex 07, France. TEL 49-26-42-74. Ed. Antoine Mares.

301   US   ISSN 0730-840X
HM1
CLINICAL SOCIOLOGY REVIEW. 1982. a. $30. Sociological Practice Association, c/o Hugh McCain, Jacksonville State University, Jacksonville, AL 36265-9982. TEL 205-782-5315. Ed. W. David Watts. bk.rev. circ. 750. **Indexed:** Psychol.Abstr., Soc.Work Res.& Abstr., Sociol.Abstr. (1965-). **Document type:** academic/scholarly publication.
  —BLDSC (3286.382000).
   Description: Publishes essays concerning the practice of sociology.

301   SP
COLECCION FUNDACION F O E S S A. SERIE ESTUDIOS. 1969. irreg. (Fundacion Fomento de Estudios Sociales y Sociologia Aplicada) Euramerica, S.A., Mateo Inurria, 15, Madrid-16, Spain. bibl.; charts.

COLORADO KAIROS. see *RELIGIONS AND THEOLOGY*

COLUMBIA JOURNAL OF LAW AND SOCIAL PROBLEMS. see *LAW*

COLUMBIANA; bioregional journal for the Intermountain Northwest. see *CONSERVATION*

COMMON GROUND. see *RELIGIONS AND THEOLOGY*

301.45   US   ISSN 0010-3772
COMMUNITY (CHICAGO). 1941. q. $4. Friendship House, 1746 W. Division Ave., Chicago, IL 60622. TEL 312-227-5065. FAX 312-227-5065. Ed. Albert Schorsch, III. adv.; bk.rev.; illus. circ. 2,500. (also avail. in microform from UMI)
  —UMI.
   Description: External house organ for Friendship House, serving the homeless and needy. Focuses on race relations.

360 301.34   AT   ISSN 0814-401X
COMMUNITY QUARTERLY; leading journal of community development case studies. 1984. q. Aus.$28 to individuals; institutions Aus.$34; students Aus.$20 (foreign Aus.$42) (effective 1995). P.O. Box 275, St. Kilda, Vic. 3182, Australia. TEL 61-3-525-3384. FAX 61-3-534-3998. (Co-sponsor: Employ-Working Effectively Inc.) Ed. Fae Dent; Pub. Chris Morris. adv.: page Aus.$100; adv. contact: Chris Morris. bk.rev. circ. 1,000. **Document type:** bulletin.
  —UnCover.
   Description: Publishes practical articles about community development.

300   US   ISSN 0277-6189
COMMUNITY SERVICE NEWSLETTER. 1943. q. $25 (foreign $30) (effective 1995 & 1996). Community Service, Inc., Box 243, Yellow Springs, OH 45387. TEL 513-767-2161. Ed. Jane Morgan. bk.rev.; circ. 350 (controlled). (back issues avail.) **Indexed:** New Per.Ind. **Document type:** newsletter.
   Formerly: Community Comments (ISSN 0010-3780)
   Description: Essays, commentary, book reviews, and announcements pertaining to the growth of small communities as a basic social institution that encompasses units of economic, social, and spiritual development.

301   US   ISSN 0195-6310
HM1
COMPARATIVE SOCIAL RESEARCH. 1978. a. $63.50 to institutions. J A I Press Inc., 55 Old Post Rd., No. 2, Box 1678, Greenwich, CT 06836-1678. TEL 203-661-7602. Ed. Richard A. Tomasson. **Indexed:** Lang.& Lang.Behav.Abstr.
  —BLDSC (3363.820000); Faxon. CCC.
   Formerly (until vol.2): Comparative Studies in Sociology (ISSN 0164-1247)

300 900   UK   ISSN 0010-4175
H1
COMPARATIVE STUDIES IN SOCIETY AND HISTORY.
1959. q. £62($86) (effective 1996). Cambridge University Press, Edinburgh Bldg., Shaftesbury Rd., Cambridge CB2 2RU, England. TEL 01223-312393. FAX 01223-315052. TELEX 851817256. (N. American addr.: Cambridge University Press, 40 W. 20th St., New York, NY 10011. TEL 212-924-3900. FAX 212-691-3239) Ed. Raymond Grew. adv.; bk.rev.; bibl.; charts; illus.; index. (also avail. in microform from UMI; back issues avail.) Indexed: A.B.C.Pol.Sci., A.I.C.P., Acad.Ind., Amer.Hist.& Life, Anthropol.Lit., Arts & Hum.Cit.Ind., Asian-Pac.Econ.Lit., ASSIA, Curr.Cont., E.I., Geo.Abstr., Hist.Abstr., Hum.Ind., IMFL, Int.Polit.Sci.Abstr., Lang.& Lang.Behav.Abstr., Mid East: Abstr.& Ind., Per.Islam. (1991-), Polit.Sci.Abstr., Rural Recreat.Tour.Abstr., Sociol.Abstr., SSCI, World Agri.Econ.& Rural Sociol.Abstr. **Document type:** academic/scholarly publication.
—BLDSC (3363.850000); Faxon; Genuine Article; SWETS; UMI; UnCover. **CCC.**
Description: Compares change and stability in societies all over the world and in all eras: topics such as slavery, colonialism, revolution, religious movements and women's roles.

301   US   ISSN 0892-5569
HT110   CODEN: CUCEEK
COMPARATIVE URBAN AND COMMUNITY RESEARCH. a. $19.95. Transaction Publishers, Transaction Periodicals Consortium, Department 3092, Rutgers University, New Brunswick, NJ 08903. TEL 908-445-2280. FAX 908-445-3138. Ed. Michael Smith. **Document type:** academic/scholarly publication.
—BLDSC (3363.878000); Faxon; UMI; UnCover.
Description: Provides an interdisciplinary review of theoretical, empirical, and applied research on the process of urbanization and community change throughout the world.

301   AG   ISSN 0327-7860
CONCEPTOS BOLETIN. 1912. bi-m. Museo Social Argentino, Corrientes 1723, 1042 Buenos Aires, Argentina. Ed.Bd. bk.rev.; abstr.; bibl
Formerly (until 1987): Museo Social Argentino. Boletin (ISSN 0045-3331)

301.2 942   UK
CONFLICT AND CHANGE IN BRITAIN - A NEW AUDIT. 1990. irreg., latest 1993. £10.95 (hardcover edition £28). Athelone Press Ltd., 1 Park Dr., London NW11 7SG, England. TEL 0181-458-0888. FAX 0181-201-8115. (Dist. in the U.S. by: Athelone Press, 165 First Ave., Atlantic Highlands, NJ 07781. TEL 908-872-1441) Eds. Paul Rock, David Downes. (back issues avail.) **Document type:** monographic series.
Description: Reports on areas of British life conventionally conceived to be conflict laden. Assesses the scale and character of the conflict in these areas, considers new evidence, and attempts to reach balanced judgments by placing such conflict in its historical and social contexts.

301   US   ISSN 0899-9910
CONFLICT AND CONSCIOUSNESS: STUDIES IN WAR, PEACE AND SOCIAL THOUGHT. irreg. Peter Lang Publishing, Inc., 62 W. 45th St., 4th Fl., New York, NY 10036. TEL 212-302-6740. FAX 212-302-7574. Ed. Charles P. Webel. **Document type:** academic/scholarly publication, monographic series.
Description: Discusses topics on individual consciousness, personal and collective belief systems, and social practices involving coercion and violence.

CONFRONTATION - CHANGE REVIEW. see *BUSINESS AND ECONOMICS*

CONGRESSO BRASILEIRO DE ECONOMIA E SOCIOLOGIA RURAL. ANAIS. see *AGRICULTURE* — *Agricultural Economics*

CONSERVATIVE REVIEW. see *POLITICAL SCIENCE*

CONTEMPORARY FAMILY THERAPY; an international journal. see *PSYCHOLOGY*

CONTEMPORARY GERMAN STUDIES: OCCASIONAL PAPERS. see *LITERATURE*

301   UK   ISSN 0069-942X
CONTEMPORARY ISSUES SERIES. 1969. a. Peter Owen Ltd., 73 Kenway Rd., London SW5 0RE, England. TEL 071-373-5628. FAX 071-373-6760. (Dist. in U.S. by: Dufour Editions, Inc., Box 449, Chester Springs, PA 19425. TEL 215-458-5005)

301.15   US
CONTEMPORARY STUDIES IN APPLIED BEHAVIORAL SCIENCE. 1983. irreg., vol.4, 1986. $58.50 to institutions. J A I Press Inc., 55 Old Post Rd., No. 2, Box 1678, Greenwich, CT 06836-1678. TEL 203-661-7602. Ed. Louis A. Zurcher. bibl.; index.

301   US
CONTEMPORARY STUDIES IN SOCIOLOGY. irreg., vol.6, 1986. $58.50 to institutions. J A I Press Inc., 55 Old Post Rd., No. 2, Box 1678, Greenwich, CT 06836-1678. TEL 203-661-7602. Ed. John Clark.

301   US   ISSN 1056-1072
H1   CODEN: CDSSEN
CONTENTION; a journal of debates in society, culture, and science. 1991. 3/yr. $25 to individuals; institutions $45. Indiana University Press, Journals Division, 601 N. Morton St., Bloomington, IN 47404. TEL 812-855-9449. FAX 812-855-7931. Ed. Nikki Keddie. **Document type:** academic/scholarly publication.
—BLDSC (3425.330000); Faxon; UnCover.
Description: Provides a forum for debates on issues and trends in the social sciences, humanities, and natural sciences. The emphasis is on controversies to increase understanding of key issues.

CONTINUITY AND CHANGE; a journal of social structure, law and demography in past societies. see *POPULATION STUDIES*

301.4   US   ISSN 0147-1023
CONTRIBUTIONS IN FAMILY STUDIES. 1977. irreg., no.22, 1992. price varies. Greenwood Press, Inc. (Subsidiary of: Greenwood Publishing Group Inc.), 88 Post Rd. W., Box 5007, Westport, CT 06881-5007. TEL 203-226-3571. FAX 203-222-1502. Ed. Carol V.R. George.
—BLDSC (3458.470000).

301.4   US   ISSN 0147-1031
CONTRIBUTIONS IN INTERCULTURAL AND COMPARATIVE STUDIES. 1976. irreg. price varies. Greenwood Press, Inc. (Subsidiary of: Greenwood Publishing Group Inc.), 88 Post Rd. W., Box 5007, Westport, CT 06881-5007. TEL 203-226-3571. FAX 203-222-1502. Ed. Ann M. Pescatello. **Document type:** monographic series.

301   US   ISSN 0084-9278
CONTRIBUTIONS IN SOCIOLOGY. 1970. irreg., no.97, 1992. price varies. Greenwood Press, Inc. (Subsidiary of: Greenwood Publishing Group Inc.), 88 Post Rd. W., Box 5007, Westport, CT 06881-5007. TEL 203-226-3571. FAX 203-222-1502. Ed. Don Martindale.
—BLDSC (3461.440000).

301   II   ISSN 0069-9667
CONTRIBUTIONS TO INDIAN SOCIOLOGY. (Text in English) N.S. 1957. s-a. $39 to individuals; instituions $91 (effective Sep. 1995). (Institute of Economic Growth) Sage Publications India Pvt. Ltd., P.O. Box 4215, New Delhi 110 048, India. TEL 91-11-6444958. FAX 91-11-6472426. (Overseas subscr. to: Sage Publications Ltd., 6 Bonhill St., London EC2A 4PU, England; N. American subscr. to: Sage Publications, Inc., Box 5084, Thousand Oaks, CA 91356) Ed. T.N. Madan. adv.; bk.rev. circ. 900. Indexed: A.I.C.P., Anthropol.Lit., IMFL, Int.Polit.Sci.Abstr., Rural Devel.Abstr., Sociol.Abstr. (1985-). **Document type:** academic/scholarly publication.
—Genuine Article; SWETS.
Description: Provides an international forum for research on Indian and Southeast Asian societies.

CONTRIBUTIONS TO THE STUDY OF POPULAR CULTURE. see *ANTHROPOLOGY*

362 301.4   US
CO-OP NETWORKER. bi-m. free. St. John's Mercy Medical Center, 615 S. New Ballas Rd., St. Louis, MO 63141. TEL 314-569-6010. Ed. Richard P. Johnson.

334   JA
COOPERATIVE LIFE/GEKKAN KYODOTAI. (Text in Japanese) 1963. m. 1000 Yen($5) Japanese Commune Movement, 2083 Sakae-cho, Imaichi-shi, Tochigi-ken 321-12, Japan. Ed. Hisao Okumura. adv.; bk.rev.; abstr.; charts; stat.; index. circ. 1,000.
Formerly: Gekkan Kibbutz (ISSN 0016-5956)

301   US
CORPORATE COMMUNITY RELATIONS NEWSLETTER; the newsletter for the community relations professional. 1986. m. (except combined May-Jun., Jul-Aug.). $115. Boston College, Center for Corporate Community Relations, 36 College Rd., Chestnut Hill, MA 02167-3835. TEL 617-552-4545. FAX 617-552-8499. E-mail: labanca@hermes.bc.edu. Ed. Lisa LaBanca. bk.rev.; cum.index: 1989-1994. circ. 1,500. (back issues avail.) **Document type:** trade publication, newsletter.
Description: Trends and issues affecting corporations and their involvement in the community, corporate citizenship, and corporporate social responsibility.

301   IT
CORSO DI SOCIOLOGIA. 1974; N.S. 1992. m. L.60000($60) (effective 1995 & 1996). Centro Studi Terzo Mondo, Via G.B. Morgagni 39, 20129 Milan, Italy. TEL 39-2-29409041. Ed. Dr. Umberto Melotti. adv. contact: Elena Sala. circ. 4,000. **Document type:** monographic series.
Description: Covers sociological, anthropological and sociobiological issues at the center of today's debate.

301   US
COUNTRY LADY'S DAYBOOK - COUNTRY CLASSIFIED.* 1975. m. $5. c/o Schultz, 12270 Volver Ave., Felton, CA 95018-8947. bibl.; illus.
Formerly: Country Lady's Daybook; **Incorporates:** Country Classified.

361 300   US
COURAGE IN THE STRUGGLE FOR JUSTICE AND PEACE. 1986. 10/yr. free. United Church of Christ, Office for Church Society, 110 Maryland Ave., N.E., Washington, DC 20002. TEL 202-543-1517. bk.rev. circ. 16,000. (back issues avail.)
Description: Covers social justice issues.

CREDO. see *RELIGIONS AND THEOLOGY*

301   IT   ISSN 0011-1546
HM7
CRITICA SOCIOLOGICA. (Text in Italian; summaries in English) 1967. q. L.50000($45) (foreign L.100000($90))(effective 1992). S I A R E S, Corso Vittorio Emanuele 24, 00186 Rome, Italy. TEL 06-6786760. Ed. Franco Ferrarotti. adv.; bk.rev.; bibl.; illus. circ. 3,500. (also avail. in microform from UMI; reprint service avail. from UMI) Indexed: Lang.& Lang.Behav.Abstr., Sociol.Abstr. (1967-).
—BLDSC (3487.410000).

CRITICAL SOCIOLOGY. see *LITERARY AND POLITICAL REVIEWS*

CRITIQUE OF ANTHROPOLOGY; a journal for the critical reconstruction of anthropology. see *ANTHROPOLOGY*

309 330.9   BE   ISSN 0770-0075
CRITIQUE REGIONALE; cahiers de sociologie et d'economie regionales. 1979. irreg. 1300 BEF. (Universite Libre de Bruxelles, Institut de Sociologie) Centre de Sociologie et d'Economie Regionales, 39 rue de Bruxelles, 1400 Nivelles, Belgium. TEL 32-2-6503430. FAX 32-2-6503335. (Co-sponsor: Comite pour l'Etude des Problemes de l'Emploi et du Chomage) bk.rev. **Document type:** monographic series.
—BLDSC (3487.490400).

301.4 973   US
CROSS CURRENTS (LOS ANGELES). Issued with: Amerasia Journal (ISSN 0044-7471) s-a. free to subscribers of Amerasia Journal. University of California at Los Angeles, Asian American Studies Center, 3230 Campbell Hall, Los Angeles, CA 90095-1546. TEL 310-825-2968. FAX 310-206-9844. Ed. Glenn Omatsu. **Document type:** newsletter.

SOCIOLOGY

306.84 US ISSN 1070-6852
CROSS-TALK; transgender community news & information monthly. 1988. m. $54. Box 944, Woodland Hills, CA 91365. TEL 818-907-3053. FAX 818-347-4190. E-mail: kymmer@xconn.com. Ed. Kymberleigh Richards. adv.; bk.rev. circ. 1,500. **Document type:** consumer publication.

800 320 CN ISSN 0704-6588
CROSSCURRENTS. 1973. q. $10. Greenwich, 516 Ave. K. South, Saskatoon, Sask., Canada. TEL 306-244-0679. FAX 306-244-0795. Ed. Robert Fink. bk.rev. circ. 500. **Document type:** newsletter.
Description: A newsletter on politics, peace, the environment, music and art.

CUADERNOS C I P C A (SERIE POPULAR). see *EDUCATION — Adult Education*

301 SP ISSN 0302-7724
HN1
CUADERNOS DE REALIDADES SOCIALES. Short title: R S. 1973. s-a. 2000 ptas.($20) Instituto de Sociologia Aplicada de Madrid, Claudio Coello 141, Madrid-6, Spain. TEL 5620239. Ed. Jesus Maria Vazquez. bk.rev.; bibl. circ. 1,000. (also avail. in microform; back issues avail.) **Indexed:** Int.Polit.Sci.Abstr., Sociol.Abstr. (1973-).
Description: Covers social issues in Spain and around the world.

291 US ISSN 0892-340X
CULT OBSERVER; toward an awareness of cultism in society. 1979. 10/yr. $30. American Family Foundation, Box 2265, Bonita Springs, FL 33959. TEL 212-249-7693. Ed. Robert E. Schecter. bk.rev. circ. 1,000. (back issues avail.) **Indexed:** Per.Islam. (1991-). **Document type:** bulletin.
Formerly (until 1984): Advisor (Weston) (ISSN 0740-1167)

301 US ISSN 0748-6499
BP600
CULTIC STUDIES JOURNAL; a journal on cults and manipulative techniques of social influence. 1984. s-a. $15 to individuals; institutions $25 (foreign $29). American Family Foundation, Box 2265, Bonita Springs, FL 33959. TEL 212-249-7693. Ed. Michael D. Langune. circ. 350. **Indexed:** Per.Islam. (1991-), Psychol.Abstr. (1985-). **Document type:** newsletter.
—BLDSC (3491.616700).

301.15 152.4 US ISSN 1077-341X
▼**CULTURAL DIVERSITY AND MENTAL HEALTH.** 1995. 3/yr. $96 (foreign $114) (effective 1996). John Wiley & Sons, Inc., Journals, 605 Third Ave., New York, NY 10158. TEL 212-850-6645. FAX 212-850-6021. TELEX 12-7063. E-mail: SUBINFO@JWILEY.COM. (Subscr. outside the Americas to: John Wiley & Sons Ltd., Baffins Ln., Chichester, W. Sussex PO19 1UD, England. TEL 44-1243-779777. FAX 44-1243-776128) (also avail. in microform from UMI; back issues avail.) **Document type:** academic/scholarly publication.
Refereed Serial

CULTURAL PERSPECTIVES ON THE AMERICAN SOUTH. see *HISTORY — History Of North And South America*

301.2 UK ISSN 0950-2386
HM101 CODEN: CUSTE9
CULTURAL STUDIES. 1987. 3/yr. £24 (rest of world £26) to individuals; institutions £66 (rest of world £72). Routledge, 11 New Fetter Ln., London EC4P 4EE, England. TEL 0171-583-9855. FAX 0171-842-2298. TELEX 263398-ROUT-G. E-mail: sample.journals@routledge.com. (Subscr. to: ITPS Ltd., Cheriton House, Andover, Hants SP10 5BE, England. TEL 01264-342919. FAX 01264-342807) Eds. Lawrence Grossberg, Janice Radway. adv.; page £175; trim 115 x 190. circ. 1,650. **Document type:** academic/scholarly publication.
—BLDSC (3491.668420); Faxon; Genuine Article; SWETS; UnCover. **CCC.**
Description: Provides a forum where academics, researchers, students and practitioners can consider and review patterns of power and meaning in contemporary culture, and focus for work in the interlocking areas of media, communication and cultural studies.

CULTURAL SURVIVAL. OCCASIONAL PAPERS. see *ANTHROPOLOGY*

CULTURAL SURVIVAL QUARTERLY. see *ANTHROPOLOGY*

CULTURAL SURVIVAL REPORT. see *ANTHROPOLOGY*

CULTURE & PSYCHOLOGY. see *PSYCHOLOGY*

301 947 FR ISSN 0765-0213
CULTURES ET SOCIETES DE L'EST. 1985. irreg., vol.21, 1995. price varies. Institut d'Etudes Slaves, 9 rue Michelet, F-75006 Paris, France. TEL 43-26-50-89. (Co-sponsor: Institut de Recherche et d'Etude des Nouvelles Institutions et Societes a l"Est) **Document type:** academic/scholarly publication.

301 US ISSN 0278-1204
HM1
CURRENT PERSPECTIVES IN SOCIAL THEORY; a research annual. 1980. a. $63.50 to institutions. J A I Press Inc., 55 Old Post Rd., No. 2, Box 1678, Greenwich, CT 06836-1678. TEL 203-661-7602. Ed. John Wilson. **Indexed:** Lang.& Lang.Behav.Abstr., Sociol.Abstr. (1980-), SSCI.
—BLDSC (3501.280440); Faxon. **CCC.**

301 UK ISSN 0011-3921
Z7161
CURRENT SOCIOLOGY/SOCIOLOGIE CONTEMPORAINE. (Text in English and French) 1952. 3/yr. £34 to individuals; institutions £99 (effective 1996). (International Sociological Association) Sage Publications Ltd., 6 Bonhill St., London EC2A 4PU, England. TEL 0171-374-0645. FAX 0171-374-8741. E-mail: market@sageltd.co.uk. Ed. Robert Brym. adv.: B&W page £200; trim 180 x 115; adv. contact: Bernie Folan. (reprint service avail. from KTO) **Indexed:** Abstr.Crim.& Pen., ASSIA, Curr.Cont., E.I., Human Resour.Abstr., Int.Bibl.Soc.Sci., Int.Lab.Doc., Int.Polit.Sci.Abstr., Key to Econ.Sci., Lang.& Lang.Behav.Abstr., Mid.East: Abstr.& Ind., Mid.East: Abstr.& Ind., P.A.I.S., Psychol.Abstr., Soc.Sci.Ind., Sociol.Abstr. (1958-), Sportsearch, SSCI. **Document type:** academic/scholarly publication.
—BLDSC (3504.033000); Faxon; SWETS; UnCover.
Description: Focuses on the theory, research and methodology of contemporary international sociology. Each issue is devoted to a substantial Trend Report on a particular sociological topic.

CZLOWIEK I SPOLECZENSTWO. see *PSYCHOLOGY*

361 US ISSN 0164-1867
D R C HISTORICAL AND COMPARATIVE DISASTERS SERIES. 1977. irreg., no.7, 1987. University of Delaware, Disaster Research Center, Newark, DE 19716. TEL 302-831-6618. FAX 302-831-2091. TELEX 70 99 85. **Document type:** monographic series.

D W D NEWSLETTER. (Dying with Dignity) see *LAW*

301.2 RU ISSN 0137-0545
DAGESTANSKII ETNOGRAFICHESKII SBORNIK. 1974. irreg. 1.49 Rub. Akademiya Nauk S.S.S.R., Dagestanskii Filial, Institut Istorii, Yazyka i Literatury, Prospekt Kalinina 77-b, kv.19, 367012 Makhachkala, Dagestan A.S., Russia. illus.

301 297 PH
DANSALAN QUARTERLY. 1979. q. P.100($10) Dansalan College Foundation, Inc., Gowing Memorial Research Center, Marawi City 9700, Philippines. **Indexed:** Ind.Phil.Per.
Description: Covers the Muslim regions of Mindanao and Sulu and the Maranao peoples.

301 DK ISSN 0905-5908
HN541 CODEN: DSOCE3
DANSK SOCIOLOGI. (Text in Danish; summaries in English) 1990. q. DKK 300 to individuals; institutions DKK 440. Danish Sociological Association, Copenhagen Business School, Linnesgade 22, DK-1361 Copenhagen K, Denmark. TEL 33-15-05-20. FAX 33-91-15-51. Ed. Heine Andersen. bk.rev. circ. 1,000. **Document type:** academic/scholarly publication.

301 301.412 615.7 BO
DE TEXTOS. irreg., no.10, 1985. price varies. Centro de Investigaciones Sociales, Casilla 6931 - Correo Central, La Paz, Bolivia.

DEATH AND DYING. see *PSYCHOLOGY*

DEATH STUDIES; education - counseling - care - law - ethics. see *PSYCHOLOGY*

301 PE ISSN 0254-9220
DEBATES EN SOCIOLOGIA. 1977. a. $15. Pontificia Universidad Catolica del Peru, Departamento de Ciencias Sociales, Fondo Editorial, Apdo. 1761, Lima 100, Peru. TEL 51-14-611785. Ed. Marcel Valcarcel C. charts; illus.
Supersedes: Revista de Debates: Debates de Sociologia.

170 US
DECENCY REPORTER. 1961. 3/yr. free. Children's Legal Foundation, 2845 E. Camelback Rd., Ste. 740, Phoenix, AZ 85016. TEL 602-381-1322. FAX 602-381-1613. Ed. Beth Sonlan. bk.rev. circ. 30,000.
Former titles: C D L Reporter; (until Jan. 1986): National Decency Reporter (ISSN 0027-9102)

DENMARK. SOCIALFORSKNINGSINSTITUTTET. PJECER. see *SOCIAL SERVICES AND WELFARE*

DESARROLLO DE BASE. see *BUSINESS AND ECONOMICS — International Development And Assistance*

DEUTSCHE JUGEND; Zeitschrift fuer die Jugendarbeit. see *CHILDREN AND YOUTH — About*

301.1 SZ ISSN 0378-7931
HM291
DEVIANCE ET SOCIETE. (Text in French; abstracts in English and German) 1977. q. 78 SFr. to individuals; institutions 138 SFr. Editions Medecine et Hygiene, Case Postale 456, CH-1211 Geneva 4, Switzerland. TEL 022-3469355. FAX 022-3475610. Ed. Philippe Robert. **Indexed:** Abstr.Crim.& Pen., Crim.Just.Abstr. **Document type:** academic/scholarly publication.
—BLDSC (3579.099700). **CCC.**

301 US ISSN 0163-9625
HM1 CODEN: DEBEDF
DEVIANT BEHAVIOR; an interdisciplinary journal. 1979. q. £88($145) (effective 1996). Taylor & Francis Inc., 1900 Frost Rd., Ste. 101, Bristol, PA 19007-1598. TEL 215-785-5800; 800-821-8312. FAX 215-785-5515. (Subscr. in Europe to: Taylor & Francis Ltd., Rankine Rd., Basingstoke, Hants. RG24 8PR, England. TEL 44-1256-840366. FAX 44-1256-479438) Ed. C. Eddie Palmer. adv.; bk.rev.; bibl.; charts; illus.; index. circ. 300. (also avail. in microfiche from UMI; back issues avail.; reprint service avail. from UMI) **Indexed:** Abstr.Crim.& Pen., Biol.Abstr., Crim.Just.Abstr., Curr.Cont., Lang.& Lang.Behav.Abstr., Psychol.Abstr. (1981-), Sociol.Abstr., SSCI. **Document type:** academic/scholarly publication.
—BLDSC (3579.099900); Faxon; Genuine Article; UnCover. **CCC.**
Description: Presents scientific findings on cultural norm violations from a wide variety of perspectives.
Refereed Serial

DHARAM NARAIN MEMORIAL LECTURE SERIES. see *BUSINESS AND ECONOMICS*

DIALOGO; quaderni europei di dialogica. see *PHILOSOPHY*

301.4 CR
DIALOGO.* q. free. Universidad de Costa Rica, Centro de Estudios Sociales y Poblacion, Ciudad Universitaria Rodrigo Facio, Apdo. 75, 2050 San Pedro Montes de Oca, San Jose, Costa Rica. Eds. Mario Julio Segura Vargas, Luis Montoya Salas. illus. **Indexed:** HR Rep.

301 320 PN ISSN 0046-0206
HN1
DIALOGO SOCIAL. 1967. m. (except Jan.). Bl.15 (US, Canada, Europe $35; Africa, Asia $40). Centro de Capacitacion Social, Apdo. 9a-192, Calle 66AE, Carasquilla, Panama. TEL 29-1542. Ed.Bd. adv.; bk.rev.; film rev.; bibl.; illus.; stat.; index, cum.index: 1967-1977; circ. 7,800 (controlled).

301 FR ISSN 0012-2297
DIALOGUER. no.10, 1969. q. 50 F. Union Feminine Civique et Sociale, 6 rue Beranger, 75003 Paris, France. FAX 40-27-08-78. Ed. Agnes Planchais. adv.; bk.rev.; bibl.; charts; illus. circ. 30,000.

349   FR   ISSN 0012-2513
DICTIONNAIRE PERMANENT: SOCIAL. 1950. 3 base vols. plus fortn. updates. 1690 F. for base vols. (updates 500 F.) (effective 1995). Editions Legislatives et Administratives, 80 ave. de la Marne, 92546 Montrouge Cedex, France. TEL 40-92-68-68. FAX 46-56-00-15. TELEX 632 855 F. bibl.; index, cum.index. circ. 14,000. (looseleaf format)
 Description: Provides information on labor laws and social security.

DIFFERENCES; a journal of feminist cultural studies. see *WOMEN'S STUDIES*

301   UK   ISSN 0392-1921
AS4
DIOGENES (ENGLISH EDITION). Chinese edition (ISSN 1000-6575); French edition: Diogene (ISSN 0419-1633); Spanish edition (ISSN 0012-3048) (Editions also avail. in: Arabic, Hindi, Italian, Japanese, Portuguese) 1953. q. $40 to individuals; institutions $80. (Unesco, International Council for Philosophy and Humanistic Studies, UN) Berg Publishers, 150 Cowley Rd., Oxford OX4 1JJ, England. TEL 01865-245104. FAX 01865-791165. Ed. Jean d'Ormesson. adv.; bk.rev. circ. 500. (also avail. in microfiche) **Indexed:** Amer.Hist.& Life, Arts & Hum.Cit.Ind., Curr.Cont., Hist.Abstr., Hum.Ind., M.L.A. **Document type:** academic/scholarly publication.
 ●Also available online. Vendor(s): University Microfilms International.
 —BLDSC (3588.750000); Faxon; SWETS; UMI; UnCover. **CCC.**

DIRECTORY OF PEACE STUDIES PROGRAMS. see *POLITICAL SCIENCE — International Relations*

DISCOURSE & SOCIETY. see *PSYCHOLOGY*

301.428   US   ISSN 0012-4230
DIVORCE CHATS.* 1961. irreg. membership. United States Divorce Reform, Inc., 5346 Bahia Blanca W., Ste. C, Laguna Hills, CA 92653-2531. TEL 707-833-2550. Ed. George Partis. bk.rev. circ. 1,500. (processed)

301.4   BO
DOCUMENTOS INSTITUCIONALES OFICIALES. 1972. irreg., no.25, 1985. price varies. Centro de Investigaciones Sociales, Casilla 6931 - C.C., La Paz, Bolivia.

DOUBLE TALK (AMELIA); newsletter for parents of multiples. see *CHILDREN AND YOUTH — About*

DROIT ET SOCIETE; revue international de theorie du droit et de sociologie juridique. see *LAW*

DUISBURGER STUDIEN; Geistes- und Gesellschaftswissenschaften. see *PHILOSOPHY*

E & Z - ENTWICKLUNG UND ZUSAMMENARBEIT. see *POLITICAL SCIENCE — International Relations*

EAST EUROPE REPORT. see *POLITICAL SCIENCE*

ECONOMIA E SOCIOLOGIA. see *BUSINESS AND ECONOMICS — Economic Situation And Conditions*

301.4 330   IT
ECONOMIA, SOCIETA E ISTITUZIONI.* 1989. 3/yr. L.50000. (Libera Universita Internazionale degli Studi Sociali) Societa Editrice Romana, Via Crimea 1, 47037 Rimini (FO), Italy. Eds. Giovanni Palmerio, Carlo Scognamiglio.

ECONOMIA Y SOCIOLOGIA DEL TRABAJO. see *BUSINESS AND ECONOMICS — Labor And Industrial Relations*

ECONOMIC DEVELOPMENT AND CULTURAL CHANGE. see *BUSINESS AND ECONOMICS — International Development And Assistance*

301   UK
EDINBURGH STUDIES IN CULTURE AND SOCIETY. irreg. (approx. 2 vols./yr.). price varies. Macmillan Press Ltd., Houndmills, Basingstoke, Hants RG21 2XS, England. TEL 0256-29242. FAX 0256-28339. Ed.Bd. **Document type:** monographic series.
 Formerly: Edinburgh Studies in Sociology.

EDUCATION AND SOCIETY. see *EDUCATION*

EDUCATION AND URBAN SOCIETY. see *EDUCATION*

EMIGRE; non-stop design - the magazine that ignores boundaries. see *ART*

301   NE
EMMAUS; honger en dorst. 1958. 3/yr. fl.10. Stichting Emmaus Nederland, P.O. Box 175, 3720 AD Bilthoven, Netherlands. circ. 2,000.
 Formerly: Honger en Dorst.
 Description: Articles about the Emmaus movement in the Netherlands and worldwide.

ENCYCLOPEDIA OF WORLD PROBLEMS AND HUMAN POTENTIAL. see *POLITICAL SCIENCE — International Relations*

301   US
ENCYCLOPEDIC DICTIONARY OF SOCIOLOGY. irreg., 3rd ed., 1985. $14.95. Dushkin Publishing Group, Sluice Dock, Guilford, CT 06437-9989. TEL 203-453-4351. FAX 203-453-6000. Ed. Richard Lachmann; Pub. Rick Connelly. illus.

ENQUIRY. see *POLITICAL SCIENCE*

301.3   US   ISSN 0013-9165
HM206   CODEN: EVBHAF
ENVIRONMENT AND BEHAVIOR. 1969. bi-m. $74 to individuals; institutions $228 (effective Sep. 1995). (Environmental Design Research Association) Sage Publications, Inc., 2455 Teller Rd., Thousand Oaks, CA 91320. TEL 805-499-0721. FAX 805-499-0871. E-mail: libraries@sagepub.com. (Overseas subscr. to: Sage Publications Ltd., 6 Bonhill St., London EC2A 4PU, England; Sage Publications India Pvt. Ltd., P.O. Box 4215, New Delhi 110 048 India) Ed. Robert B. Bechtel. adv.; abstr.; charts; illus.; index. circ. 1,500. (also avail. in microfilm from UMI; back issues avail.; reprint service avail. from UMI) **Indexed:** ASSIA, Avery Ind.Archit.Per., C.I.J.E., Curr.Adv.Ecol.Sci., Curr.Cont., Diar.Dis.Res., E.I., Energy Rev., Environ.Abstr., Environ.Per.Bibl. (1972-), Excerp.Med., Geo.Abstr., INIS Atomind., Lang.& Lang.Behav.Abstr., Mag.Ind., Mar.Aff.Bibl., PHRA, Psychol.Abstr. (1969-), Psycscan, Res.High.Educ.Abstr., Risk Abstr., Sage Fam.Stud.Abstr., Sage Urb.Stud.Abstr., Sel.Water Res.Abstr., Soc.Sci.Ind., Sociol.Abstr., SSCI. **Document type:** academic/scholarly publication.
 —BLDSC (3791.097000); Faxon; Genuine Article; SWETS; UMI; UnCover. **CCC.**
 Description: Discusses the interaction of the physical environment and human behavioral systems and covers the study, design, and control of the physical environment.

ENVIRONMENT AND PLANNING D: SOCIETY & SPACE. see *HOUSING AND URBAN PLANNING*

ERA SOCIALISTA. see *POLITICAL SCIENCE*

301   HU   ISSN 0014-0120
ERGONOMIA; munkaelettan, munkalelektan, munkaszociologia. 1967. bi-m. $34.50. Ergotop Ltd., P.O. Box 66, 1507 Budapest, Hungary. TEL 361-13-25-987. (Subscr. to: Kultura, Box 149, 1389 Budapest, Hungary) Ed. Gyorgy Garamvolgyi; Pub. Laszlo Galsa. adv.; bk.rev. circ. 2,500. **Indexed:** C.I.S. Abstr., Ergon.Abstr. **Document type:** academic/scholarly publication, trade publication.
 Description: Covers job psychology, human politics, work hygiene and recreation.

301 573   VE   ISSN 1315-0006
ESPACIO ABIERTO; cuaderno venezolano de sociologia y antropologia. 1992. s-a. Universidad del Zulia, Facultad de Ciencias Juridicas y Politicas, Ciudad Universitaria, Nucleo Humanistico, Apdo. Postal 15400, Maracaibo, Venezuela. TEL 061-418972. Ed.Bd. **Document type:** academic/scholarly publication.

ESPERANTO-DOKUMENTOJ. NOVA SERIO. see *LINGUISTICS*

309   BO
ESTUDIOS DE POBLACION Y DESARROLLO. 1974. irreg., no.29, 1985. price varies. Centro de Investigaciones Sociales, Casilla 6931 - C.C., La Paz, Bolivia.

301   BO
ESTUDIOS DE RECURSOS HUMANOS. 1978. irreg., no.10, 1985. Centro de Investigaciones Sociales, Casilla 6931 - C.C., La Paz, Bolivia.

301.4   BO
ESTUDIOS DE SOCIOLOGIA FAMILIAR. 1975. irreg., no.7, 1985. Centro de Investigaciones Sociales, Casilla 6931 - C.C., La Paz, Bolivia.

301   VE   ISSN 1013-4069
ESTUDIOS DEL DESARROLLO/DEVELOPMENT STUDIES JOURNAL. (Text in English, Spanish) 1990. a. Bs.800($25) (foreign $30) to individuals; institutions Bs.1600($40) (foreign $50) (effective 1993). Universidad Central de Venezuela, Centro de Estudios del Desarrollo, Apdo. Postal 6622, Caracas 1010-A, Venezuela. TEL 7523266. FAX 7512691. (U.S. subscr. addr: Poba International, No. 151, Box 02-5255, Miami, FL 33102-5255) Ed. Nelson Prato Barbosa. adv.; bk.rev. circ. 1,000.
 Description: Promotes discussion and thought on the present and future problems of development from an interdisciplinary perspective.

301   US   ISSN 0187-6961
ESTUDIOS FRONTIZEROS. 1983. q. Universidad Autonoma de Baja California, Instituto de investigaciones Sociales, P.O. Box 3280, Calexico, CA 92231. **Indexed:** Hisp.Amer.Per.Ind. (1986-).

ESTUDIOS MICHOACANOS. see *HISTORY — History Of North And South America*

309   DR   ISSN 1017-0596
HN216
ESTUDIOS SOCIALES. vol.11, 1978. q. $5. Centro de Investigacion y Accion Social, Apdo. 1004, Santo Domingo, Dominican Republic. Ed.Bd. bk.rev.; charts; stat. circ. 1,000. **Indexed:** Amer.Hist.& Life, Hisp.Amer.Per.Ind. (1970-), Hist.Abstr., Lang.& Lang.Behav.Abstr., Rural Devel.Abstr.

301   MX   ISSN 0185-4186
CODEN: ESSOE2
ESTUDIOS SOCIOLOGICOS. 1983. 3/yr. Mex.$57($38) to individuals (foreign $46); institutions $55 (foreign $64) (effective 1995). Colegio de Mexico, A.C., Departamento de Publicaciones, Camino al Ajusco 20, Codigo Postal 01000, Mexico, D.F., Mexico. TEL 525-6455955. FAX 525-6450464. TELEX 1777585 COLME. Ed. Vania Salles. adv. circ. 2,500. (back issues avail.) **Indexed:** Hisp.Amer.Per.Ind. (1992).

301.364   BO
ESTUDIOS URBANOS. 1973. irreg., no.6, 1979. price varies. Centro de Investigaciones Sociales, Casilla 6931 - C.C., La Paz, Bolivia.

ESTUDOS POLITICOS E SOCIAIS. see *POLITICAL SCIENCE*

301   FR
ETAT DE LA FRANCOPHONIE DANS LE MONDE. a. 130 F. (Haut Conseil de la Francophonie) Documentation Francaise, 29-31 quai Voltaire, 75344 Paris Cedex 07, France. TEL 40-15-70-00. FAX 40-15-72-30. TELEX 215 666 DOCFRAN. (Subscr. to: 124 rue Henri Barbusse, 93308 Aubervilliers Cedex, France. TEL 48-39-56-00. FAX 48-39-56-01)
 Description: Collection of information on French language, teaching, culture, communication, science and technology in the francophone communities.

301 330   US   ISSN 1065-0113
ETHICS & POLICY. 1974. q. $35 includes membership. Graduate Theological Union, Center for Ethics & Social Policy, 2400 Ridge Rd., Berkeley, CA 94709. TEL 510-649-2560. FAX 510-649-2565. Ed. Chris Adams. bk.rev. circ. 6,000. (back issues avail.) **Document type:** newsletter.
 Description: Emphasizes ethics in social policy and business ethics; provides members and others with current information on the work of the center.

ETHOS (WASHINGTON). see *ANTHROPOLOGY*

ETNOLOSKA TRIBINA. see *ANTHROPOLOGY*

ETUDES DAHOMEENNES. see *HISTORY — History Of Africa*

SOCIOLOGY

301 630 230   FR   ISSN 0014-2182
HN1
ETUDES RURALES; revue trimestrielle d'histoire, geographie, sociologie et economie des campagnes. 1961. q. 300 F. to individuals; institutions 400 F. (foreign 440 F.). Editions de l' Ecole des Hautes Etudes en Sciences Sociales, 131 bd. St. Michel, 75005 Paris, France. TEL 46-33-51-46. FAX 44-07-08-89. Ed. I. Chiva. adv.; bk.rev.; abstr.; bibl.; charts; illus.; index. circ. 800. **Indexed**: Amer.Hist.& Life, Geo.Abstr., Hist.Abstr., IDA, Int.Lab.Doc., Rural Recreat.Tour.Abstr., SSCI, World Agri.Econ.& Rural Sociol.Abstr.
—SWETS.
   Formerly: Cahiers des Etudes Rurales (ISSN 0071-2175)

301 960   SG   ISSN 0304-2774
ETUDES SENEGALAISES.* 1949. irreg. Institut Fondamental d'Afrique Noire, Chiek Anta Diop, Universite de Dakar, B.P. 206, Dakar, Senegal. illus. **Document type**: monographic series.

300   FR   ISSN 0014-2204
ETUDES SOCIALES. 1935. s-a. 200 F. to non-members (foreign 250 F.). Societe d'Economie et de Science Sociales, 80 rue Vaneau, 75007 Paris, France. TEL 42-22-44-27. Ed. Edouard Secretan. bk.rev.; charts; cum.index: 1961-1967. circ. 400. **Document type**: bulletin, academic/scholarly publication.

301   FR   ISSN 0014-2247
DX101
ETUDES TSIGANES. 1955. s-a. 230 F. to individuals; institutions 260 F.; students 160 F. Association des Etudes Tsiganes, 2 rue d'Hautpoul, 75019 Paris, France. TEL 40-40-09-05. FAX 42-06-75-11. adv.; bk.rev.; bibl.; illus.; cum.index: 1955-1980, 1981-1990. circ. 1,800.

EUROPE - ASIA STUDIES. see BUSINESS AND ECONOMICS

301   EI   ISSN 0531-2663
EUROPEAN ASPECTS, SOCIAL STUDIES SERIES; a collection of studies relating to European integration. 1959. irreg. Council of Europe, Publishing and Documentation Service, 67075 Strasbourg Cedex, France. (Dist. in U.S. by: Manhattan Publishing Co., Box 650, Croton-on-Hudson, N.Y. 10520)

309   EI
EUROPEAN FOUNDATION FOR THE IMPROVEMENT OF LIVING AND WORKING CONDITIONS. ANNUAL REPORT. a. European Foundation for the Improvement of Living and Working Conditions, Loughlinstown House, Shankill, Co. Dublin, Ireland. TEL 01-2826868. FAX 01-2826456.

301   UK   ISSN 0952-391X
EUROPEAN JOURNAL OF INTERCULTURAL STUDIES. 1990. 3/yr. £35 to individuals; institutions £60; foreign £67. Trentham Books Ltd., Westview House, 734 London Rd., Oakhill, Stoke-on-Trent, Staffs. ST4 5NP, England. TEL 01782-745567. FAX 01782-745553. Ed. Pieter Batelaan. index. circ. 1,500. **Indexed**: Sociol.Educ.Abstr. **Document type**: academic/scholarly publication.
—BLDSC (3829.730600).
   Description: Studies majority and minority communities throughout Europe.

EUROPEAN JOURNAL OF SOCIAL PSYCHOLOGY. see PSYCHOLOGY

301   UK   ISSN 0003-9756
HM1.A1
EUROPEAN JOURNAL OF SOCIOLOGY/ARCHIVES EUROPEENNES DE SOCIOLOGIE/EUROPAEISCHE ARCHIV FUR SOZIOLOGIE. (Text in English, French and German) 1960. s-a. £69($119) (effective 1996). (Centre National de la Recherche Scientifique) Cambridge University Press, Edinburgh Bldg., Shaftesbury Rd., Cambridge CB2 2RU, England. TEL 01223-312393. FAX 01223-315052. TELEX 851817256. (N. American addr.: Cambridge University Press, Journals Dept., 40 W. 20th St., New York, NY 10011. TEL 212-924-3900. FAX 212-691-3239) Ed.Bd. adv.; bk.rev.; bibl.; charts; illus.; stat.; index, cum.index. (also avail. in microform from UMI; back issues avail.; reprint service avail. from SWZ) **Indexed**: Abstr.Crim.& Pen., Amer.Hist.& Life (until 1993), ASSIA, Hist.Abstr. (until 1993), Int.Polit.Sci.Abstr., Lang.& Lang.Behav.Abstr., Soc.Sci.Ind., Sociol.Abstr. (1960-), SSCI. **Document type**: academic/scholarly publication.
—BLDSC (1634.278000); Faxon; Genuine Article; SWETS; UMI; UnCover. **CCC**.
   Description: Encourages comparative studies of societies worldwide.

301   UK   ISSN 0266-7215
HM1
EUROPEAN SOCIOLOGICAL REVIEW. 1985. 3/yr. £67($120) (effective 1996). Oxford University Press, Oxford Journals, Walton St., Oxford OX2 6DP, England. TEL 01865-267907. FAX 01865-267773. TELEX 837330-OXPRES-G. E-mail: jnlorders@oup.co.uk. (U.S. subscr. to: Oxford University Press Inc., 2001 Evans Rd., Cary, NC 27513. TEL 919-677-0977. FAX 919-677-1714) Ed. Hans Peter Blossfeld. adv. contact: Jane Parker. bk.rev. circ. 600. (back issues avail.) **Indexed**: ASSIA, Int.Polit.Sci.Abstr., Mult.Ed.Abstr., Sociol.Abstr. (1985-), Sociol.Educ.Abstr. **Document type**: academic/scholarly publication.
—BLDSC (3830.108000); Faxon; Genuine Article; SWETS; UMI; UnCover. **CCC**.
   Description: Aims to present papers in which research expertise is combined with substantive and theoretical significance.

EVALUATION COMMENT; the journal of educational evaluation. see EDUCATION — Teaching Methods And Curriculum

301   GW   ISSN 0175-3347
EXILFORSCHUNG; ein internationales Jahrbuch. 1983. a. price varies. (Gesellschaft fuer Exilforschung) Edition Text und Kritik GmbH, Levelingstr. 6a, 81673 Munich, Germany. TEL 089-432929. FAX 089-433997. **Document type**: academic/scholarly publication.

F A O ECONOMIC AND SOCIAL DEVELOPMENT PAPER. see BUSINESS AND ECONOMICS

301   SW   ISSN 0345-3405
F L S - AKTUELLT. 1960. q. SEK 70 membership (effective 1990). Foereningen Laerare i Samhaells- och Socialkunskap, c/o S. Hagstroem, Morkullev. 16 E, S-902 37 Umeaa, Sweden.
   Formerly (until 1963): F L S - Nytt.

300   YU   ISSN 0014-7052
FACTS AND TENDENCIES/FAITS ET TENDANCES; review for social questions. (Text in English and French) 1966. a. $3.35. Konferencija za Drustvenu Aktivnost Zena Jugoslavije - Conference for Social Activities of Yugoslav Women, Bulevar Lenjina 6, 11000 Belgrade, Yugoslavia. TEL 011 62-76-42. TELEX YU 1277. Ed. Dasa Sasic. bk.rev.; bibl. circ. 2,400.
   Description: Devoted to an international seminar on the status of women. Covers general issues, women in economy, agriculture and technical and technological development.

301.42 249   BL   ISSN 0014-7125
FAMILIA CRISTA; revista da paz e do amor - revista mensal para a familia. 1934. m. Cr.$160. Pia Sociedade Filhas de Sao Paulo, Rua Domingos de Morais 678, Sao Paulo 04010, Brazil. Ed. Joana Terezinha Puntel. adv.; bk.rev.; charts; illus. circ. 160,000.
   Description: General interest magazine for family living.

301.4 200 360   CK   ISSN 0120-3215
FAMILIA Y SOCIEDAD. 1976. bi-m. $25 in Latin America; elsewhere $28 (effective 1995). Centro de Pastoral Familiar para America Latina, Avda. 28 No. 37-21, Apdo. Aereo No. 54569, Bogota D.C., Colombia. TEL 55-1-368-0311. FAX 55-1-3680540. Ed. Fr. Gilberto Gomez. adv.; bk.rev. circ. 4,000. **Document type**: academic/scholarly publication.

FAMILIENDYNAMIK; interdisziplinaere Zeitschrift fuer systemorientierte Praxis und Forschung. see PSYCHOLOGY

301   US   ISSN 0272-992X
HQ536
FAMILY (BOCA RATON). (Subseries of: S I R S Social Issues (ISSN 0740-3127)) 1973. a. price varies; a. supplement $17. Social Issues Resources Series, Box 2348, Boca Raton, FL 33427-2348. TEL 407-994-0079; 800-232-7477. FAX 407-994-4704. (looseleaf format; also avail. in microfiche; back issues avail.)
   Description: Reprints articles that explore how society challenges family structure.

FAMILY CAREGIVER APPLICATIONS SERIES. see SOCIAL SERVICES AND WELFARE

301.4   US   ISSN 0892-2691
THE FAMILY IN AMERICA. (Includes supplement: New Research) 1978. m. $24 ($36 outside U.S.). Rockford Institute, Center on Family on America, 934 N. Main St., Rockford, IL 61103. TEL 815-964-5813. FAX 815-965-1826. (Subscr. to: Box 416, Mt. Morris, IL 61054) Ed. Bryce Christensen. illus. circ. 3,500. (back issues avail.) **Document type**: newsletter.
   Former titles: Persuasion at Work (ISSN 0163-5387)
   Description: Reports on social problems facing the traditional family.

301 360   AT   ISSN 1030-2646
HQ706   CODEN: FAMMEL
FAMILY MATTERS. 1980. 3/yr. Aus.$33 to individuals; libraries Aus.$36 (effective 1995). Austhalian Institute of Family Studies, 300 Queen St., Melbourne, Vic. 3000, Australia. TEL 61-3-2147888. FAX 61-3-2147839. bk.rev. circ. 2,000. **Indexed**: Aus.P.A.I.S., IMFL, Soc.Work Res.& Abstr.
   Former titles: Australian Institute of Family Studies. Newsletter (ISSN 0818-0229); Institute of Family Studies (ISSN 0159-9143)
   Description: Publishes research from the institute and by other Australian and international researchers on social, psychological, and legal issues involving families of all types.

301 360   AT   ISSN 1038-0213
FAMILY NOTES. 1992. irreg. Australian Institute of Family Studies, 300 Queen St., Melbourne, Vic. 3000, Australia. TEL 61-3-2147888. FAX 61-3-2147839. **Document type**: newsletter.
   Description: Provides information about the latest research and publications from the institute.

301 640 150   US   ISSN 0014-7311
HQ1
FAMILY PERSPECTIVE. 1966. q. $30 to individuals (foreign $55); institutions $60 (foreign $85). Brigham Young University, Center for Studies of the Family, 922 Kimball Tower, Provo, UT 84602. TEL 801-378-4452. FAX 801-378-5978. Ed. Stephen J. Bahr. illus. circ. 1,000. (also avail. in microform; back issues avail.) **Indexed**: IMFL. **Document type**: academic/scholarly publication.
—Faxon; UnCover. **CCC**.
   Description: Multidisciplinary journal publishing articles on any aspect of family life.

FAMILY PROCESS. see PSYCHOLOGY

SOCIOLOGY

301.42 US ISSN 0197-6664
HQ1 CODEN: FCOOBE
FAMILY RELATIONS; journal of applied family & child studies. 1952. q. $85 (foreign $97) (effective 1996). National Council on Family Relations, 3989 Central Ave., N.E., Ste. 550, Minneapolis, MN 55421-3921. TEL 612-781-9331. FAX 612-781-9348. Ed. Mark Fine. adv.; bk.rev.; charts; index. circ. 5,200. (also avail. in microform from UMI; reprint service avail. from UMI) **Indexed:** Abstr.Crim.& Pen., Abstr.Soc.Geront., Adol.Ment.Hlth.Abstr., Bk.Rev.Ind. (1989-), C.I.J.E., CERDIC, Child.Bk.Rev.Ind. (1989-), Child Devel.Abstr., Curr.Cont., Curr.Lit.Fam.Plan., Lang.& Lang.Behav.Abstr., Media Rev.Dig., Mid.East: Abstr.& Ind., Mult.Ed.Abstr., Psychol.Abstr., Res.High.Educ.Abstr., Sage Fam.Stud.Abstr., Soc.Sci.Ind., Soc.Work Res.& Abstr., Sociol.Abstr., SSCI, Stud.Wom.Abstr., Viol.& Abuse Abstr. **Document type:** academic/scholarly publication.
●Also available online. Vendor(s): Knight-Ridder, Inc., Ovid Technologies, University Microfilms International.
—BLDSC (3865.576100); Faxon; Genuine Article; SWETS; UMI; UnCover.
Former titles: Family Coordinator (ISSN 0014-7214); Family Life Coordinator.
Description: Covers applied scholarly articles with emphasis on family relationships across the life cycle with implications for intervention, education and public policy.

301.4 155 US
FAMILY SERVICE PERSPECTIVES; useful information for the workplace and home. 1988. q. $1. Family Service of the Cincinnati Area, 205 W. Fourth St., Cincinnati, OH 45202. TEL 513-381-6300. FAX 513-345-8551. Ed. Sheila Libecap. circ. 6,000. **Document type:** newsletter.
Description: Provides practical information for individuals and families about the workplace and home, for better management of job and family life and for nurturing healthy relationships.

FAMILY THERAPY NEWS. see PSYCHOLOGY

FANLIGHT NEWS. see MEDICAL SCIENCES

305.4 301 UK
FEMINIST PRAXIS. 1984. bi-m. £4 per no. University of Manchester, Department of Sociology, Manchester M13 9PL, England. TEL 061-275-2496. Ed. Liz Stanley. adv. circ. 500. (back issues avail.) **Indexed:** Sociol.Abstr. (1984-), Stud.Wom.Abstr.
Formerly: Studies in Sexual Politics.
Description: Feminist research within social sciences, focusing on epistemological issues and main relationship to praxis.

FILOZOFSKI FAKULTET - ZADAR. RAZDIO FILOZOFIJE, PSIHOLOGIJE, SOCIOLOGIJE I PEDAGOGIJE. RADOVI. see PHILOSOPHY

301 SW ISSN 0284-4818
FINNISH SOCIETY FOR DEVELOPMENT STUDIES. MONOGRAPH SERIES. (Text in English) 1987. irreg. price varies. Nordiska Afrikainstitutet - Scandinavian Institue of African Studies, P.O. Box 1703, S-751 47 Uppsala, Sweden. TEL 018-155480. FAX 018-695629. circ. 1,500. **Document type:** monographic series.

FIVE FINGERS REVIEW. see LITERATURE

FLORIDA PSYCHOLOGIST. see PSYCHOLOGY

FOCUS AFRIKA; I A K Diskussionsbeitraege. see POLITICAL SCIENCE

FORUM (LONDON, 1967); the journal of human relations and psycho-sexual studies. see PSYCHOLOGY

FORUM (LORENTON). see LITERARY AND POLITICAL REVIEWS

309.2 SW ISSN 0281-0492
FRAMTIDER. English edition: Framtider International (ISSN 1400-0199) 1982. q. Institutet foer Framtidsstudier (IF) - Institute for Future Studies, P.O. Box 591, S-101 31 Stockholm, Sweden. TEL 46-8-402-12-00. FAX 46-8-24-50-14. E-mail: ans@framtidsstudier.se. Ed. Ingemar Karlsson. circ. 19,500. **Document type:** academic/scholarly publication.

301 US ISSN 0736-9182
HM1
FREE INQUIRY IN CREATIVE SOCIOLOGY. 1972. s-a. $15 to individuals (foreign $20); institutions $25 (foreign $30) (effective 1995). University of Central Oklahoma, Department of Sociology and Criminal Justice, 100 N. University Dr., Edmond, OK 73034. TEL 405-744-6121. FAX 405-711-5780. E-mail: JRC1039@MVS.UCC.OKSTATE.EDU. Ed. John R. Cross. adv. circ. 300. (also avail. in microform from UMI; reprint service avail. from UMI) **Indexed:** Lang.& Lang.Behav.Abstr., RILM, Sociol.Abstr. (1972-). **Document type:** academic/scholarly publication.
—BLDSC (4033.322000); SWETS; UnCover.
Formerly (until Jan. 1979): Free Inquiry (Norman).
Description: Publishes articles of interest to a non-specialist audience.
Refereed Serial

FREE LIFE. see POLITICAL SCIENCE

FREIE UNIVERSITAET BERLIN. OSTEUROPA-INSTITUT. PHILOSOPHISCHE UND SOZIOLOGISCHE VEROEFFENTLICHUNGEN. see PHILOSOPHY

FRIENDS JOURNAL. see RELIGIONS AND THEOLOGY — Other Denominations And Sects

FRIENDS OF YOUTH NEWSLETTER. see CHILDREN AND YOUTH — About

306.7 363.49 US ISSN 1072-5644
FRIGHTEN THE HORSES; back issues avail. 1990. q. $18. Heat Seeking Publishing, 41 Sutter St., Ste. 1108, San Francisco, CA 94104. TEL 415-824-0282. Ed. Mark Pritchard. adv.: B&W page $150; adv. contact: Nishanga Bliss. bk.rev. circ. 4,000. **Document type:** consumer publication.
Description: Discusses issues modern sexuality and censorship.

FROM THE STATE CAPITALS. CIVIL RIGHTS. see POLITICAL SCIENCE — Civil Rights

301 330 BL
FUNDACAO CENTRO DE PESQUISAS ECONOMICAS E SOCIAIS DO PIAUI. RELATÓRIO DE ATIVIDADES. Cover title: Fundacao Centro de Pesquisas Economicas e Sociais do Piaui. Atividades C E P R O. irreg. Fundacao Centro de Pesquisas Economicas e Sociais do Piaui, Av. Miguel Rosa 3190-S, Caixa Postal 429, 6400 Teresina-Piaui, Brazil.

301 BL
FUNDACAO JOAQUIM NABUCO. SERIE ABOLICAO. 1988. irreg., no.21, 1991. Editora Massangana, Rua Dois Irmaos, 15, Apipucos, 52071-440 Recife, Brazil. TEL 081-268-4611. FAX 081-268-9600.

301 BL
FUNDACAO JOAQUIM NABUCO. SERIE CURSOS E CONFERENCIAS. 1974. irreg., no.51, 1993. Editora Massangana, Rua Dois Irmaos, 15, Apipucos, 52071-440 Recife, Brazil.
Formerly: Instituto Joaquim Nabuco de Pesquisas Sociais. Serie Cursos e Conferencias.

301 BL
FUNDACAO JOAQUIM NABUCO. SERIE DESCOBRIMENTOS. 1992. irreg., no.2, 1992. price varies. Editora Massangana, Rua Dois Irmaos, 15, Apipucos, 52071-440 Recife, Brazil. TEL 081-268-4611. FAX 081-268-4611.

301 BL
FUNDACAO JOAQUIM NABUCO. SERIE DOCUMENTOS. 1975. irreg., no.40, 1993. Editora Massangana, Rua Dois Irmaos, 15, Apipucos, 52071-440 Recife, Brazil. TEL 081-268-4611. FAX 081-268-9600.
Formerly: Instituto Joaquim Nabuco de Pesquisas Sociais. Serie Documentos.

301 BL
FUNDACAO JOAQUIM NABUCO. SERIE ESTUDOS E PESQUISAS. 1974. irreg., no.79, 1990. (Fundacao Joaquim Nabuco) Editora Massangana, Rua Dois Irmaos, 15, Apipucos, 25071 Recife, Brazil. **Indexed:** Rural Recreat.Tour.Abstr., World Agri.Econ.& Rural Sociol.Abstr.
Formerly: Instituto Joaquim Nabuco de Pesquisas Sociais. Serie Estudos e Pesquisas.

301 BL
FUNDACAO JOAQUIM NABUCO. SERIE OBRAS DE CONSULTA. 1981. irreg., no.12, 1991. price varies. Editora Massangana, Rua Dois Irmaos, 15, Apipucos, 52071-440 Recife, Brazil. TEL 081-268-4611. FAX 081-268-9600.

301.4 IT
FUORIMARGINE. 1989. irreg., no.7, 1993. price varies. Liguori Editore s.r.l., Via Mezzocannone, 19, 80134 Naples, Italy. TEL 081-5527139. Ed Alberto Abruzzese. **Document type:** monographic series.

FUTURES; the journal of forecasting, planning and policy. see BUSINESS AND ECONOMICS — Economic Situation And Conditions

301 FR ISSN 0337-307X
H3
FUTURIBLES; analyse-prevision-prospective. (Text in French; summaries in English, French) 1975. m. 630 F. (foreign 680 F.). Futuribles, sarl, 55 rue de Varenne, 75341 Paris Cedex 07, France. TEL 42-22-63-10. FAX 42-22-65-54. Ed. Hugues de Jouvenel. adv.: B&W page 4450 F.; trim 170 X 117; adv. contact: Corinne Roels. bk.rev.; charts; index. circ. 4,000. (also avail. in microform from UMI) **Indexed:** A.B.C.Pol.Sci., Curr.Cont., ELLIS, Int.Lab.Doc., Int.Polit.Sci.Abstr., Key to Econ.Sci., P.A.I.S.For.Lang.Ind., Rural Recreat.Tour.Abstr., Sociol.Abstr., World Agri.Econ.& Rural Sociol.Abstr.
—Faxon; SWETS. CCC.
Formed by the merger of: Analyse et Prevision (ISSN 0003-262X); Prospectives (ISSN 0033-1503)
Description: Analysis, forecasting and prospective on main contemporary problems with a multidisciplinary approach and in a middle and long-term perspective.

301 600 US ISSN 0164-1220
CB161
FUTURICS; a quarterly journal of futures research. 1977. q. $50 in U.S. and Canada; elsewhere $67. Minnesota Futurists, 365 Summit Ave., St. Paul, MN 55102. TEL 612-290-2846. FAX 612-290-2847. (Subscr. to: Minnesota Futurists, ASI, 365 Summit Ave., St. Paul, MN 55102) Ed. Earl C. Joseph. adv.; bk.rev. circ. 500. (also avail. in microform from UMI; back issues avail.; reprint service avail. from UMI) **Indexed:** Fut.Surv.
—UMI.
Description: Contains articles dealing with alternative futures from a professional viewpoint. Devoted to advancing our understanding of possible futures.

300 II ISSN 0016-4496
GANMITRAM. (Text in Hindi and Sanskrit) 1966. w. Rs.3. Basudeo Misra, Ed. & Pub., At 4 Post Khetasarai District, Janpur, Uttar Pradesh, India. circ. 1,800.

309 US ISSN 0891-2432
HQ1075
GENDER AND SOCIETY. 1987. bi-m. $54 to individuals; institutions $165 (effective Sep. 1995). (Sociologists for Women in Society) Sage Publications, Inc., 2455 Teller Rd., Thousand Oaks, CA 91320. TEL 805-499-0721. FAX 805-499-0871. E-mail: libraries@sagepub.com. (Overseas subscr. to: Sage Publications Ltd., 6 Bonhill St., London EC2A 4PU, England; Sage Publications India Pvt. Ltd., P.O. Box 4215, New Delhi 110 048, India) Ed. Beth E. Schneider. adv.; bk.rev. circ. 2,500. (back issues avail.; reprint service avail.) **Indexed:** IMFL, Mult.Ed.Abstr., Polit.Sci.Abstr., Psychol.Abstr. (1987-), Soc.Sci.Ind. (1994-), Sociol.Abstr. (1987-), Sp.Ed.Needs Abstr., Viol.& Abuse Abstr., Wom.Stud.Abstr. (1987-). **Document type:** academic/scholarly publication.
—BLDSC (4096.401500); Faxon; Genuine Article; SWETS; UMI; UnCover. CCC.
Description: Focuses on the social and structural study of gender as a basic principal of the social order and as a primary social category, with emphasis on theory and research from micro- and macrostructural perspectives.

SOCIOLOGY

320 300   US   ISSN 0161-3340
HN29
GENERAL SOCIAL SURVEYS. 1972. a. National Opinion Research Center, 1155 E. 60th St., Chicago, IL 60637. TEL 312-753-7500. FAX 312-753-7886. Ed. Tom W. Smith. (also avail. in microfiche) **Indexed:** SRI.
   Description: Presents survey of representative sample of U.S. population, attitudes and behavior.

GEOGRAFIA URBANA. see *GEOGRAPHY*

GESELLSCHAFT UND POLITIK; Zeitschrift fuer soziales und wirtschafliches Engagement. see *POLITICAL SCIENCE*

301   GH   ISSN 0435-9380
GHANA JOURNAL OF SOCIOLOGY. 1965. s-a. $5. Ghana Sociological Association, c/o Department of Sociology, University of Ghana, Legon, Ghana. **Indexed:** Lang.& Lang.Behav.Abstr.

301   PL   ISSN 0072-5013
GORNOSLASKIE STUDIA SOCJOLOGICZNE. 1963. irreg. Slaski Instytut Naukowy, Ul. Graniczna 32, 40-956 Katowice, Poland. (Dist. by: Ars Polona-Ruch, Krakowskie Przedmiescie 7, Warsaw, Poland)

GRADUATE SCHOOL JOURNAL. see *EDUCATION — School Organization And Administration*

309 334.683   AT   ISSN 0310-2890
GRASS ROOTS; craft and self-sufficiency for down to earth people. 1973. 6/yr. Aus.$35. Night Owl Publishers Pty. Ltd., P.O. Box 242, Euroa, Vic. 3666, Australia. TEL 6157-94-7274. FAX 6157-947285. Ed. Megg Miller. adv.; bk.rev. circ. 32,000. (back issues avail.) **Indexed:** Alt.Press Ind., Gdlns., Pinpointer.

GRASSROOTS DEVELOPMENT. see *BUSINESS AND ECONOMICS — International Development And Assistance*

GRAZER LINGUISTISCHE STUDIEN. see *LINGUISTICS*

301 314   UK   ISSN 0072-5765
GREAT BRITAIN. CENTRAL STATISTICAL OFFICE. SOCIAL TRENDS. 1970. a. £26 (Jan. 1993 edition). Central Statistical Office, C.S.O. Library, Cardiff Rd., Newport, Gwent NP9 1XG, Newport, Gwent NP9 1XG, Wales. TEL 01633-812973. FAX 01633-812599. TELEX 497121 BSO NPT G. (Orders to: H.M.S.O. Publications Centre, P.O. Box 276, London SW8 5DT, England. TEL 0171-873-9090. FAX 0171-873-8200) charts; stat. **Document type:** government publication.
  —CCC.
   Description: Compiles data pertaining to employment and leisure, education, health, transportation, and housing and analyzes trends.

GREAT BRITAIN. DEPARTMENT OF THE ENVIRONMENT. REPORT ON RESEARCH AND DEVELOPMENT. see *ENVIRONMENTAL STUDIES*

GREAT ISSUES OF THE DAY. see *POLITICAL SCIENCE*

051   US   ISSN 0017-3983
GREEN REVOLUTION; a voice for decentralization and balanced living. 1943. q. $20. School of Living, R.R. 1, Box 185A, Cochranville, PA 19330. TEL 215-593-6988. Ed. Virginia Green. bk.rev.; charts; illus. circ. 400. (also avail. in microform from UMI; reprint service avail. from UMI) **Indexed:** Alt.Press Ind., Energy Ind., Energy Info.Abstr., New Per.Ind.
  —UMI.
   Incorporates (1969-1979): Aquarian Research Foundation Newsletter.
   Description: Provides information for governing communities about the land. Promotes decentralization, community land trust, permaculture, intentional community, alternative education, alternative money, and geonomic transformation.

301.4   FR   ISSN 0180-9857
GROUPE FAMILIAL. 1958. q. 270 F. (foreign 290 F.). Federation Nationale des Ecole des Parents et des Educateurs, 5 impasse Bon-Secours, 75543 Paris Cedex 11, France. TEL 43-48-00-16. FAX 1-43-48-81-53. Ed. Odile Naudin. adv.; bk.rev.; bibl. circ. 5,000. **Indexed:** Bull.Signal.
   Description: For specialists in education. Covers issues on a general theme connected with family, psychology, social work.

GRUPPENDYNAMIK; Zeitschrift fuer angewandte Sozialpsychologie. see *PSYCHOLOGY*

301.4   FR
GUIDE DES FUTURS EPOUX. 1957. q. 11 bis rue du Docteur Baudin, 28004 Chartres Cedex 92, France. Ed. Pierre Delaval. circ. 400,000 (controlled).

301   US   ISSN 0091-7052
HM47.U6
GUIDE TO GRADUATE DEPARTMENTS OF SOCIOLOGY. a. $11 to individuals (foreign $13); students $6 (foreign $8). American Sociological Association, 1722 N St., N.W., Washington, DC 20036. TEL 202-833-3410. FAX 202-785-0146. (reprint service avail. from UMI) **Document type:** directory.

GUILFORD FAMILY THERAPY SERIES. see *PSYCHOLOGY*

GUILFORD SERIES ON PERSONAL RELATIONSHIPS. see *PSYCHOLOGY*

HAMBURG AFRICAN STUDIES/ETUDES AFRICAINES HAMBOURGEOISES. see *POLITICAL SCIENCE*

HANDLING CHILD CUSTODY, ABUSE, AND ADOPTION CASES. see *LAW — Family And Matrimonial Law*

301   KO   ISSN 1225-0120
HANGUK SAHOEHAK/KOREAN JOURNAL OF SOCIOLOGY. 1964. s-a. 25000 Won($32) Korean Sociological Association, 304-28, Sachik-dong, Chongro-ku, Seoul 110-054, S. Korea. FAX 02-739-3427. Ed. Hung-Tak Lee. adv.; bk.rev. circ. 1,000. **Document type:** academic/scholarly publication.

HARROWSMITH. see *AGRICULTURE*

301 900   US   ISSN 0146-5414
HN1
HARVEST BOOK SERIES. 1966. irreg. $26. Harvest Publishers, 1521 Shattuck Ave., Box 9515, N. Berkeley Sta., Berkeley, CA 94709. E-mail: karlk@cf.Berkeley.EDU. Ed. Richard Krooth. adv.; bk.rev. circ. 1,500. **Indexed:** Alt.Press Ind.
   Description: Dynamics of global social change.

360   US   ISSN 1034-5183
HARVEST NEWS. 1947. 3/yr. free. (CROP, the Community Hunger Appeal of Church World Service) Church World Service, Box 968, Elkhart, IN 46515. TEL 219-264-3102. FAX 219-294-2964. Ed. Frances Jones. bk.rev.; charts. circ. 290,000. **Document type:** newsletter.
   Formerly (until 1983): Service News (Elkhart) (ISSN 0037-2617)

301   US   ISSN 0891-7795
HEALTH, SOCIETY AND CULTURE. 1987. irreg., latest vol.2. price varies. Gordon & Breach Science Publishers, c/o International Publishers Distributor, 820 Town Center Dr., Langhorne, PA 19047. TEL 215-750-2642. FAX 215-750-6343. (Subscr. to: International Publishers Distributor, P.O. Box 90, Reading, Berkshire RG1 8JL, England. TEL 44-173-456-8316) Ed. H.A. Baer. **Document type:** monographic series.
   Refereed Serial

HEARD HERITAGE; Heard County, Georgia - a history of its people. see *GENEALOGY AND HERALDRY*

HELLING. see *POLITICAL SCIENCE*

360   NO   ISSN 0801-1842
HELSE- OG SOSIAL FORUM. 1972. 10/yr. NOK 50. Norsk Forening for Sosialt Arbeid - Norwegian Association for Social Work, Osterhausgt. 11, 0183 Oslo 1, Norway. Ed. Barbro Sveen. adv.; bk.rev.; abstr.; illus. circ. 6,000.
  —BLDSC (4286.378000).
   Former titles (until 1986): Sosialt Forum - Sosialt Arbeid (ISSN 0332-8791); Formed by the merger of (1927-1972): Sosialt Arbeid (ISSN 0038-1632); (1870-1972): Sosialt Forum (ISSN 0332-8783)

HESSISCHE STIFTUNG FRIEDENS- UND KONFLIKTFORSCHUNG. MITTEILUNGEN; Bericht ueber Organisation und laufende Forschung. see *POLITICAL SCIENCE — International Relations*

301   JA   ISSN 0912-2087
HIKAKU BUNMEI/COMPARATIVE CIVILIZATION. (Text in Japanese) 1985. a. Japan Society for Comparative Study of Civilizations, c/o Kyorisu College of Pharmacy, 1-5-30, Shiba-koen, Minato-ku, Tokyo 105, Japan. TEL 03-261-6190.

301.4 155
HISPANIC AMERICAN FAMILY MAGAZINE. (Text in English, Spanish) 1987. q. $12. Hispanic American Family of the Year Foundation, 10654 Woodbrige St., N. Hollywood, CA 91602-2717. TEL 818-500-1309. Ed. Bernard Kemp. adv. circ. 15,000. **Document type:** consumer publication.
   Description: Features articles on interests and concerns parents have and with the problems and pleasures of raising a family in today's society from the Hispanic American perspective.

HISTOIRE SOCIALE/SOCIAL HISTORY. see *HISTORY*

HISTORICA CARPATICA. see *POLITICAL SCIENCE*

HISTORICAL METHODS. see *HISTORY*

HISTORICAL SOCIAL RESEARCH/HISTORISCHE SOZIALFORSCHUNG. see *HISTORY — History Of Europe*

301   US   ISSN 0190-2067
HM1
HISTORY OF SOCIOLOGY: AN INTERNATIONAL REVIEW.* 1978. s-a. $25. Department of Sociology, 211 Oswald Tower, Penn State University, University Park, PA 16802. TEL 913-864-4111. Eds. Alan Sica, Gerd Schroeter. adv.; bk.rev. circ. 300. (reprint service avail. from SCH) **Indexed:** Amer.Hist.& Life, Hist.Abstr., Lang.& Lang.Behav.Abstr., Sociol.Abstr.
   Formerly: Journal of the History of Sociology.

301 309   EC   ISSN 1021-044X
HOMBRE Y AMBIENTE; el punto de vista indigena. 1987. q. S/1000($15) or exchange basis. Ediciones Abya - Yala, Casilla 8513, Quito, Ecuador. TEL 562633. (Dist. by: Libreria Libri Mundi, Juan Leon Mera, 851, Quito, Ecuador.) Ed. Jose E. Juncosa.

325 312   FR   ISSN 0223-3290
HOMMES ET MIGRATIONS. 1950. m. 425 F. Amis de Hommes & Migrations, 40 rue de la Duee, 75020 Paris, France. TEL 47-97-26-05. FAX 47-97-99-77. Ed. Philippe DeWitte; Pub. Francois Gremont. adv. contact: Patrice Coulon. bk.rev.; charts; illus.; stat.; index, cum.index. circ. 3,000. (tabloid format) **Indexed:** Abstr.Musl.Rel., Per.Islam. (1991-), Refug.Abstr.
  —BLDSC (4326.270000).
   Formerly: Cahiers Nord Africains (ISSN 0018-4365)

301   SP
HOMO SOCIOLOGICUS. 1974. irreg. Ediciones 62, S.A., Provenca 278, 08008 Barcelona, Spain. TEL 487-00-62.

HONG KONG SOCIAL AND ECONOMIC TRENDS. see *BUSINESS AND ECONOMICS — Economic Situation And Conditions*

HOUSTON REVIEW: HISTORY AND CULTURE OF THE GULF COAST. see *HISTORY — History Of North And South America*

HUMAN KINDNESS FOUNDATION NEWSLETTER; a little news. see *RELIGIONS AND THEOLOGY*

301   US   ISSN 0097-9783
HQ767
HUMAN LIFE REVIEW. 1975. q. $20 (foreign $25). Human Life Foundation, Inc., 150 E. 35th St., New York, NY 10016. TEL 212-685-5210. FAX 212-725-9793. Ed. J.P. McFadden. circ. 14,000. (also avail. in microfiche from UMI; reprint service avail. from UMI,WSH) **Indexed:** C.L.I., Curr.Lit.Fam.Plan., Leg.Per.
  —UMI; UnCover.
   Description: Covers abortion and related issues.

HUMAN NATURE; an interdisciplinary biosocial perspective. see *SOCIAL SCIENCES: COMPREHENSIVE WORKS*

HUMAN QUEST. see *RELIGIONS AND THEOLOGY*

HUMAN RESOURCES ABSTRACTS; an international information service. see *SOCIOLOGY — Abstracting, Bibliographies, Statistics*

301　　　　　US　　ISSN 0275-0392
JC571
HUMAN RIGHTS QUARTERLY; a comparative and international journal of the social sciences, humanities and law. 1979. q. $28 to individuals (foreign $38); institutions $76.50 (foreign $86.50). (Urban Morgan Institute for Human Rights) Johns Hopkins University Press, Journals Publishing Division, 2715 N. Charles St., Baltimore, MD 21218. TEL 410-516-6987. FAX 410-516-6968. Ed. Bert B. Lockwood, Jr. adv. contact: Tara Dorai-Berry. bk.rev. circ. 1,300. (also avail. in microform from UMI; microfiche from IDC; back issues avail.; reprint service avail. from UMI,WSH) **Indexed**: A.B.C.Pol.Sci., Abstr.Bk.Rev.Curr.Leg.Per., Amer.Bibl.Slavic & E.Eur.Stud., Amer.Hist.& Life (until 1993), BPIA, C.L.I., Curr.Cont., Foreign Leg.Per., Hist.Abstr. (until 1993), HR Rep. (1981-), Int.Lab.Doc., Int.Polit.Sci.Abstr., L.R.I., Lang.& Lang.Behav.Abstr., Leg.Cont., Leg.Per., P.A.I.S, Per.Islam. (1991-), Phil.Ind., Polit.Sci.Abstr., Refug.Abstr., Rel.Ind.One, Sociol.Abstr., SSCI. **Document type**: academic/scholarly publication.
— BLDSC (4336.441500); Faxon; Genuine Article; SWETS; UMI; UnCover. **CCC**.
Formerly (until 1981): Universal Human Rights (ISSN 0163-2647)
Description: Presents current work in rights research and policy analysis, and philosophical essays probing the fundamental nature of human rights as defined by the Universal Declaration of Human Rights.

HUMAN STRESS: CURRENT SELECTED RESEARCH. see *PSYCHOLOGY*

HUMAN STUDIES; a journal for philosophy and the social sciences. see *PHILOSOPHY*

301　　　　　US
THE HUMANIST SOCIOLOGIST. q. membership. Association for Humanist Sociology, Department of Sociology, University of North Carolina, Charlotte, NC 28223. (Subscr. to: c/o Charles McKelvey, Department of Sociology, Presbyterian College, Clinton, SC 29325)

301　　　　　US　　ISSN 0160-5976
HM1
HUMANITY & SOCIETY. 1977. q. $50 (foreign $55). Association for Humanist Sociology, c/o Donald Goodman, Department of Sociology, John Jay College of Criminal Justice, CUNY, 899 10th Ave., New York, NY 10009. Ed. Judy Aulette. adv.; bk.rev.; abstr.; index. circ. 600. (also avail. in microfiche) **Indexed**: Lang.& Lang.Behav.Abstr., Sociol.Abstr. (1977-).
— BLDSC (4336.581200); Faxon; UnCover.
Description: Provides a forum for sociologists and other scholars whose work addresses the problem of understanding social issues and creating a more humane and egalitarian society.

HUMOR; international journal of humor research. see *SOCIAL SCIENCES: COMPREHENSIVE WORKS*

616.39　　　　US　　ISSN 0740-1116
HUNGER NOTES. 1976. q. $18 to individuals (foreign $24); institutions $45 (foreign $51). World Hunger Education Service, Box 29056, Washington, DC 20017. TEL 202-298-9503. Ed. Lane Vanderslice. bk.rev.; illus.; circ. 300 (paid). **Indexed**: HR Rep. **Document type**: academic/scholarly publication.
Description: Presents facts and insights on hunger, poverty, grassroots self-help, and socioeconomic development for policy-makers, educators and activists. Acts as a guide to organizations and print resources on the specific focus of each issue.

300　　　　　BO　　ISSN 0018-8581
I B E A S.* 1966. m. free. Instituto Boliviano de Estudio y Accion Social, Casilla 3277, La Paz, Bolivia. bibl. (processed)

I D S BULLETIN. (Institute of Development Studies) see *BUSINESS AND ECONOMICS — International Development And Assistance*

I D S DISCUSSION PAPER. (Institute of Development Studies) see *BUSINESS AND ECONOMICS — International Development And Assistance*

I D S RESEARCH REPORTS. (Institute of Development Studies) see *BUSINESS AND ECONOMICS — International Development And Assistance*

301　　　　　DK　　ISSN 0105-0532
HN371
I E F INFORMATION.* 1971. irreg. Koebenhavns Universitet, Institut for Europaeisk Folkelivsforskning, Frue Plads, 1168 Copenhagen K, Denmark. illus.

I F R A DOCUMENTS IN SOCIAL SCIENCES AND HUMANITIES. (Institute Francais de Recherche en Afrique) see *POLITICAL SCIENCE — International Relations*

I F R A OCCASIONAL PUBLICATIONS. (Institut Francais de Recherche en Afrique) see *POLITICAL SCIENCE — International Relations*

I L P E S CUADERNOS. (Instituto Latinamericano y del Caribe de Planificacion Economica y Social) see *BUSINESS AND ECONOMICS — Macroeconomics*

301.2 991.4　　　PH　　ISSN 0073-9537
I P C MONOGRAPHS. (Text in English) irreg. price varies. Ateneo de Manila University, Institute of Philippine Culture, Box 154, Manila, Philippines. Ed. Alfonso De Guzman II. **Document type**: monographic series.

301.2 991.4　　　PH　　ISSN 0073-9545
I P C PAPERS. (Text in English) irreg., latest no.15. price varies. Ateneo de Manila University, Institute of Philippine Culture, Box 154, Manila, Philippines. **Document type**: monographic series.

309　　　　　PH
I P C POVERTY RESEARCH SERIES. irreg. Ateneo de Manila University, Institute of Philippine Culture, Box 154, Manila, Philippines. **Document type**: monographic series.

301　　　　　PH
I P C REPRINTS. (Text in English) irreg., latest no.23. Ateneo de Manila University, Institute of Philippine Culture, Box 154, Manila, Philippines.

301　　　　　AT
I R S A ITEMS. (Text in English; occasionally summaries in Spanish) 1977. a. membership. International Rural Sociology Association, c/o Dept. of Sociology, Michigan State University, East Lansing, MI 48824. Ed. Harry Schwarzweller. bk.rev. circ. 1,700. (tabloid format)

301　　　　　US
I S A G A NEWSLETTER. 1974. q. membership. International Simulation and Gaming Association, c/o Dr. S. Underwood, 4110 EECS bldg., University of Michigan, Ann Arbor, MI 48109-2122. TEL 313-936-2999. FAX 313-763-1674. bk.rev. circ. 1,000.
Description: Provides a forum for the exchange of ideas and knowledge on the design, applications, and use of games and simulation throughout the world.

301　　　　　CN　　ISSN 0828-6868
HC117.N4
I S E R RESEARCH AND POLICY PAPERS. 1985. irreg., latest no.21. price varies. Institute of Social and Economic Research, Memorial University, St. John's, NF A1C 5S7, Canada. TEL 709-737-8156. FAX 709-737-2041. E-mail: iser@kean.ucs.mun.ca. adv.; bk.rev. circ. 250. (tabloid format; back issues avail.) **Document type**: academic/scholarly publication.
— BLDSC (4582.842800).
Description: Features article length papers. These papers vary from basic social scientific research to various forms of applied research, to policy analysis and recommendations. Draws mainly on research conducted under the auspices and focuses on Newfoundland and North Atlantic studies.

301 320　　　　US
I S H I OCCASIONAL PAPERS IN SOCIAL CHANGE.* 1976. irreg., no.6, 1982. price varies. (Institute for the Study of Human Issues) I S H I Publications, 1530 Locust St., Ste. 80, Philadelphia, PA 19102. TEL 215-732-9729. Ed. J.M. Jutkowitz. circ. 1,000. (also avail. in microform from UMI)

IDEAS & ACTION. see *BUSINESS AND ECONOMICS — Labor And Industrial Relations*

IDENTITIES. see *ETHNIC INTERESTS*

IN SUMMARY. see *SOCIAL SCIENCES: COMPREHENSIVE WORKS*

IN THE MAKING; directory of radical cooperation. see *BUSINESS AND ECONOMICS — Cooperatives*

INDAGINI E PROSPETTIVE. see *POLITICAL SCIENCE*

301.2 294.5　　　II　　ISSN 0971-0612
INDIA CULTURES/SAMSKRITI. (Text in English) vol.22, 1965. q. Rs.10($5) Leonard Theological College, School of Research, P.O. Box 36, Jabalpur 482001, Madhya Pradesh, India. TEL 91-761-320117. FAX 91-761-321320. Ed. Rev. G.R. Singh. bk.rev.; illus. circ. 500. **Indexed**: Anthropol.Lit. **Document type**: academic/scholarly publication, monographic series.
Formerly: India Cultures Quarterly (ISSN 0019-4166)
Description: Contains articles on religions, cultures, tribals, ethnic minorities, antiquity and sociology.

301　　　　　II　　ISSN 0019-5642
HM1
INDIAN JOURNAL OF SOCIOLOGY. (Text and summaries in English) 1970. a. Rs.150($35) Indian Academy of Social Sciences, c/o Sociology House, K21, Hauz Khas Enclave, New Delhi 110016, India. Ed. Keshav Dev Sharma. adv. contact: Krishna Sharma. bk.rev.; abstr.; stat.; index. circ. 600. (tabloid format) **Indexed**: Lang.& Lang.Behav.Abstr., Sociol.Abstr. **Document type**: academic/scholarly publication.

301　　　　　US　　ISSN 1070-1400
E98.W8
INDIGENOUS WOMAN. 1991. irreg. $20 for 2 nos. Indigenous Women's Network, Box 174, Lake Elmo, MN 55042. Ed. Lisa Bellanger. circ. 4,000.
Description: Covers the issues and concerns of native women.

INDIVIDUALIST. see *PHILOSOPHY*

301　　　　　DK　　ISSN 0109-2421
INDVANDREREN. (Text in Danish; summaries in Arabic, English, Farsi, Greek, Kurdish, Serbo-Croatian, Tamil, Turkish, Urdu) 1983. 6/yr. DKK 95 to individuals; institutions DKK 125. Etniske Mindretals Sammenslutning (IND-sam) - Federation of Ethnic Minorities, Blegdamsvej 4, st., DK-2200 Copenhagen N, Denmark. TEL 45-31-39-21-43. FAX 45-35-36-24-10. Ed. Charlotte Albaek. adv.; illus. circ. 1,400.
Description: Focuses on topics for and about ethnic minorities in Denmark.

301　　　　　AT　　ISSN 1033-6273
▼**INFORMATION, THEORY AND SOCIETY**. 1994. s-a. $60 to individuals; institutions $120. James Nicholas Publishers, P.O. Box 244, Albert Park, Vic. 3206, Australia. TEL 61-3-696-5545. FAX 613-699-2040. Ed. Rea Zajda. adv.; bk.rev.; index. **Indexed**: Aus.Educ.Ind., Cont.Pg.Educ., Sociol.Abstr., Sociol.Educ.Abstr. **Document type**: academic/scholarly publication.
Description: Covers major and current issues in information research, focusing on contemporary cultural studies and problems pertaining to the information age, post-industrialism, individualism, commodities and postmodernity.

301.4　　　　GW　　ISSN 0938-0124
INFORMATIONEN FUER EINELTERNFAMILIEN. 1990. 9/yr. Verband Alleinstehender Muetter und Vaeter e.V., Von-Groote-Platz 20, 53173 Bonn, Germany. TEL 0228-352995. FAX 0228-358350. Ed. Gunhild Gutschmidt. circ. 1,350. **Document type**: newsletter.

INSIDE M S; a magazine of the National Multiple Sclerosis Society. see *MEDICAL SCIENCES — Psychiatry And Neurology*

INSIDE M S BULLETIN. see *MEDICAL SCIENCES — Psychiatry And Neurology*

INSTITUT FUER AFRIKA-KUNDE. ARBEITEN. see *POLITICAL SCIENCE*

INSTITUT ZA KRIMINOLOSKA I SOCIOLOSKA ISTRAZIVANJA. ZBORNIK. see *CRIMINOLOGY AND LAW ENFORCEMENT*

INSTITUTE FOR SOCIAL RESEARCH NEWSLETTER. see *SOCIAL SERVICES AND WELFARE*

SOCIOLOGY

951.9 II ISSN 0970-2814
DS1
INSTITUTE OF ASIAN STUDIES. JOURNAL. (Text in English) 1983. s-a. Rs.100($20) Institute of Asian Studies, 377, 10th East St., Thiruvanmiyur, Madras 600 041, India. TEL 91-44-416728. FAX 91-44-419866. Ed. Shu Hikosaka. adv.; bk.rev.; bibl.; illus.; stat. circ. 500.
●Also available online.
   Description: Cross-cultural and comparative studies of Asian languages, literatures, religions, and other disciplines of Asian perspective.

INSTITUTE OF DEVELOPMENT STUDIES. ANNUAL REPORT. see *BUSINESS AND ECONOMICS — International Development And Assistance*

INSTITUTE OF MODERN RUSSIAN CULTURE NEWSLETTER. see *ETHNIC INTERESTS*

301.45 UK
INSTITUTE OF RACE RELATIONS. ANNUAL REPORT. 1974. a. Institute of Race Relations, 2-6 Leeke St., King's Cross Rd., London WC1X 9HS, England. TEL 0171-837-0041. FAX 0171-278-0623. (Subscr. to: Race & Class, 120-126 Lavender Ave., Mitcham, Surrey CR4 3HP, England) **Document type:** corporate report.

309 PE ISSN 1019-4517
INSTITUTO DE ESTUDIOS PERUANOS. ESTUDIOS DE LA SOCIEDAD RURAL. 1967. irreg., no.12, 1994. price varies. I E P Ediciones, Horacio Urteaga 694, Lima 11, Peru. TEL 51-14-323070. FAX 51-14-324981. E-mail: postmaster@iep.org.pe.

301 340 UY
INSTITUTO INTERAMERICANO DEL NINO. JURIDICO SOCIAL. INFORMES TECNICOS. irreg. Instituto Interamericano del Nino, Avda. 8 de Octubre No. 2904, Montevideo, Uruguay.

INTEGRAL PSYKOANALYS; psykoterapi, sociologi, filosofi. see *MEDICAL SCIENCES — Psychiatry And Neurology*

INTERCHANGE. see *EDUCATION*

301.2 US ISSN 1057-7769
P94.6
INTERCULTURAL COMMUNICATION STUDIES. 1991. 2/yr. $50 (effective 1994). Institute for Cross-Cultural Research, Trinity University, No. 418, 715 Stadium Dr., San Antonio, TX 78212-7200. TEL 210-736-7369. FAX 210-736-8512. Ed. Bates L. Hoffer. adv.; bk.rev. circ. 200. (back issues avail.) **Document type:** academic/scholarly publication.
—BLDSC (4533.356033).
   Description: Offers a multidisciplinary approach to the study of culture - language problems across cultures, whether major cultural groups or ethnic - socioeconometric subgroups within a larger group.
Refereed Serial

362.7 FR ISSN 0538-5490
HV703
INTERNATIONAL CHILDREN'S CENTRE. PARIS. REPORT OF THE DIRECTOR-GENERAL TO THE EXECUTIVE BOARD. irreg. Centre International de l'Enfance - International Children's Center, Chateau de Longchamp, Bois de Boulogne, 75016 Paris, France. TEL 1-45-20-79-92. FAX 1-45-25-73-67.
   Description: Focuses on child health, with contributions from all disciplines relevant to the development of children's health services and activities.

INTERNATIONAL JOURNAL OF BEHAVIORAL MEDICINE. see *PSYCHOLOGY*

INTERNATIONAL JOURNAL OF BIOSOCIAL AND MEDICAL RESEARCH; bridging the gap between the natural and social sciences to better understand human behavior. see *NUTRITION AND DIETETICS*

301 CN ISSN 1180-3991
F1001
INTERNATIONAL JOURNAL OF CANADIAN STUDIES/REVUE INTERNATIONALE D'ETUDES CANADIENNES. (Text in English, French) 1990. s-a. Can.$30 to non-members; members Can.$20. International Council for Canadian Studies - Conseil International d'Etudes Canadiennes, 325 Dalhousie, S-800, Ottawa, ON K1N 7G2, Canada. TEL 613-789-7834. FAX 613-789-7830. E-mail: iccsciec@iccs.synapse.net. Ed. Kenneth McRoberts. adv.: page Can.$300; adv. contact: Guy Leclair. circ. 800. **Indexed:** Amer.Hist.& Life, Can.B.P.I., Hist.Abstr., Int.Polit.Sci.Abstr. **Document type:** academic/scholarly publication.
   Description: Multidisciplinary and international in scope, dedicated to the analysis of key issues of Canadian society in the social sciences and the arts as well as other disciplines.
Refereed Serial

301 NE ISSN 0020-7152
HM1
INTERNATIONAL JOURNAL OF COMPARATIVE SOCIOLOGY. 1960. 2/yr. fl.102($66) to individuals; institutions fl.158($102) (effective 1996). (York University, Department of Sociology, CN) E.J. Brill, P.O. Box 9000, 2300 PA Leiden, Netherlands. TEL 31-71-5353500. FAX 31-71-5317532. TELEX 39296 BRILL NL. E-mail: ejborders@ejbrill.com. (In N. America: E.J. Brill, 24 Hudson St., Kinderhook, NY 12106. TEL 800-962-4406. FAX 518-758-1959) Ed. K. Ishwaran. adv.; bk.rev.; charts. (also avail. in microform from SWZ; reprint service avail. from SWZ) **Indexed:** A.B.C.Pol.Sci., Curr.Cont., Geo.Abstr., IDA, Int.Polit.Sci.Abstr., Lang.& Lang.Behav.Abstr., Mid.East: Abstr.& Ind., Soc.Sci.Ind., Sociol.Abstr. (1960-), Sociol.Educ.Abstr., SSCI, Stud.Wom.Abstr. **Document type:** academic/scholarly publication.
—BLDSC (4542.173000); Faxon; Genuine Article; SWETS; UnCover. **CCC.**
   Description: Studies in different cultures on a comparative basis with view to reach a common level of abstraction.
Refereed Serial

301 FI ISSN 0019-6398
INTERNATIONAL JOURNAL OF CONTEMPORARY SOCIOLOGY. 1963. s-a. FIM 236($20) to individuals; institutions $40. c/o Dr. M'hammed Sabour, Dept. of Sociology, University of Joensuu, P.O. Box 111, SF-80101 Joensuu, Finland. TEL 358-73-1511. FAX 358-73-151-4528. Ed. Raj Mohan. adv.; bk.rev.; charts; illus.; cum.index. (also avail. in microfilm from UMI; reprint service avail. from UMI) **Indexed:** Amer.Hist.& Life (until 1991), ASSIA, Crim.Just.Abstr., Curr.Cont., Hist.Abstr. (until 1991), Lang.& Lang.Behav.Abstr., Sociol.Abstr. (1971-), Sociol.Educ.Abstr., SSCI. **Document type:** academic/scholarly publication.
—BLDSC (4542.176000); Faxon; UMI; UnCover.
   Formerly: Indian Sociological Bulletin.
   Description: Discussion of contemporary ideas and research in sociology.

301 II ISSN 0377-0141
HM1
INTERNATIONAL JOURNAL OF CRITICAL SOCIOLOGY. 1973. s-a. $12. Jaipur Institute of Sociology, II , C-168A, Bajaj Nagar, Jaipur 302 017, India. Ed. R.C. Gupta. bk.rev.; bibl.; charts. **Indexed:** Lang.& Lang.Behav.Abstr.

INTERNATIONAL JOURNAL OF GROUP TENSIONS. see *PSYCHOLOGY*

301 UK ISSN 0147-1767
GN496
INTERNATIONAL JOURNAL OF INTERCULTURAL RELATIONS. 1977. q. £210($334) (effective 1996). (Society for International Education, Training and Research) Elsevier Science Ltd., Pergamon, P.O. Box 800, Kidlington, Oxford OX5 1DX, England. TEL 44-1865-843000. FAX 44-1865-843010. E-mail: nlinfo-f@elsevier.nl; usinfo-f@elsevier.com; forinfo-kyf04035@niftyserve.or.jp; Site addr.: http://www.elsevier.nl/. (Subscr. in U.S. and Canada to: Elsevier Science, 660 White Plains Rd., Tarrytown, NY 10591-5153. TEL 914-524-9200. FAX 914-333-2444) Ed. Dan Landis. adv.; bk.rev. circ. 2,500. (also avail. in microfilm from UMI) **Indexed:** Adol.Ment.Hlth.Abstr., Amer.Bibl.Slavic & E.Eur.Stud., ASCA, ASSIA, Chic.Per.Ind., Crim.Just.Abstr., Lang.& Lang.Behav.Abstr., Mult.Ed.Abstr., Psychol.Abstr. (1977-), SSCI. **Document type:** academic/scholarly publication.
—BLDSC (4542.311000); Faxon; Genuine Article; SWETS; UMI; UnCover. **CCC.**
   Description: Dedicated to advancing knowledge and understanding of theory, practice and research in intergroup relations.
Refereed Serial

361 614 US ISSN 0280-7270
HV551.2
INTERNATIONAL JOURNAL OF MASS EMERGENCIES AND DISASTERS. 1983. 3/yr. $48 membership; with Unscheduled Events $70. International Research Committee on Disasters, Disaster Research Center, University of Delaware, Newark, DE 19716. TEL 302-831-6618. FAX 302-831-2091. TELEX 70 99 85. Eds. Neil Britton, Ron Perry. bk.rev. (back issues avail.) **Indexed:** Sociol.Abstr. (1983-). **Document type:** academic/scholarly publication.
—BLDSC (4542.332000).

INTERNATIONAL JOURNAL OF SOCIAL ECONOMICS. see *BUSINESS AND ECONOMICS*

301 US ISSN 0020-7659
HM1
INTERNATIONAL JOURNAL OF SOCIOLOGY. 1971. q. $495 to institutions (foreign $560) (effective Jul. 1995). M.E. Sharpe, Inc., 80 Business Park Dr., Armonk, NY 10504. TEL 914-273-1800; 800-541-6563. FAX 914-273-2106. Ed. Michael Weber. (back issues avail.) **Indexed:** Anthropol.Lit., ASSIA, Int.Polit.Sci.Abstr., Lang.& Lang.Behav.Abstr., Mid.East: Abstr.& Ind., Mult.Ed.Abstr., P.A.I.S., Sociol.Educ.Abstr., Stud.Wom.Abstr. **Document type:** academic/scholarly publication.
—BLDSC (4542.570000); Faxon; SWETS; UMI; UnCover. **CCC.**
   Formerly: Eastern European Studies in Sociology and Anthropology.
   Description: Provides English translations from international sources.
Refereed Serial

301 300 UK ISSN 0144-333X
HM1
INTERNATIONAL JOURNAL OF SOCIOLOGY AND SOCIAL POLICY. 1981. 12/yr. £798($1197) Barmarick Publications, Enholmes Hall, Patrington, N. Humber HU12 0PR, England. TEL 01964-630033. Ed. Barrie O. Pettman. circ. 200. (back issues avail.; reprint service avail. from SWZ) **Indexed:** ABI Inform., ASSIA, Lang.& Lang.Behav.Abstr., Sociol.Abstr. (1976-)., Sociol.Educ.Abstr. **Document type:** academic/scholarly publication.
—BLDSC (4542.571000); SWETS; UMI.
   Description: Seeks to provide research and promote the exchange of ideas and new concepts in sociology and social policy as well as evaluating the effects of the implementation of past approaches and strategies.

301.4 II ISSN 0020-7667
HQ1
INTERNATIONAL JOURNAL OF SOCIOLOGY OF THE FAMILY; journal of cross-national, cross-cultural and inter-disciplinary research. 1971. s-a. Rs.400($70) M D Publications Pvt Ltd, 11 Darya Ganj, New Delhi 110 002, India. TEL 3268645. FAX 91-11-3275542. Ed. Man Singh Das. adv.; bk.rev. circ. 1,200. (also avail. in microform; back issues avail.) **Indexed:** ASSIA, Lang.& Lang.Behav.Abstr., Popul.Ind., Sociol.Abstr. (1971-), SSCI.
—BLDSC (4542.572000); Faxon; UnCover.

INTERNATIONAL JOURNAL OF THE SOCIOLOGY OF LANGUAGE. see *LINGUISTICS*

SOCIOLOGY

INTERNATIONAL JOURNAL OF THE SOCIOLOGY OF LAW. see *LAW*

301 UN ISSN 1012-6902
INTERNATIONAL REVIEW FOR THE SOCIOLOGY OF SPORT. (Text in English) 1966. 4/yr. DM.156 (effective 1996). (Unesco, International Committee for Sociology of Sport (ICSS)) R. Oldenbourg Verlag GmbH, Rosenheimer Str. 145, 81671 Munich, Germany. Ed. Klaus Heinemann. adv.; bk.rev.; abstr.; bibl.; illus. circ. 1,000. (back issues avail.; reprint service avail. from SCH) **Indexed:** Lang.& Lang.Behav.Abstr., Sociol.Abstr. (1968-), Sportsearch (1984-). **Document type:** academic/scholarly publication.
—BLDSC (4547.744000); Faxon; SWETS; UnCover. CCC.
Formerly: International Review of Sport Sociology (ISSN 0074-7769)
Description: Forum for sports sociology, including related interdisciplinary topics such as social psychology, history and economics of sports, and philosophy.

301.4 II ISSN 0970-4841
HM1
INTERNATIONAL REVIEW OF MODERN SOCIOLOGY. 1971. s-a. Rs.400($70) M D Publications Pvt Ltd, 11 Darya Ganj, New Delhi 110 002, India. TEL 3268645. FAX 91-11-3275542. TELEX 31-61087 PRIN IN. Ed. Man Singh Das. adv.; bk.rev. circ. 1,200. (also avail. in microform from UMI; back issues avail.) **Indexed:** ASSIA, Lang.& Lang.Behav.Abstr., Sociol.Abstr. (1972-), SSCI.
—BLDSC (4547.385000); Faxon; UnCover.

INTERNATIONAL SOCIETY FOR THE SOCIOLOGY OF RELIGION. DIRECTORY. see *RELIGIONS AND THEOLOGY*

INTERNATIONAL SOCIETY FOR THE SOCIOLOGY OF RELIGION. NEWSLETTER - BULLETIN. see *RELIGIONS AND THEOLOGY*

301 US
INTERNATIONAL SOCIOLOGICAL REVIEW. 1984. q. $20. Harvest Publishers, 1521 Shattuck Ave., Box 9503, N. Berkeley Sta., Berkeley, CA 94709. E-mail: karlk@ocf.Berkeley.EDU. Ed. Richard Krooth.
Description: Sociological dimensions of race, class and ethnicity in the global milieu.

301 UK ISSN 0268-5809
HM1
INTERNATIONAL SOCIOLOGY. 1986. q. £33 to individuals; institutions £99 (effective 1996). (International Sociological Association) Sage Publications Ltd., 6 Bonhill St., London EC2A 4PU, England. TEL 0171-374-0645. FAX 0171-374-8741. E-mail: market@sageltd.co.uk. Ed. Roberto Cipriani. adv.: B&W page £200; trim 185 x 114; adv. contact: Bernie Folan. **Indexed:** Curr.Cont., Human Resour.Abstr., IBZ, Int.Polit.Sci.Abstr., Intl.Bibl.S.S.Soc.Cult.Anthro., Mult.Ed.Abstr., PAIS, Sage Fam.Stud.Abstr., Sci.Cit.Ind., Sociol.Abstr. (1986-), Sociol.Educ.Abstr., SSCI. **Document type:** academic/scholarly publication.
—BLDSC (4549.574200); SWETS; UnCover.
Description: Draws together work of cross-cultural relevance from the international community of sociologists, focusing on fundamental issues of theory and method and on new directions in empirical research.
Refereed Serial

301 NE ISSN 0074-8684
INTERNATIONAL STUDIES IN SOCIOLOGY AND SOCIAL ANTHROPOLOGY. 1963. irreg., vol.62, 1994. price varies. E.J. Brill, P.O. Box 9000, 2300 PA Leiden, Netherlands. TEL 31-71-5353500. FAX 31-71-5317532. TELEX 39296 BRILL NL. (In N. America: E.J. Brill, 24 Hudson St., Kinderhook, NY 12106. TEL 800-962-4406. FAX 518-758-1959) Ed. K. Ishwaran. **Document type:** monographic series.
—BLDSC (4549.820000).
Description: Discusses anthropological and sociological aspects of development, political change, and related issues.
Refereed Serial

INTERPRETIVE PERSPECTIVES ON EDUCATION AND POLICY. see *EDUCATION*

301 PO
INTERVENCAO SOCIAL. 1985. 3/yr. Esc.950 to individuals; institutions Esc.1200. Instituto Superior de Servico Social, Largo do Mitelo, 1, Lisbon 1000, Portugal. (Co-sponsors: Fundacao Calouste Gulbenkian; Junta Nacional de Investigacao Cientifica) Eds. Luisa Ferreira, Pedro Loff. circ. 1,000.

INVANDRARRAPPORT; invandrarnas debatt- och kulturtidskrift. see *POPULATION STUDIES*

301 AG ISSN 0020-9961
INVESTIGACIONES EN SOCIOLOGIA. 1962. a. $6. Universidad Nacional de Cuyo, Instituto de Sociologia, Casilla de Correo 345, 5500 Mendoza, Argentina. TEL 61-253010. FAX 61-380457. bk.rev.; abstr.; charts; illus.; tr.lit.; index. **Document type:** academic/scholarly publication.

IRISH AMERICA MAGAZINE. see *ETHNIC INTERESTS*

301 IE ISSN 0791-6035
HM22.I73 CODEN: IJSOEH
IRISH JOURNAL OF SOCIOLOGY. 1991. a. I£10 (outside E.U. I£12) to individuals; institutions I£15 (outside E.U. I£18). Sociological Association of Ireland, Department of Political Science and Sociology, University College Galway, Galway, Ireland. TEL 091-24411. Ed.Bd. bk.rev. **Document type:** academic/scholarly publication.
—BLDSC (4572.400000).
Refereed Serial

ISSUES IN FOCUS. see *CHILDREN AND YOUTH* — For

ITALIA COOPERATIVA. see *BUSINESS AND ECONOMICS* — *Cooperatives*

261 GW ISSN 0075-2584
HN30
JAHRBUCH FUER CHRISTLICHE SOZIALWISSENSCHAFTEN. 1960. a. price varies. (Universitaet Muenster, Institut fuer Christliche Sozialwissenschaften) Regensberg Druck und Verlag GmbH, Postfach 6667, 48035 Muenster, Germany. TEL 0251-717061. FAX 0251-717725. **Indexed:** CERDIC. **Document type:** academic/scholarly publication.

301 GW ISSN 0177-4093
JAHRBUCH FUER VERGLEICHENDE SOZIALFORSCHUNG. 1984. a. DM.48. (Berliner Institut fuer Vergleichende Sozialforschung) Edition Parabolis, Postfach 301125, 10722 Berlin, Germany. TEL 030-4441088. FAX 030-4441085. Eds. Jochen Blaschke, Jutta Aumueller. **Document type:** academic/scholarly publication.
Formerly: Jahrbuch zur Geschichte und Gesellschaft des Vorderen und Mittleren Orients.
Description: Covers ethnic relations, social comparative research, migration and refugees.

301 JA ISSN 0021-5414
JAPANESE SOCIOLOGICAL REVIEW/SHAKAIGAKU HYORON. (Text in Japanese; title and contents page in English) 1950. q. (Japanese Sociological Society - Nippon Shakai Gakkai) Yuhikaku Publishing Co. Ltd., 2-17 Kanda Jimbocho, Chiyoda-ku, Tokyo 101, Japano-ku. adv.; index. circ. 1,200. **Indexed:** Lang.& Lang.Behav.Abstr., Sociol.Abstr. (1955-).
—UnCover.

JARLIBRO. see *LINGUISTICS*

JASZKUNSAG; social and artistic journal. see *LITERATURE*

301 GW
JEDERMENSCH; Zeitung fuer soziale Dreigliederung, Umweltfragen, neue Lebensformen. 1958. m. DM.3.50. Jedermann Verlag, Hauptstr. 99, 88142 Wasserburg, Germany. Ed. Peter Schilinski. circ. 800.
Former titles: Jedefrau und Jedermann; Jedermann.

301.3 IS
JERUSALEM URBAN STUDIES. (Text in English) 1970. irreg. $2. Hebrew University of Jerusalem, Institute of Urban & Regional Studies, Jerusalem, Israel. Eds. Arieh Shahar, Erik Cohen. charts. circ. 1,000.

301 UK ISSN 0021-6534
DS101
JEWISH JOURNAL OF SOCIOLOGY. 1959. s-a. £12($23) to individuals; institutions £16($30). 187 Gloucester Pl., London NW1 6BU, England. TEL 071-262-8939. Ed. Judith Freedman. adv.; bk.rev.; bibl.; index. **Indexed:** A.I.C.P., ASSIA, Curr.Cont., Ind.Jew.Per., Int.Polit.Sci.Abstr., Lang.& Lang.Behav.Abstr., Mid.East: Abstr.& Ind., P.A.I.S., Psychol.Abstr., Sociol.Abstr. (1959-), SSCI. **Document type:** academic/scholarly publication.
—BLDSC (4668.355000); SWETS; UnCover.

JOURNAL FOR THE SCIENTIFIC STUDY OF RELIGION. see *RELIGIONS AND THEOLOGY*

301 AU ISSN 0253-3995
HM261
JOURNAL FUER SOZIALFORSCHUNG. 1961. q. S.675. European Centre for Social Welfare Policy and Research, Berggasse 17, A-1090 Vienna, Austria. TEL 0222-3194505-0. FAX 0222-319450519. Ed. Bernd Marin. adv. contact: Willem Stamatiou. bk.rev.; abstr.; stat.; cum.index every 5 yrs. circ. 600. (tabloid format) **Document type:** academic/scholarly publication.
—BLDSC (5066.085000).
Formerly: Meinung (ISSN 0025-8822)

JOURNAL OF AGING & SOCIAL POLICY; a journal devoted to aging & social policy. see *GERONTOLOGY AND GERIATRICS*

JOURNAL OF APPLIED BEHAVIORAL SCIENCE. see *PSYCHOLOGY*

950 960 NE ISSN 0021-9096
DT1
JOURNAL OF ASIAN AND AFRICAN STUDIES. 1966. 2/yr. fl.102($66) to individuals; institutions fl.158($102) (effective 1996). E.J. Brill, P.O. Box 9000, 2300 PA Leiden, Netherlands. TEL 31-71-5353500. FAX 31-71-5317532. TELEX 39296 BRILL NL. E-mail: ejborders@ejbrill.com. (In N. America: E.J. Brill, 24 Hudson St., Kinderhook, NY 12106. TEL 800-962-4406. FAX 518-758-1959) Eds. K. Ishwaran, Y.K. Malik. bk.rev. (also avail. in microform from SWZ; reprint service avail. from SWZ) **Indexed:** A.B.C.Pol.Sci., A.I.C.P., Abstr.Anthropol., Amer.Hist.& Life, Anthropol.Lit., Asian-Pac.Econ.Lit., ASSIA, Curr.Cont.Africa, Curr.Cont., E.I., Geo.Abstr., Hist.Abstr., IDA, Int.Polit.Sci.Abstr., Lang.& Lang.Behav.Abstr., Mid.East: Abstr.& Ind., Polit.Sci.Abstr., Rural Devel.Abstr., Rural Ext.Educ.& Tr.Abstr., Soc.Sci.Ind., SSCI. **Document type:** academic/scholarly publication.
—BLDSC (4947.230000); Faxon; Genuine Article; SWETS; UnCover. CCC.
Description: Scholarly accounts of man and society in the developing nations of Asia and Africa, uniting contributions from anthropology, sociology, history and related social sciences. Focuses on societies entering a phase of advanced technology.
Refereed Serial

JOURNAL OF BIOSOCIAL SCIENCE. see *BIOLOGY — Genetics*

JOURNAL OF BUSINESS & SOCIAL STUDIES. see *BUSINESS AND ECONOMICS*

JOURNAL OF COMMUNITY AND APPLIED SOCIAL PSYCHOLOGY. see *PSYCHOLOGY*

JOURNAL OF COMMUNITY PSYCHOLOGY. see *PSYCHOLOGY*

SOCIOLOGY

301.4 CN ISSN 0047-2328
HQ1 CODEN: JCFSAO
JOURNAL OF COMPARATIVE FAMILY STUDIES. (Text in English; summaries in English, French, Spanish) 1970. 3/yr. Can.$60. University of Calgary, Department of Sociology, 2500 University Dr. N.W., Calgary, AB T2N 1N4, Canada. TEL 403-220-7317. FAX 403-282-9298. E-mail: cairns@acs.ucalgary.ca. Ed. George Kurian. adv.: B&W page Can.$260. bk.rev.; abstr.; charts; stat.; cum.index. circ. 800. (processed; also avail. in microform from MIM,UMI; reprint service avail. from UMI) **Indexed:** Abstr.Pop.Cult., Anthropol.Lit., ASSIA, Curr.Cont., Curr.Lit.Fam.Plan., E.I., Excerp.Med., IMFL, Lang.& Lang.Behav.Abstr., Mid.East: Abstr.& Ind., Mult.Ed.Abstr., Popul.Ind., Psychol.Abstr. (1971-), Rural Recreat.Tour.Abstr., Sage Fam.Stud.Abstr., Sociol.Abstr. (1970-), Sp.Ed.Needs Abstr., SSCI, Stud.Wom.Abstr., World Agri.Econ.& Rural Sociol.Abstr. **Document type:** academic/scholarly publication.
●Also available online. Vendor(s): University Microfilms International.
Also available on CD-ROM.
—BLDSC (4961.930000); EMDOCS; Faxon; Genuine Article; SWETS; UMI; UnCover. **CCC.**
Description: Specializes in cross-cultural perspectives of the study of the family.
Refereed Serial

301 200 CN ISSN 1188-827X
BL60
JOURNAL OF COMPARATIVE SOCIOLOGY AND ETHICS. Abbreviated title: J C S E. 1973. a. $50. (International Sociological Research Center) S T C, P.O. Box 7305, Ottawa, ON K1L 8E4, Canada. TEL 613-831-1052. FAX 613-831-8452. Ed. Amarjit S. Sethi. adv.; bk.rev. circ. 1,000. (back issues avail.) **Indexed:** Rel.Ind.One, Sociol.Abstr. (1973-). **Document type:** academic/scholarly publication.
Formerly (until 1990): Journal of Comparative Sociology and Religion (ISSN 0709-3519)
Description: Covers social themes, the issue of ethics in an information society, religion as a source of information for comparative values in post-industrial societies and developing economies.
Refereed Serial

301.34 US ISSN 0891-2416
HT101
JOURNAL OF CONTEMPORARY ETHNOGRAPHY; a journal of ethnographic research. 1972. q. $60 to individuals; institutions $191 (effective Sep. 1995). Sage Publications, Inc., 2455 Teller Rd., Thousand Oaks, CA 91320. TEL 805-499-0721. FAX 805-499-0871. E-mail: libraries@sagepub.com. (Overseas subscr. to: Sage Publications Ltd., 6 Bonhill Rd., London EC2A 4PU, England; Sage Publications India Pvt. Ltd., P.O. Box 4215, New Delhi 110 048, India) Eds. Spencer Cahil, Donileen Loseke. adv.; bk.rev.; charts; illus.; index. circ. 1,300. (also avail. in microform from UMI; back issues avail.; reprint service avail.) **Indexed:** A.I.C.P., Abstr.Anthropol., Abstr.Pop.Cult., ASSIA, C.I.J.E., Curr.Cont., E.I., Lang.& Lang.Behav.Abstr., Mid.East: Abstr.& Ind., Mult.Ed.Abstr., P.A.I.S., Psychol.Abstr. (1991-), Sage Pub.Admin.Abstr., Sage Urb.Stud.Abstr., Soc.Sci.Ind., Sociol.Abstr., Sociol.Educ.Abstr., SSCI, Stud.Wom.Abstr. **Document type:** academic/scholarly publication.
—BLDSC (4965.228000); Faxon; Genuine Article; SWETS; UMI; UnCover. **CCC.**
Former titles: Urban Life (ISSN 0098-3039); (until vol.15): Urban Life and Culture (ISSN 0049-5662)
Description: Takes an interdisciplinary approach to ethnography and qualitative research.

JOURNAL OF CROSS-CULTURAL PSYCHOLOGY. see *PSYCHOLOGY*

JOURNAL OF DEVELOPING AREAS. see *BUSINESS AND ECONOMICS — International Development And Assistance*

JOURNAL OF DEVELOPMENT STUDIES. see *BUSINESS AND ECONOMICS — International Development And Assistance*

JOURNAL OF DIVORCE & REMARRIAGE; clinical studies and research in family therapy, family mediation, family studies and family law. see *MATRIMONY*

JOURNAL OF EARLY ADOLESCENCE. see *CHILDREN AND YOUTH — About*

JOURNAL OF EDUCATION AND SOCIAL CHANGE. see *EDUCATION — Abstracting, Bibliographies, Statistics*

JOURNAL OF EXPERIMENTAL SOCIAL PSYCHOLOGY. see *PSYCHOLOGY*

301.4 US ISSN 0363-1990
HQ503
JOURNAL OF FAMILY HISTORY; studies in family, kinship and demography. 1976. q. $60 to individuals; institutions $150 (effective Sep. 1995). (National Council on Family Relations) Sage Publications, Inc., 2455 Teller Rd., Thousand Oaks, CA 91320. TEL 805-499-0721. FAX 805-499-0871. E-mail: libraries@sagepub.com. (Overseas subscr. to: Sage Publications Ltd., 6 Bohnill St., London EC2A 4PU, England; Sagp Publications India Pvt. Ltd., P.O. Box 4125, New Delhi 110 048, India) Ed. Roderick Phillips. adv. contact: Margaret Travers. bk.rev.; charts; illus. circ. 1,400. (back issues avail.) **Indexed:** Amer.Bibl.Slavic & E.Eur.Stud., Amer.Hist.& Life, Curr.Cont., E.I., Hist.Abstr., Hum.Ind., IMFL, Mid.East: Abstr.& Ind., Mult.Ed.Abstr., Popul.Ind., Psychol.Abstr., Sage Fam.Stud.Abstr., Sage Urb.Stud.Abstr., Soc.Sci.Ind. (1994-), SSCI, Stud.Wom.Abstr. **Document type:** academic/scholarly publication.
●Also available online. Vendor(s): Ovid Technologies.
—BLDSC (4983.680000); Faxon; Genuine Article; SWETS; UMI; UnCover. **CCC.**
Supersedes: Family in Historical Perspective (ISSN 0360-3598)
Description: Focuses on historically based studies on families, kinship, and demography.

301 US ISSN 0192-513X
HQ1
JOURNAL OF FAMILY ISSUES. 1980. bi-m. $67 to individuals; institutions $221 (effective Sep. 1995). (National Council on Family Relations) Sage Publications, Inc., 2455 Teller Rd., Thousand Oaks, CA 91320. TEL 805-499-0721. FAX 805-499-0871. E-mail: libraries@sagepub.com. (Overseas subscr. to: Sage Publicatons Ltd., 6 Bonhill St., London EC2A 4PU, England; Sage Publications India Pvt. Ltd., P.O. Box 4215, New Delhi 110 048, India) Ed. Patricia A. Voydanoff. adv. circ. 1,500. (also avail. in microform from WSH,PMC; back issues avail.; reprint service avail.) **Indexed:** C.I.J.E., Curr.Cont., Curr.Lit.Fam.Plan., IMFL, Psychol.Abstr. (1990-), Sage Fam.Stud.Abstr., Soc.Work Res.& Abstr., Sociol.Abstr., SSCI, Viol.& Abuse Abstr. **Document type:** academic/scholarly publication.
●Also available online. Vendor(s): Ovid Technologies.
—BLDSC (4983.690000); Faxon; Genuine Article; SWETS; UMI; UnCover. **CCC.**
Description: Covers contemporary social issues and problems of marriage and family life.

JOURNAL OF FAMILY LAW. see *LAW — Family And Matrimonial Law*

JOURNAL OF FAMILY THERAPY. see *MEDICAL SCIENCES — Psychiatry And Neurology*

JOURNAL OF FAMILY VIOLENCE. see *CRIMINOLOGY AND LAW ENFORCEMENT*

JOURNAL OF FLUENCY DISORDERS. see *PSYCHOLOGY*

JOURNAL OF FORECASTING. see *BUSINESS AND ECONOMICS — Management*

JOURNAL OF GROUP PSYCHOTHERAPY, PSYCHODRAMA & SOCIOMETRY. see *PSYCHOLOGY*

301 US ISSN 0022-1465
R11 CODEN: JHSBA5
JOURNAL OF HEALTH AND SOCIAL BEHAVIOR. 1960. q. $40 to individuals (foreign $50); institutions $80 (foreign $90). American Sociological Association, 1722 N St., N.W., Washington, DC 20036. TEL 202-833-3410. FAX 202-785-0146. Ed. Ronald Angel. adv.; bk.rev.; charts; illus.; index. circ. 5,000. (also avail. in microform from MIM,UMI; reprint service avail. from UMI) **Indexed:** Abstr.Anthropol., Abstr.Health Care Manage.Stud., Abstr.Hyg., Adol.Ment.Hlth.Abstr., ASSIA, Biol.Abstr., CINAHL, Curr.Cont., Excerp.Med., FAMLI, Hosp.Lit.Ind., IMFL, Ind.Med., Int.Nurs.Ind., Lang.& Lang.Behav.Abstr., Mid.East: Abstr.& Ind., Mult.Ed.Abstr., Psychol.Abstr. (1960-), Sage Fam.Stud.Abstr., Sage Pub.Admin.Abstr., Soc.Sci.Ind., Soc.Work Res.& Abstr., Sociol.Abstr. (1961-), Sp.Ed.Needs Abstr., SSCI, Stud.Wom.Abstr., Trop.Dis.Bull. **Document type:** academic/scholarly publication.
●Also available online. Vendor(s): University Microfilms International.
—BLDSC (4996.730000); Faxon; Genuine Article; SWETS; UMI; UnCover.
Formerly: Journal of Health and Human Behavior (ISSN 0095-9006)
Description: Publishes reports of empirical studies, theoretical analyses, and synthesizing reviews that employ a sociological perspective to clarify aspects of social life bearing on human health and illness, both physical and mental.
Refereed Serial

301 UK ISSN 0952-1909
HM104
JOURNAL OF HISTORICAL SOCIOLOGY. 1988. q. £98($183) (foreign £118) (effective 1996). Basil Blackwell Ltd., 108 Cowley Rd., Oxford OX4 1JF, England. TEL 0865-791100. FAX 0865-791347. TELEX 837022-OXBOOK-G. (US addr.: Basil Blackwell, Journals Dept., Three Cambridge Center, Cambridge, MA 02142, US) Ed.Bd. (reprint service avail. from UMI) **Indexed:** Sociol.Abstr. (1981-).
—BLDSC (5000.493000); Faxon; Genuine Article; SWETS; UMI; UnCover. **CCC.**
Description: Provides an international forum for historically-informed reflection on human society.

JOURNAL OF HOMOSEXUALITY. see *HOMOSEXUALITY*

301 CN ISSN 0847-2971
JC578
JOURNAL OF HUMAN JUSTICE. 1989. s-a. Human Justice Collective, Dept. of Anthropology and Sociology, U. of British Columbia, 6303 N.W. Marine Dr., Vancouver, BC V6T 2B2, Canada. TEL 604-228-2240. E-mail: MACD@UBCMTSG. Ed. Brian MacLean. **Document type:** academic/scholarly publication.
—BLDSC (5003.416500).
Description: Offers a forum for progressive analyses of economic, gender, legal and political relations as they pertain to studies of social justice in Canadian society and abroad.
Refereed Serial

JOURNAL OF HUMAN VALUES. see *PHILOSOPHY*

JOURNAL OF INTERGROUP RELATIONS. see *POLITICAL SCIENCE — Civil Rights*

JOURNAL OF INTERNATIONAL STUDENT PERSONNEL. see *EDUCATION — International Education Programs*

JOURNAL OF INTERPERSONAL VIOLENCE; concerned with the study and treatment of victims and perpetrators of physical and sexual violence. see *CRIMINOLOGY AND LAW ENFORCEMENT*

JOURNAL OF LANGUAGE AND SOCIAL PSYCHOLOGY. see *PSYCHOLOGY*

JOURNAL OF MARITAL AND FAMILY THERAPY. see *PSYCHOLOGY*

306.8   US   ISSN 0022-2445
CODEN: JMFAA6
JOURNAL OF MARRIAGE AND THE FAMILY. 1939. q. $95 (foreign $110) (effective 1996). National Council on Family Relations, 3989 Central Ave., N.E., Ste. 550, Minneapolis, MN 55421-3921. TEL 612-781-9331. FAX 612-781-9348. Ed. Robert Milardo. adv.; bk.rev.; charts; index. circ. 7,400. (also avail. in microform from UMI; reprint service avail. from UMI) **Indexed:** Abstr.Crim.& Pen., Abstr.Hyg., Abstr.Soc.Work., Acad.Ind., Adol.Ment.Hlth.Abstr., ASSIA, Biog.Ind., Biol.Abstr., Bk.Rev.Ind. (1965-), C.I.J.E., CERDIC, Child.Bk.Rev.Ind. (1965-), Child Devel.Abstr., Commun.Abstr., Crim.Just.Abstr., Curr.Cont., Curr.Lit.Fam.Plan., Except.Child.Educ.Abstr., Excerp.Med., FAMLI, G.Soc.Sci.& Rel.Per.Lit., Hum.Ind., IMFL, Lang.& Lang.Behav.Abstr., Mag.Ind., Mid.East: Abstr.& Ind., Mult.Ed.Abstr., Past.Care & Couns.Abstr., Popul.Ind., Psychol.Abstr., Rehabil.Lit., Rel.Ind.One, Sage Fam.Stud.Abstr., Soc.Sci.Ind., Soc.Work Res.& Abstr., Sociol.Abstr. (1953-), SSCI, Stud.Wom.Abstr., Trop.Dis.Bull. **Document type:** academic/scholarly publication.
●Also available online. Vendor(s): Knight-Ridder, Inc., Ovid Technologies, University Microfilms International.
—BLDSC (5012.175000); Faxon; Genuine Article; SWETS; UMI; UnCover.
Formerly: Marriage and Family Living.
Description: Provides a forum covering theory, research interpretation and critical discussion on subjects related to marriage and the family.

301   UK   ISSN 1359-1835
▼**JOURNAL OF MATERIAL CULTURE.** Announced for publication in 1996. 3/yr. £26($42) to individuals; institutions £80($128) (effective 1996). Sage Publications Ltd., 6 Bonhill St., London EC2A 4PU, England. TEL 44-171-3740645. FAX 44-171-3748741. E-mail: folan@sageltd.co.uk. Ed.Bd.
Description: Explores the relationship between artefacts and social relations.

301   US   ISSN 0022-250X
HM1
JOURNAL OF MATHEMATICAL SOCIOLOGY. 1971. 8/yr. (in 2 vols., 4 nos./vol.). 200 ECU per vol. (effective 1996). Gordon and Breach Science Publishers, c/o International Publishers Distributor, 820 Town Center Dr., Langhorne, PA 19047. TEL 215-750-2624. FAX 215-750-6343. (Subscr. to: International Publishers Distributor, P.O. Box 90, Reading, Berkshire RG1 8JL, England. TEL 44-173-456-8316) Ed. Patrick Doreian. adv.; index. (also avail. in microform) **Indexed:** Compumath, Curr.Cont., INSPEC, Lang.& Lang.Behav.Abstr., Math.R., Psychol.Abstr., SSCI.
—BLDSC (5012.450000); Faxon; UnCover. **CCC.**
Refereed Serial

301   US   ISSN 1042-8224
HV3176   CODEN: JMSWE5
JOURNAL OF MULTICULTURAL SOCIAL WORK. 1991. q. $75 (foreign $105) (effective 1996). Haworth Press, Inc., 10 Alice St., Binghamton, NY 13904. TEL 607-722-5857; 800-342-9678. FAX 607-722-1424. TELEX 4932599. Ed. Paul R. Keys. (also avail. in microform from UMI; reprint service avail. from HAW) **Indexed:** IMFL, Mult.Ed.Abstr., Soc.Work Res.& Abstr.
—BLDSC (5021.058500); Haworth; UnCover.
Description: Develops knowledge and promotes understanding of the impact of culture, ethnicity, race, and class on the individual, group, organization, and community on the delivery of human services.
Refereed Serial

JOURNAL OF MULTILINGUAL & MULTICULTURAL DEVELOPMENT. see *LINGUISTICS*

300 572 370 900   PH   ISSN 0115-2408
LA1290
JOURNAL OF NORTHERN LUZON; a semi-annual research forum. 1970. s-a. $15. Saint Mary's College of Bayombong, Nueva Vizcaya 3700, Philippines. Ed. Bonifacio V. Ramos. adv.; bk.rev.; bibl. circ. 500. **Indexed:** Ind.Phil.Per. **Document type:** academic/scholarly publication.
Description: Contains articles on ethnic groups of northern Luzon, including the Bontoc, Gaddang and Ifugao.

305.9   AT   ISSN 1320-0038
JOURNAL OF OCCUPATIONAL SCIENCE: AUSTRALIA. 1993. q? Aus.$50 (in U.S. $50; Europe £35). c/o University of South Australia, N. Terrace, Adelaide, S.A. 5000, Australia. TEL 61-8-3022693. FAX 61-8-3022645. Ed. Ann Wilcock. adv.; bk.rev. circ. 200. **Document type:** academic/scholarly publication.
—BLDSC (5026.130000).
Description: Publishes discussion papers and research articles promoting the study of humans as occupational beings.
Refereed Serial

JOURNAL OF ORGANIZATIONAL BEHAVIOUR. see *PSYCHOLOGY*

301   UK   ISSN 0306-6150
HD1513.A3
THE JOURNAL OF PEASANT STUDIES. 1973. q. £45($70) to individuals; institutions £135 ($195) (effective 1996). Frank Cass, Newbury House, 890-900 Eastern Ave., Newbury Park, Ilford, Essex IG2 7HH, England. TEL 44-181-599-8866. FAX 44-181-599-0984. E-mail: 100067,1576@compuserve.com. Ed.Bd. adv.; B&W page £195 ($275); adv. contact: Anne Kidson. bk.rev.; index. (also avail. in microform from UMI; back issues avail.) **Indexed:** A.I.C.P., Abstr.Rural Dev.Trop., Amer.Hist.& Life, Anthropol.Lit., Asian-Pac.Econ.Lit., ASSIA, Cott.& Trop.Fibr.Abstr., Curr.Cont., Documentatieblad, E.I., Geo.Abstr., Hist.Abstr., IDA, Int.Lab.Doc., Int.Polit.Sci.Abstr., Lang.& Lang.Behav.Abstr., Mid.East: Abstr.& Ind., Mult.Ed.Abstr., P.A.I.S., Polit.Sci.Abstr., Rural Devel.Abstr., Rural Recreat.Tour.Abstr., SSCI, Stud.Wom.Abstr., World Agri.Econ.& Rural Sociol.Abstr. **Document type:** academic/scholarly publication.
—BLDSC (5030.150000); Faxon; Genuine Article; SWETS; UMI; UnCover. **CCC.**
Description: Examines the role of peasants in political, economic, and social change worldwide.
Refereed Serial

301   US   ISSN 0047-2697
HM1
JOURNAL OF POLITICAL AND MILITARY SOCIOLOGY. 1973. s-a. $30 to individuals; institutions $37. c/o Dr. Constantine P. Danopoulos, Department of Political Science, San Jose State University, San Jose, CA 95195-0119. (Subscr. to: George A. Kourvetaris, Department of Sociology, Northern Illinois University, Dekalb, IL 60115. TEL 815-753-6433) Eds. George A. Kourvetaris, Betty Dobratz. adv.; bk.rev.; cum.index. circ. 3,000. (also avail. in microform from UMI; reprint service avail. from SCH,UMI) **Indexed:** A.B.C.Pol.Sci., Abstr.Mil.Bibl., Air Un.Lib.Ind., Amer.Bibl.Slavic & E.Eur.Stud., Amer.Hist.& Life, Curr.Cont., Hist.Abstr., Int.Polit.Sci.Abstr., Lang.& Lang.Behav.Abstr., Mid.East: Abstr.& Ind., P.A.I.S., Polit.Sci.Abstr., PROMT, Sage Pub.Admin.Abstr., Sociol.Abstr., SSCI. **Document type:** academic/scholarly publication.
—BLDSC (5040.845000); Faxon; Genuine Article; SWETS; UMI.

JOURNAL OF RURAL DEVELOPMENT. see *POLITICAL SCIENCE*

JOURNAL OF RURAL HEALTH. see *MEDICAL SCIENCES*

301.35   UK   ISSN 0743-0167
HT401   CODEN: JRSTFW
JOURNAL OF RURAL STUDIES. 1985. q. £226($360) (effective 1996). Elsevier Science Ltd., Pergamon, P.O. Box 800, Kidlington, Oxford OX5 1DX, England. TEL 44-1865-843000. FAX 44-1865-843010. E-mail: nlinfo-f@elsevier.nl; usinfo-f@elsevier.com; forinfo-kyf04035@niftyserve.or.jp; Site addr.: http://www.elsevier.nl/. (Subscr. in U.S. and Canada to: Elsevier Science, 660 White Plains Rd., Tarrytown, NY 10591-5153. TEL 914-524-9200. FAX 914-333-2444) Ed. Paul Cloke. adv. (also avail. in microfilm from UMI) **Indexed:** Asian-Pac.Econ.Lit., Cott.& Trop.Fibr.Abstr., Curr.Adv.Ecol.Sci., Curr.Cont., Environ.Abstr., Environ.Per.Bibl. (1990-), Geo.Abstr., IDA, Risk Abstr., Rural Devel.Abstr., Soils & Fert, Triticale Abstr., World Agri.Econ.& Rural Sociol.Abstr. **Document type:** academic/scholarly publication.
—BLDSC (5052.128900); Faxon; Genuine Article; SWETS; UMI; UnCover. **CCC.**
Description: Forum for research in the broad spectrum of rural issues, including society, demography, housing, employment, education, land-use, recreation, agriculture and conservation.
Refereed Serial

301   UK
JOURNAL OF SEX. 1976. m. £12. G.S.P. Ltd., Gadoline House, Whyteleafe, Surrey, England. Ed. James Hughes. adv.; bk.rev. circ. 50,000.

JOURNAL OF SEX RESEARCH. see *PSYCHOLOGY*

JOURNAL OF SOCIAL DISTRESS AND THE HOMELESS. see *SOCIAL SERVICES AND WELFARE*

301 900   US   ISSN 0022-4529
HN1
JOURNAL OF SOCIAL HISTORY. 1967. q. $30 to individuals; institutions $70; students $20 (effective Jun. 1995). Carnegie - Mellon University Press, Schenley Park, Pittsburgh, PA 15213. TEL 412-268-2884. FAX 412-268-5288. E-mail: psoq@andrew.cum.edu. Ed. Peter N. Stearns. adv.; bk.rev.; charts; stat.; index. circ. 1,900. (also avail. in microform from MIM,UMI; reprint service avail. from UMI, SCH) **Indexed:** Amer.Bibl.Slavic & E.Eur.Stud., Amer.Hist.& Life, Arts & Hum.Cit.Ind., Bk.Rev.Ind. (1984-), Child.Bk.Rev.Ind. (1984-), Crim.Just.Abstr., Curr.Cont., Hist.Abstr., Lang.& Lang.Behav.Abstr., Mid.East: Abstr.& Ind., Sage Fam.Stud.Abstr., Soc.Sci.Ind., Sociol.Abstr., SSCI, Stud.Wom.Abstr. **Document type:** academic/scholarly publication.
●Also available online. Vendor(s): University Microfilms International.
—BLDSC (5064.754000); Faxon; Genuine Article; SWETS; UMI; UnCover. **CCC.**
Description: Covers all aspects of social history, including all time periods and geographical areas. Focuses on new topics, methodologies and comparisons.

JOURNAL OF SOCIAL ISSUES. see *PSYCHOLOGY*

301   UK   ISSN 0047-2794
HV1
JOURNAL OF SOCIAL POLICY. 1972. q. £86($149) (effective 1996). (Social Policy Association) Cambridge University Press, Edinburgh Bldg., Shaftesbury Rd., Cambridge CB2 2RU, England. TEL 01223-312393. FAX 01223-315052. TELEX 851817256. (N. American addr.: Cambridge University Press, Journals Dept., 40 W. 20th St., New York, NY 10011. TEL 212-924-3900. FAX 212-691-3239) Eds. Miriam David, Dulcie Groves. adv.; bk.rev.; index. (also avail. in microform from UMI; back issues avail.; reprint service avail. from SWZ) **Indexed:** A.B.C.Pol.Sci., Abstr.Hyg., ASSIA, Curr.Cont., Geo.Abstr., IMFL, Int.Lab.Doc., Int.Polit.Sci.Abstr., Lang.& Lang.Behav.Abstr., Med.Care Rev., Mid.East: Abstr.& Ind., P.A.I.S., PHRA, Polit.Sci.Abstr., PSI, Psychol.Abstr., Soc.Sci.Ind., Sociol.Abstr., Sociol.Educ.Abstr., SSCI, Stud.Wom.Abstr., Trop.Dis.Bull., World Bibl.Soc.Sec. **Document type:** academic/scholarly publication.
—BLDSC (5064.780000); Faxon; Genuine Article; SWETS; UMI; UnCover. **CCC.**
Description: Provides a theoretical, historical analysis of social policy worldwide, and investigation of processes and obstacles to enacting social policy at local and national levels.

SOCIOLOGY

360 301   US   ISSN 0191-5096
HN1
JOURNAL OF SOCIOLOGY AND SOCIAL WELFARE. 1973. q. $32 to individuals (foreign $38); institutions $69 (foreign $77) (effective 1995-1996). Western Michigan University, School of Social Work, c/o Gary Mathews, Manag. Ed., Kalamazoo, MI 49008-5034. TEL 616-387-3198. FAX 616-387-3217. E-mail: Gary.Mathews@wmich.edu. Ed. Robert D. Leighninger, Jr. adv.; bk.rev.; index, cum.index; circ. 650 (paid). (also avail. in microform from UMI; back issues avail.; reprint service avail. from UMI) Indexed: Adol.Ment.Hlth.Abstr., ASSIA, Lang.& Lang.Behav.Abstr., Mid.East: Abstr.& Ind., PSI, Psychol.Abstr. (1974-), Soc.Work. Res.& Abstr., Sociol.Abstr. (1973-). **Document type:** academic/scholarly publication.
●Also available online.
—BLDSC (5064.935000); Faxon; UnCover. **CCC.**
   Description: Presents articles on the analysis of social welfare institutions, policies and problems. Attempts to bridge the gap between social science theory and social work practice.
   Refereed Serial

JOURNAL OF SPORT AND SOCIAL ISSUES. see SPORTS AND GAMES

301   US   ISSN 1043-4070
HQ12   CODEN: JHSEEI
JOURNAL OF THE HISTORY OF SEXUALITY. 1990. q. $35 to individuals; institutions $82; students $24. University of Chicago Press, Journals Division, 5720 S. Woodlawn Ave., Chicago, IL 60637. TEL 312-753-3347. FAX 312-753-0811. TELEX 25-4603. (Subscr. to: Box 37005, Chicago, IL 60637) Ed. John C. Fout. **Indexed:** Amer.Hist.& Life (1993-), Hist.Abstr. (1993-).
—BLDSC (5002.050000); Faxon; Genuine Article; SWETS; UMI; UnCover. **CCC.**
   Description: Examines the history of sexuality in all its expressions, recognizing various differences of class, culture, gender, race, and sexual orientation. Provides a forum for historical, critical and theoretical research in the field. Presents original articles and critical reviews from historians and social scientists worldwide.
   Refereed Serial

301   US   ISSN 1054-1802
HT123
JOURNAL OF URBAN AND CULTURAL STUDIES. 1990. s-a. $16 to individuals; institutions $32 (typically set in June). University of Massachusetts, Boston, Department of English, 100 Morissey Blvd., Boston, MA 02125. Ed. Francisco Colina. adv.; bk.rev. (back issues avail.) **Indexed:** Alt.Press Ind., Sociol.Educ.Abstr. **Document type:** academic/scholarly publication.
—**CCC.**

JUNGE KIRCHE; Zeitschrift europaeischer Christinnen und Christen. see RELIGIONS AND THEOLOGY

301 572   MY   ISSN 0126-9518
JURNAL ANTROPOLOGI DAN SOSIOLOGI. (Text in English and Malay) 1972. a. M.$10. (National University of Malaysia, Department of Anthropology and Sociology - Universiti Kebangsaan Malaysia) Penerbit Universiti Kebangsaan Malaysia, 43600 UKM Bangi, Selangor, Malaysia. TELEX UNIKEB MA 31496. Ed. Hock-Tong Cheu. bk.rev.; bibl. circ. 500.
   Formerly (until 1974): Jernal Antropoloji dan Sosiologi.

KAILASH; an interdisciplinary journal of Himalayan studies. see HISTORY — History Of Asia

KAN ANDERS. see POLITICAL SCIENCE — International Relations

301   NR   ISSN 0567-4840
AP9
KANO STUDIES;* journal of Saharan and Sudanic research. 1973. a. £4.50. Bayero University, Kano, Nigeria. TELEX 31121 OXONIA NG. Ed. Ibrahim Yaro Yahaya. adv.; bk.rev. **Indexed:** M.L.A.
—**CCC.**
   Description: Examines Saharan and Sudanic research.

301   PH   ISSN 0115-6292
H1
KAYA TAO. (Text in English) 1980. a. P.30($10.50) (De La Salle University, Behavioral Sciences Department) De La Salle University Press, 2401 Taft Ave., Manila, Philippines. TEL 2-59-48-32. FAX 632-521-9094. adv.; bk.rev. circ. 500. **Document type:** academic/scholarly publication.
   Description: Publishes scholarly articles reflecting significant quantitative or qualitative research. Includes speeches, research reports, and "state of the art" papers.

950   US   ISSN 0898-1930
DS524.7
KHOSANA. 1976. 2/yr. $10 to individuals; institutions $15 (effective Jan. 1990). Association for Asian Studies, Thailand - Laos - Cambodia Studies Group, Department of Anthropology, Northern Illinois University, Dekalb, IL 60115. TEL 815-753-8577. (Subscr. to: Arlene B. Neher, Subscr. Mgr., Continuing Education, Northern Illinois University, DeKalb, IL 60115-2845. TEL 815-753-1458) Ed. Michael R. Rhum. bk.rev.; abstr.; bibl. circ. 300. (back issues avail.)
   Description: Contains academic news of Thai, Laotian and Cambodian studies. Includes information on conferences.

334   IS   ISSN 0334-2182
KIBBUTZ (TEL AVIV); interdisciplinary research review. (Text in English, Hebrew) 1973. a. price varies. Federation of Kibbutz Movements, 10 Dubnov St., Tel Aviv, Israel. Eds. Shimon Shur, Henry Near. circ. 1,250. **Indexed:** Lang.& Lang.Behav.Abstr. **Document type:** academic/scholarly publication.

KINDERSCHUTZ AKTUELL. see SOCIAL SERVICES AND WELFARE

300   NE
KLUWER NIJHOFF STUDIES IN HUMAN ISSUES. (Text in English) irreg. price varies. Kluwer Academic Publishers, Postbus 17, 3300 AA Dordrecht, Netherlands. TEL 31-78-392392. FAX 31-78-392254. TELEX 29245 KAPG NL. (Dist. by: Kluwer Academic Publishers Group, P.O. Box 322, 3300 AH Dordrecht, Netherlands. TEL 31-78-392392. FAX 31-78-546474; N. America dist. addr.: Box 358, Accord Sta., Hingham, MA 02018-0358. TEL 617-871-6600. FAX 617-871-6528) **Document type:** monographic series.
   Refereed Serial

301   US   ISSN 0278-1557
BD175   CODEN: KSCPDO
KNOWLEDGE AND SOCIETY; studies in the sociology of culture past and present. 1978. irreg, vol.8, 1989. $58.50 to institutions. J A I Press Inc., 55 Old Post Rd., No. 2, Box 1678, Greenwich, CT 06836-1678. TEL 203-661-7602. Eds. Henrika Kuklick, Elizabeth Long. **Indexed:** Lang.& Lang.Behav.Abstr., Sociol.Abstr. (1978-).
—BLDSC (5100.441000); UnCover. **CCC.**
   Formerly: Research in Sociology of Knowledge, Science and Art (ISSN 0163-0180)

301   DK   ISSN 0900-9922
KOBENHAVNS UNIVERSITET. SOCIOLOGISK INSTITUT. AFHANDLING. 1981. irreg. DKK 35. University of Copenhagen, Department of Sociology, Linnesgade 22, 1361 Copenhagen K, Denmark. TEL 33-150520. Ed. Birthe Hove.

KODO KEIRYOGAKU/JAPANESE JOURNAL OF BEHAVIORMETRICS. see PSYCHOLOGY

301   DK   ISSN 0900-9876
KOEBENHAVNS UNIVERSITET. SOCIOLOGISK INSTITUT. ARBEJDSPAPIR. 1979. irreg. DKK 15. Koebenhavns Universitet, Sociologisk Institut, Linnesgade 22, 1361 Copenhagen K, Denmark. TEL 33-150520. FAX 33-150520. Ed. Birthe Hove.

301 150   GW   ISSN 0023-2653
HM5
KOELNER ZEITSCHRIFT FUER SOZIOLOGIE UND SOZIALPSYCHOLOGIE. 1927. 4/yr. DM.156 (students DM.92) (effective 1996). Westdeutscher Verlag GmbH, Postfach 1546, 65005 Wiesbaden, Germany. TEL 0611-534389. FAX 0611-534430. Ed.Bd. adv.; bk.rev.; charts; illus.; index, cum.index. circ. 3,200. (reprint service avail. from SCH) **Indexed:** Abstr.Crim.& Pen., Curr.Cont., Ger.J.Psych., P.A.I.S.For.Lang.Ind., Phil.Ind., Psychol.Abstr. (1948-), RILM, Sociol.Abstr. (1952-53), SSCI. **Document type:** academic/scholarly publication.
—BLDSC (5104.500000); Genuine Article; SWETS. **CCC.**

301 320   GW
KRIEGSOPFER- UND BEHINDERTEN. RUNDSCHAU; Zeitschrift fuer Kriegsopfer und Behindertenfragen, Sozialpolitik Versorgungsbrecht und Gesellschaftspolitik. bi-m. DM.60. (Bund Deutscher Kriegs- und Wehrdienstopfer e.V.) Siegrfried Krach, Ed. & Pub., Hallplatz 15, 90402 Nuremberg, Germany. illus.
   Description: For disabled victims of war. Covers social politics, support, rights and sociology.

300   YU   ISSN 0023-5164
AP56
KULTURA; casopis za teoriju i sociologiju kulture i kulturnu politiku. (Text in Serbo-Croatian; summaries and contents in English) 1968. q. $15. Zavod za Proucavanje Kulturnog Razvitka, Rige od Fere 4, 11000 Belgrade, Yugoslavia. Ed. Branimir Stojkovic. bk.rev.; bibl.; charts; illus.; stat. circ. 1,000.

301   DK   ISSN 0904-0919
L O - UNGDOMS BLAD. (Lands Organisation) 1988. s-m. free. L O i Danmark, Rosenoernsalle 12, 1634 Copenhagen V, Denmark. TEL 45-31-35-35-41. FAX 45-35-37-03-12. Ed. Nina Aerenlund. circ. 10,000.

LABOUR MARKET AND SOCIAL POLICY OCCASIONAL PAPERS. see BUSINESS AND ECONOMICS — Labor And Industrial Relations

301   UK
LANCASTER WORKING PAPERS IN POLITICAL ECONOMY. irreg., no.47, 1994. Lancaster University, Department of Sociology, Lancaster LA1 4YL, England. **Document type:** academic/scholarly publication, monographic series.
—BLDSC (5145.860000).
   Formerly (until 1994): Lancaster Regionalism Group. Working Paper.

LAND REFORM, LAND SETTLEMENT AND COOPERATIVES. see AGRICULTURE — Agricultural Economics

LANGAGE ET SOCIETE. see LINGUISTICS

LANGUAGE, CULTURE AND CURRICULUM. see LINGUISTICS

LANGUAGE SCIENCES; a world journal of the sciences of language. see LINGUISTICS

LAVORO E SOCIETA; economia-cultura-politica-sociologia. see BUSINESS AND ECONOMICS

LAW & SOCIETY REVIEW. see LAW

LEADERSHIP QUARTERLY; an international journal of political, social and behavioral science. see BUSINESS AND ECONOMICS — Management

334   US   ISSN 0023-9836
LEAVES OF TWIN OAKS. 1967. irreg. $5 to individuals; institutions $10. Twin Oaks Community, Rte. 4, Box 169, Louisa, VA 23093. TEL 703-894-5126. Ed. Steve Kretzmann. illus. circ. 800. (also avail. in microform from UMI; reprint service avail. from UMI) **Document type:** trade publication.
—UMI.

LEISURE INFORMATION QUARTERLY. see LEISURE AND RECREATION

LEISURE STUDIES. see LEISURE AND RECREATION

LENDEMAINS; etudes comparees sur la France - vergleichende Frankreichforschung. see LITERARY AND POLITICAL REVIEWS

LESBIAN AND GAY COUNSELLING NEWS. see
HOMOSEXUALITY

301.2 700 IT
LETTERA INTERNAZIONALE. 1984. q. L.30000. Ediesse S.R.L., Via Goito 39, 00185 Rome, Italy. circ. 5,000. (back issues avail.)

301 UK ISSN 0267-7113
LIBERTARIAN ALLIANCE. SOCIOLOGICAL NOTES. 1985. irreg. £15($30) Libertarian Alliance, 25 Chapter Chambers, Esterbrooke St., London SW1P 4NN, England. TEL 0171-821-5502. FAX 0171-834-2031. E-mail: liberty@capital.demon.co.uk. **Document type:** monographic series.

LIETUVOS MOKSLU AKADEMIJA. FILOSOFIJA, SOCIOLOGIJA. see *PHILOSOPHY*

LIFE-SPAN DEVELOPMENT AND BEHAVIOR. see *PSYCHOLOGY*

350.865 FR ISSN 0753-1419
LOGEMENT ET FAMILLE; le reveil des locataires. m. Confederation Nationale du Logement, 8 rue Meriel, 93100 Montreuil, France. Ed. Jean-Pierre Giacono. **Document type:** newspaper.

LOISIR ET SOCIETE/SOCIETY AND LEISURE. see *LEISURE AND RECREATION*

LONDON JOURNAL. see *HISTORY — History Of Europe*

306.84 US
LOVING MORE. 1984. q. $30. P E P Publishing, Box 6306, Ocean View, HI 96737. TEL 808-929-9691. FAX 808-929-9831. Ed. Ryam Nearing. adv.; bk.rev.
Formerly (until 1991): P E P Talk - Group Marriage News.
Description: Focuses on topics relating to new paradigm relationships, including interviews, analysis of theories and ideas, children, finances, health concerns and related issues.

LUA NOVA; cultura e politica. see *POLITICAL SCIENCE*

301 YU ISSN 0352-4973
LUCA; casopis za filozofiju i sociologiju. 1984. 2/yr. Centar za Informativnu Djelatnost, Novice Cerovica 30, 81400 Niksic, Montenegro, Yugoslavia. (Co-sponsor: O.S.I.Z. Kulture i Naucnih Djelatnosti) circ. 1,000.

301.2 PL ISSN 0076-1435
GR1
LUD. (Text in Polish; summaries in English and German) 1895. a. price varies. Polskie Towarzystwo Ludoznawcze, Ul. Szewska 36, 50-139 Wroclaw, Poland. (Dist. by: Ars Polona, Krakowskie Przedmiescie 7, Warsaw, Poland) Ed. Zbigniew Jasiewicz. bk.rev.; index. circ. 800. **Indexed:** A.I.C.P., Anthropol.Lit.

301 SW ISSN 1102-4712
LUND DISSERTATIONS IN SOCIOLOGY. (Text in English, Swedish) 1992. irreg. price varies. Lund University Press, P.O. Box 141, S-221 00, Lund, Sweden. TEL 46-46-30-53-38. FAX 46-46-30-53-38. E-mail: Order@Studli.se. Ed. B. Gesser. **Document type:** academic/scholarly publication.

301.4 612 US ISSN 0271-0846
LUZ. 1953. m. $15. International Publishing Company, Inc., 10100 N.W. 25th St., Miami, FL 33172. Ed. Alberto Piccione. adv.; bk.rev.; film rev.; charts; illus. circ. 100,000.

MAINE PROGRESSIVE. see *POLITICAL SCIENCE*

301.4 MW
MALAWI. NATIONAL STATISTICAL OFFICE. FAMILY FORMATION SURVEY (YEAR). 1984. irreg. K.10.50. National Statistical Office, Commissioner for Census and Statistics, P.O. Box 333, Zomba, Malawi. TEL 265-50-522-377. FAX 265-50-523-130. TELEX 44015 CENSUS MI. **Document type:** government publication.

MAN AND LIFE. see *ANTHROPOLOGY*

MANUSIA DAN MASYARAKAT/MAN AND SOCIETY. see *ANTHROPOLOGY*

301 IT
LE MAPPE - CULTURA E SOCIETA. 1982. irreg., no.7, 1993. price varies. Liguori Editore s.r.l., Via Mezzocannone, 19, 80134 Naples, Italy. TEL 081-5527139. Eds. G. Bechelloni, G. Pagliano. **Document type:** monographic series.

301.4 US ISSN 0149-4929
HQ536 CODEN: MFARDJ
MARRIAGE & FAMILY REVIEW. 1978. q. $225 (foreign $315) (effective 1996). Haworth Press, Inc., 10 Alice St., Binghamton, NY 13904. TEL 607-722-5857; 800-342-9678. FAX 607-722-1424. TELEX 4932599. Ed. Marvin B. Sussman. adv.; bk.rev.; abstr.; index. circ. 435. (also avail. in microfiche from UMI; back issues avail.; reprint service avail. from HAW) **Indexed:** Adol.Ment.Hlth.Abstr., Bull.Signal., Chicago Psychoanal.Lit.Ind., IMFL, Mult.Ed.Abstr., Past.Care & Couns.Abstr., PSI, Psychol.Abstr. (1978-), Sage Fam.Stud.Abstr., Soc.Work Res.& Abstr., Sociol.Abstr., Stud.Wom.Abstr., Viol.& Abuse Abstr. **Document type:** academic/scholarly publication.
—BLDSC (5382.860000); Faxon; Genuine Article; Haworth; SWETS; UnCover.
Description: Covers marriage, family planning, and crisis counseling.
Refereed Serial

306.85 640 FI ISSN 0785-756X
MARTHABLADET. (Text in Swedish) 1903. m. FIM 105. Finlands Svenska Marthafoerbund, Lilla Robertsgatan 31 B 24, FIN-00130 Helsinki, Finland. TEL 358-90-665491. FAX 358-90-665175. Ed. Sheila Liljeberg-Elgert.
Former titles (until 1965): Marthabladet-Husmodern (ISSN 0785-7543); (until 1958): Husmodern (ISSN 0785-7535)

301 332.2 301 XR
MASARYKOVA UNIVERSITA. FILOZOFICKA FAKULTA. SBORNIK PRACI. G: RADA SOCIALNEVEDNA. 1957. irreg. (approx. a.). price varies. Masarykova Universita, Filozoficka Fakulta, A. Novaka 1, 660 88 Brno, Czech Republic. FAX 41-211241. bk.rev. **Document type:** proceedings.
Formerly: Universita J.E. Purkyne. Filozoficka Fakulta. Sbornik Praci. G: Rada Socialnevedna (ISSN 0231-5122)
Description: Offers articles about sociology and social work.

301 US ISSN 0743-7528
MATERIAL CULTURE DIRECTORIES. 1988. irreg. price varies. Greenwood Press, Inc. (Subsidiary of: Greenwood Publishing Group Inc.), 88 Post Rd. W., Box 5007, Westport, CT 06881-5007. TEL 203-226-3571. FAX 203-222-1502.

MAXINE'S PAGES. see *POLITICAL SCIENCE*

MEDIA CULTURE AND SOCIETY. see *COMMUNICATIONS — Television And Cable*

MEDIENPSYCHOLOGIE; Zeitschrift fuer Individual- und Massenkommunikation. see *PSYCHOLOGY*

301 IS ISSN 0025-8679
MEGAMOT; behavioural sciences quarterly. (Text in Hebrew; summaries in English) 1949. q. $38. Henrietta Szold Institute, 9 Columbia St., Kiryat Menachem, Jerusalem 96583, Israel. FAX 2-437698. Ed. K. Binyamini. adv.; bk.rev.; abstr.; bibl.; charts; illus.; stat.; cum.index. circ. 1,000. **Indexed:** Ind.Heb.Per., Psychol.Abstr. (1985-), SSCI.
Formerly: Child Welfare Research Quarterly.

300 NE ISSN 0025-9454
MENS EN MAATSCHAPPIJ; tijdschrift voor sociale wetenschappen. 1925. 4/yr. (plus special issue) fl.125 to individuals; students fl.67.50; institutions fl.230 (effective 1994). (Stichting Mens en Maatschappij) Bohn Stafleu Van Loghum B.V., P.O. Box 246, 3990 GA Houten, Netherlands. TEL 31-3403-95711. FAX 31-3403-50903. adv.; bk.rev.; bibl.; index. circ. 2,500. **Indexed:** A.I.C.P., Anthropol.Lit., E.I., Key to Econ.Sci., Sociol.Abstr. (1954-). **Document type:** academic/scholarly publication.
—BLDSC (5678.460000); SWETS.

SOCIOLOGY 6027

301.2 GW ISSN 0543-4726
DER MENSCH ALS SOZIALES UND PERSONALES WESEN. 1963. irreg., vol.11, 1991. price varies. Ferdinand Enke Verlag, Postfach 300366, 70443 Stuttgart, Germany. TEL 0711-135798-0. FAX 0711-135798-30. TELEX 07252275-GTV-D. Ed.Bd. (reprint service avail. from IRC) **Document type:** monographic series.

301 DK ISSN 0901-0025
MICRO PUBLICATIONS. SOCIAL SCIENCE SERIES; a Danish sociological journal. (Text in Scandinavian languages; summaries in English) 1952. 2/yr. $6. Institute for Longitudinal Studies, Peder Hvitfeldts straede 10, 1173 Copenhagen K, Denmark. Ed. Erik Hoegh. bk.rev.; index, cum.index. circ. 500. (also avail. in microfiche) **Indexed:** Amer.Hist.& Life, Hist.Abstr., Lang.& Lang.Behav.Abstr., Sociol.Abstr.
Formerly: Sociologiske Meddeleiser (ISSN 0038-0350)

301 US ISSN 0732-913X
HM1
MID-AMERICAN REVIEW OF SOCIOLOGY. 1976. s-a. $8 to individuals; institutions $20; students $6. Mid-American Review of Sociology Consortium, Department of Sociology, University of Kansas, Lawrence, KS 66045. TEL 913-864-4111. Ed. Jean Van Delinder. adv.; bk.rev. circ. 300. (also avail. in microform from UMI; reprint service avail. from UMI) **Indexed:** Curr.Cont., Psychol.Abstr., Sociol.Abstr. (1976-), SSCI.
—BLDSC (5761.313500); Faxon; UnCover.
Supersedes (as of vol.11): Kansas Journal of Sociology (ISSN 0022-8648)

301 949.7 CI ISSN 0352-5600
DR1231 CODEN: MIGTE9
MIGRACIJSKE TEME/MIGRATION THEMES; casopis za istrazivanje migracija i narodnosti. (Text in Croatian and English; summaries in English) 1985. q. $20 to individuals; institutions $30. Sveuciliste u Zagrebu, Institut za Migracije i Narodnosti - University of Zagreb, Institute for Migration and Nationalities Studies, Trg Stjepana Radica 3, P.P. 294, 41001 Zagreb, Croatia. TEL 385-41-539777. FAX 385-41-518248. Ed. Emil Hersak. bk.rev. circ. 800.
Description: Covers historical and present perspectives of migration and nationalities. Includes socio-economical and political aspects of the studies.

MIGRANTI-PRESS. see *POLITICAL SCIENCE*

301.15 GW ISSN 0721-2887
JV6004
MIGRATION; a European journal of international migration and ethnic relations. 1987. 4/yr. DM.72. Edition Parabolis, Postfach 301125, 10722 Berlin, Germany. TEL 030-4441088. FAX 030-4441085. (reprint service avail. from WSH) **Document type:** academic/scholarly publication.

301 360 AT ISSN 0311-3760
MIGRATION ACTION. (Text and summaries in English) 1974. 3/yr. Aus.$30 to individuals; institutions Aus.$40; foreign Aus.$50 (effective 1992). Ecumenical Migration Centre, 125 Leicester St., Fitzroy, Vic. 3065, Australia. TEL 03-426-0044. FAX 03-416-1827. Ed.Bd. adv.; bk.rev.; illus. circ. 1,000. (back issues avail.) **Indexed:** HR Rep. (1991-), P.A.I.S., Refug.Abstr.
Description: Covers news, views and debates on immigration, ethnic affairs, multiculturalism and community relations.

MIGRATIONS; revue des possibilites d'emploi-outre-mer, etranger. see *OCCUPATIONS AND CAREERS*

301 NE ISSN 0920-2234
MILIEU. 6/yr. fl.95 to individuals; institutions fl.142.50 (foreign fl.143.50) (effective 1994). Uitgeverij Boom, P.O. Box 400, 7940 AK Meppel, Netherlands. TEL 31-5220-57012. FAX 31-5220-53864.
—BLDSC (5767.577000); SWETS.

MINORITY RIGHTS GROUP. REPORT. see *POLITICAL SCIENCE — Civil Rights*

SOCIOLOGY

301 US
MISSISSIPPI STATE UNIVERSITY. SOCIAL RESEARCH REPORT SERIES. 1983. bi-m. free. Mississippi State University, Social Science Research Center, Box 5287, Mississippi State, MS 39762. TEL 601-325-7127. FAX 601-325-7966. Ed. J. Gipson Wells. circ. 700. **Indexed:** Sociol.Abstr. **Document type:** bulletin.
Formerly: Mississippi State University. Sociology Research Report Series.

301 BO
MONOGRAFIAS DE POBLACION Y DESARROLLO. 1974. irreg., no.23, 1985. price varies. Centro de Investigaciones Sociales, Casilla 6931 - C.C., La Paz, Bolivia. **Document type:** monographic series.

301 BO
MONOGRAFIAS DE RECURSOS HUMANOS. 1978. irreg., no.4, 1985. price varies. Centro de Investigaciones Sociales, Casilla 6931 - C.C., La Paz, Bolivia. **Document type:** monographic series.

301.4 BO
MONOGRAFIAS DE SOCIOLOGIA FAMILIAR. 1974. irreg., no.9, 1984. price varies. Centro de Investigaciones Sociales, Casilla 6931 - C.C., La Paz, Bolivia. **Document type:** monographic series.

301 572 NE ISSN 0169-9202
MONOGRAPHS AND THEORETICAL STUDIES IN SOCIOLOGY AND ANTHROPOLOGY IN HONOUR OF NELS ANDERSON. 1972. irreg., vol.28, 1989. price varies. E.J. Brill, P.O. Box 9000, 2300 PA Leiden, Netherlands. TEL 31-71-5353500. FAX 31-71-5317532. TELEX 39296 BRILL NL. (In N. America: E.J. Brill, 24 Hudson St., Kinderhook, NY 12106. TEL 800-962-4406. FAX 518-758-1959) Ed. K. Ishwaran. (back issues avail.) **Document type:** monographic series.
Refereed Serial

301 AT
MORGAN GALLUP POLLS. 1941. w. Aus.$235. Roy Morgan Research, G.P.O. Box 2282U, Melbourne, Vic. 3001, Australia. TEL 61-3-6296888. FAX 61-2-6292350.
Formerly: Australian Gallup Polls.

MULTICULTURAL ISSUES. see *CHILDREN AND YOUTH — For*

MUSIK UND GESELLSCHAFT. see *MUSIC*

301 US ISSN 0077-3212
N A A C P ANNUAL REPORT. 1910. a. $15. National Association for the Advancement of Colored People, 4805 Mt. Hope Dr., Baltimore, MD 21215-3297. TEL 410-358-8900. FAX 410-358-3818. circ. 5,000. (also avail. in microform from UMI) **Document type:** corporate report.

309.1 US ISSN 0893-5998
HM261.A1
N O R C REPORTER. 1967. 3/yr. free. National Opinion Research Center, 1155 E. 60th St., Chicago, IL 60637. TEL 312-702-1200. Ed. Jeff Hackett. circ. 2,500.
Formerly (until 1986): National Opinion Research Center. Newsletter (ISSN 0077-5266)

301 NZ
N Z T B SOCIAL RESEARCH SERIES. 1981. irreg., latest 1988. price varies. New Zealand Tourism Board, Market Research, P.O. Box 95, Wellington, New Zealand. TEL 04-4728-860. FAX 04-4781-736.
Former titles: N Z T D Social Research Series; N Z T P Social Research Series (ISSN 0112-9740)

301 US ISSN 0278-6168
HQ1
NATIONAL COUNCIL ON FAMILY RELATIONS. REPORT. 1955. q. $12. National Council on Family Relations, 3989 Central Ave., N.E., Ste. 550, Minneapolis, MN 55421-3921. TEL 612-781-9331. FAX 612-781-9348. Ed. Kathy Collins Royce. circ. 4,500. (processed) **Document type:** newsletter.
●Also available online.
Formerly: National Council on Family Relations Newsletter.
Description: Features updates on national, international and NCFR Association of councils affairs, broad family field news and current issues in marriage and family life.

NATIONAL REVIEW OF CRIMINAL SCIENCES. see *CRIMINOLOGY AND LAW ENFORCEMENT*

301 CH ISSN 0077-5851
NATIONAL TAIWAN UNIVERSITY JOURNAL OF SOCIOLOGY. Key Title: Guoli Taiwan Daxue Shehui Xuekan. (Text in Chinese and English) 1963. a. $5. National Taiwan University, Department of Sociology, 21 Hsuchow Rd., Taipei, Taiwan 10020, Republic of China. TEL 02-351-4239. Ed. Cheng-han Chang. bk.rev. circ. 500. **Indexed:** Lang.& Lang.Behav.Abstr., Sociol.Abstr. (1978-). **Document type:** academic/scholarly publication.
—BLDSC (5064.931000).

NELEN YUBU. see *RELIGIONS AND THEOLOGY*

572 301.2 HU ISSN 0541-9522
NEPI KULTURA - NEPI TARSADALOM. (Text in Hungarian; summaries in German) 1968. irreg., vol.16, 1991. (Magyar Tudomanyos Akademia, Neprajzi Kutato Csoport) Akademiai Kiado, Publishing House of the Hungarian Academy of Sciences, P.O. Box 245, H-1519 Budapest, Hungary. TEL 181-2134. FAX 166-6466. TELEX 22-6228 AKNYO H. abstr.; bibl.; illus.

301 NE ISSN 0927-0833
NETHERLANDS. SOCIAAL EN CULTUREEL PLANBUREAU. CAHIERS. Key Title: S.C.P. Cahier. (Text in Dutch) 1974. irreg., latest no.110, 1994. price varies. Sociaal en Cultureel Planbureau - Netherlands Social and Cultural Planning Office, Postbus 37, 2280 AA Rijswijk, Netherlands. TEL 31-70-3198700. FAX 31-70-3963000. (Subscr. to: Vuga Uitgeverij B.V., Postbus 16400, 2500 BK The Hague, Netherlands. TEL 31-70-361-4011) **Document type:** government publication, academic/scholarly publication.

301 NE ISSN 0922-8772
NETHERLANDS. SOCIAAL EN CULTUREEL PLANBUREAU. SOCIALE AND CULTURELE RAPPORTEN. Key Title: Sociaal en Cultureel Rapport. (Text in Dutch, English) 1975. biennial. $75. Sociaal en Cultureel Planbureau - Social and Cultural Planning Office, Postbus 37, 2280AA Rijswijk, Netherlands. TEL 31-70-3198700. FAX 31-70-3963000. (Subscr. to: Vuga Uitgeverij B.V., Postbus 16400, 2500 BK, The Hague, Netherlands. TEL 31-70-3614011) charts; stat. circ. 1,400. **Document type:** government publication, academic/scholarly publication.

301 NE
NETHERLANDS. SOCIAAL EN CULTUREEL PLANBUREAU. STUDIES. 1977. irreg., latest no.21, 1994. price varies. Sociaal en Cultureel Planbureau, Postbus 37, 2280 AA Rijswijk, Netherlands. TEL 31-70-3198700. FAX 31-70-3963000. (Subscr. to: Vuga Uitgeverij B.V., Postbus 16400, 2500 BK The Hague, Netherlands. TEL 31-70-3614011) **Document type:** government publication, academic/scholarly publication.

301 NE ISSN 0924-1477
NETHERLANDS JOURNAL OF SOCIAL SCIENCES. (Text in English) 1963. s-a. fl.95 (foreign fl.125) (effective 1994). (Netherlands Sociological and Anthropological Society - Netherlands Sociologica and Anthropological Society) Van Gorcum en Co. B.V., P.O. Box 43, 9400 AA Assen, Netherlands. TEL 31-5920-46864. FAX 31-5920-72064. Ed. K. Verrips. adv.; bk.rev.; index. circ. 3,500. **Indexed:** ASSIA, Curr.Cont., E.I., Int.Polit.Sci.Abstr., Lang.& Lang.Behav.Abstr., Mid.East: Abstr.& Ind., Mult.Ed.Abstr., Risk Abstr., Rural Recreat.Tour.Abstr., Sociol.Abstr., Sociol.Educ.Abstr., SSCI, Stud.Wom.Abstr., World Agri.Econ.& Rural Sociol.Abstr. **Document type:** academic/scholarly publication.
—BLDSC (6077.020500); Genuine Article; SWETS; UnCover. **CCC.**
Former titles (until 1989): Netherlands' Journal of Sociology (ISSN 0038-0172); (until 1975): Sociologia Neerlandica (ISSN 0920-4490)

300 GW ISSN 0028-3304
DIE NEUE ORDNUNG. 1946. 6/yr. DM.49. Institut fuer Gesellschaftswissenschaften Walberberg e.V., Simrockstr. 19, 53113 Bonn, Germany. TEL 0228-222323. FAX 0228-220244. Ed. Wolfgang Ockenfels. adv.; bk.rev.; index. circ. 2,400. (back issues avail.) **Indexed:** P.A.I.S.For.Lang.Ind. **Document type:** academic/scholarly publication.
Description: Discussion of current history, social issues and changes in society.

NEW DOCTOR. see *MEDICAL SCIENCES*

NEW ENVIRONMENT BULLETIN. see *NEW AGE PUBLICATIONS*

NEW GERMAN-AMERICAN STUDIES/NEUE DEUTSCHE-AMERIKANISCHE STUDIEN. see *HUMANITIES: COMPREHENSIVE WORKS*

NEW LIFE. see *RELIGIONS AND THEOLOGY — Roman Catholic*

301 US ISSN 1056-1439
HQ1031
NEW PEOPLE; the journal for the human race. 1990. bi-m. $25. Walker-Hollis Publishing, Box 47490, Oak Park, MI 48237. TEL 810-541-6943. E-mail: newpeople@aol.com. Ed. Yvette Walker Hollis; Pub. Yvette Walker Hollis. adv. contact: Daniel Hollis. bk.rev.; film rev.; circ. 2,000 (paid). (back issues avail.) **Document type:** consumer publication.
Description: Takes an inside, authentic look at today's multiracial life-style, interracial relationships and marriage, transracial adoption, and multiracial parents and heritage.

309 360 UK ISSN 0960-5231
NEW REVIEW. 1989. bi-m. £25 to individuals; organizations £30; institutions £75. Low Pay Unit, 29 Amwell St., London EC1R 1UN, England. TEL 0171-713-7616. FAX 0171-713-7581. Ed. Peta Lunberg. adv.; bk.rev. circ. 1,000. (back issues avail.) **Document type:** academic/scholarly publication.
—BLDSC (6087.760895).
Description: Carries reviews of research into causes, cures and the extent of poverty. Includes case histories and advice on individual rights.

NEW SCHOOL OBSERVER. see *COLLEGE AND ALUMNI*

NEW ZEALAND RATIONALIST AND HUMANIST; a journal on philosophy, science, religion, literature & society. see *PHILOSOPHY*

301 US
NEWS OF THE WEIRD. 7/yr. $11. Box 8306, St. Petersburg, FL 33738. Ed. Chuck Shepherd.

NIGERIAN JOURNAL OF ECONOMIC & SOCIAL STUDIES. see *BUSINESS AND ECONOMICS*

NINE; a journal of baseball history and social policy perspectives. see *SPORTS AND GAMES — Ball Games*

NONVIOLENT SANCTIONS; news from the Albert Einstein Institution. see *POLITICAL SCIENCE*

NORTH AMERICAN CULTURE. see *GEOGRAPHY*

NORTH AMERICAN FARMER. see *AGRICULTURE*

NORTH-EAST INDIA COUNCIL FOR SOCIAL SCIENCE RESEARCH. JOURNAL. see *POLITICAL SCIENCE*

NOTES AFRICAINES. see *POLITICAL SCIENCE*

NOUVELLE REVUE D'ETHNOPSYCHIATRIE. see *MEDICAL SCIENCES — Psychiatry And Neurology*

NOUVELLES PRATIQUES SOCIALES. see *SOCIAL SERVICES AND WELFARE*

NUOVA EUROPA. see *ART*

O P T: ONE PARENT TIMES. see *CHILDREN AND YOUTH — About*

OESTERREICHISCHE OSTHEFTE. see *POLITICAL SCIENCE*

301 AU
OESTERREICHISCHE ZEITSCHRIFT FUER SOZIOLOGIE. q. S.250. (Oesterrichische Gesellschaft fuer Soziologie) Compress Verlagsgesellschaft mbH, Jenullgasse 4, Postfach 231, A-1141 Vienna, Austria. TEL 01-8946449. FAX 01-8946523. Ed. Albert Kaufmann. adv.; bk.rev. **Document type:** academic/scholarly publication.

301　　　　　　　GW　ISSN 1011-0070
HM5
OESTERREICHISCHE ZEITSCHRIFT FUER SOZIOLOGIE. 1976. q. DM.58 (students DM.43) (effective 1996). (Verwaltungsakademie des Bundes, AU) Westdeutscher Verlag GmbH, Postfach 1546, 65005 Wiesbaden, Germany. TEL 0611-534389. FAX 0611-534430. Ed. Andreas Balog. **Document type:** academic/scholarly publication.
—BLDSC (6309.750000).

OMEGA: JOURNAL OF DEATH AND DYING. see PSYCHOLOGY

306.7 613.9　　　AT　ISSN 1036-8124
ON THE LEVEL. 1978. q. Aus.$49. Family Planning N.S.W., 328-336 Liverpool Rd., Ashfield, N.S.W. 2131, Australia. TEL 61-2-716-6099. Ed. Victoria Smith. adv.; bk.rev.; charts; illus.; index. circ. 1,500. (back issues avail.) **Indexed:** Stud.Wom.Abstr., Wom.Stud.Abstr. (1981-1990). **Document type:** academic/scholarly publication.
●Also available on CD-ROM.
—BLDSC (6256.707000); UnCover.
Former titles (until 1991): Healthright (ISSN 0725-1688); (until 1981): Family Planning Information (ISSN 0155-2449)
Description: Interdisciplinary publication on the social, psychological, and medical aspects of sexuality, contraception and health, of interest to health and welfare professionals.
Refereed Serial

ONTARIO FAMILY LAW QUANTUM SERVICE. see LAW — Family And Matrimonial Law

ONTARIO SYMPOSIA ON PERSONALITY AND SOCIAL COGNITION SERIES. see PSYCHOLOGY

OPINION. see PHILOSOPHY

301　　　　　　　SW　ISSN 0349-6546
OTTAR; om sexualitet, samlevnad, samhaelle. 1971. q. SEK 280 in Sweden; Nordic and Baltic countries SEK 315; elsewhere SEK 325. R F S U, P.O. Box 12128, S-102 24 Stockholm, Sweden. FAX 46-8-653-08-23. (Subscr. to: PROGEK, P.O. Box 31003, S-400 32 Goeteborg, Sweden. TEL 46-31-24-34-25) Ed. Ingrid Hagman.
Former titles (until 1981): R F S U - Bulletin (ISSN 0348-6419); (until 1977): R F S U - Bulletin om Sex och Samlevnad (ISSN 0346-0002)

341.1 320　　　　CN　ISSN 0030-686X
OUR GENERATION. 1961. s-a. $35 to individuals for 2 yrs.; institutions Can.$48; students Can.$30. 3981 St. Laurent Blvd., No. 888, Montreal, PQ H2W 1Y5, Canada. TEL 514-844-4076. (Subscr. to: P.O. Box 1258, Succ. Place du Parc, Montreal, PQ H2W 2R3, Canada) Ed. Dimitrios Roussopoulos. adv.; bk.rev.; film rev.; bibl.; illus.; index. circ. 8,500. circ. in microform from UMI,MML; reprint service avail. from UMI. **Indexed:** Alt.Press Ind., Can.B.P.I., Can.Per.Ind., CMI, Fut.Surv., Peace Res.Abstr., Polit.Sci.Abstr.
—BLDSC (6314.326000); UMI.
Formerly: Our Generation Against Nuclear War.
Description: An international journal of critical social theory.

301 572　　　　　CN
P.E.I. COMMUNITY STUDIES. (Prince Edward Island) 1974. irreg. price varies. University of Prince Edward Island, Department of Sociology and Anthropology, Charlottetown, PE C1A 4P3, Canada. TEL 902-566-0306. FAX 902-566-0420. Ed. Satadal Dasgupta. circ. controlled. **Document type:** academic/scholarly publication.

PARENTING STUDIES. see PSYCHOLOGY

301.4 362.7　　　GW　ISSN 0176-2982
PATEN; Mitteilung der Vereinigung der Pflege- und Adoptiveltern im Lande Nordrhein-Westfalen. 1984. q. DM.13. Vereinigung der Pflege- und Adoptiveltern im Lande Nordrhein-Westfalen e.V., Bochumer Landstr. 215, 45276 Essen, Germany. TEL 0201-501440. circ. 700. (back issues avail)
Description: Provides reports and information for the parents of adopted and fostercare children and professionals in related fields.

PEACE & CHANGE; a journal of peace research. see POLITICAL SCIENCE — International Relations

PENSIERO POLITICO; rivista di storia delle idee politiche e sociali. see POLITICAL SCIENCE

PENSIERO POLITICO. BIBLIOTECA. see POLITICAL SCIENCE

PEOPLE. see BIRTH CONTROL

PEOPLE AND EDUCATION; the human side of schools. see EDUCATION

PEOPLE SEARCHING NEWS. see SOCIAL SERVICES AND WELFARE

PERIPHERIE; Zeitschrift fuer Politik und Oekonomie in der dritten Welt. see BUSINESS AND ECONOMICS — International Development And Assistance

PERSPECTIVES IN URBAN GEOGRAPHY. see GEOGRAPHY

361.1 301　　　　US　ISSN 1047-0905
HN41
PERSPECTIVES ON SOCIAL PROBLEMS; a research annual. 1989. a. J A I Press, Inc., Box 1678, 55 Old Post Rd., No. 2, Greenwich, CT 06836. Eds. Gale Miller, James A. Holstein.
—UnCover.

PERSPEKTIVEN D S. (Demokratischen Sozialismus) see POLITICAL SCIENCE

301　　　　　　　PE　ISSN 0079-1075
PERU - PROBLEMA. 1969. irreg., no.23, 1994. price varies. (Instituto de Estudios Peruanos) I E P Ediciones, Horacio Urteaga 694, Lima 11, Peru. TEL 51-14-323070. FAX 51-14-324981. E-mail: postmaster@iep.org.pe. bk.rev.

301　　　　　　　PH　ISSN 0031-7810
HM1
PHILIPPINE SOCIOLOGICAL REVIEW. 1953. s-a. P.120($20) Philippine Sociological Society, Box 154, Manila 2801, Philippines. FAX 02-632-921-6159. TELEX INPHILCUL MANILA. Ed. Ricardo G. Abad. adv.; bk.rev.; bibl.; charts; stat.; index, cum.index: 1953-1987. circ. 500. (also avail. in microfilm; microfiche) **Indexed:** A.I.C.P., Abstr.Anthropol., Ind.Phil.Per., Lang.& Lang.Behav.Abstr., M.L.A., Sociol.Abstr. (1953-), SSCI.

PHILOSOPHY OF HISTORY AND CULTURE. see PHILOSOPHY

301　　　　　　　US　ISSN 0031-8906
E185.5
PHYLON; the Atlanta University review of race and culture. 1940-1987; resumed 1992. q. $30 to individuals (foreign $35); institutions $40 (foreign $45). Atlanta University, 223 James P. Brawley Dr., S.W., Atlanta, GA 30314. TEL 404-681-0251. Ed. Wilbur Watson. adv.; bk.rev.; index. circ. 2,200. (also avail. in microform from UMI; reprint service avail. from UMI,KTO) **Indexed:** Acad.Ind., Amer.Hist.& Life (until 1987), Bk.Rev.Ind. (1976-), C.I.J.E., Child.Bk.Rev.Ind. (1976-), Commun.Abstr., Curr.Cont., G.Soc.Sci.& Rel.Per.Lit., Hist.Abstr. (until 1987), Ind.Sel.Per., M.L.A., Mag.Ind., Mid.East: Abstr.& Ind., Mult.Ed.Abstr., P.A.I.S., Psychol.Abstr., Sage Fam.Stud.Abstr., Sage Urb.Stud.Abstr., Soc.Sci.Ind. (until 1994), SSCI. **Document type:** academic/scholarly publication.
—Faxon; UMI; UnCover.
Formerly: Phylon Quarterly.
Description: Examines issues of race and culture as they relate to social and political behaviors and to literary analysis.

PHYSICS AND SOCIETY. see PHYSICS

301 330　　　　UK　ISSN 0141-2779
PLANNING FOR SOCIAL CHANGE. 1976. a. £8000. Henley Centre for Forecasting Ltd., 2 Tudor St., Blackfriars, London EC4Y 0AA, England. TEL 071-353-9961. Ed. Michael Willmott.
Description: Analysis and forecasts of consumer attitudes, motivations and behavior in the UK.

301.2　　　　　　US　ISSN 1068-6762
GV1
PLAY THEORY AND RESEARCH. 1988. q. $55 to non-members; individual members $45 (foreign $77); institutional members $75 (foreign $85). (Association for the Study of Play) Sagamore Publishing, Inc., Box 647, Champaign, IL 61820. TEL 217-351-5076. FAX 217-351-2674. Ed. Dr. Margaret Carlisle Duncan; Pub. Joseph J. Bannon. bk.rev. **Indexed:** Anthropol.Lit., Commun.Abstr., Curr.Cont., Phys.Ed.Ind., Psychol.Abstr., Soc.Sci.Ind., Sportsearch (1988-), SSCI. **Document type:** academic/scholarly publication.
—Faxon; Genuine Article; UnCover. **CCC.**
Supersedes (in 1993): Play and Culture (ISSN 0894-4253)
Description: Stimulates and communicates research, critical thought and theory in all areas related to the topic of play.
Refereed Serial

POLICING AND SOCIETY; an international journal of research & policy. see CRIMINOLOGY AND LAW ENFORCEMENT

POLICY SCIENCES; an international journal devoted to the improvement of policy making. see POLITICAL SCIENCE

POLIS; ricerche e studi su societa e politica in Italia. see POLITICAL SCIENCE

POLISH HISTORICAL LIBRARY. ANTHOLOGIES. MONOGRAPHS. OPERA MINORA. see HISTORY — History Of Europe

301　　　　　　　PL　ISSN 1231-1413
HM1　　　　　　　　　CODEN: PSREFL
POLISH SOCIOLOGICAL REVIEW. (Text in English) 1961. q. $50. Polskie Towarzystwo Socjologiczne - Polish Sociological Association, Ul. Nowy Swiat 72, 00-330 Warsaw, Poland. TEL 48-22-267737. (Dist. by: Ars Polona, Krakowskie Przedmiescie 7, 00-068 Warsaw, Poland) Ed. Witold Morawski. adv.; bk.rev.; index. circ. 430. **Indexed:** ASSIA, Int.Polit.Sci.Abstr., Lang.& Lang.Behav.Abstr., Sociol.Abstr. (1961-), SSCI.
—BLDSC (6543.782000); SWETS.
Formerly (until no.2, 1993): Polish Sociological Bulletin (ISSN 0032-2997)
Description: Papers and reports on various aspects of sociological research and its practical application.

320　　　　　　　US　ISSN 0732-1228
GN492
POLITICAL AND LEGAL ANTHROPOLOGY. 1980. a. $34.95 cloth; paper $21.95. (Association for Political and Legal Anthropology) Transaction Publishers, Transaction Periodicals Consortium, Department 3092, Rutgers University, New Brunswick, NJ 08903. TEL 908-445-2280. FAX 908-445-3138. Ed. Myron J. Aronoff. **Document type:** academic/scholarly publication.
—BLDSC (6543.872100).
Description: Original analyses of political man. Articles cover a wide range of theoretical, conceptual, and methodological approaches to interrelationships among socioeconomic, cultural, and political phenomena.

POLITICAL POWER AND SOCIAL THEORY; a research annual. see POLITICAL SCIENCE

POLITICS AND SOCIETY. see POLITICAL SCIENCE

POLITICS AND SOCIETY IN GERMANY, AUSTRIA AND SWITZERLAND. see POLITICAL SCIENCE

POLITICS AND THE INDIVIDUAL; international journal of political socialization and political psychology. see POLITICAL SCIENCE

301　　　　　　　PL　ISSN 0079-3442
POLSKA AKADEMIA NAUK. ODDZIAL W KRAKOWIE. KOMISJA SOCJOLOGICZNA. PRACE. (Text in Polish; summaries in English, French, Russian) 1963. irreg., no.50, 1989. price varies. Polska Akademia Nauk, Oddzial w Krakowie, Komisja Socjologiczna, Ul. Slawkowska 17, 31-016 Krakow, Poland. TEL 48-12-224853. FAX 48-12-222791. **Document type:** monographic series.

SOCIOLOGY

301.4   FR   ISSN 0182-6220
POMME D'API. (Quarterly supplement avail.: Pomme d'Api Soleil) 1966. m. 365 F. (outside EC 415 F.) Bayard Presse, 3 rue Bayard, 75393 Paris Cedex 08, France. TEL 44-35-60-60. FAX 44-35-60-91. TELEX 648 094 F. (Subscr. to: B.P. 12, 99505 Paris Entreprises, France. TEL 46-30-38-00. FAX 46-30-31-67) adv. circ. 220,000.
    Description: Helps children from 3 to 7 years old become aware of their surroundings.

301   US   ISSN 0735-8741
POPULAR CULTURE ASSOCIATION. NEWSLETTER AND POPULAR CULTURE METHODS. 1971. irreg. membership. (Popular Culture Association) Popular Press, Bowling Green State University, Bowling Green, OH 43403. TEL 409-372-2981. Ed. Michael T. Marsden. adv. circ. 2,500. (also avail. in microform from UMI; reprint service avail. from UMI)
    Incorporates: Popular Culture Association Newsletter (ISSN 0048-4822)

POPULAR MUSIC & SOCIETY. see *MUSIC*

POPULATION RESEARCH LABORATORY. RESEARCH DISCUSSION PAPER SERIES. see *POPULATION STUDIES*

POPULATION TODAY. see *POPULATION STUDIES*

301   PO   ISSN 0870-4406
HD7209
PORTUGAL. INSTITUTO NACIONAL DE ESTATISTICA. ESTATISTICAS DE PROTECCAO SOCIAL, ASSOCIACOES SINDICAIS E PATRONAIS. 1938. a. Esc.2400. Instituto Nacional de Estatistica, Av. Antonio Jose de Almeida, 1078 Lisbon Codex, Portugal. (Subscr. to: Imprensa Nacional, Casa da Moeda, Direccao Comercial, rua D. Francisco Manuel de Melo 5, 1000 Lisbon, Portugal)
    Former titles (until 1985): Portugal. Instituto Nacional de Estatistica. Estatisticas de Seguranca Social, Associacoes Sindicais e Patronais. Continente, Acores e Madeira (ISSN 0870-6506); (until 1978): Portugal. Instituto Nacional de Estatistica. Estatisticas des Associqcoes Sindicais Patronais e Previdencia (ISSN 0377-211X); (until 1974): Portugal. Instituto Nacional de Estatistica. Estatisticas das Organizacoes Sindicais (ISSN 0079-4163)

POUR LA VIE; revue d'etudes familiales. see *POPULATION STUDIES*

PRACTICE (NEW YORK); the magazine of psychology and political economy. see *PSYCHOLOGY*

300   YU   ISSN 0032-6704
PRAKSA; casopis za drustvena pitanja. (Text in Serbo-Croatian) 1970. bi-m. 120 din. (Marksisticki Centar, Titograd) Pobjeda, Bulevar Revolucije, 81000 Titograd, Yugoslavia. Ed. Milija Komatina.

301   US   ISSN 0199-7505
PRIME OF LIFE. 1963. m. $10. Lutheran Social Services of Metropolitan New York, Inc., 27 Park Pl., New York, NY 10007-2502. Ed. Dorothy M. Scholz. circ. 8,000.

PRIMO MAGGIO; saggi e documenti per una storia di classe. see *POLITICAL SCIENCE*

309   BL   ISSN 0555-2176
PROBLEMAS BRASILEIROS; revista mensal de cultura. (Text in Portuguese; summaries in English) 1963. m. Cr.$150. Conselho Tecnico de Economia, Sociologia e Politica, Servico Social do Comercio, Avda. Paulista, 119, 5o andar, 01311-903 Sao Paulo, SP, Brazil. Ed. Rui Nogueira Martins. charts; illus.; stat. **Indexed:** Hisp.Amer.Per.Ind., P.A.I.S.
    —BLDSC (6617.365000).

301   ZR   ISSN 0379-3729
PROBLEMES SOCIAUX ZAIROIS. (Text in French) 1946. q. Centre d'Execution de Programmes Communautaires, 208 av. Kasa-Vubu, Box 1873, Lubumbashi, Zaire. Ed.Bd. bk.rev.; abstr.; charts; illus. **Indexed:** P.L.E.S.A., Trop.Dis.Bull.
    Formerly: Problemes Sociaux Congolais (ISSN 0032-9312)

PROBLEMI DELL'INFORMAZIONE. see *COMMUNICATIONS*

309   GP   ISSN 1141-3565
PROGRES SOCIAL. 1957. w. Rue Toussaint l'Ouverture, 97100 Basse-Terre, Guadeloupe. TEL 81-1041. Ed. Henri Rodes. circ. 5,000. (also avail. in microfilm from UMI)

PROGRESS IN TOURISM AND HOSPITALITY PRACTICE. see *TRAVEL AND TOURISM*

301   GW   ISSN 0342-8176
HB97.5
PROKLA; Zeitschrift fuer kritische Sozialwissenschaft. 1971. 4/yr. DM.58. (Vereinigung zur Kritik der Politischen Oekonomie e.V.) Verlag Westfaelisches Dampfboot, Dorotheenstr. 26a, 48145 Muenster, Germany. TEL 0251-6086080. FAX 0251-6086020. Ed.Bd. adv. circ. 2,000. **Document type:** academic/scholarly publication.
    Formerly (until 1976): Probleme des Klassenkampfs (ISSN 0342-8168)

301 100   GW   ISSN 0940-4147
PROTOSOZIOLOGIE. (Text in English, German) 1991. 2/yr. $38. Stephan-Heise-Str. 56, 60488 Frankfurt a.M., Germany. TEL 069-769461. FAX 069-7988465. Ed. Gerhard Preyer. bk.rev.; circ. 500 (paid). **Indexed:** Sociol.Abstr. **Document type:** academic/scholarly publication.

301   PL   ISSN 0033-2356
HM7
PRZEGLAD SOCJOLOGICZNY. (Text in Polish; summaries in English) 1930. s-a. $55 (effective 1996). Lodzkie Towarzystwo Naukowe, Ul. Piotrowska 179, 90-447 Lodz, Poland. TEL 48-42-361026. FAX 48-42-361995. (Dist. by: Ars Polona, Krakowskie Przedmiescie 7, 00-068 Warsaw, Poland) Ed. Jolanta Kulpinska. bk.rev.; bibl.; charts; index. **Indexed:** Amer.Hist.& Life (until 1990), Hist.Abstr. (until 1990), Lang.& Lang.Behav.Abstr., Sociol.Abstr. (1957-). **Document type:** academic/scholarly publication.
    Description: Methodological aspects of Polish modern sociology and related sciences.

PSYCHOLOGY AND SOCIOLOGY OF SPORT: CURRENT SELECTED RESEARCH. see *PSYCHOLOGY*

PUBLIC PULSE. see *BUSINESS AND ECONOMICS — Marketing And Purchasing*

PUBLIK-FORUM. see *RELIGIONS AND THEOLOGY*

Q J I. (Quarterly Journal of Ideology) see *POLITICAL SCIENCE*

301   IT   ISSN 0033-4952
HM7
QUADERNI DI SOCIOLOGIA. 1951. 3/yr. L.78000 (effective 1995). Rosenberg & Sellier, Via Andrea Doria 14, 10123 Turin, Italy. TEL 39-11-8127820. FAX 39-11-8127744. adv.; bk.rev.; bibl.; index. circ. 1,000. **Indexed:** Amer.Hist.& Life, Hist.Abstr., Int.Polit.Sci.Abstr., Lang.& Lang.Behav.Abstr., P.A.I.S.For.Lang.Ind., Sociol.Abstr. (1952-), SSCI.

QUADERNI STORICI. see *HISTORY*

301   IT   ISSN 0391-8521
QUALITA DELLA VITA. 1978. irreg., latest no.20. price varies. Edizioni Studium, Via Cassiodoro 14, 00193 Rome, Italy. **Document type:** monographic series.

301   US   ISSN 0162-0436
HM1
QUALITATIVE SOCIOLOGY. 1978. q. $265 (foreign $310) (effective 1996). Human Sciences Press, Inc. (Subsidiary of: Plenum Publishing Corp.), 233 Spring St., New York, NY 10013-1578. TEL 212-620-8000. FAX 212-463-0742. TELEX 23-421139. Eds. Jonathan B. Imber, Rosanna Hertz. adv. (also avail. in microform from UMI; reprint service avail. from UMI; back issues avail.) **Indexed:** Adol.Ment.Hlth.Abstr., IMFL, Lang.& Lang.Behav.Abstr., Mult.Ed.Abstr., Psychol.Abstr., Soc.Work Res.& Abstr., Sociol.Abstr. (1973-), Sociol.Educ.Abstr., Sp.Ed.Needs Abstr., Stud.Wom.Abstr. **Document type:** academic/scholarly publication.
    —BLDSC (7168.124500); Faxon; UMI; UnCover. CCC.
    Description: Covers research based on the qualitative interpretation of social life, including theory, fieldwork and ethnography, historical and comparative analyses, and photographic studies.
    Refereed Serial

301 519.5   NE   ISSN 0033-5177
H61   CODEN: QQEJAV
QUALITY AND QUANTITY; international journal of methodology. (Text in English) q. fl.478 to institutions; $306 to institutions in U.S. (effective 1996). Kluwer Academic Publishers, Postbus 17, 3300 AA Dordrecht, Netherlands. TEL 31-78-392392. FAX 31-78-392254. TELEX 29245 KAPG NL. E-mail: SERVICES@WKAP.NL. (Dist. by: Kluwer Academic Publishers Group, P.O. Box 322, 3300 AH Dordrecht. TEL 31-78-392392. FAX 31-78-546474; N. America dist. addr.: Box 358, Accord Sta., Hingham, MA 02018-0358. TEL 617-871-6600. FAX 617-871-6528) Ed. Vittorio Capecchi. bk.rev.; bibl.; charts; index. (also avail. in microform from UMI; back issues avail.; reprint service avail. from SWZ) **Indexed:** ASCA, ASSIA, Aus.Educ.Ind., Compumath, Curr.Cont., Ind.Med., J.Cont.Quant.Meth., Lang.& Lang.Behav.Abstr., Sociol.Abstr. (1967-), SSCI. **Document type:** academic/scholarly publication.
    —BLDSC (7168.135000); Faxon; Genuine Article; SWETS; UMI; UnCover. CCC.
    Description: Publishes papers on causal analysis, models of classification, graph theory applications, mathematical models of voting behavior and social mobility, and other topics related to the devlopment of rigorous scientific methodologies for the social sciences.
    Refereed Serial

300   US   ISSN 0033-6742
R A P. 1969. m. $10. Radicals Against Poverty, 42 Melrose Pl., Montclair, NJ 07042. Ed. Arnie Korotkin. bk.rev. circ. 1,500. (also avail. in microfilm) **Document type:** newsletter.
    Formerly: Vista R A P.

R N D. (Revue Notre-Dame) see *RELIGIONS AND THEOLOGY — Roman Catholic*

301.45   UK   ISSN 0306-3968
HT1501
RACE AND CLASS; a journal for Black and Third World liberation. 1959. q. £16($28) to individuals; institutions £22 ($48). Institute of Race Relations, 2-6 Leeke St., King's Cross Rd., London WC1X 9HS, England. TEL 0171-837-0041. FAX 0171-278-0623. (Subscr. to: Race & Class, 120-126 Lavender Ave., Mitcham, Surrey CR4 3HP, England) Eds. A. Sivanandan, E. Ahmad. adv.; bk.rev.; charts; index. circ. 4,000. **Indexed:** A.I.C.P., Alt.Press Ind., ASSIA, Br.Hum.Ind., CERDIC, Chic.Per.Ind., Curr.Cont.Africa, Documentatieblad, Geo.Abstr., HR Rep. (1985-), IDA, Lang.& Lang.Behav.Abstr., Left Ind. (1986-), Mid.East: Abstr.& Ind., Mult.Ed.Abstr., Soc.Sci.Ind. (1994-), SSCI. **Document type:** academic/scholarly publication.
    —BLDSC (7225.883000); Faxon; SWETS.
    Formerly: Race (ISSN 0033-7277)
    Description: Covers race and group relations.

301.45   UK   ISSN 0033-7358
HT1501
RACE TODAY. 1968. bi-m. £3. Race Today Collective, 165 Railton Rd., Brixton, London SE24 0LU, England. Ed. Leila Hassan. adv.; bk.rev.; index. circ. 5,000. **Indexed:** Curr.Cont.Africa.

144 335   II   ISSN 0033-7625
RADICAL HUMANIST.* (Text in English) 1937. m. Rs.60($40) D-26 Jangpura B, New Delhi 110014, India. Ed. V.M. Tarkunde. adv.; bk.rev. circ. 2,200. (also avail. in microform from UMI; reprint service avail. from UMI)
    —UMI.
    Description: Forum for the scientific study of current sociological, philosophical and cultural issues and problems in the spirit of humanism.

RADIX. see *RELIGIONS AND THEOLOGY*

301   IT   ISSN 0486-0349
RASSEGNA ITALIANA DI SOCIOLOGIA. 1960. q. L.140000. Societa Editrice Il Mulino, Strada Maggiore, 37, 40125 Bologna, Italy. TEL 39-51-256011. FAX 39-51-256034. Ed. Loredana Sciolla. adv.; B&W page L.1500000. index. circ. 1,800. (back issues avail.) **Indexed:** Amer.Hist.& Life, Hist.Abstr., Int.Polit.Sci.Abstr., Lang.& Lang.Behav.Abstr., P.A.I.S.For.Lang.Ind., Psychol.Abstr., Sociol.Abstr. (1960-), Stud.Wom.Abstr.
    —SWETS.

LA RAZA LAW JOURNAL. see *LAW*

READINGS IN SOCIAL AND POLITICAL THEORY. see *POLITICAL SCIENCE*

301   CN   ISSN 0034-1282
RECHERCHES SOCIOGRAPHIQUES. (Text in French) 1960. 3/yr. Can.$28 to individuals; institutions Can.$52; students Can.$19. Universite Laval, Departement de Sociologie, Cite universitaire, Quebec, PQ G1K 7P4, Canada. TEL 418-656-3544. FAX 418-656-3316. Ed. Andree Fortin. adv. contact: Simon Langlois. bk.rev.; abstr.; bibl.; charts; stat.; index, cum.index: 1960-1964. circ. 1,500. (also avail. in microform from BNQ,UMI) **Indexed:** Amer.Hist.& Life, Hist.Abstr., Int.Polit.Sci.Abstr., Lang.& Lang.Behav.Abstr., Pt.de Rep. (1978-), Sociol.Abstr. (1960-). **Document type:** academic/scholarly publication.
—UMI.
Description: Provides an interdisciplinary study of the society of Quebec and French Canada.

301   BE   ISSN 0771-677X
RECHERCHES SOCIOLOGIQUES. (Text in French; summaries in English) 1970. 3/yr. 1300 BEF. Universite Catholique de Louvain, Recherches Sociologiques, Place Montesquieu 1-10, B-1348 Louvain-la-Neuve, Belgium. TEL 32-10-474204. FAX 32-10-474603. E-mail: wery@usoc.ucl.ac.be. Ed. Cecile Wery. bk.rev. circ. 500. (reprint service avail. from SCH) **Indexed:** Lang.& Lang.Behav.Abstr., Sociol.Abstr. (1970-). **Document type:** academic/scholarly publication.
—BLDSC (7309.255000).
Description: Sociological analysis of social, methodological and theoretical problems.

301   US   ISSN 0894-4830
GV14.5
RECREATION: CURRENT SELECTED RESEARCH. 1988. a. $37.50. A M S Press, Inc., 56 E. 13th St., New York, NY 10003. TEL 212-777-4700. FAX 212-995-5413. Eds. James H. Humphrey, Fred Humphrey. index.
Description: Research articles which address societal challenges across the domains of leisure behavior.

RELACIONES; estudios de historia y sociedad. see *HISTORY — History Of North And South America*

RELACIONES. see *PSYCHOLOGY*

649 301   US   ISSN 0887-5480
RELATIONSHIP & FAMILY COMMUNICATIONS;* a unique guide for successful relationships. 1988. m. $16.80 to individuals; institutions $34. Relationship and Family Communications Company, c/o Gloria J. Gordon, Ed., 3409 E. Paris, Tampa, FL 33610. TEL 202-282-1979. (Subscr. to: RAFCOM Magazine, Box 1554, Washington, DC 20013-1554) adv. circ. 100,000.
Description: Discusses important issues in forming and maintaining loving relationships.

RELIGION AND AMERICAN CULTURE; a journal of interpretation. see *RELIGIONS AND THEOLOGY*

RELIGIONE E SOCIETA (ROME); storia della chiesa e dei movimenti cattolici. see *RELIGIONS AND THEOLOGY*

RELIGIONI E SOCIETA (TURIN); rivista di scienze sociali della religione. see *RELIGIONS AND THEOLOGY*

REPRESENTATIVE RESEARCH IN SOCIAL PSYCHOLOGY. see *PSYCHOLOGY*

301.34   US   ISSN 1058-5028
HT51
RESEARCH IN COMMUNITY SOCIOLOGY. 1990. a. J A I Press, Inc., 55 Old Post Rd., No. 2, Greenwich, CT 06836.
—CCC.

RESEARCH IN MELANESIA; a newsletter of anthropological and sociological research in Papua New Guinea. see *ANTHROPOLOGY*

301 350   US   ISSN 0732-1317
H97
RESEARCH IN PUBLIC POLICY ANALYSIS AND MANAGEMENT. 1978. a. $63.50 to institutions. (Association for Public Policy Analysis Management) J A I Press Inc., 55 Old Post Rd., No. 2, Box 1678, Greenwich, CT 06836-1678. TEL 203-661-7602. Ed. Stuart Nagel.
—BLDSC (7755.745000). CCC.

305.8   US   ISSN 0195-7449
GN495.4
RESEARCH IN RACE AND ETHNIC RELATIONS; a research annual. 1979. a. $58.50 to institutions. J A I Press Inc., 55 Old Post Rd., No. 2, Box 1678, Greenwich, CT 06836-2678. TEL 203-661-7602. Eds. Cora Bagley Marrett, Cheryl B. Leggon. adv.; bk.rev. **Indexed:** Lang.& Lang.Behav.Abstr., Psychol.Abstr., Sociol.Abstr. (1988-).
—BLDSC (7759.175000). **CCC.**

RESEARCH IN RELIGION AND FAMILY: BLACK PERSPECTIVES. see *RELIGIONS AND THEOLOGY*

301   US   ISSN 1057-1922
HT401
RESEARCH IN RURAL SOCIOLOGY AND DEVELOPMENT. 1984. a. $58.50 to institutions. J A I Press Inc., 55 Old Post Rd., No. 2, Box 1678, Greenwich, CT 06836-1678. TEL 203-661-7602. Ed. Harry K. Schwarzweller. **Indexed:** Sociol.Abstr. (1979-).
—BLDSC (7769.691000).

301.24   US   ISSN 0163-786X
HN1
RESEARCH IN SOCIAL MOVEMENTS, CONFLICTS AND CHANGE. 1978. a. $58.50 to institutions. J A I Press Inc., 55 Old Post Rd., No. 2, Box 1678, Greenwich, CT 06836-1678. TEL 203-661-7602. Ed. Louis Kriesberg. **Indexed:** Lang.& Lang.Behav.Abstr., Sociol.Abstr. (1984-).
—BLDSC (7770.570000); Faxon. **CCC.**

301.07   US   ISSN 0196-1152
HM1
RESEARCH IN SOCIAL PROBLEMS AND PUBLIC POLICY; a research annual. 1979. a. $58.50 to institutions. J A I Press Inc., 55 Old Post Rd., No. 2, Box 1678, Greenwich, CT 06836-1678. TEL 203-661-7602. Eds. Michael Lewis, JoAnn L. Miller. **Indexed:** Lang.& Lang.Behav.Abstr., Psychol.Abstr., Sociol.Abstr. (1978-).
—BLDSC (7770.580000). **CCC.**

305.5   US   ISSN 0276-5624
HT601
RESEARCH IN SOCIAL STRATIFICATION AND MOBILITY; a research annual. 1981. a. $63.50 to institutions. J A I Press Inc., 55 Old Post Rd., No. 2, Box 1678, Greenwich, CT 06836-1678. TEL 203-661-7602. Ed. Robert V. Robinson. **Indexed:** Lang.& Lang.Behav.Abstr., Sociol.Abstr. (1978-).
—BLDSC (7770.630000); Faxon. **CCC.**

301   US   ISSN 0272-2801
HQ1075
RESEARCH IN THE INTERWEAVE OF SOCIAL ROLES; a research annual. 1980. a. $58.50 to institutions. J A I Press Inc., 55 Old Post Rd., No. 2, Box 1678, Greenwich, CT 06836-1678. TEL 203-661-7602. Ed. Helen Z. Lopata. **Indexed:** Lang.& Lang.Behav.Abstr., Psychol.Abstr.

RESEARCH IN THE SOCIOLOGY OF HEALTH CARE; a research annual. see *MEDICAL SCIENCES*

301.34   US   ISSN 0733-558X
HM131
RESEARCH IN THE SOCIOLOGY OF ORGANIZATIONS. 1982. a. $63.50 to institutions. J A I Press Inc., 55 Old Post Rd., No. 2, Box 1678, Greenwich, CT 06836-1678. TEL 203-661-7602. Ed. Samuel B. Bacharach. **Indexed:** Lang.& Lang.Behav.Abstr., Sociol.Abstr. (1982-).
—BLDSC (7770.733000); UnCover. **CCC.**

301.1   US   ISSN 0277-2833
HD6951
RESEARCH IN THE SOCIOLOGY OF WORK. 1981. irreg. $63.50 to institutions. J A I Press Inc., 55 Old Post Rd., No. 2, Box 1678, Greenwich, CT 06836-1678. TEL 203-661-7602. Eds. Ida Harper Simpson, Richard L. Simpson. **Indexed:** Lang.& Lang.Behav.Abstr., Sociol.Abstr. (1981-).

301   US   ISSN 1047-0042
HT101   CODEN: RUSOEN
RESEARCH IN URBAN SOCIOLOGY. 1989. a. J A I Press Inc., 55 Old Post Rd., No. 2, Greenwich, CT 06836.
—BLDSC (7774.045000). **CCC.**

RESEARCH ON LANGUAGE AND SOCIAL INTERACTION. see *LINGUISTICS*

301   US   ISSN 1049-7315
HV1   CODEN: RSWPEW
RESEARCH ON SOCIAL WORK PRACTICE. 1990. q. $53 to individuals; institutions $143 (effective Sep. 1995). Sage Publications, Inc., 2455 Teller Rd., Thousand Oaks, CA 91320. TEL 805-499-0721. FAX 805-499-0871. E-mail: libraries@sagepub.com. (Overseas subscr. to: Sage Publications Ltd., 6 Bonhill St., London EC2A 4PU, England; Sage Publications India Pvt. Ltd., P.O. Boxx 4215, New Delhi 110 048, India) Ed. Bruce A. Thyer. circ. 1,200. (back issues avail.; reprint service avail.) **Indexed:** Psychol.Abstr. (1991-), Soc.Work Res.& Abstr., Viol.& Abuse Abstr.
—BLDSC (7770.680000); Genuine Article; UnCover. **CCC.**
Description: Devoted to the publication of emprical research concerning the methods and outcomes of social work practice.

320   US   ISSN 1053-0754
JC330.15   CODEN: RECOEZ
RESPONSIVE COMMUNITY; rights and responsibilities. 1990. q. $27 to individuals (foreign $34); institutions $70 (foreign $77); students $17 (foreign $24). Center for Policy Research, 2020 Pennsylvania Ave., Ste. 282, Washington, DC 20006. TEL 202-994-8142. FAX 202-994-1639. Ed. Amitai Etzioni. adv.; bk.rev. circ. 5,000. (back issues avail.) **Document type:** academic/scholarly publication.
—BLDSC (7777.695500); UnCover.
Description: Explores the relationships between individual rights and community responsibilities through the investigation of relevant social, ethical, philosophical, and moral issues.

REVIEW OF RELIGIOUS RESEARCH. see *RELIGIONS AND THEOLOGY*

REVIEW OF SOCIAL ECONOMY. see *BUSINESS AND ECONOMICS*

301   UK   ISSN 0261-0272
REVIEWING SOCIOLOGY. 1979. 3/yr. £8 to individuals; institutions £20. City of Birmingham Polytechnic, Department of Sociology and Applied Social Studies, C Block, Perry Barr, Birmingham B42 2SU, England. Ed.Bd. adv.; cum.index. circ. 800. **Indexed:** Sociol.Abstr. (1972-).
—BLDSC (7798.700000).
Description: Book review journal in the social sciences.

301   CI   ISSN 0350-154X
HM7
REVIJA ZA SOCIOLOGIJU/SOCIOLOGICAL REVIEW. (Text in Serbo-Croatian; summaries in English) 1971. s-a. $12.99. Sociolosko Drustvo Hrvatske - Croatian Sociological Association, Filozofski fakultet, Odsjek za Sociologiju, Djure Salaja 3, 41000 Zagreb, Croatia. TEL 041-513-155. Ed. Vjekoslav Afric. adv.; bk.rev.; bibl. circ. 1,000. **Indexed:** Int.Polit.Sci.Abstr., Lang.& Lang.Behav.Abstr., Sociol.Abstr. (1971-).
Description: Covers all aspects of sociology.

301   UY   ISSN 0797-5538
REVISTA DE CIENCIAS SOCIALES. 1986. a. Fundacion de Cultura Universitaria, 25 de Mayo No. 568, Casilla de Correo 1155, 11000 Montevideo, Uruguay. TEL 96-11-52. FAX 952549.

301   PE
REVISTA DE DEBATES: DEBATES EN SOCIOLOGIA. 1977. a. $6.40. Pontificia Universidad Catolica del Peru, Departamento de Ciencias Sociales, Fondo Editorial, Apdo. 1761, Lima 100, Peru. FAX 51-14-611785. Eds. Gonzalo Portocarrero, Ana Ponce.

REVISTA DE ECONOMIA E SOCIOLOGIA RURAL. see *AGRICULTURE — Agricultural Economics*

301   SP   ISSN 0425-3485
REVISTA DE ESTUDIOS COOPERATIVOS; revesco. 1963. a. 700 ptas. Asociacion de Estudios Cooperativos, Salustiano Olozaga 5, 4 dcha., 28001 Madrid, Spain. TEL 91-435-05-98. (Co-sponsor: Universidad de Madrid. Catedra Libre de Cooperacion) Ed. Jose Luis de Arco Alvarez. (also avail. in cards)

SOCIOLOGY

301   **SP**   ISSN 0303-9889
H8
REVISTA DE ESTUDIOS SOCIALES. 1960. 3/yr. 400 ptas.($11) Centro de Estudios Sociales de la Santa Cruz del Valle de los Caidos, Palacio Real, Bailen s-n, Apdo. de Correas 14158, Madrid 15, Spain. (Subscr. to: Libreria Editorial Augustinus, Gaztambide 75-77, Madrid 15, Spain) Ed. Luis Gonzalez Seara. bk.rev.; bibl.; circ. 2,000 (controlled). **Indexed:** Lang.& Lang.Behav.Abstr.
    Former titles (until 1971): Centro de Estudios Sociales del Valle de los Caidos. Boletin (ISSN 0008-9966); Centro de Estudios Sociales de la Santa Cruz del Valle de los Caidos. Boletin (ISSN 0429-8764)

301   **SP**   ISSN 0015-6043
REVISTA DE FOMENTO SOCIAL; * ciencias sociales. 1946. q. 4180 ptas.($38) E T E A, C. Escritor Castilla Aguaro, 4, Apdo. 439, 14004 Cordoba, Spain. Ed. Javier Gorosquieta. adv.; bk.rev.; abstr.; index. circ. 10,000.
    Formerly (1946-1963): Fomento Social (ISSN 0210-4113)

301   **CK**   ISSN 0120-1212
REVISTA DE SOCIOLOGIA. 1968. s-a. Universidad Pontificia Bolivariana, Facultad de Sociologia, Avda. La Playa 40-88, Apdo. 1178, Medellin, Colombia. bk.rev.; charts; bibl.; stat.

301   **SP**   ISSN 0210-5233
HM7
REVISTA ESPANOLA DE INVESTIGACIONES SOCIOLOGICAS. 1965. q. $50 (effective 1995). Centro de Investigaciones Sociologicas, Calle Montalban, 8, 28014 Madrid, Spain. TEL 91-5807614. FAX 91-5807619. Dir. Joaquin Arango Vila-Belda. adv.; bk.rev.; cum.index. circ. 3,000. **Indexed:** Amer.Hist.& Life, Hist.Abstr., Int.Polit.Sci.Abstr., Lang.& Lang.Behav.Abstr., Psychol.Abstr., SCIMP (1989-), Sociol.Abstr. (1965-). **Document type:** academic/scholarly publication.
—BLDSC (7854.005000); SWETS.
    Supersedes (in 1977): Revista Espanola de la Opinion Publica (ISSN 0034-9429)

301   **MX**   ISSN 0187-8468
REVISTA INTERAMERICANA DE SOCIOLOGIA. 1966. 3/yr. $1.60 per no. Instituto Mexicano de Cultura, Providencia 330, Col. del Valle, Mexico 12, D.F., Mexico. Ed. Lucio Mendieta y Nunez. bk.rev. **Indexed:** Hisp.Amer.Per.Ind. (1970-1975).

301   **SP**   ISSN 0034-9712
H8
REVISTA INTERNACIONAL DE SOCIOLOGIA. 1941. q. 3300 ptas. (foreign 4950 ptas.). Consejo Superior de Investigaciones Cientificas (C.S.I.C.), Instituto "J. Balmes" de Sociologia, Vitruvio, 8, 28006 Madrid, Spain. Ed. Carmelo Vinas y Mey. circ. 600. **Indexed:** Amer.Hist.& Life, Hist.Abstr., Int.Polit.Sci.Abstr., Sociol.Abstr. (1953-).
—BLDSC (7861.800000).
    Description: Covers sociology, demographics, population problems and social thought.

301 630   **VE**   ISSN 0798-1759
                  CODEN: IJSFEO
REVISTA INTERNACIONAL DE SOCIOLOGIA SOBRE AGRICULTURA Y ALIMENTOS/INTERNATIONAL JOURNAL OF SOCIOLOGY OF AGRICULTURE AND FOOD. (Text in English, Spanish) 1991. a. Bs.1000($20) to individuals; institutions Bs.2100($40) (includes s-a. newsletter) (effective 1994). Universidad Central de Venezuela, Centro de Estudios del Desarrollo, Apto. Postal 6622, Caracas 1010-A, Venezuela. TEL 7523266. FAX 582-7523520. (U.S. subscr. addr.: Poba International, No. 151, Box 02-5255, Miami, FL 33102-5255) (Co-sponsor: Asociacion Internacional de Sociologia, Comite de Investigaciones de Sociologia sobre Agricultura y Alimentos) Eds. Alessandro Bonanno, Nelson Prato Barbosa. adv. circ. 500. (back issues avail.) **Indexed:** Sociol.Abstr.
    Description: Covers themes such as: social relationships, the market, work, technology and production in agricultural and food industries.

REVISTA INTERNACIONAL DEL TRABAJO. see *BUSINESS AND ECONOMICS* — *Labor And Industrial Relations*

301   **MX**   ISSN 0188-2503
H8
REVISTA MEXICANA DE SOCIOLOGIA. 1939. q. Mex.$100($60) Universidad Nacional Autonoma de Mexico, Instituto de Investigaciones Sociales, Torre II de Humanidades, 7o piso, Villa Obregon, Ciudad Universitaria, 04510 Mexico D.F., Mexico. TEL 525-623-0234. FAX 525-616-1733. Ed. Sara Gordon Rapoport. adv. contact: Ricardo Tirado Segura. bk.rev.; abstr.; bibl.; charts; index, cum.index. circ. 2,000. (also avail. in microform from UMI; reprint service avail. from UMI) **Indexed:** Anthropol.Lit., Hisp.Amer.Per.Ind. (1970-), Int.Lab.Doc., Int.Polit.Sci.Abstr., Lang.& Lang.Behav.Abstr., P.A.I.S.For.Lang.Ind., Psychol.Abstr., Sage Urb.Stud.Abstr., Sociol.Abstr. (1952-). **Document type:** academic/scholarly publication.
—BLDSC (7866.410000); SWETS.

301   **PY**   ISSN 0035-0354
HM7
REVISTA PARAGUAYA DE SOCIOLOGIA. 1964. 3/yr. $40. Centro Paraguayo de Estudios Sociologicos, Eligio Ayala 973, Asuncion, Paraguay. TEL 21-443-734. FAX 595-21-447-128. Ed. Graziella Corvalan. bk.rev.; bibl.; charts; stat. circ. 1,000. (also avail. in microform from UMI; reprint service avail. from UMI) **Indexed:** Hisp.Amer.Per.Ind. (1970-), Int.Lab.Doc., Lang.& Lang.Behav.Abstr., Sociol.Abstr. (1964-).
—BLDSC (7869.520000); UMI.

REVUE CANADIENNE DE PSYCHO-EDUCATION. see *PSYCHOLOGY*

301 100   **FR**   ISSN 0990-5642
REVUE DU M A U S S. (Mouvement Anti-Utilitariste dans les Science Sociales) 1982. a. price varies. Editions La Decouverte, 9 bis, rue Abel-Hovelacque, 75013 Paris, France. TEL 44-08-84-00. FAX 44-08-84-19.

REVUE ECONOMIQUE ET SOCIALE. see *BUSINESS AND ECONOMICS*

301   **FR**   ISSN 0397-7870
E169.1
REVUE FRANCAISE D'ETUDES AMERICAINES. (Text in English or French) 1976. 4/yr. 320 F. (foreign 380 F.). Association Francaise d'Etudes Americaines, 14 rue Corvisart, 75013 Paris, France. TEL 1-44-08-51-70. Eds. Sophie Body-Gendist, Michel Granger. adv.: B&W page 2000 F. bk.rev.; bibl. circ. 1,000. (back issues avail.) **Indexed:** Amer.Hist.& Life, Arts & Hum.Cit.Ind., Hist.Abstr., Int.Polit.Sci.Abstr., M.L.A.
—Genuine Article.
    Description: Reference journal for American studies in France.

301   **FR**   ISSN 0035-2969
HM3
REVUE FRANCAISE DE SOCIOLOGIE. (Summaries in English, German, Russian, Spanish) 1960. q. (Centre National de la Recherche Scientifique) C N R S Editions, 20-22 rue St. Amand, 75015 Paris, France. TEL 45-33-16-00. FAX 45-33-92-13. TELEX 200 350 F. Dir. J.D. Reynaud. adv.; bk.rev.; bibl.; charts. circ. 3,000. **Indexed:** Curr.Cont., E.I., Int.Lab.Doc., Int.Polit.Sci.Abstr., Lang.& Lang.Behav.Abstr., P.A.I.S.For.Lang.Ind., Pt.de Rep. (1979-), Rural Recreat.Tour.Abstr., Sociol.Abstr. (1960-), SSCI, World Agri.Econ.& Rural Sociol.Abstr.
—BLDSC (7904.430000); SWETS; UnCover.
    Description: Includes theoretical and methodological articles recording fundamental research, trends and developments, discussions of new developments in the field of sociology, and identifying new areas for sociological research.

301 500   **FR**   ISSN 0242-5149
AS161
REVUE IMPREVUE. 2/yr. Universite de Montpellier (Universite Paul Valery), B.P. 5043, 34032 Montpellier Cedex 1, France. TEL 67-14-20-00. **Indexed:** Int.Polit.Sci.Abstr.
—BLDSC (4371.476500).

301.4   **CN**   ISSN 0707-9699
REVUE INTERNATIONALE D'ACTION COMMUNAUTAIRE; international review of community development. (Text in French; abstracts in English, French and Spanish) 1958. s-a. Can.$24 to individuals; institutions Can.$36. Forum International d'Action Communautaire, c/o Universite de Montreal, Ecole de Service Social, C.P. 6128, Succ. A, Montreal, PQ H3C 3J7, Canada. TEL 514-343-5732. FAX 514-343-2493. (Subscr. to: RIAC - Periodica, C.P. 444, Outremont, PQ H2V 4R6, Canada) Ed. Frederic Lesemann. adv.; bk.rev.; abstr.; charts; stat.; cum.index every 2 yrs. circ. 1,500. (back issues avail.) **Indexed:** Int.Polit.Sci.Abstr., Lang.& Lang.Behav.Abstr., Pt.de Rep. (1984-), Sociol.Abstr.
    Description: Critical debate on new trends in social policy: studies relationships in the social sector.

301 158   **FR**
▼**REVUE INTERNATIONALE DE PSYCHOSOCIOLOGIE.** 1994. s-a. 250 F. (foreign 280 F.) (effective 1995). Editions E S K A, 27 rue Dunois, 75013 Paris, France. TEL 44-06-80-42. FAX 44-24-06-94. **Document type:** academic/scholarly publication.
    Description: Seeks to show how this discipline is at the core of reality and change, as well as social life.

301   **UK**
REVUE INTERNATIONALE DE SOCIOLOGIE. 1895; N.S. 1990. 3/yr. £25($42) to individuals; institutions £88($148) (effective 1996). (Universita di Roma "La Sapienza") Carfax Publishing Co., P.O. Box 25, Abingdon, Oxon. OX14 3UE, England. TEL 44-1235-555335. FAX 44-1235-553559. (N. American subscr. to: Carfax Publishing Co., 875-81 Massachusetts Ave., Cambrdige, MA 02139) bk.rev. circ. 450. **Indexed:** Sociol.Abstr. (1954-). **Document type:** academic/scholarly publication.
    Refereed Serial

REVUE INTERNATIONALE DU TRAVAIL. see *BUSINESS AND ECONOMICS* — *Labor And Industrial Relations*

291.17   **IT**   ISSN 0392-1581
RICERCHE DI STORIA SOCIALE E RELIGIOSA. 1972. s-a. price varies. (Centro Studi per le Fonti della Storia della Chiesa nel Veneto) Edizioni di Storia e Letteratura s.r.l., Via Lancelloti, 18, 00186 Rome, Italy. TEL 6540556. FAX 06-6872567. (Co-sponsor: Centro Studi di Storia Sociale e Religiosa nel Mezzogiorno) Ed. Gabriele De Rosa. bk.rev.; illus. **Indexed:** CERDIC.

301   **JA**   ISSN 0913-1442
                  CODEN: RIHOEC
RIRON TO HOHO/SOCIOLOGICAL THEORY AND METHODS. (Text in Japanese; summaries in English) 1986. s-a. 2800 Yen. Japanese Association for Mathematical Sociology, Osaka University, Faculty of Human Sciences, 1-2, Yamadaoka, Suita 565, Japan. TEL 81-6-879-8068. FAX 81-6-879-8068. E-mail: sirayuki@tansei.cc.u-tokyo.ac.jp. (Subscr. to: Harvest Sha, 2-11-5 Mukoudai, Tanashi 188, Japan. TEL 81-424-67-6441. FAX 81-42-424-67-6441) Ed. Yukio Shirakura. adv.; bk.rev.; circ. 800 (paid). (back issues avail.) **Indexed:** Curr.Cont., Sociol.Abstr. **Document type:** academic/scholarly publication.
—BLDSC (8319.650170).
    Refereed Serial

301.4   **PL**   ISSN 0239-5568
HD8039.S4
ROCZNIKI SOCJOLOGII MORSKIEJ. (Text in Polish; summaries in English) 1986. a. price varies. Polska Akademia Nauk, Oddzial w Gdansku, Komisja Socjologii Morskiej - Polish Academy of Sciences, Section Gdansk, Commission of Maritime Sociology, c/o Ludwik Janiszewski, Ed., Ul. Warynskiego 17, 71-310 Szczecin, Poland. (Dist. by: Ars Polona, Krakowskie Przedmiescie 7, 00-068 Warsaw, Poland) bk.rev. circ. 550. **Document type:** academic/scholarly publication.
    Formerly (until 1987): Socjologia Morska.
    Description: Studies and monographs on sociological phenomena occurring in the social groups connected, through their professional activity, with the sea.

SOCIOLOGY

301   PL   ISSN 0080-3731
ROCZNIKI SOCJOLOGII WSI. STUDIA I MATERIAŁY. (Text in Polish; summaries in English and Russian) 1962. a. price varies. Polska Akademia Nauk, Instytut Filozofii i Socjologii, Ul. Nowy Swiat 72, 00-330 Warsaw, Poland. (Dist. by: Ars Polona-Ruch, Krakowskie Przedmiescie 7, Warsaw, Poland) Ed. F. Mleczko. bk.rev. circ. 500.
— BLDSC (8015.770000).
Description: Papers on sociological research into problems of rural communities.

301   RM   ISSN 1220-3688
ROMANIAN JOURNAL OF SOCIOLOGY. Rumanian edition: Sociologie Romaneasca (ISSN 1220-5389) (Text in English) 1956. s-a. 70 lei($45) (Academia Romana) Editura Academiei Romane, Calea Victoriei 125, 79717 Bucharest, Rumania. (Dist. by: Rompresfilatelia, Calea Grivitei 64-66, P.O. Box 12-201, 78104 Bucharest, Rumania) bk.rev. Indexed: Int.Polit.Sci.Abstr. **Document type:** academic/scholarly publication.
— BLDSC (8019.639500).
Formerly (until 1989): Revue Roumaine des Sciences Sociales. Serie de Sociologie (ISSN 0080-2646).

301   DK   ISSN 0108-2205
ROSKILDE UNIVERSITETSCENTER. INSTITUT FOR SAMFUNDSOEKONOMI OG PLANLAEGNING. ARBEJDSPAPIR. 1981. irreg., no.2, 1987. free. Roskilde Universitetscenter, Institut for Samfundsoekonomi og Planlaegning, Institut VIII, Postbox 260, 4000 Roskilde, Denmark.

RUCH PRAWNICZY, EKONOMICZNY I SOCJOLOGICZNY. see LAW

301   IT
RUE MORGUE. 1989. 3/yr. L.30000. Bulzoni Editore, Via dei Liburni 14, 00185 Rome, Italy. TEL 06-4455207. FAX 06-4450355. Ed. Alberto Abruzzese.

RUNNYMEDE BULLETIN. see POLITICAL SCIENCE — Civil Rights

RURAL DEVELOPMENT PERSPECTIVES. see AGRICULTURE

301.35   US   ISSN 0279-5957
HT401
THE RURAL SOCIOLOGIST. 1981. q. $18 (effective 1996). Rural Sociological Society, c/o Rabel J. Burdge, Treasurer, Institute for Environmental Studies, University of Illinois, 1101 W. Peabody Dr., Urbana, IL 61801-4723. TEL 217-244-8759. FAX 217-333-8046. index. circ. 1,000. (back issues avail.) Indexed: Agri.Eng.Abstr., ASSIA, Curr.Cont., Geo.Abstr., IDA, Poult.Abstr., Triticale Abstr., World Agri.Econ.& Rural Sociol.Abstr. **Document type:** academic/scholarly publication, newsletter.
— BLDSC (8052.629000); Faxon; UnCover.

301.35   US   ISSN 0036-0112
HT401   CODEN: RUSCA
RURAL SOCIOLOGY; devoted to scientific study of rural and small-town life. 1936. q. $87 (effective 1996). Rural Sociological Society, c/o Rabel J. Burdge, Treasurer, Institute for Environmental Studies, Univ. of Illinois, 1101 W. Peabody Dr., Urbana, IL 61801-4723. TEL 217-244-8759. Ed. Thomas A. Lyson. adv.; bk.rev.; adv.; bibl.; charts; stat.; index, cum.index: vols.1-20, 21-30, 31-40. circ. 3,000. (also avail. in microform from UMI; back issues avail.; reprint service avail. from SCH) Indexed: Abstr.Anthropol., Abstr.Health Care Manage.Stud., Abstr.Rural Dev.Trop., Amer.Bibl.Slavic & E.Eur.Stud., Amer.Hist.& Life, Asian-Pac.Econ.Lit., ASSIA, Bibl.Agri., Biol.& Agr.Ind., C.I.J.E., Crim.Just.Abstr., E.I., Energy Ind., Energy Info.Abstr., Geo.Abstr., Hist.Abstr., IDA, IMFL, Int.Lab.Doc., Int.Polit.Sci.Abstr., Lang.& Lang.Behav.Abstr., Mid.East: Abstr.& Ind., Mult.Ed.Abstr., P.A.I.S., Popul.Ind., Psychol.Abstr., Rural Recreat.Tour.Abstr., Sage Urb.Stud.Abstr., Sci.Cit.Ind., Soc.Sci.Ind., Soc.Work Res.& Abstr., Sociol.Abstr. (1952-), Soils & Fert., SSCI, Stud.Wom.Abstr., World Agri.Econ.& Rural Sociol.Abstr. **Document type:** academic/scholarly publication.
— BLDSC (8052.630000); Faxon; Genuine Article; SWETS; UMI; UnCover.

RUSSIA AND HER NEIGHBORS; facts and views on daily life. see ANTHROPOLOGY

RUSSIAN POLITICS AND SOCIETY; international review of Russian studies. see POLITICAL SCIENCE — International Relations

300   SZ
S G G REVUE. (Text in French and German) 1862. bi-m. 30 SFr. Schweizerische Gemeinnuetzige Gesellschaft, Schaffhauserstr. 7, CH-8042 Zurich 6, Switzerland. TEL 01-3634460. adv.; bk.rev.; bibl.; charts; illus.; index. circ. 8,000.
Formerly (until 1990): Schweizerische Zeitschrift fuer Gemeinnuetzigkeit (ISSN 0036-7826)

301   US   ISSN 0885-6729
S I N E T; social indicators network news. 1973. q. $16 (outside N. America $18); institutions $24. (International Sociological Association, Working Group on Social Indicators and Quality of Life Measurement) Abbott L. Ferriss, Ed. & Pub., Box 24064, Emory University Sta., Atlanta, GA 30322. TEL 404-373-4756. FAX 404-727-7532. adv.; bk.rev.; bibl.; circ. 300 (paid). **Document type:** academic/scholarly publication.
Former titles (until 1984): Social Indicators Newsletter (ISSN 0363-3195); Social Indicators.
Description: Brings together information on social indicator developments from Asia, the Pacific, Europe, and the Americas.

301 840   SZ
S K M.* (Schweizer Kontakt) (Text in German) bi-m. ($40) Exakt-Verlag, 8280 Kreuzlingen TG, Switzerland. illus.; tr.lit.

S P R C NEWSLETTER. (Social Policy Research Centre) see SOCIAL SERVICES AND WELFARE

S P R C REPORTS AND PROCEEDINGS. (Social Policy Research Centre) see SOCIAL SERVICES AND WELFARE

S P W. (Sozialistische Politik und Wirtschaft) see POLITICAL SCIENCE

S W S - RUNDSCHAU. (Sozialwissenschaftliche Studiengesellschaft) see SOCIAL SCIENCES: COMPREHENSIVE WORKS

301   US
SAGE STUDIES IN INTERNATIONAL SOCIOLOGY. 1976. irreg., vol.46, Oct. 1993. price varies. (International Sociological Association) Sage Publications, Inc., 2455 Teller Rd., Thousand Oaks, CA 91320. TEL 805-499-0721. FAX 805-499-0871. E-mail: libraries@sagepub.com. (Overseas subscr. to: Sage Publications Ltd., 6 Bonhill St., London EC2A 4PU, England; Sage Publications India Pvt. Ltd., P.O. Box 4215, New Delhi 110 048, India) bibl.; charts; stat. (back issues avail.) **Document type:** monographic series.

261 301 100   US   ISSN 0093-2582
AS30
ST. CROIX REVIEW. 1968. bi-m. $25. Religion and Society Inc., Box 244, Stillwater, MN 55082. Ed. Angus MacDonald. bk.rev.; charts; illus. circ. 2,000. (also avail. in microform from UMI; reprint service avail. from UMI; back issues avail.) Indexed: CERDIC. **Document type:** academic/scholarly publication.
— UMI; UnCover.
Formerly: Religion and Society (ISSN 0034-396X)
Description: Social criticism of controversial subjects, from a traditional point of view.

SAMISKE SAMLINGER. see ANTHROPOLOGY

LE SAUVEUR. see RELIGIONS AND THEOLOGY

301   SZ   ISSN 0255-9072
SCHWEIZERISCHE ZEITSCHRIFT FUER SOZIALVERSICHERUNG UND BERUFLICHE VORSORGE/REVUE SUISSE DES ASSURANCES SOCIALES ET DE LA PREVOYANCE PROFESSIONNELLE. 1957. bi-m. 97 SFr. Staempfli und Cie AG, Hallerstr. 7-9, CH-3001 Bern, Switzerland. TEL 031-3006666. FAX 031-3006688. Ed.Bd. adv.; bk.rev.; bibl.; charts; stat. Indexed: ASCA, Curr.Cont., P.A.I.S.For.Lang.Ind., SSCI, World Bibl.Soc.Sec. **Document type:** bulletin.
— CCC.
Formerly: Schweizerische Zeitschrift fuer Sozialversicherung (ISSN 0036-7877)

301   SZ   ISSN 0379-3664
HM5
SCHWEIZERISCHE ZEITSCHRIFT FUER SOZIOLOGIE/REVUE SUISSE DE SOCIOLOGIE/SWISS JOURNAL OF SOCIOLOGY. (Text in English, French or German; summaries in all 3 languages) 1975. 3/yr. 125 SFr. (effective 1996). (Swiss Sociological Association) Seismo Verlag, Raemistr. 69, Postfach 313, CH-8028 Zurich, Switzerland. TEL 01-2611094. FAX 01-2521054. Ed. Olivier Tschannen. adv. contact: Peter Rusterholz. bk.rev. circ. 900. Indexed: Int.Polit.Sci.Abstr., Lang.& Lang.Behav.Abstr., Sage Fam.Stud.Abstr., Sociol.Abstr. (1976-). **Document type:** academic/scholarly publication.
— BLDSC (7953.394000); SWETS.

301.4   NE   ISSN 0037-3087
SEKSTANT. vol.58, 1978. m. (9/yr.) fl.37.50. Nederlandse Vereniging voor Sexuele Hervorming, Nieuwe Molstraat 6, Box 64, 2501 CB The Hague, Netherlands. adv.; bk.rev.; illus. circ. 200,000.
Formerly: Verstandig Ouderschap.

301   UK   ISSN 1355-2619
▼**SELF AND AGENCY;** a journal of applied sociology. Announced for publication in 1996. s-a. £35 in Europe; N. America $60; elsewhere £40 (effective 1996). (University of Derby) Whiting & Birch Ltd., P.O. Box 872, Forest Hill, London SE23 3HL, England. TEL 44-181-2442421. FAX 44-181-2442448. E-mail: s.webb@derby.ac.uk. Eds. Pamela Abbott, Stephen Webb. **Document type:** academic/scholarly publication.

SERVIZIO MIGRANTI. see POLITICAL SCIENCE

SEX ROLES; a journal of research. see PSYCHOLOGY

SEXUAL ABUSE; a journal of research and treatment. see PSYCHOLOGY

301   JA   ISSN 0288-7126
SHAKAIGAKU NENSHI. 1956. a. Waseda Daigaku, Shakai Gakkai, c/o Waseda Daigaku Bungakubu, 42 Toyama-cho, Shinjuku-ku, Tokyo, Japan. illus.

SHAREDEBATE INTERNATIONAL; a ShareWare diskette magazine. see SOCIAL SCIENCES: COMPREHENSIVE WORKS

301 364   US
SHARING TIMES. m. free. Christ Truth Ministries, Box 610, Upland, CA 91785. TEL 909-981-2838. FAX 909-981-2839. Ed. Carl F. Davis, Jr. circ. 3,500 (controlled). (back issues avail.)
Description: Stories about changed lives of men and women in prison.

301   US   ISSN 1002-5936
SHEHUIXUE YANJIU/SOCIOLOGICAL STUDIES. (Text in Chinese) 1986? bi-m. $33.80. China Books & Periodicals, Inc., 2929 24th St., San Francisco, CA 94110. TEL 415-282-2994. FAX 415-282-0994. **Document type:** academic/scholarly publication.

301   TS
SHU'UN IJTIMA'IYYAH/JOURNAL OF SOCIAL AFFAIRS. (Text in Arabic) 1984. q. DH.40($20) to individuals; institutions DH. 100 ($40). Sociological Association of the U A E - Jam'aiyyat al-Ijtima'iyyin, P.O. Box 3745, Sharjah, United Arab Emirates. TEL 971-6-548161. FAX 971-6-522267. Ed. Abd al-Khaliq Abdullah. adv.; bk.rev. circ. 2,000. **Document type:** academic/scholarly publication.
Description: Publishes research on sociological concerns, with a focus on the U.A.E.
Refereed Serial

SIMULATION & GAMING; an international journal of theory, design and research. see COMPUTERS — Computer Simulation

301 900   UK
SLAVE AND POST-SLAVE SOCIETIES AND CULTURES. 1993. irreg. Frank Cass, Newbury House, 890-900 Eastern Ave., Newbury Park, Ilford, Essex 1G2 7HH, England. TEL 44-181-599-8866. FAX 44-181-599-0984. E-mail: 100067,1576@compuserve.com. (Dist. in the U.S. by: I.S.B.S., 5894 N.E. Hassalo St., Portland, OR 97213-3644) Eds. Gad Heuman, James Walvin. **Document type:** monographic series.
Refereed Serial

SOCIOLOGY

300 323.4 900   UK   ISSN 0144-039X
HT851
SLAVERY & ABOLITION; a journal of slave and post-slave studies. 1980. 3/yr. £35($48) to individuals; institutions £98 ($165) (effective 1996). Frank Cass, Newbury House, 890-900 Eastern Ave., Newbury Park, Ilford, Essex IG2 7HH, England. TEL 44-181-599-8866. FAX 44-181-599-0984. E-mail: 100067,1576@compuserve.com. Eds. Gad Heuman, James Walvin. adv.; B&W page £195 (£275); adv. contact: Anne Kidson. bk.rev.; index. (also avail. in microform from UMI; back issues avail.) **Indexed:** Amer.Hist.& Life, Hist.Abstr. **Document type:** academic/scholarly publication.
—BLDSC (8309.373000); Faxon; UMI; UnCover. **CCC.**
     Description: Discusses all aspects of human bondage throughout the ages. Concerned with the dismantling of slave systems and with the legacy of slavery.
     Refereed Serial

300 943.72 943.85   XR   ISSN 0037-6833
SLEZSKY SBORNIK/ACTA SILESIACA; ctvrtletnik pro vedy o spolecnosti. (Text in Czech; summaries in English, French, German, Russian) 1878. q. DM.133. Slezsky Ustav S Z M, Nadrazni Okruh 31, 746 48 Opava, Czech Republic. TEL 21-47-64. (Dist. in Western countries by: Kubon & Sagner, P.O. Box 34 01 08, 8000 Munich 34, Germany) Ed. Dan Gawrecki. bk.rev.; illus.; maps; cum.index: 1878-1952, 1953-1962. circ. 1,050. **Indexed:** Amer.Hist.& Life, Bibl.Ling., Hist.Abstr.
     Formerly (until 1935): Matice Opavska. Vestnik.
     Description: Devoted to social scientific research in Silesia and the Ostrava industrial districts, Czech-Polish relations, and the nationality problem in this area.

SLOVANSKE STUDIE. see *HISTORY — History Of Europe*

SLOVANSKY PREHLED/SLAVONIC REVIEW. see *POLITICAL SCIENCE*

SLOVENSKA AKADEMIJA ZNANOSTI IN UMETNOSTI. FILOZOFSKI VESTNIK/ACTA PHILOSOPHICA. see *PHILOSOPHY*

SMALL GROUP RESEARCH; an international journal of theory, investigation and application. see *PSYCHOLOGY*

301 649   US
SMART DADS. 1978. bi-m. (plus s-a. audio cassette tape: Dad Talk). $18.50. Family University, Box 500050, San Diego, CA 92150-0050. TEL 619-487-7099. FAX 619-487-7356. Ed. Paul Lewis. bk.rev.; circ. 9,000 (paid). (also avail. in audio cassette; talking book) **Document type:** newsletter.
     Formerly: Dads Only.
     Description: News, fathering, child development, marriage, and family living tips for busy dads.

301 320   AT   ISSN 0155-0306
HN841
SOCIAL ALTERNATIVES. 1977. q. Aus.$26 to individuals; institutions Aus.$39 (foreign Aus.$54) (effective thru 1996). c/o Department of Government, University of Queensland, Brisbane, Qld. 4072, Australia. TEL 365-2324. FAX 365-1388. Ed.Bd. adv.; bk.rev.; film rev.; circ. 2,000 (paid). **Indexed:** Alt.Press Ind., ASCA, Aus.P.A.I.S., Curr.Cont., HR Rep., Lang.& Lang.Behav.Abstr., Sociol.Abstr., SSCI. **Document type:** academic/scholarly publication.
—BLDSC (8318.041300); UnCover.
     Description: Covers a range of concerns relating to social, political, economic and cultural issues.

SOCIAL ANALYSIS; journal of cultural and social practice. see *ANTHROPOLOGY*

301 340   UK   ISSN 0964-6639
     CODEN: SLSTEK
SOCIAL AND LEGAL STUDIES. 1992. q. £32 to individuals; institutions £105 (effective 1996). Sage Publications Ltd., 6 Bonhill St., London EC2A 4PU, England. TEL 0171-374-0645. FAX 0171-374-8741. E-mail: market@sageltd.co.uk. Ed.Bd. adv.: B&W page £180; trim 185 x 114; adv. contact: Bernie Folan. bk.rev. **Indexed:** ASSIA, Crim.Pen.& Police.Sci.Abstr., Euro.LJI, IBZ, Intl.Bibl.S.S.Soc.Cult.Anthro., L.R.I., LJI, Sage Pub.Admin.Abstr., Sociol.Abstr., Stud.Wom.Abstr. **Document type:** academic/scholarly publication.
—BLDSC (8318.053530); UnCover.
     Description: Dedicated to critical work in law, jurisprudence, penality and the criminal justice system. Offers an interdisciplinary perspective that draws upon the analytical traditions of sociology, feminism, political economy, history and philosophy.
     Refereed Serial

SOCIAL AND POLICY ISSUES IN EDUCATION. see *EDUCATION*

301   II   ISSN 0049-0857
HN681
SOCIAL CHANGE. 1971. q. Rs.60($16) to individuals; institutions Rs.100($24). Council for Social Development - Sangha Rachana, 53 Lodi Estate, New Delhi 110 003, India. Ed. Amar Kumar Singh; Pub. Tilak Raj. adv. contact: R.S. Somi. bk.rev.; bibl. circ. 1,200. (back issues avail.) **Indexed:** Geo.Abstr., IDA. **Document type:** academic/scholarly publication.
—BLDSC (8318.070500); UnCover.
     Description: Promotes the studies and undertaking of social development, including: national and regional policies, planning processes, social and economic interaction in national growth, studies, research and survey techniques.

300 261   UK   ISSN 0037-7686
BL60
SOCIAL COMPASS; international review of sociology of religion. (Includes: Proceedings of the International Society for the Sociology of Religion) (Text in English, French) 1953. q. £31 to individuals; institutions £95 (effective 1996). (Groupe de Sciences Sociales des Religions, BE) Sage Publications Ltd., 6 Bonhill St., London EC2A 4PU, England. TEL 0171-374-0645. FAX 0171-374-8741. E-mail: market@sageltd.co.uk. Ed. A. Bastenier. adv.: B&W page £180; trim 185 x 114; adv. contact: Bernie Folan. bk.rev.; charts; stat.; index, cum.index: 1953-1973. **Indexed:** Arts & Hum.Cit.Ind., ASCA, CERDIC, Commun.Abstr., Curr.Cont., E.I., IBZ, Int.Polit.Sci.Abstr., Lang.& Lang.Behav.Abstr., Mid.East: Abstr.& Ind., Per.Islam., Rel.& Theol.Abstr. (1968-), Rel.Ind.One, Rel.Per., Sociol.Abstr. (1954-), SSCI. **Document type:** academic/scholarly publication.
—BLDSC (8318.075000); Faxon; SWETS; UnCover.
     Description: Forum for all scholars in sociology, anthropology, religious studies and theology concerned with the sociology of religion. Individual issues focus on a particular topic in current social scientific research on religion in society.
     Refereed Serial

301.1   UK   ISSN 0961-205X
HQ767.8
SOCIAL DEVELOPMENT. 1992. 3/yr. £91.50($132) (foreign £98.50) (effective 1996). Basil Blackwell Ltd., 108 Cowley Rd., Oxford OX4 1JF, England. TEL 0865-791100. FAX 0865-791347. TELEX 837002-OXBOOK-G. E-mail: jnlsamples@cix.compulink.co.uk. (U.S. subscr. to: Blackwell Publishers, 238 Main St., Cambridge, MA 02142. TEL 800-488-2665. FAX 617-547-0789) bk.rev. **Indexed:** Mult.Ed.Abstr., Psychol.Abstr. (1992-). **Document type:** academic/scholarly publication.
—BLDSC (8318.079100); UMI. **CCC.**
     Description: Publishes reports, debates, and commentary on theoretical and empirical issues in social development, emphasizing psychological processses in human development to adulthood.
     Refereed Serial

330.9 301.3   UN   ISSN 0251-6845
SOCIAL DEVELOPMENT NEWSLETTER. French edition: Bulletin du Developpement Social (ISSN 0255-948X); Spanish edition: Boletin Informativo sobre Desarrollo Social (ISSN 1014-8183) 1971. s-a. free. United Nations Centre for Social Development and Humanitarian Affairs, Social Development Division, Vienna International Centre, A-1400 Vienna, Austria. TEL 26 310. circ. 6,000. **Indexed:** HR Rep. **Document type:** newsletter.
—BLDSC (8318.079500).

301   US   ISSN 0037-7732
HN51   CODEN: SOFOAP
SOCIAL FORCES. 1922. q. $52 (foreign $60) (effective 1996). (University of North Carolina at Chapel Hill, Department of Sociology) University of North Carolina Press, Box 2288, Chapel Hill, NC 27515-2288. TEL 919-966-3561. FAX 919-966-3829. Ed. Richard L. Simpson. adv.; bk.rev.; bibl.; index, cum.index: 1922-1972. circ. 4,300. (also avail. in microform from UMI,MIM,PMC; reprint service avail. from UMI) **Indexed:** A.B.C.Pol.Sci., Abstr.Anthropol., Abstr.Crim.& Pen., Acad.Ind., Adol.Ment.Hlth.Abstr., Amer.Bibl.Slavic & E.Eur.Stud., Amer.Hist.& Life, ASCA, ASSIA, Bk.Rev.Ind. (1965-), Chic.Per.Ind., Child.Bk.Rev.Ind. (1965-), Commun.Abstr., Crim.Just.Abstr., Curr.Cont., Curr.Lit.Fam.Plan., E.I., Educ.Admin.Abstr., Geo.Abstr., Hist.Abstr., IMFL, Int.Polit.Sci.Abstr., Lang.& Lang.Behav.Abstr., Mid.East: Abstr.& Ind., Mult.Ed.Abstr., P.A.I.S., Popul.Ind., Psychol.Abstr. (1928-), Rural Recreat.Tour.Abstr., Sage Urb.Stud.Abstr., Soc.Sci.Ind., Soc.Work Res.& Abstr., Sociol.Abstr. (1952-), Sociol.Educ.Abstr., SSCI, Stud.Wom.Abstr. **Document type:** academic/scholarly publication.
● Also available online. Vendor(s): University Microfilms International.
—BLDSC (8318.089000); Faxon; Genuine Article; SWETS; UMI; UnCover.
     Refereed Serial

301   SW   ISSN 0283-202X
SOCIAL FORSKNING; inblick i SFRs verksamhetsomraade. 1986. q. free. Socialvetenskapliga Forskningsraadet - S F R, P.O. Box 2220, S-103 15 Stockholm, Sweden. TEL 46-8-23-77-35. FAX 46-8-21-05-43. Dir. Erland Bergman. bk.rev. circ. 4,000. **Document type:** academic/scholarly publication.

301.45 323.4   UK   ISSN 1350-4630
▼**SOCIAL IDENTITIES**. 1995. 3/yr. £40 to individuals; institutions £94 (effective 1996). Carfax Publishing Co., P.O. Box 25, Abingdon, Oxon. OX14 3UE, England. TEL 01235-555335. FAX 01235-553559. (Subscr. in N. America to: 875-81 Massachusetts Ave., Cambridge, MA 02139) Eds. Abebe Zegeye, David Theo Goldberg. **Document type:** academic/scholarly publication.
—BLDSC (8318.110450).
     Description: Provides a forum to examine aspects of social identity, such as race, nation, and ethnicity, along with racism and nationalism and their attendant forms of material exclusion and power.

301   US
SOCIAL INDICATORS. 1977. bi-m. $5. American Institutes for Research, Social Indicators Research Program, 1791 Arastradero Rd., Box 1113, Palo Alto, CA 94302. TEL 415-493-3550. Eds. Robert J. Rossi, Kevin J. Gilmartin. adv.; bk.rev. circ. 300. (looseleaf format)

301   NE   ISSN 0303-8300
HN25   CODEN: SINRDZ
SOCIAL INDICATORS RESEARCH; an international and interdisciplinary journal for quality-of-life measurement. (Text in English) 9/yr. fl.985.50 to institutions; $601 to institutions in U.S. (effective 1996). Kluwer Academic Publishers, Postbus 17, 3300 AA Dordrecht, Netherlands. TEL 31-78-392392. FAX 31-78-392254. TELEX 29245 KAPG NL. E-mail: SERVICES@WKAP.NL. (Dist. by: Kluwer Academic Publishers Group, P.O. Box 322, 3300 AH Dordrecht, Netherlands. TEL 31-78-392392. FAX 31-78-546474; N. America dist. addr.: Box 358, Accord Sta., Hingham, MA 02018-0358. TEL 617-871-6600. FAX 617-871-6528) Ed. Alex C. Michalos. adv.; bk.rev.; index. (also avail. in microform from UMI; reprint service avail. from SWZ) **Indexed**: ASCA, ASSIA, CERDIC, Curr.Cont., E.I., Fut.Surv., IMFL, Ind.Med., Lang.& Lang.Behav.Abstr., Mid.East: Abstr.& Ind., P.A.I.S., P.I.R.A., Phil.Ind., Psychol.Abstr. (1987-), Rural Recreat.Tour.Abstr., Sage Pub.Admin.Abstr., Sage Urb.Stud.Abstr., Soc.Work Res.& Abstr., Sociol.Abstr., SSCI, World Agri.Econ.& Rural Sociol.Abstr., World Bibl.Soc.Sec. Document type: academic/scholarly publication.
—BLDSC (8318.116000); Faxon; Genuine Article; SWETS; UMI; UnCover. **CCC**.
Description: Publishes results of empirical, philosophical and methodological research studies dealing with problems related to the measurement of all aspects of the quality of life.
Refereed Serial

301   UK   ISSN 0954-206X
SOCIAL INVENTIONS. 1985. a. £17($40) Institute for Social Inventions, 20 Heber Rd., London NW2 6AA, England. TEL 0181-208-2853. FAX 0181-452-6434. E-mail: rhino@bbcnc.org.uk. Ed. Nicholas Albery. bk.rev. circ. 650. (back issues avail.)
●Also available online.
—BLDSC (8318.116900).
Description: Discuses nontechnical social innovations for improving the quality of life, tackles social problems, and covers award winners in an annual competition for ideas from the public.

301   SI
SOCIAL ISSUES IN SOUTHEAST ASIA. (Text in English) 1985. irreg., no.14, 1994. price varies. Institute of Southeast Asian Studies, Heng Mui Keng Terrace, Pasir Panjang Rd., Singapore 0511, Singapore. TEL 778-0955. FAX 778-1735. TELEX RS 37068 ISEAS. E-mail: pubsunit@merlion.iseas.ac.sg. (Subscr. in U.S. to: Ashgate, Old Post Rd., Brookfield, VT 05036. TEL 802-276-3162)
Description: Publishes studies on the nature and dynamics of ethnicity, religions, urbanism, and population change in Southeast Asia.

301   US   ISSN 0885-7466
JC578   CODEN: SJREEO
SOCIAL JUSTICE RESEARCH. 1986. q. $215 (foreign $250) (effective 1996). Plenum Publishing Corp., 233 Spring St., New York, NY 10013-1578. TEL 212-620-8000. FAX 212-463-0742. TELEX 23-421139. Ed. Tom R. Tyler. adv.; bk.rev. (also avail. in microfilm from JSC; back issues avail.; reprint service avail. from WSH) **Indexed**: Curr.Cont., Polit.Sci.Abstr. Document type: academic/scholarly publication.
—BLDSC (8318.121500); Faxon; SWETS; UMI; UnCover. **CCC**.
Description: Covers the areas of sociology, anthropology, law, psychology and political science.
Refereed Serial

SOCIAL JUSTICE REVIEW; pioneer American journal of Catholic social action. see *SOCIAL SCIENCES: COMPREHENSIVE WORKS*

301   II
SOCIAL LIFE.* (Text in English) 1972. m. Rs.8. 1184 Bahadur Garh Rd., Delhi 6, India. Ed. Attar Chand. adv.; charts; stat.

301   US   ISSN 0275-7524
SOCIAL ORDERS SERIES. irreg., latest vol.4. price varies. Harwood Academic Publishers, c/o International Publishers Distributor, 820 Town Center Dr., Langhorne, PA 19047. TEL 215-750-2642. FAX 215-750-6343. (Subscr. to: International Publishers Distributor, Box 90, Reading, Berkshire RG1 8JL, England. TEL 44-173-456-8316) Eds. J. Revel, M. Auge. (also avail. in microform) Document type: monographic series.
—BLDSC (8318.127000).
Refereed Serial

364 301   US   ISSN 1073-7855
▼**SOCIAL PATHOLOGY**; a journal of reviews. Electronic edition (ISSN 1073-8118) 1995. 3/yr. $141. Harrow and Heston Publishers, Box 3934, Stuyvesant, NY 12203. TEL 518-456-4894. FAX 518-456-4894. Ed. Michael J. Lynch. adv. contact: Colin Heston. bk.rev. (also avail. in diskette format; back issues avail.)
●Also available online.
Description: Devoted to reviews of scholarly works in the areas of social problems, criminal justice, deviance, criminology, penology, and social control.

301.2   KE
SOCIAL PERSPECTIVES. irreg. Ministry of Finance and Planning, Central Bureau of Statistics, Social Statistics Section, P.O. Box 30266, Nairobi, Kenya. charts; stat. Document type: government publication.

301   US   ISSN 0037-7783
HN51
SOCIAL POLICY. 1970. 4/yr. $20 to individuals; institutions $50. (Social Policy Corporation) Union Institute, 25 W. 43rd St., Rm. 620, New York, NY 10036. TEL 212-642-2929. FAX 212-642-1956. Ed. Frank Riessman. adv. contact: Audrey Gartner. bk.rev.; illus.; circ. 4,000 (paid). (also avail. in microform from UMI,JAI; reprint service avail. from UMI) **Indexed**: A.B.C.Pol.Sci., Acad.Ind., Alt.Press Ind., Amer.Hist.& Life (until 1991), ASCA, ASSIA, C.I.J.E., Curr.Cont., Film Lit.Ind. (1990-), Fut.Surv., Hist.Abstr. (until 1991), Int.Polit.Sci.Abstr., Lang.& Lang.Behav.Abstr., Left Ind. (1982-), Med.Care Rev., MEDSOC, Mid.East: Abstr.& Ind., Pers.Lit., Polit.Sci.Abstr., Sage Pub.Admin.Abstr., Soc.Sci.Ind., Soc.Work Res.& Abstr., SSCI.
●Also available online. Vendor(s): University Microfilms International.
Also available on CD-ROM. Producer(s): H.W. Wilson.
—BLDSC (8318.130100); Faxon; Genuine Article; SWETS; UMI; UnCover.
Description: Contemporary social thought on policy issues and action.

350 658   UK   ISSN 0144-5596
H1
SOCIAL POLICY AND ADMINISTRATION. 1967. q. £110($229) (foreign £142) (effective 1996). Basil Blackwell Ltd., 108 Cowley Rd., Oxford OX4 1JF, England. TEL 0865-791100. FAX 0865-791347. TELEX 837022-OXBOOK-G. Ed. R.A.B. Leaper. adv.; bk.rev.; bibl.; charts; illus.; stat.; index. circ. 900. (reprint service avail. from SWZ) **Indexed**: Abstr.Crim.& Pen., Abstr.Hyg., Adol.Ment.Hlth.Abstr., ASCA, Asian-Pac.Econ.Lit., ASSIA, Curr.Cont., Lang.& Lang.Behav.Abstr., Med. Care Rev., Res.High.Educ.Abstr., Rural Recreat.Tour.Abstr., Sociol.Educ.Abstr., SSCI, Stud.Wom.Abstr., World Agri.Econ.& Rural Sociol.Abstr., World Bank.Abstr., World Bibl.Soc.Sec.
—BLDSC (8318.130400); Faxon; Genuine Article; SWETS; UMI; UnCover. **CCC**.
Formerly: Social and Economic Administration (ISSN 0037-7643)

301   US   ISSN 0037-7791
HN1   CODEN: SOPRAG
SOCIAL PROBLEMS. 1953. q. $85 to individuals and institutions (foreign $91) (effective 1996). (Society for the Study of Social Problems, Inc.) University of California Press, Journals Division, 2120 Berkeley Way, Berkeley, CA 94720. TEL 510-643-7154. FAX 510-642-9917. Ed. Robert Perrucci. adv.; bk.rev.; bibl.; charts; index, cum.index: vols.1-17, 1952-1970; vols.18-28, 1970-1981. circ. 3,800. (also avail. in microform from MIM,UMI; back issues avail.; reprint service avail. from UMI) **Indexed**: Abstr.Crim.& Pen., Abstr.Pop.Cult. (until 19??), Abstr.Soc.Work, Acad.Ind., Amer.Hist.& Life, ASCA, ASSIA, C.I.J.E., Commun.Abstr., Crim.Just.Abstr., Curr.Cont., Excerp.Med., Fut.Surv., Hist.Abstr., Int.Polit.Sci.Abstr., Mid.East: Abstr.& Ind., Mult.Ed.Abstr., P.A.I.S., Psychol.Abstr. (1954-), Res.High.Educ.Abstr., Soc.Sci.Ind., Soc.Work Res.& Abstr., Sociol.Abstr. (1953-), Sociol.Educ.Abstr., SSCI, Stud.Wom.Abstr. Document type: academic/scholarly publication.
●Also available online. Vendor(s): University Microfilms International.
—BLDSC (8318.136000); Faxon; Genuine Article; SWETS; UMI; UnCover. **CCC**.
Description: Provides a major forum for critical theoretical discussion and dialogue regarding controversial social issues and programs.
Refereed Serial

SOCIAL PSYCHOLOGICAL APPLICATIONS TO SOCIAL ISSUES. see *PSYCHOLOGY*

301.1   US   ISSN 0190-2725
HM1
SOCIAL PSYCHOLOGY QUARTERLY. 1937. q. $40 to individuals (foreign $50); institutions $80 (foreign $90). American Sociological Association, 1722 N St., N.W., Washington, DC 20036. TEL 202-833-3410. FAX 202-785-0146. Ed. Edward J. Lawler. adv.; bibl.; index. circ. 5,000. (also avail. in microform from MIM,UMI; reprint service avail. from UMI) **Indexed**: Adol.Ment.Hlth.Abstr., ASCA, ASSIA, Crim.Just.Abstr., Curr.Cont., Educ.Admin.Abstr., IMFL, Int.Polit.Sci.Abstr., Lang.& Lang.Behav.Abstr., M.L.A., Mid.East: Abstr.& Ind., Mult.Ed.Abstr., Psychol.Abstr. (1937-), Soc.Sci.Ind., Sociol.Abstr. (1953-), SSCI, Stud.Wom.Abstr. Document type: academic/scholarly publication.
—BLDSC (8318.146300); Faxon; Genuine Article; SWETS; UMI; UnCover.
Former titles (until 1978): Social Psychology (ISSN 0147-829X); (until 1977): Sociometry (ISSN 0038-0431)
Description: Publishes papers pertaining to the processes and products of social interaction. Includes the study of the primary relations of individuals to one another or to groups, collectives, or institutions, and the study of intra-individual processes insofar as they substantially influence, or are influenced by, social forces.

SOCIAL QUESTIONS BULLETIN. see *RELIGIONS AND THEOLOGY — Protestant*

305.5   US   ISSN 1075-3486
▼**SOCIAL REGISTER OBSERVER**. (Supplement to: Social Register) 1994. s-a. Social Register Association, 381 Park Ave. S., New York, NY 10805. TEL 212-685-2634. Ed.Bd. pp./issue: 34. Document type: newsletter.

SOCIAL SCIENCE & MEDICINE. see *MEDICAL SCIENCES*

SOCIAL SCIENCE INFORMATION. see *SOCIAL SCIENCES: COMPREHENSIVE WORKS*

301.15   SZ
SOCIAL STRATEGIES; monographs on sociology and social policy-monographien zur Soziologie und Gesellschaftspolitik. (Text in English, French and German) 1975. irreg., no.17, 1985. price varies. Social Strategies Publishers Co-Operative Society, Petersgraben 27, CH-4051 Basel, Switzerland. TEL 061-258881. Ed. Paul Trappe. adv.; bk.rev. circ. 2,000.

SOCIAL STUDIES OF SCIENCE; an international review of research in the social dimensions of science and technology. see *SCIENCES: COMPREHENSIVE WORKS*

SOCIOLOGY

301   HN1   US   ISSN 0164-2472
SOCIAL TEXT; theory, culture, ideology. 1979. 4/yr. $26 to individuals (foreign $38); institutions $66 (foreign $78) (effective 1996). Duke University Press, 6697 College Sta., Box 90660, Durham, NC 27708-0660. TEL 919-687-3600. FAX 919-688-4574. TELEX 802829. Eds. Bruce Robbins, Andrew Ross. adv.: B&W page $200. circ. 1,500. **Indexed:** Alt.Press Ind., Lang.& Lang.Behav.Abstr., Left Ind. (1984-).
—BLDSC (8318.217700); Faxon; SWETS; UnCover.

301   NE   ISSN 0926-3977
SOCIALE INTERVENTIE. 1972. bi-m. fl.75 to individuals; institutions fl.105 (foreign fl.108) (effective 1994). Uitgeverij Boom, P.O. Box 400, 7940 AK Meppel, Netherlands. TEL 31-5220-57012. FAX 31-5220-53864. circ. 1,200.
—SWETS.
  Former titles (until 1992): T V A (ISSN 0921-5271); (until 1986): Tijdschrift voor Agologie (ISSN 0168-8626)

SOCIALNI POLITIKA. see *POLITICAL SCIENCE*

301   UY   ISSN 0081-0649
SOCIEDAD URUGUAYA.* irreg. Editorial Arca, Colonia 1263, Montevideo, Uruguay.

309 360   HN281   BL   ISSN 0102-6992   CODEN: SOESE2
SOCIEDADE E ESTADO. 1986. s-a. Editora Universidade de Brasilia, Caixa Postal 04551, 70919-970 Brasilia D.F., Brazil. FAX 061-274-5352. TELEX 611083 UNBS BR.

301.34 914.603   PO
SOCIEDADE E TERRITORIO. 1984. irreg., no.20, 1994. Esc.5000 (Europe Esc.8000; elsewhere Esc.9000). Edicoes Afrontamento, Lda., Rua de Costa Cabral, 859, Apdo. 2009, 4201 Porto, Portugal. TEL 351-2-529271. FAX 351-2-591777. Ed. Antonio Fonseca Ferreira.

301   IT
LE SOCIETA. 1981. m. L.250000 (foreign L.500000). I P S O A s.r.l. (Subsidiary of: Wolters Kluwer N.V.), Strada 1, Palazzo F6, 20090 Assago Milanofiori (MI), Italy. TEL 39-2-824761. Ed. Francesco Zuzic. adv.: B&W page L.4000000; adv. contact: Luciano Alcaro Menichini. circ. 17,840.

301   IT
SOCIETA E AMBIENTE. 1991. irreg., no.4, 1992. price varies. Liguori Editore s.r.l., Via Mezzocannone 19, 80134 Naples, Italy. TEL 081-5527139. Ed. Franco Martinelli. **Document type:** monographic series.

301 320.531   FR
SOCIETE FRANCAISE. 1981. bi-m. 250 F. (foreign 500 F.). C R E S F, B.P. 226, 75018 Paris, France. Ed. Serge Melikow. adv.; bk.rev.; cum.index. circ. 2,500.

301   CN   ISSN 0537-6211
SOCIETE SAINT-JEAN-BAPTISTE DE MONTREAL. INFORMATION NATIONALE. 1962. m. Can.$5. Societe de Publication l'Information Nationale Inc., 82 rue Sherbrooke, W., Montreal, Que. H2x 1X3, Canada. TEL 514-843-8851. Ed. Pierre Lussier. adv.; bk.rev.; illus. circ. 15,000.
  Formerly: Societe Saint-Jean-Baptiste de Montreal Bulletin.

301   FR   ISSN 0765-3697
SOCIETES; revue des sciences humaines et sociales. 1984. 4/yr. 540 F. Dunod, 15 rue Gossin, 92543 Montrouge Cedex, France. TEL 33-1-40-92-65-00. FAX 33-1-40-92-65-97. TELEX 634 916 F. (Subscr. to: Centrale des Revues, 11 rue Gossin, 92543 Montrouge Cedex, France. TEL 33-1-46-56-52-66) Ed. M. Maffesoli.
—BLDSC (8319.181500). CCC.
  Description: Brings all the necessary information about research, about the different activities published in sociology, and the ways of integrating specialized knowledge in a large reflection.

301   FR   ISSN 1150-1944
SOCIETES CONTEMPORAINES. 1990. q. 280 F. (foreign 320 F.). (Institut de Recherche sur les Societes Contemporaines) Editions l' Harmattan, 77 rue Blomet, 75015 Paris, France. TEL 48-42-47-44. Eds. Alain Degenne, Edmond Preteceille.

301 572   CN   ISSN 0381-1794
SOCIETY/SOCIETE. (Text in English, French) 1977. 3/yr. Can.$94.16 (foreign Can.$98). Canadian Sociology and Anthropology Association, Concordia University, 1455 bd. de Maisonneuve W., Montreal, PQ H3G 1M8, Canada. TEL 514-848-8780. FAX 514-848-4539. E-mail: csaa@vax2.concordia.ca. Ed. Arlene McLaren. circ. 1,700. (reprint service avail. from UMI) **Indexed:** Amer.Bibl.Slavic & E.Eur.Stud., Anthropol.Lit., Sociol.Abstr. (1978-). **Document type:** newsletter.
  Description: Internal publication of official documents of the Society.

SOCIETY FOR THE SCIENTIFIC STUDY OF RELIGION. MONOGRAPH SERIES. see *RELIGIONS AND THEOLOGY*

THE SOCIETY NEWSLETTER. see *PSYCHOLOGY*

SOCIO-ECONOMIC PLANNING SCIENCES; the international journal of public sector decision-making. see *PUBLIC ADMINISTRATION*

SOCIO-ECONOMIC REVIEW OF PUNJAB. see *BUSINESS AND ECONOMICS — Economic Situation And Conditions*

SOCIO-ECONOMIC SERIES. see *AGRICULTURE*

SOCIOCRITICISM: LITERATURE, SOCIETY, AND HISTORY. see *LITERATURE*

301   NE   ISSN 0165-1676
SOCIODROME;* platform voor sociale wetenschappers. 5/yr. fl.57.50. Uitgeverij Boom, P.O. Box 400, 7940 AK Meppel, Netherlands. TEL 31-5220-57012. FAX 31-5220-53864. Ed.Bd. circ. 1,700.

309   US
SOCIOECONOMIC NEWSLETTER. 1976. 6/yr. free. Institute for Socioeconomic Studies, Airport Rd., White Plains, NY 10604. TEL 914-428-7400. Ed. B.A. Rittersporn, Jr. charts; illus.; circ. 17,500 (controlled). (also avail. in microfiche from WSH;PMC) **Indexed:** Lang.& Lang.Behav.Abstr.

301   XO   ISSN 0049-1225
SOCIOLOGIA/SOCIOLOGY. (Text in Slovak; summaries in English and Russian) 1969. bi-m. $22. Slovenska Akademia Vied, Sociologicky Ustav, Klemensova 19, 814 30 Bratislava, Slovakia. (Dist. in Western countries by: John Benjamins B.V., Amsteldijk 44, Amsterdam (Z.), Netherlands) Ed. V. Bauch.
  Description: Publishes original contributions from the theory, history and methodology of sociology and scientific communism, methods and techniques of sociologic research, critics of non-Marxist theories, problems of social development from capitalism to communism.

301   IT
SOCIOLOGIA (NAPLES). no.4, 1975. irreg. Societa Editrice Napoletana s.r.l., Corso Umberto I 34, 80138 Naples, Italy. Ed. Aurelio Paolinelli. **Indexed:** Int.Polit.Sci.Abstr., Lang.& Lang.Behav.Abstr., Sociol.Abstr. (1957-).

301   IT   ISSN 0038-0156
HM7
SOCIOLOGIA (ROME); rivista di scienze storiche e sociali. 1956. 3/yr. L.85000. Istituto Luigi Sturzo, Via delle Coppelle 35, 00186 Rome, Italy. TEL 39-6-6892390. FAX 39-6-6864704. Ed. Gabriele De Rosa. adv.; bibl. **Document type:** monographic series, proceedings.
—BLDSC (8319.598000).

301   IT
SOCIOLOGIA DEI MEDIA. 1988. irreg., no.5, 1992. price varies. Liguori Editore s.r.l., Via Mezzocannone, 19, 80134 Naples, Italy. TEL 081-5527139. Eds. Giovanni Bechelloni, Milly Buonanno. **Document type:** monographic series.

301.2   IT
SOCIOLOGIA DEI PROGRESSI CULTURALI. 1989. irreg., no.2, 1990. price varies. Liguori Editore s.r.l., Via Mezzocannone, 19, 80134 Naples, Italy. TEL 081-5527139. Ed. Giovanni Bechelloni. **Document type:** monographic series.

301   IT   ISSN 1121-1148
SOCIOLOGIA E RICERCA SOCIALE. 1980. 3/yr. L.69000 (foreign L.90000) (effective 1993). Franco Angeli Editore, Viale Monza, 106, Casella Postale 17175, 20100 Milan, Italy. TEL 02-2895762. Ed. G. Statera. **Indexed:** Sociol.Abstr. (1981-). **Document type:** academic/scholarly publication.

301.15   II
SOCIOLOGIA INDICA. (Text in English) 1977. s-a? (Indian Institute of Sociology) Pearl Publishers, 206, Bidhan Sarani, Calcutta 6, India. Ed. Swapn Kumar Bhattacharyya. adv.; bk.rev.

SOCIOLOGIA RURALIS. see *AGRICULTURE*

301   IT   ISSN 0392-4939
HM7
SOCIOLOGIA URBANA E RURALE. 1979. 3/yr. L.69000 (foreign L.90000) (effective 1993). Franco Angeli Editore, Viale Monza 106, 20127 Milan, Italy. TEL 02-28-27-651. Ed. Paolo Guidicini. **Document type:** academic/scholarly publication.

301 320   MX   ISSN 1405-096X
SOCIOLOGIA Y POLITICA. 1992. s-a. $20 (effective 1995). Universidad Iberoamericana, Departamento de Ciencias Sociales y Politicas, Prol. Paseo de la Reforma 880, Col. Lomas de Santa Fe, 0210 Mexico DF, Mexico. TEL 5-292-21-49. FAX 5-726-90-48. Ed. Silvia Narvaez. bk.rev.; illus. circ. 400. **Document type:** academic/scholarly publication.
  Description: Offers social analysis on socio-economic, political, and cultural processes from a scientific and interdisciplinary perspective.

301   MX   ISSN 0187-0173
SOCIOLOGICA. 1986. 3/yr. Mex.$60($30) in Latin America; US and Europe $50 (effective 1995). Universidad Autonoma Metropolitana, Departamento de Sociologia, Av. San Pablo 180, Azcapotzalco, 02200 Mexico, D.F., Mexico. TEL 525-724-4339. FAX 525-394-8093. Ed. Jose Othon Quiroz Trejo; Pub. Jose Hernandez Prado. bk.rev. circ. 2,000. **Document type:** academic/scholarly publication.
• Also available on CD-ROM.
  Description: Presents research in theoretical and practical sociology.

301   II   ISSN 0038-0229
HN681
SOCIOLOGICAL BULLETIN. (Text in English) 1951. s-a. $45. Indian Sociological Society, Centre for the Study of Social Systems, Jawaharlal Nehru University, New Delhi 110057, India. TEL 91-11-6863066. FAX 91-11-6865886. Ed. M.N. Panini. adv.; bk.rev.; bibl.; stat.; index, cum.index. circ. 1,500. (also avail. in microform; diskette format; back issues avail.) **Indexed:** Amer.Hist.& Life, ASSIA, Hist.Abstr., Lang.& Lang.Behav.Abstr., Sociol.Abstr. (1953-), SSCI. **Document type:** academic/scholarly publication.
—UnCover.
  Description: Contains papers all over the world to provide comparative analysis of social structures, social processes and cultures.

301   US   ISSN 0038-0237
HM1
SOCIOLOGICAL FOCUS. 1967. q. $45 to institutions (foreign $50). North Central Sociological Association, c/o Dept. of Sociology, Western Michigan University, Kalamazoo, MI 49008. TEL 616-387-3607. FAX 616-387-2882. Ed. Stanley Robbin. adv.; bk.rev.; bibl.; charts. circ. 900. (also avail. in microform from UMI,PMC; microfilm from WSH; reprint service avail. from UMI,WSH) **Indexed:** ASCA, ASSIA, C.I.I., Curr.Cont., Lang.& Lang.Behav.Abstr., Leg.Per., Mid.East: Abstr.& Ind., Sociol.Abstr. (1967-), Sp.Ed.Needs Abstr., SSCI, Stud.Wom.Abstr. **Document type:** academic/scholarly publication.
—BLDSC (8319.624500); Faxon; Genuine Article; SWETS; UMI; UnCover.
  Description: Publishes work representing all aspects of sociology and its subdisciplines, including theory, empirical studies, qualitative and quantitative research and applied work with policy implications.

SOCIOLOGY

301 US ISSN 0884-8971
HM1
SOCIOLOGICAL FORUM. 1986. q. $195 (foreign $230) (effective 1996). (Eastern Sociological Society) Plenum Publishing Corp., 233 Spring St., New York, NY 10013-1578. TEL 212-620-8000. FAX 212-463-0742. TELEX 23-421139. Ed. Stephen Cole. adv. (also avail. in microfilm from JSC) **Indexed:** IMFL, Psychol.Abstr. (1986-), Sociol.Abstr. **Document type:** academic/scholarly publication.
—BLDSC (8319.624600); Faxon; Genuine Article; SWETS; UMI; UnCover. **CCC.**
Description: Examines and presents the central interests of sociology in social organization and change as generic phenomena.
Refereed Serial

301 US ISSN 1077-5048
HM1 CODEN: SIMAEE
SOCIOLOGICAL IMAGINATION. 1960. q. $18 to individuals; libraries $25 (foreign $35) (effective 1995-1996). Wisconsin Sociological Association, University of Wisconsin at Whitewater, Department of Sociology, Whitewater, WI 53190. TEL 414-472-1133. FAX 414-472-5238. E-mail: Bergerr@uwwvax.uww.edu. Eds. Ronald J. Berger, Bruce Wiegand. adv.; bk.rev.; circ. 500 (paid). (processed) **Indexed:** Lang.& Lang.Behav.Abstr., Sociol.Abstr. (1962-). **Document type:** academic/scholarly publication.
Formerly (until 1994): Wisconsin Sociologist (ISSN 0043-6666)
Description: Covers issues pertaining all areas of sociological inquiry and practice, including basic and applied research, teaching and curriculum matters, and clinical practice.
Refereed Serial

301 US ISSN 0038-0245
HM1
SOCIOLOGICAL INQUIRY. 1930. q. $21 to individuals; institutions $43. (Alpha Kappa Delta - International Sociology Honor Society) University of Texas Press, Box 7819, Austin, TX 78713. TEL 512-471-4531. FAX 512-320-0668. TELEX 776453 UTEXPRES AUS. E-mail: leah@utpress.ppb.utexas.edu. Eds. Joane Nagle, William Staples. adv. contact: Leah Dixon. bk.rev.; abstr.; index. circ. 3,000. (also avail. in microform from UMI; reprint service avail. from SCH,UMI) **Indexed:** A.B.C.Pol.Sci., Adol.Ment.Hlth.Abstr., Amer.Hist.& Life, ASCA, ASSIA, Commun.Abstr., Crim.Just.Abstr., Curr.Cont., Educ.Admin.Abstr., Hist.Abstr., IMFL, Int.Polit.Sci.Abstr., Lang.& Lang.Behav.Abstr., Mid.East: Abstr.& Ind., Mult.Ed.Abstr., Peace Res.Abstr., Polit.Sci.Abstr., Soc.Sci.Ind., Sociol.Abstr. (1959-), Sociol.Educ.Abstr., Sp.Ed.Needs Abstr., SSCI, Stud.Wom.Abstr. **Document type:** academic/scholarly publication.
—BLDSC (8319.625000); Faxon; Genuine Article; SWETS; UMI; UnCover. **CCC.**
Description: Publishes the work of researchers and theorists in sociology.

301.01 US ISSN 0081-1750
HM24
SOCIOLOGICAL METHODOLOGY. 1969. a. $62 to individuals in N. America (elsewhere $70); institutions in N. America $73 (elsewhere $97). (American Sociological Association) Blackwell Publishers, 238 Main St., Cambridge, MA 02142. TEL 617-547-7110. FAX 617-547-0789. Ed. Peter V. Marsden. circ. 1,450. (also avail. in microform from UMI; back issues avail.; reprint service avail. from UMI) **Indexed:** Int.Polit.Sci.Abstr., Lang.& Lang.Behav.Abstr., Sociol.Abstr. (1978-).
—BLDSC (8319.629000); Genuine Article; SWETS; UMI.
Description: Publishes the best work on current issues in methodology for social research.

301 US ISSN 0049-1241
HM1
SOCIOLOGICAL METHODS & RESEARCH. Abbreviated title: S M R. 1972. q. $68 to individuals; institutions $205 (effective Sep. 1995). Sage Publications, Inc., 2455 Teller Rd., Thousand Oaks, CA 91320. TEL 805-499-0721. FAX 805-499-0871. E-mail: libraries@sagepub.com. (Overseas subscr. to: Sage Publications Ltd., 6 Bonhill St., London EC2A 4PU, England; Sage Publications India Pvt. Ltd., P.O. Box 4215, New Delhi 110 048, India) Ed. Christopher Winship. adv.; bk.rev.; charts; illus.; index. circ. 1,550. (also avail. in microform from UMI; back issues avail.; reprint service avail. from UMI) **Indexed:** ASCA, ASSIA, Commun.Abstr., Curr.Cont., Curr.Ind.Stat., IMFL, J.Cont.Quant.Meth., Lang.& Lang.Behav.Abstr., Mid.East: Abstr.& Ind., P.A.I.S., Pers.Lit., Sage Pub.Admin.Abstr., Soc.Work Res.& Abstr., Sociol.Abstr. (1975-), Sociol.Educ.Abstr., SSCI. **Document type:** academic/scholarly publication.
—BLDSC (8319.629500); Faxon; Genuine Article; SWETS; UMI. **CCC.**
Description: Disseminates quantitative research and methodology in the social sciences.

301 DK ISSN 0106-536X
SOCIOLOGICAL MICROJOURNAL. (Text in English, French and German) 1967. a. DKK 55($8) Erik Manniche and Kaare Svalastoga, Eds. & Pubs., 22 Linnegade, 1361 Copenhagen K, Denmark. (back issues avail.)

301 572 US ISSN 0149-4872
SOCIOLOGICAL OBSERVATIONS. 1977. irreg., vol.21, 1992. $20.95 (hardcover edition $42) (effective 1994). Sage Publications, Inc., 2455 Teller Rd., Thousand Oaks, CA 91320. TEL 805-499-0721. FAX 805-499-0871. E-mail: libraries@sagepub.com. (Overseas subscr. to: Sage Publications Ltd., 6 Bonhill St., London EC2A 4PU, England; Sage Publications India Pvt. Ltd., P.O. Box 4215, New Delhi 110 048, India) Ed. John M. Johnson. (back issues avail.; reprint service avail.) **Document type:** monographic series.
—BLDSC (8319.629800).

300 IS ISSN 0793-1069
SOCIOLOGICAL PAPERS. 1992. 4/yr. with a cumulation. free. (Leon Tamman Foundation for Research into Jewish Communities) Sociological Institute for Community Studies, Bar-Ilan University, Ramat Gan 52900, Israel. TEL 972-3-5344449. FAX 972-3-5351825. Eds. Ernest Krausz, Gitta Tulea. circ. 400. **Document type:** academic/scholarly publication.
Description: Presents individual research and theoretical articles concerning new developments in social life, including community life, ethnic relations, problems and developments in the fields of religion, education, the family, social stratification and mobility.
Refereed Serial

301 US ISSN 0731-1214
HM1
SOCIOLOGICAL PERSPECTIVES. 1958. q. $70 to individuals (foreign $90); institutions $170 (foreign $190) (effective 1996). (Pacific Sociological Association) J A I Press Inc., 55 Old Post Rd., No. 2, Box 1678, Greenwich, CT 06836-1678. TEL 203-661-7602. FAX 203-661-0792. (Addr. in Europe: J A I Press Ltd., The Courtyard, 28 High St., Hampton Hill, Mddx. TW12 1PD, England. TEL 44-181-943-9296. FAX 44-181-943-9317) Bd.Ed. adv.; charts; stat.; index, cum.index every 5 yrs. (also avail. in microform from UMI; back issues avail.; reprint service avail. from UMI) **Indexed:** A.B.C.Pol.Sci., Abstr.Crim.& Pen., Abstr.Soc.Work., Amer.Hist.& Life, ASCA, CERDIC, Curr.Cont., Hist.Abstr, IMFL, Int.Polit.Sci.Abstr., Lang.& Lang.Behav.Abstr., Mid.East: Abstr.& Ind., Mult.Ed.Abstr., Polit.Sci.Abstr., Psychol.Abstr. (1985-), Sage Urb.Stud.Abstr., Soc.Sci.Ind. (1994-), Soc.Work Res.& Abstr., Sociol.Abstr. (1958-), Sociol.Educ.Abstr., SSCI, Stud.Wom.Abstr. **Document type:** academic/scholarly publication.
—BLDSC (8319.629860); Faxon; Genuine Article; SWETS; UnCover. **CCC.**
Formerly (until 1982): Pacific Sociological Review (ISSN 0030-8919)

301 US ISSN 0163-8505
HM1
SOCIOLOGICAL PRACTICE. 1976. a. $30. Sociological Practice Association, c/o Mel Fein, Kennesaw State University, 4531 Blackwater, Marietta, GA 30066. TEL 404-928-1063. Ed. Mel Fein. bk.rev.; stat. circ. 500. (also avail. in microform from UMI; reprint service avail. from UMI) **Indexed:** Lang.& Lang.Behav.Abstr., Sociol.Abstr. (1976-). **Document type:** academic/scholarly publication.
—BLDSC (8319.629900); UMI; UnCover.
Formerly (1976-1977): S P: Sociological Practice (ISSN 0360-845X)

301 US ISSN 0038-0253
HM1 CODEN: SOLQAR
SOCIOLOGICAL QUARTERLY. 1960. q. $55 to individuals (foreign $65); institutions $145 (foreign $165). Midwest Sociological Society, J A I Press Inc., 55 Old Post Rd., No. 2, Greenwich, CT 06836-1678. TEL 203-661-7602. FAX 203-661-0792. (Addr. in Europe: J A I Press Ltd., The Courtyard, 28 High St., Hampton Hill, Mddx., TW12 1PD, England. TEL 44-181-943-9296. FAX 44-181-943-9317) Ed. Thomas G. Eynon. adv.; bk.rev.; charts; illus.; index, cum.index: 1953-1973, 1974-1983. circ. 2,550. (also avail. in microform from AMS,UMI,PMC; microfilm from WSH; back issues avail.; reprint service avail. from UMI,WSH) **Indexed:** A.B.C.Pol.Sci., Abstr.Crim.& Pen., Abstr.Soc.Work, Adol.Ment.Hlth.Abstr., Amer.Bibl.Slavic & E.Eur.Stud., Amer.Hist.& Life, ASCA, ASSIA, CERDIC, Commun.Abstr., Cont.Pg.Manage., Crim.Just.Abstr., Curr.Cont., E.I., Hist.Abstr, IMFL, Int.Polit.Sci.Abstr., Lang.& Lang.Behav.Abstr., Mid.East: Abstr.& Ind., Mult.Ed.Abstr., PSI, Psychol.Abstr. (1972-), Soc.Sci.Ind., Soc.Work Res.& Abstr., Sociol.Abstr. (1960-), Sociol.Educ.Abstr., SSCI, Stud.Wom.Abstr. **Document type:** academic/scholarly publication.
—BLDSC (8319.630000); Faxon; Genuine Article; SWETS; UnCover. **CCC.**
Formerly: Midwest Sociologist.

301 US ISSN 1061-0154
HX542
SOCIOLOGICAL RESEARCH; a journal of translations from scholarly Soviet sources. 1962. bi-m. $557 to institutions (foreign $630) (effective Jul. 1995). M.E. Sharpe, Inc., 80 Business Park Dr., Armonk, NY 10504. TEL 914-273-1800; 800-541-6563. FAX 914-273-2106. Ed. Murray Yanowitch. adv.; index. (back issues avail.) **Indexed:** Adol.Ment.Hlth.Abstr., Curr.Cont., P.A.I.S., Sage.Fam.Stud.Abstr., SSCI. **Document type:** academic/scholarly publication.
—BLDSC (8319.636000); Faxon; SWETS; UMI; UnCover. **CCC.**
Formerly (until 1992): Soviet Sociology (ISSN 0038-5824)
Refereed Serial

301 UK
▼**SOCIOLOGICAL RESEARCH ONLINE;** an electronic journal. Announced for publication in 1996. irreg. free. Sage Publications Ltd., 6 Bonhill St., London EC2 4PU, England. TEL 44-171-3740645. FAX 44-171-3748741. E-mail: market@sageltd.co.uk. Eds. Martin Bulmer, Liz Stanley.
●Available only online.

SOCIOLOGY

301   UK   ISSN 0038-0261
HM1
SOCIOLOGICAL REVIEW. 1908; N.S. 1953. bi-m.
£102($192) (foreign £119) (effective 1996).
(University of Keele) Basil Blackwell Ltd., 108
Cowley Rd., Oxford OX4 1JF, England.
TEL 01865-791100. FAX 01865-791347. TELEX
837022 OXBOOK G. Ed.Bd. adv.; bk.rev.; bibl.;
charts; index, cum.index. circ. 2,000. (also avail. in
microform from UMI; reprint service avail. from
UMI,KTO) **Indexed:** A.I.C.P., Adol.Ment.Hlth.Abstr.,
Amer.Hist.& Life, ASCA, ASSIA, Bk.Rev.Ind. (1965-),
Br.Hum.Ind., Child.Bk.Rev.Ind. (1965-),
Cont.Pg.Manage., Curr.Cont., Geo.Abstr., Hist.Abstr.,
IMFL, Int.Polit.Sci.Abstr., Lang.& Lang.Behav.Abstr.,
Mid.East: Abstr.& Ind., Psychol.Abstr.,
Res.High.Educ.Abstr., Risk Abstr., Soc.Sci.Ind.,
Sociol.Abstr. (1962-), Sociol.Educ.Abstr.,
Sp.Ed.Needs Abstr., SSCI, Stud.Wom.Abstr.,
Tech.Educ.Abstr.
—BLDSC (8319.640000); Faxon; Genuine Article;
SWETS; UMI; UnCover.
Description: Discusses subjects related to
sociology, with topical essays on health and work,
job training, equal opportunities and skills, social
attitudes to family relationships, and more.

301   US   ISSN 0273-2173
HM1   CODEN: SOSPDS
SOCIOLOGICAL SPECTRUM. 1980. q. £87($143)
(effective 1996). (Mid-South Sociological
Association) Taylor & Francis Inc., 1900 Frost Rd.,
Ste. 101, Bristol, PA 19007-1598.
TEL 215-785-5800; 800-821-8312.
FAX 215-785-5515. (Subscr. in Europe to: Taylor &
Francis Ltd., Rankine Rd., Basingstoke, Hants. RG24
8PR, England. TEL 44-1256-840366. FAX
44-1256-479438) Eds. Charles E. Faupel, Arthur S.
Wilke. adv.; bk.rev.; abstr.; bibl.; illus.; stat.; index.
circ. 600. (back issues avail.; reprint service avail.
from UMI) **Indexed:** ASCA, Curr.Cont., IMFL, Lang.&
Lang.Behav.Abstr., Mid.East: Abstr.& Ind.,
Sociol.Abstr. (1981-), SSCI. **Document type:**
academic/scholarly publication.
—BLDSC (8319.647800); Faxon; Genuine Article;
UMI; UnCover. **CCC.**
Formed by the merger of: Sociological Symposium
(ISSN 0038-027X); Sociological Forum (ISSN
0160-3469)
Description: Discusses current thoughts in
theoretical and applied psychology, education, social
psychology, political science, and anthropology.
Refereed Serial

SOCIOLOGICAL STUDIES. see POLITICAL SCIENCE —
International Relations

301   US   ISSN 0735-2751
HM24
SOCIOLOGICAL THEORY. 3/yr. $48 to individuals in N.
America (elsewhere $55.50); institutions in N.
America $66.50 (elsewhere $74). (American
Sociological Association) Blackwell Publishers, 238
Main St., Cambridge, MA 02142.
TEL 617-547-7110. FAX 617-547-0789. Ed. Craig
Calhoun. adv.: page $315; trim 5 x 8 1/2. circ.
2,200. **Indexed:** Sociol.Abstr. (1983-).
—BLDSC (8319.650150); Faxon; SWETS; UMI;
UnCover.
Description: Covers sociological theory, new
substantive theories, history of theory, metatheory,
and formal theory construction.

301   US   ISSN 1060-0876
SOCIOLOGICAL VIEWPOINTS. 1984. a. $5 to individuals;
institutions $10; students $3. Pennsylvania
Sociological Society, c/o University of Scranton,
Scranton, PA 18510-4605. TEL 717-941-7425.
FAX 717-941-6369. Ed. Edward J. Rielly. bk.rev.;
bibl. circ. 250. (back issues avail.) **Indexed:**
Sociol.Abstr. (1987-). **Document type:**
academic/scholarly publication.
Description: Publishes articles and critical essays
on topics in sociology, including original empirical
research, methodological and theoretical issues, and
critiques of social events.
Refereed Serial

301   BU   ISSN 0324-1572
SOCIOLOGICESKI PROBLEMI. (Contents page and
summaries in English and Russian) 1969. 6/yr.
1.50 lv. per no. (Bulgarska Akademiia na Naukite,
Institut po Sotsiologiia) Publishing House of the
Bulgarian Academy of Sciences, Acad. G. Bonchev
St., Bldg. 6, 1113 Sofia, Bulgaria. (Dist. by: Hemus,
6, Rouski Blvd., 1000 Sofia, Bulgaria) (Co-sponsor:
Bulgarska Sotsiologicheska Asotsiatsiia) Ed. Niko
Jahiel. bk.rev.; cum.index. circ. 470. (reprint service avail. from
IRC)

301   XR   ISSN 0038-0288
HM7   CODEN: SLCSB2
SOCIOLOGICKY CASOPIS/SOCIOLOGICAL REVIEW. (Text
in Czech; contents page in English, French, German
and Russian; summaries in English, Russian) 1965.
bi-m. DM.136. Ceska Akademie Ved, Sociologicky
Ustav, Jilska 1, 110 00 Prague 1, Czech Republic.
TEL 231-91-15. (Dist. in Western countries by:
Kubon & Sagner, P.O. Box 34 01 08, 8000 Munich
34, Germany) Ed. Karel Rychtarik. adv.; bk.rev.;
abstr.; bibl. **Indexed:** Abstr.Crim.& Pen., ASCA,
Bibl.Ling., Bull.Signal., Lang.& Lang.Behav.Abstr.,
Psychol.Abstr., Sociol.Abstr. (1965-), SSCI.
—Genuine Article.
Description: Covers studies devoted to general
sociology and methodology, and to specialized
sociological fields in Czechoslovakia and abroad.

SOCIOLOGIE DU TRAVAIL. see BUSINESS AND
ECONOMICS — *Labor And Industrial Relations*

301   CN   ISSN 0038-030X
HM3
SOCIOLOGIE ET SOCIETES. (Text in French; summaries
in English, French, Spanish) 1969. s-a. Can.$28 to
individuals; institutions Can.$48. Presses de
l'Universite de Montreal, C.P. 6128, Succ. A,
Montreal, PQ H3C 3J7, Canada.
TEL 514-343-6933. Ed. Louis Maheu. adv.; bibl.;
charts; stat. circ. 2,500. (also avail. in microform;
reprint service avail. from UMI) **Indexed:**
Can.Wom.Per.Ind., Curr.Cont., Int.Lab.Doc.,
Int.Polit.Sci.Abstr., Lang.& Lang.Behav.Abstr.,
P.A.I.S.For.Lang.Ind., Psychol.Abstr., Pt.de Rep.
(1979-), RAPRA, Sociol.Abstr. (1969-), SSCI.
Document type: academic/scholarly publication.
—BLDSC (8319.650800); SWETS; UMI.

301   FR   ISSN 0220-777X
SOCIOLOGIE PERMANENTE. 1978. irreg. Editions du
Seuil, 27 rue Jacob, 75261 Paris Cedex 6, France.
Dir. Alain Touraine. **Document type:**
academic/scholarly publication.

301   RM   ISSN 1220-5389
SOCIOLOGIE ROMANEASCA. English edition: Romanian
Journal of Sociology (ISSN 1220-3688) (Text in
Rumanian; summaries in English, French and
Russian) 1972. bi-m. 102 lei. (Academia Romana)
Editura Academiei Romane, Calea Victoriei 125,
79717 Bucharest, Rumania. (Dist. by:
Rompresfilatelia, Calea Grivitei 64-66, P.O. Box
12-201, 78104 Bucharest, Rumania) Ed. Sorin
Radulescu. bk.rev.; bibl. **Indexed:** Int.Polit.Sci.Abstr.,
Lang.& Lang.Behav.Abstr. **Document type:**
academic/scholarly publication.
Formerly (until 1990): Viitorul Social (ISSN
0379-3745)

301 572   YU   ISSN 0038-0318
SOCIOLOGIJA; casopis za sociologiju, socijalnu,
psihologiju i socijalnu antropologiju. (Text in
Serbo-Croatian) 1959. q. 20000 din. Jugoslovensko
Udruzenje za Sociologiju, Studentski trg 1, 11000
Belgrade, Yugoslavia. Ed. Esad Cimic. adv.; bk.rev.
circ. 1,000. **Indexed:** Int.Polit.Sci.Abstr., Lang.&
Lang.Behav.Abstr., Sociol.Abstr. (1959-).

301   CI   ISSN 0038-0326
HT401
SOCIOLOGIJA SELA. (Text in Croatian; summaries in
English and Russian) 1962. q. 50 HRK (foreign
$20). Sveuciliste u Zagrebu, Institut za Drustvena
Istrazivanja - University of Zagrab, Institut for Social
Research, P.O. Box 280, Amruseva 8-III, 41000
Zagreb, Croatia. TEL 385-41-430775.
FAX 385-41-433298. (Subscr. to: Mladost,
Export-Import, Ilica 30, 41000 Zagreb, Croatia) Ed.
Maja Stambuk. bk.rev.; cum.index. circ. 600.
Indexed: Geo.Abstr., Lang.& Lang.Behav.Abstr., Rural
Recreat.Tour.Abstr., Sociol.Abstr. (1963-), World
Agri.Econ.& Rural Sociol.Abstr.
Description: Publishes articles, research papers on
rural sociology, rural economics, history and
demography.

301   NE   ISSN 0038-0334
SOCIOLOGISCHE GIDS; tijdschrift voor sociologie en
sociaal onderzoek. (Text in Dutch, English, French or
German; summaries in English) 1953. bi-m. fl.80 to
individuals (foreign fl.121); institutions fl.142
(foreign fl.154.50) (effective 1994). Uitgeverij
Boom, P.O. Box 400, 7940 AK Meppel,
Netherlands. TEL 31-5220-57012.
FAX 31-5220-53864. adv.; bk.rev.; index. circ.
1,200. **Indexed:** Abstr.Crim.& Pen., E.I., Excerp.Med.,
Geo.Abstr., Lang.& Lang.Behav.Abstr., Sociol.Abstr.
(1953-).
—BLDSC (8319.653000); SWETS.

301   BE
SOCIOLOGISCHE VERKENNINGEN. no.2, 1972. irreg.
no.10, 1986. Leuven University Press, Krakenstraat
3, B-3000 Leuven, Belgium. TEL 32-16-324175.
FAX 32-16-323782. **Document type:**
academic/scholarly publication.

301   SW   ISSN 0038-0342
SOCIOLOGISK FORSKNING. 1964. q. SEK 300 in
Sweden; Nordic and Baltic countries SEK 335;
elsewhere SEK 345. Swedish Sociological
Association, Umeaa Universitet, S-901 87 Umea,
Sweden. FAX 090-166694. (Subscr. to: PROGEK,
P.O. Box 31003, S-400 32 Goeteborg, Sweden. TEL
46-31-24-34-25) Ed.Bd. adv.; bk.rev.; cum.index:
1964-74. circ. 1,500. **Indexed:** ASCA, Lang.&
Lang.Behav.Abstr., Sociol.Abstr. (1976-), SSCI.
—BLDSC (8319.654000); Genuine Article.

301   NR   ISSN 0081-1807
SOCIOLOGIST.* 1968. a. University of Ibadan,
Sociological Society, Ibadan, Nigeria.

301   GW   ISSN 0038-0377
HM3
SOCIOLOGUS; Zeitschrift fuer empirische
Ethnosoziologie und Ethnopsychologie. (Text in
English and German) 1951. s-a. DM.98. Duncker
und Humblot GmbH, Postfach 410329, 12113
Berlin, Germany. TEL 030-7900060.
FAX 030-79000631. Ed. W. Rudolph. bk.rev.; abstr.;
illus.; index. (reprint service avail. from KTO) **Indexed:**
A.I.C.P., Anthropol.Lit., Bibl.Ling.,
Cott.&Trop.Fibr.Abstr., E.I., Int.Polit.Sci.Abstr.,
P.A.I.S.For.Lang.Ind., Psychol.Abstr., World
Agri.Econ.& Rural Sociol.Abstr. **Document type:**
academic/scholarly publication.
—BLDSC (8319.660000); SWETS; UnCover. **CCC.**

301   UK   ISSN 0038-0385
HM1
SOCIOLOGY. q. q. £23 to individuals (foreign £28);
institutions £77.50 (foreign £85.50) (effective
1995-1996). (British Sociological Association) B S A
Publications, Ltd., 351 Station Rd., Dorridge, Solihull,
W. Midlands B93 8EY, England.
TEL 01564-772402. Eds. Joan Bushfield, Ted
Benton. adv.; bk.rev.; charts; index. circ. 3,700. (also
avail. in microform from UMI; reprint service avail.
from UMI) **Indexed:** Abstr.Crim.& Pen., Amer.Hist.&
Life, ASSIA, Br.Hum.Ind., Commun.Abstr.,
Cont.Pg.Manage., Crim.Just.Abstr., Curr.Cont.,
High.Educ.Curr.Aware.Bull., Hist.Abstr.,
Int.Polit.Sci.Abstr., Lang.& Lang.Behav.Abstr.,
Mid.East: Abstr.& Ind., Polit.Sci.Abstr.,
Res.High.Educ.Abstr., Rural Recreat.Tour.Abstr.,
SCIMP (1979-), Soc.Sci.Ind., Sociol.Abstr. (1967-),
Sociol.Educ.Abstr., Sp.Ed.Needs Abstr., SSCI,
Stud.Wom.Abstr., World Agri.Econ.& Rural
Sociol.Abstr. **Document type:** academic/scholarly
publication.
●Also available online. Vendor(s): University
Microfilms International.
—BLDSC (8319.670000); Faxon; Genuine Article;
SWETS; UMI; UnCover.
Description: Provides high-quality articles, debates,
progress reports, and news regarding sociology.

301   AT   ISSN 0156-4943
SOCIOLOGY OCCASIONAL PUBLICATIONS. 1978. irreg.
University of New England, Department of Sociology,
Armidale, N.S.W. 2351, Australia.
TEL 61-67-73-2300. FAX 61-67-73-3748. (back
issues avail.)

301 370 US ISSN 0038-0407
L11 CODEN: SCYEB7
SOCIOLOGY OF EDUCATION; a journal of research in socialization and social structure. 1927. q. $40 to individuals (foreign $50); institutions $80 (foreign $90). American Sociological Association, 1722 N St., N.W., Washington, DC 20036. TEL 202-833-3410. FAX 202-785-0146. Ed. Julia Wrigley. adv.; charts; index. circ. 5,000. (also avail. in microform from UMI,PMC; reprint service avail. from UMI,KTO) **Indexed:** Adol.Ment.Hlth.Abstr., ASCA, ASSIA, C.I.J.E., Cont.Pg.Educ., Curr.Cont., Educ.Admin.Abstr., Educ.Ind., Educ.Tech.Abstr., High.Educ.Curr.Aware.Bull., Lang.& Lang.Behav.Abstr., Mid.East: Abstr.& Ind., Mult.Ed.Abstr., P.A.I.S., Psychol.Abstr. (1929-), Soc.Sci.Ind. (1994-), Sociol.Abstr. (1952-), Sociol.Educ.Abstr., SOMA, SSCI, Stud.Wom.Abstr., Tech.Educ.Abstr. **Document type:** academic/scholarly publication.
●Also available online. Vendor(s): University Microfilms International.
—BLDSC (8319.678000); Faxon; SWETS; UMI; UnCover.
Formerly: Journal of Educational Sociology.
Description: Publishes papers on educational processes and on human development. The research may focus on the individual, institutions, and structural arrangements among institutions bearing on education and human development.

301 616.8 UK ISSN 0141-9889
RA418
SOCIOLOGY OF HEALTH AND ILLNESS. 1979. 5/yr. £129($280) (foreign £174) (effective 1996). Basil Blackwell Ltd., 108 Cowley Rd., Oxford OX4 1JF, England. TEL 0865-791100. FAX 0865-791347. TELEX 837022-OXBOOK-G. Ed. Mildred Blaxter. adv.; bk.rev.; index. circ. 950. (also avail. in microform) **Indexed:** Abstr.Health Care Manage.Stud., Abstr.Hyg., ASCA, ASSIA, Excerp.Med., I.P.A., Lang.& Lang.Behav.Abstr., Med.Care Rev., Mid.East: Abstr.& Ind., Mult.Ed.Abstr., Psychol.Abstr., Sociol.Abstr. (1979-), Sociol.Educ.Abstr., SSCI, Stud.Wom.Abstr., Tech.Educ.Abstr.
●Also available online.
—BLDSC (8319.692000); Faxon; Genuine Article; SWETS; UMI; UnCover. **CCC.**

301 US ISSN 1062-4120
SOCIOLOGY OF MUSIC SERIES. 1983. irreg., no.8, 1994. Pendragon Press, 41 Ferry St., Stuyvesant, NY 12173-9720. TEL 518-828-3008. FAX 518-828-2368. **Document type:** monographic series.

301 US ISSN 1069-4404
BL60 CODEN: SRELE2
SOCIOLOGY OF RELIGION. 1940. q. $50. Association for the Sociology of Religion, Marist Hall, Rm. 108, Catholic University of America, Washington, DC 20064. TEL 202-319-5447. adv.; bk.rev.; charts; stat.; index, cum.index: vols.1-24. circ. 1,325. (also avail. in microform from JAI,UMI; reprint service avail. from UMI) **Indexed:** Amer.Hist.& Life (until 1990), ASSIA, Cath.Ind., Curr.Cont., Curr.Lit.Fam.Plan., Hist.Abstr. (until 1990), Int.Polit.Sci.Abstr., Lang.& Lang.Behav.Abstr., Rel.& Theol.Abstr. (1989-), Rel.Ind.One, Rel.Per., Sociol.Abstr., SSCI. **Document type:** academic/scholarly publication.
●Also available online. Vendor(s): University Microfilms International.
—BLDSC (8319.695500); Faxon; Genuine Article; SWETS; UMI; UnCover.
Former titles (until vol.54, 1993): S A (Sociological Analysis) (ISSN 0038-0210); American Catholic Sociological Review.

790 US ISSN 0741-1235
SOCIOLOGY OF SPORT JOURNAL. Short title: S S J. 1984. q. $36 to individuals (foreign $40); institutions $80 (foreign $84); students $24 (foreign $28). (North American Society for the Sociology of Sport) Human Kinetics Publishers, Inc., Box 5076, Champaign, IL 61825-5076. TEL 217-351-5076. FAX 217-351-2674. Ed. Cynthia Hasbrook. adv. contact: Pamela Anderson. bk.rev.; bibl.; charts; stat.; index. circ. 910. (back issues avail.) **Indexed:** ASCA, Curr.Cont., Lang.& Lang.Behav.Abstr., Phys.Ed.Ind., Sociol.Abstr. (1984-), Sportsearch (1984-), SSCI. **Document type:** academic/scholarly publication.
—BLDSC (8319.696830); Faxon; Genuine Article; SWETS; UnCover. **CCC.**
Description: Focuses on the relationship between sport, society, and social institutions from the perspectives of social psychology, sociology and anthropology. Designed to communicate research, critical thought, and theory development.
Refereed Serial

SOCIOLOGY OF THE SCIENCES. YEARBOOK. see *SCIENCES: COMPREHENSIVE WORKS*

301 500 NE
SOCIOLOGY OF THE SCIENCES MONOGRAPHS. 1982. irreg. price varies. Kluwer Academic Publishers, Postbus 17, 3300 AA Dordrecht, Netherlands. TEL 31-78-392392. FAX 31-78-392254. TELEX 29245 KAPG NL. (Dist. by: Kluwer Academic Publishers Group, P.O. Box 322, 3300 AH Dordrecht, Netherlands. TEL 31-78-392392. FAX 31-78-546474; N. America dist. addr.: Box 358, Accord Sta., Hingham, MA 02018-0358. TEL 617-871-6600. FAX 617-871-6528) **Document type:** monographic series.
Refereed Serial

301 AT ISSN 0155-0632
SOCIOLOGY RESEARCH MONOGRAPHS. 1978. irreg. University of New England, Department of Sociology, Armidale, N.S.W. 2351, Australia. TEL 61-67-73-2300. FAX 61-67-73-3748. (back issues avail.) **Document type:** monographic series.

301 UK ISSN 0959-8499
SOCIOLOGY REVIEW. 1985. q. £17.95 (rest of Europe £23; elsewhere £28.50) (effective 1996). Philip Allan Publishers Ltd., Market Pl., Deddington, Oxon. OX15 OSE, England. TEL 01869-338652. FAX 01869-338803. Eds. John Williams, John Scott. adv. contact: Ceri Jenkins.
—BLDSC (8319.696600).
Supersedes (in 1991): Social Studies Review (ISSN 0267-0712)

301 572 SI ISSN 0129-8186
SOCIOLOGY WORKING PAPERS. (Text in English) 1972. irreg. price varies. (University of Singapore, Department of Sociology) Chopmen Publishers, Katong Shopping Centre, Mountbatten Rd., No. 05-28, Singapore 1543, Singapore. TEL 3441495. FAX 3440180. Ed. Peter S.J. Chen. circ. 500.
—BLDSC (9349.814000).

301 330 350 JA ISSN 0386-3506
SOGO TOSHI KENKYU/COMPREHENSIVE URBAN STUDIES. (Text in Japanese; abstracts in English) 1977. 3/yr. free. Tokyo Metropolitan University, Center for Urban Studies, 1-1 Minami Ohsawa, Hachioji, Tokyo 192-03, Japan. TEL 0426-77-2351. FAX 0426-77-2352. Ed. Yuetsu Takahashi. **Document type:** academic/scholarly publication.

301 SI ISSN 0217-9520
HN690.8
SOJOURN; social issues in Southeast Asia. (Text in English) 1986. s-a. $16 to individuals (Europe & N. America $19); institutions $21 (Europe & N. America $25). Institute of Southeast Asian Studies, Heng Mui Keng Terrace, Off Pasir Panjang Rd., Singapore 0511, Singapore. TEL 7780955. FAX 7781735. TELEX RS 37068 ISEAS. E-mail: pubsunit@merlion.iseas.ac.sg. (Subscr. in U.S. to: Ashgate, Old Post Rd., Brookfield, VT 05036. TEL 802-276-3162) Ed.Bd. adv.; bk.rev.; abstr.; bibl.; index. (also avail. in microform from UMI; back issues avail.; reprint service avail. from SCH) **Indexed:** Asian-Pac.Econ.Lit., Rural Devel.Abstr., World Agri.Econ.& Rural Sociol.Abstr. **Document type:** academic/scholarly publication.
—BLDSC (8327.118750); SWETS; UMI.
Description: Deals with issues of ethnicity, religion, urbanism, and population change. Includes articles, research notes, and occasional English translations of pivotal research first published in Southeast Asian languages.

301 NO ISSN 0332-6330
SOSIOLOGI I DAG. 1971. q. NOK 200($36) to individuals; institutions NOK 350 ($59) (effective 1995). Novus Forlag, P.O. Box 748 Sentrum, N-0106 Oslo, Norway. TEL 47-2272-7450. FAX 47-2271-8107. E-mail: rosset@novus.no. Ed. Elisabeth L. Fuerst.

301 NO ISSN 0804-0486
HM7
SOSIOLOGISK TIDSSKRIFT/JOURNAL OF SOCIOLOGY. (Text in English and the Scandinavian languages) 1993. q. NOK 395 in Nordic countries; elsewhere $76 (effective 1996). (Norwegian Sociological Association) Scandinavian University Press, P.O. Box 2959 Toeyen, N-0608 Oslo, Norway. TEL 47-22-57-54-00. FAX 47-22-57-53-53. Ed. Willy Martinussen.
Description: Presents articles on sociological research results in Norway.

SOURCE (SEATTLE). see *RELIGIONS AND THEOLOGY*

301 SA ISSN 0258-0144
HM1
SOUTH AFRICAN JOURNAL OF SOCIOLOGY. (Text and summaries in English) 1970. q. R.90. Foundation for Education, Science & Technology, P.O. Box 1758, Pretoria 0001, South Africa. TEL 12-322-6422. FAX 27-12-320-7803. Ed. Anna F. Steyn. adv. contact: T. Uys. bk.rev. circ. 500. **Indexed:** Anim.Breed.Abstr., Ind.S.A.Per., Lang.& Lang.Behav.Abstr., Mult.Ed.Abstr., RILM, Sociol.Abstr. (1970-), Sp.Ed.Needs Abstr., Stud.Wom.Abstr. **Document type:** academic/scholarly publication.
—BLDSC (8340.200000). **CCC.**
Description: Publishes contributions from any field of sociology.

SOUTH AFRICAN OUTLOOK; a journal dealing with ecumenical and racial affairs. see *RELIGIONS AND THEOLOGY*

301 SA ISSN 1015-1370
SOUTH AFRICAN SOCIOLOGICAL REVIEW; a journal of S A S A. 1973. s-a. R.30 (£10; $20) to individuals; institutions R.60 (£20; $40) (effective 1993). S A Sociological Association, Dept. of Sociology, University of Western Cape, Bellville 7535, South Africa. TEL 27-21-9592336. FAX 27-21-9592376. Ed. Jeff Lever. bk.rev. circ. 450. (also avail. in microfiche) **Indexed:** Sociol.Abstr. **Document type:** academic/scholarly publication.
—BLDSC (8345.675000).
Formerly (until 1988): A S S A Proceedings (Association for Sociology in South Africa).
Description: For sociologists and social scientists, both generalist and Southern Africa area specific.

SOUTH ASIA BULLETIN. see *HISTORY — History Of Asia*

SOUTH ASIA: JOURNAL OF SOUTH ASIAN STUDIES. see *HISTORY — History Of Asia*

SOUTHEAST ASIAN JOURNAL OF SOCIAL SCIENCES. see *SOCIAL SCIENCES: COMPREHENSIVE WORKS*

SOCIOLOGY

301 US ISSN 0038-4577
HM1
SOUTHERN SOCIOLOGIST. 1968. 3/yr. $15 to non-members. Southern Sociological Society, Department of Sociology and Anthropology, Mississippi State University, MS 39762. TEL 601-325-7869. FAX 601-325-4564. E-mail: jones@soc.msstate.edu; rent@grad.msstate.edu. Eds. George S. Rent, James D. Jones. adv. contact: James D. Jones. circ. 2,000 (paid). (also avail. in microform from UMI; reprint service avail. from UMI) **Indexed:** Lang.& Lang.Behav.Abstr., Sociol.Abstr. **Document type:** newsletter.

301 320.532 US ISSN 1046-1809
SOVIET STUDIES. irreg. Harwood Academic Publishers, c/o International Publishers Distributor, 820 Town Center Dr., Langhorne, PA 19047. TEL 215-750-2642. FAX 215-750-6343. (Subscr. to: International Publishers Distributor, Box 90, Reading, Berkshire RG1 8JL, England. TEL 44-173-456-8316) (also avail. in microform; reprint service avail. from SCH) **Indexed:** Int.Polit.Sci.Abstr. **Document type:** monographic series.
—BLDSC (8359.919800).
Refereed Serial

301 GW
▼**SOZIALE SYSTEME.** 1995. 2/yr. DM.85.50 (foreign DM.88) (students DM.59). Verlag Leske und Budrich GmbH, Postfach 300551, 51334 Leverkusen, Germany. TEL 02171-2079. FAX 02171-41209. **Document type:** academic/scholarly publication.

301 GW ISSN 0038-6073
H5
SOZIALE WELT; Zeitschrift fuer sozialwissenschaftliche Forschung und Praxis. 1949. q. DM.88. (Arbeitsgemeinschaft Sozialwissenschaftlicher Institute e.V.) Verlag Otto Schwartz und Co., Annastr. 7, 37075 Goettingen, Germany. TEL 0551-31051. FAX 0551-372812. Ed. Ulrich Beck. adv.; bk.rev.; charts; index. circ. 1,500. **Indexed:** Int.Polit.Sci.Abstr., Lang.& Lang.Behav.Abstr., P.A.I.S.For.Lang.Ind., Phil.Ind., RILM, Sociol.Abstr. (1953-), World Bibl.Soc.Sec. **Document type:** academic/scholarly publication.
—BLDSC (8361.070000); Genuine Article; SWETS.

301 360 GW ISSN 0724-3464
SOZIALWISSENSCHAFTEN UND BERUFSPRAXIS. 1978. q. DM.81 (foreign DM.87). (Berufsverband Deutscher Soziologen e.V.) Verlag Leske und Budrich GmbH, Postfach 300551, 51334 Leverkusen, Germany. TEL 02171-2079. FAX 02171-41209. Ed.Bd. adv.; bk.rev. circ. 400. (back issues avail.) **Document type:** academic/scholarly publication.

301 SZ ISSN 1017-6780
SOZIOGRAPHIE. (Text in German) 1988. 2/yr. 45 SFr. (effective 1996). (Forschungskomitee Soziographie) Seismo Verlag, Raemistr. 69, Postfach 313, CH-8028 Zurich, Switzerland. TEL 01-2611094. FAX 01-2521054. Ed. Andreas Volk. adv. contact: Peter Rusterholz. **Document type:** academic/scholarly publication.

301 GW ISSN 0340-918X
HM5
SOZIOLOGIE. q. DM.94 (foreign DM.100). (Deutsche Gesellschaft fuer Soziologie) Verlag Leske und Budrich GmbH, Postfach 300551, 51334 Leverkusen, Germany. TEL 02171-41209. Ed. B. Schaefers. (reprint service avail. from IRC) **Indexed:** Int.Polit.Sci.Abstr., Lang.& Lang.Behav.Abstr., Sociol.Abstr. (1975-). **Document type:** academic/scholarly publication.
—BLDSC (8361.216200).

301 GW ISSN 0081-3265
SOZIOLOGISCHE GEGENWARTSFRAGEN. NEUE FOLGE. 1957. irreg., no.52, 1992. price varies. Ferdinand Enke Verlag, Postfach 300366, 70443 Stuttgart, Germany. TEL 0711-135798-0. FAX 0711-135798-30. TELEX 07252275-GTV-D. Ed.Bd. (reprint service avail. from IRC) **Document type:** monographic series.

300 GW ISSN 0343-4109
SOZIOLOGISCHE REVUE; Besprechungen neuer Literatur. 1978. q. DM.156 (students DM.92) (effective 1996). R. Oldenbourg Verlag GmbH, Rosenheimstr. 145, 81671 Munich, Germany. TEL 089-45051-0. FAX 089-45051207. (Subscr. to: Postfach 801360, 81613 Munich, Germany) Ed.Bd. adv.; bk.rev.; index. circ. 1,200. (back issues avail.) **Indexed:** Lang.& Lang.Behav.Abstr., Sociol.Abstr. (1984-). **Document type:** academic/scholarly publication.
—BLDSC (8361.217500); SWETS.
Description: Contains critical reviews of newly published books in all fields of sociology, and the sociological aspects of law, politics, medicine, and religion.

301 333.7 AT
SPEAK. 1969. a. Aus.$0.10. c/o Audrey Windram, Ed., Conrad St., Longwood, S.A. 5153, Australia.

301 IT ISSN 0038-738X
GV1
SPETTACOLO; rassegna economica e sociale degli spettacoli e delle attivita artistiche e cu turali. (Text in Italian; summaries in English, French) 1951. q. L.25000 (foreign L.48000) (effective 1995 & 1996). Societa Italiana degli Autori ed Editori, Viale della Letteratura 30, 00144 Rome, Italy. TEL 39-6-59901. FAX 39-6-5923351. TELEX 611423. Ed. Francesco Paolo Regoli. adv.; bk.rev.; abstr.; charts; mkt.; stat.; index. circ. 2,000. (back issues avail.) **Indexed:** Film Lit.Ind. (1990-). **Document type:** consumer publication.
—BLDSC (8413.520000).

STATE, GOVERNMENT AND INTERNATIONAL RELATIONS. see *POLITICAL SCIENCE — International Relations*

STATO E MERCATO. see *POLITICAL SCIENCE*

301 US
HQ759.92
STEPFAMILIES. 1980. q. $14 to individuals; institutions $22 (foreign $16). Stepfamily Association of America, 215 Centennial Mall S., Ste. 212, Lincoln, NE 68508. TEL 402-477-7837. FAX 402-477-8317. adv.; bk.rev.; cum.index 1980-1993. circ. 1,500. (also avail. in microform from UMI; back issues avail.; reprint service avail. from UMI)
Formerly (until 1989): Stepfamily Bulletin (ISSN 0195-5969)
Description: Covers issues and concerns of stepparenting.

301 360 UK ISSN 1356-0522
▼**STRATHCLYDE PAPERS ON SOCIOLOGY AND SOCIAL POLICY.** 1994. irreg. University of Strathclyde, Department of Government, 16 Richmonc St., Glasgow G1 1XQ, Scotland. Ed. Isobel Lindsay. **Document type:** monographic series.
—BLDSC (8474.047905).

301 US ISSN 0884-870X
STRESS IN MODERN SOCIETY. 1984. irreg., no.19, 1989. $32.50. A M S Press, Inc., 56 E. 13th St., New York, NY 10003. TEL 212-777-4700. FAX 212-995-5413. index. (back issues avail.) **Document type:** monographic series.
Description: Monographs covering a broad range of topics from specific causes of stress to intervention methods.

STRUCTURAL EQUATION MODELING; a multidisciplinary journal. see *PSYCHOLOGY*

301 IT ISSN 0039-291X
HM7
STUDI DI SOCIOLOGIA. (Text in English, French and Italian) 1963. q. L.72000 (foreign L.113000 ($86)) (effective 1996). (Universita Cattolica del Sacro Cuore, Istituto di Sociologia) Vita e Pensiero, Largo Gemelli 1, 20123 Milan, Italy. TEL 39-2-72342310. FAX 39-2-72342260. TELEX 321033 UCATMI 1. Ed. Vincenzo Cesareo. adv.: B&W page L.2500000. bk.rev.; bibl.; charts; index. circ. 700. **Indexed:** Lang.& Lang.Behav.Abstr., Sociol.Abstr. (1963-). **Document type:** academic/scholarly publication.
Description: Covers current issues in sociology.

STUDI EMIGRAZIONE/ETUDES MIGRATIONS. see *POPULATION STUDIES*

STUDIA ANTHROPONYMICA SCANDINAVICA; tidskrift foer nordisk personnamnsforskning. see *LINGUISTICS*

301 PL ISSN 0039-3371
CODEN: STSOCP
STUDIA SOCJOLOGICZNE. q. $68. Polska Akademia Nauk, Instytut Filozofii i Socjologii, Ul. Nowy Swiat 72, 00-330 Warsaw, Poland. (Dist. by: Ars Polona-Ruch, Krakowskie Przedmiescie 7, Warsaw, Poland) (Co-sponsor: Polska Akademia Nauk, Komitet Nauk Socjologii) Ed. Jolanta Kulpinska. bk.rev.; bibl.; charts; index. **Indexed:** Lang.& Lang.Behav.Abstr., Psychol.Abstr., Sociol.Abstr. (1961-).
Description: Treatises on theoretical and methodological aspects of sociology.

301 320 RM
STUDIA UNIVERSITATIS "BABES-BOLYAI". SOCIOLOGIA - POLITOLOGIA. (Text in English, French, German, Rumanian) 1990. s-a. exchange basis. Universitatea "Babes-Bolyai", Biblioteca Centrala Universitara, Str. Clinicilor Nr. 2, Cluj-Napoca 3400, Rumania. TEL 36-64-197092. FAX 36-64-197633. Ed. I. Haiduc. **Document type:** academic/scholarly publication.

STUDIEN ZUR LITERATUR- UND SOZIALGESCHICHTE SPANIENS UND LATEINAMERIKAS. see *LITERATURE*

STUDIES IN AFRICAN AND AFRO-AMERICAN CULTURE. see *HISTORY — History Of Africa*

STUDIES IN BILINGUALISM. see *LINGUISTICS*

STUDIES IN FAMILY PLANNING. see *POPULATION STUDIES*

301 US ISSN 0889-3128
STUDIES IN GENDER AND CULTURE. 1988. irreg., latest vol.5. price varies. Gordon & Breach Science Publishers, c/o International Publishers Distributor, 820 Town Center Dr., Langhorne, PA 19047. TEL 215-750-2642. FAX 215-750-6343. (Subscr. to: International Publishers Distributor, P.O. Box 90, Reading, Berkshire RG1 8JL, England. TEL 44-173-456-8316) Ed. W. Martin. **Document type:** monographic series.
Refereed Serial

301 NE ISSN 0920-6221
STUDIES IN HUMAN SOCIETY. 1986. irreg., vol.9, 1994. price varies. E.J. Brill, P.O. Box 9000, 2300 PA Leiden, Netherlands. TEL 31-71-5353500. FAX 31-71-5317532. TELEX 39296 BRILL NL. (In N. America: E.J. Brill, 24 Hudson St., Kinderhook, NY 12106. TEL 800-962-4406. FAX 518-758-1959) Ed. P.J.M. Nas. (back issues avail.) **Document type:** monographic series.
—BLDSC (8490.690000).
Refereed Serial

301 US ISSN 0730-9139
NX501.5
STUDIES IN LATIN AMERICAN POPULAR CULTURE. 1982. a. $20 to individuals; institutions $50 (typically set in Apr.). c/o Charles M. Tatum, Modern Language Bldg. 345, University of Arizona, Tuscon, AZ 85721. TEL 602-621-1044. FAX 602-621-5594. Ed. Charles M. Tatum; Pubs. Harold E. Hinds, Jr., Charles M. Tatum. adv.; bk.rev.; circ. 500 (paid). (back issues avail.) **Indexed:** Chic.Per.Ind., Hisp.Amer.Per.Ind. (1982-), M.L.A., RILM. **Document type:** academic/scholarly publication.
—BLDSC (8490.831000); Faxon; Genuine Article; UnCover.
Refereed Serial

STUDIES IN LAW, POLITICS, AND SOCIETY; a research annual. see *LAW*

SOCIOLOGY

301.2   US   ISSN 0888-5753
E169.1
STUDIES IN POPULAR CULTURE. 1977. s-a. $20 (outside US $25) (effective 1994). Popular Culture Association in the South, c/o Dennis Hall, Ed., University of Louisville, Department of English, Louisville, KY 40292. (Subscr. to: Diane Calhoun-French, Academic Dean, Jefferson Community College, SW, Louisville, KY 40272) bk.rev. circ. 500. (back issues avail.) **Indexed:** Child.Lit.Abstr., Film Lit.Ind. (1989-). **Document type:** academic/scholarly publication.
—UnCover.
   Description: Publishes articles on film, literature, radio, television, music, graphics, the print media, and other aspects of popular culture from a multidisciplinary perspective.
   Refereed Serial

301   II
STUDIES IN SOCIAL CHANGE AND DEVELOPMENT. (Text in English) 1971. irreg., no.5, 1989. price varies. Institute of Economic Growth, University Enclave, New Delhi 110007, India. TEL 2522201. **Document type:** monographic series.
   Formerly (until no.4, 1980): Studies in Asian Social Development.

301   US
STUDIES IN SOCIAL DISCONTINUITY. 1974. irreg., no.51, 1985. Academic Press, Inc., 525 B St., Ste. 1900, San Diego, CA 92101-4495. TEL 619-231-0926. FAX 619-699-6715. (Subscr. to: Order Dept., 6277 Sea Harbor Dr., 4th Fl., Orlando, FL 32887. TEL 800-321-5068) Eds. C. Tilly, E. Shorter. (reprint service avail. from ISI)

301   NE   ISSN 0081-3518
STUDIES IN SOCIAL LIFE. (Text in English) 1953. irreg. price varies. Kluwer Academic Publishers, Postbus 17, 3300 AA Dordrecht, Netherlands. TEL 31-78-392392. FAX 31-78-392254. TELEX 29245 KAPG NL. (Dist. by: Kluwer Academic Publishers Group, P.O. Box 322, 3300 AA Dordrecht, Netherlands. TEL 31-78-392392. FAX 31-78-546474; N. America dist. addr.: Box 358, Accord Sta., Hingham, MA 02018-0358. TEL 617-871-6600. FAX 617-871-6528) **Indexed:** SSCI. **Document type:** monographic series.
   Refereed Serial

301   II
STUDIES IN SOCIOLOGY AND SOCIAL ANTHROPOLOGY. (Text in English) 1977. irreg., vol.35, 1995. price varies. Hindustan Publishing Corp., 4805-24, Bharat Ram Rd., Flat Nos.1 & 2, 1st Fl, Daryaganj, New Delhi 110002, India. TEL 9-11-3254401. FAX 9-11-6863511. Ed. M.N. Srinivas. **Document type:** academic/scholarly publication, monographic series.

301   US   ISSN 1058-5621
STUDIES IN SOUTHERN ITALIAN AND ITALIAN-AMERICAN CULTURE/STUDI SULLA CULTURA DELL'ITALIA MERIDIONALE E ITALO-AMERICANA. 1992. irreg. Peter Lang Publishing, Inc., 62 W. 45th St., 4th Fl., New York, NY 10036. TEL 212-302-6740. FAX 212-302-7574. Eds. Giose Rimanelli, Francis X. Femminella. **Document type:** academic/scholarly publication, monographic series.
   Description: Publishes studies of the literature, arts, spoken modes and socio-historical life of Southern Italian society, as well as studies of the culture of Italian-Americans whose ancestry stems from Southern Italy.

301.1   US   ISSN 0163-2396
HM1
STUDIES IN SYMBOLIC INTERACTION; an annual compilation of research. 1978. a. $63.50 to institutions. J A I Press Inc., 55 Old Post Rd., No. 2, Box 1678, Greenwich, CT 06836-1678. TEL 203-661-7602. Ed. Norman K. Denzin. illus. **Indexed:** Lang.& Lang.Behav.Abstr., Psychol.Abstr., Sociol.Abstr. (1978-).
—BLDSC (8491.788000). **CCC.**

STUDIES IN TECHNOLOGY AND SOCIAL CHANGE SERIES. see *TECHNOLOGY: COMPREHENSIVE WORKS*

309 960   ZA
STUDIES IN ZAMBIAN SOCIETY. 1978. irreg., no.3, 1978. price varies. University of Zambia, School of Humanities and Social Sciences, Committee on Student Publications, Box 2379, Lusaka, Zambia. Ed. L.M. van den Berg. circ. 1,000.

STUDIES OF ISRAELI SOCIETY. see *ETHNIC INTERESTS*

301   US   ISSN 0039-4394
SUBTERRANEAN SOCIOLOGY NEWSLETTER. 1967-1980; resumed 1987; N.S. 1990. irreg. $3. Subterranean Sociological Association, Department of Sociology, Eastern Michigan University, Ypsilanti, MI 48197. TEL 517-522-3551. Ed. Marcello Truzzi. bk.rev.; bibl.; circ. 600 (controlled). (processed) **Document type:** academic/scholarly publication, newsletter.

301   US
SURVEY RESEARCH. 1969. q. $10 to individuals; institutions $50-$500. University of Illinois, Survey Research Laboratory, 909 W. Oregon St., Ste. 300, Urbana, IL 61801. TEL 217-333-4273. FAX 217-244-4408. Ed. Diane O'Rourke. circ. 1,500. **Document type:** academic/scholarly publication.
   Description: Publicizes current research, personnel news, new methodological publications, and job openings in survey research.

301   US   ISSN 0273-2017
SURVIVAL TOMORROW;* resources for troubled times. (Includes Supplements) 1981. m. $60. c/o Nancy Tappan, Box 1050, Rogue River, OR 97537. Ed. Karl Hess. bk.rev. circ. 15,000. (back issues avail.)

309   US   ISSN 0733-2971
SURVIVORS.* 1980. bi-m. $10. Survivors Inc., Box 3564, Springfield, IL 62708-3564. Ed. D.L. Giles-Doering. adv.; bk.rev. circ. 100,000.

301.4   US
SURVIVORS OUTREACH SERIES. 1980. 8/yr. $24 in the U.S.; Canada $27; elsewhere $30. Theos Foundation, 717 Liberty Ave., No. 1301, Pittsburgh, PA 15222-3510. TEL 412-471-7779. FAX 412-471-7782. bk.rev. circ. 25. **Document type:** monographic series.
   Description: Helps widows and widowers cope with their grief.

301   HU   ISSN 0133-3461
HM7
SZOCIOLOGIA.* (Text in Hungarian; summaries in English, Russian) 1972. q. $28. Magyar Tudomanyos Akademia, Szociologiai Kutatointezet, Uri u. 49, 1014 Budapest, Hungary. Ed. L. Cseh-Szombathy. bk.rev.; bibl.; index. **Indexed:** Lang.& Lang.Behav.Abstr., Sociol.Abstr. (1972-), World Agri.Econ.& Rural Sociol.Abstr.

301   HU   ISSN 0082-1322
SZOCIOLOGIAI TANULMANYOK. 1966. irreg., vol.29, 1987. price varies. (Magyar Tudomanyos Akademia) Akademiai Kiado, Publishing House of the Hungarian Academy of Sciences, P.O. Box 245, H-1519 Budapest, Hungary. TEL 181-2134. FAX 166-6466. TELEX 22-6228 AKNYO H.

301   US
TAKING SIDES: CLASHING VIEWS ON CONTROVERSIAL ISSUES IN FAMILY AND PERSONAL RELATIONSHIPS. 1991. irreg. $13.95. Dushkin Publishing Group, Sluice Dock, Guilford, CT 06437-9989. TEL 203-453-4351. FAX 203-453-6000. Eds. Gloria W. Bird, Michael Sporakowski; Pub. Mimi Egan. illus. **Document type:** academic/scholarly publication.

301   US
TAKING SIDES: CLASHING VIEWS ON CONTROVERSIAL ISSUES IN MASS MEDIA AND SOCIETY. 1991. irreg. $13.95. Dushkin Publishing Group, Sluice Dock, Guilford, CT 06437-9989. TEL 203-543-4351. FAX 203-453-6000. Eds. Alison Alexander, Jarice Hanson; Pub. Mimi Egan. illus. **Document type:** academic/scholarly publication.

301   US
TAKING SIDES: CLASHING VIEWS ON CONTROVERSIAL SOCIAL ISSUES. irreg., 6th ed., 1990. $13.95. Dushkin Publishing Group, Sluice Dock, Guilford, CT 06437-9989. TEL 203-453-4351. FAX 203-453-6000. Eds. Kurt Finsterbusch, George McKenna; Pub. Mimi Egan. illus. **Document type:** academic/scholarly publication.

TAMBARA; Ateneo de Davao University journal. see *ANTHROPOLOGY*

301   HU   ISSN 0039-971X
HX8
TARSADALMI SZEMLE. (Text in Hungarian; summaries in English, French, German and Russian) 1931-1933; resumed 1946. m. 708 Ft.($26) (Foundation of Taisaddini Szemle) Kossuth Konyvkiado, Steindl I. Utca 6, 1366 Budapest 5, Hungary. (Subscr. to: Kultura, Box 149, H-1389 Budapest, Hungary) Ed. Mihaly Bihari. bk.rev. circ. 6,000. **Indexed:** Amer.Hist.& Life, Hist.Abstr., Rural Recreat.Tour.Abstr., World Agri.Econ.& Rural Sociol.Abstr.

301   US   ISSN 0092-055X
HM1
TEACHING SOCIOLOGY. 1973. q. $40 to individuals (foreign $50); institutions $80 (foreign $90). American Sociological Association, 1722 N St., N.W., Washington, DC 20036. TEL 202-833-3410. FAX 202-785-0146. Ed. Kathleen McKinney. adv.; bk.rev.; index. (back issues avail.) **Indexed:** ASCA, ASSIA, C.I.J.E., Cont.Pg.Educ., Curr.Cont., Educ.Ind., Educ.Tech.Abstr., High.Educ.Curr.Aware.Bull., Lang.& Lang.Behav.Abstr., Mid.East: Abstr.& Ind., Mult.Ed.Abstr., Res.High.Educ.Abstr., Sociol.Abstr. (1973-), SSCI, Stud.Wom.Abstr. **Document type:** academic/scholarly publication.
—BLDSC (8614.340000); Faxon; Genuine Article; SWETS; UMI; UnCover.
   Description: Publishes research articles, teaching tips, and reports on teaching sociology.

TECHNIK UND GESELLSCHAFT. see *TECHNOLOGY: COMPREHENSIVE WORKS*

TECHNOLOGICAL FORECASTING AND SOCIAL CHANGE. see *TECHNOLOGY: COMPREHENSIVE WORKS*

301   UK   ISSN 0160-791X
T14.5
TECHNOLOGY IN SOCIETY; an international journal. Previously announced as: Sociotechnology. 1979. q. £337($536) (effective 1996). Elsevier Science Ltd., Pergamon, P.O. Box 800, Kidlington, Oxford OX5 1DX, England. TEL 44-1865-843000. FAX 44-1865-843010. E-mail: nlinfo-f@elsevier.nl; usinfo-f@elsevier.com; forinfo-kyf04035@niftyserve.or.jp; Site address: http://www.elsevier.nl/. (Subscr. in U.S. and Canada to: Elsevier Science, 660 White Plains Rd., Tarrytown, NY 10591-5153. TEL 914-524-9200. FAX 914-333-2444) Eds. George Bugliarello, A. George Schillinger. adv.; bk.rev.; charts; illus.; stat.; index. circ. 2,000. (also avail. in microfilm from UMI) **Indexed:** Amer.Bibl.Slavic & E.Eur.Stud., ASCA, Biostat., CLOSS, Curr.Cont., Educ.Tech.Abstr., Excerp.Med., Fut.Surv., Geo.Abstr., IDA, Lang.& Lang.Behav.Abstr., Oper.Res.Manage.Sci., Psychol.Abstr., Qual.Contr.Appl.Stat., Sociol.Abstr. **Document type:** academic/scholarly publication.
—BLDSC (8761.023000); Ei; Faxon; Genuine Article; SWETS; UMI; UnCover. **CCC.**
   Description: Focuses on the role of technology in society, including articles on economic, political and cultural dynamics, the social forces that shape technological decisions, and the choices open to societies with respect to the uses of technology.
   Refereed Serial

301   IS   ISSN 0792-0601
TEL AVIV - YAFO. CENTER FOR ECONOMIC AND SOCIAL RESEARCH. RESEARCH AND SURVEYS SERIES/TEL AVIV - YAFO. HA-MERKAZ LE-MEKHKAR KALKALI VE-KHEVRATI. MEKHKARIM VE-SEKARIM. (Text in Hebrew) no.12, 1963. irreg. Center for Economic and Social Research, Tel Aviv - Yafo Municipality, Malkhei Israel Square, Tel Aviv 64162, Israel. TEL 972-3-6962156. Ed. M. Hadad. circ. 600. **Document type:** government publication.
   Formerly: Tel Aviv - Yafo. Research and Statistical Department. Special Surveys (ISSN 0082-2639)
   Description: Contains research reports on various social and urban topics concerning Tel Aviv - Yafo.

TEMAS AMERICANISTAS. see *HISTORY — History Of North And South America*

300   BO   ISSN 0040-2915
TEMAS SOCIALES. 1968. q. $8. Universidad Mayor de San Andres, Facultad de Derecho, Casilla 4787, La Paz, Bolivia. Ed. Mario Diez. charts.

SOCIOLOGY

| 301 | 100 320 | YU | ISSN 0353-7919 |

TEME. (Text in Serbo-Croatian; contents in English, French, German and Russian) 1977. q. 10000 din. Univerzitet u Nisu, Trg Bratstva i Jedinstva, Nis, Yugoslavia. TEL 018 25-868. FAX 18-24488. TELEX 16362 UNIUNI YU. Ed. Marko Sekulovic. bk.rev. circ. 500.
  Formerly (until June 1990): Marksisticke Teme (ISSN 0351-1685)

| 301 | | BL | ISSN 0103-2070 |
| HM22.B8 | | | |

TEMPO SOCIAL. 1989. s-a. $30. Universidade de Sao Paulo, Faculdade de Filosofia, Letras e Ciencias Humanas, Secao de Publicacoes, CP. 8105, 05508 Sao Paulo, Brazil. TEL 011-818-4593.

| 301 | | IT | |

TEORIA SOCIOLOGICA. 1993. s-a. L.60000 (foreign L.85000) (effective 1993). (Universita di Urbino, Istituto di Sociologia) Franco Angeli Editore, Viale Monza 106, 20127 Milan, Italy. TEL 2-28-27-651. Ed. G. Piazzi.

TEXT; an interdisciplinary journal for the study of discourse. see *HUMANITIES: COMPREHENSIVE WORKS*

THEOLOGY AND CULTURE NEWSLETTER. see *RELIGIONS AND THEOLOGY*

THEOLOGY AND SEXUALITY. see *RELIGIONS AND THEOLOGY*

THEORETICAL POPULATION BIOLOGY; an international journal. see *BIOLOGY*

| 301 | | NE | ISSN 0304-2421 |
| HM1 | | | CODEN: THSODL |

THEORY AND SOCIETY; renewal and critique in social theory. 1974. bi-m. fl.497 to institutions; $319 to institutions in U.S. (effective 1996). Kluwer Academic Publishers, Postbus 17, 3300 AA Dordrecht, Netherlands. TEL 31-78-392392. FAX 31-78-392254. TELEX 29245 KAPG NL. E-mail: SERVICES@WKAP.NL. (Dist. by: Kluwer Academic Publishers Group, P.O. Box 322, 3300 AH Dordrecht, Netherlands. TEL 31-78-392392. FAX 31-78-546474; N. America dist. addr.: Box 358, Accord Sta., Hingham, MA 02018-0358. TEL 617-871-6600. FAX 617-871-6528) Ed. Janet Gouldner. bk.rev.; index. (also avail. in microform from UMI; reprint service avail. from SWZ) **Indexed:** ASCA, ASSIA, Commun.Abstr., Curr.Cont, Int.Polit.Sci.Abstr., Lang.& Lang.Behav.Abstr., Left Ind. (1982-), P.A.I.S., Polit.Sci.Abstr., Sociol.Abstr. (1974-), SSCI. **Document type:** academic/scholarly publication.
  —BLDSC (8814.630000); Faxon; Genuine Article; SWETS; UMI; UnCover. **CCC.**
  Description: Publishes theoretically informed analyses of social processes, including theoretical and methodological issues, discussions of individuals and national societies and cultures from prehistory to contemporary times.
  Refereed Serial

| 301 | | UK | ISSN 0263-2764 |
| H1 | | | |

THEORY CULTURE & SOCIETY; explorations in critical social science. 1982. q. £35 to individuals; institutions £120 (effective 1996). Sage Publications Ltd., 6 Bonhill St., London EC2A 4PU, England. TEL 0171-374-0645. FAX 0171-374-8741. E-mail: market@sageltd.co.uk. Ed. Mike Featherstone. adv.: B&W page £230; trim 185 x 114; adv. contact: Bernie Folan. bk.rev. **Indexed:** A.I.C.P., Alt.Press Ind., ASCA, Curr.Cont., Human Resour.Abstr., IBZ, Int.Polit.Sci.Abstr., Left.Ind., M.L.A., Phil.Ind., Sociol.Abstr. (1982-), Sociol.Educ.Abstr., SSCI. **Document type:** academic/scholarly publication.
  —BLDSC (8814.631500); Faxon; Genuine Article; SWETS; UnCover.
  Description: Caters for the resurgence of interest in culture within contemporary social science. Features papers by and about modern social and cultural theorists.
  Refereed Serial

THESIS ELEVEN; a journal of critical social theory. see *SOCIOLOGY — Abstracting, Bibliographies, Statistics*

TIDSKRIFT FOER RAETTSSOCIOLOGI. see *LAW*

| 301 | | CK | |

TIERRA NUEVA. 1972. q. $32. Centro de Estudios para el Desarrollo e Integracion de America Latina, Carrera 90, No. 47-54, Apdo. Aereo 100572, Bogota, D.E. 10, Colombia. Ed. Maria B. Cabezas de Gonzalez. cum.index. circ. 1,000. **Indexed:** CERDIC.

| 301 | | BE | ISSN 0040-7615 |
| H8 | | | |

TIJDSCHRIFT VOOR SOCIALE WETENSCHAPPEN. (Text and summaries in English, French or German) 1956. 4/yr. 1000 Fr. to individuals; institutions 1450 Fr.; students 550 Fr. Rijksuniversiteit te Gent, Universiteitstraat 4, B-9000 Ghent, Belgium. Ed. Marthe Versichelen. bk.rev.; charts; index. circ. 700. **Indexed:** Key to Econ.Sci., Lang.& Lang.Behav.Abstr., Sociol.Abstr. (1958-).
  —BLDSC (8844.600000); SWETS.

TIKKUN MAGAZINE; a bi-monthly Jewish critique of politics, culture and society. see *ETHNIC INTERESTS*

| 301 | | UK | ISSN 0961-463X |
| | | | CODEN: TIMSEB |

TIME & SOCIETY. 1992. 3/yr. £28 to individuals; institutions £90 (effective 1996). Sage Publications Ltd., 6 Bonhill St., London EC2A 4PU, England. TEL 0171-374-0645. FAX 0171-374-8741. E-mail: market@sageltd.co.uk. Ed. Barbara Adam. adv.: B&W page £180; trim 165 x 110; adv. contact: Bernie Folan. bk.rev. **Indexed:** A.I.C.P., ASCA, Curr.Cont., IBZ, Int.Polit.Sci.Abstr., Sociol.Abstr. **Document type:** academic/scholarly publication.
  —BLDSC (8852.070000).
  Description: Publishes empirical and theoretical analyses on the subject of time, relating it to society and culture and to theories of individual and social behavior and action.
  Refereed Serial

TODAY (KENT). see *CHILDREN AND YOUTH — For*

TOPIA REVISTA; psicoanalisis, sociedad y cultura. see *PSYCHOLOGY*

IL TORCHIO ARTISTICO E LETTERARIO; organo ufficiale di stampa dell'Accademia Culturale d'Europa. see *ART*

| 301.45 | | SA | ISSN 1019-7435 |

TRACK TWO; constructive approaches to community and political conflict. (Text in English) 1992. q. R.25($25) Centre for Conflict Resolution, c/o University of Cape Town, Rondebosch 7700, South Africa. TEL 27-21-6502503. FAX 27-21-6852142. E-mail: mailbox@ccr.uct.ac.za. Ed. Fiona Adams. circ. 1,000. (back issues avail.) **Document type:** newsletter.
  Description: Promotes innovative constructive approaches to community and political conflict resolution, with an emphasis on alternative and non-governmental initiatives.

| 301.4 | | US | |

TRADITION, FAMILY AND PROPERTY. 1979. bi-m. $18 (foreign $25). American Society for the Defense of Tradition, Family and Property, Box 1868, York, PA 17405-1868. TEL 717-225-7147. FAX 717-225-7382. Ed. C. Preston Noell, III. **Document type:** bulletin.
  Formerly (until 1992): T F P Newsletter.

| 301 | | US | ISSN 1052-5017 |
| LB2361.5 | | | CODEN: TANSFT |

TRANSFORMATIONS. 1990. s-a. $15 to individuals; institutions $40 (effective 1996). New Jersey Project, c/o Ramapo College of NJ, 505 Ramapo Valley Rd., Ramapo, NJ 07430. TEL 201-529-7624. FAX 201-529-7508. E-mail: dcrawley@ultrix.ramapo.edu. Ed.s Donna Crawley, Frances Shapiro-Skrobe. adv.; bk.rev. circ. 2,000. **Document type:** academic/scholarly publication. —UnCover.
  Description: Aims to integrate issues of women and gender, race-ethnicity, class, and sexuality into the curriculum at all levels.

| 301.4 | | CN | ISSN 0049-4429 |

TRANSITION. (Text in English, French) 1970. 4/yr. Can.$30 membership to individuals; institutions Can.$65. Vanier Institute of the Family, 120 Holland Ave., Ste.300, Ottawa, Ont. K1Y 0X6, Canada. TEL 613-722-4007. FAX 613-729-5249. Ed. Ish Theilheimer. bk.rev.; film rev.; bibl.; stat. circ. 8,000. **Indexed:** Avery Ind.Archit.Per., Bank.Lit.Ind. **Document type:** bulletin.
  Description: Articles on family issues.

TRANSPORTATION PLANNING AND TECHNOLOGY. see *TRANSPORTATION*

TRAVAIL HUMAIN. see *PSYCHOLOGY*

| 301 | | AT | |

LA TROBE SOCIOLOGY PAPERS. 1973. irreg. La Trobe University, Department of Sociology, School of Social Sciences, Bundoora, Vic. 3083, Australia. circ. 300.

| 301 | | GW | ISSN 0722-494X |
| | | | CODEN: TUEXDZ |

TUEXENIA. 1928. a. DM.130. Floristisch - Soziologische Arbeitsgemeinschaft, Wilhelm-Weber-Str. 2, 37073 Goettingen, Germany. TEL 0551-395700. FAX 0551-398449. Ed. H. Dierschke. bk.rev. circ. 1,600. **Indexed:** Biol.Abstr., Fababean Abstr., Forest.Abstr., Irr.& Drain.Abstr., Soils & Fert., Triticale Abstr., Weed Abstr. **Document type:** academic/scholarly publication.
  —BLDSC (9068.584000).
  Formerly (until 1980): Floristisch - Soziologische Arbeitsgemeinschaft. Mitteilungen (ISSN 0373-7632)

TURK ETNOGRAFYA DERGISI/TURKISH REVIEW OF ETHNOGRAPHY. see *ANTHROPOLOGY*

TWENTIETH CENTURY FUND. NEWSLETTER. see *POLITICAL SCIENCE — International Relations*

| 301.45 | | SA | ISSN 0041-4794 |
| DT763 | | | |

TYDSKRIF VIR RASSE-AANGELEENTHEDE/JOURNAL OF RACIAL AFFAIRS. (Text in Afrikaans and English) 1949. q. R.40 (free to members). South African Bureau of Racial Affairs, Box 2768, Pretoria, South Africa. Ed. A.D. Pont. adv.; bk.rev.; stat. circ. 5,000. **Indexed:** CERDIC, Documentatieblad, Ind.S.A.Per.

U K ALCOHOL ALERT. see *DRUG ABUSE AND ALCOHOLISM*

| 301.01 | | DK | ISSN 0105-2691 |

UDKAST; dansk tidsskrift for kritisk samfundsvidenskab. 1973. 2/yr. DKK 140 (students DKK 105; foreign DKK 112). Dansk Psykologisk Forlag, Hans Knudsens Plads 1A, 2100 Copenhagen O, Denmark. TEL 45-31-18-27-57. FAX 45-31-18-57-58. Ed. Sven Moerch. index. circ. 500. (back issues avail.) **Indexed:** Psychol.Abstr.
  —BLDSC (9079.653800).

| 301 | | GW | ISSN 0170-2416 |

UEBERSEE-MUSEUM, BREMEN. VEROEFFENTLICHUNGEN. REIHE E: HUMAN-OEKOLOGIE. 1978. irreg., vol.3, 1980. price varies. Uebersee-Museum, Bremen, Bahnhofsplatz 13, 28195 Bremen, Germany. **Indexed:** Biol.Abstr. **Document type:** academic/scholarly publication.

UNE VILLE, UN PAYS. see *HISTORY — History Of Europe*

UNION SIGNAL. see *DRUG ABUSE AND ALCOHOLISM*

| 301 | | VE | ISSN 1012-2508 |

UNIVERSIDAD CENTRAL DE VENEZUELA. CENTRO DE ESTUDIOS DEL DESARROLLO. CUADERNOS DEL C E N D E S. (Text in Spanish; abstracts in English) 1983. 3/yr. Bs.2100($45) to individuals; institutions Bs.4200($70) (foreign $85) (effective 1993). Universidad Central de Venezuela, Centro de Estudios del Desarrollo, Apartado Postal 6622, Caracas 1010-A, Venezuela. TEL 7523266. FAX 582-7512691. (U.S. subscr. addr.: Poba International, No. 151, Box 02-5255, Miami, FL 33102-5255) Dir. sergio Arauda. adv.; bk.rev. circ. 2,000. (back issues avail.)
  Description: Covers Venezuelan development problems and those of the Third World in general.
  Refereed Serial

| 301 | | PR | |

UNIVERSIDAD DE PUERTO RICO. CENTRO DE INVESTIGACIONES SOCIALES. INFORME ANUAL. (Text in Spanish) 1974. a. free. Universidad de Puerto Rico, Centro de Investigaciones Sociales, Recinto de Rio Piedras, Apdo. 23345, Estacion UPR, San Juan, PR 00931-3345. Ed. Wenceslao Serra Deliz. bk.rev.; bibl. circ. 1,000.

SOCIOLOGY

301   PE
UNIVERSIDAD NACIONAL MAYOR DE SAN MARCOS. DEPARTAMENTO DE SOCIOLOGIA. REVISTA.* 1964. s-a. Universidad Nacional Mayor de San Marcos, Departamento de Sociologia, Avda. Republica de Chile 295, Casilla 454, Lima, Peru.

UNIVERSITE DE BORDEAUX II. CAHIERS ETHNOLOGIQUES. see *ANTHROPOLOGY*

301   BE   ISSN 0066-2380
HN501
UNIVERSITE LIBRE DE BRUXELLES. INSTITUT DE SOCIOLOGIE. ANNEE SOCIALE. Key Title: Annee Sociale - Institut de Sociologie. 1960. a. 1050 BEF to individuals (foreign 1100 BEF); institutions 1250 BEF (foreign 1300 BEF) (effective 1994). Universite Libre de Bruxelles, Institute de Sociologie, Av. Jeanne 44, B-1050 Brussels, Belgium. TEL 32-2-650-3359. FAX 32-2-650-3521. bk.rev. **Document type:** academic/scholarly publication.

301   BE   ISSN 0771-6796
H13
UNIVERSITE LIBRE DE BRUXELLES. INSTITUT DE SOCIOLOGIE. REVUE. Key Title: Revue de l'Institut de Sociologie. 1920. q. 1300 BEF (foreign 1650 BEF) (effective 1993). Universite Libre de Bruxelles, Institut de Sociologie, Ave. Jeanne 44, C.P. 124, 1050 Brussels, Belgium. Dir. Claude Javeau. adv.; bk.rev.; abstr.; bibl.; charts; index. circ. 1,150. **Indexed:** SSCI. **Document type:** academic/scholarly publication.
—SWETS.
Supersedes: Institut de Sociologie. Revue (ISSN 0020-2215)

UNIVERSITE NATIONALE DE COTE D'IVOIRE. ANNALES. SERIE F: ETHNOSOCIOLOGIE. see *ANTHROPOLOGY*

330   US
UNIVERSITY OF ALASKA. INSTITUTE OF SOCIAL AND ECONOMIC RESEARCH. RESEARCH SUMMARY. 1980. irreg., no.56, 1995. free. University of Alaska, Institute of Social and Economic Research, 3211 Providence Dr., Anchorage, AK 99508. TEL 907-786-7710. FAX 907-786-7739. Ed. Linda Leask. bk.rev.; charts; stat. circ. 1,900. (also avail. in microfiche; back issues avail.) **Document type:** monographic series.

301   NZ
UNIVERSITY OF AUCKLAND. DEPARTMENT OF SOCIOLOGY. PAPERS IN COMPARATIVE SOCIOLOGY. 1974. irreg., no.20, 1990. price varies. University of Auckland, Department of Sociology, Private Bag, Auckland, New Zealand. FAX 09-733-429. Ed. Ian Carter. circ. 100.

UNIVERSITY OF BIRMINGHAM. CENTRE FOR URBAN AND REGIONAL STUDIES. OCCASIONAL PAPERS. see *HOUSING AND URBAN PLANNING*

UNIVERSITY OF BIRMINGHAM. CENTRE FOR URBAN AND REGIONAL STUDIES. RESEARCH MEMORANDUM. see *HOUSING AND URBAN PLANNING*

UNIVERSITY OF BIRMINGHAM. CENTRE FOR URBAN AND REGIONAL STUDIES. URBAN AND REGIONAL STUDIES. see *HOUSING AND URBAN PLANNING*

UNIVERSITY OF BIRMINGHAM. CENTRE FOR URBAN AND REGIONAL STUDIES. WORKING PAPER. see *HOUSING AND URBAN PLANNING*

301   II   ISSN 0971-0663
UNIVERSITY OF CALCUTTA. DEPARTMENT OF SOCIOLOGY. JOURNAL. Key Title: Annual Journal of the Department of Sociology. (Supplement avail.) (Text in English) a. Rs.12. Dilip Kumar Mukherjee, Asutosh Building, Calcutta 700 073, India. Ed. Krishna Chakrabarty. bk.rev. circ. 1,000. **Indexed:** Int.Polit.Sci.Abstr.
—BLDSC (1087.054000).

UNIVERSITY OF CALIFORNIA AT BERKELEY. INTERNATIONAL AND AREA STUDIES. RESEARCH SERIES. see *POLITICAL SCIENCE*

301   GH
UNIVERSITY OF GHANA. DEPARTMENT OF SOCIOLOGY. CURRENT RESEARCH REPORT SERIES. suspended. irreg. University of Ghana, Department of Sociology, Legon, Accra, Ghana. TEL 233-21-775381. **Document type:** monographic series.

301   UK
UNIVERSITY OF HULL. DEPARTMENT OF SOCIOLOGY AND SOCIAL ANTHROPOLOGY. OCCASIONAL PAPERS. irreg., no.2, 1986. University of Hull, Department of Sociology and Social Anthropology, Hull HU6 7RX, England. **Document type:** monographic series.

UNIVERSITY OF LAGOS. HUMAN RESOURCES RESEARCH UNIT. MONOGRAPH. see *POPULATION STUDIES*

301   UK
UNIVERSITY OF LEEDS. DEPARTMENT OF SOCIAL POLICY AND SOCIOLOGY. RESEARCH WORKING PAPER. irreg., no.7, 1993. University of Leeds, Department of Social Policy and Sociology, Leeds LS2 9JT, England. **Document type:** monographic series.

301 330   JM
UNIVERSITY OF THE WEST INDIES. INSTITUTE OF SOCIAL AND ECONOMIC RESEARCH. WORKING PAPERS. no.7, 1975. irreg., latest no.35. University of the West Indies, Institute of Social and Economic Research, Mona Campus, Kingston 7, Jamaica, W.I. TEL 809-927-1020. FAX 809-927-2409. TELEX 2123 JA.

UNIVERSITY OF VAASA. PROCEEDINGS. DISCUSSION PAPERS. see *BUSINESS AND ECONOMICS — Economic Systems And Theories, Economic History*

UNIVERSITY OF WESTMINSTER. FACULTY OF BUSINESS, MANAGEMENT AND SOCIAL STUDIES. RESEARCH WORKING PAPER SERIES. see *BUSINESS AND ECONOMICS*

UNIVERZITET U ZAGREBU. PRAVNI FAKULTET. ZBORNIK. see *LAW*

UNIWERSYTET SLASKI W KATOWICACH. PRACE NAUKOWE. Z PROBLEMATYKI PRAWA PRACY I POLITYKI SOCJALNEJ. see *LAW*

361   US   ISSN 0042-0468
UNSCHEDULED EVENTS; research committee on disasters newsletter. 1967. q. $22 membership; with International Journal of Mass Emergencies and Disasters $70. International Research Committee on Disasters, Disaster Research Center, University of Delaware, Newark, DE 19716. TEL 302-831-6618. FAX 302-831-2091. TELEX 70 99 85. Ed. Dennis S. Mileti. adv.; bk.rev.; abstr. circ. 250. (back issues avail.) **Document type:** newsletter.

301   SW   ISSN 0502-7527
UPPSALA UNIVERSITET. DEPARTMENT OF SOCIOLOGY. RESEARCH REPORTS. (Text in English, Swedish) 1985. irreg. (4-6/yr.) SEK 200 for 5 nos. Uppsala Universitet, Department of Sociology, Box 513, S-75120 Uppsala, Sweden. TEL 018-1825-00. FAX 46-18-181170. TELEX UNIVUP-S-76024. (back issues avail.)
Description: Covers research carried out in the department.

URBAN ANTHROPOLOGY AND STUDIES OF CULTURAL SYSTEMS AND WORLD ECONOMIC DEVELOPMENT. see *ANTHROPOLOGY*

URBAN LEAGUE REVIEW. see *ETHNIC INTERESTS*

THE URBAN REVIEW; issues and ideas in public education. see *EDUCATION*

URBAN STUDIES. see *HOUSING AND URBAN PLANNING*

URBANIZACION, MIGRACIONES Y CAMBIOS EN LA SOCIEDAD PERUANA. see *ANTHROPOLOGY*

301   UK
V E S NEWSLETTER. no.12, 1981. 3/yr. £10 membership. Voluntary Euthanasia Society, 13 Prince of Wales Terrace, London W8 5PG, England. TEL 0171-937-7770. FAX 0171-376-2648. Ed. Meredith Macardle. bk.rev. **Document type:** newsletter.
Former titles: Exit; Exit News; Right to Die.
Description: News and articles on the right to self-determination in dying.

VAASAN YLIOPISTO. JULKAISUJA. TUTKIMUKSIA/UNIVERSITY OF VAASA. PROCEEDINGS. RESEARCH PAPERS. see *BUSINESS AND ECONOMICS — Economic Systems And Theories, Economic History*

301   HU   ISSN 0324-7228
AP82
VALOSAG. 1957. m. $28.50. (Tudomanyos Ismeretterjeszto Tarsulat) Hirlapkiado Vallalat, Blaha Lujza ter 3, 1959 Budapest 8, Hungary. TEL 1-382-399. TELEX 22-5554. (Subscr. to: Kultura, P.O. Box 149, H-1389 Budapest, Hungary.) Ed. Istvan Lazar. adv.; bk.rev. circ. 9,000. **Indexed:** Rural Recreat.Tour.Abstr., World Agri.Econ. & Rural Sociol.Abstr.

VICTIMS OF VIOLENCE REPORT. see *LAW — Criminal Law*

301   FR   ISSN 0042-5605
H3
VIE SOCIALE. 1964. bi-m. 275 F. (foreign 320 F.) (effective 1996). Centre d'Etudes, de Documentation, d'Information et d'Action Sociales (CEDIAS), 5 rue Las-Cases, 75007 Paris, France. TEL 45-51-66-10. Ed. B. Bouquet. bk.rev.; circ. 1,750 (controlled). (back issues avail.) **Document type:** academic/scholarly publication, bibliography, monographic series.
—BLDSC (9235.420000).
Description: A collection of stories, reflections, information and documentation.

303.6 305.4   US   ISSN 1077-8012
CODEN: VAWOFG
▼**VIOLENCE AGAINST WOMEN.** 1995. q. $48 to individuals; institutions $140 (effective Sep. 1995). Sage Publications, Inc., 2455 Teller Rd., Thousand Oaks, CA 91320. TEL 805-499-0721. FAX 805-499-0871. E-mail: libraries@sagepub.com. (Overseas subscr. to: Sage Publications Ltd., 6 Bonhill St., London EC2A 4PU, England; Sage Publications India Pvt. Ltd., Box 4215, New Delhi 110 048, India) Ed. Claire M. Renzetti. adv. (back issues avail.; reprint service avail.) **Document type:** academic/scholarly publication.
Description: Publishes empirical research, as well as cross-cultural and historical analyses, on all aspects of violence against women and girls.

301.1 364   US   ISSN 0886-6708
HV6250
VIOLENCE AND VICTIMS. 1986. q. $42 to individuals (foreign $47); institutions $79 (foreign $87) (effective 1996). Springer Publishing Company, 536 Broadway, New York, NY 10012-3955. TEL 212-431-4370. FAX 212-941-7842. Ed. Roland Maiuro. adv.; bk.rev. (back issues avail.) **Indexed:** Abstr.Crim.& Pen., Crim.Just.Abstr., Excerp.Med., IMFL, Ind.Med., Psychol.Abstr. (1986-), Sage Fam.Stud.Abstr., Sage Urb.Stud.Abstr., Sociol.Abstr., SOPODA. **Document type:** trade publication.
—BLDSC (9237.751000); Faxon; SWETS; UnCover. CCC.
Description: Provides a forum for the latest developments in theory, reserach, policy, clinical practice and social services in the areas of interpersonal violence and victimization.
Refereed Serial

301   IT
VITTORIO BACCELLI MAGAZINE. biennial. L.10000. Vittorio Baccelli, Ed. & Pub., C.P. 132, 55100 Lucca, Italy.

301 374 301.412   UK   ISSN 0260-3993
VIVE LA DIFFERENCE. 1979. q. £1.50 for 3 issues. C F W - Concern for Family & Womanhood, Campaign for the Feminine Woman, Springfield House, Chedworth, Cheltenham, Glos. GL54 4AH, England. TEL 01285-720454. Ed. David W. Stayt. circ. 5,000. **Document type:** academic/scholarly publication.
Description: Promotes and advances education in masculinity and femininity, the value and validity of the different sex roles, as well as marriage and family from a traditional, Christian perspective.

309   UK   ISSN 0957-8765
HD62.6   CODEN: VOLUE8
VOLUNTAS; international journal of voluntary and non-profit organizations. 1990. s-a. £35($50) to individuals; institutions £70($120). (Charities Aid Foundation) Manchester University Press, Oxford Rd., Manchester M13 9PL, England. TEL 061-273-5539. FAX 061-274-3346. TELEX 666517-UNIMAN. Eds. H. Anheier, M. Knapp; Pub. Francis Brooke. adv. contact: Matthew Branton. **Indexed:** Soc.Work Res.& Abstr. **Document type:** academic/scholarly publication.
—BLDSC (9254.577800).

SOCIOLOGY — ABSTRACTING, BIBLIOGRAPHIES, STATISTICS

301   GW
VON MANN ZU MANN. 1980. irreg. DM.3($30) Stiftung Aktiv Gegen Sexismus, Marburgerstr. 9, 60487 Frankfurt, Germany. Ed. Rudi Gerharz.

200 301   US   ISSN 1059-6216
WALK AWAY; the newsletter for ex-fundamentalists. 1989. q. $10 (effective 1994). Institute for First Amendment Studies, Inc., Box 589, Great Barrington, MA 01230. TEL 413-528-3800. FAX 413-528-4466. Ed. Skipp Porteous. bk.rev.; circ. 2,500 (paid). (also avail. in microfiche; back issues avail.) **Document type:** newsletter.
Description: Support newsletter for ex-fundamentalists. Publishes personal stories of those who walked away from fundamentalism.

WARSAW AGRICULTURAL UNIVERSITY. S G G W. ANNALS. AGRICULTURAL ECONOMICS AND RURAL SOCIOLOGY. see AGRICULTURE — Agricultural Economics

WEEKLY PROBES. see POLITICAL SCIENCE

301 320   NR   ISSN 0308-4450
HN820
WEST AFRICAN JOURNAL OF SOCIOLOGY AND POLITICAL SCIENCE. q. £20($40) University of Ibadan, Sociology Department, Ibadan, Nigeria. Ed. Justin Labinjon. adv.; bk.rev.; bibl. circ. 1,000. (back issues avail.) **Indexed:** Curr.Cont.Africa, Lang.& Lang.Behav.Abstr.

THE WHITE RIBBON. see DRUG ABUSE AND ALCOHOLISM

301   US
WINGED MERCURY MISSIVE.* 1981. irreg. $5. Winged Mercury Networking, Box 5010, Dept. 244, Asheville, NC 28813-5010. Ed. Gary Smith. bk.rev. circ. 288.

WISSENSCHAFTLICHE PAPERBACKS; Sozial- und Wirtschaftsgeschichte. see BUSINESS AND ECONOMICS — Economic Systems And Theories, Economic History

301   AU
DER WOHLFAHRTSDIENST; Monatsschrift fuer Fragen der Wirtschaft und des Sozialen Lebens. 1952. m. free. Oesterreichischer Wohlfahrtsdienst, Kaerntnerstr. 51-1, A-1010 Vienna, Austria. TEL 5127823. Ed. Gretl Pilz. adv.; bk.rev.; bibl.

WOMEN IN CULTURE AND SOCIETY. see WOMEN'S INTERESTS

301 150   US   ISSN 0730-8884
HT675
WORK AND OCCUPATIONS; an international sociological journal. 1974. q. $56 to individuals; institutions $167 (effective Sep. 1995). Sage Publications, Inc., 2455 Teller Rd., Thousand Oaks, CA 91320. TEL 805-499-0721. FAX 805-499-0871. E-mail: libraries@sagepub.com. (Overseas subscr. to: Sage Publications Ltd., 6 Bonhill St., London EC2A 4PU, England; Sage Publications India Pvt. Ltd., P.O. Box 4215, New Delhi 110 048, India) Ed. Daniel B. Cornfield. adv.; bk.rev.; index. circ. 1,250. (also avail. in microform from UMI; back issues avail.; reprint service avail. from UMI) **Indexed:** ABI Inform., ASSIA, BPIA, C.I.J.E., Curr.Cont., Ergon.Abstr., IMFL, Int.Lab.Doc., Lang.& Lang.Behav.Abstr., Mid.East: Abstr.& Ind., Pers.Lit., Psychol.Abstr. (1975-), Sage Fam.Stud.Abstr., Sage Pub.Admin.Abstr., Sociol.Abstr. (1976-), SSCI, Stud.Wom.Abstr., Tech.Educ.Abstr. **Document type:** academic/scholarly publication.
●Also available online. Vendor(s): University Microfilms International.
—BLDSC (9348.075000); Faxon; Genuine Article; SWETS; UMI; UnCover. **CCC.**
Formerly (until 1982): Sociology of Work and Occupations (ISSN 0093-9285)
Description: Provides an outlet for sociological research and theory in the substantive areas of work, occupations, and leisure and treats their structures and interrelationships.

301   UK   ISSN 0950-0170
HD6951
WORK, EMPLOYMENT & SOCIETY. 1987. q. £28 to non-member individuals; institutions £72 (foreign £79) (effective 1995). (British Sociological Association) B S A Publications Ltd., 351 Station Rd., Dorridge, Solihull, W. Midlands B93 8EY, England. TEL 01564-772402. Ed. R. Crompton. bk.rev. (also avail. in microform from UMI) **Indexed:** ASSIA, Cont.Pg.Manage., Int.Lab.Doc., Sociol.Abstr. (1987-), Sociol.Educ.Abstr. **Document type:** academic/scholarly publication.
—BLDSC (9348.149000); Faxon; Genuine Article; SWETS; UnCover.
Description: Contains articles on all aspects of work, employment, and unemployment; debates; and updates on works in progress.

301.34   TR
WORKING PAPERS ON CARIBBEAN SOCIETY. SERIES A: NEW PERSPECTIVES IN THEORY AND ANALYSIS. 1978. irreg. $2. University of the West Indies, Department of Sociology, St. Augustine, Trinidad & Tobago, W.I.

301.34   TR
WORKING PAPERS ON CARIBBEAN SOCIETY. SERIES C: RESEARCH FINDINGS. irreg. University of the West Indies, Department of Sociology, St. Augustine, Trinidad & Tobago, W.I.

WORKING PAPERS ON WOMEN IN INTERNATIONAL DEVELOPMENT. see BUSINESS AND ECONOMICS — International Development And Assistance

WORLD DISASTERS REPORT. see PUBLIC HEALTH AND SAFETY

WORLD FUTURES GENERAL EVOLUTION STUDIES. see SOCIAL SCIENCES: COMPREHENSIVE WORKS

WORLD LEISURE AND RECREATION. see LEISURE AND RECREATION

WORLD UNION. see POLITICAL SCIENCE — International Relations

301   US   ISSN 1068-5480
WRITING SOCIOLOGY. 1993. q. $10 to individuals; institutions $20. North Carolina State University, Department of Sociology, Raleigh, NC 27695. Eds. Michael Schwalbe, Clifford Staples. circ. 300 (paid). **Document type:** newsletter.
Description: Publishes short articles on the craft and politics of academic writing.

301   CC
XIANGGANG FENGQING/HONG KONG CUSTOMS. (Text in Chinese) bi-m. Guangdong Renmin Chubanshe, Qikan Bu - Guangdong People's Publishing House, No. 10, 4 Malu, Dashatou, Guangzhou, Guangdong 510102, People's Republic of China. TEL 335210. Ed. Liu Bansheng.

XIN WENHUA SHILIAO/HISTORICAL RECORDS OF THE NEW CULTURE. see HISTORY — History Of Asia

301 320   II   ISSN 0049-8351
YOUNG AGE;* social and cultural fortnightly. (Text in English and Hindi) 1965. s-m. Rs.5($5) 3968 Rasta M. S. B., Jaipur 302003, India. Ed. Surendra Kumar. adv.; bk.rev. circ. 2,500.

YOUTH & SOCIETY. see CHILDREN AND YOUTH — About

YUNNAN MINZU XUEYUAN XUEBAO/YUNNAN INSTITUTE OF NATIONALITIES. JOURNAL. see ORIENTAL STUDIES

301   GW   ISSN 0723-5607
Z A INFORMATION. 1977. s-a. free. Universitaet zu Koeln, Zentralarchiv fuer Empirische Sozialforschung, Bachemerstr. 40, 50931 Cologne, Germany. TEL 0221-47694-0. FAX 0221-4769444. E-mail: za@ibm.za.uni.koeln.de. Ed. Franz Bauske. adv.; bk.rev. circ. 3,500. (back issues avail.) **Document type:** newsletter.
Description: Information and studies in social science, covering methodological research and comparative analysis. Includes reports of events.

301 310   GW   ISSN 0721-8516
Z U M A - NACHRICHTEN. 1977. s-a. free. Zentrum fuer Umfragen, Methoden und Analysen e.V., Postfach 122155, 68072 Mannheim, Germany. TEL 0621-12460. FAX 0621-1246100. E-mail: name@zuma-mannheim.de. bk.rev. circ. 3,000. **Document type:** newsletter.

ZADOK CENTRE. SERIES NO.1. see RELIGIONS AND THEOLOGY

ZADOK CENTRE. SERIES NO.2. see RELIGIONS AND THEOLOGY

ZADOK CENTRE READING GUIDES. see RELIGIONS AND THEOLOGY

ZADOK PERSPECTIVES. see RELIGIONS AND THEOLOGY

ZEITSCHRIFT FUER AGRARGESCHICHTE UND AGRARSOZIOLOGIE. see AGRICULTURE

ZEITSCHRIFT FUER GANZHEITSFORSCHUNG. see PHILOSOPHY

301 340   GW   ISSN 0174-0202
ZEITSCHRIFT FUER RECHTSSOZIOLOGIE. s-a. DM.76 (students DM.58) (effective 1996). Westdeutscher Verlag GmbH, Postfach 1546, 65005 Wiesbaden, Germany. TEL 0611-534389. FAX 0611-534430. Ed. Erhard Blankenburg. (back issues avail.; reprint service avail. from SCH) **Indexed:** Lang.& Lang.Behav.Abstr., Sociol.Abstr. (1980-). **Document type:** academic/scholarly publication.
—SWETS. **CCC.**

301   GW   ISSN 0720-4361
ZEITSCHRIFT FUER SOZIALISATIONSFORSCHUNG UND ERZIEHUNGSSOZIOLOGIE. (Articles in English) 1980. q. DM.106 (foreign DM.118). Juventa Verlag GmbH, Ehretstr. 3, 69469 Weinheim, Germany. TEL 06201-61035. FAX 06201-13135. Ed. Rosemarie Nave-Herz. adv.; bk.rev.; index. circ. 800. **Indexed:** Lang.& Lang.Behav.Abstr., Mult.Ed.Abstr., Sociol.Abstr. (1983-), Sociol.Educ.Abstr. **Document type:** academic/scholarly publication.
—BLDSC (9486.375000). **CCC.**

ZEITSCHRIFT FUER SOZIALPSYCHOLOGIE. see PSYCHOLOGY

301   GW   ISSN 0340-1804
HM5
ZEITSCHRIFT FUER SOZIOLOGIE. 1972. bi-m. DM.142. Ferdinand Enke Verlag, Postfach 300366, 70443 Stuttgart, Germany. TEL 0711-135798-0. FAX 0711-135798-30. TELEX 07252275-GTV-D. Ed.Bd. adv.; bibl. circ. 1,400. (reprint service avail. from IRC) **Indexed:** Curr.Cont., Int.Polit.Sci.Abstr., Mult.Ed.Abstr., P.A.I.S.For.Lang.Ind., Sociol.Abstr. (1972-), SSCI, Stud.Wom.Abstr. **Document type:** academic/scholarly publication.
—BLDSC (9486.393000); Genuine Article; SWETS. **CCC.**

ZEITSCHRIFT FUER WIRTSCHAFTS- UND SOZIALWISSENSCHAFTEN. see BUSINESS AND ECONOMICS

301   FR
200 GROUPES FRANCAIS D'AFRIQUE NOIRE. 1980. a. 1190 F. I C Publications, 10 rue Vineuse, 75116 Paris Cedex 16, France. TEL 44-30-81-00. FAX 44-30-81-11.

360 DEGREES; the magazine with every angle. see CHILDREN AND YOUTH — For

SOCIOLOGY — Abstracting, Bibliographies, Statistics

301 500 011   UK   ISSN 0260-0552
ALTERNATIVE ALTERNATIVE. 1980. every 4 weeks. free to qualified personnel. 3 Mason Lodge, Skene, Aberdeenshire AB32 6XR, Scotland. TEL 01224-743433. Ed. Dave Parry; Pub. Dave Parry. bk.rev. circ. 120. **Document type:** newsletter.
Description: Covers relationship between science, politics, and religion.

SOCIOLOGY — ABSTRACTING, BIBLIOGRAPHIES, STATISTICS

301 011 US ISSN 0740-8978
HM261
AMERICAN PUBLIC OPINION INDEX.* 1983 (for 1981). a. $174.50. Opinion Research Service, 7200 Wisconsin Ave., Ste. 704, Bethesda, MD 20814-4811. Ed. D.A. Gilbert.
 Description: Topical listings of questions asked in national, state, local and special surveys and public opinion polls.

ARCHIVES DE SCIENCES SOCIALES DES RELIGIONS. see SOCIAL SCIENCES: COMPREHENSIVE WORKS — Abstracting, Bibliographies, Statistics

301 312 AT ISSN 1032-4003
HQ705
AUSTRALIAN FAMILY AND SOCIETY ABSTRACTS. (Not avail. in print after 1991 ed.) 1984. a. Australian Institute of Family Studies, 300 Queen St., Melbourne, Vic. 3000, Australia. TEL 61-3-2147888. FAX 61-3-2147839. Eds. Deborah Whithear, Belinda Stonehouse. **Document type:** abstracting/indexing.
●Also available online.
Also available on CD-ROM.
 Formerly: Family. Australian Family Studies Database.
 Description: A computer-based bibliographic system containing references to the literature on families and family life in Australia.

BIBLIOGRAFIE NEDERLANDSE SOCIALE WETENSCHAPPEN; vakbibliografie voor nederland en Nederlandstalig Belgie. see SOCIAL SCIENCES: COMPREHENSIVE WORKS — Abstracting, Bibliographies, Statistics

301 ISSN 0742-6895
BIBLIOGRAPHIES AND INDEXES IN SOCIOLOGY. 1984. irreg. price varies. Greenwood Press, Inc. (Subsidiary of: Greenwood Publishing Group Inc.), 88 Post Rd. W., Box 5007, Westport, CT 06881-5007. TEL 203-226-3571. FAX 203-222-1502.
 —BLDSC (1993.097540).

305.8 016 GW
BIBLIOGRAPHISCHE INFORMATIONEN ZU MIGRATION UND ETHNIZITAET. 1986. 4/yr. DM.48. Edition Parabolis, Postfach 301125, 10722 Berlin, Germany. TEL 030-4441088. FAX 030-4441085. **Document type:** bibliography.
 Formerly: Migration und Ethnizitaet (ISSN 0177-526X)

310 US ISSN 0893-8504
BIO-BIBLIOGRAPHIES IN SOCIOLOGY. 1987. irreg. price varies. Greenwood Press, Inc. (Subsidiary of: Greenwood Publishing Group Inc.), 88 Post Rd. W., Box 5007, Westport, CT 06881-5007. TEL 203-226-3571. FAX 203-222-1502.

CONTEMPORARY SOCIAL ISSUES: A BIBLIOGRAPHIC SERIES. see BIBLIOGRAPHIES

301 016 US ISSN 0094-3061
HM1
CONTEMPORARY SOCIOLOGY; a journal of reviews. 1972. bi-m. $50 to individuals (foreign $60); institutions $105 (foreign $115). American Sociological Association, 1722 N St., N.W., Washington, DC 20036. TEL 202-833-3410. FAX 202-785-0146. Ed. Walter Powell. adv.; bk.rev. circ. 10,000. (also avail. in microform from UMI; reprint service avail. from UMI) **Indexed:** Acad.Ind., Adol.Ment.Hlth.Abstr., Amer.Bibl.Slavic & E.Eur.Stud., Bk.Rev.Ind. (1965-), Chic.Per.Ind., Child.Bk.Rev.Ind. (1965-), E.I., Lang.& Lang.Behav.Abstr., Mid.East: Abstr.& Ind., Ref.Sour., Sociol.Abstr. (1980-), SSCI. **Document type:** academic/scholarly publication.
●Also available online. Vendor(s): University Microfilms International.
 —BLDSC (3425.305000); Faxon; Genuine Article; UMI; UnCover.
 Description: Publishes reviews and critical discussions of recent works in sociology and in related disciplines which merit the attention of sociologists.

300 150 370 US ISSN 0092-6361
CURRENT CONTENTS: SOCIAL & BEHAVIORAL SCIENCES. Short title: C C: S & B S. (Includes Author Index and Address Directory, Current Book Contents and Title Word Index) 1969. w. $442. Institute for Scientific Information, 3501 Market St., Philadelphia, PA 19104. TEL 215-386-0100. FAX 215-386-2291. (And: Brunel Science Park, Brunel University, Uxbridge UB8 3PQ, England) (also avail. in magnetic tape; diskette format) **Indexed:** Compumath, E.I., Ind.Sci.Rev., Popul.Ind., SSCI. **Document type:** academic/scholarly publication, bibliography.
●Also available online. Vendor(s): Knight-Ridder, Inc. (File no.440), Ovid Technologies (CTOC,CBIB,BEHA).
 —BLDSC (3496.209500).
 Formerly: C C B S E (Current Contents, Behavioral, Social and Educational Sciences) (ISSN 0011-3387)
 Description: Tables of contents of the world's leading publications covering social and behavioral sciences.

ECONOMIC AND SOCIAL STATISTICS OF SRI LANKA. see BUSINESS AND ECONOMICS — Abstracting, Bibliographies, Statistics

301 016 GR ISSN 0013-2934
EKISTIC INDEX OF PERIODICALS. 1968. s-a. $150 (effective 1996). Athens Center of Ekistics, 24 Syndesmou, 106 73 Athens, Greece. TEL 30-1-3623-216. FAX 30-1-3633-395. TELEX 215227. Ed. P. Psomopoulos. (back issues avail.) **Document type:** abstracting/indexing.

301 016 FR ISSN 1157-3716
H1
F R A N C I S. 521: SOCIOLOGIE. (Printed format ceased Jan. 1995) 1947. q. Centre National de la Recherche Scientifique, Institut de l'Information Scientifique et Technique, 2 allee du Parc de Brabois, 54514 Vandoeuvre-les-Nancy Cedex, France. TEL 83-50-46-00. FAX 83-50-46-50. adv. contact: Veronique Guinvarc'h. cum.index. **Indexed:** A.I.C.P., E.I., Popul.Ind. **Document type:** bibliography.
●Also available online. Vendor(s): Telesystemes - Questel.
Also available on CD-ROM.
 Formerly: Bulletin Signaletique. Part 521: Sociologie (ISSN 0765-1465); Supersedes in part: Bulletin Signaletique. Part 521: Sociologie - Ethnologie (ISSN 0007-5566)

309 310 FI
FINLAND. STATISTIKCENTRALEN. STATISTISKA MEDDELANDEN. LEVNADSFOERHAALLANDEN I FINLAND/FINLAND. CENTRAL STATISTICAL OFFICE. LIVING CONDITIONS IN FINLAND. 1977. irreg. FIM 89. Tilastokeskus, Annankatu 44, SF-00100 Helsinki 10, Finland.

310 US ISSN 0895-7983
HARRIS POLL. 1963. w. $325. (Creators Syndicate) Louis Harris and Associates, Inc., 630 Fifth Ave., 11th Fl., New York, NY 10111. TEL 212-698-9600. FAX 212-698-9669. stat.; index. circ. 400. (looseleaf format)
 Formerly: (until 1988): A B C News - Harris Survey (ISSN 0273-1037); Supersedes (1963-1978): Harris Survey Column Subscription (ISSN 0046-6875)
 Description: Discusses current political, social, economic and international issues. Contains tables with questions from national cross-section of population.

301 016 US ISSN 0099-2453
Z7165.U5
HUMAN RESOURCES ABSTRACTS; an international information service. 1966. q. $112 to individuals; institutions $330 (effective Sep. 1995). Sage Publications, Inc., 2455 Teller Rd., Thousand Oaks, CA 91320. TEL 805-499-0721. FAX 805-499-0871. E-mail: libraries@sagepub.com. (Overseas subscr. to: Sage Publications Ltd., 6 Bonhill Rd., London EC2A 4PU, England; Sage; Sage Publications India Pvt. Ltd., P.O. Box 4215, New Delhi 110 048, India) Ed. Paul McDowell. adv.; index. circ. 750. (also avail. in microfilm from UMI; back issues avail.; reprint service avail. from UMI) **Indexed:** Curr.Lit.Fam.Plan. **Document type:** abstracting/indexing.
 —UMI. CCC.
 Formerly: Poverty and Human Resources Abstracts (ISSN 0032-5864)
 Description: Abstracts the most important literature for persons interested in human resources development and related social and governmental policy questions.

I C S S R JOURNAL OF ABSTRACTS AND REVIEWS: SOCIOLOGY & SOCIAL ANTHROPOLOGY. (Indian Council of Social Science Research) see ANTHROPOLOGY — Abstracting, Bibliographies, Statistics

INDICE ESPANOL DE CIENCIAS SOCIALES. SERIES B: ECONOMICS, SOCIOLOGY AND POLITICAL SCIENCE. see BUSINESS AND ECONOMICS — Abstracting, Bibliographies, Statistics

301 016.3 UK ISSN 0085-2066
Z7161
INTERNATIONAL BIBLIOGRAPHY OF THE SOCIAL SCIENCES. SOCIOLOGY. Title page also reads: International Bibliography of Sociology. 1951. a. £125($230) (British Library of Political and Economic Science) Routledge, 11 New Fetter Ln., London EC4P 4EE, England. TEL 0171-583-9855. FAX 0171-583-0701. TELEX 263398 ROUT G. Ed. Lynne J. Brindley. adv. **Indexed:** A.I.C.P. **Document type:** abstracting/indexing, academic/scholarly publication, bibliography.
 —BLDSC (4537.113000).
 Description: A selective bibliography indexing monographs and the contents of over 2500 journals in the social sciences. Indexed by subject, geographical terms and author.

INVENTORY OF MARRIAGE AND FAMILY LITERATURE. see MATRIMONY — Abstracting, Bibliographies, Statistics

301.4 322.4 016 US
JOURNALS OF DISSENT AND SOCIAL CHANGE; a bibliography of titles in the California State University, Sacramento, library. 1969. irreg., 7th ed., 1993. $25. California State University, Sacramento, Library, 2000 Jed Smith Dr., Sacramento, CA 95819. TEL 916-278-7958. (Subscr. to: University Bookstore, California State Univ., Sacramento, 6000 J St., Sacramento, CA 95819) Ed. John Liberty. circ. controlled. (processed) **Document type:** bibliography.
 Description: Subject-arranged catalog to over 4000 journals in the Dissent and Social Change Collection.

301.15 016 US
N T I S ALERTS: BEHAVIOR AND SOCIETY. w. $125 (foreign $175). U.S. National Technical Information Service, 5285 Port Royal Rd., Springfield, VA 22161. TEL 703-487-4929. cum.index. (back issues avail.)
 Former titles: Abstract Newsletter: Behavior and Society (ISSN 0145-0034); Weekly Abstract Newsletter: Behavior and Society; Weekly Government Abstracts. Behavior and Society.

NIHON KODO KEIRYO GAKKAI TAIKAI HAPPYO RONBUN SHOROKUSHU. see PSYCHOLOGY — Abstracting, Bibliographies, Statistics

330.9 NO ISSN 0801-3845
NORWAY. STATISTISK SENTRALBYRAA. SOSIALE OG OEKNOMIISKE STUDIER. (Text in Norwegian; summaries in English) 1954. irreg. price varies. Statistisk Sentralbyraa, P.O. 131 Dep., N-33 Oslo 1, Norway. TEL 47-22-864500. FAX 47-22-864976. circ. 2,000. **Document type:** government publication.
 Formed by the merger of: (1954-1986): Norway. Statistisk Sentralbyraa. Samfunnsoekonomiske Studier (ISSN 0085-4344); (1957-1986): Norway. Statistisk Sentralbyraa. Artikler (ISSN 0085-431X); (1972-1986): Norway. Statistisk Sentralbyraa. Statistiske Analyser (ISSN 0333-0621)

301 US
NOTE US; news from Sociological Abstracts, Linguistics and Language Behavior Abstracts, and Social Planning-Policy & Development Abstracts. 1983. q. free. Sociological Abstracts, Inc., Box 22206, San Diego, CA 92192. TEL 619-695-8803. FAX 619-695-0416. Ed. Miriam Chall. circ. 10,000. **Document type:** newsletter.

NOTES AND ABSTRACTS IN AMERICAN AND INTERNATIONAL EDUCATION. see EDUCATION — Abstracting, Bibliographies, Statistics

NOVAYA LITERATURA PO SOTSIAL'NYM I GUMANITARNYM NAUKAM. FILOSOFIYA I SOTSIOLOGIYA; bibliograficheskii ukazatel' see PHILOSOPHY — Abstracting, Bibliographies, Statistics

SOCIOLOGY — COMPUTER APPLICATIONS

310 US ISSN 0193-2713
BF698.75
OPERANT SUBJECTIVITY; the Q methodology newsletter. 1977. q. $5 to individuals; institutions $7. Kent State University, Department of Political Science, Kent, OH 44242-0001. TEL 216-672-2060. (Ed. addr.: School of Education, University of Leicester, 21 University Rd., Leicester LE1 7RF, England) Ed. Steven R. Brown. bk.rev.; bibl. circ. 100. **Indexed**: Psychol.Abstr.
—UnCover.

PEACE RESEARCH ABSTRACTS JOURNAL. see *POLITICAL SCIENCE — Abstracting, Bibliographies, Statistics*

300 IS
PUBLICATIONS IN EDUCATION AND THE SOCIAL SCIENCES IN ISRAEL. (Print edition ceased with vol.10, no.4, 1991) (Text in Hebrew; titles and subject index in English) 1977. a. $250 (updates $100). Henrietta Szold Institute, 9 Columbia St, Kiryat Menachem, Jerusalem 96583, Israel. TEL 972-2-419191. FAX 972-2-437698. (Subscr. to: CDI Ltd., P.O. Box 45064, Jerusalem 91450, Israel. TEL 972-2-870112. FAX 972-2-870115) Ed. Shoshanna Langerman. abstr.; index. circ. 250. **Document type**: bibliography.
●Available only on CD-ROM.
Former titles (until vol.10, no.4, 1991): Current Research in the Social Sciences (ISSN 0334-7303); Current Research in Behavioral Sciences in Israel (ISSN 0334-2468)
Description: Publishes bibliographic data and abstracts on research, publications, articles, conferences and theses published in Israel and abroad by Israeli researchers.

309 330.9 016 JM
S E C I N ABSTRACTS. JOURNAL. 1982. biennial. $20. (Socio-Economic Information Network, Planning Institute of Jamaica) Documentation Center, 39-41 Barbados Ave., Kingston 5, Jamaica, W.I. circ. 150. **Document type**: abstracting/indexing.
Formerly: S E C I N Abstracts.

301 016 US ISSN 0164-0283
HQ536
SAGE FAMILY STUDIES ABSTRACTS. 1979. q. $98 to individuals; institutions $325 (effective Sep. 1995). Sage Publications, Inc., 2455 Teller Rd., Thousand Oaks, CA 91320. TEL 805-499-0721. FAX 805-499-0871. E-mail: libraries@sagepub.com. (Overseas subscr. to: Sage Publications Ltd., 6 Bonhill St., London EC2A 4PU, England; Sage Publications India Pvt. Ltd., P.O. Box 4215, New Delhi 110 048, India) Ed. Paul McDowell. circ. 750. (back issues avail.; reprint service avail.) **Indexed**: IMFL. **Document type**: abstracting/indexing.
—UMI; UnCover. **CCC**.
Description: Abstracts major articles, reports, books, and other materials on policy, theory, and research relating to the family, interpersonal relations, human development, therapy, and counseling.

SAGE RACE RELATIONS ABSTRACTS. see *POLITICAL SCIENCE — Abstracting, Bibliographies, Statistics*

SOCIAL THEORY: A BIBLIOGRAPHIC SERIES. see *BIBLIOGRAPHIES*

312 301 NZ
SOCIAL TRENDS IN NEW ZEALAND. 1977. irreg. NZ.$30.65. Department of Statistics, P.O. Box 2922, Wellington, New Zealand. (reprint service avail. from SCH)

301 016 US ISSN 0038-0202
HM1 CODEN: SOABA
SOCIOLOGICAL ABSTRACTS. 1953. bi-m. $510 (subscr. includes a. index). Sociological Abstracts, Inc., Box 22206, San Diego, CA 92192. TEL 619-695-8803. FAX 619-695-0416. (Co-sponsor: International Sociological Association) adv.; index, cum.index: vols.1-10, 11-15. circ. 1,900. (back issues avail.) **Indexed**: A.I.C.P. **Document type**: abstracting/indexing.
●Also available online. Vendor(s): DIMDI (SA63), Data-Star (SOCA), Knight-Ridder, Inc. (File no.37). Also available on CD-ROM. Producer(s): SilverPlatter Information, Inc. (Sociofile).
—BLDSC (8319.622000); UMI. **CCC**.

SOCIOLOGY OF EDUCATION ABSTRACTS. see *EDUCATION — Abstracting, Bibliographies, Statistics*

301 RU
SOTSIOLOGIYA: OTECHESTVENNAYA I ZARUBEZHNAYA LITERATURA; referativnyi zhurnal. 1972. q. $64. Rossiiskaya Akademiya Nauk, Institut Nauchnoi Informatsii po Obshchestvennym Naukam, Ul. Krasikova 28-21, 117418 Moscow V-418, Russia. Ed. V.I. Dobren'kov. **Document type**: abstracting/indexing.
Formerly (until 1991): Obshchestvennye Nauki za Rubezhom. Sotsiologiya (ISSN 0868-4448); Which superseded in part: Obshchestvennye Nauki za Rubezhom. Filosofiya i Sotsiologiya (ISSN 0132-7356)

301 015 HU ISSN 0133-2074
SZOCIOLOGIAI INFORMACIO/SOCIOLOGICAL INFORMATION; a magyar nyelvu es magyar vonatkozasu szakirodalom valogatott bibliografiaja. 1972. a. 473 Ft. Fovarosi Szabo Ervin Konyvtar, Szociologiai Dokumentacios Osztaly, Szabo Ervin ter 1, 1088 Budapest, Hungary. FAX 36-1-1185-914. (Co-sponsor: Budapest Fovaros Onkormanyzata) Ed. Maria Vagh. adv.; bk.rev.; index. circ. 300.
Description: Current national bibliography of books and articles on Hungarian sociology written by Hungarian sociologists in the country or abroad, and by foregin sociologists about Hungary and Hungarians.

301 IS ISSN 0792-0598
TEL AVIV - YAFO. CENTER FOR ECONOMIC AND SOCIAL RESEARCH. STATISTICAL YEARBOOK. (Text in English and Hebrew) 1961. a. Center for Economic and Social Research, Tel Aviv - Yafo Municipality, Malkhei Israel Square, Tel Aviv 64162, Israel. TEL 972-3-6962156. illus. **Document type**: government publication.
Former titles: Tel Aviv - Yafo. Research and Statistics Department. Yearbook; Tel Aviv Yearbook.
Description: Current statistical data on demographic, economic and social aspects of Tel Aviv - Yafo.

301 US ISSN 0725-5136
H61
THESIS ELEVEN; a journal of critical social theory. 1980. a. $35 to individuals (foreign $51); institutions $85 (foreign $101). M I T Press, 55 Hayward St., Cambridge, MA 02142. TEL 617-253-2889. FAX 617-258-6779. E-mail: journals-orders@mit.edu. (Editorial addr: Monash University, Anthropology and Sociology, Clayton, Vic. 3168, Australia) Ed.Bd. adv.; bk.rev.; cum.index. circ. 2,000. (also avail. in microform from UMI; back issues avail.; reprint service avail. from UMI) **Indexed**: Alt.Press Ind., Lang.& Lang.Behav.Abstr., Left Ind. (1984-), Sociol.Abstr. **Document type**: academic/scholarly publication.
—BLDSC (8820.095000); SWETS; UMI; UnCover. **CCC**.
Description: Covers theories of society, culture and politics, and the understanding of modernity.

303.6 340 US ISSN 1077-2197
▼**VIOLENCE & ABUSE ABSTRACTS**; current literature in interpersonal violence. 1995. q. $76 to individuals; institutions 220 (effective Sep. 1995). Sage Publications, Inc., 2455 Teller Rd., Thousand Oaks, CA 91320. TEL 805-499-0721. FAX 805-499-0871. E-mail: libraries@sagepub.com. (Overseas subscr. to: Sage Publications Ltd., 6 Bonhill St., London EC2A 4PU, England; Sage Publications India Pvt. Ltd., P.O. Box 4215, New Delhi 110 048, India) (back issues avail.; reprint service avail.) **Document type**: abstracting/indexing.
Description: Abstracts articles on the legal, medical, psychological, and social aspects all types of interpersonal violence, including child abuse, domestic violence, rape and sexual harassment, gang violence, and elder abuse.

301 UK ISSN 0140-9018
HN398.W58
WELSH SOCIAL TRENDS. 1977. irreg. Welsh Office, Statistical Directorate, New Crown Bldg., Cathays Park, Cardiff CF1 3NQ, Wales. TEL 01222-825054. FAX 01222-825350. **Document type**: government publication.

WORLD AGRICULTURAL ECONOMICS AND RURAL SOCIOLOGY ABSTRACTS; abstracts of world literature. see *AGRICULTURE — Abstracting, Bibliographies, Statistics*

SOCIOLOGY — Computer Applications

BEHAVIOUR AND INFORMATION TECHNOLOGY. see *PSYCHOLOGY*

301 US
COMPUTER STUDIES: COMPUTERS IN SOCIETY. irreg., 3rd ed., 1990. $12.95. Dushkin Publishing Group, Sluice Dock, Guilford, CT 06437-9989. TEL 203-453-4351. FAX 203-453-6000. Ed. Kathryn Schellenberg; Pub. Ian Nielsen. illus. **Document type**: academic/scholarly publication.

651.8 US ISSN 0095-2737
QA76 CODEN: CMSCD3
COMPUTERS & SOCIETY. 1968. q. $24. Association for Computing Machinery, Special Interest Group on Computers and Society, 1515 Broadway, 17th Fl., New York, NY 10036. TEL 212-869-7440. FAX 604-822-5485. Ed. Richard S. Rosenberg. bk.rev. circ. 1,500. **Indexed**: Comput.Cont., INSPEC. **Document type**: newsletter.
—BLDSC (3394.785000); Ei; Faxon; SWETS; UnCover.
Formerly: S I G C A S Newsletter.

301 004 UK ISSN 0747-5632
BF39.5 CODEN: CHBEEQ
COMPUTERS IN HUMAN BEHAVIOR. 1985. q. £287($457) (effective 1996). Elsevier Science Ltd., Pergamon, P.O. Box 800, Kidlington, Oxford OX5 1DX, England. TEL 44-1865-843000. FAX 44-1865-843010. E-mail: nlinfo-f@elsevier.nl; usinfo-f@elsevier.com; forinfo-kyf04035@niftyserve.or.jp; Site addr.: http://www.elsevier.nl/. (Subscr. in U.S. and Canada to: Elsevier Science, 660 White Plains Rd., Tarrytown, NY 10591-5153. TEL 914-524-9200. FAX 914-333-2444) Ed. Robert D. Tennyson. adv.; bk.rev. (also avail. in microfilm from UML; back issues avail.) **Indexed**: Abstr.Hum.Comp.Inter., Curr.Cont., Excerp.Med., INSPEC (1985-), Psychol.Abstr. (1985-). **Document type**: academic/scholarly publication.
—BLDSC (3394.921600); Ei; Faxon; Genuine Article; SWETS; UMI; UnCover. **CCC**.
Description: Scholary journal dedicated to examining the use of computers from a psychological perspective.
Refereed Serial

301 US ISSN 0740-445X
HV41
COMPUTERS IN HUMAN SERVICES. 1985. q. $150 (foreign $210) (effective 1996). Haworth Press, Inc., 10 Alice St., Binghamton, NY 13904. TEL 607-722-5857; 800-342-9678. FAX 607-722-1424. Ed. Dick Schoech. adv.; bk.rev.; bibl. circ. 446. (also avail. in microfiche from HAW; reprint service avail. from HAW) **Indexed**: Abstr.Health Care Manage.Stud., Abstr.Hum.Comp.Inter., Excerp.Med., INSPEC, Psychol.Abstr. (1985-), Soc.Work Res.& Abstr., Tech.Educ.Abstr. **Document type**: academic/scholarly publication.
—BLDSC (3394.922000); Ei; Faxon; Genuine Article; Haworth; SWETS; UnCover.
Incorporates (in 1991): Computer Use in Social Services Network. Newsletter (ISSN 0889-6194)
Description: Explores the potentials of computer and related technologies in mental health.
Refereed Serial

F R A N C I S. 603: INFORMATIQUE ET SCIENCES JURIDIQUES. see *LAW — Computer Applications*

310 US ISSN 1044-7318
QA76.9.H85 CODEN: IJHIEC
INTERNATIONAL JOURNAL OF HUMAN-COMPUTER INTERACTION. 1989. q. $45 to individuals; institutions $135. Ablex Publishing Corporation, 355 Chestnut St., Norwood, NJ 07648. TEL 201-767-8450. FAX 201-767-6717. TELEX 135-393. Eds. Michael Smith, Gavriel Salvendy. index. circ. 400. **Indexed**: A.I.Abstr., Abstr.Hum.Comp.Inter., INSPEC (1990-), Psychol.Abstr. (1989-). **Document type**: academic/scholarly publication.
—BLDSC (4542.288000); Ei; Genuine Article; SWETS; UnCover.
Description: Provides a forum for advancing the body of knowledge in cognitive and social sciences, ergonomics, and health as they relate to the use of computers.

301 621.381   UK   ISSN 0959-0684
NEW TECHNOLOGY IN THE HUMAN SERVICES. 1985. q. £10($20) to individuals; institutions £30 ($60). Computers in Teaching Initiative, Centre for Human Service Technology, University of Southampton, Department of Social Work Studies, Southampton, Hants. S09 5NH, England. TEL 01703-593536. FAX 01703-592779. E-mail: CTIHums@chst.soton.ac.uk. Ed. Bryan Glastonbury. adv.; bk.rev. circ. 1,000. **Indexed:** Soc.Work Res.& Abstr. **Document type:** academic/scholarly publication.
—BLDSC (6088.836000).
 Formerly (until 1988): Computer Applications in Social Work and Allied Professions (ISSN 0267-1980)
 Description: Details the use of computer applications, telecommunications, and interactive video within human services, including social work and probation
Refereed Serial

001.64 301   US   ISSN 0736-6906
H61.3   CODEN: SGBUD4
S I G C H I BULLETIN. q. $52 to non-members. Association for Computing Machinery, Special Interest Group on Computer and Human Interaction, 1515 Broadway, 17th Fl., New York, NY 10036. TEL 212-869-7440. FAX 212-302-5826. Ed. William Hefley. adv. contact: Walter Andrzejewski. bk.rev. circ. 5,700. **Indexed:** Abstr.Hum.Comp.Inter., Comput.Abstr., INSPEC. **Document type:** bulletin.
—BLDSC (8275.263000); Faxon; SWETS; UnCover.
 Formerly: S I G S O C Bulletin.
 Description: Encompasses all aspects of the computer-human interaction process, including research and development efforts leading to the design and evaluation of user interfaces.

SOFTWARE

see Computers–Software

SOLAR ENERGY

see Energy–Solar Energy

SOUND

see Physics–Sound

SOUND RECORDING AND REPRODUCTION

see also Music

621.389   JA
A E S REGIONAL CONVENTION, TOKYO PREPRINTS/A E S TOKYO KONBENSHON YOKOSHU. (Text in English, Japanese; summaries in English) biennial. 3000 Yen per no. Audio Engineering Society, Japan Section - A E S Nihon Shibu, Nihon Odio Kyokai, 14-34, Jingumae 1-chome, Shibuya-ku, Tokyo 150, Japan.

789.9   US   ISSN 0004-5438
ML1
A R S C JOURNAL. 1968. 2/yr. $30 (foreign $35) membership (includes A R S C Newsletter). Association for Recorded Sound Collections, Inc., Box 543, Annapolis, MD 21404-0543. TEL 410-757-0488. FAX 410-379-0175. Ed. Barry Ashpole; Pub. Ted Sheldon. adv.: page $100; 4 1/2 x 7 1/8; adv. contact: Gary Thalheimer. bk.rev.; rec.rev.; bibl.; illus.; stat.; cum.index. circ. 1,100. (looseleaf format) **Indexed:** Arts & Hum.Cit.Ind., Curr.Cont., M.L.A., Music Artic.Guide, Music Ind., RILM. **Document type:** academic/scholarly publication.
—Faxon; Genuine Article; UnCover.
 Incorporates (in 1989): A R S C Bulletin (ISSN 0587-1956)
 Description: Devoted to the results of research, technical developments, unusual discoveries, discographies, and articles of general interest in the field.
Refereed Serial

621.389   US   ISSN 0196-9145
A R S C NEWSLETTER. 1977. q. membership. Association for Recorded Sound Collections, Inc., Annapolis Division, c/o Peter Shambarger, Exec. Dir., Box 543, Annapolis, MD 21401. TEL 410-757-0488. FAX 410-349-0175. Ed. Laura Gayle-Green; Pub. Ted Sheldon. adv. contact: Gary Thalheimer. circ. 1,100. (back issues avail.) **Document type:** newsletter.
 Description: Provides coverage of A.R.S.C. activities, free brief notices of information desired and items offered or wanted.

780   US   ISSN 0097-1138
TK7881.4
THE ABSOLUTE SOUND. Short title: T A S. 1973. 8/yr. $49.95 includes High End guide (Canada $55; elsewhere $79). Pearson Publishing Enterprises, Box 360, Sea Cliff, NY 11579. TEL 516-676-2830; 800-222-3201. FAX 516-676-5469. Ed. Harry Pearson, Jr. adv.; bk.rev.; rec.rev.; index. circ. 33,000. (also avail. in microform from UMI) **Indexed:** Music Artic.Guide.
—UnCover.

ALLIGATOR. *see* MUSIC

ALMANACCO DI STEREO. *see* COMMUNICATIONS — Television And Cable

621.389 780   IT   ISSN 0393-0882
ALTA FEDELTA. 1957. m. L.70000 (foreign L.110000). Edisport Editoriale S.p.A., Via Gradisca 11, 20151 Milan, Italy. TEL 02-380851. FAX 02-38010393. Ed. Massimo Bacchetti. adv.: B&W page L.6300000, color page L.10900000; 185 x 258. bk.rev.; charts; illus.; index. circ. 73,500. **Document type:** consumer publication.
 Description: Consumer's electronic guide to audio, video and hi-fi equipment.

621.389 384.55   SP   ISSN 1130-4855
ALTA FIDELIDAD EN AUDIO Y VIDEO. 1990. 11/yr. 5500 ptas. M.C. Ediciones S.A., Monestir 23, 08034 Barcelona, Spain. TEL 3-280-43-44. FAX 3-280-39-74. Ed. Salvador Dangla; Pub. Susanna Cadena. adv. contact: Yolanda Cea. circ. 20,000. (paid). **Document type:** consumer publication.

ANNUAIRE O.G.M. (Office General de la Musique) *see* MUSIC

621.389 384.55   IT
ANNUARIO AUDIO & VIDEO. 1977. a. L.20000. Media Edizioni srl., Via Gaffurio 4, 20124 Milan, Italy. Ed. Edoardo Fleischner. adv. circ. 40,000.

621.389   IT
ANNUARIO SUONO.* 1972. q. L.5300($10) per no. Gruppo Editoriale Suono s.r.l., Via Capo Peloro, 30, 00141 Rome, Italy. TEL 893608. adv.; illus. circ. 95,000.

ANTENNA; rassegna mensile di tecnica elettronica. *see* COMMUNICATIONS — Television And Cable

AUDIO. *see* MUSIC

789.9   US   ISSN 0004-7546
TK7881.7
AUDIO AMATEUR. 1970. 4/yr. $20. Audio Amateur Publications, Box 576, Peterborough, NH 03458. TEL 603-924-9464. FAX 603-924-9467. Ed. Edward T. Dell, Jr. adv. contact: Martha Povey. bk.rev.; charts, illus.; index; circ. 6,000 (paid). (also avail. in microform from UMI; back issues avail.) **Indexed:** Ind.How To Do It (1970-). **Document type:** consumer publication.
—BLDSC (1787.870000).

621.389   SP
AUDIO CAR; autorradios, telefonia y alarmas. 1989. m. Alpress, S.A., Tamarit 73, 1o 1a, 08034 Barcelona, Spain. TEL 93-423-84-04. FAX 93-426-69-79. adv. contact: Jose Antonio Garcia. circ. 9,000. (back issues avail.)
 Description: Covers car radios, mobile telephones and car security systems.

621.389 780   US   ISSN 1052-5033
AUDIO CARPETORIUM; the newsletter for people who have it. 1989. irreg. $5. Audio Carpetorium, 111-32 112th St., S. Ozone Park, NY 11420-1026. TEL 718-835-1132. Ed. Jerry Nutter. circ. 1,000. (tabloid format; also avail. in diskette format; back issues avail.; reprint service avail.)

621.389   US   ISSN 0146-4701
TK7881.4
AUDIO CRITIC. 1977. q. $24. Audio Critic, Box 978, Quakertown, PA 18951. TEL 215-536-8884. Ed. Peter Aczel. adv.; rec.rev. **Document type:** consumer publication.

621.389   US   ISSN 0004-7554
TK5981   CODEN: ADIOA3
AUDIO ENGINEERING SOCIETY. JOURNAL. 1953. 10/yr. $130 to non-members. Audio Engineering Society, 60 E. 42nd St., New York, NY 10165. TEL 212-661-8528. FAX 212-661-7929. Ed. Daniel R. von Recklinghausen. adv.: B&W page $1050; color page $2700; 7 x 10; adv. contact: Flavia D. Elzinga. bk.rev./ abstr.; bibl.; charts; illus.; index. cum.index: 1953-1980; circ. 10,786 (paid). (also avail. in microfilm from UMI; reprint service avail. from UMI) **Indexed:** A.S.& T.Ind., Curr.Cont., Eng.Ind., INSPEC (1968-).
—BLDSC (4706.000000); Ei; Faxon; Genuine Article; SWETS; UMI; UnCover. CCC.
Refereed Serial

621.389   IT   ISSN 0392-2316
AUDIO GIORNALE.* 1977. m. (10/yr. plus supplement). L.25000($43) Gruppo Editoriale Suono s.r.l., Via Capo Peloro, 30, 00141 Rome, Italy. TEL 893608. adv.; illus.

621.3893   UK   ISSN 0960-7471
AUDIO MEDIA. 1990. m. £24 (Europe £30; rest of world £49). A M Publishing Ltd., Media House, 3 Burrel Rd., St. Ives, Cambs PE17 4LE, England. TEL 01480-461244. FAX 01480-492422. Ed. Dave Lockwood; Pub. Godfrey Davies. adv. contact: Nick Humbert. circ. 11,000. **Document type:** trade publication.
 Description: For professional audio production engineers and broadcast personnel.

621.38   NO
AUDIO VIDEO. 1993. 7/yr. Nordisk Fagpresse A-S, Fred. Olsensgt. 5, P.O. Box 1153 Sentrum, N-0107 Oslo, Norway. TEL 47-22-33-58-58. FAX 47-22-33-04-10. Ed. Tore Holter. adv. contact: Inga Grette. circ. 8,000. **Document type:** consumer publication.

621.389   SP
AUDIO VIDEO MAGAZINE; hi-fi video tv musica. 1986. m. Alpress, S.A., Tamarit 73 1o 1a, 08034 Barcelona, Spain. TEL 93-423-84-04. FAX 93-426-69-79. Ed. Francesco Mir. adv. contact: Jose Antonio Garcia. circ. 16,000.
 Description: For aficionados of hi-fi equipment and music.

621.389   US   ISSN 1044-7601
AUDIO WEEK; the authoritative news service of the Audio Consumer Electronics Industry. 1989. w. $554 (foreign $596). Warren Publishing, Inc., 2115 Ward Ct., N.W., Washington, DC 20037. TEL 212-686-5410. FAX 212-889-5097. TELEX 6502173616. Ed. Paul Gluckman. (looseleaf format; back issues avail.) **Document type:** trade publication.
 ●Also available online. Vendor(s): Data-Star, Knight-Ridder, Inc., NewsNet (EC93).
 Description: Devoted to the audio industry including home hi-fi systems and components, personal portables, car audio and mobile electronics, custom installations, blank tape and CD-ROM software.

621.389   IT
AUDIOCARSTEREO. 1990. m. (11/yr.). L.80000 (Europe L.165000; America L.230000). Technimedia s.r.l., Via Carlo Perrier 9, 00157 Rome, Italy. TEL 396-418921. FAX 396-41732169. Ed. Franco Gatta. adv. circ. 80,000. (back issues avail.)

620.2   US
AUDIOCRAFT; an introduction to the tools and techniques of audio production. irreg., 2nd ed., 1989. $30 (members $22). National Federation of Community Broadcasters, 666 11th St. N.W., Ste. 805, Washington, DC 20001. TEL 202-393-2355. Ed. Randy Thom.
 Description: Practical, results-oriented guide covering topics from the basic concept of sound to the production of full-scale documentaries and concert recordings.

SOUND RECORDING AND REPRODUCTION

621.389   IT
AUDIOGUIDA CAR. 1990. a. L.15000. Technimedia s.r.l., Via Carlo Perrier 9, 00157 Rome, Italy. TEL 396-418921. FAX 396-41732169. Ed. Paolo Nuti. adv. circ. 65,000. (back issues avail.)

621.389   IT
AUDIOGUIDA HI-FI. 1989. a. L.15000. Technimedia s.r.l., Via Carlo Perrier 9, 00157 Rome, Italy. TEL 396-418921. FAX 396-41732169. Ed. Paolo Nuti. adv. circ. 62,000. (back issues avail.)

621.389   UK   ISSN 0959-7697
TK7881.7
AUDIOPHILE. Variant title: Audiophile with Hi-Fi Answers. m. £70. Haymarket Magazines Ltd., 38-42 Hampton Rd., Teddington, Middx. TW11 0JE, England. TEL 081-943-5000. FAX 081-943-5098. TELEX 895-2440-HAYMRT-G. illus.
Formerly (until 1990): Hi-Fi Answers (ISSN 0269-9451)

621.389 384.5   FR   ISSN 0181-6349
AUDIOPHILE. 1977. 6/yr. E M P P S, 1 bd. Ney, 75018 Paris, France. TEL 40-36-01-97. FAX 40-36-11-96. Ed. Jean Hiraga.

621.389   IT
AUDIOREVIEW. 1981. m. (11/yr.). L.80000 (Europe L.165000; America L.230000). Technimedia s.r.l., Via Carlo Perrier, 9, 00157 Rome, Italy. TEL 396-418921. FAX 396-41732169. Ed. Paolo Nuti. adv. circ. 85,000. (back issues avail.)

621.38   SW   ISSN 1101-6698
AUDIOVISUELLA MEDIER. 1990. 11/yr. SEK 280 (effective 1991). A V M Sverige, P.O. Box 6056, S-114 86 Stockholm, Sweden.

620.2   AT   ISSN 1038-7242
AUSTRALIAN HI-FI. 1970. m. Aus.$86.70. Horwitz Publications Pty. Ltd., 55 Chandos St., St. Leonards, N.S.W. 2065, Australia. (Subscr. addr: P.O. Box 5555, St. Leonards, N.W.S. 2065, Australia) Ed. Greg Borrowman. adv.; bk.rev.; charts; illus. **Indexed:** Pinpointer. **Document type:** consumer publication.
Former titles: Australian Hi-Fi and Music Review; Australian Hi-Fi (ISSN 0159-0030)
Description: Covers hi-fidelity systems and components.

534   AT   ISSN 0310-8902
AUSTRALIAN HI-FI ANNUAL. 1971. a. Horwitz Publications Pty. Ltd., 55 Chandos St., St. Leonards, N.S.W. 2065, Australia. (Subscr. addr.: P.O. Box 5555, St. Leonards, N.S.W. 2065, Australia) Ed. Greg Borrowman. **Indexed:** Pinpointer. **Document type:** consumer publication.
Description: Hi-fidelity systems and components; technical advice.

621.389   US   ISSN 0195-0908
B.A.S. SPEAKER. 1972. bi-m. $25. Boston Audio Society, Box 211, Mattapan, MA 02126-0002. TEL 617-282-8335. Ed. Dave Moran. bk.rev. circ. 1,500. **Document type:** consumer publication, newsletter.
Description: Hi-Fi consumer network.

BEIKOKU TOKKYO SHOROKU. SOKUTEI, SEIMITSU KIKI, INSATSU, ONKYO, KYOIKU HEN/U.S. PATENT ABSTRACTS. MEASURING, PRECISION INSTRUMENT, PRINTING, SOUND RECORDING, EDUCATION. see *PATENTS, TRADEMARKS AND COPYRIGHTS — Abstracting, Bibliographies, Statistics*

BILLBOARD (NEW YORK). see *MUSIC*

BILLBOARD'S TAPE - DISC DIRECTORY. see *BUSINESS AND ECONOMICS — Trade And Industrial Directories*

621.389   SP
C D COMPACT. 1987. 11/yr. 5500 ptas. (Europe 7500 ptas.; US $109) (effective 1995). Hi-Tech, S.L, Vendrell 3, entlo. 1a, 08022 Barcelona, Spain. TEL 34-3-4184724. FAX 34-3-4184312. Ed. Jaime Rosal. adv. contact: Birgitta Sandberg. circ. 20,000. **Document type:** consumer publication.
Description: Provides information on what is new on the record market. Reviews over 150 CDs and laser discs of classical, jazz, new age, and ethnic music.

621.389   CN   ISSN 0840-6154
C I R P A NEWSLETTER. 1975. 4/yr. Can.$40($40) to non-members. Canadian Independent Record Production Association, 214 King St., W., Ste. 614, Toronto, ON M5H 3S6, Canada. TEL 416-593-1665. FAX 416-593-7563. Ed. Richard Sutherland. circ. 550. **Document type:** newsletter.

621.38 388.3   US   ISSN 0898-3720
CAR AUDIO & ELECTRONICS. 1988. m. $21.95. A V C O M Publishing, 21700 Oxnard St., Ste. 1600, Woodland Hills, CA 91367. TEL 818-593-3900. FAX 818-593-2274. Ed. William Neill. adv.; circ. 128,411 (paid). **Document type:** consumer publication.

CHRISTIAN MUSIC DIRECTORIES: RECORDED MUSIC. see *MUSIC*

COMPUTER MUSIC JOURNAL. see *MUSIC — Computer Applications*

621.389   US   ISSN 0011-7145
CODEN: DBSEDB
DB, THE SOUND ENGINEERING MAGAZINE. 1967. bi-m. $15. 203 Commack Rd., Ste. 1010, Commack, NY 11725. TEL 516-586-6530. Ed. Larry Zide. adv.; bk.rev.; charts; illus.; tr.lit. circ. 20,000. (also avail. in microfilm from UMI; reprint service avail. from UMI) **Indexed:** A.S.& T.Ind., Comput.Cont., Curr.Cont., INSPEC.
—BLDSC (3535.868150); Faxon; UMI; UnCover.

DIANYING YISHU/FILM ART. see *MOTION PICTURES*

DISC COLLECTOR. see *MUSIC*

253   US   ISSN 0192-334X
DISCOGRAPHIES. 1979. irreg., no. 48, 1992. price varies. Greenwood Press, Inc. (Subsidiary of: Greenwood Publishing Group Inc.), 88 Post Rd. W., Box 5007, Westport, CT 06881-5007. TEL 203-226-3571. FAX 203-222-1502. Ed. Michael Gray.
—BLDSC (3595.543000).

621.389 789   US   ISSN 1050-7868
E Q. 1990. m. $24.95. Miller Freeman P S N Inc. (Subsidiary of: United News & Media Co.), 2 Park Ave., 18th Fl., New York, NY 10016. TEL 212-213-3444. FAX 212-213-3484. E-mail: eqmagazine@aol.com. Ed. Martin Porter; Pub. Paul Gallo. circ. 37,000. **Document type:** consumer publication, trade publication.
Description: Covers projects recording and sound studio techniques for the professional audio market.

FEDELTA DEL SUONO. see *MUSIC*

621.3   UK
FEDERATION OF BRITISH TAPE RECORDISTS. RECORDING NEWS. 1965. bi-m. membership. Federation of British Tape Recordists, 26 Hawthorne Rd., Stapleford, Cambs. CB1 6BE, England. Ed. Robin Elmore. adv.; bk.rev. circ. 100.
Formerly: Federation of British Tape Recordists. News and Views.

FONOFORUM. see *MUSIC*

FOTO VIDEO AUDIO NEWS. see *PHOTOGRAPHY*

FOTOMUNDO. see *PHOTOGRAPHY*

621.38   JA
GEKKAN EBUI FURONTO/AUDIO VIDEO FRONT. (Text in Japanese) 1973. m. 1000 Yen. Kyodo Tsushinsha - Kyodo News Enterprise Ltd., 9-20, Akasaka 1-chome, Minato-ku, Tokyo 107, Japan.

GLASS AUDIO. see *MUSIC*

621.389   UK
GOLD BOOK. 1988. a. £90. Spotlight Publications Ltd., Ludgate House, 245 Blackfriars Rd., London SE1 9UR, England. TEL 071-620-3636. FAX 071-401-8036. Ed. Carl Snape. adv. contact: Jim Parkinson. circ. 3,000. **Document type:** directory.
Description: International directory of all companies involved in mastering, vinyl and CD pressing and tape duplication industries.

620   US   ISSN 1056-165X
ML27.U5
GRAMMY MAGAZINE. q. membership only. National Academy of Recording Arts and Sciences, 3402 Pico Blvd., Santa Monica, CA 90405-2118.
—Faxon.
Formerly: Grammy Pulse (ISSN 1056-1668)

GRAMOPHONE. see *MUSIC*

THE GRAMOPHONE CLASSICAL CATALOGUE. see *MUSIC*

THE GRAMOPHONE GOOD C D GUIDE; reviews of the best CDs you can buy. see *MUSIC*

H.M. HEAVY METAL & HARD ROCK; quindicinale di musica specializzata. see *MUSIC*

THE HANDBOOK OF U K RECORDING & DUPLICATING (YEAR). see *BUSINESS AND ECONOMICS — Trade And Industrial Directories*

621.389   PO   ISSN 0871-6188
HI-FI. 1988. 12/yr. Rua D. Estefania 32-1o, 1000 Lisbon, Portugal. TEL 1-544307. FAX 522643. TELEX 64198. Ed. Antonio Pancianelli. circ. 11,000.

621.389   DK   ISSN 0107-0274
HI-FI & ELEKTRONIK. 1980. m. DKK 34.50. Bonniers Specialmagasiner A-S, Strandboulevarden 130, 2100 Copenhagen OE, Denmark. Ed. Aksel Brinck Jensen.
Description: All about Hi-Fi equipment and consumer electronics.

621.38   DK   ISSN 0108-4658
HI-FI AND VIDEO REVYEN. a. DKK 114.50. Bonniers Specialmagasiner A-S, Strandboulevarden 130, 2100 Copenhagen OE, Denmark. Ed. Dan Melchior. adv. circ. 30,000.
Formerly: Hi-Fi Revyen.
Description: Catalogue of hi-fi products, TV sets and video equipment.

621.389   US   ISSN 0164-3258
HI FI BUYERS' REVIEW. m. $15. Hampton International Communications, Inc., 4520 E Grant Rd., Tuscon, AZ 85712-2617. adv.

621.389   UK   ISSN 0955-1115
HI-FI CHOICE. 1975. m. £25 (rest of Europe £39; elsewhere £51.50). Dennis Publishing Ltd., 19 Bolsover St., London W1E 4UZ, England. TEL 0171-631-1433. FAX 0171-323-3547. (Subscr. to: Subscriptions Department, Bradley Pavillions, Pear Tree Rd., Bradley Stoke North, Bristol, Avon BS12 0BR, England. TEL 01454-620070. FAX 01454-620080) Ed. Andy Benham. adv. circ. 35,000. **Document type:** consumer publication.
Description: Contains news and features on all hi-fi related topics, along with in-depth technical tests on hi-fi products.

621.389   IT
HI-FI STEREO; la rivista di musica e alta fedelta. 1988. m. L.80000 (foreign L.310000). Editori Associati, Via Brenta 13, 00198 Rome, Italy. TEL 39-6-8417179. Ed. Paolo De Petris. **Document type:** consumer publication.

621.38   FI   ISSN 0357-0738
HIFI. 1978. 12/yr. FIM 310. Helsinki Media Company Oy, P.O. Box 16, FIN-00381 Helsinki, Finland. TEL 358-0-120-5911. FAX 358-0-120-5799. Ed. Pekka Koistinen. adv. contact: Esa Sairio. circ. 11,365.
Description: Directed to hi-fi hobbyists.

621.389   SP
HIFI CLASS. 4/yr. Alpress, S.A., Tamarit 73, 1o 1a, 08004 Barcelona, Spain. TEL 3-325-61-66. FAX 3-325-69-83. circ. 20,000.

621.389   GW
HIFI EXKLUSIV. 1978. 6/yr. DM.96 (foreign DM.105). S Z V KG, Schellingstr. 39-43, 80799 Munich, Germany. TEL 089-23726-0. FAX 23726-125. Ed. Peter Nagy. adv. contact: Anja Rezsucha. circ. 24,000. **Document type:** consumer publication.

SOUND RECORDING AND REPRODUCTION

621.389   SW   ISSN 0346-0576
HIFI & MUSIK. 1970. m. (10/yr.) SEK 330 (effective 1994); newsstand price: SEK 38.50. Tidningen HiFi Musik AB, Birger Jarlsgatan 67, S-113 56 Stockholm, Sweden. TEL 46-8-15-01-05. FAX 46-8612-04-26. Ed. Lars-Erik Frej. adv.: B&W page SEK 14600, color page SEK 18400; trim 190 x 265. circ. 15,000. cols./p.: 4; pp./issue: 84. (also avail. in audio cassette)
    Formerly (until 1977): Stereo-hifi.

HIFI TEST. see *ELECTRONICS*

789.7   FR   ISSN 0988-7091
ML5
HIFI VIDEO; loisirs. 1969. m. 373 F. (effective 1995). (Publications Radio-Electroniques et Scientifiques (PRES)) Publications Georges Ventillard, 2 a 12 rue de Bellevue, 75940 Paris Cedex 19, France. TEL 44-84-84-84. FAX 42-41-89-40. TELEX 220 409 F. adv.; bk.rev.; illus. circ. 20,000.
    Formerly: Hifi Stereo (ISSN 0337-1891)

780   US
HIGH END. (Supplement to: The Absolute Sound (ISSN 0097-1138)) a. Pearson Publishing Enterprises, Box 360, Sea Cliff, NY 11579. TEL 516-676-2830; 800-222-3201. FAX 516-676-5469. Ed. Harry Pearson.

621.389   UK
HIGH FIDELITY. 1977. m. £65. Haymarket Magazines Ltd., 38-42 Hampton Rd., Teddington, Middx. TW11 0JE, England. TEL 081-943-5000. FAX 081-943-5098. TELEX 895-2440-HAYMRT-G. Ed. Elizabeth Hughes. adv.; illus. circ. 25,262.
    Former titles: New Hi-Fi Sound; Popular Hi-Fi; Popular Hi-Fi and Sound (ISSN 0309-5355)

621.389   US   ISSN 0277-1357
TK7881.7
HIGH PERFORMANCE REVIEW; definitive magazine for audiophiles & music lovers. 1981. q. $15. High Performance Review Publishing, Box 346, Woodbury, CT 06798. TEL 203-273-5826. FAX 203-273-5826. Ed. Steve Saunders. adv. contact: Henry Rupel. bk.rev.; rec.rev.; charts; illus. circ. 18,000. (back issues avail.) **Indexed:** M.I.A. **Document type:** consumer publication.
    —CCC.
    Description: Lab test and listening review of new audio hi-fi stereo equipment. Reviews of over 100 classical, pop and jazz recording releases.

621.389   JA
HIVI. (Text in Japanese) m. 12000 Yen. Stereo Sound Publishing Inc., 3-8-4, Moto-Azabu, Minato-ku, Tokyo 106, Japan. Ed. Koji Yamamoto; Pub. Isao Harada. adv. contact: Takazumi Arai. **Document type:** consumer publication.
    Formerly: Sound Boy.

621.389   UK   ISSN 0957-6614
TK7881.4
HOME & STUDIO RECORDING; the magazine for the recording musician. (UK Edition) 1983. m. £20 (foreign £25). Music Maker Publications Ltd., Alexander House, Forehill, Ely, Cambs CB7 4AF, England. TEL 0353-665577. FAX 44-353-662489. (U.S. addr.: Music Maker Publications Inc., 21601 Devonshire St., Ste. 212, Chatsworth, CA 91311. TEL 818-407-0744. FAX 818-407-0882) Ed. Paul White. adv.; bk.rev. circ. 20,000.
    Formerly: Home Studio Recording.
    Description: Focuses on recording for the home studio, with reviews of the latest recording equipment used in the home or project studio environment.

HORN SPEAKER; the newspaper for the hobbyist of vintage electronics and sound. see *ANTIQUES*

621.38   JA
HYPERCOM/HAIPAKOMU. (Text in Japanese) 1990. bi-m. 1500 Yen per no. Audio - Video Communication Center - Shichokaku Konsarutanto Senta, 11-15, Iidabashi 3-chome, Kodaira-shi, Tokyo 187, Japan.

621.389   SW   ISSN 1021-562X
ML26
I A S A JOURNAL. 1971. 2/yr. DM.55 to non-members; DM.40 (includes individual membership); DM.110 (includes institutional membership). International Association of Sound Archives, c/o Sven Allerstrand, A L B, P.O. Box 27890, S-115 93 Stockholm, Sweden. TEL 46-8-783-37-00. FAX 46-8-663-18-11. Ed. Helen P. Harrison. bk.rev.; bibl. circ. 450. **Indexed:** LISA. **Document type:** academic/scholarly publication.
    —BLDSC (4359.540200).
    Formerly (until 1992): Phonographic Bulletin (ISSN 0253-004X)

016.789   II   ISSN 0302-6744
ML156.4.N3
INDIAN RECORDS; film, classical, popular. (Text in English) m. price varies. Gramophone Company of India Ltd., 33 Jessore Rd., Calcutta 770 028, India. FAX 9133-280140. TELEX 021-5242. Ed. G. Vijayakumar. bibl. circ. 28,000.
    Description: Lists releases of titles available on record, audio cassette, and CD; 40 per issue.

780   US   ISSN 0889-4922
TK7881.4
INTERNATIONAL RECORDING EQUIPMENT AND STUDIO DIRECTORY. 1968. a. $50. B P I Communications, Inc. (New York), 1515 Broadway, New York, NY 10036. TEL 212-764-7300; 800-344-7199. FAX 212-944-1719. (also avail. in microfilm from KTO) **Document type:** directory.
    Former titles (until 1985): International Billboard Recording Studio and Equipment Directory (ISSN 0889-4914); Billboard International Recording Equipment and Studio Directory (ISSN 0160-7790); (until 1978): International Studio and Equipment Directory (ISSN 0889-4930); (until 1976): Billboard International Directory of Recording Studios (ISSN 0067-8627)
    Description: Listings on studio equipment, blank tape product charts and manufacturers, studio equipment manufacturers, studio services and recording studios.

IRIS; a revista que e a sua imagem. see *PHOTOGRAPHY*

621.398   JA   ISSN 0388-158X
J A S JOURNAL. (Text in Japanese) 1958. m. 500 Yen per no. Japan Audio Society - Nihon Odio Kyokai, 14-34, Jingumae 1-chome, Shibuya-ku, Tokyo 150, Japan.

KEYBOARDS MAGAZINE. see *MUSIC*

621.389   GW   ISSN 0933-0097
KLANG & TON. 1986. bi-m. DM.5.50. Michael E. Brieden Verlag GmbH, Ruhrorterstr. 9, 46049 Oberhausen, Germany. TEL 0208-85976-0. FAX 0208-8597649. Ed. Frank Urgif; Pub. Michael Brieden. adv. contact: Jutta Brandt. **Document type:** consumer publication.

LANGUAGE LEARNING JOURNAL. see *LINGUISTICS*

LIVE!. see *MUSIC*

621.389   US   ISSN 1079-0888
TK7881.9
LIVE SOUND! INTERNATIONAL. 1992. bi-m. $25 (foreign $65). Royle Publishing Corporation, 4741 Central 222, Kansas City, KS 64112-1533. TEL 913-677-8688. FAX 913-677-6621. Ed. Anthony McLean; Pub. John Weishar. **Document type:** trade publication.
    —UnCover. CCC.
    Formerly: Live Sound! and Touring Technology (ISSN 1066-0224)

M T. see *MUSIC*

MIX ANNUAL DIRECTORY OF RECORDING INDUSTRY FACILITIES AND SERVICES. see *BUSINESS AND ECONOMICS — Trade And Industrial Directories*

620.2   US   ISSN 0164-9957
HD9697.P563
MIX MAGAZINE; professional recording, sound & music production. 1977. m. $46 (foreign $61). Act III Publishing, 6400 Hollis, Ste.12, Emeryville, CA 94608. TEL 510-653-3307. FAX 510-653-5142. (Subscr. to: Box 41094, Nashville, TN 37204. TEL 800-888-5139) Ed. David M. Schwartz. adv.; bk.rev.; illus.; software rev. circ. 50,063. (back issues avail.) **Indexed:** Music Artic.Guide.

621.389   JA
MUSEN TO JIKKEN/AUDIO TECHNOLOGY. (Text in Japanese) 1924. m. 18660 Yen. Seibundo Shinkosha Publishing Co. Ltd., 13-7, Yayoi-cho 1-chome, Nakano-ku, Tokyo 164, Japan. Ed. Hiromitsu Nakazawa. circ. 60,000.

MUSIC AND SOUND RETAILER; the newsmagazine for musical instrument and sound product merchandisers. see *MUSIC*

621.389   US   ISSN 1051-5097
ML1055
N A R A S JOURNAL. 1990. s-a. membership only. National Academy of Recording Arts & Sciences, 3402 Pico Blvd., Santa Monica, CA 90405-2118.
    —UnCover.

621.389   AT   ISSN 0814-6888
NATIONAL FILM AND SOUND ARCHIVE NEWSLETTER. 1984. 3/yr. free. National Film and Sound Archive, McCoy Circuit, Acton, A.C.T. 2601, Australia. TEL 61-6-2093075. FAX 61-6-2093078. Ed. Elizabeth Courtney-Frost. circ. 3,000. **Document type:** newsletter.
    Description: News of the activities and issues involving the National Film and Sound Archive.

620.2   UK
NOSTALGIA. 1969. q. £2. c/o Charlie Wilson, 39 Leicester Rd., New Barnet, Herts. EN5 5EW, England. adv.; bk.rev.; charts; illus.
    Incorporates: Street Singer.

789.9   FR   ISSN 0397-3190
NOUVELLE REVUE DU SON. 1953. 10/yr. 250 F. (foreign 340 F.). E M P P S, 1 bd. Ney, 75018 Paris, France. TEL 40-36-01-97. FAX 40-36-11-96. (Subscr. to: 90 rue de Flandre, 75947 Paris Cedex 19, France. TEL 44-89-44-89. FAX 42-08-16-20) Ed. Jean Hiraga. adv. contact: Charles Estin. bk.rev.; rec.rev.; abstr.; bibl.; charts; illus.; tr.lit.; index. circ. 35,000. **Indexed:** Pt.de Rep.
    Formerly (until 1976): Revue du Son (ISSN 0035-2675); **Incorporates (1951-1956):** Arts et Techniques Sonores.

621.389   UK
ONE TO ONE (LONDON, 1985). 1985. bi-m. £30 (foreign £34). Spotlight Publications Ltd. (Subsidiary of: Morgan-Grampian plc), Ludgate House, 245 Blackfriars Rd., London SE1 9UR, England. TEL 071-620-3636. FAX 071-401-8036. Ed. Carl Snape. adv. contact: Jim Parkinson. charts; illus.; stat. circ. 8,000. **Document type:** trade publication.
    Description: Covers the international mastering, vinyl and CD pressing, and tape duplication industries.

PAUL'S RECORD MAGAZINE. see *MUSIC*

PHOTO VIDEO AUDIO NEWS. see *PHOTOGRAPHY*

621.389   UK   ISSN 0952-2360
PLAYBACK. 3/yr. free. The British Library, National Sound Archive, 29 Exhibition Rd., London SW7 2AS, England. TEL 0171-412-7440. FAX 0171-412-7441. Ed. Alan Ward. **Document type:** bulletin.
    —BLDSC (6539.142000).

621.389   US
POSITIVE FEEDBACK. 1990. bi-m. $25 (foreign $50). Oregon Triode Society, 4106 N.E. Glisan, Portland, OR 97232. TEL 503-235-9068. FAX 503-254-3866. Ed. David Robinson. **Document type:** consumer publication.

POST (PORT WASHINGTON); the magazine for animation, audio, film and video professionals. see *COMMUNICATIONS*

621.389   SP
PRO AUDIO. 11/yr. 3000 ptas. Cardenal Herrera Oria 171, Ciudad de los Periodistas, Ed. Azorin, Torre 2, 28034 Madrid, Spain. TEL 1-730-71-77. FAX 1-730-80-92. Ed. Marcos Manzandres. circ. 13,000.

621.389   JA
PRO AUDIO. (Text in Japanese) bi-m. 13080 Yen; newsstand price: 1800Yen. Stereo Sound Publishing Inc., 3-8-4, Moto-Azabu, Minato-ku, Tokyo 106, Japan. Ed. Susumu Nakamura. adv.
    Formerly: Tape Sound.

6050 SOUND RECORDING AND REPRODUCTION

621.389 338.4 US ISSN 0164-6338
PRO SOUND NEWS; the international newsmagazine for the professional recording & sound production industry. 1979. m. $30. Miller Freeman P S N Inc. (Subsidiary of: United News & Media Co.), 2 Park Ave., 18th Fl., New York, NY 10016. TEL 212-213-3444. FAX 212-213-3484. Ed. Tim Wetmore; Pub. Paul Gallo. adv. circ. 23,000. (tabloid format) **Document type:** trade publication.

621.389 UK ISSN 0269-4735
PRO SOUND NEWS. 1986. m. £25. Spotlight Publications Ltd., Ludgate House, 245 Blackfriars Rd., London SE1 9UR, England. TEL 071-620-3636. FAX 071-401-8036. Ed. Joe Hosken. adv. contact: Chris Baillie. bk.rev.; charts; illus. circ. 10,587. **Document type:** trade publication.
Description: News items and features on the technological, marketing and operational aspects of the European sound production industry, focusing on tour and studio equipment and production, technical developments by country, and product surveys.

621.389 780 GW
PRODUCTIV'S HANDBUCH FUER MUSIKER. 1982. biennial. Musik Productiv, Gildestr. 60, 49477 Ibbenbueren, Germany. TEL 05451-5001-0. FAX 05451-5001-40. circ. 45,000.
Description: Full listing of music equipment.

621.389 780 GW
PRODUCTIV'S SOLO. 1987. q. Musik Productiv, Gildestr. 60, 49477 Ibbenbueren, Germany. TEL 05451-5001-0. FAX 05451-5001-40. Ed. Heinz Rebellius. circ. 45,000. (back issues avail.)
Description: Tests of music equipment, stories and interviews.

621.389 US
PROFESSIONAL AUDIO DIRECTORY.* 1991. a. Professional Audio Journals, Inc., 1012 Melrose Ave., Elkins Park, PA 19027-3014. TEL 215-548-7238. FAX 215-548-3423. Ed. Jesse Klapholz. adv.: B&W page $2000, color page $2800; trim 8 x 10. circ. 19,232. **Document type:** directory.

RADIORAMA; practica electronica - t.v. - radio - hi-fi - ciencia. see COMMUNICATIONS — Television And Cable

RECORD EXCHANGER. see MUSIC

621.389 US ISSN 1078-8352
TK7881.4
RECORDING (CANOGA PARK, CA); the magazine for the recording musician. (U.S. Edition) 1987. m. $20. Music Maker Publications Inc., 7318 Topanga Canyon Blvd., Ste. 200, Canoga Pk., CA 91303-1242. TEL 818-346-3404. FAX 818-346-3597. (UK addr.: Music Maker Publications Ltd., Alexander House, Forehill, Ely, Cambs CB7 4AF, England) Ed. Nicholas Batzdorf. bk.rev. circ. 42,000. **Document type:** consumer publication, trade publication.
—UnCover.
Formerly (until 1994): Home & Studio Recording; Incorporates (1986-1990): Music Technology (ISSN 0896-7172)
Description: Focuses on recording in the home and studio environment. Features reviews of the latest available recording equipment and articles on techniques and applications.

ROOTS & RHYTHM NEWSLETTER. see MUSIC

SCHWANN OPUS. see MUSIC — Abstracting, Bibliographies, Statistics

SCHWANN SPECTRUM. see MUSIC — Abstracting, Bibliographies, Statistics

621.389 780 US ISSN 0199-4654
SENSIBLE SOUND. 1977. q. $20 (effective through 1996). 403 Darwin Dr., Snyder, NY 14226. TEL 716-681-3513. FAX 716-685-4172. Ed. Karl A. Nehring; Pub. John A. Horan. adv. contact: Donald Nowak. bk.rev.; tr.lit.; circ. 12,500 (paid). (back issues avail.) **Document type:** consumer publication.
●Also available online.
Description: Directed to audio equipment and recording gear hobbyists, as well as record and CD collectors.

621.38 JA ISSN 0915-5961
SHICHOKAKU JOHO KENKYUKAI KAIHO / AUDIO - VISUAL INFORMATION RESEARCH GROUP. NEWSLETTER. Key Title: A V I R G Kaiho. (Text in Japanese) 1964. 8/yr. membership. Shichokaku Joho Kenkyukai, c/o Denshi Gijutsu Sogo Kenkyujo, Chino Johobu Gazo Kenkyushitsu, 1-4, Umesono 1-chome, Tsukuba-shi, Ibaraki-ken 305, Japan.

SHOW MEETING. see COMMUNICATIONS

SON HI-FI VIDEO. see COMMUNICATIONS — Radio

621.389 AT ISSN 0729-9389
SONICS YEARBOOK; Australia music industry reference yearbook. 1980. a. Aus.$7.50 per issue. Federal Publishing Company, 140 Bourke Rd., Alexandria N.S.W. 2015, Australia. TEL 61-02-353-6666. FAX 61-02-353-0935. Ed. Greg Simmons. circ. 15,000. (back issues avail.)
Description: Comprehensive listing of equipment and services available to the Australian sound, lighting, music and entertainment industries.

621.389 FR ISSN 0243-4938
SONO. m. (except Aug.) 367 F. (effective 1995). Publications Georges Ventillard, 2 a 12 rue de Bellevue, 75019 Paris, France. TEL 44-84-84-84. FAX 42-41-89-40. TELEX 220 409 F.

SONORA; itinerari oltre il suono. see MUSIC

620.2 681 US ISSN 0038-1845
SOUND & COMMUNICATIONS. 1955. m. $15. Testa Communications, Inc., 25 Willowdale Ave., Port Washington, NY 11050. TEL 516-767-2500. FAX 516-767-9335. Ed. Judith Morrison. adv.; bk.rev. circ. 18,000.
Description: Covers contracting, engineering, design and construction in the sound, video, and communications fields.

SOUND & HI FI/IHOS. see MUSIC

789.9 US
SOUND & IMAGE. 1990. s-a. Hachette Magazines, Inc., 1633 Broadway, New York, NY 10009. TEL 212-767-6000. (Subscr. to: Box 55627, Boulder, CO 80322-5627) Ed. Michael Riggs. circ. 150,000.
Description: Covers videos and recordings; includes performer profiles and articles on custom installations.

621.3 778.59 US ISSN 0741-1715
SOUND & VIDEO CONTRACTOR; the international management and engineering journal for sound and video contractors. 1983. m. $27 (free to qualified personnel). Intertec Publishing Corp., 9800 Metcalf, Overland Park, KS 66212-2215. TEL 913-341-1300. FAX 913-967-1898. Ed. Ted Uzzle. adv.; tr.lit. circ. 20,500. (also avail. in microform from UMI) **Document type:** trade publication.
—BLDSC (8330.395000); UMI. **CCC.**

SOUND CHOICE. see MUSIC

SOUND ON SOUND. see MUSIC

SOUNDTRACK. see MUSIC

620.2 US ISSN 0199-7920
TK5983
SPEAKER BUILDER. 1980. 8/yr. $32. Audio Amateur Publications, Box 494, Peterborough, NH 03458. TEL 603-924-9464. FAX 603-924-9467. Ed. E.T. Dell. adv. contact: Martha Povey. bk.rev. circ. 11,500. (back issues avail.) Indexed: Ind.How To Do It (1980-). **Document type:** consumer publication.
—BLDSC (8361.870400).
Description: Contains projects, hands-on modifications for building one's own loudspeakers.

SPIN. see MUSIC

780.5 GW ISSN 0340-0778
STEREO; Hi-Fi- und Musikmagazin. 1974. m. DM.81.60 (foreign DM.87.60). S Z V KG, Schellingstr. 39-43, 80799 Munich, Germany. TEL 089-23726-0. FAX 089-23726-125. Ed. Peter Nagy. adv. contact: Kurt Erzinger. illus. circ. 113,000. **Document type:** consumer publication.

621.389 798.91 JA ISSN 0289-3622
STEREO. (Text in Japanese) 1963. m. 880 Yen. Ongaku No Tomo Sha Corp., Kagurazaka 6-30, Shinjuku-ku, Tokyo 162, Japan. TEL 03-3235-2111. FAX 03-3235-2129. adv.: B&W page 336000 Yen, color page 624000 Yen; trim 257 x 182. circ. 150,000.
Description: Aimed at lovers of record playing and audio techniques.

338.4 US ISSN 1060-8133
STEREO BUYERS' GUIDE. 1957. a. $3.95. Hachette Magazines, Inc., 1633 Broadway, New York, NY 10009. TEL 212-767-6000. (Subscr. to: Box 55627, Boulder, CO 80322-5627) Ed. William Burton. adv. circ. 200,000.
Former titles: Stereo Review's Stereo Buyers' Guide (ISSN 0736-6515); Stereo Directory and Buying Guide (ISSN 0090-6786); Stereo Hi-Fi Directory (ISSN 0081-5470)

621.389 AT ISSN 0819-0216
STEREO BUYER'S GUIDE. AUDIO YEARBOOK. 1971. a. Aus.$30. Horwitz Publications Pty. Ltd., 55 Chandos St., St. Leonards, N.S.W. 2065, Australia. (Subscr. addr.: P.O. Box 5555, St. Leonards, N.S.W. 2065, Australia) Ed. Greg Borrowman. **Document type:** consumer publication.
Formerly: Stereo Buyer's Guide. Manual (ISSN 0312-0058)
Description: Hi-fidelity component product reviews and buying advice.

621.389 AT ISSN 0819-0208
STEREO BUYER'S GUIDE. C D PLAYERS, TURNTABLES AND CASSETTES DECKS. 1971. a. Aus.$30. Horwitz Publications Pty. Ltd., 55 Chandos St., St. Leonards, N.S.W. 2065, Australia. TEL 61-2-901-6100. FAX 61-2-901-6116. (Subscr. to: P.O. Box 5555, St. Leonards, N.W.S., 2065, Australia) Ed. Greg Borrowman. **Document type:** consumer publication.
Former titles: Stereo Buyer's Guide. Turntables and Compact Disc Players; Stereo Buyer's Guide. Turntables (ISSN 0312-0066)
Description: Compact disc, turntable and cassette-deck product-reviews and buying advice.

621.387 AT ISSN 0819-0194
STEREO BUYER'S GUIDE. LOUDSPEAKERS, AMPLIFIERS AND TUNERS. 1971. a. Aus.$30. Horwitz Publications Pty. Ltd., 55 Chandos St., St. Leonards, N.S.W. 2065, Australia. (Subscr. to: P.O. Box 5555, St. Leonards, N.W.S. 2065, Australia) Ed. Greg Borrowman. **Document type:** consumer publication.
Former titles: Stereo Buyer's Guide. Amplifiers, FM Tuners and Receivers (ISSN 0727-4459); Stereo Buyer's Guide. Amplifiers.
Description: Loudspeaker, amplifier and tuner reviews, and buying advice.

621.389 NE ISSN 0928-866X
STEREO DRIVE; onafhankelijk tijdschrift voor caraudio, mobiele communication en autobeveiling. 1991. 8/yr. fl.65; newsstand price: fl.7.95. T W F Publicity, Bolestein 592, 1081 EK Amsterdam, Netherlands. TEL 31-20-6461727. FAX 31-20-6463726. Ed. E. van den Berg. adv.; illus. (back issues avail.) **Document type:** consumer publication.
Description: Covers car audio, mobile communications and car alarms.

789.9 US ISSN 0039-1220
ML1
STEREO REVIEW. 1958. m. $17.94 (foreign $25.94). Hachette Magazines, Inc., 1633 Broadway, New York, NY 10019. TEL 212-767-6000. (Subscr. to: Box 55627, Boulder, CO 80322-5627. TEL 800-876-9011) Ed. Louise Boundas. adv.; bk.rev.; rec.rev.; charts; illus.; index. circ. 475,000. (also avail. in microform from UMI) Indexed: Acad.Ind., Bk.Rev.Ind. (1977-), Child.Bk.Rev.Ind. (1977-), Consum.Ind., Mag.Ind., Music Artic.Guide, Music Ind., PMR, R.G., RILM, TOM.
●Also available online. Vendor(s): Knight-Ridder, Inc., University Microfilms International.
—Faxon; UMI; UnCover.
Incorporates (in 1989): High Fidelity (ISSN 0018-1455); **Formerly:** HiFi Stereo Review.
Description: Reviews and compares new audio components, reviews records: both classical and pop-rock releases.

338.4 US
STEREO REVIEW COMPACT DISC BUYERS' GUIDE. s-a. $3.95 per no. Hachette Magazines, Inc., 1633 Broadway, New York, NY 10009. TEL 212-767-6000. (Subscr. to: Box 55627, Boulder, CO 80322-5627)
  Description: Information on compact discs and players.

STEREO REVIEW'S VIDEO BUYERS' GUIDE. see COMMUNICATIONS — Video

621.389 JA
STEREO SOUND. (Text in Japanese) q. 10100 Yen; newsstand price: 2000Yen. Stereo Sound Publishing Inc., 3-8-4, Moto-Azabu, Minato-ku, Tokyo 106, Japan. Ed. Isao Harada; Pub. Isao Harada. adv. contact: Takazumi Arai. **Document type:** consumer publication.

621.389 SP ISSN 0211-7045
STEREOFONIA. 1980. 11/yr. 3600 ptas. Cardenal Herrera Oria 171, Ciudad de los Periodistas, Edif. Azorin, Torre 2, 28034 Madrid, Spain. TEL 1-730-71-77. FAX 1-730-80-92. Ed. J.C. Munoz de Solano. adv. circ. 20,000.

621.389 IT
STEREOGUIDA.* 1976. bi-m. (plus special issue). L.19000($36) Gruppo Editoriale Suono s.r.l., Via Capo Peloro, 30, 00141 Rome, Italy. TEL 893608. Eds. G.M. Binari, D. Caimi. adv. circ. 63,000.

STEREOPHILE; for the high-fidelity stereo perfectionist. see MUSIC

STEREOPHONY AND MUSIC. see MUSIC

780 I ISSN 1122-1747
STEREOPLAY. 1972. m. L.70000. Gruppo Editoriale Suono s.r.l., Via Capo Peloro, 30, 00141 Rome, Italy. TEL 893608. FAX 896981. TELEX 621348 EDSUON I. Ed. Daniel Caimi. adv.: B&W page L.4400000, color page L.7950000. circ. 145,000.

620.2 UK ISSN 0144-5944
TK7881.4
STUDIO SOUND & BROADCAST ENGINEERING. 1959. m. £24. Spotlight Publications Ltd. (Subsidiary of: Morgan-Grampian plc), Ludgate House, 245 Blackfriars Rd., London SE1 9UR, England. TEL 071-620-3636. FAX 071-401-8036. Ed. Tim Goodyear. adv. contact: Steve Grice. bk.rev.; charts; illus.; index. circ. 19,114. **Document type:** trade publication.
  —BLDSC (8500.629500); UnCover.
  Incorporates: Sound International (ISSN 0144-6037); Former titles: Studio Sound and Broadcasting; Studio Sound (ISSN 0039-954X).
  Description: News and feature articles on the technological state of sound engineering, with profiles, product reviews, and business analysis.

780 IT ISSN 1122-1755
SUONO STEREO HI-FI. 1971. m. L.60000. Gruppo Editoriale Suono s.r.l., Via Capo Peloro, 30, 00141 Rome, Italy. TEL 896977. FAX 896981. TELEX 621348 EDSUON I. Ed. Gianfranco Maria Binari. adv.: B&W page L.5150000, color page L.4200000; 185 x 245. circ. 114,000.

SUPER VIDEO & AUDIO. see COMMUNICATIONS — Video

621.389 IT
SUPERSTEREO AUDIO MAGAZINE. 1979. m. (11/yr.). L.32000 for 12 nos. Phono Publishing Company, Via Gaffurio 2, 20124 Milan, Italy. Ed. Piero Dametti Bonetti. adv. circ. 90,000.

621.389 UK
TALKING MACHINE REVIEW, INTERNATIONAL. 1962. q. $15. International Talking Machine Review, 105 Sturdee Ave., Gillingham, Kent ME7 2HG, England. TEL 0634-851824. Ed. John W. Booth. adv.; bk.rev.; rec.rev.; charts; illus.; pat.; index. circ. 1,000. (back issues avail.) **Document type:** consumer publication.
  Formerly: Talking Machine Review (ISSN 0039-9191)
  Description: Covers the history of sound recordings, discographies, artists, techniques and developments in archival-retrieval systems of disc, cylinder and other pre-CD-digital recordings. Provides histories of people and companies in the recording industry.

THE MUSIC INDUSTRY DIRECTORY. see BUSINESS AND ECONOMICS — Trade And Industrial Directories

621.389 338.4 US
THE TEXAS RECORDING AND PRODUCTION GUIDE. 1993. biennial. Office of the Governor, Texas Music Office, Box 13246, Austin, TX 78711. TEL 512-463-6666. FAX 512-463-4114. Ed. Deb Freeman. **Document type:** government publication, directory.

621.389 GW
TON - VIDEO REPORT. 1957. bi-m. DM.30. Ring der Tonband- und Videofreunde e.V., Wallfriedsweg 35, 45479 Muelheim-Ruhr, Germany. TEL 0208-426444. Ed. Lutz Koester. adv.; bk.rev. circ. 1,500. **Document type:** consumer publication.
  Formerly (until 1993): Ton - Report.

621.389 GW
TONMEISTER INFORMATIONEN. 1985. bi-m. Verband Deutscher Tonmeister, Wallensteinstr. 121, 90431 Nuernberg, Germany. TEL 0911-6590-482. FAX 0911-6590-199. bk.rev.

TUTTO STRUMENTI. see MUSIC

620.2 UK
VINTAGE RECORD MART. 1970. bi-m. £3.60. 16 London Hill, Rayleigh, Essex SS6 7HP, England. Ed. Frank K. Bailey. adv.; charts. circ. 400.

789.9 US ISSN 0042-8299
VOICESPONDENT. 1953. q. $5. Voicespondence Club, 1711 Bellevue Ave. D-1214, Richmond, VA 23227. Ed. Charles Owen. adv. contact: Charles Owen. circ. 500 (paid). (also avail. in audio cassette) **Document type:** newsletter.

621.389 UK ISSN 0309-3336
WHAT HI-FI?. vol.5, 1975. m. $65. Haymarket Magazines Ltd., 38-42 Hampton Rd., Teddington, Middx. TW11 0JE, England. TEL 081-943-5000. FAX 081-943-5098. TELEX 895-2440-HAYMRT-G. Ed. Mark Payton. adv.; charts; illus.; tr.lit. circ. 63,100.
  —BLDSC (9309.737000).
  Description: Hi-fi buyer's guide.

YINGYONG SHENGXUE/APPLIED ACOUSTICS. see PHYSICS — Sound

SOUND RECORDING AND REPRODUCTION — Abstracting, Bibliographies, Statistics

015 789.91 GW
DEUTSCHE NATIONALBIBLIOGRAPHIE. REIHE T. MUSIKTONTRAEGER. 1974. m. DM.1158. (Deutsche Bibliothek, Abteilung Deutsches Musikarchiv) Buchhaendler-Vereinigung GmbH, Postfach 100442, 60004 Frankfurt a.M., Germany. TEL 069-13060. FAX 069-1306201. TELEX 413573-BUCHV-D. bibl.; index. **Document type:** directory.
  Former titles: Deutsche Nationalbibliographie. Musiktontraeger-Verzeichnis; Deutsche Bibliographie. Musiktontraeger-Verzeichnis (ISSN 0170-1029); Deutsche Bibliographie. Schallplatten-Verzeichnis.

U.S. LIBRARY OF CONGRESS. MUSIC CATALOG ON MICROFICHE. see MUSIC — Abstracting, Bibliographies, Statistics

SOUND RECORDING AND REPRODUCTION — Computer Applications

SYSTEMS CONTRACTOR NEWS; serving the electronic systems industry. see ELECTRONICS

SPECIAL EDUCATION AND REHABILITATION

see Education–Special Education and Rehabilitation

SPORTS AND GAMES

see also Medical Sciences–Sports Medicine; Sports and Games–Ball Games; Sports and Games–Bicycles and Motorcycles; Sports and Games–Boats and Boating; Sports and Games–Horses and Horsemanship; Sports and Games–Outdoor Life

790.1 PO
A BOLA. 1945. 4/wk. Sociedade Vicra Desportiva Lda., Travessa da Queimada 23, R-c E. 2o D., 1294 Lisbon, Portugal. TEL 01-3463981. FAX 01-3464503. Eds. Vitor Serpa, Joaquim Rita. circ. 180,000.

794.2 790.13 US ISSN 1045-8034
A C F BULLETIN. 1952. bi-m. $20. American Checker Federation, Box 365, Petal, MS 39465. TEL 601-582-7090. Ed. Charles C. Walker. circ. 1,000. **Document type:** bulletin.
  Description: Covers news of checker events worldwide and includes annotated games of national tournament.

A C H P E R HEALTHY LIFESTYLES JOURNAL. (Australian Council for Health, Physical Education and Recreation Inc.) see EDUCATION

A F I BUYING DIRECTORY & WHO'S WHO. see BUSINESS AND ECONOMICS — Trade And Industrial Directories

658.8 US
A F I SHOT SHOW MAGAZINE. 1974. a. $10. (National Association of Federally Licensed Firearms Dealers) A F I Communications Group Inc., 2455 E. Sunrise Blvd., Ste. 916, Ft. Lauderdale, FL 33304-3118. TEL 305-561-3505. FAX 305-561-4129. Ed. Robert Lesmeister; Pub. Andrew Molchan. adv. contact: Danny Vincent. tr.lit. circ. 200,000. (back issues avail.) **Document type:** trade publication.
  Description: Provides firearms and archery information of concern to retailers, wholesalers and manufacturers.

A K C GAZETTE. (American Kennel Club, Inc.) see PETS

790.1 FR
A N O C TRIBUNE. (Text in English, French, Spanish) 2/yr. Association of National Olympic Committees, 21 rue d'Artois, 75008 Paris, France.

794.1 US
A P C T NEWS BULLETIN. 1967. 6/yr. $18 (foreign $36). American Postal Chess Tournaments, Box 305, Western Springs, IL 60558-0305. Ed. Helen Warren. adv. contact: Jim Warren. bk.rev. circ. 1,000. **Document type:** bulletin.
  Description: Reports on annotated and not annotated games. Includes "how-to-improve" articles, computer chess, and theory.

790.1 SP
A S; diario grafico deportivo. 1968. d. Semana, S.A., Paseo de Onesimo Redondo, 24, Apdo. 383, Madrid 8, Spain. Ed. Luis G. de Linares. adv. circ. 200,000.

790.1 617.1 US
A S M A NEWS. 1992. a. $50 membership. American Sports Medecine Association, Board of Certification, 660 W. Duarte Rd., Arcadia, CA 91007. TEL 818-445-1978. Ed. Tracy Zalke. adv.: page $125; adv. contact: J.R. Laver 529. bk.rev.; circ. 3,500 (controlled). (back issues avail.) **Document type:** newsletter.
  Formerly: A A T A News (American Athletic Trainers Association) (ISSN 1067-6031)
  Description: Covers sports medicine, injury prevention, athletic training, sports medicine certification.

SPORTS AND GAMES

790.1 059.927   UK   ISSN 1319-0881
AALAM AL-RIYADAH. Key Title: A'lam al-riyadat (Guddat). (Text in Arabic) 1991. w. $110 (effective 1994). Saudi Research and Marketing, Arab Press House, 184 High Holborn, London WC1V 7AP, England. TEL 44-171-831-8181. FAX 44-171-404-6311. (And: P.O. Box 4556, Jeddah 21441, Saudi Arabia. TEL 966-2-6691888. FAX 966-2-6671650; Subscr. in U.S. to: Attache International, 3050 Broacway, Ste. 300, Boulder, CO 80304-3154. TEL 303-442-8900. FAX 303-442-7979) adv.: B&W page $1333, color page $2400; trim 220 x 285. circ. 73,504 (paid). **Document type:** consumer publication.
   Description: Covers local and international sporting events for a young Arab audience.

796   SW   ISSN 0567-4573
AARETS IDROTT. a. SEK 639. Stroembergs Idrottsboecker, Box 65, 1€211 Vaellingby, Sweden.

796.9   SW   ISSN 0282-860X
AARETS ISHOCKEY. 1957. a. SEK 799. (Svenska Ishockeyfoerbundet) Stroembergs Idrottsboecker, P.O. Box 65, 162 11 Vaell ngby, Sweden. illus.
   From 1984 also published as: Ishockey (ISSN 0347-2221).

796   FR   ISSN 0065-0579
ACADEMIE DES SPORTS, PARIS. ANNUAIRE. 1965. irreg. (Academie des Sports, Paris) Editions Person, 34 rue de Penthievre, 75008 Paris, France. FAX 43-59-35-62. adv.

790.1   US
THE ACADEMY. 1978. q. free. United States Sports Academy, One Academy Dr., Daphne, AL 36526. TEL 205-626-3303. FAX 205-626-3874. Ed. Dr. Robert Lyster; Pub. Dr. Thomas P. Rosandich. circ. 10,000 (controlled). **Document type:** newsletter.
   Formerly: U S S A News.
   Description: Provides news about educational programs and activities of the U.S. Sports Academy.

790.1   US   ISSN 0893-9489
ACTION PURSUIT GAMES. 1988 m. $24.50. C F W Enterprises, Inc., 4201 W. Van Owen Pl., Burbank, CA 91505. TEL 818-845-2656. FAX 818-845-7761. (Subscr to: Box 404, Mt. Morris, IL 61054) Ed. Randy Kamiya. adv.: B&W page $1349.
   Description: Covers the sport of paintball. Includes games, strategies, personalities, and equipment.

688.76   US   ISSN 0199-4972
ACTION SPORTS RETAILER.* 1980. m. $15. Pacifica Publishing Corporation, Box 1899, Laguna Beach, CA 92652-1899. TEL 714-499-5374. Ed. Brad Bonhall. adv. circ. 15,900.
   —CCC.

790.1   US
ACTION TRACKS. 1976. a. 330 W. Division St., Box 1929, Eagle River, WI 54521. TEL 715-479-4425. FAX 715-479-6242. Ed. Kurt Krueger; Pub. Byron McNutt. adv.; circ. 25,000 (paid). **Document type:** newspaper.
   Formerly: Sno Times.

ADSUM. see MILITARY

790.1 330   US
ADVANCES IN THE ECONOMICS OF SPORT. 1992. irreg. J A I Press Inc., 55 Old Post Rd., No. 2, Box 1678, Greenwich, CT 06836-1678. TEL 203-661-7602. FAX 203-661-0792. Ed. Gerald Scully. **Document type:** monographic series.

AETHLON. see LITERATURE

AL-AHLY. see CLUBS

790.1   UA   ISSN 1110-4678
AL-AHRAM AL-RIYADI. 1990. w. $180 in N. America (effective 1994). Mu'assasat al-Ahram, Sharia al-Galaa, Cairo, Egypt. TEL 02-758333. FAX 02-745888. TELEX 20185 AHRAM UN. (In N. America: Al-Ahram International, 405 Lexington Ave., New York, NY 10174. TEL 212-972-6440. FAX 212-286-0285) adv.; illus.

796.815   JA   ISSN 1340-5624
AIKIDO JOURNAL. (Text in English) 1974. q. $35 in U.S.; Canada & Mexico $40. K.K. Aiki News, Lions Mansion No. 204, Tamagawa Gakuen 5-11-25, Machida-shi, Tokyo 194, Japan. TEL 81-427-24-8675. FAX 81-427-24-9119. E-mail: aikido@gol.com. Ed. Diane Skoss. adv.; bk.rev.; illus. circ. 12,000. (back issues avail.) **Indexed:** Sportsearch (1990-). **Document type:** consumer publication.
   Formerly (until vol.21, no.3, 1994): Aiki News (ISSN 0915-9517)
   Description: For serious practitioners of Japanese martial arts. Contains interviews with top instructors, history and philosophy, illustrated technical articles, self-defense, reviews of martial arts publications, and event announcements and reports.

799.202   CN   ISSN 0382-4373
AIM. (Text in English, French) 1968. 4/yr. Can.$7.49. Shooting Federation of Canada - Federation de Tir du Canada, 1600 James Naismith Dr., Gloucester, ON K1B 5N4, Canada. TEL 613-748-5659; 800-667-2673. FAX 613-748-5776. TELEX 053-3660. Ed. David Williams. adv. contact: John Russett. bk.rev. circ. 10,000. **Indexed:** Sportsearch (1962-). **Document type:** newsletter.

790.1   UK   ISSN 0266-4224
AIR GUNNER. 1984. m. £23($40) Romsey Publishing Co. Ltd., 4 The Courtyard, Denmark St., Wokingham, Berkshire, England. TEL 01734-771677. FAX 01734-772903. Ed. N. Allen; Pub. P. Dobson. adv. contact: D. Barnes. circ. 20,000. **Document type:** bulletin.
   Description: Covers all aspects of air gun shooting.

AIRBORNE MAGAZINE; comprehensive coverage of Australian radio control modelling sports. see HOBBIES

AIRSPORT. see AERONAUTICS AND SPACE FLIGHT

794.1   AG
AJEDREZ DE ESTILO. 1982. 24/yr. $119. Ajedrez Integral, Casilla de Correo 51, Sucursal 49, 1449 Buenos Aires, Argentina. TEL 331-6988. FAX 331-6988. Ed. Juan S. Morgado. adv.; bk.rev. circ. 2,000.
   Description: Contains almost 2000 annotated national and international games each year, theory and combinations.

794.1   CK
AJEDREZ UNIVERSAL. 1988. 12/yr. $45. Carrera 7a No. 34-61 oficina, 401 Bogota, D.E., Colombia. TEL 571-2452231. (U.S. addr.: Luis Bdo. Hoyos-Millon., 10 Bay St. Landing Apt. 6I, Staten Island, New York 10301) Dir. Jaime Lombana Ordonez. adv.; bk.rev. circ. 30,000.
   Description: Includes games, articles, news, theory, and combinations.

ALASKA'S WILDLIFE. see FISH AND FISHERIES

790   XO
ALBUM SLAVNYCH SPORTOVCOV. irreg, vol.4, 1976. price varies. Sport, Vajnorska Cesta 100-a, 892 58 Bratislava, Slovakia. illus.

797   US
ALERT DIVER. bi-m. $25. Divers Alert Network, Box 3823, Duke University Medical Center, Durham, NC 27710. TEL 919-684-2948. FAX 919-490-6630. Ed. Renee Duncan. adv. circ. 110,000.
   Description: Discusses medical issues and promotes safety in scuba diving.
   Refereed Serial

794.1   CK
ALFIL DAMA; revista colombiana de ajedrez. 6/yr. $25. Liga de Ajedrez de Antioquia, Exec. Dir., Carrera 50 No. 59-06, Medellin, Colombia. Ed.Bd.
   Description: Contains selections of national and international games, "how-to-improve" articles, scholastic chess, and problems.

ALL SPORT & LEISURE MONTHLY. see LEISURE AND RECREATION

ALLIANCE UPDATE. see PHYSICAL FITNESS AND HYGIENE

790.1   GW
ALTDORFER SPORTSPIEGEL. 1972. q. DM.675. Turnverein Altdorf e.v., Ernhofen 12, 91227 Leinburg, Germany. Ed. Horst Topp. (back issues avail.)

790.1   US   ISSN 0002-6808
GV741
AMATEUR ATHLETE. 1987. a. $2. Eliot Wineberg, Ed. & Pub., 7840 N. Lincoln Ave., Skokie, IL 60077. TEL 708-675-0200. FAX 708-675-2903. adv.; circ. 35,000. **Document type:** consumer publication.
   Description: Lists more than 800 running, bicycling, and triathalon events in the Midwest.

796   UK   ISSN 0065-6690
AMATEUR ATHLETIC ASSOCIATION. HANDBOOK. 1925. a. £4. Amateur Athletic Association, 3 Duchess Place, Hagley Rd., Edgbaston, Birmingham B16 8NM, England. TEL 021-456-4050. Ed. Barry Willis. adv. circ. 5,000.

796   US
GV563
AMATEUR ATHLETIC UNION OF THE UNITED STATES. OFFICIAL A A U CODE DIRECTORY. Cover title: A A U Code Directory. 1888. a. $10. Amateur Athletic Union of the United States, 3400 W. 86th St., Box 68207, Indianapolis, IN 46268. TEL 317-872-2900. FAX 317-875-0548. illus. **Document type:** directory.
   Formerly: Amateur Athletic Union of the United States. Official Handbook of the A A U Code (ISSN 0091-3405)

796.962   US
AMATEUR SPEEDSKATING UNION OF THE UNITED STATES. OFFICIAL HANDBOOK. 1930. biennial. $5. Amateur Speedskating Union of the United States, 1033 Shady Ln., Glen Ellyn, IL 60137. TEL 708-790-3230. Ed. Robert R. Vehe. adv. contact: Charles Kazmierski. circ. 3,000.
   Formerly: Amateur Skating Union of the United States. Official Handbook (ISSN 0516-866X)

797.21   UK
AMATEUR SWIMMING ASSOCIATION HANDBOOK. 1905. a. £4. Amateur Swimming Association, Harold Fern House, Derby Sq., Loughborough, Leics. LE11 OAL, England. TEL 44-509-230431. FAX 44-509-610720. Ed. A. Williams. circ. 3,700. **Document type:** directory, bulletin.
   Description: Contains news of the association administration; champions holding records in swimming, diving, synchronized swimming, and water polo in the UK and abroad; and updates regarding teaching and coaching certificates.

796   US   ISSN 0569-1796
AMATEUR WRESTLING NEWS. 1955. 12/yr. (Sep.-May). $28. Amateur Wrestling News, Box 54679, Oklahoma City, OK 73154. TEL 405-524-8551. FAX 405-524-8193. Ed. Ron Good. adv. contact: J Schneider. circ. 10,000. **Indexed:** Sports Per.Ind., Sportsearch.

799.202   US   ISSN 0899-5192
AMERICAN AIRGUNNER.* US. $15. Sport Shooting in America (SSIA), Box 62, Emmetsburg, IA 50536. TEL 712-852-3918. FAX 915-673-0404. adv.; bk.rev.
   Formerly: Airgun News and Report (ISSN 0885-4920)
   Description: Covers precision airguns; features new products, provides test reports, and reviews on air rifles.

795.414   US   ISSN 1071-3131
AMERICAN CONTRACT BRIDGE LEAGUE. BULLETIN. 1935. m. $12 to non-members. American Contract Bridge League, 2990 Airways Blvd., Memphis, TN 38116-3847. TEL 901-332-5586. FAX 901-398-7754. E-mail: 74431.3434@compuserve.com. Ed. Henry G. Francis. adv.; bk.rev.; charts; illus.; circ. 160,000 (controlled). **Document type:** bulletin.
   Formerly (until 1993): Contract Bridge Bulletin (ISSN 0010-7840)
   Description: Covers all contract bridge activity in North America, plus reports about foreign tournaments. Includes results, schedules, features and instructional material.

SPORTS AND GAMES

796.86 US ISSN 0002-8436
U860
AMERICAN FENCING. 1949. q. $12 to non-members (foreign $18). United States Fencing Association, Inc., 1750 E. Boulder St., Colorado Springs, CO 80909. TEL 719-578-4511. FAX 719-632-5737. Ed. Candi Macconaugha. adv.; illus.; index. circ. 10,000. (also avail. in microform from UMI) Indexed: Sports Per.Ind., Sportsearch (1980-). **Document type:** consumer publication.
—Faxon; UMI; UnCover.

658.8 338.476 US ISSN 0164-8136
AMERICAN FIREARMS INDUSTRY. 1973. m. $25. (National Association of Federally Licensed Firearms Dealers) A F I Communications Group Inc., 2455 E. Sunrise Blvd., 9th Fl., Ft. Lauderdale, FL 33304-3118. TEL 305-561-3505. FAX 305-561-4129. Ed. Robert Lesmeister; Pub. Andrew Molchan. adv. contact: Danny Vincent. bk.rev.; charts; illus.; stat.; tr.lit.; circ. 14,000 (paid); 32,000 (controlled). (back issues avail.) **Document type:** trade publication.
Description: Provides business and product information for licensed firearms dealers.

790.1 US
AMERICAN GLADIATORS. q. newsstand price: $3.95. London Publishing Co., Box 910, Ft. Washington, PA 19034. TEL 215-643-6385. FAX 215-540-0146. **Document type:** consumer publication.

793 US ISSN 0148-0243
GV1459
AMERICAN GO JOURNAL. (News supplement avail. entitled: American Go Newsletter) 1948. q. $25 membership. American Go Association, Box 397, Old Chelsea Sta., New York, NY 10113. FAX 212-477-2812. Ed. Roy J. Laird. adv. contact: Roy J. Laird. bk.rev. circ. 1,500. **Document type:** academic/scholarly publication.
Description: Contains news and instructions on the ancient oriental game of Go (Paduk, Weigi).

AMERICAN HANDGUNNER. see HOBBIES

796 US
AMERICAN HOCKEY LEAGUE OFFICIAL GUIDE AND RECORD BOOK (YEAR). a. $12.95. American Hockey League, 425 Union St., W. Springfield, MA 01089. TEL 413-781-2030. FAX 413-733-4767. Ed. Gordon Anziano. circ. 2,000. **Document type:** bulletin.
Formerly: American Hockey League Media Guide (Year); Which incorporated (in 1992): A H L Playoff Guide.
Description: History and record book of the American Hockey League; includes current team directories and records.

796 US
AMERICAN HOCKEY LEAGUE OFFICIAL RULE BOOK (YEAR). a. American Hockey League, 425 Union St., W. Springfield, MA 01089. TEL 413-781-2030. FAX 413-733-4767. **Document type:** bulletin.

796.962 US ISSN 8756-3789
GV848.4.U6
AMERICAN HOCKEY MAGAZINE. 1972. 9/yr. $12. (U S A Hockey) The Publishing Group, Inc., 1200 N. 7th St., Minneapolis, MN 55411-4000. TEL 612-522-1200. FAX 612-522-1182. Ed. Darryl Seibel. adv. circ. 325,000. (back issues avail.) Indexed: Sportsearch. **Document type:** consumer publication.
Former titles: American Hockey and Arena; United States Hockey and Arena Biz (ISSN 0162-654X); Hockey and Arena Biz; U S Hockey Biz.
Description: Covers amateur hockey: rules, profiles, referees and rink management.

794.2 US ISSN 1055-1638
AMERICAN INTERNATIONAL CHECKERS SOCIETY NEWSLETTER. 1970. m. $25. American International Checkers Society, 11010 Horde St., Wheaton, MD 20902. TEL 301-949-5920. Ed. Jack Birnman. bk.rev. circ. 130. (back issues avail.) **Document type:** newsletter.
Description: News, game analyses, and problems devoted to 100-square checkers.

AMERICAN KENNEL CLUB AWARDS; new titles and results from shows, obedience trials, tracking tests, field trials and hunting tests. see PETS

636.596 US ISSN 0003-0686
SF481
AMERICAN RACING PIGEON NEWS. 1885. m. (Sep.-July). $25. 34 E. Franklin St., Bellbrook, OH 45305-2098. TEL 513-848-4972. FAX 513-848-3012. Ed. Michael D. Reinke. adv.: B&W page $225, color page $800; 8 1/2 x 11. bk.rev.; illus. circ. 5,000.
Description: Provides "how-to" articles, news and opinions on the sport of pigeon breeding, training, racing and showing on an international basis.

799.2 US ISSN 0003-083X
SK1
AMERICAN RIFLEMAN. 1885. m. $35 (membership). (National Rifle Association of America) N R A Publications, 11250 Waples Mill Rd., Fairfax, VA 22030. TEL 703-267-1336. FAX 703-267-3971. Ed. E.G. Bell, Jr. adv.; bk.rev.; charts; illus.; pat.; stat. circ. 1,733,679. (also avail. in microform from UMI) Indexed: Consum.Ind., Mag.Ind., PMR, Sports Per.Ind., Sportsearch. **Document type:** consumer publication.
●Also available online. Vendor(s): University Microfilms International.
—Faxon; SWETS; UMI; UnCover.
Description: Membership publication covering firearms, Second Amendment issues, target shooting, gunsmithing, and gun collecting.

799.202 US ISSN 0734-5801
AMERICAN SINGLE SHOT RIFLE NEWS. 1948. bi-m. $20. American Single Shot Rifle Association, 625 Pine St., Marquette, MI 49855. TEL 906-225-1828. FAX 906-227-1819. Ed. Rudi Prusok. adv.; bk.rev. circ. 2,000. **Document type:** bulletin.

796.91 US ISSN 0744-1363
AMERICAN SKATING WORLD. 1981. m. $22.95 (foreign $34) (effective 1995). Group Publications Ltd. (Subsidiary of: Business Communications, Inc.), 1816 Brownsville Rd., Pittsburgh, PA 15210-3908. TEL 412-885-7600. FAX 412-885-7617. Ed. Robert A. Mock; Pub. Michael Romanus. adv. contact: Patricia Weber. circ. 15,000 (paid). (tabloid format) **Document type:** newspaper.
Description: Covers professional, competitive and recreational figure skating, plus a limited coverage of speed skating; as well as events, personalities and issues; and provides a forum for opinions involving all facets of figure skating, both in the US and worldwide.

790.1 US
AMERICAN SPORTS. 1984. m. $36. American Sports Network Inc., Box 6100, Rosemead, CA 91770. Ed. Steve Roguet; Pub. Louis Zwick. adv. contact: Martin Talty. circ. 292,482 (paid). **Document type:** consumer publication.
Description: Covers recreational sports.

790.1 US
AMERICAN STATISTICAL ASSOCIATION. STATISTICS IN SPORTS. PROCEEDINGS. 1993. a. $23 to non-members; members $15. American Statistical Association, 1429 Duke St., Alexandria, VA 22314-3402. TEL 703-684-1221. FAX 703-684-2037. **Document type:** proceedings.

790.1 US
AMERICAN WOMAN MOTORSCENE.* 1989. bi-m. $12. Ladylike Enterprises, Inc., 1510- 11th St., Ste. 201-B, Santa Monica, CA 90401-2906. TEL 310-829-0012. FAX 310-453-8850. Ed. Sue Elliott. adv.: B&W page $1750, color page $2550; trim 7 7/8 x 10 1/2. circ. 100,000. **Document type:** consumer publication.
Former titles: American Woman Motorsports & American Woman Magazine; American Woman Road Riding; American Woman Road Rider.
Description: An automotive lifestyle magazine geared towards working women.

790 GW ISSN 0171-7243
AMUSEMENT-INDUSTRIE; Fachzeitschrift fuer Freizeittechnologie und -management. (Text in German; summaries in English) 1970. q. DM.70 (Europe DM.73; elsewhere DM.117. Junfermann Verlag, Imadstr. 40, 33102 Paderborn, Germany. TEL 05251-34034. FAX 05251-36371. adv.; bk.rev.; abstr.; illus.; pat.; stat.; tr.lit.; index, cum.index. circ. 6,000. **Document type:** trade publication.

790.1 UK ISSN 0965-3422
ANGLO-AMERICAN SPORTS. 1991. m. $80. Greenflex Associates, 24 Notting Hill Gate, London W11 3JE, England. Ed. Richard Taylor.
Description: British - American coverage of baseball, basketball, ice hockey, and gridiron.

790.1 FR ISSN 1162-0900
ANNEE SPORTIVE U.S.M.T.. a. membership. Union Sportive Metropolitaine des Transports, 159 Bd de la Villette, Paris 10, France. adv.

796.35 CN
ANNUAL RINGETTE REVIEW. (Annual special edition avail. since 1990: Gillette "Soft and Dri" Special Edition of Ringette) (Text in English, French) 1979. a. Can.$2. Ringette Canada Publications, 1600 James Naismith Drive, Gloucester, ON K1B 5N4, Canada. TEL 613-748-5655. FAX 613-748-5860. Ed. Laura Webb. adv.; bk.rev. circ. 30,000. Indexed: Sportsearch (1982-). **Document type:** newsletter.
Formerly: Ringette Review.

ANREGUNG (MUNICH); Zeitschrift fuer Gymnasialpaedagogik. see EDUCATION — Teaching Methods And Curriculum

797.21 658 US ISSN 1058-7039
AQUATICS INTERNATIONAL; the source for facility products, services and management. 1989. 6/yr. $39 (foreign $79). Argus Inc., 6151 Powers Ferry Rd., N.W., Atlanta, GA 30339-2941. TEL 404-955-2500. FAX 404-955-0400. Ed. Terri Simmons. circ. 30,120 (controlled). (also avail. in microform from UMI; reprint service avail. from UMI) **Document type:** trade publication.
—UMI; UnCover. CCC.
Formerly: (until 1991): Aquatics (ISSN 1042-9697); Incorporates (1989-1991): Aquatics Buyers' Guide.
Description: Covers design, management, maintenance and programming of public and semi-public swimming pools, waterparks, beaches and other water-oriented facilities.

799.32 FR ISSN 1148-3652
L'ARCHER. 1848. w. (Apr.-Oct.). 150 F. (Associations d'Archers du Nord de la France) Independant du Pas-de-Calais, 14 rue des Clouteries, 62500 Saint Omer, France. TEL 21-93-73-65. FAX 21-39-72-50. adv. circ. 750.

796 US ISSN 1050-0693
ARCHERY BUSINESS. 1975. 6/yr. $24.95 free to qualified personnel. Ehlert Publishing Group, Inc., 601 Lakeshore Pkwy., Ste. 600, Minnetonka, MN 55305-5215. TEL 612-476-2200. FAX 612-476-8065. Ed. Mike Stranlund. adv.; bk.rev. circ. 11,000. (reprint service avail. from UMI) Indexed: Sportsearch (1985-). **Document type:** trade publication.
Formerly: Archery Retailer (ISSN 0191-8427)

496.72 US ISSN 1041-3251
AREA AUTO RACING NEWS. 1963. w. $35. Area Auto Racing News, Inc., 2829 S. Broad St., Trenton, NJ 08610. TEL 609-888-3618. FAX 609-888-2538. Ed. Len Sammons. adv.; bk.rev.; circ. 31,000 (paid). (tabloid format) **Document type:** trade publication.
Description: Covers all Northeast circle track auto races and all national series.

790.1 UK
ARENA (EDINBURGH). 1979. q. free. Scottish Sports Council, Caledonia House, South Gyle, Edinburgh EH12 9DQ, Scotland. TEL 0131-317-7200. FAX 0131-317-7202. Ed. Fred Pollock. illus.; circ. 2,000 (controlled). **Document type:** bulletin.
Formerly (until 1989): Scottish Sports Council. Bulletin (ISSN 0142-6761)

790.1 US ISSN 1043-3120
ARM BENDER. 1971. q. $25. (American Armwrestling Association) Boss Publications, Box 79, Scranton, PA 18504-0079. TEL 717-342-4984. FAX 717-342-1368. (Co-sponsors: World Armsport Federation, Bob O'Leary Sports Science) Ed. Richard Kimble. adv. circ. 1,500. (back issues avail.) **Document type:** trade publication.
Description: Promotes arm wrestling as a sport. Includes competition results, tips and tales of arm wrestlers.

ARMAS. see MILITARY

SPORTS AND GAMES

799.202 355   SP
ARMAS Y MUNICIONES. 1986. 12/yr. 5400 ptas.($100) Pza. Republica Ecuador 2, 1o, 28016 Madrid, Spain. TEL 1-457-53-02. FAX 1-457-93-12. Ed. Saul Braceras Haedo. adv.; bk.rev. circ. 35,000.

799.32   UK   ISSN 0144-7424
ARROWHEAD. 1958. 2/yr. £15 membership. Society of Archer-Antiquaries, c/o Doug Elmy, 61 Lambert Rd., Bridlington, Yorks YO16 5RD, England. TEL 01262-601604. bk.rev.; circ. controlled. (processed) Indexed: Sportsearch (1981-). **Document type:** newsletter.
Formerly: Society of Archer-Antiquaries. Newsletter (ISSN 0049-1187)
Description: Devoted to archery.

ARROW'S COMPLETE GUIDE TO MAIL ORDER SPORTING GOODS. see *BUSINESS AND ECONOMICS — Marketing And Purchasing*

ASSOCIATION FOR THE STUDY OF PLAY NEWSLETTER. see *PSYCHOLOGY*

796   FR   ISSN 0997-1971
ATHLERAMA. 1962. a. 90 F. Federation Francaise d'Athletisme, 33 bd. Pierre de Coubertin, 75013 Paris, France. TEL 44-79-13-06. FAX 48-00-00-39. Ed. Yves Pinaud. adv.; bk.rev. circ. 5,000.
Formerly (until 1982): Athletisme Francais (ISSN 0067-012X)

790.1   US   ISSN 1074-8547
ATHLETES IN ACTION. 1988. q. $7 (Canada & Mexico $9; elsewhere $11). Box 588, Lebanon, OH 45036-0588. TEL 513-933-2421. FAX 513-933-2424. Ed. Wendel Deyo. bk.rev. circ. 14,000. (tabloid format) **Document type:** newspaper.

790.1   US   ISSN 0747-315X
ATHLETIC BUSINESS. 1977. m. $36. Athletic Business Publications, Inc., 1846 Hoffman St., Madison, WI 53704. TEL 608-249-0186. FAX 608-249-1153. Ed. Sue Schmid. adv.; bk.rev.; circ. 40,000 (controlled). (back issues avail.) Indexed: Phys.Ed.Ind., Sportsearch (1985-). **Document type:** trade publication.
—BLDSC (1765.878750); Faxon; UnCover.
Formerly: Athletic Purchasing and Facilities (ISSN 0192-5482)
Description: For owners and operators of athletic, recreation and fitness facilities.

796   AT   ISSN 0300-4600
ATHLETIC ECHO. (Text in Greek) 1961. w. Aus.$35. Petranis Press, 8 Atkin St., North Melbourne, Vic. 3051, Australia. TEL 329-6581. Ed. Jim Bakatsoulas. adv.; bk.rev. circ. 5,000.

796   JA
ATHLETIC SPORTS MAGAZINE/RIKUJO-KYOGI MAGAZINE. (Text in Japanese) 1951. m. 8040 Yen. Baseball Magazine Sha, 3-10-10 Misaki-cho, Chiyoda-ku, Tokyo, Japan. Ed. Tadashi Otokawa.

796   CN   ISSN 0229-4966
ATHLETICS; the Canadian track & field running magazine. 1976. 9/yr. Can.$18.50($19.50) Athletics Inc., 1220 Sheppard Ave. E., Willowdale, ON M2K 2X1, Canada. TEL 416-495-4055. FAX 416-495-4052. Ed. Greg Lockhart. adv.; bk.rev.; illus. circ. 8,000. (also avail. in microform from MML) Indexed: Can.B.P.I., Can.Per.Ind., CMI, Sportsearch (1981-).
Formerly: Ontario Athletics.

796   US   ISSN 0044-9873
ATHLETICS ADMINISTRATION. Key Title: Athletic Administration. 1966. bi-m. $15 to non-members. National Association of Collegiate Directors of Athletics, Box 16428, Cleveland, OH 44116. TEL 800-527-8999. FAX 216-892-4007. Ed. Laurie Garrison. adv.; bk.rev.; charts; illus.; tr.lit. circ. 5,000. Indexed: Phys.Ed.Ind., Sports Per.Ind., Sportsearch (1978-). **Document type:** trade publication.
—Faxon; UnCover.
Description: Publishes features relating to the administration of college athletics programs.

796   UK   ISSN 0267-0267
ATHLETICS COACH; the quarterly coaching bulletin of the British Athletic Federation. 1964. q. £16 (foreign £18) (effective 1996). British Amateur Athletic Board, Caledonia House, South Byle, Edinburgh EH12 9DQ, Scotland. TEL 0131-317-7322. Ed. Andy Vince. adv.; bk.rev. circ. 1,200. Indexed: Phys.Ed.Ind., Sportsearch (1976-). **Document type:** newsletter.
—BLDSC (1765.881200).
Formerly: British Athletics (ISSN 0068-1326)
Description: Contains photo sequences of successful athletes, and articles on the technical aspects of track and field.

ATHLETICS EMPLOYMENT WEEKLY. see *OCCUPATIONS AND CAREERS*

796   UK   ISSN 0004-6671
ATHLETICS WEEKLY. 1945. w. £57.20 (foreign £80.20) (effective 1995-1996). E M A P - Pursuit Publishing, Bretton Ct., Bretton, Peterborough, Cambs. PE3 8DZ, England. TEL 01733-264666. FAX 01733-263294. TELEX 32157. (Subscr. to: Tower Publishing Services Ltd., Tower House, Sovereign Park, Lathkill St., Market Harborough, Leics. LE16 9EF, England. TEL 01858-468811. FAX 01858-432164) adv.; bk.rev.; illus. circ. 22,192. Indexed: Sportsearch (1976-). **Document type:** consumer publication.
Incorporates: Modern Athletics; Women's Athletics.

796   GW   ISSN 0004-6698
ATHLETIK;* illustrierte Fachzeitschrift fuer Schwerathletik. 1948. m. DM.35. (Deutscher Ringer-Bund) Athletik-Verlag, Gustav-Binz-Str. 8, D-7500 Karlsruhe 1, Germany. Ed. Werner Artmann. circ. 3,900.

ATLANTIC CITY ACTION. see *BUSINESS AND ECONOMICS — Investments*

796   IT
ATLETICA. 1933. m. L.30000($20) (Europe L.75000). Federazione Italiana di Atletica Leggera, Via della Camilluccia, 703, 00135 Rome, Italy. TEL 39-6-326831. FAX 39-6-3294323. TELEX 611294. Ed. Gianni Gola; Pub. Ottavio Castellini. adv.; B&W page L.1250000; color page L.2250000. bk.rev. circ. 17,000. **Document type:** consumer publication.

796   IT   ISSN 0390-6671
ATLETICASTUDI; ricerca scientifica & technica applicata all'atletica leggera. 1970. bi-m. L.30000. Federazione Italiana di Atletica Leggera (FIDAL), Via Della Camizzuccia 703, 00135 Rome, Italy. Ed. Gianni Gola. circ. 14,000. Indexed: Sportsearch (1983-).

796   NE   ISSN 0004-668X
ATLETIEKWERELD. 1934. 12/yr. fl.60. Koninklijke Nederlandse Atletiek Unie, P.O.B. 567, 3430 AN Nieuwegein, Netherlands. TEL 31-3402-32920. FAX 31-3402-43044. adv. contact: Cor Wielaard. bk.rev.; charts; illus.; stat.; index. circ. 9,000.

796.409   DK   ISSN 0905-3883
ATLETIK'EN. Variant title: Atletikken. 1989. 14/yr. DKK 190. Danish Athletic Federation, Lunden 5, DK-5540 Ullerslev, Denmark. TEL 45-65-35-11-35. FAX 45-65-35-37-35. Ed. Niels Larsen. circ. 4,000. **Document type:** bulletin.
Formerly (until 1989): Action (ISSN 0903-5680); Which was formed by the merger of (1982-1988): Motionsloeberen (ISSN 0108-3392); (1971-1988): Dansk Atletik (ISSN 0108-3384)

790.1   IT
ATTIVITA DOPOLAVORISTICHE. 1956. m. Dopolavoro Ferroviario di Torino, Via Sacchi 63, 10125 Turin, Italy. Ed. Settimo Todisco. adv. circ. 7,000.

AUSTRALIAN AIRSPORT. see *AERONAUTICS AND SPACE FLIGHT*

795.415   AT   ISSN 0045-0332
AUSTRALIAN BRIDGE. 1970. bi-m. Aus.$35. Bridge Shop, P.O. Box 654, Spit Junction, N.S.W. 2088, Australia. TEL 61-2-960-2909. FAX 61-2-967-2142. Ed. Stephen Lester. adv.; bk.rev. circ. 2,500. **Document type:** bulletin.

794.1   AT
AUSTRALIAN CHESS MAGAZINE. 1966. 6/yr. Aus.$24. (Australian Chess Federation) Peter Parr, Ed. & Pub., P.O. Box C274, Clarence St., Sydney, N.S.W. 2000, Australia. Ed. Peter Parr. adv.; bk.rev.; charts; index. circ. 1,800.
Formerly (until 1992): Chess in Australia (ISSN 0009-3343)

799.2   AT   ISSN 1321-3903
AUSTRALIAN CLAY TARGET SHOOTING NEWS. 1947. m. Aus.$25. Australian Clay Target Association Inc., P.O. Box 557, Mtn. Waverley, Vic. 3149, Australia. TEL 61-3-807-7577. FAX 61-3-8072716. Ed. Graeme Brown. adv.; B&W page Aus.$650; trim 270 x 210; adv. contact: Danni Bosnjak. bk.rev. circ. 7,500. **Document type:** newsletter.
Description: Covers shooting sports and club shooting throughout Australia and internationally.

793   AT   ISSN 0819-7806
AUSTRALIAN CORRESPONDENCE CHESS QUARTERLY. 1948. q. Aus.$12. Correspondence Chess League of Australia, G.P.O. Box 2360, Sydney, N.S.W. 2001, Australia. Ed. A.O. Holloway. adv.; bk.rev. circ. 1,500. **Document type:** newsletter.
Formerly: C C L A Record.

AUSTRALIAN GLIDING. see *AERONAUTICS AND SPACE FLIGHT*

796.41   AT
AUSTRALIAN GYMNAST. q. Aus.$25 (foreign Aus.$35) (effective 1996). Australian Gymnastic Federation, Lower Ground Fl., 416 St. Kilda Rd., Melbourne, Vic. 3004, Australia. TEL 03-866-6011. Ed. Peggy Browne. adv.; bk.rev.; circ. 3,000 (paid). (back issues avail.) Indexed: Sportsearch (1980-).

796.355   AT
AUSTRALIAN RUNNER.* 1980. bi-m. Aus.$46. P.O. Box 396, South Yarra, Vic. 3141, Australia. TEL 03-819-9225. FAX 03-891-6418. Ed. Terry O'Halloran. adv.; bk.rev. circ. 15,000. (back issues avail.)
Description: Covers track and field, road running, marathons, diet and nutrition, and training.

794.1   AT   ISSN 0155-7831
AUSTRALIAN WOMEN'S CHESS BULLETIN. 1976. 4/yr. $13 for 2 yrs. Australian Women's Chess League, 139 Fisher St., Malvern, S.A. 5061, Australia. TEL 618-271-8009. FAX 618-271-3472. Ed. Evelyn Koshnitsky. adv. circ. 300. **Document type:** bulletin.
Description: Devoted primarily to women's chess. Includes annotated games, biographies, interviews, and articles.

796.72   IT
AUTO E SPORT. 1981. w. L.140000 (foreign L.190000). Alfredo Cazzola Editore s.r.l., Via C. Colombo 21, 40131 Bologna, Italy. TEL 39-51-325991. FAX 39-51-321002. Ed. Alberto Sabatini. adv.; B&W or color page L.9000000. circ. 37,802.
Formerly (until 1994): Rombo Auto e Sport.

AUTO MOTOR SPORT. see *TRANSPORTATION — Automobiles*

AUTO MOTOR UND SPORT. see *TRANSPORTATION — Automobiles*

AUTO MOTOR UND SPORT SPEZIAL GEBRAUCHTWAGEN. see *TRANSPORTATION — Automobiles*

AUTO MOTOR UND SPORT TESTJAHRBUCH. see *TRANSPORTATION — Automobiles*

796.72   US   ISSN 0090-8029
GV1029
AUTO RACING DIGEST. 1973. bi-m. $22 (foreign $30). Century Publishing Co., 990 Grove St., Evanston, IL 60201-4370. TEL 708-491-6440. (Subscr. to: Box 568, Mt. Morris, IL 61054-0568. TEL 800-877-5893) Ed. Ken Leiker. adv.; charts; illus.; stat. circ. 60,000. (also avail. in microform from UMI; back issues avail.; reprint service avail. from UMI) Indexed: Sports Per.Ind., Sportsearch. **Document type:** consumer publication.
—UMI.
Description: For serious racing fans. Presents statistics and features on motorsports.

SPORTS AND GAMES

629.2 UK ISSN 0067-2432
AUTOCOURSE; the world's leading Grand Prix annual. 1951-1973; resumed. a. £27.50 (rest of Europe £33.50; N. and S. America, Middle East, Africa £39.50; Australasia £42.50) (effective 1995-1996). Hazleton Publishing, 3 Richmond Hill, Richmond, Surrey TW10 6RE, England. TEL 0181-948-5151. FAX 0181-948-4111. TELEX 946153. Ed. Alan Henry; Pub. Richard Poulter. adv. contact: Simon Maurice. illus. **Document type:** consumer publication.
—BLDSC (1828.130000).
Description: Reviews the events and gives the results for the previous year's Formula 1 season. Profiles top drivers.

796.72 629.2 UK
▼**AUTOCOURSE INDY CAR OFFICIAL YEARBOOK.** Short title: Indy Car Yearbook. 1994. a. £17.99 (rest of Europe £23.99; N. and S. America, Middle East, Africa £29.99; Australasia £32.99) (effective 1995-1996). Hazleton Publishing, 3 Richmond Hill, Richmond, Surrey TW10 6RE, England. TEL 0181-948-5151. FAX 0181-948-4111. TELEX 946153. Ed. Jeremy Shaw; Pub. Richard Poulter. adv. contact: Simon Maurice. illus.; stat. **Document type:** consumer publication.
Description: Reviews the previous year's Indy Car season and profiles top drivers.

796.72 FR
L'AUTOMOBILE - FORMULE 1. 1989. a. 35 F. Societe des Editions Techniques et Touristiques de France, 60-62 rue Danjou, 92100 Boulonge, France. TEL 46-09-95-96. FAX 46-09-99-85. Eds. Jean-Luc Martin, Marc Schliklin; Pub. Monique Helfenberger. adv. contact: Eric Brame. circ. 35,000. **Document type:** consumer publication.

796.72 MX
AUTOMUNDO DEPORTIVO.* sports. 1969. m. $60. Editorial Mex-Ameris, S.A., Av. Morelos 16, Mexico D.F. Ed. Jesus Gonzalez Diaz. adv.; illus. circ. 100,000.
Formerly: Automondo.

796.72 YU ISSN 0005-173X
AUTOSPORT;* specijalizovano nedeljno izdanje jugoslavenskog sportskog lista "Sport". (Text in Serbo-Croatian) 1966. w. 88 din. Borba, Trg Marksa i Engelsa 7, Belgrade, Yugoslavia. Ed. Ljubomir Lovric.

AUTOSPORT. see *TRANSPORTATION — Automobiles*

796.72 DK ISSN 0908-7648
AUTOSPORT. 1974. m. $50. Dansk Automobil Sports Union, Idraettens Hus, Broendby Stadion, 2605 Broendby, Denmark. TEL 45-53-70-21-94. FAX 45-53-70-20-32. Ed. Ib Trebbien. adv. contact: Michael Eisenberg. circ. 7,000.
Former titles: Aktuel Bilsport (ISSN 0109-6338); Auto Orienting (ISSN 0105-6468)

AUTOSPORT. see *TRANSPORTATION — Automobiles*

AUTOSPORT. see *TRANSPORTATION — Automobiles*

688.76 SP
AVANCESPORT. 12/yr. Consejo de Ciento 346, 08009 Barcelona, Spain. TEL 3-302-24-94. FAX 3-412-43-94. circ. 8,600.

790.1 IR ISSN 1021-6316
AVARD MAGAZINE. 1993. 12/yr. $30 (effective 1994). Mirza-e Shirazi Ave., 22nd St., No. 25, P.O. Box 14335-398, Tehran, Iran. TEL 98-21-8801087. FAX 98-21-2577692. Ed. Mohammed Ali Masoud. adv. contact: F. Karimi. bk.rev.; film rev. circ. 50,000 (paid). **Document type:** consumer publication.
Description: Covers boxing and all forms of martial arts. Includes interviews, articles on technique and training, and other news of interest.

B INTERNATIONAL. see *GENERAL INTEREST PERIODICALS — Hong Kong*

790.1 GW
B T V SPIEGEL. 1960. q. membership. Bremer Turnvereinigung von 1877 e.V., Gruenen Str. 19-21, 28199 Bremen, Germany. illus.; stat. circ. 1,400.

794.1 US
BADGER CHESS. 1982. bi-m. $15 (effective 1995). Bill Williams, Ed. & Pub., 4216 W. St. Paul Ave., Milwaukee, WI 53208-3765. TEL 414-933-1103. adv.; bk.rev. circ. 275. **Document type:** newsletter.
Description: Promotes chess among Wisconsin and foreign chess players.

796.345 DK ISSN 0005-3791
BADMINTON. (Text in Danish) 1949. 15/yr. DKK 200. Dansk Badminton Forbund - Danish Badminton Association, Idraettens Hus, Broendby Stadion 20, DK-2605 Broendby, Denmark. TEL 45-43-26-26026. FAX 45-43-21-50. Ed. Morten Buckhoej. adv.: Color page DKK 10000; trim 186 x 267; adv. contact: Per Legind. circ. 10,000. **Document type:** trade publication.

796.345 UK ISSN 0262-1940
BADMINTON ASSOCIATION OF ENGLAND. ANNUAL HANDBOOK. 1900. a. £2.50. Badminton Association of England, National Badminton Centre, Bradwell Rd., Loughton Lodge, Milton Keynes, Bucks. MK8 9LA, England. TEL 01908-568822. FAX 01908-566922. Ed. Geoffrey Snowdon. adv.; index. circ. 8,000.
Formerly: Badminton Association of England. Official Handbook (ISSN 0067-2882)

796.342 JA
BADMINTON MAGAZINE. (Text in Japanese) 1980. m. 6600 Yen. Baseball Magazine Sha, 3-10-10 Misaki-cho, Chiyoda-ku, Tokyo, Japan. Ed. Keiko Miyazawa.

796.345 UK
BADMINTON NOW. 1982. 10/yr. £1.50. Badminton Association of England, National Badminton Centre, Bradwell Rd., Loughton Lodge, Milton Keynes, Bucks. MK8 9LA, England. TEL 01908-568822. FAX 01908-566922. Ed. Sue Ashton. adv.; bk.rev.; illus. circ. 7,000. **Indexed:** Sportsearch (1985-).
Supersedes: Badminton Gazette (ISSN 0005-3805)

796.345 AT ISSN 0813-006X
BADMINTON SIDELINES. 1976. q. Aus.$12 (foreign Aus.$25). Victorian Badminton Association, P.O. Box 28, S. Melbourne, Vic. 3205, Australia. TEL 61-3-98674522. FAX 61-3-98209975. (Subscr. to: Badminton Sidelines, P.O. Box 28, S. Melbourne, Vic. 3205, Australia) Ed. Paul Kiteley. circ. 2,500.

BAEDER JOURNAL. see *BUSINESS AND ECONOMICS — Management*

797.21 AU ISSN 1023-8182
BAEDER- UND KOMMUNALTECHNIK; mit Hotelbad. 1987. 6/yr. S.250 (foreign S.350). Oesterreichischer Baederverband, Rosenhuegelstr. 198, A-1230 Vienna, Austria. TEL 03339-7346. FAX 03339-7346. Ed. Kurt Bruk. adv.: B&W page S.13200, color page S.21600; trim 260 x 180; adv. contact: Kurt Bruk. bk.rev.; index; circ. 3,000 (paid). (back issues avail.) **Document type:** bulletin.

797 US ISSN 0887-6061
BALLOON LIFE; the magazine for hot air ballooning. 1986. m. $30 (Canada and Mexico $33; elsewhere $66). Balloon Life Magazine, Inc., 2145 Dale Ave., Sacramento, CA 95815-3632. TEL 916-922-9648. FAX 916-922-4730. E-mail: 73232.1112@compuserve.com. Ed. Tom Hamilton. adv.; bk.rev. circ. 4,000. (back issues avail.) **Document type:** consumer publication.
Description: Covers the sport of hot air ballooning - events, issues, and people.

BALLOONING. see *AERONAUTICS AND SPACE FLIGHT*

797.21 MX
BALNEARIOS; donde ir a nadar. 1972. 3/yr. Agustin Melgar, 44-5, Col. Condesa, Mexico 11, DF, Mexico. Ed. Juan Flores Sedano. adv. circ. 30,000.

794.1 LV
BALTIISKIE SHAKHMATY. Latvian edition: Sahs Baltija. (Text in Russian) 1960-1990 (Dec.); resumed May 1991. m. $32 (typically set in Jan.). (Latvijas Saha Savienibas) Sahs Baltija, P.O. Box 241, 226050 Riga, Latvia. TEL 0132-286-864. Ed. Nikolai Zhuravlev. circ. 10,000.
Formerly (until Dec. 1990): Shakhmaty.
Description: Covers national and international chess games, opening theory, correspondence chess, "how-to-improve" articles, combinations, studies-problems and interviews.

799 CN ISSN 0045-155X
BARNET MARKSMAN. 1967. q. free. Barnet Rifle Club, 8550 Barnet Hwy., Barnet P.O., B.C. VOM 1E0, Canada. TEL 604-936-1965. Ed. Gladys E. Ball. circ. 1,000.

790.1 US ISSN 1067-0548
BAY SPORTS REVIEW; an unsensored journal of fan commentary. 1991. bi-m. $20. Bay Sports Review, Box 4520, Berkeley, CA 94704. TEL 415-751-3076; 800-552-8155. FAX 415-751-1055. E-mail: baysport@aol.com. Ed. Jessica Guynn; Pub. Christopher Weills. adv. contact: John P. Donohue. bk.rev. circ. 20,000. (tabloid format) **Document type:** newspaper.
Supersedes: San Francisco Sports Review.
Description: Contains fans' responses to and opinions on sports questions and topics. Lists wagering odds on NFL, Super Bowl, NL, AL, World Series, NBA, Stanley Cup and more.

799.202 GW
BAYERISCHER SCHUETZENZEITUNG. 1950. m. DM.36. Bayerischer Sportschuetzenbund, Olympia Schiessanlage, 85748 Garching-Hochbrueck, Germany. TEL 089-31694921. FAX 089-31694952. Ed. Claus-Peter Schlagenhauf. adv.; bk.rev.; video rev.; bibl.; illus.; circ. 7,500 (paid). (back issues avail.) **Document type:** newsletter.
Description: Provides news and information to members of shooting clubs in Bavaria.

790.1 GW ISSN 0171-9572
BAYERNSPORT. 1970. w. DM.48. Bayerischer Landessportverband e.V., Georg-Brauchle-Ring 93, 80992 Munich, Germany. TEL 089-15702-634. FAX 089-15702565. Ed. Rolf Hofmann. adv.; bk.rev.; film rev. circ. 26,500. (back issues avail)

790 GW ISSN 0005-7231
BAYERNTURNER. 1953. s-m. DM.37.50. Bayerischer Turnverband e.V., c/o Georg Brauchle, Haus des Sports, 8000 Munich 2, Germany. Ed. A.D. Bauchinger. circ. 5,000.

BECKETT FOCUS ON FUTURE STARS. see *HOBBIES*

BECKETT HOCKEY MONTHLY. see *HOBBIES*

796.72 US
▼**BECKETT RACING MONTHLY.** 1994. m. $29.95. Beckett Publications, 15850 Dallas Pkwy., Dallas, TX 75248. TEL 214-991-6657. FAX 214-992-8930. Ed. Pepper Hastings; Pub. James Beckett. adv.: B&W page $2100; adv. contact: Jeff Anthony. circ. 100,000 (paid). **Document type:** consumer publication.
Description: Provides coverage of many different types of auto racing.

796 NO ISSN 0804-0117
BEDRIFTSIDRETT. 1992. 10/yr. Norges Bedriftsidrettsforbund, Hauger Skolevej 1, N-1351 Rud, 67 154600, Norway. TEL 47-22-56-38-44. FAX 47-22-44-79-68. (Subscr. to: Jan Harbu Agentur, P.O. Box 7637 Skillebekk, N-0205 Oslo, Norway)

BEGA DISTRICT NEWS. see *GENERAL INTEREST PERIODICALS — Australia*

794.18 CC ISSN 1000-7679
BEIFANG QIYI/NORTHERN CHESS. (Text in Chinese) 1979. m. $28.70. Heilongjiang Qiyuan - Heilongjiang Chess Institute, 19 Heping Lu, Harbin, Heilongjiang 150040, People's Republic of China. TEL 229342. (Dist. in US by China Books & Periodicals, Inc., 2929 24th St., San Francisco, CA 94110. TEL 415-282-2994) Ed. Wang Jialiang.

6056 SPORTS AND GAMES

796.41   GW   ISSN 0005-9358
BERLINER TURNZEITUNG. 1950. m. DM.10. Berliner Turnerbund e.V., Vorarlberger Damm 39, 12157 Berlin, Germany. TEL 030-7849017. adv.; bk.rev. circ. 3,000.
Description: Information of the Berlin Gymnast Society. Contains coming events, past happenings, instructional material, and photos.

790.1   332   US
BETWEEN THE LINES (NEW YORK); financial newsletter for the sports world. q. free. Ernst & Young, Media and Entertainment Group, 227 Park Ave., New York, NY 10172. TEL 212-773-1634. Ed. Michael Breit.
Document type: newsletter.

BILEN MOTOR & SPORT. see *TRANSPORTATION — Automobiles*

794.72   IT
BILIARDO MATCH. 1967. m. L.20000. Federazione Italiana Biliardo Sportivo, Via De Sanctis 32, 20141 Milan, Italy. TEL 39-2-8436752. Ed. Rinaldo Rossetti. adv.: B&W page L.2000000, color page L.2600000; adv. contact: Mario Paleari. charts; illus.
Formerly (until 1978): Biliardo (ISSN 0006-2472)

793   GW   ISSN 0941-8571
BILLARD-SPORT MAGAZIN. 1923. m. DM.50. (Deutsche Billard Union e.V.) Sport-Media und Veranstaltungs GmbH, Hiberniastr. 17, 46240 Bottrop, Germany. TEL 02041-79610. FAX 02041-796111. Ed. Wolfgang Rittmann. adv. circ. 5,000. **Document type:** consumer publication.
Formerly (until 1991): Billard-Sport (ISSN 0936-2665)

796.72   SW   ISSN 1101-3168
BILSPORT RALLY MAGAZINE. 1990. q. SEK 195 (foreign SEK 231) (effective 1995). Albinsson & Sjoeberg, P.O. Box 529, S-371 23 Karlskrona, Sweden. TEL 46-0455-335325. FAX 46-0455-311715. Ed. Gert Karlsson. adv. contact: Susanne Zec. circ. 13,900 (controlled).

790.1   US
BINGO BUGLE. (76 eds. nationwide) 1980. m. Bingo Bugle, Inc., Box 527, Vashon, WA 98070. TEL 800-327-6437. FAX 206-463-5630. Ed. Tara Snowden; Pub. Roger Snowden. adv. contact: John Anderson. circ. 1,301,000. **Document type:** newspaper, consumer publication.
Description: Reports on the fundraising and entertainment aspects of bingo and gambling. Contains articles, photographs, stories and graphics.

051   CN
BINGO CALLER NEWS. bi-m. Can.$50. Nielsens' Publications Corporation, 19607 88th Ave., Langley, B.C. V3A 6Y3, Canada. TEL 604-888-7477. FAX 604-888-7489. Ed. Egon Nielsen. circ. 10,000.

790.1   US
BINGO TODAY. s-m. $50. Dart Publishing, Inc., 1550 140th Ave., N.E., Ste. 201, Bellevue, WA 98005. TEL 203-232-6071. FAX 206-643-7942. Ed. Rim Miksys. adv.; circ. 15,000 (controlled). (tabloid format) **Document type:** newspaper.

796.815   US   ISSN 0006-4106
BLACK BELT MAGAZINE. (Includes Yearbook) 1960. m. $28. Rainbow Publications, Inc., 24715 Ave. Rockefeller, Box 918, Santa Clarita, CA 91380-9018. TEL 805-257-4066. FAX 805-257-3028. (Subscr. to: Box 16298, N. Hollywood, CA 91615-6298. TEL 800-266-4066) Ed. Jim Coleman; Pub. Michael James. adv.; bk.rev.; charts; illus.; índex. circ. 100,000. **Indexed:** Phys.Ed.Ind., Sports Per.Ind., Sportsearch (1977-). **Document type:** consumer publication.
Description: Covers all martial arts.

790.1   US
BLACK COLLEGE SPORTS REVIEW. 1979. m. $15. Black Sports, Inc., 617 N. Liberty St., Winston-Salem, NC 27102. TEL 919-723-9026. adv. circ. 150,000.
Description: Contains sports profiles and features on Black college sports in division II and predominantly Black colleges and universities.

799.202   US   ISSN 1048-5066
BLACK POWDER TIMES. 1974. m. $15 in U.S.; Canada $17; elsewhere $20. Fred Holder, Ed. & Pub., Box 1131, Stanwood, WA 98292. TEL 206-387-0349. adv.; bk.rev.; illus.; tr.lit. circ. 1,000. (tabloid format) **Document type:** newspaper.
Formerly (until 1990): Then and Now (ISSN 8750-5886); Which was formed by the 1988 merger of (1980-1988): Blacksmith's Gazette; Then and Now (ISSN 0745-1385); Which was formerly: Black Powder Times.
Description: Covers shooting, history and blacksmithing.

793 510   US
BLACKJACK FORUM. 1981. q. $40. R G E Publishing, 414 Santa Clara Ave., Oakland, CA 94610. TEL 510-465-6452. FAX 510-652-4330. Ed. Arnold Snyder. adv.; bk.rev.; charts; stat. circ. 2,500. (back issues avail.) **Document type:** consumer publication.

794.1   US
BLACKMAR - DIEMER GAMBIT WORLD. 1983. 6/yr. $18 (foreign $24). Blackmar Press, c/o Tom V. Purser, Ed., 303 Cleveland St., Box 66, Headland, AL 36345. TEL 334-693-5591. E-mail: 72703.2253@compuserve.com. bk.rev.
Formerly: Tom Purser's B D G World.
Description: Devoted to the games, analyses and stories about the Gambit and other chess gambits.

790.1   US   ISSN 1070-390X
BLADES ON ICE. 1990. 6/yr. $29 (Canada $39; Europe $49; elsewhere $55). 7040 N. Mona Lisa Rd., Tucson, AZ 85741. TEL 602-575-1747. FAX 602-575-1484. Ed. Gerri Walbert; Pub. David Levinson. adv. contact: Joe Druar. illus.
Description: Includes current news stories, coverage of the latest amateur and professional competitions, and interviews with skaters.

790.1   GW
BLAU GELB. 1975. bi-m. Sportgemeinde Weiterstadt 1886 e.V., Am Aulenberg 2, 64331 Weiterstadt, Germany. TEL 06150-3886. circ. 2,000. (looseleaf format)

794.1   US   ISSN 1053-3087
BLITZ CHESS. 1988. q. $13 (membership) (foreign $15). World Blitz Chess Association, 8 Parnassus Rd., Berkeley, CA 94708. TEL 510-549-1169. FAX 510-486-8078. Ed. Walter S. Browne. adv.: page $180.
Description: Features blitz (5-minute) games, cross-tables, a quarterly rating list, and a calendar of events, including where to play in the U.S. Discusses the history of chess, chess problems, and the grand masters and covers top international events and chess matches.

371.7   US   ISSN 1067-750X
GV351
BLUE BOOK OF COLLEGE ATHLETICS OF SENIOR, JUNIOR AND COMMUNITY COLLEGES. 1930. a. $29.95. Athletic Publishing Co., Box 931, Montgomery, AL 36101-0931. TEL 205-263-4436. Ed. Christine Beazley; Pub. Allen Dees. adv. contact: John Allen Dees. circ. 10,000. **Document type:** directory.
Formerly: Blue Book of College Athletics; Incorporates (1958-1988): Blue Book of Junior and Community College Athletics.

790.1   HK
BO/EVENEMENT SPORTIF. (Text in Chinese) 1993. q. Y48. Hachette Filipacchi Asia - Pacific, Shop A8-9, Hon On St, Qyarry Bay, Kornhill, Hong Kong. TEL 852-2567-8707. FAX 852-2568-4650. Ed. Dennis Kung. adv.: color page $5000; trim 275 x 214; adv. contact: Agnes Tang. circ. 100,000. **Document type:** consumer publication.

796.8   CC
BO JI/TECHNIQUE OF SELF-DEFENSE. (Text in Chinese) m. $36.80. Shanxi Sheng Tiyu Yundong Weiyuanhui, 7, Tiyu Lu, Dayingpan, Taiyuan, Shanxi 030012, People's Republic of China. TEL 775310. (Dist. in US by: China Books & Periodicals, Inc., 2929 24th St., San Frnacsico, CA 94110. TEL 415-282-2994) Zhang Dakang.

790.1   US
BOB WATKINS SPORTS 24 MAGAZINE. 1989. m. $2 per no. Bob Watkins, Ed. & Pub., Box 124, Glendale, KY 42740. TEL 502-737-5585.
Description: Feature articles on people in sports, short features on local, regional and state athletic events, as well as opinion pieces.

BODYWISE. see *PHYSICAL FITNESS AND HYGIENE*

790.1   IO   ISSN 0852-6729
BOLA. w. Jalan Palmerah Selatan 17, Jakarta 10270, Indonesia. TEL 021-5483008. Ed. Hikmat Kusumaningrat. circ. 407,850.

790.1   BO
BOLIVIA EN EL DEPORTE.* q. Secretaria General de Deportes, La Paz, Bolivia. Ed. Enrique Sanchez. charts; illus.; stat.

796.72   US
BONNEVILLE RACING NEWS. 1990. m. $24. 35549 W. Stetson, Hemet, CA 92545. TEL 909-926-2277. FAX 909-926-4619. Ed. Wendy Jeffries. adv. circ. 20,000. **Document type:** newspaper.
Description: Covers automobile and motorcycle land speed racing at Bonneville, El Mirage and other such attempts worldwide.

790.1   US
BOSTON BRUINS YEARBOOK. a. $7.50. Phoenix Media - Communications Group, c/o Stephen M. Mindich, 126 Brookline Ave, Boston, MA 02215. TEL 617-536-5390. FAX 617-536-1463. Ed. Christopher Young. circ. 75,000.

790   US
BOSTON MARATHON. 1979. a. $4. Phoenix Media - Communications Group, c/o Stephen M. Mindich, Pub., 126 Brookline Ave, Boston, MA 02215. TEL 617-536-5390. FAX 617-536-1463. Ed. Peter Kadzis. adv. circ. 116,800.

790.1   BS
BOTSWANA SPORTS MAGAZINE. 1986. m. P.30 (foreign P.40). P.O. Box 201028, Gaborone, Botswana. TEL 267-357971. FAX 267-357971. Ed. Charles Y. Mubambe. adv.: B&W page P.1000, color page P.2000. circ. 8,000. **Document type:** consumer publication.
Description: Publicizes all sports at all levels.

794   US   ISSN 0164-9183
BOWLERS JOURNAL.* 1913. m. $18. (Billiards and Bowling Institute of America) National Bowlers Journal, Inc., 200 S. Michigan Ave., Ste. 1430, Chicago, IL 60604. Ed. Mort Luby, Jr. adv.; bk.rev.; charts; illus.; stat. circ. 20,000. **Indexed:** Phys.Ed.Ind., Sports Per.Ind., Sportsearch (1978-).
Former titles: National Bowlers Journal and Billiard Revue (ISSN 0027-8793); Bowlers Journal and Billiard Revue (ISSN 0006-8411)

790.1   US   ISSN 8750-3603
BOWLING DIGEST. 1983. bi-m. $18 (foreign $30). Century Publishing Co., 990 Grove St., Evanston, IL 60201. TEL 708-491-6440. (Subscr. to: Box 570, Mt. Morris, IL 61054-0570. TEL 800-877-5893) Ed. Ken Leiker. adv.; charts; illus.; stat.; tr.lit. circ. 110,000. (also avail. in microfilm; microfiche; back issues avail.) **Indexed:** Sports Per.Ind., Sportsearch (1985-). **Document type:** consumer publication. —UMI.
Description: For serious bowling fans and participants. Presents statistics, features, and instructional tips behind the sport.

796.8   MX   ISSN 0006-8470
BOX Y LUCHA; el mundo del ring. 1951. w. Mex.$832($29.29) Periodismo Especializado, S. A., Presidentes 187, Col. Portales, Mexico 13 D.F., Mexico. Ed. Antonio Elizarraras Corona. illus.

790.1   SW
BOXING. 6/yr. SEK 398 in Nordic countries; elsewhere SEK 498. (Svenska Boxningsfoerbundet) Cewe-Foerlaget AB, P.O. Box 77, S-890 10 Bjaesta, Sweden. TEL 0660-309-65. FAX 0660-305-17. adv. circ. 4,100.

796.332   GH
BOXING AND FOOTBALL ILLUSTRATED. 1976. m. POB 8392, Accra, Ghana. Ed. Nana O. Ampompah. circ. 10,000.

SPORTS AND GAMES

796
BOXING ILLUSTRATED. 1959. m. newsstand price: $3. International Sports Ltd., 530 Fifth Ave., 4th Fl., New York, NY 10036-5101. TEL 212-730-1374. FAX 212-730-9398. Ed. Herbert Goldman; Pub. John G. Ledes. adv. **Document type:** consumer publication.

796.83   JA
BOXING MAGAZINE. (Text in Japanese) 1956. m. 8040 Yen. Baseball Magazine Sha, 3-10-10 Misaki-cho, Chiyoda-ku, Tokyo, Japan. Ed. Isao Hara.

796.83   UK   ISSN 0956-098X
BOXING MONTHLY. 1989. m. £26 (foreign £48). Top Wave Ltd., 24 Notting Hill Gate, London W11 3JE, England. TEL 0171-229-9944. FAX 0171-727-5442. Ed. Glyn Leach; Pub. Nigel Baker. adv. contact: Johanna Eady. circ. 30,000. **Document type:** consumer publication.
Description: Focuses on big American and British personalities and up and coming prospects.

796.83   UK   ISSN 0006-8519
BOXING NEWS. 1909. w. £65. Boxing News Ltd., 21-22 Poland St., London W1V 3DD, England. TEL 071-734-4784. FAX 071-734-4975. Ed. Harry Mullan. adv.; bk.rev. circ. 30,000. (tabloid format) **Indexed:** Sportsearch. **Document type:** consumer publication.

796.83   US
BOXING U S A. 1981. q. $15. United States Amateur Boxing (USA Boxing), One Olympic Plaza, Colorado Springs, CO 80909. TEL 719-578-4506. FAX 719-632-3426. Ed. Kurt Stenerson. circ. 35,000. **Document type:** newsletter.

790.1   GW
BOXSPORT. fortn. DM.205.40. Deutscher Sportsverlag Kurt Stoof GmbH, Eintrachtstr. 110-118, 50668 Cologne, Germany. TEL 0221-1648-0. FAX 0221-1648318. Ed. Klaus Ludwiczak. adv. contact: Erhard Badtke. circ. 5,000. **Document type:** bulletin.

796.41   US   ISSN 0160-3280
GV461
BOYS GYMNASTICS RULEBOOK. a. $4. National Federation of State High School Associations, 11724 N.W. Plaza Circle, Box 20626, Kansas City, MO 64195-0626. TEL 816-464-5400. FAX 816-464-5571.

BRAILLE CHESS MAGAZINE. see HANDICAPPED — Visually Impaired

794.1   IC
BREFSKAKTIDINDI. 1979. irreg. (3-4/yr.). $16. Icelandic Correspondence Chess Federation, Grettisgata 42 B, IS-101 Reykjavik, Iceland. (Subscr. to: c/o Haimes Olafsson, Gen. Sec., Austvadsholti, 851 Hella, Iceland) Ed. Gunnar Hannesson. adv. circ. 200.

790.1   GW   ISSN 0932-8823
GV428
BRENNPUNKTE DER SPORTWISSENSCHAFT. s-a. DM.39.50. (Deutsche Sporthochschule Koeln) Academia Verlag GmbH, Postfach 1663, 53734 Sankt Augustin, Germany. TEL 02241-333349. FAX 02241-341528. **Document type:** academic/scholarly publication.
Formerly: Jahrbuecher der Deutschen Sporthochschule Koeln.
Description: Aimed at sports scientists, coaches and students.

795.414   NE   ISSN 0006-9825
BRIDGE. 1930. m. fl.52.50 (foreign fl.63). Nederlandse Bridge Bond, c/o B. Vrieling, Ed., Willem Dreeslaan 55, 3515 GB Utrecht, Netherlands. TEL 31-30-712644. FAX 31-30-711482. adv.; bk.rev.; charts; illus.; circ. 70,000 (paid). **Document type:** consumer publication.

795.414   UK   ISSN 0958-6768
BRIDGE (LONDON). 1926. m. £55. Chess & Bridge Ltd., 369 Euston Rd., London NW1 3AR, England. TEL 0171-388-2404. FAX 0171-388-2407. Ed. G. Liggins. adv.; bk.rev.; illus.; index. circ. 10,000.
Former titles: Bridge International; Bridge Magazine (ISSN 0006-9868); Incorporates: British Bridge World.
Description: Contains articles on bidding and play, instruction competitions, tournament reports and humour.

795.414   IT   ISSN 0006-985X
BRIDGE D'ITALIA. 1936. m. membership. Federazione Italiana Gioco Bridge, Via C. Menotti 11-C, 20129 Milan, Italy. TEL 39-2-70000483. Ed. Bruno Sacerdotti Coen. adv.; B&W page L.2500000, color page L.4500000. bk.rev.

795.414
BRIDGE PLUS. 1989. m. £25.50 (outside Europe £39.75). c/o Elena Jeronimidis, Ed. & Pub., P.O. Box 384, Reading, Berks. RG1 5YP, England. TEL 01734-351052. adv. contact: Ruth Edmonson. bk.rev. circ. 2,000. **Document type:** consumer publication.

795.414   SA
BRIDGE S A. 1954. 4/yr. $25 for 2 issues. South African Bridge Federation, P.O. Box 890347, Lyndhurst 2106, South Africa. TEL 27-11-3374030. FAX 27-11-4406435. Ed. Julius Butkow. adv.; bk.rev.; circ. 2,500. (controlled). (tabloid format) **Document type:** newsletter.
Former titles (until 1989): South African Bridge Bulletin; (until 1979): Bridge Bulletin (ISSN 0006-9841)

795.414   US   ISSN 1043-6383
BRIDGE TODAY; the magazine for people who love to play bridge. 1988. 6/yr. $24 (Canada $29; elsewhere $34). Granovetter Books, 3194 Oak Rd., Cleveland Heights, OH 44118-1826. TEL 216-371-5849. FAX 216-371-2941. Eds. Pamela and Matthew Granovetter. adv.: B&W page $350; trim 5 1/16 x 8; adv. contact: Linda Simpson. bk.rev. circ. 6,000. (reprint service avail.) **Document type:** consumer publication.

795.414   US   ISSN 0006-9876
BRIDGE WORLD. 1929. m. $42. Bridge World Magazine Inc., 39 W. 94th St., New York, NY 10025. TEL 212-866-5860. Eds. Edgar Kaplan, Jeff Rubens. adv.; bk.rev.; illus. circ. 9,000. (back issues avail.)
—UnCover.

795.414   FR   ISSN 0006-9914
BRIDGEUR. 1959. m. 500 F. Editions de Presse Specialisee, 28 Rue de Richelieu, 75001 Paris, France. TEL 1-42-96-25-00. FAX 1-40-20-92-34. Ed. J.P. Meyer. adv. contact: Muriel Clement. bk.rev.; illus. circ. 30,000.

799.32   UK   ISSN 0007-0289
BRITISH ARCHER; devoted to the fast growing sport of archery. 1949. 6/yr. £8.80. B.A. Publishing Co. Ltd., 43-45 Milford Rd., Reading RG1 8LG, England. FAX 0734-583899. Ed. John Histead. adv.; bk.rev.; illus. circ. 3,000. **Indexed:** Sportsearch (1977-).
Incorporates: British Field Archer.

794.1   UK   ISSN 0007-0440
GV1313
BRITISH CHESS MAGAZINE. 1881. m. £25($53) (rest of Europe £27.50; elsewhere £30.50). British Chess Magazine Ltd., The Chess Shop, 69 Masbro Rd., Kensington, London W14 0LS, England. TEL 0171-603-2877. FAX 0171-371-1477. Ed. Murray Chandler. adv.; bk.rev.; illus.; index. circ. 4,000. **Document type:** consumer publication.

796   UK   ISSN 0068-1938
GV1049
BRITISH CYCLING FEDERATION. HANDBOOK. 1959. a. £5 to non-members; members £3. British Cycling Federation, 1 Stuart St., Manchester M11 4DQ, England. TEL 0161-223-2244. FAX 0161-231-0591. Ed. James D. Hendry. adv. contact: James D. Hendry. circ. 10,000. **Document type:** directory.
Formerly: British Cycling Federation. Racing Handbook.

BRITISH HEALTH & FITNESS CLUB DIRECTORY. see BUSINESS AND ECONOMICS — Trade And Industrial Directories

598.2   UK   ISSN 0007-0777
BRITISH HOMING WORLD. 1933. w. £26.50. Royal Pigeon Racing Association, Severn Farm Industrial Estate, Severn Rd., Welshpool, Powys SY21 7DF, Wales. TEL 0938-552360. Ed. D.D. Glover. adv.; bk.rev.

636.596   UK   ISSN 0965-2264
BRITISH HOMING WORLD'S PIGEON RACING GAZETTE. 1946. m. £20. R P R A - B H W, Severn Farm Industrial Estate, Severn Rd., Welshpool, Powys SY21 7DF, Wales. TEL 01938-552360. FAX 01938-553969. Ed. D.D. Glover. adv.; bk.rev. circ. 550. **Document type:** newspaper.
Former titles (until 1992): Pigeon Racing Gazette (ISSN 0963-0031); Pigeon Racing News and Gazette (ISSN 0048-4164)

BRITISH LEISURE & SWIMMING POOL DIRECTORY. see BUSINESS AND ECONOMICS — Trade And Industrial Directories

BRITISH LEISURE CENTRE DIRECTORY. see BUSINESS AND ECONOMICS — Trade And Industrial Directories

790.1   UK
BRITISH OLYMPIC ASSOCIATION DIARY. a. £8.50. British Olympic Association, Wandsworth Plain, London SW18 1EH, England. TEL 081-871-2677. FAX 081-871-9104. TELEX 932312-BOA-G. circ. 1,000.
Formerly: British Olympic Association Year Book and Diary.

BRITISH OUTDOOR AMENITIES DIRECTORY. see BUSINESS AND ECONOMICS — Trade And Industrial Directories

796.72   UK   ISSN 0045-3137
BRITISH RACING NEWS. 1970. m. membership. British Racing & Sports Car Club, Brands Hatch Circuit, Fawkham, Dartford, Kent DA3 8NH, England. Ed. Paul Harmer. adv. contact: Dominic Ostrowski. bk.rev.; charts; illus.; stat.; circ. 4,500 (controlled). **Document type:** newsletter.

BROKEN SPOKE. see TRANSPORTATION — Automobiles

790.1   SW   ISSN 0345-1186
BROTTNING. 1968. m. (8/yr.). SEK 471 in Nordic countries; elsewhere SEK 571. (Svenska Brottningsfoerbundet) Cewe Foerlaget AB, P.O. Box 77, S-890 10 Bjaesta, Sweden. TEL 0660-309-65. FAX 0660-305-17. (Subscr. to: PK-Banken. Box 365, 891 01 Oernskoeldsvik, Sweden) adv. circ. 6,600.

796.812   DK   ISSN 0903-5524
BRYDNING/WRESTLING. 1972. 4/yr. DKK 100. Danmarks Brydeforbund - Danish Wrestling Federation, Sjaellandsgade 144, DK-7400 Herning, Denmark. TEL 45-97-22-22-15. FAX 45-97-22-03-49. TELEX 33 111 IDRAET DK. Ed. Bent Lauritsen. adv.; bk.rev.; illus. circ. 1,500.
Former titles: D A U Bladet (ISSN 0108-9013); Dansk Atlet Union, Landdsorganisation for Brydning (ISSN 0108-8998)

796.815   NE
BUDO KOERIER. 1952. bi-m. fl.10. Nederlandse Judo Ju-Jitsu Associatie, Boomstraat 153, Tilburg, Netherlands. Ed. P.F. Beljaars.
Formerly (until 1975): Judo-Koerier (ISSN 0047-2980)

796.815   GW   ISSN 0948-4124
DER BUDOKA. 1972. m. DM.42. Dachverband fuer Budotechniken Nordrhein-Westfalen e.V., Postfach 101506, 47015 Duisburg, Germany. TEL 0203-7381379. FAX 0203-7381409. adv.; bk.rev.; circ. 3,000 (paid). (back issues avail.) **Document type:** consumer publication.

796   SP   ISSN 0214-9060
BUDOKA Y SU REVISTA DE LAS ARTES MARCIALES. 1972. 11/yr. 3465 ptas.($40) Editorial Alas, Valencia 234, P.O. Box 36274, 08007 Barcelona, Spain. FAX 34-3-4537506. Ed. Jose Sala. adv.; bk.rev. circ. 12,000.
Formerly: Revista de las Artes Marciales (ISSN 0214-9052)

790.1   SZ
BUENDNER SPORT INFORMATION. m. Kasernenstr. 95, CH-7007 Chur, Switzerland. TEL 081-222843. Ed. Norbert Wasser. circ. 2,008.

SPORTS AND GAMES

796   BE   ISSN 1012-0491
BULLETIN D'INFORMATION SPORTIVE/SPORTS INFORMATION BULLETIN. Spanish edition: Boletin d'Informacion Deportiva (ISSN 1019-0910) (Text in Dutch, English, French) 1985. 3/yr. 1500 BEF. (Conseil d'Europe, Comite Directeur pour le Developpement du Sport) Clearing House Sport pour Tous, Espace du 27 Septembre, Blvd. Leopold II, 44, 1080 Brussels, Belgium. Ed. A. Remans. **Document type:** bulletin.
— BLDSC (8419.836500).
   Description: Provides information concerning the development of sport in member countries, including participation and promotion, ethics issues, economic aspects, sports legislation and sporting facilities.

769.41   AU
BUNDESTURNZEITUNG. 1954. m. S.200. (Oesterreichischer Turnerbund) Turn- und Sportartikel Handels GmbH, Schillerstr. 11, A-4020 Linz, Austria. TEL 0732-655359. FAX 0732-658671. adv.: page S.12000; adv. contact: Stefan Birek. circ. 15,000 (paid). (back issues avail.) **Document type:** newsletter.

LA BUSCA. see *BIBLIOGRAPHIES*

790.1 658.8   UK   ISSN 0951-516X
BUSINESS RATIO REPORT: BETTING AND GAMING; an industry sector analysis. 1987. a. I C C Business Ratios Ltd., Freepost, Field House, Hampton, Mddx. TW12 1BR, England. TEL 081-783-1940. FAX 081-783-1940. charts; stat. **Document type:** trade publication.

790.1   CN
C A B A NEWS BULLETIN. bi-m. Canadian Amateur Boxing Association, 333 River Road, Vanier, Ont. K1L 8H9, Canada. TEL 613-748-5608.

790.1   AT   ISSN 1033-0526
C A M S MANUAL OF MOTOR SPORT. 1959. a. Aus.$23. Confederation of Australian Motor Sport, P.O. Box 441, 382 Burke Rd., Camberwell, Vic. 3124, Australia. TEL 61-3-889-3746. FAX 61-3-809-1862. Ed. A. Lewis. adv. circ. 12,500. (back issues avail.)
   Description: Motor sport rules and policy for Australia. Covers rallies, race and club sport. Historical record of championships for reference and contemporary use.

790.1   AT
C A M S REPORT. 1966. q. Aus.$10. Confederation of Australian Motor Sport, 382 Burke Rd., Camberwell, Vic. 3124, Australia. TEL 61-3-889-3746. FAX 61-3-809-1862. Ed. A. Lewis. adv.; bk.rev. circ. 10,000. (back issues avail.)

790.1   US
C S S S DIGEST. 1989. 3/yr. $10. Center for the Study of Sport in Society, Northeastern University, 271 Huntington Ave., Ste. 244, Boston, MA 02115. TEL 617-437-4025. FAX 617-437-4566. Ed. Jeffrey P. Brown.

794.1   UK
CADOGAN CHESS AND BRIDGE BOOKS. 1960. a. free. Chess & Bridge Ltd., 369 Euston Rd., London NW1 3AR, England. TEL 0171-388-2404. FAX 0171-388-2407. Ed. Jimmy Adams.
   Former titles: Maxwell Macmillan Chess Books & Pergamon Chess Books; Chess Book List (ISSN 0069-3197)

796.5   UK   ISSN 0068-5267
CAIRNGORM CLUB JOURNAL. 1889. biennial, no.101, 1988. £2.50. Cairngorm Club, c/o Secretary R.C. Shirreffs, 18 Bon-Accord Square, Aberdeen AB9 1YE, Scotland. Ed. A.D. Chessell. adv.; bk.rev.; index. circ. 450.

794.1   US
CAISSA'S CHESS NEWS. 1983. 6/yr. $10. Box 09091, Cleveland, OH 44109-0091. Ed. E.A. Furst.
   Description: Devoted to chess combinations featuring tactical themes and check-mates.

790.1   US
CALIFORNIA CITYSPORTS MAGAZINE.* 1974. m. $17.95. CitySports, Inc. of California, 375 Ewing Ter., San Francisco, CA 94118-4410. TEL 415-626-1600. FAX 415-621-2323. Ed. Craig Bystrynski. circ. 150,000. **Document type:** consumer publication.
   Supersedes in part (in 1988): CitySports Magazine.
   Description: Covers all aspects of the California active lifestyle and participant (not professional) sports, including travel, recreation, nutrition and health, and profiles.

CAMPING-CAR. see *TRANSPORTATION*

799.32   CN   ISSN 0849-1712
CANADIAN ARCHER. (Text in English and French) 1955. m. Can.$25($35) to non-members; members Can.$15. Federation of Canadian Archers - Federation Canadienne des Archers, 1600 James Naismith Dr., Gloucester, ON K1B 5N4, Canada. TEL 613-748-5604. FAX 613-748-5785. TELEX 053-3660. Ed. Jude Hooey. adv.; bk.rev. circ. 1,000. (processed) **Indexed:** Sportsearch. **Document type:** newsletter.
   Former titles: F C A Official Newsletter (ISSN 0831-3776); Canadian Archer (ISSN 0319-2571); (until March 1974): Federation of Canadian Archers. Official Bulletin (ISSN 0014-9454)

796   CN   ISSN 0045-4427
CANADIAN ATHLETIC DIRECTOR AND COACH.* 1970. 6/yr. Can.$6. William B. Prentice & Associates, 30 Longwood Dr., Don Mills, Ont., Canada.

794.1   CN   ISSN 0045-4540
CANADIAN CHESS CHAT. 1946. 6/yr. Can.$16. Glenquaich Press Limited, P.O. Box 553, Sta. Q, Toronto, ON M4T 2M5, Canada. Ed. Michael D. Sharpe. bk.rev. circ. 1,000.
   Description: Covers national and international games, correspondence chess, endgame studies and opening theory.

796 617.1   US   ISSN 1066-7814
GV557   **CODEN:** CJAPEY
CANADIAN JOURNAL OF APPLIED PHYSIOLOGY/REVUE CANADIENNE DE PHYSIOLOGIE APPLIQUEE. Short title: C J A P - R C P A. (Text in English, French) 1976. q. $40 to individuals (foreign $45); institutions $88 (foreign $93); students $24 (foreign $29). (Canadian Society for Exercise Physiology, CN) Human Kinetics Publishers, Inc., Box 5076, Champaign, IL 61825-5076. TEL 217-351-5076. FAX 217-351-2674. Eds. Phillip Gardiner, Francois Perronet. adv. contact: Pamela Anderson. bk.rev.; abstr.; bibl.; charts; stat.; index. circ. 950. (back issues avail.) **Indexed:** Biol.Abstr., Can.B.P.I., Chem.Abstr., CMI, Curr.Cont., Ergon.Abstr., Excerpt.Med., Ind.Med., Psychol.Abstr. (1976-), Sci.Cit.Ind., Sportsearch (1987-). **Document type:** academic/scholarly publication.
— BLDSC (3028.570000); CASDDS; Genuine Article; SWETS; UMI; UnCover. **CCC.**
   Former titles (until 1992): Canadian Journal of Sport Sciences (ISSN 0833-1235); Canadian Journal of Applied Sport Science (ISSN 0700-3978)
   Description: Offers forum for applied physiology topics contributing to understanding of physical activity, health, and fitness.
   Refereed Serial

613.7 796 370   CN   ISSN 0712-9815
CANADIAN JOURNAL OF HISTORY OF SPORT/REVUE CANADIENNE DE L'HISTOIRE DES SPORTS. (Text in English, French) 1970. s-a. Can.$12. University of Windsor, Faculty of Human Kinetics, Windsor, ON N9B 3P4, Canada. TEL 519-253-4232. Eds. A. Metcalfe, M.A. Salter. bk.rev.; bibl. circ. 500. **Indexed:** Amer.Hist.& Life, Can.Wom.Per.Ind., Hist.Abstr., Phys.Ed.Ind., Sp.Ed.Needs Abstr., Sportsearch (1981-). **Document type:** academic/scholarly publication.
— BLDSC (3031.658000); Faxon; SWETS; UnCover. **CCC.**
   Formerly (until Dec. 1981): Canadian Journal of History of Sport and Physical Education (ISSN 0008-4115)

CANADIAN SPORTING GOODS & PLAYTHINGS. DIRECTORY. see *BUSINESS AND ECONOMICS — Trade And Industrial Directories*

CANADIAN SPORTSCARD COLLECTOR. see *HOBBIES*

796.8   CN   ISSN 0705-176X
CANADIAN WRESTLER/LUTTEUR CANADIEN. 1977. 4/yr. Can.$16. Canadian Amateur Wrestling Association - Association Canadienne de Lutte Amateur, 1600 James Naismith, Gloucester, ON, Canada. TEL 613-748-5686. FAX 613-748-5756. TELEX 053-3660. E-mail: Greg.Mathieu@Cdnsport.ca. Ed. Greg Mathieu. adv.; bk.rev. circ. 7,500. **Indexed:** Sportsearch (1977-). **Document type:** newsletter.

790.1 613.7   US   ISSN 1041-5742
CAPITAL SPORTS FOCUS.* (Avail. in 3 eds.: Baltimore, Philadelphia, Washington, DC) 1989. m. $15.95. Capital Sports Focus, Inc., 124 E. Diamond Ave., Ste. 7, Gaithersburg, MD 20877-3072. TEL 301-670-6717. FAX 301-670-9043. Ed. Manny Rosenberg. adv.; bk.rev.; circ. 100,000 (controlled).
   Description: Covers lifestyle, sports, health and fitness for residents of Washington, DC, the Baltimore metro area, and Philadelphia.

CAR CRAFT; the complete performance magazine. see *TRANSPORTATION — Automobiles*

793   US
CARD PLAYER; the magazine for those who play to win. 1988. fortn. $49. 3140 S. Polaris Ave., Las Vegas, NV 89102. TEL 702-871-1720. FAX 702-798-5577. Ed. Linda J. Johnson. adv. contact: Scott Rogers. bk.rev.; illus.; circ. 5,000 (paid); 40,000 (controlled). **Document type:** trade publication.
   Description: Covers casino and sports gambling, poker, and gambling industry news.

CAREER CONNECTIONS. see *OCCUPATIONS AND CAREERS*

790.1   US
CARIBBEAN SPORTS & TRAVEL. 1992. q. $8. Graphcom Publishing Co., Inc., 1995 N.E. 150 St., Ste. 107, N. Miami, FL 33181. TEL 305-945-7403. FAX 305-947-6410. Ed. V.C. Hanna. adv.: B&W page $1580, color page $2330; trim 8 x 10 3/4. bk.rev.; illus. circ. 40,000.
   Incorporates (1971-1990): Pleasure Boating.
   Description: Covers diving, cruising, fishing, charters, and golf packages in the Caribbean islands.

790.1 647.94   US   ISSN 0889-9797
CASINO CHRONICLE. 1983. w. (48/yr.). $175 (Canada $185; Mexico $190; elsewhere $225). Casino Chronicle Inc., 10880 Crescendo Circle, Boca Raton, FL 33498. TEL 407-477-3082. Ed. Ben A. Borowsky. adv.; bk.rev.; film rev.; play rev.; pat.; stat.; tr.lit. circ. 1,500. (back issues avail.) **Document type:** newsletter.
   Description: Focuses on the gaming industry in US.

790.1 910.09   US   ISSN 8755-6103
CASINO DIGEST. 1984. m. $47. Casino Digest, Inc., 1901-G Ashwood Ct., Ste. 123, Greensboro, NC 27455. TEL 919-375-6358. Ed. Joe Lawless; Pub. Joe Lawless. adv. contact: Ray Apple. circ. 40,000. (tabloid format; back issues avail.; reprint service avail.) **Document type:** newspaper.
   Description: Consumer news on casino gaming; informs consumer on all aspects of casino gaming and its related products and services.

793   US
CASINO GAMING INTERNATIONAL. m. Public Gaming Research Institute, 15825 Shady Grove Rd., No. 130, Rockville, MD 20850-4008. TEL 301-330-7600. FAX 301-330-7608. Ed. Duane Burke. circ. 11,000.

790   US
CASINO PLAYER. 1988. m. $24. Casino Journal Publishing Group, 8025 Black Horse Pike 470, Pleasantville, NJ 08232-2900. TEL 609-484-8866. FAX 609-645-1661. Pub. Glenn Fine. adv. circ. 200,000.
   Formerly (until 1990): Player (ISSN 1047-5303)
   Description: Statistics and inside information on legalized gambling, including casinos, sports, betting, and cruise ships. Includes interviews and feature stories.

CASUS BELLI. see *HOBBIES*

SPORTS AND GAMES

796.72   US
CAVALCADE OF AUTO RACING.* 1964. w. $15. Racing News, Inc., 4343 Ritchie Rd., Lincolnton, NC 28092-9575. TEL 704-399-8395. Ed. Ernie Elkins. adv.; bk.rev. circ. 23,000.

CELEBRITY BIRTHDAY GUIDE. see *MOTION PICTURES*

790.1   US   ISSN 0747-6817
CENTER FOR SPORTS SPONSORSHIP'S SPONSOR QUEST.* 1984. m. $30. Center for Sports Sponsorship, Box 280, Plainsboro, NJ 08536. Ed. Vicki Edwards.

790.1   ZR
CHAMPION DU ZAIRE. w. Cite de la Voix du Zaire, B.P. 9365, Kinshasa I, Zaire. Ed. Kasonga Tshilunde Boya Yawumwe.

796.41   UK
CHASEFORM JUMPING ANNUAL.* a. £15. Raceform Ltd., 19 Clarges Rd., London W1Y 7PG, England.

794.1   CN   ISSN 1187-3337
CHECK!. French edition: Echecs Premiere Classe (ISSN 1187-3329) 1928. bi-m. Can.$24 (U.S. $29; elsewhere $33). Canadian Correspondence Chess Association, 37 Bemersyde Dr., Etobicoke, ON M9A 2S9, Canada. TEL 416-234-0207. Ed. William Roach. adv.; bk.rev.; index. circ. 600. (back issues avail.)
   Formerly (until 1968): Canadian Correspondence Chess Association. Bulletin (ISSN 1191-4521)
   Description: Reports on national and international games and news; includes problems and studies, as well as opening articles.

790.7 371.893   US   ISSN 0893-8091
CHEER NEWS TODAY. 1987. q. $4.99. Box 508, Cordova, TN 38018. TEL 901-387-4431. Ed. Lis Buckner; Pub. Alan Savransky. adv. contact: Gregg Webb. bk.rev.; tr.lit. circ. 35,000. (back issues avail.)
   Description: News and information on high school and college cheerleading.

794.1   UK   ISSN 0964-6221
CHESS. 1935. m. $55. Chess & Bridge Ltd., 369 Euston Rd., London NW1 3AR, England. TEL 0171-288-2404. FAX 0171-388-2407. Ed. J. Adams. adv.; bk.rev.; charts; illus.; stat.; index. circ. 12,500. (tabloid format)
   Former titles: Pergamon Chess; (until vol.53, 1988): Chess (ISSN 0009-3319)
   Description: Provides reports on international events, features on players, instructional articles, competitions, and humor.

794.1   PH   ISSN 0116-2802
CHESS ASIA. 4/yr. $20. c/o Manalito M. Ferrer, Mgr. Ed., P.O. Box 1497, Makati Central P.O., Makati, Metro Manila, Philippines. Ed. Eugeno Torre.
   Description: Contains national and international games, "how-to-improve" articles, endgame and opening theory, studies and problems, and FIDE ratings.

794.1   US   ISSN 1065-8629
CHESS CHOW.* m. 375 S. End Ave., No. 6L, New York, NY 10280-1019. TEL 212-580-0343. FAX 212-592-7382. Ed. Joel Bengamin. circ. 800.

794.1   UK
CHESS COLLECTOR. 1988. 2/yr. $50 to non-members. Chess Collectors International, 35 Shepherds Hill, London N6 5QJ, England. (U.S. subscr. addr.: c/o Marylin Ezzes, 875 Fifth Ave. New York, NY 10021) Ed. Michael Mark.
   Description: Contains information about chess collectables, especially chess sets, chess art and history.

794.1   US   ISSN 0009-3327
GV1313
CHESS CORRESPONDENT. 1926. 6/yr. $16. C C L A, Box 3481, Barrington, IL 60011-3481. Ed. Joe Ganem. bk.rev. circ. 1,000. **Document type:** academic/scholarly publication.
   Description: Includes "how-to-improve" articles, theory, rating list, large annotated game section, and international news.

794.1   US   ISSN 0147-2569
CHESS HORIZONS. 1969. 6/yr. $12 (Canada and Mexico $18). Massachusetts Chess Association, c/o Steve Frymer, 64 Asbury St., Lexington, MA 02173-6521. TEL 617-862-3799. Ed. Joseph W. Sparks. adv.; bk.rev. circ. 1,900.
   Description: New England coverage emphasized but offers national and international news, games and theory.

794.1   US   ISSN 1044-8888
CHESS IN INDIANA. 1988. 6/yr. $10. Indiana State Chess Association, 1146 Strong Ave., Elkhart, IN 46514-2407. TEL 219-293-2241. Ed. John Crane; Pub. Michael Turner. adv.; charts; illus.; stat.; index. circ. 375. (back issues avail.) **Document type:** bulletin, newsletter.
   Description: News and history of chess tournaments, champions, and clubs in the state of Indiana.

794.1   SA
CHESS IN THE R S A. 12/yr. $15. c/o Charles van der Werthuizen, Co-Ed., P.O. Box 83694, South Hills, 2136 Johannesburg, South Africa. Ed. Darryl Accone.
   Description: Covers local and national games; includes articles, and studies-problems.

CHESS JOURNALIST. see *JOURNALISM*

794.1   US   ISSN 0197-260X
GV1313
CHESS LIFE. 1933. m. $45 (Canada $51; elsewhere $60); newsstand price: $3.75. United States Chess Federation, 186 Rte. 9W, New Windsor, NY 12553. TEL 914-562-8350. FAX 914-561-2437. Ed. Glenn Petersen. adv.; charts; illus.; stat.; index. circ. 70,000. (also avail. in microform from UMI; back issues avail.)
—Faxon; UMI; UnCover.
   Formerly (until 1980): Chess Life and Review (ISSN 0009-3351); Incorporates: Chess Review.
   Description: Features chess tournament reports, national and international chess news, instruction, and annotated games.

794.1   II   ISSN 0970-9142
CHESS MATE. 1983. 12/yr. $25 (effective 1993). 10E Teacher's Colony, Adyar, Madras 600 020, India. TEL 91-44-418763. FAX 91-44-2350305. TELEX 41-21060 PCO IN. Eds. Manuel Aaron, Arvind Aaron; Pub. Anand Aaron. adv.; page Rs.1500 ($50); trim 4 1/4 x 7. bk.rev.; bibl. circ. 3,000. **Document type:** newsletter.
   Description: Covers the Asian chess scene. Includes "how-to-improve" articles, theory, combinations, and interviews.

794.1   UK   ISSN 0960-1422
CHESS POST. bi-m. £9.50. British Correspondence Chess Society, 85 Hillyard Rd., London W7 1BJ, England. Ed. R. Gillman. adv.; bk.rev.

794.1   GW
CHESSBASE MAGAZIN. 6/yr. DM.195. ChessBase GmbH, Ueberseering 25, 22297 Hamburg, Germany. Ed. Gisbert Jacoby.
   Description: Covers current games, opening theory, endgame analyses, and includes articles.

794.1   UK
CHESSMOVES. m. £15. British Chess Federation, 9A Grand Parade, St. Leonards-on-Sea, E. Sussex TN38 ODD, England. TEL 01424-442500. FAX 01424-718372. Ed. Paul Buswell. **Document type:** newsletter.
   Formerly (until 1995): B C F Newsletter.

CHESSTAMP REVIEW. see *PHILATELY*

CHI SONO. see *BIOGRAPHY*

794.4   US
CHICAGO PLAYING CARD COLLECTOR. q. $15. Chicago Playing Card Collectors, Inc., 1559 W. Pratt Blvd., Chicago, IL 60626. TEL 312-274-0250. Ed. Barbara Lunaburg. **Document type:** bulletin.
   Description: Covers the study of playing cards.

790.1   US
CHICAGO SPORTS PROFILES. 1986. bi-m. $16.50. Sports Profiles, 4711 Golf St., Ste. 900, Skokie, IL 60076. TEL 708-673-0592. FAX 708-673-0633. Ed. Paula Blaine; Pub. Lisa Levine. adv. circ. 40,000. **Document type:** consumer publication.
   Description: Covers local professional and college sports teams.

790.1   CC   ISSN 0577-8948
CHINA SPORTS/ZHONGGUO TIYU. Variant title: China Sport. (Text in English) 1957. m. $39. (State Physical Culture and Sports Commission) Renmin Tiyu Chubanshe - People's Sports Publishing House, 8 Tiyuguan Lu, Chongwen Qu, Beijing, People's Republic of China. FAX 5113105. (Dist. in U.S. by: China Books & Periodicals, Inc., 2929 24th St., San Francisco, CA 94110) adv.; illus. circ. 50,000.
   Indexed: Sportsearch (1980-).
   Formerly (until 1980): China's Sports.
   Description: Covers athletic events, sports training, traditional Chinese sports and martial arts.

790.1   US
CHOKEHOLD. 1988. irreg. (2-3/m.). $1.50 per no. 507 W. 43rd Pl., Chicago, IL 60609. TEL 312-536-0909. Ed. Lance LeVine; Pub. Peter North. adv. contact: Terry Earl Bollea. circ. 300 (paid). **Document type:** newsletter.
   Description: Contains both serious and humorous stories about life in the wrestling world. Includes commentary on pop culture.

CIBLES. see *HOBBIES*

CIENCIA Y DEPORTE. see *SCIENCES: COMPREHENSIVE WORKS*

790.1   IT
CINQUE SPORT. 1988. q. L.25000 (foreign L.35000). Stedel s.r.l., Via Napo Torriani 1-A, 20124 Milan, Italy. TEL 39-2-66988070. FAX 39-2-66988130. Ed. Stefania Bevacqua. adv.; B&W page L.3000000, color page L.5000000. **Document type:** consumer publication.

796.91   CN   ISSN 0227-2091
CIRCLE.* 1979. bi-m. Can.$5 to non-members. Figure Skating Coaches of Canada, c/o Canadian Figure Skating Association, 1600 James Naismith Dr., Gloucester, ON K1B 5N4, Canada. TEL 416-438-2871. illus.
   Formerly: Professional Circle (ISSN 0227-2083)

796.72   US   ISSN 0734-5437
TL236
CIRCLE TRACK. 1982. m. $23.95. Petersen Publishing Co., 6420 Wilshire Blvd., Los Angeles, CA 90048. TEL 213-782-2000. Ed. Glen Grisson. adv. circ. 125,000. **Document type:** consumer publication.
—UMI.

791.8   US
▼**EL CLARIN DE LA BUSCA.** 1994. q. $35 (includes: La Busca). Taurine Bibliophiles America, 2567 Military Rd., Arlington, VA 22207. (Subscr. to: Donald K. Conover, Treasurer, 2171 Twining Rd., Newton, PA 18940. TEL 610-968-0608) Ed. H. Ray Turner. adv.; bk.rev.
   Description: Provides a forum for ideas on the literature of La Fiesta Brava through book reviews, criticism, and commentary.

794.1   US
CLEVELAND CHESS BULLETIN. 1943. irreg. (3 or 4/yr.). $10. Cleveland Chess Association, c/o James Thelen, Treas., 14326 Washington Blvd., University Heights, OH 44118. Ed. William Wright. adv.; bk.rev. circ. 150. **Document type:** bulletin.

790.1   US   ISSN 0160-6166
CLUB LIVING.* 1977. 10/yr. Club Living, Inc., 16 Copper Beech Cir., White Plains, NY 10605-4702. Ed. Diana Davis Lyons. adv.; circ. 51,000 (controlled).

796.21   US   ISSN 1050-2335
COACHING CONNECTION. 1990. m. membership only. Roller Skating Associations, 7301 Georgetown Rd., Ste. 123, Indianapolis, IN 46268-4157. TEL 317-875-3390. FAX 317-875-3394. **Document type:** trade publication.
   Description: For roller skating coaches and teachers.

SPORTS AND GAMES

796.077   AT   ISSN 0814-7752
COACHING DIRECTOR. 1984. 2/yr. Australian Coaching Council Inc., P.O. Box 176, Belconnen, A.C.T. 2616, Australia. Ed. Lawrie Woodman. adv. contact: Rebecca Layton. Indexed: Sportsearch (1984-). **Document type:** trade publication.
—BLDSC (3287.743000); UnCover.

790.1   CN
COAST TO COAST. (Text in English, French) 1986. q. membership. Sport Federation of Canada, 1600 James Naismith Dr., Gloucester, Ont. K1B 5NA, Canada. TEL 613-748-5670. FAX 613-748-5706. Ed. M.J. Barber. circ. 1,000.
   Description: Covers issues in national sport, government actions in sport.

790.1   IE
COIN-OP NEWS; the central and eastern European amusement trade journal. (Text in Bulgarian, Czech, English, Hungarian, Polish, Rumanian, Russian, Serbocroatian, Slovak) 1992. 10/yr. I£30. M D Associates, Enterprise Centre, Melitta Rd., Kildare, Ireland. TEL 0353-4521190. FAX 0353-4521438. Ed. Martin Dempsey. adv.: B&W page I£600, color page I£1000; trim 15 x 10; adv. contact: Susan Feery. circ. 5,000. **Document type:** trade publication.

COLLECTION PSYCHOLOGIE ET PEDAGOGIE DU SPORT. see *PSYCHOLOGY*

790.1   US
COLLECTOR'S SPORTSLOOK.* 1993. m. $24.95. Wizard Press, 151 Wells Ave., Congers, NY 10920-2036. TEL 914-426-1900. adv.: B&W page $2345. circ. 250,000.

790.1   US   ISSN 0735-0724
COLLEGE SPORTS. 1982. m. $14.95. College Sports Publishing, L.P., 51 Cragwood Rd., Ste. 300, S. Plainfield, NJ 07080. TEL 908-753-6600. Ed. Norbe Garrett; Pub. Matt Brown. adv. contact: Gary Victor. bk.rev.; circ. 100,000 (paid). **Document type:** consumer publication.

799.202 623.4   US   ISSN 1043-7584
HD9744.P58
COMBAT HANDGUNS. 1980. bi-m. Harris Publications, Inc., 1115 Broadway, 8th Fl., New York, NY 10010. TEL 212-807-7100. **Document type:** consumer publication.

796.812   US
COMBAT SPORTS. (Supplement to: New Wave Wrestling (ISSN 1060-5908) 1978. bi-m. $15 (foreign $24). Box 651, Gracie Sta., New York, NY 10028-0006. Ed. Michael O'Hara. circ. 6,100 (paid). **Document type:** newsletter, consumer publication.
   Description: Covers wrestling matches and related topics.

797.23 692.8   UK   ISSN 1351-1149
COMMERCIAL DIVER & UNDERWATER CONTRACTOR. 1993. bi-m. £31.50($67.50) (foreign £43.60) (effective 1995). Argus Business Media Ltd., Fuel and Metals Journals (Subsidiary of: Argus Press Group), Queensway House, 2 Queensway, Redhill, Surrey RH1 1QS, England. TEL 01737-768611. FAX 01737-761685. TELEX 948669 TOPJNL G. Ed. Tony Slinn. adv.: page £638; adv. contact: Paul Swain. circ. 1,200. (back issues avail.) **Document type:** trade publication.
   Description: Seeks to inform, educate and, occasionally, amuse, professional European divers.

790.1   US
COMMUNITY SPORTS NEWS; adult recreational sports. 1983. s-m. free. Community Sports News Inc., 123 Barclay Rd., Chapel Hill, NC 27516. TEL 919-968-8741. Ed. Joel S. Bulkley. adv. circ. 5,000. (tabloid format) **Document type:** newspaper.
   Description: Local sports and commentary.

790.1   UK   ISSN 0263-6697
COMPASS SPORT - ORIENTEER. 1980. bi-m. £13.50 (foreign £16). (British Orienteering Federation) Compass Sport Publications, 37 Sandycombe Rd., Twickenham, Middx. TW1 2LR, England. TEL 0181-892-9429. Ed. Ned Paul. adv.; bk.rev. circ. 5,500. (back issues avail.) Indexed: Sportsearch (1982-). **Document type:** consumer publication.
   Formed by the merger of: Compass Sport; Orienteer.

796   US   ISSN 1052-7133
GV847.5
THE COMPLETE HOCKEY BOOK. 1967. a. $18.95. Sporting News Publishing Co., 1212 N. Lindbergh Blvd., St. Louis, MO 63132. TEL 314-997-7111. FAX 314-993-7726. Ed.Bd. illus.; stat. circ. 4,000. (back issues avail.) **Document type:** consumer publication.
   Formed by the 1991 merger of: Hockey Register (ISSN 0090-2292) & Hockey Guide (1972-1991) (ISSN 0278-4955); Which was formerly: Pro and Amateur Hockey Guide (ISSN 0090-0818); Pro and Senior Hockey Guide (ISSN 0079-550X)

COMPUTER CHESS NEWS SHEET. see *COMPUTERS — Computer Games*

794.1 001.61
621.381   US
COMPUTER CHESS REPORTS. 1983. 2/yr. $18 (PR, HI, & AK $26; foreign $36) (effective 1995). Computer Chess Digest Inc., c/o I C D Corp., 21 Walt Whitman Rd., Huntington Sta., NY 11746. TEL 516-424-3300. Ed. Larry Kaufman. circ. 5,000. **Document type:** consumer publication, newsletter.
   Description: Detailed comparison of chess computer boards and programs for consumer and retailer info and clearinghouse.

COMPUTERSCHAAK. see *COMPUTERS — Computer Games*

COMUNITA SPORTIVA; settimanale di informazione e orientamento delle attivita CSI. see *CHILDREN AND YOUTH — For*

382   BL
CONFEDERACAO BRASILEIRA DE FUTEBOL. RELATORIO.
a. Confederacao Brasileira de Desportos, Rua da Alfandega, 70, Rio de Janeiro, Brazil. illus.
   Formerly (after 1983): Confederacao Brasileira de Desportos. Relatorio.

790.1   ZR
CONGO SPORTS. w. 99 rue de Tshela Com., Kinshasa, Zaire. adv.

790.1   US
CONNECTICUT CHESS MAGAZINE. 1976. s-a. $4. Connecticut Chess, Inc., Box 4726, Waterbury, CT 06704-1201. TEL 203-755-9749. adv.; bk.rev. circ. 500. **Document type:** newsletter.
   Former titles: Waterbury Chess Club Bulletin (ISSN 0894-0606); Connecticut Backgammon Magazine.
   Description: News and information from Connecticut chess clubs, including games played, ratings of players, and minutes of meetings.

CONSTRUCTIONS EQUIPEMENTS POUR LES LOISIRS. see *BUILDING AND CONSTRUCTION*

790.1   NE   ISSN 0045-8406
CONTRACTSPELER. 1961. bi-m. fl.17.50. Professional Players Union of Holland, Harderwijkweg 9, 2803 PW Gouda, Netherlands. TEL 31-1820-71172. FAX 31-1820-32732. (Co-sponsors: Professional Trotter and Jockey Union of Holland; Professional Cyclists Union of Holland) Ed. K. Jansen. adv.; bk.rev.; tr.lit. circ. 2,000. (tabloid format)

790.1   CN
CO-OPERATIVE GAME CATALOG; family pastimes, co-operative games, puzzles & books. 1970. 2/yr. free. Family Pastimes, RR 4, Perth, ON K7H 3C6, Canada. Ed. Jim Deacove. adv.; bk.rev.; illus. circ. 40,000. **Document type:** catalog.

794.1   UK   ISSN 0961-7736
CORRESPONDENCE CHESS. 1963. q. £6 to non-members. British Correspondence Chess Association, c/o J.M. Allain, Esq., 86 Mortimer Rd., London N1 4LH, England. TEL 0171-254-7912. (Affiliate: British Postal Chess Federation) Ed. J. Tait. adv.; bk.rev. circ. 600. **Document type:** consumer publication.

794.1   IT   ISSN 1121-3078
CORRESPONDENCE CHESS YEARBOOK. 1991. 3/yr. DM.95($56) (effective 1995 & 1996). S1 Editrice s.r.l., Via Porrettana 111, 40135 Bologna, Italy. TEL 39-51-6145374. FAX 39-51-6147636. (Diskette avail. from: Chessbase GmbH Uberseering, 25 Postfach 60 04 22, 22204 Hamburg, Germany. TEL 49-40-6301063. FAX 49-40-6301282) Ed. S. Curtacci. adv. contact: Sean Cogan. circ. 3,000 (paid). (also avail. in diskette format) **Document type:** consumer publication.
   Description: Contains approximately 400 games and 3 theoretical articles in each volume. Includes chess interest articles, and ranking and results tables from correspondence tournaments.

790.1   IT
CORRIERE DELLO SPORT - STADIO. d. Piazza Indipendenza 11B, 00185 Rome, Italy. TEL 6-49-921. FAX 6-499-26-90. Ed. Andrea Girelli. circ. 550,000.

790.1   IT
CORRIERE LAZIALE.* 1975. w. L.50000. Edilazio 92 coop.r.l., Via dei Limoni 59, 00172 Rome, Italy. TEL 39-6-21700590. FAX 39-6-2751173. Ed. Eraclite Corbi. adv.: page L.3000000. **Document type:** consumer publication.

COSMOS TOU TENNIS/WORLD OF TENNIS. see *SPORTS AND GAMES — Ball Games*

COST OF DOING BUSINESS FOR RETAIL SPORTING GOODS STORES. see *BUSINESS AND ECONOMICS — Domestic Commerce*

794.1   CN   ISSN 0832-0136
COUNTERPLAY. 1984. 6/yr. $16. Counterplay Publishing Association, P.O. Box 4422, Vancouver, B.C. V6B 3Z8, Canada. adv.; bk.rev. circ. 450.
   Description: Covers local chess games and news; includes occasional theory, "how-to-improve" articles, and interviews.

THE COUNTRYMAN'S WEEKLY. see *SPORTS AND GAMES — Outdoor Life*

794.1   FR   ISSN 0011-0507
COURRIER DES ECHECS; revue mensuelle d'echecs par correspondance. 1947. m. 195 F. (typically set in Sep.). (Association des Joueurs d'Echecs Par Correspondance) Marcel Bert, Esc. 1, 5 place Maurice Berteaux, 78400 Chatou, France. adv.; illus.

790.1   CM
COURRIER SPORTIF DU BENIN. w. B.P. 17, Douala, Cameroun. Ed. Henri Jong. adv.

790.01   US
CROSSWORD MAGAZINE. 1990. bi-m. $18. Crossword Magazine, Inc., 713 Francis Dr., Wantagh, NY 11793. TEL 516-679-8608. FAX 516-221-7809. Ed. J. Baxter Newgate. adv.; bk.rev.; illus. circ. 5,000.
   Description: Contains news and information of and about crossword puzzles and the people who create them.

793   SP
CUADERNOS DE LOTO Y BONOLOTO. 6/yr. Grupo Editorial Mazorca, Moratines 22, 1o, 28005 Madrid, Spain. TEL 1-227-35-23. Ed. Cristina R. Garcia.

CURATE REGENERATE. see *PHYSICAL FITNESS AND HYGIENE*

795.42   US
CURRENT BLACKJACK NEWS. 1979. m. (plus irreg. special issues). $99 (with special issues $145; fax service $199) (effective 1994). Pi Yee Press, 7910 Ivanhoe Ave., No. 34, La Jolla, CA 92037-4511. TEL 619-456-4080. FAX 619-456-8076. Ed. Stanford Wong. circ. 450 (paid). (looseleaf format) **Document type:** newsletter.
   Description: Contains news and updates on the rules and playing conditions for the casino game of blackjack in legal casinos, as well as reports on other casino games that can be beaten.

SPORTS AND GAMES

796 UK ISSN 0969-2576
CYCLE SPORT. 1993. m. £28.80 (foreign $41.40) (effective Nov. 1994). I P C Magazines, King's Reach Tower, Stamford St., London SE1 9LS. TEL 071-261-5000. FAX 071-261-7851. (Dist. by: Marketforce Ltd., Newman St., London, England. TEL 071-261-5000; Subscr. to: I P C, Haywards Heath, W. Sussex RH16 3ZA, England. TEL 0444-445555) Ed. Andrew Sutcliffe. adv. contact: Jane Wilson. bk.rev.; circ. 28,000 (paid). (back issues avail.) **Document type:** consumer publication.
Description: Covers the continental European professional bicycle racing scene.

CYCLING TIMES. see SPORTS AND GAMES — Bicycles And Motorcycles

790.1 FR ISSN 0293-4086
D.I.R.E. EN A P S. (Democratiser, Innover, Rechercher, Eduquer en Activite Physique et Sportive) 1981. 4/yr. 180 F. (foreign 220 F.). Federation Sportive et Gymnique du Travail, 14-16 Scandicci, 93508 Pantin Cedex, France.

790.1 GW
D J K - AKTIV. 1950. bi-m. free. Deutsche Jugendkraft e.V., Deutschhoeferstr. 17, 97422 Schweinfurt, Germany. TEL 09721-24163. Ed. Georg Loesch. adv.; circ. 2,500 (controlled). (back issues avail.)

797.21 GW
D L R G - AKTUELL. 1984. q. DM.8. D L R G - Kreisverband Kaufbeuren Ostallgau, Postfach 741, 87585 Kaufbeuren, Germany. FAX 049-834162876. Ed.Bd. circ. 600. **Document type:** bulletin.

790.1 GW
D L V - VOLKSSPORT-KALENDER.* 1969. a. free to qualified personnel. Deutsch Leichtathletik-Verband, Julius-Reiber-Str. 19, 64293 Darmstadt, Germany. TEL 08234-2444. (Co-sponsor: Oesterreichischer Leichtathletik-Verband) Ed. Otto Hosse. (back issues avail.)
Description: List of popular races in Germany and Austria for participants.

790.1 GW
D S B PRESSE; ein Artikel- und Informationsdienst des D S B. w. DM.150. Deutscher Sportbund, Postfach 710263, 60492 Frankfurt a.M., Germany. TEL 069-6700-0. FAX 069-674906. Ed. Harald Pieper. **Document type:** government publication, newsletter.

797 GW
D S W '12 NACHRICHTEN. 1955. m. Darmstaedter Schwimm- und Wassersportclub 1912 e.V., Alsfelderstr. 31, 64289 Darmstadt, Germany. TEL 06151-713077. adv. circ. 1,300.

794.2 NE ISSN 0011-5959
HET DAMSPEL. 1911. 5/yr. fl.25 (effective 1995-1996). Koninklijke Nederlandse Dambond - Royal Dutch Draughts Association, Postbus 100, 6990 AC Rheden, Netherlands. TEL 31-8309-52309. Dir. Joh. Haijtink. bk.rev.; bibl.; charts. circ. 8,800.

790.1 CC ISSN 1002-6169
DANGDAI TIYU/CONTEMPORARY SPORTS. (Text in Chinese) m. (Heilongjiang Sheng Tiyu Yundong Weiyuanhui) Dangdai Tiyu Zazhishe, 99 Xuanxua Jie, Nangang-qu, Harbin, Heilongjiang 150001, People's Republic of China. TEL 0451-2623578. FAX 0451-2623578. **Document type:** consumer publication.

795.414 DK ISSN 0011-6238
DANSK BRIDGE. 1941. m. DKK 120. Danmarks Bridgeforbund - Danish Bridge League, Skovledet 95 A, 3400 Hilleroed, Denmark. FAX 45-2-266789. (Subscr. to: Postboks 121, DK-3400 Hillerod, Denmark) Ed. Ib Lundby. adv.; bk.rev. circ. 14,000.

796 DK ISSN 0109-8705
DANSK KARATE FORBUND. MEDLEMSBLAD. 1984. q. membership. Dansk Karate Forbund, Idraettens Hus, Broenby Stadion 20, 2605 Broendby, Denmark. Ed. Joergen Nielsen. adv.; bk.rev.; illus.
Formerly: Dansk Karate Forbund (ISSN 0109-8691)

796.060489 DK ISSN 0908-1011
DANSK UNGDOM OG IDRAET. 1930. w. DKK 370. Danske Gymnastik- og Idraetsforeninger - Danish Gymnastic and Sport Organizations, P.O. Box 569, DK-7100 Vejle, Denmark. TEL 45-79-40-40-40. FAX 45-79-40-40-84. Ed. Jens Sejer Andersen. adv.; bk.rev. circ. 9,600.
Formed by the merger of (1939-1992): Dansk Idraet (ISSN 0109-5536); Incorporates (in 1987): Gymnastik Nyt (ISSN 0904-2342); (1989-1992): Ungdom og Idraet (ISSN 0905-2518); Formerly (1965-1988): Dansk Ungdom og Idraet (ISSN 0045-9631)

790.1 UK ISSN 0267-2286
DARTS PLAYER.* 1985. a. £3.50($5) World Magazines Ltd., 9 Kelsey Park Rd., Beckenham, Kent BR3 2LH, England. Ed. A.J. Wood. circ. 21,500. (back issues avail.)

799.32 UK ISSN 0140-6000
DARTS WORLD.* 1972. m. £16($30) World Magazines Ltd., 9 Kelsey Park Rd., Beckenham, Kent BR3 2LH, England. Ed. A.J. Wood. adv.; bk.rev. circ. 26,400. Indexed: Sportsearch.

790 QA
AL-DAWRI. 1978. w. A.H. al- Atiyah and Partners, P.O. Box 310, Doha, Qatar. TEL 328782. Ed. Rashid bin Owaid al-Thani. circ. 6,000.

797 IT
DELTA E PARAPENDIO. m. L.77000 (foreign L.96000). Editoriale Olimpia S.p.A., Viale Milton 2, 50129 Florence, Italy. TEL 39-55-473843. FAX 39-55-499195. Ed. Attilio Vallecchi. adv.; B&W page L.2200000, color page L.4400000; adv. contact: Dante Porta. circ. 20,000. **Document type:** consumer publication.

790.1 CU
DEPORTE, DERECHO DEL PUBLICO. 1968. bi-m. $22 in S. America; N. America $24; elsewhere $32. Via Blanca y Boyeros, Havana, Cuba. TEL 7-40-6838. TELEX 511583. (Dist. by: Ediciones Cubanas, Obispo No. 527, Apdo. 605, Havana, Cuba) Dir. Manuel Vaillant Carpente. circ. 15,000.

790.1 CU ISSN 0138-6611
DEPORTE - DERECHO DEL PUEBLO. 1968. m. $22. (Instituto Nacional de Deportes, Educacion Fisica y Recreacion) Ediciones Cubanas, Obispo No. 527, Apdo. 605, Havana, Cuba. illus.
Description: Presents articles, interviews and photo features on current national and international events, including information on the military, cultural, sports and recreational activities of the Armed Forces.

790.1 CL
DEPORTE TOTAL.* 1981. w. Luis Thayer Ojeda 1626, Casilla 3092, Providencia, Santiago, Chile. TEL 2-251-6236. FAX 2-204-7420. TELEX 341194. Dir. Dario Rojas Morales. illus. circ. 25,000.

796 SP
DEPORTE 2000. 1969. m. 420 ptas.($7.24) Instituto Nacional de Educacion Fisica y Deportes, Martin Fierro, Madrid-3, Spain. adv.; charts; illus.; stat.; index. (back issues avail.)

790.1 VE
DEPORTES. 1978. fortn. C.A. Editorial Hipodromo, Torre de la Prensa, Plaza del Panteon, Apartado 2976, Caracas 101, Venezuela. Dir. Raul Hernandez. circ. 71,927.

790.1 DR
DEPORTES. 1967. fortn. Publicaciones Ahora, San Martin 236, Apdo. Postal 1402, Santo Domingo, Dominican Republic. Dir. L.R. Cordero. circ. 5,000.

DEUTSCHE GEHOERLOSEN-ZEITUNG. see HANDICAPPED — Hearing Impaired

799.3 GW ISSN 0012-0707
DEUTSCHE SCHUETZENZEITUNG. 1954. m. DM.54. Deutscher Schuetzenbund e.V., Lahnstr. 120, 65195 Wiesbaden, Germany. TEL 0611-468070. FAX 0611-4680749. TELEX 4186-309. Ed. Dieter Nobbe. adv.; bk.rev. circ. 9,000. **Document type:** newsletter.

796 GW ISSN 0075-2401
GV204.G4
DEUTSCHER TURNER-BUND. JAHRBUCH DER TURNKUNST. 1906. a. DM.17. Deutscher Turner-Bund, Otto-Fleck-Schneise 8, 60528 Frankfurt a.M., Germany. adv.

793 GW
DEUTSCHES BRIDGE-VERBANDSBLATT. 1951. m. (Deutscher Bridge-Verband e.V.) Topp & Moeller Druck und Verlag, Postfach 2854, 32717 Detmold, Germany. TEL 05231-91990. circ. 22,000.

790.1 GW ISSN 0343-5318
DEUTSCHES TURNEN. 1856. m. DM.58.80 (foreign DM.79.20). (Deutscher Turner-Bund) Meyer und Meyer Verlag GmbH, Von-Coels-Str. 390, 52080 Aachen, Germany. TEL 0241-556033. FAX 0241-558281. (Subscr. to: Deutscher Turner-Bund, Zentralredaktion, Otto-Fleck-Schneise 8, 60528 Frankfurt a.M., Germany) adv. circ. 30,000. **Document type:** bulletin.

790.1 TS
AL-DHAID. 1985. m. Nadi al-Dhaid al-Riyadi - Al-Dhaid Sporting Club, P.O. Box 12532, Al-Dhaid, United Arab Emirates. TEL 0822750. FAX 822631. Ed. Muhammad bin Salim al-Qasimi. circ. 1,000.
Description: Covers local sports and cultural events.

DHANDHA. see MATHEMATICS

790.1 SP
DIA CUATRO QUE FUERA.... 1970. m. free. Junta Central de Fiestas de Moros y Cristianos, Palacio Municipal, Villena, Alicante, Spain. circ. controlled.

DIESEL; mensile di cultura, attualita, tecnica che tratta di tutte le motorizzazioni diesel per usi industriali, agricoli, nautici. see ENGINEERING — Mechanical Engineering

688.76 SP
DIFFUSION SPORT. 5/yr. 15000 ptas. Difusion Ediciones S.L., Rosellon 102, Entlo. 1a, 08029 Barcelona, Spain. TEL 3-323-57-02. FAX 3-323-60-80. Ed. Jordi Mullor. adv.: color page 125000 ptas. circ. 8,000. **Document type:** trade publication.
Description: Contains news, views, products, interviews and economics related to the sport and leisure sector.

688.76 SP
DIFFUSION SPORT GACETA. 11/yr. Rosellon 102, Entlo. 1a, 08029 Barcelona, Spain. TEL 3-323-57-02. FAX 3-323-60-80. Ed. Jordi Mullor.

793 US
DIPLOMACY WORLD. 1974. q. $400. Pandemonium Press, 1273 Crest Dr., Encinitas, CA 92024. Ed. R. C. Walker. circ. 400.

DIRECTORY OF RECREATIONAL MARINE PRODUCT DEALERS (YEAR); includes: boat dealers, marine equipment supply stores, marinas, marine distributors. see BUSINESS AND ECONOMICS — Trade And Industrial Directories

790.1 UK
DIRECTORY OF SPORT IN LONDON. 1986. a. free. Sports Council (London Region), P.O. Box 480, Crystal Palace NSC, Ledrington Rd., London SE19 2BQ, England. TEL 081-778-8600. FAX 081-676-9812. Ed. Scilla Ashdown. circ. 4,000. **Document type:** directory.

790.1 UK
DIRECTORY OF SPORT IN THE SOUTH EAST. 1986. a. free. Sports Council (London Region), P.O. Box 480, Crystal Palace NSC, Ledrington Rd., London SE19 2BQ, England. TEL 081-778-8600. FAX 081-676-9812. Ed. Scilla Ashdown. circ. 4,000. **Document type:** directory.

790.1 US ISSN 1055-4785
DISC GOLF JOURNAL; world's finest disc golf publication. 1991. bi-m. $17.97. 1801 Richardson Dr., No. 6, Urbana, IL 61801. TEL 217-344-3552. Ed. Kathleen Ignowski; Pub. Thomas A. Schlueter. adv.: page $130. **Document type:** newspaper.

790.1 DK ISSN 0107-9042
DISCINFORM. 1982. q. DKK 25. Dansk Frisbee Disc Forbund, Box 140, 3520 Farum, Denmark. illus.

SPORTS AND GAMES

797.21   **CN**
DIVE. (Text in English, French) q. free. Canadian Amateur Diving Association, 1600 James Naismith Dr., Ste.705, Gloucester, Ont. K1B 5N4, Canada. TEL 613-748-5631. Ed. Don Adams. circ. 1,500.
    Formerly: Platformance.

DIVE BOAT MAGAZINE. see SPORTS AND GAMES — Boats And Boating

797.21   **US**   **ISSN 1061-3323**
DIVE TRAINING. 1991. m. $18.95. Dive Training, Ltd., 405 Main St., Parkville, MO 64152. TEL 816-741-5155. FAX 816-741-6458. Ed. Seam Combs. adv.; bk.rev. circ. 70,000.
    Description: Contains how-to information for new divers and their instructors. Offers safety information and promotes the diving experience.

797.23   **UK**   **ISSN 0141-3465**
DIVER; the magazine of sub-aqua diving, undersea exploration and research. 1955. m. £30. Eaton Publications, 55 High St., Teddington, Mddx. TW11 8HA, England. TEL 0181-943-4288. FAX 0181-943-4312. Ed. B. Eaton. adv. contact: Jenny Webb. bk.rev.; charts; illus.; circ. 53,358 (paid). Indexed: Sportsearch. **Document type:** consumer publication.
—BLDSC (3604.270300).
    Formerly (until 1978): Triton (ISSN 0041-3119)
    Description: Covers topics in sport sub-aqua diving, including introduction to the sport, training, underwater recreation, travel, technology, equipment, wrecks and salvage, conservation, exploration, marine archaeology, marine biology, and underwater photography.

797.21   **US**   **ISSN 0273-8589**
DIVER. 1980. bi-m. $15. Taylor Publishing, Box 313, Portland, CT 06480. TEL 203-342-4730. FAX 203-342-5368. Ed. Bob Taylor; Pub. Bob Taylor. adv.; bk.rev.; circ. 2,000 (paid). Indexed: Sportsearch (1981-).
    Description: Covers everything relating to springboard and platform diving.

797 910   **CN**   **ISSN 0706-5132**
DIVER MAGAZINE. 1975. 9/yr. Can.$22.47 (foreign Can.$26.75); newsstand price: Can.$3.50. Seagraphic Publications Ltd., 295 - 10991 Shellbridge Way, Richmond, BC V6X 3C6, Canada. TEL 604-273-4333. FAX 604-273-0813. E-mail: Diver@boardbob.tor250.org. (Subscr. to: P.O. Box 1312, Delta, BC V4M 3Y8, Canada) Ed. Stephanie Bold; Pub. Peter Vassilopoulos. adv.: B&W page Can.$2379, color page Can.$3136; trim 8 1/8 x 10 7/8. bk.rev.; illus. circ. 30,000. (back issues avail.) **Document type:** consumer publication.
    Formerly: Pacific Diver and Underwater Adventure.
    Description: Covers Canadian and North American regional dive destination articles and travel features.

797.23   **AT**   **ISSN 0725-9417**
DIVING DOWN UNDER. 1978. q. Aus.$30 (effective 1996). Australian Underwater Federation, P.O. Box 44, Sans Souci, N.S.W. 2119, Australia. TEL 02-529-6496. FAX 02-580-5521. Ed. M. Sheehan. adv.; bk.rev. circ. 4,500.
    Formerly (until 1987): A U F Dive News.

796   **GW**   **ISSN 0173-0843**
DOKUMENTE ZUM HOCHSCHULSPORT. 1976. irreg., vol.26, 1991. price varies. (Freie Universitaet Berlin, Zentraleinrichtung Hochschulsport) Czwalina Verlag, Postfach 730240, 22122 Hamburg, Germany. TEL 040-6780025. FAX 040-6780051. **Document type:** monographic series.

797   **US**   **ISSN 0744-3226**
DOLPHIN DIGEST. 1974. 26/yr. $34.95 (foreign $140). Dolphin Publishing Company, 8033 N.W. 36th St., Miami, FL 33166-6609. TEL 305-594-0508. FAX 305-594-0518. Ed. Andrew Cohen; Pub. Tom Curtis. adv. contact: Ken Keidel. circ. 40,000. **Document type:** newspaper.
    Description: Football publication devoted to the Miami Dolphins and the NFL.

793   **IT**   **ISSN 1120-4389**
DOMENICA QUIZ. 1951. w. L.54000. Rizzoli Editore-Corriere della Sera, Via A. Rizzoli 2, 20100 Milan, Italy. TEL 39-2-2588. Ed. Eugenio Balduzzi. adv.: B&W page L.5200000; adv. contact: Flavio Biondi. circ. 113,401.
    Former titles (until 1957): Domenica Enigmistica (ISSN 1120-6187); Enigmistica (ISSN 1120-6179)

790.1   **IR**
DONYAYE VARZESH. (Text in Persian) 1970. w. $400 in N. America (effective 1994). Ettela'at Publications, P.O. Box 11365-9365, Tehran, Iran. TEL 98-21-328241. FAX 98-21-3111223. TELEX 212336. Ed. Gholamhossein Sha'bani. adv. circ. 250,000. **Document type:** consumer publication.
    Description: Covers sports in Iran and at the international level.

790.1   **DK**   **ISSN 0109-5595**
DRAGESPORT. 1984. bi-m. membership; libraries DKK 200. Danske Drageflyver Union, Oestre Parkvej 5A, DK-4100 Ringsted, Denmark. illus.
    Formerly: Dansk Dragesport (ISSN 0105-1245)

793   **GW**   **ISSN 0946-9826**
▼**DRAGON.** 1994. bi-m. DM.48. Katharinenstr. 15, 53757 St. Augustin, Germany. TEL 02241-311313. Ed. Holger Rinke; Pub. Uwe Koerner. adv. contact: Uwe Koerner. **Document type:** consumer publication.

DUNE BUGGIES & HOT VWS; the fun car journal. see TRANSPORTATION — Automobiles

790.1   **US**
DURHAM COMMUNITY SPORTS NEWS. 1985. m. free. Durham Community Sports News Inc., 123 Barclay Rd., Chapel Hill, NC 27516. TEL 919-968-8741. Ed. Joel S. Bulkley. adv. circ. 6,000. (tabloid format) **Document type:** newspaper.
    Description: Local sports and commentary.

790.1   **JO**
AD-DUSTOUR AL-RIYADI; riyadiyyah - usbu'iyyah - mutakhassisah. (Text in Arabic) w. Jordan Press and Publishing Co., University St., P.O. Box 591, 11118 Amman, Jordan. TEL 664153. FAX 667170. TELEX 21392 MEDIA JO. adv. contact: Yosef Ammary. circ. 100,000. **Document type:** newspaper.

794.1   **BE**   **ISSN 0012-7671**
E G. (End Game) 1965. q. fl.35. Chess Endgame Consultants & Publishers, c/o W. Stoffelen, Ed., Henrilei 59, B-2930 Brasschaat, Belgium. TEL 032-365-15860. bk.rev.; illus. circ. 450.

794.1   **NZ**
E P MAGAZINE. 1978. irreg., 1-2/yr. $12. (New Zealand Correspondence Chess Association) N Z C C A, P.O. Box 3278, Wellington, New Zealand. TEL 04-237-4753. Ed. J.W. Maxwell. circ. 250 (controlled).
    Description: Reports on national and international news, games, and studies on problems.

E P S. see EDUCATION — Teaching Methods And Curriculum

794.1   **CN**   **ISSN 0825-0049**
ECHEC PLUS. 1978. bi-m. Can.$29 (US Can.$37). (Federation Quebecoise des Echecs) Editions Echec Plus, C.P. 640, Succ. "C", Montreal, PQ H2L 4L5, Canada. TEL 514-252-3034. FAX 514-251-8038. TELEX 0582647. Ed. Richard Berlbe. adv. contact: Valentin Prahov. index. circ. 2,500. (back issues avail.) **Document type:** bulletin.
    Description: News and events: game analysis, problems, combinations.

794.1   **BE**
ECHIQUIER BELGE. (Text in Dutch, French) 1942. m. (except July-Aug. combined). $55 outside Belgium. Rue Van Waeyenberg 12, B-1140 Brussels, Belgium. Ed. Henri Muller. adv.; bk.rev. **Document type:** bulletin.
    Description: Includes annotated games, combinations, results, and studies on problems.

794.1   **FR**
ECHIQUIER ISSEN. 1987. 6/yr. 160 F.($30) Bruno San Marco, Ed. & Pub., 43 rue de Normandie, 92 240 Clamart, France. Ed. Bruno Marco.
    Description: Features annotated games, articles and theory.

790.1   **UA**
L'ECHO SPORTIF. (Text in French) w. Michel Bittar, Ed. & Pub., 7 Sharia de l'Archeveche, Alexandria, Egypt.

ECO DELLA RIVIERA. see TRAVEL AND TOURISM

790.1   **CK**   **ISSN 0120-677X**
EDUCACION FISICA Y DEPORTE. 1979. s-a. Col.500($10) Instituto Universitario de Educacion Fisica y Deporte, Apdo. Aereo 1226, Medellin, Colombia. Ed. Francisco Garcia. bk.rev. circ. 1,000.

790.1   **FR**   **ISSN 0245-8977**
EDUCATION PHYSIQUE ET SPORTIVE AU 1ER DEGRE. Abbreviated title: E P S 1. 1981. 5/yr. 100 F. (foreign 125 F.) (effective 1995-96). (Comite d'Etudes et d'Informations Pedagogiques de l'Education Physique et du Sport) Editions Revue E P S, 11 av. du Tremblay, 75012 Paris, France. TEL 1-48-08-30-87. FAX 1-43-98-37-38. Ed. Jean Vives. adv.
    Description: Helps in planning physical education classes.

790.1 778   **UA**
EGYPTE - SPORTS - CINEMA. (Text in French) w. 7 av. Hourriya, Alexandria, Egypt. Ed. Emile Assaad. adv.

796.962   **GW**   **ISSN 0932-5972**
EISHOCKEY MAGAZIN. 1973. m. DM.50 (foreign DM.60). Vereinigte Fachverlage GmbH, Lise-Meitner-Str. 2, 55129 Mainz, Germany. TEL 06131-992-0. FAX 06131-992100. Ed. Guenter Swoboda. adv. contact: Michael Spahn. circ. 35,000. **Document type:** consumer publication.

790.1   **GW**   **ISSN 0937-0218**
DER EISSTOCKSCHUETZE. 1976. s-m. DM.50($10) Deutsche Eisschuetzen Vereinigung e.V., Menzingerstr. 68, 80992 Munich, Germany. TEL 089-8111055. FAX 089-8144477. TELEX 5213199-DEV-D. Ed. Hermann Binder. adv.; bk.rev. circ. 1,950. **Document type:** bulletin.

EMPLOYEE SERVICES MANAGEMENT; the journal of employee services, recreation, health and education. see BUSINESS AND ECONOMICS — Management

794.1   **CN**   **ISSN 0822-5672**
EN PASSANT. (Text in English and French) 1973. 6/yr. Can.$15 (foreign $18). En Passant Publishers Ltd., 2212 Gladwin Cres. E-1, Ottawa, ON K1B 5N1, Canada. TEL 613-733-5209. FAX 613-733-2844. Ed. Hal Bond. adv.; bk.rev. circ. 3,000.
    Former titles: Chess Canada Echecs (ISSN 0225-7351); Chess Federation of Canada. Bulletin (ISSN 0317-8064)

794.1   **US**
EN PASSANT. 1946. 6/yr. $7. Chess Enterprises, 107 Crosstree Rd., Coraopolis, PA 15108. TEL 412-262-2138. Ed. Bobby Dudley. adv.; bk.rev. circ. 400. **Document type:** newsletter.
    Description: News and results of the club's events.

797.21   **UK**
ENGLISH SCHOOLS SWIMMING ASSOCIATION HANDBOOK. 1950. a. £1.50. English Schools Swimming Association, Beech Hurst, Forest Rd., E. Horsley, Surrey KT24 5BL, England. TEL 01483-285488. FAX 01483-285599. Ed. M.J. Bracey. adv. circ. 3,000. **Document type:** consumer publication.

790   **YU**   **ISSN 0013-8436**
ENIGMA; zabavni casopis: ukrstene reci, rebusi. 1952. w. 150 din.($13.90) Enigmatski Klub, Bulevar Vojvode Misica 67, Box 219, Belgrade, Yugoslavia. Ed. Vlasta Pavlovic.

ENTERTAINMENT & SPORTS LAW REVIEW. see LAW

ENTERTAINMENT AND SPORTS LAWYER. see LAW

790.1   **GW**   **ISSN 0932-7797**
ENTWICKLUNGSZUSAMMENARBEIT IM SPORT; Analysen - Dokumentationen - Lehrmaterialen. 1988. irreg., vol.8, 1990. price varies. Czwalina Verlag, Postfach 730240, 22122 Hamburg, Germany. TEL 040-6780025. FAX 040-6780051. Eds. Rolf Andresen, Christian Kroeger. **Document type:** monographic series.

688.76   **SP**
EQUIPAMIENTO DEPORTIVO. 2/yr. Fermin Caballero 64, Larra, 1, 6o D, 28034 Madrid, Spain. TEL 1-201-82-40. Ed. A. Duarte Palomero. circ. 10,000.

SPORTS AND GAMES

790.1   FR   ISSN 0153-1069
L'EQUIPE. 1946. w. 2650 F. 4 Rouget-de-Lisle, 92137 Issy les Moulineaux Cedex, France. TEL 40-93-20-20. FAX 40-93-20-08. Ed. Gerard Ernault. adv. circ. 317,836. Indexed: Sportsearch (1980-). Document type: newspaper.

ERNIE SAXTON'S MOTORSPORTS SPONSORSHIP - MARKETING NEWS; the latest marketing promotion & sponsorship news in all forms of motorsports. see BUSINESS AND ECONOMICS — Marketing And Purchasing

790.1   SY
ESBOU AL-RIADI. 1955. w. Firdoisse Ave., Tibi Bldg., Damascus, Syria. Ed. Kamel el-Bounni. adv.

790.1   EC
ESTADIO. 1962. fortn. $73. Editores Nacionales, Aguirre 730 y Boyaca, Casilla 1239, Guayaquil, Ecuador. TEL 4-327-200. FAX 4-320-499. TELEX 3423. Ed. Jose Calderon. circ. 70,000.

794.1   FR   ISSN 0014-2794
EUROPE-ECHECS. 1959. m. (except Jul.-Aug. combined). 305 F.($67) (foreign 335 F.). Nicky Fasquelle, Ed. & Pub., 4C1 rue X. Marmier, 25000 Besancon, France. TEL 81-51-01-26. (Subscr. to: B.P. 1397, 25006 Besancon Cedex, France) adv.; bk.rev.; play rev. circ. 31,000.
Description: Contains annotated games, national and international news, interviews, combinations, correspondence chess, and computer chess.

790.1   UK   ISSN 0267-5358
EVENTING; the international magazine for the sport of horse trials. 1985. m. £27($65.10) I P C Magazines, Specialist Magazine Group (Subsidiary of: Reed Elsevier group), King's Reach Tower, Stamford St., London SE1 9LS, England. TEL 071-261-5388. FAX 0444-440619. TELEX 892084 REEDBP G. (Dist. by: Quadrant Subscription Services, Oakfield House, Perrymount Rd., Haywards Heath, W. Sussex RH16 3DH, England. TEL 0444-441212) Ed. Kate Green. adv.: B&W page £595; adv. contact: Lorna Buchan. bk.rev. circ. 10,000. (back issues avail.) Document type: consumer publication.
Description: Aimed at participants and followers of the sport of horse trials from the local to international.

795.42   US
EXPERTS BLACKJACK NEWSLETTER. 1982. bi-m. $30. Gambling Times, Inc., 16140 Valerio St., Ste. B, Van Nuys, CA 91406-2916. TEL 818-781-9355. FAX 818-781-3125. Ed. Stanley Roberts. bk.rev.; software rev.; circ. 1,000 (paid). Document type: consumer publication, newsletter.
Description: Provides articles and research of interest to blackjack players. Reports on field conditions and other factors.

EXPLORE; Canada's outdoor adventure magazine. see SPORTS AND GAMES — Outdoor Life

790.1   US   ISSN 1067-3202 TS380
EXPLORER KNIFE JOURNAL. 1980. a. $2.50. (Gutmann Cutlery) Aqua-Field Publishing Co., Inc., 66 W. Gilbert St., Shrewsbury, NJ 07702. TEL 201-842-8300. Ed. Stephen Ferber. adv. circ. 105,000.
Former titles: Gutmann Puma-Explorer Knife Annual (ISSN 0731-1885); Gutmann Knife Annual (ISSN 0271-762X)

794.1   RU
EXPRESS - SHAKHMATY. 1955. s-m. $36.90. Fizkul'tura i Sport, Kalyaevskaya 27, 101421 Moscow, Russia. TEL 095-258-2690. FAX 096-200-1217. Ed. Yurii Averbakh. illus. circ. 25,000. (also avail. in microform)
Formerly: Shakhmatnyi Byulleten' (ISSN 0037-3230)

796   FR
FACEOFF. 1992. 7/yr. Canadian Publishers, 1465 St. James St., Winnipeg, MB R3H 0W9, Canada. TEL 204-949-6100. FAX 204-949-6122. Ed. Shawn Coates. adv.: B&W page Can.$1550, color page Can.$1900; adv. contact: Martin Rissen. circ. 40,000. Document type: consumer publication.

FACTS ON FILE. YEARBOOK. see HISTORY — History Of North And South America

FACTS ON FILE WORLD NEWS DIGEST WITH INDEX. see HISTORY

790.1   IE
FAIR PLAY; the Irish amusement trade journal. 1985. 8/yr. I£20. M D Associates, Enterprise Centre, Melitta Rd., Kildare, Ireland. TEL 0353-4521190. FAX 0353-4521438. Ed. Martin Dempsey. adv.: B&W page I£600, color page I£1000; trim 15 x 10; adv. contact: Susan Feery. circ. 2,000. Document type: trade publication.

790.1 659.152   US
FANS. 1992. q. free. Virgo Publishing, Inc., 4141 N. Scottsdale Rd., Ste. 316, Scottsdale, AZ 85251. TEL 602-990-1101. FAX 602-990-0819. Ed. Alisa Klemm.
Description: Covers the latest in licensed sports fashion. Includes apparel previews for NFL, NBA, MLB and NHL teams; articles on issues of interest surrounding your favorite teams; interviews with top athletes.

793   GW   ISSN 0935-0721
FANTASYWELT; das Fachmagazin fur Rollenspieler. 1985. bi-m. DM.48. Katharinenstr. 15, 53757 St. Augustin, Germany. TEL 02241-311313. Ed. Uwe Korner. adv. contact: Uwe Koerner. bk.rev.; film rev.; play rev.; illus. circ. 10,000. (back issues avail.) Document type: consumer publication.
Description: Role playing games, games for adults, fantasy and science fiction novels.

794   SP
FEBOX-BOXEO. no.19, 1975. m. 250 ptas.($6) Federacion Espanola Boxeo, Ferraz 16, Madrid-8, Spain.

796.86   SZ
FECHTEN/ESCRIME/SCHERMA.* 1978. q. (Schweizerischer Fechtverband - Federation Suisse d'Escrime - Federazione Svizzera di Scherma) G. Buechi Verlag, Schaffhauserstr. 439, Postfach 236, CH-8052 Zuerich, Switzerland. circ. 7,000. Indexed: Sportsearch.

796.86   GW   ISSN 0720-2229
FECHTSPORT. 1980. 8/yr. DM.82 (foreign DM.102). (Deutscher Fechter-Bund e.V.) Schluetersche Verlagsanstalt GmbH und Co., Hans-Boeckler-Allee 7, 30173 Hannover, Germany. TEL 0511-8550-0. FAX 0511-8550-100. (Subscr. to: Postfach 5440, 30054 Hannover, Germany) Ed. Andreas Schirmer. adv. contact: Heinz Buse. circ. 14,808. (back issues avail.) Document type: consumer publication.
—CCC.

796 371.17   SZ   ISSN 0428-1659
FEDERATION INTERNATIONALE DE GYMNASTIQUE. BULLETIN. 1950. q. 30 SFr. (foreign 45 SFr.). Federation Internationale de Gymnastique, c/o Norbert Bueche, Secretary, Rue des Oeuches 10, Case Postale 359, CH-2740 Moutier 1, Switzerland. TEL 032-936666. FAX 032-936671. TELEX 934961-FIG-CH. adv. Indexed: Sportsearch (1981-). Document type: bulletin.

799.3   CN   ISSN 0226-773X
FEDERATION OF CANADIAN ARCHERS. RULES BOOK. (Editions in English and French) 1984. irreg. Can.$10. Federation of Canadian Archers - Federation Canadienne des Archers, 1600 James Naismith Dr., Gloucester, ON K1B 5N4, Canada. TEL 613-748-5604. FAX 613-748-5785. TELEX 053-3660.

FELD WALD WASSER; schweizerische Jagdzeitung. see CONSERVATION

796 305.4   NE   ISSN 1381-2556
FEMINALE. 1990. 2/yr. N O C - N S F, Postbus 302, 6800 AH Arnhem, Netherlands. TEL 31-8308-34400. FAX 31-8308-21245. Document type: newsletter.
Description: Covers all aspects of women and sports.

794.1   GW   ISSN 0863-0534
FERNSCHACH DER D D R. 1979. 6/yr. Doebritscher Strasse 57B, 99441 Grosswabhausen, Germany. Ed. Hans Rabold.

FERRARI ITALIAN STYLE; periodico internazionale d'immagine, automobilismo e cultura. see TRANSPORTATION — Automobiles

796.355   US   ISSN 0275-5394 GV1017.H7
FIELD HOCKEY RULEBOOK. a. $4. National Federation of State High School Associations, 11724 N.W. Plaza Circle, Box 20626, Kansas City, MO 64195-0626. TEL 816-464-5400. FAX 816-464-5571. Ed. Susan True.

796.815   UK
FIGHTERS; the martial arts magazine. 1978. m. £18 (foreign £24). Peterson Publications Ltd., Peterson House, Northbank, Berryhill Industrial Estate, Droitwich, Worcs. WR9 9BL, England. TEL 0905-795564. FAX 0905-795905. Ed. Bruce P. Ayling. adv.; illus. circ. 26,000. (back issues avail.) Document type: consumer publication.
Formerly: Fighters Monthly (ISSN 0260-4965)
Description: Presents all martial arts styles and techniques, including reports on all major championships.

796.8   US   ISSN 0146-8812
FIGHTING WOMAN NEWS. 1975. q. $15. 6741 Tung Ave. W., Theodore, AL 36582-6233. TEL 334-653-0549. Ed. Debra Pettis. adv. contact: Debra Pettis. bk.rev.; charts; illus. circ. 4,100. Indexed: Wom.Stud.Abstr.
—CCC.
Description: Communications medium for women in martial arts, self-defense and combative sports.

790.1   US   ISSN 0147-0051
FIRE & MOVEMENT; the forum of conflict simulation. 1976. 7/yr. $25 (foreign $32). Decision Games, Box 4048, Lancaster, CA 93539. TEL 805-723-2088. Ed. David W. Nicholas; Pub. Christopher Cummins. adv. contact: Callie Cummins. bk.rev. circ. 4,000. (back issues avail.) Document type: consumer publication.
Description: Publishes reviews of historical board games and computer war games.

338 799.2082   US
FIREARMS BUSINESS. s-m. $126 (foreign $150) (effective 1996). Belvoir Publications, Inc., 75 Holly Hill Ln., Box 2626, Greenwich, CT 06836-2626. TEL 203-661-6111. FAX 203-661-4802. (Subscr. to: Box 420234, Palm Coast, FL 32142) Document type: consumer publication.

796.83   US
FISTIC FEVER; the boxing memorabilia magazine. 1992. bi-m. $30 (Canada $35, Europe $40, Asia/Pacific Rim $45). Ron Marshall, Ed. & Pub., Box 24111, Oakland, CA 94623-1111. TEL 510-874-4910. FAX 510-452-0827. adv. contact: J.D. Schwartz. circ. 600. Document type: newsletter.

FIT FOR FUN. see PHYSICAL FITNESS AND HYGIENE

FITNESS & SPORTS REVIEW INTERNATIONAL; specializing in track and field, weightlifting (weight training) and sports medicine. see MEDICAL SCIENCES — Sports Medicine

796.2 658   US
FITNESS EQUIPMENT DEALER. bi-m. Virgo Publishing, Inc., 4141 N. Scottsdale, No. 316, Scottsdale, AZ 85251. TEL 602-990-1101. FAX 602-990-0819. Ed. Michael A. Nichols.

796   RU   ISSN 0130-5670
FIZKULTURA I SPORT. 1922. m. $55 (effective 1996). Izdatel'stvo Fizkul'tura i Sport, Kalyaevskaya ul., 27, 101421, Russia. TEL 095-258-2690. FAX 095-200-1217. (Subscr. to: Sport Books, Ul. Sretenka 9, Moscow, Russia; Dist. in U.S. by: Victor Kamkin Inc., 4956 Boiling Brook Pkwy., Rockville, MD 20852. TEL 301-881-1637. FAX 301-881-1637) Ed. A.M. Chaikovksii. bibl.; illus.; index. circ. 717,000.

FLIEGER-REVUE. see AERONAUTICS AND SPACE FLIGHT

FLORAL UNDERAWL & GAZETTE TIMES. see HOBBIES

779.202   US
FOULING SHOT. 1977. bi-m. $14. Cast Bullet Association, Inc., 4103 Foxcraft Dr., Traverse City, MI 49684. TEL 314-425-2466. Ed. Glenn Latham. adv.; bk.rev.; cum.index: 1977-1988. circ. 1,600. (back issues avail.)
Description: Disseminates technology of cast lead bullets for target shooting and hunting.

SPORTS AND GAMES

790.1 FR
FRANCE. SECRETARIAT D'ETAT A LA JEUNESSE ET AUX SPORTS. BULLETIN OFFICIEL. 22/yr. 235 F. (foreign 287 F.). Centre National de Documentation Pedagogique, 29, rue d'Ulm, 75230 Paris Cedex 05, France. TEL 46-34-90-00. (Subscr. to: CNDP-Abonnements, B.P. 7, 21 Square St. Charles, 75012 Paris, France)
    Former titles: France. Ministere de la Jeunesse et des Sport. Bulletin Officiel; France. Secretariat a la Jeunesse et aux Sport. Bulletin Officiel.

796 FR ISSN 0071-9102
FRANCE - SPORTS. (Text in French; summaries in English, German, Italian and Spanish) 1954. biennial. 232 F. C E P P Publications, 1 Place d'Estienne d'Orves, 75009 Paris, France. TEL 42-80-67-62. FAX 42-82-99-30. Ed. Martine Clavel. adv. circ. 8,500.

790.1 NO ISSN 0332-9666
FRIIDRETT. m.(10/yr.). NOK 340 in Nordic countries; elsewhere $72 (effective 1996). (Norwegian Athletics Association) Scandinavian University Press, P.O. Box 2959 Toeyen, N-9698 Oslo, Norway. TEL 47-22-57-54-00. FAX 47-22-57-53-53. Ed. Morten Olsen. adv. circ. 7,500.
    —CCC.
    Description: Focuses on athletics in Norway.

796 SW ISSN 0046-5135
FRIIDROTT. 1972. 14/yr. SEK 649 in Nordic countries; elsewhere SEK 749. (Svenska Fri-Idrottsfoerbundet) Cewe-Foerlaget AB, P.O. Box 77, S-2890 10 Bjaesta, Sweden. TEL 0660-309-65. FAX 0660-305-17. (Subscr. to: PK-Banken, Box 365, 891 01 Oernskoeldsvik, Sweden) Ed. Charlie Wedin. adv.; bk.rev.

FRITID VED D S B. see *HOBBIES*

FRITIDSHANDLAREN. see *SPORTS AND GAMES — Bicycles And Motorcycles*

340 US ISSN 1054-1950
KF3989.A15
FROM THE GYM TO THE JURY. 1989. 5/yr. $55. Center for Sports Law and Risk Management, 6917 Wildglen Dr., Dallas, TX 75230. TEL 214-360-9691. Eds. Herb Appenzeller, Ronald Baron. index. *Document type:* newsletter.

794 336.1 US ISSN 1047-8493
FROM THE STATE CAPITALS. LOTTERY, PARIMUTUEL AND CASINO REGULATION. Variant title: Lottery, Parimutuel and Casino Regulation from the State Capitals. 1990. w. $295 (foreign $315). Wakeman-Walworth, Inc., 300 N. Washington St., Alexandria, VA 22314. TEL 703-549-8606. FAX 703-549-1372.
    Description: Covers regulation and development of state lottery programs, casinos and pari-mutuel wagering operations.

790.1 617.1 CC
FUJIAN TIYU KEJI/FUJIAN SPORTS SCIENCE AND TECHNOLOGY. (Text in Chinese) q. Y3. Fujiansheng Tiyu Kexue Yanjiusuo - Fujian Sports Science Institute, No. 17, Zhuangyuan Xiang, Wusi Lu, Fuzhou, Fujian 350005, People's Republic of China. TEL 554963. (Dist. overseas by: Jiangsu Publications Import & Export Corp., 56 Gao Yun Ling, Nanjing, Jiangsu, P.R.C.) (Co-sponsor: Fujian Tiyu Kexue Xuehui) Ed. He Fangsheng.
    Description: Covers sports theory, training, psychology, medicine as well as sports biophysics and biochemistry.

796 AT ISSN 0157-5295
FUN RUNNER. 1979. bi-m. Aus.$43 for 2 years. Triathlon Sports Pty. Ltd., P.O. Box 2590, Taren Point, N.S.W. 22229, Australia. TEL 02-524-1455. FAX 02-524-1454. Ed. Wayne Larden. adv.; B&W page Aus.$740, colof page Aus.$1320. bk.rev. circ. 17,500. *Indexed:* Sportsearch (1980-).
    Incorporates: Australasian Track and Field.

FUSSBALLTRAINING. see *SPORTS AND GAMES — Ball Games*

790.1 IE ISSN 0791-1521
GAELIC SPORT. 1958. m. 80p. per no. Holyrood Publications Ltd., 139a Lower Drumcondra Rd., Dublin 9, Ireland. Ed. Thomas McQuaid. adv. contact: Paul Gibson. bk.rev. circ. 42,650. *Indexed:* Sportsearch. *Document type:* consumer publication.

790.1 059.916 IE ISSN 0332-1274
GAELIC WORLD; iris oifigiuil Cumann Luthchleas Gael. 1979. m. I£18 (Europe I£30; U.S. I£45). Costar Associates, 10 Burgh Quay, Dublin 2, Ireland. TEL 679-2011. FAX 679-2016. Ed. Mick Dunne; Pub. Mick Wright. adv. contact: Mick Wright. bk.rev.; illus. *Document type:* consumer publication.

798.8 SP
GALGOS. vol.29, 1977. bi-m. 1500 ptas. (effective Apr. 1991). Federacion Espanola de Galgos, Barquillo 19, 28004 Madrid, Spain. FAX 522-43-44. adv. circ. 2,500.
    Formerly (until Oct. 1979): Federacion Espanola Galguera. Boletin Mensual Informativo.

794.1 GW ISSN 0937-5457
GAMBIT REVUE. (Text in English and German) 1987. 4/yr. DM.35. Schachverlag Manfred Maedler, Lilienthalstr. 52, 40474 Duesseldorf, Germany. TEL 0211-453186. Ed. Volker Drueke. *Document type:* consumer publication.
    Description: Includes over 450 gambits by white and black, opening theory, and information articles.

791.8 US ISSN 0016-4313
GAMECOCK. 1935. m. (Aug.-Sep. combined). $20. Marburger Publishing Co., Inc., Box 158, Hartford, AR 72938-0158. Ed. J.C. Griffiths. adv. circ. 14,300.

GAMEPRO. see *COMPUTERS — Computer Games*

790.1 US ISSN 0199-9788
GV1199
GAMES; puzzles, games, tests, contests, features. 1977-1990; resumed 1991. bi-m. $17.97 (foreign $27.97). B & P Publishing Company, Inc., 575 Boylston St., Boston, MA 02116-3607. TEL 617-536-5536. (Subscr. to: Games Magazine, Box 605, Mt. Morris, IL 61054-0605. TEL 800-827-8256; Editorial addr.: 19 W. 21st St., New York, NY 10010. TEL 212-727-7100. FAX 212-727-7661) Ed. R. Wayne Schmittberger; Pub. Alan Segal. adv.; bk.rev.; illus. *Indexed:* Jun.High.Mag.Abstr. *Document type:* consumer publication.
    Description: For people who enjoy solving puzzles and playing games.

790.1 330 US ISSN 8750-8222
HV6715
GAMING & WAGERING BUSINESS. m. $60. B M T Communications, Inc., 7 Penn Plaza, New York, NY 10001-3900. TEL 212-594-4120. FAX 212-714-0514. Ed. Paul Dworin. circ. 10,817.
    Formerly: Gaming Business (ISSN 0196-2213)

790.1 US ISSN 1071-9350
GAMING PRODUCTS AND SERVICES. 1993. m. $36 (Canada $45; elsewhere $95) (effective 1995). R C M Enterprises, Inc., 15500 Wayzata Blvd., Ste. 922, Box 720, Wayzata, MN 55391. TEL 612-473-5088. FAX 612-473-7068. Ed. Nick Motu; Pub. Robert C. Mead. adv.; B&W page $1705; adv. contact: Jim Peningroth. circ. 3,500. (back issues avail.) *Document type:* trade publication.
    Description: Covers products, services and trends affecting the gaming industry.

GAMING SYSTEMS SOURCE DIRECTORY. see *BUSINESS AND ECONOMICS — Trade And Industrial Directories*

794.1 GW
GARDEZ. 1981. 3/yr. DM.10. Seidenbenderstr. 74, 67549 Worms, Germany. TEL 06241-54488. Eds. Achim Berkes, Joerg Berkes. adv. circ. 150. *Document type:* bulletin.

790.1 PO ISSN 0870-1989
GAZETA DOS DESPORTOS. 1981. 3/w. $90. Rua dos Caetanos 26 - 1o, 1200 Lisbon, Portugal. TEL 346-05-17. FAX 346-05-44. Ed. Eugenio Queiros. *Document type:* newspaper.

790.1 BL
GAZETA ESPORTIVA. d. Fundacao Casper Libero, Av. Paulisto 900, Sao Paulo, SP, Brazil. Ed. Olimioda Silva e Sa. adv.

790.1 IT ISSN 1120-5067
GAZZETTA DELLO SPORT. 1897. d. R C S Editoriale Quotidiani S.p.A., Via Solferino 28, 20121 Milan, Italy. TEL 2-6339. FAX 2-65-98-936. TELEX 321697 G SPORT. Ed. Candido Cannavo. circ. 541,556.

790.1 GW ISSN 0343-6586
GERMANY. BUNDESINSTITUT FUER SPORTWISSENSCHAFT. SPORTWISSENSCHAFTLICHE FORSCHUNGSPROJEKTE ERHEBUNG (YEAR). 1974. a. free. Bundesinstitut fuer Sportwissenschaft - Federal Institute of Sport Science, Carl-Diem-Weg 4, 50933 Cologne, Germany. TEL 0221-4979126. FAX 0221-495164. Eds. H. Fleischer, L. Muelfarth. circ. 400. (back issues avail.) *Document type:* government publication.

796.41 IT ISSN 0017-0046
GINNASTA. (Supplement avail.: Gymnica) 1895. m. L.15000 (foreign L.20000). Federazione Ginnastica d'Italia, Palazzo delle Federazioni Sportive, Viale Tiziano 70, 00196 Rome, Italy. TEL 06-36858175. Ed. Bruno Grandi. adv.; charts; illus. circ. 1,500.
    Description: Covers gymnastics with special focus on the Italians in international competititon, as well as profiles of the athletes and coaches.

688.76 IT
GIORNALE DEGLI ARTICOLI SPORTIVI. 1966. 10/yr. Edizioni Miglio, Residenza I Portici, 20090 Segrate (Milan 2), Italy. TEL 39-2-2640989. FAX 39-2-2640989. Ed. P. Bellavista. adv.; B&W page L.2600000, color page L.4400000. circ. 6,000.

GIRLJOCK. see *HOMOSEXUALITY*

796.41 US ISSN 1069-6393
GV464
GIRLS GYMNASTICS RULES AND MANUAL. Key Title: High School Girls Gymnastics Rules and Manual. a. $4. National Federation of State High School Associations, 11724 N.W. Plaza Circle, Box 20626, Kansas City, MO 64195-0626. TEL 816-464-5400. FAX 816-464-5571.
    Former titles (until 1992): Official High School Girls Gymnastics Rules and Manual (ISSN 0739-9804); (until 1982): Girls Gymnastics Rule Book and Manual (ISSN 0731-8537); (until 1981): Girls Gymnastics Rules (ISSN 0270-2029); *Incorporates:* Girls Gymnastics Manual.

797.55 796.522 SZ
GLEITSCHIRM; Zeitschrift fuer Gleitschirmflieger. (Text in German) 10/yr. 80 SFr. (foreign 96 SFr.). Gasser AG, Kasernstr. 1, CH-7007 Chur, Switzerland. TEL 081-235249. FAX 081-235207. Ed. Notker Ledergerber. adv. circ. 25,000.
    Description: Explores paragliding.

793 JA
GO/IGO. (Text in Japanese) 1951. m. 13860 Yen. Seibundo Shinkosha Publishing Co. Ltd., 1-13-7 Yayoi-cho, Nakano-ku, Tokyo 164, Japan. Ed. Yuzaburo Takeda. circ. 55,000.

790.1 JA ISSN 0286-0376
GV1459
GO WORLD. (Text in English) 1977. q. $20 (Europe £20). Kiseido Publishing Company, C.P.O. Box 2126, Tokyo, Japan. TEL 0467-83-4369. FAX 0467-83-4710. E-mail: SGT00076@niftyserve.or.jp. (Subscr. in US to: KISEIDO, 454 Las Gallinas Ave., Ste. 255, San Rafael, CA 94903-3618. TEL 415-499-1543; Alt. addr.: 20 Bruges Pl., London NW1 0TE, England) Ed. Richard Bozulich. adv.; bk.rev.; index. circ. 10,500.
    —UnCover.
    Description: Covers all the important tournaments of Go in Japan, Korea, and China. Also contains instructional articles.

796 US
GOAL LINE.* 1965. q. $35. National Art Museum of Sport, 1220 Waterway Blvd., Indianapolis, IN 46202-2157. TEL 317-687-1715. FAX 317-687-1718. Ed.Bd. circ. 4,500. (back issues avail.)
    Formerly (until 1990): National Art Museum of Sport Newsletter.

GOL; fodbalovy a hokejovy tydenik. see *SPORTS AND GAMES — Ball Games*

790.1 GW
GOLF TENNIS POLO; magazine for sports, journeys, pastime, society and fashion. (Text in German) 1986. 3/yr. DM.32. Reinhold Sommerfeld GmbH, Kaiserstr. 9, 80801 Munich, Germany. TEL 089-399012. TELEX 5215031. circ. 30,000. (back issues avail.)

SPORTS AND GAMES

796.72 629.283   US
GOODGUYS GOODTIMES GAZETTE. 1988. m. $20. Goodguys Enterprises, Inc., Box 424, Alamo, CA 94507. TEL 510-838-9876. FAX 510-820-8241. Ed. Steve Anderson; Pub. Tim Holt. adv. contact: Jack Williams. circ. 28,000. **Document type:** consumer publication.
   Description: Covers motorsports-hobbyist activities. Includes personality profiles.

790   AG   ISSN 0017-291X
GRAFICO. 1919. w. Editorial Atlantida, S. A., Azopardo 579, 1307 Buenos Aires, Argentina. TEL 33-4591. TELEX 21163. Ed. Constancio C. Vigil. illus. circ. 127,000.

793   SP
GRANDES CASINOS DE ESPANA. 4/yr. Hermosilla 8, 28001 Madrid, Spain. TEL 1-431-84-22. FAX 1-575-18-96. Ed. Pedro Galindo Guerra. circ. 25,000.

790.1   UK
GRASP. 1981. m. £25 (foreign £30 ($50)). Trevor Low, Ed. & Pub., Main St., Bruntingthorpe, Leicestershire LE17 5QF, England. TEL 0533-478766. bk.rev. **Indexed:** Sportsearch (1983-).

796.72   AT   ISSN 0811-546X
THE GREAT RACE; official book of the Bathurst 1000. 1981. a. Aus.$45. Chevron Publishing Group Pty. Ltd., P.O. Box 206, Hornsby, N.S.W. 2077, Australia. TEL 02-476-3195. FAX 02-476-5739. Ed. Thomas B. Floyd. adv. contact: Ray Berghouse. circ. 20,000. **Document type:** consumer publication.
   Formerly: James Hardie 1000.
   Description: Describes a week in the event of a single motor race.

798.8   UK   ISSN 0017-4157
GREYHOUND. 1968. m. £17 (rest of Europe £22; elsewhere £34). Orchestrate Ltd., Pixmore Centre, Pixmore Ave., Letchworth, Herts. SG6 1JG, England. TEL 01462-679439. FAX 01462-485512. Ed. Floyd Amphlett. adv.; bk.rev.; bibl.; charts; illus.; mkt.; stat. circ. 14,760. **Document type:** newspaper.
   Description: Highlights dog racing.

GREYHOUND ADVISER. see PETS

798.8 798.8   IE
GREYHOUND NEWS. (Text in English) 1982. m. I£18($33) Meath Chronicle Ltd., Market Square, Navan, Co. Meath, Ireland. TEL 046-21442. FAX 046-23565. Ed. John Davis. circ. 6,767. (tabloid format)

GREYHOUND RECORDER. see PETS

798.8   US   ISSN 1042-4016
GREYHOUND REVIEW. 1911. m. $30. National Greyhound Association, Box 543, Abilene, KS 67410. TEL 913-263-4660. FAX 913-263-4689. Ed. Gary Guccione. adv.; bk.rev.; illus.; stat. circ. 6,000. (tabloid format)
   —UnCover.
   Formerly: Coursing News (ISSN 0045-8929)
   Description: Features greyhound racing news, regional correspondence, pedigree analyses, and records of breeding.

796.72   BL   ISSN 0104-2351
GRID. 1993. m. Editora Azul, S.A., Av. Nacoes Unidas 5777, 05479-900 Sao Paulo, Brazil. TEL 011-816-7866. FAX 011-813-9115. Ed. Jorge de Souza. adv.; charts; illus.; stat. circ. 45,000. **Document type:** consumer publication.
   Description: Details automobile racing.

791.8   US   ISSN 0017-4297
GRIT AND STEEL. 1899. m. $15. De Camp Publishing Co., Gaffney, SC 29342. TEL 803-489-2324. Ed. Mary M. Hodge. adv.; illus. circ. 6,000.
   Description: Highlights cock fighting.

794.1   GW
GROB ANGRIFF. 15. 6/yr. DM.20. Koernerstrasse 15, 34123 Kassel, Germany. Ed. Peter Elger.
   Description: Devoted exclusively to chess games and theory of the opening that was popularized by the Swiss I M, Henri Grob.

GROUNDSMAN. see SPORTS AND GAMES — Outdoor Life

790.1   IT   ISSN 1122-1712
GUERIN SPORTIVO; il settimanale di critica e politica sportiva. 1912. w. (50/yr.). L.370000 in America. Conti Editore S.p.A., Via del Lavoro, 7, 40068 San Lazzaro di Savena (BO), Italy. TEL 051-6227111. FAX 051-6257627. Ed. Marino Bartoletti. adv.: B&W page L.13500000, color page L.18000000; 185 x 252. circ. 68,309. **Document type:** consumer publication.

THE GUINNESS BOOK OF SPORTS RECORDS. see ENCYCLOPEDIAS AND GENERAL ALMANACS

GUN DIGEST. see HOBBIES

GUN REPORT; dedicated to the interests of antique and collectable gun enthusiasts everywhere. see HOBBIES

799.202   US   ISSN 0883-4431
TS532.4
GUN TRADERS GUIDE. 1953. a. $19.95. Stoeger Publishing Co., 55 Ruta Ct., S. Hackensack, NJ 07606. TEL 201-440-2700. Ed. John Traister; Pub. David C. Perkins. adv. contact: David C. Perkins. **Document type:** directory, consumer publication.

799.3   US   ISSN 0017-5641
GUN WORLD; for the firearms & hunting enthusiast. 1960. 13/yr. $20. Gallant - Charger Publishing, Inc., 34249 Camino Capistrano, Box HH, Capistrano Beach, CA 92624. TEL 714-493-2101. Ed. Dean A. Grennell. adv.; bk.rev.; illus. circ. 130,000. (also avail. in microform from UMI; reprint service avail. from UMI) **Document type:** consumer publication.
   —UMI.
   Description: Covers all facets of shooting, with emphasis on new firearms.

799.3   US   ISSN 0017-5676
GUNS; finest in the firearms field. (Annual supplement avail.) 1955. m. $19.95. Publishers' Development Corp., 591 Camino de la Reina, Ste. 200, San Diego, CA 92108. TEL 619-297-5350. FAX 619-297-5353. TELEX 695-478. Ed. Scott Farrell. adv. contact: Joe McMahon. bk.rev. circ. 205,619.
   Formerly: Guns Magazine.

799.202   AT   ISSN 0157-1729
GUNS AUSTRALIA. bi-m. Aus.$25.50 (foreign Aus.$74) (effective Feb. 1995). Yaffa Publishing Group, 17-21 Bellevue St., Surry Hills, N.S.W. 2010, Australia. TEL 61-2-281-2333. FAX 61-2-281-2750. Ed. Ray Galea. adv.: B&W page Aus.$1050, color page Aus.$1465; trim 273 x 210. circ. 11,025. **Document type:** consumer publication.
   Description: Firearm enthusiasts' magazine which concentrates on hardware, ammunition, as well as shooting techniques.

GUNS ILLUSTRATED (YEAR). see HOBBIES

GUNS REVIEW. see HOBBIES

799.202   US
GUNSITE NEWSLETTER. 1981. irreg. (approx. 12/yr.). $20. Gunsite, Box 700, Paulden, AZ 86334-0700. TEL 602-636-4565. FAX 602-636-1236. Ed. Richard Jee. circ. 600. (looseleaf format; back issues avail.)
   Formerly: Gunsite Gossip.

790.1   CC
GUOJI XIANGQI/CHESS. (Text in Chinese) bi-m. Shu-Rong Qiyi Chubanshe, 9, Qinglong Xiang, Chengdu, Sichuan 610031, People's Republic of China. TEL 28479. Ed. Liu Shancheng.

796.41   DK   ISSN 0108-3678
GYMNASTIK. 1982. m. DKK 125. Dansk Gymnastik Forbund, Idraettens Hus, 2605 Broendby, Denmark. FAX 45-43-26-26-10. TELEX 33 111 (IDRAET DK). Ed. Hans-Christian Jacobsen. adv.; bk.rev.; illus. circ. 3,000.
   Formerly (until 1982): Vidar (ISSN 0108-366X)
   Description: Reports on gymnastics competitions and informs on coming competitions; articles on gymnastics research.

796.41   NO   ISSN 0017-596X
GYMNASTIKK OG TURN. 1948. 10/yr. NOK 75. Norges Gymnastikk- og Turnforbund, Hauger Skolevei 1, 1351 Run, Norway. Ed. Thorf E. Thoresen. adv.; illus.
   —CCC.

796.41   IT
GYMNICA. (Supplement to: Il Ginnasta) vol.4, 1987. m. L.10000 (foreign L.15000). Federazione Ginnastica d'Italia, Palazzo delle Federazioni Sportive, 00196 Rome, Italy. TEL (06)36858175. Ed. Bruno Grandi. charts; illus.; stat.
   Description: Covers gymnastics with diagrams and illustrations of the various movements and gestures.

790.1   US   ISSN 0898-6894
TL1
H P V NEWS. m. $25 (foreign $30) includes Human Power. International Human-Powered-Vehicle Association, Box 51255, Indianapolis, IN 46251-0255. TEL 317-876-9478. Ed. Len Brunkalla. illus. **Indexed:** Sportsearch (1983-). **Document type:** newsletter.

790   GW   ISSN 0944-5293
H S V - JOURNAL. 1959. s-m. avail. upon request. Hamburger Sport - Verein e.V., Rothenbaumchaussee 125, 20149 Hamburg, Germany. TEL 040-4155-0. FAX 040-4155109. Ed.Bd. adv. circ. 20,000.
   Formerly: H S V - Post (ISSN 0017-6257)

AL-HADAF. see SPORTS AND GAMES — Horses And Horsemanship

790.1   US
HALL OF FAME NEWS. 1979. q. donation. International Tennis Hall of Fame, 100 Park Ave., New York, NY 10017. TEL 212-880-4179. Ed. Bettina Mikelberg. circ. 15,000. **Document type:** newsletter.
   Description: Discusses Hall of Fame activities and reports.

790   GW   ISSN 0017-6982
HAMBURGER SPORT - MITTEILUNGEN. 1949. w. DM.60. (Hamburger SportBund e.V.) Sport- und Jugend-Verlag GmbH und Co. KG, Laemmersieth 21, 22305 Hamburg, Germany. Ed. Anne Heitmann. adv.; bk.rev. circ. 5,500.

796   AU
HANDBALL IN OESTERREICH. irreg. S.80 (foreign S.120). Oesterreichischer Handball Bund, Hauslabgasse 24a, A-1050 Vienna, Austria. TEL 01-554379. FAX 01-552712. Ed. Alexandra Toncourt. adv. circ. 8,000. **Document type:** bulletin.
   Formerly (until 1988): Handball und Faustball in Oesterreich (ISSN 0072-9698)

790.1   GW   ISSN 0174-1209
HANDBUCH DES BERLINER SPORTS. 1976. a. DM.24.60. (Landessportbund Berlin e.V.) Schors-Verlags-Gesellschaft mbH, Postfach 1280, 65522 Niedernhausen, Germany. TEL 06127-8029. FAX 06127-8812. Ed. Dietrich Dolgner. circ. 19,000.

790.1   GW   ISSN 0174-1217
HANDBUCH DES BREMER SPORTS; fuer Sportler und Sportinteressierte. 1975. a. DM.24.60. (Landessportbund Bremen e.V.) Schors-Verlags-Gesellschaft mbH, Postfach 1280, 65522 Niedernhausen, Germany. TEL 06127-8029. FAX 06127-8812. Ed. Rudolf Kauer. circ. 14,000.

790.1   GW   ISSN 0174-1195
HANDBUCH DES HAMBURGER SPORTS. 1976. a. DM.24.60. (Hamburger Sport-Bund e.V.) Schors-Verlags-Gesellschaft mbH, Postfach 1280, 65522 Niedernhausen, Germany. TEL 06127-8029. FAX 06127-8812. Eds. Dirk Dieckwisch, Andreas Ohlrogge. circ. 15,000.

790.1   GW   ISSN 0174-1187
HANDBUCH DES SPORTS IN HESSEN; fuer alle Sportler und Sportinteressierte. 1977. a. DM.24.60. (Landessportbund Hessen e.V.) Schors-Verlags-Gesellschaft mbH, Postfach 1280, 6272 Niedernhausen, Germany. TEL 06127-8029. FAX 06127-8812. circ. 39,000.

799.202   US   ISSN 0746-6625
THE HANDGUNNER. bi-m. $4. U S Revolver Association, 40 Larchmont Ave., Taunton, MA 02780-1397. Ed. Brian Barer. adv. contact: Brian Barer. circ. 1,500 (paid). (tabloid format; back issues avail.) **Document type:** newsletter.
   Description: Contains information on pistol target shooting and pistol matches.

SPORTS AND GAMES

799.202 UK ISSN 0260-8693
HANDGUNNER: BRITAIN'S FOREMOST FIREARMS JOURNAL. 1980. 6/yr. £13 (rest of Europe £15; elsewhere £17($30)). Piedmont Publishing, Ltd., Seychelles House, Brightlingsea, Essex CO7 0NN, England. TEL 01206-305204. Ed. Richard A.I. Munday. adv.: B&W page £450; color page £600; adv. contact: Tony Smith. bk.rev.; illus. circ. 20,000. (back issues avail.) **Document type:** consumer publication.
  Description: Covers all aspects of modern small arms for a high-level professional readership worldwide.

HANDGUNS (YEAR). see *HOBBIES*

HANDLOADER'S DIGEST. see *HOBBIES*

796 UK ISSN 0073-0416
HARPERS GUIDE TO SPORTS TRADE. 1948. a. £88($138) (includes Harpers Sport & Leisure). Harpers Publishing, 47A High St., Bushey, Watford, Herts. WD2 1BD, England. TEL 0181-950-9522. FAX 0181-950-7998. Ed. Martin Johnson; Pub. Martin Johnson. adv. contact: Gregg Allen. circ. 3,600. **Document type:** directory.
  Description: Lists sports goods manufacturers and distributors in the U.K.

796.077 688.76 US ISSN 1051-6905
HI-TECH COACHING & TRAINING. (Includes a. Product and Service Directory) 1990. m. Publications & Communications, Inc., 12416 Hymeadow, Austin, TX 78750-1896. TEL 512-250-9023; 800-678-9724. FAX 512-331-3900. adv.: B&W page $2831, color page $3531; 10 x 13 1/4. (tabloid format) **Document type:** trade publication, directory.
  Description: Provides a handy reference guide for coaches, athletic trainers, and athletic directors.

790.1 VE
HIPODROMO. m. Apdo. 1192, Caracas, Venezuela. circ. 98,140.

790.1 US ISSN 0896-1379
GV859
HISTORICAL ROLLER SKATING OVERVIEW. 1982. bi-m. $15 membership. National Museum of Roller Skating, 4730 South St., Box 6759, Lincoln, NE 68506. TEL 402-483-7551. FAX 402-483-1465. E-mail: rllrsktmus.aol.comm. Ed. Scott A. Wilhite. illus. circ. 600. (back issues avail.) **Document type:** newsletter.
  Description: Covers skating in the history of American popular culture.

797.55 629.13 IT
HOBBY VOLO. 9/yr. L.70000. Zanfi Editori s.r.l., Via Emilia Ovest 954, 41100 Modena, Italy. TEL 39-59-981700. FAX 39-59-891701. adv.: B&W page L.1050000, color page L.1500000. circ. 27,000. **Document type:** consumer publication.
  Description: Reports on hang-gliding, paragliding, parachuting and ultralight flying.

790.1 613.7 GW
378.198
HOCHSCHULSPORT. 1953. s-a. Technische Universitaet Muenchen, Sportzentrum, Abteilung Hochschulsport, Connollystr. 32, 80809 Munich, Germany. TEL 089-35491-1. adv. circ. 70,000.

796.962 SW ISSN 0345-4347
HOCKEY. 1965. m. SEK 595 in Nordic countries; elsewhere SEK 695. (Svenska Ishockeyfoerbundet) CeWe-Foerlaget AB, P.O. Box 77, S-890 10 Bjaesta, Sweden. TEL 0660-309-65. FAX 0660-305-17. (Subscr. to: PK-Banken, Box 365, 891 01 Oernskoeldsvik, Sweden) Ed. Charlie Wedin. adv.; bk.rev.
  Incorporates (in 1974): Svenskt Ishockeymagasin (ISSN 0049-2698)

796 GW ISSN 0942-3486
HOCKEY. 1947. 42/yr. DM.187.83 (foreign DM.219.20). Sportverlag Schmidt und Dreisilker GmbH, Postfach 260, 71044 Sindelfingen, Germany. TEL 07031-862800. FAX 07031-862801. circ. 3,300. **Document type:** consumer publication.
  Former titles (until 1992): D H Z. Deutsche Hockey-Zeitung (ISSN 0936-5176); (until 1989): Deutsche Hockey-Zeitung (ISSN 0720-0765); (until 1980): Hockey (ISSN 0342-4413)

796.355 AT ISSN 0018-2982
HOCKEY CIRCLE. 1933. q. Aus.$4. (Australian Hockey Association) Sportstalk Publications, P.O. Box 127, Glen Iris, Vic. 3146, Australia. Ed. Richard E. Blaze. adv.; illus. circ. 5,000. **Indexed:** Sportsearch.

796.962 US ISSN 0046-7693
GV846
HOCKEY DIGEST. 1972. m. (8/yr.). $22 (foreign $30). Century Publishing Co., 990 Grove St., Evanston, IL 60201-4370. TEL 708-491-6440. (Subscr. to: Box 572, Mt. Morris, IL 61054-0572. TEL 800-877-5893) Ed. Ken Leiker. adv.; charts; illus.; stat. circ. 110,000. (also avail. in microform from UMI; back issues avail.; reprint service avail. from UMI) **Indexed:** Sports Per.Ind., Sportsearch. **Document type:** consumer publication.
  —UMI.
  Description: For serious NHL Hockey fans who want the statistics, features and excitement behind the action of the sport.

796 US
HOCKEY ILLUSTRATED. vol.13, 1973. 3/yr. Sterling - Macfadden Partnership, 233 Park Ave. S., New York, NY 10003. TEL 212-780-3500. FAX 212-780-3555. Ed. Stephen Ciacciarelli. adv.; charts; illus. **Indexed:** Sports Per.Ind. **Document type:** consumer publication.
  Formerly: Sport Heroes (ISSN 0049-190X)

796 US ISSN 1064-6892
GV848.4.U6
HOCKEY MAGAZINE. 1988. 7/yr. $17.95. The Publishing Group, Inc., 1200 7th St., Minneapolis, MN 55411-4000. TEL 612-522-1200. FAX 612-522-1182. adv. circ. 9,877. **Document type:** consumer publication.
  Formerly: Minnesota Hockey (ISSN 1050-740X)
  Description: Covers the NHL, plus collegiate, high school and amateur hockey, as well as history and controversial topics.

796.962 CN ISSN 0018-3016
HOCKEY NEWS; the international hockey weekly. 1947. w. (m. Jun.-Sep.). Transcontinental Sports Publications, 85 Scarsdale Rd., Ste. 100, Don Mills, ON M3B 2R2, Canada. TEL 416-445-5702. FAX 416-445-0753. (Subscr. to: Box 904, Buffalo, NY 14240) Ed. Steve Dryden. adv.; illus.; circ. 110,000 (paid). **Indexed:** Can.B.P.I., CMI, Sports Per.Ind., Sportsearch. **Document type:** consumer publication.
  —UMI.

796.962 US
HOCKEY PLAYER MAGAZINE. 1991. 12/yr. $17.95. Hockey Player Magazine L.P., Box 7494, Northridge, CA 91327-7494. TEL 800-807-2231. E-mail: HOCKEYMAG@Aol.com. Ed. Alex Casswell. adv.; circ. 20,000 (paid). **Document type:** consumer publication.
  Description: Written for and by recreational ice, roller and street hockey players. Each issue includes interviews, columns, departments, product news and playing tips to improve games.

796 UK ISSN 0073-3164
HOMING WORLD STUD BOOK. 1938. a. £2.50. Royal Pigeon Racing Association, Severn Farm Industrial Estate, Severn Rd., Welshool, Powys SY21 7DF, Wales. TEL 0938-2350. Ed. D.D. Glover. adv.

HORIZONTE; revista de educacao fisica e desporto. see *PHYSICAL FITNESS AND HYGIENE*

HOT ROD. see *TRANSPORTATION — Automobiles*

790.1 US ISSN 0898-6908
TL1
HUMAN POWER. 4/yr. $25 (foreign $30) includes H P V News. International Human-Powered-Vehicle Association, Box 51255, Indianapolis, IN 46251-0255. TEL 317-876-9478. Ed. David Gordon Wilson. illus. **Indexed:** Sportsearch (1981-). **Document type:** trade publication.
  —BLDSC (4336.363000).

790 IT ISSN 0018-7933
HURRA JUVENTUS. 1963. m. L.4000 per no. Gruppo Editoriale Fabbri, Via Mecenate 91, 20138 Milan, Italy. Ed. Giovanni Giovannini. adv.: color page L.22000000. illus. circ. 184,395.

I A S M H F NEWSLETTER. (International Association of Sports Museums and Halls of Fame) see *MUSEUMS AND ART GALLERIES*

796.72 US ISSN 1052-472X
I M S A ARROW. 1985. m. $39. International Motor Sports Association, 3502 Henderson Blvd., Tampa, FL 33609. TEL 813-877-4672. FAX 813-876-4604. Ed. Ken Breslauer. adv.: B&W page $600, color page $800; adv. contact: Kurtis Eide. bk.rev.; stat.; circ. 3,200 (paid). (back issues avail.) **Document type:** trade publication.

796.72 US
I M S A YEARBOOK. 1972. a. $29.95. International Motor Sports Association, 3502 Henderson Blvd., Tampa, FL 33609. TEL 813-877-4672. FAX 813-876-4604. adv.: B&W page $2350, color page $2950; trim 8 1/2 x 11. circ. 10,000.
  Description: Includes a photographic and statistical review of the past season, descriptions of seven racing series, historical data, race track data, market information, driver biographies, and membership and license information.

796 SZ
I S U CONSTITUTION. (Text in English) biennial; latest 1994. 10 SFr. International Skating Union, Postfach, CH-7270 Davos-Platz, Switzerland. TEL 081-437577. FAX 081-436671. **Document type:** bulletin.

796 SZ
I S U REGULATIONS. (Text in English) biennial; latest 1994. 20 SFr. International Skating Union, Postfach, CH-7270 Davos-Platz, Switzerland. TEL 081-437577. FAX 081-436671. **Document type:** bulletin.

796.962 UK
ICE HOCKEY. 1992. w. Powerplay Publications, 202a Lincoln Rd., Peterborough, Cambs. PE1 2NQ, England. **Document type:** consumer publication.

796.962 JA
ICE HOCKEY MAGAZINE. (Text in Japanese) 5/yr. 1950 Yen. Baseball Magazine Sha, 3-10-10 Misaki-cho, Chiyoda-ku, Tokyo, Japan. Ed. Kunihiro Otake.

796.962 US ISSN 0732-8117
GV847.5
ICE HOCKEY RULE BOOK. a. $4. National Federation of State High School Associations, 11724 N.W. Plaza Circle, Box 20626, Kansas City, MO 64195-0626. TEL 816-464-5400. FAX 816-464-5571. Ed. Richard G. Fawcett.

790.1 US
ICE SKATING INSTITUTE OF AMERICA. NEWSLETTER; the newsletter for rink owners and managers; skating instructors/coaches and the skating industry. Abbreviated title: I S I A Newsletter. 1961. 6/yr. $36. Ice Skating Institute of America, 355 W. Dundee Rd., Buffalo Grove, IL 60089-3500. TEL 708-808-7528. FAX 708-808-8329. Ed. Lara Lowery. adv. contact: Karen Schell. circ. 4,000 (paid). (back issues avail.) **Document type:** newsletter.
  Description: Features information on the ice skating industry, tips for instructors-coaches, concerns of rink owners-managers and explains ISIA services.

796.09489 DK ISSN 0900-8632
IDRAETSHISTORISK AARBOG. a. DKK 158.40. (Dansk Idraetshistorisk Forening) Odense University Press, Campusvej 55, DK-5230 Odense M, Denmark.

796 DK ISSN 0109-3835
IDRAETSLIV. 1949. 22/yr. DKK 250. Dansk Idraets-Forbund, Idraettens Hus, 2605 Broendby, Denmark. TEL 45-43-26-26-26. FAX 45-43-26-26-28. Ed. Morten Moelholm Hansen. adv. circ. 16.750.

796.72 SW ISSN 0345-5106
IDROTTSBLADET; motorsport. Abbreviated title: I B. 1910. fortn. SEK 375. (Svenska Bilsportfoerbundet) Idrottsbladet Foerlag AB, P.O. Box 19025, 152 25 Soedertaelje, Sweden. TEL 46-8-550-32770. FAX 46-8-550-12533. (Co-sponsor: Svenska Racerbaatfoerbundet) adv. circ. 20,000. **Document type:** newspaper.
  Incorporates: Rallysport Fart & Bilar.

796.42 US ISSN 0747-4911
ILLINOIS RUNNER.* 10/yr. Midwest Sports Publications, Inc., Box 125, Fairbury, IL 61739-0125. TEL 815-692-4636. FAX 815-692-4537. Ed. Glenn Latimer. adv. circ. 10,000.

SPORTS AND GAMES

688.76 IT
IMPIANTI SPORT; verde, ricreazione, piscine, attrezzature, turismo. 1976. 3/yr. L.45000($60) Edizioni Publipam s.r.l., Via Andrea Costa 2, 20131 Milan, Italy. TEL 39-2-2893517. FAX 39-2-2610875. adv.: &B&W page L.1690000, color page L.2250000. circ. 4,500.

793 US
IMPOSSIBILITY - CHALLENGER. 1981. q. (Sri Chinmoy Centre) Aum Publications, Box 32433, Jamaica, NY 11431. TEL 718-523-1166. Ed. David Burke.

790.1 US
IN MOTION (EUREKA). 1987. m. Compuset Desktop Publishing Services, 517 3rd St., Ste. 40, Eureka, CA 95501-0453. TEL 707-443-8602. Ed. Ted Silanpaa. adv. circ. 50,000.

354 US ISSN 1076-867X
INDIANA GAMING INSIGHT. 1993. 44/yr. $325. Box 383, Noblesville, IN 46060. TEL 317-773-8715. FAX 317-773-9998. Ed. Edward D. Feigenbaum.
  Description: Covers riverboat gaming, horse racing, Hoosier Lottery and Bingo, and raffle activity in Indiana.

796.42 US
INDIANA RUNNER.* 10/yr. 300 E. Fairlane Dr., Hartford City, IN 47348-1084. TEL 317-348-4739. Ed. Doug Osborn. circ. 7,000.

796 US ISSN 1071-1759
INDY CAR RACING MAGAZINE. 1983. m. $29 (Canada $33, elsewhere $55). I C R Publications, 617 S. 94 St., Milwaukee, WI 53214. TEL 414-774-6291. FAX 414-774-6740. E-mail: icr@icr.com. Ed. Ned Wicker. adv. contact: Robert Nawrocki. circ. 35,000 (paid). **Document type**: consumer publication.
  Description: Geared towards the Indy Car racing enthusiast.

796 US ISSN 0279-9863
INFO A A U. 1929. bi-m. $12. Amateur Athletic Union of the United States, 3400 W. 86th St., Box 68207, Indianapolis, IN 46268. TEL 317-872-2900. FAX 317-875-0548. Ed. David Morton. **Indexed**: Sports Per.Ind. **Document type**: newsletter.
  —UMI.
  Formerly: A A U News (ISSN 0199-6991)
  Description: Highlights events, athletes, individuals and news of the organization.

790.1 US ISSN 1046-4980
GV741
INFORMATION PLEASE SPORTS ALMANAC (YEAR). a. $10.95. Houghton Mifflin Co., 212 Park Ave. S., New York, NY 10003. TEL 212-420-5800. (Orders to: Houghton Mifflin Co., Wayside Rd., Burlington, MA 01803. TEL 800-225-3362) Ed. Mike Mserole. stat.
  Description: Provides comprehensive worldwide sports statistics.

790.1 GW
INFORMATIONEN FUER MITARBEITER UND VEREINE. m. DM.20. Hessischer Leicht-Athletik-Verband, Otto-Fleck-Schneise 4, 60528 Frankfurt a.M., Germany. TEL 069-6789-213.

796.21 US ISSN 1079-1035
INLINE RETAILER & INDUSTRY NEWS. 1992. m. $30 (free to qualified personnel). Inline, Inc., 2025 Pearl St., Boulder, CO 80302. TEL 303-440-5111. FAX 303-440-3313. E-mail: MShafran@aol.com. Ed. Michael W. Shafran; Pub. Daemon Filson. adv.: B&W page $2750, color page $3350; trim 10 x 13; adv. contact: Dave Kingsbury. bk.rev.; circ. 6,000 (controlled). (tabloid format) **Document type**: trade publication.

793 808.838 US
INPHOBIA. 1986. m. $28 (Canada $38; overseas $58). White Wolf, Inc., 780 Park North Rd., Clarkston, GA 30021. TEL 800-454-9653. FAX 404-292-9664. **Document type**: consumer publication.
  Formerly: White Wolf Magazine (ISSN 0897-9391)
  Description: Reviews and previews fantasy games large and small.

794.1 US ISSN 0896-8195
INSIDE CHESS. 1988. bi-w. $55 (foreign $83). International Chess Enterprises, Inc., 2005 5th Ave., Ste. 402, Seattle, WA 98109. TEL 206-448-1066; 800-262-4377. FAX 206-441-4736. E-mail: plp@halcyon.com. Ed. Michael Fronett. adv. contact: Russell Miller. bk.rev.; index, cum.index; circ. 5,500 (paid). (back issues avail.) **Document type**: consumer publication.
  Description: Covers amateur to international level player interest in the game of chess.

796 CN ISSN 0835-9806
INSIDE HOCKEY. 1987. 6/yr. Publications Transcontinental (Don Mills), 85 Scarsdale Rd., Ste. 100, Don Mills, Ont. M3B 2R2, Canada. TEL 416-445-5702. FAX 416-445-0753. Ed. Bob McKenzie. circ. 50,000.

796.815 US
INSIDE KARATE. 1980. m. $18. C F W Enterprises, Inc., 4201 W. Van Owen Pl., Burbank, CA 91505. TEL 818-845-2656. FAX 818-845-7761. (Subscr. to: Box 404, Mt. Morris, IL 61054) Ed. John Soet. circ. 100,000. **Indexed**: Sportsearch (1984-).
  Formerly: Kick Illustrated (ISSN 0273-7574)
  Description: For the serious martial artist. Spotlighting on self-defense, personalities and fitness.

790.1 US ISSN 0199-8501
INSIDE KUNG FU. 1973. m. $20. C F W Enterprises, Inc., 4201 W. Van Owen Pl., Burbank, CA 91505. TEL 818-845-2656. FAX 818-845-7761. (Subscr. to: Box 404, Mt. Morris, IL 61054) Ed. Dave Cater. adv.; bk.rev.; charts; illus. circ. 100,000. (also avail. in video cassette) **Indexed**: Sportsearch (1976-).
  Description: Martial arts coverage.

790.1 US ISSN 0195-3478
GV561
INSIDE SPORTS. 1979-1982; resumed 1983. m. $22 (foreign $34). Inside Sports, Inc., (Subsidiary of: Century Publishing Co.), 990 Grove St., Evanston, IL 60201-4370. TEL 708-491-6440. (Subscr. to: Box 346, Mt. Morris, IL 61054-0346) Ed.Bd. adv.; charts; illus.; stat. circ. 675,000. (also avail. in microform from UMI; reprint service avail. from UMI; back issues avail.) **Indexed**: Access (1981-), Sports Per.Ind., Sportsearch (1984-). **Document type**: consumer publication.
  —UMI; UnCover.
  Description: For serious sports fans. Presents statistics, stories, and excitement behind pro and college baseball, football, basketball, hockey, boxing, and auto racing.

790.1 US ISSN 1065-4682
INSIDE TAE KWON DO. 1986. m. C F W Enterprises, Inc., 4201 W. Van Owen Pl., Burbank, CA 91505. TEL 815-734-4151. FAX 818-845-7761. (Subscr. to: Box 404, Mt. Morris, IL 61054) Eds. Dave Cater, John Soet. adv.; bk.rev.; charts; illus. (also avail. in video cassette)
  Formerly (until 1991): Inside Kung Fu Presents Tae Kwon Do.
  Description: Guide to all types of martial arts. Spotlights different aspects of the martial arts world.

796.812 US ISSN 1047-9562
INSIDE WRESTLING. 1968. 13/yr. $19 for 12 issues in US & Canada (elsewhere $28.60) (effective 1994). London Publishing Co., Box 910, Fort Washington, PA 19034. TEL 215-643-6385. FAX 215-540-0146. Ed. Bill Apter. adv.; charts; illus.; tr.lit. **Document type**: consumer publication.

THE INSIDER (PHOENIX). see *OCCUPATIONS AND CAREERS*

790.1 384.554 US
INSIDERS SPORTSLETTER. 1981. bi-m. membership. American Sportscasters Association Inc., 5 Beekman St., Ste. 814, New York, NY 10038. TEL 212-227-8080. FAX 212-571-0556. Ed. Louis O. Schwartz. adv.; bk.rev. circ. 2,500. (back issues avail.)

799.2 US ISSN 0747-007X
INSIGHTS (FAIRFAX); N R A news for young shooters. 1980. m. $10. (National Rifle Association of America) N R A Publications, 11250 Waples Mill Rd., Fairfax, VA 22030. TEL 703-267-1586. FAX 703-267-3994. Ed. John Robbins. adv. contact: James L. Retzer. circ. 60,000. (back issues avail.)
  Description: Educational articles on shooting sports. Includes information on firearm safety, gun care, competition and hunting for readers aged 7-20.

797 US
INSTITUTE OF DIVING. NEWSLETTER. 1977. q. $25 membership. Institute of Diving, 17314 Back Beach Rd., Panama City Beach, FL 32413. TEL 904-235-4101. FAX 904-235-4101. Ed. Dorothy Parkinson. adv.; bk.rev. circ. 500. **Document type**: newsletter.

797.21 UK
INSTITUTE OF SWIMMING TEACHERS & COACHES DIRECTORY OF MEMBERSHIP. 1982. biennial. £22.50 membership. Institute of Swimming Teachers & Coaches, Dawson House, 63 Forest Rd., Loughborough, Leics. LE11 3NW, England. TEL 01509-264357. FAX 01509-219349. Ed. B.W. Relf. adv. contact: B.W. Relf. bk.rev. circ. 12,000. **Document type**: directory.

371.7 RM
INSTITUTUL DE SUBINGINERI ORADEA. LUCRARI STIINTIFICE: SERIA EDUCATIE FIZICA SI SPORT. (Text in Rumanian, occasionally in English or French; summaries in Rumanian, English or German) 1967. a. Institutul de Subingineri Oradea, Calea Armatei Rosii Nr. 5, 3700 Oradea, Rumania.
  Formerly: Institutul Pedagogic Oradea. Lucrari Stiintifice Seria Educatie Fizica si Sport; which continues in part (in 1973): Institutul Pedagogic Oradea. Lucrari Stiintifice: Seria Educatie Fizica, Biologie, Stiinte Medicale; which superseded in part (in 1971): Institutul Pedagogic Oradea. Lucrari Stiintifice: Seria A and Seria B; which was formerly (until 1969): Institutul Pedagogic Oradea. Lucrari Stiintifice.

796 UK ISSN 0074-137X
INTERNATIONAL ARCHERY FEDERATION. BULLETIN OFFICIEL. (Text in English and French) biennial., no.26, 1974. price varies. International Archery Federation, 46 The Balk, Walton, Wakefield, England. Ed. Mrs. I.K. Frith. adv.

796 371 JA ISSN 0074-1728
INTERNATIONAL ASSOCIATION OF PHYSICAL EDUCATION AND SPORTS FOR GIRLS AND WOMEN. PROCEEDINGS OF THE INTERNATIONAL CONGRESS. (Proceedings published by host countries) irreg., 6th, 1969, Tokyo. Japan Association of Physical Education for Women and Girls, 6-102 O.M.Y.C., 3-1 Jinen-cho Yoyogi, Shibuya-ku, Tokyo, Japan. circ. controlled. **Document type**: proceedings.

796.345 UK ISSN 0255-4437
INTERNATIONAL BADMINTON FEDERATION. ANNUAL STATUTE BOOK. 1935. a. £10 (effective 1994-1995). International Badminton Federation, 4 Manor Park, Mackenzie Way, Cheltenham, Glos. GL51 9TX, England. TEL 01242-234904. FAX 01242-221030. index. circ. 2,000.
  Formerly: International Badminton Federation. Annual Handbook (ISSN 0074-1981)
  Description: Rules and regulations of the International Badminton Federation.

790.1 NE ISSN 0378-4037
INTERNATIONAL BULLETIN OF SPORTS INFORMATION. 1977. q. $25. International Association for Sports Associations, P.O. Box 85558, 2508 CG The Hague, Netherlands. Ed.Bd. adv.; bk.rev. circ. 400. **Indexed**: Sportsearch (1977-). **Document type**: bulletin.
  —BLDSC (4538.261000).
  Description: News bulletin for library and documentation centers in the field of sports and physical education.

790.1 CN
INTERNATIONAL GAMBLERS CLUB NEWSLETTER. 1974. q. $24. International Gaming Inc., P.O. Box 73, Thornhill, Ont. L3T 3N1, Canada. TEL 416-731-5457. Ed. I. Kusyszyn. circ. 2,000. (back issues avail.) **Document type**: newsletter.

SPORTS AND GAMES

796.41 US ISSN 0276-1041
GV461
INTERNATIONAL GYMNAST MAGAZINE. 1956. 10/yr. $24 (effective Feb. 1993). Paul Ziert & Associates, Inc., 225 Brooks, Box 2450, Oceanside, CA 92051. TEL 619-722-0030. FAX 619-722-6208. Ed.Bd. adv.; bk.rev.; bibl.; illus.; index; circ. 20,000 (paid). (also avail. in microform from UMI; reprint service avail. from UMI) **Indexed:** Mid.East: Abstr.& Ind., Phys.Ed.Ind., Sports Per.Ind., Sportsearch (1976-). —BLDSC (4540.673000).
Former titles (until 1980): International Gymnast (ISSN 0162-9867); (until 1976): Gymnast (ISSN 0046-6670); Incorporates: Gymnastics World & Mademoiselle Gymnast (ISSN 0024-9408) & Modern Gymnast (ISSN 0026-7813)
Description: Covers gymnastics with in-depth competition reports, personalities and photos.

795.4 US
INTERNATIONAL HOME AND PRIVATE POKER PLAYERS NEWSLETTER. 1988. bi-m. $7. International Home & Private Poker Players' Association, 3784 Central Park Dr., No. 8, Las Vegas, NV 89109. TEL 906-341-5468. Ed. Tony Wuehle. circ. 300. (looseleaf format; back issues avail.) **Document type:** newsletter.
Description: Contains news of members and poker tournament results.

INTERNATIONAL JOURNAL OF PHYSICAL EDUCATION/INTERNATIONALE ZEITSCHRIFT FUER SPORTPAEDAGOGIK. see EDUCATION — Teaching Methods And Curriculum

790.1 UK ISSN 0952-3367
GV571
THE INTERNATIONAL JOURNAL OF THE HISTORY OF SPORT. 1984. 3/yr. £35($45) to individuals; institutions £90 ($135) (effective 1996). Frank Cass, Newbury House, 890-900 Eastern Ave., Newbury Park, Ilford, Essex IG2 7HH, England. TEL 44-181-599-8866. FAX 44-181-599-0984. E-mail: 100067,1576@compuserve.com. Ed.Bd. adv.: B&W page £195 ($275); adv. contact: Anne Kidson. bk.rev.; index. (also avail. in microfilm from UMI; back issues avail.) **Indexed:** Phys.Ed.Ind., Sportsearch (1987-). **Document type:** academic/scholarly publication.
—BLDSC (4542.282000); Faxon; SWETS; UMI; UnCover. CCC.
Formerly: British Journal of Sports History (ISSN 0264-9373)
Description: Aims to stimulate, promote, and coordinate research in the history of sport, recreation, and leisure.
Refereed Serial

796 GR ISSN 0074-7181
INTERNATIONAL OLYMPIC ACADEMY. REPORT OF THE SESSIONS. (Since 1968 issued in separate English, French and Greek vols.) 1961. a. $20 (free to qualified personnel). Hellenic Olympic Committee, 4 Kapsali St., Athens 107 64, Greece. FAX 30-1-724-2150. TELEX 219494. Ed. Fotini Karamanbaki. cum.index: 1961-69. circ. 9,000. **Indexed:** Sportsearch. **Document type:** proceedings.
Description: Covers profiles, results, statistics, training information and news, reports, text and photos.

790.1 US ISSN 0739-5396
INTERNATIONAL OLYMPIC LIFTER. 1974. bi-m. $25. I O L Publications, Box 65855, Los Angeles, CA 90065. TEL 800-328-8762. Ed. Bob Hise. adv.; bk.rev.; illus.; stat. circ. 2,000. (back issues avail.)
Description: Devoted to weight lifting, contains profiles, training information, and news reports plus cross training for other sports.

795.414 UK ISSN 0951-1555
INTERNATIONAL POPULAR BRIDGE MONTHLY. 1974. m. $50. Apsbridge Services Ltd., 455 Alfreton Rd., Nottingham NG7 5LX, England. TEL 0602-422615. FAX 0602-422359. Ed. Tony Sowter. adv.; bk.rev. circ. 3,000. **Document type:** consumer publication.
Formerly: Popular Bridge Monthly.
Description: Publication dealing with entertainment and instruction. Concentrates on top level bridge worldwide.

796 FR ISSN 0074-7645
INTERNATIONAL REFERENCE ANNUAL FOR BUILDING AND EQUIPMENT OF SPORTS, TOURISM, RECREATION INSTALLATIONS. 1970. a. price varies. Techno-Loisirs, 3 rue Sivel, Paris -14e, France. Ed. Georges E. Caille. adv. circ. 10,000. **Document type:** directory.

790.1 FR ISSN 0247-0276
INTERNATIONAL SCORES. 10/yr. Editions Symbiose, 1 chemin du Pre Carre, B.P. 135, 38244 Neylan Cedex, France. TEL 76-90-84-38. FAX 76-90-60-63. Ed. Annette Drapier. circ. 6,000.
Description: Covers new sport products and fashions.

796 SZ ISSN 0539-0168
INTERNATIONAL SKATING UNION. ICE DANCING REGULATIONS. biennial; latest 1994. 20 SFr. International Skating Union, Postfach, CH-7270 Davos-Platz, Switzerland. TEL 081-437577. FAX 081-436671. **Document type:** bulletin.

796 SZ ISSN 0535-2479
INTERNATIONAL SKATING UNION. MINUTES OF CONGRESS. (Text in English) biennial, latest 1994, Boston. 10 SFr. International Skating Union, Postfach, CH-7270 Davos-Platz, Switzerland. TEL 081-437577. FAX 081-436671. **Document type:** proceedings.

797.21 069 US
INTERNATIONAL SWIMMING HALL OF FAME HEADLINES. 1965. q. membership. International Swimming Hall of Fame, One Hall of Fame Dr., Ft. Lauderdale, FL 33316. TEL 305-462-6536. FAX 305-525-4031. Ed. Holly Heil. adv.; bk.rev. circ. 2,500. **Document type:** newsletter.
Formerly: International Swimming Hall of Fame News.
Description: Covers aquatics, news and events on the Swimming Hall of Fame.

790.1 US ISSN 0748-9668
INTERNATIONAL UNIVERSITY COLLEGIATE SPORTS REPORT. 1973. q. $300. T I U Press, 1301 S. Noland Rd., Independence, MO 64055. TEL 816-461-3633. Ed. John Wayne Johnston. circ. 1,000. (looseleaf format) **Document type:** newsletter.

799.202 SZ ISSN 1017-5547
INTERNATIONALES WAFFEN-MAGAZIN. (Text in German; summary of contents in English) 1982. 10/yr. 102 SFr. Habegger Verlag Zuerich, Morgartenstr. 6-10, Postfach 9230, CH-8036 Zurich, Switzerland. TEL 01-2981204. FAX 01-2981277. Ed. Peter Ernst Grimm. adv.; bk.rev.; charts; illus.; index. circ. 55,000. **Document type:** consumer publication.
Formerly (until Dec. 1989): Schweizer Waffen-Magazin (ISSN 0253-4878)
Description: Modern and antique firearms, shooting sports, self-defense.

790.1 IT
INTREPIDO. 1934. m. L.26000 (foreign L.41000). Casa Editrice Universo S.p.A., Via M. De Vizzi 35, 20092 Cinisello Balsamo (MI), Italy. TEL 39-2-618331. FAX 39-2-6128931. Ed. Nicola De Feo. adv.: B&W page L.11500000. circ. 60,000. **Document type:** consumer publication.

IRONMAN. see PHYSICAL FITNESS AND HYGIENE

794.1 IT ISSN 0021-2849
L'ITALIA SCACCHISTICA. 1911. m. L.70000 (foreign L.100000). Via Lamarmora 40, 20122 Milan, Italy. TEL 39-2-55019079. Ed. Adolivio Capece. adv.; bk.rev.; charts; illus.; index.
Description: Covers every aspect of the game of chess including national and international news.

790.1 IC ISSN 1017-3579
ITHROTTABLADID. 1939. bi-m. ISK 2874 (effective Jan. 1995). (Ithrottasamband Islands - Icelandic Sports Federation) Frodi Ltd., Seljavegur 2, 101 Reykjavik, Iceland. TEL 354-515-5500. FAX 354-515-5599. Ed. Thorgrimur Thrainsson. adv.: B&W page ISK 46900, color page ISK 81800; trim 19 x 27; adv. contact: Hafsteinn Vidar Jensson. circ. 7,000.

DER JAGDSPANIEL. see PETS

790.1 GW ISSN 0448-1445
JAHRBUCH DES SPORTS. 1977. a. DM.24.60. (Deutscher Sportbund) Schors-Verlags-Gesellschaft mbH, Postfach 1280, 65522 Niedernhausen, Germany. TEL 06127-8029. FAX 06127-8812. circ. 32,000.

799 NO ISSN 0800-3041
JAKT-FISKE. 1871. m. NOK 370. Norges Jeger- og Fiskerforbund, Hvalstadaasen 5, Box 94, 1364 Hvalstaad, Norway. Ed. Viggo Kristiansen. adv. circ. 79,000.
Formerly (until 1983): Jakt-Fiske-Friluftsliv (ISSN 0021-4051)

794.1 SP ISSN 0767-1970
JAQUE. 1971. 24/yr. 9900 ptas. (Europe $130; elsewhere $180). Jaque XXI, C. General Pardinas, 48, 3o, A, 28001 Madrid, Spain. TEL 34-1-3090379. FAX 34-1-3092655. Ed. Leontxo Garcia. adv. contact: Jesus J. Boyero. bk.rev./ circ. 12,450 (paid).
Description: Includes interviews with top chess players, annoted games, combinations, articles, studies, problems, and analyses.

790.1 TS
AL-JAZIRAH. 1980. m. Nadi al-Jazirah, Al-Lajna al-Thiqafiyyah - Al-Jazirah Club, Cultural Group, P.O. Box 2750, Abu Dhabi, United Arab Emirates. TEL 464455. Ed. Saif Ahmad al-Hamili. circ. 1,000.
Description: Covers club sporting activities.

790 FR ISSN 0021-6135
JEUNES. 1903. m. 220 F.($40) Federation Sportive et Culturelle de France, 22 rue Oberkampf, 75011 Paris, France. TEL 1-43-38-50-57. FAX 1-40-21-87-17. Ed. Jean-Marie Jouaret. adv. contact: Clement Schertzinger. bk.rev.; film rev.; play rev.; illus.; stat. circ. 11,000. **Indexed:** Sportsearch. **Document type:** newspaper.

JEWISH SPORTS & FITNESS. see PHYSICAL FITNESS AND HYGIENE

790.1 CN ISSN 0712-2632
JIM RENNIE'S SPORTS LETTER. 1977. w. Can.$200. Rennie Publications Inc., P.O. Box 1000, Collingwood, ON L9Y 4L4, Canada. TEL 705-445-7161. FAX 705-445-8650. Ed. Jim Rennie. circ. 1,600 (paid). **Indexed:** Sportsearch (1980-). **Document type:** consumer publication.

790.1 CC ISSN 1004-2105
JINGJI YU JIANMEI/ATHLETICS & BODY BUILDING. (Text in Chinese) 1985. bi-m. Shanghai Tiyu Xueyuan - Shanghai Institute of Physical Education, 650 Qingyuan Huanlu, Shanghai 200433, People's Republic of China. TEL 5485546. Ed. Dai Binyian. adv.: page Y4000. **Document type:** consumer publication.
Description: Introduces body-building exercises, and scientific methods for improving health, and maintaining good shape.

790.1 CC
JINGWU. (Text in Chinese) bi-m. Dangdai Tiyu Zazhishe, 99 Xuanxua Jie, Nangang-qu, Harbin, Heilongjiang 150001, People's Republic of China. TEL 0451-2611474. FAX 0451-2611474. Ed. Wang Lihei. **Document type:** consumer publication.

613.7 796.42 SW ISSN 0349-4047
JOGGING; loepartidningen. 1979. q. SEK 98 (effective 1991). Stockholm Marathon - Tjejmilen, P.O. Box 10023, S-100 55 Stockholm, Sweden.

613.7 IT
JOGGING - LE GRANDE CORSA. 1980. bi-m. L.30000 (rest of Europe L.60000; elsewhere L.90000). Publimaster s.r.l., Via Washington 50, 20146 Milan, Italy. TEL 39-2-48012903. FAX 39-2-48012293. Ed. Amedeo Stevaraglia. adv.: color page L.7000000; trim 190 x 280; adv. contact: Alessandro Zonca. circ. 25,000. (back issues avail.)
Formerly (until 1992): Jogging.
Description: Rrports news of long-distance races, marathons and adventure.
Refereed Serial

SPORTS AND GAMES

794.1   BL
JOGO ABERTO; a revista brasileira de xadrez. 1985. 6/yr. Cr.$50($15) Editora Jogo Aberto, Ltda., Rua Treze de Maio, 21, Bela Vista, 01327 Sao Paulo, Brazil. TEL 011-258-6506. Ed. Isabel Sampaio. adv.; bk.rev.; bibl.; index. circ. 3,000. (tabloid format; back issues avail.)
   Description: Covers the game of chess, emphasis is placed on the female players of the game.

790.1   SP
JORNADA DEPORTIVA. d. $1979. Avda. de Buenos Aires 71, Apdo. 714, Santa Cruz de Tenerife, Canary Islands. adv.

JOURNAL OF APPLIED BIOMECHANICS. see *MEDICAL SCIENCES — Sports Medicine*

796.215   US   ISSN 1057-8358
GV1100.69.A2
JOURNAL OF ASIAN MARTIAL ARTS. 1992. q. $32 to individuals (Canada and Mexico $38; elsewhere $40); institutions $75 (Canada and Mexico $81; elsewhere $83) (includes Physical Education Index). Via Media Publishing Co., 821 W. 24th St., Erie, PA 16502. TEL 814-455-9517; 800-455-9517. FAX 814-838-7811. Ed. Michael A. DeMarco; Pub. Michael A. DeMarco. adv.: B&W page $950; adv. contact: Michael DeMarco. bk.rev.; bibl.; index. circ. 6,000. (back issues avail.) **Document type:** academic/scholarly publication.
   Description: Provides an interdisciplinary and academic approach to further understand the cultures where various martial arts originated.
   Refereed Serial

790.1   GW   ISSN 1010-8262
GV201
JOURNAL OF COMPARATIVE PHYSICAL AND EDUCATION SPORT. s-a. DM.30. (International Society on Comparative Physical Education and Sport (ISCPES)) Verlag Karl Hofmann, Postfach 1360, 73603 Schorndorf, Germany. TEL 07181-402-0. FAX 07181-402111. **Document type:** academic/scholarly publication.
—BLDSC (4963.100000).
   Refereed Serial

JOURNAL OF GAMBLING STUDIES. see *MEDICAL SCIENCES — Psychiatry And Neurology*

JOURNAL OF RECREATIONAL MATHEMATICS. see *MATHEMATICS*

JOURNAL OF SPORT AND EXERCISE PSYCHOLOGY. see *PSYCHOLOGY*

301.15   US   ISSN 0193-7235
GV561
JOURNAL OF SPORT AND SOCIAL ISSUES. 1977. q. $48 to individuals; institutions $117 (effective Sep. 1995). (Northwestern University, Center for the Study of Sport in Society) Sage Publications, Inc., 2455 Teller Rd., Thousand Oaks, CA 91320. TEL 617-437-4025. FAX 617-437-4566. E-mail: libraries@sagepub.com. (Subscr. to: Sage Publications, Inc., Box 5084, Thousand Oaks, CA 91359; Overseas subscr. to: Sage Publications Ltd., 6 Bonhill St., London EC2A 4PU, England; Sage Publications India Pvt. Ltd., P.O. Box 4215, New Delhi 110 048, India) Ed. Lawrence A. Wenner. adv.; bk.rev. circ. 550. (back issues avail.) **Indexed:** Alt.Press Ind., Amer.Bibl.Slavic & E.Eur.Stud., Lang.& Lang.Behav.Abstr., Phys.Ed.Ind., Rural Recreat.Tour.Abstr., Sociol.Abstr. (1977-), Sportsearch (1976-). **Document type:** academic/scholarly publication.
—BLDSC (5066.184000); Faxon; SWETS; UnCover.
   Description: Publishes the latest research, discussion, and analysis on contemporary sports issues, such as race, the media, gender issues, economics, drugs, recruiting, injuries, and youth sports.

790.1 150   US   ISSN 0162-7341
GV561
JOURNAL OF SPORT BEHAVIOR. (Summaries in English and French) 1978. q. $20 (foreign $45). University of South Alabama, Department of Health, Physical Education and Leisure Services, Mobile, AL 36688. TEL 334-460-7131. FAX 334-460-7252. E-mail: WGilley@jaguar.usouthal.edu. Ed. William G. Gilley. bk.rev. circ. 400. (also avail. in microform from UMI) **Indexed:** Phys.Ed.Ind., Psychol.Abstr. (1980-), Sportsearch (1978-). **Document type:** academic/scholarly publication.
●Also available online. Vendor(s): University Microfilms International.
Also available on CD-ROM. Producer(s): University Microfilms International.
—BLDSC (5066.186000); Faxon; SWETS; UMI; UnCover. **CCC**.
   Description: Deals with the sociological, psychological, anthropological and related applications to the science of sport.
   Refereed Serial

790.1   US   ISSN 0094-1700
GV571
JOURNAL OF SPORT HISTORY. 1974. 3/yr. $40 to individuals (foreign $45); institutions $50 (foreign $55). North American Society for Sport History, 101 White Bldg., Pennsylvania State University, University Park, PA 16802. TEL 814-865-2416. Ed. Joseph Arbena. adv.; bk.rev.; illus. circ. 1,000. **Indexed:** Amer.Hist.& Life, Chic.Per.Ind., Curr.Cont., Hist.Abstr., Phys.Ed.Ind., Sportsearch (1974-), SSCI. **Document type:** academic/scholarly publication.
—BLDSC (5066.188000); Faxon; Genuine Article; SWETS; UnCover.

790.1 658   US   ISSN 0888-4773
JOURNAL OF SPORT MANAGEMENT. Abbreviated title: J S M. 1987. 3/yr. $30 to individuals (foreign $35); institutions $64 (foreign $69); students $18 (foreign $23). (North American Society for Sport Management) Human Kinetics Publishers, Inc., Box 5076, Champaign, IL 61825-5076. TEL 217-351-5076. FAX 217-351-2674. eds. Drs. Joy Desensi, Trevor Slack. adv. contact: Pamela Anderson. bk.rev.; bibl. circ. 850. (back issues avail.) **Indexed:** Phys.Ed.Ind., Sportsearch (1987-). **Document type:** academic/scholarly publication.
—BLDSC (5066.188300); Faxon; Genuine Article; SWETS; UnCover. **CCC**.
   Description: Fosters exchange of theory and application of management to sport, exercise, dance, and play.
   Refereed Serial

790.1   UK   ISSN 0264-0414
GV561   CODEN: JSSCEL
JOURNAL OF SPORTS SCIENCES. 1983. bi-m. £225 to insitiutions in the E.U. (N. America $385; elsewhere £250) (effective 1995). (British Association of Sports Sciences) E. & F.N. Spon, Journals Department (Subsidiary of: International Thomson Publishing Group), 2-6 Boundary Row, London SE1 8HN, England. TEL 0171-865-0066. FAX 0171-522-9623. TELEX 290164 CHAPMA G. E-mail: journal@chall.mhs.compuserve.com. (Dist. by: International Thomson Publishing Services Ltd., Cheriton House, North Way, Andover, Hants. SP10 5BE, England. TEL 01264-342713. FAX 01264-342807; Subscr. in N. America to: Chapman & Hall, One Penn Plaza, 41st Fl., New York, NY 10119. TEL 212-564-1060. FAX 212-564-1505) Ed. Thomas Reilly. adv. (reprint service avail.) **Indexed:** Excerpt.Med. (1992-), Ind.Med., Phys.Ed.Ind., Sportsearch (1983-). **Document type:** academic/scholarly publication.
—BLDSC (5066.350000); Genuine Article; SWETS; UMI; UnCover. **CCC**.
   Description: Provides a contact point among the separate disciplines in sports sciences. Includes contributions from the human sciences: anatomy, anthropology, behavioral sciences, physiology, and psychology. Papers cover technologies such as design of playing equipment and sports facilities, as well as applied research in training, team selection, performance prediction or modification, and stress reduction.
   Refereed Serial

797   US   ISSN 0747-5993
JOURNAL OF SWIMMING RESEARCH. 1984. a. $15 (Canada & Mexico $25; institutions and foreign $35). American Swimming Coaches Association, 301 S.E. 20th St., Fort Lauderdale, FL 33316. FAX 305-462-6280. (Co-sponsor: U.S. Swimming Sports Medicine) Ed. Rick Sharp. adv. **Indexed:** Sportsearch (1985-). **Document type:** academic/scholarly publication.
—BLDSC (5067.820000).
   Description: Examines applied swimming science and research.
   Refereed Serial

JOURNAL OF TEACHING IN PHYSICAL EDUCATION. see *EDUCATION — Teaching Methods And Curriculum*

796   US   ISSN 0094-8705
GV706   CODEN: JPSPF6
JOURNAL OF THE PHILOSOPHY OF SPORT. Abbreviated title: J P S. 1974. a. $19 to individuals (foreign $21); institutions $30 (foreign $32); students $12 (foreign $14). (Philosophic Society for the Study of Sport) Human Kinetics Publishers, Inc., Box 5076, Champaign, IL 61825-5076. TEL 217-351-5076. FAX 217-351-2674. Ed. Dr. William J. Morgan. adv. contact: Pamela Anderson. bk.rev.; bibl. circ. 500. (back issues avail.) **Indexed:** Curr.Cont., Phil.Ind., Phys.Ed.Ind., Sportsearch (1978-), SSCI. **Document type:** academic/scholarly publication.
—BLDSC (5034.520000); Genuine Article; SWETS; UnCover. **CCC**.
   Description: Aims to foster philosophic interchange among scholars interested in better understanding sport.
   Refereed Serial

796
JUCO REVIEW. 1948. 9/yr. $20. National Junior College Athletic Association, Box 7305, Colorado Springs, CO 80933-7305. TEL 719-590-9788. FAX 719-590-7324. Ed. George E. Killian. adv.; bk.rev.; stat. circ. 3,700. (processed; also avail. in microform from UMI; reprint service avail. from UMI) **Indexed:** Phys.Ed.Ind., Sports Per.Ind., Sportsearch (1977-). **Document type:** consumer publication.
—UMI.

796.815   NE
JUDO; jiu-jitsu, aikido. 1939. 6/yr. membership. (Judo Bond Nederland) Judo Magazine B.V., Blokhoeve 5, 3438 LC Nieuwegein, Netherlands. TEL 31-23-325260. FAX 31-23-342721. Ed. Robert van der Geest. adv. contact: Serge Dalhuizen. bk.rev.; illus.; circ. 60,000. (controlled). **Document type:** consumer publication.
   Former titles: Budo Echo; Judo Echo (ISSN 0022-5827)

796.815   UK   ISSN 0022-5819
GV475.J9
JUDO. 1956. m. £9. Judo Ltd., Candem House, 717 Manchester Old Rd., Rhodes, Middleton, Manchester M24 4GF, England. Ed. John Drogan. adv.; bk.rev.; charts; illus. circ. 8,000.

796.815   FR
JUDO. 1950. 6/yr. 150 F. Federation Francaise de Judo et Disciplines Associees (F.F.J.D.A.), 43, rue des Plantes, 75014 Paris, France. TEL 45-42-80-90. FAX 45-42-65-04. adv. circ. 20,000. **Indexed:** Sportsearch (1980-).

796.815   US   ISSN 1066-6257
JUDO JOURNAL. 1979. m. $25 in U.S.; Canada $34; elsewhere $62. Judo Journal Publications, Box 18485, Irvine, CA 92713. TEL 714-645-1674. FAX 714-722-9331. Ed. Mike Watts. adv. contact: U. Hashima. circ. 20,000. **Indexed:** Sportsearch (1980-). **Document type:** newspaper.

796.815   GW   ISSN 0179-3535
JUDO MAGAZIN. m. DM.42 (foreign DM.60). (Deutscher Judo Bund e.V.) Vereinigte Fachverlage GmbH, Lise-Meitner-Str. 2, 55129 Mainz, Germany. TEL 06131-992-0. FAX 06131-992100. Ed. Claus Beissner. adv. contact: Asko Kulke. circ. 11,673. **Document type:** consumer publication.

SPORTS AND GAMES

796.815   CN   ISSN 1193-7149
JUDO ONTARIO NEWSLETTER. q. Can.$16($15) Judo Ontario, 1185 Eglinton Ave. E., North York, ON M3C 3C6, Canada. TEL 416-426-7006. FAX 416-426-7390. Ed. Kevin Casey. adv. contact: Kevin Casey. circ. 1,000. **Document type:** newsletter.
    Former titles (until 1992): Ontario Judo Newsletter (ISSN 0834-2105); (until 1986): Ontario Judoka (ISSN 0823-9134); (until 1985): Ontario Judo's Newsletter; (until 1984): Ontario Judoka (ISSN 0826-0567); (until 1983): Judo Ontario's Newsletter (ISSN 0823-1087); (until 1982): Newsletter - Judo Ontario (ISSN 0229-5652).

JUGGLER'S WORLD MAGAZINE. see *HOBBIES*

790.1   DK   ISSN 0901-3334
K F U M IDRAET. 1921. m. DKK 58.60. K F U M Idraetsforbund i Danmark, Sundvej 9, 8700 Horsens, Denmark. Ed. Frands Orla Nielsen. adv. circ. 4,600.
    Formerly (until 1985): Frisk Glad Idraet (ISSN 0901-2710)

796.83   US   ISSN 1048-1516
K O. (Knock Out) 13/yr. $24.60 for 12 issues in US & Canada (elsewhere $34) (effective 1994). London Publishing Co., Box 910, Fort Washington, PA 19034. TEL 215-643-6385. FAX 215-540-0146. Ed. Steve Farhood. **Document type:** consumer publication.

796   HU   ISSN 1218-1498
GV201
KALOKAGATHIA. (Text mainly in Hungarian; summaries in English or Hungarian) 1954. 3/yr. 250 Ft. (effective 1995). Magyar Testnevelesi Egyetem, Alkotas u. 44, 1123 Budapest, Hungary. TEL 36-1-1564-444. FAX 36-1-1566-337. E-mail: linda@mte.hupe.hu. Ed. Ferenc Krasovec; Pub. Jozsef Tihanyi. adv.: B&W page 50000 Ft. bk.rev.; illus.; circ. 300 (controlled). **Document type:** academic/scholarly publication.
    Former titles: Magyar Testnevelesi Egyetem Kozlemenyei (ISSN 0866-2401); (until 1989): Testnevelesi Foiskola Kozlemeneyei (ISSN 0230-3337); (until 1981): Magyar Testnevelesi Foiskola. Tudomanyos Kozlemenyek.
    Description: Covers physical education and sport, philosophy, psychology, management, biomechanics, motor learning and development, and physiology.

796.815   UK   ISSN 0022-9008
KARATE AND ORIENTAL ARTS. 1966. bi-m. £6($12) Paul H. Crompton Ltd., 102 Felsham Rd., London SW15 1DQ, England. Ed. Paul H. Crompton. adv.; bk.rev.; film rev.; bibl.; charts; illus. circ. 20,000. **Indexed:** Sportsearch.

796.815   GW   ISSN 0179-7700
KARATE - BUDO JOURNAL. m. DM.76.80 (foreign DM.100.80). Satori Verlagsanstalt GmbH, Bergstr. 18, 47906 Kempen, Germany. TEL 02845-80593. FAX 02845-80392. Ed. Norbert Schiffer. adv. contact: Hans Simon. circ. 22,435. **Document type:** consumer publication.

796.815   FR   ISSN 1243-3853
KARATE, BUSHIDO. 1974. m. 261 F. Societe Europeene de Magazines, 2 bis, rue Merceur, 75011 Paris, France. FAX 43-67-85-80. Ed. G. Barissat. circ. 117,000.
    Formed by the merger of (1974-1988): Karate (ISSN 0335-2552); (1983-1988): Bushido (ISSN 0760-0097)

796.815   US   ISSN 1059-4752
KARATE INTERNATIONAL. 9/yr. $3.95 per no. DoJo Publishing, 28 W. 25th St., New York, NY 10010-2705. TEL 212-976-6262. FAX 212-967-6288.

796.8   US   ISSN 0888-031X
GV1114.3
KARATE - KUNG FU ILLUSTRATED. 1969. bi-m. $19.50 for 2 yrs. Rainbow Publications, Inc., 24715 Ave. Rockefeller, Box 918, Santa Clarita, CA 91380-9018. TEL 805-257-4066. FAX 805-257-3018. (Subscr. to: Box 16298, N. Hollywood, CA 91615-6298. TEL 800-266-4066) Ed. Bob Young; Pub. Michael James. adv. contact: Barbara Lessard. circ. 45,000. **Indexed:** Sportsearch. **Document type:** consumer publication.
    Formerly (until 1991): Karate Illustrated (ISSN 0022-9016)

769.41   GW   ISSN 0939-1371
KASKADE; european juggling magazine. (Text in English) 1984. q. DM.30 (overseas $30). Schoenbergstr. 92, 65199 Wiesbaden, Germany. TEL 0611-9467464. FAX 0611-9497464. E-mail: 100064,2551@compuserve.com. (Dist. by: Rudi Aderhold, Alwinenstr. 10, 65189 Wiesbaden, Germany) Eds. Gabi Keast, Paul Keast; Pubs. Gabi Keast, Paul Keast. adv.: page DM.970; trim 297 x 210; adv. contact: Gabi Keast. bk.rev.; bibl.; software rev.; circ. 4,000 (paid). (back issues avail.) **Document type:** consumer publication.

790.1   IR
KAYHAN VARZESHI. (Text in Persian) w. $318 to N. America (effective 1994). Kayhan Publications, Ferdowsi Ave., P.O. Box 11365-9631, Teheran, Iran. TEL 98-21-3110251. FAX 98-21-3114228. TELEX 212467. adv. circ. 125,000. **Document type:** consumer publication.

790.1   UK   ISSN 1356-6202
KEY NOTE MARKET REVIEW: U K SPORTS MARKET. Variant title: U K Sports Market. 1989. irreg. £375. Key Note Publications Ltd., Field House, 72 Oldfield Rd., Hampton, Middlesex TW12 2HQ, England. TEL 0181-783-0755. FAX 0181-783-1720. **Document type:** trade publication.
●Also available online.
Also available on CD-ROM.

793   UK
KEY NOTE REPORT: BETTING & GAMING. Variant title: Betting & Gaming. irreg. £185. Key Note Publications Ltd., Field House, 72 Oldfield Rd., Hampton, Middlesex TW12 2HQ, England. TEL 0181-783-0755. FAX 0181-783-1720. **Document type:** trade publication.
●Also available online.
Also available on CD-ROM.

790.1 658.8   UK
▼**KEY NOTE REPORT: HEALTH CLUBS AND LEISURE CENTRES.** Variant title: Health Clubs and Leisure Centres. 1994. irreg. £185. Key Note Publications Ltd., Field House, 72 Oldfield Rd., Hampton, Middlesex TW12 2HQ, England. TEL 0181-783-0755. FAX 0181-783-1720. Ed. Andrew Beatt. **Document type:** trade publication.
●Also available online.
Also available on CD-ROM.

790.1   UK   ISSN 0267-5005
KEY NOTE REPORT: SPORTS EQUIPMENT. Variant title: Sports Equipment. irreg. £185. Key Note Publications Ltd., Field House, 72 Oldfield Rd., Hampton, Middlesex TW12 2HQ, England. TEL 0181-783-0755. FAX 0181-783-1720. **Document type:** trade publication.
●Also available online.
Also available on CD-ROM.
—BLDSC (8419.834090).

KEYNOTES (OAK BROOK). see *BUSINESS AND ECONOMICS — Management*

790.1   II
KHEL BHARATI. (Text in Hindi) 1982. fortn. Rs.300. Bennett, Coleman & Coleman & Co. Ltd. (New Delhi), Times House 7, Bahadur Shah Zafar Marg, New Delhi 110002, India. (U.S. subscr. addr.: Ms. Kalpana, 42-75 Main St., Flushing, NY 11355)

790.1   II
KHEL HALCHAL; illustrated Hindi sports. (Text in Hindi) 1983. w. newsstand price: Rs.3. Naidunia Compound, Babu Labhchand Chhajilani Marg, Indore 452 009, India. TEL 0731-65770. FAX 0731-65770. TELEX 0735-342. Ed. Abhay Chhajlani; Pub. Ajay Chajlany. adv.: B&W page Rs.1000, color page Rs.1500; 240 x 180; adv. contact: S. Pandia. pp./issue: 44.

790.1   PK
KHEL KI DUNYA. (Text in Urdu) s-m. Jamil Ahmad, 6-13 al-Yusuf Chambers, Hayat Bros., Box 340, Karachi, Pakistan.

790.1   II
KHELA. (Text in Bengali) 1982. w. newsstand price: Rs.3. AAjkaal Publishers Ltd., 96 Raja Rammohan Sarani, Calcutta 700 009, India. TEL 33-355302. TELEX 212216. Ed. Asoke Dasgupta; Pub. Pratap Kr. Roy. adv.: B&W page Rs.2000, color page Rs.4000; trim 240 x 165. circ. 16,496.

796   GW   ISSN 0023-1290
KICKER - SPORTMAGAZIN. 1968. 2/wk. DM.224.40. Olympia Verlag GmbH, Badstr. 4-6, 90427 Nuernberg, Germany. TEL 0911-2160. FAX 0911-2162641. Eds. Rainer Holzschuh, Wolfgang Uhrig. adv.; bk.rev.; abstr.; illus. circ. 340,000. **Document type:** consumer publication.

796.812   JA   ISSN 0388-208X
KINDAI JUDO. (Text in Japanese; summaries in English, French) 1979. m. 7200 Yen. Baseball Magazine Sha, 3-10-10 Misaki-cho, Chiyoda-ku, Tokyo, Japan. Ed. Yoshinori Nagase.

794   UK   ISSN 0969-2150
KINGPIN. 1986. 3/yr. £7 in U.K.; Europe £9; elsewhere £11. 45B Empress Ave., Ilford, Essex IG1 3DE, England. TEL 0181-554-8266. Ed. Jonathan Manley. adv.; bk.rev. circ. 2,000. **Document type:** consumer publication.
    Description: Includes games, news, "how-to" articles, opening theory, endgame studies, correspondence chess, chess computers and humor.

790.1   BG
KIRAJAGAT. (Text in Bengali) 1977. w. National Sports Control Board, 62-63 Purana Paltan, Dhaka, Bangladesh. Ed. Ali Muzzaman Chowdhury. circ. 7,000.

794.1   FI   ISSN 0358-1071
KIRJESHAKKI. 1961. 12/yr. FIM 180($52) Esko Nuutilainen, Ed. & Pub., PL 61, 04401 Jarvenpaa, Finland. FAX 0-2918336. adv.; bk.rev. circ. 1,300.

790.1   GW
KLUBB NACHRICHTEN. 1950. bi-m. membership. Turn-Klubb zu Hannover, Maschstr. 16, 30169 Hannover, Germany. TEL 0511-8093483. FAX 0511-889941. Ed. Christian Baermann. adv.: page DM.1000; adv. contact: Christian Baermann. circ. 3,500. (back issues avail.) **Document type:** newsletter.

790.1   GW
KLUBNACHRICHTEN. 1925. m. membership. Klubnachrichten - R R T K, Schillerstr. 39, 93049 Regensburg, Germany. TEL 0941-21400. Ed. Ham Richter.

796.86   NE   ISSN 0047-3561
KONINKLIJKE OFFICIERS SCHERMBOND. KOS-GEBEUREN. fl.1.50($3.) W.P.P. Hartman, Rembrandtkade 260, Rijswijk (Z.H.), Netherlands. adv. circ. 800.

796   NE   ISSN 0023-3501
KONKREET. 1969. bi-m. fl.10. Federatie van Bevoegde Nederlandse Sportleiders, Carmenstraat 9, Apeldoorn, Netherlands. Ed. Th.J. Van Son. adv.; bk.rev. circ. 1,500.

790.1   UA
AL-KORA WAL-MALAEB/SOCCER AND PLAYGROUNDS. (Text in Arabic) 1976. w. Dar al-Tahrir, 24 Sharia Zakaria Ahmed, Cairo, Egypt. TEL 02-741611. FAX 02-749949. TELEX 92475 TAHRIR UN. circ. 95,000. **Document type:** newspaper.

KOVELS SPORTS COLLECTIBLES; a monthly newsletter for sports fans. see *HOBBIES*

794   SW   ISSN 1102-2671
KRYSS FOER ALLA. 1991. q. SEK 60 (effective 1991). Acadius Foerlags AB, P.O. Box 45088, S-104 30 Stockholm, Sweden.

793.7   SW   ISSN 0345-6609
KRYSSDAX. 1967. q. SEK 14.50 per no. Acadius Foerlags AB, P.O. Box 45088, S-104 30 Stockholm, Sweden.

793.7   SW   ISSN 0345-6617
KRYSSET. 1957. 13/yr. SEK 222 (effective 1991). Semic Specialpress, P.O. Box 1074, S-172 22 Sundbyberg, Sweden. (Subscr. to: Pressdata AB, P.O. Box 3217, S-103 64 Stockholm, Sweden)
    Incorporates (1958-1990): Chansen.

KULISY SPORTU. see *ETHNIC INTERESTS*

SPORTS AND GAMES

794.1   US   ISSN 0148-057X
KXE6S VEREIN CHESS SOCIETY. ADVISORY BOARD RECORD. 1976. bi-m. Kxe6s Verein Chess Society, Box 2066, Chapel Hill, NC 27514. Ed. Steven Buntin. adv.; bk.rev.; abstr.; bibl.; charts; illus.; stat.; index, cum.index. circ. 500. (tabloid format; back issues avail.)

794.1   US   ISSN 0148-0561
KXE6S VEREIN NEWSLETTER. 1975. bi-m. $10. Kxe6s Verein Chess Society, Box 2066, Chapel Hill, NC 27514. Eds. Steven Buntin, Jerry Clark. adv.; bk.rev.; bibl.; charts; illus.; stat.; index. (tabloid format; back issues avail.)

790.1   US
L A SPORTS PROFILES. (Los Angeles) 1986. bi-m. $16.50. Sports Profiles, 4711 Golf St., Ste. 900, Skokie, IL 60076. TEL 708-673-0592. FAX 708-673-0633. Ed. Paula Blaine; Pub. Lisa Levine. adv. circ. 40,000. **Document type:** consumer publication.
 Description: Covers local professional and college sports teams.

L S A NEWSLETTER. (Leisure Studies Association) see LEISURE AND RECREATION

793   IT   ISSN 0393-3970
LABIRINTO. 1948. m. (11/yr.). L.10000. Piazza del Parlamento 3, 00186 Rome, Italy. Ed. Luigi Bernabei. adv. circ. 1,000.

796.347   US   ISSN 1069-5893
GV989
LACROSSE MAGAZINE. 1978. 8/yr. $45 to individuals; students $35. Lacrosse Foundation, Inc., 113 W. University Parkway, Baltimore, MD 21210. TEL 410-366-6735. FAX 410-366-6735. Ed. Keith Maynard. adv.; illus.; stat.; tr.lit. circ. 8,000. (back issues avail.)
 —UnCover.
 Formerly: Lacrosse (ISSN 0194-7893)
 Description: Covers men's and women's lacrosse at all levels. Includes action photographs and news on the Lacrosse Foundation.

LAKELAND BOATING; the Great Lakes boating magazine. see SPORTS AND GAMES — Boats And Boating

790.1   IT   ISSN 0393-5884
LANCILLOTTO E NAUSICA; quadrimestrale di critica e storia dello sport. 1984. 3/yr. L.20000($15) La Meridiana Editore, Via Selci in Sabina, 14, I-00199 Rome, Italy. Ed.Bd. adv.; bk.rev. circ. 10,000.

LAS VEGAS ADVISOR. see TRAVEL AND TOURISM

LAS VEGAS INSIDER. see TRAVEL AND TOURISM

796.72   US   ISSN 1057-2643
LATE MODEL DIGEST. fortn. Back Porch Publications, Box 69, Marble, NC 28905-0069. TEL 704-837-9539. FAX 704-837-7718. Ed. Brian McLeod. adv.

796.3   US   ISSN 1067-4748
LEGENDS SPORTS MEMORABILIA. 1988. bi-m. $27. Legends Sports Memorabilia, Inc., 9950 Campo Rd., 202, Spring Valley, CA 91977. TEL 619-460-9219. FAX 619-460-4919. Ed. Michael Godfrey. adv.; B&W page $2500; adv. contact: Jeff Lapinski. circ. 50,000. **Document type:** trade publication.
 Description: Offers articles and price guide relating to sports collectibles; features by sports-beat writers.

796   RU   ISSN 0024-4155
GV1060.5
LEGKAYA ATLETIKA. 1955. m. $57 (effective 1996). (Soyuz Sportivnykh Obshchestv i Organizatsii) Izdatel'stvo Fizkul'tura i Sport, Kalyaevskaya ul., 27, 101421 Moscow, Russia. FAX 2001217. (Dist. in U.S. by: Victor Kamkin Inc., 4956 Boiling Brook Pkwy., Rockville, MD 20852. TEL 301-881-5973. FAX 301-881-1637) Ed. V.S. Kayurov. illus.; index. circ. 75,000.

613.7 790.1   GW   ISSN 0941-5270
LEIPZIGER SPORTWISSENSCHAFTLICHE BEITRAEGE. (Text in German; summaries in English, French, German and Russian) 1959. 2/yr. DM.58. (Fakultaet fuer Sportwissenschaft, Universitaet Leipzig) Academia Verlag GmbH, Postfach 1663, 53734 Sankt Augustin, Germany. TEL 02241-333349. FAX 02241-341528. Ed. H. Kirchgaessner. bk.rev.; illus.; index. circ. 400. (tabloid format) **Document type:** academic/scholarly publication.
 Formerly: Deutsche Hochschule fuer Koerperkultur. Wissenschaftliche Zeitschrift (ISSN 0457-3919)

790.1   GW   ISSN 0341-7387
LEISTUNGSSPORT. 1970. bi-m. DM.54 (foreign DM.60). Philippka-Verlag, Postfach 6540, 48034 Muenster, Germany. TEL 0251-23005-0. FAX 0251-23005-99. circ. 3,500. (back issues avail.) **Indexed:** Sportsearch (1972-). **Document type:** consumer publication.
 —BLDSC (5182.205000); SWETS.

LEISURE INDUSTRY REPORT. see LEISURE AND RECREATION

LEISURE MANAGEMENT. see LEISURE AND RECREATION

LEISURE SCIENCES; an interdisciplinary journal. see LEISURE AND RECREATION

LEISURE STUDIES. see LEISURE AND RECREATION

790.1   US
LET'S MAKE IT OFFICIAL. a. $3. National Federation of State High School Associations, 11724 N.W. Plaza Circle, Box 20626, Kansas City, MO 64195-0626. TEL 816-464-5400. FAX 816-464-5571.

796   US   ISSN 0889-4795
LET'S PLAY HOCKEY. 1972. 29/yr. $35. Let's Play, Inc., 2721 E. 42nd St., Minneapolis, MN 55406. TEL 612-729-0023. FAX 612-729-0259. adv.; circ. 19,500.
 Description: For youth and amateur players, parents, coaches and fans.

794.1   HU   ISSN 0230-5151
LEVELEZESI SAKKHIRADO. 1967. 6/yr. $4. Hungarian Chess Association, Correspondence Committee, H-1072 Budapest, Klauzal ter.5.II.30, Hungary. TEL 361-1213-832. Ed. Dezso Solt. adv.; bk.rev. circ. 1,000.
 Description: Covers national and international chess games and news, tables and results.

LICHAMELIJKE OPVOEDING. see EDUCATION — Teaching Methods And Curriculum

LOISIR ET SOCIETE/SOCIETY AND LEISURE. see LEISURE AND RECREATION

790.1   US
LONGBOARD QUARTERLY. bi-m. newsstand price: $5.95. 110 E. Palizada, Ste. 301, San Clemente, CA 92672. TEL 714-366-8282. FAX 714-366-8280.

795 745.1   US   ISSN 0278-4114
TJ1557
LOOSE CHANGE. 1977. 10/yr. $39. Mead Publishing Company, 1515 S. Commerce St., Las Vegas, NV 89102-2703. TEL 702-387-8750. Ed. Daniel R. Mead. adv.; bk.rev. circ. 2,600. (back issues avail.) **Document type:** consumer publication.
 Description: Covers collecting slot machines, gambling memorabilia and coin operated amusement devices, contemporary and antique.

791   II   ISSN 0024-6654
LOTTERY GAZETTE. (Text in English and Hindi) 1969. w. Rs.11($2) J.C. Gupta, Ed. & Pub., 157-E Kamla Nagar, Delhi 7, India. adv.; film rev.; play rev. circ. 12,000.

790.1   US   ISSN 0277-5565
LOTTERY PLAYER'S MAGAZINE. 1981. m. $23.97. Regal Publishing Corporation, 321 New Albany Rd., Moorestown, NJ 08057. FAX 609-273-6350. Ed. Samuel W. Valenza, Jr; Pub. Samuel W. Valenza, Jr. adv.; bk.rev.; play rev.; stat.; index. circ. 120,000. (back issues avail.) **Document type:** newspaper.

795   US
LOTTERY WINNING GUIDE. 1993. m. $18. Gibbs Publishing Company, Box 600927, N. Miami Beach, FL 33160. TEL 305-947-4393. Ed. James Calvin Gibbs. adv. circ. 11,000. **Document type:** consumer publication.

795   IT   ISSN 0024-6662
LOTTOROSCOPO; periodico mensile di previsioni sul lotto. 1970. m. L.25000. Lottoroscopo, Casella Postale 94, Via S. Nicolo 7, 43100 Parma, Italy. TEL 0521-206076. Ed. Giovanni Gatti. circ. 5,000.

790.1   US
LOTTOWORLD. 1993. bi-w. $29.97. Dynamic World Distributors, Inc., 2150 Goodlette Rd., N. Ste. 200, Naples, FL 33940-4811. TEL 941-643-1677; 800-223-6814. FAX 941-643-6670. E-mail: MRII@AOL.COM. Ed. Rich Holman. adv.; color page $7750. circ. 250,000 (paid). **Document type:** consumer publication.
 Description: General interest publication devoted to covering the U.S. lottery industry. Offers systems, strategies and tips that can increase the chances of winning a lotto jackpot.

799.2   CI   ISSN 0024-6999
LOVACKI VJESNIK. 1892. m. $8.55 (typically set in Jan.). Hrvatski Lovacki Savez, V. Nazora 61, Zagreb, Croatia. TEL 041-433 310. Ed. Tihomir Kovacevic. adv.; bk.rev. circ. 82,000.

796   US   ISSN 0024-7898
M A C GOPHER. 1915. m. $18. Minneapolis Athletic Club, 615 Second Ave. S., Minneapolis, MN 55402. TEL 612-339-3655. FAX 612-339-7923. Ed. Marilyn A. Siebert. adv. circ. 4,400.

796.8   NE   ISSN 0920-279X
M.A.S.H. MAGAZINE; vakblad voor combat, martial arts, survival en ninjitsu. (Text in Dutch) 1986. q. fl.20. Banzai Productions, Postbus 5050, 3502 JB Utrecht, Netherlands. TEL 31-30-942988. Ed. J.J.M.A. Hesselman. adv.; bk.rev. circ. 1,100 (controlled). (back issues avail.) **Document type:** newsletter.
 Description: Covers martial arts and related studies in the broadest sense.

796.215   US   ISSN 0898-4786
GV1102.7.T7
M A TRAINING. (Martial Arts) 1973. bi-m. $19.50 for 2 yrs. Rainbow Publications, Inc., 24715 Ave. Rockefeller, Box 918, Santa Clarita, CA 91380-9018. TEL 805-257-4066. FAX 805-257-3018. (Subscr. to: Box 16298, N. Hollywood, CA 91615-6298. TEL 800-266-4066) Ed. Doug Jeffries; Pub. Michael James. adv.; charts; illus. circ. 45,000. **Document type:** consumer publication.
 Former titles: M A Weapons (ISSN 0893-2514); Fighting Stars - Ninja; Fighting Stars (ISSN 0274-5178)
 Description: Covers training for the martial artist in all styles and product reviews.

796   IS
MACCABI WORLD UNION. NEWSLETTER. (Text in English; Spanish edition also available) 1951. m. free. Maccabi World Union, Kfar Hamaccabiah, Israel. Ed. Zvi Eyal. adv.; circ. 500 (controlled). (processed) **Document type:** newsletter.
 Formerly: Maccabi News Bulletin (ISSN 0541-5896)

MAGNUM; the shooters' magazine. see SPORTS AND GAMES — Outdoor Life

796.42   US   ISSN 1064-6779
MAINELY RUNNING. 1991. 10/yr. $17.50. 2 Howards Hill Rd., Brunswick, ME 04011. TEL 207-725-8680. Ed. John W. LeRoy. adv.; bk.rev. circ. 1,000. **Document type:** consumer publication.
 Description: Provides endurance sports coverage for the state of Maine.

790.1   US
MANHATTAN CHESS NEWS. 1989. q. $20. Manhattan Chess Club, 353 W. 46th St., New York, NY 10019. TEL 212-333-5888. Ed. Ross Garber. circ. 500. **Document type:** newsletter.

6072 SPORTS AND GAMES

354 CN
MANITOBA LOTTERIES CORPORATION. ANNUAL REPORT. (Report year ends Mar. 31) 1971. a. free. Manitoba Lotteries Corporation, 830 Empress St., Winnipeg, MB R3G 3H3, Canada. TEL 204-957-2500. FAX 204-957-2621. illus.; stat. circ. 2,000.
Former titles: Manitoba Lotteries Foundation. Annual Report (ISSN 0837-6840); (until 1983): Manitoba Lotteries and Gaming Control Commission. Annual Report (ISSN 0824-8508); (until 1981): Manitoba Lotteries Commission. Annual Report (ISSN 0703-0827)

790.1 US
MANY HAPPY RETURNS NEWSLETTER. 1982. q. $15 (effective Apr. 1995). United States Boomerang Association, Box 182, Delaware, OH 43015. TEL 614-363-4414. Ed. Bregg Snouffer; Pub. Betsy Miale-Gix. adv.; bk.rev. circ. 500. (back issues avail.) **Document type:** newsletter.
Description: Presents a forum for the art, sport, and history of boomerangs with information about the craftsmanship, sports results, and various applicable computer programs available.

796 IE ISSN 0047-5874
MARATHON; Ireland's international athletics magazine. 1967. bi-m. $25. Inch, Killeagh, Co. Cork, Ireland. TEL 024-95148. FAX 024-667582. Ed. Liam Kelleher. adv.; bk.rev.; illus.; stat. circ. 3,500. **Indexed:** Sportsearch. **Document type:** consumer publication.

796.42 SW ISSN 0283-1015
MARATHONLOEPAREN. 1968. bi-m. SEK 130 membership (effective 1991). Svenska Marathonsaellskapet, P.O. Box 218, S-101 22 Stockholm, Sweden.

790.1 SP
MARCA. (In regional eds. for Madrid, Valencia, Andalucia) 1941. d. newsstand price: 100 ptas. Recoletos Cia. Editorial, C. Recoletos 1, 28001 Madrid, Spain. TEL 337-32-20. FAX 337-37-71. Ed. Luis Infante Bravo. adv. contact: Jose Manuel Rodrigo. illus.; circ. 741,000 (controlled). cols./p.: 5; pp./issue: 40. (standard format) **Document type:** newspaper.

790.1 340 US ISSN 1057-6029
MARQUETTE SPORTS LAW JOURNAL. 1990. s-a. membership. (National Sports Law Institute) Marquette University, Law School, 1103 W. Wisconsin Ave., Milwaukee, WI 53233. TEL 414-288-5815. FAX 414-288-5818. adv.; bk.rev. (reprint service avail. from WSH) —BLDSC (5382.650500); UnCover.
Description: Aimed at attorneys and sports industry professionals. Devoted exclusively to sports law, sports business and sports ethics issues confronting amateur and professional sports. All material published is the product of student authors, published under the guidance of faculty members.

796.815 UK ISSN 0955-5447
MARTIAL ARTS ILLUSTRATED. 1988. m. £21.50. M A I Publications, Revenue Chambers, St. Peter's Str., Huddersfield HD1 1EL, England. TEL 01484-435011. FAX 01484-422177. Ed. Bob Sykes. adv.: B&W page £242, color page £572; adv. contact: Moira Spencer. bk.rev.; film rev. (back issues avail.) **Document type:** consumer publication.
Description: Covers all aspects of the martial arts, including karate, kung fu, kickboxing, aikido and taekwondo.

790.1 US
MASTERS OF KUNG-FU. 1992. bi-m. $3 per no. C F W Enterprises, Inc., 4201 W. Van Owen Pl., Burbank, CA 91505. TEL 818-845-2656. FAX 818-845-7761. (Subscr. to: Box 404, Mt. Morris, IL 61054) Ed. Dave Cater. adv.: B&W page $700; adv. contact: Steve Aochi. circ. 60,000. **Document type:** consumer publication.
Formerly: Kung-Fu Masters (ISSN 1068-7645)
Description: For martial artists with other interests and others with martial arts interests.

799.202 IS ISSN 0792-1586
MATARAH. 1988. m. 18 Misilat Hachashmonaim, Tel Aviv, Israel.

794.1 SP
MATE POSTAL. (Editions in English and Spanish) 1974. q. $15. Comision Permanente Ajedrez Postal, Santa Eulalia, 28, torre, 08921 Santa Coloma de Gramanet, Barcelona, Spain. (Subscr. to: c/o Valentin Torra, Calle Aneto, 3, 08251 Santpedor (Barcelona), Spain) (Affiliate: International Correspondence Chess Federation) Ed. Carlos Ros Miro.

790.1 SY
MAUKEF AL-RIADI. w. Ouehda Organization, Damascus, Syria. adv.

794.1 NE ISSN 0927-9768
MAX EUWE-CENTRUM. NIEUWSBRIEF. 1987. 4/yr. $25. Stichting Max Euwe-Centrum, Postbus 11513, 1001 GM Amsterdam, Netherlands. TEL 31-20-6257017. FAX 31-20-6392077. Ed. L.C.M. Diepstraten. bk.rev. **Document type:** newsletter.
Description: News about chess activities at the Max Euwe-Centrum.

MEDIA SPORTS BUSINESS. see *COMMUNICATIONS — Television And Cable*

MEN'S EXERCISE. see *PHYSICAL FITNESS AND HYGIENE*

THE MENTAL EDGE. see *PSYCHOLOGY*

MERCURY (LOS ANGELES). see *CLUBS*

790.1 VE
MERIDIANO. d. Meridiario, C.A., Bloque DeArmas, Final Av. San Martin, Esq. La Quebradita 34-2, Edificio Berlioz, Piso 2, Apdo. 475, Caracas, Venezuela. adv. circ. 300,000. **Document type:** newspaper.

790.1 US
METROSPORTS MAGAZINE. (In 2 eds.: New York Tri-State, Greater Boston) 1974. 11/yr. $18.95. Tate House Enterprises, Inc., 695 Washington St., New York, NY 10014. TEL 212-627-7040. FAX 212-242-3293. Eds. Miles & Julie Jaffe. adv.; bk.rev.; circ. 130,000 (controlled). (tabloid format; back issues avail.) **Document type:** consumer publication.
Supersedes in part (in 1988): CitySports Magazine.
Description: Covers all aspects of the New York and Boston areas adult recreational sports and fitness.

794.1 US
MICHIGAN CHESS. 1971. 6/yr. $12. 7500 Anthony, Dearborn, MI 48126. Ed. David Moody. adv.; bk.rev. circ. 1,000. **Document type:** newsletter.

MICHIGAN OUT-OF-DOORS. see *CONSERVATION*

MICROLIGHT FLYING. see *AERONAUTICS AND SPACE FLIGHT*

790.1 US ISSN 1071-4081
MIDWEST PLAYERS; the guide to gaming in the Midwest. 1991. 24/yr. $48 (Canada $60). R C M Enterprises, Inc., 15500 Wayzata Blvd., Ste. 922, Box 720, Wayzata, MN 55391. TEL 612-473-5088. FAX 612-473-7068. Ed. Joe Pawlowski; Pub. Robert C. Mead. adv.: B&W page $876.40; adv. contact: Jim Penningroth. bk.rev.; illus.; index. circ. 48,000. (tabloid format) **Document type:** newspaper, consumer publication.
Description: Provides news of casinos and tracks throughout the Midwest, with columns on recreational gambling, infromation on promotions and entertainment.

796.72 US ISSN 0047-732X
MIDWEST RACING NEWS. 1959. w. (Apr.-Sep.); m. (Oct.-Dec.). $20. Midwest Racing News, Inc., 6646 W. Fairview Ave., Milwaukee, WI 53213. TEL 414-778-4700. FAX 414-778-4688. Ed. James H. Wehner. adv. contact: Dean Strom. bk.rev.; illus. circ. 8,000. (tabloid format) **Document type:** consumer publication, trade publication.
Description: Discusses regional and national automobile races and drivers.

794.1 US
MINNESOTA CHESS JOURNAL. 1963. 4/yr. $15. Minnesota Chess Association, Box 11329, St. Paul, MN 55111-0329. Ed. Keith Hayward. adv.; bk.rev. circ. 800.
Description: Reports on national events with local participants, and computer programs.

796 613.7 US
MINNESOTA SPORTS. 11/yr. $15. Skyway News, 33 S. Fifth St., Minneapolis, MN 55402-1050. TEL 612-375-9222. FAX 612-375-9208. Ed. Glenn Hansen. adv.; circ. 40,000 (controlled). **Document type:** newspaper.

790.1 GW
MITGLIEDERRUNDSCHREIBEN. 1953. m. Deutscher Sportbund, Postfach 710263, 60492 Frankfurt a.M. TEL 069-6700-0. FAX 069-674906. circ. 1,400. **Document type:** abstracting/indexing, newsletter.

796.1 629.133 SW ISSN 0345-813X
MODELLFLYGNYT. 1963. bi-m. SEK 180. Sveriges Modellflygfoerbund (SMFF), P.O. Box 10022, S-600 10 Norrkoeping, Sweden. TEL 46-35-21-31-41. FAX 46-35-18-65-75. Ed. Sture Tingwall. circ. 12,000.
Former titles (until 1968): Modellnytt; (until 1966): Modellflygnytt.

799.202 US
MODERN GUN. bi-m. newsstand price: $2.95. Larry Flynt Publications, Inc., 9171 Wilshire Blvd., Ste. 300, Beverly Hills, CA 90210. TEL 310-858-7100. FAX 310-275-3857. **Document type:** consumer publication.

MONDO SOMMERSO; international magazine on nature, ecology, environment, sea diving activities, and travels. see *EARTH SCIENCES — Oceanography*

794.1 IT
MONDOSCACCHI. irreg. (4-5/yr.). A M I S, C.P. 306, 00100 Rome, Italy. Ed. A. Zichichi.
Description: Contains annotated games, "how-to-improve" articles, and national news. Some issues may be devoted exclusively to a particular technical or chess cultural theme.

796.522 SP ISSN 0027-0032
MONTANEROS DE ARAGON.* 1949. q. free. Montaneros de Aragon, Calvo Sotelo 11, Zaragoza, Spain. Ed. Miguel - Angel Garcia Lopez. adv.; bibl.; charts; illus.

796.86 JA
MONTHLY JAPANESE FENCING/GEKKAN KENDO NIPPON. (Text in Japanese) 1976. m. 9000 Yen. Ski Journal Co. Ltd., 3-11, Yotsuya, Shinjuku-ku, Tokyo, Japan. Ed. Toshiya Suzuki.

790.1 DK ISSN 0107-8976
MOTIONSGANG. 1982. bi-m. DKK 40. Sjaellandske Gangsport Foreninger, Mogens Aistrup, Baunevej 14, DK-2650 Hvidovre, Denmark.

MOTOR. see *TRANSPORTATION — Automobiles*

MOTOR SPORT. see *TRANSPORTATION — Automobiles*

796.72 SZ
MOTOR SPORT AKTUELL RENNTERMINKALENDER. 1986. a. 2.80 SFr. Powerslide AG, Kreuzstr. 60, Postfach 282, CH-8032 Zurich, Switzerland. TEL 01-2518347. FAX 01-2514851. Ed. Peter Wyss; Pubs. August Hug, Richard Stolz. adv. contact: August Hug. circ. 35,000. **Document type:** consumer publication.

796.72 UK
MOTORSCOT. 1949. m. £3. Scottish Clubman Ltd., 12 Evan St., Stonehaven, Kincardinshire, Scotland. Ed. A.J. Stephen. adv.; bk.rev.; bibl.; illus. circ. 10,000.
Formerly: Scottish Clubman (ISSN 0036-9152)
Description: Covers automobile, motorcycle and kart racing.

388.3 SZ
MOTORSPORT AKTUELL. (Text in German) 1963. w. newsstand price: 2.80 SFr. Powerslide AG, Kreuzstr. 60, Postfach 282, CH-8032 Zurich, Switzerland. TEL 01-2518347. FAX 01-2514851. Ed. Guenther Wiesinger; Pubs. August Hug, Richard Stolz. adv. contact: A. Grzegorzewski. bk.rev.; charts; illus.; stat.; index. circ. 75,000. **Document type:** consumer publication.

796.72 US ISSN 1057-0691
MOTORSPORTS. bi-m. J.L. Quinn & Assoc. Inc., Box 8389, Fresno, CA 93747-8389. TEL 209-445-8556. Ed. Jim Quinn; Pub. Jim Quinn. circ. 5,000. **Document type:** consumer publication.

SPORTS AND GAMES

MUENZAUTOMAT; Fachzeitschrift fuer die Automatenbranche. see *BUSINESS AND ECONOMICS — Management*

790.1   IT
MULTISPORT. 1987. 8/yr. L.33000 (foreign L.65000). Editoriale Sport Italia, Via Masaccio 12, 20149 Milan, Italy. TEL 39-2-4815396. FAX 39-2-4690907. Ed. Marco Marchei. adv.: B&W page L.3000000, color page L.4500000; adv. contact: Antonio Brazzit. circ. 29,500. **Document type**: consumer publication.

790.01   SP
MUNDO DEPORTIVO. 1906. d. 32000 ptas. Tallers 62-64, 4o, 08001 Barcelona, Spain. TEL 3-301-28-28. FAX 3-412-32-91. TELEX 54271. Ed. Javier Diez Serrat. adv. contact: Luis Garcia Adelantado. illus. circ. 67,025. **Document type**: newspaper.
     Description: Covers soccer, basketball and U.S. sports news.

796.72 629.2   UK
MURRAY WALKER'S GRAND PRIX YEAR. a. £11.99 (rest of Europe £13.99; N. and S. America, Middle East, Africa £15.99; Australasia £16.99) (effective 1995-1996). (Royal Dutch Shell) Hazleton Publishing, 3 Richmond Hill, Richmond, Surrey TW10 6RE, England. TEL 0181-948-5151. FAX 0181-948-4111. TELEX 946153. Ed. Murray Walker; Pub. Richard Poulter. adv. contact: Simon Maurice. charts; illus.; stat. **Document type**: consumer publication.
     Description: Reviews the past year's Grand Prix auto racing season.

790.1   CN   ISSN 0317-087X
MUSCLE MAG INTERNATIONAL; the "what's new" magazine of bodybuilding. 1974. m. $45. Canusa Products, 6465 Airport Rd., Mississauga, ON L4V 1E4, Canada. TEL 905-678-7311. FAX 905-678-9236. Ed. Robert Kennedy; Pub. Robert Kennedy. adv.: B&W page $4950; adv. contact: Gina Logan. bk.rev.; charts; illus. circ. 370,000. **Indexed**: Sportsearch. **Document type**: consumer publication.
     Description: Focuses on bodybuilding and fitness for both men and women.

MUSCLE TRAINING ILLUSTRATED. see *PHYSICAL FITNESS AND HYGIENE*

MUSCULAR DEVELOPMENT FITNESS & HEALTH. see *PHYSICAL FITNESS AND HYGIENE*

796   US   ISSN 0077-3336
N A I A HANDBOOK. 1959. biennial. $35. National Association of Intercollegiate Athletics, 6120 S. Yale Ave., No. 1450, Tulsa, OK 74136-4223. TEL 918-494-8828. FAX 918-494-8841. Ed. Wallace Schwartz. (reprint service avail. from UMI)

796   US   ISSN 0740-5995
N A I A NEWS. 1950. 11/yr. $30. National Association of Intercollegiate Athletics, 6120 S. Yale Ave., No. 1450, Tulsa, OK 74136-4223. TEL 918-494-8828. FAX 918-494-8841. Ed. Kevin Henry. bk.rev.; stat. circ. 7,000. (also avail. in microform from UMI; reprint service avail. from UMI) **Indexed**: Sportsearch (1976-).
     Former titles: N A I A News and Coach; N A I A News.

796   US
GV741
N A I A OFFICIAL CHAMPIONSHIP SUMMARIES. 1958. a. $20. National Association of Intercollegiate Athletics, 6120 S. Yale Ave., No. 1450, Tulsa, OK 74136-4223. TEL 918-494-8828. FAX 918-494-8841. Ed. Duane Dapron. index. circ. 2,500. (reprint service avail. from UMI)
     Former titles: N A I A Official Records Book and Championship Summaries; N A I A Official Records Book (ISSN 0077-3344)

796.72   US   ISSN 0898-9508
N A S C A R NEWS. 1949. fortn. $35 to non-members. National Association for Stock Car Auto Racing, Inc., 1801 West International Speedway Blvd., Daytona Beach, FL 32114-1243. TEL 904-253-0611. FAX 904-252-8804. Ed. Paul C. Schaefer. adv.; bk.rev.; charts; illus.; tr.lit.; index. circ. 40,000. **Document type**: newspaper.
     Formerly: N A S C A R Newsletter (ISSN 0027-5999)

790.1   US
N A Y S I RESOURCE LIST. irreg. free. North American Youth Sport Institute, 4985 Oak Garden Dr., Kernersville, NC 27284-9520. TEL 910-784-4926. Ed. Dr. Jack Hutslar. **Document type**: bibliography.
     Description: Covers books and materials for persons working with tots, youth and teens in sport, recreation, education, fitness and health.

790.1   US   ISSN 0162-1467
GV347
N C A A DIRECTORY. 1976. a. $8. National Collegiate Athletic Association, Circulation Department, Box 7347, Overland Park, KS 66207-0347. TEL 913-339-1900. circ. 2,500. **Document type**: directory.
     Description: Includes membership roster, with district and division listing, and provides information on NCAA committees and organizational structure.

790.1 616.86   US
N C A A DRUG TESTING PROGRAM. a. $1.50. National Collegiate Athletic Association, Circulation Department, Box 7347, Overland Park, KS 66207-0347. TEL 913-339-1900.
     Description: Establishes NCAA procedures and regulations for drug testing of student athletes, and includes a list of banned drugs.

796   US   ISSN 1053-0886
GV563
N C A A MANUAL. (Also published in editions for individual Divisions 1, 2, and 3.) 1906; 1966 as independent title. a. $13. National Collegiate Athletic Association, Circulation Department, Box 7347, Overland Park, KS 66207-0347. TEL 913-339-1900. circ. 7,500.
     Formerly: National Collegiate Athletic Association. Manual (ISSN 0077-3816)
     Description: Contains all NCAA legislation applicable to the three divisions, including constitution, operating and administrative by-laws.

799.202   US
N C A A MEN'S AND WOMEN'S RIFLE RULES. a. $5. National Collegiate Athletic Association, Circulation Department, Box 7347, Overland Park, KS 66207-0347. TEL 913-339-1900. illus.
     Description: Covers official signals, interpretations, and rulings.

797.21   US   ISSN 0736-5128
N C A A MEN'S AND WOMEN'S SWIMMING AND DIVING RULES. 1925. a. $4. National Collegiate Athletic Association, Circulation Department, Box 7347, Overland Park, KS 66207-0347. TEL 913-339-1900. illus. circ. 8,200.
     Former titles: N C A A Swimming (ISSN 0272-8095); Official National Collegiate Athletic Association Swimming Guide.
     Description: Covers official signals, interpretations, and rulings.

796   US   ISSN 0735-9195
GV847
N C A A MEN'S ICE HOCKEY RULES AND INTERPRETATIONS. 1926. a. $4. National Collegiate Athletic Association, Circulation Department, Box 7347, Overland Park, KS 66207-0347. TEL 913-339-1900. illus. circ. 10,000.
     Formerly: Official National Collegiate Athletic Association Ice Hockey Guide.
     Description: Covers official signals, interpretations, and rulings.

790.1   US   ISSN 0734-0508
GV839
N C A A MEN'S WATER POLO RULES. 1970. a. $4. National Collegiate Athletic Association, Circulation Department, Box 7347, Overland Park, KS 66207-0347. TEL 913-339-1900. illus.
     Former titles: N C A A Water Polo Rules (ISSN 0271-860X); Official National Collegiate Athletic Association Water Polo Rules.
     Description: Covers official signals, interpretations, and rulings.

796   US   ISSN 0027-6170
N C A A NEWS. 1964. 46/yr. $24. National Collegiate Athletic Association, Circulation Department, Box 7347, Overland Park, KS 66207-0347. TEL 913-339-1906. FAX 913-339-1950. Ed. David Pickle. adv.; bk.rev. circ. 20,000. (tabloid format) **Indexed**: Sports Per.Ind., Sportsearch (1977-).
     Incorporates: Football Statistics Rankings.

790.1   US   ISSN 0736-511X
GV1195
N C A A WRESTLING RULES. 1927. a. $3. National Collegiate Athletic Association, Circulation Department, Box 7347, Overland Park, KS 66207-0347. TEL 913-339-1900. illus. circ. 10,000.
     Formerly: Official National Collegiate Athletic Association Wrestling Guide.
     Description: Covers official signals, interpretations, and rulings.

796   US   ISSN 0744-1347
N C G A NEWS. 1961. q. membership only. Northern California Golf Association, 3200 Lopez Rd., Box NCGA, Pebble Beach, CA 93953. TEL 408-625-4653. FAX 408-625-0150. Ed. Ted Blofsky, Jr. adv.; circ. 150,000 (controlled).
     Formerly: Northern California Golf Association. Blue Book.
     Description: Provides news, articles, information on tournaments, courses and golfers, including association news.

790.1   US
N I R S A JOURNAL. 1977. 3/yr. $40. National Intramural-Recreational Sports Association, 850 S.W. 15th St., Corvallis, OR 97333-4145. TEL 503-737-2088. FAX 503-737-2026. Ed. Gary L. Miller. adv.; bk.rev.; index. circ. 3,000. (back issues avail.) **Indexed**: Phys.Ed.Ind., Sportsearch (1979-). **Document type**: academic/scholarly publication.

N S G A RETAIL FOCUS. (National Sporting Goods Association) see *BUSINESS AND ECONOMICS — Marketing And Purchasing*

N.S.W. SKINDIVER. (New South Wales) see *SPORTS AND GAMES — Outdoor Life*

NADI ABU DHABI AL-SIYAHI/ABU DHABI TOURIST CLUB. see *CLUBS*

NADI AL-WASL. see *CLUBS*

797.21   FR   ISSN 1141-1872
NAGER SAUVER. 1928. q. 200 F. (foreign 250 F.). Federation Francaise des Maitres-Nageurs Sauveteurs, 152 rue des Jardiniers, 69400 Villefranche sur Saone, France. TEL 74-62-34-13. FAX 74-62-97-06. adv. contact: circ. 5,000.
     Formerly (until 1952): L'Association des Professeurs de Natation de France (ISSN 1141-1864)

790.1   JA   ISSN 0287-900X
NANBA/SPORTS GRAPHIC NUMBER. (Text in Japanese) 1980. bi-w. 21060 Yen. Bungei-Shunju Ltd., 3 Kioi-cho, Chiyoda-ku, Tokyo 102, Japan. TEL 03-3265-1211. FAX 03-3239-3699. Ed. Atsuo Shitara. **Document type**: consumer publication.

AL-NASR. see *CLUBS*

797   FR   ISSN 1169-8152
NATATION. 1922. 27/yr. 260 F. (foreign 440 F.). Federation Francaise de Natation, 148 av. Gambetta, 75020 Paris, France. TEL 40-31-17-70. FAX 40-31-19-90. TELEX 215249. adv.; illus. **Indexed**: Sportsearch.

790.1   NE   ISSN 0169-1945
NATIONAAL SPORT MAGAZINE. 1980. bi-m. fl.45. (Nederlandse Sport Federatie) Drukkerij G.J. van Amerongen B.V., Postbus 205, 3800 AE Amersfoort, Netherlands. TEL 31-33-616349. FAX 31-33-616992. circ. 3,000. **Document type**: consumer publication.
     Formerly (until 1985): Sport Intermedium.

797   US   ISSN 1074-0651
NATIONAL AQUATICS JOURNAL.* 1985. q. membership. Council for National Cooperation in Aquatics, 3654 N. Mitchner Ave., Indianapolis, IN 46226-5840. Ed. Louise Priest. **Document type**: bulletin.
     —BLDSC (6016.051000).

796   US   ISSN 0077-3794
GV563
NATIONAL COLLEGIATE ATHLETIC ASSOCIATION. ANNUAL REPORTS. 1966. a. $16. National Collegiate Athletic Association, Circulation Department, Box 7347, Overland Park, KS 66207-0347. TEL 913-339-1900. circ. 2,500.

6074 SPORTS AND GAMES

796   US   ISSN 0077-3808
NATIONAL COLLEGIATE ATHLETIC ASSOCIATION. CONVENTION PROCEEDINGS. 1906; 1967 as independent title. a. $16. National Collegiate Athletic Association, Circulation Department, Box 7347, Overland Park, KS 66207-0347. TEL 913-339-1900. circ. 2,500.

796   US   ISSN 0190-4329
GV741
NATIONAL COLLEGIATE CHAMPIONSHIPS. 1954. a. $12. National Collegiate Athletic Association, Circulation Department, Box 7347, Overland Park, KS 66207-0347. TEL 913-339-1900. circ. 2,700.
   Formerly: National Collegiate Championships Record Book (ISSN 0148-9798)
   Description: Contains detailed summaries of championships of the preceding year, for both men's and women's athletics, with additional historical information.

796   US   ISSN 0547-616X
NATIONAL DIRECTORY OF COLLEGE ATHLETICS (MEN'S EDITION). 1968. a. $25.95. (National Association of Collegiate Directors of Athletics) Collegiate Directories, Inc., Box 450640, Cleveland, OH 44145. TEL 216-835-1172. FAX 216-835-8835. Ed. Kevin Cleary. circ. 18,000. **Document type:** directory.
   Description: Lists 2,100 senior and junior colleges and vital information about each athletic department. Covers men's intercollegiate athletics in the U.S. and Canada, NCAA, NAIA and NJCAA and other collegiate information.

796   US   ISSN 0739-1226
GV439
NATIONAL DIRECTORY OF COLLEGE ATHLETICS (WOMEN'S EDITION). 1973. a. $20.95. Collegiate Directories, Inc., Box 450640, Cleveland, OH 44145. TEL 216-835-1172. FAX 216-835-8835. Ed. Kevin Cleary. illus. circ. 18,000. **Document type:** directory.
   Formerly: National Directory of Women's Athletics (ISSN 0092-5489)

NATIONAL DIRECTORY OF HIGH SCHOOL COACHES. see *EDUCATION*

790.1   US   ISSN 0737-5204
GV710
NATIONAL FEDERATION HANDBOOK. a. $3. National Federation of State High School Associations, 11724 N.W. Plaza Circle, Box 20626, Kansas City, MO 64195-0626. TEL 816-464-5400. FAX 816-464-5571. (also avail. in microfiche from CIS) **Indexed:** SRI.

796 636   AT   ISSN 0310-589X
NATIONAL GREYHOUND NEWS. 1971. m. Aus.$17($37.20) (New South Wales Greyhound Breeders, Owners and Trainers Association) Greyhound News Pty. Ltd., Box 72, Waverly, N.S.W. 2024, Australia. Ed. Noel C. Christensen. adv.; bk.rev. circ. 20,000.
   Description: Covers dog racing.

798   US   ISSN 0897-9944
NATIONAL GREYHOUND UPDATE. 11/yr. Hobson Publishing, 21684 Granada Ave., Cupertino, CA 95014. TEL 408-446-0551. Ed. Pres Hobson.

790.1   US   ISSN 0192-978X
GV346
NATIONAL HIGH SCHOOL SPORTS RECORD BOOK. 1979. a. $4.95. National Federation of State High School Associations, 11724 N.W. Plaza Circle, Box 20626, Kansas City, MO 64195-0626. TEL 816-464-5400. FAX 816-464-5571. Ed. Fred Mares. (also avail. in microfiche from CIS) **Indexed:** SRI.

796.9   CN   ISSN 0316-831X
GV847.5
NATIONAL HOCKEY LEAGUE. OFFICIAL RULE BOOK. 1931. a. $9.95. National Hockey League Publishing, 194 Doversourt Rd., Toronto, ON M6J 3L8, Canada. TEL 416-531-6535. Ed. Dan Diamond. illus. **Document type:** consumer publication.
   Description: Official rules governing play in the NHL, featuring referee's signals rink diagram and new rules.

NATIONAL P A L UPDATE. see *CHILDREN AND YOUTH — For*

796.72   US   ISSN 0028-0208
NATIONAL SPEED SPORT NEWS. 1932. w. $32.50. Kay Publishing Co., Inc., 79 Chestnut St., Box 608, Ridgewood, NJ 07451. TEL 201-445-3117. FAX 201-445-7677. Ed. Chris Economaki. adv. contact: Corinne Economaki. bk.rev.; charts; illus. circ. 76,000. (tabloid format; also avail. in microfiche) **Document type:** newspaper.
   Description: Covers automobile racing.

796.72   US
NATIONAL SPEEDWAY DIRECTORY. 1975. a. $10. Slideways Publications, Box 448, Comstock Park, MI 49321. TEL 616-361-6229. Ed. Nancy L. Brown; Pub. Allan E. Brown. adv. contact: Allan E. Brown. stat. circ. 15,000. **Document type:** directory.
   Formerly: Midwest Auto Racing Guide.
   Description: Lists every oval track, dragstrip and road course in the U.S. and Canada.

688.76   US
NATIONAL SPORTING GOODS ASSOCIATION BUYING GUIDE. 1967. a. membership. National Sporting Goods Association, 1699 Wall St., Mt. Prospect, IL 60056-5780. TEL 708-439-4000. FAX 708-439-0111. adv. circ. 5,000. **Document type:** directory.
   Description: Lists more than 10000 sporting good suppliers, with names, addresses, phone and fax numbers.

790.1   US   ISSN 1054-2205
THE NATIONAL SPORTS REVIEW. a. $4.95. Sports Minded, 1638 Parker Ave., Ft. Lee, NJ 07024. TEL 201-944-4471. FAX 201-944-3193. **Document type:** consumer publication.
   Description: Reviews the year in sports.

799.202   SW   ISSN 0282-8057
NATIONELLT PISTOLSKYTTE. 1978. q. SEK 80 (effective 1991). Svenska Pistolskyttefoerbundet, Riddargatan 13, S-114 51 Stockholm, Sweden.

790.1   US   ISSN 0739-6074
HD9992.U5
NATIONWIDE DIRECTORY OF SPORTING GOODS BUYERS. 1978. a. $177. Salesman's Guide, A Reed Reference Publishing Company, Part of the Reed Elsevier group, 121 Chanlon Rd., New Providence, NJ 07974. TEL 908-464-6800. FAX 908-665-2894. TELEX 138 755. (Subscr. to: Salesman's Guide, Order Dept., Box 1009, Summit, NJ 07902. TEL 800-521-8110) Ed. Darrell Buono. index. circ. 2,000. **Document type:** directory, trade publication.
   Description: Lists 14,000 buyers and executives of 8,900 sporting goods retailers.

796.323   NE   ISSN 0028-2073
NEDERLANDS KORFBALBLAD. 1935. 20/yr. fl.37. Koninklijk Nederlands Korfbalverbond - Royal Dutch Korfbal Association, Postbus 1000, 3980 DA Bunnik, Netherlands. TEL 31-3405-70655. FAX 31-3405-67025. Ed. Wim van der Laan. adv.: B&W page fl.905, color page fl.2490; trim 210 x 297; adv. contact: Joop Bloomheuvel. bk.rev.; illus. circ. 7,200.

636.6   NE   ISSN 0028-2391
NEERLANDS POSTDUIVEN ORGAAN. 1948. w. fl.63. Postbus 256, Nieuwe Fellenoord 12, 5612 KC Eindhoven, Netherlands. TEL 040-437003. Ed. J.M.A.M. deZeeuw. adv.; illus.

799.3   US   ISSN 0195-1599
NEW GUN WEEK. 1967. w. $35. Second Amendment Foundation, Box 488, Buffalo, NY 14209. TEL 716-885-6408. FAX 716-884-4471. Ed. Joseph P. Tartaro. adv.; bk.rev.; illus. circ. 30,000. (reprint service avail.) **Document type:** consumer publication.
   Formerly: Gun Week (ISSN 0017-5633)

794.1   US   ISSN 0168-8782
NEW IN CHESS MAGAZINE; international chess information system. 1984. 8/yr. $76. Chess Combination, Inc., 2423 Noble Sta., Bridgeport, CT 06608-0423. TEL 203-367-1555. FAX 203-380-1703. Ed. J.H. Timman. adv.; bk.rev.; bibl.; charts; illus.; index. (back issues avail.) **Document type:** consumer publication.
   Description: Articles on new developments in world chess tournament play.

794.1   US   ISSN 0168-7697
GV1449.5
NEW IN CHESS YEARBOOK. 1984. q. $169 (subscr. includes data diskettes NICBASE). Chess Combination, Inc., 2423 Noble Sta., Bridgeport, CT 06608-0423. TEL 203-367-1555. FAX 203-380-1703. **Document type:** consumer publication.
   Description: Covers all major developments in chess openings, cites 4,000 selected games annually, with many annotations and theoretical analyses.

790.1   US
NEW JERSEY. CASINO CONTROL COMMISSION. ANNUAL REPORT. 1979. a. Casino Control Commission, Attn. Public Information Assistant, Arcade Bldg., Tennessee Ave. & The Boardwalk, Atlantic City, NJ 08401. TEL 609-441-3749. Ed. Michael J. Pollock. circ. 1,500. (also avail. in microfiche from CIS)
   Indexed: SRI. **Document type:** government publication.

793   US
NEW JERSEY CASINO JOURNAL. m. Casino Journal Publishing Group, 8025 Black Horse Pike 470, Pleasantville, NJ 08232-2900. TEL 609-484-8866. FAX 609-645-1661. Pub. Glenn Fine. adv. circ. 25,000. **Document type:** trade publication.

796   MC   ISSN 0961-933X
NEW STUDIES IN ATHLETICS. (Text in English; summaries in French) 1986. q. $30. International Amateur Athletic Federation (IAAF), 17 rue Princesse-Florestine, MC-98000 Monaco. (Co-sponsors: Fidal-Centro Studi & Ricerche; Bundesinstitut fur Sportwissenschaft) Ed.Bd. bk.rev.; bibl. circ. 2,500. **Indexed:** Sportsearch (1987-). —SWETS.

796.812   US   ISSN 1060-5908
NEW WAVE WRESTLING. (Supplement avail.: Combat Sports newsletter) 1992. m. $3.20 per no. (foreign $5.95). Box 651, Gracie Sta., New York, NY 10028-0006. illus. **Document type:** consumer publication.
   Description: Features interviews with prominent wrestling personalities and reports W.W.F., W.C.W. and independent news.

796.962   US
NEW YORK RANGERS YEARBOOK; official guide and records. 1926. a. $6. New York Rangers Hockey Club, Madison Square Garden, 4 Pennsylvania Plaza, New York, NY 10001. TEL 212-563-8000. FAX 212-563-8101. Ed. Barry Watkins. adv.; illus.; stat.
   Formerly: New York Rangers Blue Book.

796.42   US   ISSN 0161-7338
NEW YORK RUNNING NEWS. 1958. bi-m. membership. New York Road Runners Club, 9 E. 89th St., New York, NY 10128. TEL 212-860-4455. FAX 212-860-9754. TELEX 238-093-NYRRUR. Ed. Raleigh Mayer. adv. contact: Hermine Higgins. bk.rev.; stat. circ. 45,000. (back issues avail.) **Indexed:** Sports Per.Ind., Sportsearch. **Document type:** consumer publication.
   Supersedes: New York Runners Club Newsletter.
   Description: Regional sports magazine covering running, racewalking, nutrition and fitness.

790.1   US
NEW YORK SKATE NEWS; the latest in in-line and traditional skate happenings and issues in the New York and surrounding areas. 1990. bi-m. membership only. New York Road Skaters Association, 328 E. 94th St., New York, NY 10128. TEL 212-534-7858. FAX 212-369-6285. Ed. Lynn Sesse; Pub. Priscilla Boehme. adv. contact: John Breza. **Document type:** newsletter.

NEW ZEALAND CAR. see *TRANSPORTATION — Automobiles*

794.1   NZ
NEW ZEALAND CHESS. 1974. 6/yr. NZ.$18($20) New Zealand Chess Federation, P.O. Box 3130, Wellington, New Zealand. Ed.Bd. adv.; bk.rev. circ. 380.
   Description: Reports on local, national and international games.

SPORTS AND GAMES

790.1 GW ISSN 0940-3388
NIEDERSACHSEN TENNIS REPORT. m. DM.65. (Niedersaechsischen Tennisverbandes e.V.) Paragon Verlagsgesellschaft mbH, Misburgerstr. 119, 30625 Hannover, Germany. TEL 0511-561003. FAX 0511-571214. Ed. Walter Klemp. adv. contact: Wilfried Lehwald. **Document type:** consumer publication.

790.1 GW
NIEDERSACHSENTURNER. 1950. m. DM.45.60. (Niedersaechsischer Turner-Bund e.V.) Pohl Verlag, Postfach 3207, 29232 Celle, Germany. TEL 05141-7504-0. FAX 05141-750475. Ed. Manfred Senftleben. circ. 3,000. (back issues avail.) **Document type:** bulletin.

NIKEPHOROS; Zeitschrift fuer Sport und Kultur im Altertum. see HISTORY

796.41 MX
NOCAUT; solo Box. 1972. w. Mex.$6 per no. Anuar Maccise Dib, Ed. & Pub., Paseo Tollocan Km. 57.5, Toluca-Mexico, Mexico. adv. circ. 75,000.

790.1 DK ISSN 0900-0283
NORMTALSUNDERSOEGELSE FOR SPORTSBRANCHEN. 1983. a. DKK 305. Danmarks Sportshandler-Forening, Konsulenttjeneste, Naverland 34, 2600 Glosrup, Denmark. illus.

790.1 NO ISSN 0029-1994
NORSK IDRETT; Norwegian magazine on all kinds of sports. 1933. 6/yr. $34. Norsk Idrettsforbund - Norwegian Confederation of Sports, N-1351 Rud, Norway. Ed. Jan Morten Berger. adv.; bk.rev.; circ. 13,000 (controlled).
—CCC.

794.1 NO ISSN 0332-9771
NORSK SJAKKBLAD. 1906. 8/yr. $35. Frenningsvei 3, 0558 Oslo 5, Norway. FAX 02-710007. Ed. Geir Arne Drangeid. adv.; bk.rev.
Former titles (until 1975): Norsk Tidsskrift for Sjakk (ISSN 0048-0614); (until 1970): Norsk Sjakkblad (ISSN 0332-9917); (until 1932): Norsk Schakblad (ISSN 0332-9925)

799.3 NO ISSN 0333-4538
NORSK SKYTTERITIDENDE. 1882. 12/yr. NOK 125. Frivillige Skyttervesen, P.O. Box 293 Oekerin, N-0511 Oslo 5, Norway.

797.2 NO ISSN 0333-452X
NORSK SWOEMMING. 1947. 8/yr. NOK 255. Norges Swoemmeforbund - Norwegian Swimming Federation, P.O. Box 153, N-2301 Hamar, Norway.

790.1 973 US
NORTH AMERICAN SOCIETY FOR SPORT HISTORY. NEWSLETTER. 1973. a. membership. North American Society for Sport History, 101 White Bldg., Penn State University, University Park, PA 16802. TEL 814-865-2416. Ed. Ronald A. Smith. bk.rev.; bibl. **Indexed:** Sportsearch. **Document type:** newsletter.

796 970 980 US ISSN 0093-6235
GV571
NORTH AMERICAN SOCIETY FOR SPORT HISTORY. PROCEEDINGS. 1973. a. membership. North American Society for Sport History, 101 White Bldg., Penn State University, University Park, PA 16802. TEL 814-865-2416. adv. circ. 1,000. (back issues avail.) **Indexed:** Phys.Ed.Ind., Popul.Ind. **Document type:** proceedings.
—BLDSC (6837.985000).

790.1 US
NORTHERN CALIFORNIA SCHEDULE. 1982. m. $12. Schedule Publication, 80 Mitchell Blvd., San Rafael, CA 94903. TEL 415-472-7223. FAX 415-472-7233. Ed. Kees Tuinzing. adv.; bk.rev. circ. 50,000.
Description: Lists sports events for the coming 12 months. Includes running, bicycling, swimming, triathlons, biathlons, corporate fun runs and family orientated events.

794.1 US ISSN 0146-6941
NORTHWEST CHESS. 1947. m. $20. Box 84746, Seattle, WA 98124-6046. TEL 206-935-7186. FAX 206-441-4736. Ed. Russell Miller. adv.; circ. 800.

659.1 630 AT
NORTH WEST MAGAZINE. 1972. w. membership. North West Magazine Group, 287 Conadilly St., Gunnedah, N.S.W. 2380, Australia. TEL 067-420204. FAX 067-423603. Ed. Keith Millerd. circ. 45,000. **Document type:** newspaper.
Formerly: North West and Hunter Valley Magazine.

796.42 US ISSN 0883-7945
NORTHWEST RUNNER. 1972. m. $18.97 (Canada $34.97). 11808 Sunset Ave., N.E., Bainbridge Island, WA 98110-3459. TEL 206-780-5887. FAX 206-780-5686. Ed. Jim Whiting. adv.; circ. 7,000 (paid). **Document type:** consumer publication.
Formerly (until 1985): Nor'wester (ISSN 8750-6076)

794.1 US
NOST-ALGIA. 1960. bi-m. $17 (Canada $20; elsewhere $24) (effective 1993). Knights of the Square Table, 111 Amber St., Buffalo, NY 14220-1861. TEL 716-825-8281. Ed. Les Roselle. adv.; bk.rev. circ. 350. **Document type:** bulletin.
Description: Chess by mail.

790.1 IT
NUOVO TOTOGUIDA SPORT. 1974. w. L.3500 per no. Giroal s.r.l., Viale Mazzini 123, 00195 Roma, Italy. TEL 39-6-3725543. adv.; B&W page L.6600000. circ. 100,000.

790.1 IT
NUOVO VAI. 1977. m. (11/yr.). L.27000 (foreign L.45000). Jet Sport s.a.s., Via Spalato 3-A, 20124 Milan, Italy. TEL 39-2-66800391. FAX 39-2-66800368. Dir. Giustino Del Vecchio. adv.: B&W page L.1680000, color page L.2800000. circ. 40,000.

790.1 SW ISSN 0345-8377
NYA KRAFTSPORT. Variant title: Tidskriften Kraftsport. 1944. m. (8/yr.). SEK 273 in Nordic countries; elsewhere SEK 573. (Svenska Tyngdlyftningsfoerbundet) Cewe-Foerlaget AB, P.O. Box 77, S-890 10 Bjaesta, Sweden. TEL 0660-309-65. FAX 0660-305-17. (Subscr. to: PK-Banken, Box 365, 891 01 Oernskoeldsvik, Sweden) (Co-sponsor: Nordiska Tyngdlyftningsfoerbundet) adv. circ. 4,500.
Former titles (until 1962): Kraftsport; (until vol.3, 1956): Atletik.

790.1 CN
O H A HOCKEY NEWS. 1983. 4/yr. N C C Publishing, 222 Argyle Ave., Delhi, Ont. N4B 2Y2, Canada. TEL 519-582-2510. FAX 519-582-4040. Ed. D.G. Glendinning. adv. circ. 40,000.

O N S - MITTEILUNGEN. (Obersten Nationalen Sportkommission fuer den Automobil in Deutschland GmbH) see TRANSPORTATION — Automobiles

796.426 DK ISSN 0107-4202
O - POSTEN. 1951. 8/yr. DKK 150 to non-members; members DKK 110. Dansk Orienterings Forbund - Danish Orienteering Federation, Broendby-Stadion 20, DK-2605 Broendby, Denmark. Ed. Roald Kramer. adv.; bk.rev.; charts; illus.; stat. circ. 4,500. (back issues avail.)

794.1 SP
OCHO X OCHO; revista practica de ajedrez. m. $65. Zugarto Ediciones, S.A., Pablo Aranda, 3, 28006 Madrid, Spain. TEL 411-42-64. FAX 262-26-77. Ed. Roman Toran.
Description: Contains annotated games, "how-to-improve" articles, and combinations.

790.1 690 SP
OCIO - SPORT. 10/yr. Gamma Producciones Tecnicas, Trav. de Dalt. 25-27, Esc. A, Ent, 2a, 08024 Barcelona, Spain. TEL 3-284-70-12. FAX 3-284-70-54. Ed. F. Gutierrez Bayarri.
Description: Covers the construction, installation and management of sports facilities, leisure areas and parks.

688.76 SP
OCIO - SPORT EDICION GIMNASIOS. 4/yr. Gamma Producciones Tecnicas, Trav. de Dalt 25-27, Esc. A Ent. 2a, 08024 Barcelona, Spain. TEL 3-284-70-12. FAX 3-284-70-54. Ed. F. Gutierrez Bayarri.

797.23 US
ODYSSEY (DALY CITY). 1976. bi-m. (5/yr.). $15 membership. Central California Diving Council, Box 779, Daly City, CA 94017. TEL 415-583-8492. FAX 415-583-0614. Ed. Carol Rose. adv.: B&W page $120; 8 1/2 x 11. bk.rev. circ. 1,500. **Document type:** newsletter.
Description: Covers marine ecology, access, and legislation and underwater sports for Northern and Central Californian skin and scuba divers.

799.2 AU ISSN 0030-0012
OESTERREICHS WEIDWERK. 1928. m. S.498. (Niederoesterreichischer Landesjagdverband) Oesterreichischer Jagd- und Fischereiverlag der J F B GmbH, Wickenburggasse 3, A-1080 Vienna, Austria. TEL 01-4216360. FAX 01-42163636. Ed. Peter Lebersorger. adv.; bk.rev. circ. 46,000. **Indexed:** Biol.Abstr., Key Word Ind.Wildl.Res. **Document type:** bulletin.
Description: Covers hunting, fishing, environment and nature conservation. Includes news from Austrian hunting associations.

796.35 US
OFFICIAL RULES OF IN-LINE HOCKEY. a. $8.95. (National In-Line Hockey Association) Triumph Books, 644 S. Clark St., Chicago, IL 60605. TEL 312-939-3330. FAX 312-663-3557.
Description: Contains the rules and everything else one needs to know about this increasingly popular sport.

796.35 US
OFFICIAL RULES OF N H L. a. $8.95. (National Hockey League, CN) Triumph Books, 644 S. Clark St., Chicago, IL 60605. TEL 312-939-3330. FAX 312-663-3557.

794.1 US ISSN 0885-6583
OHIO CHESS BULLETIN. 1946. bi-m. $10. Ohio Chess Association, 621 Hal-Bar Dr., Cambridge, OH 43725. (Subscr. to: James Pechac, 7722 Lucerne Dr., Apt. N-35, Middleburg Hts., OH 44130. TEL 216-826-3054) Ed. Parley C. Long. adv.; bk.rev.; charts; illus.; stat.; index. circ. 500.

790.1 US ISSN 0279-9634
OHIO RUNNER.* 1979. m. (Apr.-Nov.); bi-m. (Dec.-Mar.). $14 (Alaska, Canada, Hawaii & U.S. Possessions $15; elsewhere $18). Barbara St. George, Inc., 4500 Dublin Rd., Columbus, OH 43221-5006. TEL 614-224-7500. Ed. Mark Hemman. adv. circ. 11,000.
Description: Covers the sport of road racing, track and field, biathlon and triathlon in Ohio, West Virginia, Western Pennsylvania, and Northern Kentucky.

790 RU ISSN 0131-2596
SK1
OKHOTA I OKHOTNICH'E KHOZYAISTVO. 1955. m. $81 (effective 1996). Izdatel'stvo Kolos, Sadovo-Spasskaya, 18, 107807 Moscow, Russia. (Dist. by: Mezhdunarodnaya Kniga, B. Yakimanka 39, 117049 Moscow, Russia) Ed. O.K. Gusev. bk.rev.; index. **Indexed:** Biol.Abstr.

796.9 CN ISSN 0833-8051
OLDTIMERS' HOCKEY NEWS. 1975. m. (Sep.-Apr.). Can.$10($12) Tatham Publications Inc., Box 951, Peterborough, ON K9J 7A5, Canada. TEL 705-743-2679. FAX 705-748-3470. Ed. Dave Tatham. adv.; bk.rev.; illus. circ. 15,000. (tabloid format)
Former titles (until 1986): Oldtimers' Sports News (ISSN 0711-5539); (until 1982): Canadian Oldtimers' Sports News (ISSN 0711-1002); (until 1981): Canadian Oldtimers' Hockey News (ISSN 0381-5013)

790.1 UK
OLEANDER GAMES AND PASTIMES SERIES. a. Oleander Press, 17 Stansgate Ave., Cambridge CB2 2QZ, England. (U.S. address: 80 Eighth Ave., Ste. 303, New York, NY 10011) **Document type:** bulletin.

SPORTS AND GAMES

790.1   RU   ISSN 0204-2177
OLIMPIISKAYA PANORAMA. English edition: Olympic Panorama (ISSN 0204-2592); French edition: Panorama Olympique (ISSN 0204-2606); German edition: Olympisches Panorama (ISSN 0204-2614); Spanish edition: Panorama Olimpico (ISSN 0204-241X) (Text in Russian) 1976-1980; resumed 1981. q. National Olympic Committee of the U.S.S.R., 5-7 Zhdanov St., Moscow 103031, Russia. TEL 924 65 23. TELEX 411287. Ed. Viacheslav Gavrilin.
    Description: Covers international competitions, interviews with championship athletes, forthcoming 1992 Olympic games, new sporting events and more.

796   AU
OLYMPIA AKTUELL. 1973. bi-m. S.10 per no. Oesterreichisches Olympisches Comite, Prinz-Eugen-Str. 12, A-1040 Vienna, Austria. TEL 0222-5053365. Ed. Heinz Jungwirth. adv.; bk.rev. circ. 750. **Document type:** bulletin.
    Former titles: Olympische Sport; Olympische Blaetter.

796   US   ISSN 0094-9787
GV721.5
OLYMPIAN (COLORADO SPRINGS). 1974. bi-m. $19.96 (overseas $40) (effective 1995-1996). United States Olympic Committee, One Olympic Plaza, Colorado Springs, CO 80909. TEL 719-632-5551. FAX 719-578-4677. Eds. Mike Moran, Frank X. Zang; Pub. H.O. Zimman. adv. contact: David Zimman. charts; illus. circ. 115,000. **Indexed:** Sports Per.Ind., Sportsearch (1977-). **Document type:** trade publication.
    —Faxon; UnCover.
    Description: Covers the news of the U.S. Olympic movement, focusing on U.S. athletes preparing for the Olympic games.

796.48   SZ   ISSN 0010-2431
OLYMPIC REVIEW (YEAR). French edition: Revue Olympique (ISSN 0251-3498); Spanish edition: Revista Olimpica (ISSN 1018-1008) (Editions in English, French and Spanish) 1967. 6/yr. 60 SFr. International Olympic Committee, Chateau De Vidy, CH-1007 Lausanne, Switzerland. TEL 021-6216111. FAX 021-6216216. TELEX 454024-ACIO-CH. Ed. Fekrou Kidane. adv.; bk.rev.; illus. circ. 6,000. **Indexed:** Phys.Ed.Ind., Sportsearch (1972-). **Document type:** bulletin.
    —BLDSC (6256.405000).
    Description: News and information concerning the Olympics and the Olympic Movement. Articles cover future games, sporting life, Olympic host cities and countries, news of National Olympic Committees.

790.06   BE
OLYMPICS NEWS. (Text in French) 1978. 2/yr. Comite Olympique et Interfederal Belge, Avenue de Bouchout 9, 1020 Brussels, Belgium. TEL 32-2-4791940. FAX 32-2-479-4656. TELEX 63760. Ed. Guido de Bondt. **Document type:** newsletter.
    Formerly: Olympics.

790.1   CN   ISSN 1188-5963
OLYMPIKA; the international journal of Olympic studies. 1992. a. Centre for Olympic Studies, Thames Hall, University of Western Ontario, London, ON N6A 3K7, Canada. TEL 519-679-2111. FAX 519-661-2008. Eds. Robert K. Barney, Klaus V. Meier. **Document type:** academic/scholarly publication.
    —BLDSC (6256.406000).
    Description: Incorporates sociocultural research studies predominantly related to the historical, philosophical and sociological dimensions of the modern Olympic games and the Olympic movement.
    Refereed Serial

790.1   GW   ISSN 0343-0235
OLYMPISCHE JUGEND. 1955. m. DM.24. (Deutschen Sportjugend) Verlag Karl Hofmann, Postfach 1360, 73603 Schorndorf, Germany. TEL 07181-402-0. FAX 07181-402111. Ed. Harald Pieper. bk.rev. circ. 3,500. **Document type:** bulletin.
    —CCC.
    Description: Information for young athletes.

790.1   GW   ISSN 0471-5640
OLYMPISCHES FEUER. bi-m. DM.30. (Deutsche Olympische Gesellschaft) Pohl Verlag, Postfach 3207, 29232 Celle, Germany. TEL 05141-7504-0. FAX 05141-750475. Ed. Harald Pieper. circ. 8,000. (back issues avail.) **Document type:** bulletin.

796.962   CN
ON ICE. 1989. q. Can.$11.97. On Ice Magazine Inc., P.O. Box 10, Sta. F, Toronto, Ont. M4Y 2L4, Canada. TEL 416-469-4367. FAX 416-360-4348. Ed. Jerry Amernic. adv.; bk.rev. circ. 25,000.
    Description: Aimed at adult recreational hockey players aged 20 plus. Keeps readers informed with tournament listings, health reports and tips for improving their game.

794.1   AT
ON THE MOVE (MELBOURNE). 6/yr. $25. Victorian Chess Association, G.P.O. Box 2690X, Melbourne, Vic. 3001, Australia. Ed. I.J. Laurie.
    Description: Covers local news (Victorian), tournament details and results, and games.

790.1   CN   ISSN 0702-7842
GV56.06
ONTARIO. MINISTERE DES AFFAIRES CULTURELLES ET DES LOIS DE L'ONTARIO. RAPPORT ANNUEL. 1983. a. Ministry of Tourism and Recreation, Parliament Bldgs., Toronto, Ont. M7A 2R9, Canada. TEL 416-965-2506. circ. 10,000.

790.1 305.3   CN   ISSN 0226-1561
ONTARIO WRESTLER MAGAZINE. 1981. bi-m. Can.$20($35) (effective 1991). Ontario Amateur Wrestling Association, 1220 Sheppard Ave. E., Willowdale, ON M2K 2X1, Canada. TEL 416-495-4170. FAX 416-495-4165. Ed. Sean Norris. adv. contact: Sean Norris. bk.rev.; illus.; stat.; circ. 2,500 (paid). **Indexed:** Sportsearch (1980-). **Document type:** newsletter.
    Description: Offers articles, tournament dates, coach and executive information, results.

794.1   BE
ORANG-UTAN (SOKOLSKY OR POLISH OPENING). (Text in Dutch, English, French, German) 1987. 3/yr. DM.15 in Europe; overseas $10. P.O. Box 71, B-9120 Beveren-Waas, Belgium. Ed. Dirk Van Esbroeck. **Document type:** consumer publication.

796.426   US
OREGON DISTANCE RUNNER. q. $25 membership. Oregon Road Runners Club, Box 549, Beaverton, OR 97075-0549. TEL 503-646-7867. FAX 503-520-0242. Ed. Bert van Gorder. adv. circ. 3,400.
    Description: Covers road and track running and walking, with a calendar of events, news articles and features, awards coverage.

796.5   US   ISSN 0030-7025
SH11
OUTDOOR CALIFORNIA. 1953. bi-m. $8. Department of Fish and Game, 1416 Ninth St., Sacramento, CA 95814. TEL 916-653-6420. (Subscr. to: Box 15087, Sacramento, CA 95851-0087) Ed. Dave Dick. illus.; map. circ. 47,000. **Indexed:** Cal.Per.Ind. (1978-), Sport Fish.Abstr.; Wild.Rev.
    —UnCover.

790.1   CN
OUTSIDE GUIDE. s-a. Solstice Publishing Inc., 19 Albany Ave., Toronto, ON M5R 3C2, Canada. TEL 416-535-0607. FAX 416-535-3419. Ed. Iain MacMillan; Pub. Paul Green. adv. contact: Paul Green. circ. 100,000. **Document type:** consumer publication.
    Formerly: Sunsports.

793   US
P B A TOUR OFFICIAL PROGRAM (YEAR). a. $5. Professional Bowlers Association of America, 1720 Merriman Rd., Box 5118, Akron, OH 44313. TEL 216-836-5568. FAX 216-836-2107. Ed. Christopher C. Bame. adv. contact: Christopher C. Bame. illus. circ. 110,000.
    Description: Presents the highlights of the previous year's PBA tournaments.

790 333.7   US
P I N.* 1989. q. $30 to non-members; members $18. National Recreation and Park Association, Northeast Service Center, 2775 S. Quincy St., Ste. 300, Arlington, VA 22206-2236. Ed. Ellen O'Sullivan.
    Description: Resource information and ideas for park and recreation activities organizers.

790.1   II
P T - SPORTS SCIENCE. 1990. m. Rs.430($30) K.K. Roy (Private) Ltd., 55 Gariahat Road, P.O. Box 10210, Calcutta 700 019, India. Ed. K.K. Roy. adv.; abstr.; bibl.; index. circ. 2,160.

796   US   ISSN 1045-8603
PACIFIC SPORT. m. G C Publishing, 12021 Wilshire Blvd., Ste. 7063, Los Angeles, CA 90025-1200. TEL 213-478-2188. FAX 213-394-7501. Ed. Andre Sapp.

790.1   US   ISSN 1043-4771
PAINTBALL; the complete guide to airgun pursuit games. 1988. m. $19.95 (effective Oct. 1990). C F W Enterprises, Inc., 4201 W. Van Owen Pl., Burbank, CA 91505. TEL 818-845-2656. FAX 818-845-7761. (Subscr. to: Box 404, Mt. Morris, IL 61054) adv.; bk.rev. circ. 50,000. (back issues avail.)
    Description: Presents coverage of the airgun pursuit games.

790.1   UK
PAINTBALL GAMES MAGAZINE. m. £14.40 (foreign £40). Aceville Publications Ltd., 89 East Hill, Colchester, Essex CO1 2QN, England. TEL 0206-871139. FAX 0206-871537. Ed. Matthew Tudor. adv.

794.1   PK
PAKISTAN CHESS MAGAZINE. (Text in English) 1987. 4/yr. $25. Mohammad Aejaz Ali Tahir, Ed. & Pub., Post Box 179, Karachi 74200, Pakistan. TEL 92-21-445742. FAX 92-21-4538539. adv.; bk.rev. circ. 7,000.
    Description: Reports on national and international games and news, opening theory, endgame studies, problems studies, interviews, and "how to improve" articles.

PALAESTRA; the forum of sport, physical education and recreation for the disabled. *see HANDICAPPED*

797.56   US   ISSN 0031-1588
GV770
PARACHUTIST. 1956. m. $21.50. United States Parachute Association, 1440 Duke St., Alexandria, VA 22314. TEL 703-836-3495. Ed. Jason Bell. adv. contact: Suzanne R. Popielec. bk.rev.; charts; illus.; circ. 27,000 (paid). **Indexed:** Sportsearch (1973-). **Document type:** trade publication.
    —UnCover.

794.1   GW
PATT. 1971. m. Schachverein Bottrop 21, Am Freitagshof 46, 46242 Bottrop, Germany. TEL 0201-29999. Ed. Gerhard Sklarz. play rev.; charts; illus.; stat. circ. 100. (looseleaf format; back issues avail.) **Document type:** consumer publication.

796.962   US   ISSN 1060-2429
PENGUINS REPORT. 1991. US. Gateway Publications, Inc., 610 Beatty Rd., Monroeville, PA 15146-1502. TEL 412-856-7400. FAX 412-856-7954. Ed. Tom McMillan. circ. 7,000 (paid).
    Description: Covers the Pittsburgh Penguins hockey team. Features a color poster of a Penguins player in each issue.

PENNSYLVANIA JOURNAL OF HEALTH, PHYSICAL EDUCATION, RECREATION AND DANCE. *see EDUCATION — Teaching Methods And Curriculum*

PERCHANCE. *see LITERATURE — Science Fiction, Fantasy, Horror*

683.4   US   ISSN 1083-804X
PERFORMANCE SHOOTER. m. $45 (foreign $57) (effective 1996). Belvoir Publications, Inc., 75 Holly Hill Ln., Box 2626, Greenwich, CT 06836-2626. TEL 203-661-6111. FAX 203-661-4802. **Document type:** consumer publication.

796.41   GW
PFAELZER TURNER; Amtliches Organ des Pfaelzer Turnerbundes. bi-w. DM.35. Pfaelzer Turnerbund e.V., Am Schlagbaum 5, 67655 Kaiserslautern, Germany. TEL 0631-42115. FAX 0631-42868. (back issues avail.) **Document type:** bulletin.

PHILEMAT. *see PHILATELY*

SPORTS AND GAMES

790.1 613.7   CN   ISSN 0843-2635
PHYSICAL EDUCATION DIGEST. 1985. 4/yr. $24. 111 Kingsmount Blvd., Sudbury, ON P3E 1K8, Canada. TEL 705-675-7055. FAX 705-675-5539. E-mail: pedigest@mcd.cn.ca. Ed. Dick Moss. adv. circ. 3,500.
     Formerly: Coaching Digest.
     Description: Helps physical educators and scholastic coaches stay up-to-date. Covers up to 35 different topics including new games, drills, coaching cues, teaching techniques, P.E. research and specific sports tips.

PHYSICAL EDUCATION NEW ZEALAND. JOURNAL. see *EDUCATION — Teaching Methods And Curriculum*

796   IT   ISSN 0390-3230
PISCINE OGGI. 1973. q. L.42000 (foreign L.130000). Editrice Il Campo, Via G. Amendola 11, 40121 Bologna, Italy. TEL 39-51-255360. Dir. Franco Maestrami. adv.: B&W page L.2700000, color page L.3200000. bk.rev. circ. 15,000.

790.1   BL   ISSN 0104-1762
PLACAR. 1970. m. $130. Editora Abril, S.A., Rua Geraldo Flausino Gomes, 61, 04573-900 Sao Paulo, Brazil. TEL 011-534-5294. FAX 011-534-5597. Ed. Juca Kfouri. adv.; charts; illus.; stat. circ. 120,000. **Document type:** consumer publication.
     Description: Covers soccer, sex and rock 'n' roll.

793   US   ISSN 0162-1343
HD9993.E453
PLAY METER. 1974. m. $50. Skybird Publishing Co., Inc., Box 24170, New Orleans, LA 70184. TEL 504-488-7003. adv.; charts; illus.; tr.lit.; index. circ. 5,000.

PLAY THEORY AND RESEARCH. see *SOCIOLOGY*

PLY: SVENSKA SCHACKDATORFOERINGEN. see *COMPUTERS — Computer Games*

790.1   US
POKER TIPS. Variant title: I H 3 P A Newsletter. 1984. bi-m. $7. International Home & Private Poker Players' Association, 3784 Central Park Dr., No.8, Las Vegas, NV 89109. TEL 702-893-9851. Ed. Edwin "Tony" Wuehle. bk.rev. circ. 300. (looseleaf format; back issues avail.)
     Description: For the home and private club poker player, with emphasis on poker tournaments.

796   NO   ISSN 0032-3357
POLITIIDRETT.* 1963. bi-m. Norwegian Police Athletic and Sports Association, Box 6384, Etlerstad., 0604 Oslo N, Norway. Ed. Leif Orehagen. adv. circ. 6,000.

790.1   CN   ISSN 0711-2998
POOL & SPA MARKETING. 1976. bi-m. Can.$20($20) Hubbard Marketing & Publishing Ltd., 270 Esna Park Dr., Unit 12, Markham, ON L3R 1H3, Canada. TEL 905-513-0090. FAX 905-513-1377. Ed. David Barnsley; Pub. Richard I. Hubbard. adv. contact: Andree Wolfe. bk.rev. circ. 8,000. **Document type:** trade publication.
     Formerly: Canadian Pool and Spa Marketing (ISSN 0227-3330)

797.21   US
POOLIFE. 1970. a. free. Olin Corporation, 120 Long Ridge Rd., Stamford, CT 06904. TEL 203-356-2000. FAX 203-356-3213. Ed. Aleene Nask. adv. circ. 750,000.
     Formerly: H T H Poolife.

797.21 613.7   US
POOLWAYS; the magazine of outdoor living (year). 1990. a. free to swimming pool owners. Coastal Industries, 225 Passaic St., Box 8600, Passaic, NJ 07055. TEL 201-473-8600. Ed. Pamela Art.
     Description: Articles on all aspcts of poolside living. Includes information on pool maintenance, new products, safety, health and beauty, and poolside entertainment.

POPULAR HOT RODDING. see *TRANSPORTATION — Automobiles*

PORSCHE PANORAMA. see *TRANSPORTATION — Automobiles*

797.21   AT
PORTSEA BOOMER. 1949. m. Aus.$20. Portsea Surf Life Saving Club Ltd., P.O. Box 270, Carnesie, Vic. 3163, Australia. TEL 61-3-95723233. Eds. Natalie Hood, Cameron Hunter. adv.; illus. circ. 1,500. (also avail. in microform)
     Description: Articles on surf lifesaving.

795.414   US   ISSN 0032-5279
POST MORTEM.* 1952. 6/yr. 1.50. Greater New York Bridge Association, 401 E. 74th St., New York, NY 10021. Ed. Thomas M. Smith. adv.; bk.rev.; illus. circ. 20,000.

794.1   NO
POSTSJAKK. 1945. 6/yr. NOK 200($30) Norges Postsjakkforbund - Norwegian Correspondence Chess Federation, Unni Kvil Nordal, Tangenveien 101, 1450 Nesoddtangen, Norway. Ed. Oeystein Sande. adv.; bk.rev.
     Description: Includes annotated correspondence chess games, theory, national and international correspondence chess news.

790.1   CI   ISSN 0350-9419
POVIJEST SPORTA. 1970. 4/yr. $12. Hrvatski Sportski Savez, Ilica 7, 41000 Zagreb, Croatia. TEL 041 423-900. Ed. Franjo Frntic. adv.; bk.rev.; bibl.; index. circ. 2,000.
     Description: Deals with the history of sports and sportsmen in Croatia and other countries and persons who have influenced the Croatian sports scene.

790.1   US
POWER HOTLINE. 1981. s-m. $28. Powerlifting U S A, Box 467, Camarillo, CA 93011. TEL 805-482-2378. Ed. M. Lambert. circ. 300.

796.72   SW   ISSN 0348-5900
POWER MAGAZINE. 1976. bi-m. SEK 210 (effective 1994). Broederna Lindstroems Foerlag, S-112 85 Stockholm, Sweden. adv. circ. 31,170.
     Formerly (until 1978): Power.

790.1 613.7   GW
POWER SPORT. 1985. 6/yr. DM.50 (foreign DM.72). Postfach 1151, 85587 Vaterstetten, Germany. TEL 08106-31675. FAX 08106-34605. Ed. Heinz Vierthaler. circ. 3,500. **Document type:** consumer publication.

790.1   US   ISSN 1044-6559
POWEREDGE MAGAZINE. 1988. m. $2.95 per no. Power Edge Group, 4201 W. Van Owen Pl., Burbank, CA 91505. TEL 213-769-6777. (Subscr. to: Box 404, Mt. Morris, IL 61504)
     Description: Features the tops in the field of skateboarding.

790.1   US   ISSN 0199-8536
POWERLIFTING U S A. 1977. m. $31.95. Powerlifting U S A, Box 467, Camarillo, CA 93011. TEL 805-482-2378. Ed. Mike Lambert. adv.; bk.rev. circ. 16,000. Indexed: Sportsearch (1983-).

793   UK   ISSN 0953-0592
PRACTICAL WARGAMER. 1987. bi-m. £12.60. Argus Specialist Publications Ltd. (Subsidiary of: Argus Press Group), Argus House, Boundary Way, Hemel Hempstead, Herts. HP2 7ST, England. TEL 01442-66551. FAX 01442-66998. (Subscr. to: Argus Subscription Services, Queensway House, 2 Queensway, Redhill, Surrey RH1 1QS, England. TEL 01737-768611) Ed. Ken Jones. adv.; bk.rev. (back issues avail.) **Document type:** consumer publication.
     Description: Contains articles for wargamers of all ages and experience from fantasy to Napoleonic wargaming.

PRAIRIE CLUB BULLETIN; organized for the promotion of outdoor recreation in the form of walks, outings, camping and canoeing. see *CONSERVATION*

799   US   ISSN 0048-5144
PRECISION SHOOTING. 1953. m. $29 (foreign $36). Precision Shooting, Inc., 222 McKee St., Manchester, CT 06040. TEL 203-645-8776. FAX 203-643-8215. (Subscr. to: 5735 Sherwood Forest Dr., Akron, OH 44319) Ed. David D. Brennan. adv.; bk.rev.; charts; illus.; tr.lit. circ. 12,000. (back issues avail.) Indexed: Sportsearch.
     Description: Focuses on the subject of extreme rifle accuracy in the target shooting disciplines.

795   US   ISSN 0199-0705
PREDICAMENT.* 1970. 10/yr. $5.50. Predicament, Inc., 8470 W. Zero, Casper, WY 82601. Eds. Tom and Julie Bishop. adv.; bk.rev.; illus.; tr.lit. circ. 2,600. (tabloid format; back issues avail.)

PRESS MAGAZINE. see *CLOTHING TRADE*

790.1   CN
PRESTIGE. 1992. 2/yr. Can.$5.90 (foreign Can.$6.40). Nowak Publishing, 291 De La Corniche, C.P. 451, Piedmont, PQ J0R 1K0, Canada. TEL 514-497-1962. FAX 514-227-3089. adv.: B&W page Can.$3350, color page Can.$8350; trim 8 1/2 x 10 3/4. circ. 72,500. **Document type:** consumer publication.

794.1   BL
PRETO & BRANCO/BRAZILIAN CHESS MAGAZINE. 6/yr. $21. Promochess Ltda., XCX Postal 2730, 80001 Curitiba, Brazil. Ed. Rubens A. Filguth.
     Description: Includes national and international news and game theory.

790.1 658.3   SW   ISSN 1101-265X
PRIMA LIV;* med Korpmotion. 1953. m. SEK 120. (Korpen, Svenska Motionsidrottsfoerbundet) Rikskorpen, Idrottens Hus, S-123 87 Farsta, Sweden. Ed. Christina Brinnen. adv. circ. 43,592.
     Formerly: Korp-Motion.
     Description: Focuses on intercompany athletics.

796.812   US   ISSN 1043-7576
PRO WRESTLING ILLUSTRATED. 13/yr. $30 for 12 issues in US & Canada (elsewhere $39.60) (effective 1994). London Publishing Co., Box 910, Fort Washington, PA 19034. TEL 215-643-6385. FAX 215-540-0146. Ed. Bill Apter. illus. **Document type:** consumer publication.

794.1   SP   ISSN 0032-9223
PROBLEMAS. 1935; 3rd series 1978. q. 2000 ptas. to individuals; institutions 1800 ptas. Sociedad Espanola de Problemistas de Ajedrez, Av. Principe Asturias 35, 4, 2a, 08012 Barcelona, Spain. (Co-sponsor: Federacion Espanola de Ajedrez) Ed. Manuel Munoz. bk.rev.; bibl.; charts; illus. circ. 500.

794.1   UK   ISSN 0032-9398
THE PROBLEMIST. 1926. bi-m. £18 (overseas £21.50). British Chess Problem Society, c/o Ivor Sanders, Hon. Treas., 123 Cockerell Close, Wimborne, Dorset BH211XR, England. TEL 01202-889810. Ed. Paul Valois. bk.rev.; illus.; cum.index every 4 yrs. circ. 700. **Document type:** academic/scholarly publication.

PROFESSIONAL RODEO U S A; official media guide. see *SPORTS AND GAMES — Horses And Horsemanship*

796.812   JA
PROFESSIONAL WRESTLING/SHU-KAN. (Text in Japanese) 1972. w. 15300 Yen. Baseball Magazine Sha, 3-10-10 Misaki-cho, Chiyoda-ku, Tokyo, Japan. Ed. Takashi Yamamoto.

PROGRAMMING TRENDS IN THERAPEUTIC RECREATION. see *EDUCATION — Special Education And Rehabilitation*

PROMOTOR. see *TRANSPORTATION — Automobiles*

791.8 798.2   US   ISSN 0161-5815
PRORODEO SPORTS NEWS. (Annual number avail.) 1952. w. (July-Sep.); bi-w. (Oct.-June). $32 (effective Nov. 1994). Professional Rodeo Cowboys Association Properties, Inc., 101 Pro Rodeo Dr., Colorado Springs, CO 80919. TEL 719-593-8840. FAX 719-548-4899. Ed. Patty Meier; Pub. Steve Fleming. adv.; bk.rev.; charts; illus.; stat.; tr.lit.; circ. 38,000. (paid). **Document type:** trade publication, newspaper.
     Formerly (until vol.26, no.11, Apr. 1978): Rodeo Sports News (ISSN 0035-7758)
     Description: Current news about professional rodeo for fans and contestants.

790.1   PL   ISSN 0137-9267
PRZEGLAD SPORTOWY. 1921. 5/w. Spoldzielnia Pracy Dziennikarzy "Przeglad Sportowy", P.O. Box 181, 02-017 Warsaw, Poland. TEL 48-22-289116. FAX 48-22-218697. Ed. Maciej Polkowski. adv.; illus. circ. 95,000. **Document type:** newspaper.

PSYCHOLOGIE UND SPORT. see *PSYCHOLOGY*

SPORTS AND GAMES

793 US ISSN 1042-1912
HG6111
PUBLIC GAMING INTERNATIONAL.* 1974. m. $75. Public Gaming Research Institute, 015825 Shady Grove, No. 130, Rockville, MD 20850. TEL 301-330-7600. FAX 301-330-7608. Ed. M.L. Koert. adv. circ. 15,000.
Formerly: Public Gaming Magazine.

796.962 US ISSN 1063-1518
THE PUCK STOPS HERE!;* diehard Boston Bruins fan magazine. 1992. 4/yr. $20 for 2 yrs. Fan Mags Inc., 386 Riverway St., No. 5, Boston, MA 02115. TEL 617-731-9871. adv.: B&W page $450, color page $650; trim 8 1/4 x 10 7/8. circ. 16,000. **Document type:** consumer publication.

790.1 US
PULL. 1978. a. World Pulling International, Inc., 6969 Worthington-Galena Rd., Ste. L-1000, Worthington, OH 43085. TEL 614-436-1761. FAX 614-436-0964. Ed. Rhdawnda Bliss. circ. 20,000. **Document type:** consumer publication.

790.1 US ISSN 8750-4219
THE PULLER. 1971. m. $25 (foreign $35). World Pulling International, Inc., 6969 Worthington-Galena Rd., Ste. L-1000, Worthington, OH 43085. TEL 614-436-1761. FAX 614-436-0964. Ed. Rhdawnda Bliss. circ. 8,000. (back issues avail.) **Document type:** consumer publication.

793 UK ISSN 0261-2224
PUZZLE MONTHLY. 1974. 13/yr. I P C Magazine Ltd., King's Reach Tower, Stamford St., London SE1 9LS, England. Ed. Dennis Winston. adv. circ. 164,824.

795.414 CC ISSN 1000-3479
QIAOPAI/BRIDGE. (Text in Chinese) 1985. q. $12.30. (Zhongguo Qiaopai Xiehui - China Bridge Association) Renmin Tiyu Chubanshe - People's Sports Publishing House, 8 Tiyuguan Lu, Chongwen Qu, Beijing 100061, People's Republic of China. TEL 5112466. FAX 7016129. (Dist. in U.S. by: China Books & Periodicals, Inc., 2929 24th St., San Francisco, CA 94110. TEL 415-282-2994)
Description: Covers the game of bridge.

QIGONG. see *PHYSICAL FITNESS AND HYGIENE*

794.1 UK
QUEEN'S FILE. 1983. 2/yr. $20. British Women's Chess Association, 50 Conyers Rd., First Fl. Flat, London SW16 6LT, England. TEL 0181-769-7909. Ed. Mairead O'Siochru. adv.; bk.rev. circ. 500. **Document type:** newsletter.

794.1 AT ISSN 1038-7536
QUEENSLAND CHESS. 1987. 4/yr. $17. Chess Association of Queensland, Inc., P.O. Box 5014, Mt. Gravatt East, Qld. 4122, Australia. TEL 61-7-3495648. E-mail: 100231.2620@compuserve.com. Ed. Ian Murray; Pub. Ian Murray. adv.; bk.rev. circ. 500. **Document type:** bulletin.
Description: Contains international, national and state news, annotated games, coaching articles, tournamet crosstables.

QUONDAM MAGAZINE. see *CLUBS*

796.77 UK
R A C MOTOR SPORTS YEAR BOOK. 1956. a. £19. R A C Motor Sports Association Ltd., Motor Sports House, Riverside Park, Colnbrook, Slough SL3 0HG, England. TEL 01753-681736. FAX 01753-682938. TELEX 847796-RACING-G. Ed. Derek Tye. adv. contact: Derek Tye. circ. 42,000. (back issues avail.) **Document type:** consumer publication, directory.
Description: Contains rules, regulations and other information on motor sports.

R & R SHOPPERS NEWS. (Rest & Relaxation) see *COMMUNICATIONS — Television And Cable*

613.7 370 NE ISSN 0926-7638
R S G. (Richting - Sport-Gericht); vakblad voor training, onderwijs en wetenschap. 1946. m. fl.72.90. Uitgeverij Isidoro B.V., Scheltuslaan 53, 2273 DM Voorburg, Netherlands. TEL 31-70-3864430. FAX 31-70-3862372. E-mail: rob.timmer@inter.nl.net. Ed. Annemiek Timmer-Min. adv.; bk.rev.; abstr.; charts; illus.; circ. 6,000 (paid). **Document type:** trade publication.
Formed by the 1991 merger of: Richting (ISSN 0035-5135); (1979-1991): Sport-Gericht (ISSN 0165-2087)
Description: Covers training theory, physical education, sport and sports sciences.
Refereed Serial

R V NEWS. (Recreational Vehicle) see *TRANSPORTATION*

797 UK ISSN 0557-661X
R Y A NEWS. 1968. 4/yr. membership. Royal Yachting Association, RYA House, Romsey Rd., Eastleigh, Hants. SO50 9YA, England. TEL 01703-627400. FAX 01703-629924. Ed. Carol Baker. adv. circ. 75,000. **Indexed:** Sportsearch (1977-). **Document type:** newsletter.

RACE BUSINESS. see *BUSINESS AND ECONOMICS — Marketing And Purchasing*

796 UK
RACEFORM FLAT ANNUAL.* 1899. a. £16. Raceform Ltd., 19 Clarges Rd., London W1Y 7PG, England. Ed. D. Corbett. adv. circ. 11,000.
Formerly: Raceform Up-to-Date Form Book Annual (ISSN 0081-377X)

796 UK
RACEFORM WEEKLY.* 1936. w. Raceform Ltd., Raceform House, 19 Clarges Rd., London W1Y 7PG, England.
Formerly: Raceform Up-to-Date (ISSN 0079-9394)

796.72 US ISSN 1066-6060
RACER; America's auto racing magazine. 1992. m. $30 (effective 1993). Racer Communications, Inc., 1371 E. Warner Ave., Ste. E, Tustin, CA 92680. TEL 714-259-8240. FAX 714-259-9377. Ed. John Zimmermann; Pub. Bill Sparks. adv.: B&W page $2530, color page $3435; trim 8 1/8 x 10 7/8; adv. contact: Paula Thornton. circ. 40,000. **Document type:** consumer publication.
Description: Covers major league auto racing people, technology and events.

796.72 NO ISSN 0802-7293
RACING. 44/yr. NOK 440. (Norsk Motor Klubb) Motor Media AS, P.O. Box 96, N-1801 Askim, Norway. TEL 9-886311. FAX 9-886332. Ed. Hallgeir Raknerud. adv.
Formerly: Racing - Revyen.

796 UK ISSN 0033-7366
RACING & FOOTBALL OUTLOOK. 1909. w. £28. Outlook Press Ltd., Kemp House, 152-160 City Rd., London EC1N 2NP, England. TEL 0171-490-1212. FAX 0171-608-3299. Ed. H.M. Joseph. adv. contact: Sylvia Meade. bk.rev. circ. 57,059. **Document type:** consumer publication.
Refereed Serial

796 UK ISSN 0262-4699
RACING AND FOOTBALL OUTLOOK: FOOTBALL ANNUAL. 1935. a. £2.50. Outlook Press, 152-160 City Rd., London EC1N 2NP, England. Ed. Hugh Joseph; Pub. Richard Williams. adv. contact: Sylvia Meade. circ. 50,000. **Document type:** consumer publication.

796 UK ISSN 0262-4680
RACING AND FOOTBALL OUTLOOK: JUMPING ANNUAL. 1950. a. £2.50. Outlook Press, 152-160 City Rd., London EC1N 2NP, England. Ed. Hugh Joseph; Pub. Richard Williams. adv. contact: Sylvia Meade. circ. 35,000. **Document type:** consumer publication.

796 UK ISSN 0079-9424
RACING AND FOOTBALL OUTLOOK: RACING ANNUAL. 1909. a. £2.50. Outlook Press, 152-160 City Rd., London EC1N 2NP, England. Ed. Hugh Joseph; Pub. Richard Williams. adv. contact: Sylvia Meade. circ. 40,000. **Document type:** consumer publication.
Formerly: Racing and Football Racing Annual.

028.5 790.1 US ISSN 1056-7623
RACING FOR KIDS. 1990. m. $25 (Canada $32). Griggs Publishing Co., Inc., 431 Copperfield Blvd., N.E., Box 500, Concord, NC 28025-0500. TEL 704-786-7134. FAX 704-782-8122. Ed. Gary McCredie; Pub. Robert E. Griggs Jr. adv. contact: Zeta Smith. **Document type:** consumer publication.
Description: For children ages 7-13. Covers all forms of automobile racing including stock car, hot rod, go-kart and soapbox derby.

790.1 SI
RACING GUIDE. (Text in Chinese, English) 1987. s-w. 1 New Industrial Rd., Times Centre, Singapore 1953, Singapore. TEL 2848844. FAX 2881186. TELEX 25713. Eds. Benny Ortega, Kuek Chiew Teong. circ. 20,000.

636.596 UK ISSN 0033-7390
RACING PIGEON; the British pigeon racing weekly. 1898. w. £34($70) Racing Pigeon Publishing Co. Ltd., Unit 13, 21 Wren St., London WC1X 0HF, England. TEL 0171-833-5959. FAX 0171-833-3151. Ed. Rick Osman. adv. contact: Steve Dunn. bk.rev. circ. 16,000. **Document type:** bulletin.
Description: News about pigeon racing results and methods.

636.96 US ISSN 0146-8383
RACING PIGEON BULLETIN. w. $30. 34 E. Franklin St., Bellbrook, OH 45305-2098. TEL 513-848-4972. FAX 513-848-3012. Ed. Michael D. Reinke. adv.: B&W page $225, color page $800. bk.rev. circ. 6,100. (tabloid format; back issues avail.)
Description: Provides "how-to" articles, news, and opinions on the sport of pigeon breeding, training and racing.

RACING POST. see *SPORTS AND GAMES — Horses And Horsemanship*

796.72 US ISSN 1062-4422
RACING WHEELS. 1962. w. (40/yr.). $30 (Canada $39; elsewhere $55) (effective 1995). Gary's Enterprises, 7502 N.E. 133rd Ave., Box 1555, Vancouver, WA 98668. TEL 360-892-5590. FAX 360-892-8021. Ed. G.S. Sterner. adv. contact: Dale Redinger. bk.rev.; illus.; stat.; circ. 11,450 (paid). (tabloid format) **Document type:** newspaper.

793 GW
RAETSEL IN GROSSER SCHRIFT. 1979. bi-w. DM.2.50. Martin Kelter Verlag, Muehlenstieg 16-22, 22041 Hamburg, Germany. TEL 6828950. Ed. Bodo Gohr. circ. 40,000.

793 AU
RAETSEL KRONE. m. S.240. Zeitungsverlag Dichand & Falk Gesellschaft MbH & Co., Muthg. 2, 1190 Vienna, Austria. Ed. Hans Dichand. circ. 127,500.

793 GW
RAETSEL SCHULE; fuer Jungen und Maedchen. 1983. m. DM.3. Martin Kelter Verlag, Muehlenstieg 16-22, 22041 Hamburg, Germany. TEL 6828950. circ. 60,000.

793 GW
RAETSELFREUND. 1975. w. DM.2. Martin Kelter Verlag, Muehlenstieg 16-22, 22041 Hamburg, Germany. TEL 6828950. Ed. Bodo Gohr. circ. 45,000.

793 GW
RAETSELFREUND DOPPELBAND. 1976. irreg. DM.3. Martin Kelter Verlag, Muehlenstieg 16-22, 22041 Hamburg, Germany. TEL 6828950. Ed. Bodo Gohr. circ. 50,000.

796.72 UK ISSN 0140-542X
RALLY SPORT. 1972. m. £22.50 (rest of Europe £42; elsewhere £62) (effective 1995). A & S Publishing Co. Ltd., Messenger House, 33-35 St. Michael's Sq., Bloucester GL1 1HX, England. TEL 01452-307181. FAX 01452-307170. adv. contact: Marianne Wulkan. bk.rev. circ. 25,000. **Document type:** consumer publication.

SPORTS AND GAMES

796.72 629.2   UK   ISSN 0265-2617
RALLYCOURSE; the world's leading rally annual. 1982. a. £26 (rest of Europe £32; N. and S. America, Middle East, Africa £38; Australasia £41) (effective 1995-1996). Hazleton Publishing, 3 Richmond Hill, Richmond, Surrey TW10 6RE, England. TEL 0181-948-5151. FAX 0181-948-4111. TELEX 946153. Ed. David Williams; Pub. Richard Poulter. adv. contact: Simon Maurice. illus.; stat. **Document type:** consumer publication.
 Description: Reviews the year's World Rally Championship and interviews and profiles the top drivers.

794.1   GW   ISSN 0724-1747
RANDSPRINGER. 1982. 6/yr. DM.25($17) Erich Muenster Verlag; Heimstaetten Strasse 53, 90411 Nuremberg, Germany. TEL 0911-528442. FAX 0911-522755. Ed. Rainer Schlenker. adv.; bk.rev.
 Description: Presents usual and unusual chess openings.

793.73   YU   ISSN 0034-0243
RAZONODA MILIONA; ukrstene reci, rebusi, zagonetke. 1958. q. 80 din.($1.70) Enigmatski Klub, Bulevar Vojvode Misica 67, Box 219, Belgrade, Yugoslavia. Ed. Vlasta Pavlovic.

790.1   US   ISSN 1069-1855
RECOGNITION REVIEW. 1979. m. $36. Awards and Recognition Association (A R A), 36 S. State St., No. 1212, Chicago, IL 60603-2605. TEL 800-344-2148. FAX 312-236-1140. Ed. Tim Noworyta; Pub. Ralph Bloch. adv. contact: Susan Powen. tr.lit. circ. 10,000. (tabloid format) **Document type:** newspaper.
 Former titles (until 1993): T D M A Today; Trophy Dealer; T D M A Newsletter (ISSN 1063-8261)

790.1   MX
RECORD; revista deportiva. 1955. fortn. Mex.$10 per no. Nicolas Sanchez, Ed. & Pub., Avda. Juarez 127-12, Mexico 1, D.F., Mexico. adv. circ. 15,000.

790.1   PO   ISSN 0870-2179
RECORD. 1949. 3/wk. Travessa dos Inglesinhos 3-1o, 1200 Lisbon, Portugal. TEL 1-3455675. FAX 1-3476279. Ed. Joao Marcelino. circ. 120,000.

797.2   UK   ISSN 0961-2580
RECREATION. 1934. 9/yr. £30. Institute of Sport and Recreation Management, Giffard House, 36-38 Sherrard St., Melton Mowbray, Leics. LE13 1XJ, England. TEL 01664-65531. FAX 01664-501155. Ed. Jonathan Wilson. adv.: B&W page £665. bk.rev.; index. circ. 3,000. **Indexed:** Sportsearch, W.R.C.Inf. **Document type:** trade publication.
—BLDSC (7326.831000).
 Former titles: Baths Service and Recreation Management (ISSN 0961-2572); (until Jan. 1978): Baths Service (ISSN 0005-626X)
 Description: Discusses pool equipment, mechanical and electrical services, chemicals and water treatment equipment, lockers, management systems, sports hall and gymnastic equipment.

RECREATION - ACCESS IN THE '90'S. see *HANDICAPPED*

RECREATION ADVISOR. see *LEISURE AND RECREATION*

RECREATION CANADA. see *LEISURE AND RECREATION*

RECREATION: CURRENT SELECTED RESEARCH. see *SOCIOLOGY*

790.1   US   ISSN 0164-4106
RECREATIONAL ICE SKATING; the magazine for ice skating/hockey enthusiasts. 1976. 4/yr. $12. Ice Skating Institute of America, 355 W. Dundee Rd., Buffalo Grove, IL 60089-3500. TEL 708-808-7528. FAX 708-808-8329. Ed. Lara Lowery. adv. contact: Karen Schell. circ. 31,575 (paid). (back issues avail.) **Document type:** consumer publication.

796   US   ISSN 0733-1436
REFEREE; magazine of sports officiating. 1976. m. $47.40. Referee Enterprises, Inc., Box 161, Franksville, WI 53126. TEL 414-632-8855. FAX 414-632-5460. Ed. Tom Hammill. adv.; bk.rev.; charts; illus.; index; circ. 35,000 (paid). **Indexed:** Phys.Ed.Ind., Sports Per.Ind., Sportsearch (1976-). **Document type:** trade publication.
—Faxon; UnCover.

RESEARCH QUARTERLY FOR EXERCISE AND SPORT. see *PHYSICAL FITNESS AND HYGIENE*

790.1   PO
REVISTA ATLETISMO. 1981. 12/yr. $65 (effective 1995 & 1996). Rua Maria Machado 128 10oE, 2700 Amadora, Portugal. TEL 1-4753411. FAX 1-4740714. Ed. M. Arons Carvalho. adv. circ. 5,000.

790.1   BL   ISSN 0101-3289
REVISTA BRASILEIRA DE CIENCIAS DO ESPORTE. 3/yr. Colegio Brasileiro de Ciencias do Esporte, Caixa Postal 20383, 01000 Sao Paulo SP, Brazil. **Indexed:** Sportsearch (1982-).
—BLDSC (7844.104930).

794.1   BL
REVISTA BRASILEIRA DE XADREZ POSTAL. 6/yr. free to qualified personnel. Clube de Xadrez Epistolar Brasileiro, Caixa Postal 317, 40001 Salvador (BA), Brazil. Ed. Paulo Gonclaves Guimaraes. circ. controlled.
 Description: Reports on national and international games and news, crosstables, results, and studies-problems.

REVISTA DE DERECHO DEPORTIVO. see *EDUCATION*

794.1   SP   ISSN 0214-8900
REVISTA INTERNACIONAL DE AJEDREZ. 1987. 12/yr. $75. Ediciones Eseuve, S.A., Batalla del Salado 34, 28045 Madrid, Spain. TEL 539-01-03. FAX 528-87-59. Ed. Antonio Gude. adv.; bk.rev.
 Description: Contains annotated games, articles, correspondence chess, and studies-problems, interviews and computer chess information.

794.1   RM   ISSN 1220-5516
REVISTA ROMANA DE SAH. 1950. m. $35. Interprinderea Rompresfilatelia, Sector Export-Import Press, Cales Grivitei 64-66, Bucharest 12, Casuta Postala 200, Rumania. Ed. Florin Gheorghiu.
 Formerly (until 1975): Revista de Sah (ISSN 1220-5575)
 Description: Contains national and international news and games, theory, correspondence chess, and studies-problems.

794.1   AG   ISSN 0326-0011
EL REY; revista argentina de ajedrez. 1980. irreg. Arg.$36($60) for 6 nos. Hector Ricardo Liso Ed. & Pub., 65 No. 5121, 1653 Villa Ballester, Argentina. adv.; bk.rev.; play rev.; bibl.; charts; illus.; index. circ. 300. (back issues avail.)

790.1   SY
RIADA. (Text in Arabic) w. B.P. 292, Damascus, Syria. Ed. Noureddine Rial. adv.

790.1   IT
RIETI-SPORT. 1973. m. L10000. Edizioni Sportive Reatine s.m.c., Via Centigliano, 15, 02100 Rieti, Italy. Ed. Zeno Fioritoni. adv. circ. 3,500. (back issues avail.)

799.3   UK   ISSN 0035-5224
RIFLEMAN. 1906. 6/yr. £12 (Europe £17; elsewhere £23). National Small-Bore Rifle Association, Lord Roberts House, Bisley Camp, Brookwood, Woking, Surrey GU24 ONP, England. TEL 01483-476969. FAX 01483-476392. Ed. B. Woodall. adv.; bk.rev.; charts; illus.; stat. circ. 7,500. **Indexed:** Sportsearch (1978-). **Document type:** newsletter.
 Description: Official journal of the U.K. governing body for .22 and airgun shooting.

790.1   JA
RIKUJO KYOGI. (Text in Japanese) 1967. m. Kodansha Ltd., 12-21 Otowa 2-chome, Bunkyo-ku, Tokyo 112, Japan. TEL 03-3235-6102. FAX 03-3235-2567. TELEX J34509 KODANSHA. Ed. Yutaka Hirose. circ. 50,000. **Document type:** consumer publication.
 Description: Track & field magazine for sports lovers.

796.83   US   ISSN 0035-5410
GV1115
THE RING; world's official boxing magazine. 1922. 13/yr. $30 for 12 issues in US & Canada (elsewhere $39.60) (effective 1994). London Publishing Co., Box 910, Fort Washington, PA 19034. TEL 215-643-6385. FAX 215-540-0146. Ed. Steve Farhood. adv.; bk.rev.; bibl.; illus.; stat. circ. 200,000. **Indexed:** Sports Per.Ind., Sportsearch (1977-). **Document type:** consumer publication.
—UMI; UnCover.

790.1   US
RING RHETORIC. 1971. q. membership. America Association for the Improvement of Boxing, Inc., 86 Fletcher Ave., Mt. Vernon, NY 10552. TEL 914-664-4571. Ed. Stephen H. Acunto. adv.; bk.rev. circ. 300. (looseleaf format; back issues avail.) **Document type:** bulletin, newsletter.
 Description: To educate the public on the improvement of boxing and advancing the sport.

796   CN
RINGETTE CANADA. OFFICIAL RULES (YEARS). (Text in English, French) 1965. every 3/yrs. Can.$5. Ringette Canada Publications, 1600 James Naismith Dr., Gloucester, ON K1B 5N4, Canada. TEL 613-748-5655. Ed. L. McQuaid. adv. circ. 10,000.
 Formerly: Ontario Ringette Association. Official Rules.

790.1   US
RINGSIDE. bi-m. O'Quinn Studios, Inc., 475 Park Ave. S., New York, NY 10016. TEL 212-689-2830.

796.83   UK   ISSN 0037-6310
RINGSPORT. 1959. bi-m. $10. Ringsport Publications, 5 Stockland St., Caerphilly, Glam., Wales. Ed. Evan R. Treharne. adv.; bk.rev.; illus. circ. 15,000.
 Indexed: Sportsearch.
 Supersedes: Skill.

RINKSIDER; independent voice of the industry! see *BUSINESS AND ECONOMICS — Management*

796   IT   ISSN 0048-8372
RIVISTA DI DIRITTO SPORTIVO. 1949. q. L.50000 (foreign L.75000). (Comitato Olimpico Nazionale Italiano) Casa Editrice Dott. A. Giuffre, Via Busto Arsizio 40, 20151 Milan, Italy. TEL 39-2-38000905. FAX 39-2-38009582. Ed. A. Gattai. adv.: page L.600000. circ. 5,600.

790.1 059.927   TS
AL-RIYADAH WAL-SHABAB. (Text in Arabic) 1981. w. Mu'assasat al-Bayan lil-Sahafah wal-Tiba'a wal-Nashr, P.O. Box 8837, Dubai, United Arab Emirates. TEL 444400. FAX 449820. TELEX 47707 PRESS EM. Ed. Khalid Muhammad Ahmad.
 Description: Covers sports news and youth activities.

790 059.927   UK   ISSN 1319-0822
AL-RIYADIYYAH. Key Title: Al-Riyadyat (Guddat). (Text in Arabic) 1988. d. $300. Saudi Research and Marketing, Arab Press House, 184 High Holborn, London WC1V 7AP, England. TEL 44-171-831-8181. FAX 44-171-831-2310. TELEX 889272. (And: P.O. Box 4556, Jeddah 21412, Saudi Arabia. TEL 966-2-6691888. FAX 966-2-6671650; Subscr. in U.S. to: Attache International, 3050 Broadway, Ste. 300, Boulder, CO 80304-3154. TEL 303-442-8900. FAX 303-442-7979) Ed. Hassan al-Sharqi. adv.: B&W page $4800; 14 x 23 3/16. circ. 84,111 (paid). cols./p.: 8. (broadsheet format) **Document type:** newspaper.
 Description: Covers the international sporting scene for an Arabic speaking audience.

794.1   GW   ISSN 0943-4356
ROCHADE EUROPA; die vielseitig-informative Schachzeitung. 1966. m. DM.60. Vogelsbergstr. 21, 63477 Maintal, Germany. TEL 06181-941001. FAX 06181-47791. Ed. C. Koehler. adv.; bk.rev.; bibl.; charts; illus. circ. 20,000. **Document type:** newsletter.
 Former titles (until 1992): Europa-Rochade (ISSN 0179-3934); (until 1984): Rochade.

796   US
ROCKY MOUNTAIN SPORTS. 1986. m. $14.97. 2025 Pearl St., Boulder, CO 80302-5323. TEL 303-440-5111. FAX 303-440-3313. Ed. Kathleen Gasperini. adv. circ. 42,000. **Document type:** consumer publication.
 Formerly: Rocky Mountain Sports and Fitness.
 Description: Covers the attitudes and lifestyle of the Rocky Mountain region, including sports, sport cultures and personalities.

797.21   US
▼**RODALE'S FITNESS SWIMMER**. 1995. bi-m. $17.97. Rodale Press, Inc., 33 E. Minor St., Emmaus, PA 18098. TEL 610-967-8603. Ed. Mary Bolster; Pub. Heidi Rodale. adv.; illus. **Document type:** consumer publication.

SPORTS AND GAMES

790.1 CN
ROD'S REFLECTOR. 10/yr. $12. R.R. No. 3, Pugwash, N.S. B0K 1L0, Canada. Ed. Rodney Leighton. **Document type:** newsletter.
Description: Contains reviews and comments on wrestling.

796.21 US ISSN 1073-4678
ROLLER SKATING BUSINESS. 1989. m. $45 to non-members. Roller Skating Associations, 7301 Georgetown Rd., Ste. 123, Indianapolis, IN 46268. TEL 317-875-3390. FAX 317-875-3394. Susan J. Snyder. adv. contact: Susan Snyder. charts; illus.; stat. **Document type:** trade publication.
Formerly (until 1994): Rink Digest (ISSN 1053-5772)
Description: Discusses new products and other topics of interest to owners and operators of roller-skating rinks, as well as roller-skating coaches.

790.1 US
ROLLER SPORTS REPORT. 1985. m. $20. RR 1, Box 265-A, Shaver Rd., W. Sand Lake, NY 12196. Ed. Martin Spencer. **Document type:** newsletter.
Description: Contains reprints and news about the attempts to revive the "roller sport".

790.1 GW
ROLLSPORT. 1976. m. DM.48. Deutscher Rollsport-Bund e.V., Thomas-Mann-Str. 6c, 60439 Frankfurt a.M., Germany. TEL 069-581084. FAX 069-572507. adv. circ. 1,000. **Document type:** newsletter.
Description: News about roller skating.

790.1 GW ISSN 0722-1088
ROLLSTUHLSPORT. 1982. m. DM.40. (Deutscher Rollstuhl Sportverband e.V.) Reha-Verlag GmbH, Roonstr. 30, 53175 Bonn, Germany. TEL 0228-352328. FAX 0228-359569. (Subscr. to: Deutscher Rollstuhl Sportverband e.V., Friedrich-Alfred-Str. 15, 41055 Duisburg, Germany) Eds. Ralf Harperath, Herbert Krah. adv.; illus. circ. 5,000. (back issues avail.) **Document type:** bulletin.

790.1 IT
ROMA. 1983. m. L.40000 (foreign L.80000). Ellepi s.r.l., Casella Postale 9062, 00100 Rome, Italy. Ed. Riccarso Viola. adv.: color page L.10000000. **Document type:** consumer publication.

790.1 IT
ROMAGNA PUNTO SPORT. 1979. m. L.50000. Romagna Sera, Via Paolo Bonoli,32, 47100 Forli, Italy. TEL 39-543-33596. Ed. Enzo Fasoli. adv. circ. 7,000.

796.815 CC
ROUDAO YU SHUAIJIAO/JUDO & WRESTLING. (Text in Chinese) 1983. bi-m. $18.50. Shanxi Sheng Tiyu Yundong Weiyuanhui, 7, Tiyu Lu, Dayingpan, Taiyuan, Shanxi 030012, People's Republic of China. TEL 775310. (Dist. in US by: China Books & Periodicals, Inc., 2929 24th St., San Francisco, CA 94110. TEL 415-282-2994) Ed. Zhang Dakang.
Description: Covers contemporary judo and wrestling in China.

790.1 AU
ROUGE ET NOIR. 1988. bi-m. V I P News Verlag GmbH, Taubstummengasse 13-4, A-1040 Vienna, Austria. TEL 01-5050801-0. FAX 01-505080121. Ed. Elisabeth Strunz. bk.rev. **Document type:** bulletin.
●Also available on CD-ROM.

790.1 GW ISSN 0945-7259
ROVER BLATT; Journal fuer Freunde gelaendegaengiger Rover. 1975. bi-m. DM.150. Deutscher Rover Club e.V., Ulmenweg 11, 64347 Griesheim, Germany. TEL 06155-4951. Ed. Roland Koch. adv. contact: Renate Herbst. circ. 900. (back issues avail.) **Document type:** consumer publication.

796 UK ISSN 0080-4242
ROYAL CALEDONIAN CURLING CLUB. ANNUAL. 1838. a. £4.50. Royal Caledonian Curling Club, Cairnie House, Ave. K, Ingliston Showground, Newbridge, Midlothian EH28 2NB, Scotland. TEL 0131-333-3003. FAX 0131-333-3323. Ed. W.J. Thomson. adv.; circ. 3,000. **Document type:** corporate report.

796.72 UK
ROYAL SCOTTISH AUTOMOBILE CLUB OFFICIAL HANDBOOK. 1907. a. £12.99. Royal Scottish Automobile Club, 11 Blythswood Sq., Glasgow G2 4AG, Scotland. TEL 041-221-3850. FAX 041-221-3805. Ed. Jonathan Lord. adv. circ. 5,000. **Document type:** directory.
Description: Motoring and touring guide.

796.35 US
RULES OF THE GAME OF FIELD HOCKEY. a. $5. International Hockey Federation, USFHA National Office, 1 Olympic Plaza, Colorado Springs, CO 80909. TEL 719-578-4567. FAX 719-532-0979. TELEX 452424. Ed.Bd. **Document type:** academic/scholarly publication.
Former titles: International Field Hockey Rules; Official Field Hockey Rules for School Girls (ISSN 0362-3270)

790.1 UK
THE RUNNER; runners magazine for the north and midlands. 1985. m. £18. Thomson Regional Newspapers, Thomson House, Newcastle upon Tyne, Tyne and Wear, England. TEL 0191-477-5599. FAX 0191-4900047. Ed. Chris White. adv. contact: Trish Roberts. bk.rev.; charts; illus.; stat. circ. 10,000. **Document type:** consumer publication.

796.426 US ISSN 1058-4889
RUNNER TRIATHLETE NEWS. 1985. m. $12.50. Offshore Data Services, Inc., Box 19909, Houston, TX 77224-1909. TEL 713-781-2713. FAX 713-781-9594. Ed. Lance Phegley. **Document type:** consumer publication.
Description: Covers road racing, cycling, duathlons and triathlons in Texas, New Mexico, Oklahoma, Arkansas and Louisiana.

796.42 US ISSN 0897-1706 GV1061
RUNNER'S WORLD. (German, South African and UK editions also avail.) 1966. m. $24. Rodale Press, Inc., 33 E. Minor St., Emmaus, PA 18098. TEL 610-967-5171. TELEX 847338. Ed. Amby Burfoot. adv.; illus. circ. 430,000. (also avail. in microform from UMI; reprint service avail. from UMI) Indexed: Acad.Ind., Hlth.Ind., Mag.Ind., Phys.Ed.Ind., PMR, Sports Per.Ind., Sportsearch (1973-). **Document type:** consumer publication.
●Also available online. Vendor(s): University Microfilms International.
—BLDSC (8052.384500); Faxon; SWETS; UMI; UnCover.
Incorporates (1978-1987): Runner (ISSN 0149-7316); **Former titles (until 1987):** Rodale's Runner's World (ISSN 0892-3744); (until 1985): Runner's World (ISSN 0035-9939); Distance Running News.
Description: Provides runners at any skill level with current training techniques, nutritional breakthroughs, equipment reviews, and race information in the United States and around the world.

796.42 UK ISSN 1350-7745
RUNNER'S WORLD. 1979. m. £25.40 (Ireland £29.30; rest of world £55). Rodale Press Ltd., 67-71 Goswell Rd., London EC1V 7EN, England. TEL 071-972-9119. FAX 071-972-9118. (Subscr. to: Runner's World, Unit 1, Hainault Rd., Romford, Essex RM6 5NP, England. TEL 081-597-7335) Ed. Nick Troop. adv. contact: Nick Williams. illus. circ. 40,000. Indexed: Sportsearch (1984-). **Document type:** consumer publication.
—BLDSC (8052.384600).
Supersedes (in Sep. 1993): Running (ISSN 0144-8560); **Incorporates:** Jogging Magazine.

796.42 SA
RUNNER'S WORLD. (Text in English) 1993. bi-m. Runner's World Magazine, 301 Foretrust Bldg., Martin Hammerschlag Way, Cape Town 8001, South Africa. TEL 27-21-217810. FAX 27-21-215118. Ed. Jonathan Sendzul. circ. 12,000. **Document type:** consumer publication.

796.42 GW ISSN 0945-3938
RUNNER'S WORLD. 1993. 11/yr. DM.75.60 (foreign DM.84). Ringier Verlag GmbH, Gustav-Heinemann-Ring 212, 81739 Munich, Germany. TEL 089-63818-0. FAX 089-63818100. Ed. Thomas Steffens. adv.: color page DM.11900; adv. contact: Michael Hackenberg. circ. 30,500. **Document type:** consumer publication.

RUNNING & FITNEWS. see PHYSICAL FITNESS AND HYGIENE

790.1 US ISSN 0147-2968 GV1061
RUNNING TIMES; the national calendar magazine for runners. 1977. m. $25 (foreign $39.95). Air Age Fitness Group, Rt. 7, 251 Danbury Rd., Wilton, CT 06897. TEL 203-834-2900. FAX 203-762-9803. (Subscr. to: Box 511, Mt. Morris, IL 61054. TEL 800-877-5402) Ed. Jim O'Brien. adv.; illus.; stat. circ. 80,000. (back issues avail.) Indexed: Sports Per.Ind., Sportsearch (1979-).

799.202 SA
S.A. MARKSMAN/S.A. SKERPSKUTTER. (Text in Afrikaans, English) 1959; N.S. 1994. q. membership only. South African Pistol Association - Suid-Afrikaanse Pistoolvereniging, P.O. Box 73989, Fairland 2030, South Africa. Ed. Hans Steyl. adv.; circ. 2,000 (controlled).

S A Z; the leading sporting goods and sports fashion trade newspaper. (Sport Artikel Zeitung) see BUSINESS AND ECONOMICS — Marketing And Purchasing

S B/SPORTS FACILITIES AND SWIMMING POOLS/EQUIPEMENT SPORTIF ET PISCINES/CONSTRUCCION DE INSTALACIONES DEPORTIVAS Y PISCINAS. (Sportstaettenbau und Baederanlagen) see BUILDING AND CONSTRUCTION

790.1 IT
S D S - RIVISTA DI CULTURA SPORTIVA. (Scuola Dello Sport) (Text in Italian; summaries in English, French, Spanish) 1982. q. L.16000. Comitato Olimpico Nazionale Italiano, Foro Italico, 00190 Rome, Italy. TEL 02-3685-9173. Ed. Mario Gulimelli. circ. 8,000. **Document type:** government publication, academic/scholarly publication.

S G M A COMPREHENSIVE QUARTERLY SALES TRENDS REPORT. (Sporting Goods Manufacturers Association) see BUSINESS AND ECONOMICS — Marketing And Purchasing

790.1 US
S G M A TODAY. bi-m. free. Sporting Goods Manufacturers Association, 200 Castlewood Dr., N. Palm Beach, FL 33408. TEL 407-842-4100. Ed. Michael May. circ. 5,000. (back issues avail.) **Document type:** trade publication.
Formerly: Action Update.

790.1 CN
S P O R T S. (Science Periodical on Research and Technology in Sport) 12/yr. $12. Coaching Association of Canada, 333 River Rd., Ottawa, Ont. K1L 8H9, Canada. TEL 613-746-5624.

794.1 SW ISSN 0347-5867
S S K K BULLETINEN. 1953. 6/yr. SEK 220 in the Nordic countries; elsewhere SEK 300. Sveriges Schackfoerbunds Korrespondensschackkommitte, P.O. Box 127, S-221 00 Lund, Sweden. FAX 46-46152915. Ed. Ragnar Wikman. adv.; bk.rev.; circ. 1,100 (paid).
Formerly (until 1974): Korrespondensschack-bulletinen.
Description: Reports on annotated games, combinations, and includes theoretical articles.

794.1 CI ISSN 0350-2570
SAHOVKI GLASNIK; organ Sahovskog saveza Hrvatske. (Text in Croatian) 1925. m. $20. (Sahovki Savez Hrvatske) Sahovska Naklada, Bogoviceva 7, 41000 Zagreb, Croatia. TEL 041 273-692. Ed. Drazen Marovic. adv.; bk.rev. circ. 5,500.

794.1 YU ISSN 0352-115X
SAHOVSKA KOMPOZICIJA; magazine for chess problem popularization. (Text in Serbo-Croatian) 1981. m. $5. Chess Problems Section "Student", P.O. Box 132, 32 102 Cacak, Yugoslavia. Ed. Ljubisa Papic. circ. 300. (back issues avail.)

794.1　　　　YU　ISSN 0351-1375
GV1313
SAHOVSKI INFORMATOR/CHESS INFORMANT/SAHMATNYJ INFORMATOR. 1966. 3/yr. $29. Francuska 31, 11001 Belgrade, Yugoslavia. TEL 630-109. FAX 11-626-583. TELEX 72677 CH INF YU. (Co-sponsor: World Chess Federation - F.I.D.E.) Ed. Aleksandar Matanovic. circ. 30,000.
—BLDSC (3172.524000).
Description: Includes a selection to the best games played by the world's greatest.

794.1　　　　LV
SAHS BALTIJA. Russian edition: Baltiiskie Shakhmaty. (Text in Latvian) 1959-1990 (Dec.); resumed Apr. 1991. m. $32 (typically set in Jan.) (Latvijas Saha Savienibas) Sahs Baltija, P.O. Box 241, 226050 Riga, Latvia. TEL 0132-286-864. Ed. Nikolai Zhuravlev. bk.rev. circ. 1,500.
Formerly (until Dec. 1990): Sahs (ISSN 0201-8101)
Description: Covers national and international chess games, opening theory, correspondence chess, "how-to-improve" articles, combinations, studies-problems, and interviews.

794.1　　　　HU　ISSN 0237-2525
SAKKELET. 1889. 6/yr. $36 (effective 1992). Nemzeti Sport Kft., c/o Andras Ozsvath, Ed., Nephadsereg u.10, 1005 Budapest 5, Hungary. TEL 0036-1-1312790. FAX 0036-1-1319738. (Dist. by: Kultura Kulkereskedelmi Vallalat, P.O. Box 149, 1389 Budapest, Hungary; U.S. subscr. addr.: Center for Hungarian Literature, 4418 16th Ave., Brooklyn, NY 11204) adv.; bk.rev.; illus. (also avail. in diskette format)
Description: Includes annotated games, computer and correspondence chess, studies-problems, and combinations. Covers chess events in Hungary.

790.1　　　　BE　ISSN 0775-7883
SAMSOM SPORTSECRETARIS. Variant title: Nieuwsbrief Sportsecretariaat. French edition: Lettre d'Information Hebdomadaire pour la Gestion d'un Cercle Sportif (ISSN 0776-9121) (Text in Flemish) 1987. w. 6059 BEF. C E D Samsom (Subsidiary of: Wolters Samsom Belgie n.v.), Kouterveld 14, B-1831 Diegem, Belgium. TEL 32-2-7231111.
Description: Provides advice of administrative and fiscal nature on how to run a sports organization.

796.815　　　　IT
SAMURAI - BUSHIDO E SUPER BANZI - PUGILATO. m. L.30000 (foreign L.120000). Sport Promotion s.r.l., Via Natale Battaglia 27, 20127 Milan, Italy. TEL 02-2856994.

797.2　　　　CN
SASKATCHEWAN SYNCHRO NEWS. q. Can.$15 membership. Synchro Saskatchewan, 1870 Lorne St., Regina, SK S4P 2L7, Canada. TEL 306-780-9227. FAX 306-781-6021. Eds. Wayne Hellquist, Margot Weiner. adv. contact: Kenda Richards. circ. 300. **Document type:** newsletter.

794.1　　　　IT
SCACCO; rivista mensile di tecnica e informazione sacchistica. 1970. 11/yr. $66. Edizione Scacco S.a.s., Corso Diaz 3, 12084 Mondovi (CN), Italy. TEL 0174-551054. Ed. Gallitto Salvatore. adv.; bk.rev.

SCANDINAVIAN JOURNAL OF MEDICINE & SCIENCE IN SPORTS. see MEDICAL SCIENCES — Sports Medicine

794.1　　　　NE
SCHAAKNIEUWS. 1986. 48/yr. fl.84 (in Belgium 1950 BEF; elsewhere fl.159) (effective 1994). Visserstraat 16B, 5612 BT Eindhoven, Netherlands. TEL 31-40-457832. FAX 31-40-439355. Ed. Johan van Mil. adv. contact: Erik Bouwmans. circ. 2,300.
Description: Includes current chess news and games, interviews, and articles of general interest.

794.1　　　　NE
SCHAAKSCHAKERINGEN. 1966. 12/yr. $24. Bestuur Nederlandse Bond van Correspondentieschakers, c/o L.C.M. Diepstraten, Pres., Heideveldweg 20, 1251 XN Laren (NH), Netherlands. Ed. R. Feytens. bk.rev. circ. 1,800.
Description: Includes annotated games, results, theory and articles.

794.1　　　　GW　ISSN 0048-9328
SCHACH. 1947. m. DM.72. Sport und Gesundheit Verlag GmbH, Lindenstr. 76, 10969 Berlin, Germany. TEL 030-25913028. FAX 030-25913085. Ed. Raj Tischbierek. adv. contact: Raj Tischbierek. bk.rev. circ. 10,000. **Document type:** consumer publication.

794.1　　　　AU
SCHACH AKTIV. 1979. 11/yr. S.360($36) Oesterreichischer Schachbund, Sackstr. 17, A-8010 Graz, Austria. TEL 0316-837758. FAX 0316-81697214. Ed. Kurt Fahrner. adv.: B&W page S.6000. circ. 2,100. **Document type:** newspaper.
Description: Contains national and international chess news and games, opening theory, correspondence chess, studies and problems.

794.1　　　　GW
SCHACH-ARCHIV. 1951. 12/yr. $30. Schachzentrale Caissa, Weidenbaumsweg 80, 21035 Hamburg, Germany. TEL 040-7244282. FAX 040-7214647. Ed. Horst Rattmann; Pub. Horst Rattmann. adv.; bk.rev. circ. 3,000. **Document type:** consumer publication.
Description: Deals with theoretical opening questions.

794.1　　　　GW
SCHACH IN BADEN. 1977. 6/yr. $15. Badischen Schachverband, c/o Frank Schmidt, Ed., Froehlichstr. 12, 68169 Mannheim, Germany. adv.; bk.rev.
Description: Newsletter for chessplayers.

794.1　　　　GW
SCHACHMAGAZIN 64 - SCHACH-ECHO. s-m. DM.76.80 (foreign DM.91.20); newsstand price: DM.4.40. Carl Ed. Schuenemann KG, Postfach 106067, 28060 Bremen, Germany. TEL 0421-36903-72. FAX 0421-36903-39. Ed. Otto Borik. circ. 13,500. **Document type:** bulletin.
—CCC.
Formed by the 1992 merger of: Schachmagazin 64 (ISSN 0721-9539); (1953-1992): Schach-Echo (ISSN 0036-5831)
Description: Contains articles on chess tournaments, theory and strategy. Includes calendar of events.

794.1　　　　SZ　ISSN 0176-2257
DIE SCHACHWOCHE; aktuelle Schachnachrichten aus aller Welt. 1982. 50/yr. 145 SFr. Schachagentur Caissa AG, Postfach 76, CH-5614 Sarmendorf, Switzerland. TEL 057-272061. FAX 057-273181. Ed. Werner Widmer. adv. circ. 9,500.
Description: Includes current international tournament information and over 2,400 games per year.

794.1　　　　SW　ISSN 0347-0377
SCHACKKORRESPONDENTEN. 1955. bi-m. SEK 360 (effective 1991). S J Fritidsfoerbund, P.O. Box 250, S-101 23 Stockholm, Sweden.

794.1　　　　SW　ISSN 0346-0770
SCHACKNYTT. 1970. 10/yr. $55 (effective 1995). Harry Schuessler, Ed. & Pub., P.O. Box 15098, S-750 15, Uppsala, Sweden. TEL 46-18-555-999. FAX 46-18-555-444. adv.; bk.rev.

794.1　　　　NE　ISSN 0036-5890
SCHAKEND NEDERLAND. 1893. m. fl.64.50. Koninklijke Nederlandse Schaakbond - Royal Dutch Chess Federation, Postbus 22739, 1100 DE Amsterdam, Netherlands. TEL 31-23-254025. FAX 31-23-254353. Ed. Minze bij de Weg. adv.; bk.rev.; charts; illus.; index. circ. 30,000.
Description: Covers chess.

796.86　　　　IT　ISSN 0036-6005
SCHERMA. 1961. m. Via I. Pettinengo 39, Rome, Italy. adv.; bk.rev.
Description: Covers fencing.

799　　　　NE　ISSN 0048-9344
SCHIETSPORT. 1890. m. fl.35($12) Koninklijke Nederlandse Schutters Associatie - Royal Dutch Shooting Association, Burg. de Widtstraat 2, 3811 LV Amersfoort, Netherlands. TEL 033-622388. FAX 033-650626. Ed. B.D.U. Barneveld. adv.; bk.rev. circ. 21,500.
Description: Covers shooting.

790.1　　　　GW
SCHLITTENPOST. 1971. s-a. Deutscher Bob- und Schlittensportverband e.V., An der Schiessstaette 6, 83471 Berchtesgaden, Germany. TEL 08652-9588-0. FAX 08652-958822. adv.; charts; illus.; stat. circ. 1,000. **Document type:** newsletter.

794.1　　　　CN　ISSN 0847-1428
SCHOLAR'S MATE. 1990. 5/yr. Can.$10. Kiril Publishing, Box 702, Sta. H, Montreal, PQ H3C 2V2, Canada. TEL 514-278-5292. FAX 514-278-5293. Ed. Tony Ficzere. adv.; bk.rev.; stat.; circ. 1,000 (paid). (back issues avail.)

794.1　　　　US　ISSN 1040-7707
SCHOOL MATES. 1987. bi-m. $15 (Canada $21; elsewhere $30); newsstand price: $2.50. United States Chess Federation, 186 Rte. 9W, New Windsor, NY 12553. TEL 914-562-8350. FAX 914-561-2437. Ed. Brian Bugbee. circ. 27,000. (back issues avail.)
Description: Presents chess on a beginner's level for young chess players. Includes profiles, analyses, instructions and puzzles.

799.202　　　　GW
DER SCHUETZE. 1965. q. Schuetzengesellschaft Pforzheim 1450 e.V., Kirschenpfad 1, 75181 Pforzheim, Germany. TEL 07231-63310. Ed. Frank Herholz. circ. 1,000.

790.1　　　　SZ
SCHWEIZER SPORT & MODE. (Text in German) m. 98 SFr. (foreign 125 SFr.). (Schweizer Sporthaendler Verband) Schweizer Sport & Mode, Raffelstr. 11, CH-8045 Zurich, Switzerland. TEL 01-4515155. FAX 01-4515166. Ed. Beat Ladner. **Document type:** trade publication.
Description: Trade paper for retailers of sporting goods.

796　　　　SZ
SCHWEIZER VOLKSPORT/SPORT POPULAIRE SUISSE.* (Text in French and German) 1974. 6/yr. 12 SFr. (Volksportverband Schweiz - Liechtenstein) Sinninger Druck, Oberredstr. 1, CH-5015 Niedererlinsbach, Switzerland. adv.; illus. circ. 2,500.

794.1　　　　SZ　ISSN 0036-7745
SCHWEIZERISCHE SCHACHZEITUNG; revue Suisse des echecs, revista scacchistica Svizzera. (Text in French, German, Italian) 1900. m. 70 SFr. Schweizerischer Schachverband, Gartenstr. 12, CH-4657 Dulliken, Switzerland. TEL 062-353365. (Subscr. to: c/o Werner Widmer, Postfach , CH-5614 Sarmenstorf, Switzerland) Eds. Markus Augst, Toni Preziuso. adv.; bk.rev.; charts; illus. circ. 10,000. **Document type:** bulletin.
Description: Covers the Swiss chess scene.

797.21
SCHWIMMSPORTVEREIN ESSLINGEN. VEREINSNACHRICHTEN. 1956. q. membership. Schwimmsportverein Esslingen e.V., Hohenackerstr. 32, 73733 Esslingen, Germany. TEL 0711-3704474. FAX 0711-3704475. Ed. Carola Waegerle. adv. contact: Manfred Kaltmaier. circ. 1,200. **Document type:** newsletter.

794.1　　　　UK
SCOTTISH CHESS. 1960. bi-m. $27. 38 Duncryne Ave., Mount Vernon, Glasgow G32 0RQ, Scotland. FAX 0141-778-4892. Ed. Douglas Bryson. adv.; bk.rev. circ. 750. **Document type:** consumer publication.
Description: Covers national and international games, articles, and combinations.

796.96　　　　UK　ISSN 0036-9160
SCOTTISH CURLER. 1954. m. (Sep.-May). £9($27) Dunfermline Press, Pitreavie Business Park, Dunfermline, Fife KY11 5QS, Scotland. TEL 0383-728201. Ed. Robin Welsh. adv.; bk.rev.; illus. circ. 10,000. **Indexed:** Sportsearch (1977-).
Description: Covers the sport of curling.

SPORTS AND GAMES

797.23 UK ISSN 0308-7379
SCOTTISH DIVER. 1960. bi-m. £11. Scottish Sub-Aqua Club, 40 Bogmoor Place, Glasgow G51 4TQ, Scotland. TEL 0141-425-1021. FAX 0141-330-4501. E-mail: gbax02@udcj.gla.ac.uk. Ed. Adam Curtis. adv. contact: Adam Curtis. bk.rev.; illus.; cum.index. circ. 2,500. **Indexed:** Sportsearch. **Document type:** newsletter.
  Description: Articles on sport-diving practices, dive sites worldwide, history of diving.

790.1 UK ISSN 0140-2803
SCOTTISH SPORTS COUNCIL. INFORMATION DIGEST. 1975. irreg. £1. Scottish Sports Council, Caledonia House, S. Gyle, Edinburgh EH12 9DQ, Scotland. TEL 0131-317-7200. FAX 0131-317-7202. **Document type:** bulletin.
  —BLDSC (4493.539050).

790.1 UK
SCOTTISH SPORTS COUNCIL. RESEARCH DIGEST. irreg., no.34, 1994. £5. Scottish Sports Council, Caledonia House, S. Gyle, Edinburgh EH12 9DQ, Scotland. TEL 0131-317-7200. FAX 0131-317-7202. Ed. Hilary Campbell. **Document type:** bulletin.

797 AT ISSN 0729-5529
SCUBA DIVER. bi-m. Aus.$29.70 (foreign Aus.$84) (effective Feb. 1995). Yaffa Publishing Group, 17-21 Bellevue St., Surry Hills, N.S.W. 2010, Australia. TEL 61-2-281-2333. FAX 61-2-281-2750. Ed. Sue Crowe. adv.: B&W page Aus.$1520, color page Aus.$1780; trim 273 x 210. circ. 7,290. **Document type:** consumer publication.
  Description: Provides comprehensive coverage of the recreational diving field.

790.1 US ISSN 0739-568X
SCUBA TIMES.* 1979. bi-m. $13. GBP, Inc., 14110 Perdido Key Dr., Pensacola, FL 32507-9529. TEL 904-478-5288. Ed. Cethie Cush. adv. circ. 50,000.

797.23 US
SCUBAPRO DIVING AND SNORKELING. 1986. q. $10. (Scubapro) Aqua-Field Publishing Co., Inc., 66 W. Gilbert St., Shrewsbury, NJ 07702. TEL 908-842-8300. (Subscr. to: 3105 E. Harcourt, Rancho Dominguez, CA 90221) Ed. Stephen Ferber. adv. circ. 95,000.

SEGAVISIONS. see *COMPUTERS — Computer Games*

790.1 GW ISSN 0930-3308
SEITENWECHSEL. 1986. s-a. free. Georg August Universitaet - Goettingen, Zentrale Einrichtung fuer den Allgemeinen Hochschulsport, Sprangerweg 2, 37075 Goettingen, Germany. Ed. Andreas Tyrock. adv.; bk.rev. circ. 7,500. **Document type:** academic/scholarly publication.
  Description: Covers university sports and past times.

790.1 US ISSN 0196-6243
SENIOR SPORTS NEWS. 1979. m. $2.50. National Senior Sports Association (NSSA), Box 882, Fairfax, VA 22030-0882. TEL 703-385-7540. Ed. Lloyd Wright. circ. 5,000.

790.1 UK ISSN 0958-3009
SERVE AND VOLLEY. m. £28. Lawn Tennis Association, The Queen's Club, W. Kensington, London W14 9EG, England. TEL 071-381-7000. FAX 071-381-6656. Ed. Henry Wancke. adv.: B&W page £1073, color page £1800; adv. contact: Roo Abando. circ. 39,200. (back issues avail.) **Document type:** bulletin.

790.1 IT
SFINGE.* 1980. m. L.11000 (foreign L.25000). Gruppo Editoriale Poker s.r.l., Via Gentile da Mogliano 142, 00176 Rome, Italy. TEL 39-6-21703891. Ed. Eraclite Corbi. adv.: page L.2200000; adv. contact: Mirco Corbi.

794.1 BU
SHAKHMATNA MISL. 12/yr. $30. Sofia - 1504, ul., Rakitin 2, Bulgaria. (Subscr. to: British Chess Magazine, 9 Market St., St Leonards-on-Sea, E. Sussex TN38 ODQ, England) Ed. P. Petkov.
  Description: Contains national and international chess game analyses, theory, combinations, studies and problems.

794.1 RU ISSN 0869-5229
SHAKHMATNYI VESTNIK. 1921. 0/yr. (effective 1996). Fiskultura i Sport, Kalyaevskaya 27, 103006 Moscow, Russia. TEL 095-258-2690. FAX 095-200-1217. (Dist. by: Mezhdunarodnaya Kniga, B. Yakimanka 39, 117049 Moscow, Russia; Dist. in U.S. by: Victor Kamkin Inc., 4956 Boiling Brook Pkwy, Rockville, MD 20852. TEL 301-881-5973) Ed. Yuri Averbakh. bk.rev.; bibl. circ. 30,000. (also avail. in microform)
  Formerly: Shakhmaty v S.S.S.R. (ISSN 0132-0947)

790.1 CC
SHANGHAI XIANGQI/SHANGHAI CHESS. (Text in Chinese) bi-m. Shanghai Wenhua Chubanshe - Shanghai Culture Press, 74 Shaoxing Lu, Shanghai 200020, People's Republic of China. TEL 372608. Ed. Hu Ronghua.

790.1 613.7 CC ISSN 1003-5176
SHAOLIN YU TAIJI. (Text in Chinese) 1984. bi-m. Y10.80. Henan Tiyu Baokan She, No. 3, Jiankang Lu, Zhengzhou, Henan 450053, People's Republic of China. TEL 0371-3923289. (Dist. overseas by: China International Book Trading Corp., P.O. Box 399, Beijing, P.R. China) Ed. Qiu Mingnan.
  Former titles (until 1989): Shaolin Wushu; Zhongzhou Wushu.
  Description: Covers traditional Chinese martial arts including shadow boxing practiced in the Shaolin Buddhist Temple.

SHARING THE VICTORY. see *RELIGIONS AND THEOLOGY*

794.1 II
SHATRANJ SAMARAT. 12/yr. $12. Chappa Nivas, Kambal Kendra Rd., Mandsaur, M.P., India. Ed. Nandkishor Joshi.

794.1 TS
AL-SHIRAH. (Text in Arabic, English) 1983. 3/yr. $30. Dubai Chess and Culture Club, P.O. Box 11354, Dubai, United Arab Emirates. TEL 281362. Ed. Khalid Ali bin Zayed. adv.; illus. circ. 2,000.
  Description: National and international coverage of games, and junior chess.

799.202 UK ISSN 0308-5236
SHOOT!. 1969. w. £50($123.50) I P C Magazines, Holborn Publishing Group (Subsidiary of: Reed Elsevier group), King's Reach Tower, Stamford St., London SE1 9LS, England. TEL 071-261-5000. FAX 0444-440619. TELEX 892084 REEDBP G. (Dist. by: Quadrant Subscription Services, Oakfield House, Perrymount Rd., Haywards Heath, W. Sussex RH16 3DH, England. TEL 0622-721555) Ed. Dave Smith. adv.: B&W page £1333; adv. contact: Julian Clark. circ. 131,000. (back issues avail.) **Document type:** consumer publication.
  Incorporates: Goal (ISSN 0017-1492)
  Description: For 11- to 17-year-old boys; contains news, features and statistics about the English and Scottish football leagues.

799.202 US ISSN 0080-9365
TS535
SHOOTER'S BIBLE. 1925. a. $21.95. Stoeger Publishing Co., 55 Ruta Ct., S. Hackensack, NJ 07606. TEL 201-440-2700. Ed. William S. Jarrett; Pub. David C. Perkins. adv. contact: David C. Perkins. **Document type:** consumer publication.
  —BLDSC (8268.240000).

799.3 US ISSN 0037-4148
SHOOTING INDUSTRY. 1956. m. $25. Publishers' Development Corp., 591 Camino de la Reina, Ste. 200, San Diego, CA 92108. TEL 619-297-5350. FAX 619-297-5353. TELEX 695-478. Ed. Bruce Hillman. adv. contact: Joe McMahon. bk.rev.; charts; illus.; pat.; stat.; tr.lit. circ. 22,500. **Indexed:** Bus.Ind., Tr.& Indus.Ind. **Document type:** trade publication.
  —UMI.

799.202 658.8 US ISSN 0887-9397
SHOOTING SPORTS RETAILER.* 1983. bi-m. $20. Karaban - Labiner Associates, 130 W. 42nd St., Ste. 1804, New York, NY 10036-7802. TEL 212-840-0660. Ed. Kristin Colongeli. adv.; tr.lit. circ. 22,500. **Document type:** trade publication.

799.2 US ISSN 1069-6822
SHOOTING SPORTS U S A. 1988. m. $15 to non-members. (National Rifle Association of America) N R A Publications, 11250 Waples Mill Rd., Fairfax, VA 22030. TEL 703-267-1585. FAX 703-267-3994. Ed. Karen Davey. circ. 25,000. (tabloid format) **Document type:** newspaper.
  Description: For the competitive and recreational shooter. Covers matches at the local, regional, national and international level. Includes how-to articles and listing of all NRA-sanctioned matches.

799.2 US ISSN 0038-8084
GV1151
SHOOTING TIMES. 1960. m. $21.98. P J S Publications, Inc., News Plaza, Box 1790, Peoria, IL 61656. TEL 309-682-6626; 800-727-4353. Ed. James W. Bequette. circ. 200,000. **Indexed:** Consum.Ind., Sports Per.Ind., Sportsearch. **Document type:** consumer publication.

799 UK ISSN 0037-4164
SHOOTING TIMES AND COUNTRY MAGAZINE.* 1882. w. £65 (foreign £79). Harmsworth Active, 3rd Fl., Astley House, 33 Notting Hill Gate, London W11 3JQ, England. Ed. T. O'Nions. adv.; bk.rev.; illus. circ. 36,108. **Indexed:** Geo.Abstr. **Document type:** consumer publication.
  Formerly: Shooting Times.

799 UK ISSN 0049-0415
SHOTGUN NEWS; trading post for anything that shoots. 1946. 3/mo. $22 (effective Jan. 1995). Snell Publishing Co., Box 669, Hastings, NE 68901. TEL 402-463-4589. FAX 402-463-3893. Ed. R. Terry Hunter; Pub. Robert M. Snell. adv. contact: Mary Kriger. illus.; tr.lit.; circ. 150,000 (paid). (tabloid format) **Document type:** trade publication.

790.5 613.7 US ISSN 0882-9640
SILENT SPORTS; mid-America's aerobic recreational sports magazine. 1984. m. $14. Waupaca Publishing Co., 717 Tenth St., Box 152, Waupaca, WI 54981. TEL 715-258-5546. FAX 715-258-8162. Ed. Greg Marr; Pub. Scott Turner. adv. contact: Jim Wendt. circ. 11,500. (back issues avail.) **Document type:** consumer publication.
  Formerly: Wisconsin Silent Sports.
  Description: Covers recreational fitness activities in the upper Midwest: bicycling, cross country skiing, running, canoeing, and backpacking.

797.21 SW
SIMFRAEMJAREN-LIVRAEDDAREN. 1935. q. SEK 50. Svenska Livraeddningssaellskapet-Simfraemjandet, Box 8346, 402 79 Goeteborg, Sweden. FAX 31-223234. Ed. Anders Werneten. adv. circ. 14,000.

794.1 IT ISSN 0037-5608
SINFONIE SCACCHISTICHE. (Text in English, French and Italian) 1965. q. L.15000($12) Associazione Problemistica Italiana, Via della Camilluccia 145, 00135 Rome, Italy. Ed. Marco Bonavoglia. bk.rev.; bibl.; charts; index. circ. 6,000.

794.1 IC ISSN 1022-6958
SKAK. 1947. m. $40. Johann Thorir Jonsson, Ed. & Pub., P.O. Box 1179, 121-Reykjavik, Iceland. TEL 354-553-1975.

794.1 DK ISSN 0037-6043
SKAKBLADET. 1904. m. DKK 196 (effective 1995). Dansk Skak Union, Kongestien 16, DK-2830-Virum, Denmark. TEL 45-45-85-64-63. FAX 45-45-85-03-13. Ed. Thorbjoern Rosenlund. adv.; bk.rev.; charts; illus.; index. circ. 10,000.

796.21 US ISSN 0037-6132
GV849.A1
SKATING. 1923. bi-m. $25 (in Canada $35; elsewhere $45) (effective Sep. 1993). United States Figure Skating Association, 20 First St., Colorado Springs, CO 80906. TEL 719-635-5200. FAX 719-635-9548. Ed. Kim Mutchler. adv.; illus. circ. 37,000. **Indexed:** Sports Per.Ind., Sportsearch (1975-).
  —UnCover.

799.313 US ISSN 0037-6140
GV1181
SKEET SHOOTING REVIEW;* covering the sport of skeet shooting world wide. 1947. m. $15 or membership. National Skeet Shooting Association, 5931 Roft rd., San Antonio, TX 78253-9261. TEL 210-688-3371. Ed. Susie Fluckiger. adv.; illus. circ. 18,000. **Indexed:** Sportsearch (1974-).
 Description: Contains information on new product and techniques.

790.1 CN
LE SKI (TORONTO, 1988). (Text in French) 1988. q. Can.$9.50. Solstice Publishing Inc., 19 Albany Ave., Toronto, ON M5R 3C2, Canada. TEL 416-535-0607. FAX 416-535-3419. Ed. Robert Choquette; Pub. Paul Green. adv. contact: Paul Green. circ. 21,000 (controlled). **Document type:** consumer publication.

790.1 US ISSN 0890-6076
SKI PATROL MAGAZINE. 1984. q. $20 (foreign $30). National Ski Patrol System, Inc., Ski Patrol Bldg., Ste. 100, 133 S. Van Gorden St., Lakewood, CO 80228. TEL 303-988-1111. FAX 303-988-3005. Ed. Rebecca W. Ayers. adv.; bk.rev.; charts; illus.; cum.index. circ. 27,000. **Document type:** trade publication.
—UnCover.
 Description: Discusses avalanche statistics, ski mountaineering, equipment, medical training, outdoor emergency care, fitness, risk management for ski patrollers. Includes ski area profiles.

796.93 US ISSN 0037-6213
SKI RACING. 1968. 20/yr. $19.95. Ski Racing International, Box 1125, Waitsfield, VT 05673-1125. TEL 802-496-7700. FAX 802-496-7704. Ed. Tim Etchells; Pub. Gary Black, Jr. adv. contact: Phil Knaub. bk.rev.; charts; illus.; stat. circ. 25,000. (tabloid format) **Indexed:** Sports Per.Ind., Sportsearch (1976-). **Document type:** consumer publication, newspaper.
 Description: Contains comprehensive race information and coverage. Includes race techniques and conditioning secrets from experts.

797.23 US ISSN 0037-6345
SH458
SKIN DIVER MAGAZINE; devoted to the underwater world. 1951. m. $19.94. Petersen Publishing Co., 6420 Wilshire Blvd., Los Angeles, CA 90048. TEL 213-782-2000. Ed. Bill Gleason. adv.; illus.; index. circ. 210,000. (also avail. in microform from UMI) **Indexed:** Cal.Per.Ind. (1990), Hlth.Ind., Mag.Ind., PMR, Sports Per.Ind., Sportsearch. **Document type:** consumer publication.
●Also available online. Vendor(s): Knight-Ridder, Inc..
—Faxon; UMI; UnCover.

796 US ISSN 1050-7078
SKYBOX. q. Dorsey Publishing, 1328 Elam Ave., Cincinnati, OH 45225-1808. TEL 513-541-0269. FAX 513-541-0057. Ed. Bill Dorsey. adv. circ. 100,275. **Document type:** consumer publication.

790.1 US ISSN 0192-7361
SKYDIVING. 1979. m. $20. Aerographics, 1725 N. Lexington Ave., DeLand, FL 32724. TEL 904-736-4793. FAX 904-736-9786. Ed. Michael F. Truffer. adv.; bk.rev.; circ. 10,470 (paid). (tabloid format; also avail. in microform from UMI; back issues avail.) **Indexed:** Sportsearch (1980-). **Document type:** consumer publication.
 Description: Presents news and information about the equipment, events, techniques, people and places of sport parachuting.

799.31 DK ISSN 0037-6663
SKYTTE-BLADET. 1937. 10/yr. DKK 200. Dansk Skytte Union, Broendby Stadion 20, DK-2605 Broendby, Denmark. Ed. Carit Volfing. adv.; bk.rev. circ. 4,000.

790.1 UK
SMALL SIDE TEAM GAMES AND POTTED SPORTS. 1935. irreg. £1.25 per no. Ministry of Defense, Army Sport Control Board, Clayton Barracks, Aldershot, England. **Document type:** consumer publication.

796.345 UK
SMYTHSON'S BADMINTON SPORTING DIARY. 1894. a. £20($37) Smythson U.K. Ltd., 44 New Bond St., London W1Y ODE, England. TEL 0171-629-8558. FAX 0171-490-2873. Ed. A.E. Friend. (back issues avail.) **Document type:** directory.

794.735 UK ISSN 0269-0756
SNOOKER SCENE. 1972. m. £15. Everton's News Agency, Cavalier House, 202 Hagley Rd., Edgbaston, Birmingham B16 9PQ, England. FAX 0121-452-1822. Ed. Clive Everton. adv.; bk.rev. circ. 18,000. **Document type:** consumer publication.

790.1 GW
SNOW; Surf Spezial. 1983. irreg. (1-2/yr.). DM.8 per no. Verlag Delius Klasing und Co., Postfach 101671, 33516 Bielefeld, Germany. TEL 0521-559280. FAX 0521-559113. TELEX 932934-DEKLA. Ed. Ulrich Stanciu. bk.rev.; circ. 70,000. **Document type:** consumer publication.
 Formerly (until 1991): Funboard.

790.1 US
SNOWMOBILE RACING YEARBOOK. a. $4.50. Ehlert Publishing Group, 601 Lakeshore Pkwy., Minnetonka, MN 55305. TEL 612-476-2200. FAX 612-476-2200. **Document type:** consumer publication.

SOARING. see *AERONAUTICS AND SPACE FLIGHT*

796.334 FR ISSN 0015-9557
SOCIETE D'EDITION DE PERIODIQUES SPORTIFS. 1955. w. 185 F. Sopusi, 10 rue du Faubourg Montmartre, 75009 Paris, France. (Subscr. to: 13 rue d'Enghien, 75010 Paris, France) Ed.Bd. adv.; circ. 175,000 (controlled). (looseleaf format)

790.1 US ISSN 0560-6152
GV1183
SOCIETY OF ARCHER-ANTIQUARIES. JOURNAL. 1958. a. £15 membership. Society of Archer-Antiquaries, c/o Doug Elmy, 61 Lambert Rd., Bridlington, Yorks YO16 5RD, England. TEL 01262-601604. Ed. E. McEwen. bk.rev.; charts; illus.; circ. controlled. **Document type:** bulletin.

SOCIOLOGY OF SPORT JOURNAL. see *SOCIOLOGY*

793.732 028.5 DK
SOFUS' LILLEBROR. 1974. m. DKK 183. Interpresse, Noerregade 7A, DK-Copenhagen K, Denmark. TEL 45-33-33-75-35. FAX 45-33-33-75-05. Ed. Tommy Andersen. adv. contact: Lars Rasmussen. circ. 18,000 (paid). (back issues avail.)
 Description: Contains crossword puzzles for children and youth.

796.72 SP
SOLO AUTO 4 X 4. 1983. m. 4250 ptas. (Europe 6400 ptas.; US 8500 ptas.). Alesport S.A., Gran Via 8-10, 08908 Hospitalet (Barcelona), Spain. TEL 34315533. FAX 34227404. Ed. Juan Porcar. adv.
 Description: Dedicated to the world of off-road cars, includes news and review of new models.

796 US ISSN 0279-3288
SOONERS ILLUSTRATED. 1980. 17/yr. $49.90. College Sports Communications, Inc., 4099 McEwen Rd., Ste. 350, Dallas, TX 75244. TEL 214-851-1770. FAX 214-490-9333. Ed. M.C. Ross. adv.; B&W page $800, color page $1200; trim 8 1/4 x 10 7/8. circ. 12,500. **Document type:** consumer publication.

797.23 US
SOURCES (MONTCLAIR); the journal of underwater education. 1960. bi-m. $45. National Association of Underwater Instructors, Diving Association, Box 14650, Montclair, CA 91763-1150. TEL 714-621-5801. FAX 714-621-6405. Ed. Mike Williams. adv.; bk.rev. circ. 12,000. **Indexed:** Sportsearch.
 Formerly: N A U I News.

SOUTH AFRICAN AERONEWS. see *AERONAUTICS AND SPACE FLIGHT*

SOUTH AFRICAN YACHTING. see *SPORTS AND GAMES — Boats And Boating*

798.4 AT ISSN 0038-2981
SOUTH AUSTRALIAN RACING CALENDAR. 1902. m. Aus.$50. South Australian Jockey Club Inc., G.P.O. Box 1695, Adelaide, S.A. 5001, Australia. TEL 61-8-295-0163. FAX 61-8-295-1830. Ed. A. MacDonald. adv.; cum.index. circ. 1,300. **Document type:** bulletin.

790.1 US
SOUTHERN GAMEPLAN.* 1989. 9/yr. $17. SportsMedia, Inc., Box 13215, Birmingham, AL 35202-3215. TEL 205-324-0460. Ed. Ben Cook. adv. circ. 100,000.
 Description: Features stories on national sports events affecting the southern U.S. and rising high school athletic stars, with emphasis on collegiate sports.

796.72 US ISSN 0049-1616
SOUTHERN MOTORACING. 1964. fortn. $15. Universal Services, Inc., Box 500, Winston-Salem, NC 27102. TEL 910-723-5227. Ed. Hank Schoolfield. adv.; bk.rev.; stat. circ. 20,500. (tabloid format)

796.42 US ISSN 0744-3439
SOUTHERN RUNNER. 1981. bi-m. $9. Box 6524, Metairie, LA 70009-6524. TEL 504-454-8247. Ed. Valerie D. Andrews; Pub. Mike Andrews. circ. 10,000.

790.1 GW ISSN 0723-6174
SOUVENIR & GESCHENK. 1963. q. DM.50($13) Bundesverband der Reiseandenken-Branche, Platterstr. 31, 65193 Wiesbaden, Germany. Ed. Juergen Schreiber. adv.; bk.rev. circ. 4,500.
—CCC.

SPEEDWAY. see *HOBBIES*

796.72 US
SPEEDWAY LIMITED EDITION. 1991. bi-m. $49.95. Adventure, 7200 Montgomery N.E., Ste. 356, Albuquerque, NM 87109. TEL 505-888-1515. FAX 505-888-0717. Ed. Marybeth D. Connelly. adv.; B&W page $1250; trim 4 x 6 3/8. circ. 50,000.
 Description: Covers NASCAR racing. Profiles 12 drivers in each issue. Contains prices for memorabilia and schedules.

796.72 US ISSN 0747-5403
SPEEDWAY SCENE. 1971. w. $35 (foreign $52). Hockomock Publishing, 50 Washington St., Box 300, N. Easton, MA 02356. TEL 508-238-7016. FAX 508-230-2381. Ed. Val LeSieur. circ. 54,900. (tabloid format) **Document type:** trade publication.
 Description: Covers circle track racing from Winston Cup to local tracks.

796 AU
SPIEL-SPORT-FREIZEIT-MODE. vol.13, 1964. m. S.592. Oesterreichischer Wirtschaftsverlag, Nikolsdorfer Gasse 7-11, A-1051 Vienna, Austria. TEL 0222-555585. TELEX 1-11669. Ed. Erhard Zagler. adv.; illus. circ. 2,600.
 Former titles: Sport-Spiel-Freizeit; Sportartikel-Sportmode (ISSN 0038-7959); Oesterreichische Sportartikel.

790.1 GW ISSN 0721-6777
SPIELBOX. bi-m. W. Nostheide Verlag GmbH, Schuetzenstr. 30, 96047 Bamberg, Germany. TEL 0951-21088. FAX 0951-21080. Ed. Harald Hemmerlein. circ. 6,100. **Document type:** bulletin.

793 GW
SPIELCASINO; Spielzeitung fuer Schueler, Eltern und Lehrer. 1979. s-a. DM.4. Adolf Reichwein Schule, Uchteweg 26, 33689 Bielefeld, Germany. TEL 0521-449467. FAX 0521-412743. Ed. Dirk Hanneforth. circ. 850.

790.1 613.7 US
SPLASH! (COLORADO SPRINGS). 1976. bi-m. $10 to non-members (foreign $20); free to members. United States Swimming, Inc., One Olympic Plaza, Colorado Springs, CO 80909. TEL 719-578-4578. FAX 719-578-4669. (Alt addr.: 1750 E. Boulder St., Colorado Springs, CO) Ed. Charlie Snyder; Pub. Ray Essick. circ. 150,000. (tabloid format) **Document type:** newsletter.
 Formed by the July 1993 merger of: Lanelines; (1944-1993): U S Swimming Notes (ISSN 0883-0347)
 Description: Conceived in the hope of improving communication among clubs, coaches, local swimming committees, U.S.S. staff, and the Board of Directors. Provides information on programs and services of U.S.S. and the people and events of the sport of swimming.

SPORTS AND GAMES

790.1 659.1 UK ISSN 0263-3809
SPONSORSHIP NEWS; the first magazine devoted to sponsorship. 1982. m. £112 (rest of Europe £120; elsewhere £140) (effective Jan. 1995). Charterhouse Business Publications, P.O. Box 66, Wokingham, Berks. RG41 5FS, England. TEL 01734-772770. FAX 01734-774522. Ed. Jonathan Gee. adv.; bk.rev. (back issues avail.)

613.7 790 BE ISSN 0038-7770
SPORT. 1958. 4/yr. 600 BEF. Ministere de la Communaute Francaise, Direction Generale du Sport et du Tourisme, Bd. Leopold II, 44, B-1080 Brussels, Belgium. FAX 32-2-4132825. Ed. Georges Gypens. adv. contact: Benjamin Stassen. bk.rev. circ. 2,500. **Indexed:** Acad.Ind., Sportsearch (1974-). **Document type:** academic/scholarly publication.

790 NO ISSN 0333-3639
SPORT. 1919. 8/yr. NOK 250. Norges Sportshandleres Forbund - Norwegian Sport Association, Drammensvn. 30, Oslo 2, Norway. Ed. Odd Frydenberg. adv. circ. 2,400.
Formerly (until 1974): Sportshandleren (ISSN 0049-1993)

790 RU ISSN 0203-1434
GV561
SPORT. (Editions in English, French, German, Hindi, Hungarian, Russian, Spanish) 1963. m. Ul. Moskvina 8, 103722 Moscow, Russia. TEL 095-229-4659. Ed. O.D. Spassky. illus.; index. **Indexed:** Sportsearch.
Formerly: Sport in the U.S.S.R. (ISSN 0038-7908)

790 US ISSN 0038-7797
GV561
SPORT. 1946. m. $19.94 (foreign $27.94). Petersen Publishing Co., 6420 Wilshire Blvd., Los Angeles, CA 90048. TEL 213-782-2000. Ed. Cameron Benty. adv.; bk.rev.; illus. circ. 931,517. (also avail. in microform from UMI; reprint service avail. from UMI) **Indexed:** Acad.Ind., Mag.Ind., PMR, Sports Per.Ind., Sportsearch (1977-), TOM. **Document type:** consumer publication.
—Faxon; UMI; UnCover.

790.1 PL ISSN 0137-9305
SPORT. 1945. 5/w. Fibak Noma Press S.A., Ul. Plebiscytowa 36, 40-041 Katowice, Poland. TEL 48-32-539995. FAX 48-32-537138. Ed. Adam Barteczko. circ. 80,000 (controlled).

073 SZ
SPORT. (Text in German) 1920. w. 136.70 SFr.; newsstand price: 3 SFr. Verlag Sport Wochenzeitung AG, Edenstr. 20, Postfach, CH-8021 Zurich, Switzerland. TEL 01-2077373. FAX 01-2021673. Ed. Peter Zwicky; Pub. Urs Zeier. adv. contact: Manuel Loureiro. **Document type:** newspaper.

790.1 ZR
SPORT AFRICAIN. m. 13e niveau Tour adm, Cite de la Voix du Zaire, B.P. 3356, Kinshasa-Gombe, Zaire. Ed. Tshimpumpu Wa Tshimpumpu.

790.1 SZ
SPORT AKTIV. French edition: Gym et Sport. Italian edition: Ginnasta. (Editions in French, German, Italian) 1988. fortn. 37 SFr. (Schweizerischer Turnverband) Vogt-Schild AG, Zuchwilerstr. 21, CH-4501 Solothurn, Switzerland. TEL 065-247247. FAX 065-247235. Ed. Ursi Gisler. adv.; B&W page 3130 SFr., color page 4230 SFr.; trim 188 x 270; adv. contact: Barbara Staugassinger. circ. 37,836. **Document type:** bulletin.

THE SPORT AMERICANA HOCKEY CARD PRICE GUIDE. see HOBBIES

SPORT & FITNESS. see PHYSICAL FITNESS AND HYGIENE

796.41 NE ISSN 1381-2572
SPORT & FITNESS; grootste fitness magazine van Nederland en Belgie. (Text in Dutch) 1983. bi-m. fl.39.90. S & F Publications, P.O. Box 1005, 6040 KA Roermond, Netherlands. TEL 31-4750-24702. FAX 31-4750-22234. Ed. Roel Schenk; Pub. Ton Maessen. adv.; B&W page fl.2360. circ. 35,000. **Document type:** consumer publication.
Description: For body-builders.

790.1 UK
SPORT & LEISURE (CARDIFF). 1984. 6/yr. free. Sports Council for Wales, National Sports Centre for Wales, Sophia Gardens, Cardiff CF1 9SW, Wales. FAX 0222-222431. adv. circ. 210,000. (tabloid format) **Indexed:** Sportsearch.
Former titles: Sport Wales; Welsh Sports Review.

790 UK ISSN 0144-7181
SPORT AND LEISURE (LONDON). 1949. bi-m. £15.20. Sports Council, 16 Upper Woburn Pl., London WC1H 0QP, England. TEL 0171-388-1277. FAX 0171-383-5740. Ed. Louise Fyfe. adv.; bk.rev.; illus. circ. 8,500. **Indexed:** ASSIA, Intl.Polym.Sci.& Tech., Phys.Ed.Ind., RAPRA, Sportsearch (1990-). **Document type:** consumer publication.
Formerly: Sport and Recreation (ISSN 0038-7819)
Description: Covers developments and new initiatives in recreation at elite and grass-roots levels, sports politics and policies.

790.1 613.7 UK ISSN 0267-3304
SPORT AND RECREATION INFORMATION GROUP BULLETIN. 1984. 2/yr. £10 to individuals; institutions £20. Sheffield Libraries and Information Services, Sports Library and Information Centre, Surrey St., Sheffield, England. TEL 0114-2735929. FAX 0114-2735009. Ed. Lesley Gunter. adv.; bk.rev. circ. 100. **Document type:** bulletin.

SPORT AND THE LAW JOURNAL. see LAW

796.72 FR ISSN 0038-7827
SPORT-AUTO; le magazine du sport automobile et de l'automobile sportive. 1962. m. 325 F. (Sport Auto) Gerpresse, 8 rue Pierre Brossolette, 92300 Levallois-Perret, France. TEL 40-87-40-85. Ed. Philippe Simon. adv.; bk.rev.; charts; illus. circ. 150,000. (tabloid format)

796.77 SP ISSN 1131-7140
SPORT AUTO. 1989. a. 800 ptas. Luike - Motorpress, C. Ancora 40, 28045 Madrid, Spain. TEL 34-1-3470100. FAX 34-1-3470204. Ed. Javier Recio. adv.; B&W page 530000 ptas., color page 750000 ptas.; adv. contact: Agustin Valero. **Document type:** consumer publication.
Description: Guide to auto racing events of the year.

797.21 GW ISSN 0344-6492
SPORT- BAEDER- FREIZEITBAUTEN; internationale Fachzeitschrift fuer Planung, Bau, Einrichtung, Betrieb und Forschung. (Text in German; summaries in English, French and Italian) 1961. 6/yr. DM.69. Krammer Verlag, Hermannstr. 3, 40233 Duesseldorf, Germany. TEL 0211-67972-0. FAX 0211-6797231. TELEX 8586639-KRVG-D. Ed. D. Fabian. adv. contact: Heinz Martin. bk.rev.; charts; illus.; tr.lit. circ. 4,500. **Indexed:** Br.Tech.Ind., Eng.Ind. **Document type:** trade publication.
—BLDSC (8419.675000).
Formerly: Sport- und Baederbauten (ISSN 0038-7924)
Description: International trade publication for the aquatic sport and recreation building industry. Covers various aspects of the construction and design of swimming pools and other sports facilities.

790.1 GW
SPORT BILD. 1988. w. (Wed.). DM.78; newsstand price: DM.1.60. Axel Springer Verlag AG, Axel-Springer-Platz 1, 20355 Hamburg, Germany. TEL 040-3470-0. FAX 040-340224. Ed. Gerhard Pietsch. adv.; B&W page DM.23776, color page DM.38042; trim 212 x 304; adv. contact: Rainer Zuelsdorff. circ. 647,875 (paid). **Document type:** consumer publication.

790.1 IT
SPORT CLUB. m. (11/yr.). L.110000 in Europe; America L.155000. Publimedia Societa Editrice, Corso Venezia 18, 20121 Milan, Italy. TEL 02-77521. FAX 02-781068.

790.1 658.7 US
SPORT CONSTRUCTION BUYER'S GUIDE.* 1988. a. International Sport Summit, 7315 Wisconsin Ave., Ste. 450N, Bethesda, MD 20814. FAX 301-718-0981. adv. circ. 7,000.
Description: For buyers of sport construction services.

790.1 FR
SPORT DANS LA CITE. 4/yr. National Federation of Municipal Sport, 40 rue Piat, 75020 Paris, France. TEL 43-66-63-13. FAX 43-66-78-77. Ed. Robert Denel.

796 IT
SPORT DEL MEZZOGIORNO. w. L.4750. Compagnia Editrice Napoletano, Via Chiatamone 65, 80121 Naples, Italy. Ed. Riccardo Cassero. adv. circ. 50,490.

797.23 US
SPORT DIVER. bi-m. newsstand price: $2.95. World Publications, Inc., 330 W. Canton, Winter Park, FL 32790. TEL 407-628-4802. FAX 407-628-7061. **Document type:** consumer publication.

790.1 PL ISSN 0867-6585
SPORT DLA KAZDEGO; rekreacja fizyczna. m. 6 Zl. per no. Plac Dabrowskiego 8, IV p., 00-055 Warsaw, Poland. Ed. Tadeusz Golabek. circ. 50,000.

SPORT & MEDICINA. see MEDICAL SCIENCES — Sports Medicine

796 300 UK ISSN 1357-3322
▼**SPORT, EDUCATION AND SOCIETY**. Announced for publication in 1996. 2/yr. £28($48) to individuals; institutions £64($108) (effective 1996). Carfax Publishing Co., P.O. Box 25, Abingdon, Oxon OX14 3UE, England. TEL 44-1235-555335. FAX 44-1235-553559. (N. American subscr. to: Carfax Publishing Co., 875-81 Massachusetts Ave., Cambridge, MA 02139) **Document type:** academic/scholarly publication.

790.1 FR ISSN 1152-9563
SPORT ET VIE. bi-m. (plus 2 special issues). 235 F. (foreign 308 F.). Editions Faton S.A., 25 rue Berbisey, 21000 Dijon, France. (Subscr. to: 1 rue des Artisans, B.P. 90, 21803 Quetigny Cedex, France. TEL 80-70-93-47)

790.1 GW
SPORT HANDBUCH WUERTTEMBERG; fuer alle Sportler und Sportinteressierte. 1979. a. DM.24.60. (Wuerttembergischer Landessportbund e.V.) Schors-Verlags-Gesellschaft mbH, Postfach 1280, 65522 Niedernhausen, Germany. TEL 06127-8029. FAX 06127-8812. Eds. Hans-Eberhard Rutzen, Eva-Maria Huebner. circ. 24,000.

790.1 GW
SPORT IM SPIEGEL. m. DM.75. Deutscher Sportbund, Postfach 710263, 60492 Frankfurt a.M., Germany. TEL 069-6700-0. FAX 069-674906. **Document type:** abstracting/indexing, government publication.

790.1 GW
SPORT IN NIEDERSACHSEN. m. Landessportbund Niedersachsen e.V., Ferdinand-Wilhelm-Fricke-Weg 10, 30169 Hannover, Germany. TEL 0511-12680. FAX 0511-889862.

790.1 GW ISSN 0178-1014
SPORT INFORM. 1969. bi-m. DM.40.80. Landessportbund Rheinland - Pfalz, Rheinallee 1, 55116 Mainz, Germany. TEL 06131-2814-0. FAX 06131-2814135. Ed.Bd. adv.; bk.rev. circ. 8,100. (back issues avail.) **Document type:** consumer publication.

790.1 BE ISSN 1013-4700
SPORT INTERNATIONAL. (Text in Arabic, French, German, Spanish) 1959. q. 480 BEF. International Military Sports Council - Conseil International du Sport Militaire, Rue Jacques Jordaens 26, 1050 Brussels, Belgium. TEL 32-2-647-6852. FAX 32-2-647-5387. TELEX 29416 CISM B. Ed. J. Wanderstein. illus. circ. 5,000. **Indexed:** Sportsearch.
Formerly: Sport International Yearbook.
Description: Contains case reports, activities of the executive committee, sports medicine section, and results of sport events fostering good will among nations.

796 NE ISSN 0169-6084
SPORT INTERNATIONAL. (Text in Dutch) 1980. m. fl.76.75; newsstand price: fl.7.95. Weekbladpers B.V., Postbus 1050, 1000 BB Amsterdam, Netherlands. TEL 31-20-5518711. FAX 31-20-6278537. Ed. J. Linse; Pub. C. van Nijnatten. adv.; circ. 42,000 (paid). **Document type:** consumer publication.

SPORTS AND GAMES

798.4   IT   ISSN 0038-7916
SPORT ITALIA.* 1948. w. L.250 per no. Sport Italia, Via Paleocapa 6, 20121 Milan, Italy. Ed. Sisal. adv.; bk.rev. circ. 20,000.
    Description: Covers horseracing.

790.1   IT
▼**SPORT ITALIANO.** 1994. m. Comitato Olimpico Nazionale Italiano, Stadio Olimpico, Curva Nord, Foro Italico, 00194 Rome, Italy. TEL 06-3685. FAX 06-7609. Ed. Mario Pescante. bk.rev.

790.1   GW
SPORT-KURIER. 2/w. DM.198 (foreign DM.354). Sport-Kurier Verlag GmbH, Curt-Frenzel-Str. 2, 86167 Augsburg, Germany. TEL 0821-701037. FAX 0821-705324. Ed. Paul Ludwig; Pub. Werner Tapper. adv. contact: Erich Lindner. circ. 44,571.
    Document type: newspaper.

790.1   AU
SPORT-MAGAZIN. m. S.360 (foreign S.426). Wirtschafts-Trend Zeitschriftenverlagsgesellschaft mbH, Marc-Aurel-Str. 10-12, A-1010 Vienna, Austria. TEL 01-53470-0. FAX 01-53470349. adv.
    Document type: consumer publication.

790.1   CN
▼**SPORT MAGAZINE.** (Text in French) 1994. 10/yr. Can.$19.95 (US Can.$29.95, elsewhere Can.$39.95). Editions Sport Magazine, 1500 boul. Jules-Poitrs, Ste. 220, Montreal, PQ H4N 1X7, Canada. TEL 514-337-3221. FAX 514-334-2982. Ed. Pierre-Louis Labelle. adv.: color page Can.$3600; trim 8 3/16 x 10 7/8; adv. contact: Richard Giguere. circ. 42,000. **Document type:** consumer publication.

796.06   US   ISSN 1061-6934
GV716
SPORT MARKETING QUARTERLY; for professionals in the business of marketing sport. 1992. q. $39 to individuals (foreign $48); institutions $85 (foreign $94). Fitness Information Technology Inc., Box 4425, University Ave., Morgantown, WV 26504. TEL 304-599-3482; 800-477-4348. Ed. Dallas Branch, Jr; Pub. Andrew S. Ostrow. adv. contact: Lori Lipson. bk.rev. (back issues avail.) **Document type:** trade publication.
    —BLDSC (8419.629000); UnCover.
    Refereed Serial

790.1 659.1   US
SPORT MEDIA BUYER'S GUIDE.* 1988. a. International Sport Summit, 7315 Wisconsin Ave., Ste. 450N, Bethesda, MD 20814. FAX 301-718-0981. adv. circ. 7,000.
    Description: For sport media buyers at advertising agencies, and sport media buyers and sponsors at corporations with directory information.

SPORT PILOT HOT KITS HOMEBUILTS; the magazine of recreational flying. see AERONAUTICS AND SPACE FLIGHT

790.1   US   ISSN 0888-9589
GV561
SPORT PLACE INTERNATIONAL; an international journal of sports geography. 1987. 3/yr. $25 to individuals (foreign $35); institutions $60 (foreign $70). Black Oak Press, 2624 Black Oak Dr., Stillwater, OK 74074. FAX 405-744-5620. Ed. John Rooney. adv.; charts; illus. circ. 200. Indexed: Sportsearch (1987-). **Document type:** academic/scholarly publication.
    —BLDSC (8419.635000); Faxon.
    Description: Explores the connections between people, their sports, and their places.

790.1   CN   ISSN 0828-9581
SPORT PLUS. (Text in French) 1981. m. $20. 1028 Marie Victorin, Laval, PQ H7E 3C1, Canada. TEL 514-661-5586. Ed. Charles Andre Marchand. adv. circ. 40,000.
    Former titles (until 1985): Marathon Plus (ISSN 0828-5853); (until 1984): Marathon (ISSN 0823-0870); (until 1982): Marathon Magazine (ISSN 0712-1784).

790.1   FR   ISSN 0992-7697
SPORT PREMIERE MAGAZINE. 1976. 11/yr. 120 F. S P E, 3 rue de Teheran, 75008 Paris, France. TEL 42-89-41-04. FAX 45-61-12-00. TELEX 640 369. Ed. Emmanuel Gravaud. adv. circ. 8,500.
    Formerly (until 1988): Loisirs Service (ISSN 0337-9353).

THE SPORT PSYCHOLOGIST. see PSYCHOLOGY

796   AT   ISSN 0816-3979
SPORT REPORT. 1980. m. Aus.$16 (foreign Aus.$20). Confederation of Australian Sport, 1 Phipps Close, Peakin, A.C.T. 2600, Australia. TEL 61-2-285-1887. FAX 06-282-3440. E-mail: Vivien.Bolton@Ausport.telememo.au. Ed. Melanie Collins. adv. contact: Melanie Dollins. circ. 5,000. (back issues avail.)
    Description: Provides information and commentary on current issues in sport. Includes interviews with leading sports administrators and political identities.

790.1 320 613.7   US   ISSN 0270-1812
SPORT SCENE; focus on youth programs. 1979. q. $16 (foreign $25). North American Youth Sport Institute, 4985 Oak Garden Dr., Kernersville, NC 27284-9520. TEL 910-784-4926. Ed. Dr. Jack Hutslar. adv.; bk.rev. circ. 15,000. Indexed: Sportsearch.
    Description: Provides current information about children and sports. Contains articles to help leaders be more effective, parents become more effective teachers and coaches, increase participation, decrease drop-outs and injuries, and show how sports can be made more fun for children.

790.1 378.198   FR   ISSN 0221-0142
SPORT SCOLAIRE. 1971. m. 170 F. Union Nationale du Sport Scolaire, 13 rue Saint Lazare, 75009 Paris, France. TEL 42-81-55-11. adv. circ. 80,000.
    Formerly (until 1978): A S S U (Association du Sport Scolaire et Universitaire) (ISSN 0184-3540)

796   US
SPORT SHOP NEWS.* m. $30 (foreign $40). 53 Sterling Rd., Trumbull, CT 06611-2301. TEL 203-378-1223. FAX 203-378-7285. Ed. James Martone; Pub. John Mortimer. adv.: B&W page $3975; adv. contact: Nick Glowatsky. circ. 23,409. **Document type:** trade publication.

790.1 613.7   GW   ISSN 0940-192X
SPORT SPECIAL - CONDITION; die Zeitschrift fuer Lauf- und Ausdauersport. 1970. 10/yr. DM.42 (foreign DM.54). Vereinigte Fachverlage GmbH, Lise-Meitner-Str. 2, 55129 Mainz, Germany. TEL 06131-992149. FAX 06131-992100. (Subscr. to: Postfach 2760, 55017 Mainz, Germany) circ. 2,700. **Document type:** consumer publication.
    Formerly (until 1991): Condition (ISSN 0340-2991)
    Description: Magazine about distance running and other endurance sports for senior citizens.

790.1   IT
SPORT SUD. w. L.4750. Compagnia Editrice Napoletano, Via Chiatamone 65, Naples 80121, Itlay. Ed. Enrico Marucci. adv.

796   US
SPORT SUPPLEMENT. q. free to qualified personnel. United States Sports Academy, 1 Academy Dr., Daphne, AL 36526. TEL 205-626-3303. FAX 205-626-3874. Ed. Dr. Robert Lyster; Pub. Dr. Thomas P. Rosandich. bk.rev. circ. 85,000.
    Description: Covers issues and problems of interest to high school and athletic administrators and coaches.

790.1   IT
SPORT TREND NEWS. 6/yr. Via N. Battaglia 10, 20127 Milan, Italy. TEL 2-26-14-12-55. FAX 2-28-22-44-6. Ed. Anna Maria Ghiotto. circ. 7,000.

SPORT TRUCK. see TRANSPORTATION — Trucks And Trucking

790.1   GW   ISSN 0176-4136
SPORT UND FITNESS. bi-m. DM.49.90. Sport und Fitness Verlag Benno Dahmen, Oppumerstr. 71, 47799 Krefeld, Germany. TEL 02151-67077. FAX 02151-26255. Ed. Benno Dahmen. adv. contact: Benno Dahmen. circ. 70,000. **Document type:** consumer publication.

790 658.8   GW   ISSN 0049-1926
SPORT UND MODE. (Text in French and German) 1948. m. DM.156. (Verband Deutscher Sportsgeschaefte e.V.) Verlag Chmielorz GmbH und Co., Marktplatz 13, 65183 Wiesbaden, Germany. TEL 0611-36098-0. FAX 0611-301303. Ed. Juergen B. Wamser. adv.; bk.rev.; abstr.; charts; illus.; pat.; stat. circ. 5,000. **Document type:** trade publication.

796   IT   ISSN 0490-5113
SPORT UNIVERSITARIO. 1951; N.S. 1969. q. free. Centro Universitario Sportivo Italiano, Via Angelo Brofferio 7, 00195 Rome, Italy. TEL 39-6-3722206. FAX 39-6-3724479. Ed. Ruggero Cornini. adv.: page L.100000. bk.rev. circ. 5,000. **Document type:** academic/scholarly publication.

790.1   GW   ISSN 0342-1724
SPORT-VORSCHAU/SPORTS PREVIEW; international. irreg. price varies. Verlag Horst Deike KG, Postfach 100452, 78404 Konstanz, Germany. TEL 07531-8155-0. FAX 07531-815581. **Document type:** consumer publication.
    —CCC.

790.1   GW
SPORT-WELT. 3/wk. Deutscher Sportsverlag Kurt Stoof GmbH, Eintrachtstr. 110-118, 50668 Cologne, Germany. TEL 0221-1648-0. FAX 0221-1648327. Eds. Frank Joyeux, Josef Kammerinke. adv. contact: Erhard Badtke. circ. 16,000. **Document type:** newspaper.

796   NE   ISSN 0922-4270
SPORTACCOM; magazine voor realisatie, beheer en onderhoud van sportaccomodaties. 1963. bi-m. fl.65. (Nederlandse Sport Federatie) Arko Uitgeverij b.v., Essenkade 4, 3992 AA Houten, Netherlands. TEL 31-3403-76933. FAX 31-3403-80600. Ed. T. van Zetten. adv.; charts; illus.; stat. **Document type:** trade publication.
    —SWETS.
    Former titles: Nederlandse Sport Federatie. Technische Mededelingen; Nederlandse Sport Federatie. Technische Bulletin (ISSN 0028-2308)
    Description: Covers all sports played indoors in the Netherlands and the maintenance of facilities necessary.

793   NE   ISSN 0077-6777
SPORTACCOMMODATIE IN NEDERLAND/SPORTS: PUBLIC ACCOMMODATION. (Text in Dutch and English) 1959. irreg. price varies. Centraal Bureau voor de Statistiek, Prinses Beatrixlaan 428, Voorburg, Netherlands. (Orders to: SDU - Publishers, Christoffel Plantijnstraat, The Hague) **Document type:** government publication.

790.1   MF
SPORTAMO; magazine-hebdomadaire tele-sport. (Text in French) w. Rs.65. Nouvelle Imprimerie Mauricienne, 5, rue Jemmapes, Port Louis, Mauritius.

688.76 658   GW   ISSN 0720-1516
SPORTARTIKEL WIRTSCHAFT. 1980. m. DM.146. Verlag Chmielorz GmbH und Co., Marktplatz 13, 65183Wiesbaden, Germany. TEL 0611-36098-0. FAX 0611-301303. Ed. Juergen Wamser. adv.; bk.rev. circ. 6,400. **Document type:** trade publication.

790.1   LI
SPORTAS. Variant title: Lietuvos Sportas. 1956. 3/wk. Gedimino pr. 37, Vilnius 232600, Lithuania. TEL (3702) 616-757. Ed. Vytautas Saulis. circ. 25,500. **Document type:** newspaper.

688.76   SP
SPORTBASE. 52/yr. Fin Ediciones S.A., Cerden 259, 08013 Barcelona, Spain. TEL 3-207-50-52. FAX 3-488-34-42. Ed. J.D. Aliaga Serrano.

790.1   US
SPORTBIL.* 1978. a. International Sport Summit, 7315 Wisconsin Ave., Ste. 450N, Bethesda, MD 20814. FAX 301-718-0981. adv. circ. 7,500.
    Description: Opinion papers and data on the business of sport, sport events, and sport facilities.

790.1   GW   ISSN 0170-2890
SPORTDOKUMENTATION. q. DM.108. Verlag Karl Hofmann, Postfach 1360, 73603 Schorndorf, Germany. TEL 07181-402-0. FAX 07181-402111. **Document type:** bulletin.
    —CCC.

797.21   SW   ISSN 0038-7967
SPORTDYKAREN. 1958. 5/yr. SEK 125 membership (effective 1991). Svenska Sportdykarfoerbundet (SSDF), Idrottens Hus, S-123 87 Farsta, Sweden. FAX 46-8-605-6372. Ed. Lennart Haak. adv.; bk.rev. circ. 16,500.
    Formerly (until vol.3, 1959): Sportdyrkarbladet.

6086 SPORTS AND GAMES

790.1 DK ISSN 0109-9787
SPORTEN; sports aarbogen. 1952. a. DKK 34.50. Carlsen Forlag A-S, Krogshoejvej 32, DK-2880 Bagsverd, Denmark. illus.
(until 1976): Sportsaarbogen (ISSN 0490-5482)

790.1 GW ISSN 0174-1152
SPORTHANDBUCH NIEDERSACHSEN; fuer alle Verbaende, Vereine und Sportinteressierte. 1979. a. DM.24.60. (Landessportbund Niedersachsen e.V.) Schors-Verlags-Gesellschaft mbH, Postfach 1280, 65522 Niedersachsen, Germany. TEL 06127-8029. FAX 06127-8812. Ed.Bd. circ. 35,000.

790.1 GW ISSN 0174-1144
SPORTHANDBUCH NORDRHEIN-WESTFALEN. 1976. a. DM.24.60. (Landessportbund Nordrhein-Westfalen e.V.) Schors-Verlags-Gesellschaft mbH, Postfach 1280, 6272 Niederhausen, Germany. TEL 06127-8029. FAX 06127-8812. Ed. Karl Hoffmann. circ. 85,000.

796 AA
SPORTI. 1935. w. $200. National Olimpic Committee (NOC), Rr. Kavajei, K. Postok 2908, Tirana, Albania. TEL 355-422-577. FAX 355-422-2260. Ed. Besnik Dizdari. adv. contact: Bashkim Tufa. **Document type**: newspaper.
Formerly: Sporti Popullor.

790.1 CN ISSN 1192-9103
SPORTIF. 1993. w. Can.$70.91. Publications de Sport Telemedia (Subsidiary of: Telemedia Communications), 4485 De Rouen, Montreal, PQ H1V 1H1, Canada. TEL 514-899-7767. FAX 514-899-5788. Ed. Yvon Pedneault. adv.: B&W page Can.$2665, color page Can.$3265. circ. 75,000.

790 PK ISSN 0038-7991
SPORTIMES;* the magazine for sportsmen. (Text in English) 1956. m. Rs.160($16) Progressive Papers Limited, Progressive Papers Bldg., Rattan Chand Rd., Lahore 7, Pakistan. Ed. Sultan F. Husain. charts; illus.; stat. Indexed: Sportsearch.

799.202 US ISSN 1061-2424
SPORTING CLAYS. 1989. m. newsstand price: $3.95. (National Sporting Clays Association) Patch Communications, 5211 S. Washington Ave., Titusville, FL 32780. TEL 407-268-5010. FAX 407-267-7216. adv. **Document type**: consumer publication.

790.1 AT ISSN 1030-0317
SPORTING GLOBE. 1922. 2/w. Herald & Weekly Times Ltd., 44-74 Flinders St., Melbourne, Vic. 3000, Australia. TEL 61-3-652-1111.
FAX 61-3-654-3133. TELEX 30104. Ed. Peter Helme. adv. contact: Frank Bressan. circ. 17,066. **Document type**: consumer publication.
Description: Contains team sporting results, race results, previews, interviews, comments and more.

790.1 US
SPORTING GOODS AGENTS ASSOCIATION. NEWSLETTER. m. Sporting Goods Agents Association, Box 998, Morton Grove, IL 60053. TEL 708-296-3670. FAX 708-827-0196. **Document type**: newsletter.

658.8 790 US ISSN 0146-0889
SPORTING GOODS BUSINESS; the national newsmagazine of the sporting goods industry. 1967. m. $65 (free to qualified personnel). Miller Freeman Inc. (New York) (Subsidiary of: United Newspapers Group), 1515 Broadway, New York, NY 10036. TEL 212-869-1300. FAX 212-302-6273. Ed. Andrew Gaffney. adv.; bibl.; charts; illus.; tr.lit. Indexed: Bus.Ind., Sportsearch (1977-), Tr.& Indus.Ind. **Document type**: trade publication.
●Also available online. Vendor(s): University Microfilms International.
—UMI. CCC.

658.8 790 US ISSN 0038-8017
GV743
SPORTING GOODS DEALER; national magazine of the sporting goods trade. 1899. m. free to qualified personnel. Cardinal Business Media, Inc., 1300 Virginia Dr., Ste. 400, Fort Washington, PA 19034-3225. Ed. Micheal Jacobsen. adv.; illus.; mkt.; tr.lit. circ. 29,775. (reprint service avail. from UMI) **Document type**: trade publication.

790.1 658 US ISSN 1060-2550
SPORTING GOODS INTELLIGENCE; news and analysis of the international market. 1989. 3/m. $365 (foreign $378) (effective 1995). Sports Management News, Inc., 442 Featherbed Ln., Glen Mills, PA 19342. TEL 610-558-1601. FAX 610-558-1650. Ed. John G. Horan; Pub. John G. Horan. **Document type**: newsletter, directory.

SPORTING GOODS MANUFACTURERS ASSOCIATION. EXECUTIVE COMPENSATION STUDY. see BUSINESS AND ECONOMICS — Labor And Industrial Relations

SPORTING GOODS MANUFACTURERS ASSOCIATION. FINANCIAL PERFORMANCE STUDY. see BUSINESS AND ECONOMICS — Labor And Industrial Relations

688.76 US
SPORTING GOODS WHOLESALER.* bi-m. membership only. National Association of Sporting Goods Wholesalers, Box 11344, Chicago, IL 60611-0344. TEL 312-565-0233. **Document type**: directory.

796 US ISSN 0038-805X
GV561
THE SPORTING NEWS; the nation's oldest and finest sports publication. 1886. w. $60. Sporting News Publishing Co. (Subsidiary of: Times Mirror Company), 1212 N. Lindbergh Blvd., St. Louis, MO 63132. TEL 314-997-7111. FAX 314-993-7726. Ed. John Rawlings. adv.; bk.rev.; illus. circ. 515,000. (tabloid format; also avail. in microfilm from UMI,BHP,KTO; reprint service avail. from UMI) Indexed: Access (1975-1987), Hlth.Ind., Mag.Ind., Sports Per.Ind., Sportsearch (1977-). **Document type**: consumer publication.
●Also available online. Vendor(s): Lexis-Nexis, University Microfilms International.
—UMI.

796.355 US ISSN 1051-6018
GV848.4.U6
THE SPORTING NEWS HOCKEY YEARBOOK. 1982. a. $4.95. Sporting News Publishing Co. (Subsidiary of: Times Mirror Company), 1212 N. Lindbergh Blvd., St. Louis, MO 63132. TEL 314-997-7111. FAX 314-993-7726. adv. **Document type**: consumer publication.
Formerly (until 1990): Sporting News Hockey Directory.

798.8 IE ISSN 0049-1942
SPORTING PRESS. 1923. w. I£65.28 (U.K. I£67.83; Europe I£79.05; Australia and U.S. I£105.57); newsstand price: I£1. (Irish Coursing Club) Greyhound & Sporting Press Ltd., Davis Rd., Clonmel County, Tipperary, Ireland. FAX 052-25018. Ed. J.L. Desmond. adv.: B&W page I£900; trim 21 x 15. illus. circ. 9,000. Indexed: Sportsearch. **Document type**: newspaper.
Description: News about dog racing.

790.1 GH
SPORTING RECORD. w. P.O. Box 7962, Accra, Ghana. Ed. L.O. Addy. adv.

790.1 NR
SPORTING RECORDS. 1961. w. £N52. Daily Times of Nigeria Ltd., Publications Division, New Isheri Rd., Agidingbi - Ikeja, P.M.B. 21340, Lagos, Nigeria. TEL 900850-9. TELEX 21333. Ed. Cyril Kappo. adv. circ. 222,975.
Description: Presents sporting reports and forecasts.

790.1 CN ISSN 0824-9849
SPORTING SCENE. 1980. m. Can.$20 (in US Can.$25). Sporting Scene, 22 Maberley Cres., West Hill, Ont. M1C 3K8, Canada. TEL 416-284-0304. FAX 416-284-1299. Ed. Peter Martens. adv.; circ. 19,800 (controlled). (tabloid format)

790.1 CN ISSN 1181-8808
SPORTING TIMES (CALGARY); voice of Alberta amateur sport. 1990. m. Can.$18 (foreign Can.$21). Quicksilver Communications, Box 42001, Acadia Postal Outlet, Calgary, AB T2J 7A6, Canada. TEL 403-255-8067. Ed. Ernest Granson. adv.: page Can.$500 (regular ed.), page Can.$575 (national ed.). illus.; circ. 3,000 (paid); 2,000. (tabloid format)

790.1 AT ISSN 0813-2577
SPORTING TRADITION. Variant title: Australian Society for Sports History. Journal. 1984. irreg. (2-3/yr.). Aus.$15 (foreign Aus.$25) membership. Australian Society for Sports History, Department of Human Movement Studies, P.O. Box 968, North Sydney, N.S.W. 2059, Australia. Ed. Richard Cashman. bk.rev. circ. 400. **Document type**: monographic series.
—BLDSC (8419.823850); UnCover.
Description: Covers history of Australasia sport and games.

796 RU ISSN 0038-8092
SPORTIVNAYA ZHIZN' ROSSII. 1957. m. $65. Soyuz Sportivnykh Obshchestv i Organizatsii, Armyanskii pereulok 13, 101000 Moscow, Russia. (Dist. in U.S. by: Victor Kamkin Inc., 4956 Boiling Brook Pkwy, Rockiville, MD 20852. TEL 301-881-5973) (Co-sponsor: Komitet po Fizkul'ture i Sportu) Ed. I.B. Maslennikov. adv.; illus.; index. circ. 488,992.

796 RU ISSN 0038-8106
SPORTIVNYE IGRY. 1955. m. 6 Rub. Izdatel'stvo Fizkul'tura i Sport, Kalycevskaya ul., 27, 101421 Moscow, Russia. TEL 095-258-2690. FAX 095-200-1217. Ed. D.L. Rishkov. illus.; index. circ. 15,000.

790.1 IT
SPORTIVO. 1981. m. L85000 (foreign L.170000). Sport Promotion s.r.l., Via Natale Battaglia 27, 20127 Milan, Italy. TEL 39-2-2856994. FAX 39-2-2890827. Ed. Ennio Falsoni. adv.: B&W page L.3400000, color page L.6100000. **Document type**: consumer publication.

796 GW ISSN 0014-6145
DER SPORTJOURNALIST. 1950. m. DM.60. (Verband Deutsche Sportprese e.V.) Verlag Rommerskirchen und Co. KG, Bennauerstr. 60, 53115 Bonn, Germany. TEL 0228-222974. FAX 0228-214917. Ed. Thomas Rommerskirchen. adv.; bk.rev.; illus. circ. 3,000.

SPORTMANAGEMENT. see BUSINESS AND ECONOMICS — Management

790.1 TU
SPORTMENCE. (Text in Turkish) w. Lefkosa - Nicosia, Mersin 10, Turkey. TEL 520-72212. Ed. Ertan Birnici.

SPORTPAEDAGOGIK; zeitschrift fuer Sport- Spiel- und Bewegungserziehung. see EDUCATION — Teaching Methods And Curriculum

790.1 GW ISSN 0173-2528
SPORTPRAXIS; die Fachzeitschrift fuer den Sportlehrer und Uebungsleiter. 1959. bi-m. DM.58. (Deutscher Sportbund) Limpert Verlag GmbH, Postfach 4027, 65030 Wiesbaden, Germany. TEL 0611-373072. FAX 0611-374351. Eds. H-J. Langen, H. Meusel. adv.; bk.rev. circ. 7,500. (back issues avail.) **Document type**: academic/scholarly publication.
Description: For sport teachers and trainers.

790.1 GW
SPORTREVUE. m. DM.79.90. Intermedia Werbe- und Verlagsgesellschaft mbH, Weyerhofstr. 71, 47805 Krefeld, Germany. TEL 02151-768780. FAX 02151-751095. Ed. Albert Busek. adv. contact: Juergen Dierich. circ. 55,719. **Document type**: consumer publication.

796 SI ISSN 0217-3123
SPORTS. (Text in English) 1972. 10/yr. S.$9. Singapore Sports Council, National Stadium, Kallang, Singapore 1439, Singapore. FAX 3409537. TELEX RG 35467-NASTAD. Ed. Ong Poh Choo. adv.; charts; illus.; stat. circ. 17,000. Indexed: Sportsearch.

790.1 GW ISSN 0932-9773
SPORTS. 1987. m. DM.72 (Europe DM.108; elsewhere DM.192.60). Gruner und Jahr AG & Co., Am Baumwall 11, 20459 Hamburg, Germany. TEL 040-3703-0. FAX 040-37035617. circ. 142,016. **Document type**: consumer publication.

SPORTS AND GAMES

790.1 US ISSN 0273-2572
GV583
SPORTS. (Subseries of: S I R S Social Issues (ISSN 0740-3127)) 1976. a. price varies; a. supplement $17. Social Issues Resources Series, Box 2348, Boca Raton, FL 33427-2348. TEL 407-994-0079; FAX 407-994-4707. (looseleaf format; also avail. in microfiche; back issues avail.)
Description: Reprints articles that examine social issues of professional and recreational sports.

790.1 US
GV583
SPORTS ADDRESS BIBLE; the comprehensive directory of sports addresses. 1980. a. $21.95 (Canada $24.95; elsewhere $30) (effective 1995) $24.95 (effective 1996). Global Sports Productions Ltd., 1223 Broadway, Ste. 102, Santa Monica, CA 90404-2707. TEL 310-454-9480. FAX 310-454-6590. Ed. Greg Andrews; Pub. Edward T. Kobak, Jr. adv. contact: Warren Walk. bk.rev. circ. 25,000. (also avail. in Braille; back issues avail.) **Document type:** directory.
Formerly: Comprehensive Directory of Sports Addresses (ISSN 0743-4561)
Description: Lists addresses, telephone and fax numbers and contact persons from Olympic, international, collegiate, professional, scholastic and amateur sports.

790.1 US
SPORTS AND RECREATIONAL PROGRAMS OF THE NATION'S UNIVERSITIES AND COLLEGES. 1958. quinquennial. $4. National Collegiate Athletic Association, Circulation Department, Box 7347, Overland Park, KS 66207-0347. TEL 913-339-1900. circ. 3,000.

790.1 340 US ISSN 0733-0669
KF4166.A59
SPORTS AND THE COURTS; physical education and sports law newsletter. 1980. 5/yr. $40 (Canada $43; outside N. America $50). Box 2836, Winston-Salem, NC 27102. TEL 919-725-7700. FAX 919-725-6777. Ed. C. Thomas Ross. **Indexed:** Sportsearch (1981-). **Document type:** newsletter.
—Faxon; UnCover.
Description: Contains some recent court decisions with editorial commentary.

SPORTS AND THE LAW. see LAW

790.1 629.132 US
SPORTS AVIATION. 1953. m. $35. Wittman Airfield, Box 3086, Oshkosh, WI 54903-3086. TEL 414-426-4800. Ed. Jack Cox. adv. circ. 130,000.

688.76 CN ISSN 0830-1921
SPORTS BUSINESS. 1973. 8/yr. Can.$58.85($105) Laurentian Media Inc., 501 Oakdale Rd., Downsview, ON M3N 1W7, Canada. TEL 613-475-3217; 800-565-8148. FAX 416-746-1421. illus. circ. 9,200. **Indexed:** Can.B.P.I., Can.B.P.I.
Formed by the merger of: Sports Marketing (ISSN 0227-8723) & Sports Trade (ISSN 0829-3716); Which was formerly: Sports Trade Canada (ISSN 0714-6175); Which was formed by the merger of: Sporting Goods Canada (ISSN 0381-8977); Sporting Goods Trade (ISSN 0381-9280)

790.1 AT ISSN 0314-5468
SPORTS COACH; Australian coaching magazine. 1976. q. Aus.$15 (foreign Aus.$20). (Australian Sports Commission) Australian Coaching Council Inc., P.O. Box 176, Belconnen, A.C.T. 2616, Australia. TEL 06-252-1550. FAX 06-252-1200. TELEX AA62400 AUSIS. (Subscr. to: Sports Coach, P.O. Box 128, Belconnen, A.C.T. 2616, Australia) Ed. Lawrie Woodman. adv. contact: Rebecca Layton. bk.rev. circ. 8,500. (back issues avail.) **Indexed:** Phys.Ed.Ind., Sportsearch (1978-). **Document type:** trade publication.
—BLDSC (8419.832000).

790 FR
SPORTS DANS LA CITE. 1962. q. 110 Fr. Federation Nationale des Offices Municipaux des Sports (F N O M S), 40 rue Piat, 75020 Paris, France. adv. circ. 18,000.

790.1 KO
SPORTS DONG-A. 1978. w. Dong-A Ilbo, 139 Sejongno, Chongno-gu, Seoul, S. Korea. TEL 02-721-7114. Ed. Kwon O-Kie. circ. 184,902.

790.1 US ISSN 0744-6276
SPORTS EYE. d. $2.50 per no. Sports Eye, Inc., 18 Industrial Park Dr., Port Washington, NY 11050. TEL 516-484-3300; 800-247-2923. Ed. Jay Bergman; Pub. Louis Sierra. **Document type:** consumer publication.
Description: Covers harness racing.

790.1 JM
SPORTS FOCUS; the Jamaican quarterly sports magazine. 1990. q. $10. M R C Services Ltd., 2 Easton Ave., Kingston 5, Jamaica, W.I. TEL 809-97-80650. FAX 908-92-65124. adv. circ. 10,000. **Document type:** consumer publication.

SPORTS GREAT BOOKS. see CHILDREN AND YOUTH — For

790.1 UK ISSN 1351-5462
SPORTS HISTORIAN. 1980? a. £7.50. British Society of Sports History, 8 Sherard Rd., London SE9 6EP, England. TEL 081-850-6805. (Alt. addr.: 13 Bradley Ln., Frodsham, Ches. WA6 6QA, England. TEL 061-200-4013) Ed. Russell Potts. adv.; abstr.; bibl. circ. 350. (back issues avail.) **Indexed:** Amer. Hist.& Life (1993-), Hist.Abstr. (1993-). **Document type:** academic/scholarly publication.
Formerly (until 1993): British Society of Sports History Bulletin (ISSN 0966-1042)
Description: Covers the history of sports, particularly in the U.K.
Refereed Serial

796 US ISSN 0038-822X
GV561
SPORTS ILLUSTRATED. 1954. w. $80.46. Time Inc. (Subsidiary of: Time Warner, Inc.), Time & Life Bldg., Rockefeller Center, 1271 Ave. of the Americas, New York, NY 10020-1393. TEL 212-522-1212. (Subscr. to: Sports Illustrated, Box 60190, Tampa, FL 33660) Ed. Mark Mulvoy. Pub. Dave Long. adv.; bk.rev.; illus.; index; circ. 3,150,000 (paid). (also avail. in microform from UMI; audio cassette) **Indexed:** Abr.R.G., Acad.Ind., Biog.Ind., Bk.Rev.Ind. (1980-), Child.Bk.Rev.Ind. (1980-), CMI, Hlth.Ind., Jun.High.Mag.Abstr., Mag.Ind., PMR, R.G., Sports Per.Ind., Sportsearch (1974-), TOM. **Document type:** consumer publication.
•Also available online. Vendor(s): CompuServe, Inc., Information Access Co., Knight-Ridder, Inc., Lexis-Nexis, University Microfilms International, VU/TEXT Information Services, Inc.
—Faxon; SWETS; UMI; UnCover.

SPORTS ILLUSTRATED FOR KIDS. see CHILDREN AND YOUTH — For

790.1 US ISSN 0896-9108
GV561
SPORTS INC.; the sports business weekly. 1987. w. $69.95. Times Mirror Magazines, Inc., 2 Park Ave., New York, NY 10016. TEL 212-779-5000. Ed. Craig Reiss. circ. 2,500.

790.1 UK ISSN 0261-5665
SPORTS INDUSTRY. 1981. m. £25 (foreign £34). Harper Trade Journals Ltd., Harling House, 47-51 Great Suffolk St., London SE1 0BS, England. TEL 0171-261-1604. FAX 0171-633-0281. adv. circ. 11,779. **Indexed:** Intl.Polym.Sci.& Tech., RAPRA. **Document type:** trade publication.
—BLDSC (8419.836000).

790.1 330 US
SPORTS INDUSTRY NEWS; management & finance, regulation & litigation, media & marketing. 1983. w. $244. Game Point Publishing, Box 946, Camden, ME 04843. TEL 207-236-8346. Ed. Ray Swan. bk.rev.; stat. (looseleaf format) **Document type:** trade publication.
Formerly: Industry News (ISSN 0742-2024)
Description: News items and briefs on management and finance, regulations and litigation, and media and marketing in amateur and professional sports, with news on negotiations and arbitration decisions on individual contracts.

SPORTS LAW & FINANCE. see LAW

658.8 790 US
SPORTS LICENSING INTERNATIONAL. 1992. m. Times Mirror Magazines, Inc., 2 Park Ave., New York, NY 10016. TEL 212-779-5556.
Description: News of licensing and marketing developments affecting the sporting goods field.

SPORTS LOISIRS TOURISME; la lettre de l'economie des equipements. see LEISURE AND RECREATION

796 JA
SPORTS MAGAZINE. 1972. 5/yr. 6480 Yen. Baseball Magazine Sha, 3-10-10 Misaki-cho, Chiyoda-ku, Tokyo, Japan. Ed. Ryusuke Takahashi. **Indexed:** R.G.

790.1 658.8 US ISSN 1055-8020
HD9992.U5
SPORTS MARKET PLACE. 1980. a. $199 (with updates $259). Sportsguide, Inc., Box 1417, Princeton, NJ 08542. TEL 609-921-8599. FAX 609-921-1276. (Subscr. to: Box 10129, Phoenix, AZ 85064. TEL 800-776-7877) Ed. Richard A. Lipsey. adv. contact: Richard A. Lipsey. index. circ. 1,500. (also avail. in diskette format) **Document type:** directory.
Formerly: Sportsguide (ISSN 0277-0296)
Description: Comprehensive listing of sports teams, leagues, governing bodies, TV and print media, sports marketing firms, corporate sports sponsors, sports information sources, and equipment, apparel and footwear suppliers.

SPORTS MARKET PLACE REGISTER. see BUSINESS AND ECONOMICS — Marketing And Purchasing

790.1 658 US ISSN 1049-5495
SPORTS MARKETING LETTER. 1989. m. $225. Sports Marketing Letter, 1771 Post Rd. E. Ste. 180, Westport, CT 06880. TEL 203-255-1787. Ed. Brian J. Murphy.

SPORTS MEDICINE DIGEST. see MEDICAL SCIENCES — Sports Medicine

SPORTS 'N SPOKES. see HANDICAPPED — Physically Impaired

SPORTS, PARKS AND RECREATION LAW REPORTER. see LAW

790.1 US
SPORTS PULSE.* 1990. bi-m. $9. Pulse Publications, Inc. (Mt. Vernon), 1730 Continental Pl., Mt. Vernon, WA 98273-5640. TEL 206-671-3933. adv. **Document type:** consumer publication.
Description: Covers sporting, recreation and fitness related activities, news, and people in Whatcom County.

SPORTS REPORTS. see CHILDREN AND YOUTH — For

658.8 790 AT
SPORTS RETAILER. 1937. bi-m. Aus.$30 (foreign Aus.$85) (effective Feb. 1995). Yaffa Publishing Group, 17-21 Bellevue St., Surry Hills, N.S.W. 2010, Australia. TEL 61-2-281-2333. FAX 61-2-281-2750. (Subscr. to: G.P.O. Box 606, Sydney, N.S.W. 2001, Australia) Ed. Brian Wood. adv.: B&W page Aus.$1415, color page Aus.$2145; trim 297 x 210. illus.; stat. circ. 3,741. **Document type:** trade publication.
Formerly: Sports and Leisure Ratailer (ISSN 1035-915X); Which supersedes in part (in 1990): Australasian Sportsgoods and Toy Retailer (ISSN 0004-8488)
Description: Features new products and general news of interest to sportsgoods retailers.

796.812 US ISSN 1073-1326
SPORTS REVIEW WRESTLING. 13/yr. $25.50 for 12 issues in US & Canada (elsewhere $35.10) (effective 1994). London Publishing Co., Box 910, Fort Washington, PA 19034. TEL 215-643-6385. FAX 215-540-0146. Ed. Bill Apter. **Document type:** consumer publication.

790.1 658.7 US
SPORTS SHOP NEWS; national magazine for sporting goods buyers and retailers. 1993. m. $36. Trade Publishing, 41 Shea Terr., Stratford, CT 06497-2422. TEL 203-380-8412. FAX 203-380-8412. Ed. John Mortimer. adv.: page $4975; adv. contact: John Mortimer. bk.rev.; film rev.; play rev.; bibl.; charts; illus.; stat.; tr.lit. circ. 28,000. (also avail. in diskette format; back issues avail.) **Document type:** trade publication.
Description: Features new sporting goods products and apparel in every category.

790.1 US
SPORTS SOUTH.* 1988. bi-m. $15. Regional Sports Publications, Box 50405, Henderson, NV 89016-0405. TEL 404-448-6226. FAX 404-368-2444. adv. circ. 40,000.
Formerly: Atlanta Sports South.

SPORTS AND GAMES

790.1
SPORTS SPONSORSHIP MANUAL SERIES. irreg. Center for Sports Sponsorship, Box 280, Plainsboro, NJ 08536. TEL 609-799-4722.

SPORTS TOP 10. see *CHILDREN AND YOUTH — For*

658.8 790   **UK**   **ISSN 0267-6354**
SPORTS TRADER. 1917. m. £38 (Europe £46; rest of world $100). Timothy Benn Publishing, 244-249 Temple Chambers, Temple Ave., London EC4Y 0DT, England. TEL 0171-583-3030. Ed. Alistair Phillips. adv.; bk.rev.; index. circ. 4,000. (back issues avail.) **Document type:** trade publication.
   Formerly: Sports Retailing (ISSN 0038-8254)

796.077   **AT**   **ISSN 1032-5506**
SPORTS TRAINERS DIGEST. 1987. q. Aus.$15 (foreign Aus.$22). Australian Sports Medicine Federation, P.O. Box 897, Belconnen, A.C.T. 2616, Australia. TEL 61-6-2516944. FAX 61-6-2531489. TELEX AUSIS 62400. Ed. Matt Reid. circ. 8,000. (back issues avail.)
   Description: Provides basic sports medicine including first aid, crisis management and injury prevention to sports participants.

658.8 790   **US**   **ISSN 0890-8745**
SPORTS TREND. 1969. m. $60. Shore Communications, Inc., 6255 Barfield Rd., N.E., Ste. 200, Atlanta, GA 30328-4300. TEL 404-252-8831. FAX 404-252-4436. Ed. Chuck Day. adv.; bk.rev.; circ. 29,102 (controlled). **Document type:** trade publication.
   —UMI. **CCC**.
   Formerly: Sports Merchandiser (ISSN 0049-1985)
   Description: Discusses the newest products and the latest trends and techniques for merchandising sporting goods.

797   **DK**   **ISSN 0901-0505**
SPORTSDYKKEREN.* 1966. bi-m. Dansk Sportsdykker Forbund, c/o Ole Galthen, Vesterled 22, DK-6400 Soenderborg, Denmark. Ed. Henning Olsen. adv. circ. 6,300.
   Description: Covers the sport of diving.

658.8 790   **GW**   **ISSN 0931-5381**
SPORTSHOP; international trade magazine for the sporting goods trade. (Supplement for ISPO Sportshop Hotline) (Text in English and German) 1949. 12/yr. DM.98 (foreign DM.102) (effective 1995). (Bundesverband der Deutschen Sportartikel-Industrie e.V. - World Federation of the Sporting Goods Industry) Meisenbach GmbH, Hainstr. 18, 96047 Bamberg, Germany. TEL 0951-861135. FAX 0951-861158. (Subscr. to: Postfach 2069, 96011 Bamberg, Germany) Ed. Thomas Pfeffer. adv.; B&W page DM.4700, color page DM.7100; trim 228 x 290; adv. contact: Fabian Irmer. bk.rev.; abstr.; illus.; stat. circ. 7,589. **Document type:** trade publication.
   Formerly (until 1987): Eurosport and Freizeitmode (ISSN 0340-739X); Formed by the merger of: Eurosport (ISSN 0014-259X); Freizeit-Mode (ISSN 0016-0938)

799.202   **SW**   **ISSN 0281-871X**
SPORTSKYTTEN; Sveriges sportskyttetidning. 1983. m. SEK 180 (effective 1991). Svenska Sportskyttefoerbundet, Idrottens Hus, S-123 87 Farsta, Sweden.

790.1   **UK**
SPORTSNEWS (BEDFORD). 3/yr. free. Sports Council (Eastern Region), Crescent House, 19 The Crescent, Bedford, Bedfordshire MK40 2QP, England. TEL 01234-345222. FAX 01234-359046. Ed. Roger Hasdell. adv. contact: Roger Hasdell. (back issues avail.) **Document type:** newsletter.

790.1   **UK**
SPORTSNEWS (LONDON). 1975. 3/yr. free. Sports Council (London Region), P.O. Box 480, Crystal Palace NSC, Ledrington Rd., London SE19 2BQ, England. TEL 081-778-8600. FAX 081-676-9812. Ed. Roy Headey. bk.rev. circ. 5,000. **Document type:** newsletter.

SPORTSTAETTEN UND SCHWIMMBAEDER; Zeitschrift fuer Einrichtung und Betrieb von Sport-, Baeder- und Freizeitanlagen. see *BUILDING AND CONSTRUCTION*

790.1 305.4 369.46   **US**
▼**SPORTSTALK**; the Women's Sports Foundation newsletter for young female athletes. 1994. q. membership. Women's Sports Foundation, Eisenhower Park, East Meadow, NY 11554. TEL 516-542-4700; 800-227-2988. FAX 516-542-4716. Ed. Lynnore Lawton. **Document type:** newsletter.
   Description: Contains stories and features written by girls and women about female athletes, sports principles, and general issues affecting girls for the organization's young members.

790.1   **II**   **ISSN 0971-359X**
SPORTSTAR. (Text in English) 1978. w. $98; newsstand price: Rs.10. Kasturi & Sons Ltd., Kasturi Bldgs., 859-860 Anna Salai, Madras 600 002, India. TEL 44-835067. FAX 44-835325. TELEX 416655. Ed. N. Ram; Pub. S.Rangarajan. adv.; B&W page Rs.20000, color page Rs.40000; bleed 262 x 187; adv. contact: K.V. Balasubramanyam. circ. 68,363. **Document type:** consumer publication.

687.1   **US**   **ISSN 0162-2242**
TT649
SPORTSTYLE. 1979. m. (s-m. in Aug.) $35 (Canada $41) (effective 1992). Fairchild Fashion & Merchandising Group (Subsidiary of: Capital Cities - A B C, Inc.), 7 W. 34th St., New York, NY 10001. TEL 212-630-4870. FAX 212-630-4879. adv.; circ. 2,000 (paid); 23,500 (controlled). (tabloid format) **Document type:** trade publication.
   ●Also available online. Vendor(s): Knight-Ridder, Inc.
   —**CCC**.
   Description: Merchandising publication for sports retailers. Coverage includes business information, as well as product and fashion trends.

790.1   **XK**   **ISSN 1010-5743**
SPORTSWATCH. 1985. q. $10. A L K I M Communication Production Company, Box MA 020, Marchand Post Office, Castries, St. Lucia, W.I. Ed. Albert De Terville. adv. circ. 5,000.
   —**CCC**.

790.1   **II**   **ISSN 0971-3654**
SPORTSWORLD. (Text in English) 1978. fortn. newsstand price: Rs.12. Ananda Bazar Patrika Ltd., 6 Prafulla Sarkar St., Calcutta 700 001, West Bengal, India. TEL 033-274880. FAX 033-303240. TELEX 021-5468. Ed. Mansur Ali Khan Pataudi. adv.: B&W page Rs.12000, color page Rs.24000; 160 x 235; adv. contact: Aloke Kumar. circ. 32,325. (back issues avail.)

797.21   **GW**   **ISSN 0172-8555**
SPORTTAUCHER. m. DM.56. (Verband Deutscher Sporttaucher e.V.) Schmidt-Roemhild Verlag, Mengstr. 16, 23552 Luebeck, Germany. TEL 0451-1605-0. FAX 0451-1605281. circ. 45,000. **Document type:** consumer publication.
   Incoporates: Delphin (ISSN 0011-796X)

790.1   **RM**   **ISSN 1220-6571**
SPORTUL ILUSTRAT. 1947. m. $25. Editura Sportrom, Str. Vasile Conta 16, Bucharest, Rumania. TEL 113288. FAX 113459. Ed. Constantin Macovei. adv.; bk.rev.; illus. circ. 50,000.

SPORTVERLETZUNG - SPORTSCHADEN. see *MEDICAL SCIENCES*

790.1   **NE**
SPORTWETENSCHAPPELIJKE ONDERZOEKINGEN. 1978. irreg. price varies. Uitgeverij de Vriesseborch, P.O. Box 5229, 2000 CE Haarlem, Netherlands. TEL 023-325620. illus. circ. 1,500.

796 371.7 613   **GW**   **ISSN 0342-2380**
SPORTWISSENSCHAFT. (Text in German; summaries in English, French, German) 1971. q. DM.72 (students DM.56). Verlag Karl Hofmann, Postfach 1360, 73603 Schorndorf, Germany. TEL 07181-402-0. FAX 07181-402111. Ed. Ommo Grupe. bk.rev.; index. circ. 3,000. **Indexed:** Sportsearch (1976-). **Document type:** academic/scholarly publication.
   —BLDSC (8419.860800); Faxon; SWETS. **CCC**.
   Description: Deals with the science and theory of sports.

796   **GW**   **ISSN 0342-457X**
SPORTWISSENSCHAFT UND SPORTPRAXIS. 1970. irreg., vol.101, 1995. price varies. Czwalina Verlag, Postfach 730240, 22122 Hamburg, Germany. TEL 040-6780025. FAX 040-6780051. Ed. Clemens Czwalina. **Document type:** monographic series.
   Formerly: Schriftenreihe fuer Sportwissenschaft und Sportpraxis (ISSN 0080-7141)

796   **GW**   **ISSN 0944-9604**
SPORTWISSENSCHAFTLICHE DISSERTATIONEN UND HABILITATIONEN. 1975. irreg., vol.35, 1995. price varies. Czwalina Verlag, Postfach 730240, 22122 Hamburg, Germany. TEL 040-6780025. FAX 040-6780051. Ed. Clemens Czwalina. **Document type:** monographic series.
   Formerly (until 1994): Sportwissenschaftliche Dissertationen (ISSN 0340-0956)

796   **KR**   **ISSN 0038-8300**
SPORTYVNA GAZETA. 1934. 156/yr. 4.68 Rub. Komitet po Fizkul'ture i Sportu - State Committee of Physical Culture and Sports, 13 Cheljuskintsev St., Kiev, Ukraine. TEL 228-09-63. Ed. Yuri Peresunjko. illus.
   Formerly (until 1966): Radjanski Sport.

796 790.019   **US**   **ISSN 0740-0802**
SPOTLIGHT ON YOUTH SPORTS. 1979. q. $4 (effective 1995). Michigan State University, Institute for the Study of Youth Sports, 213 I.M. Sports Circle Bldg., East Lansing, MI 48824. TEL 517-353-6689. FAX 517-353-5363. Ed. Vern Seefeldt. bk.rev.; charts; illus. circ. 2,000. (looseleaf format; back issues avail.) **Indexed:** Sportsearch (1980-). **Document type:** newsletter.

SPURT; Zeitschrift fuer Sport und Recht. see *LAW*

790.1   **GW**
SQUASH ETC.; nimm eins Publikation fuer Sport Mode Freizeit. 1980. m. DM.54. Werbung & Marketing, Stahlstr. 19, 47877 Willich, Germany. TEL 02154-3055. Ed. Peter Tekook. adv. circ. 6,150. (back issues avail.)

636.596   **UK**   **ISSN 0952-4541**
SQUILLS INTERNATIONAL PIGEON RACING YEAR BOOK. 1897. a. £5.70 hardcover; £3.50 softcover. Racing Pigeon Publishing Co. Ltd., Unit 13, 21 Wren St., London WC1X 0HF, England. TEL 0171-833-5959. FAX 0171-833-3151. adv. circ. 11,000. **Document type:** bulletin.

790.1   **CF**
STADE. 1985. w. B.P. 114, Brazzaville, Congo. TEL 81-47-18. TELEX 5285. Ed. Louis Ngami. circ. 12,000.

790.1 613.7   **GW**   **ISSN 0172-4029**
GV561
STADION; Internationale Zeitschrift fuer Geschichte des Sports. (Text in English, French, German) 1975. irreg. (1-2/yr.). DM.88. Academia Verlag GmbH, Postfach 1663, 53757 Sankt Augustin, Germany. TEL 02241-333349. FAX 02241-341528. Ed. Manfred Laemmer. adv.; bk.rev. circ. 400. (back issues avail.) **Indexed:** Amer.Hist.& Life, Hist.Abstr., Sportsearch (1975-). **Document type:** academic/scholarly publication.
   —BLDSC (8425.930000); SWETS; UnCover. Incorporated: Arena.

796   **IT**   **ISSN 0391-7924**
STADIUM; problemi dello sport. 1906. m. free. Centro Sportivo Italiano, Via delle Conciliazione 3, 00193 Rome, Italy. TEL 39-6-6867941. FAX 39-6-68802940. Ed. Donato Renato Mosella. adv.

790.1   **GW**
STADTHANDBUCH NORDBADEN; fuer alle Sportler und Sportinteressierte. 1980. a. DM.24.60. (Badischer Sportbund e.V.) Schors-Verlags-Gesellschaft mbH, Postfach 1280, 65522 Niederhausen, Germany. TEL 06127-8029. FAX 06127-8812. Ed. Rudi Arnold. circ. 12,000.

STAR GUIDE (YEAR); where to contact movie, TV stars and other celebrities. see *MOTION PICTURES*

SPORTS AND GAMES

796   KR   ISSN 0131-890X
START. 1922. m. $75. (Soyuz Sportivnykh Obshchestv i Organizatsii Ukrainy) Vidavnitstvo Molod, Vul. Parkhomenko 38-44, Kiev, Ukraine. TEL 044-213-1160. (Dist. in U.S. by: Victor Kamkin Inc., 4956 Boiling Brook Pkwy., Rockville, MD 20852. TEL 301-881-5973. FAX 301-881-1637) Ed. A. Chaly. circ. 115,000.

START. see PHYSICAL FITNESS AND HYGIENE

796   US   ISSN 1056-0912
STARTING LINE. 1971. q. Offshore Data Services, Inc., Box 19909, Houston, TX 77224-1909. TEL 713-781-2713. FAX 713-781-9594. Ed. Lance Phegley. circ. 1,500. **Document type:** consumer publication.
    Description: National coverage of track and field and cross-country for ages 8-18.

796.72   UK
STARTLINE. 1922. m. membership. British Automobile Racing Club, Thruxton Circuit, Andover, Hants., England. TEL 0264-772696. FAX 0264-773794. Ed. Dennis Carter. adv.; bk.rev.; illus. circ. 6,000. **Document type:** newsletter.
    Formerly (until 1981): B A R C News (ISSN 0005-2647)

STELUTIS ALPINIS. see TRAVEL AND TOURISM

790.1   US
STEPS TO SUCCESS ACTIVITY SERIES; sports instruction series. irreg. (1-2/yr.) $14.95 (Canada $19.95) per no. Human Kinetics Publishers, Inc., Box 5076, Champaign, IL 61825-5076. TEL 800-747-4457. FAX 217-351-1549.

STEZKA; mesicnik pro sport, turistiku, brannost. see CHILDREN AND YOUTH — For

790.1   US   ISSN 0890-9229
STING. 1982. 13/yr. $19.95. Coman Publishing Company, Inc., 505 S. Duke St., Ste. 504, Durham, NC 27701. TEL 919-688-0218. FAX 919-682-1532. (Subscr. to: Box 2331, Durham, NC 27702) Ed. Bill Ballew. circ. 8,000. **Document type:** consumer publication.
    Formerly (until 1985): Gold Line (ISSN 8750-748X)
    Description: For Georgia Tech University sports fans.

796.7   UK   ISSN 0049-2272
STOCK CAR.* 1967. m. British Stock Car Association, 101 Mountain Rd., Densbury, West Yorks. WF12 0BS, England. Ed. Deidre Nevett. adv. circ. 6,500.

796.72   US   ISSN 0734-7340
GV1029.9.S74
STOCK CAR RACING. 1966. m. $18.95. Stock Car Racing Publishing, Ltd. (Subsidiary of: General Media Publishing Group), 27 S. Main St., Ipswich, MA 01938. TEL 508-356-7030. FAX 508-356-2492. (Subscr. to: Box 420235, Palm Coast, FL 32142-0235) Ed. Dick Berggren. adv. contact: Christopher Ballard. illus. circ. 202,470. **Document type:** consumer publication.

796.72   US   ISSN 0112-1669
STREET RODDER. 1972. m. $15. McMullen & Yee Publishing, 774 S. Placentia Ave., Placentia, CA 92670-6846. TEL 714-572-2255. FAX 714-572-1864. Ed. Pat Ganahl. adv.; bk.rev. circ. 97,078.

790.1   US   ISSN 1059-793X
STUDENT SPORTS. 1986. m. $29. 777 Convention Way, Ste. 100, Anaheim, CA 92802. Ed. Mark Tennis; Pub. Andy Bark. adv. contact: Brentt Eads. circ. 48,600 (paid). **Document type:** consumer publication.
    Description: Contains profiles and articles of interest to students involved in sports. Deals with all aspects of their lives.

STUDIES IN SPORT, PHYSICAL EDUCATION AND HEALTH. see PHYSICAL FITNESS AND HYGIENE

SUGEI PAZURU. see MATHEMATICS

790.1   JA
SUMO WORLD. (Text and summaries in English) 1973. bi-m. 4500 Yen($30) c/o Foreign Press Club, 1-7-1 Yuraku-cho, Chiyoda-ku, Tokyo 100, Japan. TEL 03-3211-3161. FAX 03-3476-3774. Ed. Andy Adams. adv.; bk.rev. circ. 15,000. (back issues avail.) **Document type:** consumer publication.
    Description: Covers sumo wrestling in Japan.

796.812   JA
SUMO WRESTLING (TOKYO, 1949)/SUMO. (Text in Japanese) 1949. m. 8040 Yen. Baseball Magazine Sha, 3-10-10 Misaki-cho, Chiyoda-cho, Tokyo, Japan. Ed. Tatsuhiko Fukudome. **Document type:** consumer publication.

796.812   JA
SUMO WRESTLING (TOKYO, 1954). (Text in Japanese) 1954. bi-m. 670 Yen. Yomiuri Shinbun, Publication Dept., 7-1, 1-chome, Ote-machi, Chiyoda-ku, Tokyo, Japan. FAX 03-246-4904. Ed. Harunobu Kasai. adv. **Document type:** consumer publication.

SUN GUIDE TO THE FLAT. see SPORTS AND GAMES — Horses And Horsemanship

794.1   FI   ISSN 0355-8096
SUOMEN SHAKKI. 1924. 12/yr. FIM 230($45) Esko Nuutilainen, Ed. & Pub., PL 61, 04401 Jarvenpaa, Finland. FAX 0-2918336. adv.; bk.rev. circ. 2,100.
    Description: Includes national and international games, interviews, "how-to-improve" articles, theory, combinations, and studies-problems.

790   IT   ISSN 0039-5706
SUPERBA. vol.10, 1977. m. L.5000. Dopolavoro Ferroviario di Genova, Via A. Doria 13, 16126 Genoa, Italy. Ed. Millo Balduzzi. adv.; bk.rev.; charts; illus.

790   US   ISSN 0887-1035
SUPERSTAR WRESTLERS. 1986. 9/yr. $3 per no. Starlog Group, Inc., 475 Park Ave. S., New York, NY 10016. TEL 212-689-2830. FAX 212-889-7933. **Document type:** consumer publication.
    Description: Profiles famous wrestlers and important wrestling events.

790.1   GR
SURF & SKI. (Text and summaries in Greek) 1981. bi-m. Dr.1000. Liberis Publications Ltd., 49 Pericleous St., 154 51 N. Psychico, Athens, Greece. Ed. Dimitri Kanellopoulos. circ. 12,000. (back issues avail.) **Document type:** consumer publication.

799.202   US   ISSN 0268-6295
SURVIVAL WEAPONRY AND TECHNIQUES. m. £15.60 (foreign £38.50). Aceville Publications Ltd., 89 East Hill, Colchester, Essex CO1 2QN, England. TEL 0206-871139. FAX 0206-871537. Ed. Matthew Tudor. adv.

795.414   SW   ISSN 0282-4809
SVENSK BRIDGE. 1969. q. SEK 85 (effective 1990). Sveriges Bridgefoerbund, Banvaktsv. 24, S-171 48 Solna, Sweden. Eric Leijonhufvud.
    Former titles (until vol.2, 1984): Bridge Med Ungdomsnyt (ISSN 0348-6443); (until 1977): Bridge (Stockholm) (ISSN 0345-1747)

796.41   SW   ISSN 0281-5443
SVENSK GYMNASTIK. 1942. 8/yr. SEK 180. Svenska Gymnastikfoerbundet - Swedish Gymnastic Federation, Idrottens Hus, 123 87 Farsta, Sweden. Ed. C-H Segerfeldt. adv.; bk.rev.; illus.; stat. circ. 8,000.
    Formerly: Gymnastikledaren (ISSN 0017-5978)
    Description: News of events and general interest to gym leaders and provides a forum for debate and discussion.

790   SW   ISSN 0049-2663
SVENSK IDROTT. 1929. m. SEK 220 (effective 1990). Sveriges Riksidrottsfoerbund – Swedish Sports Confederation, Idrottens Hus, S-123 87 Farsta, Sweden. TEL 08-713-6000. FAX 08-94-81-89. Ed. Lars Roehne. adv.; bk.rev. circ. 37,000.

797.21   CN   ISSN 0319-0560
SWIM CANADA. 10/yr. Can.$30 (foreign Can.$65). 356 Sumach St., Toronto, ON M4X 1V4, Canada. TEL 416-368-2606. FAX 416-368-8936. Ed. N.J. Thierry. circ. 3,900. **Indexed:** Sportsearch (1974-).

797.21   US   ISSN 8755-2027
SWIM MAGAZINE.* 1984. bi-m. $15. Sports Publications, Inc., Box 2025, Sedona, AZ 86339-2025. TEL 818-304-7755. Ed. Phillip Whitten. adv.: B&W page $1610, color page $2405; trim 8 1/4 x 10 3/4; adv. contact: Peter Koch-Weser. circ. 35,725 (paid). **Document type:** consumer publication.

797.21   US
SWIMMING AND DIVING AND WATER POLO RULEBOOK. a. $4. National Federation of State High School Associations, 11724 N.W. Plaza Circle, Box 20626, Kansas City, MO 64195-0626. TEL 816-464-5400. FAX 816-464-5571.
    Former titles: Swimming and Diving Rules (ISSN 0163-2884); Swimming and Diving Case Book (ISSN 0145-3831); Which supersedes: Swimming Rules.

797.21   JA
SWIMMING MAGAZINE. (Text in Japanese) 1977. m. 6240 Yen. Baseball Magazine Sha, 3-10-10 Misaki-cho, Chiyoda-ku, Tokyo, Japan. Ed. Tomohei Tsukide.

797   UK   ISSN 1351-7791
SWIMMING POOL NEWS. bi-m. Rear of Penmark House, Woodbridge Meadows, Guildford, Surrey GU1 1BL, England. TEL 0483-306304. FAX 0483-579045. Ed. M. Cope. bk.rev. **Document type:** trade publication.
    —BLDSC (8576.080000).
    Description: Covers design and construction technology for pools and saunas.

SWIMMING POOL - SPA AGE. see BUILDING AND CONSTRUCTION

SWIMMING POOL - SPA AGE PRODUCT DIRECTORY. see BUILDING AND CONSTRUCTION

797.21   US   ISSN 0039-7415
SWIMMING TECHNIQUE.* 1964. q. $13 (foreign $19). Sports Publications, Inc., Box 2025, Sedona, AZ 86339-2025. TEL 818-304-7755. Ed. Phillip Whitten. adv. contact: Peter Koch-Weser. bk.rev.; film rev.; charts; illus.; index. circ. 8,500. (also avail. in microform from UMI; reprint service avail. from UMI) **Indexed:** Phys.Ed.Ind., Sports Per.Ind., Sportsearch (1965-). **Document type:** consumer publication.
    —BLDSC (8576.400000); Faxon; SWETS; UMI; UnCover.

797.21   UK   ISSN 0039-7423
SWIMMING TIMES. 1923. m. £20 (foreign £26). (Amateur Swimming Association) Swimming Times Ltd., Harold Fern House, Derby Square, Loughborough, Leics. LE11 0AL, England. TEL 01509-234433. FAX 01509-235049. (Co-sponsor: Institute of Swimming Teachers and Coaches) Ed. Peter Hassall. adv.: B&W page £500, color page £590; trim 265 x 183; adv. contact: Pat Coulson. bk.rev.; charts; illus. circ. 18,500. **Indexed:** Sportsearch (1977-). **Document type:** trade publication.
    Incorporates: Swim.

797.21   US   ISSN 0039-7431
GV837
SWIMMING WORLD.* Key Title: Swimming World and Junior Swimmer. 1960. m. $19 (foreign $29). Sports Publications, Inc., Box 2025, Sedona, AZ 86339-2025. TEL 818-304-7755. Ed. Phillip Whitten. adv. contact: Peter Koch-Weser. bk.rev.; film rev.; charts; illus.; stat.; index; circ. 33,143 (paid). (also avail. in microform from UMI; reprint service avail. from UMI) **Indexed:** Sports Per.Ind., Sportsearch (1973-). **Document type:** consumer publication.
    —Faxon; UMI; UnCover.
    Former titles: Junior Swimmer - Swimming World; Swimming World (ISSN 0586-2183)

796.86   UK
SWORD. 1948. q. $20. Amateur Fencing Association, 1 Baron's Gate, 15 Rastell Ave., London SW2 4XP, England. TEL 0171-261-8474. FAX 0181-674-2245. Ed. Malcolm Fare. adv. contact: Terry Kingston. bk.rev.; illus.; stat. circ. 4,000. **Indexed:** Sportsearch (1976-).

6090 SPORTS AND GAMES

796.86   US
SWORDMASTER. 1976. q. $6. U S Academy of Arms, 279 E. Northfield Rd., Livingston, NJ 07039. TEL 201-992-0202. Ed. A. John Geraci. bk.rev.; abstr.; bibl.; charts; illus.; stat.; tr.lit. circ. 1,000. (back issues avail.) **Indexed:** Sportsearch.

797.21   US   ISSN 1069-2290
SYNCHRO SWIMMING U S A. 1963. q. $15 (foreign $25). United States Synchronized Swimming, 201 S. Capitol Ave., Ste. 510, Indianapolis, IN 46225. TEL 317-237-5700. FAX 317-237-5705. Ed. Laura LaMarca. adv. contact: Laura LaMarca. circ. 5,000. **Indexed:** Sportsearch (1979-). **Document type:** trade publication.
  Former titles (until 1992): Synchro (ISSN 0746-5726); (until Apr. 1979): Synchro - Info.
  Description: Provides news and articles on technique and competitive synchronized swimming results from around the world.

794.1   PL   ISSN 1230-2309
SZACHISTA. 1991. m. $25. Res Publica Press International Ltd., Ul. Grazyny 13, 02-548 Warsaw, Poland. TEL 48-22-452655. FAX 48-22-454216. Ed. Andrzej Filipowicz. adv.; bk.rev.; charts; illus.
  Description: Contains chess news, chess history, annotated chess games, theory, combinations, studies and problems.

790.1   GW
T G M ECHO. 1975. q. Turngemeinde 1861 e.V., Kirchstr. 45, 55124 Mainz - Gonsenheim, Germany. TEL 06131-41106. Ed. Jochen Dietz. circ. 1,500. **Document type:** newspaper.

790.1   GW
T S VGG 1848 STADECKEN - ELSHEIM. VEREINSNACHRICHTEN. 1980. 3/yr. T S Vgg 1848 Stadecken - Elsheim e.V., Talstr. 56, 55271 Stadecken - Elsheim, Germany. TEL 06136-1584. Ed. Karl-Heinz Moerixbauer. adv. contact: Karl-Heinz Moerixbauer. bk.rev. circ. 1,000. (back issues avail.) **Document type:** bulletin.
  Description: Contains news and information about the local sports club and its members.

790.1   GW   ISSN 0179-0153
T U S INFO. (Turn- und Sportverein); Informationen aus dem Vereinsleben. 1985. q. DM.12($10) (T U S Stockum 1945 e.V.) Information about local sports., Postfach 7052, 58434 Witten, Germany. TEL 02302-49043. Ed. Rolf Korfmann. illus. circ. 1,250. (back issues avail.)

790.1   GW
T U S VEREINSNACHRICHTEN. 1907. q. membership. Turn- und Sportvereinigung Gaarden von 1875 e.V., Roentgenstr. 5, 24143 Kiel, Germany. TEL 0431-731176. Ed. Dieter Buenning. adv. circ. 2,000. **Document type:** newsletter.

796.41   GW
T V K 1877 ECHO. 1984. q. DM.20. Turnverein 1877 e.V. Essen-Kupferdreh, Kampmannbruecke 1, 45257 Essen, Germany. TEL 0201-488179. FAX 0201-488179. Ed. Bodo F. Schmischke. adv. contact: Bodo Schmischke. circ. 2,000. (back issues avail.) **Document type:** newsletter.
  Description: Magazine for members of the Turnverein.

790.1 384.554   US
T V SPORTSFILE. 1983. irreg. (approx 6/mo.). $295 via FAX or E-mail. Gould Media Services, Box 446, York, ME 03909. TEL 207-363-6037. FAX 207-363-7824. Ed. Dantia Gould. adv. (back issues avail.) **Document type:** newsletter.
  ●Also available online.
  Supersedes: Cablesports Newsletter; **Former titles:** Cable - Television Sports Newsletter; Cablesports Newsletter.
  Description: Covers breaking news affecting the TV sports business.

790.1   US   ISSN 1053-041X
T V WRESTLERS. 1989. q. $2.95 per no. Starlog Group, Inc., 475 Park Ave. S., New York, NY 10016. TEL 212-689-2830. FAX 212-889-7933. **Document type:** consumer publication.

796.815   US   ISSN 0741-028X
TAE KWON DO TIMES; martial arts, fitness & health. 1981. bi-m. $16. Tri - Mount Publications, 1423 18th St., Bettendorf, IA 52722. TEL 319-359-7202. FAX 319-355-7299. Ed. Rod Speidel; Pub. Chung Kim. adv. contact: Carol Hart. bk.rev.; circ. 70,000 (paid). (back issues avail.) **Document type:** consumer publication.
  Description: Features interviews, articles and information about martial arts.

790.1   GW
TAEKWONDO AKTUELL. 1977. m. DM.36($20) (Deutsche Taekwondo Union) Heinz Marx, Pub., Maximiliansplatz 12-I, 80333 Munich, Germany. TEL 089-222710. Ed.Bd. (back issues avail.)
  Description: Information on all aspects of Tae Kwon Do.

796.815   US   ISSN 1043-1047
TAEKWONDO WORLD. 1983. q. $7 (Canada $11). (American Taekwondo Association) A T A Publications, Box 898, Yankton, SD 57078-0898. TEL 605-665-9909. Ed. Milo Dailey. adv.; illus.; circ. 48,000 (paid). **Document type:** consumer publication.
  Former titles: A T A Magazine (ISSN 0884-5786); Martial Arts and Fitness.
  Description: Features martial arts, history and human interest stories.

790.1   CH
TAIWAN SPORTS GOODS BUYER'S GUIDE. (Text in English) a. $30. Trade Winds, Inc., No. 7, Lane 75, Yungkang St., Taipei, Taiwan 10602, Republic of China. TEL 02-393-2718. FAX 02-396-4022. **Document type:** directory, catalog.
  Formerly: Taiwan Sporting Goods Buyer's Guide.
  Description: Covers Taiwan's production of sportswear and goods for export.

TANZ UND GYMNASTIK. see *DANCE*

799.202   UK   ISSN 0143-8751
TARGET GUN. m. £23 (foreign £30). Peterson Publications Ltd., Peterson House, Northbank, Berryhill Industrial Estate, Droitwich, Worcs. WR9 9BL, England. TEL 0905-795564. FAX 0905-795905. Ed. Richard Adkins. adv.; bk.rev.; illus. circ. 24,500. **Document type:** consumer publication.

797.23   GW
TAUCH-BRILLE. 1986. m. DM.12. (Saarlaendischer Tauchsportbund) Kurt Huwig Druckerei, Goethestr. 50, 66292 Riegelsberg, Germany. TEL 06806-4001. Ed. Hannelore Huwig. circ. 800. (back issues avail.)
  Description: News about diving.

790.1 574 770
910.09   GW   ISSN 0170-4001
TAUCHEN; internationales Unterwasser-Magazin. 1978. m. DM.106.80. Jahr-Verlag GmbH & Co., Jessenstr. 1, 22767 Hamburg, Germany. TEL 040-38906-0. FAX 040-38906302. TELEX 2163485. Ed. Joerg Keller. adv. contact: Waltraud Jante. bk.rev.; charts; illus.; index. circ. 47,100. (back issues avail.) **Document type:** consumer publication.

793   US
TAVERN SPORTS INTERNATIONAL.* 1988. bi-m. $13. National Bowlers Journal, Inc., 200 S. Michigan Ave., Ste. 1430, Chicago, IL 60604. TEL 312-266-9499. Ed. Jocelyn Hathaway. adv. circ. 70,000.
  Description: Provides national and international coverage of the tavern-based game industry, including: billiards, darts, video games, shuffleboard and other coin-operated games and machines.

790.1 346.066   US   ISSN 1065-738X
TEAM LICENSING BUSINESS. m. Virgo Publishing, Inc., 4141 N. Scottsdale Rd., Ste. 316, Scottsdale, AZ 85251. TEL 602-990-1101. FAX 602-990-0819.
  Formerly: Team Licensing Business Magazine (ISSN 1059-5643)

688.76   US
TEAM LINE-UP. Variant title: Team Line-Up Newsletter. 1970. 4/yr. membership. National Sporting Goods Association, 1699 Wall St., Mt. Prospect, IL 60056-5780. TEL 708-439-4000. FAX 708-439-0111. Ed. Thomas B. Doyle. circ. 1,800. **Document type:** newsletter.

TEAM MARKETING REPORT. see *BUSINESS AND ECONOMICS — Marketing And Purchasing*

688.76   FR
TECHNO-LOISIRS; guide international annuel de la construction et de l'equipment pour le sport et les loisirs. (Text in various European languages and Esperanto) 1971. biennial. 250 F.($50) Editions Techno-Loisirs, 3 rue Sivel, 75014 Paris, France. TEL 45-40-9905. FAX 45-40-7893. Ed. Georges Caille. adv.; bk.rev.; play rev.; bibl.; illus.; pat.; stat.; tr.lit.; index. circ. 10,000. (also avail. in magnetic tape) **Document type:** directory.

TEE TO GREEN. see *LEISURE AND RECREATION*

794.1   IT
TELESCACCO 92. 1983. 11/yr. $22. Associazione Scacchista Italiana Giocatori per Corrispondenza, c/o Franco Mecucci, Via Vernio 49, 00138 Rome, Italy. TEL 06-880-3316. Ed. Angelo Bruni. bk.rev.; charts. circ. 2,800.
  Formerly (until 1992): Telescacco Nuovo.
  Description: Covers annotated games, "how-to-improve" articles, theory, correspondence tournaments and news.

TELOVYCHOVNY PRACOVNIK. see *EDUCATION — Teaching Methods And Curriculum*

796   YU   ISSN 0040-3024
TEMPO; ilustrovani nedeljni sportski list. (Text in Serbo-Croatian) 1966. w. 17664 din.($43) Politika, Cetinjska 1, 11000 Belgrade, Yugoslavia. TEL 11-321-075. Ed. Tomislav Markovic. circ. 180,000. (back issues avail.) **Indexed:** Music Ind.

790.1   PL   ISSN 0137-933X
TEMPO. 1948. 5/w. Sportpresse. sp. z o.o., Ul. Wielopole 1, 31-072 Krakow, Poland. TEL 48-12-222960. FAX 48-12-222960. Ed. Ryszard Niemiec. adv.; illus. circ. 75,000.
  Formerly (until 1959): Glos Sportowca.

796   NE   ISSN 0928-5504
TENNIS REVUE. 7/yr. fl.45. Sport & Business, Postbus 12, 6200 AA Maastricht, Netherlands. TEL 31-45-219913. FAX 31-45-227359. Ed. Hanco Naninck. adv.: B&W page fl.4000, color page fl.6000; trim 210 x 297. circ. 45,000. **Document type:** consumer publication.
  Supersedes in part (in 1993): Exclusive Sports and Resorts (ISSN 0928-0766); Which was previously (until 1992): Special Sports (ISSN 0925-7470); (until 1990): Tenis Revue (ISSN 0168-6488); (1981-1983): Tennisvaria (ISSN 0167-921X)

796   US   ISSN 0040-4241
TEXAS COACH. 1957. m. (except June, July & Dec.). $13. Texas High School Coaches Association, Drawer 14627, Austin, TX 78761. TEL 512-454-6709. Ed. Sheryl Honeycutt. adv.; bk.rev.; illus. circ. 10,600. **Indexed:** Phys.Ed.Ind., Sports Per.Ind., Sportsearch (1977-). —UnCover.

790.1   VN
THE THAO VAN HOA/SPORTS AND CULTURE. 1982. w. $0.12 per no. 5 Ly Thuong Kiet, Hanoi, Socialist Republic of Vietnam. TEL 84-4-267043. FAX 84-42-267447. TELEX 267043. Ed. Nauyen Huu Vinh. circ. 90,000.

790.1   VN
THE THAO VIET-NAM/VIET-NAM SPORTS. 1968. w. 5 Trinh Hoai Duc St., Hanoi, Socialist Republic of Vietnam. Ed. Tran Can.

THERAPEUTIC RECREATION JOURNAL. see *PHYSICAL FITNESS AND HYGIENE*

790.1   US   ISSN 0889-0692
THRASHER MAGAZINE. 1980. m. $18.50 (Canada $26, elsewhere $35). High Speed Productions, Inc., Box 884570, San Francisco, CA 94188-4570. TEL 415-822-3083. FAX 415-822-8359. Ed. Jake Phelps. adv. contact: Roger Browne. bk.rev. circ. 250,000. **Document type:** consumer publication.
  Description: Covers skateboarding, snowboarding, music, video, and aggressive youth-oriented lifestyle.

796.41　　　　CC　　ISSN 1000-3444
TICAO/GYMNASTICS. (Text in Chinese) 1982. q. $16.80. (Zhongguo Ticao Xiehui - China Gymnastics Association) Renmin Tiyu Chubanshe - People's Sports Publishing House, 8 Tiyuguan Lu, Chongwen Qu, Beijing 100061, People's Republic of China. TEL 5112466. FAX 7016129. (Dist. in U.S. by: China Books & Periodicals, Inc., 2929 24th St., San Francisco, CA 94110. TEL 415-282-2994) Ed. Jiang Youzhen.

794.1　　　　SW　　ISSN 0040-6848
TIDSKRIFT FOER SCHACK. 1895. 10/yr. SEK 350. Sveriges Schackfoerbund - Swedish Chess Federation, Gethornskroken 21, S-281 49 Haesslcholm, Sweden. TEL 451-12850. FAX 451-14790. Ed. Bo Plato. adv.; bk.rev.; index. circ. 2,500.

TIERWELT. see BIOLOGY — Ornithology

790.1　　　　US
TIGHT LINES.* 1981. m. $15. (Greater Delaware Valley Kite Society, Inc.) Dirt Cheap Press, Box B-2 Nets West, Long Neck, DE 19966. FAX 609-697-2285. Ed. Leonard M. Conover. adv.; bk.rev.; charts; illus.; pat.; stat.; tr.lit. rev. 500. **Document type:** newspaper.
　Description: Humorous but technical information on kite-flying, and announcements on competitions and other activities pertaining to the members of the society, which was founded on Ben Franklin's birthday.

796　796.332　XO　ISSN 0139-7753
TIP; tyzdennik pre futbal a hokej. 1969. w. (Slovak Physical Training Organization) Borissia, spol. s.r.o., Halasova 2, 831 03 Bratislava, Slovakia. TELEX 92650. Ed. Ferdinand Kralovic. circ. 60,000.

790.1　　　　GW
TIPP MIT. w. (Tue.). DM.195. Deutscher Sportsverlag Kurt Stoof GmbH, Eintrachtstr. 110-118, 50668 Cologne, Germany. TEL 0221-1648-0. FAX 0221-1648318. Ed. Charly Huehnergarth. adv. contact: Erhard Badtke. circ. 50,000. **Document type:** consumer publication.

790.1　　　　CC　　ISSN 1003-4420
TIYU AIHAOZHE/SPORTS FANS. (Text in Chinese) 1985. m. $41.30. Sichuan Sheng Tiyu Weiyuanhui, 1, Tiyuchang Lu, Chengdu, Sichuan 610015, People's Republic of China. TEL 662574. FAX 662574. (Dist. in US by: China Books & Periodicals, Inc., 2929 24th St., San Francisco, CA 94110. TEL 415-282-2994) Ed. Liu Yingping. circ. 60,000. **Document type:** consumer publication.

790.1　　　　CC
TIYU BOLAN. (Text in Chinese) m. Beijing Shi Tiyu Yundong Weiyuanhui, 2, Luchang Jie Toutiao, Xuanwu-qu, Beijing 100050, People's Republic of China. TEL 3012785. Ed. Liu Xingzhong. **Document type:** consumer publication.

790.1　　　　US　　ISSN 1002-879X
TIYU HUABAO/SPORTS PICTORIAL. (Text in Chinese) 1963. bi-m. $30.50. China Books & Periodicals, Inc., 2929 24th St., San Francisco, CA 94110. TEL 415-282-2994. FAX 415-282-0994.

790.1　　　　CC　　ISSN 1000-677X
TIYU KEXUE/SPORTS SCIENCE. (Text in Chinese; abstracts in English) 1981. bi-m. $27. (China Sports Science Society) Renmin Tiyu Chubanshe - People's Sport Publishing House, 8 Tiyuguan Lu, Chongwen Qu, Beijing 100061, People's Republic of China. TEL 5112466. FAX 7016129. (Dist. in U.S. by: China Books & Periodicals, 2929 24th St., San Francisco, CA 94110. TEL 415-282-2994) Ed. Zhang Caizhen. circ. 20,000. **Indexed:** Sportsearch (1985-).

790.1　　　　US
TODAY'S COACH.* 1975. q. $5. MacGregor Sports Education, 7001 Orchard Lake Rd., K, Ste. 420C, West Bloomfield, WI 48322-3608. TEL 414-786-0366. circ. 81,062. **Document type:** trade publication.
　Description: Deals with coaching techniques and strategies in a variety of competitive sports; includes interviews, sports medicine, physical training and sports administration.

790.1　　　　UK　　ISSN 0268-4977
TODAY'S RUNNER. 1985. m. £26.40 (foreign £33.20) (effective 1995-1996). E M A P - Pursuit Publishing, Bretton Ct., Bretton, Peterborough, Cambs. PE3 8DZ, England. TEL 01733-264666. FAX 01733-267198. TELEX 32157. (Subscr. to: Tower Publishing Services Ltd., Tower House, Sovereign Park, Lathkill St., Market Harborough, Leics. LE16 9EF, Engand. TEL 01858-468811. FAX 01858-432164) Ed. Allan Haines. circ. 25,388 (paid). **Document type:** consumer publication.

790.1　　　　IT
TOP SPORT. 1983. 6/yr. Via A. Saffi 32, 40131 Bologna, Italy. TEL 51-435-526. FAX 51-436-648. Ed. Giovanna Glionna. adv.: B&W page L.4100000, color page L.4500000. circ. 11,500.

790.1　　　　UK
TOUCHLINE; Scotland's official sports events diary. bi-m. Scottish Sports Council, Library & Information Service, Caledonia House, S. Gyle, Edinburgh EH12 9DQ, Scotland. TEL 0131-317-7200. FAX 0131-317-7202. Ed. Fred Pollock. **Document type:** bulletin.

794.1　　　　UK　　ISSN 0276-7090
GV1455
TOURNAMENT CHESS.* 1982. 6/yr. Tui Enterprises Ltd., 35 Ceres Rd., Plumstead, London SE18, England. Ed. M. Chandler. adv. (also avail. in microfilm; microfiche).
—CCC.

796.72　　　　US　　ISSN 1050-558X
TRACKSIDE. 1990. fortn. $37.50. Trackside Publications, 30 Main St., West Springfield, MA 01089. TEL 413-781-0500. FAX 413-781-1387. Ed. Dean Nardi.

613.7　　　　US　　ISSN 1058-3548
TRAINING AND CONDITIONING. 1991. 6/yr. free to qualified personnel. Mag, Inc., 438 W. State St., Ithaca, NY 14850. TEL 607-272-0265. FAX 607-273-0701. Ed. Eleanor Frankel. adv.: B&W page $2270, color page $3200; trim 8 1/8 x 10 7/8. circ. 23,295 (controlled). **Document type:** trade publication.
　Description: Provides pertinent information on the various training and conditioning techniques, trends, procedures and products to professionals involved in the training and conditioning of competitive athletes.

790.1　　　　GW
TRAMPOLIN INTERN. 1984. q. DM.18 (foreign DM.25). Verlag Christian Kemmer, Reichenbacher 53, 80469 Munich, Germany. TEL 089-2011453. FAX 089-7901621. Ed. Ralf Gehrke. adv.: B&W page DM.150; trim 148 x 210. circ. 500. **Document type:** consumer publication.
　Formerly (until 1992): Trampolinturnen.

790.1　　　　XO　　ISSN 0139-5114
TRENER;* the methodical magazine. 1957. m. (Slovak Physical Training Organization) Sport, Vajnorska Cesta 100-a, 832 58 Bratislava, Slovakia. Ed. Milan Perdoch. adv.; bk.rev.; bibl.; illus.; index.
　Formerly (until 1970): Trener a Cvicitel (ISSN 0493-8496)

790.1　　　　US　　ISSN 0898-3410
GV1060.7
TRIATHLETE;* triathlons, duathlons, multi-sport events. 1986. m. (11/yr.) $23.95. Winning International, Inc., Box 21056, Lehigh Valley, PA 18002-1056. TEL 215-266-6893. FAX 215-266-7196. Ed. Jeffrey Justice. adv. contact: Nancy Tamayo. bk.rev. circ. 105,000. **Indexed:** Sports Per.Ind., Sportsearch (1986-). **Document type:** consumer publication.
　Formed by the merger of (1984-1986): Tri-Athlete; (1983-1986): Triathlon (ISSN 0745-5917)

790.1　　　　AT
TRIATHLON SPORTS MAGAZINE. 1984. 10/yr. (8 m. issues and 2 bi-m. issues). Aus.$45. Triathlon Sports Pty. Ltd., P.O. Box 2590, Taren Point, N.S.W. 2229, Australia. TEL 2-524-1455. FAX 2-524-1454. Ed. Johanna Keating. adv. circ. 16,000. **Document type:** consumer publication.
　Description: For health-conscious adults and serious athletes who swim, bicycle and run for fitness.

SPORTS AND GAMES　　6091

790.1　　　　US　　ISSN 1068-8277
TRIATHLON TIMES; the official magazine of the national governing body for triathlon and related multi-sport events in the U.S. 1985. m. $25 (foreign $42). Triathlon Federation - USA, Box 15820, Colorado Springs, CO 80935-5820. TEL 719-597-9090. FAX 719-597-2121. Ed. Tim Yount. adv. contact: Randy Pelton. circ. 25,000. **Document type:** newsletter.

TRIBUNA DELL'IRPINIA; settimanale di attualita. see BUSINESS AND ECONOMICS

790.1　　　　RM
TRIBUNA SPORTURILOR. 1990. w. Str. George Cosbuc 38, 2400 Sibiu, Rumania. TEL 924-12810. FAX 924-12026. Ed. Mircea Bitu. circ. 20,000.

688.76 613.7　　　IT　　ISSN 1121-6913
TSPORT; impianti sportivi e ricreativi, piscine, fitness e arredo urbano. (Text in English, Italian) 1976. m. (9/yr.) L.80000 (Europe L.110000; elsewhere L.150000) (effective 1995). European Magazines & Guides s.r.l., Via G. Murat 84, 20159 Milan, Italy. TEL 39-2-6682261. FAX 39-2-66802982. Ed. Maria Carbone; Pub. Pietro Chianchiano. adv.: B&W page L.1800000, color page L.2600000; adv. contact: Antonio Busnelli. circ. 7,500. (back issues avail.) **Document type:** trade publication.

790.1　　　　SP　　ISSN 1131-7922
TURISPORT. (Text in English and Spanish) 10/yr. 4000 ptas. Sporturis S.A., Consejo de Ciento 346, 08009 Barcelona, Spain. TEL 3-488-12-50. FAX 3-488-34-42. Ed. Jose Maria Castro Andreu. circ. 7,000. **Document type:** consumer publication.

790　　　　GW　　ISSN 0945-666X
TURNEN & SPORT. 1927. m. DM.48 (foreign DM.72). Pohl Verlag, Postfach 3207, 29232 Celle, Germany. TEL 05141-7504-0. FAX 05141-750475. Eds. Rudi Luetgeharm, Manfred Senftleben. adv.; bk.rev.; illus.; index. circ. 15,500. (back issues avail.) **Document type:** bulletin.
　Formerly: T U S - Turnen und Sport (ISSN 0344-4023); Which incorporated: Leibesuebungen (ISSN 0024-0613)

790.1　　　　US
TURTLE RACING NEWS; official voice of the International Federation of the Advancement of Racing Turtles (I.F.A.R.T.). a. free. Chester Optimist Club, Box 374, Chester, NJ 07930. adv. **Document type:** newsletter.
　Description: Covers the rules and ethics of racing turtles.

790.1　　　　IT
TUTTO QUIZZY.* 1993. w. newsstand price: L.1200. Mediolanum Editori Associati, Via Telesio 2, 20154 Milan, Italy. TEL 39-2-48020311. FAX 39-2-48022786. Ed. Nicola Bovoli. adv.: color page L.8000000. circ. 75,000. **Document type:** consumer publication.

796.72　　　　IT
▼**TUTTOPISTA.** 1994. m. L.50000 (foreign L.100000). Barbero Editori s.r.l., Via G. Galilei, 3, 10023 Chieri (TO), Italy. TEL 39-11-9470400. FAX 39-11-9470577. Ed. Riccardo Barbero. **Document type:** consumer publication.

790　　　　IT　　ISSN 0041-4441
TUTTOSPORT. 1945. d. L.46500. Societa Editrice Sportiva, Corso Svizzera 185, 10147 Turin, Italy. TEL 11-31-081. Ed. Piero Dardanello. adv.; bk.rev. circ. 163,705. **Document type:** newspaper.

790.1　　　　IT
TWIRLING. 1979. q. L.15000. Federazione Italiana Sportiva Twirling, Via Marconi, I-28047 Oleggio (No), Italy.

799.3　　　　GW　　ISSN 0721-572X
U I T JOURNAL. (Text in English, French, German and Spanish) 1961. 6/yr. DM.44 (outside Europe DM.50). Union Internationale Tir, Bavariaring 21, 80336 Munich, Germany. FAX 089-5309481. TELEX 5216792-UIT-D. Ed. Wolfgang Schreiber. adv.; bk.rev.; charts; illus. circ. 4,000. **Document type:** bulletin.
　Formerly: Shooting Sport-Tir Sportif-Tiro Deportivo-Schiess-Sport (ISSN 0037-4156)

SPORTS AND GAMES

790.1 052 US
U S A B A AGENDA. 1976. 12/yr. free. United States Association for Blind Athletes, 33 N. Institute, Colorado Springs, CO 80903. TEL 719-630-0422. FAX 719-630-0616. Dir. Charlie Huebner. bk.rev. circ. 4,500. (also avail. in talking book)
Former titles: SportsScoop; U S A B A Newsletter.

796.72 US ISSN 0744-4702
U S A C NEWS. 1956. fortn. membership. United States Auto Club, 4910 W. 16th St., Indianapolis, IN 46224. TEL 317-247-5151. Ed. Dick Jordan. illus.; stat. circ. 7,500. (tabloid format) **Document type:** newsletter.
Description: Covers auto racing.

796.41 US ISSN 0748-6006
U S A GYMNASTICS. (Former name of issuing body: United States Gymnastics Federation) 1960. bi-m. $15. U S A Gymnastics, 201 S. Capitol Ave., Ste. 300, Pan American Plaza, Indianapolis, IN 46225. TEL 317-237-5050. FAX 317-237-5069. TELEX 272385-USGYM-IND. E-mail: Internet: USGF@DELPHI.COMM. Ed. Luan Peszek. adv. contact: Kim Clayton. circ. 63,000. (back issues avail.) **Document type:** consumer publication.
●Also available online.
Description: Covers national and international gymnastics leading to and including the Olympics. Covers men's, women's and rythmic gymnastics.

796 US
U S A HOCKEY. PLAYING RULES HANDBOOK. biennial. $7.95. U S A Hockey, 4965 N. 30th St., Colorado Springs, CO 80919. TEL 719-599-5500. FAX 719-599-5899. Ed. Darryl Seibel.
Former titles: U S A Hockey. Rule Book; Amateur Hockey Association of the United States. Rule Book.

796 US
GV847.5
U S A HOCKEY ANNUAL GUIDE. a. $5.95. U S A Hockey, 4965 N. 30th St., Colorado Springs, CO 80919-4102. TEL 719-599-5500. FAX 719-599-5899. Ed. Darryl Seibel. **Document type:** directory.
Former titles: U S A Hockey; Amateur Hockey Association of the United States. Official Guide (ISSN 0516-8635)

799.3 US ISSN 0738-9949
GV1187
THE U S ARCHER. 1982. bi-m. $17.50 (foreign $23.95). (National Archery Association) U S Archer, Inc., 7315 N. San Anna Dr., Tucson, AZ 85704. TEL 602-742-5846. FAX 602-742-0027. Ed. Arlyne Rhode; Pub. Arlyne Rhode. adv. circ. 3,800. **Document type:** trade publication.
Incorporates (in 1993): N A A Newsletter.
Description: Covers the sport of archery in the U.S. Provides tournament dates with application forms.

794.1 US
U S CHESS CATALOG. 3/yr. $2 per no. United States Chess Federation, 186 Rte. 9W, New Windsor, NY 12553. TEL 914-562-8350. FAX 914-561-2437. circ. 100,000 (paid). **Document type:** catalog.
Description: Offers the best in chess books, sets, boards, computer software, and accessories from around the world.

798.2 US
THE U S D F QUARTERLINE. 1973. q. $40 includes membership; libraries $8. (United States Dressage Federation, Inc.) Fleet Street Publishing, Box 6669, Lincoln, NE 68506-0669. TEL 402-434-8550. FAX 402-434-8570. Ed. Robin Urmanic. adv.; illus. circ. 24,000. (back issues avail.) **Indexed:** Sportsearch (1981-). **Document type:** consumer publication.
Formerly (until 1994): U S D F Bulletin (ISSN 0882-5130)
Description: Covers the art of riding and horse training. Includes competition results, articles, and news columns.

790.1 US ISSN 1074-9314
U S F A NATIONAL NEWSLETTER. q. membership. United States Fencing Association, Inc., 1750 E. Boulder St., Colorado Springs, CO 80909. TEL 719-578-4511. FAX 719-632-5737. adv.: B&W page $450. circ. 10,000 (paid). **Document type:** newsletter.

796.86 US
U S F A RULE BOOK: U S & INTERNATIONAL RULES. (Supplement avail.: Update) a. $15 with binder; without $8. United States Fencing Association, Inc., 1750 E. Boulder St., Colorado Springs, CO 80909. TEL 719-578-4511. FAX 719-632-5737.
Formerly: Fencing Rules for Competitions.

796.21 US ISSN 1044-0801
U S ROLLER SKATING. 1991. m. (except Aug.) $10 per no. U S Amateur Confederation of Roller Skating, Box 6579, 4730 South St., Lincoln, NE 68506. TEL 402-483-7551. FAX 402-483-1465. adv. circ. 65,000. **Indexed:** Sportsearch (1989-).
Description: Contains news on American competitive roller skating. Covers events, training tips, sports medicine and clinics.

790 910.03 US
U S SPORTS. 1988. bi-m. National Publications Sales Agency, Inc., National Plaza, P.O. Box 198516, Chicago, IL 60619-8516. TEL 312-375-6800. adv. circ. 200,000.
Description: Focuses on blacks in sports, covering achievements, families, and business interests.

796.342 US
U S T A COLLEGE TENNIS GUIDE.* 1976. biennial. $7. United States Tennis Association, 70 W. Red Oak Ln., White Plains, NY 10640. TEL 609-452-2580. FAX 609-452-2265. TELEX 62879058. circ. 5,000.
Description: Lists colleges and junior colleges in the U.S. that provide scholarships.

U S TEAM SPOTLIGHT. see HANDICAPPED — Hearing Impaired

UE; Magazin fuer Uebungsleiterinnen und Uebungsleiter. see EDUCATION — Teaching Methods And Curriculum

790.1 GW ISSN 0342-8419
DER UEBUNGSLEITER; Arbeitshilfen fuer Uebungsleiter im Deutschen Sportbund. 1967. m. DM.38.50. Limpert Verlag GmbH, Postfach 4027, 65030 Wiesbaden, Germany. TEL 0611-373072. FAX 0611-374351. Ed. Friedhelm Kreiss. circ. 78,000. (looseleaf format; back issues avail.) **Document type:** academic/scholarly publication.
Description: Practical help, tips and exercises for trainers.

797 US ISSN 0192-0871
GV840.S78
UNDERCURRENT.* 1975. m. $58. Atcom, Inc., 1541 Morris Ave., Bronx, NY 10457-8702. TEL 212-873-5900. FAX 212-799-1728. Ed. Ben Davison. adv. circ. 13,000. (reprint service avail. from UMI)
—CCC.
Description: For the sport diver featuring resort and equipment reviews, safety tips and ways to have more fun underwater.

796.83 US
UNITED STATES AMATEUR BOXING. ANNUAL GUIDE. Abbreviated title: U S A Boxing. 1981. a. $8. United States Amateur Boxing (U S A Boxing), Inc., One Olympic Plaza, Colorado Springs, CO 80909. TEL 719-578-4506. Ed. Kurt Stenenon. circ. controlled.
Formerly: U S A Amateur Boxing Federation. Media Guide.
Description: Provides a complete history and current information on Olympic-style boxing.

796.83 US
UNITED STATES AMATEUR BOXING. OFFICIAL RULES. Abbreviated title: U S A Boxing: Official Rules. 1981. s-a. $15. United States Amateur Boxing (U S A Boxing), Inc., One Olympic Plaza, Colorado Springs, CO 80909. TEL 719-578-4506. Ed. Kurt Stenerson. circ. 10,000.
Formerly: U S A Amateur Boxing Federation. Official Rules.

796.42
UNITED STATES CROSS-COUNTRY COACHES ASSOCIATION. ANNUAL BUSINESS MEETING. MINUTES. a. free. United States Cross-Country Coaches Association, c/o Ken O'Brien, Sec., Boyden Gym, University of Massachusetts, Amherst, MA 01003. TEL 413-545-2759.
Supersedes: United States Cross-Country Coaches Association. Proceedings; Which was formerly: United States Cross-Country and Distance Running Coaches Association. Proceedings (ISSN 0082-9706)

790.1 GW
UNSER WANDERBOTE. 1972. q. DM.24 to non-members. Volkssportverein Wanderfreunde Mainz 1971 e.V., Kapellenstr. 44, Karl-Geib-Haus, 55124 Mainz-Gosenheim, Germany. TEL 06131-45562. (Subscr. to: Irmgard May, Ed., Hegelstrasse 27, 6500 Mainz Germany) circ. 1,200. (back issues avail.) **Document type:** consumer publication.
Description: Covers swimming, bicycles and walking.

790.1 US ISSN 0883-4938
UROLOGIST'S SPORTSLIFE. bi-m. Medical Publishing Enterprises, 15-22 Fair Lawn, Fair Lawn, NJ 07410. TEL 201-796-6500. FAX 201-796-4562. Ed. Stephen Kaufman.
Description: Sports and recreation for physicians.

V A H P E R D JOURNAL. (Virginia Association for Health, Physical Education and Dance) see PHYSICAL FITNESS AND HYGIENE

790.1 CN ISSN 1192-1277
V CANADA. 1992. 6/yr. Can.$10. Graham Publications, 58 Silverbirch Ave., Toronto, ON M4E 3K9, Canada. TEL 416-699-1026. FAX 416-699-2649. Ed. Ted Graham. adv.: B&W page Can.$237, color page Can.$462; adv. contact: Marc Dunn. circ. 5,000. (tabloid format) **Document type:** consumer publication.

799.202 NO ISSN 0800-6016
VAAPENJOURNALEN. 1973. 8/yr. NOK 250. A-S Vaapenslitteratur, Box 1, N-1364 Hvalstad, Norway. Ed. Erik Braathen. adv.; bk.rev. circ. 10,000.
—CCC.
Formerly: Vaapen.

VEREINS PRAXIS; Arbeitshilfen fuer Fuehrungskraefte und Organisationsleiter. see CLUBS

796 US
VERMONT SPORTS TODAY. 1990. m. $15. Box 496, Waterbury, VT 05676-0496. TEL 802-244-5796. Ed. Kathryn Carter. adv. circ. 10,000. **Document type:** newspaper.

VI BILAEGARE. see TRANSPORTATION — Automobiles

796.72 US ISSN 1052-8067
VINTAGE MOTORSPORT; the journal of motor racing history. 1982. bi-m. $30. Vintage Motorsport Inc., 113 S. Florida Ave., Lakeland, FL 33801. FAX 813-682-8784. adv.: B&W page $915, color page $1370; trim 8 1/2 x 11. circ. 9,350. **Document type:** consumer publication.

796.3 BE
VLAAMSE BEDRIJFSSPORT. (Text in Dutch) 1977. 4/yr. 100 BEF. Vlaamse Liga van Bedrijfssportbonden, Stationstraat 27-9, 9300 Aalst, Belgium. FAX 32-2-5141106. (Subscr. to: V.L.B., Boomgaardstraat 22-15, 2600 Berchem, Belgium. TEL 32-3-2860736. FAX 32-2-2860742) Ed. Guy de Grauwe. adv.: B&W page fl.12500; trim 210 x 297. circ. 5,000. (back issues avail.)
Description: Covers corporate sporting events and activities in Belgium.

VOILA - RENAULT REVUE; Autos zum Leben. see TRANSPORTATION — Automobiles

790.1 FR
VOIX DES SPORTS. 1947. w. 239 F.($44) Voix du Nord, 8 place General de Gaulle, 59023 Lille Cedex, France. TEL 33-20-78-40-40. FAX 33-20-78-42-44. TELEX 120 687 F. Ed. J.L. Prevost. adv.: page 29750 F.; adv. contact: Michel Marin. circ. 80,000. cols./p.: 5; pp./issue: 64. (tabloid format) **Document type:** newspaper.

SPORTS AND GAMES

790.1 US ISSN 8756-7792
W W F MAGAZINE. 1983. m. (World Wrestling Federation) Titan Sports, Inc., 1241 E. Main St., Box 3857, Stamford, CT 06902. TEL 203-352-8600. FAX 203-359-5118. adv.: B&W page $5450, color page $6872; trim 8 1/4 x 10 3/4. circ. 300,000 (paid). **Document type:** consumer publication.

790.1 US ISSN 1051-5038
W W F WRESTLING SPOTLIGHT. 1988. q. newsstand price: $2.25. (World Wrestling Federation) Titan Sports, Inc., 1241 E. Main St., Stamford, CT 06902. TEL 203-352-8600. Ed. Vince Russo; Robert Mitchell, Gen. Mgr. adv.; circ. 76,000 (paid). **Document type:** consumer publication.
Description: Each issue focuses on a superstar of the W.W.F.

797.21 US
WAKE BOARDING. q. newsstand price: $2.95. World Publications, Inc., 330 W. Canton, Winter Park, FL 32790. TEL 407-628-4802. FAX 407-628-7061. **Document type:** consumer publication.

790.1 LE
WATAN AL RIYADI. (Text in Arabic) 1979. m. P.O. Box 615, Beirut, Lebanon. Ed. Antoine Chouery. adv. circ. 150,000.

797 US
WATER SAFETY JOURNAL. 1978. q. $4. National Water Safety Congress, 96 Sheila Dr., Oxford, MS 38655. FAX 601-234-1828. circ. 4,500.
Former titles: National Water Safety Congress Journal; Water Safety Journal.

797 NE ISSN 0920-3532
WATERSKI. 1964. bi-m. fl.35. (Nederlandse Waterski Bond) Waterski, Langsom 18, 1066 EW Amsterdam, Netherlands. TEL 31-20-6694748. FAX 31-20-6694554. adv.; illus.; circ. 4,500 (paid). **Document type:** consumer publication.
Formerly (until 1986): Aqua-Vite (ISSN 0003-7222)

790.1 US
▼**WEEKEND SPORTS.** 1994. bi-m. $18. Cascade-Pacific Media, Inc., 141 N. State St., Ste. 164, Lake Oswego, OR 97034. TEL 503-636-0062. Ed. Rod O'Dell; Pub. Rod O'Dell. adv.: B&W page $3638. circ. 150,000 (controlled). **Document type:** consumer publication.

WEIGHTLIFTING U S A. see PHYSICAL FITNESS AND HYGIENE

794.2 CC ISSN 1002-8706
WEIQI TIANDI. (Text in Chinese) m. $36.80. Xin Tiyu Zazhishe, 8 Tiyuguan Lu, Beijing 100061, People's Republic of China. TEL 415-282-2994; 7012603. FAX 415-282-0994. (Dist. in US by: China Books & Periodicals, Inc., 2929 24th St., San Francisco, CA 94110. TEL 415-282-2994) Ed. Hao Keqiang. **Document type:** consumer publication.
Description: Covers the Chinese board game of weiqi.

790.1 UK
WELSH AMATEUR SWIMMING ASSOCIATION. HANDBOOK. 1897. every 4 yrs. £10. Welsh Amateur Swimming Association, Wales Empire Pool, Wood St., Cardiff, S. Glam CF1 1PP, Wales. FAX 01222-342201. adv. circ. 500. (looseleaf format) **Document type:** bulletin.

796.815
WHO'S WHO IN KARATE AND THE OTHER MARTIAL ARTS AND DIRECTORY OF BLACK BELTS.* a. Who's Who in Karate, Box 490, Grimesland, NC 27837-0490. Ed. Jerri Harris. **Document type:** directory.

793 US ISSN 1047-854X
GV1301
WIN. 1977. m. $44 (foreign $51). Gambling Times, Inc., 16140 Valerio St., Ste. B, Van Nuys, CA 91406-2916. TEL 818-781-9355. FAX 818-781-3125. adv.; bk.rev.; charts; illus.; stat.; circ. 50,000 (paid). (also avail. in microfiche from UMI; back issues avail.)
—UnCover.
Formerly: Gambling Times (ISSN 0149-0214)
Description: Offers news, views, advice, strategy, and statistics on gaming. Includes betting guides, reviews on casino conditions, and information on the casino and hotel entertainment scene.

WINCHESTER COLLECTOR. see HOBBIES

790.1 US
WINDY CITY SPORTS. 1987. 12/yr. $15. Chicago Sports Resources, Inc., 1450 W. Randolph, Chicago, IL 60607. TEL 312-421-1551. FAX 312-421-1454. Ed. Jeff Banowetz; Pub. Mary Thorne. adv. contact: Doug Kaplan. bk.rev. circ. 100,000. (tabloid format) **Document type:** consumer publication.

WINGED FOOT. see PHYSICAL FITNESS AND HYGIENE

790.1 US ISSN 1055-7830
GV1049
WINNING (ALLENTOWN).* m. $2.50 per no. Winning Productions, Inc., Box 21130, Lehigh Valley, PA 18002-1130. TEL 610-821-6864. **Indexed:** Sportsearch (1987-).

796.72 US ISSN 0744-4869
WINSTON CUP ILLUSTRATED. 1982. m. $40 (effective Jan. 1992). American City Business Journals (Charlotte), 128 S. Tyron St., Ste. 2275, Charlotte, NC 28205. TEL 704-371-3966. FAX 704-371-3990. Ed. Steve Waid. adv. contact: Brett Underwood. circ. 20,000. (back issues avail.) **Document type:** consumer publication.
—CCC.
Description: Contains interviews and stories about the people in the NASCAR Winston Cup Series.

796.72 US ISSN 1053-461X
WINSTON CUP SCENE. 1976. w. American City Business Journals, 128 Tryon St., Ste. 2275, Charlotte, NC 28202. TEL 704-371-3966. FAX 704-371-3980. adv.: B&W page $2041, color page $3217; trim 10 1/4 x 13. circ. 85,352.
—CCC.

790.1 613.7 US
WISCONSIN IN MOTION. 1991. bi-m. $7.95. K.J. Gladstone, Ed. & Pub., 9231 W. Bonniwell Rd., Mequon, WI 53092. TEL 414-241-5994. FAX 414-255-7939. adv.; B&W page $647; trim 11 x 17; adv. contact: Mary Zettel. circ. 25,000. **Document type:** consumer publication.
Description: Dedicated to sports and fitness.

790.1 US ISSN 0273-8945
WOLFPACKER. 1980. 20/yr. $27.95. Coman Publishing Company, Inc., 505 S. Duke St., Ste. 504, Durham, NC 27701. TEL 919-688-0218. FAX 919-682-1532. (Subscr. to: Box 2331, Durham, NC 27702) Ed. Todd McGee. circ. 13,500. **Document type:** consumer publication.
Description: For N C State University sports fans.

790.1 US ISSN 1048-9940
WOLVERINE. 1989. $39.95. Coman Publishing Company, Inc., 505 S. Duke St., Ste. 504, Durham, NC 27701. TEL 919-688-0218. FAX 919-682-1532. (Subscr. to: Box 2331, Durham, NC 27702) Eds. John Borton, Paul Dodd. adv.: B&W page $400, color page $600; 10 x 13 1/2. circ. 13,650. **Document type:** consumer publication.
Description: For University of Michigan sports fans.

799.3 US ISSN 1045-7704
GV1151
WOMEN & GUNS MAGAZINE. 1989. m. $24.00. Second Amendment Foundation, Box 488, Buffalo, NY 14209. TEL 716-885-6408. FAX 716-884-4771. Ed. Peggy Tartaro. circ. 18,000. **Document type:** consumer publication.
Description: For female gun owners who want to learn more about pleasure shooting and self-defense. Provides information on legislative issues, competition shooting and differences between types of guns.

WOMEN IN SPORT AND PHYSICAL ACTIVITY JOURNAL. see WOMEN'S STUDIES — Abstracting, Bibliographies, Statistics

790.1 US ISSN 8750-653X
GV709
WOMEN'S SPORTS AND FITNESS. 1974. 8/yr. $19.97. 2025 Pearl St., Boulder, CO 80302. TEL 303-440-5111. FAX 303-440-4313. (Subscr. to: Box 472, Mt. Morris, IL 61054) Ed. Mary Duffy; Pub. Jane McConnell. adv. contact: Annie Weber. bk.rev.; illus.; circ. 155,000 (paid). (also avail. in microform from UMI; back issues avail.) **Indexed:** Acad.Ind., Hlth.Ind., Jun.High.Mag.Abstr., Mag.Ind., PMR, Sports Per.Ind., Sportsearch (1985-). **Document type:** consumer publication.
●Also available online. Vendor(s): University Microfilms International.
Also available on CD-ROM. Producer(s): University Microfilms International.
—BLDSC (9343.545000); Faxon; UMI; UnCover. CCC.
Formerly (until 1984): Women's Sports (ISSN 0163-7428)
Description: Provides profiles, how-to articles, equipment reviews, travel articles, and reports about various women's sports issues.

790.1 301.412 US ISSN 1061-1568
WOMEN'S SPORTS EXPERIENCE. 1985. bi-m. membership. Women's Sports Foundation, Eisenhower Park, East Meadow, NY 11554-1000. TEL 516-542-4700; 800-227-3988. FAX 516-542-4716. Ed. Lynnore Lawton. adv. circ. 9,000. (back issues avail.) **Document type:** newsletter.
Formerly (until 1992): Headway (ISSN 1044-7377)
Description: Covers all areas of women in sports, with emphasis on issues that affect women's participation in or leadership of sports.

796.47 AT ISSN 1038-6963
WORLD ACROBATICS. 1954. m. Aus.$19($25) Association of Acrobats, Unit 84, 10 Minkara Rd., Bayview, N.S.W. 2104, Australia. TEL 61-2-99991851. Ed. R.P.H. Samuels. adv.; bk.rev.; dance rev.; play rev.; charts; illus. circ. 1,500. **Indexed:** Sportsearch. **Document type:** trade publication, newsletter, bibliography.
Supersedes: Acrobatic.

737 UK ISSN 0255-4429
WORLD BADMINTON. 1970. q. £6 in the U.K. and Ireland; overseas £8 (effective 1994-1995). International Badminton Federation, 4 Manor Park, Mackenzie Way, Cheltenham, Glos. GL51 9TX, England. TEL 01242-234904. FAX 01242-221030. Ed. R. Ward. adv. contact: Kate Killworth. circ. 9,000. **Indexed:** Sportsearch. **Document type:** consumer publication.
Description: Contains articles on the world of badminton: news, international events, tournaments and results.

796.83 US ISSN 1051-9033
WORLD BOXING. 7/yr. $24.60 includes Boxing (outside US & Canada $34) (effective 1994). London Publishing Co., Box 910, Fort Washington, PA 19034. TEL 215-643-6385. FAX 215-540-0146. Ed. Steve Farhood. adv.; illus. **Indexed:** Sports Per.Ind. **Document type:** consumer publication.

790.1 US
WORLD GAMING REPORT. 18/yr. $60. 2265 Westwood Blvd., Ste. B214, Los Angeles, CA 90064.

796.355 UK ISSN 0964-0681
WORLD HOCKEY. (Text in English) 1969. q. £7 (foreign £10). (International Hockey Federation, BE) Harrow Press, Unit E6, Aladdin Workspace, 426 Long Dr., Greenford, Mddx. UB6 8UH, England. TEL 0181-575-3121. FAX 0181-575-1320. TELEX 63393 FIH G. Ed. Chris Moore. adv. contact: Peter J. Luck. bk.rev.; illus. circ. 3,500. **Indexed:** Sportsearch (1975-). **Document type:** consumer publication.
Description: Contains color photographs, full reports on all major world events, results, fixtures, and features.

WORLD LEISURE AND RECREATION. see LEISURE AND RECREATION

SPORTS AND GAMES

790.1 613.7   US   ISSN 0380-4712
THE WORLD OF A S P. 1974. q. $5. American Self-Protection Association, 825 Greengate Oval, Sagamore Hills, OH 44067. TEL 216-467-7110. FAX 216-457-6834. Eds. Nellie D. Baltazzi, Gary A. Cook. bk.rev.; circ. 55 (paid). (looseleaf format) **Document type:** newsletter.
    Description: Covers self-defense, combative sports, body-mind coordination, wellness, and fitness.
    Refereed Serial

790.1   GW
WORLD OF SPORT. 3/yr. Strebel Zielgruppen Verlag GmbH, Hoehenstr. 17, 70736 Fellbach, Germany. TEL 0711-5206-1. FAX 0711-5281424. Ed. Guenter Bayer. adv.; illus.
    Formerly (until 1990): Sport und Freizeit.

796.812   US   ISSN 1052-0899
THE WRESTLER. 1968. 13/yr. $19 for 12 issues in US & Canada (elsewhere $28.60) (effective 1994). London Publishing Co., Box 910, Fort Washington, PA 19034. TEL 215-643-6385. FAX 215-540-0146. Ed. Bill Apter. adv.; charts; illus.; tr.lit. **Document type:** consumer publication.

790.1   US   ISSN 0885-8551
WRESTLING ALL STARS HEROES AND VILLAINS. 1982. 8/yr. newsstand price: $2.95. Starlog Group, Inc., 475 Park Ave. S., New York, NY 10016. TEL 212-689-2830. FAX 212-889-7933. adv.; bk.rev. **Document type:** consumer publication.
    Formerly (until 1985): Wrestling All Stars (ISSN 0742-518X)

790.1   US
WRESTLING ALL STARS SCRAPBOOK. s-a. newsstand price: $4.50. Starlog Group, Inc., 475 Park Ave. S., New York, NY 10016. TEL 212-689-2830. FAX 212-889-7933. **Document type:** consumer publication.

790.1   US
WRESTLING CHATTERBOX. 1991. m. $25 (foreign $40). Georgiann Makroupolos, Ed. & Pub., 23-44 30th Dr., Astoria, NY 11102-3252. TEL 718-721-2369. FAX 718-721-5334. adv. contact: Georgiann Makroupolos. bk.rev.; illus. circ. 482. **Document type:** newsletter.
    Description: Covers wrestlers and wrestling match results, contests, wrestling nostalgia and most other topics related to wrestling.

790.1   US   ISSN 1060-0523
WRESTLING CLASSICS. 1989. q. newsstand price: $2.50. London Publishing Co., Box 910, Ft. Washington, PA 19034. TEL 215-643-6385. FAX 215-628-3571. **Document type:** consumer publication.

790.1   US
WRESTLING MANUAL AND CASE BOOK. biennial. $4. National Federation of State High School Associations, 11724 N.W. Plaza Circle, Box 20626, Kansas City, MO 64195-0626. TEL 816-464-5400. FAX 816-464-5571.
    Supersedes: Wrestling Officials Manual.

790.1   US   ISSN 0891-0707
THE WRESTLING NEWS. 1972. s-a. $12 (foreign $16). (Pro Wrestling Enterprises) Norman Kietzer, Ed. & Pub., Rt. 1, Box 103, Vernon Center, MN 56090. adv. circ. 9,000.

796.8   US
WRESTLING OBSERVER NEWSLETTER. 1982. w. $72. Dave Meltzer, Ed. & Pub., Box 1228, Campbell, CA 95009. TEL 408-379-8067. FAX 408-379-6562. circ. 5,600. **Document type:** newsletter.
    Description: Examines the business aspects of pro-wrestling.

790.1   US
WRESTLING PERSPECTIVE. 1990. m. $18 (effective 1996); newsstand price: 1.50. Box 351, Lyndon Center, VT 05850-0351. TEL 315-478-8052. Eds. Paul MacArthur, Davids Kolnik. bk.rev. circ. 150. **Document type:** newsletter.
    Description: Contains commentaries on wrestling, covers future developments of wrestling promotional strategies, and includes essays and interviews with classic wrestlers.

790.1   US   ISSN 0964-6701
WRESTLING RINGSIDE. 1991. bi-m. newsstand price: $2.95. Starlog Group, Inc., 475 Park Ave. S., New York, NY 10016. TEL 212-689-2830. FAX 212-889-7933. **Document type:** consumer publication.

790.1   US
WRESTLING RULEBOOK. a. $4. National Federation of State High School Associations, 11724 N.W. Plaza Circle, Box 20626, Kansas City, MO 64195-0626. TEL 816-464-5400. FAX 816-454-5571.

790.1   US   ISSN 0743-2720
WRESTLING SCENE PRESENTS RINGSIDE. 1983. 8/yr. $11.99. Starlog Group, Inc., 475 Park Ave. S., New York, NY 10016. TEL 212-689-2830. FAX 212-889-7933. Ed. Michael Benson.

790.1   US   ISSN 1042-5284
WRESTLING SUPERSTARS. q. newsstand price: $2.95. London Publishing Co., Box 910, Ft. Washington, PA 19034. TEL 215-643-6385. FAX 215-628-3571. **Document type:** consumer publication.

790.1   US
WRESTLING - THEN & NOW. 1990. m. $18 (overseas $30). Evan Ginzburg, Ed. & Pub., Box 640417, Oakland Gardens Sta., Flushing, NY 11364. TEL 718-740-4138. adv.; bk.rev. circ. 200. **Document type:** newsletter.
    Description: Contains anecdotes, clippings, and interviews regarding the old-days wrestling business and stories of new developments.

790.1   US   ISSN 0199-6258
WRESTLING U.S.A. MAGAZINE. 1964. m. $27 (foreign $37). 109 Apple House Ln., Missoula, MT 59802-3324. TEL 406-549-4448. FAX 406-549-4879. Ed. Lanny Bryant; Pub. Cody Bryant. adv. contact: Lanny Bryant. circ. 13,000. (also avail. in microform) **Document type:** consumer publication.
    —UnCover.
    Formerly: Scholastic Wrestling News.
    Description: Geared to wrestling coaches and amateur wrestlers.

796.812   US
WRESTLING WORLD. bi-m. Sterling - Macfadden Partnership, 233 Park Ave. So., New York, NY 10003. TEL 212-780-3500. FAX 212-780-3555. Ed. Stephen Ciacciarelli. adv.; illus.

796.8   CC
WUHUN/SOUL OF MARTIAL ARTS. (Text in Chinese) bi-m. $18.50. (Beijing Tiyu Yundong Weiyuanhui - Beijing Sports Society) Wuhun Zazhishe, 2 Luchangjie Toutiao, BeiweiLu, Xuanwuqu, Beijing 100050, People's Republic of China. TEL 3012785. (Dist. in US by: China Books & Periodicals, Inc., 2929 24th St., San Francisco, CA 94110. TEL 415-282-2994) Ed. Liu Xingzhong.

796.8   CC   ISSN 1000-7318
WULIN/MARTIAL ARTS. (Text in Chinese) 1980. m. $35.90. (Guangdong Sheng Wushu Xuehui - Guangdong Martial Arts Association) Guangdong Kexue Puji Chubanshe, 3 Xingping Li, Dahua Jie, Yingyuan Lu, Guangzhou, Guangdong 510047, People's Republic of China. (Dist. in US by: China Books & Periodicals, Inc., 2929 24th St., San Francisco, CA 94110. TEL 415-282-2994) Ed. Wang Guohui. circ. 200,000. **Document type:** consumer publication.
    ●Also available on CD-ROM.
    Description: Covers the developments in various martial arts styles, martial arts tournaments and other activities.

796.8 613.7   CC   ISSN 1002-8730
WUSHU JIANSHEN/HEALTH THROUGH MARTIAL ARTS. (Text in Chinese) bi-m. $20.70. Xin Tiyu Zazhishe, 8 Tiyuguan Lu, Beijing 100061, People's Republic of China. TEL 751761. (Dist. in US by: China Books & Periodicals, 2929 24th St., San Francisco, CA 94110. TEL 415-282-2994) Ed. Yang Dingxin. **Document type:** consumer publication.

794.18   CC
XIANG QI/CHINESE CHESS. (Text in Chinese) m. $17. China Books & Periodicals, 2929 24th St., San Francisco, CA 94110. TEL 415-282-2994. FAX 415-282-0994. **Document type:** consumer publication.

794.18   CC   ISSN 1002-1906
XIANGQI YANJIU/STUDIES IN CHINESE CHESS. (Text in Chinese) 1977. bi-m. Y1 per no. (Harbin Tiyu Yundong Weiyuanhui - Harbin Sports Commission) Xiangqi Yanjiu Bianjibu, Renmin Tiyuchang - People's Stadium, Harbin, Heilongjiang 150020, People's Republic of China. TEL 4687911. (Dist. in US by: China Books & Periodicals, Inc., 2929 24th St., San Francisco, CA 94110. TEL 415-282-2994) Ed. Jin Qichang. **Document type:** consumer publication.

796   CC   ISSN 0441-3679
XIN TIYU/NEW SPORTS. (Text in Chinese) 1950. m. $41.30. Xin Tiyu Zazhishe, 8 Tiyuguan Lu, Beijing 100061. TEL 751402. (Dist. in US by: China Books & Periodicals, Inc., 2929 24th St., San Francisco, CA 94110. TEL 415-282-2994) Ed. Hao Keqiang. **Document type:** consumer publication.

Y M C A WEEKLY NEWS (VANCOUVER, BC). (Vancouver Downtown Young Men's Christian Association) see *PHYSICAL FITNESS AND HYGIENE*

794.1   UK   ISSN 0305-5132
YEAR BOOK OF CHESS. 1919. a. £9.99. (British Chess Federation) B T Batsford Books Ltd., 4 Fitzhardinge St., London W1H 0AH, England. TEL 0171-486-8484. Ed. John Poole. adv. contact: Grete White. stat.; index. circ. 2,500. **Document type:** consumer publication, directory.
    Description: Covers historical records and results. Includes club directory.

797.21   CC   ISSN 1000-3495
YOUYONG/SWIMMING. (Text in Chinese) 1983. bi-m. $25.20. (Zhongguo Youyong Xiehui - China Swimming Association) Renmin Tiyu Chubanshe - People's Sports Publishing House, 8 Tiyuguan Lu, Chongwen Qu, Beijing 100061, People's Republic of China. TEL 5112466. FAX 7016129. (Dist. in U.S. by: China Books & Periodicals, Inc., 2929 24th St., San Francisco, CA 94110. TEL 415-282-2994)

ZAJI YU MOSHU/ACROBATICS AND MAGIC. see *HOBBIES*

ZAMBIA. MINISTRY OF YOUTH AND SPORT. DEPARTMENT OF YOUTH DEVELOPMENT. ANNUAL REPORT. see *CHILDREN AND YOUTH — Abstracting, Bibliographies, Statistics*

796   ZA
ZAMBIA. MINISTRY OF YOUTH AND SPORT. REPORT. 1968. a. K.100 (effective 1992). Zambia Government Printing Department, P.O. Box 30136, Lusaka, Zambia. **Document type:** government publication.
    Formerly: Zambia. Sports Directorate. Report (ISSN 0084-506X)

799.2   GW   ISSN 0044-2887
    CODEN: ZEJAAA
ZEITSCHRIFT FUER JAGDWISSENSCHAFT. (Text in German; summaries in English, French and German) 1955. q. DM.211($156) to individuals in Europe (rest of world DM.223($165)); institutions in Europe DM.331($245) (rest of world DM.343($254)) (effective 1996). Blackwell Wissenschaft, Kurfuerstendamm 57, 10707 Berlin, Germany. TEL 030-32790634. FAX 030-32790610. Ed. E. Ueckermann. adv.; bk.rev.; illus.; index. (reprint service avail. from ISI; back issues avail.) **Indexed:** Apic.Abstr., Biol.Abstr., Chem.Abstr., Curr.Adv.Ecol.Sci., Curr.Cont., Excerp.Med., Forest.Abstr., Forest Prod.Abstr., Geo.Abstr., Helminthol.Abstr., Ind.Vet., Key Word Ind.Wildl.Res., Protozool.Abstr., Sport Fish.Abstr., Vet.Bull., Wild.Rev., Zoo.Rec. **Document type:** academic/scholarly publication.
    —BLDSC (9467.400000); Genuine Article. **CCC**.

790.1   US
ZHONGGUO TIYU BAO/CHINA'S SPORTS NEWS. (Text in Chinese) 4/w. $364.50. China Books & Periodicals, Inc., 2929 24th St., San Francisco, CA 94110. TEL 415-282-2994. FAX 415-282-0994. **Document type:** newspaper.

796.8   CC   ISSN 1000-3525
GV1100.7.A2
ZHONGHUA WUSHU/CHINESE MARTIAL ARTS. (Text in Chinese) 1982. m. $41.30. (Zhongguo Wushu Xiehui - China Wushu Association) Renmin Tiyu Chubanshe - People's Sports Publishing House, 8 Tiyuguan Lu, Chongwen Qu, Beijing 100061, People's Republic of China. TEL 5112466. FAX 7016129. (Dist. in U.S. by: China Books & Periodicals, Inc., 2929 24th St., San Francisco, CA 94110. TEL 415-282-2994)

790.1   SZ
ZUERCHER LEICHTATHLET. 6/yr. Postfach 568, CH-8039 Zurich, Switzerland. TEL 01-325370. FAX 01-4621915. circ. 3,500.

794.1   RU
64; shakhmatnoe obozrenie. 24/yr. $35. Kalinina Prospect, d 7-6, Moscow 121019, Russia. Ed. A.E. Karpov.
    Description: Provides current chess news and includes articles.

790.1   UK   ISSN 0959-969X
90 MINUTES. 1990. w. £50. I P C Magazines, Specialist Magazine Group (Subsidiary of: Reed Elsevier plc), King's Reach Tower, Stamford St., London SE1 9LS, England. TEL 0171-261-5000. FAX 01444-440619. TELEX 892084 REEDBP G. (Dist. by: Quadrant Subscription Services, Oakfield House, Perrymount Rd., Haywards Heath, W. Sussex RH16 3DH, England. TEL 01622-721555) adv. contact: Julian Clark. circ. 67,000. (back issues avail.) **Document type:** consumer publication.
    Description: For 16- to 34-year-olds; contains news, features and statistics about the English and Scottish soccer league team and players.

SPORTS AND GAMES — Abstracting, Bibliographies, Statistics

796.323   US
BASKETBALL STATISTICIANS' MANUAL. a. $2.75. National Collegiate Athletic Association, Circulation Department, Box 7347, Overland Park, KS 66207-0347. TEL 913-339-1900. stat.
    Description: Provides official statistics rules, interpretations, and special rulings.

796.93   US
BIBLIOGRAPHY OF SKIING STUDIES. irreg., 8th edition, 1989. $25. University of Colorado, Business Research Division, Campus Box 420, Boulder, CO 80309-0420. TEL 303-492-8227. FAX 303-492-3620. Ed. C.R. Goeldner. circ. 200. **Document type:** bibliography.

797   FR   ISSN 0067-8260
BIBLIOTHEQUE DE LA MER. 1970. irreg. price varies. Tchou Editeur, 6 rue du Mail, 75002 Paris, France. **Document type:** bibliography.

796.95 310   US   ISSN 0163-7207
GV776.A2
BOATING REGISTRATION STATISTICS. a. $20. National Marine Manufacturers Association, 401 N. Michigan Ave., Chicago, IL 60611. TEL 312-836-4747. stat. Indexed: SRI.
    Description: State-by-state analysis of registered pleasure boats by length, hull material and propulsion system.

796.95   US
BOATING STATISTICS. 1960. a. free. U.S. Coast Guard, Commandant G-NAB, 2100 Second St., S.W., Washington, DC 20593-0001. TEL 202-267-0955. stat. circ. 7,000. **Document type:** government publication.
    Formerly: U.S. Coast Guard Boating Statistics (ISSN 0565-1530)

790.1   GW   ISSN 0941-6633
C D - R O M SPORTWISSENSCHAFT. (Text in English, German) 1990. a. DM.1200. (Bundesinstitut fuer Sportwissenschaft) Czwalina Verlag, Postfach 730240, 22122 Hamburg, Germany. TEL 040-6780025. FAX 040-6780051. **Document type:** bibliography.
● Available only on CD-ROM.

C F L FACTS, FIGURES AND RECORDS. (Canadian Football League) see SPORTS AND GAMES — Ball Games

CENTRE FOR SPORTS SCIENCE AND HISTORY. SERIAL HOLDINGS. see EDUCATION — Abstracting, Bibliographies, Statistics

790.1   UK   ISSN 0142-1484
CHARTERED INSTITUTE OF PUBLIC FINANCE AND ACCOUNTANCY. CHARGES FOR LEISURE SERVICES. ACTUALS. 1979. a. £42. Chartered Institute of Public Finance and Accountancy, 3 Robert St., London WC2N 6BH, England. TEL 071-895-8823. FAX 071-895-8825. (back issues avail.)
—BLDSC (3129.913100).

790.1   UK   ISSN 0141-187X
CHARTERED INSTITUTE OF PUBLIC FINANCE AND ACCOUNTANCY. LEISURE AND RECREATION STATISTICS. ESTIMATES. 1977. a. £63. Chartered Institute of Public Finance and Accountancy, Statistical Information Service, 3 Robert St., London WC2N 6BH, England. TEL 0171-895-8823. FAX 0171-895-8825. stat. (back issues avail.)
—BLDSC (5182.210000).
    Formerly: Chartered Institute of Public Finance and Accountancy. Leisure Estimate Statistics.

790.1   UK
CHARTERED INSTITUTE OF PUBLIC FINANCE AND ACCOUNTANCY. LEISURE CHARGES STATISTICS. ACTUALS. a. £44. Chartered Institute of Public Finance and Accountancy, Statistical Information Service, 3 Robert St., London WC2N 6BH, England. TEL 0171-895-8823. FAX 0171-895-8825. (back issues avail.)

EL CLARIN DE LA BUSCA. see SPORTS AND GAMES

790   US
GV53
CONGRESS FOR RECREATION AND PARKS. SYMPOSIUM FOR LEISURE RESEARCH. ABSTRACTS. a. $20. National Recreation and Park Association, 2775 S. Quincy St., No. 300, Arlington, VA 22206. TEL 703-820-4940. FAX 703-671-6772. index. **Document type:** abstracting/indexing.
    Supersedes in part: Congress for Recreation and Parks. Proceedings (ISSN 0069-8903)

796.358   UK
CRICKET STATISTICIAN. 1973. q. £12. Association of Cricket Statisticians, 3 Radcliffe Rd., West Bridgford, Nottingham NG2 5FF, England. TEL 01602-455407. Ed. Philip J. Bailey. adv.; bk.rev.; stat. circ. 1,500. (back issues avail.) **Document type:** consumer publication.
    Description: Covers historical research articles and cricket statistical analyses.

796.357   US
CURRENT BASEBALL PUBLICATIONS. vol.8, no.2, 1993. q. (plus a. summary). $8 (Canada $10; overseas $12). Society for American Baseball Research, Box 93183, Cleveland, OH 44101. TEL 216-575-0500. Ed. Richard Arpi. adv. contact: Morris Eckhouse. **Document type:** bibliography.
    Description: Lists new books and periodicals dealing with all facets of baseball.

796.420684   DK   ISSN 0107-4547
D A F I TAL. 1977. a. DKK 100 in Denmark; Europe DKK 140; elsewhere DKK 160. Dansk Atletik Forbund, Idraettens Hus, Broendby Stadion 20, 2605 Broendby, Denmark. TEL 45-43-26-26-26. FAX 45-43-26-23-25. illus.
    Formerly: Dansk Atletik Forbund. Statistik.

790.1 016   UK   ISSN 1352-3201
DIRECTORY OF EUROPEAN SPORTS ORGANISATIONS. 1992. irreg. £48($96). C.B.D. Research Ltd., 15 Wickham Rd., Beckenham, Kent BR3 2JS, England. TEL 0181-650-7745. FAX 0181-650-0768. (Dist. in the U.S. by: Gale Research Co., 835 Penobscot Bldg., Detroit, MI 48226. TEL 313-961-2242. FAX 313-961-6083) **Document type:** directory.
    Description: Lists 1,500 national sports organizations based in Europe.

790.1 616   CN   ISSN 1192-1420
DRUG FILE UPDATE; a current awareness index to publications on drugs and doping in sport. s-a. $45. Sport Information Resource Centre (SIRC) - Centre de Documentation pour le Sport, 1600 James Naismith Dr., Gloucester, ON K1B 5N4, Canada. TEL 613-748-5658. FAX 613-748-5701. TELEX 053-3660. (Co-sponsor: Canadian Centre for Drug-Free Sport) **Document type:** abstracting/indexing.
    Description: Reflects the latest literature and concerns about drugs and doping in sport from around the world. References grouped by individual sport and country.

FISHERIES REVIEW; an indexing service for fishery research and management. see FISH AND FISHERIES — Abstracting, Bibliographies, Statistics

688.76   US
FITNESS IN AMERICA. 1987. biennial. $65. National Sporting Goods Association, 1699 Wall St., Mt. Prospect, IL 60056-5780. TEL 708-439-4000. FAX 708-439-0111. Ed. Thomas B. Doyle.
    Description: Analysis of adult participation in 7 fitness activities, with geographical and demographic information.

796.332   US
FOOTBALL STATISTICIAN'S MANUAL. a. $2.75. National Collegiate Athletic Association, Circulation Department, Box 7347, Overland Park, KS 66207-0347. TEL 913-339-1900. stat.
    Description: Provides official statistics rules, interpretations, and special rulings.

HEALTH, PHYSICAL EDUCATION AND RECREATION MICROFORM PUBLICATIONS BULLETIN. see PHYSICAL FITNESS AND HYGIENE — Abstracting, Bibliographies, Statistics

790.1 011   US   ISSN 1041-2859
GV583
INDEX TO THE SPORTING NEWS. (Coverage starts from 1975) 1991. triennial. John Gordon Burke Publisher, Inc., Box 1492, Evanston, IL 60204-1492. TEL 708-866-8625. **Document type:** abstracting/indexing.
● Also available online.
    Description: Subject index to the Sporting News.

688.76   US
LIFESTYLE CHARACTERISTICS OF SPORTING GOODS CONSUMERS. a. $195. National Sporting Goods Association, 1699 Wall St., Mt. Prospect, IL 60056-5780. TEL 708-439-4000. FAX 708-439-0111. Ed. Thomas B. Doyle.
    Description: Provides geographical and demographic analysis of sporting goods consumers, for individual products as well as product groupings.

N C A A BASEBALL & SOFTBALL. (National Collegiate Athletic Association) see SPORTS AND GAMES — Ball Games

N C A A FOOTBALL. (National Collegiate Athletic Association) see SPORTS AND GAMES — Ball Games

688.76   US   ISSN 1073-0818
N S G A TEAM LICENSED & SPORTS CLOTHING DIARY. 1991. a. $395 to non-members. National Sporting Goods Association, 1699 Wall St., Mt. Prospect, IL 60056-5780. TEL 708-439-4000. FAX 708-439-0111. Ed. Thomas B. Doyle. **Document type:** trade publication.
    Former titles: N S G A Sports Clothing Diary; N S G A Sports Apparel Diary.
    Description: Analyzes sport and nonsport apparel purchases, with demographic data of purchasers for several product categories.

SPORTS AND GAMES — BALL GAMES

796.9 CN ISSN 0828-6647
GV847.8.N3
NATIONAL HOCKEY LEAGUE. OFFICIAL GUIDE & RECORD BOOK. 1932. a. $21. National Hockey League Publishing, 194 Doversourt Rd., Toronto, ON M6J 3L8, Canada. TEL 416-531-6535. (Issued in the U.S. by: Triumph Books, 644 S. Clark St., Chicago, IL 60605. TEL 312-939-3330. FAX 312-663-3557) Eds. Greg Inglis, Dan Diamond. **Document type:** consumer publication.
  Formed by the 1985 merger of: National Hockey League. Official Guide (ISSN 0826-5038); National Hockey League. Official Record Book (ISSN 0826-0214); Which was formerly (until 1983): National Hockey League Guide (ISSN 0316-8174); (until 1965): National Hockey League Press and Radio Guide (ISSN 0466-2997)
  Description: Statistics of contemporary and historic achievements in the National Hockey League. Contains a complete register of all professional players and prospects.

629.227 NE ISSN 0168-5864
NETHERLANDS. CENTRAAL BUREAU VOOR DE STATISTIEK. PRODUKTIESTATISTIEKEN: RIJWIEL- EN MOTORRIJWIELINDUSTRIE. (Text in Dutch; summaries in English) a. Centraal Bureau voor de Statistiek, Prinses Beatrixlaan 428, Voorburg, Netherlands. (Subscr. to: SDU - Publishers, Christoffel Plantijnstraat, The Hague, Netherlands) **Document type:** government publication.

790 314 NE ISSN 0168-4248
NETHERLANDS. CENTRAAL BUREAU VOOR DE STATISTIEK. STATISTIEK VAN DE INKOMSTEN EN UITGAVEN DER OVERHEID VOOR CULTUUR EN RECREATIE/NETHERLANDS. CENTRAL BUREAU OF STATISTICS. STATISTICS OF GOVERNMENT EXPENDITURE ON CULTURE AND RECREATION. (Text in Dutch and English) 1964. a. Centraal Bureau voor de Statistiek, Prinses Beatrixlaan 428, Voorburg, Netherlands. (Dist. by: SDU - Publishers, Christoffel Plantijnstraat 2, Postbus 20014, 2500 EA The Hague, Netherlands) **Document type:** government publication.
  Formerly: Netherlands. Centraal Bureau voor de Statistiek. Statistiek van de Uitgaven der Overheid voor Cultuur en Recreatie (ISSN 0077-7196)

OFFICIAL N C A A BASKETBALL. see *SPORTS AND GAMES — Ball Games*

OFFICIAL N C A A FINAL FOUR RECORDS BOOK. see *SPORTS AND GAMES — Ball Games*

OFFICIAL RULES OF BASKETBALL (YEAR). see *SPORTS AND GAMES — Ball Games*

OFFICIAL S E C FOOTBALL GUIDE. see *SPORTS AND GAMES — Ball Games*

796.5 388.344 US ISSN 0744-9569
R V BUSINESS. (Recreational Vehicle) 1972. m. (plus a. directory). $48. T L Enterprises, Inc., 3601 Calle Tecate, Camarillo, CA 93012. TEL 805-389-0300. FAX 805-389-0484. E-mail: 76062,1371@compuserve.com. Ed. Stephen Boilon; Pub. Michael Schneider. adv.: B&W page $2890; color page $4165; trim 8 x 10 3/4; adv. contact: Janet Van Bibber. charts; stat.; tr.lit.; circ. 13,510 (controlled). (also avail. in microfiche from CIS) **Indexed:** Bus.Ind., SRI, Tr.& Indus.Ind. **Document type:** trade publication.
  Incorporates: R V Business. Annual R V Industry Directory (ISSN 0893-6501); Former titles (until 1983): Recreational Vehicle Dealer (ISSN 0886-0041); (until 1982): R V Dealer (ISSN 0190-6747); Which incorporated (in 1980): R V R - Recreational Vehicle Retailer (ISSN 0090-3841)
  Description: Provides statistics about the economical and business aspects of the industry.

REFERATOVY VYBER ZE SPORTOVNI MEDICINY A LECEBNE REHABILITACE/ABSTRACTS OF SPORTS MEDICINE AND REHABILITATION. see *MEDICAL SCIENCES — Abstracting, Bibliographies, Statistics*

380 796 310 CN ISSN 0318-9422
SANFORD EVANS GOLD BOOK OF SNOWMOBILE DATA AND USED PRICES. 1972. a. Can.$16.50. Sanford Evans Communications Ltd., 1700 Church Ave., Box 6900, Winnipeg, MB R3C 3B1, Canada. TEL 204-694-2022. FAX 204-694-3040. Ed. Gary Henry; Pub. Gary Henry.
  Description: Current model year and previous thirteen model years listed with weight, length, track width and engine statistics. Factory suggested price and current resale values are featured.

688.76 US ISSN 1073-080X
SPORT CLOTHING EXPENDITURES IN (YEAR). a. $195 to non-members. National Sporting Goods Association, 1699 Wall St., Mt. Prospect, IL 60056-5780. TEL 708-439-4000. FAX 708-439-0111. Ed. Thomas B. Doyle.
  Description: Demographic and financial analysis of clothing purchases related to sports participation.

790.1 CN ISSN 0831-6317
SPORT THESAURUS; the thesaurus of terminology used in the Sport Database. irreg. $65. Sport Information Resource Centre (SIRC) - Centre de Documentation pour le Sport, 1600 James Naismith Dr., Gloucester, ON K1B 5N4, Canada. TEL 613-748-5658. FAX 613-748-5701. TELEX 053-3660. Ed.Bd.
  ●Also available online. Vendor(s): Ovid Technologies.

688.76 US ISSN 0193-8401
HD9992.U5
SPORTING GOODS MARKET. 1973. a. $195. National Sporting Goods Association, 1699 Wall St., Mt. Prospect, IL 60056-5780. TEL 708-439-4000. FAX 708-439-0111. Ed. Thomas B. Doyle. (also avail. in microform; back issues avail.) **Indexed:** SRI.
  Description: Reports consumer purchases of sports equipment and footwear, with channels of distribution and demographic information on age, sex, income, education and census region.

SPORTS DOCUMENTATION MONTHLY BULLETIN. see *EDUCATION — Abstracting, Bibliographies, Statistics*

796 US ISSN 1073-0826
SPORTS EQUIPMENT EXPENDITURES. 1993. a. $195. National Sporting Goods Association, 1699 Wall St., Mt. Prospect, IL 60056-5780. TEL 708-439-4000. FAX 708-439-0111. Ed. Thomas B. Doyle.
  Description: Provides total dollar sporting goods equipment expenditures for 21 sports, including total number of households, average dollar expenditures per household, and household demographics.

688.76 US
SPORTS PARTICIPATION IN (YEAR): LIFECYCLE DEMOGRAPHICS. a. $195. National Sporting Goods Association, 1699 Wall St., Mt. Prospect, IL 60056-5780. TEL 708-439-4000. FAX 708-439-0111. Ed. Thomas B. Doyle.
  Description: Analyzes sports participation by economic status of the participants.

688.76 US ISSN 0882-8210
GV583
SPORTS PARTICIPATION IN (YEAR): SERIES 1. a. $195. National Sporting Goods Association, 1699 Wall St., Mt. Prospect, IL 60056-5780. TEL 708-439-4000. FAX 708-439-0111. Ed. Thomas B. Doyle.
  Description: Publishes results of research studies on participation in 26 of the most popular sports, with frequency distributions, average days of participation and extensive demographic data on participants.

688.76 US
SPORTS PARTICIPATION IN (YEAR): SERIES 2. a. $195. National Sporting Goods Association, 1699 Wall St., Mt. Prospect, IL 60056-5780. TEL 708-439-4000. FAX 708-439-0111. Ed. Thomas B. Doyle.
  Description: Publishes results of research studies on participation in 21 activities from archery to waterskiing. Includes frequency levels, average days of participation and demographic data by age, sex, income and region of the country.

688.76 US
SPORTS PARTICIPATION IN (YEAR): STATE BY STATE. a. $195. National Sporting Goods Association, 1699 Wall St., Mt. Prospect, IL 60056-5780. TEL 708-439-4000. FAX 708-439-0111. Ed. Thomas B. Doyle.
  Description: Projects sports participation on a state by state basis for 34 sports ranging from aerobics and bowling to skiing, tennis and volleyball.

790.1 016 613.7 CN ISSN 0882-553X
GV561
SPORTSEARCH. (Text in English, French) 1974. m. $130 to individuals; institutions $240. Sport Information Resource Centre (SIRC) - Centre de Documentation pour le Sport, 1600 James Naismith Drive, Gloucester, ON K1B 5N4, Canada. TEL 613-748-5658. FAX 613-748-5701. Ed.Bd. **Document type:** abstracting/indexing.
  ●Also available online. Vendor(s): Ovid Technologies (SFDB), Data-Star, Knight-Ridder, Inc.
  Also available on CD-ROM. Producer(s): SilverPlatter Information, Inc..
  Former titles (until 1985): Sport and Fitness Index (ISSN 0826-7537); (until 1984): Sport and Recreation Index - Index de la Litterature des Sports et des Loisirs (ISSN 0705-6095); (until 1977): Sport Articles.

798.4 UK ISSN 0307-0093
STATISTICAL RECORD. 1971. 3/yr. £100. Weatherbys, Sanders Rd., Wellingborough, Northants. NN8 4BX, England. TEL 01933-440077. FAX 01933-440807. TELEX 311582-ODECS. adv. contact: Steve Boxall. stat. circ. 1,000. **Document type:** bulletin.

315.61 TU
TURKEY. DEVLET ISTATISTIK ENSTITUSU. SPOR KULUPLERI/TURKEY. STATE INSTITUTE OF STATISTICS. SPORTS CLUBS. (Text in English, Turkish) 1972. a., latest 1987. Devlet Istatistik Enstitusu - State Institute of Statistics, Necatibey Caddesi No. 114, 06100 Ankara, Turkey. TEL 90-312-4185027. FAX 90-312-4170432. **Document type:** government publication.

799 310 US ISSN 0736-6450
SK41
U.S. FISH AND WILDLIFE SERVICE. NATIONAL SURVEY OF FISHING, HUNTING, AND WILDLIFE-ASSOCIATED RECREATION. 1955. irreg., 6th, 1982. U.S. Fish and Wildlife Service, Washington, DC 20240. TEL 303-226-9403. charts; illus.; stat.
  Formerly (until 1980): U.S. Fish and Wildlife Service. National Survey of Hunting, Fishing and Wildlife-Associated Recreation (ISSN 0191-6947)

WILDLIFE REVIEW (FORT COLLINS); an indexing service for wildlife management. see *CONSERVATION — Abstracting, Bibliographies, Statistics*

SPORTS AND GAMES — Ball Games

796.323 US ISSN 0733-0448
A C C BASKETBALL HANDBOOK. (Atlantic Coast Conference) 1974. a. $6. U M I Publications, Inc., 1135 N. Tryon St., Box 30036, Charlotte, NC 28230. TEL 704-374-0420. FAX 704-374-0729. Ed. Ivan Mothershead; Pub. Ivan Mothershead. adv. contact: Mark R. Cantey. circ. 110,000. (back issues avail.)

796.332 AT
A C T A F L FOOTBALL RECORD. 1946. w. Aus.$30 (effective 1996). A C T Australian Football League, P.O. Box 364, Woden, A.C.T. 2606, Australia. TEL 06-282-4620. FAX 06-281-6136. Ed. Stephen Dobbie. adv. circ. 400. **Document type:** newsletter.
  Description: Provides team lists, results, predictions, League news, and advertising of sponsors products and services.

794.6 US ISSN 0001-1754
GV909
A L B A BOWLS. 1962. q. $3. American Lawn Bowls Association, 445 Surfview Dr., Pacific Palisades, CA 90272. Ed. Ferrell Burton, Jr. adv.; illus.; index. circ. 6,000. **Indexed:** Sportsearch (1977-).

796.3 US ISSN 0890-5649
A P B A JOURNAL. 1967. m. $27. Eric Naftaly, Ed. & Pub., Box 5405, San Francisco, CA 94083-5405. TEL 415-757-1122. FAX 415-757-1122. E-mail: 70303.3063@cis.com. adv.; charts; stat; circ. 2,500 (paid). (processed) **Document type:** newsletter.
  Description: Covers sports table games and computer games produces by APBA Game Company and allied companies.

796 SW ISSN 0567-4565
AARETS FOTBOLL. 1956. a. SEK 861 (effective 1990). (Svenska Fotbollfoerbundet) Stroemberg - Brunnhage, P.O. Box 65, 162 11 Vaellingby, Sweden.

SPORTS AND GAMES — BALL GAMES

796.334   UK
THE ABSOLUTE GAME; a Scottish football fanzine. 1987. bi-m. £6 (N. America £12). Absolute Game Ltd., P.O. Box 303, Southern D.O., Edinburgh EH9 1NE, Scotland. (Alt. addr.: 4 Gladstone Terr., Edinburgh EH9 1LX, Scotland) Ed. Archie MacGregor. bk.rev. circ. 3,000. (back issues avail.) **Document type:** consumer publication.
    Description: Covers soccer for fans.

796.342   US   ISSN 0149-4082
GV991
ADDVANTAGE MAGAZINE. 1974. m. membership. United States Professional Tennis Association, 1 USPTA Centre, 3535 Briarpark Dr., Houston, TX 77042. TEL 713-978-7782. FAX 713-978-7780. Ed. Tim Heckler. adv. circ. 10,000. (back issues avail.) **Indexed:** Sportsearch (1981-). **Document type:** trade publication.
    Description: Provides tennis-teaching professionals with educational pieces on all aspects of teaching and coaching, as well as information on U.S.P.T.A. programs and events.

796.3   UK   ISSN 0967-5477
AFRICAN SOCCER. 1992. bi-m. £15($33) (foreign £18). African Tele Promotion, Cannon Collins House, 64 Essex Rd., London N1 8LR, England. TEL 0171-226-8719. FAX 0171-704-6300. Ed. Emmanuel Maradas. adv.: Color page £3100; adv. contact: Nim Caswell. circ. 35,000 (paid). (back issues avail.) **Document type:** consumer publication.
    Description: Covers soccer throughout Africa, as played by Africans in their own countries and abroad.

796.334   IT
AGENDA DELLO SPORT. 1975. a. L.60000. Maurizio Longega, Ed. & Pub., Casella Postale 6291, 00195 Rome, Prati, Italy. TEL 39-330-734215. adv.; bk.rev. circ. 1,986. **Document type:** bulletin.

796.3   US   ISSN 1066-405X
AGGIES ILLUSTRATED. 1992. 17/yr. $49.90. College Sports Communications, Inc., 4099 McEwen Rd., Ste. 350, Dallas, TX 75244. TEL 214-851-1770. FAX 214-490-9333. adv.: B&W page $800, color page $1200; trim 8 1/4 x 10 7/8. circ. 5,750. **Document type:** consumer publication.
    Description: Covers Texas A&M University sports.

796.352   US
AL BARKOW'S GOLF REPORT;* the game's most comprehensive newsletter. 1992. m. $40. Al Barkow's Golf Report, Inc., 16 Seymour St., Montclair, NJ 07042-3340. TEL 201-746-2191. Ed. Al Barkow. bk.rev.; circ. 300 (paid). (back issues avail.) **Document type:** newsletter.

796.352   CN
▼**ALBERTA GOLFING NEWS.** 1994. 6/yr. Distinct News Publications Ltd., 600-1105 109 St., Edmonton, AB T5J 1M8, Canada. TEL 403-496-9007; 800-424-8163. FAX 403-420-6570. Ed. Denis Burns. adv.: B&W page Can.$845; trim 11 3/8 x 16 7/8; adv. contact: Dennis Burns. circ. 15,000. **Document type:** consumer publication.

796.3   SZ
ALMANACCO CALCISTICO SVIZZERO. (Text in Italian) 1950. a. 20 Fr. (Giornale del Popolo) Armando Libotte, Casella Postale, CH-6976 Castagnola, Switzerland. Ed.Bd. adv.; stat. circ. 2,000.

796.357   US   ISSN 0002-6816
AMATEUR BASEBALL NEWS. 1958. 7/yr. $5. American Amateur Baseball Congress Inc., Box 467, 118-119 Redfield Plaza, Marshall, MI 49068. TEL 616-781-2002. FAX 616-781-2060. Ed. Joseph P. Cooper. adv.; bk.rev.; film rev.; illus. circ. 10,000. (tabloid format) **Indexed:** Sportsearch.

796.352   UK   ISSN 0955-2332
AMATEUR GOLF. 1960. m. (11/yr.) £20 (overseas £35). (English Golf Union) Fore Golf Publications Ltd., 129A High St., Dovercourt, Harwich, Essex CO12 3AX, England. TEL 01255-507526. FAX 01255-508483. (EGU addr.: 1-3 Upper King St., Leicester LE1 6XF, England. TEL 0116-255-3042) Ed. Paul M. Baxter; Pub. Michael Coffey. adv.: B&W page £750; color page £1100; adv. contact: Michael Coffey. bk.rev.; circ. 11,500 (paid). **Document type:** consumer publication.
    Former titles: English Amateur Golf; Incorporates: Golf Course (ISSN 0953-6043); Supersedes: Golf News and Fixtures; English Golf Union. News and Fixtures (ISSN 0300-4260); Which was formerly titled (until 1987): Greenkeeper; Incorporates: Golf Greenkeeping; Golf Greenkeeping and Course Maintenance; British Golf Greenkeeper (ISSN 0007-0742).
    Description: Covers all aspects of amateur golf - the game and the equipment.

796.352   US
AMATEUR GOLF REGISTER. 1983. m. $12. Amateur Golfers' Association of America, Inc., 5555 Hollywood Blvd., Hollywood, FL 33021. TEL 800-327-9789. Ed. Davis Lundy. adv. circ. 25,000.

796.357   US
AMATEUR SOFTBALL ASSOCIATION OF AMERICA. RULES OF SOFTBALL. 1933. a. $8.95. (Amateur Softball Association of America) Triumph Books, 644 S. Clark St., Chicago, IL 60605. TEL 312-939-3330. FAX 312-663-3557. circ. 350,000. **Document type:** trade publication.
    Formerly: Amateur Softball Association of America. Official Guide and Rule Book (ISSN 0065-6739)
    Description: Provides the rules for both fast- and slow-pitch softball.

796.332   US
AMERICAN FOOTBALL COACHES ASSOCIATION DIRECTORY. a. (American Football Coaches Association) Collegiate Directories, Inc., Box 450640, Cleveland, OH 44145. TEL 216-835-1172. FAX 216-835-8835. **Document type:** directory.
    Description: Lists college coaches, professional personnel, bowl games, coaches associations and more.

796.33   FR
ANNEE DU FOOTBALL. 1973. a. price varies. Editions Calmann-Levy, 3 rue Auber, 75009 Paris, France. Ed. Jacques Thibert. illus.

796.33   FR   ISSN 0990-1760
ANNEE DU RUGBY. 1973. a. price varies. Editions Calmann-Levy, 3 rue Auber, 75009 Paris, France. Ed. Christian Montaignac. illus.

796.342   FR   ISSN 0242-4878
ANNEE DU TENNIS. 1979. a. price varies. Editions Calmann-Levy, 3 rue Auber, 75009 Paris, France. Ed.Bd. illus.

796.334   IT   ISSN 0003-7907
ARBITRO. 1967. m. free to qualified personnel. Federazione Italiana Giuoco Calcio, Via Gregorio Allegri 14, 00198 Rome, Italy. Ed. Giuseppe Adami. charts; illus.; circ. 20,000 (controlled). **Document type:** trade publication.
    Description: For football referees.

796.332   UK
AROUND FOOTBALL. 1982. m. £4.05. Corvus Publishing, King St., Royston, Herts. SG8 9BD, England. Ed. T.M. Grote. adv. circ. 20,000.

796.352   UK
ARTISAN GOLFER. 1947. q. 10 Brooklands Gardens, Potters Bar, Herts., England. Ed. Peter Ellis.

796.334   UK   ISSN 0263-0354
ASSOCIATION OF FOOTBALL STATISTICIANS. ANNUAL. 1981. a. £15. Association of Football Statisticians, c/o R.J. Spiller, Ed., 22 Bretons, Basildon, Essex, England. TEL 01268-416020. FAX 01268-543559. adv.; bk.rev. circ. 1,600.

796.3   US   ISSN 1056-1641
ATHLON'S BASEBALL. 1988. a. $4.99. Athlon Sports Communications, Inc., 220 25th Ave. N., Nashville, TN 37203. TEL 615-327-0747. FAX 615-327-1149. **Document type:** consumer publication.

796.3   US
ATHLON'S COLLEGE FOOTBALL. a. $4.99. Athlon Sports Communications, Inc., 220 25th Ave. N., Nashville, TN 37203. TEL 615-327-1149. FAX 615-327-1149. **Document type:** consumer publication.

796.3   US   ISSN 0734-2888
GV937
ATHLON'S PRO FOOTBALL. 1982. a. $4.99. Athlon Sports Communications, Inc., 220 25th Ave. N., Nashville, TN 37203. TEL 615-327-0747. FAX 615-327-1149. **Document type:** consumer publication.

796.352   US
AUSTAD'S. (Text in English, Japanese) m. Austad's Co. Inc., 4500 E. 10th St., Sioux Falls, SD 57196. TEL 605-336-3135. FAX 605-339-0362. circ. 1,200,000. **Document type:** catalog.
    Description: Golf equipment, supplies sold primarily to the consumer.

796   AT
AUSTRALIAN CRICKET TOUR GUIDE. 1970. a. Aus.$4.95. Mason Stewart Publishing Pty. Ltd., P.O. Box 747, Darlinghurst, N.S.W. 2010, Australia.
    Formerly: Australian Cricket Yearbook (ISSN 0084-7291)

796.354   AT   ISSN 0817-6604
AUSTRALIAN CROQUET GAZETTE. 1951. q. Aus.$15 (effective 1996). Australian Croquet Association, P.O. Box 3409, Weston, A.C.T. 2611, Australia. FAX 61-2-2880914. Ed. Mark Senior. adv.; bk.rev.; circ. 1,200 (paid). **Indexed:** Sportsearch (1980-).
    Description: Provides news on Australian croquet; general articles on coaching and history.

796.352   AT
AUSTRALIAN GOLF DIGEST. 1970. m. Aus.$52. Federal Publishing Company, 180 Bourke Rd., Alexandria, N.S.W. 2015, Australia. Ed. Phil Tresidder. circ. 22,200. **Indexed:** Sportsearch (1985-). **Document type:** consumer publication.
    Former titles: Australian Golf (Year); Australian Golf Instructional (ISSN 0311-0400); Australian Golf (ISSN 0004-9212)

796.342   AT
AUSTRALIAN TENNIS MAGAZINE; Asia and the Pacific. 1976. m. Aus.$50 (foreign Aus.$55). Nicholson Media Group Pty. Ltd., 1/457 Malvern Rd., South Yarra, Vic. 3141, Australia. TEL 61-3-826-8448. FAX 61-3-827-8808. Ed. Suzi Petkovski. adv. circ. 18,800. (back issues avail.) **Document type:** consumer publication.
    Formerly: Tennis Australia (ISSN 0313-4407)
    Description: Presents news, views on the international and Australian Tennis scene. Features regular instruction, complete records, and the psychological side of tennis.

794.72   AU
AUSTRIAN BILLIARD NEWS. m. Tera GmbH, Hauptstr. 53, A-5600 St. Johann, Austria. TEL 06412-7635. FAX 06412-763615. Ed. Ralf Teppan. adv.: B&W page DM.8300, color page DM.11600; trim 210 x 297; adv. contact: Matthias Holzmann. charts; tr.lit. circ. 4,000. **Document type:** consumer publication.

B B I A MEMBERSHIP AND PRODUCT INFORMATION GUIDE. (Billiard and Bowling Institute of America) see BUSINESS AND ECONOMICS — Trade And Industrial Directories

794.6 381   US
B B I A NEWSLINE. q. free. Billiard and Bowling Institute of America, 200 Castlewood Dr., N. Palm Beach, FL 33408. TEL 407-840-1120. Ed. Sebastian Dicasoli. stat. **Document type:** newsletter.
    Formerly: B B I A Flashes.

794.72   US
B C A BREAK. q. membership. Billiard Congress of America, 1700 S. First Ave., Ste. 25A, Iowa City, IA 52240-7049. TEL 319-351-2112. FAX 319-351-7767. circ. 2,500. **Document type:** consumer publication.
    Formerly: Billiard Congress of America Bulletin.

B T V SPEIGEL. (Bremer Turnvereinigung von 1877 e.V.) see SPORTS AND GAMES

SPORTS AND GAMES — BALL GAMES

796.352   US
BACK NINE; northwest golf magazine. 1987. every 6 wks. $9. Back Nine Publishing Co., Inc., 24219-77th Pl., W. Edmonds, WA 98026. TEL 206-367-8094. Ed. Alan A. Wentzel. adv. circ. 13,000. **Document type:** consumer publication.
Description: Covers golf courses, players and tournaments in the Pacific Northwest.

796.352   CN
BACKSPIN MANITOBA'S GOLF NEWSPAPER. 1990. 5/yr. Canadian Publishers, 1465 St. James St., Winnipeg, MB R3H 0W9, Canada. TEL 204-949-6100. FAX 204-949-6122. Ed. Brian Eastwood; Pub. Gerald L. Dorge. adv.: B&W page Can.$925, color Can.$1225; adv. contact: Scott Kaisaris. **Document type:** consumer publication.

796.345   CN   ISSN 0711-124X
BADMINTON CANADA. 1981-1986; N.S. 1988. 6/yr. Can.$6($8) Badminton Canada, 1600 Prof. James Naismith Dr., Gloucester, Ont. K1B 5N4, Canada. TEL 613-748-5605. FAX 613-748-5695. Ed. Roy Roberts. adv. circ. 3,000.
Description: Covers badminton in Canada.

796.352   GW   ISSN 0178-2436
BAHNENGOLFER. 1973. 6/yr. DM.20.50 (foreign DM.23). Deutscher Bahnengolf-Verband, Bernkastelerstr. 33a, 54472 Brauneberg, Germany. TEL 06534-1279. Ed. Thomas Grashof. adv.; bk.rev.; circ. 1,300 (controlled). **Document type:** bulletin.
Description: Information about competition in mini-golfing.

796.35   US
BALLS & STRIKES SOFTBALL. 1933. 6/yr. $16. Amateur Softball Association of America, 2801 N.E. 50th St., Oklahoma City, OK 73111. TEL 405-424-5266. FAX 405-424-3855. Ed. Ronald A. Babb. adv.; illus.; stat. circ. 320,000. **Indexed:** Sports Per.Ind., Sportsearch.
Formerly: Balls and Strikes (ISSN 0199-2406)

BALLSTREET NEWS; the consolidated baseball card pocket price guide. see *HOBBIES*

796.334   MX   ISSN 0005-4410
BALON; futbol mundial. 1963. w. Mex.$832($34.84) Periodismo Especializado, S.A., Presidentes 187, Col. Portales, Mexico, 13, D.F., Mexico. Ed. Antonio Elizarraras Corona.
Description: Covers world soccer news.

796.357   US   ISSN 0228-6033
GV863.A1
BASEBALL AMERICA. 1981. 26/yr. $43.95. Baseball America, Inc., Box 2089, Durham, NC 27702. TEL 919-682-9635; 800-835-2726. FAX 919-682-2880. Ed. Allan Simpson; Pub. Dave Chase. adv. contact: Kris Grubbs. bk.rev. circ. 70,000. **Document type:** consumer publication.
Formerly (until 1982): All-America Baseball News.

796.357   US   ISSN 0270-4218
GV877
BASEBALL CASE BOOK. a. $4. National Federation of State High School Associations, 11724 N.W. Plaza Circle, Box 20626, Kansas City, MO 64195-0626. TEL 816-464-5400. FAX 816-464-5571.

796.357   US   ISSN 0005-609X
GV862
BASEBALL DIGEST. 1941. m. $22 (foreign $30). Century Publishing Co., 990 Grove St., Evanston, IL 60201-4370. TEL 708-491-6440. (Subscr. to: Box 360, Mt. Morris, IL 61054-0360. TEL 800-877-5893) Ed. John Kuenster. adv.; charts; illus.; stat. circ. 350,000. (also avail. in microform from UMI; back issues avail.; reprint service avail. from UMI) **Indexed:** Cath.Ind., Sports Per.Ind., Sportsearch. **Document type:** consumer publication. —UMI.
Description: For serious baseball fans. Provides statistics and stories behind the sport.

796.357   US
BASEBALL FORECAST (YEAR). a. Sterling - Macfadden Partnership, 233 Park Ave. S., New York, NY 10003. TEL 212-780-3500. FAX 212-780-3555. Ed. Stephen Ciacciarelli. adv.; charts; illus. **Document type:** consumer publication.

796.357   US   ISSN 0067-4273
BASEBALL GUIDE. 1965. a. $2.50. Kwik-Fax Books (Subsidiary of: Martin Frederick, Inc.), Box 14613, Surfside Beach, SC 29587. TEL 803-238-3513. FAX 803-238-4074. Ed. Malcolm DeWitt. circ. 500,000.

796.357   US   ISSN 0199-946X
BASEBALL HOBBY NEWS. 1979. m. $19.95. 4540 Kearny Villa Rd., Ste. 215, San Diego, CA 92123. TEL 619-565-2848. FAX 619-565-6608. Ed. Frank Barning. adv.; bk.rev.; circ. 91,000 (controlled).

796.357   US   ISSN 0883-1033
GV863.A1
BASEBALL ILLUSTRATED (YEAR). a. Sterling - Macfadden Partnership, 230 Park Ave. S., New York, NY 10003. TEL 212-780-3500. FAX 212-780-3555. Ed. Stephen Ciacciarelli. adv.; charts; illus. **Document type:** consumer publication.

796.31   US
BASEBALL INSIGHT; inside stats for serious fans. 1982. 27/yr. (w. Apr.-Oct.). $139 (includes a. Pitcher and Team Report). Parrish Publications, Box 23205, Portland, OR 97223. TEL 503-244-8975. Ed. Phil Erwin. bk.rev.; charts; stat. circ. 600. (looseleaf format; back issues avail.) **Document type:** newsletter.

796.357   JA
BASEBALL MAGAZINE. (Text in Japanese) 1946. w. 14070 Yen. Baseball Magazine Sha, 3-10-10 Misaki-cho, Chiyoda-ku, Tokyo, Japan. Ed. Takao Ouchi.

796.357   US   ISSN 1066-2448
BASEBALL QUARTERLY REVIEWS; the ideal baseball research journal. 1986. q. $28 (effective 1995). H O K Enterprises, Box 9343, Schenectady, NY 12309. TEL 518-399-7890. Ed. Herman Krabbenhoft. circ. 200 (paid). (back issues avail.)
Description: Provides authoritative reports and comprehensive summaries of in-depth baseball research on topics of historical interest and statistical significance.
Refereed Serial

796.357   US   ISSN 0734-6891
GV862
BASEBALL RESEARCH JOURNAL. 1972. a. $35 membership. Society for American Baseball Research, Inc., Box 93183, Cleveland, OH 44101. TEL 216-575-0500. FAX 216-575-0502. adv. circ. 6,500. (back issues avail.) **Indexed:** Amer.Hist.& Life, Hist.Abstr., Phys.Ed.Ind., Sportsearch (1981-). **Document type:** academic/scholarly publication.

BASEBALL ROOKIE RUN DOWN (YEAR); a unique rookie card - subset card guide. see *HOBBIES*

796.357   US   ISSN 0270-1537
GV877
BASEBALL RULEBOOK. a. $4. National Federation of State High School Associations, 11724 N.W. Plaza Circle, Box 20626, Kansas City, MO 64195-0626. TEL 816-464-5400. FAX 816-464-5571.

796.357   US
BASEBALL UMPIRES MANUAL. biennial. $4. National Federation of State High School Associations, 11724 N.W. Plaza Circle, Box 20626, Kansas City, MO 64195-0626. TEL 816-464-5400. FAX 816-464-5571.

796.323   GW   ISSN 0178-9279
BASKETBALL. 1962. s-m. DM.69.40. Goettinger Tageblatt, Maschmuehlenweg 8-10, 37073 Goettingen, Germany. TEL 0551-4990520. FAX 0551-4990530. Ed. Alexander Gutowski. adv.; bk.rev.; circ. 9,000.

796.32   US   ISSN 0525-4663
GV885.45
BASKETBALL CASE BOOK. a. $4. National Federation of State High School Associations, 11724 N.W. Plaza Circle, Box 20626, Kansas City, MO 64195-0626. TEL 816-464-5400. FAX 816-464-5571. adv.; illus. circ. 300,000.

796.323   US   ISSN 0098-5988
GV885.5
BASKETBALL DIGEST. 1973. 8/yr. $22 (foreign $30). Century Publishing Co., 990 Grove St., Evanston, IL 60201-4370. TEL 708-491-6440. (Subscr. to: Box 569, Mt. Morris, IL 61054-0569. TEL 800-877-5893) Ed. Ken Leiker. adv.; bibl.; charts; illus.; stat. circ. 150,000. (also avail. in microform from UMI; reprint service avail. from UMI) **Indexed:** Sports Per.Ind. **Document type:** consumer publication. —UMI.
Description: For serious basketball fans who want the statistics, features, and excitement behind the action of pro and college basketball.

796.323   US   ISSN 0160-5747
GV885.6
BASKETBALL FORECAST (YEAR). a. Sterling - Macfadden Partnership, 233 Park Ave. S., New York, NY 10003. TEL 212-780-3500. FAX 212-780-3555. Ed. Stephen Ciacciarelli. adv.; charts; illus. **Document type:** consumer publication.

796.323   US
BASKETBALL GUIDE. 1971. a. $2.50. Kwik-Fax Books (Subsidiary of: Martin Frederick, Inc.), Box 14613, Surfside Beach, SC 29587. TEL 803-238-3513. FAX 803-238-4074. Ed. Malcolm DeWitt. circ. 300,000.
Formerly: Pro Basketball Guide (ISSN 0079-5518)

796.323   US
BASKETBALL HALL OF FAME NEWSLETTER. 1979. q. Basketball Hall of Fame, 1150 W. Columbus Ave., Box 179, Springfield, MA 01101-0179. TEL 413-781-6500. FAX 413-781-1939. Ed. Robin Deutsch. circ. 4,500. **Document type:** newsletter.

796.323   US
BASKETBALL HALL OF FAME YEARBOOK. 1972. irreg. $11.50. Basketball Hall of Fame, 1150 W. Columbus Ave., Box 179, Springfield, MA 01101-0179. TEL 413-781-6500. FAX 413-781-1939. Ed. Robin Deutsch.

796.323   US
BASKETBALL HANDBOOK. biennial. $4. National Federation of State High School Associations, 11724 N.W. Plaza Circle, Box 20626, Kansas City, MO 64195-0626. TEL 816-464-5400. FAX 816-464-5571.

796.323   US   ISSN 0270-4226
GV885.2
BASKETBALL OFFICIALS MANUAL. biennial. $4. National Federation of State High School Associations, 11724 N.W. Plaza Circle, Box 20626, Kansas City, MO 64195-0626. TEL 816-464-5400. FAX 816-464-5571.

796.323   US   ISSN 0270-8280
GV885.45
BASKETBALL RULEBOOK. a. $4. National Federation of State High School Associations, 11724 N.W. Plaza Circle, Box 20626, Kansas City, MO 64195-0626. TEL 816-464-5400. FAX 816-464-5571.

796.323   US   ISSN 0737-5212
GV885.45
BASKETBALL - SIMPLIFIED & ILLUSTRATED RULES. a. $4. National Federation of State High School Associations, 11724 N.W. Plaza Circle, Box 20626, Kansas City, MO 64195-0626. TEL 816-464-5400. FAX 816-464-5571.

796.323   US   ISSN 0005-6170
BASKETBALL WEEKLY. 1967. w. (during season). $34.95 for 20 nos. Curtis Publishing Co. (Miami), 8033 N.W. 36th St., Miami, FL 33166. TEL 305-594-0508. FAX 305-594-0518. (Subscr. to: Box 526600, Miami, FL 33152. TEL 800-334-4005) Ed. Kevin Kaminski. adv.; bk.rev.; illus.; stat.; circ. 55,000 (paid). (tabloid format) **Indexed:** Sports Per.Ind., Sportsearch.

796.342   GW   ISSN 0342-8915
BAYERN TENNIS. 1977. m. DM.55. Eisenheimerstr. 59, 80687 Munich, Germany. TEL 089-573277. Ed. Ludwig Rembold. circ. 15,000.

SPORTS AND GAMES — BALL GAMES

796.332 US ISSN 1056-4284
BEAR REPORT. 26/yr. (w. during football season). $29.95. Royle Publications, Inc., 112 Market St., Sun Prairie, WI 53590. TEL 608-837-2200. FAX 608-825-3053. Ed. Larry Mayer; Pub. John Weishar. adv. circ. 17,500. **Document type:** newspaper.
  Description: Covers the Chicago Bears and the NFL. Includes game stories, statistics, coaches' comments and player profiles.

BECKETT BASEBALL CARD MONTHLY. see *HOBBIES*

BECKETT BASEBALL CARD PRICE GUIDE. see *HOBBIES*

BECKETT BASKETBALL MONTHLY. see *HOBBIES*

BECKETT FOOTBALL CARD MONTHLY. see *HOBBIES*

794.6 UK
BEDFORDSHIRE COUNTY BOWLING ASSOCIATION. HANDBOOK. 1914. a. £1.20. c/o F.G. Pedder, Pub., 6 Greenacre Park, Clayhall Rd., Kensworth, Beds. LU6 3RE, England. TEL 0582-872675. adv. circ. 1,900. **Document type:** bulletin.

796.352 JA
BEIJING GOLF CLUB NEWS. a. Pan Asia Corporation, 17-3 Ueno 1-chome, Taito-ku, Tokyo 110, Japan. TEL 03-8374140. FAX 03-8374217.

796.342 GW ISSN 0723-1407
BEITRAEGE ZUR THEORIE UND PRAXIS DES TENNISUNTERRICHTS UND -TRAININGS. irreg., vol.17, 1993. price varies. (Deutscher Tennis Bund Sportwissenschaftlicher Beirat) Czwalina Verlag, Postfach 730240, 22122 Hamburg, Germany. TEL 040-6780025. FAX 040-6780051. **Document type:** monographic series.

796.357 UK ISSN 0264-3871
BENSON AND HEDGES CRICKET YEAR.* 1981. a. £18.99. Hodder - Headline plc, 79 Great Titchfield St., London W1P 7FN, England. Ed. David Lemmon.
  Description: Illustrated record of first-class games played world-wide.

769.323 US
BETWEEN THE LINES (SYRACUSE);* for the year round baseball enthusiast. 1989. 12/yr. (plus 2 special eds.). $15. 247 Arlington Ave., Syracuse, NY 13207-1603.
  Description: Provides a forum for the exchange of ideas between fans.

796.333 AT ISSN 0311-175X
BIG LEAGUE.* 1957? w. Aus.$10($30) New South Wales Rugby League, 165 Phillip St., Sydney, N.S.W. 2000, Australia. Ed. G. Lester.
  Formerly: Rugby League News.

796.332 US
BIG TEN CONFERENCE OFFICIAL FOOTBALL GUIDE. a. $7.95. (Big Ten Conference) Triumph Books, 644 S. Clark St., Chicago, IL 60605. TEL 312-939-3330. FAX 312-663-3557. (Orders also to: Big Ten Conference, 1500 Higgins Rd., Park Ridge, IL 60068-5742. TEL 708-696-1010. FAX 708-696-1100) stat.
  Description: Supplies team rosters and contains team and individual profiles, along with extensive statistical information.

796.325 US
BIG TEN NEWSLETTER. q. $10. Big Ten Conference, 1500 Higgins Rd., Park Ridge, IL 60068-5742. TEL 708-696-1010. FAX 708-696-1110. **Document type:** newsletter.

796.325 US
(YEAR) BIG TEN RECORDS BOOK. a. $10. Big Ten Conference, 1500 Higgins Rd., Park Ridge, IL 60068-5742. TEL 708-696-1010. FAX 708-696-1110.

796.357 US ISSN 1054-2248
GV863.A1
BILL MAZEROSKI'S BASEBALL. a. $5.95. Sports Minded, 1638 Parker Ave., Ft. Lee, NJ 07024. TEL 201-944-4471. FAX 201-944-3193. **Document type:** consumer publication.
  Description: Previews the forthcoming season from insiders in the game.

794.6 US ISSN 0164-761X
BILLIARDS DIGEST.* 1978. bi-m. $13. (National Bowlers Journal, Inc.) Luby Publishing, 200 S. Michigan Ave., K, Ste. 1430, Chicago, IL 60604-2404. TEL 312-266-7179. FAX 312-266-7215. Ed. Michael Panozzo. adv.; illus. circ. 18,000.
  Description: Dedicated to the fine art of billiards.

794.72 US ISSN 1047-2444
GV891.A1
BILLIARDS: THE (YEAR) OFFICIAL B C A RULES & RECORDS BOOK. 1948. a. $6.95. Billiard Congress of America, c/o Bruce Cottew, Ed., 1700 S. First Ave., Ste. 25A, Iowa City, IA 52240-7049. TEL 319-351-2112. FAX 319-351-7767. charts; illus.; stat. circ. 100,000. **Document type:** consumer publication.
  Description: Contains rules for games of billiards, competition records, instruction, Hall of Fame listings, and history.

796.342 US
BLACK TENNIS. 1977. m. $15. Black Tennis Magazine, Inc., Box 210767, Dallas, TX 75211. Ed. Marcus A. Freeman, Jr. adv.; bk.rev. circ. 15,000. (back issues avail.)

796.357 US
BOOK OF BASEBALL RECORDS. a. $11.95. Seymour Siwoff, Ed. & Pub., 500 Fifth Ave., New York, NY 10036. TEL 212-869-1530.

796.346 DK ISSN 0109-6761
BORDTENNIS AARBOGEN. 1982. a. DKK 55 (effective 1975). Dansk Bord-Tennis Union, Idraettens Hus, DK-2605 Broendby, Denmark. TEL 45-43-26-21-11. FAX 45-43-26-21-15. TELEX 00945. Ed.Bd. adv.; illus. circ. 3,000.

796.357 US ISSN 1075-8542
BOSTON BASEBALL. 1990. m. $1995; newsstand price: $1.95. Sports Underground, Inc., 115 Freeman St., Brookline, MA 02146. TEL 617-277-0208. Ed. M. Rutstein. adv.: B&W page $400; 8 x 10; adv. contact: M. Rutstein. **Document type:** consumer publication.
  Formerly (until 1994): Boston Baseball Underground (ISSN 1070-5678)
  Description: Gives an overview of the Major and Minor League Boston Red Sox.

796.323 US ISSN 0361-6894
GV885.52.B67
BOSTON CELTICS YEARBOOK. a. $7.50. Phoenix Media - Communications Group, c/o Stephen M. Mindich, 126 Brookline Ave., Boston, MA 02215. TEL 617-536-5390. FAX 617-536-1463. Eds. Joyce Kosofsky, Tod Rosenweig. adv. circ. 75,000.

794.6 SW ISSN 1101-3273
BOWLAREN MAGAZINET. 1922. s-m. Svenska Bowlingfoerbundet, Johanneshov, Sweden. adv. circ. 32,000.
  Formerly (until 1990): Bowlaren (ISSN 0345-1682)

794.6 UK
BOWLER.* 1973. m. £4.50. Academy Organisation (Magazines) Ltd., 57 Blythe St., Belfast BT12 5HX, N. Ireland. Ed. Bert Graham. adv.

794.6 UK ISSN 0962-8096
BOWLERS' WORLD. 1977. m. £10.50. Judgewise Ltd., 64-68 Greenfield Rd., St. Helens, Merseyside WA1D 6SL, England. TEL 0744-31314. FAX 0744-27586. Ed. Terry Magee. adv.; bk.rev. circ. 13,000. **Document type:** newsletter.

794.6 658.8 US ISSN 0068-0559
BOWLING AND BILLIARD BUYERS GUIDE.* Title varies: Bowling Buyers Guide. 1961. a. $10. National Bowlers Journal, Inc., 200 S. Michigan Ave., Ste. 1430, Chicago, IL 60604. Eds. Keith Hall, Lydia Rypincki.

794.6 US ISSN 0162-0274
GV901
BOWLING MAGAZINE. 1934. 6/yr. $11. American Bowling Congress, 5301 S. 76th St., Greendale, WI 53129. TEL 414-421-6400. FAX 414-421-7977. Ed. Bill Vint. adv.; bk.rev.; illus. circ. 140,000. Indexed: Sports Per.Ind., Sportsearch (1977-). **Document type:** consumer publication.
  Description: Covers the world of bowling.

794.6 US
BOWLING MAGAZINE A B C MEMBERS ONLY EDITION. 1992. a. $2.50 per no. American Bowling Congress, 5301 S. 76th St., Greendale, WI 53129. TEL 414-421-6400. FAX 414-421-1164. Ed. Bill Vint. adv.: B&W page $20000, color page $25000; trim 8 1/4 x 10 7/8. circ. 2,500,000. **Document type:** consumer publication.
  Formerly: Bowling Magazine Special Edition.

794.6 US
BOWLING NEWS. 1940. w. $25. Bowling News, Inc., 2606 W. Burbank Blvd., Burbank, CA 91505. TEL 818-849-4664. FAX 818-845-6321. Ed. Al Sabo. adv. contact: Lillian Oak. bk.rev. circ. 14,000. (tabloid format) **Document type:** consumer publication.
  Formerly: California Bowling News (ISSN 0008-0918)
  Description: Bowling news for and about bowling and bowler.

794.6 IT ISSN 0006-8438
BOWLING NOTIZIE;* mensile dello sport del bowling. 1966. m. L.3000 to non-members. Federazione Bowling Italiana, Via Marco d'Agrate No. 23, 20139 Milan, Italy.

794.6 IT
BOWLING OPEN. 1990. q. L.20000 (foreign L.35000) (effective 1995-96). Editrice Bowling Open S.n.c., Via Camozzi 130, 24121 Bergamo, Italy. TEL 035-244472. Ed. Gustavo Vitali. adv.: B&W page L.1000000, color page L.1600000; 210 x 297. circ. 12,100. **Document type:** trade publication.

794.6 US ISSN 0006-8446
BOWLING PROPRIETOR. 1954. m. (June & July combined). membership. Bowling Proprietors' Association of America, Box 5802, Arlington, TX 76005. TEL 817-649-5105. FAX 817-633-2940. Ed. Daniel W. Burgess. adv.; bk.rev.; illus.; circ. 4,500. (controlled). (also avail. in microform from UMI; reprint service avail. fromn UMI) Indexed: Sportsearch (1978-).
  —UMI.

794.6 US
THE BOWLING REVIEW. 1970. s-m. $5. Red Bud Media Inc., 427 Chez Paree, Hazelwood, MO 63042. TEL 314-831-4000. FAX 314-831-3610. Ed. Bill Winders; Pub. Bill Winders. adv. circ. 30,000.
  Formerly: St. Louis Bowling Review (ISSN 0193-5321)

796.31 AT ISSN 1038-5401
BOWLS ALIVE. 1992. m. Aus.$20. Royal New South Wales Bowling Association, Inc., P.O. Box A2186, S. Sydney, N.S.W. 2000, Australia. TEL 02-283-4555. FAX 02-283-4252. Ed. Rex Davies. adv. contact: Angela Cornek. bk.rev. circ. 141,044. **Indexed:** Sportsearch. **Document type:** consumer publication.
  Formed by the merger of: N.S.W. Bowls News; (1936-1991): Bowls in N.S.W. (ISSN 0006-8454)
  Description: Covers lawn bowling.

796.3 UK ISSN 0262-6942
BOWLS INTERNATIONAL. 1981. m. £20.50 (foreign £21). Key Publishing Ltd., P.O. Box 100, Stamford, Lincs. PE9 1QX, England. TEL 01780-55131. FAX 01780-57261. TELEX 265871-MONREF-G. Ed. Melvyn Beck. adv.; bk.rev.; charts; illus. circ. 11,173. **Document type:** bulletin.

796.3 AT
BOWLS - NEWS AND VIEWS. 1954. 9/yr. $1. Victorian Ladies' Bowling Association, 109 Commercial Rd., South Yarra 3141, Australia. Ed. E. McLean. adv.; illus. circ. 15,800.

796.334 AT ISSN 0817-1203
BRITISH SOCCER WEEK. 1986. w. Aus.$89 (foreign Aus.$110). Westways Publishing Co. Pty. Ltd., 103 Gt. Eastern Hwy., Rivervale, W.A. 6103, Australia. TEL 61-9-362-4344. FAX 61-9-470-3162. (Subscr. to: P.O. Box 609, Cloverdale, W.A. 6105, Australia) Ed. Terry Jones; Pub. Bill Cranny. adv. contact: Rosemarie Cranny. circ. 16,900 (paid). (back issues avail.) **Document type:** consumer publication, newspaper.
  Description: Match reports and news of players and clubs in UK. Detailed results and league standings published in Australia four days after matches are played.

6100 SPORTS AND GAMES — BALL GAMES

796.357   US
BULLPEN. q. Babe Ruth League, 1770 Brunswick Ave., Box 5000, Trenton, NJ 09638. TEL 609-695-1434. FAX 609-695-2505. adv.; circ. 32,000 (controlled).
Description: Regulation amateur youth baseball and softball program.

796.334 658.8   UK   ISSN 0269-9125
BUSINESS RATIO REPORT: FOOTBALL CLUBS; an industry sector analysis. 1986. a. I C C Business Ratios Ltd., Freepost, Field House, Hampton, Mddx. TW12 1BR, England. TEL 081-783-0977. FAX 081-783-0977. charts; stat. **Document type:** trade publication.
—BLDSC (1746.685670).

796.352 658.7   US
BUYING HABITS OF GOLF COURSE SUPERINTENDENTS. 1990. a. $945. Golf Course Superintendents Association of America, Center for Golf Course Management, 1421 Research Park Dr., Lawrence, KS 66049. TEL 913-841-2240. FAX 913-832-4433. Ed. Robert Shively. circ. 4,500. **Document type:** corporate report.

796.323   US
C B A NEWSLETTER.* 1978. w. (Nov.-Apr.) $40 for 22 nos. Continental Basketball Association, 701 Market St., Ste. 140, St. Louis, MO 63101-1824. TEL 303-331-0404. FAX 303-377-9452. Eds. Greg Anderson, Brett Meister. adv. circ. 1,500. **Document type:** newsletter.
Former titles: C B A Update; C B A Newsweekly.

796.332   ISSN 0831-3202
C F L FACTS, FIGURES AND RECORDS. 1966. a. $14.95. (Canadian Football League, CN) Triumph Books, 644 S. Clark St., Chicago, IL 60605. TEL 312-939-3330. FAX 312-663-3557. (Membership addr.: 110 Eglinton Ave., W., 5th Fl., Toronto, ON M4R 1A3, Canada) stat. circ. 9,000. (back issues avail.)
Former titles (until 1985): Canadian Football League. Official Rules and Information Manual (ISSN 0708-6784); (until 1975): C F L Official Yearbook (ISSN 0318-9775); (until 1974): Canadian Football League. Official Record and Information Manual (ISSN 0318-9783); (until 1969): Canadian Football League. Official Record Manual (ISSN 0318-9791).
Description: Contains information, statistics, records, rules, and facts about the League.

796.352   CN
C P G A OF ONTARIO DIARY - DIRECTORY. 1993. a. Kenilworth Publishing Inc., 80 W. Beaver Creek, Ste. 18, Richmond Hill, ON L4B 1H3, Canada. TEL 905-771-7333. FAX 905-771-7336. adv.: B&W page Can.$1450, color page Can.$2385; adv. contact: Jim Meecham. circ. 778. **Document type:** directory.

796.352   CN
CADILLAC GOLF CLASSIC. 1988. a. Media Enterprises, 3 Ainsley Gardens, Islington, Ont. M9A 1M5, Canada. TEL 416-233-2171. FAX 416-233-2171. Ed. Julie Cohen. adv.: B&W page Can.$4950; trim 8 1/8 x 10 3/4. circ. 9,000.

796.334   IT
CALCIO OGGI. 1990. m. L.40000. Italy Novanta s.a.s., Via Montebello 17, 00185 Rome, Italy. TEL 39-6-4870474. FAX 39-6-4825164. Ed. Stefano Petrucci. adv.: B&W page L.2800000, color page L.5000000. circ. 25,000. **Document type:** consumer publication.

796.332   US
CALIFORNIA ANGELS OFFICIAL YEARBOOK. 1983. a. $7. Woodford Publishing, 660 Market St., Ste. 206, San Francisco, CA 94104-5011. TEL 415-397-1853. FAX 415-399-0942. Ed. Jon Rochmis. adv. contact: David Lilienstein. illus. circ. 40,000. **Document type:** consumer publication.

796.352   US   ISSN 1070-3187
GV975
CALIFORNIA FAIRWAYS. 1992. bi-m. $15. (California Golf Course Superintendents Association) Adams Publishing Corp., 68-860 Perez Rd., Ste. J, Cathedral City, CA 92234-7248. TEL 619-770-4370. FAX 619-770-8019. adv.: B&W page $995, color page $1495; trim 8 1/4 x 10 7/8. circ. 3,483.

796.352   CN   ISSN 0316-8131
CANADIAN AND PROVINCIAL GOLF RECORDS. 1972. a. Royal Canadian Golf Association, Golf House, R.R. 2, Oakville, ON L6J 4Z3, Canada. TEL 416-844-1800. FAX 416-845-7040. circ. 1,500. **Document type:** academic/scholarly publication.
Formerly: Royal Canadian Golf Association. National Tournament Records (ISSN 0316-8212)
Description: Complete records for all provincial and national golf tournaments in Canada since the 1880's.

796.352   CN   ISSN 0084-8565
CANADIAN LADIES' GOLF ASSOCIATION. YEAR BOOK.* (Text in English, French) 1947. a. Can.$3. Canadian Ladies' Golf Association, Glen Abbey Golf House, 1333 Dorval Dr., Oakville, ON L6J 4Z3, Canada. TEL 905-849-2542. Ed. Jennifer McGuinness. adv.; bk.rev.; illus.; stat.; index. circ. 10,000. **Document type:** newsletter.

796.325   CN   ISSN 0834-2946
CANADIAN VOLLEYBALL ASSOCIATION. RULE BOOK. French edition: Association Canadienne de Volley-ball. Regle de Jeu (ISSN 0834-2938) a. Can.$8. Canadian Volleyball Association, 1600 James Naismith Dr., Gloucester, ON K1B 5N4, Canada. TEL 613-748-5681. FAX 613-748-5727. TELEX 053-3660 SPORTREC. adv. circ. 12,000.
Former titles (until 1987): Canadian Volleyball Association. Rule Book and Annual (ISSN 0831-8794); Canadian Volleyball Annual and Rule Book (ISSN 0576-6346)

796   VE
CANCHA. 1971. m. Urbanization Horizonte, 2da Traversal, Qta. Mabel, Caracas, Venezuela. adv.

CARD NEWS & PRICE GUIDE. see HOBBIES

796.332   UK   ISSN 0966-3061
CELTIC VIEW. 1965. w. £27 (U.S. £52). Celtic Football Club, 18 Kerrydale St., Glasgow G40 3RW, Scotland. TEL 041-551-8103. FAX 041-554-2376. Ed. Ken McNab. adv.; bk.rev. circ. 27,000.

794.6   US   ISSN 0009-3513
CHICAGO BOWLER;* bowling weekly. 1934. w. $10. Chicago Bowler Inc., 11 W. 17th St., 350 W. 22nd St., Ste. 109, Lombard, IL 60148-6137. TEL 708-629-7665. Ed. Terri M. Weglarz. adv. circ. 5,700. (tabloid format)

196.332   US
CHICAGO CUBS OFFICIAL YEARBOOK. 1985. a. $7. Woodford Publishing, 660 Market St., Ste. 206, San Francisco, CA 94104-5011. TEL 415-397-1853. FAX 415-399-0942. Ed. Jon Rochmis. adv. contact: David Lilienstein. illus. circ. 40,000. **Document type:** consumer publication.

796.352   US
CHICAGO DISTRICT GOLFER. (Includes annual Directory) 1990. q. $12. (Chicago District Golf Association) The Publishing Group, Inc., 1200 N. 7th St., Minneapolis, MN 55411-4000. TEL 612-522-1200. FAX 612-522-1182. Ed. Bill Daniels. adv. circ. 90,000.
Description: Includes news and trends, local courses and private clubs, previews of tournaments, personalities and history.

796.352   US
CHICAGO METRO GOLFER. 6/yr. Golf Publishing Inc., 516 N. York Rd., Bensonville, IL 60106-1607. TEL 708-860-5444. Ed. Gary Holaway. circ. 20,000.

796.352   US
CHICAGOLAND GOLF. 1989. 15/yr. $14. Chicagoland Golf Publishing Co., Box 4116, Wheaton, IL 60189. TEL 708-719-1000. FAX 708-719-1030. Ed. Roberta Krause; Pub. Phil Kosin. adv.; bk.rev. circ. 45,000. **Document type:** newspaper.
Description: Provides information, previews, photographs and reporting on the PGA events in the area. Covers area courses, travel, teaching techniques and interviews.

796.357   UK
CLUB CRICKET CONFERENCE OFFICIAL HANDBOOK. 1915. a. £25. Club Cricket Conference, 361 West Barnes Ln., New Malden, Surrey KT3 6JF, England. TEL 0181-949-4001. FAX 0181-336-0537. Ed. A.E.F. Stevens. adv. circ. 3,500.

796.323   US   ISSN 0009-9880
GV711
COACHING CLINIC. 1962. 10/yr. $35. Princeton Educational Publishers, Box 280, Plainsboro, NJ 08536. TEL 908-297-6920. FAX 908-297-6921. Ed. Barry Pavalec. charts; illus. circ. 7,000. **Indexed:** Phys.Ed.Ind., Sports Per.Ind., Sportsearch (1974-). **Document type:** newsletter.
Incorporates: Basketball Clinic (ISSN 0146-5007) & Women's Coaching Clinic (ISSN 0146-1133)

796.357   US   ISSN 1047-5206
COACHING DIGEST. s-a. membership only. American Baseball Coaches Association, 108 S. University Ave., Ste. 3, Mt. Pleasant, MI 48858-2327. TEL 517-775-3300. FAX 571-775-3600. Ed. Craig Rutter. circ. 6,000. **Document type:** trade publication.
Description: To assist members in increasing their education and awareness of the sport of baseball.

796.342   US   ISSN 0279-1153
COLLEGE AND JUNIOR TENNIS. 1972. q. $18. Junior Tennis, Inc., 100 Harbor Rd., Port Washington, NY 11050. TEL 516-883-6601. FAX 516-883-5241. TELEX 293185. Ed. Marcia Frost. adv. contact: Madeline Fischbach. bk.rev.; illus. circ. 5,000. (back issues avail.) **Document type:** consumer publication.
Description: Covers college and junior tennis, coverage, draw sheets, schedules, stories, photos, rankings, and results.

796.323   US
COLLEGE & PRO BASKETBALL ACTION. a. $4.95. Sports Eye, Inc., 18 Industrial Park Dr., Port Washington, NY 11050. TEL 516-484-3300; 800-247-2923. Pub. Louis Sierra. **Document type:** consumer publication.

794.6   US   ISSN 1070-1885
COLLEGE BOWLING NEWS. 1989. 2/yr. $5. Young American Bowling Alliance, 5301 S. 76th St., Greendale, WI 53129. TEL 414-421-4700. FAX 414-421-1301. circ. 19,000. (tabloid format)
Description: Covers different collegiate bowling programs and news in the U.S. and Canada.

796.31   US   ISSN 0530-9751
COLLEGIATE BASEBALL. 1957. 14/yr. $18. Collegiate Baseball Newspaper Inc., c/o Lou Pavlovich, Ed., Box 50566, Tucson, AZ 85703. TEL 520-623-4530. FAX 520-624-5501. adv.; illus. circ. 9,500. (also avail. in microfilm from UMI) **Document type:** newsletter.
—UMI.
Description: For baseball players, coaches, students. Covers the latest baseball products, innovative instructional clinics; provides feature stories on baseball personalities, and national college and high school polls.

COMBO MAGAZINE. see HOBBIES

796.357   US   ISSN 0885-9183
GV877
THE COMPLETE BASEBALL RECORD BOOK. Variant title: Sporting News Official Baseball Record Book. 1949. a. $17.95. Sporting News Publishing Co., 1212 N. Lindbergh Blvd., St. Louis, MO 63132. TEL 314-997-7111. FAX 314-993-7726. Ed. Craig Carter. **Document type:** consumer publication.
Former titles (until 1985): Official Baseball Record Book (ISSN 0162-5438); (until 1982): Sporting News Official Baseball Record Book (ISSN 0882-8237); (until 1973): Sporting News Baseball Record Book (ISSN 0882-8903); Baseball's One for the Book (ISSN 0067-429X); Official Baseball Record Book (ISSN 0078-4605)

796.33   US   ISSN 0361-2988
GV955
COMPLETE HANDBOOK OF PRO FOOTBALL. 1975. a. Penguin U S A, New American Library, 375 Hudson St., New York, NY 10014. TEL 212-366-2000. Ed. Zander Hollander. illus. **Document type:** consumer publication.

796.342   GR
COSMOS TOU TENNIS/WORLD OF TENNIS. 1982. bi-m. Dr.800. Liberis Publications Ltd., 49 Pericleous St., 154 51 N. Psychico, Athens, Greece. Ed. Dimitri Kanellopoulos. adv. circ. 10,000. (back issues avail.)

SPORTS AND GAMES — BALL GAMES

796.352   **SP**   ISSN 1133-7346
COSTAGOLF; Spain's magazine for golf and leisure. (Text in English and Spanish) 1975. m. 4500 ptas. (Europe 6000 ptas.; elsewhere 7500 ptas.) (effective 1995). Golf Area, S.A., Loma de los Riscos, 1, Apdo. 358, Torremolinos, Malaga, Spain. TEL 34-52-381542. FAX 34-52-381569. Ed. Silvia Gomez; Pub. Jose Gomez Bofill. adv. contact: Jack Nusbaum. bk.rev.; illus.; stat.; tr.lit. circ. 18,000. (back issues avail.) **Document type:** consumer publication.

796.352   **US**   ISSN 1041-2042
HS2581
COUNTRY CLUB. 1986. bi-m. Golf Club Publications, 16 Forest St., New Canaan, CT 06840. TEL 203-972-3892. Ed. E. MacFarlan Moore. adv. circ. 150,275.
   Formerly: Golf Club.
   Description: Conveys the beauty, grandeur, history and pleasures of golf. Includes profiles of country clubs.

796.358   **NE**   ISSN 0011-1236
CRICKET. 1930. 19/yr. (w. during summer). fl.55. Koninklijke Nederlandse Cricket Bond, Nieuwe Kalfjeslaan 21B, 1182 AA Amstelveen, Netherlands. TEL 31-20-6451705. FAX 31-20-6451715. Ed. G. de Grooth. adv.; bk.rev.; illus.; stat. circ. 1,600. **Document type:** bulletin.

796.358   **AT**   ISSN 0310-9356
CRICKET QUADRANT. 1973. irreg. Aus.$0.40 per no. Australian Cricket Society, A.C.T. Branch, 91 Gouger St., Torrens, A.C.T. 2607, Australia. Ed. Julian Oakley.

796.358   **II**
CRICKET SAMRAT. (Text in Hindi) 1978. m. Dewan Publications Pvt. Ltd., L-1, Kanchan Lhouse, Near Milan Cinema, Najafgarh Rd., Commercial Complex, New Delhi 110 015, India. TEL 11-591175. Ed. P. Anand Dewan. adv.: B&W page Rs.12000, color page Rs.24000; trim 24 x 16.5; adv. contact: Prakash Mahendru. circ. 87,270.

796.358   **UK**
THE CRICKETER. 1921. m. £28.20 (rest of Europe £40.80; elsewhere £46.90). Sporting Magazines and Publishing Ltd, Groombridge Rd., Beech Hanger, Ashurst, Nr. Tunbridge Wells, Kent TN3 9ST, England. TEL 01892-740256. FAX 01897-740588. Ed. Richard Hutton. adv. contact: Mary Lungley. illus. **Indexed:** Sportsearch (1977-). **Document type:** consumer publication.
   Former titles (until 1995): Cricketer International (ISSN 0266-7398); Cricketer (ISSN 0011-1260)
   Description: Covers all aspects of the game of cricket, including techniques, player profiles, reports on series.

796.358   **PK**
THE CRICKETER. (Text in English) 1973. m. Rs.275($11) Spencers Bldg., 1St Fl., I.I. Chundrigar Rd., G.P.O. Box 3721, Karachi, Pakistan. TEL 92-21-210355. FAX 92-21-2637185. Ed. Hanif Mohammad. adv.: B&W page Rs.3500, color page Rs.7000; trim 9 1/2 x 6 3/4; adv. contact: Riaz Ahmed Mansuri. charts; illus.; stat. circ. 18,000. **Indexed:** Sportsearch (1981-). **Document type:** consumer publication.
   Description: Covers national and international cricket, with interviews, match reports, scores and current statistics and other features of interest to players and fans.

796.3   **AT**   ISSN 1320-212X
CRICKETER. 1973. 7/yr. Aus.$29.75. David Syme & Co. Limited, 250 Spencer St., Melbourne, Vic. 3000, Australia. Ed. Ken Piesse. adv. (back issues avail.)
   Description: Covers cricket at the international and local level.

790.1   **UK**   ISSN 0266-7401
CRICKETER QUARTERLY FACTS AND FIGURES. 1973. q. £11.70 (rest of Europe £12; elsewhere £15.70). Sporting Magazines and Publishers Ltd., Beech Hanger, Groombridge Rd., Ashurst, Nr. Tunbridge Wells, Kent TN3 9ST, England. TEL 01892-740256. FAX 01892-740588. Ed. Richard Lockwood. adv. contact: C. Bazalgette. **Document type:** consumer publication.
   Description: Presents facts and figures of cricket in England, including international match results.

796.352 333.7   **US**   ISSN 1074-9276
CRITTENDEN GOLF INC. Variant title: GolfInc. 1991. m. $48. Crittenden Marketing, Inc., Box 189010, Coronado, CA 92178. TEL 619-437-6250. FAX 619-437-4204. Ed. Colleen Pestana; Pub. Alan Crittenden. adv.: B&W page $1695, color page $2295; trim 8 x 11; adv. contact: Noelle Chartier. circ. 15,000. **Document type:** trade publication.
   Formerly (until May 1993): Golf Development Magazine (ISSN 1068-6711)
   Description: For owners, developers, investors and architects involved in the building of golf courses and resorts.

796.354   **UK**   ISSN 0011-1880
CROQUET. 1901. bi-m. £13 minimum donation (overseas £60 for 3 yr.) (effective 1996). Croquet Association, Hurlingham Club, London SW6 3PR, England. TEL 0171-736-3148. FAX 0171-736-3148. Ed. Gail Curry. adv. contact: Gail Curry. bk.rev.; illus.; circ. 2,200 (Feb., Jun., Oct., Dec.); 5,200 (Apr., Aug.) (paid). **Indexed:** Sportsearch. **Document type:** newsletter.
   Formerly: Croquet Gazette.
   Description: Contains news and views on the sport of croquet; aimed at tournament, club, and casual players.

796.354   **US**
CROQUET ANNUAL. 1992. a. free. United States Croquet Association, 500 Ave. of Champions, Palm Beach Gardens, FL 33418. TEL 407-627-3999. FAX 407-624-3128. Ed. Bert Myer; Pub. Dean Reinke. adv.: B&W page $2800, color page $3500; trim 8 x 11 3/4. circ. 15,000. **Document type:** consumer publication.
   Description: Includes reports on U.S.C.A. events, facilities, and members; reviews croquet equipment; and discusses the history and other topics pertinent to the development, advancement, and promotion of croquet in the U.S.

796   **US**   ISSN 1047-3084
CUBS VINE LINE. 1986. m. $19.95. Chicago National League Ball Club, Inc., Box 1159, Skokie, IL 60076-8159. TEL 312-404-4129. Ed. Ned Colletti. adv.; bk.rev. circ. 30,000.

CURRENT BASEBALL PUBLICATIONS. see SPORTS AND GAMES — Abstracting, Bibliographies, Statistics

796.332   **US**
DALLAS COWBOYS OUTLOOK. 1967. a. $4.21. Sports Communications, Inc., P.O. Box 95, Waco, TX 76703. TEL 817-752-4351. Ed. Dave Campbell. adv. circ. 55,622.

796.352   **DK**   ISSN 0904-4019
DANSK GOLF GUIDE (YEAR). 1989. a. DKK 140. (Selvstendig Udgivervirksomhed) Art - Work Administration AS, Kalkbraenderihavnsgade 22 A, DK-2100 Copenhagen Oe, Denmark. FAX 45-31-18-02-32. Ed. Knud-Axel Nylen. adv.: B&W page DKK 18375, color page DKK 18375. circ. 38,000.
   Description: For golf players who are members of golf clubs within DGU, members of DGU and visiting foreign golf players in Denmark.

794.6   **GW**
DELMENHORSTER KEGLER ZEITUNG. 1968. q. (Sportkegler Vereins Delmenhorst) Fink Druck GmbH, Brandenburgerstr. 4, 27755 Delmenhorst, Germany. TEL 04221-2768. circ. 1,300.

796.342   **GW**   ISSN 0176-0599
DEUTSCHE TENNIS ZEITUNG. 1946. w. DM.109.50 (foreign DM.126). Sportverlag Schmidt und Dreisilker GmbH, Postfach 260, 71044 Sindelfingen, Germany. TEL 07031-862800. FAX 07031-862801. Ed. Brigitte Schurr. adv. contact: Monika Possehl. bk.rev.; charts; illus. circ. 50,000. (back issues avail.) **Document type:** consumer publication.
   Formerly (until 1981): Tennis.

796.342   **GW**   ISSN 0941-0457
DEUTSCHE TENNIS ZEITUNG AKTUELL. 1990. 10/yr. DM.109.50 (foreign DM.126). Sportverlag Schmidt und Dreisilker GmbH, Postfach 260, 71044 Sindelfingen, Germany. TEL 07031-862800. FAX 07031-862801. Ed. Brigitte Schurr. adv. contact: Monika Possehl. **Document type:** consumer publication.

790   **GW**   ISSN 0170-1509
DEUTSCHE VOLLEYBALL ZEITSCHRIFT. 1977. m. DM.67.20 (foreign DM.74.40). Philippka-Verlag, Postfach 6540, 48034 Muenster, Germany. TEL 0251-23005-0. FAX 0251-23005-99. Ed. Konrad Honig. circ. 19,000. (back issues avail.) **Document type:** consumer publication.

796.334   **GW**
DEUTSCHER FUSSBALL-BUND. AMTLICHE MITTEILUNGEN. 1952. m. DM.5. Deutscher Fussball-Bund (DFB) - German Soccer Association, Otto-Fleck-Schneise 6, 60528 Frankfurt, Germany. FAX 069-6788266. TELEX 416815. circ. 1,300.
   Description: Covers the official announcements of the West German Soccer Association.

790   **GW**   ISSN 0930-0791
DEUTSCHER TISCHTENNIS SPORT. 1946. m. DM.73.20 (foreign DM.79.80). Philippka-Verlag, Postfach 6540, 48034 Muenster, Germany. TEL 0251-23005-0. FAX 0251-23005-99. Ed. Konrad Honig. circ. 17,500. (back issues avail.) **Document type:** consumer publication.

796.357   **US**   ISSN 1070-4019
GV863.A1
DIAMOND (SCOTTSDALE).* 1993. m. $19.95. (Major League Baseball Players Alumni Association) Fans Publishing, Inc., 5725 N. Scottsdale Rd., Ste. C-195, Scottsdale, AZ 85250-5908. TEL 602-949-0100. FAX 602-949-9821. Ed. Ron Bianchi. adv.: B&W page $6930, color page $9900; trim 8 1/8 x 10 7/8; adv. contact: Michael Gilmore. circ. 250,000. **Document type:** consumer publication.

796.323   **US**   ISSN 1054-2213
DICK VITALE'S BASKETBALL.* a. $7.95. Preview Publishing, 17754 12th Ave., N.E., Seattle, WA 98155-3717. FAX 206-284-2083.
   Description: Preview of the upcoming college and professional basketball season from insiders in the game.

796.357   **US**   ISSN 0896-7970
DIEHARD. 1986. m. $24.95. Coman Publishing Company, Inc., 505 S. Duke St., Ste. 504, Durham, NC 27701. TEL 919-688-0218. FAX 919-682-1532. (Subscr. to: Box 2331, Durham, NC 27702) Ed. George Whitney. adv.: B&W page $400, color page $600; 10 x 13. circ. 12,400. **Document type:** consumer publication.
   Description: For Boston Red Sox fans.

DISCOVERY Y M C A. see SOCIAL SERVICES AND WELFARE

796.334   **SP**
DON BALON. 1975. w. 10400 ptas. (Europe 17680 ptas.; elsewhere 23400 ptas.) (effective 1993). Avda. Diagonal 435, 1o, 2A, 08036 Barcelona, Spain. TEL 93-2092000. FAX 93-2092611. Dir. Juan Pedro Martinez. adv. **Document type:** consumer publication.

796.332   **US**   ISSN 1054-2191
DON HEINRICH'S COLLEGE FOOTBALL. a. $4.95. Preview Publishing, 17754 12th Ave., N.E., Seattle, WA 98155-3717. TEL 201-944-4471. FAX 201-944-3193. **Document type:** consumer publication.

796.332   **US**   ISSN 1054-2221
DON HEINRICH'S PRO PREVIEW. a. $5.95. Sports Minded, 1638 Parker Ave., Ft. Lee, NJ 07024. TEL 201-944-4471. FAX 201-944-3193. **Document type:** consumer publication.
   Description: Previews the forthcoming N.F.L. season from an insider's viewpoint; includes statistics, analyses, and strategies.

796.355   **US**
EAGLE (COLORADO SPRINGS). 1932. q. $15. United States Field Hockey Association, Inc., USFHA National Office, 1750 E. Boulder St., Colorado Springs, CO 80909. TEL 719-578-4567. FAX 719-632-0979. adv.; charts; illus. circ. 10,000. **Indexed:** Sportsearch.
   Description: Information on field hockey and on the activities of the association.

796.323   **US**   ISSN 0195-0223
EASTERN BASKETBALL MAGAZINE.* 1976. fortn. $37. Eastern Basketball Publishers, c/o Ralph T. Pollio, Ed., 377 Hempstead Dr., 2nd Fl., West Hempstead, NY 11552-1906. TEL 516-483-9495. Ed. Ralph T. Pollio. circ. 52,000.

SPORTS AND GAMES — BALL GAMES

796.332 UK
EASTERN FOOTBALL NEWS.* 1913. w. £0.17. Eastern Counties Newspaper Group, Prospect House, Rouen Rd., Norwich, Norfolk NR1 1RE, England. TEL 44-1603-628311. FAX 44-1603-612930. TELEX ECNNCH G. Ed. K. Peel. adv.
  Description: Covers soccer teams and matches.

796.3 II
EKACH SHATKAR. (Text in Marathi) 1983. fortn. newsstand price: Rs.6. Shatkar Prakashan Pvt. Ltd., Shatkar Prakashan, Vishwavinay, 403, Bhagoji Keer Marg, Mahim, Bombay 400 016, India. TEL 465480. FAX 465103. Ed. Sandeep Patil; Pub. Nikhil M. Wagle. adv. contact: Dilip Tolkar.
  Description: Magazine on cricket.

796.334 JA
ELEVEN/IREBUN. (Text in Japanese) 1971. m. 6240 Yen. Nihon Sports Publishing Co. Ltd., 2-6, 2-chome, Hakusan, Bunkyo-ku, Tokyo, Japan. Ed. Noritake Tezuka.
  Description: Discusses soccer teams and matches.

796.357 US ISSN 1049-9555
ELYSIAN FIELDS QUARTERLY; the baseball review. 1981. q. $18.50 (Canada & Mexico $30; elsewhere $52). Elysian Fields Press, Box 45618, Madison, WI 53744-5618. TEL 608-273-1444. Ed. Stephen Lehman. adv. contact: Brett Apold. bk.rev.; illus.; circ. 1,100 (paid). (back issues avail.)
  Formerly (until Jan. 1992): Minneapolis Review of Baseball.

796.334 DK ISSN 0109-1417
ENGELSK FODBOLD. 1982; ceased same year. m. membership. Supporters of English Football, c/o Kim Madsen, Faegangsvej 3, Boennerup Strand, 8585 Glaesborg, Denmark. illus.

794.72 AU ISSN 1021-6472
EUROPEAN BILLIARD NEWS. (Text in English, German) 1992. bi-m. DM.66; newsstand price: DM.7. (European Pocket Billiard Federation) Tera GmbH, Hauptstr. 53, A-5600 St. Johann, Austria. TEL 06412-7635. FAX 06412-763615. Ed. Ralf Teppan. adv.: B&W page DM.2950, color page DM.4130; trim 210 x 297; adv. contact: Matthias Holzmann. circ. 20,000. **Document type:** consumer publication.

796.334 UK
EUROPEAN FOOTBALL YEARBOOK. 1990. a. Sports Projects Ltd., 188 Lightwoods Hill, Smethwick, Warley, W. Midlands B67 5EH, England. Ed. Mike Hammond; Pub. Bernard Gallagher. **Document type:** bulletin.

796.3 UK
EVENING TIMES WEE RED BOOK; the football annual. 1920. a. 1.20. George Outram & Co. Ltd., 195 Albion St., Glasgow G1 1HP, Scotland. TEL 0141-552-6255. FAX 0141-553-1355. TELEX 779818. Ed. John B. Scott. adv. contact: Nigel Boyd. circ. 40,000. **Document type:** newspaper.

796.352 US ISSN 0194-2387
EXECUTIVE GOLFER. 1972. bi-m. $9. Pazdur Publishing Co., 2171 Campus Dr., Irvine, CA 92715. TEL 714-752-6474. FAX 714-752-0398. Ed. Edward F. Pazdur. adv.; bk.rev.; illus. circ. 100,000. **Indexed:** Sportsearch.
  Formerly: Country Club Golfer.

796.334 SZ
F I F A. HANDBOOK. a. 40 SFr. Federation Internationale de Football Association, P.O. Box 85, CH-8030 Zurich, Switzerland. TEL 01-3849595. FAX 01-3849696. TELEX 817240-FIF-CH. Ed.Bd. **Document type:** bulletin.
  Description: Contains directory of committees and international referees as well as laws, association and competitions regulations plus guides for referees. Focuses on football (soccer).

796.334 SZ
F I F A. OLYMPIC FOOTBALL TOURNAMENT. (Subseries of: F I F A. Technical Studies) (Text in English, French, German, Spanish) 1980. quadrennial. 20 SFr. Federation Internationale de Football Association, P.O. Box 85, CH-8030 Zurich, Switzerland. TEL 01-3849595. FAX 01-3849696. TELEX 817240-FIF-CH. Ed.Bd. **Document type:** bulletin.

764.334 SZ
F I F A. TECHNICAL REPORTS. (Series of: World Cup, World Youth Championship, Worls Championship, U-17 World Championship, Worls Championship for Women's Football, and Olympic World Tournament) (Text in English, French, German, Spanish) irreg. price varies. Federation Internationale de Football Association, P.O. Box 85, CH-8030 Zurich, Switzerland. TEL 01-3849595. FAX 01-3849696. TELEX 817240-FIF-CH. Ed.Bd. **Document type:** monographic series.
  Formerly: F I F A. Technical Notes.

796.334 SZ
F I F A. U-17 WORLD CHAMPIONSHIP. (Subseries of: F I F A. Technical Studies) (Text in English, French, German, Spanish) 1985. biennial. 20 SFr. Federation Internationale de Football Association, P.O. Box 85, CH-8030 Zurich, Switzerland. TEL 01-3849595. FAX 01-3849696. TELEX 817240-FIF-CH. Ed.Bd. **Document type:** bulletin.
  Formerly: F I F A. U-17 World Tournament.

796.334 SZ
F I F A. WORLD CUP. (Text in English, French, German, Spanish) 1978. quadrennial. 80 SFr. Federation Internationale de Football Association, P.O. Box 85, CH-8030 Zurich, Switzerland. TEL 01-3849595. FAX 01-3849696. TELEX 817240-FIF-CH. Ed.Bd. **Document type:** bulletin.
  Description: Includes official reports of matches.

796.334 SZ
F I F A. WORLD YOUTH CHAMPIONSHIP. Variant title: F I F A - Coca-Cola Cup. (Subseries of: F I F A. Technical Studies) (Text in English, French, German, Spanish) 1981. biennial. price varies. Federation Internationale de Football Association, P.O. Box 85, CH-8030 Zurich, Switzerland. TEL 01-3849595. FAX 01-3849696. TELEX 817240-FIF-CH. Ed.Bd. **Document type:** bulletin.

746.334 SZ
F I F A. MAGAZINE. (Text in English, French, German, Spanish) irreg. 3-4/yr. 50 SFr. for Europe (foreign 80 SFr.). Federation Internationale de Football Association, P.O. Box 85, CH-8030 Zurich, Switzerland. TEL 01-3849595. FAX 01-3849696. TELEX 817240-FIF-CH. (Co-publisher: Unesco) Ed.Bd. **Indexed:** Sportsearch (1986-). **Document type:** bulletin.
  Description: Provides information on federation activities.

796.334 SZ
F I F A NEWS. (Editions in English, French, German, Spanish) 1963. m. 50 SFr. for Europe (foreign 80 SFr.). Federation Internationale de Football Association, P.O. Box 85, CH-8030 Zurich, Switzerland. TEL 01-3849595. FAX 01-3849696. TELEX 817240-FIF-CH. bk.rev. circ. 12,000. **Document type:** newsletter.
  Superseded: F I F A Official Bulletin (ISSN 0427-8321)

FANTASY BASEBALL. see HOBBIES

796.332 US
FANTASY FOOTBALL.* 1987. a. $4.95 ($5.95 in Canada). Preview Publishing, 17754 12th Ave., N.E., Seattle, WA 98155-3717. FAX 206-284-2083.

796.357 US
FASTPITCH SOFTBALL NEWS BULLETIN.* 8/yr. $10 in U.S.; Canada and Mexico $20. 1255 Kistler St., Bethlehem, PA 18015-4726.

796 GW ISSN 0323-3138
FAUSTBALL. 1956. m. DM.7.20 (foreign DM.13.80). Deutscher Faustball-Verband, Grosse Plauensche Str. 17, 01069 Dresden, Germany. (Subscr. to: Buchexport, Postfach 160, 7010 Leipzig, Germany) Ed. Frank Stein.

796 FR ISSN 0071-4267
FEDERATION INTERNATIONALE DE RUGBY AMATEUR. ANNUAIRE. 1965. a. free. International Amateur Rugby Federation, 7 Cite d'Antin, 75009 Paris, France. FAX 45-26-19-19. TELEX 660787. adv.; circ. 700 (controlled).

796 GW ISSN 0323-3189
FEDERBALL.* m. DM.13.80. Saarlaendischer Badminton Verband, Saarruferstr. 16, 6600 Saarbruecken, Germany.

796.334 IT
FIORENTINA. 1981. m. L.40000. Fiorentina S.r.l., Via Pico della Mirandola 2, 50132 Florence, Italy. TEL 39-55-572625. (V.le dei Mille 66, Florence, Italy) Ed. Roberto Gamucci. adv.: color page L.5000000. circ. 25,000. **Document type:** consumer publication.

796.332 UK ISSN 0953-4202
FIRST DOWN. 1986. w. £57.40 (effective 1992). Mediawatch Ltd., Spendlove Centre, Charlbury, Oxford OX7 3PQ, England. TEL 011-44-608-811266. FAX 011-44-608-811830. TELEX 837883-SPEND-G. adv.; bk.rev. circ. 20,000. (tabloid format; back issues avail.)
  Description: Covers American football, including detailed game reviews and previews, player and team profiles and news from the USA, the UK and Europe.

796.334 US
FLAG & TOUCH FOOTBALL RULEBOOK AND OFFICIAL'S MANUAL. 1983. biennial. $5. National Intramural-Recreational Sports Association, 850 S.W. 15th St., Corvallis, OR 97333-4145. TEL 503-737-2088. FAX 503-737-2026. Eds. Bruce L. Maurer, Jim Potter. adv.
  Description: Provides football rules and information manual for game officials.

796.352 US
FLORIDA GOLF REPORTER. 1989. 6/yr. $9.95. Golf Reporter Enterprises Inc., Box 951422, Lake Mary, FL 32795-1422. FAX 407-767-5748. Ed. Mike Jamison. adv.; circ. 20,000 (controlled).
  Description: Covers all state amateur and all PGA section golf events in Florida. Includes travel tips and updates on new courses and real estate instruction.

796.352 US
FLORIDA GOLFER.* 1987. m. $17.50. Florida Golfer, Inc., 1460 Golden Gate Pky., Ste. 103, Naples, FL 33942-3128. TEL 813-643-4994. FAX 813-643-6581. adv. **Document type:** consumer publication.
  Description: Covers current and upcoming events. Profiles amateur and professional golfers.

796.334 DK ISSN 0109-9876
FODBOLD, DANSKE KAMPE; fodbold aarbogen. 1968. a. Carlsen Forlag A-S, Krogshoejvej 32, DK-2880 Bagsvaerd, Denmark. TEL 45-44-44-32-33. FAX 45-44-44-36-33.
  Formerly (until 1984): Fodboldaarbogen (ISSN 0109-9868)

796.334 DK ISSN 0905-4006
FODBOLD, INTERNATIONALE KAMPE; aarets bedste fodbold. a. Carlsen Forlag A-S, Krogshoejvej 32, DK-2880 Bagsvaerd, Denmark. TEL 45-44-44-32-33. FAX 45-44-44-36-33.
  Former titles (until 1989): Fodbold, Udenlandske Kampe (ISSN 0109-9892); (until 1984): Fodbold, Aarets Bedste (ISSN 0109-9884)

796.334 US
FOOTBAG WORLD. 1983. q. $5 (foreign $15). World Footbag Association, 1317 Washington Ave., Ste. 7, Golden, CO 80401. TEL 303-278-9797. FAX 303-278-9841. Ed. Bruce Guettich. adv.; bk.rev. circ. 5,000. (back issues avail.) **Indexed:** Sportsearch (1986-). **Document type:** consumer publication.
  Description: Covers footbag games and its players. Includes a calendar of events, tournament results, stories, coaching advice and health tips.

796.332 US ISSN 0197-1891
GV937
FOOTBALL ACTION. 1975. s-a. $5.95. Sports Eye, Inc., 18 Industrial Park Dr., Port Washington, NY 11050. TEL 516-484-3300; 800-247-2923. Ed. Peter Hayes; Pub. Louis Sierra. adv. **Document type:** consumer publication.
  Description: Covers sports betting.

796.332 UK ISSN 0071-724X
FOOTBALL ASSOCIATION YEAR BOOK.* 1979. a. £5.99. Macmillan Ltd., 18-21 Cavaye Pl., London SW10 9PG, England. adv. **Indexed:** Br.Hum.Ind.
  Description: Reviews of the English season plus fixtures for the forthcoming one.

SPORTS AND GAMES — BALL GAMES

796.332   US   ISSN 0163-6200
GV955
FOOTBALL CASE BOOK. a. $4. National Federation of State High School Associations, 11724 N.W. Plaza Circle, Box 20626, Kansas City, MO 64195-0626. TEL 816-464-5400. FAX 816-464-5571.

796.334   US   ISSN 0015-6760
FOOTBALL DIGEST. 1971. 10/yr. $22 (foreign $30). Century Publishing Co., 990 Grove St., Evanston, IL 60201-4370. TEL 708-491-6440. (Subscr. to: Box 571, Mt. Morris, IL 61054-0571. TEL 800-877-5893) Ed. Ken Leiker. adv.; bk.rev.; illus. circ. 200,000. (also avail. in microform from UMI; reprint service avail. from UMI) **Indexed:** Sports Per.Ind., Sportsearch. **Document type:** consumer publication.
—UMI.
    Description: For serious adult football fans who want the statistics, features and excitement behind pro and college football.

796.332   US   ISSN 0364-8273
GV955.5.N35
FOOTBALL FORECAST (YEAR). a. Sterling - Macfadden Partnership, 233 Park Ave. So., New York, NY 10003. TEL 212-780-3500. FAX 212-780-3555. Ed. Stephen Ciacciarelli. adv.; charts; illus. **Document type:** consumer publication.

796.332   US   ISSN 0069-5548
FOOTBALL GUIDE. 1963. a. $2.50. Kwik-Fax Books (Subsidiary of: Martin Frederick, Inc.), Box 14613, Surfside Beach, SC 29587. TEL 803-238-3513. FAX 803-238-4074. Ed. Malcolm DeWitt. circ. 10,000,000.
    Formerly: College and Pro Football Guide.

796.332   US
FOOTBALL HANDBOOK. biennial. $4. National Federation of State High School Associations, 11724 N.W. Plaza Circle, Box 20626, Kansas City, MO 64195-0626. TEL 816-464-5400. FAX 816-464-5571.

796.332 378.198   US
(YEAR) FOOTBALL MEDIA GUIDE. 1982. a. $10. Big Ten Conference, 1500 Higgins Rd., Park Ridge, IL 60068-5742. TEL 708-696-1010. FAX 708-696-1110. charts; illus.; stat. circ. 4,000.
    Formerly: Big Ten Football Yearbook.

796.332   US   ISSN 0161-9020
FOOTBALL NEWS. 1939. w. (during season). $39.95 for 20 nos. 8033 N.W. 36th St., Miami, FL 33152. TEL 305-594-0508. (Subscr. to: Box 526600, Miami, FL 33152. TEL 800-334-4005) Ed. Andrew Cohen; Pub. Tom Curtis. adv. contact: Ken Keidel. bk.rev.; stat. circ. 86,000. (tabloid format) **Document type:** newspaper.
    Description: Devoted to college and pro football.

796.332   US
FOOTBALL OFFICIALS HANDBOOK. biennial. $4. National Federation of State High School Associations, 11724 N.W. Plaza Circle, Box 20626, Kansas City, MO 64195-0626. TEL 816-464-5400. FAX 816-464-5571.

796.332   US   ISSN 0163-6219
GV954.35
FOOTBALL OFFICIALS MANUAL. biennial. $4. National Federation of State High School Associations, 11724 N.W. Plaza Circle, Box 20626, Kansas City, MO 64195-0626. TEL 816-464-5400. FAX 816-464-5571.

796.332   US   ISSN 1054-0164
FOOTBALL PREVIEW (YEAR). a. Sterling - Macfadden Partnership, 233 Park Ave. So., New York, NY 10003. TEL 212-780-3500. FAX 212-780-3555. Ed. Stephen Ciacciarelli. adv.; charts; illus. **Document type:** consumer publication.
    Formerly: N F L Preview (Year).

796.334   AT   ISSN 0015-6795
FOOTBALL RECORD. 1912. w. (30/yr., Apr.-Sep.). Aus.$87. Australian Football League, MCG, Yarra Park, Jolimont , Vic. 3002, Australia. Ed. Greg Hobbs. adv.; bk.rev.; charts; stat. circ. 100,000.

796.334   UK
FOOTBALL REFEREE. 1974. 8/yr. £0.50 per no. Referees' Association, 37 George St., Whitefield, Manchester M45 7SZ, England. Ed. Paul Gresty. adv.; bk.rev.; circ. 8,000 (controlled). **Document type:** trade publication.
    Description: Discusses soccer matches and teams, and refereeing matters.

796.332   US   ISSN 0731-9533
GV956.8
FOOTBALL RULES - SIMPLIFIED AND ILLUSTRATED. a. $4. National Federation of State High School Associations, 11724 N.W. Plaza Circle, Box 20626, Kansas City, MO 64195-0626. TEL 816-464-5400. FAX 816-464-5571.
    Formerly: Official High School Football Rules Simplified and Illustrated for Officials, Coaches, Players, Spectators (ISSN 0163-6472)

796.332   AT   ISSN 0156-2916
FOOTBALL TIMES. 1976-1992. w., (Mar.-Oct.). Aus.$55. Messenger Press, 1 Baynes Pl., Port Adelaide, S.A. 5015, Australia. TEL 08-475722. FAX 08-475267. (Subscr. to: P.O. Box 197, Port Adelaide, SA, Australia) Ed. Ashley Hornsey. adv.; bk.rev. circ. 12,000. (back issues avail.) **Document type:** consumer publication.

796.336 028.5   AT   ISSN 1036-2940
FOOTY STARS. 1991. 3/yr. (during football season: May, June, July). Text Magazine Company, Level 5, 171 La Trobe St., Melbourne, Vic. 3000, Australia. TEL 03-272-4700. FAX 03-272-4799. Ed. Michael Roberts. adv. contact: Steven Hogan. circ. 37,500. (back issues avail.) **Document type:** consumer publication.
    Description: For children from early to mid-teens about Australian rules football.

796.342   AT
FORD AUSTRALIAN OPEN OFFICIAL SOUVENIR PROGRAM. 1987. a. Nicholson Media Group Pty. Ltd., P.O. Box 206, Hawksburn, Vic. 3142, Australia. TEL 61-3-826-8448. FAX 61-3-827-8808. Ed. Alan Trengove. adv.; B&W page Aus.$2300, color page Aus.$3100; adv. contact: Vivienne Christie. circ. 50,000. **Document type:** trade publication.
    Description: Contains news and information on players, personnel, the event and the sport.

796.352   US   ISSN 0300-8509
FORE. 1968. bi-m. $1. Southern California Golf Association, 3740 Cahuenga Blvd., North Hollywood, CA 91604. TEL 818-980-3630. FAX 818-980-1808. Ed. Robert D. Thomas. adv.; bk.rev.; illus. circ. 130,000. **Indexed:** Sportsearch. **Document type:** trade publication.

796.352   UK   ISSN 0969-9953
FORE. 1993. m. £26.50 (foreign £38) (effective 1995-1996). E M A P - Pursuit Publishing, Bretton Ct., Bretton, Peterborough, Cambs. PE3 8DZ, England. TEL 01733-264666. FAX 01733-263267. TELEX 32157. (Subscr. to: Tower Publishing Services Ltd., Tower House, Sovereign Park, Lathkill St., Market Harborough, Leics. LE16 9EF, England. TEL 01858-468811. FAX 01858-432164) adv. **Document type:** consumer publication.

796.332   US
FOREST DAVIS' SOUTHERN FOOTBALL RECRUITING.* 1990. a. Box 380723, Birmingham, AL 35238-0723. TEL 205-854-4785.

796.334   IT
FORZA MILAN!. 1962. m. L.28000 (foreign L.41000). Silvio Berlusconi Editore S.p.A., Corso Europa 5-7, 20122 Milan, Italy. TEL 39-2-77941. Ed. Gigi Vesigna. adv.; color page L.17600000. circ. 113,970. **Document type:** consumer publication.

796.334   NO   ISSN 0333-4341
FOTBALL. 1933. 8/yr. Hjemmet Mortensens Forlag AS, Soerkedalsveien 10A, N-0369 Oslo, Norway. TEL 47-2-961-500. FAX 47-2-961-382. adv.; B&W page NOK 16300, color page NOK 21400. circ. 86,354 (controlled).

796.334   SW   ISSN 0347-2752
FOTBOLL (STOCKHOLM). 1957. a. SEK 880 (effective 1990). (Svenska Fotbollfoerbundet) Stroemberg - Brunnhage, P.O. Box 65, S-162 11 Vaellingby, Sweden.

796.334   SW   ISSN 0349-8484
FOTBOLLBOKEN; med Svenska Fotbollfoerbundets taevlingskalender. 1932. a. SEK 99 (effective 1990). (Svenska Fotbollfoerbundet) Futurum Media, P.O. Box 1802, S-171 21 Solna, Sweden.
    Formerly (until 1972): Nya Fotbollboken.

796.334   SW   ISSN 0284-2319
FOTBOLLMAGASINET; officielt organ foer Svenska Fotbollfoerbundet. 1987. 10/yr. SEK 295 (effective 1990). (Svenska Fotbollfoerbundet) Futurum Media, P.O. Box 1802, S-171 21 Solna, Sweden. (Subscr. to: Pressdata, P.O. Box 3263, S-103 65 Stockholm, Sweden)

796.333   FR
FRANCE FOOTBALL. 12/yr. 415 F. Amaury Group, 4 rue Rouget-de-Lisle, 92137 Issy-les-Moulineaux Cedex, France. TEL 1-40-93-20-20. FAX 1-40-93-20-08. TELEX 203 004. illus. circ. 158,553. **Indexed:** Sportsearch. **Document type:** consumer publication.
    Formerly: Football Magazine.

796.3   FR   ISSN 1156-4954
FRANCE TENNIS DE TABLE JOURNAL. 1944. m. 255 F. Federation Francaise de Tennis de Table, 4 rue Guillot, 92120 Montrouge, France. FAX 42-53-85-96. Ed. Jean Devys. adv. circ. 5,000. **Indexed:** Sportsearch (1977-).
    Formerly (until 1989): France Tennis de Table (ISSN 1249-2752)

796.323   NE   ISSN 1380-9962
FULL COURT PRESS. (Text in Dutch) 1985. m. fl.57.50($60) (Dutch Basketball Association) Het Urkerland B.V., Postbus 29, 8320 AA Urk, Netherlands. TEL 31-5277-4455. FAX 31-5277-4695. Ed. Mart Smeets; Pub. A. Brouwer. adv.; B&W page fl.1260; trim 210 x 297; adv. contact: A. Schurink. circ. 5,000 (paid).
    Description: Covers basketball in the Netherlands, European competitions, the NBA and NCAA.

796   GW   ISSN 0009-9600
FUSSBALL CLUB PFORZHEIM. CLUB-NACHRICHTEN. 1952. m. membership. J. Esslinger Druckerei und Verlag, Poststr. 5, 75172 Pforzheim, Germany. adv. circ. 1,500.

796.334   GW
FUSSBALL-WELTZEITSCHRIFT. 1986. 4/yr. DM.80 (foreign DM.100). International Federation of Football History and Statistics, Graf-von-Galen-Str. 72, 65197 Wiesbaden, Germany. **Document type:** bulletin.
    Formerly: 11 - Zeitschrift fuer Internationale Fussball-Geschichte und -Statistik.

796.07   GW   ISSN 0016-3228
DER FUSSBALLTRAINER. 1950. m. DM.55.80. Achalm-Verlag, Postfach 1642, 72706 Reutlingen, Germany. TEL 07121-302590. adv.; bk.rev.; illus.; index. circ. 3,500. **Document type:** trade publication.
    Description: Devoted to news and information for soccer trainers and coaches. Articles cover various aspects of soccer, tips for training, tactics, personal stories.

796.334   GW   ISSN 0174-6227
FUSSBALLTRAINING. 1983. m. DM.67.20 (foreign DM.74.40). Philippka-Verlag, Postfach 6540, 48034 Muenster, Germany. TEL 0251-23005-0. FAX 0251-23005-99. circ. 17,000. (back issues avail.) **Document type:** bulletin.

796.332   FI   ISSN 0359-4378
FUTARI.* 1982. 8/yr. Erikoislehedt Oy Business Publications, P.O. Box 16, SF-00381 Helsinki, Finland. Ed. Matti Sovijaervi. circ. 58,697.

796.334   GW   ISSN 0323-8407
FUWO.* 1949. 2/w. DM.78. Axel-Springer-Platz 1, 20355 Hamburg, Germany.

796.332   US
GIANTS EXTRA. 30/yr. $29.95. Giants Extra, 927 Washington Ave., N., Green Brook, NJ 08812. TEL 908-968-0033. Eds. Bobby Duhon, Chuck Mercein. illus.; stat.
    Description: Features previews of games, player interviews, statistics of the team.

SPORTS AND GAMES — BALL GAMES

796.332 US ISSN 0279-0238
THE GIANTS NEWSWEEKLY. Running title: T G N. 1981. 28/yr. (w. (Aug.-Dec.), m. (Jan.-July)). $29.95 (Canada $79.95; elsewhere $160.95); newsstand price: $2.50. Pro Publishing, Inc., Box 816, Red Bank, NJ 07701. TEL 908-747-1085; 800-562-2198. FAX 908-741-6905. Ed. Rick Maddock. adv.; illus.; stat. circ. 66,000. (tabloid format; back issues avail.) **Document type:** newspaper, consumer publication.
 Description: News of the New York Giants football team from training camp through regular season.

796.323 IT ISSN 1122-1801
GIGANTI DEL BASKET. 1966. w. L.180000 (America L.37000). Conti Editore S.p.A, Via del Lavoro 7, 40068 San Lazzaro di Savena (BO), Italy. TEL 39-51-6258566. FAX 39-51-6258692. Ed. Paolo Facchinetti. adv.: B&W page L.4000000, color page L.6000000; 206 x 251. bk.rev. circ. 12,552. **Document type:** consumer publication.
 Description: Discusses various aspects of basketball.

796.334 IT
GOALFLASH!. 1984. m. L.55000. Forte Editore s.r.l., Via Asiago 114, 20128 Milan, Italy. TEL 39-2-2594241. Ed. Enrico Crespi. adv.: B&W page L.3000000, color page L.4000000. **Document type:** consumer publication.

796.334 796.962 XR ISSN 0323-0686
GOL; fodbalovy a hokejovy tydenik. 1968. w. 130 Kc.($78) Olympia a.s., Klimentska 1, 115 88 Prague 1, Czech Republic. (Dist. by: Artia, Ve Smeckach 30, 111 27 Prague 1, Czech Republic) Ed. K. Zelnicek. illus.; index. circ. 55,000.
 Description: Focuses on soccer and hockey.

796.332 US
GOLDEN STATE WARRIORS OFFICIAL YEARBOOK. 1993. a. $7. Woodford Publishing, 660 Market St., Ste. 206, San Francisco, CA 94104-5011. TEL 415-397-1853. FAX 415-399-0942. Ed. Jon Rochmis. adv. contact: David Lilienstein. illus. circ. 40,000. **Document type:** consumer publication.

796.352 DK ISSN 0902-8927
GOLF. 1943. 8/yr. DKK 320. Dansk Golf Union, Idraettens Hus, DK-2605 Broendby, Denmark. TEL 45-43-26-27-00. FAX 45-43-26-27-01. Ed. Poul Bjerrum. adv.; bk.rev.; illus. circ. 45,000. **Indexed:** Sportsearch.

796.352 SP ISSN 0432-0549
GOLF. 1954. m. 6600 ptas. (effective Jan. 1994). Ediciones Golf, Rodriguez San Pedro 8, 28015 Madrid, Spain. TEL 91-4461512. FAX 91-4485807. (Dist. by: A & D Distribuciones, C. E. Torroja 37, 28940 Fuenlabrada, Madrid, Spain. TEL 91-6159611) Pub. Enrique Meijide. adv. contact: Gina Ruizdelvall. circ. 40,000.
 Description: Covers golf news, lessons, tournaments, tourism, and sporting goods.

796.352 BE
GOLF. (Text in Dutch, French) 1946. m. (10/yr.). 950 BEF. (Federation Royale Belge de Golf) Belgame S.A., 167 Ave. Montjoie, 1180 Brussels, Belgium. TEL 32-2-3430845. FAX 32-2-3435772. adv. circ. 12,000. **Document type:** consumer publication.

796.352 CN ISSN 1193-7106
GOLF ALBATROS. 1983. 6/yr. Can.$19.50. Golf Albatros, 4850 Cote des neiges, No. 904, Montreal, PQ H3V 1G5, Canada. TEL 514-737-4050. FAX 514-343-4653. Ed. Gilles Gareau. adv.; bk.rev. circ. 60,000. (back issues avail.)
 Formerly (until 1992): Albatros (ISSN 0828-7791)
 Description: Features news on golf tournaments, profiles of golfers, tips on technique, information on golf equipment, resorts and clubs.

GOLF AND SPORTS TURF. see AGRICULTURE — Crop Production And Soil

796.352 IT
▼**GOLF & TURISMO**. 1994. 10/yr. L.80000 (foreign L.120000). Go.Tu. s.r.l., Via Pergolesi 22, 20124 Milan, Italy. TEL 39-2-67070873. FAX 39-2-67070879. Ed. Giorgio Mistretta. adv.: color page L.9500000; adv. contact: Lorenzo Barbieri. circ. 21,000. **Document type:** consumer publication.

796.352 AT ISSN 0818-5077
GOLF AUSTRALIA. 1987. m. Aus.$48. Horwitz Publications Pty. Ltd., 55 Chandos St., St. Leonards, N.S.W. 2065, Australia. TEL 61-2-901-6100. FAX 61-2-901-6116. (Subscr. to: Golf Australia, P.O. Box 3355, St. Leonards, N.S.W. 2065, Australia) Ed. Nigel Wall. adv. contact: Howard Jenkins. circ. 15,000. (back issues avail.) **Document type:** consumer publication.
 Description: Covers all aspects of the sport: players, tournaments, instruction, travel, equipment, features, results, etc.

796.352 GW ISSN 0931-573X
GOLF CLUB MAGAZIN. 1972. m. DM.50. Kopp Public, Hohenzollernstr. 33, 30161 Hannover, Germany. TEL 0511-337010. FAX 0511-311043. Ed. Hubert Kopp. adv.: B&W page DM.6150, color page DM.11200; trim 183 x 250. bk.rev. circ. 27,176. **Document type:** consumer publication.

796.352 658 UK ISSN 0267-1166
GOLF CLUB MANAGEMENT & EQUIPMENT NEWS.* 1933. bi-m. £30. Association of Golf Club Secretaries, Woodbury House, Jouldings Lane, Farley Hill, Reading, Berks RG1 1UR, England. Ed. N.G. Osman. adv.; bk.rev. circ. 2,500. **Indexed:** Sportsearch.

796.352 US
GOLF CLUBMAKER. 1978. q. $20 membership (foreign $24). Professional Golf Club Repairmen's Association, 2295 Ben Hogan Dr., Dunedin, FL 34698. TEL 813-733-9241. FAX 813-787-4361. Ed. Michael L. Bowers. adv.; illus.; pat.; stat.; circ. 1,000. circ. 1,000 (paid). **Indexed:** Sportsearch (1984-). **Document type:** trade publication, newsletter.
 Description: Provides information on repair and maintenance. Includes developments in the industry and association as well as research results.

GOLF COURSE BUILDERS ASSOCIATION OF AMERICA. DIRECTORY. see BUILDING AND CONSTRUCTION

796.352 US ISSN 0192-3048
GV975 CODEN: GCMAEA
GOLF COURSE MANAGEMENT. 1926. m. $30 (foreign $42). Golf Course Superintendents Association of America, 1421 Research Park Dr., Lawrence, KS 66049. TEL 913-841-2240. FAX 913-832-4466. Ed. Clay Loyd. adv.; illus. circ. 24,000. **Indexed:** Sportsearch (1979-). **Document type:** trade publication.
 —Faxon; UnCover.
 Former titles: Golf Superintendent (ISSN 0017-1840); Golf Course Reporter.

796.352 US
GOLF COURSE MANAGEMENT LETTER.* irreg. membership. Public Golf Management Association, 8030 Cedar, Ste. 215, Minneapolis, MN 55425. TEL 612-854-8482.

796.352 US ISSN 1054-0644
GOLF COURSE NEWS.* 1989. 9/yr. United Publications, Inc. (St. Petersburg), 227 Second Ave., N., St. Petersburg, FL 33701-3317. TEL 813-576-7077. adv. circ. 20,000.
 Description: Provides information on golf course management and maintenance for supervisors, golf directors, architects, developers and builders.

658 US ISSN 0436-1474
GV975
GOLF COURSE SUPERINTENDENTS ASSOCIATION OF AMERICA. MEMBERSHIP DIRECTORY; who's who in golf course management. Key Title: Membership Directory of the Golf Course Superintendents Association of America. Spine title: G C S A A Membership Directory. a. Golf Course Superintendents Association of America, 1421 Research Park Dr., Lawrence, KS 66049. TEL 913-841-2240. FAX 913-832-4466. circ. 12,000. **Document type:** directory.

796.352 US ISSN 0072-4947
GOLF COURSE SUPERINTENDENTS ASSOCIATION OF AMERICA. PROCEEDINGS OF THE INTERNATIONAL GOLF COURSE CONFERENCE AND SHOW. a. $50 to non-members. Golf Course Superintendents Association of America, 1421 Research Park Dr., Lawrence, KS 66049. TEL 913-841-2240. FAX 913-832-4466. circ. 4,500. **Document type:** proceedings.

796.352 US ISSN 0017-176X
GV961
GOLF DIGEST. (Editions in various languages) 1950. m. $27.94. New York Times Company Magazine Group, Sports - Leisure Division, 5520 Park Ave., Box 395, Trumbull, CT 06611-0395. TEL 203-373-7000. Ed. Jerry Tarde. adv.; bk.rev.; charts; illus.; tr.lit. circ. 1,465,494. (also avail. in microfilm from UMI; back issues avail.) **Indexed:** Consum.Ind., Phys.Ed.Ind., PMR, Sports Per.Ind., Sportsearch (1974-). **Document type:** consumer publication.
 —Faxon; UMI; UnCover.
 Description: Gives advice from players and experienced teachers.

796.352 FR
GOLF EN FRANCE; guide des terrains de golf francais. 1969. a. 90 F. Editions Person, 34 rue de Penthievre, 75008 Paris, France.

796.352 US
GOLF FOR WOMEN. 1988. bi-m. $15.97; newsstand price: $.3.50. Meredith Corporation, 1716 Locust St., Des Moines, IA 50336. TEL 515-284-2484. FAX 515-284-2700. Ed. Patricia Baldwin. circ. 440,000.
 Description: Covers instruction, equipment, vacation ideas and tournament listings and results.

796.352 US
GOLF GEORGIA. 1988. 6/yr. membership. (Georgia State Golf Association) Moorhead Publications, 810 S. Waukegan Rd., Ste. 200, Lake Forest, IL 60045. TEL 404-988-8864. Ed. Bill Gregory; Pub. Thomas J. Moorhead. circ. 72,500.
 Formerly (Aug. 1993-Feb. 1994): Fairways & Greens.
 Description: Features news, information and feature articles on people and events related to golf in Georgia and golf in general.

796.352 IT
GOLF GREEN. 1990. m. L.8000 per no. Editoriale Golf Green, Corso Garibaldi 95, 20121 Milan, Italy. TEL 39-2-29000504. FAX 39-2-6598379. Ed. Giorgio Mistretta. adv.: page L.9800000. **Document type:** consumer publication.

796.352 US ISSN 0072-4955
GOLF GUIDE. 1963. a. $2.50. Kwik-Fax Books (Subsidiary of: Martin Frederick, Inc.), Box 14613, Surfside Beach, SC 29587. TEL 803-238-3513. Ed. Joseph Gambatese.

796.352 CN ISSN 1184-6291
GOLF GUIDE; annual golf course directory, British Columbia, Alberta, Saskatchewan & Manitoba. 1984. a. Can.$4.95. Golf Guide Inc., 16410 - 137 Ave., Edmonton, AB T5L 4H8, Canada. TEL 403-447-2128; 800-661-1606. FAX 403-447-1933. Ed. Gord Ladbrook; Pub. Paul McCracken. adv.: B&W page Can.$2075, color page Can.$2395; trim 10 5/8 x 8 1/4. illus. circ. 50,000. (back issues avail.) **Document type:** directory.
 Former titles: Golf Courses of Alberta; Alberta Golf Guide (ISSN 0832-8803); Incorporates: British Columbia Golf Guide (ISSN 0848-8398)
 Description: Directory of more than 900 golf courses in British Columbia, Alberta and Saskatchewan and Manitoba.

796.352 UK ISSN 0263-4066
GOLF GUIDE - WHERE TO PLAY AND WHERE TO STAY. 1977. a. £8.50. F H G Publications Ltd., Abbey Mill Business Centre, Seedhill, Paisley PA1 1JN, Scotland. TEL 0141-887-0428. FAX 0141-889-7204. adv.; stat.; index. circ. 12,000. **Document type:** consumer publication.

796.352 SW ISSN 0347-237X
GOLF I SVERIGE. 1965. a. SEK 150 (effective 1995). Zinderman, P.O. Box 11385, S-404 28 Goeteborg, Sweden.

796.352 US
GOLF IDAHO MAGAZINE. 1991. a. $3.50. (Idaho Golf Association) Peak Media, Inc., Box 925, 418 N. River St., Hailey, ID 83333. TEL 208-788-4500. FAX 208-788-5098. adv.: B&W page $2145, color page $2860; trim 8 3/8 x 11. circ. 20,000.

SPORTS AND GAMES — BALL GAMES

796.352 US ISSN 0160-6808
GV961
GOLF ILLUSTRATED. 1914. bi-m. $15.95. Natcom, Inc., 5300 CityPlex Tower, 2448 E. 81st St., Tulsa, OK 74137-4207. TEL 918-491-6100. (Subscr. to: Box 50073, Boulder, CO 80322. TEL 800-554-1999) Ed. Simon McCaffery. adv.; bk.rev.; illus. circ. 200,000. **Indexed:** Sports Per.Ind. **Document type:** consumer publication.
Description: Covers all aspects of the game of golf including equipment, instruction, travel, fashion, fitness, etc.

796.352 AT ISSN 0312-9195
GOLF IN VICTORIA. 1959. 10/yr. Aus.$17. (Victorian Golf Association) V I P Printing Pty. Ltd., 43 De Haviland Rd., Mordialloc, Vic. 3195, Australia. TEL 03-8896731. (Subscr. to: Victorian Golf Association, 15 Bardolph St., Burwood, Vic. 3125, Australia) Ed. Garry Mansfield. adv. contact: Susan Shields. circ. 15,000. **Document type:** bulletin.
Formerly (until 1975): Victorian Golf (ISSN 0312-9187)

796.352 US
GV962
GOLF INDEX. 1980. s-a. $40. Ingledue Travel Publications, 444 Burchett St., Glendale, CA 91203. TEL 818-247-5530. FAX 818-247-5535. Ed. Ronald Ingledue; Pub. Ronald Ingledue. adv. circ. 10,000. **Document type:** directory, trade publication.
Formerly (until 1992): International Golf Directory (ISSN 0272-1775)

796 US ISSN 0160-6824
HD9993.G65
GOLF INDUSTRY.* 1975. 9/yr. $27. Sterling Southeast, Inc., 3301 Ponce De Leon Blvd., No.300, Coral Gables, FL 33134-7273. TEL 305-893-8771. FAX 305-893-8783. TELEX 510-6009280. Ed. Jerry Renninger. adv.; circ. 16,692 (controlled). **Indexed:** Sportsearch (1979-).

796.352 UK
GOLF INDUSTRY NEWS. 1899? m. £35 (rest of Europe £40; elsewhere £67) (effective 1995-1996). E M A P - Pursuit Publishing, Bretton Ct., Bretton, Peterborough, Cambs. PE3 8DZ, England. TEL 01733-264666. FAX 01733-263294. TELEX 32157. (Subscr. to: Tower Publishing Services Ltd., Tower House, Sovereign Park, Lathkill St., Market Harborough, Leics. LE16 9EF, England. TEL 01858-468811. FAX 01858-432164) adv. **Document type:** trade publication.

796.352 CN ISSN 1189-4830
GOLF INTERNATIONAL. (Text in French) 1992. 6/yr. Can.$28 (US Can.$36, elsewhere Can.$44) per 10 nos. (effective 1996). 798 Arthur Sauve, P.O.Box 91022, St-Eustache, Que. J7R 6V9, Canada. TEL 514-386-2927. FAX 514-974-2212. Ed. Jacques Landry; Pub. Jacques Landry. adv.: B&W page Can.$1950, color page Can.$2800; trim 8 1/8 x 10 7/8; adv. contact: Russell Miller. circ. 27,100. **Document type:** consumer publication.

796.352 US
GOLF INTERNATIONAL MAGAZINE.* 1990. bi-m. $19.95. Golf International, Inc., 2796 Quail St., Lakewood, CO 80215-7138. TEL 303-779-4803. FAX 303-779-9431. Ed. Jennifer C. Phillips. adv. circ. 55,000. **Document type:** trade publication.
Description: For the golf industry, from the novice to the professional. Features include PGA and LPGA player profiles, instruction, apparel and equipment reviews, and the best courses and resorts worldwide.

796.352 IT
GOLF ITALIANO. m. $110. Flaminia Editrice, Via A. Pollaiolo, 3, 00197 Rome, Italy. Ed. Piero Pucci.

796.352 US ISSN 0017-1794
GV961
GOLF JOURNAL. 1947. 9/yr. $25 includes membership (effective 1993). United States Golf Association, Golf House, Box 708, Far Hills, NJ 07931. TEL 908-234-2300. FAX 908-781-1112. Ed. Brett Avery. bk.rev.; illus.; index. circ. 500,000. (also avail. in microform from UMI; reprint service avail. from UMI) **Indexed:** Sports Per.Ind., Sportsearch. —UMI.
Formerly: U S G A Golf Journal.
Description: Emphasizes the game's history, its lore and U.S.G.A. championships, as well as issues such as environment and turfgrass research, equipment, course maintenance, and personalities.

796.352 GW ISSN 0933-8470
GOLF JOURNAL. 1982. 11/yr. DM.79.20. Atlas Verlag und Werbung GmbH, Karlstr. 41, 80333 Munich, Germany. TEL 089-55241201. FAX 089-55241288. Ed. Ulrich Kaiser. adv.; bk.rev.; charts; illus. circ. 28,984. **Document type:** consumer publication.
Incorporates (1972-1988): Golf - Contact.

796.352 IT
GOLF LAZIALE. bi-m. $40. Flaminia Editrice, Via A. Pollaiolo 3, 00197 Rome, Italy.

796.352 JA ISSN 0432-0573
GOLF MAGAZINE. Key Title: Gorufu Magajin. 1952. m. 10920 Yen. Golf Magazine Sha, 1-63 Kanda-Jimbo Cho, Chiyoda-ku, Tokyo, Japan. Ed. Shingo Hama. **Document type:** consumer publication.

796.352 FR ISSN 0181-2750
GOLF MAGAZINE.* 1976. 11/yr. Promogolf, 4 rue Sentou, 92150 Suresnes, France. TEL 47-72-28-10. FAX 40-99-98-05. Ed. Gilbert Constans. adv.; illus. circ. 25,000.

796.352 US ISSN 1056-5493
GV961
GOLF MAGAZINE (NEW YORK). 1959. m. $19.94 (effective 1993). Times Mirror Magazines, Inc., 2 Park Ave., New York, NY 10016. TEL 212-779-5000. (Subscr. to: Box 53733, Boulder, CO 80322-3733. TEL 800-876-7726) Ed. George Peper. adv.; illus. circ. 878,869. (also avail. in microform from UMI; reprint service avail. from UMI) **Indexed:** Access (1976-1987), Mag.Ind., Phys.Ed.Ind., PMR, Sports Per.Ind., Sportsearch (1974-). **Document type:** consumer publication. —Faxon; UMI; UnCover.
Former titles (until 1991): Golf (New York) (ISSN 1056-5485); (until 1986): Golf Magazine (ISSN 0017-1808)

796.352 FR
GOLF MANAGEMENT. 6/yr. 142 rue d'Aguesseau, 92100 Boulogne, France. TEL 46-03-15-54. FAX 46-03-97-67. TELEX 204 125 F. Ed. Pierre Boudka. circ. 2,700.

796.352 330 US
GOLF MARKET TODAY. 1972. bi-m. membership. National Golf Foundation, 1150 S. U.S. Hwy. One, Jupiter, FL 33477. TEL 407-744-6006. FAX 407-744-6107. Ed. Bill Burbaum. circ. 9,000 (controlled). **Document type:** newsletter.
Description: Publishes golf industry news, profiles of industry leaders, research findings and current trends in golf participation and golf course development and management in the U.S. and around the world.

796.352 UK ISSN 0017-1816
GOLF MONTHLY. 1911. m. £18.50($28) I P C Magazines, Specialist Magazine Group (Subsidiary of: Reed Elsevier group), King's Reach Tower, Stamford St., London SE1 9LS, England. TEL 071-261-7237. FAX 0444-440619. TELEX 892084 REEDBP G. (Dist. by: Quadrant Subscription Services, Oakfield House, Perrymount Rd., Haywards Heath, W. Sussex RH16 3DH, England. TEL 0444-440421) Ed. Colin Callander. adv. contact: Neil Gray. illus. circ. 74,471. **Indexed:** Sportsearch. **Document type:** consumer publication.

796.352 AT
GOLF NEWS. 1961. m. Aus.$48. New South Wales Golf Association, P.O. Box 704, Darlinghurst, N.S.W. 2010, Australia. TEL 02-264-8433. FAX 02-261-4750. Ed. Marea Allen. adv.; bk.rev. circ. 24,400. (reprint service avail.)
Formerly: N.S.W. Golf.
Description: Contains golf news, instructions, results, golf feature articles.

796.352 IT ISSN 1120-8007
GOLF NEWS. (Text in Italian) 1982. 10/yr. L.10000 (effective 1995 & 1996). Golf News, s.r.l., Via Scarlatti, 30, 20124 Milan, Italy. TEL 39-2-6692299. FAX 39-2-6692306. (Dist by: Parrini Distribuzione, Piazza Indipendenza, 11B Rome, Italy) Ed. Nicola Montanaro; Pub. Pat Nesi. adv.: page L.12000000; adv. contact: Giampaola Corsini. circ. 27,000.
Formerly (until 1989): Golf Magazine.
Refereed Serial

796.352 KE
GOLF NEWS. bi-m. free. Golf Publications, P.O. Box 31283, Nairobi, Kenya.

796.352 US
GOLF NEWS MAGAZINE. 1984. m. $15. Dan & Joan Poppers, Eds. & Pubs., Box 1040, Rancho Mirage, CA 92270. TEL 619-836-3700. FAX 619-836-3703. adv. circ. 23,000. **Document type:** consumer publication.
Description: Covers golf in Southern California. Provides news of events, tournaments, and courses.

796.352 NE ISSN 0927-5290
GOLF NIEUWS. 1936. m. fl.47.50. Media Bloemendaal B.V., P.B. 135, 2060 AC Bloemendaal, Netherlands. TEL 028-270044. FAX 028-274084. Ed. J.K. Kokke. adv.; charts; illus. circ. 7,000. **Indexed:** Sportsearch.
Former titles (until 1992): Golf (Amsterdam) (ISSN 0927-5282); (until 1988): Golf Benelux (ISSN 0927-5274); (until 1987): Golf (ISSN 0017-1727)

GOLF PRO MERCHANDISER. see BUSINESS AND ECONOMICS — Marketing And Purchasing

796.352 US ISSN 1079-3178
GOLF PRODUCT NEWS. 1990. 8/yr. $72. 11-15 River Rd., Fair Lawn, NJ 07410. TEL 201-796-6031. FAX 201-796-5206. Ed. Bob Seligman; Pub. Robert Nitkewicz. adv. circ. 19,300. **Document type:** trade publication.

GOLF PROPERTY. see REAL ESTATE

796.3 AU ISSN 1017-8457
GOLF REVUE. 1978. 8/yr. S.300. Orac Zeitschriftenverlag GmbH, Graben 17, A-1014 Vienna, Austria. TEL 01-54621-1210. FAX 01-5462113. (Subscr. to: Christine Hojsa, Schoenbrunnerstr. 59-61, A-1051 Vienna, Austria. TEL 01-546212006) Ed. Robert Sperl. adv.: page S.58140; adv. contact: Wolfgang Hermeneit. circ. 33,100. (back issues avail.) **Document type:** consumer publication.
Formerly (until 1994): Golf Gazette.

796.352 US ISSN 0017-1824
GOLF SHOP OPERATIONS. 1963. 10/yr. $72. New York Times Company Magazine Group, Sports - Leisure Division, 5520 Park Ave., Box 395, Trumbull, CT 06611-0395. TEL 203-373-7000. Ed. Mark Godich. illus.; stat. circ. 16,000. (tabloid format) **Indexed:** Sportsearch. **Document type:** trade publication.
Formerly: Pro Shop Operations.

796.352 GW
GOLF SPORT. m. DM.81.60 (foreign DM.88.80); newsstand price: DM.8. Top Special Verlag GmbH, Nebendahlstr. 16, 22041 Hamburg, Germany. TEL 040-3470-0. FAX 040-34725588. Ed. Dieter Genske. adv.: B&W page DM.6527, color page DM.12158; trim 180 x 250; adv. contact: Beate Asmus. circ. 25,471 (paid). **Document type:** consumer publication.

796.352 US ISSN 1051-7758
GOLF TIPS. 9/yr. $17.94. Werner Publishing Corporation, 12121 Wilshire Blvd., No.1220, Los Angeles, CA 90025-1175. TEL 310-820-1500. FAX 310-826-5008. circ. 200,000. **Indexed:** Sports Per.Ind. **Document type:** consumer publication.

796.352 US ISSN 0191-717X
GV975
GOLF TRAVELER. 1976. bi-m. $12. Affinity Group, Inc., 3601 Calle Tecate, Camarillo, CA 93012. TEL 805-389-0300. FAX 805-389-0363. Ed. Valerie Law; Pub. Robert Helms. adv. contact: Terry Thompson. bk.rev.; tr.lit. circ. 10,000. (reprint service avail.) **Document type:** consumer publication.
Description: Focuses on golf and travel for members of the Golf Card, an affiliation of 2800 golf courses that offer discounted greens fees to members.

6106 SPORTS AND GAMES — BALL GAMES

796.352　　　SI　　ISSN 0218-0987
GOLF VACATIONS. (Text in English) 1986. 2/yr. S.12. Pacom Publications Pte. Ltd., 190 Middle Rd. 14-07, Fortune Centre, Singapore 0718, Singapore. TEL 65-3370255. FAX 65-3394857. Ed. Guy Goh. adv.: B&W page S.2800, color page S.4700; trim 286 x 210. circ. 15,000 (controlled). (back issues avail.) **Document type:** consumer publication.
Description: Reviews selected golf courses, golf resorts around the world. Provides guide to golf equipment and accessories, golf tours and packages.

796.352　　　IT
GOLF WEEK. 1980. 15/yr. 20000. Via Montenapoleone 8, Milan, Italy. TEL 2-76002207. FAX 2-76013026. Ed. Enrico Magatti. adv. circ. 15,000.

796.352　　　UK
GOLF WEEKLY. 1890. w. £55 (rest of Europe £95; elsewhere £110) (effective 1995-1996). E M A P - Pursuit Publishing, Bretton Ct., Bretton, Peterborough, Cambs. PE2 9DA, England. TEL 01733-264666. FAX 01733-263294. TELEX 32157. (Subscr. to: Tower Publishing Services Ltd., Tower House, Sovereign Park, Lathkill St., Market Harborough, Leics. LE16 9EF, England) adv.; charts; illus.; tr.lit. **Indexed:** Sportsearch.
Formerly: Golf Illustrated (ISSN 0262-0340)

796.352　　　UK　　ISSN 0017-1883
GOLF WORLD. 1962. m. £35 (foreign £48) (effective 1995-1996). E M A P - Pursuit Publishing, Bretton Ct., Bretton, Peterborough, Cambs. PE3 9DZ, England. TEL 01733-264666. FAX 01733-263294. TELEX 32157. (Subscr. to: Tower Publishing Services Ltd., Tower House, Sovereign Park, Lathkill St., Market Harborough, Leics. LE16 9EF, England. TEL 01858-468811. FAX 01858-432164) adv.; bk.rev.; charts; illus.; stat.; tr.lit. circ. 90,253. **Indexed:** Sportsearch. **Document type:** consumer publication.

796.352　　　US　　ISSN 0017-1891
GV961
GOLF WORLD. 1947. w. (Jan.-Sep.), bi-w. (Oct.-Dec.). $43.94. New York Times Company Magazine Group (Subsidiary of: Sports - Leisure Division), 5520 Park Ave., Box 395, Trumbull, CT 06611-0395. TEL 203-373-7000. Ed. Terry Galvin. adv.; illus. circ. 142,832. **Indexed:** Sports Per.Ind., Sportsearch (1977-).
—Faxon.
Description: Contains news of the game and business of golf.

796.352　　　GW
GOLF ZEITUNG; Informationen fuer Entscheidungstraeger. 1988. m. DM.120. Verlag Egon Stengl, Triesterstr. 79, 81669 Munich, Germany. TEL 089-492097. FAX 089-492727. circ. 1,000. (back issues avail.)

610　　　IE　　ISSN 0791-5357
GOLFER'S COMPANION. 1973. 4/yr. £5. Sports Enterprises Ltd., Box 14, Dun Laoghaire, Dublin, Ireland. Ed. Pat Ruddy. adv.; bk.rev. circ. 20,000.

796　　　UK　　ISSN 0072-498X
GOLFER'S HANDBOOK. 1897. a. £16.99. Macmillan Press Ltd., Houndmills, Basingstoke, Hants RG21 2XS, England. TEL 0256-29242. FAX 0256-28339. Ed. Laurence Viney. adv. circ. 10,000. **Document type:** consumer publication.

796.352　　　UK　　ISSN 0953-0215
GOLFERS NEWS. 1985. m. £13.50. Alcester Rd., Portway, Birmingham B48 7HX, England. TEL 0564-822877. FAX 0564-824712. Ed. D. Lawrenson. adv.; bk.rev.; tr.lit. circ. 75,000. (back issues avail.) **Document type:** consumer publication.
Description: Covers golf with news, reviews, features, and competition results.

796.352　　　DK　　ISSN 0906-1851
GOLFHAANDBOGEN.* 1984. a. DKK 30. (Dansk Golf Union) MassMedia, c/o Release, Hollufgaard Moelle, 5220 Odense SOE, Denmark. illus.
Formerly: Dansk Golfhaandbog (ISSN 0109-5994)

796.352　　　UK
GOLFING IN BRITAIN; the definitive and essential guide for golfers in Britain. 1986. a. £6.95. Peerage Publications, P.O. Box 5135, Strand-on-the-Green, Chiswick, London W4 3WN, England. TEL 0181-747-0385. Ed. Sara Marden-King; Pub. Bruce Duncan. adv.: B&W page £460, color page £830; trim 210 x 148. circ. 100,000. **Document type:** directory.
Formerly (until 1994): England for Golf.

796.352　　　UK
GOLFING IN EUROPE; the definitive and essential guide to European golf. a. £6.95. Peerage Publications, P.O. Box 5135, Strand-on-the-Green, Chiswick, London W4 3WN, England. TEL 0181-747-0385. Ed. Sara Marden-King; Pub. Bruce Duncan. adv.: B&W page £460, color page £830; trim 210 x 148. **Document type:** directory.
Formerly: Europe for Golf.

796.352　　　UK
GOLFING YEAR. 1948. a. £6. English Golf Union, 1-3 Upper King St., Leicester, LE1 6XF, England. TEL 0113-255-3042. FAX 0116-247-1322. Ed. P.M. Baxter. adv.; bk.rev. circ. 2,500. **Document type:** consumer publication.

796　　　GW　　ISSN 0017-1735
GOLFMAGAZIN. 1961. m. DM.114. Jahr-Verlag GmbH & Co., Jessenstr. 1, 22767 Hamburg, Germany. TEL 040-38906-0. FAX 040-38906302. TELEX 2163485. Ed. Gunther Marks. adv. contact: Wolfgang Vogler. bk.rev. circ. 28,600. **Document type:** consumer publication.
Formerly: Where to Golf in Europe (ISSN 0083-9213)

796.352　　　US　　ISSN 0890-3514
GOLFWEEK.* 1975. w. $49.95. Golfweek L.P., 7657 Commerce Center Dr., Orlando, FL 32819-8923. TEL 813-294-5511. FAX 813-294-5511. Ed. Steve Ellis. adv. circ. 45,000.
Description: Contains news on pros, amateurs, equipment, courses, industry, travel, and real estate.

796.352　　　US
GOVERNMENT RELATIONS BRIEFING. 1989. m. free. Golf Course Superintendents Association of America, 1421 Research Park Dr., Lawrence, KS 66049. TEL 913-841-2240. FAX 913-832-4466. Ed. Kirk Kahler. circ. 13,700. (back issues avail.) **Document type:** newsletter.

796.352　　　IT
GRANDE GOLF. 1992. q. L.60000 (foreign L.150000). D M K Editrice s.r.l., Via Boscovich 14, 20124 Milan, Italy. TEL 39-2-6693050. FAX 39-2-6702736. Ed. Massimo Di Marco. adv.: B&W page L.7400000, color page L.10200000; adv. contact: Alessandro Zonca. **Document type:** consumer publication.

796.342　　　IT　　ISSN 1121-2675
GRANDE TENNIS. 1991. q. L.50000 (foreign L.150000). Gruppo Editoriale Grandi Periodici s.r.l., Via Boscovich 14, 20124 Milan, Italy. TEL 39-2-6693050. FAX 39-2-6702736. Ed. Massimo Di Marco. adv.: B&W page L.7000000, color page L.9800000; adv. contact: Franca Marmonti. **Document type:** consumer publication.

GREEN KEEPER. see *GARDENING AND HORTICULTURE*

796.352 635　　　CN　　ISSN 0380-3333
GREENMASTER. 1966. 6/yr. Can.$36. (Canadian Golf Superintendents Association - Association Canadienne des Surintendants de Golf) Kenilworth Publishing Inc., 80 W. Beaver Creek, Ste. 18, Richmond Hill, ON L4B 1H3, Canada. TEL 905-771-7333. FAX 905-771-7336. Ed. Dennis Mellersh. adv.: B&W page Can.$1250, color page Can.$2000; trim 8 1/8 x 10 3/4. bk.rev. circ. 2,000. **Indexed:** Sportsearch (1981-).
Description: Covers such topics as pest management, winter recovery, course architecture and design, nutrition techniques and programs, water management, continuing education, course construction, maintenance and remodeling, cultural techniques and turfgrass management.

796.332　　　UK
GRIDIRON WORLD; for the best in American football. 1984. m. £21.95. Mediawatch Ltd., Spendlove Centre, Charlbury, Oxon OX7 3PQ, England. TEL 0608-811266. FAX 0608-811380. TELEX 873883-SPEND-G. Ed. David Smith. adv.; bk.rev. circ. 10,000. (back issues avail.)
Formerly: Gridiron (ISSN 0269-0675)

796.352　　　US　　ISSN 0889-4825
GULF COAST GOLFER. 1984. 12/yr. $16. Golfer Magazines, Inc., 9182 Old Katy Rd., Ste. 212, Houston, TX 77055. TEL 713-464-0308. FAX 713-464-0129. Ed. Steve Hunter. adv.: B&W page £1630, color page $2380; 10 1/4 x 13; adv. contact: Paul Boyd. bk.rev.; circ. 30,000 (controlled). **Document type:** newspaper.
Description: Provides information to golfers in South Texas on quality of courses, better playing techniques, upcoming tournaments, and area tournament results. Includes an alphabetical list of golf courses in that region every other month.

796.31　　　NE　　ISSN 0927-7315
HANDBAL MAGAZINE. 1942. 11/yr. fl.40. (Nederlands Handbal Verbond) Verbondsbureau N.H.V., Postbus 104, 3980 CC Bunnik, Netherlands. TEL 31-3405-70775. FAX 31-3405-64743. Ed. J. Notermans. adv. circ. 7,000. **Document type:** consumer publication.
Formerly (until 1991): Handbal (ISSN 0017-7180)

796.3　　　US　　ISSN 0046-6778
HANDBALL. 1951. bi-m. $25. U S Handball Association, 2333 N. Tucson Blvd., Tucson, AZ 85716. FAX 602-745-8114. Ed. Vern Roberts. adv.; bk.rev.; charts; illus. circ. 10,000. (also avail. in microform from UMI; reprint service avail. from UMI) **Indexed:** Phys.Ed.Ind., Sports Per.Ind., Sportsearch (1977-). **Document type:** consumer publication.
—UMI; UnCover.
Formerly: Ace.

796.31　　　IT
HANDBALL. 1982. m. L.25000. Federazione Italiana Giuoco dell'Handball, Viale Tiziano 78, 00196 Rome, Italy. TEL 39-6-36858144. FAX 39-6-3230708. Ed. Flavio Guzzone. adv.: B&W page L.1800000, color page L.2500000. circ. 18,000. **Document type:** consumer publication.

796.31　　　GW
HANDBALL (DORTMUND); Amtliches Jahrbuch des Deutschen Handball-Bundes. 1987. a. DM.7.80. Deutscher Handball-Bund Verlags und Vertriebs GmbH, Westfalendamm 77, 44145 Dortmund, Germany. TEL 0231-94248-0.

796　　　GW　　ISSN 0138-1296
HANDBALL (RAUGSDORF). m. DM.15.20 (foreign DM.22). Deutscher Handball-Verband, Kurparkallee 114, 15834 Raugsdorf, Germany. (Subscr. to: Buchexport, Postfach 160, 7010 Leipzig, Germany)

790　　　GW　　ISSN 0178-2983
HANDBALL MAGAZIN. 1984. m. DM.67.20 (foreign DM.74.40). Philippka-Verlag, Postfach 6540, 48034 Muenster, Germany. TEL 0251-23005-0. FAX 0251-23005-99. Ed. Konrad Honig. circ. 15,000. **Document type:** consumer publication.

790.1　　　GW　　ISSN 0172-2476
HANDBALLTRAINING. 1979. m. DM.67.20 (foreign DM.74.40). Philippka-Verlag, Postfach 6540, 48034 Muenster, Germany. TEL 0251-23005-0. FAX 0251-23005-99. Ed. Konrad Honig. circ. 115,000. (back issues avail.) **Document type:** bulletin.
Formerly: Lehre und Praxis des Handballspiels.

796.325　　　SW　　ISSN 0345-4479
HANDBOLL. Variant title: Tidningen Handboll. 1961. m. (10/yr.). SEK 530 in Nordic countries; elsewhere SEK 630. (Svenska Hanbollfoerbundet) CeWe-foerlaget AB, P.O. Box 77, S-890 10 Bjaesta, Sweden. TEL 0660-309-65. FAX 0660-305-17. (Subscr. to: PK-Banken, Box 365, 891 01 Oernskoeldsvik, Sweden) adv. circ. 11,700.
Formerly (until 1968): Handbollskontakten.

SPORTS AND GAMES — BALL GAMES

796.352   US   ISSN 1073-5712
HARVEY PENICK'S LITTLE RED GOLF LETTER. m. $60 (foreign $72) (effective 1996). Belvoir Publications, Inc., 75 Holly Hill Ln., Box 2626, Greenwich, CT 06836-2626. TEL 203-661-6111. FAX 203-661-4802. (Subscr. to: Box 420234, Palm Coast, FL 32142) **Document type:** consumer publication.

796.3   US   ISSN 1066-1239
HAWGS ILLUSTRATED. 1992. 17/yr. $49.90. College Sports Communications, Inc., 4099 McEwen Rd., Ste. 350, Dallas, TX 75244. TEL 214-851-1770. FAX 214-490-9333. adv.: B&W page $800, color page $1200; trim 8 1/4 x 10 7/8. circ. 7,600. **Document type:** consumer publication.
Description: Covers University of Arkansas sports.

796.3   UK   ISSN 0085-1566
HOCKEY ASSOCIATION. OFFICIAL HANDBOOK. 1900. a. £5. Hockey Association, Norfolk House, 102 Saxon Gate W., Milton Keynes MK9 2EP, England. TEL 0908-241100. FAX 0908-241106. Ed. S. Baines. adv.; index, cum.index. circ. 4,000. **Document type:** bulletin.

796.3   UK   ISSN 0950-9550
HOCKEY DIGEST. 1975. 10/yr. £20 (rest of Europe £27.50; elsewhere £37.50-£41). Harrow Press, Unit E6, Aladdin Workspace, 426 Long Dr., Greenford, Mddx. UB6 8UH, England. TEL 0181-575 3121. FAX 0181-575-1320. TELEX 63393 FIH FA. Ed. Peter J. Luck. adv. contact: Peter J. Luck. bk.rev. circ. 6,500. **Indexed:** Sportsearch (1980-). **Document type:** consumer publication.
Incorporates: Hockey Field (ISSN 0018-3008); Indoor Hockey News.
Description: Includes articles, features, club and international news of topical interest to field hockey enthusiasts in Great Britain.

796.357   GW   ISSN 0945-523X
HOMERUN; das offizielle Baseball- und Softballsportmagazin. 1993. bi-m. DM.34. (Deutscher Baseball und Softball Verband e.V.) Meyer und Meyer Verlag GmbH, Von-Coels-Str. 390, 52080 Aachen, Germany. TEL 0241-556033. FAX 0241-558281. adv.: B&W page DM.1400; trim 182 x 252; adv. contact: Irmgard Jaeger. **Document type:** bulletin.

796.323   US   ISSN 0749-5285
GV885.515.N37
HOOP - N B A TODAY. 1984. 8/yr. $20.95. (National Basketball Association) Hoop Magazine, Box Hoop, Lowell, MA 01852. TEL 508-452-6310.
Formerly: N B A Today (ISSN 0279-1935)

796.323   US
HUBIE BROWN'S PRO BASKETBALL.* 1993. a. Preview Sports Publications, 210 Rte. 4 E., Paramus, NJ 07652. TEL 201-843-5656. adv.: B&W page $10867.50, color page $12075; trim 9 3/4 x 12. circ. 110,000. **Document type:** consumer publication.

796.332   GW
HUDDLE. 1989. w. DM.178 (U.S. DM.248); newsstand price: DM.4. Huddle Verlags GmbH, Am Treptower Park 28-30, 12435 Berlin, Germany. TEL 030-68834224. Ed. Michael Auerbach. adv.: B&W page DM.2100, color page DM.2100; adv. contact: Gregor Wittig. circ. 12,000. (back issues avail.) **Document type:** consumer publication.

796.332 378.198   US   ISSN 0279-3474
HUSKERS ILLUSTRATED. 1981. m. (Jan.-Apr., Aug.); w. (Sep.-Nov.). $49.90. College Sports Communications, Inc., 4099 McEwen Rd., Ste. 350, Dallas, TX 75244. TEL 214-851-1770. FAX 214-490-9333. (Subscr. to: Box 83222, Lincoln, NE 68501) Ed. M.C. Ross. adv.: B&W page $1090, color page $1640; trim 8 1/4 x 10 7/8. circ. 12,500. (back issues avail.) **Document type:** consumer publication.
Description: Carries stories and information on athletics at the University of Nebraska, with special emphasis on football.

796.357   SZ
I B A REPORT.* 1989. bi-m. International Baseball Association, Case Postale 131, Ave. de Mon-Repos 24, 1000 Lausanne 5, Switzerland. **Document type:** consumer publication.

796   SW   ISSN 1100-7303
IDROTTENS AFFAERER. 1988. 7/yr. Futurum Media, P.O. Box 1802, S-171 21 Solna, Sweden. (Subscr. to: Pressdata, P.O. Box 3263, S-103 65 Stockholm, Sweden)

796   SW   ISSN 0347-2744
IDROTTSBOKEN; aarets idrott. Spine title: Aarets Idrott. 1945. a. SEK 861 (effective 1990). Stroemberg - Brunnhage, P.O. Box 65, S-162 11 Vaellingby, Sweden.
Incorporates (in 1989): Aarets Idrott.

796   SW   ISSN 0348-9787
IDROTTSFORSKAREN; tidskrift foer svensk bteendevetenskaplig idrottsforskning. 1976. s-a. SEK 250 to individuals; libraries SEK 250; organizations SEK 300. S V E B I - Svensk Foerening foer Beteendevetenskaplig Idrottsforskning - Swedish Association for Behavioral Sport Science, c/o A. Oestnaes, Musketoersgraenden 3, S-226 39 Lund, Sweden. TEL 046-14-10-45. Ed.Bd.

796.352 917.704   US
ILLINOIS GOLFER'S TRAVEL GUIDE. 1991. a. $9.95. R S G Publishing, Inc., Box 700612, Plymouth, MI 48170-0612. TEL 313-416-5300. FAX 313-416-5389. Ed. Betty Rasmussen.
Description: Presents information on public and private golf courses in Illinois, including address and telephone, course description, facilities, and more.

796.352 917.704   US
INDIANA GOLFER'S TRAVEL GUIDE. 1991. a. $9.95. R S G Publishing, Inc., Box 700612, Plymouth, MI 48170-0612. TEL 313-416-5300. FAX 313-416-5389. Ed. Betty Rasmussen.
Description: Presents information on public and private golf courses in Indiana, including address and telephone, course description, facilities, and more.

796.342   US
INSIDE TENNIS. 1981. m. $14. William Simons, Ed. & Pub., 3561 Lakeshore Ave., Oakland, CA 94610. TEL 510-836-4556. FAX 510-836-4563. adv. circ. 40,000.

796.334   IT
INTER FOOTBALL CLUB. 1962. m. (11/yr.). L.38000 (foreign L.60000). G.E.MI. s.r.l., Foro Buonaparte 63, 20121 Milan, Italy. TEL 39-2-8051030. Ed. Valberto Miliani. adv.: color page L.14000000. circ. 80,000.

793   GW
INTERNATIONAL BASKETBALL FEDERATION. OFFICIAL REPORT OF THE WORLD CONGRESS. 1932. irreg., 15th, 1994, Toronto. International Basketball Federation, Postfach 700607, 81306 Munich, Germany. TEL 089-783036. FAX 089-7853596. TELEX 5213054-FIBA-D. circ. 300 (controlled). **Document type:** corporate report.
Formerly: International Amateur Basketball Federation. Official Report of the World Congress (ISSN 0534-6622)

794.6   US
INTERNATIONAL BOWLING INDUSTRY. 1993. m. $32 (Canada & Mexico $44; elsewhere $52). Crown Publications, 660 Hampshire Rd., No. 200, Westlake Village, CA 91361-2504. TEL 805-371-7877. FAX 805-371-7885. Ed. Bob Johnson; Pub. Allen Crown. adv.: B&W page $1465, color page $2095; trim 8 1/4 x 10 7/8. adv. contact: Scott Frager. circ. 9,776 (controlled). **Document type:** trade publication.

796.332   UK   ISSN 0074-610X
INTERNATIONAL FOOTBALL BOOK. 1959. a. £7.95. Souvenir Press Ltd., 43 Great Russell St., London WC1B 3PA, England. TEL 01-580 9307. Ed. Gordon Hallam. circ. 7,000.

796.357   US
INTERNATIONAL SOFTBALL CONGRESS (YEAR) WORLD CHAMPIONSHIP GUIDE. 1953. a. $3.50. International Softball Congress, 6007 E. Hillcrest Circle, Anaheim Hills, CA 92807. TEL 714-998-5694. FAX 714-282-7902. Ed. Ed Kirner; Pub. Milt Stark. adv. contact: Linda Nathan. circ. 10,000. **Document type:** directory.
Formerly: International Softball Congress (Year) Official Yearbook and Guide.

IO. see ANTHROPOLOGY

796.332   US   ISSN 1069-7276
IRON GAME HISTORY. 1990. bi-m. $20 (foreign $25). University of Texas at Austin, McLean Sport History Fellowship, Rm. 217, Gregory Gymnasium, Austin, TX 78712. TEL 512-447-3635. FAX 512-443-0381. E-mail: jantodd@utxum.cc.utexas.edu. Eds. Terry & Jan Todd. circ. 500. (back issues avail.) **Indexed:** Sportsearch (1990-). **Document type:** academic/scholarly publication.
Description: Examines physical culture.
Refereed Serial

794   CN   ISSN 0849-1623
JOURNAL QUEBEC QUILLES. (Text mainly in French, occasionally in English) 1988. 7/yr. Can.$11.95. Quebec Quilles Enr., C.P. 126, Succ. Anjou, Anjou, PQ H1K 4N7, Canada. TEL 514-351-5224. FAX 514-351-6818. Ed. Gilles Poulin; Pub. Yves Larocque. adv.: B&W page Can.$1395; trim 11 3/8 x 15; adv. contact: Gil Legault. circ. 25,000. (tabloid format) **Document type:** newspaper.

794.6   GW
KEGELN UND BOWLING. 1946. m. DM.44. Verlag Wolfgang Wildner, Kaulbachstr. 29, 34454 Arolsen, Germany. TEL 05691-1379. FAX 05691-6587. Ed. Wolfgang Wildner. adv.; bk.rev. circ. 7,100. (back issues avail.)

796.332   CN
KICK OFF. m. $25. Kick Off Publications, 28-88 South Park Dr., Winnipeg, Man. R3T 2M1, Canada. TEL 204-269-5724. Ed. Will Oliver. adv. circ. 50,000.

796.334   US
KICKOFF. q. members only. Major Indoor Soccer League Players Association, 2021 L St., N.W., Ste. 407, Washington, DC 20036. Ed. Will Bray. circ. 125.
Description: Covers collective bargaining of the league, player benefits, and soccer news.

796.334   SA   ISSN 1022-3819
▼**KICKOFF.** 1994. m. R.30. Touchline Media, P.O. Box 16368, Vlaeberg 8018, South Africa. illus. **Document type:** consumer publication.

796.342   UK
L T A HANDBOOK. 1980. a. £4.50. Lawn Tennis Association, The Queen's Club, W. Kensington, London W14 9EG, England. TEL 071-381-7000. FAX 071-381-6656. Ed. Jon Siddall. adv. contact: Roo Abando. circ. 6,000. **Document type:** bulletin.
Former titles: Tennis Great Britain; Lawn Tennis Association Handbook.

796.347   UK   ISSN 0023-7086
LACROSSETALK. 1948. 8/yr. £7.80. All England Women's Lacrosse Association, 4 Western Ct., Bromley St., Digbeth, Birmingham 9, England. TEL 021-7734422. Ed. G. Wilkerson. adv.; illus. circ. 1,500. **Indexed:** Sports Per.Ind., Sportsearch. **Document type:** consumer publication.
●Also available online.
Formerly (until 1989): Lacrosse.
Description: Includes articles and comment on both women's and men's lacrosse in the UK.

796.352   UK   ISSN 0307-4366
GV966
LADY GOLFER'S HANDBOOK. 1893. a. £5. Ladies Golf Union, The Scores, St. Andrews, Fife KY16 9AT, Scotland. TEL 01334-475811. FAX 01334-472818. adv. circ. 3,500. **Document type:** directory.

796.323   CC   ISSN 1000-3460
LANQIU/BASKETBALL. (Text in Chinese) 1981. bi-m. $18.50. (Zhongguo Lanqiu Xiehui - China Basketball Society) Renmin Tiyu Chubanshe - People's Sports Publishing House, 8 Tiyuguan Lu, Chongwen Qu, Beijing 100061, People's Republic of China. TEL 5112466. FAX 7016129. (Dist. in U.S. by: China Books & Periodicals, Inc., 2929 24th St., San Francisco, CA 94110. TEL 415-282-2994) Ed. Mou Zuoyun. **Document type:** consumer publication.

796.352   US
LEADER BOARD. 1991. q. $24. Golf Course Superintendents Association of America, Center for Golf Course Management, 1421 Research Park Dr., Lawrence, KS 66049. TEL 913-841-2240. FAX 913-832-4466. Ed. Carol Robertson. charts; illus. circ. 1,100. **Document type:** newsletter.

SPORTS AND GAMES — BALL GAMES

796.3 US ISSN 0892-9440
LET'S PLAY SOFTBALL. 1986. 12/yr. $12. Let's Play, Inc., 2721 E. 42nd St., Minneapolis, MN 55406. TEL 612-729-0023. FAX 612-729-0259. adv. circ. 12,000.
  Description: For players, parents, coaches, fans and officials.

796.332 US
LINDY'S A C C FOOTBALL ANNUAL. (Atlantic Coast Conference) 1987. a. $4.95. D M D Publications, Inc., 2700 Highway 280, Ste. 108, Birmingham, AL 35223. TEL 205-871-1182. Ed. Don Borst; Pub. Lindy Davis. adv. contact: Tom Myers. circ. 25,000. **Document type:** consumer publication.

796.332 US
LINDY'S BIG 8 FOOTBALL ANNUAL. 1987. a. $4.95. D M D Publications, Inc., 2700 Highway 280, Ste. 108, Birmingham, AL 35223. TEL 205-871-1182. Ed. Don Borst; Pub. Lindy Davis. adv. contact: Tom Myers. circ. 20,000.

796.332 US
LINDY'S BIG 10 FOOTBALL ANNUAL. 1987. a. $4.95. D M D Publications, Inc., 2700 Highway 280, Ste. 108, Birmingham, AL 35223. TEL 205-871-1182. Ed. Don Borst; Pub. Lindy Davis. adv. contact: Tom Myers. circ. 25,000. **Document type:** consumer publication.

796.332 US
LINDY'S PAC 10 FOOTBALL ANNUAL. 1987. a. $4.95. D M D Publications, Inc., 2700 Highway 280, Ste. 108, Birmingham, AL 35223. TEL 205-871-1182. Ed. Don Borst; Pub. Lindy Davis. adv. contact: Tom Myers. circ. 20,000. **Document type:** consumer publication.

796.332 US ISSN 1062-4198
GV937
LINDY'S PRO EDITION FOOTBALL ANNUAL. 1987. a. $4.95. D M D Publications, Inc., 2700 Highway 280, Ste. 108, Birmingham, AL 35223. TEL 205-871-1227. Ed. Howard Balzar; Pub. Lindy Davis. circ. 200,000. **Document type:** consumer publication.

796.332 US
LINDY'S S E C FOOTBALL ANNUAL. (Southeast Conference) 1982. a. $4.95. D M D Publications, Inc., 2700 Highway 280, Ste. 108, Birmingham, AL 35223. TEL 205-871-1182. Ed. Don Borst; Pub. Lindy Davis. adv. contact: Tom Myers. circ. 75,000. **Document type:** consumer publication.

796.332 US
LINDY'S SOUTHWEST FOOTBALL ANNUAL. a. $4.95. D M D Publications, Inc., 2700 Highway 280, Ste. 108, Birmingham, AL 35223. TEL 205-871-1182. Ed. Don Borst; Pub. Lindy Davis. adv. contact: Tom Myers. circ. 15,000. **Document type:** consumer publication.

796.352 US
LINKS; The Best of Golf. 1988. 7/yr. $12. Southern Links Magazine Publishing Associates, 1040 William Hilton Pkwy., Hilton Head Island, SC 29938. TEL 803-842-6200. FAX 803-842-6233. (Subscr. to: 57199 Boulder, CO 80323-7199. TEL 800-388-5205) Ed. George Fuller; Pub. John R. Purcell, Jr. adv. contact: Owen J. Hochreiter. circ. 260,000. (back issues avail.) **Document type:** consumer publication.
  Formed by the 1993 merger of: Southern Links (ISSN 1043-6375) & Western Links (ISSN 1052-3219)
  Description: Describes classic golf courses and hidden gems; features interviews with golf legends and leaders, and covers trends and controversial issues.

796.3 UK
A LOAD OF BULL; an alternative view of Wolverhampton Wanderers. 1989. q. £4($16) (effective June 1993). Box 277, 52 Call Ln., Leeds, W. Yorks. LS1 6DT, England. Ed. Dave Worton. bk.rev.; charts; illus.; play rev.; stat. circ. 3,000. (back issues avail.) **Document type:** trade publication.
  Description: Contains both serious and humorous articles, reviews, criticism, and collages pertaining to the Wolverhampton Wanderers football (soccer) club.

796.31 US
LOGBOOK (YEAR). a. $12.95. Parrish Publications, Box 23205, Portland, OR 97223. TEL 503-244-8975. Ed. Phil Erwin. **Document type:** newsletter.

196.332 US
LOS ANGELES RAMS OFFICIAL YEARBOOK. 1983. a. $7. Woodford Publishing, 660 Market St., Ste. 206, San Francisco, CA 94104-5011. TEL 415-397-1853. FAX 415-399-0942. Ed. Jon Rochmis. adv. contact: David Lilienstein. illus. circ. 40,000. **Document type:** consumer publication.

796.352 US
LYNX PLAY GOLF!. 1989. a. $2.50. (Lynx Golf, Inc.) Aqua-Field Publishing Co., Inc., 66 W. Gilbert St., Shrewsbury, NJ 07702. TEL 908-842-8300. Ed. Stephen Ferber. adv. circ. 135,000.

796.334 IT
MAGLIAZZURRA. 1970. bi-m. membership. Associazione Nazionale Azzurri d'Italia, Foro Italico, 00194 Rome, Italy. TEL 39-6-36851. FAX 39-6-36857106. Ed. Giorgio Lo Giudice. adv.: B&W page L.1800000, color page L.2500000. **Document type:** consumer publication.

796.357 US
MAJOR LEAGUE BASEBALL OFFICIAL (YEAR) PREVIEW. (In 3 regional editions and 1 national edition.) 1990. a. $4.95 per no. Hachette Magazines, Inc., 1633 Broadway, 45th Fl., New York, NY 10009. TEL 212-767-6000. Ed. Barry Shapiro. circ. 250,000.
  Description: Features interviews, profiles, plus complete batting and statistical averages; each regional issue features a local celebrity.

796.352 US
MARKET INSIGHT. 1991. m. membership. Golf Course Superintendents Association of America, Center for Golf Course Management, 1421 Research Park Dr., Lawrence, KS 66049. TEL 913-841-2240. FAX 913-841-2240. **Document type:** corporate report.

796.352 US
MASSACHUSETTS GOLFER.* q. Massachusetts Golf Association, 175 Highland Ave., Ste. 3, Needham, MA 02194-3034. TEL 617-891-4300. Ed. Rick Dunfey. circ. 50,000.

796.3 UK ISSN 1358-8958
MASTERSTROKE. 3/yr. (Bank of Scotland (Transnational)) Mediamark Publishing International Ltd., 35 Gresse St., Rathbone Pl., London W1P 1PN, England. TEL 0171-580-3105. FAX 0171-580-1695. Ed. Sally Lane; Pub. Peter Moore. circ. 50,000. **Document type:** consumer publication.

796.342 IT ISSN 0393-2842
MATCH-BALL; la rivista del tennis giovane. 1970-1985; resumed. bi-␣w. L.115000. Via C. Colombo 21, 40131 Bologna, Italy. TEL 39-51-325991. FAX 39-51-324326. Ed. roberto Mazzanti. adv.: B&W page L.3000000, color page L.5000000. bk.rev. circ. 38,731.

796.334 UK
MATCH FOOTBALL. 1979. w. £61.60 (foreign £67.60) (effective 1995-1996). E M A P - Pursuit Publishing, Bretton Ct., Bretton, Peterborough, Cambs. PE3 8DZ, England. TEL 01733-264666. FAX 01733-267198. TELEX 32157. (Subscr. to: Tower Publishing Services Ltd., Tower House, Sovereign Park, Lathkill St., Market Harborough, Leics. LE16 9EF, England. TEL 01858-468811. FAX 01858-432164) Ed. Chris Hunt. adv.; illus, stat.; circ. 113,202 (paid). **Document type:** consumer publication.
  Formerly: Match Weekly.
  Description: Covers world soccer round-up, "MatchFacts," weekend results and star ratings, and star player interviews.

796.3 FR ISSN 0754-2712
MAXI BASKET. 1982. m. (11/yr.). 359 F. Societe d'Edition Maxi B, 16 rue Gambetta, BP 221, 72005 Le Mans Cedex, France. TEL 43-39-16-20. FAX 43-24-95-64. Ed. Pascale Legendre; Pub. Pierre Texier. adv. contact: Vincent Henry. circ. 80,000. (back issues avail.)
  Description: Covers French, European and American basketball.

796.352 US
(YEAR) MEN'S BASKETBALL GUIDE. a. $10. Big Ten Conference, 1500 Higgins Rd., Park Ridge, IL 60068-5742. TEL 708-696-1010. FAX 708-696-1110.

796.352 US ISSN 1042-7678
MET GOLF. 1983. q. Times Mirror Magazines, Inc., Sports Marketing Group, 2 Park Ave., No.6, New York, NY 10016-5691. TEL 212-779-5000. adv. circ. 100,000.
  Description: For amateur and professional golfers in the New York metropolitan area. Covers events, tournaments, travel, fashion and personalities.

796.352 US ISSN 1063-2425
METRO GOLF;* a magazine for Washington area golfers. 1991. 8/yr. $14.95. Summerville Press, Inc., 1733 King St., 3rd Fl., Alexandria, VA 22314-2720. TEL 202-663-9015. FAX 202-663-9016. Ed. John Holmes; Pub. Margaret B. Heinbold. adv. contact: Frank Riggins. bk.rev. circ. 60,000. **Document type:** consumer publication.
  Description: Contains men's and women's fashions, travel in the Mid-Atlantic and Southeast regions, Kemper Open news, a holiday gift guide, and equipment reviews.

796.352 US ISSN 1080-3874
METROLINA GOLF MAGAZINE; serving the Charlotte metropolitan area. 1992. 8/yr. $8. Tayside Publishing Co., Inc., Box 9122, Hickory, NC 28603-9122. TEL 704-327-4332. FAX 704-328-4344. Ed. Gil Capps; Pub. Gil Capps. adv. contact: Gil Capps. circ. 25,000. (tabloid format; back issues avail.) **Document type:** consumer publication.
  —CCC.
  Description: Covers news and events of interest to golfers living in or visiting North and South Carolina. Profiles local players and covers regional tournaments. Reviews area golf courses and travel destinations.

796.352 US ISSN 1071-2313
MICHIGAN GOLFER. 1980. 6/yr. $10. Great Lakes Sports Publications, Inc., 7990 W. Grand River, Ste. C, Brighton, MI 48116. TEL 810-227-4200. Ed. Terry Moore; Pub. Art McCafferty. circ. 18,000. **Document type:** consumer publication.
  Description: Covers golf events and news; includes calendar of events, technical advice, new products, and travel information.

796.352 917.704 US
MICHIGAN GOLFER'S MAP & GUIDE. 1981. a. $17.95. R S G Publishing, Inc., Box 700612, Plymouth, MI 48170-0612. TEL 313-416-5300. FAX 313-416-5389. Ed. Roy Rasmussen. circ. 25,000. **Document type:** directory.
  Description: Presents information on public golf courses in Michigan, N.W. Ohio, and S.W. Ontario, Canada, including address and telephone, course description, facilities, fees, and more.

796.352 917.704 US
MICHIGAN GOLFER'S TRAVEL GUIDE. 1991. a. $9.95. R S G Publishing, Inc., Box 700612, Plymouth, MI 48170-0612. TEL 313-416-5300. FAX 313-416-5389. Ed. Roy Rasmussen. circ. 10,000. **Document type:** directory.
  Description: Presents information on public and private golf courses in Michigan, including address and telephone, course description, facilities, and more.

796.342 US
MID-AMERICA SENIOR TENNIS. 1983. m. $28. Box 465, Aurora, IL 60507. Ed. John W. Bartlett. circ. 150. **Document type:** newsletter.
  Description: Publishes tennis tournament news for senior citizen players everywhere.

796.334 US
▼**MID-ATLANTIC SOCCER.** 1994. bi-m. $19.95; newsstand price: $2.95. Cadmus Communications Corp., 1974 E. Parham Rd., Richmond, VA 23228. TEL 804-260-0140; 800-899-8833. FAX 804-264-4205. Ed. Michael J. Stott. adv.: B&W page $2000. circ. 20,000. **Document type:** consumer publication.

796.352 US
MIDWEST GOLF NEWS. m. Box 529, Anna, IL 62906. TEL 618-833-2158. Ed. Mike Fitzgerald.

SPORTS AND GAMES — BALL GAMES

796.352 US ISSN 1062-1105
MINNESOTA GOLFER. (Includes annual Directory) 1973. bi-m. $12. (Minnesota Golf Association) The Publishing Group, Inc., 1200 N. 7th St., Minneapolis, MN 55411-4000. TEL 612-522-1200. FAX 612-522-1182. Ed. Chris Geer. adv.: B&W page $2400, color page $2950; trim 8 1/2 x 11. circ. 50,000. Document type: consumer publication.
Description: Reports on players, courses, events and news in the state.

796.334 US
MINNESOTA SOCCER TIMES. 1991. 9/yr. $12.95. (Minnesota Youth Soccer Association) Varsity Publications, 13540 Lake City Way, N.E., Ste. 3, Seattle, WA 98125. TEL 206-367-2420. adv. circ. 27,431. Document type: consumer publication.
Description: Covers tournament rules and profiles outstanding players.

796.352 917.704 US
MINNESOTA - WISCONSIN GOLFER'S TRAVEL GUIDE. 1991. a. $6.95. R S G Publishing, Inc., Box 700612, Plymouth, MI 48170-0612. TEL 313-416-5300. FAX 313-416-5389. Ed. Eric Rasmussen.
Description: Presents information on public and private golf courses in Minnesota and Wisconsin, including address and telephone, course description, facilities, and more.

796.352 IT
MONDO DEL GOLF. 1981. m. L.63000 (typically set in Oct.). Casa Editrice Scode S.p.A., Corso Monforte 36, 20122 Milan, Italy. TEL 02-76006973. FAX 02-76004905. Ed. Carlo Gandini. adv.: B&W or color page L.11300000; trim 166 x 244. bk.rev.; illus. circ. 15,000.
Formerly: Golf Digest Italia.

796.352 US
MOTOROLA WESTERN OPEN (YEAR). a. $4. Western Golf Association, 1 Briar Rd., Golf, IL 60029. TEL 708-724-4600. FAX 708-724-7133. Ed. Gary J. Holaway. adv. contact: Jim Moorhead. circ. 20,000.
Description: Covers Chicago's own golf tournament.

796.352 US
MYRTLE BEACH GOLF. 1992. m. $9. Sun Publishing Company, 914 Frontage Rd. E., Myrtle Beach, SC 29577. TEL 803-626-8555. FAX 803-626-0356. Ed. John Braiser. adv. contact: John Cioni. (tabloid format; also avail. in microfilm; back issues avail.) Document type: newspaper.
Description: Informs visitors to Myrtle Beach golf courses on packages and events; profiles local golf pros.

796.4 US ISSN 0363-2504
GV881
N A G W S GUIDE. SOFTBALL. 1938-1990. a. (American Alliance for Health, Physical Education, Recreation, and Dance, National Association for Girls and Women in Sport) Kendall - Hunt Publishing Co., 2460 Kerber Blvd., Dubuque, IA 52001. TEL 800-338-5578. circ. 8,000. Indexed: ERIC.
Description: Current rules and articles on sport.

796.325 US ISSN 0065-7050
N A G W S GUIDE. VOLLEYBALL. 1938. a. (National Association for Girls and Women in Sport) Kendall - Hunt Publishing Co., 2460 Kerber Blvd., Dubuque, IA 52001. TEL 800-338-5578. circ. 17,000. Indexed: ERIC.
Description: Rules and officiating techniques.

796.323 US ISSN 1067-5159
N B A INSIDE STUFF. 1992. bi-m. $12.99. (National Basketball Association, N B A Properties) Quarton Group Publishers, Inc., 888 W. Big Beaver Rd., Ste. 600, Troy, MI 48084. TEL 810-362-7400. E-mail: instuff@aol.com. (Subscr. to: Box 1919, Marion, OH 43305-1919. TEL 800-249-4NBA) Ed. Vince Aversano; Pub. James C. Small. adv.: B&W page 26250; trim 8 1/2 x 10; adv. contact: Scott Miller. video rev.; illus. circ. 750,000. (back issues avail.) Document type: consumer publication.
●Also available online.
Description: Promotes a positive view of NBA basketball among youth ages 8-17.

796.357 US
N C A A BASEBALL & SOFTBALL. a. $7. National Collegiate Athletic Association, Circulation Department, Box 7347, Overland Park, KS 66207-0347. TEL 913-339-1900. stat.
Formerly: N C A A Baseball.
Description: Contains individual and team records, and statistical leaders.

796 US ISSN 0736-5209
GV877
N C A A BASEBALL RULES. 1974. a. $4. National Collegiate Athletic Association, Circulation Department, Box 7347, Overland Park, KS 66207-0347. TEL 913-339-1900. illus.
Former titles: N C A A Baseball Annual Guide; Official National Collegiate Athletic Association Baseball Guide (ISSN 0466-1478)
Description: Covers official signals, interpretations, and rulings.

796.332 US ISSN 0735-5475
GV937
N C A A FOOTBALL. 1969. a. $10. National Collegiate Athletic Association, 644 S. Clark St., Chicago, IL 60605. TEL 312-939-3330. FAX 312-663-3557. (Orders to: N.C.A.A. Circulation Department, Box 7347, Overland Park, KS 66207-0347. TEL 913-339-1900) stat. circ. 4,000.
Incorporates: N C A A Football Guide; Former titles: N C A A Football Records; College Football Modern Record Book (ISSN 0092-881X)
Description: Contains individual and team records, statistical leaders, all-America teams, game results from the preceding year, with schedules for the current year.

796.33 US ISSN 0736-5160
GV956.8
N C A A FOOTBALL RULES AND INTERPRETATIONS. 1961. a. $4. National Collegiate Athletic Association, Circulation Department, Box 7347, Overland Park, KS 66207-0347. TEL 913-339-1900. illus. circ. 24,000.
Formerly: Official National Collegiate Athletic Association Football Rules and Interpretations (ISSN 0094-5226)
Description: Covers official signals, interpretations, and rulings.

796.32 US ISSN 1042-3877
GV885.45
N C A A MEN'S AND WOMEN'S BASKETBALL RULES AND INTERPRETATIONS. 1967. a. $4. National Collegiate Athletic Association, Circulation Department, Box 7347, Overland Park, KS 66207-0347. TEL 913-339-1900. illus. circ. 25,000.
Supersedes: N C A A Men's Basketball Rules and Interpretations (ISSN 0736-5187); Formerly: N C A A Basketball Rules and Interpretations; Official National Collegiate Athletic Association Basketball Rules and Interpretations (ISSN 0163-2817); Official National Collegiate Athletic Association Basketball Rules (ISSN 0094-5234)
Description: Covers official signals, interpretations, and rulings.

796.32 US ISSN 1042-3869
GV885.45
N C A A MEN'S AND WOMEN'S ILLUSTRATED BASKETBALL RULES. a. $4. National Collegiate Athletic Association, Circulation Department, Box 7347, Overland Park, KS 66207-0347. TEL 913-339-1900. illus.
Former titles: N C A A Men's Illustrated Basketball Rules; N C A A Illustrated Men's Rules (ISSN 0736-5179) & N C A A Illustrated Basketball Rules (ISSN 0272-5754)
Description: Covers official signals, interpretations, and rulings.

796.334 US
GV943.4
N C A A MEN'S AND WOMEN'S SOCCER RULES. 1927. a. $4. National Collegiate Athletic Association, Circulation Department, Box 7347, Overland Park, KS 66207-0347. TEL 913-339-1900. illus. circ. 11,700.
Supersedes: N C A A Men's Soccer Rules (ISSN 0735-0368); Formerly: Official National Collegiate Athletic Association Soccer Guide.
Description: Covers official signals, interpretations, and rulings.

796 US ISSN 0736-7775
N C A A MEN'S LACROSSE RULES. a. $4. National Collegiate Athletic Association, Circulation Department, Box 7347, Overland Park, KS 66207-0347. TEL 913-339-1900. illus.
Former titles: N C A A Lacrosse Guide (ISSN 0732-9059); Official N C A A Lacrosse Guide.
Description: Covers official signals, interpretations, and rulings.

796.323 US ISSN 0736-5195
GV885.45
N C A A MEN'S READ-EASY BASKETBALL RULES. 1973. a. $1.50. National Collegiate Athletic Association, Circulation Department, Box 7347, Overland Park, KS 66207-0347. TEL 913-339-1900. illus. circ. 5,200.
Formerly: Official Read-Easy Basketball Rules.
Description: Contains a popularized version of the official NCAA rules.

796.332 US ISSN 1069-9341
GV956.8
N C A A READ-EASY FOOTBALL RULES. 1969. a. $1.50. National Collegiate Athletic Association, Circulation Department, Box 7347, Overland Park, KS 66207-0347. TEL 913-339-1900.
Formerly (until 1990): Official Read-Easy Football Rules (ISSN 0277-559X)
Description: Contains a popularized version of the official NCAA rules.

796.332 US
N F L EXCLUSIVE. (National Football League); the official magazine of the NFL season ticket holder. 1991. a. Sports Image Inc., 2107 Elliott, Apt. 302, Seattle, WA 98121-2159. TEL 206-728-7200. FAX 206-728-7200. Ed. Mike Olson; Pub. James C. Heckman. adv.: B&W page $23500, color page $29500; trim 8 1/8 x 10 1/2; adv. contact: Craig Olson. circ. 420,000.

796.357 US ISSN 0278-1867
GV863.A1
NATIONAL BASEBALL HALL OF FAME & MUSEUM YEARBOOK. 1981. a. National Baseball Hall of Fame, Main St., Box 590, Cooperstown, NY 13326. TEL 607-547-7200. Ed. William J. Guilfoile. circ. 30,000.

794.7 US ISSN 0747-3265
NATIONAL BILLIARD NEWS. m. Box 807, Northville, MI 48167. TEL 313-348-0053. FAX 313-348-7828. Ed. Conrad J. Burkman. circ. 14,500.

796.35 US ISSN 1047-6474
NATIONAL CROQUET CALENDAR. 1988. a. $30 (foreign $45). Garth Eliassen, Ed. & Pub., Box 208, Monmouth, OR 97361. TEL 503-838-5697. adv.; circ. 450 (paid). Document type: consumer publication.
Description: Covers championship croquet. Features national and international news, strategy articles, product information, and tournament schedules and results.

796.352 US ISSN 1067-0807
GV981
NATIONAL GOLF COURSE DIRECTORY. 1993. a. $49.95. Sports Directories, 1313 E. Montclair St., Springfield, MO 65804-4244. Pub. John Reynolds. Document type: directory.

796.352 US
NATIONAL GOLF MAGAZINE. 1992. 10/yr. Score Gulf Inc., 33 Plan Way, Ste. 3A, Warwick, RI 02886-1013. TEL 401-738-1265. FAX 401-739-0390. adv.: B&W page $1440, color page $1900; trim 8 3/8 x 10 7/8. circ. 15,000.
Description: Covers men's and women's pro and amateur tour information, fashion, club profiles, tips and nostalgia.

NATIONAL HOCKEY LEAGUE. OFFICIAL GUIDE & RECORD BOOK. see SPORTS AND GAMES — Abstracting, Bibliographies, Statistics

796.357 US ISSN 0734-6905
GV863.A1
NATIONAL PASTIME. 1982. a. membership. Society for American Baseball Research, Inc., Box 98183, Cleveland, OH 44101. TEL 216-575-0500. FAX 216-575-0502. adv. circ. 6,500. Indexed: Sportsearch (1982-).

6110 SPORTS AND GAMES — BALL GAMES

796.333   CN
NATIONAL RUGBY POST. 1985. 6/yr. Can.$20 (in US Can.$27; elsewhere Can.$39). (Canadian Rugby Union) National Rugby Post, 13228-76 St., Edmonton, AB T5C 1B6, Canada. TEL 403-476-0268. FAX 403-473-1066. Ed. Don Whidden; Pub. D. Graham. adv.; bk.rev. circ. 6,000. (tabloid format) **Document type:** newspaper.

796.323
NATIONAL WHEELCHAIR BASKETBALL ASSOCIATION. DIRECTORY. 1960. a. $50. National Wheelchair Basketball Association, 110 Seaton Bldg., University of Kentucky, Lexington, KY 40506. Ed. Stan Labanowich. circ. 350. **Document type:** directory.

796.323   US
NATIONAL WHEELCHAIR BASKETBALL ASSOCIATION. NEWSLETTER. s-w. (Nov.-Mar.) membership only. National Wheelchair Basketball Association, 110 Seaton Bldg., University of Kentucky, Lexington, KY 40506. **Document type:** newsletter.

796.342   US
NET FRIEND NEWS. 1978. bi-m. membership. American Tennis Federation, 200 Castlewood Dr., North Palm Beach, FL 33408. TEL 407-848-1026. FAX 407-863-8984. Ed. Brad Patterson. circ. 200 (controlled). **Document type:** newsletter.

796.342   US
NET NEWS. 1992. bi-m. $5 (effective 1994). (Atlanta Lawn Tennis Association) New South Publishing, 7840 Roswell Rd., Ste. 328, Atlanta, GA 30350-4867. TEL 404-512-0016. FAX 404-512-0504. Pub. Susan Thompson. adv.: B&W page $2590, color page $3760; trim 8 1/8 x 10 7/8. bk.rev.; circ. 50,000 (paid). **Description:** Covers leagues and scores, profiles personalities.

796.32   UK   ISSN 0144-0810
NETBALL. 1933-1937; resumed 1944. q. £6 (rest of Europe £11; elsewhere £14). All England Netball Association, Netball House, 9 Paynes Park, Hitchin, Herts. SG5 1EH, England. TEL 01462-442344. FAX 01462-442343. Ed. G. Harrold. adv.: color page £450; adv. contact: G. Harrold. bk.rev. circ. 6,000. Indexed: Sportsearch (1977-). **Document type:** consumer publication.

796.352   US
NEW ENGLAND GOLF MAGAZINE.* 1989. bi-m. $19.97. New England Golf Magazine, Inc., 148 Old Westminster Rd., Hubbardstown, MA 01452-1419. TEL 800-627-7012. FAX 508-840-3209. Pub. Mark Mitchell. adv. circ. 50,000. **Document type:** consumer publication.
Description: Focuses on local events, tournaments, courses and players.

796.332   US
NEW YORK JETS OFFICIAL YEARBOOK. 1971. a. $7 per copy. (New York Jets Football Club Inc.) New York Jets, 1000 Fulton Ave., Hempstead, NY 11550. Ed. Brooks Thomas. charts; illus.; stat. circ. 100,000. **Document type:** consumer publication.

796.323   US
NEW YORK KNICKS YEARBOOK; official guide and record book. 1947. a. $8 per no. (New York Knickerbockers Basketball Club) Madison Square Garden Corporation (Subsidiary of: Paramount Communications), 2 Pennsylvania Plaza, New York, NY 10121. TEL 212-465-6000. FAX 212-465-6498. Ed. John Cirillo. adv.; charts; illus.; stat. circ. 13,000. (reprint service avail.)

796.357   US   ISSN 0887-5863
NEW YORK METS INSIDE PITCH. 1985. m. $24.95. Coman Publishing Company, Inc., 505 S. Duke St., Ste. 504, Durham, NC 27701. TEL 919-688-0218. FAX 919-682-1532. (Subscr. to: Box 2331, Durham, NC 27702) Ed. Todd McGee. adv.: B&W page $400, color page $600; 10 x 13. circ. 19,000. **Document type:** consumer publication.

796.334   UK   ISSN 0305-4780
NEWS OF THE WORLD FOOTBALL ANNUAL. 1887. a. £3.99. Invincible Press, 77-78 Fulham Palace Rd., London W6 8JB, England. TEL 081-741-7070. Eds. Bill Bateson, Albert Sewell. circ. 80,000.
Description: Covers teams, leagues, results of games and other football information for the season.

796.352 330   US
NEWSLINE (LAWRENCE). 1975. m. $210 includes membership. Golf Course Superintendents Association of America, 1421 Research Park Dr., Lawrence, KS 66049. TEL 913-841-2240. FAX 913-832-4466. Ed. Carol Robertson. charts; illus. circ. 12,000. (back issues avail.) **Document type:** newsletter.

796.342   GW
NIEDERRHEIN TENNIS. 11/yr. (Tennis-Verband Niederrhein e.V.) Druck- und Verlagshaus Enger GmbH, An der Kollenburg 9-15, 47877 Willich, Germany. TEL 02156-918-0. Ed. Klaus Molt. adv. contact: Hermann Roehlen. circ. 24,252. **Document type:** bulletin.

796.357 301   CN   ISSN 1188-9330
NINE; a journal of baseball history and social policy perspectives. 1992. s-a. $30. B K Publishing, 11007 83rd St., Ste. 1105, Edmonton, AB T6G 0T9, Canada. TEL 403-492-0409. FAX 403-492-5774. (Subscr. to: 8625 112th St., Ste., 300 Edmonton, AB T6G 1K8, Canada. TEL 403-492-0409) Ed. Bill Kirwin. adv.; bk.rev.; film rev.; illus.; stat.; circ. 500 (paid). (back issues avail.) **Document type:** academic/scholarly publication.
Description: Promotes the study of all historical aspects of baseball, and centers on social policy implications wherever baseball is played in the world.
Refereed Serial

796.352   US   ISSN 0889-2377
NORTH TEXAS GOLFER. 1986. 12/yr. $16. Golfer Magazines, Inc., 9182 Old Katy Rd., Ste. 212, Houston, TX 77055. TEL 713-464-0308. FAX 713-464-0129. Ed. Steve Hunter. adv.: B&W page $1600, color page $2350; 10 1/4 x 13; adv. contact: Paul Boyd. circ. 28,000 (controlled). **Document type:** newspaper.
Description: Provides information to golfers in Texas above the 31st parallel on quality of courses, better playing techniques, upcoming tournaments, and tournament results. Includes an alphabetical list of golf courses in that area every other month.

796.334   IT   ISSN 1121-3256
NUOVO CALCIO. 1991. m. L.40000 (foreign L.70000). Editoriale Sport Italia, Via Masaccio 12, 20149 Milan, Italy. TEL 39-2-4815396. FAX 39-2-4690907. Ed. Marco Marchei. adv.: B&W page L.5000000, color page L.7500000; adv. contact: Antonio Brazzit. circ. 50,000. **Document type:** consumer publication.

796.342   IT
NUOVO TENNIS. 1988. m. L.38000. N.T.P. Edizioni s.r.l., Via Des Ambrois 2 bis., 10123 Turin, Italy. TEL 39-11-8123096. FAX 39-11-8123042. Ed. Marco Azzollini. adv.: B&W page L.1800000, color page L.2500000. **Document type:** consumer publication.

796.357   US   ISSN 0078-3838
GV877
THE OFFICIAL BASEBALL GUIDE. 1942. a. $13.95. Sporting News Publishing Co., 1212 N. Lindbergh Blvd., St. Louis, MO 63132. TEL 314-997-7111. FAX 314-993-7726. Eds. Craig Carter, Dave Sloan. **Document type:** consumer publication.

796.357   US   ISSN 0162-542X
THE OFFICIAL BASEBALL REGISTER. 1940. a. $13.95. Sporting News Publishing Co., 1212 N. Lindbergh Blvd., St. Louis, MO 63132. TEL 314-997-7111. FAX 314-993-7726. Eds. George Puro, Kyle Veltrop. **Document type:** consumer publication.
Formerly: Baseball Register (ISSN 0067-4281)

796.357   US   ISSN 0078-3846
OFFICIAL BASEBALL RULES. 1950. a. $4.95. Sporting News Publishing Co., 1212 N. Lindbergh Blvd., St. Louis, MO 63132. TEL 314-997-7111. FAX 314-997-7726. **Document type:** consumer publication.

796.323   US
OFFICIAL BIG TEN BASKETBALL MEDIA GUIDE. a. $7.95. (Big Ten Conference) Triumph Books, 644 S. Clark St., Chicago, IL 60605. TEL 312-939-3330. FAX 312-663-3557. (Membership addr.: Big Ten Conference, 1500 Higgins Rd., Park Ridge, IL 60068-5742) stat.
Description: Includes individual and team profiles and provides statistical data for the season.

796.323   US
(YEAR) OFFICIAL C B A GUIDE AND REGISTER.* 1978. a. $15.95. Continental Basketball Association, 701 Market St., Ste. 140, St. Louis, MO 63101-1824. TEL 303-331-0404. FAX 303-377-9452. Eds. Greg Anderson, Brett Meister. adv. circ. 6,000.
Formerly: C B A Media Guide Yearbook.

796.352   US
OFFICIAL GUIDE TO THE P G A CHAMPIONSHIPS. a. $16.95. (Professional Golfers Association) Triumph Books, 644 S. Clark St., Chicago, IL 60605. TEL 312-939-3330. FAX 312-663-3557.
Description: Provides in-depth coverage of professional golf championship events all the way back to 1916.

796.332   US   ISSN 0747-9808
GV956.8
OFFICIAL HIGH SCHOOL FOOTBALL RULES. a. $4. National Federation of State High School Associations, 11724 N.W. Plaza Circle, Box 20626, Kansas City, MO 64195-0626. TEL 816-464-5400. FAX 816-464-5571.
Formerly: Football Rulebook (ISSN 0891-3285)

796.3   US
OFFICIAL LAWN BOWLS ALMANAC. 1964. irreg. $1.50 to non-members. American Lawn Bowls Association, 445 Surfview Dr., Pacific Palisades, CA 90272. TEL 213-454-2775.
Former titles (until 1984): Official Lawn Bowls Handbook (ISSN 0065-9053); Lawn Bowler's Handbook.

796.3   US   ISSN 0078-3862
GV885
THE OFFICIAL N B A GUIDE. 1958. a. $13.95. (National Basketball Association) Sporting News Publishing Co., 1212 N. Lindbergh Blvd., St. Louis, MO 63132. TEL 314-997-7111. FAX 314-993-7726. Eds. Craig Carter, Alex Sachare. **Document type:** consumer publication.
Formerly: Official National Basketball Association Guide.

796.323   US   ISSN 1063-1089
GV885.45
OFFICIAL N C A A BASKETBALL. 1923. a. $10. (National Collegiate Athletic Association) Triumph Books, 644 S. Clark St., Chicago, IL 60605. TEL 312-939-3330. FAX 312-663-3557. (Orders to: N.C.A.A. Circulation Department, Box 7347, Overland Park, KS 66207-0347. TEL 913-339-1900) stat. circ. 12,000.
Former titles: N C A A Basketball (ISSN 0276-1017); Incorporates: N C A A Basketball Records; Which was formerly (until 1980): Official National Collegiate Athletic Association Basketball Guide.
Description: Contains individual and team records, statistical leaders, all-America teams, game results from the preceding year, with schedules for the current year.

796.33   US
OFFICIAL N C A A FINAL FOUR RECORDS BOOK. a. $9.95. (National Collegiate Athletic Association) Triumph Books, 644 S. Clark St., Chicago, IL 60605. TEL 312-939-3330. FAX 312-663-3557. stat.
Description: Provides an official statistical history of the Final Four.

796.323   US
OFFICIAL OHIO STATE UNIVERSITY MEN'S BASKETBALL PROGRAM. irreg. (published for each men's home basketball game). (Ohio State University) Zimmerman Publishing Company, Inc., 929 Harrison Ave., Ste. 202, Columbus, OH 43215. TEL 614-294-8878. FAX 614-294-4831. adv. (back issues avail.)
Description: The official game day program for the Ohio State University men's basketball team. Includes player and coach profiles, alumni news etc.

796.3   UK
OFFICIAL PREMIER LEAGUE YEARBOOK. 1992. a. (F.A. Premier League) Stanley Paul and Co. Ltd., 20 Vauxhall Bridge Rd., London SW1V 2SA, England. **Document type:** bulletin.

SPORTS AND GAMES — BALL GAMES

796.357 US
OFFICIAL RULES OF BASEBALL (YEAR). a. $8.95. (Major League Baseball) Triumph Books, 644 S. Clark St., Chicago, IL 60605. TEL 312-939-3330. FAX 312-663-3557.
Description: Lays out all the rules of the game.

796.323 US
OFFICIAL RULES OF BASKETBALL (YEAR). a. $8.95. (National Collegiate Athletic Association) Triumph Books, 664 S. Clark St., Chicago, IL 60605. TEL 312-939-3330. FAX 312-663-3557.

796.352 US
OFFICIAL RULES OF GOLF. a. $9.95. (United States Golf Association) Triumph Books, 644 S. Clark St., Chicago, IL 60605. TEL 312-939-3330. FAX 312-663-3557.
Description: Details the official rules of the game.

796.334 US
OFFICIAL RULES OF SOCCER. a. $8.95. (Federation Internationale de Football) Triumph Books, 644 S. Clark St., Chicago, IL 60605. TEL 312-939-3330. FAX 312-663-3557.

796.332 US
OFFICIAL RULES OF THE N F L. a. $8.95. (National Football League) Triumph Books, 644 S. Clark St., Chicago, IL 60605. TEL 312-939-3330. FAX 312-663-3557.

796.325 US
GV1017.V6
OFFICIAL RULES OF VOLLEYBALL. 1920. a. $8.95. U S A Volleyball, 644 S. Clark St., Chicago, IL 60605. TEL 312-939-3330. FAX 312-663-3557. (Membership addr.: U S A Volleyball, 3595 E. Fountain Blvd., Ste. I-2, Colorado Springs, CO 80910-1740. TEL 719-637-8300. FAX 719-597-6307) adv.; bk.rev.; index. circ. 41,000. (also avail. in microfiche)
Former titles: U S A Volleyball. Official Volleyball Rule Book; United States Volleyball Association. Official Volleyball Guide (ISSN 0083-3592)
Description: Covers all aspects of both in- and outdoor volleyball in detail, including special rules for co-ed play, scorekeeping, and official hand signals.

796.332 US
OFFICIAL S E C FOOTBALL GUIDE. a. $14.95. (Southeastern Conference) Triumph Books, 644 S. Clark St., Chicago, IL 60605. TEL 312-939-3330. FAX 312-663-3557. stat.
Description: Covers the games and teams of the strongest conference in college football.

796.342 UK
THE OFFICIAL WIMBLEDON ANNUAL. 1983. a. £17.99 (rest of Europe £21.99; N. and S. America, Middle East, Africa £25.99; Australasia £27.99) (effective 1995-1996). Hazleton Publishing, 3 Richmond Hill, Richmond, Surrey TW10 6RE, England. TEL 0181-948-5151. FAX 0181-948-4111. TELEX 946153. Ed. John Parsons; Pub. Richard Poulter. adv. contact: Simon Maurice. illus. Document type: consumer publication.
Description: Captures the drama of the world-famous tennis championships.

796.352 US
OHIO GOLFERS MAP & GUIDE. 1992. a. $12.95. R S G Publishing, Inc., Box 700612, Plymouth, MI 48170. TEL 313-416-5300. FAX 313-416-5389. Ed. Eric Rasmussen. adv.: B&W page $475, color page $984; trim 5 1/4 x 8 1/4. circ. 10,000.
Description: Lists addresses and statistics of public golf facilities in the state.

796.352 917.704 US
OHIO GOLFER'S TRAVEL GUIDE. 1990. a. $9.95. R S G Publishing, Inc., Box 700612, Plymouth, MI 48170-0612. TEL 313-416-5300. FAX 313-416-5389. Ed. Betty Rasmussen. circ. 10,000.
Description: Presents information on public and private golf courses in Ohio, including address and telephone, course description, facilities, and more.

796.342 CN ISSN 0824-6629
ON COURT. 1982. 8/yr. Can.$12. Fourhand II, Inc., 1200 Sheppard Ave. E., Ste. 400, Willowdale, Ont. M2K 2S5, Canada. TEL 416-497-1370. FAX 416-494-5343. Ed. Tom Mayenknecht. adv.; bk.rev.; circ. 50,000 (controlled).

796.352 CN ISSN 0710-2801
ONTARIO GOLF NEWS. 1980. 5/yr. Can.$9. Ontario Golf News Inc., 2 Billingham Rd., Ste. 400, Toronto, ON M9B 6E1, Canada. TEL 416-232-2380. FAX 416-232-9291. Ed. Charles Halpin. adv. contact: Ken McKenzie. bk.rev.; circ. 40,000 (controlled). Document type: trade publication, consumer publication.
Description: Contains coverage of all the major tournaments played in Ontario and golf highlights across Canada. Lists all golf courses in Ontario plus instructional articles and golf rules.

796.342 CN
ONTARIO TENNIS. 1969. bi-m. Can.$9.95. Ontario Tennis Association, 1220 Sheppard Ave. E., Willowdale, Ont. M2K 2X1, Canada. TEL 416-495-4215. FAX 416-495-4222. Ed. David Dunkelman. adv.; bk.rev.; stat. circ. 10,000. (tabloid format; back issues avail.)

796.3 UK ISSN 0958-5427
OPEN RUGBY. 1976. m. £26. Munro House, York St., Leeds LS9 8AP, England. TEL 0532-451560. FAX 0532-426255. Ed. Harry Edgar. adv.; bk.rev. circ. 33,000. (back issues avail.) Document type: consumer publication.

796.352 US ISSN 0161-1259
GV961
P G A MAGAZINE.* 1920. m. $23.95 to non-members. (Professional Golfers' Association of America) Quarton Group Publishers, Inc., 888 W. Big Beaver Rd., Ste. 600, Troy, MI 48084-4737. TEL 313-649-1110. FAX 313-649-2306. Ed. Lynn Henning. adv.; bk.rev.; illus. circ. 35,000. Indexed: Sports Per.Ind., Sportsearch.
Formerly (until Oct. 1977): Professional Golfer (ISSN 0033-0132)

796.352 UK
P G A PROFILE. m. (Professional Golfers' Association) In Focus Publishing, 52 Mere Green Rd., Sutton Coldfield, W. Midlands B75 5BT, England. TEL 021-323-3073. FAX 021-323-2911. (Dist. by: Warners Midlands plc., The Maltings, Manor Ln., Bourne, Lincs., England. TEL 078-423931) Ed. Jane Carter. adv. contact: Jo Holmes. bk.rev.; circ. 5,500 (controlled). (back issues avail.)

796.352 US ISSN 1042-8798
P G A TOUR BOOK. a. $12.95. (Professional Golfers Association) Triumph Books, 644 S. Clark St., Chicago, IL 60605. TEL 312-939-3330. FAX 312-663-3557.
Formerly: Offical P G A Tour Media Guide (ISSN 0193-9653)
Description: Presents inside information on the greatest players and games in the P.G.A. Tour.

796.352 US
P G M A NEWSLETTER.* (Former name of sponsoring body: Golf Course Association) 10/yr. membership. Public Golf Management Association, 8030 Cedar, Ste. 215, Minneapolis, MN 55425. TEL 612-854-8482. Document type: newsletter.
Formerly: G C A Newsletter.

796.352 CN
▼**PACIFIC GOLF.** 1994. 6/yr. Can.$12.95. Canada Wide Magazines Ltd., 401-4180 Lougheed Hwy., Burnaby, BC V5C 6A7, Canada. TEL 604-299-7311. FAX 604-299-9188. Ed. Bonnie Irving; Pub. Peter Legge. adv.: B&W page Can.$1350, color page Can.$2100; trim 8 1/8 x 10 7/8; adv. contact: Stephen Thomas. circ. 16,000. Document type: consumer publication.

796.332 US ISSN 1049-1902
PACKER REPORT. 1973. 26/yr. (w. during football season). $29.95. Royle Publications, Inc., 112 Market St., Sun Prairie, WI 53590. TEL 608-837-2200. FAX 608-825-3053. Ed. Beth Zeise; Pub. John Weishar. adv. circ. 34,000. Document type: newspaper.
Description: Devoted to coverage of the Green Bay Packers and the NFL. Contains game stories, statistics, coaches' comments, player profiles, photos and line-ups.

796.3 CN
PADDLE NEWS. q. Can.$10 to individuals; institutions Can.$25. Alberta Table Tennis Association, 11759 Groat Rd., Edmonton, AB T5M 3K6, Canada. TEL 403-453-8657. FAX 403-453-8553. Ed. David Jackson. adv.: page Can.$75; adv. contact: Rosanne Prinsen. circ. 150. (looseleaf format; back issues avail.) Document type: newsletter.
Description: Provides upd-to-date table tennis news from the province, country and world levels.

796.358 PK
PAKISTAN BOOK OF CRICKET. (Text in English) 1976. a. Rs.10. Q. Ahmed, Pub., Spencers Bldg., 3rd Fl., I.I. Chundrigar Rd., G.P.O. Box 3721, Karachi, Pakistan. charts; illus.

796.352 JA
PAR GOLF. (Text in Japanese) 1969. m. 8160 Yen. Gakken Co. Ltd., 40-5, 4-chome, Kamiikedai, Ohta-ku, Tokyo 145, Japan. Ed. Kenichi Shiono.

796.352 IT
PARLIAMO DI GOLF. 1980. m. (9/yr.) L.50000 membership (effective 1995). Editoriale Country and Sport, Via Pietro Mascagni 21, 20122 Milan, Italy. TEL 39-2-795600. FAX 39-2-795646. Ed. Lio Selva. adv.: color page L.8000000. charts; illus.; stat. circ. 19,000. Document type: consumer publication.
Description: Covers the sport of golf, includes list of competitions throughout Italy and worldwide.

796.323 US ISSN 1059-5805
GV885.4
PETERSEN'S COLLEGE BASKETBALL. 1991. a. newsstand price: $4.95. Petersen Publishing Co., 6420 Wilshire Blvd., Los Angeles, CA 90048. TEL 213-782-2000. FAX 213-782-2718. adv. Document type: consumer publication.
Description: Previews the upcoming season, including predictions, schedules, ratings, and stats.

796.332 US ISSN 0276-2129
GV937
PETERSEN'S COLLEGE FOOTBALL. Running title: College Football. N.S. 1991. a. newsstand price: $4.95. Petersen Publishing Co., 6420 Wilshire Blvd., Los Angeles, CA 90048. TEL 213-782-2000. FAX 213-782-2718. adv. circ. 180,000. Document type: consumer publication.

796.357 US ISSN 0148-3153
GV875.A1
PETERSEN'S PRO BASEBALL. 1977. a. newsstand price: $4.50. Petersen Publishing Co., 6420 Wilshire Blvd., Los Angeles, CA 90048. TEL 213-782-2000. FAX 213-782-2718. adv. circ. 196,000. Document type: consumer publication.
Description: Includes predictions, ratings, draft review, schedules and stats. Reviews the past season.

792.323 US ISSN 0192-2238
GV885.7
PETERSEN'S PRO BASKETBALL. 1977. a. newsstand price: $4.50. Petersen Publishing Co., 6420 Wilshire Blvd., Los Angeles, CA 90048. TEL 213-782-2000. FAX 213-782-2718. Ed. Al Hall. circ. 157,486. Document type: consumer publication.

796.352 US
PHILADELPHIA GOLF MAGAZINE. 1986. 5/yr. $8. Philadelphia Golf Publishing Co., 1583 Maple Ave., Paoli, PA 19301-1249. TEL 215-647-4692. adv. circ. 70,000. Document type: consumer publication.
Description: Provides news, entertainment and information about Philadelphia area golf. Covers pro and amateur tournaments.

796.357 US ISSN 8750-4278
PHILLIES REPORT; the exclusive Philadelphia Phillies newspaper. 1983. fortn. $22.95. Sports Press, Inc., Box 157, Springfield, PA 19064. TEL 610-543-4077. FAX 610-544-4013. Ed. Richard N. Westcott. adv.; bk.rev. circ. 12,000. (tabloid format; back issues avail.) Document type: newspaper.
Description: Contains features and news about Philadelphia's home team.

SPORTS AND GAMES — BALL GAMES

796.346 CC ISSN 1000-3452
PINGPANG SHIJIE/TABLE TENNIS WORLD. (Text in Chinese) 1982. q. $12.30. (Zhongguo Pingpang Xiehui - China Table Tennis Association) Renmin Tiyu Chubanshe - People's Sports Publishing House, 8 Tiyuguan Lu, Chongwen Qu, Beijing 100061, People's Republic of China. TEL 5112466. FAX 7016129. (Dist. in U.S. by: China Books & Periodicals, Inc., 2929 24th St., San Francisco, CA 94110. TEL 415-282-2994) **Document type:** consumer publication.

796.334 US
THE PITCH (CARROLLTON). 1989. m. $18. North Texas State Soccer Association, 1740 S. Interstate 35, Ste. 105, Carrolton, TX 75006. TEL 214-323-1323. FAX 214-242-3600. adv.: B&W page $1790, color page $2690; trim 9 5/8 x 13 1/2. circ. 90,000. **Document type:** newspaper.
Description: Contains association news, events, announcements and coaching hints for administrators and coaches.

796.31 US
PITCHER AND TEAM REPORT (YEAR). a. $10.95 (free with subscr. to: Baseball Insight). Parrish Publications, Box 23205, Portland, OR 97223. TEL 503-244-8975. Ed. Phil Erwin. **Document type:** newsletter.

796.352 BE ISSN 0775-9878
PLAY GOLF (NEDERLANDSE EDITIE). French edition: Play Golf (Edition Francaise) (ISSN 0776-023X) 1988. m. 950 BEF (effective 1994). Play Golf S.A., Rue du Chatelain 49, 1050 Brussels, Belgium. TEL 32-2-6471750. FAX 32-2-6482989. Ed. Bernard de Wasseige. adv.; illus.; circ. controlled. **Document type:** consumer publication.

796.358 UK ISSN 0079-2314
PLAYFAIR CRICKET ANNUAL. a. £4.50. Headline Book Publishing, 338 Euston Rd., London NW1 3BH, England. TEL 0171-387-6000. FAX 0171-387-6121. Ed. Bill Frindall. circ. 70,000. **Document type:** bulletin.

796.3 UK ISSN 0079-2322
PLAYFAIR FOOTBALL ANNUAL. 1948. a. £4.50. Headline Book Publishing, 338 Euston Rd., London NW1 3BH, England. TEL 0171-387-6000. FAX 0171-387-6121. Ed. J. Rollin. circ. 25,000. **Document type:** bulletin.

796.352 CN ISSN 0821-2023
POCKET PRO GOLF MAGAZINE. 1978. 17/yr. $85 W. Wilmot St., Unit 14, Richmond Hill, ON L4B 1K7, Canada. TEL 905-764-5409. Ed. Bruce A. Longhurst. adv. circ. 400,000. **Document type:** consumer publication.
Formerly: Pro Pocket Guide Golf Magazine (ISSN 0711-4079)

796.353 US ISSN 0146-4574
GV1010
POLO. 1975. 10/yr. $30 (Canada $42.10; elsewhere $60) (effective 1994). Polo Publications, Inc., 656 Quince Orchard Rd., Gaithersburg, MD 20878-1472. TEL 301-977-0200. FAX 301-990-9015. Ed. Martha LeGrand. adv. contact: Beth Carey. bk.rev.; illus.; circ. 5,600 (paid). **Indexed:** Sports Per.Ind., Sportsearch (1977-). **Document type:** consumer publication.
Formerly: Polo News.
Description: news on the sport of polo: tournament coverage, instructional articles and player profiles.

796.357 US
PONY BASEBALL. BLUE BOOK. 1959. triennial. $4. Pony Baseball, Inc., Box 225, Washington, PA 15301. TEL 412-225-1060. Ed.Bd. circ. 20,000.
Formerly: Boys Baseball. Blue Book (ISSN 0068-0575)
Description: Guide for operating a youth baseball or softball program for the entire community.

796.357 US
PONY BASEBALL RULES AND REGULATIONS. (In 3 editions: Shetland, Pinto & Mustang Rules; Bronco, Pony, Colt & Palomino Rules; Girls Softball) 1951. a. $0.50. Pony Baseball, Inc., Box 225, Washington, PA 15301. TEL 412-225-1060. Ed. Abraham L. Key. circ. 150,000.
Description: Rulebooks for different age level baseball and softball leagues.

796.357 US
PONY BASEBALL - SOFTBALL EXPRESS. 1952. q. $1. Pony Baseball, Inc., Box 225, Washington, PA 15301. TEL 412-225-1060. Ed.Bd. adv.; illus. circ. 29,000. (tabloid format) **Document type:** newspaper.
Former titles: Pony Baseball Express; Pony Baseball Newsletter; Boys Baseball Newsletter; Boys Baseball Bulletin (ISSN 0006-856X)
Description: Covers current news in organized baseball and softball for boys and girls from ages 5-18, including items for organizers and teams.

794.7 US ISSN 1049-2852
POOL & BILLIARD MAGAZINE. 1983. m. $31.95 (Canada and Mexico $41.95; elsewhere $71.95). Sports Publications Ltd., 1701 Bloomingdale Rd., Glendale Heights, IL 60139-2130. TEL 708-260-8500. FAX 708-260-8566. Eds. Karin Kaltofen, Shari J. Stauch; Pub. Harold L. Simonsen. adv. contact: Paul Bennema. bk.rev. circ. 15,000. **Document type:** consumer publication.
Incorporates (in 1982): Games and Leisure Inc.
Description: Dedicated to the sport of Pool and Billiards with instructional articles, tournament coverage, and industry news. Also includes new products and trends.

796.332 US
POST-SEASON FOOTBALL HANDBOOK. 1989. a. Kwik-Fax Books (Subsidiary of: Martin Frederick, Inc.), Box 14613, Surfside Beach, SC 29587. TEL 803-238-3513. Ed. Martin Frederick.

796.352 US
PRIVATE COUNTRY CLUB GUEST POLICY DIRECTORY. 1976. a. $25. Pazdur Publishing Co., 2171 Campus Dr., Irvine, CA 92715. TEL 714-752-6474. FAX 714-752-0398. Ed. Edward F. Pazdur. adv. circ. 100,000. **Document type:** directory.
Supersedes (1976-1979): Golf and Country Club Guest Policy Directory.

796.322 US
PRO BASKETBALL ILLUSTRATED (YEAR). a. Sterling - Macfadden Partnership, 233 Park Ave. S., New York, NY 10003. TEL 212-780-3500. FAX 212-780-3555. Ed. Stephen Ciacciarelli. charts; illus. **Document type:** consumer publication.

796.3305 US ISSN 0079-5526
PRO FOOTBALL (LOS ANGELES). 1960. a. newsstand price: $4.50. Petersen Publishing Co., 6420 Wilshire Blvd., Los Angeles, CA 90048. TEL 213-782-2000. **Document type:** consumer publication.
Formerly: Petersen's Pro Football Annual (ISSN 0079-1156)

796.332 US ISSN 1054-0156
GV954
PRO FOOTBALL ILLUSTRATED (YEAR). a. Sterling - Macfadden Partnership, 233 Park Ave. S., New York, NY 10003. TEL 212-780-5000. FAX 212-780-3555. Ed. Stephen Ciacciarelli. adv. **Document type:** consumer publication.

796.332 US
GV939.A1
PRO FOOTBALL REGISTER. 1966. a. $13.95. Sporting News Publishing Co., 1212 N. Lindbergh Blvd., St. Louis, MO 63132. TEL 314-997-7111. FAX 314-993-7726. Eds. George Puro, Kyle Veltrop. **Document type:** consumer publication.
Formerly: Football Register (ISSN 0071-7258)

796.332 US ISSN 0032-9053
PRO FOOTBALL WEEKLY. 1968. 30/yr. (w. during football season, m. off-season). $59.95. 666 Dundee Rd., Ste. 1101, Northbrook, IL 60062. TEL 708-272-1237. Ed. Hub Arkush. adv.; bk.rev.; charts; illus./ stat. circ. 100,000.

796.352 UK ISSN 1355-2740
PRO SHOP EUROPE. 1984. m. £45 (foreign £60). Mark Allen Publishing Ltd., Snow Hill, Dinton, Salisbury, Wiltshire SP3 5HN, England. TEL 01722-716996. FAX 01722-716926. Ed. Robert Fairbairn; Pub. Mark Allen. adv.: B&W page £793, color page £1100; trim 297 x 210; adv. contact: Michael Forde. circ. 6,850. **Document type:** trade publication.

796.3 US
PROBASKETBALL. 1993. a. Atlantic Publication Group, Inc., Box 61719, Charleston, SC 29419-1719. TEL 803-747-0025. FAX 803-744-0816. **Document type:** directory.

796.352 BE
PROGRAMME OFFICIEL DES CONCOURS DE GOLF. (Text in Dutch, French) 1945. a. Belgame S.A., Ave. Montjoie 167, 1180 Brussels, Belgium. TEL 32-2-3430845. FAX 32-2-3435772. circ. 20,000. **Document type:** directory.
Description: Lists Belgian golf competitions and information on Belgian golf courses.

796.352 US ISSN 1041-5785
PUTT-PUTT WORLD; forthefunofit! 1958. 3/yr. free. Putt-Putt Golf Courses of America, Inc., 3007 Ft. Bragg Rd., Box 35237, Fayetteville, NC 20303. TEL 910-485-7131. FAX 910-485-1122. Ed. Donna Clayton Lloyd. adv. contact: Michelle Garrison. circ. 70,000. **Document type:** consumer publication.
Description: Deals with accomplishments in the sport of putting and developments in miniature golf.

796.352 US
PUTTERS WORLD. 1993. a. $2. Professional Putters Association, 3007 Fort Bragg Rd., Box 35237, Fayetteville, NC 28303. TEL 910-485-7131. FAX 910-485-1122. Ed. Donna Lloyd. circ. 75,000. **Document type:** consumer publication.
Description: Deals with the accomplishments and opportunities for competitive putters in the sport of miniature golf.

796.335 CN ISSN 0228-6351
QUEBEC SOCCER. m. Promotions Soccer Inc., Box 1000, Sta. M, Montreal, Que. H1V 3R2, Canada. TEL 514-252-3070. FAX 514-252-3162. Ed. Pascal Cifarelli. circ. 10,000.

796.333 AT
QUEENSLAND RUGBY LEAGUE NEWS. irreg. Magazine Publishing Company, 4 Wandoo St., Fortitude Valley, Qld. 4006, Australia. TEL 61-7-252-9677. FAX 61-7-252-4667. Ed. Ross Livermore. adv.: B&W page Aus.$1560, color page Aus.$1950; trim 275 x 210; adv. contact: Trevor Kirk. circ. 15,000.
Description: Official match program for selected Rugby League games.

RACING AND FOOTBALL OUTLOOK: FOOTBALL ANNUAL.
see SPORTS AND GAMES

RACING AND FOOTBALL OUTLOOK: JUMPING ANNUAL.
see SPORTS AND GAMES

RACING AND FOOTBALL OUTLOOK: RACING ANNUAL.
see SPORTS AND GAMES

796.342 US ISSN 0273-9194
RACQUET (NEW YORK). 1980. 6/yr. $24 (Canada $30, elsewhere $32. Heather & Pine International, 42 W. 38 St., Ste. 1202, New York, NY 10018. TEL 212-768-8360. Ed. H.K. Pickens; Pub. H.K. Pickens. adv.: B&W page $7398, color page $9847; trim 8 3/8 x 10 7/8; adv. contact: Elizabeth Visconti. circ. 154,220. **Document type:** consumer publication.
Description: Concentrates on people, travel, fashion, humor, and equipment.

796.343 US
RACQUETBALL AROUND OHIO. 1982. bi-m. $10. Ohio Racquetball Association, 374 Slate Run Dr., Powell, OH 43065. TEL 614-548-4188. FAX 614-548-5079. Ed. Steve Lerner. adv. circ. 2,500. **Document type:** consumer publication.
Description: Features events, schedules and rankings. Includes national and professional news and event coverage.

796.343 US ISSN 1060-877X
RACQUETBALL MAGAZINE. 1990. bi-m. $20 (foreign $35) membership. American Amateur Racquetball Association, 1685 W. Uintah, Colorado Springs, CO 80904-2921. TEL 719-635-5396. FAX 719-635-0685. Ed. Linda Mojer. adv. contact: Steve Lerner. circ. 35,000. **Document type:** trade publication.
Description: Covers international events, national championships, state and regional news, industry reports, schedules and rankings.

796.357 US ISSN 1057-9540
REDS REPORT. 1988. m. $24.95. Coman Publishing Company, Inc., 505 S. Duke St., Ste. 504, Durham, NC 27701. TEL 919-688-0218. FAX 919-682-1532. (Subscr. to: Box 2331, Durham, NC 27702) Ed. Mark Schmetzer. adv.: B&W page $400, color page $600; 10 x 13. circ. 11,400. **Document type:** consumer publication.
Description: For Cincinnati Reds fans.

SPORTS AND GAMES — BALL GAMES

796.352   US
ROCHESTER GOLF WEEK & SPORTS LEDGER. 1988. w. $17.50. Expositor Ledger Newspapers, 2535 Brighton-Henrietta Town Line Rd., Rochester, NY 14623-2711. TEL 716-427-2468. FAX 716-271-8521. Ed. George Morgenstern. adv.; bk.rev.; illus. circ. 26,000. (tabloid format; reprint service avail.) **Document type:** newspaper.
   Description: Serves the golf sport market.

796.3   UK   ISSN 0080-4088
ROTHMANS FOOTBALL YEARBOOK. 1970. a. £16.99 for paperback; hardcover £27.50. (Rothmans (U.K.) Ltd.) Headline Book Publishing, 338 Euston Rd., London NW1 3BH, England. TEL 0171-387-6000. FAX 0171-387-6121. Ed. Jack Rollin. adv. circ. 40,000. **Document type:** bulletin.
   —BLDSC (8025.359400).

796.333   UK   ISSN 0262-4745
ROTHMANS RUGBY LEAGUE YEARBOOK. 1981. a. £15.99. (Rothmans (U.K.) Ltd.) Headline Book Publishing, 338 Euston Rd., London NW1 3BH, England. TEL 0171-387-6000. FAX 0171-387-6121. Eds. David Howes, Raymond Fletcher. illus. circ. 7,500. **Document type:** bulletin.

796.333   US   ISSN 0162-1297
RUGBY. 1975. 11/yr. $29 (Canada $34; elsewhere $42). Rugby Press, Ltd., 2350 Broadway, Ste. 220, New York, NY 10024. TEL 212-787-1160. FAX 212-595-0934. Ed. Edward Hagerty. adv. contact: Andy Koepfler. bk.rev.; circ. 10,500 (paid). (back issues avail.) **Indexed:** Sportsearch (1979-). **Document type:** consumer publication.
   Description: In-depth coverage of all U.S. championships, news on the world rugby scene, including Canada, Europe, South Africa, Australia, New Zealand and the South Pacific. Profiles of clubs and personalities, tournaments, and includes regular coverage of topics from fitness and nutrition to refereeing.

796.333   UK
RUGBY ANNUAL FOR WALES. 1968. a. £4.95. Welsh Brewers Ltd., Maesycoed Rd., Cardiff CF4 4UW, Wales. Ed. Arwyn Owen. adv. **Document type:** bulletin.

796.3   UK   ISSN 0080-4827
RUGBY FOOTBALL LEAGUE OFFICIAL GUIDE. a. £7. Rugby Football League, 180 Chapeltown Rd., Leeds LS7 4HT, England. TEL 0532-624637. FAX 0532-623386. **Document type:** consumer publication.

790.1   UK
RUGBY LEADER. 1949. w. Lancaster Publications, Martland Mill Lane, Wigan, Manchester WN5 0LX, England. TEL 0942-228000. FAX 0942-214004. Ed. John Huxley. adv. circ. 18,000. (back issues avail.)

796.333   PP
RUGBY LEAGUE NEWS. 1979. 28/yr. (during season). Word Publishing Co. Pty. Ltd., Box 1982, Boroko, Papua New Guinea. Ed. Sikio Oyassi. adv.; illus. circ. 6,000.

796.333   AT   ISSN 0035-9742
RUGBY LEAGUE WEEK. 1970. w. during season. Aus.$122.10. A C P Publishing Pty. Ltd., 54-58 Park St., Sydeny, N.S.W. 2000, Australia. TEL 02-282-8000. FAX 02-282-8111. Ed. Norm Tasker. circ. 53,047. (tabloid format)

796.333   UK
RUGBY LEAGUER. 1949. 2/wk. £60. Lancashire Publications, Martland Mill Ln., Wigan WN5 0LX, England. TEL 0942-228000. FAX 0942-214004. Ed. Steve Brady. adv. contact: Richard Woods. bk.rev.; illus.; stat. (tabloid format; back issues avail.) **Document type:** newsletter.
   Description: Contains news and features on Rugby League teams and matches.

796.333   JA
RUGBY MAGAZINE. (Text in Japanese) 1972. m. 7440 Yen. Baseball Magazine Sha, 3-10-10 Misaki-cho, Chiyoda-ku, Tokyo, Japan. Ed. Yoshinori Hamabe. **Document type:** consumer publication.

796.333   NE   ISSN 0166-9648
RUGBY NIEUWS. 1977. 10/yr. fl.50. Dutch Rugby Union, Brinklaan 74C, 1404 GL Bussum, Netherlands. TEL 31-2159-38087. FAX 31-2159-18145. Ed. E. Voet. adv.; bk.rev. circ. 7,500. **Document type:** bulletin, newspaper.
   Description: Covers national and international matches.

796.333   SA   ISSN 1022-2499
RUGBY REVIEW. Cover title: South Africa Rugby Review. 1993. a. R.19.95. Sports Publications & Promotions, P.O. Box 201535, Durban North 4016, South Africa. illus.; maps. **Document type:** consumer publication.

796.333   UK
RUGBY WORLD. 1960. m. £26 (foreign £34). I P C Magazines, King's Reach Tower, Stamford St., London SE1 9LS, England. TEL 0171-261-6830. FAX 0171-261-5419. (Subscr. to: P.O. Box 142, Reading RG4 9DX, England) Ed. Peter Bills. adv. contact: Andy McDuff. bk.rev.; illus. circ. 52,000. **Indexed:** Sportsearch (1985-). **Document type:** consumer publication.
   Formerly: Rugby World and Post (ISSN 0268-9804); Which Incorporates: Rugby Post; Rugby World (ISSN 0035-9777); Rugby Wales.

811   US   ISSN 0882-018X
RUNDY'S JOURNAL AND CONFEDERATION COURIER. 1976. s-a. $8 for 4 issues. Rundy's Journal, 217 Elizabeth St., No. 7, New York, NY 10012. TEL 212-966-1233. Ed. John A. Craig. circ. 350. (back issues avail.)
   Description: Covers baseball.

796.357   US
S A B R BULLETIN. 1971. 9/yr. Society for American Baseball Research, Inc., Box 93183, Cleveland, OH 44101. TEL 216-575-0500. FAX 216-575-0502. Ed. Morris Eckhouse. adv. circ. 6,000. **Document type:** bulletin.

796.357   SA   ISSN 1021-3570
S.A. BASEBALL DIGEST. (Text in English) 1993. q. R.37.40. (Christian Media Network) K & F Colour, P.O. Box 260272, Excom 2023, South Africa. illus. **Document type:** consumer publication.

796.325   US
S C O U T. (Student Collegiate Outlook of USA Talent) a. U S A Volleyball, 3595 E. Fountain Blvd., Ste. I-2, Colorado Springs, CO 80910-1740. TEL 719-637-8300. FAX 719-597-6307. TELEX 187258. circ. (controlled).
   Description: Contains information for volleyball coaches.

796.332   US
SAN DIEGO CHARGERS OFFICIAL YEARBOOK. 1993. a. $7. Woodford Publishing, 660 Market St., Ste. 206, San Francisco, CA 94104-5011. TEL 415-397-1853. FAX 415-399-0942. Ed. Jon Rochmis. adv. contact: David Lilienstein. illus. circ. 40,000. **Document type:** consumer publication.

796.332   US
SAN DIEGO PADRES OFFICIAL YEARBOOK. 1984. a. $7. Woodford Publishing, 660 Market St., Ste. 206, San Francisco, CA 94104-5011. TEL 415-397-1853. FAX 415-399-0942. Ed. Jon Rochmis. adv. contact: David Lilienstein. illus. circ. 40,000. **Document type:** consumer publication.

196.332   US
SAN FRANCISCO 49ERS OFFICIAL YEARBOOK. 1982. a. $7. Woodford Publishing, 660 Market St., Ste. 206, San Francisco, CA 94104-5011. TEL 415-397-1853. FAX 415-399-0942. Ed. Jon Rochmis. adv. contact: David Lilienstein. illus. circ. 40,000. **Document type:** consumer publication.

796.332   US
SAN JOSE SHARKS MAGAZINE. 1991. 6/yr. (Oct.-Apr.) $24. Woodford Publishing, 660 Market St., Ste. 206, San Francisco, CA 94104-5011. TEL 415-397-1853. FAX 415-399-0942. Ed. Jon Rochmis. adv. contact: David Lilienstein. illus. circ. 40,000. **Document type:** consumer publication.

796   QA
AL-SAQR AL-RIYADI. 1977. m. $20 to individuals; institutions $25. Al- Saqr Magazine, P.O. Box 4925, Doha, Qatar. TEL 320476. Ed. M. Kazem. adv.; bk.rev.; illus. circ. 120,000. (back issues avail.)
   Formerly: Saqer - Falcon.

796.334   SP
SCIENCE AND FOOTBALL. (Text in English) no.8, July 1994. irreg. Po. Manuel Girona 49, 7-2, 08034 Barcelona, Spain. Ed.Bd.

796.352   CN   ISSN 0711-3226
SCORE; Canada's golf magazine. (Text in English) 1981. 7/yr. Can.$16. Canadian Controlled Media Communications, 287 MacPherson Ave., Toronto, ON M4V 1A4, Canada. TEL 416-928-2909. FAX 416-928-1357. Ed. Bob Weeks. adv.; bk.rev.; illus. circ. 125,000.

796.352   UK
SCOTLAND HOME OF GOLF. 1970. a. £3.95. Pastime Publications Ltd., 6 York Pl., Edinburgh EH1 3EP, Scotland. TEL 0131-556-1105. FAX 0131-556-1129. adv. contact: Diane Gibson. circ. 30,000. **Document type:** consumer publication.

796.352   US
SENIOR P G A TOUR MEDIA GUIDE. a. $12.95. (Professional Golfers Association) Triumph Books, 644 S. Clark St., Chicago, IL 60605. TEL 312-939-3330. FAX 312-663-3557.
   Description: Provides in-depth coverage of the P.G.A. Senior Tour.

796.357   US   ISSN 1054-2183
GV863.A1
THE SHOW.✱ 1990. a. Preview Publishing, 17754 12th Ave., N.E., Seattle, WA 98155-3717. FAX 206-284-2083.
   Description: Includes profiles of players, managers and owners, as well as strategy, scouting, prospects, statistics and history.

796.357   US
SIDEKICKS. 1993. bi-m. $9.97. Southern Media Corporation, 9625 W. Sample Rd., Coral Springs, FL 33065. TEL 304-344-0332. Ed. Steve Hanks; Pub. Frank Genovese. adv.: B&W page $2400, color page $3000. circ. 25,000. **Document type:** consumer publication.
   Description: Contains information on all aspects of soccer for players at all levels.

796.3   UK
SKY BLUE PROGRAMME. 1970. w. £1.20. Coventry City Football Club Ltd., Highfield Road Stadium, King Richard St., Coventry CV2 4FW, England. TEL 0203-223535. FAX 0203-630318. adv. circ. 10,000. **Document type:** newsletter.

796.3   US
SLO-PITCH GAME. 1970. 7/yr. $6. United States Slo-Pitch Softball Association, 13540 Lake City Way, N.E., Ste. 3, Seattle, WA 98125. TEL 206-367-2420. FAX 206-367-2636. Ed. Al Ramsey. adv.: B&W page $3995, color page $5195; trim 10 5/16 x 13 5/16; adv. contact: Kirk Tortillotte. circ. 114,500 (paid). **Document type:** newspaper.

796.3   US
SLO-PITCH NEWS. 1985. m. $12. Varsity Publications, 13540 Lake City Way, N.E., Ste. 3, Seattle, WA 98125-3665. TEL 206-367-2420. FAX 206-367-2636. Ed. Dick Stephens. adv. circ. 26,000. (tabloid format; back issues avail.)
   Description: Covers slo-pitch softball with statistics and rankings on a national level.

796.342   SZ
SMASH; swiss tennis magazine. 1971. m. 72 SFr. (Swiss Tennis Association) Smash Verlag, Baslerstr. 81, CH-8048 Zurich, Switzerland. TEL 01-4011500. FAX 01-4011353. (Subscr. to: Zollikofer AG, Fuerstenlandstr. 122, 9001 St. Gallen, Switzerland) adv.: B&W page 4180 SFr., color page 6760 SFr. circ. 30,000. (back issues avail.)
   Formerly (until 1977): Tennis.

796.325   CN
SMASH. (Text in French) 1970. 2/yr. Can.$15. Federation de Volley-Ball du Quebec, 4545 ave. Pierre de Coubertin, C.P. 1000, Sta. M, Montreal, PQ H1V 3R2, Canada. TEL 514-252-3065. FAX 514-252-3176. Ed. Claude Pelletier. adv.; bk.rev. circ. 2,500. (looseleaf format) **Document type:** newspaper, bulletin.

SPORTS AND GAMES — BALL GAMES

796.3   US
SOCCER. 9/yr. Patch Communications, 5211 S. Washington Ave., Titusville, FL 32780. TEL 407-268-5010. FAX 407-267-7216. **Document type:** consumer publication.

796.334   US   ISSN 0163-4070
SOCCER AMERICA. 1971. 46/yr. $49.97. Berling Communications, Inc., Box 23704, Oakland, CA 94623. TEL 510-528-5000. FAX 510-528-5177. Ed. Lynn Berling-Manuel. adv. contact: John Hooper. bk.rev.; illus.; circ. 40,000 (paid). (also avail. in microform from UMI; reprint service avail. from UMI) **Indexed:** Sports Per.Ind., Sportsearch (1976-). **Document type:** consumer publication.
—Faxon; UMI.
Formerly: Soccer West.
Description: Delivers comprehensive, national soccer news and information to the sophisticated soccer fan. Covers U.S. national teams, the pros and college action. Also features international soccer, a monthly soccer events calendar, information and tips for adults working in youth soccer.

796.334   US
SOCCER CALIFORNIA.* 1980. 5/yr. $4. California Youth Soccer Association, 1249 Quarry Ln., Ste. 140, Pleasanton, CA 94566-8446. TEL 415-847-9111. adv. circ. 98,000.
Description: Contains news of tournaments and events, standings and scores, playing techniques and news of world soccer.

796.334   US   ISSN 0149-2365
GV942
SOCCER DIGEST. 1978. bi-m. $11.95 (foreign $30). Century Publishing Co., 990 Grove St., Evanston, IL 60201-4370. TEL 708-491-6440. (Subscr. to: Box 349, Mt. Morris, IL 61054-0349. TEL 800-877-5893) Ed. Ken Leiker. adv.; bk.rev.; charts; illus.; stat. circ. 65,000. (also avail. in microform from UMI; back issues avail.; reprint service avail. from UMI) **Indexed:** Sports Per.Ind. **Document type:** consumer publication.
—UMI.
Description: Presents statistics and features on the sport for serious soccer fans.

796.334   US   ISSN 0560-3617
SOCCER JOURNAL. 1956. 6/yr. $50 membership (Europe $70). National Soccer Coaches Association of America, East Gymnasium, Binghamton University, Binghamton, NY 13902-6000. TEL 607-777-2133. FAX 607-777-4467. Ed. Tim Schum. adv.; bk.rev.; illus. circ. 10,500. **Indexed:** Phys.Ed.Ind., Sports Per.Ind., Sportsearch (1979-).
—BLDSC (8318.021640); UnCover.

796.334 028.5   US   ISSN 1060-9911
SOCCER JR.; the soccer magazine for kids. 1992. bi-m. $14.97. Triplepoint, Inc., 27 Unquowa Rd., Fairfield, CT 06430. TEL 203-259-5766. FAX 203-256-1119. Ed. Joe Provey; Pub. Thomas L. Mindrum. adv.; color page $4950. bk.rev. circ. 100,000. **Document type:** consumer publication.
Description: Aimed at a 8-16-year-old audience. Includes profiles of stars; news of soccer at the youth, college, and national levels; health and fitness articles; tips; short fiction; historic profiles; and entertainment.

796.334   JA
SOCCER MAGAZINE. (Text in Japanese) 1966. m. 6360 yen. Baseball Magazine Sha, 3-10-10 Misaki-cho, Chiyoda-ku, Tokyo, Japan. Ed. Keiichi Chino.

796.334   US   ISSN 1070-9754
SOCCER MAGAZINE. 1993. 12/yr. Patch Communications, 5211 S. Washington Ave., Titusville, FL 32780. TEL 407-268-5010. FAX 407-269-2025. Pub. Azi Khan. adv.; B&W or color page $2995; trim 10 x 8 1/8. circ. 60,000. **Document type:** consumer publication.

796.357   UK
SOCCER PRODUCTS & SERVICES. 1985. q. Soccer Products & Services, 66 High St., Henley in Arden, Solihull, W. Midlands B95 5BX, England. TEL 0564-79-3232. Ed. Chris Rodman. circ. 32,000.

796.334   US   ISSN 0731-9541
GV943.4
SOCCER RULEBOOK. a. $4. National Federation of State High School Associations, 11724 N.W. Plaza Circle, Box 20626, Kansas City, MO 64195. TEL 816-464-5400. FAX 816-464-5571.
Formerly: National Federation of State High School Associations. Soccer Rules (ISSN 0163-4763)

796.334   US
SOCCER U.S.A.* (Text in English, Spanish) 1991. m. $2.75 per no. Box 742149, Houston, TX 77274-2149. TEL 713-597-8083. FAX 713-597-8078. adv.: B&W page $2195, color page $4175; trim 8 1/2 x 11. circ. 60,000.

796.3   UK   ISSN 0081-038X
SOCCER YEAR BOOK FOR NORTHERN IRELAND. 1966. a. £1.50. Howard Publications, 39 Boucher Rd., Belfast BT12 6UT, Northern Ireland. Ed. Malcolm Brodie.

796.334   UK   ISSN 0967-1064
SOCCERSTARS. 1992. m. £14.25($38.95) I P C Magazines, Specialist Magazine Group (Subsidiary of: Reed Elsevier group), King's Reach Tower, Stamford St., London SE1 9LS, England. TEL 071-261-5000. FAX 0444-440619. TELEX 892084 REEDBP G. (Dist. by: Quadrant Subscription Services, Oakfield House, Perrymount Rd., Haywards Heath, W. Sussex RH16 3DH, England. TEL 0622-721555) adv. contact: Julian Clark. circ. 73,000. (back issues avail.) **Document type:** consumer publication.
Description: For 7- to 11-year-old boys; contains posters, pin-ups and interviews with star players in the English and Scottish football leagues.

796.3   CN   ISSN 0849-5564
SOFTBALL B.C. MAGAZINE; the voice of the British Columbia Amateur Softball Association. 1980. q. Can.$10 (effective Jan. 1992). Softball British Columbia, P.O. Box 45570 Sunnyside Mall, Surrey, B.C. V4A 9N3, Canada. TEL 604-531-0044. FAX 604-531-8831. Ed. Penny Gardner. adv. circ. 7,000. (back issues avail.)
Description: Contains membership information and articles of sport related interest.

796.323   US
SOFTBALL ILLUSTRATED; slowpitch softball instructional series. 1981. q. $19.95. G E D Publications, Box 304, Lima, OH 45805. Ed. Glen Eley.
Description: Provides how-to-info on improving your game in the second largest team sport in America.

796.357   US   ISSN 0732-2844
GV881
SOFTBALL RULE BOOK. a. $4. National Federation of State High School Associations, 11724 N.W. Plaza Circle, Box 20626, Kansas City, MO 64195-0626. TEL 816-464-5400. FAX 816-464-5571. Ed. Bradley A. Rumble.
Formerly: National Federation of State High School Associations. Softball Rules (ISSN 0146-8286)

796.357   US
SOFTBALL WORLD. 1977. m. $16.25. Sporting World, Box 10151, Oakland Lake Sta., Oakland, CA 94610. TEL 510-428-2000. Ed. George Epstein. adv.; bk.rev. **Document type:** newspaper.

796.332   AT
SOUTH AUSTRALIAN FOOTBALL BUDGET. 1914. w. Aus.$90. South Australian National Football League, P.O. Box One, West Lakes, S.A. 5021, Australia. TEL 61-8-268-2088. FAX 61-8-45-7385. Ed. Shane Fuller. adv.; bk.rev. circ. 5,000. (back issues avail.) **Document type:** consumer publication.
Description: Contains statistics on football, and articles on players, clubs and current issues.

796.342   AT
SOUTH AUSTRALIAN TENNIS NEWS. 1948. m. Aus.$7. South Australia Hard Court Tennis League, P.O. Box 202, Goodwood, S.A. 5034, Australia. TEL 61-8-2932347. FAX 61-8-2938024. Ed. L. Tapp. adv. contact: Peter Wyatt. bk.rev.; illus.; circ. 7,000 (controlled). (back issues avail.) **Document type:** newsletter.

796.352   US
SOUTHPAW ACTIVITIES.* 1961. bi-m. membership. National Association of Left-Handed Golfers, 2010 Southwick St., Houston, TX 77080-6315. TEL 713-464-8683. Ed. Ken Ahrens.
Description: News of golf tournaments, golf courses, members' activities.

794.6   US
SPARES AND STRIKES. 1957. w. $25. Box 428, Clarence, NY 14031. TEL 716-741-2479. FAX 716-741-2468. Ed. Allen Appleford. adv. circ. 4,000. **Document type:** newspaper.
Description: Bowling newspaper.

SPITBALL; the literary baseball magazines. see *LITERATURE*

THE SPORT AMERICANA BASEBALL ADDRESS LIST. see *HOBBIES*

THE SPORT AMERICANA BASKETBALL CARD PRICE GUIDE AND ALPHABETICAL CHECKLIST. see *HOBBIES*

THE SPORT AMERICANA FOOTBALL CARD PRICE GUIDE. see *HOBBIES*

794.6   FR   ISSN 0398-8341
SPORT BOWLING.* 1963. 9/yr. 80 F.($18) Bowling de Paris, Jardin d'Acclimation, 75116 Paris, France. Eds. Michel Chollet & Bernard Mora. adv.; illus. circ. 3,000. **Indexed:** Sportsearch (1976-1983).

796.357   US   ISSN 0275-0732
GV863.A1
THE SPORTING NEWS BASEBALL YEARBOOK. a. $4.95. Sporting News Publishing Co., 1212 N. Lindbergh Blvd., St. Louis, MO 63132. TEL 314-997-7111. FAX 314-997-7726. Ed. Mike Nahrstedt. adv. **Document type:** consumer publication.

796.323   US   ISSN 0895-0598
THE SPORTING NEWS COLLEGE BASKETBALL YEARBOOK. a. $4.95. Sporting News Publishing Co., 1212 N. Lindbergh Blvd., St. Louis, MO 63132. TEL 314-997-7111. FAX 314-997-7726. adv. **Document type:** consumer publication.

796.332   US   ISSN 0733-2823
THE SPORTING NEWS COLLEGE FOOTBALL YEARBOOK. a. $4.95. Sporting News Publishing Co., 1212 N. Lindbergh Blvd., St. Louis, MO 63132. TEL 314-997-7111. FAX 314-997-7726. Ed. Mike Nahrstedt. adv. **Document type:** consumer publication.

796.357   US   ISSN 1052-7591
THE SPORTING NEWS FANTASY BASEBALL OWNERS MANUAL. 1991. a. $6.95. Sporting News Publishing Co., 1212 N. Lindbergh Blvd., St. Louis, MO 63132. TEL 314-997-7111. FAX 314-993-7726. **Document type:** consumer publication.
Formerly: Sporting News Fantasy Baseball Yearbook.

796.332   US
▼**THE SPORTING NEWS PRO FOOTBALL YEARBOOK**. 1994. a. $5.95. Sporting News Publishing Co., 1212 N. Lindbergh Blvd., St. Louis, MO 63132. TEL 314-997-7111. FAX 314-997-7726. Ed. Mike Nahrstedt. adv. **Document type:** consumer publication.

796.323   US   ISSN 0739-3067
GV885.515.N37
THE SPORTING NEWS OFFICIAL N B A REGISTER. a. $13.95. Sporting News Publishing Co., 1212 N. Lindbergh Blvd., St. Louis, MO 63132. TEL 314-997-7111. FAX 314-997-7726. Ed.Bd. **Document type:** consumer publication.
Formerly: Sporting News National Basketball Association Register (ISSN 0271-8170)

SPORTS AND GAMES — BALL GAMES

796.323 US ISSN 0895-0601
GV885.7
THE SPORTING NEWS PRO BASKETBALL YEARBOOK. a. $4.95. Sporting News Publishing Co., 1212 N. Lindbergh Blvd., St. Louis, MO 63132. TEL 314-997-7111. FAX 314-997-7726. Ed. Mike Nahrstedt. adv. **Document type:** consumer publication.
  Formerly: Sporting News Pro College Basketball Yearbook (ISSN 0733-6047)

796.332 US ISSN 0732-1902
GV937
THE SPORTING NEWS PRO FOOTBALL GUIDE. 1970. a. $13.95. Sporting News Publishing Co., 1212 N. Lindbergh Blvd., St. Louis, MO 63132. TEL 314-997-7111. FAX 314-997-7726. Eds. Craig Carter, Dave Sloan. **Document type:** consumer publication.
  Formerly: Sporting News' National Football Guide (ISSN 0081-3788)

796.332 US ISSN 0276-2307
GV937
THE SPORTING NEWS PRO FOOTBALL YEARBOOK. a. $4.95. Sporting News Publishing Co., 1212 N. Lindbergh Blvd., St. Louis, MO 63132. TEL 314-997-7111. FAX 314-997-7726. Ed. Mike Nahrstedt. adv. **Document type:** consumer publication.

SPORTS CARD PRICE GUIDE MONTHLY. see HOBBIES

796.3 US ISSN 1050-365X
GV568.5
SPORTS CARD TRADER. 1990. m. $29.95 (foreign $41.95). Century Publishing Co., 990 Grove St., Evanston, IL 60201-4370. TEL 708-491-6440. (Subscr. to: Box 443, Mt. Morris, IL 61054-0443. TEL 800-877-5893) Ed. Douglas Kale. **Document type:** consumer publication.
  Description: Features a "buy and sell" guide for baseball, football, basketball and hockey cards from 1933 to present; plus articles on how to make money in collecting sports cards.

SPORTS CARDS. see HOBBIES

SPORTS COLLECTORS DIGEST. see HOBBIES

794.6 US
SPORTS REPORTER. 1940. w. $25. Pat McDonough, 761 Second Street, Seacaucus, NJ 07094. TEL 201-866-1803. FAX 201-866-1803. E-mail: ELAuwit37AOL.COM. Ed. Dan McDonough. adv. circ. 4,000. (tabloid format) **Document type:** newspaper.
  Description: Covers bowling in the metropolitan New York region, with tournament results and announcements of upcoming competitions.

796.332 US
SPORTS WEEKLY NEWSLETTER. FOOTBALL ANALYST.* 1968. w. $100. R.W. Livingston, Ed. & Pub., Box 60008, N. Charleston, SC 29419-0008. TEL 803-797-6173. charts; stat. circ. 3,000.

796.357 US
SPORTS WEEKLY NEWSLETTER - BASEBALL.* 1968. w. $120. R.W. Livingston, Ed. & Pub., Box 60008, N. Charleston, SC 29419-0008. TEL 803-797-6173. **Document type:** newsletter.

796.323 US
SPORTS WEEKLY NEWSLETTER - BASKETBALL.* w. $100. R.W. Livingston, Ed. & Pub., Box 60008, N. Charleston, SC 29419-0008. TEL 803-797-6173. **Document type:** newsletter.

631 796.357 US ISSN 1061-687X
SPORTSTURF. 1985. m. $33. Gold Trade Publications, Inc., 68-860 Perez Rd., Ste. J, Cathedral City, CA 92234-7248. TEL 818-781-8300. Ed. Mike Augsdorfer. adv. circ. 21,371. **Document type:** trade publication.
  Former titles: Golf and Sportsturf (ISSN 1049-0000); Sportsturf (ISSN 0890-0167)

796.357 US ISSN 0894-2889
GV875.A1
SPRING TRAINING; baseball yearbook. 1988. a. $6. Spring Training, Inc., Box 667, Chapel Hill, NC 27514. TEL 919-967-2420. FAX 919-967-6294. Ed. Myles Friedman; Pub. Merle Thorpe. adv.; circ. 125,000 (paid). **Document type:** consumer publication.
  Description: Focuses on Major League Baseball's exhibition season in Florida and Arizona with team and schedule information. Gives full information about the upcoming regular season.

796.342 DK ISSN 0909-0274
SQUASH. 1980. q. DKK 100. Dansk Squash Forbund - Danish Squash Association, Idraettens Hus, Broendby Stadion 20, DK-2605 Broendby, Denmark. TEL 45-43-26-24-75. FAX 45-43-26-24-76. Ed. Oluf Joergensen. illus.
  Formerly (until 1983): Dansk Squash (ISSN 0107-2242)

796 UK
SQUASH & FITNESS. q. £2.50. Squash Rackets Association Ltd., Westpoint, 33-34 Warple Way, Acton, London W3 ORQ, England. TEL 0181-746-1616. FAX 0181-746-0580. circ. 10,000. **Document type:** newsletter.
  Formerly: Squash News (ISSN 0263-2640)

796.345 CN ISSN 0821-025X
SQUASH LIFE. (Annual supplement avail.: Squash Ontario Handbook (ISSN 1191-8624)) 1977. 4/yr. Can.$15. Squash Ontario, 1185 Eglinton Ave. E., North York, ON M3C 3C6, Canada. TEL 416-426-7201. FAX 416-426-7393. Ed. Sherry Funston; Pub. Roman Lehecka. adv. contact: Harry Allan Jr. bk.rev.; charts; illus. circ. 5,000. (back issues avail.) **Indexed:** Sportsearch (1982-). **Document type:** newsletter.
  Formerly (until 1981): Let Point (ISSN 0821-0241)
  Description: News about squash tournaments and clubs, playing tips.

796.343 IT
SQUASH MAGAZINE. 1987. q. L.30000 (Europe L.40000). Giorgio Bernardini Editore, Viale Bianca Maria 11, Milan, Italy. TEL 39-2-76003908. FAX 39-2-76015856. Ed. Tuomo Kettunen. adv.: B&W page L.4000000, color page L.5000000. circ. 34,000. **Document type:** consumer publication.

796.31 US ISSN 0164-7148
SQUASH NEWS. 1978. m. (except July-Aug.). $20 (effective 1994). Squash News, Inc., 186 Arcadia Rd., Hope Valley, RI 02832. TEL 401-539-2381. FAX 401-539-2490. Ed. Hazel White Jones. adv.; bk.rev. circ. 16,000. (tabloid format; back issues avail.) **Document type:** consumer publication.
  Description: Full coverage of the game on both the amateur and professional level; includes features, instruction, personalities and upcoming events.

796.343 IT
SQUASH NEWS ITALIANO. 8/yr. L.3500 per no. (Associazione Proprietari di Squash Club) Squash Forever, Piazza Mercato 30, 32100 Bellumo, Italy. TEL 39-437-942027. FAX 39-437-942027. Ed. Francesco Palchetti. adv.: B&W page L.1000000, color page L.1500000. circ. 11,500. **Document type:** consumer publication.

796.345 CN ISSN 1191-8624
SQUASH ONTARIO HANDBOOK. 1982. a. Squash Ontario, 1185 Eglinton Ave. E., North York, ON M3C 3C6, Canada. TEL 416-426-7201. FAX 416-426-7393. Ed. Sherry Funston; Pub. Roman Lehecka.
  Formerly (until 1992): Squash Ontario Yearbook (ISSN 0836-3552)

796.3 GW ISSN 0930-6641
SQUASH PLAYER. 10/yr. DM.40 (foreign DM.48). Fachverlag Dr. Fraund GmbH, Postfach 1329, 61364 Friedrichsdorf, Germany. TEL 06172-7106-0. FAX 06172-710610. Ed. Thomas Klein. adv. contact: Peter Weck. circ. 14,600. **Document type:** consumer publication.

796 UK ISSN 0262-4338
SQUASH PLAYER INTERNATIONAL. 1971. 10/yr. £20.85. Stonehart Leisure Magazines, 67-71 Goswell Rd., London EC1V 7EN, England. TEL 03727-41411. FAX 03727-44493. Ed. Nick Troop. adv. circ. 9,476. **Indexed:** Sportsearch (1977-).
  Description: Articles and comment for squash players plus reports of important competitions.

796 UK
SQUASH RACKETS ASSOCIATION. ANNUAL. 1930. a. £8.75. Squash Rackets Association Ltd., West Point, 33-34 Warple Way, Acton, London W3 ORQ, England. TEL 0181-746-1616. FAX 0181-746-0580. adv. circ. 10,000. **Document type:** newsletter.
  Formerly: Squash Rackets Association. Handbook (ISSN 0081-3885)

796.34 UK ISSN 0952-8512
SQUASH WORLD.* 1986. 9/yr. £15 (foreign £21). Stonehart Leisure Magazines, 67-71 Goswell Rd., London EC1V 7EN, England. TEL 03727-41411. FAX 03727-44493. Ed. Larry Halpin. circ. 10,000. (back issues avail.)
  Description: Articles on coaching, fitness, diet, and injuries. Includes tournament reports and previews.

796.357 US
STARTEC BASEBALL REPORT.* 1992. 9/yr. $4.50 per no. StarTec Publishing, 2385 Arborview Dr., Columbus, OH 43229. TEL 614-792-9988. FAX 614-792-9116. Ed. Geoff Schurech. adv.: B&W page $950, color page $1250; trim 8 1/2 x 10 7/8. circ. 60,000. **Document type:** consumer publication.

796.257 US ISSN 0161-2018
GV877
STREET & SMITH'S BASEBALL.* Variant title: Sport's Official Baseball Yearbook. 1941. a. $4.50. Street & Smith's Sports Group (Subsidiary of: Conde Nast Publications, Inc.), 140 E. 45th St., 36th Fl., New York, NY 10017-3144. TEL 212-880-8698. FAX 212-490-7927. Ed. Gerard Kavanagh. adv. circ. 261,000.
  —UMI.
  Formerly: Street and Smith's Baseball Yearbook (ISSN 0491-1520)
  Description: Provides information regarding teams representing the National, American, and Minor Leagues. Includes official National and American League schedules - official statistics, rosters, recap of league championship series, World Series, and individual records of hitters and pitchers. Player and team profiles, historical and topical features, and a review of the past season and a preview of the coming season.

796.33 US ISSN 0091-9977
GV956.8
STREET & SMITH'S COLLEGE FOOTBALL.* Variant title: Sport's Official College Football Yearbook. a. $3.95. Street & Smith's Sports Group, 140 E. 45th St., 36th Fl., New York, NY 10017-3144. TEL 212-880-8698. FAX 212-490-7927. Ed. Gerard Kavanagh. adv.; illus. circ. 273,559.
  Description: Furnishes analyses of more than 270 college football teams. Schedules include teams from each major conference. Player and team profiles, historical and topical features, review of past season and preview of coming season.

796.323 US
STREET & SMITH'S COLLEGE - PREP BASKETBALL.* a. $4.50. Street & Smith's Sports Group (Subsidiary of: Conde Nast Publications, Inc.), 140 E. 45th St., 36th Fl., New York, NY 10017-3144. TEL 212-880-8698. FAX 212-490-7972. Ed. Gerard Kavanagh. circ. 243,953.
  Description: Covers major college teams, conferences, independents with over 450 scouting reports, team and conference schedules, team and individual statistics, TV-radio listings, as well as pre-season ratings. Includes All America teams on the collegiate and scholastic level.

796.32 US ISSN 0149-7103
GV885.7
STREET & SMITH'S PRO BASKETBALL.* Variant title: Sport's Official Pro Basketball Yearbook. a. $3.95. Street & Smith's Sports Group (Subsidiary of: Conde Nast Publications, Inc.), 140 E. 45th St., 36th Fl., New York, NY 10017-3144. TEL 212-880-8698. FAX 212-490-7927. Ed. Jim O'Brien. adv.; illus. circ. 241,810.
  Formerly: Street and Smith's College and Pro Official Basketball Yearbook (ISSN 0092-511X)
  Description: For coaches, players and avid basketball enthusiasts. Covers scouting reports, team and conference schedules, individual statistics, TV-radio listings as well as pre-season ratings.

SPORTS AND GAMES — BALL GAMES

796.33 US ISSN 0092-3214
GV937
STREET & SMITH'S PRO FOOTBALL.* Variant title: Sport's Official Pro Football Yearbook. a. $3.95. Street & Smith's Sports Group (Subsidiary of: Conde Nast Publications, Inc.), 140 E. 45th St., 36th Fl., New York, NY 10017-3144. TEL 212-880-8698. FAX 212-490-7927. Ed. Gerard Kavanagh. adv.; illus. circ. 311,484. (reprint service avail. from UMI) —UMI.
 Description: Provides information regarding teams representing the National Football conference, American Football conference, and Canadian Football League. Includes NFL rosters, schedules, individual player records, review of past season and preview of coming season.

796.342 US
STRINGER'S ASSISTANT. 1975. m. $59. United States Racquet Stringers Association, 337 S. Cedros, Ste. D, Solana Beach, CA 92075. TEL 619-481-3545. FAX 619-481-0624. adv. contact: Jill Fonte. circ. 8,012. **Indexed:** Sportsearch (1984-). **Document type:** trade publication.
 Description: Covers new products, industry trends, technical product information, and stringing techniques.

796.352 GW
STROKESAVER. 1988. 5/yr. H und K Sportmarketing GmbH, Am Schlosspark 3-5, 65203 Wiesbaden, Germany. TEL 0611-609070. Eds. Kurt Kunz, Thomas Huebner. adv. (back issues avail.) **Document type:** directory.
 Description: Provides information on various golf courses throughout Germany.

STUDENT PULSEN. see COLLEGE AND ALUMNI

796.342 US
SUN TENNIS.* 1983. m. $15 (effective 1994). Field Publishing Co., 4110 N. Goldwater Blvd., Ste. 209, Scottsdale, AZ 85251-3826. TEL 602-941-3935. FAX 602-941-3936. Ed. Tammy Thomas; Pub. Mark I. Field. adv.: B&W page $1870, color page $2320; trim 11 x 14. circ. 20,000.

796.323 IT ISSN 0393-7852
SUPERBASKET. 1978-198?; resumed. 45/yr. (plus supplements). L.180000 (foreign L.250000). Alfredo Cazzola Editore s.r.l., Via C. Colombo 21, 40131 Bologna, Italy. TEL 39-51-325991. FAX 39-51-323182. Ed. Enrico Campana. adv.: page L.6000000. circ. 33,204.

796.358 SA
SUPERSPORT CRICKET BOOK; Australia, New Zealand & South Africa. 1993. irreg. R.9.95. J T Publishing, P.O. Box 17134, Doornfontein 2028, South Africa. illus. **Document type:** consumer publication.

796.334 SW ISSN 0346-2080
SVENSK FOTBOLL. 1973. m. (10/yr.). SEK 531 in Nordic countries; elsewhere SEK 631. (Svenska Fotbollfoerbundet) CeWe-Foerlaget AB, P.O. Box 77, S-890 10 Bjaesta, Sweden. TEL 0660-309-65. FAX 0660-305-17. (Subscr. to: PK-Banken, Box 365, 891 01 Oernskoeldsvik, Sweden) adv. circ. 36,500.
 Formerly (until vol.7, 1975): Svensk Fotbolltidning.

796.352 SW ISSN 0346-2102
SVENSK GOLF. 1946. 13/yr. SEK 295. Swedish Golf Federation, P.O. Box 84, 182 11 Danderyd, Sweden. TEL 46-8-622-15-00. FAX 46-8-622-6930. Ed. Anders Nordlund. adv. contact: Anders Westerlund. circ. 210,000.

796.342 SW ISSN 1101-6469
SVENSK TENNIS/SWEDISH TENNIS. 1991. 10/yr. SEK 240 (foreign price varies) (effective 1996). I C A Foerlaget, S-721 85 Vaesteraas, Sweden. TEL 46-21-19-40-00. FAX 46-21-19-42-21. Hans Mejdevi. adv. contact: Lennart Carlsson. circ. 85,100.
 Formerly: Tennistidningen.
 Description: Covers tennis in Sweden and worldwide.

796.357 JA
SYUKAN BASEBALL. (Text in Japanese) 1958. w. 13770 Yen. Baseball Magazine Sha, 3-10-10 Misaki-cho, Chiyoda-ku, Tokyo, Japan. Ed. Takao Ouchi.

796.346 UK ISSN 0039-8799
TABLE TENNIS NEWS. 1966. 8/yr. £12. English Table Tennis Association, 3rd Fl., Queensbury House, Havelock Rd., Hastings, E. Sussex TN34 1HF, England. TEL 0424-722525. FAX 0424-422103. Ed. John Wood. adv.; bk.rev.; illus. circ. 3,000. **Document type:** consumer publication.
 Description: Gives up-to-date information on national and international table tennis events and activities.

796.346 US ISSN 1068-5782
TABLE TENNIS TODAY. 1933. bi-m. $15. United States Table Tennis Association, National Table Tennis Center, 15916 Indianola Dr., Derwood, MD 20855-2103. TEL 301-330-4334. FAX 301-330-2945. Ed. Larry Hodges. adv.; bk.rev.; charts; illus. circ. 7,000. (processed) **Indexed:** Sportsearch. **Document type:** newsletter.
 Former titles (until 1992): Table Tennis Topics (ISSN 0887-6576); Spin Magazine (ISSN 0746-1801); (until 1983): Table Tennis News (ISSN 0273-8538)
 Description: Contains feature articles, player profiles, coaching tips, club profiles and soft news.

796.3 CH
TAIWAN GOLF EQUIPMENT BUYERS' GUIDE. (Text in English) a. $10. Trade Winds, Inc., No.7, Lane 75, Yungkang St., Taipei, Taiwan 10602, Republic of China. TEL 886-2-3913251. FAX 886-2-3964022. **Document type:** directory, catalog.
 Description: Product catalogs and supplier directories for golf clubs, golf balls and accessories.

796.334 IR ISSN 1024-2244
TAMASHAGARAN; mahnameh futbol Iran. (Text in Persian) 1992. m. IRI.1500 per issue. Tamashagaran Publications, No.15, 3rd Fl., Golriz St., Mottahari Ave., P.O. Box 15875-5564, Tehran, Iran. TEL 98-21-837060. FAX 98-21-832905. Ed. Ali Ashgar Ramezanpoor; Pub. Nader Davoodi. adv.; illus.; circ. 25,000 (paid). **Document type:** consumer publication.
 Description: Covers the soccer scene inside Iran and at the international level. Publishes reports on domestic games and Asian tournaments, articles and commentary on the state of the game today, and interviews with players, coaches and officials.

796.334 UK
THE TARTAN SPECIAL SCOTTISH FOOTBALL LEAGUE REVIEW. 1980. a. £4.95. Scottish Football League, 188 West Regent St., Glasgow G2 4RY, Scotland. TEL 0141-248-3844. FAX 0141-221-7450. Ed. David C. Thomson. adv.; illus. circ. 25,000.
 Former titles: Scottish Football League Review; B & Q Scottish Football League Review; Clydesdale Bank Scottish Football League Review (ISSN 0260-8804)

TEE TIME. see PHILATELY

796.342 XR ISSN 0862-6766
TENIS; prvni cesky tenisovy magazin. (Text in Czech or Slovak) 1990. m. 120 Kc.($41.50) (Cesky Svaz Telesne Vychovy) Olympia a.s., Klimentska 1, 115 88 Prague 1, Czech Republic. TEL 231-5583. (Dist. by: Artia, Ve Smeckach 30, 111 27 Prague 1, Czech Republic) Ed. Karel Blaha.

796.342 US ISSN 0040-3423
GV991
TENNIS. 1965. m. $23.94. New York Times Company Magazine Group, Sports - Leisure Division, 5520 Park Ave., Box 395, Trumbull, CT 06611-0395. TEL 203-373-7000. Ed. Donna Doherty. adv.; bk.rev.; charts; illus. circ. 800,000. (also avail. in microfilm from UMI) **Indexed:** Consum.Ind., Mag.Ind., Phys.Ed.Ind., PMR, Sports Per.Ind., Sportsearch (1977-). **Document type:** consumer publication. —Faxon; UMI; UnCover.

796.342 IT
TENNIS. 1978. m. L.18000. Federazione Italiana Tennis, Viale dei Gladiatori 31, 00194 Rome, Italy. TEL 39-6-3219850. Ed. Giuliano Annibali. adv.: B&W page L.3500000, color page L.5000000. circ. 90,000.

796.342 DK ISSN 0903-921X
TENNIS AARBOGEN. 1981. a. Dansk Tennis Forbund, Broendby Stadion 20, DK-2605 BroendbyK, Denmark. illus.
 Formerly (until 1987): Tennis Jul (ISSN 0109-4939)

796.342 US
TENNIS BUYERS GUIDE. 1984. 6/yr. $36. New York Times Company Magazine Group, Sports - Leisure Division, 5520 Park Ave., Box 395, Trumbull, CT 06611-0395. TEL 203-373-7000. adv.; bk.rev.; illus.; stat. circ. 10,000. (tabloid format) **Document type:** trade publication.

796.342 BE
TENNIS ECHO. (Editions in Dutch, French) 1982. bi-m. $80. Tennis Promotion, Bergstraat 18, B-2280 Grobbendonk, Belgium. TEL 32-13-531093. FAX 32-13-531092. Ed. Roger Vekemans. adv. contact: Roger Vekemans. illus. circ. 50,000. (back issues avail.) **Document type:** consumer publication.
 Description: Covers international tennis matches and topics of interest to tennis players, including fitness and health, equipment, tactics, and how to improve your game.

796 IT ISSN 0393-0890
TENNIS ITALIANO. 1929. m. L.77000 (foreign L.115000). Edisport S.p.A, Via Gradisca 11, 20151 Milan, Italy. TEL 39-2-380851. FAX 39-2-38010393. Ed. Giacinto Spadetta. adv.: B&W page L.6100000, color page L.10000000. bk.rev.; illus.; index. circ. 72,000.
 Description: Covers news about tennis, international and regional sports news, tests of rackets and shoes.

796.342 GW
TENNIS-JAHRBUCH. 1952. a. DM.25. Deutscher Tennis Bund e.V., Hallerstr. 89, 20149 Hamburg, Germany. TEL 040-411780. FAX 040-41178222. (Subscr. to: Buch- und Offsetdruckerei Sass und Co., Reinhard-Rube-Str. 7, 37077 Goettingen, Germany) Ed. Jens-Peter Hecht. adv. circ. 4,500. **Document type:** consumer publication.

796.342 JA
TENNIS JOURNAL. (Text in Japanese) 1982. m. 8880 Yen. Ski Journal Co., Ltd., 3-11, Yotsuya, Shinjuku-Ku, Tokyo, Japan. Ed. Seiji Miyashita.

796.342 DK ISSN 0907-9661
TENNIS MAGASINET. 1920. 7/yr. DKK 75. Dansk Tennis Forbund, Broendby-Stadion 20, DK-2605 Broendby, Denmark. FAX 45-02-456245. TELEX 33111. Ed. Chr. Weide Larsen. adv.; bk.rev. circ. 5,000. **Indexed:** Consum.Ind.
 Former titles (until 1992): Tennis-Avisen (ISSN 0900-7105); (until 1985): Tennis (ISSN 0900-7091)

796.342 GW ISSN 0176-8794
TENNIS MAGAZIN. 1976. m. DM.71.40 (foreign DM.78.60); newsstand price: DM.7. Top Special Verlag GmbH, Nebendahlstr. 16, 22041 Hamburg, Germany. TEL 040-3470-0. FAX 040-34725588. Ed. Lutz Luettig. adv.: B&W page DM.7912, color page DM.14596; trim 180 x 250; adv. contact: Beate Asmus-Fuegert. circ. 76,411. **Document type:** consumer publication.

796.342 JA
TENNIS MAGAZINE. (Text in Japanese) 1970. bi-w. 9360 Yen. Baseball Magazine Sha, 3-10-10 Misaki-cho, Chiyoda-ku, Tokyo, Japan. Ed. Koishi Nemoto. **Indexed:** Mag.Ind. **Document type:** consumer publication.

796.342 FR ISSN 0396-6267
TENNIS MAGAZINE. 1976. m. (11/yr.). 235 F. (outside EEC 336 F.). Societe d'Etude et de Developpement de la Presse Periodique, 23-25 rue de Berri, 75388 Paris Cedex 08, France. TEL 16-1-44-89-44-89. (Subscr. to: 90 rue de Flandre, 75947 Paris Cedex 19, France. TEL 16-1-40-34-35-00) Ed. Jean Couvercelle. adv.; illus. circ. 150,000.

796.342 UK ISSN 0262-9224
TENNIS MAGAZINE. 1981. m. £34. South of England Newspaper, 85 Castle Lane W., Bournemouth, Dorset BH9 3LH, England. TEL 0202-517555. FAX 0202-536439. Ed. C. Elder. adv. circ. 15,000.
 Description: Provides coverage of tournaments in the UK and abroad, product reviews and tests, player profiles and coaching articles.

796.342 US
TENNIS MIDWEST. bi-m. Box 24379, Edina, MN 55424-0379. TEL 612-920-8947. FAX 612-927-7155. Ed. Geoff Gorvin. adv. circ. 12,000.

SPORTS AND GAMES — BALL GAMES

796.342 US
TENNIS NORTHEAST.* 1988. 8/yr. Regional Sports Publications, Box 50405, Henderson, NV 89016-0405. TEL 404-448-6626. FAX 404-368-2444. adv. circ. 30,000.

796.342 IT
TENNIS OGGI. 1980. m. L.50000 (effective 1995 & 1996). Edizioni Sportive Italiane s.r.l., Via della Balduina 88, 00136 Rome, Italy. TEL 39-6-35344859. FAX 39-6-35454503. Ed. Michela Rossi. adv.: color page L.6000000; adv. contact: Sergio Rossi. circ. 30,000. **Document type:** consumer publication.

796.342 GW ISSN 0722-947X
TENNIS REVUE. m. DM.49.20 (foreign DM.61.20); newsstand price: DM.4.80. Top Special Verlag GmbH, Nebendahlstr. 16, 22041 Hamburg, Germany. TEL 040-3473901. FAX 040-34725588. Ed. Dieter Schoen; Pub. Ulrich Kaiser. adv.: B&W page DM.6120, color page DM.11020; trim 180 x 250; adv. contact: Michael Holzapfel. circ. 48,824 (paid). **Document type:** consumer publication.

796.342 US
TENNIS SOUTH.* 1986. 8/yr. $12. Regional Sports Publications, Box 50405, Henderson, NV 89015-0405. TEL 404-448-6226. FAX 404-368-2444. adv. circ. 40,000.

796.342 SZ
TENNIS TICINESE. 1975. m. 25 Fr. Federazione Ticinese Tennis, Casella Postale 88, 6906 Lugano 6, Switzerland. Ed. O. Mellini.

796.342 US
TENNIS U S T A. (In 4 regional eds.) 1990. m. membership. (U S Tennis Association) New York Times Magazine Group, Sports - Leisure Division, 5520 Park Ave., Box 395, Trumbull, CT 06611. TEL 203-373-7155. FAX 203-371-2199. Ed. Bob Moseley. circ. 400,000 (controlled). **Document type:** consumer publication.
Description: Includes news of the association's events on the national, regional and sectional level, with feature stories.

796.342 US ISSN 0194-9098
TENNIS WEEK. 1974. 20/yr. $40 (effective 1995). 341 Madison Ave., New York, NY 10017. TEL 212-808-4750. FAX 212-983-6302. Ed. Eugene L. Scott. adv. contact: Carole Graebner. bk.rev.; illus.; circ. 80,167 (paid). (tabloid format) **Document type:** consumer publication.
Formerly: Tennis News.

796.342 US
TENNIS WEST.* 1983. 8/yr. $12. Regional Sports Publications, Box 50405, Henderson, NV 89016-0405. TEL 404-448-6226. FAX 404-368-2444. adv. circ. 80,000.

796.346 UK ISSN 0040-3474
TENNIS WORLD. 1969. m. £21.50 (foreign £37.50). Presswatch Ltd., Spendlove Centre, Enstone Rd., Charlbury, Oxford OX7 3PQ, England. TEL 01608-811446. FAX 01608-811380. Ed. Alastair McIver; Pub. David Wynne-Morgan. adv. contact: David Johnston. bk.rev.; illus. circ. 13,104. Indexed: Sportsearch (1976-). **Document type:** consumer publication.
Description: Features interviews, profiles, tournament reports and previews.

793.342 613.7 US
TENNISPRO. 1988. bi-m. free to qualified personnel. U S Professional Tennis Registry, Box 4739, Hilton Head Island, SC 29938. TEL 803-785-7244. FAX 803-686-2033. Ed. Jeff Dalpiaz. adv. contact: Julie Jilly. bk.rev. circ. 9,600. (back issues avail.) **Document type:** trade publication.
Description: Educational trade publication for tennis teachers worldwide. Includes sport science, programming, sports medicine, new drills and product reviews.

796.342 GW ISSN 0937-9681
TENNISSPORT; Tennis in Theorie und Praxis. 1990. bi-m. DM.54.80 (foreign DM.66). Sportverlag Schmidt und Dreisilker GmbH, Postfach 260, 71044 Sindelfingen, Germany. TEL 07031-862800. FAX 07031-862801. Ed.Bd. adv. contact: Monika Possehl. circ. 7,500. **Document type:** consumer publication.

796.332 US
TEXAS FOOTBALL MAGAZINE. 1960. a. $6.95. Host Communications, Inc., 904 N. Broadway, Lexington, KY 40505-8162. TEL 606-252-6681. (Subscr. to: Box 3071, Lexington, KY 40596) Ed. Dave Campbell. adv. circ. 199,562. (back issues avail.) **Document type:** consumer publication.

796.342 US
TEXAS TENNIS.* 1987. 8/yr. $12. Regional Sports Publications, Box 50405, Henderson, NV 89016-0405. TEL 404-448-6226. FAX 404-368-2444. adv. circ. 30,000.

796.3 UK ISSN 1358-7374
▼ **THIRD MAN.** 1995. m. Mediamark Publishing International Ltd., 35 Gresse St., Rathbone Pl., London W1P 1PN, England. TEL 0171-580-3105. Ed. Ian MacQuillin; Pub. Peter Moore. circ. 60,000. **Document type:** consumer publication.

796.342 SW ISSN 0281-5338
TIDSKRIFT I GYMNASTIK OCH IDROTT. 1874. 10/yr. SEK 300 to non-members; members SEK 200. Svenska Gymnastiklaerarsaellskapet, Fridhemsgatan 44, S-112 40 Stockholm, Sweden. TEL 46-8-652-63-27. (Subscr. to: Peter Bengtstroem, Klarinettvaegen 205, S-434 47 Kungsbacka, Sweden) Ed. Lena Eliasson. adv.: B&W page SEK 1900. bk.rev. circ. 3,500.
Description: Covers areas of interest to physical education teachers.

TIME OUT. see *BUSINESS AND ECONOMICS — Labor And Industrial Relations*

TIP; tyzdennik pre futbal a hokej. see *SPORTS AND GAMES*

796.342 GW ISSN 0938-1910
TISCHTENNIS LEHRE. 1986. 6/yr. DM.27.30. B U G Verlag, Steppenbergallee 41, 52074 Aachen, Germany. TEL 02421-15568. FAX 02421-15285. Ed. Bernd Ulrich Gross. circ. 2,000. (back issues avail.)

796.346 AU ISSN 0040-814X
TISCHTENNIS-SCHAU. 1965. 6/yr. S.75. Verein zur Foerderung des Tischtennissports in Oesterreich, Neulerchenfelderstr. 5-7, A-1160 Vienna, Austria. adv.; bk.rev. circ. 800.

796.352 UK ISSN 0955-4939
TODAY'S GOLFER. m. £34.50 (foreign £46.50) (effective 1995-1996). E M A P - Pursuit Publishing, Bretton Ct., Bretton, Peterborough, Cambs. PE3 8DZ, England. TEL 01733-264666. FAX 01733-26364. TELEX 32157. (Subscr. to: Tower Publishing Services Ltd., Tower House, Sovereign Park, Lathkill St., Market Harborough, Leics. LE16 9EF, England. TEL 01858-468811. FAX 01858-462164) adv. **Document type:** consumer publication.

796.357 US ISSN 1065-1950
TOMAHAWK (DURHAM). 1995. m. $24.95. Coman Publishing Company, Inc., 505 S. Duke St., Ste. 504, Durham, NC 27701. TEL 919-688-0218. FAX 919-682-1532. (Subscr. to: Box 2331, Durham, NC 27702) Ed. Todd McGee. adv.: B&W page $400, color page $600; 10 x 13. circ. 11,500. **Document type:** consumer publication.
Description: For Atlanta Braves fans.

796.332 UK
TOPICAL TIMES FOOTBALL BOOK. 1959. a. £2.05. D.C. Thomson & Co. Ltd., 185 Fleet St., London EC4A 2HS, England.

796.334 US
TOUCHLINE. 1971. s-a. free to members. Soccer Association for Youth USA, 4903 Vine St., Cincinnati, OH 45217. TEL 513-242-4263. FAX 513-242-1178. Ed. Roland Bedard. adv.; circ. 100,000 (controlled). (tabloid format; back issues avail.) **Document type:** newsletter.
Description: Contains news items of interest to coaches, referees, administrators, and players.

796.352 US
TOUR. 1978. a. (P G A Tour) Times Mirror Magazines, 2 Park Ave., New York, NY 10016. TEL 212-779-5200. FAX 212-481-8085. adv.: B&W page $45260, color page $79000; trim 8 x 10 3/4. circ. 500,000 (paid). **Document type:** consumer publication.

TRADING CARDS. see *HOBBIES*

796.333 SA
TRANSVAAL RUGBY. (Text in Afrikaans and English) 1972. 12/yr. $30. (Transvaal Rugby Football Union) Pieter Coetzee Promotions, P.O. Box 6842, Brackendowns 1454, South Africa. TEL 011-902-4656. Ed. P.H. Coetzee. adv.; bk.rev. circ. 80,000. **Document type:** consumer publication.

796.334 SZ
U E F A FLASH. (Editions in English, French and German) 1991. m. free. Union of European Football Associations - Union des Associations Europeennes de Football, Chemin de la Redoute 54, Case postale 303, CH-1260 Nyon, Switzerland. TEL 022-9944444. FAX 022-9944488. TELEX 419706-UEF-CH. **Document type:** newsletter.

796.323 US
U M I'S BIG EAST. a. U M I Publications, Inc., 1135 N. Tryon St., Box 30036, Charlotte, NC 28230. TEL 704-374-0420. FAX 704-374-0729. Pub. Ivan Mothershead. circ. 85,000.

796.323 US
U M I'S BIG 8. a. U M I Publications, Inc., 1135 N. Tryon St., Box 20026, Charlotte, NC 28230. TEL 704-374-0420. FAX 704-374-0729. Pub. Ivan Mothershead. circ. 45,000.

796.323 US
U M I'S BIG 10. a. U M I Publications, Inc., 1135 N. Tryon St., Charlotte, NC 28230. TEL 704-374-0420. FAX 704-274-0729. Pub. Ivan Mothershead. circ. 80,000.

796.334 IT
U R B S INFORMAZIONI. w. L.60000. Maurizio Longega, Ed. & Pub., Casella Postale 6291, 00195 Rome, Prati, Italy. TEL 39-330-734215. adv.; bk.rev. **Document type:** bulletin.

796.357 US ISSN 1057-9532
U S A TODAY BASEBALL WEEKLY. 1991. w. $39.95. U S A Today (Subsidiary of: Gannett Newspapers), 1000 Wilson Blvd., Arlington, VA 22229. TEL 800-USA-1415. Ed. Paul White; Pub. Keith Cutler. adv. contact: Jim Schiekofer. **Document type:** newspaper.
—UMI.

796.325 US
U S A VOLLEYBALL OFFICIATING GUIDEBOOK. a.? $6. U S A Volleyball, 3595 E. Fountain Blvd., Ste. I-2, Colorado Springs, CO 80910-1740. TEL 719-637-8300. FAX 719-597-6307. TELEX 187258.

796.325 US
U S A VOLLEYBALL. SPORTS QUOTES. irreg., 6th ed., 1993. $14.95. U S A Volleyball, 3595 E. Fountain Blvd., Ste. I-2, Colorado Springs, CO 80910-1740. TEL 719-637-8300. FAX 719-597-6307. TELEX 187258.
Description: Contains inspirational sports quotations.

796.325 US
U S A VOLLEYBALL. VOLLEYBALL CASE BOOK. Cover title: Volleyball Case Book. biennial. $14.95. U S A Volleyball, 3595 E. Fountain Blvd., Ste. I-2, Colorado Springs, CO 80910-1740. TEL 719-637-8300. FAX 719-597-6307. TELEX 187258.
Description: Contains official U.S. rules interpretations for junior olympic volleyball coaches.

796.323 US ISSN 0041-5472
U S B W A TIP-OFF. 1959. m. (Nov.-Apr.). membership. United States Basketball Writers Association, c/o Joe Mitch, Ed., 803 Wildview Lane, St. Louis, MO 63101. TEL 703-780-8577. circ. 1,000. (processed)

796.35 US
U S CROQUET GAZETTE. 2/yr. Farsight Communications, Inc., 7100-24 Fairway Dr., Palm Beach Gardens, FL 33418-3763. TEL 407-627-4077. FAX 407-624-3040. Ed. Jack R. Osborn. circ. 10,000.

SPORTS AND GAMES — BALL GAMES

796.352 US ISSN 0041-5502
GV975
U S G A GREEN SECTION RECORD. 1963. bi-m. $12. United States Golf Association, Golf House, Box 708, Far Hills, NJ 07931. TEL 908-234-2300. FAX 908-234-1513. Ed. James T. Snow. bk.rev.; illus.; index. circ. 6,000. **Indexed:** Sportsearch (1977-).
—UnCover.
Formerly: Turf Management Affairs Section of U S G A Journal and Turf Management.

796.352 US
U S OPEN MAGAZINE. a. Times Mirror Magazines, Inc., Sports Marketing Group, 2 Park Ave., No. 6, New York, NY 10016-5691. TEL 203-849-5040. Ed. George Pepper. adv. circ. 300,000.

796.352 US
U S SENIOR OPEN MAGAZINE. 1991. a. $5. (United States Golf Association) Times Mirror Magazines, Inc., Sports Marketing Group, 2 Park Ave., 5th Fl., New York, NY 10016. TEL 212-779-5000. Ed. George Pepper. adv. circ. 350,000.
Description: Covers the U S G A event, its history and past champions, and its present course and players.

796.357 US
U S Y S A NATIONAL DIRECTORY.* 1988. s-a. free. United States Youth Soccer Association, Inc., 899 Presidential Dr., Ste. 117, Richardson, TX 75081-2953. TEL 214-235-4499. FAX 214-235-4480. Ed. Ray Thompsett. circ. 700. **Document type:** directory.

796.334 US
U S Y S A NETWORK.* 1987. q. free to qualified personnel. United States Youth Soccer Association, Inc., 899 Presidential Dr., Ste. 117, Richardson, TX 75081-2953. TEL 303-987-3944. FAX 303-987-3998. Ed. Jon Destefano. adv.; bk.rev.; illus.; stat. circ. 150,000. (tabloid format) **Document type:** newsletter.
Description: National and regional news of and for young soccer players, their referees, coaches, and parents.

796 SZ ISSN 0501-1590
UNION OF EUROPEAN FOOTBALL ASSOCIATIONS. BULLETIN. q. includes its Press Releases. Chemin de la Redoute 54, Case postale 303, CH-1260 Nyon, Switzerland. TEL 022-9944444. FAX 022-9944488. TELEX 419796-UEF-CH. **Document type:** bulletin.
Description: Includes association news, reports and results of events, championships, tournaments, international news, coming events, meetings, and new books.

796 SZ ISSN 0570-2070
UNION OF EUROPEAN FOOTBALL ASSOCIATIONS. HANDBOOK OF U E F A. (Text in English, French and German) 1959. base vol. 100 SFr. for base vol. Chemin de la Redoute 54, Case postale 303, CH-1260 Nyon, Switzerland. TEL 022-9944444. FAX 022-9944488. TELEX 419706-UEF-CH. bk.rev. circ. 2,500. **Document type:** trade publication.

796.352 US
U.S. WOMEN'S OPEN MAGAZINE. a. (United States Golf Association) Times Mirror Magazines, Inc., Sports Marketing Group, 2 Park Ave., 5th Fl., New York, NY 10016. TEL 212-779-5000. Ed. George Peper. adv. circ. 200,000.
Description: Covers the history of the event and the site, profiles of past champions, and analysis of the golf course.

796.353 US ISSN 0083-3118
UNITED STATES POLO ASSOCIATION. YEARBOOK. 1890. a. $25. United States Polo Association, 4059 Iron Works Pike, Lexington, KY 40511. FAX 606-231-9738. adv. circ. 3,000.

796.343 US ISSN 0083-3398
UNITED STATES SQUASH RACQUETS ASSOCIATION. OFFICIAL YEAR BOOK. 1925. a. $6. United States Squash Racquets Association, Box 1216, Bala-Cynwyd, PA 19004. TEL 610-667-4006. FAX 610-667-6539. Ed. Craig W. Brand. adv.; index. circ. 10,000.

796.342 US ISSN 0196-5425
UNITED STATES TENNIS ASSOCIATION. YEARBOOK. 1937. a. $16. H.O. Zimman, Inc., 152 Lynnway Seaport Landing, Lynn, MA 01902-3419. Ed. John Donahue. adv. circ. 15,000.
Formerly: United States Lawn Tennis Association. Yearbook (ISSN 0083-1557)

796.323 AT
VICTORIAN NETBALLER. 1981. q. Aus.$25. Netball Victoria, P.O. Box 60, N. Melbourne, Vic. 3051, Australia. TEL 61-3-329-7766. FAX 61-3-329-8175. Ed. Leigh Mawby. adv. contact: Leigh Mawby. circ. 20,000. **Document type:** newsletter.
Description: Covers administration, events, coaching tips for all those interested in netball.

THE VINTAGE & CLASSIC BASEBALL COLLECTOR; the magazine for the serious collector of baseball items. see HOBBIES

796.334 NE ISSN 0042-7977
VOETBAL INTERNATIONAL. 1965. w. fl.137.10; newsstand price: fl.3.95. Weekbladpers B.V., Postbus 1050, 1000 BB Asterdam, Netherlands. TEL 31-20-5518711. FAX 31-20-6278537. (Editorial addr.: Postbus 817, 2900 AV Capelle aan den IJssel, Netherlands. TEL 31-10-4587799. FAX 31-10-4421950) Ed. C. van Cuilenborg; Pub. C. van Nijnatten. adv.; illus.; circ. 205,000 (paid). **Document type:** consumer publication.

796.334 NE ISSN 0166-929X
VOETBAL TOTAAL. 1972. m. fl.47.50. Koninklijke Nederlandsche Voetbalbond - Royal Dutch Football Federation, P.O. Box 515, 3700 AM Zeist, Netherlands. TEL 31-3439-9211. FAX 31-3439-1397. (U.S. subscr. addr.: IPC Business Press Inc., 205 E. 42nd St., New York, NY 10017) adv.; illus.; stat.; circ. 30,500 (controlled).
Formed by the 1978 merger of: Spreekbuis (ISSN 0922-6850); K N V Ber (ISSN 0922-7237); Which was formerly: Nederlands Voetbal (ISSN 0047-9284)
Description: Covers amateur soccer teams and matches.

796.3 US ISSN 0892-7421
VOICE OF THE HAWKEYES. 25/yr. College Sports Communications, 4099 McEwen Rd., Ste. 350, Dallas, TX 75244. TEL 214-851-1770. FAX 214-490-9333. adv.; bk.rev. page $750; trim 10 x 13. circ. 12,500. **Document type:** consumer publication.
Description: Covers University of Iowa sports.

796.325 NE ISSN 0167-0247
VOLLEYBAL. 1952. m. fl.38.50 (foreign fl.89.50). Nederlandse Volleybal Bond - Dutch Vollyeball Association, Postbus 70, 3440 AB Woerden, Netherlands. TEL 31-3480-11994. FAX 31-3480-20809. Eds. H. v.d. Ploeg, Chr. Mast. adv.; B&W page fl.1210, color page fl.2155; trim 215 x 285. bk.rev. circ. 10,500. **Document type:** consumer publication.
Formerly: Volley Kroniek (ISSN 0049-6731)
Description: Technical and general coverage of national and international volleyball affairs.

796.325 US ISSN 1058-4668
VOLLEYBALL. 1990. m. $19.95. A V C O M Publishing (Subsidiary of: Consolidated Press Holdings), 21700 Oxnard St., Ste. 1600, Woodland Hills, CA 91367. TEL 818-593-3900. FAX 818-593-2274. Ed. R. Hazeltine. adv.; circ. 52,552 (paid). **Document type:** consumer publication.
Description: Contains instruction from coaches, players and pros. Covers competition including high school, Olympic and pro beach tours and profiles top talent and equipment.

796.325 US ISSN 0274-6662
GV1015
VOLLEYBALL MAGAZINE. 1976. q. (American National Volleyball Association) Straight Down, Inc., 1318 Chorro St., San Luis Obispo, CA 93401-4006. Ed. David Kraft. adv.; bk.rev. circ. 40,000. **Indexed:** Sportsearch.
Incorporates (in Dec. 1994): Volleyball Monthly (ISSN 0889-1990)

796.325 US ISSN 0882-1372
GV1017.V6
VOLLEYBALL RULEBOOK. a. $4. National Federation of State High School Associations, 11724 N.W. Plaza Circle, Box 20626, Kansas City, MO 64195-0626. TEL 816-464-5400. FAX 816-464-5571.

796.325 US
VOLLEYBALL U S A. 1972. q. $16 (foreign $20) (effective Jan. 1993). U S A Volleyball, Inc., 3595 E. Fountain Blvd., Ste. I-2, Colorado Springs, CO 80910-1740. TEL 719-637-8300. FAX 719-597-6307. Ed. Richard Wanninger. adv. contact: David Zimman. bk.rev. circ. 85,000. **Document type:** trade publication.
Former titles: Inside U S A Volleyball (ISSN 1059-8227); Volleyball U S A.
Description: Reviews activities of the association, U.S. Olympic teams and volleyball in general.

794.6 US ISSN 1078-2958
GV901
W B. 1936. 4/yr. $6 membership (typically set in Aug.). Women's International Bowling Congress, Inc., 5301 S. 76th St., Greendale, WI 53129. TEL 414-421-9000. FAX 414-421-3013. Ed. Jeffrey Nowak. adv.; illus. circ. 120,000. **Indexed:** Sports Per.Ind., Sportsearch (1977-). **Document type:** consumer publication.
Formerly (until 1994): Woman Bowler (ISSN 0043-7255)

796.334 US
WASHINGTON STATE YOUTH SOCCER NEWS. 1985. m. $12. Varsity Publications, 13540 Lake City Way, Seattle, WA 98125-3665. TEL 206-367-2420. FAX 206-367-2636. adv.: B&W page $895, color page $1795; trim 10 x 15 1/2. circ. 12,000.
Description: Contains association news, events, and coaching hints for administrators, coaches, and players.

796.342 GW
WESTFALEN TENNIS.* 1982. m. DM.50. Vereinigte Zeitungsverlage, Sudbrackstr. 14, 33611 Bielefeld, Germany. circ. 10,000.

796.3 UK ISSN 0959-0048
WHEN SATURDAY COMES. 1986. m. £15. When Saturday Comes Ltd., 2 Pear Tree Court, 4th Fl., London EC1R 0DS, England. TEL 0171-251-8595. FAX 0171-490-1598. (Distr. by: Comag, Tavistock Rd., W. Drayton, Middlesex UB7 7QE, England. TEL 0895-444055) Ed. Andy Lyons. adv.: B&W page £900, color page £1500; trim 297 x 210; adv. contact: Jonathan Westbrook. bk.rev. circ. 36,063. (back issues avail.) **Document type:** consumer publication.
Description: Presents football issues from both serious and humorous perspectives.

796.357 US
WHO RUNS PROFESSIONAL SPORTS - MAJOR LEAGUE BASEBALL. 1992. a. $9.70. Forster-Long, Inc., 3280 Ramos Circle, Sacramento, CA 95827. TEL 916-362-3276. FAX 916-362-5643. Ed. Jeffrey E. Long. **Document type:** directory, trade publication.
Description: Contains capsule biographies of Major League Baseball's decision makers: owners, presidents, vice presidents, general managers, and field managers.

796.323 US
WHO RUNS PROFESSIONAL SPORTS - THE N B A. 1992. a. $9.70. Forster-Long, Inc., 3280 Ramos Circle, Sacramento, CA 95827. TEL 916-362-3276. FAX 916-362-5643. Ed. Jeffrey E. Long. **Document type:** directory, trade publication.
Description: Contains capsule biographies of pro-basketball's decision makers: owners, presidents, vice presidents, general managers, and coaches.

796.332 US
WHO RUNS PROFESSIONAL SPORTS - THE N F L. 1992. a. $9.70. Forster-Long, Inc., 3280 Ramos Circle, Sacramento, CA 95827. TEL 916-362-3276. FAX 916-362-5643. Ed. Jeffrey E. Long. **Document type:** directory, trade publication.
Description: Contains capsule biographies of pro-football's decision makers: owners, presidents, vice presidents, general managers and coaches.

794.6 US ISSN 1066-596X
WINDY CITY BOWLING NEWS.* 1990. s-m. $12. N7788 Carver School Rd., East Troy, WI 53120-2541. TEL 414-642-3989. FAX 414-642-5138. Ed. Lisa Vint. adv.: B&W page $350; trim 11 3/8 x 14. circ. 20,000.

796.332 US
WINNING POINTS.* 1972. 19/yr. $30. Starpoint Publishing Corporation, 438 W. 37th St., New York, NY 10018. TEL 212-279-4619. adv.; charts; stat. circ. 20,000.

796.352 US ISSN 1042-6620
WISCONSIN GOLF. 1989. 7/yr. $12.95. Killarney Press, 2317 International Lane, Ste. 117, Madison, WI 53704. TEL 608-224-2600. FAX 608-224-2603. adv. circ. 10,000.
Description: Features local golf personalities, tournaments, and courses. Covers travel, environmental issues, equipment and apparel, and instruction.

796.352 US
WISCONSIN GOLF DIRECTORY. a. Killarney Press, 2317 International Lane, Ste. 117, Madison, WI 53704. TEL 608-244-2600. FAX 608-244-2603. adv. circ. 150,000. **Document type**: directory.
Description: Lists public access golf courses in Wisconsin.

796.334 US
WISCONSIN SOCCER POST. 1992. 6/yr. $9.95. (Wisconsin Youth Soccer Association) The Publishing Group, Inc., 1200 N. 7th St., Minneapolis, MN 55411-4000. TEL 612-522-1200. FAX 612-522-1182. Ed. Jess Myers.
Description: Covers youth soccer in Wisconsin, including tournament rules and regulations, soccer camps and profiles of outstanding players.

796.35 UK ISSN 0263-9041
WISDEN CRICKET MONTHLY. 1979. m. £27.50. Wisden Cricket Magazines Ltd., 25 Down Rd., Merrow, Guildford, Surrey GU1 2PY, England. FAX 01483-33153. (Subscr. to: 120-126 Lavender Ave., Mitcham, Surrey CR4 3HP, England) Ed. David Frith. adv.; bk.rev.; illus.; stat. circ. 38,000. **Document type**: newsletter.
Description: Features, reviews, reports, analysis, comment, scores and statistics on first class cricket past and present.

796.352 052 UK ISSN 0963-9276
WOMEN & GOLF. 1991. m. £27. Women & Golf Ltd., The Publishing House, 52 Mere Green Rd., Sutton Coldfield, W. Midlands B75 5BT, England. TEL 021-323-3073. FAX 021-323-2911. Ed. Jane Carter. adv.: B&W page £1000, color page £1250; trim 297 x 210; adv. contact: Jo Holmes. bk.rev.; circ. 20,000. (paid). (back issues avail.) **Document type**: consumer publication.
Description: Contains news and information aimed at the growing number of women golfers.

796.323 US
(YEAR) WOMEN'S BASKETBALL GUIDE. a. $8. Big Ten Conference, 1500 Higgins Rd., Park Ridge, IL 60068-5742. TEL 708-696-1010. FAX 708-696-1110.

796.357 US ISSN 0899-5508
WOMEN'S FASTPITCH WORLD. 1988. m. $39.99. Windmill Publishers, Box 326, St. Charles, IL 60174. TEL 708-377-7917. FAX 708-377-3681. circ. 10,000 (paid).
Description: Emphasizes coaching material about women's and girls' fast-pitch softball.

796.325 659.1 US
(YEAR) WOMEN'S VOLLEYBALL MEDIA GUIDE. a. $8. Big Ten Conference, 1500 Higgins Rd., Park Ridge, IL 60068-5742. TEL 708-696-1010. FAX 708-696-1110.

796.352 US
WORLD AMATEUR GOLF COUNCIL. RECORD BOOK. 1958. biennial. membership. World Amateur Golf Council, Golf House, Box 708, Far Hills, NJ 07931-0708. TEL 908-234-2300. FAX 908-234-9687. circ. 1,000.
Description: Covers world amateur team championships in golf.

796.31 SZ ISSN 1040-5216
WORLD BASEBALL.* (Text in English, Spanish) 1983. 3/yr. $10. International Baseball Association, Ave. de Mon-Repos 24, Case Postale 131, 1000 Lausanne 5, Switzerland. Ed. E. David Osinski. adv.; charts; stat. circ. 6,500. (back issues avail.) **Document type**: consumer publication.
Description: News on baseball around the world. Includes coverage of world tournaments and developments in the association's 81 member countries.

794.6 UK ISSN 0966-9884
WORLD BOWLS. 1954. m. £17. World Bowls Magazine Ltd., P.O. Box 247, Canterbury, Kent CT2 7XA, England. TEL 0227-781573. FAX 0227-764744. Ed. Patrick Sullivan. adv. contact: Nick Larner. bk.rev.; charts; illus.; tr.lit. circ. 10,000. (also avail. in microform from UMI) **Indexed**: Sportsearch (1973-). **Document type**: consumer publication.
Formerly: World Bowls Magazine (ISSN 0043-8278); Incorporates: Bowling Times; British Bowls.

796.342 UK ISSN 0305-6325
WORLD OF TENNIS. 1969. a. £9.99. (International Tennis Federation) Harper Collins Publishers, 77-85 Fulham Palace Rd., London W6 8JB, England. FAX 081-307-4558. Ed. John Barrett. adv.; index. circ. 5,000.

796.334 UK ISSN 0043-9037
GV942
WORLD SOCCER. 1960. m. $51. I P C Magazines, Specialist Magazine Group (Subsidiary of: Reed Elsevier group), King's Reach Tower, Stamford St., London SE1 9LS, England. TEL 071-261-6287. FAX 0444-440619. TELEX 892084 REEDBP G. (Dist. by: Quadrant Subscription Services, Oakfield House, Perrymount Rd., Haywards Heath, W. Sussex RH16 3DH, England. TEL 0444-440421) Ed. Philip Rising. adv.; illus. circ. 25,000. **Indexed**: Sportsearch (1973-). **Document type**: consumer publication. —SWETS.
Incorporates: Soccer Star (ISSN 0037-7546)

794.6 028.5 US ISSN 1072-463X
Y A B A FRAMEWORK. 1964. 6/yr. $10. Young American Bowling Alliance, 5301 S. 76th St., Greendale, WI 53129. TEL 414-421-4700. FAX 414-421-1301. Ed. Jennifer Kress. adv.; circ. 25,000 (controlled). (tabloid format) **Indexed**: Sportsearch. **Document type**: newsletter.
Former titles (until 1990): Y A B A World; Junior Bowler.
Description: Provides information and recognition for sanctioned Y.A.B.A. coaches, association secretaries, bowling centers, and members.

796.357 JA
YAKYO-TO/BASEBALL FANS.* (Text in Japanese) 1977. m. 6600 Yen. Nihon Sports Publishing Co. Ltd., 2-6, 2-chome, Hakusan, Bunkyo-ku, Tokyo, Japan. Ed. Yukio Koyanagi.

796.357 US ISSN 0744-0006
YANKEES MAGAZINE. 1980. m. $18; newsstand price: $3. New York Yankees, Yankee Stadium, 161st St. & River Ave., Bronx, NY 10451. TEL 718-579-4495. FAX 718-538-5769. Ed. Gregg Mazzola; Pub. Tom Bannon. adv. contact: David Mosca. illus.; circ. 31,000 (paid). **Document type**: consumer publication.
Description: Official publication of the New York Yankees baseball team. Covers baseball past and present.

796.3 US
YEARBOOK OF THE N C A A BASKETBALL TOURNAMENT.* (National Collegiate Athletic Association); the college basketball fan's complete independent guide to March madness. a. $9.99 (Canada $12.99). N C A A, 6201 College Blvd., Overland Park, KS 66211-2422.

796.352 338 US
▼**YELLOW PAGES OF GOLF**; for North America. 1994. a. $14.95. Activity Directories International, Inc., 8122 South Park Ln., Ste. 200, Littleton, CO 80120. TEL 303-730-3030. FAX 303-730-3092. Ed. Jerry Baines. adv. contact: Charlie Messina. **Document type**: trade publication.
Description: Lists golf related businesses including courses, retailers, and manufacturers.

796.334 US
YOUTH SOCCER LETTER; a monthly newsletter for adults working with youth soccer. (Issued with: Soccer America) 1981. m. $47.97 (effective 1995). Soccer America, 301 Post Rd., Westport, CT 06880. TEL 203-227-1755. FAX 203-226-6087. Ed. Dan Woog; Pub. Clay Berling. circ. 35,000. (also avail. in microfiche; back issues avail.) **Document type**: newsletter.

796.334 US
YOUTH SOCCER NEWS. 1985. m. $9. Varsity Publications, 13540 Lake City Way, N.E., Ste. 3, Seattle, WA 98125-3665. TEL 203-367-2420. FAX 206-367-2636. adv. circ. 28,600.
Description: Covers tournaments and leagues, youth soccer throughout southern California, Washington, Nevada, and Arizona. Includes coaching information and player profiles.

796.325 CC
ZHONGGUO PAIQIU/CHINA'S VOLLEYBALL. (Text in Chinese) q. $13.80. Xin Tiyu Zazhishe, 8 Tiyuguan Lu, Beijing 100061, People's Republic of China. TEL 751402. (Dist. in US by: China Books & Periodicals, Inc., 2929 24th St., San Francisco, CA 94110. TEL 415-282-2994) Ed. Yuan Weimin.

796.33 CC ISSN 1000-3517
ZUQIU SHIJIE/FOOTBALL WORLD. (Text in Chinese) 1981. bi-w. $35. (Zhongguo Zuqiu Xiehui - China Football Association) Renmin Tiyu Chubanshe - People's Sports Publishing House, 8 Tiyuguan Lu, Chongwen Qu, Beijing 100061, People's Republic of China. TEL 5112466. FAX 7016129. (Dist. in U.S. by: China Books & Periodicals, Inc., 2929 24th St., San Francisco, CA 94110. TEL 415-282-2994) Ed. Lu Guang.

796 CN
20 - 20. (Text in English, French) 1987. 4/yr. Can.$20 (typically set in Sep.). Canadian Table Tennis Association, 1600 James Naismith Dr., Gloucester, ON K1B 5N4, Canada. TEL 613-748-5675. FAX 613-748-5705. Ed. Adham Sharara. adv.; illus.; circ. 3,000 (controlled). (also avail. in diskette format; back issues avail.) **Document type**: newsletter, consumer publication.
Description: Contains articles on and results of Canadians involved in table tennis from local to international levels.

796.334 US
90 MINUTES. 1981. m. $25. National Soccer Hall of Fame, 11 Ford Ave., Oneonta, NY 13820. TEL 607-432-3351. FAX 607-432-8429. Ed. Brett Buzzy. bk.rev. circ. 4,000. **Document type**: newsletter.
Formerly: National Soccer Hall of Fame News.

SPORTS AND GAMES — Bicycles And Motorcycles

796.7 UK
A C U NEWSLINE. 1988. q. £8. Auto Cycle Union, ACU House, Wood St., Rugby, Warks. CV21 2YX, England. TEL 0788-540519. FAX 0788-573585. adv.; bk.rev. circ. 30,000. **Document type**: consumer publication.
Description: Contains information about all aspects of British motorcycle sports.

796.75 US
A M A SUPERCROSS SOUVENIR YEARBOOK. 1993. a. $5. (American Motorcyclist Association) C N Publishing Group, 2201 Cherry Ave., Long Beach, CA 90806. TEL 310-427-7433. FAX 310-427-6685. Ed. Jack Magnus. adv.: B&W page $3000, color page $4300; trim 8 1/8 x 10 3/4. circ. 100,000.

796.6 910.09 US
ADVENTURE CYCLIST. 1975. 9/yr. $25 includes membership. Adventure Cycling Association, Box 8308, Missoula, MT 59807-8308. TEL 406-721-1776. Ed. Daniel D'Ambrosio. adv.; bk.rev. circ. 40,000. **Indexed**: Sportsearch.
Formerly: BikeReport.
Description: Includes technical information, product news, articles concerning nutrition and training, and bicycling travel.

SPORTS AND GAMES — BICYCLES AND MOTORCYCLES

796.75   SW   ISSN 0345-0813
ALLT OM M C (MotorCyclar) 1965. 6/yr. SEK 175 (foreign SEK 231) (effective 1995); newsstand price: SEK 36. Albinsson & Sjoeberg Foerlags AB, P.O. Box 529, S-371 23 Karlskrona, Sweden. TEL 46-455-3353-30. FAX 46-455-311715. Ed. Peter Toernqvist. adv.; bk.rev.; circ. 35,900 (controlled). (back issues avail.) **Document type:** consumer publication.
     Formerly (until 1973): Racingsport.

388.347 796.7   IT
ALMANACCO LA MOTO. 1976. a. L.10000. Edigamma s.r.l., Piazza dei Sanniti 9, 00185 Rome, Italy. TEL 06-4928412. FAX 06-4940719. Ed. Renato Circi. adv.: B&W page L.7800000. circ. 90,000.

388.47   US
AMERICAN ASSOCIATION OF BICYCLE IMPORTERS. NEWSLETTER. q. American Association of Bicycle Importers, c/o Philip Kamler, 234 Schuyler Ave., Kearney, NJ 07032. TEL 201-991-8200. **Document type:** newsletter.

629.227   US   ISSN 0002-7677
AMERICAN BICYCLIST & MOTORCYCLIST.* 1879. m. $34 to qualified personnel; others $75 (effective Nov. 1990). Cycling Press, Inc., 400 Skokie Blvd., Northbrook, IL 60062-2816. TEL 212-206-7230. FAX 212-633-0079. TELEX 220378 ABM. Ed. Chris Peterson. adv.; bk.rev.; illus.; tr.lit. circ. 11,500. **Indexed:** Sportsearch (1976-). **Document type:** trade publication.
—UnCover.
     Description: Trade publication for the bicycle industry: dealers, wholesale distributors, importers, and manufacturers.

796.7   US
AMERICAN BIG TWIN DEALER. 1989. bi-m. $10 (free to qualified personnel) Advanstar Communications, Inc. (Santa Ana), 201 Sandpointe Ave., Ste. 600, Santa Ana, CA 92707-5761. TEL 714-513-8400. FAX 714-513-8414. Ed. Robin Hartfiel. adv.; circ. 5,000 (controlled). **Document type:** directory, trade publication.

796.7   US   ISSN 1059-7891
AMERICAN IRON MAGAZINE; for people who love Harley-Davidsons. 1989. m. $25. T A M Communications, Inc., 6 Prowitt St., Norwalk, CT 06855. TEL 203-855-0008. FAX 203-852-9980. (Subscr. to Box 506, Mt. Morris, IL 61054. TEL 815-734-1101) Ed. Jonathan Gourlay. adv.: B&W page $3413, color page $5250; bleed 8 3/8 x 11 1/8; adv. contact: Bob Petit. circ. 85,000 (paid). **Document type:** consumer publication.
     Description: Showcases restored and customized Harleys, tests new models and aftermarket products, covers club news throughout the U.S., technical and repair topics, as well as travel and touring items, and other issues of interest to Harley-Davidson enthusiasts.

796.7   US   ISSN 0277-9358
AMERICAN MOTORCYCLIST. 1947. m. $12.50 (foreign $15). American Motorcyclist Association, 33 Collegeview, Westerville, OH 43081-1463. TEL 614-891-2425. FAX 614-891-5012. Ed. Greg Harrison. adv.: B&W page $4950. bk.rev.; illus. circ. 177,649. **Document type:** consumer publication.
     Former titles (until Sep. 1977): A M A News (ISSN 0003-0074); American Motorcycling.
     Description: Focuses on the races and roadriding events sanctioned by the AMA each year, as well as motorcycle-related legislation at the various levels of government.

796.75   US
AMERICAN RACING MOTORCYCLES. 12/yr. Can.$20. 141 N. Meridian Rd., Youngstown, OH 44509.

796.7   US
AMERICAN RIDER. 1993. bi-m. $14.95. T L Enterprises, Inc., 3601 Calle Tecate, Camarillo, CA 93012. TEL 805-389-0300. Ed. Buzz Buzzelli; Pub. Joe McNeill. adv. contact: John Schmidt. **Document type:** consumer publication.
     Description: Publishes articles, road-tests, interviews, and features relating to Harley-Davidson motorcycles.

796.6   FR
ANNEE DU CYCLISME. 1974. a. price varies. Editions Calmann-Levy, 3 rue Auber, 75009 Paris, France. illus.

796.6   SP
ANUARIO CICLISTA. a. 750 ptas. Luike - Motorpress, C. Ancora 40, 28045 Madrid, Spain. TEL 34-1-3470100. FAX 34-1-3470204. Ed. Francisco Chico. adv.: B&W page 275000 ptas., color page 350000 ptas.; adv. contact: Agustin Valero. **Document type:** consumer publication.

796.7 659.1   AT   ISSN 0155-378X
AUSTRALASIAN DIRT BIKE. 1976. m. Aus.$50. A D B Holdings Pty. Ltd., P.O. Box 515, Narrabeed, N.S.W. 2101, Australia. TEL 02-979-7502. FAX 02-979-7576. Ed. Tony Kirby. adv. contact: Tom Foster. circ. 15,000 (paid). **Indexed:** Pinpointer. **Document type:** consumer publication.

796.6   AT   ISSN 1034-3016
AUSTRALIAN CYCLIST. 1976. bi-m. Aus.$22 in Australia; New Zealand $33; elsewhere $36 (effective 1996). Bicycle Federation of Australia, c/o P.O. Box 869, Artarmon, N.S.W. 2064, Australia. TEL 61-2-419-5419. FAX 61-2-415-1913. Ed. Neil Irvine. adv. contact: David Turner. bk.rev. circ. 16,781. (back issues avail.) **Document type:** consumer publication.
     Formerly: Push On (ISSN 0157-0994)
     Description: Covers all aspects of cycling, emphasising recreation and transportation.

796.75   AT   ISSN 0158-4138
AUSTRALIAN MOTOR RACING YEAR. 1971. a. Aus.$45. Chevron Publishing Group Pty. Ltd., P.O. Box 206, Hornsby, N.S.W. 2077, Australia. FAX 02-476-5739. Ed. Thomas B. Floyd. adv. contact: Ray Berghouse. circ. 15,000. (back issues avail.) **Document type:** consumer publication.
     Description: Reviews Australian and major overseas motor sport championships.

796   AT
AUSTRALIAN RACING DRIVERS CLUB NEWSLETTER. 1971. 6/yr. Aus.$7. Australian Racing Drivers Club, Amaroo Park Raceway, Annangrove, N.S.W. 2156, Australia. FAX 61-2-679-1184. Ed. H. Ivan Stibbard. adv.; bk.rev. circ. 2,000. **Document type:** newsletter.
     Formerly: Australian Racing Drivers Club Journal (ISSN 0311-0346)

796.7   AT
AUSTRALIAN TRAIL & TRACK MONTHLY. 1973. m. Aus.$22. L.W. & T.S. Nominees, Tootal Park, Tootal Rd., Dingley, Vic. 3172, Australia. Ed. Les Swallow. adv.; bk.rev. circ. 24,000.
     Formerly: Australian Trail and Track.

AUTO & MOTORRAD OLDTIMER. see TRANSPORTATION — Automobiles

AUTORAMA; panoramica mensile delle attivita motoristiche. see TRANSPORTATION — Automobiles

AUTOREVUU. see TRANSPORTATION — Automobiles

796.7   US   ISSN 0195-0320
B M X PLUS. (Bicycle Motocross) m. $18.98. Hi-Torque Publications, Inc., Box 957, Valencia, CA 91380-9057. TEL 818-365-6831.

796   UK
B T I. (Bicycle Trade and Industry) 1980. 18/yr. £30. 97 Front St., Wickham, Newcastle-upon-Tyne NE16 4JL, England. TEL 091-488-1947. FAX 091-488-6718. Ed. Peter Lumly. bk.rev. circ. 3,500 (controlled).
     Description: Contains news and current affairs of interest to anyone dealing with the British bicycle trade.

BACK STREET HEROES. see TRANSPORTATION — Automobiles

796.75   GW   ISSN 0724-7192
BAHNSPORT AKTUELL; Sandtrack - Speedway - Long Track - Ice Speedway. 1971. m. DM.80. Verlag Bahnsport Aktuell oHG, Industriestr. 8, 63517 Rodenbach, Germany. TEL 06184-51051. FAX 06184-51004. Ed. Christian Kalabis. adv.; illus.; stat. circ. 15,000. (back issues avail.) **Document type:** consumer publication.
     Supersedes in part (in 1983): Bahnsport Moto Cross und Enduro Aktuell (ISSN 0723-2535); Which was formerly (until 1982): Bahnsport Aktuell (ISSN 0171-8940)
     Description: International sports magazine for motorcycle racing. Features racing on sand courses, grass courses, on ice and speedways. Includes reports and results of events and championships, news, letters from readers, and future events.

BEST MOTORING. see HOBBIES

796.6   IT
BICI DA MONTAGNA. 1990. m. L.86000 (foreign L.180000). La Cuba s.r.l., Via della Maratona 66, 00194 Rome, Italy. TEL 39-6-36308996. FAX 39-6-36309950. Ed. Calogero Cascio. adv.: B&W page L.3600000, color page L.5800000. **Document type:** consumer publication.

796.6   IT
BICICLETTA. 1984. m. L.75000 (foreign L.160000). La Cuba s.r.l., Via Orti della Farnesina 137, 00194 Rome, Italy. TEL 39-6-36309977. FAX 39-6-36309950. Ed. Calogero Cascio. adv.: B&W page L.3400000, color page L.5600000. adv. contact: Giuliana Antuono. **Document type:** consumer publication.

796.6   SP
BICISPORT. 1989. m. 4320 ptas. (Europe 7770 ptas.; elsewhere 10570 ptas.); newsstand price: 450 ptas. Luike - Motorpress, C. Ancora 40, 28045 Madrid, Spain. TEL 34-1-3470100. FAX 34-1-3470204. Ed. Francisco Chico Perez; Pub. Jose Luis Samaranch. adv.: B&W page 275000 ptas., color page 350000 ptas.; adv. contact: Antonino Berges. circ. 21,000. **Document type:** consumer publication.

796.6   IT
BICISPORT. 1976. m. L.70000 (foreign L.85000). Compagnia Editoriale s.r.l., Via Capogrossi 50, 00155 Rome, Italy. TEL 39-6-2285728. FAX 39-6-2285915. Ed. Sergio Neri. adv.: B&W page L.3300000, color page L.4302000. circ. 62,000. **Document type:** consumer publication.

796.6   SP
▼**BICITECH.** 1995. s-a. newsstand price: 750 ptas. Luike - Motorpress, C. Ancora 40, 28045 Madrid, Spain. TEL 34-1-3470100. FAX 34-1-3470204. Ed. Francisco Chico Perez. adv.: B&W page 275000 ptas., color page 350000 ptas.; adv. contact: Agustin Valero. **Document type:** consumer publication.

796.6   US   ISSN 0745-8126
BICYCLE BUSINESS JOURNAL. 1947. m. $14. Quinn Publications, Inc. (Ft. Worth), 1904 Wenneca, Fort Worth, TX 76102. FAX 817-332-1619. adv.; charts; illus.; stat.; tr.lit.; index. circ. 10,000. **Indexed:** Sportsearch (1983-). **Document type:** trade publication.
—UnCover.
     Formerly: Bicycle Journal (ISSN 0006-2065)

380.1   US   ISSN 0361-381X
HD9999.B43
BICYCLE DEALER SHOWCASE. Short title: B D S. 1971. m. $35. Miramar Publishing Co., Box 3640, Culver City, CA 90231-3640. TEL 310-337-9717. Ed. Ron Piechota. adv.; bk.rev.; illus. circ. 10,382. **Indexed:** Sportsearch (1983-).
     Description: For bicycle and fitness equipment dealers with articles on selling and merchandizing.

796.6   US   ISSN 0361-381X
BICYCLE DEALER SHOWCASE BUYERS GUIDE. 1971. a. $35. Miramar Publishing Co., Box 3640, Culver City, CA 90231-3640. TEL 310-337-9717. (Subscr. to: 1 E. First St., Duluth, MN 55802) Ed. Ron Piechota. adv. circ. 10,382.
     Description: Annual buyers' guide for bicycle and fitness equipment dealers.

BICYCLE FORUM. see TRANSPORTATION

SPORTS AND GAMES — BICYCLES AND MOTORCYCLES

796.6 US ISSN 0889-289X
GV1040
BICYCLE GUIDE. 1984. m. $19.90 (Canada $24.90; elsewhere $39.90) (effective 1993); newsstand price: $2.95. Petersen Publishing Co., 6420 Wilshire Blvd., Los Angeles, CA 90048. TEL 213-782-2000. FAX 213-782-2866. Ed. Charlie Morey. adv.; bk.rev.; circ. 165,000 (paid). **Indexed:** Sportsearch (1987-). **Document type:** consumer publication.
Incorporates (in 1987): Bicycle Rider.

796.6 CN
BICYCLE HANDBOOK. 1977. a. Can.$3. Cycling British Columbia, 332-1367 West Broadway, Vancouver, BC V6H 4A9, Canada. Ed. Danelle Laidlaw. adv. circ. 6,000.

796.6 US ISSN 0742-8308
BICYCLE PAPER;* the voice of Northwest cycling. 1972. m. (Mar.-Sep.); plus winter issue. $8. Northwest Classics, 1535 Eleventh Ave., Ste. 302, Seattle, WA 98122-3933. Ed. Dave Shaw. adv.; bk.rev.; illus. circ. 7,500. (tabloid format) **Document type:** consumer publication.
Formerly: Great Bicycle Conspiracy.
Description: Touring, racing, personality features. Includes calendar of events in the Northwest for bicycle enthusiasts.

796.6 658 US ISSN 1069-8493
BICYCLE RETAILER AND INDUSTRY NEWS. 1992. 18/yr. $26 (Canada and Mexico $42; Europe and Far East $89). JayWalker Publication, 1547 S. St Francis Dr., Santa Fe, NM 87505. TEL 505-988-5099. FAX 505-988-7224. Ed. Marc Sani; Pub. Bill Tanler. adv.; B&W page $2805, color page $3540; adv. contact: Terry Moyes. bk.rev.; circ. 14,000 (controlled). (tabloid format) **Document type:** trade publication.
Description: Keeps retailers current on industry trends, new technology and marketing strategies.

796.6 US ISSN 0747-0371
GV1045
BICYCLE U S A. (Includes special ed.: Bicycle U S A Almanac) 1965. 6/yr. $30 to individuals; libraries $20. League of American Bicyclists, 190 W. Ostend St., Ste. 120, Baltimore, MD 21230-3755. TEL 410-539-3399. FAX 410-539-3496. E-mail: bikeleague@aol.com. Ed. Donald W. Tighe. adv. contact: Curt Dewees. bk.rev. circ. 22,000. **Indexed:** Sportsearch (1984-). **Document type:** consumer publication.
Former titles (until 1984): American Wheelmen (ISSN 0199-2139); (until 1979): League of American Wheelmen Bulletin (ISSN 0192-6063)

796.6 US ISSN 0006-2073
GV1040
BICYCLING. 1962. 10/yr. $16.97. Rodale Press, Inc., 33 E. Minor St., Emmaus, PA 18098. TEL 610-967-8663. FAX 610-967-8960. TELEX 847338. Ed. Bill Strickland. adv.; bk.rev.; illus.; index. circ. 330,000. (also avail. in microform from UMI; reprint service avail. from UMI) **Indexed:** Acad.Ind.; Access (1976-1988), Consum.Ind., Hlth.Ind., Ind.How To Do It (1990-), Mag.Ind., Phys.Ed.Ind., PMR, R.G. (1988-), Sports Per.Ind., Sportsearch (1974-).
•Also available online. Vendor(s): University Microfilms International.
—Faxon; UMI; UnCover. **CCC**.
Formerly: American Cycling Magazine; Which incorporates (in 1981): American Cyclist.
Description: Features fitness, training, nutrition, touring, racing, equipment, clothing, bike maintenance and new-product review.

796.6 UK ISSN 0140-4547
BIKE. 1971. m. £28.20 (foreign £41.60) (effective 1995-1996). E M A P - National Publications, Bushfield House, Orton Centre, Peterborough, Cambs. PE2 0EW, England. TEL 01733-237111. FAX 01733-239127. (Subscr. to: Tower Publishing Services Ltd., Tower House, Sovereign Park, Lathkill St., Market Harborough, Leics. LE16 9EF, England. TEL 01858-468811. FAX 01858-432164) Ed. Martyn Moore. adv.; bk.rev.; circ. 67,000 (paid). **Document type:** consumer publication.
—**CCC**.

796.6 GW ISSN 0936-7624
BIKE. 1989. 11/yr. DM.75 (foreign DM.98). Verlag Delius, Klasing und Co., Postfach 101671, 33516 Bielefeld, Germany. TEL 0521-559283. FAX 0521-559113. Ed. Ulrich Stanciu. adv. contact: Jutta Heidemann. circ. 128,393. **Document type:** consumer publication.

796.6 SP ISSN 1131-9585
BIKE; la revista de la bici de montana. 1992. m. 4560 ptas. (Europe 10060 ptas.; elsewhere 14760 ptas.); newsstand price: 475 ptas. Luike - Motorpress, C. Ancora 40, 28045 Madrid, Spain. TEL 34-1-3470100. FAX 34-1-3470204. Ed. Francisco Chico Perez; Pub. Jose Luis Samaranch. adv.; B&W page 275000 ptas., color page 350000 ptas.; adv. contact: Antonino Berges. **Document type:** consumer publication.

796.6 US ISSN 1072-4869
GV1040
▼**BIKE MAGAZINE**. 1994. 9/yr. $15.95; newsstand price: $3.95. Surfer Publications, Inc., 33046 Calle Aviador, San Juan Capistrano, CA 92675. TEL 714-496-5922. FAX 714-496-7849. (Subscr. to: Box 59269, Boulder, CO 80321-9269. TEL 800-765-5501) Ed. Steve Casimiro. adv. contact: Michael Foley. circ. 71,549 (paid). (back issues avail.) **Document type:** consumer publication.
Description: Covers all aspects of mountain biking.

796.6 SA ISSN 0378-9128
BIKE S.A.. 1975. m. R.34 (foreign R.49). Bike Promotions (Pty) Ltd., P.O. Box 894, Johannesburg 2000, South Africa. TEL 27-11-782-5521. FAX 27-11-888-3431. Ed. Simon Fourie. adv. contact: Simon Fourie. bk.rev.; illus. circ. 24,000. **Document type:** consumer publication.
Description: Information on motor bikes, bike gear and maintenance, courses and competitions.

388.347 US ISSN 1058-7926
GV1059.5
BIKER; lifestyle magazine of events, news and bikes. 9/yr. $29.95 (foreign $41.95) (effective 1995 & 1996); newsstand price: $3.99. Paisano Publications, Inc., Box 1050, Agoura Hills, CA 91376-1050. TEL 818-889-8740. FAX 818-889-4726. circ. 61,769 (paid). **Document type:** consumer publication.
Former titles: Easyriders Presents Biker (ISSN 1046-1604); Biker Lifestyle (ISSN 0745-3604)

796.7 GW
BIKERS LIVE. 1992. bi-m. DM.43; newsstand price: DM.8.50. Huber Verlag GmbH, Ottenhoeferstr. 8, 68239 Mannheim, Germany. TEL 0621-483610. FAX 0621-4836195. Ed. Stephan Schneider; Pub. Guenther Brecht. adv.; B&W page DM.2415, color page DM.3565; trim 256 x 184; adv. contact: Heiner Roth. circ. 23,814. **Document type:** consumer publication.

796.7 GW
BIKERS NEWS. m. Huber Verlag GmbH, Ottenhoeferstr. 8, 68239 Mannheim, Germany. TEL 0621-48361-0. FAX 0621-478485. Ed. Hans Baumann; Pub. Guenther Brecht. adv. contact: Michael Mosthaf. circ. 38,943. **Document type:** consumer publication.

796.7 AT
BORN TO SIN; the Abominator's bike magazine. 1989. 4/yr. Aus.$66. U C P Publishing Pty. Ltd., 30 George St., Redfern, N.S.W 2016, Australia. TEL 02-319-5655. FAX 02-317-5727. Ed. Boris Mihailovic. circ. 40,000.
Description: Covers custom motorcycles and Australian biker lifestyle.

796.7 UK ISSN 0955-0976
BRITISH BIKE MAGAZINE; the true spirit of classic motorcycling. 1987. m. £23.40($39) (rest of Europe £33; overseas £48) (effective 1994); newsstand price: £1.95 ($3.50). Traplet Publications Ltd., Traplet House, Severn Dr., Upton-upon-Severn, Worc. WR8 0JL, England. TEL 01684-594505. FAX 01684-594586. (Dist. by: Seymour, Winsor House, 1270 London Rd., London SW16 4DH, England. TEL 0181-679-1899. FAX 0181-379-8907; U.S. subscr. to: Motorsport, 550 Honey Locust Rd., Jonesburg, MO 63351-9600. TEL 314-488-3113) Eds. Tim Holmes, Rebekka Norvik-Smith. adv. contact: Jane Stephenson. bk.rev. circ. 15,000. (back issues avail.) **Document type:** consumer publication.
Incorporates: Ace Magazine.
Description: Covers the collecting, restoration and riding of classic motorcycles. Technical information is balanced by readers' travel experiences and road tests of new and classic bikes.

BRITISH CAR. see TRANSPORTATION — Automobiles

796.6 UK ISSN 0965-0776
C T & C. (Cycle Touring & Campaigning) 1878. bi-m. £15. Cyclists' Touring Club, 69 Meadrow, Godalming, Surrey GU7 3HS, England. TEL 01483-417217. FAX 01483-426994. Ed. Tim Hughes. adv.; B&W page £867, color page £1220; trim 297 x 210; adv. contact: Lisa Warburton. bk.rev.; illus.; circ. 33,045 (paid). **Indexed:** Sportsearch. **Document type:** consumer publication.
Formerly (until 1988): Cycletouring.
Description: Contains articles and other features for cycling enthusiasts.

796.6 US
CALIFORNIA BICYCLIST. 1983. m. (11/yr.). $50. Yellow Jersey Emterprises, 490 2nd St., Ste. 304, San Francisco, CA 94107. TEL 415-546-7291. FAX 415-546-9106. Ed. Kimberly Grob. adv.; B&W page $3630, color page $4680. bk.rev. circ. 175,000.
Description: Publishes news, features & events calendar for the California bicycling community.

796.7 CN ISSN 0820-8344
CANADIAN BIKER MAGAZINE. 1980. 8/yr. Can.$27 (in US Can.$35, elsewhere Can.$40). Western Biker Publications Ltd., 735 Market St., Victoria, BC V8T 2E2, Canada. TEL 604-384-0333. FAX 604-384-1832. Ed. W.L. Creed. adv. circ. 16,000. (back issues avail.)
Description: Covers touring, off-road cycling, and news for motorcycle enthusiasts.

796.6 CN ISSN 1180-1352
CANADIAN CYCLIST. 1990. a. Editions Tricycle, 3575 boul. Saint-Laurent, Bur. 310, Montreal, PQ H2X 2T7, Canada. TEL 514-847-8356. FAX 514-847-0242. Ed. Pierre Hamel. adv. circ. 30,000.

796.6 AT ISSN 1030-4770
CANBERRA CYCLIST. 1975. bi-m. Aus.$18. Pedal Power A.C.T., Inc., G.P.O. Box 581, Canberra, A.C.T. 2601, Australia. TEL 06-248-7995. FAX 06-207-3199. Ed. Neville Reece. adv.; bk.rev.; illus. circ. 300. (back issues avail.) **Document type:** newsletter.
Formerly: Pedal Power (ISSN 0313-4334)
Description: Includes rides calendar, ride reports, discounters list, new designs, letters to the editor, policy and planning reports.
Refereed Serial

796 AT ISSN 0311-1717
CAT-A-LOG. 1970. m. Aus.$1. Jaguar Car Club of Victoria, P.O. Box 161, Ringwood, Vic. 3134, Australia. Ed. John Howard Jones. adv.; bk.rev. circ. 750.

796.6 SP ISSN 1131-9593
CATALOGO BICISPORT. 1990. a. 800 ptas. Luike - Motorpress, C. Ancora 40, 28045 Madrid, Spain. TEL 34-1-3470100. FAX 34-1-3470204. Ed. Francisco Chico Perez; Pub. Jose Luis Samaranch. adv.; B&W page 275000 ptas., color page 350000 ptas.; adv. contact: Agustin Valero. circ. 18,000. **Document type:** catalog.

SPORTS AND GAMES — BICYCLES AND MOTORCYCLES

629.227 796.7 US ISSN 1050-0251
TL444
CHILTON'S MOTORCYCLE AND A T V REPAIR MANUAL.
(All-Terrain Vehicle); from 1945-1985. 1974. irreg. price varies. Chilton Co., Automotive Editorial Department, Chilton Way, Radnor, PA 19089. **Document type:** trade publication.
 Incorporates: Chilton's Motorcycle Repair Manual.

796.6 IT
CICLOTURISMO. 1988. m. L.60000. Compagnia Editoriale s.r.l., Via Capogrossi 50, 00155 Rome, Italy. TEL 06-2285728. FAX 06-2285915. Ed. Sergio Neri. adv.: B&W page L.2670000, color page L.4215000; adv. contact: Alberto Giacopello. **Document type:** consumer publication.

796.6 388.347 CN ISSN 1183-7543
CITIZENS FOR SAFE CYCLING NEWSLETTER. 1986. irreg. Citizens for Safe Cycling, Box 248, Sta. B, Ottawa, ON K1P 6C4, Canada. TEL 613-722-4454. FAX 613-729-2207. Ed. Brett Delmage. **Document type:** newsletter.
 Formerly (until 1986): Share the Road (ISSN 1185-6513)

796.6 US
CITY CYCLIST. 1974. bi-m. $25 membership (includes Auto Free Press). Transportation Alternatives, 92 St. Marks. Pl., New York, NY 10012. TEL 212-475-4600. FAX 212-475-4551. E-mail: Transalt@echonyc.com. Ed. Jesse Kalb. adv.; bk.rev. circ. 14,000. **Indexed:** Sportsearch. **Document type:** newsletter.
 Formerly: New York City Cyclist (ISSN 1063-0880)
 Description: Covers bicycle transportation and environmental issues in New York City.

796 UK ISSN 0142-890X
CLASSIC BIKE. 1978. m. £26.40 (foreign £38.70) (effective 1995-1996). E M A P - National Publications, Bushfield House, Orton Centre, Peterborough, Cambs. PE2 5UW, England. TEL 01733-237111. FAX 01733-239127. (Subscr. to: Tower Publishing Services Ltd., Tower House, Sovereign Park, Lathkill St., Market Harborough, Leics. LE16 9EF, England. TEL 01733-237111. FAX 01733-239127) Ed. John Pearson. adv.; circ. 60,060 (paid). **Document type:** consumer publication.

796.7 UK ISSN 0959-7123
CLASSIC BIKE GUIDE. Abbreviated title: C B G. 1990. m. £26.40 (foreign £32). Myatt McFarlane plc, Trident House, Heath Rd., Hale, Altrincham, Cheshire WA14 2UJ, England. TEL 0161-928-3480. FAX 0161-929-0534. (U.S. addr.: Motorsport, 550 Honey Locust Rd., Jonesburg MO 63351-9600) Ed. Claire Leavey; Pub. Steven Myatt. adv. contact: Chris Dowell. bk.rev. circ. 34,000. (back issues avail.) **Document type:** consumer publication.
 Description: Presents a forum for the appreciation of old or classic British, European, and Japanese motorcycles with stories, facts, figures, price guides, and free advertisements.

796.7 UK
THE CLASSIC MOTORCYCLE. m. £24 (foreign £35.40) (effective 1995-1996). E M A P - National Publications, Bushfield House, Orton Centre, Peterborough, Cambs. PE2 0EW, England. TEL 01733-237111. (Subscr. to: Tower Publishing Services Ltd., Tower House, Sovereign Park, Lathkill St., Market Harborough, Leics. LE16 9EF, England. TEL 01858-468811. FAX 01858-432164) adv. **Document type:** consumer publication.

COMMERCE-REPARATION AUTOMOBILE. see TRANSPORTATION — Automobiles

CONTRACTSPELER. see SPORTS AND GAMES

796.7 GW ISSN 0933-7792
CROSS MAGAZIN. 1986. m. Verlag Juergen Tietze GmbH, Hauptstr. 25, 91341 Roettenbach, Germany. TEL 09195-3530. FAX 09195-8703. Ed. Juergen Tietze. adv. contact: Juergen Hirchenheim. circ. 15,000. **Document type:** consumer publication.

388.347 FR
LE CYCLE. m. 455 F. Societe EDI 92, B.P. 184, 89 rue Carnot, 92305 Levallois Cedex, France. TEL 47-48-05-50. FAX 47-48-05-35. Ed. Pascal Litt. circ. 47,000. **Indexed:** Acad.Ind.

796 CN ISSN 0319-2822
CYCLE CANADA. French edition: Moto Journal (ISSN 0319-2865) 1971. 10/yr. Can.$29.95. Turbopress Inc., 86 Parliament St., Ste. 3B, Toronto, ON M5A 246, Canada. TEL 416-362-7966. FAX 416-362-3950. Ed. Bruce Reeve; Pub. Jean Pierre Belmonte. adv.; bk. circ. 27,000. **Indexed:** Can.B.P.I., CMI. **Document type:** consumer publication.

796.7 US
CYCLE NEWS; America's weekly motorcycle newspaper. w. $35. C N Publishing Group, 2201 Cherry Ave., Box 498, Long Beach, CA 90801. TEL 310-427-7433. FAX 310-427-6685. Ed. Jack Mangus. adv.; bk.rev.; film rev.; charts; illus. circ. 38,000. **Document type:** consumer publication.
 Formed by the merger of: Cycle News - West and Cycle News - East; Cycle News - Central Edition.
 Description: Provides news on all aspects of motorcycling.

629.2 US ISSN 0272-8923
TL440
CYCLE STREET AND TOURING GUIDE.* 1980. a. $2.95. Hachette Magazines, Inc. (Newport Beach), 1499 Monrovia Ave., Newport Beach, CA 92663. illus.

796.6 UK ISSN 0955-8535
CYCLE TRADER. 1982. bi-m. £44. Robjohns Farm, Vicarage Rd., Finchingfield, Essex CM7 4LS, England. TEL 01371-810433. FAX 01371-811065. Ed. Mark Corless. adv. **Document type:** consumer publication.

796 016 US ISSN 0011-4286
TL440
CYCLE WORLD. 1961. m. $19.94 (Europe $27.94; Canada $26.94). Hachette Magazines, Inc., 1499 Monrovia Ave., Newport Beach, CA 92663. TEL 714-720-5300. FAX 714-631-0651. (Subscr. to: Box 51222, Boulder, CO 80321-1222. TEL 800-456-3084) Ed. David Edward. adv. contact: John Dawson. bk.rev. circ. 333,454. (also avail. in microform from UMI; reprint service avail. from UMI; back issues avail.) **Indexed:** Acad.Ind., Consum.Ind., Mag.Ind., PMR, R.G., Sportsearch. **Document type:** consumer publication.
 ●Also available online. Vendor(s): University Microfilms International.
 —BLDSC (3506.412000); Faxon; UMI; UnCover.
 Incorporates (in Oct. 1991): Cycle (New York, 1952) (ISSN 0574-8135)

796 US ISSN 1060-8389
TL440
CYCLE WORLD MOTORCYCLE BUYER'S GUIDE. 1971. a. $3.50. Hachette Magazines, Inc., 1499 Monrovia Ave., Newport Beach, CA 92663. TEL 714-720-5300. Ed. Paul Dean. adv. contact: John Dawson. bk.rev.; charts; illus.; tr.lit. **Document type:** consumer publication.
 Former titles: Cycle World (Year) Annual and Buyer's Guide (ISSN 0270-2746); Cycle World Buyer's Guide; Cycle World Road Test Annual.

796.7 US ISSN 1067-4470
CYCLE WORLD'S AMERICAN BIG TWIN. Variant title: American Big Twin. 1993. a. $5.95. Hachette Magazines, Inc., 1499 Monrovia Ave., Newport Beach, CA 92663. TEL 714-720-5300. Ed. Paul Dean. adv. contact: John Dawson. illus. **Document type:** consumer publication.
 Description: For Harley-Davidson enthusiasts.

796.75 CN ISSN 0835-0612
CYCLE 1. French edition: Motocycliste. 8/yr. Jarco Publishing Co., 2021 Union St., Ste. 1150, Montreal, Que. H3A 2S9, Canada. TEL 514-284-1732. FAX 514-289-9257. adv.: B&W page $2500, color page $3500. circ. 59,473.

796.6 JA
CYCLERACE MAGAZINE. (Text in Japanese) 1978. m. 6240 Yen. Baseball Magazine Sha, 3-10-10 Misaki-cho, Chiyoda-ku, Tokyo, Japan. Ed. Yoshihiro Shimotori.

796.6 UK
CYCLESPORT. 1993. m. £26.40($60.45) I P C Magazines, Specialist Magazine Group (Subsidiary of: Reed Elsevier group), King's Ranch Tower, Stamford St., London SE1 9LS, England. TEL 071-261-6208. FAX 0444-440619. TELEX 892084 REEDBP G. (Dist. by: Quadrant Subscription Services, Oakfield House, Perrymount Rd., Haywards Heath, W. Sussex RH16 3DH, England. TEL 0444-440421) Ed. A. Sutcliffe. adv. contact: Keith Foster. (back issues avail.) **Document type:** consumer publication.
 Description: For fans of professional cycle racing.

796.6 CN
CYCLING: B.C. NEWS. m. Can.$17 membership. Cycling British Columbia, 332-1367 W. Broadway, Vancouver, B.C. V6H 4A9, Canada. TEL 604-737-3034. FAX 604-738-7175. Ed. Jeff Hohner. **Document type:** newsletter.

796.6 US
CYCLING TIMES. 1991. 10/yr. $12. Wrubel Communications, 12-32 River Rd., Fair Lawn, NJ 07410. TEL 201-796-8634. FAX 201-796-5083. E-mail: CycleTimes@aol.com. Ed. Robert Wrubel; Pub. Robert Wrubel. adv. contact: Paul Smolenski. bk.rev. circ. 24,000. (tabloid format; back issues avail.) **Document type:** newspaper.
 Description: Covers news and events of interest to cyclists, both on- and off-road, in the New York metropolitan area.

796.6 UK ISSN 1351-0142
CYCLING TODAY. 1988. m. Stonehart Leisure Magazines, 67-71 Goswell Rd., London EC1V 7EN, England. TEL 071-410-9410. FAX 071-410-9440. Ed. Jim McGurn. circ. 31,041. **Document type:** consumer publication.
 Incorporates (1988-1993): New Cyclist (ISSN 0953-038X)

796.6 US ISSN 0274-4813
CYCLING U.S.A. 1980. m. $15. U.S. Cycling Federation, 1 Plympic Plaza, Colorado Springs, CO 80909. TEL 719-578-4628. FAX 719-578-4628. Ed. Jason Anderson. adv. contact: Mary Ellen Davis. bk.rev.; illus. circ. 35,000. **Document type:** consumer publication.
 Description: Offers federation-related news reports and releases, feature articles on all aspects of bicycle racing, profiles of coaches and cyclists, and information on events and programs of interest to federation members.

796.6 UK ISSN 0951-5852
CYCLING WEEKLY. 1891. w. £45. I P C Magazines, Specialist Magazine Group (Subsidiary of: Reed Elsevier group), King's Reach Tower, Stamford St., London SE1 9LS, England. TEL 071-261-5588. FAX 0444-440619. TELEX 892084 REEDBP G. (Dist. by: Quadrant Subscription Services, Oakfield House, Perrymount Rd., Haywards Heath, W. Sussex RH16 3DH, England. TEL 0444-440421) Ed. Martin Ayres. adv.; bk.rev.; illus. circ. 38,970. **Indexed:** Sportsearch. **Document type:** consumer publication.
 Former titles (until 1986): Cycling (ISSN 0011-4316); (until 1964): Cycling and Mopeds; Incorporates (1982-1985): Cyclist Monthly (ISSN 0263-5550)
 Description: Covers all aspects of competitive cycle racing in the UK and abroad.

796 UK ISSN 0143-0238
CYCLING WORLD. 1979. m. £20 (foreign £30). Stone Leisure Ltd., Andrew House, 2a Granville Rd., Sidcup, Kent DA14 4BN, England. TEL 0181-302-6150. FAX 0181-300-2315. Ed. Robert Griffiths. adv. circ. 10,000. **Document type:** consumer publication.
 Description: Cycling magazine for touring in Europe.

388.347 AT ISSN 1034-960X
CYCLING WORLD; the Australian bicycling magazine. 1977. bi-m. (with 2 special issues). Aus.$22.27. Mason Stewart Publishing Pty. Ltd., P.O. Box 746, Darlingurst, N.S.W. 2010, Australia. FAX 02-360-5367. Ed. Chuck Smeeton. adv.; bk.rev. circ. 16,000. (back issues avail.) **Indexed:** Aus.Rd.Ind., Pinpointer, Sportsearch (1990-). **Document type:** consumer publication.
 Formerly (until 1990): Freewheeling (ISSN 0156-4579)

SPORTS AND GAMES — BICYCLES AND MOTORCYCLES

796.6 US
CYCLIST. vol.3, 1986. 9/yr. $14.97. Cyclist Magazine Publishing Corp., c/o Cyclist Reader Service, Box 993, Farmingdale, NY 11737-0001. TEL 213-328-5700. Ed. John Francis.

796.6 US
CYCLISTS' YELLOW PAGES. a. membership only. Adventure Cycling Association, 150 E. Pine St., Missoula, MT 59802-4515. TEL 406-721-1776. (Subscr. to: Box 8308, Missoula, MT 59807-8308) maps. **Document type:** consumer publication.
Description: Information resource for bicyclists covering all 50 states, all Canadian provinces and territories, and 58 foreign countries; includes listings of hostels, bike shops, tour operators, cycling books and videos, tips on transporting bicycles (including airline regulations), getting in shape, and places to go mountain biking.

796.6 FR ISSN 1167-4075
CYCLO MAGAZINE; le magazine des passionnes du velo. Cover title: Cyclo 2000. 1926. 7/yr. 170 F. Cyclo 2000, 19 rue de Boeuf, 69005 Paris, France. TEL 78-42-44-08. adv.; bk.rev.; illus. circ. 5,000.
Former titles (until 1992): Cyclo 2000 (ISSN 1167-4067); (until 1972): Sports, Culture et Tourisme (ISSN 1167-4059); (until 1964): Cyclotouriste (ISSN 1167-4040)

796.6 FR ISSN 0981-101X
CYCLOTOURISME. 1929. m. 280 F. (effective 1995). Federation Francaise de Cyclotourisme, 8 rue Jean Marie Jego, 75013 Paris, France. TEL 44-16-88-88. Ed. Joelle Briot. adv. contact: Evelyne Bacquet. bk.rev. circ. 35,000.
Description: Presents the regions of France to bicyclists.

796.6 DK ISSN 0107-7805
CYKLE-JUL. 1936. a. DKK 48. Joergen Beyerholm, Ed. & Pub., Vestervang 35, DK-3450 Blovstroed, Denmark. illus.
Formerly: Cyclen.
Description: Cycling magazine with Scandinavian championship results. Photos and stories of recent bicycling developments and racing history.

796.6 DK ISSN 0109-4211
CYKLEN. 1982. 6/yr. DKK 58.50. Ole Jensen, Gothersgade 157-159, 1123 Copenhagen K, Denmark. Ed. Jan Marker. adv.; bk.rev.; illus. circ. 15,000.

796 SW ISSN 0280-3038
CYKLING. 1935. q. SEK 90. Cykelfraemjandet - Swedish Cycling Promotion Institute, P.O. Box 6027, S-102 31 Stockholm, Sweden. TEL 8-101086. Ed. Lars Thoerngren. adv.; bk.rev.; illus. circ. 11,000.
Former titles (until 1981): Cykel- och Mopednytt (ISSN 0011-4391); (until 1954): Cyklisten.

796.6 388.34 DK ISSN 0109-2790
CYKLISTER. 1933. bi-m. DKK 150. Dansk Cycklist Forbund, Roemersgade 7, DK-1362 Copenhagen K, Denmark. TEL 45-33-32-31-21. FAX 45-33-32-76-83. Ed. Poul Jensen. adv.: B&W page DKK 8500; adv. contact: Helle Bueddal. circ. 22,000. (paid). **Document type:** consumer publication, newsletter.

796.7 DK ISSN 0109-3649
D M C - BLADET. 1982. bi-m. membership. Danske Motorcyklisters Raad, P.O. Box 10, DK-4420 Regstrup, Denmark. TEL 45-98-37-36-93. FAX 45-98-37-28-81. Ed. Rolf Skovloekke. adv.: B&W page DKK 2950, color page DKK 4500; trim 297 x 210. bk.rev.; illus. **Document type:** consumer publication.
Formerly (until Nov. 1983): D M C Nyt (ISSN 0107-8984)

629.227 US ISSN 0893-2522
TL440
DEALERNEWS; the voice of the power sports vehicle industry. 1965. m. $25 (free to qualified personnel). Advanstar Communications, Inc., 7500 Old Oak Blvd., Cleveland, OH 44130. TEL 216-826-2839. FAX 216-891-2726. (Subscr. to: 131 W. First St., Duluth, MN 55802. TEL 800-346-0085) Ed. Robin Hartfiel. adv.; circ. 14,203 (controlled). (also avail. in microform from UMI) Indexed: Bus.Ind., Tr.& Indus.Ind. **Document type:** trade publication.
—UMI. **CCC.**
Former titles: Motorcycle DealerNews (ISSN 0888-4234); Dealer News (ISSN 0887-0950); Motorcycle Dealer News (ISSN 0192-0219)
Description: For dealers in the powersports industry. Includes dealer profiles, comprehensive new product information, industry research.

388.347 640.73 US ISSN 0893-2522
DEALERNEWS BUYERS GUIDE. a. $25. Advanstar Communications, Inc., 7500 Old Oak Blvd., Cleveland, OH 44130. TEL 216-826-2839. FAX 216-891-2726. (Subscr. to: 131 W. First St., Duluth, MN 55802. TEL 800-346-0085) Ed. Robin Hartfiel. (also avail. in microform from UMI) **Document type:** trade publication.
Formerly: Motorcycle Dealernews Buyers Guide.

796.7 US ISSN 0364-1546
TL440
DIRT BIKE. 1971. m. $18.98. Hi-Torque Publications, Inc., Box 957, Valencia, CA 91380-9057. TEL 818-365-6831. Ed. Ron Lawson. adv. circ. 176,062. Indexed: Jun.High.Mag.Abstr., Sportsearch.

796.6 US
DIRT BIKE CRASH AND BURN. 3/yr. $3.50 per no. Hi-Torque Publications, Inc., Box 957, Valencia, CA 91380-9057. TEL 818-365-6831.

796.7 US ISSN 0735-4355
DIRT RIDER MAGAZINE. 1982. m. $19.94. Petersen Publishing Co., 6420 Wilshire Blvd., Los Angeles, CA 90048. TEL 213-782-2000; 800-800-3478. Ed. Richard P. Lague. adv.; illus. circ. 159,900. (also avail. in microfilm from UMI) Indexed: Ind.How To Do It (1990-). **Document type:** consumer publication.
—UMI.

796.6 US ISSN 1060-4804
DIRT WHEELS. m. $18.98. Hi-Torque Publications, Inc., Box 957, Valencia, CA 91380-9057. TEL 818-365-6831.
Formerly: Dirt Wheels Magazine (ISSN 0745-0192)

796.6 AU
DRAHTESEL. 1984. bi-m. S.130. A R G U S - Arbeitsgemeinschaft Umweltfreundlicher Stadtverkehr, Frankenberggasse 11, A-1040 Vienna, Austria. TEL 0222-5058435. FAX 0222-5050907. adv.; bk.rev. (back issues avail.) **Document type:** consumer publication.

796.7 US ISSN 1077-8020
▼**EARLYRIDERS.** 1994. q. $19.95 (effective 1995 & 1996); newsstand price: $5.99. Paisano Publications, Inc., Box 1050, Agoura Hills, CA 91376-1050. TEL 818-889-8740. FAX 818-889-4726. adv.; illus. **Document type:** consumer publication.

796 US ISSN 0046-0990
GV1059.5
EASYRIDERS. 1971. m. $39.95 (foreign $51.95) (effective 1995 & 1996); newsstand price: $4.99. Paisano Publications, Inc., Box 1050, Agoura Hills, CA 91376-1050. TEL 818-889-8740. FAX 818-889-4726. Ed. Keith Ball. adv.: page $8000; adv. contact: Lizette Hotinger. bk.rev.; charts; illus.; tr.lit.; circ. 367,065 (paid). **Document type:** consumer publication.

796.7 GW
ENDURO. m. Enduro Verlagsgesellschaft mbH, Wallenstr. 57, 73529 Schwaebisch Gmuend, Germany. TEL 07171-40807. FAX 07171-44536. Ed. Norbert Bauer. adv. contact: Manfred Jahn. circ. 21,311. **Document type:** consumer publication.

796.7 US ISSN 0027-2167
ENTHUSIAST. Title varies: Motorcycle Enthusiast. 1916. 3/yr. free. Harley-Davidson Motor Co., Inc., Box 653, Milwaukee, WI 53201. TEL 414-342-4680. FAX 414-935-4806. Ed. Dan Klemencic. adv.; illus. circ. 350,000. **Document type:** consumer publication.

796 US
EXPLORE MINNESOTA BIKING. a. Office of Tourism, 100 Metro Square, 121 7th Pl. E., St. Paul, MN 55101. TEL 800-657-3700. circ. 60,000.

796 SZ ISSN 0071-4283
FEDERATION INTERNATIONALE MOTOCYCLISTE. ANNUAIRE. (Including International Motorcycle Sporting Calendar) (Text in English and French) 1912. a. 26 SFr. International Motorcycle Federation, 11 route Suisse, CH-1295 Mies, Switzerland. TEL 022-9509500. FAX 022-9509501. adv.; bk.rev. circ. 10,000. **Document type:** bulletin.

796.6 NE ISSN 0922-1824
FIETS. (Text in Dutch) 1982. 11/yr. fl.64.50. Uitgeverij Fiets b.v., Postbus 937, 1000 AA Amsterdam, Netherlands. TEL 31-20-6237223. FAX 31-20-6221608. Ed. G.V.D. Beek. adv.; bk.rev. circ. 45,000. (back issues avail.) **Document type:** consumer publication.
Description: Bicycle magazine with buyer's guide.

796.6 910.202 US
FODOR'S SPORTS: CYCLING. irreg. $12. Fodor's Travel Publications, Inc. (Subsidiary of: Random House, Inc.), 201 E. 50th St., New York, NY 10022. TEL 800-733-3000. (Dist. by: Random House, Inc., 400 Hahn Rd., Westminster, MD 21577) Eds. Arlene Plevin, Michael Spring.

796.6 FR ISSN 0245-0429
FRANCE CYCLISTE. 1946. m. 60 F. Federation Francaise de Cyclisme, 5 rue de Rome, Rosny-sous-Bois Cedex, France. adv.

FREIE FAHRT. see *TRANSPORTATION — Automobiles*

796 SW
FRITIDSHANDLAREN. 1935. m. (11/yr.) SEK 250. Cykel- och Sporthandlarnes Riksfoerbunds Serviceaktiebolag, Kungsgatan 19, S-105 61 Stockholm 2, Sweden. FAX 46-8-24-96-16. Ed. Roland Nordlander. adv.; charts; illus.; stat.; tr.lit. circ. 1,750.
Former titles: Fritidshandlaren Cykel och Sport (ISSN 1100-052X); (until 1988): Cykel och Sportfritidshandlaren; (until vol.4, 1984): Cykel- och Sporthandlaren.

G V A MITGLIEDERVERZEICHNIS. (Gesamtverband Autoteile-Handel e.V.) see *TRANSPORTATION — Automobiles*

796.7 GW
GEBRAUCHT MOTORRAD UND ZUBEHOER KATALOG. 1981. a. DM.9.80. Motor Technik Verlag, Strausstaffel 3, 70184 Stuttgart, Germany. TEL 0711-16850-0. FAX 0711-1685054. (back issues avail.)

GENTE MOTORI. see *TRANSPORTATION — Automobiles*

338.476 UK
GLASS'S GUIDE TO MOTOR CYCLE VALUES. 1950. m. £65. Glass's Information Services Ltd., Elgin House, St. George's Ave., Weybridge, Surrey KT13 0BX, England. TEL 01932-823823.
FAX 01932-846564. (Subscr. to: Sales and Marketing, St. Martins Ct., 37 Queens Rd., Weybridge, Surrey KT13 9TU, England) Ed. Johnathan Brown. adv. contact: Keith Mackenzie. circ. 2,664 (paid). **Document type:** trade publication.
Formerly: Glass's Guide to Used Motor Cycle Values.
Description: Offers motorcycle dealers data on the values of new and used machines.

388.347 UK
GLASS'S MOTOR CYCLE CHECK BOOK. a. £18. Glass's Information Services Ltd., Elgin House, St. George's Ave., Weybridge, Surrey KT13 0BX, England. TEL 01932-823823. FAX 01932-846564. (Orders to: Sales and Marketing, St. Martins Ct., 37 Queens Rd., Weybridge, Surrey KT13 9TU, England) adv. **Document type:** trade publication.

SPORTS AND GAMES — BICYCLES AND MOTORCYCLES

388.347 396.7
388.3   IT
GUERIN SPORTIVO MESE. 1982. m. L.40000. Editoriale Master s.r.l., Via dell'Industria 6, 40068 San Lazzaro di Savena (Bologna), Italy. Ed. Italo Cucci. adv.; bk.rev. circ. 95,000.
    Formerly: Master.

796.7   US   ISSN 1055-033X
HACK'D; the magazine for and about sidecarists. 1984. q. $21. J & C Enterprises, Box 813, Buckhannon, WV 26201. TEL 304-472-6146. Ed. Jim Dodson. adv.; bk.rev.; index. circ. 3,000. (back issues avail.) **Document type**: consumer publication.
    Description: Covers motorcycle sidecars.

796.7   US
HARLEY LOVER'S CHRISTMAS. 1993. a. (Ed. Aimee Hartnett) T A M Communications, Inc., 6 Prowitt St., Norwalk, CT 06855. TEL 203-855-0008. FAX 203-852-9980. adv. contact: Mike Stankiewicz. circ. 55,000 (paid). **Document type**: consumer publication.
    Description: Annual buyer's guide for Harley-Davidson enthusiasts. Publishes articles showing how to use the various items.

796.7   US   ISSN 0893-6447
HARLEY WOMEN; dedicated to all women motorcycle enthusiasts. 1985. bi-m. $14 (foreign $19). Asphalt Angels Publications, Inc., Box 374, Steamwood, IL 60107. TEL 708-888-2645. FAX 708-888-2954. Ed. Linda Jo Giovannoni. adv. contact: Bonnie Freese. circ. 20,000. **Document type**: consumer publication.
    Description: Features male and female riders, and motorcycle events nationwide. Includes new products and clothing, fiction and poetry.

796.7   UK
HEAVY DUTY. 1992. m. £26.95 (foreign £39.95). Stone Leisure Ltd., Andrew House, 2a Granville Rd., Sidcup, Kent DA14 4BN, England. TEL 0181-302-6069. FAX 0181-300-2315. Ed. Stu Garland; Pub. Bob Griffiths. circ. 26,000. **Document type**: consumer publication.
    Description: Motorcycle magazine for Harley Davidson enthusiasts.

HORSELESS CARRIAGE GAZETTE. see *ANTIQUES*

796   US   ISSN 0046-8045
HOT BIKE. 1969. m. $20.95. McMullen & Yee Publishing, 774 S. Placentia Ave., Placentia, CA 92670-6846. TEL 714-572-2255. FAX 714-533-9979. (Dist. by: ICD - Hearst, 250 W. 55th St., New York, NY 10019) Ed. Buck Lovell. illus. circ. 62,552.
    Description: Covers high-performance motorcycles.

796.7   US
▼**HOTTEST CUSTOM IRON**. 1994. bi-m. $14.95. (Ed. Karen Berman) T A M Communications, Inc., 6 Prowitt St., Norwalk, CT 06855. TEL 203-855-0008. FAX 203-852-9980. (Subscr. to: Fulco, Box 3000, Denville, NJ 07834-9375. TEL 800-875-2997. FAX 201-627-5872) adv. contact: Mike Stankiewicz. illus.; circ. 50,000 (paid). **Document type**: consumer publication.
    Description: Presents a hands-on approach on how and why to customize Harley-Davidson motorcycles. Publishes product reviews, along with technical articles.

338.347   US
I B F NEWS. 1986. s-a. free. International Bicycle Fund, 4887 Columbia Dr. S., Seattle, WA 98108-1919. TEL 206-628-9314. E-mail: intlbike@seanews.akita.com. Ed. David Mozer. circ. 5,000. **Document type**: bulletin.
    Description: News on bicycle transportation policy, programs and philosophy.

796.7   IT   ISSN 1122-1720
IN MOTO. m. L.80000 (America L.180000). Conti Editore S.p.A., Via del Lavoro 7, 40068 S. Lazzaro di Savena, Bologna, Italy. TEL 051-6227111. FAX 051-6255418. Ed. Tommaso Valentinetti. adv.: B&W or color page L.10000000; 206 x 251. circ. 55,029. **Document type**: consumer publication.
    Description: Covers production and racing bikes.

796.6   US   ISSN 1059-759X
IN THE WIND. 1979. bi-m. $24.95 (foreign $36.95) (effective 1995 & 1996); newsstand price: $4.99. Paisano Publications, Inc., Box 1050, Agoura Hills, CA 91376-1050. TEL 818-889-8740. FAX 818-889-4726. circ. 105,676 (paid). **Document type**: consumer publication.
    Formerly: Easyriders in the Wind (ISSN 0884-5131)

796.7   US
INDIAN MOTORCYCLE ILLUSTRATED. 1993. bi-m. $24. T A M Communications, Inc., 6 Prowitt St., Norwalk, CT 06855. TEL 203-855-0008. FAX 203-852-9980. (Subscr. to: Fulco, Box 3000, Denville, NJ 07834-3000. TEL 800-875-2997. FAX 201-627-5872) adv.: B&W page $1879, color page $2865; bleed 8 3/8 x 11 1/8; adv. contact: Mike Stankiewicz. illus.; circ. 45,000 (paid). **Document type**: consumer publication.
    Description: Contains articles and news about the antique Indian motorcycle marque, of interest to collectors and motorcycle enthusiasts.

629.227   IT   ISSN 0073-7291
INDUSTRIA ITALIANA DEL CICLO E DEL MOTOCICLO. ANNUARIO. (Text in English, French, German, Italian and Spanish) 1960. a. free. Associazione Nazionale Ciclo, Motociclo e Accessori, Via Mauro Macchi, 32, Milan, Italy. TEL 02-66981818. FAX 02-66982072. TELEX 315694 ANCMA I. adv.; bk.rev.; index. circ. 12,000.
    Description: Forum covering the production of motorcycles, bicycles, mopeds, motoscooters, component parts and accessories.

796.7   UK   ISSN 0020-6504
INTERNATIONAL CYCLE SPORT. 1968. m. $60. Kennedy Brothers (Publishing) Ltd., Goulbourne St., Keighley, West Yorkshire, England. Ed. J.D. Fretwell. adv.; charts; illus.; tr.lit. **Indexed**: Sportsearch.
    Supersedes: Sporting Cyclist.

796.7   US
IRON BIKER NEWS. 1990. m. $15. Steel Publications, Box 201, Landisville, NJ 08326. TEL 609-697-1335. FAX 609-697-8387. adv. circ. 25,000. **Document type**: newspaper.

796.6   US
IRON HORSE YEARBOOK.* a. $4.95. Scott Magazines, 28 W. 25th St., New York, NY 10010. TEL 212-967-6262. FAX 212-967-6288. **Document type**: consumer publication.

796.7   US   ISSN 1063-5661
IRONWORKS; alternative reading for lifelong motor cyclists. 1991. 9/yr. $24.50. Hatton - Brown Publishers, Inc., 225 Hanrick St., Montgomery, AL 36104. TEL 205-834-1170. FAX 205-834-4525. Ed. Dennis Stemp. adv. contact: Dave Ramsey. bk.rev.; film rev.; illus. (also avail. in Braille; back issues avail.) **Document type**: consumer publication.
    Formerly: Iron Trader News.

796.76   UK   ISSN 0956-411X
KART AND SUPERKART MAGAZINE. 1979. m. £15.50. Kart and Superkart Ltd., Pindar Rd., Hoddesdon, Hertfordshire EN11 0DE, England. TEL 0992-444 201. FAX 0992-447327. TELEX 266343 G ZIP. Ed. Ed. McCormick. adv.; bk.rev. circ. 6,000. (back issues avail.)

796.6   SZ   ISSN 1022-3770
KATZENAUGE. 1981. 17/yr. 20 SFr. Postfach 745, CH-8021 Zurich, Switzerland. TEL 01-4629080. Ed. Rene-Jacques Weber. adv.; bk.rev. circ. 2,000. **Document type**: bulletin.

796.6 658.8   UK
KEY NOTE REPORT: BICYCLES. Variant title: Bicycles. 5th ed., 1987. irreg. £185. Key Note Publications Ltd., Field House, 72 Oldfield Rd., Hampton, Middlesex TW12 2HQ, England. TEL 0181-783-0755. FAX 0181-783-1720. **Document type**: trade publication.
●Also available online.
Also available on CD-ROM.
    Description: Provides an overview of the bicycle industry, including industry structure, market size and trends, developments, prospects, and major company profiles.

796.7   GW
KURVE. m. Syburger Verlag GmbH, Hertingerstr. 60, 59423 Unna, Germany. TEL 02303-98550. FAX 02303-98559. circ. 15,000. **Document type**: consumer publication.

796.7   IT   ISSN 1121-7146
LEGEND BIKE/MOTOCICLETTE DA LEGGENDA. 1992. m. L.100000 (foreign L.200000). Gruppo B Editore, Via Don Vercesi 19, 20091 Bresso (MI), Italy. TEL 39-2-66503000. FAX 39-2-66503060. Ed. Angelo Berto. adv.: B&W page L.7000000; adv. contact: Marzio Bardi. circ. 62,000. **Document type**: consumer publication.

796.6   SP
LIBRO DE ORO DE MOUNTAIN BIKE. a. 800 ptas. Luike - Motorpress, C. Ancora 40, 28045 Madrid, Spain. TEL 34-1-3470100. FAX 34-1-3470204. Ed. Francisco Chico Perez. adv.: B&W page 275000 ptas., color page 350000 ptas.; adv. contact: Agustin Valero. **Document type**: consumer publication.

796.6   SA   ISSN 1015-6488
LIFE CYCLE. 1989. 6/yr. (South African Pedal Power Association) W.J. Flesch & Partners (Pty) Ltd., P.O. Box 3473, Cape Town 8000, South Africa. TEL 27-21-461-7472. FAX 27-21-461-3758. E-mail: 100077.260@COMPUSERVE.COM. Ed. Penny Krohn. adv.; circ. 18,000 (paid). **Document type**: consumer publication.
    Description: News and information of interest to recreational cyclists.

796.7 629.227   SW   ISSN 0281-7403
M C - FOLKET. 1964. 6/yr. SEK 130. Sveriges Motorcyklisters Centralorganisation, P.O. Box 318, S-792 25 Mora, Sweden. TEL 46-250-395-10. FAX 46-250-395-19. Eds. Nisse Schmidt, Henrik Aaslund. adv.: SEK 760000, color page SEK 1070000; trim 270 x 270. circ. 42,000. cols./p.: 4; pp./issue: 84.
    Formerly (until 1981): S M C - Bladet (ISSN 0346-0517)

796.7 629.227   SW   ISSN 0282-9134
M C M; motorcykelmagasinet. 1985. 6/yr. SEK 218; newsstand price: 44. M C M Foerlag, St. Goeransgatan 62, S-112 33 Stockholm, Sweden. TEL 46-8-651-53-60. FAX 46-8-650-23-49. Ed. Inge Persson-Carleson. adv.: B&W page SEK 8000, color page SEK 10900; trim 190 x 275; adv. contact: Tomas Lofterud. circ. 23,600. cols./p.: 4; pp./issue: 80.

796   SW   ISSN 0024-7995
M C - NYTT. 1959. m. SEK 105. Broederna Lindstroms Foerlags, Box 35, 44300 Lerum, 443 01 Lerum 1, Sweden. Ed. Thommy Bernguist. adv.; bk.rev.; illus.; stat. circ. 39,896.
    Incorporates (in 1975): M C - Sport (ISSN 0025-6250)

796.7   DK   ISSN 0107-0606
M C REVYEN. (Text in Danish) a. DKK 114.50. Bonniers Specialmagasiner A-S, Strandboulevarden 130, 2100 Copenhagen OE, Denmark. Ed. Dan Melchior. circ. 25,000. **Document type**: catalog.
    Description: Catalogue of all motorbikes sold on the Danish market.

796   UK
M S A NEWSLINK. bi-m. (Motor Schools Association of Great Britain) Integral Publishing Co. Ltd., Castlefield Ho., Liverpool Rd., Castlefield, Manchester M60 9BF, England. Ed. John Lepine. bk.rev. circ. 7,500. **Document type**: trade publication.

388.347 640.73   US
MASS CYCLIST. 1979. bi-m. $25 includes membership. Bicycle Coalition of Massachusetts, Box 1015, Kendall Square Branch, Cambridge, MA 02142-0008. TEL 617-491-RIDE. bk.rev.; charts; illus.; tr.lit. circ. 600. (back issues avail.) **Document type**: newsletter.
    Former titles (until 1993): Boston Cyclist; Spoke 'n Word.
    Description: Newsletter of the Coalition, a bicycle advocacy group working to promote the safe and practical use of the bicycle for both transportation and recreation.

SPORTS AND GAMES — BICYCLES AND MOTORCYCLES

796.7 CN
MASTERLINK. 8/yr. Can.$19.95($19.95) for 12 nos. Western Biker Publications Ltd., 2750 Rock Bay Ave., Victoria, B.C. V8X 3X4, Canada. TEL 604-384-0333. FAX 604-384-1832. (Subscr. to: P.O. Box 4122, Stn. A, Victoria, B.C. V8X 3X4, Canada) Ed. Len Creed. adv.; illus.

796.7 UK ISSN 1352-8483
MILLER'S CLASSIC MOTORCYCLE PRICE GUIDE. 1993. a. Reed International, Michelin House, 81 Fulham Rd., London SW3 6RB, England. **Document type:** catalog.

796.7 GW
MOPPED; die etwas andere Motorrad-Zeitschrift. 1993. m. DM.36; newsstand price: DM.2.50. Vereinigte Motor-Verlage GmbH und Co. KG, Leuschnerstr. 1, 70174 Stuttgart, Germany. TEL 0711-18201. FAX 0711-1821781. Ed. Volker Koerdt; Pub. Peter-Paul Pietsch. adv.: B&W page DM.9400, color page DM.14100; trim 185 x 248; adv. contact: Claus Schlosser. circ. 102,489. **Document type:** consumer publication.

388.347 796.7 IT ISSN 0392-3681
MOTITALIA. 1947. m. L.18000. Federazione Motociclistica Italiana, Piazza dei Carracci, 1, 00196 Rome, Italy. FAX 06-3960091. Ed. F. Zerbi. adv.; bk.rev. circ. 110,000.
Description: Deals with motorcycle racing in Italy; includes biographies of racers, activities of racing groups, and details of competitions.

388.347 796.7 IT ISSN 0390-0304
MOTO. 1976. m. L.75000. Edigamma s.r.l., Piazza dei Sanniti 9, 00185 Rome, Italy. TEL 06-4928412. FAX 06-4940719. Ed. Claudio Porrozzi. adv. circ. 210,000.

796.7 SZ
MOTO. m. Postfach 19, CH-3000 Bern 12, Switzerland. TEL 031-454493. FAX 031-462820. Ed. Rolf Von Niederhausern. circ. 19,350.

796.7 SP
LA MOTO. 1990. m. 3840 ptas. (Europe 5600 ptas., elsewhere 10200 ptas.); newsstand price: 400 ptas. Luike - Motorpress, C. Ancora 40, 28045 Madrid, Spain. TEL 34-1-3470100. FAX 34-1-3470204. Ed. Javier Herrero; Pub. Jose Luis Samaranch. adv.: B&W page 285000 ptas., color page 430000 ptas.; adv. contact: Antonino Berges. circ. 19,000. **Document type:** consumer publication.

796.7 FR
MOTO CRAMPONS SUPERCROSS SPECIAL. 1986. a. 29 F. Societe des Editions Techniques et Touristiques de France, 60-62 rue Danjou, 92100 Boulonge, France. TEL 46-09-95-96. FAX 46-09-99-85. Ed. Jacques Bussillet; Pub. Monique Helfenberger. adv. contact: Bernard Potut. circ. 45,000. **Document type:** consumer publication.

796.7 GW ISSN 0724-7206
MOTO CROSS ENDURO AKTUELL. 1971. m. DM.88.50. Verlag Bahnsport Aktuell oHG, Industriestr. 8, 63517 Rodenbach, Germany. TEL 06184-51051. FAX 06184-51004. Ed. Christian Kalabis. adv.; bk.rev. circ. 39,000. **Document type:** consumer publication.
Supersedes in part (in 1983): Bahnsport Moto Cross und Enduro Aktuell (ISSN 0723-2535); Which was formerly (until 1982): Bahnsport Aktuell (ISSN 0171-8940)
Description: Sports magazine for all motocross enthusiasts. Features reports, results and announcements of events, championships, national and international news, and new products.

796.7 IT
MOTO GIOVANI. 1988. m. L.6000 per no. Edizioni Eden, Via Achile Grandi 1, 20017 Mazzo di Rho (MI), Italy. TEL 39-2-93509854. FAX 39-2-93506378. Ed. Gianni Eusebio. adv.: color page L.11800000. circ. 75,000. **Document type:** consumer publication.

796 CN ISSN 0319-2865
MOTO JOURNAL. English edition: Cycle Canada (ISSN 0319-2822) (Editions in English, French) 1972. 10/yr. Can.$29.95. Turbopress Inc., 86 Parliament St., Ste. 3B, Toronto, ON M5A 246, Canada. TEL 514-738-9439, FAX 738-4929. (Or: 5000 Rue Buchan, Bureau 600A, Montreal, PQ H4P 1T2) Ed. Claude Leonard; Pub. Jean Pierre Belmonte. adv. circ. 11,000.

796.7 IT ISSN 1121-6263
MOTO JUNIOR. m. L.2500 per no. Edigamma s.r.l., Piazza dei Sanniti 9, 00185 Rome, Italy. TEL 39-6-4462841. FAX 39-6-4940719. Ed. Claudio Porrozzi. adv.: B&W page L.6300000, color page L.11800000. circ. 68,500. **Document type:** consumer publication.

796.7 629.222 FR ISSN 1155-2069
MOTO LEGENDE. 1990. m. 280 F. (foreign 380 F.). Retro-Viseur, B.P. 67, 77301 Fontainebleau, France. TEL 60-71-55-55. FAX 60-72-22-37. adv.; cum. index. circ. 45,000. cols./p.: 3; pp./issue: 80. (back issues avail.)
Description: Covers classic motorcycles.

796 FR ISSN 0047-8180
MOTO REVUE. 1913. 48/yr. 580 F. (foreign 844 F.). Editions Lariviere, 15-17 Quai de l'Oise, 75166 Paris Cedex 19, France. TEL 1-40-34-22-07. FAX 1-40-35-84-41. TELEX 211 678 F. Ed. Eric Breton. adv.; abstr.; illus.; stat. circ. 100,000.

796.7 SZ
MOTO SPORT SCHWEIZ. French edition: Moto Sport Suisse. (Text in German) 1972. w. 95 SFr. (foreign 123 SFr.). Buechler Grafino AG, Dammweg 9, Postfach 5635, CH-3001 Bern, Switzerland. TEL 031-3303222. FAX 031-3303427. adv. contact: Elisabeth Rohrer. circ. 22,000. **Document type:** consumer publication.

796.7 SZ
MOTO SPORT SUISSE. German edition: Moto Sport Schweiz. (Text in French) 1986. 2/m. 43 SFr. (foreign 73 SFr.). Buechler Grafino AG, Dammweg 9, Postfach 5635, CH-3001 Bern, Switzerland. TEL 031-3303421. FAX 031-3303427. adv. contact: Elisabeth Rohrer. circ. 4,000. **Document type:** consumer publication.

796.7 SP
MOTO VERDE. 1987. m. 3750 ptas. (Europe 6400 ptas.; elsewhere 8500 ptas.); newsstand price: 375 ptas. Luike - Motorpress, C. Ancora 40, 28045 Madrid, Spain. TEL 34-1-3470100. FAX 34-1-3470204. Ed. Javier Herrero; Pub. Jose Luis Samaranch. adv.: B&W page 150000 ptas., color page 230000 ptas.; adv. contact: Antonino Berges. circ. 18,000. **Document type:** consumer publication.

796.75 FR
MOTO VERTE. m. 270 F. (foreign 352 F.). Editions Lariviere, 15-17 Quai de l'Oise, 75166 Paris Cedex 19, France. TEL 1-40-34-22-07. FAX 1-40-35-84-41. TELEX 211 678 F. Ed. Gilles Mallet. adv.

796.7 BE
MOTO 80. (Text in French) 1980. bi-w. 2400 BEF($75) (effective Oct. 1993). Moto 80 s.p.r.l., 15 rue Abbe Michel Renard, B-1400 Nivelles, Belgium. TEL 32-67-216001. FAX 32-67-221050222. Ed. Luc Paquier. circ. 22,000. **Document type:** consumer publication.
Description: Covers all types of motorcycle racing in Belgium and Europe, as well as road tests of new models, travel and other related topics.

796.7 IT ISSN 0027-1691
MOTOCICLISMO. 1914. m. L.99000 (foreign L.151000). Edisport Editoriale S.p.A., Via Gradisca 11, 20151 Milan, Italy. TEL 02-380851. FAX 02-38010393. Ed. Francesco Tietrangolo. adv.: B&W page L.9100000, color page L.15000000. bk.rev.; charts; illus.; mkt.; index. circ. 212,000.
—SWETS.
Description: News about two and three-wheel motor vehicles including test results, industrial information, prices.

796.7 SP
MOTOCICLISMO. 1951. w. 17300 ptas. (Europe 31800 ptas.; elsewhere 40300 ptas.); newsstand price: 375 ptas. Luike - Motorpress, C. Ancora 40, 28045 Madrid, Spain. TEL 91-3470100. FAX 91-3470119. Ed. Javier Herrero; Pub. Jose Luis Samaranch. adv.: B&W page 345000 ptas., color page 540000 ptas.; adv. contact: Antonino Berges. circ. 49,000. **Document type:** consumer publication.

796.7 PO
MOTOCICLISMO. 1991. m. newsstand price: Esc. 500. Motorpress Lisboa, Av. Afonso III, Lote 2, Loja B, 1900 Lisbon, Portugal. TEL 351-1-8151134. FAX 351-1-8151542. Ed. Vitor de Sousa; Pub. Luis Penha e Costa. adv. contact: Pedro Santos. circ. 28,000. **Document type:** consumer publication.

796.6 SP ISSN 1131-785X
MOTOCICLISMO CATALOGO. 1980. a. 900 ptas. Luike - Motorpress, C. Ancora 40, 28045 Madrid, Spain. TEL 34-1-3470100. FAX 34-1-3470204. Ed. Javier Herrero; Pub. Jose Luis Samaranch. adv.: B&W page 345000 ptas., color page 540000 ptas.; adv. contact: Agustin Valero. circ. 39,000. **Document type:** catalog.
Description: Presents information on current motorcycle models.

796.7 SP
▼**MOTOCICLISMO CUSTOM.** 1995. s-a. newsstand price: 400 ptas. Luike - Motorpress, C. Ancora 40, 28045 Madrid, Spain. TEL 34-1-3470100. FAX 34-1-3470204. Ed. Juan Hernandez. adv.: B&W page 345000 ptas., color page 540000 ptas.; adv. contact: Agustin Valero. **Document type:** consumer publication.

796.7 SP
MOTOCICLISMO ESPECIAL PRUEBAS. 1981. a. 800 ptas. Luike - Motorpress, C. Ancora 40, 28045 Madrid, Spain. TEL 34-1-3470100. FAX 34-1-3470204. Ed. Javier Herrero; Pub. Jose Luis Samaranch. adv.: B&W page 345000 ptas., color page 540000 ptas.; adv. contact: Agustin Valero. circ. 35,000. **Document type:** consumer publication.
Description: Presents test results on over 100 motorcycles, grouped into 10 categories.

796.7 SP
MOTOCICLISMO GRANDES PREMIOS. a. 800 ptas. Luike - Motorpress, C. Ancora 40, 28045 Madrid, Spain. TEL 34-1-3470100. FAX 34-1-3470204. Ed. Juan Hernandez. adv.: B&W page 345000 ptas., color page 540000 ptas.; adv. contact: Agustin Valero. **Document type:** consumer publication.

388.347 UK ISSN 0309-4642
MOTOCOURSE; the world's leading Grand Prix annual. 1976. a. £26 (rest of Europe £32; N. and S. America, Middle East, Africa £38; Australasia £41) (effective 1995). Hazleton Publishing, 3 Richmond Hill, Richmond, Surrey TW10 6RE, England. TEL 0181-948-5151. FAX 0181-948-4111. TELEX 946153. Ed. Michael Scott; Pub. Richard Poulter. adv. contact: Simon Maurice. illus. **Document type:** consumer publication.
—BLDSC (5969.745000).
Description: Provides detailed coverage of the previous year's motorcycle Grand Prix season and other championships and profiles championship riders.

388.347 796.7 IT
MOTOCROSS. 1971. m. L.70000 (foreign L.92000) (effective 1993). Editrice Diamante Soc. Coop. Gior., Via Cusani 10, 20121 Milan, Italy. TEL 39-2-809606. FAX 39-2-809609. Ed. Ruggero Upiglio. adv.: B&W page L.7700000, color page L.12320000. circ. 200,000.

796.77 US ISSN 0146-3292
GV1060
MOTOCROSS ACTION. 1973. m. $19.98. Hi - Torque Publications, Inc., Box 957, Valencia, CA 91380-9057. TEL 818-365-6831. Ed. Jody Weisel. adv. circ. 90,734. (back issues avail.) **Indexed:** Sportsearch.

796.7 FR ISSN 1168-609X
MOTOCROSS MAGAZINE; cross - supercross - minicross. 1992. m. 250 F.($50); newsstand price: 30 F. Sportissimo Productions et Publications, 43 bd. des Tilleuls, 04100 Manosque, France. TEL 92-72-24-65. FAX 92-87-35-73. Ed. Alain Kuligowski. adv.: B&W page 4500 F.; color page 6500 F.; adv. contact: Alain Kuligowski. circ. 6,000 (paid). (back issues avail.) **Document type:** consumer publication.
Description: Covers national and international motorcycle races and contains championship reports concerning motocross, supercross, and minicross for professionals and young fans of the sport.

SPORTS AND GAMES — BICYCLES AND MOTORCYCLES

796.7 XR ISSN 1210-1419
MOTOCYKL. 1990. m. Motorpress Praha Spol.s.t.o., Voctarova 3, 18000 Prague 8, Czech Republic. TEL 02-6844619. FAX 02-6844791. Ed. Antonin Matejka; Pub. Dietmar Metzger. adv. contact: Vera Peskova. circ. 18,000. **Document type:** consumer publication.

796.7 NE ISSN 0027-1721
MOTOR. 1913. w. fl.135. (Royal Dutch Motorcycle Union (KNMV)) Wegener Tijl Tijdschriften Groep B.V., Postbus 9943, 1006 AP Amsterdam, Netherlands. TEL 31-20-5182828. FAX 31-20-5182843. Ed. G. te Lintelo. adv.; bk.rev. circ. 31,120. **Document type:** consumer publication.
—SWETS.

MOTOR. see *TRANSPORTATION — Air Transport*

796.7 796.6 DK ISSN 0107-7554
MOTOR - BLADET. 1928. m. (11/yr.). DKK 150. Danmarks Motor Union, Vejrmosegaards Alle 80, 7000 Fredericia, Denmark. Ed. Joergen Dorscheus. adv. circ. 8,300.

796.7 HU ISSN 0865-7165
MOTOR KATALOGUS. 1990. a. 528 Ft. Motor-Presse Kiado Kft Budapest, Rakospatak ut. 70-72, H-1142 Budapest, Hungary. TEL 01-1835168. FAX 01-1830585. Ed. Imre Paulovits; Pub. Dietmar Metzger. adv. contact: Dietmar Metzger. circ. 25,000. **Document type:** consumer publication.

MOTOR MUNDIAL. see *TRANSPORTATION*

796.7 HU ISSN 0865-4131
MOTOR REVUE. 1989. m. newsstand price: 108 Ft. Motor-Presse Kiado Kft Budapest, Rakospatak ut. 70-72, H-1142 Budapest, Hungary. TEL 01-1835168. FAX 01-1830585. Ed. Imre Paulovits; Pub. Dietmar Metzger. adv. contact: Dietmar Metzger. circ. 25,000. **Document type:** consumer publication.

380.1 US ISSN 0091-3774
HD9710.5.U5
MOTORCYCLE BLUE BOOK. Variant title: Hap Jones Motorcycle Blue Book. 1952. s-a. $18. Hap Jones, Ed. & Pub., Box 32368, San Jose, CA 95152. FAX 408-432-1926.

796 UK
MOTORCYCLE DEALER. m. 20-22 Sta. Rd., Kettering, Northants NN15 7HH, England. TEL 0536-414444. FAX 0536-513582. Ed. Colin Mayo. bk.rev. circ. 3,741. **Document type:** trade publication.
Description: Covers all trade and industry motorcycle news.

796.7 CN ISSN 0705-2030
MOTORCYCLE DEALER AND TRADE. 6/yr. avail. only to dealers, distributors and manufacturers in the motorcycling industry. Turbopress Inc., 86 Parliament St., Ste. 3B, Toronto, ON M5A 246, Canada. TEL 416-362-7966. FAX 416-362-3950. Ed. Larry Tate. adv. contact: John Gale. **Document type:** trade publication.

796.75 SA ISSN 0258-5073
MOTORCYCLE DEALERS' GUIDE. 1979. q. R.57.60. Mead & McGrouther (Pty) Ltd., P.O. Box 1240, Randburg 2125, South Africa. Ed. O. Peruch. circ. 300. **Document type:** trade publication.

796.7 UK ISSN 0884-626X
MOTORCYCLE INDUSTRY MAGAZINE. 1980. m. free to qualified personnel. Industry Shopper Publishing, Inc., Box 160, Gardnerville, NV 89410-0160. TEL 702-782-0222. FAX 702-782-0266. Ed. Rick Campbell. adv.; bk.rev.; circ. 13,200 (controlled). **Document type:** trade publication.
Former titles: Motorcycle Industry Shopper (ISSN 0274-5437); Motorcycle Industry Magazine.

796.7 UK ISSN 0268-7151
MOTORCYCLE INTERNATIONAL. 1987. m. £30 (foreign £45). Myatt McFarlane plc, Trident House, Heath Rd., Hale, Altrincham, Cheshire WA14 2UJ, England. TEL 0161-928-3480. FAX 0161-941-6897. Ed. Frank Westworth; Pub. Steven Myatt. adv. contact: Jason Cook. circ. 30,000 (paid). (back issues avail.) **Document type:** consumer publication.
—BLDSC (5978.119000).

MOTORCYCLE JAPAN; annual guide to Japan's motorcycle industry. see *TRANSPORTATION*

796.7 UK ISSN 0027-1853
MOTORCYCLE NEWS. 1952. w. £94 (foreign £99.50) (effective 1995-1996). E M A P - National Publications, Bushfield House, Orton Centre, Peterborough, Cambs. PE2 0EW, England. TEL 01733-237111. FAX 01733-239127. (Subscr. to: Tower Publishing Services Ltd., Tower House, Sovereign Park, Lathkill St., Market Harborough, Leics. LE16 9EF, England. TEL 01858-468811. FAX 01858-432164) adv.; illus.; tr.lit. circ. 132,000. (tabloid format) **Document type:** consumer publication.
—CCC.

796.7 US ISSN 0164-8349
MOTORCYCLE PRODUCT NEWS.* 1974. m. $18. M H West, Inc. (Subsidiary of Maclean Hunter Publishing Co.), 5743 Corsa Ave., Ste. 220, Westlake Village, CA 91362-4027. TEL 818-997-0664. FAX 818-997-1058. (29 N. Wacker Dr., Chicago, IL 60606) Ed. Bob Jackson. adv.; illus.; circ. 12,951 (controlled).
—UMI. CCC.
Description: Serves the trade selling, servicing, manufacturing, distributing, importing and exporting of motorcycles, motorscooters, mopeds, ATV's, personal watercraft, and parts and accessories.

MOTORCYCLE PRODUCT NEWS TRADE DIRECTORY. see *BUSINESS AND ECONOMICS — Trade And Industrial Directories*

796.7 US ISSN 0736-6116
MOTORCYCLE RED BOOK. 2/yr. $56.50. Maclean Hunter Market Reports, Inc., 29 N. Wacker Dr., Chicago, IL 60606-3297. TEL 312-726-2802. FAX 312-726-2574. (back issues avail.)

796.7 UK ISSN 0306-1647
MOTORCYCLE RIDER. 1964. 6/yr. £13. British Motorcyclists Federation (Enterprises) Ltd., P.O. Box 17, Hertford SG14 3UW, England. TEL 0992-504124. FAX 081-949-6215. Ed. Roger Shufflebottom. adv.; bk.rev. circ. 12,000. **Document type:** consumer publication.
Description: Explores all aspects of motorcycling, including politics, touring, roadtests, product reviews, and owners' reports.

796.7 US ISSN 1056-1455
MOTORCYCLE ROAD RACER ILLUSTRATED; the high performance racing and riding magazine. 1988. a. $3.95. C N Publishing Group, 2201 Cherry Ave., Long Beach, CA 90806. TEL 310-427-7433. FAX 310-427-6685. Ed. Paul Carruthers. circ. 130,000.
Description: Covers both motorcycle racing and championship competitions internationally, and national road racing competitions.

796.7 US ISSN 1075-2447
MOTORCYCLE SHOPPER. 1990. m. $19.95 (Canada $42; elsewhere $60) (effective through 1996). Payne Corp., 1353 Herndon Ave., Deltona, FL 32725-9046. TEL 407-860-1989; 800-982-4599. FAX 407-574-1014. E-mail: 74047,624@COMPUSERVE.COM. Pub. Luis Hernandez, Jr. adv.: B&W page $731.25, color page $1250; trim 8 1/8 x 10 3/4. bk.rev.; circ. 45,000 (paid). **Document type:** consumer publication.
●Also available online.
Description: Marketplace for buyers, sellers and rebuilders of motorcycles of every make and model, including vintage, stock and custom.

796.7 UK ISSN 0955-9116
MOTORCYCLE SPORT. m. £17 (foreign £18). Ravenhill Publishing Co. Ltd., Standard House, Bonhill St., London EC2A 4DA, England. TEL 071-628-4741. FAX 071-638-8497. TELEX 888602-MONEWS-G. Ed. C.J. Ayton. adv. circ. 17,428. **Document type:** consumer publication.

796.7 910.202 US ISSN 1069-2797
MOTORCYCLE TOUR & TRAVEL; adventure in style. 1993. bi-m. $11.97 (foreign $16.97). T A M Communications, Inc., 6 Prowitt St., Norwalk, CT 06855. TEL 203-855-0008. FAX 203-852-9980. (Subscr. to: Box 610, Mt. Morris, IL 61054. TEL 815-734-1101) Ed. Aimee Hartnett. adv.: B&W page $3250, color page $5000; adv. contact: Mike Steinkiewicz. bk.rev.; charts; illus.; circ. 35,000 (paid). **Document type:** consumer publication.
Description: Upscale tour and travel magazine from a motorcyclists' perspective. Also discusses places to go and what to see there and contains helpful information for the long-distance rider.

796 UK ISSN 0264-8504
MOTORCYCLE TRADER. m. £25.50 (foreign £36.50). (Motorcycle Retailers Association) Seven Kings Publications Ltd., Garden Hall House, Wellesley Rd., Sutton, Surrey SM2 5UF, England. TEL 081-661-1626. FAX 081-661-1173. Ed. N. Asten. circ. 2,500. **Document type:** consumer publication.

796.7 US ISSN 0027-2205
TL1
MOTORCYCLIST. 1912. m. $19.94. Petersen Publishing Co., 6420 Wilshire Blvd., Los Angeles, CA 90048. TEL 213-782-2000. Ed. Mitch Boehm. adv.: B&W page $6010, color page $9955. bk.rev. circ. 241,542. (also avail. in microform from UMI). Indexed: Consum.Ind., Info.How To Do It (1990-), Sportsearch. **Document type:** consumer publication.
—UMI; UnCover.
Incorporates (1970-1988): Motorcycle Buyer's Guide (ISSN 0077-1678)

796.7 US ISSN 0164-9256
MOTORCYCLIST'S POST. 1967. m. $15. (New England Motorcycle Dealers Association) Motorcyclists Post Publishing Co., Box 154, Rochdale, MA 01542. TEL 508-885-5221. FAX 508-752-5733. Ed. Robert F. Frink. adv. contact: Steve Henry. bk.rev. circ. 9,895. (tabloid format; back issues avail.) **Document type:** consumer publication, trade publication, newspaper.

MOTORNOVITA INTERNATIONAL. see *TRANSPORTATION — Automobiles*

388.3 GW ISSN 0027-237X
DAS MOTORRAD. 1920. fortn. DM.142; newsstand price: DM.6. Vereinigte Motor-Verlage GmbH und Co. KG, Leuschnerstr. 1, 70174 Stuttgart, Germany. TEL 0711-18201. FAX 0711-1821156. Ed. Friedhelm Fiedler; Pub. Paul Pietsch. adv.: B&W page DM.14320, color page DM.26492; trim 185 x 248; adv. contact: Claus Schlosser. bk.rev.; illus. circ. 201,128. **Document type:** consumer publication.

796.7 SZ
MOTORRAD. 24/yr. Villa Mueslischreck, CH-6042 Dietwil, Switzerland. TEL 041-912950. Ed. Alfred Wepf. circ. 25,000.

796.7 GW ISSN 0937-9495
MOTORRAD CLASSIC. 1987. bi-m. DM.45.90; newsstand price: DM.9. Vereinigte Motor-Verlage GmbH und Co. KG, Leuschnerstr. 1, 70174 Stuttgart, Germany. TEL 0711-18201. FAX 0711-1821156. Ed. Friedhelm Fiedler; Pub. Peter-Paul Pietsch. adv.: B&W page DM.4880, color page DM.9028; trim 185 x 248; adv. contact: Claus Schlosser. illus. circ. 30,418. **Document type:** consumer publication.

796.7 GW
MOTORRAD KATALOG. 1970. a. DM.15. Vereinigte Motor-Verlage GmbH und Co. KG, Leuschnerstr. 1, 70174 Stuttgart, Germany. TEL 0711-18201. FAX 0711-1821669. (Subscr. to: Postfach 106036, 70049 Stuttgart, Germany) Ed. Friedhelm Fiedler; Pub. Peter-Paul Pietsch. adv.: B&W page DM.9536, color page DM.17642; adv. contact: Claus Schlosser. illus. circ. 200,000. **Document type:** catalog.

796.7 GW ISSN 0723-2616
MOTORRAD MAGAZIN M O. 1978. m. Motor Technik Verlag, Strausstaffel 3, 70184 Stuttgart, Germany. TEL 0711-16850-0. FAX 0711-1685064. Ed. Franz Josef Schermer; Pub. Franz Josef Schermer. circ. 65,528. (back issues avail.) **Document type:** consumer publication.
Former titles (until 1982): Mofa, Motorrad, Test, Sport (ISSN 0722-3196); (until 1981): Motorrad, Mokick, Mofa und Sport (ISSN 0172-1410)

796.7 GW
MOTORRAD MARKT. 1991. m. DM.54; newsstand price: DM.4.50. A M F Verlag GmbH, Sattlerstr. 7, 23556 Luebeck, Germany. TEL 0451-898814. FAX 0451-8966211. Ed. Juergen Koslowski. adv. circ. 190,000. **Document type:** consumer publication.

796.7 GW
MOTORRAD NEWS; das Magazin fuer Sachsen-Anhalt und Thueringen. m. Syburger Verlag GmbH, Hertingerstr. 60, 59423 Unna, Germany. TEL 02303-98550. FAX 02303-98559. circ. 8,000. **Document type:** consumer publication.

SPORTS AND GAMES — BICYCLES AND MOTORCYCLES 6127

796.7 GW
MOTORRAD OLDTIMER KATALOG; Marktuebersicht fuer klassische Motorraeder. 1988. a. DM.29.80. Heel-Verlag GmbH, Hauptstr. 354, 53639 Koenigswinter, Germany. TEL 02223-23026. FAX 02223-23028. (Dist. by: I P V, Wendenstr. 27, 20097 Hamburg, Germany. TEL 040-237110. FAX 040-23711235) Ed. Stefan Knittel. adv.: page DM.2200; trim 185 x 266; adv. contact: Sabine Tschiersch. circ. 5,000 (paid). (back issues avail.) **Document type:** catalog.

796.7 GW ISSN 0934-1951
MOTORRAD, REISEN UND SPORT. 1983. m. DM.72. Heinrich Bauer Spezialzeitschriftenverlag, Industriestr. 16, 50735 Cologne, Germany. TEL 0221-7709148. FAX 0221-7124228. (Subscr. to: Postfach 300545, 20302 Hamburg, Germany) Ed. Knut Briel; Pub. Guenter Wiechmann. adv. contact: Kay Ruedebusch. circ. 62,000. (back issues avail.) **Document type:** consumer publication.
Description: Features on motorcycle tests, touring reports, motorcycles sports, classic motorcycles.

796.7 GW
MOTORRAD SPIEGEL; das Baden-Wuerttemberger Motorrad Magazin. m. Syburger Verlag GmbH, Hertingerstr. 60, 59423 Unna, Germany. TEL 02303-98550. FAX 02303-98559. circ. 20,000. **Document type:** consumer publication.

796.7 GW
MOTORRAD SZENE; das Magazin der Motorradfahrer. m. Syburger Verlag GmbH, Hertingerstr. 60, 59423 Unna, Germany. TEL 02303-98550. FAX 02303-98559. circ. 20,000. **Document type:** consumer publication.

796.75 GW
MOTORRAD TEST (YEAR); Katalog. 1983. a. DM.14. MO-Verlag GmbH, Straussstaffel 3, 70184 Stuttgart, Germany. TEL 0711-16850-0. FAX 0711-16850-64. Ed. Franz Josef Schermer; Pub. Franz Josef Schermer. adv. contact: Stephan Koehn. circ. 120,000. **Document type:** catalog.

796.75 GW ISSN 0935-7645
MOTORRADFAHRER; Test und Technik fuer die Praxis. 1988. m. Reiner H. Nitschke Verlags GmbH, Pastor-Berg-Str. 4, 53539 Duempelfeld, Germany. TEL 02695-1009. FAX 02695-1400. Ed. Reiner H. Nitschke. adv. contact: Martina Jonas. **Document type:** consumer publication.

796.7 GW
MOTORRADSZENE BAYERN. m. Syburger Verlag GmbH, Hertingerstr. 60, 59423 Unna, Germany. TEL 02303-98550. FAX 02303-98559. circ. 17,000. **Document type:** consumer publication.

796.7 GW
MOTORRADTREFF SPINNER; das Motorradmagazin fuer Berlin, Brandenburg und Mecklenburg. m. Syburger Verlag GmbH, Hertingerstr. 60, 59423 Unna, Germany. TEL 02303-98550. FAX 02303-98559. circ. 10,000. **Document type:** trade publication.

796.7 GW
MOTORSPORT AKTUELL. 1964. w. newsstand price: DM.2.80. Vereinigte Motor-Verlage GmbH und Co. KG, Leuschnerstr. 1, 70174 Stuttgart, Germany. TEL 0711-1821226. FAX 0711-1821349. (Subscr. to: Postfach 106036, 70049 Stuttgart, Germany) Ed. Guenther Wiesinger; Pubs. August Hug, Richard Stolz. adv.: B&W page DM.6400, color page DM.10560; trim 205 x 280; adv. contact: A. Grzegorzewski. circ. 87,076. **Document type:** consumer publication.

388.347 396.7 IT ISSN 1122-1739
MOTOSPRINT. 1976. w. (51/yr.) L.140000 (America L.370000). Conti Editore S.p.A., Via del Lavoro 7, 40068 S. Lazzaro di Savena (Bologna), Italy. TEL 051-6227111. FAX 6256191. Ed. Tommaso Valentinetti. adv.: B&W page L.6900000, color page L.10400000; 185 x 252. bk.rev. circ. 66,493. **Document type:** consumer publication.

796.7 IT
MOTOTRENTINO; mototre, motolombardia, mototoscano. m. L.40000 (foreign L.50000). Edigrafica s.n.c., Loc. Centochiari, 33-1, 38100 Trento, Italy. TEL 39-461-820711. FAX 39-461-823042. Ed. Mario Facchini. adv.: B&W page L.2134000, color page L.4235000.

796.7 IT
MOTOTURISMO; il piacere di andare in moto. 1987. bi-m. L.30000 (foreign L.60000). Editore L' Isola, Piazza Roma, 1, Lurago Marinone (CO), Italy. TEL 031-937736. FAX 031-937362. Ed. Tiziano Cantatore. adv.: B&W page L.2500000, color page L.4000000. bk.rev. circ. 40,000.
Description: Covers footage on motorcycle trips, history of motorbikes and includes information on organized tours for motorcyclists.

796.7 CC ISSN 1002-6754
MOTUO CHE/MOTORCYCLE. (Text in Chinese) 1985. m. Renmin Youdian Chubanshe - People's Posts and Telecommunications Publishers, 27 Dongchang'anjie, Beijing 100740, People's Republic of China. TEL 5138139. Ed. Yu Xiaochuan.

796.6 US ISSN 1046-4875
MOUNTAIN AND CITY BIKING. m. $27.95. Challenge Publications, Inc., 7950 Deering Ave., Canoga Park, CA 91304-5007. TEL 818-887-0550. FAX 818-883-1343. Ed. Brian Hemsworth. circ. 103,000. **Document type:** consumer publication.

796.6 US ISSN 0897-5213
MOUNTAIN BIKE. bi-m. $11.97. Rodale Press, Inc., 33 E. Minor St., Emmaus, PA 18098. TEL 610-967-5171. TELEX 847338. **Document type:** consumer publication.
—UMI; UnCover.
Description: Adventure travel magazine for all-terrain cyclists featuring new products, riding techniques, event reports and previews.

796.6 GW ISSN 0946-2996
MOUNTAIN BIKE. 1993. m. DM.73.20 (foreign DM.187.20). Ringier Verlag GmbH, Gustav-Heinemann-Ring 212, 81739 Munich, Germany. TEL 089-63818-0. FAX 089-63818100. Ed. Tom Bierl. adv.: color page DM.14180; adv. contact: Christian Czerny. circ. 78,000. **Document type:** consumer publication.

796 US ISSN 0895-8467
MOUNTAIN BIKE ACTION. 1986. m. $19.98. Hi-Torque Publications, Inc., Box 957, Valencia, CA 91380-9057. FAX 805-295-1910. Ed. Jody Weisel. adv. **Document type:** consumer publication.

796.6 US ISSN 1062-2918
MOUNTAIN BIKING. 1987. 18/yr. $13.95 (effective Oct. 1994). Challenge Publications, Inc., 7950 Deering Ave., Canoga Park, CA 91304. TEL 818-887-0550. FAX 818-883-3019. (Subscr. to: ox 16149, N. Hollywood, CA 91615. TEL 818-760-8983) Ed. Mark Langton; Pub. Edwin Schnepf. circ. 86,000. **Document type:** consumer publication.
Description: Covers all aspects of the sport and recreation of mountain biking, including product reviews, bike tests, racing coverage, how-tos, interviews with industry reps and racers, and travel.

388.347 796.95 US
N A D A MOTORCYCLE - SNOWMOBILE - A T V - PERSONAL WATERCRAFT APPRAISAL GUIDE. 3/yr. $45. (National Automobile Dealers Association) N.A.D.A. Appraisal Guides, Box 7800, Costa Mesa, CA 92628-7800.
Supersedes: N A D A Motorcycle Appraisal Guide (ISSN 0095-6953).

796 SW ISSN 0048-1211
NYA CYKLISTEN. 1970. 8/yr. SEK 470 in Nordic countries; elsewhere SEK 570. (Svenska Cykelfoerbundet) Cewe-Foerlaget AB, P.O. Box 77, S-890 10 Bjaesta, Sweden. TEL 0660-309-65. FAX 0660-305-17. (Subscr. to: PK-Banken, Box 365, 891 01 Oernskeoldsvik, Sweden) Ed. Charlie Wedin. adv.; bk.rev.

796 FR ISSN 1240-8751
OFFICIEL DU CYCLE ET DE LA MOTO; seule revue de la profession. 1890. m. 740 F. (typically set in Nov.). (Federation Nationale du Commerce et de la Reparation du Cycle & Motocycle) Societe EDI 92, B.P. 184, 89 rue Carnot, 92305 Levallois Cedex, France. TEL 47-48-05-50. FAX 47-48-05-35. Ed. D.J. Presse. adv.; bk.rev.; charts; stat. circ. 13,500.
Former titles: Officiel du Cycle et du Motocycle (ISSN 0751-994X); Officiel du Cycle, du Motocycle et de la Motoculture (ISSN 0030-0519)
Description: Reviews the cycle and motorcycle industry.

796.7 US ISSN 1072-7213
OLD BIKE JOURNAL. 1989. 17/yr. $24.95 (foreign $37.95). T A M Communications Inc., 6 Prowitt St., Norwalk, CT 06855. TEL 203-855-0008. FAX 203-852-9980. (Subscr. to: Box 391, Mt. Morris, IL 61054. TEL 815-734-1101) Ed. Greg Bastek. adv.: B&W page $1769, color page $2671; bleed 8 3/8 x 11 1/8; adv. contact: Phil Milano. illus.; circ. 30,000 (paid). **Document type:** consumer publication.
Former titles (until Nov. 1993): Bike Journal International; (until 1992): Bike Journal (ISSN 1056-8441); Old Bike Journal.
Description: Features material of interest to enthusiasts of classic and collectible motorcycles. Includes restoration and technical tips.

796.6 US ISSN 0893-4606
ON ONE WHEEL. 1972. q. $15 in the U.S.; Mexico and Canada $20; elsewhere $25. Unicycling Society of America, Inc., Box 40534, Redford, MI 48240. TEL 313-661-0334. Ed. Constance Cotter. adv.; bk.rev. circ. 800. (back issues avail.)
Description: Information about all phases of unicycling including building techniques, tricks, and meets.

796.6 US ISSN 1044-4327
ON THE ROAD (NEW YORK). q. $3.95 per no. Outlaw Biker Enterprises, Inc., 450 Seventh Ave., Ste. 2305, New York, NY 10123. TEL 212-564-0112. FAX 212-465-8350. **Document type:** consumer publication.

796 US ISSN 0885-2030
OUTLAW BIKER. 1985. m. $29.95. Outlaw Biker Enterprises, Inc., 450 Seventh Ave., Ste. 2305, New York, NY 10123. TEL 212-564-0112. FAX 212-465-8350. Ed. Casey Exton. adv. circ. 150,000. (back issues avail.) **Document type:** consumer publication.

796.6 US
OUTSPOKIN'. m. $100. National Bicycle Dealers Association, 2240 University Dr., No. 130, Newport Beach, CA 92660-3319. TEL 714-722-6909. circ. 1,300. **Document type:** newsletter.
Description: Covers news and concerns of the bicycle trade.

796.7 AT ISSN 0155-4360
OZBIKE; thunder down under. 1981. 12/yr. Aus.$50. U C P Publishing Pty. Ltd., 30 George St., Redfern, N.S.W. 2016, Australia. TEL 61-2-319-6557. FAX 61-2-319-5727. Ed. Boris Mihailovic. adv. circ. 46,000. (back issues avail.)
Description: Covers custom motorcycles and Australian biker lifestyle.

796.6 NO ISSN 0801-0986
PAA HJUL. (Text in Norwegian) 1980. 6/yr. NOK 150. Norges Cykleforbund, Hanger Skolevei 1, N-1351 Rud, Norway. FAX 02-132989. TELEX 78586 NIF. Ed. Per Furseth. adv.; bk.rev. circ. 8,500.

796.6 AU
PEDAL; Bike for Fun. 9/yr. S.310 (foreign S.360). Leo Karner Verlags GmbH, A-3100 Neidling 23, Austria. TEL 02742-51567. FAX 02742-515674. Ed. Leo Karner. adv.: B&W page S.26200, color page S.41900; trim 185 x 252. circ. 35,000. **Document type:** consumer publication.

796 CN ISSN 1191-2685
PEDAL. Variant title: Canadian Cycling News. 1986. 8/yr. (m. Mar.-Nov.) Can.$22.25 (US $30; elsewhere US$34.50). (Canadian Cycling Association) Pedal Magazine, 2 Pardee Ave., Ste. 204, Toronto, ON M6K 3H5, Canada. TEL 416-530-1350. FAX 416-530-4155. Ed. Benjamin Sadavoy. adv. contact: Benjamin Sadavoy. bk.rev. circ. 20,000. **Document type:** consumer publication.
Description: Provides wide-range coverage of cycling including competitive events both national and international for road and track - mountain biking, interviews, recreational stories, product reviews, training, technique, repair and maintenance tips.

ULRICH'S INTERNATIONAL PERIODICALS DIRECTORY 1996

SPORTS AND GAMES — BICYCLES AND MOTORCYCLES

796.7   UK   ISSN 0268-4942
PERFORMANCE BIKES. m. £26.40 (foreign £40) (effective 1995-1996). E M A P - National Publications, Bushfield House, Orton Centre, Peterborough, Cambs. PE2 0EW, England. TEL 01733-237111. FAX 01733-239127. (Subscr. to: Tower Publishing Services Ltd., Tower House, Sovereign Park, Lathkill St., Market Harborough, Leics. LE16 9EF, England. TEL 01858-468811. FAX 01858-432164) adv. circ. 102,000. **Document type:** consumer publication.
Formerly (until 1985): Mechanics (ISSN 0263-8274); Which incorporated (1980-1983): Biker (ISSN 0260-5147); Former titles (until 1982): Motor Cycle Mechanics (ISSN 0262-5822); (until 1972): Motor Cycle, Scooter and Three-Wheeler Mechanics (ISSN 0027-2183)

796.7   US   ISSN 0162-3214
TL235.6
PETERSEN'S 4 WHEEL & OFF-ROAD. 1977. m. $19.94. Petersen Publishing Co., 6420 Wilshire Blvd., Los Angeles, CA 90048. TEL 213-782-2000. Ed. Drew Hardin. adv. circ. 300,000. (also avail. in microfiche) **Document type:** consumer publication. —UMI; UnCover.
Formerly: Hot Rod Magazine's 4 Wheel and Off-Road.

796   CN
PRAIRIE PEDALER. 1985. q. free to members. Saskatchewan Cycling Association, 2205 Victoria Ave., Regina, Sask. S4P 0S4, Canada. TEL 306-780-9289. FAX 306-525-4009. Ed. Denise Eberte; Pub. Denise Eberte. adv. contact: Denise Eberte. circ. 400. **Document type:** newsletter.

(YEAR) PRO BIKE DIRECTORY. see TRANSPORTATION

PRO BIKE NEWS. see TRANSPORTATION

796.7   NE
PROMOTOR. 1990. 10/yr. fl.83.50. Koninklijke Nederlandse Toeristenbond ANWB - Royal Dutch Tourist Club, Wassenaarseweg 220, Postbus 93200, 2509 BA The Hague, Netherlands. TEL 31-70-3146119. FAX 31-70-3242509. adv.: B&W page fl.3888, color page fl.5910; trim 265 x 327; adv. contact: J.W. Boersen. illus. circ. 32,000. **Document type:** consumer publication.
Description: For motorcycle enthusiasts.

796.7   US
▼**QUICK THROTTLE.** 1995. bi-m. $16.50 (effective 1995 & 1996); newsstand price: $3.99. Paisano Publications, Inc., Box 1050, Agoura Hills, CA 91376-1050. TEL 818-889-8740. FAX 818-889-4726. adv.; illus. **Document type:** consumer publication.

796.6   GW   ISSN 0720-8545
RADFAHREN; Zeitschrift fuer die Freunde des Fahrrads. 1980. bi-m. DM.64. Bielefelder Verlagsanstalt GmbH und Co. KG, Niederwall 53, 33602 Bielefeld, Germany. TEL 0521-595530. FAX 0521-595531. Eds. Michael Bollschweiler, Peter Toennishoff. adv. contact: Heinz Hussing. circ. 72,617. **Document type:** consumer publication.

796.75   GW
RADL MAGAZIN; trekking bike. 1990. 4/yr. DM.39 (foreign DM.54) for 6 nos. Reiner H. Nitschke Verlags GmbH, Pastor-Berg-Str. 4, 53520 Duempelfeld, Germany. TEL 02695-1222. FAX 02695-1400. Ed. Reiner H. Nitschke. adv. contact: Martina Jonas. **Document type:** consumer publication.

629.227   GW   ISSN 0033-8540
RADMARKT; deutsche Fachzeitschrift der Zweiradwirtschaft. 1879. m. DM.138. Bielefelder Verlagsanstalt GmbH & Co. KG, Niederwall 53, 33602 Bielefeld, Germany. TEL 0521-595-520. adv.; bk.rev.; charts; illus.; mkt.; pat.; tr.lit.; tr.mk.; index. circ. 6,000. **Document type:** trade publication.
Description: Trade publication for the bicycle market. Covers the latest information concerning bicycles, motorcycles, scooters, and foreign trade. Includes letters to the editor and list of advertisers.

796.6   GW
RADSPORT. w. (Wed.). DM.304.20. Deutscher Sportsverlag Kurt Stoof GmbH, Eintrachtstr. 110-118, 50688 Cologne, Germany. TEL 0221-1648-0. FAX 0221-1648318. Ed. Charly Huehnergarth. adv. contact: Erhard Badtke. circ. 10,879. **Document type:** newspaper.

796.7   GW   ISSN 0138-1393
RADSPORTLER. 1949. w. DM.26.40. Deutscher Radsport-Verband der DDR, Muelenweg 12, 1635 Wuensdorf, Germany. Ed. Lothar Branzke. (tabloid format)

796.7   AU
RADWELT. 7/yr. S.209. Wengerweg 10, Postfach 80, A-4950 Altheim, Austria. TEL 07723-3739. FAX 07722-4242. Ed. Wolfgang Hirschl; Pub. Arnold Hirschl. adv.: B&W page S.9700, color page S.13600; trim 185 x 250; adv. contact: Arnold Hirschl. circ. 5,000. **Document type:** consumer publication.

796   US
RECUMBENT CYCLIST NEWS. (Buyers Guide avail.) 6/yr. $28 (Canada Can.$45; elsewhere $50) (effective 1995). (Recumbent Bicycle Club of America) Recumbent Cyclist International, Box 58755, Renton, WA 98058-1755. TEL 206-852-8149. FAX 206-631-5728. Ed. Robert J. Bryant. adv.: B&W page $550; trim 8 1/2 x 11. circ. 2,500 (paid). (back issues avail.) **Document type:** consumer publication.
Former titles (until June 1993): Recumbent Cyclist Magazine; (until 1991): Recumbent Cyclist Newsletter.
Description: Fosters communication between recumbent bicycle enthusiasts, dealers and manufacturers.

796.7   SA   ISSN 1022-4580
▼**REDLINE MOTORCYCLE NEWS.** (Text in English) 1994. m. R.71.40. Redline Motorcycle News CC, P.O. Box 990429, Kibler Heights 2091, South Africa. TEL 27-11-4932729. FAX 27-11-4931794. Ed. Kenn Slater. adv.: B&W page R.2610, color page R.3250. illus. **Document type:** consumer publication.
Description: Covers motorcycles news and events nationally and internationally, and includes road tests and price information.

796.7   GW
REISE MOTORRAD. 1991. s-a. DM.9.80. Motor Technik Verlag, Straussstaffel 3, 70184 Stuttgart, Germany. TEL 0711-16850-0. FAX 0711-1685054.

796.7   AU
DER REITWAGEN.* 10/yr. An der Viehoferin 35, A-3021 Pressbaum, Austria. Ed. Andreas Werth. circ. 28,000.

796.7 629.222   FR   ISSN 0992-5007
RETROVISEUR. 1988. m. 330 (foreign 455 F.). Retro-Viseur, B.P. 67, 77301 Fontainebleau, France. TEL 60-71-55-55. FAX 60-72-22-37. adv.; illus. cols./p.: 3; pp./issue: 160. (back issues avail.) **Document type:** newspaper.
Description: Covers classic motorcycles and automobiles.

796.7   AT   ISSN 0027-2175
REVS MOTORCYCLE NEWS. 1967. fortn. Aus.$75. Federal Publishing Company, 180 Bourke Rd., Alexandria, N.S.W. 2015, Australia. Ed. Bob Gontrip. circ. 12,000.
Description: Deals with motorcycle racing and riding.

629.227   FR   ISSN 0150-7214
REVUE MOTO TECHNIQUE. 1969. q. 315 F. (foreign 350 F.). Editions Techniques pour l'Automobile et l'Industrie (ETAI), 20-22 rue de la Saussiere, 92100 Boulogne Billancourt, France. TEL 46-04-81-13. FAX 48-25-56-92. TELEX ETAIRTA 204 850 F. Ed. Christian Rey. charts; illus. circ. 15,000. —CCC.
Description: Each issue deals with 2 motorcycles and explains how to dismantle and repair them.

796.6   UK   ISSN 0967-1234
RIDE B M X MAGZINE. 1992. bi-m. £14 (foreign £20). 4130 Publishing Ltd., P.O. Box 1300, Dorchester, Dorset DT1 1FN, England. TEL 01305-251263. FAX 01305-251263. (Dist. by: UMD, 16-28 Tabernacle St., London EC2A 4BW, England. TEL 0171-638-4666) Ed. Mark Noble. adv.; bk.rev. circ. 17,500. (back issues avail.) **Document type:** consumer publication.
Formerly (until 1992): Invert.

RIDE ON!. see CONSERVATION

796.7   US   ISSN 0095-1625
GV1059.5
RIDER; motorcycle touring & sport touring. 1974. m. $15.98 (foreign $25.98). T L Enterprises, Inc., 3601 Calle Tecate, Camarillo, CA 93012. TEL 805-389-0300. Ed. Mark Tuttle, Jr; Pub. Joe McNeil. illus. circ. 117,707. **Document type:** consumer publication. —UnCover.
Description: Devoted to the motorcycle touring enthusiast, including bike tests, new-product evaluations, touring adventures, and buyer's guides.

796.6   US   ISSN 1069-2649
ROAD BIKE ACTION. 1993. m. Hi-Torque Publications, Inc., Box 957, Valencia, CA 91380-9057. TEL 818-365-6831. adv.: B&W page $2270, color page $3465; trim 8 x 10 3/4; adv. contact: Robert Rex. circ. 145,000 (paid). **Document type:** consumer publication.

796.7   US   ISSN 0035-7243
TL440.5
ROAD RIDER; America's first motorcycle touring magazine. 1969. m. $19.97. Fancy Publications, 2401 Beverly Blvd., Los Angeles, CA 90057. TEL 714-855-8822. FAX 714-855-3045. (Subscr. to: Box 488, Mt. Morris, IL 61054) Ed. Bob Carpenter. adv.; bk.rev.; illus.; index. circ. 50,000. (back issues avail.) **Document type:** consumer publication.
Description: For the traveling motorcyclists in search of two-wheeled adventure. Focuses on various aspects of motorcycle touring; foreign or domestic journeys, long distances or short weekenders.

ROADRACING WORLD & MOTORCYCLE TECHNOLOGY. see TRANSPORTATION

796.7   GW
▼**ROLLER.** 1994. a. DM.4; newsstand price: DM.4. Vereinigte Motor-Verlage GmbH und Co. KG, Leuschnerstr. 1, 70162 Stuttgart, Germany. TEL 0711-1821226. FAX 0711-1821349. Ed. Friedhelm Fiedler; Pub. Peter-Paul Pietsch. adv.: B&W page DM.6400, color page DM.11200; adv. contact: Claus Schlosser. circ. 90,000. **Document type:** consumer publication.

796.75   IT   ISSN 1122-634X
RUOTE IN PISTA INTERNATIONAL. 1982. m. (10/yr.). L.80000. Editoriale Sportquattro S.r.l., Via del Don 2, 20123 Milan, Italy. TEL 39-2-58310013. FAX 39-2-583210071. Ed. Claudio Casaroli. adv.: color page L.9000000. circ. 50,000.
Formerly (until 1989): Ruote in Pista (ISSN 1122-6226)

796.7   US   ISSN 1051-0613
SAFE CYCLING. 1980. q. $15 per no. Motorcycle Safety Foundation, 2 Jenner St., Ste. 150, Irvine, CA 92718-3812. TEL 714-727-3227. FAX 714-727-4217. Ed. Nate Rauba. bk.rev.; charts; illus.; stat.; tr.lit.; circ. 6,500 (controlled). **Document type:** newsletter.
Description: Motorcycle safety information for instructors and individuals.

388   CN   ISSN 0705-1840
SANFORD EVANS GOLD BOOK OF MOTORCYCLE DATA & USED PRICES. 1977. a. Can.$17.50. Sanford Evans Communications Ltd., 1700 Church Ave., Box 6900, Winnipeg, MB R3C 3B1, Canada. TEL 204-694-2022. FAX 204-694-3040. Ed. G.B. Henry; Pub. Gary Henry.
Description: Valuation guide features trade-in value of motorcycles, vehicle identification numbers, weight, over-all length.

796.7   GW
SCHERMER'S MOTORRAD KATALOG. 1989. a. DM.12. Motor Technik Verlag, Straussstaffel 3, 7000 Stuttgart 1, Germany. TEL 0711-16850-0. FAX 0711-1685054. (back issues avail.)

796.7   SP
SCOOTER. s-a. newsstand price: 400 ptas. Luike - Motorpress, C. Ancora 40, 28045 Madrid, Spain. TEL 34-1-3470100. FAX 34-1-3470204. Ed. Juan Hernandez. adv.: B&W page 345000 ptas., color page 540000 ptas.; adv. contact: Agustin Valero. **Document type:** consumer publication.

796.7 IT
SCOOTER MAGAZINE. 1991. q. L.20000 (foreign L.40000) (effective 1992). Editore L' Isola, Piazza Roma, 1, Lurago Marinone (CO), Italy. TEL 031-937736. FAX 031-937362. Ed. Tiziano Cantatore. adv. circ. 30,000.
Description: Covers new, vintage, and custom scooters, accessories, trips, technical tips, and news from clubs.

796.5 UK ISSN 0140-4512
SCOTTISH HOSTELLER. 1976. s-a. free. Scottish Youth Hostels Association, 7 Glebe Crescent, Stirling FK8 2JA, Scotland. TEL 01786-451181. FAX 01786-450198. Ed. E. Gardiner. adv.; bk.rev. circ. 45,000. **Document type:** newsletter.

796.6 SP
SOLO BICI. 1975. m. 4500 ptas. (Europe 6500 ptas.; US 8500 ptas.). Alesport S.A., Gran Via 8-10, 08908 Hospitalet (Barcelona), Spain. TEL 34315533. FAX 34227404. adv.; bk.rev.
Description: Dedicated to the off-road bicyclist, includes news and reports of new products and some sport coverage.

796.7 SP
SOLO MOTO ACTUAL. 1975. 52/yr. 16500 ptas. (Europe 28000 ptas.; America 37000 ptas.; Far East 52000 ptas.). Alesport S.A., Gran Via 8-10, 08908 Hospitalet (Barcelona), Spain. TEL 34315533. FAX 34227404. Ed. Enric Clara. adv. circ. 18,000.
Description: Dedicated to the motorcyclist, includes reviews of new products and sports coverage.

796.7 SP
SOLO MOTO 30. 1983. 12/yr. 4500 ptas. (Europe 6500 ptas.; US 8500 ptas.). Alesport S.A., Gran Via 8-10, 08908 Hospitalet (Barcelona), Spain. TEL 34315533. FAX 34227404. Ed. Enric Clara. adv. contact: Nelo Dreshite. bk.rev.; video rev. circ. 26,000. **Document type:** consumer publication.
Description: Dedicated to the motocyclist, with reviews of new products and some sports coverage.

796.7 AT ISSN 0310-446X
SPEEDWAY RACING NEWS. 1971. m. Aus.$52($40) (typically set in Feb.). Marine Publications Pty. Ltd., P.O. Box 767, Narrabeen, N.S.W. 2101, Australia. TEL 61-2-9132288. FAX 61-2-9131199. Ed. Tony Loxley. adv.: Andrew/Galwey. circ. 10,000. (back issues avail.) **Document type:** consumer publication.
Description: Sporting magazine for speedway enthusiasts. Covers 150 speedway tracks in Australia and New Zealand.

796.7 US
SPORT BIKE. 1991. a. $5.95. Hachette Magazines, Inc., 1499 Monrovia Ave., Newport Beach, CA 92663. TEL 714-720-5300. Ed. Paul Dean. adv. contact: John Dawson. **Document type:** consumer publication.

796.7 GW
SPORT MOTORRAD KATALOG. 1989. a. DM.9.80. Motor Technik Verlag, Straussaffel 3, 70184 Stuttgart, Germany. TEL 0711-16850-0. FAX 0711-1685054. (back issues avail.)

796.7 US ISSN 1065-7649
SPORT RIDER. 1993. bi-m. Petersen Publishing Co., 6420 Wilshire Blvd., Los Angeles, CA 90048. TEL 213-782-2000. Ed. Nick Ienatsch. adv.; illus. **Document type:** consumer publication.

796.6 US ISSN 1060-8419
SPORTBIKES. 1991. a. $3.95. Hachette Magazines, Inc., 1633 Broadway, 45th Fl., New York, NY 10009. TEL 212-767-6000.

796.7 US
STREET BIKE NEWSMAGAZINE. 1991. m. $14 (effective 1996); newsstand price: $1.75. R P M Publishing, 6514 Glade Ave., Canoga Park, CA 91303. TEL 818-888-4921. Ed. S. Alan Melamed. adv.: B&W page $900, color page $1850; trim 8 3/8 x 10 7/8. circ. 28,000. **Document type:** consumer publication.
Formerly: CA Bike - U S Bike.

796.7 UK ISSN 0961-9453
STREETFIGHTERS. 1992. bi-m. £13.50. Myatt McFarlane plc, Trident House, Heath Rd., Hale, Altrincham, Cheshire WA14 2UJ, England. TEL 0161-928-3480. FAX 0161-941-6897. Ed. Steven Myatt; Pub. Steven Myatt. adv. contact: Garry Burns. circ. 25,000. (paid). (back issues avail.) **Document type:** consumer publication.

796.6 DK ISSN 0905-4766
STYRET. 1899. 10/yr. membership. Koebenhavns Cykelhandlerforening, Ny Kongensgade 20, DK-1557 Copenhagen K, Denmark. TEL 45-33-11-40-03. FAX 45-33-12-64-19. Ed. Erik Svebolle. adv.; B&W page DKK 1950; trim 183 x 263. bibl.; mkt.; index. circ. 500. **Document type:** trade publication.
Former titles: Cykelbranchen; (until Jan. 1978): Styret (ISSN 0039-4319); Cykelhandleren.

629.227 IT ISSN 1121-3892
SUPER MOTOTECNICA. Key Title: Supermoto Tecnica. 1987. m. L.43000 (foreign L.90000). N.P.M. s.r.l., Via Molise, 3, 20085 Locate Triulzi (MI), Italy. TEL 02-90780478. FAX 02-9077862. Ed. Sandro Colombo. adv.; B&W page L.2395000, color page L.4305000; trim 185 x 264.

796 UK ISSN 0262-8457
SUPERBIKE. m. £32. Link House Magazines Ltd., Link House, Dingwall Ave., Croydon, Surrey CR9 2TA, England. TEL 0181-686-2599. FAX 0181-760-0973. (Subscr. to: R F S, 120-126 Lavender Ave., Mitcham, Surrey CR4 3HP, England) Ed. Grant Leonard. adv. circ. 28,593. **Document type:** consumer publication.
Description: Information and feature articles on street motorcycling touring, drag racing, tuning features, reviews of machinery and equipment and profiles of enthusiasts.

388.347 US ISSN 0162-3923
TL440
SUPERCYCLE. m. $27.95 (foreign $37.95). Larry Flynt Publications, Inc., 9171 Wilshire Blvd., Ste. 300, Beverly Hills, CA 90210. TEL 310-858-7100. FAX 310-274-7985. Ed. Elliot Borin. adv. **Document type:** consumer publication.
Description: Covers American motorcycles and their riders.

796.7 GW
DER SYBURGER; das nordrheinwestfaelische Motorrad-Magazin. 1980. m. DM.25. Syburger Verlag GmbH, Hertingerstr. 60, 59423 Unna, Germany. TEL 02303-98550. FAX 02303-98559. Eds. V. Heimann, G. Wagner. adv.; bk.rev. circ. 30,000. **Document type:** consumer publication.

796.6 US
▼**TANDEM MAGAZINE.** 1994. q. $12.95 (foreign $20.95) (effective 1995). Petzold Publishing, 26895 Petzold Rd., Eugene, OR 97402. TEL 503-485-5262. FAX 503-341-0788. E-mail: tandem@efn.org; Site addr.: http://tandem.efn.org/. (Subscr. to: Box 2939, Eugene, OR 97402) Ed. Greg Shepherd; Pub. Marlen Shepherd. adv.; illus. circ. 30,000. (back issues avail.) **Document type:** consumer publication.
Description: Covers all aspects of tandem cycling, with accounts of travel, reviews of tandem bicycles and related products.

796.6 US
TEXAS BICYCLIST.* 1989. 9/yr. $12. Yellow Jersey Enterprises, 12814 Azalea Creek Trail, Houston, TX 77095-4209. TEL 713-782-1661. (Subscr. to: Box 49788, Austin, TX 78765) Ed. Kim Grob. adv.; bk.rev.; circ. 45,000 (controlled). **Document type:** consumer publication.
Description: Provides information on local cycling tours, equipment and safety.

796.7 US
▼**THUNDER ALLEY.** 1994. bi-m. $14.00. T A M Communications, Inc., 6 Prowitt St., Norwalk, CT 06855. TEL 203-855-0008. FAX 203-852-9980. (Subscr. to: Fulco, Box 3000, Denville, NJ 07834-9375. TEL 800-875-2997. FAX 201-627-5872) Ed. Josh Cho. adv. contact: Mike Stankiewicz. circ. 55,000 (paid). **Document type:** consumer publication.
Description: Covers high-performance Harley-Davidson bikes. Offers real-world comparisons of motorcycle products and publishes technical and how-to articles on how to improve a Harley's performance.

796.6 GW ISSN 0936-0905
TOUR; das Rad Magazin. m. DM.79.80 (foreign DM.94.20). Atlas Verlag und Werbung GmbH, Karlstr. 41, 80333 Munich, Germany. TEL 089-55241200. FAX 089-55241288. Eds. Stefan Engert, Uwe Geissler; Pub. Hajo Artope. adv. contact: Michael Holzapfel. circ. 82,543. **Document type:** consumer publication.

796.75 GW ISSN 0933-4440
TOUREN-FAHRER; Reportagen - Test - Technik. 1981. 10/yr. DM.65 (foreign DM.90). Reiner H. Nitschke Verlags GmbH, Pastor-Berg-Str. 4, 53520 Duempelfeld, Germany. TEL 02695-1009. FAX 02695-1400. Ed. Reiner H. Nitschke. **Document type:** consumer publication.

796.7 DK ISSN 0106-1925
TOURING NYT. 1966. 8/yr. DKK 190. M C Touring Club, Oddervej 79, DK-8270 Hojbjerg, Denmark. TEL 45-86-27-25-15. FAX 45-86-27-31-19. Ed. Gunnar Skrydstrup. adv. contact: Jensen Wettlavfer. bk.rev. circ. 12,500. **Document type:** consumer publication.

796.7 US ISSN 0892-3922
TRAIL RIDER MAGAZINE. 1970. m. $18. Box 129, Medford, NJ 08055. TEL 609-953-7805. FAX 609-953-7312. Pub. Paul Clipper. adv. contact: Paul Clipper. circ. 3,000 (paid). (back issues avail.) **Document type:** consumer publication.
Description: Covers off-road motorcycling throughout the Northeast.

796.7 UK
TRAIL RIDERS FELLOWSHIP BULLETIN. 1970. q. £10($18) Trail Riders Fellowship, c/o Mrs. Rosemary Marsoton, Ed., 4 Surrey Rd., Woolston, Southampton SO1 9ED, England. TEL 0703 420813. adv.; bk.rev. circ. 2,000. (back issues avail.) **Document type:** newsletter.
Description: Newsletter of the National Club for the encouragement of non-competitive green roads motorcycling and maintenance of rights of way, in England and Wales.

796.7 UK ISSN 0958-4226
TRIALS AND MOTOCROSS NEWS. 1977. w. 55p. per no. Lancaster and Morecambe Newspapers Ltd., Victoria St., Morecambe, Lancs. LA4 4AG, England. Ed. Bill Lawless. adv.; bk.rev. circ. 30,000. **Document type:** newspaper.

796.6 IT ISSN 1120-5873
TUTTO MOUNTAIN BIKE. 1989. m. L.70000 (foreign L.140000). Gruppo B Editore, Via Don Vercesi 19, 20091 Bresso (MI), Italy. TEL 39-2-66503000. FAX 39-2-66503060. Ed. Angelo Berto. adv.: page L.6000000; adv. contact: Marzio Bardi. circ. 55,000. **Document type:** consumer publication.

796 IT ISSN 1121-3884
TUTTOCICLISMO. w. L.50000 (foreign L.60000). Federazione Ciclistica Italiana, Via dei Mille 6, 00185 Rome, Italy. TEL 39-6-4452630. FAX 39-6-4440010. Ed. Agostino Omini. adv. contact: Roberto Binda. circ. 15,000.

TUTTOFOURISTRADA OSSERVATORE MOTORISTICO. see TRANSPORTATION — Automobiles

338.347 796.7 IT ISSN 0393-7879
TUTTOMOTO. 1978. m. L.62400 (foreign L.90000). Rusconi Editori S.p.A., Servizio Abbonamenti, Viale Sarca 235, 20126 Milan, Italy. TEL 02-66191. FAX 02-6619-2737. Ed. Giulio Palumbo. adv.: page L.20000000. circ. 108,595.

629.227 IT
TUTTORALLY. 1983. m. L.80000 (foreign L.160000). Barbero Editori S.r.l., Via Galileo Galilei 3, 10023 Chieri (TO), Italy. TEL 39-11-9470400. FAX 39-11-9470577. Ed. Nanni Barbero. adv.: color page L.9400000. circ. 69,000.

629.227 NE ISSN 0165-1943
TWEEWIELER; maandblad voor de tweewielerbranche. 1921. m. Misset (Subsidiary of: Reed Elsevier plc), Postbus 4, 7000 BA Doetinchem, Netherlands. TEL 31-8340-49911. FAX 31-8340-63638. Ed. Jack Oortwijn. adv.: B&W page fl.3331, color page fl.6381; trim 215 x 285; adv. contact: Cor van Nek. abstr.; illus.; mkt.; stat. circ. 4,940. Indexed: Key to Econ.Sci. **Document type:** trade publication.
Description: Supplies information about current developments of interest to bicycle, scooter and motorcycle retailers.

SPORTS AND GAMES — BOATS AND BOATING

796   AT   ISSN 0041-4700
TWO WHEELS. m. Aus.$47. Federal Publishing Company, 180 Bourke Rd., Alexandria, N.S.W. 2015, Australia. Ed. Mick Matheson. circ. 23,500. **Indexed:** Aus.Rd.Ind., Pinpointer.
   Description: Information on latest meodels, road tests and equipment for motorcycles.

UNSER WANDERBOTE. see *SPORTS AND GAMES*

796.7   US   ISSN 1073-581X
▼ **V Q**. (V-Twin Quarterly) 1994. q. $19.95 (effective 1995 & 1996); newsstand price: $5.99. Paisano Publications, Inc., Box 1050, Agoura Hills, CA 91376-1050. TEL 818-889-8740. FAX 818-889-4726. adv.; illus. **Document type:** consumer publication.

796.7   US   ISSN 1042-5365
V-TWIN. 1989. m. $39.95 (foreign $51.95) (effective 1995 & 1996); newsstand price: $4.99. Paisano Publications, Inc., Box 1050, Agoura Hills, CA 91376-1050. TEL 818-889-8740. FAX 818-889-4726. adv.; illus. **Document type:** consumer publication.

796.6   CN   ISSN 1180-1360
VELO MAG. 6/yr. Can.$24.27. Editions Tricycle, 3575 boul. Saint-Laurent, Bur. 310, Montreal, PQ H2X 2T7, Canada. TEL 514-847-8356. FAX 514-847-0242. Ed. Pierre Hamel. adv. contact: F. Tremblay. **Indexed:** Pt.de Rep. (1989-).

796.6   FR   ISSN 0222-7797
VELO MAGAZINE. 1979. m. 215 F. S N C L'Equipe, 10 rue du Fg. Montmartre, 75009 Paris, France. Ed. J.M. Leblanc. adv.; bk.rev.
   Formerly: Cyclisme.

796.6   FR   ISSN 1157-4011
VELO TONIC. 1991. m. (11/yr.). 281 F. (foreign 347 F.). Ediregie, B.P. 86, 94420 Le Plessis-Trevise, France. TEL 45-93-72-72. FAX 45-93-25-93. TELEX EDIGIE 262 572 F. **Document type:** consumer publication.

796.6   US   ISSN 0161-1798
VELONEWS; the journal of competitive cycling. 1972. 20/yr. $37.97. Inside Communications, 1830 N. 55th St., Boulder, CO 80301-2700. TEL 303-440-0601. FAX 303-444-6788. Ed. John Wilcockson. adv.; bk.rev.; film rev.; charts; illus.; stat.; index. circ. 47,000. (tabloid format; also avail. in microfilm from UMI; back issues avail.) **Indexed:** Sports Per.Ind., Sportsearch (1977-). **Document type:** consumer publication.
   Former titles (until 1974): Cyclenews; (until 1972): Northeast Bicycle News.
   Description: Reports on major bicycle races in U.S. and Europe and includes a complete calendar of U.S.-Canada races. Provides articles on training, products, physiology and mountain biking.

VIE DE L'AUTO. see *ANTIQUES*

VIE DE LA MOTO. see *ANTIQUES*

796.7   UK
VINTAGE MOTOR CYCLE. 1948. m. £18. (Vintage Motor Cycle Club) Dalton Watson Fine Books Ltd., P.O. Box 2, Belton, Loughborough, Leics. LE12 9UW, England. TEL 01530-223569. Ed. David Styles. adv.; bk.rev. circ. 10,600. **Document type:** consumer publication.
   Formerly: Vintage Motor Cycle Club Magazine.

VOGELVRIJE FIETSER. see *TRANSPORTATION*

796.6 052   UK
W O W MAGAZINE. (Women on Wheels) 4/yr. Womens Cycle Racing Association, 27 Parkhill Rd., Sidcup, Kent DA15 7NJ, England. Ed. M. Ivatts. **Document type:** newsletter.

796.7   US   ISSN 1051-8088
WALNECK'S CLASSIC CYCLE TRADER. m. $24. Walneck's Inc., 7923 Janes Ave., Woodridge, IL 60517. TEL 708-985-4995.

796.6   UK   ISSN 0955-4912
WHAT BIKE?. m. £26.40 (foreign £35.90) (effective 1995-1996). E M A P National Publications Ltd., Bushfield House, Orton Centre, Peterborough, Cambs. PE2 0EW, England. TEL 01733-237111. FAX 01733-239127. (Subscr. to: Tower Publishing Services Ltd., Tower House, Sovereign Park, Lathkill St., Market Harborough, Leics. LE16 9EF, England. TEL 01858-468811. FAX 01858-462164) Pub. Charles Davies. adv. **Document type:** consumer publication.
   Formerly (until 1986): Bike Buyer (ISSN 0266-8092)

796.6   AT
WHEELS (ALEXANDRIA). bi-m. Aus.$60. Federal Publishing Company, 180 Bourke Rd., Alexandria, N.S.W. 2015, Australia. adv. circ. 7,516.
   Formerly: Bike Australia (ISSN 0810-2872)

796.6   US
WINNING BICYCLING ILLUSTRATED.* 1983. m. (11/yr.). $23.95. Winning International, Inc., Box 21056, Lehigh Valley, PA 18002-1056. TEL 215-266-6893. FAX 215-266-7196. Ed. Richard G. Carlson. adv. contact: Nancy Tamayo. circ. 59,264. **Document type:** consumer publication.
   Formerly: Winning Bicycle Racing Illustrated.
   Description: Features various forms of competitive bicycle racing.

629.227   CC   ISSN 1000-999X
ZHONGGUO ZIXINGCHE/CHINA BICYCLE. (Text in Chinese) 1972. bi-m. Y100($80) Bicycle Information Centre of China, China Bicycle Association, No.6, Alley 360, Anyuan Road, Shanghai 200060, People's Republic of China. TEL 021-2584696. FAX 021-2550918. Ed. Yang Huide; Pub. Sheng Aiguo. adv.; B&W page $400, color page $1000. software rev.; illus. circ. 10,000.
   Refereed Serial

796.7   SZ
ZWEIRAD SCHWEIZ.* (Text in French and German) 1900. fortn. Schweizerischer Fahrrad- und Motorrad-Gewerbe Verband - Union Suisse des Mecaniciens en Cycles et Motos, Weststr. 9, CH-3000 Bern 6, Switzerland. adv.; illus.; stat.; index. circ. 2,100. **Document type:** consumer publication.
   Former titles (until 1989): Fahrrad- und Motorrad Gewerbe; (until 1969): F M G Fachblatt (ISSN 0014-5955)

796.7   SZ
2 RAD SCHWEIZ (BERN). m. S F M G V, Zentral Sekretariat, Weststr. 9, CH-3000 Bern 6, Switzerland. TEL 031-3516660. **Document type:** consumer publication.

796.7   SZ
2-RAD SCHWEIZ (ZURICH). 24/yr. Seefeldstr. 110, CH-8008 Zurich, Switzerland. TEL 031-221500. FAX 031-3834802. Ed. Harro Lang. circ. 2,000.

796.7   GR   ISSN 1105-1299
2 TROCHI/2 WHEELS. (Text in Greek) 1988. m. $28. Technical Press, S.A., 31 Praxitelous St., 167 77 Athens, Greece. TEL 30-1-9961-861. FAX 30-1-9961-864. Ed. Costas Cavvathas; Pub. Sophie Cavvatha. circ. 20,000. **Document type:** consumer publication.
   Description: Covers motorcycles in general.

3 & 4 WHEEL ACTION. see *TRANSPORTATION — Automobiles*

SPORTS AND GAMES — Boats And Boating

796.95   US
A B Y C NEWS. q. membership only. American Boat & Yacht Council, Inc., 3069 Solomon Island Rd., Edgewater, MD 21037-1416. TEL 410-956-1050. FAX 410-956-2737. Ed. Louise Lincoln. **Document type:** newsletter.
   Description: Articles on technical and safety issues related to recreational boating.

796.95   US
A S A AFFILIATE AND INSTRUCTOR NEWS. 1983. q. membership. American Sailing Association, 13922 Marquesas Way, Marina Del Rey, CA 90292. TEL 310-822-7171. FAX 310-822-4741. Ed. Harry Munns. circ. 10,000. (looseleaf format; back issues avail.) **Document type:** newsletter.
   Description: Business topics relating to boating businesses.

796   UK   ISSN 0144-1396
A Y R S JOURNAL. 1956. irreg. (approx. 2-3/yr). £15($30) Amateur Yacht Research Society, BCM - AYRS, London WC1N 3XX, England. TEL 0752-812003. (U.S. addr.: Mr. M. Badham, Amateur Yacht Research Society, R F D No.2, P.O. Box 180, Bath, ME 04530) Ed. R.M. Ellison. bk.rev. circ. 1,400.

796.95   UK   ISSN 0964-0932
ADMARINE. 1983. m. £12. Compass Rose Ltd., 92 The Avenue, Sunbury-on-Thames, Middlesex TW16 5EX, England. adv.; bk.rev.; circ. 20,000 (controlled). (tabloid format) **Document type:** trade publication.
   Description: Reports on all aspects of the marine leisure industry.

797.14   AT   ISSN 1034-6651
THE ALFRED'S YACHTSMAN. q. (Royal Prince Alfred Yacht Club) National Publications Pty. Ltd., P.O. Box 297, Homebush West, N.S.W. 2140, Australia. TEL 02-764-1111. FAX 02-763-1699. circ. 3,000.
   Formerly (until 1989): Alfred's Navigator's Notebook (ISSN 0311-0990)
   Description: Covers all club events plus major yachting and sailing news.

797.1   US
AMERICAN POWER BOAT ASSOCIATION. A P B A RULE - REFERENCE BOOK. (In 4 vols; Parts 1-3: Racing Rules; Part 4: Racing Records, Commissions, Membership Directory) 1903. a. $10 for each part to non-members. American Power Boat Association, 17640 E. Nine Mile Rd., Box 377, Eastpointe, MI 48021. TEL 313-773-9700. FAX 313-773-6490. Ed. Michele Weston. index.
   Formerly: American Power Boat Association. A P B A Rule Book (ISSN 0065-9797)

797.123   US   ISSN 0888-1154
GV790.6
AMERICAN ROWING. 1969. bi-m. $40 membership. United States Rowing Association, 201 S. Capitol Ave., Ste. 400, Indianapolis, IN 46225-1054. TEL 317-237-5656. FAX 317-237-5646. Ed. Susan Lezotte. adv. contact: Susan Lezotte. bk.rev.; illus.; index. circ. 15,000. **Indexed:** Phys.Ed.Ind., Sports Per.Ind., Sportsearch (1986-). **Document type:** trade publication.
   Former titles: Rowing U S A (ISSN 0744-4788); Oarsman.

796.95   US
AMERICAN SAILING. q. American Sailing Association, 13922 Marquesas Way, Marina Del Rey, CA 90292. TEL 310-822-7171. FAX 310-822-4741.

797.1   US   ISSN 0279-9553
AMERICAN SAILOR. 1980. m. membership. U S Yacht Racing Union, Box 843, Franklin, TN 37064. TEL 615-791-1780. adv. circ. 28,000. **Indexed:** Sportsearch (1981-).

797.1   US   ISSN 0300-7626
AMERICAN WHITE WATER. 1967. bi-m. $20. American Whitewater Affiliation, Box 85, Phoenicia, NY 12464. TEL 914-688-5569. Ed. Beb Gedekoh. adv.; B&W page $350; trim 8 1/4 x 10 3/4; adv. contact: Phyllis B. Horowitz. bk.rev.; circ. 5,000 (paid). **Indexed:** Sportsearch (1978-). **Document type:** newsletter.
—UnCover.
   Description: Covers canoeing and kayaking and river conservation.

797   FR   ISSN 0758-6639
ANNUAIRE NAUTISME. 1963. a. 160 F.($27) Editions de Chabassol, 30 rue de Gramont, 75002 Paris, France. TEL 42-97-50-30. FAX 42-86-02-81. Ed. B. Laloup. adv.

797.1   IT
ANNUARIO DELLA NAUTICA. 1977. a. L.10000. Nautica Editrice, Via Tevere 44, 00198 Rome, Italy. TEL 39-6-8413060. FAX 39-6-8543653. TELEX 611613 NAUTIC I. adv.; B&W page L.6400000. illus.

SPORTS AND GAMES — BOATS AND BOATING

797.1 US ISSN 0003-5904
ANTIQUE OUTBOARDER. 1966. q. $45 (Canada $63; elsewhere $67) 2 yrs. membership. Antique Outboard Motor Club, Inc., Box 09293, Milwaukee, WI 53209-0293. adv.; illus.; stat. circ. 1,000. (tabloid format)
Description: Covers history, restoration, technical reports, antique outboard racing, special features, and chapter news.

623.82 FR ISSN 0395-1804
ARGUS DU BATEAU ET DE TOUT LE MATERIEL NAUTIQUE. 1966. 4/yr. Editions Kerfan, 97-103 ave. Semeria, B.P. 18, 06230 St. Jean Cap Ferrat, 53 France. Ed. D. Garnier-Gougenheim. adv. circ. 35,000.
Formerly (until 1975): Cote Inter-Europe du Bateau d'Occasion (ISSN 0395-1812)

791.95 AT
AUSTRALIAN CHARTER GUIDE. a. A.B. Organisation Pty. Ltd., P.O. Box 319, Avalon Beach, N.S.W. 2107, Australia. TEL 02-918-8322. FAX 02-918-8884. (Dist. by: Gordon & Gotch, 25-37 Huntingdale Rd., Burwood, Vic. 3125, Australia) circ. 24,000.
Description: Includes wide-ranging feature articles with an annual survey of charter fleets, their rates, season factors and booking information.

796.95 AT ISSN 0313-766X
AUSTRALIAN POWERBOAT. 1976. 6/yr. Aus.$29.70 (foreign Aus.$84) (effective Feb. 1995). Yaffa Publishing Group, 17-21 Bellevue St., Surry Hills, N.S.W. 2010, Australia. TEL 61-2-281-2333. FAX 61-2-281-2750. Ed. Stephen Hurworth. adv.: B&W page Aus.$1660, color page Aus.$2110; trim 273 x 210. circ. 5,580. **Document type:** consumer publication.
Description: For the informed enthusiast who owns a power boat or intends to acquire one.

797.123 AT ISSN 0727-3126
AUSTRALIAN ROWING. 1978. q. Aus.$14 (foreign Aus.$24). Australian Rowing Council Inc., 31 Alsace St., Carine, W.A. 6020, Australia. TEL 61-9-4472220. FAX 61-9-4472220. Ed. Ken Matts. adv.: B&W page Aus.$350; adv. contact: K.I. Matts. bk.rev. circ. 2,000. **Indexed:** Sportsearch (1983-). **Document type:** newsletter.

797.1 AT ISSN 0726-5646
AUSTRALIAN SAILING. m. Aus.$57 (foreign Aus.$152) (effective Feb. 1995). Yaffa Publishing Group, 17-21 Bellevue St., Surry Hills, N.S.W. 2010, Australia. TEL 61-2-281-2333. FAX 61-2-281-2750. Ed. Bob Ross. adv.: B&W page Aus.$1550, color page Aus.$2005; trim 273 x 210. circ. 7,150. **Document type:** consumer publication.
Description: Covers the whole spectrum of sailing from dinghies to maxi yachts - for racing or pleasure. Includes coverage of major yachting events from around the world.

796.95 AT ISSN 1035-3852
AUSTRALIAN YACHTING. 1983. m. Aus.$42 (foreign Aus.$115) (effective Feb. 1995). Yaffa Publishing Group, 17-21 Bellevue St., Surry Hills, N.S.W. 2010, Australia. TEL 61-2-281-2333. FAX 61-2-281-2750. Ed. Neil Baird. adv.: B&W page Aus.$1240, color page Aus.$1515; trim 297 x 210. bk.rev. circ. 5,000.
Former titles: Nautical News (ISSN 1034-4179) & Australian Nautical News (ISSN 0812-163X)
Description: Includes boat reviews, news on yacht races, product information and feature articles.

797.1 FR ISSN 0988-1956
AVIRON. 1886. 7/yr. 120 F. (foreign 170 F.). Aviron France Promotion, 17 bl. de la Marne, 94736 Nogent sur Marne Cedex, France.
TEL 33-1-45-14-26-70. FAX 33-1-48-75-78-80. Ed. D. Roudy. adv.; bk.rev.; illus. **Indexed:** Sportsearch (1977-).

796.95 US ISSN 0279-5949
B O A T - U S REPORTS. 1966. bi-m. $12.50. Boat Owners Association of the United States, 880 S. Pickett St., Alexandria, VA 22304.
TEL 703-461-2864. FAX 703-461-2845. Ed. Michael G. Sciulla. bk.rev. circ. 510,000. **Document type:** consumer publication.
Description: Covers legislative, regulatory and consumer issues of interest to recreational boat owners.

797.1 DK ISSN 0525-4515
BAAD-REVYEN. a. DKK 114.50. Bonniers Specialmagasiner A-S, Strandboulevarden 130, 2100 Copenhagen OE, Denmark. circ. 25,000.
Document type: catalog.
Description: Full color catalogue of more than 500 sailboats and motorboats for private use available on the Scandinavian market.

796.95 DK
BAADNYT. m. DKK 38.50. Bonniers Specialmagasiner A-S, Strandboulevarden 130, 2100 Copenhagen OE, Denmark. TEL 45-39-29-55-00.
FAX 45-39-29-01-99. Ed. Ben Melchior. circ. 21,419.
Description: Tests, cruising articles and do-it-yourself material on boats in Denmark.

796.95 SW ISSN 1102-2272
BAAT-REVYN. 1991. a. SEK 118.50 (effective 1991). Fogtdal, S-205 50 Malmoe, Sweden.

796.95 SW ISSN 1100-5580
BAATAR TIL SALU; koep, saelj, hyr allt foer sjoen. 1988. fortn. SEK 356. Baatar til Salu, S-112 85 Stockholm, Sweden. TEL 46-8-692-01-75. FAX 46-8-650-37-20. Ed. Emma Roos. adv. **Document type:** trade publication.

797.95 SW ISSN 0282-3934
BAATLIV. 1971. 5/yr. SEK 149 (effective 1991). Svenska Baatunionen (SBU), Af Pontins vaeg 6, S-115 21 Stockholm, Sweden. (Subscr. to: P.O. Box 3217, S-103 64 Stockholm, Sweden)
Formerly (until vol.3, 1983): Fritidsbaaten.

797.1 SW ISSN 0005-6308
BAATNYTT/BOATING NEWS. 1958. m. SEK 394. Bonniers Specialtidningar AB, P.O. Box 70452, S-107 26 Stockholm, Sweden. Ed. Bo Joensson. adv.: B&W page SEK 22000, color page SEK 25900. bk.rev.; illus.; mkt.; index. circ. 50,700.
Formerly (until 1962): Motorbaatsnytt.

797.1 NO ISSN 0803-6187
BAATNYTT. 1975. m. NOK 474. Bonniers, P.O. Box 253, N-1360 Nesbru, Norway.
TEL 47-66-84-60-60. FAX 47-66-84-85-85. (Subscr. to: P.O. Box 2716, St. Hanshaugen, N-0131 Oslo, Norway. TEL 47-22-3843-88) Ed. Morten Jensen. adv. contact: Viggo Ryhjell. circ. 27,000.

797.14 SW ISSN 1101-4253
BAATRACING. 1989. 3/yr. Svenska Racerbaatfoerbundet (SVERA), Idrottens Hus, S-123 87 Farsta, Sweden.

796.95 SW ISSN 1101-0088
BAATTURIST; gaesthamnar, service, sevaerdheter, koepguide. 1990. a. SEK 30 (effective 1990). Svenska Turistfoereningen, P.O. Box 25, S-101 20 Stockholm, Sweden.

796.95 SW ISSN 0283-5770
BAATVAERLDEN. 1987. a. SEK 89 per no. Baatbranchens Riksfoerbund, Ljusstoeparbakken 20, S-117 65 Stockholm, Sweden.
TEL 46-8-744-02-22. FAX 46-8-744-18-29. circ. 20,000.
Incorporates: Alla Baatar (ISSN 0284-9437)

796.95 IT ISSN 1121-1865
BARCHE E CATALOGO. 1980. m. (8/yr.) L.43000. Gruppo Editoriale Commerciale, Via G. Galilei, 6, 20124 Milan, Italy. TEL 02-29097-1.
FAX 02-29097-209. Ed. Giorgia Gessner. adv.: B&W page L.3500000, color page L.5500000; trim 185 x 243. bk.rev.; circ. 26,000 (controlled).
Description: Covers national and international boat shows, boat tests, news, techniques, and includes a catalog of all boats built or imported in Italy.

796.95 AG
BARCOS. 1976. m. $9 per no. Editorial Barcos S.R.L., Blanco Encalada 121, 1642 San Isidro, Buenos Aires, Argentina. TEL 54-1-7354407.
FAX 54-1-7354404. Ed. Adrian von Friedberg; Pub. Roberto Garcia Guevara. adv.: B&W page $1800, color page $4395; 220 x 280. bk.rev.; circ. 5,000 (paid); 8,000 (controlled). **Document type:** consumer publication.
Description: Covers commercial craft, luxury yachts, powercruisers, sailboards, sailing dinghies, sailing yachts, sportsboats, jet skis, cruising, sailing vacations, adventure, regattas, products, design, and technical notes.

796.95 US
▼**BASS & WALLEYE BOATS.** 1994. 5/yr. $11.97. Poole Publications, Inc., 20700 Belshaw Ave., Carson, CA 90746. TEL 310-537-6322. FAX 310-537-8735. Ed. Bruce Smith; Pub. Wiley Poole. adv.: B&W page $2770, color page $4395; trim 8 x 10 3/4. circ. 125,000. **Document type:** trade publication.
Description: For boat owners, marine retailers, distributors, wholesalers and jobbers, boat builders, marina and boatyard management, and others.

BASSMASTER CLASSIC REPORT. see *SPORTS AND GAMES — Outdoor Life*

797.1 FR ISSN 0005-6235
BATEAUX. 1958. m. 250 F. Ami Des Jardins, S.A., 8-10 rue Pierre Brossolette, 92300 Levallois Perret, France. Ed. Philippe Simon. adv.; bk.rev.; bibl.; charts; illus.; mkt.; tr.lit.; index, cum.index. circ. 74,081.
Description: Features true stories from the high seas, navigation guides, nautical instruction, marine charts, etc.

796.95 FR ISSN 0984-4899
BATO LOC INTERNATIONAL. 1964. 4/yr. 70 F. Editions Kerfan, 97-103 ave. Semeria, B.P. 18, 06230 St. Jean Cap Ferrat, France. TEL 93-011-037. adv.; stat.; tr.lit.; index. circ. 12,000.
Formerly (until 1987): Marche Europeen du Bateau d'Occasion.

797.1 US
BAY & DELTA YACHTSMAN. 1965. m. $16. Recreation Publications, 2033 Clement Ave., Ste. 100, Alameda, CA 94501. TEL 510-865-7500. FAX 510-865-0186. Ed. Connie Skoog; Pub. Don Abbott. adv. circ. 20,000. **Document type:** consumer publication.
Former titles (until 1993): Yachtsman (ISSN 1065-7398); (until 1992): Bay and Delta Yachtsman (ISSN 0191-4731)
Description: For boating and yachting enthusiasts.

796.95 UK
BLAKES BOATING HOLIDAY BOOKS. a. free. Blakes Holidays Ltd., Wroxham, Norwich NR12 8DH, England. TEL 01603-782141.
FAX 01603-782871. TELEX 97114. Ed. T.E. Howes. adv. circ. 30,000. **Document type:** consumer publication.

BLAKES HOLIDAY BOATING IN BRITAIN AND ABROAD. see *TRAVEL AND TOURISM*

797.1 GW ISSN 0006-4637
DER BLAUE PETER; Zeitschrift fuer Segeln und Seefahrt. 1925. 4/yr. (Deutscher Hochseesportverband Hansa e.V.) Verlag Delius, Klasing und Co., Postfach 101671, 33516 Bielefeld, Germany.
TEL 0521-559-0. FAX 0521-559113. TELEX 932934-DEKLA. adv.; illus. circ. 15,000. **Document type:** consumer publication.

796.95 US ISSN 0163-7452
GV811.63.W56
BOARD & SAIL MAGAZINE. 1978. bi-m. $10. 5109 Esmeralda St., Sacramento, CA 95820.
TEL 916-456-2130. (Subscr. to: Box 8108, Sacramento, CA 95818) Ed. David M. Yost. adv.; bk.rev. circ. 10,000.

796.95 UK ISSN 0950-7337
BOARDS. 1982. m. £28 (foreign £34). Yachting Press Ltd., 196 Eastern Esplanade, Southend-on-Sea, Essex SS1 3AB, England. Ed. Bill Dawes. adv.; bk.rev. circ. 21,490. **Document type:** bulletin.

387.2 380.1 US ISSN 0006-5366
HF6201.B3
BOAT & MOTOR DEALER. 1959. m. $20. Preston Publications, Inc., 7800 N. Merrimac Ave., Box 48312, Niles, IL 60714-3426.
TEL 708-937-1810. FAX 708-965-7639. Ed. Larry Hooper; Pub. S. Tinsley Preston. adv. contact: Jerry Burns. bk.rev. circ. 32,000. **Document type:** trade publication.

796.95 658.8 US
BOAT BROKER. m. $19. Summit Services, Inc., 8365 Old Dairy Rd., Juneau, AK 99801.
TEL 907-789-5581. FAX 907-789-0987. Ed. Riley Woodford; Pub. Renda Heimbinger. adv.: page $615, trim 6 x 9 1/2; adv. contact: Kristen Hammond. circ. 10,000. **Document type:** trade publication.

SPORTS AND GAMES — BOATS AND BOATING

796.95 380.1   CN   ISSN 0826-2802
BOAT GUIDE. s-a. Formula Publications Ltd., 447 Speers Rd., Ste. 4, Oakville, ON L6K 3S7, Canada. TEL 905-842-6591. FAX 905-842-6843. Ed. Lizanne Madigan. **Document type:** consumer publication.
   Description: Official program for Toronto and London boat show. Lists Canadian prices, photos, specifications on all new power boats and engines. Includes editorials covering sport fishing, boating trends, electronics and an index of manufacturers.

796.95   UK   ISSN 0956-6589
BOAT MART INTERNATIONAL. 1986. m. £13.20 (foreign £34.50). Aceville Publications Ltd., 89 East Hill, Colchester, Essex CO1 2QN, England. TEL 0206-871450. FAX 0206-871537. Ed. David Bridle. (back issues avail.)
   Description: For budget and small craft enthusiasts; also covers accessories.

796.95   US   ISSN 0888-1561
BOAT PENNSYLVANIA. 1984. q. Pennsylvania Fish & Boat Commission, Box 67000, Harrisburg, PA 17106-7000. Ed. Art Michaels.

623.82   US   ISSN 0886-0254
BOATBUILDER; the journal of boat design and construction. vol.6, 1988. bi-m. $30 (foreign $36) (effective 1996). Belvoir Publications, Inc., 75 Holly Hill Ln., Box 2626, Greenwich, CT 06836-2626. TEL 203-661-6111. FAX 203-661-4802. (Subscr. to: Box 420234, Palm Coast, FL 32142) Ed. Keith E. Lawrence. **Document type:** consumer publication.

623.82   US
BOATBUILDER'S INTERNATIONAL DIRECTORY; the boatbuilder's source book of designers, kit makers and suppliers. 1980. a. $7.50. Saffron Publishing, 1001 Bridgeway, Dept. 621, Sausalito, CA 94965. Ed. Peter Whyte. adv.; bk.rev. circ. 10,000. **Document type:** directory.

797.1   US   ISSN 0006-5374
GV771
BOATING. 1956. m. $26. Hachette Magazines, Inc., 1633 Broadway, 43rd Fl., New York, NY 10009. TEL 212-767-6000. FAX 212-767-5618. (Subscr. to: Box 2886, Boulder, CO 80322) Ed. John Owens. adv.: B&W page 14075. bk.rev.; charts; illus.; index. circ. 200,000. (also avail. in microform from UMI,MIM) Indexed: Access (1975-), Consum.Ind., Mag.Ind., Sports Per.Ind.
   ●Also available online. Vendor(s): Knight-Ridder, Inc., University Microfilms International.
   —UMI.
   Incorporates (1973-1980): Motorboat (ISSN 0093-6782); which incorporates (in 1975): Family Housebeating (ISSN 0014-7273); Formerly: Popular Boating.

796.95   US
BOATING ALMANAC, VOLUME 1: RHODE ISLAND, MASSACHUSETTS, MAINE, NEW HAMPSHIRE. 1961. a. $12.50. Boating Almanac Co., Inc., 203 McKinsey Rd., Severna Park, MD 21146. TEL 410-647-0084. FAX 410-647-0440. Ed. Peter A. Geis. adv.; charts.

796.95   US
BOATING ALMANAC, VOLUME 2: LONG ISLAND, CONNECTICUT, RHODE ISLAND, SOUTHERN MASSACHUSETTS. 1961. a. $12.50. Boating Almanac Co., Inc., 203 McKinsey Rd., Severna Park, MD 21146. TEL 410-647-0084. FAX 410-647-0440. Ed. Peter A. Geis. adv.; charts.

796.95   US
BOATING ALMANAC, VOLUME 3: NEW JERSEY, DELAWARE BAY, HUDSON RIVER, LAKE CHAMPLAIN, ERIE CANAL. 1961. a. $12.50. Boating Almanac Co., Inc., 203 McKinsey Rd., Severna Park, MD 21146. TEL 410-647-0084. FAX 410-647-0440. Ed. Peter A. Geis. adv.; charts.

796.95   US
BOATING ALMANAC, VOLUME 4: CHESAPEAKE BAY, DELAWARE, MARYLAND, DISTRICT OF COLUMBIA, VIRGINIA. 1961. a. $12.50. Boating Almanac Co., Inc., 203 McKinsey Rd., Severna Park, MD 21146. TEL 410-647-0084. FAX 410-647-0440. Ed. Peter A. Geis. adv.; charts.

796.95   UK   ISSN 0260-9452
BOATING BUSINESS. 1981. m. £20 (rest of Europe £30; elsewhere £40). Rushton Marine Press Ltd., Woodside, Burnhams Rd., Little Bookham, Leatherhead, Surrey KT23 3BA, England. TEL 01372-453316. FAX 01372-459974. Ed. Iain Sutherland. adv.: B&W page £1000, color page £1350; trim 305 x 224. illus.; circ. 8,500 (controlled). **Document type:** trade publication.
   Description: Provides a medium through which suppliers to the trade can establish and maintain contact with their sales outlets. Covers the U.K. and European markets.

796.95   CN   ISSN 0702-7524
BOATING BUSINESS. 1976. 6/yr. Formula Publications Ltd., 447 Speers Rd., Ste. 4, Oakville, ON L6K 3S7, Canada. TEL 905-842-6591. FAX 905-842-6843. Ed. Lizanne Madigan. adv. circ. 4,700. **Document type:** trade publication.

796.95   UK   ISSN 0967-5086
BOATING BUSINESS AND MARINE BUYERS GUIDE. 1989. a. Rushton Marine Press Ltd., Woodside, Burnhams Rd., Little Bookham, Leatherhead, Surrey KT23 2BA, England. TEL 01372-453316. FAX 01372-459974. Ed. Marishelle Gibson; Pub. Robert Hall. **Document type:** directory.
   Formerly (until 1991): Boating Business and Marine Trades Directory (ISSN 0957-5219)

796.95 910.09   US
BOATING IN THE SAN JUAN ISLANDS. a. free. Islands' Sounder, Box 758, Eastsound, WA 98245. circ. 75,000.
   Description: Provides boating and tourist information on the San Juan islands.

387.2   US   ISSN 0006-5404
HD9993.B633
BOATING INDUSTRY; the management magazine of the boating industry. (Supplement avail.: Boating Industry Marine Buyers' Guide) 1937. m. $34 (foreign $96). Argus Inc., 6151 Powers Ferry Rd., N.W., Atlanta, GA 30339-2941. TEL 404-955-2500. FAX 404-955-0400. (And: 5 Penn Plaza, New York, NY 10001. TEL 212-613-9700) Ed. Richard W. Porter. adv.; charts; illus.; tr.lit. circ. 31,248. (also avail. in microform from UMI; reprint service avail. from UMI) Indexed: Bus.Ind., SRI, Tr.& Indus.Ind. **Document type:** trade publication.
   —UMI. CCC.
   Incorporates: Marine Business (ISSN 0147-8923)
   Description: Presents ideas, role models, and guidance for boat retailers to operate their businesses more effectively and profitably. Includes information on marine management, merchandising and selling, market analysis, and industry trends.

BOATING INDUSTRY MARINE BUYERS' GUIDE. see BUSINESS AND ECONOMICS — Trade And Industrial Directories

796.95   CN   ISSN 0700-7388
BOATING NEWS. 1970. m. Can.$12.84. Tyrell Publishing, 1252 Burrard St., Ste. 201, Vancouver, BC V6Z 1Z1, Canada. TEL 604-684-1643. Ed. Don Tyrell; Pub. P.C. Tyrell. adv. contact: Jacquie McMaster. bk.rev. circ. 11,000. **Document type:** newspaper.
   Description: Covers commercial and pleasure boating.

797   US   ISSN 1059-5155
VM320
BOATING WORLD. 1979. 10/yr. $18 (Canada and overseas $45). Trans World Publishing, Inc., 2100 Powers Ferry Rd., Atlanta, GA 30339. TEL 404-955-5656. FAX 404-952-0669. Ed. Billy R. Sims. adv.; bk.rev.; charts; index. circ. 159,900. (back issues avail.) Indexed: Ind.How To Do It (1986-). **Document type:** consumer publication.
   —UMI.
   Former titles: Boat Journal (ISSN 1050-8945); Small Boat Journal (ISSN 0192-7396)
   Description: For owners of boats up to 30 feet in length; provides information for family boaters, fishermen, cruising boaters, and other watersports enthusiasts need to select equipment, maintain, and enjoy their boats.

797.1   NZ   ISSN 1171-7270
BOATINGWORLD. 1992. m. NZ.$55 (foreign NZ$145) (typically set in Sep.). New Zealand Magazines Ltd., Cnr. Halsey & Madden Streets, Freemans Bay, Auckland, New Zealand. FAX 09-309-6361. Ed. Geoff Green. adv.; bk.rev.; charts; illus.; index. circ. 24,000. (back issues avail.)
   Formed by the merger of (1984-1992): New Zealand Powerboat (ISSN 0112-4412); (1945-1992): Sea Spray (ISSN 0037-0037); Which incorporated: Boating World (ISSN 1171-7300)
   Description: Covers general boating, cruising, yachting, amateur boat building, race reports, test reports.

796.95   UK   ISSN 0966-1514
THE BOATMAN. 1992. 10/yr. £25 (U.S. $62.50); newsstand price: £2.95. Waterside Publications Ltd., Waterside House, P.O. Box 1992, Falmouth, Cornwall TR11 3RU, England. TEL 01326-375757. FAX 01326-378551. (Dist. by: MMC, Octagon House, Whitehart Meadows, Ripley, Surrey GU23 6HR, England. TEL 01483-211222) Ed. Pete Greenfield. adv.: B&W page £500, color page £750; trim 295 x 216; adv. contact: David Bryant. bk.rev. (back issues avail.) **Document type:** consumer publication.
   Description: Covers the world of traditional boats and boat craftsmanship.

796.95   US   ISSN 0739-2257
BOATS & HARBORS. 1971. 36/yr. $4. Crossville, TN 38555. TEL 615-484-6100. Ed. Edwin Donnelly. adv.; charts; illus.; tr.lit.

797.1   IT   ISSN 1121-3108
BOLINA; andar per mare. 1985. m. L.52000 (foreign L.65000). Editrice Incontri Nautici s.r.l., Piazza delle Coppelle 62, 00186 Rome, Italy. TEL 39-6-6896745. FAX 39-6-6872414. Ed. Giorgio Casti; Pub. Hilde Bianchi. adv.: B&W page L.2500000, color page L.3500000; adv. contact: Sandro Angeloni. circ. 40,000 (paid). **Document type:** trade publication.
   Description: Covers sailing, yachts, classic boats and tourism.

797.1   GW   ISSN 0006-7636
BOOTE; das Motorbootmagazin. 1965. m. DM.77 (foreign DM.99). Verlag Delius, Klasing und Co., Postfach 101671, 33516 Bielefeld, Germany. TEL 0521-559-283. FAX 0521-559113. TELEX 932934-DEKLA. Ed.Bd. adv.; illus. circ. 88,000. **Document type:** consumer publication.
   —CCC.

623.82   GW   ISSN 0006-7644
BOOTSWIRTSCHAFT. 1964. 4/yr. DM.25 (foreign DM.50). (Deutscher Boots- und Schiffbauer-Verband) Verlag fuer Bootswirtschaft GmbH, Postfach 301227, 20305 Hamburg, Germany. FAX 040-344227. Ed. Fritz Hartz. adv. contact: Klaus Fahrenkroog. bk.rev.; charts; illus.; index. circ. 2,000. **Document type:** consumer publication.

797   UK   ISSN 0309-1252
BRISTOW'S BOOK OF YACHTS. 1963. a. £3.95. Navigator Publishing Ltd., Moorhouse Farmhouse, Lower Kingston, Ringwood, Hants, England. Ed. Philip Bristow. circ. 5,000.
   Formed by the merger of: Bristow's Book of Motor Cruisers & Bristow's Book of Sailing Cruisers.

797.123   UK
BRITISH ROWING ALMANACK. A R A YEARBOOK. 1861. a. £16 to non-members. Amateur Rowing Association, 6 Lower Mall, London W6 9DJ, England. TEL 0181-748-3632. FAX 0181-741-4658. Ed. Keith L. Osborne. bk.rev.; index. **Document type:** directory.
   Formerly: British Rowing Almanack (ISSN 0068-2446)

797   UK   ISSN 0068-290X
BROWN'S NAUTICAL ALMANAC. 1858. a. £36 (effective 1995). Brown, Son and Ferguson Ltd., 4-10 Darnley St., Glasgow G41 2SD, Scotland. TEL 0141-429-5922. FAX 0141-420-1694. Eds. T. Nigel Brown, Capt. A.N. Cockroft. adv. contact: David H. Provan. circ. 15,000. **Document type:** consumer publication.

BUSINESS RATIO REPORT: THE BOAT BUILDING INDUSTRY; an industry sector analysis. see TRANSPORTATION — Ships And Shipping

SPORTS AND GAMES — BOATS AND BOATING

797.102 **UK**
BUY A BOAT (FOR UNDER 10,000 POUNDS). 1993. m. £18; newsstand price: £1.50. Freedom House Publishing Co. Ltd., P.O. Box 93, Chichester, W. Sussex PO19 1HF, England. TEL 01243-533394. FAX 01243-532025. (Dist. by: Comag, Tavistock Rd., West Drayton, Mddx., England. TEL 01895-444055) Pub. Clare Willison. adv.: color page £400; adv. contact: Clare Willison. circ. 12,000 (paid). (back issues avail.) **Document type:** catalog.
   Description: Lists boats for sale that cost less than 10,000 pounds.

797.124 **CN** **ISSN 0045-4494**
CANADIAN BOATING. 1926. 9/yr. Can.$19. Arthurs Creative Services, Box 149 Rockwood Mall, 4141 Dixie Rd., Mississauga, Ont. L4W 1V5, Canada. TEL 416-625-9660. FAX 416-625-9604. Ed. Gary Arthurs. adv.; bk.rev. circ. 17,000. **Indexed:** Can.B.P.I., CMI, CS Ind., Sportsearch.
   Incorporates: Canadian Power and Sail.

197.124 **CN** **ISSN 0832-8080**
CANADIAN SAILING REVIEW/REVUE CANADIENNE DE VOILE. 1983. bi-m. membership. Canadian Yachting Association - Association Canadienne de Yachting, 1600 James Naismith Dr., Gloucester, ON K1B 5N4, Canada. TEL 613-748-5687. FAX 613-748-5688. Ed. Brian Lane. circ. 20,000. **Indexed:** Sportsearch (1985-). **Document type:** newsletter.

796.95 **CN** **ISSN 0384-0999**
CANADIAN YACHTING. 1976. bi-m. Can.$14.18($34) Kerrwil Publications Ltd., 395 Matheson Blvd. E., Mississauga, ON L4Z 2H2, Canada. TEL 905-890-1846. FAX 905-890-5769. Ed. Jones Graham; Pub. Hugh Forbes. adv.; bk.rev. circ. 15,000. **Indexed:** Can.B.P.I., Can.Per.Ind., Sportsearch (1986-). **Document type:** consumer publication.

797.1 **UK** **ISSN 0141-2302**
CANAL & RIVERBOAT MONTHLY. 1978. m. £22 (foreign £31) (effective 1996). A.E. Morgan Publications Ltd., Stanley House, 9 West St., Epsom, Surrey KT18 7RL, England. TEL 01372-741111. FAX 01372-744493. Ed. Norman Alborough; Pub. Terence Morgan. adv. contact: Bill Sherry. bk.rev. circ. 15,000. **Document type:** consumer publication.

797.122 **IT**
CANOA FLUVIALE. 1977. 4/yr. L.30000 (foreign L.35000). Federazione Italiana Canoa Fluviale, Via Ernesto Breda 19-c, 20126 Milan, Italy. TEL 02-257-6638. adv. bk.rev. circ. 5,000.

797.122 **US**
GV781
CANOE & KAYAK. 1973. bi-m. $17.97. Canoe America Associates, Box 3146, Kirkland, WA 98083. TEL 206-827-6363. Ed. David Harrison; Pub. Judy Harrison. adv. contact: Glen Bernard. bk.rev.; charts; illus.; tr.lit. circ. 68,000. **Indexed:** Phys.Ed.Ind., Sportsearch (1977-). **Document type:** consumer publication.
   —UMI; UncOver.
   Formerly: Canoe (ISSN 0360-7496); Supersedes (in 1978): American Canoeist.
   Description: Articles and features include adventure paddling destination, equipment reviews, paddling techniques, paddling environemnt, the people, ideas, issues, and events that shape the sport of paddling.

797.122 **UK** **ISSN 0008-5626**
CANOE - CAMPER. 1938. 3/yr. £4.50 to non-members. Canoe Camping Club, 25 Waverly Road, South Norwood, London SE25 4HT, England. TEL 01-654-1835. Ed. Jill Griffin. adv.; bk.rev.; abstr.; charts; illus. circ. 700.

797.122 **UK** **ISSN 0953-010X**
CANOE FOCUS. 1976. bi-m. £2 to non-members. British Canoe Union, Adbolton Ln., W. Bridgford, Nottingham NG2 5AS, England. TEL 01602-821100. FAX 01602-821797. Ed. Kevin Danforth. adv. contact: Dean Coulter. bk.rev.; circ. 22,000 (controlled). **Document type:** newsletter.
   Description: Covers canoeing news, events, expeditions, equipment and books.

797.122 **FR**
CANOE KAYAK MAGAZINE. 6/yr. 175 F. (foreign 205 F.). Editions Faton S.A., 25 rue Berbisey, 21000 Dijon, France. (Subscr. to: 1 rue des Artisans, B.P. 90, 21803 Quetigny Cedex, France. TEL 80-70-93-48)

797.122 **UK** **ISSN 0269-9982**
CANOEIST. 1953. m. £26.40 (foreign £37.92) (effective 1996). S.T. & R.J. Fisher, 4 Sinodun Row, Appleford, Oxon. OX14 4PE, England. TEL 02135-847270. FAX 02135-847520. Ed. S. Fisher. adv.; bk.rev.; index. **Document type:** consumer publication.
   Description: Covers all aspects of canoes and kayaks, competitive and recreational.

797.123 **IT**
CANOTTAGGIO. 1922. m. L.35000($35) Industria Grafica Romana s.r.l., Via Cancelliera 24, 00040 Cecchina (RO), Italy. TEL 39-6-9342686. Ed. Gian Antonio Romanini. adv.: B&W page L.600000.

797.1 658 **US**
CHARTER INDUSTRY; management magazine for the marine charter industry. 1985. bi-m. $26.50 (effective 1995 & 1996). Charter Industry Services, Inc., 43 Kindred St., Stuart, FL 34994. TEL 407-288-1066. Ed. Paul McElroy. adv. contact: Mich McElroy. cum.index: 1985-1994; circ. 10,000 (paid); 750 (controlled). (back issues avail.) **Document type:** trade publication.
   Description: Informs the marine charter industry's professionals about ways to improve their business operations. Covers insurance, promotion, advertising, taxes, legal issues, and personnel issues.

917 796.95 **US** **ISSN 0045-656X**
CHESAPEAKE BAY MAGAZINE. 1971. m. $22.95. Chesapeake Bay Communications, Inc., 1819 Bay Ridge Ave., Annapolis, MD 21403. TEL 301-263-2662. Ed. Jean Waller. adv.; bk.rev.; charts; illus. circ. 33,000. (also avail. in microfiche) **Document type:** consumer publication.
   —UnCover.
   Description: Covers boating, history, environment, ecology and the culture of the bay from the C-and-D Canal to Norfolk, VA.

796.95 **US** **ISSN 1070-9290**
CLASSIC BOATING. 1984. bi-m. $20 (Canada $27; elsewhere S45). 280 Lac La Belle Dr., Oconomowoc, WI 53066-1648. TEL 414-567-4800. Ed. Jim Wangard; Pub. Norm Wangard. adv. contact: Terri Wangard. circ. 9,000 (paid). **Document type:** consumer publication.
   Formerly (until 1987): Antique and Classic Boat.

796.95 **AT** **ISSN 0817-8585**
CLUB MARINE. 1982. m. Aus.$50($25) Club Marine Ltd., 40 The Esplanade, Brighton, Vic. 3186, Australia. TEL 03-593-1144. FAX 03-592-7783. Ed. Andrew J. Woodley. adv.; bk.rev. circ. 37,000. (back issues avail.)

796.95 910.202 **US** **ISSN 0897-750X**
COASTAL CRUISING. 1985. 6/yr. $16.50. Nautilus Publishing, Inc., 108 Middle Ln., Beaufort, NC 28516. TEL 919-728-2233. FAX 919-726-6715. Ed. Ted Jones. adv.; bk.rev. circ. 25,000.
   Formerly (until 1988): Carolina Cruising (ISSN 0893-3723)

796.95 **UK**
CRUISING ASSOCIATION. MAGAZINE. 1910. q. membership. Cruising Association, C A House, 1 Northey St., Limestone Basin, London E14 8BT, England. TEL 0171-537-2828. FAX 0171-537-2266. Ed. Charles Ford. adv.; bk.rev.; circ. 5,000 (controlled). **Document type:** consumer publication.
   Formerly: Cruising Association. Bulletin.

796.95 **UK**
CRUISING ASSOCIATION HANDBOOK. 1909. a. membership. Cruising Association, C A House, 1 Northey St., Limestone Basin, London E14 8BT, England. TEL 0171-537-2828. FAX 0171-537-2266. circ. 5,000 (controlled). **Document type:** consumer publication.
   Formerly: Cruising Association Yearbook.

797.14 **AT** **ISSN 0812-4086**
CRUISING HELMSMAN. 1982. m. Aus.$57 (foreign Aus.$152) (effective Feb. 1995). Yaffa Publishing Group, 17-21 Bellevue St., Surry Hills, N.S.W. 21010, Australia. TEL 61-2-281-2333. FAX 61-2-281-2750. Ed. Robert Keeley. adv.: B&W page Aus.$1515, color page Aus.$1910; trim 273 x 210. circ. 8,380. **Document type:** consumer publication.
   Description: Covers the adventure, drama and romance of yacht cruising.

797.124 **US** **ISSN 0098-3519**
GV771
CRUISING WORLD. 1974. m. $28. Cruising World Publications, Inc., Box 3400, Newport, RI 02840-0992. TEL 401-847-1588. FAX 401-848-5048. (Subscr. to: Box 3045, Harlan, IA 51537-3045) Ed. Bernadette Brennan Bernon. adv.; bk.rev.; charts; illus.; tr.lit.; index. circ. 147,000. (also avail. in microform from UMI; back issues avail.; reprint service avail. from UMI) **Indexed:** Mag.Ind. **Document type:** consumer publication.
   —UMI.

796.95 **US** **ISSN 1073-158X**
CURRENT (NAPLES). 1992. bi-m. $35 (free to members). Electric Boat Association of the Americas, Inc., Box 11197, Naples, FL 33941. TEL 813-649-1779. E-mail: 71644,1214@compuserve.com. Ed. Kenneth Matthews. adv.; bk.rev. circ. 1,000. (back issues avail.) **Document type:** newsletter.

797.1 **US**
CURRENTS (COLORADO SPRINGS). 1979. q. $20. National Organization for River Sports, 212 W. Cheyenne Mountain Blvd., Colorado Springs, CO 80906-3712. TEL 719-473-2466. FAX 719-576-6238. Ed. Greg Moore. adv.; bk.rev. circ. 5,000. (back issues avail.)
   Description: Covers whitewater rivers and river running internationally, with emphasis on the United States.

797.1 **DK**
DANSK SOESPORTSKALENDER. a. H A Reklameforlag, Strandvangsvej 9 C, DK-2650 Hvidovre, Denmark. adv. circ. 70,000.

796.95 **US**
DIRECTORY OF AMERICAN SAILING SCHOOLS AND CHARTER OPERATORS. 1982. irreg. $250. National Association of Sailing Instructors and Sailing Schools, 15 Renier Ct., Middletown, NJ 07748. TEL 908-671-6190. Ed. Richard Herbst. **Document type:** directory.
   Description: Information on how to locate and select a sailing school or charter operator.

797.1 **US**
DIVE BOAT MAGAZINE. 1985. bi-m. $18 (foreign $36) (effective 1996). Total Marketing, 425 East Arrow Hwy. No. 214, Glendora, CA 91740. TEL 818-852-2028. Ed. Darren Douglass. adv. contact: Stacey C. Douglass. circ. 8,000. **Document type:** consumer publication.
   Formerly: Dive Boat Calendar and Travel Guide; Which was formed by the merger of: Dive Boat Calendar and Travel Guide: Pacific Coast Edition (ISSN 1044-9159); Dive Boat Calendar and Travel Guide: Florida - Caribbean Edition.
   Description: Provides current boat diving and travel information for scuba divers.

796.95 **US**
EMBASSY'S COMPLETE BOATING GUIDE TO FLORIDA'S EAST COAST. 1991. a. $39.95. Embassy Imprint Inc., 142 Ferry Rd., Ste. 16, Old Saybrook, CT 06475. TEL 203-395-0188. FAX 203-395-0410. E-mail: MBCMarPub@aol.com. adv. circ. 10,000. **Document type:** trade publication.
   Description: Includes navigational charts, color photographs of every harbor, yacht club, marina and boat yard listings, sightseeing ideas and fishing tips.

796.95 **US**
EMBASSY'S COMPLETE BOATING GUIDE TO LONG ISLAND SOUND. a. $39.95. Embassy Imprint Inc., 142 Ferry Rd., Ste. 16, Old Saybrook, CT 06475. TEL 203-395-0188. FAX 203-395-0410. E-mail: MBCMarPub@aol.com. adv. circ. 10,000. **Document type:** trade publication.
   Description: A comprehensive reference guide to cruising Long Island Sound from the Hudson and East Rivers to Block Island and Rhode Island in New York.

SPORTS AND GAMES — BOATS AND BOATING

796.95 US
EMBASSY'S COMPLETE BOATING GUIDE TO RHODE ISLAND AND MASSACHUSETTS. a. $39.95. Embassy Imprint Inc., 142 Ferry Rd., Ste. 16, Old Saybrook, CT 06475. TEL 203-395-0188. FAX 203-395-0410. E-mail: MBC MarPub@aol.com. adv. circ. 10,000. **Document type:** trade publication.
 Description: Contains information for cruising or sailing from Block Island, Rhode Island to Portsmouth, N.H., including information on marinas, boat yards, yacht clubs and the services and facilities they offter.

797.1 IT
FARE VELA. 1985. m. L.45000 (foreign L.80000). Publiedit s.r.l., Via Margutta 47-A, 00186 Rome, Italy. TEL 39-6-3212454. FAX 39-6-3212602. Ed. Fabio Colivicchi. adv.: B&W page L.2400000, color page L.3800000; adv. contact: Jacopo Galli. circ. 19,800. **Document type:** consumer publication.

797 FR ISSN 0071-4194
FEDERATION FRANCAISE DE NATATION. ANNUAIRE. 1921. a. 250 F. Federation Francaise de Natation, 148 Ave. Gambetta, 75020 Paris, France. TEL 40-31-17-70. FAX 40-31-19-90. TELEX 215429.

623.82 UK
FINANCIAL SURVEY. COMPANY DATA FOR SUCCESS: BOAT BUILDERS & MARINE ENGINEERS. a. I C C Financial Surveys Ltd., Field House, 72 Oldfield Rd., Hampton, Mddx. TW12 2HQ, England. TEL 081-783-0977. FAX 081-783-1940. charts; stat. **Document type:** trade publication.
 Formerly (until 1990): Financial Survey Company Directory. Boat Builders and Marine Engineers (ISSN 0952-5289)

623.8 FI ISSN 0356-7753
FINNISH BOATBUILDING INDUSTRY. (Text in English, German, French) 1971. irreg. free. Suomen Vene- ja Moottoriyhdistys - Finnish Boat and Motor Association, Mariankatu 26 B 19, 00170 Helsinki 17, Finland.

FISHING BUSINESS INTERNATIONAL. see *FISH AND FISHERIES*

797.124 910.202 US
FODOR'S SPORTS: SAILING. irreg. $12. Fodor's Travel Publications, Inc. (Subsidiary of: Random House, Inc.), 201 E. 50th St., New York, NY 10022. TEL 800-733-3000. (Dist. by: Random House, Inc., 400 Hahn Rd., Westminster, MD 21157) Eds. Michael B. McPhee, Michael Spring.

623.82 IT ISSN 0015-8666
FORZA 7; revista mensile di nautica. 1968. m. (10/yr.). L.100000 in Europe; America L.140000. Publimedia Societa Editrice, Corso Venezia 18, 20121 Milan, Italy. TEL 02-77521. FAX 02-781068. Ed. Giorgia Gessner. adv.; bk.rev.; charts; illus.; tr.lit. circ. 35,000.

797.124 FI ISSN 0359-6648
FRISK BRIS. 1903. 6/yr. FIM 200. Frisk Bris Grafisk Industri AB, Mannerheimvagen 18, FIN-00100 Helsingfors, Finland. TEL 358-0-643-445. FAX 358-0-640-648. Ed. Kari Wilen. adv.; bk.rev. circ. 3,000.
 Description: Devoted to yachting, cruising, racing; old boats and life in archipelago.

797.1 DK ISSN 0905-9741
FRITID TIL SOES. 1960. m. free. (Danish Motorboat Federation) Fogeds Forlag, P.O. Box 265, Asgaard 11, DK-360 Frederikssund, Denmark. TEL 45-42-31-28-92. FAX 45-42-31-20-25. Ed. Harly Foged. adv.: B&W page DKK 5780, color page DKK 8770; trim 195 x 270; adv. contact: Kurt Tvaerkaer. illus. circ. 8,500. **Document type:** newsletter.
 Formerly: Motor-Soesport.
 Description: Covers everything both large and small, local and international, that is of interest to "people of the sea" and the members of the Danish Motorboat Federation.

797.1 CN ISSN 0016-4259
GAM ON YACHTING. 1957. 10/yr. Can.$12 (foreign $20). Gam on Yachting Inc., 250 The Esplanade, Ste. 202, Toronto, ON M5A 1J2, Canada. TEL 416-368-1559. FAX 416-368-2831. Ed. Karin Larson. adv.; bk.rev.; illus. circ. 22,000. **Indexed:** Sportsearch.

GENTE MOTORI. see *TRANSPORTATION — Automobiles*

797.124 IT ISSN 1122-3073
GIORNALE DELLA VELA. 1975. m. L.110000. Editrice Portoria S.r.l., Via Chiosetto, 1, 20122 Milan, Italy. TEL 39-2-783541. FAX 39-2-782601. Ed. Luca Oriani. adv.: B&W page L.6000000, color page L.8990000. bk.rev. circ. 30,000.

797.125 IT ISSN 1120-799X
GIORNALE DELLE BARCHE A MOTORE. 1990. m. L.70400 (foreign L.135000). Editrice Portoria s.r.l., Via Chiossetto 1, 20122 Milan, Italy. TEL 39-2-760711. Ed. Mario Oriani. adv.: B&W page L.5780000, color page L.8670000. circ. 28,000. **Document type:** consumer publication.

796.95 IT ISSN 1120-2262
GOMMONE E LA NAUTICA PER TUTTI. 1977. 10/yr. L.56000 (foreign L.112000). (effective 1995). Stammer SpA., Via della Liberazione 1, 10068 Peschiera Borromeo (MI), Italy. TEL 02-55302606. FAX 02-55302700. Ed. Girolamo Bellina. adv.: B&W page L.2300000, color page L.3680000; trim 190 x 250. circ. 30,000.
 Former titles: Gommone; Gommone e le Piccole Barche.

796.95 US ISSN 1063-7656
GORGE GUIDE. 1982. a. $3.95. Gorge Publishing, Inc., 500 Morton Rd., Box 918, Hood River, OR 97031. TEL 503-386-7440. FAX 503-386-7480. Ed. Carol York; Pub. Pete Fotheringham. adv.: B&W page $1575, color page $2555; trim 8 3/8 x 10 7/8. circ. 30,000. **Document type:** consumer publication.
 Description: Guide to windsurfing in the Columbia Gorge River.

796.95 US
GREAT LAKES BOATING MAGAZINE. 1981. m. free. Chicago Boating Publications, Inc., 4717 5th Ave., Kenosha, WI 53140-3401. TEL 312-266-8400. Ed. Jean Van Dyke; Pub. Ned Dikmen. adv.; bk.rev. circ. 42,000. **Document type:** consumer publication.
 Description: Covers boating news, racing events, adventures, and ecology.

797.124 US ISSN 0892-5410
GREAT LAKES SAILOR. 1987. m. (except Jan.-Feb. combined). $17.95 (Canada $25.95). Great Lakes Sailor, Inc., 2132 E Ninth St., Ste. 310, Cleveland, OH 44115-1245. TEL 216-861-1777. FAX 216-861-1790. Ed. Thomas Gibbons. adv. circ. 22,000.

797 US ISSN 0017-4629
GROSSE POINTER. 1939. bi-m. $25. Kolka & Robb, Inc., 30700 Telegraph Rd., Ste. 1401, Bingham Farms, MI 48025-4524. TEL 810-642-9580. Eds. Vicki Robb, Katie Elsila. adv. contact: Lisa LaRaia. circ. 1,100. (back issues avail.)

910.202 US
GUIDE TO CRUISING THE CHESAPEAKE BAY. 1974. a. $29.50. Chesapeake Bay Communications, Inc., 1819 Bay Ridge Ave., Annapolis, MD 21403. TEL 301-263-2662. Ed. Dick Goertemiller. **Document type:** consumer publication.
 Description: Contains photographs, drawings and narratives to guide yachtsman to anchorages and ports of call along the bay from the C&D Canal to Norfolk, VA.

796.95 621.381 US
GUIDE TO MARINE ELECTRONICS. a. $2.50. Cahners Publishing Co. (Subsidiary of: Reed Elsevier group), 475 Park Ave. S., New York, NY 10016-6901. TEL 212-545-5315. FAX 212-545-5356.

797.1 US ISSN 1042-1009
HEARTLAND BOATING. 1989. 7/yr. $16.95. Inland Publications, Inc., Box 1067, Martin, TN 38237. TEL 901-587-6791. FAX 901-587-6893. Ed. Molly Lightfoot Blom; Pub. Douglas Blom. adv.: B&W page $1255; adv. contact: Tasha Blakney. bk.rev. circ. 16,000. **Document type:** consumer publication.
 Description: Provides stories about boating on the Tennessee, Ohio, Cumberland and Mississippi rivers, the inland lakes and the Tenn-Tom waterway. Includes houseboating, sailing and cruising features, and marina profiles.

797 AT
HERON NEWSLETTER. 1964. q. Aus.$2.80. National Heron Sailing Association of Australia, 1 Ethel St., Balgowlah, N.S.W. 2093, Australia. Ed. Bruce Morrissey. adv. circ. 1,750.

910.2 UK
HOSEASONS BOATING HOLIDAYS. 1946. a. free. (Hoseasons Holidays) James Hoseason, Ed. & Pub., Sunway House, Lowestoft, Suffolk NR32 2LW, England. TEL 01502-500505. FAX 01502-500532. **Document type:** consumer publication.
 Formerly: Hoseasons Holiday Boats and Bungalows Hire (ISSN 0073-3431)

796.95 US ISSN 0892-8320
HOT BOAT. vol.7, 1985. m. $22.95 (foreign $32.95). Larry Flynt Publications, Inc., 9171 Wilshire Blvd., Ste. 300, Beverly Hills, CA 90210. TEL 310-858-7100. FAX 310-274-7985. adv. **Document type:** consumer publication.
 Formerly: Hot Boat Magazine (ISSN 0745-6077)
 Description: Focuses on motorized family water sporting events, personalities, "how-to" and technical data.

797.1 US
HOUSEBOAT MAGAZINE; the family magazine for American Houseboaters. 1990. 6/yr. $16.95. Harris Publishing, Inc., 520 Park Ave., Idaho Falls, ID 83402. TEL 208-524-7000. Ed. Steve Janes; Pub. Darryl W. Harris. adv. contact: Mike Harris. circ. 20,000.

796.95 US ISSN 1073-1032
HOUSEBOAT NEWS. 1971. 6/yr. $15. Houseboat Association of America, 4940 N. Rhett Ave., Charleston, SC 29405. TEL 803-744-6581. Ed. Robert E. Perkins. adv. circ. 500. (looseleaf format; back issues avail.) **Document type:** newsletter.
 Formerly (until 1990): Houseboat Association of America. Newsletter.
 Description: News about houseboating and new products.

623.82 GW ISSN 0020-921X
I B N. (Internationale Bodensee & Boot Nachrichten); internationales Bodensee Wassersport Magazin. 1964. s.m. DM.95. Druck & Verlagshaus Hermann Daniel GmbH & Co. KG, Gruenewaldstr. 15, 72336 Balingen, Germany. TEL 07433-266100. FAX 07433-266118. Ed. Ernst-Ruediger von Dunker. adv.; bk.rev.; illus.; index. circ. 8,000. **Document type:** consumer publication.

797.14 US
I C Y R A N A DIRECTORY. a. free. Intercollegiate Yacht Racing Association of North America, Box 6597, San Antonio, TX 78209-0597. Ed. George H. Griswold. circ. 400.

623.82 FR ISSN 0019-9389
INDUSTRIES NAUTIQUES. 1965. q. 160 F.($27) (Federation des Industries Nautiques) Editions de Chabassol, 30 rue de Gramont, 75012 Paris, France. TEL 42-97-50-30. FAX 42-86-02-81. Ed. B. Laloup. adv.; bk.rev.; illus.; stat.; index. circ. 2,000.

387.2 HD9999.B5 UK ISSN 0020-6172
INTERNATIONAL BOAT INDUSTRY. 1968. bi-m. £33($66) Boating Publications, Ltd., Link House, Dingwall Ave., Croydon, Surrey CR9 T2A, England. TEL 44-81-686-2599. FAX 44-81-781-6065. Ed. Robert Greenwood. adv.; bk.rev. circ. 9,450. **Document type:** trade publication.
 Formerly: International Boating.

797.124 US
INTERNATIONAL ETCHELLS CLASS NEWSLETTER. 1970. q. membership. International Etchells Class Association, Box 534, Wall Street Sta., New York, NY 10268. TEL 212-943-5757. Ed. Pamela P. Smith. adv. circ. 1,400. **Document type:** proceedings.
 Formerly: International E-22 Class Newsletter.
 Description: For owners of Etchells class yachts in fleets worldwide.

797.124 US
INTERNATIONAL ETCHELLS CLASS YEARBOOK. 1970. biennial. membership. International Etchells Class Association, Box 534, Wall Street Sta., New York, NY 11268. TEL 212-943-5757. Ed. Pamela P. Smith. adv. circ. 4,000.
 Formerly: International E-22 Class Yearbook.
 Description: For owners of Etchells class yachts.

797.124 UK ISSN 0307-4706
INTERNATIONAL FIREBALL. 1970. 2/yr. membership. Fireball International, 47 Chiswick Quay, London W4 3UR, England. FAX 0392-410432. Ed. Richard Hughes. adv. circ. 2,500.

SPORTS AND GAMES — BOATS AND BOATING

796.95 330 US
INTERNATIONAL MARINE BUSINESS JOURNAL; the voice of the marine industries worldwide. 1989. 2/yr. Marine Business Journal, 1766 Bay Rd., Miami Beach, FL 33139. TEL 305-538-0700. Ed. Jim Murphy. circ. 33,000. (tabloid format; back issues avail.) **Document type:** trade publication.
Description: Trade magazine about the U.S. marine industry. Covers products and services.

796.95 GW
INTERNATIONALES BODENSEE-JAHRBUCH DER SPORTSCHIFFAHRT. 1959. a. DM.18. (Bodensee Segler Verband) Druck & Verlagshaus Hermann Daniel GmbH & Co. KG, Gruenewaldstr. 15, 72336 Balingen, Germany. TEL 07433-266100. FAX 07433-266118. (Co-sponsor: Bodensee Motorboot Verband) circ. 12,000. **Document type:** bulletin.
Incorporates: Internationales Bodensee Regatta Programm.

797.1 IT ISSN 0021-2857
ITALIA SUL MARE; mensile internazionale di nautica e di turismo marinaro. (Includes: 5 annual supplements) 1955. m. L.55000 (foreign L.100000). (Salone Nautico Internazionale di Genoa) Vito Bianco, Ed. & Pub., Via Messina, 31, 00198 Rome, Italy. TEL 39-6-8554962. FAX 39-6-8844703. adv.: B&W page L.2600000, color page L.3640000. bk.rev.; charts; illus.; cum.index. circ. 20,000.
Description: Covers boating, tourism, sea sports and sea fashion.

796.95 US
JAVELIN CLASS ASSOCIATION YEARBOOK. (Supplement avail.) 1976. quinquennial (plus a. supplement). membership. Javelin Class Association, 874 Beecher's Brook Rd., Mayfield Village, OH 44143. TEL 216-461-8511. Ed. G.T. Reiber. circ. 250.

796.95 US
JAVELIN CLASS ASSOCIATION YEARBOOK. SUPPLEMENT. (Supplement to: Javelin Class Association Yearbook) 1977. a. membership. Javelin Class Association, 874 Beecher's Brook Rd., Mayfield Village, OH 44143. TEL 216-461-8511. Ed. G.T. Reiber.

797.1 US
JETSPORTS MAGAZINE. 1982. 5/yr. $10. Pfanner Communications, Inc., 1371 E. Warner Ave., Ste. E, Tustin, CA 92680-6442. TEL 714-259-8240. FAX 714-259-9377. adv. circ. 40,515.
Formerly: JetSkier Magazine.
Description: Includes reports and photo stories on competitions, personalities, safety articles and a directory to products and services.

796.95 387 CN ISSN 0839-105X
JIB GEMS. q. Marine Museum Great Lakes - Kingston, 55 Ontario St., Kingston, ON K7L 2Y2, Canada. Ed. Maurice Smith. (looseleaf format) **Document type:** newsletter.

797.122 NE ISSN 0928-1495
KANO-SPORT. 1980. bi-m. fl.42. Nederlandse Kano Bond, Postbus 1160, 3800 BD Amersfoort, Netherlands. TEL 31-33-622341. FAX 31-33-612714. Ed. Lo van der Rest. adv.: bk.rev. circ. 10,000. **Document type:** consumer publication.
Formerly: Kano-Bulletin.

797.122 SW ISSN 0022-8397
KANOT-NYTT. 1948. m. SEK 60. Svenska Kanotfoerbundet - Swedish Canoe Federation, Skeppsbron 11, 611 35 Nykoeping, Sweden. TEL 0155-69808. FAX 0155-18780. TELEX 14179-SPORT-S. Ed. K. Loefgen. adv.; bk.rev.; illus. circ. 4,000.

797.122 GW ISSN 0022-8923
KANU SPORT. 1919. m. DM.60. Deutscher Kanu Verband - Wirtschafts- und Verlags GmbH, Bertaallee 8, 47005 Duisburg, Germany. TEL 0203-99759-0. FAX 0203-9975960. Ed. Dieter Reinmuth. adv.: B&W page DM.1700; trim 185 x 265; adv. contact: Wolfgang Over. bk.rev.; illus. circ. 11,500. **Document type:** consumer publication.

797.127 GW
▼**KANUMAGAZIN**; Magazin fuer Kajak und Kanadier. 1994. bi-m. DM.45.90. Rotpunkt Verlag, Ziegeleistr. 16, 71384 Weinstadt, Germany. TEL 07151-999902-0. FAX 07151-999029. Ed. Stephan Glocker; Pub. Juergen Linsenmaier. adv.: B&W page DM.3680, color page DM.6400; trim 172 x 250; adv. contact: Karsten Heyder. circ. 50,000. **Document type:** consumer publication.

797.1 RU ISSN 0320-9199
KATERA I YAKHTY. 1963. q. $41 (effective 1996). Izdatel'stvo Shipbuilding, Ul. Gogola 8, 191065 St. Petersburg, Russia. (Dist. by: Mezhdunarodnaya Kniga, B. Yakimanka 39, 117049 Moscow, Russia) Ed. V.V. Ermolin.

797.1 JA ISSN 0389-1771
KAZI/SAIL AND POWERBOAT MAGAZINE. (Text in Japanese) 1932. m. 980 Yen per no. Kazi Co., Ltd., 2-17, Hamamatsu-cho 1-chome, Minato-ku, Tokyo 105, Japan. TEL 81-3-3434-5181. FAX 81-3-3434-5184. Ed. Masami Takubo; Pub. Yoshio Doi. adv. contact: Buko Negishi. bk.rev. **Document type:** consumer publication.

797.1 FI ISSN 0780-5373
KIPPARI. (Text in English, Finnish, Swedish) 1982. 8/yr. FIM 215. Yhtyneet Kuvalehdet Oy - United Magazines Ltd., Maistraatinportti 1, SF-00240 Helsinki, Finland. TEL 358-0-156-6524. FAX 358-0-156-6505. Ed. Vesa Leppa. adv.: B&W page FIM 6700, color page FIM 9900; trim 217 x 280. circ. 14,364. **Document type:** consumer publication.
Description: For users of motorboats, from small boats to luxury yachts. Has detailed, expert and wide-ranging tests and presentations of boats, motors and gear.

797 GW ISSN 0075-627X
KLASINGS BOOTSMARKT INTERNATIONAL; YACHTEN UND BOOTE ZUBEHOER, AUSRUESTUNG, MOTOREN. 1968. a. DM.24.80. Verlag Delius, Klasing und Co., Postfach 101671, 33516 Bielefeld, Germany. TEL 0521-559-280. FAX 0521-559113. TELEX 932934-DEKLA. Ed. Hans Donath. adv. **Document type:** consumer publication.

797.1 US ISSN 0744-9194
LAKELAND BOATING; the Great Lakes boating magazine. 1946. 11/yr. $19.94. O'Meara - Brown Publications, 1560 Sherman Ave., Ste. 1220, Evanston, IL 60201. TEL 708-869-5400. FAX 708-869-5989. Ed. Randall Hess. adv. contact: Douglas Leik. bk.rev.; illus. circ. 36,133. (also avail. in microform from UMI) **Indexed:** Consum.Ind., Mich.Mag.Ind., Sportsearch. **Document type:** consumer publication.
—UMI.
Former titles (until 1983): Lakeland Boating Incorporating Sea (ISSN 0274-9076); (until 1980): Lakeland Boating (ISSN 0023-7345); Lakeland Yachting.

623.829 UK ISSN 0024-3086
VK1300
LIFEBOAT. 1852. q. £3. Royal National Lifeboat Institution, West Quay Rd., Poole, Dorset BH15 1HZ, England. Ed. Norman Hicks. adv.; bk.rev.; illus. circ. 145,000. (also avail. in microfilm from UMI)

797.1 UK ISSN 0024-5062
THE LITTLE SHIP. 1928. q. membership. Little Ship Club, Bell Wharf Ln., Upper Thames St., London EC4R 3TB, England. TEL 0171-236-7729. FAX 0171-236-9100. Ed. P.A. Rickwood. adv.; bk.rev.; charts; illus. circ. 2,000. **Document type:** newsletter.

796.95 US
THE LOG AND SAN DIEGO LOG. 1971. fortn. $24.95. Log Newspapers, 1025 Rosecrans St., San Diego, CA 92106. TEL 619-226-1608. FAX 619-226-0573. Ed. Kevin Featherly III. adv.; bk.rev. circ. 60,000. **Document type:** newsletter.
Formerly: San Diego Log (ISSN 0193-3183)
Description: Covers boating in Southern California and Western Arizona.

LOG OF MYSTIC SEAPORT. see *MUSEUMS AND ART GALLERIES*

797.14 US ISSN 0076-0455
LOG OF THE STAR CLASS; official rule book. 1921. a. membership. International Star Class Yacht Racing Association, 1545 Waukegan Rd., Glenview, IL 60025. TEL 312-729-0630. FAX 312-729-0718. Ed. Richard L. Munson. adv. circ. 3,970.

797.124 FR ISSN 0047-5017
LOISIRS NAUTIQUES; architecture et construction navales. 1967. m. 319 F. (foreign 379 F.). 71 rue Amedee St. Germain, 33800 Bordeaux, France. Ed. Emmanuel de Toma. adv. circ. 56,000. (also avail. in microform)

797.1 US
M R A A NEWSLETTER. 1972. m. membership. Marine Retailers Association of America, 150 E. Huron, Ste. 802, Chicago, IL 60611. TEL 312-938-0359. FAX 312-938-9035. Ed. Kermit Small. adv. circ. 16,000. **Document type:** newsletter.
Description: For members who are experienced professional marine dealers, with up-to-date information on industry trends.

796.95 BL
MAR: VELA E MOTOR. 1976. m. $60. Editora Groupo 1 Ltda., Avda. Marechal Camara, 271-603, CEP 20020, Rio de Janeiro, Brazil. TEL (021) 533-1415. TELEX 02137398 RYCB. Ed. Roberto Falcao. adv.; bk.rev. circ. 40,000.
Formed by the merger of: Vela e Motor & Mar.

796.95 US ISSN 1079-1930
MARINA DOCK AGE. 1988. bi-m. $20. Preston Publications, Inc., 7800 N. Merrimac Ave., Box 48312, Niles, IL 60714-3426. TEL 312-967-1810. FAX 708-965-0056. Larry Hooper; Pub. S. Tinsley Preston. adv. contact: Jerry Burns. circ. 18,000. **Document type:** trade publication.
Description: Covers the marina and boatyard business.

MARINE ELECTRONICS. see *ENGINEERING — Electrical Engineering*

MARINE SERVICE CENTER. see *TRANSPORTATION — Ships And Shipping*

796.95 677 US ISSN 1051-5100
MARINE STORE MERCHANDISING; magazine of boating accessory, parts & service merchandising. 1990. 9/yr. $28 (Canada $35; elsewhere $95). R C M Enterprises, Inc., 15500 Wayzata Blvd., Ste. 922, Box 720, Wayzata, MN 55391. TEL 612-473-5088. FAX 612-473-7068. Ed. Joe Pawlowski; Pub. Robert C. Mead. adv.: B&W page $2215; adv. contact: Jim Penningroth. index. circ. 7,500. (back issues avail.) **Document type:** trade publication.

797.124 CN ISSN 0705-8993
MARINE TRADES. 1955. q. Can.$19. Arthurs Creative Services, Box 149 Rockwood Mall, 4141 Dixie Rd., Mississauga, Ont. L4W 1V5, Canada. TEL 416-526-9660. FAX 416-625-9604. Ed. Gary Arthurs.
Formerly: Marine and Outdoor Trades (ISSN 0047-5939)

623.82 796.95 US ISSN 1052-4282
MARINEFACTS; topical directory of marine information. 1990. q. $895 (effective 1995). Running End Ltd., Box 257, Crownsville, MD 21032-0257. TEL 410-923-1325. Ed. Charles Tuten. bk.rev.; abstr.; bibl. (back issues avail.) **Document type:** directory.
●Also available online.
Also available on CD-ROM.
Description: Comprehensive bibliographic reference for marine business and mariners, from books, videos, periodicals, computer software and government publications.

797.1 US
THE MARINER. 1981. bi-w. $25 for 17 nos. Chesapeake Publishing Co. (Elkton), Box 429, Elkton, MD 21922-0429. TEL 410-398-3311. FAX 410-398-4044. Ed. Ira Black. adv.; bk.rev. circ. 24,000. (tabloid format) **Document type:** newspaper.
Description: Recreational boating on the Chesapeake Bay.

MARITIME STUDIES. see *TRANSPORTATION — Ships And Shipping*

SPORTS AND GAMES — BOATS AND BOATING

796.95 US ISSN 0749-2006
MARLIN; the international sportfishing magazine. 1982. bi-m. $24.95. World Publications, Box 2456, Winter Park, FL 32790-2456. TEL 407-628-4802. Ed. David Ritchie. adv.; bk.rev. circ. 30,000. (back issues avail.) **Document type:** consumer publication.
Description: Provides international coverage of the sport of offshore fishing.

796.95 US
MESSING ABOUT IN BOATS. 1983. s-m. $24 (Canada $36). Cycle Sport Publishing, 29 Burley St., Wenham, MA 01984. TEL 508-774-0906. Ed. Bob Hicks. adv.; bk.rev. circ. 4,000. (back issues avail.) **Document type:** consumer publication.
Description: Small boat owner news.

797 AT
MIRROR CLASS ASSOCIATION OF AUSTRALIA. YEARBOOK. 1969. a. Aus.$20. Mirror Class Association of Australia, 47 Gowrie St., South Oakleigh, Vic. 3167, Australia. Ed. W. Dooley. adv. circ. 400.
Supersedes in part: Mirror Class Association of Australia. Constitution-Rules of Measurement.

623.82 UK ISSN 0144-2910
MODEL BOATS. 1951. m. £23.40. Argus Specialist Publications Ltd. (Subsidiary of: Argus Press Group), Argus House, Boundary Way, Hemel Hempstead, Herts. HP2 7ST, England. TEL 01442-66551. FAX 01442-66998. (Subscr. to: Argus Subscription Services, Queensway House, 2 Queensway, Redhill, Surrey RH1 1QS, England. TEL 01737-768611) Ed. J. Cundell. adv.; charts; illus.; index. **Indexed:** Ind.How To Do It (1979-).
Formerly: Model Maker and Model Boats (ISSN 0026-7333)
Description: Contains articles and plans for builders of working model boats.

797.1 AT ISSN 0811-0697
MODERN BOATING. 1965. m. Aus.$52. Federal Publishing Company, 180 Bourke Rd., Alexandria, N.S.W. 2015, Australia. Ed. Mark Rothfield. adv.; bk.rev.; illus.; index. circ. 9,100. (processed) **Indexed:** Pinpointer.
Description: Covers sail and power boats, basic hints to electronic navigation and all types of boating throughout Australia and New Zealand.

797.1 IT
MONDO BARCA. (Text in English, Italian) 1988. m. L.80000 (foreign L.120000). Media Sea Communication S.r.l., Via G.A. Amadeo 41, 20133 Milan, Italy. TEL 39-2-70100020. FAX 39-2-70101709. Ed. Fabrizio de Checchi. adv.: B&W page L.6000000, color page L.9500000. circ. 38,500. (back issues avail.) **Document type:** consumer publication.
Description: Deals with sail and motor boats, yachts, new products, equipment and sports events.

797 FR ISSN 0994-964X
MOTEUR BOAT MAGAZINE. 1988. 11/yr. 289 F. (foreign 355 F.). Editions Lariviere, 15-17 Quai de l'Oise, 75166 Paris Cedex 16, France. TEL 1-40-34-22-07. FAX 1-40-35-84-41. TELEX 211 678 F.

796.95 IT
MOTONAUTICA. 1981. m. L.100000 (Europe $152, elsewhere $224). Renoma Editrice S.p.A., Via IV Novembre 54, 20019 Seguro di Settimo Milanese (MI), Italy. TEL 39-2-33500337. FAX 39-2-33501391. Ed. Claudia Muggieri. adv.: B&W page L.4950000, color page L.8500000.

MOTOR. see *TRANSPORTATION — Automobiles*

797.1 UK ISSN 0027-1780
MOTOR BOAT & YACHTING. 1904. m. $44. I P C Magazines, Specialist Magazine Group (Subsidiary of: Reed Elsevier group), King's Reach Tower, Stamford St., London SE1 9LS, England. TEL 071-261-5308. FAX 0444-440619. TELEX 892084 REEDBP G. (Dist. by: Quadrant Subscription Services, Oakfield House, Perrymount Rd., Haywards Heath, W. Sussex RH16 3DH, England. TEL 0444-440421) Ed. Alan Harper. adv. contact: Chris Rogers. bk.rev.; charts; illus.; tr.lit.; s-a. index. circ. 35,315. (also avail. in microform from UMI) **Indexed:** Br.Tech.Ind. **Document type:** consumer publication.
—UMI.
Description: Boat tests, cruising guides, advice on seamanship and navigational information for the committed boater.

797.1 US ISSN 0027-1799
VM320
MOTOR BOATING & SAILING. (Annual Show issues Jan., Sept.) 1907. m. $15.97. Hearst Magazines, Motor Boating & Sailing, 250 W. 55th St., 4th Fl., New York, NY 10019. TEL 212-649-4092. FAX 212-489-9258. (Subscr. to: C.D.S., 1901 Bell Ave., Des Moines, IA 50315) Ed. Peter Janssen. adv.: B&W page $9000, color page $14600. bk.rev.; charts; illus.; stat.; index. circ. 143,010. (also avail. in microform from UMI; back issues avail.) **Indexed:** Consum.Ind., Mag.Ind., PMR, R.G., Sports Per.Ind., Sportsearch. **Document type:** consumer publication.
—Faxon; UnCover.
Formerly: Motor Boating.

MOTOR MUNDIAL. see *TRANSPORTATION*

623.82 UK ISSN 0027-3155
MULTIHULL INTERNATIONAL. 1964. m. £21($54) (overseas £27) (effective 1996). Chandler Publications Ltd., 10 South St., Totnes, Devon TQ9 5DZ, England. TEL 01803-864668. FAX 01803-865649. Ed. Jack R.D. Heming; Pub. Jack R.D. Heming. adv.; charts; illus.; tr.lit. circ. 6,500. **Document type:** trade publication.
Incorporates (in 1968): Marine Product Guide.
Description: Provides news and views on catamarans, trimarans, and proas.

796.95 US ISSN 0749-4122
MULTIHULLS. 1975. bi-m. $21 (foreign $27). Chiodi Advertising & Publishing, Inc., 421 Hancock St., N. Quincy, MA 02171. TEL 617-328-8181. FAX 617-471-0118. Ed. Ava M. Burgess; Pub. Charles K. Chiodi. adv. contact: J. Vivian Brown. bk.rev.; film rev.; charts; tr.lit. circ. 49,000. (back issues avail.) **Document type:** consumer publication.

797.1 387 FR ISSN 1161-3904
MULTIHULLS WORLD. (Text in English; summaries in English, French) 1986. bi-m. 210 F.($43) Multicoques, Centre Commercial du Nautisme, 28 A Port St. Pierre, 83400 Hyeres, France. TEL 94-38-31-09. FAX 94-38-46-74. Ed. Andre Manchon. adv.: B&W page $3700, color page $5200; trim 280 x 210. circ. 19,000. cols./p.: 3; pp./issue: 80. (back issues avail.)
Refereed Serial

797.122 US
N A C L O NEWS. 1979. m. membership. National Association of Canoe Liveries and Outfitters, Box 248, Butler, KY 41006-0248. TEL 606-472-2205. FAX 606-472-2030. adv.; bk.rev.; circ. 750 (controlled). **Document type:** trade publication.
Description: Promotes safety, protection of waterways, and public rights of access and use of waterways.

796.95 US ISSN 1055-1972
HD9993.B63
N A D A LARGE BOAT APPRAISAL GUIDE. 3/yr. $60. (National Automobile Dealers Association) N.A.D.A. Appraisal Guides, Box 7800, Costa Mesa, CA 92628-7800.
Supersedes in part: N.A.D.A. Boat Appraisal Guide.

N A D A MOTORCYCLE - SNOWMOBILE - A T V - PERSONAL WATERCRAFT APPRAISAL GUIDE. (National Automobile Dealers Association) see *SPORTS AND GAMES — Bicycles And Motorcycles*

796.95 US ISSN 1055-1964
HD9993.B63
N A D A SMALL BOAT APPRAISAL GUIDE. 3/yr. $85. (National Automobile Dealers Association) N.A.D.A. Appraisal Guides, Box 7800, Costa Mesa, CA 92628-7800.
Supersedes in part: N A D A Boat Appraisal Guide.

796.95 US
N A S I S S NEWSLETTER. 1981. q. $10 per no. National Association of Sailing Instructors and Sailing Schools, 15 Renier Ct., Middletown, NJ 07748. TEL 908-671-6190. Ed. Richard Herbst. (looseleaf format; back issues avail.) **Document type:** newsletter.
Description: Covers subjects dealing with the operation of sailing schools, charters, and the training of its customers to sail or charter boats.

797.1 US
N M M A CERTIFICATION HANDBOOK. 1956. a. National Marine Manufacturers Association, 401 N. Michigan Ave., Chicago, IL 60611. TEL 312-836-4747. index.
Former titles: B I A Certification Handbook (ISSN 0067-9402); Boating Industry Associations Engineering Manual of Recommended Practices.

796.95 US ISSN 0363-1354
VM361
NATIONAL BOAT BOOK. a. $110. Maclean Hunter Market Reports, Inc., 29 N. Wacker Dr., Chicago, IL 60606-3297. TEL 312-726-2802. FAX 312-726-2574. (back issues avail.)

796.95 AT ISSN 1030-2425
NATIONAL MARINA SURVEY. 1987. a. A.B. Organisation Pty. Ltd., P.O. Box 319, Avalon Beach, N.S.W. 2107, Australia. TEL 02-918-8322. FAX 02-918-8884. adv.
Description: Catalogues the cost and facilities of marinas throughout Australia and New Zealand.

NATIONAL MARINE BANKERS ASSOCIATION. SUMMARY ANNUAL REPORT. see *BUSINESS AND ECONOMICS — Banking And Finance*

796.95 330 US ISSN 1045-5329
NATIONAL MARINE BUSINESS JOURNAL; the voice of the marine industries nationwide. 1986. 6/yr. $15. Marine Business Journal, 1766 Bay Rd., Miami Beach, FL 33139. TEL 305-538-0700. Ed. Jim Murphy. circ. 33,000. (tabloid format; back issues avail.) **Document type:** trade publication.
Former titles: Southern Marine Business Journal; Florida Marine Business Journal.
Description: Trade magazine about the marine industry. Covers political issues, new technologies and products. Includes export, management and insurance.

796.95 FR ISSN 0151-2846
NAUT ARGUS. 1977. q. 245 F. Societe d'Etude et de Developpement de la Presse Periodique, 23-25 rue de Berri, 75008 Paris Cedex 08, France. TEL 16-1-44-89-44-89. (Subscr. to: 90 rue de Flandre, 75947 Paris Cedex 19, France. TEL 16-1-40-34-35-00) Ed. Michel Koutsikides. adv.; illus. circ. 25,000.

797.1 IT ISSN 0392-369X
NAUTICA. 1962. m. L.160000. Nautica Editrice, Via Tevere 44, 00198 Rome, Italy. TEL 39-6-8413060. FAX 39-6-8543653. TELEX 611613 NAUTIC I. Ed. Lucio Petrone. adv.: B&W page L.6400000. bk.rev.; charts; illus.

796.95 BL
NAUTICA MAGAZINE. 1976. m. $50 (foreign $60) (effective 1995). G R 1 Editora, Rua Mateus Grou 282, 05415-040 Sao Paulo SP, Brazil. TEL 55-11-2822355. FAX 55-11-8830991. (US addr.: Nautical Network International, Karlene Pack, 1300 S.E. 17th St., Ste. 217, Fort Lauderdale, FL 33316. TEL 305-463-9000. FAX 305-524-4913) Ed. Denise Godoy; Pub. Ernani Paciornik. adv. contact: Ernani Paciornik. **Document type:** consumer publication.
Formerly: Mar - Vela e Motor.

NAUTICAL RESEARCH JOURNAL. see *TRANSPORTATION — Ships And Shipping*

SPORTS AND GAMES — BOATS AND BOATING

796.95 US
NAUTIQUE NEWS. 1961. 3/yr. free. Correct Craft, Inc., 6100 S. Orange Ave., Orlando, FL 32809. TEL 407-855-4141. FAX 407-851-7844. TELEX 56-7424 CORRCRAFT. Ed. Teresa "Terry" Dunagin. adv. circ. 80,000. **Document type:** newsletter.
 Formerly: Correct Craft Tribune.
 Description: News for boating and water sports enthusiasts, with special emphasis on Correct Craft boats.

796.95 SP
NAVEGAR. 1990. m. 5760 ptas. (Europe 10860 ptas., color page 15360 ptas.); newsstand price: 600 ptas. Luike - Motorpress, C. Ancora 40, 28045 Madrid, Spain. TEL 34-1-34701000. FAX 34-1-3470204. Ed. Javier Pedroche; Pub. Jose Luis Samaranch. adv.: B&W page 195000 ptas., color page 250000 ptas.; adv. contact: Carlos Canada. circ. 10,000. **Document type:** consumer publication.
 Description: Covers recreational sailing, boating, technical information and related topics.

797.1 SW ISSN 0028-1603
NAVIS; Navigationsselskaepets medlemsblad. 1926. 6/yr. SEK 65 (effective 1991). Navigationssaellskapet, c/o H. Breide, Af Points vaag 6, 115 21 Stockholm, Sweden. Ed. Sture Gaerdshagen. illus. circ. 1,000.

796.95 FR ISSN 0762-7378
NEPTUNE YACHTING. 1962. 11/yr. 219 F. (outside EEC 312 F.). Societe d'Etude et de Developpement de la Presse Periodique, 23-25 rue de Berri, 75008 Paris, France. TEL 16-1-44-89-44-89. (Subscr. to: 90 rue de Flandre, 75947 Paris Cedex 19, France. TEL 16-1-40-34-35-00) Ed. Alain Corroler. adv.; illus. circ. 50,000. **Indexed:** Sportsearch.
 Former titles: Neptune Nautisme; Cahiers du Yatching; Helice (ISSN 0037-6205)

NEW HAMPSHIRE MOTOR VEHICLE AND BOATING LAWS. see *LAW — Judicial Systems*

NEW ZEALAND FISHERMAN. see *SPORTS AND GAMES — Outdoor Life*

796.95 US
NEWSWAVE.* 1986. s-a. Marine Challenge, Inc., 6418 U.S Highway 41 N., Ste. 266, Apollo Beach, FL 33572-1803. TEL 813-822-4749. FAX 813-822-0972. Ed. Ardith Bonnar. bk.rev.; tr.lit. circ. 150,000. (tabloid format; back issues avail.)
 Description: Contains information on marine safety and survival.

623.82 796.95 JA
NIHON SHUTEI KOGYOKAIHO/JAPAN BOATING INDUSTRY ASSOCIATION. NEWS. (Text in Japanese) 1970. bi-m. Nihon Shutei Kogyokai - Japan Boating Industry Association, 5-1, Ginza 2-chome, Chuo-ku, Tokyo 104, Japan.

NORSK BAATINDUSTRI. see *TRANSPORTATION — Ships And Shipping*

NORTHERN MARINER. see *HISTORY*

796.95 US ISSN 1063-8164
NORTHWEST SAILBOARD. 1981. 6/yr. $9.97. Extreme Publishing, 3702 W. Valley Hwy. N., Ste. 312, Auburn, WA 98002. Ed. Carol York. adv.: B&W page $1130, color page $1775; trim 3 8/8 x 10 7/8. circ. 25,000. **Document type:** consumer publication.
 Description: Covers windsurfing in the Northwest and beyond; including instruction, products and vocations.

796.95 US ISSN 0739-747X
NOR'WESTING. 1965. m. $15. Nor'westing Publications Inc., 6044 Seaview Ave., N.W., Seattle, WA 98107. TEL 206-783-8939. FAX 206-783-9011. Ed. Gloria A. Kruzner; Pub. Peter Worthington. bk.rev.; charts; illus.; tr.lit. circ. 6,500 (paid). **Document type:** consumer publication.
 Description: Covers recreational boating, boat club news, racing and related activities and events in the Pacific Northwest, from Oregon to Alaska, with a focus on the Puget Sound area.

796.95 US ISSN 0886-0149
VK555
OCEAN NAVIGATOR; marine navigation and ocean voyaging. 1985. 7/yr. $24. Navigator Publishing Corp., Box 569, Portland, ME 04112-0569. TEL 207-772-2466. Ed. Tim Queeney; Pub. Alex Agnew. adv. contact: Alex Agnew. bk.rev. circ. 41,000. **Document type:** consumer publication. —CCC.
 Formerly (until Dec. 1985): Navigator.

769.95 US
O'DAY TODAY.* 1985. 3/yr. membership. O'Day Corporation, 1 Federal St., 13th fl., Boston, MA 02110-2003. Ed. Paulie Rebello. circ. 6,000.
 Description: For owners of O'Day boats.

797.1 AU
OESTERREICHS KANUSPORT. 1948. 5/yr. S.100. Oesterreichischer Kanu-Verband, Berggasse 16, A-1090 Vienna, Austria. TEL (0222)93645. Ed. Guenter Goldbach. adv.; bk.rev.; abstr.; bibl.; charts; illus.; stat.; tr.lit. circ. 5,000.
 Formerly: Oesterreichs Paddelsport (ISSN 0029-9995)
 Description: News on canoes, sports events, canoe associations and canoe trips.

796.95 US
OFFSHORE (NEEDHAM). 1976. m. $18.95. Offshore Publications, Inc., Box 817, Needham, MA 02194. TEL 617-449-6204. FAX 617-449-9702. Ed. Jack Goodman, Jr. adv.; bk.rev.; illus.; circ. 36,000 (paid).
 Formerly: New England Offshore (ISSN 0274-9394)

797 AT
OFFSHORE AUSTRALIAN YACHTING. 1969. bi-m. Aus.$30.70. (Cruising Yacht Club of Australia) National Publications Pty. Ltd., P.O. Box 297, Homebush, N.S.W. 2140, Australia. TEL 02-764-1111. FAX 02-763-1699. Ed. Peter Campbell. adv.; bk.rev.; charts; illus. circ. 7,500. (back issues avail.) **Indexed:** Tr.& Indus.Ind.
 Former titles: Offshore Yacht Racing and Cruising (ISSN 0819-7458); (until 1987): Offshore.
 Description: Covers all local, national and international offshore and inshore yachting; yacht racing, yacht tests and reviews, boats and boating.

797.1 CN
ONTARIO WHITEWATER. a. Can.$3. Ontario Wildwater Affiliation, c/o Canoe Ontario, 1185 Eglinton Ave. E., Ste. 104, North York, Ont. M3C 3C6, Canada. TEL 416-426-7170. FAX 416-426-7363. Ed. Kevin Brough. adv. contact: Kevin Brough. circ. 400 (paid). **Document type:** newsletter, bulletin, catalog.
 Formerly: Ontario Wildwater Affiliation. Race Book.
 Description: Covers whitewater races in Ontario and selected national and international races, instructors courses, and Ontario Whitewater training camps.

797.1 SW ISSN 0345-9667
PAA KRYSS TILL RORS. 1930. 10/yr. SEK 260 (effective 1991). Svenska Kryssarklubben - Swedish Cruising Association, Karlavagen 67, S-114 49 Stockholm, Sweden. TEL 46-8-663-18-60. FAX 46-8-662-95-18. Ed. Erling Matz. adv. contact: Raymond Emtemark. bk.rev.; circ. 40,000 (controlled).
 Formerly (until vol.7, 1986): Paa Kryss och Till Rors; Formed by the 1972 merger of: Till Rors med Segel och Motor (ISSN 0040-7682); Paa Kryss.

797.1 US ISSN 0193-3515
GV776.C2
PACIFIC BOATING ALMANAC. NORTHERN CALIFORNIA & NEVADA. 1965. a. $19.95. Pacific Boating Almanac, Box 341668, Los Angeles, CA 90034-1668. TEL 310-577-9575. FAX 310-577-9272. Ed. Peter L. Griffes. illus. **Document type:** directory.
 Formerly: Sea Boating Almanac. Northern California and Nevada (ISSN 0363-7700)

797.9 US ISSN 0276-8771
GV776.N76
PACIFIC BOATING ALMANAC. PACIFIC NORTHWEST EDITION. (In 2 vols.) vol.1 a., vol.2 biennial. $19.95 per vol. Pacific Boating Almanac, Box 341668, Los Angeles, CA 90034-1668. TEL 310-577-9575. FAX 310-577-9272. Ed. Peter L. Griffes. illus. **Document type:** directory.
 Former titles: Pacific Boating Almanac. Oregon, Washington, British Columbia and Southeastern Alaska; Pacific Almanac. Pacific Northwest and Alaska (ISSN 0148-1177); Sea Boating Almanac. Pacific Northwest and Alaska (ISSN 0363-7999)

797.1 US
GV776.C22
PACIFIC BOATING ALMANAC. SOUTHERN CALIFORNIA & MEXICO. a. $19.95. Pacific Boating Almanac, Box 341668, Los Angeles, CA 90034-1668. TEL 310-577-9575. FAX 310-577-9272. Ed. Peter L. Griffes. illus. **Document type:** directory.
 Former titles: Pacific Boating Almanac. Southern California, Arizona and Baja (ISSN 0193-3507); (until 1977): Sea Boating Almanac. Southern California, Arizona, Baja (ISSN 0363-6712)

797.1 CN ISSN 0030-8986
PACIFIC YACHTING. 1968. m. Can.$34. O P Publishing Ltd., 1132 Hamilton St., Ste. 202, Vancouver, BC V6B 2S2, Canada. TEL 604-687-1581. FAX 604-687-1925. Ed. John Shinnick. adv.: B&W page Can.$2000, color page Can.$2575; trim 203 x 273; adv. contact: Stephen Fountaine. bk.rev.; charts; illus. circ. 17,141. **Indexed:** Can.B.P.I., Can.Per.Ind. **Document type:** consumer publication.
 Formerly: Pacific Yachting Journal.

797.122 US ISSN 1058-5710
PADDLER.* 1981. 6/yr. $15. Paddling Group, P.O. Box 1341, Eagle, ID 83616-1341. TEL 619-633-2293. FAX 619-630-1270. Ed. Eugene Buchanan. adv.; bk.rev. circ. 100,000. **Indexed:** Sportsearch (1984-).
 Formerly: River Runner (ISSN 8896-9197)
 Description: Covers whitewater canoeing, rafting, and kayaking within the U.S. and internationally. Provides information on equipment, technique, conservation and other related sports, destinations, activities and issues.

796.95 GW ISSN 0936-5877
PALSTEK; Technisches Wassersport Journal. 1985. bi-m. DM.36. Der Palstek Verlag GmbH, Bismarckstr. 84, 20253 Hamburg, Germany. TEL 040-4208725. FAX 040-4206560. Ed. Ulrich Kronberg. adv. contact: Lothar Richter. circ. 28,000. **Document type:** consumer publication.

PENNSYLVANIA ANGLER. see *SPORTS AND GAMES — Outdoor Life*

797.14 CN ISSN 0834-809X
PERFORMANCE RACING NEWS. 1989. m. Can.$24.98. Buy & Sell - Bargain Hunter Newspaper Ltd., 593 Yonge St., Toronto, ON M4Y 1Z4, Canada. TEL 416-922-7223. FAX 416-922-8001. Ed. John Hopkins; Pubs. Blake Breslin, Perry Breslin. adv.: B&W page Can.$2100; trim 10 1/2 x 15 3/4; adv. contact: David Weber. illus./ circ. 30,000 (paid). (tabloid format; back issues avail.) **Document type:** consumer publication.
 Description: Provides coverage of many forms of motorsports racing.

797.124 AT ISSN 1033-8195
PERFORMANCE SAILING. 1988. m. Aus.$3.98 per issue. A.B. Organisation Pty. Ltd., P.O. Box 319, Avalon Beach, N.S.W. 2107, Australia. TEL 02-918-8322. FAX 02-918-8884. (Dist. by: Network Distribution Company, 54-58 Park St., Sydney, N.S.W. 2000, Australia) circ. 10,000.
 Description: Directed at the performance sailing community.

797.1 US ISSN 1041-567X
PERSONAL WATERCRAFT ILLUSTRATED; the personal watercraft recreation magazine. 1987. m. $18.95. C N Publishing Group, 2201 Cherry Ave., Long Beach, CA 90806. TEL 310-427-7433. FAX 310-427-6685. Ed. Paul Carruthers. circ. 68,115. **Document type:** consumer publication.
 Description: Covers all aspects of the sport and recreational use of personal watercraft.

SPORTS AND GAMES — BOATS AND BOATING

796.95   CN   ISSN 0820-5086
PLAISANCIERS. 1986. 5/yr. Can.$12. 970 Montee de Liesse, Ville St-Laurent, PQ H4T 1W7, Canada. TEL 514-856-0788. Ed. Claude Leonard; Pub. W.E. Leonard. adv. contact: Roy J. Baird, Jr. circ. 20,000 (controlled). **Document type:** consumer publication.

796.95   CN   ISSN 0830-8705
PORT HOLE/HUBLOT. (Text in English, French) q. Can.$8($10) Canadian Power & Sail Squadrons - Escadrilles Canadiennes de Plaisance, 26 Golden Gate Crt., Scarborough, ON M1P 3A5, Canada. TEL 416-293-2438; 800-268-3579. FAX 416-293-2445. Ed. Diana Zonnenberg. adv.; bk.rev. circ. 24,000. **Document type:** newsletter.
   Description: Promotes safe boating through education. Keeps members informed of CPS activities, legal and legislative matters, new products and equipment. Entertains with amusing cruising yarns, timely marine maintenance, safety articles. Serves as a forum for lively exchange of opinions and ideas.

797.1   SP   ISSN 0213-3059
PORT NAUTIC PRESS; nautica deportiva. Variant title: Nautic Press. 1982. m. 3900 ptas. Diario Maritimas, S.A., Paseo de Colon 24, 08002 Barcelona, Spain. TEL 34-93-301-5646. FAX 34-93-318-6645. Ed. Juan Cardona. circ. 32,000. **Document type:** newspaper.

796.95   US   ISSN 0886-4411
POWER AND MOTORYACHT. 1985. m. $19.95 (Canada $29.95; elsewhere $39.95). (Power and Motoryacht Association) Cahners Publishing Company (New York), Consumer Division, Division of Reed Elsevier Inc., 245 W. 17th St., New York, NY 10000. TEL 212-645-0067. FAX 212-463-6435. (Dist. by: Neodata Services, Box 2971, Boulder, CO 80329. TEL 800-388-4511) Ed. Richard Thiel. adv. contact: John Bean. circ. 156,000. (back issues avail.) **Document type:** consumer publication.
—UMI.
   Description: For owners of powerboats 24 feet or larger. Articles covers engines, electronics, financing, fishing and operation.

797.14   CN   ISSN 0838-0872
POWER BOATING CANADA. 6/yr. Power Boating - Camping Canada, 2585 Skymark Ave., Ste. 306, Mississauga, Ont. L4W 4L5, Canada. TEL 416-624-8218. FAX 416-624-6764. Ed. Darryl Simmons. adv. circ. 40,000.

797.122   CN
POWER STROKE. irreg. (3-5/yr.). membership. Saskatoon Canoe Club, Box 7764, Saskatoon, Sask. S7K 4J1, Canada. TEL 306-933-4460. Ed. Greg Fenty. circ. 150. (looseleaf format) **Document type:** newsletter.
   Description: Covers upcoming events and reports on completed events. Relates to recreational canoeing, marathon canoe racing and whitewater kayaking.

797.1   US   ISSN 0032-6089
GV835.9
POWERBOAT. 1968. m. (11/yr.) $27 (foreign $38). Nordskog Publishing, Inc., 1691 Spinnaker Dr., Ste. 206, Ventura, CA 93001-4378. TEL 805-639-2222. FAX 805-639-2220. (Subscr. to: Box 462926, Excondido, CA 92046-9843. TEL 800-731-5586) Ed. Eric Colby; Pub. Gerald Nordskog. adv.; illus.; circ. 62,575 (paid). **Indexed:** Sportsearch. **Document type:** consumer publication.

623.82   US   ISSN 1040-3663
POWERBOAT REPORTS; the consumer resource for the powercraft owner. 1988. m. $68 (foreign $80). Belvoir Publications, Inc., 75 Holly Hill Ln., Box 2626, Greenwich, CT 06836-2626. TEL 203-661-6111. FAX 203-661-4802. (Subscr. to: Box 420234, Palm Coast, FL 32142) Ed. Timothy H. Cole. **Document type:** consumer publication.

797.1   UK   ISSN 0032-6348
VM320
PRACTICAL BOAT OWNER. 1967. m. $35.20. I P C Magazines, Specialist Magazine Group (Subsidiary of: Reed Elsevier group), King's Reach Tower, Stamford St., London SE1 9LS, England. TEL 0202-680593. FAX 0444-440619. TELEX 892084 REEDBP G. (Dist. by: Quadrant Subscription Services, Oakfield House, Perrymount Rd., Haywards Heath, W. Sussex RH16 3DH, England. TEL 0444-440421) Ed. George Taylor. adv. contact: John Arthur. bk.rev.; index. circ. 66,830. **Document type:** consumer publication.
—BLDSC (6593.964000). CCC.

796.95   US   ISSN 0161-8059
PRACTICAL SAILOR. 1970. s-m. $96 (foreign $120) (effective 1996). Belvoir Publications, Inc., 75 Holly Hill Ln., Box 2626, Greenwich, CT 06836-2626. TEL 203-661-6111. FAX 203-661-4802. (Subscr. to: 11 Commerce Blvd., Palm Coast, FL 32137) Ed. Dan Spurr. circ. 40,000. **Indexed:** Sportsearch (1984-). **Document type:** consumer publication.

623.82   US   ISSN 1043-2035
PROFESSIONAL BOATBUILDER. 1989. bi-m. free to qualified personnel. WoodenBoat Publications, Inc., Box 78, Brooklin, ME 04616. TEL 207-359-4651. FAX 207-359-8920. Ed. paul Lazarus; Pub. Gail Cramer. circ. 21,000 (controlled). **Document type:** trade publication.
   Description: Contains articles of interest to boat construction, repair, design and surveying company executives.

796.95   US   ISSN 0194-6218
PROPELLER. m. membership. American Power Boat Association, 17640 E. Nine Mile Rd., Box 377, Eastpointe, MI 48021. TEL 313-773-9700. FAX 313-773-6490. Ed. Michele Weston.
   Description: Features accounts of racing events, technology, safety and racing accomplishments.

797.14 797.124   FI   ISSN 0355-6980
PURJEHTIJA/SEGLAREN. (Text in Finnish and Swedish) 1974. bi-m. Fmk.80($25) Finnish Yachting Association - Suomen Purjehtijiliitto, Radiokatu 20, SF-00240 Helsinki, Finland. TEL 358-0-1582350. FAX 358-0-1582369. TELEX 121797-SVUL. Ed. Raimo Raeikkoenen. adv.; bk.rev.; circ. 31,000 (controlled). (back issues avail.)

797.1   CN   ISSN 0833-918X
QUEBEC YACHTING, VOILE ET MOTEUR. (Text in French) 1978. 6/yr. Can.$15.78. Publications Transcontinental Inc., 1100 Boul. Rene Levesque W., 24th Fl., Montreal, PQ H3B 4X9, Canada. TEL 514-392-9000. FAX 514-392-4726. Ed. Henri Rene de Cotret. adv.; bk.rev.; charts; illus. circ. 10,000. **Indexed:** Can.Per.Ind., Pt.de Rep. (1985-), Sportsearch. **Document type:** consumer publication.
   Former titles: Quebec Yachting et Voile (ISSN 0829-3198); Quebec Yachting (ISSN 0705-243X)

796.95   US
QUIMBY'S CRUISING GUIDE. 1962. a. $15.95. Waterways Journal, Inc., 319 Fourth St., 650 Security Bldg., St. Louis, MO 63102. TEL 314-241-7354. FAX 314-241-4207. Ed. Nelson Spencer. adv. circ. 5,000.
   Description: Tells where to get gas and overnight dockage on inland waterways. Lists marinas, includes columns.

RADIO CONTROL BOAT MODELER. see HOBBIES

RADIO CONTROL BOAT MODELLER. see HOBBIES

797   UK
REGATTA. 1987. 10/yr. £20 (rest of Europe £26; elsewhere £32). Amateur Rowing Association, 6 Lower Mall, London W6 9DJ, England. TEL 0181-748-3632. FAX 0181-741-4658. Ed. Chris J. Dodd. **Indexed:** Sportsearch (1987-). **Document type:** trade publication.
   Formerly (until 1987): A.R.A. Club News.

797.1   FR   ISSN 0035-5720
RIVIERE. q. 10 F. Canoe Kayak Club de France, 47 Quai Fuber, 94360 Bry sur Marne, France. bk.rev.

797.123   NE   ISSN 0048-8518
ROEIEN. 1938. m. fl.37 (effective 1995). Koninklijke Nederlandsche Roeibond, Bosbaan 6, 1182 AC Amstelveen, Netherlands. TEL 31-20-6462740. FAX 31-20-6463881. Ed. Hans Perree. adv.; illus.; index. circ. 5,000.
   Description: Reports on regattasin Holland and abroad (including results and records), rowing eevents, touring, rowing equipment, education and training.

796.95   UK   ISSN 0485-5175
ROVING COMMISSIONS; anthology of cruising logs. 1960. a. price varies. Royal Cruising Club, c/o Sue Kimber, 11 Charlwood Terrace, London SW15 1NZ, England. TEL 0181-788-5497. Ed. Peter Cumberlidge. bk.rev. circ. 1,000. **Document type:** bulletin.

797.1   UK   ISSN 0035-9041
ROYAL NAVAL SAILING ASSOCIATION JOURNAL. 1936. s-a. membership. Royal Naval Sailing Association, c/o Royal Naval Club & Royal Albert Yacht Club, 17 Pembroke Rd., Portsmouth, Hants P01 2NT, England. Ed. Lt. Col. P.R. Thomas. adv.; bk.rev.; illus. circ. 6,800.

796.95   GW   ISSN 0342-8281
RUDERSPORT. 1883. every 8 days (May-Sept.), every 14 days (Oct.-Apr.). DM.111. (German Rowing Association) Limpert Verlag GmbH, Postfach 4027, 65030 Wiesbaden, Germany. TEL 0611-373072. FAX 0611-374351. Ed. Rolf Ziel. adv. **Document type:** bulletin.

797.124   US   ISSN 0036-2700
GV811
SAIL. 1970. m. $23.94 (Canada $30.94; elsewhere $33.94). Cahners Publishing Company (Newton), Consumer Division, Division of Reed Elsevier Inc., 275 Washington St., Newton, MA 02158-1630. TEL 617-964-3030. FAX 617-630-3737. (Dist. by: Neodata Services, Box 56397, Boulder, CO 80321-6397. TEL 800-745-7245) Ed. Patience Wales; Pub. Donald A. Macaulay. adv. contact: Richard Devlin. bk.rev.; charts; illus.; tr.lit.; circ. 178,468 (paid); 5,000 (controlled). (also avail. in microform from UMI; back issues avail.; reprint service avail. from UMI) **Indexed:** Consum.Ind., Mag.Ind., PMR, R.G., Sports Per.Ind., Sportsearch (1976-). **Document type:** consumer publication.
—Faxon; UMI; UnCover. CCC.
   Description: For sailors at various levels: cruisers and racers, from novices to experts, actively involved in the development of their sailing skills.

796.95   US   ISSN 1063-8180
SAILBOARD RETAILER. 1989. 6/yr. $20. Extreme Publishing, 3702 W. Valley Hwy. N., Ste. 312, Auburn, WA 98002. Ed. Carol York. adv.: B&W page $975; trim 8 3/8 x 10 7/8. circ. 4,500 (controlled). **Document type:** trade publication.
   Description: Includes retail selling tips and windsurfing industry and product news.

797.124   US
SAILBOAT BUYERS GUIDE. 1967. a. $4.95. Cahners Publishing Company (Newton), Division of Reed Elsevier Inc., 275 Washington St., Newton, MA 02158-1630. TEL 617-964-3030. FAX 617-630-3737. (Subscr. to: Box 7820, Torrance, CA 90504-9220. TEL 800-362-8433) (Co-publisher: Sail Publications) Ed. Patience Wales. adv.; bk.rev.; illus. circ. 95,000. **Document type:** consumer publication, directory.
   Former titles (until 1994): Sailboat and Equipment Directory (ISSN 0148-8732); (until 1970): Sailboat Directory (ISSN 0581-3115)
   Description: Provides the sailing community, the public and the trade with a reference guide to the sailboats and sailboat products available in the US and Canada.

797.124   US   ISSN 0036-2719
SAILING; the beauty of sail. 1966. m. $24.95. Port Publications, Inc., 125 E. Main St., Port Washington, WI 53074. TEL 414-284-3494. FAX 414-284-0067. Ed. Wm. F. Schanen III; Pub. Wm. F. Schanen III. adv. contact: Kenneth Quant. bk.rev.; illus.; circ. 35,000 (paid). (also avail. in microform from UMI; reprint service avail. from UMI) **Document type:** consumer publication.
—UMI.
   Formerly: Lake Michigan Sailing.

SPORTS AND GAMES — BOATS AND BOATING

797.124   CN
SAILING CANADA.* 6/yr. Gam on Yachting Inc., 250 The Esplanade., Ste. 202, Toronto, ON M5A 1J2, Canada. TEL 416-368-1559. FAX 416-368-2831. Ed. Donna Fairey Carter. adv. contact: Peter Rumgay. **Indexed:** Can.B.P.I.

797.124   US
SAILING SCENE. m. New York Times Company, 5 John Clarke Rd., Newport, RI 02840-5641. TEL 401-847-1588. FAX 401-848-5048. Ed. Jane Tracy.

797.1   US   ISSN 0889-4094
GV811.8
SAILING WORLD; the authority on performance sailing. 1962. m. $24. Cruising World Publications, Inc. (Subsidiary of: New York Times Co.), Box 3400, Newport, RI 02840-0992. TEL 401-847-1588. FAX 401-848-5048. (Subscr. to: Box 3213, Harlan, IA 51537) Ed. John Burnham. adv.; bk.rev.; illus. circ. 61,000. (also avail. in microform from UMI; back issues avail.; reprint service avail. from UMI) **Indexed:** Sportsearch (1990-). **Document type:** consumer publication.
    Former titles: Yacht Racing and Cruising (ISSN 0190-7956); Yacht Racing (ISSN 0276-2935); One-Design and Offshore Yachtsman (ISSN 0030-2511)
    Description: For the active sailor who races or cruises. Covers sailboat design, sailing technique and equipment, charter cruising, seamanship, racing events and news.

797.1   US
SANTANA. 1987. m. $20. Santana Publications, Inc., 5969 Engineer Dr., Huntington Beach, CA 92649-1129. TEL 714-379-3070. adv. circ. 25,000.
    Description: Covers racing and cruising sailing

797.1   US   ISSN 0746-8601
GV811.8
SEA; best of boating in the west. Variant title: Sea Magazine. (Covers the 13 Western United States; British Columbia, Canada, and West of coast Mexico). 1908. m. $19.94 (foreign $29.94). Duncan McIntosh Co. Inc., 17782 Cowan, Irvine, CA 92714-6012. TEL 714-660-6150. FAX 714-660-6172. Ed. Eston Ellis. adv.; bk.rev.; charts; illus.; tr.lit. (also avail. in microform from UMI; reprint service avail. from UMI) **Indexed:** PMR, Sportsearch.
—UMI.
    Formerly (until 1984): Sea and Pacific Skipper (ISSN 0274-905X); Incorporates (in 1977): Rudder (ISSN 0274-9068); Which supersedes: Sea, Eastern Edition (ISSN 0163-7533); Sea and Pacific Motor Boat (ISSN 0036-9969)
    Description: Profiles boating personalities, cruise destinations, analysis of marine environmental issues, technical information, seamanship, and news from western harbors.

796.5   GR
SEA & YACHTING; the Greek monthly yachting magazine. (Text in Greek) 1977. m. Dr.9000($85) (foreign Dr.15000). International Marine Publications, 22 Akti Themistokleous, 185 36 Piraeus, Greece. TEL 30-1-4281-923. FAX 30-1-4137-805. TELEX 21 2000 VAL GR. (N. American addr.: 7254 Fir Rd., Ambler, PA 19002. TEL 800-223-3845) Ed. Kiki Pentheroudakis; Pub. John Papadopoulos. adv. contact: Alekos Paleopoulos. circ. 20,000. (back issues avail.) **Document type:** consumer publication.
    Description: Presents articles about pleasure boats and yachts. Includes information on racing, professional or pleasure yachting, technical features, presentation and tests concerning new models of yachts and equipment, reports on the major international Greek events, and other general information.

796.95 900   US   ISSN 0270-5524
SEA HERITAGE NEWS. 1980. q. $25. Sea Heritage Foundation, 254-26 75 Ave., Glen Oaks, NY 11004. TEL 718-343-9575. Ed. Bernie Klay. adv.; bk.rev. circ. 50,000.
    Description: Covers all aspects of sea history and culture.

796.95   US   ISSN 0829-3279
GV788.5
SEA KAYAKER. 1984. bi-m. $20.95. Box 17170, Seattle, WA 97170-0870. TEL 206-789-6413. FAX 206-781-1141. (Subscr. to: Sea Kayaker, Inc., 7001 Seaview Ave. N.W., Seattle, WA 98117) Ed. Chris Cunningham; Pub. Michael Collins. adv. contact: Arnie Zapolski. bk.rev. circ. 95,000. (back issues avail.) **Indexed:** Sportsearch (1987-). **Document type:** consumer publication.
    Description: Explores kayak touring on sea and lakes, safety techniques, health, destinations, history and much more.

797.14   UK   ISSN 0143-246X
SEAHORSE. 1969. m. £30 (Europe £35; elsewhere £45). Fairmead Communications Ltd., 2 River Court, Gosport St., Lymington, Hampshire SO41 9BG, England. TEL 01590-671898. FAX 01590-671116. (Subscr. to: Computer Posting Group Ltd., 120-126 Lavendar Ave., Mitcham, Surrey CR4 3HR, England. TEL 0181-640-9418) Ed. Andrew Hurst. adv.: B&W page £910; color page £1425; trim 270 x 188; adv. contact: Graham Beeson. circ. 20,000. (back issues avail.) **Indexed:** Abstr.Engl.Stud. **Document type:** consumer publication.
    Description: Contains information on yacht design and technology, as well as international race coverage.

796.5   SZ
SEEMEILE. 1982. bi-m. 48 SFr. Seemeile Verlag, Sunneberg 3, CH-8634 Hombrechtikon, Switzerland. TEL 01-55424387. FAX 01-7806211. Ed. H. Neuhaus. adv.: B&W page 2400 SFr.; adv. contact: H. Neuhaus. bk.rev.; circ. 10,000. (paid). (back issues avail.) **Document type:** consumer publication.
Refereed Serial

797.124   GW   ISSN 0342-7528
SEGELN; das Magazin fuer Fahrtensegler. 1979. m. DM.88.20. Jahr-Verlag GmbH & Co., Jessenstr. 1, 22767 Hamburg, Germany. TEL 040-38906-0. FAX 040-38906302. Ed. Thomas Dieck. adv. contact: Bernd Hacker. circ. 26,600. **Document type:** consumer publication.

797.1   SW   ISSN 0037-0916
SEGLARBLADET; Vaestkustens baattidning. 1911. 7/yr. SEK 200 (effective 1991). Goeteborgs Kungliga Segelsaellskap, P.O. Box 5039, S-421 05 Vaestra Froelunda, Sweden. Ed. Malin Schroeder. adv.; bk.rev.; charts; illus. circ. 5,000.

797.124   GW   ISSN 0930-2891
SEGLER ZEITUNG; Informationen fuer Sport Skipper. 1981. m. Segler Zeitung Verlag GmbH, Birkenallee 36, 23669 Timmendorfer Strand, Germany. TEL 04503-5071. FAX 04503-3701. Ed. Horst Schlichting.

797.124   NO   ISSN 0802-3018
SEILSPORT. 1968. 6/yr. $55. (Norges Seilforbund) Seilsport Maritimt Forlag AS, Box 24 Voksenskogen, N-0708 Oslo 7, Norway. Ed. Tore Thjomoe. adv. circ. 24,816.

SELF-CATERING AND FURNISHED HOLIDAYS. see *TRAVEL AND TOURISM*

796.95   UK
SELL'S MARINA GUIDE. biennial. £8 (overseas £18). Miller Freeman Business Information Services (Subsidiary of: United News & Media), Riverbank House, Angel Ln., Tonbridge, Kent TN9 1SE, England. TEL 01732-362666. FAX 01732-770483. TELEX 957829. **Document type:** directory.
    Formerly (until 1989): Britain and Holland Marina Guide.
    Description: Provides boat owners with a list of coastal and inland marinas and their services. Covers Britain, Ireland, the Channel Islands, and the French coastal harbors.

623.82   UK
SELL'S MARINE INDUSTRY BUYERS' GUIDE. Variant title: Marine Industry Buyers' Guide. (Supplement avail.: County Guide to Marine Companies (ISSN 0260-7093)) 1978. a. £45 (rest of Europe £62; elsewhere £70-£75). Miller Freeman Business Information Services (Subsidiary of: United News & Media), Riverbank House, Angel Ln., Tonbridge, Kent TN9 1SE, England. TEL 01732-362666. FAX 01732-367301. TELEX 957829. Ed. Gwen Young. adv. contact: Elaine Soni. **Document type:** directory.
    Former titles: Sell'gs Marine Market International; Sell's Marine Market (ISSN 0143-1153)
    Description: Lists marine products and services.

SERRA E MAR/MOUNTAINS AND SEA. see *SPORTS AND GAMES — Outdoor Life*

SHIP & BOAT INTERNATIONAL. see *TRANSPORTATION — Ships And Shipping*

796.95   US   ISSN 0749-9361
SHOWBOAT CENTENNIALS NEWSLETTER. 1979. irreg., no.40, 1995. free. Showboat Centennials, 76 Glen Dr., Worthington, OH 43085. TEL 614-431-9422. Ed. Donald T. McDaniel; Pub. Donald T. McDaniel. bk.rev.; circ. 150 (controlled). (looseleaf format; back issues avail.) **Document type:** monographic series, newsletter.
    Description: Comprises monographs on the history of floating theaters and related river history.

796.95   US   ISSN 0749-2952
SHOWBOATS INTERNATIONAL. 1982. bi-m. $24. Hachette Magazines, Inc., 1633 Broadway, 45th Fl., New York, NY 10009. TEL 212-767-6000. adv.: color page $7480; trim 8 3/4 x 11 7/8. circ. 54,224. **Document type:** consumer publication.
—UMI.

797.1   NO   ISSN 0037-6000
SJOESPORT. 1961. 10/yr. NOK 155. Sjoesport A-S, P.O. Box 576, 5001 Bergen, Norway. adv.; bk.rev.; circ. 21,000 (controlled).
—CCC.

343.09 797   US   ISSN 1066-2383
SMALL CRAFT ADVISORY. 1985? bi-m. National Association of State Boating Law Administrators, c/o Mississippi Department of Wildlife, Fisheries and Parks, P.O. Box 451, Jackson, MS 39205. TEL 601-362-9212. FAX 601-961-4337.
    Description: Promotes boating safety.

797.1   UK
SOLENT BOOK; solent cruising & racing association year book. 1910. a. £6. (Solent Cruising & Racing Association) Isle of Wight County Press Ltd., Brannon House, 123 Pyle St., Newport, Isle of Wight PO30 1ST, England. FAX 01983-527204. Ed. R.L. Bradbeer. adv.; charts. circ. 5,000. **Document type:** consumer publication.
    Description: Provides information to all yachting and boating users of the Solent Cruising & Racing Association; includes classes, programme of events, navigational information.

796.95   US
SOUNDINGS (ESSEX); the nation's boating newspaper. 1963. m. $19.97. Soundings Publications, Inc., Pratt St., Essex, CT 06426-1122. TEL 203-767-3200. FAX 203-767-1048. Ed. Marleah Ross; Pub. John Turner. adv. contact: Russell Lennon. bk.rev.; illus. circ. 90,000. (tabloid format) **Indexed:** Amer.Hum.Ind., CERDIC. **Document type:** newspaper, consumer publication.

796.95   US   ISSN 0194-8369
SOUNDINGS TRADE ONLY. 1981. m. $25. Soundings Publications, Inc., Pratt St., Essex, CT 06426-1122. TEL 203-767-3200. FAX 203-767-1048. Ed. David Eastman; Pub. John Turner. adv. contact: Russell Lennon. circ. 35,000. (tabloid format) **Document type:** newspaper, trade publication.
    Formerly: Trade Only.
    Description: The boating business newspaper.

SPORTS AND GAMES — BOATS AND BOATING

797.1   SA
SOUTH AFRICAN YACHTING. 1957. m. R.64($25) Yachting News (Pty) Ltd., P.O. Box 3473, Cape Town 8000, South Africa. TEL 27-21-4617472. FAX 27-21-4613758. Ed. Neil Rusch. adv. contact: Bill Stymonds. bk.rev.; illus. circ. 7,500. **Document type:** consumer publication.
  Former titles: South African Yachting, Sail, Power and Waterski (ISSN 0256-7431); South African Yachting, Powerboats, Sailing, Waterski (ISSN 0038-2817); South African Yachting, Power and Sail.
  Description: News, features and technical articles on dinghy and keelboat sailing.

796.95   US   ISSN 0192-3579
SOUTHERN BOATING. 1972. m. $15. Southern Boating and Yachting, Inc., c/o Skip Allen, Ed. & Pub., 1766 Bay Rd., Miami Beach, FL 33139-1414. TEL 305-538-0700. FAX 305-532-8657. adv. contact: Steve Beck. bk.rev.; illus. circ. 33,000. **Document type:** consumer publication.
  Description: Provides general boating and cruising information for the Southeastern U.S. and Caribbean.

797.124   US
SPEARHEAD (MAYFIELD). 1970. bi-m. membership. Javelin Class Association, 874 Beecher's Bl, Mayfield Village, OH 44143. TEL 216-461-8511. Ed. G.T. Reiber. illus. circ. 250. (tabloid format)
  Description: Covers education and information about Javelin sailboats: accepted and approved modifications, social activities as well as racing.

797.124   NE   ISSN 0165-5132
SPIEGEL DER ZEILVAART. 1977. 10/yr. fl.60 (foreign fl.75) (effective 1994). Stichting Spiegel der Zeilvaart, Van Oosten de Bruijnstr. 13, 2014 VL Haarlem, Netherlands. TEL 31-23-341801. FAX 31-23-317399. (Subscr. to: Abo, Postbus 653, 2003 RR Haarlem, Netherlands) Ed. Wim de Bruijn. adv.; bk.rev.; illus. circ. 10,000.
  —SWETS.

796.95   US   ISSN 0898-8951
SPLASH (PLACENTIA). 1987. m. $39. McMullen & Yee Publishing, 774 S. Placentia Ave., Placentia, CA 92670-6846. TEL 714-572-2255. FAX 714-572-1864. adv. circ. 78,121.

797.124   IT
SPORT VELA. m. Organo Ufficiale della Federazione Italiana Vela, Viale Brigata Bisagno 2-17, Genoa, Italy. TEL 010-589431. FAX 010-592864. Ed. Rodolfo Cardellini.

796.95   US
STANDARDS AND RECOMMENDED PRACTICES FOR SMALL CRAFT. 1965. base vol. plus a. supplement. $250 for base vol.; supplements $75. American Boat & Yacht Council, Inc., 3069 Solomons Islands Rd., Edgewater, MD 21037-1416. TEL 410-956-1050. FAX 410-956-2737. Ed. Thomas Hale, circ. 3,300. (looseleaf format) **Document type:** trade publication.
  Description: Standards and recommended practices for the design and construction of recreational boats and their equipment.

797.1   GW   ISSN 0038-9706
STANDER; Boot und Motor und Wassersport. 1959. m. DM.78. (Deutscher Motoryachtverband e.V.) Westdeutsche Verlagsanstalt GmbH, Ahmser Str. 190, 32052 Herford, Germany. TEL 05221-775-0. FAX 05221-775215. Ed. Claus Breitenfeld. adv.; bk.rev.; charts; illus.; index. circ. 60,033. **Document type:** consumer publication.
  Description: Information about navigation techniques and accessories.

797.1   US   ISSN 0038-9927
STARLIGHTS. 1921. m. $8. International Star Class Yacht Racing Association, 1545 Waukegan Rd., Glenview, IL 60025. TEL 312-729-0630. FAX 312-729-0718. Ed. Richard L. Munson. adv.; bk.rev.; charts; stat.; tr.lit. circ. 3,970.

STATION LOG. see *MUSEUMS AND ART GALLERIES*

796.95   US   ISSN 1056-6422
STEAMBOATING; steamboater's handbook. 1985. q. $25. (International Steamboat Society) Bill Warren Mueller, Ed. & Pub., Rt. 1, Box 262, Middlebourne, WV 26149-9748. TEL 304-386-4434. adv.; bk.rev.; charts; illus. circ. 1,300. (back issues avail.) **Indexed:** Ind.How To Do It (1990-). **Document type:** consumer publication.
  Formerly: Steamboat News.
  Description: For owners and operators of boats powered by steam engines and boilers.

797.1   IT
SUB. 1984. m. L.63000 (foreign L.110000). Adventures s.r.l., Via A. Anfossi 20, Milan, Italy. TEL 39-2-55188494. FAX 39-2-5464407. Ed. Guido Pfeiffer. adv.: B&W page L.3500000, color page L.5500000. **Document type:** consumer publication.

797.14   AT
SYDNEY TO HOBART YACHT RACE PROGRAMME. a. National Publications Pty. Ltd., P.O. Box 297, Homebush West, N.S.W. 2140, Australia. TEL 02-764-1111. FAX 02-763-1699. circ. 7,500.
  Description: Contains the full details of previous Sydney to Hobart races including the list of entries.

796.95   CN
TANZER TALK; newsletter of the Tanzer 22 class. 1971. bi-m. $25. Tanzer 22 Class Association, P.O. Box 22, Ste. Anne de Bellevue, PQ H9X 3L4, Canada. TEL 514-457-3929. FAX 514-457-1589. Ed. John G. Charters. circ. 500. (back issues avail.) **Document type:** newsletter.
  Formerly: Tanzer 22 Newsletter.
  Description: All news and information related to yachts and yachting.

796.95   US
THOROUGHBRED. 1980. q. $25. Century Boat Club, Inc., 936 Jackman Ave., Pittsburgh, PA 15202-2808. TEL 412-761-6307. FAX 412-766-0914. (Subscr. to: Box 761, Manistee, MI 49660) Ed. Frank G. Miklos. adv.: page $150. cum.index; circ. 1,500 (paid). (back issues avail.) **Document type:** trade publication.
  Description: Covers classical and antique Century boats.

623.8   SW   ISSN 0347-0652
TRAEBITEN. 1970. a. SEK 125. Foereningen Allmoge Baatar, P.O. Box 6046 Bassholmen, S-451 06 Uddevalla, Sweden. TEL 46-31-42-64-35.
  Description: Devoted to preserving the unique Old-Nordic style of boatbuilding.

797.1   US   ISSN 0300-6557   GV776.A2
TRAILER BOATS. 1971. m. $19.97. Poole Publications, Inc., 20700 Belshaw Ave., Carson, CA 90746. TEL 310-537-6322. FAX 310-537-8735. Ed. Randy Scott; Pub. Wiley Poole. adv.: B&W page $4330, color page $6895. bk.rev.; index. circ. 87,000. (also avail. in microform from UMI) **Indexed:** Consum.Ind., Mag.Ind. **Document type:** consumer publication.
  •Also available online. Vendor(s): University Microfilms International.
    —UMI.
  Description: Covers recreational boating topics, including boat and trailer tests, marine electronics, waterskiing, product evaluations, and boating destinations.

791.95   AT
TRAILERS TOWING & 4WD. 1980. a. A.B. Organisation Pty. Ltd., P.O. Box 319, Avalon Beach, N.S.W. 2107, Australia. TEL 02-918-8322. FAX 02-918-8884. (Dist. by: Gordon & Gotch, 25-37 Huntingdale Rd., Burwood, Vic. 3125, Australia) circ. 20,000.
  Description: For trailerboat owners. Deals with the problems of launching and retrieving, trailer maintenance, state rules and regulations and evaluates four wheel drives in relation to the trailer owner.

797.124   GW
TRANS-OCEAN. 1968. q. DM.60 membership. Verein zur Foerderung des Hochseesegelns e.V., Postfach 728, 27457 Cuxhaven, Germany. TEL 04721-51800. FAX 04721-51874. Ed. Helmut Bellmer. adv.; bk.rev. circ. 2,800. (back issues avail.) **Document type:** bulletin.

623.82   GW
TRAUMBOOT REAL. 1987. bi-m. DM.15. Heinz Hueffel Verlag, Mittelstr. 2, 53562 St. Katharinen, Germany. TEL 02645-3959. FAX 02645-4827. circ. 5,000.

797.1   US
U S SAILING DIRECTORY. 1925. a. membership. United States Sailing Association, Box 209, Newport, RI 02840. TEL 401-849-5200. FAX 401-849-5208. TELEX 704592-USYRU-NORT-UD. Eds. Patricia Linn, Dana Marnane. adv. contact: Dana Marnane. circ. 30,000. **Document type:** directory.
  Former titles: U S Y R U Directory; U S Y R U Yearbook; N A Y R U Yearbook.
  Description: Provides reference material and results of each year's championships and notices of races and contains a reference list of all committee and council members.

797.124   GW
UNSERE ALTE LIEBE. 1926. q. DM.150. Segler Vereinigung Cuxhaven, Postfach 672, 27456 Cuxhaven, Germany. TEL 04721-22280. Ed. Folker Weiss. circ. 1,000. **Document type:** bulletin.

796.95   US   ISSN 0735-973X   HD9993.B633
USED BOAT PRICE GUIDE. Spine title: B U C Used Boat Price Guide. 1961. s-a. $169 per 3-vol. set. B U C International Corp., 1314 N.E. 17th Ct., Fort Lauderdale, FL 33305. TEL 305-565-6715. Ed. Walter J. Sullivan III. stat. **Document type:** directory.
  Former titles: Older Boat Price Guide (ISSN 0197-212X); Used Boat Directory.

796.95   US
VAPOR TRAIL'S BOATING NEWS & INTERNATIONAL YACHTING & CRUISER AND MANUFACTURERS REPORT. 1966. m. $24. Gemini Productions, Ltd., 8962 Bainford Drive, Huntington Beach, CA 92646. TEL 714-833-8003. Ed. Patricia Collins. circ. 25,000.
  Formed by the merger of: Vapor Trail's Yachting and Cruiser News; Vapor Trail's Boating News and Manufacturing Report; Which was formerly titled: Vapor Trail's Competition News and Manufacturing Report (ISSN 0042-2630)

796.95   BE   ISSN 0775-8553
VAREN. 1969. m. 1000 BEF. Aco, Liersestwg. 237, 2547 Lint, Belgium. TEL 32-3-4892072. FAX 32-3-4890219. circ. 20,000.
  Description: Covers all aspects of yachting, sailing and motorboating.

797.1   IT   ISSN 0042-3181
VELA E MOTORE. 1923. m. L.77000 (foreign L.125000). Edisport Editoriale S.p.A., Via Gradisca 11, 20151 Milan, Italy. TEL 39-2-380851. FAX 39-2-38010393. Ed. Piero Bacchetti. adv.: B&W page L.6600000. bk.rev.; charts; illus.; index. circ. 55,200.
  Description: News about sailboats and powerboats, instruments, regattas, marinas and ports.

797.1   FI   ISSN 0042-3343
VENE. (Text in Finnish) 1966. 10/yr. FIM 280. Yhtyneet Kuvalehdet Oy, Maistraatinportti 1, FIN-00240 Helsinki, Finland. TEL 358-0-156-6524. FAX 358-0-156-6505. TELEX 121364. Ed. Matti Murto. adv.: B&W page FIM 9000, color page FIM 13200. bk.rev.; illus. circ. 27,793.

797.1   FI   ISSN 0783-5124
VENEMAAILMA. 1985. 9/yr. FIM 258. Helsinki Media Company OY, Sport, P.O. Box 16, 00381 Helsinki, Finland. TEL 358-0-120-5911. FAX 358-0-120-5959. Ed. Markku Vento. adv. contact: Esa Sairio. circ. 17,340.

797.124   FR   ISSN 0751-5405
VOILES ET VOILIERS. m. 409 F. Societe d'Edition de Revues Nationales Specialisees, 21 rue du Faubourg St. Antoine, 75550 Paris Cedex 11, France. TEL 1-40-02-62-62. Ed. Pierre Lavialle. adv.; illus.

796.95   GW   ISSN 0940-3183
WASSERSKI MAGAZIN. 1975. bi-m. DM.33. Ostallee 49b, 54290 Trier, Germany. Pub. Franz Kirsch. circ. 10,000. (back issues avail.) **Document type:** consumer publication.
  Description: News about waterskiing.

WATER SKIER. see *SPORTS AND GAMES — Outdoor Life*

SPORTS AND GAMES — BOATS AND BOATING

797 US ISSN 1075-4792
WATERCRAFT ACTION. 1993. 8/yr. $9.95. Ehlert Publishing Group, Inc., 601 Lakeshore Pkwy., Ste. 600, Minnetonka, MN 55305. TEL 612-476-2200. FAX 612-476-8065. (Subscr. to: Box 690, Mt. Morris, IL 61054-7571. TEL 800-877-6118) Ed. Joel Johnson. adv. contact: Dave Christensen. circ. 12,000. (back issues avail.) **Document type:** newspaper.
Description: Covers watercraft races and performances.

797.1 US ISSN 1079-3119
WATERCRAFT BUSINESS. 1987. 6/yr. $12 (Canada $18; elsewhere $22) (free to qualified personnel). Ehlert Publishing Group, Inc., 601 Lakeshore Pkwy., Ste. 600, Minnetonka, MN 55305-5215. TEL 612-476-2200. FAX 612-476-8065. Ed. Glenn Hanson. adv. circ. 6,000. **Document type:** trade publication.
Formerly: Water Scooter Business (ISSN 1061-3196)

797 US
WATERCRAFT DEALER.* q. 201 Sandpointe Ave., Ste. 600, Santa Ana, CA 92707-5761. TEL 714-252-5300. FAX 714-261-9700. Ed. Paul Smith. adv.

796.95 US ISSN 1073-3191
WATERCRAFT WORLD. 1987. 9/yr. $17.95 (Canada $29.95; elsewhere 31.95). Ehlert Publishing Group, Inc., 601 Lakeshore Pkwy., Minnetonka, MN 55305. TEL 612-476-2200. FAX 612-476-2200. Ed. Glenn Hanson. **Document type:** consumer publication.
Formerly (until 1993): Water Scooter (ISSN 0899-9775)

796.95 917.504 US ISSN 8756-0038
WATERFRONT NEWS; South Florida's nautical newspaper. 1984. m. $12. Ziegler Publishing Co., Inc., 1523 South Andrews Ave., Ft. Lauderdale, FL 33316. TEL 305-524-9450. FAX 035-524-9464. Ed. Jennifer Heit. adv. contact: John Ziegler. bk.rev. circ. 42,000. (tabloid format; back issues avail.) **Document type:** newspaper.
Description: Covers South Florida's sailing, power boating, nautical history, diving, fishing and waterfront community news.

796.95 US
WATERFRONT NORTHWEST NEWS. 1993. m. Duncan McIntosh Co. Inc., 17782 Cowan Ste. C, Irvine, CA 92714. TEL 714-660-6150. FAX 714-660-6172. adv.; B&W page $925, color page $1250; trim 10 1/4 x 13 1/2. circ. 7,700 (paid); 27,300 (controlled). **Document type:** consumer publication.

796.95 US
WATERFRONT SOUTHERN CALIFORNIA NEWS. 1993. m. Duncan McIntosh Co. Inc., 17782 Cowan, Ste. C, Irvine, CA 92714. TEL 714-660-6150. adv.; B&W page $1050, color page $1375; trim 10 1/4 x 13 1/2. circ. 7,000 (paid); 35,500 (controlled). **Document type:** consumer publication.

797.1 NE ISSN 0043-1451
WATERKAMPIOEN. 1927. 24/yr. fl.124 to non-members. Koninklijke Nederlandse Toeristenbond ANWB - Royal Dutch Touring Club, Wassenaarseweg 220, Postbus 93200, 2509 BA The Hague, Netherlands. TEL 31-70-3146119. FAX 31-70-3242509. Ed. Robert Olieroock. adv.; B&W page fl.4368, color page fl.7862; trim 215 x 285; adv. contact: J.W. Boersen. bk.rev.; charts; illus.; index. circ. 60,200. **Indexed:** Key to Econ.Sci., Rural Recreat.Tour.Abstr., World Agri.Econ. & Rural Sociol.Abstr. **Document type:** consumer publication.
—SWETS.
Description: Covers water sports and travel related topics.

387.2 US ISSN 0509-917X
GV835
WATERWAY GUIDE - MID-ATLANTIC. a. $33.95. Argus Inc., 6151 Powers Ferry Rd., N.W., Atlanta, GA 30339-2941. TEL 404-955-2500. FAX 404-955-0400. Ed. Judith Powers. adv.; charts. **Document type:** directory, consumer publication.
Description: Navigation and travel guide for recreational boaters who cruise the Chesapeake Bay, Delmarva Coast, and the inter-costal waterway from Norfolk to the Georgia - Florida border.

387.2 US ISSN 0090-712X
WATERWAY GUIDE - NORTHERN. a. $33.95. Argus Inc., 6151 Powers Ferry Rd., N.W., Atlanta, GA 30339-2941. TEL 404-955-2500. FAX 404-955-0400. Ed. Judith Powers. adv.; charts. **Document type:** directory, consumer publication.
Description: Navigation and travel guide for recreational boaters who cruise the waters of the Delaware Bay, New Jersey coast, Long Island Sound, and the coasts of Connecticut, Massachusetts and Maine.

387.2 US ISSN 0511-3806
WATERWAY GUIDE - SOUTHERN. a. $33.95. Argus Inc., 6151 Powers Ferry Rd., N.W., Atlanta, GA 30339-2941. TEL 404-955-2500. FAX 404-955-0400. Ed. Judith Powers. adv.; charts. **Document type:** directory, consumer publication.
Description: Navigation and travel guide for recreational boaters who cruise the east and west coast of Florida, Bahamas, Gulf Coast to Mexico and the Tenn-Tom Waterway.

796.95 UK ISSN 0969-0654
WATERWAYS. 1946. 3/yr. membership. Inland Waterways Association, 26 Chaseview Rd., Alrewas, Burton-on-Trent, Staffordshire DE13 7EL, England. Ed. Harry Arnold. adv.; bk.rev. circ. 14,500.
—BLDSC (9279.751000).
Formerly (until 1991): I W A Waterways (ISSN 0308-583X)

796.95 US ISSN 0273-4699
WEST COAST SAILORS. m. Sailors' Union of the Pacific, 450 Harrison St., San Francisco, CA 94105. TEL 415-362-8363.

WESTCOAST MARINER. see TRANSPORTATION — Ships And Shipping

797.1 CN ISSN 0826-5003
WINDSPORT. 1982. 4/yr. Can.$16.50($19.50) 2255 B Queen St. E., Ste. 3266, Toronto, ON M4E 1G3, Canada. TEL 416-698-0138. FAX 416-698-8080. Ed. Steve Jarrett; Pub. Steve Jarrett. adv.; bk.rev.; charts; illus.; stat. circ. 15,500. (back issues avail.) **Indexed:** Sportsearch (1984-). **Document type:** consumer publication.

797.1 UK ISSN 0958-5508
WINDSURF. 1980. 10/yr. £36 in Europe; rest of world £48. The Blue Barn, Tew Ln., Wootton, Woodstock OX7 1HA, England. TEL 01993-811181. FAX 01993-811481. Ed. Mark Kasprowicz. adv. contact: Jim Peskett. illus. circ. 25,000. **Document type:** consumer publication.
Former titles: Windsurf and Boardsailing; Come Board Sailing.

797.1 IT ISSN 1120-5865
WINDSURF ITALIA. 1983. m. L.60000. Gruppo B Editore, Via Don Vercesi 19, 20091 Bresso (MI), Italy. TEL 39-2-66503000. FAX 39-2-66503060. Ed. Angelo Berto. adv.; page L.5200000. circ. 43,800. **Document type:** consumer publication.

797.124 US
WINDWARD LEG. 3/yr. $30 membership. United States Sunfish Class Association, Box 300128, Drayton Plains, MI 48330-0128. TEL 407-777-4711. FAX 407-777-3258. E-mail: ltill 75358@AOL.com. (Co-sponsor: International Sunfish Class Association) Ed. Linda Tillman. adv. contact: Linda Tillman. bk.rev. circ. 2,000. (back issues avail.) **Document type:** newsletter.
Description: Provides coverage for world and North American championships in all categories - men's, women's, and juniors' - as well as regional and local regattas.

623.82 US ISSN 0095-067X
VM320
WOODENBOAT; the magazine for wooden boat owners, builders and designers. 1974. bi-m. $24.95. WoodenBoat Publications, Inc., Box 78, Brooklin, ME 04616. TEL 207-359-4651. FAX 207-359-8920. Ed. Matthew P. Murphy; Pub. Gail Cramer. adv.; bk.rev.; illus.; index. circ. 105,000. **Indexed:** Ind.How To Do It (1981-). **Document type:** consumer publication, trade publication.
—Faxon.
Description: Contains articles of interest to those who build, design, and own wooden boats.

WORKBOAT. see TRANSPORTATION — Ships And Shipping

797.1 GW ISSN 0043-9932
YACHT; Deutschlands fuehrende Yacht-Zeitschrift. 1904. fortn. DM.149.50 (foreign DM.190). Verlag Delius, Klasing und Co., Postfach 101671, 33516 Bielefeld, Germany. TEL 0521-559-280. FAX 0521-559113. TELEX 932934-DEKLA. Ed. Joerg Neupert. adv.; illus. circ. 140,000. **Document type:** consumer publication.
—CCC.

797.1 IT ISSN 1120-7663
YACHT CAPITAL. 1990. m. L.60000. Rizzoli Editore, Via G. Gozzi 1-A, 20129 Milan, Italy. TEL 39-2-700231. FAX 39-2-70100336. Ed. Vincenzo Zaccagnino. adv.; page L.14010000; adv. contact: Flavio Biondi. circ. 22,000. **Document type:** consumer publication.

797.1 IT ISSN 0394-3143
YACHT DIGEST; la rivista dell'armatore da diporto. 1987. 6/yr. L.40000. Casa Editrice Scode S.p.A., Corso Monforte 36, 20122 Milan, Italy. TEL 39-2-76006973. FAX 39-2-76004905. Ed. Riccardo Villarosa. adv.; B&W page L.4700000, color page L.7300000; trim 174 x 244. bk.rev.; illus. circ. 12,000.

797.1 SZ
YACHTING. (Text in French and German) 1945. m. 95 SFr. Buechler Grafino AG, Postfach 5635, CH-3001 Bern, Switzerland. TEL 031-3303366. FAX 031-3303371. Ed. Johannes Kornacher. adv.; bk.rev.; illus.; mkt.; stat.; tr.lit.; tr.mk. circ. 22,000. **Indexed:** Access, Consum.Ind., Sportsearch. **Document type:** newsletter.
Former titles: Yachting News; Yachting (ISSN 0043-9959)

797.1 US ISSN 0043-9940
GV771
YACHTING; power and sail. 1907. m. $19.98. Times Mirror Magazines, Inc., 2 Park Ave., New York, NY 10016. TEL 212-779-5000; 800-999-0869. FAX 212-725-1035. Ed. Charles Barthold. adv.; bk.rev.; charts; illus.; tr.lit.; circ. 147,489. (also avail. in microform from UMI) **Indexed:** Access, Bk.Rev.Ind. (1965-), Child.Bk.Rev.Ind. (1965-), Consum.Ind., Mag.Ind., PMR, R.G., Sports Per.Ind.
—Faxon; UMI; UnCover.

797.1 IT
YACHTING ITALIANO; mensile di nautica e cultura marinaresca. 1948. m. (11/yr.) L.22000. Nautilus s.r.l., Via Tadino 29, 20124 Milan, Italy. Ed. Sandro Pellegrini. adv.; charts; illus. circ. 50,000.
Formerly: Yachting Italiano-Atomare (ISSN 0043-9975)

796.95 UK ISSN 0958-6393
YACHTING LIFE. 1977. m. £12. K.A.V. Publicity (Glasgow) Ltd., 113 West Regent St., Glasgow G2 2RU, Scotland. TEL 0141-226-3861. Ed. Alistair M. Vallance. adv.; bk.rev. circ. 8,000. **Document type:** consumer publication.

797.1 UK ISSN 0043-9983
YACHTING MONTHLY. 1906. m. $32. I P C Magazines, Specialist Magazine Group (Subsidiary of: Reed Elsevier group), King's Reach Tower, Stamford St., London SE1 9LS, England. TEL 071-261-6076. FAX 0444-440619. TELEX 892084 REEDBP G. (Dist. by: Quadrant Subscription Services, Oakfield House, Perrymount Rd., Haywards Heath, W. Sussex RH16 3DH, England. TEL 0444-440421) Ed. Geoff Pack. adv. contact: David Williams. bk.rev.; charts; illus.; tr.lit.; index. circ. 49,141. **Document type:** consumer publication.
—CCC.

797.1 BE ISSN 0774-0670
YACHTING SUD - SUR L'EAU. (Text in French) 1923. 10/yr. 800 BEF (Europe 1000 BEF; elsewhere 1200 BEF). (Ligue Regionale du Yachting Belge) Editions Bertels, Rue Caroly 37, B-1040 Brussels, Belgium. FAX 32-2-5131104. Ed.Bd. adv.; B&W page 23500 BEF, color page 33500 BEF; trim 275 x 215. bk.rev. circ. 8,000. **Document type:** consumer publication.
Formerly (until 1982): Sur l'Eau (ISSN 0039-5994)
Description: Covers regional, national and international yachting developments.

SPORTS AND GAMES — HORSES AND HORSEMANSHIP

797.1 UK ISSN 0043-9991
GV811.8
YACHTING WORLD. 1894. m. $44. I P C Magazines, Specialist Magazine Group (Subsidiary of: Reed Elsevier group); King's Reach Tower, Stamford St., London SE1 9LS, England. TEL 071-261-6800. FAX 0444-440619. TELEX 892084 REEDBP G. (Dist. by: Quadrant Subscription Services, Oakfield House, Perrymount Rd., Haywards Heath, W. Sussex RH16 3DH, England. TEL 0444-440421) Ed. Andrew Bray. adv. contact: Allan Warren. bk.rev.; illus. circ. 41,028. (also avail. in microform from UMI) **Indexed:** Sportsearch. **Document type:** consumer publication.
—UMI.

797.1 US ISSN 0094-8136
GV825
YACHTING YEAR BOOK OF NORTHERN CALIFORNIA. 1922. a. $9.50. Pacific Inter-Club Yacht Association of Northern California, Publication Office, 391 Miller Ave., Ste. 102, Mill Valley, CA 94941. TEL 415-388-8327. FAX 415-388-8361. Ed. Burnett Tregoning. adv.; illus. circ. 10,000. **Document type:** directory.

796.95 AU ISSN 1013-7823
YACHTREVUE. 1976. m. S.420. Orac Zeitschriftenverlag GmbH, Schoenbrunnerstr. 59-61, A-1050 Vienna, Austria. TEL 01-54621-0. FAX 01-5462178. Ed. Luis Gazzari. adv.; B&W page S.43440, color page S.73848; trim 185 x 250. bk.rev. circ. 52,200. (back issues avail.) **Document type:** consumer publication.

797.1 UK ISSN 0044-0000
YACHTS AND YACHTING. 1947. fortn. £50 (foreign £56). Yachting Press Ltd., 196 Eastern Esplanade, Southend-on-Sea, Essex SS1 3AB, England. Ed. Frazer Clark. adv.; bk.rev.; charts; illus. circ. 21,500. **Indexed:** Sportsearch (1973-). **Document type:** bulletin.

769.95 910.202 US
YACHTSMAN'S GUIDE TO THE BAHAMAS. 1950. a. $28.95. Tropic Isle Publishers, Inc., Box 610938, N. Miami, FL 33261-0938. TEL 305-893-4277. FAX 305-893-4278. Ed. Meredith Fields. adv. contact: Gerri Schardt. circ. 15,000. **Document type:** consumer publication.
  Description: Cruising guide with sketch charts, charter planning, resort, restaurant, diving and marina information. Covers the history of the islands.

797.14 US ISSN 0084-3261
YACHTSMAN'S GUIDE TO THE CARIBBEAN. 1964. irreg., latest issue 1975. $6.75. Seaport Publishing Co., c/o Ed. Clifford M. Montague, 843 Delray Ave., Grand Rapids, MI 49506. TEL 616-949-0048. index.

797.14 US ISSN 0084-327X
YACHTSMAN'S GUIDE TO THE GREAT LAKES. 1956. a. $15. Seaway Publishing Co., 18-22 S. Elm St., Zeeland, MI 49464. TEL 616-772-2132. Ed. Paul E. Van Koevering. adv. contact: Paul E. Van Koevering. index. circ. 5,000. **Document type:** trade publication.
  Description: Provides a guide to Great Lakes harbors.

796.95 US
GV817.V5
YACHTSMAN'S GUIDE TO THE VIRGIN ISLANDS. 1968. a. $15.95. Tropic Isle Publishers, Inc., Box 610938, N. Miami, FL 33261-0938. TEL 305-893-4277. FAX 305-893-4278. Ed. Meredith Fields. adv. contact: Gerri Schardt. **Document type:** consumer publication.
  Former titles: Yachtsman's Guide to the Virgin Islands and Puerto Rico (ISSN 0735-9020); Which supersedes (in 1987): Yachtsman's Guide to the Greater Antilles (ISSN 0162-7635)
  Description: Cruising guide with sketch charts, charter planning, resorts, diving, restaurants, and marina information; also covers the history of the islands.

796.95 SP
YATE. 1965. m. 4580 ptas.($46) M C Ediciones, Monestir 23, 08034 Barcelona, Spain. TEL 3-280-43-44. FAX 3-280-39-74. Ed. German de Soler; Pub. Susana Cadena. adv. contact: Josep Anton Romera. bk.rev.; bibl.; charts; illus. circ. 12,000. (back issues avail.)
  Formerly: Yate y Motonautica (ISSN 0210-0320)

797.1 PL
ZAGLE; magazyn sportow wodnych. m. 20000 Zl. per no. Warszawskie Towarzystwo Wioslarskie, Ul. Mariusza Zaruskiego 12, 00468 Warsaw, Poland. Ed. Slawomir Cieslinski.

797.1 US
48 DEGREES NORTH; the Northwest sailing magazine. 1981. m. $15. Boundless Enterprises, Inc., 6327 Seaview Ave., N.W., Seattle, WA 98107. TEL 206-789-7350. FAX 206-789-6392. Ed. Rich Hazelton; Pub. Chuck Streatch. adv.; B&W page $800; trim 7 1/4 x 10; adv. contact: Michael Collins. bk.rev. circ. 25,000. **Document type:** consumer publication.
  Description: Reports boating activities and racing for the Northwest.

796 UK
505 GREAT BRITAIN.* 1972. s-a. £6. International 505 Class, British Association, 3 the Embankment, Wraysbury, Staines, Middlesex, England. Ed. Terry Lawton. adv.; bk.rev. circ. 1,250. (back issues avail.)

SPORTS AND GAMES — Horses And Horsemanship

798.2 362.4 US
A H A NEWS. 1992. q. membership. North American Riding for the Handicapped Association, Inc., American Hippotherapy Association, Box 33150, Denver, CO 80233. TEL 800-369-7433. FAX 303-252-4610. **Indexed:** InterActions Bibl. (1992-). **Document type:** newsletter.

636.1 US
A H C NEWSLETTER. 1969. bi-m. membership only. American Horse Council, Inc., 1700 K St., N.W., Ste. 300, Washington, DC 20006. TEL 202-296-4031. FAX 202-296-1970. Ed. Lisa Kovner. circ. 3,200. **Document type:** newsletter.
  Description: Provides news of AHC activities.

636.1 US
A H P A NEWS. 1966. s-a. $20. American Horse Protection Association, Inc., 1000 29th St., N.W., Ste. T100, Washington, DC 20007. TEL 202-965-0500. Ed. Robin C. Lohnes. circ. 15,000. **Document type:** newsletter.
  Formerly: American Horse Protection Association Newsletter.

798 US
A M H A NEWS & MORGAN SALES NETWORK. m. free. American Morgan Horse Association, Box 960, Shelburne, VT 05482-0960. TEL 802-985-4944. FAX 802-985-8897. Ed. Paula Brown. adv. circ. 15,000. (looseleaf format)
  Incorporates (1975-1994): Morganizer; Former titles: Morgan Sales Network; (until 1992): A M H A Newsletter.

798 790.31 US ISSN 1079-3690
AMERICAN COWBOY. 1931-198?; resumed 1994. bi-m. $16.95. American Cowboy, LLC, 650 Westdale Dr., Ste. 200, Wichita, KS 67209. E-mail: Subscribe@cowboy.com. Ed. Jesse Mullins; William E. Bales. adv. contact: Sandra L. Bales. charts; illus.; circ. 80,000 (paid). **Document type:** consumer publication.
  Former titles: American Cowboy Magazine (ISSN 0738-9795); (until 1979): Hoof and Horn (ISSN 0018-4713)
  Description: Covers all aspects of the Western life-style: personalities; issues; rodeo; music, art and poetry; and homes.

636.1 US
AMERICAN FARRIER'S ASSOCIATION NEWSLETTER. bi-m. membership. American Farrier's Association, 4059 Iron Works Pike, Lexington, KY 40511. TEL 606-233-7411. FAX 606-231-7862. E-mail: afa@world.std.com. Ed. Charles Orlando. circ. 2,200 (paid). **Document type:** newsletter.

636.1 US ISSN 0274-6565
AMERICAN FARRIERS JOURNAL. 7/yr. $42.95 (typically set in July). Lessiter Publications, Box 624, Brookfield, WI 53008. TEL 414-782-4480. FAX 414-782-1252. circ. 7,000. **Document type:** trade publication.
  —BLDSC (0814.780000); UnCover.
  Description: Articles on horse anatomy and physiology, leg pathology and therapy, shoeing, blacksmithing and horse handling.

798 336.2 US
AMERICAN HORSE COUNCIL TAX BULLETIN. 1970. bi-m. $100. American Horse Council, Inc., 1700 K St., N.W., Ste. 300, Washington, DC 20006. TEL 202-296-4031. FAX 202-296-1970. Ed. Thomas A. Davis. circ. 2,800. **Document type:** bulletin.
  Description: Reviews tax cases and other tax issues affecting those owning horses as a business.

636.1 US
AMERICAN INDIAN HORSE NEWS. 1979. q. $15. Rte. 3, Box 64, Lockhart, TX 78644-9713. TEL 512-398-6642. Ed. N. Falley. adv.; bk.rev. circ. 500. **Document type:** newsletter.

798 US ISSN 0746-6153
THE AMERICAN SADDLEBRED. 1983. bi-m. $45 membership. American Saddlebred Horse Association, 4093 Iron Works Pike, Lexington, KY 40511. TEL 606-259-2742. FAX 606-259-1628. Ed. Lynn P. Weatherman. adv. contact: Gayle Strickroot. bk.rev.; illus.; index. circ. 7,200. **Document type:** consumer publication.
  —UnCover.
  Description: Provides information on equine health, international activities, legal, taxes, champions of the breed.

791.8 US
AMERICAN SHETLAND PONY CLUB. JOURNAL.* 1948. bi-m. $15. American Shetland Pony Club, 6740 N. Frostwood Pkwy., Peoria, IL 61615-2402. TEL 309-691-9661. Ed. James H. Roberts. adv.; circ. 3,200. (paid). (back issues avail.)
  Formerly: Pony Journal (ISSN 0199-5537)

636.1 US ISSN 0730-2975
AMERICAN TRAKEHNER. 1975. q. $20. American Trakehner Association, 1520 W. Church St., Newark, OH 43055. TEL 614-344-1111. FAX 614-344-3225. (Dist. addr.: 631 N.W. Tyler Ct., Ste. 301, Topeka, KS 66608) Ed. Helen K. Gibble. adv. contact: Kim Tulypan. circ. 1,400 (paid). (back issues avail.) **Document type:** trade publication.
  Description: Promotes the Trakehner breed of horse in the United States.

798.4 US ISSN 0003-1445
AMERICAN TURF MONTHLY. 1946. m. $16. Star Publishing Corporation, 438 W. 37th St., New York, NY 10018. TEL 212-279-4619. Ed. Howard Rowe. adv.; bk.rev.; illus. circ. 30,000.

798.2 NE
L'ANNEE HIPPIQUE; international equestrian yearbook. (Text in English, German, French) a. (Federation Equestre Internationale) Best Communications and Management B.V., Postbus 245, 5680 AE Best, Netherlands. TEL 31-4998-98115. FAX 31-4998-90923. Ed. Joep Bartels; Pub. Henk Bruger. illus.; circ. 44,000 (paid). **Document type:** consumer publication.
  Description: Reports the equestrian highlights of the preceding year.

636.1 US ISSN 0892-385X
APPALOOSA JOURNAL. 1946. m. $20 to non-members; members $15. Appaloosa Horse Club, Box 8403, Moscow, ID 83843. TEL 208-882-5578. FAX 208-882-8150. Ed. Debbie Pitner Moors. adv. contact: Gretchen Naccarato. illus. circ. 14,000. (also avail. in microform from UMI) **Document type:** bulletin.
  —UMI; UnCover.
  Formerly: Appaloosa News (ISSN 0003-665X)
  Description: Promotes the breed; provides informative articles; presents features and profiles that show all facets of the breed's talents.

791.8 US ISSN 0273-6519
APPALOOSA WORLD. 1980. m. Drawer 291310, Dayton Beach, FL 32029. TEL 904-767-6284. Ed. Gerald A. Matacale. index. (back issues avail.)

798.2 UK ISSN 0402-7493
ARAB HORSE SOCIETY NEWS. 1935. s-a. £13 (overseas £22). Arab Horse Society, Windsor House, Ramsbury, Marlborough, Wilts. SN8 2PE, England. TEL 01672-20782. FAX 01672-20880. adv.; illus. circ. 4,250. (tabloid format) **Document type:** consumer publication.

SPORTS AND GAMES — HORSES AND HORSEMANSHIP

798   UK
ARAB HORSE STUD BOOK. 1919. quadrennial. price varies. Arab Horse Society, Windsor House, Ramsbury, Marlborough, Wilts. SN8 2PE, England. TEL 01672-20782. FAX 01672-20880. James Carine. circ. 1,000. (tabloid format)

636.1
ARABIAN HORSE COUNTRY. 1981. m. $20. BeAnCa Publications, 4346 S.E. Division St., Portland, OR 97206. bk.rev. circ. 39,504. (reprint service avail.)

636.121   US   ISSN 0194-6803
ARABIAN HORSE EXPRESS.* 1976. m. $25. 512 Green Bay Rd., Kenilworth, IL 60043-1073. TEL 316-251-7340. FAX 316-251-4717. Eds. Kathleen Gallagher, Valarie Peruski. bk.rev. circ. 7,500. **Document type:** trade publication.

798.4   US   ISSN 0279-8425
ARABIAN HORSE TIMES. 1970. m. $25. Adams Corp., 1050 8th St., N.E., Waseca, MN 56093. TEL 507-835-3204. FAX 507-835-5138. Ed. Lynn Wright. adv.; bk.rev. circ. 25,000. **Document type:** trade publication.

636.1   US   ISSN 0003-7494
ARABIAN HORSE WORLD; the magazine for owners, breeders and admirers of fine horses. 1960. m. $36 (Canada $60; elsewhere $75). Jay Shuler Co., Inc., 824 San Antonio Ave., Palo Alto, CA 94303. TEL 415-856-0500. FAX 415-856-2831. Ed. Denise Hearst; Pubs. Nat Gorham, Jan Schuler. adv. contact: Wendy Flynn. bk.rev.; illus.; index. circ. 12,000. **Document type:** consumer publication.

798.2   AT
ARABIAN STUDS AND STALLIONS MAGAZINE; Australia's leading Arabian magazine. 1974. a. Aus.$15. (Horse World Publications) Horse World Publications, P.O. Box 8369, Woolloongabba, Qld. 4102, Australia. TEL 61-7-3914490. FAX 61-7-3915118. Ed. Bev Hayes. adv. contact: Michael Vink. bk.rev. circ. 12,500. (back issues avail.) **Document type:** trade publication.

798   US   ISSN 0164-8047
ARENA NEWS;* a Texas journal of horse events. 1977. m. $15. Box 16229, Austin, TX 78761-6229. TEL 512-328-3266. Ed. Ruth Dawson. adv. circ. 2,000.

798.2   US
ARIZONA HORSE CONNECTION. 1987. m. $12. Arizona Horse Connection, Inc., 301 W. Marlboro Dr., Chandler, AZ 85224. TEL 602-988-2111. Ed. Patti E. Trueba. adv. circ. 10,000. (back issues avail.) **Document type:** trade publication.
 Description: For all horse enthusiasts; features articles on ranches, trainers, horses of notable interest, and all types of riding disciplines.

798.2   CN   ISSN 1182-5472
ATLANTIC HORSE & PONY. 1987. bi-m. Can.$13 (foreign Can.$19) (effective 1995). D v L Publishing, P.O. Box 1509, Liverpool, NS B0T 1K0, Canada. TEL 902-354-3321. Ed.Bd; Pub. Dirk van Loon. adv.; bk.rev. circ. 4,000. **Document type:** consumer publication.
 Formerly (until 1989): Eastern Horse and Pony (ISSN 0848-8444)
 Description: For horse and pony owners, trainers and enthusiasts in the Atlantic region.

798.4   CN   ISSN 0226-627X
ATLANTIC POST CALLS. 1979. 40/yr. Can.$40. Cumberland Publishing Ltd., 14 Lawrence St., Amherst, NS B4H 3G5, Canada. TEL 902-667-3469. FAX 902-667-0377. Ed. Doug Harkness. adv. contact: Dorothy Brown. circ. 2,400. **Document type:** consumer publication.

798.2   AT
▼**AUSTRALIAN ARABIAN HORSE EXPRESS**. 1994. m. Aus.$24. (Australian Arabian Society) Horse World Publications, P.O. Box 8369, Woolloongabba, Qld. 4102, Australia. TEL 61-7-3914490. FAX 61-7-3915118. Ed. Bev Hayes. adv. contact: Michael Vink. circ. 10,000. **Document type:** trade publication.

798.2   AT   ISSN 0727-4092
AUSTRALIAN ARABIAN HORSE NEWS. 1974. q. Aus.$22. (Australian Arabian Society) Horse World Publications, P.O. Box 8369, Woolloongabba, Qld. 4102, Australia. TEL 61-7-3914490. FAX 61-7-3915118. Ed. Bev Hayes. adv. contact: Michael Vink. bk.rev. circ. 12,500. (back issues avail.) **Document type:** trade publication.
 Formerly (until 1976): Arabian Horse News (ISSN 0312-0791)

798.4   AT   ISSN 0084-7402
AUSTRALIAN HORSE RACING ANNUAL.* 1969. a. $7. Playfair Publishing Group, Box 52, Northbridge, N.S.W. 2063, Australia.

798.2   AT   ISSN 0817-8550
AUSTRALIAN STOCK HORSE JOURNAL. 1975. bi-m. free to members. P.O. Box 288, Scone, N.S.W. 2337, Australia. TEL 61-65-451122. FAX 61-65-452165. Ed. Joan Starr. adv.; B&W page Aus.$395, color page Aus.$995; adv. contact: Brian Brown. circ. 6,500 (controlled). **Document type:** trade publication.
 Formerly (until 1985): Australian Stock Horse (ISSN 0314-9056)

636.1   AT   ISSN 0005-0350
AUSTRALIAN THOROUGHBREDS; Australia's only national magazine devoted to the breeding of thoroughbred horses. 1950. bi-m. Aus.$56. Australian Thoroughbreds Magazine, Box 561, Liverpool, N.S.W. 2170, Australia. Ed. Mike Davis. adv.; bk.rev.; illus.; stat. circ. 12,000. (tabloid format)

636.1   US   ISSN 0005-366X
SF335.U6
BACKSTRETCH. 1962. bi-m. $14. United Thoroughbred Trainers of America Inc., 19899 W. Nine Mile Rd., Southfield, MI 48075. TEL 810-354-3232. FAX 810-354-3157. Ed. Harriet Dalley. Pub. Harriet H. Dalley. adv. contact: Barbara Kauer. bk.rev.; illus. circ. 12,000. **Document type:** trade publication.

798.2   GW   ISSN 0174-0512
BAYERNS PFERDE ZUCHT UND SPORT; Reiten - Pferdepraxis - Fahren. 1980. m. DM.102.80. B L V Verlagsgesellschaft mbH, Lothstr. 29, 80797 Munich, Germany. TEL 089-127050. FAX 089-12705354. Ed. Juergen Kemmler. circ. 16,000. **Document type:** bulletin.
—CCC.

798.4   NZ
BEST BETS. w. News Media Ltd., Glenside Crescent, P.O. Box 1327, Auckland, New Zealand. Ed. Bob Lovett. circ. 45,000.

636.1   US   ISSN 1050-5741
BIT AND BRIDLE. 1964. m. $18 (foreign $28). Box 336, Bellevue, NE 68005-0336. TEL 402-357-3504. FAX 402-357-2497. Ed. Lori Knutson. adv.; bk.rev.; charts. circ. 4,000. **Document type:** newspaper.
 Formerly (until Mar. 1989): Midwest Bridle and Bit (ISSN 0006-3851); **Incorporates:** Separator.

636.1 798.4   US   ISSN 0006-4998
SF277
THE BLOOD-HORSE. 1916. w. $125. (Thoroughbred Owners and Breeders Association) The Blood-Horse, Inc., 1736 Alexandria Dr., Box 4038, Lexington, KY 40544-4038. TEL 606-278-2361. FAX 606-276-4450. Ed. Raymond S. Paulick; Pub. Stacy Bearse. adv.; B&W page $1313; adv. contact: Greg Medley. bk.rev.; charts; illus.; stat.; index. circ. 23,500. (also avail. in microform from UMI) **Indexed:** Sports Per.Ind. **Document type:** trade publication.
—UMI; UnCover.
 Description: Covers thoroughbred horse breeding and racing.

798.4 636.1   UK   ISSN 0067-9224
BLOODSTOCK BREEDERS' REVIEW. 1912. a. £65. Sagittarius Bloodstock Associates Ltd., Beauvale Abbey Farm, New Rd., Newthorpe, Nottinghamshire NG16 2AA, England. TEL 01773-713060. FAX 01773-714937. Ed. Susan Cameron. bk.rev. circ. 1,400. **Document type:** academic/scholarly publication.
 Description: Contains a review of thoroughbred racing in approximately 38 countries with editorial, photographic, and statistical coverage.

798   US
BRAYER; voice of the donkey & mule world. 1968. q. $18 membership only. American Donkey and Mule Society, Inc., 2901 N. Elm St., Denton, TX 76207-7631. Ed. Betsy Hutchins. adv.; bk.rev.; tr.lit. circ. 6,000. (back issues avail.) **Document type:** consumer publication.

798   UK   ISSN 0144-7203
THE BRITISH DIRECTORY. (Supplement avail.) 1979. a. £15.95($27) Equestrian Management Consultants Ltd., Wothersome Grange, Bramham, Wetherby, Yorks. LS23 6LY, England. TEL 01532-892267. FAX 01532-893352. Ed. Antony Wakeham. adv.: B&W page £825, color page £995; 195 x 126. circ. 5,000. **Document type:** directory.
 Incorporates: Changes: An Editorial Update of Important Equestrian Developments.
 Description: Lists 18,000 breeders, retailers, riding schools, vets, farriers, trainers and holidays in Great Britain.

798   UK
BRITISH HORSE. 1985. 3/yr. membership. British Horse Society, British Equestrian Centre, Kenilworth, Warks. CV8 2LR, England. TEL 01203-696697. FAX 01203-692351. TELEX BEFKEN 311152 G. Ed. Judith Draper. adv. circ. 65,000. **Document type:** consumer publication.
 Formerly (until 1992): Horseshoe.
 Description: Aims to further the art of riding and driving and to encourage horsemastership and the welfare of horses and ponies.

798   UK   ISSN 0951-1776
BRITISH HORSE SOCIETY MEMBERS' YEAR BOOK. 1967. a. membership. British Horse Society, British Equestrian Centre, Stoneleigh, Kenilworth, Warks. CV8 2LR, England. TEL 01203-696697. FAX 01203-692351. TELEX BEFKEN 311152 G. adv. circ. 65,000. **Document type:** directory.
 Former titles (until 1987): British Horse Society Year Book (ISSN 0269-1000); (until 1983): British Horse Society Year Book & Diary (ISSN 0068-2063)

798.4   US
CAL-WESTERN APPALOOSA RACING. 1966. m. (9/yr.) $12 (effective Jan. 1990). 3097 Willow, Ste. 15, Clovis, CA 93612. TEL 209-291-0103. FAX 209-291-2039. adv.; circ. 200 (paid).
 Formerly: Cal-Western Appaloosa (ISSN 0091-4827)
 Description: Promotes Appaloosa race horses.

798.46   US   ISSN 0091-441X
CALIFORNIA HORSE REVIEW. 1963. m. $19.95 (foreign $50). Box 1238, Rancho Cordova, CA 95741-9885. TEL 916-638-1519. FAX 916-638-1784. Ed. Diane Cranz; Pub. Jennifer Forsberg Meyer. adv.; bk.rev.; circ. 6,500 (paid). **Document type:** consumer publication.

636.1   CN   ISSN 0008-2864
CANADIAN ARABIAN NEWS. 1960. bi-m. Can.$26.75($32) (effective 1995 & 1996). Canadian Arabian Horse Registry, 801 Terrace Plz., 4445 Calgary Tr. S., Edmonton, AB T6H 5R7, Canada. TEL 403-436-4244. FAX 403-438-2971. Ed. Peggy Arthurs. adv.; B&W & color, B&W page Can.$282; 9 1/2 x 7 1/2. bk.rev.; illus. circ. 2,200. **Indexed:** Sportsearch. **Document type:** consumer publication.
 Description: For purebred and partbred Arabian owners and enthusiasts. Includes articles on bloodlines, Arabians and their trainers-owners, horse health, show results and training.

798   CN   ISSN 0838-1704
CANADIAN EQUESTRIAN FEDERATION. BULLETIN. (Text in English, French) 1978. q. membership. Canadian Equestrian Federation, 1600 James Naismith Dr., Ottawa, ON K1B 4S8, Canada. TEL 613-748-5632. FAX 613-747-2920. Ed. Allison Neill. adv.; circ. 10,000 (controlled). **Document type:** bulletin.
 Description: Covers rule changes, dates of clinics-seminars, current topics in horse health, riding techniques, coaching information, show dates, affiliate organization news.

636.1   CN   ISSN 0382-5795
CANADIAN HACKNEY STUD BOOK. 1905. irreg. Canadian Hackney Society, c/o Canadian Livestock Records Corporation, Ottawa, Ont. K1V 0M7, Canada. TEL 613-731-7110. adv.; illus.

SPORTS AND GAMES — HORSES AND HORSEMANSHIP

636.1   CN   ISSN 0840-6200
CANADIAN HORSEMAN. (Includes annual supplement: Directory of Canadian Horse Industry and Buyers Guide) 1982. bi-m. Can.$18.95($27.95) Canadian Horseman Magazine, Inc., 225 Industrial Pkwy. S., P.O. Box 670, Aurora, ON L4G 4J9, Canada. TEL 905-727-0107. FAX 905-841-1530. Ed. Lee Benson; Pub. Susan Jane Anstey. adv. contact: Vicki Mosher-Tessier. bk.rev. circ. 10,000. **Indexed:** Sportsearch (1989-). **Document type:** consumer publication.
    Formerly (until 1988): Horse Sense (ISSN 0821-5073)
    Description: Offers general information for recreational and western riders.

791.8   CN   ISSN 0317-7785
CANADIAN RODEO NEWS. 1964. m. Can.$21.40($20) (Canadian Professional Rodeo Association) Canadian Rodeo News Ltd., 223, 2116 27th Ave. N.E., Calgary, AB T2E 7A6, Canada. TEL 403-250-7292. FAX 403-250-6926. Ed. P. Kirby Meston. adv.: B&W page Can.$520; trim 11 1/2 x 17; adv. contact: Vicki Mowat. bk.rev. circ. 4,000. **Indexed:** Sportsearch. **Document type:** newspaper.
    Description: Promotion of professional rodeo in Canada.

791.8   CN   ISSN 0008-5073
CANADIAN SPORTSMAN. 1870. w. (June-Oct.); bi-w. (Nov.-May). Can.$43($55) Canadian Sportsman, 25 Old Plank Rd., P.O. Box 129, Straffordville, ON N0J 1Y0, Canada. TEL 519-866-5558. FAX 519-866-5596. Ed. Gary Foerster. circ. 6,500. (back issues avail.)

798.4   CN   ISSN 0830-0593
CODEN: IRCCEP
CANADIAN THOROUGHBRED; journal of racing and breeding. (Includes annual supplement: Directory of the Canadian Horse Industry (ISSN 0831-5183)) 1961. bi-m. Can.$39.95($54.95) Canadian Throroughbred Publishing, Inc., 225 Industrial Pkwy. S., P.O. Box 670, Aurora, ON L4G 4J9, Canada. TEL 905-727-0107. FAX 905-841-1530. Ed. Lee Benson; Pub. Susan Jane Anstey. adv. contact: Annette Wamarillo-Pascoe. bk.rev.; charts; pat.; stat.; tr.lit. circ. 4,300. (back issues avail.) **Indexed:** Sportsearch. **Document type:** consumer publication.
    Former titles: Thoroughbred Review; Canadian Horse (ISSN 0008-378X)
    Description: Covers Canadian racing and breeding statistics, major races and profiles.

798   UK   ISSN 0958-1820
CARRIAGE DRIVING. 1986. bi-m. £15($36) Willington Management Ltd., 22 Bedwin St., Salisbury, Wilts. SP1 3UT, England. TEL 01722-422107. Ed. Richard James. adv.; bk.rev.; charts; illus. (back issues avail.) **Document type:** bulletin.
    Description: Covers all types of carriage driving and related subjects.

798.2   US   ISSN 0899-756X
CASCADE HORSEMAN. m. $12. Klamath Publishing, Box 788, Klamath Falls, OR 97601. TEL 503-883-4000. circ. 8,000.
    Description: West Coast horse industry publication.

798   IT   ISSN 1121-3809
CAVALLI E CAVALIERI. 1989. m. L.70000 (foreign L.130000). Mio Cavallo, Via Pergolesi 8, 20124 Milan, Italy. TEL 39-2-66715150. FAX 39-2-66715171. Ed. Gaetano Manti. adv.: page L.2950000. circ. 15,000. **Document type:** consumer publication.

CAVALLO MAGAZINE; mensile di natura, politica e cultura. see *ANIMAL WELFARE*

798   AG   ISSN 0008-8986
CENTAUROS; revista de polo, turf, equitacion, pato y troto. 1955. irreg., vol.40, 1978. Arg.$15. San Martin 66, Buenos Aires, Argentina. Eds. Jorge Oliva & Manuel Caramelo Gomex. **Indexed:** SSCI.

798.4   UK
CHASEFORM NOTE-BOOK.* w. £70. Raceform Ltd., 19 Clarges Rd., London W1Y 7PG, England. Ed. Dan Corbett. circ. 4,000.
    Description: Covers jump racing in UK.

796.42   UK
CHASERS AND HURDLERS. 1975. a. £65. Portway Press Ltd., Timeform House, Northgate, Halifax, West Yorkshire HX1 1XE, England.
    Description: Essays and notes on the performances of horses.

798.2   FR   ISSN 0245-3614
CHEVAL MAGAZINE. 1971. m. 280 F. (foreign 380 F.) (effective 1995). Optipress, B.P. 60, 78490 Montfort l'Amaury, France. TEL 34-86-29-22. FAX 34-86-78-79. adv.

798   FR   ISSN 1145-6000
CHEVAL PRATIQUE. 1990. m. 280 F. Editions Lariviere, 15-17 quai de l'Oise, 75019 Paris, France. TEL 40-34-22-07. FAX 40-35-84-47. circ. 80,000. (back issues avail.) **Document type:** consumer publication.
    Description: Practical information and sports articles for young riders who own their own horses.

798.2   FR   ISSN 1148-201X
CHEVAL STAR. 1987. m. 150 F. (foreign 210 F.) (effective 1995). Optipress, B.P. 60, 78490 Montfort l'Amaury, France. TEL 34-86-29-09. FAX 34-86-78-79. Ed. Jerome Chehu. adv.
    Former titles: Cheveaux de Penny & Cheval Infos.
    Description: Illustrated stories on horses and ponies for kids and adolescents.

798.4   US   ISSN 0009-5990
SF321
CHRONICLE OF THE HORSE; the horse in sport--steeplechasing, horse shows, foxhunting, etc. 1937. w. $42 (effective 1995 & 1996). Chronicle of the Horse, Inc., Box 46, Middleburg, VA 22117. TEL 703-687-6341. FAX 703-687-3937. Ed. John Strassburger; Pub. Robert L. Banner, Jr. adv. contact: Nancy Comer. bk.rev.; illus.; s-a. index; circ. 24,000 (paid). (also avail. in microform from UMI) **Indexed:** Sports Per.Ind. **Document type:** trade publication. —UMI.
    Description: Sporting magazine covering the major English equestrian disciplines on a regional, national and international basis; also includes feature and training articles.

636.1   UK
CLYDESDALE STUD BOOK. 1877. a. £6. Clydesdale Society of Great Britain and Ireland, Castlepark, The Castleton, Auchterarder, Perthshire PH3 1JR, Scotland. TEL 01764-664925. Ed. Fiona C. Roebuck. circ. 300. **Document type:** directory.

798.4   SA   ISSN 1016-6416
COMPUTAFORM. Variant title: Transvaal Computaform. Eastern Cape edition (ISSN 1017-1363) 1946. w. Times Media Limited, P.O. Box 1138, Johannesburg 2000, South Africa. adv.; stat.; cum.index. circ. 4,000.
    Former titles (until 1972): Duff's Turf Guide (Incorporating Computaform); Duff's Turf Guide (ISSN 0012-7035)

CONTRACTSPELER. see *SPORTS AND GAMES*

798.2   CN   ISSN 0829-2930
CORINTHIAN HORSE SPORT. (Includes annual supplement: Directory of the Canadian Horse Industry (ISSN 0831-5183)) 1968. m. Can.$27.95($42.85) Corinthian Publishing Co. Ltd., 225 Industrial Pkwy. S., P.O. Box 670, Aurora, ON L4G 4J9, Canada. TEL 905-727-0107. FAX 905-841-1530. Ed. Susan Safford; Pub. Susan Jane Anstey. adv. contact: Vicki Mosher Tessier. bk.rev.; charts; pat.; stat.; tr.lit. circ. 10,000. (back issues avail.) **Indexed:** Can.B.P.I., Sportsearch. **Document type:** consumer publication.
    Former titles: Corinthian Horse Sport in Canada; Corinthian: Horse Sport; Corinthian (ISSN 0319-7581)
    Description: Features show results, training techniques, profiles, international news.

798.2   UK   ISSN 1351-8305
COUNTRY AND DISTANCE RIDER. 1990. bi-m. £14.25 (Europe £17.25; elsewhere £19.95). Champions International, Roses Farm, Childerditch Ln., Little Warley, Brentwood, Essex CM13 3EE, England. TEL 0277-810708. Ed. Clare Wilde. adv.; bk.rev.
    Description: Covers long-distance and endurance riding, pleasure riding.

798   ISSN 0847-2173
COURRIER HIPPIQUE. 1983. 6/yr. Can.$15. Sportam Inc., 4545 Pierre-de-Coubertin, Box 1000, Sta. M, Montreal, Que. H1V 3R2, Canada. TEL 514-252-3053. FAX 514-252-3165. adv.

636.1   ISSN 0300-5607
COURSES ET ELEVAGE. 1954. 10/yr. 660 F. Union Nationale Interprofessionnelle du Cheval (UNIC), 22, rue de Penthievre, 75008 Paris, France. TEL 45-62-00-52. FAX 42-25-96-75. TELEX 650 913F EQUUS. adv.; bk.rev.; illus. circ. 9,300.

798   US   ISSN 0887-2406
CURLY CUES. 1975. s-a. membership. American Bashkir Curly Registry, Box 246, Ely, NV 89301. TEL 702-289-4999. Ed. Sunny Martin. circ. 1,500. **Document type:** newsletter.
    Description: Promotes the rare curly-coated horse, near to extinction in the US.

798   US   ISSN 1081-0951
CUTTING HORSE CHATTER. 1948. m. membership. National Cutting Horse Association, 4704 Hwy. 377, S., Ft. Worth, TX 76116-8805. TEL 817-244-6188. FAX 817-244-2015. Ed. Karl R. Little. adv.; bk.rev. circ. 10,326. (back issues avail.)
    Former titles (until Apr. 1993): Cutting Horse (ISSN 1061-3986); (until 1991) Cuttin' Hoss Chatter (ISSN 0090-8711)

798.2   GW
DEUTSCHE REITERLICHE VEREINIGUNG. REPORT. 1920. w. DM.150. F N - Verlag, Postfach 110363, 48205 Warendorf, Germany. TEL 02581-7696. FAX 02581-633146. circ. 2,400. **Document type:** newsletter.
    Description: Reports and articles on horses and riding.

798.2   CN   ISSN 0831-5183
DIRECTORY OF THE CANADIAN HORSE INDUSTRY. (Supplement to: Corinthian Horse Sport (ISSN 0829-2930); Canadian Thoroughbred (ISSN 0830-0593); Canadian Horseman (ISSN 0840-6200)) 1983. a. Can.$7.95 (effective Jan. 1995). Corinthian Publishing Co. Ltd., 225 Industrial Pkwy. S., Box 670, Aurora, ON L4G 4J9, Canada. TEL 905-727-0107. FAX 905-841-1530. Ed. Susan Jane Anstey. circ. 20,000. (back issues avail.) **Document type:** directory.

DONKEY DIGEST. see *ANIMAL WELFARE*

DRAFT HORSE JOURNAL. see *AGRICULTURE — Poultry And Livestock*

798.2   US   ISSN 0147-796X
SF309.5
DRESSAGE & C T. 1971. m. $25 (foreign $35). Sport Horse Publishing, Inc., 211 W. Main St., New London, OH 44851. TEL 419-929-6781. FAX 419-929-3800. Ed. Ivan I. Bezugloff, Jr; Pub. Ivan I. Bezugloff, Jr. adv. contact: Phyllis Johnson. bk.rev.; bibl.; charts; illus.; tr.lit.; cum.index vols. 1-5; circ. 10,000 (paid). (back issues avail.) **Indexed:** Sportsearch (1977-). **Document type:** consumer publication. —UnCover.
    Former titles: Dressage and Combined Training (ISSN 0147-7951); Dressage (ISSN 0046-0680)
    Description: Contains technical articles on the Olympic equestrian disciplines of dressage and combined training. Covers major national and international competitions, profiles and interviews.

798.2   UK   ISSN 0958-1804
DRESSAGE MAGAZINE; the key to good riding. 1987. m. £27($53) Cecile Park Publishing Ltd., 55-63 Goswell Rd., London EC1V 7EN, England. TEL 0171-490-3398. FAX 0171-490-3394. adv.; bk.rev.; charts; illus. (back issues avail.)
    Formerly: Dressage Review.
    Description: Covers all aspects of dressage.

798.2   US   ISSN 0276-7074
DRIVING DIGEST MAGAZINE; driving for every equine. bi-m. $13.50. Box 467, Brooklyn, CT 06234. Ed. Catherine Taylor.

798   FR   ISSN 0981-3411
L'EPERON - INFORMATION HIPPIQUE. 1957. m. (11/yr.). 150 F. 174 av. Charles de Gaulle, Neuilly-sur-Seine, France. Ed. Roger-Louis Thomas. adv.; bk.rev.; illus. circ. 16,000.
    Formerly (until 1982): Information Hippique (ISSN 0245-9892)

SPORTS AND GAMES — HORSES AND HORSEMANSHIP

798   UK
EQUESTRIAN TRADE NEWS. 1978. m. £55 (rest of Europe £60; elsewhere £72. Equestrian Management Consultants Ltd., Wothersome Grange, Bramham, Wetherby, Yorks LS23 6LY, England. TEL 01532-892267. FAX 01532-893352. Ed. A.C. Wakeham. adv.: B&W page £560, color page £1050; 267 x 187. bk.rev. circ. 3,500.
  Description: Reports news on trade matters relating to saddlery, riding, clothing, feedstuffs and equipment, both overseas and in the U.K.

798   US   ISSN 0013-9831
EQUESTRIAN TRAILS. vol.24, 1970. m. membership. Equestrian Trails, Inc., 13741 Foothill Blvd., Ste. 220, Sylmar, CA 91342-3105. FAX 818-362-9443. Ed. Holly E. Carson. adv.; bk.rev.; charts; illus.; tr.lit. circ. 5,000. **Document type:** newspaper.

798   CN
EQUILIFE. (Text in English, French) s-m. P.O. Box 164, Dalkeith, Ont. K0B 1E0, Canada. TEL 613-874-2219. Ed. Diane Coombs. circ. 7,000.

EQUINE ATHLETE; the equine sports medicine newsjournal. see VETERINARY SCIENCE

798   UK
EQUINE BEHAVIOUR. 1978. s-a. £6. Equine Behaviour Study Circle, Leyland Farm, Gawcott, Buckingham, Bucks., England. Ed. Moyra Williams. bk.rev.; abstr.; bibl.; charts; illus. circ. 150. (back issues avail.)
  Description: Includes observations, reports and analyses on all aspects of equine behavior from worldwide sources.

636.1   US   ISSN 1056-8212
EQUINE TIMES. 1980. m. $13.95. Camden Publications, 331 E. Bell St., Box 8, Camden, MI 49232-0008. TEL 517-368-0365. FAX 517-368-5131. Ed. John Snyder; Pub. Kurt Greenhoe. adv. contact: Jay Sliker. bk.rev.; circ. 6,000 (paid). (tabloid format) **Document type:** newsletter.
  Description: Serves the horse enthusiast in Michigan, Indiana and Ohio.

798   US
THE EQUINE TRADE JOURNAL. 1993. bi-m. Box 5299, Laguna Beach, CA 92652. TEL 714-494-2033. FAX 714-376-8891. E-mail: Equinetrad@aol.com. Pub. Ann Abbott. **Document type:** trade publication.
  Description: Provides a medium for trainers and breeders of sport horses to market their stock directly to the attention of other equine professionals.

798 636.089   CN   ISSN 0828-864X
EQUINEWS; serving the horse industry - all breeds, all disciplines. 1980. m. Can.$15 (foreign $22). John Whittle, Ed. & Pub. (Subsidiary of: Westview Publications), Site 15, C.5, R.R.6, Vernon, BC V1T 6Y5, Canada. TEL 604-542-2002. FAX 604-549-7099. adv. (tabloid format; back issues avail.)
  Formerly (until 1984): Hoof Beats.

798   SP
EQUITACION; deporte e industria hipica. 1993. m. 5000 ptas. (effective 1995). Servicios Industriales Pesqueros S.A., Policarpo Sanz 22-3o, 36202 Vigo, Spain. TEL 34-86-437004. FAX 34-86-430625. TELEX 83058 IBISA E. Ed. Alfonso Paz-Andrade. adv.; B&W page 75000 ptas., color page 115000 ptas.; trim 185 x 260; adv. contact: Pilar Sarabia. circ. 15,000. **Document type:** consumer publication, trade publication.

798.2 501   US   ISSN 0149-0672
SF277
EQUUS. 1977. m. $24. Fleet Street Publishing Corp., 656 Quince Orchard Rd., Gaithersburg, MD 20878. TEL 301-977-3900. (Subscr. to: Neodata, Box 57919, Boulder, CO 80322-7919) Ed. Ami Shinitzky. adv.; index. circ. 134,125. (also avail. in microform from UMI; reprint service avail. from UMI) **Indexed:** Farm & Garden Ind., Sports Per.Ind., Sportsearch (1978-).
  —Faxon; UMI; UnCover.

798.2   UK
EUROPEAN PATTERN BOOK. (Text in English, French) a. £25. (British Horseracing Board) Weatherbys, Sanders Rd., Wellingborough, Northants. NN8 6UJ, England. FAX 01933-440077. circ. 5,000. **Document type:** trade publication.
  Description: Outlines all group-classified horse races and their conditions.

636.1 798.4   UK   ISSN 0260-7468
EUROPEAN RACEHORSE. 1949. 4/yr. £24($48) Turf Newspapers Ltd., 19 Clarges St., London W1Y 7PG, England. Ed. Richard Onslow. adv.; bk.rev.; illus.; index.
  Incorporates: British Racehorse (ISSN 0007-1706)

636.1   DK   ISSN 0108-7738
FJORDHESTEN. 1982. q. membership. Fjordhesteavlen, Landskontoret for Heste, Udkaersvej 15, Skejby, 8200 Aarhus N, Denmark. illus.

798.2   GW   ISSN 0342-4758
FREIZEIT IM SATTEL; die Fachzeitschrift fuers Freizeitreiten. 1958. m. DM.73.20. F S Verlag GmbH, Droste-Huelshoff-Str. 3, 53129 Bonn, Germany. TEL 0228-236622. FAX 0228-235274. Ed. Erika Mueller. adv.: B&W page DM.3490, color page DM.6864; trim 185 x 260; adv. contact: Erika Ingendahl. bk.rev. circ. 27,944. **Document type:** consumer publication.

798.4   VE   ISSN 0016-3775
GACETA HIPICA. 1950. w. Bs.156. Editora de Revistas, C.A., Avda. Principal los Ruices, Adpo. 2935, Caracas 101, Venezuela. Eds. Benigno Martin Pinedo, Jaime Martin Pinedo. adv. circ. 158,600.

798   US   ISSN 1062-7510
GAITWAY MAGAZINE. 1991. m. $23.95 (effective Jan. 1994). Gaitway Magazine, Inc., Box 31306, Lafayette, LA 70593-1306. TEL 318-237-3988. FAX 318-237-3983. Ed. Patricia Zeitoun. adv.: B&W page $275; 7 x 9 1/2; adv. contact: Tissa Porter. circ. 5,500 (paid). **Document type:** trade publication.
  Description: Covers training, breeding, activities and veterinary care of smooth-gaited saddle horses. Includes personality features and life-style articles.

798   UK   ISSN 0072-078X
GENERAL STUD BOOK. 1773. q. £165. Weatherbys, Sanders Rd., Wellingborough, Northants. NN8 48X, England. TEL 01933-440077. FAX 01933-440807. TELEX 311582-ODECS. Ed. David Aitken. adv. contact: Paul Jones. stat. circ. 1,000. **Document type:** directory.
  —BLDSC (4111.450000).

791.8   US
GIRLS' RODEO ASSOCIATION NEWS.* 1964. m. $5. Girls' Rodeo Association, c/o Ed. Lydia Moore, Rt. 5, Box 698, Blanchard, OK 73010-9805. illus.

GOLF TENNIS POLO; magazine for sports, journeys, pastime, society and fashion. see SPORTS AND GAMES

636.1   SP   ISSN 0085-1337
GUIA DE LOS CABALLOS VERIFICADOS EN ESPANA. 1875. a. 4500 ptas. Sociedad de Fomento de la Cria Caballar de Espana, Hipodromo de la Zarzuela, Aravaca, 28023 Madrid, Spain. TEL 207 07 51. TELEX 48 260 SFCCE. circ. 2,000.

798   FR   ISSN 0765-0116
GUIDE DU CHEVAL ARABE EN FRANCE. 1964. a. 150 F. price varies. Guides Equestres, 5 rue Alexandre Cabanel, 75015 Paris, France. FAX 33-47-34-94-94. Ed. Caroline Elgosi. adv. circ. 8,000.
  Formerly: Ou Monter a Cheval (ISSN 0078-7035)

636.1   UK
HACKNEY HORSE SOCIETY YEAR BOOK. a. £7 to non-members. Hackney Horse Society, Clump Cottage, Chitterne, Nr. Warminster, Wilts. BA12 0LL, England. TEL 01985-850906.

636.1   US   ISSN 0046-6700
HACKNEY JOURNAL.* 1970. bi-m. $9. Hackney Publications Inc., 56 Seventh Ave., Apt.10-A, New York, NY 10011-6672. Ed. Paul E. Bolton, Jr. adv.; bk.rev. circ. 1,500. (tabloid format)

636.1   UK
HACKNEY STUD BOOK. quadrennial. £25. Hackney Horse Society, Clump Cottage, Chitterne, Nr. Warminster, Wilts, BA12 0LL, England. TEL 01985-850906.

636.295 798.4   TS
AL-HADAF. (Text in Arabic) 1988. w. Mu'assasat Galadari lil-Tiba'ah wal-Nashr, P.O. Box 11243, Dubai, United Arab Emirates. TEL 582400. FAX 582238. TELEX 46832. Ed. Abd al-Latif Galadari. adv. contact: Kamal Raj Shah. circ. 20,000.
  Description: Covers all sporting activities within the U.A.E., with a focus on traditional Arab pursuits such as camel racing and horse racing.

636.1   SW   ISSN 1100-9799
HAEST- OCH PONNYBOKEN; alla haestvaenners aarsbok. 1968. a. Semic Press AB, P.O. Box 1074, S-172 22 Sundbyberg, Sweden.

798.2 636.1   SW   ISSN 0345-486X
HAESTEN/HORSE; foer avel och sport. (Text in Swedish) 1920. m. SEK 390. Tidskriften Haesten, Pl 566 Kampavall, S-540 17 Lerdala, Sweden. Ed. Maria Cidh. adv.: B&W page SEK 4950, color page SEK 7750. circ. 10,000.
  Formerly (until 1945): Svensk Ryttartidning.

798.2   SW   ISSN 0280-7777
HAESTSPORT; magasin foer trav och galopp. 1982. bi-m. SEK 175 (effective 1990). Haestsport, P.O. Box 28088, S200 28 Malmoe, Sweden.

798   AU   ISSN 1018-3698
HAFLINGERSPORT. 1986. bi-m. S.250. Reitclub St. Erhard, Haymogasse 19, A-1238 Vienna, Austria. TEL 01-8827224. Ed. Erika Bruhns. adv.; bk.rev.; circ. 1,500. (back issues avail.) **Document type:** newsletter.

636.1   GW
DER HANNOVERANER. 1922. bi-m. membership. Verband Hannoverscher Warmblutzuechter e.V., Lindhooperstr. 92, 27283 Verden, Germany. TEL 04231-6730. FAX 04231-67312. Ed. Ludwig Christmann. adv.; bk.rev.; bibl.; charts; illus.; stat. circ. 18,000. **Document type:** newsletter.
  Formerly: Hannoversches Pferd (ISSN 0017-7474)

798.46   AT   ISSN 0818-2442
HARNESS RACER. 1948. m. Aus.$48. Harness Racing Board, 740 Mt. Alexander Rd., Moonee Ponds, Vic. 3039, Australia. TEL 03-375 4255. FAX 02-370-4299. Ed. Robert Pangho. adv. circ. 5,500. (back issues avail.)
  Formerly (until 1986): Gazette (Melbourne) (ISSN 0729-879X)
  Description: Promotion and information guide for harness racing.

636.1   UK   ISSN 0951-2640
HEAVY HORSE WORLD; the only magazine for heavy horse owners and enthusiasts in the U.K. 1987. q. $34. Park Cottage, West Dean, Chichester, W. Sussex PO18 ORX, England. TEL 01243-811364. Eds. Christopher Zeuner, Diana Zeuner; Pubs. Christopher Zeuner, Diana Zeuner. adv.; bk.rev. circ. 2,500. (back issues avail.) **Document type:** consumer publication.
  Formerly: Heavy Horse.

636.1   NE
HENGSTENBOEK. s-a. fl.50. Misset (Subsidiary of: Reed Elsevier plc), Postbus 4, 7000 BA Doetinchem, Netherlands. TEL 31-8340-49911. FAX 31-8340-43839. TELEX 45481. illus. circ. 2,000. (looseleaf format)
  Description: Details about all the stallions approved for breeding in the Netherlands.

798   DK
HIPPOLOGISK. 1888. m. DKK 386. (Sportsrideklubben i Koebenhavn) Landsbladet, V. Farimagsgade 6, 1606 Copenhagen, Denmark. TEL 33-112222. FAX 33-323046. Ed. Helle Sydendal. adv. contact: Tove Madsen. bk.rev. circ. 15,100. **Document type:** consumer publication.
  Formerly: Hippologisk Tidsskrift (ISSN 0018-201X)

S

SPORTS AND GAMES — HORSES AND HORSEMANSHIP

798.4   NE   ISSN 0046-7715
HOEFSLAG; geillustreerd weekblad voor paardenvrienden. (Includes supplements: Paarden & Cap & Hoefslag Jaarboek) 1949. w. fl.187. Best Communications & Management B.V., Postbus 245, 5680 AE Best, Netherlands. TEL 31-4998-98115. FAX 31-4998-90923. Ed. M.C.M. Jurgens. adv.: B&W page fl.1995; trim 185 x 248. bk.rev. circ. 28,500. **Document type:** consumer publication.
   Description: Covers all aspects of the equestrian world, for recreational riders, stable-owners, competition riders, stud owners.

798.4   US   ISSN 0018-4683
HOOF BEATS. 1933. m. $10 to members; non-members $18. United States Trotting Association, 750 Michigan Ave., Columbus, OH 43215. TEL 614-224-2291. Ed. Dean A. Hoffman. adv. contact: Richard Dakin. illus. circ. 22,000. **Document type:** trade publication.
   —UnCover.
   Description: Features horse racing.

798   US
HOOF PRINT.* 1975. bi-m. $10. North American Trail Ride Conference, Box 338, Sedalia, CO 80135-0338. TEL 619-588-7245. Ed. Ruth Bourgeois. adv. circ. 2,500. **Document type:** newspaper.

798   US   ISSN 0094-3355
HORSE AND HORSEMAN; the nation's finest horse magazine. 1971. m. $18. Gallant - Charger Publishing, Inc., 34249 Camino Capistrano, Box HH, Capistrano Beach, CA 92624. TEL 714-493-2101. Ed. Jack Lewis. adv.; bk.rev.; illus.; tr.lit. circ. 96,000. (reprint service avail.) **Indexed:** Farm & Garden Ind.
   Incorporating: International Rider and Driver (ISSN 0044-1090)
   Description: Covers all facets of horsemanship with emphasis on breeds and training.

636.1 798   UK   ISSN 0018-5140
HORSE AND HOUND. 1884. w. £63($119) I P C Magazines, Specialist Magazine Group (Subsidiary of: Reed Elsevier group), King's Reach Tower, Stamford St., London SE1 9LS, England. TEL 071-261-6315. FAX 0444-440619. TELEX 892084 REEDBP G. (Dist. by: Quadrant Subscription Services, Oakfield House, Perrymount Rd., Haywards Heath, W. Sussex RH16 3DH, England. TEL 0444-440421) Ed. Michael Clayton. adv.: B&W page £1530; adv. contact: Darryl Sherer. bk.rev.; illus. circ. 80,000. (back issues avail.) **Document type:** consumer publication.
   —CCC.
   Description: Covers all British equestrian sports and international championships including racing, horse trials, dressage, polo, show jumping, showing, hunting, pony club.

798   UK
HORSE AND PONY (PETERBOROUGH). 1971. fortn. £33.40 (foreign £38.50) (effective 1995-1996). E M A P - Pursuit Publishing, Bretton Ct., Bretton, Peterborough, Cambs. PE3 8DZ, England. TEL 01733-264666. FAX 01733-261984. TELEX 32157. (Subscr. to: Tower Publishing Services Ltd., Tower House, Sovereign Park, Lathkill St., Market Harborough, Leics. LE16 9EF, England. TEL 01858-468811. FAX 01858-432164) Ed. Andrea Oakes; Pub. Melvyn Bagnell. adv. contact: Karen Barsberry-Woods. bk.rev./ circ. 61,123 (paid). **Document type:** consumer publication.

636.1   UK
HORSE & RIDER. 1950. m. £33.60. D.J. Murphy (Publishers) Ltd., Haslemere House, Lower St., Haslemere, Surrey GU27 2PE, England. TEL 01428-651551. FAX 01428-653888. Ed. Kate Austin. adv.; bk.rev.; illus. circ. 35,000. **Indexed:** Farm & Garden Ind., Jun.High.Mag.Abstr., Sportsearch. **Document type:** consumer publication.
   Formerly: Light Horse (ISSN 0024-3329)

798 636.1   US   ISSN 0018-5159
SF277
HORSE & RIDER.* 1968. m. $19.95. Horse & Rider, Inc. (Subsidiary of: Cowles Media Company), 12265 W Bayaud Ave., Carewood, CO 80228-2116. TEL 714-361-1955. FAX 714-361-0333. Ed. Sue Copeland. adv.; bk.rev.; charts; illus.; tr.lit. circ. 160,000. **Indexed:** PMR, Sportsearch (1984-).
   —UnCover.
   Incorporates (1981-1991): Performance Horseman (ISSN 0744-3633)
   Description: For the competitive horse owner, breeder and trainer. Covers training tips, techniques, feeding, Western fashion and lifestyle, riding equipment, medical reports, and special events.

798   CN
HORSE CENTS. q. membership. Canadian Thoroughbred Horse Society, Alberta Division, 410, 1501 - 1 St., S.W., Calgary, AB T2R 0W1, Canada. TEL 403-266-2248. FAX 403-233-8085. Ed. Rennie J. Gellner. adv. contact: Rennie Geller. circ. 500 (controlled). (back issues avail.) **Document type:** newsletter.
   Description: Keeps membership up-to-date with the industry.

798.2   CN   ISSN 0847-9984
HORSE CHRONICLE. 1989. bi-m. Can.$15. Kennedy Publishing Inc., R.R. 5, Georgetown, ON L7G 4S8, Canada. TEL 905-877-2058. FAX 905-877-2058. Ed. Leslie A. Kennedy. adv. contact: Marion Todd Kennedy. circ. 5,500. **Document type:** newspaper.

798.2 630   US
HORSE CONNECTION. 1989. m. $18. Virginia Horse Council, Box 72, Riner, VA 24149. TEL 703-382-3071. E-mail: aalley@bev.net. Ed. Louise St. Amour. circ. 550 (paid). **Document type:** consumer publication.
   Description: Covers southwestern Virginia horsemanship: people, places, and events.

636.1   US   ISSN 0145-9791
SF277
HORSE ILLUSTRATED. 1976. m. $21.97; newsstand price: $2.50. Fancy Publications, 2401 Beverly Blvd., Los Angeles, CA 90057. TEL 213-385-2222. FAX 714-855-3045. (Subscr. to: Box 57549, Boulder, CO 80322-7549) Ed. Sharon Lemon Ralls. adv.; bk.rev.; illus. circ. 90,000.
   Description: For families caring for one or more pleasure horses and who ride both English and Western (all breeds). Covers the care, health and performance of the horse, as well as regular features on training, conditioning, feeding and showing.

636.1   US   ISSN 0890-233X
SF278.5   CODEN: AESSE8
HORSE INDUSTRY DIRECTORY. 1972. a. $20. American Horse Council, Inc., 1700 K St, N.W., Ste. 300, Washington, DC 20006. TEL 202-296-4031. FAX 202-296-1970. Ed. Lisa Kovner. **Document type:** directory.

798.2   NE
HORSE INTERNATIONAL; sport & breeding. (Text in English) 1993. 10/yr. Best Communications & Management B.V., Postbus 245, 5680 AE Best, Netherlands. TEL 31-4998-98115. FAX 31-4998-90923. adv.: B&W page fl.3500, color page fl.4500; trim 297 x 420; adv. contact: R. van der Kuil. illus. circ. 8,500. **Document type:** consumer publication.
   Formerly (until Dec. 1994): Horse Sport International (ISSN 1352-6006)

798 336   US
HORSE OWNERS AND BREEDERS TAX MANUAL. 1975. a. $90. American Horse Council, Inc., 1700 K St., N.W., Ste. 300, Washington, DC 20006. TEL 202-296-4031. FAX 202-296-1970. circ. 4,300. (looseleaf format; back issues avail.) **Document type:** bulletin.

798   UK
HORSE RACING QUIZ BOOK.* a. £1.50. Raceform Ltd., 19 Clarges Rd., London W1Y 7PG, England.

THE HORSE REPORT. see *VETERINARY SCIENCE*

798   US
HORSE SHOW. 1937. m. $25. American Horse Shows Association, Inc., 220 E. 42nd St., 4th Fl., New York, NY 10017-5876. TEL 212-972-2472. FAX 212-983-7286. TELEX 7105813811 AMHORSE NYK. Ed. Norine Dworkin. adv.; bk.rev. circ. 58,000. **Document type:** trade publication.
   Description: Provides information on ruling, policies and officials and profiles top horsemen and horsewomen who compete at AHSA-recognized events.

636.1   US   ISSN 0018-5191
HORSE WORLD; feature-oriented show-horse specialty publication. 1933. m. $35. Dabora, Inc., Box 1007, Shelbyville, TN 37160. TEL 615-684-8123. Ed. David L. Howard. adv.; bk.rev. circ. 5,000. **Indexed:** Sportsearch.

798.2   US   ISSN 0018-523X
HORSEMAN AND FAIR WORLD; devoted to the trotting and pacing horse. 1877. w. $40. Horseman Publishing Co. Inc., Box 11688, Lexington, KY 40577. TEL 606-254-4026. Ed. Harold Monaghan. adv.; illus.; stat. circ. 10,000.
   Description: Discusses harness horse racing and breeding.

636.1 798.4   US   ISSN 0018-5256
HORSEMEN'S JOURNAL. 1949. m. $24. (Horsemen's Benevolent and Protective Association) Horsemen's Journal, Inc., 2800 Grand Rte. St. John St., New Orleans, LA 70119-3023. Ed. William Anderson. adv.; bk.rev.; bibl.; charts; illus.; stat.; index. circ. 45,000. (also avail. in microform from UMI; back issues avail.)
   —UMI.
   Description: Discusses horse breeding and racing.

798   US   ISSN 0092-6353
HORSEPLAY. 1973. m. $22.97. H P Partnership, 11 Park Ave., Box 545, Gaithersburg, MD 20877. TEL 301-840-1866. FAX 301-840-5722. Ed. Lisa Kiser; Pub. John Raaf. adv. contact: Carol Shiro. bk.rev. circ. 48,000. **Document type:** consumer publication.
   Description: Specializes in the Olympic equestrian disciplines, plus fox hunting and recreational riding.

798.2   CN   ISSN 0840-6715
HORSEPOWER; magazine for young horse lovers. 1988. bi-m. Can.$15.95($19.95) (effective 1991). Corinthian Publishing Co. Ltd., 225 Industrial Pkwy. S., Box 670, Aurora, ON L4G 4J9, Canada. TEL 905-727-0101. FAX 905-841-1530. Ed. Susan Stafford. adv.: B&W page $400, color page $850; adv. contact: Cheryl Prezuiso. circ. 10,000. (back issues avail.) **Document type:** consumer publication.
   Description: Presents short stories, horse care information, caption contests, riding hints, crosswords, humor

636.1   US   ISSN 0046-7936
HORSES. 1962. bi-m. $29.95 (foreign $39.95). Horses Publishing Co., 21 Greenview, Carlsbad, CA 92009. TEL 619-931-9958. FAX 619-931-0650. Ed. John Quirk. adv.; bk.rev.; film rev.; stat. circ. 10,000. **Indexed:** Sportsearch. **Document type:** consumer publication.
   Description: Covers international equestrian events.

798.2   CN   ISSN 0225-4913
HORSES ALL; the magazine dedicated to horses and their people. 1977. m. Can.$15. (Quarter Horse Association of Alberta) North Hill Publications, 4000 - 19th St. N.E., Calgary, AB T2E 6P8, Canada. TEL 403-250-6633. FAX 403-291-0703. Ed. Mickey Dumont; Pub. Eric Prosser. adv.: B&W page Can.$545; adv. contact: Pamela Bryan. bk.rev.; film rev.; illus. circ. 9,000. (tabloid format) **Document type:** newspaper.
   Description: Official publication of 39 national and regional associations including light horse, heavy horse, rodeo, and jumping. Includes veterinarian and health news.

636.1   US   ISSN 0018-5264
HORSETRADER. (Consists of all advertising; contains no editorial matter) 1960. m. $15. Horsetrader, Inc., Box 728, Middlefield, OH 44062. TEL 216-632-5266. FAX 216-632-5631. Ed. Jerry Goldberg. adv. contact: Richard Briggs. illus. circ. 34,224. **Document type:** trade publication.

SPORTS AND GAMES — HORSES AND HORSEMANSHIP

798 UK
HOUNDS. 1984. m. £20($40) Ravensworld Ltd., Hunters Moon, Exford, Minehead, Somerset TA24 7PP, England. TEL 01643-831695. FAX 01643-831576. Ed. Bryan Jackson. adv.: color page £400; adv. contact: Bryan Jackson. bk.rev.; illus. circ. 10,800. **Document type:** consumer publication.

798 US ISSN 1057-8501
HUNTER & SPORT HORSE. 1991. 7/yr. $15.99. Midwest Hunter, Inc., 12204 Covington Rd., Fort Wayne, IN 46804-9720. TEL 219-625-4030. FAX 219-625-3480. Ed. Laura Allen. adv.: Carol/Craig. circ. 28,000. **Document type:** consumer publication.
Formerly (until 1992): Midwest Hunter & Sport Horse (ISSN 1056-8182)
Description: Covers dressage, combined training, hunter/jumper, and related equestrian sports.

798.4 US
ILLINOIS RACING NEWS. 1972. m. $24. (Illinois Thoroughbred Breeders and Owners Foundation) Midwest Outdoors Ltd., 111 Shore Dr., Hinsdale, IL 60521. TEL 708-887-7722. FAX 708-887-1958. Ed. Joan Colby. adv.; bk.rev.
Description: Covers thoroughbred horse racing and breeding.

INSIDE EQUINE; news from the Equine Research Centre. see VETERINARY SCIENCE

636.1 US ISSN 0894-0614
INSIDE INTERNATIONAL; the official publication of the Arabian breeds. 1979. bi-m. $18. International Arabian Horse Association, Box 33696, Denver, CO 80233. TEL 303-450-4774. FAX 303-450-5127. Ed. Shelley Bowling. adv. circ. 7,000.

INTERNATIONAL GAMBLERS CLUB NEWSLETTER. see SPORTS AND GAMES

798.2 US ISSN 1062-7146
INTERNATIONAL SADDLERY AND APPAREL JOURNAL. 1983. m. $100 (free to qualified personnel). EEMG, Inc, Box 3039, Berea, KY 40403-3039. FAX 606-986-1770. Ed. Janet Buell. adv. contact: Anne Crawtree. circ. 8,261 (controlled). (also avail. in microfilm) **Document type:** trade publication.
Formerly (until Jan. 1992): Horse Digest (ISSN 0733-1339)
Description: Addresses current business and marketing issues, trends, and practices in the equestrian and equine goods industries.

IPPOLOGIA. see VETERINARY SCIENCE

636.1 798.4 IE ISSN 0021-1184
IRISH FIELD. 1870. w. I£82.16 (U.K. I£84.76; elsewhere I£93.60). Irish Times Ltd., 10-15 D'Olier St., Dublin 2, Ireland. TEL 01-6792022. FAX 01-6793029. Ed. Valentine Lamb. adv.; bk.rev.; illus. circ. 10,512. (also avail. in microfilm) **Document type:** newspaper.
Description: Covers horse breeding, racing and show jumping.

798.2 GW ISSN 0173-8208
JAHRBUCH ZUCHT; Leistungen und Daten der Deutschen Pferdezucht. 1911. a. DM.84. (Deutsche Reiterliche Vereinigung e.V.) F N - Verlag, Postfach 110363, 48205 Warendorf, Germany. TEL 02581-7696. FAX 02581-633146. circ. 3,000. **Document type:** directory.
Former titles: Jahrbuch fuer Pferdeleistungspruefungen. Tiel 2, Zucht (ISSN 0173-8194); Leistunshengste der Deutschen Warmblutzucht (ISSN 0173-8178)
Description: German stallion data, including lists of breeders.

798 XO ISSN 0231-9039
JAZDECTVO.* (Text in Czech, Slovak) 1953. m. (Slovak Technical University, Physical Education Organization) Sport, Vajnorska Cesta 100-a, 832-58 Bratislava, Slovakia. (back issues avail.)

798.4 AG ISSN 0021-7115
JOCKEY CLUB.* (Text in English, Spanish) 1966. q. Arg.$35($12) Jockey Club de Buenos Aires, Cerrito 1353, 2 Piso, Buenos Aires, Argentina. (U.S. subscr. to: Franklin Square Subscription Agency, 545 Cedar Ln., Teaneck, NJ 07666) Ed. Eduardo Botta. adv.; illus.

798.2 CN ISSN 0380-3554
JR. RIDER. 1977. q. Can.$3($3.25) National Sport and Recreation Centre, Inc., c/o Jan Fewster, Ed., R.R. 1, Kemptville, Ont. K0G 1J0, Canada. TEL 613-746-0060. adv.; illus.

798.2 US ISSN 1041-2786
JUST HORSIN' AROUND; news and advice for the Tennessee horseman. 1988. m. $25. Jordan Hills Enterprises, Jordan Hills Farm, Rt. 10 Jordan Rd., Franklin, TN 37064. TEL 615-791-5656. Ed. Margo Isom. circ. 12,000. (tabloid format; back issues avail.)

798 US
KANSAS HORSEMAN.* 1980. m. $15. Kansas Horseman, RR 2, Box 35, Beverly, KS 67423-9603. TEL 913-227-3339. Ed. Terry Galloway. adv.; bk.rev. circ. 2,000. (tabloid format; back issues avail.)

798 SZ
KAVALLO; Zeitschrift fuer Pferdesport und Pferdezucht. (Text in German) 1911. 19/yr. 95 SFr. Schuetzenhausstr. 5, CH-8330 Pfaeffikon ZH, Switzerland. TEL 01-9503011. FAX 01-9501089. Ed. Georges Zehnder. adv. contact: Helmut Froehlich. bk.rev. circ. 17,200.
Formerly: Schweizer Kavallerist (ISSN 0036-7389)

798 636.1 PL ISSN 0137-1487
KON POLSKI. (Supplements avail: Ujezdzanie; Wyniki; Informator) 1966. bi-m. $18 (effective June 1995). Kon Polski Sp. z o.o., Zlota 63a m.6, 00-819 Warsaw, Poland. TEL 48-22-209817. FAX 48-22-243628. (Subscr. to: Centurii 3, 04-944 Warsaw, Poland) Ed. Tomasz A. Szymanski. adv. circ. 10,000.

636.1 798 RU ISSN 0023-3285
KONEVODSTVO I KONNYI SPORT. 1842. bi-m. $45 (effective 1996). Izdatel'stvo Kolos, Sadovo-Spasskaya, 18, 107807 Moscow, Russia. TEL 207-17-90. FAX 207-28-70. (Subscr. to: Mezhdunarodnaya Kniga, Moscow, G-200, Russia) Ed. Nikolai A. Moiseenko. bk.rev.; index. circ. 15,000. **Indexed:** Anim.Breed.Abstr.; Nutr.Abstr. —BLDSC (0092.100000).

798.2 US ISSN 0047-4088
THE LARIAT. 1949. m. $14. Lariat, 12675 S.W. First St., Beaverton, OR 97005. TEL 503-644-2233. FAX 503-644-2213. Ed. Barbara Zellner. adv.; bk.rev.; illus. circ. 7,500. (tabloid format; back issues avail.) **Document type:** newspaper.
Description: General interest tabloid for Northwest horsepeople. Covers all breeds of horses, news of individuals, clubs, and competitions.

636.1 798 US ISSN 0892-6271
LONE STAR HORSE REPORT. 1983. m. $15. Lone Star Horse Report, 5129 E. Belknap, Box 14767, Fort Worth, TX 76117. TEL 817-838-8642. FAX 817-838-6410. Henry L. King, Ed. & Pub. adv.; bk.rev. circ. 10,000. (back issues avail.) **Document type:** consumer publication.
Description: Dedicated to the distribution of information about horses, horsemen, events and places in the Texas-Oklahoma horse market.

354 CN ISSN 0317-7262
SF335.C2
MANITOBA. HORSE RACING COMMISSION. ANNUAL REPORT. a. free. Horse Racing Commission, P.O. Box 46086, Winnipeg, Man. R3R 3S3, Canada. TEL 204-885-7770. FAX 204-831-0942. stat. circ. 200. **Document type:** government publication.

636.1 US ISSN 0025-4274
SF277
THE MARYLAND HORSE. 1936. bi-m. $20 (foreign $29). Maryland Horse Breeders Association, Box 427, Timonium, MD 21094. TEL 410-252-2100. FAX 410-560-0503. Ed. Richard W. Wilcke. adv.: B&W page $400; color page $1000; adv. contact: Barry Reightler. bk.rev.; charts; illus.; stat. circ. 4,600. **Indexed:** Sportsearch. **Document type:** trade publication.
Description: Promotes Maryland's equine industry, covering the entire, diverse spectrum with concentration on the breeding and racing of thoroughbreds. Intended both as information and entertainment for all those interested in equestrian activities and events in Maryland.

798.2 US ISSN 1073-5704
MICHAEL PLUMB'S HORSE JOURNAL. m. $45 (foreign $57) (effective 1996). Belvoir Publications, Inc., 75 Holly Hill Ln., Greenwich, CT 06836-2626. TEL 203-661-6111. FAX 203-661-4802. (Subscr. to: Box 420234, Palm Coast, FL 32142) **Document type:** consumer publication.

798 US
MICHIGAN QUARTER HORSE JOURNAL. 1955. m. $35 membership. Michigan Quarter Horse Association, Box 248, Bath, MI 48808-0248. TEL 616-781-5766. Ed. Diane Graves. adv.; illus. circ. 2,500. (back issues avail.) **Document type:** trade publication.
Description: Articles on the advancement and improvement of the breeding and performance of the quarter horse.

636.1 US ISSN 1056-3245
SF293.T5
MID-ATLANTIC THOROUGHBRED. 1991. bi-m. $20 (foreign $29). Maryland Horse Breeders Association, Box 427, Timonium, MD 21094. TEL 410-252-2100. FAX 410-560-0503. Ed. Richard Wilke. adv.: B&W page $600; color page $1200; adv. contact: Kristen Mowery. bk.rev. circ. 10,000. **Document type:** trade publication.
Description: Promotes thoroughbred racing and breeding in the Mid-Atlantic region. Directed to horse breeders, trainers, owners and enthusiasts.

798 US
MID-SOUTH HORSE REVIEW. 1992. m. $15 (effective Apr. 1992). Box 519, Somerville, TN 38068. TEL 901-465-4042. FAX 901-465-5493. Ed. Anne Fordyce. adv.; bk.rev. circ. 12,500. (tabloid format; back issues avail.) **Document type:** trade publication.

MIN HEST. see CHILDREN AND YOUTH — For

798 IT ISSN 1121-3183
MIO CAVALLO. 1990. m. L.60000 (foreign L.115000). Mio Cavallo, Via G.B. Pergolesi 8, 20124 Milan, Italy. TEL 39-2-66715150. FAX 39-2-66715171. Ed. Gaetano Manti. adv.: color page L.4900000. circ. 31,681. **Document type:** consumer publication.

798.2 US ISSN 0747-1424
SF291
MODERN HORSE BREEDING;* the leading advisory resource for the breeding industry. 1984. m. (10/yr.) $29.95. Round Table Publishing, Inc., 13017 Wisteria Dr. No. 324, Germantown, MD 20874-2675. TEL 301-977-3900. Ed. Bobbie Lieberman. adv.; bk.rev. circ. 6,000. **Indexed:** Farm & Garden Ind.
—UnCover.

636.1 US ISSN 0027-1098
SF293.M8
THE MORGAN HORSE. 1941. m. $27.50 (effective Sep. 1991). American Morgan Horse Association, Box 960, Shelburne, VT 05482-0960. TEL 802-985-4944. FAX 802-985-8897. Ed. Suzy Lucine. adv.; bk.rev.; illus. circ. 9,000.
—Faxon; UnCover.

798 US
MOUNTAIN RIDERS. 1989. m. $15. South By Southwest Ranch, 15190 Tierra Rejada, Moor Park, CA 93021. TEL 805-523-9334. Ed. Kate Poss. circ. 5,000 (controlled).
Description: For all horse owners, breeders and riders, with information on equestrian events, politics and personalities.

798.2 362.4 US ISSN 1067-5876
N A R H A NEWS. 1970. 6/yr. $20 membership ($60 outside N. America). North American Riding for the Handicapped Association, Inc., Box 33150, Denver, CO 80233. TEL 303-452-1212; 800-369-7433. FAX 303-252-4610. Ed. William Scebbi. adv.; bk.rev. circ. 3,500. (back issues avail.) **Indexed:** InterActions Bibl., Sportsearch (1983-). **Document type:** newsletter.
Description: Provides news and technical information for people who assist the physically and mentally disabled to ride horses for therapy and recreation.

SPORTS AND GAMES — HORSES AND HORSEMANSHIP

798.4 AT ISSN 0726-1799
NATIONAL BUCKSKIN SOCIETY. NEWSLETTER. 1973. q. Aus.$30 membership. National Buckskin Society Inc., P.O. Box 27, Berwick, Vic. 3806, Australia. TEL 61-56-292722. Ed. A. Thirkell. adv.; bk.rev. circ. 200. (back issues avail.) Document type: newsletter.
  Description: Provides information on dressage, turnout, showing, and caring for horses.

798 US
NATIONAL CUTTING HORSE ASSOCIATION. RULE BOOK. 1946. a. membership. National Cutting Horse Association, 4704 Hwy. 377, S., Fort Worth, TX 76116-8805. TEL 817-244-6188. FAX 817-244-2015. Ed. Karl R. Little. circ. 10,326.

636.1 US ISSN 0027-9455
NATIONAL HORSEMAN. 1865. m. $38. 14455 N. Hayden Rd., Ste. 208, Scottsdale, AZ 85260-6948. TEL 602-922-5202. FAX 602-922-5212. Ed. Raymond E. Sheffield. adv.; illus.; circ. 3,000 (paid). —UnCover.
  Description: Focuses on show horses.

798.2 AT ISSN 1320-2081
NATIONAL TROTTING WEEKLY. 1975. w. Aus.$115. David Syme & Co. Limited, 250 Spencer St., Melbourne, Vic. 3000, Australia. TEL 03-601-4222. Ed. Richard Trembath. adv. circ. 15,000. (tabloid format; back issues avail.)
  Description: Harness racing in the eastern states of Australia.

798.2 910.202 US
SF285.35
NATIONWIDE OVERNIGHT STABLING DIRECTORY & EQUESTRIAN VACATION GUIDE. 1982. a. $29.45 (effective Jan. 1995). Equine Travelers of America, Inc., 1026 W. Ash, Box 322, Arkansas City, KS 67005-0322. TEL 316-442-8131. FAX 316-442-8215. Eds. James L. McDaniel, Janice J. Nelson. adv. circ. 5,000. Document type: directory.
  Formerly (until 1990): Nationwide Overnight Stabling Directory (ISSN 0886-5647)

636.1 NZ ISSN 0028-8209
NEW ZEALAND HORSE & PONY. 1959. m. NZ.$45. Independent News (Auckland) Ltd., P.O. Box 1327, Auckland, New Zealand. FAX 64-9-309-2279. Ed. Joan Gilchrist. adv.; bk.rev. circ. 7,500. Document type: consumer publication.
  —CCC.

636.1 US ISSN 1067-5884
NORTHEAST EQUINE JOURNAL. 1988. m. $14. Turley Publications, 29 Water St., Palmer, MA 01069. TEL 603-357-4271. FAX 603-357-7851. Ed. Janice R. Montgomery; Pub. Pat Turley. adv.; bk.rev. circ. 16,000.
  Description: Features articles on horses and horse people, all breeds, and discipline, a calendar of equestrian events, tips on teaching and training techniques, and articles on equine healthcare, and notes from around the the New York and New England regions.

798.2 US
NUESTRO CABALLO. 1970. q. membership only. Peruvian Paso Horse Registry of North America, 1038 Fourth St., No. 4, Santa Rosa, CA 95404-4319. TEL 707-579-4394.

798.2 AU
OESTERREICHISCHE REITER - ZEITUNG. 8/yr. S.150. Steiger-Werbung Verlags- und Werbegesellschaft mbH, Hermanngasse 25, A-1070 Vienna, Austria. Ed. Hedwig Giesser. adv.; illus. circ. 5,000.

798 US
OHIO THOROUGHBRED. 1971. bi-m. $21. (Ohio Thoroughbred Breeders and Owners) Centaurus, Inc., 920 Race St., Ste. 201, Cincinnati, OH 45202. TEL 513-241-9112. FAX 513-421-4011. Ed. Gayle Babst. adv. contact: Gregory Babst. bk.rev. circ. 1,500. (back issues avail.) Document type: trade publication.
  Description: Contains information pertaining to the thoroughbred industry in Ohio.

636.1 798 GW ISSN 0030-2066
DAS OLDENBURGER SPORTPFERD. 1969. 6/yr. DM.30. Verband der Zuechter des Oldenburger Pferdes e.V., Donnerschweerstr. 72-80, 26123 Oldenburg, Germany. TEL 0441-980610. FAX 0441-82416. Ed. Claus Schridde. adv.; bk.rev.; illus.; stat. circ. 4,000. Document type: newsletter.

798.4 UK ISSN 0265-0452
OWNERS, TRAINERS & BREEDERS. 1980. bi-m. £18($40) Arrowhead Ltd., Nr. Borden, Hants., England. (Subscr. to: 50 High St., Eton, Berkshire SL4 6BL, England) Ed. David Watkinson. circ. 12,000.
  Formerly (until Jan. 1983): Owners.

798 US
P O A. 1956. m. $22. Pony of the Americas Club Inc., 5240 Elmwood Ave., Indianapolis, IN 46203. TEL 317-788-0107. FAX 317-788-0108. Ed. Susan Adams. adv.; bk.rev. circ. 1,300.
  Formerly (until 1985): Pony of the Americas.
  Description: Covers horse care, training, show results, and club events.

798.2 NE
PAARDEN. (Supplement to: Hoefslag) m. fl.57.50. Best Communications & Management B.V., Postbus 245, 5680 AE Best, Netherlands. TEL 31-4998-98115. FAX 31-4998-90923. adv.; B&W page fl.1995; trim 215 x 285. illus. Document type: trade publication.

798.4 NE ISSN 0039-1387
PAARDESPORT IN REN EN DRAF. 1880. s-w. (Tue. & Thu.). fl.275. (Nederlandse Draf- en Rensport) Publico B.V., Postbus 273, 2501 GB The Hague, Netherlands. TEL 31-70-3021536. FAX 31-70-3021535. adv.; bk.rev.; charts. circ. 6,600. Document type: trade publication.
  Formed by the merger of: Stichting Nederlandse Draf- en Rensport. Officieel Bulletin; Draver en Volbloed.

798 US ISSN 0894-4458
PACIFIC COAST JOURNAL (SACRAMENTO).* 1963. m. $20. Pacific Coast Quarter Horse Association, 560 Wall St., Ste. A, Auburn, CA 95603-3931. TEL 916-924-7265. Ed. Kate Riordan. adv. circ. 5,082.
  Description: Focuses on equine breeding, taxes and laws, coverage of upcoming events and championship standings.

636.1 798 US ISSN 0164-5706
PAINT HORSE JOURNAL. 1962. m. $26 to non-members; members $21. American Paint Horse Association, Box 961023, Ft. Worth, TX 76161-0023. TEL 817-439-3400. FAX 817-439-3484. Ed. Darrell Dodds. adv.; bk.rev.; circ. 20,000 (paid). adv. (back issues avail.)
  Description: For those interested in riding, training, breeding, exhibiting or racing American Point Horses.

636.1 US ISSN 0031-045X
PALOMINO HORSES. 1942. m. $17.50. Palomino Horse Breeders of America, Inc., 15253 E. Skelly Dr., Tulsa, OK 74116-2637. TEL 800-647-6672. Ed. Tracy Thompson. adv.; bk.rev. circ. 5,600.

798.2 US
PALOMINO PARADE. 1937. bi-m. $15 (foreign $20). Palomino Horse Association, HC 63, Box 24, Dornsife, PA 17823. TEL 717-758-3067. Ed. Linda Tullis. Document type: newsletter.
  Description: News and information of interest to Palomino horse owners.

798.4 FR
PANORAMA TIERCE.* 1960. w. Editions en Direct, Chemin Blague, 13290 Les Milles, France. Ed. Jean Maizoue. adv.; illus.

636.1 GW ISSN 0932-3570
PFERD UND SPORT IN SCHLESWIG-HOLSTEIN UND HAMBURG. 1960. m. DM.42.60. (Verband der Zuechter des Holsteiner Pferdes) Verlag Wartenberg und Soehne GmbH, Theodorstr. 41, 22761 Hamburg, Germany. adv.; bk.rev.; illus.; stat. circ. 3,000.
  Former titles (until 1986): Pferde (ISSN 0932-3562); (until 1971): Holsteiner Pferd (ISSN 0018-3709)
  Description: Covers all aspects of horse breeding.

798.2 AU ISSN 1016-9733
PFERDEREVUE. 1990. m. S.420. Orac Zeitschriftenverlag GmbH, Schoenbrunnerstr. 59-61, A-1050 Vienna, Austria. TEL 01-54621-0. FAX 01-5462178. Ed. Leopold Pingitzer. adv.; B&W page S.31800, color page S.54060; trim 185 x 250. circ. 38,800. (back issues avail.) Document type: consumer publication.

636.1 US ISSN 0031-9937
PINTO HORSE. 1985. q. $20 to non-members; members $15. Pinto Horse Association of America Inc., 1900 Samuels Ave., Fort Worth, TX 76102. TEL 817-336-7842. FAX 817-336-7416. adv.; charts; illus.; stat. circ. 2,500.
  Supersedes: Pinto Horse International.

POLO. see SPORTS AND GAMES — Ball Games

636.1 798.2 UK ISSN 0032-4256
PONY. 1949. m. £23.40. D.J. Murphy (Publishers) Ltd., Haslemere House, Lower St., Haslemere, Surrey GU27 2PE, England. TEL 01428-651551. FAX 01428-653888. Ed. Kate Austin. adv.; bk.rev.; illus. circ. 35,000. Document type: consumer publication.

798.2 US ISSN 0090-8762
PRACTICAL HORSEMAN. 1973. m. $24.95. Cowles Media Company, Box 589, Unionville, PA 19375. TEL 215-380-8977. FAX 215-380-8304. adv.; illus. circ. 67,473. **Indexed:** Sports Per.Ind., Sportsearch (1977-).
  —UnCover.

791.8 798.2 US
PROFESSIONAL RODEO U S A; official media guide. a. $12.95. (Professional Rodeo Cowboys Association) Triumph Books, 644 S. Clark St., Chicago, IL 60605. TEL 312-939-3330. FAX 312-663-3557. Document type: trade publication.
  Description: Covers the personalities and drama of professional rodeo events across the nation.

798 SA ISSN 1021-8157
PROGRESSIVE RACING; promoting the sport of kings. 1993. m. (13/yr.). R.150. Progressive Racing Systems, P.O. Box 184, Pinetown 3600, South Africa. adv.; illus. Document type: consumer publication.

PRORODEO SPORTS NEWS. see SPORTS AND GAMES

798.4 SI ISSN 0129-2552
PUNTERS' WAY - SINGAPORE EDITION. (Malaysia edition avail.) (Text in Chinese, English) 1977. s-w. 42 MacTaggart Road, 06-02 MacTaggart Bldg., Singapore 1336, Singapore. TEL 2866733. FAX 02895413. Ed. T.S. Phan. adv.: B&W page S$500, color page S$1450; trim 215 X 148. circ. 60,000.
  Description: Provides information required by racegoers for reference in punting on horses, including photo-finish and computerised speed rating. Also publishes regular racing news from Australia and New Zealand.

636.1 US ISSN 0164-6656
SF293.Q3
QUARTER HORSE JOURNAL. 1948. m. $21 (foreign $42). American Quarter Horse Association, Box 200, Amarillo, TX 79168. FAX 806-376-8364. (Subscr. to: Box 32470, Amarillo, TX 79120) Ed. Audie Rackley. adv.; bk.rev.; illus. circ. 74,000. (also avail. in microfiche from UMI) **Indexed:** PMR. —Faxon; UnCover.
  Description: Covers horse show results, business opportunities, and all other news of interest related to the association.

636.1 US
QUARTER HORSE NEWS. 1978. s-m. $24. Quarter Horse News Inc., Morris Communications Corp., Box 9707, Ft. Worth, TX 76147. TEL 817-335-5128. FAX 817-335-2062. Ed. Glory Ann Kurtz. adv.: B&W page $495, color page $845; 10 1/4 x 13 1/2; adv. contact: Don Mayer. circ. 12,700. (tabloid format; back issues avail.) Document type: newspaper.
  Description: Covers all facets and interests of the Quarter Horse industry, includes both professional and amateur aspects.

798.2 US
QUARTER HORSE TRACK. 1975. m. Quarter Horse Track Publishing, Inc., Box 9648, Ft. Worth, TX 76107. TEL 817-332-3801. Eds. Jerry McAdams, Ben Hudson. adv.; bk.rev. circ. 8,611.

SPORTS AND GAMES — HORSES AND HORSEMANSHIP

798.4   US   ISSN 0899-3130
THE QUARTER RACING JOURNAL. 1988. m. $19 (foreign $38). American Quarter Horse Association, Box 200, Amarillo, TX 79168. TEL 806-376-4811. FAX 806-376-8364. (Subscr. to: Box 32470, Amarillo, TX 79120) Ed. Jim Jennings. adv.; bk.rev. circ. 10,500. (back issues avail.) **Document type:** trade publication.
—UnCover.
   Description: Records and preserves the pedigree of the American Quarter horse. Covers the American Quarter horse racing industry.

636.1 798.4   US   ISSN 0091-7516
SF357.3
QUARTER RACING RECORD;* the magazine of quarter horse racing. 1961. m. $18. Quarter Racing Publishers, Inc., 2033 Heritage Park Dr., Oklahoma City, OK 73120-7502. Ed. H. David Smith. adv.; bk.rev.; charts; stat. circ. 9,000.

798.4   AT
QUEENSLAND RACING CALENDAR. m. Aus.$60. (Queensland Principal Club) Magazine Publishing Company, 4 Wandoo St., Fortitude Valley, Qld. 4006, Australia. TEL 61-7-252-9677. FAX 61-7-252-4667. Ed. Larelle Stephens. adv.: B&W page Aus.$605, color page Aus.$1045; trim 275 x 210; adv. contact: Trevor Kirk. circ. 2,500. **Document type:** trade publication.
   Description: Covers news and legislation pertaining to the horse racing industry. Includes events, lists trainers, jockeys, etc.

798.4   UK   ISSN 0955-1751
RACEFORM HANDICAP BOOK.* 1944. w. £0.85 per issue. Raceform Ltd., 19 Clarges Rd., London W1Y 7PG, England. Ed. Len Bell. adv.; bk.rev. circ. 43,000. (tabloid format)
   Incorporates: Racehorse (ISSN 0048-6523).

798   UK   ISSN 0081-3761
RACEFORM "HORSES IN TRAINING".* 1891. a. £9. Raceform Ltd., 19 Clarges Rd., London W1Y 7PG, England. Ed. L. Bell. adv. circ. 13,000.
   Formerly: Sporting Chronicle "Horses in Training".

798   UK   ISSN 0079-9408
RACEHORSES. 1948. a. £68. Portway Press Ltd., Timeform House, Northgate, Halifax, Yorkshire HX1 1XE, England. Ed. J.D. Newton. adv. circ. 8,000.
   Description: Essays and notes on the performances of horses in the flat racing category.

798.2   FR   ISSN 0224-7534
RACING. 1946. m. (Racing Club de France) Editions Arcadiennes, 5 rue Eble, 75007 Paris, France. adv.; illus.

798   UK   ISSN 0968-3364
RACING POST. 1986. d. (Mon.-Sat.). £660; newsstand price: £0.75. Racing Post, 120 Coombe Ln., Raynes Park, London SW20 0BA, England. TEL 0181-879-3377. FAX 0181-947-2652. Ed. Alan Byrne. adv. contact: Jim Solks. bk.rev.; circ. 47,000 (paid). pp./issue: 60. (tabloid format; back issues avail.) **Document type:** newspaper.
   Description: Covers horse racing, greyhound racing and general sports betting.

798.4   US   ISSN 0033-7439
RACING STAR WEEKLY. 1932. w. $45. Star Publishing Corporation, 438 W. 37th st., New York, NY 10018. TEL 212-279-4619. Ed. Bob Smith. adv.; bk.rev.; stat. circ. 12,000. (tabloid format)

798.2   US
RACING UPDATE. 1977. s-m. $200. Racing Update, Inc., Box 11052, Lexington, KY 40512. TEL 606-231-7966. Ed. William J. Oppenheim. circ. 1,500. (back issues avail.)

636.1   US   ISSN 0744-6829
THE RACKING REVIEW. 1975. s-m. $20. c/o Ann O. Yeiser, Box 777, Waynesboro, TN 38485. TEL 615-722-3688. FAX 615-722-3689. illus.

798.2   US
RANGERBRED NEWS. 1965. bi-m. free to members. Colorado Ranger Horse Association, Inc., Rd. No. 1, Box 1290, Wampum, PA 16157. TEL 412-535-4841. Ed. Laurel Kosior. adv. circ. 450. **Document type:** newsletter.
   Description: Contains information about CRHA, and happenings elsewhere in the horseworld.

636.1   US   ISSN 8750-5630
RECORD HORSEMAN. 1966. bi-w. $35. R S Livestock Publishers, Box 1209, 4800 Wadsworth, CO 80034-1209. TEL 303-425-5777. FAX 303-431-7545. Ed. Dan Green; Pub. Harry Green Jr. adv. contact: Ann Meyers. circ. 10,000. (tabloid format) **Document type:** newspaper.
   Incorporates: Capital Horseman (ISSN 8750-152X); Straight from the Horse's Mouth.
   Description: General interest, all-breed publication for the Rocky Mountain area horse enthusiast.

636.1   UK   ISSN 0307-0638
REGISTER OF NON-THOROUGHBRED MARES. 1974. a. £15. Weatherbys, Sanders Rd., Wellingborough, Northants. NN8 4BX, England. TEL 01933-440077. FAX 01933-440807. TELEX 311582-ODECS. **Document type:** directory.

791.8 658   US
REGISTRY NEWS. 1968. q. membership only. Arabian Horse Registry of America, Inc., 12000 Zuni St., Westminster, CO 80234. TEL 303-450-4748. tr.lit. circ. 25,000.
   Description: Updates the members of rules and policy changes related to registration and transfer records of purebred Arabian horses as well as activities of the registry.

798.4   GW   ISSN 0944-5854
REITEN UND FAHREN ST. GEORG; Magazin fuer Pferdesport und Pferdezucht. 1899. m. DM.112.20. Jahr-Verlag GmbH & Co., Jessenstr. 1, 22767 Hamburg, Germany. TEL 040-38906-0. FAX 040-38906302. TELEX 2163485. Ed. Hermann Kothe. adv. contact: Heike Tiedemann. circ. 45,950. (back issues avail.) **Document type:** consumer publication.
   Formerly: Reiten - St. Georg (ISSN 0720-1524)

798   GW   ISSN 0034-3692
REITER REVUE INTERNATIONAL. 1958. m. DM.108. Zeitschriftenverlag R B D V Rheinisch-Bergische Druckerei- und Verlagsgesellschaft mbH, Postfach 1135, 40196 Duesseldorf, Germany. TEL 0211-5052620. FAX 0211-5052662. Ed. Irina Ludewig. adv. contact: Herbert Kroeppel. bk.rev.; tr.lit.; index. circ. 41,000. **Document type:** consumer publication.
—CCC.

636.1   GW   ISSN 0343-6861
REITER UND PFERDE IN WESTFALEN. 1976. m. DM.63 (foreign DM.84.60). Landwirtschaftsverlag GmbH, Huelsebrockstr. 2, 48165 Muenster, Germany. TEL 02051-80-10. FAX 02501-801-204. TELEX 8-92665-LANDV-D. (Subscr. to: Postfach 480249, 48079 Muenster, Germany) adv. circ. 26,200. **Document type:** bulletin.
   Description: Horse breeding and riding information.

798.2   GW   ISSN 0173-2404
REITERJOURNAL; Fachmagazin fuer Pferdzucht und Reitsport in Baden-Wuerttemberg. 1980. m. DM.101.40. Matthaes Verlag GmbH, Olgastr. 87, 70180 Stuttgart, Germany. TEL 0711-2133-0. Ed. Hugo Matthaes. index. circ. 25,000. (back issues avail.) **Document type:** newspaper.

798.2   GW   ISSN 0344-4295
REITSPORT IN WESER - EMS. 1975. m. DM.6. Landwirtschaftsverlag Weser - Ems GmbH, Postfach 3440, 26024 Oldenburg, Germany. TEL 0441-75055. FAX 0441-7780653. Ed. Bernd Keine. circ. 7,000. **Document type:** consumer publication.

798.2   GW   ISSN 0940-8282
REITSPORT MAGAZIN. m. DM.75. (Reiterverbandes Hannover - Bremen) Paragon Verlagsgesellschaft mbH, Misburgerstr. 119, 30625 Hannover, Germany. TEL 0511-561003. FAX 0511-571214. Ed. Frauke Heidtmann. adv. contact: Wilfried Lehwald. **Document type:** consumer publication.

798.2   CN   ISSN 0820-571X
THE RIDER. 1970. m. (10/yr.). Can.$25 (foreign Can.$30) (effective 1995). Golden Arc Publishing and Typesetting Ltd., 491 Book Rd. W., Ancaster, ON L9G 3L1, Canada. TEL 905-648-2035. FAX 905-648-6977. Ed. Aidan W. Finn; Pub. Aidan W. Finn. adv. contact: Barry Finn. bk.rev. circ. 10,000. (tabloid format) **Indexed:** Sportsearch. **Document type:** newspaper.
   Formed by the Sep. 1994 merger of: English Rider (ISSN 1182-9958) & Western Rider (ISSN 0702-9071); Which was formerly: Canadian Rider; Incorporates: Canadian Quarter Horse Journal (ISSN 0319-6348)
   Description: Covers all aspects of horsemanship, primarily in Ontario and the U.S. Midwest, but also elsewhere.

798   UK   ISSN 0963-7028
RIDERS JOURNAL. 1989. m. £20. Leisure and Equestrian Publications, Hopes House, Longyester, Gifford EH41 4PL, Scotland. TEL 01620-810596. FAX 01620-810788. (Dist. by: S & M Distribution, 6 Leigham Court Rd., London SW16 2PG, England. TEL 0181-677-8111) Ed. Alison Rae. adv. contact: Alison Rae. bk.rev. circ. 7,000. (back issues avail.) **Document type:** consumer publication.
   Description: Information aimed at horse owners, equestrian center proprietors, and stud owners.

798.2   UK   ISSN 0035-516X
RIDING. 1936. m. Scott Publications Ltd., Corner House, Foston, Grantham, Lincs NG32 2JU, England. TEL 0400-82032. FAX 0400-82275. Ed. Peter Churchill. adv.: B&W page £648. bk.rev.; illus. circ. 36,918. **Indexed:** Sportsearch.
—CCC.

798   US
RIDING INSTRUCTOR. 1985. q. $35. American Riding Instructors Association, Box 282, Alton Bay, NH 03810-0282. TEL 603-875-4000. FAX 603-875-7771. adv.: B&W page $265; trim 7 x 9 3/4.

798.2   SW   ISSN 0345-973X
RIDSPORT. 1973. bi-m. SEK 595 (includes Ridsport Special). Tidnings AB Ridsport, P.O. Box 14, S-619 00 Trosa, Sweden. TEL 46-156-132-40. FAX 46-156-120-29. **Document type:** newsletter.

798.2   SW   ISSN 1100-9721
RIDSPORT SPECIAL. 1989. s-a. SEK 595 (includes Ridsport). Tidnings AB Ridsport, P.O. Box 14, S-619 00 Trosa, Sweden. TEL 46-156-132-40. FAX 46-156-120-29.

798.2   US   ISSN 0738-8381
ROCKY MOUNTAIN QUARTER HORSE MAGAZINE. 1963. m. $20 (effective 1995-1996). Rocky Mountain Quarter Horse Association, 318 Livestock Exchange Bldg., Denver, CO 80216. TEL 303-296-1143. FAX 303-297-8576. Eds. Darlene Goodwin, Ann McLarty. adv. contact: Darlene Goodwin. circ. 1,500. (back issues avail.) **Document type:** trade publication.

796   US   ISSN 0149-6425
RODEO NEWS; focussing on an American tradition. 1961. m. $24. Rodeo News, Inc., 721 N. Cedar, Box 598, Pauls Valley, OK 73075. TEL 405-238-3310. FAX 405-238-3725. Ed. Misti Ashford; Pub. Janet Smith. adv. contact: Paul Beck. bk.rev.; illus.; stat. circ. 14,000. **Document type:** consumer publication.
   Description: Covers the sport of rodeo in all areas and at all levels.

798.4   UK
RUFF'S GUIDE TO THE TURF AND THE SPORTING LIFE WHO'S WHO IN RACING. 1842. a. £40. The Sporting Life, One Canada Sq., Canary Wharf, London E14 5AP, England. TEL 0171-510-3000. FAX 0171-293-3758. Ed. Martin Pickering. adv. **Document type:** directory.
   Formerly: Ruff's Guide to the Turf and the Sporting Life Annual (ISSN 0080-4819)

798.2   SW   ISSN 0284-690X
RYTTAR-MAGASINET. 1987. q. SEK 160 (effective 1991). Ryttar-magasinet, P.O. Box 220, S-182 52 Djursholm, Sweden.

SPORTS AND GAMES — HORSES AND HORSEMANSHIP

636.1 US ISSN 0036-2271
SF277
SADDLE AND BRIDLE. 1927. m. $40. Saddle and Bridle, Inc., 375 N. Jackson Ave., St. Louis, MO 63130. TEL 314-725-9115. FAX 314-725-6440. Pub. Jeffrey Thomson. adv. contact: Christopher Thompson. bk.rev.; illus.; circ. 5,500 (paid). **Document type:** trade publication.
Description: Directed to owners and trainers of various breeds of English show horses. Provides information on training, management, veterinary care and horse show history.

798 US
SADDLE HORSE REPORT. 1976. w. $50. Dabora, Inc., Box 1007, Shelbyville, TN 37160. TEL 615-684-8123. Ed. David Howard. circ. 4,000.

636.1 SZ
SCHWEIZER PFERDE. (Text in German) bi-m. 5.50 Fr. per no. Roro-Press Verlag, Schwamendingenstr. 80, CH-8050 Zurich, Switzerland. Ed.Bd. illus.

636.1 UK
SHETLAND PONY STUD-BOOK SOCIETY MAGAZINE. 1968. a. £20. 6 King's Pl., Perth PH2 8AD, Scotland. TEL 01738-23471. FAX 01738-36436. Ed. D.W.H. Dick. adv. contact: D.W.H. Dick. circ. 1,500. **Document type:** directory.

798 UK
SHIRE HORSE SHOW CATALOGUE. 1897. a. £2.50. Shire Horse Society, East of England Showground, Peterborough PE2 6XE, England. TEL 0733-390696. FAX 0733-390720. Ed. Stephen Stagg. adv. circ. 3,000. **Document type:** catalog.

636.1 UK
SHIRE HORSE STUD BOOK. a. £15. Shire Horse Society, East of England Showground, Peterborough PE2 6XE, England. TEL 0733-390696. FAX 0733-390720. circ. 3,000. **Document type:** directory.

798.2 US ISSN 0744-3056
SIDE-SADDLE NEWS. 1974. 6/yr. $35. International Side-Saddle Organization, Box 282, Alton Bay, NH 03810-0282. TEL 603-875-4000. FAX 603-875-7771. Ed. Charlotte B. Kneeland. adv.; bk.rev.; index. circ. 450. **Indexed:** Sportsearch. **Document type:** newsletter.

636.1 798.4 SA
THE SOUTH AFRICAN RACEHORSE. 1953. bi-m. R.35. Horseman Publications (Pty) Ltd., P.O. Box 78220, Sandton, 2146 Transvaal, South Africa. TEL 27-11-444-4566. FAX 27-11-444-7888. Ed. Alison MacKenzie. adv.; bk.rev.; stat. circ. 7,000.
Former titles: South African Racehorse and Horseman; Which was formed by the 1981 merger of: South African Racehorse (ISSN 0038-2590); South African Horseman.
Description: Offers authoritative and balanced coverage of racing and breeding.

798 US ISSN 0093-3929
SOUTHERN HORSEMAN. 1962. m. $15. Southern Publishing, 3839 Business Hwy., 45 N., Box 71, Meridian, MS 39302-0071. TEL 601-693-6607. Ed. Tracy Thompson; Pub. Thelma Thompson. adv.: B&W page $528, color page $935; adv. contact: Jeanette Pinkham. circ. 26,000. **Document type:** consumer publication.

798.4 US
SF321
SPEEDHORSE - RACING REPORT. 1969. w. $39. Speedhorse, Inc., Box 1000, Norman, OK 73070-1000. TEL 405-573-1050. FAX 405-573-1059. Ed. Diane Garloni; Pub. Constance Golden. adv. contact: Andrew Golden. bk.rev. circ. 9,100. **Document type:** trade publication. **Incorporates** (in 1990): Racing Report; Which was formerly: Speedhorse Tabloid; **Incorporates** (in 1990): Speedhorse (ISSN 0364-9237); Which was formerly: Quarter Racing World (ISSN 0048-6124)

798.2 IT
SPORT EQUESTRI (ROME). 1960. bi-m. L.6000($10) Atena S.p.A., Via di Val Tellina 47, 00151 Rome, Italy. Ed. Romelo Renolini. adv.; illus.; index. circ. 5,000.

798 AT ISSN 1038-9601
SPORTSMAN. 1900. s-w. Aus.$150. News Ltd., 2 Holt St., Surry Hills, N.S.W. 2010, Australia. TEL 02-288-2528. FAX 02-288-3453. Ed. Wayne Hickson. adv.; bk.rev. circ. 25,000.

798.4 US ISSN 0098-5422
SF277
SPUR; the magazine of thoroughbred and country life. 1965. bi-m. $24. Spur Publications, Inc., 725 Broad St., Augusta, GA 30901. TEL 706-722-6060. FAX 706-724-3873. Ed. Cathy Laws. adv.; bk.rev.; charts; illus. circ. 15,000. **Indexed:** Sportsearch. **Document type:** consumer publication.
Formerly (until 1974): Spur of Virginia (ISSN 0038-8688)
Description: Contains articles of interest to owners, breeders, riders, trainers and enthusiasts of racing, steeplechasing, polo, fox hunting and jumping and the country life-style that surrounds these spots.

636.1 US ISSN 1055-2979
SF293.T5
STALLION DIRECTORY. a. Thoroughbred Times Company Inc., 496 Southland Dr., Box 8237, Lexington, KY 40503. TEL 606-260-9800. FAX 606-260-9812. **Document type:** directory.
Incorporates: Sire Book (ISSN 0272-3786)

636.1 DK ISSN 0107-3818
STAMBOG. a. DKK 73.20. (Dansk Varmblod, Dansk Rideheste Avlsforbund) Landsudvalget for Hesteavl, Vesterbrogade 6D, 1620 Copenhagen V, Denmark. illus. **Document type:** trade publication.
Formerly: Dansk Sportsheste Avlsforbunds Stambog.
Description: Studbook for stallions and mares.

636.160948 DK ISSN 0900-5846
STAMBOG OVER SHETLAND PONYER. a. DKK 150. Avlsforeningen for Shetlandsponyer, c/o Else Enemark, Riisvej 24, DK-4540 Faareveje, Denmark. **Document type:** trade publication.

798 CN ISSN 0834-0110
STANDARDBRED NEWS. 1971. fortn. Can.$35($50) Wicklow Hills Publishing Co. Inc., Box 150, Acton, ON L7J 2M3, Canada. TEL 519-853-5100. FAX 519-853-5040. Ed. Paul Nolan. adv. contact: Paul Nolan. bk.rev.; illus. circ. 5,000. **Indexed:** Sportsearch. **Document type:** trade publication.
Former titles: Standardbred (ISSN 0705-2553); Standardbred Magazine.
Description: For serious standardbred horse owners and breeders: features Canadian race results and industry news and comment.

798 AT ISSN 0311-8215
STUD AND STABLE. 1971. irreg. Aus.$0.10. Percival Publishing Co. Pty. Ltd., 862 Elizabeth St., Waterloo, NSW 2017, Australia.
Formerly: Australasian Stud and Stable (ISSN 0310-6403)

636.1 UK
SUFFOLK STUD BOOK. 1880. a. £10. Suffolk Horse Society, Market Hill, Woodbridge, Suffolk IP12 4LU, England. TEL 01394-380643. Ed. Philip Ryder-Davies. adv. circ. 500. **Document type:** directory.

798 UK ISSN 0955-0488
SUN GUIDE TO THE FLAT. a. £3.99. Invincible Press, 78-85 Fulham Palace Rd., London W6 8JB, England. TEL 081-741-7070. Ed. Ben Newton. circ. 40,000.
Description: Contains news on jockeys, tracks, races and horses for thoroughbred racing in the UK.

798 US
T E A M CLUB NEWSLETTER. (Tellington-Jones Equine Awareness Method) 1981. q. $25 membership. T.E.A.M News International, Box 3793, Santa Fe, NM 87501-0793. TEL 505-455-2945. Ed. Robyn Hood. circ. 4,000. **Document type:** newsletter.

798 IT ISSN 1121-4139
T E AMICO CAVALLO. (Tutto Equitazione) 1991. m. L.40000. Ediset s.r.l., Via Zandonai 61, 00194 Rome, Italy. TEL 39-6-4441179. FAX 39-6-4441604. Ed. Massimo De Biase. adv.: B&W page L.2200000, color page L.3980000. circ. 20,000. **Document type:** consumer publication.

798.2 US
TACK 'N TOGS BOOK; directory for retailers of apparel, equipment and supplies for horse and rider. 1971. a. $15. Miller Publishing Co., 12400 Whitewater Dr., Ste. 160, Box 2400, Minnetonka, MN 55343-2524. TEL 612-931-0211. FAX 612-931-0910. Ed. Dan DeWeese. adv.; charts; stat.; tr.lit. circ. 22,023 (controlled). (reprint service avail. from UMI) **Document type:** consumer publication.

688.76 US ISSN 0149-3442
TACK 'N TOGS MERCHANDISING; for retailers of apparel, equipment and supplies for horse and rider. 1970. m. $25 (free to qualified personnel). Miller Publishing Co., 12400 Whitewater Dr., Ste. 160, Box 2400, Minnetonka, MN 55343-2524. TEL 612-931-0211. FAX 612-931-0910. Ed. Dan DeWeese. adv.; charts; illus.; stat.; tr.lit. circ. 22,023 (controlled). (also avail. in microform from UMI; reprint service avail. from UMI)
—UMI. CCC.

798.4 US ISSN 0164-6168
THE TEXAS THOROUGHBRED. (Former name of issuing body: Texas Thoroughbred Breeders Association) vol.4, 1979. q. $30. Texas Thoroughbred Association, Box 14967, Austin, TX 78761. TEL 512-458-6133. FAX 512-453-5919. E-mail: 76737,2731@compuserve.com; Brooksie66@aol.com; YUJN29A@prodigy.com. Ed. Brock Sheridan. adv.; illus. circ. 2,800. **Document type:** trade publication.

798.2 615.8 GW ISSN 0942-7546
THERAPEUTISCHES REITEN. 1982. q. Deutsches Kuratorium fuer Therapeutisches Reiten, c/o F. Delius, Ed., Wasserfuhr 47D, 66319 Bielefeld, Germany. TEL 0521-160380. FAX 0521-101487. **Indexed:** InterActions Bibl. (1994-).
Formerly (until 1992): Therapeutisches Reiten in Medizin, Paedagogik, Sport (ISSN 0935-5804)

636.1 AT ISSN 0311-8347
THOROUGHBRED BREEDERS' HANDBOOK; stallion pedigrees for Australia and New Zealand. 1975. irreg. (3-4/yr.), 4th ed., 1988. Aus.$19.95. Libra Books Pty. Ltd., G.P.O. Box 10, Hobart, Tas. 7001, Australia. TEL 61-02-311754. FAX 61-02-341426. Ed. B.M. Wicks. circ. 2,000. (back issues avail.)
—CCC.

636.1 798 US ISSN 0049-3821
SF293.T5
THOROUGHBRED OF CALIFORNIA. 1941. m. $42. California Thoroughbred Breeders Association, 201 Colorado Place, Arcadia, CA 91007. TEL 818-445-7800. FAX 818-574-0852. Ed. Nat Wess. adv.; bk.rev.; charts; illus.; index. circ. 7,000. (also avail. in microform from UMI; reprint service avail. from UMI)
—UMI; UnCover.

798 US ISSN 0082-4240
THOROUGHBRED RACING ASSOCIATIONS. DIRECTORY AND RECORD BOOK. 1955. a. $15 to non-members. Thoroughbred Racing Associations, 420 Fair Hill Dr., No.1, Elkton, MD 21921-2573. FAX 410-398-1366. Ed. Conrad Sobkowiak. circ. 3,000 (controlled). **Document type:** directory.

798.4 US ISSN 0887-2244
SF293.T5
THOROUGHBRED TIMES. 1985. w. $75. Thoroughbred Times Company Inc., 496 Southland Dr., Box 8237, Lexington, KY 40503. TEL 606-260-9800. FAX 606-260-9812. Ed. Mark Simon. adv.; bk.rev. circ. 20,000. (tabloid format; also avail. in microform; back issues avail.)
Description: Covers breeding, racing and public auction news of the thoroughbred industry.

798 UK
TIMEFORM BLACK BOOK. 1940. w. price varies. Portway Press Ltd., Timeform House, Halifax HX1 1XE, England. Ed. J.D. Newton.
Formerly: Timeform.
Description: Contains individual dossiers of facts and opinions for every racehorse in Britain.

SPORTS AND GAMES — HORSES AND HORSEMANSHIP

798.46 US
TIMES: ALMANAC. a. included with Times: in harness. Times: standard inc., 8125 Jonestown Rd., Harrisburg, PA 17112. TEL 717-469-2000. FAX 717-469-2005.
Description: Reviews public auctions, major races, statistics for breeders, owners and horsemen, pedigree pages for the upcoming breeding season and a directory of industry-related services and products.

798.46 US ISSN 1046-9974
TIMES: IN HARNESS. 1989. w. $68. Times: standard inc., 8125 Jonestown Rd., Harrisburg, PA 17112. TEL 717-469-2000. FAX 717-469-2005. Ed. Frank Cotolo. adv. circ. 7,000. (tabloid format) **Document type:** newspaper, trade publication.
Description: Covers national and international harness racing. Includes major harness racing events, race previews, and controversial topics.

798 UK
TODAY'S HORSE. m. £15.60 (foreign £34). Aceville Publications Ltd., 89 East Hill, Colchester, Essex CO1 2QN, England. TEL 0206-871450. FAX 0206-871537. Ed. Kate Finlayson. adv.

798.2 CN
TRAIL RIDERS OF THE CANADIAN ROCKIES NEWSLETTER. 1962. 3/yr. membership. Trail Riders of the Canadian Rockies, P.O. Box 6742, Sta. "D", Calgary, Alta. T2P 2E6, Canada. TEL 403-264-8656. FAX 403-264-8657. Ed. Nancy Maguire. adv. circ. 230. (looseleaf format) **Document type:** newsletter.

798.2 GW ISSN 0720-9150
TRAKEHNER HEFTE. 1982. 6/yr. DM.53 (foreign DM.68). Symposion Verlag, Wagnerstr. 12, 73728 Esslingen, Germany. TEL 0711-350001. FAX 0711-3508766. Eds. Betty Finke, Lars Gehrmann. adv. contact: Hans Juergen Maier. circ. 8,900. **Document type:** consumer publication.
—CCC.

798.2 GW ISSN 0935-7483
TRAUMPFERDE. 1978. m. DM.70 (foreign DM.106). Symposion Verlag, Wagnerstr. 12, 73728 Esslingen, Germany. TEL 0711-350001. FAX 0711-3508766. Ed. Gudrun Waiditschka. adv. contact: Hans Juergen Maier. bk.rev. circ. 60,000. (back issues avail.) **Document type:** consumer publication.
Formerly (until 1993): Pferde Heute (ISSN 0176-490X)

798.4 DK ISSN 0109-2308
TRAVSPORT FOR FAGFOLK. 1983. q. DKK 78.40. Bent Kim Jepsen, Ed. & Pub., Faarupvej 102, 8381 Mundelstrup, Denmark. adv.; illus.

798.4 CN ISSN 0704-0733
TROT. (Text in English and French) 1975. m. Can.$22 to non-members. Canadian Trotting Association, 2150 Meadowvale Blvd., Mississauga, Ont. L5N 6R6, Canada. TEL 416-858-3060. FAX 416-858-3111. Ed. Harold Howe. adv.; B&W & color, B&W page Can.$600; trim 8 1/8 x 10 7/8. bk.rev. circ. 25,000. **Indexed:** Sportsearch.
Former titles: Maple Leaf Trot; Canadian Trot Canadien (ISSN 0045-5504)

798 IT
TROTTATORE. 1953. bi-m. L.50000. Associazione Nazionale Allevatori del Cavallo Trottatore (ANACT), Viale del Policlinico 131, I-00161 Rome, Italy. TEL 06 844-24-21. charts; illus.; stat. circ. 2,300. (back issues avail.)

798 US ISSN 0083-3509
TROTTING AND PACING GUIDE; official handbook of harness racing. 1947. a. $10. United States Trotting Association, 750 Michigan Ave, Columbus, OH 43215. TEL 614-224-2291. Ed. John Pawlak. index. circ. 5,500.

798 IT
TROTTO SPORTSMAN. 1946. 3/wk. L.250000. Editrice Trotto Italiano s.r.l., Piazza Cavour 2, 20121 Milan, Italy. TEL 39-2-796794. FAX 39-2-76002795. TELEX 323511. Ed. Gaetano Manti. adv.; B&W page L.4800000. bk.rev. circ. 65,000.
Description: Offers starting lists and results of all official horse races in Italy. Includes the concerns of the horse racing world.

798.4 AT ISSN 0726-8254
TURF MONTHLY. 1952. m. Aus.$100. Turf Monthly Pty. Ltd., P.O. Box 426, Round Corner, N.S.W. 2158, Australia. TEL 61-2-651-4700. FAX 61-2-651-4988. Ed. Warwick Hobson. adv. contact: Mark Brassel. bk.rev. circ. 25,000. (back issues avail.)
Description: Covers all aspects of horse racing: breeding, punting, personalities and topicalities.

798.2 AU
TURF SPORT;* die Wochenzeitung fuer den Pferderennsport. 1979. s-w. S.1380. Walter Zwierschuelz, Ed. & Pub., Stroheckgane 1, A-1090 Vienna, Austria. circ. 2,500. (back issues avail.)
Formerly: Turf Aktuell.

798 US ISSN 0744-0103
U S C T A NEWS. 1973. bi-m. $15. United States Combined Training Association, Box 2247, Leesburg, VA 22075-7596. TEL 508-887-9090. FAX 508-887-9001. adv.; bk.rev. circ. 10,000. (back issues avail.) **Document type:** trade publication.
Description: Informs members of proper treatment and training of horses, features rider and horse profiles, and provides updates of national and international rules.

798 US
U S E T NEWS.* 1956. irreg. (5-6/yr.). membership. United States Equestrian Team, c/o Bill Landsman Associates, 77 7th Ave. 10 Fl., New York, NY 10011-6626. TEL 212-370-4160. Ed. Bill Landsman. circ. 15,000.

798 US
U S T A SIRES AND DAMS; the register. 1948. a. $60. United States Trotting Association, 750 Michigan Ave, Columbus, OH 43215. TEL 614-224-2291. Ed. David Carr. index. circ. 9,000. **Document type:** directory.
Formerly: Sires and Dams (ISSN 0083-3495)

798 US ISSN 0083-3517
SF325
U S T A YEAR BOOK. 1939. a. $15. United States Trotting Association, 750 Michigan Ave., Columbus, OH 43215. TEL 614-224-2291. Ed. David Carr. index. circ. 8,000.

798.2 636.1 GW ISSN 0342-7331
UNSER PFERD; Fachzeitschrift fuer Pferdesport und Pferdezucht in Hessen. m. DM.28. Verlag G. Grandpierre, Obergasse 16, 65510 Idstein, Germany. Ed. W. Blum. circ. 4,500.

636.1 SW ISSN 0346-4687
VAAR PONNY. 1959. q. SEK 65. Svenska Ponnyavelsforbundet - Swedish Pony Breeding Society, Tjaerbyhus, S-312 00 Laholm, Sweden. TEL 430-10633. Ed. Birgitta Dyrsch. adv.; bk.rev.; illus. circ. 4,100. **Document type:** trade publication.
Formerly: Ponny (ISSN 0032-4213)
Description: Stud books for all pony breeds in Sweden, articles about pony breeding and shows.

792.4 DK ISSN 0042-2118
VAEDDELOEBSBLADET. Variant title: V6 Magasinet. 1913. w. DKK 185. Vaeddeloebsbladet, Charlottenlund, Copenhagen V, Denmark. Eds. J. Hecht-Neilsen, Lavs Donatzky. adv.; illus. circ. 6,000.

636.1 FI ISSN 0781-5638
VILLIVARSA. 1984. m. FIM 138. Yhtyneet Kuvalehdet Oy - United Magazines Ltd., Maistraatinportti 1, SF-00240 Helsinki, Finland. TEL 358-0-156-6524. FAX 358-0-156-6505. Ed. Hannelise Willberg. adv.; B&W page FIM 1950, color page FIM 4800; trim 190 x 265; adv. contact: Kauko Kanerva. circ. 24,393. **Document type:** consumer publication.

630 798.2 US
VIRGINIA HORSE COUNCIL NEWS. 1973. m. (11/yr.). $10 membership. Virginia Horse Council, Box 72, Riner, VA 24149. TEL 703-382-3071. E-mail: aalley@bev.net. Ed. Alice Alley. adv. contact: Alice Alley. circ. 550. **Document type:** newsletter.
Formerly: Virginia Horse.
Description: Features articles on horse health; includes updates, 4-H recognitions, legislative issues, and industry events in Virginia.

798.4 US ISSN 0505-8813
VOICE OF THE TENNESSEE WALKING HORSE; a national publication devoted exclusively to the breed. 1962. m. (except Sep.). $18. Tennessee Walking Horse Breeders' & Exhibitors' Association, Box 286, Lewisburg, TN 37091. TEL 615-359-1567. FAX 615-359-2539. Ed. P.J. Wamble. adv. contact: David Kranich. circ. 16,000.
—UnCover.
Description: Provides information for those who own, breed, train, or ride Tennessee Walking Horses, whether for show or pleasure. Covers industry events, personality profiles, health care, and farm management and includes training-related articles.

798 US ISSN 0093-6928
SF293.T4
WALKING HORSE REPORT. 1971. w. $50. Dabora, Inc., Box 1007, Shelbyville, TN 37160. TEL 615-684-8123. Ed. David Howard. circ. 5,500.

798 US ISSN 1079-4433
WARMBLOOD NEWS. 1989. bi-m. $24 (foreign $37). American Warmblood Registry, Inc., Box 15167, Tallahassee, FL 32317-5167. TEL 904-893-4089. FAX 904-893-8255. Ed. C.M. Frank; Pub. Sonsa K. Lowenfish. adv.; bk.rev.; video rev.; charts; illus.; stat. circ. 3,000. (back issues avail.)
Description: Presents auction results, sales statistics, performance results, breed and registry news, breed profiles, pedigree analysis, government regulations.

798 US
WEEKLY TRACK TOPICS. 1963. fortn. Harness Tracks of America, Inc., 4640 E Sunrise Dr., Ste. 200, Tucson, AZ 85718-4576. Ed. Stanley F. Bergstein. adv. contact: Tammy Gantt. circ. 2,000. (back issues avail.) **Document type:** newsletter.
Description: Covers topics of interest to management of race tracks and racing associations.

636.1 US
WELARA JOURNAL. 1982. s-a. $4 (foreign $5); free with membership. Welara Pony Society, Box 401, Yucca Valley, CA 92286. TEL 619-364-2048. FAX 619-364-2048. Ed. John H. Collins. adv.; B&W page $30 (members $25), color page $50 (members $45). bk.rev. circ. 1,400.
●Also available online.

798 UK
WELSH PONY AND COB SOCIETY JOURNAL. 1962. a. £20.43. (Welsh Pony and Cob Society - Cymdeithas y Merlod a'r Cobiau Cymreig) Cambrian Printers Ltd., Llanbadarnfawr, Aberystwyth, Dyfed SY23 1HS, Wales. TEL 01970-617501. FAX 01970-625401. Ed. E. Wynne Davies. adv. contact: E. Wynne Davies. circ. 7,000. (back issues avail.) **Document type:** directory.

798 US ISSN 1062-3914
WESTERN HORSE.* 1980. m. $15.97. Frontier Publishing Co., 1150 Trails End, Prescott Valley, AZ 86303. Ed. Richard Gibson. adv. circ. 70,000.

798.2 GW ISSN 0933-9345
WESTERN HORSE; Zucht - Haltung - Western Reiten. 1988. m. DM.78 (foreign DM.89). Verlag Ute Kierdorf, Gut Dohrgaul, 51688 Wipperfuerth, Germany. TEL 02267-4495. FAX 02267-4458. Ed. Hardy Oelke. adv.; bk.rev. circ. 24,000. (back issues avail.) **Document type:** consumer publication.

636.1 US ISSN 0043-3837
SF277
WESTERN HORSEMAN; devoted mainly to Western horses. 1936. m. $18 (foreign $25). Western Horseman, Inc., Box 7980, Colorado Springs, CO 80933-7980. TEL 719-633-5524. FAX 719-633-1392. (Subscr. to: Box 542, Mt. Morris, IL 61054-0542. TEL 800-877-5278) Ed. Pat Close; Andy Witte. adv. contact: Corliss Palmer. index. circ. 230,322. (also avail. in microform from UMI; reprint service avail. from UMI) **Indexed:** Access, Biol.& Agr.Ind., PMR, Sports Per.Ind., Sportsearch. **Document type:** consumer publication.
—Faxon; UMI; UnCover.
Description: Covers Western riding, training, veterinary care, saddles and equipment, endurance riding, reining, rodeo, cowboy history and poetry, working ranches, Western art, packing and outfitting.

SPORTS AND GAMES — OUTDOOR LIFE

798.2   US
WHIP. 1974. q. $45. American Driving Society, Box 160, Metamora, MI 48455. TEL 810-664-8666. Ed. Ann L. Pringle. adv. circ. 2,500. (back issues avail.) **Document type:** newsletter.

798   ISSN 0192-5210
YANKEE HORSETRADER; voice of the eastern horseman. 1978. m. $10. Yankee Horsetrader Inc., 54 Birch Grove Rd., R.R. 3, Pittsfield, MA 01201. Ed. David E. Scribner. adv.; bk.rev.; illus. circ. 8,500.

051   US   ISSN 1069-6105
YIPPY YI YEA MAGAZINE; western style, coast to coast. 1992. q. $3.95 per no. Long Publications, Inc., 8393 E. Holly Rd., Holly, MI 48442. TEL 810-634-9675. FAX 810-634-0301. Ed. Cheryl Anderson. adv.: B&W page $795; color page $795; trim 8 1/8 x 10 1/2; adv. contact: Karen Brace. circ. 300,000. **Document type:** consumer publication.

636.1   UK   ISSN 0266-4119
YOUR HORSE. 1983. m. £24 (foreign £32) (effectie 1995-1996). E M A P Pursuit Publishing Ltd., Bretton Ct., Bretton, Peterborough, Cambs. PE3 8DZ, England. TEL 01733-264666. FAX 01733-261984. TELEX 32157. (Subscr. to: Tower Publishing Services Ltd., Tower House, Sovereign Park, Lathkill St., Market Harborough, Leics. LE16 9EF, England. TEL 01858-468811. FAX 01858-432164) Ed. Lesley Eccles; Pub. Melvyn Bagnell. adv. contact: Karen Barsberry-Woods. circ. 56,119 (paid). **Document type:** consumer publication.

SPORTS AND GAMES — Outdoor Life

796.42   US   ISSN 0361-347X
GV1060.67
A A U OFFICIAL TRACK AND FIELD HANDBOOK, RULES AND RECORDS. a. $5. Amateur Athletic Union of the United States, 3400 W. 86th St., Box 68207, Indianapolis, IN 46268. TEL 317-872-2900. FAX 317-875-0548. **Document type:** bulletin.

796.5 910   GW   ISSN 0179-6089
A D A C CAMPINGFUEHRER. BAND 1: SUEDEUROPA. 1951. a. DM.28. (Allgemeiner Deutscher Automobil-Club e.V.) A D A C Verlag GmbH, Am Westpark 8, 81373 Munich, Germany. TEL 089-7676-0. Ed. H. Nitschke. adv. circ. 185,000. **Document type:** bulletin.
   Supersedes in part: Internationaler Campingfuehrer (ISSN 0074-9753)

796.5 910   GW   ISSN 0179-6046
A D A C CAMPINGFUEHRER. BAND 2: DEUTSCHLAND, MITTEL- UND NORDEUROPA. 1952. a. DM.28. (Allgemeiner Deutscher Automobil-Club e.V.) A D A C Verlag GmbH, Am Westpark 8, 81373 Munich, Germany. TEL 089-7676-0. adv. circ. 150,000. **Document type:** bulletin.

796.93   GW   ISSN 0936-5192
A D A C SKI-ATLAS ALPEN. 1984. a. DM.52. (Allgemeiner Deutscher Automobil-Club e.V.) A D A C Verlag GmbH, Am Westpark 8, 81373 Munich, Germany. TEL 089-7676-0. **Document type:** bulletin.
   Formerly (until 1988): Grosse A D A C Ski Atlas (ISSN 0179-5538)

796.552   US   ISSN 1067-5604
G505
A M C OUTDOORS. 1907. 10/yr. membership only. Appalachian Mountain Club, 5 Joy St., Boston, MA 02108. TEL 617-523-0636. FAX 617-523-0722. Ed. Catherine Buni. adv. contact: Perry Allison. bk.rev.; circ. 63,000 (paid). (back issues avail.) **Document type:** consumer publication.
   —Faxon; UnCover.
   Formerly: Appalachia Bulletin (ISSN 1052-5319); Which superseded: A M C Times.
   Description: Provides club members and the public with coverage of how to protect and enjoy the Northeast outdoors.

796.93   US
A S F WASHINGTON LETTER. 1982. m. $200. American Ski Federation, 207 Constitution Ave., N.E., Washington, DC 20002. TEL 202-543-1595.

A Z U R CAMPING MAGAZIN. see TRAVEL AND TOURISM

796   SW   ISSN 0348-1379
AAKA SKIDOR; ski & adventure magazine. Variant title: Aaka Skidor - Skid och Fjaellmagazinet. Variant title: Nya Aaka Skidor. 1974. 5/yr. SEK 159 in Sweden; rest of Europe SEK 192; elsewhere SEK223. Hummelgren & Almebaeck Foerlag AB, P.O. Box 8014, S-104 20 Stockholm, Sweden. TEL 46-8-650-05-25. FAX 46-8-650-04-07. (Subscr. to: Titeldata AB, S-112 86 Stockholm, Sweden. TEL 46-8-652-43-00) Ed. Anders Tapper. adv. contact: Magnus Oehman. bk.rev.; circ. 56,000. **Document type:** consumer publication.
   Incorporates (in1990): Skid och Flaellmagazinet; (in 1988): Ski Alp.
   Description: Devoted to Alpine skiing, mountain biking, mountain climbing, and adventure sports.

796.52   US   ISSN 0065-082X
GV199.8
ACCIDENTS IN NORTH AMERICAN MOUNTAINEERING. 1948. a. $7. American Alpine Club, 710 10th St., Golden, CO 80401-1022. Ed. John E. Williamson. circ. 8,000. (reprint service avail. from UMI)
   Formerly: Accidents in American Mountaineering.

799   IT   ISSN 0392-3061
ACQUASPORT. 1978. m. Organo Ufficiale della Federazione Italiana Pesca Sportiva e Attivita Subacquee, Viale Milton 7, Florence, Italy. TEL 055-473843. FAX 055-499195. Ed. Alessandro Menchi.

796.552 796.5   AT
ACTION OUTDOOR. 1983. bi-m. Aus.$22. Australian Sport Publications, 54 Schutt St., Newport, Vic. 3015, Australia. Ed. Ron Moon. adv.; bk.rev. circ. 33,000. (back issues avail.)

796.522   US   ISSN 0001-8236
F127.A2
ADIRONDAC. 1945. 6/yr. $20 to non-members. Adirondack Mountain Club, Inc., RR 3, Box 3055, Lake George, NY 12845. TEL 518-668-4447. FAX 518-668-3746. Ed. Neal Burdick. adv.: B&W page $395; trim 8 1/8 x 10 7/8; adv. contact: Karen L. Brooks. bk.rev.; illus.; index. circ. 12,000. **Indexed:** Acid Pre.Dig., Energy Ind., Energy Info.Abstr., Environ.Abstr. **Document type:** consumer publication.
   —CIS; UnCover.
   Description: Features articles on conservation, nature, history, wilderness trips, use of equipment, places to go in Adirondack and Catskill Parks; club-sponsored outings and workshops.

917   US   ISSN 0001-8252
F127.A2
ADIRONDACK LIFE. 1970. 7/yr. $17.95. Box 97, Jay, NY 12941. TEL 518-946-2191. FAX 518-946-7461. Ed. Elizabeth Folwell; Pub. Tom Hughes. adv. contact: Jo'el P. Kramer. bk.rev.; bibl.; charts; illus. circ. 50,000. **Indexed:** Acid Pre.Dig., Amer.Hist.& Life, Hist.Abstr. **Document type:** consumer publication.
   Description: Provides news and information about the Adirondack region.

ADVENTURE EDUCATION AND OUTDOOR LEADERSHIP. see CHILDREN AND YOUTH — About

ADVENTURE WEST. see TRAVEL AND TOURISM

AIRFLOW. see AERONAUTICS AND SPACE FLIGHT

ALABAMA CONSERVATION. see CONSERVATION

799.3   US   ISSN 0279-6783
ALABAMA GAME & FISH. m. $14.97. Game & Fish Publications, Inc., 2250 Newmarket Pkwy., Ste. 110, Box 741, Marietta, GA 30061-0741. TEL 404-953-9222. FAX 404-933-9510. Ed. Jimmy Jacobs. circ. 15,928.

ALABAMA WILDLIFE. see CONSERVATION

354.9   US   ISSN 0362-6962
SK367
ALASKA. DIVISION OF WILDLIFE CONSERVATION. ANNUAL REPORT OF SURVEY - INVENTORY ACTIVITIES. Key Title: Annual Report of Survey - Inventory Activities. 1970. a. free. Department of Fish and Game, Division of Wildlife Conservation, Box 22526, Juneau, AK 99802-2526. TEL 907-465-4190. Ed. Susan Abbott. illus. circ. 250. **Document type:** government publication.
   Formerly (until 1991): Alaska. Division of Game. Annual Report of Survey - Inventory Activities.

799.1   US   ISSN 1047-5176
THE ALASKA ANGLER. 1986. bi-m. $49 (Canada $59; elsewhere $69). Alaska Angler Publications, Box 83550, Fairbanks, AK 99708. TEL 907-455-8000. FAX 907-455-6691. Ed. Chris Batin. adv.; bk.rev.; charts; illus.; stat. (looseleaf format; back issues avail.) **Document type:** consumer publication.
   Description: Covers Alaska sportfishing.

799.2   US   ISSN 1047-5184
THE ALASKA HUNTER. 1987. bi-m. $49 (Canada $59; elsewhere $69). Alaska Angler Publications, Box 83550, Fairbanks, AK 99708. TEL 907-455-8000. FAX 907-455-6691. Ed. Chris Batin. adv.; bk.rev.; charts; illus.; stat. (looseleaf format; back issues avail.) **Document type:** consumer publication.
   Description: Provides information on where to hunt in Alaska.

796   US
ALASKA OUTDOOR TIMES. 1993. bi-w. Alaska Outdoor Development Corp., Box 443, 200 Albrecht, Palmer, AK 88645. TEL 907-746-3324. adv. circ. 50,000. **Document type:** consumer publication.

799   CN   ISSN 0318-4943
ALBERTA FISHING GUIDE. 1972. a. Can.$4.95. Barry Mitchell Publications, Ltd., 6C, 5571-45 St., Red Deer, AB T4N 1L2, Canada. TEL 403-347-5079. FAX 403-341-5454. Ed. Ann Mitchell. adv.: B&W page Can.$1565; color page Can.$2035; trim 8 1/4 x 10 3/4; adv. contact: Barry Mitchell. bk.rev.; illus. circ. 30,000. **Document type:** consumer publication.
   Description: Includes a comprehensive guide to 1300 sportfishing waters in Alberta, comes with current and detailed directions, species, size of fish, and facilities.

ALL AROUND KENTUCKY. see AGRICULTURE

796.5   SW   ISSN 0346-9190
ALLT OM HUSVAGN OCH CAMPING. 1976. m. SEK 296. Caravan Press AB, P.O. Box 1263, S-171 24 Solna, Sweden. TEL 46-8-730-54-85. FAX 46-8-735-57-10. Ed. Lars-Erik Paulsson. adv. contact: Monica Sved. bk.rev.; circ. 25,600 (controlled). **Document type:** consumer publication.

799.2   SW   ISSN 1101-1904
ALLT OM JAKT; & vapen. 1983. m. SEK 336; newsstand price: SEK 39.50. Bonniers Specialtidning AB, P.O. Box 70452, S-107 26 Stockholm, Sweden. TEL 46-8-736-37-00. FAX 46-8-32-04-40. (Subscr. to: Pressdata AB, P.O. Box 3217, S-103 64 Stockholm, Sweden) Ed. Eric Wallin. adv.: B&W page SEK 12300, color page SEK 16500; trim 190 x 265; adv. contact: Bosse Fritzen. circ. 49,200. cols./p.: 4; pp./issue: 72.
   Former titles (until vol.9, 1989): Allt om Jakt och Vapen (ISSN 1100-0147); (until vol.7, 1987): Jakt och Vapen (ISSN 0281-675X)

796.5   IT   ISSN 1121-7200
ALMANACCO CARAVAN & CAMPER. a. L.10000. Edimedia s.r.l., Via Sant'Erasmo 11, 00184 Rome, Italy. TEL 39-6-70000718. FAX 39-6-7001802. Ed. Maurizio Testa. adv.: B&W page L.4620000, color page L.8250000. circ. 40,000.

796.5   IT
ALMANACCO ROULOTTE. 1977. a. Edigamma s.r.l., Piazza dei Sanniti 9, 00185 Rome, Italy. TEL 06-4928412. FAX 06-4940719. Ed. Renato Circi.

796.93   IT
ALP. 1985. m. L.90000 (foreign L.115000) (effective 1995). Vivalda Editori s.r.l., Via Invorio 24-A, 10146 Turin, Italy. TEL 39-11-7720444. FAX 39-11-7720499. Ed. Enrico Camanni; Pub. Giorgio Vivalda. adv.: B&W page L.4300000, color page L.6900000; adv. contact: Mario Dalmaviva. cum.index: nos.1-100. **Document type:** consumer publication.
   Description: Covers mountaineering.

796.522   SZ   ISSN 0002-6336
ALPEN/ALPES. (Text in French, German) 1892. m. 58 SFr. Club Alpin Suisse - Swiss Alpine Club, Helvetiaplatz 4, CH-3005 Bern, Switzerland. FAX 031-3526063. adv.; bk.rev.; charts; illus. circ. 75,000. **Document type:** bulletin.
   —CCC.
   Description: Contains articles on mountaineering and maps.

SPORTS AND GAMES — OUTDOOR LIFE

796   **AU**
ALPENVEREIN GRAZ. NACHRICHTEN. s-a. Oesterreichischer Alpenverein, Sektion Graz, Sackstr. 16, A-8010 Graz, Austria. TEL 0316-822266. FAX 0316-81247415. Ed. Franz Wolkinger. circ. 9,000. **Document type:** newsletter.

796.522   **IT**   **ISSN 0002-6468**
ALPI VENETE. 1947. s-a. L.8000. Club Alpino Italiano Sezioni Trivenete, C.P. 514, 30170 Mestre PT (Venice), Italy. Ed. Armando Scandellari. adv.; bk.rev.; bibl.; charts; illus.

796.522 796.93   **GW**   **ISSN 0177-3542**
ALPIN. 1963. m. DM.76.80 (foreign DM.84). Olympia Verlag GmbH, Badstr. 4-6, 90427 Nuernberg, Germany. Ed. Georg Schimke. adv. contact: Claudia Popp. **Document type:** consumer publication.
—CCC.
Formerly (until 1984): Alpin-Magazin (ISSN 0722-7884); Which incorporates: Bergwelt (ISSN 0340-1294); Alpinismus (ISSN 0002-6484)

796   **UK**   **ISSN 0065-6569**
DQ821
ALPINE JOURNAL; a record of mountain adventure and scientific observation. 1863. a. £18.50. Alpine Club, 55 Charlotte Rd., London EC2A 3QT, England. TEL 44-71-613-0755. Ed. Johanna Merz. adv.; bk.rev.; index. circ. 1,500. **Indexed:** Br.Hum.Ind., GeoRef., Sportsearch.
—BLDSC (0802.150000).
Incorporates (in 1982): Alpine Climbing; (in 1977): Ladies Alpine Club. Journal.

799.31   **US**   **ISSN 0065-6747**
AMATEUR TRAPSHOOTING ASSOCIATION. OFFICIAL TRAPSHOOTING RULES. 1923. a. $12 membership. Amateur Trapshooting Association, 601 W. National Rd., Vandalia, OH 45377-0458. TEL 513-898-4638. FAX 513-898-5472. index. circ. 100,000.

799.1   **DK**   **ISSN 0900-2650**
AMATOERFISKEREN. 1979. q. membership. Dansk Amatoerfisker Forening, c/o Bent Wissing, Barsoevej 170, Loeft Kirkeby, DK-62-- Aabenraa, Denmark. illus.

796.52   **US**   **ISSN 0065-6925**
GV199.8
AMERICAN ALPINE JOURNAL.* 1929. a. $25. American Alpine Club, 710 10th St., Golden, CO 80401-1022. TEL 212-722-1628. Ed. H. Adams Carter. bk.rev.; index. circ. 6,000. (also avail. in microform from UMI; reprint service avail. from UMI). **Indexed:** GeoRef.
—UMI; UnCover.

796.552   **US**   **ISSN 0147-9288**
AMERICAN ALPINE NEWS.* 1950. 4/yr. $4. American Alpine Club, 710 10th St., Golden, CO 80401-1022. TEL 212-722-1628. Ed. Ruth Mendenhall. adv.; bk.rev. circ. 2,000. (reprint service avail. from UMI). **Indexed:** Sportsearch.
Formerly: A A C News.
Description: Contains articles on mountaineering and maps.

799.1   **US**   **ISSN 1055-6737**
SH451
AMERICAN ANGLER. 1978. bi-m. $20. Abenaki Publishers, Inc., Box 4100, Bennington, VT 05201-4100. TEL 802-447-1518. FAX 802-447-2471. Ed. Jack Russell; Pub. Joe Migliore. adv.: B&W page $1660, color page $2095; trim 8 1/8 x 10 7/8; adv. contact: Kathryn Fox. bk.rev.; stat.; tr.lit.; circ. 36,000 (paid). (back issues avail.)
Former titles: American Angler and Fly Tyer; American Fly Tyer; Fly Tyer (ISSN 0164-730X)

799.32   **US**   **ISSN 1077-8284**
AMERICAN BOWHUNTER. 1983. 6/yr. $9. International Bowhunting Publications, Inc., Box 67, Pillager, MN 56473-0067. TEL 218-746-3333. FAX 218-746-3307. Ed. Johnny E. Boatner. adv.: B&W page $1513, color page $2176; adv. contact: Johnny Boatner. bk.rev.; film rev.; bibl.; charts; illus.; stat.; tr.lit. circ. 65,000. (back issues avail.) **Document type:** consumer publication, newsletter.
Formerly: International Bowhunter (ISSN 0739-0696)

799.2   **US**   **ISSN 0002-807X**
AMERICAN COONER. 1970. m. $11. George O. Slankard, Ed. & Pub., 16 E. Franklin, Sesser, IL 62884. TEL 618-625-2711. adv.; illus. circ. 22,000.

799.2   **US**   **ISSN 0002-8452**
SK1
AMERICAN FIELD; the sportsman's newspaper of America. 1874. w. $30. American Field Publishing Co., 542 S. Dearborn St., Chicago, IL 60605-1508. TEL 312-663-9797. FAX 312-663-5557. Ed. B.J. Matthys. adv.; bk.rev.; illus. circ. 12,000. (tabloid format)
Description: Devoted to pointing dog field trials and upland game bird hunting, conservation and propagation.

799.3   **US**   **ISSN 1060-0892**
AMERICAN GUNSMITH. m. $49 (foreign $60) (effective 1996). Belvoir Publications, Inc., 75 Holly Hill Ln., Box 2626, Greenwich, CT 06836-2626. TEL 203-661-6111. FAX 203-661-4802. Ed. Dave Tinicek. adv. contact: Danice Grkinich. **Document type:** consumer publication.

799   **US**
AMERICAN HANDGUNNER'S ANNUAL BOOK OF HANDGUNS. a. Publisher's Development Corp., 591 Camino de la Reina, Ste. 200, San Diego, CA 92108. TEL 619-297-8520. FAX 609-297-5353. TELEX 695-478. Ed. Cameron Hopkins. adv. contact: Joe McMahon. illus. circ. 90,000.
Description: Contains detailed specifications, photos, catalog guides, prices and editorial descriptions and information on firearms that qualify as handguns.

796.5   **US**   **ISSN 0279-9472**
AMERICAN HIKER. 1977. bi-m. $25. American Hiking Society, Box 20160, Washington, DC 20041-2160. TEL 703-255-9304. FAX 703-255-9308. Ed. Dane Lillard. adv.: B&W page $550, color page $900; trim 8 1/2 x 11. circ. 5,000. **Document type:** consumer publication.
Formerly (until 1993): American Hiker News (ISSN 0164-5722)
Description: Covers hiking, trails, new products, camping and the environment.

799.2   **US**   **ISSN 0092-1068**
SK1
AMERICAN HUNTER. 1973. m. $35 (membership). (National Rifle Association of America) N R A Publications, 11250 Waples Mill Rd., Fairfax, VA 22030. TEL 703-267-1336. FAX 703-267-3971. Ed. Tom Fulgham. adv.; bk.rev.; illus. circ. 1,534,423. **Document type:** consumer publication.
—UMI; UnCover.
Description: Membership publication covering hunting, technique, equipment, places to hunt, wildlife management and Second Amendment issues.

796.93 640.73   **US**   **ISSN 1055-0615**
AMERICAN SKIER.* 1976. 4/yr. $1 per no. American Ski Association, Box 480067, Denver, CO 80248-0067. TEL 303-397-7676. adv. circ. 83,000.
Formerly (until 1990): Skiers Advocate.

388.3   **US**
AMERICAN SNOWMOBILER. 6/yr. Recreational Publications, Inc., 7582 Currell Blvd., St. Paul, MN 55125-2220. TEL 612-738-1953. FAX 612-738-2302. Ed. Jerry Bassett. adv. circ. 40,000.

AMUSEMENT BUSINESS; international newsweekly for live entertainment and amusement industry. see *THEATER*

799   **AU**   **ISSN 0003-2824**
ANBLICK; Zeitschrift fuer Jagd, Fischerei, Jagdhundwesen und Naturschutz. 1946. m. S.426. Steirische Landesjaegerschaft, Heinrichstr. 125-4, A-8010 Graz, Austria. TEL 0316-31248. Ed. Hannes Kollar. adv.; TLX.rev.; index. circ. 14,700. **Indexed:** Key Word Ind.Wildl.Res.
Description: Focuses on fishing and hunting.

799.1   **GW**   **ISSN 0179-843X**
ANGELWOCHE; deutsche Sportfischer-Zeitung. 1984. fortn. DM.77.50 (foreign DM.92.50). Jahr-Verlag GmbH & Co., Jessenstr. 1, 22767 Hamburg, Germany. TEL 040-38906131. FAX 040-38906302. TELEX 2163485-JJV-D. Ed. Rolf Schwarzer; Pub. Alexander Jahr. adv. contact: Werner Schloetcke. circ. 84,110. **Document type:** consumer publication.

799.1   **UK**   **ISSN 0003-3243**
ANGLER'S MAIL. (Supplement avail.: Angler's Mail Annual) 1964. w. £34. I P C Magazines, Specialist Magazine Group (Subsidiary of: Reed Elsevier group), King's Reach Tower, Stamford St., London SE1 9LS, England. TEL 0171-261-5778. FAX 0171-261-6963. TELEX 892084 REEDBP G. (Dist. by: Quadrant Subscription Services, Oakfield House, Perrymount Rd., Haywards Heath, W. Sussex RH16 3DH, England. TEL 01444-440421) Ed. Roy Westwood. adv. contact: Kevin Attridge. bk.rev.; illus. circ. 55,343. **Document type:** consumer publication.
—CCC.
Description: Aimed at the avid fisherman.

799.1   **UK**
ANGLERS MAIL ANNUAL. (Supplement to: Anglers Mail (ISSN 0003-3243)) 1975. a. £3.25. I P C Magazines, Specialist Magazine Group (Subsidiary of: Reed Elsevier group), King's Reach Tower, Stamford St., London SE1 9LS, England. TEL 0171-261-5778. FAX 0171-261-7851. Ed. J. Ingham. circ. 30,000.

799.1   **US**
ANGLING AMERICA MAGAZINE; the official freshwater tournament angling publication of America. 1987. bi-m. $12.95. Angling America, Inc., 635 Green Rd., Box 961, Madison, IN 47250. TEL 812-273-1612. Ed. Tonia Gordon. adv. circ. 20,000.
Description: Multi-species publication featuring bass, crappie, bluegill, walleye and catfish. Covers significant freshwater tournament events in America.

799.1   **UK**   **ISSN 0956-5477**
ANGLING GUIDE. 1970. irreg., latest 1993. £1.30. Department of Agriculture, Fisheries Division, Hut 5, Castle Grounds, Stormont Estate, Belfast BT4 3PW, Northern Ireland. TEL 01232-523434. FAX 01232-423121. adv. circ. 12,000. **Document type:** government publication.
Description: Provides information on the Department of Agriculture fisheries.

799.1   **UK**
ANGLING PLUS. m. £26.20 (foreign £29.70) (effective 1995-1996). E M A P - Pursuit Publishing, Bretton Ct., Bretton, Peterborough, Cambs. PE3 8DZ, England. TEL 01733-264666. FAX 01733-263294. TELEX 332157. (Subscr. to: Tower Publishing Services Ltd., Tower House, Sovereign Park, Lathkill St., Market Harborough, Leics. LE16 9EF, England. TEL 01858-468811. FAX 01858-432164) adv. **Document type:** consumer publication.

799.1   **US**   **ISSN 1045-3539**
THE ANGLING REPORT. 1988. m. $39 (Canada and Mexico $45; elsewhere $60). Oxpecker Enterprises, Inc., 9300 S. Dadeland Blvd., Ste. 605, Miami, FL 33156-2721. TEL 305-670-1361. FAX 305-670-1376. Ed. Don Causey; Pub. Don Causey. adv. contact: Milton Aquino. circ. 3,800. (looseleaf format; back issues avail.) **Document type:** newsletter.
Description: Serves the angler who travels.

799.1   **UK**   **ISSN 0003-3308**
ANGLING TIMES. 1953. w. £52 (foreign £60) (effective 1995-1996). E M A P - Pursuit Publishing, Bretton Ct., Bretton, Peterborough, Cambs. PE3 8DZ, England. TEL 01733-264666. FAX 01733-263294. TELEX 32157. (Subscr. to: Tower Publishing Services Ltd., Tower House, Sovereign Park, Lathkill St., Market Harborough, Leics. LE16 9EF, England. TEL 01858-468811. FAX 01858-432164) Ed. Keith Higgenbottom; Pub. Robert MacDonald. adv. contact: Julie Ingamells. bk.rev.; illus.; tr.lit.; circ. 111,503 (paid). **Document type:** consumer publication.
—CCC.
Description: Contains news about game and sea fishing.

SPORTS AND GAMES — OUTDOOR LIFE

796.42 AT
ANNUAL ALMANAC OF RECORDS AND RESULTS. 1958. a. Aus.$5. Athletics Australia, P.O. Box 1400, N. Melbourne, Vic. 3051, Australia. TEL 61-3-329-1400. FAX 61-3-329-1500. adv. circ. 4,000.
  Description: Covers records and results of the previous seasons Track and Field performances in Australia.

799 CN
ANNUEL DE CHASSE OU ANNUEL DE PECHE. 1987. a. Can.$4.95. Groupe Polygone Editeurs Inc., 11450 Blvd. Albert-Hudon, Montreal, PQ H1G 3J9, Canada. TEL 514-327-4464. FAX 514-327-0514. Ed. Michel Bibeau; Pub. Luc Lemay. adv. contact: Jose Cristofaro. circ. 50,000. (back issues avail.)
  Description: Articles on fishing, hunting, outdoor life and the environment.

799.1 745.1 US ISSN 0744-3749
ANTIQUE ANGLER; a quarterly newsletter-history of fishing-collectible tackle, etc. 1979. q. $7.50. Antique Angler, Inc., Box K, Stockton, NJ 08559. TEL 609-397-1577. Ed. Paul J. Webber. adv.; bk.rev. circ. 2,000.
  Description: Provides a forum for exchanging information among fishing tackle collectors of U.S. and abroad.

796.522 US ISSN 0003-6587
G505
APPALACHIA JOURNAL. 1876. s-a. $10. Appalachian Mountain Club, 5 Joy St., Boston, MA 02108. TEL 617-523-0636. FAX 617-523-0722. Ed. Sandy Stott. adv.; bk.rev.; abstr.; bibl.; illus.; stat.; index, cum.index. circ. 11,000. **Indexed:** Amer.Hist.& Life, Biol.Abstr., Curr.Cont., GeoRef., Hist.Abstr. **Document type:** newsletter.
—BLDSC (1569.000000); Faxon.

796.5 US ISSN 0003-6641
F106
APPALACHIAN TRAILWAY NEWS. 1939. 5/yr. $15. Appalachian Trail Conference, Box 807, Harpers Ferry, WV 25425. TEL 304-535-6331. FAX 304-535-2667. Ed. Judith Jenner. bk.rev.; circ. 25,000. (paid). **Indexed:** GeoRef. **Document type:** newsletter.
  Description: Features Appalachian trail news and features.

796.93 IT ISSN 0392-2375
L'APPENNINO. 1873. m. L.10000. Club Alpino Italiano, Sezione di Roma, Piazza S. Andrea della Valle 3, 00186 Rome, Italy. TEL 39-6-68803424. Ed. Carlo Alberto Pinelli. adv.: B&W page L.1000000.
Document type: consumer publication.

797 FR ISSN 0154-179X
AQUA MAGAZINE; revue du water-polo et des sports aquatiques. 1978. m. 180 F. 37 rue des Mathurins, 75008 Paris, France. Ed. Gerard Daguin. adv. circ. 12,000.

799.2 IT
ARCO. 1989. bi-m. L.35000 (foreign L.40000). Greentime s.r.l., Via Barberia 11, 40123 Bologna, Italy. TEL 39-51-584020. FAX 39-51-585000. Ed. Olga Misley. adv.: B&W page L.2800000, color page L.3600000. circ. 45,000. **Document type:** newspaper.

796 799 US ISSN 1069-0298
ARIZONA GREAT OUTDOORS. 1989. q. $8. Interpersonal Enterprises, Inc., Box 6243, Scottsdale, AZ 85261. TEL 602-945-6746. FAX 602-945-3766. Ed. Janet Jacobsen. adv.: B&W page $800; trim 11 3/8 x 14; adv. contact: Janet L. Jacobsen. maps. circ. 23,000. cols./p.: 4; pp./issue: 12. (tabloid format; back issues avail.) **Document type:** newspaper.
  Description: Reports on conservation, hiking, camping and other self-propelled outdoor recreation activities in the state of Arizona.

799 US ISSN 0888-840X
ARIZONA HUNTER AND ANGLER.* 1984. m. $18. S & S Publications, Inc., Box 859, Mesa, AZ 85211-0859. TEL 602-890-2547. Ed. Tom Stiles. adv. circ. 18,810. **Document type:** consumer publication.
  Description: Features where-to-go and how-to-do-it articles on fishing and hunting in the state.

ARKANSAS OUTDOORS. see *CONSERVATION*

799.3 US
ARKANSAS SPORTSMAN. m. Game & Fish Publications, Inc., 2250 Newmarket Pkwy., Ste. 110, Box 741, Marietta, GA 30061-0741. TEL 404-953-9222. FAX 404-933-9510. Ed. Bob Borgwat. circ. 10,500.

ARKANSAS WILDLIFE. see *CONSERVATION*

799 IT
ARMI E PESCA. 1955. m. L.35000 (foreign L.60000). (Italian Association of Traders and Dealers of Arms, Hunting and Fishing) Gest. Ed. di Daniele Paolucci, Via Redi, 22, 20129 Milan, Italy. TEL 02-29512541. FAX 02-294049500. adv.: B&W page L.1400000, color page L.1950000. bk.rev. circ. 5,000.
  Formerly: Armieri (ISSN 0004-2412)
  Description: Focuses on firearms and other weapons.

799 IT
ARMI E TIRO; rivista di armi tiro, caccia e turismo. 1988. m. L.88000 (foreign L.130000). Edisport Editoriale S.p.A., Via Gradisca 11, 20151 Milan, Italy. TEL 02-380851. FAX 02-38010393. adv.: B&W page L.5700000, color page L.9700000. bk.rev.; charts; illus.; index. circ. 79,500.
  Description: Covers weapon tests and archery used in hunting.

ARMY - NAVY STORE & OUTDOOR MERCHANDISER. see *CLOTHING TRADE*

799.2 683.4 FI ISSN 0781-2124
ASE JA ERA/GUN AND GAME. 1984. 8/yr. FIM 275; newsstand price: FIM 28. Karprint Ky Eero Ahola, FIN-03150 Huhmari, Finland. TEL 358-90-269-481. FAX 358-269466. Ed. Juna Anola. adv.: B&W page FIM 5600, color page FIM 7900; trim 215 x 302; adv. contact: Kari Rautiainen. bk.rev. circ. 16,000. (back issues avail.) **Document type:** consumer publication.
  Description: Oriented towards gun enthusiasts, collectors, hunters.

796.5 296 US
ASSOCIATION OF JEWISH SPONSORED CAMPS. CAMP DIRECTORY. 1963. a. free. Association of Jewish Sponsored Camps, 130 E. 59th St., New York, NY 10022. TEL 212-751-0477. circ. 2,000. **Document type:** directory.

796.93 US ISSN 0199-1574
ATLANTA SKIER.* 1967. q. $10 to nonmembers; members $5. Atlanta Ski Club, Inc., 6303 Barfield Rd., Ste. 120, Atlanta, GA 30328-4236. Ed. Joe Hatchell.

ATLANTIC INFLIGHT. see *AERONAUTICS AND SPACE FLIGHT*

ATLANTIC SALMON JOURNAL. see *FISH AND FISHERIES*

796.42 SP
ATLETISMO ESPANOL. 1951. m. 5500 ptas.($55) Real Federacion Espanola de Atletismo, C. Miguel Angel, 16, 28010 Madrid, Spain. TEL 341-310-3677. FAX 341-308-5912. Ed. Fernando Marquina. adv. contact: Juan Carlos Garcia de Polavieja. bk.rev.; bibl. circ. 10,000. (back issues avail.) **Document type:** consumer publication.
  Description: Provides results of track and field events, calendar of events, interviews with athletes, and training techniques.
  Refereed Serial

799.2 AT ISSN 0810-5928
AUSTRALASIAN SPORTING SHOOTER. 1963. m. Aus.$48 (foreign Aus.$130) (effective Feb. 1995). (Sporting Shooters Association of Australia) Yaffa Publishing Group, 17-21 Bellevue St., Surry Hills, N.S.W. 2010, Australia. TEL 61-2-281-2333. FAX 61-2-281-2750. Ed. Ray Galea. adv.: B&W page Aus.$1775, color Aus.$2255; trim 273 x 210. bk.rev.; illus. circ. 19,750. **Indexed:** Sportsearch (1978-). **Document type:** consumer publication.
  Former titles (until 1982): Australian Shooters Journal (ISSN 0005-0245); Sporting Shooter (ISSN 0038-8076)
  Description: Explores the world of guns and hunting.

796 AT
AUSTRALIAN LADIES GOLF UNION. OFFICIAL YEARBOOK.* 1932. a. Aus.$7.50. Australian Ladies Golf Union, 355 Moray St., S. Melbourne, Vic. 3205, Australia. Ed. Maisie Mooney. adv. circ. 16,000.

796 AT ISSN 0818-6510
AUSTRALIAN ORIENTEER. 1979. bi-m. Aus.$25 (foreign Aus.$28). Orienteering Federation of Australia Inc., P.O. Box 263, Jamison Centre, A.C.T. 2614, Australia. TEL 06-251-3885. FAX 06-253-1574. Ed. David Hogg. adv.; bk.rev. circ. 1,500. (back issues avail.) **Document type:** newsletter.
  Description: Covers the sport of orienteering in Australia.

AUSTRALIAN PARKS & RECREATION. see *CONSERVATION*

796.93 AT ISSN 0084-7593
AUSTRALIAN SKI YEARBOOK. 1928. a. Aus.$5 per no. Mason Stewart Publishing Pty. Ltd., P.O. Box 746, Darlinghurst, N.S.W. 2010, Australia. TEL 02-331-5006. FAX 02-360-5367. Ed. Teresa Curman. adv.: B&W page Aus.$1515, color page Aus.$1945; trim 273 x 210. bk.rev. circ. 8,100.
  Description: Equipment guide and the year's round up.

796.93 AT ISSN 0818-9307
AUSTRALIAN SKIING. 1969. 5/yr. Aus.$50. (N.S.W. Ski Association) Mason Stewart Publishing Pty. Ltd., P.O. Box 746, Darlinghurst, N.S.W. 2010, Australia. TEL 02-331-5006. FAX 02-360-5367. adv.: B&W page Aus.$1515, color page Aus.$1945; trim 273 x 210. bk.rev. circ. 10,790.
  Formerly (until 1986): Fall-Line Ski Magazine (ISSN 0818-9315)
  Description: Explores the world of Australian skiing.

796 AU
AUSTRIA SKI. 9/yr. S.300 (foreign S.400). Oesterreichische Skiverband, Olympiastr. 10, A-6021 Innsbruck, Austria. TEL 0512-59501-0. FAX 0512-584697. circ. 110,000. **Document type:** consumer publication.

AUTO CARAVAN NOTIZIE. see *TRAVEL AND TOURISM*

799.1 US ISSN 0274-7936
B.A.S.S. TIMES. (Bass Anglers Sportsman Society) 1970. m. $12. B.A.S.S., Inc., Box 17900, Montgomery, AL 36141-0900. TEL 205-272-9530. FAX 205-279-7148. Ed. Matt Vincent. adv.: B&W page $4515, color page $5675; trim 11 x 17. circ. 60,000. **Document type:** consumer publication.

796.5 CN ISSN 0045-3013
B C OUTDOORS. (British Columbia) 1945. 8/yr. Can.$23.95. O P Publishing Ltd., 1132 Hamilton St., Ste. 202, Vancouver, BC V6B 2S2, Canada. TEL 604-687-1581. FAX 604-687-1925. Ed. Karl Bruhn. adv.: B&W page $2853, color page $3428; trim 203 x 273; adv. contact: Mark White. bk.rev. circ. 39,374. **Indexed:** Can.Per.Ind., CMI, Key Word Ind.Wildl.Res., Sportsearch. **Document type:** consumer publication.
  Formerly: B.C. Digest.
  Description: Covers fishing, hunting and outdoor recreation

799.1 CN ISSN 0827-2042
B.C. SPORT FISHING MAGAZINE. 1981. bi-m. Can.$17.12($17) P.M. Marketing Ltd., 909 Jackson Crescent, New Westminister, BC V3L 4S1, Canada. TEL 604-521-4901. Ed. Rikk Taylor. adv.: B&W page Can.$1950, color page Can.$2330; trim 8 x 10 7/8. circ. 20,500 (paid).

SPORTS AND GAMES — OUTDOOR LIFE

796.5 US ISSN 0277-867X
GV199.6
BACKPACKER; the magazine of wilderness adventure. 1973. bi-m. $19.97. Rodale Press, Inc., 33 E. Minor St., Emmaus, PA 18098. TEL 610-967-5171. TELEX 847338. (Subscr. to: Box 2784, Boulder, CO 80322) Ed. James Gorman. adv.: B&W page $7215, color page $10135; trim 7 7/8 x 10 1/2. bk.rev. circ. 248,329. (also avail. in microform from UMI) **Indexed:** Acad.Ind., Access, Consum.Ind., Mag.Ind., Phys.Ed.Ind., PMR, Sportsearch (1976-). **Document type:** consumer publication.
●Also available online. Vendor(s): University Microfilms International.
—Faxon; UMI; UnCover.
Former titles (until 1980): Backpacker Including Wilderness Camping (ISSN 0199-3097); (until 1979): Backpacker (1973) (ISSN 0160-3329); **Incorporates** (1971-19??): Wilderness Camping (ISSN 0043-5430)
Description: Includes articles on the latest equipment, destinations and how to get the most out of your trips.

769.552 US
BACKPACKING NEWSLETTER. 1976. m. $20. Frank Ashley, Ed. & Pub., Box 79, Spickard, MO 64679-0079. TEL 816-485-6648. bk.rev. (looseleaf format) **Document type:** newsletter.

799 US ISSN 0005-3775
BADGER SPORTSMAN. 1943. m. $8. Vercauteren Publishing Inc., 19 E. Main St., Chilton, WI 53014. TEL 414-849-7036. FAX 414-849-4651. adv. circ. 26,800. (tabloid format)
Description: Covers the outdoors in Wisconsin.

BAILY'S HUNTING DIRECTORY. see BUSINESS AND ECONOMICS — Trade And Industrial Directories

799.1 US
BASS AND FRESHWATER FISHING. 1979. a. $2.70. Times Mirror Magazines, Inc., 2 Park Ave., New York, NY 10016. TEL 212-779-5000. Ed. Vin T. Sparano. circ. 150,000. (reprint service avail. from UMI)
Former titles: Southern Fishing by Outdoor Life & Outdoor Life's Guide to Fishing the South.

BASSIN'; official magazine of the weekend angler. see FISH AND FISHERIES

799.1 796.95 US
BASSMASTER CLASSIC REPORT. 1981. a. $2.95. (Bass Anglers Sportsman Society) B.A.S.S., Inc., Box 17900, Montgomery, AL 36141-0900. TEL 205-272-9530. FAX 205-279-7148. Ed. Dave Precht. adv.: B&W page $3230, color page $4720; trim 8 1/8 x 10 7/8. circ. 125,000. **Document type:** consumer publication.
Description: Press guide and program of the Bass Masters Classic.

779.1 US
BASSMASTER MAGAZINE. 1968. 10/yr. $20. (Bass Anglers Sportsman Society) B.A.S.S., Inc., Box 17900, Montgomery, AL 36117-0900. TEL 334-272-9530. FAX 334-279-7148. Ed. Dave Precht. adv.: B&W page $14750, color page $21570; trim 8 1/8 x 10 7/8. bk.rev.; charts; illus. circ. 570,060. **Document type:** consumer publication.
Description: How-to, where-to and when-to information for bass fishermen.

799.2 US
BEARDS & SPURS. s-a. $2.95 per no. Buckmasters, Box 24422, Montgomery, AL 36124-4022. TEL 334-215-3337. FAX 334-215-3535.

796.5 GW ISSN 0179-1419
BERG (YEAR); Alpenvereins-Jahrbuch. 1869. a. DM.34.80. Deutscher Alpenverein, Von-Kahr-Str. 2-4, 80997 Munich, Germany. (Co-sponsor: Oesterreichischer Alpenverein) index. **Indexed:** GeoRef. **Document type:** consumer publication.

796 GW ISSN 0005-8963
DER BERGSTEIGER. 1932. m. DM.96.60. F. Bruckmann Muenchen Verlag und Druck GmbH, Nymphenburgerstr. 86, 80636 Munich, Germany. TEL 089-125701. FAX 089-1257269. adv.; bk.rev. **Document type:** consumer publication.
Description: Covers mountaineering and skiing.

796.522 NE ISSN 0005-898X
BERGVRIEND. 1952. bi-m. membership. Nederlandse Bergsportvereniging, Van Aerssenstraat 178, 2582 JT The Hague, Netherlands. Ed. C. Tamminga. adv.; bk.rev.; illus. circ. 13,500.

799.1 JA
BEST FISHING. (Text in Japanese) 1977. m. 3970 Yen. Nihon Journal Press, 11-8, 2-chome, Higashi-Shimbashi, Minato-ku, Tokyo, Japan. Ed. Ichitaro Midorigawa.

796.93 US
THE BEST OF CROSS COUNTRY SKIING. 1990. a. $3. Cross Country Ski Areas Association, 259 Bolton Rd., Winchester, NH 03470. TEL 603-239-4341. FAX 603-239-6387. Ed. Chris Frado. circ. 10,000. **Document type:** directory, newsletter.
Description: Lists over 250 cross country ski areas in the US and selected areas in Canada. Includes information on groomed kilometers, ski services, lodging, and ski areas amenities and programs.

BICYCLING. see SPORTS AND GAMES — Bicycles And Motorcycles

799.2 US
BIG GAME GUIDE. 1991. a. Ehlert Publishing Group, Inc., 601 Lakeshore Pkwy., Ste. 600, Minnetonka, MN 55305-5215. TEL 612-476-2200. FAX 612-476-8065. **Document type:** consumer publication.
Description: Features bowhunting adventure stories.

799.2 US
SK301
BIG GAME HUNTING. Cover title: Petersen's Complete Guide to Hunting. 1977. a. newsstand price: $6.95. Petersen Publishing Co., 6420 Wilshire Blvd., Los Angeles, CA 90048. TEL 213-782-2000. **Document type:** consumer publication.
Formerly: Deer Hunting (Los Angeles) (ISSN 0270-0069)

796.93 CC
BINGXUE YUNDONG. (Text in Chinese) bi-m. Heilongjiang Sheng Tiyu Kexue Yanjiusuo - Heilongjiang Institute of Sport Science, 21, Xuanxi Jie, Nangang-qu, Harbin, Heilongjiang 141, People's Republic of China. TEL 221683. Ed. Sun Jingguo.

BIRD WATCHING. see BIOLOGY — Ornithology

DER BLAUE PETER; Zeitschrift fuer Segeln und Seefahrt. see SPORTS AND GAMES — Boats And Boating

799.1 GW ISSN 0720-4116
BLINKER; internationale Sportfischerzeitschrift. 1969. m. DM.94.80. Jahr-Verlag GmbH & Co., Jessenstr. 1, 22767 Hamburg, Germany. TEL 040-38906-0. FAX 040-38906302. TELEX 2163485. Ed. Karl Koch; Pub. Alexander Jahr. adv. contact: Werner Schloetcka. circ. 113,100. (back issues avail.) **Document type:** consumer publication.

796.93 914 US ISSN 1067-3938
GV854.8.E9
BLUE BOOK OF EUROPEAN SKI RESORTS. 1993. a. $15. (SwissAir, Company Des Alpes) Inter-Ski Services, Inc., Box 9595, Washington, DC 20016. TEL 202-342-0886. FAX 202-338-1940. Ed.Bd. circ. 8,000. **Document type:** directory.
Description: Complete listing of ski areas with facilities, rates, statistics and telephone numbers.

799.1 UK ISSN 0958-3602
BOAT ANGLER. 1990. bi-m. £14.70 (foreign £23.10) (effective 1995-1996). E M A P - Pursuit Publishing, Bretton Ct., Bretton, Peterborough, Cambs. PE3 8DZ, England. TEL 01733-264666. FAX 01733-263294. TELEX 32157. (Subscr. to: Tower Publishing Services Ltd., Tower House, Sovereign Park, Lathkill St., Market Harborough, Leics. LE16 9EF, England. TEL 01733-264666. FAX 01733-363294) adv. contact: Pete Truman. **Document type:** consumer publication.

799 US
BOB ELLSBERG'S HUNTER & FISHERMAN'S PLANNING YEARBOOK; a complete guidebook, calendar & journal for the outdoorsman. a. $12.95. Outdoor Enterprises, 1048 Valley St., Astoria, OR 97103. TEL 503-325-5573. Ed. Paul F. Barnum. illus.

796.172 US ISSN 1047-2223
GV840.S8
BODY BOARDING. 1985. q. $9.95. Western Empire Publications, 950 Calle Amanecer, Ste. C, Box 3010, San Clemente, CA 92672. TEL 714-498-6485. Ed. N. Carroll. adv.; bk.rev. **Document type:** consumer publication.
Formerly (until 1987): Surfing Magazine's Body Boarding (ISSN 0896-7318)

799.32 US ISSN 0894-7856
GV1183
BOW AND ARROW HUNTING; the world's leading archery magazine. 1963. bi-m. $18. Gallant - Charger Publishing, Inc., 34249 Camino Capistrano, Box HH, Capistrano Beach, CA 92624. TEL 714-493-2101. Ed. Jack Lewis. adv.; bk.rev.; illus. circ. 98,000. (back issues avail.) **Indexed:** Sportsearch. **Document type:** consumer publication.
—UnCover.
Formerly (until 1985): Bow and Arrow (ISSN 0006-8403)
Description: Concentrates on bowhunting with emphasis on North American species.

799.2 US
BOW & ARROW MAGAZINE'S BOWHUNTER'S ANNUAL. Spine title: Bowhunter's Annual. 1975. a. $3.95. Gallant - Charger Publishing, Inc., 34249 Camino Capistrano, Box HH, Capistrano Beach, CA 92624. TEL 714-493-2101. Ed. Jack Lewis. adv.; bk.rev. circ. 108,000. **Document type:** consumer publication.

799.32 US ISSN 0273-7434
BOWHUNTER; the magazine for the hunting archer. 1971. 8/yr. $24. Cowles Magazines, Inc. (Subsidiary of: Cowles Media Company), 6405 Flank Dr., Box 8200, Harrisburg, PA 17105-8200. TEL 717-657-9556. FAX 717-657-9526. Ed. M.R. James. adv.; bk.rev. circ. 184,203. (also avail. in microform from UMI; reprint service avail. from UMI) **Indexed:** Sportsearch. **Document type:** consumer publication.
—UMI.
Description: Features bow and arrow hunting adventure, how-to, safety and ethics.

799.32 US ISSN 1049-9768
BOWHUNTING. 8/yr. $15.95. Petersen Publishing Co., 6420 Wilshire Blvd., Los Angeles, CA 90048. TEL 213-782-2000. Ed. Greg Tinsley. adv.; illus. circ. 110,000. **Document type:** consumer publication.
—UMI.

799.32 US ISSN 1066-7148
BOWHUNTING NEWS. 1989. m. $15. Eastern Publishing & Distributing, Inc., 1-B Airport Dr., Hopedale, MA 01747. TEL 508-478-4754. FAX 508-478-3541. Ed. Christina Goodwin; Pub. Roy Goodwin. adv.: B&W page $805, color page $1105; 10 1/8 x 15 1/4; adv. contact: Steve Clark. bk.rev. circ. 26,000. (tabloid format) **Document type:** newspaper.
Formerly (until 1992): Eastern Bowhunting.
Description: Official newspaper of 12 statewide bowhunting organizations. Contains 14ories by bowhunters relating actual hunting experiences, and industry news, hunting programs and updates on pending legislation.

799.32 US ISSN 1043-5492
BOWHUNTING WORLD. 1952. 8/yr. $20 (Canada $28; elsewhere $30). Ehlert Publishing Group, Inc., 601 Lakeshore Pkwy., Ste. 600, Minnetonka, MN 55305-5215. TEL 612-476-2200. FAX 612-476-8065. Ed. Mike Strandlun. adv.; bk.rev.; charts; illus.; mkt.; pat.; tr.lit.; tr.mk.; index. circ. 145,000. (also avail. in microform from UMI; reprint service avail. from UMI) **Indexed:** Consum.Ind., Mag.Ind., Phys.Ed.Ind., Sports Per.Ind., Sportsearch.
—UMI; UnCover.
Formerly (until 1989): Archery World (ISSN 0003-827X)

799.2 US
BOWMASTERS. bi-m. newsstand price: $2.95. Thicket Publishing, 2100 Riverchase Center, Ste. 118, Birmingham, AL 35244-1852. TEL 205-987-6007. FAX 205-987-2882. **Document type:** consumer publication.

SPORTS AND GAMES — OUTDOOR LIFE

796   UK
BRITAIN'S BEST BEACHES; the comprehensive guide to the blue beaches in Britain. 1986. a. £6.95. Peerage Publications, P.O. Box 5135, Strand-on-the-Green, Chiswick, London W4 3WN, England. TEL 0181-747-0385. Ed. Sara Marden-King; Pub. Bruce Duncan. adv.: B&W page £460, color page £830; trim 210 x 148. **Document type**: directory.
    Formerly (until 1994): England's Seaside.

796.5
BRITAIN'S BEST CAMPING AND CARAVANNING PARKS. a. £7.99. (Automobile Association) A A Publishing, Norfolk House, Priestly Rd., Basingstoke, Hants. RG24 9NY, England. TEL 01256-20123. FAX 01256-22575. adv. **Document type**: consumer publication.
    Former titles: Camping and Caravanning in Britain; Camping and Caravanning in the U.K.

796.522   CN   ISSN 0045-2998
BRITISH COLUMBIA MOUNTAINEER. 1917. biennial. Can.$10. British Columbia Mountaineering Club, P.O. Box 2674, Vancouver, BC V6B 3W8, Canada. TEL 604-737-3000. Ed. M.C. Feller. adv.: bk.rev. circ. 500. **Document type**: consumer publication.

799.2   US
BROWNING DEER HUNTING. 1986. a. $2.50. (Browning Arms) Aqua-Field Publishing Co., Inc., 66 W. Gilbert St., Shrewsbury, NJ 07702. TEL 201-842-8300. Ed. Stephen Ferber. adv. circ. 100,000.

796.5   CN   ISSN 0383-9249
BRUCE TRAIL NEWS. 1963. q. Can.$12($12) (Bruce Trail Association) Trail News Inc., 17 Marlborough Ave., Toronto, Ont. M5R 1X5, Canada. TEL 416-964-7281. Ed. Norman Day. adv.: B&W page $600, color page $9000; trim 8 1/4 x 11. bk.rev.; illus.; circ. 10,000 (controlled). (back issues avail.)
    Description: News about outdoor life, camping and the environment.

799.2   US
BUCKMASTERS WHITETAIL. bi-m. $3.95 per no. Buckmasters, Box 244022, Montgomery, AL 36124-4022. TEL 334-215-3337. FAX 334-215-3535. Ed. Russell Thornberry; Pub. Jack C. Bushman. adv. contact: Margaret Ann Swearingen. circ. 180,425 (paid). **Document type**: consumer publication.

BUGLE (MISSOULA); journal of elk and the hunt. see CONSERVATION

796 910.2   NE   ISSN 0007-3768
BUITENSPOOR. 1918. m. membership. Nederlandse Toeristen Kampeerclub, Kerkstraat 28, 5301 EJ Zaltbommel, Netherlands. Ed. J.H. Sanders. adv.; bk.rev.; charts; illus.; index. circ. 5,000.

799.202   CN
BULLSEYE. (Text in English or French) 1946. q. free. Royal New Brunswick Rifle Association, c/o M.E. MacGillivray, 156 Glengary Pl., Fredericton, N.B. E3B 5Z9, Canada. TEL 506-455-8213. Ed. Conrad Leroux. adv.: bk.rev. circ. 600.

799   US
C A D A GUN JOURNAL. 1991. m. $29.95. Blue Book Publications, 1 Appletree Sq., Minneapolis, MN 55425. TEL 612-853-1338; 800-368-2232. FAX 612-853-1486. Ed. Julie Lindermann. adv.; bk.rev. **Document type**: consumer publication.

796.5   UK   ISSN 0008-2406
C S E NEWS. 1962. m. £30. Camping & Sports Equipment Ltd., 4 Spring St., London W2 3RB, England. TEL 071-262-2886. FAX 071-706-0360. Ed. P. Moloney. adv.; bk.rev.; abstr.; illus.; mkt.; pat.; stat.; tr.lit. circ. 6,011. **Document type**: trade publication.
    Incorporating: Camping and Sports Equipment.
    Description: Trade journal for the camping and outdoor leisure sector: camping, caravaning, outdoor equipment and accessories.

C T & C. (Cycle Touring & Campaigning) see SPORTS AND GAMES — Bicycles And Motorcycles

C T P A NEWS. (California Travel Parks Association, Inc.) see TRAVEL AND TOURISM

799.2   IT
CACCIA E CANI. 1967. m. L.55000. Silvio Basile Editore, Lungo Bisago Istria 34, 16141 Genoa, Italy. TEL 39-10-852151. FAX 39-10-83550555. Ed. Guseppe Negri. adv.: B&W page L.2520000, color page L.4520000. circ. 25,000. **Document type**: consumer publication.

799   IT   ISSN 0574-9913
CACCIA E PESCA. 1967. m. L.35000. Editoriale Bertacchi s.r.l., Via Bertacchi 2, Milan, Italy. Ed. Giuseppe Negri. adv. circ. 65,000.
    Description: Covers fishing and hunting, sports and outdoor games.

799.2   IT
CACCIATORE ITALIANO. m. (Federazione Italiana Caccia) Editoriale Olympia, Viale Milton 7, Florence, Italy. TEL 39-55-490-750. Ed. Ruggero Faccin. adv.: B&W page L.10000000, color page L.15000000; trim 185 x 254. circ. 790,000.

799.1   US   ISSN 8750-8907
SH473
CALIFORNIA ANGLER.* 1985. m. $18. Box 15631, Santa Ana, CA 92705-0631. TEL 714-261-9779. FAX 714-261-9853. Ed. John Skrabo. adv. circ. 33,500.
    Formed by the merger of (1974-1985): Angler (ISSN 0745-3817); (1981-1985): Western Saltwater Fisherman (ISSN 0277-0644)
    Description: Focuses on primarily fresh and saltwater fishing in California, the Baja Peninsula, Mexico mainland and the Pacific Basin.

796 975   US   ISSN 0164-8748
CALIFORNIA EXPLORER. 1978. bi-m. $28.50. J B K Enterprises Inc., 1135 Terminal Way, Ste. 209, Reno, NV 89502. TEL 707-942-6249. Ed. Kay Graves. adv. contact: Harold Chevrier. cum. index. circ. 7,509. (back issues avail.) **Document type**: consumer publication.
    Description: Covers the backroads, hiking trails and history of the West.

CALIFORNIA FISH AND GAME. see CONSERVATION

799.1   US   ISSN 1071-5673
CALIFORNIA FLY FISHER. 1992. bi-m. $14.50. Box 40429, San Francisco, CA 94140. TEL 415-284-0313. FAX 415-284-0321. Ed. Richard Anderson. adv. contact: Richard Anderson. bk.rev.; index; circ. 6,000 (paid). (tabloid format) **Document type**: consumer publication.
    Description: Dedicated to exploring fly fishing opportunities in and around California.

CAMINOS DA TERRA. see CONSERVATION

796.5   GW   ISSN 0724-4215
CAMP; Magazin fuer Caravan und Reisemobil. 1977. m. Top Special Verlag GmbH, Nebendahlstr. 16, 22041 Hamburg, Germany. TEL 040-3470-0. FAX 040-34725588. Ed. Joachim Kalkowsky. adv. contact: Beate Asmus-Fuegert. circ. 37,924. **Document type**: consumer publication.

CAMPBOOK: CALIFORNIA - NEVADA. see TRAVEL AND TOURISM

CAMPBOOK: EASTERN CANADA. see TRAVEL AND TOURISM

CAMPBOOK: GREAT LAKES. see TRAVEL AND TOURISM

CAMPBOOK: MIDEASTERN. see TRAVEL AND TOURISM

CAMPBOOK: NORTH CENTRAL. see TRAVEL AND TOURISM

CAMPBOOK: NORTHWESTERN. see TRAVEL AND TOURISM

CAMPBOOK: SOUTH CENTRAL. see TRAVEL AND TOURISM

CAMPBOOK: SOUTHEASTERN. see TRAVEL AND TOURISM

CAMPBOOK: SOUTHWESTERN. see TRAVEL AND TOURISM

796.5   IT   ISSN 0008-2325
CAMPEGGIO ITALIANO. 1958. m. L.25000 (foreign L.30000). Federazione Italiana del Campeggio e del Caravanning, Via Vittorio Emanuele 11, 50041 Calenzano (FI), Italy. TEL 39-55-882391. FAX 39-55-8825918. Ed. Giancarlo Ceci. adv.: B&W page L.1600000, color page L.1960000. circ. 25,000. (back issues avail.)

796   US   ISSN 0410-4889
CAMPFIRE CHATTER. 1957. m. $12. North American Family Camps Association, Inc., Box 328, Concord, VT 05824-0328. TEL 802-695-2563. Ed. Pat O'Malley. adv. circ. 2,500.

796.5   US   ISSN 0162-3796
CAMPGROUND MANAGEMENT; business publication for profitable outdoor recreation. Variant title: Woodall's Campground Management. 1969. m. $24.95. Woodall Publishing Co., 13975 W. Polo Trail Dr., Lake Forest, IL 60045. TEL 708-362-6700; 800-323-9076. FAX 708-362-8776. Ed. Mike Byrnes; Pub. Deborah A. Spriggs. adv.: B&W page $2250, color page $2700; adv. contact: Mary Sgaraglino. bk.rev.; charts; illus.; stat.; tr.lit.; circ. 14,000 (controlled). (tabloid format; back issues avail.) **Document type**: trade publication.
    Formerly: Campground Management and R V Park Management.
    Description: Contains information for the development, rehabilitation, maintenance, operation and management of a campground.

CAMPGROUNDATA; national newsletter for campground buyers & owners. see BUSINESS AND ECONOMICS — Small Business

796.5   DK   ISSN 0045-4125
CAMPING. 1926. m. membership. Dansk Camping Union - Danish Camping Union, Gl. Kongevej 74 D, DK-1850 Frederiksberg C, Denmark. TEL 31-21-06-00. FAX 31-210108. Ed. Joergen Froehlich. adv.; bk.rev.; film rev.; charts; illus. circ. 50,000. **Document type**: consumer publication.

796.5   GW
CAMPING; illustrierte Zeitschrift fuer Caravan-, Zelt-, Motor-Touristik und Wassersport. m. (Deutscher Camping Club e.V.) D C C-Wirtschaftsdienst und Verlag GmbH, Postfach 400428, 80704 Munich, Germany. TEL 089-380142-0. FAX 089-334737. adv. circ. 40,000. **Document type**: consumer publication.

796.5   UK
CAMPING & CARAVANNING. 1907. m. membership. Camping and Caravanning Club, Greenfields House, Westwood Way, Coventry, Warks. CV4 8JH, England. TEL 01203-694995. FAX 01203-694886. Ed. Peter Frost. adv.; bk.rev.; illus. circ. 109,539. **Document type**: consumer publication.
    Formerly: Camping and Outdoor Life.

796.5   US   ISSN 0896-5706
CAMPING AND R V MAGAZINE. 1985. m. $17.95. Box 458, Washburn, WI 54891-0458. TEL 715-373-5556. FAX 715-373-5003. Eds. Bob Miller, Jerry Wasley; Pub. Ruth K. Radtke. adv.: B&W page $984, color page $1584; trim 8 1/4 x 10 7/8. bk.rev. circ. 20,000. **Document type**: consumer publication.
    Description: Covers camping and recreation. Features new products, maintainance, campground reviews, humor, fiction, and destinations.

796.5   CN   ISSN 0384-9856
CAMPING CANADA. 1971. 7/yr. Can.$17.12 (in US Can.$37.35, elsewhere Can.$53.50). Camping Canada Magazine, 2585 Skymark Ave., Unit 306, Mississauga, ON L4W 4L5, Canada. TEL 905-624-8218. FAX 905-624-6764. Ed. Diane Batten; Pub. William E. Taylor. adv.; bk.rev. circ. 50,000. Indexed: Sportsearch. **Document type**: consumer publication.

CAMPING CARAVANNING AND SPORTS EQUIPMENT TRADES DIRECTORY. see BUSINESS AND ECONOMICS — Trade And Industrial Directories

SPORTS AND GAMES — OUTDOOR LIFE

796.5   SZ   ISSN 0008-2414
CAMPING-CARAVANNING-REVUE. (Text in French, German, Italian) 1937. 10/yr. 22.50 SFr. Schweizerischer Camping- und Caravanning-Verband - Federation Suisse de Camping et de Caravanning, Case Postale 24, CH-6000 Luzern 4, Switzerland. TEL 041-2104822. FAX 041-2100002. Ed.Bd. adv.; bk.rev. circ. 11,093. **Document type:** consumer publication.

674.9448908   DK   ISSN 0108-7355
GV191.48.D4
CAMPING DANMARK; godkendte campingpladser i Danmark. (Forms part of: Nordiske Officielle Campingfortegnelser) (Text in Danish, English, French and German) 1968. a. DKK 36 (effective 1986). Campingraadet, Hesseloegade 16, DK-2100 Copenhagen Oe, Denmark. illus.
Formerly: Godkendte Campingpladser i Danmark.

796.5   CN   ISSN 0829-4844
CAMPING IN ONTARIO. 1975. a. Ontario Private Campground Association, 40 University Ave., Ste. 1116, Toronto, ON M5J 1T1, Canada. TEL 416-977-0454. FAX 416-977-3299. Dir. Fred Gray. adv. circ. 120,000. **Document type:** directory, consumer publication.
Former titles (until 1985): Ontario Private Campground Association. Camping Directory (ISSN 0827-4223); (until 1981): Camp Ontario (ISSN 0827-4231)

796.5   UK
CAMPING MAGAZINE. 1961. m. £29.20. Link House Magazines Ltd., Link House, Dingwall Ave., Croydon CR9 2TA, England. TEL 0181-686-2599. FAX 0181-760-0973. (Subscr. addr.: R F S,120-126 Lavender Ave., Mitcham, Surrey CR4 3HP, England) Ed. John Lloyd. adv.; bk.rev.; charts. (back issues avail.) **Document type:** consumer publication.
Former titles: Camping and Walking (ISSN 0952-5106); (until 1986): Camping and Trailer (ISSN 0266-7878); Camping (ISSN 0032-4469)
Description: Family-oriented information about camping and walking.

796.54   US   ISSN 0740-4131
SK601.A1
CAMPING MAGAZINE. 1926. 6/yr. $18.95 (effective till Jul.-Aug. 1994). American Camping Association, Inc., 5000 State Rd. 67 N., Martinsville, IN 46151-7902. TEL 317-342-8456. FAX 317-342-2065. Ed. Nancy LaMarca Gordon. adv.; charts; illus.; stat.; tr.lit.; index. circ. 8,000. (also avail. in microform from UMI; back issues avail.; reprint service avail. from UMI) **Indexed:** Mag.Ind., R.G., Rehabil.Lit., Sports.Per.Ind., Sportsearch. **Document type:** consumer publication.
●Also available online.
Also available on CD-ROM.
—Faxon; SWETS; UMI; UnCover.

796 658   US
CAMPING PRODUCTS MERCHANDISER.* bi-m. Hanley Publishing Co., 32 W. Grand Ave., Fox Lake, IL 60020-1224. TEL 708-677-8151. Ed. Gloria Krolski. circ. 10,000. **Document type:** consumer publication.

796.5   AU
CAMPING REVUE; Magazin des Oesterreichischen Camping Clubs. 1967. 6/yr. membership. (Oesterreichischer Camping Club) Oe A M T C Verlag GmbH, Hoelzlgasse 66, A-3400 Klosterneuburg, Austria. TEL 01-711991293. FAX 01-711991498. TELEX 133907. Ed. Friedrich Wilhelm. adv.: B&W page S.23000, color page S.32200; trim 185 x 255; adv. contact: Reinhart Rosner. bk.rev.; abstr.; charts; illus.; stat. circ. 15,000. **Document type:** consumer publication.
Former titles: Sport Review; Oesterreichische Camping Revue; Oesterreichische Camping and Caravaning Revue (ISSN 0029-8972); Camping und Sport Revue.

796   US   ISSN 8750-1465
CAMPING TODAY. 1983. m. $20 membership. Family Campers & R Vers, 4804 Transit Rd., Bldg. 2, Depew, NY 14043. TEL 716-668-6242. Ed. DeWayne Johnson; Pub. Don Wright. adv. contact: Thad Wright. circ. 20,000 (paid). **Document type:** consumer publication.
Formerly: Tent and Trail.
Description: For camper and RV owners. Also covers wildlife and conservation.

796.52   CN   ISSN 0068-8207
F1090   CODEN: CNAJA6
CANADIAN ALPINE JOURNAL. 1907. a. Can.$24.95. Alpine Club of Canada, Box 2040, Canmore, AB T0L 0M0, Canada. TEL 403-678-3200. FAX 403-678-3224. Ed. Geoff Powter. bk.rev.; illus.; index, cum.index: 1907-1987. circ. 3,500. (back issues avail.) **Indexed:** GeoRef., Sportsearch.
—UnCover.

796   CN   ISSN 0710-9326
CANADIAN R V DEALER. 1975. bi-m. Can.$11. Power Boating - Camping Canada, 2585 Skymark Ave., Ste. 306, Mississagua, Ont. L4W 4L5, Canada. TEL 416-624-8218. FAX 416-624-6764. Ed. Norman Rosen. adv.; tr.lit. **Indexed:** Sportsearch, Tr.& Indus.Ind.
Formerly: Canadian Camping and R V Dealer.

796.93   CN   ISSN 0844-594X
CANADIAN SKI PRO/SKI PRO CANADIEN. (Text in English and French) 1983. 4/yr. membership. Canadian Ski Instructors' Alliance, 774 Decarie Blvd., Ste. 310, Ville St-Laurant, PQ, Canada. TEL 514-748-2648. FAX 514-748-2476. Ed. Carolyn Paquette. adv. circ. 20,000. **Document type:** bulletin.
Formerly: Profile (ISSN 0835-4375)

799.1   CN   ISSN 0842-1412
CANADIAN SPORTFISHING. 1988. 6/yr. Can.$19.95 (foreign Can.$24.95). 937 Centre Rd., Dept. 2020, Waterdown, ON L0R 2H0, Canada. TEL 905-689-1112. FAX 905-689-2065. Ed. Kerry Knudsen. adv.: B&W page Can.$4150, color page Can.$5150; trim 8 1/8 x 10 7/8; adv. contact: Henry Waszczuk. circ. 60,000. **Document type:** consumer publication.

797.56   CN   ISSN 0319-3896
CANPARA. 1961. 6/yr. Can.$26.75 (foreign Can.$35). Canadian Sport Parachuting Association, 4185 Dunning Rd., Navan, ON K4B 1J1, Canada. TEL 613-835-3731. FAX 613-835-3731. Ed. Andrew Haines. adv.: B&W page Can.$250, color page Can.$600. bk.rev. circ. 4,500. **Indexed:** Sportsearch. **Document type:** newsletter.
Former titles: Canadian Parachutist (ISSN 0045-5245); Parachute Club of Canada. Newsletter.

796.5   IT
CARA CARAVAN CAMPER. 1978. s-a. L.6500 per no. Di Baio Editore s.r.l., Via Settembrini 11, 20124 Milan, Italy. Ed. G.M. Jonghi Lavarini. adv.

796.5   GW   ISSN 0930-0309
CARAVAN; Zeitschrift fuer Camper, Caravaner, Touristen. 1957. m. DM.54 (foreign DM.66) (effective 1995). Westdeutsche Verlagsanstalt GmbH, Ahmser Str. 190, 32052 Herford, Germany. TEL 05221-775-0. FAX 05221-775215. Ed. Norbert M. Hoyer. adv.; illus. circ. 40,000. **Document type:** consumer publication.
Former titles: Caravan Camping-Journal (ISSN 0343-2912); Camping Journal (ISSN 0008-2449)
Description: Information about travelling, new accessories and techniques.

CARAVAN AND OUTDOOR LIFE. see TRAVEL AND TOURISM

796.5   SW   ISSN 0008-6169
CARAVAN BLADET. 1958. bi-m. SEK 100. Caravan Club of Sweden, Traengkaarsvaegen 39, 703 57 Oerebro, Sweden. TEL 19-137668. FAX 19-116082. Ed. Rune Petterson. adv.; illus. circ. 13,000. **Document type:** consumer publication.

CARAVAN CAMPING DIRECTORY. see BUSINESS AND ECONOMICS — Trade And Industrial Directories

CARAVAN INDUSTRY SUPPLIES & SERVICES DIRECTORY. see BUSINESS AND ECONOMICS — Trade And Industrial Directories

796.5   UK
CARAVAN MOTORCARAVAN & CAMPING. m. £13.20 (foreign £35.50). Aceville Publications Ltd., 89 East Hill, Colchester, Essex CO1 2QN, England. TEL 0206-871450. FAX 0206-871537. Ed. David Bridle. adv. **Document type:** consumer publication.

680 796   FR   ISSN 0399-7715
LE CARAVANIER. 1965. 7/yr. (plus special issue). 182 F. (foreign 246 F.) (effective 1994-1995). Ediregie, B.P. 86, 94420 Le Plessis Trevise, France. TEL 45-93-72-72. FAX 45-93-25-93. TELEX EDIGIE 262 572 F. Dir. Jean Rousseau. adv.; illus. circ. 100,000. **Document type:** consumer publication.

CARAVANING. CARAVAN & CAMPER; vacanze turismo auto. see TRAVEL AND TOURISM

799.1   IT
CARPFISHING. 4/yr. Editoriale Olimpia S.p.A., Viale Milton 7, 50129 Florence, Italy. TEL 39-55-473843. FAX 39-55-499195. **Document type:** consumer publication.

799.1   UK   ISSN 0957-8528
CARPWORLD. 1988. m. £46.50. Angling Publications, 1 Grosvenor Sq., Sheffield, S. Yorks. S2 4MS, England. TEL 01742-580812. FAX 01742-582725. Ed. Tim Paisley. adv. contact: Mary Paisley. circ. 18,500. (back issues avail.) **Document type:** consumer publication.

796.172   UK   ISSN 1354-5086
CARVE SURFING MAGAZINE. q. £9. Orca Publications Ltd., 11 Cliff Rd., Newquay, Cornwall TR7 2NE, England. TEL 01637-878074. FAX 01637-878074. (Dist. by: UMD, 16-28 Tabernacle St., London EC2A 4BN, England) Ed. Chris Power. adv. contact: Chris Power. (back issues avail.) **Document type:** consumer publication.
Formerly (until 1994): Groundswell.
Description: General interest magazine for surfers, including travel photo-stories, news, international and British competition coverage, and 'how to' features.

CATALOGUE OF CANADIAN RECREATION AND LEISURE RESEARCH. see LEISURE AND RECREATION

799   SP   ISSN 0212-5625
CAZA Y PESCA; revista mensual de caza, pesca, tiro, armas y guarderia. 1943. m. 6000 ptas. (foreign 8000 ptas.). Joaquin Espana Pena, Jose Abascal, 24, 1 Izda., 28003 Madrid, Spain. TEL 34-14473484. FAX 34-14474163. adv.; bk.rev.; charts; illus. circ. 42,000. (back issues avail.)

799   VE
CAZA Y PESCA NAUTICA. 1954. m. $25. P.O. Box 60.764, Caracas 1060 A, Venezuela. Ed. Heinz R. Doebbel. adv. circ. 25,500.
Description: Cover fishing, hunting and water sports.

799.2   US   ISSN 0009-1952
CHASE; a full cry of hunting. 1920. m. $20. Chase Publishing Co., Inc., 1150 Industry Rd., Box 55090, Lexington, KY 40555. TEL 606-254-4262. Ed. Jo Ann Stone. adv.: B&W page $121. bk.rev.; illus. circ. 3,000. **Document type:** trade publication.
Description: Includes listings, registrations, results of field trials, plus articles and stories.

CHATAR & CHALUPAR; casopis pro kutily, chatare a chalupare. see ARCHITECTURE

790   US   ISSN 0893-195X
GV191.4
CHEVY OUTDOORS. Key Title: Outdoors. 1986. q. $8. Aegis Group - Publishers (Subsidiary of: Lintas - Ceco Communications), 30400 Van Dyke Ave., Warren, MI 48093. TEL 810-574-9100. FAX 810-558-5897. Ed. Michael Brudenell. adv. circ. 1,000,000.
Formerly: Chevy Camper.
Description: Features, information, and events pertaining to all forms of outdoor recreation and leisure, with tips on fishing, cooking, boating recreational vehicles and personality profiles.

796.552   US
CHICAGO MOUNTAINEER. 1945. s-a. $10. (Chicago Mountaineering Club) Data Base Management Services, 998 Lake Country Ct., Oconomowoc, WI 53066. TEL 414-567-1110. (Subscr. to: Chicago Mountaineering Club, 22 S. Thurlow St., Hinsdale, IL 60921) Ed. David L. Harrison. bk.rev.; bibl. circ. 350.
Description: Covers technical rock climbing. Includes reports on expeditions and personal experiences.

6158 SPORTS AND GAMES — OUTDOOR LIFE

796   US
CHOCONUT FOUNDATION NEWSLETTER. 1985. 4/yr. $10 membership. Choconut Foundation, H C R No. 19, Stephentown, NY 12168. (Subscr. to: Urko Wood, Treas., 105 S. Narberth Ave., Narberth, PA 19072. TEL 215-668-9397) Ed. Dan Lorber. (looseleaf format) **Document type:** newsletter.
   Supersedes (1896-1985): Choconut News.
   Description: News of foundation activities in outdoor education and recreation, with announcements of meetings and reports from members.

796.42   JA
CITY RUNNER. (Text in Japanese) 1983. m. 4560 Yen. Gakken Co., Ltd., 40-5, 4 chome, Kamiikedai, Ohta-ku, Tokyo 145, Japan. Ed. Masahiro Onuma.

796.522   UK   ISSN 0955-3045
CLIMBER AND HILLWALKER. 1961. m. £30. Caledonian Magazines Ltd., The Plaza Tower, East Kilbride, Glasgow G74 1LW, Scotland. TEL 013552-46444. FAX 013552-63013. Ed. Peter Evans. adv.; bk.rev.; charts; illus.; tr.lit. circ. 15,549. **Indexed:** Geo.Abstr., Sportsearch. **Document type:** consumer publication. —UnCover.
   Former titles: Climber; Climber and Rambler (ISSN 0009-8973); Climber.

796.522   US   ISSN 0045-7159
GV199.4
CLIMBING. 1970. 8/yr. $28. (Climbing, Ltd.) Elk Mountain Press, Inc., Box 339, 1101 Village Rd., Ste. LL-1-B, Carbondale, CO 81623. TEL 970-963-9449. FAX 970-963-9442. E-mail: climbing@infosphere.com. Ed. Michael Kennedy; Pub. Michael Kennedy. adv.: B&W page $1595, color page $2425; trim 8 3/8 x 10 7/8. bk.rev.; charts; illus.; circ. 45,000 (paid). **Indexed:** Sportsearch. **Document type:** consumer publication. —UnCover.
   Description: Discusses rock-climbing and mountaineering.

796.552   US   ISSN 1073-4988
CLIMBING ART. 1986. s-a. $20 (foreign $30) (effective 1995 & 1996). Fairfield Communications, 5620 S. 49th St., Lincoln, NE 68516. TEL 800-755-0024. FAX 402-421-1268. Ed. Scott Titterington. adv.; bk.rev. circ. 1,800. (back issues avail.) **Document type:** consumer publication.
   Description: Covers mountaineering and rock climbing. Focuses on biographies, short stories, essays, and poetry about the essence of the climbing experience.

796.522   IT
CLUB ALPINO ITALIANO. RIVISTA. 1874. m. L.50000 to non-members; members L.20000; foreign L.80000 (effective 1994). Club Alpino Italiano, Via E. Fonseca Pimentel 7, 20127 Milan, Italy. TEL 39-2-26141378. FAX 39-2-26141395. Ed. Alessandro Giorgetta. adv.: B&W page L.6000000, color page L.7800000. bk.rev.; abstr.; bibl.; charts; illus.; stat.; tr.lit.; index. circ. 200,000. (tabloid format) **Indexed:** GeoRef.
   Formerly (until 1979): Club Alpino Italiano. Rivista Mensile (ISSN 0009-9511)

796   US
COLEMAN CAMPING AND OUTDOOR ADVENTURES. 1977. a. $2. Aqua-Field Publishing Co., Inc., 66 W. Gilbert St., Shrewsbury, NJ 07702. TEL 201-842-8300. Ed. Steve Ferber. adv.: B&W page $1740, color page $2675; trim 8 1/4 x 10 7/8. circ. 171,517. **Document type:** consumer publication.
   Former titles: Coleman Outdoor Annual; Coleman Camping Annual.

799.1   US
COLORADO HUNTING, FISHING & OUTDOOR GUIDE;* official Colorado-Wyoming fishing guide. 1954-1990 (18th ed.); suspended. biennial. $12.95. Rocky Mountain Angling Club, 1699 S. Quebec, Ste. 102, Englewood, CO 80111. TEL 303-793-1993.
   Former titles: Tim Kelley's Fishing Guide; Official Colorado-Wyoming Fishing Guide.

799   US   ISSN 0010-1699
SK351
COLORADO OUTDOORS. 1952. bi-m. $8.50. Division of Wildlife, 6060 Broadway, Denver, CO 80216. TEL 303-291-7469. Ed. Russell C. Bromby. charts; illus.; index. circ. 60,000. **Indexed:** Key Word Ind.Wildl.Res., Sport Fish.Abstr., Wild.Rev. —UnCover.

799.2   US
COLUMBIA DUCK & GOOSE SHOOTING. 1985. a. $2.50. (Columbia Sportswear) Aqua-Field Publishing Co., Inc., 66 W. Gilbert St., Shrewsbury, NJ 07702. TEL 201-842-8300. Ed. Stephen Ferber. adv. circ. 115,000.

COMMONS, OPEN SPACES AND FOOTPATHS PRESERVATION SOCIETY. ANNUAL REPORT. see CONSERVATION

333   UK
COMPACT TRACTOR & TURF MACHINERY. q. 63 Ulcombe Gardens, Canterbury, Kent CT2 7QZ, England. TEL 0227-470317. FAX 0227-471700. Ed. M. Rose. bk.rev. circ. 4,500.
   Description: Surveys the compact tractor and professional turf and domestic garden machinery industries.

796.5   PO   ISSN 0010-3969
COMPANHEIROS. 6/yr. free. Clube de Campismo de Lisboa, Rua de Misericordia 137, 2 Andar, Lisbon, Portugal. Ed. Armando Almeida Henriques. bk.rev.; illus.

796.5   US   ISSN 1047-1669
COMPETITION ANGLER. 1989. m. $15. 2160 Renwick Dr., Poland, OH 44514. TEL 216-757-8171. Ed. Jack Wollitz. adv. contact: Barb Wollitz. bk.rev.; circ. 500 (controlled). **Document type:** newsletter.
   Description: For tournament-style bass fishermen, primarily in Ohio. Covers bass tournaments, schedules and related bass fishing news.

799.1   SA
COMPLETE FLY FISHERMAN; South Africa's fresh and salt water fly fishing magazine. 1993. m. P.O. Box 3083, Pretoria 0001, South Africa. adv.; illus. **Document type:** consumer publication.

799.3   US   ISSN 1058-3785
SK274
COMPLETE SPORTSMAN: GUNS & HUNTING. bi-m. Harris Publications, Inc., 1115 Broadway, 8th Fl., New York, NY 10010. TEL 212-807-7100. FAX 212-627-4678. Ed. Lamar Underwood.

711
CONGRESS IN PARK AND RECREATION ADMINISTRATION. REPORTS. triennial. International Federation of Park and Recreation Administration, General Secretary, The Grotto, Lower Basildon, Reading, Berkshire RG8 9NE, England. TEL 0491-874222. FAX 0491-874059.
   Formerly: World Congress in Public Park Administration. Reports (ISSN 0510-8225)

799.2   FR
CONNAISSANCE DE LA CHASSE. m. 300 F. (foreign 396 F.). Editions Lariviere, 15-17 Quai de l'Oise, 75166 Paris Cedex 19, France. TEL 1-40-34-22-07. FAX 1-40-35-84-41. TELEX 211 678 F. Ed. Jean Capiod. adv.

333.7   US   ISSN 0092-5764
SD1
CONNECTICUT WALK BOOK. 1937. irreg., 17th ed., 1993. $17. Connecticut Forest and Park Association, Inc., Middlefield, 16 Meriden Rd., Rockfall, CT 06481-2961. TEL 203-346-2372. illus.
   Description: Guide to hiking trails in Connecticut.

796   SP
CONSEJO SUPERIOR DE INVESTIGACIONES CIENTIFICAS. GRUPOS DE MONTANA DE ACCION CULTURAL. BOLETIN INFORMATIVO.* (Text in Spanish; summaries in English, French, Spanish) 1972. s-a. 200 ptas. per no. Consejo Superior de Investigaciones Cientificas (C.S.I.C.), Grupos de Montana de Accion Cultura, Seranno, 117, 28006 Madrid, Spain. adv.; bk.rev.; abstr.; bibl.; illus.; stat.; tr.lit.; index, cum.index. circ. 500.

CONSERVATIONIST. see CONSERVATION

799.3   US
COON-HOUND CORNER. bi-m. 2298 S. Elliott Rd., S.W., Stockport, OH 43787. TEL 614-557-3248. FAX 614-557-3253. Ed. Katherine A. Janson. circ. 9,000.

COUNTRY SPORTS DIRECTORY. see BUSINESS AND ECONOMICS — Trade And Industrial Directories

796   UK   ISSN 0953-2757
COUNTRY WALKING. 1987. m. £26.40 (foreign £33.10) (effective 1995-1996). E M A P - Pursuit Publishing, Bretton Ct., Bretton, Peterborough, Cambs. PE3 8DZ. TEL 01733-264666. FAX 01733-261984. TELEX 32157. (Subscr. to: Tower Publishing Services Ltd., Tower House, Sovereign Park, Lathkill St., Market Harborough, Leics. LE16 9EF, England. TEL 01858-468811. FAX 01858-462164) Ed. Lynne Maxwell; Pub. Melvyn Bagnell. adv. contact: Jane Gray. bk.rev.; circ. 41,017 (paid). (back issues avail.) **Document type:** consumer publication.

799.2   UK   ISSN 1350-9683
THE COUNTRYMAN'S WEEKLY. 1983. w. £49.40. Countrywide Periodical Publishing Ltd., Yelverton, Devon PL20 7PE, England. Ed. Jayne Willcocks; Pub. Vic Gardner. adv. contact: Ruth Isaac. bk.rev. (back issues avail.) **Document type:** newspaper.
   Former titles: Shooting News and Country Weekly; Shooting News and Weekly (ISSN 0954-8718)

COUNTRYSIDE. see CONSERVATION

799.1   US   ISSN 1066-3975
CRAPPIE. 1989. 6/yr. $13.95. NatCom, Inc., 5300 CityPlex Tower, 2448 E. 81st St., Tulsa, OK 74137-4207. TEL 918-491-6100. Ed. Simon McCaffery. adv. contact: Ellie Shimer. circ. 100,000. **Document type:** consumer publication.

796.93   US   ISSN 0278-9213
GV854.4
CROSS COUNTRY SKIER. 1976. 5/yr. $14.97. Collins Chase Publications, Inc., 1823 Fremont Ave. S., Minneapolis, MN 55403. TEL 612-377-0312. Ed. Jim Chase. adv.; bk.rev. circ. 75,000. **Indexed:** Sports Per.Ind., Sportsearch (1981-). —UnCover.
   Formerly (until 1981): Nordic Skiing.
   Description: Devoted to cross country skiing. Provides information for both novice and expert skiers in tuning up techniques, buying equipment, and finding new places to ski.

796.96   CN
CURLING NEWS. 1957. 6/yr. Can.$22. 401 Richmond St. E., Ste. 102, Toronto, ON M5V 1X3, Canada. TEL 800-553-8003. FAX 416-595-9617. Ed. George Karryls; Pub. Brian Cooke. adv. contact: Reid Ferguson. bk.rev. circ. 40,000. **Indexed:** Sportsearch. **Document type:** consumer publication.
   Formerly: Canadian Curling News (ISSN 0045-4648)
   Description: Provides national and international curling news.

796.552   GW
D A V LUDWIGSBURG. MITTEILUNGSBLATT. 1972. a. D A V Ludwigsburg, Deutscher Alpenverein, Sektion Ludwigsburg, Postfach 304, 71603 Ludwigsburg, Germany. TEL 07141-927893. circ. 2,500. (back issues avail.)
   Description: Covers mountaineering and hiking.

D C C - CARAVAN UND MOTORCARAVAN MODELLFUEHRER. (Deutscher Camping Club e.V.) see TRANSPORTATION — Automobiles

796   GW
D V V - KURIER. 1971. m. DM.16. Deutscher Volkssportverband e.V., Fabrikstr. 8, 84503 Altoetting, Germany. TEL 08671-8071. FAX 08671-8377. adv. circ. 12,000. (back issues avail.) **Document type:** newsletter.

D W J - INFO; Mitteilungen des Bundesverbandes. (Deutsche Waldjugend) see FORESTS AND FORESTRY

799   US   ISSN 0194-5769
DAKOTA COUNTRY. 1979. m. $14.95. Mitzel Outdoor Publications, Inc., Box 2714, Bismarck, ND 58502. TEL 701-255-3031. FAX 701-224-1412. Ed. William A. Mitzel. adv. contact: Sylvia Shockman. circ. 11,255. **Document type:** consumer publication.
   Description: Focuses on fishing and hunting in the Dakotas.

SPORTS AND GAMES — OUTDOOR LIFE

799 US ISSN 0891-902X
DAKOTA OUTDOORS. 1976. m. $10. Hipple Publishing Co., Inc., 333 W. Dakota, Box 669, Pierre, SD 57501-0669. TEL 605-224-7301. FAX 605-224-9210. Ed. Kevin Hipple. adv. contact: Terrly Hipple. bk.rev.; tr.lit. circ. 6,597. (also avail. in microfilm; back issues avail.) **Document type:** consumer publication.
  Formerly (until 1986): Dakota Fisherman.
  Description: Covers all spects of hunting and fishing as well as outdoor news, legislative, governmental and regulatory actions. Also provides product information, hints, tips.

779.2 US
DEER AND BIG GAME. 1977. a. $2.75. Times Mirror Magazines, Inc., 2 Park Ave., New York, NY 10016. TEL 212-779-5000. Ed. Vin T. Sparano. adv.; illus. circ. 150,000. (reprint service avail. from UMI)
  Former titles: Midwest Fishing by Outdoor Life; Outdoor Life's Guide to Fishing the Midwest.

799.2 US ISSN 0164-7318
DEER & DEER HUNTING; practical & comprehensive information for white-tailed deer hunters. 1977. 8/yr. $17.95. Krause Publications, Inc., 700 E. State St., Iola, WI 54990. TEL 715-445-2214. FAX 715-445-4087. TELEX 556461 KRAUSE PUB UD. Ed. Pat Durkin. adv. contact: Dave Larsen. bk.rev. circ. 247,000.

799.2 US
DEER TRAIL. 1983. 5/yr. $20 includes membership. Whitetails Unlimited, Inc., Box 720, Sturgeon Bay, WI 54235-0720. TEL 414-743-6777. adv. circ. 35,000. **Document type:** consumer publication.

799.2 US
DEER UNLIMITED MAGAZINE.* 1978. bi-m. $7. Deer Unlimited of America, Inc., Box 1129, Abbeville, SC 29620-1129. Ed. Jim Edens. circ. 9,000.
  Description: Gives hunting tips.

DEL-MAR-VA HEARTLAND. see *AGRICULTURE*

796.525 UK ISSN 0046-0036
DESCENT; the magazine for cavers. 1969. bi-m. £14.10($22) Ambit Publications, Fuller Ct., Ste. 1, Lower Quay St., Gloucester GL2 2LW, England. FAX 01452-423430. Ed. Chris Howes; Pub. Keith Creighton. adv. contact: Sue Dwyer. bk.rev.; charts; illus. circ. 3,000. **Indexed:** Sportsearch.
  —BLDSC (3555.750000).
  Description: Covers the sprot of caving and speleology.

DESIGN. see *ARCHITECTURE*

799.2 GW ISSN 0724-2654
DEUTSCHE JAGD-ZEITUNG; Forum fuer Jaeger und Naturfreunde. 1983. m. DM.98. Mittelrhein Verlag GmbH, Feldstr. 6, 56377 Nassau, Germany. TEL 02604-97010. FAX 02604-970130. Ed. Walterpeter Twer. circ. 51,000. **Document type:** bulletin.

796.522 GW ISSN 0012-1088
DEUTSCHER ALPENVEREIN; Mitteilungen-Jugend am Berg. 1948. bi-m. DM.6 membership. Deutscher Alpenverein, Von-Kahr-Str. 2-4, 80997 Munich, Germany. Ed. Elmar Landes. adv.; bk.rev.; illus.; index. **Indexed:** GeoRef. **Document type:** consumer publication.
  Description: Covers mountaineering in the Alps.

799 AG ISSN 0012-2327
DIANA.* 1935. m. Tacuari 237, Buenos Aires, Argentina. Ed. Dir. Francisco Jose Cabrera. adv.; charts; illus.; mkt.
  Description: Focuses on fishing and hunting.

799.2 IT ISSN 0012-2343
DIANA (FLORENCE); rivista del cacciatore. 1906. q. L.103000 (foreign L.137000). Editoriale Olimpia S.p.A., Viale Milton 7, 50129 Florence, Italy. TEL 39-55-473843. FAX 39-55-499195. TELEX 573084 EDOL I. Ed. Dir. Giuliano Incerpi. adv.; B&W page L.4200000, color page L.7650000. illus.; index. circ. 92,000. **Document type:** academic/scholarly publication.

796 US
DIRECTIONS (CHICAGO). 1976. m. $20 (foreign $25). Live Free, Inc., 11123 St. Lawrence Ave., Chicago, IL 60628. TEL 312-821-5483. (Subscr. to: Box 1743, Harvey, IL 60426) Eds. James C. Jones, Joe Wieser. adv.; bk.rev.; illus. circ. 1,212. (back issues avail.) **Document type:** newsletter.
  Description: Articles, classified advertisements, and announcements on family and self-reliance and emergency survival tactics and products.

790.1 551.44 UK ISSN 0264-4975
DIRECTORY OF BRITISH CAVING CLUBS (YEAR). 1982. a. £5. Rhychydwr, Crymych, Dyfed SA41 3RB, Wales. TEL 0239-831-371. Ed. Tony Oldham. adv. circ. 3,000. (back issues avail.) **Document type:** directory.

792 US ISSN 0361-4255
T391
DIRECTORY OF NORTH AMERICAN FAIRS, FESTIVALS AND EXPOSITIONS. Variant title: Amusement Business's Directory North American Fairs. 1888. a. $50. B P I Communications, Amusement Business Division, Box 24970, Nashville, TN 37202. TEL 615-321-4250. FAX 615-327-1575. circ. 1,600. **Document type:** directory.
  Formerly (until 1972): Cavalcade and Directory of Fairs (ISSN 0069-1291)
  Description: Lists over 3,500 state and county fairs, festivals and public expositions in the U.S. and Canada that run three days or more. Contains general and statistical data plus chronological cross references.

796 362.4 US ISSN 1067-098X
DISABLED OUTDOORS MAGAZINE. 1987. q. $14 (Canada $20). John Kopchik, Jr., HC 80, Box 395 Grand Marais, MN 55604. TEL 218-387-9100. FAX 218-387-9100. Ed. Carolyn Dohme. adv.; bk.rev. circ. 7,800. **Document type:** consumer publication.
  Description: Covers outdoor sports such as fishing, camping, sky diving and water skiing for disabled people.

796.352 US ISSN 0892-2357
DISC GOLF WORLD NEWS. 1984. q. $15 in U.S.; Canada $20; Europe $21; elsewhere $23. Disc Golf World, Box 4474, Overland Park, KS 66204-0474. TEL 913-648-1905. FAX 913-648-1116. Eds. Lynne & Rick Rothstein. adv. contact: Rick Rothstein. bk.rev.; charts; illus.; stat. circ. 950.
  Formerly: Columbia Disc Golf News.
  Description: Review and preview of disc golf events, equipment and promotions, results, interviews, cartoons, and instructional pieces.

799.1 US ISSN 1071-6432
DISCOVERING AND EXPLORING NEW JERSEY'S FISHING STREAMS AND THE DELAWARE RIVER. 1991. a. $10.95 (effective 1994). New Jersey Sportsmen's Guides, Box 100, Somerdale, NJ 08083. TEL 609-665-8350. FAX 609-665-8656. Ed. Steve Perrone; Pub. Steve Perrone. illus.; maps. circ. 7,500. **Document type:** consumer publication.
  Formerly (until 1993): Discovering and Exploring New Jersey's Fishing Streams (ISSN 1058-5761)
  Description: Covers stream and river fishing in New Jersey.

796.552 790.1 US ISSN 1069-6660
DIVIDENDS. 1980. s-a. $5. Continental Divide Trail Society, Box 30002, Bethesda, MD 20824. TEL 410-235-9610. Ed. Gary Grey. bk.rev. circ. 250. **Document type:** newsletter.
  Description: Reports on progress in developing and managing the Continental Divide National Scenic Trail.

799.2 US ISSN 0737-0105
TS536.6.M8
DIXIE GUN WORKS BLACKPOWDER ANNUAL. a. $2.95. Dixie Gun Works, Box 684, Union City, TN 38281. TEL 901-885-0374. FAX 901-885-0440. Ed. Butch Winter. adv. circ. 100,000. (back issues avail.)
  Description: Covers hunting, history, modern uses of black powder, and topics relating to the black powder era.

796.93 UK ISSN 0070-718X
DOWNHILL ONLY JOURNAL. 1936. a. membership. Downhill Only Club, c/o D.F. Ryan, Brigadier, Lodwick, Monxton, Hants SP11 8AW, England. adv.; bk.rev.; index. circ. 1,700.

352.7 799 US
DWELLING PORTABLY. 1980. 3/yr. $1 per no. Light Living Library, Box 190-UR, Philomath, OR 97370. Eds. Holly & Bert Davis. adv.; bk.rev. circ. 1,300. (back issues avail.) **Document type:** newsletter.
  Former titles: Portable Dwelling; Message Post.
  Description: Emphasis on long-period backpack camping.

769.93 US
E S R BUYERS' GUIDE. a. Eastern Ski Representatives Association, H.C.R. 1, Box 7, White Haven, PA 18661. TEL 717-443-7180. **Document type:** consumer publication.

796.93 US
E S R NEWSLETTER. irreg. Eastern Ski Representatives Association, H.C.R. 1, Box 7, White Haven, PA 18661. TEL 717-443-7180. **Document type:** newsletter.

799.1 US ISSN 0899-0506
EAST COAST ANGLER.* 1987. w. $15. East Coast Angler, Inc., P.O. Box 280, Somerville, NJ 08876-0280. TEL 800-333-4744. FAX 201-295-2008. Ed. Mickey Cooper. adv.; bk.rev. circ. 10,000. (back issues avail.)
  Description: Reports on fresh and saltwater fishing.

796.93 330 US ISSN 1070-9231
GV854.8.N58
ECONOMIC ANALYSIS OF UNITED STATES SKI AREAS. 1971. a. $150. University of Colorado, Business Research Division, Campus Box 420, Boulder, CO 80309-0420. TEL 303-492-8227. FAX 303-492-3620. **Indexed:** SRI.
  Formerly (until 1994): Economic Analysis of North American Ski Areas (ISSN 0147-4243)

796.5 UK
EN ROUTE. 1963. 7/yr. membership. Caravan Club, East Grinstead House, E. Grinstead, W. Sussex RH19 1UA, England. Ed. David Hunter. adv.; bk.rev. circ. 190,000.

796 US
THE EQUIPMENT GUIDE. a. $3.95. Ehlert Publishing Group, Inc., 601 Lakeshore Pkwy., Minnetonka, MN 55305. TEL 612-476-2200. **Document type:** consumer publication.

796 799 FI ISSN 0356-3464
ERA. 1977. m. FIM 315. Yhtyneet Kuvalehdet Oy, Maistraatinportti 1, FIN-00240 Helsinki, Finland. TEL 358-0-156-6524. FAX 358-0-156-6505. TELEX 121364. Ed. Seppo Suuronen. adv.; B&W page FIM 7800, color page FIM 11500. circ. 45,437.
  Description: Focuses on camping, fishing and hunting. Each issues carries a special theme.

799 FI ISSN 1236-5548
ERAMIES. 1946. bi-m. FIM 60. Suomen Metsastaja ja Kalastajaliitto r.y., Hiekkakuja 1C, 33230 Tampere, Finland. TEL 35831-2126543. FAX 35831-223356. Ed. Kalervo Saarinen. adv.: B&W page FIM 4200, color page FIM 6600; trim 180 x 245. bk.rev. circ. 12,000.
  Description: Includes stories, technical reports, hunting and fishing tips.

ESCAPEES. see *TRANSPORTATION — Automobiles*

ESCAPEES CLUB. ANNUAL DIRECTORY. see *TRANSPORTATION — Automobiles*

797.173 VE
ESQUI ACUATICO Y OTROS DEPORTES. 1975. 6/yr. Av. Lisboa, Ota La Caromotana 5-01-19-28, Calif. Norte, Caracas 1070, Venezuela. adv. circ. 10,000.

796 US
ESQUIRE SPORTSMAN; the good life for men. 1992. q. $3.95 per no. Hearst Corporation, Esquire, 250 W. 55th St., New York, NY 10019. TEL 212-459-7500. Ed. Terry McDonell. adv.; illus.
  Description: Articles, fiction, celebrity profiles and equipment reviews focusing on outdoor life, hunting and fishing.

6160 SPORTS AND GAMES — OUTDOOR LIFE

796 333.7   BE
EURO-UNION GICEF. 1972. Allard Robert Cie, c/o Art et Nature, Route d'Orval 44, 6823 Florenville, Belgium. TEL 32-61-312726. FAX 32-61-312709. adv.: B&W page 21600 BEF, color page 29500 BEF.
   Formerly: Foret Chasse Peche Environnement.
   Description: Covers topics relating to outdoor recreation, hunting, fishing, conservation and matters of interest to land and forest owners.

796.5   GW   ISSN 0071-2272
EUROPA CAMPING UND CARAVANING. INTERNATIONALER FUEHRER. (Text in English, French and German) 1959. a. DM.22.80. Drei Brunnen Verlag und Co., Postfach 101154, 7000 Stuttgart 10, Germany. FAX 0711-2576217. Ed. Ursel Wunder-Gessler.

796.93   IT
EUROSKI. 1967. a. L.4500. Ideapiu S.r.l., Via Durini 3, 20122 Milan, Italy. Ed. Paolo De Michele. adv. circ. 26,000.

790.1   CN   ISSN 0714-816X
EXPLORE; Canada's outdoor adventure magazine. 1981. 6/yr. Can.$24($26.70) Thompson & Gordon Publishing Co. Ltd., 301 14th St., N.W., No. 420, Calgary, AB T2N 2A1, Canada. FAX 403-270-7922. Ed. Marion Harrison. adv.: B&W page Can.$1945, color page Can.$2915; 8 3/16 x 10 7/8. bk.rev. circ. 30,000. (also avail. in microfiche; reprint service avail. from MML; back issues avail.). **Indexed:** Can.B.P.I., Can.Per.Ind., CMI. **Document type:** consumer publication.
   Formerly: Explore Alberta.
   Description: Focuses on backpacking, bicycling, canoeing and skiing featuring Canadian destinations. Covers ecotourism, the environment, outdoor photography, sports medicine, equipment and new products for the outdoor recreationist.

EXPLORE MINNESOTA CAMPGROUND GUIDE. see *TRAVEL AND TOURISM*

796.95 796.42   US
EXPLORE MINNESOTA CROSS-COUNTRY SKIING. a. free. Office of Tourism, 100 Metro Square, 121 7th Pl. E., St. Paul, MN 55101. TEL 800-657-3700. circ. 15,000. **Document type:** consumer publication.

796   US
EXPLORE MINNESOTA DOWNHILL SKIING. a. free. Office of Tourism, 100 Metro Square, 121 7th Pl. E., St. Paul, MN 55101. TEL 800-657-3700. circ. 13,000.

EXPLORE MINNESOTA HIKING. see *TRAVEL AND TOURISM*

796.93   SZ   ISSN 0425-5291
F I S BULLETIN. (Text in English, French, German) q. 32 SFr. (International Ski Federation) Hallwag AG, Nordring 4, CH-3000 Bern, Switzerland. TEL 031-3323131. FAX 031-3314133. TELEX 912661-CH. circ. 1,709. (back issues avail.) **Indexed:** Sportsearch (1973-). **Document type:** bulletin.

FAIR CHASE. see *CONSERVATION*

FAIRS AND FESTIVALS (YEAR). see *ARTS AND HANDICRAFTS*

910.2   UK   ISSN 0957-7327
FAMILY SITES GUIDE. 1966. a. £3. Haymarket Magazines Ltd., 38-42 Hampton Rd., Teddington, Middx. TW11 0JE, England. TEL 081-943-5000. TELEX 895-2440-HAYMRT-G.
   Former titles: Camper Sites Guide; Practical Camper's Sites Guide; Camping Sites in Britain and France (ISSN 0068-6980)
   Description: Lists and evaluates over 1500 camper sites.

FANG; Fuehrungszeitschrift. see *FORESTS AND FORESTRY*

FARM POND HARVEST. see *FISH AND FISHERIES*

796.552 910.09   IC   ISSN 1022-1271
FARVIS - AFANGAR; timarit um ferdamal. 1979. q. ISK 600 per no. Farvegur hf, Bolholti 4, 105-Reykjavik, Iceland. TEL 354-568-0699. FAX 354-568-0649. Ed. Thorunn Gestsdottir. circ. 6,000.
   Formerly (until 1988): Afangar (ISSN 1017-3501)
   Description: Focuses on outdoor living and traveling in Iceland and abroad.

799   US   ISSN 0015-0673
SK1
FIELD & STREAM. 1895. m. $15.94. Times Mirror Magazines, Inc., 2 Park Ave., New York, NY 10016. TEL 212-779-5000. FAX 212-725-3836. (Subscr. to: Box 54734, Boulder, CO 90321-4734. TEL 800-289-0639) Ed. Duncan Barnes. adv.; bk.rev.; charts; illus. circ. 2,000,000. (also avail. in microform from UMI; reprint service avail. from UMI) **Indexed:** Abr.R.G., Biog.Ind., Consum.Ind., Jun.High.Mag.Abstr., Mag.Ind., PMR, R.G., Sports Per.Ind., TOM.
   •Also available online. Vendor(s): University Microfilms International. —UMI.
   Description: Gives hunting and fishing tips.

799.17   US   ISSN 0163-5468
SH681
FIELD & STREAM BASS FISHING ANNUAL.* Short title: Bass Fishing. 1977. a. $2.50 (newstand sales only). Times Mirror Magazines, Inc., 2 Park Ave., New York, NY 10016-5675. TEL 212-779-5000. Ed. Glenn Sapir. circ. 200,000.

799   US   ISSN 1057-6428
SK301
FIELD & STREAM DEER HUNTER'S GUIDE.* Short title: Deer Hunting. 1978. a. $2.50 (newstand sales only). Times Mirror Magazines, Inc., 2 Park Ave., New York, NY 10016-5675. TEL 212-779-5000. Ed. Glenn Sapir. circ. 250,000.
   Formerly: Field & Stream Deer Hunting Annual (ISSN 0163-5042)

799.1   US   ISSN 0362-6385
SH401
FIELD & STREAM FISHING ANNUAL.* Short title: Fishing. 1976. a. $2.50 (newstand sales only). Times Mirror Magazines, Inc., 2 Park Ave., New York, NY 10016-5675. TEL 212-779-5000. Ed. Glenn Sapir. illus. circ. 250,000.

799.2   US   ISSN 0361-3011
SK1
FIELD & STREAM HUNTING ANNUAL.* Short title: Hunting Annual (New York). 1975. a. $2.50 (newstand sales only). Times Mirror Magazines, Inc., 2 Park Ave., New York, NY 10016-5675. TEL 212-779-5000. Ed. Glenn Sapir. illus. circ. 250,000.

799.2   US   ISSN 1062-1091
FIGHTING KNIVES. 1989. bi-m. $14.95. Larry Flynt Publications, Inc., 9171 Wilshire Blvd., Ste. 300, Beverly Hills, CA 90210. TEL 310-858-7100. FAX 310-274-7985. Ed. Gregory A. Walker. adv.; bk.rev. **Document type:** consumer publication.
   Description: Contains complete reviews of custom knives and their makers, combat and field use evaluations of custom and commercial knives, and coverage of knife accessories and related areas.

796.42   SW   ISSN 0345-3332
FINAL; Svenska skolidrottsfoerbundets tidning. 1949. 5/yr. SEK 60 (effective 1991). Svenska Skolidrottsfoerbundet, Idrottens Hus, 123 87 Farsta, Sweden. adv. circ. 6,000.

799.2   IT
FIRE-ARMS MADE IN ITALY. 1990. a. Albatros Pubblicita s.r.l., Via Ausonio 12, 20123 Milan, Italy. TEL 39-2-89408053. FAX 39-2-89408199. Ed. Giancarlo Lubner. adv.: B&W page L.1000000, color page L.1800000; adv. contact: Giancarlo Lubner. circ. 5,000. **Document type:** catalog.

799.1   GW   ISSN 0015-2838
FISCH UND FANG; Erlebnis Magazin fuer Angler. 1960. m. DM.68.40($46) Verlag Paul Parey (Hamburg), Spitalerstr. 12, 20095 Hamburg, Germany. TEL 040-33969-0. FAX 040-33969-199. TELEX 2161291-PARV-D. Ed. Thomas Wendt. adv.; illus.; index. circ. 85,000. (reprint service avail. from ISI) **Document type:** consumer publication.
   Formerly: Fischwaid (ISSN 0722-706X)

799.1
FISH AND GAME FINDER. (In 22 regional editions.) 1973. m. free. Fish and Game Finder Magazines, Inc., 1233 W. Jackson St., Orlando, FL 32805. TEL 407-425-0045. FAX 407-425-1529. circ. 300,000. (controlled).
   Formerly: Fish Finder.
   Description: Promotes the various types of fishing and hunting for the active outdoorsman.

799.1   US   ISSN 0747-3397
THE FISH SNIFFER; for the northern California, Nevada, and Oregon angler. (Includes bi-monthly feature supplement Gamefishing West.) 1982. bi-w. $35. Northern California Angler Publications, Inc., Box 994, Elk Grove, CA 95759-0994. TEL 916-685-2245. FAX 916-685-1498. Ed. Daniel K. Bacher. adv.; circ. 21,500 (paid). (tabloid format; back issues avail.)
   Description: Up-to-date news and features covering recreational fishing and conservation in the West.

799.1   US
FISHERMAN. (In 5 regional editions: Florida (ISSN 1059-5295); Long Island & Metro New York (1040-0109); Mid-Atlantic (1040-0133); New England (1040-0125); New Jersey (1040-0117)) 1966. w. $20. L I F Publishing Corp., 14 Ramsey Rd., Shirley, NY 11967. TEL 516-345-5200. Ed. Fred Golofaro. adv.; bk.rev.; bibl.; illus.; tr.lit.
   Formerly: Long Island Fisherman.
   Description: Provides regional coverage of recreational fishing.

799.1   IT
FISHERMAN E DIPORTO. 1992. q. L.27000 (Europe L.57000, elsewhere L.77000). ED.A.I. s.r.l., Via G. Guinicelli 4, 50133 Florence, Italy. TEL 39-55-574774. FAX 39-55-570103. Ed. Ugo Passalacqua. adv.: B&W page L.3300000, color page L.4150000. circ. 40,000. **Document type:** consumer publication.

799   US   ISSN 0015-301X
FISHING AND HUNTING NEWS. (Ten editions avail. covering 13 Western states) 1944. bi-w. $49.95. Outdoor Empire Publishing, Inc., 511 Eastlake Ave. E., Box C 19000, Seattle, WA 98109. TEL 206-624-3845. FAX 206-340-9816. Ed. Pat McGann. adv.; bk.rev.; charts; illus.; stat. circ. 110,000. (tabloid format)

799.1   US
FISHING FACTS. Northern edition (ISSN 0899-9597); Southern edition (ISSN 0899-9589) 1963. 7/yr. $14.97. Fishing Facts, Inc., 312 E. Buffalo St., Milwaukee, WI 53202. TEL 414-287-4333. Eds. Spencer Petros, Carl Malz. adv.; charts; stat.; illus.; index. circ. 125,000. **Indexed:** Sports Per.Ind.
   Formerly: Fishing News.

799.1   US   ISSN 1063-1577
SH559
FISHING HOLES.* 1974. m. Fishing Holes Magazine, 14505 N.E. 91st St., Redmondon, WA 98052-6585.

796   UK
FISHING IN BRITAIN; the definitive and essential guide for anglers in Britain. 1986. a. £6.95. Peerage Publications, P.O. Box 5135, Strand-on-the-Green, Chiswick, London W4 3WN, England. TEL 0181-747-0385. Ed. Sara Marden-King; Pub. Bruce Duncan. adv.: B&W page £460, color page £830; trim 210 x 148. circ. 100,000. **Document type:** directory.
   Formerly: England for Fishing.

799.1   US   ISSN 0164-0941
SH505
FISHING IN MARYLAND. 1953. a. $6.95. Fishing in Maryland, Inc., Box 201, Phoenix, MD 21131. TEL 410-561-3720. Ed. Bill Burton; Pub. W. Cary de Russy. adv. contact: W. Cary de Russy. illus. circ. 29,000. **Document type:** consumer publication.
   Supersedes in part: Fishing in the Mid-Atlantic; Fishing in Maryland and Virginia (ISSN 0363-8898)

FISHING MAGAZINE FOR YOUNG BOY. see *CHILDREN AND YOUTH — For*

SPORTS AND GAMES — OUTDOOR LIFE

799.1   AT   ISSN 0816-7885
FISHING NEWS; the newsmagazine of Australian angling. 1970. 10/yr. Aus.$33.15. Mason Stewart Publishing Pty. Ltd., P.O. Box 746, Darlinghust, N.S.W. 2010, Australia. TEL 02-331-5006. FAX 02-360-5367. Ed. Paul B. Kidd. circ. 14,500. (back issues avail.) **Document type:** consumer publication.
    Description: For amateur anglers. Advises where and how to catch fish in Australia.

799.1   US
FISHING SMART. 1987. a. $2.50. (Mercury Marine) Aqua-Field Publishing Co., Inc., 66 W. Gilbert St., Shrewsbury, NJ 07702. TEL 201-842-8300. Ed. Stephen Ferber. adv. circ. 110,000.

799.1   US   ISSN 8750-1287
FISHING TACKLE RETAILER. 1980. 11/yr. free to qualified personnel. B.A.S.S., Inc., Box 17900, Montgomery, AL 36117-0900. TEL 205-272-9530. FAX 205-279-7148. Ed. Dave Ellison. adv. circ. 21,000. **Document type:** consumer publication.
    Former titles: Fishing Tackle Retailer Magazine (ISSN 0745-8169); Fishing Tackle Retailer (ISSN 0274-788X)

799.1   US   ISSN 0015-3060
FISHING TACKLE TRADE NEWS. 1952. m. $45. Fishing Tackle Trade News, Inc., Div. Vickers Communications, Box 2669, Vancouver, WA 98668-2669. TEL 360-693-4721. FAX 360-693-3997. Ed. John Kirk; Pub. Bob Vickers. adv. contact: Bob Vickers. bk.rev.; illus.; circ. 21,500 (controlled). **Document type:** trade publication.
    Description: Serves retailers of tackle and fishing products; wholesalers, jobbers, distributors, buying groups; importers and exporters of fishing products and sporting goods.

799.1   AT   ISSN 1320-2839
FISHING WORLD. 1969. m. Aus.$57 (foreign Aus.$152) (effective Feb. 1995). Yaffa Publishing Group, 17-21 Bellevue St., Surry Hills, N.S.W. 2010, Australia. TEL 61-2-282-2333. FAX 61-2-281-2750. Ed. G. Schott. adv.: B&W page Aus.$1645, color page Aus.$1825; trim 273 x 210. charts; illus.; tr.lit. circ. 22,505. **Document type:** consumer publication.
    Former titles: Australian Angler's Fishing World (ISSN 0158-572X); Australian Angler (ISSN 0045-0235)
    Description: Highlights various fishing methods.

799.1   US   ISSN 0015-3079
SH401
FISHING WORLD. 1955. 6/yr. $14.95. (Fishing Club of America) K C Publishing Inc., 700 W. 74th St., Ste. 310, Kansas City, MO 64112. TEL 816-531-5730. FAX 816-531-3873. Ed. Chuck Harper. adv.; bk.rev.; illus.; index. circ. 270,000. (back issues avail.) **Document type:** consumer publication.
    Description: Covers all phases of sport fishing in both fresh and Saltwater environments.

799   CN   ISSN 0847-9992
FISH'N CANADA NEWS. 1988. 4/yr. Can.$9.95 (US $9.95 elsewhere Can.$20). Fish'n Canada News Ltd., 1240 Phillip Murray Ave., Ste. 1, Oshawa, ON L1J 6Z9, Canada. TEL 416-571-3223. FAX 416-571-3328. Ed. Mary-Anne King. adv. circ. 127,000. (tabloid format)

799.1   DK   ISSN 0109-1581
FISK & FRI; alt om lystfiskeri. 1983. m. DKK 270. Kronprinsessegade 42, DK-1306 Copenhagen K, Denmark. Ed. Svend Erik Vardrup. adv.; illus. circ. 20,000.

799.1   SW   ISSN 1100-3626
FISKE FOER ALLA. 1988. 8/yr. SEK 273. Bonniers Specialtidningar AB, P.O. Box 70452, S-107 26 Stockholm, Sweden. (Subscr. to: Pressdata AB, P.O. Box 3217, S-103 64 Stockholm, Sweden) Ed. Johnny Albertsson. adv.: B&W page SEK 11500, color page 13500.

FISKERIBLADET. see FISH AND FISHERIES

796.5   SW   ISSN 1104-6503
FJAELLET. 1956. q. SEK 100. Svenska Fjaellklubben (SFK) - Swedish Alpine Club, Tegeluddsv. 30, S-115 40 Stockholm, Sweden. FAX 46-8-358-972. Ed. Goeran Fagerstroem. adv.: B&W page SEK 1200; adv. contact: Grethe Broberg. bk.rev.; circ. 1,500 (paid). **Document type:** newsletter.
    Formerly (until 1994): Fjaellklubbsnytt (ISSN 0348-5013)
    Description: Concentrates on all aspects of mountaineering.

796.552   NO   ISSN 0332-8775
FJELL OG VIDDE. 1967. q. Norske Turistforening, Stortingsgate 28, N., Oslo 1, Norway. adv.; bk.rev. circ. 115,000.

799.1   GW   ISSN 0178-0409
FLIEGENFISCHEN; internationales Magazin fuer Flugangler. 1984. 6/yr. DM.89.40. Jahr-Verlag GmbH & Co., Jessenstr. 1, 22767 Hamburg, Germany. TEL 040-38906-0. FAX 040-38906302. TELEX 2163485. Ed. Bernd Kuleisa; Pub. Alexander Jahr. adv. contact: Bernd Hacker. circ. 12,500. (back issues avail.) **Document type:** consumer publication.

799.1   GW   ISSN 0176-2087
DER FLIEGENFISCHER. 1975. bi-m. DM.76($42) Verlag J. Schueck, Lohhofer Str. 11, 90453 Nuernberg, Germany. (Subscr. addr.: P.O. Box 1170, 8504 Stein, Germany) adv.; bk.rev.; index. circ. 5,000. (back issues avail.)
    Description: Covers fly fishing.

799   US   ISSN 0889-3322
FLORIDA GAME & FISH. 1986. m. $14.97. Game & Fish Publications, Inc., 2250 Newmarket Pkwy., Ste. 110, Box 741, Marietta, GA 30061-0741. TEL 404-953-9222. FAX 404-933-9510. Ed. Jimmy Jacobs. circ. 13,518. (back issues avail.)
    Description: Covers hunting and fishing in Florida.

799   US   ISSN 0015-3885
FLORIDA SPORTSMAN. 1969. m. $18.95 (effective 1994-1995). Wickstrom Publishers, Inc., 5901 S.W. 74th St., Ste. 310, Miami, FL 33143. TEL 305-661-4222. FAX 305-284-0277. Pub. Karl Wickstrom. adv. contact: Bob Mitchell. bk.rev.; charts; illus.; circ. 105,665 (paid). **Indexed:** Acid Rain Abstr., Acid Rain Ind.
    Formerly (until 1971): Florida and Tropic Sportsman.
    Description: For fisherman both visiting and residing in Florida, the Bahamas, and the American tropics. Covers fishing, hunting, boating.

FLORIDA WILDLIFE. see CONSERVATION

799.3   US
FLORIDA WOODS & WATERS MAGAZINE.* 1984. 4/yr. $16. NewTech Solutions, Inc., 800 N. Magnolia Ave., Ste. 1650, Orlando, FL 32803-3256. TEL 407-629-2393. FAX 407-629-5448. Ed. Paul Andrea. adv. circ. 21,000. **Document type:** consumer publication.

796.172   BL   ISSN 0104-155X
FLUIR. (Supplement avail.: Fluir Bodyboard) 1987. m. $130. Editora Azul, S.A., Av. Nacoes Unidas, 5777, 05479-900 Sao Paulo SP, Brazil. TEL 11-816-7866. FAX 11-813-9115. (Subscr. to: Rua do Curtume 769, 05065-900 Sao Paulo SP, Brazil. TEL 011-823-9100) Ed. Jorge de Souza. adv.: color page $8096; 208 x 274. charts; illus. circ. 19,000. **Document type:** consumer publication.
    Description: Covers surfing: championships, equipment and fashions.

FLY AND GLIDE. see AERONAUTICS AND SPACE FLIGHT

799.1   US   ISSN 0015-4741
SH401
FLY FISHERMAN. 1969. 6/yr. $24. Cowles Magazines, Inc. (Subsidiary of: Cowles Media Company), 6405 Flank Dr., Box 8200, Harrisburg, PA 17105-8200. TEL 717-657-9555. FAX 717-657-9526. Ed. John Randolph. adv.; bk.rev.; cum.index vols. 1-16. circ. 130,000. (reprint service avail. from UMI) **Document type:** consumer publication.
    —Faxon; UMI; UnCover.

799.1   US
FLY FISHING MADE EASY. 1984. a. $2.95. (Scientific Anglers) Aqua-Field Publishing Co., Inc., 66 W. Gilbert St., Shrewsbury, NJ 07702. TEL 201-842-8300. Ed. Stephen Ferber. adv. circ. 130,000.

799.1   US   ISSN 1045-0149
FLY ROD & REEL. 1979. 6/yr. $14.97. Down East Enterprise, Inc., Box 679, Camden, ME 04843. TEL 207-594-9544. FAX 207-594-7215. Ed. Jim Butler. adv. circ. 52,429.
    Formerly: Rod and Reel (ISSN 0194-925X)
    Description: Covers conservation and fly-fishing how-to, equipment reviews and travel.

799   US
FLY TACKLE DEALER. 6/yr. Down East Enterprise, Inc., Box 679, Camden, ME 04843. TEL 207-594-9544. FAX 207-594-7215. Ed. Jim Butler. adv.; bk.rev. circ. 10,500. (back issues avail.) **Document type:** trade publication.
    Description: Trade magazine for makers and sellers of fly-fishing equipment.

799.1   US   ISSN 0147-8834
SH456
FLYFISHER. 1968. q. membership. Federation of Fly Fishers, Box 722, Sandpoint, ID 83864. TEL 208-263-3573. Ed. Dennis G. Bitton. adv.: page $1035. bk.rev.; tr.lit. circ. 15,000. (back issues avail.)
    Description: Covers articles on fly fishing, where, how, why, and news from what's happening in the Federation.

799.1   UK   ISSN 0046-4228
FLYFISHERS JOURNAL. 1911. s-a. £17. Flyfishers' Club, 24A Old Burlington St., London W.1., England. Ed. Kenneth Robson. adv.; bk.rev.; index. circ. 1,400. **Document type:** consumer publication.
    —BLDSC (4754.230000).

799.1   US   ISSN 0744-7191
FLYFISHING. 1978. 5/yr. $15.95. Frank Amato Publications, Box 82112, Portland, OR 97282. TEL 503-653-8151. FAX 503-653-2766. Ed. Marty Sherman. adv. contact: Sherry Gullings. bk.rev.; circ. 36,649 (paid). **Document type:** consumer publication.
    Description: Covers casting, fly tying, knots, best places to fish, conservation, new product services and domestic and foreign news.

799.3 333.7
FOCUS (INDIANAPOLIS). bi-m. Department of Natural Resources, 402 W. Washington, Rm. W273, Indianapolis, IN 46204. TEL 317-232-4080. FAX 317-232-8150. Ed. Jon Marshall. circ. 32,000. **Document type:** newsletter.

FODOR'S SKIING IN THE U S A & CANADA. see TRAVEL AND TOURISM

796.5 910.202   US
FODOR'S SPORTS: HIKING. irreg. $12. Fodor's Travel Publications, Inc. (Subsidiary of: Random House, Inc.), 201 E. 50th St., New York, NY 10022. TEL 800-733-3000. (Dist. by: Random House, Inc., 400 Hahn Rd., Westminster, MD 21157) Eds. Cindy Ross, Michael Spring.

796.42 910.202   US
FODOR'S SPORTS: RUNNING. irreg. $12. Fodor's Travel Publications, Inc. (Subsidiary of: Random House, Inc.), 201 E. 50th St., New York, NY 10022. TEL 800-733-3000. (Dist. by: Random House, Inc., 400 Hahn Rd., Westminster, MD 21157) Eds. John Schubert, Michael Spring.

796.552 790.1   US   ISSN 1064-0681
THE FOOTPRINT. 1966. bi-m. membership only. Florida Trail Association, Box 13708, Gainesville, FL 32604. Eds. Don Meinders, Marie Meinders.

FRANCE - SPORTS. see SPORTS AND GAMES

797   NZ
FREE FALL KIWI.* 1972. bi-m. NZ.$7. New Zealand Federation of Parachute Clubs, Inc., 30a Grange Rd., Honick, Auckland, New Zealand. adv.; charts; illus.

SPORTS AND GAMES — OUTDOOR LIFE

796.172   AT   ISSN 0727-615X
FREESAIL. 1982. q. Mason Stewart Publishing Pty. Ltd., P.O. Box 746, Darlinghursty, N.S.W. 2010, Australia. TEL 02-331-5006. FAX 02-360-5367. Ed. Michael McGrath. adv. contact: Steven Kay. video rev. circ. 16,000.
  Description: Covers windsurfing: pictorials, travel, news, technique tips, product information.

796.5   GW
FREIZEIT - CARAVAN - CAMPING MAGAZIN. 1976. m. DM.20. F C C Verlag, Blumenweg 13, 30900 Wedemark, Germany. adv.; bk.rev.; illus. circ. 209,000.

FRIENDS OF PARKS & RECREATION. see CONSERVATION

796   SW   ISSN 0283-9571
FRILUFTSLIV, I ALLA VAEDER. 1947. m. SEK 140. Friluftsfraemjandet, P.O. Box 708, 101 30 Stockholm 1, Sweden. TEL 08-23-43-50. FAX 08-241903. Ed. Per Goethlin. adv.; bk.rev. circ. 80,000. (also avail. in audio cassette)
  Formerly (until 1987): I Alla Vaeder (ISSN 0345-5017)
  Description: Articles for the whole family on outdoor life; trekking, canoing, walking, skiing, skating, etc.

FRITID I SVERIGE. see LEISURE AND RECREATION

799.2   US   ISSN 0016-2620
FULL CRY; published exclusively for the American coon hound and trail hound enthusiast. 1939. m. $16. Gault Publications, Inc., Box 10, Boody, IL 62514. TEL 217-865-2332. FAX 217-865-2334. Ed. Seth Gault. adv.: B&W page $250. bk.rev. circ. 25,754. **Document type**: consumer publication.
  Description: For coon, bear, lion, bobcat and squirrel hunters.

799   US   ISSN 0016-2922
FUR - FISH - GAME. HARDING'S MAGAZINE. 1925. m. $15.95. A.R. Harding Publishing Co., 2878 E. Main St., Columbus, OH 43209. TEL 614-231-9585. Ed. Mitch Cox; Pub. Jeff Kirn. adv. contact: Kurt Herrmann. bk.rev.; illus.; tr.lit. circ. 105,000.
  Description: Presents hunting, trapping and fishing advice for practical outdoorsmen.

796.552   JA
GAKUJIN/ALPINIST. (Text in Japanese) 1947. m. Tokyo Shimbun Publications Dept., 2-3-13, Konan, Minato-ku, Tokyo 108, Japan. Ed. Takao Nakazono. circ. 150,000.

799   US   ISSN 1066-0577
THE GAME MANAGER. 1987. q. $20. Multiple Use Managers, Inc., Box 1330, West Point, CA 95255-1330. TEL 209-293-7087. FAX 209-293-7087. Ed. Wayne Long. adv. **Document type**: newsletter.
  Formerly (until 1989): Hunting Ranch Business.
  Description: Designed for land owners and game managers.

799.2   FR   ISSN 1142-9437
GAZETTE OFFICIELLE DE LA CHASSE ET DE LA NATURE. every 8 d. 980 F. (foreign 1140 F.) (effective 1995). Office des Nouvelles Internationales, 18 rue de Folin, 64200 Biarritz, France. TEL 59-43-80-45. FAX 59-43-80-41. TELEX 570061 F. Ed. Dominique Laporte. adv. contact: Jacques Darrigrand. **Document type**: newspaper.
  Description: Contains articles and features of interest to hunters.

639.2   FR   ISSN 0046-5542
GAZETTE OFFICIELLE DE LA PECHE ET DE L'EAU. 1959. every 10 d. 900 F. (foreign 1050 F.) (effective 1995). Office des Nouvelles Internationales, 18 rue de Folin, 64200 Biarritz, France. TEL 59-43-80-45. FAX 59-43-80-41. TELEX 570061 F. Ed. Jacques Darrigrand. adv. contact: Jacques Darrigrand. (processed) **Document type**: newspaper.
  Description: Contains articles and features of interest to anglers.

799   US   ISSN 0895-3295
GEORGIA OUTDOOR NEWS. 1986. m. $11.95. Georgia Outdoor News, Inc., 1625 Williams Dr., Ste. 208, Marietta, GA 30066. TEL 404-425-0990. FAX 404-425-0998. adv.: B&W page $725, color page $1075; trim 7 3/4 x 10 7/8; adv. contact: Phil Barnet. circ. 34,145. **Document type**: consumer publication.
  Description: Focuses on fishing and hunting throughout Georgia.

799   US   ISSN 0199-6517
GEORGIA SPORTSMAN. 1976. m. $14.95. Game & Fish Publications, Inc., 2250 Newmarket Pkwy., Ste. 110, Box 741, Marietta, GA 30061-0741. TEL 404-953-9222. FAX 404-933-9510. Ed. J. Jacobs. circ. 40,000.

796.5   SA   ISSN 1013-8390
GETAWAY. (Text in English) 1989. m. R.100 overseas. Ramsay, Son & Parker (Pty) Ltd., P.O. Box 180, Howard Place 7450, South Africa. TEL 27-21-5311391. FAX 27-21-5313846. Ed. D. Steele. adv. circ. 102,000. **Document type**: consumer publication.
  Description: Publishes articles on outdoor places of interest, game parks, nature conservation, photography, trailing and caravaning.

799.2   IT
GIORNALE DEL CACCIATORE. 1951. bi-m. free. Federazione Italiana della Caccia, Associazione Cacciatori Alto Adige, Via Rossmini 51, 39100 Bozen, Italy. TEL 39-471-975608. FAX 39-471-973786. Ed. Ferrari Auer. adv.; bk.rev. circ. 1,100.

GLEITSCHIRM; Zeitschrift fuer Gleitschirmflieger. see SPORTS AND GAMES

796.93   BE   ISSN 0774-6849
GO SKIING. French edition (ISSN 0774-6830) (Text in Flemish) 1983. a. 100 BEF. Event S.A., Rue du Chatelain 49, 1050 Brussels, Belgium. TEL 32-2-6471750. FAX 32-2-6482989. Ed. Marie Dominique Spinoit. adv.; illus. **Document type**: consumer publication.
  Description: Covers all aspects of skiing, for beginners and pros, including competition results, travel features, interviews and more.

797.1   BE   ISSN 0772-5949
GO SURFING; het belgische surf & fun magazine. French edition (ISSN 0772-5957) (Text in Flemish) 1977. 3/yr. 600 BEF. (Landelijke Windsurfing Federatie) Event S.A., Rue du Chatelain 49, 1050 Brussels, Belgium. TEL 32-2-6471750. FAX 32-2-6482989. Ed. Marie-Dominique Spinoit. adv. contact: Bernard de Wasseige. bk.rev.; illus. circ. 30,000. **Document type**: consumer publication.
  Formerly: De Windsurfer.
  Description: Covers all aspects of windsurfing, speedsail, speedtrials, regattas, sports fashion and the surf life-style.

GOLD PROSPECTOR. see MINES AND MINING INDUSTRY

GOOD BEACH GUIDE; indicates which beaches are likely to be polluted and which are believed to be free from sewage pollution. see ENVIRONMENTAL STUDIES

GOOD CAMPS GUIDE BRITAIN (YEAR). see TRAVEL AND TOURISM

GOOD CAMPS GUIDE EUROPE (YEAR). see TRAVEL AND TOURISM

GOOD CAMPS GUIDE FRANCE (YEAR). see TRAVEL AND TOURISM

796.93   UK   ISSN 0958-0735
GOOD SKI GUIDE; A-Z of world resorts. 1981. irreg. £20. Hill Publications, 1-2 Dawes Court, 93 High St., Esher, Surrey KT10 9QD, England. Ed. John Hill. adv.; charts; illus.; stat.; tr.lit. circ. 200,000. (back issues avail.)

796.93   UK
GOOD SKI RESORTS GUIDE. 1983. a. £2.50. Hill Publications, 1-2 Dawes Court, 93 High St., Esher, Surrey KT10 8AQ, England. TEL 0372-69799. adv.; charts; illus.; stat.; tr.lit. circ. 40,000. (back issues avail.)

799   US   ISSN 0273-6691
GV191.2
GRAY'S SPORTING JOURNAL. 1975. 6/yr. $35.95. Box 1207, Augusta, GA 30903-1207. TEL 800-458-4010. FAX 706-724-3873. Ed. David C. Foster. adv. contact: Lea Cockerham. bk.rev. circ. 30,000. **Document type**: consumer publication.
  Description: Hunting and fishing oriented literary magazine.

796.93   US
GREAT LAKES SKIER. 1980. 3/yr. $5. Great Lakes Sports Publications, Inc., 7990 W. Grand River, Ste. C, Brighton, MI 48116. TEL 810-227-4200. Ed. Jim Neff; Pub. Art McCafferty. adv. contact: Ann Neff. circ. 11,000. (tabloid format) **Document type**: consumer publication.
  Description: Covers alpine and nordic skiing in the Great Lakes area. Includes a race calendar and coverage, travel tips and new product information.

796.5   UK   ISSN 0140-7570
THE GREAT OUTDOORS. 1978. m. £30. Caledonian Magazines Ltd., The Plaza Tower, East Kildride, Glasgow G74 1LW, Scotland. TEL 013552-46444. FAX 013552-63013. Ed. Cameron McNeish. circ. 27,112. **Document type**: consumer publication.

333.78   UK   ISSN 0017-4696
GROUNDSMAN. 1947. m. £30. (Institute of Groundsmanship) Adam Publishing Ltd., 42 West End Avenue, Pinner, Middlesex HA5 1BJ, England. TEL 081-868-3600. FAX 081-429-2374. Ed. Gene Price. adv.; bk.rev.; illus.; circ. 6,000. (controlled).
  Indexed: Sportsearch (1979-).
  —BLDSC (4220.150000).

796 914.5   IT   ISSN 0072-792X
GUIDA CAMPING D'ITALIA. 1958. a. L.11000. Federazione Italiana del Campeggio e del Caravanning, Casella Postale 23, 50041 Calenzano (Florence), Italy. adv.

796.5   FR   ISSN 0765-7005
GUIDE OFFICIEL CAMPING - CARAVANING. a. 75 F. in France and abroad (effective 1995). (Federation Francaise de Camping et de Caravaning) Edirégie, B.P. 86, 94420 Le Plessis Trevise, France. TEL 45-93-72-72. FAX 45-93-25-93. TELEX EDIGIE 262 572 F. adv. circ. 135,000. **Document type**: consumer publication, directory.

796.54   US   ISSN 1046-5774
GV193
GUIDE TO ACCREDITED CAMPS (YEAR). 1952. a. $12.95 (with subscr. to Camping Magazine $6.55). American Camping Association, Inc., 5000 State Rd. 67 N., Martinsville, IN 46151-7902. TEL 317-342-8456. FAX 317-342-2065. index. circ. 14,000. **Document type**: directory, consumer publication.
  Formerly: Parents' Guide to Accredited Camps; Which was formed by the merger of: Parents' Guide to Accredited Camps. West Edition; Parents' Guide to Accredited Camps. South Edition; Parents' Guide to Accredited Camps. Northeast Edition; Parents' Guide to Accredited Camps. Midwest Edition.
  Description: Lists over 2,000 camps accredited by the American Camping Association throughout the United States (and some abroad).

GUIDE TO CARAVAN AND CAMPING HOLIDAYS. see TRAVEL AND TOURISM

GUIDE TO EATING ONTARIO SPORT FISH. see FISH AND FISHERIES

799.1   US   ISSN 0164-3746
GULF COAST FISHERMAN. Variant title: Harold Wells Gulf Coast Fisherman. 1976. q. $11.75. Harold Wells Gulf Coast Fisherman, Inc., Drawer P, Port Lavaca, TX 77979. FAX 512-552-8864. Ed. Gary M. Ralston; Pub. Gary M. Ralston. adv.; bk.rev.; circ. 12,000. (paid).
  Description: Covers all aspects of saltwater fishing from Florida to Texas.

799.2   US   ISSN 0739-4403
GUN DIGEST HUNTING ANNUAL. 1983. a. D B I Books, Inc., 4092 Commercial Ave., Northbrook, IL 60062. TEL 708-767-6310; 800-767-6310. FAX 708-272-2051.

SPORTS AND GAMES — OUTDOOR LIFE

799.2 636.7 US ISSN 0279-5086
GUN DOG; upland bird and waterfowl dogs. 1981. bi-m. $23.95. Stover Publishing Co., Inc., 1901 Bell Ave., Ste. 4, Des Moines, IA 50315-1030. TEL 515-243-2472. FAX 515-243-0233. (Subscr. to: Box 343, Mt. Morris, IL 61054) Ed. Bob Wilbanks; Pub. Carrell Bunn. adv.: B&W page $2310, color page $3118; adv. contact: Mary Stearns. bk.rev.; illus. circ. 56,855. **Document type:** consumer publication.
Description: Provides tips for upland bird and waterfowl hunter-gunners involved with pointing, flushing, and retrieving breeds of bird dogs.

GUN SHOW CALENDAR. see ANTIQUES

799.202 US ISSN 1042-6450
TS534.5
GUN TESTS; the consumer resource for the serious shooter. 1989. m. $72 (foreign $84) (effective 1996). Belvoir Publications, Inc., 75 Holly Hill Ln., Box 2626, Greenwich, CT 06836-2626. TEL 203-661-6111. FAX 203-661-4802. (Subscr. to: Box 420234, Palm Coast, FL 32142) Ed. Dave Tinker. **Document type:** consumer publication.

799.2 US ISSN 0362-2495
TS532
GUN WORLD ANNUAL. 1973. a. $3.95. Gallant - Charger Publishing, Inc., 34249 Camino Capistrano, Box HH, Capistrano Beach, CA 92624. TEL 714-493-2101. Ed. Jack Lewis. adv.; bk.rev.; illus. circ. 126,000. (also avail. in microfilm from UMI) **Document type:** consumer publication.
Formerly: Gun World Hunting Guide (ISSN 0362-4749)

799.3 US ISSN 0017-5684
TS535
GUNS & AMMO. 1958. m. $21.94. Petersen Publishing Co., 6420 Wilshire Blvd., Los Angeles, CA 90048. TEL 213-782-2000. Ed. Kevin Steele. adv.: B&W page $15880. bk.rev.; charts; illus.; index. circ. 575,000. (also avail. in microform from UMI; reprint service avail. from UMI) **Indexed:** Consum.Ind., Mag.Ind., PMR, Sports Per.Ind. **Document type:** consumer publication.
●Also available online. Vendor(s): Knight-Ridder, Inc. —SWETS; UMI.

799.3 US ISSN 0883-9468
SK274
GUNS & AMMO ACTION SERIES. 1983. bi-m. Petersen Publishing Co., 6420 Wilshire Blvd., Los Angeles, CA 90048. TEL 213-782-2839. FAX 213-782-2839. **Document type:** consumer publication.

799.3 US ISSN 1059-1672
TS537
GUNS AND AMMO HANDGUN ANNUAL. a. Petersen Publishing Co., 6420 Wilshire Blvd., Los Angeles, CA 90048. TEL 213-782-2853. FAX 213-782-2839. **Document type:** consumer publication.
Supersedes (in 1984): Guns and Ammo Annual (ISSN 0072-906X)

797 US ISSN 0895-433X
HANG GLIDING. 1970. m. $35 (Canada and Mexico $40; elsewhere $50) (effective 1994-1995). U.S. Hang Gliding Association, Inc., Box 8300, Colorado Springs, CO 80933-8300. TEL 719-632-8300. FAX 719-632-6417. Ed. Gil Dodgen. adv. contact: Jeff Elgart. bk.rev.; bibl.; charts; illus. circ. 10,500. **Indexed:** Sportsearch (1978-). **Document type:** consumer publication.
—UnCover.
Formerly (until 1976): Ground Skimmer.

796.5 790.01 UK ISSN 0263-8134
HARPERS SPORTS & LEISURE. 1930. every 3 wks. £88($138) (includes Harpers Guide to Sports Trade). Harpers Publishing, 47A High St., Bushey, Watford, Herts. WD2 1BD, England. TEL 0181-950-9522. FAX 0181-950-7998. Ed. Martin Johnson; Pub. Martin Johnson. adv. contact: Gregg Allen. bk.rev.; film rev. circ. 3,900. **Document type:** trade publication.
Former titles: Harpers Sports; Harpers Sports and Camping (ISSN 0141-142X)
Description: Contains articles for the U.K. sports trade.

HELPING OUT IN THE OUTDOORS; a directory of volunteer jobs and internships in parks and forests nationwide. see BUSINESS AND ECONOMICS — Trade And Industrial Directories

799.1 NE
HENGELSPORT NIEUWS. 1977. bi-m. membership. Stichting Public Relations Hengelsport Friesland, Postbus 350, 8600 AJ Sneek, Netherlands. TEL 05154-9876. FAX 05154-9899. Ed. F. Meijer. adv.; bk.rev. circ. 14,000.

919.4 796.74 AT ISSN 0085-1477
HERALD CARAVANNING GUIDE. 1931. a. Aus.$1. Herald Travel Bureau, Newspaper House, 247 Collins St., Melbourne, Vic. 3000, Australia. Ed. D. H. Day.

HIGH ADVENTURE; a Royal Rangers magazine for boys. see CHILDREN AND YOUTH — For

796.552 UK ISSN 0962-2667
HIGH MOUNTAIN SPORTS. 1982. m. £27 (foreign $32). (British Mountaineering Council) High Magazine Ltd., 164 Barkby Rd., Leicester LE4 7LF, England. TEL 0533-460722. FAX 0533-460748. Ed. Geoff Birtles. adv. contact: Sue Barklie. bk.rev. circ. 16,903. (back issues avail.) **Document type:** consumer publication.
—UnCover.
Formerly: High Magazine (ISSN 0951-8940)
Description: Contains international and UK coverage of rock climbing, mountaineering, serious hill walking and related mountain sports.

796 US
HIGHWAYS. (In 4 regional editions: Region 1: Northwest (1045-5922); Region 2 Southwest (1047-0840); Regions 3 & 4: Central (1047-0859); Region 5: Northwest (1047-0867); Region 6: Southeast (ISSN 1047-0875)) 1966. 10/yr. $3 to members. (Good Sam Club) T L Enterprises, Inc., 3601 Calle Tecate, Camarillo, CA 93012. TEL 805-389-0300. Ed. R. Epstein; Pub. Joe McNeil. adv. circ. 912,584. **Document type:** consumer publication.
Formerly (until 1989): Good Sam's Hi-Way Herald (ISSN 0194-9764)
Description: Aimed at campers and owners of recreational vehicles.

796.552 II
HIMALAYAN JOURNAL. (Text in English) 1928. a. Rs.295 (effective till 1996). Himalayan Club, P.O. Box 1905, Bombay 400 001, India. TEL 91-22-204-1268. FAX 91-22-202-1029. Ed. Harish Kapadia. adv.; bk.rev.; charts; illus.; index, cum.index: vols.1-50, 1929-1994. circ. 1,500. (tabloid format) **Indexed:** Helminthol.Abstr. **Document type:** academic/scholarly publication, abstracting/indexing.
Refereed Serial

796.522 II ISSN 0018-1897
HIMAVANTA; India's only mountaineering monthly. (Text in English) 1969. m. Rs.50($12) (effective 1996). Himalayan Federation, 63E Mohanirban Rd., Calcutta 700 029, India. TEL 74-1424. Ed. Kamal K. Guha. adv. contact: Dasarthi Sarkar. bk.rev. circ. 11,000. (looseleaf format) **Document type:** newsletter.
Description: Covers climbs, high altitude treks, explorations, glaciology, meteorology, climatology, environment, communications, archaeology, sociology and anthropology of the Himalayas.

799.2 GW
HIRSCHMANNBRIEF. 1961. a. $5. Verein Hirschmann e.V., Schriftfuehrer, Dr. Wolf-Eberhard Barth, 3424 Oderhaus Post St. Andreasberg, Germany. circ. 550.

796.5 NE
HOLLAND CAMPING.* 1965. a. fl.14. Camping Media BV, Postbus 234, 6710 BE Ede, Netherlands. adv. circ. 15,000.
Formerly: Camping Benelux.

799.1 US
HOOKS AND LINES. bi-m. membership. International Women's Fishing Association, Drawer 3125, Palm Beach, FL 33480. Ed. Joan Willmott. **Document type:** newsletter.

796 US ISSN 0018-4780
SK75
HOOSIER OUTDOORS. 1967. bi-m. $7.50. High Point Communications, Box 447, Cloverdale, IN 46120. TEL 317-795-6312. Ed. Philip E. Junker. adv.; bk.rev. circ. 8,000. (back issues avail.)
Description: Outdoor activities in Indiana such as hunting, camping, fishing, boating and skiing.

HOUNDS. see SPORTS AND GAMES — Horses And Horsemanship

796.552 CI ISSN 0354-0650
HRVATSKI PLANINAR/CROATIAN MOUNTAINEER. 1898. bi-m. $15. Hrvatski Planinarski Savez - Croation Mountaineering Association, Kozarceva 22, 41000 Zagreb, Croatia. TEL 041-448-774. TELEX 041-441-088. Ed. Dr. Zeljko Poljak. adv.; bk.rev.; charts; illus.; index; cum.index. circ. 2,300.
Former titles (until Mar. 1991): Nase Planine (ISSN 0027-819X); (until 1944): Hrvatski Planinar.

796.95 US
HUMMER TRAIL AND TOURING GUIDE. 1973. 5/yr. (m., Sep.-Jan.). $7.95. Royle Publications, Inc., 112 Market St., Sun Prairie, WI 53590. TEL 608-825-6315. FAX 608-825-3053. Ed. Cathy Hanson. adv.: B&W page $2630, color page $3030; trim 8 3/8 x 10 7/8; adv. contact: Cathy Hanson. circ. 20,000. **Document type:** consumer publication.
Description: Covers travel, trails, new products, events and personalities for snowmobilers in the Midwest.

799.2 US ISSN 1066-3460
HUNTER EDUCATION INSTRUCTOR. 1973. 8/yr. $12. Outdoor Empire Publishing, Inc., 511 Eastlake Ave. E., Box C 19000, Seattle, WA 98109. TEL 206-624-3845. Ed. Maureen Liang. adv.; film rev.; charts; illus.; stat.; tr.lit.; index; circ. 10,000 (controlled). (tabloid format)
Former titles (until 1989): Hunter Safety Instructor (ISSN 0737-6227); (until 1983): Hunter Safety News.

796.93 US
HUNTER MOUNTAIN NEWS. 1970. 12/yr. $15. (Hunter Mountain Ski Bowl) Hunter Mt. News Corp., Box 110, Syosset, NY 11791. TEL 516-496-4588. Ed. Paul E. Pepe. adv.; bk.rev.; charts; illus. circ. 25,000.

799.2 CN
HUNTER'S GUIDE TO PROFESSIONAL OUTFITTERS. 1988. a. Can.$19.95. Hines Proguide, 50 Eglinton Ave. W., Ste. 1009, Mississauga, ON L5R 3P5, Canada. TEL 905-967-4319. FAX 905-964-1553. Ed. Sherman Hines. adv. contact: Anne Marie Townsend. circ. 3,000.

799.2 US ISSN 0018-7860
HUNTER'S HORN. 1921. m. $10. Hunter's Horn, 114-120 E. Franklin Ave., Box 707, Sesser, IL 62884. TEL 618-625-2711. Ed. George Slankard. adv.; bk.rev.; illus. circ. 9,800.
Description: Describes fox and wolf hunting.

799.2 US
HUNTING ANNUAL (LOS ANGELES). 1980. a. newsstand price: $6.95. Petersen Publishing Co., 6420 Wilshire Blvd., Los Angeles, CA 90048. TEL 213-782-2000. Ed. Todd Smith. adv. circ. 110,000. **Document type:** consumer publication.

799.2 US
HUNTING GUNS BY OUTDOOR LIFE & JIM CARMICHEL. 1984. a. $2.75. Times Mirror Magazines, Inc., 2 Park Ave., New York, NY 10016. TEL 212-779-5000. Ed. Vin T. Sparano. adv.

799.2 US ISSN 1059-3837
SK274
HUNTING HORIZONS. 1992. a. $34. Wolfe Publishing Co., 6471 Airpark Dr., Prescott, AZ 86301. TEL 602-445-7810; 800-899-7810. FAX 602-778-5124. adv.: B&W page $1617, color page $2611; trim 8 1/8 x 10 7/8. circ. 45,000. **Document type:** consumer publication.
Description: Focuses on the life-style of the sophisticated sportsman, or upscale hunter-shooter.

799.2 US ISSN 1053-4466
THE HUNTING REPORT: EDITION II - FOR BIRDSHOOTERS AND WATERFOWLERS. 1989. m. $45 (Canada and Mexico $51; elsewhere $66). Oxpecker Enterprises, Inc., 9300 S. Dadeland Blvd., Ste. 605, Miami, FL 33156-2721. TEL 305-670-1361. FAX 305-670-1376. Ed. Don Causey; Pub. Don Causey. adv. contact: Milton Aquino. circ. 1,500. (looseleaf format; back issues avail.) **Document type:** newsletter.
Description: A where-to-go information source for the hunter who travels for his sport.

SPORTS AND GAMES — OUTDOOR LIFE

799.2 US ISSN 1052-4746
THE HUNTING REPORT FOR BIG GAME HUNTERS; serving the hunter who travels. 1981. m. $60 (Canada and Mexico $66; elsewhere $81). Oxpecker Enterprises, Inc., 9300 S. Dadeland Blvd., Ste. 605, Miami, FL 33156-2721. TEL 305-670-1361. FAX 305-670-1376. Ed. Don Causey; Pub. Don Causey. adv. contact: Milton Aquino. bk.rev. circ. 3,500. (looseleaf format; back issues avail.) **Document type:** newsletter.

711 UK ISSN 1012-7720
I F P R A BULLETIN. q. International Federation of Park and Recreation Administration, General Secretary, The Grotto, Lower Basildon, Reading, Berkshire RG8 9NE, England. TEL (0491)-874222. FAX 0491-874059.

796.93 US
I LOVE NEW YORK WINTER TRAVEL AND SKI GUIDE. a. free. Department of Economic Development, 1 Commerce Plaza, Albany, NY 12245. TEL 518-474-4116. FAX 518-486-6416. Ed. Mary Ellen Walsh. **Document type:** consumer publication.
Formerly: I Love New York Skiing and Winter Adventures.
Description: Lists downhill and cross-country skiing centers and facilities, events, festivals and package tours.

796.172 US
I S L SURFWORLD. 1987. m. $35. (International Surfing Committee) Surfhouse, Box 299, Beverly Hills, CA 90213. Ed. Winston Holt; Pub. Gary F. Filona II. bk.rev. circ. 1,081,000.
Description: Covers all 6 events in surfing.

799.1 US
I W F A YEARBOOK. 1955. a. membership. International Women's Fishing Association, Drawer 3125, Palm Beach, FL 33480. Ed. Joan S. Willmott. adv. circ. 300.

799.2 US
ILLINOIS DEER & TURKEY SHOW PREVIEW. 1992. a. Target Communications Corp., 7626 W. Donges Bay Rd., Mequon, WI 53097-3400. TEL 414-242-3990; 800-324-3337. FAX 414-242-7391. Ed. Glenn Helgeland; Pub. Glenn Helgeland. adv.: B&W page $450, color page $738; trim 8 3/8 x 10 7/8; adv. contact: Lynn Anderson. circ. 30,000 (controlled). **Document type:** consumer publication.
Description: Previews shows, events, seminars, and new products for hunters in Illinois.

333.78 US ISSN 0019-2155
ILLINOIS PARKS & RECREATION. 1970. bi-m. $20. Illinois Association of Park Districts, 211 E. Monroe, Springfield, IL 62701. TEL 217-523-4554. (Co-sponsor: Illinois Park and Recreation Association) Ed. Ann M. Londrigan. adv.; bk.rev.; illus.; stat. circ. 4,600.
Formerly: Illinois Park and Recreation Quarterly.

799.1 UK ISSN 0959-9606
IMPROVE YOUR COURSE FISHING. m. £25.60 (foreign £29.10) (effective 1995-1996). E M A P - Pursuit Publishing, Bretton Ct., Bretton, Peterborough, Cambs. PE3 8DZ, England. TEL 01733-264666. FAX 01733-263294. TELEX 32157. (Subscr. to: Tower Publishing Services Ltd., Tower House, Sovereign Park, Lathkill St., Market Harborough, Leics. LE16 9EF, England. TEL 01858-468811. FAX 01858-432164) adv. **Document type:** consumer publication.

799.1 UK ISSN 0965-0261
IMPROVE YOUR SEA ANGLING. m. £22 (foreign £27) (effective 1995-1996). E M A P - Pursuit Publishing, Bretton Ct., Bretton, Peterborough, Cambs. PE3 8DZ, England. TEL 01733-264666. FAX 01733-263294. TELEX 32157. (Subscr. to: Tower Publishing Services Ltd., Tower House, Sovereign Park, Lathkill St., Market Harborough, Leics. LE16 9EF, England. TEL 01858-468811. FAX 01858-263294) adv. **Document type:** consumer publication.

799.1 US ISSN 0276-9905
SH401
IN-FISHERMAN; the journal of freshwater fishing. 1975. 7/yr. $16. In-Fisherman Communications Network, 2 In-Fisherman Dr., Brainerd, MN 56401-0999. TEL 218-829-1648. FAX 218-829-3091. Ed. Doug Stange. adv.: B&W page $9800, color page $12740; adv. contact: Stu LeGaard. circ. 334,101. **Indexed:** Access (1981-), Sports Per.Ind. **Document type:** consumer publication.

799.1 US
IN-FISHERMAN - WALLEYE GUIDE. 1983. a. In-Fisherman Communications Network, 2 In-Fisherman Dr., Brainerd, MN 56401-0999. TEL 218-829-1648. FAX 218-829-3091. Ed. Doug Stange. adv.: B&W page $3500, color page $4725; adv. contact: Stu LeGaard. circ. 204,000. **Document type:** consumer publication.

796 US
IN-FISHERMANS WALLEYE IN-SIDER. 1990. 6/yr. In-Fisherman Communications Network, 2 In-Fisherman Dr., Brainerd, MN 56401-0999. TEL 218-829-1648. FAX 218-829-3091. Ed. Doug Stange. adv.: B&W page $2750, color page $3710. circ. 50,801. **Document type:** consumer publication.

796.552 II ISSN 0971-426X
INDIAN MOUNTAINEER. (Text in English) 1978. s-a. Rs.10. Indian Mountaineering Foundation, c/o Director, Headquarters Complex, Benito Juarez Rd., Anand Niketan, New Delhi 110021, India. TEL 91-11-671211. FAX 91-11-6883412. adv.; bk.rev. circ. 2,000.

790.1 US ISSN 1066-4092
INLINE. 1991. 9/yr. $25.97. InLine, Inc., 2025 Pearl St., Boulder, CO 80302-4429. TEL 303-440-5111. FAX 303-440-3313. (Subscr. to: Box 527, Mt. Morris, IL 61054. TEL 800-877-5281) Ed. Natalie Kurylko; Pub. Daemon Filson. adv. **Document type:** consumer publication.
Description: For in-line roller skating enthusiasts.

796.42 US ISSN 1042-3664
INSIDE TEXAS RUNNING. 1977. 10/yr. $11 (foreign $25) (effective 1996). Joanne Schmidt, Ed. & Pub., 9514 Bristlebrook, Houston, TX 77083. TEL 713-498-3208. FAX 713-879-9980. adv. contact: John Eilert. circ. 10,000 (paid).
Description: Covers running and running-related events in Texas.

796 US
INSIDE TRIATHLON. 1986. 12/yr. $29.95. Inside Communications, 1830 N. 55th St., Boulder, CO 80301-2700. TEL 303-440-0601. FAX 303-444-6788. Ed. Chris Newbound. adv.; bk.rev. circ. 18,000. **Document type:** consumer publication.
Formerly: Triathlon Today (ISSN 1051-9564)

796.93 US ISSN 1070-2172
INSIDERS SKI LETTER. 1989. 10/yr. $33. Skiletter, Inc., 115 Lilly Pond Ln., Katonah, NY 10536. TEL 914-232-5094. Ed. Greg Berry. **Document type:** newsletter.
●Also available online.
Description: Covers skiing for serious skiers.

790.1 US
INTERNATIONAL AMUSEMENT INDUSTRY BUYERS GUIDE. 1986. a. $45. B P I Communications, Amusement Business Division, Box 24970, Nashville, TN 37202. TEL 615-321-4250. FAX 615-327-1575. circ. 8,500. **Document type:** directory.
Former titles: Amusement Industry Buyers Guide; Amusement Rides and Game Buyers Guide.
Description: Contains comprehensive listings of manufacturers, importers and suppliers of all types of rides, games and merchandise as well as food and drink equipment and suppliers.

799.1 US ISSN 0257-1420
INTERNATIONAL ANGLER. 1973. bi-m. membership. International Game Fish Association, 1301 E. Atlantic Blvd., Pompano Beach, FL 33060-6744. TEL 305-941-3474. Ed. Ray Crawford. bk.rev.; illus.; stat. circ. 25,000. **Document type:** newsletter.
Formerly: International Marine Angler.
Description: Game fish world records, articles relating to recreational fishing, conservation and statistics on fishing.

INTERNATIONAL CYCLE SPORT. see SPORTS AND GAMES — Bicycles And Motorcycles

796.5 GW ISSN 0074-7122
INTERNATIONAL NATURIST GUIDE/INTERNATIONALER FKK-REISEFUEHRER/GUIDE NATURISTE INTERNATIONALE. a. DM.6.80. (International Naturist Federation) Richard Danehl's Verlag, Postfach 500344, 2000 Hamburg 50, Germany. adv.

796.355 796.42 US ISSN 0897-3571
INTERNATIONAL TRACK & FIELD ANNUAL. 1988. a. $19.95. (Association of Track & Field Statisticians) Lyons & Burford, Publishers, 31 W. 21st St., New York, NY 10010. TEL 800-836-0510. Ed. Peter Matthews.
Description: Includes over 200,000 entries for men's and women's events, over 700 biographic entries and indexed for more than 8000 athletes.

INTERNATIONAL UNION OF ALPINE ASSOCIATIONS. BULLETIN/UNION INTERNATIONALE DES ASSOCIATIONS D'ALPINISME. BULLETIN. see TRAVEL AND TOURISM

IOWA SIERRAN. see CLUBS

IRON DOG TRACKS. see ANTIQUES

796.52 IC ISSN 1021-108X
ISALP; arsrit Islenska Alpaklubbsins. 1985. a. ISK 2700. Islenski Alpaklubburinn, P.O. Box 1054, IS-121 Reykjavik, Iceland. TEL 354-581-1700. Ed. Torfi Hjaltason. adv.; illus. circ. 300. (back issues avail.)

797 AT
IT. 1968. irreg. Aus.$0.10 per no. Canberra Bushwalking Club, Box 160, Canberra City, A.C.T. 2601, Australia.

796.552 JA
IWA-TO-YUKI/ROCK AND SNOW. (Text in Japanese) 1958. bi-m. 7700 Yen. Yama-kei Publishers Company, 1-1-33, Shiba-Daimon, Minato-ku, Tokyo 105, Japan. TEL 03-3436-4026. FAX 03-5472-4430. Ed. Tsunemichi Ikeda. adv. contact: Isamu Arai. circ. 50,000.

JACHT EN NATUURBEHEER. see CONSERVATION

799.2 DK ISSN 0906-415X
JAEGER. Key Title: Jaeger (Frederiksberg). 1884. m. DKK 350 (typically set in July). Jaegerne, Danmarks Jaegerforbund, Hoejnaesvej 56, DK-2610 Roedovre, Denmark. TEL 45-38 33 29 11. FAX 45-31-19-02-41. Ed. Martin Dahl-Hansen. adv.; bk.rev.; charts; illus.; stat.; index; circ. controlled.
Formed by the 1991 merger of: Dansk Jagt (ISSN 0106-9500) & Strandjaegeren (ISSN 0039-212X) & Jagt og Fiskeri (ISSN 0021-3977)

799.2 GW ISSN 0720-4523
JAEGER; Zeitschrift fuer das Jagdrevier. 1883. m. DM.123. Jahr-Verlag GmbH & Co., Jessenstr. 1, 22767 Hamburg, Germany. TEL 040-38906-0. FAX 040-38906302. TELEX 2163485. Ed. Horst Rohleder. adv. contact: Waltraud Jante. illus. circ. 26,100. **Indexed:** Key Word Ind.Wildl.Res. **Document type:** consumer publication.
Formerly: Deutsche Jaeger-Zeitung (ISSN 0012-0324)
Description: Discusses all aspects of hunting.

796 GW
JAEGER UND FISCHER. m. DM.12. (Landesjagdverband und Landessportfischerverband Schleswig-Holstein e.V.) Schmidt-Roemhild Verlag, Mengstr. 16, 23552 Luebeck, Germany. TEL 0451-1605-0. FAX 0451-1605253. **Document type:** consumer publication.

379.2 IT
JAEGERZEITUNG. (Text in German) 1951. q. free. Suedtiroler Jagdverband, Rosministrasse 51, 39100 Bozen, Italy. TEL 39-471-975608. FAX 39-471-973786. adv.; bk.rev. circ. 4,700.

799.2 GW
JAGD IN BAYERN. 1952. m. Landesjagdverband Bayern e.V., Implerstr. 25, 81371 Munich, Germany. Ed. Alfred Preisser. circ. 43,000.
Description: Examines wild animal welfare, guns, and pistols for the hunter.

SPORTS AND GAMES — OUTDOOR LIFE 6165

799.2　　　　　　GW　ISSN 0021-3926
JAGD UND JAEGER IN RHEINLAND-PFALZ. 1964. m. membership. (Landesjagdverband Rheinland-Pfalz) Verlag Dieter Hoffmann (Mainz), Senefelder Str. 25, 55129 Mainz, Germany. Ed. Nis Wagner. adv.; bk.rev. circ. 17,500.
　Description: Emphasis is on hunting.

799.2　　　　　　GW　ISSN 0021-3942
DER JAGDGEBRAUCHSHUND. 1965. m. DM.74. (Jagdgebrauchshundverband) B L V Verlagsgesellschaft mbH, Lothstr. 29, 80797 Munich, Germany. TEL 089-12705-0. FAX 089-12705354. Ed. Karl Walch. adv. contact: Henning Stemmler. bk.rev.; abstr.; illus. **Document type:** bulletin.
　—CCC.

799.2　　　　　　GW　ISSN 0943-9773
JAGEN WELTWEIT. 1990. bi-m. DM.66. Mittelrhein Verlag GmbH, Feldstr. 6, 56377 Nassau, Germany. TEL 02604-97010. FAX 02604-970130. Ed. Andreas Rockstroh. adv. contact: Ralf Clemens. circ. 19,000. **Document type:** consumer publication.

799.2　　　　　　DK　ISSN 0900-0488
JAGTHUNDEN. 1942. 10/yr. membership. Skovbjergvej 35, 7280 S. Felding, Denmark. adv. circ. 6,000.

799　　　　　　SW　ISSN 0345-5629
JAKT OCH JAEGARE. KRING LAEGERELDEN. 1940. m. SEK 200 (effective 1995). Jaegarnas Riksfoerbund - Landsbygdens Jaegare, Saltsjoegatan 15, S-151 32 Soedertaelje, Sweden. TEL 46-8-550-336-59. FAX 46-8-550-651-77. Ed. Bengt Tandberg. adv. contact: Monica Wistedt. bk.rev. circ. 15,600.
　Formed by the 1969 merger of: Kring Laegerelden; (until 1969): Jakt och Jaegare.
　Description: Focuses on fishing and hunting.

799.2　　　　　　SW　ISSN 0345-5637
JAKTJOURNALEN. (Text in Swedish) 1970. m. SEK 325. AB Jaktjournalen, P.O. Box 10184, 434 22 Kungsbacka, Sweden. FAX 0300-16310. Ed. John Duff. adv.; bk.rev. circ. 46,900.
　Description: Covers all aspects of hunting.

799　　　　　　SW　ISSN 0021-406X
JAKTMARKER OCH FISKEVATTEN. (Supplement avail.: Jakt och Fiske) 1913. 11/yr. SEK 349. Bo Svensson, Ed. & Pub., Vaestra Torggatan 18, S-652 24 Karlstad, Sweden. TEL 46-54-10-03-70. adv.: B&W page SEK 15000; color page SEK 18000; trim 185 x 267. bk.rev. circ. 57,400. cols./p.: 4; pp./issue: 100.
　Formerly (until vol.3, 1962): Fraan Jaktmarker och Fiskevatten.
　Description: Covers all aspects of fishing and hunting.

JERSEY SIERRAN. see CONSERVATION

799　　　　　　FR　ISSN 0755-7140
JOURNAL DU CHASSEUR. 1950. bi-m. 105 F. Federation Departementemerale des Chasseurs de la Gironde, Rue du petit Barail - B.P. 231, 33028 Bordeaux Cedex, France. TEL 56-39-88-23. Ed. Claude Businelli. adv.; bk.rev. circ. 14,000.

JOURNAL OF APPLIED RECREATION RESEARCH. see LEISURE AND RECREATION

796.5　　　　　　US　ISSN 0021-9649
JOURNAL OF CHRISTIAN CAMPING. 1969. bi-m. $24.95 (foreign $26.95). Christian Camping International, Box 62189, Colorado Springs, CO 80962-2189. TEL 719-260-9400. FAX 719-260-6398. Ed. Dean Ridings. adv.; bk.rev.; illus.; stat.; index.
　Formerly: Camps and Conferences Magazine.
　Description: For camping professionals, primarily for those whose camps, conference centers, and retreat centers are part of the Association.

JOURNAL OF LEISURE RESEARCH. see LEISURE AND RECREATION

333.7 658　　　　　US　ISSN 0735-1968
GV181.5
JOURNAL OF PARK AND RECREATION ADMINISTRATION. 1986. q. $35 to individuals; institutions $40 (foreign $45). Sagamore Publishing Inc., 302 W. Hill St., Box 647, Champaign, IL 61824-0647. TEL 217-359-5940. FAX 217-359-5979. bk.rev.; circ. 720 (controlled). **Indexed:** Sportsearch (1986-). **Document type:** trade publication.
　—BLDSC (5029.145000); Faxon; UnCover.
　Description: Scholarly articles for the leisure service practitioner, focusing on planning, finance, organizational practice, personnel evaluation, programming, and marketing and promotion.

K O A DIRECTORY ROAD ATLAS AND CAMPING GUIDE. (Kampgrounds of America, Inc.) see BUSINESS AND ECONOMICS — Trade And Industrial Directories

799　　　　　　AU
KAERNTNER JAEGER. 1971. q. membership. Kaerntner Jaegerschaft, Bahnhofstr. 38B, A-9020 Klagenfurt, Austria. Ed. G. Anderluh. adv.; bk.rev.; illus. **Indexed:** Key Word Ind.Wildl.Res.
　Description: Covers all aspects of hunting.

796.5　　　　　　BE　ISSN 0775-8545
KAMPEERTOERIST. 1952. m. (11/yr.) 1185 BEF. (Vlaamse Kampeertoeristen) Making Magazines, Baudelostraat 29, B-9000 Ghent, Belgium. TEL 32-9-2338463. FAX 32-9-2338087. (Co-sponsor: Sportfederatie Vlaamse Kampeerders) adv.: B&W page 25000 BEF, color page 36000 BEF; trim 275 x 198. bk.rev. circ. 13,700.
　Description: For campers and outdoor sports enthusiasts.

KANSAS WILDLIFE & PARKS. see CONSERVATION

KASHSHAFAT AL-IMARAT/EMIRATES BOY SCOUTS. see CLUBS

790 333.78　　　　US　ISSN 1059-9177
SK1
KENTUCKY AFIELD; the magazine. 1945. bi-m. $5. Department of Fish and Wildlife Resources, Division of Information and Education, 1 Game Farm Rd., Frankfort, KY 40601. TEL 502-564-4336. FAX 502-564-6508. Eds. Carolyn Lynn, Norm Minch. bk.rev.; charts; illus. circ. 45,000. **Indexed:** Sport Fish.Abstr.; Wild.Rev. **Document type:** government publication, consumer publication.
　—Faxon; UnCover.
　Formerly (until 1992): Kentucky Happy Hunting Ground (ISSN 0023-0235)
　Description: Covers all aspects of wildlife-associated outdoor recreation and conservation related programs administered by the Department.

KEY NOTE REPORT: CAMPING & CARAVANNING. see LEISURE AND RECREATION

790　　　　　　US　ISSN 0192-3439
TL759.A1
KITELINES; quarterly journal of the worldwide kite community. 1977. q. $16 (foreign $22) (effective Feb. 1995). Aeolus Press, Inc., Box 466, Randallstown, MD 21133-0466. TEL 410-922-1212. FAX 410-922-4262. Ed. Valerie Govig; Pub. Valerie Govig. adv.; bk.rev.; charts; illus.; index; circ. 13,000 (paid). (also avail. in microfiche; back issues avail.) **Indexed:** Ind.How To Do It. **Document type:** consumer publication.
　Supersedes: Kite Tales (ISSN 0192-3420)
　Description: Comprehensive full-color magazine of kite news, reviews, plans, tips and in-depth feature articles.

796.93 330　　　　US　ISSN 1079-5839
KOTTKE NATIONAL END OF SEASON SURVEY. 1979. a. $100 to non-members; members $25. National Ski Areas Association, 133 S. Van Gordon St., Ste. 300, Lakewood, CO 80288. TEL 303-987-1111. FAX 303-986-2345.
　Formerly (until 1993): End of Season National Business Survey.
　Description: Examines changes and trends in skier visits for the domestic ski industry. Analyzes influence of season length, lift capacity, night skiing, and snow-making on business volume.

796.5　　　　　　SW
KULTRYCKET. 1966. 6/yr. SEK 60 membership. M H F Husvagns Club, Moeregatan 34, S-382 00 Nybro, Sweden. TEL 46-481-114-84. Ed. Bertil Aastroem; Pub. Jan Wilhelmsson. adv.: B&W page SEK 320, color page SEK 530; trim 185 x 264; adv. contact: Kurt Ohlson. circ. 2,600. cols./p.: 4; pp./issue: 28.

LAND AND WATER CONSERVATION FUND GRANTS MANUAL. see CONSERVATION

796.42　　　　　　GW　ISSN 0047-4355
LEICHTATHLETIK. 1926. w. DM.224. B & W Bartels & Wernitz Sportverlag GmbH, Am Eichgarten 15, 12167 Berlin, Germany. Ed. Heinz Vogel. adv.; bk.rev.; index. circ. 10,000.
　—CCC.

LEISURE MANAGER. see LEISURE AND RECREATION

LIVING AMONG NATURE DARINGLY!; how to for trappers, farmers, and homesteaders. see GARDENING AND HORTICULTURE

796.93　　　　　　US
LONG ISLAND SKI. 1981. irreg. free. Leah S. Dunaief, Ed. & Pub., Box V.T., Setauket, NY 11733. TEL 516-751-1550. adv. circ. 60,000.

796　　　　　　US
LONG TRAIL NEWS. 1922. q. $24 membership or exchange basis. Green Mountain Club, Inc., Rte. 100, RR 1, Box 650, Waterbury Center, VT 05677-9735. TEL 802-244-7037. FAX 802-244-5867. Ed. Sylvia Plumb. adv.; bk.rev. circ. 6,000. **Document type:** newsletter.
　Formerly (until 1925): Green Mountain News.
　Description: News, information, letters, and announcements pertaining to the members and activities of the Green Mountain Club, which promotes hiking and conservation activities in this Vermont mountain range.

799　　　　　　US　ISSN 1060-7617
LONGHUNTER JOURNAL. 1989. q. $10. National Muzzle Loading Rifle Association, Box 67, Friendship, IN 47021. TEL 812-667-5131; 800-745-1493. FAX 812-667-5136. Ed. Jon Withol. adv. contact: Joyce Vogel. bk.rev. **Document type:** newsletter.

LOUISIANA CONSERVATIONIST. see CONSERVATION

799.2　　　　　　US　ISSN 0744-3692
LOUISIANA GAME AND FISH. 1981. m. $14.97. Game & Fish Publications, Inc., 2250 Newmarket Pkwy., Ste. 110, Box 741, Marietta, GA 30061-0741. TEL 404-953-9222. FAX 404-933-9510. Ed. Bob Borgwat. circ. 13,438.

799.2 333.7　　　BU　ISSN 0324-0541
LOV I RIBOLOV. (Text in Bulgarian) 1895. m. 180 lv.($17) Nasluka Ltd., Lov i Ribolov, 31-33 Vitosha Blvd., 1040 Sofia, Bulgaria. TEL 00359-02-881492. FAX 00359-02-803633. (Subscr. addr.: Klokotnitsa 24, Sofia, Bulgaria. TEL 00359-02-318024) Ed. Stefan Landjev. adv. contact: Lidia Lukanova. charts, illus. circ. 50,000. **Document type:** consumer publication.
　Description: Includes articles, short stories about hunting, animals, predominantly wild animals and nature, conservation, ecology, international hunting tourism.

799.2　　　　　　XV　ISSN 0024-7014
LOVEC. (Text in Slovenian) 1918. m. 200 din.($10.45) Lovska Zveza Slovenije, Zupanciceva 9, Ljubljana, Slovenia. Eds. Tone Svetina, France Cvenkel.
　Description: Discusses hunting.

799.2 891.87 641.5　XO　ISSN 0541-8836
MAGAZIN POLOVNIKA. a. Priroda, Krizkova 9, 815 34 Bratislava, Slovakia. TEL 472-41-45. illus.

799.2　　　　　　SA
MAGNUM; the shooters' magazine. (Text mainly in English, some articles in Afrikaans) 1976. m. R.95 (foreign R.130) (effective through July 1996). South Africa Man Pty. Ltd., P.O. Box 35204, Northway 4065, South Africa. TEL 27-31-526551. FAX 27-31-5628389. Ed. Ronald K. Anger. adv. contact: Dorothy Wessels. bk.rev.; index; circ. 30,000 (paid). (back issues avail.)
　Formerly: Man.

S

SPORTS AND GAMES — OUTDOOR LIFE

799   US   ISSN 0199-0365
MAINE SPORTSMAN. 1977. m. $12. All Outdoors, Box 365, Augusta, ME 04330. (Subscr. to: Box 507, Yarmouth, ME 04096) Ed. Harry Vanderweide. circ. 30,000.

799   FR
MAISON DE LA CHASSE ET DE LA NATURE. REVUE. 1969. a. per no. to non-members. (Maison de la Chasse et de la Nature) Editions Person, 34 rue de Penthievre, 75008 Paris, France. Ed. J.H. Person. adv.; bk.rev. circ. 2,500.
    Formerly: Maison de la Chasse et de la Nature. Bulletin d'Information (ISSN 0987-741X)

MANITOBA NATURALISTS SOCIETY BULLETIN. see *CONSERVATION*

796.42   GW   ISSN 0179-5597
MARATHON AKTUELL. 1981. m. DM.48($25) Sportverlag, Derfflinger Str. 34, 40470 Duesseldorf, Germany. Ed. Burkhard Swara. adv.; bk.rev. circ. 6,000. (back issues avail.)

MARINE RECREATIONAL FISHERIES. see *FISH AND FISHERIES*

MASSACHUSETTS SIERRAN. see *CONSERVATION*

MATKAILU/TOURISM. see *TRAVEL AND TOURISM*

799.2   IT   ISSN 0392-3665
IL MESE DI CACCIA. 1964. m. (10/yr.). Associazione Nazionale Libera Caccia, Via Cavour 183-B, 00184 Rome, Italy. Ed. Mario Pagnoncelli. adv. circ. 150,000.

METSASTAJA. see *CONSERVATION*

799   FI   ISSN 0026-1629
METSASTYS JA KALASTUS. m. FIM 360. Yhtyneet Kuvalehdet Oy, Maistraatinportti 1, FIN-00240 Helsinki, Finland. TEL 358-0-156-6524. FAX 358-0-156-6505. TELEX 121364. Ed. Jussi Soikkanen. adv.; B&W page FIM 7500, color page FIM 10900. illus. circ. 34,702.
    Description: Concerns hunting and fishing.

199.2   US
MICHIGAN DEER & TURKEY SHOW PREVIEW. 1989. a. Target Communications Corp., 7626 W. Donges Bay Rd., Mequon, WI 53097-3400. TEL 414-242-3990; 800-324-3337. FAX 414-242-7391. Ed. Glenn Helgeland; Pub. Glenn Helgeland. adv.; B&W page $521, color page $849; trim 8 3/8 x 10 7/8; adv. contact: Lynn Anderson. circ. 35,000 (controlled). **Document type:** consumer publication.
    Description: Previews events, shows, seminars and new products of interest to hunters in Michigan.

799.1   US   ISSN 1057-2856
MICHIGAN HUNTING & FISHING. 8/yr. $15.97 (effective 1994). Northwoods Publications, Inc., 430 N. Front St., Box 90, Lemoyne, PA 17043. TEL 717-761-1400. FAX 717-761-4579. (Subscr. to: Box 977, E. Lansing, MI 48826. TEL 517-351-5957) Ed. Kenny Darwin. adv.; circ. 29,000 (paid). **Document type:** consumer publication.
    Formerly (until 1991): Michigan Fisherman (ISSN 0274-4783)
    Description: News and information for hunters and fishing enthusiasts in Michigan.

MICHIGAN NATURAL RESOURCES MAGAZINE. see *CONSERVATION*

796.42   US   ISSN 0279-1773
MICHIGAN RUNNER. 1979. 9/yr. $13.50. Great Lakes Sports Publications, Inc., 7990 W. Grand River, Ste. C, Brighton, MI 48116. TEL 810-227-4200. Ed. Dave Foley; Pub. Art McCafferty. adv. contact: Ann Neff. circ. 10,000. (tabloid format) **Document type:** consumer publication.
    Description: Includes medical advice, calendar of running events and news.

796.94   US   ISSN 0746-2298
MICHIGAN SNOWMOBILER. 1967. 6/yr. $8. Box 417, E. Jordan, MI 49727-0417. TEL 616-536-2371. FAX 616-536-7691. Ed. Lyle Shipe. adv. circ. 29,800. **Document type:** newspaper.
    Description: Covers all aspects of snowmobiling from trail riding to racing.

799 614   US   ISSN 0539-8908
SK91
MICHIGAN SPORTSMAN. 1976. m. $14.95. Game & Fish Publications, Inc., 2250 Newmarket Pkwy., Ste. 110, Box 741, Marietta, GA 30061-0741. TEL 404-953-9222. FAX 404-933-9510. Ed. Dennis Schmidt. circ. 25,000. **Indexed:** Mich.Mag.Ind.

799.2   US
MIDWEST BOWHUNTER. 1985. bi-m. $7.95 (foreign $13.95). 405 Pearl St., Sioux City, IA 51101. TEL 712-255-5132. Ed. Ritch A. Stolpe. adv.; bk.rev. circ. 5,000. **Document type:** newspaper.
    Description: For the hunting archer. Provides hunter success stories and photos, conservation news and information on new products.

799   US   ISSN 0747-3648
MIDWEST OUTDOORS. 1967. m. $11.95. Midwest Outdoors Ltd., 111 Shore Dr., Hinsdale, IL 60521. TEL 708-887-7722. FAX 708-887-1958. Ed. Eugene M. Laulunen. adv.; bk.rev.; charts; illus. circ. 49,000. (tabloid format) **Document type:** consumer publication.

799   US   ISSN 0274-8622
MINNESOTA SPORTSMAN. 1977. m. $14.95. Game & Fish Publications, Inc., 2250 Newmarket Pkwy., Ste. 110, Box 741, Marietta, GA 30061-0741. TEL 404-953-9222. FAX 404-933-9510. Ed. Dennis Schmidt. adv.; illus. circ. 32,000.

799   US   ISSN 0744-4192
MISSISSIPPI GAME & FISH. m. $14.97. Game & Fish Publications, Inc., 2250 Newmarket Pkwy., Ste. 110, Box 741, Marietta, GA 30061-0741. TEL 404-953-9222. FAX 404-933-9510. Ed. Bob Borgwat. adv. circ. 12,775.

MISSISSIPPI OUTDOORS. see *CONSERVATION*

MISSOURI CONSERVATIONIST. see *CONSERVATION*

796.42   AT   ISSN 0047-7672
MODERN ATHLETE AND COACH. 1962. q. Aus.$25 (effective thru 1996). Australian Track & Field Coaches Association, 1 Fox Ave., Athelstone, S.A. 5076, Australia. TEL 61-8-337-4510. Ed. Jess Jarver. adv.; bk.rev. circ. 2,500. **Indexed:** Phys.Ed.Ind., Sportsearch (1974-).
    —BLDSC (5883.690000).
    Description: Covers coaching on all track and field events, and related subjects such as nutrition, physiology, psychology, and bio-mechanics.

796.522   FR   ISSN 0047-7923
MONTAGNE ET ALPINISME. 1955. 4/yr. 136 F. Club Alpin Francais, 24, av. de Laumiere, 75019 Paris, France. Ed. Annie Bertholet. adv.; bk.rev.; illus.; charts. circ. 75,000.
    Description: Covers all aspects of mountaineering.

639.9   US   ISSN 0027-0016
MONTANA OUTDOORS. 1970. bi-m. $7. Department of Fish, Wildlife and Parks, 1420 E. Sixth, Helena, MT 59620. TEL 406-444-2474. Ed. Dave Books. bk.rev.; charts; illus. (back issues avail.) **Indexed:** Sport Fish.Abstr., Wild.Rev.
    —UnCover.

MOTOR CARAVAN WORLD. see *TRANSPORTATION*

796.5   UK
MOTOR CARAVANNER. 1960. m. membership. Motor Caravanners' Club, 71 Cricklewood Broadway, London NW2 3JR, England. Ed. Bill Brooks. adv.; bk.rev.; circ. controlled.

796.5   UK   ISSN 0141-9269
MOTORCARAVAN & MOTORHOME MONTHLY. Variant title: M M M. 1966. m. £25.20 (Europe £35; elsewhere £42.50). Sanglier Publications Ltd., The Maltings, West St., Bourne, Lincs. PE10 9PH, England. TEL 01778-393313. FAX 01778-425437. Ed. Penny Smith. adv.; B&W page £905, color page £1185; trim 275 x 190; adv. contact: Paul Barnett. bk.rev.; circ. 23,569. **Document type:** consumer publication.
    Incorporates: (in 1978): Motor Caravan and Camping (ISSN 0027-1829)

796.5 388.346   US   ISSN 0744-074X
TX1100
MOTORHOME. 1968. m. $26. T L Enterprises, Inc., 3601 Calle Tecate, Camarillo, CA 93012. TEL 805-389-0300. Ed. Bill Estes; Pub. Joe McNeil. adv.; illus.; mkt.; tr.mk. circ. 150,000. **Indexed:** Consum.Ind. **Document type:** consumer publication.
    Former titles: Motorhome Life (ISSN 0164-503X); Motorhome Life and Camper Coachman (ISSN 0361-1043); Which was formed by the merger of: Motorhome Life (ISSN 0027-2221); Camper Coachman; **Incorporating:** Van Life and Family Trucking (ISSN 0160-6107)
    Description: Devoted exclusively to the motorhome enthusiast's life-style. Includes vehicle tests, travel features, buyer's guides, new-product previews, and technical tips.

MOUNT BULLER NEWS. see *TRAVEL AND TOURISM*

796.5   KE
MOUNTAIN CLUB OF KENYA. BULLETIN. 1903. a. Mountain Club of Kenya, P.O. Box 46741, Nairobi, Kenya. **Indexed:** P.L.E.S.A. (1987-). **Document type:** bulletin.

796.552   SA   ISSN 0258-0101
MOUNTAIN CLUB OF SOUTH AFRICA. JOURNAL. (Text in Afrikaans, English) 1894. a. R.24. Mountain Club of South Africa, 97 Hatfield St., Cape Town 8001, South Africa. TEL 021-453-412. Ed. A. Hutton. adv.; bk.rev. circ. 2,800.

MOUNTAIN VISITOR. see *TRAVEL AND TOURISM*

796.522   US   ISSN 0027-2620
F886
MOUNTAINEER (SEATTLE); to explore, study, preserve and enjoy the natural beauty of Northwest America. 1907. m. (plus special issues). $15. Mountaineers, Inc., 300 Third Ave., W., Seattle, WA 98119-4117. TEL 206-284-6310. FAX 206-284-4977. Ed. Brad Stracener. adv.; bk.rev. circ. 15,000. **Indexed:** GeoRef. **Document type:** bulletin.
    —UnCover.

799.3   US   ISSN 1041-6366
MUSKY HUNTER MAGAZINE. 1989. bi-m. $18.95. Outlook Publishing, Box 147, 8554 US Hwy. 51, Ste.1, Minocqua, WI 54548. TEL 715-356-6301. FAX 715-358-2807. Ed. Jim Saric. adv.; B&W page $855, color page $1075; trim 8 1/2 x 11. circ. 16,000. **Document type:** consumer publication.

799.3   US   ISSN 0027-5360
MUZZLE BLASTS. 1939. m. $30. National Muzzle Loading Rifle Association, Box 67, Friendship, IN 47021. TEL 812-667-5131. FAX 812-667-5137. adv.; bk.rev.; bibl.; charts; illus.; index. circ. 27,000. **Document type:** consumer publication.

796.552   US   ISSN 0274-5720
TS536.6.M8
MUZZLELOADER. 1974. bi-m. $18 (foreign $22.50) (effective 1996). Scurlock Publishing Co., Inc., Route 5, Box 347M, Texarkana, TX 75501-9805. TEL 903-832-4726; 800-228-6389. FAX 903-831-3177. Ed. Bill Scurlock. adv.; bk.rev.; index; circ. 20,500 (paid). (back issues avail.) **Document type:** consumer publication.
    Description: Focuses on building, shooting, and hunting with muzzleloading guns, and on the history of muzzleloading guns in North America.

MYSLIVOST. see *CONSERVATION*

796.42   US   ISSN 0736-7783
GV1060.6
N C A A MEN'S AND WOMEN'S CROSS COUNTRY AND TRACK & FIELD RULES. 1922. a. $4. National Collegiate Athletic Association, Circulation Department, Box 7347, Overland Park, KS 66207-0347. TEL 913-339-1900. illus. circ. 10,000.
    Formerly: Official National Collegiate Athletic Association Track and Field Guide (ISSN 0196-9358)
    Description: Covers official signals, interpretations, and rulings.

SPORTS AND GAMES — OUTDOOR LIFE

796.93   US   ISSN 0741-9279
GV854.A1
N C A A MEN'S AND WOMEN'S SKIING RULES. 1963. a. $5. National Collegiate Athletic Association, Circulation Department, Box 7347, Overland Park, KS 66207-0347. TEL 913-339-1900. illus. circ. 1,000.
Former titles: N C A A Skiing Rules; (until 1980): Official National Collegiate Athletic Association Skiing Rules; National Collegiate Athletic Association. Official Skiing Rules (ISSN 0469-8592)
Description: Covers official signals, interpretations, and rulings.

799   UK   ISSN 0028-0070
N R A JOURNAL. 1860. q. £12 (Europe £15.25; Australia and New Zealand £24; elsewhere £22). National Rifle Association, Bisley Camp, Brookwood, Woking, Surrey GU24 0PB, England. TEL 01483-797777. FAX 01483-797285. Ed. P.F. Hicks. adv. contact: C.J. Judge. bk.rev. circ. 6,000.
Indexed: Sportsearch. Document type: proceedings.
Description: News and informational articles pertaining to the activities and membership of the NRA with results of competitions, personal profiles, agendas of meetings, and announcements of events.

N S R A NEWSLETTER. (National Ski Retailers Association) see BUSINESS AND ECONOMICS — Marketing And Purchasing

797   AT
N.S.W. SKINDIVER. (New South Wales) 1950. 4/mo. Aus.$20 (effective 1996). Australian Underwater Federation, N.S.W. Branch Sydney Metropolitan Zone, P.O. Box 44, Sans Souci, N.S.W. 2219, Australia. TEL 02-529-6496. Ed. M.V. Sheehan. adv.; bk.rev.; illus. circ. 4,500.
Former titles: Skin Diving News from New South Wales; Australian Skindivers (ISSN 0005-0253); N.S.W. Skindiver.

796.42   US   ISSN 0744-2416
NATIONAL MASTERS NEWS. 1977. m. $26. National Masters News, Box 50098, Eugene, OR 97405. TEL 503-343-7716. FAX 818-782-1135. Ed. Al Sheahen. adv.; bk.rev.; stat. circ. 6,000. (tabloid format; back issues avail.) Document type: consumer publication.
Description: Covers running and track and field for athletes forty and over.

796.5   US   ISSN 0734-7960
E160
NATIONAL PARK GUIDE.* 1966. a. $12.95. Prentice Hall Travel Directories (Subsidiary of: Simon & Schuster), 15 Columbus Cir., New York, NY 10023-7706. TEL 708-945-3737. FAX 708-945-3786. adv.: B&W page $1350, color page $1620; trim 8 x 10 3/4. circ. 25,000.
Former titles: Allstate Motor Club National Park Guide; Rand McNally National Park Guide (ISSN 0079-9629)

799.31   US   ISSN 0077-5738
NATIONAL SKEET SHOOTING ASSOCIATION. RECORDS ANNUAL.* 1947. a. $15. National Skeet Shooting Association, 5931 Roft Rd., San Antonio, TX 78253-9261. TEL 210-688-3371. Ed. Susie Fluckiger. adv.; index. circ. 18,000.

NATIONAL WILDLIFE; dedicated to the wise use of our natural resources. see CONSERVATION

796   SZ
NATUERLICH; Chrueteregge. 1981. 11/yr. 68 SFr. A T Zeitschriftenverlag, Bahnhofstr. 39-43, CH-5001 Aarau, Switzerland. TEL 064-266161. FAX 064-266293. Ed. Walter Hess. adv. circ. 75,000. Document type: consumer publication.

799   IT
NATURA OGGI. m. L.72000. Rizzoli Editore-Corriere della Sera, Via A. Rizzoli 2, 20132 Milan, Italy. TEL 02-2588. TELEX 312119 RIZZMI. Ed. L. Grandori.

796 333.7   GW   ISSN 0943-4607
NATURFREUNDE. 1949. bi-m. DM.11. Naturfreunde Bundesgruppe Deutschland e.V., Postfach 600441, 70304 Stuttgart, Germany. TEL 0711-336914-0. FAX 0711-3369144. adv. contact: Joerg Munder. Document type: bulletin.
Formerly (until 1992): Wandern und Bergsteigen (ISSN 0342-6432)

NEBRASKALAND. see CONSERVATION

799   IT
NEGOZIANTE CACCIA PESCA SPORT. 11/yr. Piazza S. Camillo de Lellis 1, 20124 Milan, Italy. TEL 39-2-66984880. FAX 39-2-66984771. Ed. Roberto Galimberti. adv.: B&W page L.3200000, color page L.4500000. circ. 9,600.

796.93   IT   ISSN 0028-4114
TD868
NEVE INTERNATIONAL. 1959. q. L.24000 (foreign L.35000). Publitec, Corso Massimo d'Azeglio 60, 10126 Turin, Italy. TEL 011-687093. FAX 011-6509801. Ed. Carlo G. Bertolotti. adv. circ. 10,000.
Description: Covers maintenance and management of wintersport resorts, snowmaking and ski slopes and lifts.

796   US   ISSN 0894-1203
NEW ENGLAND OUT-OF-DOORS. m. 510 King St., Littleton, MA 01460-1250. TEL 508-486-4785. Ed. Bryant Chaplin. circ. 23,000. Document type: consumer publication.
Formerly: Massachusetts and New Hampshire Out-of-Doors (ISSN 8750-1295)

796.42   US   ISSN 1041-4800
NEW ENGLAND RUNNER. 1983. 7/yr. $24.95. New England Sports Publications, Box 252, Boston, MA 02113. TEL 617-891-1844. FAX 617-899-0481. Ed. Bob FitzGerald; Pub. John McGrath. adv. circ. 14,575. Document type: consumer publication.
Formerly: Boston Running News (ISSN 8750-8621); Which incorporates: New England Running (ISSN 0737-0385)
Description: Covers running, triathalons, and track and field events in the six New England States and New York.

796.93   US
NEW ENGLAND SKIERS' GUIDE. 1983. a. $2.95. Ski Racing International, Box 1125, Waitsfield, VT 05673-1125. TEL 802-496-7700. FAX 802-496-7704. Ed. Tim Etchells; Pub. Gary Black, Jr. adv. contact: Phil Knaub. circ. 90,000 (controlled). Document type: consumer publication.
Description: Lists more than 150 alpine and nordic resorts in New England.

797.124   US
NEW ENGLAND WINDSURFING JOURNAL. 1983. 11/yr. $12. Buzzwords, Box 2120, Southbury, CT 06488. TEL 203-264-9463. FAX 203-264-9467. Ed. Peter Bogucki.
Formerly (until 1991): New England Sailboard Journal.

NEW HAMPSHIRE FISH AND GAME LAWS. see LAW — Judicial Systems

799.1   US   ISSN 1066-1379
NEW HAMPSHIRE WILDLIFE JOURNAL. 1969. 11/yr. $10. Fish and Game Department, 2 Hazen Dr., Concord, NH 03301. TEL 603-271-3211. FAX 603-271-1438. Ed. Judy S. Cummings. circ. 5,000.
Former titles (until Nov. 1992): Fish and Game Highlights of New Hampshire (ISSN 1041-4762); (until 1986): New Hampshire Natural Resources (ISSN 0028-5285); Which superseded: Field Notes (Concord) (ISSN 0739-5663)
Description: Publishes stories and information about wildlife, fishing, hunting, department programs and subjects of interest to outdoor enthusiasts.

799.1   US   ISSN 1054-4623
NEW JERSEY LAKE SURVEY FISHING MAPS GUIDE. 1989. a. $9.95 (effective 1994). New Jersey Sportsmen's Guides, Box 100, Somerdale, NJ 08083. TEL 609-665-8350. FAX 609-665-8656. Ed. Steve Perrone; Pub. Steve Perrone. adv.; illus.; maps. circ. 7,500. Document type: consumer publication.
Formerly (until 1991): New Jersey Lake Survey Map Guide (ISSN 1043-6405)
Description: Covers fishing and exploring New Jersey lakes, with information on fish species, lake depths, and more.

796   US
NEW YORK OUTDOORS. 1992. m. $19.95 (effective 1996). Allsport Publishing Corp., 51 Atlantic Ave., Floral Park, NY 11001. TEL 516-352-9700. FAX 516-437-6841. Ed. Scott Shane. adv. circ. 50,000.
Description: Covers outdoor activities in the greater New York Area.

799   US   ISSN 1044-7571
NEW YORK SPORTSMAN. 1972. 8/yr. $15.97. Northwoods Publications, Inc., 430 N. Front St., Box 90, Lemoyne, PA 17043. TEL 717-761-1400. FAX 717-761-4579. adv. circ. 48,000. Document type: consumer publication.
Description: Editorial features include hunting, fishing and trapping articles, as well as where-to and how-to within the regional scene. Includes news items and conservation.

799.1 797.1   NZ   ISSN 0113-9606
NEW ZEALAND FISHERMAN. 1988. m. NZ.$35 (foreign NZ.$130). New Zealand Magazines Ltd., Cnr. Halsey & Madden Streets, Freemans Bay, Auckland, New Zealand. TEL 09-3098-292. FAX 09-3096-361. Ed. William B. Kirk. circ. 25,000. (tabloid format; back issues avail.)
Description: Covers sport fishing, boat and landbased, inland fresh water and ocean fishing, and conservation.

799.2   NZ   ISSN 1171-6568
NEW ZEALAND HUNTING & WILDLIFE. 1962. q. NZ.$20. New Zealand Deerstalkers' Association Inc., P.O. Box 6514, Te Aro, Wellington 6035, New Zealand. TEL 64-3-570-5666. FAX 64-3-570-5888. Ed. T. Orman. adv.: B&W page NZ.$700, color page NZ.$900; trim 296 x 210. bk.rev.; charts; illus.; cum.index; circ. 4,000 (paid).
—CCC.
Formerly: New Zealand Wildlife (ISSN 0028-8802)
Description: Provides hunting articles on instruction, memories and conservation issues.

799   GW   ISSN 0048-0339
NIEDERSAECHSISCHER JAEGER. 1950. s-m. DM.85.80. (Landesjagdverband Niedersachsen) Landbuch-Verlag GmbH, Kabelkamp 6, 30179 Hannover, Germany. adv.; bk.rev.
—CCC.
Description: Covers cultural, historical, social, economical and ecological aspects of the region. Includes list of events and exhibitions.

799.2   US
NIKON HUNTER'S WORLD. 1987. a. $2.50. (Nikon, Inc.) Aqua-Field Publishing Co., Inc., 66 W. Gilbert St., Shrewsbury, NJ 07702. TEL 201-842-8300. Ed. Stephen Ferber. adv. circ. 110,000.
Formerly: Nikon's Big Game Hunting.

796   IT   ISSN 1121-6379
NO LIMITS WORLD; l'unica rivista dedicata all'estremo. 1992. m. L.70000 (foreign L.180000). No Limits World s.r.l., Via Corridoni 11, 20122 Milan, Italy. TEL 39-2-76005205. FAX 39-2-76007174. Ed. Antonio Soccol. adv.: B&W page L.9700000, color page L.15000000. circ. 106,525. Document type: consumer publication.
Description: Includes features on people who live life to the extreme. Covers various forms of adventure: rock climbing, deep-sea diving, small plane piloting, skiing.

796.93 910.09 380   US
NORDIC NETWORK. 1976. q. $25. Cross Country Ski Areas Association, 259 Bolton Rd., Winchester, NH 03470. TEL 603-239-4341. FAX 603-239-6387. Ed. Chris Frado. adv.; bk.rev. circ. 450. Document type: directory, newsletter.
Formerly: Cross Country Ski Areas of America Newsletter.

NORSK FISKARALMANAKK. see FISH AND FISHERIES

799.1   US   ISSN 1043-2450
NORTH AMERICAN FISHERMAN. 1988. bi-m. $18. North American Outdoor Group, Inc., 12301 Whitewater Dr., Box 3403, Minnetonka, MN 55343. TEL 612-936-0555. FAX 612-936-9755. Ed. Steve Pennaz. adv.; bk.rev. circ. 400,000. Document type: consumer publication.
Description: A forum for avid fishermen.

SPORTS AND GAMES — OUTDOOR LIFE

799.2   US   ISSN 0194-4320
SK40
NORTH AMERICAN HUNTER. 1979. 7/yr. $18. North American Outdoor Group, Inc., 12301 Whitewater Dr., Box 3401, Minnetonka, MN 55343. TEL 612-936-9333. FAX 612-936-9755. Ed. Bill Miller. adv.; bk.rev. circ. 600,000. **Document type:** consumer publication.
—UnCover.
Description: A forum for avid hunters.

NORTH AMERICAN PYLON; dedicated to sports car autocrossing. see *TRANSPORTATION — Automobiles*

799.2   US   ISSN 0746-6250
NORTH AMERICAN WHITETAIL. 8/yr. $14.95. Game & Fish Publications, Inc., 2250 Newmarket Pkwy., Ste. 110, Box 741, Marietta, GA 30061-0741. TEL 404-953-9222. FAX 404-933-9510. Ed. Gordon Whittington. adv. circ. 170,000.

799   US   ISSN 0897-8816
NORTH CAROLINA GAME & FISH. m. $14.97. Game & Fish Publications, Inc., 2250 Newmarket Pkwy., Ste. 110, Box 741, Marietta, GA 30061-0741. TEL 404-953-9222. FAX 404-933-9510. Ed. Jeff Samsel. circ. 16,571.

NORTH DAKOTA OUTDOORS. see *CONSERVATION*

790 333.7   US
NORTHEAST MEMO.* 1966. q. free. U.S. Heritage Conservation and Recreation Service, Northeast Regional Office, c/o National Park Service, 2nd Chestnut St, No. 260 Custom House, Philadelphia, PA 19106. Ed. Roslyn H. Brewer. circ. 4,300. (processed; back issues avail.)
Formerly: Northeast Outdoor Memo.

796.5   US   ISSN 0199-8463
NORTHEAST OUTDOORS. 1968. m. $8. Northeast Outdoors, Inc., 70 Edwin Ave., Box 2180, Waterbury, CT 06722. TEL 203-755-0158. FAX 203-755-3480. Ed. Mike Griffith. adv.: B&W page $1485; 10 x 14; adv. contact: Linda Herrmann. bk.rev.; circ. 14,000 (paid). (tabloid format) **Document type:** newspaper.
Description: Describes campgrounds and tourist regions in the Northeastern U.S for family campers and those with RVs, with advice and new product information.

769.93   US
NORTHWEST SKIER. 1958. m. $7.95. Cascade Communications, Inc., Box 99666, Seattle, WA 98199. TEL 206-329-4795. (Subscr. to: Box 23070, Seattle, WA 98102-0370) Ed. Jenny Peterson. adv.; bk.rev. circ. 30,000. (back issues avail.) **Indexed:** Sportsearch.
Former titles: Northwest Skier and Northwest Sports (ISSN 0274-9149); Northwest Skier (ISSN 0029-3458)
Description: Covers skiing in Alaska, Idaho, Montana, Oregon, Washington and British Columbia.

799   FR   ISSN 0048-0835
NOS CHASSES. 1958. m. 20 F.($5) Editions Chasse Sports, 28 rue de l'Ermitage, 75020 Paris, France. Ed. Marc Lambert. adv. circ. 32,000 (controlled).

799.2   IT   ISSN 0029-4365
NOTIZIARIO DI CACCIA E PESCA - TIRO A VOLO. 1947. w. L.195000. Greentime s.r.l., Via Barberia 11, 40123 Bologna, Italy. Ed. Olga Misley. adv.: B&W page L.1800000, color page L.2600000; adv. contact: Gian Luigi Zanettin. bk.rev.; illus. circ. 50,000. **Document type:** newspaper.
Description: Covers hunting, fishing and clay pigeon shooting.

796   GW
O P N - OUTDOOR PROFESSIONAL NEWS. q. Rotpunkt Verlag, Ziegeleistr. 16, 71384 Weinstadt, Germany. TEL 07151-99902-0. FAX 07151-999029. Pub. Juergen Linsenmaier. adv.: B&W page DM.3920, color page DM.6900; trim 172 x 250; adv. contact: Karsten Heyder. **Document type:** consumer publication.

OESTERREICHISCHE TOURISTENZEITUNG. see *TRAVEL AND TOURISM*

796   AU   ISSN 0029-8840
OESTERREICHISCHER ALPENVEREIN. AKADEMISCHE SEKTION GRAZ. MITTEILUNGEN. 1892. a. membership. Oesterreichischer Alpenverein, Akademische Sektion Graz, Rechbauerstr. 12, A-8010 Graz, Austria. TEL 0316-329753. Ed. Norbert Hauer. adv.; bk.rev.; illus. circ. 1,000. **Document type:** bulletin.

796.522   AU   ISSN 0029-9715
OESTERREICHISCHER ALPENVEREIN. MITTEILUNGEN. 1863. bi-m. membership. Oesterreichischer Alpenverein, Wilhelm-Greil-Str. 15, A-6010 Innsbruck, Austria. TEL 0512-59547-0. FAX 0512-575528. Ed. Gerold Benedikter. adv.; bk.rev.; index. circ. 127,000. **Indexed:** Bibl.Cart. **Document type:** newsletter.
Description: Covers mountain climbing and hiking, tourism, travel reports, expeditors, skiing, forestry, environmental planning and protection, history, and new publications. Includes readers' letters.

796 680   FR   ISSN 0987-3201
L'OFFICIEL DES TERRAINS DE CAMPING ET DE CARAVANING. 1972. 9/yr. 265 F. (foreign 328 F.) (effective 1994-1995). Ediregie, B.P. 86, 94420 Le Plessis Trevise, France. TEL 45-93-72-72. FAX 45-93-25-93. TELEX EDIGIE 262 572 F. Ed. Jacques Gout. adv. circ. 11,000. **Document type:** consumer publication.

799.2   US
OHIO DEER & TURKEY SHOW PREVIEW. 1992. a. Target Communications Corp., 7626 W. Donges Bay Rd., Mequon, WI 53097-3400. TEL 414-242-3990; 800-324-3337. FAX 414-242-7391. Ed. Glenn Helgeland; Pub. Glenn Helgeland. adv.: B&W page $521, color page $849; trim 8 3/8 x 10 7/8; adv. contact: Lynn Anderson. circ. 35,000 (controlled). **Document type:** consumer publication.
Description: Previews shows, seminars, and new products of interest to hunters in Ohio.

799.1   US   ISSN 0889-2407
OHIO FISHERMAN.* m. 41 S. Grant Ave., Ste. 202, Columbus, OH 43215-3927. TEL 614-445-7506. Ed. Dan Armitage.

799.1   US
OHIO FISHWRAPPER. 1986. m. $8.95. Fremont Messenger Co. (Subsidiary of: Gannett Co., Inc.), 1700 Cedar St., Fremont, OH 43420. TEL 419-332-5511. FAX 419-332-9750. adv. circ. 40,000.

799   US   ISSN 0746-6013
OKLAHOMA GAME & FISH. 1982. m. $14.97. Game & Fish Publications, Inc., 2250 Newmarket Pkwy., Ste. 110, Box 741, Marietta, GA 30061-0741. TEL 404-953-9222. FAX 404-933-9510. Ed. Nick Gilmore. circ. 10,000.

796.552   UK   ISSN 1352-0571
ON THE EDGE MAGAZINE. 1987. bi-m. £20($40) Climbing Company Ltd., P.O. Box 21, Buxton, Derbys. SK17 9BR, England. TEL 0298-72801. FAX 0298-72801. (Dist. by: Warners Group Distribution, The Maltings, Manor Ln., Bourne, Lincs. PE10 9PH, England. TEL 0778-393652) Ed. Gill Kent. adv. contact: Simon Moody. bk.rev.; abstr.; film rev.; play rev.; circ. 12,000 (paid). (back issues avail.) **Document type:** consumer publication.
Description: Covers climbing in its entirety, with sections on training, technique, and equipment.

ON THE LINE (PENSACOLA). see *LEISURE AND RECREATION*

796   US
ON THE TRAIL. m. $14. Box 456, E. Syracuse, NY 13057-0456. TEL 315-437-9296. Ed. Janel Hansen. **Document type:** newspaper.

797   NE   ISSN 0048-1696
ONDERWATERSPORT. 1970. m. fl.40($20) Nederlandse Onderwatersport Bond, Nassaustraat 12, 3583 XG Utrecht, Netherlands. TEL 31-30-517014. FAX 31-30-510773. Ed. G.G.M. van Oosterhout. adv.; bk.rev.; charts; illus.; tr.lit. circ. 15,000. **Document type:** consumer publication.
Incorporates: Onderwaterwereld (ISSN 0923-2184); Which was formerly (until 1980): Duiksport (ISSN 0923-2176); (until 1979): Sportduiker (ISSN 0166-9745)

ONTARIO FARM & COUNTRY ACCOMMODATIONS DIRECTORY. see *TRAVEL AND TOURISM*

799.1   CN   ISSN 0822-8736
ONTARIO FISHERMAN. 1979. bi-m. Can.$19. Transcontinental Sports Publications, 85 Scarsdale Rd., Ste. 400, Don Mills, ON M3B 2R2, Canada. TEL 416-445-5702. FAX 519-445-0753. Ed. Matt Nicholls. adv. contact: Esther Sumka. circ. 22,000 (paid). **Document type:** consumer publication.

799   CN   ISSN 0707-3178
ONTARIO OUT OF DOORS. 1969. 10/yr. Can.$23. MacLean Hunter Ltd., 227 Front St. E., Toronto, ON M5A 1E8. TEL 416-368-0185. FAX 416-941-9113. Ed. Burt Myers. adv.: B&W page $3326, color page $3655; 8 1/4 x 11. bk.rev.; illus. circ. 100,000. **Indexed:** Can.B.P.I., Can.Per.Ind., CMI.
Description: Directed to the Ontario outdoor enthusiasts of with information about fishing, hunting, and camping activities. Includes where-to and how-to articles, and examines conservation of natural resources.

796.95   CN   ISSN 0383-7009
ONTARIO SNOWMOBILER. 1986. 5/yr. Can.$17($22) (Ontario Federation of Snowmobile Clubs) Ontario Snowmobiler Publishing Ltd., RR 3, Centre Road, Mount Albert, ON L0G 1M0, Canada. TEL 905-473-7009. FAX 905-473-5217. Eds. Mark Lester, Kent Lester; Pub. Terrence D. Kehoe. adv. contact: John Hildebrandt. maps. circ. 72,000. (back issues avail.) **Document type:** consumer publication, trade publication.
Description: News about snowmobiling and the snowmobile industry.

797.1   CN   ISSN 0226-5702
ONTARIO WATER SKIER. 1974. 4/yr. Can.$12. Ontario Water Ski Association, 1185 Eglinton Ave. E., N. York, ON M3C 3C6, Canada. TEL 416-426-7092. FAX 416-426-7378. adv.: B&W page Can.$240; trim 7 1/2 x 10. bk.rev.; illus. circ. 1,500. **Indexed:** Sportsearch (1978-). **Document type:** newsletter.
Description: Articles on water skiing, equipment, technique, events and activities in recreational and competitive forms of the sport.

796   NE   ISSN 0168-3845
OP PAD. 1983. 9/yr. fl.67.50. Koninklijke Nederlandse Toeristenbond ANWB - Royal Dutch Touring Club, Wassenaarseweg 220, Postbus 93200, 2509 BA The Hague, Netherlands. TEL 31-70-3146119. FAX 31-70-3242509. adv.: B&W page fl.4080, color page fl.7344; trim 215 x 285; adv. contact: J.W. Boersen. illus.; circ. 52,000 (paid). **Document type:** consumer publication.
Description: For well-to-do campers, hikers, cyclists, canoeists and mountaineers.

OPEN SPACES. see *CONSERVATION*

790.1   US   ISSN 0886-1080
GV200.4
ORIENTEERING NORTH AMERICA. 1985. m. $23.50. (United States Orienteering Federation) S M & L Berman Publishing Co., 23 Fayette St., Cambridge, MA 02139-1111. TEL 617-868-7416. FAX 617-876-8186. (Alt. addr.: Box 1444, Forest Park, GA 30051) Eds. Sara Mae Berman; Pub. Lawrence J. Berman. adv.; bk.rev. circ. 1,850. (back issues avail.) **Document type:** consumer publication.
Description: Covers all aspects of the sport of orienteering. Geared towards all levels of interest.

OUT AND ABOUT SMITH MOUNTAIN LAKE. see *TRAVEL AND TOURISM*

OUT WEST. see *TRAVEL AND TOURISM*

796.5   GW   ISSN 0935-3356
OUTDOOR; das andere Reisemagazin. 1988. bi-m. DM.45.90 (foreign DM.51.90). Rotpunkt Verlag, Ziegeleistr. 16, 71384 Weinstadt, Germany. TEL 07151-99902-0. FAX 07151-999029. (Subscr. to: Zenit Pressevertrieb GmbH, Postfach 810640, 70523 Stuttgart, Germany) Eds. Gunnar Homann, Robert Bartscher; Pub. Juergen Linsenmaier. adv.: B&W page DM.3920, color page DM.6900; trim 172 x 250; adv. contact: Karsten Heyder. bk.rev.; index. circ. 58,100. (back issues avail.) **Document type:** consumer publication.

SPORTS AND GAMES — OUTDOOR LIFE

796   GW
OUTDOOR & TREKKING AUSRUESTUNGSHANDBUCH (YEAR). a. Rotpunkt Verlag, Ziegeleistr. 16, 71384 Weinstadt, Germany. TEL 07151-999902-0. FAX 07151-999029. Pub. Juergen Linsenmaier. adv.: B&W page DM.4160, color page DM.7400; trim 172 x 250; adv. contact: Karsten Heyder. **Document type:** catalog.

796 917.1 333.7   CN   ISSN 0315-0542
OUTDOOR CANADA. 1972. 8/yr. Can.$24. Outdoor Canada Publishing Ltd., 703 Evans Ave., Ste. 202, Toronto, ON M9C 5E9, Canada. TEL 416-695-0311. FAX 416-695-0381. Ed. Teddi Brown. adv.: B&W page Can.$6840, color page Can.$7950; trim 7 x 10; adv. contact: Ildiko Marshall. illus.; tr.lit. circ. 95,000. (also avail. in microform) **Indexed:** Can.B.P.I., Can.Per.Ind., CMI, Sportsearch. **Document type:** consumer publication.
—UnCover.
Description: For active, outdoor Canadians and their families. Covers fishing, canoeing, hiking, hunting, exploring, boating, photography, wildlife and winter sports.

799.06   CN   ISSN 0700-9909
OUTDOOR CREST. 1975. irreg. free. Toronto Sportsmen's Association, 17 Mill St., Willowdale, ON M2P 1B3, Canada. TEL 416-487-4477. Ed. Peter Edwards. illus. circ. 1,200. **Document type:** newsletter.
Formerly: Outdoor Crest Newsletter (ISSN 0700-9895)

799   US   ISSN 0030-7076
SK1
OUTDOOR LIFE. 1898. m. $30. Times Mirror Magazines, Inc., 2 Park Ave., New York, NY 10016. TEL 212-779-5000. FAX 212-686-6877. (Subscr. to: Box 54733, Boulder, CO 80322. TEL 800-365-1580) Ed. Vin. T. Sparano. adv.; illus. circ. 1,350,000. (also avail. in microform from UMI; reprint service avail. from UMI) **Indexed:** Consum.Ind., Jun.High.Mag.Abstr., Mag.Ind., PMR, R.G., Sports Per.Ind., TOM.
●Also available online. Vendor(s): Knight-Ridder, Inc., University Microfilms International.
Also available on CD-ROM. Producer(s): University Microfilms International.
—Faxon; UMI; UnCover.
Description: Concentrates on hunting and fishing.

796.5   US
OUTDOOR LIFE GUIDES. q. $2.75 per no. Times Mirror Magazines, Inc., 2 Park Ave., New York, NY 10016. TEL 212-779-5000.

OUTDOOR NEWS. see CONSERVATION

OUTDOOR NEWS BULLETIN. see CONSERVATION

OUTDOOR OKLAHOMA. see CONSERVATION

799   US   ISSN 0739-0602
OUTDOOR PRESS. 1966. w. $30. Outdoor Press, N. 2012 Ruby St., Spokane, WA 99207. TEL 509-328-9292. FAX 509-327-9861. Ed. Fred C. Peterson II. adv.: B&W page $700, color page $1200; 11 1/2 x 14 1/2. bk.rev.; circ. 6,000 (paid). (tabloid format) **Document type:** newspaper.
Description: Reports on hunting and fishing in the Pacific Northwest.

796   US
OUTDOOR PURSUITS SERIES. irreg. (1-2/yr.) $12.95 (Canada $17.50) per no. Human Kinetics Publishers, Box 5076, Champaign, IL 61825-5076. TEL 800-747-4457. FAX 217-351-1549.

OUTDOOR REPORT. see LEISURE AND RECREATION

796   US   ISSN 0279-8107
OUTDOOR RETAILER.* 1980. m. $15. Pacifica Publishing Corporation, 31652 Second Ave., Box 1899, Laguna Beach, CA 92652-1899. TEL 714-499-4591. FAX 714-499-5092. Ed. Pam Montgomery. adv.: B&W page $1400, color page $1850; 8 3/8 x 10 7/8. circ. 12,000 (controlled).
—CCC.

790.1   AT
OUTDOOR SHOWMAN. 1949. q. Aus.$32 (effective 1995 & 1996). Victorian Showmen's Guild, Box 36, Ascot Vale, Vic. 3032, Australia. TEL 61-3-376-8544. FAX 61-3-3760505. Ed. V.A. Hilton. adv. circ. 1,000. **Document type:** trade publication.

OUTDOOR SINGLES NETWORK. see SINGLES' INTERESTS AND LIFESTYLES

796.5   UK
OUTDOOR TRADE AND INDUSTRY. 1984. bi-m. £5. 97 Front St., Whickham, Newcastle-upon-Tyne NE16 4JL, England. Ed. Peter Lumley. adv.; circ. controlled.
Incorporates: Camping and Outdoor Leisure Trader.

796   US
OUTDOORS ILLUSTRATED.* q. Market Focus Publications, 1001 Hawkins St., Nashville, TN 37203-4773. TEL 615-256-8844. Ed. Bill Hudgins. circ. 250,000.

OUTDOORS UNLIMITED. see CONSERVATION

796   US   ISSN 0278-1433
GV191.2
OUTSIDE (SANTA FE). 1976. m. $18. Mariah Media Inc., Outside Plaza, 400 Market St., Santa Fe, NM 87501. TEL 505-989-7100. FAX 505-898-4700. (Subscr. to: Box 51733, Boulder, CO 80321-1733. TEL 800-678-1131) Ed. Mark Bryant. adv.: B&W page $20229, color page $29235; 8 1/4 x 10 7/8. bk.rev.; illus. circ. 450,000. (also avail. in microfilm from UMI; reprint service avail. from UMI) **Indexed:** Access (1980-), Sportsearch (1980-). **Document type:** consumer publication.
—UMI; UnCover.
Former titles (until 1980): Mariah - Outside (ISSN 0194-4371); (until 1979): Mariah (ISSN 0149-7790)
Description: Inspires people to enjoy fuller, more rewarding lives through year-round participation in sports, travel, events, photography, and politics of the world.

796   US
▼**OUTSIDE'S SPORT & TRAVEL GUIDES.** 1995. q. (includes a. Buyer's Guide). Mariah Media Inc., Outside Plaza, 400 Market St., Santa Fe, NM 87501. TEL 505-989-7100. FAX 505-989-4700. adv.; illus.; circ. 200,000 (paid). **Document type:** consumer publication.

796   US
▼**OVER THE EDGE.** 1994. bi-m. newsstand price: $3.99. H G Publications, Inc., 9171 Wilshire Blvd., Ste. 300, Beverly Hills, CA 90210. TEL 310-858-7100. FAX 310-275-3857. adv. **Document type:** consumer publication.
Description: Aimed at the adventure sports enthusiast.

799.1   US   ISSN 1069-0689
PACIFIC FISHERMAN. 1989. m. $25. Barana Publishing, 23182 Alcalde, Ste. K, Laguna Hills, CA 92653. TEL 714-830-2290. FAX 714-830-5108. Ed. Peter Barana. adv. contact: Tony Garza. circ. 16,846 (paid). (back issues avail.) **Document type:** consumer publication.
Description: Covers saltwater fishing in Alaska, Washington, Oregon, California and Baja California. Includes how-to techniques and travel.

799.3   UK   ISSN 0955-9124
PAINTBALL ADVENTURES. 1989. m. £20.50. Penn Publishing Co., 20 Hill Farm Way, Hazlemere, Bucks HP15 7SY, England. TEL 0494-814418. FAX 0494-812746. Ed. Stuart Wall. adv. contact: David Smith. bk.rev. (back issues avail.) **Document type:** consumer publication.

333.78   UK   ISSN 0954-3880
PARKS, GOLF COURSES AND SPORTS GROUNDS. 1935. m. £25 (foreign £27) (effective 1996). Clarke & Hunter (London) Ltd., 250 London Rd., Staines, Mddx. TW18 4JQ, England. TEL 01784-461326. FAX 01784-462073. Ed. Alan Guthrie; Pub. Dudley Penrose. adv. contact: Jennifer Archer. bk.rev.; abstr.; bibl.; charts; illus.; stat.; index. circ. 6,580. **Indexed:** Hort.Abstr., Sportsearch (1976-). **Document type:** trade publication.
—BLDSC (6406.821000).
Formerly (until 1975): Parks and Sports Grounds (ISSN 0031-224X)
Description: Concentrates on design, construction and maintenance of turf areas in parks, recreation areas and sports grounds.

PATHWAYS ACROSS AMERICA; a newsletter for national scenic and historic trails. see HISTORY — History Of North And South America

PEAK AND PRAIRIE. see CONSERVATION

796.42   UK   ISSN 0962-0184
PEAK PERFORMANCE. 1990. m. £35. Stonehart Leisure Magazines, 67-71 Goswell Rd., London EC1V 7EN, England. TEL 0171-250-1881. FAX 0171-410-9440. (Subscr. to: Hainault Rd., Romford, Essex RM6 5NP, England. TEL 0181-597-7335) Ed. Nick Troop. circ. 2,000.
—BLDSC (6413.796100).

799   SZ
PECHEUR ROMAND. 1936. m. 42 Fr. (foreign 52 Fr.). Presses Centrales Lausanne SA, Rue de Geneve 7, 1003 Lausanne, Switzerland. Ed. A. Quartier. adv.; bk.rev.; charts; illus.; tr.lit.; index; cum.index. circ. 6,500.
Former titles: Nature Information; Pecheur et Chasseur Suisses (ISSN 0031-3734)
Description: Covers fishing and hunting.

796.5   US   ISSN 0031-434X
SH1
PENNSYLVANIA ANGLER.* 1931. m. $5. Fish Commission, Box 67000, Harrisburg, PA 17106-7000. Ed. Art Michaels. bk.rev. circ. 65,000. **Indexed:** Sport Fish.Abstr., Wild.Rev.
—Faxon; UnCover.
Description: Covers fishing, boating and camping.

799.2   US
▼**PENNSYLVANIA DEER & TURKEY SHOW PREVIEW.** 1994. a. Target Communications Corp., 7626 W. Donges Bay Rd., Mequon, WI 53097-3400. TEL 414-242-3990; 800-324-3337. FAX 414-242-7391. Ed. Glenn Helgeland; Pub. Glenn Helgeland. adv.: B&W page $521, color page $849; trim 8 3/8 x 10 7/8; adv. contact: Lynn Anderson. circ. 35,000 (controlled). **Document type:** consumer publication.
Description: Previews shows, conferences, and new products of interest to hunters in Pennsylvania.

799   US   ISSN 0897-8808
PENNSYLVANIA GAME & FISH. 1982. m. $14.97. Game & Fish Publications, Inc., 2250 Newmarket Pkwy., Ste. 110, Box 741, Marietta, GA 30061-0741. TEL 404-953-9222. FAX 404-933-9510. Ed. Stephen Carpenteri. adv. circ. 19,702.
Formerly: Pennsylvania Outdoors (ISSN 0745-225X)

799.2   US   ISSN 0031-451X
SK351
PENNSYLVANIA GAME NEWS. 1931. m. $9. Game Commission, 2001 Elmerton Ave., Harrisburg, PA 17110-9797. TEL 717-787-3745. FAX 717-772-2411. Ed. Bob Mitchell. bk.rev.; illus.; index. circ. 150,000. (also avail. in microform from UMI; reprint service avail. from UMI) **Indexed:** Biol.Abstr., Biol.Dig.
—UMI.

799   US   ISSN 0274-6336
PENNSYLVANIA SPORTSMAN. 1959. 8/yr. $12. Northwoods Publications, Inc., 430 N. Front St., Box 90, Lemoyne, PA 17043. TEL 717-761-1400. FAX 717-761-4579. Ed. Lou Hoffman. adv. circ. 63,000. **Document type:** consumer publication.
Formerly: Pennsylvania's Outdoor People.
Description: Covers hunting, fishing, and trapping, as well as conservation for the outdoorsman.

SPORTS AND GAMES — OUTDOOR LIFE

799.1   IT   ISSN 1121-3639
PESCA A MOSCA; tecnica attrezzature itinerari. 1991. m. L.70000 (Europe L.100000; elsewhere L.110000). Ed.A.I. s.r.l. (Edizioni Aeronautiche Italiane), Casella Postale 1550, 50100 Florence, Italy. Ed. Antonio Del Campana. **Document type:** consumer publication.

799.1 614.7   IT   ISSN 0394-090X
PESCA IN. m. L.65000 (Europe L.95000; elsewhere L.100000). Ed.A.I. s.r.l. (Edizioni Aeronautiche Italiane), V. Guinicelli 4, 50133 Florence, Italy. TEL 39-55-574774. FAX 39-55-570103. TELEX 580217 EDAI I. Ed. Riccardo Galigani. adv.: B&W page L.3800000, color page L.5650000. circ. 64,500. **Document type:** consumer publication.
    Description: Covers freshwater fishing. Contains competition reports, scientific articles and environmental issues.

799.1   IT   ISSN 0394-0918
PESCA IN MARE. m. L.75000 (Europe L.95000; elsewhere L.100000). Ed.A.I. s.r.l. (Edizioni Aeronautiche Italiane), V. Guinicelli 4, 50133 Florence, Italy. TEL 39-55-574774. FAX 39-55-570103. TELEX 580217 EDAI I. Ed. Fabrizio Bonanni. adv.: B&W page L.3800000, color page L.5650000. circ. 81,200. **Document type:** consumer publication.
    Description: Covers fishing, fishing boats, nautical environmental issues.

PESCA NOTIZIE. see *FISH AND FISHERIES*

799.1   IT   ISSN 0031-6091
PESCARE; la rivista dei pescatori. 1962. m. L.75000 (foreign L.106000). Editoriale Olimpia S.p.A., Viale Milton 7, 50129 Florence, Italy. TEL 055-473843. FAX 055-499195. TELEX 573084 EDOL I. Ed. Antonio Brandi. adv.: B&W page L.4000000, color page L.7300000; adv. contact: Alessandro Menchi. charts; illus.; index. circ. 40,200. **Document type:** consumer publication.

799.1   IT   ISSN 1121-3647
PESCARE M & S. (Mosca e Spinning) 1991. m. L.25500 (foreign L.38000). Editoriale Olimpia S.p.A., Viale Milton 7, 50129 Florence, Italy. TEL 39-55-473843. FAX 39-55-499195. Ed. Sandro Conti. adv.: B&W page L.3650000, color page L.6600000; adv. contact: Alessandro Menchi. **Document type:** consumer publication.

799.1   IT   ISSN 1121-3833
PESCARE MARE. 1989. m. L.75000 (foreign L.106000). Editoriale Olimpia S.p.A., Viale Milton 7, 50129 Florence, Italy. TEL 39-55-473843. FAX 39-55-499195. Ed. Sandro Conti. adv.: B&W page L.4000000, color page L.7300000; adv. contact: Alessandro Menchi.

799.1   IT
PESCASUB. 1988. m. L.45000 (foreign L.90000). Adventures s.r.l., V.la A. Antossi 20, 20135 Milan, Italy. TEL 39-2-55188494. FAX 39-2-5464407. Ed. Guido Pfeiffer. adv.: B&W page L.3500000, color page L.5500000. **Document type:** consumer publication.

739.7   US   ISSN 1040-1865
PETERSEN'S HANDGUNS. m. $23.94. Petersen Publishing Co., 6420 Wilshire Blvd., Los Angeles, CA 90048. TEL 213-782-2000. Ed. J. Libourel. circ. 150,800. **Document type:** consumer publication.

799.2   US   ISSN 0146-4671
SK1
PETERSEN'S HUNTING. 1973. m. $19.94. Petersen Publishing Co., 6420 Wilshire Blvd., Los Angeles, CA 90048. TEL 213-782-2000. Ed. Todd Smith. adv.; bk.rev.; illus. circ. 345,521. (also avail. in microform from UMI) **Document type:** consumer publication.
    —UMI.

799.1   SZ   ISSN 0031-6318
PETRI-HEIL. Schweizerische Fischereizeitung. 1950. m. 72.20 SFr. Weka Verlag AG, Hermetschloostr. 77, CH-8010 Zurich, Switzerland. TEL 01-4320456. FAX 01-4329436. Ed. H. Dietiker. circ. 20,000. **Document type:** newspaper.

799.2   US
PHEASANTS FOREVER. 1982. 5/yr. $20. Pheasants Forever Inc., Box 75473, St. Paul, MN 55175. TEL 612-481-7142. FAX 612-481-0715. adv. circ. 68,962.
    Description: For pheasant hunters and enthusiasts. Focuses on conservation and the importance of wildlife, specifically upland birds.

799.2   GW   ISSN 0340-7829
DIE PIRSCH; Magazin fuer Jagd, Wild, Natur. 1948. fortn. DM.166.70. B L V Verlagsgesellschaft mbH, Lothstr. 29, 80797 Munich, Germany. TEL 089-12705-0. FAX 089-12705354. Ed. Michael Lewicki. adv. contact: Henning Stemmler. bk.rev.; illus. **Indexed:** Key Word Ind.Wildl.Res. **Document type:** consumer publication.
    —CCC.
    Formed by merger of: Pirsch (ISSN 0032-0269); Deutscher Jaeger (ISSN 0012-1118)

796.5   FR   ISSN 0048-427X
PLAISIRS DE LA CHASSE. 1952. 12/yr. 300 F. Imprimerie de Champagne, 14, rue du Patronage Laique, 52003 Chaumont Cedex, France. Ed. Antoine Cohen-Potin. adv. circ. 55,000.

799.1   FR   ISSN 0032-0501
PLAISIRS DE LA PECHE. (Not published 1987-1988) 1953. bi-m. 200 F. (foreign 270 F.). Editions du Cameleon, 11 rue Vauthier, 92100 Boulogne Billancourt, France. TEL 46-04-48-84. FAX 46-04-26-48. Ed. Jean Tesseyre; Pub. Jean Tesseyre. adv. contact: Virginie Merlin. bk.rev./; circ. 35,000 (paid). **Document type:** newspaper.
    Description: Covers freshwater and saltwater fly fishing, ecology, and freshwater management.

796   FR
PLANCHE A VOILE.* q. Message S.A., 49 rue Camdronne, 75015 Paris, France. **Indexed:** Sportsearch (1984-).

796   FR   ISSN 0242-6986
PLANCHE MAGAZINE.* m. Message S.A., 49 rue Camdronne, 75105 Paris, France. **Indexed:** Sportsearch (1988-).

THE POINTING DOG JOURNAL. see *AGRICULTURE — Poultry And Livestock*

799   XO   ISSN 0231-8768
POL'OVNICTVO A RYBARSTVO/HUNTING AND FISHING. 1949. m. $51. (Slovensky Polovnicky Zvaz - Slovak Hunters' Union) Rada S P Z a Rada S R Z, Kocel'ova 17, 821 08 Bratislava, Slovakia. (Co-sponsor: Slovensky Rybarsky Zvaz - Slovak Fishermen's Union) **Indexed:** Ind.Vet., Poult.Abstr.

POOLWAYS; the magazine of outdoor living (year). see *SPORTS AND GAMES*

796.522   US   ISSN 0092-2226
F217.B6
POTOMAC APPALACHIAN. 1932. m. $6. Potomac Appalachian Trail Club, Inc., 118 Park St., S.E., Vienna, VA 22180-4609. Ed. Kathryn Wolff. adv.; bk.rev.; illus. circ. 3,800. **Indexed:** Sportsearch.
    Incorporates (in 1972): Potomac Appalachian Forecast; Formerly (until 1971): Potomac Appalachian Trail Club. Bulletin (ISSN 0032-5635)
    Description: Covers hiking and mountaineering.

796.93   US   ISSN 0145-4471
GV854.A1
POWDER. 1971. 7/yr. $12.95. Surfer Publications, Inc., 33046 Calle Aviador, San Juan Capistrano, CA 92675. TEL 714-496-5922. FAX 714-496-7849. (Subscr. to: Box 50239, Boulder, CO 80322-8144. TEL 800-289-8983) Ed. Steve Casimiro. adv. contact: Ben Warner. illus. circ. 115,000. **Indexed:** Sports Per.Ind., Sportsearch (1979-). **Document type:** consumer publication.
    —UnCover.

796.93   SA   ISSN 1018-1385
POWER BOAT AND SKI. 1988. bi-m. R.28($14) Yachting News (Pty) Ltd., P.O. Box 3473, Cape Town 8000, South Africa. TEL 27-21-4617472. FAX 27-21-4613758. Ed. Geoff Dekenah. adv. contact: Bill Stymonds. circ. 4,500. **Document type:** consumer publication.
    Formerly (until Nov. 1991): Power and Ski (ISSN 1012-3288)

POWER STROKE. see *SPORTS AND GAMES — Boats And Boating*

799.1   AT   ISSN 1039-0952
POWERBOAT FISHING. 1992. 6/yr. Aus.$29.70 (foreign Aus.$84) (effective Feb. 1995). Yaffa Publishing Group, 17-21 Bellevue St., Surry Hills, N.S.W. 2010, Australia. TEL 61-2-281-2333. FAX 61-2-281-2750. Ed. Mark Arblaster. adv.: B&W page Aus.$1545, color page Aus.$1965; trim 273 x 210. circ. 8,090. **Document type:** consumer publication.
    Description: Aimed at all boat sportfishermen slanted to the more affluent fishermen.

796   UK   ISSN 0269-9427
PRACTICAL CARAVAN. 1966. m. £55. Haymarket Magazines Ltd., 38-42 Hampton Rd., Teddington, Middx. TW11 OJE, England. TEL 081-943-5000. TELEX 895-2440-HAYMRT-G. Ed. Bruce Black. circ. 51,529.
    Description: Product tests and tips about caravans.

799   US   ISSN 1067-5914
PRACTICAL SPORTSMAN; hunting, fishing and the shooting sports. Key Title: Fred Trost's Practical Sportsman. bi-m. $20 includes membership. (Practical Sportsman Club) Practical Sportsman, Inc., 14099 Webster Rd., Bath, MI 48808. TEL 517-641-6701. FAX 517-641-6061. (Subscr. to: Box 1001, Bath, MI 48808-1001) Ed. Jo Ann Cribley; Pub. Fred Trost. adv. contact: Matt Radzialowski. circ. 25,000. (back issues avail.) **Document type:** consumer publication.
    Former titles (until 1992): Fred Trost's Outdoor Digest (ISSN 0884-9137); (until 1985): Michigan Outdoors Club. Club Digest (ISSN 8750-1996)
    Description: Information, news and events of interest to active hunters and sportsmen.

PSYCHOLOGY AND SOCIOLOGY OF SPORT: CURRENT SELECTED RESEARCH. see *PSYCHOLOGY*

799   CN
GV585.3.Q4
QUEBEC (PROVINCE). MINISTERE DE L'ENVIRONNEMENT ET FAUNE. RAPPORT ANNUEL. (Editions in English, French) 1980. a. price varies. (Ministere de l'Environnement et Faune) Publications du Quebec, C.P. 1005, Quebec, PQ G1K 7B5, Canada. TEL 418-643-5150.
    Former titles: Quebec (Province). Ministere du Loisir de la Chasse et de la Peche. Rapport Annuel (ISSN 0229-3811); Quebec (Province). Department of Tourism, Fish and Game. Annual Report (ISSN 0481-2786)

QUINNEHTUKQUT. see *CONSERVATION*

776.5 658   US
R V PARK & CAMPGROUND REPORT.* (Former name of issuing body: National Campground Owners Association) 1981. m. $25. National Association of R V Parks & Campgrounds, 8605 Westwood Center Dr., Ste. 201, Vienna, VA 22182-2231. TEL 703-471-0143. FAX 703-481-9661. Ed. Dina Lewis. adv.; bk.rev. circ. 3,300.
    Formerly (until 1993): N C O A News.
    Description: Covers news in the commercial campground and resort park industry.

796.95   US   ISSN 1170-9081
RACE & RALLY. 1968. q. $12 (effective 1995-1996). Snowmobiler Publications, Inc., c/o Kevin Beilke, Ed., Box 993, Alexandria, MN 56308. TEL 612-763-5411. FAX 612-763-5411. Pub. Jim Beilke. adv. circ. 100,000. **Indexed:** Sportsearch. **Document type:** consumer publication.
    Formerly: Snowmobiler's Race and Rally.

796.42   UK   ISSN 1351-833X
RACE WALKING RECORD. 1941. m. £3.50. Race Walking Association, 65 Lordship Lane, London SE22, England. Ed. John Hedgethorne. circ. 1,000.

796.42   US   ISSN 1049-3956
RACETIME.* 1989. m. $11.95. 351 N. Newport Blvd., Ste. 556, Newport Beach, CA 92663-4120. Ed. Bill Johnson. circ. 5,000.
    Description: Covers racing events shown on the three major networks and cable stations.

RAMBLING TODAY. see *CONSERVATION*

SPORTS AND GAMES — OUTDOOR LIFE

796.5   CN   ISSN 0845-4418
RATHERBY. 9/yr. Can.$10. Keeper Publications, 28 Fairy Ave., Box 2849, Huntsville, Ont. P0A 1K0, Canada. TEL 705-789-6600. FAX 705-789-6600. adv. circ. 14,000.
    Description: Calendar, folklore and nature magazine for Muskoka Cottagers.

333.78   NE   ISSN 0165-4179
RECREATIE EN TOERISME. 1968. 11/yr. fl.112 to non-members. Arko Uitgeverij b.v., Essenkade 4, 3992 AA Houten, Netherlands. TEL 31-3403-76933. FAX 31-3403-80600. (Subscr. to: P.O. Box 616, 3430 AP Nieuwegein, Netherlands) Ed. Joop Janssen. adv.; bk.rev.; illus. circ. 2,500. Indexed: Dok.Str., HRIS, Rural Recreat.Tour.Abstr., World Agri.Econ.& Rural Sociol.Abstr.
—BLDSC (7326.760000); SWETS.
    Formerly (until 1983): Recreatievoorzieningen (ISSN 0926-6941)

RECREATION AND OUTDOOR LIFE DIRECTORY; a guide to national and international organizations. see *BUSINESS AND ECONOMICS — Trade And Industrial Directories*

RECREATION EXECUTIVE REPORT. see *LEISURE AND RECREATION*

RECREATION NEWS. see *TRAVEL AND TOURISM*

796.93   US   ISSN 0746-4541
RECREATIONAL SKIER. 1969. 5/yr. membership. Skier Education Foundation, c/o U.S. Recreational Ski Association, Box 25469, Anaheim, CA 92825-5469. TEL 714-634-1050. FAX 714-634-2305. Ed. Jan Schneider; Pub. Ed McArthur. adv. contact: Rosalie Brown. bk.rev.; illus. circ. 32,000. (tabloid format) **Document type:** newspaper.
    Former titles: U S Ski News; Far West Ski News; Far West News (ISSN 0014-7648)

796.54   CN   ISSN 0316-1226
REPERTOIRE DES CAMPS DE VACANCES/DIRECTORY OF ACCREDITED CAMPS. (Text in English, French) 1963. a. free. Quebec Camping Association, 4545 Ave. Pierre-de-Coubertin, Montreal, PQ H1V 3R2, Canada. TEL 514-252-3113. FAX 514-252-1650. adv. **Document type:** directory.

796.552   GW
REUTLINGER ALPINIST; Magazin der Sektion Reutlingen im Deutschen Alpenverein. 1984. q. Werbe-Design-Service GmbH, Tuebingerstr. 96, 72762 Reutlingen, Germany. TEL 07121-320987. bibl.; charts; stat.; index.
    Description: Description of adventures in the mountains, climbing and tourist excursions.

796.9   FR   ISSN 1158-2634
REVUE ALPINE.* 1878. q. 60 F. (Club Alpin Francais, Section Rhone-Alpes) Publications Periodiques Specialisees, 11, rue d'Algerie, 69001 Lyon, France. adv. circ. 6,000.
    Supersedes in part (in 1894): Section Lyonnaise du Club Francais (ISSN 1158-2642)

799.2   FR   ISSN 0035-3752
REVUE NATIONALE DE LA CHASSE. m. 270 F. (La Chasse) Gerpresse, 8 rue Pierre Brossolette, 92300 Levallois-Perret, France. TEL 40-87-40-85. Ed. Jacques Simeon. adv.; bibl.; illus. circ. 135,000.

799.2   GW   ISSN 0171-0796
RHEINISCHE-WESTFAELISCHER JAEGER. 1947. m. DM.63 (foreign DM.80.20). (Landesjagdverband Nordrhein-Westfalen e.V.) Landwirtschaftsverlag GmbH, Huelsebrockstr. 2, 48165 Muenster, Germany. TEL 02501-801-0. FAX 0251-801-204. (Subscr. to: Postfach 480249, 48079 Muenster, Germany) adv. circ. 63,700. (back issues avail.) **Document type:** consumer publication.

799.1   BN   ISSN 0035-4953
RIBARSKI LIST. 1926. q. 200 din. per no. Sportsko-Ribovolvni Savez Bosne i Hercegovine, Stevana Sindelica 1-II, 71000 Sarajevo, Bosnia Hercegovina. Ed. Mustafa Lagumdzija. adv.; bk.rev. circ. 35,000.

799.1   CI   ISSN 0350-6789
RIBOLOV. (Text in Serbo-Croatian) 1953. bi-m. free. Hrvatski Sportsko Ribolovni Savez - Croatian Sports Fishing Association, Trg Sportova 11, Zagreb, Croatia. FAX 041-325864. Ed. Damir Valdgoni. adv. circ. 35,000.
    Formerly: Sportski Ribolov (ISSN 0038-8289)

796   US   ISSN 0162-3583
SK274
RIFLE; the sporting firearms journal. 1968. bi-m. $19. Wolfe Publishing Co., 6471 Airpark Dr., Prescott, AZ 86301. TEL 602-445-7810; 800-899-7810. FAX 602-778-5124. Ed. Dave Scovill. adv.; bk.rev.; charts; illus.; mkt.; pat.; stat.; index, cum.index every 2 yrs. circ. 76,000.
    Formerly: Rifle Magazine (ISSN 0035-5216)

799   US
RIFLE & SHOTGUN ANNUAL. a. Petersen Publishing Co., 6420 Wilshire Blvd., Los Angeles, CA 90048. TEL 213-782-2000. adv.; illus. **Document type:** consumer publication.

RING JUNGER BUENDE. MITTEILUNGEN. see *CHILDREN AND YOUTH — About*

796.552   IT   ISSN 0393-4217
RIVISTA DELLA MONTAGNA. 1970. m. L.75000 (foreign L.100000). Centro di Documentazione Alpina, Corso Turati 49, 10134 Turin, Italy. TEL 39-11-3197827. FAX 39-11-3197823. Ed. Roberto Mantovani. adv.; B&W page L.3500000, color page L.5300000. bk.rev.; illus.; index, cum.index. circ. 36,000. (back issues avail.)

799.1   IT
RIVISTA DI PESCA - MOSCA E SPINNING. 1990. m. L.63000 (foreign L.100000). Valle Editori s.r.l., Via Campo d'Arrigo 6 A-R, 50137 Florence, Italy. TEL 39-55-661722. FAX 39-55-661534. Ed. Edugenio Cecioni. adv.; B&W page L.2330000, color page L.4130000. circ. 18,000. **Document type:** consumer publication.

796.42   US   ISSN 0739-3784
ROAD RACE MANAGEMENT NEWSLETTER. 1982. 11/yr. $97 (foreign $112). Road Race Management, Inc., 4904 Glen Cove Pkwy., Bethesda, MD 20816-3006. TEL 301-320-6865. FAX 301-3210-9164. Ed. Phil Stewart. adv. circ. 500. (back issues avail.) **Indexed:** Sportsearch (1985-). **Document type:** newsletter.
    Description: For sponsors, directors and organizers of long-distance running events.

ROAD SMART. see *TRAVEL AND TOURISM*

796.522   AT   ISSN 0816-2425
ROCK (PRAHRAN); Australia's climbing magazine. 1978-1980; resumed 1983. q. Aus.$31.80($35.40) Wild Publications Pty. Ltd., P.O. Box 415, Prahran, Vic. 3181, Australia. Ed. Chris Baxter. adv. circ. 6,000.

796.552   US   ISSN 0885-5722
ROCK & ICE. 1984. bi-m. $24 (Canada and Mexico $34; elsewhere $36.50). Eldorado Publishing, Box 3595, Boulder, CO 80307. TEL 303-499-8410. Ed. George Bracksieck. adv.: B&W page $1695, color page $2395; trim 8 3/8 x 10 7/8; adv. contact: Wendy Levison. bk.rev.; charts; illus. circ. 45,000. (back issues avail.) **Document type:** consumer publication.
—UnCover.
    Description: Covers international climbing and other related outdoor adventures.

797.2   US   ISSN 1060-9563
GV840.S78
RODALE'S SCUBA DIVING. 1992. 10/yr. $14.97 (Canada $19.97; elsewhere $24.97). Rodale Press, Inc., 33 Minor St., Emmaus, PA 18098. TEL 610-967-5171. FAX 610-967-8963. (Subscr. to: Box 7576, Red Oak, IA 51591. TEL 800-666-0016) Ed. Steven Blount; Pub. David S. McAfee. adv.; illus. circ. 200,000. (back issues avail.) **Document type:** consumer publication.
    Incorporates (1987-1992): Fisheye View Scuba Magazine.
    Description: Covers all aspects of scuba diving for both enthusiasts and professionals, including equipment, techniques, fitness, travel destinations, environmental issues.

796.552   GW   ISSN 0935-3372
ROTPUNKT; das Klettermagazin. 1985. bi-m. DM.52.80 (foreign DM.58.80). Rotpunkt Verlag, Ziegeleistr. 16, 71384 Weinstadt, Germany. TEL 07151-99902-0. FAX 07151-999029. (Subscr. to: Rotpunkt Leserservice, Postfach 810640, 70523 Stuttgart, Germany) Ed. Peter Schindler; Pub. Juergen Linsenmaier. adv.: B&W page DM.3200, color page DM.5300; trim 172 x 250; adv. contact: Karsten Heyder. bk.rev.; bibl.; color. circ. 38,200. (back issues avail.) **Document type:** consumer publication.
    Description: Focuses on climbing and mountaineering.

796   US
ROYAL OUTDOOR SPORTSMAN. a. Aqua-Field Publishing Co., Inc., 66 W. Gilbert St., Shrewsbury, NJ 07702. TEL 908-899-4200. adv.

796.42   US   ISSN 0892-5038
RUNNING JOURNAL. 1984. m. $22. Carolina Runner, Inc., Box 157, Greeneville, TN 37744. TEL 615-638-4177. FAX 615-638-3328. adv.; bk.rev. circ. 12,000.
    Formerly: Racing South.
    Description: Covers running in the Southeast, along with race walking, bi- and triathloning. Includes a calendar of events covering 13 states.

RUNNING WILD; the trailrunner's magazine. see *LEISURE AND RECREATION*

799.1   GW
RUTE UND ROLLE. 1949. m. newsstand price: DM.5. Top Special Verlag GmbH, Nebendahlstr. 16, 22041 Hamburg, Germany. TEL 040-3470-0. FAX 040-34725588. Ed. Heinz Foerster. adv.: B&W page DM.5433, color page DM.9830; trim 180 x 250; adv. contact: Beate Asmus-Fuegert. circ. 80,779. **Document type:** consumer publication.
    Formerly: Deutscher Angelsport (ISSN 0323-3472)

RYBARSTVI. see *FISH AND FISHERIES*

799.1   US
S C FISH & GAME FINDER MAGAZINE. 1973. m. $15. Fish Finder Industries, Inc. (Subsidiary of: Wiley Publishing Enterprises Inc.), Box 545, Summerville, SC 29484-0545. TEL 803-875-2490. FAX 803-875-9301. Ed. Ed Wiley. adv.: page $592.50; 7 1/4 x 9 3/4. circ. 20,000. **Document type:** consumer publication.
    Formerly: Carolina Fish Finder Magazine.
    Description: Contains pictures and reports on fishing and hunting in South Carolina.

799   US
S H O T BUSINESS. (Shooting, Hunting & Outdoor Trade) 1993. bi-m. $25. National Shooting Sports Foundation, 11 Mile Hill Rd., Newtown, CT 06470-2359. TEL 203-426-1320. FAX 203-426-1087. Ed. Mike Schwarz; Pub. Robert Deltny. adv.: B&W page $2750, color page $3350; trim 10 7/8 x 14 1/2. circ. 20,000. (controlled).

799.2   US   ISSN 0199-5316
SK1
SAFARI; the journal of big game hunting. 1971. bi-m. $30 in N. America; elsewhere $55. Safari Club International, 4800 W. Gates Pass Rd., Tucson, AZ 85745. TEL 520-620-1220. FAX 520-622-1205. William R. Quimby, Dir. of Publications. adv. contact: Eric Hubbell. bk.rev.; illus. circ. 23,000. **Document type:** consumer publication.

799.2   FR   ISSN 0036-2867
SAINT HUBERT. 1901. m. 280 F. (foreign 380 F.). M.T.E., 17, place de General de Gaulle, 93100 Montreuil, France. Ed. J. Sire. adv.; bk.rev.; bibl.; illus.

SALAR. see *FISH AND FISHERIES*

799.1   CN   ISSN 0703-5810
SALMO SALAR. 1976. bi-m. Association des Pecheurs Sportifs de Saumons du Quebec, 7525 Place Martin, Charlesbourg, PQ, Canada.

799.1   US   ISSN 0029-3431
SALMON - TROUT STEELHEADER. 1967. bi-m. $14.95. Frank Amato Publications, Box 82112, Portland, OR 97282. TEL 503-653-8108. FAX 503-653-2766. Ed. Nick Amato. adv. contact: Sherry Gullings. bk.rev.; illus.; circ. 30,381 (paid). **Document type:** consumer publication.
    Formerly: Northwest Salmon - Trout Steelheader.

SPORTS AND GAMES — OUTDOOR LIFE

799.1   US
SALT WATER FISHING. a. Times Mirror Magazines, Inc., 2 Park Ave., New York, NY 10016. TEL 212-779-5000.

799.1   US   ISSN 0036-3618
SALT WATER SPORTSMAN. 1939. m. $24.95. (Salt Water Sportsman, Inc.) Times Mirror Magazines, Inc., Salt Water Sportsman, 77 Franklin St., Boston, MA 02210-1510. TEL 617-439-9977. FAX 617-338-2309. (Subscr. to: Box 54358, Boulder, CO 80322) Ed. C.M. Cunningham; Pub. E.F. Andersen. adv. contact: Jaye McAuliffe. bk.rev.; illus.; index; circ. 141,000 (paid). (also avail. in diskette format) **Indexed:** Consum.Ind., PMR, Sportsearch. **Document type:** consumer publication, newspaper.
—UMI.
   Description: Covers marine sport fishing.

SANFORD EVANS GOLD BOOK OF SNOWMOBILE DATA AND USED PRICES. see *SPORTS AND GAMES — Abstracting, Bibliographies, Statistics*

799   FR   ISSN 0751-9907
SAUVAGINE ET SA CHASSE. 1935. m. 200 F. Association Nationale des Chasseurs de Gibier d'Eau, 124 av. du Wagram, 75017 Paris, France. TEL 47-63-02-32. FAX 46-22-82-53. Ed. Raymond Pouget. adv.; bk.rev. circ. 30,000.

796.93   IT
SCARPONE. 1931. m. L.50000 to non-members; members L.20000; foreign L.80000. Club Alpino Italiano, Via E. Fonseca Pimentel 7, 20127 Milan, Italy. TEL 39-2-26141378. FAX 39-2-26141395. Ed. Teresio Valsesia. adv.: B&W page L.4500000. circ. 200,000. **Document type:** newsletter.

DER SCHUETZE. see *SPORTS AND GAMES*

799   SZ   ISSN 0036-8016
SCHWEIZER JAEGER. 1915. 12/yr. 80 SFr. (Schweizerischer Patentjaeger- und Wildschutzverband) Druckerei Marcel Kuerzi AG, Werner-Kaelin-Str. 11, CH-8840 Einsiedeln, Switzerland. adv.; bk.rev.; illus.; stat.; index. circ. 9,000. **Indexed:** Key Word Ind.Wildl.Res. **Document type:** consumer publication.

796.93   IT   ISSN 0036-8040
SCI; rivista degli sport invernali. 1957. 10/yr. L.60000. Casa Editrice Scode S.p.A., C.so Monforte 36, 20121 Milan, Italy. TEL 02-76006973. FAX 02-76004905. Ed. Gianni Bianco. adv.: B&W page L.6400000, color page L.9800000; trim 176 x 245. bk.rev.; illus. circ. 18,381.

796.93   IT
SCI FONDO. 1957. 5/yr. L.20000. Casa Editrice Scode S.p.A., Corso Monforte 36, 20122 Milan, Italy. TEL 02-76006973. FAX 02-76004905. Ed. Riccardo Villarosa. adv.: B&W page L.2800000, color page L.4100000; trim 174 x 244. bk.rev.; illus. circ. 10,000.

796.93   IT
SCIARE. 1966. s-m. L.60000. D M K Editrice s.r.l., Via Boscovich 14, Milan, Italy. TEL 39-2-66986694. FAX 39-2-6702736. Ed. Massimo di Marco. adv.: B&W page L.6100000, color page L.8200000. circ. 85,000. **Document type:** consumer publication.

797.173   IT
SCINAUTICO. 1978. 4/yr. Federazione Italiana Scinautico, Via Piranesi 44-B, Milan, Italy. adv. circ. 15,000.

917.1   CN   ISSN 0225-8315
SCOPE CAMPING NEWS. 1965. 6/yr. Can.$15. Merton Publications Ltd., Box 39, Hyde Park (London), ON NOM 1Z0, Canada. Ed. Harold Merton. adv.; illus. circ. 30,000. **Document type:** consumer publication.
   Formerly: Scope: Recreational Vehicle and Camping News (ISSN 0048-9743)
   Description: Provides travel articles and camping activities for the recreational vehicle user in Canada.

799.1   UK
SCOTLAND FOR FISHING. 1970. a. £3.95. Pastime Publications Ltd., 6 York Pl., Edinburgh EH1 3EP, Scotland. TEL 0131-556-1105. FAX 0131-556-1129. adv. contact: Diane Gibson. circ. 30,000. **Document type:** consumer publication.

796.522   UK   ISSN 0080-813X
G505
SCOTTISH MOUNTAINEERING CLUB. JOURNAL. 1890. a. £6.95. (Scottish Mountaineering Club) Cordee, 3a De Montfort St., Leicester LE1 7HD, England. TEL 0533-543579. FAX 0533-471176. Ed. W.D. Brooker. adv.; bk.rev.
—BLDSC (8210.930000).

796.5   GW   ISSN 0176-4624
SCOUTING; Zeitschrift fuer Pfadfinderinnen und Pfadfinder. 1984. q. DM.22. Deutscher Spurbuchverlag, Hemmerleinsleite 46, 96148 Baunach, Germany. TEL 09544-1561. FAX 09544-809. Ed. Paul-Thomas Hinkel. adv.; bk.rev. circ. 3,000. (back issues avail.) **Document type:** bulletin.

799.1   UK   ISSN 0306-6568
SEA ANGLER. 1972. m. £23.40 (foreign £33) (effective 1995-1996). E M A P - Pursuit Publishing, Bretton Ct., Bretton, Peterborough, Cambs. PE3 8DZ, England. TEL 01733-264666. FAX 01733-263294. TELEX 32157. (Subscr. to: Tower Publishing Services Ltd., Tower House, Sovereign Park, Lathkill St., Market Harborough, Leics. LE16 9EF, England. TEL 01858-468811. FAX 01858-432164) Ed. Mel Russ; Pub. Andy Benham. adv. contact: Kate Brown. bk.rev.; charts; illus.; stat.; tr.lit.; circ. 50,121 (paid). **Document type:** consumer publication.
—CCC.

799.1   UK   ISSN 0265-024X
SEA FISHING TODAY. 1983. q. Goodhead Publications Ltd., 27 Murdock Rd., Bicester, Oxon. OX6 7RG, England. adv.

797.17   US
SELLING SCUBA.* bi-m. Diving Equipment Manufacturers Association, 27071 Cabot Rd., Ste. 103, Laguna Hills, CA 92653-7009. TEL 714-744-5284. **Document type:** newsletter.
   Formerly (until Feb. 1989): D E M A Newsletter.

799   CN   ISSN 0711-7957
SENTIER CHASSE - PECHE. 1971. m. (11/yr.). Can.$34.95 (foreign Can.$55). Groupe Polygone Editeurs Inc., 11450 Blvd. Albert-Hudon, Montreal, PQ H1G 3J9, Canada. TEL 514-327-4464. FAX 514-327-0514. Ed. Michel Bibeau; Pub. Luc Lemay. adv. contact: Jose Cristofaro. circ. 67,000. (back issues avail.) **Indexed:** Pt.de Rep. (1979-).
   Formerly: Quebec Chasse et Peche (ISSN 0315-260X)
   Description: Articles on fishing, hunting, outdoor life and the environment.

796.552 797.1   PO
SERRA E MAR/MOUNTAINS AND SEA. 12/yr. Rua Dr. Antonio Menano, 6370 Formos de Algodres, Portugal. TEL 71-99476. Ed. Paulo Menano.

799.1   US
SHIMANO SPORT FISHING. 1984. a. $2.50. (Shimano American Corp.) Aqua-Field Publishing Co., Inc., 66 W. Gilbert St., Shrewsbury, NJ 07702. TEL 201-842-8300. Ed. Stephen Ferber. adv. circ. 120,000.

799.2   UK
SHOOTING GAZETTE. m. £17.50 to members (foreign £24). (Game Conservancy) B P G Ltd., 2 West St., Bourne, Lincs. PE10 9NE, England. TEL 0778-393747. FAX 0778-425453. **Document type:** consumer publication.
   Description: Covers every aspect of game and rough shooting and reviews good places to hunt.

799.2   US   ISSN 0744-3773
SHOTGUN SPORTS. 1976. 10/yr. $26. Box 6810, Auburn, CA 95604. TEL 916-889-2220. FAX 916-889-9106. Ed. Frank Kodl. adv. circ. 108,000.

SIERRA ATLANTIC. see *CONSERVATION*

SIERRA REPORT. see *CONSERVATION*

796.5 917.9   US   ISSN 8750-1600
GV199.42.N69
SIGNPOST FOR NORTHWEST TRAILS. 1966. m. $25. Washington Trails Association, 1305 4th Ave., No. 512, Seattle, WA 98101-2401. TEL 206-625-1367. Ed. Dan Nelson. adv.: B&W page $260; 8 1/2 x 11. bk.rev.; illus.; index. circ. 3,000.
   Formerly: Signpost for Northwest Hikers (ISSN 0583-2594)

796.93   IT   ISSN 1120-5881
SKATE SNOW BOARD. 1990. m. Gruppo B Editore, Via Don Vercesi 19, 200091 Bresso (MI), Italy. TEL 02-66503000. FAX 02-66503060. **Document type:** consumer publication.

796.93   US   ISSN 0037-6159
GV854
SKI. 1936. 8/yr. $13.94. Times Mirror Magazines, Inc., 2 Park Ave., New York, NY 10016. TEL 212-779-5000. Ed. Edward Pitoniak. adv.; illus. circ. 434,500. (also avail. in microform from UMI; reprint service avail. from UMI) **Indexed:** Consum.Ind., Phys.Ed.Ind., PMR, Sports Per.Ind., Sportsearch (1974-).
—Faxon; UMI; UnCover.
   Incorporates: Ski Life.

796.93   US
SKI AMERICA. 1973. 4/yr. free. Ski America Enterprises, Inc., 370 Wahconah St., Box 1140, Pittsfield, MA 01202-1140. TEL 413-637-9810. Ed. Joseph B. Hollister. adv.; bk.rev.; charts; illus. circ. 300,000.

796.93   US   ISSN 0037-6175
GV854.A1
SKI AREA MANAGEMENT. 1962. bi-m. $26. Beardsley Publishing Corp., Box 644, Woodbury, CT 06798. FAX 203-266-0452. Ed. David Rowan. adv.; bk.rev.; index. circ. 4,010. **Indexed:** Hospit.Ind., Sportsearch (1974-). **Document type:** trade publication.
—UnCover.

796.93   CN   ISSN 0702-701X
SKI CANADA. 1972. bi-m. Can.$14.99. Solstice Publishing Inc., 19 Albany Ave., Toronto, ON M5R 3C2, Canada. TEL 416-535-0607. FAX 416-535-3419. Ed. Iain MacMillan; Pub. Paul Green. adv. contact: Paul Green. circ. 55,000. **Indexed:** Can.B.P.I., CMI, Sportsearch (1979-). **Document type:** consumer publication.
   Formerly: Ski Canada Journal.

796.93   FR   ISSN 0399-2055
SKI FRANCAIS. 1940. 5/yr. 120 F. (foreign 180 F.). (Federation Francaise de Ski) Publiski, 15-17 chemin de la Capuche, 38100 Grenoble, France. TEL 76-87-83-62. FAX 76-87-74-33. Ed. Gilles Chappaz. adv. contact: Stephanie Alcaraz. bk.rev.; illus. circ. 60,000.

796.93   US   ISSN 0197-3479
SKI INDUSTRY LETTER. 1979. m. $298 (foreign $349). Skiletter, Inc., 115 Lilly Pond Ln., Katonah, NY 10536. TEL 914-232-5094. Ed. Greg Berry. bk.rev. (avail. only by fax) **Document type:** newsletter.
   Description: Covers the ski trade.

796.93   JA
SKI JOURNAL. (Text in Japanese) 1966. m. 9360 Yen. Ski Journal Co. Ltd., 3-11, Yotsuya, Shinjuku-KU, Tokyo, Japan. Ed. Seiji Miyashita.

796.93   FR
SKI MAGAZINE. 1963. m. Edimonde-Loisirs, 23-25 rue de Berri, 75388 Paris Cedex 08, France. TEL 40-34-35-00. TELEX EDIMOND 642970F. (Subscr. to: 90 rue de Flandre, 75947 Paris Cedex 19, France) **Document type:** consumer publication.
   Formerly (until 1984): Ski-Flash Magazine (ISSN 0293-9673); Which was formed by the 1972 merger of: Ski Flash (ISSN 0765-5533); Ski Magazine (ISSN 0765-5541); Which was previously (until 1968): Neige et Glace (ISSN 0028-2545)

SPORTS AND GAMES — OUTDOOR LIFE

796.93   NE   ISSN 0169-2364
SKI MAGAZINE. 1953. 7/yr. (Sep.-Mar.) fl.62.50 membership. (Dutch Ski Federation) Management Media B.V., P.O. Box 1932, 1200 BX Hilversum, Netherlands. TEL 31-35-232756. FAX 31-35-232401. Ed. J.W.J. van Waaijen. adv.: B&W page fl.6195. circ. 100,000. **Document type:** consumer publication.
Incorporates (1988-1991): Ski Plus (ISSN 0923-3237); **Formerly (until 1983):** Ski (ISSN 0165-6902)
Description: Contains articles on skiing and winter sports activities, travel suggestions, product information.

796.93   CN   ISSN 0037-6221
SKI RUNNER. 1926. 4/yr. membership. (Toronto Ski Club) Frank McNulty Publishing, 100 Mountain Road, Unit 3, Collingwood, Ont. L9Y 3Z8, Canada. TEL 705-445-5024. Ed. Deena Dolan. adv.; bk.rev. circ. 400. **Indexed:** Sportsearch.

796.93   SZ   ISSN 0037-623X
SKI - SCHWEIZER SKISPORT/SKI SUISSE/SCI SVIZZERO. (Text in French, German and Italian) 1968. 7/yr. 27 SFr. (Schweizerischer Ski-Verbandes) Habegger AG Druck und Verlag, Gutenbergstr. 1, CH-4552 Derendingen, Switzerland. TEL 065-411151. FAX 065-422632. Ed. Joseph Weibel. adv. contact: Paul Meier. bk.rev.; circ. 114,000 (controlled).
—CCC.

796.93   UK   ISSN 0954-9765
SKI SPECIAL. 1975. 3/yr. £7.50. Activity Associates Ltd., 27 Belsize Ln., London NW3 5AS, England. TEL 0171-435-5472. FAX 0171-431-3742. TELEX 295441 BUSYB G. Ed. Christopher Thomas. adv.: B&W page £940, color page £1450; trim 298 x 210; adv. contact: Cathy Fourie. bk.rev. circ. 70,000. **Document type:** consumer publication.
Description: Information on skiing holidays worldwide, equipment and clothing.

796.93   NO   ISSN 0333-3973
SKI-SPORT. Variant title: SkiSport. 1959. 9/yr. Skiforum A-S, P.O. Box 6, N-1355 Baerum Postterminal, Norway. TEL 47-67-56-56-90. FAX 47-67-56-56-99. Ed. Allan Aabec. adv.: B&W page NOK 9500, color page NOK 13300; adv. contact: Per Stenberg. circ. 16,000. (back issues avail.) **Document type:** consumer publication.
Supersedes in part (in 1981): Alpin-Sport (ISSN 0332-8252); Ski-Idrett (ISSN 0332-9720)
Description: Devoted to everything relevant to skiing in Norway.

796.93   UK   ISSN 0955-8225
SKI SURVEY. 1972. 5/yr. £11 (Europe £14; elsewhere £20). Ski Club of Great Britain, 118 Eaton Sq., London SW1W 9AF, England. TEL 0171-245-1033. FAX 0171-245-1258. TELEX 291608-SKIDOM-G. (Dist. by: Comag Specialist Division, Merany Centre, Central Way, Feltham, Middlesex TW14 0RX, England) Ed. Gillian Williams. adv.; bk.rev.; cum.index every 3 yrs. circ. 22,677. **Indexed:** Sportsearch. **Document type:** consumer publication.

796.93   US   ISSN 1058-3246
SKI TECH. 1986. 5/yr. $16. Ski Racing International, Box 1125, Waitsfield, VT 05673-1125. TEL 802-496-7700. FAX 802-496-7704. Ed. Perkins Miller; Pub. Gary Black, Jr. adv. contact: Phil Knaub. circ. 13,421. **Document type:** trade publication.
Description: Provides product information on ski equipment, ski wear and accessories for owners, managers, buyers, sales and service personnel of ski shops, instructors, and consumers.

796.93   CN
SKI THE WEST. 1987. a. Can.$5. Kootenay Advertiser Ltd., 1510 2nd St. N., Cranbrook, BC V1C 3L2, Canada. FAX 604-489-3743. Ed. Daryl Shellborn. circ. 40,450. **Document type:** consumer publication.
Description: For visitors who wish to ski in Southeast B.C., Northwest Montana and Northern Idaho.

796.93   IT
SKI TIME. 1988. w. (Nov.-Apr.). L.3500 per no. Casa Editrice Scode S.p.A., Corso Monforte 36, 20122 Milan, Italy. TEL 39-2-76006973. FAX 39-2-76004905. Ed. Guido Pietroni. adv.: page L.6900000; adv. contact: Gisella Cigognani. circ. 30,000. **Document type:** consumer publication.

796.93   US
SKI WATCH ATLAS. a. $3.95. C R N International, Inc., One Circular Ave., Hamden, CT 06514. TEL 203-288-2002. FAX 203-281-3291. Ed. Gary Zenobia; Pubs. Barry Beeman, Richard Kalt. adv.: B&W page $4000, color page $5000; trim 8 3/8 x 10 7/8; adv. contact: Patrick Kane. circ. 100,000 (controlled). **Document type:** directory.

796.93   US
SKI WEEK. 1972. w. (during winter). Mountain Media, 111 Main St., Plymouth, NH 03264. Ed. Patricia Cowdery. adv. circ. 25,000.

SKI WRITERS BULLETIN. see JOURNALISM

796.93   US   ISSN 0161-1054 GV855
SKI X - C. (Cross - Country) 1978. a. $3.95. Rodale Press, Inc., 33 E. Minor St., Emmaus, PA 18098. TEL 610-967-5171. adv. circ. 160,000.

796.93   US
SKIER. * (Former name of issuing body: U S - Ski Association) 1964. 10/yr. $6. United States Skiing, Box 100, Park City, UT 84060. Ed. Elmar Baxter. adv.; bk.rev.; film rev. circ. 37,000. (tabloid format) **Indexed:** Sportsearch.
Former titles: Southwest Skier (ISSN 0049-1667); Southern California Skier.

796.93   UK   ISSN 0951-5941
SKIER. 1983. bi-m. £15. Hollanden Publishing Ltd., 26c London Rd., Sevenoaks, Kent TN13 1AP, England. TEL 01732-743644. FAX 01732-743647. Ed. Frank Baldwin. adv. contact: Peter Phillips. bk.rev. circ. 30,000. **Indexed:** Sportsearch (1978-). **Document type:** consumer publication.
Incorporates: British Ski Magazine.
Description: All aspects of ski and snowboard related subjects: racing, equipment and travel.

796.93   US
SKIER'S POCKET GUIDE. (15 regional editions avail.) 1983. a. free. Pocket Guide Publications, Inc., 9650 Clayton Rd., St. Louis, MO 63124. TEL 314-991-5222. FAX 314-991-8911. Ed. Jackson D. Waterbury. adv.: color page $26900. circ. 1,100,000 (controlled). **Document type:** consumer publication.
Description: Provides tips and advice on skiing, maps and local information on more than 70 ski areas.

796.93   US   ISSN 0037-6264 GV854.A1
SKIING. 1948. 7/yr. $13.94. Times Mirror Magazines, Inc., 2 Park Ave., New York, NY 10016. TEL 212-779-5000. (Subscr. to: Box 54180, Boulder, CO 80322. TEL 800-825-5552) Ed. Rick Kahl. adv.; bk.rev.; illus.; index. circ. 449,500. (also avail. in microform from UMI) **Indexed:** Acad.Ind., Mag.Ind., PMR, R.G., Sports Per.Ind., Sportsearch (1976-), TOM. **Document type:** consumer publication.
●Also available online. Vendor(s): University Microfilms International.
—Faxon; UMI; UnCover.

796.93   US
SKIING FOR WOMEN. 1993. a. Times Mirror Magazines, Inc., 2 Park Ave., New York, NY 10016. TEL 212-779-5000.

796.93   US   ISSN 0037-6299 GV854.A1
SKIING TRADE NEWS. 1964. 8/yr. $15. Times Mirror Magazines, Inc., 2 Park Ave., New York, NY 10016. TEL 212-779-5465. Ed. William Grout. adv.; charts; illus.; mkt.; stat.; tr.lit. circ. 11,529. (reprint service avail.) **Indexed:** Bus.Ind., Tr.& Indus.Ind. **Document type:** trade publication.
●Also available online. Vendor(s): Knight-Ridder, Inc.
Former titles: Skiing Trade Monthly News; Wintersports Trade Magazine.

796.93   GW   ISSN 0930-1194
SKILAEUFER. 7/yr. DM.35. Brinkmann Verlag GmbH, Eberg 16-18, 51709 Marienheide, Germany. TEL 02264-7061. FAX 02264-3510. Ed. Herbert Klose. circ. 40,166. **Document type:** consumer publication.

796.93   GW   ISSN 0944-6281
SKILANGLAUF - TRIATHLON - MARATHON. 7/yr. DM.35. Brinkmann Verlag GmbH, Eberg 16-18, 51709 Marienheide, Germany. TEL 02264-7062. FAX 02264-3510. Ed. Herbert Klose. adv. contact: Hans Martin Brinkmann. circ. 4,748. **Document type:** consumer publication.
Formerly: Skilanglauf (ISSN 0178-1901)

796.93   GW
SKILEHRER MAGAZIN. 1980. bi-m. Deutscher Skilehrerverband e.V., Sohnckestr. 17, 81479 Munich, Germany. TEL 089-799051. FAX 089-7901851. illus. circ. 8,000.

796.93   GW   ISSN 0583-4724
SKIMAGAZIN. 1977. 6/yr.; newsstand price: DM.7. Top Special Verlag GmbH, Nebendahlstr. 16, 22041 Hamburg, Germany. TEL 040-3470-0. FAX 040-34725588. Ed. Klaus Steffensen. adv.: B&W page 5979, color page DM.11360; trim 180 x 250; adv. contact: Beate Asmus-Fuegert. circ. 45,398. **Document type:** consumer publication.

796.93   FI   ISSN 0359-0569
SKIMBAAJA. 1977. 7/yr. FIM 243. Helsinki Media Company Oy, P.O. Box 16, 00381 Helsinki, Finland. TEL 358-0-120-5911. FAX 358-0-120-5959. Ed. Jari Stroemberg. circ. 13,784.

796   GW   ISSN 0721-4472
SKIPPER. m. DM.60 (foreign DM.90). Freizeit und Wassersport Verlag GmbH, Am Windfeld 15, 83714 Miesbach, Germany. TEL 08025-294243. FAX 08025-294271. Ed. Hans Lienau. adv. contact: Rainer Matthe. circ. 28,037. **Document type:** consumer publication.

796.93   CN   ISSN 1191-2677
SKITRAX. 1990. q. Can.$8.56($12.15) 2 Pardee Ave., Ste. 204, Toronto, ON M6K 3H5, Canada. TEL 416-530-1350. FAX 416-530-4155. Ed. Benjamin A. Sadavoy. adv.; bk.rev. circ. 15,000. **Document type:** consumer publication.
Description: Takes a look at the spectrum of the competitive cross-country ski scene and covers the recreational side of the sport. Includes buyer's guide, product reviews, feature articles and columns.

796.42 333.78   SW   ISSN 0346-1297
SKOGSSPORT. 1947. 10/yr. SEK 245. Svenska Orienteringsfoerbundet, Idrottens Hus, S-123 87 Farsta, Sweden. TEL 46-8-605-00. FAX 46-8-724-93-38. Ed. Ola Gustafsson; Pub. Maria Nimvik. adv.: B&W page SEK 6700, color page SEK 8900; trim 185 x 267. circ. 11,600. cols./p.: 4; pp./issue: 58.
Formerly (until 1969): Tidning foer Skogssport.

796.552 790.1   CN
SKYLINER. 1972. m. membership. Skyline Hikers of the Canadian Rockies, 114 Brantford Crescent, NW, Calgary, Alta. T2L 1N8, Canada. Ed. Virginia Klatzel.

797.5   UK
SKYWINGS. 1975. m. £27 (rest of Europe £32). British Hang Gliding and Paragliding Association Ltd., Old Schoolroom, Loughborough Rd., Leicester LE4 5PJ, England. TEL 0114-267-9227. Ed. Joe Schofield. adv. contact: Paul Henry. bk.rev.; adv. 8,000 (paid). (back issues avail.) **Document type:** consumer publication.
Former titles (until 1994): Wings! (ISSN 0951-5712); Illustrated British Flypaper.
Description: Covers new products, news, competitions, safety, travel techniques and theoretical issues.

796   US
SNO WEST. 4/yr. Harris Publishing, Inc. (Idaho Falls), 520 Park Ave., Idaho Falls, ID 83402-3516. TEL 208-524-7000. FAX 208-522-5241. Ed. Steve Janes. adv. contact: Mel Erickson. circ. 21,000. **Document type:** consumer publication.

796.95   SW   ISSN 0348-1867
SNOESKOTER. 1973. 6/yr. SEK 200; newsstand price: SEK 38. (Snofed) Liwall Foerlags AB, P.O. Box 23, S-901 02 Umeaa, Sweden. TEL 46-90-14-11-40. Ed. Lars Wallmark. adv.: B&W page SEK 11250, color page SEK 15600; trim 188 x 265. circ. 18,000. cols./p.: 4; pp./issue: 86.

SPORTS AND GAMES — OUTDOOR LIFE

796   **US**
SNOW ACTION. 6/yr. Harris Publishing, Inc. (Idaho Falls), 520 Park Ave., Idaho Falls, ID 83402-3516. TEL 208-524-7000. FAX 208-522-5241. Ed. Steve Janes; Pub. Darryl Harris. adv. contact: Mel Erickson. (tabloid format) **Document type:** consumer publication, newspaper.

796.93   **US**   **ISSN 0896-758X**
GV191.4
SNOW COUNTRY; alpine skiing, freestyle, cross-country, snowboarding, apres-ski. 1988. 8/yr. $13.97. New York Times Company Magazine Group, Sports - Leisure Division, 5520 Park Ave., Box 395, Trumbull, CT 06611-0395. TEL 203-373-7000; 800-333-2299. (Subscr. to: P.O. Box 2071, Harlan, IA 51593-2270) Ed. Roger Toll. circ. 460,000. **Document type:** consumer publication.
Description: Provides travel and instructional advice for skiing, mountain climbing, golf, tennis, backpacking, white water rafting, biking, hang gliding, hiking, sailboarding and flyfishing.

796.93   **US**
SNOW COUNTRY BUSINESS. 1961. bi-m. $30 (Canada $35; elsewhere $65) (effective 1994). New York Times Magazine Group, Sports - Leisure Division, 5520 Park Ave., Box 395, Trumbull, CT 06611-0395. TEL 203-373-7059. FAX 203-371-2127. Ed. John Fry. adv.: B&W page $4180; adv. contact: Nick Hock. illus. tr.lit. circ. 14,000. (also avail. in microform from UMI; reprint service avail. from UMI) **Indexed:** Sportsearch. **Document type:** trade publication.
Formerly: Ski Business (ISSN 0037-6191)

796.95   **CN**   **ISSN 0711-6454**
SNOW GOER; snowmobiling. 1979. 4/yr. Camar Publications Ltd., 130 Spy Court, Markham, ON L3R 5H6, Canada. TEL 416-485-8440. FAX 416-475-9246. Ed. Chris Knowles. adv.; circ. 150,000 (controlled). **Document type:** consumer publication.

796.95   **US**   **ISSN 1056-4209**
SNOW GOER. 1990. 5/yr. $13.97 (foreign $23.97; Canada $19.97). Ehlert Publishing Group, Inc., 601 Lakeshore Pkwy., Ste. 600, Minnetonka, MN 55305-5215. TEL 612-476-2200. FAX 612-476-8065. Ed. Dan Hauser. adv. circ. 104,000. **Document type:** consumer publication.
Description: Provides information on new machines, travel, new products, performance, personalities, do-it-yourself projects and events.

796.93   **CN**   **ISSN 1192-3776**
SNOWBOARD CANADA. 1992. 3/yr. Can.$19.95 for 6 nos. 2255 B Queen St. E., Ste. 3266, Toronto, ON M4E 1G3, Canada. TEL 416-698-0138. FAX 416-698-8080. Ed. Steve Jarrett. adv. contact: Leslie Atkin. bk.rev.; charts; illus. **Document type:** consumer publication.

796.93   **NE**
▼**SNOWBOARD MAGAZINE.** (Text in Dutch) 1995. 3/yr. (Oct.-Jan.) fl.62.50 membership includes Ski Magazine. (Dutch Ski Federation, Snowboard Holland) Management Media B.V., P.O. Box 1932, 1200 BX Hilversum, Netherlands. TEL 31-35-232756. FAX 31-35-232401. adv. circ. 100,000. **Document type:** consumer publication.
Description: Articles and product information relating to snowboarding.

796.93   **US**   **ISSN 1046-0403**
SNOWBOARDER. 1989. 7/yr. $13.95. Surfer Publications, Inc., 33046 Calle Aviador, San Juan Capistrano, CA 92675. TEL 714-496-5922. FAX 714-496-7849. (Subscr. to: Box 53964, Boulder, CO 80322-3964. TEL 800-765-5501) Ed. Doug Paladini. adv. circ. 80,000. **Document type:** consumer publication.
—UnCover.
Description: Provides technique and equipment tips, equipment reviews, as well as profiles of ski areas that allow snowboarding.

796.9   **US**   **ISSN 0274-8363**
SNOWMOBILE. 1980. 4/yr. (during winter). $11.80 (Canada $17.80; elsewhere $21.80). Ehlert Publishing Group, Inc., 601 Lakeshore Pkwy., Ste. 600, Minnetonka, MN 55305-5215. TEL 612-476-2200. FAX 612-476-8065. Ed. Dan Hauser. adv.; bk.rev. circ. 600,000. (reprint service avail. from UMI) **Document type:** consumer publication.
Incorporates (1966-1985): Snow Goer (ISSN 0191-8095); **Formed by the 1980 merger of:** SnoTrack (ISSN 0049-0822); Midwest Snowmobiler.

796.95   **US**   **ISSN 0883-8259**
SNOWMOBILE BUSINESS. 1967. 6/yr. $15 to qualified personnel. Ehlert Publishing Group, Inc., 601 Lakeshore Pkwy., Ste. 600, Minnetonka, MN 55305-5215. TEL 612-476-2200. FAX 612-476-8065. Ed. Don Dan Hauser. adv.; charts; illus.; stat. circ. 6,000.
Formerly (until 1985): Snow Goer Trade.

790.1   **US**   **ISSN 0164-6540**
SNOWMOBILE WEST MAGAZINE. Short title: Snowest. 1974. 4/yr. (Aug.-Nov.). $14.95. Harris Publishing, Inc. (Idaho Falls), 520 Park Ave., Idaho Falls, ID 83402. TEL 208-524-7000. FAX 208-522-5241. Ed. Steve Janes. circ. 161,000. (back issues avail.)
Description: Contains articles on the sport of snowmobiling in the Western United States. Includes areas of trail riding, snowmobile previews, industry updates, some aspects of racing and other items related to snowmobiling.

796.93   **US**   **ISSN 0892-9963**
SNOWSHOE. 1983. a. $100. United States Snowshoe Association, R.D. 1, Corinth, NY 12822. TEL 518-654-7165. Ed. Candice Bowen Bosworth. **Document type:** consumer publication.

796   **US**
SOBEK. 1976. q. $5. 6267 Robin Hood Way, Oakland, CA 94611. TEL 209-736-0226. FAX 415-834-1166. TELEX 3775709 SOBEK. Richard Bangs, Dir. adv.; bk.rev. circ. 5,000. **Document type:** catalog.
Formerly: Bush League.

796.4   **SA**   **ISSN 0256-0569**
SOUTH AFRICAN RUNNER. 1977. m. R.30. Box 32083, Bramfontein 2017, Johannesburg, South Africa. adv.; bk.rev. circ. 15,000.

SOUTH AFRICAN 4 X 4. see **TRANSPORTATION — Automobiles**

799   **US**   **ISSN 0897-9154**
SOUTH CAROLINA GAME & FISH. m. $14.97. Game & Fish Publications, Inc., 2250 Newmarket Pkwy., Ste. 110, Box 741, Marietta, GA 30061-0741. TEL 404-953-9222. FAX 404-933-9510. Ed. Jeff Samsel. circ. 12,000.

SOUTH CAROLINA OUT-OF-DOORS. see **CONSERVATION**

799   **US**
SOUTH CAROLINA RULES AND REGULATIONS FOR HUNTING AND FISHING LICENSES. 1992. a. free. Atlantic Publication Group, Inc., Box 61719, Charleston, SC 29419-1719. TEL 803-747-0025. FAX 803-744-0816. adv. contact: Delphine Lisignoli. circ. 400,000 (controlled). **Document type:** government publication, consumer publication.
Description: Covers regulations for hunting, wildlife management areas, freshwater and saltwater fishing for purchasers of licenses.

SOUTH CAROLINA WILDLIFE. see **CONSERVATION**

799.1   **US**
SOUTH FLORIDA'S ANGLER'S GUIDE. 1983. bi-m. $10. Don Simunek Enterprises, Inc., Box 6170, Lake Worth, FL 33466. TEL 407-968-2004. FAX 407-969-7943. adv. circ. 25,000.
Description: Covers freshwater and saltwater fishing.

799.1   **US**   **ISSN 0199-3372**
SK1
SOUTHERN OUTDOORS. 1946. 9/yr. $15. (Bass Anglers Sportsman Society) B.A.S.S., Inc., Box 17900, Montgomery, AL 36141. TEL 334-272-9530. FAX 334-279-7148. Ed. Larry Teague. adv.: B&W page $6685, color page $9990; trim 7 x 10. bk.rev.; illus. circ. 257,000. **Indexed:** PMR. **Document type:** consumer publication.
Formerly: Southern Outdoors - Gulf Coast Fisherman (ISSN 0038-4399)
Description: How-to, when-to and where-to information on fishing, hunting, boating and travel for southern sportsmen.

SOUTHERN SIERRAN. see **CONSERVATION**

796.552   **US**   **ISSN 0734-5895**
SPELEONEWS. 1953. q. $12. (National Speleological Society, Nashville and Chattanooga Grottoes) Nashville Grotto, c/o Barbara Munson, 4138 Dark Hollow Rd., McMinnville, TN 37110. TEL 615-668-3925. FAX 615-780-2210. Eds. Chuck Mangelsdorf, Rodger Ling. bk.rev.; illus. circ. 200. **Document type:** newsletter.
Description: News articles and historical notes on explorations of and expeditions to grottoes and caves.

799.1   **IT**
SPINNING; techniche di pesca con esche artificiali. 1991. q. L.27000 (Europe L.57000; elsewhere L.67000). Ed.A.I. s.r.l. (Edizioni Aeronautiche Italiane), Casella Postale 1550, 50100 Florence, Italy. **Document type:** consumer publication.

SPORT AVIATION. see **AERONAUTICS AND SPACE FLIGHT**

796.5   **FR**   **ISSN 0397-4707**
SPORT ET PLEIN AIR. 1952. m. (11/yr.). 125 F. (foreign 240 F.). Federation Sportive et Gymnique du Travail, 14-16 rue Scandicci, 93508 Pantin Cedex, France. Ed.Bd. adv. circ. 70,000. **Indexed:** Sportsearch.

799.1   **US**   **ISSN 0896-7369**
SPORT FISHING. 1986. 9/yr. $18.97. World Publications, Inc., 330 W. Canton, Box 2456, Winter Park, FL 32789. TEL 407-628-4802. FAX 407-628-7061. Ed. Dean Travis-Clarke. adv. circ. 113,215. **Document type:** consumer publication.
Description: Includes how-to and product information relating to offshore sport fishing.

796.9   **IT**
SPORT INVERNALI. 1946. m. (Sep.-May). Federazione Italiana Sport Invernali, Via Piranesi 44-B, 20137 Milan, Italy. TEL 39-2-75731. Ed. Carlo Valentino. adv.: B&W page L.4500000, color page L.6800000; adv. contact: Roberto Binda. circ. 140,463. **Document type:** consumer publication.

797   **UK**   **ISSN 0584-9217**
SPORT PARACHUTIST. 1964. bi-m. £18($18.40) British Parachute Association, Wharf Way, Glen Parva, Leicester LE2 9TF, England. TEL 071-403-6753. FAX 071-378-1208. Ed. Ola Soyinka. adv.; bk.rev.; illus. circ. 6,500. **Indexed:** Sportsearch (1976-). **Document type:** consumer publication.

799.1   **FR**
SPORT PRO MER. 7/yr. J.M. Editions, 6 av. des Andes, ZA de Courtaboeuf, 91952 Les Ulis Cedex, France. TEL 64-46-39-60. FAX 69-07-62-62. Ed. Joel Jordy. circ. 3,000.

799   **AT**   **ISSN 1322-4883**
SPORTDIVING IN AUSTRALIA AND THE SOUTH PACIFIC. 1968. bi-m. Aus.$37.50 (foreign Aus.$70) (effective 1996). Mountain, Ocean & Travel Publications Pty. Ltd., P.O. Box 167, Narre Warren, Vic. 3805, Australia. TEL 61-59-443774. FAX 61-59-444024. Ed. Barry Andrewartha. adv.; bk.rev.; illus.; index. circ. 16,000. (back issues avail.) **Document type:** consumer publication.
Formerly: Skindiving in Australia and the South Pacific (ISSN 0313-4954)
Description: Covers dive travel, wrecks, marine natural history, equipment overviews, technical and diver safety articles.

799.2 UK ISSN 0141-7053
SPORTING GUN. 1978. m. £26.40 (foreign £35) (effective 1995-1996). E M A P - Pursuit Publishing, Bretton Ct., Bretton, Peterborough, Cambs. PE3 8DZ, England. TEL 01733-264666. FAX 01733-263294. TELEX 32157. (Tower Publishing Services Ltd., Tower House, Sovereign Park, Lathkill St., Market Harborough, Leics. LE16 9EF, England. TEL 01858-468811. FAX 01858-432164) Ed. Robin Scott; Pub. Ian Beacham. adv.; bk.rev.; illus.; tr.lit.; circ. 31,880 (paid). **Document type:** consumer publication.

797.56 629.132 NE ISSN 0921-8017
SPORTPARACHUTIST. (Text in Dutch) 1959. bi-m. fl.45 to non-members. Koninklijke Nederlandse Vereniging voor Luchtvaart, Afdeling Parachutespringen - Royal Netherlands Aeronautical Association, Department of Parachuting, Jozef Israelsplein 8, 2596 AS The Hague, Netherlands. TEL 31-70-3245457. FAX 31-70-3240230. Ed. Nathalie Chudiak. adv.; B&W page fl.780, color page fl.1530; 210 x 297. bk.rev.; illus. circ. 3,500.
Formerly: Swing Through the Air (ISSN 0039-7458)
Description: Covers technical (equipment, instruction, regulations) and social (competitions, shows, clubs and people) aspects of skydiving.

796 US ISSN 0038-8149
SPORTS AFIELD. 1887. m. $13.97. Hearst Magazines, Sports Afield, 250 W. 55th St., New York, NY 10019. TEL 212-649-4000. (Subscr. to: Box 7166, Read Oak, IA 51591) Ed. Terry McDonell. adv.; bk.rev.; charts; illus. circ. 530,000. (also avail. in microform from UMI) **Indexed:** Access (1975-), Consum.Ind., Mag.Ind., PMR, Sports Per.Ind. **Document type:** consumer publication.
—Faxon; UnCover.
Former titles: Sports Afield with Rod and Gun; Sports Afield.
Description: Hands-on magazine for outdoor enthusiasts. Covers hunting, fishing, shooting, and boating, along with off-road activities, nature and conservation issues, and practical tips.

799.1 US
SPORTS FISHING. 9/yr. $18.97. World Publications, Inc., Box 2456, Winter Park, FL 32790. TEL 407-628-4802. FAX 407-628-7061. **Document type:** consumer publication.

799 CN
SPORTS NATURE PLEIN AIR CHASSE-PECHE. 1991. 8/yr. Can.$18.95. Groupe Polygone Editeurs Inc., 11450, Bvd. Albert-Hudon, Montreal-Nord, QC H1G 3J9, Canada. TEL 514-327-4464. FAX 514-327-0602. Ed. Jean Page. adv. contact: Guy LePage. circ. 105,000. (tabloid format) **Document type:** consumer publication.
Formerly (until 1994): Parlons Plein Air Chasse et Peche (ISSN 1191-4335)

799 NE ISSN 1380-2135
SPORTVISSERSMAGAZINE BEET. 1976. m. fl.69.50 (1300 BEF) (effective 1995). Vipmedia Publishing en Services, Willemstraat 23, 4811 AJ Breda, Netherlands. TEL 31-76-211272. FAX 31-76-144531. (Subscr. to: Postbus 7164, 4800 GD Breda, Netherlands; Subscr. in Belgium to: Vipmedia, Bredamaan 852, 2170 Merksem, Belgium. TEL 32-3-6454294) Eds. Pierre Bronsgeest, Guido Vinck. illus. circ. 60,000. **Document type:** consumer publication.
Formerly (until 1992): Sportvissers Magazine (ISSN 0924-3763); Which was formed by the merger of (1984-1989): Visblad Extra (ISSN 0921-7010); Which was formerly (until 1986): Sportvissers Journaal (ISSN 0921-7088); (1976-1989): Beet (ISSN 0166-6827); Which incorporates (1970-1985): Vissport (ISSN 0165-3431)

STEZKA; mesicnik pro sport, turistiku, brannost. see CHILDREN AND YOUTH — For

796.522 NO ISSN 0049-2248
STI OG VARDE. 1970. q. NOK 90 (effective 1995). Bergen Turlag, C. Sundtsgt. 3, 5004 Bergen, Norway. FAX 47-55-32-81-15. Ed. Torill Refsdal Aase. adv.; bk.rev.; illus. circ. 10,000.
—CCC.

799.1 UK ISSN 0966-2766
STILLWATER TROUT ANGLER. 1992. m. £21.60($52.80) I P C Magazines, Specialist Magazine Group (Subsidiary of: Reed Elsevier group), King's Reach Tower, Stamford St., London SE1 9LS, England. TEL 071-261-5829. FAX 0444-440619. TELEX 892084 REEDBP G. (Dist. by: Quadrant Subscription Services, Oakfield House, Perrymount Rd., Haywards Heath, W. Sussex RH16 3DH, England. TEL 0444-440421) Ed. Roy Westwood. adv. contact: Kevin Attridge. circ. 30,000. (back issues avail.) **Document type:** consumer publication.
Description: Covers trout fishing methods and prospects at leading UK reservoirs and small stillwaters.

799.1 SA ISSN 0040-7399
STYWE LYNE. English edition: Tight Lines (ISSN 0040-7739) (Text in Afrikaans, English) 1960. m. P.O. Box 3083, Pretoria 0001, South Africa. (Co-sponsor: S.A. Angler Union)

797 FR ISSN 0990-0845
SUBAQUA. 1958. bi-m. 160 Fr. (foreign 250 F.). Federation Francaise d'Etudes et de Sports Sous-Marins, 24 quai de Rive Neuve, 13007 Marseille, France. TEL 91-54-92-23. FAX 91-54-77-43. Ed. Francis Imbert. adv. contact: Max Walker. bk.rev.; charts; film rev.; illus.; index. circ. 35,000. **Indexed:** Sportsearch.
Formerly: Etudes et Sports Sous-Marins (ISSN 0425-5054); Incorporates (in 1981): Aventure Sous-Marine (ISSN 0005-1977)

796.522 US ISSN 0039-5056 G505
SUMMIT: THE MOUNTAIN JOURNAL. 1955. bi-m. $24.95 (effective 1995-1996). Summit Publications, Inc., 1221 May St., Hood River, OR 97031-1549. TEL 503-387-2200. FAX 503-387-2223. (Dist. by: Curtis Circulation, 433 Hackensack, Hackensack, NJ 07601; Subscr. to: SUM, Box 3000, Denville, NJ 07834. TEL 800-387-2200) Ed. John Harlin, III; Pub. Cari Breitinger. adv.; B&W page $2080, color page $3250; adv. contact: Steve Hutchins. bk.rev.; illus. circ. 35,000. **Indexed:** Sportsearch. **Document type:** consumer publication.
—UMI; UnCover.
Description: Covers international and U.S. highcountry culture, environment, sport, history, photography, literature and travel.

799.1 FI ISSN 0789-6638
SUOMEN KALAPAIKKAOPAS. (Text in Finnish; summaries in English, German, Swedish) 1966. irreg., approx. biennial. FIM 49. Kalatalouden Keskusliitto - Federation of Finnish Fisheries Associations (Centralfoerbundet foer Fiskerihushaallning), Koydenpunojankatu 7 B 23, 00180 Helsinki 18, Finland. TEL 358-0-640-126. FAX 358-0-608-309. Ed. Markku Myllyla. adv.: B&W page FIM 2900; trim 158 x 230; adv. contact: Jouko Poutanen. index. circ. 10,000. **Document type:** catalog.
Former titles: Kalapaikkaopas; Kalapaikat; Kalastuspaikkaopas (ISSN 0075-4684)
Description: Guide to angling in Finland.

796.72 US ISSN 0039-5692
SUPER STOCK & DRAG ILLUSTRATED. 1964. m. $17.95. Super Stock & Drag Illustrated Publishing, Ltd. (Subsidiary of: General Media Publishing Group), 6728 Eton Ave., Canoga Park, CA 91303. TEL 818-992-4777. FAX 818-992-0775. (Subscr. to: Box 420235, Palm Coast, FL 32142-0235) Ed. John Stewart. adv. contact: Christopher Ballard. bk.rev.; illus.; stat. circ. 55,937. (back issues avail.) **Document type:** consumer publication.

796.95 CN
SUPERTRAX INTERNATIONAL. (Text in English and French) 1989. 3/yr. Can.$12.95($9.95) (Canadian Council of Snowmobile Organizations) Supertrax Publishing Inc., Box 20219, 856 Upper James St., Hamilton, ON L9C 7M8, Canada. TEL 905-575-1621. FAX 905-575-8283. Ed. Kent Lester; Pub. Terrence Kehoe. adv. contact: John Hildebrandt. circ. 295,000. **Document type:** consumer publication.
Formerly: Supertrax.
Description: News, tests and specifications about snowmobiles and the industry across Canada.

796.172 IT
SURF. 1980. L.22500. Nautilus s.r.l., Via Tadino 29, 20124 Milan, Italy. Ed. Silvio Mursia. adv. circ. 50,000.

796.3 SP
SURF A VELA; revista mensual de windsurf. 1984. m. 4000 ptas.($60) (effective 1996). Editorial Noray, S.A., San Gervasio de Cassolas, 79, bajo, 08022 Barcelona, Spain. TEL 34-3-211-11-46. FAX 34-3-212-79-11. Ed. Panxo Pi-Suner; Pub. Pablo Zendrera. adv. contact: Irene Cereceda. circ. 23,000. (back issues avail.) **Document type:** consumer publication.
Description: Covers the world of windsurfing: travel, races, equipment, people and industry. Includes snowboarding in the wintertime.

796.172 GW
SURF-MAGAZIN. 1977. 10/yr. DM.60 (foreign DM.79). Verlag Delius, Klasing und Co., Postfach 101671, 33516 Bielefeld, Germany. TEL 0521-559280. FAX 0521-559113. TELEX 932934-DEKLA. Ed. Gerd Kloos. adv.; illus. circ. 135,000. **Document type:** consumer publication.
Formerly (until 1988): Surf (ISSN 0342-7560)

796.172 UK
SURF MAGAZINE. 1989. bi-m. £15 (foreign £30). Stone Leisure Ltd., Andrew House, 2a Granville Rd., Sidcup, Kent DA14 4BN, England. TEL 0181-302-6150. FAX 0181-300-2315. Ed. Mark Griffiths. adv. circ. 15,000. (back issues avail.) **Document type:** consumer publication.
Formerly: On Board Surf Magazine (ISSN 0956-019X)
Description: Covers the best of European and international surfing.

797.172 US ISSN 0270-2630
SURF REPORT; journal of international surfing destinations. 1980. m. $35 (foreign $42). Box 1028, Dana Point, CA 92629. TEL 714-496-5922. FAX 714-496-7849. Ed. Donna Oakley. adv. **Document type:** newsletter.

797.172 US ISSN 0039-6036 GV840.S8
SURFER; the international surfing magazine. 1960. m. $20.95. Surfer Publications, Inc., 33046 Calle Aviador, San Juan Capistrano, CA 92675. TEL 714-496-5922. FAX 714-496-7849. (Subscr. to: Box 58122, Boulder, CO 80321-8122. TEL 800-765-5501) Ed. Steve Hawk. adv.; illus. circ. 133,000. **Indexed:** Mag.Ind., Sports Per.Ind., Sportsearch (1977-). **Document type:** consumer publication.

797.172 US ISSN 1062-3892
THE SURFER'S JOURNAL. 1992. q. $35. Steve Pezman, Ed. & Pub., 1050 Calle Cordillera, Unit 106, San Clemente, CA 92672. TEL 714-361-0331. FAX 714-361-2417. adv.; B&W page $4200. circ. 12,000 (paid).

797.172 US ISSN 0194-9314
SURFING. 1964. m. $19.95. Western Empire Publications, 950 Calle Amanecer, Ste. C, Box 3010, San Clemente, CA 92672. TEL 714-492-7873. FAX 714-498-6485. Ed. N. Carroll. adv.; bk.rev.; illus. circ. 103,967. **Indexed:** Cal.Per.Ind. (1990), Sportsearch (1978-). **Document type:** consumer publication.

796.172 IT ISSN 1120-0227
SURFING. 1988. a. L.12000. Hi Promotion s.r.l., Via San Marco 48, 20121 Milan, Italy. TEL 39-2-6572441. FAX 39-2-6572468. Ed. Cristiano Zanni. adv.: color page L.3800000; adv. contact: Ferrante Lavorato. **Document type:** consumer publication.

796.96 SW ISSN 0346-2048
SVENSK CURLING. 1961. q. SEK 60 in Sweden; other Nordic countries SEK 80; Europe SEK 100; elsewhere SEK 120 (effective 1995. Svenska Curlingfoerbundet, Idrottens Hus, 123 87 Farsta, Sweden. FAX 46-86-04-70-78. Ed. Haakan Sundstrom. adv.; illus. circ. 5,000.
Formerly (until vol.4, 1971): Curling (ISSN 0011-3107)

SPORTS AND GAMES — OUTDOOR LIFE

799   **SW**   **ISSN 0039-6583**
SVENSK JAKT. (Supplements avail.) 1863. m. SEK 320. Svenska Jaegarefoerbundet - Swedish Hunters Association, P.O. Box 1, S-163 21 Spaanga, Sweden. TEL 46-8-795-33-00. FAX 46-8-761-20-15. Ed. Bertil Lundvik. adv. contact: Lena Gardmo. bk.rev.; charts; illus.; circ. 175,800 (controlled).
   Description: Focuses on nature; covers shooting, hunting and dog-breeding.

797.21 613.7   **US**
SWIMMING POOLS TODAY. 1985. q. $5. National Swimming Pool Owner's Association (NSPOA), 1213 Ridgecrest Circle, Denton, TX 76205. Ed. Tom A. Doron. bk.rev. circ. 100,000. (looseleaf format) **Document type:** newsletter.
   Description: Featuring the swimming pool: safety, chemistry, cleaning, repair, and new products; swimming for fitness and health; entertainment at the poolside.

SYLVANIAN. see *CONSERVATION*

796.42   **JA**
T. TENNIS; tennis magazine. (Text in Japanese) 1983. m. 4200 Yen. Gakken Co., Ltd., 40-5, 4 chome, Kamiikedai, Ohta-ku, Tokyo 145, Japan. Ed. Kunio Suganuma.

799.2   **IT**
TACARMI; tiro, armi, caccia. 1964. m. L.120000. Editrice Leone s.r.l., Via E. DeAmicis 25, 20123 Milan, Italy. TEL 39-2-8373768. FAX 39-2-89403518. Ed. Paolo Tagini. adv.: B&W page L.1750000, color page L.2900000. bk.rev. circ. 30,000.

688.7   **UK**   **ISSN 0015-3052**
TACKLE & GUNS. 1957. m. £13.50. Frontline Ltd. (Subsidiary of: E M A P - Haymarket Ltd.), Park House, 117 Park Rd., Peterborough PE1 2TR, England. TEL 0733-555161. FAX 62788. TELEX 329292 FRONTG. Ed. Cyril Holbrook. adv.; bk.rev.; illus.; stat.; tr.lit.
—CCC.
   Formerly: Fishing Tackle Dealer.

799.1   **US**
TACKLE TIMES (BARRINGTON). 1979. 6/yr. membership. American Sportfishing Association, 1033 N. Fairfax St., Ste. 200, Alexandria, VA 22314-1540. TEL 703-519-9691. FAX 703-519-1872. Ed. Norville S. Prosser. bk.rev.; circ. 2,000 (controlled). **Document type:** bulletin.
   Formerly: Top of the Week.

799   **US**
TAIL TRACKS. 1971. q. $25 (effective through 1996). American Trails, Box 200787, Denver, CO 80220. TEL 303-321-6606. FAX 303-321-6858. E-mail: AmerTrails@AOL.COM. Ed. Skye Ridley. adv.; bk.rev. circ. 4,000. **Document type:** newsletter.
   Former titles: American Trails Newsletter & National Trails Council. Newsletter.
   Description: Provides information on trail issues and events.

796   **AT**
TANDANYA. 1971. q. membership. Adelaide Bushwalkers Inc., Box 178, Unley, S.A. 5061, Australia. Ed. G. Oats. adv. circ. 220. **Document type:** newsletter.

797   **AT**   **ISSN 0157-2938**
TASMANIAN TRAMP. 1933. biennial. price varies. Hobart Walking Club, G.P.O. Box 753H, Hobart, Tas. 7001, Australia. Ed.Bd. adv.; cum.index: 1933-1963; 1966-1979. circ. 1,300.

TEAM AND TRAIL; the musher's monthly news. see *PETS*

796   **CN**
TELEGRAPH (SASKATOON). 1972. bi-w. Can.$37.45. Turner-Warwick Publications Inc., 892 104th St., P.O. Box 1029, N. Battleford, SK S9A 3E6, Canada. TEL 306-445-7261. FAX 306-445-3223. Ed. Lois Walsh. adv.; bk.rev. circ. 5,000. **Indexed:** Sportsearch. **Document type:** newspaper.
   Formerly (until 1988): Take Five (ISSN 0821-0160); Supersedes (in 1983): Recreation Saskatchewan (ISSN 0708-0743)

796   **BE**   **ISSN 0779-3324**
TEMPO RUNNING. (Editions in Dutch, French) 1986. 6/yr. 800 BEF (foreign 1200 BEF). Publirun, 190 rue Victor Hugo, Bte. 1, 1040 Brussels, Belgium. TEL 32-2-735-2160. FAX 32-2-7352314. Ed. Andre Selleslagh. adv.: B&W page 66000 BEF; adv. contact: Nicolas Poncelet. circ. 15,000 (paid).
   Formerly (until 1993): Joggings et Marathons (ISSN 0775-0951)

TENNESSEE CONSERVATIONIST; nature, environmental issues. see *CONSERVATION*

799.2   **US**
TENNESSEE DEER & TURKEY SHOW & PREVIEW. 1990. a. Target Communications Corp., 7626 W. Donges Bay Rd., Mequon, WI 53097-3400. TEL 414-242-3990; 800-324-3337. FAX 414-242-7391. Ed. Glenn Helgeland; Pub. Glenn Helgeland. adv.: B&W page $450, color page $738; trim 8 3/8 x 10 7/8; adv. contact: Lynn Anderson. circ. 30,000 (controlled). **Document type:** consumer publication.
   Description: Previews trade shows, conferences, and new products for hunters in Tennessee.

790.1   **US**   **ISSN 0161-3871**
TENNESSEE SPORTSMAN. 1980. m. $14.95. Game & Fish Publications, Inc., 2250 Newmarket Pkwy., Ste. 110, Box 741, Marietta, GA 30061-0741. TEL 404-953-9222. FAX 404-933-9510. Ed. Bill Hartlage.

799   **US**
TEXAS FISH & GAME.* 10/yr. $15. Highland Publishing Co., 7600 W. Tidwell Rd., Ste. 708, Houston, TX 77040-5719. TEL 512-693-5725. (Subscr. to: 4550 Post Oak Place Rd., Ste. 150, Houston TX 77027. TEL 713-626-3474)
   Incorporates (1973-1991): Texas Fisherman.
   Description: Covers hunting and fishing activities.

799.1   **US**
TEXAS FISHING GUIDE. a. free. Parks and Wildlife Department, 4200 Smith School Rd., Austin, TX 78744. TEL 512-389-4800; 800-792-1112. adv. contact: Greg Long. illus. **Document type:** consumer publication, government publication.
   Description: Outlines Texas state laws on fresh- and saltwater fishing, offers advice on catching and preparing fish, and tells anglers where to obtain further information.

799.2   **US**
TEXAS HUNTING GUIDE (YEAR). a. free. Parks and Wildlife Department, 4200 Smith School Rd., Austin, TX 78744. TEL 512-389-4800. **Document type:** government publication, consumer publication.

799 796.5   **US**
TEXAS OUTDOOR GUIDE MAGAZINE. 1968. bi-m. $12. Smith Publishing Co., Inc., Box 55573, Houston, TX 77055. Ed. Linda Peek Smith. adv.; bk.rev.; charts; illus.; stat.; tr.lit. circ. 100,000. (back issues avail.)

799.1   **US**
TEXAS RECREATIONAL FRESH AND SALTWATER FISHING GUIDE (YEAR). a. free. Park and Wildlife Department, 4200 Smith School Rd., Austin, TX 78744. TEL 512-389-4990. FAX 512-389-4894. adv. circ. 2,000,000. **Document type:** government publication.
   Description: Summary of fishing regulations.

799   **US**   **ISSN 0279-8875**
TEXAS SPORTSMAN. m. Game & Fish Publications, Inc., 2250 Newmarket Pkwy., Ste. 110, Box 741, Marietta, GA 30061-0741. TEL 404-953-9222. FAX 404-933-9510. Ed. Nick Gilmore. circ. 20,000.

796.552   **JA**
THE-YAMA-TO-KEIKOKU/MOUNTAIN AND VALLEY. (Text in Japanese) 1930. m. Yama-Kei Publishers Co., 1-1-33, Shiba-Daimon, Minato-ku, Tokyo 105, Japan. TEL 03-3436-4023. Ed. Akira Yamaguchi. circ. 230,000.

799.2   **US**
THICKETS HUNTING - FISHING GUIDE.* q. newsstand price: $4.95. Thickets Publishing, 2100 Riverchase Center, Ste. 118, Birmingham, AL 35244. TEL 205-987-6007. FAX 205-987-2882. **Document type:** consumer publication.

796.42   **UK**
THROWER. 1977. q. £12 for 2 yrs. National Athletics Coach, 152 Longdon Rd., Knowle, Solihull, W. Midlands B93 9HU, England. TEL 01564-772557. Ed. Max Jones. adv. circ. 1,000. **Indexed:** Sportsearch (1984-). **Document type:** bulletin.
   Formerly: Circle.

796.42   **CC**   **ISSN 1000-3509**
TIANJING/TRACK & FIELD. (Text in Chinese) 1981. bi-m. $18.50. (Zhongguo Tianjing Xiehui - China Track and Field Association) Renmin Tiyu Chubanshe - People's Sports Publishing House, 8 Tiyuguan Lu, Chongwen Qu, Beijing 100061, People's Republic of China. TEL 5112466. FAX 7016129. (Dist. in U.S. by: China Books & Periodicals, Inc., 2929 24th St., San Francisco, CA 94110)

TIDE. see *CONSERVATION*

796.5   **GW**   **ISSN 0941-5076**
TOPMOBIL; Magazin fuer Caravan und Reisemobil. (Text in English, German) 1989. bi-m. Top Special Verlag GmbH, Nebendahlstr. 16, 22041 Hamburg, Germany. TEL 040-347-3901. FAX 040-34725588. Ed. Joachim Kalkowsky. adv. contact: Manfred Ruopp. circ. 33,821. **Document type:** consumer publication.

799.1   **AT**   **ISSN 1031-9344**
TOURNAMENT FISHERMAN. 1988. q. Aus.$5.95. A.B. Organisation Pty. Ltd., P.O. Box 319, Avalon Beach, N.S.W. 2107, Australia. TEL 02-918-8322. FAX 02-918-8884. (Dist. by: Network Distribution Company, 54-58 Park St., Sydney, N.S.W. 2000, Australia) adv.

TRACES (JACKSON). see *CLUBS*

796.42   **US**
TRACK AND FIELD CASE BOOK. biennial. $4. National Federation of State High School Associations, 11724 N.W. Plaza Circle, Box 20626, Kansas City, MO 64195-0626. TEL 816-464-5400. FAX 816-464-5571. Ed. Thomas E. Frederick.

796.42   **US**
GV1060.6
TRACK AND FIELD COACHES REVIEW. 1927. q. $20 (foreign $30) (effective 1995). United States Track Coaches Association, 1330 N.W. Sixth St., Ste. D, Gainesville, FL 32601. TEL 904-955-2120. Ed. T.J. Juskiewicz; Pub. Jimmy Carnes. adv.; bk.rev.; charts; illus.; index, cum.index. circ. 2,200. (also avail. in microfilm from UMI; reprint service avail. from UMI) **Indexed:** Phys.Ed.Ind., Sportsearch (1976-). **Document type:** academic/scholarly publication.
—UMI; UnCover.
   Former titles (until 1995): Track and Field Quarterly Review (ISSN 0041-0292); (until 1964): Clinic Notes.
   Description: Includes educational and technical articles by and for track and field coaches and athletes.

796.42   **US**   **ISSN 0041-0284**
TRACK & FIELD NEWS. 1948. m. $33 (foreign $41). Track & Field News, 2570 El Camino Real, No. 606, Mountain View, CA 94040. TEL 415-948-8188. FAX 415-948-9445. Ed. Garry Hill. adv.; bk.rev.; illus.; mkt. circ. 28,000. (also avail. in microform from UMI) **Indexed:** Sports Per.Ind., Sportsearch (1974-). **Document type:** consumer publication.
—Faxon; SWETS; UMI; UnCover.
   Description: Provides complete coverage of the sport from high school to the Olympic level. Includes news, features, interviews, and action photos.

796.42   **US**
TRACK AND FIELD OFFICIALS MANUAL. biennial. $4. National Federation of State High School Associations, 11724 N.W. Plaza Circle, Box 20626, Kansas City, MO 64195-0626. TEL 816-464-5400. FAX 816-464-5571. Ed. Frank Kovaleski.

796.42   **US**   **ISSN 0270-4129**
GV1060.67
TRACK AND FIELD RULEBOOK. a. $4. National Federation of State High School Associations, 11724 N.W. Plaza Circle, Box 20626, Kansas City, MO 64195-0626. TEL 816-464-5400. FAX 816-464-5571.
   Formerly: Track and Field Rules and Records.

SPORTS AND GAMES — OUTDOOR LIFE

796.42 US ISSN 0041-0306
TRACK NEWSLETTER. 1955. 42/yr. $49 (foreign $75). Track & Field News, 2570 El Camino Real, No. 606, Mountain View, CA 94040. TEL 415-948-8188. FAX 415-949-9445. Ed. Garry Hill. circ. 600. **Indexed:** Sportsearch. **Document type:** newsletter.
   Description: Latest track and field, results and summaries.

796.42 US ISSN 0742-3918
GV561
TRACK TECHNIQUE: OFFICIAL TECHNICAL PUBLICATION. 1960-1981; resumed 1983. q. $15 (foreign $16). (Athletics Congress - U S A) Track & Field News, 2570 El Camino Real, No. 606, Mountain View, CA 94040. TEL 415-948-8188. FAX 415-948-9445. Ed. Kevin McGill. bk.rev.; bibl.; charts; illus. circ. 3,500. (also avail. in microform from UMI) **Indexed:** Phys.Ed.Ind., Sports Per.Ind., Sportsearch. **Document type:** academic/scholarly publication.
   —UMI; UnCover.
   Formerly (until 1981): Track Technique (ISSN 0041-0314)
   Description: Covers technique and training for all events, injury care and prevention, biomechanics and physiology, motivation and coaching psychology, diet and nutrition, strength training, racing tactics.

797.172 AT ISSN 1032-3317
TRACKS. 1970. m. Aus.$39.60. Mason Stewart Publishing Pty. Ltd., P.O. Box 746, Darlinghurst, N.S.W. 2010, Australia. TEL 02-331-5006. FAX 02-360-5367. Ed. Gary Dunne. adv. circ. 35,000. **Document type:** consumer publication.

796.15 US
TRADEWINDS. q. membership only. Kite Trade Association International, 50 First St., No.300, San Francisco, CA 94105. TEL 415-764-4908. FAX 415-764-4915. Ed. Traci Davis Souza.
   Description: For those involved in various aspects of the kite industry.

796.522 US ISSN 0041-0756
F782.R6
TRAIL AND TIMBERLINE. 1918. m. $10 to non-members (foreign $13). Colorado Mountain Club, 710 10th St., Ste. 200, Golden, CO 80401-1022. TEL 303-279-3080. FAX 303-279-9690. Ed. Marilyn Peterson. adv.: B&W page $230; 5 1/2 x 8 1/2. bk.rev.; charts; illus.; maps; index, cum.index every 10 yrs. circ. 9,000. **Document type:** consumer publication.
   —UnCover.
   Description: Membership magazine for the Colorado Mountain Club with news on mountain sports and conservation.

799.3 US
TRAIL TALK. q. Whitetails Unlimited, Inc., Box 720, Sturgeon Bay, WI 54235-0720. TEL 414-743-6777. Ed. Dale G. Deckman. **Document type:** consumer publication.

796 333.7 US ISSN 0749-1352
TRAIL WALKER; news of hiking and conservation. 1963. bi-m. $18 membership (libraries $12.50). New York - New Jersey Trail Conference, Inc., 232 Madison Ave., New York, NY 10016. TEL 212-685-9699. FAX 212-779-8102. adv.; bk.rev. circ. 10,000. **Document type:** newspaper.

796.5 UK
TRAIL WALKER. m. £26.40 (foreign £33.10) (effective 1995-1996). E M A P - Pursuit Publishing, Bretton Ct., Bretton, Peterborough, Cambs. PE3 8DZ, England. TEL 01733-264666. FAX 01733-263294. TELEX 32157. (Subscr. to: Tower Publishing Services Ltd., Tower House, Sovereign Park, Lathkill St., Market Harborough, Leics. LE16 9EF, England. TEL 01858-468811. FAX 01858-432164) adv. **Document type:** consumer publication.

796.5 DK ISSN 0108-6758
TRAILER. (Text in Danish and Swedish) 1983. m. DKK 19.75. Fut & Fart, Vejlevej 49, 7330 Brande, Denmark.

796.5 388.344 US ISSN 0041-0780
TX1100
TRAILER LIFE. 1941. m. $11.98. T L Enterprises, Inc., 3601 Calle Tecate, Camarillo, CA 93012. TEL 805-389-0300. Ed. Bill Estes; Pub. Joe McNeil. illus.; mkt. circ. 290,035. (also avail. in microform from UMI) **Indexed:** Consum.Ind., Mag.Ind., PMR. **Document type:** consumer publication.
   —UMI; UnCover.
   Description: RV magazine for travel trailers, motorhome and truck campers. Travelogues, buyer's guides, vehicle tests, technical tips, and more.

TRAILER LIFE CAMPGROUND AND R V SERVICES DIRECTORY. see BUSINESS AND ECONOMICS — Trade And Industrial Directories

796 US ISSN 0748-7401
TRANSWORLD SKATEBOARDING. 1983. m. $19.95 to individuals (foreign $52.95); libraries $14.97 (foreign $33.77). Transworld Publications, Inc., 353 Airport Rd., Oceanside, CA 92054. TEL 619-722-7777. FAX 619-722-0653. (Subscr. to: Box 469006, Escondido, CA 92046. TEL 800-334-8152) Ed. Dave Swift; Pubs. Larry Balma, Peggy Covens. adv. contact: Sheri Roberts. **Document type:** consumer publication.
   Description: Contains interviews with leading skaters, contests, features about the local skating scene, worldwide travel stories, skating skills, and choosing a board.

796.93 US ISSN 1046-4611
TRANSWORLD SNOWBOARDING. 7/yr (Oct.-Apr.). $14.95 to individuals (foreign $25.80); libraries $11.21 (foreign $22.06). Times Mirror Magazines, Inc., 2 Park Ave., New York, NY 10016. TEL 212-779-5000. FAX 212-725-3836. (Subscr. to: Box 54734, Boulder, CO 90321-4734. TEL 800-289-0639) Ed. Kevin Kinnear. adv. contact: Sheri Roberts. **Document type:** consumer publication.

799 US ISSN 0041-1760
TRAP & FIELD. 1890. m. $25. Curtis Magazine Group, Inc., 1200 Waterway Blvd., Indianapolis, IN 46202. TEL 317-633-8800. FAX 317-264-2192. Ed. Bonnie Nash. adv.; illus. circ. 16,500. **Indexed:** Sportsearch (1977-). **Document type:** consumer publication.

799.2 US ISSN 8750-233X
SK283
TRAPPER AND PREDATOR CALLER. 1974. m. $16.95. Krause Publications, Inc., 700 E. State St., Iola, WI 54990. TEL 715-445-2214. FAX 715-445-4087. TELEX 556461 KRAUSE PUB UD. Ed. Gordy Krahn. circ. 35,437. (tabloid format)
   Description: Focuses on the newest trapping and calling techniques, equipment, and animal lures. Includes reports on activities state by state. Includes information on products helpful to outdoorsmen and on muzzle loading.

796.42 GW ISSN 0931-3850
TRIATHLON UND SPORTWISSENSCHAFT. 1987. irreg., vol.9, 1994. price varies. (Sportswissenschaftlicher Beirat der Deutschen Triathlon Union) Czwalina Verlag, Postfach 730240, 22122 Hamburg, Germany. TEL 040-6780025. FAX 040-6780051. **Document type:** monographic series.

799 333.7 SP
TROFEO; caza - pesca - naturaleza. 1970. m. 5000 ptas. Prensa Espanola, S.A., Telemaco 37, 28027 Madrid, Spain. TEL 91-3203299. FAX 91-3203557. Dir. J. Delibes. circ. 35,000.
   Description: Covers hunting, fishing and nature conservation.

799.1 UK ISSN 0041-3372
TROUT AND SALMON; a journal for game fishermen. 1955. m. £25.20 (foreign £39.70) (effective 1995-1996). E M A P - Pursuit Publishing, Bretton Ct., Bretton, Peterborough, Cambs. PE3 8DZ, England. TEL 01733-264666. FAX 01733-263294. TELEX 32157. (Subscr. to: Tower Publishing Services Ltd., Tower House, Sovereign Park, Lathkill St., Market Harborough, Leics. LE16 9EF, England. TEL 01858-468811. FAX 01858-432164) Ed. Sandy Leventon; Pub. Robert MacDonald. adv. contact: Julie Goodwin. illus.; circ. 43,017 (paid). **Document type:** consumer publication.
   —CCC.

799.1 UK ISSN 0142-9108
TROUT FISHERMAN. m. £24. E M A P Pursuit Publishing Ltd., Bretton Court, Bretton, Peterborough, Cambs. PE3 8DZ, England. TEL 01733-264666. FAX 01733-263294. Ed. Chris Dawn; Pub. Robert MacDonald. adv. contact: Julie Goodwin. bk.rev.; illus.; circ. 38,563 (paid). **Document type:** consumer publication.
   Description: Directed to the stillwater game fisherman.

799.2 US ISSN 8750-0205
TURKEY & TURKEY HUNTING. 1983. 6/yr. $12.95. Krause Publications, Inc., 700 E. State St., Iola, WI 54990. TEL 715-445-2214. FAX 715-445-4087. TELEX 556461. Ed. Gerry Blair. adv. contact: Debbie Knauer. circ. 95,000.
   Description: Guide to U.S. turkey hunting. Includes calling tips, first-hand hunting experiences, contest results, calendar of events and bow and gun techniques.

799.2 IT
TUTTO TIRO. m. L.81500 (foreign L.109000). Editoriale Olimpia S.p.A., Viale Milton 7, 50129 Florence, Italy. TEL 39-55-473843. FAX 39-55-499195. adv.: B&W page L.2650000, color page L.4850000. circ. 20,075 (paid). **Document type:** consumer publication.

796 US
TWISTED (WOODBRIDGE). m. $1 per no. 11698 Howitzer Lane, Woodbridge, VA 22192. Ed. Jamie Early.
   Description: Contains stories and photos of skateboarding.

799.1 US ISSN 0883-6841
U S A OUTDOORS. 1975. bi-m. membership. Bassing America Corp., 4398 Sunbelt Dr., Dallas, TX 75248. TEL 214-380-2656. FAX 214-380-2621. Ed. John Brett. adv.: B&W page $970; 8 1/2 x 11. bk.rev. circ. 57,000. (back issues avail.)
   Description: For tournament bass fishermen.

U S SKI WRITERS ASSOCIATION NEWSLETTER. see JOURNALISM

ULTRALIGHT FLYING!; international magazine of ultralight aviation. see AERONAUTICS AND SPACE FLIGHT

796.42 US ISSN 0744-3609
GV1065.2
ULTRARUNNING. 1981. 10/yr. $25 (foreign $32). 300 N. Main St., Box 481, Sunderland, MA 01375. TEL 413-665-7573. Ed. Peter Gagarin; Pub. Peter Gagarin. adv. contact: Fred Pilon. circ. 5,200 (paid). **Indexed:** Sportsearch (1987-). **Document type:** consumer publication.

U.S. FISH AND WILDLIFE SERVICE. NATIONAL SURVEY OF FISHING, HUNTING AND WILDLIFE-ASSOCIATED RECREATION. see SPORTS AND GAMES — Abstracting, Bibliographies, Statistics

799.2 GW ISSN 0566-2621
UNSERE JAGD. m. B L V Verlagsgesellschaft mbH, Lothstr. 29, 80797 Munich, Germany. TEL 089-12705-0. FAX 089-12705541. Ed. H.-D. Willkomm. adv. contact: Hennig Stemmler. illus. circ. 37,980. (tabloid format) **Indexed:** Key Word Ind.Wildl.Res. **Document type:** consumer publication.

796 SW ISSN 0281-2932
UTE-MAGASINET.* 1980. bi-m. SEK 175. Milvus Forlags AB, P.O. Box 147, S-83005 Jaerpen, Sweden. FAX 0642-11411. Ed. Marion Areng. adv.; bk.rev. circ. 24,000.

799.1 799.2 IC
VEIDIMADURINN. 1984. 2/yr. ISK 5628 (effective Jan. 1995). Frodi Ltd., Seljavegur 2, 101 Reykjavik, Iceland. TEL 354-515-5500. FAX 354-51505599. Ed. Gylfi Palsson. adv.: B&W page ISK 46900, color page ISK 81800; trim 19 x 27; adv. contact: Ingolfur Asgeirsson. circ. 6,000.
   Formerly: A Veidum (ISSN 1017-3625)
   Description: Focuses on sport fishing, hunting and shooting.

VERMONT FISH AND WILDLIFE REGULATIONS. see LAW

SPORTS AND GAMES — OUTDOOR LIFE

796.522 SP ISSN 0042-4420
VERTEX.* (Text in Catalan; summaries in French, Spanish) 1966. bi-m. 195 ptas. Federacion Catalana de Montanismo, Ramblas 61, 1-2, Barcelona 12, Spain. adv.; bk.rev.; bibl.; charts; illus.; index; cum.index. circ. 4,000.

796.42 AT ISSN 0310-4745
VETERAN ATHLETE. 1986. m. Aus.$24($40) Mipen Enterprises Pl., McInnes Rd., Tynong North, Vic. 3813, Australia. TEL 059-428344. Ed. Mike Hall. adv. circ. 1,000. (back issues avail.)

796.5 CN ISSN 0844-1804
VIE EN PLEIN AIR. (Text in French) 1970. q. 3592 Poirier Blvd., Ville St-Laurent, PQ H4R 2J5, Canada. TEL 514-856-0788. Ed. Claude Leonard.

796.5 CN ISSN 0710-2054
VIE ET CAMPING. (Text in French) 1976. 2/yr. free. Vie en Plein Air, 3592 Poirier Blvd., Ville St-Laurent, PQ H4R 2J5, Canada. TEL 514-856-0788. FAX 514-856-0790. adv. circ. 25,000. **Indexed:** Sportsearch.

796.5 799 NO ISSN 0332-7442
VILLMARKSLIV. 1972. m. NOK 387. Hjemmet Mortensen AS, P.O. Box 5928, Majorstua, N-0308 Oslo, Norway. TEL 47-22-96-14-07. FAX 47-22-96-13-09. Ed. Dag Kjelsaas. adv.; B&W page NOK 1245, color page NOK 20000. bk.rev. circ. 95,000.
Description: For people who are intersted in outdoor life, fishing and hunting.

799 RM
VINATORUL SI PESCARUL ROMAN. 1948. m. 360 lei($6) Association of Hunters and Anglers, Calea Mosilor 128, Bucharest, Rumania. FAX 136804. Ed. Victor Tarus. adv.; bk.rev. circ. 25,000.

790.1 US
VIRGINIA OUTDOORS PLAN (YEAR). 1965. quinquennial. $10. Department of Conservation & Recreation, Division of Planning and Recreation Resources, 203 Governor St., Ste. 326, Richmond, VA 23219. TEL 804-786-2556. FAX 804-786-6141. illus.; tr.lit.
Formerly (1965 report): Virginia's Common Wealth.
Description: Attempts to project to project future needs and identify emerging trends and issues that may effect open space, natural resources and recreation resources planning and management.

VIRGINIA WILDLIFE. see CONSERVATION

VIRGINIA WILDLIFE FEDERATION. FEDERATION RECORD. see CONSERVATION

797.23 US
VISIBILITY. 1959. bi-m. $20 membership (institutions $50). Underwater Society of America, Box 628, Daly City, CA 94017. TEL 415-583-8492. FAX 415-294-3496. Ed. Carol Rose. adv.; B&W page $100; trim 8 1/2 x 11; adv. contact: Carol Rose. bk.rev.; bibl. circ. 2,500. **Document type:** newsletter.
Formerly: Underwater Reporter (ISSN 0199-5189)
Description: Covers all issues of underwater diving.

799 GW ISSN 0138-1601
VISIER. 1975. m. DM.87. Visier Verlag GmbH, Olgastr. 86, 70180 Stuttgart, Germany. TEL 0711-237570. FAX 0711-235730. (Subscr. to: Visier Leserservice, Spitalerstr. 12, 20095 Hamburg, Germany. TEL 040-33969188. FAX 040-33969136) Ed. David Schiller; Pub. Hannes Scholten. adv.; B&W page DM.3985, color page DM.5313; adv. contact: Dirk Schoenfeld. circ. 65,000. **Document type:** publication.

VOL A VOILE MAGAZINE. see AERONAUTICS AND SPACE FLIGHT

799 BE
VOOR EN DOOR DE VISSER; internationaal hengelsportblad. (Text in Dutch) 1964. m. 915 BEF (fl.49). De Scheemaecker b.v.b.a, Boechoutsesteenweg 178, 2540 Hove, Belgium. TEL 32-3-4552299. FAX 32-3-4540475. (In Netherlands: Postbus 9, 5600 AA Eindhoven, Netherlands. TEL 31-40-811420) Ed. Oscar Van Nooten; Pub. Alfred De Scheemaecker. adv.; B&W page 22800 BEF, color page 41000 BEF; trim 212 x 146; adv. contact: M. Mertens. circ. 30,000.
Description: Covers sport fishing.

VOYAGEUR TRAIL NEWS. see LEISURE AND RECREATION

796.552 613.7 US ISSN 0739-4497
WALKING! JOURNAL;* the art, science and sport of walking. 1983. q. $8. Walking Journal, Inc., 37 Pleasant St., Concord, NH 03301-4005. Ed. Kevin Kelly. adv.; bk.rev.; charts; illus. circ. 4,000. (back issues avail.) **Document type:** consumer publication.

799.1 US ISSN 0744-1266
WALLEYE. 1980. 6/yr. $12.50. Walleye International, Box 40210, Cleveland, OH 44140. TEL 216-333-9494. FAX 216-777-7803. Ed. H.B. Riser. adv. circ. 48,066.
Description: Covers fishing techniques, conditions, uses of new tackle, boats, equipment, new books, cooking and environmental issues.

796.5 GW ISSN 0178-1677
WANDERMAGAZIN. 1985. bi-m. DM.38.50. Verlag Andrea Saenger, Moltkestr. 95, 53173 Bonn, Germany. TEL 0228-351259. FAX 0228-353207. Ed. Michael Saenger. adv.; bk.rev. circ. 70,000. (back issues avail.)

796 US
WARP; the surf - skate - snow experience. 1992. bi-m. $19.95. TransWorld Publications, Inc., 353 Airport Rd., Oceanside, CA 92054. TEL 619-722-7777. FAX 619-722-0653. (Subscr. to: Box 469014, Escondido, CA 92046. TEL 800-334-8152) Ed. Kevin Kinnear; Pubs. Larry Balma, Peggy Covens. adv. contact: Sheri Roberts. illus. **Document type:** consumer publication.
Description: Covers surfing, skateboarding and snowboarding, and music.

797.173 US ISSN 0883-7813
WATER SKI. 1976. 10/yr. $18.97. World Publications, Inc., 330 W. Canton Ave., Box 2456, Winter Park, FL 32790. TEL 407-628-4802; 800-879-0495. FAX 407-628-7601. Ed. Erik Calonius. adv.; illus. circ. 114,775. **Document type:** consumer publication. **Incorporates:** Spray's Water Ski Magazine (ISSN 0273-7892); Which was formerly (until vol.4, no.7, 1980): Spray (ISSN 0164-9722).

797.173 US ISSN 0049-7002 GV840.S5
WATER SKIER. 1951. 7/yr. $8 (foreign $12). American Water Ski Association, 799 Overlook Dr., Winter Haven, FL 33884. TEL 813-324-4341. FAX 813-325-8259. Ed. Greg Nixon. adv.; charts; illus.; tr.lit.; circ. 25,000 (controlled). (also avail. in microfiche; reprint service avail.) **Indexed:** Mag.Ind., Sportsearch (1974-).

799 US ISSN 0897-9162
WEST VIRGINIA GAME & FISH. m. $14.97. Game & Fish Publications, Inc., 2250 Newmarket Pkwy., Ste. 110, Box 741, Marietta, GA 30061-0741. TEL 404-953-9222. FAX 404-933-9510. Ed. Ken Freel.

799 US ISSN 0049-7479
WESTERN OUTDOOR NEWS. 1954. w. $34.95. Western Outdoors Publications, 3197E Airport Loop Dr., Costa Mesa, CA 92626. TEL 714-546-4370. (Or: Box 2027, Newport Beach, CA 92659-1027) Ed. Pat McDonell. adv. circ. 75,000. (tabloid format)

796.5 US ISSN 0043-4000 SK1
WESTERN OUTDOORS. 1960. 9/yr. $14.95. Western Outdoors Publications, 3197E Airport Loop Dr., Costa Mesa, CA 92626. TEL 714-546-4370. FAX 714-662-3486. (Or: Box 2027, Newport Beach, CA 92659-1027) Ed. Jack Brown. adv.; bk.rev.; illus. circ. 128,000. **Indexed:** Cal.Per.Ind. (1978-), PMR.
—UnCover.

796.93 CN ISSN 1184-2679
WESTERN SKIER. 1972. 6/yr. Can.$10($15) McIntosh Publishing Co. Ltd., Box 430, North Battleford, Sask. S9A 2Y5, Canada. TEL 306-445-4401. FAX 306-445-1977. Ed. Rod McDonald. circ. 38,100.
Former titles: Saskatchewan Skier (ISSN 0849-6927); (until 1989): Saskatchewan Ski Journal.
Description: Covers skiing in western Canada and the US, resort features, fashions, technique improvement, club news, and press releases.

799 CN ISSN 0709-1532
WESTERN SPORTSMAN. 1969. bi-m. Can.$15.95. Western Sportsman Ltd., Box 737, Regina, SK S4P 3A8, Canada. TEL 306-352-2773. FAX 306-565-2440. Ed. Roger Francis. adv.; bk.rev.; charts; illus.; stat. circ. 28,000.
Formerly: Fish and Game Sportsman (ISSN 0015-2897); Which was formed by the merger of: Fish and Game of Alberta; Saskatchewan Sportsman.

WHEELERS R V RESORT AND CAMPGROUND GUIDE: NORTH AMERICAN EDITION. see TRAVEL AND TOURISM

799.1 UK
WHERE TO FISH. vol. 84, 1994. biennial. £19.95. Thomas Harmsworth Publishing, Old Rectory Offices, Stoke Abbott, Beaminster, Dorset DT8 3JT, England. TEL 01308-868118. FAX 01308-868995. Ed. D.A. Orton. adv. circ. 12,000. **Document type:** directory.
Description: Directory of fishing in the rivers, lakes, and reservoirs of England, Scotland, Wales, and Northern Ireland and overseas.

796.93 917 US ISSN 0163-9684 GV854.4
WHITE BOOK OF SKI AREAS. U S AND CANADA. 1976. a. $16. Inter-Ski Services, Inc., Box 9595, Friendship Sta., Washington, DC 20016. TEL 202-342-6084. FAX 202-338-1940. Ed. Robert G. Enzel. circ. 12,000. **Document type:** directory.
Formerly: White Book of U S Ski Areas (ISSN 0145-6075)
Description: Complete listing of ski areas with facilities, rates, statistics, and telephone numbers.

790 CN ISSN 0043-5015
WHITESHELL ECHO.* 1956. m. Can.$2($3) (Whiteshell District Association) Lance Publishing Co. Ltd., 56 Elm Park, Winnipeg, Man., Canada. Ed. Wes Rowson. circ. 4,000. (tabloid format)

799.2 US
WHITETALE JOURNAL. 8/yr. newsstand price: $2.95. Thicket Publishing, 2100 Riverchase Center, Ste. 118, Birmingham, AL 35244-1852. TEL 205-987-6007. FAX 205-987-2882. **Document type:** consumer publication.
Formerly: Buckhunter's Whitetail.

799 US
WHOOP 'N' HOLLER. q. membership. West Virginia Scenic Trails Association, 633 W. Virginia Ave., Morgantown, WV 26505. TEL 304-296-5158. Ed. George L. Rosier. circ. 200. **Document type:** newsletter.
Description: Covers hiking, backpacking, and club news.

796 AT ISSN 0726-2809
WILD; Australia's wilderness adventure magazine. 1981. q. Aus.$27.80($36.80) Wild Publications Pty. Ltd., P.O. Box 415, Prahran, Vic. 3181, Australia. TEL 61-3-826-8482. Ed. Chris Baxter. charts; illus.; film rev.; index. circ. 19,685. (back issues avail.)
Description: Covers hiking, cross-country skiing, canoeing, mountaineering and caving in Australia.

799.1 GW ISSN 0043-5422
WILD UND HUND; Zeitschrift fuer Jaeger und andere Naturfreunde. 1895. fortn. DM.151. Verlag Paul Parey (Hamburg), Spitalerstr. 12, 20095 Hamburg, Germany. TEL 040-33969-0. FAX 040-33969-199. TELEX 2161391-PARV-D. Ed. Horst Reetz. adv.; bk.rev.; illus. circ. 88,000. (reprint service avail. from ISI) **Indexed:** Ind.Vet., Key Word Ind.Wildl.Res., Vet.Bull. **Document type:** consumer publication.
—CCC.

WILDERNESS AND ENVIRONMENTAL MEDICINE. see MEDICAL SCIENCES — Sports Medicine

SPORTS AND GAMES — OUTDOOR LIFE

799.2 US ISSN 0886-0637
WILDFOWL; the magazine for duck & goose hunters. 1985. bi-m. $23.95. Stover Publishing Co., Inc., 1901 Bell Ave., Ste. 4, Des Moines, IA 50315. TEL 515-243-2472. FAX 515-243-0233. (Subscr. to: Box 372, Mt. Morris, IL 61054) Ed. Bob Wilbanks; Pub. Carrell Bunn. adv.: B&W page $1611; color page $2343; adv. contact: Mary Stearns. circ. 32,522. (back issues avail.) **Document type:** consumer publication.
   Description: For waterfowl hunters.

799 CN ISSN 0043-5457
WILDLIFE CRUSADER. 1944. 6/yr. Can.$10. Manitoba Wildlife Federation, 1770 Notre Dame Ave., Winnipeg, Man., Canada. TEL 204-633-5967. FAX 204-632-5200. Ed. Denis Corneau. adv.; bk.rev.; charts; illus.; stat. circ. 32,468.

799.2 US ISSN 0886-3458
WILDLIFE HARVEST. 1970. m. $35 (effective Oct. 1995). (North American Gamebird Association, Inc.) Wildlife Harvest Publications, Box 96, Goose Lake, IA 52750. TEL 319-242-3046. FAX 319-242-3046. Ed. John Mullin; Pub. John M. Mullin. adv.: B&W page $270; adv. contact: Peggy Mullin Boehmer. bk.rev.; circ. 2,943 (paid). **Document type:** trade publication.
   Description: Covers the market for shooting and hunting supplies, clothing and equipment, shotguns, shotshells, clay-targets and sporting clay traps.

797.173 US ISSN 0279-9359
GV811.63.W56
WIND SURF.* 1971. m. $21. 1341 Ocean Ave., Ste. 534, Santa Monica, CA 90401-1066. TEL 714-661-4888. FAX 714-661-0487. Ed. Drew Kampion. adv.; bk.rev.; tr.lit. circ. 56,750. (reprint service avail.) Indexed: Sports Per.Ind., Sportsearch (1984-).

790 CN ISSN 0049-7681
WINDSOR SPORTSMEN'S NEWS.* m. Windsor Sportsmen's Club, 2401 Dougall Rd., Box 452, Windsor, Ont., Canada. **Indexed:** Sportsearch.

796.172 US
GV811.63.W56
WINDSURFING; the nation's leading windsurfing magazine. 1981. 8/yr. $18.97. World Publications, Inc., 330 W. Canton, Box 2456, Winter Park, FL 32790. TEL 407-628-4802. FAX 407-628-7601. (Subscr. to: Box 183, Mt. Morris, IL 61054. TEL 800-394-6006) Ed. Debbie Z. Snow. adv. contact: Sue Gilman. circ. 92,991. **Document type:** consumer publication.
—UnCover.
   Formerly: WindRider (ISSN 0279-4659)

976.17 US ISSN 1063-8172
WINDSURFING CALIFORNIA. 1990. 7/yr. $9.97. Extreme Publishing, 3702 W. Valley Hwy. N., Ste. 312, Auburn, WA 98002. Ed. Carol York. adv.: B&W page $1130, color page $1775; trim 8 3/8 x 10 7/8; adv. contact: Marie Cordell. circ. 25,000. **Document type:** consumer publication.
   Description: Covers windsurfing in California and the Southwest; includes features, tips, events, products and locations.

799.2 US ISSN 0892-1849
WING & SHOT; the magazine for upland bird hunters. 1986. bi-m. $23.95. Stover Publishing Co., Inc., 1901 Bell Ave., Ste. 4, Des Moines, IA 50315. TEL 515-243-2472. FAX 515-243-0233. Ed. Bob Wilbanks; Pub. Carrell Bunn. adv.: B&W page $1463; color page $2128; adv. contact: Mary Stearns. bk.rev. circ. 17,968. **Document type:** consumer publication.
   Description: For upland bird hunters.

799.2
WISCONSIN DEER & TURKEY SHOW PREVIEW. 1989. a. Target Communications Corp., 7626 W. Donges Bay Rd., Mequon, WI 53092-3400. TEL 414-242-3990; 800-324-3337. FAX 414-242-7391. Ed. Glenn Helgeland; Pub. Glenn Helgeland. adv.: B&W page $595, color page $970; trim 8 3/8 x 10 7/8; adv. contact: Lynn Anderson. circ. 40,000 (controlled). **Document type:** consumer publication.
   Description: Previews shows, events, seminars, and new products of interest to hunters in Wisconsin.

WISCONSIN NATURAL RESOURCES. see *CONSERVATION*

796 US ISSN 0893-5769
WISCONSIN OUTDOOR JOURNAL. 1987. 8/yr. $15.95. Krause Publications, Inc., 700 E. State St., Iola, WI 54990. TEL 715-445-2214. FAX 715-445-4087. Ed. Brian Lovett. adv. circ. 40,000.
   Description: Offers information on hunting, fishing, camping and the sporting life in the state of Wisconsin. Covers natural resource management, natural history, outdoor-related news and legislation.

796.95 US ISSN 0745-161X
WISCONSIN SNOWMOBILE NEWS. 1987. 7/yr. (m., Sep.-Mar.). $7. (Association of Wsiconsin Snowmobile Clubs) Royle Publications, Inc., 112 Market St., Sun Prairie, WI 53590. TEL 608-825-6315. FAX 608-825-3053. Ed. Cathy Hanson. adv.: B&W page $2630, color page $3030; trim 8 3/8 x 10 7/8; adv. contact: Cathy Hanson. circ. 23,966. **Document type:** consumer publication.
   Description: Contains association news, legislative actions, and travel articles. Covers new products and personalities.

796 US ISSN 0361-9451
SK143
WISCONSIN SPORTSMAN. 1972. m. $14.95. Game & Fish Publications, Inc., 2250 Newmarket Pkwy., Ste. 110, Box 741, Marietta, GA 30061-0741. TEL 404-953-9222. FAX 404-933-9510. Ed. Dennis Schmidt. adv.; bk.rev. circ. 33,000.

WOMEN OUTDOORS. see *WOMEN'S INTERESTS*

796 US
WOMEN'S OUTDOOR JOURNAL. Abbreviated title: W O J. 6/yr. Liberty Ridge Publishing, R.R.3, Box 72, Rockport, IN 47635. TEL 812-359-5293. Ed. Rebecca A. Hinton. circ. 4,000.

WONDERFUL WEST VIRGINIA. see *CONSERVATION*

796.5 US
WOODALL'S CAMP-ORAMA. 1974. m. Woodall Publishing Co., 13975 W. Polo Trail Dr., Lake Forest, IL 60045-9952. TEL 708-362-6700; 800-323-9076. FAX 616-754-8410. Pub. Deborah A. Spriggs. adv.: B&W page $1042; adv. contact: Mary Sgaraglino. circ. 32,000. **Document type:** consumer publication.

WOODALL'S CAMPERWAYS; the Middle Atlantic campers' newspaper. see *TRAVEL AND TOURISM*

917.59 US ISSN 0162-7406
WOODALL'S CAMPGROUND DIRECTORY. EASTERN EDITION. a. $11.95. Woodall Publishing Co., 13975 W. Polo Trail Dr., Lake Forest, IL 60045. TEL 708-362-6700; 800-323-9076. FAX 708-362-8776. Pub. Deborah A. Spriggs. adv. contact: Mary Sgaraglino. **Document type:** directory.
   Supersedes in part: Woodall's Campground Directory (ISSN 0362-3823); Which was formerly: Woodall's Trailering Parks and Campgrounds (ISSN 0084-1110)
   Description: Annual directory of campgrounds in the eastern states.

917.59 US
WOODALL'S CAMPGROUND DIRECTORY. NORTH AMERICAN EDITION. a. $17.95. Woodall Publishing Co., 13975 W. Polo Trail Dr., Lake Forest, IL 60045. TEL 708-362-6700; 800-323-9076. FAX 708-362-8776. Pub. Deborah A. Spriggs. adv. contact: Mary Sgaraglino. bk.rev.; bibl.; charts; illus.; tr.lit. circ. 450,000. **Document type:** directory.
   Former titles: Woodall's Campground Directory. North American - Canadian Edition (ISSN 0146-1362); Woodall's Campground Directory. North American Edition; Which supersedes in part: Woodall's Campground Directory (ISSN 0362-3823); Which was formerly: Woodall's Trailering Parks and Campgrounds (ISSN 0084-1110)
   Description: Lists more than 12,000 campgrounds throughout the U.S., Canada, and Mexico, using a two-tier rating system. Includes information about facilities and recreation.

917.59 US ISSN 0162-7414
WOODALL'S CAMPGROUND DIRECTORY. WESTERN EDITION. a. $11.95. Woodall Publishing Co., 13975 W. Polo Trail Dr., Lake Forest, IL 60045. TEL 708-362-6700; 800-323-9076. FAX 708-362-8776. Pub. Deborah A. Spriggs. adv. contact: Mary Sgaraglino. **Document type:** directory.
   Supersedes in part: Woodall's Campground Directory (ISSN 0362-3823); Which was formerly: Woodall's Trailering Parks and Campgrounds (ISSN 0084-1110)
   Description: Lists campgrounds in the western United States.

796.5 US
WOODALL'S PLAN IT - PARK IT - GO. 1984. a. $12.95. Woodall Publishing Co., 13975 W. Polo Trail Dr., Lake Forest, IL 60045. TEL 708-362-6700; 800-323-9076. FAX 708-362-8776. Pub. Deborah A. Spriggs. adv. contact: Mary Sgaraglino. tr.lit. circ. 170,000. **Document type:** directory.
   Former titles: Woodall's Tent Camping Guide; Woodall's Tenting Directory (ISSN 0742-3977)
   Description: Lists all the campgrounds in the U.S. and Canada that welcome tent campers, includes editorials on tenting accessories and tents, cooking recommendations, travel tips and attractions, as well as checklists explaining how to pack.

388 US
WOODALL'S SOUTHERN R V. 1981. m. Woodall Publishing Co., 13975 W. Polo Trail Dr., Lake Forest, IL 60045-9952. TEL 708-362-6700; 800-323-9076. FAX 708-362-8776. Pub. Deborah A. Spriggs. adv.: B&W page $1003; adv. contact: Mary Sgaraglino. **Document type:** consumer publication.

796.5 917.704 US
WOODALL'S TRAILS-A-WAY. 1970. m. $8. Woodall Publishing Co., 13975 W. Polo Trail Dr., Lake Forest, IL 60045-9952. TEL 708-362-6700; 800-323-9076. FAX 708-362-8776. Pub. Deborah Spriggs. adv.: B&W page $1097; adv. contact: Mary Sgaraglino. bk.rev. circ. 35,000. (tabloid format) **Document type:** consumer publication.

796.5 US
WOODSWOMEN NEWS. 1982. q. $20 to non-members. Woodswomen Adventure Travel for Women, 25 West Diamond Lake Rd., Minneapolis, MN 55419. TEL 612-822-3809. FAX 612-822-3814. Ed. Liz Ohle. adv. contact: Liz Olds. bk.rev. circ. 10,000. (tabloid format; back issues avail.) **Document type:** newsletter.
   Description: Acts as a forum for this national organization, which provides adventure travel and active vacations for women of all ages.

799.2 US
WORLD BOWHUNTERS. 1989. bi-m. $22 (effective 1993). 4133 W. Michigan Ave., Jackson, MI 49202. TEL 517-750-9060. FAX 517-750-3640. Ed. Ted Nugent. adv. circ. 15,000.
   Formerly: Ted Nugent World Bowhunters

WORLD RECORD GAME FISHES. see *FISH AND FISHERIES*

796.93 338 US
YELLOW PAGES OF SKIING. (year) North American planner & directory. 1993. a. $14.95. Activity Directories International, Inc., 8122 South Park Ln., Ste. 200, Littleton, CO 80120. TEL 303-730-3030. FAX 303-730-3092. Ed. Jerry Baines. adv. contact: Charlie Messina. circ. 160,000. **Document type:** trade publication.
   Description: A compilation of ski areas and associated businesses, including accommodations, transportation and restaurants. Serves as a travel planner and industry buying guide.

796.54 UK ISSN 1355-7491
YOUR BIG SITES BOOK: CAMPING AND CARAVANNING CLUB SITES LIST; camping sites yearbook. 1920. biennial. membership. Camping and Caravanning Club, Greenfields House, Westwood Way, Coventry, Warks. CV4 8JH, England. TEL 01203-694995. FAX 01203-694886. Ed. Peter Frost. circ. 109,539. **Document type:** consumer publication.
   Supersedes in part (in 1989): Camping and Caravanning Club Handbook and Sites List; Which was formerly: Camping Club Handbook and Sites List; Camping Club of Great Britain and Ireland. Year Book with List of Camp Sites (ISSN 0068-6956)

SPORTS MEDICINE

796.54   UK   ISSN 1355-3348
YOUR PLACE IN THE COUNTRY: A GUIDE TO CAMPING AND CARAVANNING CLUB SITES. 1920. a. membership. Camping and Caravanning Club, Greenfields House, Westwood Way, Coventry, Warks. CV4 8JH, England. TEL 01203-694995. FAX 01203-694886. Ed. Peter Frost. circ. 109,569. **Document type:** consumer publication.
Supersedes in part (in 1989): Camping and Caravanning Club Handbook and Sites List; Which was formerly: Camping Club Handbook and Sites List; Camping Club of Great Britain and Ireland. Year Book with List of Camp Sites (ISSN 0068-6956)

799.1   CC   ISSN 1000-3487
ZHONGGUO DIAOYU/ANGLING IN CHINA. (Text in Chinese) 1984. m. $12.60. (Zhongguo Diaoyu Xiehui - China Angling Association) Renmin Tiyu Chubanshe - People's Sport Publishing House, 8 Tiyuguan Lu, Chongwen Qu, Beijing 100061, People's Republic of China. TEL 5112466. FAX 7016129. (Dist. in U.S. by: China Books & Periodicals, Inc., 2929 24th St., San Francisco, CA 94110. TEL 415-282-2994) Ed. Lu Guang. adv. circ. 200,000.

797.172   SA   ISSN 1021-0032
ZIGZAG BODYBOARDING. (Text in English) 1993. q. R.6 per issue. Zigzag Promotions, P.O. Box 11, Westville 3630, South Africa. adv.; illus. **Document type:** consumer publication.

796.5 910.202   IT
2 C PLEIN AIR; cultura e strumenti del turismo all'aria aperta. 1971. m. (11/yr.). L.60000 (foreign L.100000). Edizioni Plein Air snc., Largo San Pio V, 16, 00165 Rome, Italy. TEL 39-6-6632628. FAX 39-6-6237266. Ed. Lucia Jannucci. adv.: B&W page L.6500000, color page L.11000000; adv. contact: Franco ossati. bk.rev. circ. 72,000. **Document type:** consumer publication, trade publication.
Formerly (until 1987): 2C Caravan e Camping.
Description: Includes nature, vacations, traveling, outdoor sports and life.

796   US   ISSN 1079-9184
3-D & TARGET ARCHERY. 6/yr. $16.95 (Canada $24.95; elsewhere $26.95). Ehlert Publishing Group, Inc., 601 Lakeshore Pkwy., Minnetonka, MN 55305. TEL 612-476-2200. **Document type:** consumer publication.

SPORTS MEDICINE

see *Medical Sciences-Sports Medicine*

STATISTICS
see also specific subjects

A A M A INDUSTRY STATISTICAL REVIEW AND FORECAST. (American Architectural Manufacturers Association) see *BUILDING AND CONSTRUCTION — Abstracting, Bibliographies, Statistics*

A G A GAS STATS; monthly gas utility statistical report. see *PETROLEUM AND GAS — Abstracting, Bibliographies, Statistics*

A H A HOSPITAL STATISTICS (YEAR). see *HOSPITALS — Abstracting, Bibliographies, Statistics*

A M P S METER WEEKLY REPORTS. (All Media and Product Survey) see *ADVERTISING AND PUBLIC RELATIONS — Abstracting, Bibliographies, Statistics*

A M P S RADIO DIARY. (All Media and Product Survey) see *COMMUNICATIONS — Abstracting, Bibliographies, Statistics*

310 001.64   US
A P D U NEWSLETTER. 1976. m. $325 membership. Association of Public Data Users, Princeton University Computing Center, 87 Prospect Ave., Princeton, NJ 08544. TEL 609-258-6025. FAX 609-258-3943. E-mail: apdu@princeton.edu. Ed. Susan Anderson. cum.index: 1976-1991. circ. 500. (back issues avail.) **Document type:** newsletter.
Description: Designed to inform readers of issues and policies that affect the collection and dissemination of public data by the federal government, and availability of data products in various media formats (print, CD-ROM).

310   GW
AACHEN. STATISTISCHES AMT. STATISTISCHE KURZINFORMATION. 1982. irreg. DM.4 per no. Statistisches Amt, Roemerstr. 10, 52064 Aachen, Germany. TEL 0241-4321235. FAX 0241-4322874. circ. 400. (back issues avail.) **Document type:** government publication.
Description: Each issue devoted to one area of statistics. Covers vital statistics, election statistics, and population statistics.

310   DK   ISSN 0107-7120
AARHUS KOMMUNES STATISTISKE KONTOR. INFORMATION. 1970. irreg. (approx. 50/yr.). free. Aarhus Kommunes Statistiske Kontor, Raadhuset, 8100 Aarhus C, Denmark. TEL 45-89-40-21-81. FAX 45-89-40-21-21. (looseleaf format)

310   II
ABSTRACT OF STATISTICS FOR TAMIL NADU. (Text in English) 1956. a. Rs.4 per no. Director of Statistics, Madras 600006, India. (Subscr. to: Government Publication Dpot, 166 Anna Rd., Madras 600002, India) circ. controlled. (back issues avail.)

ACCIDENT - INCIDENT REPORTING A D R E P. see *TRANSPORTATION — Abstracting, Bibliographies, Statistics*

ACTIVIDADES DE INVESTIGACION Y DESARROLLO EXPERIMENTAL. see *TECHNOLOGY: COMPREHENSIVE WORKS — Abstracting, Bibliographies, Statistics*

ACTUARIAL REVIEW. see *INSURANCE — Abstracting, Bibliographies, Statistics*

ADVANCED STUDIES IN THEORETICAL AND APPLIED ECONOMETRICS. see *BUSINESS AND ECONOMICS — Economic Systems And Theories, Economic History*

ADVANCES IN RISK ANALYSIS. see *PUBLIC HEALTH AND SAFETY — Abstracting, Bibliographies, Statistics*

ADVANCES IN STATISTICAL ANALYSIS AND STATISTICAL COMPUTING. see *COMPUTERS*

AEROSPACE FACTS AND FIGURES. see *AERONAUTICS AND SPACE FLIGHT — Abstracting, Bibliographies, Statistics*

318   MX   ISSN 0186-0453
AGENDA ESTADISTICA. 1967. a. Mex.$8500. Instituto Nacional de Estadistica, Geografia e Informatica, Secretaria de Programacion y Presupuesto, Prol. Heroe de Nacozari 2301 Sur, Puerta 11 Acceso, 20270 Aguascalientes, Ags., Mexico. TEL 91-49-181948. FAX 491-807-39. circ. 11,000. **Document type:** government publication.

AGRICULTURA SI SILVICULTURA ROMANIEI IN PROFIL TERITORIAL/ROMANIA'S AGRICULTURE AND SYLVICULTURE AT THE TERRITORIAL LEVEL. see *AGRICULTURE — Abstracting, Bibliographies, Statistics*

AGRICULTURAL STATISTICS OF GREECE. see *AGRICULTURE — Abstracting, Bibliographies, Statistics*

AGRICULTURAL STATISTICS SERIES NO.3: EUROPEAN COMMUNITIES INDEX OF AGRICULTURAL PRICES. see *AGRICULTURE — Abstracting, Bibliographies, Statistics*

AIR CARRIER INDUSTRY SCHEDULE SERVICE TRAFFIC STATISTICS. MEDIUM REGIONAL CARRIERS. see *TRANSPORTATION — Abstracting, Bibliographies, Statistics*

AIR CARRIER OPERATIONS IN CANADA/OPERATIONS DES TRANSPORTEURS AERIENS AU CANADA. see *AERONAUTICS AND SPACE FLIGHT — Abstracting, Bibliographies, Statistics*

AIR CARRIER TRAFFIC AT CANADIAN AIRPORTS. see *TRANSPORTATION — Abstracting, Bibliographies, Statistics*

314.8   DK   ISSN 0109-8047
HA1461
AKTUELL NORDISK STATISTIK/CURRENT NORDIC STATISTICS. (Text in Scandinavian languages) 1984. s-a. DKK 30. Nordisk Statistisk Sekretariat - Nordic Statistical Secretariat, Sejroegade 11, Dk-2100 Copenhagen OE, Denmark. TEL 45-39-17-39-82. FAX 45-31-18-51-22. circ. 750. **Document type:** bulletin.
●Also available on CD-ROM.

ALABAMA LABOR MARKET NEWS. see *BUSINESS AND ECONOMICS — Abstracting, Bibliographies, Statistics*

ALABAMA'S VITAL EVENTS. see *PUBLIC ADMINISTRATION — Abstracting, Bibliographies, Statistics*

ALASKA. AGRICULTURAL STATISTICS SERVICE. AGRICULTURAL STATISTICS. see *AGRICULTURE — Abstracting, Bibliographies, Statistics*

ALASKA FARM REPORTER. see *AGRICULTURE — Abstracting, Bibliographies, Statistics*

316   AE   ISSN 1111-0376
ALGERIA. OFFICE NATIONAL DES STATISTIQUES. ANNUAIRE STATISTIQUE DES WILAYATE DU CENTRE. Key Title: Annuaire Statistique des Wilayate du Centre. (Text in French) 1982. a. price varies. Office National des Statistiques - Al-Diwan al-Watani lil-Ihsa'iyat, 8 & 10 rue des Moussebiline, B.P. 202 Ferhat Boussad, Algiers, Algeria. TEL 213-64-77-90. **Document type:** government publication.

316   AE   ISSN 1111-7680
ALGERIA. OFFICE NATIONAL DES STATISTIQUES. ANNUAIRE STATISTIQUE DES WILAYATE DE L'EST. Key Title: Annuaire Statistique des Wilayate de l'Est. (Text in French) 1983. a. price varies. Office National des Statistiques, 8 & 10 rue des Moussebiline, B.P. 202 Ferhat Boussad, Algiers, Algeria. TEL 213-64-77-90. **Document type:** government publication.

316   AE   ISSN 1111-0368
ALGERIA. OFFICE NATIONAL DES STATISTIQUES. ANNUAIRE STATISTIQUE DES WILAYATE DE L'OUEST. Key Title: Annuaire Statistique des Wilayate de l'Ouest. (Text in French) 1981. a. price varies. Office National des Statistiques - Al-Diwan al-Watani lil-Ihsa'iyat, 8 & 10 rue des Moussebiline, B.P. 202 Ferhat Boussad, Algiers, Algeria. TEL 213-64-77-90. **Document type:** government publication.

316   AE   ISSN 1111-5696
ALGERIA. OFFICE NATIONAL DES STATISTIQUES. BULLETIN DE STATISTIQUES COURANTES. (Text in French) 1987. 6/yr. 500 din. Office National des Statistiques - Al-Diwan al-Watani lil-Ihsa'iyat, 8 & 10 rue des Moussebiline, B.P. 202 Ferhat Boussad, Algiers, Algeria. TEL 213-64-77-90. (back issues avail.) **Document type:** government publication.

316   AE   ISSN 1111-0392
ALGERIA. OFFICE NATIONAL DES STATISTIQUES. COLLECTIONS STATISTIQUES. (Text in French) 1985. irreg. price varies. Office National des Statistiques - Al-Diwan al-Watani lil-Ihsa'iyat, 8 & 10 rue des Moussebiline, B.P. 202 Ferhat Boussad, Algiers, Algeria. TEL 213-64-77-90. (back issues avail.) **Document type:** government publication.

316   AE   ISSN 1111-5939
ALGERIA. OFFICE NATIONAL DES STATISTIQUES. DONNEES STATISTIQUES. (Text in French) 1985. m. 500 din. Office National des Statistiques - Al-Diwan al-Watani lil-Ihsa'iyat, 8 & 10 rue des Moussebiline, B.P. 202 Ferhat Boussad, Algiers, Algeria. TEL 213-64-77-90. (back issues avail.) **Document type:** government publication.

ALGERIA. OFFICE NATIONAL DES STATISTIQUES. INDICES DES PRIX A LA CONSOMMATION. see *BUSINESS AND ECONOMICS — Abstracting, Bibliographies, Statistics*

316   AE   ISSN 1111-7001
ALGERIA. OFFICE NATIONAL DES STATISTIQUES. INFORMATIONS STATISTIQUES SUR LA CONJONCTURE. (Text in French) 1989. q. 250 din. (foreign 1250 din). Office National des Statistiques - Al-Diwan al-Watani lil-Ihsa'iyat, 8 & 10 rue des Moussebiline, B.P. 202 Ferhat Boussad, Algiers, Algeria. TEL 213-64-77-90. (back issues avail.) **Document type:** government publication.

316   AE   ISSN 1111-0384
ALGERIA. OFFICE NATIONAL DES STATISTIQUES. STATISTIQUES (REVUE TRIMESTRIELLE). Key Title: Statistiques - Office National des Statistiques. 1949; N.S. 1983. q. 100 din. (foreign 500 din.) (effective 1994). Office National des Statistiques - Al-Diwan al-Watani lil-Ihsa'iyat, 8 & 10 rue des Moussebiline, B.P. 202 Ferhat Boussad, Algiers, Algeria. TEL 213-64-77-90. TELEX 67190. cum.index: nos.1-35. (back issues avail.) **Document type:** government publication.
   Supersedes (in 1983): Algeria. Direction des Statistiques et de la Comptabilite Nationale. Bulletin Trimestriel de Statistiques; Former titles: Algeria. Direction des Statistiques. Bulletin Trimestriel de Statistiques; Algeria. Sous-Direction des Statistiques. Bulletin de Statistiques Generales (ISSN 0002-5305); Algeria. Service de Statistique Generale. Bulletin Mensual.

316   AE   ISSN 1010-1284
L'ALGERIE EN QUELQUES CHIFFRES. (Supplement to: Annuaire Statistique de l'Algerie (ISSN 1111-0355X)) (Text in French) irreg. (approx a.). 150 din. Office National de Statistiques - Al-Diwan al-Watani lil-Ihsa'iyat, 8 & 10 rue des Moussebiline, B.P. 202 Ferhat Boussad, Algiers, Algeria. TEL 213-64-77-90. **Document type:** government publication.

311   II   ISSN 0971-0388
ALIGARH JOURNAL OF STATISTICS. 1981. a. Rs.35($15) to individuals; institutions Rs.50 ($20). Aligarh Muslim University, Department of Statistics, Aligarh 202002, India. TELEX 564-230 AMU IN. circ. 300. **Indexed:** Biostat., Oper.Res.Manage.Sci., Qual.Contr.Appl.Stat., Stat.Theor.Meth.Abstr.
—BLDSC (0787.822000).

ALL MEDIA & PRODUCT SURVEY. see *ADVERTISING AND PUBLIC RELATIONS — Abstracting, Bibliographies, Statistics*

314   GW   ISSN 0002-6018
HA1   CODEN: ALSAAX
ALLGEMEINES STATISTISCHES ARCHIV. (Text in German; summaries in English) 1890. q. DM.128. (Vorstand der Deutschen Statistischen Gesellschaft) Vandenhoeck und Ruprecht, Robert-Bosch-Breite 6, 37079 Goettingen, Germany. TEL 0551-6959-26. FAX 0551-695917. (Subscr. to: 37070 Goettingen, Germany) Ed. Horst Rinne. adv.; bk.rev.; bibl.; charts; index. circ. 620. (reprint service avail. from KTO) **Indexed:** Biol.Abstr., J.Cont.Quant.Meth., P.A.I.S.For.Lang.Ind., Stat.Theor.Meth.Abstr. **Document type:** academic/scholarly publication.
—SWETS. **CCC.**

AMERICAN JOURNAL OF MATHEMATICAL AND MANAGEMENT SCIENCES. see *MATHEMATICS*

AMERICAN PETROLEUM INSTITUTE. MONTHLY STATISTICAL REPORT. see *PETROLEUM AND GAS — Abstracting, Bibliographies, Statistics*

AMERICAN RADIO. see *COMMUNICATIONS — Abstracting, Bibliographies, Statistics*

AMERICAN SALARIES AND WAGES SURVEY. see *BUSINESS AND ECONOMICS — Abstracting, Bibliographies, Statistics*

310   AS
AMERICAN SAMOA STATISTICAL DIGEST (YEAR). a. $5 (foreign $6.50). American Samoa Government, Economic Development Planning Office, Research and Statistics Division, Pago Pago, 96799, American Samoa. Ed. Vai Filigan. **Document type:** government publication.

AMERICAN STATISTICAL ASSOCIATION. GOVERNMENT STATISTICS SECTION. PROCEEDINGS. see *PUBLIC ADMINISTRATION — Abstracting, Bibliographies, Statistics*

AMERICAN STATISTICAL ASSOCIATION. PHYSICAL AND ENGINEERING SCIENCES. PROCEEDINGS. see *ENGINEERING*

AMERICAN STATISTICAL ASSOCIATION. SECTION ON STATISTICAL EDUCATION. PROCEEDINGS. see *EDUCATION — Abstracting, Bibliographies, Statistics*

310   US   ISSN 0149-9963
QA276.4
AMERICAN STATISTICAL ASSOCIATION. STATISTICAL COMPUTING SECTION. PROCEEDINGS (OF THE ANNUAL MEETING). 1976. a. $45 to non-members; members $30. American Statistical Association, 1429 Duke St., Alexandria, VA 22314-3402. TEL 703-684-1221. FAX 703-684-2037. stat. **Indexed:** Curr.Ind.Stat. **Document type:** proceedings.
—BLDSC (6636.300000).

AMERICAN STATISTICAL ASSOCIATION. STATISTICS IN SPORTS. PROCEEDINGS. see *SPORTS AND GAMES*

311   US   ISSN 0733-5830
QA276.A1
AMERICAN STATISTICAL ASSOCIATION. SURVEY RESEARCH METHODS. PROCEEDINGS. 1978. a. $66 to non-members; members $44. American Statistical Association, 1429 Duke St., Alexandria, VA 22314-3402. TEL 703-684-1221. FAX 703-684-2037. **Indexed:** Curr.Ind.Stat. **Document type:** proceedings.
—BLDSC (6811.510000); Faxon.
   Formerly: American Statistical Association. Statistical Section. Proceedings.

311   US   ISSN 0003-1305
HA1   CODEN: ASTAAJ
AMERICAN STATISTICIAN. 1947. q. $55. American Statistical Association, 1429 Duke St., Alexandria, VA 22314-3402. TEL 703-684-1221. FAX 703-684-2037. (also avail. in microform from KTO,MIM,UMI,PMC; reprint service avail. from SWZ) **Indexed:** Biostat., Chem.Abstr., Child Devel.Abstr., Compumath, Comput.Abstr., Curr.Cont., Curr.Ind.Stat., Deep Sea Res.& Oceanogr.Abstr., Ind.Sci.Rev., INSPEC, J.Cont.Quant.Meth., Math.R., Oper.Res.Manage.Sci., P.A.I.S., Qual.Contr.Appl.Stat., Risk Abstr., Sci.Cit.Ind., Soc.Sci.Ind., SSCI, Stat.Theor.Meth.Abstr.
—BLDSC (0857.650000); Faxon; Genuine Article; SWETS; UMI; UnCover. **CCC.**

016   US   ISSN 0091-1658
Z7554.U5
AMERICAN STATISTICS INDEX; a comprehensive guide and index to the statistical publications of the U.S. Government. (CD-ROM title: Statistical Masterfile) 1974. m. (with q. and a. cumulations). price varies. Congressional Information Service, Part of the Reed Elsevier group, 4520 East-West Hwy., Bethesda, MD 20814-3389. TEL 301-654-1550; 800-638-8380. FAX 301-654-4033. Ed. Ben Pitkin. abstr.; stat.; index; cum.index: 1974-79; 1980-84; 1985-88; 1989-1992. **Indexed:** Mid.East: Abstr.& Ind., Noise Pollut.Publ.Abstr., Popul.Ind. **Document type:** abstracting/indexing.
•Also available online. Vendor(s): Knight-Ridder, Inc. (File no.102).
Also available on CD-ROM.
   Description: Abstracts and index of U.S. government statistical publications by subject, name, type of data breakdown, title and report number.

THE AMERICAN WOMAN (YEAR); a status report. see *WOMEN'S STUDIES — Abstracting, Bibliographies, Statistics*

310   519.54   US   ISSN 0163-9617
AMSTAT NEWS. 1974. 11/yr. $40. American Statistical Association, 1429 Duke St., Alexandria, VA 22314-3402. TEL 703-684-1221. FAX 703-684-2037. Ed. Marilyn J. Humm. adv. circ. 19,000. (also avail. in microform from UMI; back issues avail.)
—SWETS; UMI.

ANGOLA. DIRECCAO DOS SERVICOS DE ESTATISTICA. ANUARIO ESTATISTICO. see *PUBLIC ADMINISTRATION — Abstracting, Bibliographies, Statistics*

316   AO   ISSN 0003-3413
ANGOLA. DIRECCAO DOS SERVICOS DE ESTATISTICA. BOLETIM MENSAL.* (Text in Portuguese) N.S. 1942. m. Esc.180. Direccao dos Servicos de Estatistica, Caixa Postal 1215, Luanda, Angola. adv.; stat. circ. 15,200. **Document type:** government publication, bulletin.

ANGOLA. DIRECCAO DOS SERVICOS DE ESTATISTICA. INFORMACOES ESTATISTICAS. see *PUBLIC ADMINISTRATION — Abstracting, Bibliographies, Statistics*

STATISTICS   6181

519.5   US   ISSN 0090-5364
HA1   CODEN: ASTSC7
ANNALS OF STATISTICS. 1973. 6/yr. $150. Institute of Mathematical Statistics, Business Office, 3401 Investment Blvd., Ste. 7, Hayward, CA 94545-3819. TEL 510-783-8141. FAX 510-783-4131. E-mail: IMS@STAT.BERKELEY.EDU. circ. 4,300 (paid). (also avail. in microform from UMI) **Indexed:** Biostat., Compumath, Curr.Cont., Curr.Ind.Stat., Ind.Sci.Rev., J.Cont.Quant.Meth., Math.R., Oper.Res.Manage.Sci., Qual.Contr.Appl.Stat., Risk Abstr., Sci.Cit.Ind., SSCI, Stat.Theor.Meth.Abstr. **Document type:** academic/scholarly publication.
—BLDSC (1044.400000); Faxon; Genuine Article; SWETS; UMI; UnCover. **CCC.**
   Supersedes in part: Annals of Mathematical Statistics (ISSN 0003-4851)

ANNOTATED ACCESSIONS LIST OF STUDIES AND REPORTS IN THE FIELD OF SCIENCE STATISTICS. see *BIBLIOGRAPHIES*

ANNUAIRE DES STATISTIQUES DU COMMERCE EXTERIEUR DU TOGO. see *BUSINESS AND ECONOMICS — Abstracting, Bibliographies, Statistics*

316.6   DM
ANNUAIRE STATISTIQUE DE BENIN. a., latest 1975. 2000 Fr.CFA. Institut National de la Statistique et de l'Analyse Economique, B.P. 323, Cotonou, Benin.
   Formerly: Annuaire Statistique du Dahomey.

316   AE   ISSN 1111-035X
ANNUAIRE STATISTIQUE DE L'ALGERIE/STATISTICAL YEARBOOK OF ALGERIA. (Supplement avail.: L'Algerie en Quelques Chiffres (ISSN 1010-1284)) (Text in French) a. 2750 din. Office Nationale des Statistiques - Al-Diwan al-Watani lil-Ihsa'iyat, 8 & 10 rue des Moussebiline, B.P. 202 Ferhat Boussad, Algiers, Algeria. TEL 213-64-77-90. **Document type:** government publication.

314   BE   ISSN 0770-0415
HA1393
ANNUAIRE STATISTIQUE DE LA BELGIQUE. Dutch edition: Statistisch Jaarboek van Belgie (ISSN 0770-7673) (Text in French) 1870. a. 1250 BEF (foreign 1560 BEF) (effective 1993). Institut National de Statistique, 44 rue de Louvain, B-1000 Brussels, Belgium. TEL 32-2-5486211. FAX 32-2-5486367. **Document type:** government publication.
—BLDSC (1073.482500).
   Formerly (until 1960): Annuaire Statistique de la Belgique et du Congo Belge (ISSN 0770-2221)

314   FR   ISSN 0066-3654
HA1213
ANNUAIRE STATISTIQUE DE LA FRANCE. 1878. a. 590 F.($97) Institut National de la Statistique et des Etudes Economiques, 18 bd. Adolphe Pinard, 75675 Paris Cedex 14, France. TEL 41-17-50-50. FAX 41-17-66-66. circ. 3,000. (reprint service avail. from SCH) **Document type:** government publication.
—BLDSC (1073.483000).
   Description: Presents statistics showing trends in demographics, the economy and society. Includes commentary, definitions and methodology.

316   TI   ISSN 0066-3689
HA4684
ANNUAIRE STATISTIQUE DE LA TUNISIE. a. Institut National de la Statistique, 70 rue Echcham, Tunis, Tunisia. **Document type:** government publication.

316   MR   ISSN 0851-089X
ANNUAIRE STATISTIQUE DU MAROC. (Editions in Arabic, French) 1917. a. DH.165. Direction de la Statistique, B.P. 178, Rabat, Morocco. TEL 212-7-77-36-06. FAX 212-7-77-32-17. TELEX 36714. (also avail. in microfiche) **Document type:** government publication.
   Incorporates: Morocco. Direction de la Statistique. Statistiques Retrospectives; Parc Automobile du Maroc.

316.7   CD   ISSN 0577-5000
ANNUAIRE STATISTIQUE DU TCHAD.* (Text in French) a, latest 1976. 3000 Fr.CFA. Ministere du Development Rural, Direction de la Promotion des Productions Agricole et de la Securite Alimentaire, Division de la Statistique Agricole, N'djamena, Chad. illus.; stat.

STATISTICS

316.6   TG
ANNUAIRE STATISTIQUE DU TOGO. 1966. a., latest 1987. 4000 Fr.CFA. Direction de la Statistique, Boite Postale 118, Lome, Togo. illus.; stat. **Document type:** government publication.

ANNUAL BULLETIN OF COAL STATISTICS FOR EUROPE AND NORTH AMERICA. see *MINES AND MINING INDUSTRY — Abstracting, Bibliographies, Statistics*

ANNUAL BULLETIN OF ELECTRIC ENERGY STATISTICS FOR EUROPE. see *ENERGY — Abstracting, Bibliographies, Statistics*

ANNUAL BULLETIN OF GAS STATISTICS FOR EUROPE/BULLETIN ANNUEL DE STATISTIQUES DE GAZ POUR L'EUROPE. see *PETROLEUM AND GAS — Abstracting, Bibliographies, Statistics*

ANNUAL BULLETIN OF GENERAL ENERGY STATISTICS FOR EUROPE. see *ENERGY — Abstracting, Bibliographies, Statistics*

ANNUAL BULLETIN OF HOUSING AND BUILDING STATISTICS FOR EUROPE. see *BUILDING AND CONSTRUCTION — Abstracting, Bibliographies, Statistics*

ANNUAL BULLETIN OF STEEL STATISTICS FOR EUROPE. see *METALLURGY — Abstracting, Bibliographies, Statistics*

ANNUAL BULLETIN OF TRADE IN CHEMICAL PRODUCTS. see *BUSINESS AND ECONOMICS — Production Of Goods And Services*

ANNUAL BULLETIN OF TRANSPORT STATISTICS FOR EUROPE. see *TRANSPORTATION — Abstracting, Bibliographies, Statistics*

519.5 006 003   UA
ANNUAL CONFERENCE ON STATISTICS, COMPUTER SCIENCE AND OPERATIONS RESEARCH. PROCEEDINGS. (In 5 vols.) (Text and summaries in Arabic, English) a. $50. Cairo University, Institute of Statistical Studies and Research, Tharwat St., Orman, Cairo, Egypt. FAX 3482533. TELEX 94372. Ed. M.R. Mahmoud. (back issues avail.) **Document type:** proceedings.

310   UK   ISSN 1351-444X
ANNUAL REGISTRARS SERVICE. 1953. a. including cum.supplements. Extel Financial Ltd., Fitzroy House, 13-17 Epworth St., London EC2A 4DL, England. TEL 01-251-3333. FAX 01-608-3514. TELEX 884319.
     Formerly (until 1993): Register of Registrars (ISSN 0482-1319)

ANNUAL REPORT ON THE CONSUMER PRICE INDEX (YEAR). see *CONSUMER EDUCATION AND PROTECTION — Abstracting, Bibliographies, Statistics*

ANNUAL REPORT ON TOBACCO STATISTICS. see *TOBACCO — Abstracting, Bibliographies, Statistics*

ANNUARIO GEOECONOMICO MONDIALE; commercio e produzioni. see *BUSINESS AND ECONOMICS — Abstracting, Bibliographies, Statistics*

314   IT   ISSN 0066-4545
HA1367
ANNUARIO STATISTICO ITALIANO. a. L.55000 (effective 1993). Istituto Nazionale di Statistica, Via Cesare Balbo 16, 00100 Rome, Italy. FAX 06-46735198. circ. 4,700. **Document type:** government publication.

ANNUARIUM STATISTICUM ECCLESIAE/STATISTIQUE DE L'EGLISE/STATISTICAL YEARBOOK OF THE CHURCH. see *RELIGIONS AND THEOLOGY — Abstracting, Bibliographies, Statistics*

314.6   SP   ISSN 1130-166X
ANUARI ESTADISTIC DE CATALUNYA. (Text in Catalan) 1984. a. Institut d'Estadistica de Catalunya, Via Laietana 58, 08003 Barcelona, Spain. TEL 39-3-4120088. FAX 39-3-4123145. circ. 4,000.

ANUARIO DE ESTADISTICAS DEL MEDIO AMBIENTE. see *ENERGY — Abstracting, Bibliographies, Statistics*

317.2   MX
ANUARIO DE ESTADISTICAS ESTATALES. 1984. a. Mex.$2000($5.50) Instituto Nacional de Estadistica, Geografia e Informatica, Secretaria de Programacion y Presupuesto, Prol. Heroe de Nacozari, 2301, Puerta 11 Acceso, 20270 Aguascalientes, Ags., Mexico. TEL 91-49-18-19-48. FAX 91-491-80739. circ. 1,000. **Document type:** government publication.

ANUARIO DE ESTADISTICAS LABORALES. see *BUSINESS AND ECONOMICS — Abstracting, Bibliographies, Statistics*

ANUARIO DE JUSTICIA. see *LAW — Abstracting, Bibliographies, Statistics*

ANUARIO DE TRANSPORTE Y COMUNICACIONES. see *TRANSPORTATION — Abstracting, Bibliographies, Statistics*

318   UN   ISSN 1014-0697
ANUARIO ESTADISTICO DE AMERICA LATINA Y EL CARIBE/STATISTICAL YEARBOOK FOR LATIN AMERICA AND THE CARIBBEAN. (Text in English and Spanish) 1969. a. $65. Comision Economica para America Latina y el Caribe - Economic Commission for Latin America and the Caribbean, Casilla 179-D, Santiago, Chile. (Subscr. to: United Nations Publications, Sales Section, Rm. DC2-0853, New York, NY 10017 (212-754-8302); or Distribution and Sales Section, Palais des Nations, 1211 Geneva 10, Switzerland) charts. (also avail. in microfiche from CIS; back issues avail.) **Indexed:** IIS, P.A.I.S.
—BLDSC (8452.885000).
     Former titles (until 1985): Anuario Estadistico de America Latina; (until 1973): Boletin Estadistico de America Latina (ISSN 0251-9445)

317.2   MX
ANUARIO ESTADISTICO DE BAJA CALIFORNIA. a. Instituto Nacional de Estadistica, Geografia e Informatica, Secretaria de Programacion y Presupuesto, Prol. Heroe de Nacozari 2301 Sur, Puerta 11 Acceso, 20270 Aguascalientes Ags., Mexico. TEL 91-49-18-19-48. FAX 491-807-39. **Document type:** government publication.

317.2   MX
ANUARIO ESTADISTICO DE BAJA CALIFORNIA SUR. a. Instituto Nacional de Estadistica, Geografia e Informatica, Secretaria de Programacion y Presupuesto, Prol. Heroe de Nacozari 2301 Sur, Puerta 11 Acceso, 20270 Aguascalientes Ags., Mexico. TEL 49-18-19-48. FAX 491-807-39. circ. 600. **Document type:** government publication.

317.2   MX
ANUARIO ESTADISTICO DE CAMPECHE. a. Instituto Nacional de Estadistica, Geografia e Informatica, Secretaria de Programacion y Presupuesto, Prol. Heroe de Nacozari 2301 Sur, Puerta 11 Acceso, 20270 Aguascalientes Ags., Mexico. TEL 49-18-19-48. FAX 491-807-39. **Document type:** government publication.

317   CU   ISSN 0574-6132
ANUARIO ESTADISTICO DE CUBA. English edition: Statistical Yearbook Compendium of the Republic of Cuba. 1952. a. $15 in N. America; S. America $17; Europe $18; others $20. Comite Estatal de Estadisticas, Centro de Informacion Cientifico-Tecnica, Almendares No. 156, esq. a Desague, Gaveta Postal 6016, Havana, Cuba. (Dist. by: Ediciones Cubanas, Obispo No. 527, Apdo. 605, Havana, Cuba) circ. 1,000. **Document type:** government publication.

317.2   MX
ANUARIO ESTADISTICO DE DURANGO. a. Instituto Nacional de Estadistica, Geografia e Informatica, Secretaria de Programacion y Presupuesto, Prol. Heroe de Nacozari 2301 Sur, Puerta 11, Acceso, 20270 Aguascalientes Ags., Mexico. TEL 49-18-19-48. FAX 491-807-39. **Document type:** government publication.

317.2   MX
ANUARIO ESTADISTICO DE GUANAJUATO. a. Instituto Nacional de Estadistica, Geografia e Informatica, Secretaria de Programacion y Presupuesto, Prol. Heroe de Nacozari 2301 Sur, Puerta 11, Acceso, 20290 Aguascalientes Ags., Mexico. TEL 49-18-19-48. FAX 491-807-39. **Document type:** government publication.

317.2   MX   ISSN 0185-7126
ANUARIO ESTADISTICO DE LOS ESTADOS UNIDOS MEXICANOS. 1894. a. Mex.$29500($10) Instituto Nacional de Estadistica, Geografia e Informatica, Secretaria de Programacion y Presupuesto, Prol. Heroe de Nacozari 2301 Sur, Puerta 11, Acceso, 20270 Aguascalientes Ags., Mexico. TEL 49-18-19-48. FAX 491-807-39. circ. 5,000. **Document type:** government publication.
     Formerly (until 1938): Anuario Estadistico de la Republica Mexicana (ISSN 0187-8581)

317.2   MX
ANUARIO ESTADISTICO DE NAYARIT. a. Instituto Nacional de Estadistica, Geografia e Informatica, Secretaria de Programacion y Presupuesto, Prol. Heroe de Nacozari 2301 Sur, Puerta 11, Acceso, 20270 Aguascalientes Ags., Mexico. TEL 49-18-19-48. FAX 491-807-39. **Document type:** government publication.

317.2   MX
ANUARIO ESTADISTICO DE SONORA. a. Instituto Nacional de Estadistica, Geografia e Informatica, Secretaria de Programacion y Presupuesto, Prol. Heroe de Nacozari 2301 Sur, Puerta 11, Acceso, 20270 Aguascalientes Ags., Mexico. TEL 49-18-19-48. FAX 491-807-39. circ. 1,000. **Document type:** government publication.

317.2   MX
ANUARIO ESTADISTICO DE TLAXCALA. a. Instituto Nacional de Estadistica, Geografia e Informatica, Secretaria de Programacion y Presupuesto, Prol. Heroe de Nacozari 2301 Sur, Puerta 11, Acceso, 20270 Aguascalientes Ags., Mexico. TEL 49-18-19-48. FAX 491-807-39. **Document type:** government publication.

317.2   MX
ANUARIO ESTADISTICO DE ZACATECAS. a. Instituto Nacional de Estadistica, Geografia e Informatica, Secretaria de Programacion y Presupuesto, Prol. Heroe de Nacozari 2301 Sur, Puerta 11, Acceso, 20270 Aguascalientes Ags., Mexico. TEL 49-18-19-48. FAX 491-807-39. **Document type:** government publication.

314.6   SP   ISSN 1133-4258
ANUARIO ESTADISTICO DEL AREA METROPOLITANA DE VALENCIA. 1990. a. Camara Oficial de Comercio Industria y Navegacion de Valencia, Poeta Querol 15, 46002 Valencia, Spain. TEL 34-6-3511301. FAX 34-6-3516349.

317.2   MX
ANUARIO ESTADISTICO DEL DISTRITO FEDERAL. a. Instituto Nacional de Estadistica, Geografia e Informatica, Secretaria de Programacion y Presupuesto, Prol. Heroe de Nacozari 2301 Sur, Puerta 11, Acceso, 20270 Aguascalientes Ags., Mexico. TEL 49-18-19-48. FAX 491-807-39. **Document type:** government publication.

317.2   MX
ANUARIO ESTADISTICO DEL ESTADO DE AGUASCALIENTES. a. Instituto Nacional de Estadistica, Geografia e Informatica, Secretaria de Programacion y Presupuesto, Prol. Heroe de Nacozari 2301 Sur, Puerta 11, Acceso, 20270 Aguascalientes Ags., Mexico. TEL 49-18-19-48. FAX 491-807-39. **Document type:** government publication.

317.2   MX
ANUARIO ESTADISTICO DEL ESTADO DE CHIAPAS. a. $22. Instituto Nacional de Estadistica, Geografia e Informatica, Secretaria de Programacion y Presupuesto, Prol. Hereo de Nacozari, 2301, Puerta 11, Acceso, 20270 Aguascalientes, Ags., Mexico. TEL 91-49-18-19-48. FAX 91-491-80739. **Document type:** government publication.

317.2   MX
ANUARIO ESTADISTICO DEL ESTADO DE CHIHUAHUA. (In 2 vols.) a. $28.50. Instituto Nacional de Estadistica, Geografia e Informatica, Secretaria de Programacion y Presupuesto, Prol. Heroe de Nacozari, 2301, Puerta 11, Acceso, 20270 Aguascalientes Ags., Mexico. TEL 91-49-18-19-48. FAX 91-491-80739. **Document type:** government publication.

STATISTICS

317.2   MX
ANUARIO ESTADISTICO DEL ESTADO DE COAHUILA. a. Instituto Nacional de Estadistica, Geografia e Informatica, Secretaria de Programacion y Presupuesto, Prol. Heroe de Nacozari 2301 Sur, Puerta 11, Acceso, 20270 Aguascalientes, Ags., Mexico. TEL 49-18-19-48. FAX 491-807-39. **Document type:** government publication.

317.2   MX
ANUARIO ESTADISTICO DEL ESTADO DE COLIMA. a. Instituto Nacional de Estadistica, Geografia e Informatica, Secretaria de Programacion y Presupuesto, Prol. Heroe de Nacozari 2302 Sur, Puerta 11, Acceso, 20270 Aguascalientes Ags., Mexico. TEL 49-18-19-48. FAX 491-807-39. **Document type:** government publication.

317.2   MX
ANUARIO ESTADISTICO DEL ESTADO DE GUERRERO. a. Instituto Nacional de Estadistica, Geografia e Informatica, Secretaria de Programacion y Presupuesto, Prol. Heroe de Nacozari 2301 Sur, Puerta 11, Acceso, 20270 Aguascalientes Ags., Mexico. TEL 49-18-19-48. FAX 491-807-39. circ. 750. **Document type:** government publication.

317.2   MX
ANUARIO ESTADISTICO DEL ESTADO DE HIDALGO. a. Instituto Nacional de Estadistica, Geografia e Informatica, Secretaria de Programacion y Presupuesto, Prol. Heroe de Nacozari 2302 Sur, Puerta 11, Acceso, 20270 Aguascalientes Ags., Mexico. TEL 49-18-19-48. FAX 491-807-39. **Document type:** government publication.

317.2   MX
ANUARIO ESTADISTICO DEL ESTADO DE JALISCO. a. Instituto Nacional de Estadistica, Geografia e Informatica, Secretaria de Programacion y Presupuesto, Prol. Heroe de Nacozari 2301 Sur, Puerta 11, Acceso, 20270 Aguascalientes, Ags., Mexico. TEL 49-18-19-48. FAX 491-807-39. **Document type:** government publication.

317.2   MX
ANUARIO ESTADISTICO DEL ESTADO DE MEXICO. a. Instituto Nacional de Estadistica, Geografia e Informatica, Secretaria de Programacion y Presupuesto, Prol. Heroe de Nacozari 2301 Sur, Puerta 11, Acceso, 20270 Aguascalientes Ags., Mexico. TEL 49-18-19-48. FAX 491-807-39. **Document type:** government publication.

317.2   MX
ANUARIO ESTADISTICO DEL ESTADO DE MORELOS. a. Instituto Nacional de Estadistica, Geografia e Informatica, Secretaria de Programacion y Presupuesto, Prol. Heroe de Nacozari 2301 Sur, Puerta 11, Acceso, 20270 Aguascalientes Ags, Mexico. TEL 49-18-19-48. FAX 491-807-39. **Document type:** government publication.

317.2   MX
ANUARIO ESTADISTICO DEL ESTADO DE NUEVO LEON. a. Instituto Nacional de Estadistica, Geografia e Informatica, Secretaria de Programacion y Presupuesto, Prol. Heroe de Nacozari 2301 Sur, Puerta 11, Acceso, 20270 Aguascalientes Ags., Mexico. TEL 49-18-19-48. FAX 491-308-39. **Document type:** government publication.

317.2   MX
ANUARIO ESTADISTICO DEL ESTADO DE OAXACA. a. Mex.$35000($12) Instituto Nacional de Estadistica, Geografia e Informatica, Secretaria de Programacion y Presupuesto, Prol. Heroe de Nacozari 2301 Sur, Puerta 11, Acceso, 20270 Aguascalientes Ags., Mexico. TEL 91-49-18-19-48. FAX 91-491-80739. **Document type:** government publication.

317.2   MX
ANUARIO ESTADISTICO DEL ESTADO DE PUEBLA. a. Mex.$22($43) Instituto Nacional de Estadistica, Geografia e Informatica, Secretaria de Programacion y Presupuesto, Prol. Heroe de Nacozari 2301 Sur, Puerta 11, Acceso, 20270 Aguascalientes Ags., Mexico. TEL 91-49-18-19-48. FAX 91-491-80739. circ. 1,000. **Document type:** government publication.

317.2   MX
ANUARIO ESTADISTICO DEL ESTADO DE QUERETARO. a. Instituto Nacional de Estadistica, Geografia e Informatica, Secretaria de Programacion y Presupuesto, Prol. Heroe de Nacozari 2301 Sur, Puerta 11, Acceso, 20270 Aguascalientes Ags., Mexico. TEL 49-18-19-48. FAX 491-807-39. **Document type:** government publication.

317.2   MX
ANUARIO ESTADISTICO DEL ESTADO DE QUINTANA ROO. a. Instituto Nacional de Estadistica, Geografia e Informatica, Secretaria de Programacion y Presupuesto, Prol. Heroe de Nacozari 2301 Sur, Puerta 11, Acceso, 20270 Aguascalientes Ags., Mexico. TEL 49-18-19-48. FAX 491-807-39. **Document type:** government publication.

317.2   MX
ANUARIO ESTADISTICO DEL ESTADO DE SAN LUIS POTOSI. a. Instituto Nacional de Estadistica, Geografia e Informatica, Secretaria de Programacion y Presupuesto, Prol. Heroe de Nacozari 2301 Sur, Puerta 11, Acceso, 20270 Aguascalientes Ags., Mexico. TEL 49-18-19-48. FAX 491-807-39. **Document type:** government publication.

317.2   MX
ANUARIO ESTADISTICO DEL ESTADO DE SINALOA. a. Instituto Nacional de Estadistica, Geografia e Informatica, Secretaria de Programacion y Presupuesto, Prol. Heroe de Nacozari 2301 Sur, Puerta 11, Acceso, 20270 Aguascalientes Ags., Mexico. TEL 49-18-19-48. FAX 491-807-39. **Document type:** government publication.

317.2   MX
ANUARIO ESTADISTICO DEL ESTADO DE TABASCO. a. Instituto Nacional de Estadistica, Geografia e Informatica, Secretaria de Programacion y Presupuesto, Prol. Heroe de Nacozari 2301 Sur, Puerta 11, Acceso, 20270 Aguascalientes Ags., Mexico. TEL 49-18-19-48. FAX 491-807-39. **Document type:** government publication.

317.2   MX
ANUARIO ESTADISTICO DEL ESTADO DE TAMAULIPAS. a. Instituto Nacional de Estadistica, Geografia e Informatica, Secretaria de Programacion y Presupuesto, Prol. Heroe de Nacozari 2301 Sur, Puerta 11, Acceso, 20270 Aguascalientes Ags., Mexico. TEL 49-18-19-48. FAX 491-807-39. circ. 750. **Document type:** government publication.

317.2   MX   ISSN 0187-4764
ANUARIO ESTADISTICO DEL ESTADO DE VERACRUZ. a. Instituto Nacional de Estadistica, Geografia e Informatica, Secretaria de Programacion y Presupuesto, Prol. Heroe de Nacozari 2302 Sur, Puerta 11, Acceso, 20270 Aguascalientes Ags., Mexico. TEL 49-18-19-48. FAX 491-807-39. **Document type:** government publication.

317.2   MX
ANUARIO ESTADISTICO DEL ESTADO DE YUCATAN. a. Instituto Nacional de Estadistica, Geografia e Informatica, Secretaria de Programacion y Presupuesto, Prol. Heroe de Nacozari 2301 Sur, Puerta 11, Acceso, 20270 Aguascalientes Ags., Mexico. TEL 49-18-19-48. FAX 491-807-39. **Document type:** government publication.

318   PY   ISSN 0252-8932
ANUARIO ESTADISTICO DEL PARAGUAY. 1886. a. exchange basis. Direccion General de Estadistica y Censos, Humaita 463, Asuncion, Paraguay. (Subscr. to: Casilla de Correo 1118, Asuncion, Paraguay) Ed. Jose Diaz de Bedoya. circ. 1,500. **Document type:** government publication.

318   BL   ISSN 0100-1299
HA971
ANUARIO ESTATISTICO DO BRASIL/STATISTICAL YEARBOOK OF BRAZIL. 1916. a. $150. Fundacao Instituto Brasileiro de Geografia e Estatistica, Centro de Documentacao e Disseminacao de Informacoes, Rua General Canabarro 666, 2o andar, Maracana 20271-201 Rio de Janeiro, Brazil. TEL 55-21-2645424. FAX 55-21-2289575. bk.rev.; charts. circ. 10,000. **Document type:** government publication.

318   BL   ISSN 0100-8730
HA988.S2
ANUARIO ESTATISTICO DO ESTADO DE SAO PAULO. 1979. a. $69.10. Fundacao Sistema Estadual de Analise de Dados, Av. Casper Libero, 464, 01033 Sao Paulo, Brazil. charts. circ. 1,000. **Document type:** government publication.
    Description: Characterizes the social, economic, demographic and physical aspects of the state.

318.11   BL   ISSN 0103-5274
ANUARIO ESTATISTICO DO ESTADO DO PARA. 1977. a. $1. Instituto do Desenvolvimento Economico-Social do Para, Coordenadoria de Estatistica Estadual, Av. Nazare 871, 66040 Belem, Para, Brazil. TEL 55-91-2244411. FAX 55-91-2253414. bibl.; charts; stat.
    Description: Discusses socio-economic issues of the state.

318   BL   ISSN 0100-381X
HC188.R4
ANUARIO ESTATISTICO DO RIO GRANDE DO SUL. 1972. a. Cr.$30 (effective 1995). Fundacao de Economia e Estatistica, Rua Duque de Caxias, No. 1691, CEP 90010-283 Porto Alegre RS, Brazil. TEL 55-512-259455. FAX 55-512-25006. TELEX 0515042. (also avail. in diskette format) **Document type:** government publication.
    Formerly (until 1967): Anuario da Producao Agropecuaria.
    Description: Covers information and statistics on the municipal level. Looks at physical, demographic, and socio-economic aspects of the state of Brazil.

ANUARIO FINANCIERO (YEAR). see *BUSINESS AND ECONOMICS — Abstracting, Bibliographies, Statistics*

314   RM   ISSN 1220-3246
ANUARUL STATISTIC AL ROMANIEI/STATISTICAL YEARBOOK OF ROMANIA. (Text in English, Rumanian) 1902. a. $75 (effective 1995 & 1996). Comisia Nationala pentru Statistica - National Commission for Statistics, Bd. Libertatii 16, Sector 5, 70542 Bucharest, Rumania. TEL 40-1-6143371. FAX 40-1-3124873. **Document type:** government publication.
    Description: Presents statistical data in many areas. Includes comments, explanations and graphs.

310   GW   ISSN 0066-5673
ARBEITEN ZUR ANGEWANDTEN STATISTIK. 1967. irreg., vol.36, 1992. Physica-Verlag GmbH und Co., Postfach 105280, 69042 Heidelberg, Germany. TEL 06221-487492. FAX 06221-413982. (Subscr. to: Springer-Verlag GmbH, Postfach 311340, 10643 Berlin, Germany. TEL 030-8214092) Ed.Bd. **Indexed:** Math.R. **Document type:** monographic series.
    Formerly: Berlin. Freie Universitaet. Institut fuer Statistik und Versicherungsmathematik. Berichte (ISSN 0067-5865)

314   GW   ISSN 0072-162X
DAS ARBEITSGEBIET DER BUNDESSTATISTIK. (Issued in two parts) (Editions in English, German) a. DM.19.80 for German ed.; English ed. DM.17.80. Statistisches Bundesamt, 65180 Wiesbaden, Germany. TEL 0611-75-1. FAX 0611-724000. TELEX 61186-STBA-D. **Document type:** government publication.

314.95   FA   ISSN 0906-3323
ARBOK FYRI FOEROYAR; statistical yearbook for the Faroe Islands. 1976. a. DKK 75($13) Hagstova Foeroya, P.O. Box 355, FR-110 Torshavn, Faroe Islands. TEL 298-14636. FAX 298-18696. Ed. Hans Pauli Stroem. circ. 800.
    Formerly (until 1990): Arsfragreiding fyri Foeroyar (ISSN 0105-6794)
    Description: Publishes the official statistics for the Faroe Islands.

318   AG
ARGENTINA. CENTRAL DE ESTADISTICAS NACIONALES. INFORME. 1976. irreg. $240. Central de Estadisticas Nacionales, Av. De Mayo 953, 1084 Buenos Aires, Argentina. Ed. Carlos A. Canta Yoy. circ. 10,500. **Document type:** newsletter.

ARGENTINA. INSTITUTO NACIONAL DE ESTADISTICA Y CENSOS. ANUARIO ESTADISTICO. see *POPULATION STUDIES — Abstracting, Bibliographies, Statistics*

STATISTICS

310   AG   ISSN 0326-6230
ARGENTINA. INSTITUTO NACIONAL DE ESTADISTICA Y CENSOS. DOCUMENTO DE TRABAJO. irreg., no.21, 1994. price varies. Instituto Nacional de Estadistica y Censos, Avda. Julio A. Roca 609 P.B., 1067 Buenos Aires, Argentina. TEL 54-1-3499662. FAX 54-1-3499621. **Document type:** government publication, monographic series.

318   AG   ISSN 0326-6214
HB235.A7
ARGENTINA. INSTITUTO NACIONAL DE ESTADISTICA Y CENSOS. ESTADISTICA MENSUAL. m. Arg.$50($97) (effective 1994). Instituto Nacional de Estadistica y Censos, Avda. Julio A. Roca 609 P.B., 1067 Buenos Aires, Argentina. TEL 54-1-3499662. FAX 54-1-3499621. **Document type:** government publication.
   Former titles (until 1984): Argentina. Instituto Nacional de Estadistica y Censos. Boletin de Estadistica y Censos (ISSN 0325-1950); Argentina. Direccion Nacional de Estadistica y Censos. Boletin Mensual de Estadistica (ISSN 0518-4673)

ARIZONA STATISTICAL ABSTRACT. see *BUSINESS AND ECONOMICS — Abstracting, Bibliographies, Statistics*

ARKANSAS. EMPLOYMENT SECURITY DEPARTMENT. STATISTICAL REVIEW. see *BUSINESS AND ECONOMICS — Abstracting, Bibliographies, Statistics*

ARKANSAS VITAL STATISTICS. see *POPULATION STUDIES — Abstracting, Bibliographies, Statistics*

315   UN   ISSN 1014-3750
ASIA - PACIFIC IN FIGURES. 1987. a. United Nations Economic and Social Commission for Asia and the Pacific (ESCAP), United Nations Bldg., Rajadamnern Ave., Bangkok 10200, Thailand.

ASPHALT ROOFING. see *BUILDING AND CONSTRUCTION — Abstracting, Bibliographies, Statistics*

AUDIT BUREAU OF CIRCULATIONS. ANNUAL REPORT. see *ADVERTISING AND PUBLIC RELATIONS — Abstracting, Bibliographies, Statistics*

AUDIT BUREAU OF CIRCULATIONS. SUPPLEMENTAL DATA REPORTS. see *ADVERTISING AND PUBLIC RELATIONS — Abstracting, Bibliographies, Statistics*

314   GW   ISSN 0004-7953
AUGSBURG IN ZAHLEN. 1946. q. DM.16. Amt fuer Stadtentwicklung und Statistik, Schmiedberg 6, 86152 Augsburg, Germany. TEL 0821-3246850. FAX 0821-3246877. Ed. Kurt Forner. stat. circ. 500. (also avail. in microform) **Document type:** government publication.

310   GW
AUSLANDSSTATISTIK. VIERTELJAHRESHEFTE. q. DM.89.20. Statistisches Bundesamt, 65180 Wiesbaden, Germany. TEL 0611-75-1. FAX 0611-724000. TELEX 61186-STBA-D. **Document type:** government publication.
   Formerly: Internationale Monatszahlen.

AUSTRALIA. AIR TRANSPORT STATISTICS. AIRPORT TRAFFIC DATA. see *TRANSPORTATION — Abstracting, Bibliographies, Statistics*

AUSTRALIA. AIR TRANSPORT STATISTICS. COMMUTER AIRLINES. see *TRANSPORTATION — Abstracting, Bibliographies, Statistics*

AUSTRALIA. AIR TRANSPORT STATISTICS. DOMESTIC AIRLINES (ANNUAL). see *TRANSPORTATION — Abstracting, Bibliographies, Statistics*

AUSTRALIA. AIR TRANSPORT STATISTICS. DOMESTIC AIRLINES (QUARTERLY). see *TRANSPORTATION — Abstracting, Bibliographies, Statistics*

AUSTRALIA. AIR TRANSPORT STATISTICS. INTERNATIONAL SCHEDULED AIR TRANSPORT. see *TRANSPORTATION — Abstracting, Bibliographies, Statistics*

AUSTRALIA. AIR TRANSPORT STATISTICS. MONTHLY PROVISIONAL STATISTICS OF INTERNATIONAL SCHEDULED AIR TRANSPORT. see *TRANSPORTATION — Abstracting, Bibliographies, Statistics*

AUSTRALIA. AIR TRANSPORT STATISTICS. SURVEY OF HOURS FLOWN. see *TRANSPORTATION — Abstracting, Bibliographies, Statistics*

AUSTRALIA. BUREAU OF STATISTICS. A GUIDE TO THE AUSTRALIAN NATIONAL ACCOUNTS. see *BUSINESS AND ECONOMICS — Abstracting, Bibliographies, Statistics*

AUSTRALIA. BUREAU OF STATISTICS. AGRICULTURAL INDUSTRIES, FINANCIAL STATISTICS, AUSTRALIA. see *AGRICULTURE — Abstracting, Bibliographies, Statistics*

AUSTRALIA. BUREAU OF STATISTICS. AGRICULTURAL INDUSTRIES, FINANCIAL STATISTICS, AUSTRALIA, PRELIMINARY ESTIMATES. see *AGRICULTURE — Abstracting, Bibliographies, Statistics*

AUSTRALIA. BUREAU OF STATISTICS. AGRICULTURE, AUSTRALIA. see *AGRICULTURE — Abstracting, Bibliographies, Statistics*

AUSTRALIA. BUREAU OF STATISTICS. AGSTATS MANUAL. see *AGRICULTURE — Abstracting, Bibliographies, Statistics*

AUSTRALIA. BUREAU OF STATISTICS. ANNUAL STATISTICS ON FINANCIAL INSTITUTIONS. see *BUSINESS AND ECONOMICS — Abstracting, Bibliographies, Statistics*

AUSTRALIA. BUREAU OF STATISTICS. APPARENT CONSUMPTION OF SELECTED FOODSTUFFS, AUSTRALIA, PRELIMINARY. see *PUBLIC ADMINISTRATION — Abstracting, Bibliographies, Statistics*

AUSTRALIA. BUREAU OF STATISTICS. ASSETS OF SUPERANNUATION FUNDS AND APPROVED DEPOSIT FUNDS. see *BUSINESS AND ECONOMICS — Abstracting, Bibliographies, Statistics*

AUSTRALIA. BUREAU OF STATISTICS. ATTENDANCE AT SELECTED CULTURAL VENUES, AUSTRALIA. see *SOCIAL SCIENCES: COMPREHENSIVE WORKS — Abstracting, Bibliographies, Statistics*

319.4   AT   ISSN 1031-0541
AUSTRALIA. BUREAU OF STATISTICS. AUSTRALIA AT A GLANCE. 1971. a. Aus.$1 (foreign Aus.$1.90). Australian Bureau of Statistics, P.O. Box 10, Belconnen, A.C.T. 2616, Australia. circ. 2,409. **Document type:** government publication.
   Description: Contains information about demography and manpower, finance, production and retail sales, price indexes, national accounts, overseas transactions, transport and building.

AUSTRALIA. BUREAU OF STATISTICS. AUSTRALIAN BUSINESS EXPECTATIONS. see *BUSINESS AND ECONOMICS — Abstracting, Bibliographies, Statistics*

319.4   AT   ISSN 0815-3523
AUSTRALIA. BUREAU OF STATISTICS. AUSTRALIAN CAPITAL TERRITORY AT A GLANCE. 1984. a. Aus.$1 (foreign Aus.$1.90). Australian Bureau of Statistics, P.O. Box 10, Belconnen, A.C.T. 2616, Australia. **Document type:** government publication.
   Description: Contains information about population, vital statistics, education, health, welfare, crime and justice, income, labor force, prices, retail, trade, building, agriculture, tourist, finance, manufacturing, transport and climate.

AUSTRALIA. BUREAU OF STATISTICS. AUSTRALIAN CAPITAL TERRITORY BUSINESS INDICATORS. see *BUSINESS AND ECONOMICS — Abstracting, Bibliographies, Statistics*

AUSTRALIA. BUREAU OF STATISTICS. AUSTRALIAN CAPITAL TERRITORY COURTS. see *LAW — Abstracting, Bibliographies, Statistics*

319   AT   ISSN 1039-6594
HA3008.A9
AUSTRALIA. BUREAU OF STATISTICS. AUSTRALIAN CAPITAL TERRITORY IN FOCUS. 1963. a. Aus.$28. Australian Bureau of Statistics, P.O. Box 10, Belconnen, A.C.T. 2616, Australia. circ. 194. **Document type:** government publication.
   Formerly: Australian Capital Territory Statistical Summary (ISSN 0067-1754)
   Description: Contains statistical information for A.C.T., including climate, demography, social matters, education, employment, earnings, prices, household expenditure, agriculture, manufacturing, retail trade, construction, transport, finance and tourism.

AUSTRALIA. BUREAU OF STATISTICS. AUSTRALIAN CONSUMER PRICE INDEX: CONCEPTS, SOURCES AND METHODS. see *BUSINESS AND ECONOMICS — Abstracting, Bibliographies, Statistics*

AUSTRALIA. BUREAU OF STATISTICS. AUSTRALIAN ECONOMIC INDICATORS. see *BUSINESS AND ECONOMICS — Abstracting, Bibliographies, Statistics*

AUSTRALIA. BUREAU OF STATISTICS. AUSTRALIAN HOUSING IN BRIEF. see *HOUSING AND URBAN PLANNING — Abstracting, Bibliographies, Statistics*

AUSTRALIA. BUREAU OF STATISTICS. AUSTRALIAN LABOUR MARKET. see *BUSINESS AND ECONOMICS — Abstracting, Bibliographies, Statistics*

AUSTRALIA. BUREAU OF STATISTICS. AUSTRALIAN NATIONAL ACCOUNTS: CAPITAL STOCK. see *BUSINESS AND ECONOMICS — Abstracting, Bibliographies, Statistics*

AUSTRALIA. BUREAU OF STATISTICS. AUSTRALIAN NATIONAL ACCOUNTS: FINANCIAL ACCOUNTS. see *BUSINESS AND ECONOMICS — Abstracting, Bibliographies, Statistics*

AUSTRALIA. BUREAU OF STATISTICS. AUSTRALIAN NATIONAL ACCOUNTS: MULTIFACTOR PRODUCTIVITY. see *BUSINESS AND ECONOMICS — Abstracting, Bibliographies, Statistics*

AUSTRALIA. BUREAU OF STATISTICS. AUSTRALIAN NATIONAL ACCOUNTS: STATE ACCOUNTS (ANNUAL). see *BUSINESS AND ECONOMICS — Abstracting, Bibliographies, Statistics*

AUSTRALIA. BUREAU OF STATISTICS. AUSTRALIAN NATIONAL ACCOUNTS: STATE ACCOUNTS (QUARTERLY). see *BUSINESS AND ECONOMICS — Abstracting, Bibliographies, Statistics*

AUSTRALIA. BUREAU OF STATISTICS. AUSTRALIAN SOCIAL TRENDS. see *SOCIAL SCIENCES: COMPREHENSIVE WORKS — Abstracting, Bibliographies, Statistics*

AUSTRALIA. BUREAU OF STATISTICS. AUSTRALIAN WINE AND GRAPE INDUSTRY. see *BEVERAGES — Abstracting, Bibliographies, Statistics*

AUSTRALIA. BUREAU OF STATISTICS. AUSTRALIAN WOMEN'S YEAR BOOK. see *WOMEN'S STUDIES — Abstracting, Bibliographies, Statistics*

AUSTRALIA. BUREAU OF STATISTICS. AUSTRALIANS AND THE ENVIRONMENT. see *ENVIRONMENTAL STUDIES — Abstracting, Bibliographies, Statistics*

AUSTRALIA. BUREAU OF STATISTICS. AVERAGE MONTHLY EXCHANGE RATES. see *BUSINESS AND ECONOMICS — Abstracting, Bibliographies, Statistics*

AUSTRALIA. BUREAU OF STATISTICS. AVERAGE RETAIL PRICES OF SELECTED ITEMS, EIGHT CAPITAL CITIES. see *BUSINESS AND ECONOMICS — Abstracting, Bibliographies, Statistics*

AUSTRALIA. BUREAU OF STATISTICS. AVERAGE WEEKLY EARNING, AUSTRALIA, PRELIMINARY. see *BUSINESS AND ECONOMICS — Abstracting, Bibliographies, Statistics*

AUSTRALIA. BUREAU OF STATISTICS. AVERAGE WEEKLY EARNINGS, STATE AND AUSTRALIA. see *BUSINESS AND ECONOMICS — Abstracting, Bibliographies, Statistics*

AUSTRALIA. BUREAU OF STATISTICS. BALANCE OF PAYMENTS, AUSTRALIA (ANNUAL). see *BUSINESS AND ECONOMICS — Abstracting, Bibliographies, Statistics*

AUSTRALIA. BUREAU OF STATISTICS. BALANCE OF PAYMENTS, AUSTRALIA (CANBERRA, 1976). see *BUSINESS AND ECONOMICS — Abstracting, Bibliographies, Statistics*

AUSTRALIA. BUREAU OF STATISTICS. BALANCE OF PAYMENTS, AUSTRALIA - CONCEPTS, SOURCES AND METHODS. see *BUSINESS AND ECONOMICS — Abstracting, Bibliographies, Statistics*

AUSTRALIA. BUREAU OF STATISTICS. BALANCE OF PAYMENTS, AUSTRALIA (QUARTERLY). see *BUSINESS AND ECONOMICS — Abstracting, Bibliographies, Statistics*

AUSTRALIA. BUREAU OF STATISTICS. BALANCE OF PAYMENTS, AUSTRALIA - SUMMARY OF CONCEPTS, SOURCES AND METHODS. see *BUSINESS AND ECONOMICS — Abstracting, Bibliographies, Statistics*

AUSTRALIA. BUREAU OF STATISTICS. BUILDING ACTIVITY, AUSTRALIA: DWELLING UNIT COMMENCEMENTS, PRELIMINARY. see *BUILDING AND CONSTRUCTION — Abstracting, Bibliographies, Statistics*

AUSTRALIA. BUREAU OF STATISTICS. BUILDING ACTIVITY, AUSTRALIAN CAPITAL TERRITORY. see *BUILDING AND CONSTRUCTION — Abstracting, Bibliographies, Statistics*

AUSTRALIA. BUREAU OF STATISTICS. BUILDING AND CONSTRUCTION ACTIVITY, AUSTRALIA. see *HOUSING AND URBAN PLANNING — Abstracting, Bibliographies, Statistics*

AUSTRALIA. BUREAU OF STATISTICS. BUILDING APPROVALS, AUSTRALIA. see *HOUSING AND URBAN PLANNING — Abstracting, Bibliographies, Statistics*

AUSTRALIA. BUREAU OF STATISTICS. BUSINESS OPERATIONS AND INDUSTRY PERFORMANCE, AUSTRALIA. see *BUSINESS AND ECONOMICS — Abstracting, Bibliographies, Statistics*

310 AT ISSN 1036-9570
AUSTRALIA. BUREAU OF STATISTICS. CANBERRA STATISTICAL AREA SUMMARY. 1991. a. Aus.$17.50. Australian Bureau of Statistics, P.O. Box 10, Belconnen, A.C.T. 2616, Australia. **Document type:** government publication.
 Description: Summarizes information relating to area, population, births, deaths, building activity, retail trade, manufacturing, tourism, traffic accidents and education.

350 319 AT ISSN 0813-1317
AUSTRALIA. BUREAU OF STATISTICS. CATALOGUE OF SMALL AREA STATISTICS. 1983. s-a. Aus.$17.50 (foreign Aus.$22.50)(effective 1991). Australian Bureau of Statistics, P.O. Box 10, Belconnen, A.C.T. 2616, Australia. TEL 062-527911. FAX 062-51009. **Document type:** government publication.
 Description: Contains a subject index, an area index and a list of ABS publications containing small-area data. Also includes data on those small areas not covered in the data released on magnetic tape and microfiche formats.

AUSTRALIA. BUREAU OF STATISTICS. CHILDREN'S HEALTH SCREENING. see *MEDICAL SCIENCES — Abstracting, Bibliographies, Statistics*

AUSTRALIA. BUREAU OF STATISTICS. CHILDREN'S IMMUNISATION. see *MEDICAL SCIENCES — Abstracting, Bibliographies, Statistics*

AUSTRALIA. BUREAU OF STATISTICS. COMPANY PROFITS, AUSTRALIA. see *BUSINESS AND ECONOMICS — Abstracting, Bibliographies, Statistics*

AUSTRALIA. BUREAU OF STATISTICS. CONSTANT PRICE ESTIMATES OF MANUFACTURING PRODUCTION, AUSTRALIA. see *BUSINESS AND ECONOMICS — Abstracting, Bibliographies, Statistics*

AUSTRALIA. BUREAU OF STATISTICS. CONSUMER PRICE INDEX. see *BUSINESS AND ECONOMICS — Abstracting, Bibliographies, Statistics*

AUSTRALIA. BUREAU OF STATISTICS. CONSUMER PRICE INDEX: EFFECT OF CHANGES IN PRICES OF IMPORTED ITEMS. see *BUSINESS AND ECONOMICS — Abstracting, Bibliographies, Statistics*

AUSTRALIA. BUREAU OF STATISTICS. COST OF ENVIRONMENT PROTECTION, AUSTRALIA: SELECTED INDUSTRIES. see *ENVIRONMENTAL STUDIES — Abstracting, Bibliographies, Statistics*

AUSTRALIA. BUREAU OF STATISTICS. DEMOGRAPHY, AUSTRALIAN CAPITAL TERRITORY. see *POPULATION STUDIES — Abstracting, Bibliographies, Statistics*

AUSTRALIA. BUREAU OF STATISTICS. DIRECTORY OF ENERGY RELATED STATISTICS. see *PUBLIC ADMINISTRATION — Abstracting, Bibliographies, Statistics*

AUSTRALIA. BUREAU OF STATISTICS. DIRECTORY OF HOUSING RELATED STATISTICS. see *HOUSING AND URBAN PLANNING — Abstracting, Bibliographies, Statistics*

AUSTRALIA. BUREAU OF STATISTICS. DIRECTORY OF INDUSTRIAL RELATIONS STATISTICS. see *BUSINESS AND ECONOMICS — Abstracting, Bibliographies, Statistics*

AUSTRALIA. BUREAU OF STATISTICS. DIRECTORY OF LABOUR MARKET AND SOCIAL SURVEY DATA. see *BUSINESS AND ECONOMICS — Abstracting, Bibliographies, Statistics*

AUSTRALIA. BUREAU OF STATISTICS. DIRECTORY OF TOURISM STATISTICS. see *TRAVEL AND TOURISM — Abstracting, Bibliographies, Statistics*

AUSTRALIA. BUREAU OF STATISTICS. DISTRIBUTION AND COMPOSITION OF EMPLOYEE EARNINGS AND HOURS, AUSTRALIA, PRELIMINARY. see *BUSINESS AND ECONOMICS — Abstracting, Bibliographies, Statistics*

AUSTRALIA. BUREAU OF STATISTICS. DISTRIBUTION AND COMPOSITION OF EMPLOYEE EARNINGS AND HOURS, STATES AND AUSTRALIA - DATA SERVICE. see *BUSINESS AND ECONOMICS — Abstracting, Bibliographies, Statistics*

AUSTRALIA. BUREAU OF STATISTICS. EMPLOYED WAGE AND SALARY EARNERS, AUSTRALIA. see *BUSINESS AND ECONOMICS — Abstracting, Bibliographies, Statistics*

AUSTRALIA. BUREAU OF STATISTICS. EMPLOYER TRAINING EXPENDITURE, AUSTRALIA. see *BUSINESS AND ECONOMICS — Abstracting, Bibliographies, Statistics*

AUSTRALIA. BUREAU OF STATISTICS. ENVIRONMENTAL ISSUES: PEOPLE'S VIEWS AND PRACTICES. see *ENVIRONMENTAL STUDIES — Abstracting, Bibliographies, Statistics*

AUSTRALIA. BUREAU OF STATISTICS. ESTIMATED RESIDENT POPULATION BY AGE AND SEX IN STATISTICAL LOCAL AREAS, AUSTRALIAN CAPITAL TERRITORY. see *POPULATION STUDIES — Abstracting, Bibliographies, Statistics*

AUSTRALIA. BUREAU OF STATISTICS. ESTIMATED RESIDENT POPULATION IN STATISTICAL LOCAL AREAS, AUSTRALIAN CAPITAL TERRITORY. see *POPULATION STUDIES — Abstracting, Bibliographies, Statistics*

AUSTRALIA. BUREAU OF STATISTICS. EXPORT PRICE INDEX, AUSTRALIA. see *BUSINESS AND ECONOMICS — Abstracting, Bibliographies, Statistics*

319 AT ISSN 1323-5966
▼**AUSTRALIA. BUREAU OF STATISTICS. HISTORICAL PUBLICATIONS ON C D - R O M.** 1994. a. Australian Bureau of Statistics, P.O. Box 10, Belconnen, A.C.T. 2616, Australia. **Document type:** government publication, abstracting/indexing.
 ●Available only on CD-ROM.
 Description: Contains images of every printed publication produced by ABS.

AUSTRALIA. BUREAU OF STATISTICS. HOUSE PRICE INDEXES: EIGHT CAPITAL CITIES. see *REAL ESTATE — Abstracting, Bibliographies, Statistics*

AUSTRALIA. BUREAU OF STATISTICS. HOUSING, AUSTRALIA: A STATISTICAL OVERVIEW. see *HOUSING AND URBAN PLANNING — Abstracting, Bibliographies, Statistics*

AUSTRALIA. BUREAU OF STATISTICS. HOUSING FINANCE FOR OWNER OCCUPATION, AUSTRALIA. see *BUSINESS AND ECONOMICS — Abstracting, Bibliographies, Statistics*

AUSTRALIA. BUREAU OF STATISTICS. IMPORT PRICE INDEX, AUSTRALIA. see *BUSINESS AND ECONOMICS — Abstracting, Bibliographies, Statistics*

AUSTRALIA. BUREAU OF STATISTICS. INCOME DISTRIBUTION, AUSTRALIA. see *BUSINESS AND ECONOMICS — Abstracting, Bibliographies, Statistics*

319 016 AT ISSN 1038-6300
AUSTRALIA. BUREAU OF STATISTICS. INDEX TO THE HISTORICAL MICROFICHE SERIES - STATISTICAL PUBLICATIONS SINCE FEDERATION. irreg. Aus.$90. Australian Bureau of Statistics, P.O. Box 10, Belconnen, A.C.T. 2616, Australia. **Document type:** government publication, abstracting/indexing.
 Formerly: Catalogue of Historical Microfiche Series - Statistical Publications.
 Description: Lists publications released by the Central Office of the ABS since 1901 and publications issued by the State Office since 1985.

AUSTRALIA. BUREAU OF STATISTICS. INDUSTRIAL DISPUTES, AUSTRALIA (MONTHLY). see *BUSINESS AND ECONOMICS — Abstracting, Bibliographies, Statistics*

AUSTRALIA. BUREAU OF STATISTICS. INFORMATION PAPER: MEASURING EMPLOYMENT AND UNEMPLOYMENT. see *BUSINESS AND ECONOMICS — Abstracting, Bibliographies, Statistics*

310 AT ISSN 0817-9344
AUSTRALIA. BUREAU OF STATISTICS. INFORMATION PAPER: NATIONAL HEALTH SURVEY, SAMPLE FILE ON MAGNETIC MEDIA. 1978. irreg., latest 1990. Australian Bureau of Statistics, P.O. Box 10, Belconnen, A.C.T. 2616, Australia. **Document type:** government publication.
 Description: Provides technical details of the sample file, information about the data content together with conditions of issue and how to order.

AUSTRALIA. BUREAU OF STATISTICS. INTERNATIONAL INVESTMENT POSITION, AUSTRALIA (ANNUAL). see *BUSINESS AND ECONOMICS — Abstracting, Bibliographies, Statistics*

AUSTRALIA. BUREAU OF STATISTICS. INTERNATIONAL INVESTMENT POSITION. AUSTRALIA: AUSTRALIAN SECURITIES HELD BY NOMINEES ON BEHALF OF NON-RESIDENTS. see *BUSINESS AND ECONOMICS — Abstracting, Bibliographies, Statistics*

AUSTRALIA. BUREAU OF STATISTICS. INTERNATIONAL INVESTMENT POSITION, AUSTRALIA: PURCHASES AND SALES OF PORTFOLIO CORPORATE EQUITIES BY NON-RESIDENTS. see *BUSINESS AND ECONOMICS — Abstracting, Bibliographies, Statistics*

AUSTRALIA. BUREAU OF STATISTICS. INTERNATIONAL INVESTMENT POSITION, AUSTRALIA (QUARTERLY). see *BUSINESS AND ECONOMICS — Abstracting, Bibliographies, Statistics*

AUSTRALIA. BUREAU OF STATISTICS. INTERNATIONAL INVESTMENT POSITION, AUSTRALIA: SUPPLEMENTARY COUNTRY STATISTICS. see *BUSINESS AND ECONOMICS — Abstracting, Bibliographies, Statistics*

AUSTRALIA. BUREAU OF STATISTICS. INTERNATIONAL MERCHANDISE TRADE, AUSTRALIA. see *BUSINESS AND ECONOMICS — Abstracting, Bibliographies, Statistics*

AUSTRALIA. BUREAU OF STATISTICS. JOB VACANCIES AND OVERTIME, AUSTRALIA. see *OCCUPATIONS AND CAREERS — Abstracting, Bibliographies, Statistics*

AUSTRALIA. BUREAU OF STATISTICS. LABOUR COSTS, AUSTRALIA. see *BUSINESS AND ECONOMICS — Abstracting, Bibliographies, Statistics*

STATISTICS

AUSTRALIA. BUREAU OF STATISTICS. LABOUR FORCE, AUSTRALIA. see *BUSINESS AND ECONOMICS — Abstracting, Bibliographies, Statistics*

AUSTRALIA. BUREAU OF STATISTICS. LABOUR FORCE, AUSTRALIA, PRELIMINARY. see *BUSINESS AND ECONOMICS — Abstracting, Bibliographies, Statistics*

AUSTRALIA. BUREAU OF STATISTICS. LABOUR STATISTICS IN BRIEF, AUSTRALIA. see *BUSINESS AND ECONOMICS — Abstracting, Bibliographies, Statistics*

AUSTRALIA. BUREAU OF STATISTICS. LIVESTOCK PRODUCTS, AUSTRALIA. see *AGRICULTURE — Abstracting, Bibliographies, Statistics*

AUSTRALIA. BUREAU OF STATISTICS. MANAGED FUNDS, AUSTRALIA. see *BUSINESS AND ECONOMICS — Abstracting, Bibliographies, Statistics*

AUSTRALIA. BUREAU OF STATISTICS. MANUFACTURING INDUSTRY, AUSTRALIA, PRELIMINARY. see *BUSINESS AND ECONOMICS — Abstracting, Bibliographies, Statistics*

AUSTRALIA. BUREAU OF STATISTICS. MANUFACTURING PRODUCTION, AUSTRALIA, PRELIMINARY. see *BUSINESS AND ECONOMICS — Abstracting, Bibliographies, Statistics*

AUSTRALIA. BUREAU OF STATISTICS. MANUFACTURING PRODUCTION, AUSTRALIA: PRINCIPAL COMMODITIES PRODUCED. see *BUSINESS AND ECONOMICS — Abstracting, Bibliographies, Statistics*

AUSTRALIA. BUREAU OF STATISTICS. MERCHANDISE IMPORTS, AUSTRALIA: BALANCE OF PAYMENTS BASIS. see *BUSINESS AND ECONOMICS — Abstracting, Bibliographies, Statistics*

AUSTRALIA. BUREAU OF STATISTICS. MIGRATION, AUSTRALIA. see *POPULATION STUDIES — Abstracting, Bibliographies, Statistics*

AUSTRALIA. BUREAU OF STATISTICS. MINING INDUSTRY, AUSTRALIA, PRELIMINARY. see *MINES AND MINING INDUSTRY — Abstracting, Bibliographies, Statistics*

AUSTRALIA. BUREAU OF STATISTICS. MINING TECHNOLOGY STATISTICS, AUSTRALIA. see *MINES AND MINING INDUSTRY — Abstracting, Bibliographies, Statistics*

AUSTRALIA. BUREAU OF STATISTICS. MONTHLY STATISTICS FOR CORPORATIONS REGISTERED UNDER THE FINANCIAL CORPORATIONS ACT. see *BUSINESS AND ECONOMICS — Abstracting, Bibliographies, Statistics*

310　　　　AT　　ISSN 0727-1689
AUSTRALIA. BUREAU OF STATISTICS. MONTHLY SUMMARY OF STATISTICS, AUSTRALIA. 1937. m. Aus.$22 per no. Australian Bureau of Statistics, P.O. Box 10, Belconnen, A.C.T. 2616, Australia. TEL 062-527911. FAX 062-516009. stat. circ. 935. **Document type:** government publication.
Formerly: Monthly Review of Business Statistics (ISSN 0027-0539)
Description: Includes statistical data on population and vital statistics, employment and unemployment, wages and price, production, building, national accounts, finance, internal trade, foreign trade, balance of payments and transport.

AUSTRALIA. BUREAU OF STATISTICS. MOTOR VEHICLE HIRE INDUSTRY, AUSTRALIA. see *TRANSPORTATION — Abstracting, Bibliographies, Statistics*

AUSTRALIA. BUREAU OF STATISTICS. N I F - 10S MODEL DATA BASE MANUAL. see *BUSINESS AND ECONOMICS — Abstracting, Bibliographies, Statistics*

AUSTRALIA. BUREAU OF STATISTICS. NATIONAL CRIME STATISTICS. see *LAW — Abstracting, Bibliographies, Statistics*

AUSTRALIA. BUREAU OF STATISTICS. NEW MOTOR VEHICLE REGISTRATIONS, AUSTRALIA, PRELIMINARY. see *TRANSPORTATION — Abstracting, Bibliographies, Statistics*

AUSTRALIA. BUREAU OF STATISTICS. NEW SOUTH WALES OFFICE. BUILDING APPROVALS, NEW SOUTH WALES. see *HOUSING AND URBAN PLANNING — Abstracting, Bibliographies, Statistics*

AUSTRALIA. BUREAU OF STATISTICS. NEW SOUTH WALES OFFICE. BUILDING ACTIVITY, NEW SOUTH WALES. see *BUILDING AND CONSTRUCTION — Abstracting, Bibliographies, Statistics*

AUSTRALIA. BUREAU OF STATISTICS. NEW SOUTH WALES OFFICE. CRIME AND SAFETY SURVEY, NEW SOUTH WALES. see *LAW — Abstracting, Bibliographies, Statistics*

AUSTRALIA. BUREAU OF STATISTICS. NEW SOUTH WALES OFFICE. DWELLING UNIT COMMENCEMENTS REPORTED BY APPROVING AUTHORITIES, NEW SOUTH WALES. see *HOUSING AND URBAN PLANNING — Abstracting, Bibliographies, Statistics*

AUSTRALIA. BUREAU OF STATISTICS. NEW SOUTH WALES OFFICE. ECONOMIC INDICATORS, NEW SOUTH WALES. see *BUSINESS AND ECONOMICS — Abstracting, Bibliographies, Statistics*

AUSTRALIA. BUREAU OF STATISTICS. NEW SOUTH WALES OFFICE. ESTIMATED RESIDENT POPULATION BY AGE AND SEX IN STATISTICAL LOCAL AREAS, NEW SOUTH WALES. see *POPULATION STUDIES — Abstracting, Bibliographies, Statistics*

AUSTRALIA. BUREAU OF STATISTICS. NEW SOUTH WALES OFFICE. ESTIMATED RESIDENT POPULATION OF STATISTICAL LOCAL AREAS, NEW SOUTH WALES, PRELIMINARY. see *POPULATION STUDIES — Abstracting, Bibliographies, Statistics*

319.4　　　AT　　ISSN 0725-5039
AUSTRALIA. BUREAU OF STATISTICS. NEW SOUTH WALES OFFICE. NEW SOUTH WALES IN BRIEF. 1977. a. Aus.$1. Australian Bureau of Statistics, New South Wales Office, St. Andrews House, Sydney Square, George St., Sydney, N.S.W. 2000, Australia. **Document type:** government publication.
Description: Provides information about N.S.W.: its population, health, education, law, labor, transport, agriculture, finance, trade, and tourism.

319　　　　AT　　ISSN 0810-9338
DU150
AUSTRALIA. BUREAU OF STATISTICS. NEW SOUTH WALES OFFICE. NEW SOUTH WALES YEAR BOOK. 1904. s-a. Aus.$31. Australian Bureau of Statistics, New South Wales Office, St. Andrews House, Sydney Square, George St., Sydney, N.S.W. 2000, Australia. **Document type:** government publication.
Formerly: Official Year Book of New South Wales (ISSN 0085-4441)
Description: Provides extensive information about the state: history, geography, government, demography, labor, transport, communications, construction, agriculture, mining and energy, manufacturing, commerce and finance.

AUSTRALIA. BUREAU OF STATISTICS. NEW SOUTH WALES OFFICE. PRINCIPAL AGRICULTURAL COMMODITIES, NEW SOUTH WALES, PRELIMINARY. see *AGRICULTURE — Abstracting, Bibliographies, Statistics*

310　　　　AT　　ISSN 0818-2272
AUSTRALIA. BUREAU OF STATISTICS. NEW SOUTH WALES OFFICE. REGIONAL STATISTICS, NEW SOUTH WALES. 1956. a. Aus.$20. Australian Bureau of Statistics, New South Wales Office, St. Andrews House, Sydney Square, George St., Sydney, N.S.W. 2000, Australia. **Document type:** government publication.
Formerly: Handbook of Local Statistics, New South Wales.
Description: Contains principal statistics on population, births, deaths, building, agriculture, manufacturing, tourist acommodation and government finances.

AUSTRALIA. BUREAU OF STATISTICS. NEW SOUTH WALES OFFICE. RETAILING IN NEW SOUTH WALES. see *BUSINESS AND ECONOMICS — Abstracting, Bibliographies, Statistics*

AUSTRALIA. BUREAU OF STATISTICS. NEW SOUTH WALES OFFICE. THE LABOUR FORCE, NEW SOUTH WALES AND AUSTRALIAN CAPITAL TERRITORY. see *BUSINESS AND ECONOMICS — Abstracting, Bibliographies, Statistics*

AUSTRALIA. BUREAU OF STATISTICS. NEW SOUTH WALES OFFICE. TOURIST ACCOMMODATION, NEW SOUTH WALES. see *HOTELS AND RESTAURANTS — Abstracting, Bibliographies, Statistics*

AUSTRALIA. BUREAU OF STATISTICS. NORTHERN TERRITORY OFFICE. AGRICULTURE AND FISHING, NORTHERN TERRITORY. see *AGRICULTURE — Abstracting, Bibliographies, Statistics*

AUSTRALIA. BUREAU OF STATISTICS. NORTHERN TERRITORY OFFICE. BUILDING ACTIVITY, NORTHERN TERRITORY. see *BUILDING AND CONSTRUCTION — Abstracting, Bibliographies, Statistics*

AUSTRALIA. BUREAU OF STATISTICS. NORTHERN TERRITORY OFFICE. BUILDING APPROVALS, NORTHERN TERRITORY. see *HOUSING AND URBAN PLANNING — Abstracting, Bibliographies, Statistics*

AUSTRALIA. BUREAU OF STATISTICS. NORTHERN TERRITORY OFFICE. DEMOGRAPHY, NORTHERN TERRITORY. see *POPULATION STUDIES — Abstracting, Bibliographies, Statistics*

AUSTRALIA. BUREAU OF STATISTICS. NORTHERN TERRITORY OFFICE. MANUFACTURING INDUSTRY, NORTHERN TERRITORY. see *BUSINESS AND ECONOMICS — Abstracting, Bibliographies, Statistics*

319.4　　　AT　　ISSN 0815-3809
AUSTRALIA. BUREAU OF STATISTICS. NORTHERN TERRITORY OFFICE. NORTHERN TERRITORY AT A GLANCE. 1983. a. Aus.$1. Australian Bureau of Statistics, Northern Territory Office, MLC Bldg., 6th Fl., 81 Smith St., Darwin, N.T. 0800, Australia. circ. 9,000. **Document type:** government publication.
Description: Contains a wide range of statistical information on the Northern Territory, including physical data, population, vitals, employment and wages, price indices, agriculture and fishing, mineral production, manufacturing, building, foreign trade and tourism.

AUSTRALIA. BUREAU OF STATISTICS. NORTHERN TERRITORY OFFICE. NORTHERN TERRITORY BUSINESS INDICATORS. see *BUSINESS AND ECONOMICS — Abstracting, Bibliographies, Statistics*

319　　　　AT　　ISSN 1037-1176
AUSTRALIA. BUREAU OF STATISTICS. NORTHERN TERRITORY OFFICE. NORTHERN TERRITORY IN FOCUS. 1960. a. Aus.$28. Australian Bureau of Statistics, Northern Territory Office, MLC Bldg., 6th Fl., 81 Smith St., Darwin, N.T. 0800, Australia. TEL 062-527911. FAX 516009.
Formerly: Northern Territory Statistical Summary (ISSN 0067-0855)
Description: Detailed information about the territory including chronological table of important events, list of representatives and officials; population and vital statistics, occupied dwellings, employment, wages, trade unions, industrial disputes and more.

AUSTRALIA. BUREAU OF STATISTICS. NORTHERN TERRITORY OFFICE. RESIDENT POPULATION ESTIMATES FOR STATISTICAL LOCAL AREAS, NORTHERN TERRITORY, PRELIMINARY. see *POPULATION STUDIES — Abstracting, Bibliographies, Statistics*

AUSTRALIA. BUREAU OF STATISTICS. OVERSEAS ARRIVALS AND DEPARTURES, AUSTRALIA (MONTHLY). see *POPULATION STUDIES — Abstracting, Bibliographies, Statistics*

319　　　　AT　　ISSN 0727-145X
AUSTRALIA. BUREAU OF STATISTICS. POCKET YEAR BOOK, AUSTRALIA. 1913. a. Aus.$10. Australian Bureau of Statistics, P.O. Box 10, Belconnen, A.C.T. 2616, Australia. TEL 062-527911. FAX 062-516009. circ. 1,141. **Document type:** government publication.
Formerly: Pocket Compendium of Australian Statistics (ISSN 0079-239X)
Description: Provides comprehensive basic statistics of Australia.

AUSTRALIA. BUREAU OF STATISTICS. POPULATION SURVEY MONITOR. see *POPULATION STUDIES — Abstracting, Bibliographies, Statistics*

AUSTRALIA. BUREAU OF STATISTICS. PRICE INDEX OF MATERIALS USED IN BUILDING OTHER THAN HOUSE BUILDING, SIX STATE CAPITAL CITIES AND CANBERRA. see *BUILDING AND CONSTRUCTION — Abstracting, Bibliographies, Statistics*

AUSTRALIA. BUREAU OF STATISTICS. PRICE INDEX OF MATERIALS USED IN HOUSE BUILDING, SIX STATE CAPITAL CITIES AND CANBERRA. see *BUILDING AND CONSTRUCTION — Abstracting, Bibliographies, Statistics*

AUSTRALIA. BUREAU OF STATISTICS. PRICE INDEXES OF ARTICLES PRODUCED BY MANUFACTURING INDUSTRY, AUSTRALIA. see *BUSINESS AND ECONOMICS — Abstracting, Bibliographies, Statistics*

AUSTRALIA. BUREAU OF STATISTICS. PRICE INDEXES OF COPPER MATERIALS, AUSTRALIA. see *METALLURGY — Abstracting, Bibliographies, Statistics*

AUSTRALIA. BUREAU OF STATISTICS. PRICE INDEXES OF MATERIALS USED IN COAL MINING, AUSTRALIA. see *MINES AND MINING INDUSTRY — Abstracting, Bibliographies, Statistics*

AUSTRALIA. BUREAU OF STATISTICS. PRICE INDEXES OF MATERIALS USED IN MANUFACTURING INDUSTRIES, AUSTRALIA. see *BUSINESS AND ECONOMICS — Abstracting, Bibliographies, Statistics*

AUSTRALIA. BUREAU OF STATISTICS. PRINCIPAL AGRICULTURAL COMMODITIES, AUSTRALIA, PRELIMINARY, AGRICULTURAL PRODUCTION AND FARMERS' INTENTIONS FOR (NEXT) SEASON. see *AGRICULTURE — Abstracting, Bibliographies, Statistics*

AUSTRALIA. BUREAU OF STATISTICS. PRIVATE HOSPITALS, AUSTRALIA. see *HOSPITALS — Abstracting, Bibliographies, Statistics*

AUSTRALIA. BUREAU OF STATISTICS. PRIVATE NEW CAPITAL EXPENDITURE AND EXPECTED EXPENDITURE, AUSTRALIA. see *BUSINESS AND ECONOMICS — Abstracting, Bibliographies, Statistics*

AUSTRALIA. BUREAU OF STATISTICS. PRODUCER AND FOREIGN TRADE PRICE INDEXES: CONCEPTS, SOURCES AND METHODS. see *BUSINESS AND ECONOMICS — Abstracting, Bibliographies, Statistics*

AUSTRALIA. BUREAU OF STATISTICS. PROFILES OF AUSTRALIAN BUSINESS. see *BUSINESS AND ECONOMICS — Abstracting, Bibliographies, Statistics*

AUSTRALIA. BUREAU OF STATISTICS. PUBLIC SECTOR FINANCIAL ASSETS AND LIABILITIES, AUSTRALIA. see *BUSINESS AND ECONOMICS — Abstracting, Bibliographies, Statistics*

319   AT   ISSN 1032-0512
AUSTRALIA. BUREAU OF STATISTICS. PUBLICATIONS TO BE RELEASED IN (YEAR). 1982. a. free. Australian Bureau of Statistics, P.O. Box 10, Belconnen, A.C.T. 2616, Australia. FAX 06-253-1404. stat. circ. 40,000. **Document type:** government publication.
Formerly: Lists of Publications to be Released by the Canberra and State Office of the A B S During (Year).
Description: Lists all ABS publications to be released by central and state offices in each year.

AUSTRALIA. BUREAU OF STATISTICS. QUARTERLY INDEXES OF INDUSTRIAL PRODUCTION, AUSTRALIA. see *BUSINESS AND ECONOMICS — Abstracting, Bibliographies, Statistics*

AUSTRALIA. BUREAU OF STATISTICS. QUEENSLAND OFFICE. AGRICULTURE, QUEENSLAND. see *AGRICULTURE — Abstracting, Bibliographies, Statistics*

AUSTRALIA. BUREAU OF STATISTICS. QUEENSLAND OFFICE. DEMOGRAPHY, QUEENSLAND. see *POPULATION STUDIES — Abstracting, Bibliographies, Statistics*

AUSTRALIA. BUREAU OF STATISTICS. QUEENSLAND OFFICE. ESTIMATED RESIDENT POPULATION, QUEENSLAND. see *POPULATION STUDIES — Abstracting, Bibliographies, Statistics*

319   AT   ISSN 0048-6396
AUSTRALIA. BUREAU OF STATISTICS. QUEENSLAND OFFICE. MONTHLY SUMMARY OF STATISTICS, QUEENSLAND. 1961. m. Aus.$12 per no. Australian Bureau of Statistics, Queensland Office, 313 Adelaide St., Brisbane, Qld. 4000, Australia. circ. 700. **Document type:** government publication.
Description: Contains summaries of up-to-date statistics on a wide range of subjects.

319   AT   ISSN 0085-5316
AUSTRALIA. BUREAU OF STATISTICS. QUEENSLAND OFFICE. QUEENSLAND POCKET YEAR BOOK. 1950. a. Aus.$10. Australian Bureau of Statistics, Queensland Office, 313 Adelaide St., Brisbane, Qld. 4000, Australia. TEL 07-222-6022. FAX 07-229-6171. TELEX AA 40271. index. circ. 2,500. **Document type:** government publication.
Description: Pocket-sized reference to the State's official statistics.

319   AT   ISSN 1030-7389
AUSTRALIA. BUREAU OF STATISTICS. QUEENSLAND OFFICE. QUEENSLAND YEAR BOOK. a. Aus.$40. Australian Bureau of Statistics, Queensland Office, 313 Adelaide St., Brisbane, Qld. 4000, Australia. index. circ. 2,500. **Document type:** government publication.
Former titles (until 1965): Queensland Government Statistician. Official Year Book of Queensland (ISSN 1030-7370); (until 1957): Queensland Government Statistician. Queensland Year Book (ISSN 0085-5359); (until 1937): Queensland Government Statistician. Queensland Official Year Book (ISSN 0810-719X); Which was formerly (until 1901): Year Book of Queensland (ISSN 0810-7203).
Description: Covers the history, environment, government, economy, finance, law, population, education, agriculture, transport and industrial conditions of Queensland.

319   AT   ISSN 1322-2368
AUSTRALIA. BUREAU OF STATISTICS. QUEENSLAND OFFICE. REGIONAL STATISTICS, QUEENSLAND. 1994. a. Aus.$22. Australian Bureau of Statistics, Queensland Office, 313 Adelaide St., Brisbane, Qld. 4000, Australia. TEL 07-222-6022. FAX 07-229-6171. TELEX AA 40271. **Document type:** government publication.
Formed by the merger of (1980-1993): Brisbane City Statistical Summary (ISSN 0726-2019) & Local Government Areas Statistical Summary, Queensland (ISSN 1030-4789); Which was formerly (until 1987): Local Authority Areas Statistical Summary, Queensland (ISSN 0727-1808)
Description: Contains summary of information for each legal local government area, statistical division and statistical district: area, population, births, deaths, building, manufacturing establishments, pre-school and child care centers, schools, agricultural industry and production, acute public hospitals, motor vehicles registered and road traffic accidents.

AUSTRALIA. BUREAU OF STATISTICS. REAL ESTATE AGENTS INDUSTRY, AUSTRALIA. see *REAL ESTATE — Abstracting, Bibliographies, Statistics*

AUSTRALIA. BUREAU OF STATISTICS. REGIONAL POPULATION GROWTH, AUSTRALIA. see *POPULATION STUDIES — Abstracting, Bibliographies, Statistics*

310   AT   ISSN 0818-3856
HA37
AUSTRALIA. BUREAU OF STATISTICS. REGISTER OF COMMONWEALTH STATISTICAL COLLECTIONS. 1985. triennial. Aus.$20 per no. Australian Bureau of Statistics, P.O. Box 10, Belconnen, A.C.T. 2616, Australia. **Document type:** government publication.
Description: A list of statistical collections conducted by Commonwealth agencies. Each entry lists the collecting organization, collection title, geographic coverage, and geographic detail, etc.

310   AT   ISSN 0729-5022
AUSTRALIA. BUREAU OF STATISTICS. RESEARCH AND EXPERIMENTAL DEVELOPMENT, ALL SECTOR SUMMARY, AUSTRALIA. 1978. biennial. Aus.$20 per no. Australian Bureau of Statistics, P.O. Box 10, Belconnen, A.C.T. 2616, Australia. **Document type:** government publication.
Description: Presents summary statistics on the level and distribution of expenditure and human resources devoted to research and experimental development carried out by business enterprises, government, higher education and private non-profit sectors.

AUSTRALIA. BUREAU OF STATISTICS. RESEARCH AND EXPERIMENTAL DEVELOPMENT, ALL SECTOR SUMMARY (INTER-YEAR SURVEY), AUSTRALIA. see *BUSINESS AND ECONOMICS — Abstracting, Bibliographies, Statistics*

AUSTRALIA. BUREAU OF STATISTICS. RESEARCH AND EXPERIMENTAL DEVELOPMENT, BUSINESS ENTERPRISES, AUSTRALIA. see *BUSINESS AND ECONOMICS — Abstracting, Bibliographies, Statistics*

AUSTRALIA. BUREAU OF STATISTICS. RESEARCH AND EXPERIMENTAL DEVELOPMENT, BUSINESS ENTERPRISES, AUSTRALIA, PRELIMINARY. see *BUSINESS AND ECONOMICS — Abstracting, Bibliographies, Statistics*

AUSTRALIA. BUREAU OF STATISTICS. RESEARCH AND EXPERIMENTAL DEVELOPMENT, GENERAL GOVERNMENT AND PRIVATE NON-PROFIT ORGANISATIONS, AUSTRALIA. see *BUSINESS AND ECONOMICS — Abstracting, Bibliographies, Statistics*

AUSTRALIA. BUREAU OF STATISTICS. RESEARCH AND EXPERIMENTAL DEVELOPMENT, HIGHER EDUCATION ORGANISATIONS, AUSTRALIA. see *EDUCATION — Abstracting, Bibliographies, Statistics*

AUSTRALIA. BUREAU OF STATISTICS. RETAIL INDUSTRY, AUSTRALIA. see *BUSINESS AND ECONOMICS — Abstracting, Bibliographies, Statistics*

AUSTRALIA. BUREAU OF STATISTICS. RETAIL TRADE, AUSTRALIA. see *BUSINESS AND ECONOMICS — Abstracting, Bibliographies, Statistics*

AUSTRALIA. BUREAU OF STATISTICS. RETAIL TRADE, AUSTRALIA: COMMODITY DETAILS. see *BUSINESS AND ECONOMICS — Abstracting, Bibliographies, Statistics*

AUSTRALIA. BUREAU OF STATISTICS. RETAILING IN AUSTRALIA. see *BUSINESS AND ECONOMICS — Abstracting, Bibliographies, Statistics*

AUSTRALIA. BUREAU OF STATISTICS. SHEEP AND WOOL, AUSTRALIA, PRELIMINARY. see *AGRICULTURE — Abstracting, Bibliographies, Statistics*

AUSTRALIA. BUREAU OF STATISTICS. SMALL BUSINESS IN AUSTRALIA. see *BUSINESS AND ECONOMICS — Abstracting, Bibliographies, Statistics*

AUSTRALIA. BUREAU OF STATISTICS. SOUTH AUSTRALIAN OFFICE. BUILDING APPROVALS, SOUTH AUSTRALIA. see *HOUSING AND URBAN PLANNING — Abstracting, Bibliographies, Statistics*

AUSTRALIA. BUREAU OF STATISTICS. SOUTH AUSTRALIAN OFFICE. DWELLING UNIT COMMENCEMENTS REPORTED BY APPROVING AUTHORITIES, SOUTH AUSTRALIA. see *HOUSING AND URBAN PLANNING — Abstracting, Bibliographies, Statistics*

AUSTRALIA. BUREAU OF STATISTICS. SOUTH AUSTRALIAN OFFICE. ESTIMATED RESIDENT POPULATION BY AGE AND SEX IN STATISTICAL LOCAL AREAS, SOUTH AUSTRALIA. see *POPULATION STUDIES — Abstracting, Bibliographies, Statistics*

AUSTRALIA. BUREAU OF STATISTICS. SOUTH AUSTRALIAN OFFICE. LIVESTOCK AND LIVESTOCK PRODUCTS, SOUTH AUSTRALIA. see *AGRICULTURE — Abstracting, Bibliographies, Statistics*

310   AT
AUSTRALIA. BUREAU OF STATISTICS. SOUTH AUSTRALIAN OFFICE. LOCAL GOVERNMENT AREA STATISTICS, SOUTH AUSTRALIA. 1970. irreg., latest 1995. Aus.$22. Australian Bureau of Statistics, South Australian Office, G.P.O. Box 2272, Adelaide, S.A. 5001, Australia. **Document type:** government publication.
Formerly: Divisional Statistics, South Australia.

AUSTRALIA. BUREAU OF STATISTICS. SOUTH AUSTRALIAN OFFICE. MANUFACTURING INDUSTRY, SOUTH AUSTRALIA. see *BUSINESS AND ECONOMICS — Abstracting, Bibliographies, Statistics*

STATISTICS

319 AT ISSN 0079-2446
AUSTRALIA. BUREAU OF STATISTICS. SOUTH AUSTRALIAN OFFICE. POCKET YEAR BOOK OF SOUTH AUSTRALIA. 1917. a. Aus.$10. Australian Bureau of Statistics, South Australian Office, G.P.O. Box 2272, Adelaide, S.A. 5001, Australia. FAX 08-237-7566. **Document type:** government publication.
Description: Contains compact tables covering most types of statistical information collected by the ABS. Also lists the State Government Ministry.

AUSTRALIA. BUREAU OF STATISTICS. SOUTH AUSTRALIAN OFFICE. PRINCIPAL AGRICULTURAL COMMODITIES, SOUTH AUSTRALIA, PRELIMINARY. see *AGRICULTURE — Abstracting, Bibliographies, Statistics*

310 AT ISSN 0814-0871
AUSTRALIA. BUREAU OF STATISTICS. SOUTH AUSTRALIAN OFFICE. SOUTH AUSTRALIA AT A GLANCE. 1979. a. Aus.$1. Australian Bureau of Statistics, South Australian Office, G.P.O. Box 2272, Adelaide, S.A. 5001, Australia. **Document type:** government publication.
Description: Contains information on South Australia compared with Australia, tourist accommodation, population, education, welfare services, prices, labor force, finance, trade, transport, agriculture, mining and building, etc.

AUSTRALIA. BUREAU OF STATISTICS. SOUTH AUSTRALIAN OFFICE. SOUTH AUSTRALIAN ECONOMIC INDICATORS. see *BUSINESS AND ECONOMICS — Abstracting, Bibliographies, Statistics*

319 AT ISSN 0085-6428
AUSTRALIA. BUREAU OF STATISTICS. SOUTH AUSTRALIAN OFFICE. SOUTH AUSTRALIAN YEAR BOOK. 1966. a. Aus.$30. Australian Bureau of Statistics, South Australian Office, G.P.O. Box 2272, Adelaide, S.A. 5001, Australia. FAX 08-237-7566. **Document type:** government publication.
Description: Provides comprehensive statistical information about South Australia, its physiography, history, institutions and social and economic conditions.

AUSTRALIA. BUREAU OF STATISTICS. SOUTH AUSTRALIAN OFFICE. TOURIST ACCOMMODATION, SOUTH AUSTRALIA. see *TRAVEL AND TOURISM — Abstracting, Bibliographies, Statistics*

AUSTRALIA. BUREAU OF STATISTICS. STATE ESTIMATES OF PRIVATE NEW CAPITAL EXPENDITURE. see *BUSINESS AND ECONOMICS — Abstracting, Bibliographies, Statistics*

AUSTRALIA. BUREAU OF STATISTICS. STOCKS, SELECTED INDUSTRY SALES AND EXPECTED SALES, AUSTRALIA. see *BUSINESS AND ECONOMICS — Abstracting, Bibliographies, Statistics*

AUSTRALIA. BUREAU OF STATISTICS. TASMANIAN OFFICE. AGRICULTURE STATISTICS - SELECTED SMALL AREA DATA, TASMANIA. see *AGRICULTURE — Abstracting, Bibliographies, Statistics*

AUSTRALIA. BUREAU OF STATISTICS. TASMANIAN OFFICE. DWELLING UNIT COMMENCEMENTS REPORTED BY APPROVING AUTHORITIES, TASMANIA. see *HOUSING AND URBAN PLANNING — Abstracting, Bibliographies, Statistics*

AUSTRALIA. BUREAU OF STATISTICS. TASMANIAN OFFICE. GOVERNMENT FINANCE STATISTICS, TASMANIA. see *BUSINESS AND ECONOMICS — Abstracting, Bibliographies, Statistics*

AUSTRALIA. BUREAU OF STATISTICS. TASMANIAN OFFICE. HOUSEHOLD EXPENDITURE SURVEY AT A GLANCE, TASMANIA. see *HOME ECONOMICS — Abstracting, Bibliographies, Statistics*

AUSTRALIA. BUREAU OF STATISTICS. TASMANIAN OFFICE. POPULATION STATISTICS, TASMANIA. see *POPULATION STUDIES — Abstracting, Bibliographies, Statistics*

AUSTRALIA. BUREAU OF STATISTICS. TASMANIAN OFFICE. PRINCIPAL AGRICULTURAL COMMODITIES, TASMANIA, PRELIMINARY. see *AGRICULTURE — Abstracting, Bibliographies, Statistics*

310 AT ISSN 0813-5487
AUSTRALIA. BUREAU OF STATISTICS. TASMANIAN OFFICE. TASMANIA AT A GLANCE. 1982. a. Aus.$1. Australian Bureau of Statistics, Tasmanian Office, G.P.O. Box 66A, Hobart, Tas. 7001, Australia. **Document type:** government publication.
Description: Contains information on Tasmania's geography, population, social and vital statistics, labor force, wages, price indexes, agriculture, mining, manufacturing, building, trade, transport, finance, and tourism.

319 AT ISSN 1031-9573
AUSTRALIA. BUREAU OF STATISTICS. TASMANIAN OFFICE. TASMANIAN POCKET YEARBOOK. 1913. a. Aus.$10. Australian Bureau of Statistics, Tasmanian Office, G.P.O. Box 66A, Hobart, Tas. 7001, Australia. circ. 3,300. **Document type:** government publication.
Formerly (until 1988): Pocket Year Book of Tasmania (ISSN 0314-1640)
Description: Presents a basic statistical summary of Tasmania.

319.4 AT ISSN 1034-1803
AUSTRALIA. BUREAU OF STATISTICS. TASMANIAN OFFICE. TASMANIAN STATISTICAL INDICATORS. 1987. m. Aus.$12 per no. Australian Bureau of Statistics, Tasmanian Office, G.P.O. Box 66A, Hobart, Tas. 7001, Australia. stat. circ. 600. **Document type:** government publication.
Formed by the merger of (1978-1987): Monthly Summary of Statistics, Tasmania (ISSN 0314-2094); (1983-1987): Major Economic Indicators, Tasmania (ISSN 0812-6763); (1981-1987): Miscellaneous Indicators of Production, Tasmania (ISSN 0726-3546)
Description: Contains tables dealing with: population and vital statistics, employment and unemployment, wages and prices, production statistics, building, finance, trade, retail sales, tourism, motor vehicle registrations and road traffic accidents.

AUSTRALIA. BUREAU OF STATISTICS. TAXATION REVENUE, AUSTRALIA. see *BUSINESS AND ECONOMICS — Abstracting, Bibliographies, Statistics*

AUSTRALIA. BUREAU OF STATISTICS. TOURISM INDICATORS, AUSTRALIA. see *TRAVEL AND TOURISM — Abstracting, Bibliographies, Statistics*

AUSTRALIA. BUREAU OF STATISTICS. TOURIST ACCOMMODATION, AUSTRALIA. see *HOTELS AND RESTAURANTS — Abstracting, Bibliographies, Statistics*

AUSTRALIA. BUREAU OF STATISTICS. TOURIST ACCOMMODATION, AUSTRALIAN CAPITAL TERRITORY. see *HOTELS AND RESTAURANTS — Abstracting, Bibliographies, Statistics*

AUSTRALIA. BUREAU OF STATISTICS. TRAINING AND EDUCATION EXPERIENCE, AUSTRALIA. see *BUSINESS AND ECONOMICS — Abstracting, Bibliographies, Statistics*

AUSTRALIA. BUREAU OF STATISTICS. VALUE OF PRINCIPAL AGRICULTURAL COMMODITIES PRODUCED, AUSTRALIA, PRELIMINARY. see *AGRICULTURE — Abstracting, Bibliographies, Statistics*

AUSTRALIA. BUREAU OF STATISTICS. VICTORIAN OFFICE. AGRICULTURAL LAND USE AND SELECTED INPUTS, VICTORIA. see *AGRICULTURE — Abstracting, Bibliographies, Statistics*

AUSTRALIA. BUREAU OF STATISTICS. VICTORIAN OFFICE. AGRICULTURE STATISTICS - SELECTED SMALL AREA DATA, VICTORIA. see *AGRICULTURE — Abstracting, Bibliographies, Statistics*

AUSTRALIA. BUREAU OF STATISTICS. VICTORIAN OFFICE. BUILDING ACTIVITY, VICTORIA. see *BUILDING AND CONSTRUCTION — Abstracting, Bibliographies, Statistics*

AUSTRALIA. BUREAU OF STATISTICS. VICTORIAN OFFICE. BUILDING APPROVALS BY STATISTICAL LOCAL AREAS, VICTORIA - SMALL AREA SUMMARY DATA REPORTS. see *HOUSING AND URBAN PLANNING — Abstracting, Bibliographies, Statistics*

AUSTRALIA. BUREAU OF STATISTICS. VICTORIAN OFFICE. BUILDING APPROVALS, VICTORIA. see *HOUSING AND URBAN PLANNING — Abstracting, Bibliographies, Statistics*

AUSTRALIA. BUREAU OF STATISTICS. VICTORIAN OFFICE. CROPS, PASTURES AND FRUIT, VICTORIA. see *AGRICULTURE — Abstracting, Bibliographies, Statistics*

AUSTRALIA. BUREAU OF STATISTICS. VICTORIAN OFFICE. DEMOGRAPHY, VICTORIA. see *POPULATION STUDIES — Abstracting, Bibliographies, Statistics*

AUSTRALIA. BUREAU OF STATISTICS. VICTORIAN OFFICE. DWELLING UNIT COMMENCEMENTS REPORTED BY APPROVING AUTHORITIES, VICTORIA. see *HOUSING AND URBAN PLANNING — Abstracting, Bibliographies, Statistics*

AUSTRALIA. BUREAU OF STATISTICS. VICTORIAN OFFICE. ESTIMATED RESIDENT POPULATION IN STATISTICAL LOCAL AREAS, VICTORIA, PRELIMINARY. see *POPULATION STUDIES — Abstracting, Bibliographies, Statistics*

AUSTRALIA. BUREAU OF STATISTICS. VICTORIAN OFFICE. LABOUR FORCE, VICTORIA. see *BUSINESS AND ECONOMICS — Abstracting, Bibliographies, Statistics*

AUSTRALIA. BUREAU OF STATISTICS. VICTORIAN OFFICE. LIVESTOCK AND LIVESTOCK PRODUCTS, VICTORIA. see *AGRICULTURE — Abstracting, Bibliographies, Statistics*

AUSTRALIA. BUREAU OF STATISTICS. VICTORIAN OFFICE. MANUFACTURING INDUSTRY, VICTORIA. see *BUSINESS AND ECONOMICS — Abstracting, Bibliographies, Statistics*

319 AT ISSN 0158-202X
AUSTRALIA. BUREAU OF STATISTICS. VICTORIAN OFFICE. MONTHLY SUMMARY OF STATISTICS, VICTORIA. 1960. m. Aus.$12 per no. Australian Bureau of Statistics, Victorian Office, G.P.O. Box 2796Y, Melbourne, Vic. 3001, Australia. circ. 320. **Document type:** government publication.
Supersedes in part (in 1994): Economic Indicators, Victoria (ISSN 0810-7521); Victorian Monthly Statistical Review (ISSN 0049-6162)
Description: Covers Victorian population, employment, wages and prices, production, building, finance, trade, transport and communications.

AUSTRALIA. BUREAU OF STATISTICS. VICTORIAN OFFICE. PRINCIPAL AGRICULTURAL COMMODITIES, VICTORIA, PRELIMINARY. see *AGRICULTURE — Abstracting, Bibliographies, Statistics*

AUSTRALIA. BUREAU OF STATISTICS. VICTORIAN OFFICE. RETAIL INDUSTRY: DETAILS OF OPERATIONS, VICTORIA. see *BUSINESS AND ECONOMICS — Abstracting, Bibliographies, Statistics*

AUSTRALIA. BUREAU OF STATISTICS. VICTORIAN OFFICE. TOURIST ACCOMMODATION, VICTORIA. see *HOTELS AND RESTAURANTS — Abstracting, Bibliographies, Statistics*

AUSTRALIA. BUREAU OF STATISTICS. VICTORIAN OFFICE. VALUE OF AGRICULTURAL COMMODITIES PRODUCED, VICTORIA. see *AGRICULTURE — Abstracting, Bibliographies, Statistics*

310 AT ISSN 0725-1181
AUSTRALIA. BUREAU OF STATISTICS. VICTORIAN OFFICE. VICTORIA AT A GLANCE. 1980. a. Aus.$1. Australian Bureau of Statistics, Victorian Office, G.P.O. Box 2796Y, Melbourne, Vic. 3001, Australia. **Document type:** government publication.
Description: Contains information about demography, education, welfare services, overseas trade, finance, labor force, income, prices, manufacturing, tourism, transport, and Victorian data compared with Australia.

994 319   AT   ISSN 0067-1223
AUSTRALIA. BUREAU OF STATISTICS. VICTORIAN OFFICE. VICTORIAN YEARBOOK. 1873. a. Aus.$38 for hard cover; soft cover Aus.$31. Australian Bureau of Statistics, Victorian Office, G.P.O. Box 2796Y, Melbourne, Vic. 3001, Australia. adv.; bk.rev.; bibl.; index. circ. 2,000. **Document type:** government publication.
   Description: Provides comprehensive statistical information about Victoria, including history, geography, government, demography, labor, education, health, agriculture, manufacturing, mining, commerce, finance, construction and transport.

AUSTRALIA. BUREAU OF STATISTICS. WESTERN AUSTRALIAN OFFICE. BUILDING ACTIVITY, WESTERN AUSTRALIA. see *HOUSING AND URBAN PLANNING — Abstracting, Bibliographies, Statistics*

AUSTRALIA. BUREAU OF STATISTICS. WESTERN AUSTRALIAN OFFICE. DEMOGRAPHY, WESTERN AUSTRALIA. see *POPULATION STUDIES — Abstracting, Bibliographies, Statistics*

AUSTRALIA. BUREAU OF STATISTICS. WESTERN AUSTRALIAN OFFICE. DWELLING UNIT COMMENCEMENTS REPORTED BY APPROVING AUTHORITIES, WESTERN AUSTRALIA. see *HOUSING AND URBAN PLANNING — Abstracting, Bibliographies, Statistics*

AUSTRALIA. BUREAU OF STATISTICS. WESTERN AUSTRALIAN OFFICE. ESTIMATED RESIDENT POPULATION BY AGE AND SEX IN STATISTICAL LOCAL AREAS, WESTERN AUSTRALIA. see *POPULATION STUDIES — Abstracting, Bibliographies, Statistics*

AUSTRALIA. BUREAU OF STATISTICS. WESTERN AUSTRALIAN OFFICE. ESTIMATED RESIDENT POPULATION IN STATISTICAL LOCAL AREAS, WESTERN AUSTRALIA, PRELIMINARY. see *POPULATION STUDIES — Abstracting, Bibliographies, Statistics*

AUSTRALIA. BUREAU OF STATISTICS. WESTERN AUSTRALIAN OFFICE. ESTIMATED STOCKS OF DWELLING, WESTERN AUSTRALIA. see *BUILDING AND CONSTRUCTION — Abstracting, Bibliographies, Statistics*

AUSTRALIA. BUREAU OF STATISTICS. WESTERN AUSTRALIAN OFFICE. MANUFACTURING INDUSTRY, WESTERN AUSTRALIA. see *BUSINESS AND ECONOMICS — Abstracting, Bibliographies, Statistics*

319.4   AT   ISSN 0727-2367
AUSTRALIA. BUREAU OF STATISTICS. WESTERN AUSTRALIAN OFFICE. MONTHLY SUMMARY OF STATISTICS, WESTERN AUSTRALIA. 1958. m. Aus.$12 per no. Australian Bureau of Statistics, Western Australian Office, 30 Tarrace Rd., E. Perth, W.A. 6004, Australia. circ. 312. (processed) **Document type:** government publication.
   Incorporates (1989-1993): Economic Indicators, Western Australia (ISSN 1031-7155); Formerly: Monthly Statistical Summary, Western Australia (ISSN 0004-8542)
   Description: Covers business activities, population, employment, wages and prices, building, production, finance, trade, tourism and transport.

AUSTRALIA. BUREAU OF STATISTICS. WESTERN AUSTRALIAN OFFICE. PRICE INDEX OF WESTERN AUSTRALIAN PRODUCED HARDWOODS. see *FORESTS AND FORESTRY — Abstracting, Bibliographies, Statistics*

AUSTRALIA. BUREAU OF STATISTICS. WESTERN AUSTRALIAN OFFICE. PRINCIPAL AGRICULTURAL COMMODITIES, WESTERN AUSTRALIA, PRELIMINARY. see *AGRICULTURE — Abstracting, Bibliographies, Statistics*

310   AT
AUSTRALIA. BUREAU OF STATISTICS. WESTERN AUSTRALIAN OFFICE. WESTERN AUSTRALIA'S ABORIGINAL PEOPLE. 1986. irreg., latest 1991. Aus.$20. Australian Bureau of Statistics, Western Australian Office, 30 Terrace Rd., E. Perth, W.A. 6004, Australia. **Document type:** government publication.
   Description: Presents a range of statistics on Western Australia's Aboriginal population.

310   AT   ISSN 0727-2022
AUSTRALIA. BUREAU OF STATISTICS. WESTERN AUSTRALIAN OFFICE. WESTERN AUSTRALIA IN BRIEF. 1979. a. Aus.$1. Australian Bureau of Statistics, Western Australian Office, 30 Terrace Rd., E. Perth, W.A. 6004, Australia. **Document type:** government publication.

AUSTRALIA. BUREAU OF STATISTICS. WHOLESALE INDUSTRY, AUSTRALIA. see *BUSINESS AND ECONOMICS — Abstracting, Bibliographies, Statistics*

AUSTRALIA. BUREAU OF STATISTICS. WOMEN'S HEALTH. see *WOMEN'S HEALTH — Abstracting, Bibliographies, Statistics*

AUSTRALIA. BUREAU OF STATISTICS. WORKING PAPERS IN ECONOMETRICS AND APPLIED STATISTICS. see *BUSINESS AND ECONOMICS — Abstracting, Bibliographies, Statistics*

319   AT   ISSN 0810-8633
HA3001
AUSTRALIA. BUREAU OF STATISTICS. YEAR BOOK AUSTRALIA. 1908. a. Aus.$70. Australian Bureau of Statistics, P.O. Box 10, Belconnen, A.C.T. 2616, Australia. TEL 062-527911. FAX 062-516009. circ. 1,861. **Document type:** government publication.
   Former titles (until 1975): Official Year Book of Australia (ISSN 0312-4746); (until 1973): Official Year Book of the Commonwealth of Australia (ISSN 0078-3927)
   Description: General statistical reference work, containing comprehensive information on demography, prices and household expenditures, labor and industry, social welfare, public health, law and order, education, agriculture and rural industry, and more.

AUSTRALIA. LIFE INSURANCE GROUP. HALF YEARLY FINANCIAL BULLETIN ON LIFE INSURANCE. see *INSURANCE — Abstracting, Bibliographies, Statistics*

AUSTRALIAN BUREAU OF AGRICULTURAL AND RESOURCE ECONOMICS. AUSTRALIAN FISHERIES STATISTICS (YEAR). see *FISH AND FISHERIES — Abstracting, Bibliographies, Statistics*

AUSTRALIAN BUREAU OF AGRICULTURAL AND RESOURCE ECONOMICS. QUARTERLY FOREST PRODUCTS STATISTICS. see *FORESTS AND FORESTRY — Abstracting, Bibliographies, Statistics*

AUSTRALIAN BUREAU OF AGRICULTURAL AND RESOURCE ECONOMICS. QUARTERLY MINERAL STATISTICS. see *MINES AND MINING INDUSTRY — Abstracting, Bibliographies, Statistics*

AUSTRALIAN BUREAU OF AGRICULTURAL ECONOMICS. COMMODITY STATISTICAL BULLETIN (YEAR). see *BUSINESS AND ECONOMICS — Abstracting, Bibliographies, Statistics*

310   AT   ISSN 0004-9581
HA1   CODEN: AUJSA3
AUSTRALIAN JOURNAL OF STATISTICS. 1959. 3/yr. Aus.$75($70) (Statistical Society of Australia) Australian Statistical Publishing Association, Inc., G.P.O. Box 573, Canberra, A.C.T. 2601, Australia. Ed. I.R. James. adv.; bk.rev.; charts; index. circ. 1,500. (also avail. in microform from SWZ; back issues avail.; reprint service avail. from SWZ) **Indexed:** Biostat., Curr.Ind.Stat., J.Cont.Quant.Meth., Math.R., Oper.Res.Manage.Sci., Qual.Contr.Appl.Stat., SSCI, Stat.Theor.Meth.Abstr.
   —BLDSC (1812.700000); Faxon; SWETS; UnCover.

AUSTRALIAN WOOL SALE STATISTICS. STATISTICAL ANALYSIS. PART A & B & C & D. see *TEXTILE INDUSTRIES AND FABRICS — Abstracting, Bibliographies, Statistics*

AUSTRIA. STATISTISCHES ZENTRALAMT. DEMOGRAPHISCHES JAHRBUCH OESTERREICHES. see *POPULATION STUDIES — Abstracting, Bibliographies, Statistics*

AUSTRIA. STATISTISCHES ZENTRALAMT. INDUSTRIE UND GEWERBESTATISTIK PART 1. see *BUSINESS AND ECONOMICS — Abstracting, Bibliographies, Statistics*

310   AU
AUSTRIA. STATISTISCHES ZENTRALAMT. MIKROZENSUS; JAHRESERGEBNISSE. (Subseries of its Beitraege zur Oesterreichischen Statistik) 1969. a. S.250. Oesterreichisches Statistisches Zentralamt, Hintere Zollamtsstr. 2b, A-1033 Vienna, Austria. TEL 0222-71128-0. FAX 0222-7156828. stat. circ. 370. **Document type:** government publication.
   Description: Information on population, employment and stock of dwellings.

310   AU
AUSTRIA. STATISTISCHES ZENTRALAMT. PUBLIKATIONSANGEBOT. 1978. a. free. Oesterreichisches Statistisches Zentralamt, Hintere Zollamtsstr. 2b, A-1033 Vienna, Austria. TEL 0222-71128-0. FAX 0222-7156828. Eds. Margret Mitteregger, Marion Bretterecker. (back issues avail.) **Document type:** government publication.
   Description: Publications list and prices.

310   AU
AUSTRIA. STATISTISCHES ZENTRALAMT. STATISTISCHE NACHRICHTEN. 1923. a. S.1450. Oesterreichisches Statistisches Zentralamt, Hintere Zollamtsstr. 2b, A-1033 Vienna, Austria. TEL 0222-71128-0. FAX 0222-7156828. Ed. Kurt Klein. **Indexed:** P.A.I.S.For.Lang.Ind. **Document type:** government publication.
   Description: Data on all censuses in Austria.

AVERAGE ANNUAL PAY BY STATE AND INDUSTRY. see *BUSINESS AND ECONOMICS — Economic Situation And Conditions*

AVERAGE ANNUAL PAY LEVELS IN METROPOLITAN AREAS (YEAR). see *BUSINESS AND ECONOMICS — Economic Situation And Conditions*

B A C M I STATISTICAL YEARBOOK. see *BUILDING AND CONSTRUCTION — Abstracting, Bibliographies, Statistics*

B F S AKTUELL. (Bundesamt fuer Statistik) see *PUBLIC ADMINISTRATION*

B L S RELEASES: DEMOGRAPHIC DATA BOOK FOR STATES AND LARGE METROPOLITAN AREAS. (U.S. Bureau of Labor Statistics) see *BUSINESS AND ECONOMICS — Economic Situation And Conditions*

B L S REPORTS ON EMPLOYEE BENEFITS IN THE UNITED STATES. (U.S. Bureau of Labor Statistics) see *BUSINESS AND ECONOMICS — Economic Situation And Conditions*

B L S UPDATE. (U.S. Bureau of Labor Statistics) see *BUSINESS AND ECONOMICS — Economic Situation And Conditions*

B P I STATISTICAL HANDBOOK. (British Phonographic Industry) see *MUSIC — Abstracting, Bibliographies, Statistics*

B S R I A STATISTICS BULLETIN. (Building Services Research and Information Association) see *HEATING, PLUMBING AND REFRIGERATION — Abstracting, Bibliographies, Statistics*

314   GW   ISSN 0408-1714
HA1320.B2
BADEN - WUERTTEMBERG. STATISTISCHES LANDESAMT. STATISTISCH-PROGNOSTISCHER BERICHT; Daten - Analysen - Perspektiven. 1973. a. Statistisches Landesamt, Postfach 106033, 70049 Stuttgart, Germany. TEL 0711-6410. FAX 0711-6412440. Ed. Dr. Leibing. circ. 1,200. **Document type:** government publication.

314   GW
BADEN - WUERTTEMBERG. STATISTISCHES LANDESAMT. STATISTISCHE BERICHTE. m. Statistisches Landesamt, Postfach 106030, 70049 Stuttgart, Germany. TEL 0711-6410. FAX 0711-6412440. Ed. Dr. Leibing. circ. 1,000. (back issues avail.) **Document type:** government publication.

314   GW   ISSN 0721-1821
BADEN - WUERTTEMBERG IN WORT UND ZAHL. 1953. m. DM.68.40. Statistisches Landesamt, Postfach 106033, 70049 Stuttgart, Germany. TEL 0711-641-0. FAX 0711-6412440. Ed. Dr. Leibing. bk.rev. circ. 1,100. **Document type:** government publication.

STATISTICS

318 BF
BAHAMAS. DEPARTMENT OF STATISTICS. STATISTICAL ABSTRACT. 1969. a. $5. Department of Statistics, P.O. Box N 3904, Nassau, Bahamas. **Document type:** government publication, abstracting/indexing.

318 BF
BAHAMAS. DEPARTMENT OF STATISTICS. STATISTICAL SUMMARY. 1971. q. $2. Department of Statistics, P.O. Box N 3904, Nassau, Bahamas. **Document type:** government publication.

BAHRAIN. MONETARY AGENCY. QUARTERLY STATISTICAL BULLETIN. see *BUSINESS AND ECONOMICS — Abstracting, Bibliographies, Statistics*

BALANCE SHEETS. see *BUSINESS AND ECONOMICS — Abstracting, Bibliographies, Statistics*

BANCO CENTRAL DE VENEZUELA. ANUARIO DE BALANZA DE PAGOS. see *BUSINESS AND ECONOMICS — Abstracting, Bibliographies, Statistics*

BANCO CENTRAL DE VENEZUELA. ANUARIO DE CUENTAS NACIONALES. see *BUSINESS AND ECONOMICS — Abstracting, Bibliographies, Statistics*

BANCO CENTRAL DE VENEZUELA. ANUARIO DE ESTADISTICAS INTERNACIONALES. see *BUSINESS AND ECONOMICS — Abstracting, Bibliographies, Statistics*

BANCO CENTRAL DE VENEZUELA. ANUARIO DE ESTADISTICAS PRECIOS Y MERCADO LABORAL. see *BUSINESS AND ECONOMICS — Abstracting, Bibliographies, Statistics*

BANCO DE MEXICO. INDICADORES DEL SECTOR EXTERNO. see *BUSINESS AND ECONOMICS — Abstracting, Bibliographies, Statistics*

BANCO DE MEXICO. INDICE DE PRECIOS. see *BUSINESS AND ECONOMICS — Abstracting, Bibliographies, Statistics*

BANCO DE PORTUGAL. ESTATISTICA E ESTUDOS ECONOMICOS. see *BUSINESS AND ECONOMICS — Abstracting, Bibliographies, Statistics*

BANGLADESH BANK. STATISTICS DEPARTMENT. ANNUAL BALANCE OF PAYMENTS. see *BUSINESS AND ECONOMICS — Abstracting, Bibliographies, Statistics*

BANK OF GREECE. MONTHLY STATISTICAL BULLETIN. see *BUSINESS AND ECONOMICS — Banking And Finance*

BANK OF ISRAEL. ANNUAL STATISTICS OF ISRAEL'S BANKING SYSTEM. see *BUSINESS AND ECONOMICS — Abstracting, Bibliographies, Statistics*

BANK OF ISRAEL. CURRENT BANKING STATISTICS. see *BUSINESS AND ECONOMICS — Abstracting, Bibliographies, Statistics*

BANK OF ISRAEL. EXCHANGE RATES. see *BUSINESS AND ECONOMICS — Abstracting, Bibliographies, Statistics*

BANK OF ISRAEL. MAIN ISRAELI ECONOMIC DATA. see *BUSINESS AND ECONOMICS — Abstracting, Bibliographies, Statistics*

BARBADOS. STATISTICAL SERVICE. BULLETIN. OVERSEAS TRADE. see *BUSINESS AND ECONOMICS — Abstracting, Bibliographies, Statistics*

317.29 BB ISSN 0378-8873
HA865
BARBADOS. STATISTICAL SERVICE. MONTHLY DIGEST OF STATISTICS. 1974. m. B.$0.50. Statistical Service, National Insurance Bldg., 3rd Fl., Fairchild St., Bridgetown, Barbados, W.I. illus.

310 BB
BARBADOS. STATISTICAL SERVICE. SURVEY OF ACCOMMODATION ESTABLISHMENTS. irreg. Statistical Service, National Insurance Bldg., 3rd Fl., Fairchild St., Bridgetown, Barbados, W.I.

BASIC AND CLINICAL BIOSTATISTICS. see *MATHEMATICS*

314 GW
BAYERISCHES LANDESAMT FUER STATISTIK UND DATENVERARBEITUNG. ZEITSCHRIFT - BAYERN IN ZAHLEN. 1869. m. DM.88. Bayerisches Landsamt fuer Statistik und Datenverarbeitung, Neuhauserstr. 8, 80288 Munich, Germany. TEL 089-2119205. Ed. K. Witte. adv.; charts; tr.lit.; index. circ. 1,000. (back issues avail.) **Document type:** government publication.
   Formerly: Bayern in Zahlen (ISSN 0005-7215)

519.5 US ISSN 0959-2083
BAYESIAN STATISTICS. Represents: Proceedings of the Valencia International Meeting. irreg. price varies. Oxford University Press, 200 Madison Ave., New York, NY 10016. TEL 212-679-7300. **Indexed:** Curr.Ind.Stat. **Document type:** proceedings.
   —BLDSC (1871.234000).

BEER STATISTICS NEWS. see *BEVERAGES*

310 DK ISSN 0107-5071
BEFOLKNINGEN I KOEBENHAVN 1 JANUAR. (Subseries: Tal fra Koebenhavns Statistiske Kontor) 1977. a. DKK 20. Koebenhavns Kommune, Oekonomidirektoratet, Statistisk Kontor, Vester Voldgade 87, DK-1552 Copenhagen V, Denmark. (Dist. by: Danske Boghandleres Kommissionsanstalt, Siljangade 6-8, 2300 Copenhagen S, Denmark)
   Formerly: Befolkningen i Januar.

314 AU ISSN 0067-2319
BEITRAEGE ZUR OESTERREICHISCHEN STATISTIK. 1953. irreg. price varies. Oesterreichisches Statistisches Zentralamt, Hintere Zollamtsstr. 2b, A-1033 Vienna, Austria. TEL 0222-71128-0. FAX 0222-7156828. **Document type:** government publication.
   Description: Publications from all branches of statistics collection.

BELGIUM. INSTITUT NATIONAL DE STATISTIQUE. ACCIDENTS DE LA CIRCULATION SUR LA VOIE PUBLIQUE AVEC TUES ET BLESSES. see *PUBLIC HEALTH AND SAFETY — Abstracting, Bibliographies, Statistics*

314.93 BE ISSN 0770-0369
HA1393
BELGIUM. INSTITUT NATIONAL DE STATISTIQUE. ANNUAIRE DE STATISTIQUES REGIONALES. Key Title: Annuaire de Statistiques Regionales - Institut National de Statistique. Dutch edition: Regionaal Statistisch Jaarboek - Nationaal Instituut voor de Statistiek (ISSN 0770-772X) 1976. a. 500 BEF (foreign 625 BEF) (effective 1993). Institut National de Statistique, 44 rue de Louvain, B-1000 Brussels, Belgium. TEL 32-2-5486211. FAX 32-2-5486367. charts; stat. **Document type:** government publication.

314 BE ISSN 0067-5431
BELGIUM. INSTITUT NATIONAL DE STATISTIQUE. ANNUAIRE STATISTIQUE DE POCHE. Dutch edition: Statistisch Zakjaarboek - Nationaal Instituut voor de Statistiek. (Text in French) 1965. a. 150 BEF (foreign 185 BEF) (effective 1993). Institut National de Statistique, 44 rue de Louvain, B-1000 Brussels, Belgium. TEL 32-2-5486211. FAX 32-2-5486367. **Document type:** government publication.

314 BE ISSN 0045-1703
BELGIUM. INSTITUT NATIONAL DE STATISTIQUE. BULLETIN DE STATISTIQUE. Dutch edition: Statistisch Tijdschrift. (Text in French) 1909. 11/yr. 1410 BEF (foreign 1760 BEF) (effective 1993). Institut National de Statistique, 44 rue de Louvain, B-1000 Brussels, Belgium. TEL 32-2-5486211. FAX 32-2-5486367. charts. **Indexed:** P.A.I.S.For.Lang.Ind. **Document type:** government publication.

330 BE
BELGIUM. INSTITUT NATIONAL DE STATISTIQUE. CATALOGUE DES PRODUITS ET SERVICES. Dutch edition: Catalogus van de Produkten en Diensten van het Nationaal Instituut voor de Statistiek. (Text in French) a. free. Institut National de Statistique, Rue de Louvain 44, B-1000 Brussels, Belgium. TEL 32-2-5486211. FAX 32-2-5486367. **Document type:** government publication, catalog.
   Supersedes: Belgium. Institut National de Statistique. Catalogue des Publications (ISSN 0376-7736)

310 BE ISSN 0069-8075
BELGIUM. INSTITUT NATIONAL DE STATISTIQUE. ETUDES STATISTIQUES. Key Title: Etudes Statistiques - Institut National de Statistique. Dutch edition: Statistische Studien - Nationaal Instituut voor de Statistiek (ISSN 0772-1838) (Includes subseries: Belgium. Institut National de Statistique. Comptes Nationaux de la Belgique) 1966. irreg. (2-4/yr.). price varies. Institut National de Statistique, 44 rue de Louvain, B-1000 Brussels, Belgium. TEL 32-2-5486211. FAX 32-2-5486367. **Indexed:** P.A.I.S.For.Lang.Ind. **Document type:** government publication.

BELGIUM. INSTITUT NATIONAL DE STATISTIQUE. STATISTIQUE DE LA NAVIGATION INTERIEURE. see *TRANSPORTATION — Abstracting, Bibliographies, Statistics*

BELGIUM. INSTITUT NATIONAL DE STATISTIQUE. STATISTIQUE DU TOURISME ET DE L'HOTELLERIE. see *TRAVEL AND TOURISM — Abstracting, Bibliographies, Statistics*

BELGIUM. INSTITUT NATIONAL DE STATISTIQUE. STATISTIQUE DU TRAFIC INTERNATIONAL DES PORTS (U.E.B.L.). see *TRANSPORTATION — Abstracting, Bibliographies, Statistics*

BELGIUM. INSTITUT NATIONAL DE STATISTIQUE. STATISTIQUES AGRICOLES. see *AGRICULTURE — Abstracting, Bibliographies, Statistics*

BELGIUM. INSTITUT NATIONAL DE STATISTIQUE. STATISTIQUES DE LA CONSTRUCTION ET DU LOGEMENT. see *BUILDING AND CONSTRUCTION — Abstracting, Bibliographies, Statistics*

BELGIUM. INSTITUT NATIONAL DE STATISTIQUE. STATISTIQUES DEMOGRAPHIQUES. see *POPULATION STUDIES — Abstracting, Bibliographies, Statistics*

BELGIUM. INSTITUT NATIONAL DE STATISTIQUE. STATISTIQUES DU COMMERCE INTERIEUR ET DES TRANSPORTS. see *TRANSPORTATION — Abstracting, Bibliographies, Statistics*

BELGIUM. INSTITUT NATIONAL DE STATISTIQUE. STATISTIQUES INDUSTRIELLES. see *BUSINESS AND ECONOMICS — Abstracting, Bibliographies, Statistics*

BELGIUM. INSTITUT NATIONAL DE STATISTIQUE. STATISTIQUES JUDICIAIRES. see *LAW — Abstracting, Bibliographies, Statistics*

BELGIUM. INSTITUT NATIONAL DE STATISTIQUE. VEHICULES A MOTEUR NEUFS MIS EN CIRCULATION. see *TRANSPORTATION — Abstracting, Bibliographies, Statistics*

BELGIUM. MINISTERE DE L'EDUCATION, DE LA RECHERCHE ET DE LA FORMATION. ANNUAIRE STATISTIQUE. see *EDUCATION — Abstracting, Bibliographies, Statistics*

BELGIUM. MINISTERE DE LA SANTE PUBLIQUE ET DE L'ENVIRONNEMENT. ADMINISTRATION DES ETABLISSEMENTS DE SOINS. ANNUAIRE STATISTIQUE DES HOPITAUX/BELGIUM. MINISTERIE VAN VOLKSGEZONDHEID EN LEEFMILIEU. BESTUUR VOOR DE VERZORGINGSINSTELLINGEN. STATISTISCH JAARBOEK VAN DE ZIEKENHUIZEN. see *PUBLIC HEALTH AND SAFETY — Abstracting, Bibliographies, Statistics*

314 BE ISSN 0771-0410
HA1393
BELGIUM. NATIONAAL INSTITUUT VOOR DE STATISTIEK. WEEKBERICHT. French ed.: Belgium. Institut National de Statistique. Communique Hebdomadaire (ISSN 0772-6341) (Text in Dutch) 1945. w. 1400 BEF (foreign 1750 BEF) (effective 1993). Institut National de Statistique - Nationaal Instituut voor de Statistiek, 44 rue de Louvain, B-1000 Brussels, Belgium. TEL 32-2-5486211. FAX 32-2-5486367. **Document type:** government publication.
   Supersedes (in 1982): Communique Hebdomadaire - Institut National de Statistique (Bilingual Edition) (ISSN 0771-0364)

317.2 BH
BELIZE. CENTRAL STATISTICAL OFFICE. ABSTRACT OF STATISTICS. a. $20. Ministry of Finance, Central Statistical Office, Belmopan, Belize. TEL 08-22207. FAX 08-23206. **Document type:** government publication.
   Description: Contains data relating to the social, demographic, economic, agricultural and climatic situation of Belize.

BELIZE FAMILY HEALTH SURVEY. see *MEDICAL SCIENCES — Abstracting, Bibliographies, Statistics*

317.2 BH
BELIZE IN FIGURES. a. free. Ministry of Finance, Central Statistical Office, Belmopan, Belize. TEL 08-22207. FAX 08-23206. **Document type:** government publication, bulletin.
   Description: Provides a quick reference on the social, demographic, economic, agricultural and climatic situation of Belize.

310 GW ISSN 0005-9331
BERLINER STATISTIK. (Supplements avail.) 1947. m. DM.54($18) (Statistisches Landesamt) Kulturbuch Verlag GmbH, Postfach 470449, 12313 Berlin, Germany. TEL 030-6618484. FAX 030-6617828. bk.rev.; charts; mkt.; stat. circ. 1,500. **Indexed:** P.A.I.S.For.Lang.Ind. **Document type:** government publication.

BIBLIOGRAPHY OF ECONOMIC AND STATISTICAL PUBLICATIONS ON TANZANIA. see *BUSINESS AND ECONOMICS — Abstracting, Bibliographies, Statistics*

BILDUNG IM ZAHLENSPIEGEL. see *EDUCATION — Abstracting, Bibliographies, Statistics*

BILDUNGSSTATISTIK SCHLUESSEL FUER BERUFSAUSBILDUNG/STATISTIQUE SCOLAIRE CODE DE LA FORMATION PROFESSIONELLE. see *EDUCATION — Adult Education*

310 US ISSN 8750-0434
BIOMETRIC BULLETIN.* 1984. q. $10. International Biometric Society - Internationale Biometrische Gesellschaft - Societe Internationale de Biometrie, 808 17th St., N.W., Washington, DC 20006-3910. TEL 703-836-8311. E-mail: tomasson@inapg.inra.fr. Ed. Richard Tomassone. abstr.; circ. 6,400. circ. 2,088.980,000 (paid). (back issues avail.) **Document type:** bulletin.
   —BLDSC (2088.980000).

310 574 US ISSN 0006-341X
CODEN: BIOMB6
BIOMETRICS. (Text in English, French, German) 1945. q. $100 (effective 1996). Biometric Society, 808 17th St., N.W., Washington, DC 20006-3910. TEL 202-223-9669. FAX 202-223-9569. adv.; bk.rev.; charts; illus.; stat.; index, cum.index: vols.1-20, 1945-1964. circ. 8,600. (also avail. in microform from UMI,PMC; microfiche from BHP; reprint service avail. from UMI) **Indexed:** Abstr.Anthropol., Agri.Eng.Abstr., Anim.Breed.Abstr., Appl.Mech.Rev., Biol.Abstr., Biol.& Agr.Ind., Biostat., C.I.S.Abstr., Chem.Abstr., Compumath, Comput.Abstr., Comput.Cont., Curr.Adv.Ecol.Sci., Curr.Cont., Curr.Ind.Stat., Dairy Sci.Abstr., Deep Sea Res.& Oceanogr.Abstr., Dent.Ind., Ecol.Abstr., Excerp.Med., Food Sci.& Tech.Abstr., Forest.Abstr., Forest Prod.Abstr., Geo.Abstr., Helminthol.Abstr., Herb.Abstr., Hort.Abstr., IDA, Ind.Med., Ind.Sci.Rev., Ind.Vet., INIS Atomind., INSPEC (1982-1985), J.Cont.Quant.Meth., Math.R., Nutr.Abstr., Oper.Res.Manage.Sci., Plant Breed.Abstr., Qual.Contr.Appl.Stat., Risk Abstr., Sci.Cit.Ind., Soils & Fert., Sorghum & Millets Abstr., Sport Fish.Abstr., Stat.Theor.Meth.Abstr., Triticale Abstr., Vet.Bull., W.R.C.Inf., Wild.Rev., Zoo.Rec. **Document type:** academic/scholarly publication.
   —BLDSC (2088.000000); Ei; Faxon; Genuine Article; SWETS; UMI; UnCover. **CCC.**
   Refereed Serial

BIOMETRIKA. see *BIOLOGY — Abstracting, Bibliographies, Statistics*

BLUE BOOK OF FOOD STORE OPERATORS & WHOLESALERS. see *FOOD AND FOOD INDUSTRIES — Abstracting, Bibliographies, Statistics*

BOATING STATISTICS. see *SPORTS AND GAMES — Abstracting, Bibliographies, Statistics*

BOLETIN DE ESTADISTICAS LABORALES. see *BUSINESS AND ECONOMICS — Abstracting, Bibliographies, Statistics*

318 BO
BOLIVIA. CAMARA DE DIPUTADOS. ESTADISTICAS SOCIO-ECONOMICAS. 1987? a. Muller & Asociados, Edif. Camara de Comercio, Ofc. 1305, Casilla 608, La Paz, Bolivia. TEL 378970.

BOLIVIA. INSTITUTO NACIONAL DE ESTADISTICA. ANUARIO DE COMERCIO EXTERIOR. see *BUSINESS AND ECONOMICS — Abstracting, Bibliographies, Statistics*

BOLIVIA. INSTITUTO NACIONAL DE ESTADISTICA. ANUARIO DE ESTADISTICAS INDUSTRIALES. see *BUSINESS AND ECONOMICS — Abstracting, Bibliographies, Statistics*

BOLIVIA. INSTITUTO NACIONAL DE ESTADISTICA. ESTADISTICAS REGIONALES DEPARTAMENTALES. see *PUBLIC ADMINISTRATION — Abstracting, Bibliographies, Statistics*

318 BO ISSN 0302-5217
HA965
BOLIVIA EN CIFRAS. 1972. a. Instituto Nacional de Estadistica, Casilla de Correo No. 6129, La Paz, Bolivia.

310 GW
BONNER MONATSZAHLEN; Statistik aktuell. 1981. m. Buerger- und Standesamt, Statistikstelle, Bottlerplatz 1, 53103 Bonn, Germany. TEL 0228-773480. FAX 0228-772281. TELEX 886861-SKBN-D. Ed. Klaus Kosack. circ. 1,000. (back issues avail.) **Document type:** government publication.

BOOK OF THE STATES. see *PUBLIC ADMINISTRATION*

BOTSWANA. CENTRAL STATISTICS OFFICE. DEMOGRAPHIC AND HEALTH SURVEY. see *BUSINESS AND ECONOMICS — Abstracting, Bibliographies, Statistics*

BOTSWANA. CENTRAL STATISTICS OFFICE. EXTERNAL TRADE STATISTICS. see *BUSINESS AND ECONOMICS — Abstracting, Bibliographies, Statistics*

BOTSWANA. CENTRAL STATISTICS OFFICE. HEALTH STATISTICS REPORT. see *MEDICAL SCIENCES — Abstracting, Bibliographies, Statistics*

BOTSWANA. CENTRAL STATISTICS OFFICE. HOUSEHOLD INCOME AND EXPENDITURE SURVEY. see *BUSINESS AND ECONOMICS — Abstracting, Bibliographies, Statistics*

BOTSWANA. CENTRAL STATISTICS OFFICE. LABOUR STATISTICS. see *BUSINESS AND ECONOMICS — Abstracting, Bibliographies, Statistics*

BOTSWANA. CENTRAL STATISTICS OFFICE. STATISTICAL BULLETIN. see *BUSINESS AND ECONOMICS — Abstracting, Bibliographies, Statistics*

BOTSWANA. CENTRAL STATISTICS OFFICE. TOURIST STATISTICS. see *TRAVEL AND TOURISM — Abstracting, Bibliographies, Statistics*

BOTSWANA. CENTRAL STATISTICS OFFICE. TRANSPORT STATISTICS. see *TRANSPORTATION*

BOTSWANA. MINISTRY OF AGRICULTURE. AGRICULTURAL STATISTICS. see *AGRICULTURE — Abstracting, Bibliographies, Statistics*

BOTSWANA. MINISTRY OF AGRICULTURE. FARM MANAGEMENT SURVEY RESULTS. see *AGRICULTURE — Agricultural Economics*

BOTSWANA. MINISTRY OF AGRICULTURE. LIVESTOCK MANAGEMENT SURVEY RESULTS. see *AGRICULTURE — Poultry And Livestock*

318.1 BL ISSN 0103-9288
HA973
BRASIL EM NUMEROS/BRAZIL IN FIGURES. (Editions in English, Portuguese) 1960. a. $80. Fundacao Instituto Brasileiro de Geografia e Estatistica, Centro de Documentacao e Disseminacao de Informacoes, Rua General Canabarro 666, 2o andar, Maracana 20272-201 Rio de Janeiro, Brazil. TEL 55-21-264-5424. FAX 55-21-21289575.
   Supersedes (in 1992): Brasil: Series Estatisticas Retrospectivas (ISSN 0068-0842); Which was formerly (until 1970): Brasil em Numeros (ISSN 0524-2010)

BRAZIL. FUNDACAO INSTITUTO BRASILEIRO DE GEOGRAFIA E ESTADISTICA. ESTATISTICAS DO REGISTRO CIVIL. see *POPULATION STUDIES — Abstracting, Bibliographies, Statistics*

BRAZIL. SERVICO SOCIAL DO COMERCIO. ANUARIO ESTATISTICO. see *PUBLIC ADMINISTRATION — Abstracting, Bibliographies, Statistics*

BRITISH AID STATISTICS; STATISTICS OF U.K. ECONOMIC AID TO DEVELOPING COUNTRIES. see *BUSINESS AND ECONOMICS — Abstracting, Bibliographies, Statistics*

317 CN
BRITISH COLUMBIA. MINISTRY OF GOVERNMENT SERVICES. 12/yr. Can.$50. Ministry of Government Services, B C Stats, 553 Superior St., Victoria, BC V8V 1X4, Canada. TEL 604-387-1502. FAX 604-387-0329. **Document type:** government publication.
   Formerly: British Columbia. Ministry of Finance and Corporate Relations. Current Statistics.
   Description: Lists the latest monthly and annual data on the labour force, consumer price index and production.

BRITISH COLUMBIA. MINISTRY OF MUNICIPAL AFFAIRS, RECREATION AND HOUSING. MUNICIPAL STATISTICS, INCLUDING REGIONAL DISTRICTS. see *PUBLIC ADMINISTRATION — Abstracting, Bibliographies, Statistics*

BRITISH FOOTWEAR MANUFACTURERS FEDERATION. STATISTICS. see *SHOES AND BOOTS — Abstracting, Bibliographies, Statistics*

BRITISH JOURNAL OF MATHEMATICAL AND STATISTICAL PSYCHOLOGY. see *PSYCHOLOGY*

BRITISH TOURIST AUTHORITY. DIGEST OF TOURIST STATISTICS. see *TRAVEL AND TOURISM — Abstracting, Bibliographies, Statistics*

BRITISH VIRGIN ISLANDS. STATISTICS OFFICE. BALANCE OF PAYMENTS. see *BUSINESS AND ECONOMICS — Abstracting, Bibliographies, Statistics*

BRITISH VIRGIN ISLANDS. STATISTICS OFFICE. NATIONAL INCOME AND EXPENDITURE. see *BUSINESS AND ECONOMICS — Abstracting, Bibliographies, Statistics*

947 314 HU ISSN 0521-4882
BUDAPEST STATISZTIKAI EVKONYVE. a. 325 Ft. (Kozponti Statisztikai Hivatal) Statisztikai Kiado Vallalat, Kaszasdulo u. 2, Box 99, 1300 Budapest 3, Hungary. TEL 688-635. TELEX 22-6699. (Subscr. to: Kultura, Box 149, H-1389 Budapest, Hungary) circ. 800.

947 314 HU ISSN 0438-2242
HA1208
BUDAPEST STATISZTIKAI ZSEBKONYVE. a. 99 Ft. (Kozponti Statisztikai Hivatal) Statiqum Kiado es Nyomda Kft., Kaszasdulo u. 2, Box 99, 1300 Budapest 3, Hungary. TEL 361-180-3311. FAX 361-168-8635. TELEX 22-6699. (Subscr. to: Kultura, Box 149, 1389 Budapest, Hungary) circ. 1,000.

314 HU ISSN 0133-2449
BUDAPESTI STATISZTIKAI TAJEKOZTATO. q. (Kozponti Statisztikai Hivatal) Statisztikai Kiado Vallalat, Kaszasdulo u. 2, P.O. Box 99, 1300 Budapest 3, Hungary. TEL 688-635. TELEX 22-6699. (Subscr. to: Kultura, Box 149, H-1389 Budapest, Hungary)

BUREAU OF JUSTICE STATISTICS REPORTS. JUSTICE EXPENDITURE AND EMPLOYMENT. see *CRIMINOLOGY AND LAW ENFORCEMENT*

STATISTICS

316 316   BD
BURUNDI. INSTITUT DE STATISTIQUES ET D'ETUDES ECONOMIQUES. ANNUAIRE STATISTIQUE. a. $45. Institut de Statistiques et d'Etudes Economiques, B.P. 156, Bujumbura, Burundi.
Formerly: Burundi. Departement des Etudes et Statistiques. Bulletin Annuaire.

316   BD
BURUNDI. INSTITUT DE STATISTIQUES ET D'ETUDES ECONOMIQUES. BULLETIN MENSUEL DES PRIX. m. $270. Institut de Statistiques et d'Etudes Economiques, B.P. 1156, Bujumbura, Burundi.
Formerly: Burundi. Departement des Etudes et Statistiques. Informations Statistiques Mensuelles.

316   BD
BURUNDI. INSTITUT DE STATISTIQUES ET D'ETUDES ECONOMIQUES. BULLETIN STATISTIQUE TRIMESTRIEL. Title varies slightly. (Supplement avail.) 1965. q. $60. Institut de Statistiques et d'Etudes Economiques, B.P. 1156, Bujumbura, Burundi. stat. **Indexed:** P.A.I.S.For.Lang.Ind.
Formerly: Burundi. Departement des Etudes et Statistiques. Bulletin Trimestriel; **Supersedes:** Burundi. Ministere du Plan. Departement des Statistiques. Bulletin de Statistique (ISSN 0525-2539)

BUSINESS MONITOR. RETAIL PRICES INDEX. see *BUSINESS AND ECONOMICS — Abstracting, Bibliographies, Statistics*

BUSINESS MONITOR: ASSETS AND LIABILITIES OF FINANCE HOUSES AND OTHER CONSUMER CREDIT COMPANIES. see *BUSINESS AND ECONOMICS — Abstracting, Bibliographies, Statistics*

BUSINESS MONITOR: CATERING AND ALLIED TRADES. see *HOTELS AND RESTAURANTS — Abstracting, Bibliographies, Statistics*

BUSINESS MONITOR: COMPANY FINANCE. see *BUSINESS AND ECONOMICS — Abstracting, Bibliographies, Statistics*

BUSINESS MONITOR: COMPUTER SERVICES. see *COMPUTERS — Computer Industry*

BUSINESS MONITOR: CREDIT BUSINESS. see *BUSINESS AND ECONOMICS — Abstracting, Bibliographies, Statistics*

BUSINESS MONITOR: GUIDE TO THE CLASSIFICATION OF OVERSEAS TRADE STATISTICS. see *BUSINESS AND ECONOMICS — Abstracting, Bibliographies, Statistics*

BUSINESS MONITOR: MOTOR TRADES. see *TRANSPORTATION — Abstracting, Bibliographies, Statistics*

BUSINESS MONITOR: OVERSEAS TRADE STATISTICS OF THE UNITED KINGDOM (ANNUAL REVISION). see *BUSINESS AND ECONOMICS — Abstracting, Bibliographies, Statistics*

BUSINESS MONITOR: OVERSEAS TRADE STATISTICS OF THE UNITED KINGDOM (QUARTERLY REVISION). see *BUSINESS AND ECONOMICS — Abstracting, Bibliographies, Statistics*

BUSINESS MONITOR: OVERSEAS TRANSACTIONS. see *BUSINESS AND ECONOMICS — Abstracting, Bibliographies, Statistics*

BUSINESS MONITOR: OVERSEAS TRAVEL AND TOURISM. see *TRAVEL AND TOURISM — Abstracting, Bibliographies, Statistics*

BUSINESS MONITOR: RETAIL SALES. see *BUSINESS AND ECONOMICS — Abstracting, Bibliographies, Statistics*

BUSINESS MONITOR: RETAILING. see *BUSINESS AND ECONOMICS — Abstracting, Bibliographies, Statistics*

BUSINESS MONITOR: SERVICE TRADES. see *BUSINESS AND ECONOMICS — Abstracting, Bibliographies, Statistics*

BUSINESS MONITOR: WHOLESALING. see *BUSINESS AND ECONOMICS — Abstracting, Bibliographies, Statistics*

C A B AIR CARRIER TRAFFIC STATISTICS. (Civil Aeronautics Board) see *TRANSPORTATION — Abstracting, Bibliographies, Statistics*

C A T M O G. (Concepts and Techniques in Modern Geography) see *GEOGRAPHY*

319   TR
C.S.O. STATISTICAL BULLETINS. 1972. irreg. price varies. Central Statistical Office, 35-41 Queen St., P.O. Box 98, Port-of-Spain, Trinidad & Tobago, W.I. TEL 809-625-3705. (Dist. by: Government Printing Office, 2-4 Victoria Ave., Port-of-Spain, Trinidad & Tobago, W.I.) **Document type:** government publication.

310   II   ISSN 0008-0683
HA1   CODEN: CSTBAA
CALCUTTA STATISTICAL ASSOCIATION. BULLETIN. (Text in English) 1947. q. Rs.60($16) Calcutta Statistical Association, Calcutta University, New Science Bldg., 35 B.C. Rd., Calcutta 19, India. Ed. S.K. Chatterjee. adv.; bk.rev.; charts; stat.; index. circ. 400. **Indexed:** Curr.Ind.Stat., J.Cont.Quant.Meth., Math.R., Stat.Theor.Meth.Abstr. **Document type:** bulletin. —Faxon; SWETS; UnCover.

312   US
CALIFORNIA COUNTY FACT BOOK. 1960. a. $30. California State Association Counties, 1100 K St., Ste. 101, Sacramento, CA 95814. TEL 916-327-7500. charts; stat. circ. 1,000.
Description: Statistical compilation on: agriculture, land use and natural resources, budget, revenue and expenditures, court and law enforcement, county jails, transportation and public works, employment, building activity, elected officials.

CALIFORNIA COUNTY PROJECTIONS (YEAR); regional market update and projections. see *BUSINESS AND ECONOMICS — Abstracting, Bibliographies, Statistics*

CALIFORNIA ECONOMIC GROWTH (YEAR); regional market update and projections. see *BUSINESS AND ECONOMICS — Abstracting, Bibliographies, Statistics*

CALIFORNIA POPULATION CHARACTERISTICS (YEAR); regional market update and projections. see *POPULATION STUDIES — Abstracting, Bibliographies, Statistics*

CALIFORNIA WORK INJURIES AND ILLNESSES. see *OCCUPATIONAL HEALTH AND SAFETY — Abstracting, Bibliographies, Statistics*

318   CK   ISSN 0120-6338
CAMBIO Y PROGRESO. 1985. irreg., latest no.2. $30. Departamento Administrativo Nacional de Estadistica, Banco Nacional de Datos, Avda. El Dorado, Apdo. Aereo 80043, Bogota D.C., Colombia. TEL 2223273. FAX 2222305. TELEX 44573.

310   CM
CAMEROON. DIRECTION DE LA STATISTIQUE ET DE LA COMPTABILITE NATIONALE. BULLETIN MENSUEL DE STATISTIQUE. 1974. m. 12000 Fr.CFA. Direction de la Statistique et de la Comptabilite Nationale, B.P. 660, Yaounde, Cameroon. TEL 220-445. circ. 500.

CAMEROON. DIRECTION DE LA STATISTIQUE ET DE LA COMPTABILITE NATIONALE. NOTE ANNUELLE DE STATISTIQUE. see *BUSINESS AND ECONOMICS — Abstracting, Bibliographies, Statistics*

316   CM
CAMEROON. PROVINCIAL STATISTICAL SERVICE OF THE SOUTH WEST. ANNUAL STATISTICAL REPORT, SOUTH WEST PROVINCE. a. Service Provincial de la Statistique du Sud-Ouest, Box 93, Buea, Cameroon.

CANADA. STATISTICS CANADA. AGGREGATE PRODUCTIVITY MEASURES. see *BUSINESS AND ECONOMICS — Abstracting, Bibliographies, Statistics*

CANADA. STATISTICS CANADA. AIR CHARTER STATISTICS. see *TRANSPORTATION — Abstracting, Bibliographies, Statistics*

CANADA. STATISTICS CANADA. AIR PASSENGER ORIGIN AND DESTINATION. CANADA - UNITED STATES REPORT. see *TRANSPORTATION — Abstracting, Bibliographies, Statistics*

CANADA. STATISTICS CANADA. AVIATION STATISTICS CENTRE. SERVICE BULLETIN/CANADA. CENTRE DES STATISTIQUES DE L'AVIATION. BULLETIN DE SERVICE. see *TRANSPORTATION — Abstracting, Bibliographies, Statistics*

CANADA. STATISTICS CANADA. BEVERAGE AND TOBACCO PRODUCTS INDUSTRIES. see *TOBACCO — Abstracting, Bibliographies, Statistics*

CANADA. STATISTICS CANADA. BUILDING PERMITS. see *BUILDING AND CONSTRUCTION — Abstracting, Bibliographies, Statistics*

CANADA. STATISTICS CANADA. BUILDING PERMITS. ANNUAL SUMMARY. see *BUILDING AND CONSTRUCTION — Abstracting, Bibliographies, Statistics*

CANADA. STATISTICS CANADA. CABLE TELEVISION. see *COMMUNICATIONS — Abstracting, Bibliographies, Statistics*

CANADA. STATISTICS CANADA. CANADA'S MINERAL PRODUCTION: PRELIMINARY ESTIMATES. see *MINES AND MINING INDUSTRY — Abstracting, Bibliographies, Statistics*

CANADA. STATISTICS CANADA. CLOTHING INDUSTRIES. see *CLOTHING TRADE — Abstracting, Bibliographies, Statistics*

CANADA. STATISTICS CANADA. COAL AND COKE STATISTICS. see *MINES AND MINING INDUSTRY — Abstracting, Bibliographies, Statistics*

CANADA. STATISTICS CANADA. COAL MINES. see *MINES AND MINING INDUSTRY — Abstracting, Bibliographies, Statistics*

CANADA. STATISTICS CANADA. COMMUNICATIONS SERVICE BULLETIN. see *COMMUNICATIONS — Abstracting, Bibliographies, Statistics*

CANADA. STATISTICS CANADA. COMMUNITY COLLEGES AND RELATED INSTITUTIONS, POSTSECONDARY ENROLMENT AND GRADUATES. see *EDUCATION — Abstracting, Bibliographies, Statistics*

CANADA. STATISTICS CANADA. CONSUMER PRICES AND PRICE INDEXES. see *BUSINESS AND ECONOMICS — Abstracting, Bibliographies, Statistics*

CANADA. STATISTICS CANADA. CORPORATION FINANCIAL STATISTICS. see *BUSINESS AND ECONOMICS — Abstracting, Bibliographies, Statistics*

CANADA. STATISTICS CANADA. CORPORATION TAXATION STATISTICS. see *BUSINESS AND ECONOMICS — Abstracting, Bibliographies, Statistics*

CANADA. STATISTICS CANADA. CREDIT UNIONS. see *BUSINESS AND ECONOMICS — Abstracting, Bibliographies, Statistics*

CANADA. STATISTICS CANADA. CRUDE PETROLEUM AND NATURAL GAS INDUSTRY. see *PETROLEUM AND GAS — Abstracting, Bibliographies, Statistics*

CANADA. STATISTICS CANADA. DIRECT SELLING IN CANADA. see *BUSINESS AND ECONOMICS — Abstracting, Bibliographies, Statistics*

CANADA. STATISTICS CANADA. ELEMENTARY - SECONDARY SCHOOL ENROLMENT. see *EDUCATION — Abstracting, Bibliographies, Statistics*

CANADA. STATISTICS CANADA. EMPLOYMENT, EARNINGS AND HOURS. see *BUSINESS AND ECONOMICS — Abstracting, Bibliographies, Statistics*

CANADA. STATISTICS CANADA. ESTIMATES OF LABOUR INCOME. see *BUSINESS AND ECONOMICS — Abstracting, Bibliographies, Statistics*

CANADA. STATISTICS CANADA. EXPORTS, MERCHANDISE TRADE H S BASED. see *BUSINESS AND ECONOMICS — Abstracting, Bibliographies, Statistics*

CANADA. STATISTICS CANADA. FABRICATED METAL PRODUCTS INDUSTRIES. see *METALLURGY — Abstracting, Bibliographies, Statistics*

CANADA. STATISTICS CANADA. FAMILY INCOMES, CENSUS FAMILIES. see BUSINESS AND ECONOMICS — Abstracting, Bibliographies, Statistics

CANADA. STATISTICS CANADA. FARM PRODUCTS PRICE INDEX. see AGRICULTURE — Abstracting, Bibliographies, Statistics

CANADA. STATISTICS CANADA. FIELD CROP REPORTING SERIES. see AGRICULTURE — Abstracting, Bibliographies, Statistics

CANADA. STATISTICS CANADA. FINANCIAL STATISTICS OF EDUCATION. see EDUCATION — Abstracting, Bibliographies, Statistics

CANADA. STATISTICS CANADA. FOOD INDUSTRIES. see FOOD AND FOOD INDUSTRIES — Abstracting, Bibliographies, Statistics

CANADA. STATISTICS CANADA. FRUIT AND VEGETABLE PRODUCTION. see AGRICULTURE — Abstracting, Bibliographies, Statistics

CANADA. STATISTICS CANADA. GAS UTILITIES, TRANSPORT AND DISTRIBUTION SYSTEMS. see PETROLEUM AND GAS — Abstracting, Bibliographies, Statistics

CANADA. STATISTICS CANADA. GENERAL REVIEW OF THE MINERAL INDUSTRIES, MINES, QUARRIES AND OIL WELLS. see MINES AND MINING INDUSTRY — Abstracting, Bibliographies, Statistics

CANADA. STATISTICS CANADA. GYPSUM PRODUCTS. see BUILDING AND CONSTRUCTION — Abstracting, Bibliographies, Statistics

CANADA. STATISTICS CANADA. HEALTH REPORTS. SUPPLEMENT. see HOSPITALS — Abstracting, Bibliographies, Statistics

CANADA. STATISTICS CANADA. HIGHWAY, ROAD, STREET AND BRIDGE CONTRACTORS. see ENGINEERING — Abstracting, Bibliographies, Statistics

CANADA. STATISTICS CANADA. HISTORICAL LABOUR FORCE STATISTICS, ACTUAL DATA, SEASONAL FACTORS, SEASONALLY ADJUSTED DATA. see BUSINESS AND ECONOMICS — Abstracting, Bibliographies, Statistics

CANADA. STATISTICS CANADA. HOUSEHOLD FACILITIES AND EQUIPMENT. see HOME ECONOMICS — Abstracting, Bibliographies, Statistics

CANADA. STATISTICS CANADA. IMPORTS, MERCHANDISE TRADE H S BASED. see BUSINESS AND ECONOMICS — Abstracting, Bibliographies, Statistics

CANADA. STATISTICS CANADA. INDUSTRIAL CORPORATIONS, FINANCIAL STATISTICS. see BUSINESS AND ECONOMICS — Abstracting, Bibliographies, Statistics

310   CN   ISSN 0380-0547
HC111
CANADA. STATISTICS CANADA. INFOMAT. French edition (ISSN 0380-0563) (Catalogue 11-002) (Editions in English and French) 1932. w. $156. Statistics Canada, Publications Division, Ottawa, ON K1A 0T6, Canada. TEL 613-951-7277; 800-267-6677. FAX 613-951-1584. Ed. Greg Thomson. (also avail. in microform from MML)
   Formerly: Statistics Canada Weekly (ISSN 0380-0555)
   Description: Highlights major Statistics Canada reports, reference papers and other releases.

CANADA. STATISTICS CANADA. INTERNATIONAL TRAVEL. see TRAVEL AND TOURISM — Abstracting, Bibliographies, Statistics

310   CN   ISSN 0228-5134
Z7554.C2
CANADA. STATISTICS CANADA. LISTING OF SUPPLEMENTARY DOCUMENTS. (Catalogue 11-207) (Text in English and French) 1980. a. Can.$32($38) (foreign $45). Statistics Canada, Communications Division, 3rd Floor, R.H. Coats Bldg., Ottawa, Ont. K1A 0T6, Canada. TEL 613-951-7277. FAX 613-951-1584. (Subscr. to: Publications Sales and Services, Ottawa, Ont. K1A 0T6, Canada)
   Description: Systematic inventory of supplementary Statistics Canada documents available to the public, includes technical papers, memoranda, discussions and working papers.

CANADA. STATISTICS CANADA. LIVESTOCK AND ANIMAL PRODUCTS STATISTICS. see AGRICULTURE — Abstracting, Bibliographies, Statistics

CANADA. STATISTICS CANADA. MANUFACTURING INDUSTRIES OF CANADA: SUB-PROVINCIAL AREAS. see BUSINESS AND ECONOMICS — Abstracting, Bibliographies, Statistics

CANADA. STATISTICS CANADA. MARKET RESEARCH HANDBOOK. see BUSINESS AND ECONOMICS — Abstracting, Bibliographies, Statistics

CANADA. STATISTICS CANADA. MECHANICAL TRADE CONTRACTORS. see ENGINEERING — Abstracting, Bibliographies, Statistics

CANADA. STATISTICS CANADA. MERCHANDISING INVENTORIES. see BUSINESS AND ECONOMICS — Abstracting, Bibliographies, Statistics

CANADA. STATISTICS CANADA. MINERAL WOOL INCLUDING FIBROUS GLASS INSULATION. see BUILDING AND CONSTRUCTION — Abstracting, Bibliographies, Statistics

CANADA. STATISTICS CANADA. MOTION PICTURE THEATRES AND FILM DISTRIBUTORS. see MOTION PICTURES — Abstracting, Bibliographies, Statistics

CANADA. STATISTICS CANADA. NATIONAL INCOME AND EXPENDITURE ACCOUNTS. see BUSINESS AND ECONOMICS — Abstracting, Bibliographies, Statistics

CANADA. STATISTICS CANADA. NON-METALLIC MINERAL PRODUCTS INDUSTRIES. see CERAMICS, GLASS AND POTTERY — Abstracting, Bibliographies, Statistics

CANADA. STATISTICS CANADA. NON-RESIDENTIAL GENERAL CONTRACTORS AND DEVELOPERS. see BUILDING AND CONSTRUCTION — Abstracting, Bibliographies, Statistics

CANADA. STATISTICS CANADA. OILS AND FATS/HUILES ET CORPS GRAS. see FOOD AND FOOD INDUSTRIES — Abstracting, Bibliographies, Statistics

CANADA. STATISTICS CANADA. OTHER MANUFACTURING INDUSTRIES. see BUSINESS AND ECONOMICS — Abstracting, Bibliographies, Statistics

CANADA. STATISTICS CANADA. PASSENGER BUS AND URBAN TRANSIT STATISTICS. see TRANSPORTATION — Abstracting, Bibliographies, Statistics

CANADA. STATISTICS CANADA. PASSENGER BUS AND URBAN TRANSIT STATISTICS. see TRANSPORTATION — Abstracting, Bibliographies, Statistics

CANADA. STATISTICS CANADA. PENSION PLANS IN CANADA. see INSURANCE — Abstracting, Bibliographies, Statistics

CANADA. STATISTICS CANADA. PRIMARY IRON AND STEEL. see METALLURGY — Abstracting, Bibliographies, Statistics

CANADA. STATISTICS CANADA. PRIMARY METAL INDUSTRIES. see METALLURGY

CANADA. STATISTICS CANADA. PRINTING, PUBLISHING AND ALLIED INDUSTRIES. see PRINTING — Abstracting, Bibliographies, Statistics

CANADA. STATISTICS CANADA. PRIVATE AND PUBLIC INVESTMENT IN CANADA, INTENTIONS. see BUSINESS AND ECONOMICS — Abstracting, Bibliographies, Statistics

CANADA. STATISTICS CANADA. PRIVATE AND PUBLIC INVESTMENT IN CANADA. REVISED INTENTIONS. see BUSINESS AND ECONOMICS — Abstracting, Bibliographies, Statistics

CANADA. STATISTICS CANADA. PRODUCTION OF POULTRY AND EGGS. see AGRICULTURE — Abstracting, Bibliographies, Statistics

CANADA. STATISTICS CANADA. PRODUCTS SHIPPED BY CANADIAN MANUFACTURERS. see BUSINESS AND ECONOMICS — Abstracting, Bibliographies, Statistics

CANADA. STATISTICS CANADA. PROVINCIAL GOVERNMENT ENTERPRISE FINANCE: INCOME AND EXPENDITURE, ASSETS, LIABILITIES AND NET WORTH. see BUSINESS AND ECONOMICS — Abstracting, Bibliographies, Statistics

CANADA. STATISTICS CANADA. QUARTERLY ESTIMATES OF TRUSTEED PENSION FUNDS. see BUSINESS AND ECONOMICS — Abstracting, Bibliographies, Statistics

CANADA. STATISTICS CANADA. QUARTERLY REPORT ON ENERGY SUPPLY. DEMAND IN CANADA. see ENERGY — Abstracting, Bibliographies, Statistics

CANADA. STATISTICS CANADA. RADIO AND TELEVISION BROADCASTING. see COMMUNICATIONS — Abstracting, Bibliographies, Statistics

CANADA. STATISTICS CANADA. RAILWAY CARLOADINGS. see TRANSPORTATION — Abstracting, Bibliographies, Statistics

CANADA. STATISTICS CANADA. RAILWAY OPERATING STATISTICS. see TRANSPORTATION — Abstracting, Bibliographies, Statistics

CANADA. STATISTICS CANADA. REFINED PETROLEUM AND COAL PRODUCTS INDUSTRIES. see PETROLEUM AND GAS — Abstracting, Bibliographies, Statistics

CANADA. STATISTICS CANADA. REPORT ON FUR FARMS. see LEATHER AND FUR INDUSTRIES — Abstracting, Bibliographies, Statistics

CANADA. STATISTICS CANADA. RESTAURANT, CATERER AND TAVERN STATISTICS. see HOTELS AND RESTAURANTS — Abstracting, Bibliographies, Statistics

CANADA. STATISTICS CANADA. RETAIL CHAIN AND DEPARTMENT STORES. see BUSINESS AND ECONOMICS — Abstracting, Bibliographies, Statistics

CANADA. STATISTICS CANADA. ROAD MOTOR VEHICLES, FUEL SALES. see TRANSPORTATION — Abstracting, Bibliographies, Statistics

CANADA. STATISTICS CANADA. ROAD MOTOR VEHICLES, REGISTRATIONS. see TRANSPORTATION — Abstracting, Bibliographies, Statistics

CANADA. STATISTICS CANADA. RUBBER AND PLASTIC PRODUCTS INDUSTRIES. see RUBBER — Abstracting, Bibliographies, Statistics

CANADA. STATISTICS CANADA. SECURITY TRANSACTIONS WITH NON-RESIDENTS. see BUSINESS AND ECONOMICS — Abstracting, Bibliographies, Statistics

CANADA. STATISTICS CANADA. SHIPPING IN CANADA. see TRANSPORTATION — Abstracting, Bibliographies, Statistics

CANADA. STATISTICS CANADA. SURFACE AND MARINE TRANSPORT. see TRANSPORTATION — Abstracting, Bibliographies, Statistics

CANADA. STATISTICS CANADA. SURVEY OF CANADIAN NURSERY TRADES INDUSTRY. see GARDENING AND HORTICULTURE — Abstracting, Bibliographies, Statistics

CANADA. STATISTICS CANADA. SYSTEM OF NATIONAL ACCOUNTS. CANADA'S INTERNATIONAL INVESTMENT POSITION. see *BUSINESS AND ECONOMICS — Abstracting, Bibliographies, Statistics*

CANADA. STATISTICS CANADA. TELECOMMUNICATIONS STATISTICS. see *COMMUNICATIONS — Abstracting, Bibliographies, Statistics*

CANADA. STATISTICS CANADA. TELEPHONE STATISTICS. see *COMMUNICATIONS — Abstracting, Bibliographies, Statistics*

CANADA. STATISTICS CANADA. TEXTILE PRODUCTS INDUSTRIES. see *TEXTILE INDUSTRIES AND FABRICS — Abstracting, Bibliographies, Statistics*

CANADA. STATISTICS CANADA. THE LABOUR FORCE. see *BUSINESS AND ECONOMICS — Abstracting, Bibliographies, Statistics*

CANADA. STATISTICS CANADA. TRUSTEED PENSION FUNDS - FINANCIAL STATISTICS. see *BUSINESS AND ECONOMICS — Abstracting, Bibliographies, Statistics*

CANADA. STATISTICS CANADA. VENDING MACHINE OPERATORS. see *MACHINERY — Abstracting, Bibliographies, Statistics*

CANADA. STATISTICS CANADA. WHOLESALE TRADE. see *BUSINESS AND ECONOMICS — Abstracting, Bibliographies, Statistics*

CANADA. STATISTICS CANADA. WOOD INDUSTRIES. see *FORESTS AND FORESTRY — Abstracting, Bibliographies, Statistics*

971   CN   ISSN 0840-6014
HC115
CANADA, A PORTRAIT. 1980. biennial. Can.$25($29.95) (effective Apr. 1991). Statistics Canada, Publications Division, Ottawa, Ont. K1A 0T6, Canada. TEL 613-951-7277. FAX 613-951-1584.
    Description: Presents current and historical information to form a portrait of Canada.

971 317   CN   ISSN 0068-8142
HA744
CANADA YEARBOOK. French edition: Annuaire du Canada. (Catalog 11-202) (Text in English) 1867. biennial. $72. Statistics Canada, Publications Division, Ottawa, ON K1A 0T6, Canada. TEL 800-267-6677. FAX 613-951-1582. (also avail. in microfilm from MML) **Document type:** government publication.
    Description: Offers comprehensive and timely data on economy, arts, sports, government, geography, demography.

CANADIAN ECONOMIC OBSERVER/OBSERVATEUR ECONOMIQUE CANADAIEN. see *BUSINESS AND ECONOMICS — Abstracting, Bibliographies, Statistics*

CANADIAN FISHERIES. STATISTICAL HIGHLIGHTS. see *FISH AND FISHERIES — Abstracting, Bibliographies, Statistics*

CANADIAN FISHERIES ANNUAL STATISTICAL REVIEW. see *FISH AND FISHERIES*

CANADIAN GRAINS INDUSTRY STATISTICAL HANDBOOK. see *AGRICULTURE — Abstracting, Bibliographies, Statistics*

310   CN   ISSN 0319-5724
CANADIAN JOURNAL OF STATISTICS/REVUE CANADIENNE DE STATISTIQUE. (Text in English, French) 1973. q. Can.$99. Statistical Society of Canada, Rm 4356 Herzberg Bldg., Carleton University, Ottawa, ON K1S 5B6, Canada. TEL 613-788-3988. Ed. Nancy Reid. adv. contact: Dan Krewski. bk.rev.; stat.; index. circ. 1,350. (back issues avail.) **Indexed:** Biostat., Compumath, Curr.Ind.Stat., J.Cont.Quant.Meth., Math.R., Oper.Res.Manage.Sci., Qual.Contr.Appl.Stat., Qual.Contr.Appl.Stat., Ref.Zh., Risk Abstr., Stat.Theor.Meth.Abstr. **Document type:** academic/scholarly publication.
    —BLDSC (3035.760000); Faxon; Genuine Article; SWETS; UnCover. **CCC.**
    Description: Publishes original articles on both theoretical and applied statistics.

CANADIAN PULP AND PAPER ASSOCIATION. MONTHLY NEWSPRINT STATISTICS/ASSOCIATION CANADIENNE DES PATES ET PAPIERS. STATISTIQUES MENSUELLES SUR LE PAPIER JOURNAL. see *PAPER AND PULP*

310   CN   ISSN 0831-5698
HN101
CANADIAN SOCIAL TRENDS. French edition: Tendances Sociales Canadiennes (ISSN 0831-5701) (Catalogue 11-008) (Editions in English and French) 1982. q. Can.$34($40) (foreign $48). (Ministry of Industry and Science) Statistics Canada, Publications Division, Ottawa, ON K1A 0T6, Canada. TEL 613-951-7277; 800-267-6677. FAX 613-951-1584. Ed. Cynthia Silver. adv.; charts; illus.; stat. **Indexed:** Amer.Hist.& Life, Can.B.P.I., Can.Per.Ind., Hist.Abstr., Pt.de Rep. (1991-). **Document type:** government publication.
    Description: Discusses the social, economic and demographic changes affecting the lives of Canadians and contains the latest figures for major social indicators.

CAPITAL PUNISHMENT (YEAR). see *CRIMINOLOGY AND LAW ENFORCEMENT*

CARIBBEAN TOURISM ORGANIZATION. STATISTICAL NEWS. see *TRAVEL AND TOURISM — Abstracting, Bibliographies, Statistics*

CASUALTY ACTUARIAL SOCIETY. DISCUSSION PAPER PROGRAM. see *INSURANCE — Abstracting, Bibliographies, Statistics*

CASUALTY ACTUARIAL SOCIETY. FORUM. see *INSURANCE — Abstracting, Bibliographies, Statistics*

CASUALTY ACTUARIAL SOCIETY. PROCEEDINGS. see *INSURANCE — Abstracting, Bibliographies, Statistics*

CASUALTY ACTUARIAL SOCIETY. YEARBOOK. see *INSURANCE — Abstracting, Bibliographies, Statistics*

016   MX   ISSN 0186-0437
CATALOGO (YEAR) PRODUCTOS DEL I N E G I. 1987. a. free. Instituto Nacional de Estadistica, Geografia e Informatica, Secretaria de Programacion y Presupuesto, Prol. Heroe de Nacozari 2301 Sur, Puerta 11, Acceso, 20270 Aguascalientes Ags., Mexico. TEL 49-18-19-48. FAX 491-807-39. circ. 4,000. **Document type:** catalog.
    Former titles (until 1977): Catalogo de Informacion Estadistica y Geografica; (until 1976): Sistema Nacional de Informacion. Catalog Historico de Publicasione.

310 338.9   JA   ISSN 0301-9837
Z7164.U5
CATALOGUE OF STATISTICAL MATERIALS OF DEVELOPING COUNTRIES. (Text in English, Japanese) biennial. 5000 Yen. Institute of Developing Economies - Ajia Keizai Kenkyusho, 42 Ichigaya-Hommura-cho, Shinjuku-ku, Tokyo 162, Japan. **Document type:** catalog.

319   CJ
CAYMAN ISLANDS. STATISTICS OFFICE. COMPENDIUM OF STATISTICS. 1975. a. $25. Statistics Office, Government Administration Bldg., Grand Cayman, Cayman Islands, British W.I. TEL 809-949-0940. FAX 809-949-8782. TELEX 4260 CIGOVT. **Document type:** government publication, abstracting/indexing.
    Formerly: Statistical Abstract of the Cayman Islands; Statistical Abstract of the Government of the Cayman Islands.

CENSO DE POBLACION Y VIVIENDAS. see *POPULATION STUDIES — Abstracting, Bibliographies, Statistics*

001.4   US
HA203
CENSUS AND YOU; monthly news form the U.S. Bureau of the Census. 1966. m. $21 (foreign $26.25). U.S. Bureau of the Census, Data User Services Division, Washington, DC 20233. TEL 301-457-1584. FAX 301-457-4714. (Subscr. to: Superintendent of Documents, U.S. Government Printing Office, Box 371974, Pittsburgh, PA 15250-9754. TEL 202-512-1800. FAX 202-512-2250) Ed. Neil Tillman. charts; stat.; index. circ. 8,000. (also avail. in microfiche from CIS; back issues avail.; reprint service avail. from CIS and the Census Bureau) **Indexed:** Amer.Stat.Ind. (1975-), Ind.U.S.Gov.Per., PROMT. **Document type:** government publication, newsletter.
    •Also available online. Vendor(s): CompuServe, Inc., Knight-Ridder, Inc.
    Former titles: U.S. Bureau of the Census. Data User News (ISSN 0096-9877); U.S. Bureau of the Census. Small Area Data Activities; U.S. Bureau of the Census. Small Area Data Notes.
    Description: Presents news on the most recent demographic and economic reports and information on data released online and on computer, magnetic tape, and CD-ROM. Uses of electronic data products, the 1990 census, economic censuses, and data for business and market research are emphasized.

CENSUS OF AGRICULTURE. see *AGRICULTURE — Abstracting, Bibliographies, Statistics*

CENSUS OF AGRICULTURE: FINAL REPORTS. see *AGRICULTURE — Abstracting, Bibliographies, Statistics*

CENSUS OF MANUFACTURING INDUSTRIES OF PUERTO RICO. see *BUSINESS AND ECONOMICS — Production Of Goods And Services*

CENSUS OF PRIVATE NON-PROFIT MAKING INSTITUTIONS IN FIJI. A REPORT. see *BUSINESS AND ECONOMICS — Abstracting, Bibliographies, Statistics*

CENTRAL BANK OF ICELAND. ECONOMIC STATISTICS. see *BUSINESS AND ECONOMICS — Abstracting, Bibliographies, Statistics*

CENTRAL BANK OF SOMALIA. BULLETIN/BANKIGA DHEXE EE SOOMAALIYA. FAAFIN. see *BUSINESS AND ECONOMICS — Abstracting, Bibliographies, Statistics*

CENTRAL BANK OF SRI LANKA. SOCIO ECONOMIC DATA. see *BUSINESS AND ECONOMICS — Abstracting, Bibliographies, Statistics*

CENTRAL BANK OF TRINIDAD AND TOBAGO. MONTHLY STATISTICAL DIGEST. see *BUSINESS AND ECONOMICS — Abstracting, Bibliographies, Statistics*

CENTRAL BANK OF TRINIDAD AND TOBAGO. QUARTERLY STATISTICAL DIGEST. see *BUSINESS AND ECONOMICS — Abstracting, Bibliographies, Statistics*

318   UY
CENTRO DE ESTADISTICAS NACIONALES Y COMERCIO INTERNACIONAL DEL URUGUAY. COSTO DE LA VIDA. s-a. $35 per no. (effective Jan. 1993). Centro de Estadisticas Nacionales y Comercio Internacional del Uruguay, Misiones 1361, Casilla de Correo 1510, 11200 Montevideo, Uruguay. TEL 95-29-30. FAX 95-45-78. **Document type:** bulletin.
    Description: Provides indices and comparative percentage variations of prices, services, salaries, and the value of the dollar.

310   XR
CESKA STATISTIKA. irreg. price varies. Cesky Statisticky Urad, Sokolovska 142, 186 04 Prague 8, Czech Republic. TEL 42-2-6604-2451. FAX 42-2-6631-0429. **Document type:** government publication.
    Description: Provides the outcome of large-scale statistical projects and yearly reports for individual branch statistics including descriptions, non-recurrent surveys and balance summaries.

519.5 004   US   ISSN 0933-2480
QA276.A1   CODEN: CNDCE4
CHANCE; new directions for statistics and computers. 1988. q. $75 (effective 1996). (American Statistics Association) Springer-Verlag, Journals, 175 Fifth Ave., New York, NY 10010. TEL 212-460-1612. FAX 212-473-6272. (N. American subscr. to: Journal Fulfillment Services, Box 2485, Secaucus, NJ 07096-2491. TEL 800-777-4643. FAX 201-348-4505; Elsewhere: Heidelberger Platz 3, 14197 Berlin, Germany. TEL 030-8207-1. FAX 030-8214091) Ed. John E. Rolph. (also avail. in microform from UMI; reprint service avail.) **Indexed:** Biostat., Curr.Ind.Stat. **Document type:** academic/scholarly publication.
—BLDSC (3129.632370); SWETS; UnCover. **CCC.**
Description: Aimed at persons using statistical methods and approaches in market research, demographics, social sciences, and medicine.
Refereed Serial

CHARITY TRENDS. see *SOCIAL SERVICES AND WELFARE — Abstracting, Bibliographies, Statistics*

CHARTERED INSTITUTE OF PUBLIC FINANCE AND ACCOUNTANCY. ARCHIVES STATISTICS. ESTIMATES. see *BUSINESS AND ECONOMICS — Abstracting, Bibliographies, Statistics*

CHARTERED INSTITUTE OF PUBLIC FINANCE AND ACCOUNTANCY. CAPITAL EXPENDITURE AND DEBT FINANCING STATISTICS. ACTUALS. see *BUSINESS AND ECONOMICS — Abstracting, Bibliographies, Statistics*

CHARTERED INSTITUTE OF PUBLIC FINANCE AND ACCOUNTANCY. CEMETERIES STATISTICS. ACTUALS. see *PUBLIC HEALTH AND SAFETY — Abstracting, Bibliographies, Statistics*

CHARTERED INSTITUTE OF PUBLIC FINANCE AND ACCOUNTANCY. CHARGES FOR LEISURE SERVICES. ACTUALS. see *SPORTS AND GAMES — Abstracting, Bibliographies, Statistics*

CHARTERED INSTITUTE OF PUBLIC FINANCE AND ACCOUNTANCY. COUNCIL TAX STATISTICS. ESTIMATES. see *BUSINESS AND ECONOMICS — Abstracting, Bibliographies, Statistics*

CHARTERED INSTITUTE OF PUBLIC FINANCE AND ACCOUNTANCY. COUNTY FARMS STATISTICS. ACTUALS. see *AGRICULTURE — Abstracting, Bibliographies, Statistics*

CHARTERED INSTITUTE OF PUBLIC FINANCE AND ACCOUNTANCY. CREMATORIA STATISTICS. ACTUALS. see *PUBLIC HEALTH AND SAFETY — Abstracting, Bibliographies, Statistics*

CHARTERED INSTITUTE OF PUBLIC FINANCE AND ACCOUNTANCY. DIRECT SERVICE ORGANISATION STATISTICS. ACTUALS. see *BUILDING AND CONSTRUCTION — Abstracting, Bibliographies, Statistics*

CHARTERED INSTITUTE OF PUBLIC FINANCE AND ACCOUNTANCY. EDUCATION STATISTICS. ACTUALS. see *EDUCATION — Abstracting, Bibliographies, Statistics*

CHARTERED INSTITUTE OF PUBLIC FINANCE AND ACCOUNTANCY. EDUCATION STATISTICS. ESTIMATES. see *EDUCATION — Abstracting, Bibliographies, Statistics*

CHARTERED INSTITUTE OF PUBLIC FINANCE AND ACCOUNTANCY. ENVIRONMENTAL HEALTH STATISTICS. ACTUALS. see *PUBLIC HEALTH AND SAFETY — Abstracting, Bibliographies, Statistics*

CHARTERED INSTITUTE OF PUBLIC FINANCE AND ACCOUNTANCY. FINANCE AND GENERAL STATISTICS. ESTIMATES. see *BUSINESS AND ECONOMICS — Abstracting, Bibliographies, Statistics*

CHARTERED INSTITUTE OF PUBLIC FINANCE AND ACCOUNTANCY. FIRE STATISTICS. ACTUALS & ESTIMATES. see *FIRE PREVENTION — Abstracting, Bibliographies, Statistics*

CHARTERED INSTITUTE OF PUBLIC FINANCE AND ACCOUNTANCY. HIGHWAYS AND TRANSPORTATION. ACTUALS. see *TRANSPORTATION — Abstracting, Bibliographies, Statistics*

CHARTERED INSTITUTE OF PUBLIC FINANCE AND ACCOUNTANCY. HIGHWAYS AND TRANSPORTATION STATISTICS. ESTIMATES & ACTUALS. see *TRANSPORTATION — Abstracting, Bibliographies, Statistics*

CHARTERED INSTITUTE OF PUBLIC FINANCE AND ACCOUNTANCY. HOMELESSNESS STATISTICS. see *HOUSING AND URBAN PLANNING — Abstracting, Bibliographies, Statistics*

CHARTERED INSTITUTE OF PUBLIC FINANCE AND ACCOUNTANCY. HOUSING REVENUE ACCOUNT STATISTICS. ESTIMATES & ACTUALS. see *HOUSING AND URBAN PLANNING — Abstracting, Bibliographies, Statistics*

CHARTERED INSTITUTE OF PUBLIC FINANCE AND ACCOUNTANCY. HOUSING RENTS STATISTICS. ACTUALS. see *HOUSING AND URBAN PLANNING — Abstracting, Bibliographies, Statistics*

CHARTERED INSTITUTE OF PUBLIC FINANCE AND ACCOUNTANCY. LEISURE AND RECREATION STATISTICS. ESTIMATES. see *SPORTS AND GAMES — Abstracting, Bibliographies, Statistics*

CHARTERED INSTITUTE OF PUBLIC FINANCE AND ACCOUNTANCY. LEISURE CHARGES STATISTICS. ACTUALS. see *SPORTS AND GAMES — Abstracting, Bibliographies, Statistics*

CHARTERED INSTITUTE OF PUBLIC FINANCE AND ACCOUNTANCY. LOCAL AUTHORITY AIRPORTS. ACCOUNTS AND STATISTICS. ACTUALS. see *TRANSPORTATION — Abstracting, Bibliographies, Statistics*

CHARTERED INSTITUTE OF PUBLIC FINANCE AND ACCOUNTANCY. LOCAL GOVERNMENT COMPARATIVE STATISTICS. ESTIMATES. see *PUBLIC ADMINISTRATION — Abstracting, Bibliographies, Statistics*

CHARTERED INSTITUTE OF PUBLIC FINANCE AND ACCOUNTANCY. PERSONAL SOCIAL SERVICES STATISTICS. ACTUALS. see *SOCIAL SERVICES AND WELFARE — Abstracting, Bibliographies, Statistics*

CHARTERED INSTITUTE OF PUBLIC FINANCE AND ACCOUNTANCY. PERSONAL SOCIAL SERVICES STATISTICS. ESTIMATES. see *SOCIAL SERVICES AND WELFARE — Abstracting, Bibliographies, Statistics*

CHARTERED INSTITUTE OF PUBLIC FINANCE AND ACCOUNTANCY. PLANNING AND DEVELOPMENT STATISTICS. ESTIMATES & ACTUALS. see *HOUSING AND URBAN PLANNING — Abstracting, Bibliographies, Statistics*

CHARTERED INSTITUTE OF PUBLIC FINANCE AND ACCOUNTANCY. POLICE STATISTICS. ACTUALS. see *CRIMINOLOGY AND LAW ENFORCEMENT — Abstracting, Bibliographies, Statistics*

CHARTERED INSTITUTE OF PUBLIC FINANCE AND ACCOUNTANCY. POLICE STATISTICS. ESTIMATES. see *CRIMINOLOGY AND LAW ENFORCEMENT — Abstracting, Bibliographies, Statistics*

CHARTERED INSTITUTE OF PUBLIC FINANCE AND ACCOUNTANCY. PROBATION. ESTIMATES & ACTUALS. see *SOCIAL SERVICES AND WELFARE — Abstracting, Bibliographies, Statistics*

CHARTERED INSTITUTE OF PUBLIC FINANCE AND ACCOUNTANCY. PUBLIC LIBRARIES STATISTICS. ACTUALS. see *LIBRARY AND INFORMATION SCIENCES — Abstracting, Bibliographies, Statistics*

CHARTERED INSTITUTE OF PUBLIC FINANCE AND ACCOUNTANCY. PUBLIC LIBRARIES STATISTICS. ESTIMATES. see *LIBRARY AND INFORMATION SCIENCES — Abstracting, Bibliographies, Statistics*

CHARTERED INSTITUTE OF PUBLIC FINANCE AND ACCOUNTANCY. REVENUE COLLECTION STATISTICS. ACTUALS. see *BUSINESS AND ECONOMICS — Abstracting, Bibliographies, Statistics*

CHARTERED INSTITUTE OF PUBLIC FINANCE AND ACCOUNTANCY. TRADING STANDARDS STATISTICS. ACTUALS & ESTIMATES. see *BUSINESS AND ECONOMICS — Abstracting, Bibliographies, Statistics*

CHARTERED INSTITUTE OF PUBLIC FINANCE AND ACCOUNTANCY. WASTE COLLECTION STATISTICS. ACTUALS. see *PUBLIC ADMINISTRATION — Abstracting, Bibliographies, Statistics*

CHARTERED INSTITUTE OF PUBLIC FINANCE AND ACCOUNTANCY. WASTE DISPOSAL STATISTICS. ACTUALS. see *PUBLIC ADMINISTRATION — Abstracting, Bibliographies, Statistics*

318   CL
CHILE. INSTITUTO NACIONAL DE ESTADISTICAS. COMPENDIO ESTADISTICO. 1971. a. Esc.2700 (US $16.60; elsewhere $21.10) (effective 1994). Instituto Nacional de Estadisticas, Av. Bulnes 418, Casilla 498, Correo 3, Santiago, Chile. stat.

CHILE. INSTITUTO NACIONAL DE ESTADISTICAS. INDICADORES DE EMPLEO, POR SEXO Y GRUPOS DE EDAD, TOTAL NACIONAL. see *BUSINESS AND ECONOMICS — Abstracting, Bibliographies, Statistics*

CHILE. INSTITUTO NACIONAL DE ESTADISTICAS. INDICE DE PRECIOS AL CONSUMIDOR. see *BUSINESS AND ECONOMICS — Abstracting, Bibliographies, Statistics*

318   CL
CHILE. INSTITUTO NACIONAL DE ESTADISTICAS. INFORMATIVO ESTADISTICO V REGION. 1974. a. Esc.1050 (US $7.30; elsewhere $8.40) (effective 1994). Instituto Nacional de Estadisticas, Casilla 498, Correos 3, Santiago, Chile.

CHILE. SERVICIO NACIONAL DE PESCA. ANUARIO ESTADISTICO DE PESCA. see *FISH AND FISHERIES*

CHINA FACTS AND FIGURES ANNUAL. see *POLITICAL SCIENCE*

CHINA MONTHLY STATISTICS. see *BUSINESS AND ECONOMICS — Abstracting, Bibliographies, Statistics*

315   CH   ISSN 0577-8670
CHINA, REPUBLIC. EXECUTIVE YUAN. DIRECTORATE-GENERAL OF BUDGET, ACCOUNTING & STATISTICS. MONTHLY BULLETIN OF STATISTICS. (Text in English) 1975. m. $30. Executive Yuan, Directorate-General of Budget, Accounting & Statistics, 2 Kwang-Chow Street, Taipei, Taiwan, Republic of China. TEL 02-363-6140. FAX 02-362-6029. (Subscr. to: China Culture Service, No. 5, Lane 333, Roosevelt Rd. Sec. 3, Taipei, Taiwan, R.O.C.) stat. circ. 1,452.

310 011   CH   ISSN 0257-5736
HN747.7
CHINA, REPUBLIC. EXECUTIVE YUAN. DIRECTORATE-GENERAL OF BUDGET, ACCOUNTING & STATISTICS. SOCIAL INDICATORS (YEAR). (Text in Chinese, English; summaries in Chinese) 1979. a. NT.$350. Executive Yuan, Directorate-General of Budget, Accounting & Statistics, 2, Kwang-Chow St., Taipei, Taiwan, Republic of China. TEL 02-381-4910. (Subscr. to: China Cultural Service, No. 5, Lane 333, Sec. 3, Roosevelt Rd., Taiwan, R.O.C.) circ. 800.

CHINA, REPUBLIC. MINISTRY OF FINANCE. DEPARTMENT OF STATISTICS. MONTHLY STATISTICS OF EXPORTS AND IMPORTS/CHIN CH'U K'OU MAO I T'UNG CHI YUEH PAO. see *BUSINESS AND ECONOMICS — Abstracting, Bibliographies, Statistics*

CHINA, REPUBLIC. TOURISM BUREAU. REPORT ON TOURISM STATISTICS (YEAR). see *TRAVEL AND TOURISM — Abstracting, Bibliographies, Statistics*

315.1   US   ISSN 1050-351X
HA4631
CHINA STATISTICAL ABSTRACT. (Text in English) 1988. a. (State Statistical Bureau, CC - Guojia Tongji Ju) Praeger Publishers (Subsidiary of: Greenwood Publishing Group Inc.), 88 Post Rd. W., Box 5007, Westport, CT 06881-5007. TEL 203-226-3571. FAX 203-222-1502. (Dist. in China by: China Statistical Information and Consultancy Service Centre, 38 Yuetan Nanjie, Sanlihe, Beijing, P.R. China. TEL 86-1-8015074) **Indexed:** SRI. **Document type:** abstracting/indexing.

STATISTICS

315   HK   ISSN 1052-9225
HA4631
CHINA STATISTICAL YEARBOOK. Chinese edition: Zhongguo Tongji Nianjian. (Text in English) 1981. a. HK.$650($125) for English ed.; Chinese ed. HK.$350 ($65). Economic Information & Agency, 342 Hennessy Rd., 10-16 Fl., Wanchai, Hong Kong. TEL 5-738217. FAX 852-8388304. TELEX 86990 EIA HX. (back issues avail.)
—BLDSC (3180.234633).
   Formerly: Statistical Yearbook of China (ISSN 0255-6766)

315.1   US   ISSN 1040-7979
HA4631
CHINA STATISTICS SERIES. 1989. irreg. price varies. Praeger Publishers (Subsidiary of: Greenwood Publishing Group Inc.), 88 Post Rd. W., Box 5007, Westport, CT 06881-5007. TEL 203-226-3571. FAX 203-222-1502. **Document type:** monographic series.

CIVIL AVIATION STATISTICS OF THE WORLD (YEAR). see *TRANSPORTATION* — Abstracting, Bibliographies, Statistics

CIVILIAN MANPOWER STATISTICS. see *BUSINESS AND ECONOMICS* — Abstracting, Bibliographies, Statistics

CLASIFICACION MEXICANA DE OCUPACIONES. see *OCCUPATIONS AND CAREERS* — Abstracting, Bibliographies, Statistics

COAL STATISTICS INTERNATIONAL. see *MINES AND MINING INDUSTRY* — Abstracting, Bibliographies, Statistics

COLOMBIA. DEPARTAMENTO ADMINISTRATIVO NACIONAL DE ESTADISTICAS. ANUARIO DE ESTADISTICAS INDUSTRIALES. see *BUSINESS AND ECONOMICS* — Abstracting, Bibliographies, Statistics

318   CK
COLOMBIA. DEPARTAMENTO ADMINISTRATIVO NACIONAL DE ESTADISTICA. ANUARIO DE JUSTICIA.* a. Departamento Administrativo Nacional de Estadistica, Banco Nacional de Datos, Centro Administrativo Nacional-Avda. El Dorado, Apdo. Aereo 80043, Bogota, Colombia. **Document type:** government publication.
   Formerly: Colombia. Departamento Administrativo Nacional de Estadistica. Anuario General de Estadistica - Justicia.

COLOMBIA. DEPARTAMENTO ADMINISTRATIVO NACIONAL DE ESTADISTICA. ANUARIO GENERAL DE ESTADISTICA - TRANSPORTES Y COMUNICACIONES. see *TRANSPORTATION* — Abstracting, Bibliographies, Statistics

318   CK   ISSN 0120-6281
HA1011
COLOMBIA. DEPARTAMENTO ADMINISTRATIVO NACIONAL DE ESTADISTICA. BOLETIN DE ESTADISTICA. (Includes supplement) 1951. m. Col.$4000($200) Departamento Administrativo Nacional de Estadistica, Banco Nacional de Datos, Centro Administrativo Nacional, Avda. El Dorado, Apdo. Aereo 80043, Bogota D.E., Colombia. FAX 2222305. TELEX 44573. Ed. Saul Ojeda Gomez. charts; illus.; stat.; index. circ. 3,000. **Indexed:** P.A.I.S.For.Lang.Ind. **Document type:** government publication.
   Formerly (until Dec. 1984): Colombia. Direccion General de Estadistica. Boletin Mensual de Estadistica (ISSN 0120-0836); And (until 1952): Colombia. Direccion General de Estadistica. Boletin Informativo.

318   CK
COLOMBIA. DEPARTAMENTO ADMINISTRATIVO NACIONAL DE ESTADISTICA. ESTADISTICAS HISTORICAS. irreg. Departamento Administrativo Nacional de Estadistica, Banco Nacional de Datos, Apartado Aereo 80043, Avda. Eldovado, Bogota, Colombia. **Document type:** government publication.

318   CK   ISSN 0120-6443
COLOMBIA ESTADISTICA. 1979. a. $60. Departamento Administrativo Nacional de Estadistica, Banco Nacional de Datos, Avda. El Dorado, Apdo. Aereo 80043, Bogota D.E., Colombia. FAX 2222305. TELEX 44573. **Document type:** government publication.

COMERCIO EXTERIOR DE MEXICO. INFORMACION PRELIMINAR. see *BUSINESS AND ECONOMICS* — Abstracting, Bibliographies, Statistics

COMERTUL EXTERIOR AL ROMANIEI/FOREIGN TRADE OF ROMANIA. see *BUSINESS AND ECONOMICS* — Abstracting, Bibliographies, Statistics

COMMERCE EXTERIEUR DE LA GRECE/EXOTERIKON EMPORION TOS ELLADOS. see *BUSINESS AND ECONOMICS* — Abstracting, Bibliographies, Statistics

COMMODITY PRICE STATISTICS MONTHLY. see *BUSINESS AND ECONOMICS* — Abstracting, Bibliographies, Statistics

COMMODITY TRADE STATISTICS; according to the Standard International Trade Classification. see *BUSINESS AND ECONOMICS* — Abstracting, Bibliographies, Statistics

314   IT
COMMUNE DI GENOVA. NOTIZIARIO STATISTICO MENSILE. 1928. m. free. Comune di Genova, Via Garibaldi, 9, Genova, Italy. TEL 010-261242. FAX 010-257143. stat. circ. 700. **Document type:** government publication.
   Formerly: Genova Statistica (ISSN 0016-691X)

310   IO
COMMUNICATION STATISTICS. (Text in Indonesian) 1965. a. Rps.3000($1.50) Central Bureau of Statistics - Biro Pusat Statistik, Jalan Dr. Sutomo No. 8, Box 3, Jakarta Pusat, Indonesia. TEL 21-372808. circ. 300. **Document type:** government publication.

519.5   US   ISSN 0361-0926
QA276.A1   CODEN: CSTMDC
COMMUNICATIONS IN STATISTICS. PART A: THEORY AND METHODS. 1973. 12/yr. $1395. Marcel Dekker Journals, 270 Madison Ave., New York, NY 10016. TEL 212-696-9000. FAX 212-685-4540. TELEX 421419. (Subscr. to: Box 5017, Monticello, NY 12701) Ed. W.B. Smith. adv.; charts. (also avail. in microform from RPI; reprint service avail. from SWZ) **Indexed:** Biostat., Compumath, Curr.Cont., Curr.Ind.Stat., Ind.Sci.Rev., INSPEC (1976-), J.Cont.Quant.Meth., Math.R., Oper.Res.Manage.Sci., Qual.Contr.Appl.Stat., Risk Abstr., Sci.Cit.Ind., Stat.Theor.Meth.Abstr. **Document type:** academic/scholarly publication.
—BLDSC (3363.432000); Ei; Faxon; Genuine Article; SWETS; UMI; UnCover. **CCC.**
   Supersedes in part (with vol.5, 1976): Communications in Statistics (ISSN 0090-3272)
   Refereed Serial

519.5 621.319   US   ISSN 0361-0918
QA276.A1   CODEN: CSSCDB
COMMUNICATIONS IN STATISTICS. PART B: SIMULATION AND COMPUTATION. 1976. 4/yr. $550. Marcel Dekker Journals, 270 Madison Ave., New York, NY 10016. TEL 212-696-9000. FAX 212-685-4540. TELEX 421419. (Subscr. to: Box 5017, Monticello, NY 12701) Ed. W.B. Smith. (also avail. in microform from RPI; reprint service avail. from SWZ) **Indexed:** Biostat., Compumath, Curr.Cont., Curr.Ind.Stat., Ind.Sci.Rev., INSPEC (1976-), J.Cont.Quant.Meth., Math.R., Oper.Res.Manage.Sci., Qual.Contr.Appl.Stat., Sci.Cit.Ind., Stat.Theor.Meth.Abstr. **Document type:** academic/scholarly publication.
—BLDSC (3363.431000); Ei; Faxon; Genuine Article; SWETS; UMI; UnCover. **CCC.**
   Supersedes in part (with vol.5, 1976): Communications in Statistics (ISSN 0090-3272)
   Refereed Serial

519.5   US   ISSN 0882-0287
QA274.A1   CODEN: CSSME8
COMMUNICATIONS IN STATISTICS. PART C: STOCHASTIC MODELS. 1985. 4/yr. $425 ($1939 with parts A&B). Marcel Dekker Journals, 270 Madison Ave., New York, NY 10016. TEL 212-696-9000. FAX 212-685-4540. TELEX 421419. (Subscr. to: Box 5017, Monticello, NY 12701) (Co-publisher: Operations Research Society of America (ORSA)) Ed. Marcel Neuts. (also avail. in microform from RPI; reprint service avail. from SWZ) **Indexed:** Biostat., Curr.Ind.Stat., Stat.Theor.Meth.Abstr. **Document type:** academic/scholarly publication.
—BLDSC (3363.431500); Faxon; SWETS; UMI; UnCover. **CCC.**

COMPANHIA PARANAENSE DE ENERGIA. INFORME ESTATISTICO ANUAL. see *ENERGY* — Abstracting, Bibliographies, Statistics

318   GT
COMPENDIO ESTADISTICO SOBRE VARIABLES ECONOMICO-SOCIALES. a. Instituto Nacional de Estadistica, 8A Calle no. 9-55, Zona 1, Guatemala, Guatemala.

314   IT   ISSN 0069-7958
COMPENDIO STATISTICO ITALIANO. a. L.27000 (effective 1993). Istituto Nazionale di Statistica, Via Cesare Balbo 16, 00100 Rome, Italy. FAX 06-46735198. circ. 12,250. **Document type:** government publication.
   Formerly: Compendio Statistico (ISSN 0390-640X)

COMPENSATION AND WORKING CONDITIONS. see *BUSINESS AND ECONOMICS* — Economic Situation And Conditions

519.5   NE   ISSN 0253-018X
COMPSTAT SYMPOSIUM. PROCEEDINGS. (Computational Statistics) Key Title: Compstat. (Text in English) 1974. biennial. DM.120. (International Association for Statistical Computing, European Section) International Statistical Institute, Prinses Beatrixlaan 428, Postbus 950, 2270 AZ Voorburg, Netherlands. TEL 31-70-3375737. FAX 31-70-3860025. (Orders to: Physica-Verlag, c/o Springer GmbH, Auslieferungs-Gesellschaft, Haberstr. 7, 6900 Heidelberg-Rohrbach, Germany) Ed.Bd. abstr. **Indexed:** Stat.Theor.Meth.Abstr. **Document type:** proceedings.
—BLDSC (3368.400000).
   Description: Publishes papers reflecting current interests in computational statistics.

519.5   GW   ISSN 0943-4062
QA276.4
COMPUTATIONAL STATISTICS. (Text in English) 1982. q. DM.378($274) (effective 1996). Physica-Verlag GmbH und Co., Postfach 105280, 69042 Heidelberg, Germany. TEL 06221-487492. FAX 06221-487177. (Subscr. to: Springer-Verlag GmbH, Auftragsbearbeitung, Postfach 311340, 10643 Berlin, Germany. TEL 030-8207424; Dist. in North America by: Springer-Verlag New York Inc., 175 Fifth Ave., New York, NY 10010, U.S.A.. TEL 212-460-1500) Eds. W. Haerdle, D.W. Scott. (also avail. in microform from UMI) **Indexed:** Curr.Ind.Stat., Cyb.Abstr., INSPEC (1992-), J.Cont.Quant.Meth., Math.R., Stat.Theor.Meth.Abstr., Zent.Math. **Document type:** academic/scholarly publication.
—BLDSC (3390.624200); Ei; Faxon; SWETS; UMI; UnCover. **CCC.**
   Formerly: C S Q - Computational Statistics Quarterly (ISSN 0723-712X)
   Description: Covers computational aspects of new and existing statistical techniques.

314   GR   ISSN 0069-8245
CONCISE STATISTICAL YEARBOOK OF GREECE. (Text in English and Greek) 1954. a. $15. National Statistical Service of Greece, Statistical Information and Publications Division - Ethniki Statistiki Yperesia tes Ellados, 14-16 Lykourgou, 101 66 Athens, Greece. TEL 30-1-3244-748. FAX 30-1-3222-205. TELEX 216734 ESYE GR. (back issues avail.)

CONCRETE PIPE INDUSTRY STATISTICS. see *ENGINEERING* — Abstracting, Bibliographies, Statistics

316   CF   ISSN 0010-5805
CONGO. CENTRE NATIONAL DE LA STATISTIQUE ET DES ETUDES ECONOMIQUES. BULLETIN MENSUEL DE LA STATISTIQUE. 1958. m. 12000 Fr.CFA. Centre National de la Statistique et des Etudes Economiques, B.P. 2031, Brazzaville, Congo. charts; mkt. circ. 500. (processed)

314   IT
CONOSCERE L'ITALIA/INTRODUCING ITALY. a. free. Istituto Nazionale di Statistica, Via Cesare Balbo 16, 00100 Rome, Italy. FAX 06-46735198. **Document type:** government publication.

CONSUMER EXPENDITURE SURVEY. see *BUSINESS AND ECONOMICS* — Economic Situation And Conditions

CONSUMER EXPENDITURE SURVEY: QUARTERLY DATA FROM THE INTERVIEW SURVEY. see *BUSINESS AND ECONOMICS* — Economic Situation And Conditions

CONSUMER EXPENDITURES IN (YEAR). see *BUSINESS AND ECONOMICS* — Economic Situation And Conditions

CONSUMER PRICE INDEX. see *BUSINESS AND ECONOMICS — Economic Situation And Conditions*

CONSUMER PRICE INDEX: WASHINGTON, DC. see *BUSINESS AND ECONOMICS — Economic Situation And Conditions*

COST OF DOING BUSINESS SURVEY: OPERATING PERFORMANCE COMPARISONS FOR MUSIC PRODUCT DEALERS. see *MUSIC*

COST SURVEY. see *MEDICAL SCIENCES*

317.2   CR
COSTA RICA. DIRECCION GENERAL DE ESTADISTICA Y CENSOS. ESTADISTICA VITAL; poblacion, nacimientos, defunciones, matrimonios. a. Direccion General de Estadistica y Censos, Apdo. 10163, 1000 San Jose, Costa Rica.

310   CR   ISSN 0589-8544
COSTA RICA. DIRECCION GENERAL DE ESTADISTICA Y CENSOS. INVENTARIO DE LAS ESTADISTICAS NACIONALES. 1964. irreg., latest 1970. exchange basis. Direccion General de Estadistica y Censos, Apdo. 10163, San Jose, Costa Rica.

310   US   ISSN 0890-1627
COUNCIL OF PROFESSIONAL ASSOCIATION ON FEDERAL STATISTICS. NEWS. Key Title: New from C O P A F S. 1982. q. $30. Council of Professional Association on Federal Statistics, 1429 Duke St., Ste. 402, Alexandria, CA 22314-3402. Ed. Edward J. Span. circ. 500. **Document type:** newsletter.

317   US   ISSN 0082-9455
HA202
COUNTY AND CITY DATA BOOK. 1944. irreg. for 1994 edition (foreign $50). U.S. Bureau of the Census, Data User Services Division, Washington, DC 20233. TEL 301-457-4100. FAX 301-457-4714. (Subscr. to: Superintendent of Documents, U.S. Government Printing Office, Box 371954, Pittsburgh, PA 15250-7954. TEL 202-783-3238. FAX 202-512-2233; Or: Bernan, 4611-F Assembly Dr., Lanham, MD 20706. TEL 301-459-7666. FAX 301-459-0056) (also avail. in microfiche) **Document type:** government publication.
●Also available online. Vendor(s): CompuServe, Inc., Knight-Ridder, Inc.
Also available on CD-ROM.

310 312   US   ISSN 1059-9096
HA203
COUNTY AND CITY EXTRA; annual metro, city and county data book. 1992. a. $89.95. (Kraus Organization, Ltd.) Bernan Press, 4611-F Assembly Dr., Lanham, MD 20706-4391. TEL 301-459-7666. FAX 301-459-0056. Eds. George E. Hall, Courtenay M. Slater.
●Also available on CD-ROM.
  Description: General reference that lists a wide range of statistical data for every state, county, city, and metropolitan area in the United States. Incorporates data obtained from the Census Bureau, Bureau of Economic Analysis, FBI, National Weather Service, and others.

COUNTY PENETRATION REPORTS; a tabulation of county circulation data for daily and weekly newspapers. see *ADVERTISING AND PUBLIC RELATIONS — Abstracting, Bibliographies, Statistics*

CRIME AND DELINQUENCY IN CALIFORNIA. see *CRIMINOLOGY AND LAW ENFORCEMENT — Abstracting, Bibliographies, Statistics*

CRIME STATE RANKINGS; crime in the 50 United States. see *CRIMINOLOGY AND LAW ENFORCEMENT — Abstracting, Bibliographies, Statistics*

CRIMINAL VICTIMIZATION IN THE UNITED STATES. see *CRIMINOLOGY AND LAW ENFORCEMENT*

CUADERNOS DE BIOESTADISTICA Y SUS APLICACIONES INFORMATICAS. see *BIOLOGY — Abstracting, Bibliographies, Statistics*

519.5   SP   ISSN 0211-853X
CUADERNOS DE ESTADISTICA MATEMATICA. 1980. s-a. free. Universidad de Granada, Facultad de Ciencias, Departamento de Estadistica Matematica, Fuentenueva, s-n, 18001 Granada, Spain. **Indexed:** Stat.Theor.Meth.Abstr.

318   UN   ISSN 0251-9437
CUADERNOS ESTADISTICOS DE LA C E P A L. 1976. irreg., no.19, 1993. Comision Economica para America Latina y el Caribe - Economic Commission for Latin America and the Caribbean, Casilla 179-D, Santiago, Chile. FAX 562480252.

317.28   CU
CUBA. COMITE ESTATAL DE ESTADISTICAS. REVISTA ESTADISTICA. (Text in Spanish; summaries in English and Russian) 1979. s-a. Comite Estatal de Estadisticas, Centro de Informacion Cientifico-Tecnica, Almendares No. 156, esq. a Desague, Gaveta Postal 6016, Havana, Cuba. Ed. Ramon Sabadi Rodriquez. bk.rev.; bibl.; charts.

CUBA EN CIFRAS. see *BUSINESS AND ECONOMICS — Abstracting, Bibliographies, Statistics*

CUBA QUARTERLY ECONOMIC REPORT. see *BUSINESS AND ECONOMICS — Abstracting, Bibliographies, Statistics*

CULTURA Y MEDIOS DE COMUNICACION. see *COMMUNICATIONS — Abstracting, Bibliographies, Statistics*

CURRENT BUSINESS REPORTS: MONTHLY WHOLESALE TRADE, SALES AND INVENTORIES. see *BUSINESS AND ECONOMICS — Domestic Commerce*

CURRENT INDEX TO STATISTICS; applications-methods-theory. see *MATHEMATICS — Abstracting, Bibliographies, Statistics*

CURRENT INDUSTRIAL REPORTS: BROADWOVEN FABRICS (GRAY). see *TEXTILE INDUSTRIES AND FABRICS — Abstracting, Bibliographies, Statistics*

CURRENT INDUSTRIAL REPORTS: FATS AND OILS. OILSEED CRUSHINGS. see *FOOD AND FOOD INDUSTRIES — Abstracting, Bibliographies, Statistics*

CURRENT INDUSTRIAL REPORTS: FATS AND OILS. PRODUCTION, CONSUMPTION, AND STOCKS. see *FOOD AND FOOD INDUSTRIES — Abstracting, Bibliographies, Statistics*

CURRENT INDUSTRIAL REPORTS: NONFERROUS CASTINGS. see *METALLURGY — Abstracting, Bibliographies, Statistics*

CYPRUS. DEPARTMENT OF STATISTICS AND RESEARCH. AGRICULTURAL STATISTICS. see *AGRICULTURE — Abstracting, Bibliographies, Statistics*

CYPRUS. DEPARTMENT OF STATISTICS AND RESEARCH. CENSUS OF COTTAGE INDUSTRY. see *BUSINESS AND ECONOMICS — Abstracting, Bibliographies, Statistics*

CYPRUS. DEPARTMENT OF STATISTICS AND RESEARCH. CENSUS OF INDUSTRIAL PRODUCTION.. see *BUSINESS AND ECONOMICS — Abstracting, Bibliographies, Statistics*

CYPRUS. DEPARTMENT OF STATISTICS AND RESEARCH. CENSUS OF POULTRY. see *AGRICULTURE — Abstracting, Bibliographies, Statistics*

CYPRUS. DEPARTMENT OF STATISTICS AND RESEARCH. CRIMINAL STATISTICS. see *CRIMINOLOGY AND LAW ENFORCEMENT — Abstracting, Bibliographies, Statistics*

CYPRUS. DEPARTMENT OF STATISTICS AND RESEARCH. DEMOGRAPHIC REPORT. see *POPULATION STUDIES — Abstracting, Bibliographies, Statistics*

CYPRUS. DEPARTMENT OF STATISTICS AND RESEARCH. DEMOGRAPHIC SURVEY. (YEAR). see *POPULATION STUDIES — Abstracting, Bibliographies, Statistics*

CYPRUS. DEPARTMENT OF STATISTICS AND RESEARCH. ECONOMIC INDICATORS. see *BUSINESS AND ECONOMICS — Economic Situation And Conditions*

CYPRUS. DEPARTMENT OF STATISTICS AND RESEARCH. ECONOMIC REPORT. see *BUSINESS AND ECONOMICS — Abstracting, Bibliographies, Statistics*

CYPRUS. DEPARTMENT OF STATISTICS AND RESEARCH. FUNCTIONS AND SERVICES. see *PUBLIC ADMINISTRATION — Abstracting, Bibliographies, Statistics*

CYPRUS. DEPARTMENT OF STATISTICS AND RESEARCH. HOUSEHOLD INCOME AND EXPENDITURE SURVEY. see *BUSINESS AND ECONOMICS — Abstracting, Bibliographies, Statistics*

CYPRUS. DEPARTMENT OF STATISTICS AND RESEARCH. IMPORTS AND EXPORTS STATISTICS. see *BUSINESS AND ECONOMICS — Abstracting, Bibliographies, Statistics*

CYPRUS. DEPARTMENT OF STATISTICS AND RESEARCH. INDUSTRIAL STATISTICS. see *BUSINESS AND ECONOMICS — Abstracting, Bibliographies, Statistics*

CYPRUS. DEPARTMENT OF STATISTICS AND RESEARCH. MULTI-ROUND DEMOGRAPHIC SURVEY. MIGRATION IN CYPRUS. see *POPULATION STUDIES — Abstracting, Bibliographies, Statistics*

310   CY
CYPRUS. DEPARTMENT OF STATISTICS AND RESEARCH. QUESTIONNAIRES FOR CENSUSES AND SURVEYS. (Text in English, Greek) 1982. irreg. £C3. Ministry of Finance, Department of Statistics and Research, 13 Lord Byron Ave., Nicosia, Cyprus. TEL 357-2-302349. FAX 357-2-456712. **Document type:** government publication.
  Description: Summarizes all questionnaires used by the Department of Statistics and Research in conducting censuses, surveys, and other statistical inquiries.

CYPRUS. DEPARTMENT OF STATISTICS AND RESEARCH. STATISTICAL ABSTRACT. see *SOCIAL SCIENCES: COMPREHENSIVE WORKS — Abstracting, Bibliographies, Statistics*

CYPRUS. DEPARTMENT OF STATISTICS AND RESEARCH. STATISTICS OF IMPORTS AND EXPORTS. see *BUSINESS AND ECONOMICS — Abstracting, Bibliographies, Statistics*

CYPRUS. DEPARTMENT OF STATISTICS AND RESEARCH. TOURISM, MIGRATION AND TRAVEL STATISTICS. see *TRAVEL AND TOURISM — Abstracting, Bibliographies, Statistics*

310   XR
CZECH REPUBLIC. CESKY STATISTICKY URAD. AKTUALITY. (In 2 vols.) m. $108. Cesky Statisticky Urad, Sokolovska 142, 186 04 Prague 8, Czech Republic. TEL 42-2-6604-2451. FAX 42-2-6631-0429. **Document type:** government publication.
  Description: The first volume includes the results of price statistics, developments in the cost of living, unemployment, agriculture, tourism and cash receipts and expenditures of the state budget. The second volume covers the results of industry, construction, transport, internal and external expenditures of the population, and the preliminary results of financial performance. It also includes the latest results from business cycle surveys.

310   XR
CZECH REPUBLIC. CESKY STATISTICKY URAD. EDICE - AKTUALNI INFORMACE/CZECH REPUBLIC. CZECH STATISTICAL OFFICE. SERIES - LATEST STATISTICAL INFORMATION. (Text in Czech, English) m. price varies. Cesky Statisticky Urad, Sokolovska 142, 186 04 Prague 8, Czech Republic. TEL 42-2-6604-2451. FAX 42-2-6631-0429. **Document type:** government publication.
  Description: Presents review tables with methodological explanations, brief analytical commentary and graphic supplement.

310   XR
CZECH REPUBLIC. CESKY STATISTICKY URAD. EDICE - STATISTICKE INFORMACE/CZECH REPUBLIC. CZECH STATISTICAL OFFICE. SERIES - STATISTICAL INFORMATION. (Consists of 38 series) m. and q. (plus a. cumulation). price varies. Cesky Statisticky Urad, Sokolovska 142, 186 04 Prague 8, Czech Repubic. TEL 42-2-6604-2451. FAX 42-2-6631-0429. **Document type:** government publication.
  Description: Includes the results of statistical surveys of periodicity shorter than one year and preliminary yearly results. It is divided into individual series corresponding to branch statistics.

STATISTICS

314.37 947   XR
CZECH REPUBLIC. CESKY STATISTICKY URAD. STATISTICKE PREHLEDY. 1967. m. $96. Cesky Statisticky Urad - Czech Statistical Office, Sokolovska 142, 186 04 Prague 8, Czech Republic. TEL 42-2-6604-2451. FAX 42-2-6631-0429. Ed. Jan Fischer.
    Formerly: Czech Republic. Federalni Statisticky Urad. Statisticke Prehledy (ISSN 0322-7537).
    Description: Regular as well as irregular statistical information on various fields of economic, social and cultural development of Czech Republic.

CZECH REPUBLIC. CESKY STATISTICKY URAD. STATISTICKY BULLETIN. see *BUSINESS AND ECONOMICS — Abstracting, Bibliographies, Statistics*

CZECH REPUBLIC. CZECH STATISTICAL OFFICE. BULLETIN. see *BUSINESS AND ECONOMICS — Abstracting, Bibliographies, Statistics*

317   CN   ISSN 0827-0465
HC111
THE DAILY. 1932. d. Can.$120($144) (foreign $168). Statistics Canada, Publications Division, Ottawa, Ont. K1A 0T6, Ontario. TEL 613-951-7277. FAX 613-951-1584.
    Description: Contains news summaries and announcements of reports, reference papers and a list of titles of the publications released.

DAIRY MARKET STATISTICS: ANNUAL SUMMARY. see *AGRICULTURE — Abstracting, Bibliographies, Statistics*

DAIRY STATISTICS. see *AGRICULTURE — Abstracting, Bibliographies, Statistics*

314.89   DK   ISSN 0107-7139
HA1473
DANMARK I TAL. English edition: Data on Denmark (ISSN 0107-7961) 1981. a. DKK 40 free to educational establishments). Danmarks Statistik, Sejroegade 11, 2100 Copenhagen OE, Denmark. TEL 01-29 82 22. illus.

016.31489   DK   ISSN 0905-5851
Z7554.D3
DANMARKS STATISTIK. PUBLIKATIONER. English edition: Publications Issued by Danmarks Statistik (ISSN 0905-586X) 1984. s-a. free. Danmarks Statistik, Sejroegade 11, DK-2100 Copenhagen Oe, Denmark. TEL 45-39-17-39-17. FAX 45-31-18-48-01. Ed.Bd. illus. circ. 800. **Document type:** catalog.

310   DK   ISSN 0417-0164
DENMARK. DANMARKS STATISTIK. DETAILPRISER. 1963. q. DKK 64.75. Danmarks Statistik, Sejroegade 11, 2100 Copenhagen OE, Denmark. TEL 31-298222. FAX 31-184801. TELEX 16236. (back issues avail.)

DENMARK. DANMARKS STATISTIK. PRISSTATISTIK. see *BUSINESS AND ECONOMICS — Abstracting, Bibliographies, Statistics*

314.89   DK   ISSN 0070-3567
HA1477
DENMARK. DANMARKS STATISTIK. STATISTISK AARBOG. (Text in Danish; notes in English) 1896. a. DKK 208. Danmarks Statistik, Sejroegade 11, 2100 Copenhagen OE, Denmark. TEL 45-31-29-82-22. FAX 45-31-18-48-01. TELEX 16236. cum.index: 1769-1972.
    Description: Consists of tables (without explanatory text) with principal results of most censuses and surveys conducted by Danmarks Statistik.

314.89   DK   ISSN 0070-3583
HA1472
DENMARK. DANMARKS STATISTIK. STATISTISK TIARS-OVERSIGT/DENMARKS STATISTICS. STATISTICAL TEN-YEAR REVIEW. 1961. a. DKK 96. Danmarks Statistik, Sejroegade 11, 2100 Copenhagen OE, Denmark. TEL 45-31-29-82-22. FAX 45-31-18-48-01. (also avail. in diskette format)
    Description: Presents comparable annual statistics for the past ten years, thus revealing both trends and structural changes. Adapted to the educational sector.

314.89   DK   ISSN 0106-6439
DENMARK. DANMARKS STATISTIK. STATISTISKE MEDDELELSER. 1852. irreg. price varies. Danmarks Statistik, Sejroegade 11, DK-2100 Copenhagen OE, Denmark. TEL 45-31-29-82-22. FAX 45-31-18-48-01. TELEX 16236.

314.89   DK   ISSN 0039-0682
DENMARK. DANMARKS STATISTIK. STATISTISKE UNDERSOGELSER. 1958. irreg. price varies. Danmarks Statistik, Sejroegade 11, 2100 Copenhagen OE, Denmark. TEL 31-298222. FAX 31-184801. TELEX 16236. **Document type:** monographic series.

016.31489   DK   ISSN 0109-8314
Z7554.D3
DENMARK. DANMARKS STATISTIK. VEJVISER I STATISTIKKEN. 1978. irreg. DKK 195. Danmarks Statistik, Sejroegade 11, DK-2100 Copenhagen OE, Denmark. TEL 45-31-29-82-22. FAX 45-31-18-48-01. TELEX 16236.
    Formerly (until 1984): Denmark. Danmarks Statistik. Vejvisser i Danmarks Statiske Publikationer (ISSN 0107-1009)

DEPARTMENT STORE INVENTORIES. see *BUSINESS AND ECONOMICS — Economic Situation And Conditions*

DEUTSCHE BUNDESBANK. MONATSBERICHTE. STATISTISCHE BEIHEFTE. REIHE 5: DEVISENKURSSTATISTIK. see *BUSINESS AND ECONOMICS — Abstracting, Bibliographies, Statistics*

DIGEST OF UNITED KINGDOM ENERGY STATISTICS. see *ENERGY — Abstracting, Bibliographies, Statistics*

310   UK   ISSN 0262-8295
DIGEST OF WELSH STATISTICS. 1954. a. £7. Welsh Office, Statistical Directorate, New Crown Bldg., Cathays Park, Cardiff CF1 3NQ, Wales. TEL 01222-825044. FAX 01222-825350. TELEX 487228. Ed. E. Swires-Hennessy. stat. circ. 800. **Document type:** government publication. —BLDSC (3588.335000). CCC.
    Description: Specifics on social conditions, labor, education, production, distribution, transport and finance.

310   US   ISSN 0278-405X
HA1
DIRECTORY OF STATISTICIANS. triennial. $125. American Statistical Association, 1429 Duke St., Alexandria, VA 22314-3402. TEL 703-684-1221. FAX 703-684-2037. **Document type:** directory.
    Formerly: Statisticians and Others in Allied Professions (ISSN 0081-508X)

DISPLACED WORKERS. see *BUSINESS AND ECONOMICS — Economic Situation And Conditions*

DISTRIBUTION OF HIGH SCHOOL GRADUATES AND COLLEGE GOING RATE, NEW YORK STATE. see *EDUCATION — Abstracting, Bibliographies, Statistics*

DJIBOUTI. DIRECTION NATIONALE DE LA STATISTIQUE. BULLETIN DE STATISTIQUE ET DE DOCUMENTATION. see *PUBLIC ADMINISTRATION — Abstracting, Bibliographies, Statistics*

DONNEES STATISTIQUES SUR LE LIVRE BELGE DE LANGUE FRANCAISE. see *PUBLISHING AND BOOK TRADE — Abstracting, Bibliographies, Statistics*

314   GW   ISSN 0418-1263
DUESSELDORF IN ZAHLEN. 1902. q. DM.40. Landeshauptstadt Duesseldorf, Amt fuer Statistik und Wahlen, Postfach 101120, 40200 Duesseldorf, Germany. TEL 0211-8993314. FAX 0211-8929076. stat. circ. 650. (looseleaf format) **Document type:** government publication.

EARNINGS - INDUSTRY AND SERVICES. see *BUSINESS AND ECONOMICS — Abstracting, Bibliographies, Statistics*

310   US
EAST TENNESSEE DEVELOPMENT DISTRICT ECONOMIC STATISTICS. 1981. q. $1 per county ($10 per book). East Tennessee Development District, 5616 Kingston Pike, Box 19806, Knoxville, TN 37939-2806. TEL 615-584-8553. FAX 615-584-5159. **Document type:** government publication.
    Description: Summarizes various federal, state and local sources which provide economic data for East Tennessee Development District region.

ECONOMIC AND SOCIAL STATISTICS OF SRI LANKA. see *BUSINESS AND ECONOMICS — Abstracting, Bibliographies, Statistics*

ECONOMIC INDICATORS OF THE FARM SECTOR. PRODUCTION AND EFFICIENCY STATISTICS. see *AGRICULTURE — Agricultural Economics*

ECUADOR. INSTITUTO NACIONAL DE ESTADISTICA Y CENSOS. ENCUESTA ANUAL DE COMERCIO INTERNO. see *BUSINESS AND ECONOMICS — Abstracting, Bibliographies, Statistics*

ECUADOR. INSTITUTO NACIONAL DE ESTADISTICA Y CENSOS. ENCUESTA ANUAL DE EDIFICACIONES. see *BUILDING AND CONSTRUCTION — Abstracting, Bibliographies, Statistics*

ECUADOR. INSTITUTO NACIONAL DE ESTADISTICA Y CENSOS. ENCUESTA ANUAL DE MIGRACION INTERNACIONAL. see *POPULATION STUDIES — Abstracting, Bibliographies, Statistics*

ECUADOR. INSTITUTO NACIONAL DE ESTADISTICA Y CENSOS. ENCUESTA ANUAL DE RESTAURANTES, HOTELES Y SERVICIOS. see *HOTELS AND RESTAURANTS — Abstracting, Bibliographies, Statistics*

318 370   EC
ECUADOR. INSTITUTO NACIONAL DE ESTADISTICA Y CENSOS. ENCUESTA ANUAL DE RECURSOS Y ACTIVIDADES DE SALUD. 1967. a. Esc.16000($16) Instituto Nacional de Estadistica y Censos, 10 de Agosto No. 229, Quito, Ecuador. TEL 593-2-591900. FAX 593-2-580041.

318.6   EC
ECUADOR: DATOS E INDICADORES BASICOS/ECUADOR: BASIC DATA AND INDICATORS. a. Consejo Nacional de Desarrollo, Apdo. Postal 22114, Quito, Ecuador. TEL 563-666 ext. 150. FAX 593-2-563002.

EDIFICACION. see *BUILDING AND CONSTRUCTION — Abstracting, Bibliographies, Statistics*

EDUCACAO; indicadoes sociais. see *EDUCATION — Abstracting, Bibliographies, Statistics*

EDUCATION IN CANADA; a statistical review. see *EDUCATION — Abstracting, Bibliographies, Statistics*

EDUCATION STATISTICS, NEW YORK STATE; prepared especially for members of the Legislature. see *EDUCATION — Abstracting, Bibliographies, Statistics*

315.6   UA
EGYPT. CENTRAL AGENCY FOR PUBLIC MOBILISATION AND STATISTICS. STATISTICAL YEARBOOK. (Text in Arabic and English) 1961. a. ££14. Central Agency for Public Mobilisation and Statistics, Box 2086, Nasr City, Cairo, Egypt.
    Formerly: Statistical Handbook of Egypt.

318   ES   ISSN 0080-5661
EL SALVADOR. DIRECCION GENERAL DE ESTADISTICA Y CENSOS. ANUARIO ESTADISTICO. a. free or exchange basis. Direccion General de Estadistica y Censos, 1 Calle Poniente y 43 Avenida Norte, San Salvador, El Salvador.

317.284   ES   ISSN 0013-404X
EL SALVADOR. DIRECCION GENERAL DE ESTADISTICA Y CENSOS. BOLETIN ESTADISTICO. 1951. q. free or exchange basis. Direccion General de Estadistica y Censos, 1 Calle Poniente y 43 Avenida Norte, San Salvador, El Salvador. mkt.; stat.

EL SALVADOR. MINISTERIO DE PLANIFICACION Y COORDINACION DEL DESARROLLO ECONOMICO Y SOCIAL. ENCUESTA NACIONAL DE INGRESOS Y GASTOS DE LOS HOGARES URBANOS. see *HOME ECONOMICS — Abstracting, Bibliographies, Statistics*

STATISTICS

318   ES   ISSN 0581-4111
EL SALVADOR. MINISTERIO DE PLANIFICACION Y COORDINACION DEL DESARROLLO ECONOMICO Y SOCIAL. INDICADORES ECONOMICOS Y SOCIALES. 1962. irreg., latest 1987-89. Ministerio de Planificacion y Coordinacion del Desarrollo Economico y Social, Seccion de Investigaciones Estadisticas, Casa Presidential, San Salvador, El Salvador. Ed.Bd. stat.; charts. **Indexed:** P.A.I.S.For.Lang.Ind.
   Description: Covers El Salvador's public health, education, social security, employment, commerce, banking, public finance, construction, transportation, communication, agriculture and manufacture.

EL SALVADOR. MINISTERIO DE TRABAJO Y PREVISION SOCIAL. ESTADISTICAS DEL TRABAJO. see *BUSINESS AND ECONOMICS — Abstracting, Bibliographies, Statistics*

ELECTRICITE DE FRANCE. STATISTIQUES DE LA PRODUCTION ET DE LA CONSOMMATION. see *ENGINEERING — Abstracting, Bibliographies, Statistics*

EMPLOYEE BENEFITS IN MEDIUM AND LARGE FIRMS. see *BUSINESS AND ECONOMICS — Economic Situation And Conditions*

EMPLOYER COSTS FOR EMPLOYEE COMPENSATION. see *BUSINESS AND ECONOMICS — Economic Situation And Conditions*

EMPLOYMENT AND EARNINGS. see *BUSINESS AND ECONOMICS — Economic Situation And Conditions*

EMPLOYMENT AND EARNINGS: CHARACTERISTICS OF FAMILIES. see *BUSINESS AND ECONOMICS — Economic Situation And Conditions*

EMPLOYMENT AND EARNINGS: STATES AND AREAS. see *BUSINESS AND ECONOMICS — Economic Situation And Conditions*

EMPLOYMENT AND EARNINGS: UNITED STATES. see *BUSINESS AND ECONOMICS — Economic Situation And Conditions*

EMPLOYMENT AND WAGES ANNUAL AVERAGES. see *BUSINESS AND ECONOMICS — Economic Situation And Conditions*

EMPLOYMENT COST INDEX. see *BUSINESS AND ECONOMICS — Economic Situation And Conditions*

EMPLOYMENT COST INDEXES AND LEVELS. see *BUSINESS AND ECONOMICS — Economic Situation And Conditions*

EMPLOYMENT, HOURS, AND EARNINGS: UNITED STATES. see *BUSINESS AND ECONOMICS — Economic Situation And Conditions*

EMPLOYMENT IN PERSPECTIVE: MINORITY WORKERS. see *BUSINESS AND ECONOMICS — Economic Situation And Conditions*

EMPLOYMENT IN PERSPECTIVE: WOMEN IN THE LABOR FORCE. see *BUSINESS AND ECONOMICS — Economic Situation And Conditions*

THE EMPLOYMENT SITUATION. see *BUSINESS AND ECONOMICS — Economic Situation And Conditions*

ENCUESTA NACIONAL AGROPECUARIA. RESULTADOS DE LA PRODUCCION AGRICOLA. see *AGRICULTURE — Abstracting, Bibliographies, Statistics*

317.2   MX
ENCUESTA NACIONAL DE INGRESOS Y GASTOS DE LOS HOGARES. irreg. Instituto Nacional de Estadistica, Geografia e Informatica, Secretaria de Programacion y Presupuesto, Av. Prol. Hereo de Nacozari 2301 S., Puerta 11, planta baja, Aguascalientes 20290, Ags., Mexico.

ENCUESTA NACIONAL DE NUTRICION. see *NUTRITION AND DIETETICS — Abstracting, Bibliographies, Statistics*

ENCUESTA NACIONAL DEL EMPLEO. see *BUSINESS AND ECONOMICS — Abstracting, Bibliographies, Statistics*

ENERGIEVERSORGUNG OESTERREICHS. see *ENERGY — Abstracting, Bibliographies, Statistics*

ENQUETE ANNUELLE SUR L'ACTIVITE DES ORGANISMES DE SECURITE SOCIALE. see *SOCIAL SERVICES AND WELFARE — Abstracting, Bibliographies, Statistics*

314   GW
ENTWICKLUNGEN IN NORDRHEIN-WESTFALEN IM JAHRE (YEAR). 1972. a. Landesamt fuer Datenverarbeitung und Statistik Nordrhein-Westfalen, Postfach 101105, 40002 Duesseldorf, Germany. TEL 0211-9449-01. FAX 0211-442006. circ. 7,000. **Document type:** government publication.
   Description: Statistics of all areas of life in Nordrhein-Westfalen: employment, industry, agriculture, schools, traffic, etc.

ENVIRONMENTAL AND ECOLOGICAL STATISTICS. see *ENVIRONMENTAL STUDIES — Abstracting, Bibliographies, Statistics*

ESTABLECIMIENTOS MANUFACTURERAS EN PUERTO RICO. see *BUSINESS AND ECONOMICS — Abstracting, Bibliographies, Statistics*

310   US   ISSN 0014-1735
HA1   CODEN: ESTDA4
ESTADISTICA. (Text in English, French, Portuguese and Spanish) 1943. s-a. $7. Organization of American States, Department of Publications, 1889 F St., N.W., Washington, DC 20006. TEL 703-941-1617. Ed. M. Alicia Monzon De Madariaga. bibl.; charts; index, cum.index: 1943-1953. circ. 2,300. (also avail. in microfilm from UMI; reprint service avail. from UMI) **Indexed:** Geo.Abstr., Math.R., Popul.Ind.—BLDSC (3812.530000); UMI; UnCover.

319   PN   ISSN 0259-6725
ESTADISTICA PANAMENA. BOLETIN. 1963. irreg. free. Direccion de Estadistica y Censo, Apdo. 5213, Panama 5, Panama. FAX 507-69-7294. circ. 850. **Document type:** government publication.
   Description: Presents preliminary data from the regular series, or a study on a specific theme.

ESTADISTICA PANAMENA. SITUACION CULTURAL. SECCION 511. EDUCACION. see *EDUCATION — Abstracting, Bibliographies, Statistics*

ESTADISTICA PANAMENA. SITUACION DEMOGRAFICA. SECCION 221. ESTADISTICAS VITALES. see *POPULATION STUDIES — Abstracting, Bibliographies, Statistics*

ESTADISTICA PANAMENA. SITUACION ECONOMICA. SECCION 312. PRODUCCION PECUARIA. see *AGRICULTURE — Abstracting, Bibliographies, Statistics*

ESTADISTICA PANAMENA. SITUACION ECONOMICA. SECCION 312. SUPERFICIE SEMBRADA Y COSECHA DE ARROZ, MAIZ Y FRIJOL DE BEJUCO. see *AGRICULTURE — Abstracting, Bibliographies, Statistics*

ESTADISTICA PANAMENA. SITUACION ECONOMICA. SECCION 312. SUPERFICIE SEMBRADA Y COSECHA DE CAFE, TABACO Y CANA DE AZUCAR. see *AGRICULTURE — Abstracting, Bibliographies, Statistics*

ESTADISTICA PANAMENA. SITUACION ECONOMICA. SECCION 331. COMERCIO. ANUARIO DE COMERCIO EXTERIOR. see *BUSINESS AND ECONOMICS — Abstracting, Bibliographies, Statistics*

ESTADISTICA PANAMENA. SITUACION ECONOMICA. SECCION 351. INDICE DE PRECIOS AL POR MAYOR Y AL CONSUMIDOR. see *BUSINESS AND ECONOMICS — Abstracting, Bibliographies, Statistics*

ESTADISTICA PANAMENA. SITUACION ECONOMICA. SECCION 351. PRECIOS PAGADOS POR EL PRODUCTOR AGROPECUARIO. see *AGRICULTURE — Abstracting, Bibliographies, Statistics*

ESTADISTICA PANAMENA. SITUACION ECONOMICA. SECCION 351. PRECIOS RECIBIDOS POR EL PRODUCTOR AGROPECUARIO. see *AGRICULTURE — Abstracting, Bibliographies, Statistics*

ESTADISTICA PANAMENA. SITUACION ECONOMICA. SECCION 351. PRECIOS RECIBIDOS POR EL PRODUCTOR AGROPECUARIO. COMPENDIO. see *AGRICULTURE — Abstracting, Bibliographies, Statistics*

ESTADISTICA PANAMENA. SITUACION ECONOMICA. SECCION 352. HOJA DE BALANCE DE ALIMENTOS. see *AGRICULTURE — Abstracting, Bibliographies, Statistics*

ESTADISTICA PANAMENA. SITUACION POLITICA, ADMINISTRATIVA Y JUSTICIA. SECCION 631. JUSTICIA. see *LAW — Abstracting, Bibliographies, Statistics*

ESTADISTICA PANAMENA. SITUACION SOCIAL. SECCION 431. SERVICIOS DE SALUD. see *SOCIAL SERVICES AND WELFARE — Abstracting, Bibliographies, Statistics*

ESTADISTICA PANAMENA. SITUACION SOCIAL. SECCION 451. ACCIDENTES DE TRANSITO. see *TRANSPORTATION — Abstracting, Bibliographies, Statistics*

310 330   CL
ESTADISTICA Y ECONOMIA. 1990. s-a. Esc.2250 (US $15.60; elsewhere $18.25) (effective 1994). Instituto Nacional de Estadisticas, Av. Bulnes 418, Casilla 498, Correo 3 Santiago, Chile. Ed. Gabriela Ahumada.

ESTADISTICAS DE EDUCACION EXTRAESCOLAR. see *EDUCATION — Abstracting, Bibliographies, Statistics*

ESTADISTICAS DEL COBRE Y OTROS MINERALES ANUARIO. see *MINES AND MINING INDUSTRY — Abstracting, Bibliographies, Statistics*

ESTADISTICAS PECUARIAS. see *AGRICULTURE — Abstracting, Bibliographies, Statistics*

ESTADISTICAS POLICIALES. POLICIA DE INVESTIGACIONES DE CHILE. see *CRIMINOLOGY AND LAW ENFORCEMENT — Abstracting, Bibliographies, Statistics*

ESTIMATED RESIDENT POPULATION BY AGE AND SEX IN STATISTICAL LOCAL AREAS, VICTORIA. see *POPULATION STUDIES — Abstracting, Bibliographies, Statistics*

ETESIA STATISTIKE. EREVNA TOU KARKINOU/ANNUAL STATISTICAL SURVEY OF CANCER. see *MEDICAL SCIENCES — Abstracting, Bibliographies, Statistics*

311   MR   ISSN 0851-9722
ETUDES DE CONJONCTURE: EVOLUTIONS ET TENDANCES. q. DH.66. Direction de la Statistique, B.P. 178, Rabat, Morocco. TEL 212-7-77-36-06. FAX 212-7-77-32-17. TELEX 36714. **Indexed:** P.A.I.S.For.Lang.Ind. **Document type:** government publication.
   Former titles (until 1991): Conjoncture Economique (ISSN 0851-5921); (until 1988): Conjoncture Economique au Maroc (ISSN 0851-0989); Morocco. Direction de la Statistique. Etude de Conjoncture.

380 310   UK   ISSN 0953-0258
EUROPEAN DIRECTORY OF NON-OFFICIAL STATISTICAL SOURCES. 1988. irreg., 2nd edition, 1993. £160($335) (effective 1996). Euromonitor, 60-61 Britton St., London EC1M 5NA, England. TEL 0171-251-8024. FAX 0171-608-3149. (Addr. in N. America: Euromonitor International, 122 S. Michigan Ave., Ste. 1200, Chicago, IL 60603. TEL 312-922-1115. FAX 312-922-1157) **Document type:** directory.
   Description: Includes more than 2,000 published statistical reports from various sources, including trade and professional associations, banks, stockbrokers, market researchers, academic institutions, and private companies.

EUROSTAT. RAPID REPORTS. AGRICULTURE, FORESTRY AND FISHERIES. see *AGRICULTURE — Abstracting, Bibliographies, Statistics*

EVALUATING YOUR FIRM'S INJURY & ILLNESS RECORD. CONSTRUCTION INDUSTRIES. see *OCCUPATIONAL HEALTH AND SAFETY*

EVALUATING YOUR FIRM'S INJURY & ILLNESS RECORD. SERVICE INDUSTRIES. see *OCCUPATIONAL HEALTH AND SAFETY*

EVALUATING YOUR FIRM'S INJURY & ILLNESS RECORD. TRANSPORTATION & PUBLIC UTILITIES INDUSTRIES. see *OCCUPATIONAL HEALTH AND SAFETY*

6200 STATISTICS

EVALUATING YOUR FIRM'S INJURY & ILLNESS RECORD. WHOLESALE & RETAIL TRADE INDUSTRIES. see *OCCUPATIONAL HEALTH AND SAFETY*

EXPORT STATISTICS OF AFGHANISTAN/IHSA'IYAH-I AMUAL-I SADIRATI-I AFGHANISTAN. see *BUSINESS AND ECONOMICS — Abstracting, Bibliographies, Statistics*

EXTERNAL TRADE STATISTICS OF GHANA (ANNUAL). see *BUSINESS AND ECONOMICS — Abstracting, Bibliographies, Statistics*

EXTERNAL TRADE STATISTICS OF GHANA (HALF-YEARLY). see *BUSINESS AND ECONOMICS — Abstracting, Bibliographies, Statistics*

EXTERNAL TRADE STATISTICS OF GHANA (QUARTERLY). see *BUSINESS AND ECONOMICS — Abstracting, Bibliographies, Statistics*

F H A TRENDS OF HOME MORTGAGE CHARACTERISTICS; section 203(b) mortgages insured (year). see *HOUSING AND URBAN PLANNING*

FACT BOOK; a statistical handbook. see *EDUCATION — Abstracting, Bibliographies, Statistics*

FACTORY SALES OF ELECTRIC STORAGE BATTERIES. see *BUSINESS AND ECONOMICS — Abstracting, Bibliographies, Statistics*

FACTS ABOUT FAMILY PRACTICE. see *MEDICAL SCIENCES — Abstracting, Bibliographies, Statistics*

315.4   II
FACTS ABOUT HARYANA. 1967. irreg. Director of Public Relations, Chandigarh, India. stat. circ. 3,000.

315   IS
FAMILY EXPENDITURE SURVEY. (Text in English and Hebrew) 1969. irreg. price varies. Central Bureau of Statistics, Box 13015, Hakirya Romema, Jerusalem 91 130, Israel. TEL 02-553400. stat. (back issues avail.)
    Description: Research on consumption patterns, income and savings levels of urban families.

FAMILY SAVING SURVEY (YEAR). see *BUSINESS AND ECONOMICS — Abstracting, Bibliographies, Statistics*

FARM BUSINESS STATISTICS FOR SOUTH EAST ENGLAND. see *AGRICULTURE — Abstracting, Bibliographies, Statistics*

FEDERAL CIVILIAN WORKFORCE STATISTICS. EMPLOYMENT AND TRENDS. see *BUSINESS AND ECONOMICS — Abstracting, Bibliographies, Statistics*

FEDERAL MILK ORDER MARKET STATISTICS. see *AGRICULTURE — Abstracting, Bibliographies, Statistics*

FERTILISER ASSOCIATION OF INDIA. FERTILISER STATISTICS. see *AGRICULTURE — Abstracting, Bibliographies, Statistics*

FIJI. BUREAU OF STATISTICS. AIRCRAFT STATISTICS. see *AERONAUTICS AND SPACE FLIGHT — Abstracting, Bibliographies, Statistics*

FIJI. BUREAU OF STATISTICS. CENSUS OF BUILDING AND CONSTRUCTION. see *BUILDING AND CONSTRUCTION — Abstracting, Bibliographies, Statistics*

FIJI. BUREAU OF STATISTICS. CENSUS OF DISTRIBUTION AND SERVICES. see *BUSINESS AND ECONOMICS — Abstracting, Bibliographies, Statistics*

FIJI. BUREAU OF STATISTICS. CENSUS OF INDUSTRIES. see *BUSINESS AND ECONOMICS — Abstracting, Bibliographies, Statistics*

FIJI. BUREAU OF STATISTICS. CURRENT ECONOMIC STATISTICS. see *BUSINESS AND ECONOMICS — Abstracting, Bibliographies, Statistics*

FIJI. BUREAU OF STATISTICS. ECONOMIC AND FUNCTIONAL CLASSIFICATION OF GOVERNMENT ACCOUNTS. see *BUSINESS AND ECONOMICS — Abstracting, Bibliographies, Statistics*

FIJI. BUREAU OF STATISTICS. EMPLOYMENT SURVEY OF FIJI. see *BUSINESS AND ECONOMICS — Abstracting, Bibliographies, Statistics*

FIJI. BUREAU OF STATISTICS. FIJI FERTILITY SURVEY. see *POPULATION STUDIES — Abstracting, Bibliographies, Statistics*

FIJI. BUREAU OF STATISTICS. FIJI HOUSEHOLD INCOME AND EXPENDITURE SURVEY. see *BUSINESS AND ECONOMICS — Abstracting, Bibliographies, Statistics*

FIJI. BUREAU OF STATISTICS. NATIONWIDE UNEMPLOYMENT SURVEY. see *BUSINESS AND ECONOMICS — Abstracting, Bibliographies, Statistics*

FIJI. BUREAU OF STATISTICS. POPULATION OF FIJI; monograph for the U N World population. see *POPULATION STUDIES — Abstracting, Bibliographies, Statistics*

310   FJ   ISSN 0256-4149
FIJI. BUREAU OF STATISTICS. STATISTICAL NEWS. 1979. m. $33 (effective 1995 & 1996). Bureau of Statistics, P.O. Box 2221, Suva, Fiji. **Document type:** government publication.

FIJI. BUREAU OF STATISTICS. SURVEY OF DISTRIBUTIVE TRADE. see *BUSINESS AND ECONOMICS — Abstracting, Bibliographies, Statistics*

FIJI. BUREAU OF STATISTICS. TOURISM AND MIGRATION STATISTICS. see *TRAVEL AND TOURISM — Abstracting, Bibliographies, Statistics*

FIJI. BUREAU OF STATISTICS. TRADE REPORT. see *BUSINESS AND ECONOMICS — Abstracting, Bibliographies, Statistics*

FIJI. BUREAU OF STATISTICS. VITAL STATISTICS. see *BUSINESS AND ECONOMICS — Abstracting, Bibliographies, Statistics*

FIJI FACTS AND FIGURES. see *BUSINESS AND ECONOMICS — Abstracting, Bibliographies, Statistics*

FINANCIAL STATISTICS OF MAJOR INVESTOR-OWNED ELECTRIC UTILITIES (YEAR). see *ENERGY — Abstracting, Bibliographies, Statistics*

FINANCIAL STATISTICS OF MAJOR PUBLICLY OWNED ELECTRIC UTILITIES (YEAR). see *ENERGY — Abstracting, Bibliographies, Statistics*

FINANCIAL STATISTICS OF UNIVERSITIES AND COLLEGES/STATISTIQUES FINANCIERES DES UNIVERSITES ET COLLEGES. see *EDUCATION — Abstracting, Bibliographies, Statistics*

FINANZAS. see *BUSINESS AND ECONOMICS — Abstracting, Bibliographies, Statistics*

FINANZAS PUBLICAS ESTATALES Y MUNICIPALES DE MEXICO. see *BUSINESS AND ECONOMICS — Abstracting, Bibliographies, Statistics*

FINLAND. STATISTIKCENTRALEN. STATISTISKA MEDDELANDEN. LEVNADSFOERHAALLANDEN I FINLAND/FINLAND. CENTRAL STATISTICAL OFFICE. LIVING CONDITIONS IN FINLAND. see *SOCIOLOGY — Abstracting, Bibliographies, Statistics*

311   FI   ISSN 0355-2063
HA1
FINLAND. TILASTOKESKUS. KAESIKIRJOJA/FINLAND. STATISTIKCENTRALEN. HANDBOECKER/FINLAND. CENTRAL STATISTICAL OFFICE. HANDBOOKS. (Text in Finnish and sometimes in English and Swedish) 1971. irreg. price varies. Tilastokeskus, Annankatu 44, SF-00100 Helsinki 10, Finland.

314.71   FI   ISSN 0015-2390
HA1450.5
FINLAND. TILASTOKESKUS. TILASTOKATSAUKSIA/FINLAND. STATISTIKCENTRALEN. STATISTISKA OEVERSIKTER/FINLAND. CENTRAL STATISTICAL OFFICE. BULLETIN OF STATISTICS. (Text in English, Finnish and Swedish) 1924. q. FIM 110. Tilastokeskus, Annankatu 44, SF-00100 Helsinki 10, Finland. (Subscr. to: Government Printing Centre, Box 516, SF-00100 Helsinki 10, Finland) charts; stat. circ. 2,350.

FINLAND. TILASTOKESKUS. TILASTOTIEDOTUS. PALKAT LONER/FINLAND. CENTRAL STATISTICAL OFFICE. WAGES AND SALARIES. see *BUSINESS AND ECONOMICS — Abstracting, Bibliographies, Statistics*

314   FI   ISSN 0357-0614
Z7554.F5
FINLAND. TILASTOKESKUS. VALTION TILASTOJULKAISUT/FINLAND. STATISTIKCENTRALEN. STATENS STATISTISKA PUBLIKATIONER/FINLAND. CENTRAL STATISTICAL OFFICE. GOVERNMENT STATISTICS. (Text in English, Finnish and Swedish) 1978. a. FIM 60. Tilastokeskus, Annankatu 44, SF-00100 Helsinki 10, Finland.

FIRE STATISTICS UNITED KINGDOM. see *FIRE PREVENTION — Abstracting, Bibliographies, Statistics*

FISHERIES MARKET NEWS REPORT. see *FISH AND FISHERIES — Abstracting, Bibliographies, Statistics*

310   GW
FLENSBURGER ZAHLENSPIEGEL (YEAR). 1951. a. DM.7.50. Stadt Flensburg, Amt fuer Stadtentwicklung, Postfach 2742, 24917 Flensburg, Germany. circ. 500. **Document type:** government publication.

FLORIDA LONG-TERM ECONOMIC FORECAST. see *BUSINESS AND ECONOMICS — Abstracting, Bibliographies, Statistics*

FLORIDA STATISTICAL ABSTRACT. see *BUSINESS AND ECONOMICS — Abstracting, Bibliographies, Statistics*

FLORIDA VITAL STATISTICS. see *POPULATION STUDIES — Abstracting, Bibliographies, Statistics*

FOOD INDUSTRY STATISTICS DIGEST. see *FOOD AND FOOD INDUSTRIES — Abstracting, Bibliographies, Statistics*

FOOTWEAR INDUSTRY STATISTICAL REVIEW. see *SHOES AND BOOTS — Abstracting, Bibliographies, Statistics*

FOREIGN TRADE STATISTICS OF AFRICA. SERIES A: DIRECTION OF TRADE. see *BUSINESS AND ECONOMICS — Abstracting, Bibliographies, Statistics*

FRANCE. CONSEIL NATIONAL DU CREDIT. STATISTIQUES MENSUELLES. see *BUSINESS AND ECONOMICS — Abstracting, Bibliographies, Statistics*

FRANCE. CONSEIL NATIONAL DU CREDIT. STATISTIQUES TRIMESTRIELLES. see *BUSINESS AND ECONOMICS — Abstracting, Bibliographies, Statistics*

314   FR   ISSN 0007-4713
FRANCE. INSTITUT NATIONAL DE LA STATISTIQUE ET DES ETUDES ECONOMIQUES. BULLETIN MENSUEL DE STATISTIQUE. 1911. m. 346 F. (foreign 562 F.); microfiche 176 F. (foreign 349 F.). Institut National de la Statistique et des Etudes Economiques, 18 bd. Adolphe Pinard, 75675 Paris Cedex 14, France. TEL 41-17-50-50. FAX 41-17-66-66. stat. circ. 7,600. (also avail. in microfiche) **Indexed:** P.A.I.S.For.Lang.Ind.
    —BLDSC (2877.730000).
    Formerly (until 1949): Statistique Generale de la France. Bulletin.
    Description: Statistics on employment, industry, business, prices and finance in France and other countries.

311.2   FR   ISSN 0151-9514
FRANCE. INSTITUT NATIONAL DE LA STATISTIQUE ET DES ETUDES ECONOMIQUES. COURRIER DES STATISTIQUES. 1977. 4/yr. 135 F. (foreign 234 F.). Institut National de la Statistique et des Etudes Economiques, 18 bd. Adolphe Pinard, 75675 Paris Cedex 14, France. TEL 41-17-50-50. FAX 41-17-66-66.
    Description: Presents a global image of the life of the public statistical system.

FRANCE. MINISTERE DE L'AGRICULTURE ET DE LA PECHE. ANALYSES ET ETUDES. CAHIERS. see *AGRICULTURE — Abstracting, Bibliographies, Statistics*

FRANCE. MINISTERE DE L'URBANISME ET DU LOGEMENT. STATISTIQUES ET ETUDES GENERALES. see *HOUSING AND URBAN PLANNING — Abstracting, Bibliographies, Statistics*

FRANCE. SERVICE D'ETUDE DES STRATEGIES ET DES STATISTIQUES INDUSTRIELLES. LA SITUATION DE L'INDUSTRIE. PREMIERS RESULTATS. see *BUSINESS AND ECONOMICS — Abstracting, Bibliographies, Statistics*

314 GW
FRANKFURT AM MAIN. AMT FUER STATISTIK, WAHLEN UND EINWOHNERWESEN. STATISTISCHES JAHRBUCH. 1951. a. DM.39. Amt fuer Statistik, Wahlen und Einwohnerwesen, 60275 Frankfurt a.M., Germany. TEL 069-212-33667. FAX 069-212-37888. circ. 800. **Document type:** government publication.
Formerly: Frankfurt am Main. Statistisches Amt und Wahlamt. Statistisches Jahrbuch (ISSN 0071-9218)
Description: Covers complete statistical information of the town. Includes population, economy, housing, public health, finance, culture and elections.

310 GW ISSN 0177-7351
FRANKFURTER STATISTISCHE BERICHTE. 1936. q. DM.33. Amt fuer Statistik, Wahlen und Einwohnerwesen, 60275 Frankfurt a.M., Germany. TEL 069-212-33667. FAX 069-212-37888. circ. 600. **Document type:** government publication.
Description: Covers complete statistics of the town: vital, population, economical, financial, public health, cultural, housing and more.

FROZEN FISHERY PRODUCTS. ANNUAL SUMMARY. see *FISH AND FISHERIES — Abstracting, Bibliographies, Statistics*

310 GW
FULDA. STATISTISCHER BERICHT. 1974. a. free. Magistrat der Stadt Fulda, Abt. 103, Postfach 1020, 36010 Fulda, Germany. TEL 0661-102198. FAX 0661-79153. TELEX 6619707-STDFD. circ. 1,000.

310 GO
GABON. DIRECTION GENERALE DE L'ECONOMIE. BULLETIN MENSUEL DE STATISTIQUE. m. Direction de la Statistique et des Etudes Economiques, B.P. 179, Libreville, Gabon.
Former titles: Gabon. Direction de la Statistique et des Etudes Economique. Bulletin Mensuel de Statistique; Gabon. Service National de la Statistique. Bulletin Mensuel de Statistique.

GAMBIA. CENTRAL STATISTICS DEPARTMENT. EDUCATION STATISTICS. see *EDUCATION — Abstracting, Bibliographies, Statistics*

GAMBIA. CENTRAL STATISTICS DEPARTMENT. MONTHLY SUMMARY OF EXTERNAL TRADE STATISTICS. see *BUSINESS AND ECONOMICS — Abstracting, Bibliographies, Statistics*

GAMBIA. CENTRAL STATISTICS DEPARTMENT. SUMMARY OF TOURIST STATISTICS. see *TRAVEL AND TOURISM — Abstracting, Bibliographies, Statistics*

GAMBIA. CENTRAL STATISTICS DEPARTMENT. TOURIST STATISTICS. see *TRAVEL AND TOURISM — Abstracting, Bibliographies, Statistics*

GAS AND FUEL CORPORATION OF VICTORIA. STATISTICS. see *PETROLEUM AND GAS — Abstracting, Bibliographies, Statistics*

GAS INDUSTRY STATISTICS (YEAR). see *PETROLEUM AND GAS — Abstracting, Bibliographies, Statistics*

314 GW
GEMEINDEN NORDRHEIN-WESTFALENS; Informationen aus der amtlichen Statistik. 1976. a. DM.15. Landesamt fuer Datenverarbeitung und Statistik Nordrhein-Westfalen, Postfach 101105, 40002 Duesseldorf, Germany. TEL 0211-9449-01. FAX 0211-442006. circ. 1,200. (back issues avail.) **Document type:** government publication.

DIE GENOSSENSCHAFTEN IN DER BUNDESREPUBLIK DEUTSCHLAND. STATISTIK. see *BUSINESS AND ECONOMICS — Cooperatives*

GEOGRAPHIC PROFILE OF EMPLOYMENT AND UNEMPLOYMENT. see *BUSINESS AND ECONOMICS — Economic Situation And Conditions*

GEOGRAPHICAL CODE OF GREECE; by department, eparchy, municipality, commune and locality. see *GEOGRAPHY — Abstracting, Bibliographies, Statistics*

GEORGIA DESCRIPTIONS IN DATA. see *POPULATION STUDIES — Abstracting, Bibliographies, Statistics*

GEORGIA STATISTICAL ABSTRACT. see *BUSINESS AND ECONOMICS — Abstracting, Bibliographies, Statistics*

GERMANY. BUNDESANSTALT FUER ARBEIT. BERUFSBERATUNG. ERGEBNISSE DER BERUFSBERATUNGSSTATISTIK. see *BUSINESS AND ECONOMICS — Abstracting, Bibliographies, Statistics*

310 GW ISSN 0433-7344
GERMANY. BUNDESMINISTERIUM FUER ERNAEHRUNG, LANDWIRTSCHAFT UND FORSTEN. STATISTISCHER MONATSBERICHT. 1949. m. DM.190. Bundesministerium fuer Ernaehrung, Landwirtschaft und Forsten, Planungskoordination und -grundlagen, Postfach 140270, 53107 Bonn, Germany. TEL 0228-529-0. FAX 0228-5294262. TELEX 886844-BML-D. (Subscr. to: Bundesamt fuer Landwirtschaft und Ernaehrung, Adicksallee 40, 60322 Frankfurt a.M., Germany) Ed. M. Schmidt. circ. 1,050. **Document type:** government publication.

GERMANY. STATISTISCHES BUNDESAMT. AUSGEWAEHLTE ZAHLEN FUER DIE BAUWIRTSCHAFT. see *BUILDING AND CONSTRUCTION — Abstracting, Bibliographies, Statistics*

GERMANY. STATISTISCHES BUNDESAMT. BEVOELKERUNG UND ERWERBSTAETIGKEIT. REIHE 1: GEBIET UND BEVOELKERUNG. see *POPULATION STUDIES — Abstracting, Bibliographies, Statistics*

GERMANY. STATISTISCHES BUNDESAMT. FACHSERIE 2, UNTERNEHMEN UND ARBEITSSTAETTEN, REIHE 4.1: INSOLVENZVERFAHREN. see *BUSINESS AND ECONOMICS — Abstracting, Bibliographies, Statistics*

GERMANY. STATISTISCHES BUNDESAMT. FACHSERIE 3, LAND- UND FORSTWIRTSCHAFT, FISCHEREI; REIHE 3: BETRIEBS-, ARBEITS- UND EINKOMMENSVERHAELTNISSE. see *AGRICULTURE — Abstracting, Bibliographies, Statistics*

GERMANY. STATISTISCHES BUNDESAMT. FACHSERIE 4, PRODUZIERENDES GEWERBE, REIHE 3.1: PRODUKTION IM PRODUZIERENDEN GEWERBE. see *BUSINESS AND ECONOMICS — Abstracting, Bibliographies, Statistics*

GERMANY. STATISTISCHES BUNDESAMT. FACHSERIE 5, BAUTAETIGKEIT UND WOHNUNGEN, REIHE 1: BAUTAETIGKEIT. see *BUILDING AND CONSTRUCTION — Abstracting, Bibliographies, Statistics*

GERMANY. STATISTISCHES BUNDESAMT. FACHSERIE 5, BAUTAETIGKEIT UND WOHNUNGEN, REIHE 2: BEWILLIGUNGEN IM SOZIALEN WOHNUNGSBAU. see *BUILDING AND CONSTRUCTION — Abstracting, Bibliographies, Statistics*

GERMANY. STATISTISCHES BUNDESAMT. FACHSERIE 6, HANDEL, GASTGEWERBE, REISEVERKEHR; REIHE 3: EINZELHANDEL. see *BUSINESS AND ECONOMICS — Abstracting, Bibliographies, Statistics*

GERMANY. STATISTISCHES BUNDESAMT. FACHSERIE 6, HANDEL, GASTGEWERBE, REISEVERKEHR; REIHE 6: INNERDEUTSCHER WARENVERKEHR. see *BUSINESS AND ECONOMICS — Abstracting, Bibliographies, Statistics*

GERMANY. STATISTISCHES BUNDESAMT. FACHSERIE 7, AUSSENHANDEL, REIHE 7: AUSSENHANDEL NACH LAENDERN UND GUETERGRUPPEN DER PRODUKTIONSSTATISTIKEN (SPEZIALHANDEL). see *BUSINESS AND ECONOMICS — Abstracting, Bibliographies, Statistics*

GERMANY. STATISTISCHES BUNDESAMT. FACHSERIE 7, AUSSENHANDEL, REIHE 3: AUSSENHANDEL NACH LAENDERN UND WARENGRUPPEN (SPEZIALHANDEL). see *BUSINESS AND ECONOMICS — Abstracting, Bibliographies, Statistics*

GERMANY. STATISTISCHES BUNDESAMT. FACHSERIE 7, AUSSENHANDEL, REIHE 2: AUSSENHANDEL NACH WAREN UND LAENDERN (SPEZIALHANDEL). see *BUSINESS AND ECONOMICS — Abstracting, Bibliographies, Statistics*

GERMANY. STATISTISCHES BUNDESAMT. FACHSERIE 7, AUSSENHANDEL, REIHE 1: ZUSAMMENFASSENDE UEBERSICHTEN FUER DEN AUSSENHANDEL. see *BUSINESS AND ECONOMICS — Abstracting, Bibliographies, Statistics*

GERMANY. STATISTISCHES BUNDESAMT. FACHSERIE 8, VERKEHR, REIHE 2: EISENBAHNVERKEHR. see *TRANSPORTATION — Abstracting, Bibliographies, Statistics*

GERMANY. STATISTISCHES BUNDESAMT. FACHSERIE 8, VERKEHR, REIHE 3.3: VERKEHRSUNFAELLE. see *TRANSPORTATION — Abstracting, Bibliographies, Statistics*

GERMANY. STATISTISCHES BUNDESAMT. FACHSERIE 8, VERKEHR, REIHE 4: BINNENSCHIFFAHRT. see *TRANSPORTATION — Abstracting, Bibliographies, Statistics*

GERMANY. STATISTISCHES BUNDESAMT. FACHSERIE 8, VERKEHR, REIHE 5: SEESCHIFFAHRT. see *TRANSPORTATION — Abstracting, Bibliographies, Statistics*

GERMANY. STATISTISCHES BUNDESAMT. FACHSERIE 8, VERKEHR, REIHE 6: LUFTVERKEHR. see *TRANSPORTATION — Abstracting, Bibliographies, Statistics*

GERMANY. STATISTISCHES BUNDESAMT. FACHSERIE 10. RECHTSPFLEGE. see *LAW — Abstracting, Bibliographies, Statistics*

GERMANY. STATISTISCHES BUNDESAMT. FACHSERIE 11: BILDUNG UND KULTUR. see *EDUCATION — Abstracting, Bibliographies, Statistics*

GERMANY. STATISTISCHES BUNDESAMT. FACHSERIE 16, LOEHNE UND GEHAELTER, REIHE 3: ARBEITERVERDIENSTE IM HANDWERK. see *BUSINESS AND ECONOMICS — Abstracting, Bibliographies, Statistics*

GERMANY. STATISTISCHES BUNDESAMT. FACHSERIE 16, LOEHNE UND GEHAELTER, REIHE 5: LOEHNE, GEHAELTER UND ARBEITSKOSTEN IM AUSLAND. see *BUSINESS AND ECONOMICS — Abstracting, Bibliographies, Statistics*

GERMANY. STATISTISCHES BUNDESAMT. FACHSERIE 17, PREISE, REIHE 1: PREISE UND PREISINDIZES FUER DIE LAND- UND FORSTWIRTSCHAFT. see *AGRICULTURE — Abstracting, Bibliographies, Statistics*

GERMANY. STATISTISCHES BUNDESAMT. FACHSERIE 17, PREISE, REIHE 2: PREISE UND PREISINDIZES FUER GEWERBLICHE PRODUKTE. ERZEUGERPREISE. see *BUSINESS AND ECONOMICS — Abstracting, Bibliographies, Statistics*

GERMANY. STATISTISCHES BUNDESAMT. FACHSERIE 17, PREISE, REIHE 3: PREISINDEX FUER DEN WARENEINGANG DES PRODUZIERENDEN GEWERBES. see *BUSINESS AND ECONOMICS — Abstracting, Bibliographies, Statistics*

GERMANY. STATISTISCHES BUNDESAMT. FACHSERIE 17, PREISE, REIHE 4: MESSZAHLEN FUER BAULEISTUNGSPREISE UND PREISINDIZES FUER BAUWERKE. see *BUSINESS AND ECONOMICS — Abstracting, Bibliographies, Statistics*

GERMANY. STATISTISCHES BUNDESAMT. FACHSERIE 17, PREISE, REIHE 8: PREISE UND PREISINDIZES FUER DIE EIN- UND AUSFUHR. see *BUSINESS AND ECONOMICS — Abstracting, Bibliographies, Statistics*

GERMANY. STATISTISCHES BUNDESAMT. FACHSERIE 17, PREISE, REIHE 9: PREISE UND PREISINDIZES FUER VERKEHRSLEISTUNGEN. see *TRANSPORTATION — Abstracting, Bibliographies, Statistics*

GERMANY. STATISTISCHES BUNDESAMT. FACHSERIE 17, PREISE, REIHE 10: INTERNATIONALER VERGLEICH DER PREISE FUER DIE LEBENSHALTUNG. see *BUSINESS AND ECONOMICS — Abstracting, Bibliographies, Statistics*

6202 STATISTICS

GERMANY. STATISTISCHES BUNDESAMT. FACHSERIE 17, PREISE, REIHE 11: PREISE UND PREISINDIZES IM AUSLAND. see *BUSINESS AND ECONOMICS — Abstracting, Bibliographies, Statistics*

318 GW
GERMANY. STATISTISCHES BUNDESAMT. LAENDERBERICHTE. (Subseries of its Allgemeine Statistik des Auslandes; avail. for approx. 30 countries) irreg. DM.515. 65180 Wiesbaden, Germany. TEL 0611-75-1. FAX 0611-724000. TELEX 61186-STBA-D. **Document type:** government publication.

GERMANY. STATISTISCHES BUNDESAMT. WARENVERZEICHNIS FUER DIE AUSSENHANDELSSTATISTIK. see *BUSINESS AND ECONOMICS — Abstracting, Bibliographies, Statistics*

310 GW ISSN 0072-4114
GERMANY. STATISTISCHES BUNDESAMT. ZAHLENKOMPASS/STATISTICAL COMPASS. (Editions in English, German) a. DM.9.80. 65180 Wiesbaden, Germany. TEL 0611-75-1. FAX 0611-724000. TELEX 61186-STBA-D. **Document type:** government publication.

GHANA. STATISTICAL SERVICE. ECONOMIC SURVEY. see *BUSINESS AND ECONOMICS — Abstracting, Bibliographies, Statistics*

GHANA. STATISTICAL SERVICE. MOTOR VEHICLE REGISTRATION. see *TRANSPORTATION — Abstracting, Bibliographies, Statistics*

GHANA. STATISTICAL SERVICE. POPULATION CENSUS - DEMOGRAPHIC AND ECONOMIC CHARACTERISTICS. see *POPULATION STUDIES — Abstracting, Bibliographies, Statistics*

GHANA. STATISTICAL SERVICE. POPULATION CENSUS - SPECIAL REPORT ON LOCALITIES. see *POPULATION STUDIES — Abstracting, Bibliographies, Statistics*

316 GH ISSN 0855-0662
GHANA. STATISTICAL SERVICE. QUARTERLY DIGEST OF STATISTICS. 1952. q. $60. Statistical Service, Information Section, Box 1098, Accra, Ghana. TEL 233-21-663578. FAX 233-21-667069. TELEX 2205 MIFAEP GH. **Document type:** government publication.
Formerly: Ghana. Central Bureau of Statistics. Quarterly Digest of Statistics (ISSN 0435-8864)

GHANA INDUSTRIAL CENSUS. DIRECTORY OF INDUSTRIAL ESTABLISHMENTS. see *BUSINESS AND ECONOMICS — Abstracting, Bibliographies, Statistics*

GHANA INDUSTRIAL CENSUS. PHASE II REPORT. see *BUSINESS AND ECONOMICS — Abstracting, Bibliographies, Statistics*

GHANA LIVING STANDARDS SURVEY. ROUND REPORT. see *BUSINESS AND ECONOMICS — Abstracting, Bibliographies, Statistics*

GHANA LIVING STANDARDS SURVEY. RURAL COMMUNITIES IN GHANA. see *BUSINESS AND ECONOMICS — Abstracting, Bibliographies, Statistics*

310 SW ISSN 0072-5110
GOETEBORGS UNIVERSITET. STATISTISKA INSTITUTIONEN. SKRIFTSERIE. PUBLICATIONS. (Text in English or Swedish) 1954. irreg. price varies. A W I International AB, P.O. Box 4627, S-116 91 Stockholm, Sweden. TEL 468-640-8800. FAX 468-641-1180. Ed. Sture Holm.

318.1 BL
GOIAS, BRAZIL. SECRETARIA DO PLANEJAMENTO E COORDENACAO. BOLETIM ESTADISTICO. (Includes comparative data for previous years) irreg? Secretaria do Planejamento e Coordenacao, Goiania, Brazil.
Continues: Goias, Brazil. Departamento Estadual de Estatistica. Boletim Estatistico.

GRANT ASSISTANCE PROGRAM. FISCAL YEAR STATISTICAL SUMMARIES. see *TRANSPORTATION — Abstracting, Bibliographies, Statistics*

314 UK ISSN 0072-5730
HA1122
GREAT BRITAIN. CENTRAL STATISTICAL OFFICE. ANNUAL ABSTRACT OF STATISTICS. 1948. a. £22.50 (Feb. 1993 edition). Central Statistical Office, C.S.O. Library, Government Bldgs., 155 Cardiff Rd., Newport, Gwent NP9 1XG, Wales. TEL 01633-812973. FAX 01633-812599. TELEX 497121 BSO NPT G. (Orders to: H.M.S.O. Publications Centre, P.O. Box 276, London SW8 5DT, England. TEL 0171-873-9090. FAX 0171-873-8200) circ. 5,500. (reprint service avail. from KTO,SCH) **Document type:** government publication.
—BLDSC (1073.850000). **CCC.**
Description: Compiles the latest economic, financial, and social figures from the C.S.O. monthly and annual publications.

GREAT BRITAIN. CENTRAL STATISTICAL OFFICE. ANNUAL CENSUS OF PRODUCTION REPORTS. see *BUSINESS AND ECONOMICS — Abstracting, Bibliographies, Statistics*

GREAT BRITAIN. CENTRAL STATISTICAL OFFICE. FAMILY EXPENDITURE SURVEY. see *BUSINESS AND ECONOMICS — Macroeconomics*

GREAT BRITAIN. CENTRAL STATISTICAL OFFICE. FINANCIAL STATISTICS. see *BUSINESS AND ECONOMICS — Abstracting, Bibliographies, Statistics*

314 UK ISSN 0261-1791
GREAT BRITAIN. CENTRAL STATISTICAL OFFICE. GUIDE TO OFFICIAL STATISTICS. 1976. irreg., latest 1990. £24. Central Statistical Office, C.S.O. Library, Government Bldgs., 155 Cardiff Rd., Newport, Gwent NP9 1XG, Wales. TEL 01633-812973. FAX 01633-81599. TELEX 497121 BSO NPT G. (Orders to: H.M.S.O. Publications Centre, P.O. Box 276, London SW8 5DT, England. TEL 0171-873-9090. FAX 0171-873-8200) **Document type:** government publication.
—BLDSC (4229.755000). **CCC.**
Description: Traces primary sources of statistics for the past five years for areas ranging from weather to wages, finance to forestry, production to police.

314.1 UK ISSN 0951-9092
GREAT BRITAIN. CENTRAL STATISTICAL OFFICE. KEY DATA. Key Title: Key Data. 1986. a. £5.50 (1993-1994 edition). Central Statistical Office, C.S.O. Library, Government Bldgs., Cardiff Rd., Newport, Gwent NP9 1XG, Wales. TEL 01633-812973. FAX 01633-812599. TELEX 497121 BSO NPT G. (Avail. from: H.M.S.O. Publications Centre, P.O. Box 276, London SW8 5DT, England. TEL 0171-873-9090. FAX 0171-873-8200) Ed.Bd. charts; stat. (back issues avail.) **Document type:** government publication.
—BLDSC (5091.822400).
Description: Compiles U.K. business and social statistics on trade and industry, employment, health and social security, education, environment and energy, law and order, and defense.

314 UK ISSN 0308-6666
GREAT BRITAIN. CENTRAL STATISTICAL OFFICE. MONTHLY DIGEST OF STATISTICS. 1946. m. £88 (includes a. supplement) (effective 1994). Central Statistical Office, C.S.O. Library, Government Bldgs., 155 Cardiff Rd., Newport, Gwent NP9 1XG, Wales. TEL 01633-812973. FAX 01633-812599. TELEX 497121 BSO NPT G. (Orders to: H.M.S.O. Publications Centre, P.O. Box 276, London SW8 5DT, England. TEL 0171-873-9090. FAX 0171-873-8200) stat. **Document type:** government publication.
—BLDSC (5937.400000); UMI. **CCC.**
Description: Provides information on demographics, employment, energy, engineering, transport, international finance, and other topics.

314 325 UK ISSN 0261-1783
GREAT BRITAIN. CENTRAL STATISTICAL OFFICE. REGIONAL TRENDS. 1965. a. £26 (for Jul. 1993 edition). Central Statistical Office, C.S.O. Library, Government Bldgs., 155 Cardiff Rd., Newport, Gwent NP9 1XG, Wales. TEL 01633-812973. FAX 01633-812599. TELEX 497121 BSO NPT G. (Orders to: H.M.S.O. Publications Centre, P.O. Box 276, London SW8 5DT, England. TEL 0171-873-9090. FAX 0171-873-8200) charts; stat. **Document type:** government publication.
—BLDSC (7336.786000). **CCC.**
Former titles: Great Britain. Central Statistical Office. Regional Statistics (ISSN 0308-146X); Great Britain. Central Statistical Office Abstracts of Regional Statistics (ISSN 0072-5749)
Description: Compiles detailed demographic statistics for each standard region of the U.K.

GREAT BRITAIN. CENTRAL STATISTICAL OFFICE. SOCIAL TRENDS. see *SOCIOLOGY*

GREAT BRITAIN. CENTRAL STATISTICAL OFFICE. STANDARD INDUSTRIAL CLASSIFICATION OF ECONOMIC ACTIVITIES (YEAR). see *BUSINESS AND ECONOMICS — Abstracting, Bibliographies, Statistics*

314 UK ISSN 0017-3630
CODEN: STANE2
GREAT BRITAIN. CENTRAL STATISTICAL OFFICE. STATISTICAL NEWS; developments in British official statistics. 1968. q. £20. Central Statistical Office, C.S.O. Library, Government Bldgs., 155 Cardiff Rd., Newport, Gwent NP9 1XG, Wales. TEL 01633-812973. FAX 01633-812599. TELEX 497121 BSO NPT G. (Orders to: H.M.S.O. Publications Centre, P.O. Box 276, London SW8 5DT, England. TEL 0171-873973. FAX 0171-873-8200) (also avail. in microform from UMI; reprint service avail. from UMI) **Document type:** government publication.
—BLDSC (8448.575000); Faxon; UMI; UnCover. **CCC.**

311 UK ISSN 0081-8313
GREAT BRITAIN. CENTRAL STATISTICAL OFFICE. STUDIES IN OFFICIAL STATISTICS. irreg. price varies. Central Statistical Office, C.S.O. Library, Government Bldgs., 155 Cardiff Rd., Newport, Gwent NP9 1XG, Wales. TEL 01633-812973. FAX 01633-81259. TELEX 497121 BSO NPT G. (Orders to: H.M.S.O. Publications Centre, P.O. Box 276, London SW8 5DT, England. TEL 0171-873-9090. FAX 0171-873-8200) **Document type:** government publication.
—**CCC.**

GREAT BRITAIN. CENTRAL STATISTICAL OFFICE. UNITED KINGDOM BALANCE OF PAYMENTS. see *BUSINESS AND ECONOMICS — Abstracting, Bibliographies, Statistics*

GREAT BRITAIN. CENTRAL STATISTICAL OFFICE. UNITED KINGDOM NATIONAL ACCOUNTS. see *BUSINESS AND ECONOMICS — Abstracting, Bibliographies, Statistics*

GREAT BRITAIN. CIVIL AVIATION AUTHORITY. ANNUAL PUNCTUALITY STATISTICS - FULL ANALYSIS (YEAR). see *TRANSPORTATION — Abstracting, Bibliographies, Statistics*

GREAT BRITAIN. CIVIL AVIATION AUTHORITY. ANNUAL PUNCTUALITY STATISTICS - SUMMARY ANALYSIS (YEAR). see *TRANSPORTATION — Abstracting, Bibliographies, Statistics*

GREAT BRITAIN. CIVIL AVIATION AUTHORITY. PUNCTUALITY STATISTICS HEATHROW, GATWICK, MANCHESTER, BIRMINGHAM, LUTON AND STANSTEAD - FULL ANALYSIS. see *TRANSPORTATION — Abstracting, Bibliographies, Statistics*

GREAT BRITAIN. CIVIL AVIATION AUTHORITY. PUNCTUALITY STATISTICS HEATHROW, GATWICK, MANCHESTER, BIRMINGHAM, LUTON AND STANSTEAD - SUMMARY ANALYSIS. see *TRANSPORTATION — Abstracting, Bibliographies, Statistics*

GREAT BRITAIN. CIVIL AVIATION AUTHORITY. U.K. AIRLINES ANNUAL OPERATING, TRAFFIC & FINANCIAL STATISTICS. see *TRANSPORTATION — Abstracting, Bibliographies, Statistics*

GREAT BRITAIN. CIVIL AVIATION AUTHORITY. U.K. AIRLINES MONTHLY OPERATING & TRAFFIC STATISTICS. see TRANSPORTATION — *Abstracting, Bibliographies, Statistics*

GREAT BRITAIN. CIVIL AVIATION AUTHORITY. U.K. AIRPORTS ANNUAL STATEMENTS OF MOVEMENTS, PASSENGERS AND CARGO (YEAR). see TRANSPORTATION — *Abstracting, Bibliographies, Statistics*

GREAT BRITAIN. CIVIL AVIATION AUTHORITY. U.K. AIRPORTS MONTHLY STATEMENTS OF MOVEMENTS, PASSENGERS AND CARGO. see TRANSPORTATION — *Abstracting, Bibliographies, Statistics*

GREAT BRITAIN. DEPARTMENT FOR EDUCATION. STATISTICS OF EDUCATION. see EDUCATION — *Abstracting, Bibliographies, Statistics*

GREAT BRITAIN. DEPARTMENT FOR EDUCATION. STATISTICS OF EDUCATION. FURTHER AND HIGHER EDUCATION. STUDENT - STAFF RATIOS AND UNIT COSTS. see EDUCATION — *Abstracting, Bibliographies, Statistics*

GREAT BRITAIN. DEPARTMENT OF HEALTH AND SOCIAL SECURITY. SOCIAL SECURITY STATISTICS. see SOCIAL SERVICES AND WELFARE — *Abstracting, Bibliographies, Statistics*

GREAT BRITAIN. GOVERNMENT STATISTICAL SERVICE. ABORTION STATISTICS. see BIRTH CONTROL — *Abstracting, Bibliographies, Statistics*

GREAT BRITAIN. GOVERNMENT STATISTICAL SERVICE. CANCER STATISTICS REGISTRATIONS. ENGLAND AND WALES. see MEDICAL SCIENCES — *Abstracting, Bibliographies, Statistics*

GREAT BRITAIN. GOVERNMENT STATISTICAL SERVICE. CONGENITAL MALFORMATION STATISTICS NOTIFICATIONS. see MEDICAL SCIENCES — *Abstracting, Bibliographies, Statistics*

GREAT BRITAIN. GOVERNMENT STATISTICAL SERVICE. SUMMARY OF BED AVAILABILITY. ENGLAND - FINANCIAL YEAR (YEAR). see HOSPITALS — *Abstracting, Bibliographies, Statistics*

GREAT BRITAIN. H M TREASURY. CIVIL SERVICE STATISTICS. see PUBLIC ADMINISTRATION — *Abstracting, Bibliographies, Statistics*

GREAT BRITAIN. HOME OFFICE. STATISTICS OF THE MISUSE OF DRUGS: SEIZURES AND OFFENDERS DEALT WITH, UNITED KINGDOM (YEAR). see MEDICAL SCIENCES — *Abstracting, Bibliographies, Statistics*

GREECE. NATIONAL STATISTICAL SERVICE. AGRICULTURAL AND LIVESTOCK PRODUCTION (YEAR). see AGRICULTURE — *Abstracting, Bibliographies, Statistics*

GREECE. NATIONAL STATISTICAL SERVICE. ANNUAL STATISTICAL SURVEY ON MINES, QUARRIES AND SALTERNS. see MINES AND MINING INDUSTRY — *Abstracting, Bibliographies, Statistics*

GREECE. NATIONAL STATISTICAL SERVICE. CULTURAL STATISTICS. see ART — *Abstracting, Bibliographies, Statistics*

GREECE. NATIONAL STATISTICAL SERVICE. ENVIRONMENTAL STATISTICS. see ENVIRONMENTAL STUDIES — *Abstracting, Bibliographies, Statistics*

GREECE. NATIONAL STATISTICAL SERVICE. GREEK INDUSTRIAL CLASSIFICATION. see BUILDING AND CONSTRUCTION — *Abstracting, Bibliographies, Statistics*

GREECE. NATIONAL STATISTICAL SERVICE. HOUSEHOLD EXPENDITURE SURVEY. see BUSINESS AND ECONOMICS — *Abstracting, Bibliographies, Statistics*

GREECE. NATIONAL STATISTICAL SERVICE. LABOUR FORCE SURVEY. see BUSINESS AND ECONOMICS — *Abstracting, Bibliographies, Statistics*

314   GR   ISSN 0028-0240
HA1351
GREECE. NATIONAL STATISTICAL SERVICE. MONTHLY STATISTICAL BULLETIN. (Text in English, Greek) m. $84. National Statistical Service of Greece, Statistical Information and Publications Division - Ethniki Statistiki Yperesia tes Ellados, 14-16 Lykourgou, 101 66 Athens, Greece. TEL 30-1-3244-748. FAX 30-1-3222-205. TELEX 216734 ESYE GR. **Document type:** government publication, bulletin.

GREECE. NATIONAL STATISTICAL SERVICE. PRODUCTION OF MANUFACTURED ITEMS. see BUSINESS AND ECONOMICS — *Abstracting, Bibliographies, Statistics*

GREECE. NATIONAL STATISTICAL SERVICE. PROVISIONAL NATIONAL ACCOUNTS OF GREECE. see BUSINESS AND ECONOMICS

GREECE. NATIONAL STATISTICAL SERVICE. PUBLIC FINANCE STATISTICS. see BUSINESS AND ECONOMICS — *Abstracting, Bibliographies, Statistics*

GREECE. NATIONAL STATISTICAL SERVICE. QUARTERLY NATIONAL ACCOUNTS OF GREECE. see BUSINESS AND ECONOMICS — *Abstracting, Bibliographies, Statistics*

GREECE. NATIONAL STATISTICAL SERVICE. RESULTS OF SEA FISHERY SURVEY BY MOTOR VESSELS. see FISH AND FISHERIES — *Abstracting, Bibliographies, Statistics*

GREECE. NATIONAL STATISTICAL SERVICE. REVISED AGRICULTURAL PRICE INDICES. see AGRICULTURE — *Abstracting, Bibliographies, Statistics*

GREECE. NATIONAL STATISTICAL SERVICE. REVISED CONSUMER PRICE INDEX. see BUSINESS AND ECONOMICS — *Abstracting, Bibliographies, Statistics*

GREECE. NATIONAL STATISTICAL SERVICE. REVISED PRICE INDICES OF NEW BUILDING DWELLINGS CONSTRUCTION (YEAR). see BUILDING AND CONSTRUCTION — *Abstracting, Bibliographies, Statistics*

GREECE. NATIONAL STATISTICAL SERVICE. SHIPPING STATISTICS. see TRANSPORTATION — *Abstracting, Bibliographies, Statistics*

GREECE. NATIONAL STATISTICAL SERVICE. SOCIAL WELFARE AND HEALTH STATISTICS. see SOCIAL SERVICES AND WELFARE — *Abstracting, Bibliographies, Statistics*

GREECE. NATIONAL STATISTICAL SERVICE. STANDARD CLASSIFICATION OF THE BRANCHES OF ECONOMIC ACTIVITY. see BUSINESS AND ECONOMICS — *Abstracting, Bibliographies, Statistics*

GREECE. NATIONAL STATISTICAL SERVICE. STATISTICS OF THE DECLARED INCOME OF LEGAL ENTITIES AND ITS TAXATION. see BUSINESS AND ECONOMICS — *Abstracting, Bibliographies, Statistics*

GREECE. NATIONAL STATISTICAL SERVICE. STATISTICS ON CIVIL, CRIMINAL AND REFORMATORY JUSTICE. see CRIMINOLOGY AND LAW ENFORCEMENT — *Abstracting, Bibliographies, Statistics*

GREECE. NATIONAL STATISTICAL SERVICE. STATISTICS ON THE DECLARED INCOME OF PHYSICAL PERSONS AND ITS TAXATION. see BUSINESS AND ECONOMICS — *Abstracting, Bibliographies, Statistics*

GREECE. NATIONAL STATISTICAL SERVICE. STATISTIQUES DU TRAVAIL. see BUSINESS AND ECONOMICS — *Abstracting, Bibliographies, Statistics*

GREECE. NATIONAL STATISTICAL SERVICE. TOURIST STATISTICS. see TRAVEL AND TOURISM — *Abstracting, Bibliographies, Statistics*

GREECE. NATIONAL STATISTICAL SERVICE. TRANSPORT AND COMMUNICATION STATISTICS. see TRANSPORTATION — *Abstracting, Bibliographies, Statistics*

GREEK ECONOMY IN FIGURES (YEAR). see BUSINESS AND ECONOMICS — *Abstracting, Bibliographies, Statistics*

309.1982   DK   ISSN 0106-228X
GROENLAND (COPENHAGEN)/KALAALLIT NUNAAT. (Text in Danish and English) 1968. a. DKK 70. Statsministeriet, Groenlandsafdelingen, Hausergade 3, 1128 Copenhagen K, Denmark. FAX 33-936815. TELEX 27125-MFG. circ. 3,800.

317   CN   ISSN 0711-852X
HC120.I5
GROSS DOMESTIC PRODUCT BY INDUSTRY. 1987. m. Can.$127($152) (foreign $178). Statistics Canada, Publications Division, Ottawa, Ont. K1A 0T6, Canada. TEL 613-951-7277. FAX 613-951-1584.
  Description: Contains monthly, quarterly, and annual estimates of GDP for 183 industries, including aggregates and special industry groupings.

GROUPEMENT DES INDUSTRIES ELECTRONIQUES. STATISTIQUES ANNUELLES. see ELECTRONICS

GUANGDONG SOCIOECONOMIC STATISTICS MONTHLY. see BUSINESS AND ECONOMICS — *Abstracting, Bibliographies, Statistics*

310   CC
GUANGXI TONGJI/GUANGXI STATISTICS. (Text in Chinese) bi-m. Guangxi Tongji Ju - Guangxi Bureau of Statistics, 22 Xinzhu Lu, Nanning, Guangxi 530022, People's Republic of China. TEL 22368. Ed. Su Xiaohan.

318   GT
GUATEMALA. DIRECCION GENERAL DE ESTADISTICA. ENCUESTA DE LA INDUSTRIA MANUFACTURERA FABRIL. Variant title: Encuesta Industrial. 1972. a., latest 1987. $15. Instituto Nacional de Estadistica, Departamento de Estudios Especiales y Estadisticas Continuas, 8A Calle No. 9-55, Zona 1, Guatemala, Guatemala.
  Formerly: Guatemala. Direccion General de Estadistica. Departamento de Estudios Especiales y Estadisticas Continuas. Produccion, Venta y Otros Ingresos de la Encuesta Anual de la Industria Manufacturera Fabril.

310   CN
GUIDE TO STATISTICS CANADA'S PROGRAMS AND PRODUCTS. (Catalogue 12-575) (Text in English, French) irreg. Can.$85($110) Statistics Canada, Publications Division, Ottawa, ON K1A 0T6, Canada. TEL 800-267-6677. FAX 613-951-1582. **Document type:** government publication.
  Description: Profiles over 400 individual surveys conducted by Statistics Canada, providing survey content, frequency and the resulting products.

310   US   ISSN 0434-9067
Z7554.U5
GUIDE TO U S GOVERNMENT STATISTICS. biennial. $215. Documents Index, Inc., 7900 Sudley Rd., Ste. 405, Manassas, VA 22110-2806. TEL 703-257-4844. Eds. Donna Andriot, Jay Andriot. **Document type:** abstracting/indexing.
  Description: Entries include classification numbers, title, beginning and closing dates, frequency and annotations, as well as detailed bibliographic information, with an extensive index by title, subject, area and agency.

HACETTEPE BULLETIN OF NATURAL SCIENCES AND ENGINEERING. see SCIENCES: COMPREHENSIVE WORKS

314.912   IC   ISSN 0254-4733
HAGSKYRSLUR ISLANDS/STATISTICS OF ICELAND. (Text in Icelandic; tableheadings in English) 1914. irreg. Hagstofa Islands - Statistical Bureau of Iceland, Skuggasund 3, IS-150 Reykjavik, Iceland. TEL 354-560-9800. FAX 354-562-8865. E-mail: hagstofa@hag.stjr.is. Dir. Hallgrimur Snorrason. (back issues avail.)

314.912   IC   ISSN 0019-1078
HAGTIDINDI/MONTHLY STATISTICS. 1914. m. $45. Hagstofa Islands - Statistical Bureau of Iceland, Skuggasund 3, IS-150 Reykjavik, Iceland. TEL 354-560-9800. FAX 354-562-8865. E-mail: hagstofa@hag.stjr.is. Dir. Hallgrimur Snorrason. stat.; index. circ. 2,200. (back issues avail.)
  Description: Includes statistics on population, work force, foreign trade, prices and production.

STATISTICS

HAGTOELUR MANADARINS. see BUSINESS AND ECONOMICS — Abstracting, Bibliographies, Statistics

HAIGUAN TONGJI/CUSTOMS STATISTICS. see BUSINESS AND ECONOMICS — Abstracting, Bibliographies, Statistics

317.29 HT ISSN 0017-6788
HA881
HAITI. INSTITUT HAITIEN DE STATISTIQUE. BULLETIN TRIMESTRIEL DE STATISTIQUE. 1952. a. (with q. supplement). free. Institut Haitien de Statistique et d'Informatique, Departement des Finances et des Affaires Economique, Blvd. Harry Truman, Port-au-Prince, Haiti, W. Indies. Dir. Raymond Gardiner. charts; mkt.; stat. circ. 500. **Indexed:** P.A.I.S.For.Lang.Ind.

314 GW ISSN 0017-6877
HAMBURG IN ZAHLEN. 1947. m. DM.50. Statistisches Landesamt Hamburg, Steckelhoern 12, 20457 Hamburg, Germany. TEL 040-3681-1766. FAX 040-36811700. TELEX 212121-SENAT-D. Ed. Erhard Hruschka. charts; stat. circ. 1,100. **Document type:** government publication.
Formerly: Hamburger Monatszahlen.

315 II ISSN 0072-9728
HANDBOOK OF BASIC STATISTICS OF MAHARASHTRA STATE. (Editions in English and Marathi) 1960. a. Rs.40. Directorate of Economics and Statistics, MHADA Bldg., Kalanagar, Baudra (E), Bombay 400051, India. Ed. V.B. Mujumdar.

HANDBOOK OF INTERNATIONAL TRADE AND DEVELOPMENT STATISTICS - UNITED NATIONS/MANUEL DE STATISTIQUES DU COMMERCE INTERNATIONAL ET DU DEVELOPMENT - NATIONS UNIES. see BUSINESS AND ECONOMICS — Abstracting, Bibliographies, Statistics

HANDBOOK OF LABOR STATISTICS. see BUSINESS AND ECONOMICS — Economic Situation And Conditions

HANDBOOK OF NUMERICAL ANALYSIS. see MATHEMATICS

HANDBOOK OF STATE TRADING ORGANIZATIONS OF DEVELOPING COUNTRIES/REPERTOIRE DES ORGANISMES DE COMMERCE D'ETAT DES PAYS EN DEVELOPPEMENT/REPERTORIO DE LAS ORGANIZACIONES COMERCIALES ESTATALES DE PAISES EN DESARROLLO/DALIL AL-HAY'AT AT-TIGANIYYA AL-HUKUMIYYA FI AL-BULDAN AN-NAMIYA. see BUSINESS AND ECONOMICS — Abstracting, Bibliographies, Statistics

HANDBUCH DER OESTERREICHISCHEN SOZIALVERSICHERUNG. see INSURANCE — Abstracting, Bibliographies, Statistics

HANDELSHOCHSCHULE LEIPZIG. WISSENSCHAFTLICHE ZEITSCHRIFT. see BUSINESS AND ECONOMICS

310 DK ISSN 0106-8490
HANDELSHOEJSKOLEN I AARHUS. SKRIFTSERIE. no.3, 1982. irreg. price varies. Aarhus Graduate School of Management, Department of Information Science, Fuglesangsalle 4, 8210 Aarhus V, Denmark. TEL 06-155588. FAX 06-150188. Ed. Kai Kristensen. illus.

311.3 FI ISSN 0788-1576
Z674.5.F5
HELSINGIN KAUPUNGIN TIETOKESKUKSEN NELJANNESVUOSIJULUAISU. KVARTTI/HELSINGFORS STADS FAKTCENTRALS KVARTALSOEVERSIKT/QUARTERLY FROM THE CITY OF HELSINKI INFORMATION MANAGEMENT CENTRE. Key Title: Kvartti. 1979. q. FIM 160 (typically set in Dec.). Helsingin Kaupungin Tietokeskus - City of Helsinki Information Management Centre, P.O. Box 303, SF-00171 Helsinki, Finland. FAX 358-0-169-3777. Ed. Eero Holstila. bk.rev.; circ. 800 (controlled).
Former titles (until 1990): Helsingin Kaupungin Teilastokeksuksen Neljannesvuosijulkaisu (ISSN 0781-0490); Helsingin Kaupungin Tilastokeskuksen Neljannesvuosikatsaus (ISSN 0357-3362); Tilastollisia Kuukaustitietoja Helsingista (ISSN 0040-7658)

310 FI ISSN 0785-8736
HA1449.H4
HELSINGIN KAUPUNGIN TILASTOLLINEN VUOSIKIRJA. (Text in Finnish and Swedish) 1908. a. FIM 110. Helsingin Kaupungin Tietokeskus, Helsingfors Stads Faktacentral - City of Helsinki, Information Management Centre, Aleksanterinkatu 16-18, FIN-00171 Helsinki, Finland. TEL 90-1693193. FAX 90-1693200. Ed. Anneli Pulkkinen. stat. circ. 1,300. (back issues avail.) **Document type:** monographic series.
Formerly (until 1988): Helsingin Kaupunki Tilastollinen Vuosikirja (ISSN 0356-9489)

314 GW
HESSISCHE KREISZAHLEN. 1956. s-a. DM.16. Hessisches Statistisches Landesamt, Rheinstr. 35-37, 65185 Wiesbaden, Germany. TEL 0611-38020. FAX 0611-3802990. **Document type:** government publication.
Description: Government publication covering extensive vital statistics.

HIGHER EDUCATION ABSTRACTS; abstracts of periodical literature, monographs and conference papers on college students, faculty and administration. see EDUCATION — Higher Education

HIGHWAY SAFETY PERFORMANCE. FATAL AND INJURY ACCIDENT RATES ON PUBLIC ROADS IN THE UNITED STATES. see TRANSPORTATION — Abstracting, Bibliographies, Statistics

317 US ISSN 0073-2664
HISTORICAL STATISTICS OF THE UNITED STATES. 1949. irreg. price varies. U.S. Bureau of the Census, Data User Services Division, Washington, DC 20233. TEL 301-457-4100. FAX 301-457-4714. **Document type:** government publication.

HOME-GROWN CEREALS AUTHORITY. CEREALS STATISTICS. see AGRICULTURE — Abstracting, Bibliographies, Statistics

318 HO
HONDURAS. SECRETARIA DE HACIENDA Y CREDITO PUBLICO. DIRECCION GENERAL DE PRESUPUESTO. PRESUPUESTO GENERAL DE INGRESOS Y EGRESOS DE LA REPUBLICA. a. Secretaria de Hacienda y Credito Publico, Direccion General de Presupuesto, Tegucigalpa, M.D.C., Honduras.

318 HO
HONDURAS. SECRETARIA DE PLANIFICACION, COORDINACION Y PRESUPUESTO. ANUARIO ESTADISTICO. a. Secretaria de Planificacion, Coordinacion y Presupuesto, Direccion General de Estadistica y Censos, Tegucigalpa D.C., Honduras. **Document type:** government publication.

HONDURAS. SECRETARIA DE PLANIFICACION COORDINACION Y PRESUPUESTO. DIRECCION GENERAL DE ESTADISTICA Y CENSOS. ENCUESTA PERMANENTE DE HOGARES DE PROPOSITOS MULTIPLES. see HOUSING AND URBAN PLANNING — Abstracting, Bibliographies, Statistics

318 HO
HONDURAS EN CIFRAS. 1965. a. free. Banco Central de Honduras, Departamento de Estudios Economicos, 1a Calle, 6a y 7a avenida, Tegucigalpa, D.C., Honduras. TEL 37-2270. TELEX 1121. charts; stat.

315 HK ISSN 1011-4033
HONG KONG. ANNUAL DIGEST OF STATISTICS. (Text in English) 1978. a. HK.$98. Census and Statistics Department, Wanchai Tower, 12 Harbour Rd., Hong Kong. TEL 852-25988197. FAX 852-25987482. (Subscr. to: Director of Information Services, Information Services Department, 28F Siu On Centre, 188 Lockhart Rd., Wanchai, Hong Kong.) charts; stat. **Document type:** government publication. —BLDSC (4326.347800).

310 330.9 HK
HONG KONG. CENSUS AND STATISTICS DEPARTMENT. CONSUMER PRICE INDEX. ANNUAL REPORT. (Text in English) a. price varies. (Census and Statistics Department) Government Publication Centre, G.P.O. Bldg., Ground Fl., Connaught Place, Hong Kong, Hong Kong. (Subscr. to: Director of Information Services, Information Services Dept., 1 Battery Path, G-F, Central, Hong Kong) Ed.Bd. **Document type:** government publication.

310 330.9 HK
HONG KONG. CENSUS AND STATISTICS DEPARTMENT. CONSUMER PRICE INDEX. REPORT. (Text in English) m. HK.$42. (Census and Statistics Department) Government Publication Centre, G.P.O. Bldg., Ground Fl., Connaught Pl., Hong Kong, Hong Kong. (Subscr. to: Director of Information Services, Information Services Dept., 1 Battery Path, G-F, Hong Kong, Hong Kong) Ed.Bd. (back issues avail.) **Document type:** government publication.

310 657 HK
HONG KONG. CENSUS AND STATISTICS DEPARTMENT. DIRECTOR OF AUDITS. REPORT. (Editions in Chinese, English) irreg., latest 1988. price varies. Government Publication Centre, G.P.O. Bldg., Ground Fl., Connaught Place, Hong Kong, Hong Kong. (Subscr. to: Director of Information Services, Information Services Dept., 1 Battery Path, G-F, Central, Hong Kong) Ed.Bd. **Document type:** government publication.

HONG KONG. CENSUS AND STATISTICS DEPARTMENT. ESTIMATES OF GROSS DOMESTIC PRODUCT. see BUSINESS AND ECONOMICS — Abstracting, Bibliographies, Statistics

HONG KONG. CENSUS AND STATISTICS DEPARTMENT. HALF-YEARLY REPORT OF WAGE STATISTICS. see BUSINESS AND ECONOMICS — Abstracting, Bibliographies, Statistics

310 330.9 HK
HONG KONG. CENSUS AND STATISTICS DEPARTMENT. MONTHLY SURVEY OF RETAIL SALES. REPORT. (Text in English) m. HK.$12. (Census and Statistics Department) Government Publication Centre, G.P.O. Bldg., Ground Fl., Connaught Pl., Hong Kong, Hong Kong. (Subscr. to: Director of Information Services, Information Services Dept., 1 Battery Path, G-F, Central, Hong Kong) Ed.Bd. **Document type:** government publication.

HONG KONG. CENSUS AND STATISTICS DEPARTMENT. QUARTERLY REPORT ON GENERAL HOUSEHOLD SURVEY. see BUSINESS AND ECONOMICS — Abstracting, Bibliographies, Statistics

HONG KONG. CENSUS AND STATISTICS DEPARTMENT. SALARIES AND EMPLOYEE STATISTICS. REPORT. MANAGERIAL AND PROFESSIONAL EMPLOYEES (EXCLUDING TOP MANAGEMENT). see BUSINESS AND ECONOMICS — Abstracting, Bibliographies, Statistics

HONG KONG. CENSUS AND STATISTICS DEPARTMENT. SHIPPING STATISTICS. see TRANSPORTATION — Abstracting, Bibliographies, Statistics

310 HK
HONG KONG. CENSUS AND STATISTICS DEPARTMENT. YEARBOOK (YEAR). (Editions in Chinese, English) 1984. a. HK.$38. Government Publication Centre, G.P.O. Building, Ground Fl., Connaught Pl., Hong Kong. (Subscr. to: Director of Information Services, Information Services Dept., 1 Battery Path, G-F, Central, Hong Kong) Ed.Bd. **Document type:** government publication.

HONG KONG ECONOMIC TRENDS. see BUSINESS AND ECONOMICS — Abstracting, Bibliographies, Statistics

315 HK
HONG KONG IN FIGURES. 1976. a. free. Census and Statistics Department, Wanchai Tower, 12 Harbour Rd., Hong Kong. TEL 851-25988197. FAX 852-25987482. (Subscr. to: Director of Information Services, Information Services Department, 28F Siu On Centre, 188 Lockhart Rd., Wanchai, Hong Kong) **Document type:** government publication.

315 HK ISSN 0300-418X
HA1950.H6
HONG KONG MONTHLY DIGEST OF STATISTICS. 1970. m. HK.$50. Census and Statistics Department, Wanchai Tower, 12 Harbour Rd., Hong Kong. TEL 852-25988197. FAX 852-25987482. (Subscr. to: Director of Information Services, Information Services Department, 28F Siu On Centre, 188 Lockhart Rd., Wanchai, Hong Kong) Ed.Bd. stat. circ. 2,000. **Document type:** government publication.

314　　　　RM　　ISSN 1223-7566
HOUSEHOLD LABOUR FORCE SURVEY. a. $8 (effective 1995 & 1996). Comisia Nationala Pentru Statistica - National Commission for Statistics, Bd. Liberatii 16, Sector 5, 70542 Bucharesti, Rumania. TEL 40-1-6143371. FAX 40-1-3124873. **Document type:** government publication.
　Description: Presents data and commentaries regarding the active employed and unemployed population and the in-active population.

HOUSEHOLD PROJECTIONS FOR THE COUNTIES OF WALES. see *HOUSING AND URBAN PLANNING — Abstracting, Bibliographies, Statistics*

HOUSING MARKET STATISTICS. see *BUSINESS AND ECONOMICS — Abstracting, Bibliographies, Statistics*

HOUSING SURVEY OF JAPAN (YEAR). see *HOUSING AND URBAN PLANNING — Abstracting, Bibliographies, Statistics*

HUMAN SETTLEMENTS BASIC STATISTICS/STATISTIQUES DE BASE ETABLISSEMENTS HUMAINS/ESTADISTICAS BASICAS DE ASENTAMIENTOS HUMANOS. see *HOUSING AND URBAN PLANNING — Abstracting, Bibliographies, Statistics*

310　　　　HU　　ISSN 0441-4713
HUNGARY. KOZPONTI STATISZTIKAI HIVATAL. NEMZETKOZI STATISZTIKAI EVKONYV. quadrennial. 371 Ft. Statiqum Kiado es Nyomda Kft., Kaszasdulo u. 2, P.O. Box 99, 1300 Budapest 3, Hungary. TEL 361-180-3311. FAX 361-168-8635. TELEX 22-6699. (Subscr. to: Kultura, Box 149, 1389 Budapest, Hungary) circ. 3,000.

314　　　　HU　　ISSN 0018-781X
HUNGARY. KOZPONTI STATISZTIKAI HIVATAL. STATISZTIKAI HAVI KOZLEMENYEK. 1957. m. 3480 Ft.($60) Komaromi Myomda es Kiado Kft., Igmandi ut 1, P.O. Box 21, 2901 Komarom 1, Hungary. TEL 3634-342248. FAX 3634-342361. Ed. Lorinc Soos. adv. contact: Peter Zoltan. charts; stat. circ. 1,350. **Document type:** bulletin.

314　　　　HU　　ISSN 0039-0690
HUNGARY. KOZPONTI STATISZTIKAI HIVATAL. STATISZTIKAI SZEMLE. 1923. m. 396 Ft.($52) Statisztikai Kiado Vallalat, Kaszasdulo u. 2, P.O.B.99, 1300 Budapest 3, Hungary. TEL 688-635. TELEX 22-6699. (Subscr. to: Kultura, Box 149, H-1389 Budapest, Hungary) Ed. Maria Visi Lakatos. cum.index 1923-1962. circ. 1,500. **Indexed:** Popul.Ind.
　Formerly: Magyar Statisztikai Szemle.

314.391　　HU　　ISSN 0018-7828
HUNGARY. KOZPONTI STATISZTIKAI HIVATAL. TERULETI STATISZTIKA. (Text in Hungarian; contents page in English & Russian) 1957. bi-m. 198 Ft.($21.50) Statisztikai Kiado Vallalat, Kaszasdulo u. 2, P.O.B.99, 1300 Budapest 3, Hungary. TEL 688-635. TELEX 22-6699. (Subscr. to: Kultura, Box 149, H-1389 Budapest, Hungary) Ed. Tibor Kordcs. bk.rev. circ. 1,320.
　Formerly: Megyei es Varosi Statisztikai Ertesito.

947 314　　HU　　ISSN 0303-5344
HUNGARY. KOZPONTI STATISZTIKAI HIVATAL TERULETI STATISZTIKAI EVKONYV. a. 201 Ft. Statisztikai Kiado Vallalat, Kaszasdulo u. 2, P.O.B.99, 1300 Budapest 3, Hungary. TEL 688-635. TELEX 22-6699. (Subscr. to: Kultura, Box 149, H-1389 Budapest, Hungary)

319.4 333.91 330.9 AT　ISSN 0729-5030
HUNTER VALLEY RESEARCH FOUNDATION. WORKING PAPERS. 1969. irreg. Hunter Valley Research Foundation, P.O. Box 23, Tighes Hill, N.S.W. 2297, Australia. TEL 049-69-4566. FAX 049-614981. Ed. W.E.J. Paradice. charts. (back issues avail.)

I C C O QUARTERLY BULLETIN OF COCOA STATISTICS. (International Cocoa Organization) see *FOOD AND FOOD INDUSTRIES*

I C E S FISHERIES STATISTICS/BULLETIN STATISTIQUE DES PECHES MARITIMES. see *FISH AND FISHERIES — Abstracting, Bibliographies, Statistics*

310　　　　AG　　ISSN 0326-6249
I N D E C ESTUDIOS. 1984. irreg., no.23, 1993. price varies. Instituto Nacional de Estadistica y Censos, Avda. Julio A. Roca, 609 P.B., 1067 Buenos Aires, Argentina. TEL 54-1-3499662. FAX 54-1-3499621. **Document type:** government publication, monographic series.

310　　　　AG　　ISSN 0326-6222
I N D E C METODOLOGIAS. 1978. irreg., no.7, 1991. price varies. Instituto Nacional de Estadistica y Censos, Avda. Julio A. Roca 609 P.B., 1067 Buenos Aires, Argentina. TEL 54-1-3499662. FAX 54-1-3499621. **Document type:** government publication, monographic series.

310　　　　AG
I N D E C NORMAS. 1988. irreg., no.3, 1991. price varies. Instituto Nacional de Estadistica y Censos, Avda. Julio A. Roca, 609 P.B., 1067 Buenos Aires, Argentina. TEL 54-1-3499662. FAX 54-1-3499621. **Document type:** government publication, monographic series.

I N S E E PICARDE RELAIS. (Institut National de la Statistique et des Etudes Economiques) see *BUSINESS AND ECONOMICS — Abstracting, Bibliographies, Statistics*

IDAHO. DEPARTMENT OF HEALTH AND WELFARE. ANNUAL SUMMARY OF VITAL STATISTICS. see *PUBLIC HEALTH AND SAFETY — Abstracting, Bibliographies, Statistics*

310　　　　US　　ISSN 1053-3443
HC107.I3
ILLINOIS STATISTICAL ABSTRACT. 1987. a. $40 for paperback edition (diskette $50; both $75). University of Illinois at Urbana-Champaign, Bureau of Economic and Business Research, 428 Commerce Bldg., W., 1206 S. Sixth St., Champaign, IL 61820. TEL 217-333-2330. FAX 217-233-7410. (also avail. in diskette format)
　Description: Presents a wide range of statistics for the state, counties, metropolitan areas and the US.

IMPORTS & EXPORTS OF CRUDE OIL AND PETROLEUM PRODUCTS. see *PETROLEUM AND GAS*

IMPORTS STATISTICS OF AFGHANISTAN/IHSA'IYAH-I AMUAL-I VARIDATI-I AFGHANISTAN. see *BUSINESS AND ECONOMICS — Abstracting, Bibliographies, Statistics*

310　　　　IT
INDAGINE STATISTICA NAZIONALE. a. (Associazione Nazionale dei Produttori di Piastrelle di Ceramica) Edi. Cer S.r.l., Viale Monte Santo, 40, 41049 Sassuolo (Modena), Italy. TEL 0536-818111. FAX 0536-806510. TELEX 511050.

310　　　　US　　ISSN 0737-4461
Z7552
INDEX TO INTERNATIONAL STATISTICS. (CD-ROM title: Statistical Masterfile) 1983. m. (with q. and a. cumulations). $1620 (effective 1995). Congressional Information Service, Part of the Reed Elsevier group, 4520 East-West Hwy., Bethesda, MD 20814-3389. TEL 301-654-1550; 800-638-8380. FAX 301-654-4033. Ed. Polly A. Bosch. abstr.; index, cum.index: 1983-87, 1988-1991. (back issues avail.) **Document type:** abstracting/indexing.
●Also available on CD-ROM.
—BLDSC (4380.455200).
　Description: Identifies, catalogues, describes and indexes statistical publications of international, intergovernmental organizations.

317　　　　CN　　ISSN 0843-6142
Z7554.C2
INDEX TO STATISTICS CANADA SURVEYS AND QUESTIONNAIRES. (Text in English, French) 1981. a. Can.$26($31) (foreign $36). Statistics Canada, Publications Division, Ottawa, Ont. K1A 0T6, Canada. TEL 613-951-7277. FAX 613-951-1584.
　Description: Lists all the questionnaire-based surveys of Statistics Canada and the questionnaires used in conducting the surveys, under the Division of Statistics Canada that is resonsible for the survey.

STATISTICS　6205

315　　　　II
INDIA. CENTRAL STATISTICAL ORGANIZATION. ANNUAL REPORT. (Text in English) 1949. a. price varies. Central Statistical Organization, Sardar Patel Bhavan, Sansad Marg, New Delhi 110001, India. adv. circ. 400. **Document type:** government publication.
　Formerly: India. Central Statistical Organization. Sample Surveys of Current Interest in India. Report (ISSN 0073-6163)

315.4　　　II　　ISSN 0019-4174
INDIA. CENTRAL STATISTICAL ORGANIZATION. MONTHLY ABSTRACT OF STATISTICS. (Text in English and Hindi) 1948. m. Rs.648($233.28) Central Statistical Organization, Sardar Patel Bhavan, Sansad Marg, New Delhi 1, India. bk.rev.; charts. circ. 650. **Document type:** government publication.

315　　　　II　　ISSN 0073-6155
HA1713
INDIA. CENTRAL STATISTICAL ORGANIZATION. STATISTICAL ABSTRACT. (Text in English) 1951. a. Rs.253.50($91.26) Central Statistical Organization, Sardar Patel Bhavan, Sansad Marg, New Delhi 110001, India. **Document type:** government publication, abstracting/indexing.

INDIA. DEPARTMENT OF RURAL DEVELOPMENT. ADMINISTRATIVE INTELLIGENCE DIVISION. PROGRESS REPORT ON SMALL FARMERS DEVELOPMENT AGENCY PROGRAMME. see *AGRICULTURE — Abstracting, Bibliographies, Statistics*

INDIA. DEPARTMENT OF RURAL DEVELOPMENT. ADMINISTRATIVE INTELLIGENCE DIVISION. SOME SPECIAL PROGRAMMES OF RURAL DEVELOPMENT. STATISTICS. see *AGRICULTURE — Abstracting, Bibliographies, Statistics*

INDIA. MINISTRY OF HOME AFFAIRS. VITAL STATISTICS DIVISION. SAMPLE REGISTRATION BULLETIN. see *POPULATION STUDIES — Abstracting, Bibliographies, Statistics*

INDIA. MINISTRY OF HOME AFFAIRS. VITAL STATISTICS DIVISION. SURVEY OF CAUSES OF DEATH (RURAL). see *POPULATION STUDIES — Abstracting, Bibliographies, Statistics*

INDIAN PETROLEUM AND NATURAL GAS STATISTICS. see *PETROLEUM AND GAS — Abstracting, Bibliographies, Statistics*

310 003　　II　　ISSN 0250-9636
INDIAN SOCIETY OF STATISTICS AND OPERATIONS RESEARCH. JOURNAL. (Text in English) 1980. a. Rs.150 to Indian libraries; $60 to foreign libraries. Indian Society of Statistics and Operations Research, M.S. College, Department of Mathematics, P.O. Box 65, Saharanpur 247001, India. TEL 25407. Eds. S.U. Khan, P.L. Maggu. adv.; bk.rev.; abstr.; bibl.; stat.; index. (back issues avail.) **Indexed:** Math.R., Zent.Math.
—BLDSC (4769.020000).

310　　　　II　　ISSN 0073-6686
INDIAN STATISTICAL INSTITUTE. ANNUAL REPORT. 1933. a. free. Indian Statistical Institute, 203 Barrackpore Trunk Rd., Calcutta 700 035, India. TEL 52-6694. TELEX 21-2210 STAT IN. circ. 2,000.

310　　　　II　　ISSN 0258-1736
INDIAN STATISTICAL INSTITUTE. LECTURE NOTES. 1961. irreg. price varies. Indian Statistical Institute, 203 Barrackpore Trunk Rd., Calcutta 700035, India. (also avail. in microfilm)
　Formerly: Indian Statistical Institute. Research and Training School. Publications.

310 519　　II　　ISSN 0073-6716
INDIAN STATISTICAL INSTITUTE. STATISTICS AND PROBABILITY SERIES. RESEARCH MONOGRAPHS. irreg. Statistical Publishing Society, 204-1 Barrackpore Trunk Rd., Calcutta 700035, India. Ed. R.R. Rao.

310　　　　II　　ISSN 0073-6724
INDIAN STATISTICAL SERIES. irreg., nos.24-25, 1970. price varies. Indian Statistical Institute, 203 Barrackpore Trunk Rd., Calcutta 700 035, India. TEL 52-6694. TELEX 21-2210 STAT IN.

INDIANA FACTBOOK. see *ENCYCLOPEDIAS AND GENERAL ALMANACS*

ULRICH'S INTERNATIONAL PERIODICALS DIRECTORY 1996

6206 STATISTICS

318   CK   ISSN 0120-9299
HC196
INDICADORES DE COYUNTURA. 1987. m. $120. Departamento Administrativo Nacional de Estadistica, Banco Nacional de Datos, Centro Administrativo Nacional, Avda. El Dorado, Apdo. Aereo 80043, Bogota D.E., Colombia. FAX 2222305. TELEX 44573. **Document type:** government publication.

317.2   PN   ISSN 0250-4332
INDICADORES ECONOMICOS Y SOCIALES DE PANAMA. a. free. Direccion de Estadistica y Censo, Contraloria General, Apdo. 5213, Panama 5, Panama. FAX 507-69-7294.
Description: A brief statistical extract of demographic, economic and social data.

310   CR
INDICE DE PRECIOS AL CONSUMIDOR DE INGRESOS MEDIOS Y BAJOS DEL AREA METROPOLITANA DE SAN JOSE. 1989. m. Direccion General de Estadistica y Censos, Apdo. 10163, San Jose, Costa Rica.

339   PR   ISSN 0019-7017
INDICE DE PRECIOS AL CONSUMIDOR PARA FAMILIAS OBRERAS EN PUERTO RICO. (Text in English and Spanish) 1966. m. free. Department of Labor, Bureau of Labor Statistics, 505 Munoz Rivera Ave., Hato Rey, PR 00918. Ed. Guillermo Solla Velez. charts; stat. (processed) **Document type:** government publication.

INDICE DE PRECIOS AL POR MAYOR. see *BUSINESS AND ECONOMICS — Abstracting, Bibliographies, Statistics*

310   IO
INDONESIA. WELFARE INDICATORS. (Text in English, Indonesian) 1972. a. Rps.10000($7) Central Bureau of Statistics - Biro Pusat Statistik, Jalan Dr. Sutomo No. 8, Box 3, Jakarta Pusat, Indonesia. TEL 21-372808. circ. 200. **Document type:** government publication.
Formerly: Indonesia. Social Welfare Indicators.

INDONESIA OIL STATISTICS/STATISTIK PERMINYAKAN INDONESIA. see *PETROLEUM AND GAS — Abstracting, Bibliographies, Statistics*

INDONESIA STATISTICS. see *BUSINESS AND ECONOMICS — Abstracting, Bibliographies, Statistics*

INDUSTRIA MOLINERA. TRIGO. see *AGRICULTURE — Abstracting, Bibliographies, Statistics*

INDUSTRIAL TRENDS. see *BUSINESS AND ECONOMICS — Abstracting, Bibliographies, Statistics*

INDUSTRY REVIEW. see *BUSINESS AND ECONOMICS — Abstracting, Bibliographies, Statistics*

INDUSTRY WAGE SURVEYS. see *BUSINESS AND ECONOMICS — Economic Situation And Conditions*

310   UK
INFO (YEAR); today's yearbook & factfinder. a. (Hutchinson Gallup) Helicon Publishing Ltd., 42 Hythe Bridge St., Oxford OX1 2EP, England. Ed. Denise Dresner.

318   BO
INFORMACION ESTADISITICA REGIONAL COCHABAMBA. a.? free. Instituto Nacional de Estadistica, Casilla de Correo 6129, La Paz, Bolivia. circ. 1,000.

318   UY
INFORMACIONES Y ESTADISTICAS NACIONALES AND INTERNACIONALES. bi-m. $140 (effective Jan. 1993). Centro de Estadisticas Nacionales y Comercio Internacional del Uruguay, Misiones 1361, Casilla de Correo 1510, 11200 Montevideo, Uruguay. TEL 95-29-30. FAX 95-45-78. **Document type:** bulletin.
Description: Provides data on production, demographics, economic indicators and trade.

310   CL
INFORME SOBRE CHILE. 1979. a. $220. Editorial Gestion, Rafael Canas 114, Casilla 16485, Correo 9 Santiago, Chile. TEL 562-2356959. FAX 562-2361114. adv. circ. 10,000.

314   AU
INNSBRUCK. STATISTISCHES JAHRBUCH. 1952. a. S.125. Stadtmagistrat Innsbruck, Innrain 10, A-6020 Innsbruck, Austria. TEL 0512-5360522. FAX 0512-5360521. index. circ. 500. **Document type:** bulletin.
Description: Statistical yearbook of the city of Innsbruck.

INSTITUTE OF STATISTICAL MATHEMATICS. ANNALS. see *MATHEMATICS*

INSTITUTO INTERAMERICANO DEL NINO. ESTADISTICA E INFORMATICA. INFORMES TECNICOS. see *SOCIAL SERVICES AND WELFARE*

INSURANCE REGULATORY INFORMATION SYSTEM RATIO RESULTS. see *INSURANCE — Abstracting, Bibliographies, Statistics*

INSURANCE STATISTICS (YEARS). see *INSURANCE — Abstracting, Bibliographies, Statistics*

INTER-INDUSTRY STUDY OF THE NEW ZEALAND ECONOMY. see *BUSINESS AND ECONOMICS — Abstracting, Bibliographies, Statistics*

INTERNAL TRADE OF IRAN. see *BUSINESS AND ECONOMICS — Domestic Commerce*

INTERNATIONAL CIVIL AVIATION OGANIZATION. DIGESTS OF STATISTICS. SERIES OFOD. ON-FLIGHT ORIGIN AND DESTINATION/ORGANISATION DE L'AVIATION CIVILE INTERNATIONALE. RECEUIL DE STATISTIQUES. SERIE OFOD. ORIGINE ET DESTINATION PAR VOL/MEZHDUNARODNAYA ORGANIZATSIYA GRAZHDANSKOI AVIATSII. STATISTICESKI SBORNIK. SERIYA OFOD. NASALNY I KONESNY PUNKTY POLETA/ORGANIZACON DE AVIACION CIVIL INTERNACIONAL. COMPENDIO ESTADISTICO. SERIE OFOD. ORIGEN Y DESTINO POR VUELO. see *TRANSPORTATION — Abstracting, Bibliographies, Statistics*

INTERNATIONAL CIVIL AVIATION ORGANIZATION. DIGESTS OF STATISTICS. SERIES AF. AIRPORT AND ROUTE FACILITIES. FINANCIAL DATA AND SUMMARY TRAFFIC DATA/ORGANISATION DE L'AVIATION CIVILE. RECEUIL DE STATISTIQUES. SERIE AF. INSTALLATIONS ET SERVICES D'AEROPORT ET DE ROUTE. DONNES FINANCIERES ET STATISTIQUES DE TRAFFIC SOMMAIRES/MEZHDUNARODNAYA ORGANIZATSIYA GRAZHDANSKOI AVIATSII. STATISTICHESKI SBORNIK. SERIYA AF. AEROPORTNOE I MARSHRUTNOE OBORUDOVANIE. FINANSOVYE IZLOZHENIYA DANNYKH PO PERENOZHKAM/ORGANIZACON DE AVIACION CIVIL INTERNACIONAL. COMPENDIO ESTADISTICO. SERIE AF. INSTALACIONES Y SERVICIOS DE AEROPUERTO Y EN RUTA. DATOS FINANCIEROS Y RESUMEN DE DATOS DE TRAFICO. see *TRANSPORTATION — Abstracting, Bibliographies, Statistics*

INTERNATIONAL CIVIL AVIATION ORGANIZATION. DIGESTS OF STATISTICS. SERIES AT. AIRPORT TRAFFIC. see *TRANSPORTATION — Abstracting, Bibliographies, Statistics*

INTERNATIONAL CIVIL AVIATION ORGANIZATION. DIGESTS OF STATISTICS. SERIES F. FINANCIAL DATA - COMMERCIAL AIR CARRIERS. see *TRANSPORTATION — Abstracting, Bibliographies, Statistics*

INTERNATIONAL CIVIL AVIATION ORGANIZATION. DIGESTS OF STATISTICS. SERIES FP. FLEET - PERSONNEL - COMMERCIAL AIR CARRIERS. see *TRANSPORTATION — Abstracting, Bibliographies, Statistics*

INTERNATIONAL CIVIL AVIATION ORGANIZATION. DIGESTS OF STATISTICS. SERIES TF. TRAFFIC BY FLIGHT STAGE. see *TRANSPORTATION — Abstracting, Bibliographies, Statistics*

INTERNATIONAL CIVIL AVIATION ORGANIZATION. DIGESTS OF STATISTICS. SERIES T. TRAFFIC, COMMERCIAL AIR TRAFFIC. see *TRANSPORTATION — Abstracting, Bibliographies, Statistics*

INTERNATIONAL COMMISSION FOR THE CONSERVATION OF ATLANTIC TUNAS. STATISTICAL BULLETIN. see *FISH AND FISHERIES — Abstracting, Bibliographies, Statistics*

INTERNATIONAL COMPARISONS OF MANUFACTURING PRODUCTIVITY AND UNIT LABOR COST TRENDS (YEAR). see *BUSINESS AND ECONOMICS — Economic Situation And Conditions*

INTERNATIONAL COTTON INDUSTRY STATISTICS. see *TEXTILE INDUSTRIES AND FABRICS — Abstracting, Bibliographies, Statistics*

INTERNATIONAL JOURNAL OF MATHEMATICAL AND STATISTICAL SCIENCES. see *MATHEMATICS*

382 665.5   US   ISSN 1044-1816
HD9560.1
INTERNATIONAL PETROLEUM STATISTICS REPORT. 1989. m. $47 (foreign $58.75). U.S. Energy Information Administration, National Energy Information Center, EI-231, James Forrestal Bldg., Rm. 1F-048, 1000 Independence Ave., S.W., Washington, DC 20585. TEL 202-586-8800. (Subscr. to: Superintendent of Documents, U.S. Government Printing Office, Box 371954, Pittsburgh, PA 15250-7954. TEL 202-512-1800. FAX 202-512-2250) Ed. Michael J. Maloney. (back issues avail.) **Document type:** government publication. —CIS.
Description: Presents data on international oil production, consumption, imports, exports, and stocks.

INTERNATIONAL PHOTO PROCESSING INDUSTRY REPORT. see *PHOTOGRAPHY — Abstracting, Bibliographies, Statistics*

INTERNATIONAL RAYON AND SYNTHETIC FIBRES COMMITTEE. STATISTICAL YEARBOOK. see *TEXTILE INDUSTRIES AND FABRICS — Abstracting, Bibliographies, Statistics*

310   NE   ISSN 0074-8609
HA11   CODEN: BIISAR
INTERNATIONAL STATISTICAL INSTITUTE. BULLETIN. PROCEEDINGS OF THE BIENNIAL SESSIONS. (Edited by local organizing committees in the respective host country) (Text in English) 1885. biennial, 49th, 1993, Florence. fl.175. International Statistical Institute, Prinses Beatrixlaan 428, Postbus 950, 2270 AZ Voorburg, Netherlands. TEL 31-70-3375737. FAX 31-70-3860025. **Indexed:** Math.R., Stat.Theor.Meth.Abstr. **Document type:** proceedings.
Description: Proceedings of the biennial sessions of the ISI, including the text of all invited papers covering the spectrum of the statistical profession: statistical theory and method, applied statistics, and other topics.

519.5   NE   ISSN 0306-7734
CODEN: ISTRDP
INTERNATIONAL STATISTICAL REVIEW. 1933. 3/yr. $76.10. International Statistical Institute, Prinses Beatrixlaan 428, Postbus 950, 22270 Voorburg, Netherlands. TEL 31-70-3375737. FAX 31-70-3860025. Eds. D.J. Trewin, B.W. Silverman. adv.; bk.rev.; charts; illus.; stat.; index. circ. 4,000. (reprint service avail. from SWZ) **Indexed:** Biostat., Compumath, Cont.Pg.Manage., Curr.Cont., Curr.Ind.Stat., Ind.Vet., INSPEC, J.Cont.Quant.Meth., Math.R., Oper.Res.Manage.Sci., Qual.Contr.Appl.Stat., Sci.Cit.Ind., Stat.Theor.Meth.Abstr., Vet.Bull. **Document type:** academic/scholarly publication.
—BLDSC (4549.660000); Faxon; SWETS; UnCover.
Formerly: International Statistical Institute Review (ISSN 0020-8779)
Description: Provides a view of work in statistics, covering the spectrum of the statistical profession and including the most relevant aspects of probability.

INTERNATIONAL STEEL STATISTICS - AUSTRALIA. see *METALLURGY — Abstracting, Bibliographies, Statistics*

INTERNATIONAL STEEL STATISTICS - AUSTRIA. see *METALLURGY — Abstracting, Bibliographies, Statistics*

INTERNATIONAL STEEL STATISTICS - BELGIUM, LUXEMBOURG. see *METALLURGY — Abstracting, Bibliographies, Statistics*

INTERNATIONAL STEEL STATISTICS - BRAZIL. see *METALLURGY — Abstracting, Bibliographies, Statistics*

STATISTICS

INTERNATIONAL STEEL STATISTICS - CANADA. see
METALLURGY — Abstracting, Bibliographies,
Statistics

INTERNATIONAL STEEL STATISTICS - DENMARK. see
METALLURGY — Abstracting, Bibliographies,
Statistics

INTERNATIONAL STEEL STATISTICS - FINLAND. see
METALLURGY — Abstracting, Bibliographies,
Statistics

INTERNATIONAL STEEL STATISTICS - FRANCE. see
METALLURGY — Abstracting, Bibliographies,
Statistics

INTERNATIONAL STEEL STATISTICS - GERMANY,
FEDERAL REPUBLIC. see METALLURGY —
Abstracting, Bibliographies, Statistics

INTERNATIONAL STEEL STATISTICS - GREECE. see
METALLURGY — Abstracting, Bibliographies,
Statistics

INTERNATIONAL STEEL STATISTICS - IRISH REPUBLIC.
see METALLURGY — Abstracting, Bibliographies,
Statistics

INTERNATIONAL STEEL STATISTICS - ITALY. see
METALLURGY — Abstracting, Bibliographies,
Statistics

INTERNATIONAL STEEL STATISTICS - JAPAN. see
METALLURGY — Abstracting, Bibliographies,
Statistics

INTERNATIONAL STEEL STATISTICS - KOREA (SOUTH).
see METALLURGY — Abstracting, Bibliographies,
Statistics

INTERNATIONAL STEEL STATISTICS - NETHERLANDS.
see METALLURGY — Abstracting, Bibliographies,
Statistics

INTERNATIONAL STEEL STATISTICS - NORWAY. see
METALLURGY — Abstracting, Bibliographies,
Statistics

INTERNATIONAL STEEL STATISTICS - PORTUGAL. see
METALLURGY — Abstracting, Bibliographies,
Statistics

INTERNATIONAL STEEL STATISTICS - SELECTED
CENTRAL AND SOUTH AMERICAN COUNTRIES. see
METALLURGY — Abstracting, Bibliographies,
Statistics

INTERNATIONAL STEEL STATISTICS - SPAIN. see
METALLURGY — Abstracting, Bibliographies,
Statistics

INTERNATIONAL STEEL STATISTICS - SUMMARY TABLES.
see METALLURGY — Abstracting, Bibliographies,
Statistics

INTERNATIONAL STEEL STATISTICS - SWEDEN. see
METALLURGY — Abstracting, Bibliographies,
Statistics

INTERNATIONAL STEEL STATISTICS - SWITZERLAND. see
METALLURGY — Abstracting, Bibliographies,
Statistics

INTERNATIONAL STEEL STATISTICS - TAIWAN. see
METALLURGY — Abstracting, Bibliographies,
Statistics

INTERNATIONAL STEEL STATISTICS - U S A. see
METALLURGY — Abstracting, Bibliographies,
Statistics

INTERNATIONAL STEEL STATISTICS - UNITED KINGDOM.
see METALLURGY — Abstracting, Bibliographies,
Statistics

INTERNATIONAL SUGAR ORGANIZATION. MARKET
REPORT AND PRESS SUMMARY. see FOOD AND
FOOD INDUSTRIES

INTERNATIONAL SUGAR ORGANIZATION. PROCEEDINGS.
see FOOD AND FOOD INDUSTRIES

INTERNATIONAL SUGAR ORGANIZATION. QUARTERLY
MARKET REVIEW. see FOOD AND FOOD INDUSTRIES

INTERNATIONAL SUGAR ORGANIZATION. STATISTICAL
BULLETIN. see FOOD AND FOOD INDUSTRIES —
Abstracting, Bibliographies, Statistics

INTERNATIONAL TEXTILE MACHINERY SHIPMENT
STATISTICS. see TEXTILE INDUSTRIES AND
FABRICS — Abstracting, Bibliographies, Statistics

INTERNATIONAL TRADE STATISTICS YEARBOOK. see
BUSINESS AND ECONOMICS — Abstracting,
Bibliographies, Statistics

INTERNATIONAL WHEAT COUNCIL. WORLD GRAIN
STATISTICS (YEAR). see AGRICULTURE —
Abstracting, Bibliographies, Statistics

INTERNATIONAL YEARBOOK OF INDUSTRIAL STATISTICS.
see BUSINESS AND ECONOMICS — Abstracting,
Bibliographies, Statistics

IOWA CROP REPORT. see AGRICULTURE — Abstracting,
Bibliographies, Statistics

IOWA OFFICIAL REGISTER. see POLITICAL SCIENCE —
Abstracting, Bibliographies, Statistics

IOWA STATE UNIVERSITY. STATISTICAL LABORATORY.
ANNUAL REPORT. see MATHEMATICS —
Abstracting, Bibliographies, Statistics

IRAN. MINISTRY OF ECONOMY. BUREAU OF STATISTICS.
SERIES. see BUSINESS AND ECONOMICS —
Abstracting, Bibliographies, Statistics

IRANIAN INDUSTRIAL STATISTICS. see BUSINESS AND
ECONOMICS — Abstracting, Bibliographies,
Statistics

IRANIAN MINERAL STATISTICS. see MINES AND MINING
INDUSTRY — Abstracting, Bibliographies, Statistics

IRELAND. CENTRAL STATISTICS OFFICE. CENSUS OF
INDUSTRIAL PRODUCTION. see BUSINESS AND
ECONOMICS — Abstracting, Bibliographies,
Statistics

314   IE   ISSN 0075-062X
IRELAND (EIRE) CENTRAL STATISTICS OFFICE.
TUARASCAIL AR STAIDREAMH BEATHA - REPORT ON
VITAL STATISTICS. 1864. q. £15. Stationery Office,
Dublin, Ireland. TEL 01-6613111.
FAX 01-4752760. (Subscr. to: Government
Publication Office, Trade and Postal Sales, 4-5
Harcourt Rd., Dublin 2, Ireland) Document type:
government publication.
  Formerly: Detailed Annual Report of the Registrar
General for Ireland.

314   IE   ISSN 0790-8970
IRELAND. STATIONERY OFFICE. STATISTICAL ABSTRACT.
1931. a. Stationery Office, Dublin, Ireland.
TEL 01-6613111. FAX 01-4752760. (Subscr. to:
Government Supplies Agency, Trade and Postal
Sales, 4-5 Harcourt Rd., Dublin 2, Ireland) circ.
2,000. Document type: abstracting/indexing.
  Formerly (until 1986): Statistical Abstract of
Ireland (ISSN 0081-4660)

314   IE   ISSN 0790-8334
HF189
IRELAND. STATIONERY OFFICE. STATISTICAL BULLETIN.
1925. q. £85. Stationery Office, Dublin, Ireland.
TEL 01-6613111. FAX 01-4752760. (Subscr. to:
Government Supplies Agency, Publications Section,
4-5 Harcourt Rd., Dublin 2, Ireland) charts; mkt.;
stat. Indexed: Curr.Lit.Fam.Plan., P.A.I.S., PROMT,
Rehabil.Lit. Document type: government publication.
—BLDSC (8447.458540).
  Former titles: Irish Statistical Bulletin (ISSN
0021-1370); Irish Trade Journal and Statistical
Bulletin.
  Description: Presents detailed results of all
short-term economic series with retrospection.
Periodic articles on annual inquiries and
methodology are also included.

IRON & MANGANESE ORE DATABOOK. see MINES AND
MINING INDUSTRY — Abstracting, Bibliographies,
Statistics

IRON AND STEEL YEARLY STATISTICS. see
METALLURGY — Abstracting, Bibliographies,
Statistics

ISRAEL. CENTRAL BUREAU OF STATISTICS.
AGRICULTURAL STATISTICS QUARTERLY. see
AGRICULTURE — Abstracting, Bibliographies,
Statistics

ISRAEL. CENTRAL BUREAU OF STATISTICS. CAUSES OF
DEATH. see POPULATION STUDIES — Abstracting,
Bibliographies, Statistics

315   IS   ISSN 0021-1982
HA1931
ISRAEL. CENTRAL BUREAU OF STATISTICS. MONTHLY
BULLETIN OF STATISTICS. (Text in English and
Hebrew) 1949. m. $60 includes supplement.
Central Bureau of Statistics, P.O.B. 13015,
Jerusalem 91 130, Israel. TEL 02-21 12 11. stat.

310 016   IS   ISSN 0334-3278
ISRAEL. CENTRAL BUREAU OF STATISTICS. NEW
STATISTICAL PROJECTS AND PUBLICATIONS IN
ISRAEL. (Text in Hebrew; summaries in English)
1970. q. $20. Central Bureau of Statistics, Box
13015, Jerusalem 91 130, Israel. TEL 02-21 12
11. bibl.; index. (back issues avail)

312   IS
ISRAEL. CENTRAL BUREAU OF STATISTICS. QUARTERLY
STATISTICS OF THE ADMINISTERED TERRITORIES.
(Text mainly in Hebrew; occasionally in English)
1968. q. price varies. Central Bureau of Statistics,
Box 13015, Jerusalem 91 130, Israel. TEL 02-21
12 11. stat. (back issues avail.) Document type:
government publication.

ISRAEL. CENTRAL BUREAU OF STATISTICS. STAFF IN
UNIVERSITIES. see EDUCATION — Abstracting,
Bibliographies, Statistics

315.69   IS   ISSN 0081-4679
HA1931
ISRAEL. CENTRAL BUREAU OF STATISTICS. STATISTICAL
ABSTRACT OF ISRAEL/SHENATON STATISTI
LE-YISRAEL. (Text in English and Hebrew) 1949. a.
$27. Central Bureau of Statistics, Box 13015,
Jerusalem 91 130, Israel. TEL 02-21 12 11.
Document type: abstracting/indexing.
—BLDSC (8447.414000).

ISRAEL. CENTRAL BUREAU OF STATISTICS. SUICIDES
AND ATTEMPTED SUICIDES. see POPULATION
STUDIES — Abstracting, Bibliographies, Statistics

ISRAEL. CENTRAL BUREAU OF STATISTICS. VITAL
STATISTICS. see POPULATION STUDIES —
Abstracting, Bibliographies, Statistics

314   IT
ITALIAN STATISTICAL ABSTRACT. (Text in English) a.
L.27000 (effective 1993). Istituto Nazionale di
Statistica, Via Cesare Balbo 16, 00100 Rome, Italy.
FAX 06-46735198. Document type: government
publication.
  Description: Provides results of principal statistical
works on the social and economic situation in Italy.

310
ITALIAN STATISTICAL SOCIETY. JOURNAL. (Text in
English) 1992. 3/yr. L.70000 (foreign L.110000)
(effective 1992). (Societa Italiana di Statistica)
Giardini Editori e Stampatori, Via delle Sorgenti 23,
56010 Agnano Pisano (PI), Italy. TEL 050-934242.
FAX 050-934200. Ed. A. Zuliani. Document type:
academic/scholarly publication.

ITALY. CENTRO PER LA STATISTICA AZIENDALE. INDEX.
see BUSINESS AND ECONOMICS — Abstracting,
Bibliographies, Statistics

314   IT   ISSN 0021-3136
HA1360
ITALY. ISTITUTO NAZIONALE DI STATISTICA. BOLLETTINO
MENSILE DI STATISTICA. 1925. m. L.130000
(foreign L.160000) (effective 1993). Istituto
Nazionale di Statistica, Via Cesare Balbo 16, 00100
Rome, Italy. FAX 06-46735198. charts; stat.; index.
circ. 5,000. Indexed: P.A.I.S.For.Lang.Ind.
  Description: Detailed data of demographic, social,
economic and financial phenomena.

314   IT   ISSN 1120-8953
ITALY. ISTITUTO NAZIONALE DI STATISTICA. COLLANA
D'INFORMAZIONE. 1977. irreg. price varies. Istituto
Nazionale di Statistica, Via Cesare Balbo 16, 00100
Rome, Italy. FAX 06-46735198. Document type:
government publication.

STATISTICS

314 IT ISSN 0390-6620
HA1363
ITALY. ISTITUTO NAZIONALE DI STATISTICA. INDICATORI MENSILI. m. L.33000 (foreign L.43000) (effective 1993). Istituto Nazionale di Statistica, Via Cesare Balbo 16, 00100 Rome, Italy. FAX 06-46735198. circ. 3,200.

314 IT
ITALY. ISTITUTO NAZIONALE DI STATISTICA. RAPPORTO ANNUALE: LA SITUAZIONE DEL PAESE. a. free. Istituto Nazionale di Statistica, Via Cesare Balbo 16, 00100 Rome, Italy. FAX 06-46735198.

ITALY. ISTITUTO NAZIONALE DI STATISTICA. STATISTICA ANNUALE DEL COMMERCIO CON L'ESTERO. TOMO 1: DATI GENERALI E RIASSUNTIVI. see *BUSINESS AND ECONOMICS — Abstracting, Bibliographies, Statistics*

ITALY. ISTITUTO NAZIONALE DI STATISTICA. STATISTICA ANNUALE DEL COMMERCIO CON L'ESTERO. TOMO 2: MERCI PER PAESI. see *BUSINESS AND ECONOMICS — Abstracting, Bibliographies, Statistics*

ITALY. ISTITUTO NAZIONALE DI STATISTICA. STATISTICA TRIMESTRALE DEL COMMERCIO CON L'ESTERO. see *BUSINESS AND ECONOMICS — Abstracting, Bibliographies, Statistics*

ITALY. ISTITUTO NAZIONALE DI STATISTICA. STATISTICHE DEI TRASPORTI MARITTIMI. see *TRANSPORTATION — Abstracting, Bibliographies, Statistics*

ITALY. ISTITUTO NAZIONALE DI STATISTICA. STATISTICHE DEL COMMERCIO INTERNO. see *BUSINESS AND ECONOMICS — Abstracting, Bibliographies, Statistics*

ITALY. ISTITUTO NAZIONALE DI STATISTICA. STATISTICHE DELLA PREVIDENZA, DELLA SANITA E DELL'ASSISTENZA SOCIALE. see *SOCIAL SERVICES AND WELFARE — Abstracting, Bibliographies, Statistics*

ITALY. ISTITUTO NAZIONALE DI STATISTICA. STATISTICHE DEMOGRAFICHE. see *POPULATION STUDIES — Abstracting, Bibliographies, Statistics*

ITALY. ISTITUTO NAZIONALE DI STATISTICA. STATISTICHE GIUDIZIARIE. see *LAW — Abstracting, Bibliographies, Statistics*

ITALY. ISTITUTO NAZIONALE DI STATISTICA. STATISTICHE INDUSTRIALI. see *BUSINESS AND ECONOMICS — Abstracting, Bibliographies, Statistics*

ITALY. ISTITUTO NAZIONALE DI STATISTICA. STATISTICHE METEOROLOGICHE. see *METEOROLOGY — Abstracting, Bibliographies, Statistics*

IVORY COAST. MINISTERE DE L'AGRICULTURE. ANNUAIRE DE STATISTIQUES AGRICOLES. see *AGRICULTURE — Abstracting, Bibliographies, Statistics*

519.5 US ISSN 0162-1459
HA1 CODEN: JSTNAL
J A S A. (Journal of the American Statistical Association) 1888. q. $60. American Statistical Association, 1429 Duke St., Alexandria, VA 22314-3402. TEL 703-684-1221. FAX 703-684-2037. E-mail: asainfo@asa.mhs.compuserve.com. adv.; bk.rev.; bibl.; index. circ. 16,000. (also avail. in microform from UMI,KTO,PMC; reprint service avail. from SWZ,UMI) **Indexed:** Abstr.Hyg., B.P.I., Biol.Abstr., Biostat., Bus.Ind., Child Devel.Abstr., Compumath, Comput.Rev., Cont.Pg.Manage., Curr.Cont., Curr.Ind.Stat., Excerp.Med., Hort.Abstr., J.Cont.Quant.Meth., J.of Econ.Lit., Mark.Res.Abstr. (1963-), Math.R., Oper.Res.Manage.Sci., Popul.Ind., Psychol.Abstr., Qual.Contr.Appl.Stat., Risk Abstr., SSCI, Stat.Theor.Meth.Abstr., Tr.& Indus.Ind., Trop.Dis.Bull., World Bank.Abstr. **Document type:** academic/scholarly publication.
—BLDSC (4694.000000); Faxon; Genuine Article; SWETS; UMI; UnCover. **CCC.**
  Formerly: American Statistical Association. Journal (ISSN 0003-1291)
  Description: Focuses on statistical applications, theory, and methods in economic, social, physical, engineering, and health sciences and on new methods of statistical education.

314 NE
JAARBOEK EINDHOVEN. 1957. a. fl.28. Gemeente Eindhoven, Afdeling Onderzoek en Statistiek, P.O. Box 90150, 5600 RB Eindhoven, Netherlands. TEL 31-40-382338. FAX 31-40-433585. TELEX 51365 NL. Ed.Bd. stat.; illus.; index. circ. 500. **Document type:** government publication.

310 GW ISSN 0408-1706
JAHRBUECHER FUER STATISTIK UND LANDESKUNDE VON BADEN-WUERTTEMBERG. 1863. a. DM.16.10. Statistisches Landesamt, Postfach 106033, 70049 Stuttgart, Germany. TEL 0711-6410. FAX 0711-6412440. Ed. Dr. Leibing. bibl.; charts; stat.; cum.index: 1977-1983. circ. 850. (back issues avail.) **Document type:** government publication.
  Formerly (until 1953): Wuerttembergische Jahrbucher fuer Statistik und Landeskunde (ISSN 0721-1589)

315.4 II ISSN 0303-9234
HA1728.K35
JAMMU AND KASHMIR. DIRECTORATE OF ECONOMICS AND STATISTICS. DIGEST OF STATISTICS. (Text in English) q. Directorate of Economics and Statistics, Planning and Development Department, Jammu and Kashmir, India.

JAPAN. MANAGEMENT AND COORDINATION AGENCY. STATISTICS BUREAU. EMPLOYMENT STATUS SURVEY. see *BUSINESS AND ECONOMICS — Abstracting, Bibliographies, Statistics*

JAPAN. MINISTRY OF HEALTH AND WELFARE. STATISTICS AND INFORMATION DEPARTMENT. HANDBOOK OF HEALTH AND WELFARE STATISTICS. see *PUBLIC HEALTH AND SAFETY — Abstracting, Bibliographies, Statistics*

315 JA ISSN 0385-969X
JAPAN. MINISTRY OF HEALTH AND WELFARE. STATISTICS AND INFORMATION DEPARTMENT. MONTHLY REPORT ON VITAL STATISTICS. Key Title: Jinko Dotai Tokei Geppo, Gaisu. m. 618 Yen per no. (Dec. 1030 Yen). Ministry of Health and Welfare, Statistics and Information Department - Koseisho Daijin Kanbo Tokei Johobu, 7-3 Ichigaya Honmura-cho, Shinjuku-ku, Tokyo 162, Japan. TEL 03-3260-3181. FAX 03-3260-8824. (Subscr. to: Health and Welfare Statistics Association, 5-13-14 Roppongi, Minato-ku, Tokyo, Japan. TEL 03-3586-3361. FAX 03-3584-4710) **Document type:** government publication.
  Formerly (until 1970): Jinko Dotai Tokei Maigetsu Gaisu (ISSN 0385-9681)

JAPAN. MINISTRY OF HEALTH AND WELFARE. STATISTICS AND INFORMATION DEPARTMENT. REPORT ON ACTIVITIES OF PUBLIC HEALTH CENTERS. see *MEDICAL SCIENCES — Abstracting, Bibliographies, Statistics*

JAPAN. MINISTRY OF HEALTH AND WELFARE. STATISTICS AND INFORMATION DEPARTMENT. REPORT ON SURVEY OF NATIONAL MEDICAL CARE INSURANCE SERVICES. see *INSURANCE — Abstracting, Bibliographies, Statistics*

JAPAN. MINISTRY OF HEALTH AND WELFARE. STATISTICS AND INFORMATION DEPARTMENT. REPORT ON SURVEY OF OCCUPATIONAL STATISTICS ON VITAL EVENTS. see *OCCUPATIONS AND CAREERS — Abstracting, Bibliographies, Statistics*

JAPAN. MINISTRY OF HEALTH AND WELFARE. STATISTICS AND INFORMATION DEPARTMENT. REPORT ON SURVEY OF PUBLIC ASSISTANCE. see *SOCIAL SERVICES AND WELFARE — Abstracting, Bibliographies, Statistics*

JAPAN. MINISTRY OF HEALTH AND WELFARE. STATISTICS AND INFORMATION DEPARTMENT. REPORT ON SURVEY OF SOCIO-ECONOMIC ASPECTS ON VITAL EVENTS. see *POPULATION STUDIES — Abstracting, Bibliographies, Statistics*

JAPAN. MINISTRY OF HEALTH AND WELFARE. STATISTICS AND INFORMATION DEPARTMENT. REPORT ON SURVEY OF SOCIAL WELFARE INSTITUTIONS. see *SOCIAL SERVICES AND WELFARE — Abstracting, Bibliographies, Statistics*

JAPAN. MINISTRY OF HEALTH AND WELFARE. STATISTICS AND INFORMATION DEPARTMENT. STATISTICAL REPORT ON COMMUNICABLE DISEASES. see *PUBLIC HEALTH AND SAFETY — Abstracting, Bibliographies, Statistics*

JAPAN. MINISTRY OF HEALTH AND WELFARE. STATISTICS AND INFORMATION DEPARTMENT. STATISTICAL REPORT ON FOOD POISONINGS. see *PUBLIC HEALTH AND SAFETY — Abstracting, Bibliographies, Statistics*

JAPAN. MINISTRY OF HEALTH AND WELFARE. STATISTICS AND INFORMATION DEPARTMENT. STATISTICAL REPORT ON PUBLIC HEALTH ADMINISTRATION AND SERVICES/EISEI GYOSEI GYOMU HOKOKU. see *PUBLIC HEALTH AND SAFETY — Abstracting, Bibliographies, Statistics*

JAPAN. MINISTRY OF HEALTH AND WELFARE. STATISTICS AND INFORMATION DEPARTMENT. STATISTICAL REPORT ON SOCIAL WELFARE ADMINISTRATION AND SERVICES. see *SOCIAL SERVICES AND WELFARE — Abstracting, Bibliographies, Statistics*

312 JA ISSN 0075-3270
JAPAN. MINISTRY OF HEALTH AND WELFARE. STATISTICS AND INFORMATION DEPARTMENT. VITAL STATISTICS. Key Title: Jinko Dotai Tokei. Variant title: Vital Statistics Japan. 1899. a. (in 3 vols.). 9785 Yen for vol.1; vol.2 11330 Yen; vol.3 12360 Yen. Ministry of Health and Welfare, Statistics and Information Department - Koseisho Daijin Kanbo Tokei Johobu, 7-3 Ichigaya-Honmura-cho, Shinjuku-ku, Tokyo 162, Japan. TEL 03-3260-3181. FAX 03-3269-8824. (Subscr. to: Health & Welfare Statistics Association, 5-13-14, Roppongi, Minato-ku, Tokyo, Japan. TEL 03-3586-3361. FAX 03-3584-4710) **Document type:** government publication.
—BLDSC (9241.860000).
  Formerly: Nihon Teikoku Jinko Dotai Tokei - Vital Statistics of the Japanese Empire.

JAPAN. POCKET SIZE STATISTICS OF SUGAR PRODUCTS. see *FOOD AND FOOD INDUSTRIES — Abstracting, Bibliographies, Statistics*

JAPAN. STATISTICS BUREAU. ANNUAL REPORT ON FAMILY INCOME AND EXPENDITURE SURVEY. see *HOME ECONOMICS — Abstracting, Bibliographies, Statistics*

JAPAN. STATISTICS BUREAU. NEWS BULLETIN. see *POPULATION STUDIES — Abstracting, Bibliographies, Statistics*

315 JA ISSN 0389-3502
HC461
JAPAN: AN INTERNATIONAL COMPARISON. Variant title: Japan (Year). (Text in English) a. 900 Yen($9) Keizai Koho Center, Otemachi Bldg., 6-1 Ote-machi 1-chome, Chiyoda-ku, Tokyo 100, Japan. FAX 03-3201-1418. Ed. Nabeshima Michihisa.
  Description: Pocket-sized statistical profile of Japan in comparison with other nations. Covers population and area, national income, agriculture and food supply, industry and services, foreign trade, balance of payments, exchange rates, employment, wages, and productivity.

JAPAN EXPORTS & IMPORTS: COMMODITY BY COUNTRY. see BUSINESS AND ECONOMICS — Abstracting, Bibliographies, Statistics

JAPAN STATISTICAL ASSOCIATION. MONTHLY REPORT OF RETAIL PRICES. CONSUMER PRICE INDEX. see BUSINESS AND ECONOMICS — Abstracting, Bibliographies, Statistics

JAPAN STATISTICAL ASSOCIATION. MONTHLY REPORT OF RETAIL PRICES. PRICES OF CONSUMER GOODS AND SERVICES. see BUSINESS AND ECONOMICS — Abstracting, Bibliographies, Statistics

JAPAN STATISTICAL ASSOCIATION. MONTHLY REPORT ON THE FAMILY INCOME AND EXPENDITURE SURVEY. see BUSINESS AND ECONOMICS — Abstracting, Bibliographies, Statistics

JAPAN STATISTICAL ASSOCIATION. MONTHLY REPORT ON THE LABOUR FORCE SURVEY. see BUSINESS AND ECONOMICS — Abstracting, Bibliographies, Statistics

315.2   JA   ISSN 0549-4680
JAPAN STATISTICAL ASSOCIATION. MONTHLY STATISTICS OF JAPAN. (Text and summaries in English and Japanese) 1947. m. 1150 Yen per no. Nihon Tokei Kyokai - Japan Statistical Association, Crest 21, 6-21, Yocho-machi, Shinjuku-ku, Tokyo 162, Japan. TEL 03-5269-3058. FAX 03-5269-3058. Document type: government publication.

JAPAN STATISTICAL ASSOCIATION. POPULATION CENSUS OF JAPAN. see POPULATION STUDIES — Abstracting, Bibliographies, Statistics

315   JA   ISSN 0389-9004
JAPAN STATISTICAL YEARBOOK. (Text in English and Japanese) 1949. a. 14500 Yen. Nihon Tokei Kyokai - Japan Statistical Association, Crest 21, 6-21, Yocho-machi, Shinjuku-ku, Tokyo 162, Japan. TEL 03-5269-3051. FAX 03-5269-3058. circ. 800.
—BLDSC (4650.173000).

519.5 510.28   JA   ISSN 0915-2350
JAPANESE SOCIETY OF COMPUTATIONAL STATISTICS. JOURNAL. (Text in English) 1988. a. $30. Japanese Society of Computational Statistics, University of Tsukuba, Institute of Socio-Economic Planning, 1-1-1 Tennodai, Tsukuba, Ibaraki 305, Japan. TEL 0298-53-5008. FAX 0298-55-3849. E-mail: onishi@shako.sk.tsukuba.ac.jp. Ed. Haruo Onishi. circ. 400. Document type: academic/scholarly publication.
—BLDSC (4809.419300).
Description: Publishes papers on new statistical methods in which computation plays an important role, new computational techniques in statistics, new philosophy, development or evaluation of statistical software.
Refereed Serial

JEWISH EDUCATIONAL STATISTICS. see EDUCATION — Abstracting, Bibliographies, Statistics

310   JA   ISSN 0910-9684
JIDOSHA HOYU SHARYOSU. 1973. m. 4320 Yen (typically set in April). Jidosha Kensa Toroku Kyoryokukai, Toranomon Kiyoshi Bldg., 3-10, 4-chome, Toranomon, Minato-ku, Tokyo 105, Japan. TEL 03-3432-5611. FAX 03-3432-1044. Ed. Isamu Seki. bk.rev. circ. 1,500. (back issues avail.) Document type: newsletter.

315   JO   ISSN 0075-4013
HA4561
JORDAN. DEPARTMENT OF STATISTICS. ANNUAL STATISTICAL YEARBOOK. (Text in Arabic and English) 1950. a. $25 (effective Oct. 1993). Department of Statistics, P.O. Box 2015, Amman, Jordan. TEL 842171. FAX 833518. TELEX 24117 STATIS JO. Document type: government publication.
Incorporates (1960-1988): Jordan. Department of Statistics. National Accounts (ISSN 0449-1513)

JORDAN. DEPARTMENT OF STATISTICS. SERVICES SURVEY. see BUSINESS AND ECONOMICS — Abstracting, Bibliographies, Statistics

JOURNAL CONTENTS IN QUANTITATIVE METHODS. see BUSINESS AND ECONOMICS — Abstracting, Bibliographies, Statistics

JOURNAL OF APPLIED STATISTICAL SCIENCE. see MATHEMATICS

519.5   UK   ISSN 0266-4763
QA276.A1
JOURNAL OF APPLIED STATISTICS. Online edition (ISSN 1360-0532) 1975. bi-m. £96 to individuals; institutions £272 (effective 1996). Carfax Publishing Co., P.O. Box 25, Abingdon, Oxon. OX14 3UE, England. TEL 01235-555335. FAX 01235-553559. (U.S. subscr. to: Carfax Publishing Co., 875-81 Massachusetts Ave., Cambridge, MA 02139) Ed. Gopal K. Kanji. adv.; bk.rev. (also avail. in microfiche; back issues avail.) Indexed: Biostat., Comput.Abstr., Curr.Ind.Stat., J.Cont.Quant.Meth., Oper.Res.Manage.Sci., Stat.Theor.Meth.Abstr. Document type: academic/scholarly publication.
●Also available online.
—BLDSC (4947.110000); Ei; Faxon; SWETS; UMI; UnCover. CCC.
Formerly (until 1984): Bulletin in Applied Statistics.
Refereed Serial

JOURNAL OF BIOPHARMACEUTICAL STATISTICS. see PHARMACY AND PHARMACOLOGY

JOURNAL OF BUSINESS AND ECONOMIC STATISTICS. see BUSINESS AND ECONOMICS — Abstracting, Bibliographies, Statistics

JOURNAL OF COMPUTATIONAL AND GRAPHICAL STATISTICS. see MATHEMATICS

JOURNAL OF ECONOMETRICS. see BUSINESS AND ECONOMICS — Economic Systems And Theories, Economic History

519.5   NE   ISSN 0747-9662
H62.A1   CODEN: JEMEEZ
JOURNAL OF ECONOMIC AND SOCIAL MEASUREMENT. (Text in English) 1974. q. fl.376($209) (effective 1995). I O S Press, Van Diemenstraat 94, 1013 CN Amsterdam, Netherlands. TEL 31-20-6382189. FAX 31-20-6203419. E-mail: marie-louise.kok@ios.nl. (In N. America: Box 10558, Burke, VA 22009-0558. TEL 703-323-5554. FAX 703-250-4705) Ed. Charles G. Renfro. (also avail. in microform) Indexed: ASSIA, Chic.Per.Ind., Curr.Cont., Hosp.Lit.Ind., Human Resour.Abstr., INSPEC, J.of Econ.Lit., Lang.& Lang.Behav.Abstr., P.A.I.S., Popul.Ind., Sociol.Abstr., SSCI, Stat.Theor.Meth.Abstr., Urb.Aff.Abstr. Document type: academic/scholarly publication.
—BLDSC (4972.607000); Faxon; UnCover. CCC.
Formerly (until 1985): Review of Public Data Use (ISSN 0092-2846)
Description: Investigates all aspects of data production, distribution, and use with primary focus on economic and sociological data.

311   SW   ISSN 0282-423X
HA1523   CODEN: JOFSEA
JOURNAL OF OFFICIAL STATISTICS; an international review. (Text in English) 1860. q. SEK 400($65) Statistics Sweden, S-115 81 Stockholm, Sweden. TEL 46-8-783-43-00. FAX 46-8-783-42-88. TELEX 015261 SWESTAT S. (Subscr. to: Journal of Official Statistics, SCB-Distribution, S-701 89 Oerebro, Sweden) Ed. Lars Lyberg. adv.; bk.rev.; charts; illus.; stat.; index. circ. 1,100. (back issues avail.) Indexed: Biostat., Curr.Ind.Stat., J.Cont.Quant.Meth., Oper.Res.Manage.Sci., Popul.Ind., Qual.Contr.Appl.Stat., Stat.Theor.Meth.Abstr.
—BLDSC (5026.235000); SWETS.
Formerly (until 1985): Sweden. Statistiska Centralbyraan. Statistisk Tidskrift (ISSN 0039-7261)
Description: Specializes in issues pertinent to survey sampling with emphasis on the methodology and applications used by statistical agencies in the production of official statistics.

319.14   PH   ISSN 0022-3603
HA1821
JOURNAL OF PHILIPPINE STATISTICS. (Text in English) 1940. q. $10. National Statistics Office, Ramon Magsaysay Blvd., Box 779, Manila, Philippines. FAX 610794. Ed. Preciosa Astillero. charts; stat. circ. 250. Indexed: Asian-Pac.Econ.Lit., Ind.Phil.Per., P.A.I.S.

JOURNAL OF RISK AND UNCERTAINTY. see PSYCHOLOGY

JOURNAL OF STATISTICAL COMPUTATION AND SIMULATION. see COMPUTERS — Computer Simulation

JOURNAL OF STATISTICAL PHYSICS. see PHYSICS

519.5   NE   ISSN 0378-3758
QA276.A1   CODEN: JSPIDN
JOURNAL OF STATISTICAL PLANNING AND INFERENCE. (Text in English) 1977. 21/yr. fl.2961($1806) (effective 1996). North-Holland (Subsidiary of: Elsevier Science B.V.), P.O. Box 211, 1000 AE Amsterdam, Netherlands. TEL 31-20-4853911. FAX 31-20-4853598. TELEX 18582 ESPA NL. (Subscr. in U.S. and Canada to: Elsevier Science Inc., Box 882, Madison Sq. Sta., New York, NY 10159. TEL 212-989-5800. FAX 212-633-3990) Ed. S.S. Gupta. (also avail. in microform from UMI; back issues avail.; reprint service avail. from SWZ) Indexed: Biostat., BPIA, Bus.Ind., Compumath, Comput.Abstr., Curr.Cont., Curr.Ind.Stat., Ind.Sci.Rev., INSPEC, J.Cont.Quant.Meth., Math.R., Oper.Res.Manage.Sci., Qual.Contr.Appl.Stat., Stat.Theor.Meth.Abstr. Document type: academic/scholarly publication.
—BLDSC (5066.842000); Ei; Faxon; Genuine Article; SWETS; UnCover. CCC.
Description: Provides information on statistics, with special emphasis on statistical planning and the related areas of combinatorial mathematics and probability theory.
Refereed Serial

311   BG   ISSN 0256-422X
JOURNAL OF STATISTICAL RESEARCH. 1967. s-a. $25 (effective 1996). University of Dhaka, Institute of Statistical Research and Training, Ramna, Dhaka 1000, Bangladesh. TEL 880-2-501298. FAX 880-2-865583. Ed. Ehsanes Saleh. bk.rev.; charts; stat. Indexed: Math.R. Document type: academic/scholarly publication.
Supersedes: University of Dhaka. Institute of Statistical Research and Training. Bulletin (ISSN 0020-3165)

JUSTIZ IN ZAHLEN. see LAW — Abstracting, Bibliographies, Statistics

JUVENILE COURT STATISTICS. see LAW — Abstracting, Bibliographies, Statistics

316   NR
KADUNA STATE STATISTICAL YEARBOOK. 1975. a. Ministry of Economic Planning and Rural Development, Economic Planning Division, P.M. Bag 2032, Kaduna, Nigeria.
Formerly: North Central State Statistical Yearbook.

KANO (STATE). MOTOR VEHICLE STATISTICS. see TRANSPORTATION — Abstracting, Bibliographies, Statistics

KANO (STATE). STATISTICAL YEAR-BOOK. see BUSINESS AND ECONOMICS — Abstracting, Bibliographies, Statistics

316.69   NR
KANO (STATE). STATISTICS DIVISION. AREA CODES. a. price varies. Statistics Division, Budget Department, Director of Statistics, P.M.B. 3291, Kano, Nigeria. Document type: government publication, directory.
Formerly: Northern Nigeria Area Code Publication.

519.5   JA   ISSN 0914-8930
KEISANKI TOKEIGAKU/BULLETIN OF THE COMPUTATIONAL STATISTICS OF JAPAN. (Text in Japanese; summaries in English and Japanese) 1988. a. Nihon Keisanki Tokei Gakkai - Japanese Society of Computational Statistics, c/o Okayama Daigaku Kyoyobu, Tokeigaku Kyoshitsu, 1-1, Tsushima 2-chome, Okayama-shi, Okayama-ken 700, Japan. abstr. Indexed: Stat.Theor.Meth.Abstr.
—BLDSC (2458.143200).

KENTUCKY. CABINET FOR HUMAN RESOURCES. VITAL STATISTICS REPORT. see PUBLIC HEALTH AND SAFETY — Abstracting, Bibliographies, Statistics

KENYA. CENTRAL BUREAU OF STATISTICS. AGRICULTURAL CENSUS (LARGE FARM AREAS). see AGRICULTURE — Abstracting, Bibliographies, Statistics

KENYA. CENTRAL BUREAU OF STATISTICS. DEVELOPMENT ESTIMATES. see BUSINESS AND ECONOMICS — Abstracting, Bibliographies, Statistics

6210 STATISTICS

KENYA. CENTRAL BUREAU OF STATISTICS. EMPLOYMENT AND EARNINGS IN THE MODERN SECTOR. see BUSINESS AND ECONOMICS — *Abstracting, Bibliographies, Statistics*

KENYA. CENTRAL BUREAU OF STATISTICS. ESTIMATES OF RECURRENT EXPENDITURES. see BUSINESS AND ECONOMICS — *Abstracting, Bibliographies, Statistics*

KENYA. CENTRAL BUREAU OF STATISTICS. ESTIMATES OF REVENUE EXPENDITURES. see BUSINESS AND ECONOMICS — *Abstracting, Bibliographies, Statistics*

316.76 KE
KENYA. CENTRAL BUREAU OF STATISTICS. STATISTICAL ABSTRACT. 1961. a. (latest 1993). KShs.200. Central Bureau of Statistics, Ministry of Finance and Planning, P.O. Box 30266, Nairobi, Kenya. (Subscr. to: Government Press, Haile Selassie Ave., P.O. Box 30128, Nairobi, Kenya. TEL 254-2-334075) stat. (back issues avail.) **Document type:** government publication.
  Formerly: Kenya. Ministry of Economic Planning and Development. Statistics Division. Statistical Abstract (ISSN 0075-5850)

KENYA. CENTRAL BUREAU OF STATISTICS. SURVEYS OF INDUSTRIAL PRODUCTION. see BUSINESS AND ECONOMICS — *Abstracting, Bibliographies, Statistics*

316.76 KE ISSN 0453-6002
KENYA STATISTICAL DIGEST. 1963. q. price varies. Ministry of Finance and Planning, Central Bureau of Statistics, P.O. Box 30266, Nairobi, Kenya. (Subscr. to: Government Press, Haile Selassie Ave., P.O. Box 30128, Nairobi, Kenya. TEL 254-2-334075) stat. **Document type:** government publication.

KEY STATISTICAL INDICATORS FOR HEALTH IN WALES/DANGOSYDDION YSTADEGOL ALLWEDDOL AR GYFER LECHYD YNG NGHYMRU. see PUBLIC HEALTH AND SAFETY — *Abstracting, Bibliographies, Statistics*

KNITSTATS; yearly statistical bulletin for the hosiery and knitwear industry. see TEXTILE INDUSTRIES AND FABRICS — *Abstracting, Bibliographies, Statistics*

KNOW MORE ABOUT OIL: WORLD STATISTICS. see PETROLEUM AND GAS — *Abstracting, Bibliographies, Statistics*

310 DK ISSN 0106-3839
HA1489.C6
KOBENHAVNS STATISTISKE AARBOG; for Koebenhavn og Frederiksberg samt Hovedstadsregionen. (Text in Danish and English) 1919. a. DKK 200. Statistisk Kontor - Copenhagen Statistical Office, Vester Voldgade 87, 1552 Copenhagen V, Denmark. (Subscr. to: Danske Boghandleres Kommissionsanstalt, Siljangade 6-8, 2300 Copenhagen S, Denmark) circ. 2,400.

KOREA (REPUBLIC). NATIONAL STATISTICAL OFFICE. ANNUAL REPORT ON THE INTERNAL MIGRATION STATISTICS. see POPULATION STUDIES — *Abstracting, Bibliographies, Statistics*

KOREA (REPUBLIC). NATIONAL STATISTICAL OFFICE. POPULATION & HOUSING CENSUS REPORT. see POPULATION STUDIES — *Abstracting, Bibliographies, Statistics*

315 KO ISSN 0075-6873
HA4630.5
KOREA STATISTICAL YEARBOOK/HANGUK TONGGYE YONGAM. (Text in English, Korean) 1952. a. 16500 Won($33) National Statistical Office, Hanta Bldg., 647-15, Yoksam-dong, Kangnam-gu, Seoul 135-080, S. Korea. TEL 02-222-1971. (Subscr. to: the Korean Statistical Association, Room 302, Chungok Building, 561-30, Sinsa-dong, Gangnam-gu, Seoul 135-120, S. Korea. TEL 02-517-0382. FAX 02-725-4347) circ. 1,500.
  Formerly (until 1961): Daihan Mingug Tongyei Nyengam (ISSN 0253-3014)

KOSTEN EN FINANCIERING VAN DE GEZONDHEIDZORG IN NEDERLAND/COST OF HEALTH CARE IN THE NETHERLANDS. see PUBLIC HEALTH AND SAFETY — *Abstracting, Bibliographies, Statistics*

314 GW
KREFELD. AMT FUER STATISTIK UND STADTENTWICKLUNG. STATISTISCHES JAHRBUCH. 1926. a. DM.15. Amt fuer Statistik und Stadtentwicklung, Bleichpfad 3, 47727 Krefeld, Germany. TEL 02151-862153. FAX 02151-608482. Ed.Bd. bk.rev. circ. 450. **Document type:** government publication.

314 GW
KREISSTANDARDZAHLEN NORDRHEIN-WESTFALEN; statistische Angaben fuer kreisfreie Staedte und Kreise. 1951. a. DM.10. Landesamt fuer Datenverarbeitung und Statistik Nordrhein-Westfalen, Postfach 101105, 40002 Duesseldorf, Germany. TEL 0211-9449-01. FAX 0211-442006. circ. 1,300. (back issues avail.) **Document type:** government publication.

KULTUR- UND STADTNACHRICHTEN AUS WEITRA. see HISTORY

KUWAIT. CENTRAL STATISTICAL OFFICE. AGRICULTURAL STATISTICS BULLETIN/KUWAIT. AL-IDARAH AL-MARKAZIYYAH LIL-IHSA'. NASHRAH AL-IHSA'AT AL-ZIRA'IYYAH. see AGRICULTURE — *Abstracting, Bibliographies, Statistics*

KUWAIT. CENTRAL STATISTICAL OFFICE. ANNUAL BULLETIN OF FOREIGN TRADE STATISTICS/KUWAIT. AL-IDARAH AL-MARKAZIYYAH LIL-IHSA'. AL-NASHRAH AL-SANAWIYYAH LI-IHSA'AT AL-TIJARAH AL-KHARIJIYYAH. see BUSINESS AND ECONOMICS — *Abstracting, Bibliographies, Statistics*

315.367 KU ISSN 0259-532X
KUWAIT. CENTRAL STATISTICAL OFFICE. ANNUAL STATISTICAL ABSTRACT. Key Title: Al-Majmu'ah al-Ihsa'iyyah al-Sanawiyyah - Wizarat al-Takhtit, al-Idarah al-Markaziyyah. (Text in Arabic, English) 1964. a., latest 1993. Central Statistical Office - Al-Idarah al-Markaziyyah lil-Ihsa', P.O. Box 26188, Safat 13122, Kuwait. TEL 965-2428200. FAX 965-2430464. TELEX 22468 TAKHTET KT. circ. 450. **Document type:** government publication.

KUWAIT. CENTRAL STATISTICAL OFFICE. ANNUAL STATISTICAL BULLETIN FOR TRANSPORT AND COMMUNICATION/KUWAIT. AL-IDARAH AL-MARKAZIYYAH LIL-IHSA'. AL-NASHRAH AL-IHSA'IYYAH AL-SANAWIYYAH LIL-NAQL WAL-MUWASALAT. see TRANSPORTATION — *Abstracting, Bibliographies, Statistics*

KUWAIT. CENTRAL STATISTICAL OFFICE. ANNUAL SURVEY OF ESTABLISHMENTS - CONSTRUCTION/KUWAIT. AL-IDARAH AL-MARKAZIYYAH LIL-IHSA'. AL-BAHTH AL-SANAWI LIL-MANSHAAT - AL-TASHYID WAL-BINA'. see BUILDING AND CONSTRUCTION — *Abstracting, Bibliographies, Statistics*

KUWAIT. CENTRAL STATISTICAL OFFICE. ANNUAL SURVEY OF ESTABLISHMENTS - INDUSTRIAL/KUWAIT. AL-IDARAH AL-MARKAZIYYAH LIL-IHSA'. AL-BAHTH AL-SANAWI LIL-MANSHAAT - AL-SINA'AH. see BUSINESS AND ECONOMICS — *Abstracting, Bibliographies, Statistics*

KUWAIT. CENTRAL STATISTICAL OFFICE. ANNUAL SURVEY OF ESTABLISHMENTS - SERVICES/KUWAIT. AL-IDARAH AL-MARKAZIYYAH LIL-IHSA'. AL-BAHTH AL-SANAWI LIL-MANSHAAT - AL-KHADAMAT. see BUSINESS AND ECONOMICS — *Abstracting, Bibliographies, Statistics*

KUWAIT. CENTRAL STATISTICAL OFFICE. ANNUAL SURVEY OF ESTABLISHMENTS - WHOLESALE & RETAIL TRADE/KUWAIT. AL-IDARAH AL-MARKAZIYYAH LIL-IHSA'. AL-BAHTH AL-SANAWI LIL-MANSHAAT - TIJARAH AL-JUMLAH WAL-TAJZI'AH. see BUSINESS AND ECONOMICS — *Abstracting, Bibliographies, Statistics*

KUWAIT. CENTRAL STATISTICAL OFFICE. BUILDINGS AND DWELLINGS CENSUS/KUWAIT. AL-IDARAH AL-MARKAZIYYAH LIL-IHSA'. TA'DAD AL-MABANI WAL-MASAKIN. see BUSINESS AND ECONOMICS — *Abstracting, Bibliographies, Statistics*

KUWAIT. CENTRAL STATISTICAL OFFICE. CONSTRUCTION STATISTICS RESULTS/KUWAIT. AL-IDARAH AL-MARKAZIYYAH LIL-IHSA'. NATA'IJ IHSA'AT AL-TASHYID WAL-BINA'. see BUILDING AND CONSTRUCTION — *Abstracting, Bibliographies, Statistics*

KUWAIT. CENTRAL STATISTICAL OFFICE. ESTABLISHMENT CENSUS/KUWAIT. AL-IDARAH AL-MARKAZIYYAH LIL-IHSA'. TA'DAD AL-MUNSHAAT. see BUSINESS AND ECONOMICS — *Abstracting, Bibliographies, Statistics*

KUWAIT. CENTRAL STATISTICAL OFFICE. FAMILY BUDGET SURVEY - FINAL RESULTS/KUWAIT. AL-IDARAH AL-MARKAZIYYAH LIL-IHSA'. MIZANIYYAT AL-USRAH - AL-NATA'IJ AL-TAJMI'IYYAH AL-NIHA'IYYAH. see BUSINESS AND ECONOMICS — *Abstracting, Bibliographies, Statistics*

KUWAIT. CENTRAL STATISTICAL OFFICE. FINANCIAL STATISTICS/KUWAIT. AL-IDARAH AL-MARKAZIYYAH LIL-IHSA'. AL-IHSA'AT AL-MAALIYYAH. see BUSINESS AND ECONOMICS — *Abstracting, Bibliographies, Statistics*

KUWAIT. CENTRAL STATISTICAL OFFICE. FISHING STATISTICS BULLETIN/KUWAIT. AL-IDARAH AL-MARKAZIYYAH LIL-IHSA'. NASHRAH IHSA'AT AL-THARWAH AL-SAMAKIYYAH. see FISH AND FISHERIES — *Abstracting, Bibliographies, Statistics*

KUWAIT. CENTRAL STATISTICAL OFFICE. GENERAL POPULATION CENSUS/KUWAIT. AL-IDARAH AL-MARKAZIYYAH LIL-IHSA'. AL-TA'DAD AL-AAM LIL-SUKKAN. see POPULATION STUDIES — *Abstracting, Bibliographies, Statistics*

KUWAIT. CENTRAL STATISTICAL OFFICE. GOVERNMENT FINANCIAL STATISTICS/KUWAIT. AL-IDARAH AL-MARKAZIYYAH LIL-IHSA'. AL-IHSA'AT AL-MAALIYYAH LIL-HUKUMAH. see BUSINESS AND ECONOMICS — *Abstracting, Bibliographies, Statistics*

KUWAIT. CENTRAL STATISTICAL OFFICE. MONTHLY BULLETIN OF FOREIGN TRADE STATISTICS/KUWAIT. AL-IDARAH AL-MARKAZIYYAH LIL-IHSA'. AL-NASHRAH AL-SHAHRIYYAH LI-IHSA'AT AL-TIJARAH AL-KHARIJIYYAH. see BUSINESS AND ECONOMICS — *Abstracting, Bibliographies, Statistics*

KUWAIT. CENTRAL STATISTICAL OFFICE. MONTHLY CONSUMER PRICE INDEX NUMBERS. see BUSINESS AND ECONOMICS — *Abstracting, Bibliographies, Statistics*

310 KU ISSN 0023-5768
KUWAIT. CENTRAL STATISTICAL OFFICE. MONTHLY DIGEST OF STATISTICS/KUWAIT. AL-IDARAH AL-MARKAZIYYAH LIL-IHSA'. AL-NASHRAH AL-IHSA'IYYAH AL-SHAHRIYYAH. (Text in Arabic, English) 1965; N.S. 1980. m. Central Statistical Office - Al-Idarah al-Markaziyyah lil-Ihsa', P.O. Box 26188, Safat 13122, Kuwait. TEL 965-2428200. FAX 965-2430464. TELEX 22468 TAKHTET KT. **Document type:** government publication.
  Supersedes: Kuwait. Central Statistical Office. Monthly Statistical Bulletin.

KUWAIT. CENTRAL STATISTICAL OFFICE. NATIONAL ACCOUNTS STATISTICS/KUWAIT. AL-IDARAH AL-MARKAZIYYAH LIL-IHSA'. IHSA'AT AL-HISABAT AL-QAWMIYYAH. see BUSINESS AND ECONOMICS — *Abstracting, Bibliographies, Statistics*

KUWAIT. CENTRAL STATISTICAL OFFICE. PRELIMINARY RESULTS OF LABOUR FORCE BY SAMPLE. see BUSINESS AND ECONOMICS — *Abstracting, Bibliographies, Statistics*

KUWAIT. CENTRAL STATISTICAL OFFICE. PROVISIONAL ESTIMATES - NATIONAL ACCOUNTS. see BUSINESS AND ECONOMICS — *Abstracting, Bibliographies, Statistics*

KUWAIT. CENTRAL STATISTICAL OFFICE. SOCIAL STATISTICS BULLETIN/KUWAIT. AL-IDARAH AL-MARKAZIYYAH LIL-IHSA'. NASHRAT AL-IHSA'AT AL-IJTIMA'IYYAH. see SOCIAL SERVICES AND WELFARE — *Abstracting, Bibliographies, Statistics*

KUWAIT. CENTRAL STATISTICAL OFFICE. VITAL STATISTICS - A SUMMARISED ANALYSIS BULLETIN/KUWAIT. AL-IDARAH AL-MARKAZIYYAH LIL-IHSA'. TAHLIL AL-IHSA'AT AL-HAYAWIYYAH. see POPULATION STUDIES — *Abstracting, Bibliographies, Statistics*

KUWAIT. CENTRAL STATISTICAL OFFICE. VITAL STATISTICS - BIRTHS AND DEATHS/KUWAIT. AL-IDARAH AL-MARKAZIYYAH LIL-IHSA'. AL-IHSA'AT AL-HAYAWIYYAH - AL-MAWALID WAL-WAFAYAT. see POPULATION STUDIES — Abstracting, Bibliographies, Statistics

KUWAIT. CENTRAL STATISTICAL OFFICE. VITAL STATISTICS - MARRIAGE AND DIVORCE/KUWAIT. AL-IDARAH AL-MARKAZIYYAH LIL-IHSA'. AL-IHSA'AT AL-HAYAWIYYAH - AL-ZAWAJ WAL-TALAQ. see MATRIMONY — Abstracting, Bibliographies, Statistics

KUWAIT. CENTRAL STATISTICAL OFFICE. WHOLESALE PRICE INDEX NUMBERS/KUWAIT. AL-IDARAH AL-MARKAZIYYAH LIL-IHSA'. AL-ARQAM AL-QIYASIYYAH LI-AS'AR AL-JUMLAH. see BUSINESS AND ECONOMICS — Abstracting, Bibliographies, Statistics

KUWAIT. CENTRAL STATISTICAL OFFICE. YEARLY BULLETIN OF TRANSIT STATISTICS/KUWAIT. AL-IDARAH AL-MARKAZIYYAH LIL-IHSA'. NASHRAH IHSA'AT AL-TRANSIT. see BUSINESS AND ECONOMICS — Abstracting, Bibliographies, Statistics

LABOR FORCE AND NONAGRICULTURAL EMPLOYMENT ESTIMATES. see BUSINESS AND ECONOMICS — Abstracting, Bibliographies, Statistics

LABOUR FORCE AND MIGRATION SURVEY. see POPULATION STUDIES — Abstracting, Bibliographies, Statistics

LABOUR FORCE SITUATION IN INDONESIA: PRELIMINARY FIGURES/KEADAAN ANGKATAN KERJA DI INDONESIA: ANGKA SEMENTARA. see BUSINESS AND ECONOMICS — Abstracting, Bibliographies, Statistics

LANDBOUW-ECONOMISCH INSTITUUT. ONDERZOEKVERSLAG. see AGRICULTURE

314 AU
LANDESHAUPTSTADT INNSBRUCK. STATISTISCHER VIERTELJAHRESBERICHT. 1950. q. S.120. Stadtmagistrat Innsbruck, Innrain 10, A-6020 Innsbruck, Austria. TEL 0512-5360523. FAX 0512-5360521. index. circ. 100. Document type: bulletin.
 Description: Statistical information on the Austrian city of Innsbruck.

314.912 IC ISSN 1017-6683
LANDSHAGIR/STATISTICAL ABSTRACT OF ICELAND. (Text in Icelandic, tableheadings in English) 1984. a. $40. Hagstofa Islands - Statistical Bureau of Iceland, Skuggasund 3, IS-150 Reykjavik, Iceland. TEL 354-560-9800. FAX 354-562-8865. E-mail: hagstofa@hag.stjr.is. Dir. Hallgrimur Snorrason. circ. 2,500. (also avail. in diskette format; back issues avail.)

LAW ENFORCEMENT MANAGEMENT AND ADMINISTRATIVE STATISTICS (YEAR). see CRIMINOLOGY AND LAW ENFORCEMENT — Abstracting, Bibliographies, Statistics

315.692 LE ISSN 0023-9860
LEBANON. DIRECTION CENTRALE DE LA STATISTIQUE. BULLETIN STATISTIQUE MENSUEL. (Text in Arabic and French) 1963. m. free. Direction Centrale de la Statistique, Ministere du Plan, Beirut, Lebanon. mkt.; stat. circ. 1,900.
 Formerly: Lebanon. Service de Statistique Generale. Bulletin Statistique Mensuel.

315 LE ISSN 0075-8388
LEBANON. DIRECTION CENTRALE DE LA STATISTIQUE. RECUEIL DE STATISTIQUES LIBANAISES.* (Text in Arabic and French) 1963. a. free. Direction Centrale de la Statistique, Ministere du Plan, Beirut, Lebanon.

310 US ISSN 0930-0325
LECTURE NOTES IN STATISTICS. 1980. irreg. price varies. Springer-Verlag, 175 Fifth Ave., New York, NY 10010. TEL 212-460-1500. FAX 212-473-6272. (Also: Berlin, Heidelberg, Tokyo and Vienna) Ed.Bd. (reprint service avail. from ISI) Indexed: INSPEC. Document type: monographic series. —BLDSC (5180.422000).

311 MH
LEGISLACAO DO SISTEMA DE INFORMACAO ESTATISTICA DE MACAU/LAW OF MACAO STATISTICAL INFORMATION SYSTEM. (Text in Chinese, Portuguese) 1989. irreg. free. Direccao dos Servicos de Estatistica e Censos, Rua Inacio Baptista, No. 4-6, P.O. Box 3022, Macao. TEL 853-3995311. FAX 853-307825. Document type: government publication.

LENGTH OF STAY BY DIAGNOSIS & OPERATION, UNITED STATES. see HOSPITALS — Abstracting, Bibliographies, Statistics

LENGTH OF STAY BY DIAGNOSIS & OPERATION, UNITED STATES, NORTH CENTRAL REGION. see HOSPITALS — Abstracting, Bibliographies, Statistics

LENGTH OF STAY BY DIAGNOSIS & OPERATION, UNITED STATES, NORTHEASTERN REGION. see HOSPITALS — Abstracting, Bibliographies, Statistics

LENGTH OF STAY BY DIAGNOSIS & OPERATION, UNITED STATES, SOUTHERN REGION. see HOSPITALS — Abstracting, Bibliographies, Statistics

LENGTH OF STAY BY DIAGNOSIS & OPERATION, UNITED STATES, WESTERN REGION. see HOSPITALS — Abstracting, Bibliographies, Statistics

LETTERE D'AFFARI. see BUSINESS AND ECONOMICS — Abstracting, Bibliographies, Statistics

314.89 DK ISSN 0900-2499
LEVEVILKAAR I DANMARK/LIVING CONDITIONS IN DENMARK; statistisk oversigt. (Text in Danish and English) 1976. quadrennial. DKK 196. Danmarks Statistik, Sejroegade 11, DK-2100 Copenhagen OE, Denmark. TEL 45-31-29-82-22. FAX 45-31-18-48-01. TELEX 16236. (Dist. by: Danske Boghendleres Kommissionsanstalt, Siljangade 6, 2300 Copenhagen S, Denmark)
 Description: Compendium of social statistics concerning main aspects of the Danish population's living conditions.

LIBRARY AND INFORMATION SCIENCE EDUCATION STATISTICAL REPORT. see LIBRARY AND INFORMATION SCIENCES — Abstracting, Bibliographies, Statistics

LIBYA. CENSUS AND STATISTICAL DEPARTMENT. TRENDS OF EXTERNAL TRADE. see BUSINESS AND ECONOMICS — Abstracting, Bibliographies, Statistics

LIBYA. CENSUS AND STATISTICS DEPARTMENT. AGRICULTURAL CENSUS. see AGRICULTURE — Abstracting, Bibliographies, Statistics

LIBYA. CENSUS AND STATISTICS DEPARTMENT. EXTERNAL TRADE INDEX. see BUSINESS AND ECONOMICS — Abstracting, Bibliographies, Statistics

LIBYA. CENSUS AND STATISTICS DEPARTMENT. EXTERNAL TRADE STATISTICS. see BUSINESS AND ECONOMICS — Abstracting, Bibliographies, Statistics

339.42 LY ISSN 0023-1630
LIBYA. CENSUS AND STATISTICS DEPARTMENT. MONTHLY COST OF LIVING INDEX FOR TRIPOLI TOWN. (Text in Arabic and English) 1964. m. free. Secretariat of Planning, Census and Statistics Department, P.O. Box 600, Tripoli, Libya. charts; stat. Document type: government publication.

LIBYA. CENSUS AND STATISTICS DEPARTMENT. REPORT OF THE ANNUAL SURVEY OF PETROLEUM MINING INDUSTRY. see PETROLEUM AND GAS — Abstracting, Bibliographies, Statistics

LIBYA. CENSUS AND STATISTICS DEPARTMENT. REPORT OF THE ANNUAL SURVEY OF UNITS PROVIDING TECHNICAL SERVICES TO THE PETROLEUM MINING INDUSTRY. see PETROLEUM AND GAS — Abstracting, Bibliographies, Statistics

315 LY ISSN 0075-9287
LIBYA. CENSUS AND STATISTICS DEPARTMENT. STATISTICAL ABSTRACT. (Text in Arabic and English) 1958. a. free. Secretariat of Planning, Census and Statistics Department, P.O. Box 600, Tripoli, Libya. Document type: government publication.

LIFETIME DATA ANALYSIS; an international journal devoted to the methods and applications of reliability and survival analysis. see INSURANCE

318 PE
LIMA - CALLAO COMPENDIO ESTADISTICO. irreg., 2nd ed., 1991. Instituto Nacional de Estadistica e Informatica, Av. 28 de Julio No. 1056, Lima, Peru.

LLOYD'S REGISTER OF SHIPPING. STATISTICAL TABLES. see TRANSPORTATION — Abstracting, Bibliographies, Statistics

LUXEMBOURG. SERVICE CENTRAL DE LA STATISTIQUE ET DES ETUDES ECONOMIQUES. ANNUAIRE STATISTIQUE. see BUSINESS AND ECONOMICS — Abstracting, Bibliographies, Statistics

LUXEMBOURG. SERVICE CENTRAL DE LA STATISTIQUE ET DES ETUDES ECONOMIQUES. ANNUAIRE STATISTIQUE (YEAR). see BUSINESS AND ECONOMICS — Abstracting, Bibliographies, Statistics

LUXEMBOURG. SERVICE CENTRAL DE LA STATISTIQUE ET DES ETUDES ECONOMIQUES. INDICATEURS RAPIDES. SERIE A2: INDICES DES PRIX DE LA CONSTRUCTION. see BUILDING AND CONSTRUCTION — Abstracting, Bibliographies, Statistics

LUXEMBOURG. SERVICE CENTRAL DE LA STATISTIQUE ET DES ETUDES ECONOMIQUES. STATISTIQUES RETROSPECTIF (1839-1989). see BUSINESS AND ECONOMICS — Abstracting, Bibliographies, Statistics

MAANDSTATISTIEK VAN HET FINANCIEWEZEN. see BUSINESS AND ECONOMICS — Abstracting, Bibliographies, Statistics

MACAO. DIRECCAO DOS SERVICOS DE ESTATISTICA E CENSOS. ANUARIO ESTATISTICO DO COMERCIO EXTERNO/MACAO. CENSUS AND STATISTICS DEPARTMENT. YEARBOOK OF EXTERNAL TRADE STATISTICS. see BUSINESS AND ECONOMICS — Abstracting, Bibliographies, Statistics

310 MH ISSN 0870-5615
MACAO. DIRECCAO DOS SERVICOS DE ESTATISTICA E CENSOS. ANUARIO ESTATISTICO/MACAO. CENSUS AND STATISTICS DEPARTMENT. YEARBOOK OF STATISTICS. (Text in Chinese, English and Portuguese) 1932. a. free. Direccao dos Servicos de Estatistica e Censos, Rua Inacio Baptista, No. 4-6, P.O. Box 3022, Macao. TEL 853-3995311. FAX 853-307825. Document type: government publication.

MACAO. DIRECCAO DOS SERVICOS DE ESTATISTICA E CENSOS. AVALIACAO DAS NECESSIDADES DE MAO-DE-OBRA. see BUSINESS AND ECONOMICS — Abstracting, Bibliographies, Statistics

MACAO. DIRECCAO DOS SERVICOS DE ESTATISTICA E CENSOS. BALANCO ENERGETICO (ANUAL)/MACAO. CENSUS AND STATISTICS DEPARTMENT. BALANCE OF ENERGY (ANNUAL). see ENERGY — Abstracting, Bibliographies, Statistics

314 MH ISSN 0872-461X
MACAO. DIRECCAO DOS SERVICOS DE ESTATISTICA E CENSOS. BOLETIM MENSAL/MACAO. CENSUS AND STATISTICS DEPARTMENT. MONTHLY DIGEST. (Text in Chinese, Portuguese) 1976. m. free. Direccao dos Servicos de Estatistica e Censos, Rua Inacio Baptista, No. 4-6, P.O. Box 3022, Macao. TEL 853-3995311. FAX 853-307825. Document type: government publication.
 Formerly (until 1986): Macao. Direccao dos Servicos de Estatistica e Censos. Boletim Mensal de Estatistica (ISSN 0870-5569)

MACAO. DIRECCAO DOS SERVICOS DE ESTATISTICA E CENSOS. BOLETIM MENSUAL DO COMERCIO EXTERNO/MACAO. CENSUS AND STATISTICS DEPARTMENT. MONTHLY BULLETIN OF EXTERNAL TRADE. see BUSINESS AND ECONOMICS — Abstracting, Bibliographies, Statistics

MACAO. DIRECCAO DOS SERVICOS DE ESTATISTICA E CENSOS. CENSOS DA POPULACAO/MACAO. CENSUS AND STATISTICS DEPARTMENT. POPULATION CENSUS. see POPULATION STUDIES — Abstracting, Bibliographies, Statistics

STATISTICS

MACAO. DIRECCAO DOS SERVICOS DE ESTATISTICA E CENSOS. ESTATISTICAS DA PESCA/MACAO. CENSUS AND STATISTICS DEPARTMENT. STATISTICS OF FISHERY. see FISH AND FISHERIES — *Abstracting, Bibliographies, Statistics*

MACAO. DIRECCAO DOS SERVICOS DE ESTATISTICA E CENSOS. ESTATISTICAS DEMOGRAFICAS/MACAO. CENSUS AND STATISTICS DEPARTMENT. DEMOGRAPHIC STATISTICS. see POPULATION STUDIES — *Abstracting, Bibliographies, Statistics*

MACAO. DIRECCAO DOS SERVICOS DE ESTATISTICA E CENSOS. ESTATISTICAS DE CONSTRUCAO/MACAO. CENSUS AND STATISTICS DEPARTMENT. CONSTRUCTION STATISTICS. see REAL ESTATE — *Abstracting, Bibliographies, Statistics*

MACAO. DIRECCAO DOS SERVICOS DE ESTATISTICA E CENSOS. ESTATISTICAS DE ENERGIA/MACAO. CENSUS AND STATISTICS DEPARTMENT. ENERGY STATISTICS. see ENERGY — *Abstracting, Bibliographies, Statistics*

MACAO. DIRECCAO DOS SERVICOS DE ESTATISTICA E CENSOS. ESTATISTICAS DA JUSTICA E DA CRIMINALIDADE/MACAO. CENSUS AND STATISTICS DEPARTMENT. STATISTICS OF JUSTICE AND CRIMINALITY. see LAW — *Abstracting, Bibliographies, Statistics*

MACAO. DIRECCAO DOS SERVICOS DE ESTATISTICA E CENSOS. ESTATISTICAS DAS SOCIEDADES/MACAO. CENSUS AND STATISTICS DEPARTMENT. STATISTICAL DATA CONCERNING COMPANIES. see REAL ESTATE — *Abstracting, Bibliographies, Statistics*

MACAO. DIRECCAO DOS SERVICOS DE ESTATISTICA E CENSOS. ESTATISTICAS DO TURISMO/MACAO. CENSUS AND STATISTICS DEPARTMENT. TOURISM STATISTICS. see TRAVEL AND TOURISM — *Abstracting, Bibliographies, Statistics*

MACAO. DIRECCAO DOS SERVICOS DE ESTATISTICA E CENSOS. ESTIMATIVAS DO PRODUTO INTERNO BRUTO/MACAO. CENSUS AND STATISTICS DEPARTMENT. GROSS DOMESTIC PRODUCT ESTIMATIONS. see BUSINESS AND ECONOMICS — *Abstracting, Bibliographies, Statistics*

MACAO. DIRECCAO DOS SERVICOS DE ESTATISTICA E CENSOS. ESTIMATIVAS DA POPULACAO RESIDENTE EM MACAO/MACAO. CENSUS AND STATISTICS DEPARTMENT. ESTIMATION OF RESIDENT POPULATION IN MACAO. see POPULATION STUDIES — *Abstracting, Bibliographies, Statistics*

MACAO. DIRECCAO DOS SERVICOS DE ESTATISTICA E CENSOS. ESTUDOS DO COMERCIO EXTERNO/MACAO. CENSUS AND STATISTICS DEPARTMENT. STUDIES OF EXTERNAL TRADE. see BUSINESS AND ECONOMICS — *Abstracting, Bibliographies, Statistics*

MACAO. DIRECCAO DOS SERVICOS DE ESTATISTICA E CENSOS. INDICADORES DO COMERCIO EXTERNO/MACAO. CENSUS AND STATISTICS DEPARTMENT. INDICATORS OF EXTERNAL TRADE. see BUSINESS AND ECONOMICS — *Abstracting, Bibliographies, Statistics*

MACAO. DIRECCAO DOS SERVICOS DE ESTATISTICA E CENSOS. INDICADORES DO TURISMO/MACAO. CENSUS AND STATISTICS DEPARTMENT. TOURISM INDICATORS. see TRAVEL AND TOURISM — *Abstracting, Bibliographies, Statistics*

MACAO. DIRECCAO DOS SERVICOS DE ESTATISTICA E CENSOS. INDICE DE PRECOS NO CONSUMIDOR/MACAO. CENSUS AND STATISTICS DEPARTMENT. CONSUMER PRICE INDEX. see BUSINESS AND ECONOMICS — *Abstracting, Bibliographies, Statistics*

MACAO. DIRECCAO DOS SERVICOS DE ESTATISTICA E CENSOS. INDICE DE PRECOS NO CONSUMIDOR (RELATORIO ANUAL)/MACAO. CENSUS AND STATISTICS DEPARTMENT. CONSUMER PRICE INDEX (ANNUAL REPORT). see BUSINESS AND ECONOMICS — *Abstracting, Bibliographies, Statistics*

MACAO. DIRECCAO DOS SERVICOS DE ESTATISTICA E CENSOS. INDICES DE PRECOS DOS MATERIAS DE CONSTRUCAO. see BUILDING AND CONSTRUCTION — *Abstracting, Bibliographies, Statistics*

MACAO. DIRECCAO DOS SERVICOS DE ESTATISTICA E CENSOS. INDICES DE PRECOS E QUANTIDADES DO COMERCIO EXTERNO. see BUSINESS AND ECONOMICS — *Abstracting, Bibliographies, Statistics*

MACAO. DIRECCAO DOS SERVICOS DE ESTATISTICA E CENSOS. INDICES E SALARIOS DA CONSTRUCAO CIVIL/MACAO. CENSUS AND STATISTICS DEPARTMENT. INDICES AND WAGES OF THE CONSTRUCTION INDUSTRY. see BUSINESS AND ECONOMICS — *Abstracting, Bibliographies, Statistics*

MACAO. DIRECCAO DOS SERVICOS DE ESTATISTICA E CENSOS. INQUERITO AO EMPREGO. see BUSINESS AND ECONOMICS — *Abstracting, Bibliographies, Statistics*

MACAO. DIRECCAO DOS SERVICOS DE ESTATISTICA E CENSOS. INQUERITO AO ENSINO/MACAO. CENSUS AND STATISTICS DEPARTMENT. EDUCATION SURVEY. see EDUCATION — *Abstracting, Bibliographies, Statistics*

MACAO. DIRECCAO DOS SERVICOS DE ESTATISTICA E CENSOS. INQUERITO AS DESPESAS DOS VISITANTES/MACAO. CENSUS AND STATISTICS DEPARTMENT. VISITOR EXPENDITURE SURVEY ANNUAL REPORT. see TRAVEL AND TOURISM — *Abstracting, Bibliographies, Statistics*

MACAO. DIRECCAO DOS SERVICOS DE ESTATISTICA E CENSOS. INQUERITO AS EMBARCACOES DE PESCA/MACAO. CENSUS AND STATISTICS DEPARTMENT. SURVEY OF FISHING VESSELS. see FISH AND FISHERIES — *Abstracting, Bibliographies, Statistics*

MACAO. DIRECCAO DOS SERVICOS DE ESTATISTICA E CENSOS. INQUERITO DOS SALARIOS E BENEFICIOS. see BUSINESS AND ECONOMICS — *Abstracting, Bibliographies, Statistics*

MACAO. DIRECCAO DOS SERVICOS DE ESTATISTICA E CENSOS. OPERACOES SOBRE IMOVEIS/MACAO. CENSUS AND STATISTICS DEPARTMENT. TRANSACTIONS CONCERNING REAL ESTATE. see REAL ESTATE — *Abstracting, Bibliographies, Statistics*

315   MH
MACAO. DIRECCAO DOS SERVICOS DE ESTATISTICA E CENSOS. PLANO DE ACTIVIDADES/MACAO. CENSUS AND STATISTICS DEPARTMENT. ACTIVITIES PLAN. (Text in Chinese, Portuguese) 1988. a. free. Direccao dos Servicos de Estatistica e Censos, Rua Inacio Baptists, No. 4-6, P.O. Box 3022, Macao. TEL 853-3995311. FAX 853-307825. **Document type:** government publication.

MACAO. DIRECCAO DOS SERVICOS DE ESTATISTICA E CENSOS. PRINCIPAIS INDICADORES DAS ESTATISTICAS DO TRABALHO. see BUSINESS AND ECONOMICS — *Abstracting, Bibliographies, Statistics*

315   MH
MACAO. DIRECCAO DOS SERVICOS DE ESTATISTICA E CENSOS. PRINCIPAIS INDICADORES ESTATISTICOS. (Text in Chinese, English, Portuguese) 1993. m. free. Direccao dos Servicos de Estatistica e Censos, Rua Inacio Baptista, No. 4-6, P.O. Box 3022, Macao. TEL 853-3995311. FAX 853-307825. **Document type:** government publication.

MACAO. DIRECCAO DOS SERVICOS DE ESTATISTICA E CENSOS. RECENSEAMENTO AOS RESTAURANTES, HOTEIS E ESTABELECIMENTOS SIMILARES/MACAO. CENSUS AND STATISTICS DEPARTMENT. CENSUS OF RESTAURANTS, HOTELS AND SIMILAR ESTABLISHMENTS. see HOTELS AND RESTAURANTS — *Abstracting, Bibliographies, Statistics*

MACAO. DIRECCAO DOS SERVICOS DE ESTATISTICA E CENSOS. RECENSEAMENTO DOS ALOJAMENTOS INFORMAI/MACAO. CENSUS AND STATISTICS DEPARTMENT. CENSUS OF INFORMAL ACCOMODATION. see POPULATION STUDIES — *Abstracting, Bibliographies, Statistics*

MACAO. DIRECCAO DOS SERVICOS DE ESTATISTICA E CENSOS. RECENSEAMENTO GERAL A HABITACAO/MACAO. CENSUS AND STATISTICS DEPARTMENT. GENERAL CENSUS OF HOUSING. see HOUSING AND URBAN PLANNING — *Abstracting, Bibliographies, Statistics*

MACAO. DIRECCAO DOS SERVICOS DE ESTATISTICA E CENSOS. RECENSEAMENTO INDUSTRIAL/MACAO. CENSUS AND STATISTICS DEPARTMENT. INDUSTRIAL CENSUS. see BUSINESS AND ECONOMICS — *Abstracting, Bibliographies, Statistics*

315   MH   ISSN 0872-4237
MACAO. DIRECCAO DOS SERVICOS DE ESTATISTICA E CENSOS. RELATORIO DE ACTIVIDADES/MACAO. CENSUS AND STATISTICS DEPARTMENT. ACTIVITIES REPORT. (Text in Chinese, Portuguese) 1986. a. free. Direccao dos Servicos de Estatistica e Censos, P.O. Box 3022, Macao. TEL 853-3995311. FAX 853-307825. **Document type:** government publication.

MACAO. DIRECCAO DOS SERVICOS DE ESTATISTICA E CENSOS. TRANSPORTE DE MERCADORIAS POR VIAS DE UTILIZACAO. see BUSINESS AND ECONOMICS — *Abstracting, Bibliographies, Statistics*

310   MH   ISSN 0870-6778
MACAU EM NUMEROS/MACAO IN FIGURES. (Text in Chinese, English, Portuguese) 1985. a. free. Direccao dos Servicos de Estatistica e Censos, Rua Inacio Baptista, No. 4-6, P.O. Box 2033, Macao. TEL 853-3995311. FAX 853-307825. **Document type:** government publication.

314.9   PO
MADEIRA. DIRECCAO REGIONAL DE ESTATISTICA. BOLETIM TRIMESTRAL DE ESTATISTICA. 1972. q. Esc.2000 (effective Jan. 1992). Direccao Regional de Estatistica, Calcada de Santa Clara No. 38, 9000 Funchal, Madeira, Portugal. circ. 150. **Document type:** government publication, bulletin.
     Former titles: Portugal. Instituto Nacional de Estatistica. Delegacao do Funchal. Anuario Estatistico - Regiao Autonoma de Madeira; Portugal. Instituto Nacional de Estatistica. Delegacao do Funchal. Boletim Trimestral de Estatistica - Arquipelago de Madeira (ISSN 0303-1705)

314   HU   ISSN 1215-7864
HA1201   CODEN: STEVEC
MAGYAR STATISZTIKAI EVKONYV. English edition: Hungarian Statistical Yearbook (ISSN 1215-8941) 1871. a. 550 Ft. (English ed. 1100 Ft.). Statiqum Kiado es Nyomda Kft., Kaszasdulo u. 2, P.O. Box 99, 1300 Budapest 3, Hungary. TEL 361-168-8635. FAX 361-168-8635. TELEX 22-6699. (Subscr. to: Kultura, Box 149, 1389 Budapest, Hungary) —BLDSC (5345.503000).
     Formerly (until 1990): Hungary. Kozponti Statisztikai Hivatal. Statistikai Evkonyv (ISSN 0073-4039)

314   HU   ISSN 0133-5847
MAGYAR STATISZTIKAI ZSEBKONYV. English edition: Statistical Pocket Book of Hungary (ISSN 0441-473X); German edition: Statistisches Taschenbuch Ungarns (ISSN 0139-4231); Russian edition: Vengerski Statisticheski Spravochnik (ISSN 0505-1975) 1933. a. 48 Ft. (language editions 300 Ft.). (Kozponti Statisztikai Hivatal) Statiqum Kiado es Nyomda Kft., Kaszasdulo u. 2, P.O.B. 99, 1300 Budapest 3, Hungary. TEL 361-180-3311. FAX 361-168-8635. TELEX 22-6699. (Subscr. to: Kultura, Box 149, 1389 Budapest, Hungary) circ. 1,200 (Eng. ed.).

310   HU   ISSN 0230-5828
MAGYARORSZAG. English edition: Hungary (ISSN 0230-5755) German edition: Ungarn (ISSN 0230-5909); Russian edition: Vengria v Godu (ISSN 0230-5925) 1964. a. 80 Ft. (language editions 110 Ft.). (Kozponti Statisztikai Hivatal) Statiqum Kiado es Nyomda Kft., Kaszasdulo u. 2, Box 99, 1300 Budapest 3, Hungary. TEL 361-180-3311. FAX 361-168-8635. TELEX 22-6699. (Subscr. to: Kultura, Box 149, 1389 Budapest, Hungary) Ed. Jozsef Palfy. circ. 200,000. **Indexed:** PROMT.

519.5 UA ISSN 0542-1748
AL-MAJALLAH AL-IHSA'IYYAH AL-MISRIYYAH/EGYPTIAN STATISTICAL JOURNAL. Abbreviated title: E S J. (Text and summaries in Arabic and English) 1957. 2/yr. $15. Cairo University, Institute of Statistical Studies and Research, Tharwat St., Orman, Cairo, Egypt. FAX 3482533. TELEX 94372. Ed. M.R. Mahmoud. (back issues avail.) **Indexed:** Curr.Ind.Stat., Math.R., Stat.Theor.Meth.Abstr. **Document type:** academic/scholarly publication.

MAJOR COLLECTIVE BARGAINING SETTLEMENTS IN PRIVATE INDUSTRY. see *BUSINESS AND ECONOMICS — Economic Situation And Conditions*

MAJOR COLLECTIVE BARGAINING SETTLEMENTS IN STATE AND LOCAL GOVERNMENT. see *BUSINESS AND ECONOMICS — Economic Situation And Conditions*

MAJOR PROGRAMS. see *BUSINESS AND ECONOMICS — Economic Situation And Conditions*

MALAWI. NATIONAL STATISTICAL OFFICE. ANNUAL STATEMENT OF EXTERNAL TRADE. see *BUSINESS AND ECONOMICS — Abstracting, Bibliographies, Statistics*

MALAWI. NATIONAL STATISTICAL OFFICE. ANNUAL SURVEY OF ECONOMIC ACTIVITIES. see *BUSINESS AND ECONOMICS — Abstracting, Bibliographies, Statistics*

MALAWI. NATIONAL STATISTICAL OFFICE. BALANCE OF PAYMENTS. see *BUSINESS AND ECONOMICS — Public Finance, Taxation*

MALAWI. NATIONAL STATISTICAL OFFICE. EMPLOYMENT AND EARNINGS: ANNUAL REPORT. see *BUSINESS AND ECONOMICS — Abstracting, Bibliographies, Statistics*

MALAWI. NATIONAL STATISTICAL OFFICE. FAMILY FORMATION SURVEY (YEAR). see *SOCIOLOGY*

316 MW
MALAWI. NATIONAL STATISTICAL OFFICE. MONTHLY STATISTICAL BULLETIN. m. K.200. National Statistical Office, Commissioner for Census and Statistics, P.O. Box 333, Zomba, Malawi. TEL 265-50-522-377. FAX 265-50-523-130. TELEX 44015 CENSUS MI. **Document type:** government publication, bulletin.

310 MW ISSN 0076-3284
MALAWI. NATIONAL STATISTICAL OFFICE. NATIONAL ACCOUNTS REPORT. 1967. a. K.125. National Statistical Office, Commissioner for Census and Statistics, P.O. Box 333, Zomba, Malawi. TEL 265-50-522-377. FAX 265-50-523-130. TELEX 44015 CENSUS MI. **Document type:** government publication.

MALAWI. NATIONAL STATISTICAL OFFICE. NATIONAL SAMPLE SURVEY OF AGRICULTURE. see *AGRICULTURE — Abstracting, Bibliographies, Statistics*

MALAWI. NATIONAL STATISTICAL OFFICE. POPULATION CENSUS FINAL REPORT. see *POPULATION STUDIES — Abstracting, Bibliographies, Statistics*

MALAWI. NATIONAL STATISTICAL OFFICE. SURVEY OF HANDICAPPED PERSONS. see *HANDICAPPED — Abstracting, Bibliographies, Statistics*

MALAWI. NATIONAL STATISTICAL OFFICE. TRANSPORT STATISTICS. see *TRANSPORTATION — Abstracting, Bibliographies, Statistics*

MALAWI. NATIONAL STATISTICAL OFFICE. URBAN HOUSEHOLD EXPENDITURE SURVEY. see *POPULATION STUDIES — Abstracting, Bibliographies, Statistics*

MALAWI. NATIONAL STATISTICAL OFFICE. URBAN HOUSING SURVEY. see *HOUSING AND URBAN PLANNING*

316 MW
MALAWI STATISTICAL YEARBOOK. 1965. a. K.40. National Statistical Office, Commissioner for Census and Statistics, P.O. Box 333, Zomba, Malawi. TEL 265-50-522-377. FAX 265-50-523-130. TELEX 44015 CENSUS MI.
Supersedes: Malawi. National Statistical Office. Compendium of Statistics (ISSN 0076-3268)

MALAWI TOURISM REPORT. see *TRAVEL AND TOURISM — Abstracting, Bibliographies, Statistics*

MALAYSIA. DEPARTMENT OF MINES. STATISTICS RELATING TO THE MINING INDUSTRY OF MALAYSIA. see *MINES AND MINING INDUSTRY — Abstracting, Bibliographies, Statistics*

310 MY ISSN 0127-4732
HA4600.6.Z9
MALAYSIA. DEPARTMENT OF STATISTICS. ANNUAL STATISTICAL BULLETIN SARAWAK. (Text in English) 1964. a. M.$8. Department of Statistics - Jabatan Perangkaan, Wisma Statistik, Jalan Cenderasari, 50514 Kuala Lumpur, Malaysia. (Dist. by: Department of Statistics, Malaysia (Sarawak Branch), 5th Fl., Bangunan Tun Datuk, Patinggi Tuanku Hj. Bujang, 93514 Kuching, Sarawak, Malaysia) **Document type:** government publication.
Formerly (until 1971): Malaysia. Department of Statistics. Annual Bulletin of Statistics. State of Sarawak (ISSN 0080-6439)

315 330 MY
MALAYSIA. DEPARTMENT OF STATISTICS. BALANCE OF PAYMENTS REPORT MALAYSIA. (Text in English, Malay) irreg., latest 1990-92. M.$13. Department of Statistics - Jabatan Perangkaan, Wisma Statistik, Jalan Cenderasari, 50514 Kuala Lumpur, Malaysia. TEL 03-2922133. **Document type:** government publication.

310 MY ISSN 0127-8363
HD9987.M3
MALAYSIA. DEPARTMENT OF STATISTICS. CENSUS OF SELECTED SERVICE INDUSTRIES. (Text in Bahasa Malaysia, English) 1971. a. M.$25 (effective Apr.1993). Department of Statistics, Wisma Statistik, Block E, Jalan Cenderasari, 50514 Kuala Lumpur, Malaysia. TEL 03-2922133. **Document type:** government publication.
Description: Contains statistics on shipping, real estate, transportation, tourism, advertising, banking and financial service industries.

MALAYSIA. DEPARTMENT OF STATISTICS. HANDBOOK OF COCOA, COCONUT AND TEA STATISTICS MALAYSIA. see *AGRICULTURE — Abstracting, Bibliographies, Statistics*

315 MY
MALAYSIA. DEPARTMENT OF STATISTICS. MONTHLY BULLETIN OF STATISTICS, SABAH. (Text in English) m. M.$5 per no. Department of Statistics - Jalan Cenderasari, Wisma Statistik, Jalan Cenderasari, 50514 Kuala Lumpur, Malaysia. TEL 03-2922133. (Subscr. to: Department of Statistics (Sabah Branch), 1st Fl., Federal House, Jalan Mat Salleh, 88000 Kota Kinabalu, Sabah, Malaysia. TEL 088-232277) **Document type:** government publication.

315 330 MY
MALAYSIA. DEPARTMENT OF STATISTICS. MONTHLY CONSUMER PRICE INDEX FOR MALAYSIA. (Text in English, Malay) m. M.$5. Department of Statistics - Jabatan Perangkaan, Wisma Statistik, Jalan Cenderasari, 50514 Kuala Lumpur, Malaysia. TEL 03-2922133. **Document type:** government publication.

MALAYSIA. DEPARTMENT OF STATISTICS. MONTHLY RUBBER STATISTICS OF MALAYSIA. see *RUBBER — Abstracting, Bibliographies, Statistics*

310 MY
MALAYSIA. DEPARTMENT OF STATISTICS. MONTHLY STATISTICAL BULLETIN, MALAYSIA/SIARAN PERANGKAAN BULANAN SEMENANJUNG MALAYSIA. (Text in English, Malay) 1949. m. M.$15 per no. Department of Statistics - Jabatan Perangkaan, Wisma Statistik, Jalan Cenderasari, 50514 Kuala Lumpur, Malaysia. TEL 03-2922133. FAX 03-2937018. **Document type:** government publication.
Former titles (until 1990): Monthly Statistical Bulletin, Peninsular Malaysia; (until 1977): Monthly Statistical Bulletin of West Malaysia (ISSN 0542-3686)

315 MY ISSN 0127-9238
MALAYSIA. DEPARTMENT OF STATISTICS. MONTHLY STATISTICAL BULLETIN, SARAWAK. (Text in English) m. M.$12 per no. Department of Statistics, Wisma Statistik, Jalan Cenderasari, 50514 Kuala Lumpur, Malaysia. TEL 03-2922133. FAX 03-2937018. (Subscr. to: Department of Statistics (Sarawak Branch), 5th Fl., Bangunan Tun Datuk, Patinggi Tuanku HJ. Bujang, 93514 Kuching, Sarawak, Malaysia. TEL 082-240287) **Document type:** government publication.

MALAYSIA. DEPARTMENT OF STATISTICS. MONTHLY TIN STATISTICS OF MALAYSIA. see *MINES AND MINING INDUSTRY — Abstracting, Bibliographies, Statistics*

315 MY ISSN 0126-7086
HC445.5.Z9
MALAYSIA. DEPARTMENT OF STATISTICS. NATIONAL ACCOUNTS STATISTICS, MALAYSIA. (Text in English) 1982. irreg. M.$14. Department of Statistics, Wisma Statistik, Jalan Cenderasari, 50514 Kuala Lumpur, Malaysia. TEL 03-2922133. **Document type:** government publication.

MALAYSIA. DEPARTMENT OF STATISTICS. RUBBER STATISTICS HANDBOOK, MALAYSIA. see *RUBBER — Abstracting, Bibliographies, Statistics*

MALAYSIA. DEPARTMENT OF STATISTICS. VITAL STATISTICS MALAYSIA (YEAR). see *POPULATION STUDIES — Abstracting, Bibliographies, Statistics*

315.95 MY ISSN 0127-2624
HA1791
MALAYSIA. DEPARTMENT OF STATISTICS. YEARBOOK OF STATISTICS. (Text in English) 1965. a. M.$23. Department of Statistics - Jabatan Perangkaan, Wisma Statistik, Jalan Cenderasari, 50514 Kuala Lumpur, Malaysia. TEL 03-2922133. FAX 03-2937018. **Document type:** government publication.
Former titles (until 1989): Malaysia. Department of Statistics. Statistics Handbook Malaysia; (until 1984): Malaysia. Department of Statistics. Annual Bulletin of Statistics (ISSN 0542-3570)

316.6 ML
MALI. SERVICE DE LA STATISTIQUE GENERALE, DE LA COMPTABILITE NATIONALE ET DE LA MECANOGRAPHIE. BULLETIN MENSUEL DE STATISTIQUE. m. 4000 F. Direction Nationale de la Statistique et de l'Information, B.P. 12, Bamako, Mali.

314 MM ISSN 0256-8047
HA1117.M3
MALTA. CENTRAL OFFICE OF STATISTICS. ANNUAL ABSTRACT OF STATISTICS. a. L.2. Central Office of Statistics, Auberge d'Italie, Merchants' St., Valletta, Malta. FAX 356-248483. (Subscr. to: Publication Bookshop, Auberge de Castille, Valletta, Malta) **Document type:** government publication.
Formerly: Statistical Abstract of the Maltese Islands (ISSN 0081-4733)

MALTA. CENTRAL OFFICE OF STATISTICS. DEMOGRAPHIC REVIEW. see *POPULATION STUDIES — Abstracting, Bibliographies, Statistics*

MALTA. CENTRAL OFFICE OF STATISTICS. EDUCATION STATISTICS. see *EDUCATION — Abstracting, Bibliographies, Statistics*

314.585 MM ISSN 0025-1437
MALTA. CENTRAL OFFICE OF STATISTICS. QUARTERLY DIGEST OF STATISTICS. 1960. q. £0.75. Central Office of Statistics, Auberge d'Italie, Merchants' St., Valletta, Malta. FAX 356-248483. (Subscr. to: Publications Bookshop, Auberge de Castille, Valletta, Malta) (processed) **Document type:** government publication.

MALTA. CENTRAL OFFICE OF STATISTICS. SHIPPING AND AVIATION STATISTICS. see *TRANSPORTATION — Abstracting, Bibliographies, Statistics*

MALTA. DEPARTMENT OF INFORMATION. REPORTS ON THE WORKING OF GOVERNMENT DEPARTMENTS. see *PUBLIC ADMINISTRATION — Abstracting, Bibliographies, Statistics*

MANAGED HEALTH CARE OVERVIEW. see *INSURANCE — Abstracting, Bibliographies, Statistics*

STATISTICS

317.127   CN   ISSN 0700-2971
MANITOBA STATISTICAL REVIEW. 1972. q. Can.$55. Bureau of Statistics, 333 - 260 St. Mary Ave., Winnipeg, MB R3C 0M6, Canada. TEL 204-945-2985. FAX 204-945-0695. illus. circ. 220. **Indexed:** CS Ind. **Document type:** government publication.
    Incorporates (in Jan. 1979): Manitoba Price Statistics; **Formerly:** Manitoba Digest of Statistics.

330.9 316   MR   ISSN 0851-0946
LE MAROC EN CHIFFRES. (Editions in Arabic, French) 1961. a. DH.33. Direction de la Statistique, B.P. 178, Rabat, Morocco. TEL 212-7-77-36-06. FAX 212-7-77-32-17. TELEX 36714. (Co-sponsor: Banque Marocaine du Commerce Exterieur, Direction du Developpement) circ. 20,000 (6,000 Arabic Ed., 14,000 French Ed.). (also avail. in microfiche) **Document type:** government publication.

310   MQ   ISSN 0399-242X
HA918.9
MARTINIQUE. INSTITUT NATIONAL DE LA STATISTIQUE ET DES ETUDES ECONOMIQUES. BULLETIN DE STATISTIQUE. Key Title: Bulletin de Statistique (Martinique). 1964. a. Institut National de la Statistique et des Etudes Economiques, Service de Statistique de la Martinique, Pointe de Jaham, B.P. 7212, 97233 Schoelcher Cedex, Martinique. **Document type:** government publication.
    Formerly (until 1965): Martinique. Institut National de la Statistique et des Etudes Economiques. Bulletin Mensuel de Statistique (ISSN 0399-2411)

MASSACHUSETTS TAXPAYERS FOUNDATION. STATE BUDGET TRENDS. see *BUSINESS AND ECONOMICS — Abstracting, Bibliographies, Statistics*

316.6   MU   ISSN 0543-1433
MAURITANIA. DIRECTION DE LA STATISTIQUE ET DES ETUDES ECONOMIQUES. BULLETIN MENSUEL STATISTIQUE. (Text in French) m. 20 Fr.CFA. Direction de la Statistique et des Etudes Economiques, B.P. 240, Nouakchott, Mauritania. illus.

316.982   MF   ISSN 1013-6061
MAURITIUS. CENTRAL STATISTICAL OFFICE. ANNUAL DIGEST OF STATISTICS. 1961. a. Rs.100 (effective June 1995). Central Statistical Office, Toorawa Centre, Cr. S.S. R & J. Mosque Sts., Port Louis, Mauritius. TEL 230-234-5294. FAX 230-208-4011. (Subscr. to: Government Printing Office, Ramtoolah Bldg., Sir S. Ramgoolam St., Port Louis, Mauritius) stat. **Document type:** government publication.
    Former titles (until 1984): Mauritius. Central Statistical Office. Bi-Annual Digest of Statistics; Mauritius. Central Statistical Office. Quarterly Digest of Statistics; Mauritius. Central Statistical Office. Bi-Annual Digest of Statistics; Mauritius. Central Statistical Office. Quarterly Digest of Statistics (ISSN 0025-6056)

MAURITIUS. CENTRAL STATISTICAL OFFICE. DIGEST OF AGRICULTURAL STATISTICS. see *AGRICULTURE — Abstracting, Bibliographies, Statistics*

MAURITIUS. CENTRAL STATISTICAL OFFICE. DIGEST OF DEMOGRAPHIC STATISTICS. see *POPULATION STUDIES — Abstracting, Bibliographies, Statistics*

MAURITIUS. CENTRAL STATISTICAL OFFICE. DIGEST OF EDUCATIONAL STATISTICS. see *EDUCATION — Abstracting, Bibliographies, Statistics*

MAURITIUS. CENTRAL STATISTICAL OFFICE. DIGEST OF INDUSTRIAL STATISTICS. see *BUSINESS AND ECONOMICS — Abstracting, Bibliographies, Statistics*

MAURITIUS. CENTRAL STATISTICAL OFFICE. DIGEST OF LABOUR STATISTICS. see *BUSINESS AND ECONOMICS — Abstracting, Bibliographies, Statistics*

MAURITIUS. CENTRAL STATISTICAL OFFICE. DIGEST OF PUBLIC FINANCE STATISTICS. see *BUSINESS AND ECONOMICS — Abstracting, Bibliographies, Statistics*

MAURITIUS. CENTRAL STATISTICAL OFFICE. DIGEST OF ROAD TRANSPORT STATISTICS. see *TRANSPORTATION — Abstracting, Bibliographies, Statistics*

MAURITIUS. CENTRAL STATISTICAL OFFICE. EXTERNAL TRADE STATISTICS. see *BUSINESS AND ECONOMICS — Abstracting, Bibliographies, Statistics*

MAURITIUS. CENTRAL STATISTICAL OFFICE. INTERNATIONAL TRAVEL AND TOURISM STATISTICS. see *TRAVEL AND TOURISM — Abstracting, Bibliographies, Statistics*

316.982   MF
MAURITIUS. CENTRAL STATISTICAL OFFICE. STATISTICAL SUMMARY. 1978. a. Rs.30 (effective Jun. 1995). Central Statistical Office, Toorawa Centre, Cr. S.S. R & J. Mosque Sts., Port Louis, Mauritius. (Subscr. to: Government Printing Office, Ramtoolah Bldg., Sir S. Ramgoolam St., Port Louis, Mauritius). TEL 230-234-5294. FAX 230-208-4011) **Document type:** government publication.

MEASUREMENT METHODS FOR THE SOCIAL SCIENCES SERIES. see *METROLOGY AND STANDARDIZATION*

MENTAL HEALTH STATISTICAL NOTES. see *SOCIAL SERVICES AND WELFARE — Abstracting, Bibliographies, Statistics*

314   YU   ISSN 0350-4247
MESECNI STATISTICKI PREGLED. (Text in Serbian) 1952. m. 120 din.($15) Republicki Zavod za Statistiku, Bulevar Lenjina 4, Titograd, Yugoslavia. Ed. Andreja Stokic. circ. 310.

METALL STATISTIK. see *METALLURGY — Abstracting, Bibliographies, Statistics*

519.5   GW   ISSN 0026-1335
QA276.A1   CODEN: MTRKA8
METRIKA; international journal for theoretical and applied statistics. (Text in English) 1953. 6/yr. (in 2 vols., 3 nos./vol.). DM.498($361) (effective 1996). Physica-Verlag GmbH und Co., Postfach 105280, 69042 Heidelberg, Germany. TEL 06221-487492. FAX 06221-487177. (Subscr. to: Springer Verlag GmbH, Postfach 311540, 10643 Berlin, Germany. TEL 030-8207-424; Dist. in North America by: Springer-Verlag New York Inc., 175 Fifth Ave., New York, NY 10010, U.S.A.. TEL 212-460-1500) Eds. W. Uhlmann, F. Pukelsheim. adv.; bk.rev.; charts; index. circ. 1,000. (also avail. in microform from UMI; back issues avail.; reprint service avail. from SWZ) **Indexed:** Biostat., Curr.Cont., Curr.Ind.Stat., INSPEC, Int.Abstr.Oper.Res., J.Cont.Quant.Meth., Math.R., Stat.Theor.Meth.Abstr., Zent.Math. **Document type:** academic/scholarly publication.
    —BLDSC (5748.700000); Faxon; SWETS; UMI; UnCover. **CCC.**
    Description: Covers statistical methods and mathematical statistics: statistical quality control, sampling control, sampling theory, design of experiments.
    Refereed Serial

310   US
METRO MILWAUKEE MUNICIPAL DATA BOOK. a. $7 to members; non-members $15. Metropolitan Milwaukee Association of Commerce, Council of Small Business Executives, 756 N. Milwaukee St., Milwaukee, WI 53202. TEL 414-287-4100.
    Description: Features a detailed look of the Milwaukee market at the municipal level. Provides information on population trends, housing data, education and taxes.

519.5   IT   ISSN 0026-1424
HA1   CODEN: MRONAM
METRON; rivista internazionale di statistica. (Text in various European languages) 1920. s-a. DM.190 (typically set in Dec.). Universita degli Studi di Roma, Facolta di Scienze Statistiche Demografiche ed Attuariali, Dipartimento di Statistica, Probabilita e Stat. Applicate, Citta Universitaria, 00185 Rome, Italy. FAX 00396-4747743. (Dist. by: E S I A Books and Journals, Via Palestro, 30, 00185 Rome, Italy) Ed. Mario Badaloni. adv.; bk.rev.; abstr.; charts; stat.; index, cum.index. circ. 1,000. **Indexed:** Biol.Abstr., Curr.Cont., Math.R., Stat.Theor.Meth.Abstr. **Document type:** academic/scholarly publication.
    —BLDSC (5748.930000); Faxon; SWETS; UnCover.
    Description: Articles by mathematicians, statisticians and economists in the topics of demography, physics, biology and medicine.

310   US   ISSN 0741-9767
HG8963.M5
METROPOLITAN LIFE INSURANCE COMPANY. STATISTICAL BULLETIN S B. 1920. q. $50 to individuals (foreign $60); libraries $40. Metropolitan Life Insurance Company, 1 Madison Ave., New York, NY 10010. FAX 212-213-0577. Ed. Charles G. Hertz, M.D. charts; stat.; index. circ. 20,000. (also avail. in microfilm from UMI,BLH; microfiche from CIS; reprint service avail. from UMI) **Indexed:** B.P.I., Biol.Abstr., BPIA, Bus.Ind., Curr.Cont., Nutr.Abstr., P.A.I.S., SRI. **Document type:** bulletin.
    —Faxon; UMI; UnCover.
    Former titles (1982-1983): Metropolitan Life Foundation. Statistical Bulletin (ISSN 0736-4822); **(until 1981):** Statistical Bulletin - Metropolitan Life (ISSN 0026-1513)
    Description: Demographic and medical care data on health care coverage, focusing on charges across the nation, mortality trends, life table analyses, and profiles of major population groups.

MEXICO. INSTITUTO NACIONAL DE ESTADISTICA, GEOGRAFIA E INFORMATICA. ENCUESTA INDUSTRIAL MENSUAL; 129 clases de actividad. see *BUSINESS AND ECONOMICS — Abstracting, Bibliographies, Statistics*

317   MX   ISSN 0186-2707
HA37
MEXICO. INSTITUTO NACIONAL DE ESTADISTICA, GEOGRAFIA E INFORMATICA. REVISTA DE ESTADISTICA. 1938. irreg., vol.3, no.6, 1989. free. Instituto Nacional de Estadistica, Geografia e Informatica, Secretaria de Programacion y Presupuesto, Prol. Heroe de Nacozari 2301 Sur, Puerta 11, Acceso, 20270 Aguascalientes Ags., Mexico. TEL 49-18-19-48. FAX 491-807-39. (Subscr. to: Direccion General de Estudios del Territorio Nacional, Balderas 71, Col. Centro, Mexico 1, D.F., Mexico) mkt.; stat.; index. circ. 1,000.
    Formerly: Mexico. Direccion General de Estadistica. Revista de Estadistica y Geografia (ISSN 0026-1769)

MILLION DOLLAR PROJECT PLANNED LIST. see *ARCHITECTURE*

MINAS GERAIS, BRAZIL. DEPARTAMENTO DE ESTRADAS DE RODAGEM. SERVICO DE TRANSITO. ESTATISTICA DE TRAFEGO E ACIDENTES. see *TRANSPORTATION — Abstracting, Bibliographies, Statistics*

316   MZ
MOCAMBIQUE - INFORMACAO ESTATISTICA. 1982. m. (Comissao Nacional do Plano) Centro de Documentacao Economica, C.P. 2051, Maputo, Mozambique.

MONTANA. DEPARTMENT OF SOCIAL AND REHABILITATION SERVICES. STATISTICAL REPORT. see *SOCIAL SERVICES AND WELFARE — Abstracting, Bibliographies, Statistics*

MONTHLY ACTS TABLES & TABLE OF UNREPEALED PRINCIPAL ACTS. see *LAW — Abstracting, Bibliographies, Statistics*

MONTHLY LABOR REVIEW. see *BUSINESS AND ECONOMICS — Economic Situation And Conditions*

MONTHLY REPORT ON TOURISM - REPUBLIC OF CHINA/KUAN KUANG TZU LIAO. see *TRAVEL AND TOURISM — Abstracting, Bibliographies, Statistics*

315   BG   ISSN 0377-1555
HA1730.8
MONTHLY STATISTICAL BULLETIN OF BANGLADESH. (Supplement avail.: annual data) (Text in English) 1972. m. Tk.660($168) (effective Jan. 1995). Ministry of Planning, Statistics Division, Bureau of Statistics, Secretariat, Dhaka 2, Bangladesh. TEL 409871. Ed. Tgul Islam. circ. 300. **Document type:** government publication.
    Supersedes: Bangladesh. Bureau of Statistics. Monthly Bulletin of Statistics (ISSN 0012-849X)
    Description: Presents current data on performance of family planning, labor and employment, wages, agriculture, meteorology, industrial production, transport and communication, foreign trade, national income accounts, as well as public finance and accounting.

315.19   KO   ISSN 0027-0563
MONTHLY STATISTICS OF KOREA. (Text in English, Korean) 1958. m. 3000 Won($6) National Statistical Office, Hanta Bldg., 647-15, Yoksam-dong, Kangnam-gu, Seoul 135-080, S. Korea. TEL 02-222-1971. (Subscr. to: the Korean Statistical Association, Room 302, Chungok Building, 561-30, Sinsa-dong, Gangnam-gu, Seoul 135-120, S. Korea. TEL 02-517-0382. FAX 02-725-4347) stat.; index. circ. 1,800.

MONTHLY STATUTORY RULES TABLES & TABLE OF UNREVOKED PRINCIPAL STATUTORY RULES. see *LAW* — *Abstracting, Bibliographies, Statistics*

310   382   MJ   ISSN 0303-447X
MONTSERRAT. STATISTICS OFFICE. OVERSEAS TRADE REPORT. Key Title: Overseas Trade (Plymouth). irreg. Statistics Office, Plymouth, Monserrat. **Document type:** government publication.

312   MR   ISSN 0256-9159
HC810.A1
MOROCCO. DIRECTION DE LA STATISTIQUE. BULLETIN MENSUEL DES STATISTIQUES. (Text in Arabic, French) q. DH.363. Direction de la Statistique, B.P. 178, Rabat, Morocco. TEL 212-7-77-36-06. FAX 212-7-77-32-17. TELEX 36714. **Document type:** government publication.

MOROCCO. DIRECTION DE LA STATISTIQUE. INDICE DES PRIX A LA PRODUCTION INDUSTRIELLE, ENERGETIQUE ET MINIERE. see *BUSINESS AND ECONOMICS* — *Abstracting, Bibliographies, Statistics*

MOROCCO. DIRECTION DE LA STATISTIQUE. INDICE DU COUT DE LA VIE. see *BUSINESS AND ECONOMICS* — *Abstracting, Bibliographies, Statistics*

MOROCCO. DIRECTION DE LA STATISTIQUE. POPULATION ACTIVE URBAINE, PREMIERS RESULTATS. see *POPULATION STUDIES* — *Abstracting, Bibliographies, Statistics*

MOROCCO. DIRECTION DE LA STATISTIQUE. POPULATION ACTIVE URBAINE, RESULTATS DETAILLES. see *POPULATION STUDIES* — *Abstracting, Bibliographies, Statistics*

MOTORFAHRZEUGE IN DER SCHWEIZ. EINGEFUEHRTE MOTORFAHRZEUGE/VEHICULES A MOTEUR EN SUISSE. VEHICULES A MOTEUR IMPORTES. see *TRANSPORTATION* — *Abstracting, Bibliographies, Statistics*

MOTORFAHRZEUGE IN DER SCHWEIZ. MOTORFAHRZEUGBESTAND IN DER SCHWEIZ AM 30. SEPTEMBER (YEAR)/VEHICULES A MOTEUR EN SUISSE. EFFECTIF DES VEHICULES A MOTEUR EN SUISSE AU 30 SEPTEMBRE (YEAR). see *TRANSPORTATION* — *Abstracting, Bibliographies, Statistics*

MOVERS STATISTICAL PROFILE (YEAR); demographic, economic and financial data of the moving industry. see *TRANSPORTATION* — *Abstracting, Bibliographies, Statistics*

MUSIC U S A; annual statistical review of the musical instrument industry. see *MUSIC*

310   PH   ISSN 0115-2092
HA1821
N S O MONTHLY BULLETIN OF STATISTICS. (Text in English) m. $6 per no. National Statistics Office, Ramon Magsaysay blvd., P.O. Box 779, Manila, Philippines. FAX 610794. circ. 250. **Indexed:** Ind.Phil.Per.

N Z T B VISITOR STATISTICS RESEARCH SERIES. (New Zealand Tourism Board) see *TRAVEL AND TOURISM* — *Abstracting, Bibliographies, Statistics*

NARCOTIC DRUGS: ESTIMATED WORLD REQUIREMENTS FOR (YEAR). see *PHARMACY AND PHARMACOLOGY* — *Abstracting, Bibliographies, Statistics*

310   RU
NARODNOE KHOZYAISTVO ALTAISKOGO KRAYA. 1967. every 5 yrs. (Tsentral'noe Statisticheskoe Upravlenie) Redaktsionno-Poligraficheskoe Proizvodstvennoe Ob'edinenie "Soyuzblankoizdat", Altaiskoe Redaktsionno-Proizvodstvennoe Otdelenie, B. Olonskaya 28, Barnaul, Russia. Ed. Olga Zamiatina. stat. circ. 5,000.

NATIONAL ACCOUNTS OF THE MALTESE ISLANDS. see *BUSINESS AND ECONOMICS* — *Public Finance, Taxation*

NATIONAL AGRICULTURAL STATISTICS SERVICE. CATTLE ON FEED. see *AGRICULTURE* — *Abstracting, Bibliographies, Statistics*

NATIONAL BANK OF LIBERIA. QUARTERLY STATISTICAL BULLETIN. see *BUSINESS AND ECONOMICS* — *Banking And Finance*

NATIONAL COAL ASSOCIATION. WEEKLY STATISTICAL SUMMARY. see *MINES AND MINING INDUSTRY* — *Abstracting, Bibliographies, Statistics*

NATIONAL INCOME AND PRODUCT ACCOUNTS OF THE UNITED STATES: STATISTICAL TABLES. see *BUSINESS AND ECONOMICS* — *Abstracting, Bibliographies, Statistics*

NATIONAL SURVEY OF PROFESSIONAL, ADMINISTRATIVE, TECHNICAL AND CLERICAL PAY. see *BUSINESS AND ECONOMICS* — *Economic Situation And Conditions*

318   AG
NATIONAL TERRITORY OF TIERRA DEL FUEGO, ANTARCTICA AND ISLANDS OF THE SOUTH ATLANTIC. MINISTERIO DE ECONOMIA Y HACIENDA. ANUARIO ESTADISTICO. a. free. Ministerio de Economia y Hacienda, San Martin 450 PB, Of. 119, 9410 Ushuaia, Argentina.

NAVAL RESEARCH LOGISTICS: AN INTERNATIONAL JOURNAL. see *MILITARY* — *Abstracting, Bibliographies, Statistics*

NEBRASKA STATISTICAL HANDBOOK. see *PUBLIC ADMINISTRATION* — *Abstracting, Bibliographies, Statistics*

634.9   NE
NEDERLANDSE BOSSTATISTIEK. 1952. irreg. Centraal Bureau voor de Statistiek, Prinses Beatrixlaan 428, Voorburg, Netherlands. (Dist. by: SDU - Publishers, Christoffel Plantijnstraat, The Hague, Netherlands) circ. 650. **Document type:** government publication.

NEDERLANDSE JEUGD EN HAAR ONDERWIJS/NETHERLANDS YOUTH AND ITS EDUCATION. see *EDUCATION* — *Abstracting, Bibliographies, Statistics*

315.49   NP
NEPAL. CENTRAL BUREAU OF STATISTICS. STATISTICAL POCKET BOOK. (Text in English) 1974. biennial. $1. Central Bureau of Statistics, Ramshah Path, Thapathali, Kathmandu, Nepal. TEL 977-1-213413. FAX 977-1-227720. illus. circ. 7,000.

310   NP
NEPAL AND THE WORLD; a statistical profile. (Text in English) 1992. a. Rs.300($6) Federation of Nepalese Chambers of Commerce and Industry, P.O. Box 269, Teku, Kathmandu, Nepal. TEL 977-1-233196. FAX 977-1-227322. TELEX 2786 FNCCI NP. Ed. Binod H. Hoshi. **Document type:** trade publication.
    Description: Contains wide range of statistics related to trade, industry, tourism and planning of Nepal. Compares Nepal's economy with the South Asian nations and the rest of the world.

NETHERLANDS. CENTRAAL BUREAU VOOR DE STATISTIEK. CIVIL AND ADMINISTRATIVE JURISDICTION. BURGERLIJKE EN ADMINISTRATIEVE RECHTSPRAAK. see *LAW*

NETHERLANDS. CENTRAAL BUREAU VOOR DE STATISTIEK. CRIMINALITEIT STRAFRECHTSPLEGING. see *CRIMINOLOGY AND LAW ENFORCEMENT* — *Abstracting, Bibliographies, Statistics*

NETHERLANDS. CENTRAAL BUREAU VOOR DE STATISTIEK. INSTITUTIONELE BELEGGERS. see *BUSINESS AND ECONOMICS* — *Abstracting, Bibliographies, Statistics*

NETHERLANDS. CENTRAAL BUREAU VOOR DE STATISTIEK. JAARSTATISTIEK VAN DE BEVOLKING/NETHERLANDS. CENTRAL BUREAU OF STATISTICS. ANNUAL POPULATION STATISTICS. see *POPULATION STUDIES* — *Abstracting, Bibliographies, Statistics*

NETHERLANDS. CENTRAAL BUREAU VOOR DE STATISTIEK. KWARTAALBERICHT RECHTSBESCHERMING EN VEILIGHEID/NETHERLANDS. CENTRAL BUREAU OF STATISTICS. QUARTERLY BULLETIN ON JUSTICE AND SECURITY STATISTICS. see *LAW* — *Abstracting, Bibliographies, Statistics*

314.92   NE   ISSN 0166-0268
NETHERLANDS. CENTRAAL BUREAU VOOR DE STATISTIEK. MAANDSCHRIFT. (Title and contents page in Dutch and English) 1906. m. fl.100. Centraal Bureau voor de Statistiek, Prinses Beatrixlaan 428, Voorburg, Netherlands. (Dist. by: SDU - Publishers, Christoffel Plantijnstraat, The Hague, Netherlands) **Document type:** government publication.

NETHERLANDS. CENTRAAL BUREAU VOOR DE STATISTIEK. MAANDSTATISTIEK VAN DE BEVOLKING. see *POPULATION STUDIES* — *Abstracting, Bibliographies, Statistics*

NETHERLANDS. CENTRAAL BUREAU VOOR DE STATISTIEK. MAANDSTATISTIEK VAN DE LANDBOUW. see *AGRICULTURE* — *Abstracting, Bibliographies, Statistics*

NETHERLANDS. CENTRAAL BUREAU VOOR DE STATISTIEK. NEDERLANDSE ENERGIEHUISHOUDING. see *ENVIRONMENTAL STUDIES* — *Abstracting, Bibliographies, Statistics*

NETHERLANDS. CENTRAAL BUREAU VOOR DE STATISTIEK. PRODUKTIESTATISTIEKEN: VEEVOEDERINDUSTRIE. see *AGRICULTURE* — *Abstracting, Bibliographies, Statistics*

314   NE   ISSN 0168-3756
NETHERLANDS. CENTRAAL BUREAU VOOR DE STATISTIEK. REGIONAAL STATISTISCH ZAKBOEK. a. Centraal Bureau voor de Statistiek, Prinses Beatrixlaan 428, Voorburg, Netherlands. (Dist. by: SDU - Publishers, Christoffel Plantijnstraat, The Hague, Netherlands) **Document type:** government publication.

310   NE
NETHERLANDS. CENTRAAL BUREAU VOOR DE STATISTIEK. STATISTICAL STUDIES. 1953. irreg. price varies. Centraal Bureau voor de Statistiek, Prinses Beatrixlaan 428, Voorburg, Netherlands. **Document type:** government publication.

NETHERLANDS. CENTRAAL BUREAU VOOR DE STATISTIEK. STATISTIEK DER BRANDEN/NETHERLANDS. CENTRAL BUREAU OF STATISTICS. FIRE STATISTICS. see *FIRE PREVENTION* — *Abstracting, Bibliographies, Statistics*

NETHERLANDS. CENTRAAL BUREAU VOOR DE STATISTIEK. STATISTIEK VAN DE VAARWAGEN. see *TRANSPORTATION* — *Abstracting, Bibliographies, Statistics*

NETHERLANDS. CENTRAAL BUREAU VOOR DE STATISTIEK. STATISTIEK VAN DE ZEEVAART/NETHERLANDS. CENTRAL BUREAU OF STATISTICS. STATISTICS OF SEABORNE SHIPPING. see *TRANSPORTATION* — *Abstracting, Bibliographies, Statistics*

NETHERLANDS. CENTRAAL BUREAU VOOR DE STATISTIEK. STATISTIEK VAN DE INTERNATIONALE BINNENVAART/NETHERLANDS. CENTRAL BUREAU OF STATISTICS. STATISTICS OF THE INTERNATIONAL INLAND SHIPPING. see *TRANSPORTATION* — *Abstracting, Bibliographies, Statistics*

NETHERLANDS. CENTRAAL BUREAU VOOR DE STATISTIEK. STATISTIEK VAN DE INVESTERINGEN IN VASTE ACTIVA IN DE NIJVERHEID/NETHERLANDS. CENTRAAL BUREAU OF STATISTICS. STATISTICS ON FIXED CAPITAL FORMATION IN INDUSTRY. see *BUSINESS AND ECONOMICS* — *Abstracting, Bibliographies, Statistics*

6216 STATISTICS

NETHERLANDS. CENTRAAL BUREAU VOOR DE STATISTIEK. STATISTIEK VAN DE KOOPVAARDIJVLOOT/NETHERLANDS. CENTRAL BUREAU OF STATISTICS. STATISTICS OF THE MERCHANT MARINE. see *TRANSPORTATION — Abstracting, Bibliographies, Statistics*

NETHERLANDS. CENTRAAL BUREAU VOOR DE STATISTIEK. STATISTIEK VAN HET ERKENDE SCHRIFTELIJK ONDERWIJS/NETHERLANDS. CENTRAL BUREAU OF STATISTICS. STATISTICS ON CORRESPONDENCE COURSES. see *EDUCATION — Teaching Methods And Curriculum*

NETHERLANDS. CENTRAAL BUREAU VOOR DE STATISTIEK. STATISTIEK VAN HET PERSONENVERVOER/NETHERLANDS. CENTRAL BUREAU OF STATISTICS. STATISTICS OF PASSENGER TRANSPORT. see *TRANSPORTATION — Abstracting, Bibliographies, Statistics*

NETHERLANDS. CENTRAAL BUREAU VOOR DE STATISTIEK. STATISTIEK VAN HET BINNENLANDS GOEDERENVERVOER. STATISTICS OF INTERNAL GOODS TRANSPORT IN THE NETHERLANDS. see *TRANSPORTATION — Abstracting, Bibliographies, Statistics*

310　　　　NE　ISSN 0166-9680
NETHERLANDS. CENTRAAL BUREAU VOOR DE STATISTIEK. STATISTISCH BULLETIN. irreg. Centraal Bureau voor de Statistiek, Prinses Beatrixlaan 428, Voorburg, Netherlands. (Dist. by: CBS, P.O. Box 959, 2270 AZ Voorburg, Netherlands) circ. 3,500. **Document type:** government publication.
—SWETS.

310　　　　NE　ISSN 0168-3705
NETHERLANDS. CENTRAAL BUREAU VOOR DE STATISTIEK. STATISTISCH ZAKBOEK/NETHERLANDS. CENTRAL BUREAU OF STATISTICS. POCKET YEARBOOK. (Text in Dutch, English) 1944. a. Centraal Bureau voor de Statistiek, Prinses Beatrixlaan 428, Voorburg, Netherlands. (Dist. by: SDU - Publishers, Christoffel Plantijnstraat 2, Postbus 20014, 2500 EA The Hague, Netherlands) **Document type:** government publication.

NETHERLANDS. CENTRAAL BUREAU VOOR DE STATISTIEK. STATISTISCHE ONDERZOEKINGEN. see *BUSINESS AND ECONOMICS — Abstracting, Bibliographies, Statistics*

314　　　　NE　ISSN 0922-5897
NETHERLANDS. CENTRALE COMMISSIE VOOR DE STATISTIEK. JAARVERSLAG. 1899. a. free. Centrale Commissie voor de Statistiek, P.O. Box 4000, 2270 JM Voorburg, Netherlands. FAX 31-70-3877453. TELEX 32692-CBS-NL. Ed. J.R. Nobel. circ. 900. **Document type:** government publication.
Description: Covers activities and meetings of the commission and its sub-commissions.

NEW BRUNSWICK. TOURISM RECREATION & HERITAGE. TECHNICAL SERVICES BRANCH. PROVINCIAL PARK STATISTICS. see *CONSERVATION — Abstracting, Bibliographies, Statistics*

NEW CALEDONIA. INSTITUT TERRITORIAL DE LA STATISTIQUE ET DES ETUDES ECONOMIQUES. BULLETIN DE CONJONCTURE. see *BUSINESS AND ECONOMICS — Abstracting, Bibliographies, Statistics*

NEW CALEDONIA. INSTITUT TERRITORIAL DE LA STATISTIQUE ET DES ETUDES ECONOMIQUES. INDICES DES PRIX A LA CONSOMMATION. see *BUSINESS AND ECONOMICS — Abstracting, Bibliographies, Statistics*

330.9 319　　　NL　ISSN 0336-4062
HA4007.N4
NEW CALEDONIA. INSTITUT TERRITORIAL DE LA STATISTIQUE ET DES ETUDES ECONOMIQUES. INFORMATIONS STATISTIQUES RAPIDES. 1972. m. CFPF2600 (foreign CFPF4400). Institut Territorial de la Statistique et des Etudes Economiques, P.O. Box 823, Noumea, New Caledonia. TEL 27-54-81. FAX 28-81-48. Ed. Ph. Maesse. adv. circ. 1,200. **Document type:** government publication.
Formerly: New Caledonia. Service de la Statistique. Nouvelle Caledonie et Dependences. Bulletin de Statistique. (ISSN 0336-3945)

NEW CALEDONIA. INSTITUT TERRITORIAL DE LA STATISTIQUE ET DES ETUDES ECONOMIQUES. TABLEAUX DE L'ECONOMIE CALEDONIENNE. see *BUSINESS AND ECONOMICS — Abstracting, Bibliographies, Statistics*

NEW HAMPSHIRE VITAL STATISTICS. see *POPULATION STUDIES — Abstracting, Bibliographies, Statistics*

NEW JERSEY PUBLIC LIBRARY STATISTICS FOR (YEAR). see *LIBRARY AND INFORMATION SCIENCES — Abstracting, Bibliographies, Statistics*

NEW SOUTH WALES COAL YEARBOOK (YEAR). see *MINES AND MINING INDUSTRY — Abstracting, Bibliographies, Statistics*

NEW TRENDS IN PROBABILITY AND STATISTICS. see *MATHEMATICS*

NEW YORK (STATE). DEPARTMENT OF SOCIAL SERVICES. SOCIAL STATISTICS. see *SOCIAL SERVICES AND WELFARE — Abstracting, Bibliographies, Statistics*

317　　　　US　ISSN 0077-9334
HA541
NEW YORK STATE STATISTICAL YEARBOOK. 1967. a. $54. Nelson A. Rockefeller Institute of Government, 411 State St., Albany, NY 12203-1003. FAX 518-443-5788. Ed. Michael Cooper. index. circ. 3,000. (also avail. in microfiche from CIS) **Indexed:** SRI. **Document type:** government publication.
Description: Contains statistical information on New York State, as well as select U.S. data. Gives complete descriptions of each state agency and the name and phone number of a contact at each agency.

NEW ZEALAND. DEPARTMENT OF STATISTICS. CONSUMER EXPENDITURE. see *BUSINESS AND ECONOMICS — Abstracting, Bibliographies, Statistics*

NEW ZEALAND. DEPARTMENT OF STATISTICS. DEMOGRAPHIC TRENDS. see *POPULATION STUDIES — Abstracting, Bibliographies, Statistics*

NEW ZEALAND. DEPARTMENT OF STATISTICS. INCOMES. see *BUSINESS AND ECONOMICS — Abstracting, Bibliographies, Statistics*

319　　　　NZ　ISSN 0114-2119
HA3032
NEW ZEALAND. DEPARTMENT OF STATISTICS. KEY STATISTICS; a monthly abstract of statistics. m. (except Jan.). NZ$295. Department of Statistics, P.O. Box 2922, Wellington, New Zealand. charts; mkt.; stat. circ. 2,400. **Document type:** government publication.
—CCC.
Formerly: New Zealand. Department of Statistics. Monthly Abstract of Statistics (ISSN 0027-0180)

NEW ZEALAND. DEPARTMENT OF STATISTICS. POPULATION CENSUS: INTERNAL MIGRATION. see *POPULATION STUDIES — Abstracting, Bibliographies, Statistics*

NEW ZEALAND. DEPARTMENT OF STATISTICS. POPULATION CENSUS: TOTAL POPULATION STATISTICS. see *POPULATION STUDIES — Abstracting, Bibliographies, Statistics*

NEW ZEALAND. HEALTH STATISTICAL SERVICES. CLIENT SERVICES NEWSLETTER. see *PUBLIC HEALTH AND SAFETY*

NEW ZEALAND HEALTH INFORMATION SERVICE. FETAL AND INFANT DEATHS. see *POPULATION STUDIES — Abstracting, Bibliographies, Statistics*

311　　　　NZ　ISSN 0111-9176
NEW ZEALAND STATISTICIAN. 1966. 2/yr. NZ$37 (foreign NZ$48) (effective 1995). New Zealand Statistical Association (Inc.), P.O. Box 1731, Wellington, New Zealand. TEL 64-6-350-4265. FAX 64-6-350-5611. E-mail: H.Morton@massey.ac.nz. Ed. R.H. Morton. adv.; bk.rev.; abstr.; stat. circ. 350. **Indexed:** Curr.Ind.Stat. **Document type:** academic/scholarly publication.
—BLDSC (6099.425000). **CCC.**
Refereed Serial

318.6　　　　NQ
NICARAGUA EN CIFRAS. irreg., latest 1991. Instituto Nacional de Estadisticas y Censos, Apdo. Postal 4031, Managua, Nicaragua. circ. 2,000. **Document type:** government publication.

316.6　　　　NG
NIGER. DIRECTION DE LA STATISTIQUE ET DES COMPTES NATIONAUX. BULLETIN TRIMESTRIEL DE STATISTIQUE. q. 1200 F. Direction de la Statistique et des Comptes Nationaux, Ministere du Plan, Niamey, Niger. illus.
Former titles: Niger. Ministere du Developpement et de la Cooperation. Direction de la Statistique. Bulletin de Statistique; Niger. Service de la Statistique. Bulletin Trimestriel de Statistique (ISSN 0545-9516)

NIGERIA. FEDERAL MINISTRY OF LABOUR AND PRODUCTIVITY. QUARTERLY BULLETIN OF LABOUR STATISTICS. see *BUILDING AND CONSTRUCTION — Abstracting, Bibliographies, Statistics*

316　　　　NR　ISSN 0078-0626
HA1977.N5
NIGERIA. FEDERAL OFFICE OF STATISTICS. ANNUAL ABSTRACT OF STATISTICS. (Text in English) a. $25. Federal Office of Statistics, P.M.B. 12528, Nigeria.

NIGERIA. FEDERAL OFFICE OF STATISTICS. BUILDING AND CONSTRUCTION SURVEY. see *BUILDING AND CONSTRUCTION — Abstracting, Bibliographies, Statistics*

316　　　　NR　ISSN 0029-0017
NIGERIA. FEDERAL OFFICE OF STATISTICS. DIGEST OF STATISTICS. 1952. q. £N15($15) Federal Office of Statistics, P.M.B. 12528, Nigeria. stat.

NIGERIA. FEDERAL OFFICE OF STATISTICS. INDUSTRIAL SURVEY. see *BUSINESS AND ECONOMICS — Abstracting, Bibliographies, Statistics*

NIGERIA. FEDERAL OFFICE OF STATISTICS. REPORT ON GENERAL CONSUMER SURVEY REPORT. see *BUSINESS AND ECONOMICS — Abstracting, Bibliographies, Statistics*

NIGERIA. FEDERAL OFFICE OF STATISTICS. REPORT ON GENERAL HOUSEHOLD. see *BUSINESS AND ECONOMICS — Abstracting, Bibliographies, Statistics*

NIGERIA. FEDERAL OFFICE OF STATISTICS. REPORT ON GENERAL HOUSEHOLD SURVEY. see *HOUSING AND URBAN PLANNING — Abstracting, Bibliographies, Statistics*

NIGERIA. FEDERAL OFFICE OF STATISTICS. REPORT ON NATIONAL CONSUMER SURVEY. see *BUSINESS AND ECONOMICS — Abstracting, Bibliographies, Statistics*

NIGERIA. FEDERAL OFFICE OF STATISTICS. REPORT ON URBAN HOUSEHOLD SURVEY. see *HOUSING AND URBAN PLANNING — Abstracting, Bibliographies, Statistics*

NIGERIA. FEDERAL OFFICE OF STATISTICS. SOCIAL STATISTICS IN NIGERIA. see *SOCIAL SCIENCES: COMPREHENSIVE WORKS — Abstracting, Bibliographies, Statistics*

NIGERIA. KANO (STATE) PUBLIC FINANCE STATISTICS OF KANO STATE & LOCAL GOVERNMENT COUNCILS. see *BUSINESS AND ECONOMICS — Abstracting, Bibliographies, Statistics*

NIGERIA. NATIONAL UNIVERSITIES COMMISSION. STATISTICAL DIGEST. see *EDUCATION — Higher Education*

NIHON SUGAKKAI KOEN ABUSUTORAKUTO. TOKEI SUGAKU BUNKAKAI. see *MATHEMATICS — Abstracting, Bibliographies, Statistics*

519.5 US ISSN 1048-5252
QA278.8 CODEN: NOSTEK
NONPARAMETRIC STATISTICS. 1991. 4/yr. 116 ECU (effective 1996). Gordon and Breach Science Publishers, c/o International Publishers Distributor, 820 Town Center Dr., Langhorne, PA 19047. TEL 215-750-2642. FAX 215-750-6343. (Subscr. to: International Publishers Distributors, P.O. Box 90, Reading, Berkshire RG1 8JL, England. TEL 44-173-456-8316) Ed. Ibrahim A. Ahmad. (also avail. in microform) **Indexed:** Curr.Ind.Stat. —BLDSC (5022.842200); SWETS. **CCC.**
 Refereed Serial

314 DK ISSN 0078-1088
DL1
NORDISK STATISTISK AARSBOK/YEARBOOK OF NORDIC STATISTICS. (Subseries of: NORD) (Text in English and Swedish) 1962. a. DKK 248 (typically set in Feb.- Mar.). Nordic Council of Ministers, Store Strandstraede 18, DK-1255 Copenhagen Oe, Denmark. TEL 45-39-17-39-17. FAX 45-31-18-48-01. (Dist. by: Allmaenna Foerlaget AB, 106 47, Stockholm, Sweden) (Co-sponsor: Nordic Statistical Secretariat, Sejroegade 11, DK-2100, Copenhagen Oe, Denmark) Ed. Harry de Sharengrad. (also avail. in microfiche from CIS) **Indexed:** IIS.
 Description: Presents statistical information on the five Nordic countries; Denmark, Finland, Iceland, Norway and Sweden, including selected data for Greenland, the Faroe Islands and Aaland.

310 DK ISSN 0106-9039
HA1461
NORDISK STATISTISK SEKRETARIAT. TEKNISKE RAPPORTER/NORDIC STATISTICAL SECRETARIAT. TECHNICAL REPORTS. (Text in Scandinavian languages; summaries in English) 1968. irreg., no.60, 1995. Nordisk Statistisk Sekretariat - Nordic Statistical Secretariat, Sejroegade 11, DK-2100 Copenhagen OE, Denmark. TEL 45-39-17-39-82. FAX 45-31-18-51-22.

314.8 DK ISSN 0078-1096
HD7198
NORDISK STATISTISK SKRIFTSERIE/STATISTICAL REPORTS OF THE NORDIC COUNTRIES. (Text in Scandinavian languages; editions occasionally in English) 1954. irreg., no.64, 1993. price varies. Nordisk Statistisk Sekretariat - Nordic Statistical Secretariat, Sejroegade 11, DK-2100 Copenhagen OE, Denmark. TEL 45-39-17-39-82. FAX 45-31-18-51-22. circ. 3,000. **Document type:** monographic series.

NORDRHEIN-WESTFAELISCHEN INDUSTRIE- UND HANDELSKAMMER. STATISTISCHES JAHRBUCH. see *BUSINESS AND ECONOMICS — Abstracting, Bibliographies, Statistics*

310 GW ISSN 0468-656X
NORDRHEIN-WESTFALEN. STATISTISCHES JAHRBUCH. 1949. a. DM.48. Landesamt fuer Datenverarbeitung und Statistik Nordrhein-Westfalen, Postfach 101105, 40002 Duesseldorf, Germany. TEL 0211-9449-01. FAX 0211-442006. circ. 2,000. **Document type:** government publication. —BLDSC (8454.826000).
 Formerly: Duesseldorf. Statistisches Jahrbuch.

NORTH CAROLINA. DIVISION OF SOCIAL SERVICES. STATISTICAL JOURNAL. see *SOCIAL SERVICES AND WELFARE — Abstracting, Bibliographies, Statistics*

NORTH CAROLINA REPORTED PREGNANCIES. see *BIRTH CONTROL — Abstracting, Bibliographies, Statistics*

NORTH CAROLINA VITAL STATISTICS. see *POPULATION STUDIES — Abstracting, Bibliographies, Statistics*

NORTH DAKOTA. JUDICIAL SYSTEM. ANNUAL REPORT. see *LAW — Abstracting, Bibliographies, Statistics*

NORTH PACIFIC ANADROMOUS FISH COMMISSION. STATISTICAL YEARBOOK. see *FISH AND FISHERIES — Abstracting, Bibliographies, Statistics*

NORWAY. STATISTISK SENTRALBYRAA. ARBEIDSMARKEDSTATISTIKK - LABOUR MARKET STATISTICS. see *BUSINESS AND ECONOMICS — Abstracting, Bibliographies, Statistics*

NORWAY. STATISTISK SENTRALBYRAA. BEFOLKNINGSSTATISTIKK HEFTE 2/NORWAY. CENTRAL BUREAU OF STATISTICS. POPULATION STATISTICS VOL.2. see *POPULATION STUDIES — Abstracting, Bibliographies, Statistics*

NORWAY. STATISTISK SENTRALBYRAA. FISKERISTATISTIKK. see *FISH AND FISHERIES — Abstracting, Bibliographies, Statistics*

NORWAY. STATISTISK SENTRALBYRAA. HELSEINSTITUSJONER. see *MEDICAL SCIENCES — Abstracting, Bibliographies, Statistics*

NORWAY. STATISTISK SENTRALBYRAA. HELSEPERSONELLSTATISTIKK. see *MEDICAL SCIENCES — Abstracting, Bibliographies, Statistics*

NORWAY. STATISTISK SENTRALBYRAA. HELSESTATISTIKK/HEALTH STATISTICS. see *PUBLIC HEALTH AND SAFETY — Abstracting, Bibliographies, Statistics*

NORWAY. STATISTISK SENTRALBYRAA. INDUSTRISTATISTIKK VOL.1/INDUSTRIAL STATISTICS. VOL.1. see *BUSINESS AND ECONOMICS — Abstracting, Bibliographies, Statistics*

NORWAY. STATISTISK SENTRALBYRAA. JORDBRUKSSTATISTIKK/AGRICULTURAL STATISTICS. see *AGRICULTURE — Abstracting, Bibliographies, Statistics*

NORWAY. STATISTISK SENTRALBYRAA. KOMMUNESTYREVALGET/NORWAY. CENTRAL BUREAU OF STATISTICS. MUNICIPAL AND COUNTY ELECTIONS. see *PUBLIC ADMINISTRATION — Abstracting, Bibliographies, Statistics*

NORWAY. STATISTISK SENTRALBYRAA. KRIMINALSTATISTIKK/CRIMINAL STATISTICS. see *CRIMINOLOGY AND LAW ENFORCEMENT — Abstracting, Bibliographies, Statistics*

NORWAY. STATISTISK SENTRALBYRAA. LOENNSSTATISTIKK/WAGE STATISTICS. see *BUSINESS AND ECONOMICS — Abstracting, Bibliographies, Statistics*

NORWAY. STATISTISK SENTRALBYRAA. NASJONALREGNSKAP/NATIONAL ACCOUNTS STATISTICS. see *BUSINESS AND ECONOMICS — Abstracting, Bibliographies, Statistics*

NORWAY. STATISTISK SENTRALBYRAA. REISELIVSTATISTIK/STATISTICS ON TRAVEL. see *TRAVEL AND TOURISM — Abstracting, Bibliographies, Statistics*

NORWAY. STATISTISK SENTRALBYRAA. SAMFERDSELSSTATISTIKK/NORWAY. CENTRAL BUREAU OF STATISTICS. TRANSPORT AND COMMUNICATION STATISTICS. see *TRANSPORTATION — Abstracting, Bibliographies, Statistics*

NORWAY. STATISTISK SENTRALBYRAA. SKOGSTATSTIKK. see *FORESTS AND FORESTRY — Abstracting, Bibliographies, Statistics*

314.81 NO ISSN 0377-8908
HA1501
NORWAY. STATISTISK SENTRALBYRAA. STATISTISK AARBOK/STATISTICAL YEARBOOK. (Subseries of its Norges Offisielle Statistikk) (Text in English, Norwegian) 1880. a. NOK 95. Statistisk Sentralbyraa, P.O. Box 8131 Dep., N-0033 Oslo, Norway. TEL 47-22-864500. FAX 47-22-864976. circ. 35,000. **Document type:** government publication.

314.81 NO ISSN 0029-3636
NORWAY. STATISTISK SENTRALBYRAA. STATISTISK MAANEDSHEFTE/MONTHLY BULLETIN OF STATISTICS. (Text in English, Norwegian) 1882. m. NOK 430. Statistisk Sentralbyraa, P.O. Box 8131 Dep., N-0033 Oslo, Norway. TEL 47-22-864500. FAX 47-22-864976. stat. circ. 3,350. **Document type:** government publication.

NORWAY. STATISTISK SENTRALBYRAA. STORTINGSVALG/NORWAY. CENTRAL BUREAU OF STATISTICS. PARLIAMENTARY ELECTIONS. see *PUBLIC ADMINISTRATION — Abstracting, Bibliographies, Statistics*

314.81 NO ISSN 0804-0524
HA1503
NORWAY. STATISTISK SENTRALBYRAA. UKENS STATISTIKK. 1960. w. NOK 620. Statistisk Sentralbyraa, P.O. Box 8131-Dep., N-0033 Oslo, Norway. TEL 47-22-864500. FAX 47-22-864976. stat. circ. 2,100. **Document type:** government publication.
 Formerly (until 1992): Norway. Statistisk Sentralbyraa. Statistiske Ukehefte (ISSN 0550-0567)

NORWAY. STATISTISK SENTRALBYRAA. UTDANNINGSSTATISTIKK. OVERSIKT. see *EDUCATION — Abstracting, Bibliographies, Statistics*

NORWAY. STATISTISK SENTRALBYRAA. UTENRIKSHANDEL/NORWAY. CENTRAL BUREAU OF STATISTICS. EXTERNAL TRADE. see *BUSINESS AND ECONOMICS — Abstracting, Bibliographies, Statistics*

NORWAY. STATISTISK SENTRALBYRAA. VAREHANDELSSTATISTIKK/WHOLESALE AND RETAIL TRADE STATISTICS. see *BUSINESS AND ECONOMICS — Abstracting, Bibliographies, Statistics*

314.81 NO ISSN 0801-079X
NORWAY. STATISTISK SENTRALBYRAA. VEJVISER I NORSK STATISTIKK/GUIDE TO NORWEGIAN STATISTICS. 1963. irreg. free. Statistisk Sentralbyraa - Central Bureau of Statistics, P.O. Box 8131 Dep., N-0033 Oslo 1, Norway. TEL 47-22-86-45-00. FAX 47-22-86-49-73. Eds. Elly Lie, Liv Argel. circ. 10,000. **Document type:** government publication.
 Description: Presents a survey of official Norwegian statistics, systematically arranged according to the classification by subject matters of the CBS. Covers statistics compiled by the CBS or by other government agencies.

O E C D EXTERNAL DEBT STATISTICS. see *BUSINESS AND ECONOMICS — Abstracting, Bibliographies, Statistics*

310 330.9 AQ ISSN 1021-7274
O E C S ANNUAL DIGEST OF STATISTICS. 1984. irreg. EC$25($10) Organisation of Eastern Caribbean States, Economic Affairs Secretariat, P.O. Box 822, St. John's, Antigua, W.I. TEL 809-462-3500. FAX 809-462-1537. stat. circ. 350. **Document type:** bulletin.
 Description: Summarizes statistics in the member countries.

O E C S ENERGY REVIEW. (Organisation of Eastern Caribbean States) see *ENERGY — Abstracting, Bibliographies, Statistics*

310 330.9 AQ ISSN 1021-7339
O E C S NATIONAL ACCOUNTS DIGEST. 1985. irreg. EC$25($10) Organisation of Eastern Caribbean States, Economic Affairs Secretariat, P.O. Box 822, St. John's, Antigua, W.I. TEL 809-462-3500. FAX 809-462-1537. charts; stat. circ. 350. **Document type:** bulletin.
 Description: Covers the national income and expenditure of OECS member countries.

310 330.9 AQ ISSN 1021-7290
O E C S STATISTICAL POCKET DIGEST. 1983. irreg. EC$5($2) Organisation of Eastern Caribbean States, Economic Affairs Secretariat, P.O. Box 822, St. John's, Antigua, W.I. TEL 809-462-3500. FAX 809-462-1537. stat. circ. 1,500. **Document type:** bibliography.
 Description: Reference guide to statistics and basic information about OECS member countries.

OCCUPATIONAL COMPENSATION SUMMARIES. see *BUSINESS AND ECONOMICS — Economic Situation And Conditions*

OCCUPATIONAL COMPENSATION SURVEYS. see *BUSINESS AND ECONOMICS — Economic Situation And Conditions*

OCCUPATIONAL DISEASE IN CALIFORNIA. see *OCCUPATIONAL HEALTH AND SAFETY — Abstracting, Bibliographies, Statistics*

OCCUPATIONAL INJURY & ILLNESS INFORMATION. see *OCCUPATIONAL HEALTH AND SAFETY — Abstracting, Bibliographies, Statistics*

STATISTICS

OCCUPATIONAL OUTLOOK HANDBOOK. see *OCCUPATIONS AND CAREERS*

OCCUPATIONAL OUTLOOK QUARTERLY. see *OCCUPATIONS AND CAREERS*

DER OEFFENTLICHE VERKEHR/TRANSPORTS PUBLICS. see *TRANSPORTATION — Abstracting, Bibliographies, Statistics*

310   AU
OESTERREICHISCHE ZEITSCHRIFT FUER STATISTIK. 1972. s-a. Oesterreichische Statistische Gesellschaft, Universitaet Innsbruck, Institut fuer Statistik, Christoph-Probst-Platz, A-6020 Innsbruck, Austria. E-mail: oezstat@stat-nov.uibk.ac.at. Ed. Gilg Seeber. circ. 3,200. **Document type:** academic/scholarly publication.
    Former titles (until 1995): Oesterreichische Zeitschrift fuer Statistik und Informatik (ISSN 1015-0811); Oesterreichische Statistische Gesellschaft. Mitteilungsblatt.

OHIO. DEPARTMENT OF HUMAN SERVICES. CHILD WELFARE STATISTICS. see *SOCIAL SERVICES AND WELFARE — Abstracting, Bibliographies, Statistics*

OIL AND ENERGY TRENDS: ANNUAL STATISTICAL REVIEW. see *ENERGY — Abstracting, Bibliographies, Statistics*

OKLAHOMA BUSINESS BULLETIN. see *BUSINESS AND ECONOMICS — Abstracting, Bibliographies, Statistics*

ONTARIO PUBLIC SECTOR; of official personnel in federal, provincial and municipal governments in the province of Ontario. see *PUBLIC ADMINISTRATION — Abstracting, Bibliographies, Statistics*

OPERANT SUBJECTIVITY; the Q methodology newsletter. see *SOCIOLOGY — Abstracting, Bibliographies, Statistics*

317   US   ISSN 1050-0383
HN90.P8
OPINIONS (YEAR). a. $129. Gale Research Inc., 835 Penobscot Bldg., Detroit, MI 48226-4094. TEL 313-961-2242. FAX 313-961-6083. TELEX 810-221-7086. Eds. Chris John Miko, Edward Weilant.
    Description: Contains extracts from public opinion surveys and polls conducted by business, government, professional and news organizations.

OREGON DEPARTMENT OF REVENUE. INCOME AND INHERITANCE TAX LAW ABSTRACTS. see *BUSINESS AND ECONOMICS — Abstracting, Bibliographies, Statistics*

OREGON PROPERTY TAX STATISTICS. see *BUSINESS AND ECONOMICS — Abstracting, Bibliographies, Statistics*

OREGON PUBLIC HEALTH STATISTICS REPORT. see *PUBLIC HEALTH AND SAFETY — Abstracting, Bibliographies, Statistics*

310   US   ISSN 0250-6289
HA755
ORGANIZATION OF AMERICAN STATES. STATISTICAL BULLETIN. 1979. q. $12. Organization of American States, General Secretariat, 1889 F St., N.W., Washington, DC 20006. TEL 703-941-1617. charts; stat. circ. 1,000. (also avail. in microfiche from CIS; back issues avail.) Indexed: IIS, P.A.I.S.

318.4   BO
ORURO EN CIFRAS. irreg. Bs.5($2.50) Universidad Boliviano de Oruro, Instituto de Investigaciones Economicas, Casilla 441, Oruro, Bolivia. TEL 591-52-55503. adv.; charts. **Document type:** bulletin.
    Description: Reflects economic, socio-cultural, and population aspects of Oruro.

OXFORD BULLETIN OF ECONOMICS AND STATISTICS. see *BUSINESS AND ECONOMICS*

519.5   US   ISSN 0952-9942
OXFORD STATISTICAL SCIENCE SERIES. 1987. irreg. price varies. Oxford University Press, 200 Madison Ave., New York, NY 10016. TEL 212-679-7300. **Document type:** monographic series.
—BLDSC (6321.021300).

519.5   JA   ISSN 0285-0370
OYO TOKEIGAKU/JAPANESE JOURNAL OF APPLIED STATISTICS. (Text and summaries in Japanese) 1971. 3/yr. 6000 Yen. Oyo Tokei Gakkai - Japanese Society of Applied Statistics, Dept. of Mathematics, Keio University, 14-1, Hiyoshi 3-chome, Kohoku-ku, Yokohama-shi, Kanagawa-ken 223, Japan. FAX 81-45-562-4442. Ed. Isao Yoshimura. **Document type:** academic/scholarly publication.

P M A STATISTICAL FACTBOOK; pharmaceuticals, in-vivo diagnostic. (Pharmaceutical Manufacturers Association) see *PHARMACY AND PHARMACOLOGY — Abstracting, Bibliographies, Statistics*

PACIFIC ASIA TRAVEL ASSOCIATION. ANNUAL STATISTICAL REPORT. see *TRAVEL AND TOURISM — Abstracting, Bibliographies, Statistics*

PACIFIC ASIA TRAVEL ASSOCIATION. QUARTERLY STATISTICAL REPORT. see *TRAVEL AND TOURISM — Abstracting, Bibliographies, Statistics*

PAKISTAN. CENTRAL BUREAU OF EDUCATION. EDUCATIONAL STATISTICS BULLETIN SERIES. see *EDUCATION — Abstracting, Bibliographies, Statistics*

PAKISTAN INSTITUTE OF DEVELOPMENT ECONOMICS. STATISTICAL PAPERS SERIES. see *BUSINESS AND ECONOMICS — Abstracting, Bibliographies, Statistics*

315   PK   ISSN 0078-8473
PAKISTAN STATISTICAL ASSOCIATION. PROCEEDINGS. (Text in English) a. Rs.2. Pakistan Statistical Association, Institute of Statistics, University of the Punjab, Lahore, Pakistan. **Document type:** proceedings.

318   PN   ISSN 0078-8996
PANAMA EN CIFRAS. 1953. a. Bl.1 (foreign Bl.3.50) (effective 1995). Direccion de Estadistica y Censo, Contraloria General, Apartado 5213, Panama 5, Panama. FAX 507-69-7294. circ. 8,000. **Document type:** government publication.
    Description: Contains demographic, economic and social statistical information.

319   PP   ISSN 0310-5377
PAPUA NEW GUINEA. NATIONAL STATISTICAL OFFICE. ABSTRACT OF STATISTICS. 1967. q. K.7 (foreign K.8). National Statistical Office, P.O. Wards Strip, Papua New Guinea. FAX 675-255057. TELEX FINANCE NE 22312. Ed. Nick Suvulo. charts. circ. 500. **Document type:** government publication, abstracting/indexing.
    Supersedes: Papua and New Guinea. Quarterly Summary of Statistics (ISSN 0031-1537)
    Description: Includes monthly or quarterly figures drawn from most of the economic statistical series compiled by the NSO and some by the Bank of Papua New Guinea.

PAPUA NEW GUINEA. NATIONAL STATISTICAL OFFICE. BUILDING STATISTICS. see *BUILDING AND CONSTRUCTION — Abstracting, Bibliographies, Statistics*

PAPUA NEW GUINEA. NATIONAL STATISTICAL OFFICE. CENSUS OF EMPLOYMENT. see *BUSINESS AND ECONOMICS — Abstracting, Bibliographies, Statistics*

339 319   PP   ISSN 1017-6500
PAPUA NEW GUINEA. NATIONAL STATISTICAL OFFICE. CONSUMER PRICE INDEX. 1964. q. K.7 (foreign K.8). National Statistical Office, P.O. Wards Strip, Papua New Guinea. FAX 675-255057. TELEX FINANCE NE 22312. Ed. Nick Suvulo. circ. 440.
    Supersedes: Papua New Guinea. Bureau of Statistics. Quarterly Retail Price Index (ISSN 0031-1529)
    Description: Covers six urban areas and contains price indexes, for groups and major subgroups of household 3xpenditures, and retail prices of major domestic commodities.

PAPUA NEW GUINEA. NATIONAL STATISTICAL OFFICE. DOMESTIC FACTOR INCOMES, BY REGION AND PROVINCE. see *BUSINESS AND ECONOMICS — Abstracting, Bibliographies, Statistics*

PAPUA NEW GUINEA. NATIONAL STATISTICAL OFFICE. ECONOMIC INDICATORS. see *BUSINESS AND ECONOMICS — Abstracting, Bibliographies, Statistics*

PAPUA NEW GUINEA. NATIONAL STATISTICAL OFFICE. EXPORT PRICE INDEXES. see *BUSINESS AND ECONOMICS — Abstracting, Bibliographies, Statistics*

PAPUA NEW GUINEA. NATIONAL STATISTICAL OFFICE. GOVERNMENT FINANCE STATISTICS. see *BUSINESS AND ECONOMICS — Abstracting, Bibliographies, Statistics*

PAPUA NEW GUINEA. NATIONAL STATISTICAL OFFICE. GROSS DOMESTIC PRODUCT AND EXPENDITURE. see *BUSINESS AND ECONOMICS — Abstracting, Bibliographies, Statistics*

PAPUA NEW GUINEA. NATIONAL STATISTICAL OFFICE. IMPORT PRICE INDEXES. see *BUSINESS AND ECONOMICS — Abstracting, Bibliographies, Statistics*

PAPUA NEW GUINEA. NATIONAL STATISTICAL OFFICE. INTERNATIONAL TRADE - EXPORTS. see *BUSINESS AND ECONOMICS — Abstracting, Bibliographies, Statistics*

PAPUA NEW GUINEA. NATIONAL STATISTICAL OFFICE. INTERNATIONAL TRADE - IMPORTS. see *BUSINESS AND ECONOMICS — Abstracting, Bibliographies, Statistics*

PAPUA NEW GUINEA. NATIONAL STATISTICAL OFFICE. PRODUCTION STATISTICS. see *BUSINESS AND ECONOMICS — Abstracting, Bibliographies, Statistics*

PAPUA NEW GUINEA. NATIONAL STATISTICAL OFFICE. RURAL INDUSTRIES. see *BUSINESS AND ECONOMICS — Abstracting, Bibliographies, Statistics*

PAPUA NEW GUINEA. NATIONAL STATISTICAL OFFICE. RURAL INDUSTRIES. AGRICULTURE LARGEHOLDINGS (PRELIMINARY). see *BUSINESS AND ECONOMICS — Abstracting, Bibliographies, Statistics*

PAPUA NEW GUINEA. NATIONAL STATISTICAL OFFICE. SECONDARY INDUSTRIES (PRELIMINARY STATEMENT). see *BUSINESS AND ECONOMICS — Abstracting, Bibliographies, Statistics*

PAPUA NEW GUINEA. NATIONAL STATISTICAL OFFICE. SECONDARY INDUSTRIES. see *BUSINESS AND ECONOMICS — Abstracting, Bibliographies, Statistics*

PAPUA NEW GUINEA. NATIONAL STATISTICAL OFFICE. STATISTICAL BULLETIN: CAPITAL EXPENDITURE BY PRIVATE BUSINESSES. see *BUSINESS AND ECONOMICS — Abstracting, Bibliographies, Statistics*

PAPUA NEW GUINEA. NATIONAL STATISTICAL OFFICE. STATISTICAL BULLETIN: CENSUS OF RETAIL SALES AND SELECTED SERVICES. see *BUSINESS AND ECONOMICS — Abstracting, Bibliographies, Statistics*

PAPUA NEW GUINEA. NATIONAL STATISTICAL OFFICE. STATISTICAL BULLETIN: REGISTERED MOTOR VEHICLES. see *TRANSPORTATION — Abstracting, Bibliographies, Statistics*

PAPUA NEW GUINEA. NATIONAL STATISTICAL OFFICE. TAXATION STATISTICS. PRELIMINARY BULLETIN. see *BUSINESS AND ECONOMICS — Abstracting, Bibliographies, Statistics*

PAPUA NEW GUINEA HANDBOOK. see *BUSINESS AND ECONOMICS — Abstracting, Bibliographies, Statistics*

PAPUA NEW GUINEA INTERNATIONAL ARRIVALS AND DEPARTURES. see *POPULATION STUDIES — Abstracting, Bibliographies, Statistics*

STATISTICS

318.92   PY   ISSN 0031-1677
PARAGUAY. DIRECCION GENERAL DE ESTADISTICA Y CENSOS. BOLETIN ESTADISTICO. (Supplement to Anuario Estadistico de la Republica del Paraguay) 1957. s-a. free. Direccion General de Estadistica y Censos, Humaita 463, Casilla de Correo 1118, Asuncion, Paraguay. Ed. Jose Diaz de Bedoya. mkt.; stat. circ. 1,000.

PECHAT BELARUSI/BYELORUSSIAN PUBLICATIONS. see *PUBLISHING AND BOOK TRADE* — Abstracting, Bibliographies, Statistics

PEDIATRIC LENGTH OF STAY BY DIAGNOSIS AND OPERATION, UNITED STATES. see *HOSPITALS* — Abstracting, Bibliographies, Statistics

PENNSYLVANIA. AGRICULTURAL STATISTICS SERVICE. CROP AND LIVESTOCK ANNUAL SUMMARY. see *AGRICULTURE — Crop Production And Soil*

PENNSYLVANIA. BOARD OF PROBATION AND PAROLE. MONTHLY STATISTICAL REPORT. see *CRIMINOLOGY AND LAW ENFORCEMENT* — Abstracting, Bibliographies, Statistics

PERSONALE- OG OEKONOMISTATISTIK FOR SYGEHUSVAESENET. see *HOSPITALS* — Abstracting, Bibliographies, Statistics

310   SP   ISSN 1134-0444
PERSPECTIVA ECONOMICA DE CATALUNYA. 1963. bi-m. 5000 ptas. Cambra Oficial de Comerc, Industria i Navegacio de Barcelona, Diagonal, 452, 08006 Barcelona, Spain. TEL 34-3-4169300. FAX 34-3-4169301. stat. Indexed: P.A.I.S.For.Lang.Ind.
    Former titles (until 1993): Boletin de Estadistica y coyuntura (ISSN 0210-1580); (until 1972): Boletin Estadistico Coyuntural (ISSN 0522-3806)

PESQUISA ANUAL DO TRANSPORTE RODOVIARIO. see *TRANSPORTATION* — Abstracting, Bibliographies, Statistics

318   BL   ISSN 0101-6822
HD7323.A3
PESQUISA NACIONAL POR AMOSTRA DE DOMICILIOS. 1967. a. Fundacao Instituto Brasileiro de Geografia e Estatistica, Centro de Documentacao e Disseminacao de Informacoes, Rua General Canabarro 66, 2o Andar, Maracana 20271-201 Rio de Janeiro, Brazil. TEL 55-21-2645424. FAX 55-21-2289575. **Document type:** government publication.

PETROLEUM INFORMATION INTERNATIONAL. see *PETROLEUM AND GAS*

PETROLEUM MARKET INTELLIGENCE. see *PETROLEUM AND GAS* — Abstracting, Bibliographies, Statistics

PHARMACEUTICAL MANUFACTURERS ASSOCIATION. ANNUAL SURVEY REPORT. see *PHARMACY AND PHARMACOLOGY* — Abstracting, Bibliographies, Statistics

PHILIPPINE STATISTICAL YEARBOOK. see *BUSINESS AND ECONOMICS* — Abstracting, Bibliographies, Statistics

PHILIPPINES. BUREAU OF LABOR AND EMPLOYMENT STATISTICS. OCCUPATIONAL WAGES SURVEY. see *BUSINESS AND ECONOMICS* — Abstracting, Bibliographies, Statistics

PHILIPPINES. NATIONAL STATISTICS OFFICE. ANNUAL SURVEY OF ESTABLISHMENTS. see *BUSINESS AND ECONOMICS* — Abstracting, Bibliographies, Statistics

PHILIPPINES. NATIONAL STATISTICS OFFICE. DIRECTORY OF LARGE ESTABLISHMENTS. see *BUSINESS AND ECONOMICS* — Abstracting, Bibliographies, Statistics

315   PH   ISSN 0116-2624
PHILIPPINES. NATIONAL STATISTICS OFFICE. INTEGRATED SURVEY OF HOUSEHOLDS BULLETIN. q. $100. National Statistics Office, Ramon Magsaysay Blvd., Box 779, Manila, Philippines. FAX 610794. circ. 300.
    Formerly: Philippines. National Census and Statistics Office. Sample Survey of Households Bulletin.

PHILIPPINES. NATIONAL STATISTICS OFFICE. VITAL STATISTICS REPORT. see *POPULATION STUDIES* — Abstracting, Bibliographies, Statistics

310   GW
PIRMASENS ZAHLEN UND FAKTEN: STATISTISCHE JAHRBUCH STADT PIRMASENS. 1979. a. Stadtplanungsamt, Bahnhofstr. 41, 66953 Pirmasens, Germany. TEL 06331-842433. FAX 06331-842540. TELEX 452286. circ. 200.
Document type: government publication.

310 312   US   ISSN 1073-0001
HA203
PLACES, TOWNS AND TOWNSHIPS. 1993. a. $69.95. (Kraus Organization, Ltd.) Bernan Press, 4611-F Assembly Dr., Lanham, MD 20706-4391. TEL 301-459-7666; 800-274-4447. FAX 301-459-0056.
    Description: Provides an in-depth look at a wide range of statistical data for U.S. towns and townships.

318   CL
PLAN NACIONAL DE RECOPILACION ESTADISTICA. 1983. a. Instituto Nacional de Estadisticas, Av. Bulnes 418, Casilla 498, Correo 3 Santiago, Chile.

POCKET BOOK OF TRANSPORT STATISTICS OF INDIA. see *TRANSPORTATION* — Abstracting, Bibliographies, Statistics

310   PL   ISSN 0006-4025
HA1451   CODEN: BSTAEY
POLAND. GLOWNY URZAD STATYSTYCZNY. BIULETYN STATYSTYCZNY. (Contents page in English and Russian) 1957. m. $21. Zaklad Wydawnictw Statystycznych, Al. Niepodleglosci 208, 00-925 Warsaw, Poland. TEL 48 22 25-03-45. (Dist. by: Ars Polona Ruch, Krakowskie Przedmiescie 7, Warsaw, Poland) charts; stat.; index. circ. 2,500.

314   PL   ISSN 0079-2608
HA1451   CODEN: MRSTEU
POLAND. GLOWNY URZAD STATYSTYCZNY. MALY ROCZNIK STATYSTYCZNY/POLAND. CENTRAL STATISTICS OFFICE. CONCISE STATISTICAL YEARBOOK. (Editions in English, French, German, Polish and Russian) 1958. a. 30 Zl. Zaklad Wydawnictw Statystycznych, Al. Niepodleglosci 208, 00-925 Warsaw, Poland. TEL 48 22 25-03-45.

POLAND. GLOWNY URZAD STATYSTYCZNY. RAPORT O STANIE, ZAGROZENIU I OCHRONIE SRODOWISKA (YEAR). see *ENVIRONMENTAL STUDIES* — Abstracting, Bibliographies, Statistics

314   PL   ISSN 0079-2780
POLAND. GLOWNY URZAD STATYSTYCZNY. ROCZNIK STATYSTYCZNY/POLAND. CENTRAL STATISTICS OFFICE. STATISTICAL YEARBOOK. (Text in Polish; summaries in English and Russian) 1921. a. Zaklad Wydawnictw Statystycznych, Al. Niepodleglosci 208, 00-925 Warsaw, Poland. TEL 48 22 25-03-45.
Document type: government publication.
—BLDSC (8005.600000).

314   PL   ISSN 0043-518X
HA1451
POLAND. GLOWNY URZAD STATYSTYCZNY. WIADOMOSCI STATYSTYCZNE. (Text in Polish; contents page and summaries in English, Russian) 1985. m. $21. Zaklad Wydawnictw Statystycznych, Al. Niepodleglosci 208, 00-925 Warsaw, Poland. TEL 48 22 25-03-45. (Dist. by: Ars Polona · Ruch, Krakowskie Przedmiescie 7, Warsaw, Poland) charts; stat.; index. circ. 3,400.

310   PL   ISSN 0867-0854
POLAND. GLOWNY URZAD STATYSTYCZNY. ZESZYTY METODYCZNE I KLASYFIKACJE. 1966. irreg. price varies. Zaklad Wydawnictw Statystycznych, Al. Niepodleglosci 208, 00-925 Warsaw, Poland. TEL 48 22 25-03-45. (Dist. by: Ars Polona-Ruch, Ul. Krakowskie Przedmiescie 7, Warsaw, Poland)
    Former titles (until 1990): Poland. Glowny Urzad Statystyczny. Zeszyty Metodyczne (ISSN 0208-9726); (until 1974): Poland. Glowny Urzad Statystyczny. Zeszyty Metodologiczne (ISSN 0079-2829)

POLLING REPORT. see *POLITICAL SCIENCE* — Abstracting, Bibliographies, Statistics

310   US   ISSN 1041-3782
POPULAR STATISTICS SERIES. 1983. irreg., vol.6, 1993. price varies. Marcel Dekker, Inc., 270 Madison Ave., New York, NY 10016. TEL 212-696-9000. FAX 212-658-4540. TELEX 421419.
—BLDSC (6551.198000).

314   PO   ISSN 0871-8741
HA1575
PORTUGAL. INSTITUTO NACIONAL DE ESTATISTICA. ANUARIO ESTATISTICO. CONTINENTE, ACORES E MADEIRA. Key Title: Anuario Estadistico de Portugal. (Text in French and Portuguese) 1875. a. Esc.6700. Instituto Nacional de Estatistica, Av. Antonio Jose de Almeida, 1078 Lisbon Codex, Portugal. (Orders to: Imprensa Nacional, Casa da Moeda, Direccao Comercial, Rua D. Francisco Manuel de Melo 5, 1000 Lisbon, Portugal)
    Formerly: Portugal. Instituto Nacional de Estatistica. Anuario Estatistico (ISSN 0079-4112)

314   PO
PORTUGAL. INSTITUTO NACIONAL DE ESTATISTICA. BOLETIM MENSAL DE ESTATISTICA: CONTINENTE, ACORES E MADEIRA. (Text in English, Portuguese) 1929. m. Esc.2500. Instituto Nacional de Estatistica, Av. Antonio Jose de Almeida, 1078 Lisbon Codex, Portugal. (Dist. by: Imprensa Nacional, Casa da Moeda, Direccao Comercial, rua D. Francisco Manuel de Melo 5, 1000 Lisbon, Portugal) bibl.; stat. circ. 1,450. Indexed: P.A.I.S.For.Lang.Ind.
    Formerly: Portugal. Instituto Nacional de Estatistica. Boletim Mensal (ISSN 0032-5082)

PORTUGAL. INSTITUTO NACIONAL DE ESTATISTICA. ESTATISTICAS DOS TRANSPORTES E COMMUNICACOES: CONTINENTE, ACORES E MADEIRA. see *TRANSPORTATION* — Abstracting, Bibliographies, Statistics

314   PO   ISSN 0378-3227
PORTUGAL. INSTITUTO NACIONAL DE ESTATISTICA. SERIE ESTATISTICAS REGIONAIS. 1970. irreg. Instituto Nacional de Estatistica, Av. Antonio Jose de Almeida, 1078 Lisbon Codex, Portugal. (Orders to: Imprensa Nacional, Casa da Moeda, Direccao Comercial, rua D. Francisco Manuel de Melo 5, 1000 Lisbon, Portugal) stat.; circ. controlled.

314   PO   ISSN 0871-8725
PORTUGAL EM NUMEROS. (Editions in English and Portuguese) 1969. a. Esc.120. Instituto Nacional de Estatistica, Av. Antonio Jose de Almeida, 1078 Lisbon Codex, Portugal.
    Former titles: Portugal (Year) (ISSN 0377-2470); (until 1977): Portugal. Instituto Nacional de Estatistica. Sinopse de Dados Estatisticos: Continente Ilhas Adjacentes.

314.6   PO   ISSN 0871-4614
HC391
PORTUGAL EM NUMEROS; SITUACAO SOCIO-ECONOMICA. English edition: Portugal; Economic and Social Indicators (ISSN 0871-4622) 1987. a. free. Ministerio do Planeamento e Administracao Territorio, Departamento de Prospectiva e Planeamento, Avda. D. Carlos I, 126, 1200 Lisbon, Portugal. **Document type:** government publication.

POULTRY MARKET STATISTICS. see *AGRICULTURE* — Abstracting, Bibliographies, Statistics

PRAGUE CONFERENCE ON INFORMATION THEORY, STATISTICAL DECISION FUNCTIONS, RANDOM PROCESSES. TRANSACTIONS. see *COMPUTERS* — Information Science And Information Theory

PRICE AND WAGE STATISTICS OF SRI LANKA. see *BUSINESS AND ECONOMICS* — Abstracting, Bibliographies, Statistics

314.97   XV   ISSN 0032-8227
PRIKAZI IN STUDIJE. (Text in Slovenian) 1955. m. 18 din. per no. Zavod SR Slovenije za Statistiko, Vozarski Pot 12, Ljubljana, Slovenia. Ed. Branko Mlinar. charts; stat. (processed)

PROBABILITY AND MATHEMATICAL STATISTICS. see *MATHEMATICS*

PROBATION AND PAROLE (YEAR). see *CRIMINOLOGY AND LAW ENFORCEMENT*

6220 STATISTICS

PRODUCCION AGRICOLA - PERIODO DE VERANO. see AGRICULTURE — Abstracting, Bibliographies, Statistics

PRODUCER PRICE INDEXES. see BUSINESS AND ECONOMICS — Economic Situation And Conditions

PRODUCTION OF CANADA'S LEADING MINERALS. see MINES AND MINING INDUSTRY — Abstracting, Bibliographies, Statistics

PRODUCTIVITY AND COSTS: BUSINESS, NONFARM BUSINESS, MANUFACTURING, AND NONFINANCIAL CORPORATIONS. see BUSINESS AND ECONOMICS — Economic Situation And Conditions

PRODUCTIVITY BY INDUSTRY (YEAR). see BUSINESS AND ECONOMICS — Economic Situation And Conditions

PRODUCTIVITY MEASURES FOR SELECTED INDUSTRIES. see BUSINESS AND ECONOMICS — Economic Situation And Conditions

PROFILES OF EARNINGS IN CYPRUS: BY EDUCATION, OCCUPATION, EXPERIENCE, AGE, SEX AND SECTOR. see BUSINESS AND ECONOMICS — Abstracting, Bibliographies, Statistics

PROPANE MARKET FACTS; statistical handbook of the LP-gas industry. see PETROLEUM AND GAS — Abstracting, Bibliographies, Statistics

310   PL   ISSN 0033-2372
HA1   CODEN: PZSTAD
PRZEGLAD STATYSTYCZNY. 1954. q. $54. (Polska Akademia Nauk, Komitet Statystyki i Ekonometrii) Wydawnictwo Naukowe P W N, Miodowa 10, 00-251 Warsaw, Poland. Ed. Michal Kolupa. bk.rev.; charts; illus.; index. circ. 1,000. Indexed: INSPEC, Int.Abstr.Oper.Res., Math.R.
—BLDSC (6944.850000).

PUBLIC EDUCATION FINANCES. see EDUCATION — Abstracting, Bibliographies, Statistics

PUBLIC LIBRARIES IN WESTERN AUSTRALIA. STATISTICAL BULLETIN. see LIBRARY AND INFORMATION SCIENCES — Abstracting, Bibliographies, Statistics

PUERTO RICO. DEPARTMENT OF HEALTH. INFORME ANUAL DE ESTADISTICAS INSTITUCIONALES. see PUBLIC HEALTH AND SAFETY — Abstracting, Bibliographies, Statistics

PUERTO RICO. DEPARTMENT OF HEALTH. OFFICE OF HEALTH STATISTICS. DIVISION OF STATISTICS AND REPORTS. ANNUAL VITAL STATISTICS REPORT/INFORME ANUAL DE ESTADISTICAS VITALES. see POPULATION STUDIES — Abstracting, Bibliographies, Statistics

PUERTO RICO. DEPARTMENT OF LABOR. BUREAU OF LABOR STATISTICS. EMPLOYMENT HOURS AND EARNINGS IN THE MANUFACTURING ESTABLISHMENTS PROMOTED BY THE ECONOMIC DEVELOPMENT ADMINISTRATION OF THE PUERTO RICAN INDUSTRIAL DEVELOPMENT COMPANY. see BUSINESS AND ECONOMICS — Abstracting, Bibliographies, Statistics

PUERTO RICO. DEPARTMENT OF LABOR. DIRECTORIO DE ORGANIZACIONES DEL TRABAJO. see LABOR UNIONS

PUERTO RICO. DEPARTMENT OF LABOR. EMPLEO, HORAS Y SALARIOS EN LAS INDUSTRIAS MANUFACTURERAS/PUERTO RICO. DEPARTMENT OF LABOR. EMPLOYMENT, HOURS AND EARNINGS IN THE MANUFACTURING INDUSTRIES. see BUSINESS AND ECONOMICS — Abstracting, Bibliographies, Statistics

QATAR YEARBOOK. see PUBLIC ADMINISTRATION — Abstracting, Bibliographies, Statistics

QUALITY AND QUANTITY; international journal of methodology. see SOCIOLOGY

310   330.072   US   ISSN 1043-8262
HB135
QUANTITY AND QUALITY IN ECONOMIC RESEARCH. 1985. a. $53. (International Society of Statistical Science in Economics) University Press of America, 4720 Boston Way, Ste. A, Lanham, MD 20706. TEL 301-451-3366. Ed. R.Ch. Brown. **Document type:** academic/scholarly publication.
—BLDSC (7168.348000).

310   US
QUANTITY AND QUALITY IN STATISTICAL RESEARCH. 1985. biennial. $35.50. International Society of Statistical Science, 536 Oasis Dr., Santa Rosa, CA 95407. TEL 707-575-3529. Ed. R. Brown. adv. contact: M. Zanzarov. **Document type:** academic/scholarly publication.

QUARTERLY OPERATING STATISTICS; of major household goods carriers. see TRANSPORTATION — Abstracting, Bibliographies, Statistics

310   AF
QUARTERLY REVIEW OF AFGHAN STATISTICS/SHMAYR SIRANAH-YI IHSA'IYAH. (Text in Persian) 1976. q. Central Statistical Office, Nader Shah Minah, Block No. 4, Box 2002, Kabul, Afghanistan. stat.

QUARTERLY STATISTICAL BULLETIN/BULLETIN STATISTIQUE TRIMESTRIEL. see BUSINESS AND ECONOMICS — Abstracting, Bibliographies, Statistics

317   CN   ISSN 0834-5252
HA747
QUEBEC STATISTIQUE. 1914-1980; resumed 1986. a. Can.$9.95. (Bureau of Statistics) Ministere des Communications, Direction de la Communication, 1500-D boul. Charest Ouest, 1er, Sainte-Foy, PQ G1N 2E5, Canada. TEL 418-643-5150. index. circ. 6,000. **Document type:** government publication.
   Former titles (until 1986): Annuaire du Quebec - Quebec Yearbook (ISSN 0066-3018); (until 1962): Annuaire Statistique. Quebec (ISSN 0704-3651); Which incorporated (1914-1934): Statistical Year Book (Quebec. English Edition) (ISSN 0704-3643)

310   SP
QUESTIIO. Variant title: Quaderns d'Estadistica i Investigacio Operativa. (Text in Catalan, English, French; summaries in English) 3/yr. 2700 ptas. (effective 1995). Institut d'Estadistica de Catalunya, Via Laietana 58, 08003 Barcelona, Spain. TEL 34-3-4121730. FAX 34-3-4123145. Eds. Enric Ripoll, Carles M. Cuadras; Co-sponsors: Universitat de Barcelona, Universitat Politecnica de Catalunya. adv. contact: Eduard Bonet. Indexed: Curr.Ind.Stat., Stat.Theor.Meth.Abstr. **Document type:** academic/scholarly publication, government publication.
—BLDSC (7216.222600); Ei.
   Former titles (until 1992): Quaderns d'Estadistica, Sistemes, Informatica i Investigacio Operativa (ISSN 0210-8054); Formerly (until 1977): Cuadernos de Estadistica Aplicada e Investigacion Operativa.
   Refereed Serial

310   SW   ISSN 0283-3654
QVARTILEN. 1986. q. SEK 100 membership (effective 1995). Svenska Statistikersamfundet, Statistiska Institutionen, P.O. Box 7008, S-220 07 Lund, Sweden. TEL 46-8-780-49-16. FAX 46-8-783-43-28. E-mail: k.lindell@sub.se. Ed. Kajsa Lindell. circ. 1,000. **Document type:** newsletter.

R I A QUARTERLY STATISTICS REPORT - ROBOTICS. (Robotic Industries Association) see COMPUTERS — Robotics

316.8   SA
R S A STATISTICS IN BRIEF. a., latest 1994. free. Central Statistical Service - Sentrale Statistiekdiens, Private Bag X44, Pretoria 0001, South Africa. TEL 27-12-310-8911. FAX 27-12-310-8500. **Document type:** government publication.

311   UK   ISSN 1351-0657
R S S NEWS. 1974. 10/yr. membership. Royal Statistical Society, 12 Errol St., London EC1Y 8LX, England. TEL 0171-638-8998. FAX 0171-256-7598. E-mail: rss@bristol.ac.uk. Ed. Frank Duckworth. adv.: B&W page £560; trim 270 x 190; adv. contact: Marie-Claire Hislop. circ. 6,500. **Document type:** newsletter.
   Formerly: R S S News and Notes.
   Description: News of events in the field of statistics and of the Royal Statistical Society.

R V BUSINESS. (Recreational Vehicle) see SPORTS AND GAMES — Abstracting, Bibliographies, Statistics

310   UK   ISSN 0268-6376
RADICAL STATISTICS. 1975. 3/yr. £12 to individuals; libraries £20. Radical Statistics Group, c/o London Hazards Centre, Headland House, 3rd Fl., 308 Grays Inn Rd., London WC1X 8DS, England. adv.; bk.rev. circ. 450. **Document type:** academic/scholarly publication.
   Description: A forum for radical ideas in the political development and exploitation of statistical methods and in the uses and abuses of statistics.

RAJASTHAN, INDIA. DIRECTORATE OF ECONOMICS AND STATISTICS. BASIC STATISTICS. see BUSINESS AND ECONOMICS — Abstracting, Bibliographies, Statistics

RAUMFORSCHUNG UND RAUMORDNUNG. see HOUSING AND URBAN PLANNING — Abstracting, Bibliographies, Statistics

REAL EARNINGS. see BUSINESS AND ECONOMICS — Economic Situation And Conditions

314   FR   ISSN 0990-2562
REGARDS SUR L'ILE-DE-FRANCE. 1979. q. 185 F. Institut National de la Statistique et des Etudes Economiques (INSEE), Direction Regionale d'Ile-de-France, 7 rue Stephenson, Montigny-le-Bretonneux, 78188 Saint-Quentin-en-Yvelines Cedex, France. TEL 30-96-90-00. FAX 30-96-90-01. Ed. Alain Godinot. adv. circ. 1,500.
   Formerly (until 1988): Aspects Statistiques de l'Ile de France.

318   PE
REGION ANDRES AVELINO CACERES COMPENDIO ESTADISTICO. Instituto National de Estadistica e Informatica, Av. 28 de Julio 1056, Lima, Peru. circ. 200. **Document type:** government publication.

318   PE
REGION AREQUIPA COMPENDIO ESTADISTICO. a. Instituto Nacional de Estadistica e Informatica, Av. 28 de Julio No. 1056, Lima, Peru.

318   PE
REGION CHAVIN COMPENDIO ESTADISTICO. a.? Instituto Nacional de Estadistica e Informatica, Av. 28 de Julio No. 1056, Lima, Peru. circ. 200.
   Description: Contains geographical, demographical, social and economic statistics of the region.

318   PE
REGION INKA COMPENDIO ESTADISTICO. irreg. Instituto Nacional de Estadistica e Informatica, Av. 28 de Julio 1056, Lima, Peru. circ. 200. **Document type:** government publication.

318   PE
REGION JOSE CARLOS MARIATEGUI COMPENDIO ESTADISTICO. irreg., 3rd ed., 1991. Instituto Nacional de Estadistica e Informatica, Av. 28 de Julio 1056, Lima, Peru. **Document type:** government publication.

318   PE
REGION LORETO COMPENDIO ESTADISTICO. irreg., 3rd ed., 1991. Instituto Nacional de Estadistica e Informatica, Av. 28 de Julio 1056, Lima, Peru. **Document type:** government publication.

318   PE
REGION LOS LIBERTADORES - WARI COMPENDIO ESTADISTICO. irreg., 2nd ed., 1991. Instituto Nacional de Estadistica e Informatica, Av. 28 de Julio 1056, Lima, Peru. circ. 200. **Document type:** government publication.

318   PE
REGION NOR ORIENTAL DEL MARANON COMPENDIO ESTADISTICO. irreg. Instituto Nacional de Estadistica e Informatica, Av. 28 de Julio No. 1056, Lima, Peru. **Document type:** government publication.

318   PE
REGION SAN MARTIN - LA LIBERTAD COMPENDIO ESTADISTICO. irreg. Instituto Nacional de Estadistica e Informatica, Av. 28 de Julio 1056, Lima, Peru. **Document type:** government publication.

314	IT

REGIONI IN CIFRE. a. Istituto Nazionale di Statistica, Via Cesare Balbo 16, 00100 Rome, Italy. FAX 06-46735198. **Document type:** government publication.

REPORT ON PASSENGER ROAD TRANSPORT IN ZAMBIA. see TRANSPORTATION — Abstracting, Bibliographies, Statistics

REPORT ON TOURISM STATISTICS IN TANZANIA. see TRAVEL AND TOURISM — Abstracting, Bibliographies, Statistics

RESEARCH AND STUDIES. see EDUCATION — Abstracting, Bibliographies, Statistics

318	BL	ISSN 0102-0226
HC188.R4		

RESENHA ESTATISTICA DO RIO GRANDE DO SUL. (Text in English, Portuguese, Spanish) 1977. a. Cr.$6 (effective 1995). Fundacao de Economia e Estatistica, Rua Duque de Caxias, 1691, CEP 90010-283 Porto Alegre RG, Brazil. TEL 55-512-259455. FAX 55-512-25006. TELEX 0515042.

RETAIL FOOD PRICE INDEX: WASHINGTON, D C. see BUSINESS AND ECONOMICS — Economic Situation And Conditions

THE REVIEW OF ECONOMICS AND STATISTICS. see BUSINESS AND ECONOMICS

314	BL	ISSN 0034-7175
HA984		

REVISTA BRASILEIRA DE ESTATISTICA/BRAZILIAN STATISTICAL JOURNAL. (Text in Portuguese; summaries in English) 1940. s-a. $120. Fundacao Instituto Brasileiro de Geografia e Estatistica, Rua General Canabarro 666, 2o andar, Maracana 20271-201 Rio de Janeiro, Brazil. TEL 55-21-2645424. FAX 55-21-2289575. bk.rev.; bibl.; charts; illus.; stat.; index. circ. 1,000. **Indexed:** Popul.Ind. **Document type:** government publication.

REVISTA DE ECONOMIA Y ESTADISTICA. see BUSINESS AND ECONOMICS

REVISTA ECONOMIA; nueva etapa. see BUSINESS AND ECONOMICS

314.98	RM	ISSN 1018-046X

REVISTA ROMANA DE STATISTICA. (Text in Rumanian; summaries in English)) 1952. m. $140 (effective 1995 & 1996). Comisia Nationala pentru Statistica - National Commission for Statistics, 16 Bd. Libertatii, Sector 5, 70542 Bucharest, Rumania. TEL 40-1-6143371. FAX 40-1-3124873. (Dist. by: Rodipet S.A., P.O. Box 33-57, Piata Presei Libere 1, Sector 1, Bucharest, Rumania) circ. 2,700. **Indexed:** Rural Recreat.Tour.Abstr., World Agri.Econ.& Rural Sociol.Abstr.
—BLDSC (7870.514900).
Formerly (until 1989): Revista de Statistica (ISSN 0556-6398)
Description: Provides official figures from the commission's papers.

310	FR	ISSN 0035-175X
		CODEN: RVSTA7

REVUE DE STATISTIQUE APPLIQUEE. 1953. q. 650 F. (effective 1996). Societe de Statistique de France (ASU), Institut Henri Poincare, 11 rue Pierre et Marie Curie, 75231 Paris Cedex 05, France. TEL 44-27-66-60. FAX 44-07-04-74. Ed. Pierre Cazes. adv. contact: Jean-Marie Grosbras. bk.rev.; bibl.; charts; stat.; index, cum.index: vols. 1-17. circ. 800. (reprint service avail. SWZ) **Indexed:** Biostat., Math.R., Oper.Res.Manage.Sci., Qual.Contr.Appl.Stat., SSCI.
—Faxon; SWETS.

REVUE DROMOISE. see ARCHAEOLOGY

314	IT	ISSN 0035-7960

ROMA E PROVINCIA ATTRAVERSO LA STATISTICA; dati mensili e annuali. 1956. a. L.800. per no. Camera di Commercio Industria Artigianato e Agricoltura di Roma, Via De'Burro 147, 00186 Rome, Italy. Ed. Leonida Attili. bk.rev.; charts; stat.; index, cum.index; circ. controlled.

314.891	DK	ISSN 0105-8339

ROSKILDE KOMMUNE. STATISTIKKEN. 1970. a. free. Roskilde Kommune, Planlaegningssekretarietet, Sct. Ols Straede 1, 4000 Roskilde, Denmark. circ. 425.

310	UK	ISSN 0964-1998
HA1		CODEN: JSTAAG

ROYAL STATISTICAL SOCIETY. JOURNAL. SERIES A: STATISTICS IN SOCIETY. 1838. 3/yr. £52($95) (foreign £59) (effective 1996). Basil Blackwell Ltd., 108 Cowley Road, Oxford OX4 1JF, England. TEL 44-1865-791100. FAX 44-1865-791347. Eds. D. Holt, S.M. Gore. adv.; bk.rev.; bibl.; index. circ. 5,700. (also avail. in microfilm from BHP) **Indexed:** Abstr.Hyg., Appl.Mech.Rev., Biostat., Compumath, Cont.Pg.Manage., Curr.Cont., Curr.Ind.Stat., Deep Sea Res.& Oceanogr.Abstr., High.Educ.Curr.Aware.Bull., Ind.Vet., Int.Polit.Sci.Abstr., J.Cont.Quant.Meth., J.of Econ.Lit., Mark.Res.Abstr. (1963-), Math.R., Oper.Res.Manage.Sci., P.A.I.S., Popul.Ind., Qual.Contr.Appl.Stat., Res.High.Educ.Abstr., Rural Recreat.Tour.Abstr., SSCI, Trop.Dis.Bull., World Agri.Econ.& Rural Sociol.Abstr., World Bank.Abstr. **Document type:** academic/scholarly publication.
—BLDSC (4866.000000); Faxon; Genuine Article; SWETS. **CCC.**
Formerly (until 1988): Royal Statistical Society. Journal. Series A: General (ISSN 0035-9238)
Description: Contains papers on economic, social and governmental issues, historical, biographical, philosophical, demographical and medical statistics. **Refereed Serial**

311	UK	ISSN 0035-9246
HA1		CODEN: JSTBAJ

ROYAL STATISTICAL SOCIETY. JOURNAL. SERIES B: METHODOLOGICAL. 1934. q. £52($95) (foreign £59) (effective 1996). Basil Blackwell Ltd., 108 Cowley Road, Oxford OX4 1JF, England. TEL 0865-791100. FAX 0865-791347. Eds. J.T. Kent, R.L. Smith. adv.; bibl.; index. circ. 4,500. **Indexed:** Abstr.Hyg., Appl.Mech.Rev., Biostat., Compumath, Curr.Cont., Curr.Ind.Stat., Hort.Abstr., Int.Polit.Sci.Abstr., J.Cont.Quant.Meth., Mark.Res.Abstr. (1963-), Math.R., SSCI, Stat.Theor.Meth.Abstr., Trop.Dis.Bull. **Document type:** academic/scholarly publication.
—BLDSC (4867.000000); Faxon; Genuine Article; SWETS; UMI; UnCover. **CCC.**
Description: Addresses theory and development of new statistical methods and applications of established methods.

519.5	UK	ISSN 0035-9254
HA1		CODEN: APSTAG

ROYAL STATISTICAL SOCIETY. JOURNAL. SERIES C: APPLIED STATISTICS. 1952. q. £52($95) (foreign £59) (effective 1996). Basil Blackwell Ltd., 108 Cowley Rd., Oxford OX4 1JF, England. TEL 0865-791100. FAX 0865-791347. (Subscr. to: Journals Subscription Department, Marston Book Services, P.O. Box 87, Oxford OX2 ODT, England) Eds. I.R. Dunsmore, D.J. Hand. adv.; bk.rev.; bibl.; index. circ. 5,400. (back issues avail.) **Indexed:** Biostat., Br.Archaeol.Abstr., Br.Tech.Ind., C.I.S. Abstr., Compumath, INSPEC (1968-1982), Int.Polit.Sci.Abstr., J.Cont.Quant.Meth., Mark.Res.Abstr. (1963-), Math.R., Nutr.Abstr., Oper.Res.Manage.Sci., Qual.Contr.Appl.Stat., RAPRA Risk Abstr., SSCI, W.R.C.Inf. **Document type:** academic/scholarly publication.
—BLDSC (1580.000000); Ei; Faxon; Genuine Article; SWETS; UMI; UnCover. **CCC.**
Description: Discusses the application of statistical methods to practical problems including computer algorithms.

RUBBER STATISTICAL BULLETIN. see RUBBER

314	RM	ISSN 1223-7507

RUMANIA. COMISIA NATIONALA PENTRU STATISTICA. BULETIN STATISTIC LUNAR. English edition: Rumania. National Commission for Statistics. Monthly Statistical Bulletin (ISSN 1221-7069) (Editions in English and Rumanian) m. $85 (effective 1995 & 1996). Comisia Nationala pentru Statistica - National Commission for Statistics, Bd. Libertatii 16, Sector 5, 70542 Bucharest, Rumania. TEL 40-1-6143371. FAX 40-1-3124873. **Document type:** government publication.
Description: Presents statistical information referring to the main fields of economic and social activity.

314	RM	ISSN 1221-7034

RUMANIA. COMISIA NATIONALA PENTRU STATISTICA. BULETIN STATISTIC TRIMESTRIAL/RUMANIA. NATIONAL COMMISSION FOR STATISTICS. QUARTERLY STATISTICAL BULLETIN. (Text in English, Rumanian) q. $35 (effective 1995 & 1996). Comisia Nationala pentru Statistica - National Commission for Statistics, Bd. Libertatii 16, Sector 5, 70542 Bucharest, Rumania. TEL 40-1-6143371. FAX 40-1-3124873. **Document type:** government publication.
Description: Presents data on the main fields of economic and social activity, by months and quarters.

RUSSIA & EURASIA ARMED FORCES REVIEW ANNUAL. see MILITARY

RUSSIA & EURASIA FACTS & FIGURES ANNUAL. see POLITICAL SCIENCE — Abstracting, Bibliographies, Statistics

316.7	RW	ISSN 0256-7229
HA4695		

RWANDA. DIRECTION GENERALE DE LA STATISTIQUE. BULLETIN DE STATISTIQUE. (Supplement avail.) 1964. q. $48 (effective Aug. 1991). Direction Generale de la Statistique, B.P. 46, Kigali, Rwanda. **Document type:** government publication.
Former titles (until 1976): Rwanda. Direction de la Statistique et de la Documentation. Bulletin de Statistique (ISSN 0304-9426); (until 1972): Rwanda. Direction de l'Office Generale des Statistiques. Bulletin de Statistique (ISSN 0557-5583)

S A R STATISTICS. (Search and Rescue) see TRANSPORTATION — Abstracting, Bibliographies, Statistics

310	XK

ST. LUCIA. STATISTICAL DEPARTMENT. ANNUAL STATISTICAL DIGEST. 1960. a. EC$15. Statistical Department, New Government Bldg., Block C, 2nd Fl., Conway, Castries, St. Lucia, W.I. TEL 809-45-22697. FAX 809-45-31648. TELEX 6394 FORAFF. Ed. Bryan Boxill. **Document type:** government publication.

310	XK

ST. LUCIA. STATISTICAL DEPARTMENT. STATISTICAL POCKET DIGEST. 1979. a. EC$2($2) Statistical Department, New Government Bldg., Block C, 2nd Fl., Conway, Castries, St. Lucia, W.I. TEL 809-45-22697. FAX 809-45-31648. TELEX 6394 FORAFF. Ed. Bryan Boxill. **Document type:** government publication.

311	II	ISSN 0581-4790

SAMVADADHVAM. (Text in Bengali, English and Hindi) 1956. irreg. Indian Statistical Institute, 203 Barrackpore Trunk Rd., Calcutta 700035, India. Ed. Bd. bk.rev.; bibl.; charts; illus.; stat.; circ. 2,500 (controlled).

SANFORD EVANS GOLD BOOK OF SNOWMOBILE DATA AND USED PRICES. see SPORTS AND GAMES — Abstracting, Bibliographies, Statistics

311	II	ISSN 0581-572X
		CODEN: SANABS

SANKHYA. SERIES A; Indian journal of statistics. (Text in English) 1933. q. Statistical Publishing Society, 204-1 Barrackpore Trunk Rd., Calcutta 700035, India. Ed.Bd. adv.; bibl.; index. circ. 1,500 (combined). (also avail. in microfilm from PMC; microfiche from PMC) **Indexed:** Biol.Abstr., Biostat., Chem.Abstr., Curr.Ind.Stat., J.Cont.Quant.Meth., Math.R., P.A.I.S., SSCI, Stat.Theor.Meth.Abstr.
—BLDSC (8075.003000); Genuine Article; SWETS; UnCover.

310	II	ISSN 0581-5738
		CODEN: SANBBV

SANKHYA. SERIES B; Indian journal of statistics. (Text in English) 1933. q. Statistical Publishing Society, 204-1 Barrackpore Trunk Rd., Calcutta 700035, India. Ed.Bd. adv.; bibl.; stat. circ. 1,500 (combined). (also avail. in microform from PMC) **Indexed:** Biol.Abstr., Chem.Abstr., Curr.Ind.Stat., P.A.I.S., SSCI, Stat.Theor.Meth.Abstr.
—BLDSC (8075.005000); Genuine Article; SWETS; UnCover.

6222 STATISTICS

314   SF
SAO TOME E PRINCIPE. REPARTICAO PROVINCIAL DOS SERVICOS DE ESTATISTICA. BOLETIN TRIMESTRAL DE ESTATISTICA. 1971. q. Reparticao Provincial dos Servicos de Estatistica, Caixa Postal No. 256, Sao Tome, Sao Tome e Principe.

315   II
SARVEKSHANA. (Text in English and Hindi) 1977. q. Rs.100($36) National Sample Survey Organisation, Sardar Patel Bhavan, Parliament St., New Delhi 110001, India. (Subscr. to.: Controller of Publications, Civil Lines, Delhi 110 054, India) stat. circ. 1,000. (back issues avail.)

319   SU   ISSN 0581-8605
HA1681
SAUDI ARABIA. CENTRAL DEPARTMENT OF STATISTICS. STATISTICAL YEARBOOK. (Text in Arabic, English) 1965. a. sR.30. Central Department of Statistics, Box 3735, Riyadh 11118, Saudi Arabia. **Document type:** government publication.
   Description: Presents a picture of economic and social development in the kingdom on the basis of scientifically organized studies.

SAUDI ARABIA. MINISTRY OF EDUCATION. EDUCATIONAL STATISTICS. see *EDUCATION — Abstracting, Bibliographies, Statistics*

519.5   UK   ISSN 0303-6898
QA276.A1   CODEN: SJSADG
SCANDINAVIAN JOURNAL OF STATISTICS; theory and applications. (Supplements avail.) (Text in English) 1974. q. £87($148) (foreign £92) (effective 1996). Basil Blackwell Ltd., 108 Cowley Rd., Oxford OX4 1JF, England. TEL 0865-791100. FAX 0865-791347. TELEX 837022-OXBOOK-G. adv.; abstr.; illus.; index. circ. 700. **Indexed:** ASCA, Biostat., Compumath, Curr.Cont., Curr.Ind.Stat., J.Cont.Quant.Meth., Math.R., Oper.Res.Manage.Sci., Qual.Contr.Appl.Stat., Risk Abstr., Stat.Theor.Meth.Abstr.
   —BLDSC (8087.549000); Faxon; Genuine Article; SWETS; UMI; UnCover. **CCC.**

SCHWEIZERISCHE STRASSENVERKEHRSZAEHLUNG/COMPTAGE SUISSE DE LA CIRCULATION ROUTIERE. see *TRANSPORTATION — Abstracting, Bibliographies, Statistics*

SCHWEIZERISCHE VERKEHRSSTATISTIK/STATISTIQUE SUISSE DES TRANSPORTS. see *TRANSPORTATION — Abstracting, Bibliographies, Statistics*

SCHWEIZERISCHE ZEITSCHRIFT FUER VOLKSWIRTSCHAFT UND STATISTIK/REVUE SUISSE D'ECONOMIE POLITIQUE ET DE STATISTIQUE. see *BUSINESS AND ECONOMICS*

SCOTLAND. REGISTRAR GENERAL. ANNUAL REPORT. see *POPULATION STUDIES — Abstracting, Bibliographies, Statistics*

314   UK
SCOTTISH ABSTRACT OF STATISTICS. 1971. a. £34. Scottish Office, New St. Andrew's House, Rm. 5-52, Edinburgh EH1 3TG, Scotland. TEL 0131-244-4987. FAX 0131-244-4785. circ. 800. **Document type:** abstracting/indexing, government publication.
   Supersedes (in 1971): Digest of Scottish Statistics.
   Description: Major reference volume of statistics of life in Scotland.

SCOTTISH EDUCATION DEPARTMENT. SOCIAL WORK SERVICES GROUP. STATISTICAL BULLETIN. see *SOCIAL SERVICES AND WELFARE*

SCOTTISH EDUCATION DEPARTMENT. STATISTICAL BULLETIN. see *EDUCATION — Abstracting, Bibliographies, Statistics*

SCOTTISH HOME AND HEALTH DEPARTMENT. STATISTICAL BULLETIN. see *PUBLIC HEALTH AND SAFETY — Abstracting, Bibliographies, Statistics*

SECURITE ROUTIERE. see *TRANSPORTATION — Abstracting, Bibliographies, Statistics*

SELECTED VITAL STATISTICS AND HEALTH STATISTICS INDICATORS. ANNUAL REPORT. see *POPULATION STUDIES — Abstracting, Bibliographies, Statistics*

519.5   US   ISSN 0747-4946
QA279.7   CODEN: SEANEX
SEQUENTIAL ANALYSIS. 1982. 4/yr. $40 to individuals; institutions $385. Marcel Dekker Journals, 270 Madison Ave., New York, NY 10016. TEL 212-696-9000. FAX 212-685-4540. TELEX 421419 MARDEEK. (Subscr. to: Box 5017, Monticello, NY 12701) Eds. B.K. Ghosh, P.K. Sen. abstr. (also avail. in microform from RPI; reprint service avail. from SWZ) **Indexed:** Biostat., Curr.Ind.Stat., J.Cont.Quant.Meth., Oper.Res.Manage.Sci., Qual.Contr.Appl.Stat., Stat.Theor.Meth.Abstr., Zent.Math. **Document type:** academic/scholarly publication.
   —BLDSC (8242.279500); Faxon; SWETS; UMI; UnCover. **CCC.**
   Formerly: Communications in Statistics. Part C: Sequential Analysis.

SEYCHELLES. DEPARTMENT OF FINANCE. ECONOMIC INDICATORS. see *BUSINESS AND ECONOMICS — Abstracting, Bibliographies, Statistics*

SEYCHELLES. DEPARTMENT OF FINANCE. NATIONAL ACCOUNTS. see *PUBLIC ADMINISTRATION — Abstracting, Bibliographies, Statistics*

310   SE
SEYCHELLES. DEPARTMENT OF FINANCE. STATISTICAL BULLETIN.. 1980. q. R.25. Department of Finance, Statistics Division, P.O. Box 206, Independence House, Victoria, Republic of Seychelles. stat. (back issues avail.)

310   SE
SEYCHELLES. DEPARTMENT OF FINANCE. STATISTICS DIVISION. STATISTICAL ABSTRACT. 1977. a. 60 Fr. Department of Finance, Statistics Division, P.O. Box 206, Victoria, Mahe, Seychelles. circ. 250. **Document type:** government publication, abstracting/indexing.

SEYCHELLES. MANAGEMENT AND INFORMATION SYSTEMS DIVISION. TOURISM AND MIGRATION STATISTICS. see *TRAVEL AND TOURISM — Abstracting, Bibliographies, Statistics*

SEYCHELLES. PRESIDENT'S OFFICE. STATISTICS DIVISION. CENSUS. see *POPULATION STUDIES — Abstracting, Bibliographies, Statistics*

SEYCHELLES. PRESIDENT'S OFFICE. STATISTICS DIVISION. EMPLOYMENT & EARNINGS. see *BUSINESS AND ECONOMICS — Abstracting, Bibliographies, Statistics*

SEYCHELLES. PRESIDENT'S OFFICE. STATISTICS DIVISION. EXTERNAL TRADE. see *BUSINESS AND ECONOMICS — Abstracting, Bibliographies, Statistics*

SEYCHELLES. PRESIDENT'S OFFICE. STATISTICS DIVISION. POPULATION AND VITAL STATISTICS. see *POPULATION STUDIES — Abstracting, Bibliographies, Statistics*

SEYCHELLES. PRESIDENT'S OFFICE. STATISTICS DIVISION. PRODUCTION INDICATORS. see *BUSINESS AND ECONOMICS — Abstracting, Bibliographies, Statistics*

SEYCHELLES. PRESIDENT'S OFFICE. STATISTICS DIVISION. RETAIL PRICES. see *BUSINESS AND ECONOMICS — Abstracting, Bibliographies, Statistics*

SEYCHELLES. PRESIDENT'S OFFICE. STATISTICS DIVISION. STATISTICAL ABSTRACT. see *BUSINESS AND ECONOMICS — Abstracting, Bibliographies, Statistics*

SEYCHELLES. STATISTICS DIVISION. STATISTICAL BULLETIN. TOURISM. see *TRAVEL AND TOURISM — Abstracting, Bibliographies, Statistics*

SEYCHELLES. STATISTICS DIVISION. STATISTICAL BULLETIN. VISITOR SURVEY. see *TRAVEL AND TOURISM — Abstracting, Bibliographies, Statistics*

310   CC
SHANGHAI TONGJI/SHANGHAI STATISTICS. (Text in Chinese) m. (Shanghai Shi Tongji-ju - Shanghai Municipal Bureau of Statistics) Shanghai Tongji Bianjibu, 1008 Dong Changzhi Road, Shanghai 200082, People's Republic of China. TEL 5458253. Ed. Yan Delun. **Document type:** government publication.

SHENZHEN TONGJI NIANJIAN (YEAR)/SHENZHEN STATISTICAL YEARBOOK. see *BUSINESS AND ECONOMICS — Abstracting, Bibliographies, Statistics*

SHIPPING STATISTICS AND ECONOMICS. see *TRANSPORTATION — Abstracting, Bibliographies, Statistics*

310   NE   ISSN 0254-7694
SHORT BOOK REVIEWS. (Text in English) 1980. 3/yr. $27.67. International Statistical Institute, Prinses Beatrixlaan 428, Postbus 950, 2270 AZ Voorburg, Netherlands. TEL 31-70-3375737. FAX 31-70-3860025. Ed. Dr. A.M. Herzberg. adv.; bk.rev. circ. 4,300. **Document type:** academic/scholarly publication.
   Description: Provides a rapid book review service for statisticians covering books on statistics and related subjects published throughout the world.

315   MY
SIARAN PERANGKAAN TAHUNAN - SABAH. 1964. a. M.$10. Department of Statistics - Jabatan Perangkaan, Wisma Statistik, Jalan Cenderasari, 50514 Kuala Lumpur, Malaysia. TEL 088-232277. (Subscr. to: Dept. of Statistics, Malaysia (Sabah Branch), 1st Fl., Federal House, Jalan Mat Salleh, 88000 Kota Kinabalu, Sabah, Malaysia) circ. 465. **Document type:** government publication.
   Formerly (until 1969): Malaysia. Department of Statistics. Annual Bulletin of Statistics Sabah (ISSN 0080-5203)

310   CC
SICHUAN TONGJI NIANJIAN/STATISTICAL YEARBOOK OF SICHUAN. (Text in Chinese) a. Y38. (Sichuan Tongji Ju) Zhongguo Tongji Chubanshe - China Statistics Publishing House, 38 Yuetan Nanjie, Sanlihe, Beijing 100826, People's Republic of China. TEL 8217162. TELEX 22778-FASSB-CN. **Document type:** government publication.

316   SL
SIERRA LEONE. CENTRAL STATISTICS OFFICE. ANNUAL STATISTICAL DIGEST. 1969? a. Le.8. Central Statistics Office, Tower Hill, Freetown, Sierra Leone.

310   SL   ISSN 0080-9535
SIERRA LEONE IN FIGURES. a. free. Bank of Sierra Leone, P.O. Box 30, Freetown, Sierra Leone. TEL 232-22-226501. FAX 232-22-224764. TELEX 3232 FREETOWN.

314   EI   ISSN 1018-5739
HA1107.5
SIGMA. (Editions in English, French) 1976. q. free. Statistical Office of the European Communities, L-2985 Luxembourg, Luxembourg. (Dist. in U.S. by: European Community Information Service, 210 M. St., N.W., Ste. 707, Washington, DC 20037) Ed. J. Drappier. **Indexed:** IIS, Int.Lab.Doc., Rural Recreat.Tour.Abstr., World Agri.Econ.& Rural Sociol.Abstr., World Bank.Abstr.
   —BLDSC (8275.367000).
   Formerly (until 1991): Eurostat News (ISSN 0378-4207)
   Description: Seeks to provide up-to-date information on the progress of measures taken in the run up towards European integration.

314   LU
SIGMA; the bulletin of European statistics. bi-m. free. Statistical Office of the European Communities, Bureau d'Information, Batiment Jean Monnet, L-2920 Luxembourg, Luxembourg. Ed. J. Drappier.

338 315   SI   ISSN 0037-5640
SINGAPORE. DEPARTMENT OF STATISTICS. MONTHLY DIGEST OF STATISTICS.. 1962. m. S.$7.70. Department of Statistics, 8 Shenton Way 10-01 Treasury Bldg., Singapore 0106, Singapore. TEL 3209702. FAX 3209689. TELEX RS 63001 STAT. **Document type:** government publication.
   Description: Provides current data relating to the demographic, economic and social characteristics of Singapore.

SINGAPORE. DEPARTMENT OF STATISTICS. REPORT ON THE SURVEY OF SERVICES (YEAR). see *PUBLIC ADMINISTRATION — Abstracting, Bibliographies, Statistics*

SINGAPORE. DEPARTMENT OF STATISTICS. REPORT ON THE SURVEY OF WHOLESALE TRADE, RETAIL TRADE, RESTAURANTS & HOTELS (YEAR). see *HOTELS AND RESTAURANTS — Abstracting, Bibliographies, Statistics*

SINGAPORE MONTHLY TRADE STATISTICS: IMPORTS & EXPORTS. see *BUSINESS AND ECONOMICS — Abstracting, Bibliographies, Statistics*

315   SI   ISSN 0583-3655
HA1797.S5
SINGAPORE YEARBOOK OF STATISTICS. a. S.$13.40. Department of Statistics, 8 Shenton Way 10-01 Treasury Bldg., Singapore 0106, Singapore. TEL 3209702. FAX 3209689. TELEX RS-63001 STAT. charts.
    Description: Provides important data on the demographic, economic and social characteristics of Singapore.

SISTER COMMUNITIES HEALTH PROFILES OF THE U S - MEXICO BORDER/PERFILES DE SALUD DE LAS COMUNIDADES HERMANAS DE LA FRONTERA MEXICO - ESTADOS UNIDOS. see *PUBLIC HEALTH AND SAFETY — Abstracting, Bibliographies, Statistics*

SITUATION ET STATISTIQUES MONDIALES DU SECTEUR VITICOLE. see *BEVERAGES — Abstracting, Bibliographies, Statistics*

SOCIAL INDICATORS BY PREFECTURE (YEAR). see *SOCIAL SERVICES AND WELFARE — Abstracting, Bibliographies, Statistics*

SOCIAL TRENDS IN NEW ZEALAND. see *SOCIOLOGY — Abstracting, Bibliographies, Statistics*

310   FR
SOCIETE DE STATISTIQUE DE PARIS. JOURNAL; la revue internationale des statisticiens d'expression Francaise. 1869. q. 500 F. to individuals (foreign 600 F.); institutions 1,000 F.(foreign 1,200 F.). Societe de Statististique de Paris, 15 bd. Gabriel Peri, B.P. 100, 92244 Malakoff Cedex, France. TEL 38-41-72-61. FAX 38-41-73-80. Ed. G. Gallais-Hamonno. bk.rev.; bibl.; charts; stat. circ. 1,000. (also avail. in microfiche from BHP; reprint service avail. from KTO) **Indexed:** J.Cont.Quant.Meth., P.A.I.S.For.Lang.Ind. **Document type:** academic/scholarly publication.
    Former titles: Societe de Statistique de Paris et de France. Journal; Societe de Statistique de Paris. Journal (ISSN 0037-914X)

316   SO
SOMALIA IN FIGURES. triennial. free. Ministry of National Planning, Direction of Statistics, P.O. Box 1742, Mogadisho, Somalia.
    Description: Contains statistics on the population, livestock, agriculture, fishery, economy, transportation, education and health trends and conditions in Somalia.

310   JA   ISSN 0446-5849
SOMUCHO. TOKEIKYOKU KENKYU IHO/MANAGEMENT AND COORDINATION AGENCY. STATISTICS BUREAU. RESEARCH MEMOIR. (Text in Japanese; summaries in English) 1950. s-a. Somucho, Tokeikyoku - Management and Coordination Agency, Statistics Bureau, 19-1, Wakamatsu-cho, Shinjuku-ku, Tokyo 162, Japan. **Document type:** government publication.

SOURCEBOOK OF CRIMINAL JUSTICE STATISTICS. see *CRIMINOLOGY AND LAW ENFORCEMENT — Abstracting, Bibliographies, Statistics*

SOUTH AFRICA. CENTRAL STATISTICAL SERVICE. AGRICULTURAL SURVEY. see *AGRICULTURE — Abstracting, Bibliographies, Statistics*

316.8   SA
SOUTH AFRICA. CENTRAL STATISTICAL SERVICE. ANNUAL REPORT/SOUTH AFRICA. SENTRALE STATISTIEKDIENS. JAARVERSLAG. a. free. Central Statistical Service - Sentrale Statistiekdiens, Private Bag X44, Pretoria 0001, South Africa. TEL 27-12-310-8911. FAX 27-12-310-8500. **Document type:** government publication.
    Formerly: South Africa. Department of Statistics. Annual Report of the Statistics Advisory Council and of the Secretary of Statistics.

SOUTH AFRICA. CENTRAL STATISTICAL SERVICE. BIRTHS. see *POPULATION STUDIES — Abstracting, Bibliographies, Statistics*

SOUTH AFRICA. CENTRAL STATISTICAL SERVICE. BUILDING PLANS PASSED AND BUILDINGS COMPLETED. see *BUILDING AND CONSTRUCTION — Abstracting, Bibliographies, Statistics*

316.8   SA   ISSN 0034-5024
HA1991
SOUTH AFRICA. CENTRAL STATISTICAL SERVICE. BULLETIN OF STATISTICS. Key Title: Bulletin van Statistiek. (Text in Afrikaans, English) 1967. q. R.20 per no. (foreign R.27.40) (effective 1994). Central Statistical Service - Sentrale Statistiekdiens, Private Bag X44, Pretoria 0001, South Africa. TEL 27-12-310-8911. FAX 27-12-310-8500. (Orders to: Government Printing Works, Private Bag X85, Pretoria 0001, South Africa) circ. 1,200. **Document type:** government publication, bulletin.
    Former titles: South Africa. Department of Statistics. Bulletin of Statistics; South Africa. Department of Statistics. Monthly Bulletin of Statistics.

SOUTH AFRICA. CENTRAL STATISTICAL SERVICE. CENSUS OF ARCHITECTS AND QUANTITY SURVEYORS. see *ARCHITECTURE — Abstracting, Bibliographies, Statistics*

SOUTH AFRICA. CENTRAL STATISTICAL SERVICE. CENSUS OF BUSINESS SERVICES - ACCOUNTING, AUDITING AND BOOKKEEPING SERVICES. see *BUSINESS AND ECONOMICS — Abstracting, Bibliographies, Statistics*

SOUTH AFRICA. CENTRAL STATISTICAL SERVICE. CENSUS OF BUSINESS SERVICES - ADVERTISING PRACTITIONERS AND ALLIED SERVICES AND MARKETING RESEARCH SERVICES. see *ADVERTISING AND PUBLIC RELATIONS — Abstracting, Bibliographies, Statistics*

SOUTH AFRICA. CENTRAL STATISTICAL SERVICE. CENSUS OF BUSINESS SERVICES - CONSULTING ENGINEERS. see *BUSINESS AND ECONOMICS — Abstracting, Bibliographies, Statistics*

SOUTH AFRICA. CENTRAL STATISTICAL SERVICE. CENSUS OF BUSINESS SERVICES - DATA PROCESSING SERVICES. see *BUSINESS AND ECONOMICS — Abstracting, Bibliographies, Statistics*

SOUTH AFRICA. CENTRAL STATISTICAL SERVICE. CENSUS OF BUSINESS SERVICES - EMPLOYMENT PLACEMENT AGENCIES, RECRUITING ORGANISATIONS AND LABOUR BROKERS SERVICES. see *BUSINESS AND ECONOMICS — Abstracting, Bibliographies, Statistics*

SOUTH AFRICA. CENTRAL STATISTICAL SERVICE. CENSUS OF BUSINESS SERVICES - LEGAL SERVICES. see *BUSINESS AND ECONOMICS — Abstracting, Bibliographies, Statistics*

SOUTH AFRICA. CENTRAL STATISTICAL SERVICE. CENSUS OF CONSTRUCTION. see *BUILDING AND CONSTRUCTION — Abstracting, Bibliographies, Statistics*

SOUTH AFRICA. CENTRAL STATISTICAL SERVICE. CENSUS OF ELECTRICITY, GAS AND STEAM. see *ENERGY — Abstracting, Bibliographies, Statistics*

SOUTH AFRICA. CENTRAL STATISTICAL SERVICE. CENSUS OF ESTATE AGENCIES, RENT COLLECTORS, APPRAISERS AND VALUERS. see *REAL ESTATE — Abstracting, Bibliographies, Statistics*

SOUTH AFRICA. CENTRAL STATISTICAL SERVICE. CENSUS OF HOSPITALS, CLINICS, AND OTHER HEALTH SERVICE ESTABLISHMENTS. see *HOSPITALS — Abstracting, Bibliographies, Statistics*

SOUTH AFRICA. CENTRAL STATISTICAL SERVICE. CENSUS OF LETTING OF OWN FIXED PROPERTY. see *REAL ESTATE — Abstracting, Bibliographies, Statistics*

SOUTH AFRICA. CENTRAL STATISTICAL SERVICE. CENSUS OF LICENSED RESTAURANTS. see *HOTELS AND RESTAURANTS — Abstracting, Bibliographies, Statistics*

SOUTH AFRICA. CENTRAL STATISTICAL SERVICE. CENSUS OF MANUFACTURING - MATERIALS PURCHASED AND MANUFACTURES SOLD. see *BUSINESS AND ECONOMICS — Abstracting, Bibliographies, Statistics*

SOUTH AFRICA. CENTRAL STATISTICAL SERVICE. CENSUS OF MANUFACTURING - PRINCIPAL STATISTICS ON A REGIONAL BASIS. see *BUSINESS AND ECONOMICS — Abstracting, Bibliographies, Statistics*

SOUTH AFRICA. CENTRAL STATISTICAL SERVICE. CENSUS OF MANUFACTURING - REGISTER OF MANUFACTURERS ACCORDING TO PRODUCTS MANUFACTURED IN SOUTH AFRICA. see *BUSINESS AND ECONOMICS — Abstracting, Bibliographies, Statistics*

SOUTH AFRICA. CENTRAL STATISTICAL SERVICE. CENSUS OF MANUFACTURING - STATISTICS ACCORDING TO MAJOR GROUPS AND SUBGROUPS. see *BUSINESS AND ECONOMICS — Abstracting, Bibliographies, Statistics*

SOUTH AFRICA. CENTRAL STATISTICAL SERVICE. CENSUS OF MEDICAL, DENTAL AND OTHER HEALTH SERVICES - CHIROPRACTORS, HOMEOPATHS, NATUROPATHS, OSTEOPATHS AND HERBALISTS. see *MEDICAL SCIENCES — Abstracting, Bibliographies, Statistics*

SOUTH AFRICA. CENTRAL STATISTICAL SERVICE. CENSUS OF MEDICAL, DENTAL AND OTHER HEALTH SERVICES - DOCTORS. see *MEDICAL SCIENCES — Abstracting, Bibliographies, Statistics*

SOUTH AFRICA. CENTRAL STATISTICAL SERVICE. CENSUS OF MEDICAL, DENTAL AND OTHER HEALTH SERVICES - DENTISTS. see *MEDICAL SCIENCES — Abstracting, Bibliographies, Statistics*

SOUTH AFRICA. CENTRAL STATISTICAL SERVICE. CENSUS OF MEDICAL, DENTAL AND OTHER HEALTH SERVICES - SUPPLEMENTARY HEALTH SERVICES AND DENTAL TECHNICIANS. see *MEDICAL SCIENCES — Abstracting, Bibliographies, Statistics*

SOUTH AFRICA. CENTRAL STATISTICAL SERVICE. CENSUS OF MINING. see *MINES AND MINING INDUSTRY — Abstracting, Bibliographies, Statistics*

SOUTH AFRICA. CENTRAL STATISTICAL SERVICE. CENSUS OF MOTOR TRADE AND REPAIR SERVICES. see *BUSINESS AND ECONOMICS — Abstracting, Bibliographies, Statistics*

SOUTH AFRICA. CENTRAL STATISTICAL SERVICE. CENSUS OF RENTING AND LEASING OF MACHINERY AND EQUIPMENT. see *MACHINERY — Abstracting, Bibliographies, Statistics*

SOUTH AFRICA. CENTRAL STATISTICAL SERVICE. CENSUS OF RETAIL TRADE. see *BUSINESS AND ECONOMICS — Abstracting, Bibliographies, Statistics*

SOUTH AFRICA. CENTRAL STATISTICAL SERVICE. CENSUS OF SOCIAL, RECREATIONAL AND PERSONAL SERVICES - HAIRDRESSING AND BEAUTY SERVICES. see *BEAUTY CULTURE — Abstracting, Bibliographies, Statistics*

SOUTH AFRICA. CENTRAL STATISTICAL SERVICE. CENSUS OF SOCIAL, RECREATIONAL AND PERSONAL SERVICES - LAUNDRY, CLEANING AND DYEING SERVICES. see *CLEANING AND DYEING — Abstracting, Bibliographies, Statistics*

SOUTH AFRICA. CENTRAL STATISTICAL SERVICE. CENSUS OF SOCIAL, RECREATIONAL AND PERSONAL SERVICES - MOTION PICTURE AND VIDEO PRODUCTION. see *MOTION PICTURES — Abstracting, Bibliographies, Statistics*

SOUTH AFRICA. CENTRAL STATISTICAL SERVICE. CENSUS OF SOCIAL, RECREATIONAL AND PERSONAL SERVICES - MOTION PICTURE DISTRIBUTION AND PROJECTION AND VIDEO DISTRIBUTION SERVICES. see *MOTION PICTURES — Abstracting, Bibliographies, Statistics*

SOUTH AFRICA. CENTRAL STATISTICAL SERVICE. CENSUS OF SOCIAL, RECREATIONAL AND PERSONAL SERVICES - PHOTOGRAPHIC STUDIOS. see *PHOTOGRAPHY — Abstracting, Bibliographies, Statistics*

SOUTH AFRICA. CENTRAL STATISTICAL SERVICE. CENSUS OF SOCIAL, RECREATIONAL AND PERSONAL SERVICES - UNDERTAKERS AND CREMATORIUM SERVICES. see *FUNERALS — Abstracting, Bibliographies, Statistics*

STATISTICS

SOUTH AFRICA. CENTRAL STATISTICAL SERVICE. CENSUS OF SOCIAL, RECREATIONAL AND PERSONAL SERVICES - WELFARE ORGANISATIONS. see *SOCIAL SERVICES AND WELFARE* — *Abstracting, Bibliographies, Statistics*

SOUTH AFRICA. CENTRAL STATISTICAL SERVICE. CENSUS OF TOWNSHIP DEVELOPMENT. see *HOUSING AND URBAN PLANNING* — *Abstracting, Bibliographies, Statistics*

SOUTH AFRICA. CENTRAL STATISTICAL SERVICE. CENSUS OF TRANSPORT AND ALLIED SERVICES. see *TRANSPORTATION* — *Abstracting, Bibliographies, Statistics*

SOUTH AFRICA. CENTRAL STATISTICAL SERVICE. CENSUS OF VETERINARY SERVICES, ANIMAL HOSPITALS AND CARE CENTRES. see *VETERINARY SCIENCE* — *Abstracting, Bibliographies, Statistics*

SOUTH AFRICA. CENTRAL STATISTICAL SERVICE. CENSUS OF WHOLESALE TRADE, COMMERCIAL AGENTS AND ALLIED SERVICES. see *BUSINESS AND ECONOMICS* — *Abstracting, Bibliographies, Statistics*

SOUTH AFRICA. CENTRAL STATISTICAL SERVICE. CRIMES: PROSECUTIONS AND CONVICTIONS WITH REGARD TO CERTAIN OFFENCES. see *LAW* — *Abstracting, Bibliographies, Statistics*

SOUTH AFRICA. CENTRAL STATISTICAL SERVICE. CURRENT POPULATION SURVEY - COLOUREDS AND ASIANS. see *POPULATION STUDIES* — *Abstracting, Bibliographies, Statistics*

SOUTH AFRICA. CENTRAL STATISTICAL SERVICE. DEMOGRAPHIC STATISTICS. see *POPULATION STUDIES* — *Abstracting, Bibliographies, Statistics*

SOUTH AFRICA. CENTRAL STATISTICAL SERVICE. FINAL SOCIAL ACCOUNTING MATRIX FOR SOUTH AFRICA. see *PUBLIC ADMINISTRATION* — *Abstracting, Bibliographies, Statistics*

SOUTH AFRICA. CENTRAL STATISTICAL SERVICE. FINANCIAL STATISTICS OF COMPANIES (YEAR). see *BUSINESS AND ECONOMICS* — *Abstracting, Bibliographies, Statistics*

SOUTH AFRICA. CENTRAL STATISTICAL SERVICE. FINANCIAL STATISTICS OF LOCAL GOVERNMENTS. see *PUBLIC ADMINISTRATION* — *Abstracting, Bibliographies, Statistics*

SOUTH AFRICA. CENTRAL STATISTICAL SERVICE. INPUT OUTPUT TABLES. see *BUSINESS AND ECONOMICS* — *Abstracting, Bibliographies, Statistics*

SOUTH AFRICA. CENTRAL STATISTICAL SERVICE. LOCAL GOVERNMENT STATISTICS. see *PUBLIC ADMINISTRATION* — *Abstracting, Bibliographies, Statistics*

SOUTH AFRICA. CENTRAL STATISTICAL SERVICE. MANPOWER SURVEY (OCCUPATIONAL INFORMATION). see *BUSINESS AND ECONOMICS* — *Abstracting, Bibliographies, Statistics*

SOUTH AFRICA. CENTRAL STATISTICAL SERVICE. NEW VEHICLES REGISTERED. see *TRANSPORTATION* — *Abstracting, Bibliographies, Statistics*

SOUTH AFRICA. CENTRAL STATISTICAL SERVICE. POPULATION CENSUS. ADJUSTMENT FOR UNDERCOUNT. see *POPULATION STUDIES* — *Abstracting, Bibliographies, Statistics*

SOUTH AFRICA. CENTRAL STATISTICAL SERVICE. POPULATION CENSUS. AGE BY DEVELOPMENT REGION, STATISTICAL REGION AND DISTRICT (URBAN AND NON-URBAN). see *POPULATION STUDIES* — *Abstracting, Bibliographies, Statistics*

SOUTH AFRICA. CENTRAL STATISTICAL SERVICE. POPULATION CENSUS. DURATION OF STAY BY DEVELOPMENT REGION, STATISTICAL REGION AND DISTRICT. see *POPULATION STUDIES* — *Abstracting, Bibliographies, Statistics*

SOUTH AFRICA. CENTRAL STATISTICAL SERVICE. POPULATION CENSUS. DWELLINGS. see *POPULATION STUDIES* — *Abstracting, Bibliographies, Statistics*

SOUTH AFRICA. CENTRAL STATISTICAL SERVICE. POPULATION CENSUS. ECONOMIC CHARACTERISTICS OF THE POPULATION. see *POPULATION STUDIES* — *Abstracting, Bibliographies, Statistics*

SOUTH AFRICA. CENTRAL STATISTICAL SERVICE. POPULATION CENSUS. ECONOMIC SECTOR BY DEVELOPMENT REGION, STATISTICAL REGION AND DISTRICT. see *POPULATION STUDIES* — *Abstracting, Bibliographies, Statistics*

SOUTH AFRICA. CENTRAL STATISTICAL SERVICE. POPULATION CENSUS. GEOGRAPHICAL DISTRIBUTION OF THE POPULATION. see *POPULATION STUDIES* — *Abstracting, Bibliographies, Statistics*

SOUTH AFRICA. CENTRAL STATISTICAL SERVICE. POPULATION CENSUS. HOME LANGUAGE BY DEVELOPMENT REGION, STATISTICAL REGION AND DISTRICT. see *POPULATION STUDIES* — *Abstracting, Bibliographies, Statistics*

SOUTH AFRICA. CENTRAL STATISTICAL SERVICE. POPULATION CENSUS. HOUSEHOLDS. see *POPULATION STUDIES* — *Abstracting, Bibliographies, Statistics*

SOUTH AFRICA. CENTRAL STATISTICAL SERVICE. POPULATION CENSUS. INCOME BY DEVELOPMENT REGION, STATISTICAL REGION AND DISTRICT. see *POPULATION STUDIES* — *Abstracting, Bibliographies, Statistics*

SOUTH AFRICA. CENTRAL STATISTICAL SERVICE. POPULATION CENSUS. LEVEL OF EDUCATION BY DEVELOPMENT REGION, STATISTICAL REGION AND DISTRICT (URBAN AND NON-URBAN). see *POPULATION STUDIES* — *Abstracting, Bibliographies, Statistics*

SOUTH AFRICA. CENTRAL STATISTICAL SERVICE. POPULATION CENSUS. OCCUPATION BY DEVELOPMENT REGION, STATISTICAL REGION AND DISTRICT. see *POPULATION STUDIES* — *Abstracting, Bibliographies, Statistics*

SOUTH AFRICA. CENTRAL STATISTICAL SERVICE. POPULATION CENSUS. RELIGION BY DEVELOPMENT REGION, STATISTICAL REGION AND DISTRICT. see *RELIGIONS AND THEOLOGY* — *Abstracting, Bibliographies, Statistics*

SOUTH AFRICA. CENTRAL STATISTICAL SERVICE. POPULATION CENSUS. SELECTED STATISTICAL REGIONS. see *POPULATION STUDIES* — *Abstracting, Bibliographies, Statistics*

SOUTH AFRICA. CENTRAL STATISTICAL SERVICE. POPULATION CENSUS. SOCIAL CHARACTERISTICS OF THE POPULATION. see *POPULATION STUDIES* — *Abstracting, Bibliographies, Statistics*

SOUTH AFRICA. CENTRAL STATISTICAL SERVICE. POPULATION CENSUS. SUMMARISED RESULTS AFTER ADJUSTMENT FOR UNDERCOUNT. see *POPULATION STUDIES* — *Abstracting, Bibliographies, Statistics*

SOUTH AFRICA. CENTRAL STATISTICAL SERVICE. POPULATION CENSUS (YEAR). see *POPULATION STUDIES* — *Abstracting, Bibliographies, Statistics*

SOUTH AFRICA. CENTRAL STATISTICAL SERVICE. PROJECTIONS. see *POPULATION STUDIES* — *Abstracting, Bibliographies, Statistics*

316.8   SA
▼**SOUTH AFRICA. CENTRAL STATISTICAL SERVICE. PROVINCIAL STATISTICS PART 1 - WESTERN CAPE.** (Report no. 00-90-01) 1994. a. R.10 (foreign R.11). Central Statistical Service - Sentrale Statistiekdiens, Private Bag X44, Pretoria 0001, South Africa. TEL 27-12-310-8911. FAX 27-12-310-8500. (Orders to: Government Printing Works, Private Bag X85, Pretoria 0001, South Africa) **Document type:** government publication.
   Description: Provides statistical data on demography, housing, education, health, industries, gross geographical product and price indices for the Western Cape province.

316.8   SA
▼**SOUTH AFRICA. CENTRAL STATISTICAL SERVICE. PROVINCIAL STATISTICS PART 2 - EASTERN CAPE.** (Report no. 00-90-02) 1994. a. R.10 (foreign R.11). Central Statistical Service, Private Bag X44, Pretoria 0001, South Africa. TEL 27-12-310-8911. FAX 27-12-310-8500. (Orders to: Government Printing Works, Private Bag X85, Pretoria 0001, South Africa) **Document type:** government publication.
   Description: Provides statistical data on demography, housing, education, health, industries, gross geographic product and price indices for the Eastern Cape province.

316.8   SA
▼**SOUTH AFRICA. CENTRAL STATISTICAL SERVICE. PROVINCIAL STATISTICS PART 3 - NORTHERN CAPE.** (Report no. 00-90-03) 1994. a. R.10 (foreign R.11). Central Statistical Service, Private Bag X44, Pretoria 0001, South Africa. TEL 27-12-310-8911. FAX 27-12-310-8500. (Orders to: Government Printing Works, Private Bag X85, Pretoria 0001, South Africa) **Document type:** government publication.
   Description: Provides statistical data on demography, housing, education, health, industries, gross geographic product and price indices for the Northern Cape province.

316.8   SA
▼**SOUTH AFRICA. CENTRAL STATISTICAL SERVICE. PROVINCIAL STATISTICS PART 4 - ORANGE FREE STATE.** (Report no. 00-90-04) 1994. a. R.10 (foreign R.11). Central Statistical Service - Sentrale Statistiekdiens, Private Bag X44, Pretoria 0001, South Africa. TEL 27-12-310-8911. FAX 27-12-310-8500. (Orders to: Government Printing Works, Private Bag X85, Pretoria 0001, South Africa) **Document type:** government publication.
   Description: Provides statistical data on demography, housing, education, health, industries, gross geographic product and price indices for the Orange Free State.

316.8   SA
▼**SOUTH AFRICA. CENTRAL STATISTICAL SERVICE. PROVINCIAL STATISTICS PART 5 - KWAZULU - NATAL.** (Report no. 00-90-05) 1994. a. R.10 (foreign R.11). Central Statistical Service - Sentrale Statistiekdiens, Private Bag X44, Pretoria 0001, South Africa. TEL 27-12-310-8911. FAX 27-12-310-8500. (Orders to: Government Printing Works, Private Bag X85, Pretoria 0001, South Africa) **Document type:** government publication.
   Description: Provides statistical data on demography, housing, education, health, industries, gross geographic product and price indices for KwaZulu - Natal.

316.8   SA
▼**SOUTH AFRICA. CENTRAL STATISTICAL SERVICE. PROVINCIAL STATISTICS PART 6 - NORTH-WEST.** (Report no. 00-90-06) 1994. a. R.10 (foreign R.11). Central Statistical Service, Private Bag X44, Pretoria 0001, South Africa. TEL 27-12-310-8911. FAX 27-12-310-8500. (Orders to: Government Printing Works, Private Bag X85, Pretoria 0001, South Africa) **Document type:** government publication.
   Description: Provides statistical data on demography, housing, education, health, industries, gross geographic product and price industries for the North-West province.

316.8   SA
▼**SOUTH AFRICA. CENTRAL STATISTICAL SERVICE. PROVINCIAL STATISTICS PART 7 - PRETORIA - WITWATERSRAND - VEREENIGING.** (Report no. 00-90-07) 1994. a. R.10 (foreign R.11). Central Statistical Service - Sentrale Statistiekdiens, Private Bag X44, Pretoria 0001, South Africa. TEL 27-12-310-8911. FAX 27-12-310-8500. (Orders to: Government Printing Works, Private Bag X85, Pretoria 0001, South Africa) **Document type:** government publication.
   Description: Provides statistics on demography, housing, education, health, industries, gross geographical product and price indices for the PWV province.

316.8　　　　SA
▼SOUTH AFRICA. CENTRAL STATISTICAL SERVICE. PROVINCIAL STATISTICS PART 8 - EASTERN TRANSVAAL. (Report no. 00-90-08) 1994. a. R.11 (foreign R.11). Central Statistical Service, Private Bag X44, Pretoria 0001, South Africa. TEL 27-12-310-8911. FAX 27-12-310-8500. (Orders to: Government Printing Works, Private Bag X85, Pretoria 0001, South Africa) Document type: government publication.
Description: Provides statistical data on demography, housing, education, health, industries, gross geographic product and price indices for the Eastern Transvaal.

316.8　　　　SA
▼SOUTH AFRICA. CENTRAL STATISTICAL SERVICE. PROVINCIAL STATISTICS PART 9 - NORTHERN TRANSVAAL. (Report no. 00-90-09) 1994. a. R.10 (foreign R.11). Central Statistical Service, Private Bag X44, Pretoria 0001, South Africa. TEL 27-12-310-8911. FAX 27-12-310-8500. (Orders to: Government Printing Works, Private Bag X85, Pretoria 0001, South Africa) Document type: government publication.
Description: Provides statistical data on demography, housing, education, health, industries, gross geographic product and price indices for the Northern Transvaal.

316.8　　　　SA
▼SOUTH AFRICA. CENTRAL STATISTICAL SERVICE. PROVINCIAL STATISTICS PART 10 - REPUBLIC OF SOUTH AFRICA. (Report No. 00-90-10) 1994. a. R.10 (foreign R.11). Central Statistical Service - Sentral Statistiekdiens, Private Bag X44, Pretoria 0001, South Africa. TEL 27-12-310-8911. FAX 27-12-310-8500. (Orders to: Government Printing Works, Private Bag X85, Pretoria 0001, South Africa) Document type: government publication.
Description: Provides statistical data on demography, housing, education, health, industries and the gross geographic product for South Africa.

SOUTH AFRICA. CENTRAL STATISTICAL SERVICE. REGISTERED VEHICLES AS AT 30 JUNE. see *TRANSPORTATION* — Abstracting, Bibliographies, Statistics

316.8　　　　SA　　ISSN 0258-0616
SOUTH AFRICA. CENTRAL STATISTICAL SERVICE. REPORT/SOUTH AFRICA. SENTRALE STATISTIEKDIENS. VERSLAG. (Text in Afrikaans, English) irreg. Central Statistical Service - Sentrale Statistiekdiens, Private Bag X44, Pretoria 0001, South Africa. TEL 27-12-310-8911. FAX 27-12-310-8500. (Orders to: Government Printing Works, Private Bag X85, Pretoria 0001, South Africa) Document type: government publication.

SOUTH AFRICA. CENTRAL STATISTICAL SERVICE. REPORT ON MARRIAGES AND DIVORCES - WHITES, COLOUREDS AND ASIANS - SOUTH AFRICA. see *POPULATION STUDIES* — Abstracting, Bibliographies, Statistics

SOUTH AFRICA. CENTRAL STATISTICAL SERVICE. ROAD TRAFFIC COLLISIONS. see *TRANSPORTATION* — Abstracting, Bibliographies, Statistics

SOUTH AFRICA. CENTRAL STATISTICAL SERVICE. SOUTH AFRICAN LIFE TABLES. see *POPULATION STUDIES* — Abstracting, Bibliographies, Statistics

SOUTH AFRICA. CENTRAL STATISTICAL SERVICE. STANDARD CODE LIST FOR STATISTICAL REGIONS, MAGISTERIAL DISTRICTS, CITIES, TOWNS, AND NON-URBAN AREAS. see *METROLOGY AND STANDARDIZATION*

SOUTH AFRICA. CENTRAL STATISTICAL SERVICE. STANDARD INDUSTRIAL CLASSIFICATION OF ALL ECONOMIC ACTIVITIES. see *METROLOGY AND STANDARDIZATION*

316.8　　　　SA
SOUTH AFRICA. CENTRAL STATISTICAL SERVICE. STATISTICAL RELEASE. (Series of 135 news releases, Nos. P0002 - P9504) irreg. free. Central Statistical Service - Sentrale Statistiekdiens, Private Bag X44, Pretoria 0001, South Africa. TEL 27-12-310-8911. FAX 27-12-310-8500. Document type: government publication.
Formerly: South Africa. Department of Statistics. Statistical News Releases.
Description: Provides summary statistical data on all aspects of South African life for which statistics are collected, including population censuses, vital statistics, business surveys, and government financial statisitics.

SOUTH AFRICA. CENTRAL STATISTICAL SERVICE. STATISTICAL RELEASE. ACTUAL AND ANTICIPATED CAPITAL EXPENDITURE OF THE PUBLIC SECTOR. see *BUSINESS AND ECONOMICS* — Abstracting, Bibliographies, Statistics

SOUTH AFRICA. CENTRAL STATISTICAL SERVICE. STATISTICAL RELEASE. ACTUAL AND ANTICIPATED CONSTRUCTION EXPENDITURE OF THE PUBLIC SECTOR BY REGION. see *BUSINESS AND ECONOMICS* — Abstracting, Bibliographies, Statistics

SOUTH AFRICA. CENTRAL STATISTICAL SERVICE. STATISTICAL RELEASE. AGRICULTURAL SURVEY. see *AGRICULTURE* — Abstracting, Bibliographies, Statistics

SOUTH AFRICA. CENTRAL STATISTICAL SERVICE. STATISTICAL RELEASE. AVERAGE RETAIL PRICES OF FOOD. see *BUSINESS AND ECONOMICS* — Abstracting, Bibliographies, Statistics

SOUTH AFRICA. CENTRAL STATISTICAL SERVICE. STATISTICAL RELEASE. BUILDING INDUSTRY ADVISORY COUNCIL CONTRACT PRICE ADJUSTMENT PROVISIONS - WORKGROUP INDICES (HAYLETT). see *BUILDING AND CONSTRUCTION* — Abstracting, Bibliographies, Statistics

SOUTH AFRICA. CENTRAL STATISTICAL SERVICE. STATISTICAL RELEASE. BUILDING PLANS PASSED AND BUILDINGS COMPLETED. see *BUILDING AND CONSTRUCTION* — Abstracting, Bibliographies, Statistics

SOUTH AFRICA. CENTRAL STATISTICAL SERVICE. STATISTICAL RELEASE. BUILDING STATISTICS - PRIVATE SECTOR. see *BUILDING AND CONSTRUCTION* — Abstracting, Bibliographies, Statistics

SOUTH AFRICA. CENTRAL STATISTICAL SERVICE. STATISTICAL RELEASE. CENTRAL GOVERNMENT: REVENUE OF THE STATE REVENUE AND OTHER REVENUE ACCOUNTS. see *PUBLIC ADMINISTRATION* — Abstracting, Bibliographies, Statistics

SOUTH AFRICA. CENTRAL STATISTICAL SERVICE. STATISTICAL RELEASE. CENSUS OF ACCOUNTING, AUDITING AND BOOKKEEPING SERVICES (YEAR). see *BUSINESS AND ECONOMICS* — Abstracting, Bibliographies, Statistics

SOUTH AFRICA. CENTRAL STATISTICAL SERVICE. STATISTICAL RELEASE. CENSUS OF AUXILIARY, HEALTH SERVICES AND DENTAL TECHNICIANS (YEAR). see *MEDICAL SCIENCES* — Abstracting, Bibliographies, Statistics

SOUTH AFRICA. CENTRAL STATISTICAL SERVICE. STATISTICAL RELEASE. CENSUS OF ADVERTISING PRACTITIONERS AND ALLIED SERVICES AND MARKETING RESEARCH SERVICES. see *ADVERTISING AND PUBLIC RELATIONS* — Abstracting, Bibliographies, Statistics

SOUTH AFRICA. CENTRAL STATISTICAL SERVICE. STATISTICAL RELEASE. CENSUS OF BUSINESS SERVICES - LEGAL SERVICES (YEAR). see *BUSINESS AND ECONOMICS* — Abstracting, Bibliographies, Statistics

SOUTH AFRICA. CENTRAL STATISTICAL SERVICE. STATISTICAL RELEASE. CENSUS OF CONSTRUCTION. see *BUILDING AND CONSTRUCTION* — Abstracting, Bibliographies, Statistics

SOUTH AFRICA. CENTRAL STATISTICAL SERVICE. STATISTICAL RELEASE. CENSUS OF CHIROPRACTORS AND HOMEOPATHS. see *MEDICAL SCIENCES* — Abstracting, Bibliographies, Statistics

SOUTH AFRICA. CENTRAL STATISTICAL SERVICE. STATISTICAL RELEASE. CENSUS OF CONSULTING ENGINEERING SERVICES (YEAR). see *BUSINESS AND ECONOMICS* — Abstracting, Bibliographies, Statistics

SOUTH AFRICA. CENTRAL STATISTICAL SERVICE. STATISTICAL RELEASE. CENSUS OF DATA PROCESSING SERVICES (YEAR). see *BUSINESS AND ECONOMICS* — Abstracting, Bibliographies, Statistics

SOUTH AFRICA. CENTRAL STATISTICAL SERVICE. STATISTICAL RELEASE. CENSUS OF DOCTORS (YEAR). see *MEDICAL SCIENCES* — Abstracting, Bibliographies, Statistics

SOUTH AFRICA. CENTRAL STATISTICAL SERVICE. STATISTICAL RELEASE. CENSUS OF DENTISTS (YEAR). see *MEDICAL SCIENCES* — Abstracting, Bibliographies, Statistics

SOUTH AFRICA. CENTRAL STATISTICAL SERVICE. STATISTICAL RELEASE. CENSUS OF ELECTRICITY, GAS AND STEAM. see *ENERGY* — Abstracting, Bibliographies, Statistics

SOUTH AFRICA. CENTRAL STATISTICAL SERVICE. STATISTICAL RELEASE. CENSUS OF EMPLOYMENT PLACEMENT AGENCIES, RECRUITING ORGANISATIONS AND LABOUR BROKERS SERVICES. see *BUSINESS AND ECONOMICS* — Abstracting, Bibliographies, Statistics

SOUTH AFRICA. CENTRAL STATISTICAL SERVICE. STATISTICAL RELEASE. CENSUS OF HOSPITALS, CLINICS AND OTHER HEALTH SERVICE ESTABLISHMENTS (YEAR). see *HOSPITALS* — Abstracting, Bibliographies, Statistics

SOUTH AFRICA. CENTRAL STATISTICAL SERVICE. STATISTICAL RELEASE. CENSUS OF LETTING OF OWN FIXED PROPERTY (YEAR). see *REAL ESTATE* — Abstracting, Bibliographies, Statistics

SOUTH AFRICA. CENTRAL STATISTICAL SERVICE. STATISTICAL RELEASE. CENSUS OF MINING. see *MINES AND MINING INDUSTRY* — Abstracting, Bibliographies, Statistics

SOUTH AFRICA. CENTRAL STATISTICAL SERVICE. STATISTICAL RELEASE. CENSUS OF MANUFACTURING. see *BUSINESS AND ECONOMICS* — Abstracting, Bibliographies, Statistics

SOUTH AFRICA. CENTRAL STATISTICAL SERVICE. STATISTICAL RELEASE. CENSUS OF SOCIAL, RECREATIONAL AND PERSONAL SERVICES (YEAR). see *SOCIAL SERVICES AND WELFARE* — Abstracting, Bibliographies, Statistics

SOUTH AFRICA. CENTRAL STATISTICAL SERVICE. STATISTICAL RELEASE. CENSUS OF TRANSPORT AND ALLIED SERVICES. see *TRANSPORTATION* — Abstracting, Bibliographies, Statistics

SOUTH AFRICA. CENTRAL STATISTICAL SERVICE. STATISTICAL RELEASE. CENSUS OF TOWNSHIP DEVELOPERS. see *REAL ESTATE* — Abstracting, Bibliographies, Statistics

SOUTH AFRICA. CENTRAL STATISTICAL SERVICE. STATISTICAL RELEASE. CONSTRUCTION AND TOWNSHIP DEVELOPERS: WORK ON HAND AND WORK DONE. see *BUILDING AND CONSTRUCTION* — Abstracting, Bibliographies, Statistics

SOUTH AFRICA. CENTRAL STATISTICAL SERVICE. STATISTICAL RELEASE. CONSUMER PRICE INDEX. see *BUSINESS AND ECONOMICS* — Abstracting, Bibliographies, Statistics

SOUTH AFRICA. CENTRAL STATISTICAL SERVICE. STATISTICAL RELEASE. CONSUMER PRICE INDEX BASE. see *BUSINESS AND ECONOMICS* — Abstracting, Bibliographies, Statistics

SOUTH AFRICA. CENTRAL STATISTICAL SERVICE. STATISTICAL RELEASE. CONTRACT PRICE INDEX FOR BUILDINGS. see *BUILDING AND CONSTRUCTION* — Abstracting, Bibliographies, Statistics

STATISTICS

SOUTH AFRICA. CENTRAL STATISTICAL SERVICE. STATISTICAL RELEASE. CONSUMER PRICE INDEX WEIGHTS. see *BUSINESS AND ECONOMICS — Abstracting, Bibliographies, Statistics*

SOUTH AFRICA. CENTRAL STATISTICAL SERVICE. STATISTICAL RELEASE. ELECTRICITY AVAILABLE FOR DISTRIBUTION. see *ENERGY — Abstracting, Bibliographies, Statistics*

SOUTH AFRICA. CENTRAL STATISTICAL SERVICE. STATISTICAL RELEASE. EXCHEQUER ACCOUNT - FINAL. see *PUBLIC ADMINISTRATION — Abstracting, Bibliographies, Statistics*

SOUTH AFRICA. CENTRAL STATISTICAL SERVICE. STATISTICAL RELEASE. EXCHEQUER ACCOUNT (FIRST PUBLICATION). see *PUBLIC ADMINISTRATION — Abstracting, Bibliographies, Statistics*

SOUTH AFRICA. CENTRAL STATISTICAL SERVICE. STATISTICAL RELEASE. EXPENDITURE BY THE GENERAL GOVERNMENT. see *PUBLIC ADMINISTRATION — Abstracting, Bibliographies, Statistics*

SOUTH AFRICA. CENTRAL STATISTICAL SERVICE. STATISTICAL RELEASE. EXPENDITURE OF THE CENTRAL GOVERNMENT. see *PUBLIC ADMINISTRATION — Abstracting, Bibliographies, Statistics*

SOUTH AFRICA. CENTRAL STATISTICAL SERVICE. STATISTICAL RELEASE. FINANCIAL STATISTICS OF BLACK LOCAL AUTHORITIES. see *PUBLIC ADMINISTRATION — Abstracting, Bibliographies, Statistics*

SOUTH AFRICA. CENTRAL STATISTICAL SERVICE. STATISTICAL RELEASE. FINANCIAL STATISTICS OF COMPANIES. see *BUSINESS AND ECONOMICS — Abstracting, Bibliographies, Statistics*

SOUTH AFRICA. CENTRAL STATISTICAL SERVICE. STATISTICAL RELEASE. FINANCIAL STATISTICS OF EXTRABUDGETARY ACCOUNTS AND FUNDS. see *BUSINESS AND ECONOMICS — Abstracting, Bibliographies, Statistics*

SOUTH AFRICA. CENTRAL STATISTICAL SERVICE. STATISTICAL RELEASE. FINANCIAL STATISTICS OF LOCAL AUTHORITIES AND REGIONAL SERVICES COUNCILS AND JOINT SERVICES BOARDS. see *PUBLIC ADMINISTRATION — Abstracting, Bibliographies, Statistics*

SOUTH AFRICA. CENTRAL STATISTICAL SERVICE. STATISTICAL RELEASE. FINANCIAL STATISTICS OF LOCAL GOVERNMENTS (YEAR). see *PUBLIC ADMINISTRATION — Abstracting, Bibliographies, Statistics*

SOUTH AFRICA. CENTRAL STATISTICAL SERVICE. STATISTICAL RELEASE. FINANCIAL STATISTICS OF PROVINCIAL ADMINISTRATIONS. see *PUBLIC ADMINISTRATION — Abstracting, Bibliographies, Statistics*

SOUTH AFRICA. CENTRAL STATISTICAL SERVICE. STATISTICAL RELEASE. FINANCIAL STATISTICS OF UNIVERSITIES AND TECHNIKONS. see *EDUCATION — Abstracting, Bibliographies, Statistics*

SOUTH AFRICA. CENTRAL STATISTICAL SERVICE. STATISTICAL RELEASE. FOREIGN TRADE STATISTICS. see *BUSINESS AND ECONOMICS — Abstracting, Bibliographies, Statistics*

SOUTH AFRICA. CENTRAL STATISTICAL SERVICE. STATISTICAL RELEASE. GROSS DOMESTIC PRODUCT AT CONSTANT PRICES. see *BUSINESS AND ECONOMICS — Abstracting, Bibliographies, Statistics*

SOUTH AFRICA. CENTRAL STATISTICAL SERVICE. STATISTICAL RELEASE. GROSS GEOGRAPHIC PRODUCT AT FACTOR INCOMES. see *BUSINESS AND ECONOMICS — Abstracting, Bibliographies, Statistics*

SOUTH AFRICA. CENTRAL STATISTICAL SERVICE. STATISTICAL RELEASE. HOUSEHOLD EXPENDITURE. see *BUSINESS AND ECONOMICS — Abstracting, Bibliographies, Statistics*

SOUTH AFRICA. CENTRAL STATISTICAL SERVICE. STATISTICAL RELEASE. INDICES OF THE PHYSICAL VOLUME OF MANUFACTURING PRODUCTION - PRELIMINARY. see *BUSINESS AND ECONOMICS — Abstracting, Bibliographies, Statistics*

SOUTH AFRICA. CENTRAL STATISTICAL SERVICE. STATISTICAL RELEASE. LABOUR STATISTICS: BUILDING SOCIETIES, BANKING INSTITUTIONS AND INSURANCE COMPANIES. see *BUSINESS AND ECONOMICS — Abstracting, Bibliographies, Statistics*

SOUTH AFRICA. CENTRAL STATISTICAL SERVICE. STATISTICAL RELEASE. LABOUR STATISTICS: EMPLOYMENT AND SALARIES AND WAGES - WHOLESALE, RETAIL, MOTOR TRADE AND HOTELS. see *BUSINESS AND ECONOMICS — Abstracting, Bibliographies, Statistics*

SOUTH AFRICA. CENTRAL STATISTICAL SERVICE. STATISTICAL RELEASE. LABOUR STATISTICS: INDICES OF WAGE RATES AND LABOUR COSTS IN THE METAL AND ENGINEERING INDUSTRIES. see *BUSINESS AND ECONOMICS — Abstracting, Bibliographies, Statistics*

SOUTH AFRICA. CENTRAL STATISTICAL SERVICE. STATISTICAL RELEASE. MANUFACTURING AND CONSTRUCTION (EMPLOYMENT AND EARNINGS). see *BUSINESS AND ECONOMICS — Abstracting, Bibliographies, Statistics*

SOUTH AFRICA. CENTRAL STATISTICAL SERVICE. STATISTICAL RELEASE. MANUFACTURING - CAPITAL EXPENDITURE ON NEW ASSETS. see *BUSINESS AND ECONOMICS — Abstracting, Bibliographies, Statistics*

SOUTH AFRICA. CENTRAL STATISTICAL SERVICE. STATISTICAL RELEASE. MANUFACTURING - FINANCIAL STATISTICS. see *BUSINESS AND ECONOMICS — Abstracting, Bibliographies, Statistics*

SOUTH AFRICA. CENTRAL STATISTICAL SERVICE. STATISTICAL RELEASE. MANUFACTURING - FINANCIAL STATISTICS (QUARTERLY). see *BUSINESS AND ECONOMICS — Abstracting, Bibliographies, Statistics*

SOUTH AFRICA. CENTRAL STATISTICAL SERVICE. STATISTICAL RELEASE. MANUFACTURING PRODUCTION. see *BUSINESS AND ECONOMICS — Abstracting, Bibliographies, Statistics*

SOUTH AFRICA. CENTRAL STATISTICAL SERVICE. STATISTICAL RELEASE. MANUFACTURING - PRODUCTION AND SALES. see *BUSINESS AND ECONOMICS — Abstracting, Bibliographies, Statistics*

SOUTH AFRICA. CENTRAL STATISTICAL SERVICE. STATISTICAL RELEASE. MANUFACTURING STATISTICS: BASIC METAL AND FABRICATED METAL PRODUCTS, MACHINERY AND EQUIPMENT, MOTOR VEHICLES AND PARTS AND MISCELLANEOUS PRODUCTS. see *BUSINESS AND ECONOMICS — Abstracting, Bibliographies, Statistics*

SOUTH AFRICA. CENTRAL STATISTICAL SERVICE. STATISTICAL RELEASE. MANUFACTURING STATISTICS: CHEMICAL, RUBBER, PLASTIC, GLASS AND NON-METALLIC MINERAL PRODUCTS. see *BUSINESS AND ECONOMICS — Abstracting, Bibliographies, Statistics*

SOUTH AFRICA. CENTRAL STATISTICAL SERVICE. STATISTICAL RELEASE. MANUFACTURING STATISTICS: PRODUCTS MANUFACTURED: FOODS, BEVERAGES AND TOBACCO PRODUCTS. see *BUSINESS AND ECONOMICS — Abstracting, Bibliographies, Statistics*

SOUTH AFRICA. CENTRAL STATISTICAL SERVICE. STATISTICAL RELEASE. MANUFACTURING STATISTICS: PRODUCTS MANUFACTURED: TEXTILES, CLOTHING, LEATHER AND LEATHER PRODUCTS, WOOD AND WOOD PRODUCTS, PAPER AND PAPER PRODUCTS AND PRINTING. see *BUSINESS AND ECONOMICS — Abstracting, Bibliographies, Statistics*

SOUTH AFRICA. CENTRAL STATISTICAL SERVICE. STATISTICAL RELEASE. MARRIAGES AND DIVORCES. see *POPULATION STUDIES — Abstracting, Bibliographies, Statistics*

SOUTH AFRICA. CENTRAL STATISTICAL SERVICE. STATISTICAL RELEASE. MID-YEAR ESTIMATES (POPULATION). see *POPULATION STUDIES — Abstracting, Bibliographies, Statistics*

SOUTH AFRICA. CENTRAL STATISTICAL SERVICE. STATISTICAL RELEASE. MINING - FINANCIAL STATISTICS. see *MINES AND MINING INDUSTRY — Abstracting, Bibliographies, Statistics*

SOUTH AFRICA. CENTRAL STATISTICAL SERVICE. STATISTICAL RELEASE. MINING - PRODUCTION AND SALES. see *MINES AND MINING INDUSTRY — Abstracting, Bibliographies, Statistics*

SOUTH AFRICA. CENTRAL STATISTICAL SERVICE. STATISTICAL RELEASE. MINING, QUARRYING, MANUFACTURING, CONSTRUCTION, ELECTRICITY (EMPLOYMENT AND EARNINGS). see *BUSINESS AND ECONOMICS — Abstracting, Bibliographies, Statistics*

SOUTH AFRICA. CENTRAL STATISTICAL SERVICE. STATISTICAL RELEASE. MOTOR TRADE - FINANCIAL STATISTICS. see *BUSINESS AND ECONOMICS — Abstracting, Bibliographies, Statistics*

SOUTH AFRICA. CENTRAL STATISTICAL SERVICE. STATISTICAL RELEASE. NEW AND USED VEHICLES REGISTERED - NATAL. see *TRANSPORTATION — Abstracting, Bibliographies, Statistics*

SOUTH AFRICA. CENTRAL STATISTICAL SERVICE. STATISTICAL RELEASE. NEW AND USED VEHICLES REGISTERED - ORANGE FREE STATE. see *TRANSPORTATION — Abstracting, Bibliographies, Statistics*

SOUTH AFRICA. CENTRAL STATISTICAL SERVICE. STATISTICAL RELEASE. NEW AND USED VEHICLES REGISTERED - TRANSVAAL. see *TRANSPORTATION — Abstracting, Bibliographies, Statistics*

SOUTH AFRICA. CENTRAL STATISTICAL SERVICE. STATISTICAL RELEASE. NEW VEHICLES REGISTERED. see *TRANSPORTATION — Abstracting, Bibliographies, Statistics*

SOUTH AFRICA. CENTRAL STATISTICAL SERVICE. STATISTICAL RELEASE. POPULATION CHARACTERISTICS (YEAR); Boipatong, Bophelong, Evaton, Orange Farm, Sebokeng and Sharpeville. see *POPULATION STUDIES — Abstracting, Bibliographies, Statistics*

SOUTH AFRICA. CENTRAL STATISTICAL SERVICE. STATISTICAL RELEASE. PRELIMINARY RESULTS POPULATION CENSUS (YEAR). see *POPULATION STUDIES — Abstracting, Bibliographies, Statistics*

SOUTH AFRICA. CENTRAL STATISTICAL SERVICE. STATISTICAL RELEASE. PRICE INDICES FOR THE CIVIL ENGINEERING INDUSTRY. see *BUSINESS AND ECONOMICS — Abstracting, Bibliographies, Statistics*

SOUTH AFRICA. CENTRAL STATISTICAL SERVICE. STATISTICAL RELEASE. PRODUCTION PRICES - ALL ITEMS. see *BUSINESS AND ECONOMICS — Abstracting, Bibliographies, Statistics*

SOUTH AFRICA. CENTRAL STATISTICAL SERVICE. STATISTICAL RELEASE. PRODUCTION PRICE INDEX. see *BUSINESS AND ECONOMICS — Abstracting, Bibliographies, Statistics*

SOUTH AFRICA. CENTRAL STATISTICAL SERVICE. STATISTICAL RELEASE. PRODUCTION PRICE INDEX BASE (YEAR). see *BUSINESS AND ECONOMICS — Abstracting, Bibliographies, Statistics*

SOUTH AFRICA. CENTRAL STATISTICAL SERVICE. STATISTICAL RELEASE. PUBLIC ROAD TRANSPORT (NON-GOVERNMENTAL INSTITUTIONS) OF PASSENGERS AND GOODS - FINANCIAL STATISTICS. see *TRANSPORTATION — Abstracting, Bibliographies, Statistics*

SOUTH AFRICA. CENTRAL STATISTICAL SERVICE. STATISTICAL RELEASE. PUBLIC SECTOR (EMPLOYMENT AND EARNINGS). see *BUSINESS AND ECONOMICS — Abstracting, Bibliographies, Statistics*

STATISTICS

SOUTH AFRICA. CENTRAL STATISTICAL SERVICE. STATISTICAL RELEASE. RECORDED BIRTHS. see *POPULATION STUDIES — Abstracting, Bibliographies, Statistics*

SOUTH AFRICA. CENTRAL STATISTICAL SERVICE. STATISTICAL RELEASE. RECORDED DEATHS. see *POPULATION STUDIES — Abstracting, Bibliographies, Statistics*

SOUTH AFRICA. CENTRAL STATISTICAL SERVICE. STATISTICAL RELEASE. REGISTERED HOTELS - FINANCIAL STATISTICS. see *HOTELS AND RESTAURANTS — Abstracting, Bibliographies, Statistics*

SOUTH AFRICA. CENTRAL STATISTICAL SERVICE. STATISTICAL RELEASE. REGIONAL MID-YEAR ESTIMATES - REPUBLIC OF SOUTH AFRICA. see *POPULATION STUDIES — Abstracting, Bibliographies, Statistics*

SOUTH AFRICA. CENTRAL STATISTICAL SERVICE. STATISTICAL RELEASE. RETAILERS IN MOTOR VEHICLES AND ACCESSORIES - TRADING REVENUE: EXPECTED VALUES. see *BUSINESS AND ECONOMICS — Abstracting, Bibliographies, Statistics*

SOUTH AFRICA. CENTRAL STATISTICAL SERVICE. STATISTICAL RELEASE. RETAIL PRICES - ALL ITEMS. see *BUSINESS AND ECONOMICS — Abstracting, Bibliographies, Statistics*

SOUTH AFRICA. CENTRAL STATISTICAL SERVICE. STATISTICAL RELEASE. RETAIL TRADE - FINANCIAL STATISTICS. see *BUSINESS AND ECONOMICS — Abstracting, Bibliographies, Statistics*

SOUTH AFRICA. CENTRAL STATISTICAL SERVICE. STATISTICAL RELEASE. RETAIL TRADE IN MOTOR VEHICLES AND ACCESSORIES - TRADING REVENUE (FINAL). see *BUSINESS AND ECONOMICS — Abstracting, Bibliographies, Statistics*

SOUTH AFRICA. CENTRAL STATISTICAL SERVICE. STATISTICAL RELEASE. RETAIL TRADE SALES. see *BUSINESS AND ECONOMICS — Abstracting, Bibliographies, Statistics*

SOUTH AFRICA. CENTRAL STATISTICAL SERVICE. STATISTICAL RELEASE. RETAIL TRADE SALES - EXPECTED SALES. see *BUSINESS AND ECONOMICS — Abstracting, Bibliographies, Statistics*

SOUTH AFRICA. CENTRAL STATISTICAL SERVICE. STATISTICAL RELEASE. RETAIL TRADE SALES (FINAL). see *BUSINESS AND ECONOMICS — Abstracting, Bibliographies, Statistics*

SOUTH AFRICA. CENTRAL STATISTICAL SERVICE. STATISTICAL RELEASE. RETAIL TRADE SALES - PRELIMINARY. see *BUSINESS AND ECONOMICS — Abstracting, Bibliographies, Statistics*

SOUTH AFRICA. CENTRAL STATISTICAL SERVICE. STATISTICAL RELEASE. ROAD TRAFFIC COLLISIONS. see *TRANSPORTATION — Abstracting, Bibliographies, Statistics*

SOUTH AFRICA. CENTRAL STATISTICAL SERVICE. STATISTICAL RELEASE. ROAD TRAFFIC COLLISONS AND NUMBER OF PERSONS KILLED DURING THE HOLIDAY SEASON. see *TRANSPORTATION — Abstracting, Bibliographies, Statistics*

SOUTH AFRICA. CENTRAL STATISTICAL SERVICE. STATISTICAL RELEASE. STATISTICS OF CIVIL CASES FOR DEBT. see *LAW — Abstracting, Bibliographies, Statistics*

SOUTH AFRICA. CENTRAL STATISTICAL SERVICE. STATISTICAL RELEASE. STATISTICS OF DEVELOPMENT BOARDS. see *PUBLIC ADMINISTRATION — Abstracting, Bibliographies, Statistics*

SOUTH AFRICA. CENTRAL STATISTICAL SERVICE. STATISTICAL RELEASE. STATISTICS OF DEVELOPMENT BOARDS. see *PUBLIC ADMINISTRATION — Abstracting, Bibliographies, Statistics*

SOUTH AFRICA. CENTRAL STATISTICAL SERVICE. STATISTICAL RELEASE. STATISTICS OF LIQUIDATIONS AND INSOLVENCIES. see *LAW — Abstracting, Bibliographies, Statistics*

SOUTH AFRICA. CENTRAL STATISTICAL SERVICE. STATISTICAL RELEASE. STATISTICS OF MOTOR AND OTHER VEHICLES AS AT 30 JUNE - ALL VEHICLES. see *TRANSPORTATION — Abstracting, Bibliographies, Statistics*

SOUTH AFRICA. CENTRAL STATISTICAL SERVICE. STATISTICAL RELEASE. STATISTICS OF REGISTERED HOTELS. see *HOTELS AND RESTAURANTS — Abstracting, Bibliographies, Statistics*

SOUTH AFRICA. CENTRAL STATISTICAL SERVICE. STATISTICAL RELEASE. STATISTICS OF REGISTERED HOTELS: BEDNIGHTS - FOREIGN TOURISTS. see *HOTELS AND RESTAURANTS — Abstracting, Bibliographies, Statistics*

SOUTH AFRICA. CENTRAL STATISTICAL SERVICE. STATISTICAL RELEASE. STATISTICALLY UNRECORDED ACTIVITIES OF COLOUREDS, INDIANS AND BLACKS. see *BUSINESS AND ECONOMICS — Abstracting, Bibliographies, Statistics*

SOUTH AFRICA. CENTRAL STATISTICAL SERVICE. STATISTICAL RELEASE. STOCK OF PRIMARY STEEL PRODUCTS ON HAND. see *METALLURGY — Abstracting, Bibliographies, Statistics*

SOUTH AFRICA. CENTRAL STATISTICAL SERVICE. STATISTICAL RELEASE. SUMMARY LABOUR STATISTICS. see *BUSINESS AND ECONOMICS — Abstracting, Bibliographies, Statistics*

SOUTH AFRICA. CENTRAL STATISTICAL SERVICE. STATISTICAL RELEASE. SURVEY OF ARCHITECTS AND QUANTITY SURVEYORS. see *BUSINESS AND ECONOMICS — Abstracting, Bibliographies, Statistics*

SOUTH AFRICA. CENTRAL STATISTICAL SERVICE. STATISTICAL RELEASE. SURVEY OF FLATS. see *HOUSING AND URBAN PLANNING — Abstracting, Bibliographies, Statistics*

SOUTH AFRICA. CENTRAL STATISTICAL SERVICE. STATISTICAL RELEASE. SURVEY OF HOUSES, SECTIONAL TITLE UNITS AND DOMESTIC WORKERS. see *HOUSING AND URBAN PLANNING — Abstracting, Bibliographies, Statistics*

SOUTH AFRICA. CENTRAL STATISTICAL SERVICE. STATISTICAL RELEASE. TOTAL VALUE OF WHOLESALE TRADE SALES - EXPECTED SALES. see *BUSINESS AND ECONOMICS — Abstracting, Bibliographies, Statistics*

SOUTH AFRICA. CENTRAL STATISTICAL SERVICE. STATISTICAL RELEASE. TOURISM - JAN SMUTS, D F MALAN AND LOUIS BOTHA AIRPORTS. see *TRAVEL AND TOURISM — Abstracting, Bibliographies, Statistics*

SOUTH AFRICA. CENTRAL STATISTICAL SERVICE. STATISTICAL RELEASE. TRANSPORT OF GOODS BY ROAD AND RAIL. see *TRANSPORTATION — Abstracting, Bibliographies, Statistics*

SOUTH AFRICA. CENTRAL STATISTICAL SERVICE. STATISTICAL RELEASE. TRANSPORT OF PASSENGERS BY BUS AND TRAIN. see *TRANSPORTATION — Abstracting, Bibliographies, Statistics*

SOUTH AFRICA. CENTRAL STATISTICAL SERVICE. STATISTICAL RELEASE. TRANSFERS OF RURAL IMMOVABLE PROPERTY. see *REAL ESTATE — Abstracting, Bibliographies, Statistics*

SOUTH AFRICA. CENTRAL STATISTICAL SERVICE. STATISTICAL RELEASE. USED VEHICLES REGISTERED. see *TRANSPORTATION — Abstracting, Bibliographies, Statistics*

SOUTH AFRICA. CENTRAL STATISTICAL SERVICE. STATISTICAL RELEASE. UTILIZATION OF PRODUCTION CAPACITY. see *BUSINESS AND ECONOMICS — Abstracting, Bibliographies, Statistics*

SOUTH AFRICA. CENTRAL STATISTICAL SERVICE. STATISTICAL RELEASE. WAGE RATES: BUILDING INDUSTRY. see *BUSINESS AND ECONOMICS — Abstracting, Bibliographies, Statistics*

SOUTH AFRICA. CENTRAL STATISTICAL SERVICE. STATISTICAL RELEASE. WAGE RATES: CIVIL ENGINEERING INDUSTRY. see *BUSINESS AND ECONOMICS — Abstracting, Bibliographies, Statistics*

SOUTH AFRICA. CENTRAL STATISTICAL SERVICE. STATISTICAL RELEASE. WHOLESALE TRADE - FINANCIAL STATISTICS. see *BUSINESS AND ECONOMICS — Abstracting, Bibliographies, Statistics*

SOUTH AFRICA. CENTRAL STATISTICAL SERVICE. STATISTICAL RELEASE. WHOLESALE TRADE SALES. see *BUSINESS AND ECONOMICS — Abstracting, Bibliographies, Statistics*

SOUTH AFRICA. CENTRAL STATISTICAL SERVICE. STATISTICS OF DIVISIONAL COUNCILS. see *PUBLIC ADMINISTRATION — Abstracting, Bibliographies, Statistics*

SOUTH AFRICA. CENTRAL STATISTICAL SERVICE. SURVEY OF HOUSEHOLD EXPENDITURE. see *BUSINESS AND ECONOMICS — Abstracting, Bibliographies, Statistics*

SOUTH AFRICA. CENTRAL STATISTICAL SERVICE. SURVEY OF THE ACCOUNTS OF COMPANIES.. see *BUSINESS AND ECONOMICS — Abstracting, Bibliographies, Statistics*

SOUTH AFRICA. CENTRAL STATISTICAL SERVICE. TOURISM AND MIGRATION. see *POPULATION STUDIES — Abstracting, Bibliographies, Statistics*

316.8 SA
SOUTH AFRICA. CENTRAL STATISTICAL SERVICE. USER'S GUIDE. Afrikaans edition: Gebruikersgids. (Text in English) q. free. Central Statistical Service - Sentrale Statistiekdiens, Private Bag X44, Pretoria 0001, South Africa. TEL 27-12-310-8911. FAX 27-12-310-8500. **Document type:** government publication, catalog.

SOUTH AFRICA. DEPARTMENT OF AGRICULTURE AND FISHERIES. DIVISION OF ECONOMIC SERVICES. ABSTRACT OF AGRICULTURAL STATISTICS/KORTBEGRIP VAN LANDBOUSTATISTIEKE. see *AGRICULTURE — Abstracting, Bibliographies, Statistics*

SOUTH AFRICA. OFFICIAL YEARBOOK OF THE REPUBLIC OF SOUTH AFRICA. see *HISTORY — Abstracting, Bibliographies, Statistics*

SOUTH AFRICAN LABOUR STATISTICS. see *BUSINESS AND ECONOMICS — Abstracting, Bibliographies, Statistics*

519.5 SA ISSN 0038-271X
QA276.A1 CODEN: SASSB5
SOUTH AFRICAN STATISTICAL JOURNAL/SUID-AFRIKAANSE STATISTIESE TYDSKRIF. (Text in Afrikaans, English; summaries in English) 1967. s-a. $50 (effective 1993). South African Statistical Association - Suid-Afrikaanse Statistiese Vereniging, P.O. Box 27321, Sunnyside 0132, South Africa. TEL 27-11-716-2686. FAX 27-11-339-1697. Ed. J.S. Galpin. adv.; index. circ. 350. **Indexed:** ASCA, Biostat., Compumath, Curr.Ind.Stat., Ind.S.A.Per., J.Cont.Quant.Meth., Math.R., Oper.Res.Manage.Sci., Qual.Contr.Appl.Stat., SSCI, Stat.Theor.Meth.Abstr. **Document type:** academic/scholarly publication.
—BLDSC (8346.450000); Faxon; Genuine Article; SWETS; UnCover.
Description: Covers topics in theoretical mathematical statistics and applications.

316.8 SA ISSN 0081-2544
HA1991
SOUTH AFRICAN STATISTICS. (Text in Afrikaans, English) 1968. a., latest 1994. R.60 (foreign R.64.50 (effective 1994). Central Statistical Service - Sentrale Statistiekdiens, Private Bag X44, Pretoria 0001, South Africa. TEL 27-12-310-8911. FAX 27-12-310-8500. (Orders to: Government Printing Works, Private Bag X85, Pretoria 0001 South Africa) **Document type:** government publication.
—BLDSC (8346.500000).
Formerly (until 1966): South Africa. Department of Statistics. Statistical Year Book.

STATISTICS

317.57 US ISSN 0739-9308
HA621
SOUTH CAROLINA STATISTICAL ABSTRACT. 1972. a. $20. Budget and Control Board, Division of Research & Statistical Services, Rembert C. Dennis Bldg., Rm. 425, 1000 Assembly St., Columbia, SC 29201. TEL 803-734-3788. FAX 803-734-3619. bk.rev.; stat. circ. 1,400. (also avail. in microfiche) **Indexed:** SRI. **Document type:** abstracting/indexing.
Description: Presents data on factors impacting on the state's social and economic development: manufacturing, wholesale and retail trade, construction, housing, business and industry employment, agriculture, banking and finance, income, education, tourism, and population.

SOUTH DAKOTA. DEPARTMENT OF REVENUE. ANNUAL STATISTICAL REPORT. see BUSINESS AND ECONOMICS — Abstracting, Bibliographies, Statistics

SOUTH DAKOTA. STATE DEPARTMENT OF SOCIAL SERVICES. ANNUAL STATISTICAL REPORT. see SOCIAL SERVICES AND WELFARE — Abstracting, Bibliographies, Statistics

310 NL ISSN 0377-2039
SOUTH PACIFIC COMMISSION. STATISTICAL BULLETIN. (Text in English and French) 1973. irreg., no.45, 1995. South Pacific Commission, B.P. D5, Noumea, Cedex, New Caledonia. TEL 687-262000. FAX 687-263818. TELEX 3139 NM SOPACOM. **Document type:** monographic series.
—BLDSC (8447.971200).

SOUTH PACIFIC ECONOMIES: STATISTICAL SUMMARY. see BUSINESS AND ECONOMICS — Abstracting, Bibliographies, Statistics

314 SP ISSN 0066-5177
SPAIN. INSTITUTO NACIONAL DE ESTADISTICA. ANUARIO ESTADISTICO: EDICION EXTENSA. 1912. a. Instituto Nacional de Estadistica, P. de la Castellana, 183, 28071 Madrid, Spain.

314 SP
SPAIN. INSTITUTO NACIONAL DE ESTADISTICA. BOLETIN MENSUAL DE ESTADISTICA. 1918. m. Instituto Nacional de Estadistica, P. de la Castellana, 183, 28071 Madrid, Spain. charts; stat.; index. circ. 3,100. **Indexed:** P.A.I.S.For.Lang.Ind.
Formerly (until 1992): Spain. Instituto Nacional de Estadistica. Boletin de Estadistica (ISSN 0038-6391)

314 SP ISSN 0014-1151
HA1 CODEN: ESTEA7
SPAIN. INSTITUTO NACIONAL DE ESTADISTICA. ESTADISTICA ESPANOLA. Key Title: Estadistica Espanola. 3/yr. 3200 ptas. Instituto Nacional de Estadistica, P. de la Castellana, 183, 28071 Madrid, Spain. bk.rev.; bibl.; charts; illus.; stat. circ. 1,000. **Indexed:** Ind.SST, Stat.Theor.Meth.Abstr.

314 SP ISSN 0213-7410
SPAIN. INSTITUTO NACIONAL DE ESTADISTICA. INDICES DE PRECIOS DE CONSUMO. BOLETIN INFORMATIVO. 1971. q. Instituto Nacional de Estadistica, P. de la Castellana, 183, 28071 Madrid, Spain.
Formerly: Spain. Instituto Nacional de Estadistica. Indice del Coste de la Vida.

SPAIN. MINISTERIO DE AGRICULTURA, PESCA Y ALIMENTACION. BOLETIN MENSUAL DE PRECIOS. see AGRICULTURE — Agricultural Economics

310 SP
SPAIN. MINISTERIO DE ECONOMIA Y HACIENDA. MEMORIA ESTADISTICA. SEGUROS PRIVADOS. 1953. a. 8000 ptas. Ministerio de Economia y Hacienda, Direccion General de Seguros, Paseo de la Castellana 44, 28046 Madrid, Spain. TEL 91-575-48-00. FAX 91-431-44-35. circ. 500. **Document type:** government publication.

314.5 IT
LO SPETTACOLO IN ITALIA; annuario statistico. 1936. a. L.25000 (effective 1995 & 1996). Societa Italiana degli Autori ed Editori, Viale della Letteratura 30, 00144 Rome, Italy. TEL 39-6-59901. FAX 39-6-5923351. TELEX 611423. Ed. Francesco Paolo Regoli. bk.rev. (back issues avail.) **Document type:** consumer publication.

310 US ISSN 0172-7397
SPRINGER SERIES IN STATISTICS. 1979. irreg. price varies. Springer-Verlag, 175 Fifth Ave., New York, NY 10010. TEL 212-460-1500. FAX 212-473-6272. (Also: Berlin, Heidelberg, Tokyo and Vienna) Ed.Bd. (reprint service avail. from ISI) **Indexed:** INSPEC, Math.R. **Document type:** monographic series.

314 GW ISSN 0344-5550
HC287.H4
STAAT UND WIRTSCHAFT IN HESSEN. 1946. m. DM.45. Hessisches Statistisches Landesamt, Rheinstr. 35-37, 65185 Wiesbaden, Germany. TEL 0611-38020. FAX 0611-3802990. bk.rev.; charts. **Document type:** government publication.
Description: Government publication including economic and vital statistics.

STADT DUISBURG. BERUFSBILDUNGSBERICHT (YEAR). see EDUCATION — School Organization And Administration

310 GW ISSN 0930-2034
STADT REMSCHEID STATISTISCHES JAHRBUCH. 1949. a. DM.25. Amt fuer Stadtentwicklung und Statistik, Hindenburgstr. 52-58, 42853 Remscheid, Germany. Ed. Hoffmann. bk.rev. circ. 450. (back issues avail.)

STANDARD & POOR'S STATISTICAL SERVICE. CURRENT STATISTICS. see BUSINESS AND ECONOMICS — Investments

STANDARD & POOR'S STATISTICAL SERVICE. SECURITY PRICE INDEX. see BUSINESS AND ECONOMICS — Investments

STATE AND LOCAL STATISTICS SOURCES. see PUBLIC ADMINISTRATION

317.3 US ISSN 0276-6566
HA202
STATE AND METROPOLITAN AREA DATA BOOK. (Supplement avail.) irreg. price varies. U.S. Bureau of the Census, Data User Services Division, Washington, DC 20233. TEL 301-457-4100. FAX 301-457-4714. (Orders to: Superintendent of Documents, U.S. Government Printing Office, Box 371954, Pittsburgh, PA 15250-7954. TEL 202-512-1800. FAX 202-512-2250; Or: Bernan, 4611-F Assembly Dr., Lanham, MD 20706, TEL 301-459-7666. FAX 301-459-0056) (also avail. in microfiche) **Document type:** government publication.
●Also available online. Vendor(s): CompuServe, Inc., Knight-Ridder, Inc.

STATE AND METROPOLITAN AREA EMPLOYMENT AND UNEMPLOYMENT. see BUSINESS AND ECONOMICS — Economic Situation And Conditions

STATE OF THE INDUSTRY REPORT. see BUSINESS AND ECONOMICS — Abstracting, Bibliographies, Statistics

317.56 US
STATE PLANNING NEWSLETTER. 1994. q. free. Office of State Planning, 116 W. Jones St., Raleigh, NC 27603-8003. TEL 919-733-4131. FAX 919-715-3562. Ed. Stephanie Fowler. circ. 2,700 (controlled). **Document type:** government publication.
Supersedes (1979-1994): North Carolina. State Data Center. Newsletter.
Description: Provides news of the activities and publications of the State Data Center, State Demographer, and the Center for Geographic Information and Analysis.

310 IT ISSN 0390-590X
CODEN: STATDJ
STATISTICA. 1941. q. L.60000 (foreign L.85000) (effective 1994). Cooperativa Libraria Universitaria Editrice Bologna, Via Marsala 24, 40126 Bologna, Italy. TEL 051-220736. FAX 051-237758. Ed. P. Fortunati. adv.; bk.rev.; bibl.; index. circ. 2,500. (also avail. in microform from UMI) **Indexed:** J.Cont.Quant.Meth., Math.R., Popul.Ind.

519.5 UK ISSN 0039-0402
HA1
STATISTICA NEERLANDICA. (Text in English) 1952. 3/yr. £88($142) (foreign £88) (effective 1996). (Vereniging voor Statistiek, NE - Netherlands Society for Statistics and Operations Research) Basil Blackwell Ltd., 108 Cowley Rd., Oxford OX4 1JF, England. TEL 44-865-791100. FAX 44-865-791347. (Subscr. to: Box 87, Oxford OX2 0DT, England. TEL 44-865-791155. FAX 44-865-791927; In N. America: Blackwell Publishers, 238 Main St., Cambridge, MA 02142. TEL 617-547-7110. FAX 617-547-0789) adv.; bk.rev.; stat.; index. circ. 1,300. (also avail. in microform from UMI; reprint service avail. from SWZ) **Indexed:** Biostat., Curr.Ind.Stat., Int.Abstr.Oper.Res., J.Cont.Quant.Meth., Key to Econ.Sci., Math.R., Oper.Res.Manage.Sci., Qual.Contr.Appl.Stat., Stat.Theor.Meth.Abstr. **Document type:** academic/scholarly publication.
—BLDSC (8447.390000); Faxon; SWETS; UMI; UnCover. **CCC.**

STATISTICAL ABSTRACT OF LATIN AMERICA. see HISTORY — Abstracting, Bibliographies, Statistics

315 II ISSN 0081-4709
STATISTICAL ABSTRACT OF MAHARASHTRA STATE. (Text in English) a. Rs.250. Directorate of Economics and Statistics, MHADA Bldg., Kalanagar, Bandra (E), Bombay 400051, India.

310 II ISSN 0081-4717
STATISTICAL ABSTRACT OF RAJASTHAN. (Text in English) 1958. a. Rs.130. Directorate of Economics and Statistics, Tilak Marg, Jaipur, Rajasthan, India. **Document type:** government publication, abstracting/indexing.
Description: Provides information on different sectors of the State's economy with break-ups in regard to space, time and important characteristics.

315 CE ISSN 0259-8086
STATISTICAL ABSTRACT OF THE DEMOCRATIC SOCIALIST REPUBLIC OF SRI LANKA. (Text in English) 1949. irreg., latest 1993. Rs.300. Department of Census and Statistics, Ministry of Plan Implementation, P.O. Box 563, No. 6, Albert Crescent, Colombo 7, Sri Lanka. TEL 94-1-695291. FAX 94-1-695291. (Subscr. to: Superintendent, Government Publications Bureau, Colombo, Sri Lanka) index. circ. 1,878. **Document type:** government publication.
Formerly: Statistical Abstract of Ceylon (ISSN 0081-4636)

317.3 US ISSN 0081-4741
HA202 CODEN: SASTDA
STATISTICAL ABSTRACT OF THE UNITED STATES (YEAR). 1878. a. $32 for softcover edition (foreign $40); hardcover edition $38 (foreign $47.50). U.S. Bureau of the Census, Data User Services Division, Washington, DC 20233. TEL 301-457-4100. FAX 301-457-4714. (Orders to: Superintendent of Documents, U.S. Government Printing Office, Box 371954, Pittsburgh, PA 15250-7954. TEL 202-512-1800. FAX 202-512-2250; Or: National Technical Information Service, 5285 Port Royal Rd., Springfield, VA 22161. TEL 703-487-4650. FAX 703-321-8547; Also dist. by: Reference Press, Inc., 6448 Hwy. 290E, Ste. E-104, Austin, TX 78723; TEL 800-486-8666, FAX 512-454-9401; And: Bernan, 4611-F Assembly Dr., Lanham, MD; TEL 800-274-4447, FAX 301-459-0056) (also avail. in microfiche; microfilm from UMI;BHP; reprint service avail. from UMI) **Document type:** government publication.
●Also available online. Vendor(s): CompuServe, Inc., Knight-Ridder, Inc.
—BLDSC (8447.421000); CASDDS; UMI.
Description: Contains an extensive collection of the latest vital statistics and industry trends and an important summary of statistics on the social, political, and economic organization of the U.S.

330.9 US ISSN 0898-3879
HA661
STATISTICAL ABSTRACT OF UTAH. 1947. irreg. (approx. every 3 yrs.) University of Utah, Bureau of Economic and Business Research, Salt Lake City, UT 84112. TEL 801-581-6333. FAX 801-581-3354. (back issues avail.) **Document type:** monographic series.
Former titles (until 1987): Utah Statistical Abstract (ISSN 0278-3770); (until 1979): Statistical Abstract of Utah (ISSN 0095-6961)

311   IE   ISSN 0081-4776
STATISTICAL AND SOCIAL INQUIRY SOCIETY OF IRELAND. JOURNAL. 1846. a. I£10. Statistical and Social Inquiry Society of Ireland, c/o Central Statistics Office, Ardee Rd., Rathmines, Dublin 6, Ireland. TEL 01-4977144. FAX 01-4972360. Ed. Aidan Punch. cum.index: 1847-1947, 1947-1979. circ. 700. **Indexed:** C.R.E.J., P.A.I.S., Rural Recreat.Tour.Abstr., World Agri.Econ.& Rural Sociol.Abstr. **Document type:** academic/scholarly publication.
—BLDSC (4903.690000).
   Refereed Serial

STATISTICAL ANNUALS: LIST OF I E G LIBRARY HOLDINGS. see BIBLIOGRAPHIES

310   TH   ISSN 0858-1886
STATISTICAL BUDGET AND ACTIVITIES IN THAILAND. (Text in Thai) 1966. a. National Statistical Office, Statistical Techniques Division, Larn Luang Road, Bangkok Metropolis 10100, Thailand.
  Description: List of statistical organizations and units under different ministries and departments having submitted their own budgets through the National Statistical Office each year.

317.3   US
STATISTICAL FORECASTS OF THE UNITED STATES. 1993. biennial. $89.50. Gale Research Inc., 835 Penobscot Bldg., Detroit, MI 48226. TEL 313-961-2242. FAX 313-961-6083. Ed. James E. Person, Jr.
  Description: Compiles 1000 charts, graphs, tables and other statistical illustrations collected from a broad range of sources.

315   JA   ISSN 0081-4792
HA1832
STATISTICAL HANDBOOK OF JAPAN. (Text in English) 1958. a. 1400 Yen. Nihon Tokei Kyokai - Japan Statistical Association, Crest 21, 6-21, Yocho-machi, Shinjuku-ku, Tokyo 162, Japan. TEL 81-3-5269-3051. FAX 81-3-5269-3058. **Document type:** government publication.

315   II
STATISTICAL HANDBOOK OF TAMIL NADU. (Text in English) 1969. a. Rs.6. Director of Statistics, Madras 600006, India. (Subscr. to: Government Publication Depot, 166 Anna Rd., Madras 600002, India)

315   TH   ISSN 0857-9466
STATISTICAL HANDBOOK OF THAILAND. (Text in English) 1964. a. price varies. National Statistical Office, Statistical Data Bank and Information Dissemination Division, Larn Luang Rd., Bangkok 10100, Thailand. TEL 622-281-0333. FAX 662-2813814. circ. 1,000. **Document type:** government publication.
—BLDSC (8448.522000).
  Description: Area, geography, climate, population, public health and vital statistics, education, agriculture, forestry, mining, public finance and national income, money and banking.

310   PH
STATISTICAL HANDBOOK OF THE PHILIPPINES. (Text in English) a. $9. National Statistics Office, Ramon Magsaysay Blvd., P.O. Box 779, Manila, Philippines. FAX 610794.
  Description: Reference book that contains all statistical information possible.

316.67   GH
STATISTICAL HANDBOOK OF THE REPUBLIC OF GHANA. a. NC.1.70. Information Services Department, Box 745, Accra, Ghana.

STATISTICAL INDICATOR REPORTS. see BUSINESS AND ECONOMICS — Abstracting, Bibliographies, Statistics

STATISTICAL INDICATORS FOR ASIA AND THE PACIFIC. see BUSINESS AND ECONOMICS — Abstracting, Bibliographies, Statistics

310   AF
STATISTICAL INFORMATION OF AFGHANISTAN/MA'LUMAT-I IHSA'IVI-I AFGHANISTAN. (Text in Persian or Pushto) no. 3, 1975. irreg. Central Statistical Office, Nader Shah Minah, Block No. 4, Box 2002, Kabul, Afghanistan. stat.

STATISTICAL INFORMATION PACKAGE. see OCCUPATIONS AND CAREERS — Abstracting, Bibliographies, Statistics

STATISTICAL INSTITUTE OF JAMAICA. DEMOGRAPHIC STATISTICS. see POPULATION STUDIES — Abstracting, Bibliographies, Statistics

STATISTICAL INSTITUTE OF JAMAICA. MONETARY STATISTICS REPORT. see BUSINESS AND ECONOMICS — Abstracting, Bibliographies, Statistics

STATISTICAL INSTITUTE OF JAMAICA. NATIONAL INCOME AND PRODUCT. see BUSINESS AND ECONOMICS — Abstracting, Bibliographies, Statistics

319   JM
STATISTICAL INSTITUTE OF JAMAICA. POCKETBOOK OF STATISTICS. 1976. a. $15.50. Statistical Institute of Jamaica, 9 Swallowfield Rd., Kingston 5, Jamaica, W.I. FAX 809-92-64859. circ. 573.
  Formerly (until 1978): Jamaica. Department of Statistics. Pocketbook of Statistics.

317   JM
STATISTICAL INSTITUTE OF JAMAICA. STATISTICAL ABSTRACT. 1972. a. (published 9 months after year to which it relates). $21. Statistical Institute of Jamaica, 9 Swallowfield Rd, Kingston 5, Jamaica, W.I. FAX 809-92-64859. circ. 117. **Document type:** abstracting/indexing.
  Former titles: Jamaica. Department of Statistics. Statistical Abstract; Jamaica. Department of Statistics. Annual Abstract of Statistics (ISSN 0075-2983)
  Description: Presents a wide cross-section of data in both the economic and social fields.

319   JM
STATISTICAL INSTITUTE OF JAMAICA. STATISTICAL REVIEW. q. $14 per no. Statistical Institute of Jamaica, 9 Swallowfield Rd., Kingston 5, Jamaica, W.I. FAX 809-92-64859. circ. 148.
  Formerly (until 1981): Jamaica. Department of Statistics. Statistical Review.

519.502461   UK   ISSN 0962-2802
R853.S7
STATISTICAL METHODS IN MEDICAL RESEARCH. 1992. q. £51($91) to individuals; institutions £107 ($209) (effective 1996). Arnold (Subsidiary of: Hodder Headline plc.), 338 Euston Rd., London NW1 3BH, England. TEL 0171-873-6000. FAX 0171-873-6325. (Subscr. to: Turpin Distribution Services Ltd., Blackhorse Rd., Letchworth, Herts 5G6 1HN England. TEL 01462-672555. FAX 01462-480947) **Indexed:** Curr.Ind.Stat., Ind.Med. (1993-), Stat.Theor.Meth.Abstr. **Document type:** academic/scholarly publication.
—BLDSC (8448.573050); SWETS. **CCC.**

315   IS
STATISTICAL MONTHLY OF ISRAEL. (Text in English and Hebrew) 1950. m. Central Bureau of Statistics, P.O. Box 13015, Jerusalem 91 130, Israel. TEL 02-21 12 11. (back issues avail.) **Indexed:** Ind.Heb.Per.

310   JA   ISSN 0561-922X
STATISTICAL NOTES OF JAPAN. (Text in English) 1953. irreg., no.45, 1991. free. International Statistical Affairs Division, Statistical Standards Department, Statistics Bureau, Management and Coordination Agency, 19-1 Wakamatsu-cho, Shinjuku-ku, Tokyo, Japan. FAX 81-3-5273-1181. circ. 550 (controlled).

519.5   GW   ISSN 0932-5026
HA15   CODEN: STPAE4
STATISTICAL PAPERS/STATISTISCHE HEFTE. (Text in English and German) 1960. 4/yr. DM.298($216) (effective 1996). Springer-Verlag, Heidelberger Platz 3, 14197 Berlin, Germany. TEL 030-8207-0. FAX 030-8214091. E-mail: orders@springer.de. (Subscr. in N. America to: Springer-Verlag New York, Inc., 44 Hartz Way, Secaucus, NJ 07096-2491. TEL 201-348-4033. FAX 201-348-4505) Ed.Bd. adv.; bk.rev.; charts; illus. circ. 800. (also avail. in microform from UMI; reprint service avail. from ISI,SCH) **Indexed:** Curr.Ind.Stat., J.Cont.Quant.Meth., Math.R., P.A.I.S.For.Lang.Ind., Stat.Theor.Meth.Abstr. **Document type:** academic/scholarly publication.
—BLDSC (8448.620000). Genuine Article; SWETS; UMI. **CCC.**
  Formerly (until 1988): Statistische Hefte (ISSN 0039-0631)
  Description: Forum for the presentation and critical assessment of statistical methods, particularly for discussion of their methodological foundations and potential applications.

315   II   ISSN 0081-5012
STATISTICAL POCKET BOOK: INDIA. (Text in English) 1956. a. Rs.45($15.50) Central Statistical Organization, Sardar Patel Bhavan, Sansad Marg, New Delhi 110001, India.
  Formerly: Statistical Pocket Book of the Indian Union.

315.8   AF   ISSN 0302-2099
STATISTICAL POCKET-BOOK OF AFGHANISTAN. 1972. irreg. Department of Statistics, Kabul, Afghanistan. illus.

315   CE   ISSN 0585-1777
HA1697
STATISTICAL POCKET BOOK OF THE DEMOCRATIC SOCIALIST REPUBLIC OF SRI LANKA. (Editions in English, Sinhalese, Tamil) 1966. a. Rs.50 for English ed.; Rs.175 for Sinhalese, Tamil eds. Department of Census and Statistics, Ministry of Plan Implementation, Box 563, Colombo 7, Sri Lanka. (Dist. by: Superintendent, Government Publications Bureau, Colombo, Sri Lanka) circ. 2,457. (back issues avail.) **Document type:** government publication.
  Former titles: Statistical Pocket Book of Sri Lanka; Statistical Pocket Book of Ceylon.

310   YU   ISSN 0585-1815
STATISTICAL POCKET-BOOK OF YUGOSLAVIA. (Text in English) 1955. a. Savezni Zavod za Statistiku - Federal Statistical Office, Kneza Milosa 20, Belgrade, Yugoslavia.

310   BG
STATISTICAL POCKETBOOK OF BANGLADESH. (Text in English) 1978. a. Tk.60($14) Bureau of Statistics, Secretariat, Dhaka 2, Bangladesh. charts; stat. circ. 5,000.
  Description: Information on Bangladesh's statistics for population, agriculture, industry and banking.

315.98   IO   ISSN 0126-3595
HA1811
STATISTICAL POCKETBOOK OF INDONESIA/BUKU SAKU STATISTIK INDONESIA. (Subseries of its Statistik Tahunan) (Text in English and Indonesian) 1940. a. Rps.7500($5) Central Bureau of Statistics - Biro Pusat Statistik, Jalan Dr. Sutomo 8, Box 3, Jakarta Pusat, Indonesia. TEL 21-372808. circ. 1,500. **Document type:** government publication.
  Supersedes: Statistik Indonesia.

317   US
STATISTICAL PROFILE OF IOWA. biennial. free. Iowa Department of Economic Development, 200 E. Grand Ave., Des Moines, IA 50309. TEL 515-242-4878. FAX 515-242-4918. index. **Indexed:** SRI. **Document type:** directory.
  Description: Details on Iowa's business community.

STATISTICAL PROFILE OF THE SOFT DRINK INDUSTRY. see BEVERAGES — Abstracting, Bibliographies, Statistics

STATISTICAL QUARTERLY; Higher Education Unit Services unit salary and vacancy survey. see OCCUPATIONS AND CAREERS — Abstracting, Bibliographies, Statistics

310 011   US   ISSN 0278-694X
Z7554.U5
STATISTICAL REFERENCE INDEX. CD-ROM edition: Statistical Masterfile. 1980. m. (with q. and a. cumulations). price varies. Congressional Information Service, Part of the Reed Elsevier group, 4520 East-West Hwy., Bethesda, MD 20814-3389. TEL 301-654-1550; 800-638-8380. FAX 301-654-4033. Ed. Lynn K. Marble. abstr.; stat.; index, cum.index: 1980-85, 1986-89; 1990-93. (back issues avail.) **Document type:** abstracting/indexing.
• Also available on CD-ROM.
  Description: Indexes and abstracts statistics contained in publications from more than 1,000 leading American sources.

319   IR   ISSN 1010-9617
HA4570.2
STATISTICAL REFLECTION OF THE ISLAMIC REPUBLIC OF IRAN. Persian edition: Iran Dar A'inah-i Amar (ISSN 1010-9633) (Text in English) 1981. a. Statistical Centre of Iran, Dr. Fatemi Ave., Tehran 14144, Iran. TEL 655061. FAX 653451. TELEX 213233 AMAR IR. charts; stat. **Document type:** government publication.

6230 STATISTICS

STATISTICAL REPORT ON VISITOR ARRIVALS TO INDONESIA. see *TRAVEL AND TOURISM — Abstracting, Bibliographies, Statistics*

STATISTICAL REVIEW OF GOVERNMENT IN UTAH. see *PUBLIC ADMINISTRATION — Abstracting, Bibliographies, Statistics*

519.5   US   ISSN 0883-4237
QA276.A1   CODEN: STSCEP
STATISTICAL SCIENCE; a review journal. 1986. q. $75. Institute of Mathematical Statistics, 3401 Investment Blvd., Ste. 7, Hayward, CA 94545-3819. TEL 510-783-8141. FAX 510-783-4131. E-mail: IMS@STAT.BERKELEY.EDU. Ed. Paul Switzer. bk.rev. (also avail. in microform from UMI) **Indexed:** Biostat., Curr.Ind.Stat., Oper.Res.Manage.Sci., Qual.Contr.Appl.Stat., Stat.Theor.Meth.Abstr. —BLDSC (8448.953000); Ei; Faxon; Genuine Article; SWETS; UMI; UnCover. **CCC.**
  Refereed Serial

310   AT   ISSN 0314-6820
STATISTICAL SOCIETY OF AUSTRALIA. NEWSLETTER. 4/yr. Aus.$8($10) (Statistical Society of Australia) Australian Statistical Publishing Association, Inc., G.P.O. Box 573, Canberra, A.C.T. 2601, Australia. **Document type:** newsletter.

STATISTICAL THEORY AND METHOD ABSTRACTS. see *MATHEMATICS — Abstracting, Bibliographies, Statistics*

STATISTICAL TRENDS IN TRANSPORT. see *TRANSPORTATION — Abstracting, Bibliographies, Statistics*

STATISTICAL YEARBOOK FOR ASIA AND THE PACIFIC/ANNUAIRE STATISTIQUE POUR L'ASIE ET LE PACIFIQUE. see *BUSINESS AND ECONOMICS — Abstracting, Bibliographies, Statistics*

315   BG   ISSN 0302-2374
STATISTICAL YEARBOOK OF BANGLADESH. (Text in English) 1964. a. Tk.200($40) Bureau of Statistics, Secretariat, Dhaka 2, Bangladesh. **Document type:** government publication.
  Formerly: Statistical Digest of Bangladesh.
  Description: Data on population, agriculture, industry, foreign trade and banking in Bangladesh.

314   GR   ISSN 0081-5071
STATISTICAL YEARBOOK OF GREECE. (Text in English, Greek) 1955. a. $27. National Statistical Service of Greece, Statistical Information and Publications Division - Ethniki Statistiki Yperesia tes Ellados, 14-16 Lykourgou, 10166 Athens, Greece. TEL 30-1-3244-748. FAX 30-1-3222-205. TELEX 216734 ESYE GR. (back issues avail.) **Document type:** government publication.

STATISTICAL YEARBOOK OF GUANGDONG (YEAR). see *BUSINESS AND ECONOMICS — Abstracting, Bibliographies, Statistics*

319.55   IR   ISSN 1017-2564
STATISTICAL YEARBOOK OF IRAN. Key Title: Salnamah-i Amari-i Kishvar. (Text in Persian) 1967. a. Statistical Centre of Iran, Dr. Fatemi Ave., Teheran 14144, Iran. TEL 655061. FAX 653451. TELEX 213233 AMAR IR. charts; illus.; stat. **Document type:** government publication.

317.292   JM   ISSN 0304-0992
STATISTICAL YEARBOOK OF JAMAICA. 1973. a. 42. Statistical Institute of Jamaica, 9 Swallowfield Rd., Kingston 5, Jamaica, W.I. FAX 809-92-64859. illus. circ. 155.

310   LH   ISSN 0259-4676
STATISTICAL YEARBOOK OF LIECHTENSTEIN/STATISTISCHES JAHRBUCH FUERSTENTUM LIECHTENSTEIN. 1977. a. free. Amt fuer Volkswirtschaft, Vaduz FL-9490, Liechtenstein. FAX 41-75-66289. Ed.Bd. circ. 1,200. (back issues avail.) **Document type:** government publication.

315   TH   ISSN 0857-9067
HA1781
STATISTICAL YEARBOOK OF THAILAND. (Text in English, Thai) 1909. a. price varies. National Statistical Office, Statistical Data Bank and Information Dissemination Division, Larn Luang Rd., Bangkok 10100, Thailand. TEL 622-281-0333. FAX 662-2813814. circ. 1,000. **Document type:** government publication.
  Description: Information on the geography, climate, population, public health and vital statistics of Thailand.

310   NE   ISSN 0303-6448
HA1381
STATISTICAL YEARBOOK OF THE NETHERLANDS. 1942. a. Centraal Bureau voor de Statistiek, Prinses Beatrixlaan 428, Voorburg, Netherlands. (Orders to: SDU - Publishers, Christoffel Plantijnstraat, The Hague, Netherlands) **Document type:** government publication.

STATISTICAL YEARBOOK OF THE REPUBLIC OF CHINA. see *BUSINESS AND ECONOMICS — Abstracting, Bibliographies, Statistics*

314   BU
STATISTICHESKI GODISHNIK NA NARODNA REPUBLIKA BULGARIA. 1909. a. price varies. (Ministerstvo na Informatsiiata i Suobshteniiata, Komitet za Socialna Informacia v N.R. Bulgaria) Foreign Trade Co. "Hemus", 1B Raiko Daskalov Sq., 1000 Sofia, Bulgaria. TEL 359-2-801575. FAX 359-2-883419. stat. circ. 2,000.

311   UK   ISSN 0039-0526
HA1   CODEN: STTNAP
THE STATISTICIAN. 1950. q. £125($233) (foreign £145) (effective 1996). (Institute of Statisticians) Basil Blackwell Ltd., 108 Cowley Rd., Oxford OX4 1DF, England. TEL 44-865-791100. (Subscr. to: P.O. Box 87, Oxford OX2 0DT, England. TEL 44-865-791155. FAX 44-865-791927; In N. America: Blackwell Publishers, 238 Main St., Cambridge, MA 02142. TEL 617-547-7110. FAX 617-547-0789) Ed. Nigel Smeeton. adv.; bk.rev.; charts. (also avail. in microfiche; microform from UMI; back issues avail.) **Indexed:** ASCA, Biostat., Compumath, Cont.Pg.Manage., Curr.Cont., Curr.Ind.Stat., Excerp.Med., Geo.Abstr., Geol.Abstr., INSPEC, J.Cont.Quant.Meth., Oper.Res.Manage.Sci., P.A.I.S., Qual.Contr.Appl.Stat., SSCI. **Document type:** academic/scholarly publication.
  —BLDSC (8453.200000); Faxon; Genuine Article; SWETS; UMI; UnCover. **CCC.**
  Refereed Serial

STATISTICKA ROCENKA CESKE REPUBLIKY. see *BUSINESS AND ECONOMICS — Abstracting, Bibliographies, Statistics*

310   YU   ISSN 0585-1920
HA1631   CODEN: SGJUEB
STATISTICKI GODISNJAK JUGOSLAVIJE. 1954. a. Savezni Zavod za Statistiku, Kneza Milosa 20, Belgrade, Yugoslavia.

310   YU   ISSN 0352-3349
STATISTICKI KALENDAR JUGOSLAVIJE. 1955. a. Savezni Zavod za Statistiku, Savremena Administracija, Kneza Milosa 20, Belgrade, Yugoslavia.

314.97   BN   ISSN 0039-0542
STATISTICKI PREGLED SOCIJALISTICKE REPUBLIKE BOSNE I HERCEGOVINE. (Text in Serbo-Croatian) 1953. m. $10.45. Republicki Zavod za Statistiku, Jugoslavenske Narodne Armije 54, Sarajevo, Bosnia Hercegovina. Ed. Nedjo Kovacevic.

519.5   US   ISSN 0233-1888
QA276.A1
STATISTICS; a journal of theoretical and applied statistics. (Text in English, French, German or Russian) 1949. 8/yr. 116 ECU (effective 1996). Gordon & Breach Science Publishers, c/o International Publishers Distributor, 820 Town Center Dr., Langhorne, PA 19047. TEL 215-750-2642; 800-545-8398. FAX 215-750-6343. (Subscr. to: International Publishers Distributor, P.O. Box 90, Reading, Berkshire RG1 8JL, England. TEL 44-173-456-8316) Ed. Olaf Bunke. **Indexed:** INSPEC, J.Cont.Quant.Meth., Math.R., Stat.Theor.Meth.Abstr. **Document type:** academic/scholarly publication.
  —BLDSC (8453.505000); Faxon; SWETS; UnCover. **CCC.**
  Formerly (until 1984): Series Statistics (ISSN 0323-3944); Which supersedes in part (from 1977): Mathematische Operationsforschung und Statistik (ISSN 0047-6277)
  Refereed Serial

STATISTICS (YEAR) ROAD ACCIDENTS JAPAN. see *TRANSPORTATION — Abstracting, Bibliographies, Statistics*

519.5 001.6   UK   ISSN 0960-3174
                             CODEN: STACE3
STATISTICS AND COMPUTING. q. £49($89) to individuals; institutions in the E.C. £120 (N. America $199; elsewhere £130) (effective 1995). Chapman & Hall, Journals Department (Subsidiary of: International Thomson Publishing Group), 2-6 Boundary Row, London SE1 8HN, England. TEL 0171-865-0066. FAX 0171-522-9623. TELEX 290164 CHAPMA G. E-mail: journal@chall.mhs.compuserve.com. (Dist. by: International Thomson Publishing Services Ltd., Cheriton House, North Way, Andover, Hants. SP10 5BE, England. TEL 01264-342713. FAX 01264-342807; Subscr. in N. America to: Chapman & Hall, Journals Promotion Department, One Penn Plaza, 41st Fl., New York, NY 10019. TEL 212-564-1060. FAX 212-564-1505) Ed. David J. Hand. adv.; bk.rev.; software rev. (reprint service avail.) **Indexed:** Compumath, Curr.Ind.Stat., INSPEC (1992-), Stat.Theor.Meth.Abstr. **Document type:** academic/scholarly publication.
  —BLDSC (8453.516500); Genuine Article; SWETS. **CCC.**
  Description: Covers the entire range of interaction between statistics and computing.
  Refereed Serial

519.5   NE   ISSN 0167-7152
QA276.A1   CODEN: SPLTDC
STATISTICS & PROBABILITY LETTERS. (Text in English) 1982. 20/yr. fl.1775($1082) (effective 1996). North-Holland (Subsidiary of: Elsevier Science B.V.), P.O. Box 211, 1000 AE Amsterdam, Netherlands. TEL 31-20-4853911. FAX 31-20-4853598. TELEX 18582 ESPA NL. (Subscr. in U.S. and Canada to: Elsevier Science Inc., Box 882, Madison Sq. Sta., New York, NY 10159. TEL 212-989-5800. FAX 212-633-3990) Ed. Richard A. Johnson. (also avail. in microform from UMI; back issues avail.; reprint service avail. from SWZ) **Indexed:** ASCA, Compumath, Curr.Ind.Stat., J.Cont.Quant.Meth., Math.R., Stat.Theor.Meth.Abstr. **Document type:** academic/scholarly publication.
  —BLDSC (8453.518000); Ei; Genuine Article; SWETS; UnCover. **CCC.**
  Description: Covers all fields of statistics and probability, and provides an outlet for rapid publication of short communications in the field.
  Refereed Serial

STATISTICS - EUROPE; sources for market research. see *BUSINESS AND ECONOMICS — Abstracting, Bibliographies, Statistics*

STATISTICS FOR IRON AND STEEL INDUSTRY IN INDIA. see *METALLURGY — Abstracting, Bibliographies, Statistics*

STATISTICS IN MEDICINE. see *MEDICAL SCIENCES — Abstracting, Bibliographies, Statistics*

STATISTICS OF EDUCATION IN WALES: HIGHER & FURTHER EDUCATION. see *EDUCATION — Abstracting, Bibliographies, Statistics*

STATISTICS OF JAPANESE NON-LIFE INSURANCE BUSINESS. see *INSURANCE — Abstracting, Bibliographies, Statistics*

STATISTICS OF LIFE INSURANCE BUSINESS IN JAPAN. see INSURANCE — *Abstracting, Bibliographies, Statistics*

STATISTICS OF ROAD TRAFFIC ACCIDENTS IN EUROPE AND NORTH AMERICA. see TRANSPORTATION — *Abstracting, Bibliographies, Statistics*

STATISTICS OF SOUTHERN COLLEGE AND UNIVERSITY LIBRARIES. see LIBRARY AND INFORMATION SCIENCES — *Abstracting, Bibliographies, Statistics*

STATISTICS OF WORLD TRADE IN STEEL. see METALLURGY — *Abstracting, Bibliographies, Statistics*

STATISTICS ON SCIENTIFIC AND TECHNOLOGICAL ACTIVITIES/IHSA'AT AL-ANSHITAH AL-'ILMIYYAH WAL-TEKNOLOJIYYAH FI DAWLAT AL-KUWAYT. see SCIENCES: COMPREHENSIVE WORKS — *Abstracting, Bibliographies, Statistics*

STATISTICS RELATING TO REGIONAL AND MUNICIPAL GOVERNMENTS IN BRITISH COLUMBIA. see PUBLIC ADMINISTRATION — *Abstracting, Bibliographies, Statistics*

310 016   US   ISSN 0585-198X
Z7551
STATISTICS SOURCES; a subject guide to data on industrial, business, social, educational, financial and other topics for the U.S. and selected foreign countries. 1960. a. $360. Gale Research Inc., 835 Penobscot Bldg., Detroit, MI 48226. TEL 313-961-2242; 800-877-4253. FAX 313-961-6083. TELEX 810-221-7086. Eds. Jacqueline Wasserman O'Brien, Steven R. Wasserman.
Description: Lists over 2000 national and international statistics sources.

314   SW
STATISTICS SWEDEN. QUARTERLY FOREIGN TRADE STATISTICS S I T C. (Contents page and summaries in English) 1954. q. SEK 250 (effective 1992). Statistiska Centralbyraan, Distribution, S-701 89 Oerebro, Sweden. circ. 1,250.
Formerly (until 1990): Sweden. Statistiska Centralbyraan. Utrikeshandel. Maanadsstatistik (ISSN 0373-2649)

310   US   ISSN 1040-0672
                    CODEN: STMOEV
STATISTICS: TEXTBOOKS AND MONOGRAPHS SERIES. 1972. irreg., vol.439, 1995. price varies. Marcel Dekker, Inc., 270 Madison Ave., New York, NY 10016. TEL 212-696-9000. FAX 212-685-4540. TELEX 421419.
—BLDSC (8453.613000).

STATISTIK OVER REGISTRERING AF NYE AUTOMOBILER I DANMARK. see TRANSPORTATION — *Abstracting, Bibliographies, Statistics*

314.8   DK   ISSN 1395-0126
STATISTIK UDEN GRAENSER/STATISTIKK UTEN GRENSER/STATISTICS UNLIMITED. Variant title: Nordic Statistics on C D - R O M. (Text in English and the Nordic languages) 1992. a. $220. (Nordisk Statistisk Sekretariat - Nordic Statistical Secretariat) Danmarks Statistik, Sejroegade 11, DK-2100 Copenhagen Oe, Denmark. TEL 45-31-29-82-22. FAX 45-31-18-48-01. (back issues avail.) **Document type:** government publication.
●Available only on CD-ROM.

STATISTIQUE ANNUELLE DE LA NAVIGATION INTERIEURE. see TRANSPORTATION — *Abstracting, Bibliographies, Statistics*

STATISTIQUES DU COMMERCE EXTERIEUR DE L'UNION ECONOMIQUE BELGO-LUXEMBOURGEOISE. see BUSINESS AND ECONOMICS — *Abstracting, Bibliographies, Statistics*

STATISTIQUES FINANCIERES DES INSTITUTIONS DE DEPOT. see BUSINESS AND ECONOMICS — *Abstracting, Bibliographies, Statistics*

314.92   NE
STATISTISCH OVERZICHT HILVERSUM. 1954. s-a. fl.30. Bureau voor Onderzoek en Statistiek, Koninginneweg 5, Hilversum, Netherlands. Ed. R.W. de Jong. charts. circ. 250.
Former titles: Statistisch Jaaroverzicht Hilversum; Statistisch Kwartaaloverzicht Hilversum (ISSN 0028-291X); Incorporates: Population Statistics Hilversum (ISSN 0032-4736)

STATISTISCHE MONATSHEFTE SCHLESWIG-HOLSTEIN. see PUBLIC ADMINISTRATION — *Abstracting, Bibliographies, Statistics*

310   GW   ISSN 0934-6767
HA1320.N6
STATISTISCHE RUNDSCHAU NORDRHEIN-WESTFALEN. 1949. m. DM.48. Landesamt fuer Datenverarbeitung und Statistik Nordrhein-Westfalen, Postfach 101105, 40002 Duesseldorf, Germany. TEL 0211-9449-01. FAX 0211-442006. circ. 720. (back issues avail.) **Document type:** government publication.

STATISTISCHER BERICHT DER STADT FRANKENTHAL. see PUBLIC ADMINISTRATION — *Abstracting, Bibliographies, Statistics*

STATISTISCHER VIERTELJAHRESBERICHT HANNOVER. see PUBLIC ADMINISTRATION — *Abstracting, Bibliographies, Statistics*

314   GW   ISSN 0177-2554
STATISTISCHER WOCHENDIENST. w. DM.140. Statistisches Bundesamt, 65180 Wiesbaden, Germany. TEL 0611-75-1. FAX 0611-724000. TELEX 61186-STBA-D. **Document type:** government publication.

310   AU
STATISTISCHES AMT DER STADT WIEN. STATISTISCHE MITTEILUNGEN. 1876. q. S.200. Statistisches Amt der Stadt Wien, Volksgartenstr. 3, A-1016 Vienna, Austria. TEL 4000-88611. FAX 4000-9988610. (Subscr. to: Herold Druck und Verlags mbH, Faradaygasse 6, A-1032 Vienna, Austria) Ed. Peter Pokay. bk.rev.; stat. circ. 800. **Document type:** government publication.
Formerly (until 1985): Mitteilungen aus Statistik und Verwaltung der Stadt Wien (ISSN 0026-6876)
Description: Statistical tables and analyses concerning population, economy, social statistics and education in the city of Vienna.

314   GW   ISSN 0081-5322
STATISTISCHES JAHRBUCH BERLIN. 1945. a. DM.55. (Statistisches Landesamt) Kulturbuch Verlag GmbH, Postfach 470449, 12312 Berlin, Germany. TEL 030-6618484. FAX 030-6617828. (back issues avail.) **Document type:** government publication.
Supersedes: Berlin in Zahlen.

314   SZ   ISSN 0081-5330
HA1593
STATISTISCHES JAHRBUCH DER SCHWEIZ/ANNUAIRE STATISTIQUE DE LA SUISSE. 1891. a. price varies. (Statistisches Amt) Neue Zuercher Zeitung, Falkenstr. 11, CH-8021 Zurich, Switzerland. TEL 01-2581392. FAX 01-2581677. **Document type:** bulletin.

314   GW   ISSN 0931-9239
STATISTISCHES JAHRBUCH DER STADT AUGSBURG. 1953. irreg. DM.28. Amt fuer Stadtentwicklung und Statistik, Schmiedberg 6, 86152 Augsburg, Germany. TEL 0821-3246850. FAX 0821-3246877. Ed. Kurt Forner. circ. 400. **Document type:** government publication.

STATISTISCHES JAHRBUCH DER STADT KOELN. see PUBLIC ADMINISTRATION — *Abstracting, Bibliographies, Statistics*

310   AU   ISSN 0259-6083
STATISTISCHES JAHRBUCH DER STADT WIEN. 1883. a. S.400. Statistisches Amt der Stadt Wien, Volksgartenstr. 3, A-1016 Vienna, Austria. TEL 4000-88611. FAX 4000-9988610. (Subscr. to: Jugend und Volk Verlagsgesellschaft mbH, Anschuetzgasse 1, A-1150 Vienna, Austria) adv.; charts; index. circ. 800. (back issues avail.) **Document type:** government publication.
Description: Statistical data on the city of Vienna, including statistics of city districts and suburban areas.

STATISTISCHES JAHRBUCH DEUTSCHER GEMEINDEN. see PUBLIC ADMINISTRATION — *Abstracting, Bibliographies, Statistics*

314   GW   ISSN 0943-5743
HA1232
STATISTISCHES JAHRBUCH FUER DIE BUNDESREPUBLIK DEUTSCHLAND. 1952. a. DM.128. Statistisches Bundesamt, 65180 Wiesbaden, Germany. TEL 0611-75-1. FAX 0611-724000. TELEX 61186-STBA-D. **Document type:** government publication.
Formerly (until 1992): Statistisches Jahrbuch fuer das Vereinte Deutschland (ISSN 0941-3774); Which was formed by the 1991 merger of: Statistisches Jahrbuch fuer die Bundesrepublik Deutschland (ISSN 0081-5357); Statistisches Jahrbuch der Deutschen Demokratischen Republik (ISSN 0323-4258); Which superseded: Statistisches Jahrbuch der Hauptstadt der Deutschen Demokratischen Republik Berlin (ISSN 0435-6314)

314   AU   ISSN 0081-5314
STATISTISCHES JAHRBUCH FUER DIE REPUBLIK OESTERREICH. 1882. a. S.670. Oesterreichisches Statistisches Zentralamt, Hintere Zollamtstr. 2b, A-1033 Vienna, Austria. TEL 0222-71128-0. FAX 0222-7156828. adv. circ. 2,700. **Document type:** government publication.
Formerly (until 1950): Statistisches Handbuch fuer die Republik Oesterreich.

310   GW   ISSN 0077-2062
STATISTISCHES JAHRBUCH MUENCHEN. 1969. a. DM.25. Amt fuer Statistik und Datenanalyse, Tal 30, 80331 Munich, Germany. Ed. Egon Dheus.

310   GW
STATISTISCHES LANDESAMT HAMBURG. DATEN UND INFORMATIONEN FALTBLATT. English edition: Hamburg State Bureau of Statistics. Facts and Figures. 1977. a. free. Statistisches Landesamt Hamburg, Steckelhoern 12, 20457 Hamburg, Germany. TEL 040-3681-1766. FAX 040-36811700. TELEX 212121-SENATD. circ. 45,000. **Document type:** government publication.

310   AU   ISSN 0259-7985
STATISTISCHES TASCHENBUCH DER STADT WIEN. 1884. a. S.80. Statistisches Amt der Stadt Wien, Volksgartenstr. 3, A-1016 Vienna, Austria. TEL 4000-88611. FAX 4000-9988610. (Subscr.to: Jugend und Volk Verlagsgesellschaft mbH, Anschuetzgasse 1, A-1150 Vienna, Austria) adv.; charts; stat.; index. circ. 1,500. (back issues avail.) **Document type:** government publication.

314.891   DK   ISSN 0906-2211
STATISTISK AARBOG FOR HOVEDSTADSREGIONEN/STATISTICAL YEARBOOK FOR THE COPENHAGEN REGION. (Text in Danish and English) 1977. a. DKK 150. Hovedstadsregionens Statistikkontor, Vester Voldgade 87, 4, DK-1552 Copenhagen, Denmark. TEL 45-33-66-24-24. FAX 45-33-91-05-02. E-mail: hovpfl@unidhp.uni-c.dk. Ed. N.H. Johansen. illus.; circ. 1,000 (controlled).
Formerly (until 1990): Statistik for Hovedstadsregionen (ISSN 0106-2344)

310   SW   ISSN 0081-5381
HA1523
STATISTISK AARSBOK FOER SVERIGE/ABSTRACT OF SWEDISH STATISTICS. 1914. a. SEK 410. Statistiska Centralbyraan, Publishing Unit, S-701 89 Oerebro, Sweden. circ. 12,300.

STATISTISK TIAARS-OVERSIGT FOR KOEBENHAVNS KOMMUNE. see PUBLIC ADMINISTRATION — *Abstracting, Bibliographies, Statistics*

STATS - MONTHLY STATISTICAL AND MARKETING DIGEST. see BUSINESS AND ECONOMICS — *Abstracting, Bibliographies, Statistics*

314   AU   ISSN 0039-1093
HA1188.S8
STEIRISCHE STATISTIKEN. 1957. q. S.120. Amt der Steiermaerkischen Landesregierung, Landesamtsdirektion - Referat Statistik, Burgring 4, A-8010 Graz, Austria. FAX 0877-2339. TELEX 311838-LGRGZ-A. Ed. Ernst Burger. charts; stat.; index. circ. 500. (tabloid format) **Document type:** bulletin.

STATISTICS

310   GW
STOCHASTIK IN DER SCHULE. 1981. 3/yr. DM.25. Verein zur Foerderung des Schulischen Statistikunterrichts e.V., Kammannstr. 13, 58097 Hagen, Germany. Ed.Bd. adv.; bk.rev.; bibl.; cum.index: 1979-1989. (back issues avail.). **Document type:** academic/scholarly publication. *Refereed Serial*

STUDIES IN BAYESIAN ECONOMETRICS AND STATISTICS. see *BUSINESS AND ECONOMICS — Economic Systems And Theories, Economic History*

STUDIES IN PROBABILITY, OPTIMIZATION AND STATISTICS. see *MATHEMATICS — Computer Applications*

STUDIES IN PSEPHOLOGY. see *POPULATION STUDIES — Abstracting, Bibliographies, Statistics*

STUDIES IN STATISTICAL MECHANICS. see *PHYSICS — Mechanics*

314   GW   ISSN 0072-3967
STUDIES ON STATISTICS. (Text in English) 1957. irreg. price varies. Statistisches Bundesamt, 65180 Wiesbaden, Germany. TEL 0611-75-1. FAX 0611-724000. TELEX 61186-STBA-D. **Document type:** government publication.

SUDAN. DEPARTMENT OF STATISTICS. FOREIGN TRADE STATISTICS. see *BUSINESS AND ECONOMICS — Abstracting, Bibliographies, Statistics*

310   SJ
SUDAN. DEPARTMENT OF STATISTICS. STATISTICAL YEARBOOK. (Text in English) 1973. a. Department of Statistics, Box 700, Khartoum, Sudan.

SUMMARY OF RATE SCHEDULES OF NATURAL GAS PIPELINE COMPANIES. see *ENERGY — Abstracting, Bibliographies, Statistics*

314   FI   ISSN 0081-5063
SUOMEN TILASTOLLINEN VUOSIKIRJA/STATISTISK AARSBOK FOER FINLAND/STATISTICAL YEARBOOK OF FINLAND. (Text in English, Finnish, Swedish) 1879. a. FIM 265 in Scandinavia; Europe FIM 265; elsewhere FIM 300. Tilastokeskus, Annankatu 44, SF-00100 Helsinki 10, Finland. (Subscr. to: Statisti Finland, P.O. Box 504, SF-00100 Helsinki, Finland) circ. 5,000.
—BLDSC (8452.850000).

318   SR
SURINAME. ALGEMEEN BUREAU VOOR DE STATISTIEK. NATIONALE REKENINGEN. (Subseries of: Suriname in Cijfers) irreg. Algemeen Bureau voor de Statistiek, Paramaribo, Surinam.

317   CN   ISSN 0714-0045
HA31.2
SURVEY METHODOLOGY. 1975. s-a. Can.$30($36) (foreign $42). Statistics Canada, Publications Division, Ottawa, Ont. K1A 0T6, Canada. TEL 613-951-7277. FAX 613-951-1584. **Indexed:** Curr.Ind.Stat., Oper.Res.Manage.Sci., Qual.Contr.Appl.Stat.
—BLDSC (8550.560000). CCC.
Description: Presents articles dealing with various aspects of statistical development relevant to a statistical agency and evaluation of specific methodologies as applied to actual data collection or the data themselves.

314   GW   ISSN 0562-6927
SURVEY OF GERMAN FEDERAL STATISTICS/APERCU DE LA STATISTIQUE FEDERALE ALLEMANDE. (Editions in English and French) 1957. irreg. DM.17.80. Statistisches Bundesamt, 65180 Wiesbaden, Germany. TEL 0611-75-1. FAX 0611-724000. TELEX 61186-STBA-D. **Document type:** government publication.
Formerly (1957-1970): Germany (Federal Republic, 1949-). Statistisches Bundesamt Arbeiten (ISSN 0072-1611)

SURVEY OF HOUSEHOLD ECONOMIC ACTIVITIES (YEAR). see *BUSINESS AND ECONOMICS — Economic Situation And Conditions*

SURVEY ON GRADUATING STUDENTS ABROAD. see *EDUCATION — Abstracting, Bibliographies, Statistics*

316   SQ   ISSN 0586-1357
SWAZILAND. CENTRAL STATISTICAL OFFICE. ANNUAL STATISTICAL BULLETIN. 1966. a. E.2. Central Statistical Office, Box 456, Mbabane, Swaziland. TEL 43765. illus. circ. 800. **Document type:** government publication, bulletin.

316   SQ
SWAZILAND. CENTRAL STATISTICAL OFFICE. ANNUAL SURVEY OF SWAZI NATION LAND. 1972. a., latest 1982. free. Central Statistical Office, Box 456, Mbabane, Swaziland. TEL 43765. stat. circ. 500. **Document type:** government publication.

SWAZILAND. CENTRAL STATISTICAL OFFICE. CENSUS OF INDIVIDUAL TENURE FARMS. see *AGRICULTURE — Abstracting, Bibliographies, Statistics*

SWAZILAND. CENTRAL STATISTICAL OFFICE. CENSUS OF INDUSTRIES. see *BUSINESS AND ECONOMICS — Abstracting, Bibliographies, Statistics*

SWAZILAND. CENTRAL STATISTICAL OFFICE. EDUCATION STATISTICS. see *EDUCATION — Abstracting, Bibliographies, Statistics*

316   SQ
SWAZILAND. CENTRAL STATISTICAL OFFICE. STATISTICAL NEWS. 1967. q. free. Central Statistical Office, P.O. Box 456, Mbabane, Swaziland. TEL 43765. circ. 600. (processed) **Document type:** government publication.
Former titles (until 1974): Swaziland. Central Statistical Office. Quarterly Digest of Statistics; Swaziland. Central Statistical Office. Statistical News and Economic Indicators (ISSN 0302-3907); And: Swaziland Statistical News (ISSN 0586-1403).

SWAZILAND. CENTRAL STATISTICAL OFFICE. TIMBER STATISTICS. see *FORESTS AND FORESTRY — Abstracting, Bibliographies, Statistics*

SWEDEN. LUFTFARTSVERKET. AARSBOK. see *TRANSPORTATION — Abstracting, Bibliographies, Statistics*

SWEDEN. LUFTFARTSVERKET. CHARTERSTATISTIK. see *TRANSPORTATION — Abstracting, Bibliographies, Statistics*

SWEDEN. LUFTFARTSVERKET. FLYGPLATSSTATISTIK. see *TRANSPORTATION — Abstracting, Bibliographies, Statistics*

314   SW   ISSN 0039-7253
HA1523
SWEDEN. STATISTISKA CENTRALBYRAAN. ALLMAAN MAANADSSTATISTIK/MONTHLY DIGEST OF SWEDISH STATISTICS. (Contents page and summaries in English) 1963. m. (plus a. supplement). SEK 580 (effective 1992). Statistiska Centralbyraan, Distribution, S-701 89 Oerebro, Sweden. circ. 4,000. **Document type:** government publication.

314   SW   ISSN 0280-7629
SWEDEN. STATISTISKA CENTRALBYRAAN BIBLIOTEK. STATISTIK FRAAN INTERNATIONELLA ORGAN. 1974. a. SEK 40. Statistics Sweden Library, S-115 81 Stockholm, Sweden. circ. 200.
Formerly (until 1983): Aktuell Internationell Statistik i SCBs Bibliotek.

309   SW   ISSN 0347-7193
HD7731
SWEDEN. STATISTISKA CENTRALBYRAAN. LEVNADSFOERHAALLANDEN. RAPPORT. (Text in English, Swedish) 1975. irreg. Statistiska Centralbyraan, Distribution, S-701 89 Oerebro, Sweden. illus.
Formerly: Sweden. Statistiska Centralbyraan. Living Conditions Reports.

314   SW   ISSN 0082-0229
SWEDEN. STATISTISKA CENTRALBYRAAN. MEDDELANDEN I SAMORDNINGSFRAAGOR/REPORTS ON STATISTICAL CO-ORDINATION. Variant title: Mis. 1966. irreg. (1-4/yr.). price varies. Statistiska Centralbyraan (SCB), S-115 81 Stockholm, Sweden. TEL 46-8-783-40-00. FAX 46-8-783-45-99. (Dist. by: S C B Distribution, 701 89 Oerebro, Sweden) **Document type:** monographic series.

SWEDEN. STATISTISKA CENTRALBYRAAN. STATISTISKA MEDDELANDEN. SERIE BO, BOSTAEDER OCH BYGGNADER. see *BUILDING AND CONSTRUCTION — Abstracting, Bibliographies, Statistics*

314   SW   ISSN 0082-0350
SWEDEN. STATISTISKA CENTRALBYRAAN. URVAL SKRIFTSERIES - SELECTION SERIES. (Text in Swedish; summaries in English) 1969. irreg. price varies. Statistiska Centralbyraan, Publishing Unit, S-701 89 Oerebro, Sweden. circ. 750.

314   SW   ISSN 0039-727X
SWEDEN. STATISTISKA CENTRALBYRAAN. UTRIKESHANDEL. KVARTALSSTATISTIK. (Contents page and summaries in English) 1961. q. SEK 950. Statistiska Centralbyraan, Distribution, S-701 89 Oerebro, Sweden. circ. 1,400.

SWITZERLAND. BUNDESAMT FUER STATISTIK. BILANZ DER WOHNBEVOELKERUNG IN DEN GEMEINDEN DER SCHWEIZ - BILAN DEMOGRAPHIQUE DES COMMUNES SUISSES. see *POPULATION STUDIES — Abstracting, Bibliographies, Statistics*

SWITZERLAND. BUNDESAMT FUER STATISTIK. SCHUELERINNEN, SCHUELER UND STUDIERENDE - ELEVES ET ETUDIANTS. see *EDUCATION — Abstracting, Bibliographies, Statistics*

SWITZERLAND. DIRECTORATE GENERAL OF CUSTOMS. ANNUAL REPORT. see *BUSINESS AND ECONOMICS — Abstracting, Bibliographies, Statistics*

SWITZERLAND. DIRECTORATE GENERAL OF CUSTOMS. ANNUAL STATISTICS. see *BUSINESS AND ECONOMICS — Abstracting, Bibliographies, Statistics*

SWITZERLAND. DIRECTORATE GENERAL OF CUSTOMS. MONTHLY STATISTICS. see *BUSINESS AND ECONOMICS — Abstracting, Bibliographies, Statistics*

315   SY   ISSN 0081-4725
SYRIA. CENTRAL BUREAU OF STATISTICS. STATISTICAL ABSTRACT. (Text in Arabic, English) 1948. a. $75 in Arab countries; elsewhere $100 (effective 1995). Central Bureau of Statistics, Damascus, Syria. FAX 3322292. TELEX STC 411093 SY. **Document type:** government publication.
Description: Various current statistics of different sectors.

SYRIA. CENTRAL BUREAU OF STATISTICS. SUMMARY OF FOREIGN TRADE. see *BUSINESS AND ECONOMICS — Abstracting, Bibliographies, Statistics*

T V PROGRAM STATS. see *COMMUNICATIONS — Abstracting, Bibliographies, Statistics*

310   II   ISSN 0082-1578
TAMIL NADU. DEPARTMENT OF STATISTICS. ANNUAL STATISTICAL ABSTRACT. (Text in English) 1954. a. Rs.11. Director of Statistics, Madras 600006, India. (Subscr. to: Government Publication Depot, 166 Anna Rd., Madras 600002, India) **Document type:** government publication, abstracting/indexing.

316.78   TZ   ISSN 0039-9469
TANZANIA. BUREAU OF STATISTICS. QUARTERLY STATISTICAL BULLETIN. q. EAs.4 per no. Bureau of Statistics, Box 796, Dar es Salaam, Tanzania. (Orders to: Government Publications Agency, Box 1801, Dar es Salaam, Tanzania) mkt. **Document type:** government publication.

TANZANIA. BUREAU OF STATISTICS. SURVEY OF EMPLOYMENT. see *BUSINESS AND ECONOMICS — Abstracting, Bibliographies, Statistics*

TANZANIA. BUREAU OF STATISTICS. SURVEY OF INDUSTRIAL PRODUCTION. see *BUSINESS AND ECONOMICS — Abstracting, Bibliographies, Statistics*

314   SZ
TASCHENSTATISTIK (YEAR). (Text in English, French, German and Italian) a. Bundesamt fuer Statistik, Schwarztorstr. 96, CH-3003 Bern, Switzerland. TEL 031-3236011. FAX 031-3236061. **Document type:** government publication.

TASMANIAN TRANSPORT STATISTICS. see *TRANSPORTATION — Abstracting, Bibliographies, Statistics*

TAX BURDEN ON TOBACCO. see *TOBACCO — Abstracting, Bibliographies, Statistics*

TEACHING STATISTICS; an international journal for teachers of pupils aged 9 to 19. see EDUCATION — *Abstracting, Bibliographies, Statistics*

519.5 003   DK   ISSN 0906-9992
TECHNICAL UNIVERSITY OF DENMARK. INSTITUTE OF MATHEMATICAL STATISTICS AND OPERATIONS RESEARCH. TECHNICAL REPORT. irreg. Technical University of Denmark, Institute of Mathematical Statistics and Operations Research, Bldg. 321, DK-2800 Lyngby, Denmark. FAX 45-42-88-13-97. illus.
Former titles (until 1992): Technical University of Denmark. Institute of Mathematical Statistics and Operations Research. Research Report (ISSN 0107-3826); Institut for Matematisk Statistik og Operationsanalyse. Working Paper (ISSN 0107-5233)

TENNESSEE PUBLIC LIBRARY DIRECTORY AND STATISTICS (YEAR). see LIBRARY AND INFORMATION SCIENCES — *Abstracting, Bibliographies, Statistics*

317   US   ISSN 0082-2760
HA641
TENNESSEE STATISTICAL ABSTRACT. 1969. a. $32. University of Tennessee at Knoxville, Center for Business and Economic Research, Knoxville, TN 37996-4170. TEL 615-974-5441. FAX 615-974-3100. TELEX 557461 UTSUPBLST. Ed. Betty B. Vickers. circ. 1,400. (also avail. in microfiche from BHP,CIS) **Indexed:** SRI.

314   SP   ISSN 1133-0686
HA1
TEST. (Text in English) 1950. 2/yr. (in 1 vol.). 12000 ptas. Sociedad de Estadistica e Investigacion Operativa, Hortaleza 104, 2o Izda., 28004 Madrid, Spain. TEL 34-1-3082474. adv.; bk.rev.; abstr.; bibl.; charts; stat.; tr.lit.; index. circ. 600. **Indexed:** Ind.SST, Int.Abstr.Oper.Res., Math.R.
Formerly (until 1992): Trabajos de Estadistica (ISSN 0213-8190); Supersedes in part (in 1986): Trabajos de Estadistica e Investigacion Operativa (ISSN 0041-0241); Which was formerly (until 1963): Trabajos de Estadistica (ISSN 0210-5675).

310 976.4   US   ISSN 0363-4248
AY311.D3
TEXAS ALMANAC AND STATE INDUSTRIAL GUIDE. Cover title: Texas Almanac. 1857. biennial. $16.95 hardbound; paperbound $10.95. Dallas Morning News, Box 655237, Dallas, TX 75265. TEL 214-977-8261. (Dist. by: Andrews & McMeel, 4900 Main St., Kansas City, MO 64112. TEL 800-642-6480. FAX 816-932-6706) Ed. Mike Kingston. adv.; charts; illus.; stat.; index. circ. 50,000. (also avail. in microform) **Indexed:** SRI.
Former titles (until 1967): Texas Almanac (ISSN 0363-423X); (1904-1955): Texas Almanac and State Industrial Guide (ISSN 0363-4221)

TEXAS BLUE BOOK OF LIFE INSURANCE STATISTICS. see INSURANCE — *Abstracting, Bibliographies, Statistics*

TEXAS PETRO FACTS. see PETROLEUM AND GAS — *Abstracting, Bibliographies, Statistics*

TEXAS PUBLIC LIBRARY STATISTICS. see LIBRARY AND INFORMATION SCIENCES — *Abstracting, Bibliographies, Statistics*

016 315   TH   ISSN 0857-9164
THAILAND. NATIONAL STATISTICAL OFFICE. ANNOTATED STATISTICAL BIBLIOGRAPHY. (Text in English) 1961. irreg., latest 1990-1991 ed. price varies. National Statistical Office, Statistical Data Bank and Information Dissemination Division, Larn Luang Rd., Bangkok 10100, Thailand. TEL 622-281-0333. FAX 622-2813814. circ. 1,000. **Document type:** government publication, bibliography.
Description: List of statistical publications published officially by Thai government agencies.

310   TH   ISSN 0858-2696
THAILAND. NATIONAL STATISTICAL OFFICE. ANNUAL REPORT. (Text in Thai) 1963. a. National Statistical Office, Statistical Data Bank and Information Dissemination Division, Larn Luang Rd., Bangkok 10100, Thailand. TEL 662-281-0333. FAX 662-2813814. circ. 1,000. **Document type:** government publication.
Description: Results of work following the program of the National Statistical Office administration in general for the reported year.

315.93   TH   ISSN 0857-9482
HA4600.55
THAILAND. NATIONAL STATISTICAL OFFICE. QUARTERLY BULLETIN OF STATISTICS. (Text in English and Thai) 1952. q. price varies. National Statistical Office, Statistical Data Bank and Information Dissemination Division, Larn Luang Rd., Bangkok 10100, Thailand. TEL 662-281-0333. FAX 662-281-3814. charts; stat. circ. 1,000. **Document type:** government publication, bulletin.
Description: Statistical tables on climate, population and vital statistics, social statistics, production, transport and communication.

315   TH
THAILAND. NATIONAL STATISTICAL OFFICE. RESEARCH PAPER. 1975. irreg. National Statistical Office, Statistical Information Division, Larn Luang Rd., Bangkok, Thailand. FAX 2813814.

THEORY AND DECISION LIBRARY. SERIES B: MATHEMATICAL AND STATISTICAL METHODS. see MATHEMATICS

310 658.3   US
TIMING ANALYSIS PROJECTION. Short title: T A P. 1971. s-m. to clients only. Covato Research Corporation, Manor Oak II, Ste. 333, 1910 Cochran Rd., Pittsburgh, PA 15220. TEL 412-341-3700. FAX 412-341-8922. Ed. Phillip R. Covato. index. circ. 100. (back issues avail.) **Document type:** trade publication.

316.6   TG
TOGO. DIRECTION DE LA STATISTIQUE. BULLETIN MENSUEL DE STATISTIQUE. m. 5600 Fr.CFA. Direction de la Statistique, Boite Postale 118, Lome, Togo.

TOGO. MINISTRY OF ECONOMY AND FINANCE. BULLETIN DE STATISTIQUES. see BUSINESS AND ECONOMICS — *Abstracting, Bibliographies, Statistics*

310   JA   ISSN 0285-7677
TOKEI. (Text in Japanese) 1947. m. 8100 Yen. Nihon Tokei Kyokai - Japan Statistical Association, Crest 21, 6-21, Yocho-machi, Shinjuku-ku, Tokyo 162, Japan. TEL 03-5269-3051. FAX 03-5269-3058.

TOKEI SURI KENKYUZYO KENKYU RIPOTO/INSTITUTE OF STATISTICAL MATHEMATICS. RESEARCH REPORT. GENERAL SERIES. see MATHEMATICS

310   CC   ISSN 0496-4225
TONGJI YANJIU/STATISTICS RESEARCH. (Text in Chinese) bi-m. Zhongguo Tongji Chubanshe - China Statistics Publishing House, 38 Yuetan Nanjie, Sanlihe, Beijing 100826, People's Republic of China. TEL 217162. Ed. Mo Rida.

310   JA
TOYO KEIZAI. STATISTICS MONTHLY. (Text in Japanese) 1939. m. Toyo Keizai Inc., 1-2-1, Nihonbashi Hongoku-cho, Chuo-ku, Tokyo 103, Japan. TEL 03-3246-5575. FAX 03-3242-4068. Ed. Naoto Tamaoka. circ. 15,000.

TRANSPORT STATISTICS GREAT BRITAIN. see TRANSPORTATION — *Abstracting, Bibliographies, Statistics*

TRANSPORTE, COMUNICACIONES, TURISMO. see TRANSPORTATION — *Abstracting, Bibliographies, Statistics*

311   TR   ISSN 0082-6502
TRINIDAD AND TOBAGO. CENTRAL STATISTICAL OFFICE. ANNUAL STATISTICAL DIGEST. 1951. a. T.T.$10. Central Statistical Office, 35-41 Queen St., P.O. Box 98, Port-of-Spain, Trinidad & Tobago, W.I. TEL 809-625-5370. (Dist. by: Government Printer, 2-4 Victoria Ave., Port-of-Spain, Trinidad & Tobago, W.I.) **Document type:** government publication.

TRINIDAD AND TOBAGO. CENTRAL STATISTICAL OFFICE. BUSINESS SURVEYS. see BUSINESS AND ECONOMICS — *Abstracting, Bibliographies, Statistics*

TRINIDAD AND TOBAGO. CENTRAL STATISTICAL OFFICE. ECONOMIC INDICATORS. see BUSINESS AND ECONOMICS — *Abstracting, Bibliographies, Statistics*

TRINIDAD AND TOBAGO. CENTRAL STATISTICAL OFFICE. ESTIMATED INTERNAL MIGRATION. BULLETIN.. see POPULATION STUDIES — *Abstracting, Bibliographies, Statistics*

TRINIDAD AND TOBAGO. CENTRAL STATISTICAL OFFICE. FINANCIAL STATISTICS. see BUSINESS AND ECONOMICS — *Abstracting, Bibliographies, Statistics*

TRINIDAD AND TOBAGO. CENTRAL STATISTICAL OFFICE. INTERNATIONAL TRAVEL REPORT. see TRAVEL AND TOURISM — *Abstracting, Bibliographies, Statistics*

TRINIDAD AND TOBAGO. CENTRAL STATISTICAL OFFICE. LABOUR FORCE BY SEX. see BUSINESS AND ECONOMICS — *Abstracting, Bibliographies, Statistics*

TRINIDAD AND TOBAGO. CENTRAL STATISTICAL OFFICE. OVERSEAS TRADE. ANNUAL REPORT. see BUSINESS AND ECONOMICS — *Abstracting, Bibliographies, Statistics*

TRINIDAD AND TOBAGO. CENTRAL STATISTICAL OFFICE. OVERSEAS TRADE. BI-MONTHLY REPORT. see BUSINESS AND ECONOMICS — *Abstracting, Bibliographies, Statistics*

317   TR
TRINIDAD AND TOBAGO. CENTRAL STATISTICAL OFFICE. POCKET DIGEST. 1973. a. T.T.$100. Central Statistical Office, 35-41 Queen St., P.O. Box 98, Port-of-Spain, Trinidad & Tobago, W.I. TEL 809-625-3705. (Dist. by: Government Printing Office, 2-4 Victoria Ave., Port-of-Spain, Trinidad & Tobago, W.I.) **Document type:** government publication.

TRINIDAD AND TOBAGO. CENTRAL STATISTICAL OFFICE. POPULATION AND VITAL STATISTICS; REPORT. see POPULATION STUDIES — *Abstracting, Bibliographies, Statistics*

TRINIDAD AND TOBAGO. CENTRAL STATISTICAL OFFICE. QUARTERLY ECONOMIC REPORT. see BUSINESS AND ECONOMICS — *Abstracting, Bibliographies, Statistics*

TRINIDAD AND TOBAGO. CENTRAL STATISTICAL OFFICE. QUARTERLY TRAVEL. see TRAVEL AND TOURISM — *Abstracting, Bibliographies, Statistics*

310   TR
TRINIDAD AND TOBAGO. CENTRAL STATISTICAL OFFICE. STAFF PAPERS. 1967. irreg. free. Central Statistical Office, 35-41 Queen St., P.O. Box 98, Port-of-Spain, Trinidad & Tobago, W.I. TEL 809-625-3705. (Dist. by: Government Printing Office, 2-4 Victoria Ave., Port-of-Spain, Trinidad & Tobago, W.I.) **Document type:** monographic series, government publication.

TUNGSTEN STATISTICS. see METALLURGY — *Abstracting, Bibliographies, Statistics*

316.11   TI   ISSN 0041-4115
TUNISIA. INSTITUT NATIONAL DE LA STATISTIQUE. BULLETIN MENSUEL DE STATISTIQUE. (Text in Arabic, French) 1954. m. 22 din. Institut National de la Statistique, 70 rue Echcham, Tunis, Tunisia. **Indexed:** P.A.I.S.For.Lang.Ind. **Document type:** government publication.

TUNISIA. OFFICE DES PORTS NATIONAUX. BULLETIN ANNUEL DES STATISTIQUES. see TRANSPORTATION — *Abstracting, Bibliographies, Statistics*

TURISMO; estadisticas de turismo y movimiento internacional de viajeros. see TRAVEL AND TOURISM — *Abstracting, Bibliographies, Statistics*

TURISMUL IN ROMANIA/TOURISM IN ROMANIA. see TRAVEL AND TOURISM — *Abstracting, Bibliographies, Statistics*

TURKEY. DEVELT ISTATISTIK ENSTITUSU. TOPTAN FIYAT ISTATISTIKLERI/TURKEY. STATE INSTITUTE OF STATISTICS. WHOLESALE PRICE STATISTICS. see BUSINESS AND ECONOMICS — *Abstracting, Bibliographies, Statistics*

TURKEY. DEVLET ISTATISTIK ENSTITUSU. ADALET ISTATISTKLERI/TURKEY. STATE INSTITUTE OF STATISTICS. JUDICIAL STATISTICS. see LAW — *Abstracting, Bibliographies, Statistics*

TURKEY. DEVLET ISTATISTIK ENSTITUSU. AYLIK DIS TICARET OZETI/TURKEY. STATE INSTITUTE OF STATISTICS. MONTHLY SUMMARY OF FOREIGN TRADE. see *BUSINESS AND ECONOMICS — Abstracting, Bibliographies, Statistics*

TURKEY. DEVLET ISTATISTIK ENSTITUSU. AYLIK EKONOMIK GOSTERGELER/TURKEY. STATE INSTITUTE OF STATISTICS. MONTHLY ECONOMIC INDICATORS. see *BUSINESS AND ECONOMICS — Abstracting, Bibliographies, Statistics*

315.61   TU   ISSN 0041-4263
TURKEY. DEVLET ISTATISTIK ENSTITUSU. AYLIK ISTATISTIK BULTENI/TURKEY. STATE INSTITUTE OF STATISTICS. MONTHLY BULLETIN OF STATISTICS. Key Title: Aylik Istatistik Bulteni - Istatistik Enstitusu. (Text in English, Turkish) 1952. m. $17.60. Devlet Istatistik Enstitusu - State Institute of Statistics, Necatibey Caddesi No. 114, 06100 Ankara, Turkey. TEL 90-312-4175027. FAX 90-312-4170432. charts; stat. circ. 3,000. **Document type:** government publication.
Description: Monthly statistical and evaluation bulletin.

TURKEY. DEVLET ISTATISTIK ENSTITUSU. BINA INSAAT ISTATISTIKLERI/TURKEY. STATE INSTITUTE OF STATISTICS. BUILDING CONSTRUCTION STATISTICS. see *BUILDING AND CONSTRUCTION — Abstracting, Bibliographies, Statistics*

TURKEY. DEVLET ISTATISTIK ENSTITUSU. BOSANMA ISTATISTIKLERI/TURKEY. STATE INSTITUTE OF STATISTICS. DIVORCE STATISTICS. see *MATRIMONY — Abstracting, Bibliographies, Statistics*

TURKEY. DEVLET ISTATISTIK ENSTITUSU. BUTCELER - BELEDIYELER, IL OZEL IDARLER VE KOYLER/TURKEY. STATE INSTITUTE OF STATISTICS. BUDGETS - MUNICIPAL AND SPECIAL PROVINCIAL ADMINISTRATIONS AND VILLAGES. see *PUBLIC ADMINISTRATION — Abstracting, Bibliographies, Statistics*

TURKEY. DEVLET ISTATISTIK ENSTITUSU. CIFTCININ ELINE GECEN FIYATLAR/TURKEY. STATE INSTITUTE OF STATISTICS. PRICES RECEIVED BY FARMERS. see *AGRICULTURE — Abstracting, Bibliographies, Statistics*

TURKEY. DEVLET ISTATISTIK ENSTITUSU. DENIZ TASITLARI ISTATISTIKLERI (18 VE DAHA YUKARI GROS TONILATOLUK)/TURKEY. STATE INSTITUTE OF STATISTICS. STATISTICS OF SEA VESSELS (18 GROSS TONNAGES AND OVER). see *TRANSPORTATION — Abstracting, Bibliographies, Statistics*

TURKEY. DEVLET ISTATISTIK ENSTITUSU. DIS TICARET ISTATISTIKLERI/TURKEY. STATE INSTITUTE OF STATISTICS. FOREIGN TRADE STATISTICS. see *BUSINESS AND ECONOMICS — Abstracting, Bibliographies, Statistics*

TURKEY. DEVLET ISTATISTIK ENSTITUSU. DONEMLER ITIBARIYLE IMALAT SANAYII: ISTIHDAM - ODEMELER - URETIM EGILIM (GECICI SONUCLAR)/TURKEY. STATE INSTITUTE OF STATISTICS. MANUFACTURING INDUSTRY (QUARTERLY) EMPLOYMENT - PAYMENTS - PRODUCTION - EXPECTATIONS (PROVISIONAL RESULTS). see *BUSINESS AND ECONOMICS — Abstracting, Bibliographies, Statistics*

TURKEY. DEVLET ISTATISTIK ENSTITUSU. EVLENME ISTATISTIKLERI/TURKEY. STATE INSTITUTE OF STATISTICS. MARRIAGE STATISTICS. see *MATRIMONY — Abstracting, Bibliographies, Statistics*

315.61   TU
TURKEY. DEVLET ISTATISTIK ENSTITUSU. GAP IL ISTATISTIKLERI/TURKEY. STATE INSTITUTE OF STATISTICS. S E A P PROVINCIAL STATISTICS. (Text in English, Turkish) a., latest 1993. $40. Devlet Istatistik Enstitusu, Necatibey Cad. No. 114, 06100 Ankara, Turkey. TEL 90-312-4185027. FAX 90-312-4170432. (also avail. in diskette format) **Document type:** government publication.
Description: Provides statistical information on provinces of the South Eastern Anatolian Project, including demographic, economic, environmental and other types of data.

TURKEY. DEVLET ISTATISTIK ENSTITUSU. GAYRI SAFI MILLI HASILA, HABER BULTENI/TURKEY. STATE INSTITUTE OF STATISTICS. GROSS NATIONAL PRODUCT RESULTS, NEWS BULLETIN. see *BUSINESS AND ECONOMICS — Abstracting, Bibliographies, Statistics*

TURKEY. DEVLET ISTATISTIK ENSTITUSU. GAZ VE SU ISTATISTIKLERI/TURKEY. STATE INSTITUTE OF STATISTICS. GAS AND WATER STATISTICS. see *ENERGY — Abstracting, Bibliographies, Statistics*

TURKEY. DEVLET ISTATISTIK ENSTITUSU. GENEL NUFUS SAYIMI. GECICI SONUCLAR/TURKEY. STATE INSTITUTE OF STATISTICS. CENSUS OF POPULATION. PRELIMINARY RESULTS. see *POPULATION STUDIES — Abstracting, Bibliographies, Statistics*

TURKEY. DEVLET ISTATISTIK ENSTITUSU. GENEL NUFUS SAYIMI. IDARI BOLUNUS/TURKEY. STATE INSTITUTE OF STATISTICS. CENSUS OF POPULATION. ADMINISTRATIVE DIVISION. see *POPULATION STUDIES — Abstracting, Bibliographies, Statistics*

TURKEY. DEVLET ISTATISTIK ENSTITUSU. GENEL NUFUS SAYIMI. NUFUSAN SOSYAL VE EKONOMIK NITELIKLERI/TURKEY. STATE INSTITUTE OF STATISTICS. CENSUS OF POPULATION. SOCIAL AND ECONOMIC CHARACTERISTICS OF POPULATION. see *POPULATION STUDIES — Abstracting, Bibliographies, Statistics*

TURKEY. DEVLET ISTATISTIK ENSTITUSU. GENEL TARIM SAYIMI/TURKEY. STATE INSTITUTE OF STATISTICS. GENERAL AGRICULTURAL CENSUS. see *AGRICULTURE — Abstracting, Bibliographies, Statistics*

TURKEY. DEVLET ISTATISTIK ENSTITUSU. GEVRE ISTATISTIKLERI - HAVA KIRLILIGI/TURKEY. STATE INSTITUTE OF STATISTICS. ENVIRONMENTAL STATISTICS - AIR POLLUTION. see *ENVIRONMENTAL STUDIES — Abstracting, Bibliographies, Statistics*

315.61   TU
TURKEY. DEVLET ISTATISTIK ENSTITUSU. IL VE BOLGE ISTATISTIKLERI/TURKEY. STATE INSTITUTE OF STATISTICS. PROVINCIAL AND REGIONAL STATISTICS. (Text in English, Turkish) a., latest 1993 $65 (effective 1994). Devlet Istatistik Enstitusu - State Institute of Statistics, Necatibey Caddesi No. 114, 06100 Ankara, Turkey. TEL 90-312-4185027. FAX 90-312-4174032. (also avail. in diskette format) **Document type:** government publication.
Description: Provides statistics at the regional and provincial level for population, industry, energy, transportation, health, education and many other subjects.

TURKEY. DEVLET ISTATISTIK ENSTITUSU. INTIHAR ISTATISTIKLERI/TURKEY. STATE INSTITUTE OF STATISTICS. SUICIDE STATISTICS. see *POPULATION STUDIES — Abstracting, Bibliographies, Statistics*

315.61   TU
TURKEY. DEVLET ISTATISTIK ENSTITUSU. ISTATISTIK GOSTERGELER/TURKEY. STATE INSTITUTE OF STATISTICS. STATISTICAL INDICATORS. (Text in English, Turkish) 1991. a., latest 1991. $90. Devlet Istatistik Enstitusu - State Institute of Statistics, Necatibey Caddesi No. 114, 06100 Ankara, Turkey. TEL 90-312-4185027. FAX 90-312-4170432. (also avail. in diskette format) **Document type:** government publication.
Description: Provides statistical tables and data from the earliest years of the Turkish Republic, from 1923 to the present.

TURKEY. DEVLET ISTATISTIK ENSTITUSU. KABOTAJ VE ULUSLARARASI DENIZ TASIMASI ISTATISTIKLERI/TURKEY. STATE INSTITUTE OF STATISTICS. STATISTICS OF COASTAL AND INTERNATIONAL SEA TRANSPORTATION. see *TRANSPORTATION — Abstracting, Bibliographies, Statistics*

TURKEY. DEVLET ISTATISTIK ENSTITUSU. KAMU KURUMU VE KURULUSLARI HIZMET ONCESI VE HIZMET ICI EGITIM ISTATISTIKLERI/TURKEY. STATE INSTITUTE OF STATISTICS. STATISTICS ON TRAINING IN STATE INSTITUTIONS. see *EDUCATION — Abstracting, Bibliographies, Statistics*

TURKEY. DEVLET ISTATISTIK ENSTITUSU. KARAYOLU TRAFIK KAZA ISTATISTIKLERI/TURKEY. STATE INSTITUTE OF STATISTICS. ROAD TRAFFIC ACCIDENTS STATISTICS. see *TRANSPORTATION — Abstracting, Bibliographies, Statistics*

TURKEY. DEVLET ISTATISTIK ENSTITUSU. KESIN HESAPLAR - BELEDIYELER VE IL OZEL IDARELERI/TURKEY. STATE INSTITUTE OF STATISTICS. FINAL ACCOUNTS - MUNICIPALITIES AND SPECIAL PROVINCIAL ADMINISTRATIONS. see *PUBLIC ADMINISTRATION — Abstracting, Bibliographies, Statistics*

306.021   TU   ISSN 1300-1167
TURKEY. DEVLET ISTATISTIK ENSTITUSU. KULTUR ISTATISTIKLERI/TURKEY. STATE INSTITUTE OF STATISTICS. CULTURAL STATISTICS. Key Title: Kultur Istatistikleri. (Text in English, Turkish) 1936. a., latest 1991. $30. Devlet Istatistik Enstitusu - State Institute of Statistics, Necatibey Caddesi No. 114, 06100 Ankara, Turkey. TEL 90-312-4185027. FAX 90-312-4170432. circ. 1,130. **Document type:** government publication.

TURKEY. DEVLET ISTATISTIK ENSTITUSU. MADEN ISTATISTIKLERI/TURKEY. STATE INSTITUTE OF STATISTICS. MINING STATISTICS. see *MINES AND MINING INDUSTRY — Abstracting, Bibliographies, Statistics*

TURKEY. DEVLET ISTATISTIK ENSTITUSU. MAHALLI IDARELER SECIMI SONUCLARI/TURKEY. STATE INSTITUTE OF STATISTICS. RESULTS OF ELECTIONS OF LOCAL ADMINISTRATIONS. see *POLITICAL SCIENCE — Abstracting, Bibliographies, Statistics*

TURKEY. DEVLET ISTATISTIK ENSTITUSU. MILLETVEKILI GENEL SECIMI SONUCLARI/TURKEY STATE INSTITUTE OF STATISTICS. RESULTS OF GENERAL ELECTION OF REPRESENTATIVES. see *POLITICAL SCIENCE — Abstracting, Bibliographies, Statistics*

TURKEY. DEVLET ISTATISTIK ENSTITUSU. MILLI EGITIM ISTATISTIKLERI ORGUN EGITIM/TURKEY. STATE INSTITUTE OF STATISTICS. NATIONAL EDUCATIONAL STATISTICS FORMAL EDUCATION. see *EDUCATION — Abstracting, Bibliographies, Statistics*

TURKEY. DEVLET ISTATISTIK ENSTITUSU. MILLI EGITIM ISTATISTIKLERI: OGRETIM YILI BASI. see *EDUCATION — Abstracting, Bibliographies, Statistics*

TURKEY. DEVLET ISTATISTIK ENSTITUSU. MILLI EGITIM ISTATISTIKLERI YAYGIN EGITIM/TURKEY. STATE INSTITUTE OF STATISTICS. NATIONAL EDUCATION STATISTICS ADULT EDUCATION. see *EDUCATION — Abstracting, Bibliographies, Statistics*

TURKEY. DEVLET ISTATISTIK ENSTITUSU. MOTORLU KARA TASITLARI ISTATISTIKLERI/TURKEY. STATE INSTITUTE OF STATISTICS. MOTOR VEHICLE STATISTICS. see *TRANSPORTATION — Abstracting, Bibliographies, Statistics*

TURKEY. DEVLET ISTATISTIK ENSTITUSU. OLUM ISTATISTIKLERI (IL VE ILCE MERKEZLERINDE)/TURKEY. STATE INSTITUTE OF STATISTICS. DEATH STATISTICS (IN PROVINCIAL AND DISTRICT CENTERS). see *POPULATION STUDIES — Abstracting, Bibliographies, Statistics*

TURKEY. DEVLET ISTATISTIK ENSTITUSU. PERAKENDE FIYAT ISTATISTIKLERI/TURKEY. STATE INSTITUTE OF STATISTICS. RETAIL PRICE STATISTICS. see *BUSINESS AND ECONOMICS — Abstracting, Bibliographies, Statistics*

TURKEY. DEVLET ISTATISTIK ENSTITUSU. SANAYI URETIM INDEKSI (DONEMLER ITIBARIYLE)/TURKEY. STATE INSTITUTE OF STATISTICS. INDUSTRIAL PRODUCTION INDEXES (QUARTERLY). see *BUSINESS AND ECONOMICS — Abstracting, Bibliographies, Statistics*

STATISTICS

315.61   TU
TURKEY. DEVLET ISTATISTIK ENSTITUSU. SAYILARLA TURKIYE/TURKEY. STATE INSTITUTE OF STATISTICS. TURKEY IN FIGURES. (Text in English, Turkish) 1975. a., latest 1991. free. Devlet Istatistik Enstitusu - State Institute of Statistics, Necatibey Caddesi No. 114, 06100 Ankara, Turkey. TEL 90-312-4185027. FAX 90-312-4170432. circ. 20,000. **Document type:** government publication.
   Description: Provides brief statistical information on Turkey, including finance and national accounts, foreign trade, industrial production, agriculture, energy, population, climate and geography.

TURKEY. DEVLET ISTATISTIK ENSTITUSU. SIRKETLER KOOPERATIFLER VE FIRMA ISTATISTIKLERI/TURKEY. STATE INSTITUTE OF STATISTICS. COMPANIES, COOPERATIVES AND FIRMS STATISTICS. see *BUSINESS AND ECONOMICS — Abstracting, Bibliographies, Statistics*

TURKEY. DEVLET ISTATISTIK ENSTITUSU. SPOR KULUPLERI/TURKEY. STATE INSTITUTE OF STATISTICS. SPORTS CLUBS. see *SPORTS AND GAMES — Abstracting, Bibliographies, Statistics*

TURKEY. DEVLET ISTATISTIK ENSTITUSU. SU URUNLERI ISTATISTIKLERI/TURKEY. STATE INSTITUTE OF STATISTICS. FISHERY STATISTICS. see *FISH AND FISHERIES — Abstracting, Bibliographies, Statistics*

TURKEY. DEVLET ISTATISTIK ENSTITUSU. TARIM ISTATISTIKLERI OZETI/TURKEY. STATE INSTITUTE OF STATISTICS. SUMMARY OF AGRICULTURAL STATISTICS. see *AGRICULTURE — Abstracting, Bibliographies, Statistics*

TURKEY. DEVLET ISTATISTIK ENSTITUSU. TARIMSAL URETIM DEGERI/TURKEY. STATE INSTITUTE OF STATISTICS. VALUE OF AGRICULTURAL PRODUCTION. see *AGRICULTURE — Abstracting, Bibliographies, Statistics*

TURKEY. DEVLET ISTATISTIK ENSTITUSU. TARIMSAL YAPI VE URETIM/TURKEY. STATE INSTITUTE OF STATISTICS. AGRICULTURAL STRUCTURE AND PRODUCTION. see *AGRICULTURE — Abstracting, Bibliographies, Statistics*

TURKEY. DEVLET ISTATISTIK ENSTITUSU. TICARET, OTEL, LOKANTA VE HIZMET ISTATISTIKLERI/TURKEY. STATE INSTITUTE OF STATISTICS. STATISTICS OF TRADE, HOTELS, RESTAURANTS AND SERVICES. see *HOTELS AND RESTAURANTS — Abstracting, Bibliographies, Statistics*

TURKEY. DEVLET ISTATISTIK ENSTITUSU. TOPTAN ESYA VE TUKETICI FIYATLARI AYLIK INDEKS BULTENI/TURKEY. STATE INSTITUTE OF STATISTICS. WHOLESALE AND CONSUMER PRICE INDEXES MONTHLY BULLETIN. see *BUSINESS AND ECONOMICS — Abstracting, Bibliographies, Statistics*

TURKEY. DEVLET ISTATISTIK ENSTITUSU. TURIZM ISTATISTIKLERI/TURKEY. STATE INSTITUTE OF STATISTICS. TOURISM STATISTICS. see *TRAVEL AND TOURISM — Abstracting, Bibliographies, Statistics*

TURKEY. DEVLET ISTATISTIK ENSTITUSU. TURKIYE EKONOMISI ISTATISTIK VE YORUMLAR/TURKEY. STATE INSTITUTE OF STATISTICS. TURKISH ECONOMY STATISTICS AND EVALUATIONS. see *BUSINESS AND ECONOMICS — Abstracting, Bibliographies, Statistics*

315.61   TU   ISSN 0259-3491
TURKEY. DEVLET ISTATISTIK ENSTITUSU. TURKIYE ISTATISTIK YILLIGI/TURKEY. STATE INSTITUTE OF STATISTICS. STATISTICAL YEARBOOK OF TURKEY. Key Title: Istatistik Yilligi, Bag-kur. 1929. a. $95 (effective 1994). Devlet Istatistik Enstitusu - State Institute of Statistics, Necatibey Caddesi No. 114, 06100 Ankara, Turkey. TEL 90-312-4185027. FAX 90-312-4170432. circ. 3,115. **Document type:** government publication.
   Formerly (until 1972): Turkiye Istatistik Yilligi (ISSN 0082-691X)

TURKEY. DEVLET ISTATISTIK ENSTITUSU. TURKIYE NUFUS ARASTIRMASI/TURKEY. STATE INSTITUTE OF STATISTICS. TURKISH DEMOGRAPHIC SURVEY. see *POPULATION STUDIES — Abstracting, Bibliographies, Statistics*

TURKEY. DEVLET ISTATISTIK ENSTITUSU. ULASTIRMA ISTATISTIKLERI OZETI/TURKEY. STATE INSTITUTE OF STATISTICS. SUMMARY STATISTICS ON TRANSPORTATION - COMMUNICATION. see *TRANSPORTATION — Abstracting, Bibliographies, Statistics*

315.61   TU
▼**TURKEY. DEVLET ISTATISTIK ENSTITUSU. YAYINLAY VE ELEKTRONIK HIZMETLER KATALOGU.** English edition: Turkey. State Institute of Statistics. Publications and Electronic Services Catalogue. 1994. irreg. free. Devlet Istatistik Enstitusu, Necatibey Caddesi No. 114, 06100 Ankara, Turkey. TEL 90-312-4185027. FAX 90-312-4170432. illus. **Document type:** government publication, catalog.
   Description: Presents information on available statistical publications covering social and economic conditions in Turkey.

TURKEY. DEVLET ISTATISTIK ENSTITUSU. YILLIK IMALAT SANAYI ISTATISTIKLERI/TURKEY. STATE INSTITUTE OF STATISTICS. ANNUAL MANUFACTURING INDUSTRY STATISTICS. see *BUSINESS AND ECONOMICS — Abstracting, Bibliographies, Statistics*

TURKEY. STATE INSTITUTE OF STATISTICS. CENSUS OF INDUSTRY AND BUSINESS ESTABLISHMENTS - 1ST STAGE RESULTS. see *BUSINESS AND ECONOMICS — Abstracting, Bibliographies, Statistics*

TURKEY. STATE INSTITUTE OF STATISTICS. CENSUS OF INDUSTRY AND BUSINESS ESTABLISHMENTS - 2ND STAGE RESULTS, LARGE SCALE MANUFACTURING INDUSTRIES. see *BUSINESS AND ECONOMICS — Abstracting, Bibliographies, Statistics*

TURKEY. STATE INSTITUTE OF STATISTICS. CENSUS OF INDUSTRY AND BUSINESS ESTABLISHMENTS - 2ND STAGE RESULTS, SERVICE, HOTEL, RESTAURANT, GUEST HOUSE, CAFE. see *BUSINESS AND ECONOMICS — Abstracting, Bibliographies, Statistics*

TURKEY. STATE INSTITUTE OF STATISTICS. CENSUS OF INDUSTRY AND BUSINESS ESTABLISHMENTS - 2ND STAGE RESULTS, SMALL-SCALE MANUFACTURING INDUSTRIES. see *BUSINESS AND ECONOMICS — Abstracting, Bibliographies, Statistics*

TURKEY. STATE INSTITUTE OF STATISTICS. CENSUS OF INDUSTRY AND BUSINESS ESTABLISHMENTS - 2ND STAGE RESULTS, TRADE. see *BUSINESS AND ECONOMICS — Abstracting, Bibliographies, Statistics*

TURKEY. STATE INSTITUTE OF STATISTICS. CENSUS OF POPULATION. INTERNAL MIGRATION BY PERMANENT RESIDENCE. see *POPULATION STUDIES — Abstracting, Bibliographies, Statistics*

TURKEY. STATE INSTITUTE OF STATISTICS. CONSUMPTION EXPENDITURES. see *BUSINESS AND ECONOMICS — Abstracting, Bibliographies, Statistics*

TURKEY. STATE INSTITUTE OF STATISTICS. HOUSEHOLD LABOR FORCE SURVEY RESULTS. see *BUSINESS AND ECONOMICS — Abstracting, Bibliographies, Statistics*

TURKEY. STATE INSTITUTE OF STATISTICS. INCOME DISTRIBUTION. see *BUSINESS AND ECONOMICS — Abstracting, Bibliographies, Statistics*

TURKEY. STATE INSTITUTE OF STATISTICS. METHODOLOGY EXPLANATION OF TRADE PRICE AND QUANTITY INDEXES. see *BUSINESS AND ECONOMICS — Abstracting, Bibliographies, Statistics*

315.61   TU
TURKEY. STATE INSTITUTE OF STATISTICS. PROVINCIAL INDICATORS. (Text in English) irreg. $44. Devlet Istatistik Enstitusu - State Institute of Statistics, Necatibey Caddesi No. 114, 06100 Ankara, Turkey. TEL 90-4-4176440. FAX 90-4-4253387. **Document type:** government publication.

TURKEY. STATE INSTITUTE OF STATISTICS. RESULTS OF GENERAL ELECTION OF REPRESENTATIVES. B: PROVINCE. see *POLITICAL SCIENCE — Abstracting, Bibliographies, Statistics*

THE U K ELECTRICITY INDUSTRY: ELECTRICITY SERVICES & COSTS. see *ENERGY — Abstracting, Bibliographies, Statistics*

U K EXPORTS OF IRON AND STEEL (YEAR). see *METALLURGY*

U K IMPORTS OF IRON AND STEEL (YEAR). see *METALLURGY*

U K IRON AND STEEL INDUSTRY. ANNUAL STATISTICS. see *METALLURGY — Abstracting, Bibliographies, Statistics*

THE U K REGULATED INDUSTRIES: FINANCIAL FACTS (YEAR). see *BUSINESS AND ECONOMICS — Abstracting, Bibliographies, Statistics*

THE U K TOURIST: STATISTICS (YEAR). see *TRAVEL AND TOURISM — Abstracting, Bibliographies, Statistics*

THE U K WATER INDUSTRY: CHARGES FOR WATER SERVICES (YEAR). see *WATER RESOURCES — Abstracting, Bibliographies, Statistics*

THE U K WATER INDUSTRY: WATER SERVICES & COSTS (YEAR). see *WATER RESOURCES — Abstracting, Bibliographies, Statistics*

U N C T A D COMMODITY YEARBOOK. (United Nations Conference on Trade and Development) see *BUSINESS AND ECONOMICS — Abstracting, Bibliographies, Statistics*

U S CHEMICAL INDUSTRY STATISTICAL HANDBOOK. see *CHEMISTRY — Abstracting, Bibliographies, Statistics*

U S COAL PLANT STATISTICS. see *ENERGY — Abstracting, Bibliographies, Statistics*

U S NUCLEAR PLANT STATISTICS. see *ENERGY — Abstracting, Bibliographies, Statistics*

UKAZATELEU SOCIALNIHO A HOSPODARSKEHO VYVOJE CESKE REPUBLIKY/INDICATORS OF SOCIAL AND ECONOMIC DEVELOPMENT IN THE CZECH REPUBLIC. see *BUSINESS AND ECONOMICS — Abstracting, Bibliographies, Statistics*

UNEMPLOYMENT IN STATES. see *BUSINESS AND ECONOMICS — Economic Situation And Conditions*

310 060   UN   ISSN 0082-7533
UNESCO STATISTICAL REPORTS AND STUDIES. (Editions in English and French) 1955. irreg., no.32, 1992. price varies. Unesco, 7-9 Place de Fontenoy, 75700 Paris, France. TEL 45-77-16-10. (Dist. in U.S. by: Unipub, 4611-F Assembly Dr., Lanham, MD 20706-4391)
   —BLDSC (8448.722000).

310   UN   ISSN 0082-7541
    CODEN: SYUNDY
UNESCO STATISTICAL YEARBOOK. (Text in English, French and Spanish) 1952. a., latest 1991. $80. Unesco, 7-9 Place de Fontenoy, 75700 Paris, France. TEL 577-16-10. (Dist. in U.S. by: Unipub, 4611-F Assembly Dr., Lanham, MD 20706-4391) (also avail. in microfiche from CIS) **Indexed:** IIS.
   —BLDSC (9090.220000); CASDDS.

UNION LABOR IN CALIFORNIA. see *LABOR UNIONS — Abstracting, Bibliographies, Statistics*

310   IT
UNIONE REGIONALE CAMERE DI COMMERCIO DELL'EMILIA-ROMAGNA. STATISTICHE REGIONALI. 1970. q. L.50000. Unione Regionale Camere di Commercio dell'Emilia-Romagna (C.E.R.E.S.), Via Montegrappa 4-D, 40121 Bologna, Italy. TEL 39-51-223030. FAX 39-51-234945. Dir. Claudio Pasini. circ. 1,200. **Document type:** bulletin.

UNITED NATIONS. DEPARTMENT OF INTERNATIONAL ECONOMIC AND SOCIAL AFFAIRS. STATISTICAL OFFICE. CONSTRUCTION STATISTIC YEARBOOK. see *BUILDING AND CONSTRUCTION — Abstracting, Bibliographies, Statistics*

STATISTICS

310 519   NE   ISSN 0167-8000
HA1   CODEN: SJUED4
UNITED NATIONS. ECONOMIC COMMISSION FOR EUROPE. STATISTICAL JOURNAL. Key Title: Statistical Journal of the United Nations Economic Commission for Europe. (Text in English) 1982. q. fl.451($251) (effective 1995). I O S Press, Van Diemenstraat 94, 1013 CN Amsterdam, Netherlands. TEL 31-20-6382189. FAX 31-20-6203419. E-mail: marie-louise.kok@ios.nl. (In N. America: Box 10558, Burke, VA 22009-0558. TEL 703-323-5554. FAX 703-250-4705) Ed T. Griffin. adv.; bk.rev. **Indexed:** IIS, INSPEC (1989-), J.Cont.Quant.Meth., J.of Econ.Lit. **Document type:** academic/scholarly publication.
—BLDSC (8448.552200); Ei; Faxon; SWETS. **CCC.**
    Description: Provides information for the professional world of statisticians and establishes a forum for critical discussion of the entire range of problems facing statistical services.

UNITED NATIONS. NATIONAL ACCOUNTS STATISTICS. ANALYSIS OF MAIN AGGREGATES. see *BUSINESS AND ECONOMICS* — *Abstracting, Bibliographies, Statistics*

UNITED NATIONS. NATIONAL ACCOUNTS STATISTICS. GOVERNMENT ACCOUNTS AND TABLES. see *BUSINESS AND ECONOMICS* — *Abstracting, Bibliographies, Statistics*

UNITED NATIONS. NATIONAL ACCOUNTS STATISTICS. MAIN AGGREGATES AND DETAILED TABLES. see *BUSINESS AND ECONOMICS* — *Abstracting, Bibliographies, Statistics*

310   UN   ISSN 0082-8459
HA12.5   CODEN: STYBDH
UNITED NATIONS. STATISTICAL YEARBOOK. (Text in English and French) 1949. a. price varies. (United Nations Statistical Office) United Nations Publications, Room DC2-853, New York, NY 10017. TEL 212-963-3802; 800-253-9646. FAX 212-963-3489. (Or: Distribution and Sales Section, Palais des Nations, CH-1211 Geneva 10, Switzerland) (also avail. in microfiche from CIS) **Indexed:** IIS.
●Also available on CD-ROM.
—BLDSC (8452.800000); CASDDS.

310   UN   ISSN 0041-7432
HC57
UNITED NATIONS STATISTICAL OFFICE. MONTHLY BULLETIN OF STATISTICS. (Supplement avail.) (Text in English, French; supplement in English, French or Spanish) 1947. m. $225. United Nations Publications, Rm. DC2-853, New York, NY 10017. TEL 212-963-8302; 800-263-9646. FAX 212-963-3489. charts; mkt. (also avail. in microfiche from CIS) **Indexed:** IIS, Nutr.Abstr.
—BLDSC (5935.430000); UMI.
    Description: Provides monthly statistics on 74 subjects from over 200 countries and territories, including special tables that graphically portray important economic developments.

U.S. BUREAU OF LABOR STATISTICS. AREA WAGE SURVEYS. see *BUSINESS AND ECONOMICS* — *Economic Situation And Conditions*

U.S. BUREAU OF LABOR STATISTICS. BULLETINS. see *BUSINESS AND ECONOMICS* — *Economic Situation And Conditions*

U.S. BUREAU OF LABOR STATISTICS. C P I DETAILED REPORT. see *BUSINESS AND ECONOMICS* — *Economic Situation And Conditions*

U.S. BUREAU OF LABOR STATISTICS. NATIONAL OFFICE NEWS RELEASES. see *BUSINESS AND ECONOMICS* — *Economic Situation And Conditions*

U.S. BUREAU OF LABOR STATISTICS. REPORTS. see *BUSINESS AND ECONOMICS* — *Economic Situation And Conditions*

U.S. BUREAU OF LABOR STATISTICS. REPRINT SERIES. see *BUSINESS AND ECONOMICS* — *Economic Situation And Conditions*

U.S. BUREAU OF LABOR STATISTICS. SOUTHWEST STATISTICAL SUMMARY. see *BUSINESS AND ECONOMICS* — *Abstracting, Bibliographies, Statistics*

310   US   ISSN 0082-9544
U.S. BUREAU OF THE CENSUS. TECHNICAL PAPERS. Key Title: Technical Papers - U.S. Department of Commerce, Bureau of the Census. 1953. irreg. price varies. U.S. Bureau of the Census, Data User Services Division, Washington, DC 20233. TEL 301-457-4100. FAX 301-457-4714. (Orders to: Superintendent of Documents, U.S. Government Printing Office, Box 371954, Pittsburgh, PA 15250-7954. TEL 202-512-1800. FAX 202-512-2250) **Document type:** government publication.

310   US   ISSN 0082-9552
U.S. BUREAU OF THE CENSUS. WORKING PAPERS. 1954. irreg. U.S. Bureau of the Census, Data User Services Division, Washington, DC 20233. TEL 301-457-4100. FAX 301-457-4714. (Subscr. to: Superintendent of Documents, U.S. Government Printing Office, Box 371954, Pittsburgh, PA 15250-7954. TEL 202-512-1800. FAX 202-512-2250) **Document type:** government publication.

U.S. CENTERS FOR DISEASE CONTROL. TUBERCULOSIS STATISTICS IN THE UNITED STATES. see *MEDICAL SCIENCES* — *Respiratory Diseases*

U.S. DEPARTMENT OF AGRICULTURE. AGRICULTURAL STATISTICS. see *AGRICULTURE* — *Abstracting, Bibliographies, Statistics*

U.S. DEPARTMENT OF AGRICULTURE. AGRICULTURAL STATISTICS BOARD REPORT: AGRICULTURAL PRICES. see *AGRICULTURE* — *Abstracting, Bibliographies, Statistics*

U.S. DEPARTMENT OF AGRICULTURE. AGRICULTURAL STATISTICS BOARD REPORT: CATTLE. see *AGRICULTURE* — *Abstracting, Bibliographies, Statistics*

U.S. DEPARTMENT OF AGRICULTURE. AGRICULTURAL STATISTICS BOARD REPORT: CHICKENS AND EGGS. see *AGRICULTURE* — *Abstracting, Bibliographies, Statistics*

U.S. DEPARTMENT OF AGRICULTURE. AGRICULTURAL STATISTICS BOARD REPORT: CROP PRODUCTION. see *AGRICULTURE* — *Abstracting, Bibliographies, Statistics*

U.S. DEPARTMENT OF AGRICULTURE. AGRICULTURAL STATISTICS BOARD REPORT: CATFISH PROCESSING AND CATFISH PRODUCTION. see *FISH AND FISHERIES* — *Abstracting, Bibliographies, Statistics*

U.S. DEPARTMENT OF AGRICULTURE. AGRICULTURAL STATISTICS BOARD REPORT: COLD STORAGE. see *AGRICULTURE* — *Abstracting, Bibliographies, Statistics*

U.S. DEPARTMENT OF AGRICULTURE. AGRICULTURAL STATISTICS BOARD REPORT: DAIRY PRODUCTS. see *AGRICULTURE* — *Abstracting, Bibliographies, Statistics*

U.S. DEPARTMENT OF AGRICULTURE. AGRICULTURAL STATISTICS BOARD REPORT: EGG PRODUCTS. see *AGRICULTURE* — *Abstracting, Bibliographies, Statistics*

U.S. DEPARTMENT OF AGRICULTURE. AGRICULTURAL STATISTICS BOARD REPORT: HOGS AND PIGS. see *AGRICULTURE* — *Abstracting, Bibliographies, Statistics*

U.S. DEPARTMENT OF AGRICULTURE. AGRICULTURAL STATISTICS BOARD REPORTS: LIVESTOCK SLAUGHTER. see *AGRICULTURE* — *Abstracting, Bibliographies, Statistics*

U.S. DEPARTMENT OF AGRICULTURE. AGRICULTURAL STATISTICS BOARD REPORT: MILK PRODUCTION. see *AGRICULTURE* — *Abstracting, Bibliographies, Statistics*

U.S. DEPARTMENT OF AGRICULTURE. AGRICULTURAL STATISTICS BOARD REPORTS: NONCITRUS FRUITS AND NUTS. see *AGRICULTURE* — *Abstracting, Bibliographies, Statistics*

U.S. DEPARTMENT OF AGRICULTURE. AGRICULTURAL STATISTICS BOARD REPORT: POTATOES AND POTATO STOCKS. see *AGRICULTURE* — *Abstracting, Bibliographies, Statistics*

U.S. DEPARTMENT OF AGRICULTURE. AGRICULTURAL STATISTICS BOARD REPORT: POULTRY SLAUGHTER. see *AGRICULTURE* — *Abstracting, Bibliographies, Statistics*

U.S. DEPARTMENT OF AGRICULTURE. AGRICULTURAL STATISTICS BOARD REPORT: PEANUT STOCKS AND PROCESSING. see *AGRICULTURE* — *Abstracting, Bibliographies, Statistics*

U.S. DEPARTMENT OF AGRICULTURE. AGRICULTURAL STATISTICS BOARD REPORT: RICE STOCKS. see *AGRICULTURE* — *Abstracting, Bibliographies, Statistics*

U.S. DEPARTMENT OF AGRICULTURE. AGRICULTURAL STATISTICS BOARD REPORT: VEGETABLES. see *AGRICULTURE* — *Abstracting, Bibliographies, Statistics*

U.S. DEPARTMENT OF AGRICULTURE. RURAL BUSINESS AND COOPERATIVE DEVELOPEMENT SERVICE. COMPARATIVE STATISTICS. see *AGRICULTURE* — *Abstracting, Bibliographies, Statistics*

U.S. DEPARTMENT OF EDUCATION. NATIONAL CENTER FOR EDUCATION STATISTICS. ACADEMIC LIBRARIES. see *EDUCATION* — *Abstracting, Bibliographies, Statistics*

U.S. DEPARTMENT OF EDUCATION. NATIONAL CENTER FOR EDUCATION STATISTICS. COMPLETIONS IN INSTITUTIONS OF HIGHER EDUCATION. see *EDUCATION* — *Abstracting, Bibliographies, Statistics*

U.S. DEPARTMENT OF EDUCATION. NATIONAL CENTER FOR EDUCATION STATISTICS. DIGEST OF EDUCATION STATISTICS. see *EDUCATION* — *Abstracting, Bibliographies, Statistics*

U.S. DEPARTMENT OF EDUCATION. NATIONAL CENTER FOR EDUCATION STATISTICS. FALL ENROLLMENT IN HIGHER EDUCATION. see *EDUCATION* — *Abstracting, Bibliographies, Statistics*

U.S. DEPARTMENT OF EDUCATION. NATIONAL CENTER FOR EDUCATION STATISTICS. PUBLIC ELEMENTARY AND SECONDARY STATE AGGREGATE DATA, BY STATE. see *EDUCATION* — *Abstracting, Bibliographies, Statistics*

U.S. DEPARTMENT OF EDUCATION. NATIONAL CENTER FOR EDUCATION STATISTICS. STATE HIGHER EDUCATION PROFILES. see *EDUCATION* — *Abstracting, Bibliographies, Statistics*

U.S. DEPARTMENT OF HOUSING AND URBAN DEVELOPMENT. CHARACTERISTICS OF F H A SINGLE-FAMILY MORTGAGES: SELECTED SECTIONS OF NATIONAL HOUSING ACT. (Federal Housing Administration) see *HOUSING AND URBAN PLANNING*

U.S. DEPARTMENT OF HOUSING AND URBAN DEVELOPMENT. F H A HOMES; data for states on characteristics of FHA operations under Section 203. see *HOUSING AND URBAN PLANNING*

U.S. DEPARTMENT OF HOUSING AND URBAN DEVELOPMENT. F H A HOME MORTGAGE INSURANCE OPERATIONS: STATE, COUNTY AND M S A - P M S A. (Federal Housing Administration) see *HOUSING AND URBAN PLANNING*

U.S. DEPARTMENT OF HOUSING AND URBAN DEVELOPMENT. F H A HOMES (SUPPLEMENT). see *HOUSING AND URBAN PLANNING*

U.S. DEPARTMENT OF HOUSING AND URBAN DEVELOPMENT. F H A MONTHLY REPORT OF OPERATIONS. PROJECT INSURANCE PROGRAMS. (Federal Housing Administration) see *HOUSING AND URBAN PLANNING*

U.S. DEPARTMENT OF HOUSING AND URBAN DEVELOPMENT. F H A REPORT OF INSURANCE OPERATIONS UNDER HOME MORTGAGE PROGRAMS FOR (MONTH). (Federal Housing Administration) see *HOUSING AND URBAN PLANNING*

U.S. DEPARTMENT OF HOUSING AND URBAN DEVELOPMENT. F H A TRENDS OF HOME MORTGAGE CHARACTERISTICS. (Federal Housing Administration) see *HOUSING AND URBAN PLANNING*

STATISTICS 6237

U.S. DEPARTMENT OF TRANSPORTATION. NATIONAL TRANSPORTATION STATISTICS. ANNUAL; a supplement to the summary of national transportation statistics. see TRANSPORTATION — Abstracting, Bibliographies, Statistics

U.S. FEDERAL HIGHWAY ADMINISTRATION. HIGHWAY STATISTICS. see TRANSPORTATION — Abstracting, Bibliographies, Statistics

U.S. FISH AND WILDLIFE SERVICE. NATIONAL SURVEY OF FISHING, HUNTING AND WILDLIFE-ASSOCIATED RECREATION. see SPORTS AND GAMES — Abstracting, Bibliographies, Statistics

U.S. IMPORT AND EXPORT PRICE INDEXES. see BUSINESS AND ECONOMICS — Economic Situation And Conditions

U.S. INTERNAL REVENUE SERVICE. STATISTICS OF INCOME, FINAL CORPORATION INCOME TAX RETURNS. see BUSINESS AND ECONOMICS — Public Finance, Taxation

U.S. NATIONAL CENTER FOR HEALTH STATISTICS. MONTHLY VITAL STATISTICS REPORT. see POPULATION STUDIES — Abstracting, Bibliographies, Statistics

U.S. NATIONAL CENTER FOR HEALTH STATISTICS. VITAL AND HEALTH STATISTICS. SERIES 2. DATA EVALUATION AND METHODS RESEARCH. see PUBLIC HEALTH AND SAFETY — Abstracting, Bibliographies, Statistics

U.S. NATIONAL CENTER FOR HEALTH STATISTICS. VITAL AND HEALTH STATISTICS. SERIES 3. ANALYTICAL STUDIES. see PUBLIC HEALTH AND SAFETY — Abstracting, Bibliographies, Statistics

U.S. NATIONAL CENTER FOR HEALTH STATISTICS. VITAL AND HEALTH STATISTICS. SERIES 5. COMPARATIVE INTERNATIONAL VITAL AND HEALTH STATISTICS REPORTS. see PUBLIC HEALTH AND SAFETY — Abstracting, Bibliographies, Statistics

U.S. NATIONAL CENTER FOR HEALTH STATISTICS. VITAL AND HEALTH STATISTICS. SERIES 6. COGNITION AND SURVEY MEASUREMENT. see PUBLIC HEALTH AND SAFETY — Abstracting, Bibliographies, Statistics

U.S. NATIONAL CENTER FOR HEALTH STATISTICS. VITAL AND HEALTH STATISTICS. SERIES 10. DATA FROM THE HEALTH INTERVIEW SURVEY. see PUBLIC HEALTH AND SAFETY — Abstracting, Bibliographies, Statistics

U.S. NATIONAL CENTER FOR HEALTH STATISTICS. VITAL AND HEALTH STATISTICS. SERIES 11. DATA FROM THE HEALTH AND NUTRITION EXAMINATION SURVEY. see PUBLIC HEALTH AND SAFETY — Abstracting, Bibliographies, Statistics

U.S. NATIONAL CENTER FOR HEALTH STATISTICS. VITAL AND HEALTH STATISTICS. SERIES 14. DATA ON HEALTH RESOURCES. see PUBLIC HEALTH AND SAFETY — Abstracting, Bibliographies, Statistics

U.S. NATIONAL CENTER FOR HEALTH STATISTICS. VITAL AND HEALTH STATISTICS. SERIES 20. DATA ON MORTALITY. see PUBLIC HEALTH AND SAFETY — Abstracting, Bibliographies, Statistics

U.S. NATIONAL CENTER FOR HEALTH STATISTICS. VITAL AND HEALTH STATISTICS. SERIES 21. DATA ON NATALITY, MARRIAGE, AND DIVORCE. see PUBLIC HEALTH AND SAFETY — Abstracting, Bibliographies, Statistics

U.S. NATIONAL CENTER FOR HEALTH STATISTICS. VITAL AND HEALTH STATISTICS. SERIES 23. DATA FROM THE NATIONAL SURVEY OF FAMILY GROWTH. see PUBLIC HEALTH AND SAFETY — Abstracting, Bibliographies, Statistics

U.S. NATIONAL CENTER FOR HEALTH STATISTICS. VITAL AND HEALTH STATISTICS. SERIES 24. COMPILATIONS OF DATA ON NATALITY, MORTALITY, DIVORCE, AND INDUCED TERMINATIONS OF PREGNANCY. see PUBLIC HEALTH AND SAFETY — Abstracting, Bibliographies, Statistics

U.S. NATIONAL INSTITUTE ON DRUG ABUSE. STATISTICAL SERIES D. DATA FROM THE CLIENT ORIENTED DATA ACQUISITION PROCESS. QUARTERLY REPORT. PROVISIONAL DATA. see PHYSICAL FITNESS AND HYGIENE — Abstracting, Bibliographies, Statistics

U.S. RAILROAD RETIREMENT BOARD. MONTHLY BENEFIT STATISTICS. see BUSINESS AND ECONOMICS — Labor And Industrial Relations

U.S. RURAL ELECTRIFICATION ADMINISTRATION. ANNUAL STATISTICAL REPORT. RURAL ELECTRIFICATION BORROWERS. see ENGINEERING — Electrical Engineering

UNITED STATES TELEPHONE ASSOCIATION. STATISTICS OF THE LOCAL EXCHANGE CARRIERS. see COMMUNICATIONS — Abstracting, Bibliographies, Statistics

339　　　　UY　ISSN 0041-8439
UNIVERSIDAD DE LA REPUBLICA. FACULTAD DE CIENCIAS ECONOMICAS Y DE ADMINISTRACION. INSTITUTO DE ESTADISTICA. INDICE DE PRECIOS AL CONSUMIDOR. 1962. m. Urg.$3.40. Universidad de la Republica, Facultad de Ciencias Economicas y de Administracion, Instituto de Estadistica, Montevideo, Uruguay. stat. (processed)

UNIVERSIDADE FEDERAL DO RIO DE JANEIRO. INSTITUTO DE MATEMATICA. MEMORIAS DE MATEMATICA. see MATHEMATICS — Abstracting, Bibliographies, Statistics

519.5　　　　DK　ISSN 0105-9645
UNIVERSITETETS STATISTISKE INSTITUT. RESEARCH REPORT. 1976. irreg. free. (University of Copenhagen, Institute of Statistics) Universitetets Statistiske Institute, Studiestraede 6, DK-1455 Copenhagen K, Denmark. TEL 45-35-32-32-50. FAX 45-35-32-32-59.
Formerly: Koebenhavns Universitet. Statistiske Institut. Afhandlinger. Graa Serie.

UNIVERSITY OF CALIFORNIA AT BERKELEY. CAMPUS STATISTICS. see EDUCATION — Abstracting, Bibliographies, Statistics

UNIVERSITY OF GHANA. INSTITUTE OF STATISTICAL, SOCIAL AND ECONOMIC RESEARCH. DISCUSSION PAPERS. see SOCIAL SCIENCES: COMPREHENSIVE WORKS

330　　　　AT　ISSN 0157-0188
UNIVERSITY OF NEW ENGLAND. DEPARTMENT OF ECONOMETRICS. WORKING PAPERS IN ECONOMETRICS AND APPLIED STATISTICS. 1979. 10/yr. free. University of New England, Department of Econometrics, Armidale, N.S.W. 2351, Australia. TEL 61-67-732276. FAX 61-67-733607. E-mail: dchotika@metz.une.edu.au. Ed. D. Chotikapanich. cum.index. circ. 100. (looseleaf format; back issues avail.) Document type: academic/scholarly publication.
Description: Mainly covers research results in econometric theory and applied statistics.

310　　　　US　ISSN 0078-1495
UNIVERSITY OF NORTH CAROLINA, CHAPEL HILL. INSTITUTE OF STATISTICS. MIMEO SERIES. 1947. irreg. (approx. 3/mo.). price varies. University of North Carolina at Chapel Hill, Department of Statistics, Chapel Hill, NC 27514. TEL 919-962-2307. cum.index.

URUGUAY. DIRECCION GENERAL DE ESTADISTICA Y CENSOS. INDICE MEDIO DE SALARIOS. see BUSINESS AND ECONOMICS — Abstracting, Bibliographies, Statistics

USUAL WEEKLY EARNINGS OF WAGE AND SALARY WORKERS. see BUSINESS AND ECONOMICS — Economic Situation And Conditions

UTAH AGRICULTURAL STATISTICS. see AGRICULTURE — Abstracting, Bibliographies, Statistics

UTAH MARRIAGE AND DIVORCE ANNUAL REPORT. see POPULATION STUDIES — Abstracting, Bibliographies, Statistics

315.4　　　　II　ISSN 0042-1626
UTTAR PRADESH. STATE PLANNING INSTITUTE. QUARTERLY BULLETIN OF STATISTICS. (Text in English and Hindi) 1966. q. Rs.35. State Planning Institute, Economic and Statistics Division, Uttar Pradesh, India. stat. circ. 640. (processed) Document type: bulletin, government publication.
Description: Statistics relating to industry, labor, prices, agriculture, transportation, population, and communications.

VANUATU. STATISTICS OFFICE. MONETARY AND BANKNG STATISTICS. see BUSINESS AND ECONOMICS — Abstracting, Bibliographies, Statistics

VANUATU. STATISTICS OFFICE. STATISTICAL INDICATORS. see BUSINESS AND ECONOMICS — Abstracting, Bibliographies, Statistics

VENEZUELA. MINISTERIO DE AGRICULTURA Y CRIA. DIRECCION DE ECONOMICA Y ESTADISTICA AGROPECUARIA. ANUARIO ESTADISTICO AGROPECUARIO. see AGRICULTURE — Abstracting, Bibliographies, Statistics

VENEZUELA. MINISTERIO DE AGRICULTURA Y CRIA. DIRECCION DE PLANIFICACION Y ESTADISTICA. ESTADISTICAS AGROPECUARIAS DE LAS ENTIDADES FEDERALES. see AGRICULTURE — Abstracting, Bibliographies, Statistics

VENEZUELA. MINISTERIO DE ENERGIA Y MINAS. ANUARIO ESTADISTICO MINERO. see MINES AND MINING INDUSTRY — Abstracting, Bibliographies, Statistics

VENEZUELA. MINISTERIO DE ENERGIA Y MINAS. APENDICE ESTADISTICO. see ENERGY — Abstracting, Bibliographies, Statistics

VENEZUELA. MINISTERIO DE ENERGIA Y MINAS. COMPENDIO ESTADISTICO DEL SECTOR ELECTRICO. see ENERGY — Abstracting, Bibliographies, Statistics

VENEZUELA. MINISTERIO DE ENERGIA Y MINAS. PETROLEO Y OTROS DATOS ESTADISTICOS. see PETROLEUM AND GAS — Abstracting, Bibliographies, Statistics

330　　　　VE　ISSN 0254-7317
VENEZUELA. OFICINA CENTRAL DE ESTADISTICA E INFORMATICA. ANUARIO ESTADISTICO. 1984. a. Bs.900 (for 1992 edition). Oficina Central de Estadistica e Informatica, Apdo. de Correos 4593, Carmelitas, Caracas 1010A, Venezuela. TEL 58-2-782-11-33. FAX 58-2-781-13-80. TELEX 21241. Document type: government publication.

330　　　　VE
VENEZUELA ESTADISTICA E INFORMATICA. 1974-1978; N.S. 1986. s-a. free or on exchange basis. Oficina Central de Estadistica e Informatica, Apdo. de Correos 4593, Carmelitas, Caracas 1010A, Venezuela. TEL 58-2-782-11-33. FAX 58-2-781-13-80. Document type: government publication.
Formerly: Estadistica Venezolana.

VERKEERSVEILIGHEID. see TRANSPORTATION — Abstracting, Bibliographies, Statistics

314.7　　　　RU　ISSN 0042-4692
VESTNIK STATISTIKI. 1949. m. 31.80 Rub. (Tsentral'noe Statisticheskoe Upravlenie pri Sovete Ministrov) Izdatel'stvo Statistika, Ul. Kirova, 39, Moscow K-450, Russia. index. circ. 35,000. (reprint service avail. from KTO) Indexed: Curr.Dig.Sov.Press, Rural Recreat.Tour.Abstr., World Agri.Econ.& Rural Sociol.Abstr.

VINNUMARKADUR/LABOR MARKET STATISTICS. see BUSINESS AND ECONOMICS — Abstracting, Bibliographies, Statistics

VIRGIN ISLANDS (U.S.). DEPARTMENT OF LABOR. BUREAU OF LABOR STATISTICS. LABOR MARKET REVIEW. see BUSINESS AND ECONOMICS — Labor And Industrial Relations

VITAL STATISTICS OF IOWA. see POPULATION STUDIES — Abstracting, Bibliographies, Statistics

VITAL STATISTICS OF THE UNITED STATES. see PUBLIC HEALTH AND SAFETY — Abstracting, Bibliographies, Statistics

STATISTICS

WASHINGTON (STATE). DEPARTMENT OF NATURAL RESOURCES. ANNUAL FIRE STATISTICS. see *FORESTS AND FORESTRY* — *Abstracting, Bibliographies, Statistics*

WASHINGTON (STATE). DEPARTMENT OF REVENUE. RESEARCH DIVISION. TAX STATISTICS. see *BUSINESS AND ECONOMICS* — *Public Finance, Taxation*

WASHINGTON (STATE). EMPLOYMENT SECURITY DEPARTMENT. MONTHLY JOB SERVICE STATISTICS. see *OCCUPATIONS AND CAREERS* — *Abstracting, Bibliographies, Statistics*

WASHINGTON AGRICULTURAL STATISTICS. see *AGRICULTURE* — *Abstracting, Bibliographies, Statistics*

WEATHER AND FORECASTING. see *METEOROLOGY*

WELSH HOUSE CONDITION SURVEY. see *HOUSING AND URBAN PLANNING* — *Abstracting, Bibliographies, Statistics*

WELSH HOUSING STATISTICS. see *HOUSING AND URBAN PLANNING* — *Abstracting, Bibliographies, Statistics*

WEST BENGAL. ANNUAL FINANCIAL STATEMENT (BUDGET). see *BUSINESS AND ECONOMICS* — *Abstracting, Bibliographies, Statistics*

WEST BENGAL. BUREAU OF APPLIED ECONOMICS AND STATISTICS. STATISTICAL HANDBOOK. see *BUSINESS AND ECONOMICS* — *Abstracting, Bibliographies, Statistics*

WEST VIRGINIA RESEARCH LEAGUE. STATISTICAL HANDBOOK; a digest of selected data on state and local government in West Virginia. see *BUSINESS AND ECONOMICS* — *Public Finance, Taxation*

WIRTSCHAFT UND STATISTIK. see *BUSINESS AND ECONOMICS*

310 GW
WIRTSCHAFT UND VERKEHR NORDRHEIN-WESTFALENS IN ZAHLEN. 1984. m. DM.25. Landesamt fuer Datenverarbeitung und Statistik Nordrhein-Westfalen, Postfach 101105, 40002 Duesseldorf, Germany. TEL 0211-9449-01. FAX 0211-442006. circ. 400. (back issues avail.) **Document type:** government publication.

WISCONSIN. DIVISION OF CORRECTIONS. OFFICE OF INFORMATION MANAGEMENT. ADMISSIONS TO JUVENILE INSTITUTIONS. see *CRIMINOLOGY AND LAW ENFORCEMENT* — *Abstracting, Bibliographies, Statistics*

WORLD COUNCIL OF CREDIT UNIONS. ANNUAL AND STATISTICAL REPORT. see *BUSINESS AND ECONOMICS* — *Banking And Finance*

WORLD MINERAL STATISTICS; world production, exports and imports. see *MINES AND MINING INDUSTRY* — *Abstracting, Bibliographies, Statistics*

WORLD POPULATION PROJECTIONS; estimates and projections with related demographic statistics. see *POPULATION STUDIES* — *Abstracting, Bibliographies, Statistics*

WORLD RUBBER STATISTICS HANDBOOK. see *RUBBER* — *Abstracting, Bibliographies, Statistics*

WORLD SHIPPING STATISTICS (YEAR). see *TRANSPORTATION* — *Abstracting, Bibliographies, Statistics*

WORLD STEEL EXPORTS. see *METALLURGY* — *Abstracting, Bibliographies, Statistics*

WORLD STEEL EXPORTS - STAINLESS, HIGH SPEED & OTHER ALLOY. see *METALLURGY* — *Abstracting, Bibliographies, Statistics*

WORLD WROUGHT COPPER STATISTICS. see *METALLURGY* — *Abstracting, Bibliographies, Statistics*

310 CC
XINJIANG PRODUCTION AND CONSTRUCTION CORP. STATISTICAL YEARBOOK/XINJIANG SHENGCHAN JIANSHE BINGTUAN TONGJI NIANJIAN. (Text in Chinese) a. Y50. (Xinjian Production and Construction Corp.) Zhongguo Tongji Chubanshe - China Statistics Publishing House, 38 Yuetan Nanjie, Sanlihe, Beijing 100826, People's Republic of China. TEL 8217162.

YAMAGUCHIKEN EISEI KOGAI KENKYU SENTA NENPO. see *PUBLIC HEALTH AND SAFETY* — *Abstracting, Bibliographies, Statistics*

YEARBOOK OF AGRICULTURAL STATISTICS OF BANGLADESH. see *AGRICULTURE* — *Abstracting, Bibliographies, Statistics*

330 314.97 YU ISSN 0019-3585
HA1531
YUGOSLAVIA. SAVAZNI ZAVOD ZA STATISTIKU. INDEKS; mesecni pregled privredne statistike SFR Jugoslavije. (English and French translations of texts and terms avail. on request) 1952. m. 400 din.($23.33) Savezni Zavod za Statistiku, Kneza Milosa 20, Belgrade, Yugoslavia. TEL 681-999. Ed. Ibrahim Latific. mkt.; stat. circ. 4,400.

YUGOSLAVIA. SAVAZNI ZAVOD ZA STATISTIKU. DEMOGRAFSKA STATISTIKA. see *POPULATION STUDIES* — *Abstracting, Bibliographies, Statistics*

310 YU ISSN 0351-0603
YUGOSLAVIA. SAVEZNI ZAVOD ZA STATISTIKU. METODOLOSKE STUDIJE, RASPRAVE I DOKUMENTACIJA. 1973. irreg. Savezni Zavod za Statistiku, Kneza Milosa 20, Belgrade, Yugoslavia. TEL 38-11-681999. **Document type:** government publication.

310 YU ISSN 0513-6547
HA37.Y8
YUGOSLAVIA. SAVEZNI ZAVOD ZA STATISTIKU. METODOLOSKI MATERIJALI. irreg. Savezni Zavod za Statistiku, Kneza Milosa 20, Belgrade, Yugoslavia. TEL 38-11-681999. **Document type:** government publication.

310 YU
YUGOSLAVIA. SAVEZNI ZAVOD ZA STATISTIKU. RADNE ORGANIZACIJE PREMA VISINI NAJNIZEG I NAJVISEG NETO LICNOG DOHOTKA. (Subseries of: Statisticki Bilten) s-a. 20 din. Savezni Zavod za Statistiku, Kneza Milosa 20, Belgrade, Yugoslavia. TEL 38-11-681999. circ. 1,000. **Document type:** government publication.

314 YU ISSN 0039-0534
YUGOSLAVIA. SAVEZNI ZAVOD ZA STATISTIKU. STATISTICKA REVIJA. (Summaries in English and French) 1954. q. 160 din.($8.88) Savezni Zavod za Statistiku, Kneza Milosa 20, Belgrade, Yugoslavia. TEL 38-11-681999. (Co-sponsor: Jugoslovensko Statisticko Drustvo) Ed. Branislav Ivanovic. bk.rev.; bibl.; index. circ. 1,000. **Document type:** government publication.

314 YU ISSN 0084-4365
HA1631
YUGOSLAVIA. SAVEZNI ZAVOD ZA STATISTIKU. STATISTICKI BILTEN. (Text in Serbian with English, French and Russian translation) 1950. w. 600 din.($66.67) Savezni Zavod za Statistiku, Kneza Milosa 20, Belgrade, Yugoslavia. TEL 38-11-681999. Ed. Ibragim Catific. **Document type:** government publication.

310 YU ISSN 0513-6555
HA37.Y8
YUGOSLAVIA. SAVEZNI ZAVOD ZA STATISTIKU. STUDIJE, ANALIZE I PRIKAZI. 1953. irreg. Savezni Zavod za Statistiku, Kneza Milosa 20, Belgrade, Yugoslavia. **Document type:** government publication.
Formerly (until 1960): Yugoslavia. Savezni Zavod za Statistiku. Studije i Analize.

Z U M A - NACHRICHTEN. (Zentrum fuer Umfragen, Methoden und Analysen e.V.) see *SOCIOLOGY*

310 ZR
ZAIRE. INSTITUT NATIONAL DE LA STATISTIQUE. BULLETIN TRIMESTRIEL DES STATISTIQUES GENERALES. q. Institut National de la Statistique, Direction des Services Generaux, B.P. 20, Kinshasa, Zaire.

ZAMBIA. CENTRAL STATISTICAL OFFICE. AGRICULTURAL AND PASTORAL PRODUCTION (COMMERCIAL FARMS). see *AGRICULTURE* — *Abstracting, Bibliographies, Statistics*

ZAMBIA. CENTRAL STATISTICAL OFFICE. AGRICULTURAL AND PASTORAL PRODUCTION (NON-COMMERCIAL). see *AGRICULTURE* — *Abstracting, Bibliographies, Statistics*

ZAMBIA. CENTRAL STATISTICAL OFFICE. BALANCE OF PAYMENTS STATISTICS. see *BUSINESS AND ECONOMICS* — *Abstracting, Bibliographies, Statistics*

ZAMBIA. CENTRAL STATISTICAL OFFICE. CONSUMER PRICE STATISTICS. see *BUSINESS AND ECONOMICS* — *Abstracting, Bibliographies, Statistics*

ZAMBIA. CENTRAL STATISTICAL OFFICE. FISHERIES STATISTICS (NATURAL WATERS). see *FISH AND FISHERIES* — *Abstracting, Bibliographies, Statistics*

316 ZA ISSN 0027-0377
ZAMBIA. CENTRAL STATISTICAL OFFICE. MONTHLY DIGEST OF STATISTICS. 1964. m. $32. Central Statistical Office, P.O. Box 31908, Lusaka, Zambia. TEL 260-1-211231. stat. **Document type:** government publication.
Description: For the study of social and economic conditions in Zambia.

ZAMBIA. CENTRAL STATISTICAL OFFICE. QUARTERLY AGRICULTURAL STATISTICAL BULLETIN. see *AGRICULTURE* — *Abstracting, Bibliographies, Statistics*

316 ZA ISSN 0084-4551
HA1977.R48
ZAMBIA. CENTRAL STATISTICAL OFFICE. STATISTICAL YEAR BOOK. 1967. a. K.3. Central Statistical Office, P.O. Box 31908, Lusaka, Zambia. TEL 260-1-211231. **Document type:** government publication.

ZAMBIA. CENTRAL STATISTICAL OFFICE. TRANSPORT STATISTICS. see *TRANSPORTATION* — *Abstracting, Bibliographies, Statistics*

ZAMBIA. CENTRAL STATISTICAL OFFICE. VITAL STATISTICS. see *POPULATION STUDIES* — *Abstracting, Bibliographies, Statistics*

315 CC ISSN 1002-4557
HA1
ZHONGGUO TONGJI/CHINA STATISTICS. (Text in Chinese) 1980. m. $15 (foreign $39.50). (State Statistical Bureau - Guojia Tongji Ju) Zhongguo Tongji Chubanshe - China Statistics Publishing House, 38 Yuetan Nanjie, Sanlihe, Beijing 100826, People's Republic of China. TEL 8217162. TELEX 22778-FASSB-CN. (Dist. in US by: China Books & Periodicals, Inc., 2929 24th St., San Francisco, CA 94110. TEL 415-282-2994) circ. 150,000. (back issues avail.)
Description: Covers government statistical organization, practice and research on statistics.

ZHUHAI TONGJI NIANJIAN (YEAR)/ZHUHAI STATISTICAL YEARBOOK. see *BUSINESS AND ECONOMICS* — *Abstracting, Bibliographies, Statistics*

ZIMBABWE. CENTRAL STATISTICAL OFFICE. AGRICULTURAL PRODUCTION IN PURCHASE LANDS: NATIONAL AND PROVINCIAL TOTALS. see *AGRICULTURE* — *Abstracting, Bibliographies, Statistics*

ZIMBABWE. CENTRAL STATISTICAL OFFICE. AGRICULTURAL PRODUCTION IN TRIBAL TRUST LAND IRRIGATION SCHEMES AND TILCOR ESTATES. see *AGRICULTURE* — *Abstracting, Bibliographies, Statistics*

ZIMBABWE. CENTRAL STATISTICAL OFFICE. CENSUS OF PRODUCTION. see *BUSINESS AND ECONOMICS* — *Abstracting, Bibliographies, Statistics*

ZIMBABWE. CENTRAL STATISTICAL OFFICE. CROP PRODUCTION OF LARGE-SCALE COMMERCIAL AGRICULTURAL UNITS. see *AGRICULTURE* — *Abstracting, Bibliographies, Statistics*

ZIMBABWE. CENTRAL STATISTICAL OFFICE. INCOME TAX STATISTICS; analysis of assessments and loss statements. see *BUSINESS AND ECONOMICS — Abstracting, Bibliographies, Statistics*

ZIMBABWE. CENTRAL STATISTICAL OFFICE. MONTHLY MIGRATION AND TOURIST STATISTICS. see *TRAVEL AND TOURISM — Abstracting, Bibliographies, Statistics*

316   RH   ISSN 1012-649X
ZIMBABWE. CENTRAL STATISTICAL OFFICE. QUARTERLY DIGEST OF STATISTICS. Key Title: Quarterly Digest of Statistics - Central Statistical Office. 1964. q. Central Statistical Office, P.O. Box 8063, Causeway, Harare, Zimbabwe. circ. 1,100. Document type: government publication.
Supersedes: Zimbabwe. Central Statistical Office. Monthly Digest of Statistics (ISSN 0556-8706)

ZIMBABWE. CENTRAL STATISTICAL OFFICE. QUARTERLY POULTRY CENSUS. see *AGRICULTURE — Abstracting, Bibliographies, Statistics*

SURGERY

see *Medical Sciences–Surgery*

TAXATION

see *Business and Economics–Public Finance, Taxation*

TEACHING METHODS AND CURRICULUM

see *Education–Teaching Methods and Curriculum*

TECHNOLOGY: COMPREHENSIVE WORKS

600 301   US   ISSN 1066-3878
A B Q CORRESPONDENT. 1985. bi-m. $30. A B Q Communications Corporation, Box 1432, Corrales, NM 87048. TEL 505-897-0822. FAX 505-898-6525. E-mail: correspo@swcp.com. Ed. Nelson B. Winkless III. circ. 100 (controlled). (back issues avail.) Document type: newsletter.
Description: Emphasizes technology and its social impact.

A F P SCIENCES; bulletin information scientifique, technique, medicale. (Agence France-Presse) see *MEDICAL SCIENCES*

A S T C NEWSLETTER. (Association of Science-Technology Centers) see *MUSEUMS AND ART GALLERIES*

A S T I S CURRENT AWARENESS BULLETIN. (Arctic Science & Technology Information System) see *TECHNOLOGY: COMPREHENSIVE WORKS — Abstracting, Bibliographies, Statistics*

600   SP   ISSN 1132-9327
A T: ACTUALIDAD TECNOLOGICA; periodico de equipos y tecnologia. 1988? 11/yr. 5000 ptas.($79) (effective 1995). Editorial Alcion, S.A., Triana 53, 28016 Madrid, Spain. TEL 34-1-345-64-00. FAX 34-1-345-39-45. TELEX 49236 QUMI E. Ed. Pedro de la Pezuela. adv. contact: Francisco Lillo. bk.rev.; illus.; tr.lit. circ. 30,000. (tabloid format) Document type: newspaper.
Formerly (until 1992): Actualidad Tecnologica (ISSN 1132-6492)

A T E A JOURNAL. (American Technical Education Association, Inc.) see *EDUCATION*

500   LO
A T S NEWSLETTER. 1987. 2/yr. Appropriate Technology Section, P.O. Box 686, Maseru 100, Lesotho. Indexed: P.L.E.S.A. Document type: newsletter.

ACADEMIA DE STIINTE A REPUBLICA MOLDOVA. BULETINUL. FIZICA SI TEHNICA. see *PHYSICS*

620   HU   ISSN 0001-7035
T4   CODEN: ATSHA8
ACADEMIA SCIENTIARUM HUNGARICA. ACTA TECHNICA. (Text in English) 1950. 8/yr. (in 2 vols.) $80 (effective 1992). (Magyar Tudomanyos Akademia) Akademiai Kiado, Publishing House of the Hungarian Academy of Sciences, P.O. Box 245, H-1519 Budapest, Hungary. TEL 181-2134. FAX 166-6466. TELEX 22-6228 AKNYO H. Ed. Pal Michelberger. adv.; bk.rev.; bibl.; charts; illus.; index. (back issues avail.) Indexed: Appl.Mech.Rev., Curr.Cont., GeoRef., INSPEC (1968-), Int.Aerosp.Abstr., ISMEC, Met.Abstr., World Alum.Abstr. Document type: academic/scholarly publication.
—BLDSC (0664.000000); CASDDS; UnCover. CCC.
Description: Covers mechanics, material testing, architecture, building technology, highway and railway construction, thermodynamics, mechanical engineering, mechanical technology, metallurgy, electrical engineering, electronics, automation and telecommunication.

ACTA BOREALIA; A Nordic journal of circumpolar societies. see *EARTH SCIENCES*

ACTA HISTORIAE SCIENTIARUM BALTICA/BALTIJAS ZINATNU VESTURES APCEREJUMI. see *SCIENCES: COMPREHENSIVE WORKS*

600   MX   ISSN 0515-3085
T78   CODEN: APTMAY
ACTA POLITECNICA MEXICANA. (Text in Spanish; summaries in English, French, German) 1959. q. Mex.$150($10) Instituto Politecnico Nacional, Comision de Operacion y Fomento de Actividades Academicas, Apdo. Postal 42-161, Prolongacion de S. Diaz Miron y Plan de San Luis, Mexico 17, D.F., Mexico. Ed. Rafael Nevero Zuloaga. bibl.; charts; cum.index. Indexed: Biol.Abstr., Chem.Abstr., INSPEC (1970-).

ADVANCES IN ENVIRONMENTAL SCIENCE AND ENGINEERING. see *ENVIRONMENTAL STUDIES*

ADVANCES IN NATURAL AND TECHNOLOGICAL HAZARDS RESEARCH. see *PUBLIC HEALTH AND SAFETY*

ADVANCES IN UNDERWATER TECHNOLOGY, OCEAN SCIENCE AND OFFSHORE ENGINEERING. see *EARTH SCIENCES — Oceanography*

AEROSPACE TESTING SEMINAR. PROCEEDINGS. see *AERONAUTICS AND SPACE FLIGHT*

600   UN   ISSN 1010-5263
CODEN: ASTTEC
AFRICAN JOURNAL OF SCIENCE AND TECHNOLOGY. SERIES A. TECHNOLOGY. 1982. 2/yr. African Network of Scientific and Technical Institutions - Reseau Africain d'Instituts Scientifiques et Techniques, ANSTI-RAIST Secretariat, UNESCO ROSTA, P.O. Box 30592, Nairobi, Kenya. Indexed: P.L.E.S.A. Document type: academic/scholarly publication.
—CASDDS.
Supersedes in part (in 1986): African Journal of Science and Technology.

600 330   UK   ISSN 0954-6782
T1
AFRICAN REVIEW OF BUSINESS AND TECHNOLOGY. 1964. m. (11/yr.) £55($93.50) (effective 1995). Alain Charles Publishing Ltd., 27 Wilfred St., London SW1E 6PR, England. TEL 0171-834-7676. FAX 0171-973-0076. TELEX 297165 ACPLTD G. Ed. Jonquil L. Phelan. adv. contact: Jane Wellman. circ. 17,403. (back issues avail.) Indexed: RICS. Document type: trade publication.
—BLDSC (0732.925000).
Former titles: African Technical Review (ISSN 0266-6677); West African Technical Review ABC (ISSN 0043-3039)
Description: For personnel in executive and managerial capacities in government, industry and commerce operating in Africa.

600   US   ISSN 1050-0014
T174.3
AFRICAN TECHNOLOGY FORUM. 1988. 3/yr. $9.60 to individuals in Africa (elsewhere $19.20); institutions in Africa $12 (elsewhere $24). African Technology Forum, M I T Branch, Box 171, Cambridge, MA 02139. TEL 617-225-0339. FAX 617-252-3330. Ed. Mawuli Tse. adv.; bk.rev. circ. 3,623. Indexed: Documentatieblad.
Description: Covers the development of science and technology as it affects the African continent.

AGRICULTURAL RESEARCH ORGANIZATION. SCIENTIFIC ACTIVITIES. see *AGRICULTURE*

620   AI
TA4.A35   CODEN: IATNAK
AKADEMIYA NAUK ARMENII. IZVESTIYA. SERIYA TEKHNICHESKIKH NAUK/HAYASTANI HANRAPETUTIAN GITUTSUNNERI AZGAIN ACADEMIAY TEKHNIKAKAN GITUTSUNNERY HANDES. (Text in Armenian, English, Russian) 1957. bi-m. 300 dram. Akademiya Nauk Armenii, Pr. Marshala Bagramayana, 24, 375019 Erevan, Armenia. TEL 52-45-80. TELEX 243344. Ed. R.M. Martirossian. charts; index. Indexed: INIS Atomind., INSPEC, Math.R. Document type: academic/scholarly publication.
—CASDDS.
Formerly: Akademiya Nauk Armyanskoi S.S.R. Izvestiya. Seriya Tekhnicheskikh Nauk (ISSN 0002-306X)

AKADEMIYA NAUK AZERBAIJANA. IZVESTIYA. SERIYA FIZIKO-TEKHNICHESKIKH I MATEMATICHESKIKH NAUK. see *PHYSICS*

600   UZ
CODEN: IUZTA4
AKADEMIYA NAUK UZBEKISTANA. IZVESTIYA. SERIYA TEKHNICHESKIKH NAUK. (Text in Russian) 1957. bi-m. 11.10 Rub. Izdatel'stvo Fan, Ul. Gogolya 70, k. 105, 700000 Tashkent, Uzbekistan. Indexed: Chem.Abstr., INIS Atomind., INSPEC, Met.Abstr., World Alum.Abstr.
—CASDDS.
Formerly: Akademiya Nauk Uzbekskoi S.S.R. Izvestiya. Seriya Tekhnicheskikh Nauk (ISSN 0516-2629)

AKADEMIYA NAVUK BELARUSI. VESTSI. SERIYA FIZIKA-TEKHNICHNYKH NAVUK. see *PHYSICS*

600   SZ
AKTUELLE TECHNIK. m. B & L Verlags AG, Steinwiesenstr. 3, CH-8952 Schlieren, Switzerland. TEL 01-7304066. FAX 01-7305841. Ed. Peter Boll. circ. 18,000. Document type: trade publication.

600   CN   CODEN: RCAIAN
ALBERTA GEOLOGICAL SURVEY. INFORMATION SERIES. 1947. irreg. price varies. Alberta Geological Survey, Information Sales, 9945 108 St., Edmonton, AB T5K 2G6, Canada. TEL 403-422-3767. FAX 403-422-1918. Indexed: Chem.Abstr., Eng.Ind. Document type: academic/scholarly publication, monographic series.
Formerly: Alberta Research Council. Information Series (ISSN 0034-5180)
Description: Covers indices, symposia proceedings and reports of applied studies.

600   CN
ALBERTA GEOLOGICAL SURVEY. REPORTS. 1919. irreg. price varies. Alberta Geological Survey, Information Sales, 9945 108 St., Edmonton, AB T5K 2G6, Canada. TEL 403-422-3767. FAX 403-422-1918. Indexed: GeoRef.
Former titles: Alberta Research Council. Reports; Research Council of Alberta. Report (ISSN 0080-1607)

600   SP   ISSN 0213-5558
ALTA TECNOLOGIA; ilustrada. 1986. m. 2750 ptas.($29) Tecnologia y Prensa S.A., Ctra. de Irun, Km. 12,400, 28049 Madrid, Spain. (Distr. in U.S. by: High Technology Publishing Corporation, 38 Commercial Wharf, Boston, MA 02110; Tel. 617-227-4700) Ed. Norberto Gallego. adv.; charts; illus.; stat. circ. 20,000. (back issues avail.)

TECHNOLOGY: COMPREHENSIVE WORKS

600 970 500   US   ISSN 8756-7296
T1   CODEN: AHETEU
AMERICAN HERITAGE OF INVENTION & TECHNOLOGY. 1985. 4/yr. $15. (General Motors) Forbes, Inc., Forbes Bldg., 60 Fifth Ave., New York, NY 10011. TEL 212-206-5500. FAX 212-620-2332. Ed. Frederick Allen. illus. circ. 210,000.
—BLDSC (0817.734000); Faxon; UnCover. **CCC.**

AMERICAN PETROLEUM INSTITUTE. HEALTH AND ENVIRONMENTAL SCIENCES DEPARTMENT. REPORTS AND OTHER PUBLICATIONS, INDEX AND ABSTRACTS. see PUBLIC HEALTH AND SAFETY — Abstracting, Bibliographies, Statistics

AMERICAN POWER CONFERENCE. PROCEEDINGS. see ENERGY

338   US
AMERON NEWS. 1970. q. Ameron, 245 S. Los Robles Ave., Pasadena, CA 91101. FAX 818-683-4060. Ed. S.D. Stracner. charts; illus.; circ. 10,000 (controlled). **Document type:** newsletter.

600   US
ANNUAL MEMBRANE TECHNOLOGY - PLANNING CONFERENCE PROCEEDINGS (YEAR). a. $350. Business Communications Co., Inc. (Norwalk), 25 Van Zant St., Ste. 13, Norwalk, CT 06855. TEL 203-853-4266. FAX 203-853-0348. TELEX 6502934929 WUI. **Document type:** proceedings.

658.5   GW   ISSN 0003-6099
ANTRIEBSTECHNIK. (Includes: Antriebstechnik-Handbuch) (Text in German; index in English and German) 1962. m. DM.230 (foreign DM.240). (Forschungsvereinigung Antriebstechnik e. V.) Vereinigte Fachverlage GmbH, Lise-Meitner-Str. 2, 55129 Mainz, Germany. TEL 06131-992-01. FAX 06131-992-100. TELEX 04187752. (Subscr. to: Postfach 2760, 55017 Mainz, Germany) Ed. Prof. Winter. adv.; bk.rev.; abstr.; charts; illus. circ. 16,000. (back issues avail.) **Indexed:** Excerp.Med., Fluidex, ISMEC, Met.Abstr., World Alum.Abstr.
—SWETS.

APPLIED ERGONOMICS; human factors in technology and society. see ENGINEERING

APPLIED RESEARCH. see SCIENCES: COMPREHENSIVE WORKS

600 338.4   II   ISSN 0970-4663
APPROPRIATE TECHNOLOGY DOCUMENTATION BULLETIN. (Text in English) 1974. bi-m. Rs.75($40) National Institute of Small Industry Extension Training, Yousufguda, Hyderabad 500045, India. TELEX 425-6381-SIET-IN. Ed. M.V. Seetharam. **Document type:** abstracting/indexing.

600   NO   ISSN 0802-7676
ARBEIDSLEDEREN. bi-m. NOK 40. Norges Arbeidslederforbund, Drammensveien 40, Postboks 2523 Solli, Oslo 2, Norway. Ed. Gunnar J. Larsen. adv. circ. 11,114.

658.5   GW   ISSN 0003-780X
ARBEITSVORBEREITUNG; Zeitschrift fuer Planung und Steuerung der Fertigung. 1964. bi-m. DM.103.80. Carl Hanser Verlag, Kolbergerstr. 22, 81679 Munich, Germany. TEL 089-998300. FAX 089-984809. (Subscr. to: Postfach 860420, 81631 Munich, Germany) Ed.Bd. adv.; bk.rev. circ. 6,000. **Document type:** trade publication.
—SWETS. **CCC.**

600   AG   ISSN 0326-8101
ARGENTINA TECNOLOGICA. 1986. bi-m. free. Banco de la Provincia de Buenos Aires, San Martin 137, 1004 Buenos Aires, Argentina. TEL 331-8375-9 (Int. 1289). circ. 20,000.

ARQUEOLOGIA INDUSTRIAL. see ARCHAEOLOGY

ARTE. see ART

ARTS AND SCIENCES NEWSLETTER. see SCIENCES: COMPREHENSIVE WORKS

600 500   AT   ISSN 1036-3769
T29.A1
ASCENT TECHNOLOGY MAGAZINE. 1991. q. Aus.$15 (Asia Aus.$23; N. America Aus.$31.50; Europe Aus.$37). (Department of Industry, Science adj Technology) Australian Government Publishing Service, G.P.O. 84, Canberra, A.C.T. 2601, Australia. TEL 61-6-295-4411. FAX 61-6-295-4455. TELEX AA62013. Ed. P.R. Section. **Document type:** government publication.
Formed by the merger of (1983-1990): Ascent (ISSN 0810-7688); (1987-1990): Australian Technology Magazine (ISSN 0819-3916)
Description: Covers the sciencific and technological developments, and industry policies in Australia.

600   TH
ASIAN INSTITUTE OF TECHNOLOGY. ANNUAL RESEARCH AND ACTIVITIES REPORT. 1962. a. free. Asian Institute of Technology, c/o Academic Secretary, P.O. Box 2754, Bangkok 10501, Thailand. TEL 66-2-516-0110-29. FAX 66-2-516-2126. TELEX 84276 AIT TH. Ed. Roger A. Hawkey. circ. 1,000. (microfiche). **Indexed:** GeoRef. **Document type:** bulletin, academic/scholarly publication.
Formerly: Asian Institute of Technology. Research Summary (ISSN 0572-4198)

600 330   UK   ISSN 0956-3784
ASIAN REVIEW OF BUSINESS AND TECHNOLOGY. 1979. m. (11/yr.). £55($93.50) (effective 1995). Alain Charles Publishing Ltd., Alain Charles House, 27 Wilfred St., London SW1E 6PR, England. TEL 0171-834-7676. FAX 0171-973-0076. TELEX 297165 ACPLTD G. Ed. Jonquil Phelan. adv. contact: Sally Ann Hayes. circ. 10,722 (paid). (back issues avail.) **Document type:** trade publication.
—BLDSC (1742.745050).
Formerly: Far Eastern Technical Review (ISSN 0144-8218)
Description: Serves the senior business executives and government officials throughout the Pacific Rim.

ASSOCIATED SCIENTIFIC AND TECHNICAL SOCIETIES OF SOUTH AFRICA. ANNUAL PROCEEDINGS. see SCIENCES: COMPREHENSIVE WORKS

600   FR   ISSN 0066-9288
ASSOCIATION FRANCAISE DES EXPERTS DE LA COOPERATION TECHNIQUE INTERNATIONALE. ANNUAIRE. 1965. a. $2. Association Francaise des Experts de la Cooperation Technique Internationale, 12, rue Mesnil, 75116 Paris, France. TEL 45-53-41-16.

AUSTRALASIAN SCIENCE. see SCIENCES: COMPREHENSIVE WORKS

AUSTRALIAN SCIENCE AND TECHNOLOGY NEWSLETTER. see SCIENCES: COMPREHENSIVE WORKS

600   AU
AUSTRIA INNOVATIV. 1986. 4/yr. S.328. Bohmann Druck und Verlag GmbH & Co. KG, Leberstr. 122, A-1110 Vienna, Austria. TEL 0222-74095-0. FAX 0222-74095183. Ed. Harald Thurnher. adv.: B&W page S.34600, color page S.48600; trim 185 x 250; adv. contact: Christina Ruckenbauer. bk.rev. circ. 12,500. **Document type:** academic/scholarly publication.
Description: Covers new technological research and experiments in industry and universities.

620   PL   ISSN 0239-6440
   CODEN: TCMYAH
AUTO-TECHNIKA MOTORYZACYJNA. m. $162. S I M A D Spolka z o.o., Wal Miedzyszynski 646, 03-994 Warsaw, Poland. (Subscr. to: Auto-Technika Motoryzacyjna, ul. Bartycka 20, 00-716 Warsaw, Poland) Ed. Marian Karwas. circ. 100,000. **Indexed:** Chem.Abstr., ISMEC.
—CASDDS.
Formerly: Technika Motoryzacyjna (ISSN 0040-1153)

AWISHKARA. see SCIENCES: COMPREHENSIVE WORKS

B B R; Wasser und Rohrbau. see WATER RESOURCES

607   CN
B C I T ANNUAL REPORT. 1975. a. British Columbia Institute of Technology, Marketing & Development, Information & Community Relations, 3700 Willingdon Ave., Burnaby, B.C. V5G 3H2, Canada. TEL 604-434-5734. Ed. Carol Dion. illus.
Former titles: B C I T: The Career Campus (ISSN 0707-3291); British Columbia Institute of Technology. Annual Report (ISSN 0381-260X)

600 378   CN
B C I T UPDATE. w. free. British Columbia Institute of Technology, Marketing & Development, Information & Community Relations, 3700 Willingdon Ave., Burnaby, BC V5G 3H2, Canada. TEL 604-434-5734. Ed. Carol Dion.

B L A S T. see LAW

B M F T FORKAT. (Bundesministerium fuer Forschung und Technologie) see SCIENCES: COMPREHENSIVE WORKS

600   GW   ISSN 0724-0856
B M F T JOURNAL. 1973. 6/yr. free. Bundesministerium fuer Forschung und Technologie, Heinemannstr. 2, 53175 Bonn, Germany. TEL 0228-593516. FAX 0228-593601. Ed. Steffen Isensee. circ. 70,000. **Document type:** government publication.
Former titles (until 1984): B M F T Mitteilungen (ISSN 0170-9615); Mitteilungen aus dem B M F T (ISSN 0170-9593)
Description: Government publication covering events, information on research and technology.

600 500   BL   ISSN 0100-1949
T4   CODEN: BTCPDY
BAHIA, BRAZIL (STATE). CENTRO DE PESQUISAS E DESENVOLVIMENTO. BOLETIM TECNICO. (Text in Portuguese; summaries in English) s-a. $15 or exchange basis. Centro de Pesquisas e Desenvolvimento, Km 0 da BA 512, Caixa Postal 09, 42800 Camacari BA, Brazil. TEL 071-832-1111. FAX 071-832-2095. bibl.; charts; illus.; index. **Indexed:** Chem.Abstr., Eng.Ind., Food Sci.& Tech.Abstr., Met.Abstr., World Alum.Abstr.
—CASDDS.
Formerly (until 1975, vol. 2): C E P E D. Boletim Tecnico. Serie Tecnologia de Alimentos.
Description: Covers various themes such as: agriculture, chemistry, environment, energy, mining, metallurgy, materials and petrochemistry.

600 510   US
BALSKRISHNAN - NEUSTADT SERIES.* irreg. price varies. Holt, Rinehart and Winston, Inc., c/o Harcourt Brace Javonovich, Orlando, FL 32887. TEL 407-345-2500.

500 600   GW   ISSN 0932-7541
BATTELLE INFORMATION. 1967. 3/yr. free. Battelle Europe, Am Roemerhof 35, 60486 Frankfurt a.M., Germany. FAX 069-7908-80. TELEX 411966. (U.S. address: Battelle Memorial Institute, 505 King Ave., Columbus OH 43201) Ed. Doris Jessen. bk.rev.; cum.index. circ. 7,500. **Indexed:** Excerp.Med., Int.Packag.Abstr., Paper & Bd.Abstr.
Former titles (until April, 1987): Battelle Aktuell; (until 1978): Battelle Information.
Description: Features Battelle research centers in Europe, devoted to research and development in electronic systems, engineering, advanced materials, biological and environmental sciences, and technology management.

TECHNOLOGY: COMPREHENSIVE WORKS

605 US ISSN 0145-8477
CODEN: BATODH
BATTELLE TODAY. 1976. q. free to qualified personnel. Battelle Memorial Institute, Communications Office, Attn: Harriet A. Craig, Ed., 505 King Ave., Columbus, OH 43201. TEL 614-424-5336. FAX 614-424-3889. E-mail: craig@battelle.org. bk.rev.; illus.; circ. 36,000 (controlled). (back issues avail.; reprint service avail. from UMI) **Indexed:** Biol.Abstr., CAD CAM Abstr., Chem.Abstr., Graph.Arts Lit.Abstr., Int.Packag.Abstr., Intl.Polym.Sci.& Tech., Met.Abstr., Paper & Bd.Abstr., Print.Abstr., PROMT, RAPRA.
—Genuine Article; UMI.
Supersedes (in 1976): Battelle Memorial Institute. Research Outlook (ISSN 0092-1122); Which was formerly: Battelle Research Outlook (ISSN 0522-4810)
Description: Highlights of Battelle's worldwide activity in innovative research, technology commercialization and management of large technical programs.

BESSATSU SAIENSU. see *SCIENCES: COMPREHENSIVE WORKS*

BIBLIOGRAPHIC GUIDE TO TECHNOLOGY. see *BIBLIOGRAPHIES*

BIO-TECHNOLOGY; the international monthly for industrial biology. see *BIOLOGY — Biotechnology*

BIOPROCESS TECHNOLOGY SERIES. see *BIOLOGY*

600 US ISSN 0067-9127
T15.A1
BLAETTER FUER TECHNIKGESCHICHTE. 1932. irreg. price varies. (Technisches Museum fuer Industrie und Gewerbe, Forschungsinstitut fuer Technikgeschichte, AU) Springer-Verlag, 175 Fifth Ave., New York, NY 10010. TEL 212-460-1500. (Also: Berlin, Heidelberg, Tokyo, Vienna) **Indexed:** Amer.Hist.& Life, Hist.Abstr. **Document type:** monographic series.

BOLETIN S I N I C Y T. (Sistema Nacional de Informacion Cientifica y Tecnologia) see *SCIENCES: COMPREHENSIVE WORKS*

BOMBAY TECHNOLOGIST. see *CHEMISTRY*

600 UK ISSN 0140-766X
BRITISH ELECTROTECHNICAL APPROVALS BOARD. ANNUAL LIST OF APPROVED ELECTROTECHNICAL EQUIPMENT. (Monthly supplement avail.) 1966. a. free. B E A B, Mark House, the Green, 9-11 Queen's Rd., Hersham, Walton-on-Thames, Surrey KT12 5NA, England. TEL 01932-244401. FAX 01932-226603. E-mail: 100433,1226. circ. 10,000 (controlled). **Document type:** catalog.

BRITISH STANDARDS MICROFILE. see *ENGINEERING*

BUILDING SERVICES ENGINEERING RESEARCH & TECHNOLOGY. see *BUILDING AND CONSTRUCTION*

THE BULLETIN OF SCIENCE, TECHNOLOGY & SOCIETY. see *SCIENCES: COMPREHENSIVE WORKS*

600 PL ISSN 0068-4597
BYDGOSKIE TOWARZYSTWO NAUKOWE. WYDZIAL NAUK TECHNICZNYCH. PRACE. SERIA Z (PRACE ZBIOROWE). 1966. irreg. price varies. Bydgoskie Towarzystwo Naukowe, Jezuicka 4, Bydgoszcz, Poland. (Dist. by: Ars Polona-Ruch, Krakowskie Przedmiescie 7, Warsaw, Poland)

600 500 620 US
C I R A S NEWS. 1966. q. $10 (outside Iowa). Iowa State University, Center for Industrial Research and Service, I S U Research Park, Ste. 500, 2501 N. Loop Dr., Ames, IA 50010-8286. TEL 515-294-3420. FAX 515-294-4925. Ed. William R. Berkland; Pub. Jerald Rounds. circ. 6,306. (tabloid format; back issues avail.) **Document type:** newsletter.
Description: Provides Iowa manufacturing executives with information about methods for improving their management techniques and manufacturing and processing operations. Also describes services available to them from the CIRAS and other service agencies.

600 IT
C I S E NEWSLETTER. (Centro Informazioni Studi Esperienze) (Editions in English & Italian) 1980. q. free. C I S E - Tecnologie Innovative, Casella Postale 12081, 20134 Milan, Italy. FAX 39-2-21672620. TELEX 311643 CISE I. Ed. Paolo Civardi. circ. 5,000 (2,000 English ed.; 3,000 Italian ed.) **Document type:** newsletter.
Description: Covering development and innovation in the industrial field with emphasis on electric power generation.

C I S T I NEWS INTERNATIONAL. (Canadian Institute for Scientific and Technical Information) see *SCIENCES: COMPREHENSIVE WORKS — Computer Applications*

C L S U SCIENTIFIC JOURNAL. (Central Luzon State University) see *AGRICULTURE*

C O S T E D NEWSLETTER. (Committee on Science and Technology in Developing Countries) see *SCIENCES: COMPREHENSIVE WORKS*

C P S T OCCASIONAL PAPERS. (Commission on Professionals in Science & Technology) see *SCIENCES: COMPREHENSIVE WORKS*

C R I C RAPPORT DE RECHERCHE. see *SCIENCES: COMPREHENSIVE WORKS*

C S I R ANNUAL REPORT - TECHNOLOGY IMPACT. see *SCIENCES: COMPREHENSIVE WORKS*

CAHIERS DE LA RECHERCHE SCIENTIFIQUE ET TECHNIQUE. see *SCIENCES: COMPREHENSIVE WORKS*

600 500 BL
CALENDARIO DE EVENTOS EM CIENCIA E TECNOLOGIA. q. $9.80. Instituto Brasileiro de Informacao em Ciencia e Tecnologia, SAS Quadra 2, Lote 6, Bloco H, 70070-000 Brasilia, D.F., Brazil. TEL 2176161. FAX 2262677.
Former titles: Eventos em Politica Cientifica e Tecnologica; Calendario de Eventos Tecnico-Cientificos Realizados no Brazil (ISSN 0100-3399)

CALIFORNIA TECHNOLOGY REGISTER. see *BUSINESS AND ECONOMICS — Trade And Industrial Directories*

600 CN
CANADIAN CORPORATE R & D DIRECTORY. 1992. a. (plus updates 10/yr.) Can.$495. Evert Communications Limited, 1296 Carling Ave., 2nd Fl., Ottawa, ON K1Z 7K8, Canada. TEL 613-728-4621. FAX 613-728-0385. Ed. Natalie Gallimore; Pub. Gordon Hutchison. (looseleaf format; also avail. in diskette format) **Document type:** directory.
Description: Overviews about 300 Canadian R and D intensive companies and organizations.

CANADIAN R & D DIRECTORY. see *BUSINESS AND ECONOMICS — Trade And Industrial Directories*

600 001.3 GW ISSN 0176-0629
CAROLO-WILHELMINA MITTEILUNGEN. 1966. s-a. Technische Universitaet Braunschweig, Postfach 3329, 38023 Braunschweig, Germany. Ed. Lutz Tantow. bibl.; charts; illus. **Document type:** academic/scholarly publication.
Formerly (until 1986): Technische Universitaet Braunschweig. Mitteilungen.

CENTAURUS; international magazine of the history of mathematics, science and technology. see *SCIENCES: COMPREHENSIVE WORKS*

CENTRALE VIDENSKABSETISKE KOMITE. BERETNING/CENTRAL SCIENTIFIC - ETHICAL COMMITTEE OF DENMARK. REPORT. see *PHILOSOPHY*

658.5 FR ISSN 1156-7104
T2
CENTRALIENS. Variant title: Arts et Manufactures Centraliens. 10/yr. 25 F. Association des Anciens Eleves de l'Ecole Centrale des Arts et Manufactures, 8 rue Jean-Goujon, 75008 Paris, France. TEL 42-25-02-37. FAX 49-53-08-21. Ed. Pierre Chappaz. circ. 11,477. **Indexed:** Met.Abstr., World Alum.Abstr.
—BLDSC (1736.301000).
Formerly (until 1990): Arts et Manufactures (ISSN 0004-3990)

600 MG
CENTRE D'INFORMATION ET DE DOCUMENTATION SCIENTIFIQUE ET TECHNIQUE. RECHERCHES POUR LE DEVELOPPEMENT. SERIE SCIENCES TECHNOLOGIQUES. 2/yr. 60 F.($10) Centre d'Information et de Documentation Scientifique et Technique, B.P. 6224, Antananarivo 101, Madagascar. TEL 33288.

600 500 BE ISSN 0069-1968
T10.65.B4 CODEN: CDORBV
CENTRE NATIONAL DE DOCUMENTATION SCIENTIFIQUE ET TECHNIQUE. RAPPORT D'ACTIVITE. 1964. biennial. free. Centre National de Documentation Scientifique et Technique - National Center for Scientific and Technical Documentation, 4, Bd. de l'Empereur, B-1000 Brussels, Belgium. Dir. A. Cockx. index; circ. 1,000 (controlled). **Indexed:** Bull.Signal.
Description: Offers a concise evaluation of activities and accomplishments of the year. Also reports on results of the previous years, to illuminate long-term projects.

600 IT ISSN 0392-8225
LA CERAMICA MODERNA ED ANTICA; mensile di informazione tecnica. 1979. m. (11/yr.). L.45000 (foreign L.67000). Gruppo Editoriale Faenza Editrice s.p.a., Via Pier. de Crescenzi, 44, 48018 Faenza RA, Italy. TEL 39-546-663488. FAX 39-546-660440. adv.: B&W page L.4160000. circ. 4,730.
Formerly: Ceramica Moderna.

CEYLON INSTITUTE OF SCIENTIFIC & INDUSTRIAL RESEARCH. ANNUAL REPORT. see *SCIENCES: COMPREHENSIVE WORKS*

CEYLON INSTITUTE OF SCIENTIFIC AND INDUSTRIAL RESEARCH. NEWS BULLETIN. see *SCIENCES: COMPREHENSIVE WORKS*

CHEMICAL ENGINEERING WORLD; India's foremost technical journal. see *ENGINEERING — Chemical Engineering*

CHINA CENTER OF ADVANCED SCIENCE AND TECHNOLOGY SERIES. see *SCIENCES: COMPREHENSIVE WORKS*

CHINA REPORT: SCIENCE AND TECHNOLOGY. see *SCIENCES: COMPREHENSIVE WORKS*

CHONGQING KEJI/CHONGQING SCIENCE AND TECHNOLOGY. see *SCIENCES: COMPREHENSIVE WORKS*

CHUBU UNIVERSITY. COLLEGE OF ENGINEERING. MEMOIRS/CHUBU DAIGAKU KOGAKUBU KIYO. see *ENGINEERING*

CHUO DAIGAKU RIKOGAKUBU KIYO/CHUO UNIVERSITY. FACULTY OF SCIENCE AND ENGINEERING. BULLETIN. see *SCIENCES: COMPREHENSIVE WORKS*

CIENCIA INTERAMERICANA. see *SCIENCES: COMPREHENSIVE WORKS*

CIENCIA PARA TODOS. see *SCIENCES: COMPREHENSIVE WORKS*

CIENCIA Y DESARROLLO. see *SCIENCES: COMPREHENSIVE WORKS*

600 500 CU ISSN 0253-7397
CODEN: CTFMDH
CIENCIAS TECNICAS FISICAS Y MATEMATICAS. 1981. s-a. $26 in S. America; N. America $30; elsewhere $36. Academia de Ciencias de Cuba, Apartado 2291, Zona 2, Havana, Cuba. (Dist. by: Ediciones Cubanas, Obispo No. 461, Apdo. 605, Havana, Cuba) Ed. Jose Altshuler. circ. 1,500. **Indexed:** INSPEC (1983-).
—BLDSC (3198.205655); CASDDS.

600 UK ISSN 0305-6120
CODEN: CIWODV
CIRCUIT WORLD. 1973. q. £44.80($90) (Institute of Interconnection Technology) Wela Publications Ltd., Asahi House, 10 Church Rd., Port Erin IM99 8HD, Isle of Man. TEL 01624-836044. FAX 01624-835400. (Co-sponsor: Printed Circuit Interconnection Federation) Ed. William Goldie. adv.; bk.rev. (back issues avail.) **Indexed:** Copper Abstr., INSPEC (1975-). **Document type:** academic/scholarly publication.
—BLDSC (3198.839000); Ei; SWETS; UnCover. CCC.

TECHNOLOGY: COMPREHENSIVE WORKS

600   US
CLOVERVIEW. q. Virginia Polytechnic Institute and State University, 202 Media Bldg., Blacksburg, VA 24061. TEL 703-961-7370.

600   NE   ISSN 0165-232X
GB641   CODEN: CRSTDL
COLD REGIONS SCIENCE AND TECHNOLOGY. 1979. q. fl.670($409) (effective 1996). Elsevier Science B.V., P.O. Box 211, 1000 AE Amsterdam, Netherlands. TEL 31-20-4853911. FAX 31-20-4853598. TELEX 18582 ESPA NL. E-mail: nlinfo-f@elsevier.nl; usinfo-f@elsevier.com; forinfo-kyf04035@niftyserve.or.jp; Site addr.: http://www.elsevier.nl/. (Subscr. in U.S. and Canada to: Elsevier Science Inc., Box 882, Madison Sq. Sta., New York, NY 10159. TEL 212-989-5800. FAX 212-633-3990) Ed. M. Mellor. (also avail. in microform from UMI) Indexed: Appl.Mech.Rev., Chem.Abstr., Curr. Cont., E&P Hlth. (1993-), Eng.Ind., Forest Prod.Abstr., Gas Process.& Ppl. (1993-), Geo.Abstr., Geol.Abstr., GeoRef., Geotech.Abstr., Irr.& Drain.Abstr., Meteor.& Geoastrophys.Abstr., Off.Tech. (1993-), Petrol.Abstr. (1993-), Soils & Fert. **Document type:** academic/scholarly publication.
—BLDSC (3295.760000); CASDDS; Ei; Faxon; Genuine Article; UnCover. **CCC.**
Description: Deals with the scientific and technical problems of cold environments, including both natural and artificial environments.
Refereed Serial

600 070   US   ISSN 1062-6727
COLE PAPERS; technology, journalism, publishing. 1989. m. $117. 2590 Greenwich St., Ste. 9, San Francisco, CA 94123-3333. TEL 415-673-2424. FAX 415-673-2449. E-mail: cole@plink.geis.com. Ed. David M. Cole. bk.rev.; charts; illus. **Document type:** newsletter.
Description: Discusses technologies publishers can use to put out newspapers, magazines and books.

600   US   ISSN 1074-519X
COMPOSITES NEWS: INFRASTRUCTURE. no.4, 1994. s-m. $287. (Composites Worldwide) Composites News International, 991 Lomas Santa Fe Dr., C469, Solana Beach, CA 92075-7010. TEL 619-755-1372. FAX 619-755-5271. E-mail: 71520.623@compuserve. Ed. Steve Loud. **Document type:** newsletter.
—CCC.
Description: Provides information about composites used in infrastructure, construction and civil engineering, buildings, applications and markets.

660 677   UK   ISSN 0266-3538
TA418.9.C6   CODEN: CSTCEH
COMPOSITES SCIENCE AND TECHNOLOGY. 1968. m. £1060($1686) (effective 1996). Elsevier Science Ltd., P.O. Box 800, Kidlington, Oxford OX5 1DX, England. TEL 44-1865-843000. FAX 44-1865-843010. E-mail: nlinfo-f@elsevier.nl; usinfo-f@elsevier.com; forinfo-kyf04035@niftyserve.or.jp; Site addr.: http://www.elsevier.nl/. (Subscr. in U.S. and Canada to: Elsevier Science, 660 White Plains Rd., Tarrytown, NY 10591-5153. TEL 914-524-9200. FAX 914-524-9200) Eds. B. Harris, Tsu-Wei Chou. adv.; bk.rev.; illus.; index. (also avail. in microform from UMI; back issues avail.) Indexed: Abstr.Bull.Inst.Pap.Chem., Chem.Abstr., Curr.Cont., Eng.Ind., Excerp.Med., INSPEC (1988-), Int.Aerosp.Abstr., Intl.Polym.Sci.& Tech., J.of Ferroc., Met.Abstr., RAPRA, Sci.Cit.Ind., Text.Tech.Dig., World Alum.Abstr., World Text.Abstr. **Document type:** academic/scholarly publication.
—BLDSC (3365.650000); CASDDS; Ei; Faxon; Genuine Article; SWETS; UnCover. **CCC.**
Incorporates (in 1985): Fibre Science and Technology (ISSN 0015-0568)
Description: Publishes original articles, occasional review papers, and letters, on all aspects of the fundamental and applied science of engineering composites.
Refereed Serial

600   PH
CON - SCIENCE. (Text in English and Pilipino; summaries in English) 1979. bi-m. P.1. Industrial Technology Development Institute, P. Gil, Taft Ave., P.O. Box 774, Manila, Philippines. FAX 632-592275. TELEX ITT 40404. Ed. Ronand Henson. bk.rev. circ. 750.
Formerly: N I S T Newsletter.

CONFERENCE ON SPACE SIMULATION. PROCEEDINGS. see *AERONAUTICS AND SPACE FLIGHT*

600   US
CONFERENCE ON U S TECHNOLOGY POLICY. PROCEEDINGS. Variant title: I E E E Conference on U S Technology Policy. Proceedings. 1977. biennial. price varies. (I E E E, Technical Activities Board) Institute of Electrical and Electronics Engineers, Inc., 345 E. 47th St., New York, NY 10017. TEL 212-705-7900. FAX 212-705-7682. (Subscr. to: IEEE Service Center, Box 1331, 445 Hoes Lane, Piscataway, NJ 08855-1331) (Co-sponsor: IEEE, United States Activities Board) **Document type:** proceedings.
Formerly (until 1979): Conference on U S Technological Policy. Proceedings.
Description: Discusses policies in the areas of energy, national resources, information systems and public understanding.

CONFIGURATIONS; a journal of literature, science and technology. see *LITERATURE*

600   CR   ISSN 0253-2492
Q180.C75
CONSEJO NACIONAL PARA INVESTIGACIONES CIENTIFICAS Y TECNOLOGICAS, COSTA RICA. INFORME ANUAL. 1975. a. free. Consejo Nacional para Investigaciones Cientificas y Tecnologicas, Departamento de Informacion y Documentacion, Apdo. 10318, San Jose, Costa Rica. circ. 1,000.

CONSUMER INFORMATION APPLIANCE; the platform for enhanced services. see *COMMUNICATIONS — Telephone And Telegraph*

CONTEMPORARY TRENDS IN EUROPEAN SOCIAL SCIENCES. see *SOCIAL SCIENCES: COMPREHENSIVE WORKS*

CORPTECH DIRECTORY OF TECHNOLOGY COMPANIES. see *BUSINESS AND ECONOMICS — Trade And Industrial Directories*

CORROSION PREVENTION AND CONTROL. see *METALLURGY*

COURT TECHNOLOGY BULLETIN. see *LAW — Judicial Systems*

CRITICAL REVIEWS IN MULTIPHASE SCIENCE & TECHNOLOGY. see *SCIENCES: COMPREHENSIVE WORKS*

CROSSROADS; Halacha and the modern world. see *RELIGIONS AND THEOLOGY — Judaic*

CURRENT AWARENESS. S D I SERVICE. see *MEDICAL SCIENCES*

600   NE
CURRENT ISSUES IN PRODUCTION ECOLOGY. (Text in English) 1993. irreg., vol.2, 1994. price varies. Kluwer Academic Publishers, Postbus 17, 3300 AA Dordrecht, Netherlands. TEL 31-78-392392. FAX 31-78-392254. TELEX 29245 KAPG NL. (Dist. by: Kluwer Academic Publishers Group, P.O. Box 322, 3300 AH Dordrecht, Netherlands. TEL 31-78-392392. FAX 31-78-546474; N. America dist. addr.: Box 358, Accord Sta., Hingham, MA 02018-0358. TEL 617-871-6600. FAX 617-871-6528) **Document type:** monographic series.
Refereed Serial

600 340   GW
D I N. CATALOGUE OF TECHNICAL RULES. VOL 1: GERMAN STANDARDS AND TECHNICAL RULES. German edition: D I N - Katalog fuer Technische Regeln. Band 1: Deutsche Normen (ISSN 0722-9313) (Text in English, German) 1926. a. DM.298. (Deutsches Institut fuer Normung e.V. (D I N)) Beuth Verlag GmbH, Burggrafenstr. 6, 10787 Berlin, Germany. TEL 030-2601-0. FAX 030-26011260. TELEX 183622-BVB-D. (Dist. in US by: Global Engineering Documents, 2805 McGaw Ave., Box 19539, Irvine, CA 92714) circ. 10,000. **Document type:** catalog.
Supersedes in part (in 1993): D I N. Catalogue of Technical Rules.

600 340   GW   ISSN 0945-1080
D I N. CATALOGUE OF TECHNICAL RULES. VOL. 2: INTERNATIONAL STANDARDS AND TECHNICAL RULES. German edition: D I N. Katalog fuer Technische Regeln. Band 2: Internationale Normen und Ausgewaehlte Auslaendische Normen. (Text in English, German) 1926. a. DM.148. (Deutsches Institut fuer Normung e.V. (D I N)) Beuth Verlag GmbH, Burggrafenstr. 6, 10787 Berlin, Germany. TEL 030-2601-0. FAX 030-26011260. TELEX 183622-BVB-D. (Dist. in US by: Global Engineering Documents, 2805 McGaw Ave., Box 19539, Irvine, CA 92714) circ. 4,000. **Document type:** catalog.
Supersedes in part (in 1993): D I N. Catalogue of Technical Rules.

DAEDALUS. see *MUSEUMS AND ART GALLERIES*

600   US   ISSN 1070-1893
DALLAS - FORT WORTH TECHNOLOGY.* 1991. m. $8.95. T M C, Inc., 801 E. Campbell Rd., Ste. 170, Richardson, TX 75081-1856. TEL 214-907-9977. FAX 214-783-8546. Ed. Tom Mattos. adv.: B&W page $1530, color page $2130; trim 10 5/8 x 13 1/2; adv. contact: Cathy Rentzel. circ. 25,000.
Description: Covers news in high technology affecting area businesses.

DANESHMAND. see *SCIENCES: COMPREHENSIVE WORKS*

600   SA   ISSN 0256-8934
DATAWEEK; electronics technology. (Text in English) fortn. R.30. Technews (Pty) Ltd., P.O. Box 626, Kloof 3640, South Africa. TEL 27-31-764-0593. FAX 27-31-764-0386. Ed. R.K. Beaumont. circ. 3,482 (controlled). (tabloid format) **Document type:** trade publication.
Description: Covers electronic technology: components, design, manufacture, testing and maintenance.

DEFENCE SCIENCE JOURNAL. see *MILITARY*

DENGEN KAIHATSU K.K. CHOSA SHIRYO/ELECTRIC POWER DEVELOPMENT. STUDY REPORT. see *ENGINEERING — Electrical Engineering*

600   US
DENTAL PRODUCTS REPORT EUROPE. 1980. 6/yr. $30. Medical Economics Publishing Co., Inc., Five Paragon Dr., Montvale, NJ 07645. TEL 201-358-7200. FAX 201-573-1045. Ed. Jeanne K. Matson. adv. circ. 40,000. (tabloid format; also avail. in microform from UMI) **Document type:** trade publication.
Formerly: Dental Products Report International.
Description: Introduces dental materials, equipment, and service available to dentists and their laboratory technicians.

600   MX
DESARROLLO TECNOLOGICO. (Text in Spanish; summaries in English, Spanish) 1992. irreg. (2-3/yr.). Mex.$8 per no. Universidad Nacional Autonoma de Mexico, Instituto de Investigaciones en Matematicas Aplicadas en y Sistemas, Apdo. Postal 20-726, Del. V.A. Obregon, 01000 Mexico D.F., Mexico. TEL 622-35-62. FAX 550-00-47. Ed. Maria Ochoa Macedo. bibl.; charts. circ. 500. **Document type:** academic/scholarly publication.
Description: Specializes in electronics and computer sciences.
Refereed Serial

DESIGN & DRAFTING NEWS. see *ENGINEERING*

DESIGN & TECHNOLOGY FILE. see *EDUCATION — Teaching Methods And Curriculum*

745.209489   DK   ISSN 0906-9194
DESIGN DK. (Text in Danish, English) 1980. 6/yr. DKK 375 in Scandinavia; Europe DKK 444; elsewhere DKK 490. Danish Design Council, H.C. Andersen Blvd. 18, DK-1553 Copenhagen V, Denmark. TEL 45-33-14-66-88. FAX 45-33-32-00-48. Eds. Jens Bernsen, Susanne Schenstroem. bk.rev.; illus. circ. 6,000. Indexed: DAAI. **Document type:** bulletin, trade publication.
Former titles (until 1991): Design (ISSN 0900-3517); (until 1988): D D Bulletin (ISSN 0107-0908)
Description: Gives an up-to-date review of the developments taking place in Danish and international industrial design and graphic communication.

TECHNOLOGY: COMPREHENSIVE WORKS

745.2 US ISSN 0011-9407
TA175 CODEN: DIGNAO
DESIGN NEWS; news for OEM design engineers. 1946. 24/yr. $95 (Canada $150; Mexico $140; elsewhere $180). Cahners Publishing Company (Newton), Division of Reed Elsevier Inc., 275 Washington St., Newton, MA 02158-1630. TEL 617-964-3030. FAX 617-558-4402. (Subscr. to: 44 Cook St., Denver, CO 80206. TEL 800-662-7776) Ed. Lawrence D. Maloney. adv.: B&W page $8620. abstr.; charts; illus.; pat.; tr.lit.; index. circ. 170,193. (also avail. in microform; reprint service avail. from UMI) Indexed: A.I.Abstr., A.S.& T.Ind., Bus.Ind., CAD CAM Abstr. (until 1992), Chem.Abstr., DM & T, Energy Info.Abstr., Hlth.Ind., Ind.Sci.Rev., INSPEC, Mag.Ind., Met.Abstr., PMR, PROMT, Robomat. (until 1992), Sh.& Vib.Dig., Tel.Abstr., Text.Tech.Dig., Tr.& Indus.Ind., World Alum.Abstr. **Document type**: trade publication.
—BLDSC (3560.000000); CIS; Ei; Faxon; Genuine Article; SWETS; UMI; UnCover. **CCC**.
Description: For design engineers and engineering management. Provides information on power transmission, fastening, computers and CAD-CAM, fluid power, electrical and electronic design, new materials, new processes and new patents. Emphasis is on both mechanical and electrical-electronic design.
Refereed Serial

DESIGN PRODUCTS AND APPLICATION. see *ENGINEERING*

745.2 GW ISSN 0932-3724
DESIGN-REPORT. bi-m. Rat fuer Formgebung, Ludwig-Erhard-Anlage 1, 60327 Frankfurt a.M., Germany. TEL 069-747919. FAX 069-7410911. circ. 1,200. Indexed: DAAI.
—SWETS.

600 UK ISSN 0964-6566
DESIGN REVIEW. 1990. q. £16. (Chartered Society of Designers) Tradevine Ltd., 26 Cramer St., London W1M 3HE, England. TEL 071-486-7419. FAX 071-486-1451. (Subscr. to: 29 Bedford Sq., London WC1B 3EG, England. TEL 071-631-1510) Ed. David Redhead. adv. contact: Simon Turner. bk.rev. circ. 10,000. Indexed: DAAI. **Document type**: trade publication.
—BLDSC (3560.177000).

DESIGN STUDIES. see *ARCHITECTURE*

600 US ISSN 0192-1312
HN980
DEVELOPMENT COMMUNICATION REPORT. 1972. q. $10 (free to qualified personnel). (Institute for International Research) Clearinghouse on Development Communication, 1815 N. Ft. Myer Dr., Ste. 600, Arlington, VA 22209. TEL 703-527-5546. FAX 703-527-4661. (Co-sponsor: U.S. Agency for International Development) bk.rev.; circ. 7,000 (controlled). Indexed: Educ.Tech.Abstr., ERIC, Rural Ext.Educ.& Tr.Abstr., Rural Recreat.Tour.Abstr., World Agri.Econ.& Rural Sociol.Abstr. **Document type**: newsletter.
Formerly (until 1976): Instructional Technology Report.
Description: Each issue focuses on a different aspect of communications and is targeted to professionals in developing countries. Includes articles on communication and specific sectors, such as health, agriculture, the environment, population and family planning, education, and women and development.
Refereed Serial

600 US
DEVELOPNET NEWS; online news and views on technology transfer in international development. 1990. m. free. Volunteers in Technical Assistance, Inc., 1600 Wilson Blvd., Ste. 500, Arlington, VA 22209. TEL 703-276-1800. FAX 703-243-1865. TELEX 440192 VITAUI. Ed. Vicki Tsiliopoulos. bk.rev. **Document type**: newsletter.
●Available only online.
Description: Specializes in information dissemination and communications technology; offers services in the areas of sustainable agriculture, food processing, renewable energy applications, water sanitation and supply, small enterprise development and information management.

007 US ISSN 0886-0076
T176 CODEN: DARTEB
DIRECTORY OF AMERICAN RESEARCH AND TECHNOLOGY; organizations active in product development for business. 1986. a., 29th edition, 1994. $329.95. R.R. Bowker, A Reed Reference Publishing company, 121 Chanlon Rd., New Providence, NJ 07974. TEL 908-464-6800. FAX 908-665-6688. TELEX 138 755. (Subscr. to: Order Dept., Box 31, New Providence, NJ 07974-9003. TEL 800-521-8110) (also avail. in magnetic tape) Indexed: Copper Abstr. **Document type**: bibliography, directory.
●Also available on CD-ROM. Producer(s): Bowker - Reed Reference Electronic Publishing.
—BLDSC (3592.596900). **CCC**.
Formerly (until 1986): Industrial Research Laboratories of the United States (ISSN 0073-7623)
Description: Profiles more than 11,000 U.S. and Canadian corporate and nonprofit, independent, and university research facilities. Lists key personnel, contact information, staff size, and research activities. Includes a Personnel Index and a Classification Index that cross-references organizations under 33 fields and 1,500 subfields.

600 II
DIRECTORY OF EXTRAMURAL RESEARCH AND DEVELOPMENT PROJECTS APPROVED FOR FUNDING BY CENTRAL GOVERNMENT. 1991. a. Department of Science and Technology, Technology Bhavan, New Mehrauli Rd., New Delhi 110016, India. TEL 0091-651912. FAX 0091-6862418. Ed. A.R. Rajeswari. circ. 3,000. **Document type**: government publication, directory.

DIRECTORY OF JAPANESE TECHNICAL RESOURCES IN THE UNITED STATES. see *BUSINESS AND ECONOMICS — Trade And Industrial Directories*

600 US
DIRECTORY OF MEMBRANE & HIGH TECH SEPARATIONS (YEAR). a. $300. Business Communications Co., Inc. (Norwalk), 25 Van Zant St., Ste. 13, Norwalk, CT 06855. TEL 203-853-4266. FAX 203-853-0348. TELEX 6502934929 UWI. **Document type**: directory.
Formerly: Yearbook and Directory of Members and Separation Technology.

600 II
DIRECTORY OF RESEARCH AND DEVELOPMENT INSTITUTIONS. 1980. irreg. Department of Science and Technology, Technology Bhavan, New Mehrauli Rd., New Delhi 110016, India. TEL 0091-651912. FAX 0091-6862418. Ed. A.R. Rajeswari. circ. 2,000. **Document type**: government publication, directory.

DIRECTORY OF THE SCIENTISTS, TECHNOLOGISTS, AND ENGINEERS OF THE P C S I R. see *SCIENCES: COMPREHENSIVE WORKS*

DISCOVER (BURBANK). see *SCIENCES: COMPREHENSIVE WORKS*

600 US
DISSONANCE. 1990. 4/yr. $2 per no. Box 1431, Burlington, VT 05402-1431. TEL 802-860-6285. E-mail: hunneman@aol.com. Ed. Leif Hunneman. adv.: page $100; 8 1/2 x 11. bk.rev. circ. 3,000. **Document type**: newsletter.
Description: Discusses the advancement of human condition through the marriage of art, humor and technology.

600 500 CC ISSN 0253-4258
T4 CODEN: THYPDK
DONGBEI GONGXUEYUAN XUEBAO/NORTHEAST INSTITUTE OF TECHNOLOGY. JOURNAL. (Text in Chinese) q. $1.50 per no. Dongbei Gongxueyuan - Northeast Institute of Technology, No.1, Wenhua Lu 1 Duan, Heping-qu, Shenyang, Liaoning 110006, People's Republic of China. (Dist. outside China by: China International Book Trading Corp., P.O. Box 399, Beijing, P.R.C.) Indexed: Chem.Abstr., Math.R. **Document type**: academic/scholarly publication.
—CASDDS.

658.507 DK ISSN 0108-6707
DRIFTSTEKNIKERBOGEN. 1974. a. DKK 100. Danmarks Tekniske Universitet, Driftsteknisk Institut, Bygn. 423, DK-2800 Lyngby, Denmark. TEL 45-93-44-66. FAX 45-93-44-67. illus. circ. 300.
Formerly: Driftsteknikerdag.

DZALUU DZOHION BUTEEGCH/YOUNG INVENTOR. see *SCIENCES: COMPREHENSIVE WORKS*

600 FR ISSN 0756-0737
E A O. (Enseignement Assiste par Ordinateur) 1983. 18/yr. 2200 F. A Jour, 11 rue du Marche St. Honore, 75001 Paris, France. TEL 42-96-67-22. FAX 40-20-07-75. TELEX TELEXEL 615887 F.

E D A. (Electronic Design Automation Ltd.) see *ELECTRONICS*

600 UK ISSN 0954-6154
E D I UPDATE. (Electronic Data Interchange) 1988. 10/yr. £259($499) I B C Publishing, Gilmoora House, 57-61 Mortimer St., London W1N 7TD, England. TEL 0171-637-4383. FAX 0171-636-6414. (Subscr. in the U.S. to: IBC (USA), 290 Eliot St., Box 91004, Ashland, MA 01721-9104. TEL 508-881-2000. FAX 508-881-0982) Ed. Ken Cottrill. bk.rev. (looseleaf format; back issues avail.) **Document type**: trade publication.
Description: Covers the most recent international developments for electronic data interchange. Concentrates on the news, analysis, case studies, marketplace information, and a diary of major events.

600 US ISSN 1082-5452
E M F - E M I CONTROL. 1982. bi-m. $49 (foreign $67) includes the EMC-EMF Buyers' Guide. E E C Press, 6193 Finchingfield Rd., Gainesville, VA 22065. TEL 804-483-0700. FAX 804-493-9386. Ed. Don White. adv.; bk.rev.; charts; illus.; stat.; index; circ. 35,000 (paid). (back issues avail.) **Document type**: trade publication.
●Also available on CD-ROM.
Formerly (until 1994): E M C Technology (ISSN 0278-4270)
Description: Focuses on controlling the electric equipment and system emission and susceptibility and the electromagnetic environment to reduce human exposure.

E N E A NOTIZIARIO - ENERGIA E INNOVAZIONE; mensile di informazione sulle nuove tecnologie, l'energia, e l'ambiente. (Ente per le Nuove Tecnologie, l'Energie e l'Ambiente) see *ENERGY*

600 US
E O S - E S D TECHNOLOGY. (Electrical Overstress - Electrostatic Discharge); the magazine for ESD-control professionals in the electronics industry. 1989. bi-m. $65. Brinton Group Inc., 49 Eaton Rd., Ste. 100, Framingham, MA 01701. TEL 508-877-7958. FAX 508-877-3457. TELEX 6503201857 MCIUW. Ed. Lisa Gillette. adv. circ. 30,000. (also avail. in microfiche; microfilm) **Document type**: trade publication.

600 US ISSN 1069-1987
E R C UPDATE. 1988. q. Engineering Research Center, University of Maryland, Potomac Bldg., No. 092, College Park, MD 20742. TEL 301-405-3906. FAX 301-403-4105. E-mail: jm31@umail.umd.edu. Ed. Judith Mays. circ. 15,000. (back issues avail.) **Document type**: newsletter.
Description: Covers research projects as well as research capabilities available to Maryland industry and others.

E R I C - I I UPDATE. (Educational Resources Information Center - Information and Technology) see *LIBRARY AND INFORMATION SCIENCES — Computer Applications*

620 FR
ECOLE NATIONALE SUPERIEURE DE TECHNIQUES AVANCEES. RAPPORT D'ACTIVITE SUR LES RECHERCHES. 1972. biennial. free. Ecole Nationale Superieure de Techniques Avancees, Direction des Recherches, 32, Bd. Victor, 75015 Paris, France. TEL 45-52-54-11. FAX 45-52-55-87. bk.rev. circ. 1,200.

TECHNOLOGY: COMPREHENSIVE WORKS

600　　　　　　US　　ISSN 1043-8599
HC79.T4　　　　　　CODEN: EINTEO
ECONOMICS OF INNOVATION AND NEW TECHNOLOGY. 1990. 4/yr. 72 ECU (effective 1996). Harwood Academic Publishers, c/o International Publishers Distributor, 820 Town Center Dr., Langhorne, PA 19047. TEL 215-750-2642. FAX 215-750-6343. (Subscr. to: International Publishers Distributor, PO Box 90, Reading, Berkshire, RG1 8JL, England. TEL 44-173-456-8316) Eds. Peter Swann, W. Edward Steinmuller. (also avail. in microform)
—BLDSC (3657.021000); SWETS. **CCC.**
　　Refereed Serial

600　338　　　　NE
▼**ECONOMICS OF SCIENCE, TECHNOLOGY AND INNOVATION.** (Text in English) 1994. irreg., vol.3, 1995. Kluwer Academic Publishers, Postbus 17, 3300 AA Dordrecht, Netherlands. TEL 31-78-392392. FAX 31-78-392254. TELEX 29245 KAPG NL. (Dist. by: Kluwer Academic Publishers Group, P.O. Box 322, 3300 AH Dordrecht, Netherlands. TEL 31-78-392392. FAX 31-78-546474; N. America dist. addr.: Box 358, Accord Sta., Hingham, MA 02018-0358. TEL 617-871-6600. FAX 617-871-6528) (back issues avail.) **Document type:** monographic series.
　　Refereed Serial

EDUCATION AND TRAINING. see *EDUCATION*

EDUCATIONAL TECHNOLOGY; the magazine for managers of change in education. see *EDUCATION*

600　　　　　JA　　ISSN 0387-7434
EDUCATIONAL TECHNOLOGY RESEARCH. s-a. $22. Educational Technology Journal Association of Japan, 4-1-1, Nukui-kita Machi, Koganei-shi, Tokyo 184, Japan. (Dist. by: Business Center for Academic Societies Japan, 5-16-9 Honkomagome, Bunkyo-ku, Tokyo 113, Japan. TEL 03-5814-5811)

EMBASSY OF SWITZERLAND BULLETIN. see *SCIENCES: COMPREHENSIVE WORKS*

EN T A NEWSLETTER. (Environmental Technology Assessment) see *ENVIRONMENTAL STUDIES*

ENCYCLOPEDIA OF PHYSICAL SCIENCE & TECHNOLOGY YEARBOOK. see *SCIENCES: COMPREHENSIVE WORKS*

ENERGIE; das Magazin fuer Wirtschaft, Forschung, Technik, Umwelt. see *ENERGY*

ENERGY CONSERVATION AND UTILIZATION TECHNOLOGIES. see *CONSERVATION*

604.2　　　　US　　ISSN 0046-2012
ENGINEERING DESIGN GRAPHICS JOURNAL. 1936. 3/yr. (in 1 vol.) $20 to non-members (Canada & Mexico $25; elsewhere $30); individual members $6; institutions $10 (effective 1996). American Society for Engineering Education, Engineering Design Graphics Division, c/o Mary A. Sadowski, Ed., 1419 Knoy Hall, Purdue University, W. Lafayette, IN 47907-1419. TEL 317-494-8206. FAX 317-494-0486. (Subscr. to: Department of Engineering Graphics, Ohio State University, 2070 Neil Ave., Columbus, OH 43210-1275) adv. contact: Craig Miller. bk.rev.; charts; illus.; circ. 800 (paid). (also avail. in microform from UMI; reprint service avail. from UMI; back issues avail.) **Document type:** academic/scholarly publication.
—BLDSC (3758.960000); Faxon; Genuine Article; UMI; UnCover.
　　Former titles (until vol.33, no.3, 1969): Journal of Engineering Graphics; (until vol.22, no.2, 1958): Journal of Engineering Drawing.
　　Description: Articles devoted to the fundamentals of engineering graphics education and engineering technology. Topics include engineering graphics, computer graphics, descriptive geometry, geometric modeling, computer-aided drafting and design, graphic data processing, visualization techniques, and graphics instruction.
　　Refereed Serial

ENVIRONMENTAL SCIENCE AND TECHNOLOGY (NEW YORK). see *ENVIRONMENTAL STUDIES*

600　　　　　CU
EQUIPOS Y PRODUCTOS. TECNOLOGIA. m. Academia de Ciencias, Instituto de Documentacion e Informacion Cientifico-Tecnica (I D I C T), Capitolio Nacional, Prado y San Jose, Habana 2, Havana, Cuba.

600　　　　　　NE　　ISSN 0927-4057
　　　　　　　　　　CODEN: ECATEJ
EURO COURSES. ADVANCED SCIENTIFIC TECHNIQUES. (Text in English) 1991. irreg. price varies. (Commission of the European Communities) Kluwer Academic Publishers, Postbus 17, 3300 AA Dordrecht, Netherlands. TEL 31-78-392392. FAX 31-78-392254. TELEX 29245 KAPG NL. (Dist. by: Kluwer Academic Publishers Group, P.O. Box 322, 3300 AH Dordrecht, Netherlands. TEL 31-78-392392. FAX 31-78-546474; N. America dist. addr.: Box 358, Accord Sta., Hingham, MA 02018-0358. TEL 617-871-6600. FAX 617-871-6528) **Indexed:** Zoo.Rec. **Document type:** proceedings.
　　Refereed Serial

EURO COURSES. CHEMICAL AND ENVIRONMENTAL SCIENCES. see *ENVIRONMENTAL STUDIES*

EURO COURSES. COMPUTER AND INFORMATION SCIENCE. see *COMPUTERS*

EURO COURSES. ENVIRONMENTAL IMPACT ASSESSMENT. see *ENVIRONMENTAL STUDIES*

EURO COURSES. ENVIRONMENTAL MANAGEMENT. see *ENVIRONMENTAL STUDIES*

EURO COURSES. HEALTH PHYSICS AND RADIATION PROTECTION. see *ENERGY — Nuclear Energy*

EURO COURSES. MECHANICAL AND MATERIALS SCIENCE. see *ENGINEERING — Engineering Mechanics And Materials*

EURO COURSES. NUCLEAR SCIENCE AND TECHNOLOGY. see *ENERGY — Nuclear Energy*

620　　　　　NE　　ISSN 0926-9789
　　　　　　　　　CODEN: EUCOE4
EURO COURSES. RELIABILITY AND RISK ANALYSIS. (Text in English) 1991. irreg. price varies. (Commission of the European Communities) Kluwer Academic Publishers, Postbus 17, 3300 AA Dordrecht, Netherlands. TEL 31-78-392392. FAX 31-78-392254. TELEX 29245 KAPG NL. (Dist. by: Kluwer Academic Publishers Group, P.O. Box 332, 3300 AH Dordrecht, Netherlands. TEL 31-78-392392. FAX 31-78-546474; N. America dist. addr.: Box 358, Accord Sta., Hingham, MA 02018-0358. TEL 617-871-6600. FAX 617-871-6528) **Indexed:** Chem.Abstr. **Document type:** proceedings.
—CASDDS.
　　Refereed Serial

621.36　　　　NE　　ISSN 0926-9797
EURO COURSES. REMOTE SENSING. (Text in English) 1991. irreg. vol.4, 1994. price varies. (Commission of the European Communities) Kluwer Academic Publishers, Postbus 17, 3300 AA Dordrecht, Netherlands. TEL 31-78-392392. FAX 31-78-392254. TELEX 29245 KAPG NL. (Dist. by: Kluwer Academic Publishers Group, P.O. Box 322, 3300 AH Dordrecht, Netherlands. TEL 31-78-392392. FAX 31-78-546474; N. America dist. addr.: Box 358, Accord Sta., Hingham, MA 02018-0358. TEL 617-871-6600. FAX 617-871-6528) (back issues avail.) **Document type:** proceedings.
　　Refereed Serial

600　　　　　NE　　ISSN 0927-1007
　　　　　　　　　CODEN: EUCTEJ
EURO COURSES. TECHNOLOGICAL INNOVATION. (Text in English) 1991. irreg. vol.2, 1994. price varies. (Commission of the European Communities) Kluwer Academic Publishers, Postbus 17, 3300 AA Dordrecht, Netherlands. TEL 31-78-392392. FAX 31-78-392254. TELEX 29245 KAPG NL. (Dist. by: Kluwer Academic Publishers Group, P.O. Box 322, 3300 AH Dordrecht, Netherlands. TEL 31-78-392392. FAX 31-78-546474; N. America dist. addr.: Box 358, Accord Sta., Hingham, MA 02018-0358. TEL 617-871-6600. FAX 617-871-6528) **Document type:** proceedings.
—CASDDS.
　　Refereed Serial

EUROPE - LATIN AMERICA REPORT: SCIENCE AND TECHNOLOGY. see *SCIENCES: COMPREHENSIVE WORKS*

600　　　　　SZ
EUROPEAN ORGANIZATION FOR QUALITY. CONFERENCE PROCEEDINGS. 1970. a. price varies. European Organization for Quality - Organisation Europeenne pour la Qualite, P.O. Box 5032, CH-3001 Bern, Switzerland. TEL 031-3206166. FAX 031-3206828. **Document type:** proceedings.
　　Formerly: European Organization for Quality Control. Conference Proceedings (ISSN 0071-2981)

658.5　　　　UK　　ISSN 0969-059X
　　　　　　　　　CODEN: EOQUDF
EUROPEAN QUALITY. (Text in English; summaries in French, German, Italian, Russian) 1958. bi-m. £85 (155 SFr.). (European Organization for Quality - Organisation Europeenne pour la Qualite) European Quality Publications Ltd., 9-17 St. Albans Pl., London N1 0NX, England. TEL 44-171-704-2000. FAX 44-171-704-2700. adv.; bk.rev.; abstr.; bibl.; charts; illus.; stat. circ. 2,700. (back issues avail.) **Indexed:** INSPEC, Oper.Res.Manage.Sci., P.A.I.S., Qual.Contr.Appl.Stat., Robomat. **Document type:** trade publication.
—BLDSC (3829.843280); SWETS.
　　Formerly (until 1993): E O Q Quality (ISSN 0033-5169)

EUROPEAN RESEARCH CENTRES; a directory of organizations in science, technology, agriculture and medicine. see *SCIENCES: COMPREHENSIVE WORKS*

EUROPEAN SOURCES OF SCIENTIFIC AND TECHNICAL INFORMATION. see *SCIENCES: COMPREHENSIVE WORKS*

658.5　　　　SZ　　ISSN 0014-3243
EUROTEC; European technical news. (Text in English, French and German) 1941. bi-m. 80 SFr. (overseas 95 SFr.). Hugo Buchser S.A., Route de Acacias 25, P.O. Box 30, CH-1211 Geneva 24, Switzerland. TEL 022-3003737. FAX 022-3003748. adv.; bk.rev.; bibl.; charts; illus.; mkt.; pat.; stat.; tr.lit. circ. 11,000. **Document type:** bulletin.

600　　　　　FR　　ISSN 1148-1331
EUROTECHNOLOGIE; la lettre des programmes de R&D technologique. 1991. 22/yr. 2200 F. A Jour, 11 rue du Marche St. Honore, 75001 Paris, France. TEL 42-96-67-22. FAX 40-20-07-75. TELEX 615887 AJOUR. Ed. Philippe Collier.

EVERYMAN'S SCIENCE. see *SCIENCES: COMPREHENSIVE WORKS*

EXPERIENTIA. SUPPLEMENTUM. see *BIOLOGY*

530　　　　　JA
F G M NEWS. (Functionally Gradient Materials) (Text in Japanese) q. 5000 Yen to non-members; members 2500 Yen. Society of Non-Traditional Technology - Mito Kagaku Gijutsu Kyokai, Toranomon Kotohira Kaikan, 1-2-8 Toranomon, Minato-ku, Tokyo 105, Japan. TEL 81-3-3503-4681. FAX 81-3-3597-0535.

600　　　　　US　　ISSN 0172-5203
　　　　　　　　　CODEN: FMSREE
FACHBERICHTE MESSEN - STEUERN - REGELN. 1977. irreg. price varies. Springer-Verlag, 175 Fifth Ave., New York, NY 10010. TEL 212-460-1500. FAX 212-473-6272. (Also: Berlin, Heidelberg, Tokyo and Vienna) (reprint service avail. from ISI) **Indexed:** INSPEC. **Document type:** monographic series.

658.7 621　　　AT　　ISSN 0728-9413
FACTORY EQUIPMENT NEWS. 1966. m. Aus.$73. Thomson Business Publishing, 47 Chippen St., Chippendale, N.S.W. 2008, Australia. TEL 02-699-2411. FAX 02-698-3920. Ed. Henry Pepper. adv.; illus.; tr.lit. circ. 16,404. **Indexed:** Br.Ceram.Abstr.
　　Formerly: F E N: Australian Factory Equipment News (ISSN 0014-5807)

600 500　　　UK　　ISSN 0071-4097
FAWLEY FOUNDATION LECTURES. (Not published in 1985 and in 1988) 1954. irreg. £2 per no. University of Southampton, Highfield, Southampton SO9 5NH, England. FAX 0703-593037. Ed. S.L. Headleand. circ. 3,500. **Document type:** monographic series.
—BLDSC (3901.000000).

TECHNOLOGY: COMPREHENSIVE WORKS

600 US
FEDERAL APPLIED TECHNOLOGY DATABASE. Short title: F A T D. s-m. price varies. U.S. National Technical Information Service, 5285 Port Royal Rd., Springfield, VA 22161. TEL 703-487-4630.
● Available only online. Vendor(s): Ovid Technologies.
   Description: Includes information on federal laboratory resources, technology and inventions for licensing catalogs.

600 US ISSN 0886-7836
FEDERAL TECHNOLOGY CATALOG. a. $33 in US, Canada, Mexico; elsewhere $66 (free with NTIS Tech Notes). U.S. National Technical Information Service, 5285 Port Royal Rd., Springfield, VA 22161. TEL 703-487-4630. (back issues avail.)

FERRUM; Nachrichten aus der Eisenbibliothek. see METALLURGY

668.6 II
FERTILISER TECHNOLOGY. (Text in English) 1964. q. Rs.15($6) Fertilizer (Planning & Development) India Ltd., Sindri, Dhanbad 828122, Bihar, India. Ed. Benoy K. Banerjee. bk.rev.; abstr.; stat.; cum.index. circ. 800. Indexed: Anal.Abstr., Anal.Abstr., Biol.Abstr., Chem.Abstr., Fert.Abstr., Field Crop Abstr., Herb.Abstr., Hort.Abstr., Indian Sci.Abstr., PROMT, Ref.Zh., Sci.Abstr., Soils & Fert.
   Formerly (until vol.12, no.3, 1975): Technology (ISSN 0040-1641)

FH-BO-JOURNAL. (Fachhochschule Bochum) see COLLEGE AND ALUMNI

FIBEROPTIC PRODUCT NEWS. see COMMUNICATIONS — Telephone And Telegraph

FINANCIAL TECHNOLOGY INTERNATIONAL BULLETIN. see BUSINESS AND ECONOMICS — Banking And Finance

600 US ISSN 1058-0948
FLAME RETARDANCY NEWS. 1991. m. $350 (foreign $400). Business Communications Co., Inc. (Norwalk), 25 Van Zant St., Ste. 13, Norwalk, CT 06855. TEL 203-853-4266. FAX 203-853-0348. TELEX 6502934929 WUI. Ed. Norma Corbitt.
● Also available online. Vendor(s): NewsNet (RD40).
—CCC.

FORM FUNCTION FINLAND. see ARCHITECTURE

FORNTIDA TEKNIK. see ARCHAEOLOGY

FORSKNING OCH FRAMSTEG. see SCIENCES: COMPREHENSIVE WORKS

FORUM WISSENSCHAFT; das kritische Wissenschaftsmagazine. see SCIENCES: COMPREHENSIVE WORKS

FRONTIERS OF POWER CONFERENCE. PROCEEDINGS. see ENERGY

600 340 GW ISSN 0178-8639
FUEHRER DURCH DIE BAUNORMUNG. (Text in English, French, German, Spanish) 1985. a. DM.54. (Deutsches Institut fuer Normung e.V. (D I N)) Beuth Verlag GmbH, Burggrafenstr. 6, 10787 Berlin, Germany. TEL 030-2601-0. FAX 030-26011260. TELEX 183622-BVB-D. (Dist. in U.S. by: Global Engineering Documents, 2805 McGaw Ave., Box 19539, Irvine, CA 92714) circ. 4,000. **Document type:** catalog.

600 GW ISSN 0071-9749
FUEHRER DURCH DIE TECHNISCHE LITERATUR; Katalog technischer Werke fuer Studium und Praxis. 1900. a. DM.44. Fr. Weidemanns Buchhandlung (H.Witt), Postfach 6406, 30064 Hannover, Germany. TEL 0511-16382-0. FAX 0511-1638266. Ed. Renate Boehm. adv. circ. 20,000. **Document type:** academic/scholarly publication.

600 JA
FUKUI UNIVERSITY. FACULTY OF EDUCATION. MEMOIRS. SERIES 5: APPLIED SCIENCE AND TECHNOLOGY. (Text in Japanese; summaries in English and Japanese) 1964. a. free. Fukui University, Faculty of Education, 9-1, 3-chome, Bunkyo, Fukui 910, Japan. **Document type:** academic/scholarly publication.

FUKUOKA KYOIKU DAIGAKU KIYO. DAI-3-BUNSATSU. SUGAKU, RIKA, GIJUTSUKA HEN/FUKUOKA UNIVERSITY OF EDUCATION. BULLETIN. PART 3: MATHEMATICS, NATURAL SCIENCES AND TECHNOLOGY. see SCIENCES: COMPREHENSIVE WORKS

FUORISTRADA. see ENVIRONMENTAL STUDIES

600 US
FUTURE TECHNOLOGY INTELLIGENCE REPORT. 1990. m. $150. F T I R Inc., Box 423652, San Francisco, CA 94142-3652. TEL 415-359-3757. Ed. Antony C. Sutton; Pub. M. Marseille. bk.rev.; pat.; circ. 500 (paid). (back issues avail.) **Document type:** newsletter.
   Description: Predicts future technology emphasizing little known and unpublicized developments from world network of contacts. Includes such topics as: cold fusion, weather engineering and energy medicine.

FUTURES; the journal of forecasting, planning and policy. see BUSINESS AND ECONOMICS — Economic Situation And Conditions

600 US
FUTURETECH. 1986. m. $1500 (foreign $1560). Technical Insights, Inc., 32 N. Dean St., Englewood, NJ 07631-9967. TEL 201-568-4744. FAX 201-568-8247. (Subscr. to: Box 1304, Ft. Lee, NJ 07024-9967) Ed. Peter Savage. bibl.; pat. (looseleaf format; back issues avail.) **Document type:** newsletter.
   Description: Presents strategic technologies judged capable of having an impact on broad industrial fronts.

FUTURICS; a quarterly journal of futures research. see SOCIOLOGY

THE FUTURIST; a journal of forecasts, trends, and ideas about the future. see SCIENCES: COMPREHENSIVE WORKS

500 SZ
FUTUROLOGY. (Text in English) q. 60 Fr. International Creative Center - Rencontres Creatives Internationales, 20, Ch. Colladon, CH-1211 Geneva 28, Switzerland. Ed. Dali Schindler. adv.

G A T F WORLD. (Graphic Arts Technical Foundation) see PRINTING

GATEWAY ENGINEER. see ENGINEERING

620 UZ ISSN 0130-0997 CODEN: GLOTAY
GELIOTEKHNIKA. English translation: Applied Solar Energy (US ISSN 0003-701X) 1965. bi-m. 15.60 Rub. (Akademiya Nauk Uzbekistana) Izdatel'stvo Fan, Ul. Gogolya 70, k. 105, 700000 Tashkent, Uzbekistan. Indexed: Biol.Abstr., Chem.Abstr., INIS Atomind., INSPEC.
—BLDSC (0047.060000); CASDDS.

GERMAN STANDARDS (DIN) ENGLISH LANGUAGE. see ENGINEERING

GLOBAL BIOGEOCHEMICAL CYCLES. see SCIENCES: COMPREHENSIVE WORKS

GLOBAL LINK. see AGRICULTURE — Agricultural Economics

600 IT
GOLEM. 1989. m. L.70000 (foreign L.105000) (effective 1994). (Istituto di Psicologia del C N R) Edizioni Dedalo s.r.l., Casella Postale 362, 70100 Bari, Italy. TEL 080-5311413. FAX 080-5311414. (Edit. addr.: Istituto di Psicologia del CNR, Via Nomentana 56, 00161 Rome, Italy. TEL 06-4404639. FAX 06-4403678) Dir. Danco Singer.
   Description: Provides information to those who use or want to use new technologies.

600 US ISSN 0882-3766 Q179.98
GOVERNMENT RESEARCH DIRECTORY. 1980. irreg., 6th ed., 1990. $390. Gale Research Inc., 835 Penobscot Bldg., Detroit, MI 48226. TEL 313-961-2242. FAX 313-961-6083. TELEX 810-221-7086. Ed. Annette Piccirelli. **Document type:** directory.
● Also available online. Vendor(s): Knight-Ridder, Inc. —BLDSC (4206.060300).
   Formerly: Government Research Centers Directory (ISSN 0270-4811)

GRAM SHILP. see SCIENCES: COMPREHENSIVE WORKS

GRANTS FOR SCIENCE AND TECHNOLOGY PROGRAMS. see SCIENCES: COMPREHENSIVE WORKS

GREATER LOS ANGELES TECHNOLOGY RESOURCE GUIDE (YEAR). see BUSINESS AND ECONOMICS — Trade And Industrial Directories

GREATER ORANGE COUNTY TECHNOLOGY RESOURCE GUIDE (YEAR). see BUSINESS AND ECONOMICS — Trade And Industrial Directories

600 608.7 US
GUIDE TO AVAILABLE TECHNOLOGIES; an annual guide to business opportunities in technology. 1985. a. $150. Techni Research Associates, Inc., Box T, Willow Grove, PA 19090-0922. TEL 610-657-1753. FAX 610-576-7924. Pub. Louis F. Schiffman. **Document type:** newsletter.

GUNMA UNIVERSITY, FACULTY OF EDUCATION. ANNUAL REPORT: ART, TECHNOLOGY, HEALTH & PHYSICAL EDUCATION, AND SCIENCE OF HUMAN LIVING SERIES. see EDUCATION — Higher Education

GUOJI KEJI JIAOLIU/INTERNATIONAL SCIENCE AND TECHNOLOGY EXCHANGE. see SCIENCES: COMPREHENSIVE WORKS

GUOWAI KEJI DONGTAI/FOREIGN SCIENCE AND TECHNOLOGY DEVELOPMENT. see SCIENCES: COMPREHENSIVE WORKS

600 JA ISSN 0286-5491 CODEN: HKSKDY
HAKODATE TECHNICAL COLLEGE. RESEARCH REPORTS/HAKODATE KOGYO KOTO SENMON GAKKO KIYO. (Text in Japanese; summaries in English) 1967. a. Hakodate Technical College - Hakodate Kogyo Koto Senmon Gakko, 226 Tokura-cho, 2 Hakodate 042, Japan. illus. Indexed: Chem.Abstr. —CASDDS.

HANDBUCH DER DATENBANKEN FUER NATURWISSENSCHAFT, TECHNIK, PATENTE. see COMPUTERS — Data Base Management

658.5 GW ISSN 0942-8976
HANDWERK MAGAZIN. 1947. m. DM.89 (foreign DM.110.60). Hans Holzmann Verlag GmbH, Gewerbestr. 2, 86825 Bad Woerishofen, Germany. TEL 08247-35401. FAX 08247-354170. Ed. Gerd-Ulrich Brandenburg. adv.; bk.rev. **Document type:** trade publication.
   Former titles: Handwerk; Neue Handwerk (ISSN 0028-3193)
   Description: For all craft trades. Includes news and information, features, reports of events and exhibitions.

HEALTH TECHNOLOGY MANAGEMENT. see MEDICAL SCIENCES

HEIDELBERGER ARBEITSBUECHER. see SCIENCES: COMPREHENSIVE WORKS

HEIDELBERGER JAHRBUECHER. see SCIENCES: COMPREHENSIVE WORKS

HEIDELBERGER TASCHENBUECHER. see SCIENCES: COMPREHENSIVE WORKS

HERION - INFORMATIONEN. see ENGINEERING — Hydraulic Engineering

HIGH TECH INVESTOR. see BUSINESS AND ECONOMICS — Investments

6246 TECHNOLOGY: COMPREHENSIVE WORKS

600 US ISSN 0741-0808
HIGH-TECH MATERIALS ALERT; advanced materials: their uses and manufacture. 1984. m. $570 (foreign $630). Technical Insights, Inc., 32 N. Dean St., Englewood, NJ 07631-9967. TEL 201-568-4744. FAX 201-568-8247. (Subscr. to: Box 1304, Ft. Lee, NJ 07024-1304) Ed. Alan Brown. bk.rev.; bibl.; charts; pat.; stat.; tr.lit. (back issues avail.) **Document type:** newsletter.
—BLDSC (4307.361070). **CCC.**
 Description: Details of significant developments in materials, alloys and metallic whiskers, and ceramic and graphite fibers

HIGH TECH SEPARATIONS NEWS. see *CHEMISTRY — Analytical Chemistry*

HIGH TECHNOLOGY LAW JOURNAL. see *LAW*

HISTORICAL STUDIES IN IRISH SCIENCE AND TECHNOLOGY. see *SCIENCES: COMPREHENSIVE WORKS*

HISTORY AND TECHNOLOGY. see *HISTORY*

600 UK ISSN 0307-5451
T14.7
HISTORY OF TECHNOLOGY. 1976. a. price varies. Mansell Publishing Ltd., Wellington House, 125 Strand, London WC2R 0BB. TEL 0171-420-5555. FAX 0171-240-7261. (Dist. in U.S. by: Cassell, PCS Data Processing Inc., 360 W. 31st St., New York, NY 10001) Eds. G. Hollister-Short, F.A.J.L. James. **Indexed:** Amer.Hist.& Life, Br.Archaeol.Abstr., Hist.Abstr. **Document type:** academic/scholarly publication.
—SWETS; UnCover.
 Description: Contains essays on the technical problems of different periods and societies and the measures taken to solve them.

600 UK
HISTORY OF TECHNOLOGY SERIES. 1979. irreg., vol.20, 1994. Institution of Electrical Engineers, Michael Faraday House, Six Hills Way, Stevenage, Herts SG1 2AY, England. TEL 0438-313311. FAX 0438-313465. TELEX 825578-IEESTV-G. Ed. B. Bowers. **Document type:** monographic series.

607 JA ISSN 1340-3966
T177.J3 CODEN: HKKHAG
HOKKAIDO NATIONAL INDUSTRIAL RESEARCH INSTITUTE. REPORTS/HOKKAIDO KOGYO GIJUTSU KENKYUHJO HOKOKU. 1966. irreg. Hokkaido National Industrial Research Institute - Hokkaido Kogyo Gijutsu Kenkyuhjo, 2-17 Tsukisamu-higashi, Toyohira-ku, Sapporo 062, Hokkaido, Japan. Ed. Takeshi Okutaui. **Indexed:** Chem.Abstr. **Document type:** bulletin.
—CASDDS.
 Formerly: Government Industry Development Laboratory, Hokkaido. Reports - Hokkaido Kogyo Kaihatsu Shikenjo Hokoku (ISSN 0441-0734)

600 JA
HOKKAIDO NATIONAL INDUSTRIAL RESEARCH INSTITUTE. TECHNICAL DATA/HOKKAIDO KOGYO GIJUTSU KENKYUHJO SHIRYOH. 1961. irreg. free. Hokkaido National Industrial Research Institute - Hokkaido Kogyo Gijutsu Kenkyuhjo, 2-17 Tsukisamu-higashi, Toyohira-ku, Sapporo 062, Hokkaido, Japan. TEL 81-11-857-8901. E-mail: tonooka@nniri.go.jp.
 Formerly: Government Industrial Development Laboratory, Hokkaido. Technical Data - Hokkaido Kogyo Kaihatsu Shikenjo Gijutsu.

600 PL ISSN 0137-8813
HORYZONTY TECHNIKI. 1948. m. $22. (Naczelna Organizacja Techniczna (NOT)) Edytor Ltd., Ul. Swietokrzyska 14a, Warsaw, Poland. (Dist. by: Ars Polona-Ruch, Krakowskie Przedmiescie 7, Warsaw, Poland) (Co-sponsor: Towarzystwo Wiedzy Powszechnej) Ed. Jerzy Wierzbowski. circ. 100,000.

HOSPITAL TECHNOLOGY SERIES. see *HOSPITALS*

HUANAN LIGONG DAXUE XUEBAO (ZIRAN KEXUE BAN)/SOUTH-CHINA UNIVERSITY OF SCIENCE AND ENGINEERING. JOURNAL (NATURAL SCIENCE EDITION). see *SCIENCES: COMPREHENSIVE WORKS*

HUAZHONG LIGONG DAXUE XUEBAO/CENTRAL-CHINA UNIVERSITY OF SCIENCE AND ENGINEERING. JOURNAL. see *SCIENCES: COMPREHENSIVE WORKS*

HUMAN DESIGN. see *ART*

745.2 AU ISSN 0018-7224
HUMAN INDUSTRIAL DESIGN. (Text in German) 1968. irreg. Verlag Dr. Herta Ranner, Zeismannsbrunngasse 1, A-1070 Vienna, Austria. TEL 01-935387. Ed. H. Ranner. adv.; bk.rev. **Document type:** trade publication.

HUMANISMUS UND TECHNIK. see *SOCIAL SCIENCES: COMPREHENSIVE WORKS*

I'(YEAR). (Informatika) see *LIBRARY AND INFORMATION SCIENCES*

600 US ISSN 0160-1040
T37
I A. (Industrial Archeology) 1976. s-a. $35 to individuals; institutions $40; students $20 (subscr. includes S I A Newsletter). Society for Industrial Archeology, Department of Social Sciences, Michigan Technological University, Houghton, MI 49931. Ed. Patrick E. Martin. adv.; bk.rev.; illus. circ. 1,600. (back issues avail.) **Indexed:** Avery Ind.Archit.Per. **Document type:** academic/scholarly publication.
 Description: Explores post-18th century technology and society.

600 US
I E E E CONFERENCE ON DECISION AND CONTROL. PROCEEDINGS. a. price varies. (I E E E, Control Systems Society) Institute of Electrical and Electronics Engineers, Inc., 345 E. 47th St., New York, NY 10017-2349. TEL 212-705-7900. FAX 212-705-7682. (Subscr. to: Box 1331, 445 Hoes Lane, Piscataway, NJ 08855-1331) **Indexed:** Comput.Cont.
—Ei. **CCC.**
 Formerly (until 1982): I E E E Conference on Decision and Control, Including the Symposium on Adaptive Processes. Proceedings (ISSN 0191-2216); Incorporates (as of 1970): Symposium on Adaptive Processes.

I E E E ENGINEERING IN MEDICINE AND BIOLOGY MAGAZINE. see *BIOLOGY — Bioengineering*

600 621.3 US ISSN 0278-0097
T14.5 CODEN: ITSMDC
I E E E TECHNOLOGY AND SOCIETY MAGAZINE. 1982. q. $125 to non-members (effective 1996). (I E E E, Society on Social Implications of Technology) Institute of Electrical and Electronics Engineers, Inc., 345 E. 47th St., New York, NY 10017-2394. TEL 908-981-0060. FAX 908-981-9667. (Subscr. to: Box 1331, 445 Hoes Ln., Piscataway, NJ 08855-1331) Ed. Norman Balabanian. (also avail. in microform from UMI,EEE) **Indexed:** INSPEC (1983-).
—BLDSC (4363.095000); Ei; Faxon; Genuine Article; SWETS; UMI; UnCover. **CCC.**
 Formerly: Technology and Society.

I E E E TRANSACTIONS ON INDUSTRY APPLICATIONS. see *ENGINEERING — Electrical Engineering*

600 UK ISSN 0268-6171
I E E MANAGEMENT OF TECHNOLOGY SERIES. irreg., vol.16, 1993. Institution of Electrical Engineers, Michael Faraday House, Six Hills Way, Stevenage, Herts SG1 2AY, England. TEL 0438-313311. FAX 0438-313465. TELEX 825578-IEESTV-G. Eds. G.A. Montgomerie, B.C. Twiss. **Indexed:** INSPEC. **Document type:** monographic series.
—BLDSC (4362.742200).

600 US
I F U. (Text in German) vol.51, 1980. irreg. price varies. (Universitaet Stuttgart, Institut fuer Umformtechnik, GW) Springer-Verlag, 175 Fifth Ave., New York, NY 10010. TEL 212-460-1500. FAX 212-473-6272. (Also: Berlin, Heidelberg, Tokyo and Vienna) Ed. K. Lange. (reprint service avail. from ISI) **Document type:** academic/scholarly publication.

745.2 SA
I N F O P A K MANUFACTURING. w. Council for Scientific and Industrial Research, Division of Information Services, P.O. Box 395, Pretoria 0001, South Africa. TEL 27-12-841-4942. FAX 27-12-862869.

I N T INFORMATIVO. (Instituto Nacional de Tecnologia) see *SCIENCES: COMPREHENSIVE WORKS*

600 US ISSN 1054-0229
I T E A JOURNAL OF TEST AND EVALUATION. 1983. q. $60 (foreign $80). International Test & Evaluation Association, 4400 Fair Lakes Court, Fairfax, VA 22033. TEL 703-631-6220. adv. circ. 2,000.
 Description: Articles on test and evaluation procedures, methods and philosophies used in testing both software and hardware.

I T E S T BULLETIN. (Institute for Theological Encounter with Science and Technology) see *RELIGIONS AND THEOLOGY*

I T E S T CONFERENCE PROCEEDINGS. (Institute for Theological Encounter with Science and Technology) see *RELIGIONS AND THEOLOGY*

I U E NEWS. (International Union of Electronic, Electrical, Salaried, Machine and Furniture Workers, A F L - C I O) see *LABOR UNIONS*

600 SP ISSN 0211-0776
T4
IBERICA - ACTUALIDAD CIENTIFICA. 1973. 12/yr. 3750 ptas. Apdo. 23095, 08080 Barcelona, Spain. TEL 34-3-240-32-41. Ed. Pascual Bolufer.

600 AG ISSN 0326-3878
N7
IDEAS EN ARTE Y TECNOLOGIA. 1984. 3/yr. $48. Universidad de Belgrano, Teodoro Garcia 2090, 1426 Buenos Aires, Argentina. TEL 774-2133. Ed. Avelino J. Porto. bk.rev.; bibl. circ. 1,000. (back issues avail.)
 Description: Covers architecture, engineering and computer science.

ILLUSTRERAD VETENSKAP. see *SCIENCES: COMPREHENSIVE WORKS*

600 US ISSN 1041-4320
IMAGING TECHNOLOGY REPORT. 1987. m. $168 (foreign $188). Microfilm Publishing, Inc., Box 950, Larchmont, NY 10538-0950. TEL 914-834-3044. FAX 914-834-3993. Ed. Mitchell Badler. **Indexed:** Info.Media & Tech. **Document type:** newsletter.
—BLDSC (4368.996600).
 Description: Reviews optical disk, micrographics and business imaging technologies, practices and industry developments.

600 US
IMPACT ASSESSMENT. 1981. q. $50 to individuals; institutions $65. International Association for Impact Assessment, Box 70, Belhaven, NC 27810. TEL 919-964-2338. FAX 919-964-2340. Ed. Dan Bronstein. bk.rev.; charts. circ. 2,100. (back issues avail.) **Document type:** academic/scholarly publication.
—BLDSC (4370.806545).
 Former titles (until Feb. 1993): Impact Assessment Bulletin; I A I A Bulletin (ISSN 0734-9165)
 Description: Provides a link to the latest ideas from environmentalists, planners, decision makers, private consultants and policy analysts, university professors and their students throughout the world.
 Refereed Serial

IN FOCUS (MOUNTAIN VIEW). see *HANDICAPPED — Visually Impaired*

IN TECHNOLOGY. see *BUSINESS AND ECONOMICS*

INDIA. DEPARTMENT OF SCIENCE & TECHNOLOGY. ANNUAL REPORT. see *SCIENCES: COMPREHENSIVE WORKS*

600 II ISSN 0073-6511
INDIAN INSTITUTE OF TECHNOLOGY, MADRAS. ANNUAL REPORT. (Text in English) 1960. a. Indian Institute of Technology at Madras, c/o Central Library, Madras 600 036, India.

INDIAN JOURNAL OF HISTORY OF SCIENCE. see *SCIENCES: COMPREHENSIVE WORKS*

600 338.91 II ISSN 0970-7867
T27.I42
INDIAN JOURNAL OF RURAL TECHNOLOGY. (Text in English) 1989. s-a. (2 nos./vol.). Rs.100($30) Department of Rural Development, Council for Advancement of People's Action and Rural Technology (CAPART), D-58 Pankha Rd., New Delhi 110058, India. TEL 5592313. (Subscr. to: C-21 Community Centre, Behind Janak Cinema, Janakpuri, New Delhi 110058, India) Ed. Asha Joglekar. adv.; bk.rev.; charts; stat. circ. 500. **Document type:** academic/scholarly publication.
Description: Publishes original papers, review articles, case studies, and communications on rural energy, water supply, health and medicare, industries, transport, housing, environment, and agricultural equipment.
Refereed Serial

607 II ISSN 0971-3034
INDIAN JOURNAL OF TECHNICAL EDUCATION. (Text in English) 1971. 4/yr. Rs.180 to members; non-members Rs.300; foreign $30. Indian Society for Technical Education, IIT Campus, New Delhi 110 016, India. TEL 653431. Ed.Bd. bk.rev.; illus. circ. 12,000. **Document type:** academic/scholarly publication.

600 II
INDUSTRIAL CONSULTANCY. 1978. m. Rs.450 (foreign $400). Industrial Consultancy, A-7, Pushpanjali Enclave, Pitampura, New Delhi 110 039, India. TEL 91-11-7274590. FAX 91-11-7274572. TELEX 63085 JNBR. Ed. R.C. Paliwal. adv.; bk.rev. circ. 20,000. (reprint service avail. from ISI) **Document type:** trade publication.

745.2 JA ISSN 0389-4215
INDUSTRIAL DESIGN. (Text in English, Japanese) q. $158.50. Japan Industrial Designers' Association - Nihon Indasutoriaru Dezaina Kyokai, Sekai Boeki Senta Biru Bekkan, 4F, 4-1, Hamamatsucho 2-chome, Minato-ku, Tokyo 105, Japan. (Dist. by: Intercontinental Marketing Corp., I.P.O. Box 5056, Tokyo 100-30, Japan. TEL 81-3-3661-7458. FAX 81-3367-9694) **Document type:** trade publication.

621.9 UK ISSN 0019-8145
TJ1193 CODEN: INDRA9
INDUSTRIAL DIAMOND REVIEW. 1940. bi-m. free to qualified personnel. De Beers Industrial Diamond Division Pty. Ltd., Charters, Sunninghill, Ascot, Berks SL5 9PX, England. FAX 0344-28188. TELEX 848021-DEBID-G. Ed. Paul Daniel. adv.; bk.rev.; abstr.; illus.; index. circ. 10,000. (also avail. in microfilm from UMI; reprint service avail. from UMI, ISI) **Indexed:** Br.Ceram.Abstr., Br.Tech.Ind., Chem.Abstr., Curr.Cont., Eng.Ind., Excerp.Med., ISMEC, Ref.Zh., Sci.Cit.Ind., World Alum.Abstr. **Document type:** trade publication.
—BLDSC (4450.000000); CASDDS; Ei; Faxon; UMI.
Incorporates: Industrial Diamond Abstracts.
Description: Reviews developments in the design and manufacture of diamond, CBN, PCD, and PCBN tooling; also provides applications in industry and science.

INDUSTRIAL EDUCATION. see *EDUCATION — Higher Education*

600 380.5 UK ISSN 0265-5071
INDUSTRIAL HERITAGE MAGAZINE; industry - transport - people. 1974. q. £9 (overseas £10). Book House, Ravenstonedale, Kirkby Stephen, Cumbria CA17 4NQ, England. TEL 0153-962-3634. Ed. John Keavey. adv.; bk.rev. circ. 500. (back issues avail.) **Document type:** academic/scholarly publication.
Former titles: Yesteryear Heritage & Industrial Past (ISSN 0307-1677)
Description: Contains articles on the history of technology and transport in the U.K.

616 US ISSN 0019-8447
TA401 CODEN: INDLAP
INDUSTRIAL LABORATORY. English translation of: Zavodskaya Laboratoriya (RU ISSN 0321-4265) 1958. m. $1395 (foreign $1630) (effective 1996). (Ministerstvo Chernoi Metallurgii, Tsentral'noe Upravlenie Nauchno-Tekhnicheskogo Obshchestvoi po Chernoi Metallurgii, RU) Plenum Publishing Corp., Consultants Bureau, 233 Spring St., New York, NY 10013-1578. TEL 212-620-8468. FAX 212-463-0742. TELEX 23-421139. Ed. N.P. Lyakishev. (also avail. in microfilm from JSC; back issues avail.) **Indexed:** Appl.Mech.Rev., Cadscan, Chem.Titles, Comput.& Info.Sys., Curr.Cont., Electron.& Communic.Abstr.J., Energy Res.Abstr., Eng.Ind., Excerp.Med., INIS Atomind., INSPEC (1969-), Lead Abstr., Pollut.Abstr., Solid.St.Abstr., Zincscan. **Document type:** academic/scholarly publication.
—BLDSC (0412.100000); Faxon; Genuine Article; SWETS; UMI. **CCC.**
Refereed Serial

INDUSTRIAL MATHEMATICS. see *MATHEMATICS*

338 658.5 US ISSN 0199-2074
INDUSTRIAL PRODUCT BULLETIN. 1942. m. $68 (Canada $75.97; Mexico $71; elsewhere $81) (effective 1996). Gordon Publications, Inc., Part of Cahners Publishing Company, Division of Reed Elsevier Inc., 301 Gibraltar Dr., Box 650, Morris Plains, NJ 07950-0650. TEL 201-292-5100. FAX 201-898-9281. Ed. Anita LaFond. adv.; page $7700. illus.; tr.lit. circ. 204,500. (tabloid format; also avail. in microform from UMI; reprint service avail. from UMI)
—UMI. **CCC.**
Formerly: Industrial Bulletin (ISSN 0019-8021)
Description: Serves the general US industrial field, primarily manufacturing industries classified in SIC 20-39, encompassing the processing and metalworking industries.

INDUSTRIAL PRODUCTS FINDER. see *BUSINESS AND ECONOMICS — Trade And Industrial Directories*

658.7 US ISSN 0019-8617
INDUSTRIAL PROGRESS;* a pictorial look at new industrial products and processes, plus features of interest to men. 1961. bi-m. free. (Goodyear Industrial Products Division) Donnelly Marketing (Subsidiary of: Reuben H. Donnelly Corp.), 1901 S. Meyers Rd., Ste. 700, Oakbrook Terrace, IL 60181. (Subscr. to: Goodyear Tire and Rubber Co., 1144 E. Market St., Akron, OH 44316) Ed. Frederick H. Kling. illus.; circ. 60,000 (controlled).

INDUSTRIAL TEACHER EDUCATION DIRECTORY. see *EDUCATION — Higher Education*

338 658.5 II ISSN 0019-8803
HC431
INDUSTRIAL TIMES. (Text in English) 1958. fortn. Rs.235. Eve's Weekly Ltd., J.K. Somani Bldg., Bombay Samachar Marg, Bombay 400 023, India. Ed. Sushil Silvano.

600 US ISSN 0743-3271
INDUSTRIAL WEST;* serving the machine tool & metal working industries. 1984. m. free to qualified personnel. Mitchell Publishing Co., Box 3974, Ontario, CA 91761-0990. TEL 818-442-8321. (Alt. addr.: Box 4909, El Monte, CA 91734-0909) Ed. Sid Crown. adv.; bk.rev.; tr.lit. circ. 25,000.
Description: News, articles, announcements, and items of interest to the machine tool and metal-working industries.

INDUSTRIALIZACION Y DESARROLLO TECNOLOGICO. see *BUSINESS AND ECONOMICS — International Development And Assistance*

INDUSTRIAS PESQUERAS; revista maritima quincenal. see *BUSINESS AND ECONOMICS*

338 671 GW ISSN 0019-9036
CODEN: IANZAQ
INDUSTRIE-ANZEIGER; polytechnische Zeitschrift fuer die technische Industrie. 1879. w. (plus special issues). DM.296.40 (foreign DM.343.20). (Wirtschaftsverband Eisen, Blech und Metall Verarbeitende Industrie) Konradin Verlag Robert Kohlhammer GmbH, 70771 Leinfelden-Echterdingen, Germany. TEL 0711-7594-0. FAX 0711-7594-398. Ed. R. Langbein. adv.: page DM.9280; adv. contact: Burkhard Lemke. bk.rev.; charts; illus.; mkt.; stat. circ. 54,069. **Indexed:** C.I.S. Abstr., Chem.Abstr., Cyb.Abstr., Eng.Ind., Excerp.Med., Fluidex, INIS Atomind., INSPEC, Key to Econ.Sci., Met.Abstr., Packag.Sci.Tech., World Alum.Abstr. **Document type:** trade publication.
—BLDSC (4474.620000); CASDDS; SWETS. **CCC.**
Description: For the machine industry. Provides news and information on manufacturing, technological research and new products.

600 FR ISSN 0537-5819
INDUSTRIES ET TECHNIQUES FRANCAISES; le magazine de la performance industrielle. 1957. 22/yr. 440 F. (foreign 697 F.) (effective Jan. 1991). C E P Information Technologie, Immeuble Europais, 26 rue d'Oradour sur Glane, 75504 Paris Cedex 15, France. TEL 1-44-25-31-31. FAX 1-45-57-35-06. TELEX 270 589 F. adv.; illus.; mkt.; tr.lit. circ. 41,000. **Indexed:** C.I.S. Abstr., Excerp.Med., Met.Abstr., World Alum.Abstr.
—BLDSC (4475.225000); Ei.
Former titles: Industries et Techniques (ISSN 0150-6617); Argus Manager (ISSN 0004-122X)

INDUSTRY, TRADE, AND TECHNOLOGY REVIEW. see *BUSINESS AND ECONOMICS — International Commerce*

INFORMACION CIENTIFICA Y TECNOLOGICA. see *SCIENCES: COMPREHENSIVE WORKS*

INFORMATIVO I B I C T. (Instituto Brasileiro de Informacao em Ciencia e Tecnologia) see *SCIENCES: COMPREHENSIVE WORKS*

INNOVATION: THE EUROPEAN JOURNAL OF SOCIAL SCIENCES. see *SOCIAL SCIENCES: COMPREHENSIVE WORKS*

INNOVATIONEWS; an advanced technical materials fact sheet. see *SCIENCES: COMPREHENSIVE WORKS*

600 500 GW
INNOVATIONS-NACHRICHTEN. 1980. q. free. Arbeitsgemeinschaft der Industrie- und Handelskammern in Baden-Wuerttemberg, Jaegerstr. 30, 70174 Stuttgart, Germany. TEL 0711-2005-0. FAX 0711-2005-429. circ. 4,000. (looseleaf format) **Document type:** newspaper.

600 US ISSN 0300-757X
INSIDE R & D; a weekly report on technical innovation. 1972. w. $790 (foreign $890). Technical Insights, Inc., 32 N. Dean St., Englewood, NJ 07631-9967. TEL 201-568-4744. FAX 201-568-8247. (Subscr. to: Box 1304, Ft. Lee, NJ 07024) Ed. Charles Joslin. bk.rev.; bibl.; charts; pat.; stat.; tr.lit. (back issues avail.) **Indexed:** PROMT. **Document type:** newsletter.
—BLDSC (4518.153000). **CCC.**
Description: Covers new and significant developments in technology.

L'INSTALLATORE ITALIANO; la rivista mensile degli impianti tecnici. see *HEATING, PLUMBING AND REFRIGERATION*

600 NE ISSN 0165-2990
INSTELLINGEN. 1976. m. (11/yr.). fl.68.50. Koggeschip Vakbladen B.V., Postbus 1198, 1000 BD Amsterdam, Netherlands. TEL 31-20-6916666. FAX 31-20-6960396. circ. 3,700. **Indexed:** Key to Econ.Sci. **Document type:** trade publication.
—SWETS.
Formerly: Instellingen Bouw Inrichting en Beheer.

600 DR
INSTITUTO TECNOLOGICO DE SANTO DOMINGO. BIBLIOTECA. BOLETIN DE ANALITICAS. 1983. s-a. Instituto Tecnologico de Santo Domingo, Biblioteca, Apdo. 249-2, Santo Domingo, Dominican Republican. circ. 600.

6248 TECHNOLOGY: COMPREHENSIVE WORKS

600 UK
INSTRUMENTATION REVIEW. 1980. q. free. A B B Kent plc., Lea Rd., Luton, Beds. LU1 3AE, England. Ed. P.L. Culley. circ. 20,000. (tabloid format; back issues avail.) Indexed: Fluidex, INSPEC (1992-), World Text.Abstr. Document type: trade publication.
—CCC.
Former titles (until 1992): Process Instrumentation Review; (until 1991): Kent Review (ISSN 0143-8697)

THE INTELLIGENT HOME. see *INTERIOR DESIGN AND DECORATION — Furniture And House Furnishings*

INTERNATIONAL CONGRESS ON TECHNOLOGY AND TECHNOLOGY EXCHANGE. PROCEEDINGS. see *ENGINEERING*

INTERNATIONAL FIBER SCIENCE AND TECHNOLOGY SERIES. see *CHEMISTRY — Organic Chemistry*

INTERNATIONAL JOURNAL OF INSTRUCTIONAL MEDIA. see *EDUCATION — Teaching Methods And Curriculum*

INTERNATIONAL JOURNAL OF LAW AND INFORMATION TECHNOLOGY. see *LAW*

600 SZ ISSN 0268-1900
TA401 CODEN: IJMTE2
INTERNATIONAL JOURNAL OF MATERIALS & PRODUCT TECHNOLOGY; the journal of materials innovation, failure preventive technology, product liability and technical insurance. (Abstracts in English) 1986. bi-m. $290 in N. America; elsewhere DM.500. (Unesco, UN) Inderscience Enterprises Ltd., World Trade Centre Bldg., 110 Ave. Louis Casai, Case Postale 306, CH-1215 Geneva-Aeroport, Switzerland. FAX 022-7910885. Ed. M.A. Dorgham. adv.; bk.rev.; abstr.; illus.; charts; index. circ. 7,000. (back issues avail.) Indexed: Environ.Abstr., INSPEC (1987-), Intl.Polym.Sci.& Tech., RAPRA. Document type: bulletin.
—BLDSC (4542.335500); CASDDS; Ei; Faxon; Genuine Article; SWETS.
Description: Covers the technologies of oils and lubricants, steel, aluminum, plastics and composites, electronic (solid state) materials, ceramics, corrosion resistant and finishing materials, polymers, resins and rubber products.

INTERNATIONAL JOURNAL OF POWER AND ENERGY SYSTEMS. see *ENERGY*

600 CN ISSN 1192-2575
INTERNATIONAL JOURNAL OF TECHNOLOGY ADVANCES. (Text in Arabic, English) 1993. 4/yr. Can.$400 (free to qualified personnel). Box 98029, S. Common Post, 2150 Burnhamthorpe Rd., Mississauga, ON L5L 3A0, Canada. FAX 516-277-2875. (And: Box 38552, Abdulla Al-Salem, Kuwait City 72256, Kuwait. FAX 965-489-1179) Ed. M.I. Ismail.
Description: Designed for concise, cooperative publication of simple and creative ideas.
Refereed Serial

INTERNATIONAL JOURNAL OF TECHNOLOGY AND DESIGN EDUCATION. see *EDUCATION — Teaching Methods And Curriculum*

600 658 SZ ISSN 0267-5730
T1 CODEN: IJTMEG
INTERNATIONAL JOURNAL OF TECHNOLOGY MANAGEMENT; journal of engineering and technology management, technology policy and strategy. (Text in English; abstracts in French, German, Japanese) 1986. 8/yr. $365 to N. America; elsewhere DM.630. (Unesco, UN) Inderscience Enterprises Ltd., World Trade Centre Bldg., 110 Ave. Louis Casai, Case Postale 306, CH-1215 Geneva-Aeroport, Switzerland. FAX 022-7910885. Ed. M.A. Dorgham. adv.; bk.rev.; abstr.; charts; illus.; index. circ. 20,000. (back issues avail.) Indexed: A.I.Abstr. (until 1992), ABI Inform, B.P.I., CAD CAM Abstr. (until 1992), CLOSS, Energy Info.Abstr., INSPEC (1986-), Robomat. (until 1992), Tel.Abstr., Telegen (until 1989). Document type: academic/scholarly publication.
—BLDSC (4542.693700); Ei; Faxon; Genuine Article; SWETS; UMI; UnCover.
Description: Presents conference reports, company profiles, news about technology transfer and R & D management.

INTERNATIONAL JOURNAL OF VEHICLE DESIGN; journal of vehicle engineering, automotive technology and components. see *TRANSPORTATION*

600 II
INTERNATIONAL PRESS CUTTING SERVICE: TECHNICAL NEWS REPORT. 1979. w. $85. International Press Cutting Service, Box 63, Allahabad 211001, India. Ed. Nandi Khanna. (looseleaf format)

658 US
INTERNATIONAL TRENDS IN MANUFACTURING TECHNOLOGY. 1983. irreg. price varies. Springer-Verlag, 175 Fifth Ave., New York, NY 10010. TEL 212-460-1500. FAX 212-473-6272. (Also: Berlin, Heidelberg, Tokyo and Vienna) (Co-publisher: I F S (Publications) Ltd.) Ed.Bd. Document type: academic/scholarly publication.

INTERNATIONAL UNDERWATER SYSTEMS DESIGN. see *EARTH SCIENCES — Oceanography*

600 US ISSN 1066-2472
INTERTEK; a journal about technology and society. a. $8 for 2 yrs. 13 Daffodil Ln., San Carlos, CA 94070-1552. adv.; bk.rev. Document type: academic/scholarly publication.
Description: Discusses specific aspects of the impact of technology and computers on society and the social order.

600 500 539.7 IT
INVENTIVA; periodico tecnico - scientifico - sociale. 1958. q. L.10000. Unione Italiana Inventori, Casella Postale 322, 80100 Naples, Italy. TEL 39-823-327222. Ed. Emilio C. Oberdan Vicario. adv.: page L.100000. bk.rev. circ. 4,000.

INVESTIGACION Y CIENCIA. see *SCIENCES: COMPREHENSIVE WORKS*

IRANIAN JOURNAL OF SCIENCE AND TECHNOLOGY. see *SCIENCES: COMPREHENSIVE WORKS*

ISRAEL ACADEMY OF SCIENCES AND HUMANITIES. SECTION OF HUMANITIES. PROCEEDINGS. see *HUMANITIES: COMPREHENSIVE WORKS*

338 600 IS ISSN 0334-6307
ISRAEL HIGH-TECH & INVESTMENT REPORT. (Text in English) 1985. m. IS.285($198) (effective 1994). Israel Publications Inc., P.O. Box 33633, Tel Aviv 61336, Israel. TEL 972-3-5235279. FAX 972-3-5227799. (Subscr. in U.S. to: 47 Byron Pl., Scarsdale, NY 10583. TEL 914-723-8321. FAX 914-723-8340) Ed. Joseph Morgenstern. Document type: newsletter.
Formerly: Israel High-Tech Report.
Description: Covers current business and technology issues and trends, including research and development, investment prospects, international cooperation, and regional issues.

ISSUES IN SCIENCE AND TECHNOLOGY. see *SCIENCES: COMPREHENSIVE WORKS*

600 IT ISSN 0391-738X
ITALIAN TECHNOLOGY; the journal of Italian engineering, machinery and technical products. 1975. 3/yr. $60 free. E R I S S.p.A., Via Tellini, 14, 20155 Milan, Italy. TEL 2-331-033-05. FAX 2-331-042-45. Ed. Francesco Goi. bk.rev. circ. 14,200.

600 RU ISSN 0202-7836
ITOGI NAUKI I TEKHNIKI: OBSHCHAYA MEKHANIKA. irreg., vol.7, 1990. price varies. Vsesoyuznyi Institut Nauchno-Tekhnicheskoi Informatsii (VINITI), Ul. Usievicha 20-A, 125219 Moscow A-219, Russia. (Subscr. to: Mezhdunarodnaya Kniga, Moscow 121200, Russia)
—BLDSC (0126.709000).

JAHRBUCH ARBEIT UND TECHNIK. see *SCIENCES: COMPREHENSIVE WORKS*

600 GW ISSN 0935-0292
JAHRBUCH SCHWEISSTECHNIK. 1986. a. DM.44. Deutscher Verlag fuer Schweisstechnik, Postfach 101965, 40010 Duesseldorf, Germany. TEL 0211-1591-0. FAX 0211-1591-200. TELEX 8582583. adv.; bk.rev. circ. 7,000. Document type: trade publication.

600 JA ISSN 0027-7614
 CODEN: NKGSAR
JAPAN. GOVERNMENT INDUSTRIAL RESEARCH INSTITUTE, NAGOYA. TECHNICAL NEWS. (Text in Japanese) 1952. m. Government Industrial Research Institute, Nagoya, 1 Hirate-machi, Kita-ku, Nagoya, Japan. Ed. S. Suzuki. abstr.; bibl.; index, cum.index.
—CASDDS.

600 JA ISSN 0385-5236
JAPAN JOURNAL OF EDUCATIONAL TECHNOLOGY. q. 3600 Yen. Educational Technology Journal Association of Japan, 4-1-1, Nukui-kita Machi, Koganei-shi, Tokyo 184, Japan. (Dist. by: Business Center for Academic Societies Japan, 5-16-9 Konkomagome, Bunkyo-ku, Tokyo 113, Japan. TEL 03-5814-5811)

JAPAN REPORT: SCIENCE AND TECHNOLOGY. see *SCIENCES: COMPREHENSIVE WORKS*

620.1 JA ISSN 0038-1586
 CODEN: SOKAB9
JAPAN SOCIETY FOR TECHNOLOGY OF PLASTICITY. JOURNAL/SOSEI TO KAKO. (Text in Japanese; summaries in English) 1960. m. 10500 Yen($42) Japan Society for Technology of Plasticity - Nihon Sosei Kako Gakkai, Torikatsu Bldg., 5-2-5 Roppongi, Minato-ku, Tokyo 106, Japan. TEL 03-3402-0849. FAX 03-3402-0965. Ed. Hideo Hirotsu. adv.; bk.rev.; abstr.; charts; bibl.; index, cum.index. circ. 5,000. (back issues avail.) Indexed: Chem.Abstr., JTA, Met.Abstr., World Alum.Abstr.
—BLDSC (4808.150000); CASDDS.

600 US ISSN 1060-8117
T27.J3
JAPAN TECHNOLOGY HIGHLIGHTS. English translation of: Nikkan Kogyo Shimbun. 1990. bi-w. $295. International Technology Review, Box 7445, Northridge, CA 91327. TEL 818-360-3955.
—BLDSC (4650.285000).

600 JA
JAPANESE INDUSTRY AND TECHNOLOGY. DIGEST. (Text in English) 1978. m. 1500 Yen($10) (Trade Policy Research Institute) Japan Trade & Industry Publicity, Inc., Toranomon Kotohira Kaikan, 2-8 Toranomon 1-chome, Minato-ku, Tokyo 105, Japan. (U.S. addr.: Akiwa Information Access, 247 W. 72nd St., Ste. 1RE, New York, NY 10023) Ed. Isamu Yoshina. circ. 10,000. (back issues avail.) Indexed: A.I.Abstr., CAD CAM Abstr., Energy Info.Abstr., Environ.Abstr., Key to Econ.Sci., Tel.Abstr.

600 US ISSN 1058-7314
JAPANESE TECHNOLOGY REVIEWS: NEW MATERIALS (SECTION C). 1989. 2/yr. (in 1 vol.). 60 ECU (effective 1993). Gordon and Breach Science Publishers, c/o International Publishers Distributor, 820 Town Center Dr., Langhorne, PA 19047. TEL 215-750-2642. FAX 215-750-6343. (Subscr. to: International Publishers Distributor, P.O. Box 90, Reading, Berkshire RG1 8JL, England. TEL 44-173-456-8316) Ed. Toshiaki Ikoma. (also avail. in microform)
—BLDSC (4662.120440). CCC.
Supersedes in part: Japanese Technology Review (ISSN 0898-5693)
Refereed Serial

JAPANINFO; Fernost Berichte: Deutscher Dienst fuer Wirtschaft, Politik, Technologie und Gesellschaft. see *BUSINESS AND ECONOMICS — International Commerce*

600 FR ISSN 0021-5554
LA JAUNE ET LA ROUGE. 1948. 10/yr. 280 F. (effective through 1991). Societe Amicale des Anciens Eleves de l'Ecole Polytechnique, 5 rue Descartes, 75005 Paris, France. TEL 33-1-46-33-74-25. FAX 44-07-01-69. adv.; bk.rev. circ. 13,000.
—BLDSC (4663.422000).
Description: Publications of the former students of Ecole Polytechnique Association.

600 CC ISSN 1000-5803
JIANGXI GONGYE DAXUE XUEBAO/JIANGXI INDUSTRIAL UNIVERSITY. JOURNAL. (Text in Chinese) 1985. q. Jiangxi Gongye Daxue - Jiangxi Industrial University, No.61, Beijing Donglu, Nanchang, Jiangxi 330029, People's Republic of China. TEL 333535. Ed. Liu Bingsheng. Document type: academic/scholarly publication.

TECHNOLOGY: COMPREHENSIVE WORKS

JINRI KEJI/SCIENCE AND TECHNOLOGY TODAY. see *SCIENCES: COMPREHENSIVE WORKS*

JINZHAN: GUOJI MAOYI YU KEJI JIAOLIU/PROGRESS: INTERNATIONAL EXCHANGE IN TRADE, SCIENCE AND TECHNOLOGY. see *BUSINESS AND ECONOMICS — International Commerce*

600   CC   ISSN 1002-283X
JISHU KAIFA YU YINJIN/EXPLORATION AND IMPORT OF TECHNOLOGY. (Text in Chinese) 1985. bi-m. Y3.60. Fujiansheng Keji Qingbao Yanjiusuo - Fujian Institute of Scientific and Technological Information, 52 Hudong Lu, Fuzhou, Fujian 350003, People's Republic of China. TEL 0591-557288. FAX 0591-556468. (Dist. overseas by: Jiangsu Publications Import & Export Corp., 56 Gao Yun Ling, Nanjing, Jiangsu, P.R.C.) (Co-sponsor: Science and Technology Department of Fujian Economics Committee) Ed. Ye Zhonghua. circ. 3,000.
    Description: Focuses on technology and resource development, advanced and practical technology and the latest technological and economic information in Fujian, Taiwan and Hong Kong.

600   US
JOHNS HOPKINS STUDIES IN THE HISTORY OF TECHNOLOGY. 1967; N.S. 1978. irreg. price varies. Johns Hopkins University Press, 701 W. 40th St., Ste. 275, Baltimore, MD 21211. TEL 410-516-6900. FAX 410-516-6998. (reprint service avail. from UMI)
    Refereed Serial

600   UK
JOINT FRAMEWORK FOR INFORMATION TECHNOLOGY. ANNUAL REPORT. a. Department of Trade and Industry, Technology Programmes and Services Division, 151 Buckingham Palace Rd., London SW1W 9SS, England. TEL 071-215-1345. **Document type:** government publication.

JOURNAL FOR VOCATIONAL AND SPECIALIZED EDUCATION IN SOUTH AFRICA/JOERNAAL VIR BEROEPS- EN BUITENGEWONE ONDERWYS IN SUID-AFRIKA. see *EDUCATION*

600 900   US   ISSN 0147-8885
RB43   CODEN: JOHIDN
JOURNAL OF HISTOTECHNOLOGY. 1977. q. $60 (effective 1996). National Society for Histotechnology, 4201 Northview Dr., Ste. 502, Bowie, MD 20716-1073. TEL 301-262-6221. FAX 301-262-9188. Ed. Jules Elias. adv.; bk.rev.; index. circ. 5,000. **Indexed:** Biol.Abstr., Chem.Abstr., Curr.Cont., Excerp.Med. **Document type:** trade publication.
    —BLDSC (5002.400000); CASDDS; Faxon; Genuine Article; SWETS; UnCover.
    Description: Publishes original articles, brief reports, notes on techniques, case studies dealing with anatomy, histochemistry, pathology, microscopy, and immunohistochemistry. Articles on applications and evaluations of commercially prepared kits, continuing education, and medical news.
    Refereed Serial

JOURNAL OF INDUSTRIAL TEACHER EDUCATION. see *EDUCATION — Higher Education*

600 338   US   ISSN 1062-0656
TS183   CODEN: JPMSEI
JOURNAL OF MATERIALS PROCESSING AND MANUFACTURING SCIENCE. 1992. q. $195. Technomic Publishing Co., Inc., 851 New Holland Ave., Box 3535, Lancaster, PA 17604. TEL 717-291-5609. FAX 717-295-4538. Ed. Selcuk I. Guceri. index. circ. 80. **Indexed:** Intl.Polym.Sci.& Tech., RAPRA. **Document type:** academic/scholarly publication.
    —BLDSC (5012.234000); CASDDS; Ei; Genuine Article; UMI; UnCover. CCC.
    Description: Covers developments in processing metals, polymers and composites, ceramics, powders, and specialty materials.
    Refereed Serial

JOURNAL OF PURE AND APPLIED SCIENCES/TEMEL VE UYGULAMALI BILMLER DERGISI. see *SCIENCES: COMPREHENSIVE WORKS*

JOURNAL OF SCIENCE AND TECHNOLOGY. see *SCIENCES: COMPREHENSIVE WORKS*

600   US   ISSN 1071-6084
T61
JOURNAL OF TECHNOLOGY STUDIES. 1974. s-a. $7 per no. Epsilon Pi Tau, c/o Jerry Streichler, Ed., Bowling Green State University, Bowling Green, OH 43403-0305. E-mail: bsmith@bgnet.bgsu.edu. Ed. Jerry Streichler. bk.rev.
    —BLDSC (5068.568000); UMI.
    Formerly (until 1993): Epsilon Pi Tau. Journal (ISSN 0887-9532)
    Refereed Serial

600   US   ISSN 0892-9912
T174.3
JOURNAL OF TECHNOLOGY TRANSFER.* 1976. q. $60. Technology Transfer Society, 55 S. State Ave., Ste. 3-F2, Indianapolis, IN 46201-7876. Ed. Tina McKinley. bk.rev. circ. 800. **Document type:** academic/scholarly publication.
    ●Also available online. Vendor(s): Ovid Technologies, Knight-Ridder, Inc..
    Also available on CD-ROM.
    —BLDSC (5068.570000); Faxon.
    Description: Contains articles describing methods, mechanisms, case studies and theories of technology transfer.
    Refereed Serial

600   UK   ISSN 0143-9782
QA280   CODEN: JTSADL
JOURNAL OF TIME SERIES ANALYSIS. 1980. bi-m. £38($73) (foreign £46) (effective 1996). Basil Blackwell Ltd, 108 Cowley Rd., Oxford OX4 1JF, England. Ed. M. Priestley. adv.; index. circ. 1,000. (back issues avail.; reprint service avail. from SWZ) **Indexed:** Agri.Eng.Abstr., Biostat., Curr.Ind.Stat., INSPEC, J.Cont.Quant.Meth., Math.R., Oper.Res.Manage.Sci., Qual.Contr.Appl.Stat., Stat.Theor.Meth.Abstr.
    —BLDSC (5069.400000); Faxon; SWETS; UMI; UnCover. CCC.

600   US   ISSN 1063-0732
HT101
JOURNAL OF URBAN TECHNOLOGY. 1992. 3/yr. $45 to individuals (overseas $60); institutions $54 (overseas $69) (effective 1996). Society of Urban Technology, 244-57 89th Ave., Bellerose, NY 11426. TEL 718-347-9234. (Subscr. to: 300 Jay St., Brooklyn, NY 11201) Ed. Richard E. Hanley. adv. contact: Richard E. Hanley. circ. 600. (back issues avail.) **Indexed:** Avery Ind.Archit.Per., Urb.Aff.Abstr. **Document type:** academic/scholarly publication.
    Description: Examines the interaction between cities and technologies for a general audience whose businesses, occupations, or studies require their understanding of what technologies do to cities and cities do to technologies.

600   CU   ISSN 0449-4555
T4
JUVENTUD TECNICA. 1965. m. $20 in N. America; S. America $26; Europe $29; elsewhere $41. (Union de Jovenes Comunistas, Movimento de Brigadas Tecnicas) Ediciones Cubanas, Departamento de Exportacion, Obispo No. 527, Apdo. 605, Havana, Cuba. Dir. German Fernandez Burguet. bibl.; illus. circ. 100,000.
    Description: Reflects the Technical Youth Brigades' participation in the multifaced economic development of the country. Covers articles, commentaries, photo features, and national and international sports events.

KAGAKU GIJUTSU BUNKEN SABISU/SCIENCE AND TECHNOLOGY INFORMATION SERVICE. see *SCIENCES: COMPREHENSIVE WORKS*

600 500   JA
KAGAKU GIJUTSU HAKUSHO/WHITE PAPER OF SCIENCE AND TECHNOLOGY IN JAPAN. (Text in Japanese) 1958. a. 3400 Yen (effective 1994). Okura-sho, Insatsu-kyoku - Ministry of Finance, Printing Bureau, 2-4 Toranomon 2-chome, Minato-ku, Tokyo 105, Japan. bk.rev.; stat. **Document type:** government publication.

600   JA
KAGAKU GIJUTSU HAKUSHO NO ARAMASHI. (Text in Japanese) 1987. a. 300 Yen (effective 1995). Okura-sho, Insatsu-kyoku - Ministry of Finance, Printing Bureau, 2-4 Toranomon 2-chome, Minato-ku, Tokyo 105, Japan. **Document type:** government publication.
    Description: Summary of Kagaku Gijutsu Hakusho.

600   JA   ISSN 0447-5089
Q180.J3
KAGAKU GIJUTSU KENKYU CHOSA HOKOKU/REPORT ON THE SURVEY OF RESEARCH AND DEVELOPMENT. (Text in English and Japanese) 1960. a. 4000 Yen. Somucho, Tokeikyoku - Management and Coordination Agency, Statistics Bureau, 19-1 Wakamatsu-cho, Shinjuku-ku, Tokyo 162, Japan. TEL 81-3-3203-1111. FAX 81-3-5273-1180. stat. **Document type:** government publication.

600   JA
KAGAKU GIJUTSU KENKYU CHOSA KEKKA NO GAIYO. (Text in Japanese) a. Somucho, Tokeikyoku - Management and Coordination Agency, Statistics Bureau, 19-1 Wakamatsu-cho, Shinjuku-ku, Tokyo 162, Japan. stat. **Document type:** government publication.
    Description: Contains an outline of the Kagaku Gijutsu Kenkyu Chosa Hokoku.

600   JA
KAGAKU GIJUTSU SHINKO CHOSEIHI NYUSU. (Text in Japanese) 1983. irreg. Kagaku Gijutsucho - Science and Technology Agency, 2-1 Kasumigaseki 2-chome, Chiyoda-ku, Tokyo 100, Japan. **Document type:** government publication.
    Description: Contains news of special coordination funds for promoting science and technology.

600   JA
KAGAKU GIJUTSU SHINKO CHOSEIHI SHIKEN KENKYU JISSHI KEIKAKU. (Text in Japanese) a. Kagaku Shinbunsha, 8-1 Hamamatsu-cho 1-chome, Minato-ku, Tokyo 105, Japan.
    Description: Contains planning papers of experimental studies by special coordination funds for promoting science and technology.

600   JA
KAGAKU GIJUTSUCHO NENPO. (Text in Japanese) 1957. a., latest 1995 (for the year 1993). 5000 Yen. (Kagaku Gijutsucho - Science and Technology Agency) Government Publications Service Center, 2-1, 1-chome, Kasumigaseki, Chiyoda-ku, Tokyo, Japan. **Indexed:** INIS Atomind. **Document type:** government publication.
    Description: The annual report of the agency.

600   JA   ISSN 0368-5918
                  CODEN: KKGOAG
KAGAKU TO KOGYO (OSAKA)/SCIENCE AND INDUSTRY. (Text and summaries in Japanese and English) 1926. m. Osaka Koken Kyokai - Osaka Society of Industrial Research, Osaka-shiritsu Kogyo Kenkyujo, 6-50 Morinomiya 1-chome, Joto-ku, Osaka-shi, Osaka-fu 536, Japan. abstr.
    —BLDSC (5081.110000); CASDDS.
    Description: Contains original papers, reviews, commentary, and news.

600 500   JA   ISSN 0916-1902
                  CODEN: KKDREE
KANAGAWA KOKA DAIGAKU KENKYU HOKOKU. B RIKOGAKU HEN/KANAGAWA INSTITUTE OF TECHNOLOGY. RESEARCH REPORTS. PART B. SCIENCE AND TECHNOLOGY. (Text in English and Japanese; summaries in English) 1976. a. Kanagawa Institute of Technology - Kanaguwa Koka Daigaku, 1030 Shimoogino, Atsugi-shi, Kanagawa-ken 243-02, Japan. FAX 0462-42-6111. **Indexed:** Chem.Abstr., Jap.Per.Ind. **Document type:** bulletin.
    —CASDDS.
    Formerly (until 1988): Ikutoku Kogyo Daigaku Kenkyu Hokoku. B Rikogaku Hen (ISSN 0386-1163)

620   JA   ISSN 0022-832X
                  CODEN: KDKOAL
KANAZAWA DAIGAKU KOGAKUBU KIYO/KANAZAWA UNIVERSITY. FACULTY OF TECHNOLOGY. MEMOIRS.* (Text in English, Japanese) 1952. a. exchange basis. Kanazawa Daigaku, Kogakubu - Kanazawa University, Faculty of Technology, 40-20 Kodatsuno 2-chome, Kanazawa-shi, Ishikawa-ken 920, Japan. charts; illus. circ. 800. (also avail. in microfiche) **Indexed:** Chem.Abstr., INIS Atomind., INSPEC, JCT. **Document type:** academic/scholarly publication.
    —BLDSC (5602.000000); CASDDS.

6250 TECHNOLOGY: COMPREHENSIVE WORKS

620 JA ISSN 0453-2198
TA7 CODEN: TRKUAW
KANSAI UNIVERSITY TECHNOLOGY REPORTS/KANSAI DAIGAKU KOGAKUBU KENKYU HOKOKU. (Text in English) 1959. a. exchange basis. Kansai University, Faculty of Engineering - Kansai Daigaku Kogakubu, 3-3-35 Yamate-cho, Suite 564, Osaka, Japan. Ed. Katsutaro Katsuta. bk.rev. **Indexed:** Chem.Abstr., Geo.Ref., INSPEC, JCT, JTA, Math.R.
—BLDSC (8759.600000); CASDDS; UnCover.

KE XUE. see *SCIENCES: COMPREHENSIVE WORKS*

600 500 JA
KEIO GIJUKU DAIGAKU RIKOGAKUBUHO. (Text in Japanese) 1962. a. Keio Gijuku Daigaku, Rikogakubu - Keio University, Faculty of Science and Technology, 14-1, Hiyoshi 3-chome, Kohoku-ku, Yokohama-shi, Kanagawa-ken 223, Japan.
Description: Contains news of the faculty.

600 530 JA
KEISHA KINO ZAIRYO SHINPOJUMU KOENSHU/SYMPOSIUM OF FUNCTIONALLY GRADIENT MATERIALS FORUM. PROCEEDINGS. (Text in English, Japanese) a. 8000 Yen to non-members; members 5000 Yen. Mito Kagaku Gijutsu Kyokai, Keisha Kino Zairyo - Society of Non-Traditional Technology, Functionally Gradient Materials Forum, 2-8, Toranomon 1-chome, Minato-ku, Tokyo 105, Japan. TEL 81-3-3503-4681. FAX 81-3-3597-0535.
Document type: proceedings.

KEJI DAOBAO/SCIENCE AND TECHNOLOGY HERALD. see *SCIENCES: COMPREHENSIVE WORKS*

KEJI JINBU YU DUICE. see *SCIENCES: COMPREHENSIVE WORKS*

KEJI KAIFA DONGTAI/R & D INFORMATION. see *SCIENCES: COMPREHENSIVE WORKS*

KEJI RIBAO/SCIENCE & TECHNOLOGY DAILY. see *SCIENCES: COMPREHENSIVE WORKS*

KEJI YINGYU XUEXI/LEARNING ENGLISH FOR SCIENCE & TECHNOLOGY. see *LINGUISTICS*

KEJI YU FAZHAN/SCIENCE, TECHNOLOGY AND DEVELOPMENT. see *SCIENCES: COMPREHENSIVE WORKS*

KENKYU GIJUTSU KEIKAKU/JOURNAL OF SCIENCE POLICY AND RESEARCH MANAGEMENT. see *BUSINESS AND ECONOMICS — Management*

KENYA JOURNAL OF SCIENCES. SERIES A: PHYSICAL AND CHEMICAL SCIENCES. see *SCIENCES: COMPREHENSIVE WORKS*

KENYA NATIONAL ACADEMY FOR ADVANCEMENT OF ARTS AND SCIENCES. NEWSLETTER. see *SCIENCES: COMPREHENSIVE WORKS*

KEXUE JISHU YANJIU CHENGGUO GONGBAO/BULLETIN OF SCIENTIFIC AND TECHNOLOGICAL ACHIEVEMENTS. see *SCIENCES: COMPREHENSIVE WORKS*

KEXUE JISHU YU BIANZHENGFA/SCIENCE, TECHNOLOGY, AND DIALECTICS. see *SCIENCES: COMPREHENSIVE WORKS*

KHOA HOC KY THUAT KINH TE THE GIOI/WORLD SCIENCE, TECHNOLOGY AND ECONOMY. see *SCIENCES: COMPREHENSIVE WORKS*

KINKI DAIGAKU RIKOGAKUBU KENKYU HOKOKU/KINKI UNIVERSITY. FACULTY OF SCIENCE AND TECHNOLOGY. JOURNAL. see *SCIENCES: COMPREHENSIVE WORKS*

KOBE DAIGAKU DAIGAKUIN SHIZEN KAGAKU KENKYUKA KIYO B/KOBE UNIVERSITY. GRADUATE SCHOOL OF SCIENCE AND TECHNOLOGY. MEMOIRS. SERIES B. see *SCIENCES: COMPREHENSIVE WORKS*

600 JA ISSN 0287-6507
KOBE UNIVERSITY. GRADUATE SCHOOL OF SCIENCE AND TECHNOLOGY. MEMOIRS. SERIES A/KOBE DAIGAKU DAIGAKUIN SHIZEN KAGAKU KENKYUKA KIYO. A. (Text and summaries in English) 1983. a. Kobe Daigaku, Daigakuin Shizen Kagaku Kenkyuka - Kobe University, Graduate School of Science and Technology, 1-1, Rokkodai-cho, Nada-ku, Kobe-shi, Hyogo-ken 657, Japan. abstr.
—UnCover.

600 JA
KOCHI GIJUTSU/OBVIOUS TECHNIQUE. (Text in Japanese) 1990. m. Azutekku Yugen Gaisha - Aztec Inc., 4-2-209, Azabudai 1-chome, Minato-ku, Tokyo 106, Japan.

658.5 GW ISSN 0023-4435
KRAFTHAND. 1927. bi-m. DM.94.50. Krafthand Verlag Walter Schulz, Gottlieb-Daimler-Str. 10, Postfach 1462, 86825 Bad Woerishofen, Germany. Ed. W. Schweizer. adv.; bk.rev.; charts; illus.; mkt.; tr.lit.; index. circ. 18,500.
—CCC.

KULTUR UND TECHNIK. see *MUSEUMS AND ART GALLERIES*

KULTURBERICHTE AUS NIEDEROESTERREICH. see *ART*

600 KO
KWAHAK KISUL YORAM/HANDBOOK OF SCIENCE AND TECHNOLOGY. 1970. a. Ministry of Science and Technology, Seoul, S. Korea. circ. 1,500.

KWARTALNIK HISTORII NAUKI I TECHNIKI/QUARTERLY JOURNAL OF THE HISTORY OF SCIENCE AND TECHNOLOGY. see *SCIENCES: COMPREHENSIVE WORKS*

KYOTO INSTITUTE OF TECHNOLOGY. FACULTY OF ENGINEERING AND DESIGN. MEMOIRS. see *SCIENCES: COMPREHENSIVE WORKS*

500 600 JA ISSN 0453-0357
T4 CODEN: KKDKAN
KYUSHU INSTITUTE OF TECHNOLOGY. BULLETIN: SCIENCE AND TECHNOLOGY/KYUSHU KOGYO DAIGAKU KENKYU HOKOKU: KOGAKU. (Text in Japanese; abstracts in English) 1951. s-a. exchange basis. Kyushu Institute of Technology - Kyushu Kogyo Daigaku, 1-1 Sensui-cho, Tobata, Kitakyushu 804, Japan. abstr. **Indexed:** Chem.Abstr., GeoRef., INSPEC (1971-), JTA.
—BLDSC (2601.540000); CASDDS; UnCover.

608.7 346.04 US ISSN 0047-4576
L E S NOUVELLES. 1966. 4/yr. membership; libraries $35 (foreign $50). Licensing Executives Society International, c/o Jack Stuart Ott, Ed., 1444 W. 10th St., Ste. 403, Cleveland, OH 44113. TEL 216-241-3940. FAX 216-566-9267. bk.rev.; pat.; index. circ. 8,000.
Formerly: Nouvelles (ISSN 0270-174X)

LAMY DROIT DE L'INFORMATIQUE; informatique, telematique, reseaux. see *LAW*

600 US ISSN 0075-7926
LANDOLT-BOERNSTEIN, ZAHLENWERTE UND FUNKTIONEN AUS NATURWISSENSCHAFTEN UND TECHNIK. NEUE SERIE. GROUP 4: MACROSCOPIC AND TECHNICAL PROPERTIES OF MATTER. 1974. irreg. price varies. Springer-Verlag, 175 Fifth Ave., New York, NY 10010. TEL 212-460-1500. FAX 212-473-6272. (Also: Berlin, Heidelberg, Tokyo and Vienna) Ed. K.H. Hellwege. (reprint service avail. from ISI) **Document type:** academic/scholarly publication.

600 UK
LASER. 1966. irreg. £0.30 per no. 26 Selwood Rd., Addiscombe, Croydon CR0 7JR, Surrey, England. Ed.Bd. adv.; bk.rev.; bibl.; charts; illus. circ. 100.

700 US ISSN 0749-5250
LASER DISC NEWSLETTER. 1984. m. $35 (foreign $50). Douglas Pratt, Ed. & Pub., Box 420, East Rockaway, NY 11518. TEL 516-594-9304. adv. circ. 4,000. **Document type:** newsletter.
Description: Covers consumer news on movie, cultural, and educational laser discs available in both the American and Japanese markets.

LATVIJAS FIZIKAS UN TEHNISKO ZINATNU ZURNALS/LATVIAN JOURNAL OF PHYSICS AND TECHNICAL SCIENCES. see *PHYSICS*

LAW OF HIGH TECHNOLOGY INNOVATION. see *PATENTS, TRADEMARKS AND COPYRIGHTS*

LICENSING LAW HANDBOOK. see *LAW*

600 500 US
THE LIGHTBULB; for the professional inventor. 1972. bi-m. $24.95 (Canada $34.95; elsewhere $50). Inventors Workshop International, 7332 Mason Ave., Canoga Park, CA 91306-2822. TEL 818-340-4268. FAX 818-884-8312. Eds. Melvin L. Fuller, Maggie Weisberg. adv.: B&W page $600; adv. contact: Michael Valentine. bk.rev.; pat.; circ. 7,000 (paid). (tabloid format) **Document type:** trade publication, consumer publication.
—CCC.
Former titles (until 1992): Invent! (ISSN 1040-3485); (until 1988): Lightbulb (ISSN 0883-6914)
Description: Covers a broad range of the latest developments in practically all fields of human enterprise and technological advancement.

LINDE BERICHTE AUS TECHNIK UND WISSENSCHAFT. see *SCIENCES: COMPREHENSIVE WORKS*

LIVE AND LET LIVE. see *PHILOSOPHY*

600 US ISSN 0024-5852
U168
LOGISTICS SPECTRUM. 1967. q. $50 (foreign $60). Society of Logistics Engineers, 8100 Professional Pl., Ste. 211, New Carollton, MD 20785-2225. TEL 800-695-7653. FAX 301-459-1522. TELEX 469527. Ed. Elizabeth P. Crowe. bk.rev. circ. 8,500. (reprint service avail. from UMI) **Indexed:** Abstr.Mil.Bibl., Air Un.Lib.Ind., D M & T, PROMT.
—BLDSC (5292.350000); UMI; UnCover. **CCC.**

M O - METALLOBERFLAECHE; Beschichten von Metall und Kunststoff. see *METALLURGY*

M P G SPIEGEL. (Max-Planck-Gesellschaft zur Foerderung der Wissenschaften) see *SCIENCES: COMPREHENSIVE WORKS*

M T DIALOG. (Medizin-Technischer) see *MEDICAL SCIENCES*

M T U FOCUS. (Motoren- und Turbinen-Union Muenchen GmbH) see *AERONAUTICS AND SPACE FLIGHT*

MCGRAW-HILL YEARBOOK OF SCIENCE AND TECHNOLOGY. see *SCIENCES: COMPREHENSIVE WORKS*

MACHINE VISION & APPLICATIONS. see *COMPUTERS — Cybernetics*

600 US ISSN 0899-5729
TJ153
MAINTENANCE TECHNOLOGY. 1988. m. $75 (foreign $95). Applied Technology Publications, Inc., 1300 S. Grove Ave., Barrington, IL 60010. TEL 708-382-8100. FAX 708-304-8603. Ed. Bob Boldwin; Pub. Ciro Buttacavoli. adv.; bk.rev.; circ. 72,000 (controlled). **Document type:** trade publication.
—BLDSC (5352.631000).
Description: Provides practical technical and business information to maintenance professionals (engineers, managers, and supervisors) in four broad subject areas: Maintenance of electrical systems and instrumentation, maintenance of mechanical systems, maintenance of plant facilities, and management of maintenance operations.

600 IO ISSN 0541-7406
CODEN: MJPGAI
MAJALAH PERUSAHAAN GULA. (Text in Indonesian; summaries in English) q. $25. Pusat Penelitian Perkebunan Gula Indonesia, Jl. Paulawan 25, Pasurnan 67126, Indonesia. TEL 0343-21086. FAX 0343-21178. TELEX 31008 SUGEXS IA. **Indexed:** Hort.Abstr., Sugar Ind.Abstr.
—BLDSC (5352.893000); CASDDS.

MAJALLAT AL-ULUM. see *SCIENCES: COMPREHENSIVE WORKS*

600 MY ISSN 0127-6441
MALAYSIAN TECHNOLOGIST. (Text in English) vol.24, 1974. bi-m. M.$7 per no. Technological Association of Malaysia, 46 Jalan 52-4, New Town Centre, 46200 Petaling Jaya, Selangor, Malaysia. FAX 03-756-9637. Ed. Ir. Chang Choong Kong. adv.; abstr.; charts; illus.; stat.; tr.lit.; index. circ. 1,500. (also avail. in record)
Formerly: Technical Association of Malaysia. Journal (ISSN 0040-0882)

MANAGING TECHNOLOGY TODAY. see *BUSINESS AND ECONOMICS — Management*

531 338   US   ISSN 0896-1611
TS183
MANUFACTURING REVIEW. 1988. q. $100 to non-members (foreign $120); members $36 (foreign $56). American Society of Mechanical Engineers, 22 Law Dr., Fairfield, NJ 07007-2300. TEL 201-882-1170; 800-843-2763. FAX 201-882-5155. (Co-sponsor: Institute of Industrial Engineers) Ed. Philip H. Francis. adv.; bk.rev.; charts; illus.; cum.index: 1988-1992. circ. 1,500. (back issues avail.) **Indexed:** A.I.Abstr. (until 1992), Appl.Mech.Rev., CAD CAM Abstr. (until 1992), Eng.Ind., INSPEC (1990-), Robomat. (until 1992).
—BLDSC (5367.279000); Ei; Faxon; SWETS; UMI; UnCover. CCC.
   Description: Facilitates the transition of manufacturing-related research results to applications.
   Refereed Serial

600   US   ISSN 8750-2100
MASS HIGH TECH. 1982. fortn. $28. Mass Tech Times, Inc., 500 W. Cummings Pk., Ste. 3500, Woburn, MA 01801. TEL 617-935-1100. FAX 617-935-0308. Ed. Patrick L. Porter. adv.; bk.rev.; illus. circ. 12,000. (also avail. in microfiche from UMI) **Indexed:** Energy Info.Abstr., Tel.Abstr., Telegen.
●Also available online.
—UMI.

MASSACHUSETTS TECHNOLOGY RESOURCE GUIDE (YEAR). see *BUSINESS AND ECONOMICS — Trade And Industrial Directories*

MATERIALS SCIENCE & ENGINEERING B: SOLID-STATE MATERIALS FOR ADVANCED TECHNOLOGY. see *ENGINEERING — Engineering Mechanics And Materials*

620   US   ISSN 0025-6420
MECANICA POPULAR. (Editions avail. for Central America, Argentina, Brazil, Colombia, Ecuador, Mexico, Peru, Puerto Rico, U.S., Venezuela) (Text in Spanish) m. $22.50. Editorial America, S.A., Vanidades Continental Bldg., 6355 N.W. 36th St., Virginia Gardens, FL 33166. TEL 305-871-6400. FAX 305-871-8769. Ed. Santiago Villazon. adv.; illus. circ. 173,000.

600 634.9   FR   ISSN 0339-9702
MECANISATION FORESTIERE; * activites forestieres internationales. 1975. 48/yr. 61 bd. d'Hautpoul, 14360 Trouville, France. Ed. Andre Bouchez. adv. circ. 6,000.

MECHANICAL CONTRACTOR LITERATURE SHOWCASE. see *BUILDING AND CONSTRUCTION*

600   IT   ISSN 1120-1932
MEDIAPLUSNEWS; monthly of information, culture, technological actualities. 1987. 11/yr. L.120000 in Europe; America & Asia L.170000. Media Plus s.r.l., Via Ausonio 5, 20123 Milan, Italy. TEL 39-2-8372407. FAX 39-2-58100311. Ed. Franco Marelli Coppola. adv. contact: Paola Pirogalli. bk.rev. circ. 12,000.
   Description: Presents news and articles from and towards the industrial world, with particular consideration for the technological innovations coming from the research world.
   Refereed Serial

MEDIZIN, TECHNIK UND GESELLSCHAFT. see *MEDICAL SCIENCES*

600 500   JA   ISSN 0285-8258
MEIJI DAIGAKU KAGAKU GIJUTSU KENKYUJO HOKOKU. SOGO KENKYU/MEIJI UNIVERSITY. INSTITUTE OF SCIENCE AND TECHNOLOGY. REPORT. SPECIAL PROJECT. (Text and summaries in English and Japanese) 1981. a. Meiji Daigaku, Kagaku Gijutsu Kenkyujo - Meiji University, Institute of Science and Technology, 1-1 Higashi-mita 1-chome, Tama-ku, Kawasaki-shi, Kanagawa-ken 214, Japan.

600 500   JA   ISSN 0386-4944
Q4   CODEN: MDKKDY
MEIJI DAIGAKU KAGAKU GIJUTSU KENKYUJO KIYO/MEIJI UNIVERSITY. INSTITUTE OF SCIENCE AND TECHNOLOGY. MEMOIRS. (Text in English and Japanese; summaries in English) 1962. irreg. Meiji Daigaku, Kagaku Gijutsu Kenkyujo - Meiji University, Institute of Science and Technology, 1-1 Higashi-mita 1-chome, Tama-ku, Kawasaki-shi, Kanagawa-ken 214, Japan. **Indexed:** Chem.Abstr., Jap.Per.Ind.

600 500   JA   ISSN 0543-3916
Q4   CODEN: MDKGBK
MEIJI DAIGAKU KAGAKU GIJUTSU KENKYUJO NENPO/MEIJI UNIVERSITY. INSTITUTE OF SCIENCE AND TECHNOLOGY. ANNUAL REPORT. (Text in Japanese) 1959. a. Meiji Daigaku, Kagaku Gijutsu Kenkyujo - Meiji University, Institute of Science and Technology, 1-1 Higashi-mita 1-chome, Tama-ku, Kawasaki-shi, Kanagawa-ken 214, Japan. abstr. **Indexed:** Chem.Abstr.
—CASDDS.

600   JA   ISSN 0386-4952
Q179.9   CODEN: MDRKAW
MEIJO DAIGAKU RIKOGAKUBU KENKYU HOKOKU/MEIJO UNIVERSITY. FACULTY OF SCIENCE AND TECHNOLOGY. REPORTS. (Text in Japanese; summaries in English) 1957. a. Meijo Daigaku, Rikogakubu - Meijo University, Faculty of Science and Technology, 1-501 Shiogamaguchi, Tenpaku-ku, Nagoya-shi, Aichi-ken 468, Japan. TEL 052-832-1151. abs. **Indexed:** Chem.Abstr., INSPEC, Jap.Per.Ind. **Document type:** academic/scholarly publication.
—BLDSC (7467.085000); CASDDS.

MESSTECHNISCHE BRIEFE; Zeitschrift fuer das Elektrische Messen Mechanischer Groessen. see *ENGINEERING — Mechanical Engineering*

MESTNYI PROIZVODSTVENNYI OPYT V PROMYSHLENNOSTI/LOCAL LEVEL EXPERIENCE IN THE MANUFACTURING INDUSTRY; nauchno-tekhnicheskii referativnyi sbornik. see *ENGINEERING — Mechanical Engineering*

MESTNYI PROIZVODSTVENNYI OPYT V STROITEL'STVE/LOCAL LEVEL EXPERIENCE IN THE CONSTRUCTION INDUSTRY; nauchno-tekhnicheskii referativnyi sbornik. see *BUILDING AND CONSTRUCTION*

600   UK
MICRO TECHNOLOGY. 1981. m. M T Publications, 80 Highgate Rd., London NW5 1PB, England. FAX 071-485-9030. adv. circ. 28,000.

MICROGRAVITY - SCIENCE AND TECHNOLOGY; international journal for microgravity research and applications. see *AERONAUTICS AND SPACE FLIGHT*

MILJOE & TEKNOLOGI. see *ENVIRONMENTAL STUDIES*

620 610   US   ISSN 0739-5914
Z7403   CODEN: MIMIE6
MIND: THE MEETINGS INDEX. 1984. bi-m. $450 (foreign $475). InterDok Corp., 173 Halstead Ave., Box 326, Harrison, NY 10528. TEL 914-835-3506. FAX 914-835-6757. Ed. Yvette Roper.
—BLDSC (5775.498000); CASDDS.
   Description: Lists future conferences, seminars, workshops, congresses, meetings, institutes and courses.

MINORITY - OWNED HIGH TECH BUSINESSES. see *BUSINESS AND ECONOMICS — Trade And Industrial Directories*

600   HU   ISSN 1215-0851
TA4
MISKOLCI EGYETEM. KOZLEMENYEI. III SOROZAT, GEPESZET. 1975. irreg. Miskolci Egyetem, Miskolc, Hungary.
—BLDSC (5828.622000).
   Formerly (until 1989): Nehezipari Muszaki Egyetem. Kozlemenyei. III Sorozat, Gepeszet (ISSN 0324-6728)

600   JA   ISSN 0914-627X
MITO KAGAKU GIJUTSU/SOCIETY OF NON-TRADITIONAL TECHNOLOGY. JOURNAL. (Text in Japanese) 1973. m. 500 Yen per no. Mito Kagaku Gijutsu Kyokai - Society of Non-Traditional Technology, Toranomon Kotohira Kaikan, 2-8 Toranomon 1-chome, Minato-ku, Tokyo 105, Japan. TEL 81-3-3503-4681. FAX 81-3-3597-0535.
   Description: Contains reviews, commentary, and news of the organization.

MITSUBISHI ELECTRIC ADVANCE; a quarterly survey of new products, systems and technology. see *ENGINEERING — Electrical Engineering*

600   JA   ISSN 0026-6817
    CODEN: TRMHA3
MITSUBISHI HEAVY INDUSTRIES TECHNICAL REVIEW. (Text in English) 1964. 3/yr. 3000 Yen. Mitsubishi Heavy Industries, Ltd., Technical Administration Department, 3-1, Minatomirai 3-chome, Nishi-ku, Yokohama 220-84, Japan. TEL 045-224-9050. FAX 045-224-9906. TELEX J-22282. (Subscr. to: The Ohm-sha, Ltd., 1, 3-chome Kanda-Nishiki-cho, Chiyoda-ku, Tokyo 101, Japan) circ. 4,000. **Indexed:** BMT, Chem.Abstr., Int.Aerosp.Abstr., JCT, JTA, Met.Abstr., Ocean.Abstr., Pollut.Abstr.
—BLDSC (8725.695000); CASDDS.

600   JA   ISSN 0387-2432
    CODEN: MIJGAF
MITSUBISHI JUKO GIHO. (Text in Japanese; summaries in English) 1964. 6/yr. 3000 Yen. Mitsubishi Heavy Industries, Ltd., Technical Administration Department, 3-1, Minatomirai 3-chome, Nishi-ku, Yokohama 220-84, Japan. TEL 045-224-9050. FAX 045-224-9906. TELEX J-22282. (Subscr. to: The Ohm-sha, Ltd., 1, 3-chome, Kanda-Nishiki-cho, Chiyoda-ku, Tokyo 101, Japan) circ. 11,000. **Indexed:** Chem.Abstr., JCT.
—BLDSC (5829.806000); CASDDS.

670   JA   ISSN 0540-469X
MITSUBISHI TECHNICAL BULLETIN. (Text in English) 1962. irreg. exchange basis. Mitsubishi Heavy Industries, Ltd., Technical Administration Dept., 3-1, Minatomirai 3-chome, Nishi-ku, Yokohama 220-84, Japan. TEL 045-224-9050. FAX 045-224-9906. TELEX J-22282. circ. 1,600. **Indexed:** INSPEC.
—BLDSC (5829.807000).

604.24   US
MODERN DRAFTING PRACTICES AND STANDARDS MANUAL. base vol. (plus irreg. updates 3-4/yr.). $114 (foreign $140). Genium Publishing Corp., 1 Genium Plaza, Schnectady, NY 12304-4690. TEL 518-377-8854; 800-243-6486. FAX 518-377-1891. Ed. Robert A. Roy. (looseleaf format)

745.2   IT   ISSN 0391-3635
MODO; mensile di informazione sul design. (Text in Italian; summaries in English) 1977. m. (10/yr.). L.80000 (foreign L.160000). Ricerche Design Editrice s.r.l., Via Roma 21, 20094 Corsico (Milan), Italy. TEL 39-2-4491149. FAX 39-2-4405544. Ed. C. Secondi. adv.: B&W page L.6800000, color page L.7900000. bk.rev. circ. 35,000. (back issues avail.) **Indexed:** Artbibl.Mod., Avery Ind.Archit.Per., Br.Tech.Ind., DAAI.
—BLDSC (5900.195000).
   Description: Discusses industrial design.

600 500   IR
MOKHTAREIN VA MOBTAKERIN. q. Soroush Press, 228 Mottahhari Ave., P.O. Box 15875-1163, Teheran, Iran. TEL 021-830771.

600   UK
MONITOR (LUTON); newspaper of A B B instrumentation. 1969. q. A B B Kent plc., Lea Rd., Luton, Beds. LU1 3AE, England. Ed. P.L. Culley. circ. 5,500. (tabloid format; back issues avail.) **Document type:** trade publication.
   Formerly (until 1990): Kent News.

MONOGRAFIE Z DZIEJOW NAUKI I TECHNIKI. see *SCIENCES: COMPREHENSIVE WORKS*

306.45   US   ISSN 0962-5631
MONOGRAPHS ON SCIENCE, TECHNOLOGY, AND SOCIETY. irreg. price varies. Oxford University Press, 200 Madison Ave., New York, NY 10016. TEL 212-679-7300. Ed. Sir Alec Merrison. **Document type:** monographic series.
   Refereed Serial

TECHNOLOGY: COMPREHENSIVE WORKS

600   GW   ISSN 0932-5395
MOTORIST. 1986. bi-m. DM.91. Verlag Siegfried Rohn GmbH, Stolberger Str. 84, 50933 Cologne, Germany. TEL 0221-54974. FAX 0221-5497278. Ed. Juergen Krieger. adv.: B&W page DM.4844, color page DM.8444; trim 185 x 270; adv. contact: Kathrin Schlottky. circ. 11,000. **Document type:** trade publication.
    Formerly (until 1987): Motoristen Markt und Technik (ISSN 0931-9824)

600   LY
AL-MUNTIJUN. m. P.O. Box 734, Tripoli, Libya.

N A T A NEWS. (National Association of Testing Authorities) see *SCIENCES: COMPREHENSIVE WORKS*

608   NE   ISSN 0168-132X
                      CODEN: NAESDI
N A T O ADVANCED SCIENCE INSTITUTES SERIES E: APPLIED SCIENCES. (Text in English) 1974. irreg., no.255, 1994. price varies. (North Atlantic Treaty Organization, Scientific Affairs Division, BE) Kluwer Academic Publishers, Postbus 17, 3300 AA Dordrecht, Netherlands. TEL 31-78-392392. FAX 31-78-392254. TELEX 29245 KAPG NL. (Dist. by: Kluwer Academic Publishers Group, P.O. Box 322, 3300 AH Dordrecht, Netherlands. TEL 31-78-392032. FAX 31-78-546474; N. America dist. addr.: Box 358, Accord Sta., Hingham, MA 02018-0358. TEL 617-871-6600. FAX 617-871-6528) Indexed: Biol.Abstr., Chem.Abstr., GeoRef., INSPEC, Math.R. **Document type:** monographic series.
    ●Also available online. Vendor(s): European Space Agency (File no.128).
          —CASDDS. **CCC.**
    Formerly: N A T O Advanced Study Institute Series E: Applied Sciences.
    Refereed Serial

N D T & E INTERNATIONAL; the independent journal of non-destructive testing. see *ENGINEERING — Engineering Mechanics And Materials*

N E H A BULLETIN. (Vereniging Het Nederlandsch Economisch-Historish Archief) see *BUSINESS AND ECONOMICS — Economic Systems And Theories, Economic History*

N E H A JAARBOEK. (Vereniging Het Nederlandsch Economisch-Historisch Archief) see *BUSINESS AND ECONOMICS — Economic Systems And Theories, Economic History*

N I S S A T NEWSLETTER. (National Information System for Science and Technology) see *SCIENCES: COMPREHENSIVE WORKS*

600   JA
                      CODEN: NSMNEY
N S M F NEWS. (New Superconducting Materials Forum) (Text in Japanese) bi-m. 10000 Yen to individuals; institutions 20000Yen (membership only). Society of Non-Traditional Technology - Mito Kagaku Gijutsu Kyokai, Toranomon Kotohira Kaikan, 2-8, Tokanomon 1-chome, Minato-ku, Tokyo 105, Japan. TEL 81-3-3503-4681. FAX 81-3-3597-0535.

600   FR   ISSN 0992-3020
N T I. (Nouvelles Technologies de l'Information) 20/yr. 800 F. A Jour, 11 rue du Marche St. Honore, 75001 Paris, France. TEL 42-96-67-22. FAX 40-20-07-75. TELEX 615887 AJOUR. Ed. Francois de Valence. circ. 5,000.

600   KR   ISSN 0206-3131
NADEZHNOST' I DOLGOVECHNOST' MASHIN I SOORUZHENNII; respublikanskii mezhvedomstvennyi sbornik nauchnykh trudov. (Text in Russian) 1982. s-a. (Akademiya Nauk Ukrainskoi Ukrainy, Institut Problem Prochnosti) Izdatel'stvo Naukova Dumka, c/o Yu.A. Khramov, Dir, Ul. Repina, 3, Kiev 252 601, Ukraine. (Subscr. to: Mezhdunarodnaya Kniga, Moscow, G-200, Russia) Ed. V.T. Troshchenko.

NANJING DAXUE XUEBAO (ZIRAN KEXUE BAN)/NANJING UNIVERSITY. JOURNAL (NATURAL SCIENCE EDITION). see *SCIENCES: COMPREHENSIVE WORKS*

NARODNI TECHNICKE MUZEUM. CATALOGUES OF COLLECTIONS. see *MUSEUMS AND ART GALLERIES*

NATIONAL DEFENSE ACADEMY. MEMOIRS. MATHEMATICS, PHYSICS, CHEMISTRY AND ENGINEERING/BOEI DAIGAKKO KIYO RIKOGAKU-HEN. see *SCIENCES: COMPREHENSIVE WORKS*

600 620   KO
NATIONAL INDUSTRIAL TECHNOLOGY INSTITUTE. ANNUAL REPORT. (Text in Korean; summaries in English) 1948. a. free. National Industrial Technology Institute, 2 Chungang-dong, Kwachon, Kyonggi-do, CPO Box 3300, Seoul, S. Korea. TEL 503-7981-90. TELEX MOCNDM K23231. illus.
    Formerly (until 1992): National Industrial Research Institute. Annual Report.

NATIONAL RESEARCH CENTRE. BULLETIN. see *SCIENCES: COMPREHENSIVE WORKS*

600   CN   ISSN 1183-9082
NATIONAL RESEARCH COUNCIL OF CANADA. INSTITUTE FOR INFORMATION TECHNOLOGY. ANNUAL REPORT. French edition: Conseil National de Recherches du Canada. Institut de Technologie de l'Information. Rapport Annuel (ISSN 1183-9090) 1991. a. free. National Research Council of Canada, Institute for Information Technology - Conseil National de Recherches du Canada, Institut de Technologie de l'Information, Rm. 211, M-50, Ottawa, ON K1A 0R6, Canada. TEL 613-993-1880. FAX 613-952-7998. Ed. Evelyn M. Kidd. circ. 2,200. **Document type:** government publication.
    Description: Reports on current research projects, current publications and gives an Institute profile.

NATUUR EN TECHNIEK/NATURE AND TECHNOLOGY; natuurwetenschappelijk en technisch maandblad/scientific and technical monthly. see *SCIENCES: COMPREHENSIVE WORKS*

600 600   YU   ISSN 0352-583X
NAUCNI PODMLADAK. SVESKA ZA PRIRODNO-MATEMATICKE I TEHNICKE NAUKE; strucni casopis studenata Univerziteta u Nisu. (Text in Serbo-Croatian; summaries in English) 1969. q. 2500 din.($4) Univerzitet u Nisu, Trg Bratislava i Jedinstva 2, 18000 Nis, Serbia, Yugoslavia. TEL 018 22-226. Ed. Milorad Pavlovic. adv. circ. 500. Indexed: Lang.& Lang.Behav.Abstr.
    Formerly (until 1984): Naucni Podmladak: Tehnicke Nauke (ISSN 0351-1030); Supersedes in part (in 1971): Naucni Podmladak: Tehnicke Nauke. Drustvene Nauke.

NAUKA I ZHIZN'; nauchno-populyarnyi zhurnal. see *SCIENCES: COMPREHENSIVE WORKS*

NEDERLANDSE ORGANISATIE VOOR TOEGEPAST NATUURWETENSCHAPPELIJK ONDERZOEK. JAARVERSLAG. see *SCIENCES: COMPREHENSIVE WORKS*

NETSU SHORI/JAPAN SOCIETY FOR HEAT TREATMENT. JOURNAL. see *METALLURGY*

600   IT
NEURAL; realta virtuali, network, media, suoni futuri, fantascienza, UFO. 1993. bi-m. newsstand price: L.6500. Via Giustino Fortunato 8-N, 70125 Bari, Italy. TEL 39-80-410950. E-mail: m.habens@agora.stm.it. Ed. Marcello Baraghini. **Document type:** consumer publication.

600 332.6   US   ISSN 0882-6382
NEW & EMERGING TECHNOLOGY;* executive newsreport and forecast on industrial innovation. 1983. m. $180. 120 Ausable State Rd., Bay City, MI 48706-3675. TEL 517-893-7700. FAX 517-894-5390. Ed. David L. Rogers. adv.; bk.rev.; index. circ. 5,000. (back issues avail.)
    Formerly (until 1985): Midwest Technology (ISSN 0740-8668)
    Description: Reports on new technologically-based products and companies, especially in automated manufacturing, involving robotics, machine vision and artificial intelligence; also covers socio-technical developments affecting the economy, and investment and financial market opportunities.

658.7   US   ISSN 0028-4963
      TJ1
NEW EQUIPMENT DIGEST. 1936. m. $50 (free to qualified personnel). Penton Publishing (Subsidiary of: Pittway Company), 1100 Superior Ave., Cleveland, OH 44114-2543. TEL 216-696-7000. FAX 216-696-8765. (Subscr. to: Box 95759, Cleveland, OH 44101) Ed. Robert King. adv.: bk.rev.; illus.; tr.lit.; circ. 211,000 (controlled). (also avail. in microform from UMI; reprint service avail. from UMI) —UMI. **CCC.**
    Description: Descriptions of new or significantly improved industrial products.

658.7   CN   ISSN 0028-4971
NEW EQUIPMENT NEWS. 1940. m. Can.$47.64 (foreign Can.$55.65). Canadian Engineering Publications Ltd., 20 Richmond St. W., Ste. 415, Toronto, ON M5V 1Vg, Canada. TEL 905-599-3737. FAX 905-599-3730. Ed. Barrie Lehman; Pub. Tom Monson. adv. contact: Tom Monson. abstr.; charts; illus.; tr.lit.; circ. 23,000 (controlled). (tabloid format) **Document type:** trade publication.
    Description: Provides in-plant buyers and specifiers with current information on industrial product developments.

658.7   SA   ISSN 0028-498X
NEW EQUIPMENT NEWS. Abbreviated title: N E N. 1963. m. R.93.48 (foreign R.122.40) (effective 1994). Thomson Publications (Subsidiary of: Times Media Ltd.), P.O. Box 56182, Pinegowrie 2123, South Africa. TEL 27-11-789-2144. FAX 27-11-789-3196. Ed. Gill Marsden. adv.; abstr.; illus.; tr.lit. circ. 9,036. **Document type:** trade publication.

600   US   ISSN 0740-3569
NEW FROM EUROPE; research advisory service on technological developments from Western Europe. 1979. m. $295. Prestwick Publications, Inc., 390 N. Federal Hwy., Ste. 401, Deerfield Beach, FL 33441-2209. Ed. Roy H. Roecker. bk.rev.

600   US   ISSN 0740-3550
NEW FROM JAPAN; research advisory service on Japanese technological developments. 1974. m. $295. Prestwick Publications, Inc., 390 N. Federal Hwy., Ste. 401, Deerfield Beach, FL 33441-2209. Ed. Roy H. Roecker. bk.rev.

600   US   ISSN 0740-3577
NEW FROM U S; research advisory service on U.S. technological developments. 1981. m. $295. Prestwick Publications, Inc., 390 N. Federal Hwy., Ste. 401, Deerfield Beach, FL 33441-2209. Ed. R.H. Roecker. bk.rev.

600   UK   ISSN 0265-3443
                     CODEN: NMJAE6
NEW MATERIALS - JAPAN. 1980. m. £365($581) (effective 1996). Elsevier Science Ltd., P.O. Box 800, Kidlington, Oxford OX5 1DX, England. TEL 44-1865-843000. FAX 44-1865-843010. E-mail: nlinfo-f@elsevier.nl; usinfo-f@elsevier.com; forinfo-kyf04035@niftyserve.or.jp; Site addr.: http://www.elsevier.nl/. (Subscr. in U.S. and Canada to: Elsevier Science, 660 White Plains Rd., Tarrytown, NY 10591-5153. TEL 914-524-9200. FAX 914-333-2444) Ed. N. Butler. (back issues avail.) Indexed: Intl.Polym.Sci.& Tech., Met.Abstr., RAPRA, World Alum.Abstr. **Document type:** trade publication, newsletter.
    ●Also available online. Vendor(s): Data-Star, Knight-Ridder, Inc.
      —BLDSC (6084.474590); CASDDS; SWETS. **CCC.**
    Description: Covers new materials, products, processes, manufacturing techniques, and commercial prospects originating in Japan.

600   SW   ISSN 1100-956X
NEW SCANDINAVIAN TECHNOLOGY. (Text in English) 1989. q. $60. Bjare Information AB, P.O. Box 29 124, S-100 52 Stockholm, Sweden. TEL 46-8-662-28-69. FAX 46-8-6628859. (Co-sponsors: Nordic Industrial Fund; National Agency of Industry and Trade, I&HS, Denmark; Technology Development Centre, TEKES, Finland; National Research Countil, NRC, Iceland; Royal Norwegian Council for Scientific and Industrial Research, NTNF, Norway; Swedish National Board for Industrial and Technical Development, NUTEK, Sweden) Ed. Torgny Bjare. adv. circ. 25,000. Indexed: Intl.Polym.Sci.& Tech., RAPRA.
    Description: Presents accounts of occurrences on the technical R&D front in the Nordic countries.

TECHNOLOGY: COMPREHENSIVE WORKS

600   T1   US   ISSN 0894-0789
NEW TECHNOLOGY WEEK. 1987. w. King Publishing Group, Inc., 627 National Press Bldg., Washington, DC 20045. TEL 202-638-4260. FAX 202-662-9744. Ed. Ken Jacobson. bk.rev. Indexed: Comput.Lit.Ind. **Document type:** newsletter. ●Also available online. Vendor(s): Data-Star, Knight-Ridder, Inc., Lexis-Nexis, NewsNet (RD23). —BLDSC (6088.840600). CCC.
    Description: Covers advanced and emerging technologies. Reports on business opportunities and strategies, federal policy, technology transfer, business and trade.

609.931   Q1   NZ   ISSN 0112-3890   CODEN: NZJTEI
NEW ZEALAND JOURNAL OF TECHNOLOGY. 1958; N.S. 1985. q. NZ.$40. Department of Scientific and Industrial Research, Science Information Publishing Centre, Box 9741, Wellington, New Zealand. Ed. N. Hawcroft. bibl.; charts; illus.; index. circ. 900. (back issues avail.) Indexed: Appl.Mech.Rev., Biol.Abstr., Chem.Abstr., Curr.Adv.Ecol.Sci., Curr.Cont., Dairy Sci.Abstr., Deep Sea Res.& Oceanogr.Abstr., Energy Ind., Energy Info.Abstr., Excerp.Med., Field Crop Abstr., Food Sci.& Tech.Abstr., Forest.Abstr., Forest Prod.Abstr., Geo.Abstr., Geotech.Abstr., Helminthol.Abstr., Herb.Abstr., Hort.Abstr., Ind.N.Z.Per., Ind.Sci.Rev., Ind.Vet., INSPEC (1968-1987), Math.R., Met.Abstr., Nutr.Abstr., Pig News & Info., Plant Breed.Abstr., Rev.Appl.Entomol., Rev.Plant Path., Sel.Water Res.Abstr., So.Pac.Per.Ind., Soils & Fert., Sport Fish.Abstr., Vet.Bull., Wild.Rev., Zoo.Rec. **Document type:** academic/scholarly publication.
—CASDDS. CCC.
    Supersedes (in 1985): New Zealand Journal of Science (ISSN 0028-8365)

600   UK   ISSN 0266-7533
NEWCOMEN BULLETIN. 1939. 3/yr. membership. Newcomen Society for the Study of the History of Engineering and Technology, Science Museum, South Kensington, London SW7 2DD, England. TEL 0171-589-1793. bk.rev.; bibl. **Document type:** academic/scholarly publication.

NEWCOMEN SOCIETY FOR THE STUDY OF THE HISTORY OF ENGINEERING AND TECHNOLOGY. TRANSACTIONS. see *ENGINEERING*

NEWTON/NYUTON. see *SCIENCES: COMPREHENSIVE WORKS*

NICHI-FUTSU RIKOKA KAISHI/SOCIETE FRANCO-JAPONAISE DES SCIENCES PURES ET APPLIQUEES. BULLETIN. see *SCIENCES: COMPREHENSIVE WORKS*

600 500   JA   ISSN 0369-4313   CODEN: NDRSD2
NIHON DAIGAKU RIKOGAKU KENKYUJO SHOHO/NIHON UNIVERSITY. RESEARCH INSTITUTE OF SCIENCE AND TECHNOLOGY. JOURNAL. (Text in Japanese) 1950. s-a. exchange basis. Nihon Daigaku, Rikogaku Kenkyujo - Nihon University, Research Institute of Science and Technology, 1-8 Kanda Surugadai, Chiyoda-ku, Tokyo 101, Japan. abstr.; circ. controlled. Indexed: Chem.Abstr., INSPEC, JCT, JTA. —BLDSC (4847.900000); CASDDS.

600   JA
NIHON DAIGAKU RIKOGAKUBU GAKUJUTSU KOENKAI KOEN RONBUNSHU/NIHON UNIVERSITY. RESEARCH INSTITUTE OF SCIENCE AND TECHNOLOGY. PROCEEDINGS OF MEETING. (Text in English, Japanese) a. Nihon Daigaku, Rikogakubu Rikogaku Kenkyujo - Nihon University, College of Science and Technology, Research Institute of Science and Technology, 1-8 Kanda Surugadai, Chiyoda-ku, Tokyo 101, Japan. circ. controlled. **Document type:** proceedings.
    Description: Contains proceedings from the meetings of the institute.

NIHON SEKIGAISEN GAKKAISHI/JAPAN SOCIETY OF INFRARED SCIENCE AND TECHNOLOGY. JOURNAL. see *PHYSICS — Heat*

NIHON UNIVERSITY. RESEARCH INSTITUTE OF SCIENCE AND TECHNOLOGY. REPORT. see *SCIENCES: COMPREHENSIVE WORKS*

600   JA   ISSN 0913-7912
NIIGATA KOGYO TANKI DAIGAKU KENKYU KIYO/NIIGATA TECHNICAL JUNIOR COLLEGE. JOURNAL. (Text in Japanese; summaries in English) 1971. irreg. Niigata Kogyo Tanki Daigaku - Niigata Technical Junior College, 5827 Kamishin'ei-cho, Niigata-shi, Niigata-ken 950-21, Japan.
    Description: Contains original papers.

600 620 500   Q4   JA   ISSN 0286-2743   CODEN: NKHEDR
NIIHAMA KOGYO KOTO SENMON GAKKO KIYO. RIKOGAKU HEN/NIIHAMA NATIONAL COLLEGE OF TECHNOLOGY. MEMOIRS. SCIENCE AND ENGINEERING. (Text in English and Japanese; summaries in English) 1965. a. Niihama Kogyo Koto Senmon Gakko - Niihama National College of Technology, 7-1 Yakumo-cho, Niihama-shi, Ehime-ken 792, Japan. Indexed: Chem.Abstr., INIS Atomind., Jap.Per.Ind.
—BLDSC (5629.342000); CASDDS.

NIKKEI SAIENSU. see *SCIENCES: COMPREHENSIVE WORKS*

600   JA
NIKKEI TECHNO FRONTIER. (Text in Japanese) s-m. Nihon Keizai Shimbun, Inc., 1-9-5 Otemachi, Chiyoda-ku, Tokyo 100-66, Japan. TEL 03-3270-0251. FAX 03-5255-2661. TELEX J22308 NIKKEI. **Document type:** newsletter.
    Description: Covers a wide range of high-tech topics, and new products and services.

600   JA   ISSN 0910-6227
NISHINIPPON KOGYO DAIGAKU KIYO. RIKOGAKU HEN/NISHINIPPON INSTITUTE OF TECHNOLOGY. MEMOIRS. SCIENCE AND TECHNOLOGY. (Text in English and Japanese; summaries in English) 1969. a. Nishinippon Kogyo Daigaku - Nishinippon Institute of Technology, 1633 Aratsu, Kanda-machi, Miyako-gun, Fukuoka-ken 800-03, Japan.

NORDRHEIN-WESTFAELISCHE AKADEMIE DER WISSENSCHAFTEN. VORTRAEGE NATUR-INGENIEUR-UND WIRTSCHAFTSWISSENSCHAFTEN. see *SCIENCES: COMPREHENSIVE WORKS*

NORGES TEKNISK-NATURVITENSKAPELIGE FORSKNINGSRAAD. AARSBERETNING/ROYAL NORWEGIAN COUNCIL FOR SCIENTIFIC AND INDUSTRIAL RESEARCH. ANNUAL REPORT. see *SCIENCES: COMPREHENSIVE WORKS*

338   FR   ISSN 0029-1803
NORMANDIE INDUSTRIELLE. 1939. q. 120 F. (Societe Industrielle de Rouen) Editions Lecerf, 22 rue des Bons Enfants, Rouen, France. Ed. M. Lecerf. adv.; bk.rev.; bibl.; charts; illus.; tr.lit. circ. 5,700. Indexed: C.I.S. Abstr.
—BLDSC (6133.000000).

NORTHERN PERSPECTIVES. see *ENVIRONMENTAL STUDIES*

600   CU
NOTICIERO CIENTIFICO. SERIE: TECNOLOGIA. fortn. Academia de Ciencias, Instituto de Documentacion e Informacion Cientifico-Tecnica (I D I C T), Capitolio Nacional, Prado y San Jose, Habana 2, Havana, Cuba.

NOTRE DAME TECHNICAL REVIEW. see *ENGINEERING*

600   CN   ISSN 0706-7739
NOVA SCOTIA RESEARCH FOUNDATION CORPORATION. ANNUAL REPORT. 1947. a. Nova Scotia Research Foundation Corporation, 101 Research Dr., Woodside Industrial Park, Box 790, Dartmouth, NS B2Y 3Z7, Canada. TEL 902-424-8670. FAX 902-424-4679. E-mail: bmacneill@nsrfc.ns.ca. Ed.Bd. adv. contact: R.F.(Bob) MacNeill. **Document type:** corporate report.
    Formerly (until 1976): Nova Scotia Research Foundation. Annual Report (ISSN 0078-2475)

NUEVO DE LA CIENCIA Y LA TECNICA. see *SCIENCES: COMPREHENSIVE WORKS*

600   SP   ISSN 0214-1310
NUEVO SIGLO, CUADERNOS DE LA INNOVACION. 6/yr. Puente de Deusto 7, 3o Dpto. 5, Bilbao, Spain. TEL 1-447-84-14. FAX 1-247-84-43. Ed. Javier Bustamente. circ. 104,400.

600   US
O C D DIAMOND. 1935. m. American Cyanamid Co., Organic Chemical Division, Bound Brook, NJ 08805. TEL 908-831-2000. Ed. Robert G. Meyer. circ. 6,500 (controlled).
    Formerly (until 1976): Bound Brook Diamond.

600   Q172.5.S34   FR   ISSN 1011-792X   CODEN: MSTIE9
O E C D MAIN SCIENCE AND TECHNOLOGY INDICATORS/O C D E PRINCIPAUX INDICATEURS DE LA SCIENCE ET DE LA TECHNOLOGIE. 1988. s-a. $40. Organization for Economic Cooperation and Development, 2 rue Andre-Pascal, 75775 Paris Cedex 16, France. (U.S. orders to: O.E.C.D. Publications and Information Center, 2001 L St., N.W., Ste. 700, Washington, DC 20036-4910. TEL 202-785-6323) (also avail. in microfiche from OEC,UMI,CIS) Indexed: IIS.
—BLDSC (5352.070000); CASDDS.

O R S T O M INSTITUT FRANCAIS DE RECHERCHE POUR LE DEVELOPEMENT EN COOPERATION. RAPPORT D'ACTIVITE. see *SCIENCES: COMPREHENSIVE WORKS*

O S A ANNUAL MEETING DIGEST. (Optical Society of America, Inc.) see *PHYSICS — Optics*

OAK RIDGE NATIONAL LABORATORY REVIEW. see *ENERGY*

600   CN   ISSN 0380-1969
ONTARIO TECHNOLOGIST. 1958. 6/yr. Can.$25 (foreign Can.$35) (effective 1995). Ontario Association of Certified Engineering Technicians & Technologists, 10 Four Seasons Pl., Ste. 404, Etobicoke, ON M9B 6H7, Canada. TEL 416-621-9621. FAX 416-621-8694. Ed. Ruth M. Klein. adv. contact: R.M. Klein. bk.rev. circ. 19,499. **Document type:** trade publication.

600   BL
OPEMA EM RITMO DE BRASIL JOVEM. 1968. irreg. free. (Ministerio dos Transportes, Operacao Maua) Assessoria de Relacoes Publicas, Editora, Promocoes e Publicidade Ltda., Av. Beira Mar 406, Grupo 906, Rio de Janeiro, Brazil. adv.; illus.; stat. circ. 60,000.

ORGANIZATION OF AFRICAN UNITY. SCIENTIFIC TECHNICAL AND RESEARCH COMMISSION. PUBLICATION. see *SCIENCES: COMPREHENSIVE WORKS*

600 500   T4   JA   ISSN 0375-0191   CODEN: OKDRAK
OSAKA KOGYO DAIGAKU KIYO. RIKO HEN/OSAKA INSTITUTE OF TECHNOLOGY. MEMOIRS. SERIES A. SCIENCE AND TECHNOLOGY. (Text in English and Japanese; summaries in English) 1962. 2/yr. Osaka Kogyo Daigaku - Osaka Institute of Technology, 16-1 Omiya 5-chome, Asahi-ku, Osaka 535, Japan. charts; illus. Indexed: Biol.Abstr., Chem.Abstr., INIS Atomind., Jap.Per.Ind., JCT, Math.R.
—CASDDS.

OSAKA KYOIKU DAIGAKU KIYO. DAI-3-BUMON. SHIZEN KAGAKU/OSAKA KYOIKU UNIVERSITY. MEMOIRS. SERIES 3: NATURAL SCIENCE AND APPLIED SCIENCE. see *SCIENCES: COMPREHENSIVE WORKS*

620   TA4   JA   ISSN 0030-6177   CODEN: TROUAI
OSAKA UNIVERSITY. FACULTY OF ENGINEERING. TECHNOLOGY REPORTS/OSAKA DAIGAKU KOGAKU HOKOKU. (Text in English) 1951. s-a. exchange basis. Osaka Daigaku, Kogakubu - Osaka University, Faculty of Engineering, 2-1 Yamadaoka, Suita-shi, Osaka 565, Japan. Ed. Katsuhiko Fujii. bk.rev. circ. 1,050. Indexed: Appl.Mech.Rev., Chem.Abstr., Eng.Ind., Fluidex, INSPEC, JCT, JTA, Math.R., Met.Abstr., Sci.Abstr.
—BLDSC (8759.800000); CASDDS; Ei.

TECHNOLOGY: COMPREHENSIVE WORKS

607   JA   ISSN 0369-0369
Q180.J3   CODEN: MISIAW
OSAKA UNIVERSITY. INSTITUTE OF SCIENTIFIC AND INDUSTRIAL RESEARCH. MEMOIRS/OSAKA DAIGAKU SANGYO KAGAKU KENKYUJO KIYO. (Text in European languages) 1941. a. exchange basis. Osaka Daigaku, Sangyo Kagaku Kenkyujo - Osaka University, Institute of Scientific and Industrial Research, Mihoga-oka, Ibaraki, Osaka 567, Japan. TEL 06-877-5111. FAX 06-879-8509. Ed.Bd. circ 750. **Indexed:** Chem.Abstr., Energy Info.Abstr., INIS Atomind. **Document type:** academic/scholarly publication.
—BLDSC (5620.000000); CASDDS.

OTTAWA R & D REPORT. see *ENGINEERING*

600   PK
P A S T I C TRANSLATIONS. 1957. irreg., latest 1982. Rs.10($4) Pakistan Scientific and Technological Information Centre, Quaid-i-Azam University Campus, Box No.1217, Islamabad, Pakistan. cum.index. circ. 500. (also avail. in microfilm)
Formerly: P A N S D O C Translations (ISSN 0078-8368)

P E D. (Production & Industrial Equipment Digest) see *ENGINEERING*

600   GW   ISSN 0936-0492
P T B BERICHTE. irreg. Physikalisch-Technische Bundesanstalt, Bundesallee 100, 38116 Braunschweig, Germany. TEL 0531-5920. FAX 0531-5929292. TELEX 0952822-PTB-D. (Dist. by: Wirtschaftsverlag Neue Wissenschaft GmbH, Postfach 101110, 27511 Bremerhaven, Germany. TEL 0471-46093. FAX 0471-42765) **Document type:** academic/scholarly publication.
—BLDSC (1927.042000).

PAKISTAN COUNCIL OF SCIENTIFIC AND INDUSTRIAL RESEARCH. ANNUAL REPORT. see *SCIENCES: COMPREHENSIVE WORKS*

PAKISTAN JOURNAL OF SCIENTIFIC AND INDUSTRIAL RESEARCH. see *SCIENCES: COMPREHENSIVE WORKS*

PALEOCEANOGRAPHY. see *SCIENCES: COMPREHENSIVE WORKS*

PAPUA NEW GUINEA UNIVERSITY OF TECHNOLOGY. REPORTER. see *COLLEGE AND ALUMNI*

620   HU   ISSN 0031-3750
T4
PECSI MUSZAKI SZEMLE.* 1956. q. membership. Muszaki es Termeszettudomanyi Egyesuletek Szovetsege, Baranya Megyei Szervezet, P.F. 451, HU-1372 Budapest, Hungary. Ed. Zoltan Miklosvari. charts; illus.; cum.index every 5 yrs. circ. 1,200. **Indexed:** Hung.Build.Bull.

600   001.642   US   ISSN 1065-0261
PENNSYLVANIA BUSINESS AND TECHNOLOGY. 1990. q. $19.95. Pittsburgh High Technology Council, 4516 Henry St., Pittsburgh, PA 15213-9916. TEL 412-687-2700. FAX 412-687-2791. Ed. Betsy Momich. circ. 15,000.
●Also available online. Vendor(s): University Microfilms International.
Formerly: Pennsylvania Technology.
Description: For all levels of management, and professionals in engineering, computers, marketing and sales.

600   UK
PERA NEWS. 1947. bi-m. Pera International, Melton Mowbray, Leics. LE13 0PB, England, England. TEL 44-1664-501501. FAX 44-1664-501264. **Indexed:** BMT. **Document type:** bulletin.
Formerly: P E R A Bulletin.

338   IT   ISSN 0031-5435
PERITO INDUSTRIALE. 1933. bi-m. L.30000 (foreign L.33000). Associazione Periti Industriali di Milano, Via del Carroccio 6, 20123 Milan, Italy. TEL 02-89408416. Ed. Carlo Marzari. adv.: B&W page L.500000. bk.rev. circ. 3,800. **Document type:** monographic series.

PERTANIKA JOURNAL OF SCIENCE AND TECHNOLOGY. see *SCIENCES: COMPREHENSIVE WORKS*

600   PH   ISSN 0116-7294
T1   CODEN: PTEJEB
PHILIPPINE TECHNOLOGY JOURNAL; a quarterly organ for Philippine technological researchers. 1976. q. P.260($60) Science and Technology Information Institute, Department of Science and Technology, P.O. Box 3596, Manila, Philippines. TEL 8220961. Ed. Ricardo M. Lantican. adv.; bk.rev.; cum.index every 5 yrs. circ. 2,000. (back issues avail.) **Indexed:** Chem.Abstr., Excerp.Med., Food Sci.& Tech.Abstr., Forest.Abstr., Philip.Abstr., Rural Recreat.Tour.Abstr., Soils & Fert., World Agri.Econ.& Rural Sociol.Abstr.
—CASDDS.
Former titles: D O S T Technology Journal (ISSN 0115-2777); National Science and Technology Journal; N S D B Technology Journal.

600   NE   ISSN 0923-0106
PHILOSOPHY AND TECHNOLOGY. (Text in English) 1983. irreg., vol.10, 1993. price varies. (Society for Philosophy and Technology) Kluwer Academic Publishers, Postbus 17, 3300 AA Dordrecht, Netherlands. TEL 31-78-392392. FAX 31-78-392254. TELEX 29245 KAPG NL. (Dist. by: Kluwer Academic Publishers Group, P.O. Box 322, 3300 AH Dordrecht, Netherlands. TEL 31-78-392392. FAX 31-78-546474; N. America dist. addr.: Box 358, Accord Sta., Hingham, MA 02018-0358. TEL 617-871-6600. FAX 617-871-6528) **Document type:** monographic series.
—BLDSC (6464.815000).
Refereed Serial

600   GW   ISSN 0340-4366
PHYSIKALISCH-TECHNISCHE BUNDESANSTALT. JAHRESBERICHT. 1971. a. free. Physikalisch-Technische Bundesanstalt, Bundesallee 100, 38116 Braunschweig, Germany. TEL 0531-5920. FAX 0531-5929292. TELEX 952822-PTB-D. circ. 1,800. **Document type:** corporate report.
—BLDSC (4636.360000).
Description: Describes activities of all laboratories of the PTB; includes a list of publications.

600   GW   ISSN 0341-7964
PHYSIKALISCH-TECHNISCHE BUNDESANSTALT. PRUEFREGELN. 1967. irreg. Physikalisch-Technische Bundesanstalt, Bundesallee 100, 38116 Braunschweig, Germany. TEL 0531-5920. FAX 0531-5929292. TELEX 592822-PTB-D. Ed. Helmut Klages. **Document type:** bulletin.
Description: Instructions for testing measuring instruments and working equipment, including descriptions of testing procedures, necessary standard instruments and other appliances.

620   PL   ISSN 0239-7528
CODEN: BASSEP
POLISH ACADEMY OF SCIENCES. BULLETIN. TECHNICAL SCIENCES. (Text in English, French, German and Russian) 1953. q. $100. Polska Akademia Nauk, Centrum Upowszechniania Nauki, Palac Kultury i Nauki, Pietro XXIII, pok.23-10, 00-901 Warsaw, Poland. (Dist. by: Ars Polona, Krakowskie Przedmiescie 7, 00-068 Warsaw, Poland) Ed. T. Sliwinski. adv. contact: Ewa Bartkowiak. bibl.; charts; illus.; index. circ. 260. **Indexed:** Appl.Mech.Rev., Chem.Abstr., Eng.Ind., Geotech.Abstr., INIS Atomind., INSPEC (1983-), Key Word Ind.Wildl.Res., Math.R., Met.Abstr. **Document type:** monographic series, bulletin.
—CASDDS.
Formerly (until 1983): Academie Polonaise des Sciences. Bulletin. Serie des Sciences Techniques (ISSN 0001-4125)

POLISH TECHNICAL REVIEW/PRZEGLAD POLSKIEJ TECHNIKI. see *ENGINEERING*

509   PL   ISSN 1232-9568
POLITECHNIKA KRAKOWSKA. MONOGRAFIE. SERIA: HISTORYCZNO-TECHNICZNA. (Subseries of: Politechnika Krakowska. Monografie (ISSN 0860-097X)) (Text in Polish; summaries in English, French, German, Russian) 1993. irreg. price varies. Politechnika Krakowska, Ul. Warszawska 24, 31-155 Krakow, Poland. TEL 48-12-374289. FAX 48-12-335773. TELEX 322468 PK PL. **Document type:** academic/scholarly publication, monographic series.

600   PL
POLITECHNIKA KRAKOWSKA. MONOGRAFIE. SERIA: PODSTAWOWE NAUKI TECHNICZNE. (Subseries of: Politechnika Krakowska. Monografie (ISSN 0860-097X)) (Text in Polish; summaries in English, German, French, Russian) 1985. irreg. price varies. Politechnika Krakowska, Ul. Warszawska 24, 31-155 Krakow, Poland. TEL 48-12-374289. FAX 48-12-335773. TELEX 322468 PK PL. bibl.; charts; illus. circ. 200. **Document type:** academic/scholarly publication, monographic series.

600   PL   ISSN 0137-138X
POLITECHNIKA KRAKOWSKA. ZESZYTY NAUKOWE. PODSTAWOWE NAUKI TECHNICZNE. (Text in Polish; summaries in English, French, German and Russian) 1968. irreg. price varies. Politechnika Krakowska, Ul. Warszawska 24, 31-155 Krakow, Poland. TEL 48-12-374289. FAX 48-12-335773. TELEX 322468 PK PL. bibl.; charts; illus. circ. 200. **Document type:** academic/scholarly publication.

620   US   ISSN 0032-4558
T1
POPULAR MECHANICS. 1902. m. $17.97 (effective 1995). Hearst Magazines, Popular Mechanics, 224 W. 57th St., New York, NY 10019. TEL 212-649-3076. (Subscr. to: C.D.S., 1901 Bell Ave., Des Moines, IA 50315. TEL 800-333-4948) Ed. Joe Oldham. adv.; illus. circ. 1,600,000. (also avail. in microform from UMI) **Indexed:** Abr.R.G., Acad.Ind., Art & Archaeol.Tech.Abstr., Biog.Ind., Can.B.P.I., Consum.Ind., Gdlns, HRIS, Ind.Child.Mag., Ind.How To Do It (1963-), Jun.High.Mag.Abstr., Mag.Ind., MELSA, PMR, R.G., TOM.
●Also available on CD-ROM. Producer(s): University Microfilms International.
—BLDSC (6550.600000); Faxon; UnCover.
Description: Examines new products, techniques as well as scientific and technological developments. Covers the automobile, the home, shop, outdoors, and science and technology.

620   US   ISSN 0161-7370
AP2   CODEN: PSCIEP
POPULAR SCIENCE; the what's new magazine. 1872. m. $13.94 (foreign $21.94) (effective 1992). Times Mirror Magazines, Inc., 2 Park Ave., New York, NY 10016. TEL 212-779-5000. (Subscr. to: Box 5096, Harlan, IA 51593-2596. TEL 800-289-9399) Ed. Fred Abatemarco. adv.; bk.rev.; charts; illus.; pat.; tr.lit.; index. circ. 2,000,000. (also avail. in microform from UMI,PMC; reprint service avail. from UMI) **Indexed:** A.I.Abstr. (until 1992), Abr.R.G., Acad.Ind., Acid Rain Ind., CAD CAM Abstr. (until 1992), Can.B.P.I., Consum.Ind., Energy Info.Abstr., Environ.Abstr., Gdlns., GeoRef., Ind.Child.Mag., Ind.How To Do It (1963-), Jun.High.Mag.Abstr., Mag.Ind., MELSA, PMR, R.G., Robomat. (until 1992), Tel.Abstr., TOM.
●Also available online. Vendor(s): Knight-Ridder, Inc., University Microfilms International.
Also available on CD-ROM. Producer(s): University Microfilms International.
—BLDSC (6550.990000); CIS; Faxon; SWETS; UMI; UnCover. **CCC.**
Formerly: Popular Science Monthly (ISSN 0032-4647)
Description: Comprehensive coverage of a broad range of scientific and technological topics such as computers and electronics, energy, tools and techniques, new products and inventions as well as horticulture.

POSITIVE ALTERNATIVES. see *POLITICAL SCIENCE*

POST; a magazine for the promotion of science and technology. see *SCIENCES: COMPREHENSIVE WORKS*

POUR LA SCIENCE. see *SCIENCES: COMPREHENSIVE WORKS*

600   GW
POWDER & BULK SOLIDS YEARBOOK & DIRECTORY. (Text in English) 1992. a. 96 SFr. Trans Tech Publications, Berlinerstr. 2, 38678 Clausthal-Zellerfeld, Germany. TEL 05323-9697-0. FAX 05323-969799. adv.; B&W page DM.3000, color page DM.4500; trim 270 x 180. **Document type:** directory.

600 GW ISSN 0934-7348
TS180
POWDER HANDLING & PROCESSING. 1989. q. 284 SFr. Trans Tech Publications, Berlinerstr. 2, 38678 Clausthal-Zellerfeld, Germany. TEL 05323-9697-0. FAX 05323-969799. Ed. Wolfgang Geisler. adv.: B&W page DM.3500, color page DM.5000; trim 270 x 180. circ. 5,000. **Document type:** trade publication.
—BLDSC (6571.910000); Ei; Faxon; SWETS.
Description: Explores practical problems of processing, handling, storing, packaging powder and dry particles, as well as equipment design and engineering.

PRIMARY D A T A. (Design and Technology Association) see EDUCATION — Teaching Methods And Curriculum

PRISMA (KASSEL). see SCIENCES: COMPREHENSIVE WORKS

PRO ZUKUNFT. see ENVIRONMENTAL STUDIES

607 US
PROBABLE LEVELS OF R & D EXPENDITURES: FORECAST AND ANALYSIS. 1960? a. free. Battelle Memorial Institute, Columbus Operations, 505 King Ave., Columbus, OH 43201. TEL 614-424-6424. charts; stat.; circ. controlled. (also avail. in microfiche from CIS) **Indexed:** SRI.

PROBLEME DE AUTOMATIZARE. see ENGINEERING

670 UK ISSN 0032-9762
TS200 CODEN: PRFIAT
PRODUCT FINISHING. 1948. m. $107. Sawell Publications Ltd., 127 Stanstead Rd., London SE23 1JE, England. Ed. J.E. Bean. adv.; bk.rev.; charts; illus.; pat.; tr.lit.; tr.mk.; index. circ. 4,380. (also avail. in microform from PMC) **Indexed:** Art & Archaeol.Tech.Abstr., Br.Tech.Ind., Cadscan, Chem.Abstr., Eng.Ind., Excerp.Med., Int.Packag.Abstr., Lead Abstr., Met.Abstr., World Alum.Abstr., World Surf.Coat., Zincscan.
—BLDSC (6853.000000); Ei; SWETS; UnCover.

PRODUCTS FINISHING. see PAINTS AND PROTECTIVE COATINGS

PRODUCTS FINISHING DIRECTORY. see PAINTS AND PROTECTIVE COATINGS

600 CN ISSN 0701-1687
PRODUITS POUR L'INDUSTRIE QUEBECOISE. (Text in French) 1976. 6/yr. Can.$35. Action Communications Inc., 135 Spy Ct., Markham, ON L3R 5H6, Canada. TEL 905-477-3222. FAX 905-477-4320. Ed. David Terhune. adv.; circ. 15,050 (controlled). (tabloid format; back issues avail.)

600 500 FR ISSN 0397-8060
T175 CODEN: PRTCDG
PROGRES TECHNIQUE. 1974. 5/yr. 520 F. (effective 1995). Association Nationale de la Recherche Technique, 101 av. Raymond Poincare, 75016 Paris, France. TEL 33-1-44-05-04-40. FAX 33-1-47-04-25-20. E-mail: 100322.1546@compuserve.com. Ed. Bernadette Ragot. adv. contact: Roger Pagezy. bk.rev.; bibl. circ. 3,000. **Indexed:** Met.Abstr. **Document type:** newsletter.
●Also available online.
—BLDSC (6864.938700); CASDDS.
Supersedes (in 1976): Recherche Technique (ISSN 0486-1272)

600 SZ
PROGRESS IN NUMERICAL SIMULATION FOR MICROELECTRONICS. 1991. irreg., vol.2, 1993. Birkhaeuser Verlag, P.O. Box 133, CH-4010 Basel, Switzerland. TEL 061-2717400. FAX 061-2717666. Eds. K. Merten, A. Gilg. **Document type:** monographic series.

PROJECT APPRAISAL. see BUSINESS AND ECONOMICS — Investments

600 PL ISSN 0239-3174
PROJEKTOWANIE I SYSTEMY. (Text in Polish; summaries in English, Russian) a. price varies. (Polish Academy of Sciences, Committee of Science) Ossolineum, Publishing House of the Polish Academy of Sciences, Rynek 9, 50-106 Wroclaw, Poland. TEL 48-71-386-25. FAX 48-71-448-103. TELEX 0712771 OSS PL. Ed. Wojciech Gasparski. **Document type:** academic/scholarly publication.
Description: Papers on designing process and system science.

600 PL ISSN 0137-8783
HD8536
PRZEGLAD TECHNICZNY, INNOWACJE. 1875. w. $70. (Naczelna Organizacja Techniczna) Wydawnictwo Czasopism i Ksiazek Technicznych SIGMA - NOT, Ul. Ratuszowa 11, P.O. Box 1004, 00-950 Warsaw, Poland. (Dist. by: Zaklad Kolportazu SIGMA-NOT, ul. Bartycka 20, P.O. Box 1004, 00-950 Warsaw, Poland) (Co-sponsor: Polskie Towarzystwo Ekonomiczne) Ed. Ewa Mankiewicz-Cudny. circ. 30,000. **Indexed:** C.I.S. Abstr.
Formerly (until 1977): Innowacje (ISSN 0208-5615); Which was formed by the 1974 merger of: Wektory; Przeglad Techniczny (ISSN 0033-2380)

PUBLIKATIONEN ZU WISSENSCHAFTLICHEN FILMEN. SEKTION TECHNISCHE WISSENSCHAFTEN, NATURWISSENSCHAFTEN. see MOTION PICTURES

PUROMETEUSU. see SCIENCES: COMPREHENSIVE WORKS

QUEBEC SCIENCE. see SCIENCES: COMPREHENSIVE WORKS

QUESTIONS. see EDUCATION — Teaching Methods And Curriculum

QUIDDITY; polemical review of new developments in publishing. see BUSINESS AND ECONOMICS — Marketing And Purchasing

QUIPU; revista latinoamericana de historia de las ciencias y la tecnologia. see SCIENCES: COMPREHENSIVE WORKS

610 658.8 US ISSN 1061-1894
R & D INNOVATOR; researcher's monthly tool for invention and discovery. 1992. m. $144 in N. America; elsewhere $168 (effective 1995 & 1996). Winston J. Brill Associates, 4134 Cherokee Dr., Madison, WI 53711. TEL 608-231-6766. FAX 608-231-6794. E-mail: wbrill@vms.macc.wise.edu. Ed. Winston J. Brill. bk.rev.; illus. (back issues avail.) **Document type:** newsletter.
Description: Provides a resource for productivity and creativity in research and development. Illuminates the human side of the research process.

R I S T JOURNAL OF R & D. (Research Institute of Industrial Science & Technology) see SCIENCES: COMPREHENSIVE WORKS

RADIO KIT ELETTRONICA. see HOBBIES

RAND RESEARCH PUBLICATIONS. see SCIENCES: COMPREHENSIVE WORKS

600 GW ISSN 0935-9133
RATGEBER FORSCHUNG UND TECHNOLOGIE; Foerderungsmoeglichkeiten und Beratungshilfen. 1985. a. DM.49.80. Deutscher Wirtschaftsdienst, Marienburgerstr. 22, 50968 Cologne, Germany. TEL 0221-93763-0. FAX 0221-9376399. Ed. Adolf Gaube. **Document type:** bulletin.

RECHERCHE. see SCIENCES: COMPREHENSIVE WORKS

600 FR ISSN 0765-0779
RECHERCHE TECHNOLOGIE. m. 200 F. (foreign 230 F.) Ministere de la Recherche et de la Technologie, Imprimerie Nationale, B.P. 514, 59505 Douai Cedex, France.
Description: Presents new rules, publications and services of the Ministry.

REGIONAL TECHNOLOGY GUIDE - CENTRAL U S REGION. see BUSINESS AND ECONOMICS — Trade And Industrial Directories

REGIONAL TECHNOLOGY GUIDE - EASTERN LAKES. see BUSINESS AND ECONOMICS — Trade And Industrial Directories

REGIONAL TECHNOLOGY GUIDE - GREAT LAKES. see BUSINESS AND ECONOMICS — Trade And Industrial Directories

REGIONAL TECHNOLOGY GUIDE - MID ATLANTIC REGION. see BUSINESS AND ECONOMICS — Trade And Industrial Directories

REGIONAL TECHNOLOGY GUIDE - NEW JERSEY AND DELAWARE VALLEY. see BUSINESS AND ECONOMICS — Trade And Industrial Directories

REGIONAL TECHNOLOGY GUIDE - NEW YORK METRO. see BUSINESS AND ECONOMICS — Trade And Industrial Directories

REGIONAL TECHNOLOGY GUIDE - NORTHERN CALIFORNIA. see BUSINESS AND ECONOMICS — Trade And Industrial Directories

REGIONAL TECHNOLOGY GUIDE - NORTHERN NEW ENGLAND REGION. see BUSINESS AND ECONOMICS — Trade And Industrial Directories

REGIONAL TECHNOLOGY GUIDE - NORTHWEST REGION. see BUSINESS AND ECONOMICS — Trade And Industrial Directories

REGIONAL TECHNOLOGY GUIDE - SOUTHEAST REGION. see BUSINESS AND ECONOMICS — Trade And Industrial Directories

REGIONAL TECHNOLOGY GUIDE - SOUTHERN CALIFORNIA. see BUSINESS AND ECONOMICS — Trade And Industrial Directories

REGIONAL TECHNOLOGY GUIDE - SOUTHWEST REGION. see BUSINESS AND ECONOMICS — Trade And Industrial Directories

RELIABILITY ENGINEERING AND SYSTEM SAFETY. see ENGINEERING

620 US ISSN 0034-4508
RENSSELAER ENGINEER. 1947. irreg. (2-3/yr.). $10. Rensselaer Polytechnic Institute, Rensselaer Union, Troy, NY 12180-3590. TEL 518-266-6515. Ed. Paul Singh. adv.; bk.rev.; charts; illus. circ. 4,000.
Description: Engineering, science and technology journal of the students of Rensselaer Polytechnic Institute.

REPORTERO INDUSTRIAL; new equipment, machinery and techniques for industry. see MACHINERY

REPUBLIC OF CHINA. NATIONAL SCIENCE COUNCIL PROCEEDINGS. PART D: MATHEMATICS, SCIENCE, AND TECHNOLOGY EDUCATION. see SCIENCES: COMPREHENSIVE WORKS

600 US ISSN 0746-9179
T175 CODEN: REDEEA
RESEARCH & DEVELOPMENT. Abbreviated title: R & D Magazine. 1959. m. $75 (Canada $112; Mexico $105; elsewhere $135). Cahners Publishing Company (Des Plaines), Division of Reed Elsevier Inc., 1350 E. Touhy Ave., Box 5080, Des Plaines, IL 60017-5080. TEL 708-635-8800. FAX 708-390-2618. (Subscr. to: 44 Cook St., Denver, CO 80206. TEL 800-662-7776) Ed. Rob Cassidy. adv.: B&W page 6930, color page $8250. bk.rev.; charts; illus.; stat.; index; circ. 100,000 (controlled). (also avail. in microform; microfiche from CIS) **Indexed:** Abstr.Bull.Inst.Pap.Chem., Anal.Abstr., ASCA, B.P.I., BMT, Br.Ceram.Abstr., Bus.Ind., Cadscan, Ceram.Abstr., Chem.Abstr., Curr.Cont., Curr.Pack.Abstr., Energy Ind., Energy Info.Abstr., Eng.Ind., Excerp.Med., Fluidex, Graph.Arts Lit.Abstr., Ind.Sci.Rev., INSPEC, Int.Aerosp.Abstr., Lead Abstr., Mag.Ind., Met.Abstr., PROMT, Risk Abstr., Sh.& Vib.Dig., SRI, Text.Tech.Dig., Tr.& Indus.Ind., World Alum.Abstr., Zincscan. **Document type:** academic/scholarly publication.
●Also available online. Vendor(s): Knight-Ridder, Inc.
—CASDDS; Ei; Faxon; Genuine Article; SWETS; UMI; UnCover. **CCC.**
Formerly (until 1984): Industrial Research and Development (ISSN 0160-4074); Which was formed by the merger of: Industrial Research (ISSN 0019-8722); Research - Development (ISSN 0034-5199)
Description: Technical review of applied research and development with scientific data from all industrial areas.
Refereed Serial

TECHNOLOGY: COMPREHENSIVE WORKS

600   II
RESEARCH & DEVELOPMENT IN INDUSTRY. 1976. biennial. Rs.50. Department of Science and Technology, New Mehrauli Rd., New Delhi 110016, India. Ed. A.R. Rajeswari. circ. 2,000. **Document type:** government publication.

600 500   JA   ISSN 0289-9329
RESEARCH AND DEVELOPMENT IN JAPAN AWARDED THE OKOCHI MEMORIAL PRIZE. (Text in English) 1970. a. Okochi Kinenkai - Okochi Memorial Foundation, 17-1 Toranomon 1-chome, Minato-ku, Tokyo 105, Japan. **Indexed:** Eng.Ind.

600   US
T175
RESEARCH & DEVELOPMENT PRODUCT SOURCE TELEPHONE DIRECTORY. (Published as an issue of Research & Development (ISSN 0746-9179)) a. $50. Cahners Publishing Company (Des Plaines), Division of Reed Elsevier Inc., 1350 E. Touhy Ave., Des Plaines, IL 60017-5080. TEL 708-635-8800. FAX 708-390-2618. (Subscr. to: 44 Cook St., Denver, CO 80206. TEL 800-662-7776) adv.; circ. 100,000 (controlled). (back issues avail.) **Document type:** directory.
—CASDDS; UMI. **CCC.**
Formerly (until 1992): Research and Development Telephone Directory.

620   II   ISSN 0034-513X
T1   CODEN: RSIDAO
RESEARCH AND INDUSTRY; a journal for entrepreneurs and technologists. (Text in English) 1956. q. Rs.250($100) Council of Scientific and Industrial Research, Publications & Information Directorate, Hillside Rd., New Delhi 110 012, India. TEL 91-11-5786301. FAX 91-11-5731353. TELEX 031-77271 PID IN. E-mail: pid@sirnetd.ernet.in. Eds. V.K. Sharma, M.M.S. Karki. adv.; bk.rev.; abstr.; charts; illus.; tr.lit.; index. circ. 800. **Indexed:** CAD CAM Abstr., Cadscan, Chem.Abstr., Energy Info.Abstr., Environ.Abstr., Food Sci.& Tech.Abstr., ISMEC, Lead Abstr., Soils & Fert., Tel.Abstr., Zincscan. **Document type:** academic/scholarly publication.
—BLDSC (7715.300000); CASDDS; Ei; Genuine Article.

RESEARCH ENGINEERING MANUFACTURING. see ENGINEERING

RESEARCH IN PHILOSOPHY AND TECHNOLOGY. see PHILOSOPHY

600   US   ISSN 0737-1071
HD45
RESEARCH ON TECHNOLOGICAL INNOVATION, MANAGEMENT AND POLICY. 1983. a. $63.50 to institutions. J A I Press Inc., 55 Old Post Rd., No. 2, Box 1678, Greenwich, CT 06836-1678. TEL 203-661-7602. Ed. Richard S. Rosenbloom.
—BLDSC (7773.714000). **CCC.**
Refereed Serial

667.2   UK   ISSN 0557-9325
TP890   CODEN: RWPCAG
REVIEW OF PROGRESS IN COLORATION AND RELATED TOPICS. 1970. a. £13.50. Society of Dyers and Colourists, Box 244, Perkin House, Bradford, Yorkshire BD1 2JB, England. TEL 01274-725138. FAX 01274-392888. Ed. Paul Dinsdale. circ. 3,500. (also avail. in microfilm) **Indexed:** Abstr.Bull.Inst.Pap.Chem., Art & Archaeol.Tech.Abstr., Chem.Abstr., Text.Tech.Dig., World Surf.Coat., World Text.Abstr. **Document type:** trade publication.
—BLDSC (7794.160000); CASDDS; Ei; Faxon; SWETS.
Description: Review articles on coloration.

600 500   FR
REVIEWS OF NATIONAL SCIENCE AND TECHNOLOGY POLICY. irreg. price varies. Organization for Economic Cooperation and Development, 2 rue Andre-Pascal, 75775 Paris Cedex 16, France. (U.S. orders to: O.E.C.D. Publications and Information Center, 2001 L St., N.W., Ste. 700, Washington, DC 20036-4910. TEL 202-785-6323) (also avail. in microfiche from OEC,CIS) **Indexed:** IIS.

REVISTA DE EGRESADOS. see COLLEGE AND ALUMNI

600   CU
REVISTA TECNOLOGICA. 1962-1975; resumed. s-a. $24 in S. America; N. America $26; elsewhere $30. Ministerio de Industria Basica, Avda. Carlos III No. 666, Havana, Cuba. (Dist. by: Ediciones Cubanas, Obispo No. 527, Apdo. 605, Havana, Cuba) **Indexed:** GeoRef.
Formerly: Nuestra Industria. Revista Tecnologia (ISSN 0029-5736)

REVUE D'HISTOIRE DES SCIENCES. see SCIENCES: COMPREHENSIVE WORKS

REVUE DES INGENIEURS ET TECHNICIENS EUROPEENS. see ENGINEERING

600 620   SZ   ISSN 0374-4256
LA REVUE POLYTECHNIQUE. (Text in French) 1898. m. 60 SFr. (foreign 150 SFr.). Marcel Meichtry Editions, Chemin de la Caroline 26, CH-1213 Petit-Lancy - Geneva, Switzerland. TEL 022-7921027. FAX 022-928834. TELEX 422098-HSPI-CH. Ed. Alexandre Kanel. adv. contact: Andre Almy. bk.rev.; bibl.; charts; illus.; tr.lit. circ. 10,200. **Indexed:** Cyb.Abstr. **Document type:** trade publication.
—BLDSC (7942.560000).
Description: Provides technical information of relevance to Swiss machine, electronics and information technology industries.

620   LU   ISSN 0035-4260
    CODEN: RTLXA4
REVUE TECHNIQUE LUXEMBOURGEOISE. (Text in English, French and German) 1908. q. 1800 Fr. Association Luxembourgeoise des Ingenieurs, Architectes et Industriels, 4 bd. Grande-Duchesse Charlotte, 1330 Luxembourg, Luxembourg. TEL 45-13-54. FAX 45-09-32. Ed. Michel Pundel. adv.; bk.rev.; bibl.; index. circ. 3,000. **Indexed:** Chem.Abstr., Eng.Ind., Met.Abstr., World Alum.Abstr. **Document type:** trade publication.
—CASDDS.

RIVISTA DEL CONSULENTE TECNICO. see LAW

ROCKY MOUNTAIN HIGH TECHNOLOGY DIRECTORY. see BUSINESS AND ECONOMICS — Trade And Industrial Directories

679.9   GW   ISSN 0035-7863
ROHSTOFF RUNDSCHAU; Fachblatt des gesamten Handels mit Alt- und Abfallstoffen. 1938. s-m. DM.162. Reed Elsevier Deutschland GmbH (Subsidiary of: Reed Elsevier group), Hans-Cornelius-Str. 4, 82166 Graefelfing, Germany. TEL 089-855021. FAX 089-853799. TELEX 522451. Ed. Burkhard Bierschenck. adv. contact: Elke Mueller. illus.; stat.; index. **Document type:** trade publication.
—**CCC.**

ROYAL SOCIETY NEWS. see SCIENCES: COMPREHENSIVE WORKS

600   SA
S A INSTRUMENTATION & CONTROL. (Text in English) m. R.30. Technews (Pty) Ltd., P.O. Box 626, Kloof 3640, South Africa. TEL 27-31-764-0593. FAX 27-31-764-0386. Ed. Mike Barker. circ. 5,674 (controlled). **Document type:** trade publication.
Formerly: Computech.
Description: Covers advanced industrial technology: automation, computation, instrumentation.

S & T POST. (Science and Technology) see SCIENCES: COMPREHENSIVE WORKS

600   II   ISSN 0970-8715
S E N D O C BULLETIN. PART 1: INDUSTRY AND TECHNOLOGY. (Text in English) 1973. m. Rs.150($75) National Institute of Small Industry Extension Training, Small Enterprises National Documentation Centre, Yousufguda, Hyderabad 500045, India. TEL 91-40-238544. FAX 91-40-238547. TELEX 425-6381-SIET-IN. Ed. K. Subhashini. **Document type:** abstracting/indexing.

300 600   US
S H O T NEWSLETTER. 1969. q. $5 membership. Society for the History of Technology, c/o Bruce Seely, Secretary, Michigan Technological University, Department of Social Sciences, 1400 Townsend Dr., Houghton, MI 49931-1295. TEL 906-487-2459. FAX 906-487-2468. E-mail: BSEELY@MTU.edu. adv. circ. 1,800. (back issues avail.) **Document type:** newsletter.
Description: Circulates news among members of the Society.

600 629.3   US   ISSN 0747-623X
S O L ETTER. 1966. m. (11/yr.). $15 membership. Society of Logistics Engineers, 8100 Professional Pl., No. 211, New Carollton, MD 20785-2225. TEL 800-695-7653. FAX 301-459-1522. Ed. Marya B. Anderson. adv.; tr.lit. circ. 8,500. (back issues avail.) **Document type:** academic/scholarly publication.
—**CCC.**
Description: Publishes updates of topics and events for the society, as well as the field of logistics.

600 500   JA
S T A: ITS ROLES AND ACTIVITIES. (Science and Technology Agency) (Text in English) a. free. Kagaku Gijutsu-cho, 2-1 Kasumigaseki 2-chome, Chiyoda-ku, Tokyo 100, Japan. FAX 81-3-3593-1370. **Document type:** government publication.

600   FR   ISSN 1010-5247
S T I REVIEW. (Science Technology Industry) French edition: S T I Revue (ISSN 1010-5239) 1986. s-a. 180 F.($42) Organization for Economic Cooperation and Development, 2 rue Andre-Pascal, 75775 Paris Cedex 16, France. (U.S. orders to: O.E.C.D. Publications and Information Center, 2001 L St., N.W., Ste. 700, Washington, DC 20036-4910. TEL 202-785-6323) (also avail. in microfiche from OEC,CIS) **Indexed:** Environ.Abstr., IIS, Tel.Abstr.
—BLDSC (8464.758000); UnCover.
Description: Contains reports and articles on science, technology and industry policy issues which are of current interest to the member countries of the organization.

600 500   JA   ISSN 0289-7016
S U T BULLETIN. (Text and summaries in Japanese) 1984. m. (Science University of Tokyo - Tokyo Rika Daigaku) Tokyo Rika Daigaku Shuppankai - Science University of Tokyo Press, 1-3 Kagurazaka, Shinjuku-ku, Tokyo 162, Japan.
Description: Contains reviews and commentary.

S U T NEWS. (Society for Underwater Technology) see EARTH SCIENCES — Oceanography

SALARIES OF SCIENTISTS, ENGINEERS AND TECHNICIANS; a summary of salary surveys. see OCCUPATIONS AND CAREERS

SAMUEL NEAMAN INSTITUTE FOR ADVANCED STUDIES IN SCIENCE AND TECHNOLOGY. ANNUAL REPORT. see SCIENCES: COMPREHENSIVE WORKS

SANG TAO/CREATIVITY. see BUSINESS AND ECONOMICS

658.5   JA   ISSN 0036-4371
SANGYO GIJUTSU JOHO YOKKAICHI/INDUSTRIAL AND TECHNOLOGICAL INFORMATION OF YOKKAICHI CITY. (Text in Japanese) 1961. m. free. Yokkaichi-shiritsu Toshokan - Yokkaichi City Library, 2-42 Kubota 1-chome, Yokkaichi-shi, Mie-ken 510, Japan. bk.rev.; charts; illus.; pat.; circ. controlled. (processed)

SANTA CLARA COMPUTER AND HIGH-TECHNOLOGY LAW JOURNAL. see LAW

SASKATCHEWAN RESEARCH COUNCIL. ANNUAL REPORT. see SCIENCES: COMPREHENSIVE WORKS

SAUDI-ARABIAN SASO STANDARDS MICROFILE. see ENGINEERING

SCHOOL SCENE. see EDUCATION

600   GW   ISSN 0946-7939
▼**SCHUETTGUT.** 1995. q. DM.198. Trans Tech Publications, Berlinerstr. 2, 38678 Clausthal-Zellerfeld, Germany. TEL 05323-9697-0. FAX 05323-969799. adv.: B&W page DM.3000, color page DM.4500; trim 270 x 180. circ. 7,500. **Document type:** trade publication.
Description: Interdisciplinary journal for the powder and bulk handling industries.

SCIENCE AND PUBLIC POLICY. see *SCIENCES: COMPREHENSIVE WORKS*

SCIENCE AND TECHNOLOGY. see *SCIENCES: COMPREHENSIVE WORKS*

SCIENCE AND TECHNOLOGY DESK REFERENCE. see *SCIENCES: COMPREHENSIVE WORKS*

SCIENCE AND TECHNOLOGY IN CHINA. see *SCIENCES: COMPREHENSIVE WORKS*

SCIENCE AND TECHNOLOGY IN JAPAN. see *SCIENCES: COMPREHENSIVE WORKS*

SCIENCE AND TECHNOLOGY IN JAPAN. see *SCIENCES: COMPREHENSIVE WORKS*

SCIENCE STUDIES; a Scandinavian journal. see *SCIENCES: COMPREHENSIVE WORKS*

SCIENCE, TECHNOLOGY & DEVELOPMENT; journal of the Third World Science, Technology & Development Forum. see *BUSINESS AND ECONOMICS — International Development And Assistance*

620   UK   ISSN 0141-9099
SCIENCE TECHNOLOGY JOURNAL. Cover title: Science Technology. 1955. q. membership. Institute of Science Technology, Mansell House, 22 Bore St., Lichfield, Staffs. WS13 6LP, England. TEL 01543-251346. FAX 01543-415804. Ed. Ian Gray. adv.; bk.rev.; abstr.; circ. 2,000 (controlled). **Indexed:** Art & Archaeol.Tech.Abstr. **Document type:** academic/scholarly publication.
—BLDSC (8164.830000).
Formerly (until 1989): Institute of Science Technology. Bulletin (ISSN 0020-3130)

SCIENTIFIC AND TECHNICAL INFORMATION IN FOREIGN COUNTRIES/KAIGAKI KAGAKU GIJUTSU JOHO SHIRYO. see *SCIENCES: COMPREHENSIVE WORKS*

SCIENTIFIC, ENGINEERING, TECHNICAL MANPOWER COMMENTS. see *OCCUPATIONS AND CAREERS*

600   AT   ISSN 0725-900X
SCITECH. 1981. m. Aus.$245 (foreign Aus.$275). Scitech Publication Pty. Ltd., G.P.O. Box 1915, Canberra, A.C.T. 2601, Australia. TEL 062-477-220. FAX 62-496648. Ed. Jane Ford. circ. 1,300. (back issues avail.)

621.9   UK   ISSN 0266-7428
SCOTTISH INDUSTRIAL HISTORY. 1969. a. £20. Business Archives Council of Scotland, The Archives, University of Glasgow, Glasgow G12 8QQ, Scotland. FAX 041-330-4158. TELEX 777070-UNIGLA. Ed. Lesley Richmond. adv.; bk.rev.; illus. circ. 400. (processed) **Document type:** academic/scholarly publication.
Formerly: S S I A and S S P H M Newsletter.

600 607   US   ISSN 0080-830X
SCRIPPS CLINIC AND RESEARCH FOUNDATION. ANNUAL REPORT. 1924. a. free. Scripps Clinic and Research Foundation, 10666 N. Torrey Pines Rd., La Jolla, CA 92037. TEL 619-455-9100. FAX 619-554-8841. circ. 5,000.

600   IT
SCUOLAOFFICINA; periodico di cultura tecnica. vol.11, 1992. s-a. L.10000. Casa dell'Innovazione Industriale, Via Bassanelli 9-11, 40129 Bologna, Italy. TEL 051-370367. FAX 051-353500. Ed. Roberto Curti.

600   JA   ISSN 0037-105X
CODEN: SEKEAI
SEISAN KENKYU/PRODUCTION RESEARCH. (Text in English and Japanese) 1949. m. free. University of Tokyo, Institute of Industrial Science - Tokyo Daigaku Seisan Gijutsu Kenkyujo, 7-22-1 Roppongi, Minato-ku, Tokyo, Japan. TEL 03-3402-6231. FAX 03-3423-8665. TELEX 0242-3216 IISTYO J. Ed. Michio Nagumo. charts; illus. circ. 1,980. **Indexed:** Abstr.J.Earthq.Eng., Appl.Mech.Rev., Chem.Abstr., INSPEC, Robomat. (until 1992). **Document type:** academic/scholarly publication.
—BLDSC (8219.800000); CASDDS.

SELSKOSTOPANSKA TEKHNIKA. see *AGRICULTURE — Agricultural Equipment*

SEMINAR REPORTEUR; journal of science and technology. see *SCIENCES: COMPREHENSIVE WORKS*

SENSOR BUSINESS DIGEST; the essential international business resource on sensors and instrumentation. see *BUSINESS AND ECONOMICS — Marketing And Purchasing*

600 614.7   US   ISSN 1079-3542
SERVICE INSIGHTS. 1977. m. $35. Heather Publishing Co., Box 201427, Arlington, TX 76006. TEL 817-860-2375. FAX 817-548-0004. Ed. Bill Akins. adv. contact: Donna Akins. circ. 28,500. **Document type:** trade publication.
Formerly: Exhaust News (ISSN 0192-7469)

600   RU   ISSN 0321-2653
T4   CODEN: ISSND8
SEVERO-KAVKAZSKII NAUCHNYI TSENTR VYSSHEI SHKOLY. TEKHNICHESKIE NAUKI. IZVIESTIYA/NORTH-CAUCASUS SCIENTIFIC CENTER OF HIGH SCHOOL. TECHNICAL SCIENCE. NEWS. 4/yr. 7.20 Rub. Rostovski Universitet, Ul. Pyshkinskaia 160, 344 700 Rostov-na-Donu, Russia. TEL 8-8630536411. TELEX 123520.
—BLDSC (0082.323000); CASDDS.

600 500   CC   ISSN 0253-9942
Q4   CODEN: SCTPDH
SHANGHAI JIAOTONG DAXUE XUEBAO/SHANGHAI JIAOTONG UNIVERSITY. BULLETIN. (Text in Chinese; summaries in Chinese and English) 1984. bi-m. Y1.5. Shanghai Jiaotong Daxue - Shanghai Jiaotong University, Library, 1954 Huashan Lu, Shanghai 200030, People's Republic of China. TEL 4310310. circ. 3,000. **Indexed:** Chem.Abstr., INSPEC (1987-), Math.R.
—CASDDS.
Description: Covers education, research and alumni affairs in the university.

600   CN   ISSN 1188-973X
SHIFT. 1992. q. Can.$18 ($25 in U.S.) (effective through 1996). Shift Magazine Inc., 174 Spandina Ave., Ste. 407, Toronto, ON M5T 2C2, Canada. TEL 416-504-1887. FAX 416-504-1889. E-mail: info@shift.com; Site addr.: http://www.shift.com/shift.home. Ed. Evan Solomon; Pub. Andrew Heintzman. adv.: B&W page Can.$1525; trim 10 7/8 x 8 3/8; adv. contact: Colin Ground. circ. 10,000 (paid); 10,000(controlled). **Indexed:** Can.B.P.I. **Document type:** consumer publication.

SHIJIE FAMING/REVIEW OF WORLD INVENTIONS. see *SCIENCES: COMPREHENSIVE WORKS*

SHIJIE KEXUE JISHU/WORLD SCIENCE AND TECHNOLOGY. see *SCIENCES: COMPREHENSIVE WORKS*

600   JA   ISSN 0387-0014
CODEN: SHIZAO
SHIZEN/NATURE. (Text in Japanese) 1946. m. 8450 Yen. Chuokoron-Sha, Inc., 8-7, Kyobashi 2-chome, Chuo-ku, Tokyo 104, Japan. Ed. Akihiko Okabe. **Indexed:** Chem.Abstr.
—CASDDS.

SHOW TECHNOLOGY MAGAZINE. see *COMMUNICATIONS*

600   GW   ISSN 0934-9391
SIEG TECH. 1985. 20/yr. DM.570. Sieg Tech Verlags GmbH, Gottfried-Claren-Str. 21, 53225 Bonn, Germany. TEL 0228-466034. FAX 0228-477418. Ed. Manfred Sieg. adv.; bk.rev. circ. 15,000. (back issues avail.) **Document type:** trade publication.

SMITHSONIAN. see *SOCIAL SCIENCES: COMPREHENSIVE WORKS*

SOCIEDAD LATINOAMERICANA DE HISTORIA DE LA CIENCIA Y LA TECNOLOGIA. BOLETIN INFORMATIVO. see *SCIENCES: COMPREHENSIVE WORKS*

338   FR   ISSN 0037-9441
T2
SOCIETE INDUSTRIELLE DE MULHOUSE. BULLETIN. 1828. q. 330 F. (foreign 360 F.). Societe Industrielle de Mulhouse, 10 rue de la Bourse, B.P. 1329, 68056 Mulhouse Cedex, France. FAX 89-45-46-47. Ed. Gerard Schmidt. adv.; bk.rev.; illus.; cum.index: 1946-1970. circ. 3,000. (back issues avail.)

600   US   ISSN 0160-1067
T37
SOCIETY FOR INDUSTRIAL ARCHEOLOGY NEWSLETTER. 1972. q. $35 to individuals; institutions $40; students $20 (includes Industrial Archeology). Society for Industrial Archeology, Department of Social Sciences, Michigan Technological University, Houghton, MI 49931. Ed. Robert M. Frame, III. bk.rev.; bibl. circ. 1,600. **Indexed:** Avery Ind.Archit.Per. **Document type:** newsletter.
Description: Examines current activity in the preservation of post-18th century technologies and industries.

SOCIETY FOR INFORMATION DISPLAY. SYMPOSIUM DIGEST. see *ENGINEERING*

667.2   UK   ISSN 0037-9859
TP890   CODEN: JSDCAA
SOCIETY OF DYERS AND COLOURISTS. JOURNAL. 1884. 10/yr. £130 to non-members (includes Review of Progress in Coloration and Related Topics). Society of Dyers and Colourists, Box 244, Perkin House, Grattan Rd., Bradford, Yorkshire BD1 2JB, England. TEL 01274-725138. FAX 01274-392888. Ed. Paul Dinsdale. adv.; bk.rev.; abstr.; bibl.; charts; illus.; stat.; index. circ. 3,500. (also avail. in microform from UMI) **Indexed:** A.S.& T.Ind., Anal.Abstr., Art & Archaeol.Tech.Abstr., Br.Tech.Ind., Chem.Abstr., Chem.Eng.Abstr., Curr.Cont., Curr.Leather Lit., Excerp.Med., Text.Tech.Dig., W.R.C.Inf., World Surf.Coat., World Text.Abstr. **Document type:** trade publication.
—BLDSC (4886.000000); CASDDS; Ei; Faxon; SWETS; UnCover.
Description: Research and practical papers on coloration.

600 629.13   US   ISSN 0885-3916
SOCIETY OF LOGISTICS ENGINEERS. ANNALS. 1986. a. $15 to non-members. Society of Logistics Engineers, 8100 Professional Pl., No. 211, New Carollton, MD 20785-2225. TEL 800-695-7653. FAX 301-459-1522. TELEX 469527. Ed. Benjamin Ostrofsky. circ. 2,500. **Document type:** academic/scholarly publication.
—CCC.
Description: Provides a forum for the research and exchange of scholarly opinions in the disciplines identified with logistics.

600   US   ISSN 0893-3499
SOCIETY OF LOGISTICS ENGINEERS. PROCEEDINGS. Variant title: International Logistics Symposium Proceedings. 1966. a. price varies. Society of Logistics Engineers, 8100 Professional Pl., No. 211, New Carollton, MD 20785-2225. TEL 800-695-7653. FAX 301-459-1522. (reprint service avail. from UMI) **Document type:** proceedings.
—CCC.

SOGO GAKUJUTSU KENKYU SHUKAI. see *SCIENCES: COMPREHENSIVE WORKS*

600 500   JA   ISSN 0289-5560
SOGO KENKYUJO HOKOKU. (Text in Japanese) 1984. a. Tokyo Rika Daigaku, Sogo Kenkyujo - Science University of Tokyo, Research Institute for Science and Technology, 2641 Yamazaki, Noda-shi, Chiba-ken 278, Japan.
Description: Provides news of the institute.

600 747   FR   ISSN 0339-1507
SOL ET MURS MAGAZINE. 1976. q. 70 F. S.E.P Edition, 194-196 rue Marcadet, 75018 Paris, France. Ed. Catherine Bouillon.

613.1   US   ISSN 1062-0400
SOLAR MIND. 1990. bi-m. $25 to individuals; students and non-profit organizations $12. Joe Stephenson, Ed. & Pub., 759 S. State St., No. 81, Ukiah, CA 95482.
Description: Explores alternative approaches to technology and its relationship to the environment.

604.24   SA   ISSN 0036-0643
SOUTH AFRICAN DRAUGHTSMAN/S A TEKENAAR. Variant title: S A Draughtsman. (Text in Afrikaans, English) vol.5, 1970. a. membership. South African Institute of Draughtsmen - Suid Afrikaanse Instituut van Tekenaars, P.O. Box 30, Bergvliet 7864, South Africa. TEL 27-21-750156. FAX 27-21-750156. Ed. W.H. Young. adv.; bk.rev.; charts; illus.; stat.; circ. 3,000 (controlled). **Document type:** newsletter.
Description: News of interest to members of the institute.

6258 TECHNOLOGY: COMPREHENSIVE WORKS

SOUTH AFRICAN JOURNAL OF AGRICULTURAL EXTENSION/SUID-AFRIKAANSE TYDSKRIF VIR LANDBOUVOORLIGTING. see *AGRICULTURE*

SOUTH AFRICAN JOURNAL OF ANTARCTIC RESEARCH. see *SCIENCES: COMPREHENSIVE WORKS*

SOUTH AFRICAN NATIONAL ANTARCTIC PROGRAMME. ANNUAL REPORT TO S C A R. see *SCIENCES: COMPREHENSIVE WORKS*

600 NL ISSN 0081-2862
DU1   CODEN: SPCTAW
SOUTH PACIFIC COMMISSION. TECHNICAL PAPER. French edition: Commission de Pacifique Sud. Document Technique (ISSN 0489-958X) (Text in English) 1949. irreg., no.204, 1994. South Pacific Commission, B.P. D5, Noumea, Cedex, New Caledonia. TEL 687-262000. FAX 687-263818. TELEX 3139 NM SOPACOM. **Indexed:** Rev.Plant Path. **Document type:** monographic series.
—BLDSC (8700.900000).

629.1 UK ISSN 0892-9270
TL787 CODEN: SPTEE8
SPACE TECHNOLOGY; industrial and commercial applications. 1981. bi-m. £435($692) (effective 1996). Elsevier Science Ltd., Pergamon, P.O. Box 800, Kidlington, Oxford OX5 1DX, England. TEL 44-1865-843000. FAX 44-1865-843010. E-mail: nlinfo-f@elsevier.nl; usinfo-f@elsevier.com; forinfo-kyf04035@niftyserve.or.jp; Site addr.: http://www.elsevier.nl/. (Subscr. in U.S. and Canada to: Elsevier Science, 660 White Plains Rd., Tarrytown, NY 10591-5153. TEL 914-524-9200. FAX 914-333-2444) Ed. R. Monti. adv.; pat. circ. 2,000. (also avail. in microfilm from UMI) **Indexed:** Cadscan, Curr.Cont., Deep Sea Res.& Oceanogr.Abstr., Energy Ind., Energy Info.Abstr., Environ.Per.Bibl., Geo.Abstr., INSPEC, Int.Aerosp.Abstr., Intl.Civil Eng.Abstr., Lead Abstr., Risk Abstr., Robomat., Soft.Abstr.Eng., Zincscan. **Document type:** academic/scholarly publication.
—BLDSC (8361.656000); Ei; Faxon; Genuine Article; SWETS; UMI; UnCover. **CCC.**
 Former titles: Earth-Oriented Applications of Space Technology (ISSN 0277-4488); (until 1982): Advances in Earth-Oriented Applications of Space Technology (ISSN 0191-538V)
 Refereed Serial

600 500 BL ISSN 0101-1529
SPECTRUM; jornal brasileiro ciencias. bi-m. Cr.$3600($45) Editora Spectrum Ltda., Av. Santa Ines, 836 - sala 2, 02415 Sao Paulo SP, Brazil. Eds. Eduardo Subacius, Sandra Maria Rodrigues Subacius. circ. 10,000.

SPECULATIONS IN SCIENCE AND TECHNOLOGY; an international journal devoted to speculative papers in the physical, mathematical, biological and engineering sciences. see *SCIENCES: COMPREHENSIVE WORKS*

600 NE ISSN 0168-468X
SPEUR- EN ONTWIKKELINGSWERK IN NEDERLAND/RESEARCH AND DEVELOPMENT ACTIVITIES IN THE NETHERLANDS. (Text in Dutch and English) 1959. a. Centraal Bureau voor de Statistiek, Prinses Beatrixlaan 428, Voorburg, Netherlands. (Dist. by: SDU - Publishers, Christoffel Plantijnstraat, The Hague, Netherlands) **Document type:** government publication.

600 US ISSN 0148-2203
T1
SPINOFF. a. U.S. National Aeronautics and Space Administration, Office of Space and Terrestrial Applications, Box 8756, Baltimore-Washington International Airport, MD 21240. TEL 202-755-2320. (Orders to: Supt. of Documents, Washington, DC 20402) illus. **Indexed:** Ind.How To Do It.
—Faxon.

745.2 US ISSN 0049-1888
SPOKESMAN. 1964. 5/yr. $6 to libraries and non-members. New York State Industrial Arts Association, c/o James D. Maxim, Ed., 9 Bristol St., Cuba, NY 14727. TEL 716-968-3734. adv.; bk.rev.; charts; illus. circ. 3,500.
 Incorporates: Spokesman Journal.

600 YU ISSN 0081-3974
SRPSKA AKADEMIJA NAUKA I UMETNOSTI. ODELJENJE TEHNICKIH NAUKA. GLAS. (Text in Serbo-Croatian; summaries in English, French, German or Russian) N.S. 1949. irreg. price varies. Srpska Akademija Nauka i Umetnosti, Knez Mihailova 35, 11001 Belgrade, Serbia, Yugoslavia. FAX 38-11-182-825. TELEX 72593 SANU YU. (Dist. by: Prosveta, Terazije 16, Belgrade, Serbia, Yugoslavia) circ. 500. **Indexed:** Art & Archaeol.Tech.Abstr., Chem.Abstr., INSPEC (1979-), Met.Abstr., World Alum.Abstr.

600 YU ISSN 0081-4040
SRPSKA AKADEMIJA NAUKA I UMETNOSTI. ODELJENJE TEHNICKIH NAUKA. POSEBNA IZDANJA. (Text in Serbo-Croatian; summaries in English, French, German or Russian) 1950. irreg. price varies. Srpska Akademija Nauka i Umetnosti, Knez Mihailova 35, 11001 Belgrade, Serbia, Yugoslavia. FAX 38-11-182-825. TELEX 72593 SANU YU. (Dist. by: Prosveta, Terazije 16, Belgrade, Serbia, Yugoslavia) circ. 600. **Indexed:** Ref.Zh.

600 IT ISSN 1121-063X
STAMPI; progettazione e produzione. m. L.35000 (foreign L.125000) (effective 1995). Tecniche Nuove s.p.a., Via C. Menotti, 14, 20129 Milan, Italy. TEL 02-75701. FAX 02-7610351. adv.: B&W page L.1650000, color page L.2470000; trim 185 x 266.

600 US ISSN 1049-8605
T11
STANDARDIZATION OF TECHNICAL TERMINOLOGY. 1983. irreg. American Society for Testing and Materials, 1916 Race St., Philadelphia, PA 19103.

STEEL INDIA. see *METALLURGY*

621.86 UK ISSN 0039-1832
STORAGE HANDLING DISTRIBUTION. 1953. m. £72 (foreign £89). Turret Group Plc., Turret House, 171 High St., Rickmansworth, Herts WD3 1SN, England. TEL 01923-777000. FAX 01923-771297. Ed. Lloyd Arkill. adv.; illus.; tr.lit. circ. 18,300. **Indexed:** BMT, Br.Tech.Ind., INSPEC, Int.Packag.Abstr., Packag.Sci.Tech. **Document type:** trade publication.
—BLDSC (8466.360000).

STUDIEN ZU SPRACHE UND TECHNIK. see *LINGUISTICS*

600 IS
STUDIES IN TECHNOLOGY. (Text in Hebrew) q. Ort Israel Pedagogical Center, Derech Hatayasim 28, Tel Aviv 67299, Israel. TEL 972-3-395057. FAX 972-6310282. Ed. Rafi Nachmias.

604 US ISSN 0896-1905
STUDIES IN TECHNOLOGY AND SOCIAL CHANGE SERIES. 1988. irreg., no.18, 1990. price varies. Iowa State University, Technology and Social Change Program, Ames, IA 50011. Dir. Eric Abbott.
—BLDSC (8491.790500).

620 RM ISSN 0039-4017
TA350 CODEN: SCMAA2
STUDII SI CERCETARI DE MECANICA APLICATA. 1950. 6/yr. 330 lei($69) (Academia Romana) Editura Academiei Romane, Calea Victoriei 125, 79717 Bucharest, Rumania. (Dist. by: Rompresfilatelia, Calea Grivitei 64-66, P.O. Box 12-201, 78104 Bucharest, Rumania) Ed. Ioan Anton. bk.rev.; charts; illus.; index. circ. 1,000. **Indexed:** Appl.Mech.Rev., Chem.Abstr., Math.R., Met.Abstr.
—CASDDS.

600 SP ISSN 0214-3046
SU FUTURO. 1988. 12/yr. 1300 ptas. Editorial Andina, S.A., Caridad 24, Pozuelo Estacion, 28023 Madrid, Spain. TEL 1-352-09-18. FAX 1-352-63-30. Ed. Pedro Bucher. adv. contact: Angelines Lagos. circ. 40,000.

600 JA ISSN 0387-1304
T4 CODEN: SJGHA8
SUMITOMO JUKIKAI GIHO/SUMITOMO HEAVY INDUSTRIES TECHNICAL REVIEW. (Text in Japanese; summaries in English) 1949. 3/yr. free. Sumitomo Jukikai Kogyo K.K. - Sumitomo Heavy Industries, Ltd., 2-1, Otemachi 2-chome, Chiyoda-ku, Tokyo 100, Japan. Ed. Hiroyasu Taniguthi. **Indexed:** Chem.Abstr., INIS Atomind. **Document type:** academic/scholarly publication, bulletin.
—BLDSC (8725.818000); CASDDS.

600 500 JA
SUMMARY OF WHITE PAPER ON SCIENCE AND TECHNOLOGY. (Text in English) a. (Kagaku Gijutsu-cho - Science and Technology Agency) Foreign Press Center - Forin Puresu Senta, 2-1 Uchisaiwai-cho 2-chome, Chiyoda-ku, Tokyo 100, Japan. abstr.

SUPERCONDUCTIVITY: PHYSICS, CHEMISTRY, TECHNOLOGY. see *PHYSICS*

SWAZILAND JOURNAL OF SCIENCE AND TECHNOLOGY. see *SCIENCES: COMPREHENSIVE WORKS*

SWIAT NAUKI. see *SCIENCES: COMPREHENSIVE WORKS*

600 FR ISSN 0988-5730
SYSTEMES EXPERTS. 22/yr. 2800 F. A Jour, 11 rue du Marche St. Honore, 75001 Paris, France. TEL 42-96-67-22. Ed. Cecile Cliquot de Mentque.

600 US ISSN 1041-6587
T I E S. (Technology, Innovation and Entrepreneurship for Students) 1988. bi-m. $25. Trenton State College, Hillwood Lakes, CN 4700, Trenton, NJ 08650-4700. TEL 609-771-3331. FAX 609-771-3330. (Co-sponsor: Drexel University) Ed. Patricia Hutchinson; Pub. Ronald Todd. adv. contact: Frank Nemeyer. bk.rev. circ. 44,000. **Document type:** trade publication.
 Description: Supports design and technology education from middle school through high school, with articles addressing the problem-solving nature, systems, impacts and history of technology.

T I S T R RESEARCH NEWS. (Thailand Institute of Scientific and Technological Research) see *SCIENCES: COMPREHENSIVE WORKS*

600 DK ISSN 0901-7917
T L - TEKNIKEREN. 22/yr. Teknisk Landsforbund, Noerre Voldgade 12, 1358 Copenhagen K, Denmark. Ed. Hans Daugaard. adv. circ. 21,193.
 Former titles (until 1985): T L Teknikeren (ISSN 0901-7895); (until 1966): Teknikeren (ISSN 0040-229X); (until 1929): Teknisk Landsforbund.

T N C - AKTUELLT; information fraan Tekniska Nomenklaturcentralen. (Tekniska Nomenklaturcentralen) see *LINGUISTICS*

600
T SQUARED NEWSLETTER.* m. $75. Technology Transfer Society, 55 S. State Ave., Ste. 3-F2, Indianapolis, IN 46201-7876. TEL 317-262-5022. Ed. K. Hayes. (tabloid format; back issues avail.) **Document type:** newsletter.
 Description: Methods, meetings, models, theories and results describing the management, diffusion and transfer of technology.

600 IS ISSN 0334-9527
TAGLIT. (Text in Hebrew) 1987. 8/m. free. P.O. Box 17255, Tel Aviv 61171, Israel. TEL 03-806122. FAX 03-7520698. Ed. David Butbul. circ. 10,000.

600 PH ISSN 0116-4333
TECH TIPS. 1986. bi-m. P.200 (foreign $45). Science and Technology Information Institute, Department of Science and Technology, P.O. Box 3596, Manila, Philippines. TEL 822-0954.
 Description: Profiles the current technological breakthroughs.

600 UK ISSN 1353-4904
TECH TRANSFER INTERNATIONAL. m. World Business Publications Ltd., Britannia House, 4th Fl., 960 High Rd., London N12 9RY, England. TEL 081-446-5141. FAX 081-446-3659. Ed. Susan Boobis; Pub. Lawrence Cooklin. **Document type:** trade publication.
—BLDSC (8614.726500).
 Formerly (until 1994): Technology Transfer International.

TECHNOLOGY: COMPREHENSIVE WORKS

600　　　　　　　SZ　　ISSN 0040-0866
T4　　　　　　　　　　CODEN: TCHNAR
TECHNICA; international technical review. (Text in German) 1951. 26/yr. 75 SFr. Industrie-Verlag AG, Muehlebachstr. 43, CH-8032 Zurich, Switzerland. Ed. M Gysi. adv.; bk.rev.; illus.; index. circ. 19,300. Indexed: BMT, C.I.S. Abstr., Chem.Abstr., Excerp.Med., INSPEC, Met.Abstr. **Document type:** trade publication.
—BLDSC (8614.850000); CASDDS; Ei; SWETS. **CCC.**
　Description: Devoted to research in all fields of technology in the machine industry. Covers mechanization, automation, controls, manufacturing, instruments and materials. Includes reports of events, new products, industry news, and positions available.

600　　　　　　　SZ　　ISSN 1012-294X
TC1　　　　　　　　　　CODEN: TBVEEX
TECHNICAL BULLETIN VEVEY. * 1985. a. Vevey Engineering Works Ltd., CH-1844 Villeneuve, Switzerland. **Indexed:** INSPEC (1985-).
　Formerly: Bulletin Technique Vevey.

600　　　　　　　US
TECHNICAL EMPLOYMENT NEWS; including captsule job listings. 1957. w. $51. Publications & Communications, Inc., 12416 Hymeadow Dr., Austin, TX 78750-1896. TEL 512-331-3918. FAX 512-331-3900. (Subscr. to: Box 399, Cedar Park, TX 78613-9987) Ed. Betty Craft. adv. circ. 10,000. (back issues avail.)
　Formerly: P - D News (ISSN 0478-9997)
　Description: Covers the contract technical services industry.

600　　　　　　　UK　　ISSN 0267-5307
TECHNICAL REVIEW MIDDLE EAST/AL-NASHRAH AL-TIQNIYYAH AL-SHARQ AL-AWSAT. (Text in Arabic, English, Farsi) 1984. bi-m. £44($76) (effective 1995). Alain Charles Publishing Ltd., Alain Charles House, 27 Wilfred St., London SW1E 6PR, England. TEL 0171-834-7676. FAX 0171-973-0076. TELEX 297165 ACPLTD G. Ed. Jonquil Phelan. (back issues avail.) **Document type:** trade publication.

600　　　　　　　UK　　ISSN 0960-6076
TECHNICAL UNIVERSITY OF KOSICE. TRANSACTIONS. 1991. s-a. £60. (Technical University of Kosice) Riecansky Science Publishing Co., 7 Meadow Walk, Great Abington, Cambridge CB1 6AZ, England. TEL 0223-893295.
—BLDSC (9012.150000).

600　　　　　　　XO　　ISSN 0139-715X
TECHNICKE NOVINY/TECHNICAL NEWSPAPER. (Text in Slovak) 1953. w. 312 Sk. V T N s r.o., Stefanikova 19, 812 71 Bratislava, Slovakia. TEL 42-7-492802. FAX 42-7-492-874. Ed. Pavol Marusinec. adv. contact: Lubica Chornova. circ. 15,000. **Document type:** newspaper.
　Description: For new science, technology and innovation.

600 331.88　　　XR　　ISSN 0040-1064
TECHNICKY TYDENIK; list podnikavych techniku a technickych podnikatelu. vol.21, 1973. w. 52 Kc.($33) (Ustredni Rada Odboru) Technicky Tydenki, a.s., Thakurova 7, 166 29 Prague 6, Czech Republic. (Dist. by: Artia, Ve Smeckach 30, 111 27 Prague 1, Czech Republic) Ed. Stanislav Karas. charts; illus. circ. 40,000.

620　　　　　　　GW
TECHNIK HEUTE; Monatshefte fuer technische Berufe. 1940. m. DM.62.50. Verlag Dr. Ing. Paul Christiani, Hermann-Hesse-Weg 2, 78464 Konstanz, Germany. adv.; bk.rev.; charts; illus.; index. circ. 23,000.
　Formerly: Ausbau (ISSN 0004-8097)

600 301　　　　　GW　　ISSN 1010-6138
TECHNIK UND GESELLSCHAFT. 1982. a. price varies. Campus Verlag, Heerstr. 149, 60488 Frankfurt a.M., Germany. TEL 069-976-51610. FAX 069-976-51678. Ed. Gotthard Bechmann. **Document type:** academic/scholarly publication.

TECHNIKA CHRONIKA/ANNALES TECHNIQUES. see **SCIENCES: COMPREHENSIVE WORKS**

600　　　　　　　GW
TECHNIKER AKTUELL. 1968. bi-m. DM.25 (students DM.15). Deutsche Techniker Verlag, Ahornallee 19, 31195 Lamspringe, Germany. TEL 05183-466. FAX 05183-5106. Ed. Georg von Raison. adv.; B&W page DM.7200; trim 172 x 252. bk.rev. circ. 11,000. **Document type:** trade publication.
　Formerly: Deutsche Techniker.

620　　　　　　　GW　　ISSN 0040-117X
T5　　　　　　　　　　CODEN: TECHDZ
TECHNIKGESCHICHTE. 1909. q. (Verein Deutscher Ingenieure) Kiepert KG, Hardenbergstr. 4-5, 10623 Berlin, Germany. Ed. K. Mauel. bk.rev.; bibl.; charts; illus.; index. **Indexed:** Excerp.Med., Math.R. **Document type:** trade publication.
—BLDSC (8736.835000); SWETS. **CCC.**

600　　　　　　　IS
TECHNION - ISRAEL INSTITUTE OF TECHNOLOGY. PRESIDENT'S REPORT. (Text in English) 1975. a. free to qualified personnel. Technion - Israel Institute of Technology, Division of Public Affairs, Haifa 3200, Israel. Ed. Harvey L. Brown. circ. 30,000 (controlled). **Indexed:** INSPEC.
　Formerly: Israel Institute of Technology. President's Report and Reports of Other Officers (ISSN 0072-9329)

620　　　　　　　IS　　ISSN 0792-3244
T173　　　　　　　　　　CODEN: TCNNAN
TECHNION MAGAZINE. (Text in English; summaries in French, German and Spanish) 1965. s-a. free. Technion - Israel Institute of Technology, Public Affairs Division, Technion City, Haifa 32000, Israel. FAX 04-221581. Ed. Susan Rose. adv.; bk.rev.; illus. circ. 35,000. **Indexed:** Avery Ind.Archit.Per.
　Supersedes: Technion (ISSN 0040-1188)

600　　　　　　　FR　　ISSN 0040-1250
T2　　　　　　　　　　CODEN: TEMDA2
TECHNIQUE MODERNE. 1908. bi-m. 1150 F. S I R P E, 76 rue de Rivoli, 75004 Paris, France. TEL 33-1-42-78-52-20. FAX 33-1-42-74-40-48. Ed. R. Drouhin. adv. contact: J. Drouhin. bk.rev.; abstr.; bibl.; charts; illus.; mkt.; index. circ. 3,400. (also avail. in microfilm from UMI) **Indexed:** Chem.Abstr., Excerp.Med., INSPEC, World Alum.Abstr.
—BLDSC (8741.000000); CASDDS; Ei. **CCC.**

600　　　　　　　FR　　ISSN 0082-2469
TECHNIQUES D'AUJOURD'HUI. 1970. irreg. price varies. Larousse, 17 rue du Montparnasse, 75280 Paris Cedex 06, France.
—**CCC.**

605　　　　　　　JA　　ISSN 0374-0854
TECHNIQUES INDUSTRIELLES DU JAPON. (Text in French) 1959. a. 2000 Yen. Societe-Franco-Japonaise des Techniques Industrielles - Nichifutsu Kogyo Gijutsukai, 2-3 Kanda Surugadai, Chiyoda-ku, Tokyo 101, Japan. **Document type:** academic/scholarly publication.

600　　　　　　　GW　　ISSN 0494-9390
　　　　　　　　　　　　CODEN: TMKWA3
TECHNISCHE MITTEILUNGEN KRUPP. (Editions in English and German) 1986. irreg. (2-4/yr.). free. Fried. Krupp AG Hoesch-Krupp, Postfach 101952, 45117 Essen, Germany. TEL 0201-1882822. FAX 0201-1884046. charts; illus.; index. circ. 8,000. **Indexed:** Chem.Abstr., Eng.Ind., INSPEC (1986-), Met.Abstr., World Alum.Abstr. **Document type:** trade publication.
—CASDDS. **CCC.**
　Supersedes (1920-1985): Technische Mitteilungen Krupp. Forschungsberichte; Technische Mitteilungen Krupp. Werksberichte (ISSN 0040-1463)

600　　　　　　　NE　　ISSN 0165-3202
TECHNISCHE REVUE. 1972. fortn. free to qualified personnel. Misset (Subsidiary of: Reed Elsevier plc), Postbus 4, 7000 BA Doetinchem, Netherlands. TEL 31-8340-49911. FAX 31-8340-43839. TELEX 45481. Ed. J. van Bruggen. adv. contact: Cor van Nek. illus.; tr.lit.; circ. 15,230 (controlled). **Document type:** trade publication.
　Description: For management in commercial enterprises.

600　　　　　　　GW　　ISSN 0724-1593
TECHNISCHE REVUE. 1981. 10/yr. free. Elsevier Thomas Fachverlag GmbH, Postfach 1869, 55130 Mainz, Germany. TEL 06131-80110. FAX 06131-831193. Ed. Rainer Sauer. adv. contact: Petra Panter. bk.rev. circ. 50,500. (tabloid format) **Document type:** trade publication.

600　　　　　　　SZ　　ISSN 0040-148X
TECHNISCHE RUNDSCHAU; Europaeische Industrie- und Handelszeitung. (Supplements avail.) 1908. w. 132 SFr. (foreign 240 SFr.). Hallwag AG, Nordring 4, CH-3001 Bern, Switzerland. TEL 031-3323131. FAX 031-3314133. TELEX 912661-CH. Ed. Hannes Gysling. adv.; bk.rev.; bibl.; charts; illus.; tr.lit.; index. circ. 17,000. **Indexed:** C.I.S. Abstr., Chem.Abstr., Cyb.Abstr., INSPEC. **Document type:** newspaper.
—SWETS.

620　　　　　　　GW　　ISSN 0043-6925
Q3　　　　　　　　　　CODEN: WZTUAU
TECHNISCHE UNIVERSITAET DRESDEN. WISSENSCHAFTLICHE ZEITSCHRIFT. (Text in German; summaries in English, German) 1952. bi-m. DM.130. Technische Universitaet Dresden, Wissenschaftliche Publikationen, Mommsenstr. 13, 01062 Dresden, Germany. FAX 0351-4632773. FAX 0351-4637165. Ed. Ute Hendlmeier. adv.; bk.rev.; bibl.; charts; illus.; index. circ. 1,400. (back issues avail.) **Indexed:** Bibl.Cart., Chem.Abstr., Dok.Str., Excerp.Med., Forest.Abstr., Forest Prod.Abstr., Geotech.Abstr., INSPEC (1968-), Math.R., VITIS. **Document type:** academic/scholarly publication.
—BLDSC (9339.110000); CASDDS; Ei. **CCC.**

600 380　　　　GW　　ISSN 0077-2089
Q9
TECHNISCHE UNIVERSITAET MUENCHEN. JAHRBUCH. 1952. a. DM.50. Technische Universitaet Muenchen, Arcisstr. 21, 80290 Munich, Germany. TEL 089-2105-8601. FAX 089-21058622. circ. 1,100. **Document type:** abstracting/indexing, bibliography.
—BLDSC (4628.200000).

658.5　　　　　　GW　　ISSN 0040-1552
TECHNISCHER HANDEL; Zentralblatt fuer den technischen Bedarf. 1914. m. DM.106 (foreign DM.129). (Verband der Technischen Haendler) Vincentz Verlag, Schiffgraben 43, 30175 Hannover, Germany. TEL 0511-9909865. FAX 0511-9909879. (Subscr. to: Postfach 6247, 30062 Hannover, Germany) Ed. L. Vincentz. adv.: B&W page DM.1920, color page DM.3600; trim 250 x 175. bk.rev.; abstr. circ. 2,900. (tabloid format) **Document type:** trade publication.
—CCC.

600　　　　　　　FR　　ISSN 1156-8968
TECHNO-TRANSFERT. 22/yr. 2800 F. A Jour, 11 rue du Marche St. Honore, 75001 Paris, France. TEL 42-96-67-22. FAX 40-20-07-75. TELEX 615887 AJOUR. Ed. Juliette Fauchet.
　Formerly: Innovation.

600　　　　　　　II
TECHNOCRAT. (Text in English) 1985. m. Nariman Point Building Services & Trading Pvt. Ltd., 920 Tulsiani Chambers, Nariman Point, Bombay 400 021, India. Ed. Maneck Davar. adv.: B&W page Rs.15000, color page Rs.27500; trim 265 x 195.

600 500　　　　BE　　ISSN 0771-6826
TECHNOLOGIA; historical and social studies in science, technology and industry. 1978. q. 450 BEF to non-members. Association des Ingenieurs Industriels et Ingenieurs Techniciens de Bruxelles (AIIBr), 26 av. de l'Amarante, 1020 Brussels, Belgium. Ed. Jean C. Baudet. bk.rev. circ. 1,000.
　Incorporates (in 1983): Comite Belge d'Histoire des Sciences. Notes Bibliographiques - Belgisch Komitee voor de Geschiedeis der Wetenschappen. Bibliograpische Notas (ISSN 0010-2415); **Formerly (until 1981):** Technologia Bruxellensis (ISSN 0771-7415)

TECHNOLOGY: COMPREHENSIVE WORKS

600 301.24   US   ISSN 0040-1625
T174   CODEN: TFSCB3
TECHNOLOGICAL FORECASTING AND SOCIAL CHANGE. 1969. 9/yr. $480 to institutions (effective 1996). Elsevier Science Inc., 655 Ave. of the Americas, New York, NY 10010. TEL 212-989-5800. FAX 212-633-3990. TELEX 420643 AEP UI. (Subscr. to: Box 882, Madison Sq. Sta., New York, NY 10159-0882) Ed. Harold A. Linstone. adv.; bk.rev. (also avail. in microform from UMI; reprint service avail. from SWZ) **Indexed:** ASCA, B.P.I., BPIA, Br.Tech.Ind., Bus.Ind., CLOSS, Cont.Pg.Manage., Curr.Cont., Econ.Abstr., Educ.Admin.Abstr., Educ.Tech.Abstr., Eng.Ind., Excerp.Med., Fut.Surv., Geo.Abstr., HRIS, IDA, INSPEC (1969-), Int.Abstr.Oper.Res., Int.Polit.Sci.Abstr., J.Cont.Quant.Meth., J.of Econ.Abstr., Key to Econ.Sci., Lang.& Lang.Behav.Abstr., Manage.Abstr., Mid.East: Abstr.& Ind., Risk Abstr., Sage Pub.Admin.Abstr., Sage Urb.Stud.Abstr., SCIMP, Sociol.Abstr., SSCI, Tr.& Indus.Ind. **Document type:** academic/scholarly publication.
—BLDSC (8757.351000); Ei; Faxon; Genuine Article; SWETS; UnCover. **CCC.**
Formerly: Technological Forecasting.
Description: Deals directly with the methodology and practice of technological forecasting and future studies as planning tools as they interrelate social, environmental and technological factors.
Refereed Serial

600   FR   ISSN 1145-5217
TECHNOLOGIE & SANTE. 1990. q. 1200 F. C N E H, 9 rue Antoine Chantin, 75014 Paris, France. TEL 40-44-15-15.
—BLDSC (8758.291000).

TECHNOLOGIE-NACHRICHTEN - MANAGEMENT-INFORMATIONEN. see *BUSINESS AND ECONOMICS — Management*

600   GW   ISSN 0344-9750
TECHNOLOGIE-NACHRICHTEN - PROGRAMM-INFORMATIONEN. 1970. s-m. DM.360. T N V GmbH, An den Eichen, 5202 Hennef 1, Germany. TEL 02248-1881. FAX 02248-1796. Ed. Nicola Gasterstaedt. circ. 500.

600   GW   ISSN 0932-2558
TECHNOLOGIE UND MANAGEMENT. 1951. q. DM.93. Betriebswirtschaftlicher Verlag Dr. Th. Gabler GmbH, Taunusstr. 54, 65183 Wiesbaden, Germany. TEL 0611-534-0. FAX 0611-534430. adv.; index. circ. 4,000. (back issues avail.) **Document type:** trade publication.
Formerly (until 1987): Technologie Manager.

600   IS   ISSN 0333-9521
T4
TECHNOLOGIES; Israel's magazine of high technology. 1983. m. $100 (effective 1992). Shukit Publishing Ltd., P.O. Box 39244, Tel Aviv 61392, Israel. TEL 052-581054. FAX 052-573628. Ed. Haim Amit. adv. circ. 15,000.
Description: Information on high-tech applicable to the Israeli market, both local and imported. Covers electronics, industry oriented computers, control and automation as well as tests.

600   CN
TECHNOLOGIES DE L'INFORMATION ET SOCIETE. Abbreviated title: T.I.S. (Text in French) 1988. 3/yr. Universite du Quebec a Montreal, Service des Publications, C.P.8888, Succ. A, Montreal, Que. H3C 3P8, Canada. TEL 514-282-4511. **Indexed:** Pt.de Rep. (1988-).

600   FR   ISSN 0840-4836
CODEN: TINSEG
TECHNOLOGIES DE L'INFORMATION ET SOCIETE. q. 500 F. Dunod, 15 rue Gossin, 92543 Montrouge Cedex, France. TEL 40-92-65-00. FAX 40-92-65-97. TELEX 634 916 F. (Subscr. to: Centrale des Revues, 11 rue Gossin, 92543 Montrouge Cedex, France. TEL 46-56-52-66) Ed. F. Pinchault. adv. **Indexed:** INSPEC (1993-). **Document type:** academic/scholarly publication.
—BLDSC (8758.360200).
Description: Covers economics, sociology, law, philosophy, ergonomics, psychology and the sciences of management, communication and education.

600   FR   ISSN 0297-1062
TECHNOLOGIES ET FORMATIONS. 1945. 6/yr. 420 F. (foreign 580 F.) (effective 1996). P Y C Edition, 5 ave du Verdun, B.P. 105, 94208 Ivry-sur-Seine Cedex, France. TEL 1-49-94-01-04. FAX 1-46-72-41-85. TELEX 263 424. (Subscr. to: B.S.I. 49 rue de la Vanne, 92126 Montrouge Cedex, France) Ed. B. Debette. adv.; bk.rev. circ. 2,833.
—**CCC.**
Formerly: Ingenieur et le Technicien de l'Enseignement Technique (ISSN 0046-9521)
Description: Intended for vocational schools and training managers.

600   US   ISSN 0273-2580
T14.5
TECHNOLOGY. (Subseries of: S I R S Social Issues (ISSN 0740-3127)) 1978. a. price varies; a. supplement $17. Social Issues Resources Series, Box 2348, Boca Raton, FL 33427-2348. TEL 407-994-0079; 800-232-7477. FAX 407-994-4704. (looseleaf format; also avail. in microfiche; back issues avail.)
Description: Reprints articles that explore the role of technology in society.

600   US   ISSN 1050-043X
T174.3
TECHNOLOGY ACCESS REPORT; newsletter for technology transfer, commercialization, defense conversion, technology policy and management. 1988. m. $497 (typically set in Jan.). University R & D Opportunities, Inc., 16 Digital Dr., Ste. 250, Novato, CA 94949-5760. TEL 415-883-7600; 800-733-1556. FAX 415-883-6421. E-mail: info@techaccess.com. Ed. Michael Odza; Pub. Michael Odza. adv. contact: Lauren Andersen. bk.rev.; circ. 1,000 (paid). (also avail. in diskette format; back issues avail.) **Document type:** newsletter.
●Also available online. Vendor(s): DataArkiv A.B., Knight-Ridder, Inc., NewsNet (RD38).
—**CCC.**
Formerly: Technology Access.
Description: Covers technology transfer and commercialization of research from universities, government, and independent laboratories and medical centers; defense-conversion, manufacturing modernization, technology management, industrial policy, licensing, venture capital, and cooperative research and developments for all companies in all industries.

500   US   ISSN 1054-4267
TECHNOLOGY ALERT. 1987. 6/yr. $139 (Canada $169; elsewhere $189). Merton Allen Associates, InfoTeam Inc., Box 15640, Plantation, FL 33318-5640. TEL 305-473-9560. FAX 305-473-0544. Ed. Merton Allen. **Document type:** newsletter.
●Also available online. Vendor(s): Data-Star, Knight-Ridder, Inc., NewsNet (RD09).
—**CCC.**
Formerly: Technology Alert Database Reports (ISSN 1058-8469)
Description: Presents on-line descriptions of available technical papers and reports abstracted from publishers' subscription newsletters. Contains summary and listings of available database searches on a variety of specific technological, management, marketing, and finance subjects.

600   UK   ISSN 0953-7325
HD45
TECHNOLOGY ANALYSIS & STRATEGIC MANAGEMENT. 1989. q. £50 to individuals; institutions £192 (effective 1996). Carfax Publishing Co., P.O. Box 25, Abingdon, Oxon. OX14 3UE, England. TEL 01235-555335. FAX 01235-553559. (Subscr. in N. America to: Carfax Publishing Co., 875-81 Massachusetts Ave., Cambridge, MA 02139) Ed. Harry Rothman. adv.; bk.rev. (also avail. in microfiche) **Indexed:** Geo.Abstr. **Document type:** academic/scholarly publication.
—BLDSC (8758.543000); Faxon; Genuine Article; SWETS; UMI. **CCC.**
Description: Presents international research linking the analysis of science and technology with the strategic needs of policymakers and management.
Refereed Serial

300 600   US   ISSN 0040-165X
T1
TECHNOLOGY AND CULTURE; devoted to the study of the development of technology and its relations with society and culture. 1960. q. $30 to individuals; institutions $67; students $20; emeriti $24. (Society for the History of Technology) University of Chicago Press, Journals Division, 5720 S. Woodlawn Ave., Chicago, IL 60637. TEL 312-753-3347. FAX 312-753-0811. TELEX 25-4603. (Subscr. to: Box 37005, Chicago, IL 60637) Ed. Robert C. Post. adv.; bk.rev.; bibl.; charts; illus.; index, cum.index: vols.1-10 (1959-1969). circ. 2,600. (also avail. in microform from KTO,UMI; reprint service avail. from ISI,KTO,UMI) **Indexed:** Acad.Ind., Amer.Bibl.Slavic & E.Eur.Stud., Amer.Hist.& Life, Art & Archaeol.Tech.Abstr., Arts & Hum.Cit.Ind., ASCA, ASSIA, Bk.Rev.Ind. (1989-), Br.Archaeol.Abstr., Child.Bk.Rev.Ind. (1989-), Curr.Cont., Excerp.Med., Hist.Abstr., Lang.& Lang.Behav.Abstr., Mid.East: Abstr.& Ind., Rural Recreat.Tour.Abstr., Soc.Sci.Ind. (until 1994), SSCI, World Agri.Econ.& Rural Sociol.Abstr. **Document type:** academic/scholarly publication.
—BLDSC (8758.600000); Faxon; Genuine Article; SWETS; UMI; UnCover. **CCC.**
Refereed Serial

TECHNOLOGY EDGE. see *OCCUPATIONS AND CAREERS*

TECHNOLOGY FOCUS. see *MILITARY*

600   US   ISSN 0886-0890
TECHNOLOGY FORECASTS & TECHNOLOGY SURVEYS. 1969. m. $160 (Canada and Mexico $164; elsewhere $172). Technology Forecasts, 205 S. Beverly Dr., Ste. 208, Beverly Hills, CA 90212. TEL 310-273-3486. Ed. Irwin Stambler; Pub. Willard Wilks. bk.rev. (back issues avail.) **Indexed:** PROMT. **Document type:** newsletter.
—BLDSC (8758.830000).
Description: Discusses important trends or advances in science and technology likely to have a great effect in the future.

600 370   UK   ISSN 0952-889X
TECHNOLOGY IN EDUCATION; devoted to the teaching of science and design technology including art & design, business studies, craft design technology, home economics, and information technology. 1985. 7/yr. £20. B & S Publications, 3 Crescent Terr., Cheltenham, Glos. GL50 3PE, England. TEL 01242-510760. FAX 01242-22626. Ed. Bernard Hubbard. adv.: B&W page £760, color page £995; trim 297 x 210. tr.lit.; circ. 8,000 (controlled). (back issues avail.) **Document type:** academic/scholarly publication.
Description: Presents a forum for teachers involved with sciences and technology.

620   IE   ISSN 0040-1676
T1   CODEN: TEIRDR
TECHNOLOGY IRELAND. 1969. 10/yr. I£25 (U.K. I£28.50; Europe I£32; rest of world I£45.50). Forbairt - the Irish Science and Technology Agency, Glasnevin, Dublin 9, Ireland. TEL 01-8370101. FAX 01-8367122. TELEX 32501. Eds. Tom Kennedy, Mary Mulvihill. adv.: B&W page I£750, color page I£1100; trim 267 x 190; adv. contact: Duncan Black. bk.rev.; abstr.; index. circ. 5,500. **Indexed:** Bull.Signal., Excerp.Med., Food Sci.& Tech.Abstr., Fuel & Energy Abstr., Int.Packag.Abstr., Intl.Civil Eng.Abstr., Ocean.Abstr., Paper & Bd.Abstr., Pollut.Abstr., Soft.Abstr.Eng., W.R.C.Inf. **Document type:** trade publication.
—BLDSC (8758.900000); Ei.
Description: Covers aspects of technology in engineering, construction, chemicals, electronics, plastics, energy, food, packaging, and textiles.

600   US   ISSN 1072-9240
TECHNOLOGY: JOURNAL OF THE FRANKLIN INSTITUTE, PART A. vol.331A, 1994. bi-m. $150 (foreign $186) (effective 1996). Cognizant Communication Corporation, 3 Hartsdale Rd., Elmsford, NY 10523-3701. TEL 914-592-7720. FAX 914-592-8981. Ed. A. Alan Moghissi. **Document type:** academic/scholarly publication.
—**CCC.**
Description: Encompasses all fields of applied sciences and advanced technology. Reports scientific findings, reviews developments in science, engineering and technology, including laws, regulations, judicial decisions and government actions. Also covers the economics, and environmental and health aspcts of technology, as well as historical, social and ethical aspects.

TECHNOLOGY: COMPREHENSIVE WORKS

600 658   US   ISSN 1073-4457
CODEN: TCMAEH
▼**TECHNOLOGY MANAGEMENT**; strategies & applications for practitioners. 1994. bi-m. $250 to institutions (effective 1996). Elsevier Science Inc., 655 Ave. of the Americas, New York, NY 10010. TEL 212-633-3950. FAX 212-633-3990. (Subscr. to: Box 882, Madison Sq. Sta., New York, NY 10159-0882) Ed. J. Leslie Glick. adv.; bk.rev. (also avail. in microform from UMI; back issues avail.) **Document type:** academic/scholarly publication.
—BLDSC (8758.929000). **CCC.**
    Description: Covers issues in practical, applied technology management.
    Refereed Serial

600   US   ISSN 1058-2282
TECHNOLOGY NEW YORK REPORT. 1982. bi-m. $250 individual membership (effective 1995). 1223 Peoples Ave., Troy, NY 12180. TEL 518-276-8769. FAX 518-276-6380. Ed. Ruth Fein Wallens; Pub. John C. Wallner. adv.; bk.rev. circ. 2,500. (back issues avail.) **Document type:** newsletter.
    Formerly (until 1993): Technology N Y Newsletter (ISSN 0732-7382)
    Description: Helps mangers of high-technology businesses locate and resources that can help them grow in New York State.

TECHNOLOGY OPPORTUNITIES: RESEARCHING EMERGING & CRITICAL TECHNOLOGIES. see *BUSINESS AND ECONOMICS*

TECHNOLOGY RESOURCE GUIDE - MIDWEST. see *BUSINESS AND ECONOMICS — Trade And Industrial Directories*

TECHNOLOGY REVIEW. see *SCIENCES: COMPREHENSIVE WORKS*

TECHNOLOGY, RISK AND SOCIETY; an international series in risk analysis. see *BUSINESS AND ECONOMICS — Economic Systems And Theories, Economic History*

600 613.62   US   ISSN 1059-0609
TECHNOLOGY SPECIAL INTEREST SECTION NEWSLETTER. (Consists of 11 sections: Administration and Management; Developmental Disabilities; Education; Gerontology; Home & Community Health; Mental Health; Physical Disabilities; School System; Sensory Integration; Technology; Work Programs) 1991. q. American Occupational Therapy Association, Inc., Box 31220, Bethesda, MD 20824-1220. TEL 301-652-2682. FAX 301-652-7711. **Document type:** newsletter.

745.2   US   ISSN 0746-3537
T61
TECHNOLOGY TEACHER. 1939. 8/yr. $55 to non-members and libraries (foreign $70). International Technology Education Association, 1914 Association Dr., Reston, VA 22091. TEL 703-860-2100. FAX 703-860-0353. Ed. Judy Miller. adv.; bk.rev.; abstr.; bibl.; charts; illus.; index. circ. 8,000. (also avail. in microform from UMI; back issues avail.) **Indexed:** C.I.J.E., Curr.Cont., Educ.Ind.
—BLDSC (8761.024000); Faxon; SWETS; UMI; UnCover.
    Former titles (until 1983): Man - Society - Technology (ISSN 0022-1813); Journal of Industrial Arts Education.

600   US   ISSN 1062-1784
TECHNOLOGY TRANSFER HIGHLIGHTS. 1990. q. free. Argonne National Laboratory, Industrial Technology Development Center, 9700 S. Cass Ave., Bldg. 900, Argonne, IL 60439. TEL 708-252-6393. FAX 708-252-5230. E-mail: margaret_hanley@gmgate.anl.gov. Ed. M. Margaret Hanley. cum.index. circ. 5,000. (back issues avail.) **Document type:** newsletter.
    ●Also available online.
    Description: Describes technology transfer activities at the laboratory. Each issue features an insert on a special topic: energy and the environment, materials, manufacturing, transportation, and computing.

TECHNOLOGY TRANSFER SOCIETY. INTERNATIONAL SYMPOSIUM PROCEEDINGS. see *BUSINESS AND ECONOMICS — Management*

TECHNOSCENE. see *CHILDREN AND YOUTH — For*

600   US
TECHNOTRENDS NEWSLETTER. 1985. m. $49.95 to new subscr. (Canada $54.95; elsewhere $61.95); renewal $39.95 (Canada $44.95; elsewhere $51.95). Burrus Research Associates, Inc., Box 26413, Milwaukee, WI 53226-0413. TEL 414-774-7790. FAX 414-774-8330. Ed. Patti A. Thomsen. **Document type:** newsletter.
    Formerly (until 1993): Technology Futures Newsletter.

600   UK   ISSN 0166-4972
HD45
TECHNOVATION; an international journal of technical innovation and entrepreneurship. 1981. 10/yr. £344($547) (effective 1996). Elsevier Science Ltd., P.O. Box 800, Kidlington, Oxford OX5 1DX, England. TEL 44-1865-843000. FAX 44-1865-843010. E-mail: nlinfo-f@elsevier.nl; usinfo-f@elsevier.com; forinfo-kyf04035@niftyserve.or.jp; Site addr.: http://www.elsevier.nl/. (Subscr. in U.S. and Canada to: Elsevier Science, 660 White Plains Rd., Tarrytown, NY 10591-5153. TEL 914-524-9200. FAX 914-333-2444) Eds. G. Hayward, G. Rosegger. adv. (reprint service avail. from SWZ) **Indexed:** ABI Inform., ASCA, Biostat., Cont.Pg.Manage., Curr.Cont., Eng.Ind., Manage.Cont., Risk Abstr. **Document type:** academic/scholarly publication.
—BLDSC (8761.150000); Ei; Faxon; Genuine Article; SWETS; UMI; UnCover. **CCC.**
    Description: Covers all facets of the technical innovation process: from the development of a new product or process through commercial utilization.
    Refereed Serial

TECHUMIM. see *RELIGIONS AND THEOLOGY — Judaic*

620   AG   ISSN 0040-1781
TECNICA E INDUSTRIA. 1922. m. Arg.$35($120) c/o Dante R. Marchesotti, 694 Rodriguez Pena, 5o, 1020 Buenos Aires, Argentina. TEL 46-3193. Ed. E.R. Fedele. adv.; bk.rev.; charts; illus.; mkt.; pat.; tr.lit.; tr.mk. circ. 5,000. **Indexed:** Chem.Abstr.

600   SP   ISSN 0213-7488
TECNO 2000; revista d'innovacio a l'empresa. (Annual monographic supplement avail.) (Text in Catalan) 1987. bi-m. 4000 ptas. (effective 1994). Fundacio Catalana per a la Recerca, Provenca 269, pral. 2a, 08008 Barcelona, Spain. TEL 93-2156784. FAX 93-4877131. Ed. David Segarra. adv.; bk.rev.; illus. circ. 6,000.
—BLDSC (8762.728000).
    Description: Provides information on economical management and technological innovations in and for industry.

600 338   MX   ISSN 0188-6452
HD45
TECNOINDUSTRIA. Mex.$90 (foreign $45) (effective 1995). Consejo Nacional de Ciencia y Tecnologia, Av. Constituyentes 1046, Col. Lomas Altas, 11950 Mexico D.F., Mexico. TEL 627-7400. Ed. Concepcion Garrido Barriga. adv. contact: Jose Luis Miranda Salgao.

600   CR   ISSN 0379-3982
T4
TECNOLOGIA EN MARCHA. 1978. q. $20. Instituto Tecnologico de Costa Rica, Apdo. 159, Cartago, Costa Rica. TEL 506-551-5333. FAX 506-552-5354. TELEX 8013-ITCR-CR. Ed. Mario Castillo. adv.; bk.rev.; bibl.; charts. circ. 1,500. **Document type:** academic/scholarly publication.

600   EC   ISSN 0257-1749
T4
TECNOLOGICA. 1976. q. $30. Escuela Superior Politecnica del Litoral, P.O. Box 5863, Guayaquil, Ecuador. Ed. Homero Ortiz. circ. 500. (microform)

TEHNICKE NOVINE. see *CHILDREN AND YOUTH — About*

TEKHNEMA; journal of philosophy and technology. see *POLITICAL SCIENCE*

620   RU   ISSN 0320-331X
TEKHNIKA MOLODEZHI. (Former name of issuing body: Vsesoyuznyi Leninskii Kommunisticheskii Soyuz Molodezhi, Tsentral'nyi Komitet) 1933. m. $49. Izdatel'stvo Molodaya Gvardiya, Novodmitrovskaya ul. 5A, 125015 Moscow, Russia. TEL 095-285-8883. (Dist. by: Mezhdunarodnaya Kniga, ul. Dimitrova D.39, 113095 Moscow, Russia; Dist. in U.S. by: Victor Kamkin Inc., 4957 Boiling Brook Pkwy, Rockville, MD 20852. TEL 301-881-5973) Ed. Aleksander Perevozchikov. adv.; bk.rev.; illus.; index. circ. 1,819,000. **Indexed:** Chem.Abstr.

600   FI   ISSN 0355-4287
TEKNIIKAN MAAILMA. 21/yr. FIM 495. Yhtyneet Kuvalehdet Oy, Maistraatinportti 1, FIN-00240 Helsinki, Finland. TEL 358-0-156-6524. FAX 358-0-156-6505. TELEX 121364. Ed. Mauri Salo. adv.; B&W page FIM 23900, color page FIM 35100. circ. 114,369.
    Description: Covers automobiles, home electronics, videos and cameras for the prospective buyer.

754   FI   ISSN 0785-997X
TEKNIIKKA & TALOUS/TEKNIK & EKONOMI. (Text in Finnish and Swedish) 1961. w. FIM 540. Oy Talentum Ab, Ratavartijankatu 2, 00520 Helsinki, Finland. TEL 358-0-148-801.
FAX 358-0-148-3512. Ed. Heikki Vuonamo. adv.: B&W page FIM 36900, color page FIM 55700; trim 290 x 380; adv. contact: Raija Palomaki. bk.rev. circ. 84,409. (looseleaf format) **Indexed:** C.I.S. Abstr. **Document type:** trade publication, newspaper.
    Formerly: Insinooriuutiset (ISSN 0020-2010)
    Description: Covers news and current business, as well as special fields in industry and technology.

607.489   DK   ISSN 0105-192X
TEKNISK VIDENSKABELIG FORSKNING. 1970. a. free. Undervisningsministeriets Forskningsafdeling, H.C. Andersens Blvd. 40, DK-1553 Copenhagen V, Denmark. Ed. Joachim Ferrik. illus. circ. 3,000.
    Formerly: Denmark. Statens Teknisk-Videnskabelige Forskningsraad. Beretning.

TEMPLE ENVIRONMENT LAW & TECHNOLOGY JOURNAL. see *LAW*

TENSOR. see *MATHEMATICS*

620   RU   ISSN 0869-8635
CODEN: TEAEFI
TEPLOFIZIKA I AEROMEKHANIKA. English translation: Russian Journal of Thermophysics and Aeromechanics (RU ISSN 0869-8643) (Text in English, Russian) 1963. 4/yr. 150000 Rub. Rossiiskaya Akademiya Nauk, Sibirskoe Otdelenie, Institut Teplofiziki, Pr. Akademika Lavrenteva 1, 630090 Novosibirsk, Russia. FAX 3832-356002. E-mail: tanda@otani.thermo.nsk.su. (Subscr. to: Rossiiskaya Academiay Nauk, Sibirskoe Otdelenie, Morskoy pr. 2, 630090 Novosibirsk, Russia. TEL 3832-350570) Ed. E.P. Volchkov. bk.rev.; charts; illus.; index. circ. 200. **Indexed:** Chem.Abstr., INIS Atomind., Math.R., Met.Abstr., World Alum.Abstr. **Document type:** academic/scholarly publication.
—BLDSC (0178.870000); CASDDS. **CCC.**
    Former titles (until 1994): Sibirskii Fiziko-tekhnicheskii Zhurnal (ISSN 0869-1339); (until 1990): Akademiya Nauk S.S.S.R. Sibirskoe Otdelenie. Izvestiya. Seriya Tekhnicheskikh Nauk (ISSN 0002-3434)

600 630   LE
AL-TIKNULUJIA AL-MULA'IMAH/MIDDLE EAST APPROPRIATE TECHNOLOGY NEWS. (Text in Arabic; summaries in English) 1984. irreg. (2-4/yr.). free. Markaz al-Sharq al-Awsat lil-Tiknulujia al-Mula'imah - Middle East Center for the Transfer of Appropriate Technology, P.O. Box 113-5474, Beirut, Lebanon. TEL 346465. TELEX 41224 MEEA LE. (Affiliate: Middle East Engineers and Architects S.A.R.L.) circ. 3,000. (looseleaf format) **Document type:** newsletter.
    Description: Publishes review articles on aspects of appropriate technology of interest to scientists, engineers, agricultural technicians and planners, introducing new ideas and defining a technical vocabulary in Arabic in the various fields.

TECHNOLOGY: COMPREHENSIVE WORKS

600   JA   ISSN 0919-8881
CODEN: TKKEE7
TOHOKU NATIONAL INDUSTRIAL RESEARCH INSTITUTE. REPORTS/TOHOKU KOGYO GIJUTSU KENKYUJO HOKOKU. (Text in English) 1972. a. Tohoku National Industrial Research Institute, 4-2-1, Nigatake, Miyagino-ku, Sendai 983, Japan.
—BLDSC (7619.552500); CASDDS.
Formerly (until 1994): Government Industrial Research Institute, Tohoku. Reports - Tohoku Kogyo Gijutsu Shikenjo Hokoku (ISSN 0389-939X)

620   JA   ISSN 0040-9006
T178.T635   CODEN: RIISAX
TOKYO DAIGAKU SEISAN GIJUTSU KENKYUJO HOKOKU/UNIVERSITY OF TOKYO. INSTITUTE OF INDUSTRIAL SCIENCE. REPORT.* (Text mainly in Japanese, occasionally English, French or German) 1950. irreg. (6-8/yr.) free. University of Tokyo, Institute of Industrial Science - Tokyo Daigaku Seisan Gijutsu Kenkyujo, 22-1 Roppongi 7-chome, Minato-ku, Tokyo 106, Japan. charts. circ. 900. **Indexed:** Chem.Abstr., Eng.Ind., INSPEC, JCT, JTA, Met.Abstr.
—BLDSC (7520.350000); CASDDS.

605   JA   ISSN 0495-8055
TOKYO INSTITUTE OF TECHNOLOGY. RESEARCH LABORATORY OF RESOURCES UTILIZATION. REPORT/SHIGEN KAGAKU KENKYUJO. (Text in English) a. Tokyo Kogyo Daigaku, Shigen Kagaku Kenkyujo - Tokyo Institute of Technology, Research Laboratory of Resources Utilization, 2-1, Ookayama 2-chome, Meguro-ku, Tokyo 152, Japan. **Indexed:** INSPEC.

600   JA   ISSN 0082-4747
TA7   CODEN: MTTMAO
TOKYO METROPOLITAN UNIVERSITY. FACULTY OF ENGINEERING. MEMOIRS/TOKYO-TORITSU DAIGAKU KOGAKUBU HOKOKU. (Text in English) 1951. a. free. Tokyo-toritsu Daigaku, Kogakubu - Tokyo Metropolitan University, Faculty of Engineering, 1-1 Minami Ohsawa, Hachioji, Tokyo 192-03, Japan. Ed. Masao Taki. adv. contact: Yoshitaka Sakata. bibl. circ. 800. **Indexed:** Chem.Abstr., INIS Atomind., INSPEC, JCT, JTA, Met.Abstr., World Alum.Abstr. **Document type:** academic/scholarly publication.
—BLDSC (5603.000000); CASDDS; UnCover.
Description: Contains original papers in the various fields of technology.

TOKYO-TO SHIKEN KENKYU KIKAN NO KENKYU KEIKAKU. see PUBLIC ADMINISTRATION — Municipal Government

600   JA   ISSN 0913-8897
CODEN: TTKKBH
TOKYO TORITSU KAGAKU GIJUTSU DAIGAKU KENKYU HOKOKU/TOKYO METROPOLITAN INSTITUTE OF TECHNOLOGY. MEMOIRS. (Text in English or Japanese) 1987. a. Tokyo Toritsu Kagaku Gijutsu Daigaku - Tokyo Metropolitan Institute of Technology, 6-6 Asahigaoka Hino, Tokyo 191, Japan. TEL 81-425-83-5111. FAX 81-425-83-5119. Ed.Bd. circ. 500. **Document type:** academic/scholarly publication.
—CASDDS.
Formed the merger of (1962-1987): Kenkyu Kiyo - Tokyo Toritsu Koku Kogyo Tanki Daigaku (ISSN 0387-1363); (1973-1987): Tokyo Toritsu Koka Tanki Daigaku Kenkyu Hokoku (ISSN 0387-1371)

600   388.31   GW
TRAFFIC TECH. 4/yr. DM.118. Sieg Tech Verlags GmbH, Gottfried-Claren-Str. 21, 53225 Bonn, Germany. TEL 0228-466034. FAX 0228-477418. Ed. Manfred Sieg. adv.; bk.rev. **Document type:** trade publication.

TRAFODION Y GYMDEITHAS WYDDONOL GENEDLAETHOL. see SCIENCES: COMPREHENSIVE WORKS

TRANET; transnational network for appropriate alternative technologies. see PHILOSOPHY — Abstracting, Bibliographies, Statistics

600   GW   ISSN 0178-4099
TRANSFER (WUERZBURG); magazine for industrial processes, equipment and supplies. (Text in English) 1985. 7/yr. DM.120. Vogel Verlag und Druck GmbH & Co. KG, Max-Plank-Str. 7-9, 97082 Wuerzburg, Germany. TEL 0931-4182145. FAX 0931-4182640. (Subscr. to: Vogel Verlag, 97064 Wuerzburg, Germany; Dist. in U.S. by: Vogel Europublishing, Inc., 19927 Villa Dr., Sonora, CA 95370. TEL 209-533-3555. FAX 209-533-9555) Ed. Bernd Maienschein. adv.: B&W page DM.8376, color page DM.10322; trim 270 x 190; adv. contact: Winfried Burkhard. circ. 25,000 (controlled). **Document type:** trade publication.
—CCC.

TRANSIZIONE. see POLITICAL SCIENCE

TREATISE ON MATERIALS SCIENCE & TECHNOLOGY. see ENGINEERING — Engineering Mechanics And Materials

605   PH   ISSN 0115-2157
TRENDS IN TECHNOLOGY. 1972. q. free. Economic Development Foundation, 6764 Ayala Ave., Box 370 MCC, Makati, Rizal, Philippines. illus. circ. 500.

600   UK
TREVITHICK SOCIETY. OCCASIONAL PUBLICATION. 1974. irreg., no.4, 1994. £6.50. Trevithick Society, c/o Mr. C. Rowe, Church Cove, The Lizard, Helston, Cornwall TR12 7PQ, England. TEL 01326-290051. circ. 1,000. **Document type:** monographic series.

600   JA   ISSN 0287-8585
TRIGGER. (Text in Japanese) 1982. m. Nikkan Kogyo Shinbun, 8-10, Kudan Kita, 1-chome, Chiyoda-ku, Tokyo 102, Japan. TEL 03-3263-2311. FAX 03-3262-4603. TELEX NIKKANKO-J29687. Ed. Mitsuo Lijima. circ. 100,000. **Document type:** trade publication.
Description: Offers general information on all industrial technology.

TUDOMANY. see SCIENCES: COMPREHENSIVE WORKS

TWO THIRDS. see AGRICULTURE — Agricultural Economics

600   614.7   US
U C A T NEWS AND VIEWS.* 4/yr. free. University of California, Davis, Appropriate Technology Program, 2043 Bainer Hall, Davis, CA 95616. TEL 916-752-1011. Ed. David Hills. illus.

600   PH   ISSN 0117-0155
U S M RESEARCH JOURNAL. 1968. 3/yr. P.24($56) to individuals; $84 to institutions. University of Southern Mindanao, College of Agriculture, Kabacan, Cotabato 9407, Philippines. Ed. Anacleto M. Pedrosa, Jr. abstr.; bibl.; charts; illus.; stat. circ. 2,000. (back issues avail.)
—BLDSC (9135.100203).
Formerly (until vol.7, no.2, 1977): M I T Research Journal (ISSN 0302-7937)

600   HU   ISSN 0230-6972
UJ TECHNIKA. 1967. q. $10. Szentharomsag ter 1, 1014 Budapest, Hungary. TEL 155-7122. TELEX 22-6490. circ. 35,000.

UNDERWATER TECHNOLOGY. see EARTH SCIENCES — Oceanography

600   UN
UNESCO. REGIONAL OFFICE FOR SCIENCE AND TECHNOLOGY FOR LATIN AMERICA AND THE CARIBBEAN. BOLETIN. (Text in Spanish) 1952. 2/yr. free. Unesco, Regional Office of Science and Technology for Latin America and the Caribbean, 1320 Bulevar Artigas, Casilla de Correo 859, Montevideo, Uruguay. bk.rev.; abstr.; bibl. circ. 2,000.
Formerly: Unesco. Field Science Office for Latin America. Boletin.

600   GW   ISSN 0943-5107
T3
UNI MAGAZIN HANNOVER. 1974. s-a. DM.32. Universitaet Hannover, Pressestelle, Postfach 6009, 30060 Hannover, Germany. TEL 0511-7625355. FAX 0511-715936. Eds. Hermann Reuke, Sabine Juergens. adv. circ. 8,000. **Document type:** academic/scholarly publication.
—BLDSC (4262.115100).
Former titles: Uni Hannover (ISSN 0171-2268); (until 1978): T U Hannover.
Refereed Serial

UNI REPORT. see SCIENCES: COMPREHENSIVE WORKS

UNION LIST OF SCIENTIFIC AND TECHNICAL PERIODICALS IN ZAMBIA. see BIBLIOGRAPHIES

338   600   US   ISSN 0083-2383
T176
U.S. NATIONAL SCIENCE FOUNDATION. RESEARCH AND DEVELOPMENT IN INDUSTRY. (Subseries of: U.S. National Science Foundation. Surveys of Science Resource Series) a. U.S. National Science Foundation, 4201 Wilson Blvd., Ste. 245, Arlington, VA 22230. (Also avail. from: Bernan, 4611-F, Assembly Dr., Lanham, MD 20706. TEL 800-274-4447. FAX 301-459-0056) **Document type:** government publication.

600   330   US
U.S. OFFICE OF TECHNOLOGY ASSESSMENT. REPORTS. INDUSTRY, TECHNOLOGY, AND EMPLOYMENT PROGRAM. irreg. price varies. U.S. Office of Technology Assessment, Publication Distribution, U.S. Congress, 600 Pennsylvania Ave., S.E., Washington, DC 20510-8025. TEL 202-224-8996. FAX 202-228-6098. E-mail: PUBREQUEST@OTA.GOV. (Dist. by: Superintendent of Documents, U.S. Government Printing Office, Box 371954, Pittsburgh, PA 15250-7954. TEL 202-783-3238. FAX 202-512-2250; And: National Technical Information Service, 5285 Port Royal Rd., Springfield, VA 22161. TEL 703-487-4650. FAX 703-321-8547) (also avail. in microfiche from CIS; back issues avail.; reprint service avail. from CIS) **Document type:** monographic series, government publication.
Formerly: U.S. Office of Technology Assessment. Reports. Materials Program.
Description: Reports discuss social, economic, and environmental issues U.S. industries are encountering.

U.S. OFFICE OF TECHNOLOGY ASSESSMENT. REPORTS. INTERNATIONAL SECURITY AND COMMERCE PROGRAM. see MILITARY

U.S. OFFICE OF TECHNOLOGY ASSESSMENT. REPORTS. TECHNOLOGY AND THE ECONOMIC TRANSITION PROJECT. see BUSINESS AND ECONOMICS

600   US
U.S. TECHNOLOGY ADMINISTRATION. NATIONAL CRITICAL TECHNOLOGIES PANEL. BIENNIAL REPORT. 1991. biennial. $17.50 in N. America; overseas $35. U.S. Technology Administration, National Technical Information Service, 5285 Port Royal Rd., Springfield, VA 22161. TEL 703-487-4650. FAX 703-4321-8547. **Document type:** government publication.
Description: Explains the relationship between critical technologies and the U.S. economy.

600   378   CK
UNIVERSIDAD TECNOLOGICA DEL CHOCO. REVISTA. 1976. irreg. Universidad Tecnologica del Choco, Difusion Cultural, Carrera 2 no. 25-22, Quibdo, Choco, Colombia. Ed. Giorgio M. Manzini.

600   BL
UNIVERSIDADE FEDERAL DO CEARA. CENTRO DE TECNOLOGIA. BOLETIM TRIMESTRAL. q. Universidade Federal do Ceara, Centro de Tecnologia, Campus Universitario do Pici, Bl. 713, C.P. 2574, Fortaleza, Ceara, Brazil.

600   BE   ISSN 0075-9333
T2
UNIVERSITE DE LIEGE. FACULTE DES SCIENCES APPLIQUEES. COLLECTION DES PUBLICATIONS. (Text in French; summaries in English and German) 1966. bi-m. 1200 BEF. Universite de Liege, Faculte des Sciences Appliquees, 75 rue du Val-Benoit, 4000 Liege, Belgium.

TECHNOLOGY: COMPREHENSIVE WORKS

600 AT ISSN 1030-5947
UNIVERSITY OF TECHNOLOGY, SYDNEY. CALENDAR. 1965. a. Aus.$5 (foreign Aus.$10). University of Technology, Sydney, P.O. Box 123, City Campus, Broadway, N.S.W. 2007, Australia. TEL 02-330-1990. FAX 02-330-1551. circ. 3,000.
Former titles (until 1989): New South Wales Institute of Technology Calendar (ISSN 0314-6057); (until 1970): New South Wales Institute of Technology Handbook.
Description: Contains a wide range of information about courses, officers, and the staff of the university.

600 500 AT
UNIVERSITY OF TECHNOLOGY, SYDNEY. RESEARCH REPORT. 1974. a. free. University of Technology, Sydney, P.O. Box 123, City Campus, Broadway, N.S.W. 2007, Australia. TEL 02-330-1253. FAX 02-330-1244. circ. 1,500.
Former titles: University of Technology, Sydney. Research and Consultancy Report (ISSN 1031-8682); (until 1987): University of Technology, Sydney. Research Report (ISSN 0312-5378)
Description: Compilation of graduate research projects.

658.2 FR ISSN 0042-126X
HC271
USINE NOUVELLE; technology and economics. 1896. w. (plus m. & a. supplements). 785 F. (foreign 1554 F.) (effective Jan. 1994). Groupe Usine Nouvelle, 59 rue du Rocher, 75008 Paris, France.
TEL 44-69-55-55. FAX 43-87-42-65. TELEX 285 485 F. Ed. Anne Marie Finkelstein. adv.; charts; illus.; mkt.; pat.; stat.; tr.lit. circ. 60,000. *Indexed:* C.I.S. Abstr., Chem.Abstr., ELLIS, Int.Lab.Doc., Key to Econ.Sci., Met.Abstr., PROMT, World Alum.Abstr.
—BLDSC (9134.000000); SWETS.

600 ES
UTEC. 1989. q. Universidad Tecnologica San Salvador, Extension Cultural, Calle Arce, 1020, Apdo. Postal 1770, San Salvador, El Salvador. TEL 71-5990. *Document type:* academic/scholarly publication.

600 FI ISSN 1235-0613
CODEN: VTJUEX
V T T JULKAISUJA/V T T PUBLIKATIONER. (Text in Finnish, Swedish) 1981. irreg. Valtion Teknillinen Tutkimuskeskus - Technical Research Centre of Finland, P.O. Box 2000, FIN-02044 VTT, Finland. FAX 358-0-4564374. (reprint service avail. from NTI) *Indexed:* Biol.Abstr., Chem.Abstr. *Document type:* monographic series.
—BLDSC (9258.906900); CASDDS; Ei.
Formerly (until 1992): Valtion Teknillinen Tutkimuskeskus. Tutkimuksia (ISSN 0358-5077)

V T T PUBLICATIONS. (Valtion Teknillinen Tutkimuskeskus) see *SCIENCES: COMPREHENSIVE WORKS*

600 FI ISSN 0357-9387
CODEN: VTTSE9
V T T SYMPOSIUM. (Text in official language of symposium) 1974. irreg. price varies. Valtion Teknillinen Tutkimuskeskus - Technical Research Centre of Finland, P.O. Box 2000, FIN-02044 VTT, Finland. FAX 358-0-4564374. *Indexed:* INSPEC. *Document type:* proceedings.
—BLDSC (9258.907000); CASDDS; Ei.

600 FI ISSN 1235-0605
CODEN: VTIEEE
V T T TIEDOTTEITA/V T T MEDDELANDEN/V T T RESEARCH NOTES. (Text in English, Finnish or Swedish) 1981. irreg. Valtion Teknillinen Tutkimuskeskus - Technical Research Centre of Finland, P.O. Box 2000, FIN-02044 VTT, Finland. FAX 358-0-4564374. (reprint service avail. from NTI) *Document type:* monographic series.
—BLDSC (9258.909000); CASDDS; Ei.
Formerly (until 1992): Valtion Teknillinen Tutkimuskeskus. Tiedotteita (ISSN 0358-5085)

VADEMECUM DEUTSCHER LEHR- UND FORSCHUNGSSTAETTEN. STAETTEN DER FORSCHUNG. see *SCIENCES: COMPREHENSIVE WORKS*

VEDA, TECHNIKA A MY/SCIENCE, TECHNOLOGY AND WE. see *CHILDREN AND YOUTH — For*

VIGNANA BHARATHI. see *SCIENCES: COMPREHENSIVE WORKS*

600 US ISSN 0745-7200
VIRGINIA EXTENSION. q. Virginia Polytechnic Institute and State University, 202 Media Bldg, Blacksburg, VA 24061. TEL 703-961-7370.
Description: Magazine concerning Virginia's extension activities.

VISHWAKARMA. see *ENGINEERING*

658.5 GW ISSN 0941-2360
TJ3
W T PRODUKTION UND MANAGEMENT; Zeitschrift fuer industrielle Fertigung. 1907. 12/yr. DM.458($332) (effective 1996). (Verein Deutscher Ingenieure) Springer-Verlag, Heidelberger Platz 3, 14197 Berlin, Germany. TEL 030-2807-0. FAX 030-8214091. E-mail: orders@springer.de. (Subscr. in N. America to: Springer-Verlag New York, Inc., 44 Hartz Way, Secaucus, NJ 07096-2491. TEL 201-348-4033. FAX 201-348-4505) adv. (also avail. in microform from UMI; reprint service avail. from ISI) *Indexed:* Appl.Mech.Rev., C.I.S. Abstr., Curr.Cont., Met.Abstr., Risk Abstr., World Alum.Abstr. *Document type:* academic/scholarly publication.
—Genuine Article; SWETS; UMI. **CCC.**
Former titles: W T - Werkstatttechnik (ISSN 0340-4544); Werkstatttechnik (ISSN 0043-2806)

W Z B PAPERS. (Wissenschaftszentrum Berlin fuer Sozialforschung) see *SOCIAL SCIENCES: COMPREHENSIVE WORKS*

600 US ISSN 1058-9163
WASHINGTON TECHNOLOGY. fortn. $50 in the U.S.; Canada $75 (overseas $250). TechNews, Inc., 8500 Leesburg Pike, Ste. 7500, Vienna, VA 22182-3932. TEL 703-848-2800.
FAX 703-848-2353. E-mail: esmith@technews.com. Ed. Esther T. Smith; Pub. Tim Karney. adv. circ. 40,000. *Document type:* newspaper.
Description: Delivers strategic information to systems integrators active in federal government information technology management.

600 500 GW ISSN 0172-1623
WECHSELWIRKUNG; Technik Naturwissenschaft Gesellschaft. 1979. bi-m. DM.70 (foreign DM.80). Remember e.g., Mariabrunnstr. 48, 52064 Aachen, Germany. TEL 0241-405930. FAX 0241-408461. Ed.Bd. adv.; bk.rev. circ. 6,000. (back issues avail.) *Document type:* academic/scholarly publication.
Description: New research and developments in science and technology and their social and ecological aspects. Includes list of events and exhibitions.
Refereed Serial

WEIZMANN INSTITUTE OF SCIENCE, REHOVOT, ISRAEL. SCIENTIFIC ACTIVITIES. see *SCIENCES: COMPREHENSIVE WORKS*

600 SZ
WERKMEISTER/CONTREMAITRE. (Text in French & German) 1894. fortn. 43 SFr. Schweizerischer Verband Technischer Betriebskader, Schaffhauserstr. 2-4, 8006 Zurich, Switzerland. Ed. Roger Erb. adv.; illus.; index. (tabloid format) *Indexed:* C.I.S. Abstr.
Formerly: Werkmeister und Technicche Arbeitsleiter - Contremaitre et Agent de Maitrise (ISSN 0043-2776)

WERKSTATT UND BETRIEB; Zeitschrift fuer Maschinenbau, Konstruktion und Fertigung. see *MACHINERY*

600 GW ISSN 0939-2629
WERKSTOFFE - IN DER FERTIGUNG. 1963. 6/yr. DM.84. Holz Verlag GmbH und Co. KG, Sonnenblumenring 35, 86415 Mering, Germany. adv.; bk.rev.; illus.; pat.; tr.lit.; index. *Document type:* trade publication.
Former titles: Werkstoffe - Betriebsleitung Technik (ISSN 0176-6058); Werkstoffe und Technik; Werkstoffe (ISSN 0043-2814)

600 658 US
WESTERN TECHNOLOGY & MANAGEMENT.* (Text in Chinese) 1980. m. free. (China Council for Promotion of International Trade) China Representatives Ltd., 158 Linwood Plaza, Ste. 224, Ft. Lee, NJ 07024-1704. Ed. Louis F. Sharpe. adv.; charts; illus.; stat. circ. 50,000.

600 AT ISSN 1034-7658
WHAT'S NEW IN SCIENTIFIC & LABORATORY TECHNOLOGY. 1981. bi-m. Aus.$36. Westwick-Farrow Pty. Ltd., Cnr. Fox Valley Rd. and Kiogle St., Wahroonga, N.S.W. 2076, Australia. TEL 02-487-2700. FAX 02-489-1265. Ed. Colin Francis. circ. 6,700 (controlled). (back issues avail.)
Description: Contains new product information for laboratory management.

600 500 JA
WHITE PAPER ON SCIENCE AND TECHNOLOGY (YEAR). (Text in English) a. $74. Japan Information Center of Science and Technology - Nihon Kagaku Gijutsu Joho Senta, 5-3, Yonbancho, Chiyoda-ku, Tokyo 102, Japan. TEL 03-5214-8413. FAX 03-5214-8410.
Description: Covers science and technology trends, activities, developments and policies of Japan.

WHO KNOWS WHAT: A GUIDE TO EXPERTS. see *SCIENCES: COMPREHENSIVE WORKS*

WHO'S WHO IN INDIAN ENGINEERING AND INDUSTRY. see *BIOGRAPHY*

WHO'S WHO IN TECHNOLOGY. see *BIOGRAPHY*

WILEY LIBRARIANS' NEWSLETTER. see *PUBLISHING AND BOOK TRADE*

WONDER: OBSERVING & CONFRONTING THE ENIGMAS THAT SURROUND US. see *SCIENCES: COMPREHENSIVE WORKS*

WORCESTER POLYTECHNIC INSTITUTE - STUDIES IN SCIENCE, TECHNOLOGY AND CULTURE. see *SCIENCES: COMPREHENSIVE WORKS*

WORLD TECHNOLOGY; patent licensing gazette. see *PATENTS, TRADEMARKS AND COPYRIGHTS*

WORLD TECHNOLOGY POLICIES. see *SCIENCES: COMPREHENSIVE WORKS*

891.7 PL ISSN 0860-276X
WYZSZA SZKOLA PEDAGOGICZNA IM. KOMISJI EDUKACJI NARODOWEJ W KRAKOWIE. ROCZNIK NAUKOWE-DYDAKTYCZNY. PRACE TECHNICZNE. 1973. irreg., no.5, 1992. price varies. Wydawnictwo Naukowe W S P, Ul. Karmelicka 41, 31-128 Krakow, Poland. TEL 33-78-20. (Co-sponsor: Ministerstwo Edukacji Narodowej)

339 600 CC ISSN 1001-5396
XIANDAIHUA/MODERNIZATION. (Text in Chinese; table of contents in English) 1978. m. Y2.50 per no. (Zhongguo Kexue Jishu Xiehui - China Association for Science and Technology) Xiandaihua Zazhishe, 32, Baishiqiao Lu, Beijing 100081, People's Republic of China. TEL 401-4007. FAX 401-4008. (Dist. outside China by: China International Book Trading Corp., P.O. Box 2820, Beijing, P.R.C.) Ed. Li Baoheng. adv. circ. 50,000.

605 JA ISSN 0386-3433
T1 CODEN: TRYUAY
YAMAGUCHI UNIVERSITY. FACULTY OF ENGINEERING. TECHNOLOGY REPORTS. (Text in English) 1972. a. exchange basis. Yamaguchi Daigaku, Kogakubu - Yamagachi University, Faculty of Engineering, Tokiwadai, Ube-shi 755, Japan. *Indexed:* Chem.Abstr., INSPEC (1983-), JCT, JTA.
—BLDSC (8760.200000); CASDDS; UnCover.

600 500 JA ISSN 0388-8738
YOSHIDA KAGAKU GIJUTSU ZAIDAN NYUSU/YOSHIDA FOUNDATION FOR SCIENCE AND TECHNOLOGY. NEWS. (Text in Japanese) 1975. q. Yoshida Kagaku Gijutsu Zaidan - Yoshida Foundation for Science and Technology, Rm. 502, Maison Yonbanchyo, 6, Yonban-cho, Chiyoda-ku, Tokyo 102, Japan.

Z W F - C I M. (Zeitschrift fuer Wirtschaftliche Fertigung und Automatisierung) see *MACHINERY*

ZAMBIA JOURNAL OF SCIENCE AND TECHNOLOGY. see *SCIENCES: COMPREHENSIVE WORKS*

ZENIT. see *SCIENCES: COMPREHENSIVE WORKS*

ZHONGGUO KEJI SHILIAO/CHINA HISTORICAL MATERIALS OF SCIENCE AND TECHNOLOGY. see *SCIENCES: COMPREHENSIVE WORKS*

TECHNOLOGY: COMPREHENSIVE WORKS — ABSTRACTING, BIBLIOGRAPHIES, STATISTICS

ZHONGGUO KEJI SHILIAO/HISTORICAL MATERIAL OF CHINESE SCIENCE AND TECHNOLOGY. see *SCIENCES: COMPREHENSIVE WORKS*

ZHONGGUO KEXUE JISHU DAXUE XUEBAO/CHINA UNIVERSITY OF SCIENCE AND TECHNOLOGY. JOURNAL. see *SCIENCES: COMPREHENSIVE WORKS*

ZHONGGUO ZIXINGCHE/CHINA BICYCLE. see *SPORTS AND GAMES — Bicycles And Motorcycles*

ZHONGWAI JISHU QINGBAO/CHINESE AND FOREIGN TECHNOLOGY INFORMATION. see *SCIENCES: COMPREHENSIVE WORKS*

ZIRAN BIANZHENGFA TONGXUN/JOURNAL OF DIALECTICS OF NATURE. see *SCIENCES: COMPREHENSIVE WORKS*

600 300 GW ISSN 0942-0436
ZUKUENFTE. 1991. q. DM.60; newsstand price: DM.15. (Sekretariat fuer Zukunftsforschung) Klartext Verlag, Dickmannstr. 2-4, 45143 Essen, Germany. TEL 0201-8620658. FAX 0201-8620622. adv.; bk.rev.; abstr.; bibl.; illus.; circ. 2,000. (back issues avail.) **Document type:** consumer publication.

600 US ISSN 1051-9637
TK5105.5
3TECH. 1990. q. 3Com Corporation, Box 58145, Santa Clara, CA 95052-9953.

TECHNOLOGY: COMPREHENSIVE WORKS — Abstracting, Bibliographies, Statistics

600 CN ISSN 0705-8454
A S T I S CURRENT AWARENESS BULLETIN. 1978. bi-m. Can.$85. Arctic Science & Technology Information System, Arctic Institute of North America, University of Calgary, 2500 University Dr. N.W., Calgary, AB T2N 1N4, Canada. TEL 403-284-7515. FAX 403-282-4609. Ed. C. Ross Goodwin. circ. 90. **Document type:** abstracting/indexing.
●Also available online. Vendor(s): QL Systems Ltd..
Also available on CD-ROM.
Formerly: Arctic Institute of North America. Library. Accessions List.
Description: Designed to disseminate information about new arctic literature and research projects. Records are arranged by subject, with geographic and author indexes.

ABSTRACT NEWSLETTER: URBAN AND REGIONAL TECHNOLOGY AND DEVELOPMENT. see *HOUSING AND URBAN PLANNING — Abstracting, Bibliographies, Statistics*

ABSTRACTS OF ROMANIAN SCIENTIFIC AND TECHNICAL LITERATURE. see *SCIENCES: COMPREHENSIVE WORKS — Abstracting, Bibliographies, Statistics*

600 500 JA ISSN 0914-4897
ABSTRACTS OF SCIENTIFIC AND TECHNOLOGICAL PUBLICATIONS. (Text in English) 1965. a. Ajinomoto K.K., Chuo Kenkyujo - Ajinomoto Co., Inc., Central Research Laboratories, 1-1 Suzuki-cho, Kawasaki-ku, Kawasaki-shi, Kanagawa-ken 210, Japan. **Document type:** abstracting/indexing.

600 CL
ACTIVIDADES DE INVESTIGACION Y DESARROLLO EXPERIMENTAL. 1978. a. Instituto Nacional de Estadisticas, Av. Bulnes 418, Casilla 498, Correo 3 Santiago, Chile.

AGBIOTECH NEWS AND INFORMATION. see *BIOLOGY — Abstracting, Bibliographies, Statistics*

600 FR ISSN 0994-7663
L'ANNEE TECHNOLOGIQUE. (Supplement to: l'Usine Nouvelle) a. 50 F. Groupe Usine Nouvelle, 59, rue du Rocher, 75008 Paris, France. TEL 44-69-55-55. FAX 43-87-42-65. TELEX 285 485 F. circ. 70,000.

600 016 AT ISSN 1030-4495
APPROPRIATE TECHNOLOGY INDEX. Short title: A T Index. 1980. q. Aus.$350. Noyce Publishing, G.P.O. Box 2222T, Meblourne, Vic. 3001, Australia. (back issues avail.) **Document type:** abstracting/indexing.
—BLDSC (1580.703000).
Description: Bibliographical indexing service to literature on appropriate technology and related fields.

600 318 AG
ARGENTINA. INSTITUTO DE ASUNTOS TECNICOS. ESTADISTICAS. 1974. irreg. Instituto de Asuntos Tecnicos, Direccion de Estadistica, Palacio Municipal, Cordoba, Argentina. charts.

ASLIB BOOK GUIDE; a monthly list of recommended scientific and technical books. see *SCIENCES: COMPREHENSIVE WORKS — Abstracting, Bibliographies, Statistics*

600 900 GW ISSN 0323-4355
BIBLIOGRAPHIE GESCHICHTE DER TECHNIK. (Text in German) 1971. a. DM.90. Saechsische Landesbibliothek, Marienallee 12, 01099 Dresden, Germany. TEL 0351-5630-0. FAX 0351-5630200. Eds. Michael Letocha, Peter Hesse. bk.rev. circ. 200. **Document type:** bibliography.

BIBLIOGRAPHIES ON THE HISTORY OF SCIENCE AND TECHNOLOGY. see *SCIENCES: COMPREHENSIVE WORKS — Abstracting, Bibliographies, Statistics*

BOLETIN DE TRADUCCIONES. see *SCIENCES: COMPREHENSIVE WORKS — Abstracting, Bibliographies, Statistics*

BRITISH REPORTS, TRANSLATIONS AND THESES. see *SCIENCES: COMPREHENSIVE WORKS — Abstracting, Bibliographies, Statistics*

BULLETIN ANALYTIQUE DE LA LITTERATURE SCIENTIFIQUE ET TECHNIQUE ROUMAINE. see *SCIENCES: COMPREHENSIVE WORKS — Abstracting, Bibliographies, Statistics*

600 UK ISSN 0966-8780
Z7913
C T I PLUS. (Current Technology Index) q. £875($1400) (effective 1995). Bowker - Saur Ltd., A part of Reed Reference Publishing, Maypole House, Maypole Rd., E. Grinstead, W. Sussex RH19 1HH, England. TEL 44-1342-330100. FAX 44-1342-330191. E-mail: custserv@bowker-saur.co.uk. (avail. for MS-DOS version) **Document type:** abstracting/indexing.
●Available only on CD-ROM. Producer(s): Bowker - Saur Ltd..
Description: Indexes more than 175,000 articles from some 320 technical and applied science journals published primarily in the United Kingdom between 1981 and the present.

CARINDEX: SCIENCE & TECHNOLOGY. see *SCIENCES: COMPREHENSIVE WORKS — Abstracting, Bibliographies, Statistics*

CATALOGO COLETIVO DE ANAIS DE EVENTOS. see *SCIENCES: COMPREHENSIVE WORKS — Abstracting, Bibliographies, Statistics*

600 016 UK ISSN 0261-0191
CATCHWORD AND TRADE NAME INDEX. Abbreviated title: C A T N I. (Supplement to: Current Technology Index (ISSN 0260-6593)) 3/yr. (including a. cumulation). £165($300) (outside the E.C. £175) (effective 1995). Bowker - Saur Ltd., A part of Reed Reference Publishing, Maypole House, Maypole Rd., E. Grinstead, W. Sussex RH19 1HH, England. TEL 44-1342-330100. FAX 44-1342-330191. (Subscr. to: Worldwide Subscription Service Ltd., Unit 4, Gibbs Reed Farm, Ticehurst, E. Sussex TN5 7HE, England) **Document type:** abstracting/indexing.
●Also available on CD-ROM. Producer(s): Bowker - Saur Ltd. (CTI Plus).
Description: Helps locate data on a particular product appearing in a technical journal by its brand, company or trade name.

600 JA ISSN 0577-9774
Q4
CHOSEN GAKUJUTSU TSUHO/KOREAN SCIENTIFIC INFORMATION. (Text in English, Japanese) 1964. s-a. Korean Association of Science and Technology in Japan - Zainihon Chosenjin Kagaku Gijutsu Kyokai, 33-14, Hakusan, 4-chome, Bunkyo-ku, Tokyo 112, Japan.

CIENCIA Y TECNICA; boletin bibliografico nacional y extranjero. see *SCIENCES: COMPREHENSIVE WORKS — Abstracting, Bibliographies, Statistics*

CURRENT BIBLIOGRAPHIES ON SCIENCE AND TECHNOLOGY: MECHANICAL ENGINEERING & CONSTRUCTION ENGINEERING. see *METALLURGY — Abstracting, Bibliographies, Statistics*

CURRENT LITERATURE ON SCIENCE OF SCIENCE. see *SCIENCES: COMPREHENSIVE WORKS — Abstracting, Bibliographies, Statistics*

CURRENT OPINION IN BIOTECHNOLOGY. see *BIOLOGY — Biotechnology*

600 016 UK ISSN 0260-6593
Z7913
CURRENT TECHNOLOGY INDEX. 1962. bi-m. plus a. cumulation. £635($1180) in UK & EEC; elsewhere £685 (effective 1995). Bowker - Saur Ltd., A part of Reed Reference Publishing, Maypole House, Maypole Rd., E. Grinstead, W. Sussex RH19 1HH, England. TEL 44-1342-330100. FAX 44-1342-330191. (Subscr. to: Worldwide Subscription Service Ltd., Unit 4, Gibbs Reed Farm, Ticehurst, E. Sussex, TN5 7HE) Ed. Peter Ellway. (also avail. in magnetic tape) **Indexed:** BMT, Fluidex. **Document type:** abstracting/indexing.
●Also available online. Vendor(s): Knight-Ridder, Inc. (File no.142).
Also available on CD-ROM. Producer(s): Bowker - Saur Ltd..
—BLDSC (3504.340000).
Formerly: British Technology Index (ISSN 0007-1889)
Description: Indexes British periodicals in all branches of engineering, chemical technology, instrumentation, building, transport, and computerization.

DIRECTORIO DE REVISTAS ESPANOLAS DE CIENCIA Y TECNOLOGIA. see *SCIENCES: COMPREHENSIVE WORKS — Abstracting, Bibliographies, Statistics*

DISSERTATION ABSTRACTS INTERNATIONAL. SECTION B: PHYSICAL SCIENCES AND ENGINEERING. see *SCIENCES: COMPREHENSIVE WORKS — Abstracting, Bibliographies, Statistics*

DOCUMENTATION - TECHNIQUE, SCIENTIFIQUE ET COMMERCIALE; revue d'information de l'edition francaise et etrangere. see *SCIENCES: COMPREHENSIVE WORKS — Abstracting, Bibliographies, Statistics*

600 015 EI
EURO ABSTRACTS. (Supplement avail.: Progress in Coal Steel and Related Social Research (ISSN 1015-6275)) (Text in English) 1962. m. 110 ECU (180 ECU with supplements). Commission of the European Communities, 200 rue de la Loi, B-1049 Brussels, Belgium. (Subscr. to: RTD Help Desk, European Commission, DG XIII/D-2, Luxembourg, Luxembourg. TEL 352-4301-33161. FAX 352-4301-32084) adv. contact: Rebecca Zahn. index. (also avail. in microform from UMI) **Indexed:** Anal.Abstr., Br.Ceram.Abstr. **Document type:** abstracting/indexing.
—BLDSC (3829.155000).
Formed by the 1989 merger of: Euro Abstracts. Section 1: Euratom and E E C Research (ISSN 0379-8771); Euro Abstracts. Section 2: Coal and Steel (ISSN 0378-3472); Which supersedes (in 1975): Euro Abstracts (ISSN 0014-2352)
Description: Provides abstracts of the European Commissions R and D publications.

FIBEROPTICS MARKETING INTELLIGENCE. see *PHYSICS — Optics*

600 016 GW ISSN 0343-5520
Z7403
FORSCHUNGSBERICHTE AUS TECHNIK UND NATURWISSENSCHAFTEN/REPORTS IN THE FIELDS OF SCIENCE AND TECHNOLOGY. (Text in English, German) 1973. q. DM.890.($668) (effective 1996). (Technische Informationsbibliothek, Hannover) V C H Verlagsgesellschaft mbH, Postfach 101161, 69451 Weinheim, Germany. TEL 06201-606-147. FAX 06201-606117. TELEX 465516-VCHWH-D. (U.S. addr.: V C H Publishers, Inc., 220 E. 23rd St, New York, NY 10010-4606. TEL 212-683-8333) (Co-sponsor: Fachinformationszentrum Energie Physik Mathematik) adv. contact: R. Roth. bk.rev.; index. circ. 325. (also avail. in microfilm; reprint service avail. from ISI) **Document type:** abstracting/indexing.
—CCC.
Former titles (until 1979): Deutsche Forschungsberichte (ISSN 0340-0751); Deutsche Forschungsberichte. Neueingange.

TECHNOLOGY: COMPREHENSIVE WORKS — ABSTRACTING, BIBLIOGRAPHIES, STATISTICS

600 500 016   US   ISSN 0094-4505
GUIDE TO AMERICAN SCIENTIFIC AND TECHNICAL DIRECTORIES. 1972. biennial. $65. Todd Publications, 18 N. Greenbush Rd., W. Nyack, NY 10994. TEL 914-358-6213. Ed. Barry Klein. **Document type:** bibliography.

HUNGARIAN R AND D ABSTRACTS. SCIENCE AND TECHNOLOGY. see SCIENCES: COMPREHENSIVE WORKS — Abstracting, Bibliographies, Statistics

I N S D O C. RUSSIAN SCIENTIFIC AND TECHNICAL PUBLICATIONS. ACCESSIONS LIST. (Indian National Scientific Documentation Centre) see SCIENCES: COMPREHENSIVE WORKS — Abstracting, Bibliographies, Statistics

INDEX DOCUMENTATION - ECONOMIE - SCIENCE - TECHNIQUE. see BUSINESS AND ECONOMICS — Abstracting, Bibliographies, Statistics

INDEX TO SCIENTIFIC & TECHNICAL PROCEEDINGS. see SCIENCES: COMPREHENSIVE WORKS — Abstracting, Bibliographies, Statistics

INDIA. DEPARTMENT OF SCIENCE AND TECHNOLOGY. RESEARCH AND DEVELOPMENT STATISTICS. see SCIENCES: COMPREHENSIVE WORKS — Abstracting, Bibliographies, Statistics

600 016
INDIAN INSTITUTE OF TECHNOLOGY, MADRAS. PH.D. DISSERTATION ABSTRACTS. (Text in English) a. Indian Institute of Technology at Madras, Central Library, Madras 600 036, India. **Document type:** abstracting/indexing.

500 600 016   II
INDIAN SCIENCE INDEX. SER. B: PRE-MODERN PERIOD. triennial. Rs.80 (foreign Rs.400). Centre for Asian Dokumentation, K-15, Cit Bldg., Christopher Road, Calcutta 700 014, India. Ed. S. Chaudhuri. **Document type:** abstracting/indexing.
Formerly: Indian Science Index. Ser. B Calcutta: Pre-modern Period.
Description: Covers scientific and technological journals all over the world.

INDICE ESPANOL DE CIENCIA Y TECNOLOGIA. see SCIENCES: COMPREHENSIVE WORKS — Abstracting, Bibliographies, Statistics

600 016   TZ   ISSN 0856-0404
INDUSTRIAL ABSTRACTS FOR TANZANIA. 1981. s-a. $28. Library Services Board, National Documentation Centre, P.O. Box 9283, Dar es Salaam, Tanzania. Ed. D.A. Sekimang'a. **Document type:** abstracting/indexing.

IPARI FORMATERVEZESI SZAKIRODALMI TAJEKOZTATO/INDUSTRIAL DESIGN ABSTRACTS. see ENGINEERING — Abstracting, Bibliographies, Statistics

JAPANESE PERIODICALS INDEX. SCIENCE AND TECHNOLOGY/ZASSHI KIJI SAKUIN. KAGAKU GIJUTSU HEN. see SCIENCES: COMPREHENSIVE WORKS — Abstracting, Bibliographies, Statistics

500 600 016   JA   ISSN 0022-765X
KAGAKU GIJUTSU BUNKEN TOYAMA/TOYAMA SCIENCE AND TECHNICAL DOCUMENTS. (Text in Japanese) 1959. bi-m. 200 Yen. Kagaku Gijutsu Bunken Riyo Shikokai - Promotive Association for Science and Technical Documents Utililization, c/o Toyama Prefectural Library, 206-3 Chayamachi, Toyama 930-01, Japan. bk.rev.; abstr.; bibl.; circ. 500 (controlled). (looseleaf format) **Document type:** bibliography.

600 500   JA
KAGAKU GIJUTSU FORAMU HOKOKUSHO. (Text in English and Japanese) a. Kagaku Gijutsucho, Kagaku Gijutsu Seisaku-kyoku - Science and Technology Agency, Science and Technology Policy Bureau, 2-1 Kasumigaseki 2-chome, Chiyoda-ku, Tokyo 100, Japan. abstr.
Description: Annual report of the forum on science and technology.

KOREAN SCIENTIFIC ABSTRACTS. see SCIENCES: COMPREHENSIVE WORKS — Abstracting, Bibliographies, Statistics

600 500   JA
KUNI NO SHIKEN KENKYU GYOMU KEIKAKU. (Text in Japanese) 1979. a. Kagaku Gijutsucho, Kagaku Gijutsu Seisaku-kyoku - Science and Technology Agency, Science and Technology Policy Bureau, 2-1 Kasumigaseki 2-chome, Chiyoda-ku, Tokyo 100, Japan. abstr. **Document type:** government publication.
Description: Contains information on national research projects.

016 600   PK
LISTS OF P A S T I C BIBLIOGRAPHIES. (Text in English) 1957. a. (latest 1978). Rs.10($4) Pakistan Scientific and Technological Information Centre, Quaid-i-Azam University, Box 217, Islamabad, Pakistan. Ed. Mumtaz Begum. circ. 500. (also avail. in microfilm) **Document type:** bibliography.
Formerly: Lists of P A N S Doc Bibliographies (ISSN 0078-835X)

MALAWI JOURNAL OF SCIENCE AND TECHNOLOGY. see SCIENCES: COMPREHENSIVE WORKS — Abstracting, Bibliographies, Statistics

600 016   US
N T I S ALERTS: FOREIGN TECHNOLOGY. w. $165 (foreign $225). U.S. National Technical Information Service, 5285 Port Royal Rd., Springfield, VA 22161. TEL 703-487-4630. FAX 703-321-8547. TELEX 64617. index. (back issues avail.) **Document type:** government publication, abstracting/indexing.
Formerly: Abstract Newsletter: Foreign Technology.

600 016   US
N T I S ALERTS: GOVERNMENT INVENTIONS FOR LICENSING. w. $250 (foreign $365). U.S. National Technical Information Service, 5285 Port Royal Rd., Springfield, VA 22161. TEL 703-487-4630. FAX 703-321-8547. TELEX 64617. Ed. Linda J. LaGarde. index. (back issues avail.) **Document type:** government publication, abstracting/indexing.
Former titles: Abstract Newsletter: Government Inventions for Licensing; Weekly Abstract Newsletter: Government Inventions for Licensing; Weekly Government Abstracts. Government Inventions for Licensing (ISSN 0364-6491)

600 016   US
N T I S ALERTS: MANUFACTURING TECHNOLOGY. w. $175 (foreign $245). U.S. National Technical Information Service, 5285 Port Royal Rd., Springfield, VA 22161. TEL 703-487-4630. FAX 703-321-8547. TELEX 64617. index. (back issues avail.) **Document type:** government publication, abstracting/indexing.
Formerly: Abstract Newsletter: Manufacturing Technology.

600   US
N T I S TITLE INDEX. q. U.S. National Technical Information Service, 5825 Port Royal Rd., Springfield, VA 22161. TEL 703-487-4630. index, cum.index. (microfiche; back issues avail.) **Document type:** government publication, bibliography.

600 016   XR
NARODNI TECHNICKE MUZEUM. BIBLIOGRAFIE. PRAMENY. (Text in Czech and German) 1970. irreg. exchange basis. Narodni Technicke Muzeum, Kostelni 42, 170 78 Prague 7, Czech Republic. **Document type:** bibliography.

500 600 016   JA   ISSN 0919-8768
NATIONAL DIET LIBRARY. ANNUAL LIST OF FOREIGN SCIENTIFIC AND TECHNICAL PUBLICATIONS/KAIGAI KAGAKU GIJUTSU SHIRYO UKEIRE MOKUROKU. (Text in English and Japanese) 1961. a. price varies. National Diet Library - Kokuritsu Kokkai Toshokan, 1-10-1 Nagata-cho, Chiyoda-ku, Tokyo 100, Japan. TEL 03-3581-2331. FAX 03-3597-9104. bibl. circ. 280. **Document type:** bibliography.
Former titles (until 1993): National Diet Library. Monthly List of Foreign Scientific and Technical Publications - Kaigai Kagaku Gijutsu Shiryo Geppo (ISSN 0454-1944); (until 1961): Gijutsu Bunken Nyusu (ISSN 0574-7805)

600 314.9   NE   ISSN 0470-6684
HD9735.N2
NETHERLANDS. CENTRAAL BUREAU VOOR DE STATISTIEK. MAANDSTATISTIEK VAN DE INDUSTRIE. 1953. m. fl.112. Centraal Bureau voor de Statistiek, Prinses Beatrixlaan 428, Voorburg, Netherlands. (Orders to: SDU - Publishers, Christoffel Plantijnstraat, The Hague, Netherlands) circ. 925. **Document type:** government publication.

NEW TECHNICAL BOOKS; a selective list with descriptive annotations. see SCIENCES: COMPREHENSIVE WORKS — Abstracting, Bibliographies, Statistics

NIHON KAGAKUSHI GAKKAI NENKAI KENKYU HAPPYO KOEN YOSHISHU. see SCIENCES: COMPREHENSIVE WORKS

600   JA
NIHON SANGYO GIJUTSUSHI GAKKAI NENKAI KOEN GAIYOSHU/JAPAN SOCIETY FOR THE HISTORY OF INDUSTRIAL TECHNOLOGY. ANNUAL CONFERENCE. PROCEEDINGS. (Text in Japanese) 1985. a. Nihon Sangyo Gijutsushi Gakkai - Japan Society for the History of Industrial Technology, Osaka Kogyokai Osaka Shoko Kaigisho Bldg. 5F, 58-7 Uchihon-machi, Hashizume-cho, Higashi-ku, Osaka-shi, Osaka-fu 540, Japan. abstr. **Document type:** proceedings.

600   PH   ISSN 0115-9984
Q76
R & D PHILIPPINES. s-a. P.250 (foreign $45). Science and Technology Information Institute, Department of Science and Technology, P.O. Box 3596, Manila, Philippines. TEL 822-0954. (Subscr. to: Dept. of Science and Technology, Bicutan, Taguig, P.O. Box 2131, Manila, Philippines) **Document type:** bibliography.
Description: Contains completed, on-going and pipeline R & Ds with complete bibliographic information.

745.2 016   GW   ISSN 0024-4805
RAT FUER FORMGEBUNG. LITERATURHINWEISE. 1961. q. DM.40. Rat fuer Formgebung, Ludwig-Erhard-Anlage 1, 60327 Frankfurt a.M., Germany. TEL 069-747919. FAX 069-7410911. bk.rev.; bibl. circ. 700(combined).

600   RU
REFERATIVNYI ZHURNAL. TEKHNICHESKAYA ESTETIKA I ERGONOMIKA. 1987. q. 7.55 Rub. Vsesoyuznyi Institut Nauchno-Tekhnicheskoi Informatsii (VINITI), Ul. Usievicha 20a, 125 219 Moscow, Russia. FAX 943-0060. TELEX 411249. Ed. Yu.N. Sorokin. circ. 1,369. **Document type:** abstracting/indexing.

S E A ABSTRACTS. see SCIENCES: COMPREHENSIVE WORKS — Abstracting, Bibliographies, Statistics

600   CN
SASKTECH DIRECTORY; a directory of advanced technology capabilities in Saskatchewan. (Text in English) 1991. a. free. Saskatchewan Economic Development, 206-15 Innovation Blvd., Saskatoon, SK S7N 2X8, Canada. TEL 306-933-7200. FAX 306-933-8244. **Document type:** directory.
Description: Profiles over 200 companies in advanced technology industries, including microelectronics, automation, fiber optics, computer and software development, biotechnology, space, communication, and related research.

SCIENCE AND TECHNOLOGY (PITTSBURGH); a purchase guide for libraries. see SCIENCES: COMPREHENSIVE WORKS — Abstracting, Bibliographies, Statistics

SCIENCE BOOKS & FILMS. see SCIENCES: COMPREHENSIVE WORKS — Abstracting, Bibliographies, Statistics

SCIENTIFIC AND TECHNICAL PUBLICATIONS IN BULGARIA. see SCIENCES: COMPREHENSIVE WORKS — Abstracting, Bibliographies, Statistics

SCIENTIFIC SERIALS IN THAI LIBRARIES. see SCIENCES: COMPREHENSIVE WORKS — Abstracting, Bibliographies, Statistics

SCITECH BOOK NEWS; an annotated bibliography of new books in science, technology, & medicine. see BIBLIOGRAPHIES

SCITECH REFERENCE PLUS; complete bibliographic information on SciTech books and serials, bibliographical data on science professionals, and corporate profiles of research and business facilities. see SCIENCES: COMPREHENSIVE WORKS — Abstracting, Bibliographies, Statistics

TELEPHONE AND TELEGRAPH

600   AT   ISSN 1030-4649
SCITECH TECHNOLOGY DIRECTORY. 1986. a. Aus.$145. Scitech Publication Pty. Ltd., G.P.O. Box 1915, Canberra, A.C.T. 2601, Australia. FAX 62-496648. Ed. Jane Ford. **Document type:** directory.
     Formerly: Technology Directory (ISSN 0817-9905)
     Description: Covers government assistance, technology centers, venture capital and other technology support bodies.

SELECTED RAND ABSTRACTS; a biannual guide to publications of the Rand Corporation. see *SCIENCES: COMPREHENSIVE WORKS* — *Abstracting, Bibliographies, Statistics*

SHINKU TANKU NENPO/ABSTRACTS OF THINK TANK REPORTS. see *SCIENCES: COMPREHENSIVE WORKS* — *Abstracting, Bibliographies, Statistics*

620 016   US   ISSN 0049-1209
SOCIETY OF MANUFACTURING ENGINEERS. TECHNICAL DIGEST; abstracts of technical papers on microfiche and hard copy. 1965. q. $26 to non-members; members $18. Society of Manufacturing Engineers, One SME Dr., Box 930, Dearborn, MI 48121-0930. TEL 313-271-1500. FAX 313-271-2861. TELEX 297742 SME UR (VIA RCA). circ. 1,000. **Document type:** abstracting/indexing.
     —BLDSC (8656.613000).

STANDARDS ACTION. see *METROLOGY AND STANDARDIZATION* — *Abstracting, Bibliographies, Statistics*

TECHNICAL EDUCATION & TRAINING ABSTRACTS. see *EDUCATION* — *Abstracting, Bibliographies, Statistics*

TECHNOLOGY MEDIA SOURCE. see *ADVERTISING AND PUBLIC RELATIONS* — *Abstracting, Bibliographies, Statistics*

600   US   ISSN 0732-5533
T1
TECHNOLOGY UPDATE (FOSTER CITY). w. $225 (foreign $250). Information Access Company (Subsidiary of: Thomson Corporation), 362 Lakeside Dr., Foster City, CA 94404. TEL 415-378-5200; 800-227-8431. FAX 415-358-4759. (Or: Predicasts Europe, 8-10 Denman St., London W1V 7RF, England. TEL 0171-494-3817)
     —CCC.
     Formerly: Technology Survey.
     Description: Provides abstracts of current information in 32 high-technology fields, including computers, lasers, genetic engineering, robotics, fiber optics, and medicine.

THAI ABSTRACTS, SERIES A. SCIENCE AND TECHNOLOGY. see *SCIENCES: COMPREHENSIVE WORKS* — *Abstracting, Bibliographies, Statistics*

VSESOYUZNYI INSTITUT NAUCHNO-TEKHNICHESKOI INFORMATSII. DEPONIROVANNYE NAUCHNYE RABOTY. see *SCIENCES: COMPREHENSIVE WORKS* — *Abstracting, Bibliographies, Statistics*

600 016   XR
VYBER NOVINEK BRNENSKYCH KNIHOVEN. SERIE G: TECHNIKA. 1974. 6/yr. 18 Kc. (49 Kc. for 7 vols. series: A-G). Moravska Zemska Knihovna, Kounicova 5-7, 601 87 Brno, Czech Republic. Ed. Jaromir Kubicek. circ. 300.
     Formerly: Statni Vedecka Knihovna. Vyber Novinek. Serie G: Technika.

WASEDA DAIGAKU DAIGAKUIN RIKOGAKU KENKYU IHO/WASEDA UNIVERSITY. GRADUATE SCHOOL OF SCIENCE AND ENGINEERING. SYNOPSES OF SCIENCE AND ENGINEERING PAPERS. see *ENGINEERING* — *Abstracting, Bibliographies, Statistics*

600 016   II   ISSN 0043-8944
WORLD REPORT ON TECHNICAL ADVANCEMENT. 1967. m. Rs.350($50) K.K. Roy (Private) Ltd., 55 Gariahat Rd., P.O. Box 10210, Calcutta 700 019, India. Ed. K.K. Roy. adv.; abstr.; pat.; stat.; index. circ. 1,000. (tabloid format)

TELEPHONE AND TELEGRAPH

see *Communications–Telephone and Telegraph*

TELEVISION AND CABLE

see *Communications–Television and Cable*

TEXTILE INDUSTRIES AND FABRICS

see also *Cleaning and Dyeing; Clothing Trade*

677   II   ISSN 0971-0833
                 CODEN: ATTDD4
A C T. (A T I R A Communications on Textiles) 1966. q. $8. Ahmedabad Textile Industry's Research Association, Ambawadi Vistor P.O., Ahmedabad 380015, India. FAX 079-429874. TELEX 121-6571 ATRA IN. E-mail: atiza@nictas.cznet.in. **Indexed:** Chem.Abstr., Text.Tech.Dig., World Text.Abstr. **Document type:** academic/scholarly publication.
     —BLDSC (1765.886800); CASDDS.
     Formerly: A T I R A Technical Digest (ISSN 0378-8148)

677   HK   ISSN 1015-8138
A T A JOURNAL; journal for Asia on textile & apparel. (Text in English; summaries in Chinese) 1990. bi-m. HK.$311 asia $55; elsewhere $62. Adsale Publishing Company, 14-F, Deuon House, Taikoo Place, 979 King's Rd., Quarry Bay, Hong Kong. TEL 852-2811-8897. FAX 852-2516-5119. Ed. Benjamin Heung. adv. circ. 113,500. (back issues avail.)
     Formerly: Asia Textile and Apparel.
     Description: For textile and apparel industry management in Asia.

677   US   ISSN 1047-692X
TS1312
A T I DIRECTORY. (American Textile International) Variant title: Textile Red Book. a. $109.50. Billian Publishing, Inc., 2100 Powers Ferry Rd., Ste. 300, Atlanta, GA 30339. TEL 404-955-5656. FAX 404-952-0669. **Document type:** directory.
     Formerly: Clark's Directory of Southern Textile Mills.

338.4   GW   ISSN 0170-4060
A V R. (Allgemeiner Vliestoff-Report) (Text in English and German) 1972. bi-m. DM.136.96. D P W Verlag GmbH, Postfach 1353, 63131 Heusenstamm, Germany. TEL 06104-6060. FAX 06104-606317. Ed. H. Osthus. adv.; bk.rev.; abstr.; bibl.; illus.; pat.; stat. circ. 8,000. **Indexed:** Paper & Bd.Abstr., Text.Tech.Dig., World Text.Abstr. **Document type:** trade publication.
     —BLDSC (0792.380000). CCC.

677.3   AT
ABOUT WOOL. 1978. irreg. free. Australian Wool Corporation, G.P.O. Box 4867, Melbourne, Vic. 3001, Australia. TEL 03-341-9111. FAX 03-341-9273. TELEX AA 30548 HWOOL.
     Description: Information sheets for school students.

ADVANCED COMPOSITES BULLETIN; an international newsletter. see *PLASTICS*

677   UK   ISSN 0144-7521
AFRICAN TEXTILES/TEXTILES AFRICAINS; for the African textile industry. (Text in English, French) 1978. bi-m. £43.50($75) (effective 1995). Alain Charles Publishing Ltd., Alain Charles House, 27 Wilfred St., London SW1E 6PR, England. TEL 0171-834-7676. FAX 0171-973-0076. TELEX 297165 ACPLTD G. Ed. Zsa Tebbit. circ. 8,090 (paid). (back issues avail.) **Indexed:** Cott.& Trop.Fibr.Abstr., Text.Tech.Dig., World Text.Abstr. **Document type:** trade publication.
     —BLDSC (0734.931000).

677.7   US
AGENT. s-a. Halper Publishing Company, 600 Central Ave., Ste. 226, Highland Park, IL 60035. TEL 708-831-6678. adv.

---

667 338.4   II   ISSN 0075-4005
AHMEDABAD TEXTILE INDUSTRY'S RESEARCH ASSOCIATION. JOINT TECHNOLOGICAL CONFERENCES. PROCEEDINGS. (Text in English) 1960. a. $16. Ahmedabad Textile Industry's Research Association, Polytechnic P.O., Ahmedabad 380015, India. TELEX 121-6571 ATIRA IN. circ. 1,000. **Indexed:** Text.Tech.Dig, World Text.Abstr. **Document type:** proceedings.

677   II
ALL INDIA HANDLOOM EXPORTERS GUIDE. irreg. $10 per no. c/o S. Narayanan, 11-B Ramachandra Iyer St., Madras 600017, India.

ALL PAKISTAN TEXTILE MILLS ASSOCIATION. CHAIRMAN'S REVIEW. see *BUSINESS AND ECONOMICS* — *Production Of Goods And Services*

677.028   US   ISSN 0040-490X
AMERICAN ASSOCIATION OF TEXTILE CHEMISTS AND COLORISTS. BUYER'S GUIDE. (Special (July) issue of: Textile Chemist and Colorist) 1969. a. $76 to non-members; members $41. American Association of Textile Chemists and Colorists, One Davis Dr., Box 12215, Research Triangle Park, NC 27709-2215. TEL 919-549-8141. FAX 919-549-8933. Ed. Susan H. Keesee. adv. contact: William B. Davis. circ. 9,600. **Document type:** directory.
     Formerly: American Association of Textile Chemists and Colorists. Products Buyer's Guide (ISSN 0065-7352)
     Description: Lists sources for dyes, pigments, chemical specialties, machinery and equipment.

677.028   US   ISSN 0192-4699
TP890.5   CODEN: BPNADG
AMERICAN ASSOCIATION OF TEXTILE CHEMISTS AND COLORISTS. NATIONAL TECHNICAL CONFERENCE. BOOK OF PAPERS. Key Title: Book of Papers, National Technical Conference. 1974. a. $61 to non-members; members $34. American Association of Textile Chemists and Colorists, One Davis Dr., Box 12215, Research Triangle Park, NC 27709-2215. TEL 919-549-8141. FAX 919-549-8933. (back issues avail.) **Indexed:** Chem.Abstr., Eng.Ind., Text.Tech.Dig., World Text.Abstr. **Document type:** proceedings.
     —CASDDS. **CCC.**
     Description: Published in conjunction with AATCC's International Conference & Exhibition; contains the full text of all available papers.

677   US
AMERICAN ASSOCIATION OF TEXTILE CHEMISTS AND COLORISTS. SYMPOSIA PAPERS. irreg. American Association of Textile Chemists and Colorists, One Davis Dr., Box 12215, Research Triangle Park, NC 27709-2215. TEL 919-549-8141. FAX 919-549-8933. **Document type:** proceedings.
     Description: Offers technological updates on specific segments of textile wet processing. Contains the full texts of all available technical papers.

677.028   US   ISSN 0883-4539
TP890
AMERICAN ASSOCIATION OF TEXTILE CHEMISTS AND COLORISTS. TECHNICAL MANUAL. 1924. a. $95 to non-members; members $56. American Association of Textile Chemists and Colorists, One Davis Dr., Box 12215, Research Triangle Park, NC 27709-2215. TEL 919-549-8141. FAX 919-549-8933. Ed. Susan H. Keesee. circ. 2,000. (also avail. in microform) **Document type:** proceedings.
     ●Also available on CD-ROM.
     Description: Contains all AATCC test methods plus AATCC research and administrative committee rosters and reports.

AMERICAN DYESTUFF REPORTER; devoted to textile wet-processing, dyeing, finishing, bleaching, etc., new product information, news of the industry. see *CLEANING AND DYEING*

AMERICAN FLOCK ASSOCIATION DIRECTORY. see *BUSINESS AND ECONOMICS* — *Trade And Industrial Directories*

TEXTILE INDUSTRIES AND FABRICS

677 US ISSN 0890-9970
TS1300 CODEN: ATINEE
AMERICA'S TEXTILES INTERNATIONAL. Abbreviated title: A T I. 1887. m. $43 (Canada $53; elsewhere $115). Billian Publishing, Inc., 2100 Powers Ferry Rd., Ste. 300, Atlanta, GA 30339. TEL 404-955-5656. FAX 404-952-0669. Ed. Monte G. Plott. adv.; bk.rev. circ. 35,000. (also avail. in microfilm from PMC,UMI) **Indexed:** Art & Archaeol.Tech.Abstr., Chem.Abstr., Text.Tech.Dig., Tr.& Indus.Ind., World Text.Abstr. **Document type:** trade publication.
—BLDSC (1765.882900); CASDDS; Ei; SWETS; UMI; UnCover.
Formerly (until 1983): America's Textile (ISSN 0737-0040); Incorporates: Fiber World; (1899-1984): Textile Industries (ISSN 0040-4985); (1973-1984): Fiber Producer (ISSN 0361-4921); Which superseded: Fiber Producer Buyer's Guide (ISSN 0091-6617).
Description: For the textile industry; complete fiber-to-fabric coverage in all facets of the US and global textile industry.

ANNUAL BOOK OF A S T M STANDARDS. VOLUME 07.01. TEXTILES - YARN, FABRICS, AND GENERAL TEST METHODS. see ENGINEERING — Engineering Mechanics And Materials

ANNUAL BOOK OF A S T M STANDARDS. VOLUME 07.02. TEXTILES - FIBERS, ZIPPERS. see ENGINEERING — Engineering Mechanics And Materials

677 NZ
APPAREL; to all clothing, textile and footwear manufacturers and retail clothing outlets. 1968. m. NZ.$64($100) Apparel Publishing Ltd., Box 56-071, Dominion Rd., Auckland 3, New Zealand. TEL 09-6315-685. FAX 09-6303-706. Ed. Valerie Blomfield. adv. circ. 3,200. **Indexed:** Text.Tech.Dig. **Document type:** trade publication.

677 II
APPAREL. (Text in English) 1974. m. Rs.400($160) Clothing Manufacturer's Association of India, 902 Mahalaxmi Chambers, 22 Bhulabhai Desai Rd., Bombay 400 026, India. TEL 91-22-4928245. FAX 91-22-4938547. TELEX 011-73753 CMAI IN. Ed. Dinesh Singal. bk.rev. circ. 10,000. (back issues avail.) **Document type:** trade publication.

677 US
APPAREL DIGEST.* 1934. m. $75. Institute of Textile Technology, 2551 Ivy Rd, Charlottesville, VA 22903-4614. TEL 804-296-5511. FAX 804-977-5400. Ed. Dennis Loy.
Former titles (until 1990): Apparel Needle Trades Digest; (until 1986): Apparel Digest.
Description: Contains summaries of the literature for the apparel and related industres selected from Textile Technology Digest.

APPAREL INDUSTRY. see CLOTHING TRADE

646 US ISSN 0275-8873
HD4966.C62
APPAREL PLANT WAGES SURVEY. a. $60 to non-members; members $25. American Apparel Manufacturers Association, 2500 Wilson Blvd., Ste. 301, Arlington, VA 22201. TEL 703-524-1864. FAX 703-522-6741. **Indexed:** SRI. **Document type:** trade publication.
Supersedes in part: Apparel Plant Wages and Personnel Policies (ISSN 0084-6678)

APPAREL RETAILERS OF AMERICA. BULLETIN. see CLOTHING TRADE

APPAREL TRADE DIRECTORY. see BUSINESS AND ECONOMICS — Trade And Industrial Directories

677 IT
ARREDO TESSILI COMPLEMENTI - BIANCHERIA CASA. (Supplement avail.) (Text in English and Italian; summaries in Italian) 1977. m. L.60000($100) Nuove Tecniche Editoriali S.r.l., Via San Siro 27, 20149 Milan, Italy. TEL 39-2-4812213. FAX 39-2-48193425. Ed. Tosca Bartolini. adv.: B&W page L.1900000, color page L.3200000. illus. circ. 22,000. (back issues avail.)
Formed by the 1990 merger of: Arredo Tessili Complementi (ISSN 0393-4462); Which was formerly (until 1984): 4T di Arredo Tessile & Arredo Biancheria Casa (ISSN 0393-4454); Which was formerly (until 1984): Arredo Tessile.
Description: Features articles on household linens; their fabrics, designs and manufacturing.

677 BE ISSN 0571-1924
ARTES TEXTILES: BIJRAGEN TOT DE GESCHIEDENIS VAN DE TAPIJT. (Text in Dutch) 1953. irreg. Vereniging voor de Geschiedenis van de Textiele Kunsten, Centrum Voor de Geschiedenis van de Tapijtkunst, Frans de Coninckstr. 17, 9218 Ledeberg, Belgium. bk.rev.; bibl. **Indexed:** RILA.

338.4 JA
ASIAN COTTON TEXTILE OUTLOOK. (Text in English) a. $350. Intercontinental Marketing Corp., I.P.O. Box 5056, Tokyo 100-30, Japan. TEL 81-3-3661-7458. FAX 81-3-3661-9646.

677 JA
ASIAN TEXTILE RECORD. 51/yr. $960. Intercontinental Marketing Corp., I.P.O. Box 5056, Tokyo 100-31, Japan. TEL 81-3-3661-7458. FAX 81-3-3667-9646.

677 IT
ASSOCIAZIONE NOBILITAZIONE TESSILE. NOTIZIARIO. 1945. w. free. Istituto per l'Assistenza e Servizi alle Aziende Tessili s.r.l., V.le Sarca, 223, 20126 Milan, Italy. TEL 02-66103404. FAX 02-66103444. Ed. Giovanni Frangi. bk.rev.; bibl.; mkt.; pat.; stat. (looseleaf format)
Formerly (until 1985): Associazione Italiana Industriali Tintori, Stampatori e Finitori Tessili. Notiziario (ISSN 0004-5950)

677 AT ISSN 0725-086X
AUSTRALASIAN TEXTILES. 1981. bi-m. Aus.$47 (foreign Aus.$105). (Society of Dyers & Colorists of Australia and New Zealand, Southern Australia Section of the Textile Institute) Australasian Textiles Publishers, Box 286, Belmont, Vic. 3216, Australia. TEL 052-552699. FAX 052-561668. Ed. S. Boston. adv.; bk.rev. circ. 2,300. **Indexed:** Text.Tech.Dig., World Text.Abstr. **Document type:** trade publication.
—BLDSC (1796.375000); Ei. CCC.

677.3 AT
AUSTRALIAN WOOL COMPENDIUM. m. Aus.$35 (foreign Aus.$40). Australian Wool Corporation, Market Information and Planning, G.P.O. Box 4867, Melbourne, Vic. 3001, Australia. TEL 341-9111. Ed. M. Gabrys. (looseleaf format)

667.3 332.6 AT
AUSTRALIAN WOOL EXPORT QUARTERLY REVIEW. q. Aus.$20 (foreign Aus.$30). Australian Wool Corporation, G.P.O. Box 4867, Melbourne, Vic. 3001, Australia. Ed. M. Gabrys. (also avail. in diskette format)

677.76 GW ISSN 0005-4925
BAND- UND FLECHTINDUSTRIE/NARROW FABRIC AND BRAIDING INDUSTRY. (Text in English and German) 1964. q. DM.83. (Industrieverband Deutscher Bandweber und Flechter e.V) Melliand Textilberichte GmbH, Mainzer Landstr. 251, 60326 Frankfurt a.M., Germany. TEL 069-75951722. FAX 069-75951720. Ed. Klaus Renkenberger. adv.: B&W page DM.1720, color page DM.4090; trim 180 x 260; adv. contact: Dagmar Henning. bk.rev.; bibl. circ. 1,100. **Indexed:** Excerpt.Med., Text.Tech.Dig., World Text.Abstr. **Document type:** trade publication.
—BLDSC (1861.570000). CCC.
Description: Provides information on narrow fabric waving and preparation, rope-making, trimmings production, label production and textile machinery.

677 BG ISSN 0253-5424
CODEN: BJJRD5
BANGLADESH JOURNAL OF JUTE & FIBRE RESEARCH. 1976. s-a. $5 per no. Bangladesh Jute Research Institute, Sher-e-Banglanagar, Dhaka 7, Bangladesh. Ed. Md. Harun-Ur-Rashid.
—CASDDS.

677 CC ISSN 1002-3348
BEIJING FANGZHI/BEIJING TEXTILE. (Text in Chinese) 1979. bi-m. Y10.80. Beijing Fangzhi Gongcheng Xuehui - Beijing Textile Engineering Society, 2 Shilipu, Chaoyangmenwai, Beijing 100025, People's Republic of China. TEL 5004477. FAX 5004271. TELEX 210362 FRHTL CN. Ed. Xu Xiaochun. adv.: B&W page Y3500. circ. 12,000.
Description: Covers new technical processes, development of machines and products, and research activities in dyeing and printing.

BEIKOKU TOKKYO SHOROKU. KAGAKU IPPAN, ORIMONO HEN/U.S. PATENT ABSTRACTS. GENERAL CHEMISTRY, TEXTILE. see PATENTS, TRADEMARKS AND COPYRIGHTS — Abstracting, Bibliographies, Statistics

677 GW ISSN 0005-8270
BEKLEIDUNG UND MASCHENWARE; Fachzeitschrift fuer die industrielle Fertigung und fuer den Handel. 1962. 6/yr. DM.36 (foreign DM.46.20). Zeitschriftenverlag R D B V, Postfach 1135, 4000 Duesseldorf 1, Germany. TEL 0211-5050. FAX 0211-5052555. adv.; bk.rev.; bibl.; charts; illus.; tr.lit.; index. **Indexed:** Text.Tech.Dig., World Text.Abstr. **Document type:** trade publication.
Description: Trade publication for the clothing industry, featuring manufacturing, trade, latest styles and fashions, industrial technology, industry news, reports and announcements of events.

BLACK SHEEP NEWSLETTER. see AGRICULTURE — Poultry And Livestock

LA BOBINA. see CLOTHING TRADE

677 JA ISSN 0385-7352
BOKEN REPORT. (Text in Japanese) 1951. a. 2000 Yen. Japan Spinners Inspecting Foundation, 18-15, 1-chome, Ue-machi, Chuo-ku, Osaka 540, Japan. TEL 06-762-5881. FAX 06-762-5889. Ed. Tadanori Inoko. adv. circ. 1,000. (back issues avail.)
Formerly (from vol.49, 1970): J S I F Report.

677 658.8 UK ISSN 0261-7773
BUSINESS RATIO REPORT: COTTON & MAN-MADE FIBRE PROCESSORS; an industry sector analysis. 1974. a. l C C Business Ratios Ltd., Freepost, Field House, Hampton, Mddx. TW12 1BR, England. TEL 081-783-0977. FAX 081-783-1940. charts; stat. **Document type:** trade publication.
—BLDSC (3477.725000).

BUTTERICK HOME CATALOG. see CLOTHING TRADE — Fashions

677 US
C L A GUIDELINES; management guidelines for C L A members. 1972. m. membership. Coin Laundry Association, 1315 Butterfield Rd., Ste. 212, Downers Grove, IL 60515. TEL 708-963-5547. FAX 708-963-5864. Ed. Maureen McLynn. circ. 3,000. (back issues avail.)

677.3 AT ISSN 0312-5211
C S I R O WOOL TEXTILE NEWS. 1954. irreg. free. Commonwealth Scientific and Industrial Research Organization., Division of Wool Technology, P.O. Box 21, Belmont, Vic. 3216, Australia. TEL 052-47-2611. Ed. P.T. Naughtin. circ. 2,500. **Indexed:** World Text.Abstr.

677 II ISSN 0084-8859
C.T.T.S. ANNUAL. (Text and summaries in English) 1949. a. College of Textile Technology, Serampore, Students Union, Serampore, West Bengal, India. Ed. S.C. Ukil.

CANADIAN TEXTILE DIRECTORY. see BUSINESS AND ECONOMICS — Trade And Industrial Directories

677 CN ISSN 0008-5170
CODEN: CTJOA6
CANADIAN TEXTILE JOURNAL. (Text in English, French) 1883. 7/yr. Can.$35. Canadian Textile Journal Pub. Co., 1 rue Pacifique, Ste.-Anne de Bellevue, PQ H9X 1C5, Canada. TEL 514-457-2347. FAX 514-457-2147. Ed. Gillian Crosby. adv. contact: Lumina Fillion. bk.rev.; charts; illus.; tr.lit.; index. circ. 3,500. **Indexed:** Art & Archaeol.Tech.Abstr., Can.B.P.I., Chem.Abstr., Key to Econ.Sci., Text.Tech.Dig., World Text.Abstr. **Document type:** trade publication.
—BLDSC (3045.000000); CASDDS; Genuine Article; UMI.

CARBON & HIGH PERFORMANCE FIBRES DIRECTORY AND DATABOOK. see PLASTICS

TEXTILE INDUSTRIES AND FABRICS

677 747.4 US ISSN 0192-4486
HD9937.U6
CARPET & RUG INDUSTRY. 1973. m. $42. Rodman Publications, Inc., 17 S. Franklin Tpk., Box 555, Ramsey, NJ 07446. TEL 201-825-2552. FAX 201-825-0553. Ed. Janet Herlihy. adv. contact: Robert J. Zilenziger, Jr. bk.rev.; abstr.; charts; illus.; pat.; stat. circ. 6,000. Indexed: Art & Archaeol.Tech.Abstr., Text.Tech.Dig., World Text.Abstr. **Document type:** trade publication.
—CCC.

677 US
CARPET AND RUG INSTITUTE. DIRECTORY. 1950. a. $15. Carpet and Rug Institute, 310 Holiday Ave., S., Box 2048, Dalton, GA 30720-2048. TEL 404-278-3176. FAX 404-278-8835. Ed. Truett Lomax. **Document type:** directory.
  Formerly: Carpet and Rug Institute. Directory and Report (ISSN 0069-0740)

677 US ISSN 0095-6457
TS1772
CARPET SPECIFIER'S HANDBOOK. 1974. irreg., 4th ed., 1987. $20. Carpet and Rug Institute, 310 Holiday Ave., S., Box 2048, Dalton, GA 30720-2048. TEL 404-278-3176. FAX 404-278-8835. illus.
Document type: bulletin.

CATALOGUE BIENNALE INTERNATIONALE DE LAUSANNE. see *ART*

677 FR ISSN 1016-8982
CENTRE INTERNATIONAL D'ETUDE DES TEXTILES ANCIENS. BULLETIN. Short title: Bulletin du C I E T A. (Text and summaries in English, French) 1955. a. 250 F. to members; institutions 600 F. (effective 1992). Centre International d'Etude des Textiles Anciens, 34 rue de la Charite, 69002 Lyon, France. TEL 78-37-15-05. FAX 72-40-25-12. bk.rev.; bibl.; illus. (processed) Indexed: World Text.Abstr. **Document type:** bulletin.
—BLDSC (2444.611000).
  Former titles (until 1989): Textiles Anciens (ISSN 0995-6638); (until 1987): Centre International d'Etude des Textiles Anciens. Bulletin de Liaison (ISSN 0008-980X)

677 GW
TS1300 CODEN: CFTXAJ
CHEMICAL FIBERS INTERNATIONAL; magazine for fiber polymers, fibers, texturing and spunbonds. (Text in English) 1919. bi-m. DM.198 (foreign DM.200.70). Deutscher Fachverlag GmbH, Mainzer Landstr. 251, 60326 Frankfurt a.M., Germany. TEL 069-75951722. FAX 069-75951720. (Subscr. to: Postfach 100606, 60006 Frankfurt a.M., Germany) Ed. Hans Koslowski. adv. contact: Richard Redling. bk.rev.; abstr.; charts; illus.; index. circ. 5,500. Indexed: Abstr.Bull.Inst.Pap.Chem., Art & Archaeol.Tech.Abstr., C.I.S. Abstr., Chem.Abstr., Cott.& Trop.Fibr.Abstr., Excerp.Med., Key to Econ.Sci., PROMT, Text.Tech.Dig., World Text.Abstr. **Document type:** trade publication.
—BLDSC (3146.450000); CASDDS; SWETS. CCC.
  Former titles: Chemiefasern - Textil-Industrie (ISSN 0340-3343); Chemiefasern; Textil-Anwendungstechnik.

677 330.9 HK
CHINA TEXTILE & APPAREL. (Text in Chinese; table of contents in Chinese, English) 1983. 6/yr. HK.$340($80) for Asia; elsewhere $81 (typically set in Jan.). (China Textile Information Institute, Beijing Textile Research Institute, CC) Adsale Publishing Company, 14F, Devon House, Taikoo Place, 979 King's Rd., Quarry Bay, Hong Kong. TEL 852-2811-8897. FAX 852-2516-5119. Ed. Benjamin Heung. adv. circ. 35,000. (back issues avail.)
  Formerly: China Textile - Zhongguo Fangzhi (ISSN 1021-1349)
  Description: Introduces to China advanced foreign technology, machinery and processing materials in the textile industry.

677 CC ISSN 1000-1484
CHINA TEXTILE UNIVERSITY. JOURNAL. Chinese edition: Zhongguo Fangzhi Daxue Xuebao (ISSN 1000-1476) (Text in Chinese) 1956. s-a. $30. Zhongguo Fangzhi Daxue - China Textile University, 1882 Yan'an Xilu, Shanghai 200051, People's Republic of China. TEL 2199898. adv. **Document type:** academic/scholarly publication.
—BLDSC (4729.219320).
  Description: Covers textile science and technology, fiber science, man-made fibers, mechanical engineering, applied chemistry and textile management engineering, clothing, automation & computer.

CLEANING & RESTORATION. see *CLEANING AND DYEING*

CLEO EN LA MODA. see *LEATHER AND FUR INDUSTRIES*

CLOTHING & TEXTILES RESEARCH JOURNAL. see *CLOTHING TRADE*

677.1 II ISSN 0530-0495
COIR. (Text in English) 1956. s-a. Rs.30($12.50) Coir Board, Cochin 682016, India.
  Description: Articles on India's coir industry.

677 667 UK
COLOUR INDEX. (Supplement avail.: Colour Index: Additions & Amendments) 1971. irreg., 3rd ed., 1993. $695 for 9-vol. set. Society of Dyers and Colourists, Perkin House, P.O. Box 244, Bradford, W. Yorks BD1 2JB, England. TEL 01274-7215138. FAX 01274-392888. (Co-sponsor: American Association of Textile Chemists and Colorists) **Document type:** trade publication.
●Also available on CD-ROM.

COLOURAGE. see *CLEANING AND DYEING*

677 IT
COMMERCIALE BOLLETTINO DELLA LANIERA. SUPPLEMENTO. 1924. w. L.20000. Editoriale Laniera s.r.l., Via Mure P. Castello 9, 36100 Vicenza, Italy. Ed. Felice Dall'Ara. adv. circ. 1,100.

COMPOSITES SCIENCE AND TECHNOLOGY. see *TECHNOLOGY: COMPREHENSIVE WORKS*

CONFECCION INDUSTRIAL. see *CLOTHING TRADE*

CONFECTIE. see *CLOTHING TRADE*

677 BE
CONTACT. (Text in Flemish, French) 1950. 12/yr. 2000 BEF. Belgian Knitwear Association - Federation de la Maille, Rode Beukendreef 14, 9831 Deurle, Belgium. TEL 091-82-21-11. FAX 091-82-40-21. Ed.Bd. adv.; bk.rev.; charts; stat. circ. 500. (back issues avail.)

677.2 PK
COTISTICS BI-ANNUAL COTTON STATISTICAL BULLETIN. (Text in English) 1972. q. free. Pakistan Central Cotton Committee, Marketing and Economic Research Section, Secretary, Moulvi Tamizuddin Khan Rd., Karachi 1, Pakistan. TEL 524104-6. charts; stat. **Document type:** bulletin.
  Formerly: Cotistics Quarterly Cotton Statistical Bulletin.

677.21 US
COTTON. PART 1: BI-MONTHLY REVIEW OF THE WORLD SITUATION. (Editions in English, French, Spanish) 1947. bi-m. $135. International Cotton Advisory Committee, 1629 K St. N.W., Ste. 702, Washington, DC 20006. TEL 202-463-6660. FAX 202-463-6950. TELEX 701517 ICACOM. charts; stat. circ. 3,200. (also avail. in microfiche from CIS) Indexed: IIS, Key to Econ.Sci., PROMT, World Text.Abstr.
  Formerly: Cotton. Part 1: Monthly Review of the World Situation.

COTTON. PART 2: WORLD STATISTICS. see *TEXTILE INDUSTRIES AND FABRICS — Abstracting, Bibliographies, Statistics*

677.21 US ISSN 0090-2462
  CODEN: CTDGAK
COTTON DIGEST INTERNATIONAL. 1928. m. $40. Cotton Digest Co., Inc., Box 820768, Houston, TX 77282-0768. TEL 713-977-1644. FAX 713-467-6935. Ed. Elizabeth Edwards Abbey. adv.; illus.; mkt. circ. 5,500. Indexed: Text.Tech.Dig. **Document type:** trade publication.
  Formerly: Cotton Digest (ISSN 0010-9797)

677.21 US ISSN 0010-9800
COTTON GIN AND OIL MILL PRESS; the magazine for the cotton ginning and oilseed processing industries. 1889. fortn. $10. Haughton Publishing Co. of Texas, Box 180218, Dallas, TX 75218. TEL 214-288-7511. Ed. Don Swanson. adv.; charts; illus.; stat. circ. 2,000. (also avail. in microfilm from UMI) Indexed: Chem.Abstr., Text.Tech.Dig.
—UMI.

677.21 US ISSN 0070-0673
TS1550
COTTON INTERNATIONAL. 1914. a. $25. Meister Publishing Co., 37733 Euclid Ave., Willoughby, OH 44094. TEL 216-942-2000. Ed. William Spencer. circ. 11,500. Indexed: Text.Tech.Dig. **Document type:** trade publication.
—CCC.
  Formerly: Cotton Trade Journal International.

677.21 UK
COTTON OUTLOOK. 1923. w. $715.82. Cotlook Ltd., Cotlook House, 458 New Chester Rd., Rock Ferry, Birkenhead, Merseyside L42 2AE, England. (Dist. in U.S. by: Cotlook Ltd., 5100 Poplar, Ste. 2520, Memphis, TN 38137) Ed. Ray Butler. adv.; charts; mkt.; stat. (processed)
  Formerly: Cotton and General Economic Review (ISSN 0010-9789)

677 US ISSN 1041-1119
D N R. 1892. 5/w. $62 (effective Jan. 1992). Fairchild Fashion Publication, Seven W. 34th St., New York, NY 10001. TEL 212-630-4199. FAX 212-630-4707. Ed. William Taffin. adv.; bk.rev.; illus.; mkt.; pat. circ. 29,073. (also avail. in microform from FCM,MIM) Indexed: Bus.Ind., PROMT, Text.Tech.Dig., Tr.& Indus.Ind.
●Also available online. Vendor(s): Knight-Ridder, Inc.
—CCC.
  Formerly: Daily News Record (ISSN 0011-5460)
  Description: Covers the men's and boy's apparel industry, includes articles from newspapers on textile manufacturers, clothing manufacturers, wholesalers, converters, and retailers.

677.3 GW ISSN 0942-301X
D W I REPORTS. 1952. irreg., no.115, 1995. DM.100. Deutsches Wollforschungsinstitut, Technische Hochschule Aachen, Veltmanplatz 8, 52062 Aachen, Germany. TEL 0241-4469-0. FAX 0241-4469100. E-mail: dwi@pool.informatik.rwth-aachen.de. Ed. H. Hoecker. **Document type:** academic/scholarly publication, proceedings.
—BLDSC (3633.420000).
  Formerly: Deutsches Wollforschungsinstitut. Vortraege.

667 US
DATATEXTILE. m. Industrial Fabrics Association International, 345 Cedar St., No. 800, St. Paul, MN 55101-1088. TEL 612-222-2508. FAX 612-222-8215. Ed. Kevin Jagielski. tr.lit. **Document type:** newsletter.

DAVISON'S SALESMAN'S BOOK. see *BUSINESS AND ECONOMICS — Trade And Industrial Directories*

DAVISON'S TEXTILE BLUE BOOK. see *BUSINESS AND ECONOMICS — Trade And Industrial Directories*

677.3 GW ISSN 0170-6322
  CODEN: DWTSDZ
DEUTSCHES WOLLFORSCHUNGSINSTITUT. SCHRIFTENREIHE. 1953. irreg., no.108, 1991. DM.50. Deutsches Wollforschungsinstitut, Technische Hochschule Aachen, Veltmanplatz 8, 52062 Aachen, Germany. TEL 0241-4469100. FAX 0241-4469100. E-mail: dwi@pool.informatik.rwth-aachen.de. Ed. H. Hoecker. **Document type:** monographic series.
—BLDSC (8100.978000); CASDDS.
  Formerly (until 1963): Deutsche Forschungsgemeinschaft Wolle. Schriftenreihe (ISSN 0417-1829)

TEXTILE INDUSTRIES AND FABRICS

677   II
DIRECT TEXTILE BULLETIN. q. $41.04. Government of India, Department of Publications, Civil Lines, Delhi 110 054, India. TEL 11-2512527. **Document type:** bulletin.

677 620   SP
DIRECTORY OF THE SPANISH COTTON-SYSTEM TEXTILE ENTERPRISES/DIRECTORIO EMPRESAS TEXTILES DE PROCESO ALGODONERO/DIRECTORI EMPRESES TEXTILS DE PROCES COTONER/DIRECTOIRE ENTERPRISES TEXTILES DE PROCESSUS COTONNIER. (Text in English, French, Catalan, Spanish) 1986. a. 5000 ptas.($50) Asociacion Industrial Textil de Proceso Algodonero (A.I.T.P.A.), Gran Via de les Corts Catalanes, 670, 08010 Barcelona, Spain. TEL 34-3189200. FAX 34-33026235. circ. 3,000. **Document type:** directory.

380.1
DIRECTORY OF WOOL, HOSIERY AND FABRICS. (Text in English) 1950. a. Rs.50. Commerce Publications Ltd., NKM International House, 178 Backbay Reclamation, Bombay 400020, India. Ed. Subhash Chandra Sarker. **Document type:** directory.
     Formerly: India and Pakistan Wool, Hosiery and Fabrics.

677   UK   ISSN 0012-3811
TS1828
DISPOSABLES AND NONWOVENS. bi-m. £25($70) (overseas £35) (effective 1996). Chandler Publications Ltd., 10 South St., Totnes, Devon TQ9 5DZ, England. TEL 01803-864668. FAX 01803-865649. Ed. Jack R.D. Heming; Pub. Jack R.D. Heming. adv.; bk.rev. circ. 2,000. **Indexed:** World Text.Abstr.
     —BLDSC (3598.730000).
     Description: Provides news for manufacturers, converters, and dealers in disposable and nonwoven materials.

677   US
DRAFTS & DESIGNS. 1958. 10/yr. $10. Robin and Russ Handweavers, 533 N. Adams St., McMinnville, OR 97128. TEL 503-472-5760. Ed. Russell E. Groff. adv.; charts; illus. circ. 800. (looseleaf format; back issues avail.) **Document type:** academic/scholarly publication.
     Description: Covers multiple harness patterns; sample swatch included with each issue.

677   AU   ISSN 0012-6071
DREIHAMMER. 1939. 4/yr. free. F.M. Haemmerle Textilwerke AG, A-6850 Dornbirn, Austria. TEL 05572-64561. Ed. Michael Lins. circ. 2,800.

677   FR   ISSN 0181-8120
E.T.N. REVUE DE L'ENTRETIEN DES TEXTILES ET NETTOYAGE. Key Title: E.T.N. 1969. m. 285 F. Centre Technique de la Teinture et du Nettoyage (CTTN), Chemin des Mouilles, B.P. 41, 69131 Ecully Cedex, France. FAX 78-43-34-12. TELEX 305 299 F. Ed. Marc Eglizeau. adv.; bk.rev.; circ. controlled.
     Formerly (until 1978): Entretien des Textiles, Cuirs et Tapis (ISSN 0181-8112)

ECHO. see HOME ECONOMICS

677   IT   ISSN 0012-9526
ECO DELL'INDUSTRIA TESSILE. 1948. 2/w. L.100000. Eleonora Caselli, Via Tripoli 24, 13051 Biella, Italy. Ed. Germano Caselli. adv.

677.21   UA   ISSN 0013-2403
EGYPTIAN COTTON GAZETTE. 1947. 2/yr. $8 per no. Alexandria Cotton Exporters Association, P.O. Box 433, Alexandria, Egypt. TEL 808377. FAX 4833002. Eds. Ahmed H. Youssef, Mongui Hefni. adv.; illus.; mkt.; stat. **Indexed:** Chem.Abstr.
     Incorporates: Egyptian Cotton Statistics.

677   US   ISSN 0080-6811
EMBROIDERY DIRECTORY. 1947. a. $5. Schiffli Lace and Embroidery Manufacturers Association, Inc., 8555 Tonnelle Ave., N. Bergen, NJ 07047-4738. TEL 201-868-7200. FAX 201-868-9833. Ed. l. Leonard Seiler. adv. circ. 2,100. **Document type:** directory.
     Former titles: Schiffli Digest and Directory; Schiffli Directory.

677   US
EMBROIDERY NEWS. 1955. irreg. (6-8/yr.). free to qualified personnel; others $10. Schiffli Lace and Embroidery Manufacturers Association, Inc., 8555 Tonnelle Ave., N. Bergen, NJ 07047-4738. TEL 201-868-7200. FAX 201-868-9833. Ed. l. Leonard Seiler. adv.; bk.rev. circ. 500. **Document type:** trade publication.

ENVIRONMENT & WASTE MANAGEMENT. see ENVIRONMENTAL STUDIES — Waste Management

EURO DECOR. see BUSINESS AND ECONOMICS

677.76   GW
EUROSEIL. 1879. bi-m. DM.42. (Bundesverband des Deutschen Seiler-, Segel- und Netzmacherhandwerks e.V.) Verlag Ernst Bauer, Breite Gasse 2, 89073 Ulm, Germany. TEL 0731-64051. FAX 0731-6021276. Ed. Ernst Joachim Bauer. adv.; bk.rev.; illus. circ. 800. **Document type:** trade publication.
     —CCC.
     Formerly (until 1992): Deutsche Seiler-Zeitung (ISSN 0012-0758)

677.31 382   NZ   ISSN 0114-8052
EXPORT LEVELS OF NEW ZEALAND WOOL PRODUCTS AND THEIR CURRENT MARKETS. 1984. a. NZ.$45. Wools of New Zealand, P.O. Box 3225, Wellington 1, New Zealand. TEL 64-4-472-6888. FAX 64-4-473-7872. Ed. S.E. Britland. circ. 20.
     Description: Covers in table and graph form the export destinations of yarns, carpets, rugs, fabrics, apparel, sheepskins, tops and silver.

677.2   US
F I N E X REPORT. vol.5, 1990. bi-m. New York Cotton Exchange, Financial Instrument Exchange, 4 World Trade Ctr., Ste. 5572, New York, NY 10048. TEL 212-938-2634. Ed. Richard Jaycobs. **Document type:** trade publication.

677   US   ISSN 0733-1843
FABRICNEWS. 1970. q. $24. Arthur J. Imparato Associates, 80 Park Ave., New York, NY 10016. TEL 213-274-6752. Ed. Shirley Jones. adv.; circ. 9,500 (controlled).
     Incorporates (1975-1990): Trade (New York).
     Description: Covers home sewing, needlearts and crafts.

FABRICS & ARCHITECTURE. see ARCHITECTURE

677 331.88   NO   ISSN 0800-5400
FABRIKKARBEIDEREN. 1926. 10/yr. Norsk Kjemisk Industriarbeiderforbund, Youngsgt 11, Oslo, Norway. TEL 401340.

677   SZ
FACHSCHRIFT FUER TEXTILREINIGUNG. m. Gapont 34, CH-9495 Triesen, Switzerland. TEL 075-26079. FAX 075-82024. Ed. Peter Grob. circ. 1,100.

677 687   US   ISSN 1067-7062
FAIRCHILD'S TEXTILE & APPAREL FINANCIAL DIRECTORY.* 1974. a. $60 (effective Oct. 1990). Fairchild Books (Subsidiary of: Fairchild Publications Inc.), 7 W. 34th St., New York, NY 10001. TEL 212-630-4000. FAX 212-887-1946. TELEX 232666 FAPB. Ed. Robert Benjamin. circ. 750. (also avail. in microfiche from CIS; back issues avail.) **Indexed:** SRI.

677   CC
FANGZHI XUEBAO/CHINA TEXTILE ENGINEERING ASSOCIATION. JOURNAL.* (Text in Chinese) m. $1 per no. Zhongguo Fangzhi Gongcheng Xuehui - China Textile Engineering Association, c/o China International Book Trading Corporation, P.O. Box 399, Beijing, People's Republic of China. TEL 2581667. **Indexed:** Chem.Abstr, World Text.Abstr.

677   CH   ISSN 1019-0473
FANGZHI ZHONGXIN QIKAN/CHINA TEXTILE INSTITUTE. JOURNAL. (Text in Chinese) 1991. bi-m. $35 in Taiwan; Asia $41; elsewhere $50. Zhongguo Fangzhi Gongye Yianjiu Zhongxin - China Textile Institute, No. 6, Chen-Tian Rd., Tu-Chen City, Taipei, Taiwan, Republic of China. TEL 886-2-2644720. FAX 886-2-2660321.
     —BLDSC (4729.219250).

677   IT
FASHION. 1970. w. L.185000($150) (effective Jan. 1993). Edizioni Ecomarket S.p.A., Corso Venezia 26, 20121 Milan, Italy. TEL 39-2-76007371. FAX 39-2-783012. Ed. Gianni Bertasso. adv.: B&W page L.4950000, color page L.6200000; adv. contact: Gianni Bertasso. circ. 30,000. **Document type:** consumer publication.
     Formerly: G T - Giornale Tessile.

677   US
HD9929.5.U6
FIBER ORGANON; featuring man-made fibers. 1930. m. $300 (foreign $400). Fiber Economics Bureau, Inc., 101 Eisenhower Pkwy, Roseland, NJ 07068. TEL 201-228-1107. FAX 201-228-7598. Ed. Rosemarie Frick. bk.rev.; charts; mkt.; stat.; index. circ. 3,500. **Indexed:** P.A.I.S., PROMT, SRI, Text.Tech.Dig., World Text.Abstr.
     Formerly: Textile Organon (ISSN 0040-5132)
     Description: Covers synthetic fibers.

677   US   ISSN 0071-4682
     CODEN: FSCSDC
FIBER SCIENCE SERIES. 1970. irreg., vol.8, 1979. price varies. Marcel Dekker, Inc., 270 Madison Ave., New York, NY 10016. TEL 212-696-9000. FAX 212-685-4540. Ed. L. Rebenfeld.
     —CASDDS.
     Refereed Serial

677   US   ISSN 1069-1391
THE FIBERFEST MAGAZINE. 1993. q. $20 (Canada $25; elsewhere $28). Sue Drummond, Ed. & Pub., Box 112, Hastings, MI 49058. TEL 616-765-3047. FAX 616-765-3538. adv. contact: Sue Hill. bk.rev. circ. 2,000. **Document type:** trade publication.
     Description: Covers all aspects of the business of natural fibers, including spinning, fiber preparation, dyeing, knitting, weaving, and animal husbandry.

547.85   US   ISSN 0015-0541
TS1548.5   CODEN: FICYAP
FIBRE CHEMISTRY. English translation of: Khimicheskie Volokna (RU ISSN 0023-1118) 1969. m. $1125 (foreign $1315) (effective 1996). (Russian Academy of Sciences, RU) Plenum Publishing Corp., Consultants Bureau, 233 Spring St., New York, NY 10013-1578. TEL 212-620-8468. FAX 212-463-0742. TELEX 23-421139. Ed. V.S. Metveev. (also avail. in microfilm from JSC; back issues avail.) **Indexed:** Appl.Mech.Rev., Chem.Titles, Eng.Ind., Excerp.Med. **Document type:** academic/scholarly publication.
     —BLDSC (0411.752000); Ei; Faxon; Genuine Article; SWETS; UMI. **CCC**.
     Refereed Serial

677   US   ISSN 0046-3728
FIBRE MARKET NEWS. 1963. bi-m. $126 (Canada $160; elsewhere $197) (effective Jan. 1995). (Group Interest Enterprises) G.I.E., Inc. Publishers, 4012 Bridge Ave., Cleveland, OH 44113. TEL 216-961-4130. FAX 216-961-0364. Ed. Daniel Sandoval; Pub. Richard J.W. Foster. adv. contact: James Keefe. charts; stat. circ. 1,200. **Document type:** trade publication.
     Description: Covers issues pertaining to the collection process and marketing of secondary fiber for recycling.

677 746   CN
FIBRE NORTH. 4/yr. Can.$26.75. Taylor Day Publishing, RR 5, Campbellford, ON K0L 1L0, Canada. Ed. Val Blake.
     Description: For all involved in the Canadian natural fiber industry, from breeders, suppliers and processors to spinners, weavers and knitters.

667   IT
FILATI COLLEZIONI. (Text in English, Italian) s-a. L.41000 (effective 1993). Zanfi Editori s.r.l., Via Emilia Ovest 954, 41100 Modena, Italy. TEL 059-891700. FAX 059-891701.
     Description: Presents all the lines and trends of yarns for the following year. Includes analyses on the sector and market developments for yarns and knitwear.

TEXTILE INDUSTRIES AND FABRICS

677   FR   ISSN 1146-0733
FILIERE MAILLE. 1982. bi-m. 320 F. (foreign 400 F.) (effective Sep. 1995. (Federation Francaise des Industries de la Maille et de la Bonneterie) Editions de l' Industrie Textile, 16 rue Ballu, 75311 Paris Cedex 09, France. TEL 48-74-15-96. FAX 48-74-01-89. Ed. Pierre S. Robin. adv.; bk.rev.; abstr.; bibl.; charts; illus.; pat.; stat.; index. **Indexed:** Text.Tech.Dig., World Text.Abstr.
—BLDSC (3925.644000); SWETS.
    Formerly (until 1990): Industrie Textile - Filiere Maille (ISSN 0750-4764); Which was formed by the merger of: Maille Informations (ISSN 0150-651X); Moniteur de la Maille.

677 660   US
FILTRATION CONFERENCE PAPERS. 1991. irreg. I N D A Association of the Nonwoven Fabrics Industry, 1001 Winstead Dr., Ste. 460, Cary, NC 27513. TEL 919-677-0060. FAX 919-677-0211. **Document type:** proceedings.

677   UK
FINANCIAL SURVEY. COMPANY DATA FOR SUCCESS: CARPET MANUFACTURERS & WHOLESALE DISTRIBUTORS. a. I C C Financial Surveys Ltd., Field House, 72 Oldfield Rd., Hampton, Mddx. TW12 2HQ, England. TEL 081-783-0977. FAX 081-783-1940. charts; stat. **Document type:** trade publication.
    Formerly (until 1991): Financial Survey Company Directory. Carpet Manufacturers and Wholesale Distributors (ISSN 0952-0090)

677   UK
FINANCIAL SURVEY. COMPANY DATA FOR SUCCESS: COTTON & MAN MADE FIBRE MANUFACTURERS & DISTRIBUTORS. a. I C C Financial Surveys Ltd, Field House, 72 Oldfield Rd., Hampton, Mddx. TW12 2HQ, England. TEL 081-783-0977. FAX 081-783-1940. charts; stat. **Document type:** trade publication.
    Formerly (until 1991): Financial Survey Company Directory. Cotton and Man Made Fibre Manufacturers and Distributors.

677.31   NZ   ISSN 1173-132X
▼**FINE WOOL REVIEW.** 1994. 10/yr. NZ.$25 (foreign NZ.$40); free to wool growers. Wools of New Zealand, P.O. Box 3225, Wellington 1, New Zealand. TEL 64-4-472-6888. FAX 64-473-7872. Ed. P.A. Conway. circ. 700. **Document type:** trade publication.
    Description: Covers the fine wool market, information, prices and forecasts of the New Zealand market and of international trends.

FLAX CRAFT. see *ARTS AND HANDICRAFTS*

677   GW   ISSN 0933-2316
FLOCK; international trade journal for the flock industry. German edition: Flock (ISSN 0178-3092) (Text in English) 1984. q. DM.198. International Services Publications, Postfach 1370, 63643 Buedingen, Germany. TEL 06042-2938. FAX 06042-7871. Ed. Joachim Mueller; Pub. Joachim Mueller. adv.: B&W page DM.1010, color page DM.2060; trim 258 x 170; adv. contact: Beritt Engelhardt. circ. 600 (paid). **Document type:** trade publication.

677   JA
FRATERNITY MONTHLY MAGAZINE. m. Zensen Japanese Federation of Textile, Garment, Chemical, Mercantile and Allied Industry Workers' Unions, 8-16 Kudan, Minami 4-chome, Chiyoda-ku, Tokyo 102, Japan. TEL 03-3265-5465. TELEX ZENSEN TOKYO.

677   FR
G A P. (Groupe Avant-Premiere) 1969. m. 370 F. (Societe G A P) Liaisons Convergence, 14 rue Chapal, 92309 Levallois-Perret, France. Ed. Aline Laresse. circ. 17,000.

GAAF GOED; vakblad voor de interieur-textiel-branche. see *INTERIOR DESIGN AND DECORATION — Furniture And House Furnishings*

677   AG   ISSN 0046-5364
GACETA TEXTIL. 1934. m. Gaceta Editora Coop Ltda., 25 de Mayo no. 786, piso 12, Buenos Aires, Argentina. Ed. Emma P. Zappettini. adv.; abstr.; bibl.; illus.; stat. circ. 15,000.

677   AG   ISSN 0016-3996
CODEN: GALAAL
GALAXIA. 1963. q. $60 (effective 1993). Asociacion Argentina de Quimicos y Coloristas Textiles, Bulnes 1425, 1176 Buenos Aires, Argentina. TEL 541-963-0394. Ed. Silvio Roldan. adv. contact: Nivea Surian. bk.rev.; abstr.; bibl.; charts; illus.; stat. circ. 1,500. **Indexed:** Chem.Abstr. **Document type:** academic/scholarly publication, trade publication.
—CASDDS.

GARMENT MANUFACTURER'S INDEX. see *CLOTHING TRADE*

677.028   US   ISSN 0882-4983
GEOTECHNICAL FABRICS REPORT; engineer's guide to geosynthesis. 1983. 9/yr. $30 (foreign $42). Industrial Fabrics Association International, 345 Cedar St., Ste. 800, St. Paul, MN 55101-1088. TEL 612-222-2508. Ed. Danette Fettig. adv.; tr.lit.; cum.index: 1983-1993. circ. 14,000. (reprint service avail.) **Indexed:** Geol.Abstr., World Text.Abstr. **Document type:** trade publication.
—BLDSC (4158.934000); Ei; SWETS; UnCover.
    Description: Case histories, technical papers and industry news related to fabrics and geomembranes used in civil engineering.

677   IT   ISSN 0017-1964
GOMITOLO. (Text in Italian or Spanish) 1963. 5/yr. L.20000($35) Edizioni Moderne Internazionali, Via Burlamacchi, 11, 20135 Milan, Italy. Ed. Anna Maria Pietraccini. adv. circ. 90,000.

677   IT
GUIDA ALLA MAGLIERIA E CALZETTERIA ITALIANE. (Text in English, French, German, Italian and Spanish) 1970. a. L.100000. (Italian Association of Knitwear Producers) Gesto s.r.l., Via Cesare Battisti 21, 20122 Milan, Italy. TEL 02-55187581. FAX 39-2-5465310. adv. **Document type:** directory.
    Former titles: Guida all'Industria Italiana della Maglieria e della Calzetteria; Annuario dell'Industria Italiana della Maglieria e della Calzetteria.
    Description: Directory of Italian knitwear and hosiery producers and their suppliers.

677.002294489   DK   ISSN 0908-8296
GUIDE - DANISH CLOTHING AND TEXTILE INDUSTRIES. 1983. biennial. free. Textil- og Beklaedningsindustrien, Bredgade 41, P.O. Box 507, DK-7400 Herning, Denmark. TEL 45-99-27-72-00. FAX 97-12-23-50. TELEX 62 199 JYTEX DK. **Document type:** directory, catalog, trade publication.
    Former titles (until 1991): Dansk Textil- og Beklaedningsguide (ISSN 0907-0931); (until 1989): Dansk Textil Exportguide (ISSN 0109-8586)

677.39   CC
GUOWAI SICHOU/FOREIGN SILK. (Text in Chinese) bi-m. Suzhou Sichou Gongxueyuan - Suzhou Institute of Silk Engineering, 14 Xiangmen Lu, Suzhou, Jiangsu 215005, People's Republic of China. TEL 225614. Ed. Wu Rongru.

HALI; the international magazine of antique carpet and textile art. see *ARTS AND HANDICRAFTS*

338.4   II   ISSN 0436-7316
HD9886.I42
HANDBOOK OF THE INDIAN COTTON TEXTILE INDUSTRY. (Text in English) a. Rs.15. Cotton Textiles Export Promotion Council, Engineering Centre 9, 4 Mathew Rd., Bombay, India.

667.3 332.6   AT
HARVESTING, MARKETING AND DISTRIBUTION COSTS FOR AUSTRALIAN WOOL - SHEEP'S BACK TO OVERSEAS MILL. a. Aus.$20 (foreign Aus.$23). Australian Wool Corporation, G.P.O. Box 4867, Melbourne, Vic. 3001, Australia. Ed. M. Gabrys.

677   UK   ISSN 0144-5871
HIGH PERFORMANCE TEXTILES; an international newsletter. 1980. m. £298($474) (effective 1996). Elsevier Science Ltd., P.O. Box 800, Kidlington, Oxford OX5 1DX, England. TEL 44-1865-843000. FAX 44-1865-843010.
E-mail: nlinfo-f@elsevier.nl; usinfo-f@elsevier.com; forinfo-kyf04035@niftyserve.or.jp; Site addr.: http://www.elsevier.nl/. (Subscr. in U.S. and Canada to: Elsevier Science, 660 White Plains Rd., Tarrytown, NY 10591-5153. TEL 914-524-9200. FAX 914-333-2444) Ed. Peter Lennox-Kerr. bk.rev.; stat. (also avail. in microform from UMI; back issues avail.) **Indexed:** Art & Archaeol.Tech.Abstr., Intl.Polym.Sci.& Tech., PROMT, RAPRA, Text.Tech.Dig., World Text.Abstr. **Document type:** trade publication, newsletter.
●Also available online. Vendor(s): Knight-Ridder, Inc.
—BLDSC (4307.338700); Ei; Genuine Article; SWETS. **CCC.**
    Description: For directors and senior managers responsible for technology, research and development, design, new product development, new ventures or overall corporate strategy.

677   US
HIGHLOFT CONFERENCE PAPERS. 1981. irreg. price varies. I N D A Association of the Nonwoven Fabrics Industry, 1001 Winstead Dr., Ste. 460, Cary, NC 27513. TEL 919-677-0060. FAX 919-677-0211. **Document type:** proceedings.
    Description: Focuses on new markets, technology, machinery and end-uses.

677   II
HISTORIC TEXTILES OF INDIA. (Text in English) 1972. irreg., vol.5, 1993. $95. Calico Museum of Textiles, Sarabhai Foundation, The Retreat, Shahibag, Ahmedabad 380 004, India. TEL 868172. Ed. B.N. Goswamy. adv. contact: D.S. Mehta. circ. 500. **Document type:** catalog.

HOME ECONOMICS ASSOCIATION OF VICTORIA. NEWSLETTER. see *HOME ECONOMICS*

HOME FASHIONS MAGAZINE. see *INTERIOR DESIGN AND DECORATION — Furniture And House Furnishings*

667   US
HOME TEXTILES INTERNATIONAL. q. Fairchild Fashion & Merchandising Group (Subsidiary of: Capital Cities - A B C, Inc.), 7 W. 34th St., 3rd Fl., New York, NY 10001. TEL 212-630-4199. FAX 212-630-4201. Ed. Donna Boyle Swartz. tr.lit.

677   US   ISSN 0195-3184
HOME TEXTILES TODAY; the business and fashion newspaper of the home textiles industry. 1979. w. $89.97. Cahners Business Newspapers (New York), Division of Reed Elsevier Inc., 245 W. 17th St., New York, NY 10011. TEL 212-337-6900. FAX 212-337-6922. (Subscr. to: Box 1424, Riverton, NJ 08077) Ed. Warren Shoulberg; Pub. Kevin Castellani. adv. contact: Mary Frazier. charts; illus.; stat. circ. 12,069. (tabloid format) **Document type:** trade publication.
—UMI.
    Description: For the marketing, merchandising and retailing of home textile products.

HOSIERY AND TEXTILE JOURNAL; monthly review for manufacturers and merchants. see *CLOTHING TRADE*

677   II
HOSIERY REPORT WEEKLY. (Text in English and Hindi) 1966. 3/m. Rs.450 (foreign £50). Kuldip Kumar Mehan, F-21B, New Qutab Road, Sadar Bazar, Delhi 110 006, India. TEL 91-11-526844. FAX 91-11-7772290. Ed. Shanti Saroup Mehan. adv.: B&W page $1500, color page $4000; bleed 215 x 275. circ. 5,000.
    Formerly: Hosiery (ISSN 0018-5418)

677.21   US   ISSN 1022-6303
CODEN: ICRCET
I C A C RECORDER. 4/yr. $145. International Cotton Advisory Committee, 1629 K St. N.W., Ste. 702, Washington, DC 20006. TEL 202-463-6660. FAX 202-463-6950. TELEX 4086660.

677   **US**
I D E A CONFERENCE PAPERS. 1971. every 3 yrs. price varies. I N D A Association of the Nonwoven Fabrics Industry, 1001 Winstead Dr., Ste. 460, Cary, NC 27513. TEL 919-677-0060. FAX 919-677-0211. **Document type:** proceedings.
    Description: Covers all areas of the nonwovens industry.

677   **US**   **ISSN 1049-3328**
TK4035.T4   **CODEN: ITFCFL**
I E E E ANNUAL TEXTILE, FIBER AND FILM INDUSTRY TECHNICAL CONFERENCE. a. Institute of Electrical and Electronics Engineers, Inc., 345 E. 47th St., New York, NY 10017-2394. TEL 212-705-7900. FAX 212-705-7682. (Subscr. to: Box 1331, 445 Hoes Lane, Piscataway, NJ 08855-1331) (also avail. in microfiche)
    —BLDSC (4362.803000); Ei; UMI; UnCover. **CCC.**
    Former titles: Textile Industry Technical Conference (ISSN 0094-9884); Textile Industry Technical Conference. Record (ISSN 0082-3651)

677   **US**
I N D A ASSOCIATION OF THE NONWOVEN FABRICS INDUSTRY. I N D A - TEC SYMPOSIUM PAPERS. (Former name of issuing body: International Nonwovens and Disposables Association) 1973. a. price varies. I N D A Association of the Nonwoven Fabrics Industry, 1001 Winstead Dr., Ste. 460, Cary, NC 27513. TEL 919-677-0060. FAX 919-677-0211.

677   **SZ**
I T M F COUNTRY STATEMENTS. (Text in English) 1977. a. 100 SFr. International Textile Manufacturers Federation, Am Schanzengraben 29, Postfach, CH-8039 Zurich, Switzerland. TEL 01-2017080. FAX 01-2017134. TELEX 817578. charts; illus.; stat. **Document type:** trade publication.
    Description: Provides information on the current state of the textile industry in each member country. Data relates general economic situation, textile manufacturing capacities, activities, and trade in textiles.

677   **SZ**
I T M F DIRECTORY. biennial. free. International Textile Manufacturers Federation, Am Schanzengraben 29, Postfach, CH-8039 Zurich, Switzerland. TEL 01-2017080. FAX 01-2017134. TELEX 817578. Ed. Herwig M. Strolz. **Document type:** directory.
    Formerly: I F C A T I Directory (ISSN 0445-0698)

677   **SZ**
I T M F STATE OF TRADE REPORT. 1989. 4/yr. 200 SFr. International Textile Manufacturers Federation, Am Schanzengraben 29, Postfach, CH-8039 Zurich, Switzerland. TEL 01-2017080. FAX 01-2017134. **Document type:** trade publication.
    Description: Shows country-by-country changes in the spinning and weaving sectors for production, outstanding orders and stocks.

IDAHO WOOL GROWERS BULLETIN. see
    AGRICULTURE — Poultry And Livestock

677.31   **NZ**
IMPORT LEVELS OF WOOL AND WOOL PRODUCTS INTO NEW ZEALAND. 1983. a. NZ.$45. Wools of New Zealand, P.O. Box 3225, Wellington 1, New Zealand. TEL 64-4-472-6888. FAX 64-4-473-7872. Ed. S.E. Britland. circ. 20.
    Description: Covers in table and graph form the import origins of carpets and rugs, yarns, wool fibre, fabrics, woven apparel, knitted apparel, rugs-blankets and other knitwear.

677   **II**   **ISSN 0970-3497**
INDIA. DIRECTORATE OF JUTE DEVELOPMENT. JUTE DEVELOPMENT JOURNAL. (Text and summaries in English) 1938. q. Rs.12. Directorate of Jute Development, c/o Dr. K. Chakravarty, Nizam Palace Campus, 234-4 Acharyya Jagadish Bose Rd., Calcutta 700 020, India. Ed. S. Nath. adv.; bk.rev.; abstr.; charts; illus.; stat.; index. circ. 200. (back issues avail.) **Indexed:** Abstr.Trop.Agri., Field Crop Abstr., Potato Abstr.
    Formerly: India. Directorate of Jute Development. Jute Bulletin (ISSN 0046-8940)

381   **II**   **ISSN 0970-9800**
INDIA. TEXTILES COMMITTEE. CONSUMER PURCHASES OF TEXTILES. (Text in English) 1969. q. Rs.500. Textiles Committee, Market Research Wing, Government of India, Ministry of Textile, Mahalaxmi Engineering Estate, 2nd Fl., Lady Jamshedji Cross Rd. No. 1, Mahim, Bombay 400 016, India. TELEX 76338 TCI IN. charts; stat. circ. 200.

677.21   **II**   **ISSN 0019-459X**
INDIAN COTTON MILLS FEDERATION JOURNAL. (Text and summaries in English) 1964. m. Rs.100($30) Indian Cotton Mills Federation, Textile Centre, 34 P. d'Mello Rd., Box 1449, Bombay 9, India. TEL 862043. TELEX 011-75426. Ed. C.V. Radhakrishnan. adv.; bk.rev.; stat.; index. circ. 1,300.

677   **II**   **ISSN 0971-0426**
TS1540   **CODEN: IJFRET**
INDIAN JOURNAL OF FIBRE & TEXTILE RESEARCH. (Text in English) 1976. q. Rs.200($90) Council of Scientific and Industrial Research, Publications & Information Directorate, CSIR, Hillside Rd., New Delhi 110 012, India. TEL 91-11-5786301. FAX 91-11-5787062. TELEX 031-77271 PID IN. E-mail: pid@sirnetd.ernet.in. Ed. S.K. Rastogi. **Indexed:** Abstr.Bull.Inst.Pap.Chem., Art & Archaeol.Tech.Abstr., Chem.Abstr, Cott.& Trop.Fibr.Abstr., Text.Tech.Dig., World Text.Abstr. **Document type:** academic/scholarly publication.
    —BLDSC (4412.470000); CASDDS; Ei; Genuine Article.
    Formerly: Indian Journal of Textile Research (ISSN 0377-8436)

677.39 638   **II**   **ISSN 0445-7722**
SF541   **CODEN: IJSEAH**
INDIAN JOURNAL OF SERICULTURE. (Text in English) 1962. s-a. Rs.25($20) Central Sericultural Research & Training Institute, Srirampuram, Manandavadi Road, Mysore 570 008, India. TEL 091-821-21406. FAX 091-821-28545. TELEX 0864-203-CSRI-IN. **Indexed:** Biol.Abstr., Curr.Adv.Ecol.Sci., Forest.Abstr., Trop.Oil Seeds Abstr., Weed Abstr.
    —CASDDS.
    Description: Documents research findings and the latest innovations in the textile industry.

677.13 676.14   **II**   **ISSN 0073-6562**
INDIAN JUTE MILLS ASSOCIATION. ANNUAL SUMMARY OF JUTE AND GUNNY STATISTICS. (Annual supplement to "Monthly Summary") (Text in English) 1955. a. Rs.25. Indian Jute Mills Association, Royal Exchange, 6 Netaji Subhas Rd., Calcutta 1, India. circ. 400.

677 676   **II**   **ISSN 0073-6570**
INDIAN JUTE MILLS ASSOCIATION. LOOM AND SPINDLE STATISTICS. 1941. biennial. Rs.5. Indian Jute Mills Association, Royal Exchange, 6 Netaji Subhas Rd., Calcutta 1, India. circ. 500.

677.39   **II**   **ISSN 0019-6355**
INDIAN SILK. (Text in English and Hindi) 1962. m. Rs.100($40) Ministry of Textiles, Central Silk Board, United Mansions, 2nd Fl., 39 M.G. Road, Bangalore 560 001, India. TEL 91-812-5582594. FAX 91-812-5582177. TELEX 845-2798 CSB IN. Ed. M.N. Ramesha. adv.; charts; illus.; mkt.; stat.; tr.lit. **Indexed:** Text.Tech.Dig. **Document type:** government publication.

677   **II**
INDIAN SYNTHETIC & RAYON. Short title: I S R. (Text in English) 1956. s-a. Rs.100 (foreign $20). Synthetic & Rayon Textiles Export Promotion Council, Resham Bhawan, 78 Veer Nariman Rd., Bombay 400 020, India. FAX 91-22-2048358. TELEX 011-83703 SEPC IN. Ed. O.P. Dhawan. adv. contact: E.L. Paulo. charts; illus.; stat.; tr.lit. circ. 3,000. **Document type:** trade publication.
    Formerly: Indian Silk and Rayon (ISSN 0442-736X)

677   **II**   **ISSN 0537-2666**
TS1312
INDIAN TEXTILE ANNUAL & DIRECTORY. (Text in English) 1965. a. Rs.125. Eastland Publications (Private) Ltd., 44 Chittaranjan Ave., Calcutta 700 012, India. TEL 27-3096. Ed. J.R. Dutta. adv.; bk.rev.; charts; illus.; pat. circ. 5,000. **Document type:** directory.

677   **II**   **ISSN 0970-0870**
INDIAN TEXTILE BULLETIN. (Text in English) 1964. q. Rs.41.20($14.85) Government of India, Department of Publications, Civil Lines, Delhi 110 054, India. TEL 11-2517409. **Document type:** bulletin.

677   **II**   **ISSN 0019-6436**
TS1300   **CODEN: INTJAV**
INDIAN TEXTILE JOURNAL. 1890. m. Rs.120($34) Business Press Private Ltd., Transmission House, Compartment No.82, Plot No. 6-19, Marol Co-op, Industrial Estate, M.V. Rd., Andheri East, Bombay 400 059, India. TEL 91-22-8351871. FAX 91-22-8379070. TELEX 011-78455 BPPL IN. Ed. Lawrence Mohan. adv.; bk.rev.; abstr.; charts; illus.; index. circ. 8,000. **Indexed:** Anim.Breed.Abstr., Chem.Abstr., Cott.& Trop.Fibr.Abstr., Text.Tech.Dig., World Text.Abstr.
    —BLDSC (4430.000000); CASDDS; Ei; UMI; UnCover.
    Description: Covers new products and news briefs.

677.21   **IT**   **ISSN 0019-7491**
INDUSTRIA COTONIERA. (Supplement avail.: Rapporto sulla Industria Cotoniera Italiana) 1948. 6/yr. L.88000. Istituto per Assistenza e Servizi alle Aziende Tessili s.r.l. (I.A.S.A.T.), Viale Sarca, 223, 20126 Milan, Italy. TEL 39-2-66103838. FAX 39-2-66103863. Ed. Roberto Diegi. adv. contact: Elena Giuliani. bk.rev.; charts; illus.; stat.; index. circ. 2,000. **Indexed:** Art & Archaeol.Tech.Abstr., Chem.Abstr., Text.Tech.Dig., World Text.Abstr. **Document type:** bulletin.

677   **AG**   **ISSN 0019-7742**
INDUSTRIA TEXTIL SUD AMERICANA. 1941. bi-m. Arg.$18($5) EDITESA S.A., Avda. Roque Saenz Pena 825, Buenos Aires, Argentina. Ed. Dr. Elio Gabellini. adv.; charts; illus.; mkt. circ. 2,000. **Indexed:** Chem.Abstr.

677   **RM**   **ISSN 1222-5347**
INDUSTRIA TEXTILA. (Text in Rumanian; summaries in English, French) 1950. q. 1830. Institutul de Cercetari Textile, Str. Lucretiu Patrascanu 16, 74674 Bucharest, Sect. 3, Rumania. TEL 40-0-6434402. FAX 40-1-3210015. adv. contact: Gheorghe Nagy. bk.rev.; abstr.; bibl.; charts; illus.; index. **Indexed:** C.I.S. Abstr., Chem.Abstr., Cott.& Trop.Fibr.Abstr., Curr.Leather Lit.
    —BLDSC (4442.500000).
    Former titles (until 1994): Industria Usoara - Textile, Tricotaje, Confectii Textile; Industria Textila (ISSN 0019-7750)

677   **US**   **ISSN 0019-8307**
INDUSTRIAL FABRIC PRODUCTS REVIEW. 1915. m. $34 (Canada & Mexico $39; elsewhere $90). Industrial Fabrics Association International, 345 Cedar St., Ste. 800, St. Paul, MN 55101-1088. TEL 612-222-2508. Ed. Sue Hagen. adv.; bk.rev.; illus.; tr.lit.; index. circ. 11,000. (back issues avail.) **Indexed:** Text.Tech.Dig., World Text.Abstr. **Document type:** trade publication.
    —BLDSC (4450.600000); Faxon.
    Formerly: Canvas Products Review.
    Description: Profiles, product news, how-to, industry news and other information of industrial and technical fabric product manufacturers.

677   **US**   **ISSN 0019-8307**
INDUSTRIAL FABRIC PRODUCTS REVIEW BUYER'S GUIDE; the encyclopedia of industrial fabrics. 1976. a. $30. Industrial Fabrics Association International, 345 Cedar St., Ste. 800, St. Paul, MN 55101-1088. TEL 612-222-2508. adv. circ. 11,000. **Document type:** trade publication.
    Description: Supply reference for manufacturers of industrial-technical fabric products.

677   **FR**   **ISSN 0019-9176**
    CODEN: INTPAF
INDUSTRIE TEXTILE. 1883. 11/yr. 790 F. (foreign 1090 F.) includes Filiere Maille (effective Sep. 1995). Editions de l' Industrie Textile, 16 rue Ballu, 75311 Paris Cedex 09, France. TEL 48-74-15-96. FAX 48-74-01-89. Ed. Pierre S. Robin. adv.; bk.rev.; abstr.; bibl.; charts; illus.; mkt.; pat.; stat.; index. circ. 6,000. **Indexed:** C.I.S. Abstr., Chem.Abstr., Excerp.Med., Key to Econ.Sci., PROMT, Text.Tech.Dig., World Text.Abstr.
    —BLDSC (4474.000000); CASDDS; Ei; SWETS.
    Incorporates (1936-1982): Teintex (ISSN 0040-2192)

TEXTILE INDUSTRIES AND FABRICS

677   US   ISSN 0733-8244
INSIDE TEXTILES. 1980. s-m. $167 (foreign $197). Point Publishing Co., Inc., Box 1309, Point Pleasant Beach, NJ 08742. TEL 908-295-8258. Ed. Noreen C. Heimbold. bk.rev. **Document type:** newsletter.
—CCC.

677   GW
INSTITUT FUER TEXTILTECHNIK DER RHEINISCH-WESTFAELISCHEN TECHNISCHEN HOCHSCHULE AACHEN. MITTEILUNGEN. (Text in English, German) 1953. a. DM.100. Institut fuer Textiltechnik der Rheinisch-Westfaelischen Technischen Hochschule Aachen, Eilfschornsteinstr. 18, 52062 Aachen, Germany. TEL 0241-805621. FAX 0241-8888149. Ed. B. Wulfhorst. circ. 250. **Document type:** proceedings.

677   II   ISSN 0257-4438
TS1300
INSTITUTION OF ENGINEERS (INDIA). TEXTILE ENGINEERING DIVISION. JOURNAL. (Text in English) 1978. s-a. Rs.40($5) Institution of Engineers (India), Textile Engineering Division, 8 Gokhale Rd., Calcutta 700 020, India. TEL 033-288334. FAX 033-288345. TELEX 0217885 IEIC IN. Ed. S.P. Misra. adv.; charts; illus.; index. circ. 2,000. **Document type:** academic/scholarly publication.
—BLDSC (4794.350000); Ei.
Refereed Serial

677   SP   ISSN 1131-6756
CODEN: BIIIEZ
INSTITUTO DE INVESTIGACION TEXTIL Y DE COOPERACION INDUSTRIAL. BOLETIN INTEXTER. 1956. 2/yr. 2980 ptas. (foreign 3430 ptas.) (effective 1995). Instituto de Investigacion Textil y de Cooperacion Industrial, Colon 15, 08222 Terrassa, Spain. TEL 34-3-7398277. FAX 34-3-7398272. Ed. F.J. Carrion. adv.; bk.rev.; illus.; circ. 1,000 (controlled). **Indexed:** Ind.SST, World Text.Abstr. **Document type:** bulletin.
—BLDSC (2207.411000); CASDDS. CCC.
Former titles (until 1989): Instituto de Investigacion Textil y de Cooperacion Industrial. Boletin Intextar (ISSN 0212-6699); (until 1982): Instituto de Investigacion Textil y de Cooperacion Industrial. Boletin (ISSN 0210-251X)
Refereed Serial

675   RM
CODEN: BPTPAK
INSTITUTUL POLITEHNIC DIN IASI. BULETINUL. SECTIA VIII: TEXTILE, PIELARIE. (Text in English, French, German, Italian, Russian, Spanish) 1946. s-a. exchange basis. Institutul Politehnic din Iasi, Bd. Copou 11, 6600 Jassy, Rumania. TEL 46577. FAX 40-81-47923. Eds. Alfred Braier, Hugo Rosman. adv.; bk.rev.; bibl. circ. 450. **Indexed:** Appl.Mech.Rev., Chem.Abstr., Math.R., Ref.Zh.
—CASDDS.
Formerly: Institutul Politehnic din Iasi. Buletinul. Sectia VI: Textile, Pielarie (ISSN 0253-1119)

677   UK   ISSN 0954-1438
INTERIOR. (Text in English, French, German) 1965. 3/yr. £63($170) (outside Europe £90) (effective 1995). Benjamin Dent & Co. Ltd. (Subsidiary of: I T B D Publications), 23 Bloombury Sq., London WC1A 2PJ, England. TEL 0171-637-2211. FAX 0171-637-2248. TELEX 8954884 BENDEN G. (N. American subscr. to: Box 1897, Lawrence, KS 66044-8897) Ed. Nina Hirst. circ. 9,000. (back issues avail.) **Document type:** trade publication.
Formerly (until 1988): International Textiles Interior (ISSN 0020-8922)
Description: Analyzes the rapidly expanding market for residential and commercial interior fabrics and carpeting. Previews major exhibitions and conferences.

677   UK   ISSN 0268-2966
INTERNATIONAL CARPET BULLETIN. 1970. 9/yr. £90 (foreign £145). World Textile Publications Ltd., 76 Kirkgate, Bradford, W. Yorkshire BD1 1TB, England. TEL 01274-726357. FAX 01274-735045. Ed. Jennifer Bradley. adv. contact: Julie Smith. bk.rev.; stat.; tr.lit. (back issues avail.) **Document type:** trade publication.
—BLDSC (4538.396700).
Description: Covers technical information for the carpet trade.

677   UK   ISSN 1357-5201
INTERNATIONAL CARPET YEARBOOK. 1970. a. £15 (foreign £17.50). World Textile Publications Ltd., 76 Kirkgate, Bradford, W. Yorks BD1 1TB, England. TEL 01942-731907. FAX 01942-735045. Ed. Derek Ward; Pub. Philip Owen. adv.: page £1500; adv. contact: Julie Smith. charts; illus.; stats.; tr.lit. circ. 2,000. (back issues avail.) **Document type:** trade publication.

667   338.4   US   ISSN 0095-683X
HD9869.N64
INTERNATIONAL DIRECTORY OF THE NONWOVEN FABRICS INDUSTRY. 1970. biennial. price varies. I N D A Association of the Nonwoven Fabrics Industry, 1001 Winstead Dr., Ste. 460, Cary, NC 27513. TEL 919-677-0060. FAX 919-677-0211. Ed. Peggy F. Blake. **Document type:** directory.
Formerly: Directory for the Nonwoven Fabrics and Disposable Soft Goods Industries (ISSN 0070-5020)

677 667   UK   ISSN 0020-658X
CODEN: IDBFAT
INTERNATIONAL DYER, TEXTILE PRINTER, BLEACHER AND FINISHER. 1879. m. £57 (foreign £70). World Textile Publications Ltd., 76 Kirkgate, Bradford, W. Yorkshire BD1 1TB, England. TEL 01274-726357. FAX 01274-735045. Ed. Phil Owen. adv. contact: Julie Smith. bk.rev.; abstr.; illus.; pat.; tr.lit. circ. 2,391. (reprint service avail. from UMI) **Indexed:** Br.Tech.Ind., Chem.Abstr., PROMT, Text.Tech.Dig., World Text.Abstr. **Document type:** trade publication.
—BLDSC (4539.753000); CASDDS; SWETS; UMI; UnCover.

677 546   US   ISSN 1049-801X
INTERNATIONAL FIBER JOURNAL. 1986. bi-m. $25. McMickle Publications, Inc., 2919 Spalding Dr., Atlanta, GA 30350-4628. TEL 404-394-6098. FAX 404-393-0161. Ed. Walter C. McMickle. adv.; circ. 8,900. (controlled). **Document type:** trade publication.
—BLDSC (4540.186450).
Description: For upper and middle management in polymerizers, fiber producers, texturers, nonwovens, and yarn spinning.

677 747.5   US
INTERNATIONAL HAJJI BABA SOCIETY. NEWSLETTER. m. International Hajji Baba Society, c/o Virginia Day, 6500 Pinecrest Ct., Annandale, VA 22063. TEL 703-354-4880. **Document type:** newsletter.
Description: Promotes interest in oriental rugs and textiles.

677   US
INTERNATIONAL NONWOVENS JOURNAL. q. $60 to non-members; members $48. (I N D A, Association of the Nonwoven Fabrics Industry) Rodman Publishing Corp., 17 S. Franklin Tpke., Box 555, Ramsey, NJ 07446. TEL 201-825-2552. FAX 201-825-0552. Ed. D.K. Smith. (back issues avail.) **Document type:** trade publication.
Formerly (until vol.6, no.1, 1994): I N D A Journal of Nonwovens Research.

677   II   ISSN 0047-0961
INTERNATIONAL PRESS CUTTING SERVICE: JUTE, GUNNY, HESSIAN, BURLAP, COIR. 1967. w. $65. International Press Cutting Service, Box 63, Allahabad 211001, India. Ed. N. Khanna. bk.rev.; index. circ. 1,200. (looseleaf format; also avail. in processed)

677   II   ISSN 0047-1119
INTERNATIONAL PRESS CUTTING SERVICE: TEXTILE NEWS. 1957. w. $65. International Press Cutting Service, Box 63, Allahabad 211001, India. Ed. N. Khanna. bk.rev.; index. circ. 1,200. (looseleaf format; also avail. in processed)

677   SZ   ISSN 1017-270X
HD9850.1   CODEN: IPCWE3
INTERNATIONAL PRODUCTION COST COMPARISON. 1979. biennial. 150 SFr. International Textile Manufacturers Federation, Am Schanzengraben 29, Postfach, CH-8039 Zurich, Switzerland. TEL 01-2017080. FAX 01-2017134. TELEX 817578. **Document type:** trade publication.
Description: Focuses on costs of producing yarns as well as spinning, weaving and knitting in Brazil, India, Italy, Japan, Korea, Thailand and the U.S.

677.39   FR   ISSN 0290-8271
INTERNATIONAL SILK ASSOCIATION. MONTHLY NEWSLETTER. (Text in English, French) 1975. m. membership only. International Silk Association - Association Internationale de la Soie, 34 rue de la Charite, 69002 Lyon, France. TEL 78-42-10-79. FAX 78-37-56-72. TELEX 330-949. bk.rev.; bibl.; illus.; mkt.; stat. circ. 500. **Document type:** newsletter.
Supersedes: International Silk Association. Bulletin (ISSN 0020-8698)

677 667   SZ   ISSN 1012-8417
CODEN: ITBFD8
INTERNATIONAL TEXTILE BULLETIN DYEING - PRINTING - FINISHING EDITION. (Editions in Chinese, English, French, German, Italian, Spanish) 1965. q. I T S Publishing, International Textile Service, Kesslerstr. 9, CH-8952 Schlieren, Switzerland. TEL 01-7305853. FAX 01-7305902. TELEX 82758-ITS-CH. **Indexed:** Art & Archaeol.Tech.Abstr., Text.Tech.Dig., World Text.Abstr. **Document type:** trade publication.
—Ei.
Formerly: International Textile Bulletin Dyeing - Finishing Edition (ISSN 0539-0788)

677   SZ
INTERNATIONAL TEXTILE BULLETIN NONWOVENS - INDUSTRIAL TEXTILES. (Editions in Chinese, English, French, German, Italian, Spanish) q. I T S Publishing, International Textile Service, Kesslerstr. 9, CH-8952 Schlieren, Switzerland. TEL 01-7305853. FAX 01-7305902. TELEX 82758-ITS-CH. Ed. Eugene Dempsey; Pub. Rosmarie Keller. adv. contact: Peter Frei. **Document type:** trade publication.

677   SZ
INTERNATIONAL TEXTILE BULLETIN YARN AND FABRIC FORMING EDITION. (Editions in Chinese, English, French, German, Italian, Spanish) I T S Publishing, International Textile Service, Kesslerstr. 9, CH-8952 Schlieren, Switzerland. TEL 01-7305853. FAX 01-7305902. TELEX 82758-ITS-CH. **Indexed:** Text.Tech.Dig., World Text.Abstr. **Document type:** trade publication.
Former titles: International Textile Bulletin Yarn Forming Edition; International Textile Bulletin Spinning Edition (ISSN 0539-0796)

677   UK   ISSN 0263-5879
CODEN: ITCLEW
INTERNATIONAL TEXTILE CALENDAR. 1993. bi-m. £75($130) (effective 1996). Textile Institute, 10 Blackfriars St., Manchester M3 5DR, England. TEL 0161-834-8457. FAX 0161-835-3087. TELEX 668297 TEXINS G. Ed. Paul Daniels. **Document type:** trade publication.
Description: Covers the spectrum of textiles worldwide.

677   SZ
INTERNATIONAL TEXTILE MANUFACTURING. 1960. a. 80 SFr. International Textile Manufacturers Federation, Am Schanzengraben 29, Postfach, CH-8039 Zurich, Switzerland. TEL 01-2017080. FAX 01-2017134. TELEX 817578. **Indexed:** World Text.Abstr. **Document type:** proceedings.
Supersedes: Cotton and Allied Textile Industries (ISSN 0574-2315)
Description: Contains full text of papers presented at annual conference.

677   UK   ISSN 0020-8914
TS1300
INTERNATIONAL TEXTILES; information and inspiration. (Text in English, French, German; supplement in Japanese) 1932. 10/yr. £150($445) (outside Europe £230) (effective 1995). Bejamin Dent & Co. Ltd. (Subsidiary of: I T B D Publications), 23 Bloombury Sq., London WC1A 2PJ, England. TEL 0171-637-2211. FAX 0171-637-2248. TELEX 8954884 BENDEN G. (N. American subscr. to: Box 1897, Lawrence, KS 66044-8897) adv.; bk.rev.; illus. (also avail. in microform from UMI; reprint service avail. from UMI) **Indexed:** DAAI, Key to Econ.Sci. **Document type:** trade publication.
—BLDSC (4550.550000); SWETS; UMI.
Incorporates (1973-1993): Textile Forecast (ISSN 0264-3537)
Description: Monitors the international textiles market worldwide and reports on design ideas and commercial realities.

TEXTILE INDUSTRIES AND FABRICS 6273

677   UK   ISSN 0965-7592
INTERNATIONAL WOOL TEXTILE OVERVIEW. 3/yr. £65 (overseas £90). International Wool Textile Organisation, 63 Addle Dr., London SW19 6LB, England. TEL 0181-788-8876. FAX 0181-788-5171. **Document type:** trade publication.
—BLDSC (4552.162000).

677   RU   ISSN 0021-3497
TS1300   CODEN: IVTTAF
IZVESTIYA VYSSHIKH UCHEBNYKH ZAVEDENII. SERIYA TEKHNOLOGIYA TEKSTIL'NOI PROMYSHLENNOSTI. 1957. bi-m. $97 (effective 1996). Ivanovskii Tekstil'nyi Institut, Ivanovo, Russia. charts; index. (tabloid format) **Indexed:** Chem.Abstr., Cott.& Trop.Fibr.Abstr., World Text.Abstr.
—BLDSC (0077.860000); CASDDS.

677   GW   ISSN 0944-1964
JAHRBUCH DER TEXTILEN RAUMAUSSTATTUNG. 1970. a. DM.62. Fachverlag Schiele und Schoen GmbH, Markgrafenstr. 11, 10969 Berlin, Germany. TEL 030-253752-0. FAX 030-2517248. Ed. Dirk Artz. **Document type:** trade publication.
Formerly (until 1993): Taschenbuch der Textilen Raumausstattung (ISSN 0341-9711)

677   JA   ISSN 0021-4752
                CODEN: JTENAL
JAPAN TEXTILE NEWS; vital marketing news in Japan and Asian countries. Short title: J T N Monthly. (Text in English) 1954. m. $130 (India & Korea $160). Osaka Senken Ltd., 3-4-9, Bingo-machi, Chuo-ku, Osaka 541, Japan. TEL 06-202-7891. FAX 06-226-0106. TELEX JTN J65470. adv.; charts; stat. **Indexed:** Chem.Abstr., Key to Econ.Sci., Text.Tech.Dig., World Text.Abstr.
—BLDSC (5073.812400); SWETS.

677   JA
JAPAN TEXTILE NEWS WEEKLY. Short title: J T N Weekly. (Text in English) w. $280. Osaka Senken Ltd., 3-4-9, Bingo-machi, Chuo-ku, Osaka 541, Japan. TEL 06-202-7891. FAX 06-226-0106. TELEX JTN J65470. (Subscr. in India to: Honesty Subscription Agency, 45-47, Dr. M.B. Welkar St., Kalbadevi Rd., Bombay 400 002. TEL 317604. FAX 2086959; Subscr. in Korea to: International Textile Design Co., Ltd., SI.Kangnam P.O. Box 1233, Seoul, S. Korea. TEL 562-1250. FAX 562-5856)

677 687   US
JEANSFLASH. s-a. Jeanswear Communication, 475 Park AVe. S, 17th Fl., New York, NY 10016-6901. TEL 212-689-3462. FAX 212-545-1709.
Description: Covers industry and association developments.

677   FR   ISSN 0021-8197
JOURNAL DU TEXTILE. Abbreviated title: J T. 1964. w. 965 F. (foreign 1260 F.). Editions Hennessen, 61 rue de Malte, 75541 Paris Cedex 11, France. TEL 1-43-57-21-89. FAX 1-47-00-08-35. Ed. Catherine Guyot. adv.: B&W page 22130 F., color page 38230 F.; 370 x 274; adv. contact: Blandine Courtier. illus. circ. 20,000. (tabloid format) **Indexed:** Key to Econ.Sci. **Document type:** newspaper, trade publication.
Description: Follows news of the textile trade from fabrics, home decoration and store management to fashion trends in ready-to-wear, menswear, childrenswear, sportswear and lingerie.

677.028   UK   ISSN 0267-7806
JOURNAL FOR WEAVERS, SPINNERS & DYERS. 1952. q. £12.20 (foreign £14.65) (effective 1996). Association of Guilds of Weavers, Spinners & Dyers, 38 Sandown Dr., Hereford HR4 9LU, England. TEL 01432-359066. Ed.Bd. adv.; bk.rev.; charts; illus.; mkt.; pat.; tr.mk. circ. 2,400. **Indexed:** DAAI. **Document type:** trade publication.
—BLDSC (5072.554500); UnCover.
Former titles: Weavers Journal; Guilds of Weavers, Spinners and Dyers. Quarterly Journal (ISSN 0017-5439)
Description: Provides for interchange of information on the subject, includes technical notes and reviews.

677 698   US   ISSN 0093-4658
TS1512   CODEN: JCTFAL
JOURNAL OF COATED FABRICS. 1971. q. $220. Technomic Publishing Co., Inc., 851 New Holland Ave., Box 3535, Lancaster, PA 17604. TEL 717-291-5609. FAX 717-295-4538. TELEX 230 753565 (TECHNOMIC UD). Ed. William C. Smith. bk.rev.; charts; illus.; index. circ. 400. (also avail. in microform from UMI; reprint service avail. from UMI) **Indexed:** Appl.Mech.Rev., Art & Archaeol.Tech.Abstr., Chem.Abstr., Curr.Cont., Eng.Ind., Excerp.Med., Intl.Polym.Sci.& Tech., RAPRA, Text.Tech.Dig., World Text.Abstr. **Document type:** academic/scholarly publication.
—BLDSC (4958.794000); CASDDS; Ei; Faxon; SWETS; UMI; UnCover. **CCC.**
Formerly: Journal of Coated Fibrous Materials (ISSN 0047-2298)
Refereed Serial

JOURNAL OF SERICULTURAL SCIENCE OF JAPAN/NIPPON SANSHIGAKU ZASSHI. see *BIOLOGY — Entomology*

JOURNAL OF THE COIN LAUNDRY AND DRYCLEANING INDUSTRY. see *CLEANING AND DYEING*

677.13   BG   ISSN 1010-3791
HD9156.J8
JUTE AND JUTE FABRICS - BANGLADESH. (Text in English) 1975. m. Tk.30($5) Bangladesh Jute Research Institute, Sher-e-Banglanagar, Dhaka 7, Bangladesh. Ed. Harun-Ur-Rashid. adv.; charts; stat. circ. 500. **Indexed:** Art & Archaeol.Tech.Abstr., Biol.Abstr., Chem.Abstr., Text.Tech.Dig.
Formerly (until Jan. 1975): Jute and Jute Fabrics - Pakistan (ISSN 0022-7099)

677   GW   ISSN 0047-3405
KETTENWIRK-PRAXIS. English edition (ISSN 0170-401X) (Text in German; summaries in English, French, Spanish) 1967. q. DM.57.50 (with English DM.92; with French DM.225). Karl Mayer GmbH, Postfach 1120, 63166 Obertshausen, Germany. TEL 06104-402-0. FAX 06104-43574. TELEX 0410174. Ed. Rolf Hufschlaeger. adv. contact: Rolf Hufschlaeger. bk.rev.; film rev.; abstr.; bibl.; illus.; pat.; cum.index. circ. 2,300. **Indexed:** Text.Tech.Dig., World Text.Abstr. **Document type:** trade publication.
—BLDSC (5090.610000). **CCC.**

677   UK   ISSN 0267-9051
KEY NOTE REPORT: FIBRES. Variant title: Fibres. irreg. £185. Key Note Publications Ltd., Field House, 72 Oldfield Rd., Hampton, Middlesex TW12 2HQ, England. TEL 0181-783-0755. FAX 0181-783-1720. **Document type:** trade publication.
●Also available online.
Also available on CD-ROM.
—BLDSC (3918.070000).

677.3   US   ISSN 0084-1234
KNITOVATIONS. 1939. s-a. $20. Woolknit Associates, Inc., 267 Fifth Ave., Ste. 806, New York, NY 10016. TEL 212-683-7785. Ed. Mildred Faulk. adv. circ. 5,660. **Indexed:** Text.Tech.Dig.
Formerly (until 1952): Woolknit Annual.

677   UK
KNITTING & HABERDASHERY: THE NEEDLECRAFTS REVIEW. 1959. bi-m. £18 (Ireland I£30; overseas £36) (effective 1995-1996). Arthur S. Damery, Ed. & Pub., Bates Business Centre, Church Rd., Harold Wood, Romford, Essex RM3 0JA, England. TEL 01708-379897. FAX 01708-379804. adv. contact: Peter J. Damery. bk.rev. circ. 5,000. (back issues avail.) **Document type:** trade publication, directory.
Former titles: Knitting and Haberdashery Review; Knitting Wool Review.

677   UK   ISSN 0266-8394
KNITTING INTERNATIONAL; the leading technical and management journal for hosiery, underwear, knitwear and knitted fabric manufacturers. Chinese edition: Guoji Zhengzhi. 1894. m. £75($200) (outside Europe £110) (effective 1995). Benjamin Dent & Co. Ltd. (Subsidiary of: I T B D Publications), 23 Bloombury Sq., London WC1A 2PJ, England. TEL 0171-637-2211. FAX 0171-637-2248. TELEX 8954884 BENDEN G. (N. American subscr. to: Box 1897, Lawrence, KS 66044-8897) Ed.Bd. adv.; bk.rev. circ. 6,000. **Indexed:** Br.Tech.Ind., Text.Tech.Dig., World Text.Abstr. **Document type:** trade publication.
—BLDSC (5100.364000).
Formerly: Hosiery Trade Journal.
Description: Keeps readers up to date with developments in technology, production, materials, marketing, companies and personnel, and fashions.

677 746   GW   ISSN 0947-0972
KNITTING TECHNOLOGY. German edition: Maschen-Industrie (ISSN 0946-7718); Spanish edition: Punto Tecnica y Moda (ISSN 0724-3847) 1979. bi-m. DM.135 (effective 1995). Meisenbach GmbH, Hainstr. 18, 96047 Bamberg, Germany. TEL 0951-861-135. FAX 0951-861-158. (Subscr. to: Postfach 2069, 96011 Bamberg, Germany) Ed. Lothar Rauscher. adv.: B&W page DM.2970, color page DM.5100; trim 270 x 180; adv. contact: Annelie Durniok. bk.rev.; abstr.; charts; illus.; pat.; index. circ. 4,328. (also avail. in microfilm) **Indexed:** Text.Tech.Dig., World Text.Abstr. **Document type:** trade publication.
—UMI. **CCC.**
Former titles: Knitting Technique (ISSN 0177-4875); W S T Knitting Technik (ISSN 0173-4415)
Description: Provides information on knitwear and hosiery production, including finishing, making-up and fashion trends.

677.00294489   DK   ISSN 0906-0413
KOMPASS SELECT EXPORT. TEXTILES, CLOTHING, FOOTWEAR AND LEATHER GOODS. Cover title: Euro Kompass Denmark. Textiles, Clothing and Footwear. (Text in Danish, English, French, German and Spanish) 1966. a. DKK 300 (listed companies DKK 100). Forlaget Kompass Danmark, Oevroedvej 5, DK-2840 Holte, Denmark. TEL 45-45-41-21-00. FAX 45-45-41-06-65. illus. **Document type:** directory.
●Also available on CD-ROM.
Formerly (until 1990): Kompass Select Export. Textiles, Clothing and Footwear (ISSN 0106-1224)

KONFEKSIYON & TEKNIK; specialist clothing magazine. see *CLOTHING TRADE*

KRUL'S MAANDBLAD VOOR STOOM- EN CHEMISCHE WASSERIJEN, VERVERIJEN EN WASSALONS. see *CLEANING AND DYEING*

677   IT   ISSN 0368-7406
LANIERA. 1887. bi-m. L.20000. Editoriale Laniera s.r.l., Via A. Stradivari 10, 20131 Milan, Italy. TEL 2-204-37-26. FAX 2-221-356. Ed. Felice Dall'Ara. adv.; bk.rev.; index. circ. 3,300. **Indexed:** Text.Tech.Dig.

677   US   ISSN 8756-5765
LATIN AMERICAN TEXTILE INDUSTRY DIRECTORY. (Text in English, Portuguese, Spanish) 1985. a. $150. Aquino Productions, Box 15760, Stamford, CT 06901. TEL 203-325-3138. Ed. Andres C. Aquino. adv.

677   SP   ISSN 0212-5498
LINEA ESPANOLA. 1961. q. 2200 ptas. Prensa Tecnica, S.A., Caspe 118-120, Barcelona 13, Spain. Ed. F. Canet Thomas. adv.; illus. circ. 5,000.
Former titles (until 1983): Modasport Jersey (ISSN 0211-8068); (until 1979): Jersey (ISSN 0211-805X)

LIVESTOCK, MEAT AND WOOL MARKET NEWS. see *AGRICULTURE — Poultry And Livestock*

TEXTILE INDUSTRIES AND FABRICS

677   IT
MAGLIE CALZE MODA INDUSTRIA ABBIGLIAMENTO. 1967. bi-m. L.105000. (Italian Association of Knitwear Producers) Gesto s.r.l., Via Cesare Battisti 21, 20122 Milan, Italy. TEL 39-2-55187581. FAX 39-2-5465310. Ed. Eugenio Faiella. adv.: color page L.2800000. bk.rev.; abstr.; bibl.; illus.; pat.; stat.; tr.lit.; index. **Indexed:** World Text.Abstr.
    Formerly: Maglie Calze Industria (ISSN 0024-9947)
    Description: Technical and economic news for the knitting industry.

677   HU   ISSN 0025-0309
TS1300   CODEN: MGTXAY
MAGYAR TEXTILTECHNIKA. 1948. m. $97. (Textilipari Muszaki es Tudomanyos Egyesulet) Lapkiado Vallalat, Lenin korut 9-11, 1073 Budapest 7, Hungary. TEL 222-408. (Subscr. to: Kultura, P.O. Box 149, H-1389 Budapest, Hungary) Eds. Pal Fusti, Sandor Gonci. adv.; bk.rev.; charts; illus. circ. 1,000. **Indexed:** Abstr.Bull.Inst.Pap.Chem., Art & Archaeol.Tech.Abstr., Chem.Abstr., Cott.& Trop.Fibr.Abstr., Text.Tech.Dig., World Text.Abstr.
  —BLDSC (5345.600000); CASDDS.

677.39   II   ISSN 0377-7537
TS1640   CODEN: MMTIBW
MAN-MADE TEXTILES IN INDIA. (Text in English) 1957. m. Rs.150 (foreign $50). Silk and Art Silk Mills' Research Association, Sasmira, Sasmira Marg, Worli, Bombay 400 025, India. TEL 22-493-5351. FAX 91-22-493-0225. Ed. D.B. Ajgaonkar. adv.; bk.rev.; abstr.; charts; illus.; stat.; index. circ. 1,500. **Indexed:** Chem.Abstr., Indian Sci.Ind., Text.Tech.Dig., World Text.Abstr. **Document type:** academic/scholarly publication.
  —BLDSC (5361.032000); CASDDS; Ei; UnCover.
    Formerly: Silk and Rayon Industries of India (ISSN 0037-525X)
    Description: Trade magazine about silk and silk mills industry.

677   II
MANCHESTER. (Text in Marathi) 1985. d. newsstand price: Rs.1. Vasant K. Dattawade, Ed. & Pub., 4-5, Zenda Chowk, P.B. No. 207, Ichalkaranji 416 115, Maharashtra, India. TEL 24343. adv. cols./p.: 8; pp./issue: 4. **Document type:** newspaper.

MARINE STORE MERCHANDISING; magazine of boating accessory, parts & service merchandising. see
SPORTS AND GAMES — Boats And Boating

677   US   ISSN 0885-9949
MARINE TEXTILES. 1986. 9/yr. $33 (Canada $41; elsewhere $95). R C M Enterprises, Inc., 15500 Wayzata Blvd., Ste. 922, Box 720, Wayzata, MN 55391. TEL 612-473-5088. FAX 612-473-7068. Ed. Sue Klemond; Pub. Robert C. Mead. adv.: B&W page $1807; adv. contact: Jim Penningroth. index. circ. 4,000. (back issues avail.) **Document type:** trade publication.
    Description: Covers fabric products and furnishings used in boating.

677   US
MARINE TEXTILES BUYERS' GUIDE. 1986. a. $20. R C M Enterprises, Inc., 15500 Wayzata Blvd., Ste. 922, Box 720, Wayzata, MN 55391. TEL 612-473-5088. FAX 612-473-7068. Ed. Sue Klemond; Pub. Robert C. Mead. adv. contact: Jim Penningroth. bk.rev.; index. circ. 4,000. **Document type:** trade publication.
    Description: Covers marine textiles, provides information and ideas about textiles used in boating.

677 746.92   SP
MARKET VISION MONOGRAFIAS. SERIE TEXTIL - MODA. 1982. 4/yr. Aramo Editorial, S.A., Muntaner 60, 2a 2a, 08011 Barcelona, Spain. TEL 3-453-79-38. FAX 3-323-79-26. Ed. Humberto Martinez. adv.; circ. 4,500 (controlled). **Document type:** monographic series, trade publication.

677   GW   ISSN 0946-7718
MASCHEN-INDUSTRIE. Spanish edition: Punto Tecnica y Moda (ISSN 0724-3847); English edition: Knitting Technology (ISSN 0947-0972) 1951. m. DM.185 (foreign DM.204) (effective 1995). Meisenbach GmbH, Hainstr. 18, 96047 Bamberg, Germany. TEL 0951-861-135. FAX 0951-861-158. (Subscr. to: Postfach 2069, 96011 Bamberg, Germany) Ed. Lothar Rauscher. adv.: B&W page DM.2970, color page DM.5100; trim 270 x 180; adv. contact: Annelie Durniok. bk.rev.; abstr.; charts; illus.; pat.; index. circ. 4,616. (also avail. in microfilm) **Indexed:** Art & Archaeol.Tech.Abstr., Chem.Abstr., Text.Tech.Dig., World Text.Abstr. **Document type:** trade publication.
  —SWETS; UMI. **CCC.**
    Formerly: Wirkerei- und Strickerei-Technik (ISSN 0043-6097)

MEDICAL TEXTILES; an international newsletter. see
MEDICAL SCIENCES

MEDLEMSTIDNINGEN INDUSTRIFACKET. see LABOR UNIONS

677   GW   ISSN 0341-0781
TS1300   CODEN: MTIRDL
MELLIAND TEXTILBERICHTE/INTERNATIONAL TEXTILE REPORTS. English edition (ISSN 0198-7275) (Editions in English, German) 1920. m. DM.252 (with English supplement DM.498). Melliand Textilberichte GmbH, Mainzer Landstr. 251, 60326 Frankfurt a.M., Germany. TEL 069-75951722. FAX 069-75951720. Ed. Wolfgang Moeck. adv.: B&W page DM.4096, color page DM.7036; trim 180 x 260; adv. contact: Dagmar Henning. bk.rev.; abstr.; bibl.; circ. 6,656 (controlled). **Indexed:** Abstr.Bull.Inst.Pap.Chem., Art & Archaeol.Tech.Abstr., Chem.Abstr., Cott.& Trop.Fibr.Abstr., Curr.Cont., Excerp.Med., INIS Atomind., PROMT, Text.Tech.Dig., W.R.C.Inf., World Text.Abstr. **Document type:** trade publication.
  —BLDSC (5546.020050); CASDDS; SWETS. **CCC.**
    Former titles (until 1976): Melliand Textilberichte International (ISSN 0375-9350); (until 1969): Melliand Textilberichte (ISSN 0025-8989); And (until 1923): Textil uber Wissenschaft (ISSN 0936-5575).
    Description: Provides information on all aspects of the textile industry, including weaving and knitting, washing, printing, finishing and textile machinery.
    Refereed Serial

677   US
MILL REPORT. 1976. irreg. Platt Saco Lowell, Drawer 2327, Greenville, SC 29602. TEL 803-859-3211. charts; illus.

677   SZ
MITTEX: MITTEILUNGEN UEBER TEXTILINDUSTRIE; Schweizerische Fachschrift fuer die gesamte Textilindustrie. vol. 80, 1973. m. 62 SFr. Schweizerische Vereinigung von Textilfachleuten, Lindenweg 7, 8122 Pfaffhausen-Zurich, Switzerland. Ed. Anthony U. Trinkler. adv.; bk.rev.; charts; illus.; mkt.; pat.; tr.lit.; index. circ. 3,000. **Indexed:** Chem.Abstr., Excerp.Med., Text.Tech.Dig. **Document type:** trade publication.
    Formerly: Mitteilungen ueber Textilindustrie (ISSN 0026-6949)

677.4   II   ISSN 0377-1490
HD9929.2.I5
MODERN FIBRES. (Text in English) vol. 4, 1973. q. Rs.20. Association of Man-Made Fibre Industry, Resham Bhavan, 78 Veer Nariman Rd., Bombay 400020, India. Ed. K.V. Ramaswamy. charts, stat.

677   BE   ISSN 0773-4468
MODIS. (Editions in Dutch, French) 1949. 6/yr. 1895 BEF($24) (Nationaal Verbond der Textieldetaillisten - National Association of Tailors and Retailers) Ward Bohe, Ed. & Pub., 8 Spastraat, 1040 Brussels, Belgium. TEL 32-2-2380651. FAX 32-2-2306444. adv. contact: Caroline Bels. charts; illus.; stat.; circ. 10,000 (paid). **Document type:** trade publication.
    Formerly: Navetex (ISSN 0028-1514)

MONTHLY COTTON LINTERS REVIEW. see
AGRICULTURE — Agricultural Economics

677   AG   ISSN 0027-3376
MUNDO TEXTIL ARGENTINO. 1962. m. 25 de Mayo 267-218, Buenos Aires, Argentina. Ed. Leonor F. Breitman. adv. circ. 2,800.

NATIONAL COTTONSEED PRODUCTS ASSOCIATION. TRADING RULES. see AGRICULTURE — Feed, Flour And Grain

677.3   AT
NATIONAL COUNCIL OF WOOL SELLING BROKERS OF AUSTRALIA. ANNUAL REPORT. 1938. a. free. National Council of Wool Selling Brokers of Australia, Ltd., 6st Fl., Wool Exchange House, 530 Little Collins St., Melbourne, Vic. 3000, Australia. TEL 61-3-629-6287. FAX 61-3-629-2289.
    Formerly: Wool Review (ISSN 0084-1218)

677   AT
NATIONAL COUNCIL OF WOOL SELLING BROKERS OF AUSTRALIA. NEWS BULLETIN. 1956. m. free. National Council of Wool Selling Brokers of Australia, Ltd., 6st Fl., Wool Exchange House, 530 Little Collins St., Melbourne, Vic. 3000, Australia. TEL 61-3-629-6287. FAX 61-3-629-2289. **Document type:** bulletin.

677   TZ
NATIONAL TEXTILE CORPORATION. ANNUAL REPORT AND ACCOUNTS. (Text in English) 1974. a. National Textile Corporation, Directorate of Planning and Finance, Box 9531, Dar es Salaam, Tanzania. adv. circ. 500.

NATIONAL WOOL MARKET REVIEW. see
AGRICULTURE — Poultry And Livestock

677   PL   ISSN 1230-4476
                     CODEN: PIKWAX
NATURAL FIBRES/WLOKNA NATURALNE. (Text in English, Polish) 1953. irreg. Instytut Wlokien Naturalnych - Institute of Natural Fibres, Ul. Wojska Polskiego 71 b, 60-630 Poznan, Poland. TEL 48-61-224815. FAX 48-61-417830. TELEX 0413486 PL. Ed. Ryszard Kozlowski. **Document type:** academic/scholarly publication.
  —BLDSC (6037.162500); CASDDS.
    Former titles (until 1992): Instytut Krajowych Wlokien Naturalnych. Prace (ISSN 0208-7685); (until 1973): Instytut Wlokien Lykowatych. Prace (ISSN 0551-648X)

677   US
NEEDLEPUNCH CONFERENCE PAPERS. 1990. irreg. price varies. I N D A Association of the Nonwoven Fabrics Industry, 1001 Winstead Rd., Ste. 460, Cary, NC 27513. TEL 919-677-0060. FAX 919-677-0211. **Document type:** proceedings.
    Description: Covers the applications, technology, raw materials and machinery of the needlepunch industry.

338.4   JA   ISSN 0910-8505
NIHON BOSEKI GEPPO/JAPAN SPINNERS' ASSOCIATION. MONTHLY REPORT. (Text in Japanese) 1947. m. 12000 Yen. Japan Institute of Cotton Textile Technology and Economy, Mengyo Kaikan, 5-8, 2-chome, Bingo-machi, Chuo-ku, Osaka-shi, Japan. TEL 06-203-5161. FAX 06-229-1590. TELEX 06-522-2230-SPINAS-J. Ed. Kiyonori Mayumi. adv. circ. 5,000. **Document type:** trade publication.

677 676   US   ISSN 0163-4429
HD9869.N64   CODEN: NOINDJ
NONWOVENS INDUSTRY; the international magazine for the nonwoven fabrics and disposable soft goods industry. 1970. m. $48. Rodman Publications, Inc., 17 S. Franklin Tpk., Box 555, Ramsey, NJ 07446. TEL 201-825-2552. FAX 201-825-0553. Ed. Ellen Noonan. adv. contact: Matthew Montgomery. bk.rev.; charts; illus.; pat.; stat.; tr.lit.; index. circ. 11,000. **Indexed:** Abstr.Bull.Inst.Pap.Chem., Chem.Abstr., Paper & Bd.Abstr., PROMT, Text.Tech.Dig., World Text.Abstr. **Document type:** trade publication.
  —BLDSC (6117.343000); CASDDS; Faxon; SWETS; UnCover. **CCC.**
    Former titles (until 1977): Formed Fabrics Industry (ISSN 0163-4399); Nonwovens and Disposable Soft Goods; Disposable Soft Goods (ISSN 0046-0362)

677   US   ISSN 1053-9832
                     CODEN: NMFRE3
NONWOVENS MARKETS AND FIBER STRUCTURES REPORT. 1986. s-m. $469. Miller Freeman, Inc. (Subsidiary of: United Newspapers), 600 Harrison St., San Francisco, CA 94107. TEL 415-905-2200. FAX 415-905-2232. TELEX 278273. Ed. Lydia Cain.
  —CCC.

TEXTILE INDUSTRIES AND FABRICS

677 608.7 US ISSN 1062-2780
NONWOVENS PATENT NEWS. 1990. m. $857 (effective 1995-1996). D.K. Smith, Ed. & Pub., 3112 E. Hampton Ave., Mesa, AZ 85204. TEL 602-924-0813. FAX 602-924-6966. **Document type:** newsletter.
  Description: Contains articles, patent abstracts, and diagrams of U.S., European and Japanese patents that affect the nonwoven textile industry. Includes polymers, films, tissues, processes, equipment, converted products, and related items.

677 UK ISSN 0953-1092
NONWOVENS REPORT INTERNATIONAL. 1971. m.(plus a. supplement). $160. Texpress, Merridale House, Mauldeth Rd., Stockport, Cheshire SK4 3NT, England. TEL 061-432-1005. FAX 061-443-1421. Ed. Derek T. Ward. bk.rev.; charts; pat.; stat. **Document type:** newsletter.
  —BLDSC (6117.346000).

677 US ISSN 0888-1979
NONWOVENS WORLD. 1986. 5/yr. $45 (free to qualified personnel). M T S Publications, 4100 S. Seventh St., Kalamazoo, MI 49009. TEL 616-375-1236. FAX 616-375-6710. Ed. James P. Hanson. adv.: B&W page $1850; trim 8 1/8 x 10 7/8; adv. contact: Wayne Carter. circ. 10,100. (also avail. in microform from UMI; reprint service avail. from UMI)
  —BLDSC (6117.346700). Faxon. **CCC.**

677 330.9 UK
NORTHERN IRELAND. DEPARTMENT OF ECONOMIC DEVELOPMENT. TEXTILES INDUSTRY TRAINING BOARD. REPORT AND FINANCIAL STATEMENTS. Cover title: Textiles Industry Training Board (Northern Ireland). Report and Financial Statements. a. £2.90. H.M.S.O. (N. Ireland), Chichester House, 64 Chichester St., Belfast BT1 4PS, N. Ireland. (Subscr. to: H.M.S.O. Publications Centre, P.O. Box 276, London SW8 5DT, England. TEL 0171-873-9090. FAX 0171-873-0011) charts; stat. **Document type:** corporate report, government publication.
  Formerly: Northern Ireland. Textiles Industry Training Board. Report and Statement of Accounts.

677 SP
NOTICIERO TEXTIL. 1983. 7/yr. 15000 ptas. includes supplement eds. (effective 1995). Astoria Ediciones S.L., Muntaner 40-42, 4o 3a, 08011 Barcelona, Spain. TEL 34-3-4517272. FAX 34-3-4543328. Ed. Jose Martin. circ. 5,500. **Document type:** trade publication.

677 SP
NOTICIERO TEXTIL (SUPPLEMENT). 1991. 20/yr. 15000 ptas. (subscr. includes main edition) (effective 1995). Astoria Ediciones, S.L., Muntaner, 40-42, 4o 3a, 08011 Barcelona, Spain. TEL 34-3-4517272. FAX 34-3-4543328. Ed. Jose Martin. circ. 5,500. **Document type:** trade publication.

677 IT ISSN 0391-6448
CODEN: NUSTES
NUOVA SELEZIONE TESSILE; mensile di tecnologie e sviluppi di fibre filati filatura ritorcitura tessitura nontessuti. (Supplement avail.: Nuova Selezione Tessile News) (Text in Italian) 1961; N.S. 1989. m. L.80000($135) Nuove Tecniche Editoriali S.r.l., Via San Siro 27, 20149 Milan, Italy. TEL 02-4812213. FAX 02-48193425. Ed. Tosca Bertolini. adv.; bk.rev.; bibl.; charts; illus.; index. circ. 6,500. (back issues avail.). **Indexed:** World Text.Abstr.
  —BLDSC (6184.920000); CASDDS; Ei.
  Formerly: Selezione Tessile (ISSN 0392-9809)
  Description: Features articles on the textile industry. Includes articles on textile texture, color, machinery and production.

677 FI ISSN 0029-6813
NYKYTEKSTIILI. 1954. m. FIM 510. Nykytekstiili Oy, Liisankatu 27 A 7, 00170 Helsinki 17, Finland. TEL 358-0-170028. FAX 358-0-135-5028. Ed. Monica Koskenranta. adv.; bk.rev.; illus.; mkt. circ. 6,600. (back issues avail.)

677 UK ISSN 1351-3176
O E REPORT AND FIBRE NEWS. 1976. bi-m. £50($100) (foreign £55($110)). Technical Industrial Services, 1 London Pl., New Mills, Stockport SK12 4ER, England. TEL 01663-742005. FAX 01663-747671. Ed. Peter Lennox-Kerr. bk.rev.; charts; illus. circ. 450. (back issues avail.) **Document type:** newsletter.
  Formerly (until 1993): O E Report (ISSN 0309-2097)

677 UK ISSN 0956-3792
OBZOR TEKSTIL'NOI PROMYSHLENNOSTI/TEXTILE REVIEW. (Text in Russian) 1987. q. £24($36) (effective 1995). Alain Charles Publishing Ltd., Alain Charles House, 27 Wilfred St., London SW1E 6PR, England. TEL 0171-834-7676. FAX 0171-973-0076. TELEX 297165 ACPLTD G. Ed. Zsa Tebbit. adv. contact: Sally Ann Hayes. circ. 5,500. circ. 6,500 (paid). (back issues avail.) **Document type:** trade publication.
  Formerly: Textile Review U S S R.
  Description: Aimed at senior management in textile mills, factories, ministries, and trade organizations throughout Russia and other former Soviet republics.

677 AU ISSN 0029-9545
OESTERREICHISCHE TEXTIL-MITTEILUNGEN; Unabhaengige Fachzeitung fuer die gesamte Textilwirtschaft. 1965. w. S.480. Verlag fuer Wirtschaftspraxis GmbH (Subsidiary of: Deutscher Fachverlag GmbH), Schrannengasse 4, Postfach 39, A-5027 Salzburg, Austria. TEL 0662-877108-9. FAX 0662-87710824. adv.; bk.rev. **Document type:** trade publication.

677 AU
OESTERREICHISCHE TEXTIL ZEITUNG. w. S.560. Johann L. Bondi und Sohn, Industriestr. 2, A-2380 Perchtoldsdorf, Austria. TEL 01-864921. FAX 01-86492144. adv. **Document type:** trade publication.

677 FR ISSN 0373-2010
OFFICIEL DES TEXTILES. q. B.P. 262, 3 rue de l'Arrivee, 75749 Paris Cedex 15, France. TEL 45-38-71-50. FAX 45-38-68-79. TELEX 203 630. Ed. Marc Mandel. adv. circ. 10,000.

677 GW ISSN 0931-0657
ORNAMENTE; Textiles Gestalten International. 1987. 5/yr. DM.80. Verlag M. und H. Schaper GmbH, Kalandstr. 4, 31061 Alfeld, Germany. TEL 05181-8009-0. FAX 05181-800933. (Subscr. to: Postfach 1642, 31046 Alfeld, Germany). **Document type:** trade publication.

PAKISTAN CENTRAL COTTON COMMITTEE. AGRICULTURAL SURVEY REPORT. see AGRICULTURE — Crop Production And Soil

PAKISTAN CENTRAL COTTON COMMITTEE. TECHNOLOGICAL BULLETIN. SERIES A. see AGRICULTURE — Crop Production And Soil

PAKISTAN CENTRAL COTTON COMMITTEE. TECHNOLOGICAL BULLETIN. SERIES B. see AGRICULTURE — Crop Production And Soil

677 PK
PAKISTAN TEXTILE. (Text in English) 1977. q. Rs.40. All Pakistan Textile Mills Association, Mohammadi House, 3rd Fl., I.I. Chundrigar Rd., Karachi 2, Pakistan. **Indexed:** World Text.Abstr.

677 PK ISSN 0048-2757
PAKISTAN TEXTILE JOURNAL. (Text in English) 1950. m. $80 to Asia & Europe; $95 to America & Australia. Mazhar Yusuf, Ed. & Pub., 304 Shaheen Centre, Kehkashan, Main Clifton Rd., Karachi, Pakistan. TEL 534792. FAX 572231. TELEX 25484-ITA-PK. adv.; bk.rev. circ. 2,200 (controlled). **Indexed:** Art & Archaeol.Tech.Abstr., Chem.Abstr., Text.Tech.Dig. **Document type:** trade publication.
  Description: Covers the textile industry from raw materials to finished goods, and well as ancillary products and services.

677 IT
PANORAMA FILATI E TESSUTI. 3/yr. Via Eupili 4, 20145 Milan, Italy. TEL 2-33-10-17-38. FAX 2-345-06-77. Ed. Paola Renate Riboldi. circ. 15,000.

PHILADELPHIA COLLEGE OF TEXTILES & SCIENCE. PORTFOLIO. see COLLEGE AND ALUMNI

677 746.92 SP
PINKER MODA. 1960. 11/yr. $120. Ediciones Tecnicas Doria, Avda. Puerta del Angel 7, Sobreat. A y B, 08002 Barcelona, Spain. TEL 34-3-3187489. FAX 34-3-3011105. Ed. Francisco Doria. adv.; bk.rev.; bibl.; illus.; stat.; tr.lit.; circ. 12,000. (controlled). **Document type:** trade publication.

677.21 GR ISSN 0032-0234
PIRAIKI-PATRAIKI. 1955. q. free. Piraiki-Patraiki Cotton Manufacturing Co. Inc., Dragatsaniou 8, 105 59 Athens, Greece. Ed. Haris Makrykostas. adv.; bk.rev.; charts; illus. circ. 10,000.

677 PL ISSN 0076-0331
CODEN: ZNLWAD
POLITECHNIKA LODZKA. ZESZYTY NAUKOWE. WLOKIENNICTWO. (Text in Polish; summaries in English and Russian) 1954. irreg. price varies. Wydawnictwo Politechniki Lodzkiej, Ul. Wolczanska 223, 93-005 Lodz, Poland. (Dist. by: Ars Polona-Ruch, Krakowskie Przedmiescie 7, Warsaw, Poland) Ed. Wlodzimierz Wiezlak. circ. 186. **Indexed:** Chem.Abstr., Text.Tech.Dig, World Text.Abstr. **Document type:** academic/scholarly publication.
  —BLDSC (9512.320900); CASDDS.
  Description: Spinning technology, synthetic fibers technology, weaving technology and fiber science.

677 NZ ISSN 0113-9746
PREMIER FIBRE NEWS. bi-m. NZ.$48($29) Fibre News Ltd., 130 Maunu Rd., P.O. Box 641, Whangare, New Zealand. TEL 64-9-4380335. adv.: B&W page NZ.$700; color page NZ.$1350; adv. contact: G. Minchin. circ. 8,000. (back issues avail.) **Document type:** trade publication.
  Former titles (until 1987): Fibre News (ISSN 0113-972X); New Zealand Mohair News (ISSN 0112-997X); (until 1986): N.Z. Mohair Journal (ISSN 0112-0492); (until 1982): Mohair Producers Association of New Zealand. Newsletter and Information Booklet.
  Description: Covers production and processing of goat fibre.

677 610 US
PROTECTIVE APPAREL CONFERENCE PAPERS. 1991. biennial. price varies. I N D A Association of the Nonwoven Fabrics Industry, 1001 Winstead Dr., Ste. 460, Cary, NC 27513. TEL 919-677-0060. FAX 919-677-0211. **Document type:** proceedings.
  Description: For the healthcare industry, manufacturers and suppliers in protective apparel.

677 PL ISSN 1230-0381
CODEN: PWTWEA
PRZEGLAD WLOKIENNICZY PLUS TECHNIK WLOKIENNICZY. (Text in Polish; summaries in English) 1992. m. $61. (Stowarzyszenie Wlokiennikow Polskich) Wydawnictwo Czasopism i Ksiazek Technicznych SIGMA - NOT, Ul. Ratuszowa 11, P.O. Box 1004, 00-950 Warsaw, Poland. TEL 48-22-180918. FAX 48-22-192187. TELEX 814550 SIGMA PL. (Dist. by: SIGMA NOT Ltd., Ul. Bartycka 20, 00-716 Warsaw, Poland) Ed. Jerzy Zakrzewski. adv.; bk.rev.; charts; illus.; pat.; stat. circ. 1,050. **Indexed:** Abstr.Bull.Inst.Pap.Chem., Chem.Abstr., Text.Tech.Dig, World Text.Abstr. **Document type:** trade publication.
  —BLDSC (6944.911000); CASDDS.
  Formed by the merger of (1947-1992): Przeglad Wlokienniczy (ISSN 0033-2410); (1929-1992): Technik Wlokienniczy (ISSN 0492-4851)
  Description: Covers textile industry, technology and machinery.

677 GW ISSN 0724-3847
PUNTO TECNICA Y MODA. English edition: Knitting Technology (ISSN 0947-0972); German edition: Maschen-Industrie (ISSN 0946-7718) (Text in Spanish) 1983. q. DM.114 (effective 1995). Meisenbach GmbH, Hainstr. 18, 96047 Bamberg, Germany. TEL 0951-861135. FAX 0951-861158. Ed. Lothar Rauscher. adv.: B&W page DM.2970, color page DM.5100; trim 270 x 180; adv. contact: Annelie Durniok. circ. 4,052. **Document type:** trade publication.

677.13 BG
QUARTERLY SUMMARY OF JUTE GOODS STATISTICS.* (Text in English) 1955. q. Tk.72. (Bangladesh Jute Industries Corp.) Bangladesh Jute Association, BJA Bldg., 137-Banga Bandhu Rd., P.O. Box 59, Narayanganj, Dhaka, Bangladesh.
  Formerly: Pakistan Jute Association. Monthly Summary of Jute Goods Statistics (ISSN 0027-0601)

677.2 IT
RAPPORTO SULLA INDUSTRIA COTONIERA ITALIANA. (Supplement to: Industria Cotoniera) a. free. Istituto per Assistenza e Servizi alle Aziende Tessili s.r.l. (I.A.S.A.T.), Viale Sarca, 223, 20126 Milan, Italy. TEL 39-2-66103838. FAX 39-2-66103863. Ed. Roberto Diegi. **Document type:** bulletin.

TEXTILE INDUSTRIES AND FABRICS

677 SP ISSN 0210-0800
CODEN: IITTCS
REVISTA DE LA INDUSTRIA TEXTIL. 1959. m. (10/yr.). 8500 ptas. (Camara de Directores y Mayordomos del Arte Textil) Revitextil, S.L., Cerdena 269, entlo. 2a, 08013 Barcelona, Spain. TEL 343-457-1220. Ed. Carlos Schneegluth Cugat. adv.; bk.rev.; bibl.; illus.; stat. circ. 6,000. Indexed: Ind.SST, World Text.Abstr.
—CASDDS. **CCC**.
Incorporates (1958-1992): Investigacion e Informacion Textil y de Tensioactivos (ISSN 0302-5268)

677 SP ISSN 0300-9718
RM1 CODEN: IJCPB5
REVISTA DE QUIMICA TEXTIL. 1966. q. 3000 ptas. Asociacion Espanola de Quimicos y Coloristas Textiles, Gran Via de Corts Catalanes, 670, 6, 08010 Barcelona, Spain. Ed. C. Schneegluth. adv.; bk.rev.; charts; illus. circ. 1,200. Indexed: Chem.Abstr., Ind.SST, World Text.Abstr.

677 BL ISSN 0035-0524
REVISTA TEXTIL. 1930. 6/yr. $200. (Primeira Escola de Tecelagem) R. da Silva Haydu & Cia. Ltda., Rua Parana 136, P.O. Box 10675, 03041-010 Sao Paulo, Brazil. TEL 55-11-270-9066. FAX 55-11-279-2409. TELEX 1124187. (Co-sponsor: Associacao de Tecnicos de Tecido Brasileiros) Ed. Ricardo da Silva Haydu. adv.; B&W page $1795, color page $2950; trim 200 x 280. bk.rev. circ. 10,000. Document type: trade publication, directory.
Description: Covers all sections of the textile industry, including machinery and equipment for spinning, weaving, knitting, printing, dyeing, and finishing processes.

677 US ISSN 1070-1796
T55.3.P75
SAFETY AND PROTECTIVE FABRICS. 1992. 4/yr. $24 (foreign $37). Industrial Fabrics Association International, 345 Cedar St., Ste. 800, St. Paul, MN 55101-1088. TEL 612-222-2500. FAX 612-222-8215. Ed. Jane Souba Jacobwith. circ. 6,000. Document type: trade publication.
Description: Educates specifiers and users about the benefits of and standards for protective clothing.

677 667 JA ISSN 0037-217X
CODEN: SNKAB2
SEN'I KAKO/DYEING & FINISHING. (Text in Japanese; summaries in English) 1949. m. Sen'i Kenkyusha, 4-26, Takanawa 1-chome, Minato-ku, Tokyo 108, Japan. Ed.Bd. adv.; charts; illus.; pat.; stat. circ. 26,500. Indexed: Art & Archaeol.Tech.Abstr., Chem.Abstr., Text.Tech.Dig.
—CASDDS.

677 JA ISSN 0371-0580
TS1300
SEN'I KIKAI GAKKAISHI. English edition: Textile Machinery Society of Japan. Journal (ISSN 0040-5043) (Text in Japanese) 1948-1965; N.S. 1972. m. 24180 Yen. Textile Machinery Society of Japan - Nihon Sen'i Kikai Gakkai, Osaka Science & Technology Center Bldg., Utsubo Koen, 8-4 Utsubo-Hon-machi 1-chome, Nishi-ku, Osaka 550, Japan. TEL 06-443-4691. Ed. S. Tanimura. circ. 8,000. Indexed: JTA, Text.Tech.Dig., World Text.Abstr. Document type: academic/scholarly publication.
—BLDSC (4908.499000); Ei.
First series (ISSN 0285-905X) was superseded by: Sen'i Kikai Gakkai Ronbunshi (Textile Machinery Society of Japan. Proceedings) (ISSN 0040-5051); and Sen'i Kogaku (Textile Machinery Society of Japan. Transactions) (ISSN 0040-506X); which merged in 1972 to form new series.

677 JA ISSN 0037-2072
TS1300 CODEN: SESKB9
SEN'I SEIHIN SHOHI KAGAKU/JAPAN RESEARCH ASSOCIATION FOR TEXTILE END-USES. JOURNAL. (Text in Japanese; summaries in English) 1960. m. 18460 Yen. Japan Research Association for Textile End-Uses - Nihon Sen'i Seihin Shohi Kagakkai, Rm. No. 201, Yoshin Ogimachi City Heights, 11-5, Doshin 2-chome, Kita-ku, Osaka 530, Japan. TEL 81-6-358-1441. FAX 81-6-358-1442. Ed. Seiei Tajimi. adv.; bk.rev.; charts; illus.; tr.lit.; index. circ. 6,000. Indexed: Art & Archaeol.Tech.Abstr., Chem.Abstr., JTA, Text.Tech.Dig., World Text.Abstr. Document type: academic/scholarly publication.
—BLDSC (4805.800000); CASDDS; Ei. **CCC**.

677 JA ISSN 0370-9574
CODEN: SEKOBF
SENSHOKU KOGYO/DYEING INDUSTRY. (Text in Japanese) 1953. m. 1250 Yen($220) Shikisensha Co., Ltd., 1-10, Tenjinbashi 7-chome, Oyodo-ku, Osaka-shi, Osaka 531, Japan. (Dist. by: Intercontinental Marketing Corp., I.P.O. Box 5056, Tokyo 100-30, Japan. TEL 81-3-3661-7458. FAX 81-3-3667-9646) Indexed: Chem.Abstr. Document type: trade publication.
—CASDDS.

677.39 UK ISSN 0266-0822
SERICA. 1970. s-m. £35. Silk Association of Great Britain, c/o Rheinbergs Ltd., Morley Rd., Tonbridge TN9 1RN, England. TEL 0732-351357. FAX 0732-770217. TELEX 95311. Ed. Leslie Rheinberg. circ. 150 (controlled). Document type: trade publication.
Description: Covers all aspects of silk and silk production.

677 IT
LA SETA. (Text in English or Italian; summaries in English, French, Italian) 1931. 3/yr. L.60000 (foreign L.100000). Stazione Sperimentale per la Seta, Via G. Colombo 81, 20133 Milan, Italy. TEL 39-2-2665990. FAX 39-2-2362788. Ed. Bruno Marcandalli. adv.; bk.rev.; abstr.; bibl.; charts; illus.; stat. circ. 1,000. (back issues avail.) Document type: academic/scholarly publication.
Description: Includes scientific and technological reports concerned with silk, protein, synthetic fibers and textiles.

677 CC ISSN 1001-2044
SHANGHAI FANGZHI KEJI/SHANGHAI TEXTILE SCIENCE AND TECHNOLOGY. (Text in Chinese) 1973. bi-m. Y18. Shanghai Fangzhi Kexue Yanjiuyuan - Shanghai Textile Research Institute, 545 Lazhou Lu, Shanghai 200082, People's Republic of China. TEL 021-5461341. FAX 86-021-5458418. TELEX 33365 STRI CN. Ed. Gu Boyuan. adv. circ. 7,000.

SHEEP! MAGAZINE; published for practical sheep farmers and ranchers. see AGRICULTURE — Poultry And Livestock

SHUTTLE CRAFT GUILD. MONOGRAPHS. see NEEDLEWORK

677 667 US ISSN 0049-0423
TT848
SHUTTLE, SPINDLE & DYEPOT. 1969. q. $25 (foreign $29). Handweavers Guild of America, 2402 University Ave., W., Ste. 702, Saint Paul, MN 55114-1701. TEL 612-646-0802. FAX 612-646-0806. Ed. Sandra Bowles. adv.; bk.rev.; illus. circ. 9,000. (also avail. in microform from UMI; reprint service avail. from UMI) Indexed: Art & Archaeol.Tech.Abstr., Art Ind., Ind.How To Do It (1978-), MELSA, Pinpointer, Text.Tech.Dig.
—BLDSC (8271.000000); Faxon; UMI; UnCover.

677.39 CC ISSN 1001-7003
SICHOU/SILK. (Text in Chinese) m. Zhongguo Sichou Xuehui, 121 Moganshan Lu, Hangzhou, Zhejiang 310011, People's Republic of China. TEL 881769. Ed. Sun Jinhui.

677.39 CC ISSN 1004-1265
SICHUAN SICHOU/SICHUAN SILK. (Text in Chinese) 1979. q. $40. (Sichuansheng Sichou Gongye Yanjiusuo - Sichuan Silk Manufacturing Research Institute) Sichuan Sichou Bianjibu, 33 Jinxianqiao Jie, Chengdu, Sichuan 610031, People's Republic of China. TEL 7768534. Ed. Zhao Lian. adv. contact: Wang Yuede. Document type: academic/scholarly publication.

677.39 382 II
SILK EXPORT BULLETIN. 1982. bi-m. (Central Silk Board) Bangalore Printing and Publishing Co. Ltd., 88 Mysore Rd., Bangalore 560 001, India. Ed. N. Nataraja. charts; illus.; stat. Document type: bulletin.

677 JA ISSN 0037-9875
CODEN: SENGA5
SOCIETY OF FIBER SCIENCE AND TECHNOLOGY, JAPAN. JOURNAL/SEN'I GAKKAISHI.* (Text in Japanese; summaries in English) 1944. m. $76. Society of Fiber Science and Technology - Sen'i Gakkai, c/o Japan Publications Trading Co., Box 5030, Tokyo International, Tokyo 100-31, Japan. Ed. Toshiyuki Uryu. adv.; bk.rev.; abstr.; bibl.; illus. circ. 5,000. Indexed: Art & Archaeol.Tech.Abstr., ASCA, Chem.Abstr., Excerpt.Med., JTA, Text.Tech.Dig., World Text.Abstr.
—BLDSC (3914.610000); CASDDS; Ei.

677 AT
SOFT FURNISHING TODAY. bi-m. Aus.$40. Furnishing Publications Pty. Ltd., 5 Faigh St., Mulgrave, Vic. 3170, Australia. TEL 03-562-5844. FAX 03-562-5412. Ed. Keith Dunn. adv.; charts; illus.; tr.lit. circ. 4,144. Document type: newsletter, trade publication.
Former titles: Domestic Textiles and Wallcoverings Trade Journal & Furnishing Textiles and Wallcoverings Trade Journal; Domestic Textiles and Wallcoverings Trade Journal.

677 US ISSN 0038-4607
SOUTHERN TEXTILE NEWS.* 1945. w. $15. Mullen Publications, Inc. (Charlotte), Box 241028, Charlotte, NC 28224. TEL 704-394-5111. Ed. Marjorie T. Richardson. adv.; illus.; mkt.; stat. circ. 7,200. (tabloid format; also avail. in microfilm) Indexed: Text.Tech.Dig.

377 IT ISSN 0394-8528
SPAZIO TESSILE. 10/yr. Via Villoresi 1, 20024 Garbagnate Milanese (MI), Italy. TEL 2-990-257-31. FAX 2-990-26-46-8. Ed. Marisa de Martiis. circ. 10,000.

677 UK ISSN 0950-5024
THE STOCKLISTS; for carpet and floorcovering buyers. 1975. m. £20.50. Mayville Publishing Co., Ltd., Mayville House, 142 Park Rd., Timperley, Altrincham, Cheshire WA15 6QT, England. Ed. Roy Spragg. adv. circ. 13,000.
Description: For those who buy floor coverings throughout Britain and Ireland.

STOCKLISTS COLOUR MAGAZINE. see INTERIOR DESIGN AND DECORATION — Furniture And House Furnishings

STUDIES IN TEXTILE AND COSTUME HISTORY. see HISTORY

677.2 SJ ISSN 0562-5033
SUDAN COTTON BULLETIN. (Text in English) 1960. m. Cotton Public Corporation, Department of Research and Statistics, Box 1672, Khartoum, Sudan. Ed.Bd. charts; stat. Document type: bulletin.

677 SZ
SURVEY ON COTTON CONTAMINATION, FOREIGN MATTER & STICKINESS. 1989. biennial. free. International Textile Manufacturers Federation, Am Schanzengraben 29, Postfach, CH-8039 Zurich, Switzerland. TEL 01-2017080. FAX 01-2017134. Document type: trade publication.

677.39 CC ISSN 1000-1999
SUZHOU SICHOU GONGXUEYUAN XUEBAO/SUZHOU INSTITUTE OF SILK ENGINEERING. JOURNAL. (Text in Chinese) q. Suzhou Sichou Gongxueyuan - Suzhou Institute of Silk Engineering, 14 Xiangmen Lu, Suzhou, Jiangsu 215005, People's Republic of China. TEL 225614. Ed. Wu Rongru.

677 US
SWATCHES. 1984. s-a. National Association of Decorative Fabric Distributors, 3008 Millwood Ave., Columbia, SC 29205. TEL 803-252-5646. adv.; circ. 17,000. (controlled).

T-SHIRT BUSINESS INFO MAPPING NEWSLETTER. see BUSINESS AND ECONOMICS — Small Business

677 FR ISSN 1161-9317
T U T. (Textiles a Usages Techniques); la revue des utilisateurs. (Text in French; summaries in English) 1991. q. 400 F. (foreign 460 F.) (effective Sep. 1995). Editions de l' Industrie Textile, 16 rue Ballu, 75311 Paris Cedex 09, France. TEL 48-74-15-96. FAX 48-74-01-89. Ed. Pierre S. Robin. adv. contact: Evelyne Merigot. illus.
—BLDSC (9076.170500).
Description: Directed to the end-users of technical material.

TEXTILE INDUSTRIES AND FABRICS

677 JA
T W A R O NEWS. m. Asian Regional Organisation of the International Textile, Garment and Leather Workers' Federation, Zeusen Kaikan Bldg. 8-16, Kudan Minami 4-chome, Chiyoda-ku, Tokyo, Japan. TEL 03-2655465.

677 GW ISSN 0082-1837
TASCHENBUCH DES TEXTILEINZELHANDELS. 1962. a. Deutscher Fachverlag GmbH, Mainzer Landstr. 251, 60326 Frankfurt a.M., Germany. TEL 069-7595-01. FAX 069-75952999. **Document type:** trade publication.

677 GW ISSN 0082-1896
TASCHENBUCH FUER DIE TEXTIL-INDUSTRIE. 1951. a. DM.64. Fachverlag Schiele und Schoen GmbH, Markgrafenstr. 11, 10969 Berlin, Germany. TEL 030-253752-0. FAX 030-2517248. Ed. W. Loy. adv. circ. 4,000. **Document type:** trade publication.

677 668.4 UK ISSN 0964-5993
TECHNICAL TEXTILES INTERNATIONAL. 1992. 10/yr. £121($193) (effective 1996). Elsevier Science Ltd., P.O. Box 800, Kidlington, Oxford OX5 1DX, England. TEL 44-1865-843000. FAX 44-1865-843010. E-mail: nlinfo-f@elsevier.nl; usinfo-f@elsevier.com; forinfo-kyf04035@niftyserve.or.jp; Site addr.: http://www.elsevier.nl/. (Subscr. in U.S. and Canada to: Elsevier Science, 660 White Plains Rd., Tarrytown, NY 10591-5153. TEL 914-524-9200. FAX 914-333-2444) Ed. N. Butler. (also avail. in microform from UMI; back issues avail.) **Document type:** trade publication, newsletter.
—BLDSC (8731.158000); Ei. **CCC**.
Description: Covers the latest developments in technical textiles and fiber-reinforced materials, from design to end-products, with analyses of industry trends and reports from major exhibitions and conferences.

677 GW
TECHNISCHE TEXTILIEN. (Text in English, German) 1958. q. DM.70 (foreign DM.79). Deutscher Fachverlag GmbH, Mainzer Landstr. 251, 60326 Frankfurt a.M., Germany. TEL 069-7595-01. FAX 069-75952999. circ. 5,000. **Document type:** trade publication.

677 SP ISSN 0040-1900
TECNICA TEXTIL INTERNACIONAL. 1957. m. 10000 ptas.($110) Ediciones Tecnicas Especializadas, Traversera de Gracia 15, 4, 08021 Barcelona, Spain. TEL 3-2097933. FAX 3-2096918. Ed. Juan B. Puig. adv.; bk.rev.; abstr.; bibl.; illus.; stat. circ. 7,500. (tabloid format; back issues avail.) **Indexed:** Ind.SST, Text.Tech.Dig.
Description: Covers the textile industry in Spain, Portugal and Latin America.

677 SP
TECNOFABRICS. q. 19000 ptas. Difusion Ediciones S.L., Rosellon 102, Entlo. 1a, 08029 Barcelona, Spain. TEL 3-323-57-02. FAX 3-323-60-80. Ed. Jordi Mullor. adv.: color page 125000 ptas. circ. 4,000. **Document type:** trade publication.

677 IT ISSN 0394-5413
TECNOLOGIE TESSILI. 1987. m. L.90000 (foreign L.180000) (effective 1995). Stammer S.p.A., Via della Liberazione 1, 20068 Peschiera Borromeo (MI), Italy. TEL 02-55302606. FAX 06-55302700. Ed. Girolamo Bellina. circ. 15,000.
—BLDSC (7993.451500).

677 IT
TECNORAMA TESSILI E ABBIGLIAMENTO. 2/yr. Pubblicita Edizioni Associati s.r.l., Via Simone d'Orsenigo 22, 20135 Milan, Italy. TEL 2-551-18-42. FAX 2-551-85-263. Ed. Ugo Carruti.

677 746.92 FI ISSN 0355-7898
TEKSI; the Finnish trade magazine for fashion. 1936. m. (9/yr.). FIM 430 in Finland; Scandinavia FIM 480; rest of Europe FIM 605. Tekstiilikauppiaiden Liitto r.y. - Association of the Finnish Textile Retailers, Mariankatu 26 B, SF-00170 Helsinki, Finland. TEL 358-0-135-1288. FAX 358-0-135-1384. Ed. Aimo Virtanen. adv.: B&W page FIM 8500, color page FIM 14300; trim 190 x 255; adv. contact: Marketta Hyotylainen. circ. 4,600. **Document type:** trade publication.
Formerly: Tekstiilikauppias.
Description: Covers the retail business, wholesale trade and textile industry in Finland.

677 FI ISSN 0040-2370
TEKSTIILILEHTI. 1937. 6/yr. FIM 280. Suomen Tekstiiliteknillinen Liitto r. y. - Textile-technical Association of Finland, Papinkatu 5 F 41, SF-33200 Tampere, Finland. FAX 359-31-120714. Ed. Clas Rosenberg. adv.; bk.rev.; charts; illus. circ. 2,000.

677 CI ISSN 0492-5882
CODEN: TEKTA6
TEKSTIL; savezni casopis za tekstilnu tehnologiju i konfekciju. (Text in Serbo-Croatian; abstracts in English and German) 1952. m. $30. Savez Inzenjera i Tehnicara Tekstilaca Hrvatske, Novakova 8-II, P.P. 829, Zagreb, Croatia. TEL 041 276-671. Eds. Dragutin Hoffer, Dinko Pezelj. **Indexed:** Art & Archaeol.Tech.Abstr., Bull.Signal., Chem.Abstr., Cott.& Trop.Fibr.Abstr., Ref.Zh., Text.Tech.Dig., World Text.Abstr.
—BLDSC (8779.000000); CASDDS; Genuine Article.

677 TU
TEKSTIL VE MUHENDIS. (Text and summaries in English, French, German, Turkish) 1987. bi-m. TL.90000($60) Chamber of Mechanical Engineers - T M M O B Makina Muhendisleri Odasi, Elmasbahceler Mah., Sabunevi Sok., Muhendislar Ishani No. 19, Kat 1, 16230 Bursa, Turkey. TEL 90-24-121190. FAX 90-24-121194. Ed. Yusuf Unler. adv.; bk.rev.; index. circ. 6,000. (back issues avail.)
Formerly (until 1991): Tekstil ve Makina.
Description: Covers raw materials, spinning, preparing, weaving, knitting, dyeing, printing, finishing, testing and quality control, clothing, marketing and other subjects.

677 TU
TEKSTIL & TEKNIK; tekstil ihtisas dergisi - specialist textile magazine. (Text in Turkish, summaries in Arabic, English, Russian) 1985. m. TL.3400000($100) Ihlas Holding A.S., Catalcesme Sok. No. 17, 34410 Cagaloglu - Istanbul, Turkey. TEL 90-212-5138720. FAX 90-212-5140650. Ed. Hyatai Inanc; Pub. Ferruh Isik. adv. contact: Mucahit Unlu. illus. circ. 15,750. **Document type:** trade publication.
Description: Reports on technical and commercial developments affecting the textile industry in Turkey, with special emphasis on exports of textiles.

677 500 XV ISSN 0351-3386
TEKSTILEC; glasilo slovenskih tekstilcev. (Text in Slovenian; summaries in English and German) 1957. m. $40. (Splosno Zdruzenje Tekstilne Industrije Slovenije - General Association of Slovene Textile Industry) Urednictvo Tekstilec, Snezniska 5, p.p. 311, 61000 Ljubljana, Slovenia. TEL 61 224-417. Ed. Anica Levin. adv.; bk.rev.; abstr.; illus.; stat.; index. circ. 3,000. (back issues avail.) **Indexed:** World Text.Abstr. **Document type:** trade publication.
●Also available online. Vendor(s): Knight-Ridder, Inc.
—BLDSC (8779.050000).
Description: Publishes original reports on textile development and research; news from all textile, mechanical and chemical technologies; trade in ready-made clothes and design; and information on the Slovenian textile industry.

677 659.152 NO ISSN 0332-5520
TEKSTILFORUM. 1931. 12/yr. NOK 460. Norges Tekstilforbund - Norwegian Textile Retailers Association, P.O. Box 2590, Solli, N-0203 Oslo, Norway. TEL 47-22-55-74-30. FAX 47-22-55-28-88. Eds. Live Nordby, Anna Therese Klingstedt. adv. contact: Bror Stende. bk.rev.; charts;.; illus. circ. 5,000. **Document type:** trade publication.
Former titles (until 1973): Manufaktur (ISSN 0025-259X).

677 YU ISSN 0040-2389
CODEN: TKIDBP
TEKSTILNA INDUSTRIJA. 1953. 6/yr. 1200 din. Savez Inzenjera i Tehnicara Tekstilaca SR Srbije, Kneza Milosa 7-II, 11000 Belgrade, Serbia, Yugoslavia. Ed. Branko Ilic. adv.; bk.rev.; index. circ. 2,600. **Indexed:** Chem.Abstr.
—CASDDS.

677 BU
TEKSTILNA PROMISHLENOST.* 1952. 10/yr. $22. Ministry of Industry, Trade and Services, Ul. Slovyanska 8, Sofia, Bulgaria. (Dist. by: Hemus, 6, Rouski Blvd., 1000 Sofia, Bulgaria) (Co-sponsor: Nauchno- Tekhnicheski Suiuz po Tekstil i Obleklo) Ed. A. Chervendinev. circ. 3,700. **Indexed:** Chem.Abstr., Text.Tech.Dig., World Text.Abstr.

677 RU ISSN 0040-2397
TS1300 CODEN: TTLPA2
TEKSTIL'NAYA PROMYSHLENNOST'. 1941. m. $103 (effective 1996). Ministerstvo Legkoi Promyshlennosti, Moscow, Russia. (Subscr. to: Mezhdunarodnaya Kniga, Moscow G-200, Russia) Ed. G.I. Pikovskii. adv.; bk.rev.; bibl.; charts; illus.; pat.; tr.lit. circ. 11,500. **Indexed:** Abstr.Bull.Inst.Pap.Chem., Biol.Abstr., Chem.Abstr, Cott.&Trop.Fibr.Abstr., Text.Tech.Dig., World Text.Abstr.
—BLDSC (0177.000000); CASDDS.

660 UK
TEX-FAX. d. £1200($2200) (effective 1994). Benjamin Dent & Co. Ltd. (Subsidiary of: I T B D Publications), 23 Bloomsbury Sq., London WC1A 2PJ, England. TEL 0171-637-2211. FAX 0171-637-2248. TELEX 8954884 BENDEN G. (avail. only by fax) **Document type:** bulletin.

677 BE ISSN 0770-6014
TS1300
TEX-TEXTILIS; technisch - wetenschappelijk maandblad voor de Benelux textielindustrie. (Text in Dutch and French) 1945. bi-m. 750 BEF. (National Organization for Textile Engineers and Directors) Drukkerij-Uitgeverij Vyncke, Brusselpoortstr. 10, B-2800 Mechelen, Belgium. (Co-sponsor: Dutch Textile Institute) Ed. Daniel Vyncke. adv.; bk.rev.; bibl.; charts; illus.; stat.; index. circ. 2,500. **Indexed:** Chem.Abstr., Excerp.Med., Text.Tech.Dig., World Text.Abstr. **Document type:** trade publication.
Formerly: Textilis (ISSN 0040-5280).

677 746.92 BE
TEXBEL (EDITION FRANCAISE). Dutch edition (ISSN 0770-6995) 1970. m. 1650 BEF. Diligentia Business Press, N.V., 42 av. du Houx, 1170 Brussels, Belgium. TEL 32-2-6781611. FAX 32-2-6603600. TELEX BELBUSS 23830. Ed. Chris Vermuyten; Pub. Robert Verbeek. adv. contact: Annika Lens. circ. 13,000. **Document type:** trade publication.

677 746 BE ISSN 0770-6995
TEXBEL (NEDERLANDSE EDITIE). French edition (ISSN 0770-7045) 1970. m. 1650 BEF. Diligentia Business Press, N.V., 42 av. du Houx, 1170 Brussels, Belgium. TEL 32-2-6781611. FAX 32-2-6603600. Ed. Chris Vermuyten; Pub. Robert Verbeek. adv. contact: Annika Lens. **Document type:** trade publication.

677 II ISSN 0970-5686
TEXINCON. Variant title: Textile Information Condensed. (Text in English) 1989. q. Rs.400 (foreign $50 or £25). National Information Centre for Textile and Allied Subjects, 3rd Fl., Atira, P.O. Polytechnic, Ahmedabad 380 015, India. FAX 91-079-429874. TELEX 121-6571 ATRA IN. E-mail: PCS@nictas-ernet-in. adv.; bk.rev.; abstr. circ. 1,000. (also avail. in diskette format) **Document type:** abstracting/indexing.
Description: Contains specialized articles and summaries of recent developments and publications of interest to persons in the textile industry.

677 NE ISSN 0040-4772
TEXPRESS; economic and technical weekly for the textile and clothing industry and trade in the Benelux countries. 1957. w. fl.260 (foreign fl.330). V N U Business Publications B.V., Postbus 9194, 1006 AC Amsterdam, Netherlands. TEL 31-20-5102911. FAX 31-20-6176781. Ed. J.G. Post. adv.: B&W page fl.6485, color page fl.9975; trim 313 x 472. bk.rev.; charts; illus.; mkt.; tr.lit. circ. 3,000. (tabloid format) **Indexed:** Key to Econ.Sci. **Document type:** trade publication.

6278 TEXTILE INDUSTRIES AND FABRICS

677.3   SA
TEXREPORT. 1952. irreg. $60 per no. C S I R - Division of Textile Technology, Box 1124, Port Elizabeth 6000, South Africa. TEL 27-41-532131. FAX 27-41-532325. E-mail: pitout@textek.csir.co.za. Ed. P. Horn. circ. 250. (back issues avail.; reprint service avail.) Indexed: Text.Tech.Dig., World Text.Abstr. **Document type:** academic/scholarly publication.
     Formerly (until 1989): S A W T R I Technical Report (ISSN 0081-2560)
     Description: Publishes fundamental applied research findings and reports on technology development affecting textiles and clothing.

338.4   US   ISSN 0092-3540
HD9853
TEXSCOPE: U S A TEXTILE INDUSTRY OVERVIEW. Key Title: Texscope (New York). 1974. irreg., latest 1983. Werner Management Consultants, Inc., 111 W. 40th St., New York, NY 10018. TEL 212-730-1280. Ed. Mary Scannapield. stat. circ. controlled.

677   NE
TEXTIELHISTORISCHE BIJDRAGEN. 1959. a., vol.34, 1994. 25. (Stichting Textielgeschiedenis) Uitgeverij Verloren, Larenseweg 123, 1221 CL Hilversum, Netherlands. TEL 31-35-6859856. FAX 31-35-6836557. Ed. E.J. Fischer. bk.rev. circ. 600. **Document type:** academic/scholarly publication.

677   NE   ISSN 0168-9940
TEXTIELVISIE; vakblad voor de textielbranche. 1963. 14/yr. fl.159.50. (Nederlandse Vereniging van Ondernemers in de Textielhandel (MITEX)) Misset (Subsidiary of: Reed Elsevier plc), Postbus 4, 7000 BA Doetinchem, Netherlands. TEL 31-8340-49911. FAX 31-8340-63638. Ed. Steffen van Beek. adv.; B&W page fl.2990, color page fl.5790; trim 230 x 300; adv. contact: Cor van Nek. circ. 9,940. Indexed: Key to Econ.Sci. **Document type:** trade publication.
     Former titles (until 1983): Textiel-Visie - Weekly (Amsterdam) (ISSN 0040-4810); Groothandel Weekly; Incorporates (1979-1982): Textiel-Visie. Damesmode (ISSN 0167-3483); (1979-1982): Textiel-Visie. Herenmode (ISSN 0167-353X)
     Description: Covers all sectors of the textile fashion business in the Netherlands.

677   XR   ISSN 0040-4829
TEXTIL/TEXTILE; odborny casopis pro textilni a odevni vyrobu. (Text in Czech; summaries in English, German, Russian) 1945. m. $43.80. A D V sporl. s r o., Cerna 4, 110 00 Prague 1, Czech Republic. (Dist. by: Artia, Ve Smeckach 30, 111 27 Prague 1, Czech Republic) Ed. Dimitrij Halkov. adv.; bk.rev.; illus.; pat.; index, cum.index. circ. 4,900. Indexed: C.I.S. Abstr.
—BLDSC (8800.800000).

677   VE
TEXTIL. 1976. q. Instituto de Capacitacion Textil, Avenida Urdaneta, Ibarra a Pilota, Edificio Karam, Piso 4, 403-406, Apdo. 2173, Caracas 101, Venezuela. Indexed: Text.Tech.Dig.

381.456 677   DK   ISSN 0040-4837
TEXTIL. 1935. s-a. DKK 749. (Dansk Textilunion) Specialbladsforlaget, Finsensvej 80, DK-2000 Frederiksberg, Denmark. TEL 45-38-88-32-22. FAX 45-38-88-30-38. (Textil og Beklaednigsindustrien) Ed. Lisbeth Wirgowitsch. circ. 6,880.

677   GW   ISSN 0492-9934
TEXTIL-BEKLEIDUNG. 1950. m. Gewerkschaft Textile-Bekleidung, Rossstr. 94, 40476 Duesseldorf, Germany. TEL 43091. TELEX 584365. **Document type:** trade publication.

677   SP
TEXTIL EXPRES NOTICIAS. 1983. 20/yr. 18000 ptas. (effective 1995). Aramo Editorial, S.A., Muntaner 60, 2o 2a, 08011 Barcelona, Spain. TEL 3-453-79-38. FAX 3-323-79-26. Ed. Humberto Martinez. adv. circ. 2,000. **Document type:** newsletter.
     Description: Contains economic and professional news in the textile industry. Includes information for the professional and trade personnel in the textile and garment industries.

677   SP
TEXTIL EXPRES SUPLEMENTOS. 1985. 5/yr. Aramo Editorial, S.A., Muntaner 60 2o 2a, 08011 Barcelona, Spain. TEL 3-453-79-38. FAX 3-323-79-26. Ed. Humberto Martinez. adv.; circ. 4,500 (controlled). **Document type:** trade publication.

677   GW   ISSN 0082-3627
DIE TEXTIL-INDUSTRIE UND IHRE HELFER. 1957. a. $51. Industrieschau-Verlagsgesellschaft mbH, Postfach 100262, 64202 Darmstadt, Germany. TEL 06151-3892-0. FAX 06151-33164. (U.S. subscr. to: Western Hemisphere Publishing Corp., Box 847, Hillsboro, OR 97123-0847. TEL 503-640-3736. FAX 503-640-2748) Ed. Margit Selka. circ. 3,500. **Document type:** directory.
● Also available online.
Also available on CD-ROM.

677   GW   ISSN 0342-2224
TEXTIL MITTEILUNGEN; mit dem Wirtschaftsblatt Branche und Business. 1946. w. DM.277.50. Branche und Business Fachverlag, Koenigsallee 70, 40212 Duesseldorf, Germany. TEL 0211-132375. FAX 0211-324862. circ. 35,000. (looseleaf format)

677   SZ   ISSN 0040-4861
TEXTIL-REVUE. (Text in German) 1921. 41/yr. 162 SFr. (foreign 206 SFr.). Zollikofer AG, Fuerstenlandstr. 122, CH-9001 St. Gallen, Switzerland. TEL 071-297777. FAX 071-297384. Ed.Bd. adv.; illus. circ. 7,000. Indexed: Key to Econ.Sci. **Document type:** trade publication.
     Formed by the merger of: Schweizer Textil-Zeitung; Schweizerische Textildetaillisten-Zeitung.

677   GW   ISSN 0040-487X
TEXTIL-WIRTSCHAFT. 1946. w. DM.398.50 (foreign DM.541.50). Deutscher Fachverlag GmbH, Mainzer Landstr. 251, 60326 Frankfurt a.M., Germany. TEL 069-759501. FAX 069-75952999. Ed. Joerg Hintz. adv.; bk.rev.; charts; illus.; mkt.; pat.; tr.lit.; tr.mk.; index. circ. 43,271. Indexed: PROMT. **Document type:** trade publication.

TEXTIL ZURNAL. see CLOTHING TRADE

677   US
TEXTILE ARTISTS' NEWSLETTER; a journal of the textile arts & history. 1978. q. $9. Textile Artists' Supply, 3006 San Pablo Ave., Berkeley, CA 94702. TEL 415-548-9988. Ed. Susan C. Druding. adv.; bk.rev.; charts; illus.; stat. circ. 1,500. (tabloid format) **Document type:** newsletter.

677   HK   ISSN 0049-3554
TS1399   CODEN: TASIDM
TEXTILE ASIA. 1970. m. HK.$398 in Hong Kong; Macao & China HK.$475; elsewhere $95 (effective 1995). Business Press Ltd., California Tower, 11-F, 30-32 d'Aguilar St., P.O. Box 185, Central, Hong Kong. TEL 5233744. FAX 8106966. TELEX 60275-TEXIA-HX. Ed. Kayser Sung. adv.; bk.rev.; charts; illus.; stat.; index. circ. 15,700. Indexed: Cott.& Trop.Fibr.Abstr., Text.Tech.Dig., World Text.Abstr. **Document type:** trade publication.
—BLDSC (8801.730000); CASDDS; Ei; UnCover.

677   II   ISSN 0368-4636
TS1300   CODEN: JTXAA9
TEXTILE ASSOCIATION (INDIA). JOURNAL. (Text in English) 1940. bi-m. Rs.150($75) Textile Association (India), Central Office, 72-A, Dr. M.B. Raut Rd., Shivaji Park, Dadar, Bombay 400 028, India. TEL 461145. Ed. M.D. Teli. adv.: B&W page Rs.2000, color page Rs.6500; 175 x 230. bk.rev. circ. 10,000. Indexed: Chem.Abstr., Cott.& Trop.Fibr.Abstr., Indian Sci.Abstr., Text.Tech.Dig., World Text.Abstr. **Document type:** academic/scholarly publication.
—BLDSC (4907.900000); CASDDS.
     Formerly (until 1971): Textile Digest.

677 667   US   ISSN 0040-490X
                         CODEN: TCCOB6
TEXTILE CHEMIST AND COLORIST. (Annual Buyer's Guide avail.) 1969. m. $40 to non-members (foreign $55). American Association of Textile Chemists and Colorists, One Davis Dr., Box 12215, Research Triangle Park, NC 27709-2215. TEL 919-549-8141. FAX 919-549-8933. Ed. Susan H. Keesee. adv.: B&W page $2070, color page $2420; trim 8 1/4 x 11 1/4. bk.rev.; bibl.; charts; illus.; index, cum.index. circ. 10,300. (also avail. in microform from UMI; reprint service avail. from UMI) Indexed: Abstr.Bull.Inst.Pap.Chem., ASCA, Chem.Abstr., Eng.Ind., Excerp.Med., Text.Tech.Dig., World Text.Abstr. **Document type:** academic/scholarly publication.
—BLDSC (8801.770000); CASDDS; Ei; Faxon; Genuine Article; SWETS; UMI; UnCover. **CCC**.
     Description: Contains current news and features on all phases of textile wet processing plus reporting on AATCC activities.
     Refereed Serial

677   II   ISSN 0040-4926
TP890   CODEN: TDYPAN
TEXTILE DYER AND PRINTER. (Text in English) 1967. fortn. Rs.50($35) Sevak Publications, 306 Shri Hanuman Industrial Estate, G.D. Ambekar Rd., Post Box No. 7110, Wadala, Bombay 400 031, India. Ed. Ravi Raghavan; Pub. N.R. Rajagoplan. adv.; charts; illus.; stat. circ. 4,500. Indexed: Art & Archaeol.Tech.Abstr., Chem.Abstr., Text.Tech.Dig., World Text.Abstr. **Document type:** trade publication.
—BLDSC (8801.930000); CASDDS; Ei.

677 700   AT   ISSN 0818-6308
TEXTILE FIBRE FORUM; the fibre magazine of the Australian region. 1981. 3/yr. Aus.$18($14) Australian Forum for Textile Arts Ltd., P.O. Box 38, Gap, Qld. 4061, Australia. TEL 07-300-6491. Ed. Janet De Boer. adv.; bk.rev.; index. circ. 7,200. Indexed: DAAI.
—UnCover.
     Formerly: Fibre Forum (ISSN 0725-9565)

677   GW
TEXTILE FORUM. (Text in English, German) 1982. q. DM.80. (European Textile Network) Textilwerkstatt Verlag, Postfach 5944, 30059 Hannover, Germany. TEL 0511-817007. FAX 0511-813108. Ed. Beatrijs Sterk. adv. contact: Beatrijs Sterk. bk.rev. circ. 6,000. **Document type:** trade publication.
     Former titles (until 1994): Textilforum (ISSN 0937-9797); (until 1990): Deutsches Textilforum (ISSN 0722-1258)

677   US   ISSN 0040-4950
HD9851
TEXTILE HI-LIGHTS. 1938. q. $75 (foreign $100) (effective 1995). American Textile Manufacturers Institute, Inc., 1801 K St., N.W., Ste. 900, Washington, DC 20006-1301. TEL 202-862-0500. FAX 202-862-0570. TELEX 710-822-9489. Ed. Amelia Malloy. circ. 2,500. (also avail. in microform; back issues avail.) **Document type:** trade publication.
     Description: Reports economic, statistic and trade information on the American manufacturing and textile industries.

677   UK   ISSN 0040-4969
HD9850.1
TEXTILE HISTORY.* 1968. 2/yr. £12 to individuals; institutions £24. W.S. Maney & Son Ltd., Hudson Rd., Leeds LS9 7DL, England. Ed. S.D. Chapman. adv.; bk.rev.; bibl.; charts; illus.; stat.; index. (back issues avail.) Indexed: Art & Archaeol.Tech.Abstr., Artbibl.Mod., Avery Ind.Archit.Per., Br.Archaeol.Abstr., Br.Hum.Ind., RILA, Text.Tech.Dig., World Text.Abstr.
—BLDSC (8801.990000); SWETS; UnCover. **CCC**.

TEXTILE INDUSTRIES AND FABRICS

677 660 UK ISSN 1353-6184
HD9850.1
TEXTILE HORIZONS; providing essential reading for all present and future decision makers in textiles and fashion worldwide. bi-m. £65($180) to non-members (foreign £95) (effective 1995). (Textile Institute) Benjamin Dent & Co. Ltd. (Subsidiary of: I T B D Publications), 23 Bloomsbury Sq., London WC1A 2PJ, England. TEL 0171-637-2211. FAX 0171-637-2248. TELEX 8954884 BENDEN G. (N. American subscr. to: Box 1897, Lawrence, KS 66044-8897) Ed. John Gibbon. adv.; bk.rev.; bibl.; charts; illus.; stat.; index. circ. 9,000. **Indexed:** Abstr.Bull.Inst.Pap.Chem., Appl.Mech.Rev., Art & Archaeol.Tech.Abstr., Br.Tech.Ind., Chem.Abstr., Curr.Cont., Excerp.Med., PROMT, Text.Tech.Dig., World Text.Abstr. **Document type:** trade publication.
—BLDSC (8801.992000); Ei; SWETS; UnCover.
Former titles (until 1994): Textile Horizons International (ISSN 1351-0266); (until 1991): Textile Horizons (ISSN 0260-6518); Textile Institute and Industry (ISSN 0039-8257)
Description: Caters to the professional needs of persons concerned with the management, economics, design, research, and production aspects of the textiles industry.

677 II ISSN 0970-6887
TEXTILE INDIA PROGRESS; monthly devoted to entire textile sector. (Text in English) 1964. m. Rs.300. Eastern Press Services (India), Asheerabad, 3-49 East Sion, Bombay 400 022, India. TEL 91-22-4072913. FAX 91-22-4077885. Ed. Raju V. Chandran. adv.: B&W page £1000, color page £2500; trim 250 x 180. bk.rev.; illus. circ. 20,000. **Document type:** trade publication.
Formerly: Textile India (ISSN 0040-4977)

677 SA
TEXTILE INDUSTRIES BUYERS GUIDE FOR SOUTHERN AFRICA. (Text in English) 1985. a. R.100. George Warman Publications (Pty.) Ltd., P.O. Box 3847, Cape Town 8000, South Africa. TEL 27-21-245320. FAX 27-21-261-332. Ed. Tony Walker. **Document type:** trade publication.
Description: Guide for buyers of textiles, yarns, textile machinery, and consumables.

677 SA ISSN 0254-0533
CODEN: TIDADD
TEXTILE INDUSTRIES DYEGEST SOUTHERN AFRICA. (Text in English) 1982. m. R.96. (Textile Institute - South Africa) George Warman Publications (Pty.) Ltd., Box 3847, Cape Town 8000, South Africa. TEL 27-21-245320. FAX 27-21-26.1332. Ed. Tony Walker. adv.; illus. **Indexed:** Ind.S.A.Per., Text.Tech.Dig., World Text.Abstr. **Document type:** trade publication.
—BLDSC (8802.105000); CASDDS.
Formed by the merger of (1972-1981): Dyers Dyegest (ISSN 0250-0019); (1978-1981): Textile Industries Southern Africa (ISSN 1013-8587)
Description: Technical journal of spinning, weaving, knitting and yarn preparation, dyeing and textile finishing.

677 UK ISSN 0040-5000
TS1300 CODEN: JTINA7
TEXTILE INSTITUTE. JOURNAL. 1910. q. £105($180) Textile Institute, 10 Blackfriars St., Manchester M3 5DR, England. TEL 0161-834-8457. FAX 0161-835-3087. TELEX 668297 TEXINS G. (Subscr. in U.S. and Canada to: Box 1897, Lawrence KS 66044-8897) Ed. J.W.S. Hearle. abstr.; bibl.; illus.; index, cum.index. circ. 3,700. **Indexed:** Abstr.Bull.Inst.Pap.Chem., Appl.Mech.Rev., Art & Archaeol.Tech.Abstr., Biol.Abstr., Br.Tech.Ind., Chem.Abstr., Curr.Cont., Curr.Leather Lit., Eng.Ind., Excerp.Med., Intl.Polym.Sci.& Tech., RAPRA, Text.Tech.Dig., World Text.Abstr. **Document type:** trade publication.
—BLDSC (4908.000000); CASDDS; Faxon; Genuine Article; SWETS; UnCover.

677 UK
TEXTILE INSTITUTE. WORLD CONFERENCE. a. £75($150) Textile Institute, 10 Blackfriars St., Manchester M3 5DR, England. TEL 0161-834-8457. FAX 0161-835-3087. TELEX 668297 TEXINS G. bibl.; charts; illus.; stat. **Indexed:** World Text.Abstr. **Document type:** proceedings.
Formerly: Textile Institute. Annual Conference.

677 JA ISSN 0082-366X
TEXTILE JAPAN/TEKISUTAIRU JAPAN.* (Text in English) 1957. a. $12. Nihon Sen'i Shinbunsha, 13-12, Nihonbashi Muromachi 1-chome, Chuo-ku, Tokyo 103, Japan. Ed.Bd.

677 331 US
TEXTILE LABOUR COST COMPARISON - INTERNATIONAL. 1950. a. Werner International, 111 W. 40th St., New York, NY 10018. TEL 212-642-6092. FAX 212-642-6084. Ed. Mary T. O'Rourke. stat. (looseleaf format; back issues avail.) **Document type:** trade publication.
Description: Covers the annual textile industry spinning and weaving labor costs. Includes international comparisons of hourly wages, shift premiums, holidays, and social changes.

677 SZ ISSN 1016-7536
TEXTILE LEADER. Key Title: I T S Textile Leader. (Text in English) s-a. 80 SFr. in Europe; rest of world $80. I T S Publishing, International Textile Service, Kesslerstr. 9, CH-8952 Schlieren, Switzerland. TEL 01-7305853. FAX 01-7305902. TELEX 82758-ITS-CH. Ed. Eugene Dempsey; Pub. Rosmarie Keller. adv. contact: Peter Frei. **Document type:** trade publication.
—BLDSC (8803.300000).

677 II ISSN 0040-5035
TEXTILE MACHINERY; accessories & stores. (Text in English) 1965. bi-m. Rs.30. Chary Publications, 14 Sidh Prasad, Ghatkopar Mahul Rd., Tilak Nagar, Bombay 400089, India. Ed. S.T. Chary. adv.; charts; illus.; stat. circ. 4,000. **Indexed:** Art & Archaeol.Tech.Abstr.

677 JA ISSN 0040-5043
TS1300 CODEN: JTMJAF
TEXTILE MACHINERY SOCIETY OF JAPAN. JOURNAL. Key Title: Journal of the Textile Machinery Society of Japan. Japanese edition: Sen'i Kikai Gakkaishi (ISSN 0371-0580) (Text in English) 1955. q. 8670 Yen. Textile Machinery Society of Japan - Nihon Sen'i Kikai Gakkai, Osaka Science & Technology Center Bldg., Utsubo Koen, 8-4 Utsubo-Hon-machi, 1-chome, Nishi-ku, Osaka 550, Japan. TEL 06-443-4691. Ed. K. Nakamura. adv.; bk.rev.; charts; illus. circ. 4,000. **Indexed:** Art & Archaeol.Tech.Abstr., Chem.Abstr., Eng.Ind., JTA, Text.Tech.Dig., World Text.Abstr. **Document type:** academic/scholarly publication.
—BLDSC (4908.500000); Genuine Article.

677 II ISSN 0040-5078
TS1300
TEXTILE MAGAZINE. (Text in English) 1959. m. Rs.150. (Textile Mills and Manufacturing Association) Gopali & Co., 407-408 Mount Rd., Madras 600 035, India. TEL 044-452892. FAX 044-457579. Ed. R. Kalidasan. bk.rev. circ. 15,000. **Indexed:** Key to Econ.Sci., Text.Tech.Dig.
—BLDSC (8803.790100).

677 US ISSN 1065-1713
TEXTILE MANUFACTURING; the journal of manufacturing technology. 1988. bi-m. $30 (foreign $42). Merit Publications, Inc., 12 Perimeter Park Dr., Ste. 102, Atlanta, GA 30341-1322. TEL 404-451-4990. Ed. Earl G. Whited. adv.; illus. circ. 18,250. **Document type:** trade publication.
Description: For textile plant managers, engineers and department managers.

677 UK ISSN 0040-5116
TS1300 CODEN: TXMOAW
TEXTILE MONTH. 1968. m. £70 (foreign £115). World Textile Publications Ltd., 76 Kirkgate, Bradford, W. Yorkshire BD1 1TB, England. TEL 01274-726358. FAX 01274-735045. Ed. P. Owen. adv.; bk.rev.; illus.; mkt.; tr.lit.; index. circ. 8,016. **Indexed:** Art & Archaeol.Tech.Abstr., Br.Tech.Ind., Chem.Abstr., Cott.& Trop.Fibr.Abstr., Excerp.Med., Key to Econ.Sci., PROMT, Text.Tech.Dig., World Text.Abstr. **Document type:** trade publication.
—BLDSC (8805.018000); CASDDS; Ei; Faxon; Genuine Article; SWETS; UMI.
Incorporates: Skinner's Record of the Manmade Fibres Industry; Man-Made Textiles; Textile Recorder.

TEXTILE MUSEUM BULLETIN. see MUSEUMS AND ART GALLERIES

677 700 US ISSN 0083-7407
NK8802.W3
TEXTILE MUSEUM JOURNAL. 1962. a. $15. Textile Museum, 2320 S St., N.W., Washington, DC 20008. TEL 202-667-0441. FAX 202-483-0994. Ed. Carol Bier. cum. index (1962-1992). circ. 3,000. **Indexed:** Anthropol.Lit., Art & Archaeol.Tech.Abstr., Art Ind., Artbibl.Mod., World Text.Abstr. **Document type:** academic/scholarly publication.
—BLDSC (8805.300000); Faxon.
Supersedes: Workshop Notes Washington, D.C. Textile Museum.
Description: Forum for original research on artistic and technical processes and the role of textiles in their historic and cultural contexts. Areas represented are: Near East, Central, South and Southeast Asia, and South and Central America.
Refereed Serial

677 II ISSN 0040-5124
TEXTILE NEWS. (Text in English) 1968. m. Rs.40. L. K. Pandeya, Ed. & Pub., Block F, 105c New Alipore, Calcutta 700053, India. **Indexed:** PROMT.

TEXTILE NEWSLETTER. see OCCUPATIONAL HEALTH AND SAFETY

677 UK ISSN 0040-5167
TS1300 CODEN: TXPRAM
TEXTILE PROGRESS. 1969. q. £60($105) (effective 1996). Textile Institute, 10 Blackfriars St., Manchester M3 5DR, England. TEL 0161-834-8457. FAX 0161-835-3087. TELEX 668297 TEXINS G. Ed. D.R. Buchanan. bibl.; charts; illus.; index. circ. 2,300. **Indexed:** Abstr.Bull.Inst.Pap.Chem., Chem.Abstr., Text.Tech.Dig., World Text.Abstr. **Document type:** trade publication.
—BLDSC (8805.700000); Ei; Genuine Article; SWETS; UMI; UnCover.

677 US ISSN 0040-5175
TS1300 CODEN: TRJOA9
TEXTILE RESEARCH JOURNAL. 1930. m. $195 (Canada $217; Mexico $219; S. America $226; Europe $241; elsewhere $251) (effective 1996). Textile Research Institute, 601 Prospect Ave., Box 625, Princeton, NJ 08542. TEL 609-924-3150. FAX 609-683-7836. Ed. Ludwig Rebenfeld. bk.rev.; bibl.; charts; illus.; index. circ. 2,500. (also avail. in microform from UMI; back issues avail.) **Indexed:** A.S.& T.Ind., Anim.Breed.Abstr., Appl.Mech.Rev., Art & Archaeol.Tech.Abstr., ASCA, Biol.Abstr., Chem.Abstr., Cott.& Trop.Fibr.Abstr., Curr.Cont., Eng.Ind., Excerp.Med., INSPEC, PROMT, RAPRA, Text.Tech.Dig., World Text.Abstr.
—BLDSC (8809.000000); CASDDS; Ei; Faxon; Genuine Article; SWETS; UMI; UnCover. CCC.
Description: Devoted to disseminating fundamental and applied scientific information in the physical, chemical, and engineering sciences related to the textiles and allied industries.
Refereed Serial

677 GR ISSN 1105-4069
TEXTILE REVIEW/EPITHEORISIS KLOSTOUFANTOURGIAS. (Supplement avail.: Directory: Textile Machinery, Equipments, Space Parts and Services) (Editions in Arabic, Greek) 1961. bi-m. (Greek edition); q. (Arabic edition). Irinis St., No. 9, 18547 N. Faliron, Athens, Greece. TEL 30-1-4813-515. TELEX 213379 TEXR. adv. **Document type:** trade publication.

677 NE ISSN 0920-4083
CODEN: TSTEE6
TEXTILE SCIENCE AND TECHNOLOGY. (Text in English) 1975. irreg., vol.11, 1994. price varies. Elsevier Science B.V., Books Division, P.O. Box 211, 1000 AE Amsterdam, Netherlands. TEL 31-20-4853911. FAX 31-20-4853705. TELEX 18582 ESPA NL. E-mail: nlinfo-f@elsevier.nl; usinfo-f@elsevier.com; forinfo-kyf04035@niftyserve.or.jp; Site addr.: http://www.elsevier.nl/. (Subscr. in U.S. and Canada to: Elsevier Science Inc., Box 882, Madison Sq. Sta., New York, NY 10159. TEL 212-989-5800) **Document type:** monographic series.
—CASDDS.
Refereed Serial

TEXTILE INDUSTRIES AND FABRICS

677 UK ISSN 0957-1639
TS1359
TEXTILE TIMES INTERNATIONAL. 1852. m. £6. (Irish Linen Guild) Granite Publications, 62 Castlereagh St., Belfast BT5 4NJ, N. Ireland. adv.; bk.rev.; mkt.; tr.lit. circ. 5,340. **Document type:** trade publication.
Former titles (until 1973): Textiles of Ireland and Linen Trade Circular (ISSN 0040-523X); (until 1968): Textiles of Ireland (ISSN 0957-1620); Which incorporates (in 1966): Linen Trade Circular (ISSN 0957-1612); Which was formerly (1913-1886): Irish Textile Journal.

677 II ISSN 0040-5205
TEXTILE TRENDS. (Text in English) 1958. m. $100. Eastland Publications (Private) Ltd., 44 Chittaranjan Ave., Calcutta 700 012, India. TEL 27-3096. Ed. M. Chakraborti. adv.; bk.rev.; charts; illus.; mkt.; pat.; tr.lit.; tr.mk. circ. 5,500. **Indexed:** Art & Archaeol.Tech.Abstr.

677 US ISSN 0040-5213
TS1300 CODEN: TEWOAH
TEXTILE WORLD. 1868. m. $42 (free to qualified personnel). MacLean Hunter Publishing Company, Textile Publications, 4170 Ashford-Dunwoody Rd., Ste. 420, Atlanta, GA 30319. TEL 404-847-2770. FAX 404-252-6150. (Subscr. to: 29 N. Wacker Dr., Chicago, IL 60606) Ed. McAllister Isaacs III. adv.; bk.rev.; charts; illus.; tr.lit.; circ. 28,142 (controlled). (also avail. in microform from UMI,PMC) **Indexed:** A.S.& T.Ind., ABI Inform., ASCA, B.P.I., Bus.Ind.; C.I.S. Abstr., Chem.Abstr., Cott.& Trop.Fibr.Abstr., Eng.Ind., Excerp.Med., PROMT, RAPRA, SRI, Text.Tech.Dig., Tr.& Indus.Ind., World Text.Abstr.
●Also available online. Vendor(s): University Microfilms International.
—BLDSC (8811.000000); CASDDS; Ei; Faxon; Genuine Article; SWETS; UMI; UnCover. **CCC.**
Former titles (until 1931): Textile Advance News; (until 1924): Textiles; (until 1923): Posselt's Textile Journal; (until 1915): Textile World Journal.
Description: For executives, specialists and managers. Covers yarn manufacturing, knitting, weaving, nonwovens, dyeing, chemical treatment, and fibers.

677 US
TEXTILES: LATIN AMERICAN INDUSTRIAL REPORT. (Avail. for each of 22 Latin American countries) 1985. a. $435 per country report. Aquino Productions, Box 15760, Stamford, CT 06901. TEL 203-325-3138.

677 US ISSN 0040-5140
TEXTILES PANAMERICANOS; revista para la industria textile. (Text in Spanish) 1941. q. $40 (foreign $48). Billian Publishing, Inc., 2100 Powers Ferry Rd., Atlanta, GA 30339. TEL 404-955-5656. FAX 404-952-0669. Ed. James Woodruffe. adv.; bk.rev.; charts; illus. circ. 15,000. **Indexed:** Art & Archaeol.Tech.Abstr., Text.Tech.Dig. **Document type:** trade publication.
Description: For the textile and apparel industry; offers current information on new technology, manufacturing processes, and modern management methods as well as Latin American and worldwide news.

677 SP ISSN 0211-7975
TEXTILES PARA EL HOGAR. 1967. 6/yr. 8900 ptas.($97) (effective 1995). Publica, S.A., Ecuador, 75, entlo., 08029 Barcelona, Spain. TEL 34-3-3215046. FAX 34-3-3221972. Ed. Balague Castella. adv.; illus. circ. 4,000.

677 SZ ISSN 0040-5248
TS1300
TEXTILES SUISSES. (Text in English, French and German) 1927. 4/yr. 84 SFr. Schweizerische Zentrale fuer Handelsfoerderung - Swiss Office for Trade Promotion, Case Postale 1128, CH-1001 Lausanne, Switzerland. TEL 021-3203231. FAX 021-3207337. Ed. Peter Pfister. adv.; illus. circ. 12,000. **Indexed:** DAAI, Key to Econ.Sci. **Document type:** trade publication.
Description: Features Swiss clothing fabrics and their use in international fashion industry.

677 NE ISSN 0040-5264
TEXTILIA. 1921. w. fl.217 (outside Benelux fl.358). V N U Business Publications B.V., Postbus 9194, 1006 AC Amsterdam, Netherlands. TEL 31-20-5102203. FAX 31-20-6176781. TELEX 14407 PUBLI NL. Ed. Wilma van Hattem. adv.; B&W page fl.6690, color page fl.10158; trim 313 x 473. bk.rev.; abstr.; bibl.; charts; illus.; mkt.; pat.; stat.; tr.lit. circ. 8,971. (tabloid format) **Indexed:** Key to Econ.Sci., Text.Tech.Dig. **Document type:** trade publication.
Description: Trade publication for the business in textiles, fashions, and home textiles. Features trade news and information, fashion news and trends, and international news. Includes list of events, positions available.

677 GW ISSN 0934-3342
TEXTILKUNST; Informationen fuer kreatives Gestalten. 1973. 4/yr. DM.75. Verlag M. und H. Schaper GmbH, Kalandstr. 4, 31061 Alfeld, Germany. TEL 05181-8009-0. FAX 05181-800933. (Subscr. to: Postfach 1642, 31046 Alfeld, Germany) Ed. B. Koch-Muenchmeyer. adv.; bk.rev.; illus. circ. 7,000. **Indexed:** Art & Archaeol.Tech.Abstr., Text.Tech.Dig. **Document type:** trade publication.

677 SZ ISSN 0040-5310
TS1510 CODEN: TXLVAE
TEXTILVEREDLUNG. 1946. 6/yr. 90 SFr. (foreign 107 SFr.). Swiss Society Textile and Chemistry, Postfach 146, CH-4013 Basel, Switzerland. TEL 061-4696121. FAX 061-4696501. Ed. A. Barthold. adv.; B&W page 1710 SFr.; trim 180 x 264; adv. contact: Rolf Stirnemann. bk.rev. circ. 2,800. **Document type:** trade publication.
—BLDSC (8813.762000); CASDDS; Ei; SWETS.
Formed by 1965 merger of: S V F Fachorgan Textilveredlung (ISSN 0371-4292); Textil-Rundschau (ISSN 0371-6465)

677.028 CC ISSN 1000-1557
TIANJIN FANGZHI GONGXUEYUAN XUEBAO/TIANJIN INSTITUTE OF TEXTILE SCIENCE AND TECHNOLOGY. JOURNAL. (Text in Chinese) 1982. q. $8. Tianjin Fangzhi Gongxueyuan - Tianjin Textile Engineering Institute, 63 Chenglinzhuang Rd., Tianjin 300160, People's Republic of China. TEL 86-22-4344477. FAX 86-22-4344572. TELEX 234025 TJFY. Ed. Chen Zhenyi. adv. contact: Jianguo Chen. circ. 2,000.

677 667.3 IT ISSN 0040-7984
CODEN: TINCAW
TINCTORIA (MILAN). (Text mainly in Italian; occasionally in English) 1903. m. L.125000($100) (Textile Ennobling Association) Edizioni Ariminum, Via Negroli 51, 20133 Milan, Italy. TEL 39-2-730091. FAX 39-2-717346. Ed. Giovanni Frangi. adv.; bk.rev.; abstr.; charts; illus.; pat.; tr.lit.; tr.mk.; index. circ. 3,000. (back issues avail.) **Indexed:** Art & Archaeol.Tech.Abstr., Chem.Abstr. **Document type:** trade publication.
—BLDSC (8857.100000); CASDDS.
Description: Devoted to textile wet processing, dyeing, finishing, bleaching and more.

677 US
TINTA E HILO. (Text in Spanish) 1991. q. $24 in N. America; elsewhere $50. Intertec Publishing, 7009 S. Potomac St., Englewood, CO 80112. TEL 303-397-7600. FAX 303-397-7619. Ed. Lourdes Huici. adv.; B&W page $1855; trim 8 3/8 x 10 7/8; adv. contact: Renee Hambleton. circ. 7,400. **Document type:** trade publication.
Description: Aimed at the screenprinter and commercial embroiderer in Mexico, Central and South America, and Spain.

677 JA
TORAY INDUSTRIES. ANNUAL REPORT. a. Toray Industries Inc., Zaimubu Kokusai Zaimuka, 2-2-1 Muro-machi Nihonbashi, Chuo-ku, Tokyo 103, Japan. TEL 03-3245-5222. FAX 03-3245-5818.

667 IT
TRENDS COLLEZIONI. (Text in English, Italian) q. L.210000 (effective 1993). Zanfi Editori s.r.l., Via Emilia Ovest 954, 41100 Modena, Italy. TEL 059-891700. FAX 059-891701. TELEX 522272 ZANFI I. illus. **Document type:** trade publication.
Formerly: Tessuto Collezioni.
Description: Covers trends in the textile sector, the latest fabrics, colors and patterns.

677 GW
UNFALLSCHIRM. q. Textil- und Bekleidungs-Berufsgenossenschaft, Oblatterwallstr. 18, 86153 Augsburg, Germany.

UNITED STATES: COTTON QUALITY REPORTS FOR GINNINGS. see **AGRICULTURE** — Agricultural Economics

677 US ISSN 1072-5628
TS840
UPHOLSTERY JOURNAL. 1993. m. $39 (Canada $48; elsewhere $95). R C M Enterprises, Inc., 15500 Wayzata Blvd., Ste. 922, Box 720, Wayzata, MN 55391. TEL 612-546-5225. FAX 612-473-7068. Ed. Tom Faust; Pub. Robert C. Mead. adv.; B&W page $1612; adv. contact: Jim Peningroth. circ. 7,500. (back issues avail.) **Document type:** trade publication.
Description: Covers fabrics, materials, tools, equipment and techniques used in upholstery.

UTSUKUSHII-KIMONO/BEAUTIFUL KIMONO. see **CLOTHING TRADE** — Fashions

V W D - LANDWIRTSCHAFT UND ERNAEHRUNG. see **BUSINESS AND ECONOMICS** — Investments

VAEVMAGASINET; Scandinavian weaving magazine. see **NEEDLEWORK**

677.4 XO ISSN 1335-0617
CODEN: VLTEED
VLAKNA A TEXTIL/FIBRES AND TEXTILES. (Text in English, Slovak) 1994. q. Vyskumny Ustav Chemickych Vlaken - Research Institute for Man-Made Fibres, 059 21 Svit, Okr. Poprad, Slovakia. TEL 42-92-56225. FAX 42-92-55663. Ed. Daniel Kello. circ. 500. **Indexed:** Abstr.Bull.Inst.Pap.Chem., Chem.Abstr., Text.Tech.Dig., World Text.Abstr. **Document type:** academic/scholarly publication.
—BLDSC (8800.810000); CASDDS.
Formed by the merger of (1951-1994): Chemicke Vlakna (ISSN 0528-9432); (1971-1994): Textil a Chemia (ISSN 0139-7656)

677 790.13 US
WARP & WEFT. 1949. m. (except July-Aug.). $12. Robin and Russ Handweavers, 533 N. Adams St., McMinnville, OR 97128. TEL 503-472-5760. Ed. Russell Groff. circ. 400. **Document type:** academic/scholarly publication.
Description: Covers four-harness patterns; sample swatch included with each issue.

677 GW ISSN 0043-1699
WEBE MIT; Zeitschrift fuer das Handweben. 1956. 4/yr. DM.23. Webe Mit-Verlag, 73650 Winterbach, 7065 Manolzweiler, Germany. Ed. S. Traub. adv.; bk.rev. circ. 4,000.

WIADOMOSCI PRODUKCYJNE: WLOKNO, ODZIEZ, SKORA. see **CLOTHING TRADE**

677 GW ISSN 0935-6886
WIRTSCHAFT HEUTE. 1962. m. DM.54. Nomos Verlagsgesellschaft mbH und Co. KG, Waldseestr. 3-5, 76530 Baden-Baden, Germany. TEL 07221-2104-0. FAX 07221-210427. adv.; bk.rev.; illus. **Document type:** bulletin.
Formerly (until 1989): Kaufleute (ISSN 0934-2109); Which was formed by the 1987 merger of: Junge Textilverkaeufer (ISSN 0176-7216); Jungkaufmann.

677.3 SA ISSN 0259-0182
WOLNUUS/WOOL NEWS. (Text in Afrikaans, English) 1980. w. free. S.A. Wool Board, P.O. Box 2191, Port Elizabeth 6056, South Africa. TEL 27-41-544301. FAX 27-41-546760. Ed. J.W. Gieselbach. circ. 700. **Document type:** trade publication.
Incorporates: Cape Wools Market Report; Formed by the merger of: Wool News Service; Wolnuusdiens.

677.31 II ISSN 0043-7808
CODEN: WWIDA5
WOOL AND WOOLENS OF INDIA. (Text in English) vol. 7, 1970. q. Rs.100 (foreign Rs.200). Indian Woollen Mills' Federation, Churchgate Chambers 5, 7th Fl., 5 New Marine Lines, Bombay 400 020, India. TEL 2624372. FAX 022-2624675. TELEX 91-022-2624675. Ed. K.V.A. Warrier. adv.; B&W page Rs.750; trim 21 x 16. abstr.; charts; illus.; mkt.; stat. circ. 450. **Indexed:** Chem.Abstr., Ind.Vet., Text.Tech.Dig., Vet.Bull., World Text.Abstr.
—CASDDS.

TEXTILE INDUSTRIES AND FABRICS — ABSTRACTING, BIBLIOGRAPHIES, STATISTICS

677.3 II ISSN 0970-504X
WOOL & WOOLLEN. (Text in English) 1964. m. Rs.120. Eastern Press Services (India), Asheerwad, 3-49 Sion East, Bombay 400 022, India. TEL 91-22-4072912. FAX 91-22-4077885. Ed. Raju V. Chandran. adv.; bk.rev.; illus. circ. 10,000.

677.3 AT ISSN 1320-4122
WOOL MARKET WEEKLY. 1975. 43/yr. Aus.$40 (foreign Aus.$50). Australian Wool Corporation, Box 4867, Melbourne, Vic. 3001, Australia. Ed. P. Hanson.
Formerly: Wool Market News.

677 AT ISSN 1038-4510
WOOL MONITOR. 1975. m. Aus.$40 (foreign Aus.$45). Australian Wool Corporation, Market Information & Planning Department, P.O. Box 4867, Melbourne, Vic. 3001, Australia. Ed. C. Wilcox. circ. 3,600.
Former titles: Australian Wool Corporation. Wool Market News: Monthly Perspective; Australian Wool Corporation. Bi-Monthly Market Report (ISSN 0310-1398)

677.31 II ISSN 0043-7824
WOOL NEWS. (Text in English) 1965. q. Rs.400($20) Wool & Woollens Export Promotion Council, 612-714 Ashoka Estate, 24 Barakhamba Rd., New Delhi 110001, India. TEL 011-3315512. FAX 91-011-3314626. TELEX 031-66673. Ed. Ashok K. Madhra. circ. 1,000 (controlled).

677.3 AT
WOOL NEWS. q. Australian Wool Corporation, P.O. Box 4867, Melbourne, Vic. 3001, Australia. **Indexed:** Text.Tech.Dig.
Formerly: Woolgrower.

677.31 UK ISSN 0263-6131
WOOL RECORD. 1909. m. £65 (foreign £112). World Textile Publications Ltd., 76 Kirkgate, Bradford, W. Yorkshire BD1 1TB, England. TEL 01274-726358. FAX 01274-735045. Ed. Mark Keighley. adv.; bk.rev.; mkt. **Indexed:** Art & Archaeol.Tech.Abstr., Chem.Abstr., Key to Econ.Sci., PROMT, Text.Tech.Dig., World Text.Abstr. **Document type:** trade publication.
—BLDSC (9347.300000); UnCover.
Formerly: Wool Record and Textile World (ISSN 0043-7832)

677.31 UK
WOOL RECORD WEEKLY MARKET REPORT. 1907. w. £115 (foreign £132). World Textile Publications Ltd., 76 Kirkgate, Bradford, W. Yorkshire BD1 1TB, England. TEL 01274-726358. FAX 01274-735045. Ed. H.M.F. Mallett. m. contact: Wynn Horn. charts; mkt.; index. **Indexed:** World Text.Abstr. **Document type:** trade publication.
Incorporates (in Dec. 1977): Weekly Wool Chart (ISSN 0043-2008)

677.3 NZ ISSN 0112-2908
WOOL RESEARCH ORGANISATION OF NEW ZEALAND COMMUNICATIONS. 1967. irreg. NZ.$250 per no. (typically set in July). Wool Research Organisation of New Zealand, Private Bag 4749, Christchurch, New Zealand. TEL 03-3252-421. FAX 3-325-2717. Ed. Barbara H. Vaile. circ. 300.
—BLDSC (3359.100000).
Description: Fundamental studies on New Zealand wool, including cellular, chemical and physical properties, appraisal, sale, scouring, processing, end-use performance and marketing.

677.3 NZ ISSN 0112-2851
WOOL RESEARCH ORGANISATION OF NEW ZEALAND REPORTS. 1970. irreg. NZ.$250 per no. (typically set in July). Wool Research Organisation of New Zealand, Private Bag 4749, Christchurch, New Zealand. TEL 64-3-325-2421. FAX 64-3-325-2717. Ed. Barbara H. Vaile. circ. 300.
—BLDSC (7634.730000).
Description: Practical research on New Zealand wool, including cellular, chemical and physical properties, appraisal, sale, scouring, processing, end-use performance and marketing.

677.3 NZ ISSN 0112-2754
WOOL RESEARCH ORGANISATION OF NEW ZEALAND SPECIAL PUBLICATIONS. 1976. irreg. price varies. Wool Research Organisation of New Zealand, Private Bag 4749, Christchurch, New Zealand. FAX 64-3-3252-717. Ed. B.H. Vaile. **Indexed:** Text.Tech.Dig., World Text.Abstr.
Description: Proceedings of meetings on New Zealand wool, including cellular, chemical and physical properties, appraisal, sale, scouring, processing, end-use performance and marketing.

677.31 US ISSN 0043-7840
WOOL SACK. 1931. q. $3. Mid-States Wool Growers Cooperative, Box 328, Brookings, SD 57006. TEL 605-692-2324. FAX 605-692-8182. Ed. Dick Boniface. adv. contact: Ronald Seeley. bk.rev.; illus.; mkt.; circ. 18,000 (controlled). **Document type:** newsletter.

677 UK ISSN 0260-2016
WOOL STATISTICS. £55 (overseas £80). International Wool Textile Organisation, 63 Albert Dr., London SW19 6LB, England. TEL 0181-788-8876. FAX 0181-788-5171. **Document type:** trade publication.
Formerly (until 1960): Research of the Wool Questionnaire Prepared by the Commonwealth Economic Commissioner.

WOOL TECHNOLOGY AND SHEEP BREEDING. see AGRICULTURE — Poultry And Livestock

677.31
WOOLLEN EXPORTERS DIRECTORY. (Text in English) vol.4, 1970. s-a. Rs.400($15) (free to qualified personnel). Wool & Woollens Export Promotion Council, 612-714 Ashoka Estate, Barakhamba Rd., New Delhi 110001, India. TEL 3315512. FAX 91-011-3314626. Ed. Ashok K. Madhra. adv.; illus.; mkt.; stat. circ. 1,000.
Formerly: Woollens and Worsteds of India (ISSN 0043-7883)

677.2 PK
WORLD COTTON MARKETS REVIEW. (Text in English) 1972. m. Pakistan Central Cotton Committee, Marketing and Economic Research Section, Secretary, Moulvi Tamizuddin Khan Rd., Karachi 1, Pakistan. TEL 524104-6. charts; stat.

677 IS ISSN 0372-7777
CODEN: YLTUAM
YALKUT; Israel textile journal. (Text in Hebrew; summaries in English) 1952. q. $30. Israel Textile Association, 12 Anna Frank St., P.O. Box 243, Ramat Gan 52526, Israel. TEL 972-3-7521133. FAX 972-3-7521141. Ed. S. Rozenzveig. adv.: B&W page $2750; trim 275 x 210; adv. contact: Steven Lubell. bk.rev.; abstr. circ. 2,000. **Indexed:** Chem.Abstr., World Text.Abstr. **Document type:** academic/scholarly publication.
—CASDDS.
Description: Covers developments in the textile industry in Israel and the world, including economic issues, new technology, fashions.

677 UK ISSN 0084-411X
YEARBOOK ON JUTE.* (Text in English) 1967. a. Asian Trade Publications Lte., Garavi Gujarat House, 1-2 Silex St., London SE1 0DW, England.

677 CC ISSN 1000-4017
YIN RAN/DYING AND FINISHING. (Text in Chinese, abstracts in English) m. Shanghai Fanzhi Kexue Yanjiuyuan - Shanghai Textile Research Institute, 545 Lanzhou Lu, Shanghai 200082, People's Republic of China. TEL 5460011. FAX 86-021-5458418. TELEX 33365 STRI CN. (Co-sponsor: Quanguo Yinran Gongye Keji Qingbao Zhan) Ed. Shen Anjing. adv.

677 JA
ZENSEN MONTHLY JOURNAL. m. Zensen Japanese Federation of Textile, Garment, Chemical, Mercantile and Allied Industry Workers' Unions, 8-16 Kudan, Minami 4-chome, Chiyoda-ku, Japan. TEL 03-265-5465. TELEX ZENSEN TOKYO.

677 JA
ZENSEN NEWSPAPER. w. Japanese Federation of Textile, Garment, Chemical, Mercantile and Allied Industry Workers' Union, 8-16 Kudan, Minami 4-chome, Chiyoda-ku, Tokyo 102, Japan. TEL 03-3265-5465. TELEX ZENSEN TOKYO. **Document type:** newspaper.

677.39 CC ISSN 1000-2103
CODEN: ZSGXEU
ZHEJIANG SICHOU GONGXUEYUAN XUEBAO/ZHEJIANG INSTITUTE OF SILK TEXTILES. JOURNAL. (Text in Chinese; summaries in English) 1979. q. $10. Zhejiang Sichou Gongxueyuan, 88 Wenyi Lu, Hangzhou, Zhejiang 310033, People's Republic of China. TEL 885814. Ed. Yuan Guanluo. circ. 2,000. **Document type:** academic/scholarly publication.
—CASDDS.

677 CC ISSN 0529-6013
ZHONGGUO FANGZHI/CHINESE TEXTILE. (Text in Chinese) 1950. m. $35. China National Textile Council, General Office, Rm. 302, 105 Jiangxi Zhonglu, Shanghai 200002, People's Republic of China. TEL 3233411. Ed. Wang Zhifu. adv.: page $2000. circ. 20,000(controlled).
Description: Covers business management, international trade, marketing and economic development in the field of textile.

677 US
ZHONGGUO FANGZHI BAO/CHINA TEXTILES NEWS. (Text in Chinese) 4/w. $138.50. China Books & Periodicals, Inc., 2929 24th St., San Francisco, CA 94110. TEL 415-282-2994. FAX 415-282-0994. **Document type:** newspaper.

677 CC ISSN 1000-1476
TS1300 CODEN: ZFDXEQ
ZHONGGUO FANGZHI DAXUE XUEBAO. English edition: China Textile University. Journal (ISSN 1000-1484) (Text in Chinese) 1956. 6/yr. $30. Zhongguo Fangzhi Daxue - China Textile University, 1882 Yan'an Xilu, Shanghai 200051, People's Republic of China. TEL 2199898. adv. **Document type:** academic/scholarly publication.
—BLDSC (4729.219300); CASDDS.
Former titles (until 1986): Shanghai College of Textile Technology. Journal; East China Institute of Textile Science and Technology. Journal.
Description: Academic journal of natural science and engineering, focusing on textile science and technology.

TEXTILE INDUSTRIES AND FABRICS — Abstracting, Bibliographies, Statistics

677 310 AT ISSN 0311-9882
AUSTRALIAN WOOL SALE STATISTICS. STATISTICAL ANALYSIS. PART A & B & C & D. (Issued in 4 parts) 1972. a. Aus.$85 (foreign Aus.$105). Australian Wool Corporation, P.O. Box 4867, Melbourne, Vic. 3001, Australia. Ed. W. Watkins. circ. 200. (also avail. in diskette format)
—BLDSC (1824.750000).
Former titles: Australian Wool (ISSN 0067-222X); Australian Wool Corporation. Statistical Analysis (ISSN 0084-764X)

677 CN ISSN 0319-891X
HD9864.C2
CANADA. STATISTICS CANADA. TEXTILE PRODUCTS INDUSTRIES. (Catalogue 34-251) (Text in English and French) 1960. a. Can.$35($42) (foreign $49). Statistics Canada, Publications Sales and Services, Ottawa, Ont. K1A 0T6, Canada. TEL 613-951-7277. FAX 613-951-1584. (also avail. in microform from MML)
Formerly (until 1985): Canada. Statistics Canada. Carpet, Mat and Rug Industry (ISSN 0527-4893)
Description: Annual census of manufactures.

667.2 016 UK
COLOUR INDEX: ADDITIONS & AMENDMENTS. (Supplement to: Colour Index) 1980. q. £74. Society of Dyers and Colourists, Perkin House, P.O. Box 244, Bradford, W. Yorks BD1 2JB, England. TEL 01274-725138. FAX 01274-392888. (Co-sponsor: American Association of Textile Chemists & Colorists) Ed.Bd. circ. 1,000. (back issues avail.) **Document type:** trade publication.

677.2 US
COTTON. PART 2: WORLD STATISTICS. Title varies: International Cotton Advisory Committee. Quarterly Statistical Bulletin. 1947. a. $125. International Cotton Advisory Committee, 1629 K St. N.W., Ste. 702, Washington, DC 20006. TEL 202-463-6660. FAX 202-463-6950. TELEX 701517 ICACOM. charts; stat. (also avail. in microfiche from CIS) **Indexed:** IIS, PROMT, Text.Tech.Dig., World Text.Abstr.

TEXTILE INDUSTRIES AND FABRICS — ABSTRACTING, BIBLIOGRAPHIES, STATISTICS

677 310   US   ISSN 0145-8957
HD9851
CURRENT INDUSTRIAL REPORTS: BROADWOVEN FABRICS (GRAY). (Series MQ22-T) q. online only, plus printed and online a. summary. U.S. Bureau of the Census, Data User Services Division, Washington, DC 20233. TEL 301-457-4100. FAX 301-457-4714. (also avail. in microfiche from CIS; reprint service avail. from CIS and the Census Bureau) Indexed: Amer.Stat.Ind. (1975-). **Document type**: government publication.
• Available only online. Vendor(s): CompuServe, Inc., Knight-Ridder, Inc.
Former titles: Current Industrial Reports: Finished Fabrics. Production, Inventories, and Unfilled Orders (ISSN 0272-5509); Current Industrial Reports: Woven Fabrics. Production, Inventories, and Unfilled Orders (ISSN 0145-5028)

677.028 620   US   ISSN 1049-1376
C2C ABSTRACTS: JAPAN - TEXTILES.* 1990. m. $200. Scan C2C, 1001 Pennsylvania Ave., N.W., No.1300, Washington, DC 20024-2025. TEL 800-525-3865. FAX 202-863-3855. **Document type**: abstracting/indexing.
• Also available online. Vendor(s): Data-Star (JPTC), Knight-Ridder, Inc. (File no.582), European Space Agency (File no.241), Orbit Search Service (JTEC). Also available on CD-ROM. Producer(s): Knight-Ridder, Inc.
Description: Contains abstracts of articles from Japanese scientific, business, and technical journals. Lists title, author, author affiliation, journal title, volume and number, date, page numbers, abstract, number of bibliographic references, and language.

677   US
DAVISON'S TEXTILE BLUE BOOK EUROPE. 1991. a. $125. Davison Publishing Co., Inc., Box 1289, Concord, NC 28026-1289. TEL 704-785-8700; 800-328-4766. FAX 704-785-8701. **Document type**: directory.
Description: Comprehensive directory of Western European textile companies listing weavers, knitters, spinners, nonwoven mills, dyers and finishers, as well as hosiery and carpet mills. Arranged alphabetically by country and city.

677   US   ISSN 0734-4708
HD9850.3
DAVISON'S TEXTILE BUYER'S GUIDE. 1934. a. $50. Davison Publishing Co., Inc., Box 1289, Concord, NC 28026-1289. TEL 704-785-8700; 800-328-4766. FAX 704-785-8701. Ed. Bruce W. Nealy. **Document type**: directory.
Formerly (until 1980): Davison's Textile Buyers and Buyers' Guide (ISSN 0730-5990)
Description: Directory with separate classifications for suppliers of chemicals, equipment, machinery, services and supplies used in the textile industry.

677 687   GW
EXTRAKTE: TEXTILIEN UND BEKLEIDUNG. 1966. w. DM.498 (foreign DM.560). Extrakte-Team-Verlag GmbH, Wolfgang-Doering-Str. 2-4, 40595 Duesseldorf, Germany. TEL 0211-701011. FAX 0211-701013. (Subscr. to: Postfach 180162, 40568 Duesseldorf, Germany) Ed. Dietmar Cloos. adv.; charts; stat.; tr.lit. circ. 4,000. (back issues avail.)

677   CC   ISSN 1000-3916
FANGZHI WENZHAI/TEXTILE ABSTRACT. (Text in Chinese) 1979. bi-m. Y42. Shanghai Fangzhi Kexue Yanjiuyuan - Shanghai Textile Research Institute, 545 Lanzhou Lu, Shanghai 200082, People's Republic of China. TEL 86-021-5461341. FAX 86-021-5458418. TELEX 33365 STRI CN. Ed. Gao Dequan. adv. circ. 3,000. **Document type**: abstracting/indexing.

338.4 677   II
INDIAN COTTON TEXTILE INDUSTRY; ANNUAL STATISTICAL BULLETIN. (Text in English) 1968. a. Southern India Mills' Association, Coimbatore, India. circ. 500. **Document type**: bulletin.

677.2   SZ   ISSN 0538-6829
HD9870.4
INTERNATIONAL COTTON INDUSTRY STATISTICS. 1958. a. 100 SFr. International Textile Manufacturers Federation, Am Schanzengraben 29, Postfach, CH-8039 Zurich, Switzerland. TEL 01-2017080. FAX 01-2017134. TELEX 817578. charts; stat. (also avail. in microform) **Indexed**: World Text.Abstr. **Document type**: trade publication.
Description: Covers productive capacity, machinery utilization and raw material consumption in the short-staple sector.

677   BE   ISSN 0074-7599
INTERNATIONAL RAYON AND SYNTHETIC FIBRES COMMITTEE. STATISTICAL YEARBOOK. 1965. a. 3000 BEF. International Rayon and Synthetic Fibres Committee - Comite International de la Rayonne et des Fibres Synthetiques, Av. Van Nieuwenhuyse 4, 1160 Brussels, Belgium. Dir. Colin M. Purvis. circ. 3,500.

677.2   SZ
INTERNATIONAL TEXTILE MACHINERY SHIPMENT STATISTICS. 1974. a. 200 SFr. International Textile Manufacturers Federation, Am Schanzengraben 29, Postfach, CH-8039 Zurich, Switzerland. TEL 01-2017080. FAX 01-2017134. TELEX 817578. charts; stat. **Document type**: trade publication.
Formerly: International Cotton Industry Statistics. Supplement.
Description: Provides information on spinning and weaving capacities installed in almost the entire world and effectively identifies investment trends.

677.3 310   UK   ISSN 0260-8855
KNITSTATS; yearly statistical bulletin for the hosiery and knitwear industry. 1976. a. £45. Knitting Industries' Federation, 53 Oxford St., Leicester LE1 5XY, England. TEL 0116-2541608. FAX 0116-2542273. (Dist. by: Knitstats Distribution, 10 Peacock Close, Ruddington, Nottingham NG11 6JF, England. TEL 0115-9841174. FAX 0115-9841174) Ed. J.A. Smirfitt. bk.rev.; index. circ. 700. (back issues avail.) **Indexed**: World Text.Abstr. **Document type**: bulletin.

630 677.13   II   ISSN 0027-0598
MONTHLY SUMMARY OF JUTE AND GUNNY STATISTICS. (Text in English) 1945. m. Rs.80. Indian Jute Mills Association, Royal Exchange, 6 Netaji Subhas Rd., Calcutta 1, India. stat. circ. 300.

377.4   US   ISSN 1062-0648
NATURAL FIBERS FACT BOOK. a. $15. University of Texas at Austin, Bureau of Business Research, Box 7459, Austin, TX 78713. TEL 512-471-1616. FAX 512-471-1063. (Co-sponsor: Natural Fibers Research and Information Center) **Document type**: trade publication.
Description: Serves as a statistical indicator of the domestic and international natural-fibers industries, with emphasis on Texas.

SACHGUETERERZEUGUNG SCHNELLBERICHT. see CERAMICS, GLASS AND POTTERY — Abstracting, Bibliographies, Statistics

677   JA
SEN-I KOUGYO YORAN/JAPAN TEXTILE INDUSTRY. DIRECTORY. (Text in Japanese) 1910. a. 19500 Yen for 1995 ed. Boshoku Zasshisha - Textile Journal and Book Pub. Co., 7-9, Ohnodai 1-chome, Osakasayama-si 589, Japan. TEL 81-06-633-7734. Ed. Ken-ichi Uno. adv. contact: Yoji Uno. circ. 3,000. **Document type**: directory.
Description: Covers Japanese textile manufacturers, institutes and universities. Also lists inspection and testing institutes, textile associations, and textile machinery traders and dealers in Japan.

677.39   II   ISSN 0536-695X
SILK IN INDIA. 1968? biennial. Central Silk Board, United Mansions, 2nd Fl., 39 M.G. Road, Bangalore 560 001, India. TEL 568194. stat.
Description: Statistical information on fabric production, market exports, foreign exchange earned, country output and comparison with world production.

677   AT   ISSN 1036-112X
TEXTILE AND APPAREL INDEX OF AUSTRALASIA.* 1940. irreg., 17th ed., 1990. Aus.$59.95. Morescope Publishing, P.O. Box 32, Canberwell, Vic. 3124, Australia. Ed. Ross Dunkley. adv. circ. 5,000.
Formerly: Textile and Apparel Index of Australia (ISSN 0159-0014)
Description: Comprehensive listings of all companies associated with textile, clothing and apparel industries in Australia and New Zealand.

677   HK
TEXTILE ASIA INDEX. 1982. a. HK.$120 in Hong Kong & Macau; elsewhere $19 (effective 1995). Business Press Ltd., California Tower, 11-F, 30-32 D'Aguilar St., P.O. Box 185, Central, Hong Kong. TEL 5247467. FAX 5-8106966. TELEX 60275-TEXIA-HX. Ed. Kayser Sung.

677 016.677   US   ISSN 0040-5191
TS1300   CODEN: TXTDAY
TEXTILE TECHNOLOGY DIGEST.* 1944. m. $475. Institute of Textile Technology, 2551 Ivy Rd, Charlottesville, VA 22903. TEL 804-296-5511. FAX 804-977-5400. Ed. Dennis Loy. bk.rev.; abstr.tr.lit.; tr.mk.; index. (also avail. in microform from UMI)
• Also available online. Vendor(s): Knight-Ridder, Inc. (File no.119).
Also available on CD-ROM.
—CCC.
Description: Publishes 10000 abstracts per year.

677   US
TEXTILE TECHNOLOGY DIGEST: SELECTED INFORMATION. 1990. m. $95. Institute of Textile Technology, Box 391, Charlottesville, VA 22902-0391. TEL 804-296-5511. FAX 804-977-5400. Ed. Dennis Loy.
Description: Selective dissemination of information from the parent publication "Textile Technology Digest" for fiber, yarn, fabric, carpets, environment, automation, knitting, weaving, dyeing, finishing, nonwovens and composites, mill practices, tests and test methods.

677 011   US
VITAL TEXTILE LITERATURE. 1989. bi-m. $95. Institute of Textile Technology, Box 391, Charlottesville, VA 22902-0391. TEL 804-296-5511. FAX 804-977-5400. Ed. Dennis Loy. **Document type**: abstracting/indexing.
Formerly (until 1993): Textile Technology Digest: Abstract Alert.
Description: Abstracts selected from the parent publication "Textile Technology Digest" for their importance in alerting the industry to vital information.

WOOLS OF NEW ZEALAND. STATISTICAL HANDBOOK. see AGRICULTURE — Abstracting, Bibliographies, Statistics

677 016   UK   ISSN 0043-9118
TS1300   CODEN: WTXAA
WORLD TEXTILE ABSTRACTS. 1969. m. £500($795) (effective 1996). Elsevier Science Ltd., P.O. Box 800, Kidlington, Oxford OX5 1DX, England. TEL 44-1865-843000. FAX 44-1865-843010. E-mail: nlinfo-f@elsevier.nl; usinfo-f@elsevier.com; forinfo-kyf04035@niftyserve.or.jp; Site addr.: http://www.elsevier.nl/. (Subscr. in U.S. and Canada to: Elsevier Science, 660 White Plains Rd., Tarrytown, NY 10591-5153. TEL 914-524-9200. FAX 914-333-2444) bk.rev.; index. (reprint service avail.) **Indexed**: Abstr.Bull.Inst.Pap.Chem., Anal.Abstr., Anim.Breed.Abstr., Appl.Mech.Rev., Ergon.Abstr. **Document type**: abstracting/indexing.
• Also available online. Vendor(s): Knight-Ridder, Inc. (File no.67), Orbit Search Service (WTA).
—BLDSC (9360.070000); UnCover. CCC.
Supersedes: Shirley Institute Summary of Current Literature; Textile Abstracts.
Description: Provides abstracts of scientific, technical and technico-economic literature relevant to fibre-forming polymers, textile and related industries and the applications of fibrous and textile materials in conventional textile products. Covers more than 500 periodicals on a monthly basis.

THEATER

see also Dance

792 362.7 US
A A T E NEWSLETTER. 1987. q. membership. American Alliance for Theatre & Education, Theatre Department, Arizona State University, Box 3411, Tempe, AZ 85287-3411. TEL 602-965-6064. FAX 602-965-5351. bk.rev. circ. 1,500. **Document type:** newsletter.
Description: Current information, jobs, events for educators and theater artists who work for or with youth, grants, new publications, proceedings of meetings.

A B C D E FOCUS. (Association of B.C. Drama Educators) see EDUCATION — Teaching Methods And Curriculum

792 GW
A K T. (Aktuelles Theater) 1969. 11/yr. DM.80 or membership. Frankfurter Bund fuer Volksbildung GmbH, Eschersheimer Landstr. 2, 60322 Frankfurt a.M., Germany. TEL 069-1545150. FAX 069-1545138. Eds. J. Kessler, G. Holzapfel. adv. contact: Ursula Pigge. bk.rev. circ. 15,000. **Document type:** consumer publication.

A M S STUDIES IN THE RENAISSANCE. see LITERATURE

792 US ISSN 0044-7927
PN2000
A S T R NEWSLETTER. 1972. 2/yr. membership. American Society for Theatre Research, c/o P.T. Dircks, Ed., C.W. Post College, Dept. of English, Greenvale, NY 11548. TEL 516-299-2391. adv.; circ. 600 (controlled). (processed) **Document type:** newsletter.

791.3 642.5 US
ABEL VALUE NEWS; panem et circenses/bread and circuses. 1969. m. $15. Abel News Agencies, 403 1st Ave. N., Estherville, IA 51334-2223. Ed. Peter M. Abel. adv.; bk.rev.; film rev.; play rev.; bibl.; charts; illus.; stat.; tr.lit. circ. 25,000.
Formerly (until 1983): Abel (ISSN 0001-3153)

ACADEMY PLAYERS DIRECTORY. see MOTION PICTURES

ADAM INTERNATIONAL REVIEW. see LITERATURE

AFRICAN ARTS. see ART

AGENCIES: WHAT THE ACTOR NEEDS TO KNOW. see BUSINESS AND ECONOMICS — Trade And Industrial Directories

791 PL ISSN 0065-6526
ALMANACH SCENY POLSKIEJ. 1960. a. Polska Akademia Nauk, Instytut Sztuki - Polish Academy of Science, Institut of Art, Ul. Dluga 28, 00-950 Warsaw, Poland. TEL 48-22-313271. FAX 22-48-313149. Ed. Anna Chojnacka. play rev.; index. circ. 500.

792 US
ALPHA PSI OMEGA: PLAYBILL. 1927. a. free. Alpha Psi Omega National Theatre Honorary, c/o Wabash College, Crawfordsville, IN 47933. TEL 317-364-4394. (Co-sponsor: Delta Psi Omega) Ed. James Fisher. bk.rev.; play rev.; illus.; stat.; circ. 7,000 (controlled). **Document type:** academic/scholarly publication, newsletter.

780 790 US
ALTERNATE ROOTS NEWSLETTER. 1977. q. Alternate Roots, Little Five Points Community Center, 1083 Austin Ave., Atlanta, GA 30307. TEL 404-577-1079. Ed. Kathie deNobriga. circ. 8,000. **Document type:** newsletter.

792.0222 XR ISSN 0002-6786
AMATERSKA SCENA; dvoumesicnik pro otazky amaterskeho divadla a umeleckeho prednesu. vol.2, 1965. m. 48 Kc.($44.80) (Informacni a Poradeske Stredisko pro Mistni Kulturu) Vydavatelstvi a Nakladatelstvi Nezavisly Novinar III, Vodickova 34, 120 21 Prague 2, Czech Republic. (Dist. by: Artia, Ve Smeckach 30, 111 27 Prague 1, Czech Republic) Ed. Tomas Cach. play rev.; abstr. circ. 1,600.

792.022 UK ISSN 0002-6867
AMATEUR STAGE. 1946. m. £10($20) Stacey Publications, 1 Hawthorndene Rd., Hayes, Bromley, Kent, England. Ed. Roy Stacey. adv.; bk.rev.; illus.; music rev.; play rev.; index. circ. 7,000. (also avail. in microform from UMI)
—UMI.

792 UK ISSN 0964-5470
AMATEUR THEATRE YEARBOOK. 1989. a. £15. Platform Publications Ltd., 83 George St., London W1H 5PL, England. TEL 0171-486-1732. FAX 0171-224-2215. Ed. Charles Vance. adv.: page £350; trim 120 x 190; adv. contact: Trevor Rawlins. circ. 2,000. (back issues avail.) **Document type:** directory, trade publication.

792 US ISSN 1061-0057
PS350
AMERICAN DRAMA. 1991. s-a. $15 to individuals; institutions $25 (effective 1995 & 1996). American Drama Institute, c/o English Department, ML69, University of Cincinnati, Cincinnati, OH 45221. TEL 513-556-3914. FAX 513-556-0142. Ed. Norma Jenckes. bk.rev. **Document type:** academic/scholarly publication.
—UnCover.
Description: Publishes studies of dramatic literature from the earliest to the most recent playwrights, featuring critical examination of trends and discussions of diversity in the script for stage, film, radio, and television.

792 US ISSN 8750-3255
PN2000
AMERICAN THEATRE; the monthly forum for news, features and opinion. 1984. 10/yr. $35 (foreign $50) (effective 1996). Theatre Communications Group, Inc., 355 Lexington Ave., New York, NY 10017. TEL 212-697-5230. FAX 212-983-4847. E-mail: tcg@tmn.com. (Dist. by: Eastern News Distributors, Inc., 2020 Superior St., Sandusky, OH 44870) Ed. Jim O'Quinn; Pub. Terrence Nemeth. adv. contact: Laura Romanowski. bk.rev.; play rev. circ. 60,000. (also avail. in microform from UMI; back issues avail.) **Indexed:** Access (1984-), Bk.Rev.Ind. (1989-), Chic.Per.Ind., Child.Bk.Rev.Ind. (1989-), SRI. **Document type:** trade publication.
● Also available online. Vendor(s): University Microfilms International.
—BLDSC (0857.860000); Faxon; SWETS; UMI; UnCover.
Description: Each issue features reports on plays in print, performances, and theater season schedules in the U.S. and abroad. Includes full-length play scripts 6 times per year.

792 US ISSN 0899-9880
AMERICAN UNIVERSITY STUDIES. SERIES 26. THEATER ARTS. 1990. irreg. Peter Lang Publishing, Inc., 62 W. 45th St., 4th Fl., New York, NY 10036. TEL 212-302-6740. Ed. Christopher Myers. **Document type:** academic/scholarly publication, monographic series.

791 US ISSN 0003-2344
GV1851.A3
AMUSEMENT BUSINESS; international newsweekly for live entertainment and amusement industry. 1894. w. $135 (Canada $155; elsewhere $165). B P I Communications, Amusement Business Division, Box 24970, Nashville, TN 37202. TEL 615-321-4250. FAX 615-327-1575. (Subscr. to: Box 41527, Nashville, TN 37204-1489) Ed. Karen Oerhey. adv.; illus. circ. 11,806. (also avail. in microform from UMI) **Indexed:** Bus.Ind., Tr.& Indus.Ind. **Document type:** newspaper.
● Also available online. Vendor(s): Knight-Ridder, Inc.
—UMI. CCC.

ANGLICA GERMANICA: SERIES 2. see LINGUISTICS

792 CC
ANHUI XIN XI. (Text in Chinese) bi-m. Y1.20 per no. Anhui Yishu Yanjiusuo - Anhui Art Institute, Hefei, Anhui 230001, People's Republic of China. TEL 255920. adv.

791 UK ISSN 0140-7740
ANIMATIONS; a review of puppets and related theatre. 1977. bi-m. £15 (Europe £25; elsewhere £30). Puppet Centre Trust, Battersea Arts Centre, Lavender Hill, London SW11 5TN, England. TEL 071-228-5335. Ed. Phyllida Shaw. bk.rev. circ. 800. **Document type:** bulletin.
Description: A review of puppets and related theater.

792 GW ISSN 0936-7446
APPLAUS; Muenchner Kulturmagazin. 1977. m. DM.60; newsstand price: DM.5. C. Hartmann Verlag GmbH, Severinstr. 5, 81541 Munich, Germany. TEL 089-6925333. FAX 089-6970673. Ed. Sven Precht; Pub. Christian Hartmann. adv.: color page DM.5280; adv. contact: Marc Spranger. circ. 15,000 (paid). **Document type:** consumer publication.

APPLAUSE THEATRE BOOK REVIEW & CATALOG. see LITERATURE

792 CL ISSN 0716-4440
APUNTES. 1960. s-a. Esc.6400 (US $30; Europe $36) (effective 1996). Universidad Catolica de Chile, Escuela de Teatro, Jaime Guzman Errazuriz 3300, Santiago, Chile. TEL 56-2-2744041. FAX 56-2-2232577. Ed. Maria de la Luz Hurtado. adv.; bk.rev.; bibl.; illus. circ. 1,200. **Indexed:** Rel.Ind.One. **Document type:** academic/scholarly publication, consumer publication.
Description: Presents the founding philosophy and supporting methods for theater activities. Contains a modern drama in its entirety and news of the theater in Chile and in the world.

792 IT ISSN 0066-6661
ARCHIVIO DEL TEATRO ITALIANO. 1968. irreg; latest 1982. price varies. Edizioni Il Polifilo, Via Borgonuovo 2, 20121 Milan, Italy. Ed. Giovanni Macchia.

792 IT
ARIEL. 1986. 3/yr. L.60000. (Istituto di Studi Pirandelliani) Bulzoni Editore, Via dei Liburni n.14, 00185 Rome, Italy. TEL 06-4455207. FAX 06-4450355. Ed. Alfredo Barbina.

ART AND CULTURE. see ART

ART LAW & ACCOUNTING REPORTER. see LAW

792 DK ISSN 0901-9901
ARTE NYT. 1958. 4/yr. (plus a special issue). DKK 45. Hvidkildevej 64, 2400 Copenhagen NV, Denmark. TEL 45-38-88-49-00. FAX 45-38-33-20-83. adv.: B&W page DKK 18000. circ. 52,000. **Document type:** consumer publication.

ARTES. see ART

792 UK
ARTISTES & AGENTS. a. £18.45. Richmond House Publishing Company Ltd., 3 Richmond Bldgs., London W1V 5AE, England. TEL 0171-437-9556. FAX 0171-287-3463. **Document type:** directory.

792 US ISSN 1051-9718
ARTISTS AND ISSUES IN THE THEATRE. irreg. Peter Lang Publishing, Inc., 62 W. 45th St., 4th Fl., New York, NY 10036. TEL 212-302-6740. FAX 212-302-7574. Ed. August W. Staub. **Document type:** academic/scholarly publication, monographic series.
—BLDSC (1735.283660).

792 US
ARTS ALIVE!; a magazine promoting the Arts. 1977. m. $18. Admar Associates - Theatrical Faces Inc., 548 N. New St., Bethlehem, PA 18018. TEL 215-758-8211. FAX 215-691-0234. Ed. Beth Hanson. adv. contact: Adeline Burt. circ. 15,000 (controlled). **Document type:** consumer publication.
Formerly (until 1986): Theatrical Faces.

792 CN
ARTS CLUB THEATRE ENCORE. 1984. bi-m. Arts Club Theatre, 1585 Johnston St., Vancouver, B.C. V6H 3R9, Canada. TEL 604-687-5315. FAX 604-687-3306. Ed. Lin Bennett. adv.

792 US ISSN 0004-4067
ARTS MANAGEMENT. 1962. 5/yr. $18. Radius Group Inc., 408 W. 57th St., New York, NY 10019. TEL 212-245-3850. Ed. Alvin H. Reiss. bk.rev.; stat.; index. circ. 12,000. (also avail. in microform from UMI; reprint service avail. from UMI) **Document type:** newsletter.
—UMI.
Description: National news service for those who finance, manage and communicate the arts.

ARTS MANAGEMENT WEEKLY. see BUSINESS AND ECONOMICS — Management

THEATER

792 780   CN   ISSN 0823-9746
ARTSBOARD. m. Can.$21.40. Professional Association of Canadian Theatres, PACT Communications Centre, 64 Charles St. E., 2nd Fl., Toronto, ON M4Y 1T1, Canada. TEL 416-968-3033. FAX 416-968-3035. E-mail: pact@acs.ucalgary.ca. Ed. Tracy Sigurdson. adv. circ. 800. (looseleaf format) **Document type:** bulletin.
   Description: Employment bulletin for the arts in Canada.

700   US   ISSN 0730-9023
ARTSEARCH; the national employment service bulletin for the performing arts. 1981. s-m. (23/yr.) $75 (outside N. America $125) (effective 1996). Theatre Communications Group, Inc., 355 Lexington Ave., New York, NY 10017. TEL 212-697-5230. FAX 212-983-4847. E-mail: tcg@tmn.com. Ed. Laurl G. Romanowski; Pub. Terence Nemeth. adv. circ. 5,300. (also avail. in looseleaf format) **Document type:** bulletin.
   Description: Lists jobs in theater, dance, opera companies, symphony orchestras, universities, arts councils, performing arts centers, and more.

ARTSPACE (COLUMBUS). see ART

792 950   US   ISSN 0742-5457
PN2860
ASIAN THEATRE JOURNAL. 1984. s-a. $20 to individuals (foreign $24); institutions $40 (foreign $46). (Association for Asian Performance) University of Hawaii Press, Journals Department, 2840 Kolowalu St., Honolulu, HI 96822. TEL 808-956-8833. FAX 808-988-6052. Ed. Samuel L. Leiter. adv.; bk.rev.; illus. circ. 575. (back issues avail.; reprint service avail from UMI) **Document type:** academic/scholarly publication.
   —BLDSC (1742.752300); Faxon; Genuine Article; UMI; UnCover.
   Supersedes: Asian Theatre Reports (ISSN 0161-4908)
   Description: Focuses on the performing arts of Asia.
   Refereed Serial

ASOCIACION ARGENTINA DE ACTORES. MEMORIA Y BALANCE. see LABOR UNIONS

792   IS   ISSN 0334-5963
PN2001
ASSAPH. SECTION C. STUDIES IN THE THEATRE. (Text in English) 1984. a. $10 to individuals; institutions $14.50 (effective 1995 & 1996). Tel Aviv University, Faculty of Visual and Performing Arts, Department of Theatre Arts, Ramat Aviv, Tel Aviv 69978, Israel. FAX 972-3-6409482. E-mail: rozik@ccsg.tau.ac.il. Ed. Eli Rozik. circ. 500. (back issues avail.) **Document type:** academic/scholarly publication.
   Refereed Serial

792   CN   ISSN 1193-7564
PN2009
ASSOCIATION FOR CANADIAN THEATRE RESEARCH. NEWSLETTER. 1976. s-a. Can.$50 (students Can.$20). Association for Canadian Theatre Research, c/o Department of Theatre and Film, University of British Columbia, Vancouver, BC V6T 1Z2, Canada. FAX 604-822-5985. E-mail: andrel@unixg.ubc.ca. Eds. Andre Loiselle, Richard Sutherland. circ. 250. **Document type:** newsletter.
   Formerly: Association for Canadian Theatre History. Newsletter (ISSN 0705-7989)
   Description: Contains a range of news items of interest to members, including reports of association business, conferences in related disciplines, calls for papers, annual bibliography, progress reports on research projects, abstracts from annual conference.

792 778.53   US
ASSOCIATION OF TALENT AGENTS. NEWSLETTER. m. membership. Association of Talent Agents, 9255 Sunset Blvd., Ste. 318, Los Angeles, CA 90069. TEL 310-274-0628. FAX 310-274-5063. Ed. Georgia Franklin. **Document type:** newsletter.
   Formerly: Association of Talent Agents. Bulletin.

ATOKA; Yoruba photoplay series. see LITERATURE

792 150   IT   ISSN 0392-2367
ATTI DELLO PSICODRAMMA. (Text in Italian; summaries in English) 1975. a. L.35000 for 2 years. Astrolabio-Ubaldini, Via Lungara 3, 00165 Rome, Italy. (Co-sponsor: Associazione Ricerche sullo Psicodramma Analitico di Roma) Ed. Ottavio Rosati. adv.; illus. circ. 5,000. **Indexed:** Psychol.Abstr.

792   US
AUDARENA STADIUM INTERNATIONAL GUIDE. Variant title: AudArena Stadium Guide. 1959. a. $75. B P I Communications, Amusement Business Division, Box 24970, Nashville, TN 37202. TEL 615-321-4250. FAX 615-327-1575. adv. circ. 5,000. **Indexed:** Sportsearch (1973-). **Document type:** directory.
   Former titles: Audarena Stadium Guide and International Directory (ISSN 0067-0537); Arena, Auditorium, Stadium Guide (ISSN 0518-3979)
   Description: Directory of over 5,500 arenas, auditoriums, stadiums, exhibit halls and amphitheatres in the US, Canada, and overseas. Complete data on facilities, including contracts, seating capacities, floor size and services offered.

792   US
AUDITION NEWS. m. $24.95. Chicago Entertainment Co., 6272 W. North Ave., Chicago, IL 60639. adv.; illus.

AUSTIN CHRONICLE. see MUSIC

792   AT   ISSN 0810-4123
PN3010
AUSTRALASIAN DRAMA STUDIES. 1982. s-a. Aus.$30 (foreign Aus.$40) (effective 1995). University of Queensland, c/o Department of English, St. Lucia, Qld. 4072, Australia. TEL 61-7-3642147. FAX 61-7-3652799. E-mail: enrfothe@mailbox.uq.oz.au. Eds. V. Kelly, R. Fotheringham. adv.; bk.rev. circ. 500. **Indexed:** Bibl.Engl.Lang.& Lit. **Document type:** academic/scholarly publication.
   —UnCover.
   Description: Theatre studies with an emphasis on Australian and New Zealand drama.
   Refereed Serial

800 780.6   PO
AUTORES. 1958. 4/yr. free. Sociedade Portuguesa de Autores, Av. Duque de Loule, 31, 1069 Lisbon Codex, Portugal. FAX 351-1-3530257. Dir. Dr. Luiz Francisco Rebello. charts; illus.

792   FR   ISSN 0045-1169
PN6113
AVANT SCENE THEATRE. 1949. 20/yr. 720 F. (foreign 906 F.) (effective 1996). Editions de l' Avant Scene, 6 rue Git-le-Coeur, 75006 Paris, France. TEL 1-46-34-28-20. FAX 1-43-54-50-14. **Indexed:** Arts & Hum.Cit.Ind., Curr.Cont.
   —BLDSC (1837.119000); Faxon; SWETS.

792   US
BACK STAGE; the performing arts weekly. 1960. w. $69. B P I Communications, Inc. (New York), 1515 Broadway, 14th Fl., New York, NY 10036. TEL 212-764-7300. FAX 212-536-5318. Ed. Sherry Eaker; Pub. Steve Elish. adv. contact: Scott Berg. bk.rev.; play rev.; illus.; tr.lit. circ. 30,000. (tabloid format; also avail. in microfiche from UMI; reprint service avail. from UMI) **Indexed:** Tr.& Indus.Ind. **Document type:** trade publication.
   —CCC.
   Incorporates (in 1977): Business Screen (ISSN 0007-7046)
   Description: Presents news stories, informative columns, reviews, previews of upcoming theatre seasons, listings of agents, casting directors, rehearsal spaces, personal managers, acting coaches, and casting notices for stage, screen, television and cabaret performers and staff.

792   US
BACK STAGE WEST; the performing arts weekly. w. $69. B P I Communications, Inc., 5055 Wilshire Blvd., Los Angeles, CA 90036. TEL 213-525-2356. FAX 213-965-1340. Ed. Rob Kendt; Pub. Steve Elish. adv. contact: Scott Berg. bk.rev.; play rev.; illus.; tr.lit.; circ. 7,100 (paid). (tabloid format) **Document type:** newspaper.
   Description: Presents news stories, informative columns, reviews, previews of upcoming theatre seasons, listings of agents, casting directors, rehearsal spaces, personal managers, acting coaches, and casting notices for stage, screen, television and cabaret performers and staff.

BALLET-HOO. see DANCE

792   IS   ISSN 0045-138X
BAMAH (JERUSALEM); educational theatre review. (Text in Hebrew; summaries in English) 1933. q. $40. Bamah Association, P.O. Box 24290, Jerusalem 91240, Israel. TEL 972-2-883986. FAX 972-2-883989. Eds. Amos Yovel, Dwora Gilula. adv.; bk.rev.; index, cum.index. **Indexed:** Ind.Heb.Per. **Document type:** academic/scholarly publication.

791.3   US   ISSN 0005-4968
BANDWAGON; the circusiana magazine. 1939. 6/yr. $19. Circus Historical Society, 2515 Dorset Rd., Columbus, OH 43221. TEL 614-294-5361. Ed. Fred D. Pfening, Jr. adv.; bk.rev.; illus. circ. 1,800. (also avail. in microform)

792 821   UK   ISSN 0264-6137
BARE NIBS. 1983. q. £2.60($5) Ware Arts Centre, 31 Richmond Close, Ware, Herts., England. (Subscr. addr.: 24 The Ridgeway, Ware, Herts., England) Ed. Steve Woollard. adv. circ. 150. (back issues avail.)

THE BEAT (HIGHLAND). see MUSIC

792   IT   ISSN 0045-1959
BIBLIOTECA TEATRALE; rivista di studi e ricerche sullo spettacolo. 1971-1979 (no. 23-24); resumed 1987. q. L.55000($12) (Istituto Internazionale per la Ricerca Teatrale) Bulzoni Editore, 14 via dei Liburni, 00185 Rome, Italy. TEL 06-4455207. FAX 06-4450355. Eds. Ferruccio Marotti, Cesare Molinari. adv.; bk.rev.; abstr.; bibl.; index, cum.index. (back issues avail.)

792   GW   ISSN 0006-4378
BLAETTER DER FREIEN VOLKSBUEHNE BERLIN. 1947. bi-m. DM.7. Verlag der Freien Volksbuehne Berlin e.V., Ruhrstr. 6, 10709 Berlin, Germany. Ed. Guenter Schulz. adv.; bk.rev.; play rev.; illus.; stat.; index. circ. 24,000.

792.08854   DK
BOERNETEATERAVISEN. 1972. q. DKK 98. Teatercentrum i Danmark, Frederiksborggade 20, DK-1360 Copenhagen K, Denmark. TEL 45-33-15-69-00. FAX 45-33-13-14-39. Ed. Carsten Jensen. bk.rev.; circ. 14,000 (controlled). **Document type:** consumer publication, newsletter.
   Formerly: Teater for Boern og Unge (ISSN 0901-0106)
   Description: Focuses on professional theater for children and youth. Includes articles on cultural, political and economic matters relevant to the theater world. Features reviews of plays, interviews and biographical sketches of actors.

BOMB; artists, writers, actors, directors. see ART

BORDER CROSSINGS. see ART

792   UK   ISSN 0951-5208
BRITISH PERFORMING ARTS YEARBOOK. 1987. a. £18.95. Rhinegold Publishing Ltd., 241 Shaftesbury Ave., London WC2H 8EH, England. TEL 0171-333-1762. FAX 0171-333-1769. Ed. Sheena Barbour. **Document type:** directory.
   Description: A complete guide to venues, performers, arts centers, festivals, education, support organizations and services for the arts professional.

791.53   UK
BRITISH PUPPET AND MODEL THEATRE GUILD. NEWSLETTER. 1956. m. £12 membership (includes Puppet Master, the Guild Magazine). British Puppet and Model Theatre Guild, c/o Gordon Shapley, Ed., 18 Maple Rd., Yeading, Hayes, Mddx. UB4 9LP, England. bk.rev. circ. 400. **Document type:** newsletter.
   Description: For amateur and professional puppeteers thoughout the U.K. and the world.

792 380   UK   ISSN 0306-4107
PN2595
BRITISH THEATRE DIRECTORY. 1972. a. £28.95. Richmond House Publishing Company Ltd., 3 Richmond Bldgs., London W1V 5AE, England. TEL 0171-437-9556. FAX 0171-287-3463. Ed. Samantha Blair. adv. contact: Spencer Block. **Document type:** directory.
   —BLDSC (6291.237800).

THEATER

792 US ISSN 0068-2748
BROADSIDE (NEW YORK, 1940). (Supplement avail.: Performance Arts Resources (ISSN: (0360-3814)) 1940; N.S. 1973. q. $20 to individuals; institutions $25. Theatre Library Association, 111 Amsterdam Ave., New York, NY 10023. TEL 212-870-1670. bk.rev. circ. 500. (back issues avail.) **Indexed:** Lib.Lit.
Description: Includes information regarding TLA sponsored events, articles about exhibits and collections related to the performing arts, and other items of interest in the fields of theatre, film and dance worldwide.

792 AU ISSN 0007-3075
PN2004
BUEHNE. 1923. 11/yr. S.380. Orac Zeitschriftenverlag GmbH, Schoenbrunnerstr. 59, A-1050 Vienna, Austria. TEL 01-54621-0. FAX 01-5462178. Ed. Elisabeth Hirschmann. adv.; B&W page S.36600, color page S.62220; trim 185 x 250. bk.rev.; play rev.; rec.rev.; illus.; circ. 98,400 (controlled). **Indexed:** Music Ind. **Document type:** consumer publication.

792 GW ISSN 0007-3083
BUEHNENGENOSSENSCHAFT. 1949. 10/yr. DM.56. (Genossenschaft Deutscher Buehnen-Angehoeriger) Buehnenschriften-Vertriebs-Gesellschaft, Feldbrunnenstr. 74, 20148 Hamburg, Germany. TEL 040-445185. FAX 040-456002. Ed. Hans Herdlein. adv.; bk.rev.; illus.

792 GW ISSN 0007-3091
BUEHNENTECHNISCHE RUNDSCHAU; Zeitschrift fuer Theatertechnik, Buehnenbau und Buehnengestaltung. 1907. 6/yr. DM.75. (Deutsche Theatertechnische Gesellschaft) Erhard Friedrich Verlag GmbH, Im Brande 17, 30926 Seelze, Germany. TEL 0511-40004-0. FAX 0511-4000444. Ed. Prof. W. Unruh. adv.; bk.rev.; abstr.; bibl.; charts; illus.; cum.index every 2 yrs. circ. 1,600. **Indexed:** Br.Tech.Ind. **Document type:** trade publication.
—BLDSC (2357.700000); Faxon.

792 US
BURNS MANTLE BEST PLAY ANNUAL. 1919. a. $36.95 cloth; paper $18.95. Applause Theatre Book Publishers, 211 W. 71st St., New York, NY 10023. TEL 212-595-4735. FAX 212-721-2856. Eds. Otis L. Guernsey, Jeffrey Sweet. circ. 20,000.

C A NEWS. (Christians in the Arts Networking, Inc.) see ART

792 FR ISSN 0295-9909
CAHIERS DU G I T A. 1985. a. 150 F. Universite de Montpellier (Universite Paul Valery), Groupe Interdisciplinaire du Theatre Antique, B.P. 5043, 34032 Montpellier Cedex 1, France. TEL 67-14-20-00. Ed. Paulette Ghiron-Bistagne. bk.rev. **Document type:** academic/scholarly publication.

792 CN ISSN 0045-3044
CALLBOARD. 1951. a. Can.$5 (foreign Can.$8). Nova Scotia Drama League, 1809 Barrington St., Ste. 901, Halifax, NS B3J 3K8, Canada. TEL 902-425-3876. FAX 902-422-0881. Ed. Eva J. Moore. adv.; bk.rev. circ. 1,100. **Document type:** consumer publication.

792 US ISSN 1064-0703
CALLBOARD (SAN FRANCISCO); monthly theatre news magazine. 1976. m. $35. Theatre Bay Area, 657 Mission St., Ste. 402, San Francisco, CA 94105-4116. TEL 415-957-1557. FAX 415-957-1556. Ed. Belinda Taylor. adv.; bk.rev. circ. 5,000. (back issues avail.) **Document type:** trade publication.
Description: Provides trade information for professionals in the Bay Area.

817 US
CALLIOPE (BALTIMORE). 1968. m. membership. Clowns of America, Inc, 1052 Foxwood Ln., Baltimore, MD 21221. Ed. Albert E. Sikorsky, Jr. adv.; bk.rev.; bibl. circ. 6,000.
Supersedes: Joeygram (ISSN 0021-7158)

CAMPUS ACTIVITIES PROGRAMMING. see EDUCATION — Higher Education

CANADA COUNCIL ANNUAL REPORT AND SUPPLEMENT/RAPPORT ANNUEL DU CONSEIL DES ARTS DU CANADA ET SON SUPPLEMENT. see ART

792 CN
CANADA ON STAGE. 1974. irreg. Can.$40. Professional Association of Canadian Theatres, PACT Communications Centre, 64 Charles St. E., 2nd Fl., Toronto, ON M4Y 1T1, Canada. TEL 416-968-3033. E-mail: pact@acs.ucalgary.ca. illus.; index. **Document type:** trade publication.
Former titles: Canada on Stage: The National Theatre Yearbook; Canada on Stage: Canadian Theatre Review Yearbook (ISSN 0380-9455)

792 CN ISSN 0315-0836
PN2009
CANADIAN THEATRE REVIEW. 1974. q. $32.50 to individuals; institutions $55; students $30. University of Toronto Press, Journals Department, 5201 Dufferin St., Downsview, ON M3H 5T8, Canada. TEL 416-667-7781. FAX 416-667-7881. Ed. Alan Filewood. adv.; bk.rev.; illus.; play rev.; cum.index: nos.1-16. circ. 1,088. (also avail. in microform from MML; back issues avail.) **Indexed:** Arts & Hum.Cit.Ind., Can.B.P.I., Can.Per.Ind., Can.Wom.Per.Ind., CMI, Curr.Cont., Ind.Bk.Rev.Hum., M.L.A., Mid.East: Abstr.& Ind. **Document type:** academic/scholarly publication.
—Faxon; Genuine Article; UnCover. CCC.

792 CN ISSN 0829-3627
CANPLAY. bi-m. Can.$26. Playwrights Union of Canada, 54 Wolseley St., 2nd Fl., Toronto, ON M5T 1A5, Canada. TEL 416-947-0201; 800-561-3318. FAX 416-947-0159. Ed. Jodi Armstrong. adv. contact: Jodi Armstrong. circ. 650. (back issues avail.) **Document type:** newsletter.
Former titles (until 1984): Playwrights Union of Canada. Newsletter (ISSN 0827-3073); (until 1983): Guild of Canadian Playwrights. Newsletter (ISSN 0824-5460)

792 IT ISSN 0394-9389
IL CASTELLO DI ELSINORE. 1988. 3/yr. L.65000 (Europe L.95000; elsewhere L.105000) (effective 1995). Rosenberg and Sellier, Via Andrea Doria, 14, 10123 Turin, Italy. TEL 39-11-8127820. FAX 39-11-8127744.

CASTINGDEX. see MOTION PICTURES

790.2 US
CAVALCADE OF ACTS & ATTRACTIONS. 1973. a. $55. B P I Communications, Amusement Business Division, Box 24970, Nashville, TN 37202. TEL 615-321-4250. FAX 615-327-1575. circ. 5,000. **Document type:** directory.
Formerly: Cavalcade and Directory of Acts and Attractions (ISSN 0090-2993)
Description: Directory of personal appearance artists (musical and theatrical), touring shows, carnivals and other specialized entertainment such as fireworks firms, and rodeos. Also contains listings of booking agents, personal managers, promoters and producers.

CELEBRITY ACCESS: THE DIRECTORY (YEAR); or how and where to write the rich and famous. see MOTION PICTURES

792 301.4157 US
CENTER STAGE (NEW YORK). 1987. m. $25. Lesbian & Gay Community Services Center, Inc., 208 W. 13th St., New York, NY 10011. TEL 212-620-7310. Ed. Dino Georgiou. circ. 23,000.

CENTRE CULTUREL FRANCAIS DE YAOUNDE. PROGRAMME SAISON. see ART

CHIRICU. see LITERATURE

CINEGUIA; annuario espanol del espectaculo y audiovisuales. see MOTION PICTURES

CINESCHEDARIO - LETTURE DRAMMATICHE. see MOTION PICTURES

792 NE
CIRCUS-GIDS NEDERLAND. m. fl.27.50. Piet de Jong, C.H. Petersstraat 10, 9714 CK Groningen, Netherlands. Ed. John de Vries. bk.rev. circ. 700.

790 GW
CIRCUS-PARADE. 1976. m. DM.85. Circus-Club International, Klosterhof 10, 24211 Preetz, Germany. TEL 04342-83103. Ed. Friedel Zscharschuch. adv.; bk.rev. circ. 4,000. **Document type:** bulletin.

792 US ISSN 0889-5996
CIRCUS REPORT. 1972. w. $40 (Canada and Mexico $45; elsewhere $50). 525 Oak St., El Cerrito, CA 94530-3699. TEL 510-525-3332. Ed. Don Marcks. adv.; bk.rev.; circ. 2,000 (paid). **Document type:** trade publication.

791.3 FR ISSN 0009-7373
CIRQUE DANS L'UNIVERS. 1950. q. 250 F. (foreign 300 F.). Club du Cirque, 116 rue Damremont, 75018 Paris, France. Ed. Marika Maymard. adv.; bk.rev.; illus. circ. 2,000.

792 800 US ISSN 0748-237X
CLIPPER STUDIES IN THE THEATER. 1985. irreg. (approx. 5/yr.). no.12, 1995. price varies. Borgo Press, Box 2845, San Bernardino, CA 92406. TEL 909-884-5813. FAX 909-888-4942. Ed. William L. Slout. **Document type:** monographic series.
Description: Monographs and anthologies on American and European theatre, from its beginnings to modern times.

792 BL
COLECAO TEATRO. no.2, 1974. irreg. Universidade Federal do Rio Grande do Sul, Porto Alegre, Brazil. bibl. **Document type:** monographic series.

COLOQUIO: ARTES; revista de artes visuais musica e bailado. see ART

792 FR ISSN 1164-382X
COMEDIE FRANCAISE. 1971. 4/yr. 300 F. (foreign 350 F.). Editions P.O.L, 8 villa d'Alesia, 75014 Paris, France. Ed. Jean-Loup Riviere. adv.; bk.rev.; illus. circ. 25,000.
—BLDSC (2948.095000).
Formerly (until 1991): Comedie Francaise. Les Cahiers (ISSN 0759-125X)

791 792.2 US ISSN 1065-1020
COMEDY U S A INDUSTRY GUIDE. 1989. a. $58.95 (effective 1993). Laughing Matter, Inc., Box 990, New York, NY 10156-0990. TEL 212-532-0171. Ed. Leslie Orlovsky; Pub. Barry Weintraub. circ. 5,000. **Document type:** directory, trade publication.
Description: Includes contact information for comedians, comedy writers, their agents, managers and publicists, comedy clubs, and talent coordinators.

COMMUNICATION QUARTERLY. see EDUCATION

COMMUNICATIONS FROM THE INTERNATIONAL BRECHT SOCIETY. see LITERATURE

792 US
COMPLETE CATALOGUE OF PLAYS (YEAR). 1936. a. Dramatists Play Service, Inc., 440 Park Ave. S., New York, NY 10016. TEL 212-683-8960. FAX 212-213-1539. Ed. Stephen Sultan. adv.; bk.rev. circ. 35,000. **Document type:** catalog.
Description: Lists all plays leased by the Dramatists Play Service, including title, author, quotes from reviews, cast and scenic requirements, and a description of the play.

792 CU ISSN 0010-5937
PN1608
CONJUNTO. 1964. q. $10 in N. America; S. America $12; Europe $17. (Casa de las Americas, Departamento de Teatro) Ediciones Cubanas, Obispo No. 461, Aptdo. 605, Havana, Cuba. Dir. Manuel Galich. abstr.; bibl.; illus. circ. 3,000. **Indexed:** Hisp.Amer.Per.Ind. (1970-).

CONNECTICUT POETRY REVIEW. see LITERATURE — Poetry

792.028 791.4 UK
CONSORTIUM FOR DRAMA & MEDIA IN HIGHER EDUCATION. NEWSLETTER. 2/yr. membership. British Universities Film and Video Council, 55 Greek St., London W1V 5LR, England. TEL 071-734-3687. FAX 071-287-3914. Ed. Lucy Board. bk.rev.; film rev.; play rev. circ. 5,500. (looseleaf format; back issues avail.) **Document type:** newsletter.

CONTACTS/KONTAKTE. see PUBLISHING AND BOOK TRADE

792 384.55 UK ISSN 0010-7344
CONTACTS. 1947. a. Spotlight, 7 Leicester Pl., London WC2H 7BP, England. TEL 0171-437-7631. FAX 0171-437-5881. Ed. Christine Barry. **Document type:** directory.

THEATER

792 780.65   AT   ISSN 1032-6456
CONTACTS & FACILITIES IN THE AUSTRALIAN ENTERTAINMENT INDUSTRY. 1963. a. Aus.$55 (foreign Aus.$80). Showcast Publications, P.O. Box 951, Crows Nest, N.S.W. 2065, Australia. TEL 02-4382144. FAX 02-438-2007.
   Formerly: Contacts and Facilities in the Entertainment Industry.

792   US   ISSN 1050-3919
CONTEMPORARY DRAMATISTS. 1973. irreg. St. Martin's Press, 175 5th Ave., New York, NY 10010. TEL 800-221-7945. TELEX TWX 710-581-6459.

CONTEMPORARY THEATRE, FILM & TELEVISION. see *BIOGRAPHY*

792   US   ISSN 1048-6801
PN2001   CODEN: CTHRE9
CONTEMPORARY THEATRE REVIEW; an international journal. 1991. 2/yr. (in 1 vol., 2 nos./vol.). 65 ECU (effective 1996). Harwood Academic Publishers, 820 Town Center Dr., Langhorne, PA 19047. TEL 215-750-2642. FAX 215-750-6343. (Subsc. to: International Publishers Distributor, PO Box 90, Reading, Berkshire, RG1 8JL, England. TEL 44-173-456-8316) Eds. Franc Chamberlain, Rick Tavorian. (also avail. in microform) **Document type:** proceedings.
—BLDSC (3425.307770). **CCC.**
   Description: Covers research in the field of performance, including all aspects of the theatre event.
   Refereed Serial

792   US   ISSN 1049-6513
CONTEMPORARY THEATRE STUDIES. irreg., latest vol.8. Harwood Academic Publishers, c/o International Publishers Distributor, 820 Town Center Dr., Langhorne, PA 19047. TEL 215-750-2642. FAX 215-750-6343. (Subscr. to: International Publishers Distributor, PO Box 90, Reading, Berkshire, RG1 8JL, England. TEL 44-173-456-8316) Ed. Rick Takvorian. (also avail. in microform)
   Refereed Serial

792   US   ISSN 0163-3821
CONTRIBUTIONS IN DRAMA AND THEATRE STUDIES. 1979. irreg., no.47, 1992. price varies. Greenwood Press, Inc. (Subsidiary of: Greenwood Publishing Group Inc.), 88 Post Rd. W., Box 5007, Westport, CT 06881-5007. TEL 203-226-3571. FAX 203-222-1502. Ed. Joseph Donohue.
—BLDSC (3458.310000).

792.028
THE COSTUMER. 1923. 6/yr. $30. National Costumers Association, Inc., c/o Mary Lou Landes Schultz, Ed., 811 N. Capitol Ave., Indianapolis, IN 46204. TEL 317-635-3655. FAX 317-267-8978. adv.; bk.rev. circ. 500. **Document type:** trade publication.
   Formerly: National Costumers Magazine.

792   US
COUNCIL OF JEWISH THEATRES NEWSLETTER. 1991. s-a. free. National Foundation for Jewish Culture, 330 Seventh Ave., 21st Fl., New York, NY 10001. TEL 212-629-0500. FAX 212-629-0508. play rev.; circ. 350 (controlled). (back issues avail.) **Document type:** newsletter.
   Description: Dedicated to promoting the interests of non-profit theaters in North America whose primary mission is the development and production of plays relevant to Jewish life and values.

792   IT
CRONACHE DEL TEATRO; settimanale di informazioni e rassegna stampa. 1981. w. L.190000. A G I S Lombarda, Piazza Luigi di Savoia, 24, 20124 Milan, Italy. TEL 02-6690241. film rev. circ. 250. (looseleaf format; back issues avail.)
   Description: Covers theater, critical theatrical study and Italian films viewed on Italian television.

792.022   NE   ISSN 0038-7258
D O E. 1951. bi-m. fl.17.50. Stichting "Ons Leekenspel", Gudelalaan 2, Bussum, Netherlands. Ed.Bd. bk.rev.; bibl.; illus. circ. 1,300.
   Formerly: Speel.

DAILY VARIETY; news of the entertainment industry. see *COMMUNICATIONS — Television And Cable*

792.09489   DK   ISSN 0907-4015
DAMARKS TEATERFORENINGERS TEATERSEMINAR. 1982. a. DKK 45. Danmarks Teaterforeninger, Frederiksborggade 20-3 m.f., 1360 Copenhagen K, Denmark. TEL 33-15-42-48. FAX 33-13-14-39.
   Formerly (until 1992): Teaterseminar (ISSN 0109-3363)

792   CC   ISSN 1002-2996
DANGDAI XIJU/CONTEMPORARY DRAMA; xiju - dianshi shuangyuekan. (Text in Chinese) 1983. bi-m. $23.90. Zhongguo Xijujia Xiehui, Shaanxi Fenhui - China Dramatists Association, Shaanxi Chapter, 172, Dongmutou Jie, Xi'an, Shaanxi 710001, People's Republic of China. TEL 23171. (Dist. in US by: China Books & Periodicals, Inc., 2929 24th St., San Francisco, CA 94110. TEL 415-282-2994) Ed. Du Yaomin.

792   CC   ISSN 1003-1200
DAWUTAI. (Text in Chinese) bi-m. Hebei Sheng Yishu Yanjiusuo - Hebei Art Research Institute, 41, Beima Lu, Shijiazhuang, Hebei 050071, People's Republic of China. TEL 743588. Ed. Feng Feng.

700   US
DENVER ARTS CENTER PROGRAMS. m. Publishing House, Inc., P.O. Box 215, Westminster, CO 80030-4860. TEL 303-428-9529. FAX 303-430-1676. Ed. Melanie Simonete. circ. 1,224,000.

792   GW   ISSN 0011-975X
DIE DEUTSCHE BUEHNE; Theatermagazin. 1909. m. DM.84. (Deutscher Buehnenverein) Erhard Friedrich Verlag GmbH, Im Brande 17, 30926 Seelze, Germany. TEL 0511-40004-0. FAX 0511-4000444. Ed. Wolfgang Ruf. adv.; bk.rev.; charts; illus.; play rev.; index. circ. 4,000. (reprint service avail. from KTO) **Document type:** trade publication.
   Description: Covers German and international performing arts.

792   GW   ISSN 0070-4431
PN2640
DEUTSCHES BUEHNEN-JAHRBUCH; Theatergeschichtliches Jahr- und Adressbuch. 1889. a. DM.66. (Genossenschaft Deutscher Buehnen-Angehoeriger) Buehnenschriften-Vertriebs-Gesellschaft, Feldbrunnenstr. 74, 20148 Hamburg, Germany. TEL 040-445185. FAX 040-456002. adv.

792 700   US
DIABLO ARTS MAGAZINE. 1990. q. Diablo Publications, 2520 Camino Diablo, Ste. 200, Walnut Creek, CA 94596. TEL 510-943-1111. FAX 510-943-1045. Ed. Peggy Spect. adv. contact: Barney Fonzi. circ. 65,000. (back issues avail.) **Document type:** consumer publication.
   Description: Covers art galleries and visual and performing arts.

792   PL   ISSN 0012-2041
PN1607
DIALOG; miesiecznik poswiecony dramaturgii wspolczesnej teatralnej, filmowej, radiowej i telewizyjnej. 1956. m. $60. Ul. Pulawska 61, 02-595 Warsaw, Poland. TEL 48-22-455475. FAX 48-22-453935. (Dist. by: Ars Polona-Ruch, Krakowskie Przedmiescie 7, Warsaw, Poland. TEL 48-22-267622) Ed. Jacek Sieradzki. bk.rev. circ. 3,000. Indexed: M.L.A.
   Description: Devoted to contemporary drama and theatre.

808.2   DK   ISSN 0109-9450
DIALOG (AARHUS). 1984. m. membership. Dramatikerstudio, Rosensgade 11, DK-8000 Aarhus, Denmark. Ed. Britta Lundqvist. adv.; bk.rev.

DIRECTORY OF HISPANIC TALENT. see *MOTION PICTURES*

DIRECTORY OF NORTH AMERICAN FAIRS, FESTIVALS AND EXPOSITIONS. see *SPORTS AND GAMES — Outdoor Life*

791.53   UK   ISSN 0142-3681
DIRECTORY OF PROFESSIONAL PUPPETEERS. 1976. biennial. £7.50. Puppet Centre Trust, Battersea Arts Centre, Lavender Hill, London SW11 5TN, England. TEL 071-228-5335. Ed. Phyllida Shaw. illus. circ. 2,000. (back issues avail.) **Document type:** directory.

DIRECTORY OF THE ARTS. see *ART*

792   US   ISSN 1041-7273
PN2078.U6
DIRECTORY OF THEATRE FACULTIES IN COLLEGES AND UNIVERSITIES, U S & CANADA. 1988. biennial. $55. C M S Publications, Inc., Box 8208, Missoula, MT 59807. TEL 406-728-2002; 800-729-0235. FAX 406-721-9419. E-mail: mu_cms@lewis.umt.edu. **Document type:** directory.
   Description: Lists over 7,000 faculty and over 1,100 schools or department of theatre.

DISKADALIA; ancient theater today. see *CLASSICAL STUDIES*

792   XR   ISSN 1210-471X
DIVADELNI NOVINY. fortn. 26 Kc. Dovadelni Ustav, Celetna 17, 110 01 Prague 1, Czech Republic. Ed. Helena Albertova.
   Formerly: Divadelni a Filmove Noviny (ISSN 0012-4141)

791.5   SW   ISSN 0349-9944
DOCKTEATER-EKO. 1971. q. SEK 120. Stiftelsen Dockteater-Eko, Smedjegatan 3, S-732 30 Arboga, Sweden. TEL 46-589-17-350.
   Description: Deals with everything related to the art of puppetry.

DOCTOR WHO MAGAZINE. see *COMMUNICATIONS — Television And Cable*

792   BE   ISSN 0771-8640
DOCUMENTA; tijdschrift voor theater. (Text in Dutch) 1983. q. 350 BEF. Documentatiecentrum voor Dramatische Kunst v.z.w., Rozier 44, 9000 Gent, Belgium. TEL 32-9-2643696. FAX 32-9-2644184. Ed. Jozef de Vos. adv.; bk.rev.; play rev.; abstr.; bibl.; illus. circ. 600. (back issues avail.) **Document type:** academic/scholarly publication.

792   YU   ISSN 0351-5494
DOKUMENTI - INFORMACIJE. (Text in Macedonian, Serbo-Croation, Slovenian) 1978. s-a. Sterijino Pozorje, Zmaj Jovina 22, 21000 Novi Sad, Voivodina, Yugoslavia. TEL 021-23-161. FAX 021-615-976.

792   GW
DOMSPATZ; Zeitschrift fuer Fulda. 1981. m. DM.25($30) Domspatz Verlag, Kanalstr. 14, 36037 Fulda, Germany. TEL 0661-75515. FAX 0661-78430. Ed. Johannes Guedelhoefer. adv.; film rev.; charts. (back issues avail.) **Document type:** newsletter.
   Description: News and articles about cultural events in Fulda.

792   UK   ISSN 0967-4454
DRAMA; one forum many voices. 1973. 3/yr. £15 (foreign £16.50). National Drama Publications, 6 Cornwell Ct., Castle Dene, S. Gosforth, Newcastle-upon-Tyne NE3 1TT, England. TEL 0191-284-6520. E-mail: jc@cmac.demon.co.uk. Ed. John Carey. bk.rev.; illus. circ. 1,500. **Document type:** trade publication.
   Formerly (until 1992): Drama Magazine; Incorporates (in 1990): London Drama Magazine.
   Description: Provides a forum for all drama practitioners to: share theory and practice, debate key issues, publish research, engage in critical analysis, and express opinion.

792 800   US   ISSN 1056-4349
PN1601
DRAMA CRITICISM. 1991. a. $75. Gale Research Inc., 835 Penobscot Bldg., Detroit, MI 48226-4094. TEL 313-961-2242. FAX 313-961-6083. TELEX 810-221-7086. Ed. Lawrence J. Trudeau.
   Description: Provides excerpts from significant commentary on 12-15 of the most widely studied dramatists from antiquity to contemporary times in each volume.

DRAMA-LOGUE. see *MOTION PICTURES*

DRAMASCOPE. see *PSYCHOLOGY*

792 US ISSN 0012-5989
PN3175.A1
DRAMATICS; devoted to the advancement of theatre arts in the secondary schools. 1929. 9/yr. $18. Educational Theatre Association, 3368 Central Parkway, Cincinnati, OH 45225. TEL 513-559-1996. Ed. Don Corathers. adv. contact: Claire Cundiff. bk.rev.; charts; illus.; index; circ. 35,500 (paid). (also avail. in microform from UMI; back issues avail.; reprint service avail. from UMI) Indexed: Curr.Cont. **Document type:** consumer publication.
—Faxon; SWETS; UMI; UnCover.
 Formerly: Dramatics-Dramatic Curtain.
 Description: Publishes articles on acting, directing, playwriting, tech theatre and other performing art skills. Also contains college and career information, playscripts, and features on theatre and theatre people.

792 US
DRAMATISTS GUILD NEWSLETTER. 1977. m. (except Jul., Aug.). members only. Dramatists Guild, Inc., 234 W. 44th St., New York, NY 10036. TEL 212-398-9366. Ed. Scott Segal. circ. 7,500. (tabloid format; back issues avail.) **Document type:** newsletter.
 Description: Contains announcements of all Guild activities, news and information of interest to dramatists.

792 US ISSN 0012-6004
PN2000
DRAMATISTS GUILD QUARTERLY. 1964. q. membership. Dramatists Guild, Inc., 234 W. 44th St., New York, NY 10036. TEL 212-398-9366. Ed. Ben Pesner. adv.; bk.rev. circ. 8,200. **Document type:** academic/scholarly publication.
—Faxon; UnCover.
 Description: Covers all aspects of theatre.

792 US
DRAMATISTS GUILD RESOURCE DIRECTORY. a. members only. Dramatists Guild, Inc., 234 W. 44th St., Penthouse, New York, NY 10036-3909. TEL 212-398-9366. Dir. Richard Garmise. **Document type:** directory.
 Description: Contains up-to-date information on agents, attorneys, grants, producers, playwriting contests, conferences and workshops.

800 US ISSN 0733-1606
PN2289
DRAMATISTS SOURCEBOOK. 1982. a. $15.95. Theatre Communications Group, Inc., 355 Lexington Ave., New York, NY 10017. TEL 212-697-5230. FAX 212-983-4847. E-mail: tcg@tmn.com. Ed.Bd; Pub. Terence Nemeth. index. circ. 7,000.
 Description: Lists opportunities for playwrights, translations, composers, lyricists, and librettists, in addition to screen, radio, and television writers.

792 UK ISSN 0141-1179
DRAMAU'R BYD. (Text in Welsh) 1969. irreg. price varies. (Welsh Arts Council) University of Wales Press, 6 Gwennyth St., Cathays, Cardiff CF2 4YD, Wales. TEL 01222-31919. FAX 01222-230908. Ed. William R. Lewis. **Document type:** academic/scholarly publication.
 Description: Contains major European plays translated into Welsh.

800 700 US ISSN 1048-9401
NX449
EARLY DRAMA, ART, AND MUSIC REVIEW. 1978. s-a. $8 to individuals; institutions $10. Medieval Institute Publications, Western Michigan University, Kalamazoo, MI 49008. TEL 616-387-8755. FAX 616-387-8750. Ed. Clifford Davidson. bk.rev. circ. 250. (back issues avail.)
 Incorporates: Medieval Music-Drama News; **Formerly:** E D A M Newsletter (ISSN 0196-5816)
 Description: Brief articles about, reviews of, and notes and announcements about activities of concern to the Early Drama, Art and Music project at the university.

792 US ISSN 0013-1997
EDUCATIONAL THEATRE NEWS. 1952. 6/yr. $3. Southern California Educational Theatre Association, 9811 Pounds Ave., Whittier, CA 90603. TEL 310-947-6334. FAX 310-947-6533. Ed. Lee Korf. adv.; bk.rev.; film rev.; play rev.; illus. circ. 3,100. (tabloid format) **Document type:** newspaper.
 Description: News coverage of secondary, youth, community, and college-university and international theatre activities, including conferences, legislation, and technical advances.

792 RU ISSN 0868-9024
PN1993
EKRAN. 1957. m. $77 (effective 1996). (Soyuz Kinematografistov) Ekran, Ul. Chasovaya 5, B, 125319 Moscow, Russia. TEL 152-88-21. (Dist. in U.S. by: Victor Kamkin Inc., 4956 Boiling Brook Pkwy., Rockville, MD 20852. TEL 301-881-5973) Ed. V.P. Demin. illus.; index. circ. 50,000.
 Formerly: (until no.1, 1991): Sovetskii Ekran (ISSN 0038-5123)

792 AU
ELISABETHBUEHNE MAGAZIN. 5/yr. S.35. Elisabethbuehne Salzburg, Plainstr. 42, A-5020 Salzburg, Austria. TEL 0662-880336. FAX 0662-880335. adv.; circ. 22,000. **Document type:** bulletin.

792 II ISSN 0013-6980
ENACT; monthly theatre magazine. (Text in English) 1967. m. Rs.35($12.50) Paul's Press, E44-11, Okhla Industrial Area, Phase II, New Delhi 110020, India. Ed. Rajinder Paul. adv.; bk.rev.; film rev.; play rev. circ. 48,448.

ENCORE (BLACKSBURG). see LITERATURE

791.4 UK
ENGLISH NATIONAL OPERA PROGRAMME. m. £1 per no. English National Opera, London Coliseum, St. Martin's Ln., London WC2, England. FAX 01-836-8379. Ed. Nicholas John. adv. circ. 25,000.
 Description: Each opera has separate program.

792 US
ENSEMBLE; the new variety arts review. 1987. q. $30. Corporeal Studio Ltd., One Hudson St., New York, NY 10013. TEL 212-619-0152. (Subscr. to: Box 227, Canal St. Sta., New York, NY 10013) Ed. J.R. Moore. adv.; bk.rev.; film rev.; play rev.; illus. circ. 1,500. (tabloid format; back issues avail.) **Document type:** consumer publication.
 Description: Reviews and critism of mime, clown, juggling, variety acts, dance, performance art and film.

ENTERTAINMENT LAW & FINANCE. see LAW

THE ENTERTAINMENT MAGAZINE ON-LINE. see MUSIC

ENTERTAINMENT, PUBLISHING AND THE ARTS HANDBOOK. see COMMUNICATIONS — Television And Cable

792 SW ISSN 0345-2581
ENTRE; teatertidskrift. 1974. q. SEK 200 in Sweden; elsewhere SEK 240 (incl. Teateraarsboken SEK 450 (foreign SEK 500) (effective 1996). Svenska Riksteatern - Swedish National Touring Theatre, S-145 83 Norsborg, Sweden. TEL 8-531-99-352. FAX 8-531-83-012. Ed. Claes Englund. bk.rev. circ. 3,000.
 Description: Contains theater and book reviews, general information and criticism, and a performance calendar for Sweden.

792 CN ISSN 0319-8650
ENVERS DU DECOR; la vie du theatre. (Text in French) vol.5, 1973. bi-m. free. Theatre du Nouveau Monde, 84 Ouest, rue Ste-Catherine, Montreal, Que. H2X 1Z6, Canada. TEL 514-861-0563. Ed. Roch Carrier. adv.; illus. (tabloid format; also avail. in microfilm from BNQ)

EPOCA; revista de cultura. see LITERATURE

792.028 UK
EQUITY JOURNAL; the official publication of the British Actor's Equity. 1931. q. £12 to non-members (free to members). British Actor's Equity Association, Guild House, Upper St. Martin's Ln., London WC2H 9EG, England. TEL 0171-379-6000. FAX 0171-379-7001. Ed. Ian Mcgasry. adv. contact: Vanessa Bird. circ. 45,000. **Document type:** trade publication.

792 US ISSN 0013-9890
EQUITY NEWS. 1913. m. $20 (free to qualified personnel). (Actors Equity Association) Dick Moore & Associates, Inc., 165 W. 46th St., New York, NY 10036. TEL 212-719-9570. Ed. Dick Moore. bk.rev.; illus.; circ. 36,500 (controlled). (tabloid format) **Document type:** newspaper.

792 AG
ESPACIO DE CRITICA E INVESTIGACION TEATRAL. 1986. s-a. Arg.$60($30) Fundacion de la Ranchería, Mexico 1152, 1097 Buenos Aires, Argentina. TEL 01-383-7887. FAX 01-961-1504. Ed. Eduardo Rovner. bk.rev. circ. 3,000. (back issues avail.)
 Description: Critical reviews of theatre.

ESSAYS IN POETICS. see LITERATURE

792 CN ISSN 0821-4425
ESSAYS IN THEATRE/ETUDES THEATRALES. 1982. s-a. Can.$17 to individuals; libraries Can.$22. University of Guelph, Department of Drama, Guelph, ON N1G 2W1, Canada. TEL 519-824-4120. FAX 519-824-0560. Eds. H. Lane, A. Wilson. adv. contact: Ric Knowles. bk.rev. circ. 300. Indexed: Arts & Hum.Cit.Ind., M.L.A. **Document type:** academic/scholarly publication.
—BLDSC (3811.789000); Faxon; Genuine Article; UnCover. **CCC.**

792 AA
ESTRADA.* bi-m. Ministry of Culture, Youth and Sport, Tirana, Albania.

792 410 800 375.4 US ISSN 0097-8663
ESTRENO; journal on the contemporary Spanish theater. (Text in Spanish; articles in English or Spanish) 1975. s-a. $15 to individuals; institutions $26. 350 N. Burrowes Bldg., University Park, PA 16802. TEL 814-865-1122. FAX 814-863-7944. Ed. Martha Halsey. adv.; bk.rev.; bibl.; index. circ. 600. Indexed: Arts & Hum.Cit.Ind., Curr.Cont., M.L.A. **Document type:** academic/scholarly publication.
—Faxon; UnCover.
 Description: Dedicated to post-civil-war Spanish theater.
 Refereed Serial

ETUDES CINEMATOGRAPHIQUES. see MOTION PICTURES

792 BE ISSN 0778-8738
Z2174.D7
ETUDES THEATRALES. (Text in French) 1968. 2/yr. 850 BEF (foreign 950 BEF) (effective 1995-1996). Ferme de Blocry, Place de l'Hocaille, B-1348 Louvain-La-Neuve, Belgium. TEL 32-10-472272. FAX 32-10-472237. Eds. Jean Florence, Anne Wibo. adv.; bk.rev.; bibl. circ. 1,000. **Document type:** academic/scholarly publication, monographic series.
 Former titles (until 1992): Cahiers Theatre Louvain (ISSN 0771-4653); Cahiers - Theatre (ISSN 0068-5232)
 Description: Discusses a different theme in twentieth century theatre in each issue.

EUGENE O'NEILL REVIEW. see LITERATURE

792 GW ISSN 0353-7161
PN2570
EUROMASKE; the European theatre journal. 1990. 4/yr. DM.36. L.H.B. Internationale Handelsbank A.G., Grosse Gallusstr. 16, 60014 Frankfurt a.M., Germany. Ed.Bd. adv.; illus.

792 US
EXPERIMENT THEATRE; "one minute" poetic drama. irreg. $5.50. Experiment Press, 6565 N.E. Windermere Rd., Seattle, WA 98105-2057. Ed. Carol Ely Harper.

F A R. see ART

THEATER

792   NE   ISSN 1010-2817
FIRT-IFTR-SIBMAS BULLETIN. (Editions in English, French) 1977. s-a. membership. Federation Internationale pour la Recherche Theatrale - International Federation for Theatre Research, c/o Van Eeghenstraat 113II, 1071 EZ Amsterdam, Netherlands. (Co-sponsor: Societe Internationale des Bibliotheques et Musees des Arts du Spectacle - International Association of Libraries and Museums of the Performing Arts) Eds. Eric Alexander, Liliana Alexandrescu. circ. 550. Document type: bulletin.

FACE TO FACE WITH TALENT. see COMMUNICATIONS — Television And Cable

FACILITY MANAGER. see BUSINESS AND ECONOMICS — Management

FAIRS AND FESTIVALS (YEAR). see ARTS AND HANDICRAFTS

792   AT
FANFARE. 1972. m. Aus.$20. Circus Fans Association of Australasia, Inc., P.O. Box 107, Underwood, Qld. 4119, Australia. TEL 61-7-8414633. FAX 61-7-8414523. Ed. Mike Mellare. circ. 400. (back issues avail.) Document type: newsletter.
    Description: Circus news in Australia and New Zealand.

792   CN   ISSN 0046-3256
PN2306.S77
FANFARES. 1967. q. membership. Stratford Shakespearean Festival Foundation of Canada, Box 520, Stratford, ON N5A 6V2, Canada. TEL 519-271-4040. circ. 20,000. Document type: newsletter.

FESTSPIEL - ILLUSTRIERTE. see MUSIC

791.53   SZ   ISSN 1021-3244
PN1970
FIGURA; zeitschrift fuer theater und spiel mit figuren. (Text in French and German) 1960. 4/yr. 40 SFr. Schweizerische Vereinigung fuer Puppenspiel, Roggenstr. 1, CH-4125 Riehen, Switzerland. TEL 061-6019264. FAX 061-6019264. Ed. Gustav Gysin. adv.; bk.rev. circ. 1,150. Document type: consumer publication.
    Formerly (until 1992): Puppenspiel und Puppenspieler (ISSN 0033-4405)

FILM A DIVADLO. see COMMUNICATIONS — Television And Cable

FILM, SZINHAZ, MUZSIKA. see MOTION PICTURES

792   AT
FIRST NIGHTERS' CURTAINCALL.* 1970. m. Aus.$3. Gallery First Nighters' Club, c/o Mrs. G. Fall, 33 Shirley Rd., Roseville, NSW 2069, Australia.

792   GW   ISSN 0930-5874
FORUM MODERNES THEATER. (Text in English, French and German) 1986. 2/yr. DM.60 to individuals; institutions DM.90. Gunter Narr Verlag, Postfach 2567, 72015 Tuebingen, Germany. TEL 07071-9797-0. FAX 07071-75288. Ed. Gunter Ahrends. Document type: academic/scholarly publication.
    —Genuine Article; SWETS. CCC.

792   GW   ISSN 0935-0012
FORUM MODERNES THEATER. SCHRIFTENREIHE. 1988. irreg., no.17, 1994. price varies. Gunter Narr Verlag, Postfach 2567, 72015 Tuebingen, Germany. TEL 07071-9797-0. FAX 07071-75288. Eds. Guenter Ahrends, Hans-Juergen Diller. Document type: monographic series.

FRIENDS FOCUS. see CLUBS

792   CC   ISSN 0257-0211
FUJIAN XIJU/FUJIAN THEATER. (Text in Chinese) 1979. bi-m. Y2.50($12.20) Fujiang Sheng Yishu Yanjiusuo, Fujian Xiju Bianjibu, 62 Yangqiao Lu, Fuzhou, Fujian 350001, People's Republic of China. TEL 31163. (Dist. overseas by: Jiangsu Publications Import & Export Corp., 56 Gao Yun Ling, Nanjing, P.R.C.; in US by: China Books & Periodicals, Inc., 2929 24th St., San Francisco, CA 94110. TEL 415-282-2994) Ed. Yuan Rongsheng.
    Description: Focuses on local drama and theater in Fujian Province.

792   UK   ISSN 0016-4283
PN6111
GAMBIT; an international drama magazine. 1963. irreg., no. 42-43. Calder Publications, 179 Kings Cross Rd., London WC1X 9BZ, England. TEL 0171-833-1300. Ed. John Calder. adv. contact: John Calder. bk.rev.; illus.; play rev. circ. 1,500.
    Indexed: Abstr.Engl.Stud.; Ind.Bk.Rev.Hum.
    —CCC.

792 917.306   US   ISSN 1040-483X
PQ6098.7
GESTOS; teoria y practica del teatro hispanico. (Text in English, Spanish) 1986. s-a. $20 to individuals (foreign $24); institutions $35 (foreign $39) (effective 1995). University of California at Irvine, Department of Spanish and Portuguese, Irvine, CA 92717. TEL 714-725-7171. FAX 714-725-2803. E-mail: gestos@uci.edu. Ed. Juan Villegas. adv.; bk.rev.; play rev.; circ. 700 (paid). (back issues avail.) Indexed: M.L.A. Document type: academic/scholarly publication.
    —Faxon; SWETS; UnCover.
    Description: Discusses theater theory, with emphasis on Hispanic theater. Includes essays, news and publication of plays on Hispanic theater for specialists.

GESTUS; a quarterly journal of Brechtian studies. see LITERATURE

792   VN
GIAO VIEN NHAN DAN/PEOPLE'S THEATRE. 1959. w. Ministry of Education and Training, Le Truc, Hanoi, Socialist Republic of Vietnam. TEL 52849. Ed. Nguyen Truong Thuy.

GIORNALE DELLO SPETTACOLO. see DANCE

792   US
GLOBE (MIAMI BEACH); script opportunities for dramatists in all media. 1984. m. $26.50. International Society of Dramatists, 1638 Euclid Ave., Miami Beach, FL 33139. TEL 305-538-3111. Ed. A. Delaplaine. bk.rev. circ. 8,000. (looseleaf format; back issues avail.)

792   YU   ISSN 0351-9120
PN2850
GODISNJAK JUGOSLOVENSKIH POZORISTA/YEARBOOK OF YUGOSLAV THEATERS. (Text in Albanian, Hungarian, Macedonian, Serbocroatian, Slovenian) 1978. a. $20. Sterijino Pozorje, Zmaj Jovina 22, 21000 Novi Sad, Vojvodina, Yugoslavia. TEL 021-23-161. Ed. Svetko Borovcanin.

GOETIKUSS. see EDUCATION

792 792.8   FR   ISSN 0982-9873
LE GRAND HUIT. (Text in French) 1986. 10/yr. 40 F. Le Grand Huit, B.P. 675, 35008 Rennes, France. Ed. Pierre Debauche. adv. circ. 20,000.

792   FR   ISSN 0993-5835
GROUPE INTERDISCIPLINAIRE DU THEATRE ANTIQUE. TEXTES ET DOCUMENTS. 1984. irreg. price varies. Universite de Montpellier (Universite Paul Valery), Groupe Interdisciplinaire du Theatre Antique, B.P. 5043, 34032 Montpellier Cedex 1, France. TEL 67-14-23-93. (back issues avail.)

H D K MAGAZIN. (Hochschule der Kuenste Berlin) see ART

792   US   ISSN 0898-7955
PN2289
HANDEL'S NATIONAL DIRECTORY FOR THE PERFORMING ARTS. (In 2 vols.) 1973. irreg., latest 5th edition, 1992. $250. R.R. Bowker, A Reed Reference Publishing company, 121 Chanlon Rd., New Providence, NJ 07974. TEL 800-521-8110. FAX 908-665-6688. TELEX 138 755. (Subscr. to: Order Dept., Box 31, New Providence, NJ 07974) Document type: directory.
    Description: Volume one covers performing arts organizations and facilities and is arranged alphabetically by state and city. Arts areas covered are dance, instrumental and vocal music, theatre and performing series. Volume two covers educational institutions offering courses and degrees in dance, music and theatre. Institutions are organized alphabetically by state.

HISPANIC AMERICAN ARTS; all you want or must know, about everything, in all the fields of Hispanic American arts. see ART

HOJAS LITERARIAS ILUSTRADAS. see LITERATURE

HOLLYWOOD ACTING COACHES AND TEACHERS DIRECTORY. see EDUCATION — Teaching Methods And Curriculum

HOLLYWOOD REPORTER. see MOTION PICTURES

HORISONT. see LITERATURE

HORIZONT; veszprem megyei kozmuvelodesi tajekoztato. see CLUBS

I C A MONTHLY BULLETIN. (Institute of Contemporary Arts) see ART

792 790.13   GW   ISSN 0342-4367
IN SACHEN SPIEL UND FEIER. 1949. s-m. DM.27. Hoefling Verlag Dr. V. Mayer, Carl-Benz-Str. 10, 69493 Hirschberg, Germany. Ed. Rudolf Guder. adv.; bk.rev.; play rev.; illus.; index. circ. 4,000. Document type: newsletter.
    Formerly (until 1972): Bunte Wagen.

INDEPENDENT SHAVIAN. see LITERATURE

700 780.65   US   ISSN 1069-2029
PN1561
INSIDE ARTS. 1989. 6/yr. $36. Association of Performing Arts Presenters, 1112 16th St., N.W., Ste. 400, Washington, DC 20036. TEL 202-833-2787. FAX 202-833-1543. Ed. Gayle Stamler. adv.: B&W page $925; adv. contact: Kim Kerker. bk.rev. circ. 250. Document type: trade publication.
    Description: Performing arts; feature stories on artists, facilities, events and projects of significance; first-person essays by artists; profiles of performers; special facilities vendor issue in summer, with directory.
    Refereed Serial

792   US
INSIDE THE BLACK HILLS. 1974. q. $8. Arts and Leisure Publications, Box 9008, Rapid City, SD 57709-9008. TEL 605-673-4100. FAX 605-673-4020. Ed. Ron Hagen. adv.; bk.rev. circ. 50,000. (back issues avail.) Document type: bulletin.
    Former titles (until 1990): In Performance; San Francisco Ballet; A.C.T.

INSTITUTO BRASIL - ESTADOS UNIDOS. BOLETIM. see EDUCATION

792   US
INTERMISSION (ALEXANDRIA). 1988. s-m. $12. K Communications, 6205 Redwood Lane, Alexandria, VA 22310. TEL 703-971-7530. FAX 703-971-7530. (Subscr. to in Missouri area: 135 W. Rose, Webster Grove, MO 63119) Ed. Verna A. Kerans. adv.; bk.rev. circ. 20,000. Document type: consumer publication.
    Formerly (until 1989): Review (Alexandria).
    Description: Covers theatre and related performing arts. Also reviews films and occasionally restaurants in the area.

792   US   ISSN 0538-6527
INTERNATIONAL CONGRESS OF LIBRARIES AND MUSEUMS OF THE PERFORMING ARTS. ACTS. 1954. irreg., 19th, 1992, Lisbon. International Association of Libraries and Museums of the performing Arts, c/o Jeanne T. Newlin, Sec.-Gen., Harvard Theater Collection, Harvard College Library, Cambridge, MA 02138. TEL 46-8-6651461. Document type: proceedings.

792   US
INTERNATIONAL THEATRE INSTITUTE OF THE UNITED STATES. NEWSLETTER. 1989. q. International Theatre Institute of the United States, Inc., 47 Great Jones St., New York, NY 10012-1114. TEL 212-254-4141. FAX 212-254-6814. Ed. Louis A. Rachow. bk.rev.; circ. 1,500 (controlled). (back issues avail.) Document type: newsletter.
    Description: Reports on the activities of ITI Worldwide, ITI US and the theatre professionals who are served by ITI's international programs.

THEATER

800 792   UK   ISSN 0260-7964
IRISH DRAMA SELECTIONS. 1982. irreg. price varies. Colin Smythe Ltd., P.O. Box 6, Gerrards Cross, Buckinghamshire SL9 8XA, England. TEL 01753-886000. FAX 01753-886469. (Pub. in U.S. by: Catholic University of America Press, 620 Michigan Ave. N.E., Washington, DC 20064) Eds. Joseph Ronsley, Ann Saddlemyer. (reprint service avail. from ISI) **Document type:** monographic series.
Description: Volumes of selected plays by Irish dramatists.

792   UK   ISSN 0965-1152
IRISH PERFORMING ARTS YEARBOOK. 1992. a. £6. Rhinegold Publishing Ltd., 241 Shaftesbury Ave., London WC2H 8EH, England. TEL 0171-333-1762. FAX 0171-333-1769. Ed. Sheena Barbour. **Document type:** directory.

792   IT
ISTITUZIONI CULTURALI PIEMONTESI. PUBBLICAZIONI. 1976. irreg. (Istituzioni Culturali Piemontesi) Cassa di Risparmio di Torino, Via XX Settembre 31, Turin, Italy. **Document type:** monographic series.

820   AU
JACOBEAN DRAMA STUDIES. (Text in English) 1972-198?; N.S. 1995. irreg. Universitaet Salzburg, Institut fuer Englische Sprache, Akademiestr. 24, A-5020 Salzburg, Austria. Ed. James Hogg. circ. 300. **Indexed:** M.L.A. **Document type:** monographic series.

JAHRBUCH DER BAYERISCHEN STAATSOPER. see *MUSIC*

JAMAICA PICTORIAL. see *MUSIC*

792   XO   ISSN 0323-2883
JAVISKO. 1968. m. $60. Narodne Osvetove Centrum, c/o Redakcia Javisko, Nam. S N P 12, 815 85 Bratislava, Slovakia.

792   CN   ISSN 0382-0335
PN2305.Q4
JEU; cahiers de theatre. 1976. q. Can.$40 (foreign $50) to individuals; institutions Can.$50 (foreign $61). Cahiers de Theatre Jeu Inc., 426 rue Sherbrooke Est, Bur. 202, Montreal, PQ H2L 1J6, Canada. TEL 514-288-2808. FAX 514-982-0711. Ed. Lorraine Camerlain. adv.; bk.rev.; play rev.; illus. circ. 1,400. (back issues avail.) **Indexed:** Pt.de Rep. (1983-).
Description: Informs about various tendencies of contemporary theatre in Quebec and other countries.

792   US   ISSN 1078-4802
PN2016
JOURNAL FOR STAGE DIRECTORS & CHOREOGRAPHERS. 1979. s-a. $18. Stage Directors and Choreographers Foundation, 1501 Broadway, Ste. 1701, New York, NY 10036. TEL 212-302-5359. FAX 212-302-6195. Ed. Jim O'Quinn. illus. **Document type:** trade publication.
Former titles: Stage Directors and Choreographers Foundation. Journal (ISSN 1055-6974); (until 1988): Society of Stage Directors and Choreographers. Journal (ISSN 0735-1577)
Description: Covers the concerns of stage directors and choreographers.

792   US   ISSN 1044-937X
PS332
JOURNAL OF AMERICAN DRAMA AND THEATRE. 1989. 3/yr. $12. C A S T A, City University of New York, Graduate School, 33 W. 42nd St., New York, NY 10036. TEL 212-642-2445. FAX 212-642-2221. Eds. Vera Mowry Roberts, Walter J. Meserve. circ. 3,400. **Document type:** academic/scholarly publication.
—Faxon; UnCover.

JOURNAL OF BECKETT STUDIES. see *LITERATURE*

792   US   ISSN 0888-3203
PN1601
JOURNAL OF DRAMATIC THEORY AND CRITICISM. 1986. s-a. $15 to individuals (foreign $20); institutions $25 (foreign $30); students $10 (foreign $15) (effective 1995). Hall Center for the Humanities, 211 Watkins Home, University of Kansas, Lawrence, KS 66045. TEL 913-864-4798. FAX 913-864-3126. Ed. John Gronbeck-Tedesco. adv.; bk.rev.; circ. 426 (paid). (back issues avail.) **Document type:** academic/scholarly publication.
—BLDSC (4970.200000); Faxon; UnCover.
Description: Addresses the theoretical issues associated with performance and performance texts.

792   CC   ISSN 0578-0659
JUBEN/PLAY SCRIPTS. (Text in Chinese) 1952. m. Y21.60($67.50) (Zhongguo Xijujia Xiehui - Chinese Theater Artists' Association) Zhongguo Xiju Chubanshe, 52, Dongsi Ba(8) Tiao, Beijing 100700, People's Republic of China. TEL 443661. (Dist. outside China by: China International Book Trading Corp., P.O. Box 399, Beijing, P.R.C.; Dist. in US by: China Books & Periodicals, Inc., 2929 24th St., San Francisco, CA 94110. TEL 415-282-2994) Ed. Wei Min.

792 808   BF
JUNKANOO. m. $18. Junkanoo Publications, Box N 4923, Nassau, Bahamas. Eds. John Munnings, Melanie Pintard.

792   US
JUST FOR LAUGHS. 1983. 11/yr. $18. J F L Communications, Inc., 22 Miller Ave., Mill Valley, CA 94941. TEL 415-383-4746. FAX 415-383-0142. adv.; B&W page $1500, color page $2000; trim 10 x 14. circ. 50,000. **Document type:** consumer publication.
Description: Chronicles stand-up comedy. Profiles performers, lists locations and schedules, provides stories and gossip.

792 791.4   CC   ISSN 1004-5864
JUYING YUEBAO/DRAMA & FILM MONTHLY. (Text in Chinese) 1959-1961; resumed 1980. m. $36.80. Jiangsu Sheng Wenhua Ting, 1, Qingdao Lu, Nanjing, Jiangsu 210008, People's Republic of China. TEL 025-635459. (Dist. in US by: China Books & Periodicals, Inc., 2929 24th St., San Francisco, CA 94110. TEL 415-282-2994) Ed. Wang Hong. circ. 5,000.
Formerly: Jiangsu Xiju.
Description: Contains film, drama and TV play scripts, and review articles.

792   CC   ISSN 1001-3768
JUZUOJIA/PLAYWRIGHT. (Text in Chinese) bi-m. Heilongjiang Sheng Wenhuating - Heilongjiang Provincial Bureau of Culture, Qingming Sidao, Nangang-qu, Harbin, Heilongjiang 150080, People's Republic of China. TEL 30198. Ed. Liu Shuzhang.

K & C. (Kunst en Cultuur) see *ART*

792   CI
KAZALISTE; revija za scensku glazbu i kulturu. 1965. fortn. $5.20. Hrvatsko Narodno Kazaliste u Osijeku, Prolaz Radoslava Bacica 1, Osijek, Croatia. Ed. Ljubomir Standjevic. illus.

792   UK
KING POLE CIRCUS MAGAZINE. (Supplement avail.: Circus Directory of the British Isles) 1934. q. £20 (outside Europe £26). Circus Friends' Association of Great Britain, c/o Membership Secretary, 20 Foot Wood Crescent, Shawclough, Rochdale, Lancs. OL12 6PB, England. Ed. David Jamieson. adv.; bk.rev.; illus.; stat. circ. 850. (back issues avail.)
Description: Contains articles and reviews on circus productions and personalities of past and present.

KITAB-I SUBH. see *LITERATURE — Poetry*

792   GW   ISSN 0940-4600
KOELNER MEDIENDIENST. 1981. bi-m. DM.48. (Rhein. AG Spiel und Theater im Regierungsbezirk Koeln e.V.) Maternus Verlag GmbH, Severinstr. 76, 50678 Cologne, Germany. TEL 0221-329993. FAX 0221-311337. Ed. Josef Broich. **Document type:** consumer publication.
Formerly: Kursprogramm Spiel und Theater.

L H A T BULLETIN. (League of Historic American Theatres) see *ARCHITECTURE*

792   US   ISSN 0023-8813
PN2309
LATIN AMERICAN THEATRE REVIEW; a journal devoted to the theatre and drama of Spanish & Portuguese America. (Text in English, Portuguese, Spanish; summaries in English) 1967. s-a. $20 to individuals; institutions $40. University of Kansas, Center of Latin American Studies, 107 Lippincott Hall, Lawrence, KS 66045. TEL 913-864-4111. FAX 913-864-4555. Ed. George W. Woodyard. adv. contact: Gabriela Gonzales. bk.rev.; bibl.; cum.index. circ. 1,200. (back issues avail.) **Indexed:** Arts & Hum.Cit.Ind., Chic.Per.Ind., Curr.Cont., Hisp.Amer.Per.Ind. (1970-), Ind.Bk.Rev.Hum., M.L.A. **Document type:** academic/scholarly publication.
—Faxon; UnCover.
Description: Presents interviews, theatre history, international stories, profiles, news, and articles about leading theatre companies and innovators in the field.
Refereed Serial

LAUGH-MAKERS; variety arts for family entertainment. see *HOBBIES*

LEBENDIGES DARMSTADT; Veranstaltungsvorschau. see *MUSEUMS AND ART GALLERIES*

LIAISON; la revue des arts en Ontario francais. see *ART*

LIGHTING DIMENSIONS. see *ARCHITECTURE*

792   UK   ISSN 0958-7217
PN2091.E4
LIGHTS!. 1937. 2/yr. free. Strand Lighting Ltd., Grant Way, Isleworth, Middlesex TW7 5QD, England. TEL 0181-560-3171. FAX 0181-490-0002. E-mail: lights@stranduk.com. (Dist. in Germany by: Strand Lighting GmbH, Salzbergstr. 2, 38302 Wolfenbuettel, Germany. TEL 05331-30080. FAX 05331-78883; Dist. in North America by: Strand Lighting Inc., 18111 S. Santa Fe Ave., Box 9004, Rancho Dominguez, CA 90221. TEL 310-637-7500. FAX 310-632-5519) Ed. David Brooks. bk.rev.; charts; illus. circ. 30,000. **Indexed:** Br.Tech.Ind. **Document type:** trade publication.
Former titles: (until 1990): Strandlight (ISSN 0950-0634); (until 1985): Tabs (ISSN 0306-9389)
Description: Articles and product descriptions on theater and television lighting with descriptions of projects from around the world.

792   US
LINCOLN CENTER CALENDAR OF EVENTS. 6/yr. free. Lincoln Center, 70 Lincoln Center Plaza, New York, NY 10023. TEL 212-875-5000. Ed. Sunny Levine. circ. 100,000.
Description: Covers events at Lincoln Center.

792   AU   ISSN 0024-4139
LINZER THEATERZEITUNG. 1955. m. S.100. Landestheater Linz, Promenade 39, A-4010 Linz, Austria. Ed.Bd. adv.; bk.rev. circ. 10,000. (tabloid format)

792   UK
▼**LIVE.** 1994. irreg., vol.2, 1995. £5.99. Methuen Drama, Michelin House, 81 Fulham Rd., London SW3 6RB, England. TEL 0171-581-9393. FAX 0171-225-9424. (Dist. by: Reed Book Services Ltd., P.O. Box 5, Rushden, Northants NN10 9YX, England. TEL 0933-58521) Ed. David Tushingham. **Document type:** monographic series.
Description: Focuses on specific issues in contemporary theater.

LIVE!. see *MUSIC*

792   US   ISSN 1043-6650
LONDON STAGE 1800-1900: A DOCUMENTARY RECORD AND CALENDAR OF PERFORMANCES. 1990. irreg. price varies. Greenwood Press, Inc. (Subsidiary of: Greenwood Publishing Group Inc.), 88 Post Rd. W., Box 5007, Westport, CT 06881-5007. TEL 203-226-3571. FAX 203-222-1502. **Document type:** monographic series.

792   UK
LONDON THEATRE GUIDE. (Text in Japanese) 1987. a. £6.50 (1000 Yen). (Japan Airlines) Eikoku Communications, Ste. 1, 1 Ave. Elmers, Surbiton, Surrey KT6 4SP, England. TEL 0181-399-6263. Ed. Emi Kazuko; Pub. Emi Kazuko. adv.: page £1650; trim 215 x 105; adv. contact: Denis van Mechelen. (back issues avail.) **Document type:** consumer publication.

6290 THEATER

792   US   ISSN 1064-0312
LONDON THEATRE NEWS. 1988. 10/yr. $51. 12 E. 86th St., New York, NY 10028. TEL 212-517-8608. FAX 212-249-9371. Ed. Roger B. Harris. adv. contact: Ellen Harris. bk.rev.; rec.rev. circ. 2,100. **Document type:** newsletter.
    Description: Provides reviews of shows, new and old, recommendations, interviews, restaurant reviews and current show listings for London.

792   US   ISSN 0026-7856
PN6111
M I D. (Modern International Drama); magazine for contemporary international drama in translation. 1967. s-a. $7 to individuals in the U.S. and Mexico (institutions $12.50); Canada $10 (institutions $13.50) (foreign $17.50) (effective 1994-1996). State University of New York at Binghamton, Theatre Department, Box 6000, Binghamton, NY 13902-6000. TEL 607-777-2704. Ed. George E. Wellwarth. adv. contact: George E. Wellwarth. cum.index: vols. 1-10 in vol.11, 1978; circ. 600 (paid). (tabloid format; also avail. in microform from UMI; reprint service avail. from UMI) **Indexed:** Amer.Bibl.Slavic & E.Eur.Stud.; Arts & Hum.Cit.Ind., Curr.Cont., Mid.East: Abstr.& Ind. **Document type:** academic/scholarly publication.
—Faxon; UMI; UnCover.
    Description: Devoted exclusively to the publication of previously untranslated plays.

792 380   UK
PN2595
MCGILLIVRAY'S THEATRE GUIDE. 1979. a. £14.95. Rebecca Books, Box 25, Brecon LD3 8NW, Wales. TEL 01874-636811. Ed. David McGillivray; Pub. Paddy French. adv. contact: Dan French. **Document type:** directory.
    Formerly (until 1994): British Alternative Theatre Directory (ISSN 0142-5218)

792 780   AU
MAGAZIN FESTSPIELE. 1984. a. S.40 (U.S. S.150). W i W Verlags GmbH, Walfischgasse 14, A-1010 Vienna, Austria. TEL 01-5129230. FAX 01-5139469. Ed. Peter Kupfer. adv.: page S.57600; adv. contact: Rosi Pritz. circ. 80,000. **Document type:** directory.

792   NE
MAGAZINE. 1978. 4/yr. donation. Toneelgroep Amsterdam, Marnixstraat 427, 1017 PK Amsterdam, Netherlands. TEL 31-20-5237800. FAX 31-20-5237838. Ed.Bd. adv. contact: Rene van der Pluijm. circ. 20,000. **Document type:** consumer publication.
    Former titles: Agenda; (until 1987): Publiekstheaterkrant.

"MAGISCHE" WELT; Zeitschrift fuer angewandte Tricktechnik und Wahrnehmungstaeuschung. see HOBBIES

792   GW   ISSN 0940-4767
MAINZER FORSCHUNGEN ZU DRAMA UND THEATER. 1987. irreg., vol.12, 1994. price varies. Francke Verlag GmbH, Postfach 2560, 72015 Tuebingen, Germany. TEL 07071-9797-0. FAX 07071-75288. **Document type:** monographic series.

MAJOR ATTRACTIONS. ANNUAL DIARY. see MUSIC

792   CN
MANITOBA THEATRE CENTRE. OVATION HOUSE PROGRAMME. 1958. 6/yr. free. Manitoba Theatre Centre, 174 Market Ave., Winnipeg, MB R3B 0P8, Canada. TEL 204-956-1340. FAX 204-947-3741. Ed. Blair Cosgrove. adv. contact: Cindy Yacyshen. illus. circ. 22,000. **Document type:** trade publication.
    Formerly: Stage Center.

792 791.43   CN   ISSN 0700-5008
PN1993
MARQUEE. 1976. 9/yr. Can.$21. Marquee Publications Ltd., 77 Mowat Ave., Ste. 621, Toronto, ON M6K 3E3, Canada. TEL 416-538-1000. FAX 416-538-0201. Ed. Ron Base. adv.: B&W page Can.$16720, color page Can.$20900; trim 8 x 10 3/4. illus. circ. 728,000. **Document type:** newspaper, consumer publication.

792   US   ISSN 0025-3928
MARQUEE (SPRINGFIELD). 1968. base vol. (plus q. updates). $40. Theatre Historical Society of America, 624 Wynne Rd., Springfield, PA 19064. TEL 610-543-8378. (Subscr. to: 152 N. York Rd., Elmhurst, IL 60126) Ed. Irvin R. Glazer. bk.rev.; illus.; index, cum.index: 1970-1979. circ. 1,000. (also avail. in microform from UMI; back issues avail.) **Indexed:** Avery Ind.Archit.Per. **Document type:** trade publication.
—UMI.
    Description: Features theatre buildings.

MASK. see EDUCATION — Teaching Methods And Curriculum

792   AU   ISSN 0025-4606
PN2004
MASKE UND KOTHURN; Internationale Beitraege zur Theaterwissenschaft. (Text in English, French, German and Italian) 1955. irreg. S.980. (Universitaet Wien, Institut fuer Theaterwissenschaft) Boehlau Verlag GmbH & Co.KG., Sachsenplatz 4-6, Postfach 87, A-1201 Vienna, Austria. TEL 0222-3302427-00. FAX 0222-3302432. TELEX 114-506-SPRIW-A. Ed. Wolfgang Greisenegger. adv.; bk.rev.; bibl.; illus.; index. circ. 800. **Indexed:** Arts & Hum.Cit.Ind., Curr.Cont., M.L.A. **Document type:** monographic series.
—SWETS.

792   UK   ISSN 0143-3784
PN2587
MEDIEVAL ENGLISH THEATRE. 1979. a. £7 (foreign £10). Medieval English Theatre, c/o Dept. of English, University of Lancaster, Lancaster LA1 4YT, England. TEL 01524-65201. FAX 01524-843085. E-mail: meth-ed@lancaster.ac.uk. Ed.Bd. circ. 400. **Indexed:** M.L.A. **Document type:** academic/scholarly publication.
—UnCover.
    Description: Articles on all aspects of medieval and Tudor English and continental theatres.

MEMPHIS STAR. see MUSIC

792   SZ   ISSN 0026-4385
MIMOS. (Text in French and German) q. 25 SFr. to non-members. Schweizerische Gesellschaft fuer Theaterkultur - Swiss Association for Theatre Research, Postfach 1940, CH-4001 Basel, Switzerland. TEL 061-3211060. FAX 061-3211075. **Document type:** academic/scholarly publication.

MISSOURI SPEECH & THEATRE JOURNAL. see COMMUNICATIONS

MODERN DRAMA. see LITERATURE

MOLODEZHNAYA ESTRADA. see CHILDREN AND YOUTH — For

792   US   ISSN 1065-1519
MOVEMENT THEATRE QUARTERLY. 1983. q. $20. National Movement Theatre Association, Box 1437, Portsmouth, NH 03802-1437. TEL 603-436-6660. Ed. M. William Fisher. adv.; illus.; illus. circ. 300. **Document type:** newsletter.
    Formerly: Mime News (ISSN 0892-4910)

729   GW   ISSN 0343-7604
MUENCHENER BEITRAEGE ZUR THEATERWISSENSCHAFT. 1972. irreg., vol.19, 1994. J. Kitzinger oHG, Schellingstr. 25, 80799 Munich, Germany. TEL 089-283637. FAX 089-281394. Eds. Klaus Lazarowicz, W. Passow. circ. 380 (paid). **Document type:** monographic series.

MUENCHENER KULTURFUEHRER MIT THEATERPLAN. see GENERAL INTEREST PERIODICALS — Germany

MUSICA, CINEMA, IMMAGINE, TEATRO. see MUSIC

792.022   US   ISSN 0027-4658
MUSICAL SHOW; devoted to the amateur presentation of Broadway musical shows on the stage. 1962. q. free to producers of musical shows. Tams-Witmark Music Library, Inc., 560 Lexington Ave., New York, NY 10022. TEL 212-688-2525. FAX 212-688-3232. Ed. Robert A. Hut. bk.rev. circ. 175,000.

792 782.1   GW   ISSN 0932-7118
MUSICALS; das Musicalmagazin. 1986. bi-m. DM.65. Verlag Klaus-Dieter Kraft, Balanstr. 19, 81669 Munich, Germany. TEL 089-448-9895. FAX 089-448-2858. Ed. Gerhard Knopf. adv.; bk.rev.; play rev. circ. 4,500. (back issues avail) **Document type:** consumer publication.
    Description: Provides reports and reviews on musicals and musical comedies from all over the world.

MUSIK & THEATER; die aktuelle Kulturzeitschrift. see MUSIC

N A D S A ANNUAL CONFERENCE DIRECTORY. (National Association of Dramatic and Speech Arts) see ADVERTISING AND PUBLIC RELATIONS

792 778.53   US
N A P A M A NEWS. q. $200 membership. National Association of Performing Arts Managers and Agents, c/o Mainstage Management Internal, Inc., Box 5517, Los Alamitos, CA 90721-5517. TEL 714-220-6707. FAX 714-220-6747. Ed. Luisa Cariaga. **Document type:** newsletter.
    Formerly: National Association of Performing Arts Managers and Agents. Newsletter.

N A T O NEWS. (National Association of Theatre Owners) see MOTION PICTURES

792 680   US
N Y C - ON STAGE. a. c/o Theatre Development Fund, 1501 Broadway, Rm. 2110, New York, NY 10036. TEL 212-221-0885. FAX 212-768-1563. Ed. Eve Rodriguez. circ. controlled. **Document type:** directory.
    Formerly: New York on Stage.
    Description: Contains listings of Broadway, off-Broadway, and off-off-Broadway theaters, and dance and music companies.

NASHVILLE SCENE. see MUSIC

792   UK
NATIONAL FEDERATION OF PLAYGOERS SOCIETIES. NEWSLETTER. 1957. q. free. National Federation of Playgoers Societies, 3 Gwenfo Dr., Wenvoe, Cardiff CF5 6ER, Wales. Ed. A. Morris-Janes. circ. 50 (controlled). (processed) **Document type:** newsletter.

792   JA   ISSN 0388-0648
NATIONAL THEATRE OF JAPAN. 6/yr. 4-1 Hayabusa-cho, Chiyoda-ku, Tokyo 102, Japan. TEL 03-3265-7411. FAX 03-3265-7402.

792   GW
NATIONALTHEATER MANNHEIM SPIELPLAN. 1975. m. Nationaltheater Mannheim, Mozartstr. 9, 68161 Mannheim, Germany. TEL 0621-16800. FAX 0621-1680-385. Ed. Klaus Schulz. adv.; charts; illus. circ. 15,000. (back issues avail.) **Document type:** bulletin.
    Formerly (until 1992): Nationaltheater Mannheim Theaterzeitung (ISSN 0934-9383)

792   II   ISSN 0028-1115
NATYA.* (Text in English) vol.10, 1969. q. Rs.12.($3.50) Bharatiya Natya Sangh, 34 New Central Market, New Delhi, India. Ed. A.R. Krishna. adv.; bk.rev.; dance rev.; play rev.

NE SKENEN E FEMIJEVE. see CHILDREN AND YOUTH — For

792   NE   ISSN 0929-2640
NEDERLANDS THEATERBOEK. (Text in English and Dutch) 1950. a. price varies. Theater Instituut Nederland, Herengracht 168, 1016 BP Amsterdam, Netherlands. TEL 31-20-6235104. FAX 31-20-6200051.
    Former titles (until 1982): Nederlands Theater- en Televisie Jaarboek (ISSN 0929-2292); (until 1971): Theater Jaarboek (ISSN 0929-2861)

792   NE   ISSN 0168-3519
NETHERLANDS. CENTRAAL BUREAU VOOR DE STATISTIEK. MUZIEK EN THEATER. irreg. Centraal Bureau voor de Statistiek, Prinses Beatrixlaan 428, Voorburg, Netherlands. (Subscr. to: SDU - Publishers, Christoffel Plantijnstraat, The Hague, Netherlands) **Document type:** government publication.
    Formerly: Netherlands. Centraal Bureau voor de Statistiek. Statistiek van het Gesubsidieerde Toneel.

792   AU   ISSN 0028-3096
NEUE BLAETTER DES THEATERS IN DER JOSEFSTADT.
(Text in German; occasionally in English, French)
1953. s-m. S.12. Theater in der Josefstadt,
Direktion, Josefstaedterstr. 26, A-1082 Vienna,
Austria. Ed. Gustav Kropatschek. adv.; bibl.; illus.
circ. 10,000. (tabloid format)

NEUE WEGE; Kulturzeitschrift junger Menschen. see
CHILDREN AND YOUTH — For

791.33   US
NEW CALLIOPE. 1984. 6/yr. $20 membership only.
(Clowns of America International) Olson Publishing,
Box 570, Lake Jackson, TX 77566-0570.
TEL 712-258-3075. Ed. Cal Olson. adv.; bk.rev.;
illus. circ. 5,750.
   Description: Provides articles on clowning. Photos
and illustrations include ideas for costuming,
makeup design, props, skits and magic.

NEW CULTURE; a review of contemporary African arts.
see ART

792   US   ISSN 1050-9720
PN2000
NEW ENGLAND THEATRE JOURNAL. 1990. a. $10. New
England Theatre Conference, c/o Department of
Theatre, Northeastern University, 360 Huntington
Ave., Boston, MA 02115. TEL 617-424-9275. Eds.
Jeffrey Martin, Stuart Hecht. adv.; bk.rev. circ.
1,000. **Document type:** monographic series.
   Description: Covers a broad range of subjects,
including traditional scholarship, performance theory,
and pedagogy, as well as theatre performance,
design, and technology.
   Refereed Serial

792   UK   ISSN 0266-464X
PN2001
NEW THEATRE QUARTERLY. 1971. q. £45($79)
(effective 1996). Cambridge University Press,
Edinburgh Bldg., Shaftesbury Rd., Cambridge CB2
2RU, England. TEL 01223-312393.
FAX 01223-315052. TELEX 851817256. (N.
American addr.: Cambridge University Press,
Journals Dept., 40 W. 20th St., New York, NY
10011. TEL 212-924-3900. FAX 212-691-3239)
Eds. Clive Barker, Simon Trussler. (also avail. in
microform from UMI; back issues avail.; reprint
service avail. from SWZ) **Document type:**
academic/scholarly publication.
   —BLDSC (6088.870500); Faxon; Genuine Article;
SWETS; UMI; UnCover. **CCC.**
   Formerly (until 1985): Theatre Quarterly (ISSN 0049-3600)
   Description: Subjects prevailing dramatic
assumptions to scrutiny.

792   US   ISSN 1074-0023
NEW YORK CASTING;* the casting and performing arts
journal. w. $25. Charles Charles Communications,
Inc., 110 Greene St., Apt. 800, New York, NY
10012-3836. Ed. Matthew Benn Lieppe.

792 384.55   US   ISSN 0730-9945
NEW YORK CASTING - SURVIVAL GUIDE; and datebook.
1980. a. $16.95. Peter Glenn Publications, Inc., 42
W. 38th St., Ste. 802, New York, NY 10018.
TEL 212-869-2020. FAX 212-869-3287. Ed.
Gregory James; Pub. Chip Brill. adv. contact: Michael
Henry. **Document type:** directory.
   Description: Resource tool for performing artists.

792   US   ISSN 0028-7784
PN2000
NEW YORK THEATRE CRITICS' REVIEWS. 1940. irreg.
(approx. 20/yr.) $122 (foreign $145) (effective
1993). Critics Theatre Reviews, Inc., 37-1561 St.,
Woodside, NY 11377. TEL 718-492-6674.
FAX 718-492-6672. Ed. Pat Willard. index,
cum.index: 1940-1960, 1961-1972, 1973-1986.
circ. 1,100. (looseleaf format; back issues avail.)
Indexed: Arts & Hum.Cit.Ind., Curr.Cont. **Document
type:** academic/scholarly publication.

792   US   ISSN 0160-0583
PN2266
NEW YORK TIMES THEATRE REVIEWS. 1870. biennial.
Times Books (Subsidiary of: Random House, Inc.),
201 E. 50th St., New York, NY 10022-7703.
TEL 212-751-2600. illus.

**NEWSBANK REVIEW OF THE ARTS: FILM AND
TELEVISION.** see MOTION PICTURES

792   US   ISSN 0737-3996
NEWSBANK REVIEW OF THE ARTS: PERFORMING ARTS.
1972. m. (q. and a. cumulations). price varies.
NewsBank, Inc., 58 Pine St., New Canaan, CT
06840-5426. TEL 203-966-1100.
FAX 203-966-6254. (paper index; articles on
microfiche; CD ROM index)

792 820   US   ISSN 0893-3766
PN1851
NINETEENTH CENTURY THEATRE. 1973. s-a. $12 to
individuals (foreign $14); institutions $20 (foreign
$22). University of Massachusetts at Amherst,
Nineteenth Century Theatre, c/o Department of
English, Amherst, MA 01003. TEL 413-545-0498.
FAX 413-545-3880. E-mail:
joseph.donohue@english.umass.edu. Ed. Joseph
Donohue; Pub. Joseph Donohue. adv.; bk.rev.; bibl.;
illus. circ. 400. (also avail. in microform from UMI;
back issues avail.; reprint service avail. from UMI)
Indexed: Abstr.Engl.Stud., Amer.Hum.Ind., Arts &
Hum.Cit.Ind., Curr.Cont., LCR, M.L.A. **Document type:**
academic/scholarly publication.
   —Faxon; UMI; UnCover.
   Formerly: Nineteenth Century Theatre Research
(ISSN 0316-5329)

NUOVA RASSEGNA; periodico di
attualita-lettere-arti-cinema-teatro. see LITERARY
AND POLITICAL REVIEWS

791.53   CN   ISSN 0030-3062
O P A L. (Ontario Puppetry Association Letter) 1962.
6/yr. Can.$30 (foreign Can.$35) membership.
Ontario Puppetry Association, 65 Front St. W., Ste.
116, Box 180, Toronto, ON M5J 1E7, Canada.
TEL 416-861-0202. Ed. Joan E. Tooke. adv.;
bk.rev.; play rev. circ. 350. **Document type:**
newsletter.
   Refereed Serial

792 380   UK
**OFFICIAL BRITISH THEATRE DIRECTORY SEATING PLAN
GUIDE.** 1992. triennial. £8.95. Richmond House
Publishing Company Ltd., Douglas House, 3
Richmond Bldgs., London W1V 5AE, England.
TEL 0171-437-9556. FAX 0171-287-3463. Ed.
Audrey Yates. adv.; circ. 3,000. **Document type:**
directory.

OFFICIAL CITY GUIDE. see TRAVEL AND TOURISM

792   US
ON - STAGE STUDIES. 1976. a. $15 (effective
1995-96). University of Colorado, Department of
Theatre & Dance, Box 261, Boulder, CO
80309-0261. TEL 303-492-7355.
FAX 303-492-7722. Ed. Judith Bock. circ. 500.
Document type: academic/scholarly publication.
   Formerly: Colorado Shakespeare Festival Annual
(ISSN 0198-831X)
   Description: Publishes articles focusing on
contemporary productions of pre-modern plays as
well as issues of performance and pedagogy.
   Refereed Serial

ON THE STREET. see MUSIC

OPERA AMERICA. REPERTOIRE SURVEY. see MUSIC

OPERA AMERICA NEWSLINE. see MUSIC

OVERALL THERE IS A SMELL OF FRIED ONIONS. see
MOTION PICTURES

792 910.03   US
OVERTURE (NEW YORK); a Black theatre annual. 1981.
a. $5. Audience Development Committee, Box 30,
Manhattanville Sta., New York, NY 10027. Ed. A.
Peter Bailey.

792 780   UK
OVERTURES; the magazine devoted to the musical on
stage and record. no.9, 1980. bi-m. £2.50($10) 41
Eton Ave., Sudbury, Wembley, Middx. HA0 3AZ,
England. Eds. Rexton S. Bunnett, John Muir.

800 792   UK   ISSN 0141-1752
OXFORD THEATRE TEXTS. 1972. irreg. price varies.
Colin Smythe Ltd., P.O. Box 6, Gerrards Cross,
Buckinghamshire SL9 8XA, England.
TEL 01753-886000. FAX 01753-886469. (Dist. in
U.S. by: Dufour Editions, P.O. Box 449, Chester
Springs, PA 19425) illus. circ. 1,500. (reprint
service avail. from ISI) **Document type:** monographic
series.
   Description: Plays by Francis Warner.

790   SA
P A C O F S NEWS/S U K O V S NUUS. (Text in Afrikaans
and English) 1972. q. free. Performing Arts Council,
Orange Free State, P.O. Box 1292, 9300
Bloemfontein, South Africa. FAX 51-305523. TELEX
267145 SA. Ed. Charmaine Ferreira. illus. circ.
6,000.

792 784   US
PALACE PEEPER. 1937. m. $25 (typically set in Sep.)
Gilbert and Sullivan Society of New York, 185 West
End Ave., No. 20-F, New York, NY 10023. Ed. Marc
Shepherd. circ. 350.
   Description: Contains history, criticism, humor, and
membership news.

792   PL   ISSN 0031-0522
PN2859.P6
PAMIETNIK TEATRALNY; kwartalnik poswiecony historii i
krytyce teatru. (Text in Polish; summaries in English)
1952. q. $20. Polska Akademia Nauk, Instytut
Sztuki, Ul. Dluga 28, 00-950 Warsaw, Poland.
TEL 48-22-313271. FAX 48-22-313149. (Dist. by:
AMOS, ul. Zuga 12, 01-806 Warsaw, Poland. TEL
48-22-346521) Eds. Edward Krasinski , Marek
Waszkiel. adv.; bk.rev.; bibl.; illus.; index. circ. 800.
   Description: Devoted to the history of Polish
theatre and theatrical criticism.

792 900   US   ISSN 1061-8112
THE PASSING SHOW. 1977. s-a. free. (Shubert
Foundation) Shubert Archive, 149 W. 45th St., New
York, NY 10036. TEL 212-944-3895. Ed. Mark E.
Swartz. illus.; circ. 3,000 (controlled). (back issues
avail.) **Document type:** newsletter, academic/scholarly
publication.
   Description: Serves archivists, historians, and
others interested in the history of theatrical
productions on Broadway, particularly the history of
the Shubert Theatrical Organization and its
producing activities.

792   IT
PATALOGO; annuario dello spettacolo teatro. 1979. a.
L.70000 (effective 1994-95). Edizioni Ubulibri, Via
B. Ramazzini, 8, 20129 Milan, Italy.
TEL 02-29404372. FAX 02-29510265. Eds.
Franco Quadri, Renata Molinari. adv.; bk.rev.
   Description: Presents all the spectacles staged in
Italy, includes reviews by theatrical critics.

PERFORMANCE; the international talent weekly. see
MUSIC

792   US   ISSN 0031-5222
PERFORMING ARTS; the theatre & music magazine.
1967. m. $30 (foreign $35). Performing Arts
Network, 3539 Motor Ave., Los Angeles, CA
90034-4800. TEL 310-839-8000.
FAX 310-839-5651. Ed. Dana Kraft. adv.: B&W
page $15525, color page $23288; trim
8 1/8 X 10 3/4. bk.rev.; film rev.; play rev. circ.
700,000.
   —UnCover.
   Description: Covers music, film, theatre,
audio-video, travel and real estate. Provides
synopses, cast biographies and background
information on plays and concerts.

792   CN   ISSN 1185-3433
PN1582.C3
PERFORMING ARTS AND ENTERTAINMENT IN CANADA.
1961. q. Can.$8 (foreign Can.$15). Canadian Stage
and Art Publications, 104 Glenrose Ave., Toronto,
ON M4T 1K8, Canada. TEL 416-484-4534.
FAX 416-484-6214. Ed. Karen Bell; Pub. George
Hencz. adv.: B&W page Can.$1593, color page
Can.$2343; trim 8 1/8 x 10 7/8; adv. contact:
Tom Hansen. bk.rev.; illus.; index. circ. 44,630. (also
avail. in microfiche from UMI; reprint service avail.
from MMI) **Indexed:** Arts & Hum.Cit.Ind., Can.B.P.I.,
Can.Per.Ind., CMI, Curr.Cont., Mag.Ind., Music Ind.
Document type: consumer publication.
   ●Also available online. Vendor(s): University
Microfilms International.
   —Faxon; Genuine Article; UMI; UnCover.
   Formerly: Performing Arts in Canada (ISSN 0031-5230)
   Description: Covers performing arts in Canada:
music, dance, theater and film.

PERFORMING ARTS BUYERS GUIDE: FOOTNOTES. see
DANCE

THEATER

792 US ISSN 0735-8393
PN1561
PERFORMING ARTS JOURNAL. 1976. 3/yr. $20 to individuals; institutions $42. (P A J Publications) Johns Hopkins University Press, Journals Publishing Division, 2715 N. Charles St., Baltimore, MD 21218. TEL 410-516-6988. FAX 410-516-6968. Eds. Bonnie Marranca, Gautam Dasgupta. adv. contact: Tara Dorai-Berry. bk.rev.; play rev.; illus. circ. 2,200. (also avail. in microfilm from UMI; back issues avail.) **Indexed:** Amer.Bibl.Slavic & E.Eur.Stud., Amer.Hum.Ind., Arts & Hum.Cit.Ind., Bk.Rev.Ind. (1981-), Child.Bk.Rev.Ind. (1981-), Curr.Cont., Hum.Ind. **Document type:** academic/scholarly publication.
—BLDSC (6423.893000); Faxon; Genuine Article; SWETS; UMI; UnCover. **CCC.**
Description: International critical coverage of contemporary theater, dance, music, and drama.

792 016 US ISSN 0360-3814
Z6935
PERFORMING ARTS RESOURCES. 1974. a. $20 to individuals; institutions $25. Theatre Library Association, 111 Amsterdam Ave., New York, NY 10023. Ed. Barbara Naomi Cohen-Stratyner. circ. 500. (back issues avail.) **Indexed:** M.L.A.
Description: Gathers and disseminates articles on resources materials relating to theatre, popular entertainments, film, television and radio; descriptions of collections, and essays on conservation and management.

800 IT
PICCOLO TEATRO DI MILANO. 1977. 5/yr. L.100000. Piccolo Teatro di Milano, Via Rovello 2, 20121 Milan, Italy. FAX 2-874836. TELEX 316279. Ed. Giorgio Strehler. adv.; bk.rev. circ. 60,000.

792 US ISSN 0895-9706
PR6066.I53
PINTER REVIEW: ANNUAL ESSAYS. 1987. a. $15 to individuals; institutions $25. University of Tampa, Box 11F, Tampa, FL 33606. Eds. Francis Gillen, Steven H. Gale. bk.rev. circ. 300. **Document type:** academic/scholarly publication.
Description: Publishes critical essays, notes, production reviews and commentaries on the plays, screenplays and other writings of Harold Pinter.
Refereed Serial

708 CN ISSN 0847-3366
PLACE DES ARTS. MAGAZINE. (Text in English, French) 1989. bi-m. Can.$14. Societe de la Place des Arts, 260 bd. de Maisonneuve Ouest, Montreal, PQ H2X 1Y9, Canada. TEL 514-285-4270. FAX 514-285-4272. (Subscr. to: Agence Periodica, C.P. 444, Outremont, PQ H2V 4R6, Canada) adv.: B&W page Can.$6090, color page Can.$7350; trim 4 7/8 x 6 3/4. bk.rev. circ. 200,000.

DAS PLATEAU. see *ART*

800 US ISSN 0749-9841
Z1231.D7
PLAY SOURCE. (Included in: Plays in Process (ISSN 0736-0711)) 1981. q. $20 (overseas $35) (effective 1996). Theatre Communications Group, Inc., 355 Lexington Ave., New York, NY 10017. TEL 212-697-5230. FAX 212-983-4847. E-mail: tcg@tmn.com. Ed. Wendy Winer; Pub. Terence Nemeth. **Document type:** trade publication.
Description: Gives brief descriptions of full-length, one-act, and musical theatre scripts. Includes addresses of where to write for permission to present, read, and learn about newer plays not yet licensed by the agencies that handle playscripts.

792 US ISSN 0032-146X
PLAYBILL; the national magazine of the theatre. 1884; N.S. 1982. m. $24 (effective 1993). Playbill Incorporated, 52 Vanderbilt Ave., 11th Fl., New York, NY 10017-3893. TEL 212-557-5757. FAX 212-682-2932. Ed. Judy Samuelson. adv.; illus. circ. 1,015,000. **Document type:** consumer publication.
Description: Provides information necessary to the understanding and enjoyment of each Broadway play, certain Lincoln Center and Off-Broadway productions and regional attractions served. Includes articles by and about theatre personalities, fashion, and events.

792 CN ISSN 0048-4415
PLAYBOARD; professional stage magazine. 1967. m. Can.$20 (US Can.$25). Arch-Way Publishers Ltd., 7560 Lawrence Dr., Burnaby, BC V5A 1T6, Canada. TEL 604-420-6115. FAX 604-420-6115. Ed. Chuck Davis; Pub. Harold Schiel. adv. contact: Irene Schiel. circ. 600,000. **Document type:** consumer publication.

799.022 371.3 US ISSN 0032-1540
PN1601
PLAYS; the drama magazine for young people. 1941. m. (Oct-May; except Jan.-Feb. combined) $28 (foreign $36) (effective 1995). Plays, Inc., 120 Boylston St., Boston, MA 02116-4615. TEL 617-423-3157. FAX 617-423-3168. Ed. Sylvia K. Burack. adv.: B&W page $1000. bk.rev.; index; circ. 15,000 (paid). (also avail. in microfilm from UMI; back issues avail.; reprint service avail. from UMI) **Indexed:** Biog.Ind., Ind.Child.Mag., Mag.Ind. —UMI.
Description: Provides a complete supply of royalty-free one-act plays and programs, skits and choral readings for schools, young people's clubs and libraries.

822 UK ISSN 0554-3045
PLAYS. A CLASSIFIED GUIDE TO PLAY SELECTION. 1951. a. £2.20($6) Stacey Publications, 1 Hawthornedene Road, Hayes, Bromley, Kent, England. Ed. Roy Stacey. adv.; bibl.

792 UK ISSN 0032-1559
PN2001
PLAYS & PLAYERS. m. £60. Mineco Designs Ltd., Northway House, 1379 High Rd., London N20 9LP, England. TEL 44-181-343-8515. FAX 44-181-446-1410. adv.; illus. **Indexed:** Hum.Ind.
—BLDSC (6539.232000); SWETS; UMI; UnCover.
Description: Theatre review guide, includes interviews.

800 US
PLAYS & PLAYWRIGHTS. 1985. biennial. $29.95 free. International Society of Dramatists, 1638 Euclid Ave., Miami Beach, FL 33139. TEL 305-538-3111. Ed. A. Delaplaine. circ. 5,600.

792 US ISSN 0268-2028
PLAYS INTERNATIONAL. m. £24 (foreign £53). Plays International Ltd., F6 Greenwood Ct., Harlescott, Shrewsbury, Shrops. SY1 3TB, England. TEL 01743-462303. FAX 01743-446177. Ed. Peter Roberts. adv. contact: Margaret Southgate. bk.rev. (back issues avail.) **Document type:** bulletin.
—BLDSC (6539.233000); Faxon; UnCover.

700 NE ISSN 0032-1621
PLUG; maandelijks informatieblad. 1967. m. fl.15. Culturele Raad Noordholland, Postbus 5348, 2000 GH Haarlem, Netherlands. TEL 31-23-319139. FAX 31-23-315228. Ed. Leo Veen. adv.; bk.rev.; film rev.; play rev.; abstr.; illus.; circ. 30,000 (controlled).

792 BN ISSN 0032-616X
PN2007
POZORISTE; casopis za pozorisnu umjetnost. (Text in Serbo-Croatian) 1959. bi-m. 60 din. Narodno Pozoriste, Tuzla, Bosnia Hercegovina. Ed. Mustafa Hadzialic. circ. 1,100.

PRELUDE. see *DANCE*

PRODUCTION AND CASTING REPORT. see *MOTION PICTURES*

792 375 US
PROFESSIONAL THEATRE FOR YOUNG AUDIENCES. irreg. $10. American Alliance for Theatre & Education, Theatre Department, Arizona State Department, Box 3411, Tempe, AZ 85287-3411. TEL 602-965-6064. FAX 602-965-9073.
Description: Provides a profile of professional theatre organizations that produce work for young audiences.

PROFILE (WASHINGTON). see *MUSIC*

792 PO
PROGRAMA.* 1978. Esc.50 per no. Grupo de Teatro de Campolide, 43, 2o D. Cde. Antas, Lisbon, Portugal. Ed. Joaquim Benite. bk.rev.; play rev.; illus. circ. 20,000.

792 US ISSN 0033-1007
PROLOGUE (MEDFORD). 1945. irreg. (3-4/yr.) free. Tufts University, Department of Drama & Dance, Medford, MA 02155. TEL 617-381-3524. Ed. Peter D. Arnott. play rev. circ. 5,000. **Indexed:** Amer.Bibl.Slavic & E.Eur.Stud.

792 US
PROLOGUE (MILWAUKEE). every 6 wks. free to qualified personnel. Milwaukee Repertory Theater, 108 E. Wells St., Milwaukee, WI 53202. TEL 414-224-1761. FAX 414-224-9790. Ed. Cindy Moran. circ. 10,000. **Document type:** newsletter.
Description: Articles on theater pieces produced by the Milwaukee Repertory Theater.

792 SP ISSN 0213-4918
PQ6227
PUBLICO; revista bimestral del espectaculo. 1983. bi-m. 3000 ptas. (Europe 4000 ptas., US $35, elsewhere $44) (effective 1991). Centro de Documentacion Teatral, Capitan Haya 44, 28020 Madrid, Spain. TEL 91-5723311. FAX 91-2705199. circ. 7,000.

PULSE. see *MUSIC*

791.53 UK ISSN 0033-4413
THE PUPPET MASTER; the Guild magazine. a. £12 membership (includes Newsletter). British Puppet & Model Theatre Guild, c/o Gordon Shapeley, 18 Maple Rd., Yeading, Nr. Hayes, Mddx. UB4 9LP, England.
Formerly (until 1946): Puppet and Model Theatre Guild. Wartime Bulletin.
Description: Deals with various aspects of professional and amateur puppetry.

791.53 US ISSN 0033-443X
PN1970
PUPPETRY JOURNAL. 1949. q. $35 membership; libraries $30. Puppeteers of America, 8005 Swallow Dr., Macedonia, OH 44056. (Subscr. to: 5 Cricklewood Path, Pasadena, CA 91107-1002) Eds. George & Pat Latshaw. adv.; bk.rev.; play rev.; charts; illus.; circ. 2,200 (controlled). (also avail. in microfilm from UMI; reprint service avail. from UMI) —UMI; UnCover.

791.53 US ISSN 1070-3624
▼**PUPPETRY YEARBOOK.** 1995. a. $49.95. Edwin Mellen Press, 415 Ridge St., Box 450, Lewiston, NY 14092. TEL 716-754-2788. FAX 716-754-4056. Ed. James Fisher.
Description: Examines the artistry of the puppet stage, past and present.

792 780 CC ISSN 0578-0608
PL2567
QU YI/VARIETY SHOW. (Text in Chinese) m. Y15($42.20) Zhongguo Quyijia Xiehui, Wenlian Dalou, 10 Nongzhanguan Nanli, Beijing 100026, People's Republic of China. (Dist. outside China by: China International Book Trading Corp., P.O. Box 399, Beijing, P.R.C.; Dist. in US by: China Books & Periodicals, Inc., 2929 24th St., San Francisco, CA 94110. TEL 415-282-2994) Ed. Luo Yang.

792.2 US
RAVE;* the comedy performance magazine. 1986. m. $15. Rave Communications, Inc., c/o E.M.C.I. Corp., 24 Richmond Hill Ave., Ste. 8, Stamford, CT 06901-3600. Ed. Ron Smith. circ. 250,000.

792 800 CN ISSN 0700-9283
PR641
RECORDS OF EARLY ENGLISH DRAMA NEWSLETTER. (Text in English) 1976. s-a. Can.$7.50. University of Toronto, Erindale College, English Department, Mississauga, ON L5L 1C6, Canada. TEL 416-828-3737. FAX 416-828-5328. Ed. J. Dutka. bk.rev.; bibl.; cum.index every 5 yrs. circ. 500. (back issues avail.) **Indexed:** Amer.Hist.& Life, Hist.Abstr., M.L.A. **Document type:** academic/scholarly publication.
Description: Articles and notes on English drama, ceremony and minstrelsy to 1642.
Refereed Serial

THEATER 6293

792 809 US ISSN 0486-3739
PN1785
RENAISSANCE DRAMA. 1967. a. $45.95 (effective 1994). Northwestern University Press, 625 Colfax St., Evanston, IL 60208-4210. TEL 708-491-5313. Ed. Mary Beth Rose. circ. 2,000. Indexed: Arts & Hum.Cit.Ind., Bibl.Ind.Lang.& Lit., Curr.Cont., M.L.A. **Document type:** academic/scholarly publication.
—BLDSC (7356.865200); UnCover.
Description: Collection of essays on topics in Renaissance drama.

792 778.5 UK ISSN 0142-6303
REPERTORY REPORT. 1972. m. £35. P.O. Box 11, London SW15 6AY, England. TEL 0181-789-0408. FAX 0181-780-1977. (Subscr. to: P.O. Box 100, Broadstairs, Kent CT10 1UJ, England. TEL 01843-860885) Ed. Baune Craig-Raymond. **Document type:** trade publication.
Description: Covers the regional repertory theatre scene, including specific companies, casting policies, audition plans, and program schedules.

792 UK ISSN 1356-9783
▼**RESEARCH IN DRAMA EDUCATION.** Announced for publication in 1996. 2/yr. £28($48) to individuals; institutions £64($108) (effective 1996). Carfax Publishing Co., P.O. Box 25, Abingdon, Oxon OX14 3UE, England. TEL 44-1235-555335. FAX 44-1235-553559. (N. American subscr. to: Carfax Publishing Co., 875-81 Massachusetts Ave., Cambridge, MA 02139) **Document type:** academic/scholarly publication.

RESEARCH OPPORTUNITIES IN RENAISSANCE DRAMA. see *LITERATURE*

RESTORATION & EIGHTEENTH CENTURY THEATRE RESEARCH. see *LITERATURE*

792 BL ISSN 0102-7336
REVISTA DE TEATRO. 1920. q. $40 or membership (effective 1993). Sociedade Brasileira de Autores Teatrais, Rua Quitanda, 194, Salas 1008-1010, 20091-000 Rio de Janeiro, R.J., Brazil. TEL 5521-263-7856. FAX 5521-240-7431. Ed. Maria Helena Kuhner. adv.; bk.rev. circ. 5,000. (back issues avail.) **Indexed:** Hisp.Amer.Per.Ind. (1970-1982).

792 FR ISSN 0035-2373
PN2003
REVUE D'HISTOIRE DU THEATRE. 1948. q. 360 F. (outside EC 380 F.). Societe d'Histoire du Theatre, 98 Bd. Kellermann, 75013 Paris, France. TEL 45-88-46-55. Ed. Rose Marie Moudoues. bk.rev.; charts; illus.; index, cum.index. (reprint service avail. from SWZ) **Indexed:** Amer.Hist.& Life, Arts & Hum.Cit.Ind., Curr.Cont., Hist.Abstr., M.L.A., RILM.
—BLDSC (7880.960000); Faxon; SWETS.

792 IT ISSN 0035-5186
RIDOTTO; rassegna mensile di teatro. 1951. m. L.2500. Societa Italiana Autori Drammatici, Via Po, 10, 00198 Rome, Italy. Ed. Enrico Beruari. adv.; bk.rev.; bibl.; charts; illus.; index. circ. 5,000. **Indexed:** M.L.A.

RODMAN HALL BULLETIN. see *ART*

RONDELL PROGRAMM. see *MOTION PICTURES*

RUCH MUZYCZNY; a musical review. see *MUSIC*

792 II
RUCHI. 1982. s-a. Rs.5. University of Calcutta, School of Drama, Aranattukara, Trichur, 680618. Kerala, India. circ. 500. (back issues avail.)

792.927 TS
AL-RUWALAH. (Text in Arabic) 1963. q. Sharjah National Theater, P.O. Box 5373, Sharjah, United Arab Emirates. TEL 354522. Ed. Ahmed bin Muhammad al-Qasimi. circ. 1,000.
Description: Discusses the development and status of Arab theater in the Gulf region, and provides a forum for exchange of information and experience among persons connected with the theater.

RYTME; nyt om folkemusik, rock, jazz og teater i Nordjylland. see *MUSIC*

792.02 CN
S D A JOURNAL - NEWSLETTER. 3/yr. Can.$35. (Saskatchewan Drama Association) Saskatchewan Teachers' Federation, Box 1108, Saskatoon, SK S7K 3N3, Canada. Ed. Catherine Anderson. adv. **Document type:** newsletter.

792 UK
SADLER'S WELLS THEATRE PROGRAMME. 1931. irreg. (approx. m.). £1. Sadler's Wells Trust Ltd., Rosebery Ave., London EC1R 4TN, England. TEL 071-278-6563. FAX 071-837-0965. TELEX 265871. Ed. Susanna Beaumont. adv.; bk.rev.; bibl.; illus. circ. 9,000. (back issues avail.)
Description: Details of performances, casts, synopsis, biographies and credits.

SAMUEL BECKETT TODAY - AUJOURD'HUI. see *LITERATURE*

792 US ISSN 0361-6495
SAMUEL FRENCH BASIC CATALOGUE OF PLAYS AND MUSICALS. a. Samuel French, Inc., 45 W. 25th St., New York, NY 10010. TEL 212-206-8990. FAX 212-206-1429. (Addr. in Canada: 80 Richmond St. E., Toronto, ON M5C 1P1, Canada. TEL 416-363-3536. FAX 416-363-8417) **Document type:** catalog.

792 VN
SAN KHAU/THEATRE. 1976. m. 51 Tran Hung Dao St., Hanoi, Socialist Republic of Vietnam. TEL 64423. Ed. Xuan Trinh.

SANGEET NATAK; journal of Indian music, dance, theatre. see *MUSIC*

SCANDINAVICA. see *LITERATURE*

792 YU ISSN 0036-5734
PN2007
SCENA; casopis za pozorisnu umetnost. 1965. bi-m. 50000 din. Sterijino Pozorje, Zmaj Jovina 22, 21000 Novi Sad, Yugoslavia. Ed. Radomir Putnik. bk.rev. circ. 1,250.

792 780 SA ISSN 0256-002X
SCENARIA. (Text in English) 1977. m. $90 (effective 1995-1996). Encore Publications (Pty) Ltd., P.O. Box 72161, Pakview 2122, Johannesburg, South Africa. TEL 27-11-447-1173. FAX 27-11-788-6313. Ed. Julius F. Eichbaum; Pub. Julius F. Eichbaum. adv.; bk.rev.; film rev.; play rev.; illus. circ. 10,000. (back issues avail.) **Indexed:** Ind.S.A.Per. **Document type:** consumer publication.
Incorporates: Arabesque.
Description: Discusses the performing arts in South Africa and worldwide.

SCENERY, COSTUMES, AND MUSICAL MATERIALS DIRECTORY. see *MUSIC*

SCENES MAGAZINE; mensuel suisse d'information culturelle. see *ART*

729 GW ISSN 0342-4553
SCHAUSPIELFUEHRER; der Inhalt der wichtigsten Theaterstuecke aus aller Welt. 1953. triennial, vol.15, 1992. DM.148 per vol. (Universitaet Wien, Institut fuer Theaterwissenschaft, AU) Anton Hiersemann Verlag, Rosenbergstr. 113, 70193 Stuttgart, Germany. TEL 0711-638265. FAX 0711-6369010. (Subscr. to: Postfach 140155, 70071 Stuttgart, Germany) Ed. Wolfgang Greisenegger. **Document type:** abstracting/indexing.

SCHWARZER FADEN; Vierteljahresschrift fuer Lust und Freiheit. see *POLITICAL SCIENCE*

792 SZ
SCHWEIZERISCHE GESELLSCHAFT FUER THEATERKULTUR. JAHRBUECHER. 1928. a. price varies. Schweizerische Gesellschaft fuer Theaterkultur - Swiss Association for Theatre Research, Postfach 1940, CH-4001 Basel, Switzerland. TEL 061-3211060. FAX 061-3211075. **Document type:** academic/scholarly publication.

792 SZ
SCHWEIZERISCHE GESELLSCHAFT FUER THEATERKULTUR. SCHRIFTEN. 1928. irreg. Schweizerische Gesellschaft fuer Theaterkultur - Swiss Association for Theatre Research, Postfach 1940, CH-4001 Basel, Switzerland. TEL 061-3211060. FAX 061-3211075. **Document type:** monographic series.

800 US ISSN 0748-2558
PR3091
SHAKESPEARE BULLETIN. 1982. q. $15. Lafayette College, English Department, Easton, PA 18042. TEL 215-250-5245. Eds. James P. Lusardi, June Schlueter. adv.; bk.rev.; play rev. circ. 1,000. (back issues avail.) **Indexed:** Bibl.Engl.Lang.& Lit., M.L.A. **Document type:** academic/scholarly publication.
—BLDSC (8254.582600); UnCover.
Incorporates (1976-1992): Shakespeare on Film Newsletter (ISSN 0739-6570); Formerly: New York Shakespeare Society Bulletin.
Description: Covers performance criticism and scholarship. Provides commentary on Shakespeare and Renaissance drama. Covers the U.S., Canada, U.K. and elsewhere.

SHAKESPEARE IN SOUTHERN AFRICA. see *LITERATURE*

SHAKESPEARE NEWSLETTER. see *LITERATURE*

SHAKESPEARE OXFORD SOCIETY. NEWSLETTER. see *LITERATURE*

SHAKESPEARE QUARTERLY. see *LITERATURE*

SHAKESPEARE WORLDWIDE. see *LITERATURE*

792 CC ISSN 0559-7277
SHANGHAI XIJU/SHANGHAI THEATER. (Text in Chinese) 1959. bi-m. Y9($24.30) (Shanghai Xijujia Xiehui) Shanghai Xiju Zazhishe, 238 Yan'an Xilu, Shanghai 200040, People's Republic of China. (Dist. outside China by: Guoji Shudian - China International Book Trading Corp., P.O. Box 399, Beijing, P.R.C.; Dist. in US by: China Books & Periodicals, Inc., 2929 24th St., San Francisco, CA 94110. TEL 415-282-2994) Ed. Zhao Laijing.

792 CC
SHANGHAI YISHUJIA/SHANGHAI ARTIST. (Text in Chinese) bi-m. $19.40. (Shanghai Yishu Yanjiusuo - Shanghai Art Institute) Shanghai Yishujia Bianjibu, No.2, Alley 112, Fenyang Lu, Shanghai 200031, People's Republic of China. TEL 4377362. (Dist. in US by: China Books & Periodicals, Inc., 2929 24th St., San Francisco, CA 94110. TEL 415-282-2994) Ed. Lan Fan.

SHAVIAN. see *LITERATURE*

SHOW MUSIC; the musical theatre magazine. see *MUSIC*

SHOWCALL. see *MUSIC*

792 AT ISSN 1032-6448
SHOWCAST CASTING DIRECTORY. 1963. a. Aus.$115 (foreign Aus.$185). Showcast Publications, P.O. Box 951, Crows Nest, N.S.W. 2065, Australia. TEL 02-438-2144. FAX 02-438-2007. **Document type:** directory.
Former titles: Showcast Directory; Showcast General Directory.
Description: Directory of actors and actresses.

792 647.968 UK ISSN 0265-9808
SIGHTLINE; journal of theatre technology and design. vol.24, no.4 1990. q. £12($24) to non-members. (Association of British Theatre Technicians) Theatrical Trading Ltd., 4 Great Pultneney St., London W1R 3DF, England. TEL 071-434-3901. Ed. Ian Herbert. adv.; bk.rev.
—UnCover.
Description: Covers all technical aspects of theatrical production, including design, technology, lighting, sound, training, planning, safety and regulations, and serves as a forum for issues of concern to technicians.

792 US ISSN 1048-955X
SIGHTLINES (NEW YORK). 1965. m. membership. U S Institute for Theatre Technology, Inc., 10 W. 19th St., Ste. 5A, New York, NY 10011. TEL 212-924-9088. FAX 212-924-9343. Eds. Eric & Cecelia Fielding. adv. circ. 3,600. **Document type:** newsletter.
Formerly (until 1988): U S I T T Newsletter (ISSN 0565-6311)

SINGER'S GUIDE TO THE PROFESSIONAL OPERA COMPANIES. see *MUSIC*

THEATER

016.80882   DK   ISSN 0106-665X
Z5781
SKUESPILREGISTER; supplement. 1979. a. DKK 111.20 (effective 1996). Dansk BiblioteksCenter as, Tempovej 7-11, DK-2750 Ballerup, Denmark. TEL 45-44-97-40-00. FAX 45-44-68-24-42.

792   XO   ISSN 0037-699X
PN2859.C93
SLOVENSKE DIVADLO/SLOVAK THEATER. (Text in Slovak; summaries in English and Russian) 1952. q. $20. Slovenska Akademia Vied, Kabinet Divadla a Filmu, Dubravska cesta 9, 813 64 Bratislava, Slovakia. (Dist. in Western countries by: John Benjamins B.V., Amsteldijk 44, Amsterdam (Z.), Netherlands) Ed. Milos Mistrik. bk.rev.; film rev.; play rev.; illus. Indexed: M.L.A., RILM.
    Description: Deals with the history of film, theater, radio and television art.

792.2 782.42   US   ISSN 1076-450X
▼THE SONDHEIM REVIEW; dedicated to the work of the musical theater's foremost composer and lyricist. 1994. q. $19.95 (Canada $24.95; elsewhere $29.95); newsstand price: $5.95. 2230 E. Bradford Ave., Unit G, Milwaukee, WI 53211-4059. E-mail: 74044,1351@compuserve.com. (Subscr. to: Department S-2, The Sondheim Review, Box 11213, Chicago, IL 60611-0213. TEL 800-584-1020) Ed. Paul Salsini. adv.; music rev.; play rev.; video rev. (back issues avail.)
    Description: Covers productions of plays by Stephen Sondheim.

268 792   US
SOUTHERN BAPTIST CONVENTION. NATIONAL DRAMA SERVICE. q. $35. Southern Baptist Convention, Sunday School Board, 127 Ninth Ave., N., Nashville, TN 37234. TEL 800-458-2772.

792   US   ISSN 0584-4738
SOUTHERN THEATRE. 1964. q. $10. (Southeastern Theatre Conference) Clinton Press, Box 9868, Greensboro, NC 27429-0868. TEL 919-272-3645. FAX 919-272-8810. Ed. Deanna Thompson. adv. contact: Marian A. Smith. bk.rev.; play rev.; index. circ. 3,500. (back issues avail.) Document type: consumer publication.
—UnCover.
    Description: Provides current articles on the theatre.

792   US
SPARKS (GRAND RAPIDS); the magazine of creative audio. 1989. irreg., latest vol.1, no.3. $3.50 per no. Box 3540, Grand Rapids, MI 49501-3540. TEL 616-363-8231. Eds. Michael Packer, Jim Middleton. (back issues avail.)
    Description: Designed for the radio - audio and theatre arts aficionado. Covers the activities of radio theatre producers, including profiles, current releases, technology, sources and history. Also covers activities of the Fireside Theatre.

792   FR   ISSN 0295-6047
SPECTACLES INFOS. 4/yr. Promoscience, 97 rue Reaumur, 75002 Paris, France. TEL 40-41-04-54. FAX 40-26-54-78. TELEX 214 891 PROMOSC. circ. 60,000.

792 370   UK   ISSN 0038-7142
SPEECH AND DRAMA. 1951. 2/yr. £6.50. Society of Teachers of Speech and Drama, 4 Fane Rd., Oxford OX3 OSA, England. TEL 01865-728304. Ed. Paul Ranger. adv. contact: Tony Hessey. bk.rev.; play rev.; index. circ. 2,000. (also avail. in microform from UMI; reprint service avail. from UMI) Document type: academic/scholarly publication.
—BLDSC (8411.195000); UMI.

791   IT
SPETTACOLO VIAGGIANTE. 1948. bi-m. L.10000. Associazione Nazionale Esercenti Spettacoli Vaggianti, Via di Villa Patrizi 10, 00161 Rome, Italy. Ed. Mario Faccio. adv. circ. 4,000.

792.02   GW
SPIEL & BUEHNE. 1974. 3/yr. DM.29. Bund Deutscher Amateurtheater e.V., Steinheimer Str. 7-1, 89518 Heidenheim, Germany. TEL 07321-48300. FAX 07321-48341. Ed. Ernst Sondergeld. adv.: page DM.880; trim 174 x 250. circ. 3,000. Document type: newsletter.

792   GW   ISSN 0038-7509
SPIEL UND THEATER; Zeitschrift fuer Amateurtheater, Darstellendes Kinderspiel, Schul- und Jugendtheater, Theatererziehung und Medienkunde. 1949. 2/yr. DM.18. Deutscher Theaterverlag GmbH, Postfach 100261, 69496 Weinheim, Germany. TEL 06201-51061. FAX 06201-507082. adv.; bk.rev.; play rev.; circ. controlled. (tabloid format) Document type: bulletin.
    Formerly: Laienspieler.

792   GW   ISSN 0038-7517
DER SPIELPLAN; die monatliche Theatervorschau. 1954. m. (11/yr.). DM.60. Loewendruck Bertram GmbH, Postfach 3744, 38027 Braunschweig, Germany. TEL 0531-352246. adv.; illus.

792   NO   ISSN 0333-2624
SPILLEROM; tidsskrift for scenekunst. 1981. 4/yr. NOK 100. (Norsk Kulturraad) Spillerom, c/o Jon Nyggaard, P.O. Box 49 Holmenkollen, N-0324 Oslo, Norway. TEL 47-22-49-05-06. FAX 47-22-49-05-06. Ed. Jon Nyggaard. adv.: B&W page NOK 2000. bk.rev.; play rev. circ. 2,000. Document type: academic/scholarly publication.

792 791.43   UK   ISSN 0142-8926
SPOTLIGHT CHILDRENS. 1980. a. £19.50. Spotlight, 7 Leicester Pl., London WC2H 7BP, England. TEL 0171-437-7031. FAX 0171-437-5881. Ed. Christine Barry. Document type: directory.

792   GW
STAATSTHEATER STUTTGART. MONATSVORSCHAU. m. Staatstheater Stuttgart, Oberer Schlossgarten 6, 70173 Stuttgart, Germany. TEL 0711-20320. FAX 0711-2032-389. TELEX 723777. adv. circ. 50,000.

STAD ANTWERPEN. CULTUREEL JAARBOEK. see MUSEUMS AND ART GALLERIES

791 792   UK
PN2001
THE STAGE. 1880. w. Stage Newspaper Ltd., Stage House, 47 Bermondsey St., London SE1 3XT, England. TEL 0171-403-1818. FAX 0171-403-1418. Ed. Brian Attwood. adv. contact: Colin Finlay. bk.rev.; illus.; play rev.; tele.rev. circ. 38,500. (tabloid format; also avail. in microfiche) Document type: trade publication.
    Formerly: Stage and Television Today (ISSN 0038-9099)

792   ZA
STAGE. (Text in English) 1956. irreg. price varies. Lusaka Theatre Club (Co-Op) Ltd., P.O. Box 30615, Lusaka, Zambia. Ed. Mase Mulondiwa. adv.; bk.rev.; play rev.; circ. 300 (controlled).

792   US   ISSN 1047-1901
PN2267
STAGE DIRECTIONS. 10/yr. S M W Communications, Inc., Beacon Bldg., 3101 Poplarwood Ct., No. 310, Raleigh, NC 27604-1010. TEL 919-872-7888. FAX 919-872-6888. E-mail: statedir@aol.com. Ed. Stephen Peithman; Pub. Susan Wershing. circ. 3,500. Document type: consumer publication.

792 375   US
STAGE OF THE ART. 1988. 3/yr. $25 (foreign $30). American Alliance for Theatre & Education, Theatre Department, Arizona State University, Box 853411, Tempe, AZ 85287-3411. TEL 602-965-6064. FAX 602-965-5351. Ed. Patricia Zimmer. adv.; bk.rev. circ. 1,100. Document type: consumer publication.
    Formerly (until 1995): Drama - Theatre Teacher (ISSN 1046-5022)
    Description: Practical articles on theatre education with an emphasis on classroom instruction, preschool - 12th grades.

792 791.43   IE
STAGECAST-IRISH STAGE AND SCREEN DIRECTORY. 1962. biennial. $15. Stagecast Publications, 15 Eaton Sq., Monkstown, Dublin County, Ireland. TEL 01-2808968. Ed. Derek Young. adv.; illus.; stat. circ. 500. (back issues avail.) Document type: directory.

792   US   ISSN 1041-6048
STAGES; the national theatre magazine. 1984. q. $15. Curtains, Inc., 301 W. 45th St., 5A, New York, NY 10036. TEL 212-245-9186. FAX 201-836-4107. Ed. Frank Scheck. adv.; bk.rev.; play rev.; illus. circ. 10,000. (tabloid format; back issues avail.) Document type: consumer publication.

STERZ; Zeitschrift fuer Literatur, Kunst und Kulturpolitik. see LITERATURE

STOHOLOSNYK/STOGOLOSNIK; aktualna svitova kultura. see ART

792   CN   ISSN 0085-6770
PN2306.S77
STRATFORD FESTIVAL; souvenir book. (Includes: Stratford Festival Story) 1953. a. Can.$10. Stratford Shakespearean Festival Foundation of Canada, Box 520, Stratford, ON N5A 6V2, Canada. TEL 519-271-4040. Document type: consumer publication.

STRINDBERGIANA. see LITERATURE

792   US   ISSN 0081-6051
PN2277.N5
STUBS (METRO NY); the seating plan guide for New York theatres, music halls, sports stadia. 1967. irreg. $9.95. Stubs Communications Co., 226 W. 47th St., New York, NY 10036. TEL 212-398-8370. FAX 212-398-8389. Ed. Ronald S. Lee. adv. circ. 30,000.

792   PL   ISSN 0208-404X
STUDIA I MATERIALY DO DZIEJOW TEATRU POLSKIEGO. 1957. irreg., vol.24, 1994. price varies. Polska Akademia Nauk, Instytut Sztuki, Ul. Dluga 26-29, P.O. Box 994, 00-950 Warsaw, Poland. TEL 48-22-313149. Document type: monographic series.
    Formerly: Studia i Materialy z Dziejow Teatru Polskiego (ISSN 0081-6647)
    Description: Polish theatre life in Poland.

792   US   ISSN 1062-0591
STUDIES IN FRENCH THEATRE. irreg. Peter Lang Publishing, Inc., 62 W. 45th St., 4th Fl., New York, NY 10036. TEL 212-302-6740. FAX 212-302-7574. Ed. Sharon Harwood-Gordon. Document type: academic/scholarly publication, monographic series.
    Description: Provides a forum for critical interpretation and analysis of French theatrical works and authors from the Middle Ages to the present day.

792   RM   ISSN 0039-3991
PN1609.R6
STUDII SI CERCETARI DE ISTORIA ARTEI. SERIA TEATRU, MUZICA, CINEMATOGRAFIE/STUDIES AND RESEARCH IN ART HISTORY. SERIES: THEATRE, MUSIC, CINEMATOGRAPHY. (Text in Rumanian; summaries in English, French, German and Russian) 1954. a. 35 lei($45) (Academia Romana) Editura Academiei Romane, Calea Victoriei 125, 79717 Bucharest, Rumania. (Dist. by: Rompresfilatelia, Calea Grivitei 64-66, P.O. Box 12-201, 78104 Bucharest, Rumania) bk.rev.; illus.; index. Indexed: RILM.

SUN BELT JOURNAL. see BUSINESS AND ECONOMICS

SYDNEY OPERA HOUSE. DIARY. see MUSIC

792   SZ
SZENE SCHWEIZ/SCENE SUISSE/SCENA SVIZZERA. 1973. a. 30 SFr. Schweizerische Gesellschaft fuer Theaterkultur - Swiss Association for Theatre Research, Postfach 1940, CH-4001 Basel, Switzerland. TEL 061-3211060. FAX 061-3211075. Document type: bulletin.

792   HU   ISSN 0039-8136
SZINHAZ. 1968. m. $32. (Szinhazmuveszeti Szovetseg) Lapkiado Vallalat, Lenin korut 9-11, 1073 Budapest 7, Hungary. TEL 222-408. (Subscr. to: Kultura, P.O. Box 149, H-1389 Budapest, Hungary) Ed. Ivan Boldizsar. bk.rev.; index. Indexed: M.L.A.

THEATER 6295

792 US ISSN 1060-3042
PN2000
T C I; the magazine of the business of entertainment technology & design. 1967. 10/yr. $40 (subscr. includes Industry Resource, Buyers Guide). Theatre Crafts International, 32 W. 18th St., New York, NY 10011-4612. TEL 212-229-2965. FAX 212-229-2084. (Subscr. to: Theatre Crafts, P.O. Box 470, Mt. Morris, IL 61054) Ed. David Barbour; Pub. Patricia MacKay. adv.: B&W page $2780, color page $4725; 276 x 375; adv. contact: Jacqueline Tien. bk.rev.; charts; illus.; circ. 25,000 (paid). (also avail. in microform from UMI) **Indexed:** Arts & Hum.Cit.Ind., Bk.Rev.Ind. (1978-), Child.Bk.Rev.Ind. (1978-), Curr.Cont., DAAI, Educ.Ind., Film Lit.Ind. (1988-), Mag.Ind., PMR, R.G., TOM. **Document type:** trade publication.
●Also available online. Vendor(s): University Microfilms International.
—Faxon; UMI.
   Formed by the 1992 merger of: Theatre Crafts (ISSN 0040-5469) & Theatre Crafts International; Which incorporated: Cue International; Which was formerly: Cue Technical Theatre Review (ISSN 0144-6088)
   Description: Offers an internationally scoped, in-depth coverage of design and technology for theatre, opera, and dance. Includes enhanced coverage of film and television, clubs and concerts, architecture and facility design.

792 US ISSN 1052-6765
NA1
T D & T. 1965. q. membership. U S Institute for Theatre Technology, Inc., 10 W. 19th St., Ste. 5A, New York, NY 10011-4206. TEL 212-924-9088. FAX 212-924-9343. Eds. Eric & Cecelia Fielding. adv. contact: Helen Willard. bk.rev.; play rev.; bibl.; charts; illus.; pat. circ. 3,750. (also avail. in microform from UMI; reprint service avail. from UMI) **Indexed:** Avery Ind.Archit.Per., Br.Tech.Ind., DAAI. **Document type:** trade publication.
—BLDSC (8814.343000); Faxon; SWETS; UMI; UnCover.
   Formerly: Theatre Design and Technology (ISSN 0040-5477)

792 US
T D F SIGHTLINES. 1986. q. free to qualified personnel. Theatre Development Fund, 1501 Broadway, New York, NY 10036. TEL 212-221-0885. FAX 212-768-1563. Ed. Stuart W. Little. circ. 1,800.
   Description: Covers matters of general theater interest. Includes news of the fund.

792.9 US ISSN 1054-2043
PN2000
T D R. (The Drama Review); a journal of performance studies. 1955. q. $32 to individuals (foreign $48); institutions $90 (foreign $106); students $20 (foreign $36). M I T Press, 55 Hayward St., Cambridge, MA 02142. TEL 617-253-2889. FAX 617-258-6779. E-mail: journals-orders@mit.edu. (Editorial addr.: TDR, New York University - Tisch School of the Arts, 721 Broadway, 6th fl., New York, NY 10003) Ed. Richard Schechner. adv.; bk.rev.; index. circ. 4,750. (also avail. in microform from UMI; back issues avail.; reprint service avail. from UMI) **Indexed:** Abstr.Engl.Stud., Acad.Ind., Amer.Bibl.Slavic & E.Eur.Stud., Arts & Hum.Cit.Ind., Bk.Rev.Ind. (1975-), Child.Bk.Rev.Ind. (1975-), Curr.Cont., Hum.Ind., M.L.A., Mag.Ind., Mid.East: Abstr.& Ind.
●Also available online.
—BLDSC (3623.197000); Faxon; Genuine Article; SWETS; UMI; UnCover. **CCC**.
   Former titles (until 1988): Drama Review (ISSN 0012-5962); (until 1968): T D R (ISSN 0273-4354); (until 1967): Tulane Drama Review (ISSN 0886-800X); (until 1957): Carleton Drama Review (ISSN 0161-3936)
   Description: Provides a forum for writing about performances and their social, economic, and political contexts.

T.G.I.F. CASTING NEWS. see OCCUPATIONS AND CAREERS

791 SA
T R U K P A C T INFO. (Text in Afrikaans, English) 1968. q. free. Transvaalse Raad vir die Uitvoerende Kunste - Performing Arts Council Transvaal, P.O. Box 566, Pretoria 0001, South Africa. FAX 012-322-3913. TELEX 3-20753 PACT SA. adv.: color page R.5290; adv. contact: Yvonne Eskell. circ. 40,000. **Document type:** consumer publication.
   Former titles (until 1991): Theatre Guide - Theatre Gids; (until 1990): T R U K - P A C T (ISSN 0085-7416)
   Description: Informs theatre enthusiasts of forthcoming productions and gives general theatre news.

792 028.5 US
T Y A TODAY. (Theatre for Young Audiences) 1985. s-a. $50 to individuals; libraries $30; students $25. International Association of Theatre for Children and Young People, United States Center, 2707 East Union, Seattle, WA 98122. TEL 206-860-9212. FAX 206-323-4611. Ed. Cyndi Pock. adv.; bk.rev.; play rev.; illus. circ. 1,000. (back issues avail.) **Document type:** trade publication.
   Description: Concerned with promotion and development of the professional theatre for young audiences in America and with the international inter-change of theatre artistry and research.

792 917.306 US ISSN 1062-5453
TAFT MEMORIAL FUND AND UNIVERSITY OF CINCINNATI SERIES IN LATIN AMERICAN AND U.S. LATINO THEATRE. 1992. irreg. Peter Lang Publishing, Inc., 62 W. 45th St., 4th Fl., New York, NY 10036. TEL 212-302-6740. FAX 212-302-7574. Ed. Kirsten F. Nigro. **Document type:** academic/scholarly publication, monographic series.

TAPROOT. see LITERATURE

792 DK ISSN 0900-0119
TEATERBLADET. m. DKK 152.50. Teaterfundet, Sankt Knuds Vej 26, 1903 Copenhagen V, Denmark.
   Formerly: Teater, Film og T V (ISSN 0108-6251)

792 DK ISSN 0902-8234
IN PROCESS
TEATERRAADETS INDSTILLINGER, FORSLAG OG KONKLUSIONER. 1976. a. free. Ministry of Culture, Danish Theater Council, Vesterbrogade 24, 4th, 1620 Copenhagen V, Denmark. TEL 45-1-247304.
   Formerly (until 1987): Teaterraadets Indstilling (ISSN 0107-248X)

792 SW ISSN 1101-9107
TEATERTIDNINGEN. 1977. 5/yr. SEK 185. Ek foer Nya Teatertidningen, P.O. Box 92377, S-102 73 Stockholm, Sweden. TEL 46-8-84-92-87. FAX 46-8-84-92-79. Ed. Rikard Hoogland. adv.; bk.rev. circ. 2,000.
   Formerly (until 1990): Nya Teatertidningen.

792 PL ISSN 0040-0769
TEATR. 1945. m. $11.70. Ul. Jakubowska 14, 03-902 Warsaw, Poland. TEL 48-22-175594. (Dist. by: Ars Polona-Ruch, Krakowskie Przedmiescie 7, Warsaw, Poland) Ed. Anrzej Wanat. bk.rev.; illus.; index. circ. 6,800.

792 RU ISSN 0131-6885
PN2007
TEATR; zhurnal dramaturgii i teatra. 1937. m. $181 (effective 1996). (Teatral'nyi Soyuz Rabochikh) Izdatel'stvo Izvestiya, Ul. Gertsena 49, Moscow 49, Russia. TEL (095) 291-5788. (Dist. by: Mezhdunarodnaya Kniga, B. Yakimanka 39, 117049 Moscow, Russia) (Co-sponsor: Soyuz Pisatelei) Ed. A. Salinskii. bk.rev.; dance rev.; play rev.; illus. circ. 32,600. **Indexed:** Curr.Dig.Sov.Press.

792 RU ISSN 0131-6915
TEATRAL'NAYA ZHIZN'. 1958. m. $97 (effective 1996). Teatral'noe Obschestvo - Theatrical Workers' Union, Kiselni Typik, dom 1, 103031 Moscow, Russia. (Dist. by: Mezhdunarodnaya Kniga, B. Yakimanka 39, 117049 Moscow, Russia) (Co-sponsors: Ministerstvo Kul'tury; Soyuz Pisatelei) Ed. Oleg Pivovarov. adv.; bk.rev.; illus.; index. circ. 10,000.

792 AG ISSN 0040-0793
TEATRO.* 1964. m. Arg.$500.($6) Concepcion Arenal 3932, Buenos Aires, Argentina.

792 IT
TEATRO. irreg. latest no.5. price varies. Angelo Longo Editore, Via Paolo Costa 33, 48100 Ravenna, Italy. TEL 39-544-217026. FAX 39-544-217554. circ. 2,000. **Document type:** monographic series.
   Description: Studies on theater.

792 NQ
TEATRO. 1993. irreg. C.$20. Comedia Nacional Ediciones, Ciudad Jardin F-18, Managua, Nicaragua. TEL 41268. Dir. Socorro Bonilla Castellon.

792 IT ISSN 1122-0678
TEATRO. STUDI E TESTI. 1985. irreg., no.8, 1993. price varies. Casa Editrice Leo S. Olschki, Casella Postale 66, 50100 Florence, Italy. TEL 39-55-6530684. FAX 39-55-6530214. **Document type:** monographic series.

792 AG
TEATRO C E L C I T; revista de teatrologia, tecnicas y reflexion sobre la practica teatral iberoamericana. 1987. 2/yr. $50 in America; Europe $65; elsewhere $80 (effective 1991). Centro Latinoamericano de Creacion e Investigacion Teatral, Bolivar 827, 1066 Buenos Aires, Argentina. TEL 541-361-8358. FAX 541-331-7353. Ed. Carlos A. Ianni. adv.; bk.rev. circ. 1,000. (back issues avail.)
   Supersedes: Teatro: Teoria y Practica.

792 AG
TEATRO COLON. q.? Arg.$10 per no. Tiempos Modernos Grupo Editor S.r.l., Santa Fe 2059 7o D, Buenos Aires, Argentina. TEL 824-9180.

792 780 945 IT ISSN 0394-6932
TEATRO E STORIA. 1986. a. Societa Editrice Il Mulino, Strada Maggiore, 37, 40125 Bologna, Italy. TEL 39-51-256011. FAX 39-51-256034. Ed. Nicola Savarese. adv.; index. circ. 1,100. (back issues avail.)

792 IT
TEATRO FESTIVAL. bi-m. Mucchi Editore s.r.l., Via Emilia Est 1527, 41100 Modena, Italy. Ed. Ugo Volli.

792 SP
LOS TEATROS. 1992. q. Arg.$16. Ediciones del Valle, Pasco 615, 3o B, Buenos Aires, Argentina. TEL 941-0353. Ed. Andres O. Valle.

792 RM ISSN 1220-4676
PN2844
TEATRULAZI. 1956. m. 300 lei($64) Ministerul Culturii, Piata Presei Libere 1, Sector 1, Bucharest, Rumania. (Subscr. to: Calea Grivitei 66-68, Box 12201, Bucharest, Rumania) Ed. Dumitro Solomon. adv.; bk.rev.; illus.; play rev.
   Formerly: Teatrul (ISSN 0040-0815)

792 BU ISSN 0204-6253
TEATUR. 1946. 10/yr. $72. (Komitet za Izkustvo i Kultura) Foreign Trade Co. "Hemus", 1B Raiko Daskalov Sq., 1000 Sofia, Bulgaria. TEL 359-2-801575. FAX 359-2-883419. (Co-sponsor: Suiuz na Artistite) Ed. K. Apostolova. play rev. circ. 4,046.

792 US ISSN 1053-8860
PN2091.S8
TECHNICAL BRIEF. 1982. 3/yr. $7 to individuals; institutions $10. Yale University, School of Drama, Technical Production Department, 222 York St., New Haven, CT 06520. TEL 203-432-9664. FAX 203-432-8336. Eds. Bronislaw Sammler, Don Harvey. illus.; tr.lit.; index. circ. 1,000. (looseleaf format; back issues avail.) **Document type:** newsletter.
   Description: Publishes articles by and for technical theater practitioners complete with mechanical drawings representing solutions to technical theater problems.

TEEN STAR ZINE; a newsletter for 10-18 year olds who love the performing arts. see CHILDREN AND YOUTH — For

6296 THEATER

792 US ISSN 0161-0775
PN2000
THEATER (NEW HAVEN). 1968. 3/yr. $22 to individuals; institutions $35. Yale University, School of Drama, Yale Repertory Theatre, 222 York St., New Haven, CT 06520. TEL 203-432-1568. FAX 203-432-8336. Ed. Erika Munk. adv.: page $250; adv. contact: Laraine Sammler. bk.rev.; illus.; play rev.; index. circ. 3,000. (also avail. in microfilm from UMI; back issues avail.; reprint service avail.) **Indexed:** Curr.Cont., Film Lit.Ind. (1977-), Hum.Ind., Ind.Bk.Rev.Hum., M.L.A, Mid.East: Abstr.& Ind. **Document type:** academic/scholarly publication.
—BLDSC (8814.306000); Faxon; SWETS; UMI; UnCover.
Formerly (until vol.8, no.2 & 3, 1976): Yale - Theatre (ISSN 0044-0167)
Description: Contains criticism, essays, reviews, translations, reports from abroad, and interviews. Each issue contains full text of a new play.

792 GW ISSN 0040-5418
PN2004
THEATER DER ZEIT. 1946. bi-m. DM.60. Felidae Verlagsgesellschaft mbH, Goldammerweg 16, 45134 Essen, Germany. TEL 0201-473031. FAX 0201-472590. Eds. Ingeborg Pietzsch, Kathrin Tiedemann. adv.; bk.rev.; dance rev.; play rev.; bibl.; illus.; index. **Indexed:** Curr.Cont., RILM. **Document type:** consumer publication.
—BLDSC (8814.310000).
Description: Covers all areas of theatre in the Germany: dramatic art, opera, children's theatre, musicals, ballet and puppet theatre.

792 GW ISSN 0040-5507
PN2004
THEATER HEUTE. 1960. m. DM.187.90. Erhard Friedrich Verlag GmbH, Im Brande 17, 30926 Seelze, Germany. TEL 0511-40004-0. FAX 0511-4000444. Ed.Bd. adv.; bk.rev.; illus.; circ. 20,000. (controlled). **Indexed:** Curr.Cont. **Document type:** consumer publication.
—Faxon; Genuine Article; SWETS. **CCC.**

792 GW
THEATER IM REVIER: KRITISCHE DOKUMENTATION. 1991. a. Wissenschaftlicher Verlag Trier, Bergstr. 27, 54295 Trier, Germany. Ed.Bd. **Document type:** trade publication.

792 AU
THEATER IN GRAZ.* 1952. w. S.220. Vereinigte Buehnen Graz, Kaiser-Josef-Platz 10, A-8010 Graz, Austria. Ed. Gernot Schoeppl. adv.; bk.rev.; play rev.; illus. circ. 6,000.
Formerly: Theaternachrichten (ISSN 0040-5450)

792 SZ
THEATER-KURIER. m. membership. (Theatergemeinde Baden) Buchdruckerei AG Baden, CH-5401 Baden, Switzerland. TEL 056-225504. circ. 6,000. **Document type:** bulletin.

792 GW ISSN 0040-5442
THEATER-RUNDSCHAU. 1955. m. DM.46 (foreign DM.51). (Bund der Theatergemeinden e.V.) Theater Rundschau Verlag GmbH, Bonner Talweg 10, 53113 Bonn, Germany. TEL 0228-915031. FAX 0228-9150350. adv.; bk.rev.; bibl.; illus. circ. 58,000. **Document type:** newspaper.

792 US ISSN 0896-1956
THEATER WEEK. 1987. w. $49 (foreign $74). That New Magazine, Inc., 28 W. 25th St., 4th Fl., New York, NY 10010. TEL 212-627-2120. FAX 212-727-9321. Ed. John Harris. adv.; bk.rev. circ. 12,000. (back issues avail.)
—Faxon.
Description: Covers broadway and regional theater.

792 SZ ISSN 0378-6935
THEATER-ZYTIG; Magazin fuer das Volkstheater in der Schweiz. 1972. 11/yr. 42 SFr. (Europe 52 SFr.; overseas 55 SFr.) to non-members. (Zentralverband Schweizer Volkstheater) Sauerlaender AG, Laurenzenvorstadt 89, CH-5001 Aarau, Switzerland. TEL 064-268626. FAX 064-245780. TELEX 981195-SAG-CH. Ed. Esther Staehli-Martin. adv.: B&W page 600 SFr., color page 2290.20 SFr.; trim 192 x 250. bk.rev.; bibl.; illus. **Document type:** trade publication.
—CCC.
Former titles (until 1981): Dialog; (until 1973): Laientheater.
Description: Information and calendar of Swiss amateur and national theatre.

792 GW
THEATERMAGAZIN. 1978. m. DM.52. (Niedersaechsischen Staatstheater Hannover) Schluetersche Verlagsanstalt GmbH und Co., Hans-Boeckler-Allee 7, 30173 Hannover, Germany. TEL 0511-8550-0. FAX 0511-8550400. (Subscr. to: Postfach 5440, 30054 Hannover, Germany) Ed. Sabine Hammer. circ. 25,000. (back issues avail.) **Document type:** trade publication.

792 GW
THEATERPAEDAGOGISCHE BIBLIOTHEK. 1983. irreg., vol. 8, 1993. Florian Noetzel Verlag, Heinrichshofen Buecher, Valoissr. 11, 26382 Wilhelmshaven, Germany. (Dist. in U.S. by: C.F. Peters Corp., 373 Park Ave. S., New York, NY 10016) Eds. Georg Immelmann, Rudolf Liechtenhan. **Document type:** monographic series.

792 GW ISSN 0723-1172
PN2004
THEATERZEITSCHRIFT. 2/yr. DM.10.80 per no. (students DM.8.80 per no.). (Verein zur Erfoschung Theatraler Verkehrformen e.V.) Wochenschau Verlag GmbH, Adolf-Damaschke-Str. 103-105, 65824 Schwalbach, Germany. TEL 06196-84010. FAX 06196-86060. Ed. Bernward Debus. circ. 1,700. **Document type:** trade publication.
Description: Theory and history of theatre, cinema and television.

792 GW
THEATERZEITUNG. 1988. m. Theater und Philharmonie Essen GmbH, Rolandstr. 10, 45128 Essen, Germany. TEL 0201-8122-0. FAX 0201-8122-211. Ed.Bd. adv.; play rev.; illus. circ. 180,000. (back issues avail.) **Document type:** newsletter.
Formerly (until 1992): Thema.

792 FR ISSN 1243-5139
PN2003
DU THEATRE. 1993. q. 240 F.($48) Pour le Theatre, 18 rue de Savoie, 75006 Paris, France. TEL 43-25-35-36. FAX 43-54-24-10. Ed. David Claire. adv.; bk.rev. circ. 2,000. **Document type:** bulletin.
Description: Covers contemporary theater in France and Europe, essays on theater, techniques, interviews, new plays.

792 US
THEATRE (NEW YORK). 1997. 8/yr. $12. 41 W. 72nd St., Apt. 14G, New York, NY 10023. TEL 212-221-6078. Eds. Ira J. Bilowit, Debbi Wasserman. circ. 10,000.

792 US
THEATRE & EVENTS GUIDE.* 1960. m. $24. Theatre & Events Guide, Inc., 180 West End Ave., Apt. 26D, New York, NY 10023-4725. TEL 212-799-5901. Ed. Adele Gold. circ. 35,700.

792 US ISSN 0082-3821
PN2012
THEATRE ANNUAL. 1942. a. $8 to individuals; institutions $10. College of William and Mary, Department of Theatre and Speech, Williamsburg, VA 23187. TEL 804-221-2668. FAX 804-221-1287. E-mail: wmcarr@mail.wm.edu. Ed. John V. Falconieri. circ. 400 (paid). **Indexed:** Abstr.Engl.Stud.; Arts & Hum.Cit.Ind., Curr.Cont., M.L.A. **Document type:** academic/scholarly publication.
—BLDSC (8814.335000).
Refereed Serial

792 AT ISSN 1320-9302
▼**THEATRE AUSTRALASIA.** 1994. m. Aus.$40 (effective 1996). Pellinor Pty. Ltd., Level 2, 44 Bridge St., Sydney, N.S.W. 2000, Australia. TEL 61-2-247-2264. FAX 61-2-247-2269. **Document type:** newspaper.

842 FR ISSN 0151-5713
THEATRE D'AUJOURD'HUI. 1976. irreg. price varies. Editons Klincksieck, 11 rue de Lille, 75005 Paris, France. Dir. Paul Vernois.

792 US ISSN 0271-3136
PN2289
THEATRE DIRECTORY; the annual contact resource of theatres and related organizations. 1972. a. $5.95. Theatre Communications Group, Inc., 355 Lexington Ave., New York, NY 10017. TEL 212-697-5230. FAX 212-983-4847. Ed. Steven Samuels. circ. 5,000. **Document type:** directory.

792 US ISSN 0737-0172
PN2275.C3
THEATRE DIRECTORY OF THE BAY AREA (YEAR). 1981. biennial. $25. Theatre Bay Area, 657 Mission St., No. 402, San Francisco, CA 94105-4116. FAX 415-957-1556. Ed. Belinda Taylor. adv. circ. 1,400. (back issues avail.) **Document type:** directory.
Description: Comprehensive guide to theater activities in the San Francisco Bay area for performers and theater lovers.

792 PL ISSN 0040-5493
PN2859.P6
THEATRE EN POLOGNE/THEATRE IN POLAND. (Text in English and French) 1958. q. $26 (effective 1995 & 1996). Miedzynarodowy Instytut Teatralny, Polski Osrodek - International Theatre Institute, Polish Center, Pl. Pilsudskiego 9, 00-078 Warsaw, Poland. TEL 48-22-263027. Ed. Elzbieta Wysinska. adv.: page $150. bk.rev.; abstr.; bibl.; illus.; play rev.; tr.lit.; index. circ. 1,700. (tabloid format) **Indexed:** Arts & Hum.Cit.Ind., Curr.Cont. **Document type:** bulletin.

792 FR ISSN 0049-3597
THEATRE ENFANCE ET JEUNESSE. (Text in English, French) 1963. s-a. $45. Association du Theatre pour l'Enfance et la Jeunesse, 98 Bd. Kellermann, 75013 Paris, France. illus.

792.02 FR ISSN 0398-0049
THEATRE ET ANIMATION; revue trimestrielle des spectacles non-professionnels et des techniques d'expression et d'animation. 1976. q. 130 F. (foreign 180 F.). Federation Nationale des Compagnies de Theatre et d'Animation, 12 Chaussee d'Antin, 75009 Paris, France. TEL 45-23-36-46. FAX 47-70-17-00. Ed. Marie-Lorraine Meurer-Revillon.
Incorporating: Nos Spectacles; Theatre Amateur (ISSN 0029-3741); Theatre et Spectacles Non Professionnels, Techniques d'Expression et d'Animation.

840 IT ISSN 1122-066X
THEATRE FRANCAIS DE LA RENAISSANCE; premiere serie. 1986. irreg., no.6, 1994. price varies. Casa Editrice Leo S. Olschki, Casella Postale 66, 50100 Florence, Italy. TEL 39-55-6530684. FAX 39-55-6530214. **Document type:** monographic series.

792 US ISSN 0733-2033
PN2000
THEATRE HISTORY STUDIES. 1981. a. $10 to individuals; libraries $15 (foreign $18). Mid-America Theatre Association, Theatre Program, Central College, Pella, IA 50219. TEL 515-628-5234. FAX 515-628-5316. E-mail: SCHANKER@central.edu. (Co-sponsor: University of North Dakota) Ed. Robert A. Schanke. adv.; bk.rev. circ. 1,000. **Indexed:** Arts & Hum.Cit.Ind., Bk.Rev.Ind., Hum.Ind., M.L.A. **Document type:** academic/scholarly publication.
—BLDSC (8814.347200); Faxon; Genuine Article; UnCover.
Refereed Serial

792 UK ISSN 0967-019X
PN2596.L6
THEATRE INDEX (YEAR). 1981. a. £10($20) 4 Cross Deep Gardens, Twickenham, Mddx. TW1 4QU, England. TEL 0181-892 6087. FAX 0181-744-3002. Ed. Ian Herbert. adv. **Document type:** directory.
Formerly (until 1991): London Theatre Index (Year) (ISSN 0263-2322)
Description: Annual critical review, with name index to who did what in the year's London productions.

792 US ISSN 0192-2882
PN3171
THEATRE JOURNAL (BALTIMORE). 1949. q. $22.50 to individuals (foreign $32.80); institutions $55 (foreign $65.80). Johns Hopkins University Press, Journals Publishing Division, 2715 N. Charles St., Baltimore, MD 21218. TEL 410-516-6967. FAX 410-516-6998. Eds. John Rouse, Janette Reinelt. adv. contact: Tara Dorai-Berry. bk.rev.; play rev.; bibl.; illus. circ. 3,820. (also avail. in microfiche from UMI; reprint service avail. from UMI; back issues avail.) **Indexed:** Abstr.Engl.Stud., Bk.Rev.Ind. (1980-), C.I.J.E., Chic.Per.Ind., Child.Bk.Rev.Ind. (1980-), Curr.Cont., Educ.Ind., Hum.Ind. **Document type:** academic/scholarly publication.
—BLDSC (8814.347500); Faxon; Genuine Article; SWETS; UnCover. **CCC.**
Formerly (until 1979): Educational Theatre Journal (ISSN 0013-1989)
Description: Covers a broad range of topics in the study and teaching of theater, including social and historical studies, production reviews, and theoretical inquiries that illuminate dramatic text and production.

792 CN ISSN 1186-7795
THE THEATRE LISTING. 1986. a. Can.$25 (1995-1996 edition). Professional Association of Canadian Theatres, PACT Communications Centre, 64 Charles St. E., 2nd Fl., Toronto, ON M4Y 1T1, Canada. TEL 416-968-3033. FAX 416-968-3035. E-mail: pact@acs.ucalgary.ca. Ed. Tracy Sigurdson. adv.; illus. **Document type:** directory.
Formerly (until 1989): Behind the Scenes.
Description: Directory of professional English-language Canadian theatres from coast to coast. Also includes service organizations, artists associations, government departments and agencies, and rental facilities.

792 UK ISSN 0040-5523
THEATRE NOTEBOOK; journal of the history and technique of the British theatre. 1946. 3/yr. $30. Society for Theatre Research, c/o The Theatre Museum, 1E Tavistock St., London WC2E 7PA, England. Ed. Russell Jackson. adv. contact: Geoff Davidson. bk.rev.; illus.; index, cum.index: vols. 1-25, 26-40. circ. 1,200. (also avail. in microfilm) **Indexed:** Abstr.Engl.Stud., Arts & Hum.Cit.Ind., Br.Tech.Ind., Curr.Cont., Hum.Ind., M.L.A. **Document type:** academic/scholarly publication.
—BLDSC (8814.350000); Faxon; Genuine Article; SWETS; UnCover.

THEATRE ORGAN REVIEW. see *MUSIC*

792 US ISSN 0361-7947
PN2266
THEATRE PROFILES; an illustrated reference guide to nonprofit professional theatres in the United States. 1973. biennial. $21.95. Theatre Communications Group, Inc., 355 Lexington Ave., New York, NY 10017. TEL 212-697-5230. FAX 212-983-4847. E-mail: tcg@tmn.com. Ed. Steven Samuels; Pub. Terence Nemeth. illus. (back issues avail.) **Document type:** trade publication.
—BLDSC (8814.354500).

792 FR ISSN 0335-2927
THEATRE PUBLIC. 1974. bi-m. 300 F.($55) (foreign 325 F.). Theatre de Gennevilliers, 41 av. des Gresillons, 92230 Gennevilliers, France. FAX 40-86-17-44. Ed. Alain Girault. adv.; bk.rev. circ. 2,000. (back issues avail.)

792 070 UK ISSN 0962-1792
PN2596.L6
THEATRE RECORD. 1981. fortn. £95($190) 4 Cross Deep Gardens, Twickenham, Middx. TW1 4QU, England. TEL 081-892 6087. FAX 081-744-3002. Ed. Ian Herbert. adv.; bk.rev.; play rev.; cum.index. (looseleaf format; back issues avail.) **Document type:** consumer publication.
Formerly (until 1991): London Theatre Record (ISSN 0261-5282)
Description: Reprints unabridged critical reviews and cast lists of all London and most new British theatre.

792 CN ISSN 1196-1198
PN2009
THEATRE RESEARCH IN CANADA/RECHERCHES THEATRALES AU CANADA. (Text in English, French) 1980. s-a. Can.$15 to individuals; students Can.$12; institutions Can.$22. University of Toronto, Graduate Centre for Study of Drama, 214 College St., Toronto, ON M5T 2Z9, Canada. TEL 416-978-7984. FAX 416-971-1378. (Co-sponsor: Queen's University in Kingston) Ed.Bd. bk.rev. circ. 490. **Indexed:** Arts & Hum.Cit.Ind., Can.B.P.I., Can.Lit.Ind., Can.Per.Ind., Curr.Cont. **Document type:** academic/scholarly publication.
—BLDSC (8814.370200); Faxon; Genuine Article.
Formerly (until vol.13): Theatre History in Canada (ISSN 0226-5761)

792 UK ISSN 0307-8833
PN2001
THEATRE RESEARCH INTERNATIONAL. (Text in English; summaries in French) 1958. 3/yr. £60($115) (effective 1996). (International Federation for Theatre Research) Oxford University Press, Oxford Journals, Walton St., Oxford OX2 6DP, England. TEL 01865-267907. FAX 01865-267773. TELEX 837330-OXPRES-G. E-mail: jnlorders@oup.co.uk. (U.S. subscr. to: Oxford University Press Inc., 2001 Evans Rd., Cary, NC 27513. TEL 919-677-0977. FAX 919-677-1714) Ed. Claude Schumacher. adv. contact: Jane Parker. bk.rev.; bibl.; illus.; index. circ. 1,050. (also avail. in microform from UMI) **Indexed:** Amer.Hist.& Life, Arts & Hum.Cit.Ind., Curr.Cont., Hist.Abstr., Hum.Ind., Ind.Bk.Rev.Hum., M.L.A., Mid.East: Abstr.& Ind. **Document type:** academic/scholarly publication.
—BLDSC (8814.370300); Faxon; Genuine Article; SWETS; UMI; UnCover. **CCC.**
Formerly: Theatre Research (ISSN 0040-5566)
Description: Presents history and criticism of drama conceived and the art of the theatre, providing both a medium of communication for scholars and a service to students of art, architecture, design, music and drama literature.

792.02 US ISSN 0362-0964
PN1620.O45
THEATRE STUDIES. 1955. a. $8 to individuals; institutions $10 (effective 1995-1996). Ohio State University, Theatre Research Institute, 1430 Lincoln Tower, 1800 Cannon Dr., Columbus, OH 43210. TEL 614-292-6614. FAX 614-292-3222. Ed. Beth A. Kattelman. adv.; bk.rev.; bibl.; illus.; cum.index: vols. 1-20 in vol. 20 (1973-74). circ. 500. (also avail. in microfilm; back issues avail.) **Indexed:** Abstr.Engl.Stud., Amer.Hum.Ind., Arts & Hum.Cit.Ind., Curr.Cont., G.Perf.Arts, M.L.A. **Document type:** academic/scholarly publication.
—Faxon; UnCover.
Refereed Serial

792 US ISSN 0040-5574
PN2000
THEATRE SURVEY. 1956. q. $45. American Society for Theatre Research, c/o Gordon Armstrong, Sec., Dept. of Fine Arts Ctr., Univ. of Rhode Island, Kingston, RI 02881-0824. Ed. Michael Quinn. adv.; bk.rev.; illus. circ. 860. (also avail. in microform from UMI; back issues avail.) **Indexed:** Abstr.Engl.Stud., Amer.Hist.& Life, Arts & Hum.Cit.Ind., Chic.Per.Ind., Curr.Cont., Hist.Abstr., Hum.Ind., M.L.A. **Document type:** academic/scholarly publication.
—Faxon; UMI; UnCover.
Refereed Serial

792 US ISSN 1054-8378
PN2000
THEATRE TOPICS. 1991. s-a. $17 to individuals; institutions $27. (Association for Theatre in Higher Education) Johns Hopkins University Press, Journals Publishing Division, 2715 N. Charles St., Baltimore, MD 21218. TEL 410-516-6987. FAX 410-516-6968. Ed. Suzanne Burgoyne. adv.; B&W page $215; adv. contact: Tara Dorai-Berry. circ. 2,300. **Document type:** academic/scholarly publication.
—UnCover. **CCC.**
Description: Addresses the concerns of scholars and artists in the areas of performance studies, dramaturgy, and theatre pedagogy.
Refereed Serial

792 US
THEATRE UPDATE. 1986. w. $28. E W A Publications, 275 Bay 37th St., Brooklyn, NY 11214. TEL 718-996-5406. FAX 718-373-1342. Ed. Kevin Browne. adv. contact: Adrienne Knoll. circ. 112,000. **Document type:** newspaper.

792.0973 US ISSN 0082-3856
THEATRE WORLD. a. $25. Crown Publishers, Inc., 201 E. 50th St., New York, NY 10022. TEL 212-254-1600. Ed. John Willis.

792 US ISSN 1060-5320
THEATREFORUM. 1992. s-a. $15 to individuals (Canada and Mexico $16; elsewhere $18); institutions $25 (Canada and Mexico $26; elsewhere $28); students $12 (Canada and Mexico $13; elsewhere $15). University of California at San Diego, Theatre Department, 9500 Gilman Dr., La Jolla, CA 92093-0344. TEL 619-534-6598. FAX 619-534-1080. Ed. Adele Edling Shank. **Document type:** academic/scholarly publication.
—UnCover.
Description: Documents, discusses, and disseminates innovative or provocative theatrical works, representing a wide variety of aesthetic and cultural interests.

792 UK ISSN 0265-2609
PN2001
THEATREPHILE. q. £15($30) D.F. Cheshire, Sean McCarthy, Eds. & Pubs., 5 Dryden St., Covent Garden, London WC2E 9NW, England.
—BLDSC (8814.387600).

792.9 US
THEATREWORKS.* irreg.(7-8/yr.). Latimer Publications, 617 Veterans Blvd., Ste. 213, Redwood City, CA 94063-1404. TEL 415-324-1570. FAX 415-324-4420. Ed. Merlyn Holmes; Pub. Douglas H. Latimer. circ. 11,000.
Description: Guide to theater productions in the Bay Area.

792 IT ISSN 0040-5604
THEATRON; rivista quadrimestrale di cultura, documentazione e informazione teatrale. (Text in English, French, German, Italian) 1961. 3/yr. L.30000 (foreign L.50000). Centro Internazionale di Documentazione del Teatro Universitario, Via Fabiola 1, 00152 Rome, Italy. TEL 06-58230047. Dir. Elda A. Vernara. adv.; bk.rev.; play rev.; bibl.; illus.; stat.; index, cum.index.

051 CN ISSN 0838-5696
THEATRUM. 1985. 5/yr. Can.$17 (foreign $27). Theatrum Publishing Inc., P.O. Box 688, Sta. C, Toronto, ON M6J 3S1, Canada. TEL 416-493-5740. FAX 416-493-5740. Ed. Sarah B. Hood; Pub. Katherine Goodes. adv.; bk.rev. circ. 3,000. (also avail. in microform from MML) **Indexed:** Can.B.P.I.

792 GW
THEMA - DAS THEATERMAGAZIN; Theatermagazin fuer Freunde und Foerderer des Badischen Staatstheaters Karlsruhe. 1987. m. free. Badisches Staatstheater Karlsruhe, Baumeisterstr. 11, 76137 Karlsruhe, Germany. Ed. Anna-Renate Soergel. play rev.; illus. circ. 12,000. **Document type:** consumer publication.
Formerly (until 1989): Musengaul.

TIAN WAI TIAN/SKY OUTSIDE SKY. see *MOTION PICTURES*

792 NE ISSN 0167-5516
TIJDSCHRIFT VOOR THEATERWETENSCHAP. 1979. q. fl.30 to individuals; institutions fl.40. Instituut voor Theaterwetenschap, Kromme Nieuwe Gracht 29, 3512 HD Utrecht, Netherlands. TEL 020-279709. Ed. H. Schoenmakers. adv.; bk.rev. circ. 400.
Description: Covers theater, theatrical dance, film, television with a historical and theoretical perspective.

THEATER

792 — NE — ISSN 0928-5059
PN2002
TONEEL TEATRAAL. 10/yr. fl.65. Theater Instituut Nederland, Herengracht 168, 1016 BP Amsterdam, Netherlands. TEL 31-20-6235119. FAX 31-20-6200051. Ed. L. Zonneveld. adv.; bk.rev.; play rev.; charts; illus. circ. 3,500. **Document type:** consumer publication.
—SWETS.
Former titles (until 1990): T T (ISSN 0923-246X); (until 1981): Toneel Teatraal (ISSN 0040-9170); (until 1974): Mickery Mouth en Toneel Teaatral (ISSN 0301-9292); Which was formed by the 1973 merger of: Toneel Teatraal (ISSN 1380-4383); Mickery Mouth (ISSN 1380-4375)

792 — MX — ISSN 0187-4160
TRAMOYA; cuaderno de teatro. 1975. q. $100. Universidad Veracruzana, Apdo. Postal 318, 91000 Xalapa, Veracruz, Mexico. FAX 281-72954. (U.S. addr.: Rutgers University, Department of Spanish, Camden, NJ 08102) Ed. Joaquina Soto. cum.index: 1975-1992. circ. 1,000. **Document type:** academic/scholarly publication.

TUITION, ENTERTAINMENT, NEWS, VIEWS. see *ART*

792 — US
U S OUTDOOR DRAMA. 1964. q. $12. Institute of Outdoor Drama, University of North Carolina at Chapel Hill, CB 3240 Nations Bank Plaza, Chapel Hill, NC 27599-3240. TEL 919-962-1328. FAX 919-962-4212. Ed. Cindy Biles. adv. contact: Scott Parker. bk.rev. circ. 1,000. (looseleaf format) **Document type:** newsletter.
Formerly (until 1990): Institute of Outdoor Drama Newsletter (ISSN 0020-3017).
Description: Covers news, announcements, theatre literature citations, and information on all aspects of outdoor historical drama planning and production such as writing, directing, designing, staging, promotion, auditions, and management.

790 — SW — ISSN 1104-2036
UNGA ATALANTE. 1993. 6/yr. SEK 120. Dansgruppen Rubicon, Oevre Husargatan 1, S-411 22 Goeteborg, Sweden. TEL 46-31-11-82-00. FAX 46-31-13-63-17.
Description: Acts as a guide to the interesting events in Goeteborg's cultural life. Observes, justifies and discusses entertainment and cultural events in Goeteborg and the rest of Sweden.

792 782 — US — ISSN 8756-856X
ML1699
U.S. NATIONAL ENDOWMENT FOR THE ARTS. APPLICATION GUIDELINES: OPERA - MUSICAL THEATER. Key Title: Opera - Musical Theater. a. free. U.S. National Endowment for the Arts, Public Information Office, 1100 Pennsylvania Ave., N.W., Washington, DC 20506. TEL 202-682-5400. **Document type:** government publication.
Formerly: N E A Grantmaking Programs: Opera - Musical Theater.
Description: Offers grant application guidelines.

792 — US — ISSN 8756-4335
PN2044.U6
U.S. NATIONAL ENDOWMENT FOR THE ARTS. APPLICATION GUIDELINES: THEATER. Key Title: Theater (Washington). (In 2 editions: Individuals; Organizations) a. free. U.S. National Endowment for the Arts, Public Information Office, 1100 Pennsylvania Ave., N.W., Washington, DC 20506. TEL 202-682-5400. **Document type:** government publication.
Formerly: N E A Grantmaking Programs: Theater.
Description: Grant application guidelines.

792 — SP
UNIVERSIDAD DE MURCIA. CATEDRA DE TEATRO. CUADERNOS. 1978. irreg., no.17, 1993. 600 ptas. Universidad de Murcia, Servicio de Publicaciones, P.O. Box 4021, 30080 Murcia, Spain. TEL 34-68-363014. FAX 34-68-363414. adv. contact: Mariano de Paco y Cesar Oliva. circ. 2,000. **Document type:** academic/scholarly publication.

792.07 — TZ
UNIVERSITY OF DAR ES SALAAM. THEATRE ARTS DEPARTMENT. ANNUAL REPORT. a. University of Dar es Salaam, Theatre Arts Department, P.O. Box 35091, Dar es Salaam, Tanzania.

700 — US — ISSN 0042-2738
PN2000
VARIETY. 1905. w. $167 (Canada $175; Europe $270; Asia-Pacific Rim $470; elsewhere $370). (Variety, Inc.) Cahners Publishing Company (New York), Entertainment Division, Division of Reed Elsevier Inc., 249 W. 17th St., New York, NY 10011. TEL 212-645-0067. FAX 212-337-6977. (Subscr. to: Box 6400, Torrance, CA 90504-0400. TEL 800-323-4345) Ed. Peter Bart. adv.; bk.rev.; film rev.; music rev.; play rev.; rec.rev.; tele.rev. circ. 30,036. (also avail. in microform from KTO,BHP) **Indexed:** Bus.Ind., Film Lit.Ind. (1973-), Int.Ind.Film Per., Intl.Ind.TV, Mag.Ind., Music Ind., PMR, SRI, Tr.& Indus.Ind.
—UMI. **CCC.**
Description: Covers all of the entertainment business: film, TV, cable, homevideo, legitimate theater, music and personal appearance.

792 011 — US
VARIETY'S DIRECTORY OF MAJOR U S SHOW BUSINESS AWARDS. irreg., latest 1989. $59.95. R.R. Bowker, A Reed Reference Publishing company, 121 Chanlon Rd., New Providence, NJ 07974. TEL 908-464-6800. FAX 908-665-6688. TELEX 138 755. (Subscr. to: Order Dept., Box 31, New Providence, NJ 07974-9903. TEL 800-521-8110) **Document type:** bibliography, directory.
Description: Lists names of all nominees and winners for every Oscar, Emmy, Tony, Grammy, and Pulitzer Prize for drama ever awarded. Organized chronologically.

VARIETY'S WHO'S WHO IN SHOW BUSINESS. see *BIOGRAPHY*

792 700 — UK — ISSN 0960-3662
VENUE MAGAZINE. 1982. fortn. £35. Greetlake Services, 64-65 North Rd., St. Andrews, Bristol, Avon BS6 5AQ, England. TEL 01272-428491. FAX 01272-420369. Ed. Dave Higgitt. adv.; bk.rev.; film rev.; play rev.; illus. circ. 17,000. (back issues avail.) **Document type:** consumer publication.

VLAANDEREN; tijdschrift voor kunst en letteren. see *ART*

792 — FR — ISSN 1140-5309
VOIES DE LA CREATION THEATRALE. a. price varies. C N R S Editions, 20-22 rue St. Amand, 75015 Paris, France. TEL 45-33-16-00. FAX 45-33-92-13. TELEX 200 356 F. adv.; bk.rev.; index; circ. 1,500 (controlled).

792 — RU — ISSN 0507-3952
VOPROSY TEATRA; sbornik statei i materialov. 1965. a. 1.45 Rub. Teatral'noe Obshchestvo - Theatrical Workers' Union, Kiselni Typik, dom 1, 103031 Moscow, Russia. (Co-sponsor: Institut Istorii Iskusstv) bibl.; illus.

WASHINGTON OPERA MAGAZINE. see *MUSIC*

792 — SA — ISSN 0043-1036
WAT KAN ONS OPVOER/WHAT CAN WE STAGE. 1967. s-a. free. Dramatic Artistic & Literary Rights Organisation (Pty) Ltd., SAMRO House, Cor. de Beer & Juta Streets, Braamfontein, South Africa. Eds. G.D. Roos, P.J. Roos. circ. 2,000 (controlled).

DIE WERKSTATT. see *DANCE*

WESTERN JOURNAL OF COMMUNICATION. see *LINGUISTICS*

WHAT'S ON IN LONDON. see *TRAVEL AND TOURISM*

791.3 — US — ISSN 0043-499X
WHITE TOPS; devoted exclusively to the circus. 1927. bi-m. $24 to non-members. Circus Fans Association of America, Rt. 1, Box 6735, White Stone, VA 22578. TEL 804-435-2951. FAX 804-435-6662. Ed. James E. Foster. adv. contact: Mike Marton. bk.rev.; illus.; circ. 2,500 (paid).

792 — US — ISSN 1047-1715
PN2289
WHO'S WHERE IN THE AMERICAN THEATRE; a directory of affiliated theatre artists in the U.S.A. 1990. irreg., 3rd ed. 1992. $14.95. Feedback Theatrebooks, 305 Madison Ave., Ste. 1146, New York, NY 10165. TEL 207-359-2781. Ed. Mollie Ann & Walter J. Meserve. adv. contact: Joe Walters. **Document type:** directory.
Description: Provides job titles, affiliations, addresses and phone numbers for more than 3300 individuals working in theatre in America.

792 — AU
WIENER FORSCHUNGEN ZUR THEATER UND MEDIENWISSENSCHAFT. 1972. irreg. price varies. (Universitaet Wien, Institut fuer Theaterwissenschaft) Wilhelm Braumueller, Universitaets Verlagsbuchhandlung GmbH, Servitengasse 5, A-1092 Vienna, Austria. TEL 01-3191159. FAX 01-3102805. Ed. Margaret Dietrich. index. circ. 1,000. **Document type:** monographic series.
Formerly: Vienna. Universitaet. Institut fuer Theaterwissenschaft. Wissenschaftliche Reihe (ISSN 0083-6176)

792 — AU — ISSN 0377-0745
HD8799.S9
WIENER GESELLSCHAFT FUER THEATERFORSCHUNG. JAHRBUCH. 1944. a. price varies. (Wiener Gesellschaft fuer Theaterforschung) Edition Praesens, Postfach 43, A-1166 Vienna, Austria. TEL 01-5350590. Ed. Otto G. Schindler. circ. 500. **Document type:** directory.
Description: Complete listing of all Austrian theater productions during the season.

796 301.412 — US — ISSN 0740-770X
PN1590.W64
WOMEN & PERFORMANCE; a journal of feminist theory. 1983. s-a. $14 to individuals (Canada $17; elsewhere $20); institutions $25 (Canada $28; elsewhere $31) (effective Sept. 1995). Women & Performance Project, 721 Broadway, 6th Fl., New York, NY 10003. TEL 212-998-1625. Ed. Judy Burns. adv.; bk.rev. circ. 1,300. **Indexed:** Alt.Press Ind., Left Ind. (1984-). **Document type:** academic/scholarly publication.
—BLDSC (9343.273000); Faxon.
Description: Publishes articles concerned with traditional and nontraditional performance, such as film, theatre, music, dance, and performing art.

792.02 — CC — ISSN 1003-0549
XIJU/DRAMA. Variant title: Zhongyang Xiju Xueyuan Xuebao. (Text in Chinese) q. $24. Zhongyang Xiju Xueyuan - Central Academy of Drama, 39 Dong Mianhua Lane, Jiaodaokou, Beijing, People's Republic of China. (Dist. outside China by: China International Book Trading Corp., P.O. Box 2820, Beijing, P.R.C.; Dist. in US by: China Books & Periodicals, Inc., 2929 24th St., San Francisco, CA 94110. TEL 415-282-2994) Ed. Xu Xiaozhong. bk.rev. **Document type:** academic/scholarly publication.

XIJU WENXUE/DRAMA LITERATURE. see *LITERATURE*

792 — CC
XIJU YISHU (BEIJING)/THEATRE ART. (Text in Chinese) q. Zhongguo Xiju Xueyuan, 3 Liren Jie, Xuanwu-qu, Beijing 100054, People's Republic of China. TEL 333931.

792 — CC — ISSN 0257-943X
XIJU YISHU (SHANGHAI)/THEATRE ARTS. (Text in Chinese) 1978. q. Y8($24) Shanghai Xiju Xueyuan - Shanghai Theatre Academy, 630 Huashan Lu, Shanghai 200040, People's Republic of China. TEL 021-521909. (Dist. outside China by: China International Book Trading Corp., P.O. Box 399, Beijing, P.R.C.; Dist. in US by: China Books & Periodicals, Inc., 2929 24th St., San Francisco, CA 94110. TEL 415-282-2994) circ. 5,000.

792 791.43 — CC — ISSN 1003-2681
XIJU YU DIANYING/THEATRE AND CINEMA. (Text in Chinese) 1980. m. Y12. Zhongguo Xijujia Xiehui, Sichuan Fenhui - China Dramatists Association, Sichuan Chapter, 85, Hongxing Zhonglu 2 Duan, Chengdu, Sichuan 610012, People's Republic of China. TEL 663834. adv.; bk.rev. circ. 5,000.

XPRESS. see *ART*

YINGJU XINZUO/NEW FILM AND PLAY SCRIPTS. see *LITERATURE*

792 375   US   ISSN 0892-9092
PN3157
YOUTH THEATRE JOURNAL. 1986. a. $25 (foreign $30). American Alliance for Theatre & Education, Theatre Department, Arizona State University, Box 853411, Tempe, AZ 85287-3411. TEL 602-965-6064. FAX 602-965-5361. Ed. Molloy Tudor. adv.; bk.rev. circ. 1,200. **Document type:** academic/scholarly publication.
—BLDSC (9421.582200); Faxon.
Description: Includes articles concerning theatre for young audiences and theatre and drama education.

792   CC
ZHONGGUO XIJU/CHINA'S THEATER. (Text in Chinese) bi-m. $27.50. (Zhongguo Xijujia Xiehui - China Theatre Artists' Association) Zhongguo Xiju Chubanshe, 52, Dongsi Ba(8) Tiao, Beijing 100700, People's Republic of China. (Dist. in US by: China Books & Periodicals, Inc., 2929 24th St., San Francisco, CA 94110. TEL 415-282-2994) Ed. Huo Dashou.

792   AU
ZUGABE. 1957. m. S.150. Tiroler Landestheater, Rennweg 2, Postfach 134, A-6020 Innsbruck, Austria. TEL 0512-52074. FAX 0512-52074333. Ed. Jutta Hoepfel. adv.; bk.rev.; rec.rev.; illus. circ. 10,000. **Document type:** bulletin.
Former titles (until 1992): Publicum (ISSN 0020-1642); Innsbrucker Konzertspiegel.

THEATER — Abstracting, Bibliographies, Statistics

792   US   ISSN 0360-2788
Z6935
BIBLIOGRAPHIC GUIDE TO THEATRE ARTS. a. $205 cloth. G.K. Hall & Co., c/o MacMillan Publishing USA, 866 Third Ave., 18th fl., New York, NY 10022. TEL 212-702-6789. (Subscr. to: Simon & Schuster, Library Reference Order Processing, 200 Old Tappan Rd., Old Tappan, NJ 07675. TEL 800-223-2336) **Document type:** bibliography, abstracting/indexing.
Description: Covers all aspects of the theatre. Lists materials catalogued during the past year by the New York Public Library, Theatre and Drama Collection.

800 792.8   US   ISSN 0742-6933
BIBLIOGRAPHIES AND INDEXES IN THE PERFORMING ARTS. 1984. irreg. price varies. Greenwood Press, Inc. (Subsidiary of: Greenwood Publishing Group Inc.), 88 Post Rd. W., Box 5007, Westport, CT 06881-5007. TEL 203-226-3571. FAX 203-222-1502.

792 493.3 791.43   US   ISSN 0892-5550
BIO-BIBLIOGRAPHIES IN THE PERFORMING ARTS. 1987. irreg. price varies. Greenwood Press, Inc. (Subsidiary of: Greenwood Publishing Group Inc.), 88 Post Rd. W., Box 5007, Westport, CT 06881-5007. TEL 203-226-3571. FAX 203-222-1502. **Document type:** monographic series.

F R A N C I S. 523: HISTOIRE ET SCIENCES DE LA LITTERATURE. see LITERATURE — Abstracting, Bibliographies, Statistics

792   US   ISSN 0882-9446
Z6935
INTERNATIONAL BIBLIOGRAPHY OF THEATRE. a. City University of New York, Brooklyn College, Theatre Research Data Center, Brooklyn, NY 11210. TEL 718-951-5998. FAX 718-951-4870. E-mail: rxwbc@cunyvm. **Document type:** bibliography.
Description: Contains 6,000 classed entries and over 18,000 subject references. Includes geographical-chronological and author indexes.

011   US
PERFORMING ARTS BIOGRAPHY MASTER INDEX. 1979. irreg., 2nd ed., 1982. $175. Gale Research Inc., 835 Penobscot Bldg., Detroit, MI 48226. TEL 313-961-2242. FAX 313-961-6083. TELEX 810-221-7086. Eds. Barbara McNeil, Miranda Herbert.
Formerly: Theatre, Film, and Television Biographies Master Index.

792 016   CN
PLAYWRIGHTS UNION OF CANADA CATALOGUE OF CANADIAN PLAYS. 1977. a. free. Playwrights Union of Canada, 54 Wolseley St., 2nd Fl., Toronto, ON M5T 1A5, Canada. TEL 416-947-0201. FAX 416-947-0159. Ed. Winston Smith. illus. circ. 10,000.
Formerly: Directory of Canadian Plays and Playwrights (ISSN 0707-5456)

792   IT
TEATRO ARCHIVIO; bollettino del Civico Museo Biblioteca dell'Attore. 1970. 3/yr. L.30000($26) (Civico Museo Biblioteca dell'Attore del Teatro di Genova) Bulzoni Editore, Via dei Liburni n.14, 00185 Rome, Italy. TEL 06-4455207. FAX 06-4450355. Ed. Alessandro d'Amico. illus.; cum.index. (back issues avail.)

THEORY OF COMPUTING

see Computers–Theory of Computing

TOBACCO

679.7   SP   ISSN 1134-0134
ACTUALIDAD TABAQUERA; revista del tabaco. 1964. m. (14/yr.). 2565 ptas.($75) (typically set in Jan.). Tabapress, S.A., Barquillo 7, 28004 Madrid, Spain. TEL 34-1-5229399. FAX 34-1-5325562. Ed. Teresa Conesa; Pub. Jesus Campos. adv. contact: Bernardo Vera. illus.; charts. circ. 16,000. (back issues avail.) **Document type:** trade publication.

ALCOHOL, TOBACCO AND FIREARMS BULLETIN. see LAW

658.8   IT   ISSN 0392-5773
AMICI DELLA PIPA; rivista bimestrale per la conoscenza e la diffusione della pipa. (Text in Italian; summaries in English) 1978. bi-m. L.20000($35) Amici della Pipa, C.P. 10734, 00100 Rome, Italy. TEL 513 2790. Ed. Giancarlo Fortunato. adv.; bk.rev. circ. 7,000.

679.7   FR   ISSN 0399-0206
TS2220   CODEN: ATBCAA
ANNALES DU TABAC. SECTION 1. 1963. a. free to qualified personnel. Societe Nationale d'Exploitation Industrielle des Tabacs et Allumettes, 53 quai d'Orsay, 75347 Paris Cedex 07, France. FAX 45-56-63-29. Ed. R. Geneve. bibl. circ. 1,100. **Indexed:** Chem.Abstr., Crop Physiol.Abstr., Excerp.Med., Field Crop Abstr., Herb.Abstr., Plant Breed.Abstr., Soils & Fert., Weed Abstr. **Document type:** academic/scholarly publication.
—CASDDS.

679.7   FR   ISSN 0399-0354
SB273   CODEN: ATSED2
ANNALES DU TABAC. SECTION 2. 1964. a. free to qualified personnel. Societe Nationale d'Exploitation Industrielle des Tabacs et Allumettes, 53 quai d'Orsay, 75340 Paris, France. FAX 53-63-66-08. Ed. J.C. Coussirat. bibl. circ. 1,100. **Document type:** academic/scholarly publication.
—BLDSC (1001.712000); CASDDS.

ASHTRAY JOURNAL; a newsletter for ashtray collectors. see HOBBIES

658.8 679.7   AT   ISSN 0045-0820
AUSTRALIAN RETAIL TOBACCONIST. 1940. m. Aus.$15. New South Wales Retail Tobacco Traders Association, Alexander House, 1st Fl., 107 Alexander St., Crows Nest, N.S.W. 2065, Australia.

679.73   GW   ISSN 0173-783X
TS2220   CODEN: BTAID3
BEITRAEGE ZUR TABAKFORSCHUNG INTERNATIONAL. (Text in English; summaries in English, French and German) 1961. irreg. free. Verband der Cigarettenindustrie, Koenigswintererstr. 550, 53227 Bonn, Germany. TEL 0228-449060. FAX 0228-442582. Ed. Bd. charts; illus.; stat. circ. 1,100. (also avail. in microfilm from UMI; reprint service avail. from UMI) **Indexed:** Anal.Abstr., Biol.Abstr., Chem.Abstr., Curr.Adv.Ecol.Sci., Curr.Cont., Excerp.Med., Field Crop Abstr., Helminthol.Abstr., Herb.Abstr., Sci.Cit.Ind. **Document type:** trade publication.
—CASDDS; Genuine Article; UMI. **CCC.**
Formerly (until 1978): Beitraege zur Tabakforschung (ISSN 0005-819X)
Description: Research on all aspects of tobacco plants, cultivation, manufacture of tobacco products, and the physical and chemical analysis of tobacco, tobacco smoke and human smoking behaviour.

BRANDSTAND; viewing the world of cigarette collecting. see HOBBIES

C T N. (Confectioner, Tobacconist, Newsagent) see FOOD AND FOOD INDUSTRIES — Bakers And Confectioners

633.71   CN   ISSN 0008-5189
CANADIAN TOBACCO GROWER. 1952. 4/yr. Can.$7. N C C Publishing, 222 Argyle Ave., Delhi, Ont. N4B 2Y2, Canada. TEL 519-582-2510. FAX 519-582-4040. Ed. Ben Steidman. adv.: B&W page Can.$712; trim 8 x 11; adv. contact: W.H. Arts. charts; illus.; mkt. circ. 3,920.

CANDY WORLD ILLUSTRATED. see FOOD AND FOOD INDUSTRIES — Bakers And Confectioners

679.7 658.8   FR
CAROTTE MODERNE. 1958. 4/yr. Societe Pym, 27 rue Hermel, 75018 Paris, France. TEL 42-64-86-11. FAX 42-64-08-09. Ed. Y. Mantion. adv. circ. 10,000.

633.71   II
CENTRAL TOBACCO RESEARCH INSTITUTE AND ITS REGIONAL RESEARCH STATIONS. ANNUAL REPORT. (Text in English) 1967. a. exchange basis. Indian Council of Agricultural Research, Central Tobacco Research Institute, Rajahmundry 533 105, India. TEL 71871-4. TELEX 0474-205. Ed.Bd. charts; stat. circ. 150.
Incorporates: Tobacco Research Institute. Annual Report; Tobacco Research Station, Hunsur, Report; Wrapper and Hookah Tobacco Research Station Report.

633.71   CU   ISSN 0138-8185
CIENCIA Y TECNICA EN LA AGRICULTURA. SERIE: TABACO. (Table of contents and abstracts in English) 2/yr. $14 in N. and S. America; Europe $16; others $17; or exchange basis. Centro de Informacion y Documentacion Agropecuario, Gaveta Postal 4149, Havana 4, Cuba. (Dist. by: Ediciones Cubanas, Obispo No. 527, Apdo. 605, Havana, Cuba) **Indexed:** Agrindex, Field Crop Abstr., Herb.Abstr., Seed Abstr., Soils & Fert.
Former titles (until 1978): Cuba. Centro de Informacion y Documentacion Agropecuario. Boletin de Resenas. Serie: Tabaco; Cuba. Centro de Informacion y Divulgacion Agropecuario. Boletin de Resenas. Serie: Tabaco.

394.14   US   ISSN 1063-7885
TS2260
CIGAR AFICIONADO. 1991. q. $14.95 (Canada $16.95; overseas $24.95); newsstand price: $3.95. M. Shanken Communications, 387 Park Ave. S., New York, NY 10016. TEL 212-684-4224. FAX 212-684-5424. TELEX 422687 MSHANK UI. (Subscr. to: Box 51091, Boulder, CO 80323-1091. TEL 800-992-2442) Ed. Marvin Shanken. adv.: B&W page $8160. illus. circ. 100,000. **Document type:** consumer publication.
Description: Provides information on fine cigars and other pleasures of life, such as travel, dining, the arts, collecting and hobbies. Includes personality profiles, restaurants that permit cigar smoking, and pastime activities from golf and fishing to music and literature.

6300 TOBACCO

658.8   UK
CIGARETTES: THE INTERNATIONAL MARKET. (Subseries of: Market Direction reports) a. £1595($3190) (effective 1996). Euromonitor, 60-61 Britton St., London EC1M 5NA, England. TEL 0171-251-8024. FAX 0171-608-3149. (Addr. in N. America: Euromonitor International, 122 S. Michigan Ave., Ste. 1200, Chicago, IL 60603. TEL 312-922-1115. FAX 312-922-1157) (looseleaf format) **Document type:** trade publication.
    Description: Analyzes the market for cigarettes for France, Germany, Italy, Spain, the U.K., the U.S., and Japan.

658.8   UK
CIGARS, CIGARILLOS AND SMOKING TOBACCO: THE INTERNATIONAL MARKET. (Subseries of: Market Direction reports) a. £1595($3190) (effective 1996). Euromonitor, 60-61 Britton St., London EC1M 5NA, England. TEL 0171-251-8024. FAX 0171-608-3149. (Addr. in N. America: Euromonitor International, 122 S. Michigan Ave., Ste. 1200, Chicago, IL 60603. TEL 312-922-1115. FAX 312-922-1157) (looseleaf format) **Document type:** trade publication.
    Formerly (until 1994): Cigars and Cigarillos: The International Market.
    Description: Analyzes the market for cigars, cigarillos, and smoking tobacco for France, Germany, Italy, Spain, the U.K., the U.S., and Japan.

658.8   US
COMPLEAT SMOKER. q. Compleat Smoker, Box 7036, Evanston, IL 60204. TEL 708-864-6016. FAX 708-864-1770. Ed.Bd. circ. 2,500.

616.865   US   ISSN 0361-1612
R850.A1
COUNCIL FOR TOBACCO RESEARCH, U S A REPORT. Key Title: Report of the Council for Tobacco Research - U S A, Inc. a. Council for Tobacco Research, U S A Inc., 900 Third Ave., New York, NY 10022. TEL 212-421-8885. abstr.
    —BLDSC (7411.355000).

633.71   CU
CUBATABACO. (Text in English and Spanish) 1972. s-a. $12 in S. America; N. America $14; elsewhere $16. (Ministerio de la Agricultura, Centro de Diseno de Envases y Divulgacion) Ediciones Cubanas, Obispo No. 527, Aptdo. 605, Havana, Cuba. TEL 7-61-8453. Dir. Zoila Couceyro. adv.; bk.rev. circ. 8,000.

633.71   CU
CUBATABACO INTERNACIONAL. (Text in English) 1979. s-a. Instituto de la Demanda Interna, Amargura 103, San Ignacio, 10100 Havana, Cuba. TEL 7-61-8453. Dir. Zoila Couceyro. circ. 3,000.

679.7   FR   ISSN 0994-8589
DEBITANT DE TABAC. 1904. 11/yr. Federation des Gerants de Debits de Tabac de l'Ile de France, 18 rue de St. Petersbourg, 75018 Paris, France. TEL 45-22-43-44. FAX 45-22-76-06. Ed. A. Perset. adv. circ. 6,000.

679.7   GW   ISSN 0012-0820
DER DEUTSCHE TABAKBAU. 1916. m. DM.52.50. Verlagsgruppe Rhein Main, Grosse Bleiche 44-50, 55116 Mainz, Germany. TEL 06131-144220. FAX 06131-144415. Ed. Hans-Gerd Koenen. adv.; bk.rev.; charts; illus.; stat. circ. 4,000. Indexed: Chem.Abstr. **Document type:** trade publication.

679.7   HU   ISSN 0012-4931
CODEN: DOHAAW
DOHANYIPAR. (Text in Hungarian; summaries in German) 1954. q. $14. (Magyar Elelmezesipari Tudomanyos Egyesulet) Lapkiado Vallalat, Lenin korut 9-11, 1073 Budapest 7, Hungary. TEL 222-409. (Subscr. to: Kultura, P.O. Box 149, H-1389 Budapest, Hungary) Ed. Istvan Bordacs. adv.; bk.rev.; charts; illus. circ. 1,570. Indexed: Chem.Abstr.
    —CASDDS.

DRUG ABUSE UPDATE. see DRUG ABUSE AND ALCOHOLISM

633.71 664.752   UK
FINANCIAL SURVEY. COMPANY DATA FOR SUCCESS: TOBACCO & CONFECTIONARY WHOLESALERS. a. I C C Financial Surveys Ltd., Field House, 72 Oldfield Rd., Hampton, Mddx. TW12 2HQ, England. TEL 081-783-0977. FAX 081-783-1940. charts; stat. **Document type:** trade publication.
    —BLDSC (8859.575250).
    Formerly (until 1991): Financial Survey Company Directory. Tobacco and Confectionary Wholesalers (ISSN 0953-5926)

679.7   II   ISSN 0046-4031
FLAME AND FLAVOUR. 1968. m. Rs.18. Tapan Kumar Das, Ed. & Pub., 12B 4 Indra Roy Rd., Calcutta 25, India. adv.; illus. circ. 1,900. (tabloid format)

633.71   US   ISSN 0015-4512
FLUE CURED TOBACCO FARMER; for commercial growers of flue-cured tobacco and related agribusiness. 1964. m. (Nov.-Jun.). $12 (overseas $12; free to tobacco producers). Specialized Agricultural Publications, Inc., 3000 Highwoods Blvd., Raleigh, NC 27604-1029. TEL 919-872-5040. FAX 919-872-6531. TELEX 802736. Ed. Dayton Matlick; Pub. Dayton Matlick. adv. contact: Dorothy Kuffler. charts; illus.; mkt.; pat.; tr.mk.; circ. 25,000 (controlled). **Document type:** trade publication.

630   FR   ISSN 0296-3361
FRANCE TABAC. 1946. 11/yr. 115 F. 19 rue Ballu, 75009 Paris, France. TEL 44-53-48-00. FAX 42-81-16-86. TELEX 281 504 FRANTAB. Ed. Francois Vedel. adv.; illus. circ. 18,000. (tabloid format) **Document type:** newspaper.
    —BLDSC (4032.778000).
    Formerly (until 1984): Voix des Cultures (ISSN 0296-337X)

FREE CHOICE. see POLITICAL SCIENCE — Civil Rights

679.7   II
INDIA. TOBACCO BOARD. ANNUAL REPORT. 1975. a. Tobacco Board, Box 451, Lakshmipuram, Guntur 522007, India. TELEX 32434.

679.7   II   ISSN 0047-1135
INTERNATIONAL PRESS CUTTING SERVICE: TOBACCO NEWS; cigarettes - cigars - bidis. 1967. w. $65. International Press Cutting Service, P.O. Box 63, Allahabad 211001, India. Ed. N. Khanna. bk.rev.; index. circ. 1,200. (processed)

679.7   UK   ISSN 0961-1673
KEY NOTE REPORT: CIGARETTES & TOBACCO. Variant title: Cigarettes & Tobacco. 1989. irreg. £185. Key Note Publications Ltd., Field House, 72 Oldfield Rd., Hampton, Middlesex TW12 2HQ, England. TEL 0181-783-0755. FAX 0181-783-1720. **Document type:** trade publication.
    ●Also available online.
    Also available on CD-ROM.

658.8   FR   ISSN 0755-4680
LOSANGE. 11/yr. 41 rue de Liuge, 75008 Paris, France. TEL 45-22-13-64. FAX 45-22-70-62. Ed. Bertrand Blin. circ. 45,000.

679.7 658.8   MF
MAURITIUS. TOBACCO BOARD. ANNUAL REPORT. 1932. a. free. Tobacco Board, Plaine Lauzun, Mauritius. Ed.Bd. charts. circ. 325. Indexed: Tob.Abstr.
    Description: Covers the operations and activities of the board.

633.71   NR   ISSN 0331-443X
NIGERIAN TOBACCO COMPANY. ANNUAL REPORT AND ACCOUNTS. 1961. a. free. Nigerian Tobacco Company (Plc), Corporate Affairs Department, Stallion House, 2 Ajose-Adeogun St., Victoria Island, Lagos, Nigeria. TEL 2690201-8. FAX 2690768. TELEX 21561 TOBACCO NG. Ed. Irene Ubah. circ. 50,000. **Document type:** corporate report.
    Formerly: Nigerian Tobacco Company. Report (ISSN 0078-0820)

679.7 628.5   US   ISSN 0897-9626
NONSMOKERS' VOICE. 1977. q. $25. Group to Alleviate Smoking Pollution (GASP), 2885 Aurora Ave., No. 37, Boulder, CO 80303-2252. TEL 303-444-9799. Ed. Peter Bialick. circ. 1,500. **Document type:** newspaper.
    Description: Contains new medical research on effects of second hand smoke, smoke-free discoveries, local and state legislation, tactics of the tobacco industry.

633.71   US
NORTH CAROLINA TOBACCO REPORT. 1950. a. free. Department of Agriculture, Box 27647, Raleigh, NC 27611. Ed. Carl W. Sofley. charts; stat. circ. 6,000. (back issues avail.) **Document type:** government publication.
    Description: Record of former sales, warehouse sales and quotas of tobacco growing in North Carolina.

679.7   AU   ISSN 0029-9561
OESTERREICHISCHE TRAFIKANTEN-ZEITUNG. m. S.552. Oesterreichischer Wirtschaftsverlag, Nikolsdorfer Gasse 7-11, A-1051 Vienna, Austria. TEL 0222-555585. TELEX 1-11669. (Affiliate: Tabaktrafikanten und -verleger) Ed. Josef Jerko. adv.; illus. circ. 6,800. (tabloid format)

679.7 668.4   DK   ISSN 0106-3235
PIBER & TOBAK. 1978. q. $30; newsstand price: DKK 11.85. Nordisk Tobakskollegium, c/o Leif Slot, Ellekrattet 18, DK-2950 Vedbaek, Denmark. TEL 45-42-89-44-02. FAX 45-31-22-41-50. Ed. Leif Slot. adv.: B&W page DKK 9600; trim 190 x 190. bk.rev. circ. 10,500. (back issues avail.)

658.8   GW
PIPE CLUB; Magazin fuer Tabakgeniesser. 1974. q. DM.18. Verlagsgruppe Rhein Main, Grosse Bleiche 44-50, 55116 Mainz, Germany. TEL 06131-144220. FAX 06131-144415. Ed. Hans-Gerd Koenen. adv.; bk.rev. circ. 50,000. (back issues avail.) **Document type:** consumer publication.
    Description: Magazine for pipe smokers.

658.8 679.7   US   ISSN 0032-0161
THE PIPE SMOKER'S EPHEMERIS. 1964. q. free. (Universal Coterie of Pipe Smokers) Tom Dunn, Ed.& Pub., 20-37 120th St., College Point, NY 11356-2128. adv.; bk.rev.; abstr.; bibl.; illus.; tr.lit.; index; circ. 7,500 (controlled). (processed) **Document type:** newsletter.
    Description: Carries original short stories, artwork, poetry, pipe and tobacco club news and convention information.

679.7   US   ISSN 0363-8480
CODEN: RATSDZ
RECENT ADVANCES IN TOBACCO SCIENCE; proceedings of the tobacco chemists' conference. 1974. a. $27 (outside N. America $41). (Tobacco Chemists' Research Conference Board) Tobacco Literature Service, 2314 D.H. Hill Library, Raleigh, NC 27695-8009. TEL 919-515-2836. (back issues avail.) Indexed: Chem.Abstr. **Document type:** proceedings.
    —CASDDS.

658.8 664.15   UK   ISSN 0961-5202
RETAIL NEWSAGENT TOBACCONIST CONFECTIONER. 1889. w. £50 (typically set in June). Newtrade Publishing Ltd., 11 Angel Gate, City Rd., London EC1V 2PT, England. FAX 071-837-0821. Ed. John G. Haylett. adv.; bk.rev. circ. 20,063.
    Formerly: Retail Newsagent, Bookseller and Stationer (ISSN 0034-6098)

679.7   FR   ISSN 0035-225X
REVUE DES TABACS; organe international de la culture, de l'industrie et de la vente du tabac. 1925. m. 430 F. (foreign 550 F.). Editions Litteraire, Techniques et Artistiques, 9 rue Saint Fiacre, 75002 Paris, France. FAX 42-36-04-62. Ed. Michel Burton. adv.; charts; illus.; mkt.; pat.; tr.mk. circ. 3,000. **Document type:** trade publication.

SITUATION & OUTLOOK REPORT. TOBACCO. see AGRICULTURE — Agricultural Economics

SMALL RETAILER. see FOOD AND FOOD INDUSTRIES

658.8   US
SMOKERS PIPELINE;* the journal of kapnismology. 1983. bi-m. $15 (foreign $40). American Pipe Collectors Club, Tobacco Barn 3, 6568 Springfield Mall, Springfield, VA 22150. TEL 703-971-2627. FAX 703-971-3352. Ed. C. Bruce Spencer. adv.; bk.rev. circ. 4,500. (tabloid format)
    Former titles: Pipe Smoker and Tobacciana Trader; Pipe Smoker (ISSN 0746-1380)
    Description: Contains articles on pipes, tobacco, events, history, and people; promotes pipe collecting as a hobby and for profit.

TOBACCO

658.8 US ISSN 0146-9266
SMOKESHOP. 1976. m. $32. B M T Communications, Inc., 7 Penn Plaza, New York, NY 10001-3900. TEL 212-594-4120. FAX 212-714-0514. Ed. Paul Dworin. adv. circ. 5,500.

338.1 SA
SOUTH AFRICA. TOBACCO BOARD. ANNUAL REPORT. 1939. a. Tobacco Board, P.O. Box 26100, Arcadia, Pretoria 0007, South Africa. TEL 27-12-3234152. FAX 27-12-2325907. Ed.Bd. stat. circ. 2,000. **Document type:** corporate report.

679.7 US
T M A DIRECTORY OF CIGARETTE BRANDS. 1977. base vol. (plus a. update). $125 to members; non-members $225. Tobacco Merchants Association of the United States, Inc., Box 8019, Princeton, NJ 08543-8019. TEL 609-275-4900. FAX 609-275-8379. Ed. Michael Marion. **Document type:** directory.

658.8 US
T M A EXECUTIVE SUMMARY. w. membership only. Tobacco Merchants Association of the United States, Inc., 231 Clarksville Rd., Ste. 6, Box 8019, Princeton, NJ 08543-8019. TEL 609-275-4900. FAX 609-275-8379. Ed. Farrell Delman. **Document type:** trade publication.
● Also available online.
Description: Summary of the principal industry developments occurring over the past week in the US and around the world. Serves as an index to the other TMA publications issued during the given week.

679.7 US
T M A GUIDE TO TOBACCO TAXES; summaries of key provisions of tobacco tax laws, all tobacco products, all states. 1962. base vol. (plus q. update). $795 to non-members; members $495. Tobacco Merchants Association of the United States, Inc., 231 Clarksville Rd., Ste. 6, Box 8019, Princeton, NJ 08543-8019. TEL 609-275-4900. FAX 609-275-8379. Ed. Laurie Amato. circ. controlled. (looseleaf format) **Document type:** trade publication.
Description: Compendium of federal and state tobacco tax law showing comparisons between states on all key tax variables such as excise tax rates, discount rates, sales prohibitions to minors, and other marketing related information.

658.8 US
T M A INTERNATIONAL TOBACCO GUIDE. 2 base vols. (plus a. update). $11500 to non-members; members $7500. Tobacco Merchants Association of the United States, Inc., 231 Clarksville Rd., Ste. 6, Box 8019, Princeton, NJ 08543-8019. TEL 609-275-4900. FAX 609-275-8379. Ed. Darryl Jayson. illus. **Document type:** trade publication.
Description: Volume I consists of country comparisons for the major economic and socio-political variables, as well as trade statistics for all manufactured and unmanufactured tobacco. Volume II provides a country-by-country breakdown of all the economic and socio-political variables describing the tobacco industry.

658.8 US
T M A ISSUES MONITOR. 1980. q. membership only. Tobacco Merchants Association of the United States, Inc., 231 Clarksville Rd., Ste. 6, Box 8019, Princeton, NJ 08543-8019. TEL 609-275-4900. FAX 609-275-8375. Ed. Farrell Delman. **Document type:** trade publication.
Description: Tracks the principal tobacco issues in the U.S. and worldwide and summarizes the principal economic, legislative, and regulatory developments.

679.7 US
T M A LEAF BULLETIN. 1950. bi-w. membership only. Tobacco Merchants Association of the United States, Inc., 231 Clarksville Rd., Ste. 6, Box 8019, Princeton, NJ 08543-8019. TEL 609-275-4900. FAX 609-275-8379. Ed. Thomas C. Slane. circ. controlled. (looseleaf format) **Document type:** trade publication.
Description: Furnishes tobacco auction market statistics, for all leaf types, including stabilization inventories, and provides a brief legislative and regulatory rundown on matters impacting the leaf sector.

679.7 340 US
T M A LEGISLATIVE BULLETIN. bi-w. membership only. Tobacco Merchants Association of the United States, Inc., 231 Clarksville Rd., Ste. 6, Box 8019, Princeton, NJ 08543-8019. TEL 609-275-4900. FAX 609-275-8379. Ed. James Vari. stat. circ. 350. (back issues avail.) **Document type:** bulletin.
● Also available online.
Incorporates (1924-198?): T M A State Bulletin; (1924-198?): T M A National Bulletin.
Description: Analyzes congressional and state legislative activity on all issues affecting all tobacco products and summarizes key provisions of these bills and laws.

679.7 US
T M A TOBACCO BAROMETER. 1923. m. membership only. Tobacco Merchants Association of the United States, Inc., 231 Clarksville Rd., Ste. 6, Box 8019, Princeton, NJ 08543-8019. TEL 609-275-4900. FAX 609-275-8379. Ed. Thomas C. Slane. circ. controlled. (looseleaf format) **Document type:** trade publication.
Description: Domestic industry guide to manufactured production, taxable removals, and tax-exempt removals for cigarettes, large cigars, little cigars, chewing tobacco, snuff, and pipe tobacco.

679.7 US
T M A TOBACCO BAROMETER: SMOKING, CHEWING, SNUFF. 1923. q. membership only. Tobacco Merchants Association of the United States, Inc., 231 Clarksville Rd., Ste. 6, Box 8019, Princeton, NJ 08543-8019. TEL 609-275-4900. FAX 609-275-8379. Ed. Thomas C. Slane. circ. controlled. (looseleaf format) **Document type:** trade publication.
● Also available online.
Description: Domestic industry guide to manufactured production, invoiced domestic sales, imports, and exports for chewing tobacco, snuff, and all forms of smoking tobacco, including roll-your-own tobacco. Provides seasonal adjustments.

679.7 US ISSN 0495-6753
T M A TOBACCO TRADE BAROMETER. (In 6 parts: Part 1: Balance of Trade Summary - all imports and all exports; Part 2: Exports of Leaf Tobacco - US exports by product & country; Part 3: Exports of Tobacco Products - US exports by product & country; Part 4: Imports of Leaf Tobacco - US imports by product & country; Part 5: Imports of Tobacco Products - US imports by products & country; Part 6: Imports of Smokers' Accessories - US imports by products & country) 1967. m. membership only. Tobacco Merchants Association of the United States, Inc., 231 Clarksville Rd., Ste. 6, Box 8019, Princeton, NJ 08543-8019. TEL 609-275-4900. FAX 609-275-8379. Ed. Thomas C. Slane. circ. controlled. (looseleaf format) **Document type:** trade publication.
Description: Details all imports and all exports of all tobacco leaf and products, including tobacco sundries, by product and country providing values and quantities. Compares current data to the previous year.

658.8 336 US
T M A TOBACCO WEEKLY. w. membership only. Tobacco Merchants Association of the United States, Inc., 231 Clarksville Rd., Ste. 6, Box 8019, Princeton, NJ 08543-8019. TEL 609-275-4900. FAX 609-275-8379. **Document type:** trade publication.
Description: Summary run-down on key domestic industry issues as they unfold at the federal, state, and local levels. Covers excise taxes, marketing and distribution issues, corporate finance, leaf and trade, health campaigns, and product liability.

658.8 602.7 US
T M A TRADEMARK REPORT. m. membership only. Tobacco Merchants Association of the United States, Inc., 231 Clarksville Rd., Ste. 6, Box 8019, Princeton, NJ 08543-8019. TEL 609-275-4900. FAX 609-275-8379. **Document type:** trade publication.
● Also available online.
Description: Tracks tobacco product and tobacco accessory trademarks and brand names from test markets through registration and covers renewals and cancellations.

679.7 US
T M A WORLD ALERT. w. membership only. Tobacco Merchants Association of the United States, Inc., 231 Clarksville Rd., Ste. 6, Box 8019, Princeton, NJ 08543-8019. TEL 609-275-4900. FAX 609-275-8379. Ed. F. Delman. circ. 375. (back issues avail.) **Document type:** bulletin.
● Also available online.
Formerly: International Executive Summary.
Description: Provides news-flash country by country description of key industry and corporate developments around the world including corporate finance, excise taxes, marketing and distribution issues, leaf and trade, and health campaigns.

658.8 US
T M A WORLD CONSUMPTION & PRODUCTION. a. membership only. Tobacco Merchants Association of the United States, Inc., 231 Clarksville Rd., Ste. 6, Box 8019, Princeton, NJ 08543-8019. TEL 609-275-4900. FAX 609-275-8379. stat. **Document type:** trade publication.
Description: Details country-by-country consumption and production of tobacco products over the previous 10 years.

633.71 IT CODEN: AISTD4
IL TABACCO. (Text in Italian; summaries in English) 1897. 3/yr. (in 1 vol.). L.20000 to individuals; institutions L.30000. Istituto Sperimentale per il Tabacco, Via P. Vitiello 66, 84018 Scafati (SA), Italy. TEL 39-81-8506168. FAX 39-81-8506206. Ed. Emanuel Marcelli. adv. circ. 1,000. (back issues avail.) **Indexed:** Biol.Abstr., Field Crop Abstr., Herb.Abstr., Plant Breed.Abstr., Tob.Abstr.
—CASDDS.
Former titles (until 1990): Istituto Sperimentale per il Tabacco. Annali (ISSN 0391-4836); (until 1973): Tabacco (ISSN 0039-8713)

679.7 SZ ISSN 0039-8721
TABAK/TABAC. (Text in French, German) 1903. m. 40 SFr. (Verband Schweizerischer Tabakhaendler - Federation Suisse des Marchands de Tabacs) Druckerei Leo Fuerer AG, Davidstr. 9, Postfach 634, CH-9001 St. Gallen, Switzerland. TEL 071-221842. FAX 071-227953. adv. 152 SFr. B&W page 1120 SFr. illus.; stat. circ. 1,200. **Indexed:** Field Crop Abstr., Plant Grow.Reg.Abstr., Seed Abstr. **Document type:** trade publication.

679.7 GW ISSN 0039-8748
HD9130.1
TABAK JOURNAL INTERNATIONAL. (Text in Dutch, English, French, German, Italian, Spanish) 1963. bi-m. DM.142($82) Verlagsgruppe Rhein Main, Postfach 3120, 55116 Mainz, Germany. TEL 06131-144248. FAX 06131-144415. Ed. Hans-Gerd Koenen. adv.; bk.rev.; charts; illus.; stat.; cum.index. circ. 4,000. **Indexed:** Excerp.Med. **Document type:** trade publication.
—BLDSC (8859.577650).

658.8 338 NE ISSN 0925-7543
TABAK PLUS BENELUX; vakblad voor de tabaksdetailhandel. 1939. 10/yr. fl.55. (N S O, Branche Organisatie Tabaksdetailhandel) Stichting Promotie Tabaksdetailhandel (SPT), Postbus 7268, 2701 AG Zoetermeer, Netherlands. TEL 31-79-426191. FAX 31-79-413341. Ed. Dick van Vlaardingen. adv.; B&W page fl.2025 (37000 BEF); color page fl.2835 (51800 BEF); trim 148 x 210. bk.rev.; charts; illus.; stat.; tr.lit. circ. 13,500. **Document type:** trade publication.

633.71 GW ISSN 0049-2825
DIE TABAK ZEITUNG; Fachorgan der Tabakwirtschaft. 1891. w. DM.204.40. Verlagsgruppe Rhein Main, Grosse Bleiche 44-50, 55116 Mainz, Germany. TEL 06131-144220. FAX 06131-144415. Ed. Hans-Gerd Koenen. adv.; bk.rev. circ. 9,000. (tabloid format) **Document type:** trade publication.

TOBACCIANA REPORTS; collecting items related to tobacco and its use. see ANTIQUES

658.8 US
TOBACCO AND NEW PRODUCTS WORLD. 1910. 3/yr. $18. Lott Publishing Co., Box 710, Santa Monica, CA 90405-1107. TEL 310-397-4217. Ed. Dave Lott. circ. 2,000.
Formerly: Tobacco World.

6302 TOBACCO — ABSTRACTING, BIBLIOGRAPHIES, STATISTICS

679.7 US ISSN 0082-4593
TOBACCO ASSOCIATES. ANNUAL REPORT. 1948. a. free. Tobacco Associates, Inc., 1306 Annapolis Dr., Ste. 102, Raleigh, NC 27608. TEL 919-821-7670. FAX 919-821-7674. Ed. Charlie King. charts; stat.; cum.index: 1948-1993; circ. 7,500 (controlled). **Document type:** corporate report.
Description: Provides a summary of the association's activities and of industry news.

679.7 610 UK ISSN 0964-4563
TOBACCO CONTROL; an international journal. (Text in English; summaries in Chinese, French, Spanish) 1992. q. £108($170) B M J Publishing Group, B.M.A. House, Tavistock Sq., London WC1H 9JR, England. TEL 0171-383-6270. FAX 0171-383-6402. (N. American subscr. to: Box 480, Franklin, MA 02038. TEL 800-2-FON-BMJ. FAX 800-2-FAX-BMJ) Ed. Ronald Davis. adv. contact: Sheila Rowe. bk.rev.; charts; illus.; stat.; index. (back issues avail.) **Document type:** academic/scholarly publication.
—BLDSC (8859.576550).
Description: Studies the nature and extent of tobacco use worldwide, the effects of tobacco use on health, the economy, the environment and society, and the efforts of the health community to prevent its use.
Refereed Serial

658.8 679.7 UK
HD9130.1
TOBACCO EUROPE; the management journal of tobacco trade distribution within the U.K. 1881. bi-m. £47($98) (overseas £55) (effective 1994-1995). Argus Business Media Ltd., International Trade Publications (Subsidiary of: Argus Press Group), Queensway House, 2 Queensway, Redhill, Surrey RH1 1QS, England. TEL 10737-768611. FAX 01737-761989. TELEX 948669 TOPJNL G. Ed. Jacques Cole. adv.; abstr.; charts; illus.; stat.; tr.lit.; index. circ. 4,000. **Indexed:** Chem.Abstr., Excerp.Med. **Document type:** trade publication.
Formerly: Tobacco (ISSN 0040-8271)

TOBACCO INDUSTRY LITIGATION REPORTER; the national journal of record of litigation affecting the tobacco industry. *see LAW*

679.7 US ISSN 0049-3945
HD9130.1 CODEN: TBCIAE
TOBACCO INTERNATIONAL. 1886. fortn. $32. Lockwood Trade Journal Co., Inc., 130 W. 42nd St., New York, NY 10036-7802. TEL 212-391-2060. FAX 212-827-0945. Ed. Glen John. adv.; bk.rev.; illus.; tr.lit.; circ. 3,000. (reprint service avail. from UMI) **Indexed:** Biol.Abstr., Chem.Abstr., Field Crop Abstr., Herb.Abstr., Plant Grow.Reg.Abstr., Soils & Fert., Soyabean Abstr.
—CASDDS; UMI.
Formerly: Tobacco International Weekly.

658.8 AT
TOBACCO JOURNAL. 1931. m. Aus.$0.50 per no. Retail Tobacco Sellers Association of Victoria, Box 1780, Melbourne, Vic. 3001, Australia. (Co-sponsor: Retail Tobacco Traders' Association of Tasmania)

679 918 US
TOBACCO: LATIN AMERICAN INDUSTRIAL REPORT. (Avail. for each of 22 Latin American countries) 1985. a. $435 per country report. Aquino Productions, Box 15760, Stamford, CT 06901. TEL 203-325-3138. Ed. Andres C. Aquino.

633.71 US
TOBACCO LIFE. 1992. 3/yr. free. Rural Press U S A, 7701 Six Forks Rd., Ste. 132, Raleigh, NC 27615. TEL 919-676-3276. FAX 919-676-9803. (Subscr. to: Box 150001, Raleigh, NC 27624) Ed. Jeff Tennant; Pub. Allen Williams. circ. 16,000. **Document type:** newspaper.

TOBACCO MARKETS IN LATIN AMERICA. *see BUSINESS AND ECONOMICS — Marketing And Purchasing*

679.7 RH
TOBACCO NEWS. 1977. m. Z.$64.80 (foreign Z.$82.20). Thomson Publications Zimbabwe (Pvt) Ltd., Thomson House, P.O. Box 1683, Harare, Zimbabwe. TEL 263-4-736835. FAX 263-4-752390. TELEX 24705 ZW. adv.; illus. **Document type:** trade publication.
Former titles (until 1992): Zimbabwe Tobacco Today; (until 1980): Rhodesia Tobacco Today; Rhodesian Tobacco Journal (ISSN 0035-4880); *Incorporating:* Tobacco Today; Stock and Crops (ISSN 0039-1557)
Description: Provides independent coverage of the tobacco industry in Zimbabwe.

338.1 II
TOBACCO NEWS. (Text in English) 1951. m. $7.50. Tobacco Board, P.O. Box 451, Lakshmipuram, Guntur 522007, India. **Indexed:** Field Crop Abstr.
Formerly: Indian Tobacco (ISSN 0445-8192)

679.7 US ISSN 0361-5693
HD9130.1
TOBACCO REPORTER; devoted to all segments of the international tobacco industry: processing, trading, manufacturing. 1874. m. $36 (foreign $78). Specialized Agricultural Publications, Inc., 3000 Highwoods Blvd., Ste. 300, Raleigh, NC 27604-1029. TEL 919-872-5040. FAX 919-872-6531. TELEX 802736. Ed. Dayton Matlick; Pub. Dayton Matlick. adv. contact: Ann Jeffries. bk.rev.; charts; illus.; mkt.; pat.; tr.lit. circ. 5,000. **Indexed:** Field Crop Abstr. **Document type:** trade publication.
—BLDSC (8859.578500).
Former titles: T R; Tobacco Reporter (ISSN 0040-8328); *Supersedes:* Western Tobacco Journal.

633.71 II ISSN 0379-055X
CODEN: TRESDX
TOBACCO RESEARCH. (Text and summaries in English) 1975. s-a. Rs.150($25) Indian Society of Tobacco Science, Central Tobacco Research Institute, Rajahmundry 533 105, Andhra Pradesh, India. Ed. C.V. Narasimha Rao. adv. circ. 300. (back issues avail.) **Indexed:** Biol.Abstr., Field Crop Abstr., Plant Grow.Reg.Abstr., Soils & Fert., Weed Abstr.
—CASDDS.

679.7 US ISSN 0082-4623
TOBACCO SCIENCE YEARBOOK. 1958. a. $26. Lockwood Trade Journal Co., Inc., 130 W. 42nd St., New York, NY 10036-7802. TEL 212-391-2060. index. (reprint service avail. from UMI)

332.6 US ISSN 0360-439X
HD9134
TOBACCO STOCKS. q. $5 per set. U.S. Department of Agriculture, Agricultural Marketing Service (Washington), Tobacco Division, Washington, DC 20250. TEL 202-205-0489. (also avail. in microfiche from CIS; reprint service avail. from CIS) **Indexed:** Amer.Stat.Ind. (1974-). **Document type:** government publication.
Supersedes: Tobacco Stocks Report. T O B.

633.71 381.1 NO ISSN 0804-3183
TOBAKK- OG KIOSK. 1918. 6/yr. free. Tobakk- og Kioskhandelens Landsforbund, P.O. Box 2854 Solli, N-0230 Oslo, Norway. TEL 47-22-55-54-90. FAX 47-22-55-86-70. Ed. Per-Tore Sliper. adv.: B&W page NOK 5400, color page NOK 7600; trim 185 x 260. tr.lit. circ. 1,800. **Document type:** trade publication.
Formerly: Tobakk - Frukt - Sjokolade (ISSN 0049-3961)

658.8 679.7 SW ISSN 0346-2765
TOBAKSHANDLAREN/TOBACCONIST. Abbreviated title: T. (Text in Swedish) 1911. 8/yr. SEK 350($20) membership. Tobaks- & Servicehandelns Riksfoerbund - National Union of Retail Tobacconists, Instrumentvaegen 10, P.O. Box 9025, S-126 00 Haegersten, Sweden. TEL 46-8-681-03-20. FAX 46-8-19-95-26. Ed. Catherine Nemes-Nagel. adv.: B&W page SEK 6200, color page SEK 12100; trim 172 x 124. bk.rev.; circ. 1,800 (controlled).

679.7 AU
TRAFIK-JOURNAL. 1964. 10/yr. S.220. Fachvereinigung der Trafikanten im Freien Wirtschaftsverband, Schottenfeldgasse 24, A-1070 Vienna, Austria. TELEX 136048-FWV-Z-A. Ed. Rudolf Bernkopf. circ. 1,500.
Formerly: Tabakverschleisser Oesterreichs (ISSN 0039-8772)

679.7 AU
TRAFIKANT. m. Zeitungsverlag Kuhn und Co. GmbH, Kutschkergasse 42, A-1180 Vienna, Austria. TEL 01-47686. FAX 01-4768621. Ed. Christine Pomberger. circ. 5,200. **Document type:** trade publication.

679.7 US ISSN 0897-1315
HD9130.1 CODEN: USDJEK
UNITED STATES DISTRIBUTION JOURNAL; the news publication of tobacco, confectionery, grocery distribution. 1874. m. $52. B M T Communications, Inc., 7 Penn Plaza, New York, NY 10001-3900. TEL 212-594-4120. FAX 212-714-0514. Ed. Kevin Francella. adv.; illus.; mkt.; stat. circ. 7,267. **Indexed:** Bus.Ind., Tr.& Indus.Ind.
Former titles: United States Tobacco and Candy Journal (ISSN 0741-2258); United States Tobacco Journal (ISSN 0041-8137).

658.8 679.7 US
UNITED STATES DISTRIBUTION JOURNAL SUPPLIER DIRECTORY. 1963. a. $75. B M T Communications, Inc., 7 Penn Plaza, New York, NY 10001-3900. TEL 212-594-4120. FAX 212-714-0514. Ed. Kevin Francella. adv.; index. circ. 5,000. **Indexed:** Tr.& Indus.Ind. **Document type:** directory.
Former titles: United States Tobacco and Candy Journal Supplier Directory (ISSN 0083-3479); United States Tobacco Journal Supplier Directory.

UNIVERSITY OF SALAHADDIN. COLLEGE OF AGRICULTURE. SCIENTIFIC JOURNAL "ZANCO". *see AGRICULTURE*

658.8 DK ISSN 0908-1798
VIN OG TOBAK. * m. Koebenhavns Tobakshandlerforening af 1885, Mellemdammen 18, DK-6760 Ribe, Denmark. Ed. Karsten K. Kesselring. adv. circ. 1,500.
Formerly: Tobakshandlerbladet (ISSN 0904-9061)

679.7 IT ISSN 0042-7829
LA VOCE DEL TABACCAIO. 1927. w. membership. Federazione Italiana Tabaccai, Via Leopoldo Serra 32, 00153 Rome, Italy. TEL 06-589-7151. FAX 06-5809826. TELEX 06-612223. Eds. Sergio Baronci, Ivo Tolu. adv.; illus. circ. 48,000. (tabloid format) **Document type:** trade publication.

679.7 UK ISSN 0043-9126
SB273
WORLD TOBACCO. 1963. 10/yr. £89 (overseas £98) (effective 1995). Argus Business Media Ltd., International Trade Publications (Subsidiary of: Argus Press Group), Queensway House, 2 Queensway, Redhill, Surrey RH1 1QS, England. TEL 01737-768611. FAX 01737-761989. TELEX 948669 TOPJNL G. Ed. George Gay. adv.; bk.rev.; charts; illus.; mkt.; pat.; tr.lit.; tr.mk. circ. 4,500. **Indexed:** PROMT. **Document type:** trade publication.
—BLDSC (9360.100000).

679.7 UK ISSN 0084-2273
WORLD TOBACCO DIRECTORY. 1938. a. £90 (overseas £100) (effective 1995). Argus Press Group Ltd., International Trade Publications (Subsidiary of: Argus Press Group), Queensway House, 2 Queensway, Redhill, Surrey RH1 1QS, England. TEL 01737-768611. FAX 01737-761989. TELEX 948669 TOPJNL G. adv. **Document type:** directory.

679.7 RH
ZIMBABWE. TOBACCO RESEARCH BOARD. ANNUAL REPORT AND ACCOUNTS. 1954. a. free. Tobacco Research Board, Library, Kutsaga Station, P.O. Box 1909, Harare, Zimbabwe. TEL 263-4-575289. FAX 263-4-575288. circ. 660. **Document type:** corporate report.
Formerly: Rhodesia. Tobacco Research Board. Annual Report and Accounts (ISSN 0080-2875)

TOBACCO — Abstracting, Bibliographies, Statistics

633.71 679.7 317 US ISSN 0747-5314
HD1751
ANNUAL REPORT ON TOBACCO STATISTICS. (Subseries of: U.S.D.A. Statistical Bulletin) a. $3. U.S. Department of Agriculture, Agricultural Marketing Service (Washington), Washington, DC 20250. TEL 202-205-0489. stat. (tabloid format) **Document type:** government publication.

679.7 016   FR   ISSN 0010-8723
C O R E S T A; bulletin d'information. (Text in English, French) 1957. q. membership. Centre de Cooperation pour les Recherches Scientifiques Relatives au Tabac (Coresta), 53 Quai d'Orsay, 75347 Paris Cedex 07, France.
FAX 1-45-56-62-30. TELEX 250604. Ed. Francois Jacob. bk.rev.; abstr.; charts; illus. circ. 1,000.
Indexed: Field Crop Abstr. **Document type:** bulletin.

338.4   CN   ISSN 0835-0019
HD9348.C3
CANADA. STATISTICS CANADA. BEVERAGE AND TOBACCO PRODUCTS INDUSTRIES. (Catalogue 32-251) (Text in English, French) 1918. a. Can.$35($42) (foreign $49). Statistics Canada, Publications Sales and Services, Ottawa, Ont. K1A 0T6, Canada. TEL 613-951-7277.
FAX 613-951-1584. (also avail. in microform from MML)
Formerly: Canada. Statistics Canada. Tobacco Products Industries (ISSN 0300-0249)

633.71 338 679.7 658.8   CN   ISSN 0708-336X
PRODUCTION AND DISPOSITION OF TOBACCO PRODUCTS/PRODUCTION ET DISPOSITION DES PRODUITS DU TABAC. (Text in English, French) 1979. m. Can.$50($60) Statistics Canada, Ottawa, ON K1A 0T6, Canada. TEL 613-951-3511. FAX 613-951-3522. Ed. Peter Zylstra. pp./issue: 4. (looseleaf format; also avail. in diskette format; magnetic tape; back issues avail.) **Document type:** government publication.
Description: Shows monthly and cumulative production, sales and inventory of cigarettes, cigars and cut tobacco in Canada.

658.8 336 310   US   ISSN 0563-6191
HD9130.1
TAX BURDEN ON TOBACCO. 1966. a. free. Tobacco Institute, 1875 I St., N.W., Washington, DC 20006. TEL 202-457-4800. stat. circ. 2,500. (also avail. in microfiche from CIS) **Indexed:** SRI.
Description: Annual historical compilation of federal, state and local tobacco tax collections, rates.

633.71 016   US   ISSN 0040-8298
TOBACCO ABSTRACTS; world literature on Nicotiana. 1957. bi-m. $39.50 (foreign $65). Tobacco Literature Service, 2314 D.H. Hill Library, North Carolina State University, Raleigh, NC 27695-8009. TEL 919-515-2836. E-mail: cbridges@cals1.cals.ncsu.edu (Internet) or Carolyn_Bridges@ncsu.edu. Ed. Pamela E. Puryear. index. circ. 500. (back issues avail.) **Indexed:** Field Crop Abstr., Herb.Abstr., Plant Breed.Abstr. **Document type:** abstracting/indexing.
—BLDSC (8859.575000).
Description: Covers tobacco culture, economics, genetics, chemistry, manufacture and distribution.

TOXICOLOGY AND ENVIRONMENTAL SAFETY

see Environmental Studies–Toxicology and Environmental Safety

TRADE AND INDUSTRIAL DIRECTORIES

see Business and Economics–Trade and Industrial Directories

TRANSPORTATION

see also Transportation–Air Transport; Transportation–Automobiles; Transportation–Computer Applications; Transportation–Railroads; Transportation–Roads and Traffic; Transportation–Ships and Shipping; Transportation–Trucks and Trucking

380.5   US
A A S H T O REFERENCE BOOK OF MEMBER DEPARTMENT PERSONNEL AND COMMITTEES. a. $35.50. American Association of State Highway and Transportation Officials, 444 N. Capitol St., N.W., Ste. 249, Washington, DC 20001.
TEL 202-624-5800. FAX 202-624-5806. **Document type:** directory.
Formerly: Reference Book of Highway Personnel (ISSN 0516-9445)

A B C AIR CARGO GUIDE. see TRANSPORTATION — Air Transport

380.5   US
A B F BY-LINES. 1953. m. free to qualified personnel. A B F Freight System, Inc., 3801 Old Greenwood Rd., Box 10048, Ft. Smith, AR 72917.
TEL 501-785-8946. FAX 501-785-8783. Ed. Jan Cutsinger. adv. contact: John Greer. charts; illus.; stat.; circ. 12,000 (controlled). **Document type:** newsletter.

ACCESS AMERICA. see HANDICAPPED — Visually Impaired

380.5   FR   ISSN 0339-2880
ACTUALITES SOCIALES DES TRANSPORTS; routiers et des activities auxiliaires des transports. 1965. m. 150 F. Editions Celse, 68 rue Cardinet, 75017 Paris, France. Ed. Daniel Mace. adv. circ. 2,000.

AIR TRANSPORT WORLD. see AERONAUTICS AND SPACE FLIGHT

AIRPORT BUSINESS. see AERONAUTICS AND SPACE FLIGHT

AIRPORTS INTERNATIONAL MAGAZINE. see AERONAUTICS AND SPACE FLIGHT

380.5   CN   ISSN 0836-1509
HE215.Z7
ALBERTA TRANSPORTATION AND UTILITIES. 1975. a. Alberta Transportation and Utilities, Public Communications Office, Main Floor, Twin Atria, 4999-98 Ave., Edmonton, AB T6B 2X3, Canada.
TEL 403-427-7674. FAX 403-466-3166. Ed. Ms. Terry Lotzer. adv. contact: Jayne Jeneroux. circ. 300. (also avail. in microfiche from MML) **Document type:** government publication.
Incorporates: Alberta. Department of Utilities. Annual Report; Former titles: Alberta Transportation. Annual Report (ISSN 0702-7702); Alberta Department of Transportation. Annual Report (ISSN 0318-4757); Alberta. Department of Utilities and Telecommunications. Annual Report; Alberta. Department of Utilities and Telephones. Annual Report; Alberta. Utilities Division. Annual Report (ISSN 0381-2294).

TRANSPORTATION   6303

388.346   US   ISSN 1043-5824
HD9710.37.U6
ALLSTATE MOTOR CLUB R V SALES, RENTAL AND SERVICE DIRECTORY.* 1990. a. Prentice Hall Travel Directories, 15 Columbus Cir., New York, NY 10023-7706. TEL 708-945-3737.
FAX 708-945-3786. adv. circ. 25,000. **Document type:** directory.
Description: Gives state-by-state listings of RV sales, rental and service facilities in chart format.

388.3 629.222   US
ALTERNATIVE TRANSPORTATION NEWS. 1991. bi-m. $20. Earthmind, Box 743, Mariposa, CA 95338-0743. TEL 213-396-1527. Ed. Michael Hackleman. adv.; bk.rev.; illus.
Description: Discusses the technologies and global issues shaping the search for alternatives to gasoline-powered transportation, including electric and human-powered vehicles, alternative fuels, battery innovations, activities of researchers and enthusiasts, and environmental impact questions.

380.5   US
AMERICAN PUBLIC WAREHOUSE REGISTER. a. $50 (Canada $50; elsewhere $60). Cahners Publishing Company (Newton), Division of Reed Elsevier Inc., 275 Washington St., Newton, MA 02158.
TEL 617-558-4473. FAX 617-558-4327. (Subscr. to: Box 750, Sicklerville, NJ 08081)
Description: Contains a listing of information regarding public warehouse facilities in the US, Canada and other trading partners.

388.4   AT   ISSN 1032-9145
AMONG OURSELVES. 1946. q. free. State Transport Authority, P.O. Box 2351, Adelaide, S.A. 5001, Australia. TEL 08-218-2513. FAX 08-231-2445. Ed. Cicely Findlay. illus. circ. 4,000. **Document type:** newsletter.
Description: Contains information on new developments in the organization and personal news about sport, achievements, retirements and social activities.

380.5   US   ISSN 1054-0288
ANIMAL TRANSPORTATION ASSOCIATION. INTERNATIONAL CONFERENCE. PROCEEDINGS.* 1978. a. price varies. Animal Transportation Association, Inc., P.O. Box 3565, North Potomac, MD 20885. TEL 301-990-6343.
FAX 301-990-0796. Ed. Harry Rowsell. adv.; bk.rev. circ. 400. **Document type:** proceedings.
—BLDSC (4538.736200).
Formerly: Animal Air Transportation Association. International Conference. Proceedings (ISSN 8755-9447)
Description: Covers all areas involved in the transport of animals worldwide.

380.5   FR   ISSN 1146-7355
ANNALES DE LA VOIRIE. bi-m. 390 F. Victoires - Editions, 38 rue Croix des Petits Champs, 75001 Paris, France. TEL 42-60-01-93. FAX 42-60-10-41. TELEX 615 887 F.

380.5   FR   ISSN 0066-3549
ANNUAIRE NATIONAL DES TRANSPORTS. 1948. a. 910 F. Editions Louis Johanet, 68 rue Boursault, 75017 Paris, France. adv.

380.52   BL   ISSN 0102-4671
ANUARIO ESTATISTICO DOS TRANSPORTES. 1970. a. free. Empresa Brasileira de Planejamento de Transportes, G E I P O T, SAN Quadra 3 Blocos N-O, 70040-920 Brasilia DF, Brazil. FAX 061-224-8642. TELEX 061-1316. circ. 1,200. **Document type:** government publication.
●Also available online.
Refereed Serial

380.5   SP
ASINTRA. 9/yr. Spanish Passenger Transport Managers' Federation, C. Cristobal Bordiu 35, Despacho 107, 28003 Madrid, Spain.
TEL 1-553-96-36. FAX 1-554-67-32. Ed. Lorenzo Chaco. circ. 7,500.

6304 TRANSPORTATION

380.5 US
ASTRALOG. 1964. bi-m. $25. American Society of Transportation and Logistics, Inc., 216 E. Church St., Lock Haven, PA 17745-2010. TEL 717-748-8515. Ed. Tricia Humphrey. adv. contact: Tricia Humphrey. circ. 2,000. (tabloid format) **Document type:** newsletter.
Formerly (until 1983): A S T L Newsletter.
Description: News and information on the activities of the society.

385.284 CN ISSN 0381-9345
ATLANTIC PROVINCES TRANSPORTATION COMMISSION. TIPS & TOPICS. Variant title: Tips & Topics. 1961. m. free in N. America; elsewhere Can.$15. Atlantic Provinces Transportation Commission, 1133 St-George Blvd., Ste 330, Moncton, NB E1E 4E1, Canada. TEL 506-857-2820. FAX 506-857-2835. E-mail: nstn1601@fox.nstn.ns.ca. Ed. Jack MacQuerrie. circ. 3,200. (back issues avail.) **Document type:** newsletter.

380.5 CN ISSN 0842-9596
ATLANTIC TRANSPORTATION JOURNAL. 1988. q. $18 (foreign $30). Bilby Holdings Ltd., 6029 Gottingen St., Halifax, NS B3K 1E5, Canada. TEL 902-420-0437. FAX 902-423-8212. adv. circ. 17,637. (tabloid format) **Document type:** trade publication.

380.5 AT
AUSTRALASIAN BUS AND COACH; the management magazine for bus and coach operators. 1988. m. (except Jan.). Aus.$35($70) Publishing Services (Australia) Pty. Ltd., 244 St. Paul's Terrace, Spring Hill, Brisbane, Qld. 4000, Australia. TEL 61-7-854-1286. Ed. Andrew Stewart. adv.: B&W page Aus.$1640, color page Aus.$2525; trim 25 x 45; adv. contact: Dave Rigby. circ. 5,661. (back issues avail.) **Document type:** trade publication.
Description: Covers transportation, travel and tourism for bus and coach operators.

388.322 IT
AUTOBUS.* 1977. m. L.60000. Vado e Torno Edizioni S.r.l., Via Lattanzio 77, 20137 Milan, Italy. TEL 39-2-55193629. FAX 39-2-55193660. Ed. Elio Guaglio. adv.: B&W page L.4100000, color page L.6000000. bk.rev.; charts; illus. circ. 15,000.
Former titles (until 1990): Autocarri e Autobus-Trans; Autocarri e Autobus (ISSN 0393-8239)

388.322 SP
AUTOBUSES Y AUTOCARES. 1989. m. 5500 ptas. (foreign 11400 ptas.). Tecnipublicaciones, S.A., C. Albacete 5, 28027 Madrid, Spain. TEL 34-1-3261440. FAX 34-1-3262539. Ed. Miguel Saez. circ. 7,000.
Description: Covers passenger transport and public transportation by bus.

388.322 NE
AUTOBUSKRONIEK. 1963. 11/yr. membership. Autobus Documentatie Vereniging, Penningmeester, Biterstraat 22, 8011 XL Zwolle, Netherlands. Ed. M.R.A. Velthuis. adv.; bk.rev. circ. 1,200.

388 385 IT
AUTOFERROTRANVIERE. 1955. m. L.100 per no. Federazione Provinciale Autoferrotranvieri di Milano, Corso Porta Vittoria 43, Milan, Italy. Ed. Bruno di Pol. adv. circ. 24,000.

388.3 AU ISSN 0005-0830
AUTOREVUE. 1965. m. S.450($12) Orac Zeitschriftenverlag GmbH, Schoenbrunnerstr. 59-61, A-1050 Vienna, Austria. TEL 01-54621-0. FAX 01-5462178. Ed. Herbert Voelker. adv.: B&W page S.79920, color page S.135864; trim 185 x 250. illus. circ. 128,200. (back issues avail.) **Document type:** consumer publication.

B I C - CODE. (Bureau International des Containers) see *PACKAGING*

380.5 KE
BANDARI; staff newspaper of Kenya Ports Authority. (Text in English, Swahili) 1969. q. free. Kenya Ports Authority, P.O. Box 95009, Mombasa, Kenya. FAX 254-11-311867. TELEX 21243 BANDARI. Ed. Andy Nyagah. adv.; illus.; circ. 12,000. (controlled). **Document type:** newspaper.
Formerly (until 1979): Bandari Zetu.

380.5 US ISSN 0197-307X
CODEN: BICPDP
BATTERY COUNCIL INTERNATIONAL. CONVENTION PROCEEDINGS. 1975. a. $50. Battery Council International, 401 N. Michigan Ave., Chicago, IL 60611. TEL 312-644-6610. abstr.; charts; illus.; stat. circ. 750. **Document type:** proceedings.
Formerly: Battery Council International. Convention Minutes.
Description: Contains transcript of the annual meeting.

BEIKOKU TOKKYO SHOROKU. YU'YU KIKAI, KENSETSU, DOBOKU HEN/U.S. PATENT ABSTRACTS. TRANSPORTING MACHINE, CONSTRUCTION, CIVIL ENGINEERING. see *PATENTS, TRADEMARKS AND COPYRIGHTS — Abstracting, Bibliographies, Statistics*

380.5 GW ISSN 0722-9399
BERLINER VERKEHRSBLAETTER. 1954. m. DM.33.60 (foreign DM.38.40). Arbeitskreis Berliner Nahverkehr e.V., Binger Str. 88, 14197 Berlin, Germany. adv.; bk.rev.; charts; illus.; index. circ. 4,000. (back issues avail.) **Document type:** consumer publication.
Description: Information magazine on public transportation in Berlin. Focus on traffic situation, roads, bus system and railroads.

380.5 NE
BESTELAUTO; Misset select. (Text in Dutch) a. Misset (Subsidiary of: Reed Elsevier plc), Postbus 4, 7000 BA Doetinchem, Netherlands. TEL 31-8340-49911. FAX 31-8340-43839. TELEX 45481. Ed. P.C. Wieman. adv.: B&W page fl.19941; unit 187 x 257; adv. contact: Cor van Nek. circ. 370,000. **Document type:** trade publication.
Description: Publishes road tests of vans and light trucks, for entrepreneurs and business and industrial fleet managers.

388.347 US ISSN 0193-8177
BICYCLE FORUM. 1978. q. $20 to individuals; institutions $25. Adventure Cycling Association, 150 E. Pine St., Missoula, MT 59802-4515. TEL 406-721-1776. (Subscr. to: Box 8308, Missoula, MT 59807-8308) (Co-sponsor: Bicycle Federation of America) Ed. Dan D'Ambrosio. index. **Document type:** consumer publication.
—UnCover.
Description: Offers a forum for readers and gives advice and information on issues of bicycle safety, education and facility design.

386 GW ISSN 0939-1916
HE669
BINNENSCHIFFAHRT. 1946. 22/yr. DM.151. (Bundesverband der Deutschen Binnenschiffahrt e.V.) Wirtschafts- und Verkehrsverlag Hansa GmbH, Elbchaussee 277, 22605 Hamburg, Germany. TEL 040-822807-0. FAX 040-822807-52. TELEX 213075-HANSA-D. (Subscr. to: Maximilian Verlagsgruppe, Zeitschriften Service, Steintorwall 17, 32052 Herford, Germany. TEL 05221-599146) (Co-sponsor: C.Schroedter & Co. (GmbH & Co. KG)) adv.; bk.rev.; bibl.; charts; illus.; stat. circ. 4,500. **Document type:** trade publication.
—SWETS. **CCC.**
Formed by the 1991 merger of: B W - Zeitschrift fuer Binnenschiffahrt und Wasserstrassen (ISSN 0930-7370); Which was formerly: Zeitschrift fuer Binnenschiffahrt und Wasserstrassen (ISSN 0340-3963) & Binnenschiffahrts-Nachrichten (ISSN 0179-7743); Which was formerly titled (until 1983): Binnenschiffahrts-Nachrichten. Ausgabe B (ISSN 0172-2069); Which supersedes in part (in 1952): Binnenschiffahrts-Nachrichten (ISSN 0006-2847)

380.5 GW ISSN 0173-0290
BLICKPUNKT STRASSENBAHN. 1979. bi-m. DM.42. Arbeitsgemeinschaft Blickpunkt Strassenbahn e.V., Postfach 410167, 12111 Berlin, Germany. TEL 030-8524305. FAX 030-7859208. Ed. Thomas E. Fischer. adv.; bk.rev.; cum.index: 1979-1992. circ. 3,000. (back issues avail.) **Document type:** consumer publication.

380.5 PN
BOLETIN. 1981. w. Bl.30 (America & Spain Bl.50) (effective Jul. 1995). El Boletin S.A., Apdo. 6-4092, El Dorado, Panama, Panama. TEL 507-236967. FAX 507-692789. (U.S. addr.: PTY 0233, Box 025207, Miami, FL 33102-5207) Ed. Theodore J. James. adv.: B&W page $570. bk.rev. circ. 1,200. **Document type:** newspaper, trade publication.
Description: Guide to shipping movements through Panama's ports. Includes an airline guide on direct flights to and from Tocumen International Airport.

380.5 IT ISSN 0006-7849
BORSA DEI NOLI; settimanale dei traffici marittimi, aerei e terrestri. 1962. w. L.45000. Publicrea Editrice Borsa dei Noli S.d.f., Corso Gastaldi 11, Genoa 16131, Italy. Ed. Novello Secondina. adv.; charts; illus.; stat. circ. 14,500. (tabloid format)

380.5 330.9 BS ISSN 1013-5731
BOTSWANA. CENTRAL STATISTICS OFFICE. TRANSPORT STATISTICS. a. Central Statistics Office, Ministry of Finance and Development Planning, Private Bag 0024, Gaborone, Botswana. TEL 267-352200. (Orders to: Government Printer, P.O. Box 87, Gaborone, Botswana) Ed. G.M. Charumbira; Pub. J.G. Segwe. **Document type:** government publication.

380.5 380.5 UK
BROOKLANDS SOCIETY GAZETTE. 1975. q. £12 (foreign £15). The Brooklands Society, Cleeve Cottage, Cobham Way, E. Horsley, Surrey KT24 5BH, England. TEL 01483-283565. FAX 01483-282466. Ed. Rupert Prior. adv. contact: P. Dench. bk.rev. circ. 1,500. (back issues avail.) **Document type:** bulletin.
Description: Discusses historic racing cars, motorcycles, and aircraft related to the Brooklands Motor Course and airfield.

380.5 CF
BULLETIN ANNUEL DES TRANSPORTS ET PARC AUTO. 1984. a. 3000 Fr.CFA. Centre National de la Statistique et des Etudes Economiques, B.P. 2031, Brazzaville, Congo. TEL 83-36-94.

380.5 LE
BULLETIN DES TRANSPORTS MARITIMES ET TERRESTRES.* (Text in Arabic and French) 1972. s.a. Direction Generale des Transports, Beirut, Lebanon. Ed. Adel Harfouche. charts; illus.

388.3 BE ISSN 0779-1267
BUS & COACH MAGAZINE. French edition (ISSN 0779-1305) (Text in Dutch) 1992. 6/yr. Multi Media Management, Rue des Pres 2-001, 4802 Vervier Heusy, Belgium. TEL 32-87-292929. adv.: B&W page 35500 BEF, color page 49400 BEF. circ. 2,000 (1,200 Dutch ed.; 800 French ed.). **Document type:** trade publication.

388.322 US ISSN 1070-6526
BUS CONVERSIONS. 1992. m. $24 (foreign $30). 3249 Cherry Ave., Long Beach, CA 90807. TEL 310-432-7645. FAX 310-427-9662. Ed. John Kadletz. adv. circ. 20,000. **Document type:** consumer publication.
Description: Covers bus conversions.

388.322 FR ISSN 0399-2535
BUS ET CAR MAGAZINE. 1976. 23/yr. 578 F. (foreign 663 F.) (effective 1994-95). Groupe Liaisons, BP 87, 92503 Rueil Malmaison Cedex, France. TEL 41-29-98-98. FAX 41-29-99-08. circ. 7,500.

BUS-FAHRT; internationale Fachzeitschrift fuer Omnibusverkehr. see *TRAVEL AND TOURISM*

BUS-FAHRT ZIELE. see *TRAVEL AND TOURISM*

388.322 UK ISSN 0143-9162
BUS FAYRE; the monthly magazine for everyone interested in buses. 1978. m. £24 (overseas £26). Autobus Review Publications Ltd., 42 Coniston Ave., Queensbury, Bradford, W. Yorks. BD13 2JD, England. TEL 01274-881640. Ed. K.A. Jenkinson. adv.; bk.rev. circ. 18,000. **Document type:** trade publication.
Formerly (until Apr. 1982): Fare Stage (ISSN 0143-9170)
Description: Looks at both the present and the past bus industry; appeals to bus enthusiasts and historians, as well as bus industry professionals.

TRANSPORTATION

388.322 US
BUS GARAGE INDEX. 1967. a. $25 (effective 1994). Friendship Publications, Inc., Box 1472, Spokane, WA 99210-1472. TEL 509-328-9181. FAX 509-325-0405. Ed. William A. Luke. circ. 2,000. (reprint service avail.)

380.1 US ISSN 0739-7194
BUS INDUSTRY MAGAZINE. 1963. q. $20 (foreign $30). Bus History Association, Inc., Loring M. Lawrence, Ed., 195 Lancelot Dr., Manchester, NH 03104-1420. TEL 603-669-7160. (Subscr. to: 965 McEwan, Windsor, Ont. N9B 2G1, Canada) adv.; bk.rev.; illus. circ. 400. (back issues avail.) **Document type:** academic/scholarly publication.
Former titles: Bus Review; Bus History.
Description: News and articles pertaining to city and intercity historical and contemporary bus operations.

388.322 US ISSN 1047-5001
BUS OPERATOR. 1985. bi-m. Tom Jackson & Associates, Inc., 3100 W. End Ave., Ste. 1210, Nashville, TN 37203-1348. TEL 615-242-7747. Ed. Bill Goodwin. adv. circ. 7,000. **Document type:** trade publication.
Description: Provides intercity bus operations professionals with technical and management information and regulatory and legislative news.

388.322 US ISSN 1083-5849
THE BUS PAGES. 1992. a. free. Bus Book Publishing, Inc., Box 9, McMinnville, OR 97128-0009. TEL 503-472-3536. FAX 503-472-3293. adv. circ. 50,000. (back issues avail.) **Document type:** directory.

388.322 US ISSN 0192-8902
BUS RIDE. 1965. 9/yr. $30 (effective 1995). Friendship Publications, Inc., Box 1472, Spokane, WA 99210-1472. TEL 509-328-9181. FAX 509-325-0405. Ed. William A. Luke. adv.; bk.rev. circ. 13,500. **Indexed:** HRIS.

338.3 US ISSN 0363-3764
HE5623.A45
BUS RIDE: BUS INDUSTRY DIRECTORY. Spine title: Bus Industry Directory. 1972. a. $68 (effective 1995). Friendship Publications, Inc., Box 1472, Spokane, WA 99210-1472. TEL 509-328-9181. FAX 509-325-0405. Ed. William A. Luke. circ. 1,500. **Document type:** directory.

388.322 US ISSN 0199-6096
BUS TOURS MAGAZINE. 1979. bi-m. $10 (foreign $15). National Bus Trader, Inc., 9698 Judson Rd., Polo, IL 61064. TEL 815-946-2341. FAX 815-946-2347. Ed. Larry Plachno. circ. 9,000 (controlled). (back issues avail.) **Document type:** trade publication.

385 388 GW ISSN 0341-5228
BUS UND BAHN. 1967. m. DM.27.50. (Verband Oeffentlicher Verkehrsbetriebe) Alba Fachverlag GmbH und Co. KG, Roemerstr. 9, 40474 Duesseldorf, Germany. TEL 0211-46901-0. FAX 0211-4690145. Ed. Alf Teloeken. bk.rev. circ. 5,850. (back issues avail.) **Indexed:** Dok.Str.
Document type: bulletin.
—CCC.

388.3 UK ISSN 0007-6392
BUSES. 1949. m. £25.20. Ian Allan Ltd., Coombelands House, Coombelands Ln., Addlestone, Surrey KT15 1HY, England. TEL 01932-855909. Ed. Stephen Morris. adv.; bk.rev.; charts; illus.; index. circ. 19,000. (reprint service avail. from UMI) **Indexed:** HRIS.
—CCC.
Formerly: Buses Illustrated.
Description: Publishes articles relating to the road passenger transport industry in the U.K.

388.322 US
BUSES INTERNATIONAL. 1980. q. $25 membership. (Buses International Association) Friendship Publications, Inc., Box 1472, Spokane, WA 99210-1472. TEL 509-328-9181. FAX 509-325-0405. Ed. William A. Luke. circ. 100. (back issues avail.)
Description: Focuses on bus transportation.

380.52 658.8 UK ISSN 0261-8168
BUSINESS RATIO REPORT: FREIGHT FORWARDERS; an industry sector analysis. 1978. a. I C C Business Ratios Ltd., Freepost, Field House, Hampton, Middx. TW12 2HQ, England. TEL 081-783-0977. FAX 081-783-1940. charts; stat. **Document type:** trade publication.
—BLDSC (4033.472650).
Formerly (until 1991): Financial Survey Company Directory. Freight Forwarders (ISSN 0952-777X)

380.5 GW ISSN 0942-346X
BUSMAGAZIN. 1981. m. DM.69. Kirschbaum Verlag GmbH, Siegfriedstr. 28, 53179 Bonn, Germany. TEL 0228-95453-0. FAX 0228-9545327. (Subscr. to: Postfach 210209, 53157 Bonn, Germany) adv.; bk.rev.; bibl.; charts; illus.; index. circ. 7,000. **Document type:** trade publication.
—CCC.
Formerly: Busverkehr (ISSN 0720-4507)

388.322 NO ISSN 0800-5389
BUSSEN. 1956. bi-m. NOK 100. Norsk Rutebilarbeiderforbund, Moellergt. 24, 0179 Oslo 1, Norway. FAX 02-115939. adv. circ. 5,700.

380.52 AG
C A T A C.* 1954. 6/yr. Argentine Association of Freight Transport, c/o Secretaria de Transportes, Avda. 9 de Julio 1925, 1o, 1332 Buenos Aires, Argentina. Ed. Jorge Navas. adv. circ. 3,500.

388.3 362.4 US
C T A P PUBLICATION. irreg. (U.S. Department of Health and Human Services, Community Transportation Assistance Project) Community Transportation Association of America, 1440 New York Ave., Ste. 440, Washington, DC 20005. TEL 202-628-1480; 800-527-8279. FAX 202-737-9197. (Co-sponsor: Project Action) **Document type:** monographic series, government publication.
Description: Discusses programs and technologies to make public transportation vehicles more accessible to disabled persons, in compliance with the Americans with Disabilities Act of 1990.

388.321 UK
CAB TRADE NEWS; national monthly paper of the licensed taxi trade. 1972. fortn. £6 (Europe £10). Drummond House, 203-209 N. Gower St., London NW1 2NL, England. TEL 071-387-3888. FAX 071-383-0877. Ed. Roger Trask. circ. 14,500. **Document type:** newspaper.

388 US ISSN 1082-345X
▼**CALIFORNIA CORRIDORS.** 1995. m. $125. Political Pulse, 926 J. St., Ste. 1214, Sacramento, CA 95814. TEL 916-446-3956. FAX 916-446-5302. Ed. Larry Lynch; Pubs. Larry Lynch, Bud Lembke. index; circ. 155 (paid). (looseleaf format; back issues avail.) **Document type:** newsletter.
Description: Covers the politics of California transportation issues. Covers the Legislature and Commissions and matters relating to all modes of transportation in the state.

381.41 US ISSN 0270-384X
HE199.5.F3
CALIFORNIA FRESH FRUIT AND VEGETABLE SHIPMENTS BY RAIL, TRUCK, AND AIR. a. $20. (Department of Food & Agriculture) Federal-State Market News Service (Sacramento), 1220 N St., Rm. 216, Box 942871, Sacramento, CA 94271-0001. TEL 916-654-0298. FAX 916-654-1046. stat. **Document type:** government publication.
Formerly: Movement of California Fruits and Vegetables by Rail, Truck, and Air (ISSN 0094-2790)

CALIFORNIA VEHICLE CODE. see LAW

388.346 FR ISSN 0769-3249
CAMPING-CAR. 1978. 7/yr. (plus special issue). 208 F. (foreign 272 F.) (effective 1994-1995). Ediregie, B.P. 86, 94420 Le Plessis Trevise, France. TEL 45-93-72-72. FAX 45-93-25-93. TELEX EDIGIE 262 572 F. Ed. Svend Meyzonnier. adv.; illus. circ. 70,000. **Document type:** consumer publication.
Formed by the 1985 merger of (1978-1985): Camping-Cars and Motor-Homes (ISSN 0183-4002); (1978-1985): Van le Camping-Car (ISSN 0292-6857); Which was formerly (until 1980): Camping Car et le Van (ISSN 0183-0139)

380.5 384 CN
CANADIAN NATIONAL ANNUAL REPORT. (Editions in English, French) 1923. a. Canadian National Railways, P.O. Box 8100, Montreal, PQ H3C 3N4, Canada. TEL 514-399-7212. FAX 514-399-5344. circ. 25,000.

CANADIAN RAIL/RAIL CANADIEN. see TRANSPORTATION — Railroads

621.1 CN ISSN 0045-5393
CANADIAN STEAM. 1972. q. $1. Richard L. Coulton, Ed. & Pub., Bentley, Alta. TOC OJ0, Canada. adv.; bk.rev.; illus.; index. circ. 50. (processed)

385 CN ISSN 0045-5466
CANADIAN TRANSPORT. (Text in English and French) 1909. bi-m. Can.$8.40. Canadian Brotherhood of Railway, Transport and General Workers, 2300 Carling Ave., Ottawa, ON, Canada. TEL 613-829-8764. FAX 613-824-6815. Ed. Russel Biggar. circ. 35,000. (also avail. in microfilm from UMI)
—UMI.

340 380.5 CN
CANADIAN TRANSPORTATION LAW REPORTER. 1990. m. Can.$435. C C H Canadian Ltd., 6 Garamond Ct., North York, ON M3C 1Z5, Canada. TEL 416-441-2992; 800-268-4522. FAX 416-444-9011. **Document type:** trade publication.
Description: Covers the Canadian Transportation Regulations environment, including transportation by rail, road, water, air and pipeline.

380.5 658.7 CN ISSN 1187-4295
HE1
CANADIAN TRANSPORTATION LOGISTICS. (Annual supplement avail.: Directory and Guide) 1898. m. Can.$44.89($52.95) (foreign $74). Southam Magazine Group, 1450 Don Mills Rd., Don Mills, ON M3B 2X7, Canada. TEL 416-445-6641. FAX 416-442-2261. Ed. Bonnie Toews. adv.; illus.; stat. circ. 14,000. **Indexed:** BPIA, Can.B.P.I.
—BLDSC (3046.032000); Faxon; UMI. **CCC.**
Former titles (until 1991): Canadian Transportation (ISSN 1184-1052); (until 1989): Canadian Transportation and Distribution Management (ISSN 0008-5200); (until 1968): Canadian Transportation (ISSN 0319-4388); Which incorporates: Traffic and Distribution Management.
Description: For those in charge of transportation, distribution, warehousing, inventory control and all functions of logistics including customs services and freight forwarding.

CARAVAN WORLD AND OUTDOOR LIFE. see TRAVEL AND TOURISM

388.346 GW ISSN 0008-6185
CARAVANING; mein Wohnwagen Magazin. 1959. m. DM.48.60; newsstand price: DM.4.50. Vereinigte Motor-Verlage GmbH und Co. KG, Leuschnerstr. 1, 70162 Stuttgart, Germany. TEL 0711-1821226. FAX 0711-1821349. adv.: B&W page DM.4500, color page DM.7875; trim 185 x 248. bk.rev.; bibl.; charts; illus.; mkt.; stat.; tr.lit.; index. circ. 55,000. (processed) **Document type:** consumer publication.
—CCC.

387 UK
TA1215 CODEN: CSYIBN
CARGO SYSTEMS. 1974. m. £121 (rest of Europe £138 ($207); elsewhere £167 ($253)) (effective 1996). I I R Publications Ltd., Market Towers, 2nd Fl., 1 Nine Elms Ln., London SW8 5NQ, England. TEL 0171-344-3800. FAX 0171-344-3806. E-mail: 100303,706@compuserve.com. Ed. Francis Phillips; Pub. Stuart Fryer. adv.; bk.rev. circ. 7,500. **Indexed:** BMT, Br.Rail.Bd., Excerp.Med., Fluidex. **Document type:** trade publication.
—Faxon.
Former titles (until 1994): Cargo Systems International (ISSN 0306-0985); Cargo Systems.
Description: Provides international coverage of the container, ports, and cargo-handling industries.

CARGOVISION. see TRANSPORTATION — Air Transport

338 IT ISSN 0008-6959
CARROZZIERE ITALIANO. 1962. m. L.120000. Edizioni Pubblire, Corso Garibaldi, 42, 20121 Milan, Italy. TEL 02-801529. FAX 02-801520. Ed. Maffeis Giuditta. adv.; bk.rev.; illus.; stat. circ. 10,000.

TRANSPORTATION

380.5   US   ISSN 0082-9404
CENSUS OF TRANSPORTATION, COMMUNICATIONS, AND UTILITIES: FINAL REPORTS. (Issued in 3 series) 1963. quinquennial, latest 1992. $127.50 for Truck Inventory and Use Survey (state reports and U.S. summary) (foreign $159.50); Geographic Area Statistics $13; Subject Series $11. U.S. Bureau of the Census, Data User Services Division, Washington, DC 20233. TEL 301-457-4100. FAX 301-457-4714. (Subscr. to: Superintendent of Documents, U.S. Government Printing Office, Box 371954, Pittsburgh, PA 15250-7954. TEL 202-512-1800. FAX 202-512-2250; Or: Bernan, 4611-F Assembly Dr., Lanham, MD 20706. TEL 301-459-7666. FAX 301-459-0056) (also avail. in microfiche) **Document type:** government publication.
● Also available on CD-ROM.

380.5   FR   ISSN 1241-5650
CENTRALE DU TRANSPORT ROUTIER. 1992. m. 58 rue Pottier, B.P. 93, 78151 Le Chesnay Cedex, France. TEL 39-55-36-64. FAX 39-23-30-30. Ed. Serge Marais. circ. 35,500 (paid). **Document type:** trade publication.

388   UK
CHARTERED INSITITUTE OF TRANSPORT, NORTHERN IRELAND. YEAR BOOK. a. (Chartered Institute of Transport, Northern Ireland) Main Stream Publications, 139 Thomas St., Portadown, Co. Armagh BT62 3BE, N. Ireland. TEL 01762-334272. FAX 01762-351046. **Document type:** corporate report.

380.5   NR
CHARTERED INSTITUTE OF TRANSPORT. ANNUAL. 1959. a. Chartered Institute of Transport, Nigerian Ports Authority, 51 Herbert Macauley St., Ebuke-metta, Lagos, Nigeria. adv.

331.881 388.4   DK   ISSN 0528-8967
CHAUFFOER NYT. 1973. bi-m. DKK 100. Fagbladenes Udgiverservice Amba, Oerbaekvej 739, DK-5220 Odense SOe, Denmark. TEL 45-65-97-25-02. FAX 45-65-97-24-07. Ed. Lis Agerbaek Joergensen. adv. circ. 25,000. **Document type:** newspaper.

658.8   US   ISSN 1057-9710
HF5487
CHILTON'S DISTRIBUTION; the transportation and business logistics magazine. 1901. m. $65. Chilton Co., Chilton Way, Radnor, PA 19089. TEL 215-964-4379. Ed. Thomas A. Foster. adv.; bk.rev.; charts; illus.; stat; tr.lit.; index. circ. 70,000. (also avail. in microform from UMI; microfiche from CIS; back issues avail.; reprint service avail.) **Indexed:** B.P.I., Intl.Mgmt.Info., Manage.Cont., SRI, Tr.& Indus.Ind.
● Also available online. Vendor(s): Knight-Ridder, Inc., Lexis-Nexis.
—UMI; UnCover. **CCC.**
Former titles (until 1986): Chilton's Distribution for Traffic and Transportation Decision Makers (ISSN 0273-6721); (until 1980): Chilton's Distribution (ISSN 0195-7244); (until 1979): Chilton's Distribution Worldwide (ISSN 0193-3248); (until 1977): Distribution Worldwide (ISSN 0886-3512); (until 1972): Chilton's Distribution Worldwide (ISSN 0886-3237); And (until 1970): Distribution Worldwide (ISSN 0012-3951); (until 1969): Distribution Manager (ISSN 0196-7290).
Description: Focuses on traffic management and inventory control.

380.5   US   ISSN 1049-8427
TL263
CHILTON'S GUIDE TO AUTOMATIC TRANSMISSION REPAIR. IMPORT CARS & TRUCKS. biennial. Chilton Book Co., 1 Chilton Way, Radnor, PA 19089.

380.5 915.1   HK   ISSN 0258-3259
CHINA TRANSPORT. 1985. q. $50. (China Communications and Transportation Association) China Transport Publications Ltd., 4306 China Resources Bldg., 43rd Fl., 26 Harbour Rd., Hong Kong, Hong Kong. TEL 5-8913831. TELEX 68444 HKTF HX. Ed. Oliver Wong. adv.; bk.rev. circ. 6,000.

380.5   FR   ISSN 0755-1088
CHRONIQUE DU TRANSPORTEUR. 1947. m. 270 F. (foreign 290 F.). Bureau d'Etudes et de Recherches Theoriques, 80 rue Jules Ferry, 93177 Bagnolet Cedex, France. TEL 1-43-60-02-36. FAX 1-48-97-11-88. Ed. Arlette Jaron. adv. circ. 13,000.
—**CCC.**

380.5   FR   ISSN 0765-3522
CIRCULER. 1984. 6/yr. 145 F. Prevention Routiere, 6 av. Hoche, 75008 Paris, France. TEL 44-15-27-00. FAX 44-15-27-40. Ed. J.Yves Salaun. adv.; bk.rev. circ. 8,000.

CITY CYCLIST. see *SPORTS AND GAMES — Bicycles And Motorcycles*

CIVIL PENALTY CASE DIGEST SERVICE. see *LAW — Civil Law*

388.322   UK   ISSN 0966-8438
CLASSIC BUS. bi-m. £17.40. Classic Bus Publishing Ltd., 39 Lilyhill Terr., Edinburgh EH8 7DR, Scotland. TEL 0131-652-0205. FAX 0131-652-0856. Ed. Gavin Booth. adv.; bk.rev. circ. 12,000. **Document type:** consumer publication.
—**CCC.**
Former titles (until 1992): Buses Extra (ISSN 0141-9927); (until 1977): Buses Special.
Description: Covers bus and coach nostalgia.

388.322   UK   ISSN 1351-3877
COACH & BUS WEEK. 1978. w. £45. E M A P - Response Publishing Ltd., Wentworth House, Wentworth St., Peterborough, Cambs. PE1 1DS, England. TEL 01733-63100. FAX 01733-62656. Ed. Mike Morgan. adv.; bk.rev. circ. 6,500. **Document type:** trade publication.
Former titles (until 1992): Coachmart; (until 1990): Day Trips and Short Breaks; Which incorporated: Tours and Excursions.

388.3   UK   ISSN 0009-9899
COACHING JOURNAL AND BUS REVIEW. 1932. 10/yr. £27 (foreign £42). Yandell Publishing, Ltd., 9 Vermont Pl., Tongwell, Milton Keynes MK15 8JA, England. TEL 01908-613323. FAX 01908-210656. Ed. Pamela Brook. adv. contact: Julie Smith. bk.rev.; charts; illus.; stat.; tr.lit. circ. 4,330. **Indexed:** HRIS. **Document type:** trade publication.
Description: Trade news for the coach and bus industry.

388.346   US   ISSN 1062-2349
COAST TO COAST MAGAZINE. 1982. 8/yr. $12. Affinity Group, Inc., 3601 Calle Tecate, Camarillo, CA 93012. TEL 805-389-0300. Ed. Valerie Law. circ. 300,000.
Description: Covers 500 private camping and resort clubs in N. America. Focuses on vacation, travel, recreation and the coast to coast system.

380.5   US
COMMANDANT'S BULLETIN. m. $23 (foreign $28.75). U.S. Department of Transportation, 400 Seventh St., S.W., Washington, DC 20590. TEL 202-366-5580. (Subscr. to: Superintendent of Documents, U.S. Government Printing Office, Box 371954, Pittsburgh, PA 15250-7951. TEL 202-512-1800. FAX 202-512-2250) (back issues avail.) **Document type:** government publication, bulletin,

380.5 362.4   UK   ISSN 0263-9378
COMMUNITY TRANSPORT MAGAZINE; the journal for minibus & non-profit transport operators. 1982. s-m. £12($30) Community Transport Association, Highbank, Halton St., Hyde, Cheshire SK14 2NY, England. TEL 061-351-1475. FAX 061-367-8780. Ed. Alison Shore. adv.; bk.rev. circ. 1,500. (back issues avail.) **Document type:** trade publication.

380.5 630   US   ISSN 0895-4437
COMMUNITY TRANSPORTATION REPORTER; the magazine of community transit industry. 1984. 9/yr. $35. Community Transportation Association of America, 1440 New York Ave., N.W., Ste. 440, Washington, DC 20005. TEL 202-628-1480. FAX 202-737-9197. Ed. Barbara-Rasin Price. adv.; bk.rev.; index, cum.index: 1983-1992; circ. 10,000 (controlled).
Formerly (until Jun. 1987): Rural Transportation Reporter.
Description: Funding, legislation, trends, accessibility, coordination, environmental issues, vehicles and components, and surveys in community transportation.

CONFIDENTIAL A-I-R LETTER. see *CRIMINOLOGY AND LAW ENFORCEMENT*

388   US   ISSN 0069-9039
HE28.C8
CONNECTICUT MASTER TRANSPORTATION PLAN.* 1971. a. Department of Transportation (Conndot), Box 317546, Newington, CT 06131-7546. TEL 203-566-5114. circ. 1,000.
Incorporates (in 1973): Connecticut Highway Needs Report.

380.5   JA   ISSN 0289-8322
CONTAINER AGE; the authoritative voice of intermodal transportation and distribution. (Text in Japanese) 1967. m. 6000 Yen. Container Age Ltd., 3F Ogihara Bldg., 1-13-2, Nishi-Shinbashi, Minato-ku, Tokyo 105, Japan. TEL 03-3501-0600. FAX 03-3501-0600. Ed. Eiji Niimoto. adv.; bk.rev. circ. 18,700. **Document type:** trade publication.
Description: Serves intermodal transportation industry, specifically shippers, manufacturers, carriers, and freight forwarders.

380.52 380.1   GW   ISSN 0174-2701
CONTAINER CONTACTS. 1971. a. DM.36.45. K.O. Storck Verlag, Stahltwiete 7, 22761 Hamburg, Germany. TEL 040-853292-0. FAX 040-8507758. Ed. H. Meder. **Document type:** trade publication.

658.7   UK   ISSN 0010-7379
TA1215
CONTAINERISATION INTERNATIONAL. 1967. m. £150($265) E M A P - Business Publishing Ltd., 33-39 Bowling Green Ln., London EC1R ODA, England. TEL 0171-837-1212. FAX 0171-278-9509. Ed. Mark Lambert. adv.; illus.; tr.lit. circ. 10,952. (reprint service avail. from UMI) **Indexed:** BMT, Fluidex, Int.Packag.Abstr. **Document type:** trade publication.
—BLDSC (3425.080000); Faxon; SWETS; UMI. **CCC.**

658.7   UK   ISSN 0305-7402
CONTAINERISATION INTERNATIONAL YEARBOOK. 1968. a. £180. E M A P - Business Publishing Ltd., 33-39 Bowling Green Ln., London EC1R ODA, England. TEL 0171-837-1212. FAX 0171-278-9509. Ed. Mark Lambert. adv.; illus. circ. 2,500. **Document type:** trade publication.
—BLDSC (3425.090000).

380.5   US   ISSN 1075-3621
COURIER MAGAZINE; newsmagazine of the messenger, courier, & expedited delivery industry. 1992. q. $20. Courier Magazine, Inc., 9418 Battle St., Ste. 201, Manassas, VA 22110. TEL 703-330-5600. FAX 703-330-5357. Ed. Carlene Mackereth; Pub. Bruce H. Joffe. adv. contact: Bruce H. Joffe. circ. 4,000. (back issues avail.) **Document type:** trade publication.

388.322   UK
CRONER'S COACH AND BUS OPERATIONS. 1983. q. £82.20 (subscr. includes m. newsletter) (effective 1993). Croner Publications Ltd. (Subsidiary of: Wolters Kluwer N.V.), Croner House, London Rd., Kingston, Surrey KT2 6SR, England. TEL 081-547-3333. FAX 081-547-2637. Ed. Colin Clark. (looseleaf format)
Description: Covers the rules and regulations governing coach and bus operations in the United Kingdom.

380.5   US
D M W B E ACTION NEWSLETTER. 1988. q. (Metropolitan Transportation Authority, Disadvantaged Minority and Women Business Enterprises) New York City Transit Authority, Affirmative Action Department, 81 Willoughby St., Brooklyn, NY 11201.

380.5 350   UK
D O T NEWS. 1988. m. free. Department of Transport, 2 Marsham St., London SW1P 3EB, England. TEL 0171-276-5082. FAX 0171-276-6080. Ed. Ian Fraser. adv. contact: Jack Pedersen. bk.rev. cols./p.: 7; pp./issue: 16. (tabloid format) **Document type:** newspaper, government publication.

388.1   DK   ISSN 0900-3665
D S B BLADET. 1943. m. DKK 150. Danske Statsbaner - Danish State Railways, Soelvgade 40, DK-1349 Copenhagen K, Denmark. TEL 45-33-14-04-00. FAX 45-33-32-62-54. Ed. Jesper Sejl. bk.rev. circ. 33,500. **Document type:** corporate report.
Formerly: Vingehjulet (ISSN 0042-6296)

TRANSPORTATION

629.2   DK
D V BOGEN. 1960. a. Danske Vognmaend Hovedorganisationen, Gammeltorv 18, 1457 Copenhagen K, Denmark. TEL 33-13-88-00. FAX 33-32-57-07. cum.index.
    Formerly: L D V Bogen.

380.5   GW
D V Z BRIEF. (Deutsche Verkehrs - Zeitung) w. DM.49.50. Tetzlaff Verlag GmbH, Nordkanalstr. 36, 20097 Hamburg, Germany. TEL 040-2371401. Ed. Frank Schnell. **Document type:** newspaper.

380.5   US
DAILY SHIPPING GUIDE. 1920. d. (Mon.-Fri.). $116. Guide Publishing Co., 118 Terry Pkwy., Gretna, LA 70056. TEL 504-368-6111. FAX 504-368-8999. Ed. Kenneth A. Hocke. **Document type:** newspaper.

380.5   DK   ISSN 0106-0724
DANMARKS TRANSPORT-TIDENDE. 1978. 22/yr. DKK 300. Forlaget Erik Koch Larsen ApS, Hojvangen 6, DK-3480 Fredensborg, Denmark. FAX 45-42-28-10-02. Ed. Jesper Nielsen. adv. contact: Bodil Hegnslund. circ. 11,062. **Document type:** newspaper.

388.346   DK   ISSN 0108-0709
DANSK TAXI TIDENDE. 1922. m. DKK 80. Dansk Taxi Forbund, Kildevaeldets Alle 12, 2600 Glostrup, Denmark. TEL 45-43-43-35-35. FAX 45-43-43-35-02. Ed.Bd. adv.; charts; illus. circ. 4,000.
    Formerly: Droske Tidende (ISSN 0040-0130)

355.69 380.5   US   ISSN 0011-7625
U1
DEFENSE TRANSPORTATION JOURNAL; magazine of international defense transportation and logistics. 1946. bi-m. $35 to non-members (effective 1995). National Defense Transportation Association, 50 South Pickett St., No. 220, Alexandria, VA 22304-3008. TEL 703-751-5011. FAX 703-823-8761. Ed.s Dennis L. Edwards, Joseph G. Mattingly, Jr. adv.; bk.rev.; charts; illus.; index; circ. 8,500. (also avail. in microform from UMI; reprint service avail. from UMI) **Indexed:** Abstr.Mil.Bibl.; Air Un.Lib.Ind.; DM & T, PROMT. **Document type:** trade publication.
    —BLDSC (3546.240000); Faxon; UMI; UnCover.
    Formerly: National Defense Transportation Journal.
    Description: Covers defense transportation and logistics for the government defense and commercial sectors.
    Refereed Serial

380.5   US
DELAWARE VALLEY PLANNING NEWS. (Includes: Regional Transportation & Planning News for the Delaware Valley) 1980. 4/yr. free. Delaware Valley Regional Planning Commission, Bourse Bldg., 21 S. Fifth St., Philadelphia, PA 19106. TEL 215-592-1800. FAX 215-592-9125. Ed. Candace B. Snyder. circ. 2,500. (tabloid format; back issues avail.)

380.5 309.2   US   ISSN 0896-0747
DELAWARE VALLEY REGIONAL PLANNING COMMISSION. ANNUAL REPORT. Cover title: D.V.R.P.C Annual Report. a. free. Delaware Valley Regional Planning Commission, Bourse Bldg., 21 S. Fifth St., Philadelphia, PA 19103. TEL 215-592-1800. FAX 215-592-9125. illus.
    Formerly: Delaware Valley Regional Planning Commission. Biennial Report (ISSN 0098-6232)
    Description: Overview of activities of the Delaware Valley Regional Planning Commission in areas of transportation, strategic planning and regional information services.

380.5   GW
DEUTSCHE VERKEHRSWISSENSCHAFTLICHE GESELLSCHAFT. SCHRIFTENREIHE. REIHE A. DOKUMENTATION. 1965. a. DM.45. Deutsche Verkehrswissenschaftliche Gesellschaft e.V., Bruederstr. 53, 51427 Bergisch Gladbach, Germany. TEL 02204-60027. FAX 02204-67743. Ed. K. Thielen. bk.rev. circ. 1,800. **Indexed:** Dok.Str. **Document type:** bibliography.

380.5   NE   ISSN 0924-5324
DEVELOPMENTS IN TRANSPORT STUDIES. (Text in English) 1980. irreg. price varies. Kluwer Academic Publishers, Postbus 17, 3300 AA Dordrecht, Netherlands. TEL 31-78-392392. FAX 31-78-392254. TELEX 29245 KAPG NL. (Dist. by: Kluwer Academic Publishers Group, P.O. Box 322, 3300 AH Dordrecht, Netherlands. TEL 31-78-392392. FAX 31-78-546474; N. America dist. addr.: Box 358, Accord Sta., Hingham, MA 02018-0358. TEL 617-871-6600. FAX 617-871-6528) **Document type:** monographic series.
    Refereed Serial

DIESEL; mensile di cultura, attualita, tecnica che tratta di tutte le motorizzazioni diesel per usi industriali, agricoli, nautici. see ENGINEERING — Mechanical Engineering

380.5   HK
DIRECTORY OF HONG KONG TRANSPORTS.* a. HK.$200. Hong Kong Trade and Industry Promotion Centre, c/o Hong Kong Trade Development Council, 36th-39th Fl., Office Tower, Convention Plaza, 1 Harbor Rd., Wanchai, Hong Kong. TEL 3-882708. FAX 3-7716438. **Document type:** directory.

380.5   UK   ISSN 0954-2094
DISTRIBUTION. 1988. bi-m £45 (foreign £60). Trinity Publishing Ltd., Times House, Station Approach, Ruislip, Middx. HA4 8NB, England. TEL 01895-677677. FAX 01895-676027. Ed. Malory Davies; Pub. S. Goodall. circ. 12,000. (back issues avail.) **Document type:** trade publication.

380 330   FR
DOCUMENTS TARIFAIRES TRANSPORT. (Supplements avail.) a. 1035 F. (with supplements 4584 F.)(effective 1990). Lamy S.A., 187-189 Quai de Valmy, 75490 Paris, France. (looseleaf format)

380.5   XR   ISSN 0012-5520
DOPRAVA/TRANSPORT; ctvrtletni ekonomicko-technicka revue. (Text in Czech; contents page and summaries also in French, German, Russian) 1959. q. $36.30. (Ministerstvo Dopravy Ceske Republiky) Dopravni Rozvojove Stredisko C.R., U Luzickeho Seminare 2, 118 00 Prague 1, Czech Republic. (Dist. by: Artia, Ve Smeckach 30, 111 27 Prague 1, Czech Republic) Ed. Josef Zatloukal. adv.; bibl.; illus. circ. 3,000.

629   US
DRIVER TRAINER NEWSLETTER. bi-m. $19 to non-members; members $15. National Safety Council, Periodicals Department, 1121 Spring Lake Dr., Itasca, IL 60143. TEL 708-775-2281. circ. 130,000. **Document type:** newsletter.
    Formerly: Driver Letter.
    Description: Professional driver letter for defensive driving course instructors.

380.5   NE
E W SPECIAL; transport en verpakking. no.2, 1976. irreg. fl.1 per no. Bonaventura B.V., Hoogoorddreef 60, 1101 BE Amsterdam, Netherlands. TEL 20-5674911. FAX 20-5674629. TELEX 14013 BONAV NL. Ed. J. Folkerstma.

380.5   EC
ECUADOR. INSTITUTO NACIONAL DE ESTADISTICA Y CENSOS. ANUARIO DE ESTADISTICAS DE TRANSPORTE. 1965. a. Esc.33000($58) Instituto Nacional de Estadistica y Censos, 10 de Agosto No. 229, Quito, Ecuador. TEL 593-2-581900. FAX 593-2-580041. circ. 500.

629.229   UK   ISSN 0307-577X
ELECTRIC VEHICLES.* 1914. q. Allens (Clerkenwell) Ltd., 177 Hagden Lane, Watford, Herts, England. Ed. Lloyd Arkill. adv.; bk.rev.; illus.; pat.; tr.lit. circ. 3,000.
    Former titles (until 1974): Electric Vehicles for Industry (ISSN 0013-4171); (until 1969): Electric Vehicles.
    Description: Covers battery electric vehicles.

388   IT   ISSN 1121-7995
ELEVATORI. 1972. bi-m. L.35000 (foreign L.53000). Volpe Editore, Via Pacinotti 4, 20090 Segrate, Italy. TEL 02-26922454. FAX 02-26922511. TELEX 313661. Ed. Carlo Distaso. adv. circ. 2,800. **Document type:** trade publication.
    Former titles (until 1992): Elevatori Moderni (ISSN 1120-2289); (until 1973): Elevatori (ISSN 0391-450X)

380.5 614.7   FR   ISSN 1163-2720
ENVIRONMENT MAGAZINE. m. (10/yr.). 690 F. Victoires - Editions, 38 rue Croix des Petits Champs, 75001 Paris, France. TEL 42-60-01-93. FAX 42-60-10-41. TELEX 615 887 F.

380.5   GR
EPITHEORESIS SYNKOINONIAKOU DIKAIOU. 1973. m. c/o Onoufrios Onouphriades, Ed., Metamorphoseos 3, 174 55 Kalamaki, Athens, Greece. TEL 30-1-9820-336. bk.rev. circ. 5,000.

380.5 001.5   PN   ISSN 1012-3555
HE222.A1
ESTADISTICA PANAMENA. SITUACION ECONOMICA. SECCION 333. TRANSPORTE. 1958. a. Bl.0.50 (foreign Bl.1.50) (effective 1995). Direccion de Estadistica y Censo, Contraloria General, Apdo. 5213, Panama 5, Panama. FAX 507-69-7294. circ. 1,000. **Document type:** government publication, bulletin.
    Supersedes in part (in 1985): Estadistica Panamena. Situacion Economica. Seccion 333-334. Transporte y Comunicaciones (ISSN 0378-7389)
    Description: Offers data on land transportation: cars, passengers, cargo transported, and railroads. Includes transportation by air and sea.

380   SP   ISSN 1133-2832
ESTUDIOS DE TRANSPORTES Y COMUNICACIONES. 1982. q. 1200 ptas. Ministerio de Obras Publicas y Transportes, Sec. General Tecnica, Paseo de la Castellana 67, 28071 Madrid, Spain.
    Former titles (until 1993): Estudios de Transportes (ISSN 1132-9599); (until 1992): T T C (ISSN 0213-7380); (until 1986): Spain. Ministerio de Transportes, Turismo y Comunicaciones. Revista (ISSN 0213-7372); (until 1985): Spain. Ministerio de Transportes, Turismo y Comunicaciones. Boletin de Informacion (ISSN 0212-1506)

380.5   AU
EURO-TRANS. 8/yr. Unter Viaduktgasse 6-11, A-1030 Vienna, Austria. FAX 0222-7136681. Ed. Alfred Mantl. circ. 16,200.

380.5   EI
EUROPA TRANSPORT. (Text in English, French, German) a. $65. Office for Official Publications of the European Communities, L-2985 Luxembourg, Luxembourg. (Dist. in the U.S. by: Unipub, 4611-F Assembly Dr., Lanham, MD 20706-4391. TEL 800-274-4888. FAX 301-459-0056)

347.7 385.1   BE   ISSN 0014-3154
K5
EUROPEAN TRANSPORT LAW/DROIT EUROPEEN DES TRANSPORTS/EUROPAEISCHES TRANSPORTRECHT/DIRITTO EUROPEO DEI TRASPORTI/EUROPEES VERVOERRECHT/DERECHO EUROPEO DE TRANSPORTES. (Text in Dutch, English, French, German, Italian, Spanish) 1966. bi-m. 5200 BEF (Europe 5800 BEF; elsewhere 6200 BEF) (effective 1996). European Transport Law, Maria-Henriettalei 1, B-2018 Antwerp, Belgium. TEL 32-3-2313655. FAX 32-3-2342380. TELEX 32544 LAWY B. Ed. Robert Wijffels. bk.rev.; charts; illus.; stat.; index. circ. 1,000. (back issues avail.) **Indexed:** ELLIS.
    —BLDSC (3830.320000).

380.5   IT
EUROTRANSPORTS; mensile di tecnica ed economia del trasporto. 1961. m. L.45000. Edizioni Andrea Latorre s.a.s., Via Giovanni Rotondi 3, 20145 Milan, Italy. TEL 02-4625381. FAX 02-4697561. Ed. Michele Latorre. adv.: B&W page L.3000000. bk.rev.; abstr.; bibl.; charts; illus.; mkt.; pat.; stat. circ. 25,000. **Document type:** trade publication. Incorporates: Container in Italia e nel Mondo (ISSN 0010-7352) & Eurotransports Illustrato (ISSN 0014-3251)

EVALUATING YOUR FIRM'S INJURY & ILLNESS RECORD. TRANSPORTATION & PUBLIC UTILITIES INDUSTRIES. see OCCUPATIONAL HEALTH AND SAFETY

(YEAR) EXPEDITED CARRIERS NETWORK GUIDE. see BUSINESS AND ECONOMICS — Trade And Industrial Directories

TRANSPORTATION

380.5 CN ISSN 0838-5416
EXPEDITEUR. 1988. 10/yr. Can.$35($40) Editions Bomart Ltee., 7493 TransCanada Hwy., Ste. 103, St. Laurent, PQ H4T 1T3, Canada. TEL 514-337-9043. FAX 514-337-1862. Ed. Steve Bouchard; Pub. Pierre Gravel. adv. contact: Marc Duhamel. circ. 10,792 (controlled). **Document type:** trade publication.
   Description: Covers the latest developments on the shipping scene, profiling their technical, economical or social dimensions.

388.3 340 UK
F T A YEARBOOK OF ROAD TRANSPORT LAW. 1963. a. £27. Freight Transport Association Ltd., Hermes House, St. Johns Rd., Tunbridge Wells, Kent TN4 9UZ, England. TEL 01892-26171. FAX 01892-34989. TELEX 957158. adv. circ. 21,000. **Document type:** trade publication.
   Formerly (until 1993): F T A Yearbook (ISSN 0306-1523).

320 CN
F Y I. (For Your Information) 1967. bi-m. free to qualified personnel. Trans Mountain Pipe Line Company Ltd., 1333 W Broadway, Ste. 900, Vancouver, B.C. V6H 4C2, Canada. TEL 604-739-5000. FAX 604-739-5004. Ed. E. Fitz-Morris. stat. circ. 500. (back issues avail.) **Document type:** newsletter.

388.346 US ISSN 0360-3024
TL298
FAMILY MOTOR COACHING. 1963. m. $27. (Family Motor Coach Association) Famoco Corporation, 8291 Clough Pike, Cincinnati, OH 45244. TEL 513-474-3622. FAX 513-474-2332. Ed. Pamela Kay. adv. contact: Virginia Bauman. bk.rev.; index. circ. 99,500.
   Description: Publishes travel articles of particular interest to motorhome travelers, along with technical information concerning mechanics, coach housekeeping, and the latest RV products and accessories.

380.5 US ISSN 0162-1106
FEDERAL CARRIERS REPORTS. 4 base vols. (plus fortn. updates). $1065. Commerce Clearing House, Inc., 4025 W. Peterson Ave., Chicago, IL 60646. TEL 312-583-8500.

FEMNET. see WOMEN'S INTERESTS

388.322 SP
FENEBUS. 1979. 6/yr. free. Orense 20, 2o planta, 28020 Madrid, Spain. TEL 1-555-20-93. FAX 1-555-20-95. Ed. J. Pertierra Rodriguez. adv. circ. 5,000. **Document type:** bulletin.

FIETS. see SPORTS AND GAMES — Bicycles And Motorcycles

380.5 IE ISSN 0957-7998
FLEET MANAGEMENT MAGAZINE. 1989. 10/yr. I£23. 13 Ranelagh Village, Ranelagh, Dublin 6, Ireland. TEL 01-4976050. FAX 01-4967408. Ed. Phillip O'Kelly. bk.rev. circ. 5,300. **Document type:** trade publication.
   Description: Transportation information for Ireland, circulated to fleet managers, distribution managers, and haulers.

380.5 UK ISSN 0953-8526
FLEET NEWS. 1978. w. £60. E M A P - Response Publishing Ltd., Wentworth House, Wentworth St., Peterborough, Cambs. PE1 1DS, England. TEL 01733-63100. Ed. Mike Gunnell. adv.; bk.rev. circ. 26,500. **Document type:** trade publication.

380.5 US ISSN 0547-888X
FLEET SAFETY NEWSLETTER. 1966. bi-m. $19 to non-members; members $15. National Safety Council, Periodicals Department, 1121 Spring Lake Dr., Itasca, IL 60143. TEL 708-775-2281. Ed. Kathy Henderson. **Document type:** newsletter.
   Former titles: Safety Newsletter: Fleet Safety; Safety Newsletter: Commercial Vehicle Section.

380.5 629.288 AT ISSN 0312-4681
FLEETLINE. 1976. bi-m. Aus.$34.50. Historic Commercial Vehicle Association Co-Op, G.P.O. Box 1010, Sydney, N.S.W. 2001, Australia. FAX 61-2-858-1137. Ed. Ian Hammond. adv.; bk.rev. circ. 450.
   Description: Provides current news regarding buses in Australia as well as historical articles.

388 SA
FLEETWATCH; South Africa's only fleet risk management journal. 1993. bi-m. R.8.50 per issue. (South African Transport Security Association) Newslink, P.O. Box 3097, Honeydew 2040, South Africa. adv.; illus. **Document type:** trade publication.

388.3 US ISSN 0092-0177
HE5633.F6
FLORIDA. DIVISION OF MOTOR VEHICLES. TAGS AND REVENUE. 1928. a. free. Department of Highway Safety and Motor Vehicles, Division of Administrative Services, Neil Kirkman Bldg., Tallahassee, FL 32304. TEL 904-488-6084. Ed.Bd. circ. 1,000.

FLORIDA MOTOR VEHICLE LAWS. see LAW

FOERDERMITTEL-JOURNAL; Materialfluss, Lager, Transport und Verpackung. see MACHINERY

380 SZ ISSN 0259-6768
FOERDERTECHNIK. (Text in German) 12/yr. 90 SFr. Industrie-Verlag AG, Muehlebachstr. 43, CH-8032 Zurich, Switzerland. Ed. J. Kistler. adv.; charts; illus. circ. 7,000. **Document type:** trade publication.
   Formerly: Wirtschaft und Technik im Transport (ISSN 0049-6820)

FRACHT - DIENST. see TRANSPORTATION — Ships And Shipping

380.5 380.5 GW
FRACHT UND MATERIALFLUSS. Abbreviated title: F. M. m. (with 2 double issues/yr.). Konradin-Verlag Robert Kohlhammer GmbH, Ernst-Mey-Str. 8, 70771 Leinfelden-Echterdingen, Germany. TEL 0711-7594-0. FAX 0711-7594-390. Ed. Peter Werle. adv.: B&W page DM.6780, color page DM.8760; trim 190 x 270. bk.rev.; circ. 16,333 (controlled). (back issues avail.) **Document type:** trade publication.
   Formerly: Fracht Management (ISSN 0342-3042)
   Description: Focuses on in-company and external transport, distribution, storage, transport packaging, materials handling, transshipment and logistics.

354.44 FR ISSN 1245-4699
FRANCE. MINISTERE DE L'EQUIPEMENT, DES TRANSPORTS ET DU TOURISME. BULLETIN OFFICIEL. 1956. 3/m. 338 F. Direction des Journaux Officiels, 26, rue Desaix, 75727 Paris Cedex 15, France. TEL 1-45-78-61-44.
   Former titles (until 1993): France. Ministere de l'Equipement, du Logement, des Transports et de l'Espace. Bulletin Officiel (ISSN 1158-2405); (until 1991): France. Ministere de l'Equipement et du Logement. Bulletin Officiel (ISSN 0990-5405); (until 1988): France. Ministere de l'Equipement, du Logement, de l'Amenagement du Territoire et des Transports. Bulletin Officiel (ISSN 0298-8224); (until 1986): France. Ministere de l'Urbanisme et du Logement et Ministere des Transports et Ministere de l'Environnement. Bulletin Officiel (ISSN 0292-1766); (until 1981): France. Ministere de l'Equipement et des Transports et Ministere du Logement et Ministere de l'Environnement. Bulletin Officiel (ISSN 0292-1758); 04432472278); (until 1978): France. Ministere de l'Environnement et du Cadre de Vie et Ministere des Transports. Bulletin Officiel (ISSN 0154-0033); (until 1978): France. Ministere de l'Equipement et de l'Amenagement du Territoire. Bulletin Officiel (ISSN 0399-0281); (until 1977): France. Ministere de l'Equipement. Bulletin Officiel (ISSN 0397-4731); (until 1976): Ministere de l'Equipement et Secretariat d'Etat aux Transports. Bulletin Officiel (ISSN 0337-8624); (until 1974): France. Ministere de l'Amenagement du Territoire de l'Equipement du Logement et du Tourisme et Ministere des Transports (ISSN 1147-1611); (until 1972): France. Ministere de l'Equipement et du Logement. Bulletin Officiel (ISSN 1147-1603); (until 1968): France. Ministere de l'Equipement et Construction et Logement Urbanisme. Bulletin Officiel (ISSN 1147-159X); (until 1966): France. Ministere de la Reconstruction et du Logement. Recueil de Textes (ISSN 0766-7574).

380.5 FR ISSN 0993-1953
FRANCE ROUTES. 1980. m. 2 bis, rue Mercoeur, 75011 Paris, France. TEL 43-67-64-24. FAX 43-67-85-50. Ed. Francis Reyes. circ. 79,588.
   Formerly (until 1988): France Routiers (ISSN 0248-174X)

380.5 UK ISSN 0016-0849
FREIGHT. 1945. m. £27. Freight Transport Association Ltd., Hermes House, St. John's Rd., Tunbridge Wells, Kent TN4 9UZ, England. TEL 01892-26171. FAX 01892-34989. TELEX 957158. Ed. Jack Pease. adv.; bk.rev.; circ. 14,989 (controlled). **Indexed:** BMT, HRIS. **Document type:** trade publication.
   —BLDSC (4033.460000).
   Formerly: Industrial Road Transport.

380.52
FREIGHT HANDLER. 1981. m. £15. K.A.V. Publicity (Glasgow) Ltd., 113 West Regent St., Glasgow G2 2RU, Scotland. TEL 0141-226-3861. Ed. Alistair M. Vallance. adv.; circ. 9,500 (controlled). **Document type:** trade publication.

380.5 UK ISSN 0965-4704
FREIGHT MANAGEMENT INTERNATIONAL. 1966. m. £45 (rest of Europe £49; elsewhere £59) (effective 1995). Freight Management Press Ltd., 230-234 Long Ln., London SE1 4QE, England. TEL 0171-403-4353. FAX 0171-403-0233. TELEX 884595. Ed. Ian Martin Jones. adv.: B&W page £1495, color page £1895; trim 297 x 210; adv. contact: Gavin Nagle. bk.rev. circ. 8,500. (also avail. in microform from UMI; back issues avail.) **Document type:** trade publication.
   —UMI.
   Former titles (until 1991): Freight Management and Distribution Today; Freight Management (ISSN 0016-0873).
   Description: Directed to senior executives in industry with distribution job functions.

380.5 US ISSN 1073-7383
FREIGHT MANAGEMENT REPORT; the independent monthly newsletter on issues affecting freight transportation management. 1983. m. $135. Transportation Research Associates, Box 4150, Toms River, NJ 08756-4150. TEL 908-505-0970. Ed. Thomas F. Dillon; Pub. Thomas F. Dillon. index; circ. 100 (paid). (back issues avail.) **Document type:** newsletter.
   Formerly: Freight Marketing Report (ISSN 0892-3566)

380.5 IE
THE FREIGHT OBSERVER. 10/yr. Strand House, Strand St., Malahide, Co. Dublin, Ireland. TEL 450928. Ed. Colin Walsh.

388 SA
FREIGHT WORLD'S WHO GOES WHERE; a directory of freight services in Africa. Running title: Who Goes Where Directory. 1992. a. R.60 (effective 1994). Bowford Publications, P.O. Box 835, Kempton Park 1620, South Africa. **Document type:** trade publication, directory.

380.5 UK
GARAGE & TRANSPORT SELECTOR. 1978. q. Nexus Media Ltd., Nexus House, Azalea Dr., Swanley, Kent BR8 8HY, England. TEL 01322-660070. FAX 01322-337633. circ. 48,120. **Document type:** trade publication.

380.5 GW ISSN 0016-5808
T55.3.H3
GEFAEHRLICHE LADUNG; das Gefahrgut Magazin. 1956. m DM.185.05. K.O. Storck Verlag, Stahltwiete 7, 22761 Hamburg, Germany. TEL 040-853292-0. FAX 040-8507758. Ed. Horst Meder. adv.; bk.rev.; bibl.; charts; illus.; index. **Indexed:** INIS Atomind. **Document type:** trade publication.
   —SWETS. CCC.
   Formerly: Gefaehrliche Fracht.

388 604.7 GW ISSN 0944-6117
GEFAHR-GUT. 1993. m. DM.210.80 (foreign DM.223.70) (effective 1995). Heinrich Vogel Fachzeitschriften GmbH, Neumarkterstr. 18, 81669 Munich, Germany. TEL 089-43180385. FAX 089-43180384. Ed. Walter Brickschen. adv.: page DM.4750; trim 185 x 253; adv. contact: Sofie Steuer. bk.rev.; charts; illus.; circ. 6,400. (back issues avail.) **Document type:** bulletin.
   Description: Covers the handling and transportation of hazardous materials and cargo.

380.5 VN ISSN 0866-8345
GIAO THONG-VAN TAI/TRANSPORT. 1962. w. D.1000 (effective Jan. 1995). Ministry of Communications, Transport, Posts and Telegraphs, 1 Nha Tho, Hanoi, Socialist Republic of Vietnam. Ed. Bui Cong Phieu; Pub. Ngo Duc Nguyen. **Document type:** newspaper.
Formerly: Giao thong-Van tai and Buu Dien - Communications, Transport, Posts and Telegraphs.

380.5 FR
GIRAFE; ponts et ouvrages d'art a hauteurs et charges limitees. irreg. 675 F. Lamy S.A., 187-189 Quai de Valmy, 75490 Paris Cedex 10, France. TEL 44-72-13-43. FAX 44-72-13-95. (looseleaf format)
Description: Lists, by department, limitations of bridges.

388 UK
GLASS'S COMMERCIAL VEHICLE CHECK BOOK. a. £22. Glass's Information Services Ltd., Elgin House, St. George's Ave., Weybridge, Surrey KT13 0BX, England. TEL 01932-823823. FAX 01932-846564. (Orders to: Sales and Marketing, St. Martins Ct., 37 Queens Rd., Weybridge, Surrey KT13 9TU, England) adv. **Document type:** trade publication.

GOODS IN TRANSIT. see *LAW — Corporate Law*

380.5 633 US
GRAIN TRANSPORTATION SITUATION. 1981. w. free. U.S. Department of Agriculture, AMS-T&M Division, 1405 Auditors Bldg., Washington, DC 20250. TEL 202-447-6793. Ed. William L. Dunton. (also avail. in microfiche from CIS; reprint service avail. from CIS) Indexed: Amer.Stat.Ind. (1980-). **Document type:** government publication.
Description: Features current happenings within the university community.

380.5 GR
GREECE AND INTERNATIONAL TRANSPORT/ELLAS KAI DIEDNIS METAPHORES; monthly financial magazine. (Text in Greek; summaries in English) 1974. m. Dr.8000($80) (effective 1995-1996); newsstand price: Dr. 600. Athens Publicity Center, 3 Peanon St., Nea Kypseli, 113 63 Athens, Greece. TEL 30-1-8230-631. FAX 30-1-8212-838. Ed. Yiannis E. Papadimitropoulos; Pub. Aspa I. Papadimitropoulos. adv.: B&W page $2400, color page $3400; adv. contact: Christine Zindrou. circ. 5,000. (back issues avail.) **Document type:** trade publication.
Description: Covers all forms of transportation in Greece.

GUIA AEREA Y MARITIMA. see *TRAVEL AND TOURISM*

380.5 VE
GUIA AEREA Y MARITIMA DE VENEZUELA C.A.; Aruba, Curacao y Bonaire. 1968. m. $90. Ministerio de Fomento - Ministry of Public Works, Apdo. 68121, Caracas 1062-A, Venezuela. (Dist. by: Target Group Communications Inc., 7225 N.W. 12th St., 2nd Fl., Miami, FL 33126) Ed. Gregorio Burgana. adv. circ. 5,400.

629.28 MX
GUIA AUTOMOTRIZ. 1954. m. J. Rodriguez & Cia, S.A., Sur 51 No. 118, Col. Ermita, Mexico 13, Mexico. Ed. Juan Rodriguez. adv. circ. 15,000.

388 FR
GUIDE DES COUTS DE TRANSPORT. a. 1445 F. Lamy S.A., 187-189 Quai de Valmy, 75490 Paris Cedex 10, France. TEL 44-72-13-43. FAX 44-72-13-95.

382 337 FR
GUIDE DES PROCEDURES DOUANIERES. a. 1030 F. (effective 1993). Lamy S.A., 187-189 Quai de Valmy, 75490 Paris Cedex 10, France. TEL 44-72-13-43. FAX 44-72-13-95.
Description: Covers duties still existing within the EC and between EC countries and the US, Japan, Eastern Europe and developing countries.

380.5 CN ISSN 0706-9995
GUIDE DU TRANSPORT PAR CAMION. (Text in English, French) 1938. a. Can.$75($85) Editions Bomart Ltee., 7493 TransCanada Hwy., Ste. 103, St. Laurent, PQ H4T 1T3, Canada. TEL 514-337-9043. FAX 514-337-1862. Pub. Pierre Gravel. adv. contact: Raymond Patry. circ. 5,000. **Document type:** trade publication.
Formerly: Guide du Transport.
Description: For the person who wants to receive or ship material between Montreal and most Canadian, American and foreign cities. Lists companies offering products or services related to the transportation industry.

380.5 GW
HANDBUCH DER VERKEHRSUNTERNEHMEN IM V D V. 1952. irreg. price varies. (Verband Deutscher Verkehrsunternehmen) Erich Schmidt Verlag GmbH & Co. (Bielefeld), Viktoriastr. 44A, 33602 Bielefeld, Germany. TEL 0521-583080. (Subscr. to: Postfach 102451, 33524 Bielefeld, Germany) adv. **Document type:** monographic series.
Formerly (until 1994): Handbuch Oeffentlicher Verkehrsbetriebe (ISSN 0073-019X)

380.5 UK ISSN 0143-6864
HAZARDOUS CARGO BULLETIN. 1980. m. £89 (typically set in Jan.). I I R Publications Ltd., 2nd Fl., Market Towers, 1 Nine Elms Ln., London SW8 5NQ, England. TEL 0171-344-3800. FAX 0171-344-3806. Ed. Michael Corkhill; Pub. Stuart Fryer. adv. contact: Veronica Bowden. bk.rev.; bibl.; charts; illus.; stat.; tr.lit. circ. 20,000. (back issues avail.) Indexed: Curr.Pack.Abstr., Fluidex, Int.Packag.Abstr., Packag.Sci.Tech. **Document type:** trade publication.
—BLDSC (4274.396000); SWETS.
Description: Covers the transport, storage and handling of hazardous materials worldwide.

380.5 604.7 US ISSN 0197-3177
HAZARDOUS MATERIALS TRANSPORTATION. (Subseries of: Chemical Regulation Reporter (ISSN 0148-7973)) 1977. m. $624 (effective July 1995). The Bureau of National Affairs, Inc., 1231 25th St., N.W., Washington, DC 20037. TEL 202-452-4200. FAX 202-822-8092. TELEX 285656 BNAI WSH. (Subscr. to: 9435 Key West Ave., Rockville, MD 20850. TEL 800-372-1033) Ed. Bernard S. Charbel. charts; stat. (looseleaf format; back issues avail.)
•Also available online. Vendor(s): NewsNet (EV35).
—CCC.
Description: Covers rules and regulations governing shipment of hazardous material by rail, air, ship, highway and pipeline, including DOT's Hazardous Materials Tables and EPA's rules for its hazardous waste tracking system.

HAZMAT TRANSPORT NEWS. see *ENVIRONMENTAL STUDIES — Waste Management*

380.5 SZ ISSN 1351-7848
HEAVY VEHICLE SYSTEMS. (Text in English) 1993. q. DM.400 ($215 in N. America). (International Association for Vehicle Design) Inderscience Enterprises Ltd., World Trade Centre Bldg., 110 Ave. Louiss Casai, Case Postale 306, CH-1215 Geneva-Aeroport, Switzerland. FAX 022-7910885. Ed. M.A. Dorgham. **Document type:** academic/scholarly publication.
—BLDSC (4282.165000); Ei.
Description: Provides a source of information and an international forum in the field of on-off road heavy vehicle systems.
Refereed Serial

380.52 UK ISSN 0957-1477
HEREFORD'S AIR CARGO. AMERICAS. 1979. s-a. $100. Maclean Hunter Ltd., Chalk Ln., Cockfosters Rd., Barnet, Herts EN4 0BU, England. TEL 081-975-9759. FAX 081-975-9752. adv.: B&W page £2285, color page £3010; trim 280 x 190. circ. 10,723. **Document type:** directory.
—CCC.
Formed by the merger of: Hereford's Air Freight Handbook. Latin America (ISSN 0267-2332) & Hereford's North America (ISSN 0143-5906)
Description: Lists all known airlines, freight forwarders, charter airlines, and brokers in the Americas region.

TRANSPORTATION 6309

380.52 UK
HEREFORD'S AIR CARGO. ASIA PACIFIC & MIDDLE EAST. s-a. $100. Maclean Hunter Ltd., Maclean Hunter House, Chalk Ln., Cockfosters Rd., Barnet, Herts EN4 0BU, England. TEL 081-975-9759. FAX 081-975-9752. adv.: B&W page £2285, color page £3010; trim 280 x 190. circ. 6,780. **Document type:** directory.

380.52 UK
HEREFORD'S AIR CARGO. EUROPE. s-a. $100. Maclean Hunter Ltd., Maclean Hunter House, Chalk Ln., Cockfosters Rd., Barnet, Herts EN4 0BU, England. TEL 081-975-9759. FAX 081-975-9752. adv.: B&W page £2285, color page £3010; trim 280 x 190. circ. 10,544. **Document type:** directory.

380.5 US ISSN 0161-0325
HIGHWAY & VEHICLE - SAFETY REPORT. 1974. fortn. $347 (foreign $372) (effective Sep. 1994). Stamler Publishing Co., 178 Thimble Islands Rd., Box 3367, Branford, CT 06405. TEL 203-488-9808. FAX 203-488-3129. Ed. Julie E. Marsh; Pub. Paul S. Stamler. bk.rev.; abstr.; bibl.; stat. (back issues avail.) **Document type:** newsletter.
Description: Covers new developments in transportation and vehicle safety.

I E E E TRANSACTIONS ON VEHICULAR TECHNOLOGY.
see *ENGINEERING — Electrical Engineering*

I S T A ANNUAL SAFE TRANSIT CONFERENCE. PROCEEDINGS. (International Safe Transit Association) see *PACKAGING*

I T F NEWS. (International Transport Workers' Federation) see *LABOR UNIONS*

388 UK ISSN 1357-6542
▼**I T S - INTELLIGENT TRANSPORT SYSTEMS.** 1995. q. Route One Publishing Ltd., Huntingdon House, 278-280 Huntingdon St., Nottingham NG1 3LY, England. TEL 0115-9508098. FAX 0115-9508120. Ed. David Crawford. adv. contact: John Williamson. **Document type:** trade publication.

625.7 US ISSN 0192-3994
I T S REVIEW. 1977. q. free. University of California at Berkeley, Institute of Transportation Studies, 109 McLaughlin Hall, Berkeley, CA 94720. TEL 510-642-3593. FAX 510-642-1246. Ed. Betsy Wing. illus. circ. 5,000. **Document type:** newsletter.
Supersedes: I T S Bulletin.

ILLINOIS VEHICLE CODE. see *LAW*

IN TRANSIT. see *LABOR UNIONS*

380.5 US ISSN 0888-8493
INBOUND LOGISTICS. 1981. 12/yr. Thomas Publishing Company, Five Penn Plaza, 8th Fl., 250 W. 34th St., New York, NY 10001. TEL 212-290-7336. FAX 212-629-1584. Ed. Richard S. Sexton. adv. circ. 43,000.
—CCC.
Former titles (until July 1985): Inbound Traffic Guide; Thomas Register's Inbound Traffic Guide.
Description: Controlling and buying inbound freight services and equipment.

388 II ISSN 0019-4956
INDIAN INSTITUTE OF ROAD TRANSPORT. MONTHLY BULLETIN. (Text in English) 1953. m. Rs.20($6) Indian Institute of Road Transport, Best House, P.O. Box 192, Bombay 400 039, India. Ed. C.D. Jeffereis. adv.; bk.rev.; charts; illus.; index. circ. 1,300.

380.5 II
INDIAN JOURNAL OF TRANSPORT MANAGEMENT. 1966. m. Rs.180 (foreign $45). Association of State Road Transport Undertakings, CIRT Bldg., Pune-Nasik Rd., Pune 411 026, India. TEL 0212-779177. FAX 0212-779426. TELEX 146-212 CIRT IN. Ed. M.K. Thomas. adv.: B&W page Rs.1800, color page $2400. bk.rev.; abstr.; charts; illus.; stat. circ. 2,200. **Document type:** academic/scholarly publication.
—CCC.
Formerly: Journal of Transport Management (ISSN 0970-4736); Supersedes (in Aug. 1977): State Transport News (ISSN 0039-016X)
Description: Publishes research articles and papers pertaining to all modes of transportation management with special reference to bus transport.

6310 TRANSPORTATION

INDUSTRIAL HANDLING & STORAGE. see *MACHINERY*

INFORMACION; imagen nacional e internacional de comunicaciones y transportes. see *COMMUNICATIONS*

384   FR   ISSN 0020-0298
INFORMATION TRANSPORTS; bulletin d'information marketing juridique et informatique. 1933. bi-m. 120 F. (foreign 150 F.). 57 rue de Soissons, 33000 Bordeaux, France. TEL 56-56-30-30. Ed. Alain Ricard. adv.; charts. circ. 3,500.
—CCC.

380.5   GW   ISSN 0931-1688
INFORMATIONDIENST VERKEHR. 1980. q. DM.40. Arbeitskreis Verkehr und Umwelt e.V. (Umkehr), Exerzierstr. 20, 13357 Berlin, Germany. TEL 030-4927473. FAX 030-4927972. adv.; bk.rev.; bibl.; illus.; stat. circ. 1,400. (back issues avail.) Document type: newsletter.

352.7   FR
INFOS FEDERALES. no.83, 1981. q. Federation des Travaux Publics et des Transports, 46 rue des Petites-Ecuries, 75010 Paris, France. Ed. Rene Valladon. bk.rev.; charts; illus.; stat.
Formerly: Federation des Travaux Publics et des Transports. Revue (ISSN 0046-3523)

380.5   FR   ISSN 0984-3086
INFOS - ROUTE. 1987. 10/yr. Editions Franc'Albert, 8 rue de la Bergere, 25000 Besancon, France. TEL 81-52-74-53. FAX 81-52-08-05. Ed. Frances Jurion. circ. 3,000.

INFRASTRUCTUUR, TRANSPORT EN LOGISTIEK. see *HOUSING AND URBAN PLANNING*

380.5   US
INSIDE D O T & TRANSPORTATION WEEK. w. $697 (foreign $777). King Publishing Group, Inc., 627 National Press Bldg., Washington, DC 20045. TEL 202-638-4260. FAX 202-662-9744. Ed. Rupert Welch. Document type: newsletter.
●Also available online. Vendor(s): Lexis-Nexis, NewsNet (GT41).
Description: Monitors the Dept. of Transportation, its disbursement of funds, and its regulatory policy. Follows major issues affecting mass transit, airline regulation, FAA technical requirements, commuter transportation and new technologies.

380.5   AU   ISSN 1017-2750
INSTITUT FUER VERKEHRSWESEN. MITTEILUNGEN. 1970. irreg. Universitaet fuer Bodenkultur, Institut fuer Verkehrswesen, Gregor-Mendel-Str. 33, A-1180 Vienna, Austria. TEL 01-476545300. FAX 01-476545344. Ed. Dr. E. Marx. index; circ. 400. (back issues avail.) Document type: academic/scholarly publication.
Formerly (until 1989): Institut fuer Geotechnik und Verkehrsbau. Mitteilungen (ISSN 0379-1483)

INSTITUTION OF CIVIL ENGINEERS. PROCEEDINGS. TRANSPORT. see *ENGINEERING — Civil Engineering*

388   PL
INSTYTUT TRANSPORTU SAMOCHODOWEGO. ZESZYTY NAUKOWE. (Text in Polish; contents in English, German, Russian) 1962. irreg. (approx. 2-3/yr.) free. Instytut Transportu Samochodowego, Ul. Jagiellonska 80, Warsaw, Poland. TEL 48-22-113231. FAX 48-22-110906. TELEX 813316 ITS PL. Ed. L. Stepniak. bk.rev.; illus.; stat.; pat.; circ. controlled. Document type: trade publication.

INTERCHANGE (ROCKVILLE). see *LABOR UNIONS*

380   US
INTERMODAL FORUM. q. $15. Containerization & Intermodal Institute, c/o Barbara Spector Yeninas, Exec. Dir., 185 Fairfield Ave., Ste. 2-D, Box 1593, North Caldwell, NJ 07007-1593. TEL 201-226-0160. Ed. Marc Felice. Document type: trade publication.

380.5   UK   ISSN 0953-928X
INTERMODAL NORTH AMERICA YEARBOOK. 1987. a. $160. Mundy Perry Ltd., 102-108 Clerkenwell Rd., London EC1M 5SA, England. TEL 0171-417-0073. FAX 0171-417-0075. Ed. David Robinson. circ. 6,241. (back issues avail.) Document type: trade publication.

380.52   US   ISSN 0882-8059
INTERMODAL REPORTER; news and analysis of the intermodal industry. 1985. s-m. $230 in U.S.; Canada $235; elsewhere $240. K - III Press, Inc., 424 W. 33rd St., New York, NY 10001. TEL 800-221-5488. FAX 212-695-5025. Ed. Robert J. Kursar. adv. circ. 1,100.
Description: Specializes in news, trends and analysis of the industry. Contains insight on equipment usage, rail policy, legislation, court rulings, pricing, labor liability, service innovations and technology.

658.7   US   ISSN 1076-9293
TA1215
INTERMODAL SHIPPING; serving the intermodal industry. 1965. m. $42 (foreign $102). Argus Inc., 6151 Powers Ferry Rd., N.W., Atlanta, GA 30339-2941. TEL 404-955-2500. FAX 404-955-0400. Ed. Herb Schild. adv.; bk.rev.; charts; illus.; pat.; stat.; tr.lit. circ. 22,290. (also avail. in microform from UMI; reprint service avail. from UMI) Indexed: Curr.Pack.Abstr., Int.Packag.Abstr., Key to Econ.Sci. Document type: trade publication.
—UMI. CCC.
Formerly: Container News (ISSN 0010-7360)
Description: Covers the worldwide container and intermodal shipping industry (transportation by ocean, rail, truck and air carriers).

380.5   UK   ISSN 0141-9501
INTERNATIONAL DISTRIBUTION & HANDLING REVIEW. 1971. bi-m. £98 (overseas £120). National Materials Handling Centre, Cranfield University, Cranfield, Bedford MK43 0AL, England. TEL 01234-750323. FAX 01234-752040. TELEX 825072-CITECH-G. Ed. H.P. Keeble. bk.rev.; index. Document type: abstracting/indexing.
Description: Offers information and abstracts relating to storage, handling, distribution and logistics.

343.09 341.7   NE
▼**INTERNATIONAL ENCYCLOPAEDIA OF LAWS. TRANSPORT LAW.** (Text in English) 1994. base vol. (plus irreg. updates). Kluwer Law International (Subsidiary of: Wolters Kluwer N.V.), Postbus 85889, 2508 CN The Hague, Netherlands. TEL 31-70-3081500. FAX 31-70-3081515. (Dist. by: Libresso Distribution Centre, P.O. Box 23, 7400 GA Deventer, Netherlands. TEL 31-5700-33155. FAX 31-5700-33834; In N. America: Kluwer Law International, 675 Massachusetts Ave., Cambridge, MA 02139. TEL 617-354-0140. FAX 617-354-8595) Ed. Marc A. Huybrechts. (looseleaf format) Document type: monographic series.
Description: Discusses all aspects of transport law at the international level and for individual countries, including maritime law, inland navigation, transport by air, rail, and road, and multimodal transport.

380.5   UK   ISSN 0032-5007
INTERNATIONAL FREIGHTING WEEKLY; sea, air, rail, road. 1962. w. £55. Maclean Hunter Ltd., Maclean Hunter House, Chalk Lane, Cockfosters Rd., Barnet, Herts EN4 0BU, England. TEL 081-242-3000. FAX 081-242-3185. TELEX 299072-MACHUN-G. Ed. R. Hailey. adv.; bk.rev.; charts; illus.; stat.; tr.lit. circ. 17,756. (tabloid format) Indexed: BMT, PROMT. Document type: trade publication.
—BLDSC (4540.370000).
Incorporating: Ports and Terminals - International Freighting.

629   UK   ISSN 1358-8265
▼**INTERNATIONAL JOURNAL OF CRASHWORTHINESS.** Announced for publication in 1996. q. £185($315) (effective 1996). Woodhead Publishing Ltd., Abington Hall, Abington, Cambridge CB1 6AH, England. TEL 44-1223-891358. FAX 44-1223-893694. E-mail: woodhead@dial.pipex.com. (Subscr. to: Turpin Distribution Services Ltd., Blackhorse Rd., Letchworth, Herts. SG6 1HN, England. TEL 44-1462-672555. FAX 44-1462-480947) Ed. E.C. Chirwa. Document type: academic/scholarly publication.
Description: Covers all matters relating to crashworthiness of road and rail vehicles, air and spacecraft, ships and submarines, on- and offshore installations.

380.52 658.788   UK   ISSN 0957-476X
CODEN: IJRTER
INTERNATIONAL JOURNAL OF RADIOACTIVE MATERIALS TRANSPORT. 1990. 4/yr. £96($195) (effective 1995). Nuclear Technology Publishing, P.O. Box 7, Ashford, Kent TN23 1YW, England. TEL 01233-641683. FAX 01233-610021. Ed. E.P. Goldfinch. adv. contact: L. Richmond. circ. 1,000. (back issues avail.) Indexed: Energy Info.Abstr., Environ.Abstr., INSPEC (1990-). Document type: trade publication.
—BLDSC (4542.524800); Faxon.
Description: Covers all aspects of the transport of radioactive materials including regulations, package design, safety assessments, testing, accidents and experience in the transport of all forms of radioactive materials.

380.5   IT   ISSN 0391-8440
INTERNATIONAL JOURNAL OF TRANSPORT ECONOMICS/RIVISTA INTERNAZIONALE DI ECONOMICA DEI TRASPORTI. (Text and summaries in English) 1974. 3/yr. L.80000($70) Via Ruggero Bonghi 11-B, 00184 Rome, Italy. Ed. Gianrocco Tucci. adv.; bk.rev.; index. circ. 1,000. (back issues avail.) Indexed: BPIA, C.R.E.J., Geo.Abstr., HRIS, J.of Econ.Lit. Document type: academic/scholarly publication.
—BLDSC (4542.696000); SWETS.

380.5 621   SZ   ISSN 0143-3369
TL1   CODEN: IJVDDW
INTERNATIONAL JOURNAL OF VEHICLE DESIGN; journal of vehicle engineering, automotive technology and components. (Text in English) 1979. bi-m. $290 to N. America; elsewhere DM.500. (International Association for Vehicle Design) Inderscience Enterprises Ltd., World Trade Centre Bldg., 110 Ave. Louis Casai, Case Postale 306, CH-1215 Geneva-Aeroport, Switzerland. FAX 022-7910885. (Co-sponsor: Unesco) Ed. M.A. Dorgham. adv.; bk.rev.; abstr.; charts; illus.; keyword index. circ. 10,000. Indexed: A.I.Abstr., Agri.Eng.Abstr., Appl.Mech.Rev., Br.Tech.Ind., CAD CAM Abstr., Cadscan, Curr.Cont., Energy Info.Abstr., Eng.Ind., Environ.Abstr., Ergon.Abstr., Excerp.Med., HRIS, Ind.Sci.Rev., INSPEC (1992-), Lead Abstr., Met.Abstr., Robomat., Sci.Cit.Ind., Sh.& Vib.Dig., World Alum.Abstr., Zincscan. Document type: academic/scholarly publication.
—BLDSC (4542.697500); Ei; Faxon; Genuine Article; SWETS; UnCover. CCC.
Description: Contains articles on the engineering design, research into and development of all types of self-propelled vehicles and their components. Includes reports of events, technical notes, and readers' letters.

INTERNATIONAL SYMPOSIUM ON THE AERODYNAMICS AND VENTILATION OF VEHICLE TUNNELS. PROCEEDINGS. see *ENGINEERING — Civil Engineering*

380.5   SZ
INTERNATIONAL TRANSPORT JOURNAL - OVERSEAS DIGEST. French edition: Journal pour le Transport International. German edition: Internationale Transport Zeitschrift. 1939. w. 170 SFr. Rittman Ltd., Spalentorweg 9, Postfach, CH-4003 Basel, Switzerland. TEL 061-2618830. FAX 061-2610878. TELEX 962217. adv.; B&W page 4500 SFr.; trim 184 x 268. circ. 27,900.

INTERNATIONAL TRANSPORT WORKERS' FEDERATION REPORT ON ACTIVITIES. see *LABOR UNIONS*

386   BE   ISSN 0074-9311
INTERNATIONAL UNION FOR INLAND NAVIGATION. ANNUAL REPORT. (Editions in French, German) 1953. a. free to members. International Union for Inland Navigation - Union Internationale de la Navigation Fluviale, 19 rue de la Presse, 1000 Brussels, Belgium. TEL 32-2-88362844. FAX 32-2-88370482. Document type: corporate report.

388 BE
INTERNATIONAL UNION OF PUBLIC TRANSPORT. REPORTS OF THE CONGRESSES. French edition: Union Internationale des Transports Publics. Rapports des Congres. German edition: Internationaler Verband fuer Oeffentliches Verkehrswesen. Berichte zu den Kongressen. 1885. biennial. price varies. International Union of Public Transport, Av. de l'Uruguay 19, B-1050 Brussels, Belgium. TEL 322-673-6100. FAX 322-660-1072. TELEX 63916 UITP B. Ed. P. Laconte. adv. circ. 18,000. **Document type:** proceedings.
 Formerly: International Union of Public Transport. Technical Reports of the Congresses.
 Description: Deals with all problems of the urban and regional public transport.

625.5 AU
INTERNATIONALE SEILBAHN-RUNDSCHAU/INTERNATIONAL AERIAL LIFT REVIEW. (Text in French and German) 8/yr. S.1136. (Organizzazione Internationale dei Trasporti a Fune) Bohmann Druck und Verlag GmbH & Co. KG, Leberstr. 122, A-1110 Vienna, Austria. TEL 0222-74095-0. FAX 0222-74095-183. TELEX 132312. Ed. Gerda Stockhammer. adv.; B&W page S.26200, color page S.39800; trim 185 x 270; adv. contact: Christina Ruckenbauer. abstr.; charts; illus. circ. 6,700. **Document type:** trade publication.
 Formerly: Internationale Berg- und Seilbahn-Rundschau (ISSN 0253-3715)

380.5 SZ ISSN 0020-9341
INTERNATIONALE TRANSPORT ZEITSCHRIFT/JOURNAL POUR LE TRANSPORT INTERNATIONAL/INTERNATIONAL TRANSPORT JOURNAL-OVERSEAS DIGEST. (Editions in French, German; summaries in English) 1939. w. 220 SFr. Rittman Ltd., Spalentorweg 9, Postfach, CH-4003 Basel, Switzerland. TEL 061-2618830. FAX 061-2610878. TELEX 962217-TRA-CH. adv.: B&W page 3600 SFr.; trim 184 x 268. bk.rev.; illus. circ. 20,200 (9,600 French ed.; 10,600 German ed.). **Indexed:** PROMT. **Document type:** trade publication.

380.5 SP ISSN 0213-3091
INTER-TRANSPORT. 1970. w. 14800 ptas. Publicaciones Men-Car, S.A., Paseo de Colon, 24, 08002 Barcelona, Spain. TEL 93-301-5516. FAX 93-318-6645. Eds. Juan Cardona, Manuel Cardona. adv.; illus.; stat. circ. 13,500. (back issues avail.)
 Formerly: Men-Car, Guia de Medios de Transporte Internacional.

ISTITUTO ITALIANO DI NAVIGAZIONE. ATTI. see AERONAUTICS AND SPACE FLIGHT

380.5 RU ISSN 0134-7799
HE255 CODEN: INOTE6
ITOGI NAUKI I TEKHNIKI: ORGANIZATSIYA UPRAVLENIYA TRANSPORTOM. irreg., vol.8, 1989. 5.40 Rub. Vsesoyuznyi Institut Nauchno-Tekhnicheskoi Informatsii (VINITI), Baltiiskaya ul. 14, Moscow A-219, Russia.
 —BLDSC (0128.198500).

380.52 RU ISSN 0202-7909
ITOGI NAUKI I TEKHNIKI: PROMYSHLENNYI TRANSPORT. irreg., vol.12, 1988. 6.60 Rub. Vsesoyuznyi Institut Nauchno-Tekhnicheskoi Informatsii (VINITI), Baltiiskaya ul. 14, Moscow A-219, Russia. (Subscr. to: Mezhdunarodnaya Kniga, Dimitrova ul. 39, 113095 Moscow, Russia)
 —BLDSC (0134.425000).

388.32 SW
ITRAFIK - MED BUSS I TRAFIK. 1985. 11/yr. SEK 440; newsstand price: SEK 40. Fateco Foerlag AB, Propellervaegen 4A, S-183 62 Taeby, Sweden. TEL 46-8-756-55-05. FAX 46-8-756-55-05. Ed. Tiit Tamme. adv.: B&W page SEK 13500, color page SEK 19000; trim 195 x 265; adv. contact: Rose-Marie Eriksson. circ. 6,900. cols./p.: 4; pp./issue: 80. **Document type:** trade publication.

380.5 UK ISSN 0263-8460
JANE'S URBAN TRANSPORT SYSTEMS. 1982. a. £190($300) Jane's Information Group, Sentinel House, 163 Brighton Rd., Coulsdon, Surrey CR5 2NH, England. TEL 0181-763-1030. FAX 0181-763-1006. TELEX 916907-JANES-G. E-mail: http://www.janes.com/janes.html. (U.S. & Can. subscr. to: Dept. DSM, 1340 Braddock Pl., Ste. 300, Box 1436, Alexandria, VA 22314-1651) Ed. Chris Bushell; Pub. Robert Hutchinson. adv. contact: Richard West. index. **Document type:** trade publication.
 ●Also available on CD-ROM.
 —BLDSC (4647.120000).
 Description: Comprehensive survey of urban transport systems and equipment manufacturers worldwide.

JARMUVEK, MEZOGAZDASAGI GEPEK; motorok, vasuti jarmuvek, kozuti jarmuvek, hajok, mezogazdasagi gepek, epitoipari gepek, repulogepek. see ENGINEERING — Mechanical Engineering

380.5 BL ISSN 0100-4891
JORNAL DOS TRANSPORTES.* vol.4, 1974. bi-m. Ministerio dos Transportes, Esplanado dos Ministerios, Bloco 9, Brasilia, Brazil. Ed. Walter Duarte. adv.; illus.

388 629.04 US ISSN 0197-6729
TF1300 CODEN: JATRDC
JOURNAL OF ADVANCED TRANSPORTATION. 1967. 3/yr. $80 (foreign $90). (Advanced Transit Association) Institute for Transportation, Inc., Duke University, Box 90304, Durham, NC 27706-0304. TEL 919-660-5312. FAX 919-660-8963. Eds. Charles M. Harman. abstr.; bibl.; charts; illus.; stat.; circ. 800 (paid). (also avail. in microform from MIM,UMI; reprint service avail. from UMI) **Indexed:** Appl.Mech.Rev.; Br.Rail.Bd.; Eng.Ind.; Fluidex, HRIS, Hwy.Res.Abstr. **Document type:** academic/scholarly publication.
 —Ei; Faxon; Genuine Article; SWETS; UMI; UnCover.
 Formerly (until vol.12, 1979): High Speed Ground Transportation Journal (ISSN 0018-1501)
 Description: Includes articles for practitioners and scholars principally on advances in planning, engineering, operations and economics of mass transportation.

JOURNAL OF COMMERCE, INDUSTRY & TRANSPORTATION. see BUSINESS AND ECONOMICS — Domestic Commerce

JOURNAL OF MOTOR VEHICLE LAW. see LAW

JOURNAL OF SAFETY RESEARCH. see OCCUPATIONAL HEALTH AND SAFETY

JOURNAL OF SHIPPING, CUSTOMS, AND TRANSPORT LAW. see LAW

621.9 UK ISSN 0022-4898
TE208.5 CODEN: JTRMAF
JOURNAL OF TERRAMECHANICS. 1964. bi-m. £290($462) (effective 1996). (International Society for Terrain Vehicle Systems) Elsevier Science Ltd., Pergamon, P.O. Box 800, Kidlington, Oxford OX5 1DX, England. TEL 44-1865-843000. FAX 44-1865-843010. E-mail: nlinfo-f@elsevier.nl; usinfo-f@elsevier.com; forinfo-kyf04035@niftyserve.or.jp; Site addr.: http://www.elsevier.nl/. (Subcr. in U.S. and Canada to: Elsevier Science, 660 White Plains Rd., Tarrytown, NY 10591-5153. TEL 914-524-9200. FAX 914-333-2444) Ed. John R. Radforth. adv.; bk.rev.; abstr.; charts; illus.; pat.; tr.lit.; cum.index. circ. 1,100. (also avail. in microform from UMI; back issues avail.) **Indexed:** Agri.Eng.Abstr., Appl.Mech.Rev., Curr.Cont., Excerp.Med., GeoRef, Geotech.Abstr. **Document type:** academic/scholarly publication.
 —BLDSC (5069.030000); Ei; Faxon; Genuine Article; SWETS; UMI; UnCover. CCC.
 Description: Covers recent research and developments in off-road locomotion, soil excavation, and related engineering aspects, including vehicle design, construction, maintenance and operation.
 Refereed Serial

380.5 330 UK ISSN 0022-5258
HE1 CODEN: JTEPEV
JOURNAL OF TRANSPORT ECONOMICS AND POLICY. 1967. 3/yr. £48($94) University of Bath, Claverton Down, Bath BA2 7AY, England. TEL 01225-826302. FAX 01225-826767. (Co-sponsor: London School of Economics and Political Science) Ed. S. Glaister. adv. contact: Kay Millard. bk.rev.; index. circ. 1,300. (back issues avail.) **Indexed:** ABI Inform, BMT, BPIA, Br.Rail.Bd., C.R.E.J., Curr.Cont., Geo.Abstr., HRIS, J.of Econ.Lit., P.A.I.S., Risk Abstr., Rural Recreat.Tour.Abstr., SSCI, World Agri.Econ.& Rural Sociol.Abstr. **Document type:** academic/scholarly publication.
 —BLDSC (5069.900000); Faxon; Genuine Article; SWETS; UMI; UnCover.

380.5 900 UK ISSN 0022-5266
HE1
JOURNAL OF TRANSPORT HISTORY. 1953; N.S.1971. s-a. £30($55) to individuals; institutions £65($120). Manchester University Press, Oxford Rd., Manchester M13 9PL, England. TEL 061-273-5539. FAX 061-274-3346. TELEX 666517-UNIMAN. Ed. John Armstrong; Pub. Francis Brooke. adv. contact: Matthew Branton. bk.rev.; bibl.; illus. circ. 600. (back issues avail.) **Indexed:** Amer.Hist.& Life, Br.Hum.Ind., Geo.Abstr., Hist.Abstr., Mid.East: Abstr.& Ind. **Document type:** academic/scholarly publication.
 —BLDSC (5070.000000); Faxon; SWETS; UMI. CCC.
 Description: History of transport from a social and economic perspective.

629.04 US ISSN 0733-947X
TA1001 CODEN: JTPEDI
JOURNAL OF TRANSPORTATION ENGINEERING. 1969. bi-m. $124 to non-members (foreign $137); members $31 (foreign $44). American Society of Civil Engineers, Air Transport, Highway, Pipeline, Urban Transportation Divisions, 345 E. 47th St., New York, NY 10017-2398. TEL 212-705-7288. FAX 212-980-4681. Ed. Kumares C. Sinha. circ. 4,000. **Indexed:** A.S.& T.Ind., BMT, CAD CAM Abstr., Curr.Cont., Deep Sea Res.& Oceanogr.Abstr., Dok.Str., E&P Hlth. (1993-), Energy Info.Abstr., Eng.Ind., Environ.Abstr., Environ.Per.Bibl., Excerp.Med., Fluidex, Gas Abstr., Gas Process.& Ppl. (1993-), GeoRef., HRIS, IDA, Ind.Sci.Rev., Intl.Civil Eng.Abstr., Off.Tech. (1993-), Petrol.Abstr. (1974-), Soft.Abstr.Eng., W.R.C.Inf. **Document type:** academic/scholarly publication.
 —BLDSC (5070.350000); CIS; Ei; Faxon; Genuine Article; SWETS; UMI; UnCover. CCC.
 Former titles: Journal of Transportation and Pipeline Engineering; Transportation Engineering Journal (ISSN 0569-7891); American Society of Civil Engineers. Transportation Engineering Division. Journal (ISSN 0044-801X)
 Description: Technical and professional articles on planning, design, construction, maintenance and operation of air, highway, and urban transportation, as well as pipeline facilities for water, oil and gas.
 Refereed Serial

388 SW
K F B KOMMUNIKE. 1985. bi-m. SEK 120 (students SEK 80). Kommunikationsforskningsberedningen (K F B), P.O. Box 5706, S-114 87 Stockholm, Sweden. TEL 46-8-459-17-00. FAX 46-8-662-63-90. E-mail: tina.esh@kfb.se. Ed. Tina Esh. adv.; bk.rev. circ. 5,000. **Document type:** government publication, academic/scholarly publication, trade publication.
 Former titles (until 1994): Forum foer Kommunikationsforskning; (until 1993): Transportforskningsnytt (ISSN 1101-900X); (until 1990): T F B - Nytt (ISSN 0282-8030)
 Description: Presentations of R&D sponsored by the Swedish Transport and Communications Research Board (KFB) and its other activities. Overviews of and debate on Swedish transport and communications research. The subject area covers transport, traffic, postal services and telecommunications and their impact on the environment, traffic safety and regional development.

380.5 PK ISSN 0075-5109
HE560.K3
KARACHI PORT TRUST. YEAR BOOK OF INFORMATION, PORT OF KARACHI, PAKISTAN. (Text in English) 1961. a. Rs.50. Karachi Port Trust, Post Box 4725, Karachi, Pakistan. TEL 201305. FAX 2415567. TELEX 2739 KPT PK. Ed. Kafil Ahmed Khan.

TRANSPORTATION

388.322 658.8   UK   ISSN 0963-4401
KEY NOTE REPORT: BUS & COACH OPERATORS. Variant title: Bus and Coach Operators. 1986. irreg. £185. Key Note Publications Ltd., Field House, 72 Oldfield Rd., Hampton, Middlesex TW12 2HQ, England. TEL 0181-783-0755. FAX 0181-783-1720. charts; stat. **Document type:** trade publication.
● Also available online.
Also available on CD-ROM.
—BLDSC (2933.021000).
Formerly (until 1989): Business Ratio Report: Bus and Coach Operators (ISSN 0269-6401)

380.5   UK   ISSN 1352-6952
KEY NOTE REPORT: FREIGHT FORWARDING. Variant title: Freight Forwarding. irreg. £185. Key Note Publications Ltd., Field House, 72 Oldfield Rd., Hampton, Middlesex TW12 2HQ, England. TEL 0181-783-0755. FAX 0181-783-1720. **Document type:** trade publication.
● Also available online.
Also available on CD-ROM.

KOMPASS PROFESSIONNEL. TRANSPORTS, MOYENS DE TRANSPORTS. see BUSINESS AND ECONOMICS — Trade And Industrial Directories

623.8025489   DK   ISSN 0106-1232
KOMPASS SELECT EXPORT. TRANSPORT EQUIPMENT. Cover title: Euro Kompass Denmark. Transport Equipment. (Text in Danish, English, French, German and Spanish) 1980. a. DKK 300 (listed companies DKK 100). Forlaget Kompass Danmark, Oeveroedvej 5, DK-2840 Holte, Denmark. TEL 45-45-41-21-00. FAX 45-45-41-06-65. illus. **Document type:** directory.
● Also available on CD-ROM.
Formerly: Kompass Select Denmark. Transport Equipment.

380.5   HU   ISSN 0023-4362
TA1001   CODEN: KOSZAZ
KOZLEKEDESTUDOMANYI SZEMLE. (Summaries in English, French, German, Russian) 1951. m. $38. (Kozlekedestudomanyi Egyesulet) Lapkiado Vallalat, Lenin korut 9-11, 1073 Budapest 7. TEL 222-408. (Subscr. to: Kultura, Box 149, H-1389 Budapest, Hungary) Ed. Bela Czere. charts; illus. **Indexed:** INSPEC, Rural Recreat.Tour.Abstr., World Agri.Econ.& Rural Sociol.Abstr.

380.5   GW   ISSN 0176-9049
KRAFTVERKEHRS HANDBUCH. a. DM.28.04. Verlag Heinrich Vogel, Neumarkterstr. 18, 81673 Munich, Germany. TEL 089-43180-0. FAX 089-4312837. (Subscr. to: Postfach 802020, 81620 Munich, Germany)
Former titles (until 1983): Kraftverkehrs-Kalender (ISSN 0174-1349); (until 1980): Recht des Kraftwagenspediteurs und Gueterkraftverkehrsunternehmers (ISSN 0173-9409)

380.524   DK   ISSN 0108-8335
KRAKS TRANSPORTKATALOG. 1973. a. DKK 260. Kraks Forlag AS, Virumgaardsvej 21, DK-2830 Virum, Denmark. TEL 45-45-83-45-83. FAX 45-45-83-10-11. Ed. D.B. Petersen. adv. contact: Carsten Engsig. circ. 40,000.

380.5   FI   ISSN 1237-2358
KULJETUS - LOGISTIIKKA. 1958. m. FIM 320. Finnish Society for Transport Economy, Katjanokankatu 5 D 14, FIN-00160 Helsinki, Finland. TEL 358-0-179566. FAX 358-0-177675. (Co-sponsor: Finnish Pallet Association) Ed. Kari Litja. adv.: B&W page FIM 6800, color page FIM 11600; trim 210 x 297; adv. contact: Juhani Piipponen. circ. 3,800. **Document type:** trade publication.
Formerly: Kuljetus (ISSN 0023-5091)
Description: For professionals in the transport and materials handling fields.

380.5   UK
L T NEWS. 1973. m. £7 (free to qualified personnel). London Regional Transport, 55 Broadway, Westminster, London SW1H 0BD, England. Ed. A.B. Russell. adv.; bk.rev.; illus. circ. 42,000.
Former titles (until 1990): L R T News; (until 1984): L T News.

LAMY TRANSPORT TOME 1; route. see LAW — International Law

LAMY TRANSPORT TOME 2; douane, commissionnaires de transport, transports maritime, transports par chemin de fer, transports aeriens, lexique. see LAW — International Law

LAMY TRANSPORT TOME 3; marchandises dangereuses. see LAW — International Law

LEONARD'S GUIDE. NATIONAL CONTRACT CARRIERS DIRECTORY. see BUSINESS AND ECONOMICS — Trade And Industrial Directories

LEONARD'S GUIDE. NATIONAL TRANSPORTATION BROKERS DIRECTORY. see BUSINESS AND ECONOMICS — Trade And Industrial Directories

LEONARD'S GUIDE. NATIONAL WAREHOUSE AND DISTRIBUTION DIRECTORY. see BUSINESS AND ECONOMICS — Trade And Industrial Directories

380.5   FR   ISSN 1254-2830
▼**LIAISONS TRANSPORTS.** 1994. m. (10/yr.). 350 F. (foreign 405 F.) (effective 1994-95). Groupe Liaisons, 1, Avenue Edouard Belin, 92856 Rueil-Malmaison Cedex, France. TEL 41-29-99-99. FAX 1-41-29-95-13.

380.5   FR   ISSN 0180-7811
LIAISONS TRANSPORTS EQUIPEMENT. 1977. m. 50 F. Confederation Francaise Democratique du Travail, Federation Generale des Transports et de l'Equipement, 47-49 ave Simon Bolivar, 75950 Paris Cedex 19, France.

LIBERIA. MINISTRY OF COMMERCE, INDUSTRY AND TRANSPORTATION. ANNUAL REPORT. see BUSINESS AND ECONOMICS — Production Of Goods And Services

388.342   IT   ISSN 0024-3779
LINEA Z; quindicinale d'attualita e politica dei trasporti. 1962. fortn. L.7200. Organizzazione Zeppieri, Viale Castro Preto Rio 82, Rome, Italy. Ed. Pietro Zeppieri. adv.; stat. circ. 4,000.
Description: Discusses public transportation topics.

380.5 630   ISSN 1043-1039
LIVE ANIMAL TRADE & TRANSPORT MAGAZINE. q. $20 (foreign $26). Silesia Companies, Inc., Box 441110, Ft. Washington, MD 20749-1110. TEL 301-292-1970. FAX 301-292-1781. circ. 1,750.
Description: Stories on every aspect of animal trade and transport.

380.5   UK   ISSN 0962-6220
LOCAL TRANSPORT TODAY. fortn. £56 (foreign £72). Local Transport Today Ltd. (Subsidiary of: Landor Publishing Ltd.), Quadrant House, 250 Kennington Ln., London SE11 5RD, England. TEL 0171-582-6626. FAX 0171-735-1299. E-mail: 100570,73@compuserve.com. **Document type:** trade publication.
—BLDSC (5290.048910).
Description: Provides information on urban and regional transportation from the viewpoint of planners, policy makers, traffic engineers, and economic and environmental analysts.

LOG TRUCKER. see FORESTS AND FORESTRY — Lumber And Wood

380.5 658   BE
LOGISTIC. (Text in Dutch) 1969. m. Technipress nv, A. Temermanstraat 26, 1731 Zellik, Belgium. TEL 32-2-4660655. FAX 32-2-4660920. adv. **Document type:** trade publication.
Former titles (until 1986): Transport, Handling and Packaging (ISSN 0770-6332); (until 1981): Manutention Emballages - Behandeling Verpakking (ISSN 0770-6383); (until 1974): Industrie Manutention (ISSN 0537-5630)

380.5   IT   ISSN 0394-4867
LOGISTICA; organizzazione, metodi e sistemi. 1970. 10/yr. L.85000 (foreign L.210000) (effective 1995). Tecniche Nuove s.p.a., Via C. Menotti 14, 20129 Milan, Italy. TEL 02-75701. FAX 02-7610351. Ed. G. Nardella. adv.: B&W page L.2280000, color page L.3150000; trim 185 x 266. bk.rev.; abstr.; charts; illus.; pat.; tr.lit. circ. 6,070.
Former titles: Magazzini e Trasporti - Logistica; (until 1971): Magazzini e Trasporti (ISSN 0024-9874)
Description: Information for storage, lifting and material handling technicians.

LOGISTICS AND MATERIALS HANDLING; the magazine for managers. see BUSINESS AND ECONOMICS — Management

380.5   CN   ISSN 0047-4991
U168   CODEN: LGTRA5
LOGISTICS AND TRANSPORTATION REVIEW. 1965. q. $31. University of British Columbia, Centre for Transportation Studies, Vancouver, BC V6T 1Z2, Canada. TEL 604-822-4510. FAX 604-822-8521. TELEX 04-51233. Ed. W.G. Waters. adv.; bk.rev.; charts; illus.; pat.; tr.mk.; index. circ. 1,000. (also avail. in microform; reprint service avail. from UMI) **Indexed:** ABI Inform., BPIA, Bus.Ind., Cont.Pg.Manage., Curr.Cont., Geo.Abstr., HRIS, IDA, INSPEC, J.of Econ.Lit., Maize Abstr., Manage.Cont., Tr.& Indus.Ind., Triticale Abstr., World Agri.Econ.& Rural Sociol.Abstr. **Document type:** academic/scholarly publication.
● Also available online. Vendor(s): University Microfilms International.
—BLDSC (5292.315000); Ei; Faxon; Genuine Article; SWETS; UMI; UnCover. **CCC.**
Former titles: Logistics Review (ISSN 0024-5844); Logistics Review and Military Logistics Journal.

380.5 658   SA
LOGISTICS NEWS. 1981. m. R.80($30) (£20) (effective 1995). Bolton Publications (Pty) Ltd., P.O. Box 966, Parklands 2121, South Africa. TEL 27-11-8803520. FAX 27-11-8806574. Ed. Richard Proctor-Sims. adv. contact: Kamal H. Saad. illus.; circ. 1,125 (paid); 3,408 (controlled). **Document type:** trade publication.
Description: Covers logistics, distribution & materials handling, for industry professionals and logistics executives.

LOGISTIEKKRANT. see BUSINESS AND ECONOMICS — Management

388   US
MCTRANS: CENTER FOR MICROCOMPUTERS IN TRANSPORTATION. NEWSLETTER. q. plus a. catalog. free. University of Florida, Transportation Research Center, 512 Weil Hall, Gainesville, FL 32611-2083. TEL 904-392-0378. FAX 904-392-3224. **Document type:** newsletter, catalog.
● Also available online.
Description: Updates and lists new and improved U.S. government highway transportation and transit software.

380.5   MX
MAS CAMINOS; por un sistema integral de transportes. 1970. m. free. Asociacion Mexicana de Caminos, Tiber 103, 06500 Mexico D.F., Mexico. TEL 207-46-60. adv.; charts; illus. **Indexed:** Dok.Str.
Formerly (until Dec. 1990): Caminos (ISSN 0008-2236)

380.5   US
MASS TRANSIT (BOSTON). 1974. q. $15. Association for Public Transportation, Box 1029, Boston, MA 02205. TEL 617-482-0282. Ed. Anne McKinnon. (back issues avail.) **Document type:** newsletter.
Description: Transit in and around Boston.

380.5   US   ISSN 0364-3484
HE4201
MASS TRANSIT (MELVILLE). 1974. m. $40. P T N Publishing Corp., 445 Broad Hollow Rd., Ste. 21, Melville, NY 11747-4722. TEL 516-845-2700. FAX 516-845-7109. Ed. Faye Guercio. adv.; bk.rev. circ. 18,000. **Indexed:** A.S.& T.Ind., Avery Ind.Archit.Per., B.P.I, Br.Rail.Bd., Dok.Str., HRIS, Ind.Sci.Rev., Tr.& Indus.Ind. **Document type:** trade publication.
—Faxon; SWETS; UMI; UnCover.
Description: Covers urban transportation worldwide, focusing on transit authorities, construction projects, products, suppliers and consultants.

621.86   GW   ISSN 0170-334X
MATERIALFLUSS; Zeitschrift fuer Logisitk-Management, Transport, Lager, Versand. 1969. m. DM.158 (Europe DM.194; overseas DM.254). Verlag Moderne Industrie, Justus-von-Liebig-Str. 1, 86899 Landsberg, Germany. TEL 08191-125-0. FAX 08191-125-483. Ed. Reinhard Irrgang. adv.: B&W page DM.6770; trim 257 x 178; adv. contact: Andreas Gerth. bk.rev.; illus. circ. 14,458. **Document type:** trade publication.
—SWETS. **CCC.**

658.7 380.5   CN   ISSN 0025-5343
MATERIALS MANAGEMENT & DISTRIBUTION. 1956. m. Can.$42. Maclean Hunter Ltd., Business Publication Division, Maclean-Hunter Bldg., 777 Bay St., Toronto, ON M5W 1A7, Canada. TEL 416-596-5720. Ed. Robert Robertson. adv.; bk.rev.; charts; illus.; stat.; tr.lit.; index. circ. 19,500. **Indexed:** Can.B.P.I., Excerp.Med., ISMEC.
—Faxon. CCC.
Formerly: Materials Handling in Canada.

380.5   MF   ISSN 0076-5554
MAURITIUS. MINISTRY OF WORKS AND INTERNAL COMMUNICATIONS. REPORT. a. price varies. Government Printing Office, Elizabeth II Ave., Port Louis, Mauritius. (Subscr. to: La Tour Koenig, Pointe aux Sables, Port Louis, Mauritius. TEL 2345294. FAX 2084011))

380.5   US   ISSN 1057-8196
HE5601
METRO (REDONDO BEACH). 1904. bi-m. (plus Factbook in Oct.) $28 (Canada $38; elsewhere $50). Bobit Publishing Company, 2512 Artesia Blvd., Redondo Beach, CA 90278-3210. TEL 310-376-8788. FAX 310-376-9043. Ed. Cliff Henke. adv.; charts; illus.; stat.; circ. 17,500 (controlled). **Indexed:** HRIS, SRI. **Document type:** trade publication.
—Faxon; UMI; UnCover.
Former titles (1975-1985): Metro Magazine (ISSN 0162-6221); (until 1974): Metropolitan (ISSN 0026-1467)
Description: Management information for transit bus, charter motorcoach and rail transit operations.

380.5   UK
METROLINK IMPACT STUDY. WORKING PAPER. irreg., no.6, 1992. £15. Metrolink Impact Study, University of Salford, Department of Geography, Salford M5 4WT, England. TEL 061-745-5000. FAX 061-745-5999. Co-sponsor: Greater Manchester Passenger Transport Executive) Eds. Liz Fairweather, Emilie Roberts. **Document type:** monographic series.

MICHIGAN MOTOR VEHICLE LAWS; with uniform traffic code. see *LAW*

380.5 330   UK
MIDDLE EAST TRANSPORT. 1977. 10/yr. £25($60) A.F. Productions Ltd., 4 Lindfield Close, Saltdean, Brishton BN2 8AP, England. Ed. Alan Freeman. adv.; bk.rev.; illus.; stat. circ. 6,527. (also avail. in microfilm; back issues avail.) **Indexed:** Key to Econ.SCi.
Former titles (until 1988): Middle East Transport and Telecommunications (ISSN 0268-5906); Middle East Industry and Transport (ISSN 0261-1473); Middle East Transport (ISSN 0140-8313)
Description: Provides freight handling tips.

MINI AUTO. see *HOBBIES*

380.5   UK   ISSN 1352-7754
MINIBUS AND COMMUNITY VEHICLES. 6/yr. £24 (foreign £36). Local Transport Today Ltd. (Subsidiary of: Landor Publishing Ltd.), Quadrant House, 250 Kennington Ln., London SE11 5RD, England. TEL 0171-582-6626. FAX 0171-735-1299. E-mail: 100570,73@compuserve.com. **Document type:** bulletin.
Description: Provides a forum for those involved in provision of specialist group passenger transport.

380 628.5   NE
MISSET BULK; magazine voor stortgoedtechnologie. Variant title: Bulk Benelux. 6/yr. Misset (Subsidiary of: Reed Elsevier plc), Postbus 4, 7000 BA Doetinchem, Netherlands. TEL 31-8340-49371. FAX 31-8340-43839. adv.; B&W page fl. 2973, color page fl.4923; trim 215 x 285; adv. contact: Cor van Nek. illus; circ. 5,000 (controlled). **Document type:** trade publication.
Description: Covers bulk goods handling technology, including storage and processing.

380.52   NO   ISSN 0802-5193
MODERNE TRANSPORT. 1968. 11/yr. NOK 280. Teknisk Presse A.S, Hovfaret 17, P.O. Box 235 Skoeyen, N-0212 Oslo 2, Norway. TEL 47-2-52-10-40. FAX 47-2-50-66-48. Ed. Christian Ryg. adv. circ. 9,164.
—CCC.
Former titles: Moderne Bil Transport (ISSN 0801-5384); Moderne Transport (ISSN 0332-6128)
Description: Covers logistics and transport. Also focuses on forwarding, warehousing, materials handling and packaging.

645   GW   ISSN 0047-780X
DER MOEBELSPEDITEUR. 1946. fortn. DM.150. (Arbeitsgemeinschaft Moebeltransport Bundesverband e.V.) Verlag der Moebelspediteur, Brandeis Offenbacher Str. 113a, 63263 Neu-Isenburg, Germany. Eds. Diether Kraus, Jutta Pickerd-Busch. adv. circ. 1,840.
—CCC.

MONDE DU CAMPING CAR. see *TRAVEL AND TOURISM*

388.346   UK   ISSN 0142-0011
MOTOR CARAVAN WORLD. m. £20 (foreign £30). Stone Leisure Ltd., Andrew House, 2a Granville Rd., Sidcup, Kent DA14 4BN, England. TEL 0181-302-6150. FAX 0181-300-2315. Ed. Bob Griffiths. adv.; illus. circ. 18,000. **Document type:** consumer publication.
Formerly: Motor Caravan Monthly.
Description: Magazine covering all aspects of recreational vehicles in Europe.

MOTOR CARAVANNER. see *SPORTS AND GAMES — Outdoor Life*

388.322   US   ISSN 0739-117X
HE5601
MOTOR COACH AGE. (Includes Motor Coach Today) 1948. q. $25. Motor Bus Society, Inc., Box 251, Paramus, NJ 07560-0251. Ed. Mac Sebree. illus.

388.322
MOTOR COACH TODAY. (Includes Motor Coach Age) q. $25. Motor Bus Society, Inc., Box 251, Paramus, NJ 07560-0251. Ed. Charles Sullivan.

MOTOR FREIGHT DIRECTORY. see *BUSINESS AND ECONOMICS — Trade And Industrial Directories*

380.5   AU
MOTOR MARKT. m. Scheydgasse 24, A-1210 Vienna, Austria. TEL 01-307703. FAX 01-30770326. circ. 38,500.

388.3   SP   ISSN 0210-5969
MOTOR MUNDIAL. 1944. m. (11/yr.). 2025 ptas. Motor Mundial, S.A., Velazquez 121, 7o D., 28006 Madrid, Spain. TEL 1-262-46-20. FAX 1-261-37-21. Ed. Gerardo Romero-Requejo. adv.; bk.rev.; bibl.; illus.; tr.lit. circ. 300,000.
—CCC.

380.5 340   CN   ISSN 0709-5341
KE2112.A45
MOTOR VEHICLE REPORTS. 1979. 12/yr. (in 6 vols.). Can.$118. Carswell, One Corporate Plaza, 2075 Kennedy Rd., Scarborough, ON M1T 3V4, Canada. TEL 416-609-8000. FAX 416-298-5094. Ed. Murray D. Segal. adv. contact: M. Lalani. **Indexed:** Ind.Can.L.P.L.
—CCC.
Description: Features decisions in motor vehicle law from all Canadian jurisdictions. Covers cases on Criminal Code motor vehicle offences including alcohol-related offences and Charter of Rights defences, Highway Traffic Act offences, civil actions relating to motor vehicles and registration and licensing issues.

388.322   US
MOTORCOACH MARKETER.* 1985. a. (American Bus Association) Tom Jackson & Associates, Inc., 3100 W. End Ave., Ste. 1210, Nashville, TN 37203-1348. TEL 615-242-7747. FAX 615-259-2042. adv. circ. 5,500. **Document type:** directory, trade publication.
Description: Lists bus and tour operators and suppliers of bus products and services.

380.5 296.7   JA
MOTORCYCLE JAPAN; annual guide to Japan's motorcycle industry. (Text in English) 1983. a. 6080 Yen. Jan Corporation, DIK Shibashi No. 415, Shinbashi 6-5-4, Minato-ku, Tokyo 105, Japan. TEL 03-3438-0361. FAX 03-3438-0362. Ed. Shin Sato. circ. 8,000. **Document type:** trade publication.

MOTORHOME. see *SPORTS AND GAMES — Outdoor Life*

MUJINKA GIJUTSU/DATA SYSTEMS FOR AUTOMATED PRODUCTION AND MATERIAL HANDLING. see *MACHINERY*

MUTUALISTE R A T P. see *LABOR UNIONS*

380.5   US   ISSN 1053-1203
N A F A FLEET EXECUTIVE; the magazine for vehicle management. 1957. m. membership. National Association of Fleet Administrators, Inc., 120 Wood Ave., S., Ste. 615, Iselin, NJ 08830-2709. TEL 908-494-8100. FAX 908-494-6789. Ed. Denise M. Rucci. adv.; bk.rev.; illus.; stat.; index. circ. 4,000. (also avail. in microfiche from CIS; back issues avail.) **Indexed:** SRI.
Formerly: N A F A Bulletin.
Description: Covers government legislation and regulation, survey results, interviews with prominent industry personalities, technological developments and intra-association news pertaining to car, van and light truck fleet management in the US and Canada.

380.5   US
N A F A FLEET FOCUS. vol.15, no.10, Oct. 1989. m. National Association of Fleet Administrators, Inc., 120 Wood Ave. S., Ste. 615, Iselin, NJ 08830-2709. TEL 201-494-8100. FAX 201-494-6789. **Document type:** newsletter.
Formerly: N A F A Newsletter.
Description: Features timely legislative and association news, meeting and conference notices, and technological innovations.

380.5   US
N F T A ANNUAL REPORT. 1967. a. free. Niagara Frontier Transportation Authority, Public Information Officer, 181 Ellicott St., Buffalo, NY 14203. TEL 716-855-7300. FAX 716-855-7657. circ. 500.
Description: Defines aims and goals of the NFTA, which are to maintain a transportation network for the benefit of the people of Western New York State. Reports on the NFTA's financial position.

363.73   US
N O A C A NEWS. 1969. q. free. Northeast Ohio Areawide Coordinating Agency, Atrium Office Plaza, 668 Euclid Ave., Cleveland, OH 44115-3000. TEL 216-241-2414. FAX 216-621-3024. Ed. Cheryl Onesky. bk.rev.; illus. circ. 2,500. **Document type:** newsletter.

385   US
N Y C T A FACTS & FIGURES.* 1970. a. $5. New York City Transit Authority, 370 Jay St., Box M, Brooklyn, NY 11201. TEL 718-330-3000. Ed. Ruth Fredericks.

380.5   GW   ISSN 0722-8287
NAHVERKEHR. 1983. m. DM.180. Alba Fachverlag GmbH & Co., Roemerstr. 9, 40476 Duesseldorf, Germany. Ed. A. Teloeken. adv.; bk.rev. circ. 3,000. **Indexed:** Dok.Str. **Document type:** trade publication.
—BLDSC (6015.300960); SWETS. CCC.

380.5   GW   ISSN 0179-504X
NAHVERKEHRS NACHRICHTEN. Cover title: NaNa. 1956. 3/m. Alf Teloeken, Ed. & Pub., Roemerstr. 9, 40476 Duesseldorf, Germany. TEL 0211-46901-0. FAX 0211-4690145. adv.; B&W page DM.3640, color page DM.5140; adv. contact: Sandra Beinlich. bk.rev. circ. 1,250. **Document type:** bulletin.
Description: Provides information on all aspects of public transportation.

388.322   US   ISSN 0194-939X
TL232
NATIONAL BUS TRADER; the magazine of bus equipment for the United States and Canada. 1977. m. $20 (foreign $25). National Bus Trader, Inc., 9698 Judson Rd., Polo, IL 60614. TEL 815-946-2341. FAX 815-946-2347. Ed. Larry Plachno. adv.; bk.rev. circ. 6,000. (back issues avail.) **Document type:** trade publication.
Description: Covers integral design bus vehicles, primarily inter-city coaches.

TRANSPORTATION

380.5 US ISSN 0732-4839
NATIONAL COOPERATIVE TRANSIT RESEARCH AND DEVELOPMENT PROGRAM REPORT. irreg., no.359, 1994. price varies. U.S. National Research Council, Transportation Research Board, 2101 Constitution Ave., N.W., Washington, DC 20418. TEL 202-334-3213. FAX 202-334-2519. circ. 2,100. (also avail. in microfiche) Indexed: Dok.Str. **Document type:** monographic series, government publication.
Description: Publishes formal reports issued at the conclusion of N.C.T.R.P. research projects.

NATIONAL CUSTOMS BROKERS & FORWARDERS ASSOCIATION OF AMERICA. MEMBERSHIP DIRECTORY. see *BUSINESS AND ECONOMICS — Trade And Industrial Directories*

338 UK
THE NATIONAL FREIGHT AND TRANSPORT GUIDE (YEAR). a. £20. Commerce Business Directories, Station House, Station Rd., Newport Pagnell, Milton Keynes, Bucks. MK16 0AG, England. TEL 01908-211177. FAX 01908-616441. Ed. Karen Pickwick; Pub. Maria Luisi. **Document type:** directory.
Description: Lists freight and transport firms throughout England.

380.5 US ISSN 0275-3286
NATIONAL HIGHWAY & AIRWAY CARRIERS & ROUTES. 1941. s-a. $190. National Highway Carriers Directory, Inc., Box 6099, Buffalo Grove, IL 60089. TEL 708-634-0606. FAX 708-634-1026. adv.: B&W page $1495, color page $2495; trim 9 3/8 x 10 7/8. circ. 3,000 (paid). **Document type:** directory.
Description: Provides comprehensive information on carrier routes throughout North America, including motor freight, intermodal trucking, airline cargo companies and contract carriers.

388 US
NATIONAL INDUSTRIAL TRANSPORTATION LEAGUE. NOTICE. 1936. w. membership only. National Industrial Transportation League, 1700 N. Moore St., Ste. 1900, Arlington, VA 22209-1904. TEL 703-524-5011. FAX 703-524-5017. adv.: B&W page $375. circ. 1,500 (controlled). **Document type:** newsletter.
Description: Comprehensive information on domestic and international issues.

665.7 US ISSN 1067-2494
NATURAL GAS FUELS. 1992. m. free to qualified personnel. R P Publishing, Inc., 1290 Broadway, Ste. 700, Denver, CO 80203-5607. TEL 303-863-0521. FAX 303-863-1722. E-mail: info@rppublishing.com. Ed. Ellen Pollock; Pub. Frank Rowe. adv.: B&W page $2600; adv. contact: Todd Allen. circ. 8,000 (controlled). **Document type:** trade publication.
Description: Focuses on natural gas as a transportation fuel.

387 623.89 AT
V1
NAVIGATION NEWSLETTER. 1959. q. Aus.$25. Australian Institute of Navigation, Box 2250 G.P.O, Sydney, N.S.W, Australia. TEL 61-2-264-6413. FAX 61-2-267-1682. Ed. K.C. Crompton. adv.; bk.rev. circ. 600. Indexed: Int.Aerosp.Abstr. **Document type:** newsletter.
Supersedes: Navigation (ISSN 0077-6262)

380.5 NE ISSN 0924-6584
NEDERLANDS VERVOER. 1948. 20/yr. fl.120 (foreign fl.170) (effective 1995). Koninklijke Nederlands Vervoer, Bezuidenhoutseweg 56, 2594 AW The Hague, Netherlands. TEL 31-70-3440534. FAX 31-70-3470573. Ed. H.W. Nanninga; Pub. H.W. Nanninga. adv.; index. circ. 3,500. Indexed: Excerp.Med., Key to Econ.Sci. **Document type:** trade publication.
—SWETS.
Formed by the 1990 merger of: Personenvervoer (ISSN 0376-6772) & Nederlands Transport (ISSN 0028-2219)
Description: Covers the transport of persons, including public transportation, buses and taxiscabs.

380.5 US
NETWORK (EAST PEORIA); the magazine for international material handling. 1980. m. $50 (foreign $100). Woodward Communications, 252 E. Washington, Box 2338, E. Peoria, IL 61611. TEL 309-669-4431. FAX 309-698-0801. adv.: B&W page $415; trim 11 x 13 1/4. bk.rev. circ. 14,000. **Document type:** trade publication.
Description: Covers news, manufacturers, new products, feature stories and people profiles.

380.15 GW ISSN 0934-1307
NEUE ZEITSCHRIFT FUER VERKEHRSRECHT. 1988. m. DM.220 (students DM.184). C.H. Beck'sche Verlagsbuchhandlung, Wilhelmstr. 9, 80801 Munich, Germany. TEL 089-38189-338. FAX 089-38189-398. Ed.Bd. adv.: B&W page DM.2300, color page DM.4025; trim 260 x 186. bk.rev. circ. 3,500. (back issues avail.) **Document type:** bulletin.

380.5 US
NEW JERSEY. DEPARTMENT OF TRANSPORTATION. ANNUAL REPORT. 1894. a. free. Department of Transportation, 1035 Parkway Ave., CN 600, Trenton, NJ 08625. charts; illus.
Former titles (until 1977): New Jersey. Department of Transportation. Highlight of Activities; (until 1974): New Jersey. Department of Transportation. Report of Operations (ISSN 0085-395X); (until 1970): New Jersey. Department of Transportation. Annual Report.

NEW JERSEY MOTOR VEHICLE AND TRAFFIC LAWS. see *LAW*

NEW JERSEY TRAFFIC DIRECTORY. see *BUSINESS AND ECONOMICS — Trade And Industrial Directories*

380.5 US
NEWSLINE (EVANSTON). s-a. Northwestern University Transportation Center, 1936 Sheridan Rd., Evanston, IL 60208-4040. TEL 708-491-7287. circ. 10,000. **Document type:** newsletter.
Description: Newsletter covering Transportation Center research, executive education, graduate education, alumni news and placement, industry updates.

380.52 658.788 NE ISSN 0921-4593
NIEUWSBLAD TRANSPORT. 1987. 3/w. fl.365 (foreign fl.895). Misset (Subsidiary of: Reed Elsevier plc), Postbus 4, 7000 BA Doetinchem, Netherlands. TEL 31-8340-49911. FAX 31-8340-43839. adv. contact: Cor van Nek. bk.rev. circ. 10,000. (back issues avail.) **Document type:** newspaper, trade publication.
Description: Covers transportation, distribution, export, and logistics.

380.5 910.09 GW
NIX WIE WEG; Mitfahrzentralen in Deutschland und aller Welt. (Text in English, French, German) 1980. w. Prolix Verlag GmbH, Goehtestr. 23, 79100 Freiburg, Germany. Ed. Daniel Jaeger. circ. 30,000. (back issues avail.)

380.5 FR
NORD-TRANSPORTS.* 1934. m. (11/yr.). 93 F. Nord Transports S.A.R.L., 156 rue Leon Jouhaux, B.P. 135, 59443 Wasquetal Cedex, France. TEL 20-72-38-38. FAX 20-98-47-36. TELEX 136 234. Ed. Karine Holinier. adv. circ. 800.

NORTHEAST DIRECTORY OF TRANSPORTATION SERVICES. see *BUSINESS AND ECONOMICS — Trade And Industrial Directories*

380 US ISSN 1061-8090
NORTHEAST JOURNAL OF TRANSPORTATION. 1918. w. $86 (foreign $114). Northeast Journal of Transportation, 31 Fargo St., Box 404, Boston, MA 02127. TEL 617-695-1660. FAX 617-695-1665. Ed. George Lauriat. adv. contact: William Bourbon. bk.rev.; charts; illus.; stat. circ. 3,000. (back issues avail.) **Document type:** trade publication.
Former titles (until 1991): New England Journal of Transportation; (until 1989): Boston Marine Guide.
Description: Covers all modes of cargo transportation and relevant developments in international and domestic trade for businesses in the Northeast, including Canada.

380.5 US
NORTHWESTERN UNIVERSITY. TRANSPORTATION CENTER. PUBLICATIONS LIST. 1978. a. free. Northwestern University, Transportation Center, 1936 Sheridan Rd., Evanston, IL 60208. TEL 708-492-7287. circ. 2,500. **Document type:** catalog.

380.5 US ISSN 0029-4039
NOTES FROM UNDERGROUND. 1970. m. $16 to individuals; institutions $25 (includes Task Force Reports). Committee for Better Transit, Inc., Box 3106, Long Island City, NY 11103. TEL 718-728-0091. Ed. Stephen Dobrow. bk.rev. circ. 2,500. (also avail. in microform from UMI; reprint service avail. from UMI)
—UMI.
Incorporating: Better Transit Bulletin (ISSN 0006-0240)
Description: News and views on mass transit and related areas, with emphasis on the New York-New Jersey metropolitan area.

NOTTINGHAM LICENSED TAXI OWNERS & DRIVERS ASSOCIATION. NEWSLETTER. see *BUSINESS AND ECONOMICS — Small Business*

380.5 SZ
NUTZVERKEHR MAGAZIN T I R; Transport Werkverkehr Logistik Bus Touristik. 1970. m. 72 SFr. (foreign 95 SFr.). Neue T I R Verlag AG, Dorfstr. 5, CH-3550 Langnau, Switzerland. TEL 035-21915. FAX 035-24642. circ. 12,000. **Document type:** trade publication.

380.5 MP
ODTEY BICHIG/SPECIAL DELIVERY. (Text in Mongolian) 1990. q. Ulan Bator Railway Administration, Ulan Bator, Mongolia. circ. 35,603.
Description: Published for transport and communication workers.

380.5 AU ISSN 0029-9790
OESTERREICHISCHER PERSONENVERKEHR. vol.10, 1970. m. S.568. (Fachverband und Fachgruppe fuer die Befoerderungsgewerbe mit Personenkraftwagen sowie Autobusunternehmungen Oesterreichs) Oesterreichischer Wirtschaftsverlag, Nikolsdorfer Gasse 7-11, A-1051 Vienna, Austria. TEL 0222-555585. TELEX 1-11669. Ed. Heinz Thomann. adv.; bk.rev.; stat. circ. 10,800.

388.322 US ISSN 1046-3372
HD9710.34.A1
OFFICIAL BUS BOOK MARKET REPORT. 1987. s-a. $194. Bus Book Publishing, Inc., Box 9, McMinnville, OR 97128-0009. TEL 503-472-3536. FAX 503-472-3293. circ. 1,500.
Description: Wholesale and retail bus values and replacement values for over 4,200 different makes, models and years.

380.5 US ISSN 0190-6690
OFFICIAL INTERMODAL EQUIPMENT REGISTER. 1969. q. $80. K - III Directory Corp., 424 W. 33rd St., New York, NY 10001. TEL 800-221-5488. FAX 212-695-5025. adv. circ. 2,500. (also avail. in magnetic tape)
Description: Contains dimensions and capacities for 3,000,000 containers, trailers, bogies and chassis used by the companies listed.

OFFICIAL INTERMODAL GUIDE; directory of intermodal services, facilities and personnel. see *BUSINESS AND ECONOMICS — Trade And Industrial Directories*

388.322 US ISSN 1083-5857
▼**OFFICIAL SCHOOL BUS RESALE GUIDE.** 1995. a. $98. Bus Book Publishing, Inc., Box 9, McMinnville, OR 97128-0009. TEL 503-472-3536. FAX 503-472-3293. Ed. Dave Mendenhall. circ. 300. **Document type:** trade publication.
Description: Lists wholesale and resale used school bus values.

380 US
OFFICIAL SHIPPERS GUIDE - CHICAGO MOTOR FREIGHT DIRECTORY. 1872. s-a. $47.50. Official Motor Freight Guide, Inc., 1700 W. Cortland St., Chicago, IL 60622-1150. TEL 312-278-2454. Ed. E. Eric Robison. adv.; charts; stat. **Document type:** directory.

OHIO MOTOR VEHICLE LAWS. see *LAW*

388.322 658.1   IT
OMNIBUS. 1979. q. free. Azienda Municipalizzata Trasporti Genova, Via Montaldo 2, 16137 Genoa, Italy. TEL 39-10-5997437. FAX 39-10-5997400. Ed. Franco Gimelli. adv.; bk.rev.; charts; illus.; stat. circ. 10,000.
   Description: Publishes articles on current news in the public transportation industry.

388.322   UK   ISSN 0305-9243
OMNIBUS MAGAZINE. 1931. bi-m. £9. Omnibus Society, 15 Alianore Rd., Caldicot, Newport, Gwent NP6 4DF, Wales. TEL 01291-422670. FAX 031-652-0856. Eds. Dave Bubier, Oliver Howorth. adv.; bk.rev.; bibl. circ. 800. **Document type:** consumer publication.
   —BLDSC (6256.550000).
   Description: Covers history and development of road passenger transport.

388.322   GW   ISSN 0724-7664
OMNIBUSSPIEGEL. 1979. bi-m. DM.59. Verlag Dieter Hanke, Am Weitgarten 37, 53227 Bonn, Germany. TEL 0228-440953. FAX 0228-445280. Pub. Dieter Hanke. adv.; bk.rev. circ. 1,200. **Document type:** newsletter.

380   NE
ONDERNEMINGSANALYSES TRENDS IN TRANSPORT. a. fl.89.50. Delwel Uitgeverij B.V., Postbus 19110, 2500 CC The Hague, Netherlands. TEL 31-70-3624800. FAX 31-70-3605606.
   Formerly (until 1992): Trends in Transport.
   Description: Provides information on the financial and economic performance of the transport sector in the Netherlands.

388   CN   ISSN 0842-0394
ONTARIO TRAFFIC. bi-m. Ontario Traffic Conference, 20 Carlton St., Ste. 121, Toronto, ON M5B 2H5, Canada. TEL 416-598-4138. FAX 416-598-0449. Ed. Leighton A. Peach. adv. **Document type:** trade publication.

380.5   NE   ISSN 1381-9011
OPENBAAR VERVOER (AMSTERDAM, 1958). 1958. m. fl.17 in Benelux (elsewhere fl.30). P.H. Kiers, Ed. & Pub., Assumburg 94, 1081 GC Amsterdam, Netherlands. TEL 31-20-6422979. adv.; bk.rev. circ. 1,325.
   Description: Examines trains, trams, and buses in the Netherlands and Belgium and urban rail worldwide.

388.324   AT
OWNER - DRIVER; dedicated to the success of the person behind the wheel. 1992. m. (except Jan.). Publishing Services (Australia) Pty. Ltd., 244 St. Paul's Terrace, Spring Hill, Brisbane, Qld. 4000, Australia. TEL 07-854-1286. FAX 07-525-4829. Ed. Andrew Stewart. adv.; B&W page Aus.$750, color page Aus.$1750; trim 415 x 280; adv. contact: Maree Blackley. circ. 23,000. (tabloid format) **Document type:** newspaper.
   Description: Keeps owner-drivers up-to-date with what affects them - from industry news, business aspects to equipments and services.

PACKUNG UND TRANSPORT; Fachmagazin fuer Verpackung, Materialfluss und Logistik. see *PACKAGING*

380.5 658 690   US   ISSN 1055-890X
PARKING TECHNOLOGY. 1991. m. free to qualified personnel. Witter Publishing Co., Inc., 84 Park Ave., Flemington, NJ 08822. TEL 908-788-0343. FAX 908-788-3782. adv.; circ. 25,000 (controlled).
   Description: Covers aspects of parking facilities and technology including: construction, facility operations, and management.

380.5   US   ISSN 0364-345X
HE4441
PASSENGER TRANSPORT. 1943. w. $65 (effective 1995). American Public Transit Association, Information Center, 1201 New York Ave., N.W., Ste. 400, Washington, DC 20005. TEL 202-898-4119. FAX 202-898-4095. Ed. Dennis Kouba. adv.; stat.; index; circ. 4,073 (paid). **Indexed:** HRIS. **Document type:** newspaper.
   Description: Covers full range of news affecting mass transit, from congressional and federal developments to local transit service developments.

380.5 574.5   US   ISSN 1078-7747
PAVING MORATORIUM UPDATE - AUTO-FREE TIMES. 1989. s-a. $30. Fossil Fuels Policy Action Institute, Box 4347, Arcata, CA 95521. TEL 707-826-7775. (Co-sponsor: Alliance for a Paving Moratorium) Ed. Jan Lundberg. adv. contact: Randy Ghent. bk.rev. circ. 15,000. (back issues avail.) **Document type:** newsletter.
   Former titles: Fossil Fuels Action Update & Ecodemocracy.
   Description: Contains articles, interviews and photos advocating and chronicling the road-fighting and auto-free movements internationally.

380.5   HU   ISSN 0303-7800
TA1001
PERIODICA POLYTECHNICA. TRANSPORT ENGINEERING. (Text in English) 1973. q. $16. Budapesti Muszaki Egyetem - Technical University of Budapest, Periodica Polytechnica, 1521 Budapest, Hungary. TEL 36-1-4631105. FAX 36-1-166-6808. TELEX 22-5931 MUEGY H. E-mail: perpol@tuo.bme.hu. (Dist. by: Kultura, P.O. Box 149, 1389 Budapest, Hungary) Ed. J. Marialigeti. bk.rev.; charts; illus.; index. circ. 350. **Document type:** academic/scholarly publication.
   —BLDSC (6425.550000); Ei.
   Refereed Serial

380.5   PH   ISSN 0031-7888
PHILIPPINES TRANSPORTATION.* 1952. m. P.12.($12) Manuel Vijungco, Ed. & Pub., Box 998, Manila, Philippines. adv.; illus.; mkt.; tr.lit. circ. 6,500.

380.5   RU   ISSN 0235-5116
POD'EMNO-TRANSPORTNAYA TEKHNIKA I SKLADY.* 1972. 6/yr. 1.20 Rub. per no. Izdatel'stvo Transport, Basmanny tupik 6A, 107174 Moscow, Russia. TEL 095-262-6773. Ed. G.N. Shishkin. illus. **Indexed:** C.I.S. Abstr.
   —CCC.
   Formerly (until 1989): Promyshlennyi Transport (ISSN 0131-5560)

380.5   PL   ISSN 0209-3324
POLITECHNIKA SLASKA. ZESZYTY NAUKOWE. TRANSPORT. 1983. irreg. Politechnika Slaska, Katowicka 7, 44-100 Gliwice, Poland. FAX 371655. TELEX 036304. (Dist. by: Ars Polona, Krakowskie Przedmiescie 7, 00-068 Warsaw, Poland) Ed. Barbara Maciejna. circ. 205.

388   PL   ISSN 1230-9265
POLITECHNIKA WARSZAWSKA. PRACE NAUKOWE. TRANSPORT. 1972. irreg. Politechnika Warszawska, c/o Biblioteka Glowna, Pl. Politechniki 1, 00-661 Warsaw, Poland. **Document type:** academic/scholarly publication.
   Formerly (until 1992): Politechnika Warszawska. Instytut Transportu. Prace (ISSN 0137-2289)

387   US   ISSN 0085-5030
HE554.N4
PORT OF NEW ORLEANS ANNUAL DIRECTORY. 1969. a. free to qualified personnel. Port of New Orleans, 2 Canal St., Box 60046, New Orleans, LA 70160. TEL 504-528-3234. FAX 504-524-2196. TELEX 58-7496. Ed. Don Hoffman. adv.; bk.rev.; charts; illus.; stat.; circ. 10,300 (controlled). **Document type:** directory.
   Description: Covers port administration, planned improvements, computer capabilities, intermodal connections, facilities and tariffs. Includes a listing of maritime businesses in the New Orleans area by services.

POWDER & BULK SOLIDS YEARBOOK & DIRECTORY. see *TECHNOLOGY: COMPREHENSIVE WORKS*

POWDER BULK SOLIDS; the magazine for the processing, handling, packaging and storing of dry particulates. see *ENGINEERING — Chemical Engineering*

POWDER BULK SOLIDS INDUSTRY MASTER. see *ENGINEERING — Chemical Engineering*

POWDER HANDLING & PROCESSING. see *TECHNOLOGY: COMPREHENSIVE WORKS*

POWER LETTER. see *ENERGY*

380.52   FR   ISSN 0765-6386
PRACTIC EXPORT. 1986. 40/yr. 700 F. Editions du Commerce International, 76 rue Nau, 13005 Marseille, France. TEL 91-92-47-20. FAX 91-92-40-30. Ed. Claude Mezzana. adv. circ. 6,900.

380.5   XR   ISSN 0032-7514
PREPRAVNI A TARIFNI VESTNIK/TRANSPORTATION AND TARIFF NEWS. 1945. fortn. 101.40 Kc.($8.66) (Federalni Ministerstvo Dopravy) Nakladatelstvi Dopravy a Spoju, Hybernska 5, 115 78 Prague 1, Czech Republic. (Subscr. to: PNS-Ustredni Expedice a Dovoz Tisku Prague, Administrace Vyvozu Tisku, Kovpakova 26, 16000 Prague 6, Czech Republic) Ed. Irena Hrabankova. bk.rev. circ. 9,760.

PRESHIPMENT TESTING. see *PACKAGING*

380.5   US
PRESIDENT TRANSPORT WORLD. Variant title: Transport World. 1979. q. $20. International Railroad and Transportation Postcard Collectives Club, Box 6782, Providence, RI 20940. Ed. Robert J. Andrews. adv.; page $3000. bk.rev.; video rev. circ. 500. (back issues avail.; reprint service avail.) **Document type:** bulletin.
   Description: Covers post cards showing various types of transportation.

PREVISIONS GLISSANTES DETAILLEES EN PERSPECTIVES SECTORIELLES (VOL.36): TRANSPORTS. see *BUSINESS AND ECONOMICS — Economic Situation And Conditions*

380.5   CN
PRIVILEGE. q. (Air Canada) Southam Printing Limited, Airmedia Division, 150 John St., Ste. 900, Toronto, Ont. M5V 3E3, Canada. TEL 416-591-1551. FAX 416-591-3511. Ed. Karen Hanley. adv. circ. 90,000.

388.347   US
(YEAR) PRO BIKE DIRECTORY. irreg., latest 1995. $25. Bicycle Federation of America, 1506 21st St., N.W., Ste. 200, Washington, DC 20036. TEL 202-463-6622. FAX 202-463-6625. **Document type:** directory.
   Description: Provides contact and program information for individuals, organizations, and government agencies involved in bicycling.

388.347   US   ISSN 1064-2765
PRO BIKE NEWS. 1980. m. $30 in US; Canada $32; elsewhere $35. Bicycle Federation of America, 1506 21st St., N.W., Ste. 200, Washington, DC 20036. TEL 202-463-6622. FAX 202-463-6625. Ed. Andy Clarke. bk.rev. circ. 600. (tabloid format; back issues avail.) **Document type:** newsletter.

380.5   US
PRO-DEVELOPMENT LETTER. 1983. bi-m. $25. American Society of Transportation and Logistics, Inc., 216 E. Church St., Lock Haven, PA 17745-2010. TEL 717-748-8515. Ed. Tricia Humphrey. adv. contact: Tricia Humphrey. circ. 2,000. (tabloid format; back issues avail.)
   Description: For professional development in transportation, logistics, and physical distribution management.

380.5   JA
PROBLEMS OF TRANSPORTATION IN JAPAN.* (Text in English) 1975. irreg. Institute of Transportation Economics - Un'yu Chosakyoku, 1-1, Ueno 7-chome, Taito-ku, Tokyo 110, Japan.

PROCLAIM (FORT WASHINGTON). see *INSURANCE*

388.3   SW
PROFFS. 8/yr. SEK 185; newsstand price: SEK 25. Fateco Foerlag AB, Proppelervaegen 4A, S-183 62 Taaby, Sweden. TEL 46-8-756-74-00. FAX 46-8-756-55-05. Ed. Bobby Hammerberg. adv.: B&W page SEK 23400, color page SEK 28900; trim 255 x 365; adv. contact: Pekka Tikkanen. circ. 27,000. cols./p.: 5; pp./issue: 32. (tabloid format)

380.5   ISSN 0033-2232
PRZEGLAD KOMUNIKACYJNY; miesiecznik ekonomiczno-techniczny. 1945. m. $7.20. Stowarzyszenie Inzynierow i Technikow Komunikacji (SITK), Ul. Czackiego 3-5, Warsaw, Poland. (Dist. by: Ars Polona- Ruch, Krakowskie Przedmiescie 7, Warsaw, Poland) Ed. Tadeusz Basiewicz. bk.rev.; bibl.; charts; illus.; stat.; index, cum.index. circ. 3,600.

TRANSPORTATION

388 BE ISSN 1016-796X
HE4201 CODEN: PTRIE5
PUBLIC TRANSPORT INTERNATIONAL. (Text in English, French, German) 1952. bi-m. 2000 BEF. International Union of Public Transport, Av. de l'Uruguay 19, 1050 Brussels, Belgium. TEL 32-2-6736100. FAX 32-2-6601072. TELEX 63916 UITP B. Ed. Pierre Laconte. adv.: B&W page 55000 BEF, color page 92000 BEF; adv. contact: Ina Ernst. bk.rev.; illus.; index, cum.index: 1952-1984. circ. 19,500. (back issues avail.) Indexed: Dok.Str., HRIS.
—BLDSC (6969.432000); Ei.
 Formerly: U I T P Revue (ISSN 0041-5154); Supersedes: International Union of Tramways, Light Railways and Motor Omnibuses. Review.

388 AT
QUEENSLAND TAXI. bi-m. (Taxi Council of Queensland) Magazine Publishing Company, 4 Wandoo St., Fortitude Valley, Qld. 4006, Australia. TEL 61-7-252-9677. FAX 61-7-252-4667. Ed. Alan Goodridge. adv.: B&W page Aus.$1538, color page Aus.$1850; trim 275 x 210; adv. contact: Trevor Kirk. circ. 4,000. **Document type:** trade publication.

380.5 IT
QUOTA NEVE. 6/yr. Via Panizza 12, 20144 Milan, Italy. TEL 2-498-31-20. FAX 2-498-51-57. Ed. Giorgio Marchelli. circ. 8,000.

380.5 069 US
R.E. OLDS TRANSPORTATION MUSEUM NEWSLETTER. 1980. q. membership. R.E. Olds Transportation Museum Association, Inc., 240 Museum Dr., Lansing, MI 48933. TEL 517-372-4150. adv.; bk.rev. circ. 1,200. (looseleaf format; back issues avail.) **Document type:** newsletter.
 Description: Covers topics of interest to museum members, including Lansing-built transportation (cars, airplanes, bicycles and trucks).

R M F. (Rail Miniature Flash) see *HOBBIES*

388 US
R T A P TRAINING RESOURCES CATALOG FOR RURAL AND SPECIALIZED TRANSIT SYSTEMS. irreg. (U.S. Federal Transit Administration, Rural Transit Assistance Program) R T A P National Resource Center, 1440 New York Ave., N.W., Ste. 440, Washington, DC 20005. TEL 202-628-1480; 800-527-8279. FAX 202-737-9197. **Document type:** catalog, government publication.
 Description: Catalogs and presents detailed information profiles on each of the 11 categories of T.D.M. measures.

796.5 US
R V BUYERS GUIDE. (Recreational Vehicle) 1982. a. T L Enterprises, Inc., 3601 Calle Tecate, Camarillo, CA 93012. TEL 805-389-0300. Pub. Joe McNeill. adv. circ. 100,000. **Document type:** directory.
 Description: Dispenses advice on selecting a recreational vehicle. Provides listings of more than 500 motorhomes, trailers, and campers.

388.346 US ISSN 0193-2888
R V NEWS. (Recreational Vehicle) 1975. m. $36. D & S Media Enterprises, Inc., 6125 S. Ash Ave, Ste. 8, Tempe, AZ 85283-5608. TEL 602-839-8130. FAX 602-820-0934. Ed. Don Magary. adv.: B&W page $2700, color page $3300; trim 8 3/8 x 10 7/8; adv. contact: Dan Holt. circ. 13,000 (controlled). **Document type:** trade publication.
 Description: Covers general news about the recreational vehicle industry.

380.5 MX
REALIDADES. 1955. m. Mex.$4 per no. Direccion General de Transito, Palma Norte 413-105, Mexico 1, D.F., Mexico. adv. circ. 10,000.

380.5 FR ISSN 0304-3320
HE192.5
RECHERCHE EN MATIERE D'ECONOMIE DES TRANSPORTS/RESEARCH ON TRANSPORT ECONOMICS. 1968. a. 420 F.($85) Organization for Economic Cooperation and Development, European Conference of Ministers of Transport, 2 rue Andre Pascal, 75775 Paris Cedex 16, France. FAX 45-24-97-42. (Dist. by: O.E.C.D. Publication Service, 2 rue Andre-Pascal, 75775 Paris Cedex 16, France. TEL 45-24-82-00; U.S. orders to: O.E.C.D. Publications and Information Center, 2001 L St., N.W., Suite 700, Washington, D.C. 20036-4095) adv. contact: J Short. circ. 800. (also avail. in microfiche from OEC) Indexed: BMT.
 ●Also available online. Vendor(s): European Space Agency (File no.74/TRANSDOC Subfile: RESEARCH).
—BLDSC (7773.780000).
 Description: Presents a general review of research activities undertaken in the ECMT member countries as well as a selection of American projects.

387 623.8 UK ISSN 0080-0422
REED'S NAUTICAL ALMANAC.* (In three editions: European, American East Coast & Meditteranean) 1931. a. $27.50. Thomas Reed Publications Ltd., Weir House, Hurst RD., E. Molesey, Surrey KT8 9AQ, England. TEL 081-941-8090. FAX 081-941-8046. TELEX 883526-REED-G. Ed. Jean Fowler. index.

380.5 FR
REGIE AUTONOME DES TRANSPORTS PARISIENS. BULLETIN DE DOCUMENTATION ET D'INFORMATION. Short title: Documentation, Information-R A T P. 5/yr. Regie Autonome des Transports Parisiens, Direction des Etudes Generales, 53 ter Quai des Grands Augustins, 75271 Paris Cedex 6, France. illus.
 Formerly: Regie Autonome des Transports Parisiens. Bulletin d'Information et de Documentation Generale.

380.5 658 UK ISSN 0034-4265
REMOVALS AND STORAGE. 1924. m. membership. (British Association of Removers) Quarrington-Curtis Ltd., 15-17 Canute Rd., Southampton SO1 1FJ, England. TEL 01703-635438. FAX 01703-632198. Ed. Stephen J. Webb. adv.; bk.rev.; circ. 1,800. (controlled). **Document type:** trade publication.

RESALE WEEKLY. see *BUILDING AND CONSTRUCTION*

380.5 US ISSN 0739-8859
HE1
RESEARCH IN TRANSPORTATION ECONOMICS. 1983. a. J A I Press Inc., 55 Old Post Rd., No. 2, Box 1678, CT 06836-1678. TEL 203-661-7602. FAX 203-661-0792. (Addr. in Europe: J A I Press Ltd., The Courtyard, 28 High St., Hampton Hill, Mddx. TW12 1PB, England. TEL 44-81-943-9396. FAX 44-81-943-9317) Ed.Bd. **Document type:** academic/scholarly publication.
—BLDSC (7773.785000). **CCC.**

388.3 SW
HE4881
RESOR OCH TRAFIK/TRAVELLING AND TRAFFIC. 1944. 9/yr. SEK 240 (effective 1991). Svenska Lokaltrafikfoereningen, Snoermakarvaagen 29, S-161 47 Bromma, Sweden. TEL 46-8-25-26-01. Ed. Maria Oldegard. adv.; bk.rev. circ. 3,000.
 Former titles: Svensk Lokaltrafik (ISSN 0039-6648); (until 1954): Meddelanden fraan Svenska Lokaltrafikfoereningen.

380.5 RM ISSN 1220-868X
REVISTA CAILOR FERATE ROMNE. (Text in Rumanian; summaries in English, French, German and Russian) m. $87. Ministerul Transporturilor si Telecomunicatiilor, Calea Grivitei 193b, 78141 Bucharest, Rumania. (Subscr. to: Rolpres Filatelia, Sectorul Export-Import Presa, P.O. Box 12-201, Galea Grivitei no. 64-66, 10376 Bucharest, Rumania) (Co-sponsor: Institutul de Cercetari si Proiectari Tehnologice in Transporturi) Ed. Sabin Petrean. adv.; bk.rev.; bibl.; charts; illus. Indexed: C.I.S. Abstr., Dok.Str. **Document type:** government publication.
 Formerly (until 1991): Revista Transporturilor. Cai Ferate (ISSN 1220-8663); Which supersedes in part (in 1989): Revista Transporturilor si Telecomunicatiilor (ISSN 0379-2390); Which was formed by the 1974 merger of: Posti si Telecommunicatii (ISSN 0048-492X); Transporturi Auto, Navale si Ariene (ISSN 0373-7136); Revista Cailor Ferate Romane (ISSN 0482-5020)

380.5 BL
REVISTA O CARRETEIRO. m. Rua Palacete das Aguias 284, 04635 Sao Paulo SP, Brazil. TEL 11-533-5237. Dir. Jose A. de Castro. circ. 160,000.

380.5 RM ISSN 1220-8671
REVISTA TRANSPORTURILOR. AUTO, DRUMURI, NAVIGATIE. (Text in Rumanian; summaries in English, French, German and Russian) m. Ministerul Transporturilor si Telecomunicatiilor, Calea Grivitei 193b, 78141 Bucharest, Rumania. (Subscr. to: Rompres Filatelia, Sectorul Export-Import Presa, P.O. Box 12-201, Calea Grivitei no. 64-66, 10376 Bucharest, Rumania) (Co-sponsor: Institutul de Cercetari si Proiectari Tehnologice in Transporturi) bibl.; charts; illus. Indexed: C.I.S. Abstr., Dok.Str. **Document type:** government publication.
 Supersedes in part (in 1989): Revista Transporturilor si Telecomunicatiilor (ISSN 0379-2390); Which was formed by the 1974 merger of: Posti si Telecommunicatii (ISSN 0048-492X); Transporturi Auto, Navale si Ariene (ISSN 0373-7136); Revista Cailor Ferate Romane (ISSN 0482-5020)

388.3 SZ ISSN 0005-1314
REVUE AUTOMOBILE; journal suisse de l'automobile. German ed.: Automobil Revue. (Text in French) 1906. w. 120 SFr. for German ed. (foreign 195 SFr.); French ed. 96 SFr. (foreign 151.80 SFr.). Hallwag AG, Nordring 4, CH-3001 Bern, Switzerland. TEL 031-3323131. FAX 031-3314133. TELEX 912661-CH. Ed. Hans-Ulrich Buschi. adv.; bk.rev.; charts; illus.; mkt.; stat. circ. 74,048 (French ed. 22,857; German ed. 51,191). **Document type:** consumer publication.
—CCC.

RIVISTA GIURIDICA DELLA CIRCOLAZIONE E DEI TRASPORTI. see *LAW*

363.12 358.4 US ISSN 1055-7725
ROAD AND REC;* the Air Force journal of driving and recreational safety. 1967-1986 (Aug.); resumed 1988. q. $7 (foreign $8.75). U.S. Air Force, Inspection and Safety Center, c/o Superintendent of Documents, U.S. Government Printing Office, Washington, DC 20402. (Subscr. to: Superintendent of Documents, U.S. Government Printing Office, Box 371954, Pittsburgh, PA 15250-7954. TEL 202-512-1800. FAX 202-512-2250) (also avail. in microform from UMI; back issues avail.) Indexed: Ind.U.S.Gov.Per. **Document type:** government publication.
—UMI.
 Supersedes in part (in 1988): Air Force Driver (ISSN 0002-2373)
 Description: Published for the prevention of vehicle and other ground mishaps.

380.5 JA ISSN 0917-0863
THE ROAD HOME; the International Highway Project newsletter. 1989. 6/yr. International Highway Construction Corporation, 37-13 Udagawa-cho, Shibuya-ku, Tokyo 150, Japan. TEL 03-3481-5733. FAX 03-3481-5994. Ed. Tateo Yamaoka. **Document type:** newsletter.
 Description: Reports on current research and news about the International Highway Project.

380.5 US ISSN 1056-4845
ROADRACING WORLD & MOTORCYCLE TECHNOLOGY. 1990. m. $18. 581 Birch St., Unit C, Lake Elsinore, CA 92530. TEL 909-245-6411. FAX 909-245-6417. Ed. John D. Ulrich. adv. contact: Robert Dragich. bk.rev. circ. 15,000. **Document type:** consumer publication.
 Description: Covers high-performance motorcycles, road racers and motorcycle technology, for racers and enthusiasts.

388 US ISSN 0048-8542
ROLLING ALONG. 1949. q. free. North Dakota Motor Carriers Association, Box 874, Bismarck, ND 58502. (Affiliate: American Trucking Association) Ed. LeRoy H. Ernst. adv. circ. 3,000. **Document type:** trade publication.

380.5 UK
S A P T NEWSLETTER. 1972. q. £10 to individuals. Scottish Association for Public Transport, 5 St. Vincent Pl., Glasgow G1 2HT, Scotland. TEL 0141-639-3697. Ed. A Reid. bk.rev. circ. 200. (back issues avail.) **Document type:** newsletter.

TRANSPORTATION

S C & R A NEWSLETTER. (Specialized Carriers & Rigging Association) see *TRANSPORTATION — Trucks And Trucking*

380.5 US ISSN 0486-8323
SAFE DRIVER. 1954. m. $19 to non-members; members $15. National Safety Council, Periodicals Department, 1121 Spring Lake Dr., Itasca, IL 60143. TEL 708-775-2281. Ed. Kathleen Henderson; Pub. Kevin H. Axe. circ. 190,000.
Description: Practical advice about safe driving ofr the professional bus, truck or passenger car driver.

SAFETY, INDUSTRIAL RELATIONS, AND GOVERNMENT AFFAIRS SPECIAL REPORT. see *TRANSPORTATION — Trucks And Trucking*

SAMFERDSEL. see *TRANSPORTATION — Roads And Traffic*

380.5 US ISSN 0362-2800
SAN FRANCISCO BAY AREA RAPID TRANSIT DISTRICT. ANNUAL REPORT. Key Title: Annual Report - San Francisco Bay Area Rapid Transit District. 1958. a. San Francisco Bay Area Rapid Transit District, 800 Madison St., Oakland, CA 94607. TEL 415-464-6000. Ed. Michael Healy. illus. circ. 5,000.

380.5 SZ
SANKT GALLER BEITRAEGE ZUM TOURISMUS UND ZUR VERKEHRSWIRTSCHAFT: REIHE VERKEHRSWIRTSCHAFT. 1970. irreg., no.15, 1993. price varies. (Hochschule St. Gallen fuer Wirtschafts- und Sozialwissenschaften, Institut fuer Fremdenverkehr und Verkehrswirtschaft) Paul Haupt AG, Falkenplatz 14, CH-3001 Bern, Switzerland. TEL 031-3012345. FAX 031-3014669. **Document type:** monographic series.
—CCC.
Formerly (until 1992): Sankt Galler Beitraege zum Fremdenverkehr und zur Verkehrswirtschaft: Reihe Verkehrswirtschaft (ISSN 0080-6048)

380.5 630 CN ISSN 0822-241X
HE2321.G7
SASKATCHEWAN GRAIN CAR CORPORATION. ANNUAL REPORT. 1979. a. free. Saskatchewan Grain Car Corporation, P.O. Box 2498, Melville, SK S0A 2P0, Canada. TEL 306-728-7444. (Subscr. to: Saskatchewan Agriculture and Food, Publication Distribution Centre, B5, Walter Scott Bldg., 3085 Albert St., Regina, SK S4S 0B5, Canada. TEL 306-787-6933. FAX 306-787-0216) stat. circ. 500. (also avail. in microfiche) **Document type:** corporate report, government publication.

SCHIP EN SCHADE; beslissingen op het gebied van zee- en binnenvaartrecht, transport en brandverzekeringsrecht. see *TRANSPORTATION — Ships And Shipping*

SCHIP EN SCHADE, KAARTEN. see *TRANSPORTATION — Ships And Shipping*

380.5
SCHOOL BUS BRIEFS. q. free. Department of Public Instruction, Pupil Transportation Service, 125 S. Webster St., Box 7841, Madison, WI 53707-7841. Ed. Kathleen J. Cole. circ. controlled.
Formerly: Chrome Yellow.

388.3 US ISSN 0036-6501
SCHOOL BUS FLEET. vol.15, 1970. m. (plus Factbook in Jan.) $25 (Canada $30; elsewhere $38). Bobit Publishing Company, 2512 Artesia Blvd., Redondo Beach, CA 90278-3210. TEL 310-376-8788. FAX 310-376-9043. Ed. Jody Bush. adv.; charts; illus.; stat.; circ. 20,000 (controlled). (also avail. in microfiche from CIS) **Indexed:** HRIS, SRI.
Description: Serving the universe of pupil transportation.

388.322 CN ISSN 1199-1194
SCHOOL BUS ONTARIO. 1991. a. Kenilworth Publishing Inc., 80 W. Beaver Creek, Ste. 18, Richmond Hill, ON L4B 1H3, Canada. TEL 416-771-7333. FAX 416-771-7336. Ed. Jim Barnes. adv.: B&W page Can.$1450, color page Can.$2200; trim 8 1/8 x 10 3/4. circ. 1,500.

338.322 370 US ISSN 1070-3586
SCHOOL TRANSPORTATION NEWS. 1991. 12/yr. $24. William E. Paul, Inc., 700 Torrance Blvd., Ste. C, Redondo Beach, CA 90277-3493. TEL 310-792-2226. FAX 310-792-2231. adv.; bk.rev. circ. 16,000. (tabloid format) **Document type:** trade publication.
Description: Focuses on news developments in school transportation at all academic levels.

SCHUETTGUT. see *TECHNOLOGY: COMPREHENSIVE WORKS*

388 UK ISSN 0048-9808
SCOTTISH TRANSPORT. 1963. a. £12.75 for 3 nos. Scottish Tramway and Transport Society, P.O. Box 78, Glasgow G3 6ER, Scotland. Ed. Brian T. Deans. adv.; bk.rev. circ. 1,500. (reprint service avail. from UMI) **Document type:** bulletin.
—BLDSC (8211.270000).
Formerly: Scottish Tramlines.

388 IT ISSN 0394-8471
SISTEMI DI TRASPORTO. Key Title: Bollettino di Informazione del Centro Studi sui Sistemi di Trasporto. 1978. q. Centro Studi sui Sistemi di Trasporto, Via Filangieri 48, 80121 Naples, Italy. TEL 39-81-415218. Ed. Danilo Ferrero.

380.5 DK
▼**SKANDINAVISK TRANSPORT-TIDENDE.** 1994. w. DKK 800. Forlaget Erik Koch Larsen ApS, Hojvangen 6, DK-3480 Fredensborg, Denmark.
FAX 45-42-28-10-02. Ed. Jesper Nielsen. **Document type:** newsletter.

380.5 SA ISSN 0038-2760
SOUTH AFRICAN TRANSPORT; the independent transport journal. 1969. m. R.110($50) (£35). Bolton Publications (Pty) Ltd., P.O. Box 966, Parklands 2121, South Africa. TEL 27-11-8803520. FAX 27-11-8806574. Ed. Richard Proctor-Sims. adv.: color page R.5000; trim 210 x 297; adv. contact: Kamal H. Saad. bk.rev.; charts; illus.; index; circ. 608 (paid); 5,039 (controlled). (also avail. in microform from UMI; reprint service avail. from UMI) **Indexed:** Ind.S.A.Per. **Document type:** trade publication.
Description: Covers multi-modal transport (air, road, rail and sea), for industry professionals and executives.

380.5 SP ISSN 0210-9220
HE5681
SPAIN. MINISTERIO DEL INTERIOR. DIRECCION GENERAL DE TRAFICO. BOLETIN INFORMATIVO. 1960. m. Ministerio del Interior, Direccion General de Trafico, Calle J. Valcarcel, 28, 28071 Madrid, Spain. illus.; stat. circ. 2,600.
—CCC.

380.5 SP ISSN 0213-3377
SPANISH INTERNATIONAL TRANSPORT NEWSPAPER. 1985. 12/yr. 7600 ptas.($85) Publicaciones Men-Car, S.A., Paseo de Colon 24, 08002 Barcelona, Spain. TEL 34-3-3015516. FAX 34-3-3186645. Ed. J. Cardona Delclos. **Document type:** newspaper.

380.52 GW ISSN 0342-7749
DER SPEDITEUR. 1953. m. DM.45. Deutscher Verkehrs Verlag GmbH, Nordkanalstr. 36, 20097 Hamburg, Germany. TEL 040-23714123. Ed. Bernhard Kaltz. adv.: B&W page DM.4100; trim 260 x 175; adv. contact: Werner Holders. circ. 5,877.

380.5 GW ISSN 0038-9013
STADTVERKEHR. 1956. 10/yr. DM.84 (foreign DM.87). E K Verlag GmbH, Postfach 5560, 79022 Freiburg, Germany. TEL 0761-703100. FAX 0761-7031050. Ed. Eva Kunow. adv.; bk.rev.; charts; illus.; index. circ. 6,000. **Document type:** trade publication.
—SWETS. **CCC.**
Description: Discusses public transport facilities.

380.5 UK
STEAM HERITAGE MUSEUMS & RALLY GUIDE. 1968. a. £2.50. T E E Publishing, The Fosse, Fosse Way, Radford Semele, Leamington Spa CV31 1XN, England. TEL 01926-614101. FAX 01926-614293. Ed. C.L. Deith. adv. circ. 20,000. **Document type:** directory.
Former titles (until 1992): Steam Heritage Yearbook, Preserved Transport and Industrial Archaeology Guide; Steam Year Book, Preserved Transport and Industrial Archaeology Guide; Steam and Organ Year Book and Preserved Transport Guide.

380.5 AU ISSN 0029-9073
DER STRASSENGUETERVERKEHR. m. S.592. (Gewerbliches Gueterbefoerderungswesen Oesterreichs) Oesterreichischer Wirtschaftsverlag, Nikolsdorfer Gasse 7-11, A-1051 Vienna 5, Austria. TEL 0222-555585. TELEX 1-11669. Ed. Heinz Thomann. circ. 9,200. **Indexed:** INSPEC.
Formerly: Oesterreichische Fuhrwerker-Zeitung.

380.5 AT ISSN 0810-0187
STREET MACHINE. 1977. 8/yr. Aus.$43.20. A C P Publishing Pty. Ltd., 54-58 Park St., Sydney, N.S.W. 2000, Australia. TEL 02-282-8652. FAX 02-267-9439. Ed. Tad Hallenbeck; Pub. Richard Walsh. adv. contact: John Paul. circ. 60,000. **Document type:** consumer publication.
Formerly: Van Wheels.

STRUCTURAL MOVER. see *ENGINEERING — Civil Engineering*

380.5 GW ISSN 0170-5652
STUDIEN ZUR VERKEHRSWIRTSCHAFT. 1972. irreg. price varies. I F O Institut fuer Wirtschaftsforschung, Poschingerstr. 5, 81679 Munich, Germany. TEL 089-9224-0. circ. 400.
Description: Covers transportation topics.

380.5 CN ISSN 0834-3594
SURFACE TRANSPORTATION R & D IN CANADA. 1963. a. Can.$45 to non-members; members Can.$30. Transportation Association of Canada, 2323 St. Laurent Blvd., Ottawa, ON K1G 4K6, Canada. TEL 613-736-1350. FAX 613-736-1395. Ed. C.J. Hedges. index. **Document type:** monographic series.
Former titles (until 1986): Inventory of Road and Highway Research and Development Activities in Canada (ISSN 0833-949X); (until 1984): Surface Transportation R and D in Canada (ISSN 0828-9042); (until 1983): Transportation R and D in Canada (ISSN 0709-5538); Transportation Research in Canada (ISSN 0381-8284); Road Research in Canada (ISSN 0381-8292)
Description: Summarizes research and development projects carried out by federal and provincial transport ministries, universities and the private sector.

380.5 CN
T A C NEWS; executive digest - focus. French edition: Nouvelles de l'A T C. 1975. bi-m. Can.$60 to non-members. Transportation Association of Canada, 2323 St. Laurent Boulevard, Ottawa, ON K1G 4K6, Canada. TEL 613-736-1350. FAX 613-736-1395. Ed. Marc Comeau. circ. 2,000. (back issues avail.) **Document type:** newsletter.
Formerly: R T A C News (ISSN 0317-1280)
Description: Reviews association activities and general developments and trends in transportation in Canada and abroad.

388 621 628.53 US ISSN 1073-4880
HE4401
▼**T C R P SYNTHESIS.** (Transit Cooperative Research Program) 1994. m. U.S. Federal Transit Administration, Office of Technical Assistance and Safety, Advanced Public Transportation Division, U.S. Department of Transportation, 400 7th St., S.W., Rm. 6107, Washington, DC 20590. TEL 202-366-4991. FAX 202-366-3765. **Document type:** bulletin, government publication.
Description: Compiles the best-practice use of alternative fuels in public buses.

TRANSPORTATION

388 SW ISSN 0346-2773
T H - TRANSPORT OCH HANTERING. 1971. m. (10/yr.). SEK 600 (foreign SEK 720); newsstand price: SEK 50. T.H. Foerlag, Box 45056, S-104 30 Stockholm, Sweden. TEL 46-8-23-03-70. FAX 46-8-10-46-18. Ed. John Murray. adv.: B&W page SEK 17000, color page SEK 23500; trim 192 x 276; adv. contact: Ann Waller. bk.rev.; circ. 3,400 (controlled). cols./p.: 4; pp./issue: 90.
 Incorporates: Bulkhantering; **Formerly:** Transport och Hanteringsekonomi (ISSN 0085-7327)

380.5 US
T I UPDATE. (Former name of issuing body: Transportation Brokers Conference of America) bi-m. Transportation Intermediaries Association, 5845 Richmond Hwy., No. 750, Alexandria, VA 22303-1865. TEL 703-329-1894. FAX 703-329-1898. Ed. Annette E. Petrick; Pub. Annette E. Petrick. **Document type:** newsletter.
 Formerly: T C B A Update.

380.5 US ISSN 0738-6826
TE1
T R NEWS. 1963. bi-m. $38 to N. America; elsewhere $41. U.S. National Research Council, Transportation Research Board, 2101 Constitution Ave., N.W., Washington, DC 20418. TEL 292-334-3218. FAX 202-334-2519. Ed. Nancy A. Ackerman. bk.rev.; charts; illus. circ. 10,000. **Indexed:** Br.Rail.Bd., Dok.Str., Geotech.Abstr., Intl.Civil Eng.Abstr., Noise Pollut.Publ.Abstr., Soft.Abstr.Eng. **Document type:** government publication.
 —BLDSC (8873.791000); Ei; Faxon; SWETS; UnCover.
 Former titles: Transportation Research News (ISSN 0095-2656); Highway Research News (ISSN 0018-1749)
 Description: Features articles on innovative practices and current research in all modes of transportation.

380.5 SZ
T T - REVUE. (Transport und Tourismus) 1945. m. 55 SFr. Verband Oeffentlicher Verkehr, Daehlhoelzliweg 12, CH-3000 Bern 6, Switzerland. Ed. Dr. C. Pfund. adv.; bk.rev.; abstr.; illus.; stat.; circ. controlled. **Document type:** consumer publication.
 Formerly: V S T Revue (ISSN 0042-1928)

T W U EXPRESS. (Transport Workers Union of America) see *LABOR UNIONS*

380.5 CH
TAIWAN TRANSPORTATION EQUIPMENT GUIDE. 3/yr. NT.$1000($40) in Asia, Middle East, Oceania; elsewhere $50. China Economic News Service, 561 Chunghsiao E. Rd. Sec. 4, Taipei, Taiwan 10516, Republic of China. TEL 02-642-2629. FAX 02-642-7422. TELEX 27710-CENSPC.

380.5 FR ISSN 0153-9205
TARIF PIECES DETACHEES. 1969. q. 555 F. Editions Techniques pour l'Automobile et l'Industrie (ETAI), 20-22 rue de la Saussiere, 92100 Boulogne-Billancourt, France. TEL 46-04-81-13. FAX 48-25-56-92. TELEX ETAIRTA 204850F. Ed. Daniel Thallinger.
 Description: Covers 120 domestic and import cars. Indicates prices of car parts (body as well as engine).

388.321 UK ISSN 0049-304X
TAXI; the newspaper of the taxi trade. 1968. fortn. £16. Licensed Taxi Drivers Association, 9-11 Woodfield Rd., London W9 2BA, England. TEL 0171-286-2728. FAX 0171-286-2494. Ed. Stuart Pessok. adv.; bk.rev.; illus.; tr.lit. circ. 25,000. **Document type:** newspaper.

388.321 NO ISSN 0332-5881
TAXI. m. (10/yr.). NOK 40. Norges Taxiforbund, Trondheimsvn. 100, Box 6538 R, Oslo 5, Norway. Ed. Kolbjoern Bekkelund.
 Former titles (until 1977): Norsk Drosjeeirblad (ISSN 0048-0584); (until 1929): Auto-Droschen (ISSN 0332-6985)

380.5 AT
TAXI. bi-m. members only. (N.S.W. Taxi Association) Associated Business Publications Pty. Ltd., 104-3 Smail St., Ultimo, N.S.W. 2007, Australia. TEL 02-212-2780. Ed. John Bowe. adv.; bk.rev. circ. 4,000. **Document type:** bulletin.

388.321 US
TAXI & LIVERY MANAGEMENT. 1982. q. $16 in N. America; elsewhere $26. International Taxicab and Livery Association, 3849 Farragut Ave., Kensington, MD 20895-2004. TEL 301-946-5701. FAX 301-946-4641. Ed. Irene Kiebuzinski; Pub. Alfred LaGasse. adv. contact: Irene Kiebuzinski. circ. 5,800. **Document type:** trade publication.
 Formerly: Taxicab Management.

388 SW
TAXI IDAG. 1986. 8/yr. SEK 310; newsstand price: SEK 40. (Svenska Taxifoerbundet) Wiksten & Iger Information AB, P.O. Box 44086, S-100 73 Stockholm, Sweden. TEL 46-8-744-14-15. FAX 46-8-744-16-18. Ed. Dan Wiksten. adv.: B&W page SEK 13000, color page SEK 20500; trim 185 x 270; adv. contact: Lars Goeran Fransson. circ. 8,700. cols./p.: 4; pp./issue: 40. **Document type:** trade publication.
 Incorporates (in 1990): Taxitrafiken (ISSN 0040-022X)
 Description: Publishes news and articles of interest to taxi drivers and others in the industry.

388.321 SP
TAXI LIBRE. 6/yr. Confederation of Spanish Independent Taxi Drivers, Carlos I, 82, 08018 Barcelona, Spain. TEL 3-23-94-167. Ed. M. Tomas Romero.

388.321 AT
TAXI NEWS. 1949. m. Aus.$1. (Taxi Council of Queensland) A. Webb & Sons Pty. Ltd., 60 Baxter St., Fortitude Valley 4006, Australia. Ed. C.H. Dwyer. adv. circ. 2,000. (tabloid format)

388.321 CN ISSN 0834-3489
TAXI NEWS. 1985. m. Can.$15($25) Chedmount Investment Ltd., 38 Fairmount Cres., Toronto, ON M4L 2H4, Canada. TEL 416-468-2328. FAX 416-466-4220. Ed. Bill McOuat; Pub. John A. Duffy. adv. contact: Barb Whitehurst. bk.rev. circ. 10,500. (back issues avail.) **Document type:** newspaper.
 Description: News and events affecting Toronto's taxi industry.

388.321 UK ISSN 0040-0254
TAXINEWS. 1960. 6/yr. £4. Owner Drivers Society, 21 Buckingham Palace Rd., London SW1W 0PN, England. TEL 0171-834-6541. Ed. E.S. Perry. adv.; bk.rev.; illus. circ. 12,500. **Document type:** newsletter.

380.54 US ISSN 1062-5240
TECH TRANSFER. q. University of California at Berkeley, Institute of Transportation Studies, 113 McLaughlin Hall, Berkeley, CA 94720. TEL 510-642-3593. FAX 510-642-1246. Ed. Betsy Wing. **Document type:** newsletter.

380.5 620 US ISSN 1069-3912
HE202.5
TECHLINK: TRANSPORTATION SAFETY. (Yearbook avail.) 1993. m. $200 (outside N. America $280). U.S. National Technical Information Service, 5285 Port Royal Rd., Springfield, VA 22161. TEL 703-487-4630. FAX 703-321-8547. (Co-sponsor: Engineering Information, Inc.) bibl. **Document type:** newsletter, government publication.
 Description: Draws upon the engineering and technical data on transportation safety contained in the Compendex Plus and N.T.I.S. Bibliographic databases.

380.5 620 US
TECHNOLOGY FOR ALASKAN TRANSPORTATION. 1986. q. free. (F H W A) Alaska Transportation Technology Transfer Program, DOT & PF T2 Program, 2301 Peger Rd., Fairbanks, AK 99709-5316. TEL 907-451-5320. FAX 907-451-2313. Ed. Michael Rundquist; Pub. Susan M. Earp. adv. contact: Sharon McLeos-Everette. bk.rev.; bibl.; charts; illus.; stat.; index; circ. 2,100 (controlled). **Document type:** newsletter.
 Description: Seeks to get innovative technology regarding transportation to transportation professionals throughout the state of Alaska, and also to share and work with T2 Centers throughout the US and Puerto Rico.
 Refereed Serial

388 IT
TECNICA DEL TRASPORTO. 1960. m. (11/yr.). L.48000 (foreign L.82000). Paleari Edizioni Milano, Via Andrea Doria 1, 20052 Monza, Italy. TEL 39-39-737312. Ed. Paolo Tamburi. adv.: B&W page L.2700000, color page L.4320000. circ. 8,700.

380.5 SP ISSN 0211-3341
TECNICAS DE TRANSPORTE Y ALMACENAJE. 1981. 6/yr. 5000 ptas. (outside Europe 6000 ptas.) (effective 1993-94). Tecniediciones, S.L., C. Rodriguez Marin 61, 3o, Apdo. 29072, 28080 Madrid, Spain. TEL 34-1-5630405. FAX 34-1-5630319. Ed. Javier Zamora Bonilla; Pub. Antonio Zamora Martin. adv.: B&W page 130000 ptas., color page 175000 ptas.; 210 x 297; adv. contact: Antonio Zamora Martin. circ. 6,000 (paid). (back issues avail.) **Document type:** trade publication.
 Description: Contains information about current issues on transportation, storage and material handling.

TEXAS CRIMINAL LAW & MOTOR VEHICLE HANDBOOK. see *LAW*

380.5 US ISSN 0040-4748
  CODEN: TXTRA8
TEXAS TRANSPORTATION RESEARCHER. 1965. q. free in U.S. & Canada (foreign $25). Texas Transportation Institute, Texas A & M Univ. System, College Station, TX 77843-3135. TEL 409-845-1734. FAX 409-845-7575. Ed. Susan Lancaster; Pub. Herb Richardson. illus.; index. circ. 4,300. (also avail. in microform from UMI) **Indexed:** Eng.Ind.
 —Ei.
 Description: Showcases transportation research and professional activities of the Institute.

385.2 387.54 UK ISSN 0952-620X
HE3004 CODEN: TCETEY
THOMAS COOK EUROPEAN TIMETABLE; railway and shipping services throughout Europe. (Text in English; summaries in French, German, Spanish) 1873. m. £115.20 (rest of Europe £142.80; elsewhere £159.60) (effective 1996). Thomas Cook Publishing, P.O. Box 227, Peterborough PE3 6SB, England. TEL 01733-268943. FAX 01733-267052. Ed. Brendin Fox. adv. contact: Anne Bedford. index. circ. 204,000. **Document type:** directory.
 —BLDSC (8820.230150); CASDDS.
 Former titles (until 1980): Thomas Cook Continental Timetable (ISSN 0144-7467); **Supersedes in part (in 1980):** Thomas Cook International Timetable (ISSN 0141-2701); Thomas Cook Continental Timetable; Cooks Continental Timetable (ISSN 0010-8286)
 Description: Supplies a comprehensive timetable for railway and shipping services throughout Europe, with maps, town plans, and passport and visa regulations.

385.2 387.54 UK ISSN 0144-7475
HE1805 CODEN: TCOTDF
THOMAS COOK OVERSEAS TIMETABLE; railway, road and shipping services outside Europe. (Text in English; summaries in French, German, Italian, Spanish) 1981. bi-m. £57.60 (rest of Europe £71.40; elsewhere £79.80) (effective 1996). Thomas Cook Publishing, P.O. Box 227, Peterborough PE3 6SB, England. TEL 01733-268943. FAX 01733-267052. TELEX 32581. Ed. Peter Tremlett. adv. contact: Anne Bedford. index. circ. 24,000. **Document type:** directory.
 —BLDSC (8820.230300); CASDDS.
 Supersedes in part (in 1980): Thomas Cook International Timetable (ISSN 0141-2701)
 Description: Provides comprehensive timetables for rail, bus and shipping services for virtually all countries outside Europe, with maps and town plans. Includes useful Travel Information section and index of over 7000 places.

TRANSPORTATION 6319

385.2 UK
THOMAS COOK WORLD AIRPORTS DIRECTORY. (Text in English; summaries in French, German, Italian, Spanish) 1984-1987; resumed 1990. biennial. £19.95. Thomas Cook Publishing, P.O. Box 227, Peterborough, Cambs. PE3 8BQ, England. TEL 01733-268937. FAX 01733-267052. TELEX 32581. Ed. Stephen York. adv.; index. circ. 17,000. **Document type:** directory.
 Former titles: Thomas Cook Airports Guide Europe (ISSN 0266-9404); Thomas Cook Airport Links (ISSN 0265-4415)
 Description: Provides a comprehensive guide to air travel based around a listing of the world's major airports.

380.5 NE ISSN 0040-7623
HE7 CODEN: TIVEDD
TIJDSCHRIFT VOOR VERVOERSWETENSCHAP/JOURNAL FOR TRANSPORT SCIENCE. (Text in Dutch, English) 1965. q. fl.147.50. P.O. Box 30180, 3001 DD Rotterdam, Netherlands. TEL 31-10-4053130. FAX 31-10-4046567. adv.; bk.rev.; abstr.; bibl.; charts; stat.; index. circ. 500. **Indexed:** Dok.Str., ELLIS, Excerp.Med., HRIS, Key to Econ.Sci. —SWETS.

380.5 SP ISSN 0212-8357
TODOTRANSPORTE; revista mensual del transporte. 1984. m. 6500 ptas. (foreign 11400 ptas.). Tecnipublicaciones S.A., C. Albacete 5, 28027 Madrid, Spain. TEL 34-1-3261440. FAX 34-1-3262539. adv. circ. 15,600.
 Description: Covers the transportation industry, including travel, cargo, air, railroad, ship and highway.

388 NE ISSN 0928-1576
TOPICS IN TRANSPORTATION. (Text in English) 1987. irreg., latest 1994. price varies. V S P, P.O. Box 346, 3700 AH Zeist, Netherlands. TEL 31-3404-25790. FAX 31-3404-32081. (Dist. in U.S. and Canada by: Books International Inc., Box 605, Herndon, VA 22070. TEL 703-435-7064. FAX 703-689-0660) **Document type:** monographic series.

380.5 SP
TRADIME INFORMA. 12/yr. Conde Aranda 124, Zaragoza, Spain. TEL 76-43-21-99. Ed. Manuel Martin Moros.

380.5 MW
TRAFFIC. (Text in English) q. Centraf Associates Ltd., Box 30462, Chichiri, Blantyre 3, Malawi.

388.31 US ISSN 0041-0691
HE1 CODEN: TRMADJ
TRAFFIC MANAGEMENT; for buyers of transportation services and related equipment. (Includes 2 bound-in bi-monthlies: International Shipping; Warehousing and Distribution) 1962. m. $69.95 (Canada $123; Mexico $114.95; elsewhere $119.95). Cahners Publishing Company (Newton), Division of Reed Elsevier Inc., 275 Washington St., Newton, MA 02158-1630. TEL 617-964-3030. FAX 617-558-4327. (Subscr. to: 8773 S. Ridgeline Blvd., Highlands Ranch, CO 80126. TEL 800-662-7776) Ed. Mitchell E. MacDonald. adv.; illus.; tr.lit. circ. 73,237. (also avail. in microform from UMI) **Indexed:** B.P.I., BPIA, Bus.Ind., Data Process.Dig., INSPEC, Manage.Cont., SRI, Tr.& Indus.Ind. **Document type:** trade publication.
 —BLDSC (8882.140000); Faxon; UMI; UnCover. **CCC.**
 Description: For traffic, transportation, and corporate management. Covers transportation strategies, new products and services, cost reductions, regulations and the law.

388.31 US ISSN 0041-073X
HE2714
TRAFFIC WORLD; the weekly newsmagazine of transportation and distribution. 1907. w. $159. Journal of Commerce, Inc. (Washington), 741 National Press Bldg., Washington, DC 20045. TEL 202-383-6140. FAX 202-737-3349. Ed. Jean V. Murphy; Pub. Stanford A./Erickson. adv. contact: William Lavner. illus.; stat. circ. 10,500. (also avail. in microform from UMI; reprint service avail. from UMI) **Indexed:** B.P.I., HRIS. **Document type:** trade publication.
 —UMI; UnCover. **CCC.**

TRAILER LIFE. see SPORTS AND GAMES — Outdoor Life

388.4 UK ISSN 0049-4372
TRAMWAY MUSEUM SOCIETY. JOURNAL. vol.2, 1961. q. membership. Tramway Museum Society, National Tramway Museum, Crich, Matlock, Derby OE4 5DP, England. Ed. E. Wright. adv.; bk.rev.; charts; illus. circ. 1,800.

363.12 US ISSN 0276-8852
HE5614.2
TRANPORTATION SAFETY INFORMATION REPORT. 1974. q. U.S. Department of Transportation, Office of the Secretary, 400 Seventh St., S.W., Rm. 10200, Washington, DC 20590. TEL 202-366-1111. (Co-sponsor: Transportation Systems Center) **Document type:** government publication.

380.5 GW
TRANS AKTUELL; die Zeitung fuer Transport, Verkehr und Management. 1992. fortn. DM.114.40; newsstand price: DM.4.90. EuroTransportMedia Verlags- und Veranstaltungs GmbH, Handwerkstr. 15, 70565 Stuttgart, Germany. TEL 0711-78498-0. FAX 0711-7849859. Ed. Werner Bicker; Pub. Frank Neumann. adv.: B&W page DM.16700, color page DM.25050; trim 288 x 394; adv. contact: Bernd Rostock. bk.rev. circ. 61,351. cols./p.: 6; pp./issue: 24. (back issues avail.) **Document type:** newspaper.

380.5 GW
TRANS AKTUELL EXTRA. 1993. bi-m. newsstand price: DM.4.80. EuroTransportMedia Verlags- und Veranstaltungs GmbH, Handwerkstr. 15, 70565 Stuttgart, Germany. TEL 0711-78498-0. FAX 0711-7849859. Ed. Werner Bicker; Pub. Frank Neumann. adv. contact: Bernd Rostock. circ. 65,000. **Document type:** trade publication.

380.5 GW
▼**TRANS AKTUELL SPEZIAL.** 1994. a. DM.24.80. EuroTransportMedia Verlags- und Veranstaltungs GmbH, Handwerkstr. 15, 70565 Stuttgart, Germany. TEL 0711-78498-0. FAX 0711-7849859. Ed. Werner Bicker; Pub. Frank Neumann. adv. contact: Bernd Rostock. circ. 50,000. **Document type:** trade publication.

TRANSACTION. see RELIGIONS AND THEOLOGY — Protestant

380.5 US ISSN 1067-0297
TRANSIT CALIFORNIA. 1990. m. $18. California Transit Association, 1400 K St., Ste. 301, Sacramento, CA 95814. TEL 916-446-4656. FAX 916-446-4318. Ed. Edward R. Gerber. adv. contact: Mary Foy. bk.rev.; charts; illus.; stat.; tr.lit. circ. 7,000. (back issues avail.) **Document type:** trade publication.
 Description: Covers rail; air quality and alternative fuels; public transit; transit buses; congestion management; Intermodal Surface Transportation Efficiency Act; transit legislation, ADA and more.

380.5 US
TRANSIT CONNECTIONS. 1993. q. $25. 345 Hudson St., New York, NY 10014. TEL 212-620-7236. FAX 212-633-1165. Ed. William D. Middleton; Pub. Robert S. McIlwain. adv.: B&W page $2200, color page $3050; trim 8 x 10 7/8. circ. 12,850. **Document type:** trade publication.

388 621 628.53 US ISSN 1075-8186
▼**TRANSIT COOPERATIVE RESEARCH PROGRAM. RESEARCH RESULTS DIGEST.** 1994. bi-m. U.S. Federal Transit Administration, Office of Technical Assistance and Safety, Advanced Public Transportation Division, U.S. Department of Transportation, 400 Seventh St., S.W., Rm. 6107, Washington, DC 20590. TEL 202-366-1991. FAX 202-366-3765. **Document type:** government publication.
 Description: Updates on the results of T.C.R.P. research into cleaner public transport.

TRANSIT TIMES (ATLANTA). see TRANSPORTATION — Railroads

380.5 US ISSN 0748-7347
TRANSITPULSE; news of worldwide people mover developments. 1983. bi-m. $75 (foreign $90). Trans21, Box 249, Fields Corner Sta., Boston, MA 02122. TEL 617-825-2318. FAX 617-482-7417. Ed. Lawrence J. Fabian. bk.rev. circ. 850. (tabloid format; back issues avail.) **Document type:** newsletter.
 Description: Covers worldwide developments in automated passenger transport systems for urban, suburban and airport travel.

380.5 SA
TRANSNET ANNUAL REPORT (YEAR). (Editions in Afrikaans and English) a. free. Transnet Limited, Public Relations Department, P.O. Box 72501, Parkview 2122, South Africa. TEL 27-11-488-7410. FAX 27-11-488-7129. TELEX 447224 SA. charts; illus.; stat.; index. circ. 7,000 (Afrikaans ed. 2,500; English ed. 4,500). **Document type:** corporate report.
 Formerly (until 1990): S A Transport Services Annual Report (Year).
 Description: Reports on the activities of all Transnet divisions, including the railways, ports, petroleum pipelines, and South African Airways.

380.5 MX
TRANSPOR. 1978. m. San Francisco 224, piso 5, Col. del Valle, Apdo. Postal 12879, Mexico 12, D.F., Mexico. Ed. Enrique Landgrave Villanueva. adv. circ. 5,000.

380.5 II ISSN 0041-137X
HE1
TRANSPORT; automobile, aviation, railways, shipping, tourism. (Text in English) 1951. q. Rs.3 per no. Transport Publications, 20 Noble Chambers, S.A. Brelvi Rd., Bombay 400001, India. Ed. K.H. Rau. adv.; bk.rev.; illus. circ. 5,000. (also avail. in microfilm from UMI)

380.5 UK ISSN 0144-3453
HE1
TRANSPORT. 1980. bi-m. £50 (foreign £75). (Chartered Institute of Transport) Triangle Management Services Ltd., 35-39 Castle St., High Wycombe HP13 6RN, England. TEL 01494-450054. FAX 01494-450836. Ed. Malory Davies. adv. contact: Jo Parsons. circ. 17,000. (controlled). **Indexed:** Br.Rail.Bd., Br.Tech.Ind., Geo.Abstr., HRIS, P.A.I.S. **Document type:** bulletin.
 —Faxon; SWETS.
 Supersedes: Chartered Institute of Transport. Journal (ISSN 0020-3181)
 Description: Encourages and coordinates the study and advancement of transport for transporters and physical distributors.

380.5 910.09 EC ISSN 1018-2179
TRANSPORT; guia ecuatoriana de transporte y turismo. 1963. m. $119 (effective 1993). Apartado de Correos 09-01-5603, Sucre 2204, Guayaquil, Ecuador. TEL 593-4-363848. FAX 593-4-454717. Ed. Pablo Cevallos Estarellas; Pub. Nelson Cevallos Aviles. adv. contact: Roberto Wagner. circ. 4,100 (paid). (back issues avail.) **Document type:** trade publication.
 Description: Airline and shipline guide for travel agents and others in the Ecuadorian travel industry.

380.5 LU
TRANSPORT. fortn. 5 rue C.M. Spoo, 2546 Luxembourg, Luxembourg.

380.52 US ISSN 0733-0197
TRANSPORT (DE) REGULATION REPORT. 1981. m. $167. Transportation Services, 960 S. Broadway, Hicksville, NY 11801. TEL 516-822-1183. FAX 516-822-1126. Ed. Anthony N. Nuzio; Pub. Anthony N. Nuzio. circ. 600 (paid). **Document type:** newsletter.

380.5 CN ISSN 0227-3020
TRANSPORT - ACTION; the newsletter of public transport consumers. (Text in English and French) 1975. bi-m. Can.$20. Transport 2000 Canada, P.O. Box CP-858, Sta. B, Ottawa, ON K1P 5P9, Canada. TEL 613-594-3290. FAX 613-594-3271. Ed. J. Goss. adv.; bk.rev. circ. 1,850. **Document type:** newsletter.
 —CCC.
 Formerly: Transport 2000 Canada. Bulletin.
 Description: News and opinion on urban transit, passenger rail, airlines and intercity busses for users of public transport services in Canada.

380 II ISSN 0041-1388
TRANSPORT AND COMMUNICATIONS. (Text in English) 1961. m. Rs.40. O.N. Pandeya, 105-C Block F, New Alipore, Calcutta 700053, India. Ed. L.K. Pandeya. circ. 6,787.

TRANSPORTATION

380 — UN — ISSN 0252-4392
TRANSPORT & COMMUNICATIONS BULLETIN FOR ASIA & THE PACIFIC. 1950. a. price varies. United Nations Economic and Social Commission for Asia and the Pacific (ESCAP), United Nations Bldg., Rajadamnern Ave., Bangkok 10200, Thailand. (Dist. by: United Nations Publications, Rm. DC2-0853, New York, NY 10017; or Distribution and Sales Section, Palais des Nations, CH-1211 Geneva 10, Switzerland) bk.rev.; charts; illus.; stat. (back issues avail.). **Indexed:** IIS, P.A.I.S.
—BLDSC (9025.504200).
Formerly: Transport and Communications Bulletin for Asia and the Far East (ISSN 0041-1396)

380.5 — II — ISSN 0300-449X
TRANSPORT AND TOURISM JOURNAL. (Text in English) 1967. q. Rs.15. 1969 Ganj Mearkhan, Daryaganj, New Delhi 110002, India. Ed. M.S. Gambhir. adv.; charts; illus.

388 — BE — ISSN 0775-0552
TRANSPORT ECHO (NEDERLANDS EDITIE). French edition (ISSN 0775-0544) 1945. 11/yr. (newsletter w.) 6800 BEF (foreign 7600 BEF) (effective 1995). Transmedia N.V., Cuylitsstraat 39, 2018 Antwerp, Belgium. TEL 32-3-2385836. FAX 32-3-2164488. Ed. Nicole Martinet. adv.: B&W page 66000 BEF, color page 108000 BEF; trim 210 x 297. bk.rev.; illus.; stat. circ. 18,400. **Indexed:** Key to Econ.Sci. **Document type:** trade publication.
Supersedes in part (in 1987): Transport Echo (Edition Bilingue) (ISSN 0009-6083); Which superseded (in 1970): Transportkroniek (ISSN 0770-2418)
Description: Covers issues and technical advances affecting transport management.

380.5 — UK
TRANSPORT ECONOMIST. 1973. 3/yr. £21. Transport Economist Group, 54 Greenvale Rd., London SE9 1PD, England. Ed. Laurie Baker. circ. 200. **Document type:** bulletin.

388.3 — NE — ISSN 0929-0508
TRANSPORT EN LOGISTIEK; weekblad voor het goederenvervoer. (Supplement avail.: Transport en Logistiek Extra) 1940; N.S. 1992. w. (Thu.) fl.245. Transport en Logistiek Nederland, Postbus 726, 2700 AS Zoetermeer, Netherlands. TEL 31-79-683111. FAX 31-79-383325. (Subscr. to: Postbus 3008, 2700 KS Zoetermeer, Netherlands. TEL 31-79-683239. FAX 31-79-683300) Eds. Jos N. Poels, Hans van Zwet. adv.: B&W page fl.2968, color page fl.4643; trim 210 x 297; adv. contact: Roel Koek. bk.rev.; illus.; stat.; index; circ. 10,700 (paid). **Indexed:** Excerp.Med., Key to Econ.Sci. **Document type:** trade publication.
—SWETS.
Formed by the 1992 merger of: Beroepsvervoer (ISSN 0005-9447) & Wegvervoer (ISSN 0043-2083); Incorporates: Vervoer en Transport Techniek; Formerly: Vrije Vervoerder.
Description: Covers transport logistics, trucks and trucking, roads and traffic in the Netherlands and Europe, as well as related issues and developments in management, automation and communications.

380.52 — NE — ISSN 0165-330X
TRANSPORT EN OPSLAG. 1977. 12/yr. fl.189.50. Misset (Subsidiary of: Reed Elsevier plc), Postbus 4, 7000 BA Doetinchem, Netherlands. TEL 31-8340-49911. FAX 31-8340-43839. TELEX 45481. Ed. P.P. Roessel. adv.: B&W page fl.3576; trim 215 x 285; adv. contact: Cor van Nek. bk.rev.; charts; illus.; index. circ. 11,720. **Indexed:** Key to Econ.Sci. **Document type:** trade publication.
Description: Information on materials handling, storage, distribution and warehousing.

380.5 — UK — ISSN 0020-3122
TL230.A1
TRANSPORT ENGINEER. 1945. m. £24 (£30 elsewhere). Institute of Road Transport Engineers, Pegasus House, 116-120 Golden Ln., London EC1Y OTL, England. TEL 071-251-1227. FAX 071-253-1228. Ed. John Dickson-Simpson. adv.; bk.rev. circ. 17,000. **Indexed:** Br.Tech.Ind. **Document type:** trade publication.
—BLDSC (9025.590000); Ei.

388 — BE — ISSN 1021-4127
TRANSPORT EUROPE. French edition: Europe Transports (ISSN 1021-4135) (Text in English) 1991. m. 22600 BEF (effective 1995). Europe Information Service, Rue de Geneve, 6, 1140 Brussels, Belgium. TEL 32-2-242-6020. FAX 32-2-242-9410. **Document type:** bulletin.
• Also available online. Vendor(s): Lexis-Nexis. Also available on CD-ROM.
Description: Covers EU initiatives in the field of transportation.

380 658.7 — SZ — ISSN 1015-1567
TRANSPORT, FOERDER- UND LAGERTECHNIK; Schweizerische Fachzeitschrift fuer rationellen Gueterumschlag, Logistik, Transport, Lagerhaltung und Foerdertechnik. 1945. 10/yr. 82 SFr. (foreign 115 SFr.). S H Z Fachverlag AG, Alte Landstr. 43, CH-8700 Kuesnacht, Switzerland. TEL 01-9108022. FAX 01-9105155. Ed. Rudolf Weber. adv.; bk.rev.; illus. circ. 5,150. (processed) **Document type:** trade publication.
Former titles: Transport und Lagertechnik (ISSN 0041-1574); Verpackung und Transport.
Description: Looks at freight transport and storage.

380.5 900 — UK — ISSN 0041-1469
TRANSPORT HISTORY. 1968. a. £24($48) (foreign £26($52)). Graphmitre Ltd., 1 West St., Tavistock, Devon PL19 8DS, England. adv.; bk.rev.; illus.; index. circ. 600. (back issues avail.) **Indexed:** Amer.Hist.& Life (until 1994), Br.Hum.Ind., Hist.Abstr. (until 1994). **Document type:** academic/scholarly publication.

380.5 658.7 — SW — ISSN 1103-0755
TRANSPORT I DAG. (Supplement avail.: Air Cargo Courier (ISSN 1101-4075)) 1969. 10/yr. SEK 490. Fateco Foerlag AB, Propellervaegen 4 A, S-183 62 Taeby, Sweden. FAX 46-8756-1400. Ed. Paul E. Branke. adv.; bk.rev. circ. 3,200. **Document type:** trade publication.
Former titles (until 1992): Teknik i Transport (ISSN 1100-4231); (until 1988): Transportteknik Scandinavia (ISSN 0284-074X); (until vol.6, 1986): Skandinavisk Transportteknik (ISSN 0282-2784); (until 1984): Transportteknik (ISSN 0041-154X)

341 — NE
TRANSPORT: INTERNATIONAL TRANSPORT TREATIES. (Text in English, French) 1974. base vol. (plus a. update) fl.445($255) (effective 1994). Kluwer Law International (Subsidiary of: Wolters Kluwer N.V.), Postbus 85889, 2508 CN The Hague, Netherlands. TEL 31-70-3081500. FAX 31-70-3081515. (Dist. by: Libresso Distribution Centre, P.O. Box 23, 7400 GA Deventer, Netherlands. TEL 31-5700-33155. FAX 31-5700-33834; In N. America: Kluwer Law International, 675 Massachusetts Ave., Cambridge, MA 02139. TEL 617-354-0140. FAX 617-354-8595) Ed. M.H. Claringbould. (looseleaf format)
Description: Provides a clear synopsis of global air, seal, rail, inland waterway and overland transport treaties currently in force, and those not yet ratified.

380.5 — UK
TRANSPORT JOURNAL. 1953. m. £47. (Institute of Transport Management) European Publications, 14-20 George St., Birmingham B12 6RG, England. Ed. C. Gavin. adv. contact: B. Drumm. bk.rev. circ. 17,500. **Document type:** trade publication.
Formerly: Transport Management Journal.

TRANSPORT LAW & POLICY. see *LAW*

388 658 — NE — ISSN 0929-9645
▼**TRANSPORT LOGISTICS.** (Text in English) 1995. q. DM.300 (effective 1996). V S P, P.O. Box 346, 3700 AH Zeist, Netherlands. TEL 31-30-6925790. FAX 31-30-6932081. E-mail: 100341.2372@compuserve.com. Ed. James Cooper. (back issues avail.) **Document type:** academic/scholarly publication.
Description: Provides an international forum to explore the interface between transport and logistics, including such aspects as information technology, economics, marketing, organizational behavior and simulation.

388.324 621.86 — DK — ISSN 0908-0570
TRANSPORT - MAGASINET; the periodical rallying all transport interests. (Supplement avail.: Intern Transport) 1960. 22/yr. DKK 407. Dansk Auto Media A-S, Hoejvangen 23, P.O. Box 159, DK-3480 Fredensborg, Denmark. TEL 45-42-28-51-00. FAX 45-42-28-20-15. Ed. Claus Ricku. adv.: B&W page DKK 17280, color page DKK 20880; trim 370 x 266. bk.rev. circ. 16,883. **Indexed:** C.R.E.J. **Document type:** trade publication.
Formerly (until 1991): Transport (ISSN 0041-1361); Incorporates (in 1980): Emballage (ISSN 0013-6549)

380.5 — UK
TRANSPORT MANAGEMENT. 1944. bi-m. £12 (foreign £15) (effective 1995). Institute of Transport Administration, 32 Palmerston Rd., Southampton SO1 1LL, England. FAX 01703-634165. Ed. Norman Thisley. adv.; bk.rev.; circ. 4,000 (controlled). **Document type:** newsletter.

380.5 — SA
TRANSPORT MANAGEMENT. 1980. m. R.102.60 (foreign R.130) (effective 1994). Thomson Publications (Subsidiary of: Times Media Ltd.), P.O. Box 56182, Pinegowrie 2123, South Africa. TEL 27-11-886-3720. FAX 27-11-789-3196. TELEX 4-22125. Ed. Udo Rypstra. adv.; bk.rev. circ. 4,857. **Indexed:** Ind.S.A.Per. **Document type:** trade publication.

388 — UK — ISSN 0958-1561
TRANSPORT MANAGER'S AND OPERATOR'S HANDBOOK. 1970. a. £27.50. Kogan Page Ltd., 120 Pentonville Rd., London N1 9JN, England. TEL 071-278-0433. FAX 071-837-6348. TELEX 263088 KOGAN G. Ed. David Lowe. adv.; charts; illus. **Document type:** trade publication.
Formerly: Transport Manager's Handbook (ISSN 0306-9435)
Description: UK and EEC transport legislation, major technical developments and significant changes within the transport industry.

380.5 — PL — ISSN 0137-4435
TRANSPORT MUSEUMS. (Yearbook of the International Association of Transport Museums) (Text in English) irreg., vol.10, 1986. Centralne Muzeum Morskie, Gdansk - Central Maritime Museum, Gdansk, Ul. Szeroka 67-68, 80-835 Gdansk, Poland. (Subscr. to: International Association of Transport Museums, Zeughaus Str. 1-5, Cologne, Germany) (Co-sponsor: International Association of Transport Museums) Ed. Przemyslaw Smolarek.

380.5 — UK — ISSN 0958-6385
TRANSPORT NEWS. 1977. m. £15. K.A.V. Publicity (Glasgow) Ltd., 113 West Regent St., Glasgow G2 2RU, Scotland. TEL 0141-226-3861. Ed. Alistair Vallance. adv. circ. 9,500. **Indexed:** ASCA. **Document type:** trade publication.

380.5 — UK — ISSN 0306-2252
TRANSPORT NEWS DIGEST. 1968. m. £18. Transport Press Services, Pegasus House, 116-120 Golden Ln., London EC1Y OTL, England. TEL 0171-251-1227. FAX 0171-253-1228. Ed. John Dickson-Simpson. adv. circ. 700. **Document type:** newsletter.
Description: Contains trucks, law and industry news.

380.5 — NZ — ISSN 0110-6236
TRANSPORT NEWS OF NEW ZEALAND. 1934. m. NZ.$49.50. (New Zealand Road Transport Association) Transport News of New Zealand Ltd., 3rd Fl., Newspaper House, 93 Boulcott St., Wellington, New Zealand. TEL 64-4-4774994. FAX 64-4-4774998. Ed. Ralph Lenton. adv. contact: Helen Crandon. bk.rev.; stat. circ. 5,034. (back issues avail.) **Document type:** trade publication.
—CCC.
Description: Keeps road transport industry informed of current technical, legal and industrial issues and events.

TRANSPORTATION 6321

380.5   UK   ISSN 0967-070X
HE193   CODEN: TRPOE9
TRANSPORT POLICY. 1993. q. £143($228) (effective 1996). Butterworth - Heinemann, Part of the Reed Elsevier group, Linacre House, Jordan Hill, Oxford OX2 8DP, England. TEL 01865-310366. FAX 01865-310898. TELEX 83111 BHPOXF G. (Subscr. to: Elsevier Science Ltd., P.O. Box 800, Kidlington, Oxford OX5 1DX, England. TEL 44-1865-843000. FAX 44-1865-843010; Subscr. in U.S. and Canada to: Elsevier Science, 660 White Plains Rd., Tarrytown, NY 10591-5153. TEL 914-524-9200. FAX 914-333-2444) (also avail. in microform from UMI; back issues avail.) Document type: academic/scholarly publication.
—BLDSC (9025.857730); UMI. **CCC.**

TRANSPORT PROCESSES IN ENGINEERING. see ENGINEERING — Mechanical Engineering

380.5   FR   ISSN 0397-474X
TRANSPORT PUBLIC. 1890. 11/yr. 470 F. Union des Transports Publics (UTP), 5 rue d'Aumale, 75009 Paris, France. TEL 1-48-74-63-51. FAX 44-91-94-60. Ed. Robert Viennet. adv.; bk.rev. circ. 3,000. Indexed: HRIS.
Formerly (until 1982): Revue des Transports Publics Urbain et Regionaux.
Description: Covers news, facts, events and analyses of public transportation.

380.5 613.1   UK   ISSN 0965-6707
TRANSPORT RETORT. 1977. bi-m. £18 (foreign £22). Transport 2000 Ltd., Walkden House, 10 Melton St., London NW1 2EJ, England. TEL 0171-388-8386. FAX 0171-388-2481. Ed. Lynn Sloman. adv. contact: Jane Puzey. circ. 2,000. Document type: bulletin.
Description: Aims to reduce the priority given by government for building roads and to encourage public transport, cycling and walking.

380.5   UK   ISSN 0144-1647
TRANSPORT REVIEWS. 1981. q. £136($225) (effective 1996). Taylor & Francis Ltd., Rankine Rd., Basingstoke, Hants. RG24 8PR, England. TEL 44-1256-840366. FAX 44-1256-479438. TELEX 858540. E-mail: info@tandf.co.uk. (Subscr. in N. America to: Taylor & Francis Inc., 1900 Frost Rd., Ste. 101, Bristol, PA 19007-1598. TEL 800-821-8312. FAX 215-785-5515) Ed. S.M.A. Banister. adv.; bk.rev. Indexed: Asian-Pac.Econ.Lit., Geo.Abstr., HRIS, IDA. Document type: trade publication, academic/scholarly publication.
—BLDSC (9025.933000); Faxon; Genuine Article; SWETS; UnCover. **CCC.**
Description: Covers all modes of transport. Describes transport organizations and policies in individual countries. Topics covered include major cities, modelling, education, public transport, research, and the use of computers.
Refereed Serial

TRANSPORT SALARIED STAFF JOURNAL. see BUSINESS AND ECONOMICS — Labor And Industrial Relations

380.5   UK
TRANSPORT TICKET SOCIETY. JOURNAL.* 1946. m. £4. Transport Ticket Society, 18 Villa Rd., Lutton, Beds. LU2 7NT, England. illus.; index. circ. controlled. (processed)

TRANSPORT WORKERS OF THE WORLD. see LABOR UNIONS

331.88   MY
TRANSPORT WORKERS UNION. TRIENNIAL REPORT. (Text in English) triennial. Transport Workers Union, Transport Workers House, 21 Jalan Barat, Petaling Jaya, Malaysia. TEL 03-7566115. Ed. V. David.

380.5   SW   ISSN 0492-004X
TRANSPORTARBETAREN/TRANSPORTWORKER. 1897. m. (11/yr.). SEK 100 (effective 1993). Svenska Transportarbetarefoerbundet - Swedish Transport Workers' Union, P.O. Box 714, S-101 33 Stockholm, Sweden. TEL 46-8-723-77-00. FAX 46-8-723-00-76. Ed. Martin Viredius. adv.: B&W page SEK 14500, color page SEK 22000; trim 252 x 380; adv. contact: Goesta Wahlbaerj. bk.rev.; abstr.; illus.; index; circ. 67,000 (controlled). (also avail. in microform) Document type: bulletin.
Description: Directed to the transport market; articles on politics, economy, working conditions, the environment and other current issues.

388   NE   ISSN 0049-4488
HE7   CODEN: TRPOB6
TRANSPORTATION; an international journal devoted to the improvement of transportation planning and practice. (Text in English) 1972. q. fl.423 to institutions; $271 to institutions in U.S. (effective 1996). Kluwer Academic Publishers, Postbus 17, 3300 AA Dordrecht, Netherlands. TEL 31-78-392392. FAX 31-78-392254. TELEX 29245 KAPG NL. E-mail: SERVICES@WKAP.NL. (Dist. by: Kluwer Academic Publishers Group, P.O. Box 322, 3300 AH Dordrecht, Netherlands. TEL 31-78-392392. FAX 31-78-546474; N. America dist. addr.: Box 358, Accord Sta., Hingham, MA 02018-0358. TEL 617-871-6600. FAX 617-871-6528) Ed. Martin G. Richards. bk.rev.; index. (also avail. in microform from UMI; reprint service avail. from SWZ) Indexed: ASCA, Bibl.Inl., BMT, Curr.Cont., Dok.Str., Eng.Ind., Environ.Abstr., Excerp.Med., Geo.Abstr., HRIS, IDA, Intl.Civil Eng.Abstr., Sage Urb.Stud.Abstr., Soft.Abstr.Eng., SSCI, Trans.Res.Abstr. Document type: academic/scholarly publication.
—BLDSC (9026.050000); Ei; Faxon; Genuine Article; SWETS; UMI; UnCover. **CCC.**
Description: Discusses issues related to the formulation of transportation policy, the preparation and evaluation of transportation plans, and the management of transport systems in all parts of the world.
Refereed Serial

380.5   US   ISSN 0273-2602
HE202.5
TRANSPORTATION (BOCA RATON). (Subseries of: S I R S Social Issues (ISSN 0740-3127)) 0975. a. price varies; a. supplement $17. Social Issues Resources Series, Box 2348, Boca Raton, FL 33427-2348. TEL 407-994-0079; 800-232-7477. FAX 407-994-4704. (looseleaf format; also avail. in microfiche; back issues avail.)
Description: Reprints articles that explore problems of transportation infrastructures, examine the impact of the automobile, and look at future modes of transportation.

380.5   US
TRANSPORTATION (SACRAMENTO); a resource guide to who's doing what in California. 1990. irreg. $20. California Institute of Public Affairs, Box 189040, Sacramento, CA 95818. TEL 916-442-CIPA. FAX 916-442-2478. (Affiliate: The Claremont Graduate School) circ. 500. Document type: directory.
Description: Detailed reference to governmental agencies at all levels, associations, institutes, academic programs, and transportation systems in California.

658.7 380.5   US   ISSN 0895-8548
TS149
TRANSPORTATION & DISTRIBUTION. 1960. m. $45 (free to qualified personnel). Penton Publishing (Subsidiary of: Pittway Company), 1100 Superior Ave., Cleveland, OH 44114-2543. TEL 216-696-7000. FAX 216-696-8765. (Subscr. to: Box 95759, Cleveland, OH 44101) Ed. Perry Trunick. adv.; bk.rev.; illus.; tr.lit.; circ. 74,138 (controlled). (also avail. in microform from UMI; reprint service avail. from UMI) Indexed: ABI Inform, B.P.I, BPIA, Bus.Ind., Curr.Pack.Abstr., Excerp.Med., Manage.Cont., PROMT, Tr.& Indus.Ind.
•Also available online. Vendor(s): Knight-Ridder, Inc., University Microfilms International.
—BLDSC (9026.119800); Ei; SWETS; UMI; UnCover. **CCC.**
Former titles (until 1987): Handling and Shipping Management (ISSN 0194-603X); (until vol.19, no.10, Oct. 1978): Handling and Shipping (ISSN 0017-7385)
Description: Covers shipper-carrier relationships, new systems and technology in handling and warehousing products, and information processing systems applicable to inventory management and increased productivity and customer service.

380.5   US
TRANSPORTATION CONSUMER. 1972. 6/yr. free. U.S. Department of Transportation, Office of Public and Consumer Affairs, 400 Seventh St., S.W., Washington, DC 20590. TEL 202-655-4000. bibl.; illus. circ. 6,000. Indexed: Ind.U.S.Gov.Per. Document type: government publication.
Supersedes (in 1978): Consumer Transpotopics; (in 1976): Transportation Topics for Consumers (ISSN 0364-6653)

380.5   US   ISSN 0889-0889
HE203
TRANSPORTATION IN AMERICA; a statistical analysis of transportation in the United States. 1983. 3/yr. $55 to individuals; libraries and bookstores $44. Eno Transportation Foundation, 44211 Slatestone Court, Leesburg, VA 22075. TEL 703-729-7200. FAX 703-729-7219. Ed. Rosalyn A. Wilson. adv. contact: Tracy Larkin. circ. 1,000. (back issues avail.) Indexed: SRI.
Description: Analysis of traffic and costs of commercial and private freight and passenger transport in US by all modes.

380.5   US
TRANSPORTATION INTERMEDIARY. (Former name of issuing body: Transportation Brokers Conference of America) 1980. bi-m. $70. Transportation Intermediaries Association, 5845 Richmond Hwy., Ste. 750, Alexandria, VA 22303-1865. TEL 703-329-1894. FAX 703-329-1898. E-mail: tia@wdn.com. Ed. Annette E. Petrick; Pub. Annette E. Petrick. adv.: B&W page $818, color page $1340; trim 8 1/8 x 10 7/8; adv. contact: Margaret O'Connor. circ. 2,865. Document type: trade publication.
Formerly: Professional Broker (ISSN 1040-8568)
Description: Covers the development and technical aspects of third-party transportation service providers.

380.5   US   ISSN 0041-1612
HE1   CODEN: TRNJA
TRANSPORTATION JOURNAL. 1961. q. $53. American Society of Transportation and Logistics, Inc., 216 E. Church St., Lock Haven, PA 17745-2010. TEL 717-748-8515. Ed. John C. Spychalski. bk.rev.; charts; illus.; pat.; stat. circ. 3,500. (also avail. in microform from UMI; reprint service avail. from UMI,WSH) Indexed: ABI Inform., ASCA, B.P.I, Bus.Ind., C.L.I., Curr.Cont., Energy Rev., Environ.Abstr., Environ.Per.Bibl. (1972-), HRIS, Leg.Per., Mar.Aff.Bibl., Mid.East: Abstr.& Ind., P.A.I.S., SSCI, Tr.& Indus.Ind.
•Also available online. Vendor(s): University Microfilms International.
—BLDSC (9026.250000); Faxon; Genuine Article; SWETS; UMI; UnCover.

380 918   US
TRANSPORTATION: LATIN AMERICAN INDUSTRIAL REPORT. 1985. a. $235 per country report. Aquino Productions, Box 15760, Stamford, CT 06901. TEL 203-325-3138. Ed. Andres C. Aquino.

TRANSPORTATION LAW JOURNAL. see LAW

380.5   US   ISSN 0308-1060
   CODEN: TPLTAK
TRANSPORTATION PLANNING AND TECHNOLOGY. 1972. 4/yr. 515 ECU (effective 1996). Gordon and Breach Science Publishers, c/o International Publishers Distributor, 820 Town Center Dr., Langhorne, PA 19047. TEL 215-750-2642. FAX 215-750-6343. (Subscr. to: International Publishers Distributor, P.O. Box 90, Reading, Berkshire RG1 8JL, England. TEL 44-173-456-8316) Ed. David Gillingwater. adv.; bk.rev. (also avail. in microform; back issues avail.) Indexed: Br.Rail.Bd., Eng.Ind., Geo.Abstr., HRIS. —BLDSC (9026.265000); Faxon; SWETS; UnCover. **CCC.**
Formerly: Transportation Technology (ISSN 0041-1671)
Refereed Serial

380.5   UK   ISSN 0962-7146
TRANSPORTATION PLANNING SYSTEMS. 1991. q. £60 (rest of Europe £72; elsewhere £80). Landor Publishing Ltd., Quadrant House, 250 Kennington Ln., London SE11 5RD, England. TEL 0171-582-6626. FAX 0171-735-1299. E-mail: 100570,73@compuserve.com. Eds. Peter Stonham, Nigel Harris. adv. contact: Rodney Fletcher. Document type: academic/scholarly publication.
—BLDSC (9026.265400).
Description: Contains papers about developing methodologies and philosophies in transport planning, new techniques and models for implementing these, and case studies showing how transport planning issues are being tackled around the world.

TRANSPORTATION

380.5 — US — ISSN 0278-9434
HE331 — CODEN: TRQUDV
TRANSPORTATION QUARTERLY. 1947. q. $40 (foreign $60). Eno Transportation Foundation, 44211 Slatestone Court, Leesburg, VA 22075. TEL 703-729-7200. FAX 703-729-7219. adv. contact: Tracy E. Larkin. circ. 1,500. (also avail. in microfilm; reprint service avail. from UMI) **Indexed:** A.S.& T.Ind., ASCA, Avery Ind.Archit.Per., Curr.Cont., Dok.Str., Eng.Ind., Environ.Abstr., Fut.Surv., Geo.Abstr., HRIS, IDA, Intl.Civil Eng.Abstr., Mid.East: Abstr.& Ind., P.A.I.S., Risk Abstr., Sage Urb.Stud.Abstr., Soft.Abstr.Eng., SSCI.
— BLDSC (9026.266000); Ei; Faxon; Genuine Article; UMI.
Formerly (until 1982): Traffic Quarterly (ISSN 0041-0713)
Description: Features research analyses and public policy issues. Addresses transportation issues such as planning, design, operation, and regulation.

380.5 — UK — ISSN 0965-8564
HE192.5 — CODEN: TRPPEC
TRANSPORTATION RESEARCH. PART A: POLICY & PRACTICE; an international journal. 1967. bi-m. £316($503) (effective 1996). Elsevier Science Ltd., Pergamon, P.O. Box 800, Kidlington, Oxford OX5 1DX, England. TEL 44-1865-843000. FAX 44-1865-843010. E-mail: nlinfo-f@elsevier.nl; usinfo-f@elsevier.com; forinfo-kyf04035@niftyserve.or.jp; Site addr.: http://www.elsevier.nl/. (Subscr. in U.S. and Canada to: Elsevier Science, 660 White Plains Rd., Tarrytown, NY 10591-5153. TEL 914-524-9200. FAX 914-5333-2444) Ed. Frank A. Haight. adv.; bk.rev. circ. 1,600. (also avail. in microfiche from MIM; microfilm from UMI) **Indexed:** A.S.& T.Ind., BPIA, Bus.Ind., Cont.Pg.Manage., Curr.Cont., Dok.Str., Energy Rev., Eng.Ind., Environ.Abstr., Environ.Per.Bibl. (1982-), Ergon.Abstr., Excerp.Med., Geo.Abstr., HRIS, IDA, INSPEC, Int.Abstr.Oper.Res., Manage.Cont., SSCI.
— BLDSC (9026.274604); Ei; Faxon; Genuine Article; SWETS; UMI; UnCover. **CCC.**
Formerly (until 1993): Transportation Research. Part A: General (ISSN 0191-2607); Which supersedes in part: Transportation Research (ISSN 0041-1647)
Description: Covers the management, political and socio-economic aspects of transportation. Publishes case studies, surveys and reviews, and pure and applied research into the movement of passengers and freight.
Refereed Serial

380.5 — UK — ISSN 0191-2615
HE192.5 — CODEN: TRBMDY
TRANSPORTATION RESEARCH. PART B: METHODOLOGICAL; an international journal. 1967. bi-m. £316($503) (effective 1996). Elsevier Science Ltd., Pergamon, P.O. Box 800, Kidlington, Oxford OX5 1DX, England. TEL 44-1865-843000. FAX 44-1865-843010. E-mail: nlinfo-f@elsevier.nl; usinfo-f@elsevier.com; forinfo-kyf04035@niftyserve.or.jp; Site addr.: http://www.elsevier.nl/. (Subscr. in U.S. and Canada to: Elsevier Science, 660 White Plains Rd., Tarrytown, NY 10591-5153. TEL 914-524-9200. FAX 914-333-2444) Ed. Frank A. Haight. adv.; bk.rev. (also avail. in microfiche from MIM; microfilm from UMI) **Indexed:** A.S.& T.Ind., ASCA, BPIA, Br.Rail.Bd., Energy Rev., Environ.Abstr., Environ.Per.Bibl. (1982-), Ergon.Abstr., Geo.Abstr., HRIS, INSPEC, Int.Abstr.Oper.Res., Math.R., SSCI. **Document type:** academic/scholarly publication.
— BLDSC (9026.274610); Ei; Faxon; Genuine Article; SWETS; UMI; UnCover. **CCC.**
Supersedes in part: Transportation Research (ISSN 0041-1647)
Description: Papers on all methodological aspects of transportation, with a particular focus on mathematical analysis.
Refereed Serial

380.5 — UK — ISSN 0968-090X
HE1
TRANSPORTATION RESEARCH. PART C: EMERGING TECHNOLOGIES. 1993. bi-m. £316($503) (effective 1996). Elsevier Science Ltd., Pergamon, P.O. Box 800, Kidlington, Oxford OX5 1DX, England. TEL 44-1865-843000. FAX 44-1865-843010. E-mail: nlinfo-f@elsevier.nl; usinfo-f@elsevier.com; forinfo-kyf04035@niftyserve.or.jp; Site addr.: http://www.elsevier.nl/. (Subscr. in U.S. and Canada to: Elsevier Science, 660 White Plains Rd., Tarrytown, NY 10591-5153. TEL 914-524-9200. FAX 914-333-2444) Ed. Stephen G. Ritchie. (also avail. in microfiche from MIM; microfilm from UMI; back issues avail.) **Indexed:** Geo.Abstr. **Document type:** academic/scholarly publication.
— BLDSC (9026.274620); Ei; SWETS; UMI; UnCover. **CCC.**
Description: Concerned with the development and application of new transportation technologies, including IVHS, and with the impact of these advances on the performance characteristics of transportation systems.
Refereed Serial

380.5 — US — ISSN 0097-8515
TE1 — CODEN: HWRCAI
TRANSPORTATION RESEARCH CIRCULAR. 1965. irreg., no.419, Mar. 1994. price varies. U.S. National Research Council, Transportation Research Board, 2101 Constitution Ave., N.W., Washington, DC 20418. TEL 202-334-3213. FAX 202-334-2519. (Co-sponsors: National Highway Traffic Safety Administration, Federal Highway Administration) circ. 3,600. (also avail. in microfiche) **Indexed:** Dok.Str. **Document type:** monographic series, government publication.
— CASDDS; Faxon; UnCover.
Description: Presents interim research findings and research problem statements.

388 — NE
TRANSPORTATION RESEARCH, ECONOMICS AND POLICY. (Text in English) 1993. irreg., vol.3, 1995. price varies. Kluwer Academic Publishers, Postbus 17, 3300 AA Dordrecht, Netherlands. TEL 31-78-392392. FAX 31-78-392254. TELEX 29245 KAPG NL. (Dist. by: Kluwer Academic Publishers Group, P.O. Box 322, 3300 AA Dordrecht, Netherlands. TEL 31-78-392392. FAX 31-78-546474; N. America dist. addr.: Box 358, Accord Sta., Hingham, MA 02018-0358. TEL 617-871-6600. FAX 617-871-6528) (back issues avail.) **Document type:** monographic series.
Refereed Serial

TRANSPORTATION SAFETY LAW PRACTICE MANUAL. see *LAW*

TRANSPORTATION SAFETY RECOMMENDATIONS. see *PUBLIC HEALTH AND SAFETY*

388 — US — ISSN 0041-1655
TA1001 — CODEN: TRSCBJ
TRANSPORTATION SCIENCE. 1967. q. $47 to individuals (foreign $54); institutions $100 (foreign $109) (effective 1995). Insttiue for Operations Research and the Management Sciences, 940-A Elkridge Landing Rd., Linthicum, MD 21090-2909. TEL 410-850-0300. FAX 410-684-2963. (Subscr. to: Box 64794, Baltimore, MD 21264-4794) Ed. Mark Daskin. charts; illus.; stat.; index. circ. 1,500. (also avail. in microform from KTO,WWS; back issues avail.) **Indexed:** A.S.& T.Ind., ASCA, BMT, Dok.Str., Eng.Ind., HRIS, INSPEC, Int.Abstr.Oper.Res., Intl.Civil Eng.Abstr., Math.R., Oper.Res.Manage.Sci., Qual.Contr.Appl.Stat., Soft.Abstr.Eng. **Document type:** academic/scholarly publication.
— BLDSC (9026.280000); Ei; Faxon; Genuine Article; SWETS; UMI; UnCover. **CCC.**
Description: Publishes original contributions and survey papers on the planning, design, economic, social and operational aspects of all modes of transportation.

380.5 — US — ISSN 0278-3819
TRANSPORTATION STUDIES. 1982. irreg., vol.14, 1990. Gordon & Breach Science Publishers, c/o International Publishers Distributor, 820 Town Center Dr., Langhorne, PA 19047. TEL 215-750-2642. FAX 215-750-6343. (Subscr. to: International Publishers Distributor, P.O. Box 90, Reading Berkshire RG1 8JL, England. TEL 44-173-456-8316) Eds. Norman Ashford, William G. Bell. (also avail. in microform) **Document type:** monographic series.
— BLDSC (9026.315000).
Refereed Serial

380.5 621 — US — ISSN 1058-5451
TL243
TRANSPORTATION SYSTEMS. biennial. American Society of Mechanical Engineers, Vehicle Design Committee, 22 Law Dr., Fairfield, NJ 07007-2300. TEL 800-843-2763.

TRANSPORTATION TELEPHONE TICKLER. see *BUSINESS AND ECONOMICS — Trade And Industrial Directories*

380 — US — ISSN 0094-9922
HE17
TRANSPORTATION U S A. 1974. q. $3.10. U.S. Department of Transportation, 400 Seventh St. S.W., Washington, DC 20590. TEL 202-655-4000. (Dist. by: Supt. of Documents, Washington, DC 20402) (also avail. in microform) **Indexed:** Ind.U.S. Gov.Per.

380.5 — SP
TRANSPORTE MUNDIAL. 1984. m. 3840 ptas. (Europe 7140 ptas., elsewhere 10040 ptas.); newsstand price: 375 ptas. Luike - Motorpress, C. Ancora 40, 28045 Madrid, Spain. TEL 34-1-347-01-00. FAX 34-1-347-02-04. Ed. F. Javier Pedroche; Pub. Jose Luis Samaranch. adv.: B&W page 260000 ptas., color page 375000 ptas.; adv. contact: Antonino Bergesa. circ. 12,000. **Document type:** trade publication.
Description: For the commercial trucking industry.

380.5 — US
TRANSPORTE PROFESIONAL. 12/yr. Martires Concepcionistas 10, 1o Dcha., 28006 Madrid, Spain. TEL 1-402-74-21. FAX 1-309-18-02. Ed. Carlos Marti.

380.5 — CU — ISSN 0258-6029
TRANSPORTE Y VIAS DE COMUNICACION. 1977. q. $25 in N. America; S. America $26; Europe $28. (Ministerio de Educacion Superior) Ediciones Cubanas, Obispo No. 527, Apdo. 605, Havana, Cuba.

380.5 — SP — ISSN 0210-5047
TRANSPORTE 3. 1977. 11/yr. 4100 ptas. Padilla 72, 28006 Madrid, Spain. TEL 34-1-401-69-21. FAX 34-1-401-03-15. Ed. P. Perez Cuadrado. **Document type:** newspaper.

THE TRANSPORTER. see *PETROLEUM AND GAS*

380.5 — CU — ISSN 0496-1021
TRANSPORTES.* 1962. bi-m. Ministerio del Transporte, Rancho Boyeros y Tulipan, Havana, Cuba. Ed. Sergio Farinas. illus.; pat.; tr.lit. circ. 25,000.
Incorporates: Proa y Puerto.

380.5 — PO
TRANSPORTES. 12/yr. R. Jose Estevao 129, 1100 Lisbon, Portugal. TEL 1-52-18-69. FAX 35-27-441. Ed. Jose Ezequiel. circ. 400,000.

380.5 — MX — ISSN 0188-8013
TRANSPORTES Y TURISMO. 1935. m. $100. Insurgentes Norte No. 696, Mexico 4, DF, Mexico. TEL 782-21-40. FAX 583-33-18. Dir. Dolores Marquez V. de Mejia. adv. circ. 4,000. **Document type:** consumer publication.

TRANSPORTEUR; au service du personnel dans le transport et les industries connexes. see *RELIGIONS AND THEOLOGY — Protestant*

388.3   NO   ISSN 0803-6640
TRANSPORTFORUM. (Text in English, Norwegian) 1929. m. NOK 275 to individuals; students NOK 150; other Nordic countries NOK 370; elsewhere NOK 420. Norske Transportbedrifters Landsforening, P.O. Box 5477 Majorstua, N-0305 Oslo, Norway. TEL 47-22-96-50-26. FAX 47-22-60-14-94. Ed. Einar Spurkeland. adv.: B&W page NOK 7600, color page NOK 12100; trim 185 x 260; adv. contact: Arnt Christiansen. bk.rev. circ. 5,500. **Document type:** trade publication.
—CCC.
(until 1991): Transportforum, Kollektivtraffikk og Transportservice (ISSN 0803-1916); (until 1990): Transportforum (ISSN 0802-2917); (until 1989): Rutebiltidende (ISSN 0048-8836)
Description: Directed to managers, employees in coach service, bus line service and city transit, transport of goods, ferry boat service and coastal liners.

380.5   GW   ISSN 0176-358X
TRANSPORTMARKT. (Text in English and German) 1980. m. DM.70. Transportmarkt Verlag GmbH, Ehlersberger Weg 214, 22889 Tangstedt, Germany. TEL 040-6071445. FAX 040-6072343. Ed. Friedemann Bast. adv.: B&W page DM.4105; trim 270 x 185; adv. contact: Bruno Haaks. bk.rev.; bibl.; stat. circ. 9,600. (back issues avail.) **Document type:** trade publication.

380.52   GW   ISSN 0174-559X
K24   CODEN: TRSPER
TRANSPORTRECHT; Zeitschrift fuer das gesamte Recht der Gueterbefoerderung, der Spedition, der Versicherungen des Transports, der Personenbefoerderung und der Reiseverstaltung. 1979. m. DM.286. Luchterhand Verlag, Gutenbergstr. 8, 65830 Kriftel, Germany. TEL 06192-408233. FAX 06192-408248. (Dist. by: Luchterhand Verlag, Heddesdorferstr. 31, 56564 Neuwied, Germany. TEL 02631-801313. FAX 02631-801210) Ed. Martina Weber. adv.: page DM.1400; trim 255 x 184; adv. contact: Margret Sock-Freiberg. bk.rev.; index; circ. 1,400. (back issues avail.) **Document type:** trade publication.
—SWETS.
Formerly: Transportation Law and Legislation.

380.5   FR   ISSN 0564-1373
HE3
TRANSPORTS. 1956. bi-m. 773.75 F. to individuals (foreign 904 F.); libraries 657.69 F. (foreign 768.40 F.) (effective 1996). Editions Techniques et Economiques, 3, rue Soufflot, 75005 Paris, France. TEL 46-34-10-30. FAX 46-34-55-83. TELEX 260-717 F. Ed. Genevieve Epstein. adv.; bk.rev.; bibl.; illus.; stat.; index. circ. 4,000. (back issues avail.) **Indexed:** ELLIS, HRIS, PROMT.
—Faxon; SWETS. CCC.
Description: Covers the economies of all methods of transport.

380.5   FR   ISSN 0151-5861
TRANSPORTS ACTUALITES. 1976. 39/yr. 425 F. (foreign 546 F.) (effective Jan. 1994). Groupe Information et Professions, 1 cite Bergere, 75009 Paris, France. TEL 44-69-55-50. FAX 48-01-07-68. TELEX 285 485. Eds. Philippe-Edouard Grardel, Jean-Pierre Maysonnave. circ. 10,336.

380.5   FR   ISSN 0397-6521
TRANSPORTS URBAINS; forum des transports publics. 1964. q. 280 F. (foreign 300 F.) (effective 1995). Groupement pour l'Etude des Transports Urbains Modernes, 173 rue Armand Silvestre, 92400 Courbevoie, France. E-mail: zembri@enpc.enpc.fr. Ed. Alain Sutter. adv.; bk.rev. circ. 2,000. **Document type:** academic/scholarly publication.
Formerly (until 1974): Forum des Transports Publics (ISSN 0071-8033)
Description: Looks at urban and suburban transportation news.
Refereed Serial

380.5   SA
TRANSTALK. (Text in Afrikaans, English) 1991. q. free. Transnet Limited, P.O. Box 72501, Parkview 2122, South Africa. TEL 27-11-488-7410. FAX 27-11-488-7129. TELEX 447224 SA. Ed. Alrika Hefers. illus. (tabloid format) **Document type:** newspaper.
Description: General interest magazine for Transnet employees, with health, education, sports, and environmental news.

380.5   IT   ISSN 0390-4520
TRASPORTI; diritto, economia, politica. 1973? 3/yr. L.150000 (foreign L.190000) (effective 1996). Mucchi Editori s.r.l., Via Emilia Est. 1527, 41100 Modena, Italy. FAX 39-59-223917. Ed.Bd.

380.5   IT   ISSN 1120-8732
TRASPORTI E TRAZIONE; rivista di tecnica, economia e pianificazione dei trasporti. 1988. bi-m. L.69000($113) to individuals; students L.26000 (effective 1994). Masson S.p.A., Divisione Periodici, Via Statuto 2-4, 20120 Milan, Italy. TEL 02-6367-1. FAX 02-6367-211. Ed. Ernesto Stagni. adv.: B&W page L.1100000, color page L.2180000; trim 210 x 295. circ. 2,000. **Document type:** academic/scholarly publication.

380.5   IT
TRASPORTI INDUSTRIALI E MOVIMENTAZIONE. 1955. m. L.100000 (foreign L.190000). Gruppo Editoriale Jackson S.p.A., Via Groki, 69, 20092 Cinisello B. (MI), Italy. TEL 39-2-66034205. FAX 39-2-66034238. Ed. Alberto Russo Frattasi. adv.: B&W page L.2990000, color page L.3890000; trim 181 x 270. circ. 6,302. (back issues avail.)
Formerly: Trasporti Industriali (ISSN 0041-1809)

380.5   IT
TRASPORTI NEWS. 12/yr. Piazza Duca d'Acosta 6, 20124 Milan, Italy. TEL 2-66-90-427. FAX 2-66-94-185. Ed. A.M. Boidi. circ. 120,000.

388.4   AT   ISSN 0155-1264
TROLLEY WIRE. 1952. q. Aus.$19 (foreign Aus.$25). South Pacific Electric Railway Co-Operative Society Ltd., P.O. Box 103, Sutherland, N.S.W. 2232, Australia. TEL 02-542-3646. Ed.Bd. bk.rev.; stat. circ. 1,200. (back issues avail.) **Indexed:** Aus.Rd.Ind.

388.322   UK   ISSN 0266-7452
TROLLEYBUS MAGAZINE. 1963. bi-m. £14 (foreign £15.50). National Trolleybus Association, 49 Alzey Gardens, Harpenden, Herts. AL5 5SY, England. (Subscr. to: 10 Compton Close, Flitwick, Beds. MK45 1TA, England) Ed. Roland Box. adv.; bk.rev.; illus. circ. 850. (tabloid format) **Document type:** newspaper.
Description: Covers many aspects of trolleybuses and their operation.

TRUCK AND BUS TRANSPORTATION; Australia's leading national road transport fleetowner monthly. see *TRANSPORTATION — Trucks And Trucking*

380.5   US   ISSN 0739-7100
U M T R I RESEARCH REVIEW. (Former issuing body: Highway Safety Research Institute) 1970. q. $35. University of Michigan, Transportation Research Institute, 2901 Baxter Rd., Ann Arbor, MI 48109-2150. TEL 313-764-2171. FAX 313-936-1081. E-mail: B SWEET@UMICH.EDU. Ed. Robert E. Sweet. charts; illus. circ. 2,100. (also avail. in microfilm; back issues avail.) **Indexed:** Eng.Ind., P.A.I.S., Psychol.Abstr. (1976-), Psycscan. **Document type:** academic/scholarly publication.
—BLDSC (9083.200000); UMI.
Former titles (until 1982): H S R I Research Review (ISSN 0146-8545); (until 1977): H S R I Research (ISSN 0364-3476)

353.85   US   ISSN 0092-3117
HE206.3
U.S. DEPARTMENT OF TRANSPORTATION. FISCAL YEAR BUDGET IN BRIEF. Key Title: Budget in Brief - Department of Transportation (Washington). a. U.S. Department of Transportation, Office of Budget, 400 Seventh St., S.W., Washington, DC 20590. **Document type:** government publication.

380.5   US   ISSN 0099-2267
HE192.5
U.S. DEPARTMENT OF TRANSPORTATION. OFFICE OF UNIVERSITY RESEARCH. AWARDS TO ACADEMIC INSTITUTIONS BY THE DEPARTMENT OF TRANSPORTATION. Key Title: Awards to Academic Institutions by the Department of Transportation. a. U.S. Department of Transportation, Office of University Research, 400 7th St., S.W., Washington, DC 20590. TEL 202-655-4000. **Document type:** government publication.

388   US
U.S. FEDERAL TRANSIT ADMINISTRATION. REPORT ON FUNDING LEVELS AND ALLOCATION OF FUNDS. a. free. U.S. Federal Transit Administration, Office of Policy, U.S. Department of Transportation, TBP-10, 400 Seventh St., S.W., Rm. 9300, Washington, DC 20590. TEL 202-366-4060. FAX 202-366-7116. (Also avail. from: National Technical Information Service, 5285 Port Royal Rd., Springfield, VA 22161. TEL 703-487-4650. FAX 703-321-8547) **Document type:** government publication.
Description: Provides U.S. Department of Transportation recommendations to Congress for the following fiscal year funds to be made available to build new fixed guideway systems and extensions.

388 362.4   US
U.S. NATIONAL RESEARCH COUNCIL. TRANSIT COOPERATIVE RESEARCH PROGRAM. ANNUAL REPORT. 1992. a. U.S. National Research Council, Transportation Research Board, 2101 Constitution Ave., N.W., Washington, DC 20418. TEL 202-334-3216. FAX 202-334-2519. (Co-sponsor: U.S. Federal Transit Administration. Transit Cooperative Research Program) **Document type:** government publication.
Description: Outlines the program's applied research on transportation issues.

U.S. OFFICE OF TECHNOLOGY ASSESSMENT. REPORTS. SCIENCE, EDUCATION, AND TRANSPORTATION PROGRAM. see *EDUCATION*

UNIVERSITATEA POLITEHNICA BUCURESTI. BULETIN STIINTIFIC. INGINERIE MECANICA/POLYTECHNICAL UNIVERSITY OF BUCHAREST. SCIENTIFIC BULLETIN. MECHANICAL ENGINEERING. see *ENGINEERING — Mechanical Engineering*

385.1   CN   ISSN 0841-8659
UNIVERSITY OF MANITOBA. TRANSPORT INSTITUTE. OCCASIONAL PAPER. 1968. irreg., latest 1992. University of Manitoba, Transport Institute, 612-181 Freedman Crescent, Winnipeg, MB R3T 2N2, Canada. TEL 204-474-9842. FAX 204-275-0204. **Document type:** monographic series.
Formerly: University of Manitoba. Center for Transportation Studies. Occasional Paper. (ISSN 0076-3977)

380.5   PL   ISSN 0208-4821
UNIWERSYTET GDANSKI. WYDZIAL EKONOMIKI TRANSPORTU. ZESZYTY NAUKOWE. EKONOMIKA TRANSPORTU LADOWEGO. (Text in Polish; summaries in English and Russian) 1971. irreg., latest no.21. price varies. Uniwersytet Gdanski, Wydzial Ekonomiki Transportu, c/o Biblioteka Glowna, Ul. Armii Krajowej 110, 81-824 Sopot, Poland. TEL 51-0061. TELEX 051 2247 BMOR PL. (Dist. by: Ars Polona-Ruch, Krakowskie Przedmiecie 7, 00-680 Warsaw, Poland) circ. 250. **Document type:** academic/scholarly publication.
—BLDSC (9512.433500).
Description: Covers problems of inland transport economics, organization of transport and transport policy, economic problems of particular branches of transport, such as railway, road and inland water.

380.5   IT
UOMINI E TRASPORTI. 1983. 10/yr. (Transport Federation) Federservice, Via Marconi 32, 40122 Bologna, Italy. TEL 39-51-554304. FAX 39-51-558619. TELEX 512811 FEDEBO I. Ed. Guido Tucci. adv.: B&W page L.1900000; adv. contact: Paolo Volta. circ. 20,000.

380.5   US   ISSN 0195-4695
URBAN TRANSPORT NEWS; management, funding, ridership, technology. 1973. bi-w. $312 (effective Sep. 1992). Business Publishers, Inc., 951 Pershing Dr., Silver Spring, MD 20910-4464. TEL 301-587-6300. FAX 301-585-9075. Ed. Tom Ramstack. bk.rev. (looseleaf format) **Document type:** newsletter.
•Also available online. Vendor(s): NewsNet (TS10).
—CCC.
Formerly: Public Transit Report (ISSN 0148-4087)
Description: Presents developments in urban transport that increase efficiency and safety, such as mass transit systems and battery-powered cars.

6324 TRANSPORTATION — ABSTRACTING, BIBLIOGRAPHIES, STATISTICS

388.322 US ISSN 1040-4880
URBAN TRANSPORTATION MONITOR. 1987. bi-w. $250 (foreign $275). Lawley Publications, Box 12300, Burke, VA 22009-2300. TEL 703-764-0512. FAX 703-764-0516. Ed. Daniel B. Rathbone. adv.: Clarissa/Reeves. bk.rev. circ. 1,000. **Document type:** newsletter.
  Description: Presents news and information on all aspects of urban transportation, transit, and traffic engineering. Survey conducted for each issue.

380.52 GW
V B B AKTUELL. 12/yr. Verkehrsgemeinschaft Berlin - Brandenburg, Brandruste 40, 12277 Berlin, Germany. TEL 030-7411001. FAX 030-7471840. circ. 700,000. **Document type:** consumer publication.
  Formerly (until 1994): B V G Aktuell.

380.5 AU
V C OE ZEITUNG. 1989. 8/yr. S.180. Verkehrsclub Oesterreich, Dingelstedtgasse 15, A-1150 Vienna, Austria. TEL 0222-8932697. FAX 0222-8932431. Ed. Christian Hoeller. adv.: page S.38900; trim 272 x 420; adv. contact: Christian Hoeller. bk.rev./circ. 28,000. cols./p.: 6; pp./issue: 8. (back issues avail.) **Document type:** newspaper.
  Description: Promotes means of transportation which are environmentally friendly.

380.5 SZ
V C S ZEITUNG. (Text in French, German) 11/yr. Verkehrs Club der Schweiz, Bahnhofstr. 8, CH-3360 Herzogenbuchsee, Switzerland. TEL 063-615151. Ed. Bernhard Stricker. circ. 85,500.

380.5 US
VANNING NOW. 1990. 5/yr. $10. Council of Councils, 638 Prospect Rd., Dept. UIPD, Berea, OH 44017-2744. TEL 216-234-5254. (Subscr. to: c/o Bob Rowland, 589 Old Post Rd., Virginia Beach, VA 23452-2914. TEL 804-463-3419) Ed. Brian Walker. adv.: B&W page $120. circ. 850. **Document type:** newsletter.
  Description: Covers custom vans and van events.

VEHICLE SYSTEM DYNAMICS; international journal of vehicle mechanics and mobility. see ENGINEERING — Mechanical Engineering

380.52 GW
VERBUNDFAHRPLAN. (Text in English, French, German) 1972. a. DM.5. Muenchner Verkehrs- und Tarifverbund GmbH, Thierschstr. 2, 80538 Munich, Germany. TEL 089-23803-0. FAX 089-23803-282. Ed. Paul Huber. adv. contact: Gisela Berg. circ. 120,000. (back issues avail.) **Document type:** directory.

380.5 AU ISSN 1019-7346
VERKEHR UND UMWELT. 6/yr. Erwin Schwaiger Verlag GmbH, Pichlergasse 2-10, A-1010 Vienna, Austria. TEL 01-3199126. FAX 01-3199125. Ed. Peter Sonnberger. circ. 10,000. **Document type:** trade publication.

380.5 388.31 GW ISSN 0341-2148
VERKEHRS RUNDSCHAU. 1944. w. DM.243.50 (foreign DM.293.20). Heinrich Vogel Fachzeitschriften GmbH, Neumarkterstr. 18, 81673 Munich, Germany. TEL 089-431800. FAX 089-43180398. (Subscr. to: Postfach 802020, 81620 Munich, Germany) charts; stat. circ. 114,420. **Document type:** trade publication.
  —CCC.

380.5 SZ
VERKEHRS UND STAATSPERSONAL. w. Hopfenweg 21, CH-3007 Bern, Switzerland. TEL 031-455562. Ed. Robert Andenmatten. circ. 18,529.

380.5 GW
DAS VERKEHRSGEWERBE WESTFALEN-LIPPE.* 1952. m. Verband fuer das Verkehrsgewerbe Westfalen-Lippe e.V., c/o Dr. E. Bauer, Hafenstr. 6, Postfach 7649, 4400 Muenster, Germany. circ. 2,500. (back issues avail.)

380.5 340 GW ISSN 0342-6734
VERKEHRSRECHTLICHE MITTEILUNGEN. m. DM.42. Kirschbaum Verlag GmbH, Siegfriedstr. 28, 53179 Bonn, Germany. TEL 0228-95453-0. FAX 0228-9545327. (Subscr. to: Postfach 210209, 53157 Bonn, Germany) Indexed: Dok.Str. **Document type:** trade publication.
  —CCC.

380.5 GW ISSN 0723-6689
VERKEHRSWIRTSCHAFT. 1982. m. DM.148.40 (foreign DM.162.70). Verlag VerkehrsWirtschaft Gerd Achilles, Spaldingstr. 210, 20097 Hamburg, Germany. TEL 040-230173. FAX 040-234613. Ed. Gerd Achilles. adv. contact: Anja Barenscheer. bk.rev. circ. 11,500. (back issues avail.) **Document type:** bulletin.

388 AT
VICTAXI. m. Aus.$35. (Victorian Taxi Association) Magazine Publishing Company, 4 Wandoo St., Fortitude Valley, Qld. 4006, Australia. TEL 61-7-252-9677. FAX 61-7-252-4667. Ed. Neil Sach. adv.: B&W page Aus.$1307, color page Aus.$2407; trim 275 x 210; adv. contact: Trevor Kirk. circ. 5,200. **Document type:** trade publication.

380.5 AT
VICTORIAN ROAD TRANSPORT ASSOCIATION. ANNUAL REPORT. a. free. Victorian Road Transport Association, 17 Raglan St., South Melbourne, Vic. 3205, Australia. TEL 699-8833. FAX 03-669-7437. circ. 2,000.

380.5 TE4 IT ISSN 0393-8077
VIE E TRASPORTI; rassegna di tecnica ed economia dei trasporti. 1929. bi-m. L.45000 (foreign L.54000). Casa Editrice la Fiaccola (Milan), Via Ravizza 62, 20149 Milan, Italy. TEL 02-4814355. FAX 02-4814834. TELEX 335512 COSTRU I. Dir. Giuseppe Saronni. adv.; abstr.; charts; illus.; stat.; index. circ. 8,000. (back issues avail.) Indexed: Chem.Abstr.
  Former titles: Rivista della Strada (ISSN 0035-5992); Asfalti, Bitumi, Catrami.

600 DK ISSN 0106-1666
VIRKSOMHEDS NYT. 1970. 10/yr. DKK 170. Christtreu, Strandlodsvei 48, DK-2300 Copenhagen S, Denmark. TEL 32-844848. FAX 31-582055. Ed. B. Remby. adv.; bk.rev.; illus.; charts; circ. 16,954 (controlled).
  Former titles: Materialehaandtering og Transport Nyt (ISSN 0025-5297); Materiale Haandtering.
  Description: Factory equipment, packing, storage and transportation.

658.564 658.78 DK ISSN 0109-8195
VIRKSOMHEDS NYT. LEVERANDOERREGISTER. 1984. a. Christtreu, Strandlodsvei 48, DK-2300 Copenhagen S, Denmark. TEL 32-844848. FAX 31-582055. circ. 16,954.

388 796.6 NE ISSN 0166-0276
VOGELVRIJE FIETSER. 1975. bi-m. fl.50. Fietsersbond E N F B, Postbus 2150, 3440 DD Woerden, Netherlands. TEL 31-3480-23119. FAX 31-3480-17058. Ed. Roel Bartlema. adv.: B&W page fl.1800. bk.rev.; index. circ. 30,000. (back issues avail.)
  —SWETS.
  Description: Covers issues relating to the use of the bicycle as a means of transportation.

380.5 RU
VSESOYUZNYI NAUCHNO-ISSLEDOVATEL'SKII INSTITUT TRANSPORTNOGO STROITEL'STVA. TRUDY.* vol.106, 1977. irreg. 0.83 Rub. per no. Izdatel'stvo Transport, Basmanny tupik 6A, 107174 Moscow, Russia. TEL 095-262-6773. Ed.Bd. circ. 1,000. Indexed: Chem.Abstr.

W S S A GRAPEVINE. (Wine and Spirits Shippers Association) see BEVERAGES

341 NE
WARSAW CONVENTION; international transport law - commentary. (Text in English) 1992. base vol. (plus irreg. updates, 2-3/yr.) fl.295($169) (effective 1994). Kluwer Law International (Subsidiary of: Wolters Kluwer N.V.), Postbus 85889, 2508 CN The Hague, Netherlands. TEL 31-70-3081500. FAX 31-70-3081515. (Dist. by: Libresso Distribution Centre, P.O. Box 23, 7400 GA Deventer, Netherlands. TEL 31-5700-33155. FAX 31-5700-33834; In N. America: Kluwer Law International, 675 Massachusetts Ave., Cambridge, MA 02139. TEL 617-354-0140. FAX 617-354-8595) Ed.Bd. (looseleaf format)
  Description: Detailed article by article commentary of the Warsaw Convention as amended by the Hague Protocol (1955) and successor instruments. Includes historical material, international case law and significant journal articles relating to transport law.

354 AT ISSN 1035-1671
WESTERN AUSTRALIA. DEPARTMENT OF TRANSPORT. ANNUAL REPORT. 1934. a. free. Department of Transport, 136-138 Stirling Highway, Nedlands, W.A. 6009, Australia. FAX 09-386-5119. TELEX 94521. circ. 600 (controlled).
  Formerly (until 1986): Western Australia. Transport Commission. Annual Report of the Commissioner of Transport.

380.5 630 US ISSN 1042-2633
HE9788.4.A55
WHO'S WHO IN LIVE ANIMAL TRADE & TRANSPORT. 1985. biennial. $28.50. Silesia Companies, Inc., Box 441110, Ft. Washington, MD 20749-1110. TEL 301-292-1970. FAX 301-292-1787. Ed. Dale L. Anderson. adv. (back issues avail.) **Document type:** directory.
  Formerly: Who's Who in Animal Transportation (ISSN 8755-688X)
  Description: Worldwide listing of personnel involved in the transporting of animals.

380.5 SA ISSN 0257-5426
WIEL. (Text in Afrikaans) 1978. m. R.44 (foreign R.60) (effective 1994). Thomson Publications (Subsidiary of: Times Media Ltd.), P.O. Box 56182, Pinegowrie 2123, South Africa. TEL 27-11-789-2144. FAX 27-11-789-3196. Ed. J. Herbst. adv.; bk.rev. circ. 21,925. (back issues avail.) **Document type:** trade publication.

388.346 TL298 US ISSN 0162-7368
WOODALL'S R V BUYER'S GUIDE. 1978. a. $5.95. Woodall Publishing Co., 13975 W. Polo Trail Dr., Lake Forest, IL 60045. TEL 708-362-6700; 800-323-9076. FAX 708-362-8776. Pub. Deborah A. Spriggs. adv. contact: Mary Sgaraglino. circ. 85,000. **Document type:** consumer publication.
  Description: Helps consumers select a recreational vehicle and accessories.

380.5 UK ISSN 1352-7614
▼**WORLD TRANSPORT POLICY & PRACTICE.** 1995. q. £99($149) (effective 1996). M C B University Press Ltd., 60-62 Toller Ln., Bradford, W. Yorks BD8 9BY, England. TEL 01274-499821. FAX 01274-547143. (Subscr. in N. America to: MCB University Press Ltd., Box 10812, Birmingham, AL 35201. TEL 205-995-1588. FAX 205-995-1588) Ed. John Whitelegg; Pub. Marjorie Brown. **Document type:** academic/scholarly publication.
  —BLDSC. (9360.154180).

ZHONGGUO JIAOTONG NIANJIAN/CHINA COMMUNICATIONS AND TRANSPORTATION YEARBOOK. see COMMUNICATIONS

380.5 SZ
ZUERICH NEWS. (Text in English, German) 1943. fortn. 58 SFr. Jean Frey AG, Postfach 285, CH-8021 Zurich, Switzerland. TEL 01-2078721. FAX 01-2078938. Ed. Rudolf Brosi. adv. contact: Adrienne Rothen. circ. 30,000. **Document type:** bulletin.

TRANSPORTATION — Abstracting, Bibliographies, Statistics

387.7 FR ISSN 0767-5178
A D P EN.... a. Aeroports de Paris, Service Previsions et Statistiques, Orly Sud 103, 94396 Orly Aerogare Cedex, France.

629.13 GW ISSN 0001-0987
A D V - INFORMATIONSDIENST. 1949. m. DM.58. Arbeitsgemeinschaft Deutscher Verkehrsflughaefen - German Airports' Association, Flughafen, 70621 Stuttgart, Germany. FAX 0711-9484746. Ed. Udo Wolffram. bk.rev.; stat.; index. circ. 350. **Document type:** abstracting/indexing.
  —CCC.
  Description: Summary of press publications on airports, air transportation and the aerospace industry.

TRANSPORTATION — ABSTRACTING, BIBLIOGRAPHIES, STATISTICS 6325

629.2 IT ISSN 0001-2033
A N F I A NOTIZIARIO STATISTICO. 1959. m. (11/yr.). L.430000($550) (effective 1995). Associazione Nazionale fra le Industrie Automobilistiche - Italian Automobile Manufacturers Association, Corso G. Ferraris 61, 10128 Turin, Italy. TEL 39-11-5613901. FAX 39-11-545986. stat. circ. 500. (back issues avail.) **Document type:** bulletin, trade publication.
Description: Covers statistics on the production, market and foreign trade of the Italian automobile industry.

388.3 621.382 US
A P T S PROJECT SUMMARIES. (Advanced Public Transportation Systems) (Subseries of: U.S. Federal Transit Administration. Report) irreg. free. U.S. Federal Transit Administration, Office of Technical Assistance and Safety, Advanced Public Transportation Division, U.S. Department of Transportation, 400 Seventh St., S.W., Rm. 6100, Washington, DC 20590. TEL 202-366-0201. FAX 202-366-3765. **Document type:** monographic series, government publication.
Description: Keeps the transportation community informed of the most recent A.P.T.S. program research in advanced (often computer-based) systems for mass transit applications.

387 NE ISSN 0929-2950
DE AAN- EN AFVOER VAN GOEDEREN OVER ZEE IN DE NEDERLANDSE ZEEHAVENS. 1982. q. Nationale Havenraad, Koninginnegracht 19, 2514 AB The Hague, Netherlands. TEL 31-70-3517615. FAX 31-70-3517600. (back issues avail.) **Document type:** government publication.
Formerly (until 1991): Aan- en Afvoer over Zee in de Nederlandse Zeehavens (ISSN 0924-4360)
Description: Statistical data concerning seaborne traffic in Dutch seaports.

363.12 UN ISSN 1014-4498
ACCIDENT - INCIDENT REPORTING A D R E P. French edition: Comptes Rendus d'Accident - Incident A D R E P (ISSN 1014-4501); Spanish edition: Notificacion de Accidentes – Incidentes A D R E P (ISSN 1014-451X) (Subseries of: Air Navigation. Series F: Circulars) (Also avail. in: Russian) 1981. a. price varies. International Civil Aviation Organization, Attn: Document Sales Unit, 1000 Sherbrooke St. W., Montreal, PQ H3A 2R2, Canada. TEL 514-285-8022. FAX 514-285-6769. TELEX 05-24513. (back issues avail.)

388.3 621.382 US
ADVANCED PUBLIC TRANSPORTATION SYSTEMS: STATE OF THE ART UPDATE (YEAR). (Subseries of: U.S. Department of Transportation. Technology Sharing Program. Report) a. U.S. Federal Transit Administration, Technology Sharing Program, U.S. Department of Transportation, 400 Seventh St., S.W. (M-433.2), Washington, DC 20590. (Also avail. from: National Technical Information Service, 5285 Port Royal Rd., Springfield, VA 22161. TEL 703-487-4650. FAX 703-321-8547) (Co-sponsor: Volpe National Transportation Systems Center) **Document type:** bulletin, government publication.
Description: Focuses on improving information, communications, and control strategies for transit and ridesharing. Contains the results of a limited investigation of the extent of the adoption of advanced technology in public transportation in the U.S. and Canada.

387.736 FR ISSN 0245-8756
AEROPORTS DE PARIS. BULLETIN MENSUEL DE STATISTIQUES. 1960. m. 210 F. (effective 1992). Aeroports de Paris, Service Documentation et Statistiques, Orly Sud 103, 94396 Orly Aerogare, France.

387.7 FR ISSN 0078-947X
AEROPORTS DE PARIS. SERVICE STATISTIQUE. STATISTIQUE DE TRAFIC. 1951. a. 210 F. (effective 1992). Aeroports de Paris - Paris Airport Authority, Service Previsions et Statistiques, Orly Sud 103, 94396 Orly Aerogare Cedex, France.

387.74 317 US ISSN 0002-2225
HE9803.A1
AIR CARRIER FINANCIAL STATISTICS. 1970. q. $16. U.S. Department of Transportation, Research & Special Programs Administration, Office of Aviation Information Management, 400 Seventh St., S.W., R., 8410, Washington, DC 20590. TEL 202-366-4000. circ. 500. (also avail. in microfiche from CIS; reprint service avail. from CIS) **Indexed:** Amer.Stat.Ind. (1984-). **Document type:** government publication.

387.7 US
AIR CARRIER INDUSTRY SCHEDULE SERVICE TRAFFIC STATISTICS. MEDIUM REGIONAL CARRIERS. 1970. q. $12. U.S. Department of Transportation, Research & Special Programs Administration, Office of Aviation, 400 Seventh St., S.W., Rm. 8410, Washington, DC 20590. TEL 202-366-4000. stat. circ. 700. (processed; also avail. in microfiche from CIS; reprint service avail. from CIS) **Indexed:** Amer.Stat.Ind. (1984-). **Document type:** government publication.
US#**0896-0577;** Commuter Air Carrier Traffic Statistics (ISSN 0270-448X)

387.7 CN ISSN 0701-7928
HE 9815.A1
AIR CARRIER TRAFFIC AT CANADIAN AIRPORTS. (Catalogue 51-005) (Text in English, French) 1976. q. Can.$122($146) (outside Canada and US $171). Statistics Canada, Transportation Division, Aviation Statistics Centre, Les Terrasses de la Chaudiere, 15 Eddy St., Hull, PQ K1A 0N9, Canada. TEL 819-997-1986. FAX 819-953-8499. (Subscr. to: Publications Sales and Services, Ottawa, ON K1A 0T6, Canada. TEL 800-267-6677)
—CCC.
Description: Examines trends in traffic, volume of passengers, charter services, aircraft movements and regional and local schedules.

387.7 US
AIR TRANSPORT FACTS & FIGURES (ANNUAL REPORT). a. $10 (Canada $13.75; elsewhere $18.75) (effective 1995). Air Transport Association of America, 1301 Pennsylvania Ave., N.W., Ste. 1100, Washington, DC 20004-1707. TEL 202-626-4000; 800-497-3326. FAX 202-626-4264. (Subscr. to: ATA Distribution Center, Box 511, Annapolis Junchon, MD 20701. TEL 301-490-7951)
Document type: trade publication.
Description: Highlights facts and figures drawn from all areas of the industry including financial data, domestic and international traffic statistics for both cargo and passenger operations, safety data, individual airline statistics, and aircraft operating statistics.

387.7 US
AIR TRAVEL SURVEY. a., latest 1993 ed. $75 (Canada $78.75; elsewhere $832.75) (effective 1995). Air Transport Association of America, 1301 Pennsylvania Ave., N.W., Ste. 1100, Washington, DC 20004-1707. TEL 202-626-4000. FAX 202-626-4264. (Subscr. to: ATA Distribution Center, Box 511, Annapolis, Junchon, MD 20701. TEL 800-497-3326) charts; illus. **Indexed:** SRI.
Document type: corporate report.
Description: Describes current trends in air travel demographics, including breakdown by purpose of trip, the number of trips taken annually by individuals surveyed and destination data.

388.324 US ISSN 1050-7671
AMERICAN TRUCKING ASSOCIATIONS. CURRENT ECONOMIC BULLETIN. 1990. w. $99. (American Trucking Associations) Trucking Information Services, Inc., 2200 Mill Rd., Alexandria, VA 22314. TEL 703-838-1792. FAX 703-683-9751. Ed. Michael J. Arendes. **Document type:** bulletin, corporate report.
Description: Compiles economic trend data.

338 AO
ANGOLA. DIRECCAO DOS SERVICOS DE ESTATISTICA. ESTATISTICA DOS VEICULOS MOTORISADOS. 1967. a. Direccao dos Servicos de Estatistica, Ministerio do Planeamento e Coordenacao Economica, C.P. 1215, Luanda, Angola. circ. 750.

380.5 UN ISSN 0250-9911
CODEN: ABTSEQ
ANNUAL BULLETIN OF TRANSPORT STATISTICS FOR EUROPE. (Text in English, French and Russian) 1950. a. price varies. Economic Commission for Europe (ECE), Palais des Nations, 1211 Geneva 10, Switzerland. TEL 022-917-2452. FAX 022-917-0039. TELEX 412962. (Orders in N. America to: United Nations Publications, Rm. DC2-853, New York, NY 10017. TEL 212-963-8302. FAX 212-963-3489; Or: Unipub, 4611-F Assembly Dr., Lanham, MD 20706. TEL 301-459-7666. FAX 301-459-0056) (also avail. in microfiche from CIS) **Indexed:** IIS. **Document type:** government publication, bulletin.
—BLDSC (1077.870000).
Description: Outlines trends in the European and North American transportation sectors.

387 620 UK ISSN 0261-2720
ANNUAL SUMMARY OF MERCHANT SHIPS COMPLETED IN THE WORLD. 1892. a. free. Lloyd's Register of Shipping, 71 Fenchurch St., London EC3M 4BS, England. TEL 0171-709-9166. (U.S. subscr. to: Lloyd's Register of Shipping, 17 Battery Pl., New York, NY 10004)
Former titles: Annual Summary of Merchant Ships Launched, Completed in the World; Annual Summary of Merchant Ships Launched in the World (ISSN 0066-4391)
Description: Provides a statistical summary of world completions and launches for all merchant ships of 100 gross tonnage and above.

380.5 301.16 CL
ANUARIO DE TRANSPORTE Y COMUNICACIONES. 1977. a. Esc.1750 (US $12.10; elsewhere $14.20) (effective 1994). Instituto Nacional de Estadisticas, Av. Bulnes 418, Casilla 498, Correo 3 Santiago, Chile.

387.7 SP ISSN 0213-0009
ANUARIO ESTADISTICO DEL TRANSPORTE AEREO ESPANA - (YEAR). (Comunidad Economica Europea edition avail.) 1970. a. 2500 ptas. Ministerio de Obras Publicas, Transportes y Medio Ambiente, Direccion General de Aviacion Civil, Subdireccion General de Sistemas de Navegacion Aereo y Aeroportuarios, Pza. S. Juan de la Cruz s/n, 28071 Madrid, Spain. **Document type:** government publication.
Formerly (until 1980): Estadisticas de la Aviacion Civil en Espana (ISSN 0421-4986)

621.86 016 HU ISSN 0230-5348
ANYAGMOZGATASI ES CSOMAGOLASI SZAKIRODALMI TAJEKOZTATO/ABSTRACT JOURNAL FOR MATERIALS HANDLING AND PACKAGING. 1982. m. 7000 Ft. Orszagos Muszaki Informacios Kozpont es Konyvtar (O.M.I.K.K.) - National Technical Information Centre and Library, Muzeum u. 17, Box 12, 1428 Budapest, Hungary. (Subscr. to: Kultura, Box 149, 1389 Budapest, Hungary) Eds. Felenc Hervai, Bela Kertesz. abstr.; index. circ. 350. **Document type:** abstracting/indexing.
Supersedes (1967-1982): Muszaki Lapszemle. Anyagmozatas, Csomagolas - Technical Abstracts. Materials Handling, Packaging (ISSN 0027-3023)

388 JA
ASIAN AUTO ABSTRACTS. (Text in English) w. 240000 Yen. (P.D.S. International) Dodwell Marketing Consultants, Kowa No. 35 Bldg., 1-14-14, Akasaka, Minato-ku, Tokyo 107, Japan. TEL 03-3589-0207. FAX 03-5570-7132. TELEX J22274 DODWELL. **Document type:** abstracting/indexing.
Description: Abstracts of press articles related to the Asian auto industry.

387.7 AT ISSN 0729-6096
AUSTRALIA. AIR TRANSPORT STATISTICS. AIRPORT TRAFFIC DATA. 1980. a. free. Department of Transport & Communications, Domestic Aviation Information Section, P.O. Box 594, Canberra City, A.C.T. 2601, Australia. TEL 06-274-7720. FAX 06-274-7727. charts. circ. 400.

387.7 AT ISSN 0727-6672
AUSTRALIA. AIR TRANSPORT STATISTICS. AUSTRALIAN AIR DISTANCES. 1982. irreg. free. Department of Transport & Communications, Domesitc Aviation Information Section, P.O. Box 594, Canberra City, A.C.T. 2601, Australia. TEL 06-274-7720. FAX 06-274-7727. charts. circ. 380. (back issues avail.)

TRANSPORTATION — ABSTRACTING, BIBLIOGRAPHIES, STATISTICS

387.7   AT   ISSN 1037-5937
AUSTRALIA. AIR TRANSPORT STATISTICS. COMMUTER AIRLINES. 1968. s-a. free. Department of Transport & Communications, Domestic Aviation Information Section, P.O. Box 594, Canberra City, A.C.T. 2601, Australia. TEL 06-274-7720. FAX 06-274-7727. circ. 470. (back issues avail.)
Formerly: Australia. Air Transport Statistics. Commuter Air Transport (ISSN 0727-274X)

387.7   AT   ISSN 1037-1273
AUSTRALIA. AIR TRANSPORT STATISTICS. DOMESTIC AIRLINES (ANNUAL). 1922. a. free. Department of Transport & Communications, Domestic Aviation Information Section, P.O. Box 594, Canberra City, A.C.T. 2601, Australia. circ. 780. (back issues avail.)
Formerly: Australia. Air Transport Statistics. Domestic Air Transport (ISSN 0159-396X)

387.7   AT   ISSN 0727-2782
AUSTRALIA. AIR TRANSPORT STATISTICS. DOMESTIC AIRLINES (QUARTERLY). 1967. q. free. Department of Transport & Communications, Domestic Aviation Information Section, P.O. Box 594, Canberra City, A.C.T. 2601, Australia. TEL 06-274-7720. FAX 06-274-7727. circ. 690. (back issues avail.)

387.7   AT
AUSTRALIA. AIR TRANSPORT STATISTICS. INTERNATIONAL SCHEDULED AIR TRANSPORT. 1934. s-a. free. Department of Transport & Communications, International Aviation Policy Division, P.O. Box 594, Canberra, A.C.T. 2601, Australia. circ. 400. (back issues avail.)
Formerly: Australia. Air Transport Statistics. International Air Transport (ISSN 0727-2723)

387.7   AT   ISSN 0727-2790
AUSTRALIA. AIR TRANSPORT STATISTICS. MONTHLY PROVISIONAL STATISTICS OF INTERNATIONAL SCHEDULED AIR TRANSPORT. 1981. m. free. Department of Transport & Communications, International Aviation Policy Division, P.O. Box 594, Canberra, A.C.T. 2601, Australia. Ed. I.M. Hunter. circ. 400.

387.7   AT   ISSN 0727-2766
AUSTRALIA. AIR TRANSPORT STATISTICS. SURVEY OF HOURS FLOWN. 1964. s-a. free. Department of Transport & Communications, Domestic Aviation Information Section, P.O. Box 594, Canberra, A.C.T. 2601, Australia. TEL 06-274-7720. FAX 06-274-7727. circ. 1,000. (back issues avail.)

387 310   AT   ISSN 1322-8773
▼**AUSTRALIA. BUREAU OF STATISTICS. FREIGHT MOVEMENTS, AUSTRALIA.** 1994. q. Aus.$12. Australian Bureau of Statistics, P.O. Box 10, Belconnen, A.C.T. 2616, Australia. **Document type:** government publication.
Description: Provides statistics on tonnes of freight moved in Australia between selected statistical divisions by mode (road, rail, sea and air).

380.5 310   AT
AUSTRALIA. BUREAU OF STATISTICS. MOTOR VEHICLE HIRE INDUSTRY, AUSTRALIA. 1986. irreg., latest 1992. Aus.$12.50. Australian Bureau of Statistics, P.O. Box 10, Belconnen, A.C.T. 2616, Australia. **Document type:** government publication.
Description: Contains details of employment, wages and salaries, components of income and expenses, assets and liabilities, and details of motor vehicles in rental fleet.

388   AT   ISSN 1321-9065
AUSTRALIA. BUREAU OF STATISTICS. MOTOR VEHICLE IN AUSTRALIA. 1994. a. Aus.$39. Australian Bureau of Statistics, P.O. Box 10, Belconnen, A.C.T. 2616, Australia. **Document type:** government publication.
Supersedes in part (1948-1993): Motor Vehicle Registrations, Australia (ISSN 0811-045X); (1971-1993): Motor Vehicle Census, Australia (ISSN 0728-2923)
Description: Contains the number of vehicles on register by type of vehicle, year of manufacture and make for each state and territory.

388   AT   ISSN 1323-4528
AUSTRALIA. BUREAU OF STATISTICS. NEW MOTOR VEHICLE REGISTRATIONS, AUSTRALIA, PRELIMINARY. 1953. m. Aus.$12 per no. Australian Bureau of Statistics, P.O. Box 10, Belconnen, A.C.T. 2616, Australia. **Document type:** government publication.
Formerly: Registrations of New Motor Vehicles, Australia, Preliminary (ISSN 0819-9795)
Description: Features registrations in each state and territory of new cars and station wagons, utilities, panel vans, rigid and articulated trucks, buses and motor cycles.

388   AT   ISSN 0314-1950
AUSTRALIA. BUREAU OF STATISTICS. TASMANIAN OFFICE. MOTOR VEHICLE REGISTRATIONS, TASMANIA. 1972. m. Aus.$5.50 per no. Australian Bureau of Statistics, Tasmanian Office, G.P.O. Box 66A, Hobart, Tas. 7001, Australia. **Document type:** government publication.
Description: Provides information about motor vehicles classified by make, type and tare mass, trucks by gross vehicle mass and gross combination mass, and motor cycles by make.

AUSTRALIAN ROAD RESEARCH. see *ENGINEERING — Abstracting, Bibliographies, Statistics*

388 016   US   ISSN 0145-6776
AUTO INDEX. (Includes year end cumulation issue) 1973. 6/yr. $6. 7 Clinton Pl., Suffern, NY 10901. Ed. David F. Plump. adv. contact: David F. Plump. bibl. circ. 300. **Document type:** abstracting/indexing.
Description: Index covers 14 automotive magazines for road tests, owner surveys and articles on maintenance and technical subjects.

629.283   FI   ISSN 0567-1795
AUTO JA TIE/AUTOMOBILES AND HIGHWAYS IN FINLAND (YEAR). (Text in English, Finnish) 1960. a. FIM 105. Finnish Road Association, P.O. Box 131, 00701 Helsinki, Finland. TEL 358-0-70010881. FAX 358-0-3511181. Ed. Jouko Perkkio. charts; illus.; stat.; index. circ. 1,700. (back issues avail.)

388.3
AUTOMOBILE IN CIFRE. (Text in English, Italian) 1950. a. L.75000($85) to non-members (effective 1995). Associazione Nazionale fra le Industrie Automobilistiche, Corso Galileo Ferraris 61, 10128 Turin, Italy. TEL 39-11-5613901. FAX 39-11-545986. stat. circ. 2,500. (back issues avail.)
Description: Provides data on the production, exportation and registrations of vehicles in Italy.

AUTOMOTIVE INDUSTRY DATA NEWSLETTER. see *TRANSPORTATION — Automobiles*

388   US   ISSN 0732-9350
Z5170
AUTOMOTIVE LITERATURE INDEX. 1981. quinquennial. $40. A. Wallace, Ed. & Pub., 2307 Shoreland Ave., Toledo, OH 43611. TEL 419-729-9065. bk.rev.; film rev.; play rev.; charts; illus.; cum.index. circ. 1,000. (back issues avail.) **Document type:** abstracting/indexing, academic/scholarly publication.

380.5   IT
AUTOVEICOLI CIRCOLANTI IN ITALIA. a. L.50000($40) Associazione Nazionale fra le Industrie Automobilistiche, Corso G. Ferraris 61, 10128 Turin, Italy. TEL 39-11-5613901. FAX 39-11-545956. stat. (back issues avail.) **Document type:** trade publication.
Description: Covers vehicles in use. Includes make, model, engine type, body and loading capacity.

387 380.5   UK   ISSN 0268-9650
VM1   CODEN: BMABE2
B M T ABSTRACTS. 1946. m. £220 (effective 1995). (British Maritime Technology Ltd.) B M T Ltd., Northumbria House, Davy Bank, Wallsend, Tyne and Wear NE28 6UY, England. FAX 0191-262-8754. Ed. G. Smith. bk.rev.; abstr.; index. circ. 400. **Indexed:** World Surf.Coat. **Document type:** abstracting/indexing.
●Also available online.
Formerly (until Jan. 1986): British Ship Research Association. Journal (ISSN 0007-1765)

387   SW   ISSN 0346-9387
BAATOLOGEN. 1963. bi-m. SEK 170 membership (effective 1994). Klubb Maritim, c/o T. Johanneson, Maloertsv. 11, S-260 40 Viken, Sweden. TEL 46-42-23-72-76. Ed. Tomas Johannesson. adv.; bk.rev. circ. 3,000.
Description: Features articles about merchant ships and shipping of today and the past, particularly in the Scandinavian countries.

387   II
BASIC PORT STATISTICS OF INDIA. 1970. a., latest edition in print 1977. $27.54. Ministry of Shipping and Transport, Transport Research Division, I D A Bldg., Jamnagar House, Shahjahan Rd., New Delhi 110011, India. (Orders to: Controller of Publications, Civil Lines, Delhi 110006, India)
Former titles: Port Transport Statistics of India; India Ports and Shipping Statistics.

388   II   ISSN 0067-6462
BASIC ROAD STATISTICS OF INDIA. Hindi edition: Mool Sarak Ankrey. 1948. a. Rs.79.40 for Hindi ed.; English ed. $3.78. Ministry of Shipping and Transport, Transport Research Division, I D A Bldg., Jamnagar House, Shahjahan Rd, New Delhi 110011, India. (Orders to: Controller of Publications, Civil Lines, New Delhi 110006, India)

386   BE   ISSN 0773-2805
BELGIUM. INSTITUT NATIONAL DE STATISTIQUE. STATISTIQUE DE LA NAVIGATION INTERIEURE. Key Title: Navigation Interieure. Dutch edition: Binnenscheepvaart (ISSN 0773-2813) (Text in French) 1971. a. 180 BEF (foreign 225 BEF) (effective 1993). Institut National de Statistique, 44 rue de Louvain, B-1000 Brussels, Belgium. TEL 32-2-5486211. FAX 32-2-5486367. **Document type:** government publication.
Incorporates (1949-1982): Belgium. Institut National de Statistique. Statistique de la Navigation du Rhin (ISSN 0067-5520)

387.1   BE   ISSN 0772-7739
BELGIUM. INSTITUT NATIONAL DE STATISTIQUE. STATISTIQUE DU TRAFIC INTERNATIONAL DES PORTS (U.E.B.L.). Dutch edition: Statistiek over de Internationale Trafiek (B.L.E.U.) in de Havens (ISSN 0772-800X) (Text in French) 1952. a. 500 BEF (foreign 625 BEF) (effective 1993). Institut National de Statistique, 44 rue de Louvain, B-1000 Brussels, Belgium. TEL 32-2-5486211. FAX 32-2-5486367. **Document type:** government publication.
Formerly (until 1977): Belgium. Institut National de Statistique. Statistique Annuelle du Trafic International des Ports (ISSN 0067-5482)

271   BE   ISSN 0773-4255
HF3601
BELGIUM. INSTITUT NATIONAL DE STATISTIQUE. STATISTIQUES DU COMMERCE INTERIEUR ET DES TRANSPORTS. Key Title: Statistiques du Commerce Interieur et des Transports. Dutch edition: Statistieken van Binnenlandse Handel en Vervoer (ISSN 0773-4263) (Text in French) 1972. 11/yr. 1760 BEF (foreign 2200 BEF) (effective 1993). Institut National de Statistique, Rue de Louvain 44, B-1000 Brussels, Belgium. TEL 32-2-5486211. FAX 32-2-5486367. charts; stat. **Indexed:** P.A.I.S.For.Lang.Ind. **Document type:** government publication.
Formed by the 1985 merger of: Belgium. Institut National de Statistique. Statistiques des Transports. (ISSN 0772-7755); Belgium. Institut National de Statistique. Statistiques du Commerce. (ISSN 0772-7747); Which supersedes (in 1972): Belgium. Institut National de Statistique. Statistiques du Commerce et des Transports (ISSN 0522-764X); Incorporates: Activites des Aerodromes Belges (ISSN 0067-5415)

338.4   BE   ISSN 0773-3070
BELGIUM. INSTITUT NATIONAL DE STATISTIQUE. VEHICULES A MOTEUR NEUFS MIS EN CIRCULATION. Dutch edition: Nieuwe to het Verkeer Toeglaten Motorvergtuigen (ISSN 0773-3089) (Text in French) 1955. a. 170 BEF (foreign 210 BEF) (effective 1993). Institut National de Statistique, 44 rue de Louvain, B-1000 Brussels, Belgium. TEL 32-2-5486211. FAX 32-2-5486367. **Document type:** government publication.
Formerly (until 1971): Belgium. Institut National de Statistique. Statistique des Vehicules a Moteurs Neufs Mis en Circulation (ISSN 0067-5555)

TRANSPORTATION — ABSTRACTING, BIBLIOGRAPHIES, STATISTICS

388 016   YU   ISSN 0352-6402
BILTEN DOKUMENTACIJE. SERIJA S1. SAOBRACAJ/BULLETIN OF DOCUMENTATION. SERIES S1. TRAFFIC. 1952. bi-m. $198. Jugoslovenski Centar za Tehnicku i Naucnu Dokumentaciju - Yugoslav Center for Technical and Scientific Documentation (YCTSD), Sl. Penezica-Krcuna 29-31, Box 724, 11000 Belgrade, Yugoslavia. Ed. Ljiljana Kojic-Bogdanovic.
    Formerly (until 1984): Bilten Dokumentacije. Serija E2. Saobracaj (ISSN 0351-7586)

387   EC
BOLETIN ESTADISTICO DE TRAFICO AEREO INTERNACIONAL. 1976. a. free. Direccion General de Aviacion Civil, Division de Transporte Aereo, Buenos Aires No. 149 y Avda. 10 de Agosto, Quito, Ecuador. TEL 552288. TELEX 22710 DACUIO ED. stat.
    Formerly: Ecuador. Direccion de Aviacion Civil. Estadisticas de Trafico Aereo.

388   BD
BURUNDI. INSTITUT DE STATISTIQUES ET D'ETUDES ECONOMIQUES. PARC AUTOMOBILE. biennial. $23. Institut de Statistiques et d'Etudes Economiques, B.P. 1156 Bujumbura, Burundi. **Document type:** government publication.

380.5   UK
BUSINESS MONITOR: MOTOR TRADES. (Part of the Service and Distributive Monitors series) a. Central Statistical Office, C.S.O. Library, Government Bldgs., Cardiff Rd., Newport, Gwent NP9 1XG, Wales. TEL 01633-812973. FAX 01633-812599. TELEX 497121 ALBBSONPT G. (Subscr. to: H.M.S.O. Publications Centre, P.O. Box 276, London SW8 5DT, England. TEL 0171-873-9090. FAX 0171-873-8200) charts. (back issues avail.) **Document type:** government publication.

387.74   US   ISSN 0731-3411
TL521
C A B AIR CARRIER TRAFFIC STATISTICS. (Civil Aeronautics Board) 1970. m. $52. U.S. Department of Transportation, Research & Special Programs Administration, Office of Aviation Information Management, 400 Seventh St., S.W., Rm. 8410, Washington, DC 20590. TEL 202-366-4000. circ. 500. (also avail. in microfiche from CIS; reprint service avail. from CIS) **Indexed:** Amer.Stat.Ind. (1984-). **Document type:** government publication.
    Formerly (until 1980): Air Carrier Traffic Statistics (ISSN 0098-0404)

387.7   CN   ISSN 0828-8208
HE9815.Z7
CANADA. STATISTICS CANADA. AIR CHARTER STATISTICS. (Catalogue 51-207) 1970. q. Can.$36($43) (foreign $50). Statistics Canada, Transportation Division, Aviation Statistics Centre, Les Terrasses de la Chaudiere, 15 Eddy St., Hull, PQ K1A 0N9, Canada. TEL 819-997-1986. FAX 613-951-1584. (Subscr. to: Publications Sales and Services, Ottawa, ON K1A 0T6, Canada. TEL 800-267-6677)
    —CCC.
    Formerly: Canada. Statistics Canada. International Air Charter Statistics (ISSN 0705-4297)
    Description: Examines the domestic and international air charter operations of more than 80 Canadian and foreigncarriers. Covers passenger, and cargo charter traffic.

387.7   CN   ISSN 0705-4343
HE9815.A1
CANADA. STATISTICS CANADA. AIR PASSENGER ORIGIN AND DESTINATION. CANADA - UNITED STATES REPORT. (Catalogue 51-205) (Text in English and French) 1968. a. Can.$42($50) (Statistics Canada, Transportation Division, Aviation Statistics Centre, Les Terrasses de la Chaudiere, 15 Eddy St., Hull, PQ K1A 0N9, Canada. TEL 819-997-1986. FAX 819-953-8499. (Subscr. to: Publications Sales and Services, Ottawa, ON K1A 0T6, Canada. TEL 800-267-6677) (also avail. in microform from MML)
    Description: Presents information on the volume of air passenger ttraffic between points in Canada and the US.

387.7   CN   ISSN 0703-2692
HE9815.A1
CANADA. STATISTICS CANADA. AIR PASSENGER ORIGIN AND DESTINATION. DOMESTIC REPORT. a. Can.$38($46) Statistics Canada, Transportation Division, Aviation Statistics Centre, Les Terrasses de la Chaudiere, 15 Eddy St., Hull, PQ K1A 0N9, Canada. TEL 819-997-1986. FAX 819-953-8499. (Subscr. to: Publications Sales and Services, Ottawa, ON K1A 0N9, Canada. TEL 800-267-6677) circ. 530.
    Description: Includes information on the volume of domestic air passenger traffic at Canadian cities and carried between Canadian city-pairs.

387.7   CN   ISSN 0068-7057
CANADA. STATISTICS CANADA. AVIATION STATISTICS CENTRE. SERVICE BULLETIN/CANADA. CENTRE DES STATISTIQUES DE L'AVIATION. BULLETIN DE SERVICE. (Catalog 51-004) (Text in English, French) 1968. m. Can.$93($112) (outside Canada and US $130). Statistics Canada, Transportation Division, Aviation Statistics Centre, Les Terrasses de la Chaudiere, 15 Eddy St., Hull, PQ K1A 0N9, Canada. (Subscr. to: Publications Sales and Services, Ottawa, ON K1A 0T6, Canada. TEL 800-267-6677) (also avail. in microform from MML)
    Description: Includes financial and operational advance statistics for Level I carriers. Covers the air transport industry, airports, fare basis statistics, passenger and cargo traffic.

388   CN   ISSN 0383-5766
HE5635
CANADA. STATISTICS CANADA. PASSENGER BUS AND URBAN TRANSIT STATISTICS. (Catalogue 53-215) (Text in English and French) 1956. a. Can.$36($43) (foreign $50). Statistics Canada, Publications Sales and Services, Ottawa, Ont. K1A 0T6, Canada. TEL 613-951-7277. FAX 613-951-1584. (also avail. in microform from MML)
    Description: Shows investment, operating revenues, expenses on intercity and rural bus companies and urban transit systems.

380.5   CN   ISSN 0829-1756
CANADA. STATISTICS CANADA. PASSENGER BUS AND URBAN TRANSIT STATISTICS. (Catalogue 53-003) (Text in English, French) 1955. m. Can.$71($85) (foreign $99). Statistics Canada, Publications Sales and Services, Ottawa, Ont. K1A 0T6, Canada. TEL 613-951-7277. FAX 613-951-1584.
    —CCC.
    Formerly: Canada. Statistics Canada. Urban Transit; Canada. Statistics Canada. Urban Transport (ISSN 0380-5948)
    Description: Outlines revenues, passengers carried and vehicle kilometers run on urban transit systems with gross operating revenues from urban transit operations exceeding $500,000.

385   CN   ISSN 0380-6308
CANADA. STATISTICS CANADA. RAILWAY CARLOADINGS. (Catalog 52-001) (Text in English, French) 1924. m. Can.$83($100) (foreign $116). Statistics Canada, Publications Sales and Services, Ottawa, Ont. K1A 0T6, Canada. TEL 613-951-7277. FAX 613-951-1584. (also avail. in microform from MML)
    —CCC.
    Description: Outlines 70 commodities by cars loaded and tonnes of revenue freight carried in eastern and western Canada by class I and II railways.

385   CN   ISSN 0380-5964
HE2801
CANADA. STATISTICS CANADA. RAILWAY OPERATING STATISTICS. (Catalogue 52-003) (Text in English, French) 1921. m. Can.$105($34) (foreign $147). Statistics Canada, Publications Sales and Services, Ottawa, ON K1A 0T6, Canada. TEL 613-951-7277. FAX 613-951-1584. (also avail. in microform from MML)
    —CCC.
    Description: Includes statistics on operating finances and traffic as well as information on seven railways.

388.3   CN   ISSN 0703-654X
HD9574.C2
CANADA. STATISTICS CANADA. ROAD MOTOR VEHICLES, FUEL SALES. (Catalogue 53-218) (Text in English, French) 1960. a. Can.$17($20) (foreign $24). Statistics Canada, Publications Sales and Services, Ottawa, Ont. K1A 0T6, Canada. TEL 613-951-7277. FAX 613-951-1584. (also avail. in microform from MML)
    Formerly: Canada. Statistics Canada. Motor Vehicle. Part 2. Motive Fuel Sales (ISSN 0527-5830)
    Description: Presents gross and net sales of gasolines and net fuel sales of diesel oil and liquefied petroleum gas used for automotive purposes by year and month, province and territory.

388.3   CN   ISSN 0706-067X
HE5635
CANADA. STATISTICS CANADA. ROAD MOTOR VEHICLES, REGISTRATIONS. (Catalogue 53-219) (Text in English, French) 1960. a. Can.$17($20) (foreign $24). Statistics Canada, Publications Sales and Services, Ottawa, Ont. K1A 0T6, Canada. TEL 613-951-7277. FAX 603-951-1584. (also avail. in microform from MML)
    Description: Presents data on registrations of motor vehicles by type including passenger automobiles, trucks, motorcycles, buses and trailers.

387   CN   ISSN 0835-5533
HE563.C2
CANADA. STATISTICS CANADA. SHIPPING IN CANADA. (Catalogue 54-205) (Text in English and French) 1946. a. Can.$41($49) (foreign $57). Statistics Canada, Publications Sales and Services, Ottawa, Ont. K1A 0T6, Canada. TEL 613-951-7277. FAX 613-951-1584. (also avail. in microform from MML)
    Formerly: Canada. Statistics Canada. Water Transportation (ISSN 0380-0342)
    Description: Presents domestic and international shipping activities at Canadian ports.

385   CN   ISSN 0828-2897
HE215.A15
CANADA. STATISTICS CANADA. SURFACE AND MARINE TRANSPORT. (Catalogue 50-002) (Text in English, French) 1971. irreg. Can.$75($90) (foreign $105). Statistics Canada, Publications Sales and Services, Ottawa, Ont. K1A 0T6, Canada. TEL 613-951-7277. FAX 613-951-1584. **Document type:** government publication.
    —CCC.
    Formerly (until 1984): Canada. Statistics Canada. Railway Transport. Service Bulletin (ISSN 0700-2211)
    Description: Presents analytical data, time series analysis and special tabulations covering trucking, rail, bus, urban, and marine transportation, and highway infrastructure.

380.5   CN   ISSN 0826-6026
HE9815.A1
CANADIAN CIVIL AVIATION. (Catalog 51-206) (Text in English, French) 1970. a. Can.$36 (US $43, elsewhere $50). Statistics Canada, Transportation Division, Aviation Statistics Centre, Les Terrasses de la Chaudiere, 15 Eddy St., Hull, PQ K1A 0N9, Canada. TEL 819-997-1986. FAX 819-953-8499. (Subscr. to: Publication Sales & Service, ON K1A 0T6, Canada. TEL 800-267-6677) circ. 390.
    Formerly: Air Carrier Financial Statements.
    Description: Reports on activities of over 250 air Canadian carriers operating in Canada. Includes operational and financial statistics on number of passengers carried, kilometers and hours flown, income statements and balance sheets as well as fare basis information.

387 971   CN   ISSN 0835-6963
Z6841.C2
CANADIAN MARITIME BIBLIOGRAPHY. (Text in English, French) 1986-1987. a. Can.$10. Memorial University of Newfoundland, Maritime Studies Research Unit, St. John's, NF A1C 5S7, Canada. TEL 709-737-8424. FAX 709-737-4569. TELEX 016-4677. (Subscr. to: Canadian Nautical Research Society, P.O. Box 7008, Sta. J, Ottawa, ON K2A 3Z6, Canada) Eds. Lewis R. Fischer, M. Stephen Salmon. adv. circ. 300. **Document type:** bibliography.
    Description: Bibliography of published materials on Canadian maritime history.
    Refereed Serial

TRANSPORTATION — ABSTRACTING, BIBLIOGRAPHIES, STATISTICS

387 016 UK ISSN 1359-2378
CARGO TODAY. 1978. q. £50 to non-members (effective 1996). International Cargo Handling Coordination Association, 71 Bondway, London SW8 1SH, England. TEL 0171-793-1022. FAX 0171-820-1703. adv.; bk.rev. circ. 2,000. **Document type**: abstracting/indexing.
 Former titles (until 1995): I C H C A Quarterly Bulletin; Cargo Handling Abstracts (ISSN 0141-0687)
 Description: Contains information bulletins and a comprehensive listing of upcoming international industry conferences, exhibitions and seminars.

385.1 332 US ISSN 0008-6924
CARRIER REPORTS. 1960. q. $35. Box 39, Lubec, ME 04652. Ed. Richard W. Honer. adv.; stat.

387 UK ISSN 0268-0815
HE565.A3
CASUALTY RETURN. 1891. a. $120. Lloyd's Register of Shipping, 71 Fenchurch St., London EC3M 4BS, England. TEL 0171-709-9166. (Subscr. in the U.S. to: Lloyd's Register of Shipping, 17 Battery Pl., New York, NY 10004)
 Former titles: Casualty Return Statistical Summary of Merchant Ships Totally Lost, Broken Up, Etc. (ISSN 0261-2712); Casualty Return Statistical Summary (ISSN 0008-7572); Merchant Ships Totally Lost, Broken Up, Etc.
 Description: Presents an annual statistical summary and listing of all merchant ships lost or reported broken up.

380.5 BL ISSN 0103-6610
CENSO DOS TRANSPORTES. 1985. quinquennial. $80. Fundacao Instituto Brasileiro de Geografia e Estatistica, Centro de Documentacao e Disseminacao de Informacoes, Rua General Canabarro 666, 2o andar, Maracana 20271-201 Rio de Janeiro, Brazil. TEL 55-21-2645424. FAX 55-21-2289575. **Document type**: government publication.

380.5 UK ISSN 0260-9886
CHARTERED INSTITUTE OF PUBLIC FINANCE AND ACCOUNTANCY. HIGHWAYS AND TRANSPORTATION. ACTUALS.* 1980. a. £30. Chartered Institute of Public Finance and Accountancy, 3 Robert St., London WC2N 6BH, England. TEL 071-895-8823. FAX 071-895-8825. (back issues avail.)

380.5 UK ISSN 0964-5624
HE243.A15
CHARTERED INSTITUTE OF PUBLIC FINANCE AND ACCOUNTANCY. HIGHWAYS AND TRANSPORTATION STATISTICS. ESTIMATES & ACTUALS. 1982. a. £52. Chartered Institute of Public Finance and Accountancy, Statistical Information Service, 3 Robert St., London WC2N 6BH, England. TEL 0171-895-8823. FAX 0171-895-8825. (back issues avail.)
 —BLDSC (4311.470000).
 Formerly: Chartered Institute of Public Finance and Accountancy. Highways and Transportation Statistics. Estimates (ISSN 0260-9894)

387.7 310 UK
CHARTERED INSTITUTE OF PUBLIC FINANCE AND ACCOUNTANCY. LOCAL AUTHORITY AIRPORTS. ACCOUNTS AND STATISTICS. ACTUALS. 1979. a. £39. Chartered Institute of Public Finance and Accountancy, Statistical Information Service, 3 Robert St., London WC2N 6BH, England. TEL 0171-895-8823. FAX 0171-895-8825. (back issues avail.)
 Formerly: Chartered Institute of Public Finance and Accountancy. Local Authority Airports. Accounts and Statistics (ISSN 0260-9967)

388.476 CC ISSN 1002-0918
CHINA AUTO/ZHONGGUO QICHE. (Text in English) 1991. bi-m. $150. (Zhongguo Qiche Jishu Yanjiu Zhongxin - China Automotive Technology & Research Center) Innovative Technology & Trading Co., No. 45 Zengguang Rd., Haidian, Beijing 100037, People's Republic of China. TEL 8424477. FAX 8864576. (Editorial addr.: P.O. Box 59, Tianjin 300162, P.R. China. TEL 86-22-473100. FAX 86-22-470843) Ed. Zhu Dezhao. adv. **Document type**: newsletter.
 Description: Provides comprehensive analysis of the automotive industry in China.

387.7 629.1 UN
CIVIL AVIATION STATISTICS OF THE WORLD (YEAR). (Text in: English, French, Russian, Spanish) a. $28. International Civil Aviation Organization, Attn: Document Sales Unit, 1000 Sherbrooke St. W., Montreal, PQ H3A 2R2, Canada. TEL 514-285-8022. FAX 514-285-6769. TELEX 05-24513.

318 CK
COLOMBIA. DEPARTAMENTO ADMINISTRATIVO NACIONAL DE ESTADISTICA. ANUARIO GENERAL DE ESTADISTICA - TRANSPORTES Y COMUNICACIONES. irreg.? Departamento Administrativo Nacional de Estadistica, Banco Nacional de Datos, Centro Administrativo Nacional, Avda. Eldorado, Bogota, Colombia.

380.5 FR
COMMENT EVALUER LA PART DU TRAFIC MARITIME DE NOTRE COMMERCE EXTERIEUR QUI ECHAPPE AUX PORTS FRANCAIS. 1975. a. 260 F. Ministere de Transport, Observatoire Economique et Statistique des Transports (OEST), 55 rue Brillat-Savarin, 75658 Paris Cedex 13, France.

380.5 016 US ISSN 0011-3654
Z7164.T8
CURRENT LITERATURE IN TRAFFIC AND TRANSPORTATION. 1960. q. $20 (effective 1994). Northwestern University, Transportation Library, Evanston, IL 60208-2300. TEL 708-491-5275. FAX 708-491-8601. Ed. Dorothy Ramm. bibl. circ. 550. (also avail. in microfilm from UMI; reprint service avail. from UMI) **Document type**: bibliography.
 —UMI.

614 380.5 FR
E C M T STATISTICAL REPORT ON ROAD ACCIDENTS. a. price varies. Organization for Economic Cooperation and Development, European Council of Ministers of Transport, 2 rue Andre-Pascal, 75775 Paris Cedex 16, France. (U.S. orders to: O.E.C.D. Publications and Information Center, 2001 L St., N.W., Ste. 700, Washington, DC 20036-4910. TEL 202-785-6323) (also avail. in microfiche from OEC,CIS) **Indexed**: IIS.

388 016 RU ISSN 0131-7962
EKSPRESS-INFORMATSIYA. GORODSKOI TRANSPORT. 1961. 48/yr. $179 (effective 1996). Vsesoyuznyi Institut Nauchno-Tekhnicheskoi Informatsii (VINITI), Baltiiskaya ul., 14, Moscow A-219, Russia. (Subscr. to: Mezhdunarodnaya Kniga, Dimitrova ul. 39, 113095 Moscow, Russia)
 —CCC.

625.1 016 RU
EKSPRESS-INFORMATSIYA. ORGANIZATSIYA PEREVOZOK. AVTOMATIZIROVANNIE SISTEMY UPRAVLENIA TRANSPORTOM. 1962. 48/yr. 38 Rub. Vsesoyuznyi Institut Nauchno-Tekhnicheskoi Informatsii (VINITI), Baltiiskaya ul., 14, Moscow A-219, Russia. (Subscr. to: Mezhdunarodnaya Kniga, Dimitrova ul. 39, 113095 Moscow, Russia)
 Formerly: Ekspress-Informatsiya. Organizatsiya Perevozok, Avtomatizirovanie, Telemekhanika i Svyaz' na Zheleznykh Dorogakh (ISSN 0207-5016)

380.5 016 RU ISSN 0131-0402
EKSPRESS-INFORMATSIYA. PROMYSHLENNYI TRANSPORT. 1960. 48/yr. 38 Rub. Vsesoyuznyi Institut Nauchno-Tekhnicheskoi Informatsii (VINITI), Baltiiskaya ul., 14, Moscow A-219, Russia. (Subscr. to: Mezhdunarodnaya Kniga, Dimitrova ul. 39, 113095 Moscow, Russia)
 —CCC.

380.5 FR
HE4761
ENQUETE PERMANENTE SUR L'UTILISATION DES VEHICULES DE TRANSPORT EN COMMUN DE PERSONNES EN (YEAR). 1979. a. 80 Fr. Observatoire Economique et Statistique des Transports, 55 rue Brillat-Savarin, 75658 Paris Cedex 13, France. Ed. Yves Jacquin. circ. 13,000.
 Formerly: Enquete sur l'Utilisation des Autobus et Autocars en (Year) (ISSN 0243-850X)

388.41 PN ISSN 0378-6765
ESTADISTICA PANAMENA. SITUACION SOCIAL. SECCION 451. ACCIDENTES DE TRANSITO. 1958. a. Bl.0.50 (foreign Bl.1.50) (effective 1995). Direccion de Estadistica y Censo, Contraloria General, Apdo. 5213, Panama 5, Panama. FAX 507-69-7294. circ. 850. **Document type**: government publication, bulletin.
 Description: Offers detailed information on transportation accidents in the country.

380.5 GT
ESTADISTICAS DE TRANSPORTE DE GUATEMALA. irreg., latest 1988-89. $15. Instituto Nacional de Estadistica, Ministerio de Economia, 8A Calle no.9-55, Zona 1, Guatemala, Guatemala. TEL 502-26136. (Co-sponsor: Ministerio de Comunicaciones, Transportes y Obras Publicas) **Document type**: government publication.

388.3 US ISSN 0160-4570
HE5623.A1
F & O S MOTOR CARRIER ANNUAL REPORT. (Financial and Operating Statistics); results of operations class I & II motor carriers of property; regulated by the Interstate Commerce Commission. a. $400 (including Motor Carrier Quarterly Report $495). (American Trucking Associations) Trucking Information Services, Inc., 2200 Mill Rd., Alexandria, VA 22314. TEL 703-838-1792. FAX 703-683-9751. illus. **Document type**: trade publication.
 Supersedes: F and O S (ISSN 0098-2245)

388.3 US
F & O S MOTOR CARRIER QUARTERLY REPORT. (Financial and Operating Statistics). q. $400 (including Motor Carrier Annual Report $495). (American Trucking Associations) Trucking Information Services, Inc., 2200 Mill Rd., Alexandria, VA 22314. TEL 703-838-1792. FAX 703-683-9751. **Document type**: trade publication.
 Description: Presents data and cumulative summaries based on quarterly reports filed with the I.C.C. by Class I and II carriers.

380.5 FJ ISSN 0256-8063
FIJI. BUREAU OF STATISTICS. SHIPPING STATISTICS. 1971. a., latest 1986. $5 (effective 1995 & 1996). Bureau of Statistics, P.O. Box 2221, Suva, Fiji. **Document type**: government publication.

385.1 FI ISSN 0430-5272
FINLAND. TILASTOKESKUS. LIIKENNETILASTOLLINEN VUOSIKIRJA/FINLAND. STATISTIKCENTRALEN. SAMFAERDSELSTATISTISKAARSBOK/FINLAND. CENTRAL STATISTICAL OFFICE. YEARBOOK OF TRANSPORT STATISTICS. (Section XXXVI of Official Statistics of Finland) (Text in English, Finnish and Swedish) 1958. a. FIM 68. Tilastokeskus, Annankatu 44, SF-00100 Helsinki 10, Finland.

388.31 FI ISSN 0355-2284
HE255.3.A15
FINLAND. TILASTOKESKUS. TIELIIKENNEONNETTOMUUDET/FINLAND. STATISTIKCENTRALEN. VAEGTRAFIKOLYCKOR/FINLAND. CENTRAL STATISTICAL OFFICE. ROAD TRAFFIC ACCIDENTS. (Text in English, Finnish and Swedish) 1967. a. FIM 90. Tilastokeskus, P.O. Box 504, SF-00101 Helsinki, Finland. (back issues avail.)

380.5 FR ISSN 0758-9719
HE63.A3
FRANCE. OBSERVATOIRE ECONOMIQUE ET STATISTIQUE DES TRANSPORTS. MEMENTO DE STATISTIQUES DES TRANSPORTS. a. 110 F. Ministere de l'Equipement, des Transports et du Tourisme, Observatoire Economique et Statistiques des Transports, Grande Archee, 92055 Paris la Defense Cedex 4, France. TEL 40-81-21-22. FAX 40-81-17-71.
 Formerly: France. Departement des Statistiques de Transport. Memento de Statistiques des Transports.

TRANSPORTATION — ABSTRACTING, BIBLIOGRAPHIES, STATISTICS

380.5 FR ISSN 0988-5390
FRANCE. OBSERVATOIRE ECONOMIQUE ET STATISTIQUE DES TRANSPORTS. NOTE DE CONJONCTURE. 1980. m. 600 Fr. Ministere de l'Equipement, des Transports et du Tourisme, Observatoire Economique et Statistique des Transports, Grande Archee, 92055 Paris la Defense Cedex 4, France. TEL 40-81-21-22. FAX 40-81-17-71.
Formerly (until 1987): France. Ministere des Transports, Departement des Statistiques des Transports. Note de Conjoncture (ISSN 0244-7819); Incorporates (196?-1987): France. Ministere des Transports. Departement des Statistiques des Transports. Bulletin Mensuel de Statistiques (ISSN 0758-9298); Which was formerly (until 1978): France. Ministere de l'Equipement. Bulletin Mensuel de Statistiques (ISSN 0997-4113); (until 1974): France. Ministere de l'Equipement et du Logement. Bulletin Mensuel de Statistiques (ISSN 0997-4105).

387.7 US
GENERAL AVIATION STATISTICAL DATABOOK. 1980. a. $10. General Aviation Manufacturers Association, 1400 K St., N.W., Ste. 801, Washington, DC 20005. TEL 202-393-1500. FAX 202-842-4063. stat. (also avail. in microfiche from CIS) **Indexed:** SRI.

388.413 GW ISSN 0943-1527
GERMANY. KRAFTFAHRT-BUNDESAMT. FAHR- UND FAHRLEHRERLAUBNISSTATISTIKEN. s-a. DM.21. Metzler - Poeschel Verlag, Postfach 1152, 72125 Kusterdingen, Germany. TEL 07071-935355. FAX 07071-935393. **Document type:** government publication.

388.413 GW ISSN 0943-1519
GERMANY. KRAFTFAHRT-BUNDESAMT. FAHRERLAUBNIS AUF PROBE. q. DM.18. Metzler - Poeschel Verlag, Postfach 1152, 72125 Kusterdingen, Germany. TEL 07071-935355. FAX 07071-935393. **Document type:** government publication.

388.413 GW ISSN 0943-1535
GERMANY. KRAFTFAHRT-BUNDESAMT. FAHRZEUGMAENGELSTATISTIK. s-a. DM.24. Metzler - Poeschel Verlag, Postfach 1152, 72125 Kusterdingen, Germany. TEL 07071-935355. FAX 07071-935393. **Document type:** government publication.

388.413 GW ISSN 0943-1551
GERMANY. KRAFTFAHRT-BUNDESAMT. GRENZUEBERSCHREITENDER GUETERKRAFTVERKEHR. a. DM.65. Metzler - Poeschel Verlag, Postfach 1152, 72125 Kusterdingen, Germany. TEL 07071-935355. FAX 07071-935393. **Document type:** government publication.

388.413 GW ISSN 0943-1470
GERMANY. KRAFTFAHRT-BUNDESAMT. KRAFTFAHRZEUGSTATISTIKEN. m. DM.220. Metzler - Poeschel Verlag, Postfach 1152, 72125 Kusterdingen, Germany. TEL 07071-935355. FAX 07071-935393. **Document type:** government publication.

388.413 GW ISSN 0943-1497 HE5669
GERMANY. KRAFTFAHRT-BUNDESAMT. NEUZULASSUNGEN - BESITZUMSCHREIBUNGEN - LOESCHUNGEN VON KRAFTFAHRZEUGEN UND KRAFTFAHRZEUGANHAENGERN. a. DM.65. Metzler - Poeschel Verlag, Postfach 1152, 72125 Kusterdingen, Germany. TEL 07071-935355. FAX 07071-935393. **Document type:** government publication.

388.413 GW ISSN 0943-1543
GERMANY. KRAFTFAHRT-BUNDESAMT. VERKEHRSSTATISTIKEN. m. DM.21. Metzler - Poeschel Verlag, Postfach 1152, 72125 Kusterdingen, Germany. TEL 07071-935355. FAX 07071-935393. **Document type:** government publication.

388.413 GW ISSN 0943-1500
GERMANY. KRAFTFAHRT-BUNDESAMT. VERKEHRSZENTRALREGISTER. s-a. DM.8. Metzler - Poeschel Verlag, Postfach 1152, 72125 Kusterdingen, Germany. TEL 07071-935355. FAX 07071-935393. **Document type:** government publication.

380.5 314 GW ISSN 0072-4092
GERMANY. STATISTISCHES BUNDESAMT. FACHSERIE 8, VERKEHR, REIHE 1: GUETERVERKEHR DER VERKEHRSZWEIGE. q. DM.50.80. 65180 Wiesbaden, Germany. TEL 0611-75-1. FAX 0611-724000. TELEX 61186-STBA-D. **Document type:** government publication.

385.1 314 GW ISSN 0072-4041
GERMANY. STATISTISCHES BUNDESAMT. FACHSERIE 8, VERKEHR, REIHE 2: EISENBAHNVERKEHR. m. DM.51.60. 65180 Wiesbaden, Germany. TEL 0611-75-1. FAX 0611-724000. TELEX 61186-STBA-D. **Document type:** government publication.

388 314 GW ISSN 0935-7726
GERMANY. STATISTISCHES BUNDESAMT. FACHSERIE 8, VERKEHR, REIHE 3: STRASSENPERSONENVERKEHR. q. DM.36. Statistisches Bundesamt, 65180 Wiesbaden, Germany. TEL 0611-75-1. FAX 0611-724000. TELEX 61186-STBA-D. **Document type:** government publication.
Formerly: Germany (Federal Republic, 1949-). Statistisches Bundesamt. Fachserie 8, Verkehr, Reihe 3: Strassenverkehr (ISSN 0072-405X)

614 312 GW ISSN 0937-8294
GERMANY. STATISTISCHES BUNDESAMT. FACHSERIE 8, VERKEHR, REIHE 3.3: VERKEHRSUNFAELLE. m. (plus a. cumulations). DM.132. Statistisches Bundesamt, 65180 Wiesbaden, Germany. TEL 0611-75-1. FAX 0611-724000. TELEX 61186-STBA-D. **Document type:** government publication.
Former titles (until 1989): Germany. (Federal Rupublic, 1949-). Statistisches Bundesamt. Fachserie 8, Verkehr, Reihe 3.3: Strassenverkehrsunfaelle (ISSN 0170-7752); Germany (Federal Republic, 1949-). Statistisches Bundesamt. Fachserie 8, Verkehr, Reihe 3.3: Haushaelte und Familien (ISSN 0072-4068)

387 314 GW ISSN 0072-4017
GERMANY. STATISTISCHES BUNDESAMT. FACHSERIE 8, VERKEHR, REIHE 4: BINNENSCHIFFAHRT. m. DM.108. Statistisches Bundesamt, 65180 Wiesbaden, Germany. TEL 0611-75-1. FAX 0611-724000. TELEX 61186-STBA-D. **Document type:** government publication.

387 314 GW ISSN 0072-4025
GERMANY. STATISTISCHES BUNDESAMT. FACHSERIE 8, VERKEHR, REIHE 5: SEESCHIFFAHRT. m. DM.108. 65180 Wiesbaden, Germany. TEL 0611-75-1. FAX 0611-724000. TELEX 61186-STBA-D. **Document type:** government publication.

387.7 314 GW ISSN 0072-4033
GERMANY. STATISTISCHES BUNDESAMT. FACHSERIE 8, VERKEHR, REIHE 6: LUFTVERKEHR. m. DM.177.60. 65180 Wiesbaden, Germany. TEL 0611-75-1. FAX 0611-724000. TELEX 61186-STBA-D. **Document type:** government publication.

380.5 314 GW ISSN 0072-3924
GERMANY. STATISTISCHES BUNDESAMT. FACHSERIE 17, PREISE, REIHE 9: PREISE UND PREISINDIZES FUER VERKEHRSLEISTUNGEN. a. DM.8.80. 65180 Wiesbaden, Germany. TEL 0611-75-1. FAX 0611-724000. TELEX 61186-STBA-D. **Document type:** government publication.

629 GH
GHANA. STATISTICAL SERVICE. MOTOR VEHICLE REGISTRATION. q. $20. Statistical Service, Information Section, P.O. Box 1098, Accra, Ghana. TEL 233-21-663578. FAX 233-21-667069. TELEX 2205 MIFAEP GH. **Document type:** government publication.
Formerly: Ghana. Central Bureau of Statistics. Motor Vehicle Registration.

388 US
GRANT ASSISTANCE PROGRAM. FISCAL YEAR STATISTICAL SUMMARIES. a. free. U.S. Federal Transit Administration, Ofice of Grants Management (TGM-11), Grant Assistance Program, U.S. Department of Transportation, TGM-10, 400 Seventh St., S.W., Rm. 9315, Washington, DC 20590. TEL 202-366-2053. FAX 202-366-7951. (Also avail. from: National Technical Information Service, 5285 Port Royal Rd., Springfield, VA 22161. TEL 703-487-4650. FAX 703-321-8547). **Document type:** government publication.
Description: Presents selected analyzed data on the distribution of various Grant Assistance Program Funds administered by the Federal Transit Administration.

387.736 UK
GREAT BRITAIN. CIVIL AVIATION AUTHORITY. AIRPORT SURVEYS. (Subseries of: Civil Aviation Publications) a. price varies. Civil Aviation Authority, Printing and Publication Services, Greville House, 37 Gratton Rd., Cheltenham, Glos. GL50 2BN, England. TEL 01242-235151. FAX 01242-584139. charts. (back issues avail.) **Document type:** government publication.
Description: Surveys passenger activity at selected groups of airports.

387.742 UK
GREAT BRITAIN. CIVIL AVIATION AUTHORITY. ANNUAL PUNCTUALITY STATISTICS - FULL ANALYSIS (YEAR). (Subseries of: Civil Aviation Publications) a. £43. Civil Aviation Authority, Printing and Publication Services, Greville House, 37 Gratton Rd., Cheltenham, Glos. GL50 2BN, England. TEL 01242-235151. FAX 01242-584139. (back issues avail.) **Document type:** government publication.
Description: Analyzes the on-time performance of each route to and from the monthly reports. Data are analyzed by U.K. airport and by airline for each route.

387.742 UK
GREAT BRITAIN. CIVIL AVIATION AUTHORITY. ANNUAL PUNCTUALITY STATISTICS - SUMMARY ANALYSIS (YEAR). (Subseries of: Civil Aviation Publications) a. £11. Civil Aviation Authority, Printing and Publication Services, Greville House, 37 Gratton Rd., Cheltenham, Glos. GL50 2BN, England. TEL 01242-235151. FAX 01242-584139. (back issues avail.) **Document type:** government publication.
Description: Analyzes the on-time performance of charter and scheduled air services for each airline and route.

387.742 UK ISSN 0957-5154
GREAT BRITAIN. CIVIL AVIATION AUTHORITY. PUNCTUALITY STATISTICS HEATHROW, GATWICK, MANCHESTER, BIRMINGHAM, LUTON AND STANSTEAD - FULL ANALYSIS. (Annual report avail.) m. £330. Civil Aviation Authority, Printing and Publication Services, Greville House, 37 Gratton Rd., Cheltenham, Glos. GL50 2BN, England. TEL 01242-265151. FAX 01242-584139. (back issues avail.) **Document type:** government publication.
Description: Provides a full analysis of on-time performance by route and airline (both scheduled and charter) for major U.K. airports.

387.742 UK ISSN 0957-5162
GREAT BRITAIN. CIVIL AVIATION AUTHORITY. PUNCTUALITY STATISTICS HEATHROW, GATWICK, MANCHESTER, BIRMINGHAM, LUTON AND STANSTEAD - SUMMARY ANALYSIS. Key Title: Punctuality Statistics - Summary Analysis. (Annual report avail.) 1989. m. £70. Civil Aviation Authority, Printing and Publication Services, Greville House, 37 Gratton Rd., Cheltenham, Glos. GL50 2BN, England. TEL 01242-235151. FAX 01242-584139. (back issues avail.) **Document type:** government publication.
Description: Analyzes the on-time performance of each route to and from these major U.K. airports. Data are also broken down by airline.

6330 TRANSPORTATION — ABSTRACTING, BIBLIOGRAPHIES, STATISTICS

387.71   UK
GREAT BRITAIN. CIVIL AVIATION AUTHORITY. U.K. AIRLINES ANNUAL OPERATING, TRAFFIC & FINANCIAL STATISTICS. 1973. a. £14.50. Civil Aviation Authority, Printing and Publication Services, Greville House, 37 Gratton Rd., Cheltenham, Glos. GL50 2BN, England. TEL 01242-235151. FAX 01242-584139. **Document type:** government publication.
    Supersedes in part (as of 1983): Great Britain. Civil Aviation Authority. Annual Statistics.
    Description: Analyzes the operation of U.K. airlines in such measures as passengers, passenger-kilometers, cargo-tonnage kilometers, and load factors.

387.74 310   UK
GREAT BRITAIN. CIVIL AVIATION AUTHORITY. U.K. AIRLINES MONTHLY OPERATING & TRAFFIC STATISTICS. 1973. m. £56 (overseas £68). Civil Aviation Authority, Printing and Publication Services, Greville House, 37 Gratton Rd., Cheltenham, Glos. GL50 2BN, England. TEL 01242-235151. FAX 01242-584139. **Document type:** government publication.
    Supersedes in part (in 1983): Great Britain. Civil Aviation Authority. C A A Monthly Operating and Traffic Statistics (ISSN 0265-0266); Former titles (until 1983): Great Britain. Civil Aviation Board. C A A Monthly Statistics (ISSN 0306-3577); Business Monitor Civil Aviation Series.
    Description: Analyzes the operation of U.K. airlines for number of passengers flown, passenger-kilometers, cargo tonnage-kilometers, and load factors.

387.74   UK
GREAT BRITAIN. CIVIL AVIATION AUTHORITY. U.K. AIRPORTS ANNUAL STATEMENTS OF MOVEMENTS, PASSENGERS AND CARGO (YEAR). (Subseries of: Civil Aviation Publications) 1973. a. £14. Civil Aviation Authority, Printing and Publication Services, Greville House, 37 Gratton Rd., Cheltenham, Glos. GL50 2BN, England. TEL 01242-235151. FAX 01242-584139. **Document type:** government publication.
    Supersedes in part (in 1983): Great Britain. Civil Aviation Authority. Annual Statistics.
    Description: Analyzes the number of movements, passengers, and cargo tonnage handled at some 50 U.K. airports. Data are divided intor such categories as domestic, international, scheduled, and charter.

387.74 620.3   UK
GREAT BRITAIN. CIVIL AVIATION AUTHORITY. U.K. AIRPORTS MONTHLY STATEMENTS OF MOVEMENTS, PASSENGERS AND CARGO. 1973. m. £56 (overseas £68). Civil Aviation Authority, Printing and Publication Services, Greville House, 37 Gratton Rd., Cheltenham, Glos. GL50 2BN, England. TEL 01242-235151. FAX 01242-584139. charts. **Document type:** government publication.
    Supersedes in part (in 1983): Great Britain. Civil Aviation Authority. C A A Monthly Operating and Traffic Statistics (ISSN 0265-0266)
    Description: Analyzes the number of movements, passengers, and cargo tonnage handled at 50 U.K. airports.

387   GR   ISSN 0072-7423
GREECE. NATIONAL STATISTICAL SERVICE. SHIPPING STATISTICS. (Text in English and Greek) 1967. a. $12. National Statistical Service of Greece, Statistical Information and Publications Division - Ethniki Statistiki Ypereisa tes Ellados, 14-16 Lykourgou, 101 66 Athens, Greece. TEL 30-1-3244-748. FAX 30-1-3222-205. TELEX 216734 ESYE GR. (back issues avail.) **Document type:** government publication.

301.6 380.5   GR   ISSN 0256-3657
HE250
GREECE. NATIONAL STATISTICAL SERVICE. TRANSPORT AND COMMUNICATION STATISTICS. (Text in Greek) 1967. a. $7. National Statistical Service of Greece, Statistical Information and Publications Division - Ethniki Statistiki Ypereisa tes Ellados, 14-16 Lykourgou, 101 66 Athens, Greece. TEL 30-1-3244-748. FAX 30-1-3222-205. TELEX 216734 ESYE GR. (back issues avail.) **Document type:** government publication.

388 016   HU   ISSN 0231-1941
HAJOZASI SZAKIRODALMI TAJEKOZTATO/SHIPPING ABSTRACTS. 1949. bi-m. 2700 Ft. Orszagos Muszaki Informacios Kozpont es Konyvtar (O.M.I.K.K.) - National Technical Information Centre and Library, Muzeum u. 17, Box 12, 1428 Budapest, Hungary. (Subscr. to: Kultura, Box 149, 1389 Budapest, Hungary) Ed. Nandorne Raics. abstr.; index. circ. 350. **Document type:** abstracting/indexing.
    Supersedes in part (in 1982): Muszaki Lapszemle. Kozlekedes - Technical Abstracts. Transportation (ISSN 0027-5042)

380.5 630   US
HANDBOOK OF LIVE ANIMAL TRANSPORT. 1984. q. (plus periodic suppl.). $150 for the first year; $65 thereafter. Silesia Companies, Inc., Box 441110, Ft. Washington, MD 20749-1110. TEL 301-292-1970. FAX 301-292-1787. Ed. Dale L. Anderson. index. circ. 160. (looseleaf format) **Document type:** abstracting/indexing.
    Formerly: Handbook of Animal Transportation.
    Description: Compiles articles, listings and information on all phases of transporting animals worldwide.

625 388.1 016   US   ISSN 1050-0804
TE1
HIGHWAY RESEARCH ABSTRACTS. 1968. q. $85 to N. America; elsewhere $90. U.S. National Research Council, Transportation Research Board, Highway Research Information Service, 2101 Constitution Ave., N.W., Washington, DC 20418. TEL 202-334-3218. FAX 202-334-2519. TELEX 248664 NASWUR. Ed.Bd. abstr. circ. 2,500. **Document type:** abstracting/indexing, government publication.
    ●Also available online.
    Formerly (until 1990): H R I S Abstracts (ISSN 0017-6222)
    Description: Abstracts of research reports, technical papers in conference proceedings, and journal articles on highway research related topics.

388.3   US
HIGHWAY SAFETY - ANNUAL REPORT. a. $11. U.S. Federal Highway Administration, Office of Highway Information Management, Department of Transportation, 400 Seventh St., S.W., Washington, DC 20590. TEL 202-366-0180. FAX 202-366-7742. (Subscr. to: Superintendent of Documents, U.S. Government Printing Office, Box 371954, Pittsburgh, PA 15250-7954. TEL 202-512-1800. FAX 202-512-2250; Or: Bernan, 4611-F Assembly Dr., Lanham, MD 20706. TEL 301-459-7666. FAX 301-459-0056) **Document type:** government publication.
    ●Also available online.

388.3   US   ISSN 8755-8688
HE5614.2
HIGHWAY SAFETY PERFORMANCE. FATAL AND INJURY ACCIDENT RATES ON PUBLIC ROADS IN THE UNITED STATES. a. $7.50. U.S. Federal Highway Administration, Office of Highway Information Management, Department of Transportation, 400 Seventh St., S.W., Washington, DC 20590. TEL 202-366-0180. FAX 202-366-7742. (Orders to: Superintendent of Documents, U.S. Government Printing Office, Box 371954, Pittsburgh, PA 15250-7954. TEL 202-512-1800. FAX 202-512-2250; Or: Bernan, 4611-F Assembly Dr., Lanham, MD 20706. TEL 301-459-7666. FAX 301-459-0056) **Document type:** government publication.
    ●Also available online.
    Formerly (until 1982): Fatal and Injury Accident Rates on Federal-Aid and other Highway Systems (ISSN 0565-0437)

310 385.1   HK
HONG KONG. CENSUS AND STATISTICS DEPARTMENT. SHIPPING STATISTICS. (Text in English) 1984. a. HK.$21. Government Publication Centre, G.P.O. Bldg., Ground Fl., Connaught Place, Hong Kong, Hong Kong. (Subscr. to: Director of Information Services, Information Services Dept., 1 Battery Path, G-F, Central, Hong Kong) Ed.Bd.

388.31   HU   ISSN 0237-8280
HE247.5.A15
HUNGARY. KOZPONTI STATISZTIKAI HIVATAL. KOZLEKEDESI EVKONYV. a. 310 Ft. Statisztikai Kiado Vallalat, Kaszasdulo u. 2, P.O.B. 99, 1300 Budapest 3, Hungary. TEL 1-688-635. TELEX 22-6699. (Subscr. to: Kultura, Box 149, H-1389 Budapest, Hungary) circ. 650.
    Former titles: Hungary. Kozponti Statisztikai Hivatal. Kozlekedesi Posta es Tavkozlesi; Hungary. Kozponti Statisztikai Hivatal. Kozlekedesi es Hirkozlesi Evkonyv (ISSN 0133-9133)

387   UN   ISSN 1014-5834
I C A O PUBLICATIONS AND AUDIO VISUAL TRAINING AIDS CATALOGUE. Key Title: Catalogue of I C A O Publications and Audio Visual Training Aids. (Editions avail. in English, French, Russian, Spanish) a. (plus m. updates). free. International Civil Aviation Organization, Attn: Document Sales Unit, 1000 Sherbrooke St. W., Montreal, PQ H3A 2R2, Canada. TEL 514-285-8022. FAX 514-285-6769. TELEX 05-24513. **Document type:** catalog.
    Description: Lists all I.C.A.O. publications, current and back issues, available. Includes list of discontinued titles.

388.3 621.382   US
I V H S ARCHITECTURE DEVELOPMENT PROGRAM. INTERIM STATUS REPORT. irreg. Intelligent Vehicle Highway Society of America, 400 Virginia Ave., S.W., Ste. 900, Washington, DC 20024-2730. TEL 202-484-4847. FAX 202-484-3483. (Sponsor: U.S. Department of Transportation) (back issues avail.) **Document type:** monographic series, government publication.
    Description: Presents the latest research of the National I.V.H.S. Architecture Development Program, which seeks to implement a nationally compatible intelligent transportation system to improve the efficiency and reduce the negative effects of ground transportation.

388 621.382   US   ISSN 1065-5123
I V H S JOURNAL; R&D, operational testing and deployment of intelligent vehicle highway systems. 1993. q. 91 ECU (effective 1996). (Intelligent Vehicle Highway Society of America) Gordon & Breach Science Publishers, c/o International Publishers Distributor, 820 Town Center Dr., Langhorne, PA 19047. TEL 215-750-2642; 800-545-8398. FAX 215-750-6343. (Subscr. to: International Publishers Distributor, P.O. Box 90, Reading, Berkshire RG1 8JL, England. TEL 44-173-456-8316) Ed. Kan Chen. **Document type:** academic/scholarly publication.
—BLDSC (4589.051500).

385   II   ISSN 0376-9909
HE3291
INDIAN RAILWAYS YEARBOOK. (Text in English) 1973. a. Railway Board, Directorate of Statistics and Economics, New Delhi 110001, India.

385 016   GW   ISSN 0170-2947
INFORMATION EISENBAHN; Dokumentation des Fachschrifttums. 1956. m. DM.120. Deutsche Bundesbahn, Dokumentationsdienst, Wallstr. 56, 55122 Mainz, Germany. TEL 06131-15428. FAX 06131-155924. adv.; bk.rev.; abstr.; stat.; tr.lit. circ. 2,300.
—CCC.
    Formerly: Kurzauszuege aus dem Schrifttum fuer das Eisenbahnwesen (ISSN 0023-5695)
    Description: Documentation of specialized railway publications, including abstracts.

388.3 621.382   US   ISSN 1054-2647
INSIDE I V H S; intelligent vehicle - highway systems update. 1991. fortn. £395($495) (Europe £395). Waters Information Services, Inc., Box 2248, Binghamton, NY 13902-2248. TEL 607-770-9242; 800-947-7947. FAX 607-770-9435. (European and Asian subscr. to: Waters Information Services Ltd., 57-59 Neal St., London WC2H 9PJ, England. TEL 44-171-240-2090. FAX 44-171-240-2076) Ed. Philip Alling. **Document type:** trade publication.
    ●Also available online. Vendor(s): NewsNet (TS01).

387.74   CN
INTERNATIONAL AIR TRANSPORT ASSOCIATION. MONTHLY INTERNATIONAL STATISTICS. (Text in English) 1980. m. $800 (diskette $1400). International Air Transport Association, Publications, 2000 Peel St., Montreal, PQ H3A 2R4, Canada. TEL 514-844-6311. FAX 514-844-3788. TELEX 05-267627. circ. 300. (also avail. in diskette format)
Description: Report showing traffic, capacity and passenger load factor trends of international scheduled services.

387.71   UN   ISSN 0251-267X
INTERNATIONAL CIVIL AVIATION OGANIZATION. DIGESTS OF STATISTICS. SERIES OFOD. ON-FLIGHT ORIGIN AND DESTINATION/ORGANISATION DE L'AVIATION CIVILE INTERNATIONALE. RECEUIL DE STATISTIQUES. SERIE OFOD. ORIGINE ET DESTINATION PAR VOL/MEZHDUNARODNAYA ORGANIZATSIYA GRAZHDANSKOI AVIATSII. STATISTICESKIJ SBORNIK. SERIYA OFOD. NASALNY I KONESNY PUNKTY POLETA/ORGANIZACION DE AVIACION CIVIL INTERNACIONAL. COMPENDIO ESTADISTICO. SERIE OFOD. ORIGEN Y DESTINO POR VUELO. (Text in English, French, Russian, Spanish) 1979. q. (plus a. series). price varies (diskette edition $200). International Civil Aviation Organization, Attn: Document Sales Unit, 1000 Sherbrooke St. W., Montreal, PQ H3A 2R2, Canada. TEL 514-285-8022. FAX 514-285-6769. TELEX 05-24513. (also avail. in diskette format; back issues avail.)
Description: Contains the revenue traffic performed for various city pairs.

387.71   UN   ISSN 1010-1500
INTERNATIONAL CIVIL AVIATION ORGANIZATION. DIGESTS OF STATISTICS. SERIES AF. AIRPORT AND ROUTE FACILITIES. FINANCIAL DATA AND SUMMARY TRAFFIC DATA/ORGANISATION DE L'AVIATION CIVILE. RECUEIL DE STATISTIQUES. SERIE AF. INSTALLATIONS ET SERVICES D'AEROPORT ET DE ROUTE. DONNES FINANCIERES ET STATISTIQUES DE TRAFFIC SOMMAIRES/MEZHDUNARODNAYA ORGANIZATSIYA GRAZHDANSKOI AVIATSII. STATISTICHESKI SBORNIK. SERIYA AF. AEROPORTNOE I MARSHRUTNOE OBORUDOVANIE. FINANSOVYE IZLOZHENIYA DANNYKH PO PERENOZHKAM/ORGANIZACION DE AVIACION CIVIL INTERNACIONAL. COMPENDIO ESTADISTICO. SERIE AF. INSTALACIONES Y SERVICIOS DE AEROPUERTO Y EN RUTA. DATOS FINANCIEROS Y RESUMEN DE DATOS DE TRAFICO. (Text in English, French, Russian, Spanish) no.3, 1985. irreg., no.10, 1992. $42 (diskette edition $200). International Civil Aviation Organization, Attn: Document Sales Unit, 1000 Sherbrooke St. W., Montreal, PQ H3A 2R2, Canada. TEL 514-285-8022. FAX 514-285-6769. TELEX 05-24513. (also avail. in diskette format; back issues avail.)
Description: Contains the financial data and summary traffic data for international airports and route facilities.

387   UN   ISSN 0074-2422
INTERNATIONAL CIVIL AVIATION ORGANIZATION. DIGESTS OF STATISTICS. SERIES AT. AIRPORT TRAFFIC. (Editions in English, French, Russian, Spanish) 1960. a., no.33, 1992. $32 (diskette $200). International Civil Aviation Organization, Attn: Document Sales Unit, 1000 Sherbrooke St. W., Montreal, PQ H3A 2R2, Canada. TEL 514-285-8022. FAX 514-285-6769. TELEX 05-24513. (also avail. in diskette format; magnetic tape; back issues avail.) **Indexed:** IIS.
Description: Presents statistics on airports open to international traffic.

387   UN   ISSN 0074-2430
INTERNATIONAL CIVIL AVIATION ORGANIZATION. DIGESTS OF STATISTICS. SERIES F. FINANCIAL DATA - COMMERCIAL AIR CARRIERS. (Editions in English, French, Russian, Spanish) a., no.47, 1993. $70 (Diskette version $200). International Civil Aviation Organization, Attn: Document Sales Unit, 1000 Sherbrooke St. W., Montreal, PQ H3A 2R2, Canada. TEL 514-285-8022. FAX 514-288-6769. TELEX 05-24513. (also avail. in diskette format; magnetic tape; back issues avail.) **Indexed:** IIS.
Description: Supplies the balance sheets of commercial air carriers, along with profit-and-loss statements.

387   UN
INTERNATIONAL CIVIL AVIATION ORGANIZATION. DIGESTS OF STATISTICS. SERIES FP. FLEET - PERSONNEL - COMMERCIAL AIR CARRIERS. (Classification of its Digest of Statistics, issued from 1947. Digest and Series numbering maintained separately) (Editions in English, French, Russian and Spanish) a., no.47, 1993. $37 (diskette version $200). International Civil Aviation Organization, Attn: Document Sales Unit, 1000 Sherbrooke St. W., Montreal, PQ H3A 2R2, Canada. TEL 514-285-8022. FAX 514-285-6769. TELEX 05-24513. (also avail. in diskette format; magnetic tape; back issues avail.) **Indexed:** IIS.
Formerly: International Civil Aviation Organization. Digests of Statistics. Series FP. Fleet, Personnel (ISSN 0074-2449)
Description: Provides statistical material on the number and types of aircraft, along with figures on employees.

387   UN   ISSN 0074-2457
INTERNATIONAL CIVIL AVIATION ORGANIZATION. DIGESTS OF STATISTICS. SERIES R. CIVIL AIRCRAFT ON REGISTER. (Editions in English, French, Russian, Spanish) 1961. a., no.33, 1993. $23 (diskette version $200). International Civil Aviation Organization, Attn: Document Sales Unit, 1000 Sherbrooke St. W., Montreal, PQ H3A 2R2, Canada. TEL 514-285-8022. FAX 514-285-6769. TELEX 05-24513. (also avail. in diskette format; magnetic tape; back issues avail.) **Indexed:** IIS.
Description: Compiles statistical data on registered civil aircraft heavier than 9,000 kg.

387   UN   ISSN 1014-0093
INTERNATIONAL CIVIL AVIATION ORGANIZATION. DIGESTS OF STATISTICS. SERIES TF. TRAFFIC BY FLIGHT STAGE. (Text in English, French, Spanish, Russian) a., no.108, 1993. $107 (diskette version $200). International Civil Aviation Organization, Attn: Document Sales Unit, 1000 Sherbrooke St. W., Montreal, PQ H3A 2R2, Canada. TEL 514-285-8022. FAX 514-285-6769. TELEX 05-24513. (also avail. in microfiche from CIS; diskette format; back issues avail.) **Indexed:** IIS.
Formerly: International Civil Aviation Organization. Digests of Statistics. Series TF. Traffic Flow (ISSN 0074-2473)
Description: Provides statistics on the flow of commercial air traffic from point to point.

387   UN   ISSN 1014-0077
INTERNATIONAL CIVIL AVIATION ORGANIZATION. DIGESTS OF STATISTICS. SERIES T. TRAFFIC, COMMERCIAL AIR TRAFFIC. (Editions in English, French, Russian, Spanish) 1947. a., no.53, 1989-1993. $65 (diskette version $200). International Civil Aviation Organization, Attn: Document Sales Unit, 1000 Sherbrooke St. W., Montreal, PQ H3A 2R2, Canada. TEL 514-285-8022. FAX 514-285-6769. TELEX 05-24513. (also avail. in diskette format; magnetic tape) **Indexed:** IIS.
Former titles (until 1977): International Civil Aviation Organization. Digests of Statistics. Series T. Airline Traffic (ISSN 1014-0085); (until 1975): International Civil Aviation Organization. Digests of Statistics. Series T. Traffic (ISSN 0074-2465)
Description: Presents commercial air traffic statistics for scheduled airlines provided by country.

387 629.1 016   UN   ISSN 0074-249X
Z5063.A1
INTERNATIONAL CIVIL AVIATION ORGANIZATION. INDEX OF I C A O PUBLICATIONS. ANNUAL CUMULATION. (Text in English) irreg., latest 1986. $9. International Civil Aviation Organization, Attn: Document Sales Unit, 1000 Sherbrooke St. W., Montreal, PQ H3A 2R2, Canada. TEL 514-285-8022. FAX 514-285-6769. TELEX 05-24513. (back issues avail.) **Document type:** abstracting/indexing.

385   FR
INTERNATIONAL RAILWAY STATISTICS. a. 850 F. Union Internationale des Chemins de Fer - Internationaler Eisenbahnverband, 16 rue Jean Rey, 75015 Paris, France. TEL 44-49-20-20. FAX 44-49-20-29.

385   FR   ISSN 0074-7580
INTERNATIONAL RAILWAY STATISTICS. STATISTICS OF INDIVIDUAL RAILWAYS. (Text in English, French, German) 1927. a. 600 F. Union Internationale des Chemins de Fer - International Union of Railways, 16 rue Jean Rey, 75015 Paris, France. TEL 44-49-20-20. FAX 44-49-20-29. TELEX 270835FUNINFER.
Description: Collection of statistics on lines, traction, rolling stock, personnel, traffic and finances.

385.1   BE   ISSN 0378-1968
INTERNATIONAL STATISTICAL HANDBOOK OF URBAN PUBLIC TRANSPORT/RECUEIL INTERNATIONAL DE STATISTIQUES DES TRANSPORTS PUBLICS URBAINS/INTERNATIONALES STATISTIK-HANDBUCH FUER DEN OEFFENTLICHEN STADTVERKEHR. 1964. irreg. 3700 BEF. International Union of Public Transport, Av. de l'Uruguay 19, B-1050 Brussels, Belgium. TEL 322-673-6100. FAX 322-660-1072. TELEX 63916 UITP B.
Supersedes: International Union of Public Transport. Transports Publics dans les Principales Villes du Monde (ISSN 0539-113X)
Description: Contains statistical data on 1100 networks worldwide (urban and regional public transport).

330   IE   ISSN 0444-5147
IRELAND. CENTRAL STATISTICS OFFICE. PARTICULARS OF VEHICLES REGISTERED AND LICENSED FOR THE FIRST TIME. a. I£2. Central Statistics Office, Skehard Rd., Cork, Ireland. TEL 021-359000. FAX 021-359090. (processed) **Document type:** government publication.

330   IE   ISSN 0791-346X
IRELAND. CENTRAL STATISTICS OFFICE. STATISTICS OF PORT TRAFFIC. a. I£2. Central Statistics Office, Skehard Rd., Cork, Ireland. TEL 021-359000. FAX 021-359090. (processed) **Document type:** government publication.
Description: Presents information for each harbour authority on the number of arrivals and net register tonnage of trading and passenger vessels. Includes the weight of goods and number of livestock handled and details on the type of traffic.

388.3   IS   ISSN 0075-1057
ISRAEL. CENTRAL BUREAU OF STATISTICS. MOTOR VEHICLES. (Subseries of its Special Series) (Text in Hebrew; summaries in English) irreg., no.746, 1983. price varies. Central Bureau of Statistics, Box 13015, Jerusalem 91 130, Israel. TEL 02-21 12 11.

380.3 310   IS   ISSN 0333-6050
ISRAEL. CENTRAL BUREAU OF STATISTICS. ROAD ACCIDENTS WITH CASUALTIES. (Text in English and Hebrew) 1950. a., no.761, 1984. price varies. Central Bureau of Statistics, Box 13015, Jerusalem 91 130, Israel.

ITALY. ISTITUTO NAZIONALE DI STATISTICA. STATISTICA DEGLI INCIDENTI STRADALI. see **PUBLIC HEALTH AND SAFETY — Abstracting, Bibliographies, Statistics**

387 314   IT
HE839
ITALY. ISTITUTO NAZIONALE DI STATISTICA. STATISTICHE DEI TRASPORTI MARITTIMI. 1972. a. L.25000 (effective 1993). Istituto Nazionale di Statistica, Via Cesare Balbo 16, 00100 Rome, Italy. FAX 06-46735198.
Former titles (until 1990): Italy. Istituto Nazionale di Statistica. Statistiche della Navigazione Marittima; Italy. Istituto Centrale di Statistica. Annuario Statistico della Navigazione Marittima (ISSN 0075-1898)

385   IT   ISSN 0021-3144
ITALY. MINISTERO DEI TRASPORTI E DELL'AVIAZIONE CIVILE. AZIENDA AUTONOMA DELLE FERROVIE DELLO STATO. BOLLETTINO STATISTICO MENSILE.* 1942. m. L.9000. (Azienda Autonoma delle Ferrovie dello Stato) Edizioni Richerche, Viale Ippocrate 85, Rome, Italy. charts; stat.

6332 TRANSPORTATION — ABSTRACTING, BIBLIOGRAPHIES, STATISTICS

629.286   JA
JAPAN AUTO ABSTRACTS; real time database. (Text in English) w. 840000 Yen. Dodwell Marketing Consultants, Kowa no.35, Bldg., 14-14 Akasaka 1-chome, Minato-ku, Tokyo 107, Japan. TEL 03-3589-0207. FAX 03-5570-7132. TELEX J22274 DODWELL. **Document type:** abstracting/indexing.
  Description: English abstracts of Japanese-press articles related to the Japanese auto industry.

388.41   NR
KANO (STATE). MOTOR VEHICLE STATISTICS. 1978. biennial. $30 (effective 1996). Budget & Economic Planning Directorate, Ministry of Finance, Audu Bako Secretariat, P.M.B. 3291, Kano, Nigeria. stat. **Document type:** government publication.

388   HU   ISSN 0231-0724
KOZUTI KOZLEKEDESI SZAKIRODALMI TAJEKOZTATO/ROAD TRANSPORT ABSTRACTS. 1949. m. 3200 Ft. Orszagos Muszaki Informacios Kozpont es Konyvtar (O.M.I.K.K.) - National Technical Information Centre and Library, Muzeum u. 17, P.O. Box 12, 1428 Budapest, Hungary. Ed. E. Vajda. circ. 510. **Document type:** abstracting/indexing.
  Supersedes in part (in 1982): Muszaki Lapszemle. Kozlekedes - Technical Abstracts. Transportation (ISSN 0027-5042)

388.324   GW   ISSN 0943-1489
HE5669
KRAFTFAHRT-BUNDESAMT. BESTAND AN KRAFTFAHRZEUGEN UND KRAFTFAHRZEUGANHAENGERN. 1948. a. DM.69. Metzler - Poeschel Verlag, Postfach 1152, 72125 Kusterdingen, Germany. TEL 07071-935355. FAX 07071-935393. **Document type:** government publication.

380   KU
KUWAIT. CENTRAL STATISTICAL OFFICE. ANNUAL STATISTICAL BULLETIN FOR TRANSPORT AND COMMUNICATION/KUWAIT. AL-IDARAH AL-MARKAZIYYAH LIL-IHSA'. AL-NASHRAH AL-IHSA'IYYAH AL-SANAWIYYAH LIL-NAQL WAL-MUWASALAT. (Text in Arabic, English) 1972. a., latest for years 1990-1992. Central Statistical Office - Al-Idarah al-Markaziyyah lil-Ihsa', P.O. Box 26188, Safat 13122, Kuwait. TEL 965-2428200. FAX 965-2430464. TELEX 22468 TAKHTET KT. **Document type:** government publication.
  Supersedes in part (in 1981): Kuwait. Al-Idarah al-Markaziyyah lil-Ihsa'. Nashrah Sanawiyyah li-Ihsa'at al-Khadamat al-Aamah.

380.5 011   US   ISSN 1065-0520
CODEN: LTSTEX
LITERATURE ABSTRACTS: TRANSPORTATION & STORAGE. (Part of: Literature Abstracts) m. American Petroleum Institute, Central Abstracting & Information Services, 275 Seventh Ave., New York, NY 10001-6708. TEL 212-366-4040. FAX 212-366-4298. **Document type:** abstracting/indexing.
  Formerly (until 1991): A P I Abstracts - Transportation and Storage.

387   UK   ISSN 0076-0234
HE563.A3
LLOYD'S REGISTER OF SHIPPING. STATISTICAL TABLES. 1878. a. $120. Lloyd's Register of Shipping, 71 Fenchurch St., London EC3M 4BS, England. TEL 0171-709-0166. (U.S. subscr. to: Lloyd's Register of Shipping, 17 Battery Pl., New York, NY 10004) charts. (also avail. in microfiche from BHP).
  Description: Breaks the world merchant fleet down by registration, size, age, and ship type.

388   LU   ISSN 1012-6635
LUXEMBOURG. SERVICE CENTRAL DE LA STATISTIQUE ET DES ETUDES ECONOMIQUES. INDICATEURS RAPIDES. SERIE D. IMMATRICULATIONS DE VEHICULES AUTOMOTEURS. m. Service Central de la Statistique et des Etudes Economiques, 6 bd. Royal, B.P. 304, 2013 Luxembourg, Luxembourg. TEL 478-4268. FAX 46-42-89. (looseleaf format) **Document type:** government publication.

LUXEMBOURG. SERVICE CENTRAL DE LA STATISTIQUE ET DES ETUDES ECONOMIQUES. INDICATEURS RAPIDES. SERIE F: ACCIDENTS CORPORELS DE LA CIRCULATION ROUTIERE. see *POPULATION STUDIES — Abstracting, Bibliographies, Statistics*

629.2 016   UK   ISSN 0309-0817
TL1
M I R A AUTOMOBILE ABSTRACTS. 1955. m. £230. Motor Industry Research Association, Watling St., Nuneaton, Nuneaton, Warks. CV10 0TU, England. FAX 01203-343772. Ed. J. Woodward. adv.; bk.rev.; abstr.; repts. circ. 800. Indexed: Agri.Eng.Abstr., BMT, Fluidex. **Document type:** abstracting/indexing.
  ● Also available online. Vendor(s): European Space Agency.
  —BLDSC (1831.930000).
  Former titles: M I R A Abstracts (ISSN 0305-8972); Automobile Abstracts (ISSN 0005-1357)
  Description: Abstracts technical papers relating to automotive engineering.

380.5   MW
MALAWI. NATIONAL STATISTICAL OFFICE. TRANSPORT STATISTICS. 1980. a. K.25. National Statistical Office, Commissioner for Census and Statistics, P.O. Box 333, Zomba, Malawi. TEL 265-50-522-3777. FAX 265-50-523-130. TELEX 44015 CENSUS MI. **Document type:** government publication.

387.7   MM   ISSN 0377-791X
MALTA. CENTRAL OFFICE OF STATISTICS. SHIPPING AND AVIATION STATISTICS. 1936. a. L.1. Central Office of Statistics, Auberge d'Italie, Merchants' St., Valletta, Malta. FAX 356-248483. (Subscr. to: Publications Bookshop, Auberge de Castille, Valletta, Malta) **Document type:** government publication.
  Formerly: Shipping and Aviation Statistics of the Maltese Islands (ISSN 0080-9268)

016.387   NE   ISSN 0920-1610
MARITIME INFORMATION REVIEW. (Text in English) 1976. m. (11/yr.). fl.350 (effective 1995). Netherlands Maritime Information Centre, P.O. Box 21873, 3001 AW Rotterdam, Netherlands. TEL 31-10-4130960. FAX 31-10-4112857. **Document type:** abstracting/indexing.
  ● Also available online. Vendor(s): European Space Agency.
  Description: Presents the latest additions to the MARNA (maritime specialist literature) and SHIPDES (ship descriptions) databases of the Netherlands Maritime Information Centre. Includes abstract, keywords index, and bibliographic citations.

386 382   US
MARITIME RESEARCH. WEEKLY NEWSLETTER. 1953. w. $250. Maritime Research, Inc., 499 Ernston Rd., Box 805, Parlin, NJ 08859. TEL 908-727-8040. charts; stat.

388.314   MF
MAURITIUS. CENTRAL STATISTICAL OFFICE. DIGEST OF ROAD TRANSPORT STATISTICS. 1985. a. Rs.75 (effective Jun. 1995). Central Statistical Office, Toorawa Centre, Cr. S.S. R & J. Mosque Sts., Port Louis, Mauritius. TEL 230-234-5294. FAX 230-208-4011. (Subscr. to: Government Printing Office, Ramtoolah Bldg., Sir S. Ramgoolam St., Port Louis, Mauritius) **Document type:** government publication.

387   UK   ISSN 0261-1848
MERCHANT SHIPBUILDING RETURN. 1888. q. free. Lloyd's Register of Shipping, 71 Fenchurch St., London EC3M 4BS, England. TEL 0171-709-9166. (U.S. subscr. to: Lloyd's Register of Shipping, 17 Battery Pl., New York, NY 10004)
  Description: Provides statistical summaries of all self-propelled ships of 100 gross tonnage and above under construction or on order, including analyses by country of build, size, type and registration.

318   BL
MINAS GERAIS, BRAZIL. DEPARTAMENTO DE RODAGEM. SERVICO DE TRANSITO. ESTATISTICA DE TRAFEGO E ACIDENTES. 1969. a. free. Departamento de Estradas de Rodagem, Servico de Transito, Av. Andradas, 1120, 30000 Belo Horizonte, Brazil. stat. circ. 1,000.
  Formerly: Minas Gerais, Brazil. Departamento de Estradas de Rodagem. Servico de Transito. Estatistica de Trafego.

385   II   ISSN 0027-0504
MONTHLY RAILWAY STATISTICS. (Text in English, Hindi) vol.16, 1967. m. Railway Board, Director, Statistics & Economics, Public Relations, New Delhi 110001, India. charts; stat.

629.2 016   UK   ISSN 0265-0843
MOTOR INDUSTRY MANAGEMENT. 1946. m. £30 (foreign £36). Institute of the Motor Industry, Fanshaws, Brickendon, Herts. SG13 8PQ, England. TEL 099-286521. FAX 099-286521. Ed. Chris Phillips. adv.; bk.rev.; abstr.; bibl.; charts; illus.; index, cum.index. circ. 100,000.
  Incorporates (1988-1990): Motor Industry Engineer; **Former titles:** Motor Management (ISSN 0020-2746); Institute of the Motor Industry. Journal (ISSN 0020-3173)

388.3 310   SZ
MOTORFAHRZEUGE IN DER SCHWEIZ. EINGEFUEHRTE MOTORFAHRZEUGE/VEHICULES A MOTEUR IMPORTES EN SUISSE. VEHICULES A MOTEUR IMPORTES. (Text in French and German) 1929. a. 5 SFr. Bundesamt fuer Statistik, Schwarztorstr. 96, CH-3003 Bern, Switzerland. TEL 031-3236011. FAX 031-3236061. **Document type:** government publication.
  Formerly: Eingefuehrte Motorfahrzeuge.

388.3 310   SZ
MOTORFAHRZEUGE IN DER SCHWEIZ. MOTORFAHRZEUGBESTAND IN DER SCHWEIZ AM 30. SEPTEMBER (YEAR)/VEHICULES A MOTEUR EN SUISSE. EFFECTIF DES VEHICULES A MOTEUR EN SUISSE AU 30 SEPTEMBRE (YEAR). (Text in French and German) 1951. a. 32 SFr. Bundesamt fuer Statistik, Schwarztorstr. 96, CH-3003 Bern, Switzerland. TEL 031-3236011. FAX 031-3236061. **Document type:** government publication.
  Formerly: Motorfahrzeugbestand in der Schweiz am 30. September (Year).

388.324   US
MOVERS STATISTICAL PROFILE (YEAR); demographic, economic and financial data of the moving industry. a. $35. American Movers Conference, 1611 Duke St., Alexandria, VA 22314. TEL 703-683-7410. FAX 703-683-7527. **Document type:** trade publication.
  Formerly (until 1994): Moving Industry Financial and Economic Statistics.
  Description: Covers statistics of the moving industry, including demographic section and industry wage information section, for anyone dealing with the moving business.

380.5 016   US
N T I S ALERTS: TRANSPORTATION. w. $135 (foreign $195). U.S. National Technical Information Service, 5285 Port Royal Rd., Springfield, VA 22161. TEL 703-487-4630. FAX 703-321-8547. TELEX 64617. index. (back issues avail.) **Document type:** abstracting/indexing.
  Former titles: Abstract Newsletter: Transportation (ISSN 0163-1527); Weekly Abstract Newsletter: Transportation; Weekly Government Abstracts. Transportation.

387   JA   ISSN 0469-4783
NAGOYA PORT STATISTICS ANNUAL/NAGOYAKO TOKEI NENPO. (Text in Japanese) 1958. a. free. Nagoya Port Authority - Nagoyako Kanri Kumiai, 1-8-21 Irifune, Minato-ku, Nagoya 455, Japan. TEL 052-654-7840. FAX 052-654-7995. stat. circ. 1,000. **Document type:** government publication.

387   JA   ISSN 0027-7592
NAGOYA PORT STATISTICS MONTHLY/NAGOYAKO TOKEI SOKUHO. (Text in Japanese) 1949. m. free. Nagoya Port Authority - Nagoyako Kanri Kumiai, 1-8-21 Irifune, Minato-ku, Nagoya 455, Japan. TEL 052-654-7840. FAX 052-654-7995. bk.rev.; stat. circ. 400. **Document type:** government publication.

380.5   US   ISSN 0148-849X
NATIONAL RESEARCH COUNCIL. TRANSPORTATION RESEARCH BOARD. BIBLIOGRAPHY. 1947. irreg. price varies. U.S. National Research Council, Transportation Research Board, 2101 Constitution Ave., N.W., Washington, DC 20418. TEL 202-334-3214. FAX 202-334-2519. bibl. (also avail. in microfiche) **Document type:** bibliography, government publication.
  Description: Summaries of published research findings in various transportation-related disciplines.

TRANSPORTATION — ABSTRACTING, BIBLIOGRAPHIES, STATISTICS

385   BE   ISSN 0771-517X
NATIONALE MAATSCHAPPIJ VAN BELGISCHE SPOORWEGEN. DOCUMENTATIEBULLETIN. French edition: Societe Nationale des Chemins de Fer Belges. Bulletin de Documentation (ISSN 0771-5129) (Text in Dutch) 1947. m. 1000 BEF (effective 1994). Nationale Maatschappij der Belgische Spoorwegen, Bureau 01-114, Section 80-1 - Societe Nationale des Chemins de Fer Belges, 85 rue de France, B-1070 Brussels, Belgium. TEL 32-2-525-3530. FAX 32-2-525-4045. bk.rev.; abstr.; bibl. circ. 345. **Document type:** academic/scholarly publication, bulletin.
    Formerly: Societe Nationale des Chemins de Fer Belges. Documentaire (ISSN 0012-4567).
    Description: Catalog of articles of periodicals and books especially on railway transport.

388.1   US
NEBRASKA. DEPARTMENT OF ROADS. NEBRASKA SELECTED STATISTICS. a. free. Nebraska Department of Roads, Transportation Planning Division, 1500 NE Hwy. 2, Box 94759, Lincoln, NE 68509-4759. TEL 402-479-4519. FAX 402-479-4325. illus. circ. 160. **Document type:** government publication.
    Former titles: Nebraska. Department of Roads. Highway Statistics: State and Local Road and Street Data for (Year); Nebraska Highway Statistics: State and Local Construction Mileage (ISSN 0099-0442)

331   NE   ISSN 0024-8770
NETHERLANDS. CENTRAAL BUREAU VOOR DE STATISTIEK. MAANDSTATISTIEK VERKEER EN VERVOER. 1937. m. fl.100. Centraal Bureau voor de Statistiek, Prinses Beatrixlaan 428, Voorburg, Netherlands. (Orders to: SDU - Publishers, Christoffel Plantijnstraat, The Hague, Netherlands) stat.; index. circ. 510. **Document type:** government publication.

388.3   NE   ISSN 0168-4973
NETHERLANDS. CENTRAAL BUREAU VOOR DE STATISTIEK. STATISTIEK DER MOTORVOERTUIGEN/NETHERLANDS. CENTRAL BUREAU OF STATISTICS. STATISTICS OF MOTOR VEHICLES. (Text in Dutch and English) 1966. a. Centraal Bureau voor de Statistiek, Prinses Beatrixlaan 428, Voorburg, Netherlands. (Dist. by: SDU - Publishers, Christoffel Plantijnstraat 2, Postbus 20014, 2500 EA The Hague, Netherlands) **Document type:** government publication.
    Formerly: Netherlands. Centraal Bureau voor de Statistiek. Statistiek der Motorrijtuigen (ISSN 0077-698X)

387 314.9   NE   ISSN 0168-4825
NETHERLANDS. CENTRAAL BUREAU VOOR DE STATISTIEK. STATISTIEK VAN AAN-, AF- EN DOORVOER. GOEDERENVERVOER PER GOEDERENSOORT VAN EN NAAR DE ZEEHAVENS VAN ROTTERDAM EN AMSTERDAM. 1950. a. Centraal Bureau voor de Statistiek, Prinses Beatrixlaan 428, Voorburg, Netherlands. (Orders to: SDU - Publishers, Christoffel Plantijnstraat, The Hague, Netherlands) circ. 300. **Document type:** government publication.
    Formerly: Netherlands. Centraal Bureau voor de Statistiek. Statistiek van het Internationaal Zeehavenvervoer.

386   NE   ISSN 0927-7471
HE674
NETHERLANDS. CENTRAAL BUREAU VOOR DE STATISTIEK. STATISTIEK VAN DE VAARWAGEN. Key Title: Statistiek van de Vaarwagen. 1946. a. Centraal Bureau voor de Statistiek, Prinses Beatrixlaan 428, Voorburg, Netherlands. (Orders to: S D U Uitgeverij, Christoffel Plantijnstraat 2, Postbus 20014, 2500 EA The Hague, Netherlands) **Document type:** government publication.
    Former titles (until 1992): Netherlands. Centraal Bureau voor de Statistiek. Statistiek van de Scheepvartbeweging (ISSN 0168-5279); Statistiek der Scheepvartbeweging in Nederland (ISSN 0920-9913); Statistiek der Scheepvartbeweging op de Rivieren en Kanalen in Nederland (ISSN 0920-9921)

387 310   NE   ISSN 0168-5422
HE845
NETHERLANDS. CENTRAAL BUREAU VOOR DE STATISTIEK. STATISTIEK VAN DE ZEEVAART/NETHERLANDS. CENTRAL BUREAU OF STATISTICS. STATISTICS OF SEABORNE SHIPPING. (Text in Dutch and English) 1948. a. Centraal Bureau voor de Statistiek, Prinses Beatrixlaan 428, Voorburg, Netherlands. (Dist. by: SDU - Publishers, Christoffel Plantijnstraat 2, Postbus 20014, 2500 EA The Hague, Netherlands) **Document type:** government publication.

386 314   NE   ISSN 0168-5376
NETHERLANDS. CENTRAAL BUREAU VOOR DE STATISTIEK. STATISTIEK VAN DE INTERNATIONALE BINNENVAART/NETHERLANDS. CENTRAL BUREAU OF STATISTICS. STATISTICS OF THE INTERNATIONAL INLAND SHIPPING. (Text in Dutch and English) 1948. a. Centraal Bureau voor de Statistiek, Prinses Beatrixlaan 428, Voorburg, Netherlands. (Dist. by: SDU - Publishers, Christoffel Plantijnstraat 2, Postbus 20014, 2500 EA The Hague, Netherlands) **Document type:** government publication.

387.5   NE   ISSN 0168-5473
NETHERLANDS. CENTRAAL BUREAU VOOR DE STATISTIEK. STATISTIEK VAN DE KOOPVAARDIJVLOOT/NETHERLANDS. CENTRAL BUREAU OF STATISTICS. STATISTICS OF THE MERCHANT MARINE. (Text in Dutch and English) 1949. a. Centraal Bureau voor de Statistiek, Prinses Beatrixlaan 428, Voorburg, Netherlands. (Orders to: S D U Uitgeverij, Christoffel Plantijnstraat 2, Postbus 20014, 2500 EA The Hague, Netherlands) **Document type:** government publication.

388.1   NE   ISSN 0168-5023
NETHERLANDS. CENTRAAL BUREAU VOOR DE STATISTIEK. STATISTIEK VAN DE VERKEERSONGEVALLEN OP DE OPENBARE WEG/NETHERLANDS. CENTRAL BUREAU OF STATISTICS. STATISTICS OF ROAD-TRAFFIC ACCIDENTS. (Text in Dutch and English) 1947. a. Centraal Bureau voor de Statistiek, Prinses Beatrixlaan 428, Voorburg, Netherlands. (Dist. by: SDU - Publishers, Christoffel Plantijnstraat 2, Postbus 20014, 2500 EA The Hague, Netherlands) **Document type:** government publication.

388 387   NE   ISSN 0168-5074
NETHERLANDS. CENTRAAL BUREAU VOOR DE STATISTIEK. STATISTIEK VAN HET PERSONENVERVOER/NETHERLANDS. CENTRAL BUREAU OF STATISTICS. STATISTICS OF PASSENGER TRANSPORT. (Text in Dutch and English) 1943. a. Centraal Bureau voor de Statistiek, Prinses Beatrixlaan 428, Voorburg, Netherlands. (Dist. by: SDU - Publishers, Christoffel Plantijnstraat 2, Postbus 20014, 2500 EA The Hague, Netherlands) **Document type:** government publication.

386   NE   ISSN 0168-5325
HE69
NETHERLANDS. CENTRAAL BUREAU VOOR DE STATISTIEK. STATISTIEK VAN HET BINNENLANDS GOEDERENVERVOER. STATISTICS OF INTERNAL GOODS TRANSPORT IN THE NETHERLANDS. (Text in Dutch, English) 1948. a. Centraal Bureau voor de Statistiek, Prinses Beatrixlaan 428, Voorburg, Netherlands. (Orders to: SDU - Publishers, Christoffel Plantijnstraat, The Hague, Netherlands) **Document type:** government publication.

388.3   SW
NEW CAR PRICE-LIST. bi-m. SEK 172 (effective 1993). AB Bilstatistik, Box 5514, S-114 85, Stockholm, Sweden. TEL 46-8-701-63-60. FAX 46-8-791-23-11. TELEX 119-23-BIL S.

388.3   CN   ISSN 0705-5595
HD9710.C22
NEW MOTOR VEHICLE SALES. (Text in English, French) 1932. m. Can.$144($173) (foreign $202). Statistics Canada, Publications Division, Ottawa, Ont. K1A 0T6, Canada. TEL 613-951-7277. FAX 613-951-1584.
    Description: Presents data on new motor vehicles: number and value of new passenger cars, trucks and buses sold, by month, as well as cumulatively, for both current and previous years.

388.3   SW
NEW REGISTRATIONS. m. SEK 1024. AB Bilstatistik, Box 5514, S-114 85 Stockholm, Sweden. TEL 46-8-701-63-60. FAX 46-8-791-23-11. TELEX 119-23 BIL S.

387.5   JA
NIHON SHOSEN SENPUKU TOKEI. 1972. a. free. Japanese Shipowners' Association, Research and Public Relations Division - Nihon Senshu Kyokai, c/o Kaiun Bldg., 6-4 Hirakawa-cho 2-chome, Chiyoda-ku, Tokyo 102, Japan. FAX 03-262-4760. TELEX J2322148. stat. circ. 2,800.
    Description: Statistical summary of the Japanese merchant fleet.

388   NO   ISSN 0468-8147
NORWAY. STATISTISK SENTRALBYRAA. SAMFERDSELSSTATISTIKK/NORWAY. CENTRAL BUREAU OF STATISTICS. TRANSPORT AND COMMUNICATION STATISTICS. (Subseries of its Norges Offisielle Statistikk) (Text in English and Norwegian) 1958. a. NOK 85 (effective 1996). Statistisk Sentralbyraa - Central Bureau of Statistics, P.O. Box 8131-Dep., N-0033 Oslo, Norway. TEL 47-22-864500. FAX 47-22-864976. circ. 1,100. **Document type:** government publication.

388.31 310   SZ
DER OEFFENTLICHE VERKEHR/TRANSPORTS PUBLICS. (Text in French and German) 1985. a. 29 SFr. Bundesamt fuer Statistik, Schwarztorstr. 96, CH-3003 Bern, Switzerland. TEL 031-3236011. FAX 031-3236061. **Document type:** government publication.

388 310   PP
PAPUA NEW GUINEA. NATIONAL STATISTICAL OFFICE. STATISTICAL BULLETIN: REGISTERED MOTOR VEHICLES. (Text in English) 1962. a. £1.50. Department of Transport, Database Bureau Office, c/o Database Manager, P.O. Box 457, Konedoba, Papua New Guinea. circ. 100. **Document type:** government publication.
    Description: Provides statistics on the total stock of motor vehicles in Papua New Guidea that have been registered or reregistered during the year. Registrations are broken down by vehicle type, ownership, province, make, and capacity of vehicle.

318   BL   ISSN 0103-6653
HE5653.A1
PESQUISA ANUAL DO TRANSPORTE RODOVIARIO. 1968. a. $80. Fundacao Instituto Brasileiro de Geografia e Estatistica, Centro de Documentacao e Disseminacao de Informacoes, Rua General Canabarro 666, 2o andar, Maracana 20271-201 Rio de Janeiro, Brazil. TEL 55-21-2645424. FAX 55-21-2289575.
    Formerly (until 1986): Empresas de Transporte Rodoviario (ISSN 0100-154X)

380.5   II   ISSN 0079-2381
POCKET BOOK OF TRANSPORT STATISTICS OF INDIA. 1968. a. $12.96. Ministry of Shipping and Transport, Transport Research Division, I D A Bldg., Jamnagar House, Shahjahan Rd., New Delhi 110011, India. (Orders to: Controller of Publications, Civil Lines, Delhi 110006, India)
    Formerly: India Transport Statistics.

387 317   PL
POLAND. GLOWNY URZAD STATYSTYCZNY. STATYSTYKA ZEGLUGI SRODLADOWEJ I DROG WODNYCH SRODLADOWYCH. (Subseries of its: Seria Statystyka Polski Materialy Statystyczne) a. 15 ZI. Zaklad Wydawnictw Statystycznych, Al. Niepodleglosci 208, 00-925 Warsaw, Poland. TEL 48 22 25-03-45.

315.2   JA
PORT OF YOKOHAMA. ANNUAL STATISTICS.. (Text in Japanese) no.212, Nov. 1969. a. free. Port and Harbor Bureau, Industry and Trade Center Bldg., 2 Yamashita-cho Nakaku, Yokohama, Japan. FAX 45-671-7158. (processed)
    Formerly: Port of Yokohama. Monthly Statistics. (ISSN 0032-4876)

380.5 301.16 314   PO   ISSN 0377-2292
HE77
PORTUGAL. INSTITUTO NACIONAL DE ESTATISTICA. ESTATISTICAS DOS TRANSPORTES E COMUNICACOES: CONTINENTE, ACORES E MADEIRA. 1970. a. Esc.4000. Instituto Nacional de Estatistica, Avda. Antonio Jose de Almeida 1, 1078 Lisbon Codex, Portugal.

6334 TRANSPORTATION — ABSTRACTING, BIBLIOGRAPHIES, STATISTICS

388.3 362.4   US
PROJECT ACTION PRODUCTS AND PUBLICATIONS RESOURCE GUIDE. a. free. (National Institute for Accessible Action) Project Action, 1350 New York Ave., N.W., Ste. 711, Washington, DC 20005. TEL 800-659-NIAT. FAX 202-737-7914. **Document type:** bibliography, government publication.
   Description: Lists research product and publication deliverables related to making public transportation accessible to persons with disabilities.

338.324   US
QUARTERLY OPERATING STATISTICS; of major household goods carriers. q. $85. American Movers Conference, 1611 Duke St., Alexandria, VA 22314. TEL 703-683-7410. FAX 703-683-7527. **Document type:** trade publication.
   Description: Earnings of major household goods carriers. For anyone dealing with the moving business.

385   BL   ISSN 0102-4930
R F F S A ANUARIO ESTATISTICO. 1960. a. free. Rede Ferroviaria Federal, S.A., Departamento Geral de Estatistica, Rio de Janeiro, Brazil.
   Description: Provides statistical information on the railway system of Brazil.

338 625 016   RU   ISSN 0486-2252
REFERATIVNYI ZHURNAL. AVTOMOBIL'NYE DOROGI. 1963. m. $182 (effective 1996). Vsesoyuznyi Institut Nauchno-Tekhnicheskoi Informatsii (VINITI), Baltiiskaya ul., 14, Moscow A-219, Russia. (Subscr. to: Mezhdunarodnaya Kniga, Dimitrova ul. 39, 113095 Moscow, Russia) **Document type:** abstracting/indexing.
   —CCC.

388 016   RU   ISSN 0034-2297
REFERATIVNYI ZHURNAL. AVTOMOBIL'NYI I GORODSKOI TRANSPORT. 1961. m. $456 (effective 1996). Vsesoyuznyi Institut Nauchno-Tekhnicheskoi Informatsii (VINITI), Baltiiskaya ul., 14, Moscow A-219, Russia. (Subscr. to: Mezhdunarodnaya Kniga, Dimitrova ul. 39, 113095 Moscow, Russia) **Document type:** abstracting/indexing.
   —CCC.

621.43 016   RU   ISSN 0486-2279
REFERATIVNYI ZHURNAL. DVIGATELI VNUTRENNEGO SGORANIYA. 1956. m. $194 (effective 1996). Vsesoyuznyi Institut Nauchno-Tekhnicheskoi Informatsii (VINITI), Baltiiskaya ul., 14, Moscow A-219, Russia. (Subscr. to: Mezhdunarodnaya Kniga, Dimitrova ul. 39, 113095 Moscow, Russia) **Document type:** abstracting/indexing.
   —CCC.

388.3 614 016   RU   ISSN 0202-9952
REFERATIVNYI ZHURNAL. ORGANIZATSIYA I BEZOPASNOST DOROZHNOGO DVIZHENIYA. 1973. m. $80 (effective 1996). Vsesoyuznyi Institut Nauchno-Tekhnicheskoi Informatsii (VINITI), Baltiiskaya ul., 14, Moscow A-219, Russia. (Subscr. to: Mezhdunarodnaya Kniga, Dimitrova ul. 39, 113095 Moscow, Russia) **Document type:** abstracting/indexing.
   —CCC.

REFERATIVNYI ZHURNAL. TRUBOPROVODNYI TRANSPORT. see ENGINEERING — Abstracting, Bibliographies, Statistics

387 016   RU   ISSN 0484-2545
REFERATIVNYI ZHURNAL. VODNYI TRANSPORT. 1962. m. $388 (effective 1996). Vsesoyuznyi Institut Nauchno-Tekhnicheskoi Informatsii (VINITI), Baltiiskaya ul., 14, Moscow A-219, Russia. (Subscr. to: Mezhdunarodnaya Kniga, Dimitrova ul. 39, 113095 Moscow, Russia) **Document type:** abstracting/indexing.
   —CCC.

387.7 016   RU   ISSN 0484-2561
REFERATIVNYI ZHURNAL. VOZDUSHNYI TRANSPORT. 1962. m. $320 (effective 1996). Vsesoyuznyi Institut Nauchno-Tekhnicheskoi Informatsii (VINITI), Baltiiskaya ul., 14, Moscow A-219, Russia. (Subscr. to: Mezhdunarodnaya Kniga, Dimitrova ul. 39, 113095 Moscow, Russia) **Document type:** abstracting/indexing.
   —CCC.

385.1 016   RU   ISSN 0034-2645
REFERATIVNYI ZHURNAL. VZAIMODEISTVIE RAZNYKH VIDOV TRANSPORTA I KONTEINERNYE PEREVOZKI. 1961. m. $117 (effective 1996). Vsesoyuznyi Institut Nauchno-Tekhnicheskoi Informatsii (VINITI), Baltiiskaya ul., 14, Moscow A-219, Russia. (Subscr. to: Mezhdunarodnaya Kniga, Dimitrova ul. 39, 113095 Moscow, Russia) **Document type:** abstracting/indexing.
   —CCC.

385 016   RU   ISSN 0484-2596
REFERATIVNYI ZHURNAL. ZHELEZNODOROZHNYI TRANSPORT. 1960. m. $280 (effective 1996). Vsesoyuznyi Institut Nauchno-Tekhnicheskoi Informatsii (VINITI), Baltiiskaya ul., 14, Moscow A-219, Russia. (Subscr. to: Mezhdunarodnaya Kniga, Dimitrova ul. 39, 113095 Moscow, Russia) **Document type:** abstracting/indexing.
   —CCC.

388.1   ZA
REPORT ON PASSENGER ROAD TRANSPORT IN ZAMBIA. 1968. a. $4. Central Statistical Office, P.O. Box 31908, Lusaka, Zambia. TEL 211-231.

388   HU   ISSN 0231-3928
REPULESI SZAKIRODALMI TAJEKOZTATO/AVIATION AND AIR TRANSPORT ABSTRACTS. bi-m. 3000 Ft. Orszagos Muszaki Informacios Kozpont es Konyvtar (O.M.I.K.K.) - National Technical Information Centre and Library, Muzeum u. 17, P.O. Box 12, 1428 Budapest, Hungary. (Subscr. to: Kultura, P.O. Box 149, 1389 Budapest, Hungary) Ed. Ferenc Bardosi. circ. 200. **Document type:** abstracting/indexing.
   Supersedes in part (in 1982): Muszaki Lapszemle. Kozlekedes - Technical Abstracts. Transportation (ISSN 0027-5042)

388.31   UK   ISSN 0263-9653
HE5614.5.G7
ROAD ACCIDENTS: WALES. 1983. a. Welsh Office, Statistical Directorate, New Crown Bldg., Cathays Park, Cardiff CF1 3NQ, Wales. TEL 01222-825054. FAX 01222-825350. **Document type:** government publication.
   —BLDSC (7994.240000).

016 629.2 620   US   ISSN 0741-2029
S A E TECHNICAL LITERATURE ABSTRACTS. 1965. q. $110. Society of Automotive Engineers, 400 Commonwealth Dr., Warrendale, PA 15096-0001. TEL 412-776-4841. FAX 412-776-3036. cum.index: 1965-1993. (also avail. in magnetic tape; back issues avail.) Indexed: Corros.Abstr., Fluidex, Sh.& Vib.Dig. **Document type:** abstracting/indexing.
   ●Also available online. Vendor(s): Orbit Search Service.
   —BLDSC (8062.928500). CCC.
   Supersedes (in 1985): S A E Quarterly Abstracts.

359.97   US   ISSN 0163-2833
TL553.8
S A R STATISTICS. (Search and Rescue) a. free. U.S. Coast Guard, Office of Navigation Safety and Waterway Services, 2100 Second St., S.W., Washington, DC 20593-0001. TEL 202-267-1054. E-mail: s.white/g-nrs@cgsmtp.comdt.uscg.mil. Lt. Cmdr. Steven H. White. **Document type:** government publication.
   Description: Compiles statistics on U.S. Coast Guard maritime search and rescue activities.

380.5   FR
S I T R A M TRAFFIC INTERNATIONAL RESULTATS TRIMESTRIELS. 1979. q. 261 F. Ministere de Transport, Observatoire Economique et Statistique des Transports (OEST), 55 rue Brillat-Savarin, 75658 Paris Cedex 13, France.

388.31 310   SZ   ISSN 1013-5804
SCHWEIZERISCHE STRASSENVERKEHRSZAEHLUNG/COMPTAGE SUISSE DE LA CIRCULATION ROUTIERE. (Text in French and German) 1985. every 5 yrs. 19 SFr. Bundesamt fuer Statistik, Schwarztorstr. 96, CH-3003 Bern, Switzerland. TEL 031-3236011. FAX 031-3236061. **Document type:** government publication.

388.31 310   SZ   ISSN 0258-7874
SCHWEIZERISCHE VERKEHRSSTATISTIK/STATISTIQUE SUISSE DES TRANSPORTS. (Text in French and German) 1976. a. 32 SFr. Bundesamt fuer Statistik, Schwarztorstr. 96, CH-3003 Bern, Switzerland. TEL 031-3236011. FAX 031-3236061. **Document type:** government publication.

388   BE   ISSN 0776-9636
SECURITE ROUTIERE. Dutch edition: Verkeersveiligheid (ISSN 0776-9628) (Text in French) 1986. a. Institut Belge pour la Securite Routiere - Belgisch Instituut voor de Verkeersveiligheid, Chausse de Haecht 1405, 1130 Brussels, Belgium. TEL 32-2-2441511. FAX 32-2-2164342. Dir. C. Van Den Meersschaut.
   Supersedes (1967-1985): Conseil Superieur de la Securite Routiere. Rapport (ISSN 0776-961X)
   Description: Provides detailed statistical information on traffic safety in Belgium.

623.81   JA
SEIBU ZOSENKAI RONBUN KOGAI/WEST JAPAN SOCIETY OF NAVAL ARCHITECTS. ABSTRACTS FROM RESEARCH REPORT. (Text in English, Japanese) s-a. Seibu Zosenkai, c/o Kyushu Daigaku Kogakubu Zosengaku Kyoshitsu, 10-1, Hakozaki 6-chome, Higashi-ku, Fukuoka-shi, Fukuoka-ken 812, Japan.

387   UK   ISSN 0306-1817
SHIPPING STATISTICS AND ECONOMICS. 1970. m. £530 (outside Europe £570). Drewry Shipping Consultants (Subsidiary of: Drewry International Ltd.), 11 Heron Quay, London E14 4JF, England. TEL 0171-538 0191. FAX 0171-987-9396. TELEX 21167 HPDLDN G. stat.; circ. 1,200 (paid). **Document type:** trade publication.
   —BLDSC (8262.920000).
   Description: Provides the shipping professional with numerous tables and charts supported by concise, well-written commentary on worldwide trends.

387   SI   ISSN 0218-6187
SINGAPORE PORT STATISTICS. (Text in English) 1979. m. S.$95 in Singapore; Malaysia - Brunei S$135; elsewhere S$225. Port of Singapore Authority, Research and Statistics Department, 13th Fl., PSA Bldg., 460 Alexandra Rd., Singapore 0511, Singapore. TEL 2794217. FAX 2795713. TELEX RS 21507. Ed. Mary Yeo. charts. circ. 135. (back issues avail.) **Document type:** government publication.
   Former titles (until 1994): Singapore Shipping and Cargo Statistics; (until 1989): Singapore. Department of Statistics. Shipping and Cargo Statistics (ISSN 0129-6477)
   Description: Contains 18 statistical tables on vessel movements and cargo handled at the Port of Singapore.

629.222   UK
SOCIETY OF MOTOR MANUFACTURERS AND TRADERS. MONTHLY STATISTICAL REVIEW. m. $119 to non-members. Society of Motor Manufacturers and Traders Ltd., Forbes House, Halkin St., London SW1X 7DS, England. TEL 0171-235-7000. FAX 0171-235-7112. TELEX 21628. **Document type:** trade publication.

380.5   SA
SOUTH AFRICA. CENTRAL STATISTICAL SERVICE. CENSUS OF TRANSPORT AND ALLIED SERVICES. (Report No. 71-01-01) irreg., latest 1986. R.6.60 (foreign R.7.20). Central Statistical Service - Sentrale Statistiekdiens, Private Bag X44, Pretoria 0001, South Africa. TEL 27-12-310-8911. FAX 27-12-310-8500. (Orders to: Government Printing Works, Private Bag X85, Pretoria 0001, South Africa) **Document type:** government publication.

388   SA   ISSN 0259-0409
SOUTH AFRICA. CENTRAL STATISTICAL SERVICE. NEW VEHICLES REGISTERED. (Report No. 71-51-01) a., latest 1992. R.8 (foreign R.10). Central Statistical Service - Sentrale Statistiekdiens, Private Bag X44, Pretoria 0001, South Africa. TEL 27-12-310-8911. FAX 27-12-310-8500. (Orders to: Government Printing Works, Private Bag X85, Pretoria 0001, South Africa) **Document type:** government publication.
   Former titles: South Africa. Central Statistical Service. Statistics of New Vehicles Registered; South Africa. Department of Statistics. Statistics of New Vehicles Registered; South Africa. Department of Statistics. Statistics of New Vehicles Licensed.

TRANSPORTATION — ABSTRACTING, BIBLIOGRAPHIES, STATISTICS

388.3 310　　　　SA
SOUTH AFRICA. CENTRAL STATISTICAL SERVICE. REGISTERED VEHICLES AS AT 30 JUNE. (Report No. 71-11-01) 1972. a., latest 1992. R.20 (foreign R.21.90). Central Statistical Service - Sentrale Statistiekdiens, Private Bag X44, Pretoria 0001, South Africa. TEL 27-112-310-8911. FAX 27-12-310-8500. (Orders to: Government Printing Works, Private Bag X85, Pretoria 0001, South Africa) Document type: government publication.
　Former titles: South Africa. Central Statistical Service. Statistics of Motor and Other Vehicles; South Africa. Department of Statistics. Statistics of Motor and Other Vehicles.

312.44　　　　SA　　ISSN 0258-7793
SOUTH AFRICA. CENTRAL STATISTICAL SERVICE. ROAD TRAFFIC COLLISIONS. (Report No. 71-61-01) a., latest 1992. R.25 (foreign R.27.40). Central Statistical Service - Sentrale Statistiekdiens, Private Bag X44, Pretoria 0001, South Africa. TEL 27-12-310-8911. FAX 27-12-310-8500. (Orders to: Government Printing Works, Private Bag X85, Pretoria 0001, South Africa) Document type: government publication.
　Formerly: South Africa. Department of Statistics. Road Traffic Accidents (ISSN 0584-195X)

380.5 316.8　　　　SA
SOUTH AFRICA. CENTRAL STATISTICAL SERVICE. STATISTICAL RELEASE. CENSUS OF TRANSPORT AND ALLIED SERVICES. (No. P7101) irreg., latest 1986. free. Central Statistical Service - Sentrale Statistiekdiens, Private Bag X44, Pretoria 0001, South Africa. TEL 27-12-310-8911. FAX 27-12-310-8500. Document type: government publication.

380.5 316.8　　　　SA
SOUTH AFRICA. CENTRAL STATISTICAL SERVICE. STATISTICAL RELEASE. NEW AND USED VEHICLES REGISTERED - NATAL. (No. P7151.6) m. free. Central Statistical Service - Sentrale Statistiekdiens, Private Bag X44, Pretoria 0001, South Africa. TEL 27-12-310-8911. FAX 27-12-310-8500. Document type: government publication.

380.5 316.8　　　　SA
SOUTH AFRICA. CENTRAL STATISTICAL SERVICE. STATISTICAL RELEASE. NEW AND USED VEHICLES REGISTERED - ORANGE FREE STATE. (No. P7151.4) m. free. Central Statistical Service - Sentral Statistiekdiens, Private Bag X44, Pretoria 0001, South Africa. TEL 27-12-310-8911. FAX 27-12-310-8500. Document type: government publication.

380.5 316.8　　　　SA
SOUTH AFRICA. CENTRAL STATISTICAL SERVICE. STATISTICAL RELEASE. NEW AND USED VEHICLES REGISTERED - TRANSVAAL. (No. P7151.3) m. free. Central Statistical Service - Sentral Statistiekdiens, Private Bag X44, Pretoria 0001, South Africa. TEL 27-12-310-8911. FAX 27-12-310-8500. Document type: government publication.

380.5 316.8　　　　SA
SOUTH AFRICA. CENTRAL STATISTICAL SERVICE. STATISTICAL RELEASE. NEW VEHICLES REGISTERED. (No. P7151.1) m. free. Central Statistical Service - Sentral Statistiekdiens, Private Bag X44, Pretoria 0001, South Africa. TEL 27-12-310-8911. FAX 27-12-310-8500. Document type: government publication.

380.5 316.8　　　　SA
SOUTH AFRICA. CENTRAL STATISTICAL SERVICE. STATISTICAL RELEASE. PUBLIC ROAD TRANSPORT (NON-GOVERNMENTAL INSTITUTIONS) OF PASSENGERS AND GOODS - FINANCIAL STATISTICS. (No. P7143) q. free. Central Statistical Service - Sentrale Statistiekdiens, Private Bag X44, Pretoria 0001, South Africa. TEL 27-12-310-8911. FAX 27-12-310-8500. Document type: government publication.

380.5 316.8　　　　SA
SOUTH AFRICA. CENTRAL STATISTICAL SERVICE. STATISTICAL RELEASE. ROAD TRAFFIC COLLISIONS. (No. P7161.2) m. free. Central Statistical Service - Sentrale Statistiekdiens, Private Bag X44, Pretoria 0001, South Africa. TEL 27-12-310-8911. FAX 27-12-310-8500. Document type: government publication.

380.5 316.8　　　　SA
SOUTH AFRICA. CENTRAL STATISTICAL SERVICE. STATISTICAL RELEASE. ROAD TRAFFIC COLLISONS AND NUMBER OF PERSONS KILLED DURING THE HOLIDAY SEASON. (No. P7161.3) irreg. free. Central Statistical Service - Sentrale Statistiekdiens, Private Bag X44, Pretoria 0001, South Africa. TEL 27-12-310-8911. FAX 27-12-310-8500. Document type: government publication.
　Description: Covers traffic accident statistics for the Summer, Winter and Easter holiday seasons.

380.5 316.8　　　　SA
SOUTH AFRICA. CENTRAL STATISTICAL SERVICE. STATISTICAL RELEASE. STATISTICS OF MOTOR AND OTHER VEHICLES AS AT 30 JUNE - ALL VEHICLES. (No. P7151.5) a. free. Central Statistical Service - Sentrale Statistiekdiens, Private Bag X44, Pretoria 0001, South Africa. TEL 27-12-310-8911. FAX 27-12-310-8500. Document type: government publication.
　Description: Principal statistics by type of vehicle and population group of owner.

380.5 316.8　　　　SA
SOUTH AFRICA. CENTRAL STATISTICAL SERVICE. STATISTICAL RELEASE. TRANSPORT OF GOODS BY ROAD AND RAIL. (No. P7142) m. free. Central Statistical Service - Sentrale Statistiekdiens, Private Bag X44, Pretoria 0001, South Africa. TEL 27-12-310-8911. FAX 27-12-310-8500. Document type: government publication.

380.5 316.8　　　　SA
SOUTH AFRICA. CENTRAL STATISTICAL SERVICE. STATISTICAL RELEASE. TRANSPORT OF PASSENGERS BY BUS AND TRAIN. (No. P7141) m. free. Central Statistical Service - Sentrale Statistiekdiens, Private Bag X44, Pretoria 0001, South Africa. TEL 27-12-310-8911. FAX 27-12-310-8500. Document type: government publication.

380.5 316.8　　　　SA
SOUTH AFRICA. CENTRAL STATISTICAL SERVICE. STATISTICAL RELEASE. USED VEHICLES REGISTERED. (No. P7151.2) m. free. Central Statistical Service - Sentrale Statistiekdiens, Private Bag X44, Pretoria 0001, South Africa. TEL 27-12-310-8911. FAX 27-12-310-8500. Document type: government publication.

388.314　　　　SA
SOUTH AFRICA. DIVISION OF ROADS AND TRANSPORT TECHNOLOGY. TRANSPORT STATISTICS/DIVISIE VIR PAD- EN VERVOERTEGNOLOGIE. (Text in Afrikaans, English) 1969. a. R.45. Division of Roads and Transport Technology, Box 395, Pretoria 0001, South Africa. FAX 841-32-32. TELEX 3-21312SA. (Co-sponsor: Department of Transport) Ed. C.C. Hamilton. charts; illus. circ. 1,000. Document type: government publication.
　Former titles: National Institute for Transport and Road Research. Transport Statistics & National Institute for Transport and Road Research. Road Statistics.

614.86　　　　SP　　ISSN 0085-655X
SPAIN. MINISTERIO DEL INTERIOR. DIRECCION GENERAL DE TRAFICO. BOLETIN INFORMATIVO: ACCIDENTES. 1962. a. Ministerio del Interior, Direccion General de Trafico, Gabinete de Estudios, Calle J. Valcarcel, 28, 28071 Madrid, Spain. circ. 2,000.

614.86　　　　SP　　ISSN 0304-9191
HE5081
SPAIN. MINISTERIO DEL INTERIOR. DIRECCION GENERAL DE TRAFICO. BOLETIN INFORMATIVO: ANUARIO ESTADISTICO GENERAL. 1960. a. Ministerio del Interior, Direccion General de Trafico, Gabinete de Estudios, Calle J. Valcarcel, 28, 28071 Madrid, Spain. circ. 2,500.

380.5　　　　EI　　ISSN 0257-2419
STATISTICAL OFFICE OF THE EUROPEAN COMMUNITIES. TRANSPORT, COMMUNICATIONS, TOURISME - ANNUAIRE STATISTIQUE. (Text in Dutch, French, German, Italian) a. $30. Office for Official Publications of the European Communities, L-2985 Luxembourg, Luxembourg. (Dist. in the U.S. by: Unipub, 4611-F Assembly Dr., Lanham, MD 20706-4391. TEL 800-274-4888. FAX 301-459-0056)
　Formerly: Statistical Office of the European Communities. Statistiques des Tranports. Annuaire (ISSN 0081-4962)

380.5 310　　　　FR　　ISSN 1013-0284
STATISTICAL TRENDS IN TRANSPORT. (Text in English, French) 1965. a. 160 F.($32) Organization for Economic Cooperation and Development, European Conference of Ministers of Transport, 2 rue Andre Pascal, 75775 Paris Cedex 16, France. (Dist. by: O.E.C.D. Publications Service, 2 rue Andre-Pascal, 75775 Paris Cedex 16, France. TEL 45-24-82-00; U.S. orders to: O.E.C.D. Publications and Information Center, 2001 L St., N.W., Ste. 700, Washington, DC 20036-4095) (also avail. in microfiche from CIS) **Indexed:** IIS.
　Description: Sets out the main statistical data concerning the transport sector in the 31 member countries of the ECMT.

388.31 310　　　　JA　　ISSN 1012-6430
STATISTICS (YEAR) ROAD ACCIDENTS JAPAN. a. $22. International Association of Traffic and Safety Sciences, 6-20, 2-chome, Yaesu, Chuo-ku, Tokyo 104, Japan. TEL 03-3273-7884. FAX 03-3272-7054.
　Formerly (until 1983): Statistics of Road Traffic Accidents in Japan (ISSN 0386-1708)

388.31　　　　UK　　ISSN 0267-3118
STATISTICS OF ROAD LENGTHS IN WALES. 1985. irreg. Welsh Office, Statistical Directorate, New Crown Bldg., Cathays Park, Cardiff CF1 3NQ, Wales. TEL 01222-825054. FAX 01222-825350. Document type: government publication.

388.1　　　　UN
STATISTICS OF ROAD TRAFFIC ACCIDENTS IN EUROPE AND NORTH AMERICA. 1956. a. price varies. Economic Commission for Europe (ECE), Palais des Nations, 1211 Geneva 10, Switzerland. TEL 022-917-2452. FAX 022-917-0039. TELEX 412962. (Orders in N. America to: United Nations Publications, Rm. DC2-853, New York, NY 10017. TEL 212-963-8302. FAX 212-963-3489; Or: Unipub, 4611-F Assembly Dr., Lanham, MD 20706. TEL 310-459-7666. FAX 310-459-0056) (also avail. in microfiche from CIS) **Indexed:** IIS. Document type: government publication.
　Formerly: Statistics of Road Traffic Accidents in Europe (ISSN 0497-9575)
　Description: Summarizes statistics on traffic accidents in Europe and North America, along with data on their causes, number of crashes involving intoxicated drivers, and casualties in nonfatal accidents.

388　　　　DK　　ISSN 0901-6139
STATISTIK OVER REGISTRERING AF NYE AUTOMOBILER I DANMARK. (Text in Danish; summaries in English) 1949. m. DKK 1200 (effective 1992). Automobil-Importoerernes Sammenslutning, Ryvangs Alle 68, 2900 Hellerup, Denmark. Ed. Kai Noerrung.
　Description: Data on new registration of vehicles. Listed by make-model and county of owner-user.

386　　　　FR　　ISSN 0984-6700
STATISTIQUE ANNUELLE DE LA NAVIGATION INTERIEURE. 1881. a. 279.65 F. (Ministere de l'Equipement, du Logement, des Transports et de l'Espace) Voies Navigables de France, 175 rue Ludovic Boutleux, B.P. 820, 62408 Bethune Cedex, France. TEL 21-63-24-24. FAX 21-63-24-42. TELEX 250 857.
　Formed by the merger of: Statistique Annuelle de la Navigation Interieure par Courants de Trafic (ISSN 0984-6697) & Statistique Annuelle de la Navigation Interieure par Sections de Voies Navigables (ISSN 0427-329X)

387.7　　　　SW　　ISSN 0348-2251
SWEDEN. LUFTFARTSVERKET. AARSBOK. 1976. a. SEK 42. Luftfartsverket - Board of Civil Aviation, S-601 79 Norrkoeping, Sweden. stat.

387.7　　　　SW
SWEDEN. LUFTFARTSVERKET. CHARTERSTATISTIK. 1970. s-a. SEK 84. Luftfartsverket - Board of Civil Aviation, S-601 79 Norrkoeping, Sweden.

387.7　　　　SW
SWEDEN. LUFTFARTSVERKET. FLYGPLATSSTATISTIK. m. SEK 180. Luftfartsverket - Board of Civil Aviation, S-601 79 Norrkoeping, Sweden.

TRANSPORTATION — ABSTRACTING, BIBLIOGRAPHIES, STATISTICS

380   SW   ISSN 0082-0334
HE260.A15
SWEDEN. STATISTISKA CENTRALBYRAAN. STATISTISKA MEDDELANDEN. SERIE T, TRANSPORT OCH KOMMUNIKATIONER. (Text in Swedish; table heads and summaries in English) 1969. irreg. SEK 1200. Statistiska Centralbyraan, Publishing Unit, S-701 89 Oerebro, Sweden. circ. 1,000.
    Formerly (until 1976): Sweden. Statistiska Centralbyraan. Statistiska Meddelanden. T.

388   SZ
SWITZERLAND. BUNDESAMT FUER STATISTIK. MOTORFAHRZEUGE IN DER SCHWEIZ. IN VERKEHR GESETZTE NEUE MOTORFAHRZEUGE - VEHICULES A MOTEUR EN SUISSE. VEHICULES A MOTEUR NEUFS MIS EN CIRCULATION. (Text in French and German) 1929. a. 12 SFr. Bundesamt fuer Statistik, Schwarztorstr. 96, CH-3003 Bern, Switzerland. TEL 031-3236011. FAX 031-3236061. TELEX 912871. **Document type:** government publication.
    Formerly: Switzerland. Bundesamt fuer Statistik. In Verkehr Gesetzte Neue Motorfahrzeuge - Vehicules a Moteur Neufs Mis en Circulation; Superseded in part: Switzerland. Statistisches Amt. Eingefuehrte Motorfahrzeuge: In Verkehr Gesetzte Neue Motorfahrzeuge.

387.7   AU
TAETIGKEITSBERICHT DES VERKEHRS ARBEITSINSPEKTORATES FUER DAS JAHR (YEAR). 1952. quadrennial. free. Bundesministerium fuer oeffentliche Wirtschaft und Verkehr, Gruppe Verkehrs - Arbeitsinspektorat, Radetzskystr. 2, A-1031 Vienna, Austria. TEL 0222-71162-9129. FAX 0222-7130326. circ. 1,200. **Document type:** government publication.

380.5 315   CH
TAIWAN ANNUAL STATISTICAL REPORT OF TRANSPORTATION/TAI-WAN SHENG CHIAO T'UNG T'UNG CHI NIEN PAO. (Text in Chinese and English) 1946. a. Taiwan Provincial Government, Department of Transportation - Tai-wan Sheng Cheng Fu Chiao T'ung Chu, Nantou Hsien, Taiwan, Republic of China. stat.

380.5   AT   ISSN 0819-4882
TASMANIAN TRANSPORT STATISTICS. 1971. a., latest 1989. Aus.$10. Transport and Works Department, Policy Development and Co-ordination Division, G.P.O. Box 936J, Hobart, Tas. 7001, Australia. TEL 002-336522. FAX 002-336243. Ed.Bd. charts; stat. circ. 300. **Document type:** government publication.
    Formerly: Tasmanian Transport Bulletin (ISSN 0310-7531)
    Description: Cumulation of statistics on transport in Tasmania.

315.2   JA
TETSUDO SHARYOTO SEISAN DOTAI TOKEI GEPPO/MONTHLY SURVEY ON CURRENT ROLLING STOCK PRODUCTION. (Text in Japanese) 1954. m. free. Ministry of Transport, Transport Policy Bureau - Un'Yu-sho Un'Yu-seisaku-kyoku, Information and Research Department, 2-1-3 Kasumigaseki, Chiyoda-ku, Tokyo 100, Japan.
    Formerly: Monthly Statistics of Actual Production of Railway Cars (ISSN 0040-4055)

315.2   JA
TETSUDO SHARYOTO SEISAN DOTAI TOKEI NENPO/ANNUAL SURVEY ON CURRENT ROLLING STOCK PRODUCTION. (Text in Japanese) 1954. a. free. Ministry of Transport, Transport Policy Bureau - Un'Yu-sho Un'Yu-seisaku-kyoku, Information and Research Department, 2-1-3 Kasumigaseki, Chiyoda-ku, Tokyo 100, Japan.
    Formerly: Annual Statistics of Actual Production of Railway Cars.

388.4   US
HE4441
TRANSIT PLANNING AND RESEARCH REPORTS; an annotated bibliography. 1972. s-a. free. U.S. Federal Transit Administration, Office of Technical Assistance and Safety, Advanced Public Transportation Division, U.S. Department of Transportation, 400 Seventh St., S.W., Rm. 6100, Washington, DC 20590. TEL 202-366-0201. FAX 202-366-3765. index. circ. 2,000. **Document type:** bibliography, government publication.
    Formerly: Urban Mass Transportation Abstracts (ISSN 0090-8223)
    Description: Lists and annotates government documents on public transportation, along with the address where they can be obtained.

388.411   US   ISSN 1062-9483
HE305
TRANSIT RESEARCH ABSTRACTS. 1982. a. $75 in N. America (elsewhere $78). U.S. National Research Council, Transportation Research Board, 2101 Constitution Ave., N.W., Washington, DC 20418. TEL 202-334-3213. FAX 202-334-2519. (Co-sponsor: U.S. Federal Transit Administration, Technical Assistance Program) Ed.Bd. circ. 500. (back issues avail.) **Document type:** abstracting/indexing, government publication.
●Also available online. Vendor(s): Knight-Ridder, Inc. (File no.63).
    Formerly (until 1992): Urban Transportation Abstracts (ISSN 0734-0648)
    Description: Abstracts research reports, technical papers, journal articles, and ongoing research in urban transportation and public transit.

380.5   AT   ISSN 1033-9752
TRANSPORT AND COMMUNICATIONS INDICATORS. 1976. q. Aus.$17. (Bureau of Transport and Communications Economics) Australian Government Publishing Service, G.P.O. Box 84, Canberra, A.C.T. 2601, Australia. TEL 61-6-295-4411. FAX 61-6-295-4455. TELEX AA62013. stat. circ. 500. (back issues avail.)
    Former titles (until 1988): Transport Indicators. Bulletin (ISSN 0812-0927); (until 1983): Transport Indicators (ISSN 0159-7493)
    Description: Guide to Australian transport and communications trends. Covers freight, passenger modes, fuel prices, and some general economic indicators.

388.1   UK   ISSN 0144-8021
TRANSPORT STATISTICS GREAT BRITAIN. a. price varies. (Department of Transport) H.M.S.O. Books, Publications Centre, 51 Nine Elms Ln., London SW8 5DR, England. TEL 0171-873-0011. FAX 0171-873-8463. (Subscr. to: H.M.S.O. Books, P.O. Box 276, London SW8 5DT, England. TEL 0171-873-9090. FAX 0171-873-8200) (Co-sponsors: Scottish Development Office; Welsh Office) circ. 2,000. **Document type:** government publication.
—BLDSC (9025.952000).
    Formed by the merger of (1963-1976): Great Britain. Department of the Environment. Highway Statistics (ISSN 0072-6893); (1962-1976): Passenger Transport in Great Britain (ISSN 0079-0133)

380.5   US
TRANSPORTATION ACCIDENT BRIEFS. (Consists of 5 series: Aviation, Highway, Marine, Pipeline, Railroad) irreg. price varies. (U.S. Department of Transportation, National Transportation Safety Board) U.S. National Technical Information Service, 5825 Port Royal Rd., Springfield, VA 22161. TEL 703-487-4630. FAX 703-321-8547. **Document type:** government publication.
    Description: Presents basic facts, conditions, circumstances, and probable causes in each instance. Additional statistical information is tabulated by types of accidents and casualties related to types of carriers involved and by causal factors.

387.7   US
TRANSPORTATION ACCIDENT BRIEFS. AVIATION. (Subseries of: Transportation Accident Briefs) irreg. (approx. 18/yr.) price varies. (U.S. Department of Transportation, National Transportation Safety Board) U.S. National Technical Information Service, 5825 Port Royal Rd., Springfield, VA 22161. TEL 703-487-4630. FAX 703-321-8547. **Document type:** government publication.

338.31   US
TRANSPORTATION ACCIDENT BRIEFS. HIGHWAY. (Subseries of: Transportation Accident Briefs) irreg. (approx. 3/yr.) price varies. (U.S. Department of Transportation, National Transportation Safety Board) U.S. National Technical Information Service, 5825 Port Royal Rd., Springfield, VA 22161. TEL 703-487-4630. FAX 703-321-8547. **Document type:** government publication.

387   US
TRANSPORTATION ACCIDENT BRIEFS. MARINE. (Subseries of: Transportation Accident Briefs) irreg. (approx. 4/yr.) price varies. (U.S. Department of Transportation, National Transportation Safety Board) U.S. National Technical Information Service, 5825 Port Royal Rd., Springfield, VA 22161. TEL 703-487-4630. FAX 703-321-8547. **Document type:** government publication.

TRANSPORTATION ACCIDENT BRIEFS. PIPELINE. see *PETROLEUM AND GAS* — *Abstracting, Bibliographies, Statistics*

385   US
TRANSPORTATION ACCIDENT BRIEFS. RAILROADS. (Subseries of: Transportation Accident Briefs) irreg. (approx. 4/yr.) price varies. (U.S. Department of Transportation, National Transportation Safety Board) U.S. National Technical Information Service, 5825 Port Royal Rd., Springfield, VA 22161. TEL 703-487-4630. FAX 703-321-8547. **Document type:** government publication.

380.5   US
TRANSPORTATION ACCIDENT REPORTS. (Conists of 5 series: Aviation, Highway, Marine, Pipeline, Railroad) irreg. price varies. (U.S. Department of Transportation, National Transportation Safety Board) U.S. National Technical Information Service, 5825 Port Royal Rd., Springfield, VA 22161. TEL 703-487-4630. FAX 703-321-8547. **Document type:** government publication.
    Description: Reviews investigations of selected accidents conducted by N.T.S.B. Contains, in narrative form, the board's factual findings and analysis leading to the probable cause.

387.7   US
TRANSPORTATION ACCIDENT REPORTS. AVIATION. (Subseries of: Transportation Accident Reports) irreg. (approx. 8/yr.) price varies. (U.S. Department of Transportation) U.S. National Technical Information Service, 5285 Port Royal Rd., Springfield, VA 22161. TEL 703-487-4620. FAX 703-321-8547. **Document type:** government publication.

380.5   US
TRANSPORTATION ACCIDENT REPORTS. HIGHWAY. (Subseries of: Transportation Accident Reports) irreg. (approx. 7/yr.) price varies. (U.S. Department of Transportation, National Transportation Safety Board) U.S. National Technical Information Service, 5825 Port Royal Rd., Springfield, VA 22161. TEL 703-487-4630. FAX 703-321-8547. **Document type:** government publication.

387   US
TRANSPORTATION ACCIDENT REPORTS. MARINE. (Subseries of: Transportation Accident Reports) irreg. (approx. 10/yr.) price varies. (U.S. Department of Transportation, National Transportation Safety Board) U.S. National Technical Information Service, 5825 Port Royal Rd., Springfield, VA 22161. TEL 703-487-4630. FAX 703-321-8547. **Document type:** government publication.

TRANSPORTATION ACCIDENT REPORTS. PIPELINE. see *PETROLEUM AND GAS* — *Abstracting, Bibliographies, Statistics*

385   US
TRANSPORTATION ACCIDENT REPORTS. RAILROADS. (Subseries of: Transportation Accident Reports) irreg. (approx. 10/yr.) price varies. (U.S. Department of Transportation, National Transportation Safety Board) U.S. National Technical Information Service, 5825 Port Royal Rd., Springfield, VA 22161. TEL 703-487-4630. FAX 703-321-8547. (also avail. in microfiche from CIS; reprint service avail. from CIS) **Indexed:** Amer.Stat.Ind. (1985-). **Document type:** government publication.

TRANSPORTATION ENERGY RESEARCH. see *ENERGY* — *Abstracting, Bibliographies, Statistics*

TRANSPORTATION — ABSTRACTING, BIBLIOGRAPHIES, STATISTICS

TRANSPORTATION ENERGY RESEARCH ABSTRACTS. see ENERGY — Abstracting, Bibliographies, Statistics

388.324 US
(YEAR) TRANSPORTATION FACT BOOK. a. $40. American Movers Conference, 1611 Duke St., Alexandria, VA 22314. TEL 703-683-7410. FAX 703-683-7527. **Document type:** trade publication.
  Description: Provides traffic statistics of the moving industry. For anyone who deals with the moving business.

380.5 US ISSN 0082-5956
TRANSPORTATION STATISTICS IN THE UNITED STATES. 1954. irreg. price varies. U.S. Interstate Commerce Commission, 12th St. and Constitution Ave., N.W., Washington, DC 20423. TEL 202-655-4000. (also avail. in microfilm from BHP) **Document type:** government publication.

380 910 VE
TRANSPORTE, COMUNICACIONES, TURISMO. 1989. q. Esc.650 (US $4.30. elsewhere $4.70) per no. Instituto Nacional de Estadisticas, Casilla 498, Correos 3, Santiago, Chile.

380.5 FR ISSN 0769-0584
TRANSPORTS ROUTIERS DE MARCHANDISES EFFECTUES PAR DES TRANSPORTEURS ETRANGERS SUR LE TERRITOIRE FRANCAIS. 1973. quadrennial. 260 F. Ministere de Transport, Observatoire Economique et Statistique des Transports (OEST), 55 rue Brillat-Savarin, 75658 Paris Cedex 13, France.

387.1 TI
TUNISIA. OFFICE DES PORTS NATIONAUX. BULLETIN ANNUEL DES STATISTIQUES. Cover title: Tunisia. Office des Ports Nationaux. Trafic Maritime. a. Office des Ports Nationaux, Tunis, Tunisia. **Document type:** government publication, bulletin.

387.2021 TU ISSN 1300-1698
HE565.T8
TURKEY. DEVLET ISTATISTIK ENSTITUSU. DENIZ TASITLARI ISTATISTIKLERI (18 VE DAHA YUKARI GROS TONILATOLUK)/TURKEY. STATE INSTITUTE OF STATISTICS. STATISTICS OF SEA VESSELS (18 GROSS TONNAGES AND OVER). Key Title: Deniz Tasitlari Istatistikleri. (Text in English, Turkish) 1960. a., latest 1991. $30. Devlet Istatistik Enstitusu - State Institute of Statistics, Necatibey Caddesi No. 114, 06100 Ankara, Turkey. TEL 90-312-4185027. FAX 90-312-4170432. circ. 1,100. (also avail. in diskette format) **Document type:** government publication.

387.021 TU ISSN 1300-1000
HA1971
TURKEY. DEVLET ISTATISTIK ENSTITUSU. KABOTAJ VE ULUSLARARASI DENIZ TASIMASI ISTATISTIKLERI/TURKEY. STATE INSTITUTE OF STATISTICS. STATISTICS OF COASTAL AND INTERNATIONAL SEA TRANSPORTATION. Key Title: Kabotaj ve Uluslararasi Deniz Tasimasi Istatistikleri. (Text in English, Turkish) 1959. a., latest 1991. $30. Devlet Istatistik Enstitusu - State Institute of Statistics, Necatibey Caddesi No. 114, 06100 Ankara, Turkey. TEL 90-312-4180527. FAX 90-312-4170432. circ. 1,100. (also avail. in diskette format) **Document type:** government publication.

363.125021 TU ISSN 1300-1175
TURKEY. DEVLET ISTATISTIK ENSTITUSU. KARAYOLU TRAFIK KAZA ISTATISTIKLERI/TURKEY. STATE INSTITUTE OF STATISTICS. ROAD TRAFFIC ACCIDENTS STATISTICS. Key Title: Trafik Kaza Istatistikleri. (Text in English, Turkish) 1976. a., latest 1991. $30. Devlet Istatistik Enstitusu - State Institute of Statistics, Necatibey Caddesi No. 114, 06100 Ankara, Turkey. TEL 90-312-4180527. FAX 90-312-4170432. circ. 920. (also avail. in diskette format) **Document type:** government publication.

388.3021 TU ISSN 1300-106X
TURKEY. DEVLET ISTATISTIK ENSTITUSU. MOTORLU KARA TASITLARI ISTATISTIKLERI/TURKEY. STATE INSTITUTE OF STATISTICS. MOTOR VEHICLE STATISTICS. Key Title: Motorlu Kara Tasitlari Istatistikaleri. (Text in English, Turkish) 1947. a., latest 1991. $30. Devlet Istatistik Enstitusu - State Institute of Statistics, Necatibey Caddesi No. 114, 06100 Ankara, Turkey. TEL 90-312-4180527. FAX 90-312-4170432. circ. 1,100. (also avail. in diskette format) **Document type:** government publication.

388.021 TU ISSN 1300-1019
TURKEY. DEVLET ISTATISTIK ENSTITUSU. ULASTIRMA ISTATISTIKLERI OZETI/TURKEY. STATE INSTITUTE OF STATISTICS. SUMMARY STATISTICS ON TRANSPORTATION - COMMUNICATION. Key Title: Ulastirma Istatistikleri Ozeti. (Text in English, Turkish) 1982. a., latest 1991. $30. Devlet Istatistik Enstitusu - State Institute of Statistics, Necatibey Caddesi No. 114, 06100 Ankara, Turkey. TEL 90-312-4180527. FAX 90-312-4170432. circ. 975. (also avail. in diskette format) **Document type:** government publication.
  Formerly (until 1991): Turkey. State Institute of Statistics. Transportation and Road Traffic Accidents Statistics Summary.

388.4 016 BE ISSN 1022-6915
U I T P BIBLIO-EXPRESS. (Summaries in English, French, German) 1962. 6/yr. 3000 BEF. International Union of Public Transport, Av. de l'Uruguay 19, B-1050 Brussels, Belgium. TEL 322-673-6100. FAX 322-660-10-72. TELEX 63916 UITP B. circ. 3,000.
  Formerly: U I T P Biblio-Index (ISSN 0041-5146)
  Description: Part of a computerized bibliographical database.

387.7 341.46 US
U S GOVERNMENT AFFAIRS REPORT: FEDERAL BIENNIAL LEGISLATIVE REPORT. biennial, latest 1995. $75 (Canada $78.75; elsewhere $83.75) (effective 1995). Air Transport Association of America, 1301 Pennsylvania Ave., N.W., Ste. 1100, Washington, DC 20004-1707. TEL 202-626-4000. FAX 202-626-4081. (Subscr. to: ATA Distribution Center, Box 511, Annapolis Junction, MD 20701. TEL 800-497-3326. FAX 301-206-9789) **Document type:** corporate report.
  Description: Provides summaries and a chronological listing of legislative action on issues affecting the airline industry.

387.7 FR
UNION DES CHAMBRES DE COMMERCE ET ETABLISSENENTS GESTIONNAIRES D'AEROPORT. STATISTICS ON AIRPORT TRAFFIC. a. Union des Chambres de Commerce et Etablissements Gestionnaires d'Aeroport, 86 rue de la Federation, 75015 Paris, France. TEL 40-65-98-68. FAX 47-34-16-07.

310 380.5 US ISSN 0161-8628
U.S. DEPARTMENT OF TRANSPORTATION. NATIONAL TRANSPORTATION STATISTICS. ANNUAL; a supplement to the summary of national transportation statistics. a. $13. U.S. Department of Transportation, Statistical Information Reporting Branch, Office of the Assistant Secretary for Policy, Plans, and International Affairs, Washington, DC 20590. TEL 202-655-4000. (Orders to: Superintendent of Documents, U.S. Government Printing Office, Box 371954, Pittsburgh, PA 15250-7954. TEL 202-512-1800. FAX 202-512-2250; Or: Bernan, 4611-F Assembly Dr., Lanham, MD 20706. TEL 800-274-4447. FAX 301-459-0056) illus. **Document type:** government publication.
  Formed by the 1977 merger of: U.S. Department of Transportation. Energy Statistics; U.S. Department of Transportation. Summary of National Transportation Statistics (ISSN 0360-8980)

388.3 US ISSN 0095-344X
HE355.A3
U.S. FEDERAL HIGHWAY ADMINISTRATION. HIGHWAY STATISTICS. Key Title: Highway Statistics. 1945. a. $14. U.S. Federal Highway Administration, Office of Highway Information Management, Department of Transportation, 400 Seventh St., S.W., Washington, DC 20590. TEL 202-366-0180. FAX 202-366-7742. (Orders to: Superintendent of Documents, U.S. Government Printing Office, Box 371954, Pittsburgh, PA 15250-7954. TEL 202-512-1800. FAX 202-512-2250; Or: Bernan, 4611-F Assembly Dr., Lanham, MD 20706. TEL 301-459-7666. FAX 301-459-0056) Ed. A. French. stat. circ. 5,000. **Document type:** government publication.
  ●Also available online.

388.3 629 US ISSN 1073-4872
U.S. FEDERAL TRANSIT ADMINISTRATION. TECHNOLOGY SHARING PROGRAM. REPORT. irreg. U.S. Department of Transportation, Technology Sharing Program, U.S. Department of Transportation, 400 Seventh St., S.W. (M-443.2), Washington, DC 20590. (Also avail. from: National Technical Information Center, 5285 Port Royal Rd., Springfield, VA 22161. TEL 703-487-4650. FAX 703-321-5847) **Document type:** monographic series, government publication.
  Description: Publishes technical reports concerning all aspects of public transportation.

625.7 016 US ISSN 0068-6115
UNIVERSITY OF CALIFORNIA. INSTITUTE OF TRANSPORTATION STUDIES. LIBRARY REFERENCES. 1955. irreg., no.78, 1978. price varies. University of California at Berkeley, Institute of Transportation Studies Library, 412 McLaughlin Hall, Berkeley, CA 94720. TEL 415-642-3604. FAX 415-642-1246. Eds. Catherine Cortelyou, Daniel Krummes. **Document type:** bibliography.

388 HU ISSN 0231-0767
VASUTI KOZLEKEDESI SZAKIRODALMI TAJEKOZTATO/RAILWAY TRANSPORTATION ABSTRACTS. m. 4000 Ft. Orszagos Muszaki Informacios Kozpont es Konyvtar (O.M.I.K.K.) - National Technical Information Centre and Library, Muzeum u. 17, 1428 Budapest, Hungary. (Subscr. to: Kultura, P.O. Box 149, 1389 Budapest, Hungary) Ed. Raczne Agnes Kovacs. circ. 400. **Document type:** abstracting/indexing.
  Supersedes in part (in 1982): Muszaki Lapszemle. Kozlekedes - Technical Abstracts. Transportation (ISSN 0027-5042)

387.7 FR ISSN 0291-9508
VENTILATION DU TRAFIC COMMERCIAL. m. 440 F. (effective 1992). Aeroports de Paris, Service Previsions et Statistiques, Orly Sud 103, 94396 Orly Aerogare Cedex, France.

388 BE ISSN 0776-9628
VERKEERSVEILIGHEID. French edition: Securite Routiere (ISSN 0776-9636). (Text in Dutch) 1986. a. Institut Belge pour la Securite Routiere - Belgisch Instituut voor de Verkeersveiligheid, Chaussee de Haecht 1405, 1130 Brussels, Belgium. TEL 32-2-2441511. FAX 32-2-2164342. Dir. C. Van Den Meersschaut. **Document type:** corporate report.
  Supersedes: Hoger Raad voor de Verkeersveiligheid. Verslag (ISSN 0776-9601)

012 380.5 SZ
VERKEHRSTECHNIK IN DER SCHWEIZ; Lieferantenkatalog der schweizerischer oeffentlicher Verkehrsbetriebe. 1965. a. 28 Fr.($19) Cicero Verlag AG, Postfach, CH-8021 Zurich, Switzerland. TEL 01-4888400. FAX 01-4888300. TELEX 812648-CH. Ed. P. Eggspuehler. adv. circ. 5,000.

629.2 US ISSN 0083-7229
HD9710.U5
WARD'S AUTOMOTIVE YEARBOOK. 1938. a. $275 (or included with subscr. to Ward's Automotive Reports). Ward's Communications (Subsidiary of: Intertec Publishing Corp.), 3000 Town Center, Ste. 2to, Southfield, MI 48075-1212. TEL 810-357-0800. FAX 810-357-0810. Ed. Deebe Ferris. adv.; bk.rev.; charts; illus.; stat.; index. circ. 5,087. **Document type:** trade publication.
  —CCC.
  Description: Comprehensive reference work of vital industry statistics: U.S. and worldwide auto and truck production; sales by market segment, engine size, and model year; factory-installed equipment tables; vehicle registrations; supplier directory.

TRANSPORTATION — AIR TRANSPORT

387 II
WATER TRANSPORT STATISTICS OF INDIA. 1969. a. $11.70. Ministry of Shipping and Transport, Transport Research Division, I D A Bldg., Jamnagar House, Shahjahan Rd., New Delhi 11001, India. (Orders to: Controller of Publications, Civil Lines, Delhi 110006, India)
- Formerly: India. Ministry of Shipping and Transport. Statistics of Water Transport Industries (ISSN 0081-5144)

388.31 UK ISSN 0267-8160
HE244.A15
WELSH TRANSPORT STATISTICS. 1985. a. Welsh Office, Statistical Directorate, New Crown Bldg., Cathays Park, Cardiff CF1 3NQ, Wales. TEL 01222-825054. FAX 01222-825350. Document type: government publication.
—BLDSC (9294.704200).

387 NE
WERKGELEGENHEID IN DE NEDERLANDSE ZEEHAVENS. (Not published 1993) 1989. a. free. Nationale Havenraad, Koninginnegracht 19, 2514 AB The Hague, Netherlands. TEL 31-70-3517615. FAX 31-70-3517600. Document type: government publication.
- Formerly (until 1990): Werkgelegenheidsstatistiek Nederlandse Zeehavens.
- Description: Provides statistical data relating to employment in Dutch seaports, covering the period from 1985 to the present.

388 US ISSN 0084-0572
WISCONSIN. DEPARTMENT OF TRANSPORTATION. DIVISION OF PLANNING AND BUDGET. HIGHWAY MILEAGE DATA. (Former name of issuing body: Division of Planning) 1946. a. $12. Department of Transportation, Division of Planning, Box 7913, 4802 Sheboygan Ave., Madison, WI 53707. TEL 608-266-3661. circ. 200.

388 US ISSN 0084-0580
G1416.P21
WISCONSIN. DEPARTMENT OF TRANSPORTATION. DIVISION OF PLANNING. HIGHWAY TRAFFIC. Short title: Wisconsin Highway Traffic. 1968. a. $14.50. Department of Transportation, Division of Planning, Data Development Section, 4802 Sheboygan Ave., Box 7913, Madison, WI 53707. TEL 608-266-1466. circ. 300.
- Formerly: Wisconsin. Division of Highways. System Planning Section. Highway Traffic in Wisconsin Cities (ISSN 0512-0624)

388 US ISSN 0098-0323
HE371.W6
WISCONSIN TRAFFIC DATA - AUTOMATIC TRAFFIC RECORDER; monthly average daily traffic. Short title: Wisconsin Traffic Data - A T R. 1970. a. $14.69. Department of Transportation, Division of Planning, Data Development Section, 4802 Sheboygan Ave., Box 7913, Madison, WI 53707. TEL 608-266-1466. circ. 125.
- Former titles: Wisconsin. Department of Transportation. Automatic Traffic Recorder Data; Wisconsin. Department of Transportation. Traffic Planning Section. Automatic Recorder Station Traffic Data (ISSN 0091-6080)

387.7 CN ISSN 0084-1366
TL720.A1
WORLD AIR TRANSPORT STATISTICS. 1956. a. $130. International Air Transport Association, 2000 Peel St., Montreal, PQ H3A 2R4, Canada. TEL 514-844-6311. FAX 514-844-3788. TELEX 05-267627. charts. (also avail. in diskette format; back issues avail.)
- Description: Contains the latest figures on the world's airlines' traffic, capacity, financial results and operating fleet, provides a review of air transport development, gives detailed global statistics and lists individual IATA Member airlines' results and rankings.

388.411 SZ ISSN 0444-1419
WORLD ROAD STATISTICS. (Text in English, French and German.) 1964. a. 200 SFr. International Road Federation - Federation Routiere Internationale, 63 Rue de Lausanne, CH-1202 Geneva, Switzerland. TEL 22-7317150. FAX 22-7317158. Document type: bulletin.
- Formerly: Welt-Strassen-Statistik.
- Description: Presents statistical data on transport, road networks, traffic, accidents, taxation, production, imports and exports of motor vehicles, etc.

387 UK ISSN 0959-7719
WORLD SHIPPING STATISTICS (YEAR). a. £150($260) (effective Mar. 1995). Fairplay Publications Ltd., P.O. Box 96, Coulsdon, Surrey CR5 2TE, England. TEL 0181-645-2800. FAX 0181-660-2824. TELEX 884595 FRPLAY G. (N. American subscr. to: Fairplay Publication Ltd., Box 354, Germantown, NY 12526. TEL 518-537-6682. FAX 518-537-6667) Document type: directory.
- Formerly: Fairplay World Shipping Statistics.
- Description: Analyzes supply and demand and market prices in the shipping industry.

380.5 SZ ISSN 0302-7902
WORLD TRANSPORT DATA/STATISTIQUES MONDIALES DE TRANSPORT. (Text in English and French) 1973. irreg., latest 1995. 150 SFr. International Road Transport Union, 3 rue de Varembe, B.P. 44, CH-1211 Geneva 20, Switzerland. TEL 022-9182700. FAX 022-9182741. circ. 4,000. Document type: trade publication.

384 314 YU ISSN 0513-0794
YUGOSLAVIA. SAVEZNI ZAVOD ZA STATISTIKU. SAOBRACAJ I VEZE. (Subseries of: Statisticki Bilten) (Edition also in English) 100 din.($5.56) Savezni Zavod za Statistiku, Kneza Milosa 20, Belgrade, Yugoslavia. TEL 38-11-681999. illus. circ. 1,100. Document type: government publication.

380.5 ZA ISSN 0514-5392
ZAMBIA. CENTRAL STATISTICAL OFFICE. TRANSPORT STATISTICS. q. $4. Central Statistical Office, P.O. Box 31908, Lusaka, Zambia. TEL 260-1-211231. Document type: government publication.

TRANSPORTATION — Air Transport

387.7 UK
A A I B RECOMMENDATIONS - C A A PROGRESS REPORT (YEAR). (Subseries of: Civil Aviation Publications) a. £10. Civil Aviation Authority, Printing and Publication Services, Greville House, 37 Gratton Rd., Cheltenham, Glos. GL50 2BN, England. TEL 01242-2635151. FAX 01242-584139. (back issues avail.) Document type: government publication.
- Description: Lists the year's A.A.I.B. recommendations and reports on C.A.A. action taken.

387.744 UK ISSN 0141-6529
A B C AIR CARGO GUIDE. 1958. m. £210. Reed Travel Group, Part of Reed Telepublishing (Subsidiary of: Reed Elsevier group), Church St., Dunstable, Beds. LU5 4HB, England. TEL 01582-600111. FAX 01582-695230. TELEX 82168 AIRABC G. Ed. Sarah Cranstone. circ. 7,500. Document type: directory.
- Formerly: A B C Air Cargo Guide and Directory (ISSN 0001-0391)
- Description: Provides comprehensive coverage of worldwide air cargo schedules, rates, transfer corrections and other cargo-related information to freight forwarders, commercial exporters and airlines.

387.744 UK ISSN 0959-2911
A B C EXECUTIVE FLIGHT PLANNER: ASIA, PACIFIC. 1983. m. £78. Reed Travel Group, Part of Reed Telepublishing (Subsidiary of: Reed Elsevier group), Church St., Dunstable, Beds. LU5 4HB, England. TEL 01582-600111. FAX 01582-695230. TELEX 82168 AIRABC G. Ed. R. Cooper. circ. 31,000. Document type: directory.
—BLDSC (0537.756600).
- Formerly: A B C Air Asia (ISSN 0265-4024)
- Description: Provides a regionalized guide to air schedules.

387.7 UK ISSN 0309-6157
A B C WORLD AIRWAYS GUIDE. 1946. m. £390. Reed Travel Group, Part of Reed Telepublishing (Subsidiary of: Reed Elsevier group), Church St., Dunstable, Beds. LU5 4HB, England. TEL 01582-600111. FAX 01582-695230. TELEX 82168 AIRABC G. Ed. Roger Cooper. adv. circ. 28,000. Document type: directory.
- Description: Provides a reference source for international and domestic scheduled flight and fare information worldwide.

387.7 US
A C C A EXPRESS.* q. (Air Courier Conference of America) Sage Communications, 181 Park St., Montclair, NJ 07042. TEL 201-744-5771. FAX 201-744-6353. Ed. Herb Lev. circ. 1,500.

629 US ISSN 0194-8652
HD9711.A1
A C FLYER. (Air Craft) 1972. m. $28 (foreign $46). McGraw-Hill, Inc., 1221 Ave. of the Americas, New York, NY 10020. TEL 212-512-2000. (Subscr. to: Box 516, Hightstown, NJ 08520-1450) adv. circ. 60,000.
—UMI.
- Description: Lists used aircraft for sale.

387.736 FR ISSN 0761-9286
A D P A LA UNE. 1956. 11/yr. free. Aeroports de Paris, Service Communication Programme - Paris Airport Authority, 291 Bd. Raspail, 75675 Paris cedex 14, France. Ed. Anatole Rojinski. adv.; bk.rev.; illus.; stat. circ. 6,000.
- Formerly: Propos en l'Air (ISSN 0033-1384)

A D V - INFORMATIONSDIENST. (Arbeitsgemeinschaft Deutscher Verkehrsflughaefen) see TRANSPORTATION — Abstracting, Bibliographies, Statistics

A P A HOLIDAY. (Airline Passengers Association) see TRAVEL AND TOURISM

A S U TRAVEL GUIDE; the airline employee's discount directory. (Airline Services Unlimited) see TRAVEL AND TOURISM

387.4 CN ISSN 0256-3290
A T A - I A T A RESERVATIONS INTERLINE MESSAGE PROCEDURES - PASSENGER. Key Title: AIRIMP-Passenger. 1977. a. $50 (effective 1995). International Air Transport Association, 2000 Peel St., Montreal, PQ H3A 2R4, Canada. TEL 514-844-6311. FAX 514-844-3788. TELEX 05-267627.
- Description: The official source of passenger reservations interline message procedures used worldwide.

ACCIDENT - INCIDENT REPORTING A D R E P. see TRANSPORTATION — Abstracting, Bibliographies, Statistics

387.736 GW ISSN 0931-5470
AEROGUIDE; Nationale und Internationale Flugverbindungen von ueber 180 deutschen Flughaefen. 1985. a. $20. Verlag fuer Wirtschaftliche Informationen, Malvenweg 4, 51061 Cologne, Germany. TEL 0221-963564-0. FAX 0221-96356427. circ. 10,000. Document type: directory.

387.74 UK
AERONAUTICAL INFORMATION CIRCULARS. Abbreviated title: A I C. (Also avail. as part of United Kingdom Aeronautical Information Publication) m. (13/yr.). £20 (overseas £45). Civil Aviation Authority, Printing and Publications Services, Greville House, 37 Gratton Rd., Cheltenham, Glos. GL50 2BN, England. TEL 01242-235151. FAX 01242-584139. (looseleaf format) Document type: government publication, trade publication.

387.7 UN ISSN 0443-7918
AERONAUTICAL INFORMATION SERVICES PROVIDED BY STATES/SERVICES D'INFORMATION AERONAUTIQUE ASSURES PAR LES ETATS/AERONAVIGATSIONNOE INFORMATSIONNOE OBSLUZHIVANIE, PREDOSTAVLYAEMOE GOSUDARSTVAMI/SERVICIOS DE INFORMACION AERONAUTICA SUMINISTRADOS POR LOS ESTADOS. (Text in: English, French, Russian, Spanish) 1960. irreg., 82nd ed., 1994. $20. International Civil Aviation Organization, Attn: Document Sales Unit, 1000 Sherbrooke St. W., Montreal, PQ H3A 2R2, Canada. TEL 514-285-8022. FAX 514-285-6769. TELEX 05-24513.

AEROPORTS DE PARIS. BULLETIN MENSUEL DE STATISTIQUES. see TRANSPORTATION — Abstracting, Bibliographies, Statistics

387.7 FR ISSN 0065-3721
AEROPORTS DE PARIS. RAPPORT DU CONSEIL D'ADMINISTRATION. (Editions in English and French) a. free. Aeroports de Paris - Paris Airport Authority, Service Relations Publiques et Editions, 291 Bd. Raspail, 75675 Paris, France.

AEROPORTS DE PARIS. SERVICE STATISTIQUE. STATISTIQUE DE TRAFIC. see TRANSPORTATION — Abstracting, Bibliographies, Statistics

TRANSPORTATION — AIR TRANSPORT

387.736   FR   ISSN 1240-6309
AEROPORTS DE PARIS. TRAFIC DES PRINCIPAUX AEROPORTS MONDIAUX. (Text in English and French) a. 160 F. (effective 1992). Aeroports de Paris, Service Documentation et Statistiques, Orly Sud 103, 94396 Orly Aerogare, France.

387.736   FR   ISSN 0336-626X
AEROPORTS MAGAZINE. 1968. 10/yr. 250 F. Aeroports de Paris, Service Communication, 291 Bd. Raspail, 75675 Paris Cedex 14, France. TEL 43-35-70-01. FAX 43-35-75-50. TELEX 270 803. adv. circ. 7,097.

AIR ALASKA; the northern aviator's news. see *AERONAUTICS AND SPACE FLIGHT*

387.7   UK   ISSN 0963-9993
AIR & BUSINESS TRAVEL NEWS. 1965. s-m. £25 (effective 1994). Air & Business Travel Ltd., P.O. Box 3703, Catford, London SE6 4YT, England. TEL 081-690-8833. FAX 081-314-0581. (Subscr. also to: P.O. Box 1315, Potters Bar, Herts. EN6 1PU, England. TEL 0707-665151. FAX 0707-660330) Ed. Chris Lockwood. adv. contact: Malcolm Ginsberg. bk.rev. circ. 13,000. **Document type:** trade publication.
    Former titles: Air and Business Travel; Air Travel; Air Travel and Interline News (ISSN 0264-4249); Interline and Air Travel News; Interline News.
    Description: Aimed at the professional traveler and travel market, mainly airlines and hotels.

341.46   NE   ISSN 0927-3379
K1
AIR & SPACE LAW. (Text in English) 1975. bi-m. fl.432 to institutions; $277 to institutions in U.S. (effective 1996). Kluwer Law International (Subsidiary of: Wolters Kluwer N.V.), Postbus 85889, 2508 CN The Hague, Netherlands. TEL 31-70-3081500. FAX 31-70-3081515. (Dist. by: Kluwer Aademic Publishers Group, P.O. Box 322, 3300 AH Dordrecht, Netherlands. TEL 31-78-546392. FAX 31-78-546477; In N. America: Kluwer Law International, 675 Massachusetts Ave., Cambridge, MA 02139. TEL 617-354-0140. FAX 617-354-8595) Ed.Bd. (reprint service avail. from WSH) Indexed: Abstr.Bk.Rev.Curr.Leg.Per., Abstr.Crim.& Pen., C.L.I., Euro.LJI, Int.Aerosp.Abstr., L.R.I., Leg.Per.
    —BLDSC (0774.131000); SWETS; UnCover. **CCC.**
    Formerly (until 1992): Air Law (ISSN 0165-2079)
    Description: Presents topical information on aviation policy, and the civil, commercial, administrative and penal aspects of the study of air and space law.

387.7   UK
AIR-BRITAIN AIRLINE FLEETS. 1980. a. £12. Air-Britain (Historians) Ltd., 1 East St., Tonbridge, Kent TN9 1HP, England.
    Former titles: Airline Fleets (ISSN 0262-1657) & World Airline Fleets Handbook.
    Description: Airline fleet data worldwide on over 1500 operators in 166 countries.

387.744   SW   ISSN 1101-4075
AIR CARGO COURIER. (Includes Transport i Dag) 1990. q. SEK 375 (effective 1990). Fateco Foerlag AB, Propellervaegen 4 A, S-183 62 Taeby, Sweden. FAX 46-8736-1400.

387.744   US
AIR CARGO NEWS. 1975. 12/yr. $36. Air Cargo News, Inc., Box 777, Jamaica, NY 11431. TEL 718-479-0176. Ed. Milton A. Caine. adv. circ. 42,000.

387.7   US   ISSN 1075-1742
▼**AIR CARGO REPORT;** news and analysis of the global air cargo industry. 1994. bi-w. $595 (foreign $630) (effective 1995). Phillips Business Information, Inc., 1201 Seven Locks Rd., Potomac, MD 20854. TEL 301-424-3338; 800-777-5006. FAX 301-309-3847. E-mail: pbi@phillips.com. Ed. Benet Wilson. (back issues avail.) **Document type:** newsletter.
    ●Also available online. Vendor(s): Information Access Co., NewsNet.
    Description: Covers market trends, opportunities, management and industry issues, air safety, legislation, technology and marketing strategies in the air cargo world.

387.7   US   ISSN 0745-5100
HE9788
AIR CARGO WORLD. 1910. m. $52 (foreign $112). Argus Inc., 6151 Powers Ferry Rd., N.W., Atlanta, GA 30339-2941. TEL 404-955-2500. FAX 404-955-0400. Ed. Victoria Fagouri. adv.; bk.rev.; illus.; tr.lit.; index. circ. 25,292. (also avail. in microform from UMI; reprint service avail. from UMI) **Document type:** trade publication.
    ●Also available online.
    —BLDSC (0774.750000); UMI. **CCC.**
    Former titles (until 1982): Air Cargo Magazine (ISSN 0148-7469); (until 1976): Cargo Airlift; Air Transportation (ISSN 0002-2551)
    Description: International magazine devoted to the expeditious movement of goods and information. Serves the fields of transportation, physical distribution, courier and small package shipping, import-export and bulk freight traffic in industries utilizing air as a distribution vehicle.

AIR CARRIER INDUSTRY SCHEDULE SERVICE TRAFFIC STATISTICS. MEDIUM REGIONAL CARRIERS. see *TRANSPORTATION — Abstracting, Bibliographies, Statistics*

AIR FINANCE ANNUAL. see *BUSINESS AND ECONOMICS — Banking And Finance*

387.7   US   ISSN 0092-2870
HE9788.5.U5
AIR FREIGHT DIRECTORY. 1961. bi-m. $84. Air Cargo, Inc., 1819 Bay Ridge Ave., Annapolis, MD 21403. TEL 410-280-8911. FAX 410-268-3154. Ed. Valere Zorn. adv. circ. 7,500. **Document type:** directory.
    Superseded: Air Freight Directory of Points in the United States Served Directly by Air and by Pick-up and Delivery Service and by Connecting Motor Carriers (ISSN 0515-8125)
    Description: Features comprehensive listing of ground transportation service points and rates.

AIR LINE PILOT; the magazine of professional flight deck crews. see *AERONAUTICS AND SPACE FLIGHT*

387.74 341.   UK
AIR NAVIGATION - THE ORDER AND THE REGULATIONS. (Subseries of: Civil Aviation Publications) base vol. plus irreg. amendments. £27. Civil Aviation Authority, Printing and Publication Services, Greville House, 37 Gratton Rd., Cheltenham, Glos. GL50 2BN, England. TEL 01242-235151. FAX 01242-584139. (looseleaf format) **Document type:** government publication.
    Description: Sets out the provisions of the Air Navigation Order and regulations made under it. Also publishes the provisions of the C.A.A. Regulations, the C.A.A. Schemes of Charges, Air Navigation (Noise Certification) Order, Investigations of Accidents Regulations, and Dangerous Goods Regulations.

387.7   NZ   ISSN 0065-4817
AIR NEW ZEALAND. ANNUAL REPORT. 1965. a. free. Air New Zealand Ltd, Quay Tower, 29 Customs St. West, Auckland, New Zealand. FAX 64-09-3662764. (U.S. addr: 1960 E. Grand Ave., Ste. 900, El Segundo, CA 90245) circ. 30,000.

387   AT   ISSN 0727-338X
AIR PILOT. 1952. q. free to qualified personnel. Australian Federation of Air Pilots, 132 Albert Rd., South Melbourne, Vic. 3205, Australia. TEL 03-699-8199. Ed. Terry O'Connell. adv.; bk.rev.; illus. circ. 5,000. **Document type:** newsletter.

341.46   US
AIR SERVICE RIGHTS IN U S INTERNATIONAL AIR TRANSPORT AGREEMENTS. (In 4 vols.) a. (plus updates). $75 in N. America; elsewhere $85 (effective 1995). Air Transport Association of America, 1301 Pennsylvania Ave., N.W., Ste. 1100, Washington, DC 20004-1707. TEL 202-626-4260. FAX 202-626-4159. **Document type:** corporate report.
    Description: Provides a compilation of air service rights provided by US international bilateral air transport agreements. The rights include both scheduled and charter air services.

387.7   US
AIR TRAFFIC CONTROL. biennial base vol. (plus q. updates). $70 (foreign $87.50) (effective 1995). U.S. Federal Aviation Administration, 800 Independence Ave., S.W., Washington, DC 20591. TEL 202-267-3484. (Subscr. to: Superintendent of Documents, U.S. Government Printing Office, Box 371954, Pittsburgh, PA 15250-7954. TEL 202-512-1800. FAX 202-512-2250) (looseleaf format) **Document type:** trade publication, government publication.
    Description: Prescribes air traffic control procedures and phrases for air traffic controllers.

341.46   US   ISSN 0400-1915
AIR TRAFFIC CONTROL ASSOCIATION. BULLETIN. m. membership only. Air Traffic Control Association, Inc., 2300 Clarendon Blvd., Ste. 711, Arlington, VA 22201. TEL 703-522-5717. Ed. Carol Newmaster. **Document type:** bulletin.

387.74   UK
AIR TRAFFIC CONTROL LICENSING. (Subseries of: Civil Aviation Publications) irreg., 14th ed., 1992. £7.50 per no. Civil Aviation Authority, Printing and Publication Services, Greville House, 37 Gratton Rd., Cheltenham, Glos. GL50 2BN, England. TEL 01242-235151. FAX 01242-584139. **Document type:** government publication, trade publication.
    Description: Incorporates the Certification of Competence Scheme and introduces changes to MER for the first validation of combined ratings.

387.74   US   ISSN 1064-3818
TL725.3.T7   CODEN: ATCQER
AIR TRAFFIC CONTROL QUARTERLY; an international journal of engineering and operations. 1993. q. $196 (foreign $251) (effective 1996). (Air Traffic Control Association Institute) John Wiley & Sons, Inc., Journals, 605 Third Ave., New York, NY 10158-0012. TEL 212-850-6645. FAX 212-850-6021. TELEX 12-7063. E-mail: SUBINFO@JWILEY.COM. (Subscr. outside the Americas to: John Wiley & Sons Ltd., Baffins Ln., Chichester, W. Sussex PO19 1UD, England. TEL 44-1243-779777. FAX 44-1243-776128) Ed. Anand Mundra. adv. contact: Roberta Frederick. (also avail. in microform from UMI; back issues avail.) **Document type:** academic/scholarly publication.
    —BLDSC (0776.655200).
    Refereed Serial

387.74 629.136   UK   ISSN 0969-6725
AIR TRAFFIC MANAGEMENT. 1992. bi-m. £49($120). Camrus Publishers, Nestor House, Playhouse Yard, London EC4V 5EX, England. TEL 0171-779-8866. FAX 0171-779-8867. adv.: B&W page $3375, color page $5245; trim 11 x 8; adv. contact: Rosa Bellanca. (back issues avail.) **Document type:** trade publication.
    Description: Publishes reports and features on matters of concern to air traffic control executives.

629.1 387.74   UK
AIR TRAFFIC SERVICES ENGINEERING REQUIREMENTS. (Subseries of: Civil Aviation Publications) base vol. plus irreg. updates. £45. Civil Aviation Authority, Printing and Publication Services, Greville House, 37 Gratton Rd., Cheltenham, Glos. GL50 2BN, England. TEL 01242-235151. FAX 01242-584139. (looseleaf format) **Document type:** government publication.
    Description: Establishes the requirements and guidelines for standards and practices that organizations and individuals providing or seeking to provide an air traffic service must follow.

387.7   US   ISSN 0190-552X
HE9788.5.U5
AIR TRANSPORT. 1937. a. $10. Air Transport Association of America, 1301 Pennsylvania Ave., N.W., Ste. 100, Washington, DC 20004-1707. TEL 202-626-4000. FAX 202-626-4081. (Subscr. to: ATA Distribution Center, Box 511, Annapolis Juncion, MD 20701. TEL 800-497-3326. FAX 301-206-9789) Ed.Bd. (also avail. in microfiche from CIS) Indexed: SRI. **Document type:** corporate report.
    Description: Report of the United States scheduled airline industry.

TRANSPORTATION — AIR TRANSPORT

387.7   CN   ISSN 0065-485X
AIR TRANSPORT ASSOCIATION OF CANADA. ANNUAL REPORT. 1960. a. Air Transport Association of Canada, 747 Metropolitan Life Bldg., 99 Bank St., Ottawa, Ont. K1P 6B9, Canada. TEL 613-233-7727. Ed. Donald H. Watson. circ. 1,000.

AIR TRANSPORT FACTS & FIGURES (ANNUAL REPORT). see *TRANSPORTATION — Abstracting, Bibliographies, Statistics*

AIR TRAVEL SURVEY. see *TRANSPORTATION — Abstracting, Bibliographies, Statistics*

387.744   CN   ISSN 0256-3207
AIR WAYBILL HANDBOOK. 1978. a. $39 (effective 1995). International Air Transport Association, 2000 Peel St., Montreal, PQ H3A 2R4, Canada. TEL 514-844-6311. FAX 514-844-3788. TELEX 05-267627.
    Description: Guide to the completion and issuance of the international air waybill. Contains the Resolutions and Recommended Practices related to the air waybill.

387.7   RH
AIR ZIMBABWE ANNUAL REPORT. 1968. a. free. Air Zimbabwe Corporation, P.O. Box AP. 1, Harare Airport, Harare, Zimbabwe. TEL 263-4-575111. FAX 263-4-575068. TELEX 40008 ZW. circ. 2,000. **Document type:** corporate report.
    Formerly: Air Rhodesia Annual Report.

387.7   AT
AIRCARGO ASIA - PACIFIC. 1990. 11/yr. Aus.$65. Impact Publications, 11-643 Newcastle St., Leederville, W.A. 6007, Australia. TEL 61-0-328-3711. FAX 61-9-238-3986. Ed. Chris Hurd. circ. 3,000. **Document type:** trade publication.

387.736   UN
AIRCRAFT CHARACTERISTICS DATA BANK. VOLUME 1 - SUMMARY AND EXPLANATION. (Text in English, French, Spanish, Russian) a. $14 (set of vols.1-6 $317). International Civil Aviation Organization, Attn: Document Sales Unit, 1000 Sherbrooke St. W., Montreal, PQ H3A 2R2, Canada. TEL 514-285-8022. FAX 514-285-6769. TELEX 05-24513. (also avail. in diskette format; magnetic tape)
    ●Also available online.
    Description: Contains all the information users need to understand the I.C.A.O. Aircraft Data Bank.

629.13   US   ISSN 1072-3145
AIRCRAFT MAINTENANCE TECHNOLOGY. 1989. bi-m. $40 (Canada and Mexico $55; elsewhere $120). Johnson Hill Press, Inc. (Subsidiary of: P T N Publishing Corp.), 1233 Janesville Ave., Fort Atkinson, WI 53538. TEL 414-563-6388. FAX 414-563-1701. Ed. Greg Napert. adv.; circ. 25,000. (controlled). (tabloid format)
    Formerly (until 1993): Aircraft Technician (ISSN 1044-8012)
    Description: Focuses on the technical and mechanical side of the 19-passenger and below airline industry.

363.12 629.13   UK   ISSN 0960-9261
AIRCRAFT PROXIMITY HAZARDS REPORTS. Short title: A P H A Z Reports. 1991. irreg., vol.7. £10. Civil Aviation Authority, Printing and Publication Services, Greville House, 37 Gratton Rd., Cheltenham, Glos. GL50 2BN, England. TEL 01242-2635151. FAX 01242-584139. (back issues avail.) **Document type:** government publication.
    Description: Reviews U.K. aircraft near misses.

AIRCRAFT TECHNOLOGY ENGINEERING & MAINTENANCE. see *AERONAUTICS AND SPACE FLIGHT*

AIRCRAFT TYPE DESIGNATORS/INDICATIFS DE TYPE D'AERONEF/DESIGNADORES DE TIPOS DE AERONAVE. see *BIOLOGY*

AIRCRAFT VALUE JOURNAL. see *AERONAUTICS AND SPACE FLIGHT*

387.7   US   ISSN 1071-0655
AIRCRAFT VALUE NEWSLETTER. Variant title: Aircraft Value News. 1992. bi-w. $595 (foreign $630) (effective 1995). Phillips Business Information, Inc., 1201 Seven Locks Rd., Potomac, MD 20854. TEL 301-424-3338. FAX 301-309-3847. E-mail: pbi@phillips.com. Ed. Steve Nearman. (back issues avail.) **Document type:** newsletter.
    ●Also available online. Vendor(s): Information Access Co., NewsNet.
    —CCC.

387.7 332   UK   ISSN 0143-2257
HE9782
AIRFINANCE JOURNAL. 1980. m. £138. Euromoney Publications plc., Nestor House, Playhouse Yard, London EC4V 5EX, England. TEL 0171-779-8935. FAX 0171-779-8541. TELEX 886196 EURMON G. Ed. Chris Kjelgaard. adv. circ. 4,500. (back issues avail.) **Document type:** trade publication.
    ●Also available online. Vendor(s): University Microfilms International.
    —UMI.
    Description: Aviation and aerospace financing techniques.

AIRLINE ADVERTISING PROJECT. see *ADVERTISING AND PUBLIC RELATIONS*

387.7   US   ISSN 1074-4312
▼**AIRLINE & COMMERCIAL AIRCRAFT REPORT INTERNATIONAL.** Abbreviated title: A C A R International. 1994. m. $39.95. Airways International, Inc., Box 1109, Sandpoint, ID 83864-0872. TEL 208-263-5166. FAX 208-263-3313. Ed. John Wegg. adv.: page $3000; trim 190 x 255; adv. contact: Seija Wegg-Itronen. circ. 5,000 (paid). (back issues avail.) **Document type:** newsletter.
    Description: Detailed news digest of worldwide commercial air transport.

387.7 658   UK   ISSN 0268-7615
AIRLINE BUSINESS. 1985. m. $99. Reed Business Publishing Ltd. (Subsidiary of: Reed Elsevier plc), Quadrant House, The Quadrant, Sutton, Surrey SM2 5AS, England. TEL 0181-652-4996. FAX 0181-652-8914. Ed. Richard Whitaker. adv. circ. 25,600. **Indexed:** Hospit.Ind. **Document type:** trade publication.
    ●Also available online. Vendor(s): Data-Star, Information Access Co., Reuters, Ltd.
    —BLDSC (0784.505000). **CCC.**
    Description: Covers politics, finance and business trends in the air transport industry worldwide.

387.7   CN   ISSN 1013-4050
AIRLINE CODING DIRECTORY. 1988. 3/yr. $138 (effective 1995). International Air Transport Association, 2000 Peel St., Montreal, PQ H3A 2R4, Canada. TEL 514-884-6311. FAX 514-844-3788. TELEX 05-267627. (also avail. in magnetic tape) **Document type:** directory.
    Description: The official industry source for airline designators, location identifiers and three-digit airline numeric codes. Includes ISO currency and country codes.

387.7 330.9   CN
AIRLINE ECONOMIC RESULTS AND PROSPECTS. a. $100. International Air Transport Association, Cost Committee, 2000 Peel St., Montreal, PQ H3A 2R4, Canada. TEL 514-844-6311. FAX 514-844-5286. (also avail. in diskette format)
    Description: Offers an overview of the economic performance of the industry with a detailed analysis of cost trends by route area for specified periods.

387.7   US   ISSN 1040-5410
AIRLINE FINANCIAL NEWS. 1986. w. $595 (effective 1995). Phillips Business Information, Inc., 1201 Seven Locks Rd., Potomac, MD 20854. TEL 301-424-3338. FAX 301-309-3847. E-mail: pbi@phillips.com. Ed. Benet Wilson. adv. **Document type:** newsletter.
    ●Also available online. Vendor(s): Data-Star, Knight-Ridder, Inc., NewsNet (AE25).
    —CCC.

629.13   UK   ISSN 0002-2721
AIRLINE FLEET RECORD. 3/yr. $245. Aviation Studies International, Sussex House, Parkside, Wimbledon, London SW19 5NB, England. TEL 0181-946-5082. **Document type:** directory, trade publication.
    Description: Lists by continent the fleets of 1,500 airlines.

387.7   US   ISSN 0095-4683
HE9768
AIRLINE HANDBOOK. 1972. a. $16. AeroTravel Research Publications, Box 3694, Cranston, RI 02910. TEL 401-941-6140. Ed. Paul K. Martin. illus.

387.7   US
AIRLINE INDUSTRIAL RELATIONS CONFERENCE. NEWSLETTER. bi-m. Airline Industrial Relations Conference, 1920 N St., N.W., Ste. 250, Washington, DC 20036. TEL 202-861-7550.

387.7 332   US
THE AIRLINE INDUSTRY: AN INDUSTRY OVERVIEW. 1990. a. $395. Dun & Bradstreet Information Services (Murray Hill) (Subsidiary of: Dun & Bradstreet, Inc.), One Diamond Hill Rd., Murray Hill, NJ 07974. TEL 908-665-5224. FAX 908-771-7599. Ed. Matthew Gowen.
    Description: Features an analysis of the top 25 airlines including an overview of financial conditions.

387   UK   ISSN 0966-2065
AIRLINE MAINTENANCE WORLD. 1990. bi-m. £70($180) (effective 1992). A M W Publishing Ltd., 40 Chomham Rd., Sunningdale, Berks SI5 ODX, England. TEL 344-784866. FAX 344-874543. Ed. Don Parry. adv.; circ. 12,708 (controlled). (back issues avail.)
    Description: Reports on the commercial aspects of the airline maintenance industry especially with regard to finance, third party business and new contracts. Includes world news and profiles.

387.7   US   ISSN 1071-1325
AIRLINE MARKETING NEWS. 1993. bi-w. $595 (foreign $630) (effective 1995). Phillips Business Information, Inc., 1201 Seven Locks Rd., Potomac, MD 20854. TEL 301-424-3338. FAX 301-309-3847. E-mail: pbi@phillips.com. Ed. James Brown. (back issues avail.) **Document type:** newsletter.
    —CCC.

629.13   US   ISSN 0002-2748
AIRLINE NEWSLETTER. 1967. s-m. $65. Roadcap Aviation Publications, 1030 S. Green Bay Rd., Lake Forest, IL 60045. TEL 708-234-4730. Ed. Roy R. Roadcap. cum.index. (looseleaf format)
    Formerly: World Airline Record Newsletter (ISSN 0512-2368)
    Description: News and analysis of trends in commercial air transportation.

387.7   SP
AIRLINE NINETY TWO; revista de aviacion comercial y aeropuertos. 11/yr. 5320 ptas. (Europe 8200 ptas.; America 10000 ptas.) (effective 1995). Edefa, S.A., Editorial de Publicaciones, Jorge Juan, 98-2, 28009 Madrid, Spain. TEL 1-577-49-57. FAX 577-46-70. adv.: B&W page 217000 ptas., color page 378000 ptas.; trim 187 x 267. circ. 15,000.
    Description: Covers commercial aviation and airports.

387.742   US   ISSN 0892-4236
AIRLINE, SHIP & CATERING ONBOARD SERVICES MAGAZINE; the international trade publication for the passenger service and duty free markets. (Includes Annual Industry Directory) 1974. 8/yr. $25 (foreign $65). (Airline Inflight Food Service Association) International Publishing Company of America, 665 La Villa Dr., Miami Springs, FL 33166. TEL 305-887-1700. FAX 305-885-1923. Ed. Richard Lundstrum. circ. 9,000. **Indexed:** Hospit.Ind. **Document type:** trade publication.
    Former titles: Airline and Travel Food (ISSN 0161-1755); Airline Food and Flight Service; Airline News.
    Description: Geared towards food service management of domestic and international airlines. Covers ships, railroads, catering firms and other suppliers to the travel industry.

TRANSPORTATION — AIR TRANSPORT

387.7 US ISSN 0896-6575
HE9761.1
AIRLINERS; the world's airline magazine. 1988. bi-m. $23.95; newsstand price: $4.50. World Transport Press, Inc., Box 20189, Castro Valley, CA 94546. TEL 510-732-2747. FAX 510-732-2699. (Subscr. to: Box 521238, Miami, FL 33152-1238. TEL 305-477-7163. FAX 305-599-1995) Ed. Nicholas A. Veronico. adv. contact: Michael Wilkinson. bk.rev.; circ. 32,000 (paid). **Document type:** consumer publication.
Description: Presents news, air transport trends, articles, and photography for commercial aviation enthusiasts.

387.736 UK ISSN 0268-7712
AIRPORT; travelling in style. 1985. m. free. Redwood Publishing Ltd., 101 Bayham St., London NW1 0AG, England. TEL 0171-251-8798. FAX 0171-251-8801. Ed. Alison James. adv. **Document type:** consumer publication.

387.736 UN
AIRPORT CHARACTERISTICS DATA BANK. VOLUME 2 - INDIAN OCEAN REGION. (Text in English, French, Spanish, Russian) a. $38 (set of vols.1-6 $317). International Civil Aviation Organization, Attn: Document Sales Unit, 1000 Sherbrooke St. W., Montreal, PQ H3A 2R2, Canada. TEL 514-285-8022. FAX 514-285-6769. TELEX 05-24513. (also avail. in diskette format; magnetic tape)
●Also available online.
Description: Provides information on airport facilities in and off the coast of Africa.

387.736 UN
AIRPORT CHARACTERISTICS DATA BANK. VOLUME 3 - CARRIBBEAN AND SOUTH AMERICAN REGIONS. (Text in English, French, Spanish, Russian) a. $43 (set of vols.1-6 $317). International Civil Aviation Organization, Attn: Document Sales Unit, 1000 Sherbrooke St. W., Montreal, PQ H3A 2R2, Canada. TEL 514-285-8022. FAX 514-285-6769. TELEX 05-24513. (also avail. in diskette format; magnetic tape)
●Also available online.
Description: Provides information on the main airports in South America and the Caribbean.

387.736 UN
AIRPORT CHARACTERISTICS DATA BANK. VOLUME 4 - EUROPEAN REGION. (Text in English, French, Russian, Spanish) a. $117 (set of vols.1-6 $317). International Civil Aviation Organization, Attn: Document Sales Unit, 1000 Sherbrooke St. W., Montreal, PQ H3A 2R2, Canada. TEL 514-285-8022. FAX 514-285-6769. TELEX 05-24513. (also avail. in diskette format; magnetic tape)
●Also available online.
Description: Provides information on the facilities of the main European airports.

387.736 UN
AIRPORT CHARACTERISTICS DATA BANK. VOLUME 5 - MIDDLE EAST AND ASIA REGIONS. (Text in English, French, Russian, Spanish) a. $55 (set of vols. 1-6 $317). International Civil Aviation Organization, Attn: Document Sales Unit, 1000 Sherbrooke St. W., Montreal, PQ H3A 2R2, Canada. TEL 514-285-8022. FAX 514-285-6769. TELEX 05-24513. (also avail. in diskette format; magnetic tape)
●Also available online.
Description: Provides information on facilities of the main airports in Asia and the Middle East.

387.736 UN
AIRPORT CHARACTERISTICS DATA BANK. VOLUME 6 - NORTH ATLANTIC, NORTH AMERICAN AND PACIFIC REGIONS. (Text in English, French, Russian, Spanish) a. $50 (set of vols.1-6 $317). International Civil Aviation Organization, Attn: Document Sales Unit, 1000 Sherbrooke St. W., Montreal, PQ H3A 2R2, Canada. TEL 514-285-8022. FAX 514-285-6769. TELEX 05-24513. (also avail. in diskette format; magnetic tape)
●Also available online.
Description: Provides information on facilities at the main airports in North America, as well as the North Atlantic and Pacific regions.

387.736 690 GW ISSN 0002-2802
HE9797.A1 CODEN: APFRBE
AIRPORT FORUM; airport construction and operation, air transport, air traffic control. (Text in English) 1970. bi-m. DM.175 (foreign DM.216); newsstand price: DM.29. Vereinigte Motor-Verlage GmbH und Co. KG, Leuschnerstr. 1, 70174 Stuttgart, Germany. TEL 0711-18201. FAX 0711-1821756. (Subscr. to: Postfach 106036, 70049 Stuttgart, Germany) Ed. David Woolley; Pub. Peter-Paul Pietsch. adv.: B&W page DM.3300, color page DM.5775; trim 185 x 248; adv. contact: Reinhard Wittstamm. charts; illus. circ. 14,000. Indexed: Br.Tech.Ind., Excerp.Med., INSPEC (1984-). **Document type:** consumer publication.
—Ei; SWETS. CCC.
Description: Covers airport news worldwide; latest developments and future plans.

387.74 CN ISSN 0256-3193
AIRPORT HANDLING MANUAL. a. $139 (effective 1995). International Air Transport Association, 2000 Peel St., Montreal, PQ H3A 2R4, Canada. TEL 514-844-6311. FAX 514-844-3788. TELEX 05-267627.
Description: Contains recommended industry procedures covering load control, aircraft handling messages, standard delay codes, aircraft loading and departure control systems.

387.7 US
AIRPORT HIGHLIGHTS. 1964. 26/yr. $495 (libraries $125). Airports Council International - North America, 1775 K St., N.W., Ste. 500, Washington, DC 20006. TEL 202-293-8500. FAX 202-331-1362. Ed. Victoria Pannell. bk.rev. circ. 2,000. **Document type:** trade publication.
Description: Contains the latest airport news, regulatory and Congressional developments, domestic and international aviation news, industry issues, and employment and business opportunities.

387.736 US
AIRPORT JOURNAL. m. $17. Box 273, Clarendon Hills, IL 60514-0273. TEL 708-318-6872. Ed. John S. Andrews. adv. circ. 26,500.

387.7 US ISSN 1048-2091
TL725.A1
AIRPORT MAGAZINE. 1989. bi-m. $25 (foreign $40). American Association of Airport Executives, 4212 King St., Alexandria, VA 22302. TEL 703-824-0504. FAX 703-820-1395. Ed. Ellen Horton; Pub. Joan/Lowden. adv. contact: Susan Haynes. index. circ. 7,000. (back issues avail.) **Document type:** trade publication.

614.85 387.7 US ISSN 1057-5537
AIRPORT OPERATIONS. bi-m. $60 in N. America; elsewhere $65. Flight Safety Foundation, Inc., 2200 Wilson Blvd., Ste. 500, Arlington, VA 22201-3306. TEL 703-522-8300. FAX 703-525-6047. Ed. Roger Rozelle. circ. 3,000. (reprint service avail. from UMI)
Formerly (until vol.13, no.5, 1987): Airport Operations Safety Bulletin (ISSN 0898-574X); Incorporates (in 1978): Airport Operations Ground Safety Bulletin; Airport Ground Safety Bulletin.
Description: Directs attention to ground operations that involve aircraft and other equipment, airport personnel and services, air traffic control and passengers.

387.7 US
AIRPORT PRESS. 1978. m. $32. P.A.T.I., 15 Lakeside Dr., Katonah, NY 10536. TEL 718-244-6788. FAX 718-995-3432. Ed. Dick Eisley; Pub. William Puckhaber. adv.: B&W page $4225, color page $4975; trim 11 3/8 x 15; adv. contact: Patricia Ranieri. circ. 26,117. (tabloid format) **Document type:** newspaper.
Description: Provides news and information of interest to the U.S. and overseas airport community.

387.7 US ISSN 0044-7601
AIRPORT REPORT. 1954. s-m. membership. American Association of Airport Executives, 4212 King St., Alexandria, VA 22302. TEL 703-824-0504. FAX 703-820-1395. Ed. Ellen P. Horton; Pub. Joan Lowden. adv. contact: Susan Haynes. bk.rev.; illus.; circ. controlled. (looseleaf format) **Document type:** trade publication.

387.736 UK
AIRPORT SUPPORT. 1982. m. £60 (Europe £80; elsewhere £90). Euromoney Publications plc., Nestor House, Playhouse Yard, London EC4V 5EX. TEL 071-779-8888. FAX 071-779-8617. TELEX 290700 EUROMON G. Ed. Chris Frankland. adv.; bk.rev. circ. 12,490. **Document type:** trade publication.
Description: Covers news and features on aircraft ground support, airport construction, and air traffic control.

387.7 US ISSN 1044-9469
AIRPORTS. w. $525 (foreign $585). McGraw-Hill, Inc., Aviation Week Group, 1200 G St., N.W., Ste. 200, Washington, DC 20005. TEL 202-383-2350. Ed. Avery Vise.
●Also available online. Vendor(s): Knight-Ridder, Inc. (File no.624/McGRAW-HILL PUBLICATIONS ONLINE), Dow Jones News Retrieval, Lexis-Nexis, NewsNet (AE21).
Description: Aimed at airport managers, users, and suppliers. Subjects covered include noise abatement, landing rights, curfews, franchise and rental fees, regulation, funding, FAA grants.

387.736 CN
AIRPORTS NORTH AMERICA. 1993. 4/yr. Can.$30($40) (foreign Can.$60). Baum International Media, 1625 Ingleton Ave., Burnaby, BC V5C 4L8, Canada. TEL 604-298-3004. FAX 604-291-1906. Ed. Toni Dabbs; Pub. Heri R. Baum. adv.: B&W page Can.$4070, color page Can.$5320; adv. contact: Kevin Cook. circ. 20,000. (tabloid format) **Document type:** trade publication.

387.7 SA
▼**AIRREPORT**; South Africa's aviation yearbook. 1994. a. R.59. P.O. Box 221, Morningside 2057, South Africa.

387.7 JM
AIRTEAM CIRCLE. s-a. Airports Authority of Jamaica, 64 Knutsford Blvd., Kingston 5, Jamaica, W.I. TEL 809-92-61622. Ed. Trevor Spence. adv.

387.7 UK ISSN 0306-0349
AIRTRADE. 1975. m. £55. Maclean Hunter Ltd., Maclean Hunter House, Chalk Lane, Cockfosters Rd., Barnet, Herts EN4 0BU, England. TEL 081-242-3000. FAX 081-242-3185. TELEX 299072-MACHUN-G. Ed. Chris Pocock. circ. 11,127. **Document type:** trade publication.

387.7 US ISSN 1074-4320
▼**AIRWAYS**; a global review of commercial flight. 1994. bi-m. $22.95. Airways International, Inc., Box 1109, Sandpoint, ID 83864-0872. TEL 208-263-5166. FAX 208-263-3313. Ed. John Wegg. adv.: B&W page $820, color page $1300; 7 x 10; adv. contact: Seijk Wegg-Itkonen. circ. 30,000 (paid). (back issues avail.) **Document type:** trade publication.
Description: For all interested in commercial air transport; features airlines, aircraft, personalities, issues.

387.7 US
ALL AMERICAN AVIATION ASSOCIATION NEWS. 1992. q. $50 membership. All American Aviation Association, Box 5793, Englewood, NJ 07631. TEL 201-568-8145. **Document type:** newsletter.
Description: Addresses aviation employment issues of interest to African Americans, including historical topics.

ANUARIO ESTADISTICO DEL TRANSPORTE AEREO ESPANA - (YEAR). see *TRANSPORTATION — Abstracting, Bibliographies, Statistics*

387.7 CH ISSN 1021-3740
ASIAN AIR TRANSPORT. (Text in Chinese, English) 1988. m. $80. Tzeng Brothers Information Group, P.O. Box 43-345, 7G-09 World Trade Ctr., Taipei, Taiwan 105, Republic of China. TEL 886-2-725-1904. FAX 723-8898. Ed. Robert Tzeng. adv.: B&W page $2500, color page $4000; trim 180 x 248; adv. contact: Jack Lee. circ. 11,750. **Document type:** trade publication.

TRANSPORTATION — AIR TRANSPORT

387.7   US   ISSN 1071-0663
ASIAN AVIATION NEWS. 1993. bi-w. $595 (foreign $630) (effective 1995). Phillips Business Information, Inc., 1201 Seven Locks Rd., Potomac, MD 20854. TEL 301-424-3338. FAX 301-309-3847. E-mail: pbi@phillips.com. Ed. Steve Nearman. (back issues avail.) **Document type:** newsletter.
—CCC.

387.7   US
ATLANTIC FLYER. m. $16.50 (foreign $75). 213 Evansville Ave., Meriden, CT 06451. TEL 203-238-9009. FAX 203-238-4121. Ed. Jacquelyn Lanpher. adv. circ. 84,000. (tabloid format) **Document type:** newspaper, trade publication.
Description: Features aviation news and history of interest to general-aviation pilots, historians, and restorers of antique aircraft, listing of aviation events.

ATLAS - AIR FRANCE; geographie physique et humaine - decouverte de l'homme et de la nature. see *TRAVEL AND TOURISM*

387.7   CN
AUTOMATIC IDENTIFICATION IN THE AIRLINE INDUSTRY HANDBOOK. a. $59. International Air Transport Association, 2000 Peel St., Montreal, PQ H3A 2R4, Canada. TEL 514-844-6311. FAX 514-844-3788. TELEX 05-267627.
Description: Offers a single source of quick and easy reference to the airlines' standards that use automatic identification.

387.7   US
AVIATION. bi-m. newsstand price: $2.95. Cowles Magazines Inc., 4 High Ridge Park, Stamford, CT 06905. TEL 203-322-2900. FAX 203-322-0302. **Document type:** consumer publication.

387.7 910.09   II   ISSN 0970-3578
HE9761.1
AVIATION & SPACE JOURNAL. (Text in English) 1977. q. Rs.110($25) V.J. Joseph, Ed. & Pub., C-4 Rishikesh II, Evershine Nagar, Malad West, Bombay 400 064, India. TEL 8826614. adv.; charts; illus.; stat. (reprint service avail.)
Description: Devoted to air transport, travel and tourism, as well as the trade fair and hotel industries.

THE AVIATION CONSUMER. see *AERONAUTICS AND SPACE FLIGHT*

AVIATION EDUCATION NEWS BULLETIN. see *AERONAUTICS AND SPACE FLIGHT*

629.132   FR
AVIATION & PILOTE; revue des loisirs de l'air. 1973. m. 330 F. Societe d'Edition et d'Exploitation de Supports, Aerodrome de Lognes-Emerainville, 77185 Lognes, France. TEL 1-64-62-05-06. FAX 1-64-62-11-09. Ed. Jacques Callies. adv.; bk.rev. circ. 25,000.
Former titles: Aviation et Pilote Prive; Pilote Prive; Aero-Club et le Pilote Prive.

387 629.132   US   ISSN 1058-7004
AVIATION EUROPE. 1991. w. McGraw-Hill, Inc., Aviation Week Group, 1200 G St., N.W., Ste. 200, Washington, DC 20005. TEL 202-383-2350.
•Also available online. Vendor(s): Knight-Ridder, Inc. (AE), Dow Jones News Retrieval (AE), Lexis-Nexis (AVEUR), NewsNet (AE35).

387.7   US   ISSN 0887-9877
HD9711.A1
AVIATION INTERNATIONAL NEWS; the newsmagazine of corporate/business aviation. 1972. bi-m. $36 (foreign $60). Convention News Co., Inc., 21 Cross Ave., Midland Park, NJ 07432. TEL 201-444-5075. FAX 201-444-4647. E-mail: CompuServe76451.2055. (Subscr. to: Circulation Dept., 81 Kenosia Ave., Danbury, CT 06810. TEL 203-798-2400) Ed. James Holahan. adv.; bk.rev. circ. 31,000. (tabloid format) **Document type:** trade publication.

341.46   US   ISSN 0273-7310
AVIATION LAW REPORTS. 4 base vols. plus s-m. updates. $1670. Commerce Clearing House, Inc., 4025 W. Peterson Ave., Chicago, IL 60646. TEL 312-583-8500.

AVIATION LITIGATION REPORTER; the national journal of record of aviation litigation. see *LAW*

AVIATION MEDICINE. see *MEDICAL SCIENCES*

341.46   US
AVIATION REGULATORY DIGEST SERVICE. m. $315. Hawkins Publishing Co., Inc., Box 480, Mayo, MD 21106-0480. TEL 301-798-1677. Ed. Carl R. Eyler. 90. (looseleaf format; back issues avail.) **Document type:** abstracting/indexing.
Formerly: Civil Aeronautics Board Service.

341.46   CN
AVIATION REGULATORY WATCH GROUP REPORTS. 1988. a. $55 per no. International Air Transport Association, 2000 Peel St., Montreal, PQ H3A 2R4, Canada. TEL 514-844-6311. FAX 514-844-3788. TELEX 05-267627.
Formerly: Aviation Regulatory Watch Reports.
Description: Reports on regulatory changes in the US, Europe, Latin America, Asia, Africa and the Middle East and the effects those changes have on the global aviation system.

AVIATION SAFETY; the twice-monthly journal of accident prevention. see *AERONAUTICS AND SPACE FLIGHT*

387.7   US   ISSN 1075-1378
AVIATION TELEPHONE DIRECTORY. EASTERN & SOUTHWESTERN STATES. 1946. a. $29.95. Directional Media System Inc., 515 W. Lambert Rd., Ste. D, Brea, CA 92621. TEL 714-990-5115. adv. circ. 3,000. **Document type:** directory.
Former titles: Aviation Telephone Directory: Pacific and Western States; (until 1979): Pacific Coast Aviation Directory.

387.7   US   ISSN 1075-136X
AVIATION TELEPHONE DIRECTORY. WESTERN & NORTHCENTRAL STATES. 1946. a. $29.95. Directional Media System Inc., 515 W. Lambert Rd., Ste. D, Brea, CA 92621. TEL 714-990-5115. **Document type:** directory.

629.1   II
AVION;* a monthly on aviation. 1971. m. Rs.32. 16-Park Area, New Delhi 5, India. Ed. J.K. Jain. adv.; charts; illus.

AVIONICS REVIEW. see *AERONAUTICS AND SPACE FLIGHT*

387.71   UK   ISSN 0265-3311
THE AVMARK ECONOMIST. 1984. 10/yr. £295($460) (effective Jan. 1995). Avmark Inc., 26 Eccleston Sq., London SW1V 1NS, England. TEL 0171-821-6788. FAX 0171-834-4372. Ed. Keith McMullan; Pub. Barbara Beyer. adv. contact: Emma McCrow. index. circ. 700. (back issues avail.) **Document type:** trade publication.
Description: Publishes in-depth reports on economic, financial, political, and market factors affecting airlines and aviation-related services.

387.7   UK   ISSN 1358-8893
B A A FLIGHT GUIDE. s-a. £7.50 (foreign £13.50). (British Airports Authority) Mediamark Publishing International Ltd., 35 Gresse St., Rathbone Pl., London W1P 1PN, England. TEL 0171-580-3105. FAX 0171-580-1695. (Subscr. to: Direct Mail Ad and Marketing, P.O. Box 198, Crawley W. Sussex RH10 24J, England. TEL 01293-611932) Pub. Peter Moore. circ. 120,000. **Document type:** directory.

387.7   UK
B A A NEWS. 1975. m. free to BAA staff and pensioners. (British Airport Authority) B A A plc., 130 Wilton Rd., London SW1V 1LQ, England. TEL 071-932-6736. FAX 071-932-6773. Ed. David Bland. adv. circ. 12,000. (tabloid format)
Formerly (until 1987): Airport News.

387.7   UK   ISSN 1351-4849
B A A REPORTS AND ACCOUNTS. 1966. a. (British Airports Authority) B A A plc., Corporate Office, 130 Wilton Rd., London SW1V 1LQ, England. TEL 0171-834-9449. FAX 0171-932-6699. Ed. Steven Olivant. illus. circ. 700,000. **Document type:** corporate report.
Description: Great Britain. British Airports Authority. Annual Report and Accounts (ISSN 0068-1229)

B S P DATA INTERCHANGE SPECIFICATIONS HANDBOOK. see *BUSINESS AND ECONOMICS — Banking And Finance*

BANK SETTLEMENT PLAN QUICK REFERENCE HANDBOOK. see *BUSINESS AND ECONOMICS — Banking And Finance*

387.74   GW   ISSN 0005-9242
BERLIN-FLUGPLAN. 1952. m. free. Berliner Flughafen Gesellschaft mbH, Abteilung Presse- und Oeffentlichkeitsarbeit, Flughafen Schoenefeld, 12521 Berlin, Germany. TEL 030-60911620. FAX 030-60911623. Ed. W.-D. Schultze. adv.; bk.rev.; abstr.; mkt. circ. 40,000. **Document type:** directory.
Description: Contains schedules of flights of the Berlin-Tegel, Berlin-Schoenefeld and Berlin Tempelhof Airports. Also includes airfares and airport information.

BEST FARES. see *TRAVEL AND TOURISM*

BOLETIN ESTADISTICO DE TRAFICO AEREO INTERNACIONAL. see *TRANSPORTATION — Abstracting, Bibliographies, Statistics*

387.7   UK   ISSN 0306-7041
BRITISH AIRWAYS EXECUTIVE. 1967. bi-m. free. British Airways PLC, Box 10, Heathrow Airport, Middlesex TW6 2JA, England. Ed. G. Wall. adv.; circ. 110,000 (controlled).
Incorporates: Incentive and Agenda.

387.7   UK
BRITISH AIRWAYS NEWS. 1940. w. free to staff and qualified personnel. British Airways PLC., P.O. Box 10, Heathrow Airport, Middlesex TW6 2JA, England. FAX 01-897-6230. TELEX 8813983-BAWYSC-G. Ed. Michael Blunt. adv.; bk.rev.; illus. circ. 57,000.
Former titles: B O A C News; B O A C Review (ISSN 0005-3252)

387.71 629.132   BE   ISSN 0776-7595
BUSINESS AVIATION & REGIONAL TRANSPORT. Short title: B A & R T. (Text in English) 1989. bi-m. 2400 BEF($75) Aerospace Resource Group, 23 Chemin Sainte Anne, B-1380 Ohain, Belgium. TEL 32-2-6521226. FAX 32-2-6531629. Ed. Didier Daoust; Pub. Fernand M. Francois. adv.: B&W page $2700, color page $5200; bleed 285 x 210; adv. contact: Fernand Francois. bk.rev. circ. 11,000. **Document type:** trade publication.
Incorporates: European Avianews (ISSN 0778-7502); Which was formerly titled (until 1991): Avianews International (ISSN 0772-876X); (1972-1982): Avianews.
Description: Promotes business and regional aviation. Covers the top 200 European aircraft companies and operations.

387.7   UK
BUSINESS LIFE. 1986. m. (British Airways) Premier Magazines Ltd., Haymarket House, 1 Oxendon St., London SW1Y 4EE, England. TEL 0171-925-2544. FAX 0171-839-4491. Ed. Sandra Harris. circ. 135,000. **Document type:** consumer publication.

387.7 658.8   UK   ISSN 0950-2394
BUSINESS RATIO REPORT: AIRFREIGHT AGENCIES; an industry sector analysis. 1986. a. I C C Business Ratios Ltd., Freepost, Field House, Hampton, Mddx. TW12 1BR, England. TEL 081-783-0977. FAX 081-783-1940. charts; stat. **Document type:** trade publication.
—BLDSC (0776.105000).

387.7 658   US
BUTLER AVIATION'S ECHELON;* the magazine for corporate executives. m. $36. Halsey Publishing Co., 600 Corporate Dr., Ste. 300, Fort Lauderdale, FL 33334-3604. TEL 305-893-1520. Ed. Debra Silver. adv.; illus.; circ. controlled.
Incorporates: Skylite.

BYWAYS (FAIRFAX). see *TRAVEL AND TOURISM*

387   UK
C A A SPECIFICATIONS. irreg., latest no.20. price varies. Civil Aviation Authority, Printing and Publication Services, Greville House, 37 Gratton Rd., Cheltenham, Glos. GL50 2BN, England. TEL 01242-235151. FAX 01242-584139. **Document type:** government publication, bulletin.
Description: Details specifications on aircraft safety devices.

TRANSPORTATION — AIR TRANSPORT

387.7   US
C N S FOCUS. 1986. 4/yr. membership. Cargo Network Services, 300 Garden City Plaza, Ste. 312, Garden City, NY 11530-3325. TEL 516-747-3375. FAX 516-747-3312. Ed. Tony Calabrese. adv.: B&W page $2350; adv. contact: Harry Watson. circ. 7,000 (controlled). **Document type:** trade publication.

629.13   CN   ISSN 0008-2848
CANADIAN AIRCRAFT OPERATOR; Canada's general aviation newspaper. 1964. s-m. Can.$22. Arthurs Creative Services, Box 149 Rockwood Mall, 4141 Dixie Rd., Mississauga, Ont. L4W 1V5, Canada. TEL 416-625-9660. FAX 416-625-9604. Ed. Ed Belitsky. adv.; bk.rev.; illus.; stat. circ. 8,150. (tabloid format) **Document type:** newspaper.

387.7   CN   ISSN 0829-2132
CANADIAN AVIATION NEWS. 1976. bi-w. Can.$12($21) Canadian Aviation News Ltd., Ste. 202, 1338 T - 36 Ave. N.E., Calgary, AB T2E 6T6, Canada. TEL 403-250-9833. FAX 403-291-9281. Ed. R. Engel. adv.; bk.rev. circ. 10,000. (also avail. in microfiche)
Formerly (until 1984): Canadian Western Aviation News.

387.7   CN
CANADIAN BUSINESS AIRCRAFT ASSOCIATION. NEWS BRIEF. m. free to qualified personnel. Canadian Business Aircraft Association, 50 O'Connor St., Ste. 1317, Ottawa, ON K1P 6L2, Canada. TEL 613-236-5611. FAX 613-236-2361. circ. 650. **Document type:** newsletter.
Supersedes in part: Canadian Business Aircraft Association. Newsletter.
Description: Provides items of general interest to CBAA membership and corporate aviation industry.

CANADIAN CIVIL AIRCRAFT REGISTER. see *AERONAUTICS AND SPACE FLIGHT*

CANADIAN CIVIL AVIATION. see *TRANSPORTATION — Abstracting, Bibliographies, Statistics*

CANADIAN GENERAL AVIATION NEWS. see *AERONAUTICS AND SPACE FLIGHT*

387.742   CN
CARGO AGENT'S HANDBOOK. a. $18. International Air Transport Association, 2000 Peel St., Montreal, PQ H3A 2R4, Canada. TEL 514-844-6311. FAX 514-844-5286.
Description: Sets out resolutions and other provisions which are of interest to IATA Cargo Agents in the exercise of their rights and obligations as registered Agents, and contains information of practical value in their day-to-day work.

387.744   CN
CARGO COMMUNITY SYSTEMS DIRECTORY AND GUIDELINES. a. $80. International Air Transport Association, 2000 Peel St., Montreal, PQ H3A 2R4, Canada. TEL 514-844-6311. FAX 514-844-5286.
Description: Contains a world-wide directory of cargo community systems and guidelines relating to CCS operation and interconnection standards.

387.444   US   ISSN 0278-0801
CARGO FACTS. 1981. 12/yr. $250 (foreign $295). Edwin C. Laird, 1501 4th Ave., 1620, Seattle, WA 98101-1662. TEL 206-587-6537. FAX 206-587-6540. Ed. Jon Biggs. adv. circ. 1,000. (back issues avail.) **Document type:** newsletter.

387.7   CN   ISSN 1015-8073
CARGO INTERCHANGE MESSAGE PROCEDURES MANUAL. a. $80. International Air Transport Association, 2000 Peel St., Montreal, PQ H3A 2R4, Canada. TEL 514-844-6311. FAX 514-844-3788. TELEX 05-267627.
Formerly (until 1988): Cargo I M P Manual (ISSN 0257-5019)
Description: Official source for message specifications covering space allocation, air waybill information, flight manifest, accounting, status, discrepancy, embargo and proposed airline-customs systems.

387.744   CN   ISSN 0256-3215
CARGO SERVICES CONFERENCE RESOLUTIONS MANUAL. 1980. a. $76 (effective 1995). International Air Transport Association, 2000 Peel St., Montreal, PQ H3A 2R4, Canada. TEL 514-844-6311. FAX 514-844-3788. TELEX 05-267627.
Description: Contains all the agreed procedures and documentation for international, interline air cargo transportation.

387.744   CN
CARGO TARIFF COORDINATING CONFERENCES RESOLUTIONS MANUAL. a. $120. International Air Transport Association, 2000 Peel St., Montreal, PQ H3A 2R4, Canada. TEL 514-844-6311. FAX 514-844-3788. TELEX 05-267627.
Description: Contains the text of all resolutions adopted by the Cargo Tariff Coordinating Conferences, together with details of corresponding government reservations.

387.7   NE   ISSN 0925-7748
CARGOVISION. (Text in English) 1986. bi-m. free. K L M Royal Dutch Airlines, Information and Documentation Department, Postbus 7700, 1117 ZL Schipol, Netherlands. TEL 31-20-6494545. FAX 31-20-6439261. Ed. Mairiona McInally Kier. charts; illus.; stat.; circ. 40,000. (controlled). (back issues avail.) **Document type:** trade publication.
Description: Publication from KLM Cargo covering worldwide cargo news and information, company activities, international trade and freight market, airports, and profiles of cities served by KLM Cargo.

387.7   US   ISSN 0069-1437
HE9803.A1
CENSUS OF U.S. CIVIL AIRCRAFT. 1965. a. $8.50. U.S. Federal Aviation Administration., Office of Management Systems, 800 Independence Ave., S.W., Washington, DC 20591. TEL 202-655-4000. (Orders to: National Technical Information Service, 5285 Port Royal Rd., Springfield, VA 22161. TEL 703-487-4630. FAX 703-321-8547; Or: Bernan, 4611-F Assembly Dr., Lanham, MD 20706. TEL 301-459-7666. FAX 301-459-0056) **Document type:** government publication.

CESTE I MOSTOVI/ROADS AND BRIDGES. see *ENGINEERING — Civil Engineering*

387.7   HK
CIVIL AIRCRAFT ACCIDENT REPORTS. (Text in English) irreg., latest 1979. price varies. (Civil Aviation Department) Government Publication Centre, G.P.O. Bldg., Ground Fl., Connaught Place, Hong Kong, Hong Kong. TEL 5-8428801. (Subscr. to: Director of Information Services, Information Services Dept., 1 Battery Path, G-F, Central, Hong Kong) Ed.Bd.

629.13   UK
CIVIL AIRCRAFT AIRWORTHINESS INFORMATION AND PROCEDURES. Abbreviated title: C A A I P. (Subseries of: Civil Aviation Publications) base vol. plus irreg. updates. £83. Civil Aviation Authority, Printing and Publication Services, Greville House, 37 Gratton Rd., Cheltenham, Glos. GL50 2BN, England. TEL 01242-235151. FAX 01242-584139. (looseleaf format) **Document type:** government publication.
Description: Gives general information on various matters regarding civil aircraft manufacture, overhaul, repair, maintenance, operation and policies.

387.7 331.88   UK
CIVIL AVIATION NEWS; the paper that unites all aviation workers. 1978. bi-m. £2($5) Community Centre, F.C.A., Hanworth Rd., Feltham, Middx, England. adv.; bk.rev. circ. 10,000.

CIVIL AVIATION STATISTICS OF THE WORLD (YEAR). see *TRANSPORTATION — Abstracting, Bibliographies, Statistics*

387.7   UK   ISSN 0960-9024
CIVIL AVIATION TRAINING. Short title: C A T. 1990. q. £16($32) Monch UK Ltd., 84 Alexandra Rd., Farnborough, Hants GU14 6DD, England. TEL 01252-517974. FAX 01252-512714. Ed. Trevor Nash; Pub. Andrew Smith. adv. contact: Stephen Marston. circ. 12,000 (controlled). **Document type:** trade publication.
Description: Provides reports on training within air carriers for airlines, training centers, pilot schools, and trade bodies.

CIVIL TRANSPORT DATA SHEETS. see *AERONAUTICS AND SPACE FLIGHT*

387.7   GW
COCKPIT REPORT. (Text in German) 1972. bi-m. free. Vereinigung Cockpit e.V., Lerchesbergring 24, 60598 Frankfurt a.M., Germany. TEL 069-681065. FAX 069-682678. circ. 800. **Document type:** bulletin.

387.7   US   ISSN 1040-5402
COMMUTER - REGIONAL AIRLINE NEWS. w. $595 (effective 1994). Phillips Business Information, Inc., 1201 Seven Locks Rd., Potomac, MD 20854. TEL 301-424-3338. FAX 301-309-3487. E-mail: pbi@phillips.com. Ed. Benet Wilson. adv. **Document type:** newsletter.
●Also available online. Vendor(s): Data-Star, Knight-Ridder, Inc., NewsNet (AE25).
—CCC.

387.7   US   ISSN 1056-0254
COMMUTER REGIONAL AIRLINE NEWS INTERNATIONAL. 1987. w. $595 (foreign £395) (effective 1995). Phillips Business Information, Inc., 120 Seven Locks Rd., Potomac, MD 20854. TEL 301-424-3338. FAX 301-309-3847. E-mail: pbi@phillips.com. Ed. Kristin Solheim. **Document type:** newsletter.
●Also available online. Vendor(s): NewsNet (AE26).
—CCC.

387.7   UK   ISSN 0265-4504
COMMUTER WORLD. 1984. 6/yr. £35(£70) Shephard Press Ltd., 111 High St., Burnham, Bucks. SL1 7JZ, England. TEL 01628-604311. FAX 01628-664334. Ed. Ian Harbison. circ. 11,341. **Document type:** trade publication.

CONCISE; aerospace news from the commonwealth of independent states. see *AERONAUTICS AND SPACE FLIGHT*

387.7 628   US   ISSN 1054-1241
CONSERVATION AERONAUTICS. 1975. q. $15 membership. International Association of Natural Resource Pilots, c/o Fred Kruger, Box 309, Spooner, WI 54801. TEL 715-635-4169. FAX 715-635-4105. Ed. Francis Satterlee. adv. contact: Fred Kruger. circ. 200. **Document type:** newsletter.
Formerly: Conservation Aviation.
Description: Geared toward pilots engaged in in-flight environmental observation.

387   AT
CONTACT (SOUTH YORRA). 1945. q. free. Royal Australian Air Force Association, Victoria Division, 4 Cromwell Rd., S. Yarra, Vic. 3141, Australia. TEL 61-3-8268573. FAX 61-3-8264739. adv.; bk.rev. circ. 3,500. **Indexed:** AESIS. **Document type:** newspaper.

387.7   US
CONTRACTIONS HANDBOOK. base vol. (plus irreg. updates). $66 (foreign $82.50). U.S. Federal Aviation Administration, 800 Independence Ave., S.W., Washington, DC 20591. TEL 202-267-3484. (Subscr. to: Superintendent of Documents, U.S. Government Printing Office, Box 371954, Pittsburgh, PA 15250-7954. TEL 202-512-1800. FAX 202-512-2250) (looseleaf format) **Document type:** government publication.
Description: Lists all the approved word and phrase contractions used by F.A.A. personnel and by other organizations providing air traffic control, communications, weather, and other air navigation services.

387.736   FR   ISSN 1141-4804
CONTROL; magazine international de la navigation aerienne et des aeroports. 1972. q. 110 F. (foreign 130 F.) (typically set in Sep.). Association Professionnelle de la Circulation Aerienne, Aerogare Cedex 048, F-33700 Merignac, France. TEL 56-55-63-77. FAX 56-55-63-63. Ed. Michel Drobycheff; Pub. Jean-Pierre Bernard. adv. contact: Michele Bennavail. bk.rev. circ. 4,000. **Document type:** newsletter.
Description: Acts as a channel for the exchange of ideas and information related to air traffic, airports, communication, space, training, air transport, European policies.

387.7   US
CONTROLLER. 1981. fortn. Peed Corporation, Box 85310, Lincoln, NE 68501. TEL 402-477-8900. adv. circ. 192,852. (tabloid format)

TRANSPORTATION — AIR TRANSPORT

387.7 332.6 CN
CORPORATE AIR TRAVEL SURVEY. Abbreviated title: C A T S. 1989. a. price varies. International Air Transport Association, 2000 Peel St., Montreal, PQ H3A 2R4, Canada. TEL 514-844-6311. FAX 514-844-5286.
Description: Surveys international business travellers for opinions and attitudes toward air travel.

CORPORATE AVIATION SAFETY SEMINAR. PROCEEDINGS. see AERONAUTICS AND SPACE FLIGHT

387.7 US
D F W PEOPLE - THE AIRPORT NEWSPAPER. (Dallas - Fort Worth) w. $75. Wood Publications, Inc., 400 Fuller-Wiser, Ste. 125, Euless, TX 76039. TEL 817-540-4666. FAX 817-685-7562. Ed. Bill Leader; Pub. Jim Wood. adv. contact: Janie Ross. circ. 13,000 (controlled). **Document type:** newspaper.
Description: Directed to employees at D.F.W. International, Alliance and Meacham airports.

387.7 UK ISSN 0140-3672
DANGEROUS GOODS BULLETIN. 1977. biennial. Civil Aviation Authority, Printing and Publication Services, Grevile House, 37 Gratton Rd., Cheltenham, Glos. GL50 2BN, England. TEL 01242-235151. FAX 01242-584139. **Document type:** government publication, monographic series.

341.46 CN ISSN 0256-3266
DANGEROUS GOODS TRAINING PROGRAMME. 1983. a. International Air Transport Association, 2000 Peel St., Montreal, PQ H3A 2R4, Canada. TEL 514-844-6311. FAX 514-844-3788. TELEX 05-267627.
Description: For training all categories of staff who have a legal requirement for training in the carriage of dangerous goods by air.

341.46 UK
DECISIONS ON AIR TRANSPORT LICENCE APPLICATIONS. irreg. £30 (overseas £45). Civil Aviation Authority, Printing and Publication Services, Greville House, 37 Gratton Rd., Cheltenham, Glos. GL50 2BN, England. TEL 01242-235151. FAX 01242-584139. **Document type:** government publication.

387.7 US
DELTA AIR LINES FLEET FACTS (YEAR). (Part of Fleet Facts series.) 1992. a. $12.95 (series of 6 $59.95) (effective 1995 & 1996). Bostick Publications, Box 17181, Memphis, TN 38187. TEL 901-685-3343. Ed. Brian Bostick. **Document type:** consumer publication, trade publication.
Description: Lists all the aircraft in the Delta fleet, including serial and line numbers, first flight, previous owners and operators, engine type, and airframe modifications.

387.74 US
DELTA WORLDWIDE TIMETABLE. 1947. bi-m. Delta Air Lines, Inc., 1030 Delta Blvd., Dept. 790, Atlanta, GA 30320. TEL 404-715-5299. FAX 404-715-2731. adv.: B&W & color page $29720; trim 4 x 9. circ. 700,000. **Document type:** trade publication, directory.

DESIGNATORS FOR AIRCRAFT OPERATING AGENCIES, AERONAUTICAL AUTHORITIES AND SERVICES. see BIOLOGY

387.7 910.22 US
DETROIT NEWSPAPER AGENCY. TRAVEL DIRECTORY. biennial. free. Detroit Newspaper Agency, Travel Advertising, 615 W. Lafayette, Detroit, MI 48226. TEL 313-222-2326. FAX 313-222-6015. TELEX 810-221-7448. circ. 6,000. **Document type:** directory.
Formerly: Detroit News Travel Directory.

387.7 UK
DIRECTORY OF C A A APPROVED ORGANISATIONS. (Subseries of: Civil Aviation Publications) base vol. plus irreg. updates. £24. Civil Aviation Authority, Printing and Publication Services, Greville House, 37 Gratton Rd., Cheltenham, Glos. GL50 2BN, England. TEL 01242-584139. FAX 01242-584139. (looseleaf format) **Document type:** directory, government publication.
Description: Lists the names and addresses of C.A.A.-approved organizations.

341.46 IT ISSN 0391-2434
DIRITTO E PRATICA DELL'AVIAZIONE CIVILE. 1987. s-a. price varies. Casa Editrice Dott. A. Giuffre, Via Busto Arsizio 40, 20151 Milan, Italy. TEL 02-38009582. FAX 02-38009582.

E A A EXPERIMENTER; the "how to" magazine for the aircraft builder. (Experimental Aircraft Association, Inc.) see AERONAUTICS AND SPACE FLIGHT

387 510 EC
ECUADOR. DIRECCION DE AVIACION CIVIL. MATHEMATICS. m. Direccion de Aviacion Civil, P.O. Box 2077, Quito, Ecuador.

363.12 628 UN
EMERGENCY RESPONSE GUIDANCE FOR AIRCRAFT INCIDENTS INVOLVING DANGEROUS GOODS. (Editions in: English, French, Russian, Spanish) biennial. $15 (diskette version $200) (1995-1996 edition). International Civil Aviation Organization, Attn: Document Sales Unit, 1000 Sherbrooke St. W., Montreal, PQ H3A 2R2. TEL 514-285-8022. FAX 514-285-6769. TELEX 05-24513. (also avail. in diskette format)

ENROUTE; your complementary in-flight magazine. see TRAVEL AND TOURISM

ENVIRONMENTAL MONITOR. see ENVIRONMENTAL STUDIES

ENVIRONMENTAL REVIEW. see ENVIRONMENTAL STUDIES

ESSEX COUNTY COUNCIL. PLANNING. SUBJECT MONITORING REPORTS. STANSTEAD AIRPORT. see PUBLIC ADMINISTRATION — Municipal Government

341 NE
EUROPEAN AIR LAW; texts and documents. (Text in English) 1992. base vol. (plus irreg. updates, 2-3/yr.) fl.210($114) (effective 1994). Kluwer Law International (Subsidiary of: Wolters Kluwer N.V.), Postbus 85889, 2508 CN The Hague, Netherlands. TEL 31-70-3081500. FAX 31-70-3081515. (Dist. by: Libresso Distribution Centre, P.O. Box 23, 7400 GA Deventer, Netherlands. TEL 31-5700-33155. FAX 31-5700-33834; In N. America: Kluwer Law International, 675 Massachusetts Ave., Cambridge, MA 02139. TEL 617-354-0140. FAX 617-354-8595) Eds. Elmar Giemulla, Ronald Schmid. (looseleaf format)
Description: Compilation of EC legislation and case law of the European Court of Justice pertaining to aviation law, including all important European treaties and references to relevant literature.

341 NE
EUROPEAN AIR LAW ASSOCIATION CONFERENCE PAPERS. (Text in English) 1991. irreg., vol.4, 1993. price varies. Kluwer Law International (Subsidiary of: Wolters Kluwer N.V.), Postbus 85889, 2508 CN The Hague, Netherlands. TEL 31-70-3081500. FAX 31-70-3081515. (Dist. by: Libresso Distribution Centre, P.O. Box 23, 7400 GA Deventer, Netherlands. TEL 31-5700-33155. FAX 31-5700-33834; In N. America: Kluwer Law International, 675 Massachusetts Ave., Cambridge, MA 02139. TEL 617-354-0140. FAX 617-354-8595) (Co-publisher: Sakkoulas, GR) Ed. P. Dagtoglou. (back issues avail.) **Document type:** proceedings.
Description: Presents an overview of topics discussed at association conferences, covering a variety of legal, economic and regulatory issues in European air law.

387.7 UK ISSN 0959-1311
EUROPEAN BUSINESS AIR NEWS. 1989. 9/yr. £30. Stansted News Ltd., 134 South St., Bishop Stortford, Herts CM23 3BQ, England. TEL 01279-506670. FAX 01279-755147. Ed. David Wright. adv.: B&W page $4059, color page $6039; trim 297 x 420; adv. contact: Barry Dawkins. circ. 6,374. **Document type:** trade publication.
Description: Up to date news, political and product information for the European corporate and business aircraft owner and operator.

387.7 UN ISSN 0071-2558
EUROPEAN CIVIL AVIATION CONFERENCE (REPORT OF SESSION). (Issued as a subseries of Air Transport. Series D: Reports) (Editions in English, French) 1955. triennial since 1961 with intermediate sessions; triennial 15th, 1993; intermediate 22nd 1993. free. European Civil Aviation Conference, 3 bis, Villa Emile-Bergerat, 92522 Neuilly sur Seine Cedex, France. TEL 46-37-96-45. FAX 46-24-18-18. (reprint service avail.)

387.7 UK ISSN 1352-9420
EUROPEAN HELICOPTER ASSOCIATION HANDBOOK. Key Title: European Helicopter Association Information Handbook. 1972. a. $10. (European Helicopter Association) Shephard Press Ltd., 111 High St., Burnham, Bucks. SL1 7JZ, England. TEL 01628-604311. FAX 01628-664334. Ed. Capt. E.H. Brown. adv. circ. 2,000. **Document type:** trade publication.
Formerly (until 1987): British Helicopter Advisory Board Handbook.

387.7 US ISSN 1057-9648
HE9761.1
F A A AVIATION NEWS. 1962. bi-m. $16 (foreign $20) (effective 1995). U.S. Federal Aviation Administration, 800 Independence Ave., S.W., Washington, DC 20591. TEL 202-267-8017. FAX 202-366-7060. (Subscr. to: Superintendent of Documents, U.S. Government Printing Office, Box 371954, Pittsburgh, PA 15250-7954. TEL 202-512-1800) Ed. Phyllis Duncan. charts; illus.; stat. circ. 35,000. (also avail. in microform from MIM,UMI; back issues avail.; reprint service avail. from UMI) **Indexed:** Ind.U.S.Gov.Per., Mid.East: Abstr.& Ind. **Document type:** government publication, newsletter.
—BLDSC (3863.050000); UMI.
Formerly: F A A General Aviation News (ISSN 0362-7942); **Continues:** F A A Aviation News (ISSN 0014-553X)
Description: Discusses F.A.A. regulations and directives to enhance aviation safety; also updates student and professional pilots on rule changes and contains reference information on such matters as aircraft maintenance, avionics, and accident analysis and prevention.

387.7 US ISSN 1056-2761
TL553.5
F A A AVIATION SAFETY JOURNAL. 1991. q. U.S. Federal Aviation Administration, Safety Information Staff, ASF-20, 800 Independence Ave., S.W., Washington, DC 20591. **Document type:** government publication.
—UnCover.

F A N S FACTS SHEET. (Future Air Navigation Systems) see AERONAUTICS AND SPACE FLIGHT

387.74 614.86 US
FACTS AND ADVICE FOR AIRLINE PASSENGERS. 1979. biennial. $5. Aviation Consumer Action Project, Box 19029, Washington, DC 20036. TEL 202-638-4000. Ed.Bd. **Document type:** consumer publication.
Description: Shows how to avoid or minimize the inconvenience of airline service problems.

387.73 US
FEDERAL AVIATION ADMINISTRATION: HIGH ALTITUDE POLLUTION PROGRAM. biennial. Federal Aviation Administration, Office of Environment and Energy, Washington, DC 20591.

387.7 US
FEDERAL EXPRESS FLEET FACTS (YEAR). (Part of Fleet Facts series) 1992. a. $10.95 (series of 6 $59.95). Bostick Publications, Box 17181, Memphis, TN 38187. TEL 901-685-3343. Ed. Brian Bostick. **Document type:** consumer publication, trade publication.
Description: Provides airliner enthusiasts with information on all the aircraft in the Federal Express fleet, along with serial and line numbers, date of first flight, previous owners and operators, engine types, and airframe modifications.

FLAP INTERNACIONAL; revista latinoamericana de aviacao. see AERONAUTICS AND SPACE FLIGHT

TRANSPORTATION — AIR TRANSPORT

387.82 UK ISSN 0269-3984
FLIGHT INTERNATIONAL DIRECTORY OF BRITISH AVIATION. 1977. biennial. £48($95) (N. America £60) (effective 1995). (Flight International) Flight International Directories, P.O. Box 1315, Potters Bar, Herts. EN6 1PU, England. TEL 01707-665151. FAX 01707-660330. Ed. Malcolm Ginsberg. adv.; circ. 3,000 (paid). **Document type:** directory.
  Incorporates: Who's Who in British Aviation; Formerly (until 1980): Flight Directory of British Aviation.
  Description: Lists about 1,350 U.K. companies involved in general, civil, and military aviation. Also lists important government agencies, flying clubs, and museums and organizations. Covers the Civil Aviation Authority and other U.K. government agencies.

387.7 UK ISSN 0263-7006
FLIGHT INTERNATIONAL DIRECTORY OF EUROPEAN AVIATION. 1982. biennial. £45($90) (N. America £60) (effective 1995). (Flight International) Flight International Directories, P.O. Box 1315, Potters Bar, Herts. EN6 1PU, England. TEL 01707-665151. FAX 01707-660330. Ed. Malcolm Ginsberg. adv.; circ. 2,000 (paid). **Document type:** directory.
  Incorporates: Who's Who in European Aviation; Formerly: Flight Directory of European Aviation.
  Description: Gives full information on civil and military aviation, airlines, air taxi companies, flying clubs, airports, aviation organizations, manufacturers of parts and equipment, and prominent persons in aviation.

387.7 614.8 US
FLIGHT SAFETY FOUNDATION. ANNUAL INDEX. a. Flight Safety Foundation, Inc., 2200 Wilson Blvd., Ste. 500, Arlington, VA 22201-3306. TEL 703-820-2777. FAX 703-820-9399.

387.7 341.46 US
FLIGHT SERVICES HANDBOOK. base vol. plus irreg. updates. $52 (foreign $65). U.S. Federal Aviation Administration, Office of Public Affairs, Department of Transportation, 800 Independence Ave., S.W., Washington, DC 20591. (Subscr. to: Superintendent of Documents, U.S. Government Printing Office, Box 371954, Pittsburgh, PA 15250-7954. TEL 202-512-1800. FAX 202-512-2250) (looseleaf format) **Document type:** government publication.
  Description: Prescribes procedures and phraseology for use by personnel providing flight assistance and communications services.

387.7 629.132 US
FLIGHTLINE. 1965. q. $21.50. Pilots International Association, Inc., 4000 Olson Memorial Hwy., Minneapolis, MN 55422. TEL 612-588-5175. Ed. Jason Rasmussen. circ. 6,000. (tabloid format) back issues avail.)
  Description: Covers general aviation topics. Provides membership information, safety tips.

387.742 331.8 US ISSN 0164-8691
HD6515.A43
FLIGHTLOG. 1962. bi-m. $14. Association of Flight Attendants, AFL-CIO, 1625 Massachusetts Ave., N.W., Washington, DC 20036. TEL 202-328-5400. FAX 202-328-5424. Ed. Jane Goodman. adv. contact: Darlene Dobbs. bk.rev. circ. 33,000. (back issues avail.) **Document type:** trade publication.
  Description: Covers labor union issues pertaining to member flight attendants; includes air safety and health issues, aviation industry news and trends.

387.7 GW
FLUGBEGLEITER; Bordbuch der Flugbereitschaft des Bundesministers der Verteidigung. 1991. q. free. ProPress Verlag GmbH, Am Buschhof 8, 53229 Bonn, Germany. TEL 0228-970970. FAX 0228-444296. circ. 15,000. **Document type:** government publication.

387.7 GW
FLUGBLATT; der aktuelle Report. 1969. 4/yr. Flughafen Stuttgart GmbH, Postfach 230461, 70624 Stuttgart, Germany. TEL 0711-948-0. FAX 0711-9482362. bk.rev. circ. 10,000. **Document type:** trade publication.

387.736 GW
FLUGHAFEN NACHRICHTEN DUESSELDORF. free. irreg. (6-8/yr.). Flughafen Duesseldorf GmbH, Public Relations Dept., Postfach 300363, 40403 Duesseldorf, Germany. TEL 0211-4212306. FAX 0211-4212760. TELEX 8584818. Ed. Peter Zarth. **Document type:** bulletin.
  Description: Reports about Duesseldorf Airport for airport staff and clients.

387.7 GW ISSN 0015-4563
DER FLUGLEITER. 1954. q. DM.10. Verband Deutscher Flugleiter, Schorndorferstr. 81, 73730 Esslingen a.N., Germany. TEL 0711-3160922. FAX 0711-3160922. Ed. Werner Fischbach. adv.; bk.rev.; bibl.; illus.; pat.; stat. circ. 3,000. (looseleaf format) **Document type:** newsletter.

387.7 GW
FLUGPLAN KOELN-BONN. 1952. 7/yr. free. Flughafen Koeln-Bonn GmbH, Postfach 980120, 51129 Cologne, Germany. FAX 02203-402743. Ed. Hanns Ley. adv. circ. 750,000. **Document type:** bulletin.

387.7 GW ISSN 0932-8238
FLUGUNFALL JAHRESBERICHT. 1964. a. Luftfahrt-Bundesamt, Flugunfalluntersuchungsstelle, Postfach 3054, 38020 Braunschweig, Germany. TEL 0531-2355-0. FAX 0531-2355246. **Document type:** bulletin.
  Former titles (until 1986): Ergebnisse der Fachlichen Untersuchung von Unfaellen bei dem Betrieb Deutscher Luftfahrzeuge im In- und Ausland sowie Auslaendische Luftfahrzeuge im Inland (ISSN 0178-8094); (until 1983): Ergebnisse der Fachlichen Untersuchung von Unfaellen bei dem Betrieb von Luftfahrzeugen (ISSN 0343-6594)

387.7 GW
FLUGUNFALLINFORMATION. m. DM.70. Luftfahrt-Bundesamt, Flugunfalluntersuchungsstelle, Postfach 3054, 38020 Braunschweig, Germany. TEL 0531-2355-0. FAX 0531-2355246. **Document type:** government publication.

387.7 UK
FLYER. 1990. m. £27.60 (overseas £45). Seager Publishing Ltd., The Little Theatre, St. Michael's Pl., Bath, Avon BA1 2SF, England. adv. contact: Jacqui Pitblado. (back issues avail.) **Document type:** consumer publication.
  Description: Covers all aspects of noncommercial aviation, particularly light aircraft.

387.7 PK ISSN 0046-4236
FLYER INTERNATIONAL; aviation and tourism. (Text in English) 1964. m. $75. (Azam Ali) Manhattan International Ltd., 187-3B-2 P.E.C.H. Society, Karachi 29, Pakistan. Ed. Ms. Semeen Jaffery. adv.; bk.rev.; charts; illus.; tr.lit. circ. 15,000.

387.72 SW ISSN 0015-4776
FLYGPOSTEN. Variant title: Nya Flygposten. 1954. q. SEK 45($8) (effective 1991). Svensk Pilotfoerening - Swedish Air Line Pilots Association, Olofsgatan 10, 111 36 Stockholm, Sweden. FAX 46-760-55649. Ed. Michael Agelii. adv.; illus. circ. 3,000.
  Formerly (until vol.6, 1955): Skandinavisk Flygpersonalfoerening.

387.7 UK ISSN 1355-1523
FOCUS ON COMMERCIAL AVIATION SAFETY. 1990. q. £12. (U K Flight Safety Committee) J M H Publishing, 7 Stafford Rd., Cornford Ln., Tunbridge Wells, Kent TN2 4QZ, England. TEL 01892-546446. FAX 0892-542369. Ed. R.C. Humphreyson. adv. contact: John Heath. circ. 17,500. **Document type:** bulletin.

629.13 350 UK
FOREIGN AIRWORTHINESS DIRECTIVES. C A A ADDITIONAL AIRWORTHINESS DIRECTIVES. (Subseries of: Civil Aviation Publications) 3 base vols. (plus irreg. supplements). £30.50 for vols. 1 & 2; vol. 3 £33.50. Civil Aviation Authority, Printing and Publication Services, Greville House, 37 Gratton Rd., Cheltenham, Glos. GL50 2BN, England. TEL 01242-235151. FAX 01242-584139. (looseleaf format) **Document type:** government publication.
  Description: Compiles C.A.A. Additional Airworthiness Directives for aircraft, engines, propellers, and other equipment manufactured in the U.S.

387.74 US ISSN 1046-0330
HE9803.A2
FREQUENT FLYER; for business people who must travel. 1980. m. $84 (effective 1995). Reed Travel Group, Part of the Reed Elsevier group (Subsidiary of: Reed Telepublishing), 500 Plaza Dr., Secaucus, NJ 07096. TEL 201-902-2000. FAX 201-902-1967. Ed. Laurie Berger. adv. contact: Gloria Lerner. circ. 226,000. **Document type:** consumer publication.
  ●Also available online.
  Formerly (until 1989): O A G Frequent Flyer (ISSN 0277-2108)
  Description: Provides travel tips for business people who must travel frequently.

387.7 AG
G A T A REPORT. (Guia Argentina de Trafico Aereo) w. G.A.T.A., Via Monte 723-9oD, 1053 Buenos Aires, Argentina. TEL 54-1-3228301. FAX 54-1-3220242. Ed. Raul Feldman. adv. contact: Monique Larrain. circ. 7,000 (paid). **Document type:** trade publication.

GAY AIRLINE & TRAVEL CLUB NEWSLETTER. see *HOMOSEXUALITY*

387.7 GW ISSN 0934-3571
GEFAHRGUT - DANGEROUS GOODS C D - R O M. (Issued in various editions) irreg. Springer-Verlag, Heidelberger Platz 3, 14197 Berlin, Germany. TEL 030-8207-0. FAX 030-820-7448. E-mail: orders@springer.de. (Orders in N. America to: Box 2485, Secaucus, NJ 07096-2991. TEL 800-777-4643. FAX 201-348-4505) charts; illus.; index.
  ●Available only on CD-ROM.
  Description: Offers information about environmentally risky substances from a combination of or all the following databases: Hommel, CHEMDATA, Swiss Operation Files, Merck, BAG Toxic Substances Lists, SUVA, VCI.

387.7 US
GENERAL AVIATION AIRCRAFT SHIPMENT REPORT. 1946. q. $3. General Aviation Manufacturers Association, 1400 K St., NW, Ste. 801, Washington, DC 20005. TEL 202-393-1500. FAX 202-842-4063. stat. circ. 1,500. (also avail. in microfiche from CIS; back issues avail.) **Indexed:** SRI.
  Formerly: General Aviation Airplane Shipment Report.

387.74 US
GENERAL AVIATION - HELICOPTER ACCIDENT REPORT; ongoing record of all general aviation accidents reported to the F A A. 1983. w. $1500. Andrews Publications, 1646 West Chester Pike, Box 1000, Westtown, PA 19395. TEL 610-399-6600; 800-345-1101. FAX 610-399-6610. Ed. Harry G. Armstrong. index. (looseleaf format; back issues avail.) **Document type:** newsletter.
  Formerly (until 1992): General Aviation Accident Report (ISSN 0887-7823)

GENERAL AVIATION STATISTICAL DATABOOK. see *TRANSPORTATION — Abstracting, Bibliographies, Statistics*

629.13 RU ISSN 0017-3606
CODEN: GRAVAC
GRAZHDANSKAYA AVIATSIYA. (Text in Russian) 1930. m. $68 (effective 1996). Ministerstvo Grazhdanskoi Aviatsii, Moscow, Russia. bk.rev.; illus.; index. **Indexed:** Chem.Abstr.

387.7 UK
GREAT BRITAIN. AIR TRANSPORT USERS COUNCIL ANNUAL REPORT. (Former name of issuing body (until Oct. 1993): Air Transport Users Committee) 1975. a. free. Air Transport Users Council, Kingsway House, 5th Fl., 103 Kingsway, London WC2B 6QX, England. TEL 0171-242-3882. FAX 0171-831-4132. circ. 4,000. **Document type:** corporate report.

387.742 UK
GREAT BRITAIN. CIVIL AVIATION AUTHORITY. AIR TRAVEL TRUST. ANNUAL REPORT AND ACCOUNTS. a. £8.50. Civil Aviation Authority, Printing and Publication Services, Air Travel Trust, Greville House, 37 Gratton Rd., Cheltenham, Glos. GL50 2BN, England. TEL 01242-235151. FAX 01242-584139. **Document type:** government publication.

TRANSPORTATION — AIR TRANSPORT

387.742 UK
GREAT BRITAIN. CIVIL AVIATION AUTHORITY. AIR TRAVEL TRUST COMMITTEE. ANNUAL REPORT. a. £8350. Civil Aviation Authority, Printing and Publication Services, Air Travel Trust Committee, Greville House, 37 Gratton Rd., Cheltenham, Glos. GL50 2BN, England. TEL 01242-235151. FAX 01242-584139. **Document type:** government publication.

629.13 UK
GREAT BRITAIN. CIVIL AVIATION AUTHORITY. AIRWORTHINESS NOTICES. (Subseries of: Civil Aviation Publications) base vol., plus irreg. updates. £15. Civil Aviation Authority, Printing and Publication Services, Greville House, 37 Gratton Rd., Cheltenham, Glos. GL50 2BN, England. TEL 01242-235151. FAX 01242-584139. (looseleaf format) **Document type:** government publication.
Description: Disseminates airworthiness information.

387.71 UK ISSN 0306-3569
HE9843.A1
GREAT BRITAIN. CIVIL AVIATION AUTHORITY. ANNUAL REPORT AND ACCOUNTS. 1949. a. £10. Civil Aviation Authority, Printing and Publication Services, Greville House, 37 Gratton Rd., Cheltenham, Glos. GL50 2BN, England. TEL 01242-235151. FAX 01242-584139. **Document type:** government publication, corporate report.
Formerly: Great Britain. Air Transport Licensing Board. Report (ISSN 0072-5617)

621.13 UK
GREAT BRITAIN. CIVIL AVIATION AUTHORITY. APPROVED AERIAL POSITIONS. (Subseries of: Civil Aviation Publications) base vol. plus irreg. updates. £18.45. Civil Aviation Authority, Printing and Publication Services, Greville House, 37 Gratton Rd., Cheltenham, Glos. GL50 2BN, England. TEL 0242-235151. FAX 0242-584139. (looseleaf format) **Document type:** government publication.
Description: Lists the approved antenna locations for B.C.A.R. compliance.

387.7 629.13 UK
GREAT BRITAIN. CIVIL AVIATION AUTHORITY. CIVIL AVIATION PUBLICATIONS. irreg., no.639. price varies. Civil Aviation Authority, Printing and Publication Services, Greville House, 37 Gratton Rd., Cheltenham, Glos. GL50 2BN, England. TEL 01242-235151. FAX 01242-584139. (back issues avail.) **Document type:** government publication, monographic series.
Description: Covers a wide range of technical, legal, regulatory, and professional aspects of civil aviation.

387.71 620.3 UK
GREAT BRITAIN. CIVIL AVIATION AUTHORITY. D O R A COMMUNICATION. irreg. price varies. Civil Aviation Authority, Printing and Publication Services, Greville House, 37 Gratton Rd., Cheltenham, Glos. GL50 2BN, England. TEL 01242-235151. FAX 01242-584139. **Document type:** government publication, monographic series.
Description: Covers various aspects of disturbances caused by aircraft noise.

387.71 620.3 UK
GREAT BRITAIN. CIVIL AVIATION AUTHORITY. D O R A REPORT. irreg. price varies. Civil Aviation Authority, Printing and Publication Services, Greville House, 37 Gratton Rd., Cheltenham, Glos. GL50 2BN, England. TEL 01242-235151. FAX 01242-584139. **Document type:** government publication, monographic series.
Description: Covers noise disturbance caused by aircraft.

387.71 620.3 UK
GREAT BRITAIN. CIVIL AVIATION AUTHORITY. D R REPORT. irreg. price varies. Civil Aviation Authority, Printing and Publication Services, Greville House, 37 Gratton Rd., Cheltenham, Glos. GL50 2BN, England. TEL 01242-235151. FAX 01242-584139. **Document type:** government publication, monographic series.
Description: Publishes studies on the effects of aircraft noise.

387.74 UK
GREAT BRITAIN. CIVIL AVIATION AUTHORITY. DATA SHEETS. irreg. price varies. Civil Aviation Authority, Printing and Publications Services, Greville House, 37 Gratton Rd., Cheltenham, Glos. GL50 2BN, England. TEL 0242-235151. FAX 0242-584139. **Document type:** government publication, monographic series.

387.42 UK
GREAT BRITAIN. CIVIL AVIATION AUTHORITY. DOCUMENT. Variant title: C A A Document. irreg., no.681. free. Civil Aviation Authority, Printing and Publication Services, Greville House, 37 Gratton Rd., Cheltenham, Glos. GL50 2BN, England. TEL 01242-235151. FAX 01242-584139. (back issues avail.) **Document type:** government publication, monographic series.

387.7 UK
GREAT BRITAIN. CIVIL AVIATION AUTHORITY. GENERAL AVIATION AIRMISS BULLETIN; a review of selected incidents. 3/yr. £5 (overseas £7). Civil Aviation Authority, Printing and Publication Services, Greville House, 37 Gratton Rd., Cheltenham, Glos. GL50 2BN, England. TEL 01242-235151. FAX 01242-584139. **Document type:** government publication, bulletin.
Formerly: Great Britain. Civil Aviation Authority. General Aviation Airmisses (ISSN 0144-2481)
Description: Describes near-misses involving small private aircraft.

387.7 UK ISSN 0309-667X
GREAT BRITAIN. CIVIL AVIATION AUTHORITY. GENERAL AVIATION SAFETY INFORMATION LEAFLETS. m. £12 (overseas £18). Civil Aviation Authority, Printing and Publication Services, Greville House, 37 Gratton Rd., Cheltenham, Glos. GL50 2BN, England. TEL 01242-235151. FAX 01242-584139. (looseleaf format) **Document type:** government publication.
Description: Reports on occurrences and selected aviation accidents and contains saftey information for owners and operators of small private aircraft.

387.74 UK
GREAT BRITAIN. CIVIL AVIATION AUTHORITY. GENERAL INFORMATION BULLETIN. 2/wk. £150 (£175 with subscr. to Navigation Warning Information Bulletin). Civil Aviation Authority, Printing and Publication Services, Greville House, 37 Gratton Rd., Cheltenham, Glos. GL50 2BN, England. TEL 01242-235151. FAX 01242-584139. (looseleaf format) **Document type:** government publication, bulletin.
Description: Collates current N.O.T.A.M. information.

387.7 UK
GREAT BRITAIN. CIVIL AVIATION AUTHORITY. INTERNATIONAL REGISTER OF CIVIL AIRCRAFT. (Supplements avail.) 1962. 4 base vols. (plus q. updates) (includes UK Register). £172 for base vols. (microfiche £114); UK and Irish Registers only £65; updates only £73 (microfiche £40). Civil Aviation Authority, Printing and Publication Services, Greville House, 37 Gratton Rd., Cheltenham, Glos. GL50 2BN, England. (also avail. in microfiche) **Document type:** government publication.
Description: Lists all aircraft registrations of more than 40 European and African nations. Also enumerates details of each aircraft as to its owner or operator, airworthiness certification, maximum take-off weight, and number of hours on the airframe.

387.7 UK ISSN 0141-9498
GREAT BRITAIN. CIVIL AVIATION AUTHORITY. LIBRARY BULLETIN. 1978. m. £40 (overseas £49). Civil Aviation Authority, Printing and Publication Services, Central Library, Greville House, 37 Gratton Rd., Cheltenham, Glos. GL50 2BN, England. TEL 01242-235151. FAX 01242-584139. bibl. **Document type:** government publication, bulletin, catalog.
Description: Reviews books, reports, and periodical articles available in C.A.A. libraries.

387.74 UK
GREAT BRITAIN. CIVIL AVIATION AUTHORITY. NAVIGATION WARNING INFORMATION BULLETIN. 2/wk. £75 (£175 with subscr. to General Information Bulletin). Civil Aviation Authority, Printing and Publication Services, Greville House, 37 Gratton Rd., Cheltenham, Glos. GL50 2BN, England. TEL 01242-235151. FAX 01242-584139. (looseleaf format) **Document type:** government publication, bulletin.
Description: Collates current N.O.T.A.M. information.

387.7 UK
GREAT BRITAIN. CIVIL AVIATION AUTHORITY. NEW REPORTABLE OCCURRENCES. fortn. £20 (overseas £35); with Occurrence Digest £55 (overseas £70). Civil Aviation Authority, Safety Data Analysis Unit, Fl. 2W, Aviation House, Gatwick Airport S., W. Sussex RH6 0YR, England. stat. **Document type:** government publication.

387.744 UK
GREAT BRITAIN. CIVIL AVIATION AUTHORITY. NOTICES TO A O C HOLDERS. (Air Operator's Certificate) base vol. plus irreg. updates. £18.50. Civil Aviation Authority, Printing and Publication Services, Greville House, 37 Gratton Rd., Cheltenham, Glos. GL50 2BN, England. TEL 01242-235151. FAX 01242-584139. (looseleaf format) **Document type:** government publication, trade publication, bulletin.

387.7 UK
GREAT BRITAIN. CIVIL AVIATION AUTHORITY. OCCURRENCE DIGEST. fortn. £35 (overseas £50); with New Reportable Occurrences £55 (overseas £70). Civil Aviation Authority, Safety Data Analysis Unit, Fl. 2W, Aviation House, Gatwick Airport S., W. Sussex RH6 0YR, England. stat. **Document type:** government publication.

387.7 UK ISSN 0306-4646
GREAT BRITAIN. CIVIL AVIATION AUTHORITY. OFFICIAL RECORD SERIES 1: LICENSING NOTICES. base vol. plus irreg. updates. £80 for series 1 and 2 (overseas £100); series 1-5 £95 (overseas £125). Civil Aviation Authority, Printing and Publication Services, Greville House, 37 Gratton Rd., Cheltenham, Glos. GL50 2BN, England. TEL 01242-235151. FAX 01242-235151. (looseleaf format) **Document type:** government publication.
Description: Includes legal instruments relating to air transport licenses, route licenses, and operating licenses. Also outlines C.A.A. procedures regarding these licenses.

387.7 UK ISSN 0306-4654
GREAT BRITAIN. CIVIL AVIATION AUTHORITY. OFFICIAL RECORD SERIES 2: NOTICES RELATING TO AIR TRANSPORT LICENSES, ROUTE LICENSES AND OPERATING LICENSES. base vol. plus irreg. updates. £80 for series 1 and 2 (overseas £100); series 1-5 £95 (overseas £125). Civil Aviation Authority, Printing and Publication Services, Greville House, 37 Gratton Rd., Cheltenham, Glos. GL50 2BN, England. TEL 01242-235151. FAX 01242-584139. (looseleaf format) **Document type:** government publication.

387.7 UK ISSN 0951-0036
GREAT BRITAIN. CIVIL AVIATION AUTHORITY. OFFICIAL RECORD SERIES 3: AIR TRAVEL ORGANISER LICENSING, PART 1. base vol. plus irreg. updates. £15 for series 3, parts 1 and 2 (overseas £20); series 1-5 £95 (overseas £125). Civil Aviation Authority, Printing and Publication Services, Greville House, 37 Gratton Rd., Cheltenham, Glos. GL50 2BN, England. TEL 01242-235151. FAX 01242-584139. (looseleaf format) **Document type:** government publication.
Supersedes in part: Great Britain. Civil Aviation Authority. Official Record Series 3: Air Travel Organiser Licensing (ISSN 0306-4662)
Description: Outlines A.T.O.L. requirements and procedures.

TRANSPORTATION — AIR TRANSPORT

387.7 UK ISSN 0951-0044
GREAT BRITAIN. CIVIL AVIATION AUTHORITY. OFFICIAL RECORD SERIES 3: AIR TRAVEL ORGANISER LICENSING, PART 2. base vol. plus s-a. updates. £15 for series 3, parts 1 and 2 (overseas £20); series 1-5 £95 (overseas £125). Civil Aviation Authority, Printing and Publication Services, Greville House, 37 Gratton Rd., Cheltenham, Glos. GL50 2BN, England. TEL 01242-235151. FAX 01242-584139. (looseleaf format) **Document type:** government publication, directory.
   Supersedes in part: Great Britain. Civil Aviation Authority. Official Record Series 3: Air Travel Organiser Licensing (ISSN 0306-4662)
   Description: Lists holders of Air Travel Organiser Licence holders by name, trading name, and A.T.O.L. number.

387.7 UK ISSN 0306-4670
GREAT BRITAIN. CIVIL AVIATION AUTHORITY. OFFICIAL RECORD SERIES 4: MISCELLANEOUS. base vol. plus irreg. updates. £6 for series 4 (overseas £9.50); series 1-5 £95 (overseas £125). Civil Aviation Authority, Printing and Publication Services, Greville House, 37 Gratton Rd., Cheltenham, Glos. GL50 2BN, England. TEL 01242-235151. FAX 01242-584139. (looseleaf format) **Document type:** government publication.

387.7 UK ISSN 0306-4689
GREAT BRITAIN. CIVIL AVIATION AUTHORITY. OFFICIAL RECORD SERIES 5: SCHEMES OF CHANGES. base vol. plus a. update. £95 includes series 1-4 (overseas £125). Civil Aviation Authority, Printing and Publication Services, Greville House, 37 Gratton Rd., Cheltenham, Glos. GL50 2BN, England. TEL 01242-235151. FAX 01242-584139. (looseleaf format) **Document type:** government publication.
   Description: Contains schemes to be paid to C.A.A. in connection with the performance by C.A.A. of specified functions.

387.7 UK ISSN 0951-0052
GREAT BRITAIN. CIVIL AVIATION AUTHORITY. OFFICIAL RECORD SERIES 6: AIRPORTS - ECONOMIC REGULATION, PART 1. base vol. plus irreg. updates. £12 for series 6, parts 1 and 2 (overseas £17). Civil Aviation Authority, Printing and Publication Services, Greville House, 37 Gratton Rd., Cheltenham, Glos. GL50 2BN, England. TEL 01242-235151. FAX 01242-584139. (looseleaf format) **Document type:** government publication.
   Supersedes in part: Great Britain. Civil Aviation Authority. Official Record Series 6: Airports - Economic Regulation.
   Description: Details what must be included in an application from an airport operator to levy fees.

387.7 UK ISSN 0951-0060
GREAT BRITAIN. CIVIL AVIATION AUTHORITY. OFFICIAL RECORD SERIES 6: AIRPORTS - ECONOMIC REGULATION, PART 2. base vol. plus irreg. updates. £12 for series 6, parts 1 and 2 (overseas £17). Civil Aviation Authority, Printing and Publication Services, Greville House, 37 Gratton Rd., Cheltenham, Glos. GL50 2BN, England. TEL 01242-235151. FAX 01242-584139. (looseleaf format) **Document type:** government publication.
   Supersedes in part: Great Britain. Civil Aviation Authority. Offical Record Series 6: Airports - Economic Regulation, Part 2.
   Description: Outlines C.A.A. decisions regarding applications by airport operators to levy fees.

387.74 UK
GREAT BRITAIN. CIVIL AVIATION AUTHORITY. PAPERS. Variant title: C A A Papers. irreg., no.94005. price varies. Civil Aviation Authority, Printing and Publication Services, Greville House, 37 Gratton Rd., Cheltenham, Glos. GL50 2BN, England. TEL 01242-235151. FAX 01242-584139. (back issues avail.) **Document type:** government publication, monographic series.

387.7 UK
GREAT BRITAIN. CIVIL AVIATION AUTHORITY. REPORTABLE A T C OCCURRENCES. (Air Traffic Control) m. £15 (overseas £30). Civil Aviation Authority, Safety Data Analysis Unit, Fl. 2W, Aviation House, Gatwick Airport S., W. Sussex RH6 0YR, England. stat. **Document type:** government publication.

387.7 UK
GREAT BRITAIN. CIVIL AVIATION AUTHORITY. REPORTABLE OCCURRENCES. m. £15 (overseas £30). Civil Aviation Authority, Safety Data Analysis Unit, Fl. 2W, Aviation House, Gatwick Airport S., W. Sussex RH6 0YR, England. stat. **Document type:** government publication.

621.13 UK
GREAT BRITAIN. CIVIL AVIATION AUTHORITY. TYPE CERTIFICATE DATA SHEETS. (Subseries of: Civil Aviation Publications) base vol. plus irreg. updates. £24. Civil Aviation Authority, Printing and Publication Services, Greville House, 37 Gratton Rd., Cheltenham, Glos. GL50 2BN, England. TEL 01242-235151. FAX 01242-584139. (looseleaf format) **Document type:** government publication.
   Description: Compiles Type Certificate Data Sheets, the part of the Type Certificate that signifies C.A.A. acceptance of an aircraft type for U.K. airworthiness certification.

GREAT LAKES PILOT NEWS. see *AERONAUTICS AND SPACE FLIGHT*

387.742 CC
GUANGZHOU MINHANG/GUANGZHOU CIVIL AVIATION. (Text in Chinese) bi-m. Guangzhou Minhang Baoshe, Baiyun Jichang (Airport), Guangzhou, Guangdong 510406, People's Republic of China. TEL 678901. Ed. Ma Tingwei.

387.72 MX
GUIA AEREA DE MEXICO Y CENTRO-AMERICA. 1968. m. Mex.$185($65) (effective 1994). Libros Especializados Editores, S.A., Schiller 108, Apdo. Postal 53-039, 11570 Mexico, D.F., Mexico. TEL 525-545-1628. FAX 525-2030712. Ed. Horacio Echeverria German. adv.: B&W page $1220, color page $1750; adv. contact: Sandra Lopez Arias. illus. circ. 5,500. **Document type:** trade publication.
   Description: Reference tool for travel professionals.

629.13 BL ISSN 0017-5145
GUIA AERONAUTICO. 1947. m. 1994. m. $120. Editora Guia Aeronautico Ltda., Rua Joao Alvares 27, 20220 Rio de Janeiro 14, RJ, Brazil. Ed. Ruy Costa Barros. adv.; charts. circ. 15,000.

387.74 AG ISSN 0326-1050
GUIA ARGENTINA DE TRAFICO AEREO. 1947. m. Arg.$350($350) (effective 1995 & 1996). Impresiones Newgate S.A., Viamonte 723-9oD, 1053 Buenos Aires, Argentina. TEL 54-1-3228301. FAX 54-1-3220242. Ed. Raul Feldman. adv. contact: Monique Larrain. circ. 8,000. (back issues avail.) **Document type:** trade publication.

629.133 BL
GUIA DO HELICOPTERO/HELICOPTER GUIDE. a. Aviacao em Revista Editora Ltda., Rua Ibiraja 322, 04310-020 Sao Paulo SP, Brazil. TEL 55-11-578-6277. FAX 55-11-578-6657. Pub. Helcio Estrella. adv.: B&W page $2956, color page $3300. circ. 10,000. **Document type:** directory.
   Description: Provides a review of the helicopter industry in Brazil. Lists products and services available in the Brazilian market.

387.7 BL
GUIA DO TAXI AEREO/AIR TAXI GUIDE. a. Aviacao em Revista Editora Ltda., Rua Ibiraja 322, 04310-020 Sao Paulo SP, Brazil. TEL 55-11-578-6277. FAX 55-11-578-6657. Pub. Helcio Estrella. adv.: B&W page $2956, color page $3300. circ. 10,000. **Document type:** directory.
   Description: Provides information on air taxi operation in Brazil.

387.736 IT
GUIDA AGLI AEROPORTI D'ITALIA. 1991. a. Ediman s.r.l., Corso S. Gottardo 39, 20136 Milan, Italy. TEL 39-2-58103791. FAX 39-2-58103789. Ed. Marco Biamonti. adv.: B&W page L.2800000, color page L.4300000. **Document type:** directory.

387.7 US
GUIDE TO FEDERAL AVIATION ADMINISTRATION PUBLICATIONS. a. free. U.S. Federal Aviation Administration, 800 Independence Ave., S.W., Washington, DC 20591. (Orders to: U.S. Department of Transportation, M-443.2, Washington, DC 20590. TEL 202-267-3484) **Document type:** government publication, catalog, bibliography.
   Description: Alerts pilots to new federal government publications on aviation.

GUILD NEWS. see *AERONAUTICS AND SPACE FLIGHT*

H A C TECHLINE. (Historical Aircraft Corporation) see *AERONAUTICS AND SPACE FLIGHT*

HADASHOT SAPANUT VETEUFAH - YIDION; shipping and aviation news. see *TRANSPORTATION — Ships And Shipping*

HANGKKONG ZHISHI/AEROSPACE KNOWLEDGE. see *AERONAUTICS AND SPACE FLIGHT*

387.7 US ISSN 0739-5728
HD9711.25.A1
HELICOPTER ANNUAL. 1983. a. $40 to non-members; members $20. Helicopter Association International, 1635 Prince St., Alexandria, VA 22314-2818. TEL 703-683-4646. Ed. Daniel P. Warsley. adv. contact: Melanie Beames. circ. 25,000. (also avail. in microfiche from CIS) **Indexed:** SRI. **Document type:** directory, trade publication.
   Description: A comprehensive reference guide for the civil helicopter industry. Includes helicopter specifications, industry statistics, membership directories, listings of international civil aviation contacts, aviation periodicals, and more.

387.7 629.1 US
HELICOPTER ASSOCIATION INTERNATIONAL. MAINTENANCE UPDATE. q. $50 to non-members; members $25. Helicopter Association International, 1635 Prince St., Alexandria, VA 22314-2818. TEL 703-683-4646; 800-425-4976. FAX 703-683-4745.
   Description: Provides a forum for mechanics and technicians to exchange information. Includes regulatory issues, airworthiness directives, and aircraft alerts.

387.7 US
HELICOPTER ASSOCIATION INTERNATIONAL. OPERATIONS UPDATE. m. $50 to non-members; members $25. Helicopter Association International, 1635 Prince St., Alexandria, VA 22314-2818. TEL 703-683-4646; 800-435-4976. FAX 703-683-4745. TELEX 89-615. Ed. Dan Warsley. circ. 1,000. (looseleaf format) **Document type:** trade publication.
   Description: Reports related to government and industry activities which affect helicopter operators.

HELICOPTER ASSOCIATION INTERNATIONAL. PRELIMINARY ACCIDENT REPORTS AND TECHNICAL NOTES. see *AERONAUTICS AND SPACE FLIGHT*

387.7 UK ISSN 0262-0448
HELICOPTER WORLD. 1981. m. £40($80) Shephard Press Ltd., 111 High St., Burnham, Bucks. SL1 7JZ, England. TEL 01628-604311. FAX 01628-664334. Ed. John Osmond; Pub. Ben Drew. adv. contact: Sandy Doyle. circ. 11,943. **Document type:** trade publication.

359 CN ISSN 0227-3160
HELICOPTERS. 1980. q. Can.$28($47) Corvus Publishing Group Ltd., 158 1224 Aviation Park N.E., Calgary, AB T2E 7E2, Canada. TEL 403-275-9457. FAX 403-275-3925. Ed. Paul J. Skinner. adv. contact: Paul J. Skinner. bk.rev. circ. 6,500. **Document type:** trade publication.
   Formerly: Helicopters in Canada (ISSN 0826-1237)

387.7 629.1 US ISSN 0882-6633
HELIPORT DEVELOPMENT GUIDE. biennial. $75 to non-members; members $45. Helicopter Association International, 1635 Prince St., Alexandria, VA 22314-2818. TEL 703-683-4646; 800-435-4976. FAX 703-683-4745. TELEX 89-615. **Document type:** trade publication.
   Description: Includes copies of selected FAA publications and lists consultants.

TRANSPORTATION — AIR TRANSPORT

387.7   UK   ISSN 0143-795X
HEREFORD'S AIR CARGO. European edition (ISSN 0144-3941); American edition (ISSN 0143-5906); Asia Pacific & Middle East edition (ISSN 0308-9940) 1972. s-a. Maclean Hunter Ltd., Chalk Ln., Cockfosters Rd., Barnet, Herts EN4 0BU, England. TEL 081-975-9759. FAX 081-975-9752. adv. **Document type:** directory.
—CCC.
    Formerly: Air Cargo.

387.7   UK   ISSN 0951-9637
HEREFORD'S WORLDWIDE. 1986. a. £40. MacLean Hunter Ltd., MacLean Hunter House, Chalk Lane, Cockfosters Rd., Barnet, Herts EN4 0BU, England. TEL 081-242-3000. FAX 081-242-3185. TELEX 299072-MACHUN-G. adv. circ. 7,850. **Document type:** trade publication.

387.74   HK
HONG KONG. CIVIL AVIATION DEPARTMENT. DIRECTOR'S ANNUAL REPORT. (Text in English) 1984. a. HK.$25. Government Publication Centre, G.P.O. Bldg., Ground Fl., Connaught Place, Hong Kong, Hong Kong. TEL 5-8428801. (Subscr. to: Director of Information Services, Information Services Dept., 1 Battery Path, G-F, Central, Hong Kong) Ed.Bd.

387.74   HK
HONG KONG AIRLINE TIMETABLE. (Text in English) 1978. m. HK.$240. Thomson Press Hong Kong Ltd., 202-203 Hollywood Centre, 233 Hollywood Rd., Hong Kong. TEL 815-9111. FAX 851-1933. Ed. George Wong. adv. (back issues avail.)
    Description: Contains airline flight schedules and information on hotels, consulates, holidays, events, currency conversion rates, airline codes, and airport taxes.

HUMAN FACTORS DIGEST. see BIOLOGY

387.71   CN
I A T A AIRPORT AND EN-ROUTE AVIATION CHARGES MANUAL. base vol. (plus updates 6-8/yr.) $500. International Air Transport Association, 2000 Peel St., Montreal, PQ H3A 2R4, Canada. TEL 514-844-6311. FAX 514-844-5286. (looseleaf format)
    Description: Details the airport and navigation charges made by over 200 national and supra-national authorities world-wide: landing fees, passenger services charges, parking, terminal navigation, noise, security and en route navigation charges.

387.7   CN
I A T A ANNUAL REPORT. (Director General's report to the Annual General Meeting of the International Air Transport Association) (Text in English, French and Spanish) 1945. a. free; limited distribution. International Air Transport Association, 2000 Peel St., Montreal, PQ H3A 2R4, Canada. TEL 514-844-6311. FAX 514-844-3788. TELEX 05-267627. circ. controlled.
    Formerly: State of the Air Transport Industry (ISSN 0081-4571).

387.7   CN
I A T A CITY CODE DIRECTORY. a. $360. International Air Transport Association, 2000 Peel St., Montreal, PQ H3A 2R4, Canada. TEL 514-844-6311. FAX 514-844-5286. (also avail. in magnetic tape)
    Description: World-wide list of city, country numerical and alphabetical codes, state, province or territory codes as well as currency alphabetical codes for use by the airline industry when computing tariffs and mileage.

387.7   CN   ISSN 0256-3223
I A T A DANGEROUS GOODS REGULATIONS. Key Title: Dangerous Goods Regulations. (Editions in Chinese, English, French, German, Spanish) 1957. a. $77 (effective 195). International Air Transport Association, 2000 Peel St., Montreal, PQ H3A 2R4, Canada. TEL 514-844-6311. FAX 514-844-3788. TELEX 05-267627. circ. 55,000.
—BLDSC (3518.810000).
    Description: Contains all provisions mandated by ICAO and all rules universally agreed by airlines to correctly package and safely transport dangerous goods by air.

387.7 629.1   CN   ISSN 1011-3266
I A T A - I A L AIR DISTANCES. 1974. a. $100. International Air Transport Association, 2000 Peel St., Montreal, PQ H3A 2R4, Canada. TEL 514-844-6311. FAX 514-844-3788. TELEX 05-267627.
    Description: Calculates distances between 40,000 city pairs for charter and non-scheduled flights. Also offers city coordinates and conversion tables.

387.71   CN
I A T A LIST OF TICKET AND AIRPORT TAXES AND FEES. 2 base vols. (plus q. updates) $535. International Air Transport Association, 2000 Peel St., Montreal, PQ H3A 2R4, Canada. TEL 514-844-6311. FAX 514-844-5286.
    Description: Lists more than 900 information records for over 580 different ticket and airport taxes and fees imposed in some 230 countries.

387.7   CN
I A T A PUBLICATIONS AND TRAINING MATERIAL AVAILABLE TO THE PUBLIC. (Text in English) 1979. a. free. International Air Transport Association, 2000 Peel St., Montreal, PQ H3A 2R4, Canada. TEL 514-844-6311. FAX 514-844-3788. TELEX 05-267627.
    Former titles: International Air Transport Association. Industry Automation and Finance Services Department. Publications; International Air Transport Association. Economics and Industry Finance Department. Bulletin; International Air Transport Association. Industry Research Division. Bulletin; International Air Transport Association. Industry Research Division. Service Information Bulletin.

387   CN   ISSN 0376-642X
I A T A REVIEW. (Text in English) 1966. 6/yr. free. International Air Transport Association, 2000 Peel St., Montreal, PQ H3A 2R4, Canada. TEL 514-844-6311. FAX 514-844-3788. TELEX 05-267627. circ. controlled.
    Formerly: I A T A News Review (ISSN 0085-199X)

387.74 341   UN
I C A O ABBREVIATIONS AND CODES. (Incorporates Amendments 1-20) (Editions in English, French, Russian, Spanish) irreg., 4th ed., 1989. $21. International Civil Aviation Organization, Attn: Document Sales Unit, 1000 Sherbrooke St. W., Montreal, PQ H3A 2R2, Canada. TEL 514-285-8022. FAX 514-285-6769. TELEX 05-24513.

387   UN   ISSN 1014-4412
I C A O CIRCULARS. Spanish edition: Circluar O A C I (ISSN 1014-4420); French edition: Circulaire O A C I (ISSN 1014-4439); Russian edition: Tsirkulyar I K A O (ISSN 1014-4447) 1968. irreg. price varies. International Civil Aviation Organization, Attn.: Document Sales Unit, 1000 Sherbrooke St. W., Montreal, PQ H3A 2R2, Canada. TEL 514-285-8022. FAX 514-285-3769. TELEX 05-24513. **Document type:** monographic series.

387 341   UN
THE I C A O FINANCIAL REGULATIONS. irreg., 8th ed., 1993. $4. International Civil Aviation Organization, Attn: Document Sales Unit, 1000 Sherbrooke St. W., Montreal, PQ H3A 2R2, Canada. TEL 514-285-8022. FAX 514-285-6769. TELEX 05-24513.

I C A O PUBLICATIONS AND AUDIO VISUAL TRAINING AIDS CATALOGUE. (International Civil Aviation Organization) see TRANSPORTATION — Abstracting, Bibliographies, Statistics

378 341   UN
I C A O PUBLICATIONS REGULATIONS. irreg., 7th ed., 1989. $3. International Civil Aviation Organization, Attn: Document Sales Unit, 1000 Sherbrooke St. W., Montreal, PQ H3A 2R2, Canada. TEL 514-285-8022. FAX 514-285-6769. TELEX 05-24513.

387.7   US   ISSN 0276-640X
TL501
ILLINOIS AVIATION. 1950. bi-m. $5. Department of Transportation, Division of Aeronautics, Capital Airport, Springfield, IL 62707. TEL 217-785-8516. Ed. John R. Nelson. circ. 25,000. (tabloid format) **Document type:** government publication.

INDIAN BRADSHAW. see TRANSPORTATION — Railroads

387.7 003   CN
INFORMATION TECHNOLOGY CATALOGUE. 2/yr. $220. International Air Transport Association, 2000 Peel St., Montreal, PQ H3A 2R4, Canada. TEL 514-844-6311. FAX 514-844-5286. **Document type:** catalog.
    Description: Focuses on automation products and services relevant to the airline industry.

387.74   US
INITIAL DECISIONS AND BOARD OPINIONS AND ORDERS IN SAFETY. irreg. (approx. 12/yr.) $380 in U.S., Canada, Mexico; elsewhere $760. (Department of Transportation, National Transportation and S.A., Federal Aviation Administration) U.S. National Technical Information Service, 5825 Port Royal Rd., Springfield, VA 22161. TEL 703-487-4630.
    Description: Decisions are made by the administrative law judges from the bench or in writing on whether the FAA had a right to suspend or revoke the airman certificate and whether the pilot violated regulations in a specific case.

INTER - CANADIAN. see CONSUMER EDUCATION AND PROTECTION

387.7   NE
INTERNATIONAL AIR SHOW GUIDE. (Text in English) 1981. a. fl.10. Flash Aviation, Postbus 855, 5600 AW Eindhoven, Netherlands. Ed. C. van den Heuvel. adv.; bk.rev. circ. 10,000.
    Formerly: Aviation Focus.

387.7   CN   ISSN 0303-3945
INTERNATIONAL AIR TRANSPORT ASSOCIATION. ANNUAL GENERAL MEETING. REPORTS AND PROCEEDINGS. (Text in English, French and Spanish) 1945. a. free. International Air Transport Association, 2000 Peel St., Montreal, PQ H3A 2R4, Canada. TEL 514-844-6311.
    Former titles: International Air Transport Association. Annual Report; Air Transport Association. Annual General Meeting Reports and Proceedings; International Air Transport Association. Bulletin (ISSN 0074-1329).

387.74   CN
INTERNATIONAL AIR TRANSPORT ASSOCIATION. LIST OF OPERATORS AT EACH AIRPORT. 2/yr. $35 per no. International Air Transport Association, 2000 Peel St., Montreal, PQ H3A 2R4, Canada. TEL 514-844-6311. FAX 514-844-5286.
    Description: Lists airlines that provide services at various world airports.

INTERNATIONAL AIR TRANSPORT NEWSLETTER. see OCCUPATIONAL HEALTH AND SAFETY

387.7   UK   ISSN 0443-7365
INTERNATIONAL AVIATION NEWS. 1948. m. $40. Romac Associates, 12 Nymans Court, Crawley, W. Sussex RH10 6PP, England. TEL 01293-523554. FAX 01293-523555. Ed. Richard Demmria. bk.rev. circ. 18,000. **Document type:** consumer publication.

INTERNATIONAL CIVIL AVIATION OGANIZATION. DIGESTS OF STATISTICS. SERIES OFOD. ON-FLIGHT ORIGIN AND DESTINATION/ORGANISATION DE L'AVIATION CIVILE INTERNATIONALE. RECEUIL DE STATISTIQUES. SERIE OFOD. ORIGINE ET DESTINATION PAR VOL/MEZHDUNARODNAYA ORGANIZATSIYA GRAZHDANSKOI AVIATSII. STATISTICESKI SBORNIK. SERIYA OFOD. NASALNY I KONESNY PUNKTY POLETA/ORGANIZACION DE AVIACION CIVIL INTERNACIONAL. COMPENDIO ESTADISTICO. SERIE OFOD. ORIGEN Y DESTINO POR VUELO. see TRANSPORTATION — Abstracting, Bibliographies, Statistics

387   UN   ISSN 0074-221X
K4093
INTERNATIONAL CIVIL AVIATION ORGANIZATION. AERONAUTICAL AGREEMENTS AND ARRANGEMENTS. ANNUAL SUPPLEMENT. (Text in English, French) 1965. a. $5. International Civil Aviation Organization, Attn: Document Sales Unit, 1000 Sherbrooke St. W., Montreal, PQ H3A 2R2, Canada. TEL 514-285-8022. FAX 514-285-6769. TELEX 05-24513.

TRANSPORTATION — AIR TRANSPORT

387.7   UN
INTERNATIONAL CIVIL AVIATION ORGANIZATION. AERONAUTICAL CHART CATALOGUE. (Text in: English, French, Russian, Spanish) irreg., 28th ed., 1993. $44. International Civil Aviation Organization, Attn: Document Sales Unit, 1000 Sherbrooke St. W., Montreal, PQ H3A 2R2, Canada. TEL 514-285-8022. FAX 514-285-6769. TELEX 05-24513. **Document type:** catalog.

387.74 341   UN
INTERNATIONAL CIVIL AVIATION ORGANIZATION. AIRCRAFT OPERATIONS. (Editions in English, French, Russian, Spanish) irreg. (in 2 vols.); 4th ed., 1993. $18 for Vol.1; Vol.2 $74. International Civil Aviation Organization, Attn: Document Sales Unit, 1000 Sherbrooke St. W., Montreal, PQ H3A 2R2, Canada. TEL 514-285-8022. FAX 514-285-6769. TELEX 056-24513.

387 341   UN
INTERNATIONAL CIVIL AVIATION ORGANIZATION. ANNEXES TO THE CONVENTION ON CIVIL AVIATION. (Editions in English, French, Russian, Spanish; occasionally in Arabic) irreg. price varies. International Civil Aviation Organization, Attn: Document Sales Unit, 1000 Sherbrooke St. W., Montreal, PQ H3A 2R2, Canada. TEL 514-285-8022. FAX 514-285-6769. TELEX 05-24513. (back issues avail.)

387 629.1   UN   ISSN 1014-0646
INTERNATIONAL CIVIL AVIATION ORGANIZATION. ASSEMBLY. MINUTES OF THE PLENARY MEETINGS. Arabic edition: Munazzamat al-Tayaran al-Madani al-Duwali. Al-Qararat al-Tacrir al-Wataiq. Al-Gamiyyat al-Umumiyyat (ISSN 1014-076X); French edition: Organisation de l'Aviation Civile. Assemble. Procedes Verbaux des Seances Plenieres (ISSN 1014-0662); Russian edition: Mezhdunarodnaya Organizatsiya Grazhdanskoi Aviatsii. Assambleya. Rezolutsii i Protokoly Plenarnogo Zhasedaniya (ISSN 1014-0654); Spanish edition: Organizacion de Aviacion Civil Internacional. Asamblea. Actas de las Sesiones Plenarias (ISSN 1014-0670) (Text in English) 1947. irreg., 29th, Montreal, 1992. $31. International Civil Aviation Organization, Attn: Document Sales Unit, 1000 Sherbrooke St. W., Montreal, PQ H3A 2R2, Canada. TEL 514-285-8022. FAX 514-285-6769. TELEX 05-24513. **Document type:** proceedings.

387   UN   ISSN 1014-0603
INTERNATIONAL CIVIL AVIATION ORGANIZATION. ASSEMBLY. REPORT AND MINUTES OF THE ADMINISTRATIVE COMMISSION. Arabic edition: Al-Taqrir - Munazzamat al-Tayaran al-Madani al-Duwali. Al-Gamiyyat al-Umumiyyat al-Dawarat. Al-Lagnat al-Idarriyyat (ISSN 1014-0751); French edition: Organisation de l'Aviation Civile Internationale. Assemble. Rapport et Procedes Verbaux de la Commission Administrative (ISSN 1014-0638); Mezhdunarodnaya Organizatsiya Grazhdanskoi Aviatsii. Assambleya. Doklady i Protokoly Administrativnoi Komissii (ISSN 1014-0611); Organizacion de Aviacion Civil Internacional. Asamblea. Informe y Actas de la Comision Administrativa (ISSN 1014-062X) (Text in English) 1947. irreg., 29th, Montreal, 1992. $17. International Civil Aviation Organization, Attn: Document Sales Unit, 1000 Sherbrooke St. W., Montreal, PQ H3A 2R2, Canada. TEL 514-285-8022. FAX 514-285-6769. TELEX 05-24513. **Document type:** proceedings.

387.7   UN   ISSN 0074-2376
INTERNATIONAL CIVIL AVIATION ORGANIZATION. ASSEMBLY. REPORT AND MINUTES OF THE ECONOMIC COMMISSION. (Editions in Arabic, English, French, Russian, Spanish) 1947. irreg., 29th, Montreal, 1992. $11. International Civil Aviation Organization, Attn: Document Sales Unit, 100 Sherbrooke St. W., Montreal, PQ H3A 2R2, Canada, Canada. TEL 514-285-8022. FAX 514-285-3769. TELEX 05-24513. **Document type:** proceedings.

387.7   UN   ISSN 0074-2368
INTERNATIONAL CIVIL AVIATION ORGANIZATION. ASSEMBLY. REPORT AND MINUTES OF THE LEGAL COMMISSION. Arabic edition: Al-Taqrir - Munazzamat al-Tayaran al-Umumiyyat al-Dawrat. Al Lagnat al-Qanumiyyat (ISSN 1014-045X); French edition: Organisation de l'Aviation Civile Internationale. Assemble. Rapport et Procedes de la Commission Juridique. (ISSN 1014-0417); Russian edition: Mezhdunarodnaya Organizatsiya Grazhdanskoi Aviatsii. Assembleya. Doklady i Protokoly Yuridicheskoi Komissii (ISSN 1014-0425); Organizacion de Aviacion Civil Internacional. Asamblea. Informe y Actas de la Comision Juridica (ISSN 1014-0409) 1947. irreg., 29th, Montreal, 1992. $7. International Civil Aviation Organization, Attn: Document Sales Unit, 1000 Sherbrooke St. W., Montreal, PQ H3A 2R2, Canada. TEL 514-285-8022. FAX 514-285-6769. TELEX 05-24513. **Document type:** proceedings.

387   UN   ISSN 1014-0565
INTERNATIONAL CIVIL AVIATION ORGANIZATION. ASSEMBLY. REPORTS AND MINUTES OF THE EXECUTIVE COMMITTEE. Arabic edition: Al-Taqrir - Munazzamat al-Tayaran al-Madani al-Duwali. Al-Gamiyyat al-Umumiyyat al-Dawarat. Al-Lagnat al-Tanfidiyyat (ISSN 1014-0727); French edition: Organisation de l'Aviation Civile Internationale. Assemble. Rapport et Procedes Verbaux du Comite Executif. Russian edition: Mezhdunarodnaya Organizatsiya Grazhdanskoi Aviatsii. Assambleya. Doklady i Protokoly Ispolnitel'nogo Komiteta (ISSN 1014-0581) (Text in English) 1947. irreg., 29th, Montreal, 1992. $32. International Civil Aviation Organization, Attn: Document Sales Unit, 1000 Sherbrooke W., Montreal, PQ H3A 2R2, Canada. TEL 514-285-8022. FAX 514-285-6769. TELEX 05-24513. (back issues avail.)
—BLDSC (4538.643000).

387.7   UN   ISSN 0074-235X
INTERNATIONAL CIVIL AVIATION ORGANIZATION. ASSEMBLY. RESOLUTIONS. (Editions in Arabic, English, French, Russian, Spanish) 1965, 15th. irreg., 29th, Montreal, 1982. $21. International Legal Aviation Organization, Attn: Document Sales Unit, 1000 Sherbrooke St. W., Montreal, PQ H3A 2R2, Canada. TEL 514-285-8022. FAX 514-285-3769. TELEX 05-24513.

387 341   UN
INTERNATIONAL CIVIL AVIATION ORGANIZATION. CONVENTIONS. (Text in English, French, Russian, Spanish) 1948. irreg. price varies. International Civil Aviation Organization, Attn: Document Sales Unit, 1000 Sherbrooke St. W., Montreal, PQ H3A 2R2, Canada. TEL 514-285-8022. FAX 514-285-6769. TELEX 05-24513. (back issues avail.)

387   UN
INTERNATIONAL CIVIL AVIATION ORGANIZATION. COUNCIL. ANNUAL REPORT. (Editions in Arabic, English, French, Russian, Spanish) a. $27. International Civil Aviation Organization, Attn: Document Sales Unit, 1000 Sherbrooke St. W., Montreal, PQ H3A 2R2, Canada. TEL 514-285-8022. FAX 514-288-6769. TELEX 05-24513. (also avail. in microfiche from CIS; back issues avail.) **Indexed:** IIS. **Document type:** corporate report.

INTERNATIONAL CIVIL AVIATION ORGANIZATION. COUNCIL TO CONTRACTING STATES ON CHARGES FOR AIRPORTS AND AIR NAVIGATION SYSTEMS. STATEMENTS. see BIOLOGY

INTERNATIONAL CIVIL AVIATION ORGANIZATION. DIGESTS OF STATISTICS. SERIES AF. AIRPORT AND ROUTE FACILITIES. FINANCIAL DATA AND SUMMARY TRAFFIC DATA/ORGANISATION DE L'AVIATION CIVILE. RECUEIL DE STATISTIQUES. SERIE AF. INSTALLATIONS ET SERVICES D'AEROPORT ET DE ROUTE. DONNES FINANCIERES ET STATISTIQUES DE TRAFFIC SOMMAIRES/MEZHDUNARODNAYA ORGANIZATSIYA GRAZHDANSKOI AVIATSII. STATISTICHESKI SBORNIK. SERIYA AF. AEROPORTNOE I MARSHRUTNOE OBORUDOVANIE. FINANSOVYE IZLOZHENIYA DANNYKH PO PERENOZHKAM/ORGANIZACION DE AVIACION CIVIL INTERNACIONAL. COMPENDIO ESTADISTICO. SERIE AF. INSTALACIONES Y SERVICIOS DE AEROPUERTO Y EN RUTA. DATOS FINANCIEROS Y RESUMEN DE DATOS DE TRAFICO. see TRANSPORTATION — Abstracting, Bibliographies, Statistics

INTERNATIONAL CIVIL AVIATION ORGANIZATION. DIGESTS OF STATISTICS. SERIES AT. AIRPORT TRAFFIC. see TRANSPORTATION — Abstracting, Bibliographies, Statistics

INTERNATIONAL CIVIL AVIATION ORGANIZATION. DIGESTS OF STATISTICS. SERIES F. FINANCIAL DATA - COMMERCIAL AIR CARRIERS. see TRANSPORTATION — Abstracting, Bibliographies, Statistics

INTERNATIONAL CIVIL AVIATION ORGANIZATION. DIGESTS OF STATISTICS. SERIES FP. FLEET - PERSONNEL - COMMERCIAL AIR CARRIERS. see TRANSPORTATION — Abstracting, Bibliographies, Statistics

INTERNATIONAL CIVIL AVIATION ORGANIZATION. DIGESTS OF STATISTICS. SERIES R. CIVIL AIRCRAFT ON REGISTER. see TRANSPORTATION — Abstracting, Bibliographies, Statistics

INTERNATIONAL CIVIL AVIATION ORGANIZATION. DIGESTS OF STATISTICS. SERIES TF. TRAFFIC BY FLIGHT STAGE. see TRANSPORTATION — Abstracting, Bibliographies, Statistics

INTERNATIONAL CIVIL AVIATION ORGANIZATION. DIGESTS OF STATISTICS. SERIES T. TRAFFIC, COMMERCIAL AIR TRAFFIC. see TRANSPORTATION — Abstracting, Bibliographies, Statistics

363.12 629.1   UN
INTERNATIONAL CIVIL AVIATION ORGANIZATION. GENERAL CONCEPT OF SEPARATION PANEL. REPORT OF THE MEETING. (Editions in English, French, Russian, Spanish) irreg., 7th, 1990. price varies. International Civil Aviation Organization, Attn: Document Sales Unit, 1000 Sherbrooke St. W., Montreal, PQ H3A 2R2, Canada. TEL 514-285-8022. FAX 514-285-6769. TELEX 05-24513. **Document type:** proceedings.

387.7   UN   ISSN 0074-2503
INTERNATIONAL CIVIL AVIATION ORGANIZATION. LEGAL COMMITTEE. MINUTES AND DOCUMENTS (OF SESSIONS). (Editions in English, French, Russian and Spanish) 1948. triennial, 29th, Montreal, 1994. $10. International Civil Aviation Organization, Attn: Document Sales Unit, 1000 Sherbrooke St. W., Montreal, PQ H3A 2R2, Canada. TEL 514-285-8022. FAX 514-285-6769. TELEX 05-24513. (back issues avail.) **Document type:** proceedings.

INTERNATIONAL CIVIL AVIATION ORGANIZATION. LOCATION INDICATORS. see BIOLOGY

387 341   UN
INTERNATIONAL CIVIL AVIATION ORGANIZATION. PROCEEDINGS AND ACTION. (Editions in English, French, Russian, Spanish) irreg., 122nd session. $12. International Civil Aviation Organization, Attn: Document Sales Unit, 1000 Sherbrooke St. W., Montreal H3A 2R2, Canada. TEL 514-285-8022. FAX 514-285-6769. TELEX 05-24513. (back issues avail.) **Document type:** proceedings.

387 341   UN
INTERNATIONAL CIVIL AVIATION ORGANIZATION. PROTOCOLS. irreg. price varies. International Civil Aviation Organization, Attn: Document Sales Unit, 1000 Sherbrooke St., W., Montreal, PQ H3A 2R2, Canada. TEL 514-285-8022. FAX 514-285-6769. TELEX 05-24513. (back issues avail.)

629.1   UN   ISSN 0074-2546
INTERNATIONAL CIVIL AVIATION ORGANIZATION. REPORT OF THE AIR NAVIGATION CONFERENCE. (Editions in English, French, Russian, Spanish) 1953. irreg., 10th, 1991. $37. International Civil Aviation Organization, Attn: Document Sales Unit, 1000 Sherbrooke St. W., Montreal, PQ H3A 2R2, Canada. TEL 514-285-8022. FAX 514-285-6769. TELEX 05-24513.

387 341   UN
INTERNATIONAL CIVIL AVIATION ORGANIZATION. RULES OF THE AIR AND AIR TRAFFIC SERVICES. (Incorporates Amendments 1-4) (Editions in English, French, Russian, Spanish) irreg., 12th ed., 1993. $44. International Civil Aviation Organization, Attn: Document Sales Unit, 1000 Sherbrooke St. W., Montreal H3A 2R2, Canada. TEL 514-285-8022. FAX 514-285-6769. TELEX 05-24513.

TRANSPORTATION — AIR TRANSPORT

INTERNATIONAL CIVIL AVIATION ORGANIZATION. SPECIAL COMMITTEE FOR THE MONITORING AND CO-ORDINATION OF DEVELOPMENT AND TRANSITION PLANNING FOR THE FUTURE AIR NAVIGATION SYSTEM (FANS - PHASE II). REPORT OF THE MEETING. see BIOLOGY

387.7 629.1   UN
INTERNATIONAL CIVIL AVIATION ORGANIZATION. VISUAL AIDS PANEL. REPORT OF THE MEETING. (Editions in: English, French, Russian, Spanish) irreg., 12th, 1991. $40. International Civil Aviation Organization, Attn: Document Sales Unit, 1000 Sherbrooke St. W., Montreal, PQ H3A 2R2, Canada. TEL 514-285-8022. FAX 514-285-6769. TELEX 05-24513. **Document type:** proceedings.

629.13   AT
▼**INTERNATIONAL DIRECTORY OF CIVIL AIRCRAFT (YEAR).** 1995. biennial. $17.95. Aerospace Publications Pty. Ltd., Weston Creek, A.C.T., Australia. Eds. Gerard Frawley, Jim Thorn. illus. **Document type:** directory.
   Description: Lists all civil aircraft in production and revenue service, giving for each type powerplant and performance specifications, dimensions, weights, production runs, and a brief history. Covers news and trends in civil aviation.

658   US   ISSN 0538-7442
INTERNATIONAL FEDERATION OF OPERATIONAL RESEARCH SOCIETIES. AIRLINE GROUP (A G I F O R S) PROCEEDINGS. 1961. a. $60. International Federation of Operational Research Societies, Airline Group, c/o Joe D. Hinson, Federal Express, 2831 Airways, Memphis, TN 38132. FAX 901-395-7451. circ. 300. (processed; back issues avail.) **Document type:** proceedings.

387.7
INTERNATIONAL FLIGHT ATTENDANTS ASSOCIATION NEWSLETTER. 3/yr. International Flight Attendants Association, c/o P.R. Miller, 2314 Old New Windsor Pike, New Windsor, MD 21776. **Document type:** newsletter.

387.7 387   US
INTERNATIONAL NAVIGATION ASSOCIATION NEWSLETTER. 3/yr. $35. International Navigation Association, Inc., Box 2324, Arlington, VA 22202-0324. Ed. Bob Revel. adv.: bk.rev. circ. 350. **Document type:** newsletter.
   Formerly (until 1993): International Omega Association Newsletter.
   Description: Technical, engineering and scientific interchange of information relating to long-range navigation.

INTERNATIONAL NOTICES TO AIRMEN. see AERONAUTICS AND SPACE FLIGHT

INTERNATIONAL OPERATIONS BULLETIN. see AERONAUTICS AND SPACE FLIGHT

387.7   CN
INTERNATIONAL SCHEDULED AND CHARTER FREIGHT FORECAST. a. $265. International Air Transport Association, 2000 Peel St., Montreal, PQ H3A 2R4, Canada. TEL 514-844-6311. FAX 514-844-3788. TELEX 05-267627. (also avail. in diskette format)
   Formerly: Freight Traffic Forecast.
   Description: Shows global and regional forecasts of air freight tonnage and highlights major historical and projected trends.

387.7   CN
INTERNATIONAL SCHEDULED PASSENGER FORECAST. a. $265. International Air Transport Association, 2000 Peel St., Montreal, PQ H3A 2R4, Canada. TEL 514-844-6311. FAX 514-844-3788. TELEX 05-267627. (also avail. in diskette format)
   Formerly (until 1994): Passenger Traffic Forecast.
   Description: Forecast giving a collective view of the world's major airlines on scheduled international passenger traffic prospects in the coming five years. Includes global as well as regional forecasts and highlights major historical and projected trends.

387.7   RU   ISSN 0202-7887
TL552
ITOGI NAUKI I TEKHNIKI: VOZDUSHNYI TRANSPORT. (Text in Russian) 1969. irreg., latest vol.18-19, 1989. 6.60 Rub. Vsesoyuznyi Institut Nauchno-Tekhnicheskoi Informatsii (VINITI), Baltiiskaya ul. 14, Moscow A-219, Russia. (Subscr. to: Mezhdunarodnaya Kniga, Dimitrova ul. 39, 113095 Moscow, Russia)
—BLDSC (0041.560000).

387.7 629.13   NE
341.46
J A R AMENDMENT SERVICE TO REGULATORY DOCUMENTS. irreg. £60 in the U.K. (overseas £75). Joint Aviation Authorities, J A R Headquarters, Saturnusstraat 8-10, P.O. Box 3000, 2130 KA Hoofddorp, Netherlands. TEL 31-2503-19700. FAX 31-2503-21714. (Also subscr. to: Civil Aviation Authority, Printing and Publication Services, Greville House, 37 Gratton Rd., Cheltenham, Glos. GL50 2BN, England. TEL 0242-235151. FAX 0242-584139) (also avail. in diskette format)
● Also available on CD-ROM.

387.7   SZ
J P AIRLINE FLEETS INTERNATIONAL. 1966. a. 72.50 SFr. (Europe 90 SFr.; overseas 125 SFr.). Bucher & Co., Publikationen, P.O. Box 44, CH-8058 Zurich - Airport, Switzerland. TEL 01-8741747. FAX 01-8741757. (Dist. in UK by: BuchAir (UK) Ltd., P.O. Box 89, Reigate, Surrey RH2 7FG, England. TEL 01737-224747. FAX 01737-226777; Dist. in US by: BuchAir (USA) Inc., Box 750515, Forest Hills, NY 11375-0515. TEL 718-349-4828. FAX 718-263-8748) Ed. Ulrich Klee. adv. contact: Frank E. Bucher. illus.; circ. 12,000 (paid). **Document type:** directory.
   Description: Lists for each airline each aircraft, along with serial number, year built, and airframe history.

387.7   UK
JANE'S AIR TRAFFIC CONTROL. 1982. a. £140($235) Jane's Information Group, Sentinel House, 163 Brighton Rd., Coulsdon, Surrey CR5 2NH, England. TEL 0181-763-1030. FAX 0181-763-1006. TELEX 916907-JANES-G. E-mail: http://www.janes.com/janes.html. (U.S. & Canada order from: Dept. DSM, 1340 Braddock Pl., Ste. 300, Box 1436, Alexandria, VA 22314-1651) Ed. David Rider. adv.; index. **Document type:** directory.
   Former titles (until 1993): Jane's Airport and A T C Equipment (ISSN 0264-0953); Jane's Airport Equipment.
   Description: International directory for the aviation ground support market, covering 1500 manufacturers of all categories of airport equipment with detailed product specifications.

387.736   UK   ISSN 0954-7649
HE9797.A1
JANE'S AIRPORT REVIEW. bi-m. £68($116) Jane's Information Group, Sentinel House, 163 Brighton Rd., Coulsdon, Surrey CR5 2NH, England. TEL 0181-763-1030. FAX 0181-763-1006. TELEX 916907-JANES-G. E-mail: http://www.janes.com/janes.html. **Document type:** trade publication.
   ● Also available online. Vendor(s): Knight-Ridder, Inc..
—BLDSC (4645.975000). **CCC.**
   Description: For senior executives in the airport management, airlines and air traffic control, and national and international regulatory authorities. Covers new products and services.

JANE'S AIRPORTS AND HANDLING AGENTS. see BUSINESS AND ECONOMICS — Trade And Industrial Directories

JANE'S INFORMATION UPDATE. ALL THE WORLD'S AIRCRAFT. see AERONAUTICS AND SPACE FLIGHT

387.7   UK
JANE'S WORLD AIRLINES. base vol. (plus q. updates). £595($990) Jane's Information Group, Sentinel House, 163 Brighton Rd., Coulsdon, Surrey CR5 2NH, England. TEL 0181-763-1030. FAX 0181-763-1006. TELEX 916907-JANES-G. E-mail: http://www.janes.com/janes.html. Ed. Danny Pratt; Pub. Robert Hutchinson. adv. contact: Richard West. **Document type:** trade publication.
   Description: Airline-by-airline reports covering airline structure and operations; includes fleet structure, routes operated, traffic statistics and financial data.

387.7 658.8   US   ISSN 0021-6003
JET CARGO NEWS; for air shipping decision makers. 1968. m. $30 (foreign $45). Hagall Publishing Co., Box 920952, Ste. 398, Houston, TX 77292-0952. TEL 713-681-4760. FAX 713-682-3871. Ed. Jennifer Gibson. adv.: B&W page $3480; adv. contact: Regina Michael. bk.rev.; charts; illus. circ. 23,000. (tabloid format) **Document type:** trade publication.
   Description: Dedicated to providing the air shipping industry with timely, factual news related to domestic and international movement of goods by air and the purchase of shipping equipment, services and supplies.

387.7 333   US
JET FUEL INTELLIGENCE. 1991. 51/yr. $1975 includes fax service (effective 1993). Petroleum & Energy Intelligence Weekly, Inc., 575 Broadway, 4th Fl., New York, NY 10012-3230. TEL 212-941-5500. FAX 212-941-5508. Ed. Cristina Haus; Pub. Edward Morse. **Document type:** trade publication.
   Description: Follows developments in the international aviation fuels trade, including airport by airport jet fuel and spot cargo pricing, regional trends, and other factors influencing the market.

387.7   US
JETRADER.* m. International Society of Transport Aircraft Traders, 6300 N. River Rd. Ste. 727, Rosemont, IL 60018-4226. TEL 708-698-1632. FAX 708-823-0536. TELEX 5101011287 CRNEWS ISTAT.

387.7 910.09   SZ
JETSTREAM AIR NEWS; Swiss aviation magazine. 1961. m. 42 Fr. Postfach 1130, CH-8058 Zurich-Airport, Switzerland. Ed. Martin Hirzel. adv. circ. 5,000. (back issues avail.)

387.7 629.13   NE
JOINT AVIATION AUTHORITIES. CERTIFICATION INFORMATION - PROCEDURES. base vol. plus q. updates. £90 in the U.K. (overseas £105). Joint Aviation Authorities, J A A Headquarters, Saturnusstraat 8-10, P.O. Box 3000, 2130 KA Hoofddorp, Netherlands. TEL 31-2503-79700. FAX 31-2503-21714. (Also subscr. to: Civil Aviation Authority, Printing and Publication Services, Greville House, 37 Gratton Rd., Cheltenham, Glos. GL50 2BN, England. TEL 0242-235151. FAX 0242-584139) (also avail. in diskette format)
● Also available on CD-ROM.

387.7   NE
JOINT AVIATION AUTHORITIES. GENERAL INFORMATION - PROCEDURES. INFORMATION LEAFLETS. base vol. plus q. updates. £75 in the U.K. (overseas £90). Joint Aviation Authorities, J A A Headquarters, Saturnusstraat 8-10, P.O. Box 3000, 2130 KA Hoofddorp, Netherlands. TEL 31-2503-79700. FAX 31-2503-21714. (Also avail. from: Civil Aviation Authority, Printing and Publication Services, Greville House, 37 Gratton Rd., Cheltenham, Glos. GL50 2BN, England. TEL 0242-235151. FAX 0242-584139) (also avail. in diskette format)
● Also available on CD-ROM.

387.7 629.13   NE
JOINT AVIATION AUTHORITIES. MAINTENANCE INFORMATION - PROCEDURES. base vol. plus q. updates. £80 in the U.K. (overseas £90). Joint Aviation Authorities, J A A Headquarters, Saturnusstraat 8-10, P.O. Box 3000, 2130 KA Hoofddorp, Netherlands. TEL 31-2503-79700. FAX 31-2503-21714. (Also subscr. to: Civil Aviation Authority, Printing and Publication Services, Greville House, 37 Gratton Rd., Cheltenham, Glos. GL50 2BN, England. TEL 0242-235151. FAX 0242-584139) (also avail. in diskette format)
● Also available on CD-ROM.

387.7 629.13   NE
341.46
JOINT AVIATION AUTHORITIES. NOTICE OF PROPOSED AMENDMENT SCHEME. irreg. £60 in the U.K. (overseas £85). Joint Aviation Authorities, J A A Headquarters, Saturnusstraat 8-10, P.O. Box 3000, 2130 KA Hoofddorp, Netherlands. TEL 31-2503-79700. FAX 31-2503-21714. (Also subscr. to: Civil Aviation Authority, Printing and Publication Services, Greville House, 37 Gratton Rd., Cheltenham, Glos. GL50 2BN, England. TEL 0242-235151. FAX 0242-584139) (also avail. in diskette format)
● Also available on CD-ROM.

TRANSPORTATION — AIR TRANSPORT

387.7 629.13
341.46 NE
JOINT AVIATION AUTHORITIES. REGULATORY DOCUMENTS. irreg. price varies. Joint Aviation Authorities, J A A Headquarters, Saturnusstraat 8-10, P.O. Box 3000, 2130 KA Hoofdorp, Netherlands. TEL 31-2503-79700. FAX 31-2503-21714. (Also subscr. to: Civil Aviation Authority, Greville House, 37 Gratton Rd., Cheltenham, Glos. GL50 2BN, England. TEL 0242-235151. FAX 0242-584139) (also avail. in diskette format)
●Also available on CD-ROM.

341.46 AG
JORNADAS NACIONALES DE DERECHO AERONAUTICO Y ESPACIAL. TRABAJOS. irreg. $15 per no. Universidad Nacional de Cordoba, Instituto de Derecho Aeronautico y Espacial y de las Telecomunicaciones de Cordoba, Ituzaingo 87, piso 4, Local 10, 5000 Cordoba, Argentina. TEL 43138. TELEX 51.418 LOREN AR.

JOURNAL OF AIR TRANSPORT MANAGEMENT. see BUSINESS AND ECONOMICS — Management

387.7 NE ISSN 0022-7374
K L M NEWS. (Text in Dutch, English) 1946. irreg. fl.60. K L M Royal Dutch Airlines, Information and Documentation Department, Postbus 7700, 1117 ZL Schiphol, Netherlands. Ed.Bd.

387.7 UK ISSN 0951-6735
KEY NOTE REPORT: AIRLINES. Variant title: Airlines. 1981. irreg. £185. Key Note Publications Ltd., Field House, 72 Oldfield Rd., Hampton, Middlesex TW12 2HQ, England. TEL 0181-783-0755. FAX 0181-783-1720. **Document type**: trade publication.
●Also available online.
Also available on CD-ROM.
—BLDSC (0784.537700).

387.7 UK
KEY NOTE REPORT: AIRPORTS. Variant title: Airports. irreg. £185. Key Note Publications Ltd., Field House, 72 Oldfield Rd., Hampton, Middlesex TW12 2HQ, England. TEL 0181-783-0755. FAX 0181-783-1720. **Document type**: trade publication.
●Also available online.
Also available on CD-ROM.

387.7 GW
L B A INFO. 1988. q. Luftfahrt-Bundesamt, Postfach 3054, 38020 Braunschweig, Germany. TEL 0531-2355-0. FAX 0531-2355254. Ed. Klaus Neufeldt. circ. 2,500. **Document type**: government publication.

387.7 CN
LEADING EDGE. 1992. s-a. free to qualified personnel. Canadian Business Aircraft Association, 1317 50 O'Connor St., Ottawa, ON K1P 6L2, Canada. TEL 613-236-5611. FAX 613-236-2361. Ed. Darrell Eagles. adv. contact: Janet Maslin. circ. 1,000. (back issues avail.) **Document type**: trade publication.
Description: Contains articles of association and business aviation community's activities.

387.7 385 FR ISSN 0756-8037
LETTRE CONFIDENTIELLE DES TRANSPORTS. (Text in French) 1974. w. 2132 Fr. Societe Generale d'Editions Techniques (SOGETEC), 249 rue Lecourbe, 75015 Paris, France. TEL 48-28-73-14. Ed. Elie Le Du. bk.rev. circ. 1,000.

266 387.7 US
LIFE LINK. 1945. a. free or donation. Mission Aviation Fellowship, 1849 Wabash Ave., Box 3202, Redlands, CA 92373. TEL 909-794-1151. FAX 909-794-3016. Ed. Ghislaine F. Benney. circ. 50,000. **Document type**: consumer publication.
Former titles: Mission Aviation; Missionary Aviation (ISSN 0026-6043)
Description: Covers the activities of the organization, a Christian air service operating in the Third World.

387.7 US
LIGHT AIRCRAFT MANUFACTURERS ASSOCIATION. NEWSLETTER. 1984. irreg. free. Light Aircraft Manufacturers Association, 22 Deer Oaks Ct., Pleasanton, CA 94588. TEL 510-426-9122. circ. 400.

LIGHT PLANE MAINTENANCE; the monthly maintenance report to pilots and aircraft owners. see AERONAUTICS AND SPACE FLIGHT

341.46 CN ISSN 0256-4742
LIVE ANIMALS REGULATIONS. French edition: Reglementation du Transport des Animaux Vivants (ISSN 1012-8271) (Editions in English, French and Spanish) 1975. a. $61. International Air Transport Association, 2000 Peel St., Montreal, PQ H3A 2R4, Canada. TEL 514-844-6311. FAX 514-844-3788. TELEX 05-276627.
—BLDSC (5279.270000).
Description: Describes the container to be used for carriage for each kind of animal and the precautionary measures to be taken during ground and air transportation.

LOG. see AERONAUTICS AND SPACE FLIGHT

387.7 NE ISSN 0921-7258
TL504
LUCHTVAART. 1984. 11/yr. fl.63 (foreign fl.102.50). Ten Brink Meppel B.V., Postbus 1064, 7940 KB Meppel, Netherlands. TEL 05220-54646. FAX 05220-55517. Ed. Thijs Postma. adv.; bk.rev. circ. 10,000.
—SWETS.
Formed by the 1987 merger of: Vliegtuigparade (ISSN 0165-3040); Luchtvaartwereld (ISSN 0921-724X).

387.7 GW
LUFTHANSEAT; Zeitung fuer die Mitarbeiter der Lufthansa. (Text in English, German) 1955. w. free. Deutsche Lufthansa AG, Von-Gablenz-Str. 2-6, 50679 Cologne, Germany. TEL 0221-8262392. FAX 0221-8262306. Ed. Bernd Habbel. bk.rev. circ. 57,000. **Document type**: newspaper.

387.7 MW ISSN 0076-3055
MALAWI. DEPARTMENT OF CIVIL AVIATION. ANNUAL REPORT. a. K.0.30. Government Printer, P.O. Box 37, Zomba, Malawi.

MALTA. CENTRAL OFFICE OF STATISTICS. SHIPPING AND AVIATION STATISTICS. see TRANSPORTATION — Abstracting, Bibliographies, Statistics

629.13 UK
MANDATORY AIRCRAFT MODIFICATIONS AND INSPECTIONS SUMMARY. (Subseries of: Civil Aviation Publications) base vol. plus irreg. updates. £27. Civil Aviation Authority, Printing and Publication Services, Greville House, 37 Gratton Rd., Cheltenham, Glos. GL50 2BN, England. TEL 01242-235151. FAX 01242-584139. (looseleaf format) **Document type**: government publication.
Description: Lists modifications to airworthiness directives, inspections, and service bulletins for aircraft, engines, and components of U.K. manufacture.

387.74 UK
MANUAL OF AIR TRAFFIC SERVICES - PART 1. (Subseries of: Civil Aviation Publication) base vol. plus irreg. updates. £31. Civil Aviation Authority, Printing and Publication Services, Greville House, 37 Gratton Rd., Cheltenham, Glos. GL50 2BN, England. TEL 01242-235151. FAX 01242-584139. (looseleaf format) **Document type**: government publication.

MASSACHUSETTS INSTITUTE OF TECHNOLOGY. FLIGHT TRANSPORTATION LABORATORY. F T L REPORTS AND MEMORANDA. see AERONAUTICS AND SPACE FLIGHT

MECHANIST. see AERONAUTICS AND SPACE FLIGHT

387.736 US
MICHIGAN AIRPORT DIRECTORY. 1922. a. $8. Aeronautics Commission, 2700 E. Airport Service Dr., Capital City Airport, Lansing, MI 48906. TEL 517-335-8521. FAX 517-321-6422. Ed. John L. Wagner. circ. 8,000 (controlled).

387.7 US ISSN 0194-5068
MIDWEST FLYER MAGAZINE; serving the Upper Midwest. 1978. m. $15 (effective 1995 & 1996). Flyer Publications, Inc., Box 199, Oregon, WI 53575-0199. Ed. Dave Weiman. adv.; bk.rev. circ. 22,000. **Document type**: consumer publication, trade publication.

387.7 CN
MILEAGE MANUAL. a. $2190. International Air Transport Association, 2000 Peel St., Montreal, PQ H3A 2R4, Canada. TEL 514-844-6311. FAX 514-844-5286. (also avail. in magnetic tape)
Description: Compilation of the shortest operated mileage and maximum permitted mileage between more than 700,000 specified city pairs on the world airline map.

387.71 GW ISSN 0942-3478
MOMBERGER AIRPORT INFORMATION. (Text in English) 1973. bi-w. DM.495($330) Momberger Airport Information, Postfach 1127, 71273 Rutesheim, Germany. TEL 07152-51640. FAX 07152-55005. Ed. Manfred Momberger; Pubs. Manfred Momberger, Karin Momberger. bk.rev. Indexed: Key to Econ.Sci. **Document type**: newsletter.
—CCC.
Former titles (until 1992): Airport Forum News (ISSN 0174-3279); (until 1979): Airport Forum Report (ISSN 0341-0579)

387.7 GW
MONATSBERICHT ANGEZEIGTER FLUGUNFAELLE. 1983. m. DM.80. Luftfahrt-Bundesamt, Flugunfalluntersuchungsstelle, Postfach 3054, 38020 Braunschweig, Germany. TEL 0531-2355-0. FAX 0531-2355246. circ. 100. **Document type**: government publication.
Formerly: Monatsbericht der Angezeigten Flugunfalluntersuchungsstelle.

387.7 US
MONTANA AND THE SKY. 1961. m. $5. Department of Transportation, Aeronautics Division, Box 5178, Helena, MT 59604. TEL 406-444-2506. FAX 406-444-2519. Ed. Debbie Alke. circ. 3,000. **Document type**: government publication.

387.742 AT
MORGAN INDEX ON AIRLINE TRAVEL (AUSTRALIA). 1973. q. Roy Morgan Research, Box 2282U, Melbourne, Vic. 3001, Australia. TEL 61-3-6296888. FAX 61-3-6291250.

388.3 IT
MOTOR. 1944. m. L.75000. Societa Edizioni Tecniche, Piazza A. Mancini 4-G, 00196 Rome, Italy. TEL 39-6-3220209. FAX 39-6-3233309. Ed. Sergio Favia del Core. adv.: B&W page L.7400000, color page L.10000000. bk.rev. circ. 112,243.

387.71 CN ISSN 1013-4344
MULTILATERAL INTERLINE TRAFFIC AGREEMENTS MANUAL. 3/yr. $195 (effective 1995). International Air Transport Association, 2000 Peel St., Montreal, PQ H3A 2R4, Canada. TEL 514-844-6311. FAX 514-844-3788. TELEX 05-267627.
Description: Contains the passenger and cargo Interline Agreements, which spell out the basic rules airlines follow when collecting money and issuing documents for carriage on each other's services.

387.7 US ISSN 1060-4340
N A T A NEWS. 1969. m. $50 to non-members. National Air Transportation Association, 4226 King St., Alexandria, VA 22302-1507. TEL 703-845-9000. FAX 703-845-8176. Ed. Ann Devers. adv.; charts; illus.; stat.; tr.lit. circ. 1,700. (back issues avail.) **Document type**: trade publication.
Formerly: AirTran News.

387.7 US ISSN 0745-9874
N T S B REPORTER. (National Transportation Safety Board) 1983. m. $36. Peter Katz Productions, Inc., Box 831, 9 Romar Ave., White Plains, NY 10605-0831. TEL 914-949-7443. Ed. Peter Katz. (back issues avail.)
Description: Reports on aviation accident investigations.

387.7 KE ISSN 0077-2666
NAIROBI AIRPORT. ANNUAL REPORT.* 1958. a. Director of Aerodromes, P.O. Box 19001, Nairobi, Kenya.

387.7 US
NATIONAL AIR TRANSPORTATION ASSOCIATION. ANNUAL REPORT. a. National Air Transportation Association, 4226 King St., Alexandria, VA 22302-1507. TEL 703-845-9000. FAX 703-845-8176. **Document type**: corporate report.

TRANSPORTATION — AIR TRANSPORT

387.7 US
HD4966.A482
NATIONAL AIR TRANSPORTATION ASSOCIATION. INDUSTRY COMPENSATION GUIDE. 1978. a. $95 to non-members; members $45. National Air Transportation Association, 4226 King St., Alexandria, VA 22302-1507. TEL 703-845-9000. FAX 703-845-8176. **Document type:** trade publication.
  Formerly: National Air Transportation Association. Wage and Salary Handbook (ISSN 0191-3433)

629.1 387.7 US
NATIONAL BUSINESS AIRCRAFT ASSOCIATION. MAINTENANCE AND OPERATIONS BULLETIN. irreg. National Business Aircraft Association, 1200 18th St., N.W., 2nd fl., Washington, DC 20036-2598. TEL 202-783-9000. FAX 202-331-8364.

387.7 US
NATIONAL TRANSPORTATION SAFETY BOARD DIGEST SERVICE. 1972. m. $315. Hawkins Publishing Co., Inc., Box 480, Mayo, MD 21106-0480. TEL 410-798-1677. FAX 410-798-1098. Ed. Carl R. Eyler. circ. 150. (looseleaf format) **Document type:** abstracting/indexing.

387.7 NE ISSN 0168-552X
NETHERLANDS. CENTRAAL BUREAU VOOR DE STATISTIEK. STATISTIEK VAN DE LUCHTVAART/NETHERLANDS. CENTRAL BUREAU OF STATISTICS. CIVIL AVIATION STATISTICS. (Text in Dutch and English) 1949. a. fl.25. Centraal Bureau voor de Statistiek, Prinses Beatrixlaan 428, Voorburg, Netherlands. (Subscr. to: SDU - Publishers, Christoffel Plantijnstraat, The Hague, Netherlands) **Document type:** government publication.

387.7 US ISSN 0091-6978
TL726.3.N5
NEW JERSEY AIRPORT DIRECTORY. 1968. irreg., latest 1981. $2. Department of Transportation, 1035 Parkway Ave., CN 600, Trenton, NJ 08625. illus. **Document type:** directory.

387.7 910.1 CN
NORTH ATLANTIC REPORT. a. International Air Transport Association, 2000 Peel St., Montreal, PQ H3A 2R4, Canada. TEL 514-844-6311. FAX 514-844-5286. charts; stat.
  Description: Shows developments in the North, Mid and South Atlantic air travel markets. Provides detailed information on changes in traffic for individual airlines and the total route market.

387.7 US
NORTHWEST AIRLINES FLEET FACTS (YEAR). (Part of Fleet Facts series) 1992. a. $10.95 (series of 6 $59.95). Bostick Publications, Box 17181, Memphis, TN 38187. TEL 901-685-3343. Ed. Brian Bostick. **Document type:** consumer publication, trade publication.
  Description: Lists all the aircraft in the Northwest fleet; also includes serial and line numbers, first flight, previous owners and operators, airframe modifications, and engine type used.

387.7 US
NORTHWEST PASSAGES. s-m. free to qualified personnel. Northwest Airlines, Inc., 5101 Northwest Dr., St. Paul, MN 55111-3034. TEL 612-726-7357. Ed. John F. Heenehan. adv.; circ. 54,000 (controlled). **Document type:** newspaper.
  Description: Employee newspaper with articles on the aviation industry and specifically Northwest Airlines, covering corporate developments, employee news and concerns.

341.46 UK
NOTICES TO AERODROME LICENSE HOLDERS. base vol. plus irreg. updates. £20. Civil Aviation Authority, Printing and Publication Services, Greville House, 37 Gratton Rd., Cheltenham, Glos. GL50 2BN, England. TEL 01242-235151. FAX 01242-584139. **Document type:** government publication, bulletin.

387.744 US ISSN 0191-152X
O A G AIR CARGO GUIDE. 1957. m. $110. Official Airline Guides, Part of Reed Travel Group (Subsidiary of: Reed Elsevier plc), 2000 Clearwater Dr., Oak Brook, IL 60521. TEL 708-574-6000. FAX 708-574-6091. TELEX 210144. adv.; circ. 7,600 (paid). **Document type:** directory.
  —UMI.
  Formerly: Air Cargo Guide.
  Description: Lists information on shipping freight by air, including direct and connecting cargo air services worldwide.

387.74 US ISSN 1057-0918
HE9802.A2 CODEN: ODFEEE
O A G DESKTOP FLIGHT GUIDE - NORTH AMERICAN EDITION. 1948. fortn. $285 without fares; $380 with fares. Official Airline Guides, Part of Reed Travel Group (Subsidiary of: Reed Elsevier plc), 2000 Clearwater Dr., Oak Brook, IL 60521. TEL 708-574-6000. FAX 708-574-6091. TELEX 210144. adv. circ. 113,400. **Document type:** directory.
  —CASDDS.
  Formerly (until 1991): Official Airline Guide. North American Edition (ISSN 0191-1619)
  Description: Reference guide to direct and connecting air services within the US, Canada, Mexico and the Caribbean.

387.7 US ISSN 1057-0454
HE9768 CODEN: ODGEEJ
O A G DESKTOP FLIGHT GUIDE - WORLDWIDE EDITION. m. $250. Official Airline Guides, Part of Reed Travel Group (Subsidiary of: Reed Elsevier plc), 2000 Clearwater Dr., Oak Brook, IL 60521. TEL 708-574-6000. FAX 708-574-6091. TELEX 210144. circ. 42,000. Indexed: Rehabil.Lit. **Document type:** directory.
  —CASDDS.
  Former titles (until 1991): Official Airline Guide. WorldWide Edition (ISSN 0364-3875); Official Airline Guide. International Edition (ISSN 0097-5192); Official Airline Guide. Quick Reference International Edition. Part 1.
  Description: Reference guide to international direct and connecting air services for all scheduled airlines worldwide. Does not include air services within and between the US, Canada, Mexico and Caribbean.

387.74 UK
O A G FLIGHT DISK. m. £275. Reed Travel Group, Part of Reed Telepublishing (Subsidiary of: Reed Elsevier group), Church St., Dunstable, Beds. LU5 4HB, England. TEL 01582-600111. FAX 01582-695230. TELEX 82168 AIRABC G. Ed. Janet Mathews. (diskette format) **Document type:** directory.
  Description: Via PC diskette, contains worldwide flight schedules, car rental and ground transportation contact numbers, details on frequent-flyer and lodge programs, and travel related destination data in more than 200 countries.

629.1 385 UK ISSN 1355-4980
O A G FLIGHT PLANNER: EUROPE, MIDDLE EAST & AFRICA. (Official Airline Guide) 1975. m. £92. Reed Travel Group, Part of Reed Telepublishing (Subsidiary of: Reed Elsevier group), Church St., Dunstable, Beds. LU5 4HB, England. TEL 01582-600111. FAX 01582-695230. TELEX 82168 AIRABC G. Ed. Roger Coopes. circ. 16,000. **Document type:** directory.
  —BLDSC (6196.390500).
  Former titles: A B C Executive Flight Planner: Europe, Middle East and Africa (ISSN 0959-1389); A B C Air Europe, Middle East and North Africa (ISSN 0951-6905); American Express SkyGuide Europe - Middle East; (until 1985): A B C Air - Rail Europe (ISSN 0305-8077)
  Description: An essential desktop travel planning reference for travel planners and travelers alike.

387.74 US
O A G POCKET FLIGHT GUIDE EUROPE, MIDDLE EAST, AFRICA EDITION. 1978. m. $73. Official Airline Guides, Part of Reed Travel Group (Subsidiary of: Reed Elsevier plc), 2000 Clearwater Dr., Oak Brook, IL 60521. TEL 708-574-6000. FAX 708-574-6091. circ. 23,600. **Document type:** directory.
  Former titles: O A G Pocket Flight Guide - Europe and Middle East Edition (ISSN 8750-0310); O A G Europe and Middle East Pocket Flight Guide (ISSN 0191-1546)
  Description: Pocket-size guide to direct and connecting air services to and from Europe, the Middle East, and Africa, including travel within these regions.

387.74 US
O A G POCKET FLIGHT GUIDE - LATIN AMERICAN - CARIBBEAN EDITION. m. $73. Official Airline Guides, Part of Reed Travel Group (Subsidiary of: Reed Elsevier plc), 2000 Clearwater Dr., Oak Brook, IL 60521. TEL 708-574-6000. FAX 708-574-6091. TELEX 210144. **Document type:** directory.

387.74 US ISSN 0743-8249
HE9803.A2 CODEN: ONAGDU
O A G POCKET FLIGHT GUIDE - NORTH AMERICAN EDITION. 1970. m. $73. Official Airline Guides, Part of Reed Travel Group (Subsidiary of: Reed Elsevier plc), 2000 Clearwater Dr., Oak Brook, IL 60521. TEL 708-574-6000. FAX 708-574-6091. TELEX 210144. circ. 278,700. **Document type:** directory.
  —CASDDS.
  Formerly: O A G North American Pocket Flight Guide (ISSN 0191-1538)
  Description: Pocket-size guide to direct and connecting air services for travel between the US, Canada, Mexico and the Caribbean.

387.74 US
O A G POCKET FLIGHT GUIDE - PACIFIC ASIA EDITION. 1982. m. $73. Official Airline Guides, Part of Reed Travel Group (Subsidiary of: Reed Elsevier plc), 2000 Clearwater Dr., Oak Brook, IL 60521. TEL 708-574-6000. FAX 708-574-6091. TELEX 210144. circ. 9,500. **Document type:** directory.
  Formerly: O A G Pocket Flight Guide - Pacific Area Edition (ISSN 0745-5275)
  Description: Pocket-size guide to direct and connecting air service for travel to and within all countries of the Pacific geographical region.

387.7 UK ISSN 1355-4972
▼**O A G WORLD AIRWAYS GUIDE.** 1994. m. £390. Reed Travel Group, Part of Reed Telepublishing (Subsidiary of: Reed Elsevier group), Church St., Dunstable, Beds. LU5 4HB, England. TEL 01582-600111. FAX 01582-695230. TELEX 82168 AIRABC G. Ed. Roger Cooper. circ. 32,000. **Document type:** directory.
  Description: Provides corporate travel planners with a single reference source of comprehensive, accurate airline schedules worldwide.

387.7 AU
OESTERREICHISCHE LUFTFAHRT PRESSE. 1953. s-m. S.1290. Seidengasse 32-17, A-1070 Vienna 7, Austria. FAX 5266116. Eds. Leo Froehlich, Helga Markowitsch. adv.; bk.rev. circ. 2,000.
  Formerly: Oesterreichischer Luftfahrt Pressedienst (ISSN 0029-9774)

OFFICIAL GUIDE TO FLIGHT ATTENDANTS CAREERS. see *OCCUPATIONS AND CAREERS*

OFFICIAL GUIDE TO TRAVEL AGENT & TRAVEL CAREERS. see *OCCUPATIONS AND CAREERS*

387.7 US
OFFSHORE DESIGN GUIDE: HELIPORTS. 1984. s-a. free. Helicopter Safety Advisory Conference, Box 60220, Houston, TX 77205. TEL 713-960-7654. **Document type:** trade publication.

OKECIE; airport magazine. see *TRAVEL AND TOURISM*

TRANSPORTATION — AIR TRANSPORT 6353

387.74 341.46 UK
OVERSEAS NON-SCHEDULED FLIGHT CLEARANCES GUIDE. (Subseries of: Civil Aviation Publications) base vol. plus irreg. updates. £50. Civil Aviation Authority, Printing and Publication Services, Greville House, 37 Gratton Rd., Cheltenham, Glos. GL50 2BN, England. TEL 01242-235151. FAX 01242-584139. (looseleaf format) **Document type:** government publication.
 Description: Provides charter and general-aviation operators with details of U.K. foreign entry and overflight requirements of U.S. airspace, together with useful associated information on U.K. airports, refueling, and various limitations or restrictions.

387.7 US
PACIFIC FLYER. 1977. m. $18.50 (foreign $85). 3355 Mission Ave., Ste. 213, Oceanside, CA 92054-1334. TEL 619-439-4466. FAX 619-439-9666. Ed. Wayman C. Dunlap. adv. contact: Alan Lindquist. bk.rev. (tabloid format; back issues avail.) **Document type:** trade publication.
 Description: Features aviation news and history of interest to pilots, historians, and lovers of aviation.

387.7 CN
PASSENGER AND CARGO SERVICES NEWS - INSIGHT. 6/yr. (plus 2 updates). $100. International Air Transport Association, 2000 Peel St., Montreal, PQ H3A 2R4, Canada. TEL 514-844-6311. FAX 514-844-6311. TELEX 05-267627.
 Formerly: Passenger and Cargo Services News.
 Description: Features articles on the latest developments in cargo services, passenger services, airport-ground handling activities and information on data automation services.

387.742 CN ISSN 1013-4042
PASSENGER RESERVATIONS MANUAL. 1983. a. $50 (effective 1995). International Air Transport Association, 2000 Peel St., Montreal, PQ H3A 2R4, Canada. TEL 514-844-6311. FAX 514-844-3788. TELEX 05-267627.
 Description: Contains all internationally agreed upon reservations rules and interline reservations message procedures.

387.742 CN ISSN 0256-3282
PASSENGER SERVICES CONFERENCE RESOLUTIONS MANUAL. 1981. a. $163 (effective 1995). International Air Transport Association, 2000 Peel St., Montreal, PQ H3A 2R4, Canada. TEL 514-844-6311. FAX 514-844-3788. TELEX 05-267627.
 Description: Contains all rules and regulations which have been universally accepted by airlines to process passengers and baggage in the international interline environment.

387.71 CN
PASSENGER TARIFF COORDINATING CONFERENCES RESOLUTIONS MANUAL. a. $240. International Air Transport Association, 2000 Peel St., Montreal, PQ H3A 2R4, Canada. TEL 514-844-6311. FAX 514-844-3788. TELEX 05-267627.
 Description: Contains the text of all resolutions adopted by the Passenger Tariff Coordinating Conferences together with details of corresponding Government Reservations.

387.744 HK
PAYLOAD ASIA; the air cargo - courier - express magazine for the Asia - Pacific region. 1985. m. (Federation of Asia - Pacific Aircargo Associations) Asian Media Services Ltd., P.O. Box 3580, GPO Hong Kong, Hong Kong. TEL 852-893-3676. FAX 852-893-3676. Ed. Van Fenema. adv.: B&W page $2595, color page $3315; trim 210 x 295. circ. 12,500 (controlled). **Document type:** trade publication.

387.7 GW ISSN 0175-0143
PILOT UND FLUGZEUG. 1974. m. DM.140.40. Wiesbadener Str. 59b, 61462 Koenigstein, Germany. Ed. Heiko Teegen. adv.; charts; illus. circ. 19,000. **Document type:** consumer publication.
 Formerly: Luftfahrt International.

387.7 US ISSN 1052-5580
PIPER'S MAGAZINE. m. $41. Jones Publishing Inc., Box 5000, N. 7450 Aanstad Rd., Iola, WI 54945. TEL 715-445-5000. FAX 715-445-4053. Ed. David Sakrison. adv. circ. 11,000.
 Description: For owners of Piper aircraft.

307.71 US
PORT AUTHORITY OF NEW YORK AND NEW JERSEY. AVIATION DEPARTMENT. AIRPORT STATISTICS. a. Port Authority of New York and New Jersey, Aviation Department, Aviation Economics Division, One World Trade Ctr., New York, NY 10048. TEL 212-466-7000. stat.

387.736
PORT AUTHORITY OF NEW YORK AND NEW JERSEY. AVIATION DEPARTMENT. AVIATION ANNUAL REPORT. a. Port Authority of New York and New Jersey, Aviation Department, One World Trade Ctr., New York, NY 10048.

PORT PROGRESS NEWS AND EVENTS. see TRANSPORTATION — Ships And Shipping

387.7 CN
PRINCIPLES OF CARGO HANDLING AND PERISHABLE CARGO HANDLING GUIDE. a. $48 (effective 1995). International Air Transport Association, 2000 Peel St., Montreal, PQ H3A 2R4, Canada. TEL 514-844-6311. FAX 514-844-3788. TELEX 05-267627.
 Description: Addresses such subjects as: industry co-operation and interface between participants; cargo acceptance; general and special cargo handling.

388.324 US ISSN 0032-8901
TL721.4
PRIVATE PILOT. 1965. m. $21.97; newsstand price: $2.95. Fancy Publications, 2401 Beverly Blvd., Los Angeles, CA 90057. TEL 714-855-8822. FAX 714-855-3045. (Subscr. to: Box 55064, Boulder, CO 80322-5064) Ed. Mary Silitch. adv.; bk.rev.; charts; illus.; stat. circ. 100,000.
 Description: For the owner-flyer. Focuses on those issues relevant to the serious owner and pilots of single-engined and light twin-engined aircraft. Emphasis is on new and used aircraft evaluation, new avionics products, travel, flying club activities and pilot-training programs.

387.7 US ISSN 0191-6238
TL501
PROFESSIONAL PILOT MAGAZINE. 1967. m. $36. Queensmith Communications Corporation, 3014 Colvin St., Alexandria, VA 22314. TEL 703-370-0606. FAX 703-370-7082. Ed. Mary Silitch. adv.: B&W page $8048; adv. contact: Murray Q. Smith. circ. 32,000 (controlled). **Document type:** trade publication.
 —UnCover.
 Description: Presents information of interest to corporate, charter, and commuter airlines pilots and associated personnel.

PROPLINER; the international review of piston-engined and turboprop transport aircraft. see AERONAUTICS AND SPACE FLIGHT

341.46 US
PROVISIONS IN U S INTERNATIONAL AIR TRANSPORT AGREEMENTS. 1985. 4 base vols. (plus updates). $400 in N. America; elsewhere $424 (effective 1995). Air Transport Association of America, 1301 Pennsylvania Ave., N.W., Ste. 1100, Washington, DC 20004-1707. TEL 202-626-4260. FAX 202-626-4259. (looseleaf format)
 Description: Contains the text of every Air Transport agreement between the United States and 72 foreign countries.

387.7 GR ISSN 1105-1310
PTISI/FLIGHT. 1979. m. $36. Technical Press S.A., 31 Praxitelous St, 167 77 Athens, Greece. TEL 30-1-9961-861. FAX 30-1-9961-864. Ed. Costas Cavvathas; Pub. Sophie Cavvatha. circ. 38,000. **Document type:** trade publication.
 Description: Covers aerospace technology and defense matters.

387.74 387 PR
PUERTO RICO. PORTS AUTHORITY. OFFICE OF ECONOMIC RESEARCH. STATISTICAL REPORT. (Text in English; summaries in English) 1955. q. free. Ports Authority, Office of Economic Research & Statistics, G.P.O. Box 362829, San Juan, PR 00936. stat. circ. 500. (back issues avail.) **Document type:** government publication.

QUEENSLAND FLYING DOCTOR. see HOSPITALS

387.744 388.324 US
QUICK CALLER: BOSTON AREA AIR CARGO DIRECTORY. 1976. a. $11. Fourth Seacoast Publishing Co., Inc., Box 145, St. Clair Shores, MI 48080. TEL 810-779-5570. FAX 810-779-5547. Ed. Thomas Buysse; Pub. Roger J. Buysse. circ. 10,000. **Document type:** directory.

387.7 388.324 US
QUICK CALLER: CHICAGO AREA AIR CARGO DIRECTORY. a. $11. Fourth Seacoast Publishing Co., Inc., Box 145, St. Clair Shores, MI 48080. TEL 810-779-5570. FAX 810-779-5547. Ed. Thomas Buysse; Pub. Roger Buysse. **Document type:** directory.

387.744 388.324 US
QUICK CALLER: DETROIT AREA AIR CARGO DIRECTORY. 1973. a. $11. Fourth Seacoast Publishing Co., Inc., Box 145, St. Clair Shores, MI 48080. TEL 810-779-5570. FAX 810-779-5547. Ed. Thomas Buysse; Pub. Roger Buysse. circ. 10,000. **Document type:** directory.

387.7 388.324 US
QUICK CALLER: LOS ANGELES AREA AIR CARGO DIRECTORY. a. $11. Fourth Seacoast Publishing Co., Inc., Box 145, St. Clair Shores, MI 48080. TEL 810-779-5570. FAX 810-779-5547. Ed. Thomas Buysse; Pub. Roger Buysse. **Document type:** directory.

387.744 388.324 US
QUICK CALLER: MIAMI - ORLANDO - FLORIDA AIR CARGO DIRECTORY. 1975. a. $11. Fourth Seacoast Publishing Co., Inc., Box 145, St. Clair Shores, MI 48080. TEL 810-779-5570. FAX 810-779-5547. Ed. Thomas Buysse; Pub. Roger Buysse. circ. 10,000. **Document type:** directory.
 Formerly: Quick Caller: Miami Area Air Cargo Directory.

387.744 388.324 US
QUICK CALLER: NEW YORK METRO AREA AIR CARGO DIRECTORY. 1989. a. $11. Fourth Seacoast Publishing Co., Inc., Box 145, St. Clair Shores, MI 48080. TEL 810-779-5570. FAX 810-779-5547. Ed. Thomas Buysse; Pub. Roger Buysse. circ. 15,000. **Document type:** directory.

387.744 388.324 US
QUICK CALLER: SAN FRANCISCO BAY AREA AIR CARGO DIRECTORY. 1982. a. $11. Fourth Seacoast Publishing Co., Inc., Box 145, St. Clair Shores, MI 48080. TEL 810-779-5570. FAX 810-779-5547. Ed. Thomas Buysse. circ. 10,000. **Document type:** directory.

387.74 UK
RANDOM FLIGHT PLAN A F T N ADDRESS BOOK. (Aeronautical Fixed Telecommunications Network) base vol. plus irreg. updates. £30. Civil Aviation Authority, Printing and Publication Services, Greville House, 37 Gratton Rd., Cheltenham, Glos. GL50 2BN, England. TEL 01242-235151. FAX 01242-584139. (looseleaf format) **Document type:** government publication.
 Description: Provides a guide to the selection of appropriate collective address codes to simplify addressing of flight safety messages via the A.F.T.N.

387.7 UK
REDCOAT. 1989. q. Redcoat Express Ltd., 12 Gatwick Metro Centre, Balcombe Rd., Horley, Surrey RH6 9GA, England. TEL 01293-774141. FAX 01293-774080. TELEX 87337 REDAIR.
 Description: Concerned with air communication specifically for the West African community in the diaspora.

TRANSPORTATION — AIR TRANSPORT

387.742   UK   ISSN 1070-065X
TL726
REGIONAL AIR INTERNATIONAL; the international magazine for regional, commuter, and short haul airlines. 1978. m. Shephard Press, 111 High St., Burnham, Bucks. SL1 7JE, England. TEL 01628-604311. FAX 01628-664334. adv.; bk.rev. circ. 29,500. (also avail. in microform from UMI; reprint service avail. from UMI) **Document type:** trade publication.
—UMI; UnCover. CCC.
    Former titles: Commuter Air International (ISSN 1054-7436); (until 1990): Commuter Air (ISSN 0199-2686)
    Description: Reflects the interests of the regional-commuter airline industry, its carriers, service organizations, manufacturers and vendors. Focuses on the nuts and bolts of managing an airline, with emphasis on solving a variety of problems ranging from maintenance to labor disputes.

387.7   US
REGIONAL AIRLINE ASSOCIATION. ANNUAL REPORT. 1974. a. $50 to non-members. Regional Airline Association, 1200 19th S., N.W., Ste. 300, Washington, DC 20036. TEL 202-857-1170. FAX 202-429-5113. Ed. Deborah McElroy. adv.; illus.; stat.; circ. 2,700 (controlled). **Indexed:** SRI. **Document type:** corporate report.
    Description: Provides comprehensive analysis of issues and trends affecting the US domestic regional airline industry, with company information for airlines and suppliers.

REGIONAL AIRLINE DIRECTORY. see *BUSINESS AND ECONOMICS — Trade And Industrial Directories*

387.71   UN   ISSN 1012-6538
REGIONAL DIFFERENCES IN FARES, RATES AND COSTS FOR INTERNATIONAL AIR TRANSPORT (YEAR). (Subseries of: I C A O Circulars) (Editions in: English, French, Russian, Spanish) 1979. a. $7. International Civil Aviation Organization, Attn: Document Sales Unit, 1000 Sherbrooke St. W., Montreal, PQ H3A 2R2, Canada. TEL 514-285-8022. FAX 514-285-6769. TELEX 05-24513. (back issues avail.)

387.7   FR   ISSN 0080-066X
REGISTRE AERONAUTIQUE INTERNATIONAL. 1966. a. (with q. suppl.). 1800 F. Bureau Veritas, Registre International de Classification de Navires et d'Aeronefs, 92077 Paris la Defense Cedex 44, France. TEL 33-1-42-91-52-95. TELEX 611183F BVAVO. bk.rev. circ. 1,000. (also avail. in microfiche) **Document type:** directory.

341.46   CN
REGULATORY AFFAIRS REVIEW. q. $500. International Air Transport Association, 2000 Peel St., Montreal, PQ H3A 2R4, Canada. TEL 514-844-6311. FAX 514-844-3788. TELEX 05-267627. index.
    Description: Brings together information and supporting documentation on government policies affecting the international scheduled aviation industry.

387.74   UK
REPORTABLE ACCIDENTS TO U K REGISTERED AIRCRAFT AND TO FOREIGN REGISTERED AIRCRAFT IN U K AIRSPACE (YEAR). (Subseries of: Civil Aviation Publications) 1949. a. £10. Civil Aviation Authority, Printing and Publication Services, Greville House, 37 Gratton Rd., Cheltenham, Glos. GL50 2BN, England. TEL 01242-235151. FAX 01242-584139. charts; stat. (back issues avail.) **Document type:** government publication.
    Formerly: Accidents to Aircraft on the British Register (ISSN 0306-3550)
    Description: Compiles and analyzes accidents to U.K.-registered civilian aircraft during the year.

387.71 657   CN
REVENUE ACCOUNTING MANUAL. a. $100. International Air Transport Association, 2000 Peel St., Montreal, PQ H3A 2R4, Canada. TEL 514-844-6311. FAX 514-844-3788. TELEX 05-267627.
    Description: Explains the standard billing procedures for the interline accounting of passenger, cargo, Universal Air Travel and miscellaneous revenues.

387.7 629.1   US   ISSN 1073-8274
HE9769.A3
ROTOR ROSTER. 1987. a. $29. Air Track, Box 610, Hilliard, FL 32046. TEL 912-496-3504. FAX 912-496-7513. Ed. Faye E. Nelson; Pub. Glenn Wonnacott. adv. contact: Sue B. Hill. charts; illus. circ. 10,000. (magnetic tape; back issues avail.) **Document type:** directory.
    Description: Provides worldwide listing of civil helicopter owners.

S P A WATER LANDING DIRECTORY. (Seaplane Pilots Association) see *AERONAUTICS AND SPACE FLIGHT*

SAVIA. see *TRAVEL AND TOURISM*

387.7   SZ
DIE SCHWEIZERISCHE ZIVILLUFTFAHRT; l'aviation civile Suisse. (Text in French, German) 1925. a. 12 Fr. Bundesamt fuer Zivilluftfahrt - Federal Office for Civil Aviation (Office Federal de l'Aviation Civile), Inselgasse, CH-3003 Berne, Switzerland. Ed. Daniel Ruhier. circ. 1,400.
    Supersedes (from 1975): Schweizerische Luftverkehrsstatistik - Statistique du Trafic Aerien Suisse.

341.46   UK
SHAWCROSS & BEAUMONT AIR LAW. 3 base vols. (plus q. updates). £495($990) Butterworth & Co. (Publishers) Ltd., Part of the Reed Elsevier group, Halsbury House, 35 Chancery Ln., London WC2A 1EL, England. TEL 071-400-2500. FAX 071-400-2842. (U.S. addr.: Butterworth Legal Publishers, 90 Stiles Rd., Salem, NH 03079-9981. TEL 603-898-9664) Ed.Bd. (looseleaf format) **Document type:** trade publication.
    Description: Contains an informed exposition of the principal legal rules governing the flight and operation of aircraft.

341.46   UK
SHAWCROSS & BEAUMONT AVIATION REPORTS. 3 base vols. (plus q. updates). £400($990) Butterworth & Co. (Publishers) Ltd., Part of the Reed Elsevier group, 35 Chancery Ln., London WC2A 1EL, England. TEL 071-400-2500. FAX 071-400-2842. (U.S. addr.: Butterworth Legal Publishers, 90 Stiles Rd., Salem, NH 03079-9981. TEL 603-898-9664) Eds. J.D. McClean, Elizabeth de Montlaur Martin. (looseleaf format) **Document type:** trade publication.
    Description: Contains an informed exposition of the principal legal rules governing the flight and operation of aircraft.

387.7   US
SIGHT LECTURE. a. Wings Club, 52 Vanderbilt Ave., 18th Fl., New York, NY 10017. TEL 212-867-1770.

387.7   SI
SINGAPORE CHANGI AIRPORT TIMETABLE. (Text in English) 1989. q. $8. Times Trade Directories Pte. Ltd., Times Centre, 1 New Industrial Rd., Singapore 1953, Singapore. TEL 2848844. FAX 2881186. TELEX RS 25713 TIMESS.

387.7   US
SPECTRUM NEWSLETTER (WASHINGTON). m. Air Transport Association of America, 1301 Pennsylvania Ave., N.W., Ste. 1100, Washington, DC 20004-1707. TEL 202-626-4000. FAX 202-626-4081. **Document type:** newsletter.
    Description: Provides update on SPEC 2000 developments, related events and ATA Material Management activities. Includes news of latest document revisions, service improvements, forthcoming meetings and activities, and technologies.

387.7   US   ISSN 0271-2598
SPEEDNEWS; a wwekly publication for the aviation industry. 1979. w. $547. Speednews, Inc., 1801 Ave. of the Stars, Ste. 210, Los Angeles, CA 90067-5904. TEL 310-203-9603. FAX 310-203-9352. TELEX 292674. Ed. Ann More; Pub. Gil Speed. adv. contact: Steve Costley. bk.rev.; circ. 3,000 (paid). **Document type:** trade publication, newsletter.
• Also available online. Vendor(s): NewsNet (AE15).
    Description: Keeps executives up-to-date on the week's aviation news, including new aircraft orders, leases, new product orders and innovations.

SPIC; revista de turismo. see *TRAVEL AND TOURISM*

387.74   CN
STANDARD SCHEDULES INFORMATION MANUAL. 2/yr. $275. International Air Transport Association, 2000 Peel St., Montreal, PQ H3A 2R4, Canada. TEL 514-884-6311. FAX 514-844-3788. TELEX 05-267627.
    Description: Designed to help originators and recipients of schedule information, both in terms of electronic data processing and for conventional manual processess.

387.736   CN
SUMMARY OF AIRPORT CAPACITIES. a. $140 (effective 1994). International Air Transport Association, 2000 Peel St., Montreal, PQ H3A 2R4, Canada. TEL 514-844-6311. FAX 514-844-3788. TELEX 05-267627.
    Description: Provides airport capacity information regarding selected international airports. Information includes details on hours of operation, declared capacity of the runway, apron and terminal building, terminal building profiles and planned airport developments to increase capacity.

387.71   CN
SURVEY OF REMITTANCES OF FOREIGN BALANCES. a. (plus 1 update). $200. International Air Transport Association, 2000 Peel St., Montreal, PQ H3A 2R4, Canada. TEL 514-844-6311. FAX 514-844-3788. TELEX 05-267627.
    Description: Details the worldwide industry position with respect to remittances of foreign balances. Contains individual country data, regional analyses, and executive summary and individual comments on the worst ten countries.

387.71   UN
SURVEYS OF INTERNATIONAL AIR TRANSPORT FARES AND RATES. (Subseries of: I C A O Circulars) (Editions in: English, French, Russian, Spanish) a. (issued in Sep.). $18. International Civil Aviation Organization, Attn: Document Sales Unit, 1000 Sherbrooke St. W., Montreal, PQ H3A 2R2, Canada. TEL 514-285-8022. FAX 514-285-6769. TELEX 05-24513. (back issues avail.)

380.5   CI   ISSN 0351-1898
SUVREMENI PROMET. (Text in Croatian; summaries in English) 1979. bi-m. $42. University of Zagreb, Faculty of Transportation, Vukeliceva 4, 41000 Zagreb, Croatia. TEL 041 215 767. Ed. Franko Rotim. adv.; bk.rev. circ. 1,400.

363.12 628   UN
TECHNICAL INSTRUCTIONS FOR THE SAFE TRANSPORT OF DANGEROUS GOODS BY AIR. (Editions in: English, French, Spanish, Russian) biennial. $88 (supplement $20) (1995-1996 edition). International Civil Aviation Organization, Attn: Document Sales Unit, 1000 Sherbrooke St. W., Montreal, PQ H3A 2R2, Canada. TEL 514-285-8022. FAX 514-285-6769. TELEX 05-24513.

387.74   TH   ISSN 0125-1090
THAILAND AIRLINE TIMETABLE. (Text in English) 1976. m. Advertising and Media Consultants Ltd., Silom Condominium, 12th Fl., 52-38 Soi Saladaeng 2, Bangkok, Thailand. TEL 233-9111. FAX 236-6764. TELEX 82463-LOOKEAS-TH. circ. 20,000.

387.74   CN   ISSN 0256-4459
TICKETING HANDBOOK. (Editions in English, French, Spanish) 1968. a. price varies. International Air Transport Association, 2000 Peel St., Montreal, PQ H3A 2R4, Canada. TEL 514-844-6311. FAX 514-844-3788. TELEX 05-2676276.
    Description: Explains in detail what entries are to be made on tickets, MCOs, MPDs and PTAs.

387.7   US
TRANS WORLD AIRLINES FLEET FACTS (YEAR). (Part of Fleet Facts series) 1992. a. $8.95 (series of 6 $59.95). Bostick Publications, Box 17181, Memphis, TN 38187. TEL 901-685-3343. Ed. Brian Bostick. **Document type:** consumer publication, trade publication.
    Description: Lists all the aircraft in the T.W.A. fleet; gives serial and construction numbers, first flight, engine type, previous owners and leasers, and airframe conversions.

TRAVEL AGENT'S HANDBOOK. see *TRAVEL AND TOURISM*

TRANSPORTATION — AIR TRANSPORT

387.7   UK
▼**TRAVEL INDUSTRY DIRECTORY.** 1994. a. £33 (in N. America £450). (London City Airport) Air & Business Travel News, P.O. Box 1315, Potters Bar, Herts. EN6 1PU, England. TEL 01707-665151. FAX 01707-0660330. Ed. Malcolm Ginsberg. circ. 1,500 (paid). **Document type:** directory.
    Description: Lists tourism organizations, airlines, airports, U.K. and overseas railways, cruise and ferry companies, car rental agencies, bus operators, and training companies.

387.742   DK   ISSN 0900-3606
TRAVEL MANAGER C P H. 5/yr. European Traffic Guides, Boestoftevej 70, DK-4660 Store Heddinge, Denmark. adv. circ. 8,000.
    Formerly (until 1983): Copenhagen Airline Guide.

621.13 350   UK
U K ADDITIONAL REQUIREMENTS AND SPECIAL CONDITIONS. (Subseries of: Civil Aviation Publications) base vol. plus irreg. updates. £35. Civil Aviation Authority, Printing and Publication Services, Greville House, 37 Gratton Rd., Cheltenham, Glos. GL50 2BN, England. TEL 01242-235151. FAX 01242-584139. (looseleaf format) **Document type:** government publication.
    Description: Lists C.A.A. requirements for the certification of aircraft built outside the U.K.

387.7   UK   ISSN 0951-6301
U K AIRMISSES INVOLVING COMMERCIAL AIR TRANSPORT. 1987. 3/yr. £5.30 per no. Civil Aviation Authority, Printing and Publication Services, Greville House, 37 Gratton Rd., Cheltenham, Glos. GL50 2BN, England. TEL 01242-235151. FAX 01242-584139. **Document type:** government publication.
    —BLDSC (9082.651230).

387.7   CN
U L D CONTROL MANUAL. a. $73. International Air Transport Association, 2000 Peel St., Montreal, PQ H3A 2R4, Canada. TEL 514-844-6311. FAX 514-844-5286.
    Description: Contains input and output procedures, message formats and agreements that are required to run the ULD control system.

387.74   CN   ISSN 0849-6811
U L D TECHNICAL MANUAL. (Unit Load Devices) a. $120 (effective 1995). International Air Transport Association, 2000 Peel St., Montreal, PQ H3A 2R4, Canada. TEL 514-844-6311. FAX 514-844-3788. TELEX 05-267627. illus. **Document type:** trade publication.
    Description: Contains all specifications agreed to within the airline industry and illustrates them with clear drawings.

387.7   US
U S AIR FLEET FACTS (YEAR). (Part of Fleet Facts series) 1992. a. $10.95 (series of 6 $59.95). Bostick Publications, Box 17181, Memphis, TN 38187. TEL 901-685-3343. Ed. Brian Bostick. **Document type:** consumer publication, trade publication.
    Description: Lists all the aircraft in the USAir fleet, along with serial and line numbers, first flight, previous owners and operators, engine type, and airframe conversions.

U S GOVERNMENT AFFAIRS REPORT: FEDERAL BIENNIAL LEGISLATIVE REPORT. see TRANSPORTATION — Abstracting, Bibliographies, Statistics

387.7 341.46   US
U S GOVERNMENT AFFAIRS REPORT: FEDERAL REPORT (NEWSLETTER). 25/yr. $200 (Canada $215; elsewhere $235) (effective 1995). Air Transport Association of America, 1301 Pennsylvania Ave., N.W., Ste. 1100, Washington, DC 20004-1707. TEL 202-626-4000. FAX 202-626-4081. (Subscr. to: ATA Distribution Center, Box 511, Annapolis Junctio, MD 20701. TEL 800-497-3326. FAX 301-206-9789) **Document type:** newsletter.
    Description: Covers aviation matters including regulatory proceedings and tax appropriations.

387.7   US
UNITED AIRLINES FLEET FACTS (YEAR). (Part of Fleet Facts series) 1992. a. $12.95 (series of 6 $59.95). Bostick Publications, Box 17181, Memphis, TN 38187. TEL 901-685-3343. Ed. Brian Bostick. **Document type:** consumer publication, trade publication.
    Description: Lists all aircraft in the United fleet, including serial and construction numbers, first flight and previous owners, airframe modifications, and engine type.

387.74 341.46   UK
UNITED KINGDOM AERONAUTICAL INFORMATION PUBLICATION. Abbreviated title: U K - A I P. (Subseries of: Civil Aviation Publications) base vol. with periodic updates. £475 (updates only £30). Civil Aviation Authority, Printing and Publication Services, Greville House, Cheltenham, Glos. GL50 2BN, England. TEL 01242-235151. FAX 01242-584139. (looseleaf format) **Document type:** government publication, trade publication.
    Formerly: U K Air Pilot.
    Description: Contains information on facilities, services, rules, regulations, and restrictions in U.K. airspace.

387.7   US
U.S. FEDERAL AVIATION ADMINISTRATION. NATIONAL AVIATION SYSTEM: DEVELOPMENT AND CAPITAL NEEDS. 1969. irreg. free. U.S. Federal Aviation Administration, 800 Independence Ave., S.W., Washington, DC 20591. TEL 202-655-4000. illus. circ. 3,000.
    Former titles: U.S. Federal Aviation Administration. National Aviation System: Challenges of the Decade Ahead; U.S. Federal Aviation Administration. National Aviation System Policy Summary (ISSN 0092-4555)

387.74   US
U.S. NATIONAL TRANSPORTATION SAFETY BOARD. AIRCRAFT ACCIDENT REPORTS. (Formerly issued by Department of Transportation) irreg. $35 (brief format $40). U.S. National Transportation Safety Board, Department of Transportation, Washington, DC 20590. TEL 202-426-8787. FAX 703-321-8547. (Subscr. to: National Technical Information Service, 5285 Port Royal Rd., Springfield, VA 22151) (also avail. in microfiche from CIS; reprint service avail. from CIS) **Indexed:** Amer.Stat.Ind. (1979-).

387.7   US
UNIVERSITY AVIATION ASSOCIATION. NEWSLETTER. bi-m. $35. University Aviation Association, 3410 Skyway Dr., Auburn, AL 36830. TEL 205-844-2434. FAX 205-844-2432. Ed. Gary W. Kiteley. adv. contact: Carolyn Williamson. bk.rev. circ. 650. (looseleaf format; back issues avail.) **Document type:** newsletter.

WATER FLYING. see AERONAUTICS AND SPACE FLIGHT

WATER FLYING ANNUAL. see AERONAUTICS AND SPACE FLIGHT

387.7   US   ISSN 0509-9528
WEEKLY OF BUSINESS AVIATION. 1965. w. $470 (foreign $530). McGraw-Hill, Inc., Aviation Week Group, 1200 G St., N.W., Ste. 200, Washington, DC 20005. TEL 202-383-2350. Ed. David Collogan. adv.; bk.rev.; charts; illus.; stat.; tr.lit.; q. cum.index. (looseleaf format; also avail. in microfiche from CIS) ●Also available online. Vendor(s): Knight-Ridder, Inc. (File no.624/McGRAW-HILL PUBLICATIONS ONLINE), Dow Jones News Retrieval (BA), Lexis-Nexis (WBA), NewsNet (AE20).
    Formerly: Business Aviation (ISSN 0045-3617)

WEEKLY REVIEW OF COLLECTIVE BARGAINING. see BUSINESS AND ECONOMICS — Labor And Industrial Relations

629.13   CN
WINGS. 1957. bi-m. Can.$32($52) (effective Jan. 1995). Corvus Publishing Group Ltd., 158, 1224 Aviation Park, N.E., Calgary, AB T2E 7E2, Canada. TEL 403-275-9457. FAX 403-275-3925. Ed. Paul J. Skinner. adv. contact: Paul J. Skinner. bk.rev.; illus.; index. circ. 13,500. (back issues avail.) **Document type:** trade publication.
    Former titles: Wings Magazine of Canada (ISSN 0701-1369); Canadian Wings (ISSN 0008-5367)
    Description: Provides domestic and international coverage of corporate, commercial and military aviation.

910.09   US
WINGS OF ALOHA. (Text in Japanese) 1989. q. Honolulu Publishing Company, Ltd., 36 Merchant St., Honolulu, HI 96813. TEL 808-524-7400. FAX 808-531-2306. Ed. Pat Pitzer. circ. 20,000.
    Description: In-flight magazine of Aloha Airlines and Aloha Island Air. Contains general information about Hawaii.

387.1   US   ISSN 1049-7781
WINGS WEST; the Western aviation magazine. 1985. bi-m. $18. Weisner Publishing, Inc., 7009 S. Potomac St., Englewood, CO 80112. TEL 303-778-7145. FAX 303-397-7619. Ed. Edward Huber; Pub. Edward Huber. adv.; bk.rev.; circ. 14,571 (paid). (back issues avail.) **Document type:** consumer publication.
    Description: Presents news and information for Western aircraft owners, pilots and their families.

387.7   UK   ISSN 0955-9000
WINGSPAN. m. £22.50 (overseas £28.50); newsstand price: £2.22. Wingspan Publications, 5 Riverside, Wooborn Moor, Nr. High Wycombe, Bucks. HP10 0NU, England. TEL 0628-523458. (Dist. by: S M Magazine Distribution Ltd., 6 Leiham Court Rd., Streatham, London SW16 2PG, England) Ed. Alan Forberg. adv.; bk.rev.; illus. **Document type:** consumer publication.
    Incorporates: Planes.

WOLKENRIDDER. see TRAVEL AND TOURISM

WORLD AIR TRANSPORT STATISTICS. see TRANSPORTATION — Abstracting, Bibliographies, Statistics

287.7   CN
WORLD AIRLINE COOPERATION REVIEW. q. International Air Transport Association, 2000 Peel St., Montreal, Que. H3A 2R4, Canada. TEL 514-844-6311. Dir. Gunter Eser.

387.7   UK   ISSN 0951-8673
WORLD AIRLINE FLEETS NEWS. 1977. m. £49.95. Aviation Data Centre Ltd., P.O. Box 92, Feltham, Mddx. TW13 7EQ, England. TEL 081-751-3317. (Dist. in U.S. by: World Transport Press, Inc., Box 521238, Miami, FL 33152-1238. TEL 305-477-7163. FAX 305-599-1995) adv.; bk.rev. circ. 5,000.
    Former titles (until 1987): Airline Data News (ISSN 0263-3272); World Airline Fleets Monthly (ISSN 0140-6450)
    Description: Informs airline professionals and airliner enthusiasts on airline start-ups and failures, aircraft purchased and sold, new liveries, and accidents.

629.1 387.7   US   ISSN 1059-4183
WORLD AIRLINE NEWS. 1991. w. $595 (effective 1995). Phillips Business Information, Inc., 1201 Seven Locks Rd., Potomac, MD 20854. TEL 301-424-3338. FAX 301-309-3847. E-mail: pbi@phillips.com. Ed. Jim Brown. **Document type:** newsletter.
    ●Also available online. Vendor(s): NewsNet (AE31). —CCC.

387.7   US   ISSN 0084-1374
WORLD AIRLINE RECORD. 1948. irreg., 7th ed., 1972 (with q. supplements). $43.50. Roadcap Aviation Publications, 1030 S. Green Bay Rd., Lake Forest, IL 60045. TEL 708-234-4730. Ed. Roy R. Roadcap.

387.7   US   ISSN 1078-1420
▼**WORLD AIRPORT WEEK.** 1994. w. $495 (foreign $560) (effective 1995). Phillips Business Information, Inc., 1201 Seven Locks Rd., Potomac, MD 20854. TEL 301-424-3338. FAX 301-309-3847. E-mail: pbi@phillips.com. Ed. Jim Brown. index. (back isssues avail.) **Document type:** newsletter.
    ●Also available online. Vendor(s): Information Access Co., NewsNet.
    Description: International coverage of airport finance and technology, airport and airside development.

WORLD METEOROLOGICAL ORGANIZATION. COMMISSION FOR AERONAUTICAL METEOROLOGY. ABRIDGED FINAL REPORT OF THE (NO.) SESSION. see METEOROLOGY

WORLD MILITARY AVIATION (YEAR). see AERONAUTICS AND SPACE FLIGHT

TRANSPORTATION — AUTOMOBILES

387.71 UN
THE WORLD OF CIVIL AVIATION. (Subseries of: I C A O Circulars) (Editions in: Arabic, English, French, Russian, Spanish) a. price varies. International Civil Aviation Organization, Attn: Document Sales Unit, 1000 Sherbrooke St. W., Montreal, PQ H3A 2R2, Canada. TEL 514-285-8022. FAX 514-285-6769. TELEX 05-24513. (back issues avail.)
Description: Previews 3-year periods of civil aviation.

ZAKENREIS/BUSINESS TRAVEL. see *TRAVEL AND TOURISM*

387.7 ZA
ZAMBIA. DEPARTMENT OF CIVIL AVIATION. ANNUAL REPORT. (Text in English) a. Zambia Government Printing Department, P.O. Box 30136, Lusaka, Zambia. **Document type:** government publication.

ZHONGGUO MINHANG BAO/CIVIL AVIATION ADMINISTRATION OF CHINA. JOURNAL. see *TRAVEL AND TOURISM*

387.7 US
630 NEWS.* 1978. bi-m. $39 to non-members. Independent Federation of Flight Attendants, 720 Olive St., Ste. 1700, St. Louis, MO 63101-2320. TEL 212-818-1130. FAX 212-949-4058. adv.

TRANSPORTATION — Automobiles

388.3 US
A A A MOTORIST - WEST VIRGINIA. bi-m. membership. A A A West Penn - West Virginia, 5900 Baum Blvd., Pittsburgh, PA 15206. TEL 412-365-7243. FAX 412-362-0926. Ed. Ann Reed Rose. charts; illus. circ. 72,000. (tabloid format) **Document type:** newspaper.

388.3 US
A A A MOTORIST - WESTERN PENNSYLVANIA. 1952. m. membership. A A A West Penn - West Virginia, 5900 Baum Blvd., Pittsburgh, PA 15206. TEL 412-365-7243. FAX 412-362-0926. Ed. Ann Reed Rose. adv.; bk.rev.; charts; illus.; stat.; tr.lit. circ. 440,000. (tabloid format; back issues avail.) **Document type:** newspaper.
Supersedes: Western Pennsylvania Motorist (ISSN 1066-6869)
Description: Contains information for the motorist and traveler.

A A A TODAY (CINCINNATI). (American Automobile Association) see *TRAVEL AND TOURISM*

388.3 US ISSN 0890-7471
A A A TODAY MAGAZINE.* 1927. bi-m. membership. (American Automobile Association) Automobile Club Publications, 1000 AAA Dr., Heathrow, FL 32746-5063. TEL 614-653-0912. Ed. Johanna Guzik. adv.; bk.rev.; circ. 1,700,000. (controlled). (reprint service avail.)
Formed by the merger of: Motor Travel (ISSN 0027-2086); Motorist.

796.72 US
A A A TRAVELER (ALLENTOWN). 1910. 6/yr. membership. American Automobile Association - Lehigh Valley, Box 1910, Allentown, PA 18105-1910. TEL 610-434-5141. FAX 610-778-3381. Ed. Judy Barberich. adv.; charts; illus.; stat. circ. 93,000. **Document type:** newspaper.
Former titles: A A A Motorist (Allentown) (ISSN 1056-2532); (until 1991): A A A Today (Allentown) (ISSN 0896-4874); **Supersedes** (in 1987): Lehigh Valley Motor Club News.

A A A TRAVELER (FLORHAM PARK). see *TRAVEL AND TOURISM*

388.3 US ISSN 0001-0154
HE5623.A1
A A M V A BULLETIN. 1935. bi-m. $25 in U.S.; Canada $30; elsewhere $40. American Association of Motor Vehicle Administrators, 4200 Wilson Blvd., Ste. 1100, Arlington, VA 22203. TEL 703-522-4200. FAX 703-522-1553. Ed. Jennifer Cagan Thompson. charts; illus. circ. 2,500. **Document type:** newsletter.

629.222 SA
A A MOTORSPORT NEWS. 1983; N.S. 1992. q. A A Motorsport, P.O. Box 9444, Johannesburg 2000, South Africa. illus. **Document type:** bulletin.
Former titles (until 1993): A A Motorsport. Official Bulletin; (until 1989): A A S A Motorsport. Official Bulletin; S A Motor Sport Control Bulletin (ISSN 1010-8025)

629.286 UK
A B S MANUAL. (Antilock Brake System) 1993. a. £37. Glass's Information Services Ltd., Elgin House, St. Georges Ave., Weybridge, Surrey KT13 9TU, England. TEL 01932-823823. FAX 01932-846564. (Orders to: Sales and Marketing, St. Martins Ct., 37 Queens Rd., Weybridge, Surrey KT13 9TU, England) **Document type:** trade publication.
Description: Covers all the major elements involved in the fault diagnosis and repair of automobile antilock brake systems.

388.3 910.09 GW ISSN 0943-3945
A C E LENKRAD. 1954. m. membership. (Auto Club Europa e.V.) A C E Verlag GmbH, Schmidenerstr. 233, 70374 Stuttgart, Germany. TEL 0711-5303-200. FAX 0711-5303-210. TELEX 7254873-ACEP. Ed. Ernst Bauer. adv. contact: Ursula Hoerning. bk.rev. circ. 640,000. **Document type:** consumer publication.
Description: Automobile club magazine featuring the latest news on cars, parts and accessories. Articles also cover testing, road safety and travel. Includes readers' comments.

388.3 IT ISSN 0001-0715
A C I INFORMAZIONI. 1947. m. L.4000. Automobile Club d'Italia, Via Marsala 8, Rome, Italy. Ed. C. Storri. mkt.; stat.; index. circ. 3,000.

338.3 IT
A C I NEWS. 1949. bi-m. membership. (Auto Club Italia) Edit Data, Via S. Francesco Da Paola 22, 10123 Turin, Italy. Ed. Pier Domenico Clemente. adv.: B&W page L.3600000, color page L.4200000.
Formerly: A C I News Piemonte.

388 US
A C R A ALERT. 1978. irreg. membership. American Car Rental Association, 1225 I St., N.W., Ste. 500, Washington, DC 20005-3914. TEL 202-789-2240. FAX 202-371-1467. Ed. Tom Chaplin. circ. 2,500.
Description: Informs members of legislation affecting the car rental industry, and industry events.

388 US
A C R A REPORT. 1978. q. membership. American Car Rental Association, 1225 I St., N.W. Ste. 500, Washington, DC 20005-3814. TEL 202-789-2240. FAX 202-371-1467. Ed. Tom Chaplin. adv. circ. 2,500. (back issues avail.)
Description: Contains articles about the car rental industry - legislation, management features, news stories, new members.

629.286 SZ
A C S ZURICH. m. Swiss Motor Club, International Werbung, P.O. Box, CH-8032 Zurich 1, Switzerland. circ. 15,000.

388.3 GW ISSN 0007-2842
A D A C MOTORWELT. 1925. m. membership. (Allgemeiner Deutscher Automobil-Club e.V.) A D A C Verlag GmbH, Am Westpark 8, 81373 Munich, Germany. TEL 089-7676-0. FAX 089-76766799. Ed. Theodor Siepert. adv. contact: Michael Behrend. bibl.; charts; illus.; stat. circ. 11,382,492. (processed) Indexed: Dok.Str. **Document type:** consumer publication.

629.283 GW
A D A C SIGNALE. 1988. s-a. free. (Allgemeiner Deutscher Automobil-Club e.V.) A D A C Verlag GmbH, Am Westpark 8, 81373 Munich, Germany. TEL 089-7676-0. circ. 3,000. **Document type:** bulletin.

796.77 GW ISSN 0934-7569
A D A C SPECIAL AUTO. a. DM.14.80. (Allgemeiner Deutscher Automobil-Club e.V.) A D A C Verlag GmbH, Am Westpark 8, 81373 Munich, Germany. TEL 089-7676-0. FAX 089-76762500. **Document type:** consumer publication.

388 GW ISSN 0937-2938
A D A C SPECIAL GEBRAUCHTWAGEN. a. DM.12.80. (Allgemeiner Deutscher Automobil-Club e.V.) A D A C Verlag GmbH, Am Westpark 8, 81373 Munich, Germany. TEL 089-7676-0. FAX 089-76762500. **Document type:** consumer publication.

A D A C SPECIAL REISE. (Allgemeiner Deutscher Automobil-Club e.V.) see *TRAVEL AND TOURISM*

A F A S QUARTERLY. (Automotive Fine Arts Society) see *ART*

629.286 AG
A G E S. 1925. 6/yr. Asociacion de Garajes y Estaciones de Servico, Hipolito Yrigoyen 2738, Buenos Aires, Argentina. adv. circ. 1,000.

629.286 US
A I A UPDATE. 1983. m. membership only. (Auto International Association) Sema Publications, Box 4910, Diamond Bar, CA 91765-0910. TEL 909-860-2961. FAX 909-860-1709. Ed. Sherri Collins. circ. 350. **Document type:** newsletter, trade publication.
Formerly: A I A News.
Description: Discusses imported auto parts for foreign built cars domiciled in the US.

629.2 AT ISSN 0044-5681
A I M NEWSLETTER. (Supplement avail.: A I M Ads) 1967. 23/yr. Aus.$343 (foreign Aus.$493). Automotive Industry Matters Pty. Ltd., P.O. Box 184, Albert Park, Vic. 3206, Australia. FAX 61-59-899666. Ed. Trevor Dawson-Grove. adv.: page Aus.$1250; 225 x 175. **Document type:** newsletter.

A L P C A NEWSLETTER. (Automobile License Plate Collectors Association) see *HOBBIES*

A M G B A OCTAGON. (American M G B Association) see *ANTIQUES*

A M G B A QUARTERLY. (American M G B Association) see *ANTIQUES*

796.77 UK
A M MAGAZINE. 1948. q. membership. Aston Martin Owners' Club Ltd., 22 Bank St., Braintree, Essex CM7 7UP, England. FAX 01376-551431. Ed. Brian Joscelyne. adv.; bk.rev.; circ. 4,000. (controlled).
Formerly: A M Quarterly.

796.77 IT
A M: MENSILE INTERNAZIONALE DELL'AUTOMOBILE. 1989. m. L.62000 (foreign L.140000). Editoriale Giorgio Mondadori S.p.A., Via A. Ponti, 10, 20143 Milan, Italy. TEL 39-2-89166475. FAX 39-2-89125977. Ed. Daniele Pellegrini. adv.: B&W page L.19200000, color page L.25000000; adv. contact: G. Ruccio. illus. circ. 30,000. (back issues avail.)
Description: Covers developments in the automobile world, including racing news, vintage sports cars, road tests of new cars, profiles and histories of marques, and news of products and accessories.

388.3 GW ISSN 0001-1983
A M Z. (Auto Motor Zubehoer); Fachzeitschrift fuer das gesamte Kraftfahrzeugwesen. 1912. m. DM.12. Verlagsgesellschaft Gruetter GmbH, Postfach 910708, 30427 Hannover, Germany. TEL 0511-4609300. FAX 0511-4609320. TELEX 922579-DRUCK. Ed. Konrad Hofer. adv.; bk.rev.; illus.; stat.; tr.lit.; index. circ. 25,000. **Document type:** trade publication.
—CCC.

629.286 658 AT
A P A JOURNAL. (Auto Parts Accessories) 1974. bi-m. Aus.$30($60) Glenvale Publications Pty. Ltd., 4 Palmer Court, Mt. Waverley, Vic. 3149, Australia. TEL 61-3-544-2233. FAX 61-3-543-1150. Ed. David Morley. adv.: B&W page $1250, color page $1940; adv. contact: Leon Trimmings. circ. 7,328. (back issues avail.) **Document type:** trade publication.

A P R A (YEAR) MEMBERSHIP ROSTER AND TRADE DIRECTORY. (Automotive Parts Rebuilders Association) see *BUSINESS AND ECONOMICS — Trade And Industrial Directories*

TRANSPORTATION — AUTOMOBILES

308.3 US
A R A NEWSLETTER. 1970. m. free to members only. Automotive Recyclers Association, 3975 Fair Ridge Dr., Ste. 20 N., Fairfax, VA 22033-2924. TEL 703-385-1001. Ed. Christopher Murphy. circ. 2,000. **Document type:** newsletter.
Formerly: A D R A Newsletter.

338 368 US
A S P A FLASH.* 1990. irreg. (American Salvage Pool Association) International Business Ventures Corp., Box 42450, Phoenix, AZ 85080-2450. TEL 602-272-2900. FAX 602-269-1843. circ. 195 (controlled). (back issues avail.)

388 368 US
A S P A REPORT.* 1986. q. membership. (American Salvage Pool Association) International Business Ventures Corp., Box 42450, Phoenix, AZ 85080-2450. TEL 602-272-2900. FAX 602-269-8643. circ. 3,500.

629.2 IT ISSN 0001-2661
A T A ASSOCIAZIONE TECNICA DELL'AUTOMOBILE.* (Text mainly in Italian; occasionally in English) 1948. m. $7.50. Associazione Tecnica dell'Automobile, Via Pettinati 20, 10126 Torino, Italy. adv.; bk.rev.; abstr.; bibl.; charts; illus.; pat.; index. circ. 3,000. **Indexed:** Appl.Mech.Rev.
—BLDSC (1765.400000).

388.3 IT
A T A - INGEGNERIA AUTOMOTORISTICA. 9/yr. Via Pettinati 20, 10126 Turin, Italy. TEL 11-634-630. FAX 11-630-278. Ed. F. Filippi. circ. 4,000.

629.2 GW ISSN 0001-2785
TL3 CODEN: AUTZA6
A T Z. (Automobiltechnische Zeitschrift); fuer Forschung, Entwicklung, Konstruktion, Versuch und Fertigung. 1898. m. DM.267 (foreign DM.308) (effective 1996). Franckh-Kosmos Verlags-GmbH und Co., Postfach 106011, 70049 Stuttgart, Germany. TEL 0711-2191-332. FAX 0711-2191-350. Ed. Juergen Goroncy. adv.: B&W page DM.4800, color page DM.8400; trim 185 x 256; adv. contact: Eva-Maria Lesch. bk.rev.; bibl.; charts; illus.; stat.; index, cum.index every 20 yrs. circ. 4,283. **Indexed:** Appl.Mech.Rev., C.I.S. Abstr., Eng.Ind., Excerp.Med., Fluidex, INIS Atomind., ISMEC, Met.Abstr., Sh.& Vib.Dig. **Document type:** academic/scholarly publication.
—BLDSC (1833.000000); Ei; Faxon; SWETS. **CCC.**
Description: Trade publication for the automobile industry. Features construction, development, research, production engineering, and testing. Includes industry news, reports of meetings and events.

388.3 910.09 GW
A V D AUTO BORD UND SPORT BUCH. a. DM.5 for non-members. A v D Verlag GmbH, Lyonerstr. 16, 60528 Frankfurt a.M., Germany. TEL 069-6606270. FAX 069-6606260. **Document type:** consumer publication.
Formerly: A v D Auto Bordbuch.

ACCELERATOR. see *ANTIQUES*

796.7 FR
ACTION AUTOMOBILE. 1934. m. (11/yr.) 196 F. (foreign 246 F.) (effective 1992). Excelsior Publications, 1 rue du Colonel Pierre Avia, 75503 Paris Cedex 15, France. TEL 46-48-48-48. FAX 46-48-48-09. TELEX 631 994 F. Ed. Michel Guegan. adv. contact: Gilles de Keranflech. bk.rev.; charts; illus. circ. 306,181.
Formerly: Action Automobile et Touristique (ISSN 0001-7418)

ACTION ERA VEHICLE. see *ANTIQUES*

388 SZ
ADRA REVUE.* 10/yr. Mosse Annoncen, Postfach, CH-8025 Zurich, Switzerland. Ed. Alfred Wepf. circ. 17,000.

629.2 US ISSN 0065-2555
ADVANCES IN ENGINEERING. irreg. price varies. Society of Automotive Engineers, 400 Commonwealth Dr., Warrendale, PA 15096-0001. TEL 412-776-4841. FAX 412-776-3036. **Document type:** academic/scholarly publication.
Refereed Serial

388.3 US ISSN 0892-1121
AFTERMARKET BUSINESS. 1936. 12/yr. $30. Advanstar Communications, Inc., 7500 Old Oak Blvd., Cleveland, OH 44130. TEL 216-891-2604. FAX 216-891-2574. (Subscr. to: 131 W. First St., Duluth, MN 55802. TEL 800-346-0085) Ed. Sandie Stambaugh-Cannon. adv.; charts; illus.; stat. circ. 23,180. (tabloid format; also avail. in microform from UMI) **Indexed:** Bus.Ind., PROMT, SRI, Tr.& Indus.Ind. **Document type:** trade publication.
●Also available online. Vendor(s): Knight-Ridder, Inc. —UMI. **CCC.**
Former titles: Home and Auto (ISSN 0162-8801); Home and Auto Retailer (ISSN 0018-3911)
Description: Previews of new products, industry news, merchandising trends and company and business activities of automotive aftermarket retailers.

338.476 CN ISSN 0828-6116
AFTERMARKET CANADA. 1985. m. Can.$40 (U.S. $50; elsewhere $75). S G B Communications, 2050 Speers Rd., Unit 1, Oakville, ON L6L 2X8, Canada. TEL 416-847-0277. FAX 416-847-7752. Ed. Steve Manning. adv. contact: Shirley Brown. bk.rev. circ. 11,600. **Document type:** trade publication.
Description: Industry news on the automotive aftermarket. Includes information on wholesaling and replacement parts.

338.476 US
AFTERMARKET DISTRIBUTION. 10/yr. Automotive Warehouse Distributors Association, 9140 Ward Pkwy., Kansas City, MO 64114. TEL 816-444-3500. FAX 816-444-0330. Ed. Jennie Ison. **Document type:** newsletter, trade publication.
Formerly (until 1994): A W D A News.

629.222 378.002 US ISSN 1069-9996
AFTERMARKET TRAINING GUIDE. (Special issue included in: Brake & Front End, Underhood Service, and Importcar) 1993. a. $39.95 (foreign $79.95) (effective 1995). Babcox Publications, 11 S. Forge St., Akron, OH 44304. TEL 216-536-6117. FAX 216-535-0874. Ed. Doug Kaufman. adv.: B&W page $8265, color page $10280; trim 8 x 10 7/8. circ. 110,000. **Document type:** directory, trade publication.
Description: Contains over 1,600 listings of training programs in the automotive aftermarket.

796.77 CY
TO AFTOKINITO. 1972. m. £C9. Vista Publications, P.O. Box 4890, Arsinois 86, Flat 4, Nicosia, Cyprus. Ed. Andrew Karmios. adv. circ. 10,000. (back issues avail.)

629.286 US
AIR CONDITIONING & HEATING SERVICE & REPAIR - DOMESTIC CARS, LIGHT TRUCKS & VANS. 1977. a. $39. Mitchell International, Inc., 9889 Willow Creek Rd., Box 26260, San Diego, CA 92196-0260. TEL 800-648-8010. FAX 619-578-4752. illus. (also avail. in microform)
●Also available on CD-ROM.
Description: Auto service and repair manual for professional auto technicians.

629.286 US
AIR CONDITIONING & HEATING SERVICE & REPAIR - IMPORTED CARS & TRUCKS. 1977. a. $39. Mitchell International, Inc., 9889 Willow Creek Rd., Box 26260, San Diego, CA 92196-0260. TEL 800-878-6550. FAX 619-578-4752. illus. (also avail. in microform)
●Also available on CD-ROM.
Description: Auto service and repair manual for professional auto technicians.

629.2 FI ISSN 0355-9610
AJA. 4/yr. P.O. Box 16, SF-00381 Helsinki, Finland. Ed. Jukka Miettinen. adv. circ. 100,000.

388 US ISSN 0364-930X
TL215.A35
ALFA OWNER. 1958. m. $35. (Alfa Romeo Owners Club) Pfanner Communications, Inc., 1371 E. Warner Ave., Ste. E, Tustin, CA 92680-6442. TEL 714-259-8240. FAX 714-259-9377. (Subscr. to: 2468 Gum Tree Ln., Fallbrook, CA 92028) Ed. Elyse Barrett. adv.; bk.review.; illus. circ. 5,800.

388.3 US ISSN 0898-8986
ALL CHEVY. 1987. q. $2.50 per no. McMullen & Yee Publishing, 744 S. Placentia Ave., Placentia, CA 92670-6846. TEL 714-572-2255. FAX 714-572-1864.

380.5 SW ISSN 1101-7546
ALLA BILAR; uppslagsboken med data och priser paa alla modeller. 1973. a. SEK 98 (effective 1990). (Teknikens Vaerld) Bonniers Specialtidningar AB, P.O. Box 70452, S-107 26 Stockholm, Sweden. (Subscr. to: Bonniers prenumerations Service, S-103-64 Stockholm, Sweden)

796.77 CN ISSN 0821-7505
ALMANACH DE L'AUTO. 1984. a. Can.$11.95. Publicor Inc., 7 Chemin Bates, Outremont, Que. H2V 1A6, Canada. TEL 514-270-1100. FAX 514-270-6900. Ed. Claude Bedard. adv. circ. 24,018.

ALSACE AUTOMOBILE. see *TRAVEL AND TOURISM*

ALTERNATIVE TRANSPORTATION NEWS. see *TRANSPORTATION*

796.7 NO ISSN 0802-7730
AMCAR. 1976. 10/yr. Amcar Magazine A-S, P.O. Box 6006, N-7003 Trondheim, Norway. TEL 47-72-88-84-90. FAX 47-72-88-95-04. Ed. Terje G. Aasen. adv.: Color page NOK 12750; trim 190 x 277; adv. contact: Marit Larsen. circ. 27,000. (back issues avail.)
Description: Concentrates on things of interest to enthusiasts of American automobiles.

343 US ISSN 0093-4062
KF2210.Z95
AMERICAN AUTOMOBILE ASSOCIATION. DIGEST OF MOTOR LAWS. Key Title: Digest of Motor Laws. a. $11.95. American Automobile Association, Traffic Safety Department, 1000 AAA Dr., Heathrow, FL 32746-5063. TEL 407-444-7961. FAX 407-444-7956. Ed. Charles A. Butler. circ. 80,000. **Document type:** monographic series.

388.3 US
AMERICAN CARWASH REVIEW. 1964. s-a. $12. Lott Publishing Co., Box 1107, Santa Monica, CA 90406. TEL 310-397-4217. Ed. Dave Lott. adv.; tr.lit. circ. 3,031. (tabloid format) **Document type:** trade publication, newspaper.
Formerly: Car Wash Review (ISSN 0008-607X)

629.286 US ISSN 0095-1811
HD9999.C27
AMERICAN CLEAN CAR. 1972. bi-m. $33. Crain Associated Enterprises, 500 N. Dearborn St., Chicago, IL 60610. TEL 312-337-7700. Ed. Larry Ebert. adv. circ. 16,000. (reprint service avail. from UMI)
—UMI. **CCC.**

796.77 US
AMERICAN IMPERIALIST.* 1992. bi-m. $25 (effective 1992). Imperial Club of America, 2631 E. Behrend Dr., Phoenix, AZ 85024-1923. TEL 602-488-0330. Ed. John Rosen. adv. circ. 350. (back issues avail.)
Description: Dedicated to the protection, preservation, restoration and enjoyment of Imperial automobiles.

796.77 US ISSN 1041-3138
AMERICAN RODDER. 1987. m. $34.95 (foreign $46.95) (effective 1995 & 1996); newsstand price: $3.99. Paisano Publications, Inc., Box 1050, Agoura Hills, CA 91376-1050. TEL 818-889-8740. FAX 818-889-4726. adv.; circ. 65,561 (paid). **Document type:** consumer publication.

388 US ISSN 0274-8215
AMERICAN TOWMAN. 1977. m. $40. American Towman Network, 75 N. Maple Ave., Ridgewood, NJ 07450-3247. TEL 201-612-1300. Ed. Steven Calitri; Pub. Charles Duke, III. adv.; circ. 10,600 (paid); 15,900 (controlled). **Document type:** trade publication.
Incorporates: Road Service News.

TRANSPORTATION — AUTOMOBILES

338.476   UK   ISSN 0958-2495
ANGLIA AUTO TRADER. 1988. w. £83.20; newsstand price: £0.70. Anglia Auto Trader Ltd., 84 St. Benedicts St., Norwich, Norfolk NR2 4AB, England. TEL 01603-663232. FAX 01603-624114. (Subscr. to: 18 Vulcan House, Vulcan Rd. N., Norwich, Norfolk NR6 6AQ, England. TEL 01603-486692) circ. 13,195. **Document type:** catalog.
    Description: Lists cars, trucks, and other vehicles for sale in the Anglia area.

388.3   IT
ANNUARIO ACCESSORI AUTO. 1991. a. L.15000. Edigest s.r.l., Via Brenta 13, 00198 Rome, Italy. TEL 39-6-8540121. FAX 39-6-8845585. Ed. Paolo De Petris. adv.: B&W page L.9500000, color page L.15200000. circ. 127,000. **Document type:** consumer publication.

ANTIQUE AUTOMOBILE. see *ANTIQUES*

388.3   AG   ISSN 0004-0991
ARGENTINA AUTOMOTRIZ. vol.4, 1970. 6/yr. $20. Camara Argentina del Libro - Argentine Book Association, Av. Belgrano 1580, 6 Piso, 1093 Buenos Aires, Argentina. Ed. Hugo Brik. adv.; bk.rev.; charts; stat. circ. 27,800.

388.3   FR   ISSN 0751-5545
ARGUS DE L'AUTOMOBILE ET DES LOCOMOTIONS. (Annual supplement avail.: Les Statistiques de l'Automobile) 1927. w. 500 F. (foreign 760 F.) Societe Nouvelle d'Etudes, d'Editions et de Publicite, 1 pl. Boieldieu, 75082 Paris Cedex 02, France. TEL 42-61-83-03. FAX 49-27-09-50. TELEX ARGAUTO 214633F. Ed. Florence Loste; Pub. Jaques Loste. adv. contact: Jean-Pierre Dagory. circ. 200,000. **Document type:** consumer publication, corporate report.
    Description: Reports on the results of car, van, and motorcycle tests, as we;; as new and used car prices and automotive data of the European and French markets.

ARIZONA A A A HIGHROADS. see *TRAVEL AND TOURISM*

796.77   US
ARNOLT-BRISTOL REGISTRY. 1985. s-a. $10. Box 60, Brooklandville, MD 21022. Ed. Lee Raskin. adv. circ. 275. (back issues avail.) **Document type:** directory.

388   US
ARROW (ROCHESTER). 1957. q. $25 membership. Pierce-Arrow Society, Inc., 135 Edgerton St., Rochester, NY 14607. Ed. Bernard J. Weis. illus. circ. 1,100. (processed)

388.3   NE   ISSN 0004-3966
ARTS EN AUTO. 1934. 21/yr. membership. (Vereniging van Artsen) Wegener Tijl Tijdschriften Groep B.V., Postbus 9943, 1006 AP Amsterdam, Netherlands. TEL 31-20-5182828. FAX 31-20-5182843. Ed.Bd. adv.; bk.rev.; illus.; index; circ. 57,413 (controlled). **Document type:** trade publication.

ARZT UND AUTO; der kraftfahrende Arzt. see *MEDICAL SCIENCES*

ASIAN AUTO ABSTRACTS. see *TRANSPORTATION — Abstracting, Bibliographies, Statistics*

388   UK   ISSN 1355-6118
ASIAN AUTO DIGEST. 1992. 10/yr. £375($595) (effective 1995). Newspeed - Xyst, 134 Lots Rd., Chelsea, London SW10 ORJ, England. TEL 0171-352-9220. FAX 0171-352-9110. Ed. Paul Fisher. adv. contact: Stephen Fisher. (back issues avail.) **Document type:** newsletter.
    Formerly (until 1994): Japan Auto Digest.

ASSOCIATION FOR THE ADVANCEMENT OF AUTOMOTIVE MEDICINE. PROCEEDINGS. see *MEDICAL SCIENCES*

AUBURN - CORD - DUESENBERG CLUB NEWSLETTER. see *ANTIQUES*

388 629.286   UK   ISSN 0260-664X
AUSTIN HEALEY YEAR BOOK. 1978. a. Magpie Publishing Co., Holmerise, Seven Hills Rd., Cobham, Surrey, England. illus.

AUSTRALIA. BUREAU OF STATISTICS. MOTOR VEHICLE IN AUSTRALIA. see *TRANSPORTATION — Abstracting, Bibliographies, Statistics*

AUSTRALIA. BUREAU OF STATISTICS. NEW MOTOR VEHICLE REGISTRATIONS, AUSTRALIA, PRELIMINARY. see *TRANSPORTATION — Abstracting, Bibliographies, Statistics*

AUSTRALIA. BUREAU OF STATISTICS. TASMANIAN OFFICE. MOTOR VEHICLE REGISTRATIONS, TASMANIA. see *TRANSPORTATION — Abstracting, Bibliographies, Statistics*

388.3   AT
AUSTRALIAN FLEET MAGAZINE. 1986. m. Aus.$85. M P A Group, 20-24 Stokes St., Port Melbourne, Vic. 3207, Australia. TEL 03-646-5688. FAX 03-646-8330. Ed. Elisabeth Tuckey. adv. circ. 8,000. (back issues avail.)
    Description: Industry magazine for the automotive fleet of Australia.

796.77   AT
AUSTRALIAN JAGUAR DRIVER. m. Aus.$30. Jaguar Drivers Club of Australia, P.O. Box 2, Drummoyne, N.S.W. 2047, Australia. Ed. Owen Graham. adv. circ. 700.

388.3   AT   ISSN 1036-3254
AUSTRALIAN ROAD AND TRACK. 1986. 10/yr. Aus.$70. Stop Press Publishing Pty. Ltd., 51 Jackson St., Balgowlah, N.S.W. 2093, Australia. TEL 61-2-9070133. FAX 61-2-9070195. (Also dist. by: Gordon & Gotch, 68-72 Kingsrove Rd., Bellmore, N.S.W. 2193, Australia. TEL 61-2-789-6444) Ed. Robin Luck. adv.: B&W page Aus.$1235, color page Aus.$2475; adv. contact: Bruce Raymond. bk.rev. circ. 20,000. (back issues avail.) **Document type:** consumer publication.

388.3   AT
AUSTRALIAN SERVICE STATION & CONVENIENCE STORE NEWS. 1961. 6/yr. Aus.$49 (New Zealand Aus.$80; overseas Aus.$110). Berg Bennett & Associates Pty. Ltd., 73 Mullens St.., Balmain, N.S.W. 2041, Australia. TEL 61-2-5551355. FAX 61-2-5551434. Ed. Keith Berg; Pub. Keith Berg. adv. contact: Keith Berg. circ. 10,784. **Document type:** trade publication.
    Former titles (until 1993): Service Station (ISSN 0818-2884); *(until 1985):* Automotive Service (ISSN 0005-1586)
    Description: Matters concerning government legislation, marketing and technical information, customer relations and more.

388   AU
AUSTRO CLASSIC; oesterreichische Magazin fuer Motorgeschichte. 1991. bi-m. S.340($40) Verein fuer Motorgeschichte, Raimundgasse 6, A-1020 Vienna, Austria. TEL 01-2146798. Ed. Wolfgang Buchta. circ. 6,000. **Document type:** newsletter.

629.286   SZ
AUTO. Variant title: A C S Auto. (Text in German) 1901. 10/yr. 40 SFr. (foreign 60 SFr.). (Swiss Automobile Club) Vogt-Schild AG, Zuchwilerstr. 21, CH-4501 Solothurn, Switzerland. TEL 065-247247. FAX 065-247235. Ed. Erwin Thomann. adv.: B&W page 4700 SFr., color page 6800 SFr.; trim 185 x 260; adv. contact: Veronika Wegmueller. circ. 71,146. **Document type:** consumer publication.

629.286   IT   ISSN 1122-1674
AUTO; mensile di automobilismo e tecnica automobilistica. 1985. m. L.68000 (America L.210000) (typically set in Jan.). Conti Editore S.p.A., Via del Lavoro, 7, 40068 San Lazzaro di Savena (BO), Italy. TEL 051-6227111. FAX 051-6255418. TELEX 510212. Ed. Tommaso Valentinetti. adv.: B&W or color page L.27000000; 206 x 251. bk.rev. circ. 171,017. **Document type:** consumer publication.

388   GW
AUTO. 1953. fortn. Motor-Presse Stuttgart, Leuschnerstr. 1, 70174 Stuttgart, Germany. TEL 0711-18201. FAX 0711-1821669. (Subscr. to: Postfach 106036, 70049 Stuttgart, Germany) Ed. Oskar Weber. circ. 730,000. **Document type:** trade publication.

629.222   NE
AUTO; autojaargids. 1985. a. fl.6.95. Service Pers B.V., Postbus 9044, 1800 GA Alkmaar, Netherlands. TEL 31-72-158084. FAX 31-72-157540. Ed. P. Hooft. adv.; bk.rev. **Document type:** consumer publication.

388.3   II   ISSN 0005-0709
AUTO AGE. (Text in English) 1953. bi-m. Rs.40. Agelong, B-1-440, Kalyani 741 235, India. Ed. Amalendu Syam. adv.; bk.rev.; charts; illus.; stat. circ. 20,000. (tabloid format)

338 629.2   GW   ISSN 0179-4078
AUTO AKTUELL. m. Verband der Automobilindustrie e.V., Westendstr. 61, 60325 Frankfurt a.M., Germany. TEL 069-7570-0. FAX 069-7570-261. TELEX 411293. **Document type:** trade publication.

AUTO AND FLAT GLASS JOURNAL. see *CERAMICS, GLASS AND POTTERY*

629.2   NE   ISSN 0376-6918
AUTO & MOTOR TECHNIEK. 1940. 11/yr. fl.106. Misset (Subsidiary of: Reed Elsevier plc), Postbus 4, 7000 BA Doetinchem, Netherlands. TEL 31-8340-49911. FAX 31-8340-43839. TELEX 45481. Ed. A. Cupedo. adv.: B&W page fl.2907; unit 187 x 257; adv. contact: Cor van Nek. bk.rev.; charts; illus. circ. 21,750. **Indexed:** Excerp.Med. **Document type:** trade publication.
    —SWETS.
    Formerly: A M T - V A M Orgaan; *Formed by the merger of:* Auto Service; Auto en Motor Techniek.
    Description: Technical magazine dealing with the maintenance and repair of cars.

388.3   US   ISSN 1065-6685
AUTO & TRUCK INTERNATIONAL. Spanish edition: Auto & Truck International en Espanol (ISSN 1065-6693) (Editions in English and Spanish) 1917. 6/yr. $50 (free to qualified personnel). Hunter Publishing Ltd. Partnership (Subsidiary of: Johnston International Division), 25 Northwest Point Blvd., Ste. 800, Elk Grove Village, IL 60007. TEL 708-427-9512. FAX 708-427-2013. (Subscr. to: Box 5050, Des Plaines, IL 60017) Ed. Jim Halloran; Pub. Gary Hydes. adv.; bk.rev.; charts; illus.; tr.lit. **Document type:** trade publication.
    Former titles: Automobile International - Automovil Internacional (ISSN 0005-1594); Automotive World.
    Description: For vehicle repair shops, fleets, vehicle dealers, dealers of parts, accessories and equipment and automotive manufacturers in 183 countries and territories worldwide.

629.25   DK   ISSN 0108-8971
AUTO AVISEN AUTIG.* 1960. m. (Auto-Tilbehoers Grossist-Foreningen A U T I G) Dansk Bladforlag ApS, Hellerupvej 78, 2900 Hellerup, Denmark. (Co-sponsor: Drewsen) adv. circ. 10,251.
    Formerly (until 1982): A U T I G (ISSN 0005-0679)

388   GW
AUTO BILD. w. (Sat.). Axel Springer Verlag AG, Axel-Springer-Platz 1, 20355 Hamburg, Germany. TEL 040-3470-0. FAX 040-340224. Ed. Peter Felske. adv. contact: Peter Reckow. circ. 865,266. **Document type:** consumer publication.

388.3 629.2   DK
AUTO BLADET. 1936. M. DKK 110. Centralforeningen af Autoreparatorer i Danmark, Kirkevej 1-3, 2630 Taastrup, Denmark. FAX 45-44-53-13-10. Ed. Benny Kirkegaard. index. circ. 3,300. (reprint service avail.)
    Formerly: Motor - Service og Autoteknisk Tidsskrift (ISSN 0027-1993)

388   GW
AUTO BLITZ. m. Auto Media Verlagsgruppe, Ottilienstr. 1, 90461 Nuernberg, Germany. TEL 0911-94699-0. FAX 0911-9469960. Ed. Olaf Schilling. circ. 352,000. **Document type:** consumer publication.

796.77   IT
AUTO CAPITAL. 1981. m. L.81600. Rizzoli Editore-Corriere della Sera, Via Angelo Rizzoli 2, 20132 Milan, Italy. TEL 39-6-2588. Ed. Filippo Piazzi. adv.: page L.22200000; adv. contact: Flavio Biondi. circ. 44,602. **Document type:** consumer publication.

629   SP
AUTO-CLUB. 1983. bi-m. membership. Real Automovil Club de Espana, Jose Abascal 10, 28003 Madrid, Spain. TEL 447-92-00. TELEX 45411 CIJA E. Ed. Fernando Falco. adv.; bk.rev. circ. 215,000. **Document type:** consumer publication.

TRANSPORTATION — AUTOMOBILES

388.3   IT
AUTO D'EPOCA. m. L.81000 (foreign L.112000). Edizioni Pegaso s.r.l., Viale dell Republica 247, 31100 Treviso, Italy. TEL 39-4222-66503. FAX 39-4222-421775. Ed. Maurizio Catozzi. adv.: B&W page L.6000000, color page L.9000000.

629.2   SA   ISSN 0378-522X
AUTO DATA DIGEST. 1974. a. R.37. Mead & McGrouther (Pty) Ltd., P.O. Box 1240, Randburg 2125, South Africa. Eds. O. Peruch, W. Calcutt. circ. 4,500. **Document type:** trade publication.

388.3   SP   ISSN 0214-7750
AUTO DEALER. w. Tecnipublicaciones S.A., C. Albacete 5, 28027 Madrid, Spain. TEL 34-1-3261440. FAX 34-1-3262539. Ed. Patricia Rial.

388.3   SA
AUTO DEALERS' GUIDE. 1960. m. R.76.20. Mead & McGrouther (Pty) Ltd., P.O. Box 1240, Randburg 2125, South Africa. adv. circ. 6,000. **Document type:** trade publication.
    Formerly: Auto Dealers' Digest (ISSN 0005-0733)

627.286   IT   ISSN 0393-8387
AUTO E DESIGN. (Text in English and Italian) 1979. bi-m. L.79000($127) (foreign L.132500). Auto e Design s.r.l., Corso Francia 161, 10139 Turin, Italy. TEL 39-11-766628. FAX 39-11-758810. Ed. Fulvio Cinti; Pub. Fulvio Cinti. adv.: B&W page L.5200000, color page L.7000000. bk.rev. circ. 13,000.
    Indexed: DAAI. **Document type:** consumer publication.
    —BLDSC (1827.160000); SWETS.
    Description: Designed for auto industry's design centers, design studios, major designers and specialized schools.

388.3   IT
AUTO & FOURISTRADA. 1982. 10/yr. L.62400 (foreign L.90000). Rusconi Editori S.p.A., Viale Sarca 235, 20126 Milan, Italy. TEL 02-66191. FAX 02-6619-2879. Ed. Daniele Buzzonetti. adv.: page L.20000000. circ. 85,828. (back issues avail.)
    Formerly: Auto in Fouristrada (ISSN 0393-7887)

AUTO E SPORT. see SPORTS AND GAMES

388   FR   ISSN 0150-7230
AUTO EXPERTISE. (Includes supplement: Tarif Pieces Detachees) 1966. bi-m. (with q. supplement). 615 F. (foreign 705 F.). Editions Techniques pour l'Automobile et l'Industrie (ETAI), 22 rue de la Saussiere, 92100 Boulogne Billancourt, France. TEL 46-04-81-13. FAX 48-25-56-92. TELEX ETAIRTA 204 850 F. Ed. Jacques Dubroca. circ. 10,554.
    —CCC.
    Description: Provides repair estimates for cars in accidents.

796.77   HU   ISSN 0864-9219
AUTO EXTRA. 1988. m. $45 (effective 1992). Axel Springer - Budapest Kft. (Budapest), P.O.B. 430, 1537 Budapest, Hungary. (Subscr. to: Kultura, P.O.B. 149, 1389 Budapest, Hungary) Ed. Bencze Szabo Peter.

388   SZ
AUTO FLASH. (Text in French) m. Case Postale 66, CH-1223 Cologny, Switzerland. TEL 022-482112. Ed. Gerald Henriod. circ. 30,000.

629.286   CN
AUTO HEBDO. (Text in English, French) 1976. w. 130 DeLiege St., Montreal, Que. H2P 1J2, Canada. Ed. Elio Vettes. adv. circ. 28,000.

388   PO
AUTO HOJE. 1989. w. newsstand price: Esc. 269. Motorpress Lisboa, Av. Afonso III, Lote 2, Loja B, 1900 Lisbon, Portugal. TEL 351-1-8151134. FAX 351-1-8151542. Ed. Joao Ferreira; Pub. Luis Penha e Costa. adv. contact: Rita Vidreiro. circ. 22,000. **Document type:** consumer publication.

388   SZ
AUTO ILLUSTRIERTE. 1977. m. newsstand price: 6 SFr. Powerslide AG, Kreuzstr. 60, Postfach 282, CH-8032 Zurich, Switzerland. TEL 01-2518347. FAX 01-2514851. Ed. Stefan Donat; Pubs. August Hug, Richard Stolz. adv. contact: August Hug. circ. 30,000. **Document type:** consumer publication.

629.286   US
AUTO IMPACT; journal of operations and technology for metro area body shops. 1987. m. $48 (free to qualified personnel) (effective Jan. 1994). Maxco Publications, Inc, 1275 Bloomfield Ave., No. 6-36, Fairfield, NJ 07004-2708. TEL 201-785-0764. FAX 201-785-0753. Ed. Pat McCarthy. circ. 3,700 (controlled). **Document type:** trade publication.
    Description: Offers news and guidance for owners and managers of collision repair shops.

388.3   IT   ISSN 1120-7655
AUTO IN.* ceased. bi-m. L.48000 (foreign L.81900). Edizioni Conde Nast S.p.A., Piazza Castello, 27, 20121 Milan, Italy. TEL 39-2-85611. FAX 39-2-870686. Ed. Gino Rancati. adv.: page L.8350000. circ. 14,000. **Document type:** consumer publication.

AUTO INDEX. see TRANSPORTATION — Abstracting, Bibliographies, Statistics

388.3   AT   ISSN 1322-3690
AUTO INDUSTRY AUSTRALIA. 1919. m. Aus.$55. Victorian Automobile Chamber of Commerce, 464 St. Kilda Rd., Melbourne, Vic. 3004, Australia. FAX 61-3-829-3401. adv.; bk.rev.; charts; stat.; index. circ. 5,500. (back issues avail.) **Indexed:** Aus.Rd.Ind. **Document type:** trade publication.
    Former titles: Motor Industry Journal (ISSN 0729-0799); V A C C Journal (ISSN 0004-8712); Australian Automobile Trade Journal.

380.5 001.6   UK   ISSN 0262-317X
AUTO INDUSTRY NEWSLETTER. 1979. m. $440. Industrial Newsletters Ltd., 42 Market Sq., Toddington, Dunstable, Beds. LU5 6BS, England. TEL 01525-872060. FAX 01525-874759. Ed. John Mortimer. pat.; tr.lit.; index. (back issues avail.) **Document type:** newsletter.
    Description: Provides international coverage of the car, truck, and components industries for engineers and management-level professionals. Includes information about manufacturing routes, contracts placed, design ideas, and technological developments.

629.286   FR   ISSN 1242-014X
AUTO INFOS. w. 650 F. Publi-Inter, 89 rue Carnot, 92300 Levallois-Perret, France. Ed. Jean-Pierre Thibault. adv. contact: Olivier Charron.
    Former titles (until 1992): Automobile Infos (ISSN 1145-654X); (until 1989): C R A Infos (ISSN 0755-5245)

629.222   SA   ISSN 1021-8505
AUTO ITALIANA. (Text in English) 1993. bi-m. R.42. Spartan Communication, P.O. Box 9344, Pretoria 0001, South Africa. adv.; illus.; maps. **Document type:** consumer publication.

388.3   FR   ISSN 0005-0768
TL2
AUTO-JOURNAL. 1950. s-m. 360 F. Societe EDP, 8-10, rue Pierre Brossolette, 92300 Levallois Perret, France. FAX 40-87-42-37. Dir. Jacques Hersant. adv.; bibl.; charts; illus.; circ. 400,000 (paid); 267,000 (controlled).

388.3   BE
AUTO JOURNAL; journal du XXe siecle. (Text in English, French) 26/yr. Diffusion et Publicite S.A., 318 rue Vanderkindere, B-1180 Brussels, Belgium. Ed. P. de Vanssay. adv. circ. 20,000.

629.2   GW
AUTO-KATALOG. 1956. a. DM.15. Vereinigte Motor-Verlage GmbH und Co. KG, Leuschnerstr. 1, 70174 Stuttgart, Germany. TEL 0711-18201. FAX 0711-1821756. (Subscr. to: Postfach 106036, 70049 Stuttgart, Germany) Ed. Helmut Luckner. adv.: B&W page DM.18110, color page DM.33500; adv. contact: Peter Steinbach. abstr.; index. circ. 400,000. **Document type:** catalog.
    Formerly: Auto-Modelle.
    Description: Presentation of text and pictures of new cars from around the world.

388   XR
AUTO KATALOG. 1992. a. Motorpress Praha Spol.s.t.o., Voctarova 3, 18000 Prague 8, Czech Republic. TEL 02-6844619. FAX 02-6844791. Ed. Antonin Matejka; Pub. Dietmar Metzger. adv. contact: Vera Peskova. circ. 40,000. **Document type:** consumer publication.

388   HU   ISSN 0865-3518
AUTO KATALOGUS. 1989. a. 648 Ft. Motor-Presse Kiado Kft Budapest, Rakospatak ut. 70-72, H-1142 Budapest, Hungary. TEL 01-1835168. FAX 01-1830585. Ed. Kristof Karlovitz; Pub. Dietmar Metzger. adv. contact: Dietmar Metzger. circ. 65,000. **Document type:** consumer publication.

388.3   US   ISSN 0005-0776
HD9999.C27
AUTO LAUNDRY NEWS.* 1953. m. $20. Columbia Communications, Inc., 2125 Center Ave., Ste. 305, Fort Lee, NJ 07024-5859. TEL 212-532-9290. FAX 212-779-8345. Ed. Robert Storch. adv.; charts; illus.; stat.; tr.mk. circ. 18,500.

388   GW
AUTO MAGAZIN. 1978. m. Auto Media Verlagsgruppe, Ottilienstr. 1, 90461 Nuernberg, Germany. TEL 0911-94699-0. FAX 0911-9469960. Eds. Juergen Jablonski, Volker Figura; Pub. Juergen Jablonski. adv. contact: Holger Ries. bk.rev. circ. 94,988. **Document type:** consumer publication.

388   HU   ISSN 0864-8492
AUTO MAGAZIN. 1989. m. newsstand price: 228 Ft. Motor-Presse Kiado Kft Budapest, Rakospatak ut. 70-72, H-1142 Budapest, Hungary. TEL 01-1835168. FAX 01-1830585. Ed. Kristof Karlovitz; Pub. Dietmar Metzger. adv. contact: Dietmar Metzger. circ. 30,000. **Document type:** consumer publication.

388   XR
AUTO MAGAZIN. 1993. m. Motorpress Praha Spol.s.t.o., Voctarova 3, 18000 Prague 8, Czech Republic. TEL 02-6844619. FAX 02-6844791. Ed. Antonin Matejka; Pub. Dietmar Metzger. adv. contact: Vera Peskova. circ. 32,000. **Document type:** consumer publication.

AUTO MAGAZINE. see MILITARY

388   PO
AUTO MAGAZINE. 1992. m. newsstand price: Esc. 500. Motorpress Lisboa, Av. Afonso III, Lote 2, Loja B, 1900 Lisbon, Portugal. TEL 351-1-8151134. FAX 351-1-8151542. Ed. Alfredo Lavrador; Pub. Luis Penha e Costa. adv. contact: Pedro Dantos. circ. 25,000. **Document type:** consumer publication.

658.8   US   ISSN 0192-186X
AUTO MERCHANDISING NEWS; the national business magazine for the volume aftermarket. 1971. m. $48 (free to qualified personnel). Mortimer Communications, Inc., Box 1185, Fairfield, CT 06430. TEL 203-384-9323. FAX 203-375-1463. Ed. Bill Mortimer. adv.; bk.rev.; circ. 23,224 (controlled).
    Description: Designed to help retailers and distributors of auto parts and accessories run their businesses more efficiently.

629.2   BE
AUTO-MOTO-REVUE. (Text in Dutch, French) m. 2950 BEF. Federauto a.s.b.l., Bd. de la Woluwe 46, Bte 9, B-1200 Brussels, Belgium. TEL 32-2-7786200. FAX 32-2-7786222.

388.3   HU   ISSN 0005-0792
AUTO-MOTOR. 1946. s-m. $43.50. Lapkiado Vallalat, Lenin korut 9-11, 1073 Budapest 7, Hungary. TEL 222-408. (Subscr. to: Kultura, P.O. Box 149, H-1389 Budapest, Hungary) Ed. Imre Kokai. adv.: B&W page $1603. bk.rev.; charts; illus. circ. 280,000.

388.3 796.92   PL   ISSN 0867-4000
AUTO MOTOR SPORT. 1991. w. Auto Motor Press, Ul. Kredytowa 1a, 00-950 Warsaw, Poland. TEL 48-22-268429. FAX 48-22-268427. Ed. Jerzy Borkowski. adv. contact: Grazyna Kaluzynska. circ. 145,000.
    Description: Covers motorization, tourism, road safety.

TRANSPORTATION — AUTOMOBILES

388.3 796.72 GW ISSN 0005-0806
AUTO MOTOR UND SPORT. 1946. fortn. DM.130; newsstand price: DM.5.80. Vereinigte Motor-Verlage GmbH und Co. KG, Leuschnerstr. 1, 70174 Stuttgart, Germany. TEL 0711-18201. FAX 0711-1821669. Ed. Bernd Ostmann. adv.: B&W page DM.31135, color page DM.57600; trim 185 x 248; adv. contact: Rolf Priesmann. charts; illus. circ. 503,352. **Document type:** consumer publication.
—SWETS.
  Description: Articles, tests and reports on cars and everything relating to them.

388.3 796.72 GW
AUTO MOTOR UND SPORT SPEZIAL GEBRAUCHTWAGEN. 1976. a. DM.5.80. Vereinigte Motor-Verlage GmbH und Co. KG, Leuschnerstr. 1, 70174 Stuttgart, Germany. TEL 0711-1821226. FAX 0711-1821349. Ed. Helmut Luckner; Pub. Richard Stolz. adv. contact: Peter Steinbach. charts; illus.; stat.; tr.lit. circ. 400,000. **Document type:** catalog.

388.3 796.72 GW
AUTO MOTOR UND SPORT TESTJAHRBUCH. 1984. a. DM.12.80. Vereinigte Motor-Verlage GmbH und Co. KG, Leuschnerstr. 1, 70174 Stuttgart, Germany. TEL 0711-18201. FAX 0711-1821756. (Subscr. to: Postfach 106036, 70049 Stuttgart, Germany) Ed. Helmut Luckner; Pub. Richard Stolz. adv.: B&W page DM.9500, color page DM.17500; adv. contact: Peter Steinbach. charts; illus.; stat.; tr.lit. circ. 150,000. **Document type:** catalog.

388 629.286 GW
AUTO MOTORRAD FREIZEIT. 1986. m. DM.57.60; newsstand price: DM.4.80. A M F Verlag GmbH, Sattlerstr. 7, 23556 Luebeck, Germany. TEL 0451-898814. FAX 0451-8966211. Ed. Juergen Koslowski. circ. 156,000. **Document type:** consumer publication.

629.286 IT ISSN 1120-494X
AUTO OGGI; settimanale di auto e consigli pratici sul mondo dei motori. 1986. w. L.83100 (foreign L.145500). Arnoldo Mondadori Editore S.p.A., Casella Postale 1833, 20101 Milan, Italy. TEL 3199345. Ed. Sandro Liberali. adv.: page L.22800000. circ. 164,000.

388.3 US
AUTO PARTS REPORT. 1986. s-m. $425. International Trade Services, Box 5950, Bethesda, MD 20824-5950. TEL 301-229-2077. FAX 301-229-3995. Ed. Ronald J. DeMarines. (back issues avail.) **Document type:** newsletter.
●Also available online.
  Formerly: Automotive Parts International (ISSN 0896-3614)
  Description: Reports on news and trends involving the OE and aftermarket auto parts industry worldwide.

388.3 US ISSN 1042-6205
HD9710.U5
AUTO PRICE ALMANAC. 7/yr. $26.95. Pace Publications (Milwaukee), 1020 N. Broadway, Ste. 111, Milwaukee, WI 53202. TEL 414-272-9977. FAX 414-272-9973.
  Description: Dealer's cost and manufacturer's suggested list price for all new American and foreign cars, with used car prices covering the past ten years.

388.3 US
AUTO REMARKETING. 1990. m. $19.95. Cherokee Publishing Company, c/o Ronald H. Smith & Associates, Inc., 1150 S.E. Maynard Rd., Ste. 210, Cary, NC 27511-4164. TEL 919-469-9911. FAX 919-481-2658. Ed. Ron Smith. adv. circ. 20,000. **Document type:** trade publication.
  Formerly: Used Car Merchandising.
  Description: Reports on changes in the automotive industry and their effects on the buying and selling of used cars. Covers the used car operations of franchised and independent dealers and the preparation of cars for resale.

AUTO RENTAL NEWS. see BUSINESS AND ECONOMICS — Marketing And Purchasing

388.3 US
AUTO RETAIL REPORT; independent medium interpreting news of the automotive industry. 1989. bi-w. $427. United Communications Group, 11300 Rockville Pike, Ste. 1100, Rockville, MD 20852-3030. TEL 301-816-8950. FAX 301-816-8945. Ed. Donna Lawrence. bk.rev.; stat. circ. 5,000. (processed)
  Formed by the 1989 merger of: Autoservice Profit Report; (1945-1989): Motor News Analysis (ISSN 0027-1942)

388.3 SP ISSN 0005-1691
AUTO REVISTA; semanario del motor. 1959. w. 15000 ptas. (foreign 23800 ptas.). Tecnipublicaciones, S.A., C. Albacete 5, 28027 Madrid, Spain. TEL 34-1-3261440. FAX 34-1-3262539. Ed. Carlos Monroy. adv.; bk.rev.; bibl.; charts; illus.; mkt.; pat.; stat.; tr.lit. circ. 38,000.
  Description: Covers the automobile business and industry. Contains prices and test results.

388.3 US ISSN 1068-980X
AUTO REVISTA. (Text in English, Spanish) 1988. w. free. Revista Communications, Inc., 14330 Midway Rd., Ste. 202, Dallas, TX 75244-3514. TEL 214-386-0040. FAX 214-386-4255. Ed. Jacob Lozano; Pub. Ray Lozano. adv.; circ. 35,000 (controlled). **Document type:** consumer publication.
  Description: Focuses on the retail auto market in the Dallas - Fort Worth Metroplex.

388.3 US ISSN 1053-4318
AUTO SERVICE INSIDER.* 1988. bi-w. $195. Atcom, Inc., 1541 Morris Ave., Bronx, NY 10457-8702. TEL 212-873-5900. FAX 212-799-1728. Ed. Stephen Byers. circ. 500. (back issues avail.)
  Formerly: Auto Service Today (ISSN 1042-7414)

388 IT
AUTO 70; mensile di informazione tecnica e commerciale sul motorismo. m. L.2000 per no. Via G. Verdi 53, 10124 Turin, Italy. Ed. Giacomo Gaspardo Moro. adv. circ. 32,000.

796.77 US
AUTO SHOW WEEKLY. 1991. bi-w. $19.95. Fantasy Publications, 6034 S. Lindbergh Blvd., St. Louis, MO 63123-7041. TEL 314-487-0054. FAX 314-487-7284. Ed. Robert Albright. adv. contact: James Smoot Jr. bk.rev. circ. 50,000. **Document type:** consumer publication.
  Formerly: Auto Exotica.

388.3 US ISSN 1065-0792
AUTO SOUND & SECURITY. 1990. bi-m. $2.95 per no. McMullen & Yee Publishing, 774 S. Placentia Ave., Placentia, CA 92670-6846. TEL 714-572-2255. FAX 714-572-186.

388.3 IT
AUTO SPECIAL. 1990. 3/yr. L.10000 per no. Ediauto s.r.l., Via Solferino 31, 46040 Guidizzolo (MN), Italy. TEL 39-376-840104. FAX 39-376-9911238. Ed. Sergio Massaro. adv.: B&W or color page L.8000000. **Document type:** consumer publication, monographic series.

629.286 PL ISSN 1230-8536
AUTO SUKCES. 1990. m. $1.10 per no. Inter-Media, Ul. Narbutta 1, 02-564 Warsaw, Poland. TEL 48-22-488185. FAX 48-22-486273. Ed. Krzysztof Dabrowski. adv.; illus. circ. 100,000. **Document type:** newspaper.

388 AT
AUTO SUPERMARKET. 1985. w. A C P Publishing Pty. Ltd. (Subsidiary of: Trader Division) 77 Atherton Rd., Oakleigh, Vic. 3166, Australia. TEL 03-530-4055. FAX 03-530-4077. adv. contact: Gregg Hauthorpes. **Document type:** trade publication, consumer publication.
  Description: Provides information on vehicles for sale in Victorian automotive market.

388.33 AU
AUTO TANKSTELLE GARAGE. 1930. m. S.665. Bohmann Druck und Verlag GmbH & Co. KG, Leberstr. 122, A-1110 Vienna, Austria. TEL 0222-74095-0. FAX 0222-74095-183. TELEX 132312. circ. 5,600. **Document type:** trade publication.
  Former titles: Tankstelle und Garage; Garage, Tankstelle und Servicestation (ISSN 0016-4550)

629.2 SZ ISSN 0005-0857
AUTO-TECHNIK; der Automobil-Mechaniker. 1951. m. (10/yr.). 75 Fr. Verlag Aargauer Tagblatt AG, Bahnhofstrasse 39-43, 5001 Aarau, Switzerland. Ed. J. Pfyl. adv. circ. 8,500.

388.3 AU ISSN 0001-2688
AUTO TOURING; die Oesterreichische Kraftfahrzeug-Zeitung. Abbreviated title: A.T. 1947. m. S.100. Oesterreichischer Automobil- Motorrad- und Touring-Club Betriebe Gmbh, Schubertring 1-3, A-1010 Vienna, Austria. Ed. Alfons Malushka. adv.; illus. circ. 745,000.

388.3 HK
▼**AUTO TREND.** (Text in Chinese; table of contents in Chinese, English) 1994. 6/yr. HK.$291($68) for Asia; elsewhere $74. (Ministry of Domestic Trade, China Automotive Trade Corp., CC) Adsale Publishing Company, 14F, Deuon House, Taikoo Place, 979 King's Rd., Quarry Bay, Hong Kong. TEL 852-2811-8897. FAX 852-2516-5119. (Co-sponsor: China Automotive Circulation Association) Ed. Alfred Wong. adv. circ. 15,000. (back issues avail.) **Document type:** consumer publication.
  Description: Contains information on the analysis and interpretation of different cars and market trends.

388.3 US ISSN 1049-9601
TL1
AUTO TRIM & RESTYLING NEWS; maintenance and repair of auto upholstery, etc. 1953. 12/yr. $28 (in Canada $48; elsewhere $77). National Association of Auto Trim Shops, 6255 Barfield Rd., Ste. 200, Atlanta, GA 30328-4300. TEL 404-252-8831. FAX 404-252-4436. Ed. Gary Fong. adv.; bk.rev.; charts; illus. circ. 9,400. **Document type:** trade publication.
—CCC.
  Formerly: Auto Trim News (ISSN 0005-0865)
  Description: Covers automotive and marine soft goods, restoration and replacement, upholstery, convertible tops and carpets, as well as restyling items such as sunroofs, pinstriping and aerodynamic alterations.

388 796.7 GW
AUTO & MOTORRAD OLDTIMER. 1992. m. DM.54; newsstand price: DM.4.50. A M F Verlag GmbH, Sattlerstr. 7, 23556 Luebeck, Germany. TEL 0451-898814. FAX 0451-8966211. Ed. Juergen Koslowski. adv.; circ. 50,000 (paid). **Document type:** consumer publication.
  Former titles (until 1995): Auto Motorrad Oldtimer; Cabrio und Oldtimer Markt.

614.86 GW
AUTO UND VERKEHR. 1966. bi-m. Achelis und Partner GmbH, Firedenspromenade 87, 81827 Munich, Germany. TEL 089-4309014. FAX 089-4307284. Ed. Thomas Achelis. adv. contact: Erwin Stadler. circ. 30,000. **Document type:** consumer publication.

388 AU
AUTO UND WIRTSCHAFT. 1988. m. S.990 (foreign S.1750). Elektro und Wirtschaft Verlagsgesellschaft mbH, Wilhelminenstr. 91-IIC, A-1160 Vienna, Austria. TEL 0222-453149-0. FAX 0222-469032-30. Ed. Helmut Rockenbauer. circ. 23,600. **Document type:** trade publication.

388.3 SP
AUTO VERDE; la revista del 4x4. 1992. m. 4500 ptas. (Europe 9700 ptas., elsewhere 14100 ptas.); newsstand price: 425 ptas. Luike - Motorpress, C. Ancora 40, 28045 Madrid, Spain. TEL 34-1-3470100. FAX 34-13470204. Ed. Carlos Hernandez; Pub. Jose Luis Samaranch. adv.: B&W page 325000 ptas., color page 460000 ptas.; adv. contact: Antonino Berges. circ. 18,000. **Document type:** consumer publication.
  Description: Presents news and tests of 4x4 vehicles, information on 4x4 sports and recreation.

796.77 FR ISSN 0222-3996
AUTO VERTE. m. 328 F. (foreign 449 F.). Editions Lariviere, 15-17 Quai de l'Oise, 75166 Paris Cedex 19, France. TEL 1-40-34-22-07. FAX 1-40-35-84-41. TELEX 211 678 F. Ed. Richard Verdelet. adv.

TRANSPORTATION — AUTOMOBILES

629.2 621.38   FR   ISSN 0005-0881
AUTO-VOLT; Electrauto. 1929. m. 530 F. (foreign 645 F.). Editions Techniques pour l'Automobile et l'Industrie (ETAI), 20 rue de la Saussiere, 92100 Boulogne Billancourt, France. TEL 46-04-81-13. FAX 48-25-56-92. TELEX ETAIRTA 204850 F. Ed. Loic de Parcevaux. adv.; charts; illus.; index. circ. 7,560. **Indexed:** INSPEC (1978-1992).
—BLDSC (1835.500000). CCC.
Description: Provides information on electronic equipment of cars and ways to uphold and regulate them.

388.3   GW
AUTO ZEITUNG. 1969. bi-w. DM.210. Heinrich Bauer Spezialzeitschriftenverlag, Industriestr. 16, 50735 Cologne, Germany. TEL 0221-7709157. FAX 0221-714153. Ed. G. Wiechmann. adv.; bk.rev.; charts; illus. circ. 135,000. **Document type:** consumer publication.

629.286 338.476   GW
AUTO ZUBEHOER MARKT; Fachmagazin fuer Marketing, Trends und Technik. 1988. m. DM.120($85) Goethestr. 16, 58313 Herdecke, Germany. Ed. M. Kaufhold. circ. 4,500.
Description: For car-accessory traders and producers, technical and marketing news.

AUTOBUS. see TRANSPORTATION

388.3   UK   ISSN 1355-8293
TL1
AUTOCAR. 1895. w. £75($150) Haymarket Magazines Ltd., 38-42 Hampton Rd., Teddington, Middx. TW11 0JE, England. TEL 081-943-5000. FAX 081-943-5653. TELEX 895-2440-HAYMRT-G. (Subscr. to: 3-4 Hardwick St., London EC1R 4RY, England) Ed. Bob Murray. adv.; bk.rev.; charts; illus.; stat.; index. circ. 97,080. (also avail. in microform from UMI,PMC; microfilm from BHP; back issues avail.) **Indexed:** Br.Tech.Ind., DAAI, RAPRA. **Document type:** consumer publication.
—BLDSC (1828.000000); SWETS. CCC.
Former titles (until 1994): Autocar and Motor (ISSN 0955-5889); Incorporates (1903-1988): Motor (ISSN 0143-6945); (1895-1988) Autocar (ISSN 0005-092X)

338.3   SP
AUTOCATALOGO. 1981. a. 1200 ptas. Luike - Motorpress, C. Ancora 40, 28045 Madrid, Spain. TEL 34-1-3470100. FAX 34-1-3470204. Ed. Javier Recio; Pub. Jose Luis Samaranch. adv.; B&W page 530000 ptas., color page 750000 ptas.; adv. contact: Agustin Valero. circ. 50,000. **Document type:** catalog.

629.22   BE   ISSN 0778-3574
AUTOCCASION. (Text in French) 1987. bi-w. Maxipress S.A., 52 rue Broodcoorens, 1310 La Hulpe, Belgium. TEL 32-2-6520020. FAX 32-2-6521129. adv.; circ. 35,000 (controlled). **Document type:** newspaper.

388.3   AG   ISSN 0005-0946
AUTOCLUB; revista del automovilismo, turismo e informaciones. 1961. bi-m. Automovil Club Argentino, Av. del Libertador 1850, Buenos Aires, Argentina. TEL 824-1837. Ed. Cesar C. Carman. adv.; bk.rev.; abstr.; charts; illus.; mkt.; stat.; tr.lit. circ. 710,600.

AUTOCOURSE; the world's leading Grand Prix annual. see SPORTS AND GAMES

AUTOCOURSE INDY CAR OFFICIAL YEARBOOK. see SPORTS AND GAMES

388.3   GW
AUTOFACHMANN. (Includes instructional materials) 1952. m. DM.126. (Zentralverband des Kraftfahrzeughandwerks) Vogel Verlag und Druck GmbH & Co. KG, Max-Planck-Str. 7-9, 97082 Wuerzburg, Germany. TEL 0931-418-2145. FAX 0931-4182640. (Subscr. to: Vogel Verlag, 97064 Wuerzburg, Germany; Dist. in U.S. by: Vogel Europublishing, Inc., 19927 Villa Dr., Sonora, CA 95370. TEL 209-533-3555. FAX 209-533-9555) Ed. Werner Degen. adv.; B&W page DM.8976, color page DM.14436; trim 270 x 190; adv. contact: Eberhard Boer. bk.rev.; abstr.; charts; illus.; stat.; cum.index; circ. 92,953 (controlled) **Document type:** trade publication.
Formerly: Junghandwerker im Kraftfahrzeug Betrieb (ISSN 0022-6432)

388.3   IT
AUTOGIORNALE. 1975. fortn. L.2000 per no. Publicar, Via Lorenzini 15, 25015 Desenzano (BS), Italy. TEL 39-30-9911238. Ed. Sergio Massaro. adv.: color page L.15000000. circ. 50,000.

666.1 629.286   US   ISSN 1047-2061
AUTOGLASS. Variant title: Auto Glass Magazine. 1990. bi-m. $19.95. National Glass Association, 8200 Greensboro Dr., Ste. 302, McLean, VA 22102-3881. TEL 703-442-4890. FAX 703-442-0630. Ed. Nicole Miles. adv. circ. 7,000. **Document type:** trade publication.
Description: For the automotive and other transportation glass industries. Includes industry news and provides technical, management and new product information.

388.3   IT
AUTOGUIDA.* s-a. (Unione Nazionale degli Automobilisti) Editrice Pentapolis s.r.l., Via Aurelia 641, 00165 Rome, Italy. TEL 39-6-3203942. Ed. Edoardo Roberto. adv.; B&W page L.3000000, color page L.5400000. circ. 35,000.

629.222   II
AUTOGUIDE. (Text in English) 1966. m. Rs.150 (oveaseas $30). 1010, Faiz Rd., Karol Bagh, New Delhi 110 005, India. TEL 5729250. FAX 5755225. Ed. Joginder P. Malhotra. adv.: B&W page Rs.3000, color page Rs.7500; trim 230 x 180; adv. contact: M.P. Malhotra. cols./p.: 3.

388.3   GW   ISSN 0005-0989
AUTOHAUS; Fachmagazin fuer Unternehmensfuehrung und Werkstattpraxis. 1957. fortn. DM.256.80. (Zentralverband Deutsches Kfz-Gewerbe e.V.) Autohaus Verlag GmbH, Alte Landstr. 8-10, 85521 Ottobrunn, Germany. TEL 089-60805-0. Ed. Hannes Brachat. adv.; bk.rev.; charts; illus.; tr.lit. circ. 21,000. **Document type:** trade publication.
—CCC.

629.2   US   ISSN 0199-6908
AUTOINC. 1952. m. $20. Automotive Service Association, 1901 Airport Fwy., Ste. 100, Box 929, Beford, TX 76021. TEL 817-283-6205. FAX 817-685-0225. adv.; stat.; tr.lit. circ. 14,000.
Former titles: Automotive Independent; Independent Garageman.

629.286   MX
AUTOINDUSTRIA. 1971. m. Grupo Editorial Aviare, Queretaro 229, Desp. 402, Apdo. 71339, 06700 Mexico D.F., Mexico. TEL 5-584-31-94. FAX 2-584-48-21. (In U.S.: c/o Alfredo Villagran Arnaud, Fruitland Ste. 40, Los Angeles CA 10937. TEL 818-769-42-98) Ed. Alfredo Villagran Arevalo. adv.; bk.rev. circ. 30,384.

388.3   NE   ISSN 0005-0997
AUTOKAMPIOEN. 1908. 26/yr. fl.124.80 to non-members. Koninklijke Nederlandse Toeristenbond ANWB - Royal Dutch Touring Club, Wassenaarseweg 220, Postbus 93200, 2509 BA The Hague, Netherlands. TEL 31-70-3146119. FAX 31-70-3242509. Ed. J. Vroomans. adv.: B&W page fl.4944, color page fl.9394; trim 215 x 285; adv. contact: J.W. Boersen. bibl.; charts; illus.; mkt.; stat. circ. 72,575. **Document type:** consumer publication.
—SWETS.

388.3   GW
AUTOKAUFMANN. 1983. m. DM.202. (Zentralverband des Kraftfahrzeuggewerbes) Vogel Verlag und Druck GmbH & Co. KG, Max-Planck-Str. 7-9, 97082 Wuerzburg, Germany. TEL 0931-4182145. FAX 0931-4182640. (Subscr. to: Vogel Verlag, 97064 Wuerzburg, Germany; Dist. in U.S. by: Vogel Europublishing, Inc., 19927 Villa Dr., Sonora, CA 95370. TEL 209-533-3555. FAX 209-533-9555) Ed. Juergen Rinn. adv.; B&W page DM.8976, color page DM.14436; trim 270 x 190; adv. contact: Eberhard Boer. abstr.; charts; illus.; stat.; index. circ. 92,593. **Document type:** trade publication.

388   NE
AUTOKOMPAS. 1989. m. fl.50. Auto Vakbladen Uitgeverij, Postbus 100, 4920 AC Made, Netherlands. TEL 31-1626-87600. FAX 31-1626-87444. Ed. R. Kuchler. adv. contact: M. Kuchler. circ. 22,000. (tabloid format) **Document type:** trade publication.

388.3   GW   ISSN 0937-3381
AUTOKOSTEN UND STEUERN AKTUELL; Kosten und Steuern. vol.11, 1977. a. DM.54. (Allgemeiner Deutscher Automobil-Club e.V.) A D A C Verlag GmbH, Am Westpark 8, 81373 Munich, Germany. TEL 089-7676-0. circ. 9,000. **Document type:** bulletin.
Former titles: A D A C Handbuch - Geschaeftswagen (ISSN 0931-0053); Was Kostet der Geschaeftswagen; (until vol.15, 1979-80): Was Kostet Mein Auto?

629.286   UK
AUTOMATIC TRANSMISSION MANUAL. 1989. triennial. £65. Glass's Information Services Ltd., Elgin House, St Georges Ave., Weybridge, Surrey KT13 0BX, England. TEL 01932-823823. FAX 01932-846564. (Subscr. to: Sales and Marketing, St. Martins Ct., 37 Queens Rd., Weybridge, Surrey KT13 9TU, England) **Document type:** trade publication.

AUTOMOBIEL KLASSIEK. see ANTIQUES

388.3   SA   ISSN 0304-8721
HD9710.S7
AUTOMOBIL. (Text and summaries in Afrikaans, English) 1909. m. R.48. (Motor Industries' Federation) M & M Publications, P.O. Box 8859, Johannesburg 2000, South Africa. TEL 27-11-880-5790. FAX 27-11-880-5789. Ed. R.W. Emslie. adv.; bk.rev. circ. 9,833.
Formerly: Automobile in Southern Africa (ISSN 0005-139X)

388.3   SW   ISSN 0280-1981
AUTOMOBIL. 1981. m. SEK 410; newsstand price: SEK 39.50. Broedreana Lindstroems Foerlags AB, S-112 85 Stockholm, Sweden. TEL 46-8-692-01-60. Ed. Robert Petersson. adv.: B&W page SEK 9800, color page SEK 12450; trim 190 x 280. circ. 22,200. cols./p.: 4; pp./issue: 84.

629.2   GW   ISSN 0005-1306
AUTOMOBIL-INDUSTRIE; research, design, manufacturing. 1956. 8/yr. DM.210. Vogel Verlag und Druck GmbH & Co. KG, Max-Planck-Str. 7-9, 97082 Wuerzburg, Germany. TEL 0931-4182145. FAX 0931-4182640. (Subscr. to: Vogel Verlag, 97064 Wuerzburg, Germany; Dist. in U.S. by: Vogel Europublishing, Inc., 19927 Villa Dr., Sonora, CA 95370. TEL 209-533-3555. FAX 209-533-9555) Ed. Sybille Geitel. adv.; B&W page DM.5898, color page DM.8478; trim 270 x 190; adv. contact: Eberhard Boer. bk.rev.; illus.; tr.lit.; circ. 10,000. **Indexed:** Curr.Cont. **Document type:** trade publication.
—CCC.

338.476   GW   ISSN 0934-0394
AUTOMOBIL PRODUKTION. 1987. bi-m. DM.168 (Europe DM.198; overseas DM.248). Verlag Moderne Industrie, Justus-von-Liebig-Str. 1, 86899 Landsberg, Germany. TEL 08191-125-0. FAX 08191-125279. Ed. Claus Rentschler. adv.: B&W page DM.5950; trim 257 x 178; adv. contact: Thomas Heringer. circ. 7,294. **Document type:** trade publication.
—SWETS.

629.2 796.7 388.34 XR
AUTOMOBIL REVUE;* technicky mesicnik. (Quarterly supplement avail.: Stavba Automobilu) (Text in Czech or Slovak; summaries in English, German, Russian) 1955. m. $51. Unipress, spol. s r.o., Borivojova 23, 130 00 Prague 3, Czech Republic. (Dist. by: Artia, Ve Smeckach 30, 111 27 Prague 1, Czech Republic) Ed. Milan Josif. charts; illus. circ. 60,000.
Formerly (until 1992): Automobil (ISSN 0404-3529)

629.222   GW
AUTOMOBIL- UND MOTORRAD-CHRONIK. (Includes English Supplement) 1972. m. DM.78. Motor-Presse Verlag GmbH, Leuschnerstr. 1, 70174 Stuttgart, Germany. Ed. Halwart Schrader. adv.; bk.rev.; illus.; pat.; stat.; tr.lit.; index. circ. 12,000. (back issues avail.)
Description: Looks at antique cars.

TRANSPORTATION — AUTOMOBILES

388.3   CN   ISSN 0005-1330
L'AUTOMOBILE; pour le grossiste. (Text in French) 1939. bi-m. Can.$13.91($21) (foreign $21). Southam Magazine Group, 1450 Don Mills Rd., Don Mills, ON M3B 2X7, Canada. TEL 416-445-6641. FAX 416-442-2261. Ed. Mark Beauchamp. adv.; bk.rev.; charts; illus.; stat.; tr.lit. circ. 12,000. (back issues avail.) Indexed: Pt.de Rep. (1979-).
  Description: Emphasizes the latest in technical innovations along with market trends, new products, successful business analysis and how readers can increase their bottom line.

388.3   IT   ISSN 0005-1349
AUTOMOBILE. 1945. m. L.20000 (effective 1995 & 1996). (Automobile Club d'Italia) Editrice dell' Automobile s.r.l., Viale Regina Margherita 290, 00198 Rome, Italy. TEL 39-6-4402061. FAX 39-6-44231160. Ed. Carlo Luna; Pub. Paolo Basili. adv.; B&W page L.19400000, color page L.30800000. bk.rev.; film rev.; charts; illus.; stat.; tr.lit. circ. 1,152,968.

629.2   UK   ISSN 0955-1328
AUTOMOBILE. 1982. m. £50. Enthusiast Publishing Ltd., c/o Peter Hart, Holmerise, Seven Hills Rd., Cobham, Surrey KT11 1ES, England. TEL 0932-64212. FAX 0932-862430. adv.; bk.rev. circ. 15,000.
  Description: Reports on pre-1950 cars and commercial vehicles.

388.3   US   ISSN 0894-3583
AUTOMOBILE (NEW YORK). m. $19.94 in U.S.; Canada $29.90; elsewhere $29.94. K-III Magazines, 200 Madison Ave., New York, NY 10016. TEL 212-447-4700. FAX 212-447-4778. (Subscr. to: Box 55752, Boulder, CO 80322. TEL 800-289-2886) Ed. Davis E. Davis, Jr. (reprint service avail. from UMI) Indexed: Access (1988-). Document type: consumer publication.
  Description: Provides entertaining and informative coverage of automotive subjects, from road tests and new car reviews to vintage car collecting.

AUTOMOBILE & TRACTOR; ancillary & agri equipment. see AGRICULTURE — Agricultural Equipment

AUTOMOBILE ASSOCIATION MEMBERS HANDBOOK. see TRAVEL AND TOURISM

388   RH
AUTOMOBILE ASSOCIATION OF ZIMBABWE. MEMBERS' HANDBOOK. 1923. biennial. membership. Automobile Association of Zimbabwe, Fanum House, 57 Samora Machel Ave., Harare, P.O. Box 585, Zimbabwe. FAX 752552. TELEX 22167 ZW. Ed. J.M. Rowett. adv. contact: Mrs. F.M. Steblicki. circ. 50,000.
  Description: Information on services for members.

388.3   IT
AUTOMOBILE CLUB TORINO. 1949. bi-m. membership. Automobile Club Torino, Via Giolitti 15, 10123 Turin, Italy. Ed. Tancredi Savaro. adv. circ. 129,000.

AUTOMOBILE DESIGN LIABILITY. see LAW

338   US
THE AUTOMOBILE INDUSTRY: DOMESTIC & FOREIGN AUTO MANUFACTURERS. 1992. a. $395. Dun & Bradstreet Information Services (Murray Hill) (Subsidiary of: Dun & Bradstreet, Inc.), One Diamond Hill Rd., Murray Hill, NJ 07974. TEL 908-665-5224. FAX 908-771-7599. Ed. Mike Farinella.
  Description: Profiles the major foreign and domestic automobile manufacturers with an analysis of industry issues. Also covers truck manufacturers and the impact of pending regulations.

338.476   JA
THE AUTOMOBILE INDUSTRY - TOYOTA AND JAPAN. (Text in English) 1972. a. free. Toyota Motor Corporation, International Public Affairs Division, 1-4-18, Koraku, Bunkyo-ku, Tokyo 112, Japan. TEL 03-3817-9930. FAX 03-3817-9017. charts; illus.; stat. circ. 15,000. Indexed: JCT. Document type: corporate report.
  Formerly: Motor Industry of Japan; Incorporates: Toyota in Brief.

AUTOMOBILE INSURANCE LOSSES, COLLISION COVERAGES, VARIATIONS BY MAKE AND SERIES. see INSURANCE

388   FR
L'AUTOMOBILE - LES ESSAIS. 1990. a. 39 F. Societe des Editions Techniques et Touristiques de France, 60-62 rue Danjou, 92100 Boulonge, France. TEL 46-09-95-96. FAX 46-09-99-85. Eds. Jean-Luc Martin, Marc Schliklin; Pub. Monique Helfenberger. adv. contact: Eric Brame. circ. 130,000. Document type: consumer publication.

388   FR
L'AUTOMOBILE - LES OCCASIONS. 1993. a. 34 F. Societe des Editions Techniques et Touristiques de France, 60-62 rue Danjou, 92100 Boulonge, France. TEL 46-09-95-96. FAX 46-09-95-96. Eds. Jean-Luc Martin, Marc Schliklin; Pub. Monique Helfenberger. adv. contact: Eric Brame. circ. 110,000. Document type: consumer publication.

AUTOMOBILE MAGAZINE. see TRAVEL AND TOURISM

388.3   US   ISSN 0005-1438
TL1
AUTOMOBILE QUARTERLY. 1962. q. $59.95 (foreign $63.95). Automobile Quarterly, Inc. (Subsidiary of: Kutztown Publishing Co.), Box 348, Kutztown, PA 19530. TEL 800-523-0236. FAX 610-683-3287. Dir. Jonathan A. Stein. charts; illus.; cum.index: 1962-1987, 1988-1993. circ. 17,500. (back issues avail.) Indexed: A.S.& T.Ind., Ind.Sci.Rev. Document type: consumer publication.
  —Faxon; UMI; UnCover.
  Description: Contains articles on contemporary, modern, classic, collectibles, historic, special interest, sports, racing, postwar and pre-war cars.

388   FR
L'AUTOMOBILE - TOUTES LES VOITURES DU MONDE. 1978. a. 49 F. Societe des Editions Techniques et Touristiques de France, 60-62 rue Danjou, 92100 Boulonge, France. TEL 46-09-95-96. FAX 46-09-99-85. Eds. Jean-Luc Martin, Marc Schliklin; Pub. Monique Helfenberger. adv. contact: Eric Brame. circ. 200,000. Document type: consumer publication.

629.2   SZ   ISSN 0084-7674
AUTOMOBILE YEAR/ANNEE AUTOMOBILE/AUTO-JAHR. (Editions in English, French, German) 1953. a. 85 SFr. Editions J R, P.O. Box 81, CH-1000 Lausanne 9, Switzerland. TEL 021-3116733. FAX 021-3116734. (Dist. in UK by: Vine House Distribution, Waldenbury, North Common, Chailey, E. Sussex BN8 4DR, England; Dist. in US by: Motorbooks, Box 2, Osceola, WI 54020) Ed. Ian Norris; Pub. J.-R. Piccard. adv. circ. 39,000. Document type: consumer publication.
  —BLDSC (1832.700000); UMI.

388   US
AUTOMOBILER. 1923. bi-m. $2. (Automobile Club of Hartford) Hartford Automobiler, 815 Farmington Ave., West Hartford, CT 06119. TEL 203-236-3261. adv. circ. 177,000.

388.3   FR   ISSN 0759-6065
AUTOMOBILES CLASSIQUES. 1977. bi-m. 136 F. (N. America 421 F.). Conde Nast S.A., 73 rue de Vaugirard, 75006 Paris, France. TEL 40-62-01-85. FAX 45-55-47-13. (Subscr. to: 60732 Sainte-Genevieve Cedex, France. TEL 16-44-89-50-00; In U.S. subscr. to: International Subscriptions Inc., 30 Montgomery St., yth Fl. Jersey City, NJ 07302. TEL 201-451-9420) Eds. Antoine Prunet, Rosine Bertrand. adv.; bk.rev.; circ. 25,383 (controlled).
  Formerly: Enthousiaste.

318   US
AUTOMOBILES: LATIN AMERICAN INDUSTRIAL REPORT. (Avail. for each of 22 Latin American countries) 1985. a. $435 per country report. Aquino Productions, Box 15760, Stamford, CT 06901. TEL 203-325-3138. Ed. Andres C. Aquino.

AUTOMOBILISME ARDENNAIS. see TRAVEL AND TOURISM

796.77   IT   ISSN 0394-0128
AUTOMOBILISMO. 1985. m. L.71500 (foreign L.120000). Edisport Editoriale S.p.A., Via Gradisca 11, 20151 Milan, Italy. TEL 02-380851. FAX 02-38010393. Ed. Francesco Metrangolo. adv.: B&W page L.10700000, color page L.17600000. bk.rev.; charts; illus.; index. circ. 88,000.
  Description: Provides information on cars, industrial news and results of tests. Includes technical and sport reports.

388   IT   L.20000
AUTOMOBILISTA. 1983. m. L.20000. Edizioni Pubblire, Corso Garibaldi, 20121 Milan, Italy. adv. circ. 28,000.

388   FR   ISSN 0751-557X
AUTOMOBILISTE. 1966. bi-m. 60 F. 42, rue du Bac, 75007 Paris, France. Ed. Adrien Malght. adv.; bk.rev. circ. 18,000.

388.3   IT
AUTOMONDO; mensile automobilistico di politica attualita e cultura. 1964. 11/yr. L.30000 (foreign L.60000). Automondo s.r.l., Viale Stelvio 44, 20159 Milan, Italy. TEL 39-2-66803268. FAX 39-2-66804220. Ed. Corrado Canali. adv.: B&W page L.5000000, color page L.8000000. bk.rev. circ. 35,000. (back issues avail.)

380   UK
AUTOMOTIVE. 1990. q. Lucas Industries plc, Brueton House, New Rd., Solihull, W. Midlands B91 3TX, England. TEL 021-627-5791. FAX 021-627-6066. TELEX 335334-LUCARDO-G. Ed. J. Goodwin. circ. 35,000. Document type: trade publication.
  Description: Covers news relating to petrol and diesel engines, braking systems, and electrical systems in the commercial, bus, coach, farm, and marine fields.

388.3   US   ISSN 1071-1430
▼AUTOMOTIVE & TRANSPORTATION INTERIORS. 1994. m. $30 (Canada and Mexico $51; overseas $82). Shore Communications, Inc., 6255 Barfield Rd., Ste. 200, Atlanta, GA 30328-4300. TEL 404-252-8831; 800-241-9034. FAX 404-252-4436. Ed. Richard Lebovitz; Pub. Angelo Varrone. adv.: B&W page $2965; trim 8 1/8 x 10 7/8. tr.lit.; index; circ. 12,444 (controlled). (back issues avail.) Document type: trade publication.
  —CCC.
  Description: Provides information on manufacturing, management issues, and new technologies used in fabricating interiors of automobiles and other vehicles.

629   US   ISSN 0192-0995
TL255
AUTOMOTIVE BODY REPAIR NEWS. 1962. m. $60. Chilton Co., Chilton Way, Radnor, PA 19089. TEL 610-964-4000. FAX 610-964-4981. Ed. Tony Molla. adv.; bk.rev.; circ. 60,000 (controlled). (tabloid format)
  Description: For professional businesses engaged in automotive collision repair and paint-refinish.

629.286
AUTOMOTIVE BODY REPAIR NEWS (YEAR) BUYERS GUIDE AND FACT BOOK.* 1977. a. Chilton Publishing, One Chilton Way, Radnor, PA 19089. TEL 312-332-0210. FAX 312-332-0329. Ed. Neal E. Mann. adv.; tr.lit. circ. 62,039.

388   US   ISSN 0191-6459
AUTOMOTIVE BOOSTER OF CALIFORNIA. 1928. m. $7. KAL Publications Inc., 1037 N. Lake Ave., Pasadena, CA 91104. TEL 818-398-6848. FAX 818-398-6840. Ed. Kathy Laderman. adv. contact: Lynne Kenworthy. circ. 4,700. (back issues avail.) Document type: trade publication.
  Description: Covers the automotive parts aftermarket and industry in California and the West.

338.3   US
AUTOMOTIVE CONTACT. 1945? m. Automotive Contact, Box 517, Terre Haute, IN 47808. TEL 812-232-2441. Ed. T.L. Spelman. adv.; bk.rev. circ. 5,000.

338.3   US
AUTOMOTIVE CONTACT DIRECTORY. INDIANA. a. $27.95. Automotive Contact, Box 517, Terre Haute, IN 47808. TEL 812-232-2441. Ed. T.L. Spelman. adv. circ. 3,250. Document type: directory.
  Formerly: Indiana Automotive Directory.

TRANSPORTATION — AUTOMOBILES 6363

388.3 629.2 US ISSN 0005-1497
AUTOMOTIVE COOLING JOURNAL. 1956. m. $33.
National Automotive Radiator Service Association,
Box 97, E. Greenville, PA 18041.
TEL 215-541-4500. FAX 215-679-4977. E-mail:
narsa@aol.com. (Co-sponsor: Mobile Air
Conditioning Society) Ed. Wayne Juchno. adv.: B&W
page $1150, color page $1975; bleed
8 3/4 x 11 3/8; adv. contact: Jim Fortney. bk.rev.;
index. circ. 10,200. **Document type:** trade
publication.
  Description: Management and technical articles for
the owners and operators of automotive cooling
system service and air conditioning shops.

629 330 US
AUTOMOTIVE DEALERS DIGEST. fortn. Davco, Inc., Box
1272, Ridgewood, NJ 07451-1272.
TEL 908-583-2100. Ed. Raphael Cohen.

629.2 AT
AUTOMOTIVE ENGINEER. 1933. 6/yr. Aus.$65 to
non-members. Institute of Automotive Mechanical
Engineers (Inc.), 227 Great North Rd., Fivedock,
N.S.W. 2046, Australia. TEL 02-713-4711.
FAX 02-713-2671. Ed. Ralph Goss. adv.; bk.rev.;
charts; illus.; tr.lit.; circ. 26,551 (controlled). **Indexed:**
Agri.Eng.Abstr., Fluidex, HRIS. **Document type:** trade
publication.
  Formerly: Australian Automotive Engineering and
Equipment (ISSN 0004-8720)

629.2 UK ISSN 0307-6490
TL1
AUTOMOTIVE ENGINEER; for designers of cars, vans,
trucks, etc. 1962. 6/yr. £69 within EC; US $139;
rest of world £73 (effective 1995). (Institution of
Mechanical Engineers) Mechanical Engineering
Publications Ltd., Northgate Ave., Bury St. Edmunds,
Suffolk IP32 6BW, England. TEL 01284-763277.
FAX 01284-704006. TELEX 817376. Ed. John
Fenton. adv.; bk.rev.; charts; illus.; pat.; tr.lit. circ.
8,391. **Indexed:** API Abstr., API Catal., API Hlth.&
Environ., API Oil., API Pet.Ref., API Pet.Subst., API
Transport., Aus.Rd.Ind., BMT, Br.Tech.Ind., Eng.Ind.,
Excerp.Med., Fluidex, HRIS, Intl.Polym.Sci.& Tech.,
ISMEC, Met.Abstr., RAPRA, World Alum.Abstr.
Document type: trade publication.
  —BLDSC (1833.818000); Ei; Faxon; SWETS; UMI.
CCC.
  Formed by the merger of: Automotive Design
Engineering (ISSN 0005-1500); Journal of
Automotive Engineering.
  Description: News and informational briefs and
research papers on technological, design, and
product development pertaining to the mechanical,
electronic, and operational aspects of on- and
off-highway vehicles.

629.2 US ISSN 0098-2571
TL1 CODEN: AUEGBB
AUTOMOTIVE ENGINEERING MAGAZINE. (Supplements
avail.: Off-Highway Engineering (ISSN 1074-6919);
Truck Engineering (ISSN 1048-9584)) 1905. m.
$72 (foreign $126). Society of Automotive
Engineers, 400 Commonwealth Dr., Warrendale, PA
15096. TEL 412-772-7114. FAX 412-776-4026.
Ed. Daniel Holt. adv.; illus. circ. 100,000. (also avail.
in microfiche from PMC; microfilm from PMC)
Indexed: A.S.& T.Ind., Acad.Ind., Agri.Eng.Abstr., API
Abstr., API Catal., API Hlth.& Environ., API Oil., API
Pet.Ref., API Pet.Subst., API Transport., B.C.I.R.A.,
BMT, Cadscan, Ergon.Abstr., Excerp.Med., Fluidex,
Geotech.Abstr., Ind.Sci.Rev., INIS Atomind., INSPEC
(1978-1985), Intl.Polym.Sci.& Tech., ISMEC, Lead
Abstr., Met.Abstr., PROMT, RAPRA, Rural
Recreat.Tour.Abstr., Sh.& Vib.Dig., Tr.& Indus.Ind.,
World Alum.Abstr., Zincscan. **Document type:**
academic/scholarly publication.
  ●Also available online. Vendor(s): Orbit Search
Service.
  —BLDSC (1833.820000); Ei; Faxon; Genuine
Article; SWETS; UMI. **CCC.**
  Formerly (until 1972): S A E Journal of Automotive
Engineering (ISSN 0097-711X)
  Description: Covers advances in automotive
technology that can be applied to the design of new
or improved vehicle systems for the automotive
engineer.

388.3 US ISSN 0195-1564
HD9710.U5
AUTOMOTIVE EXECUTIVE. 1917. m. $24 (foreign $30).
National Automobile Dealers Association, 8400
Westpark Dr., 10th Fl., McLean, VA 22102.
TEL 703-821-7150. FAX 703-821-7234. Ed. Marc
H. Stertz. adv. contact: Donna Beatty. illus.; index.
circ. 24,000. (back issues avail.) **Document type:**
trade publication.
  —UMI; UnCover.
  Incorporates: N A D A Newsletter; (in 1979): Cars
and Trucks (ISSN 0164-3592); **Formerly (until
1974):** N A D A Magazine.

388.3 US ISSN 0005-1519
AUTOMOTIVE FLEET. 1961. m. (plus Factbook in April).
$35 (Canada $42; elsewhere $53). Bobit
Publishing Company, 2512 Artesia Blvd., Redondo
Beach, CA 90278-3210. TEL 310-376-8788.
FAX 310-376-9043. Ed. Mike Antich. adv.; charts;
illus.; stat.; circ. 22,000 (controlled). (also avail. in
microfiche from CIS) **Indexed:** SRI. **Document type:**
trade publication.
  Description: Covers the car and light truck fleet
market.

629.2 US
AUTOMOTIVE INDUSTRIES. (Annual Statistical Number)
1895. m. $70 (foreign $129). Chilton Co., 2600
Fisher Bldg., 3011 W. Grand Blvd., Detroit, MI
48202. TEL 313-875-2090. FAX 313-875-8148.
Ed. Marge Sorge. adv.; bk.rev.; charts; illus.; tr.lit.;
s-a. index. circ. 103,050. (also avail. in microfilm
from UMI,PMC; microfiche from UMI,CIS; reprint
service avail. from UMI) **Indexed:** A.S.& T.Ind., B.P.I.,
Bus.Ind., CAD CAM Abstr. (until 1992), Educ.Ind.,
Eng.Ind., Environ.Abstr., Excerp.Med., Ind.Sci.Rev.,
ISMEC, Met.Abstr., PROMT, Robomat. (until 1992),
SRI, Tr.& Indus.Ind., World Alum.Abstr.
  ●Also available online. Vendor(s): Knight-Ridder, Inc.,
Lexis-Nexis.
  —Ei; SWETS; UMI; UnCover. **CCC.**
  Former titles: Chilton's Automotive Industries (ISSN
0273-656X); (until 1976): Automotive Industries
(ISSN 0005-1527)
  Description: Contains comprehensive information
on all aspects of the automobile industry. Subjects
covered may include new cars production
scheduling, inventory control, materials development,
personnel management techniques, robotics and
automation applications and European
manufacturing.

338.476 SA ISSN 1018-8371
AUTOMOTIVE INDUSTRIES (YEAR). (Text in English) a.
(South African Foreign Trade Organisation) SAFTO,
Publishing Division, P.O. Box 782706, Sandton
2146, South Africa. TEL 27-11-883-3737.
FAX 27-11-883-6569. TELEX 4-24111 SA. adv.
contact: Dorine Pretorius. index. **Document type:**
directory.
  Formerly: Automotive (Year).

388 US
**THE AUTOMOTIVE INDUSTRY: A LOOK AT DEALERSHIP,
REPAIR SERVICES AND AUTO PARTS RETAILERS.**
1992. a. Dun & Bradstreet Information Services
(Murray Hill) (Subsidiary of: Dun & Bradstreet, Inc.),
One Diamond Hill Rd., Murray Hill, NJ 07974.
TEL 908-665-5224. FAX 908-771-7599. Ed. Mike
Farinella.
  Description: Examines dealerships, repair services
and auto parts retailers to determine the affect of
economic conditions.

388 338.478 UK ISSN 0951-158X
AUTOMOTIVE INDUSTRY DATA NEWSLETTER. Short title:
A I D Newsletter. 1983. s-m. £355. Automotive
Industry Data Ltd., P.O. Box 4211, Tamworth, Staffs.
B79 9BY, England. TEL 01827-383144.
FAX 01827-383151. Ed. John May. stat.; s-a. index.
(back issues avail.) **Document type:** newsletter.
  Description: Provides statistical analysis of motor
industry.

380.5 II
AUTOMOTIVE INDUSTRY OF INDIA - FACTS & FIGURES.
(Text in English) 1966. a. Rs.50. Automotive
Component Manufacturers Association of India, 80
Dr. Annie Besant Rd., Worli, Bombay 400018, India.
Ed. N. Srinivasan. circ. 2,000.
  Formerly: Automotive and Ancillary Industry.

388 UK ISSN 0967-0386
AUTOMOTIVE INTERIORS INTERNATIONAL. 1990. q.
£55 (foreign £65). Turret Group Plc., Turret House,
171 High St., Rickmansworth, Herts WD3 1SN,
England. TEL 01923-777000.
FAX 01923-771297. (Subscr. to: 177 Hagden Ln.,
Watford, Herts WD1 8LN, England. TEL
01923-228577) Ed. Chris Wright. adv. contact:
Dominic Frewin. tr.lit. (back issues avail.) **Document
type:** trade publication.
  Description: International journal for the design
and equipping of automotive interiors.

629.222 UK
AUTOMOTIVE INTERNATIONAL. 1993. m. £45 in the
UK; Europe £75; elsewhere £95. 5 Blenheim Centre,
Locks Ln., Mitcham, Surrey CR4 2JX, England.
TEL 44-81-687-2340. FAX 44-81-646-7926. Ed.
Mark Bursa. adv. contact: Nick White. circ. 17,500
(controlled). **Document type:** newspaper.
  Description: Serves world automotive industry
senior managers, covering the design, production,
and distribution of motor vehicles, with emphasis on
the European market.

629.222 US ISSN 0898-2155
AUTOMOTIVE INVESTOR. m. $99.50 (foreign $137).
Mary Ann Liebert, Inc., 1651 Third Ave., New York,
NY 10128. TEL 212-289-2300.
FAX 212-289-4697. Ed. Richard M. Langworth.
charts; illus.; mkt.; tr.lit.
  Description: Financial newsletter for buyers, sellers,
and collectors of vintage, classic, and special-interest
cars, 1925 onwards. Provides contacts for technical
information, analyzes market trends and investment
opportunities.

AUTOMOTIVE LITIGATION REPORTER; the twice monthly
national reporting service of litigation concerning
common automotive defects. see LAW

380 UK
AUTOMOTIVE MANAGEMENT. m. 1 Oxted Chambers,
185-187 Station Rd. E., Oxted, Surrey RH8 0QE,
England. TEL 01883-732000.
FAX 01883-730933. Ed. Mark Catterall. adv.
contact: Richard Dye. circ. 21,913 (controlled).
Document type: newspaper, trade publication.
  Description: Serves U.K. automotive retail senior
managers as well as senior directors of vehicle
manufacturing and import firms.

388.3 US ISSN 0733-2084
AUTOMOTIVE MARKET REPORT. 1951. w. $85.
Automotive Auction Publishing, Inc., 1713 Ardmore
Blvd., Pittsburgh, PA 15221-4405.
TEL 412-242-3900. Ed. Clyde K. Hillwig. adv.; mkt.
circ. 10,000. **Indexed:** PROMT. **Document type:** trade
publication.
  Formerly: Automotive Market Report and Auto
Week (ISSN 0005-1543)

388 UK ISSN 1354-2346
AUTOMOTIVE MARKETING REVIEW. 1989. m. £180.
Sewells International Ltd., Dart Business Centre,
Dartington, Totnes, Devon TQ9 6JE, England.
TEL 01803-867070. FAX 01803-866507. Ed.
Toby Proctor. bk.rev.; stat.; circ. 500 (paid).
Document type: newsletter.
  Description: World developments in automotive
markets and marketing practice.

388.476 380.1 US
**AUTOMOTIVE MARKETING WHO'S WHO A P A A SHOW
DIRECTORY.** 1976. a. (Automotive Parts and
Accessories Association) Chilton Co., Chilton Way,
Radnor, PA 19089. TEL 215-964-4226. adv. circ.
15,000.

388.3 US ISSN 0045-1088
AUTOMOTIVE MESSENGER. 1957. m. $10. Red Bud
Media Inc., 427 Chez Paree, Hazelwood, MO
63042. TEL 314-831-4000. FAX 314-831-3610.
Ed. Bill Winders; Pub. Bill Winders. adv.; bibl.; charts;
illus.; pat.; tr.lit. circ. 11,000. (tabloid format)
Document type: newspaper, trade publication.

TRANSPORTATION — AUTOMOBILES

388.3 629.2   US   ISSN 0005-1551
TL1
AUTOMOTIVE NEWS; engineering, financial, manufacturing, sales, marketing, servicing. 1925. w. $85 (effective 1995). Crain Communications Inc. (Detroit), Automotive News, 1400 Woodbridge Ave., Detroit, MI 48207-3187. TEL 313-446-6000. (Subscr. to: 965 E. Jefferson, Detroit, MI 48207) Ed. Peter Brown. adv.; B&W page $8850; adv. contact: Tony Merpi. bk.rev.; charts; illus.; mkt.; stat.; tr.lit. circ. 80,000. (tabloid format; also avail. in microform from UMI,PMC; microfiche from CIS) Indexed: Acad.Ind., B.P.I., Bus.Ind., PROMT, SRI, Tr.& Indus.Ind.
—BLDSC (1834.100000); UMI. **CCC**.

388.3   US
▼**AUTOMOTIVE NEWS GUIDE TO AUTO INDUSTRY EVENTS**. 1994. a. $12.95. Crain Communications, Inc. (Detroit), 1400 Woodbridge Ave., Detroit, MI 48207-3187. TEL 313-446-6000. Ed. Peter Brown. circ. 77,000.

629.2   US
AUTOMOTIVE NEWS MARKET DATA BOOK. 1933. a. $37.50 (effective Jan. 1992). Crain Communications, Inc. (Detroit), Automotive News, 1400 Woodbridge Ave., Detroit, MI 48207. TEL 313-446-6000. Ed. Peter Brown. adv. circ. 77,000. (also avail. in microform from UMI; reprint service avail. from UMI)
Formerly: Automotive News Almanac (ISSN 0067-2580)

388.3   US   ISSN 0005-156X
AUTOMOTIVE NEWS OF THE PACIFIC NORTHWEST. 1919. m. $10. 14789 S.E. 82nd Dr., Clackamas, OR 97015-9624. TEL 503-656-1456. FAX 503-656-1547. Ed. William H. Boyer. adv.; bk.rev.; illus.; tr.lit. circ. 4,800.

629.288   US   ISSN 0567-2317
TL1
AUTOMOTIVE REBUILDER; the independent voice of the rebuilding industry. (Includes Purchasing Directory published in Jan.) 1964. 12/yr. $49 (foreign $98) (effective 1995). Babcox Publications, 11 S. Forge St., Box 1810, Akron, OH 44309-1810. TEL 216-535-6117. FAX 216-535-0874. Ed. Dave Wooldridge. adv.; B&W page $4280. circ. 509 (paid); 23,003 (controlled). **Document type**: trade publication.
Description: Serves engine and vehicle mechanical parts rebuilders. Discusses management topics, technical information, new products and services, legislative issues and industry news.

629   US   ISSN 1058-9376
TL154
AUTOMOTIVE RECYCLING. 1975. bi-m. $30. Automotive Recyclers Association, 3975 Fair Ridge Dr., Ste. 20 N., Fairfax, VA 22033-2924. TEL 703-385-1001. Ed. Christopher Murphy. adv. circ. 4,000. **Document type**: trade publication.
Former titles (until 1990): Dismantlers Digest (ISSN 0192-0316); Automotive Recycler and Merchandiser; Auto Wrecker.

388.3   CN   ISSN 0005-1578
AUTOMOTIVE RETAILER. 1947. m. Can.$25.68. Automotive Retailers' Publishing Co. Ltd., 4281 Canada Way, Ste.120, Burnaby, BC V5G 4P1, Canada. TEL 604-432-7987. FAX 604-432-1756. Ed. Reg Romero. adv.; bk.rev. circ. 5,000. (also avail. in microform from UMI) Indexed: Can.B.P.I. **Document type**: trade publication.

629.286   CN   ISSN 0068-9629
AUTOMOTIVE SERVICE DATA BOOK. 1935. a. Can.$28.89 (foreign Can.$27). Southam Business Communications Inc., 1450 Don Mills Rd., Don Mills, ON M3B 2X7, Canada. TEL 416-445-6641. FAX 416-442-2261. Ed. David Booth. adv.

629.286   US
AUTOMOTIVE TIMES. 1980. m. $24 (free to qualified personnel). (Auto Body Association of Rhode Island) Maxco Publications Inc., 1275 Bloomfield Ave., No. 6-36, Fairfield, NJ 07004. TEL 201-785-0764. FAX 201-785-0447. Ed. Pat McCarthy. adv. contact: Carolyn Lighty. charts; illus.; stat.; tr.lit. circ. 800. (back issues avail.) **Document type**: trade publication.
Description: Offers news and information about the collision repair industry circulated to all licensed auto body repair shops in the state.

AUTOMOTIVE, TOOLING, METALWORKING, AND ASSOCIATED INDUSTRIES NEWSLETTER. see *OCCUPATIONAL HEALTH AND SAFETY*

388.3 658   US   ISSN 0889-3918
AUTOMOTIVE WEEK. 1975. w. $140. Automotive Week Publishing Co., Box 3495, Wayne, NJ 07474-3495. TEL 201-694-7792. Ed. Chuck Laverty. adv.; s-a. index. (back issues avail.) **Document type**: newsletter, trade publication.
Formerly: Automotive Buyer.
Description: Covers merchandise, marketing, trends and fast-breaking news reports of auto replacement market retailers, wholesalers and distributors.

629.222 658.8   UK
AUTOMOTIVES: THE INTERNATIONAL MARKET. (Subseries of: Market Direction reports) a. £1595($3190) (effective 1996). Euromonitor, 60-61 Britton St., London EC1M 5NA, England. TEL 0171-251-8024. FAX 0171-608-3149. (Addr. in N. America: Euromonitor International, 122 S. Michigan Ave., Ste. 1200, Chicago, IL 60603. TEL 312-922-1115. FAX 312-922-1157) (looseleaf format) **Document type**: trade publication.
●Also available online. Vendor(s): Data-Star, Knight-Ridder, Inc.
Description: Analyzes the market for new cars in France, Germany, Italy, Spain, the U.K., the U.S., and Japan.

388   IT
AUTOMOTO GIORNALE. 1970. m. L.2500. Club de Commone, c/o Lorenzo Janni, Ed., Via Cavour 38, 20094 Corsico (Milan), Italy. adv. circ. 30,000.

388.3   AG   ISSN 0005-1608
AUTOMOTOR.* 1960. m. Arg.$5($7) Erwin Toppelberg, Santiago del Estero 643, Buenos Aires, Argentina. Ed. Diego Perez Cevallos. adv.; charts; illus.; index. circ. 13,500.

338.3   SP
AUTOMOVIL. m. 4200 ptas. (Europe 9100 ptas.; elsewhere 13100 ptas.); newsstand price: 400 ptas. Luike - Motorpress, C. Ancora 40, 28045 Madrid, Spain. TEL 34-1-3470100. FAX 34-1-3470143. Dir. Carlos Hernandez. adv.; B&W page 430000 ptas., color page 600000 ptas.; adv. contact: Antonino Berges. circ. 80,000. **Document type**: consumer publication.

388.3   VE   ISSN 0005-1616
AUTOMOVIL DE VENEZUELA. 1961. m. Bs.1200($25) Promotrix, S.R.L., Av. Caurimare, Qta. Expo., Colinas de Bello Monte, Caracas, Venezuela. TEL 58-2-751-1355. FAX 58-2-751-11-22. Ed. Armando Ortiz P. adv. contact: Maria Ortiz. circ. 7,500 (controlled). **Document type**: consumer publication, trade publication.

388.3   SP   ISSN 0005-1632
AUTOMOVILISMO EN ESPANA. (Includes special nos.) 1942. m. 2200 ptas. Editorial Borrmari, S.A., Don Ramon de la Cruz 68, 6o, 28001 Madrid, Spain. TEL 1-402-96-07. FAX 1-401-88-74. Ed. Ramon Borreda Garcia. adv.; bk.rev.; bibl.; illus.; stat.; index. circ. 16,500.

388.3   US   ISSN 1045-1978
AUTOPARTS REPORT; news and analysis of the changing autoparts industry. 1990. 24/yr. $340 (foreign $405). International Trade Services, Box 5950, Bethesda, MD 20824-5950. TEL 301-229-2077. FAX 301-229-3995. Ed. Fred Donovan. **Document type**: trade publication.
●Also available online. Vendor(s): Data-Star, Knight-Ridder, Inc., NewsNet (AU09).
Description: Provides analysis of new marketing techniques, tracks the forces of consolidation, and explains the effects of industry changes.

388   HU   ISSN 0239-0426
AUTOPIAC. 1989. m. newsstand price: 89 Ft. Motor-Presse Kiado Kft Budapest, Rakospatak ut. 70-72, H-1142 Budapest, Hungary. TEL 01-1835168. FAX 01-1830585. Ed. Tibor Tothmatyas; Pub. Dietmar Metzger. adv. contact: Dietmar Metzger. circ. 50,000. **Document type**: consumer publication.

614.86   CN   ISSN 0836-1630
AUTOPINION. 1981. a. Can.$7.20. Canadian Automobile Association, 1775 Courtwood Cres., Ottawa, ON K2C 3J2, Canada. TEL 613-226-7631. FAX 613-225-7383. Ed. David Steventon. **Document type**: consumer publication.
Description: Published for the car buyer and automobile enthusiast. Contains specifications, editorial copy and feature articles on new and used automobiles.

629.2   SP   ISSN 0567-2392
AUTOPISTA. 1957. w. 15600 ptas. Luike - Motorpress, C. Ancora 40, 28045 Madrid, Spain. TEL 34-1-3470100. FAX 34-1-3470135. Ed. Javier Recio. adv.; B&W page 530000 ptas., color page 750000 ptas.; adv. contact: Antonino Berges. circ. 90,000 (controlled). (back issues avail.) **Document type**: consumer publication.

388.3   SP
AUTOPISTA PRUEBAS. a. 800 ptas. Luike - Motorpress, C. Ancora 40, 28045 Madrid, Spain. TEL 34-1-3470100. FAX 34-1-3470204. Ed. Javier Recio. adv.; B&W page 530000 ptas., color page 750000 ptas.; adv. contact: Agustin Valero. **Document type**: consumer publication.
Description: Presents the results of tests of 70 car models.

388.3   IT   ISSN 0005-1683
AUTORAMA; panoramica mensile delle attivita motoristiche. 1958. m. L.35000 (foreign L.70000). Vega Editrice s.r.l., Via Ramazzotti 20, 20052 Monza Parco, Italy. TEL 39-39-493101. Ed. Paolo Altieri. adv.; B&W page L.4000000, color page L.7200000; 185 x 250. circ. 30,000 (paid).

388.3   NE
AUTORETAIL. (Text in Dutch) m. (10/yr.). Misset (Subsidiary of: Reed Elsevier plc), Postbus 4, 7000 BA Doetinchem, Netherlands. TEL 31-8340-49911. FAX 31-8340-63638. (Editorial addr.: Hollywoodlaan 16, 1325 Almere, Netherlands. TEL 31-36-5375220) adv.; B&W page fl.2528, color page fl.4966; trim 210 x 297; adv. contact: Cor van Nek. illus. **Document type**: trade publication.

629.2   LX
AUTOREVUE. 1948. m. B.P. 231, L-2012 Luxembourg, Luxembourg. TEL 22-99-3. Ed. Paul Neyens. illus. circ. 10,000.

796.77 796.75   ER   ISSN 0868-4405
AUTOREVUU. 1990. m. $42 (effective 1993). Kirjastus Perioodika, Parnu mnt. 8, 0090 Tallinn, Estonia. TEL 0142-441-262. FAX 0142-442-484. (Subscr. to: Akateeminen Kirjakauppa, 128 SF, 00101 Helsinki, Finland) Ed. Vello Kala. stat. circ. 4,700.

629.286   IT
AUTORIPARATORE, IL GOMMISTA, ELETTRAUTO. bi-m. L.120000. Edizioni Pubblire, Corso Garibaldi, 42, 20121 Milan, Italy. TEL 02-801529. FAX 02-801520. adv. circ. 10,000.
Formerly: Autoriparatore; Incorporates: Gommista.

388.3   IT
AUTORUOTE 4X4. 1986. m. (11/yr.) L.110000 in Europe; America L.150000. Publimedia Societa Editrice, Corso Venezia 18, 20121 Milan, Italy. TEL 02-77521. FAX 02-781068. Ed. Francesco Buffa di Perrero. (back issues avail.)

388.3   II   ISSN 0005-0695
AUTOSPARK. 1949. m. Rs.125 (foreign Rs.300). 101 Vijay Apts., C.D. Barfiwala Marg, Andheri (West), Bombay 400058, India. TEL 6212733. Ed. Vijay Kumar Vats. adv.: B&W page Rs.4000, color page Rs.8000; trim 23 x 17. bk.rev.; charts; illus.; mkt.; stat. circ. 12,000.
Description: Covers the Indian automobile industry.

AUTOSPORT; specijalizovano nedeljno izdanje jugoslavenskog sportskog lista "Sport". see *SPORTS AND GAMES*

796.72   UK   ISSN 0269-946X
AUTOSPORT. 1950. w. £135($149) Haymarket Specialist Magazines Ltd., 60 Waldegrave Rd., Teddington, Mddx. TW11 8LG, England. TEL 0181-943-5804. FAX 0181-943-5922. TELEX 895 2440 HAYMRT G. Ed. Bruce Jones. charts; illus.; stat. circ. 53,486. (processed; also avail. in microform from UMI) **Document type**: consumer publication.
Description: Details automobile racing.

TRANSPORTATION — AUTOMOBILES

796.77   IT
AUTOSPORT. 1975. m. L.10000. (Autosport) Edicentro S.r.l., Via Giuseppe Mantellini 18, Rome 00179, Italy. Ed. Anselmo Baffigi. adv. circ. 110,000.

796.77   PO
AUTOSPORT. 1977. w. Esc.7700. Medipress Sociedade Editora de Publicacoes, Lda., Av. Infante D. Henrique 334, 1800 Lisbon, Portugal. TEL 351-1-8520756. FAX 351-1-8518990. Ed. Joao Rodrigues; Pub. Rui Freire. adv.: B&W page Esc.250000, color page Esc.350000; trim 155 x 215; adv. contact: Luis Caramelo. circ. 75,000 (controlled).

388.3   IT   ISSN 0005-1748
AUTOSPRINT. 1961. w. L.140000 (America L.370000). Conti Editore S.p.A., Via del Lavoro 7, 40068 San Lazzaro di Savena, Bologna, Italy. TEL 051-6227111. FAX 051-6258310. TELEX 510272. Ed. Carlo Cavicchi. adv.: B&W page L.10600000, color page L.17600000; 185 x 252. bk.rev. circ. 101,647. **Document type:** consumer publication.
    Description: Focuses on racing cars.

796.77   IT   ISSN 1122-1828
AUTOSPRINT ANNO. 1970. a. L.8000 (foreign L.25000). Conti Editore S.p.A., Via del Lavoro 7, 40068 S. Lazzaro di Savena (Bologna), Italy. TEL 051-6227111. FAX 6255418. Ed. Carlo Cavicchi. adv.: B&W page L.11200000, color page L.16800000. circ. 60,000. **Document type:** consumer publication.
    Description: Focuses on racing cars.

388.3   AG   ISSN 0326-0380
AUTOTECNICA.* vol.37, 1972. m. Union Proprietarios de Talleres Mecanicos de Automoviles, Alsina 2540, Buenos Aires, Argentina. Ed. Jose F. Vinotto. adv.; illus.

629.286   IT   ISSN 1121-3450
AUTOTECNICA. m. (11/yr.). L.65000 (foreign L.130000). Nuovi Periodici Milanesi, Via Molise 3, 20085 Locate Triulzi (MI), Italy. TEL 02-90780478. FAX 02-9077862. Ed. Sandro Colombo. adv.: B&W page L.3025000, color page L.5445000; trim 185 x 264; adv. contact: Marco Mordonini. **Document type:** newspaper.

388   GW
AUTOTEST UND TUNING MAGAZIN. m. Auto Media Verlagsgruppe, Ottilienstr. 1, 90461 Nuernberg, Germany. TEL 0911-94699-0. FAX 0911-9469960. Ed. Juergen Jablonski; Pub. Juergen Jablonski. adv. contact: Kurt-Guenther Kohlmann. circ. 77,781. **Document type:** consumer publication.

338.476   UK   ISSN 0308-7476
AUTOTRADE. m. $185. Morgan-Grampian Technical Press Ltd. (Subsidiary of: Morgan-Grampian plc), Morgan-Grampian House, 30 Calderwood St., London SE18 6QH, England. TEL 081-855-7777. FAX 081-316-3102. Ed. Susan Gay. adv. contact: Paul Golder. circ. 31,200. **Document type:** trade publication.
    Description: Covers all aspects of the automotive trades, including service garages, bodyshops, accessory retailers and distributors.

388   GW
AUTOTUNING. m. Auto Media Verlagsgruppe, Ottilienstr. 1, 90461 Nuernberg, Germany. TEL 0911-94699-0. FAX 0911-9469960. Ed. Juergen Jablonski; Pub. Juergen Jablonski. adv. contact: Kurt-Guenther Kohlmann. circ. 84,482. **Document type:** consumer publication.

388   SP
AUTOVIA. 1990. m. 1200 ptas. (Europe 3700 ptas.; elsewhere 5600 ptas.); newsstand price: 125 ptas. Luike - Motorpress, C. Ancora 40, 28045 Madrid, Spain. TEL 34-1-3470100. FAX 34-1-3470152. Ed. Jose Luis Sarralde; Pub. Jose Luis Samaranch. adv.: B&W page 250000 ptas., color page 380000 ptas.; adv. contact: Antonino Berges. circ. 30,000. **Document type:** consumer publication.

388.3   NE   ISSN 0005-0873
AUTOVISIE. 1956. 26/yr. fl.135 (foreign fl.273) (effective 1995). B.V. Uitgeversmaatschappij Bonaventura (Subsidiary of: Elsevier N.V.), Postbus 2158, 1000 CD Amsterdam, Netherlands. TEL 31-20-6914111. FAX 31-20-5674398. Ed. N. de Jong. adv.; bk.rev. circ. 52,450. **Indexed:** Excerp.Med. **Document type:** consumer publication.
—SWETS.

388.3   US   ISSN 0005-1802
AUTOWEEK. 1958. w. $28. Crain Communications, Inc. (Detroit), 1400 Woodridge Ave., Detroit, MI 48207-3187. TEL 313-446-6000. FAX 313-446-0347. TELEX 810-221-5122. (Subscr. to: 965 E. Jefferson, Detroit, MI 48207) Ed. Matt DeLorenzo. adv.: page $14605; adv. contact: Jay McKenzie. bk.rev.; illus. circ. 280,000.
●Also available online. Vendor(s): Lexis-Nexis.
    Formerly: Autoweek and Competition Press.
    Description: Covers new domestic and imported cars and trucks. Gives driving impressions, road tests and evaluations.

629.222   NE   ISSN 1381-7973
AUTOWEEK. (Text in Dutch) 1990. w. fl.111.80. Uitgeverij Spaarnestad B.V., Postbus 1, 2000 MA Haarlem, Netherlands. TEL 31-23-304304. adv.; circ. 135,000 (paid). **Document type:** consumer publication.

388.3   UK   ISSN 0005-1829
AUTOWORLD. 1962. 4/yr. £6. Renault U.K. Ltd., Western Ave., London W3 ORZ, England. Ed. Marguerite Nudd. adv.; bk.rev.; charts. circ. 150,000.
    Formerly: Ici Renault.

388.3   GW
AUTOZEITUNG. 1969. fortn. DM.150.80 (foreign DM.220). Heinrich Bauer Verlag, Burchardstr. 11, 20095 Hamburg, Germany. TEL 040-3019-0. FAX 040-326589. Ed. Guenter Wiechmann. circ. 180,225. **Document type:** consumer publication.

629.22   US   ISSN 0149-1911
TL215.A94
AVANTI OWNERS ASSOCIATION NEWSLETTER.* Key Title: Newsletter - Avanti Owners Association. q. $7.50. Avanti Owners Association International, Box 322, Uxbridge, MA 01569. **Document type:** newsletter.

388.3   US   ISSN 1073-1903
AVENUES (LOS ANGELES). vol.62, 1970. bi-m. membership. Automobile Club of Southern California, Box 60539, Los Angeles, CA 90060. TEL 213-741-4760. FAX 213-741-3033. Ed. Gail Harrington. adv.: B&W page $2999, color page $3799; adv. contact: Bob Bradley. charts; illus. circ. 2,700,000.
    Former titles (until Nov.-Dec. 1993): Auto Club News (ISSN 0746-8504); Auto Club News Pictorial (ISSN 0005-0725)

629.2 796.7 388.3   XV   ISSN 0352-5368
AVTO MAGAZIN. 1967. fortn. Delo Czp d.o.o., Dunajska 5, 61000 Ljubljana, Slovenia. Ed. Ivan Vidic.

338.3   RU   ISSN 0005-2337
                           CODEN: AVPRA3
AVTOMOBIL'NAYA PROMYSHLENNOST. 1934. m. $103 (effective 1996). Izdatel'stvo Mashinostroenie, 4, Stromynsky per., 107076 Moscow, Russia. TEL 095-269-7141. FAX 095-269-4897. Ed. V.P. Morozov. adv.: page DM.4000. bk.rev.; bibl.; charts; illus.; index. circ. 13,600. **Indexed:** Agri.Eng.Abstr., Biol.Abstr., Chem.Abstr., Met.Abstr., World Alum.Abstr. **Document type:** academic/scholarly publication.
—CASDDS.
    Description: Introduces the reader to new developments in the theory and practice of the automobile industry as well as to the state-of-the-art and trends in the automovile industry in foreign countries.

AVTOMOBIL'NYE DOROGI. see ENGINEERING — Civil Engineering

388.3   RU   ISSN 0005-2345
TL4   CODEN: AVTRAN
AVTOMOBIL'NYI TRANSPORT. Short title: A T. 1923. m. $102 (effective 1996). (Ministerstvo Transporta) Concern " Rosavtotrans", Likhov per 3, 103051 Moscow, Russia. TEL 200-20-02. FAX 282-95-58. TELEX 411-12-51. Ed. E.P. Kuprin. charts; illus. **Indexed:** Chem.Abstr.
—BLDSC (0005.000000).
    Description: Covers all aspects of transportation.

388.3   US
B C I NEWS. q. free to members. Battery Council International, 401 N. Michigan Ave., Chicago, IL 60611. TEL 312-644-6610. Ed. Peter Wiltjer. circ. 725.

388.3   GW
B M W CLUB JOURNAL. (Text in English and German) 1984. q. DM.20. B M W Club Europa e.V., Hufelandstr. 8A, 80788 Munich, Germany. TEL 089-38224820. FAX 089-38234390. adv.; bk.rev. circ. 17,500. **Document type:** newsletter.

796.77 157.61   UK   ISSN 0267-9841
BACK STREET HEROES. 1983. m. £28.80 (foreign £45). Myatt McFarlane plc, Trident House, Heath Rd., Hale, Altrincham, Cheshire WA14 2UJ, England. TEL 0161-928-3480. FAX 0161-941-6897. (Subscr. in US to: Motorsport, 550 Honey Locust Rd., Jonesburg, MO 63351-9600) Ed. Karen Tait; Pub. Steven Myatt. adv. contact: Graham Wells. bk.rev. circ. 41,604. (back issues avail.) **Document type:** consumer publication.
    Description: Covers motorcycles with particular emphasis on customizing and performance.

388.3   FR   ISSN 0005-6197
BASSE NORMANDIE AUTOMOBILE. 1949. m. free. Chambre Syndicale Nationale du Commerce et de la Reparation Automobile, Secteur Regional Basse-Normandie, 4 rue Pasteur, B.P. No. 7, 14011 Caen Cedex, France. Ed. Jean P. Pellan. adv.; circ. 1,000 (controlled).

BATTERIES INTERNATIONAL. see ENGINEERING — Electrical Engineering

629.2 621.38   US   ISSN 0005-6359
BATTERY MAN; international journal for starting, lighting, ignition & generating systems. 1921; N.S. 1959. m. $22 (foreign $55). Independent Battery Manufacturers Association, Inc., 100 Larchwood Dr., Largo, FL 34640. TEL 813-586-1408. FAX 813-586-1400. Ed. Celwyn E. Hopkins. adv.; bk.rev.; charts; illus.; tr.lit.; index. circ. 4,200. **Indexed:** Cadscan, Lead Abstr., PROMT, Zincscan. **Document type:** trade publication.
—BLDSC (1866.620000); Faxon; UMI.
    Description: Looks at automobile electrical system servicing.

388   JA
BEST CAR. (Text in Japanese) 1978. s-m. Kodansha Ltd., 12-21 Otowa 2-chome, Bunkyo-ku, Tokyo 112, Japan. TEL 03-3943-1292. FAX 03-3943-6226. TELEX J34509 KODANSHA. Ed. Yu Katsumata. circ. 470,000. **Document type:** consumer publication.
    Formerly: Best Car Guide.
    Description: For car enthusiasts.

388.3   SA   ISSN 1022-8330
▼**BEST DEAL;** South Africa's authorative used vehicle guide for buyers, sellers and owners. 1994. bi-m. newsstand price: R.5. Mead & McGrouther (Pty) Ltd., P.O. Box 1240, Randburg 2125, South Africa. adv.; illus. **Document type:** trade publication.

388   US
BIG BIRD. 1981. bi-m. $20. Thunderbirds of America, Box 2766, Cedar Rapids, IA 52406. TEL 715-884-6546. Ed. John Draxler. adv.; bk.rev.; stat. rec. 500. (looseleaf format) **Document type:** newsletter.
    Description: Provides news and information on restoration and maintenance for the Ford Thunderbirds, 1967 and on.

TRANSPORTATION — AUTOMOBILES

388 629.2 NO ISSN 0800-5850
BIL. (Text in Norwegian) 1975. 10/yr. NOK 290. Fagbladforlaget AS, Urtegaten 9, P.O. Box 9247, Vaterland, 0134 Oslo 1, Norway. TEL 47-22-68-03-13. FAX 47-22-68-20-85. Ed. Kjell Magne Aalbergsjoe. circ. 68,000. **Document type:** consumer publication, trade publication.
—CCC.
    Description: Includes results of testing of new cars and car related products. Covers technical features, in-car entertainment equipment.

629.222 DK ISSN 0006-2332
BIL OG MOTOR. m. DKK 225 (typically set in Jan.). Danmarks Automobilforhandler Forening, Alhambravej 5, DK-1826 Frederiksberg C, Denmark. TEL 45-31-31-45-55. FAX 45-31-31-30-75. adv.: B&W page DKK 4650, color page DKK 10850; trim 297 x 210. circ. 2,200.

388.3 DK ISSN 0107-0924
BIL-REVYEN. a. DKK 114.50. Bonniers Specialmagasiner A-S, Strandboulevarden 130, 2100 Copenhagen OE, Denmark. adv. circ. 80,000.
    Description: Full color catalogue of more than 1000 cars from all over the world.

388.3 NO ISSN 0006-2367
BILBRANSJEN - BILTEKNISK FAGBLAD. 1929. m. $20. Norges Bilbransjeforbund, Drammenv. 97, Oslo 2, Norway. Ed. Oyvind Holmvik. adv.; charts; illus.; stat.; tr.lit. circ. 5,000.
—CCC.
    Formerly: Bilbransjen; **Incorporates:** Oljebladet (ISSN 0030-2120)

796.77 DK
BILEN MOTOR & SPORT. 1967. m. DKK 34.50. Bonniers Specialmagasiner A-S, Strandboulevarden 130, 2100 Copenhagen OE, Denmark. Ed. Klaus Lyngfeldt. adv.: B&W page DKK 28900, color page DKK 37100; 406 x 258.
    Former titles: Bilen (ISSN 0106-9470); Bilen, Motor og Sport; Bilen og Baaden (ISSN 0006-2464)
    Description: Publishes articles and information on automobiles, new engineering and design.

388.3 DK ISSN 0901-6120
BILISMEN I DANMARK. 1967. a. free. Automobil-Importoerernes Sammenslutning, Ryvangs Alle 68, DK-2900 Hellerup, Denmark. Ed. Kai Noerrung.
    Description: Lists new-registered vehicles and vehicles in use, by make.

388.3 IC ISSN 1017-351X
BILLINN. 1984. bi-m. ISK 2874 (effective Jan. 1995). (Icelandic AAA) Frodi Ltd., Seljavegur 2, 101 Reykjavik, Iceland. TEL 354-515-5500. FAX 354-515-5599. Ed. Leo M. Jonsson. adv.: B&W page ISK 46900, color page ISK 81800; trim 19 x 27; adv. contact: Sjoefn Sigurgeirsdottir. circ. 8,000.
    Former titles: Bilabladid Billinn; Bilabladid Oekuthor.

796.77 SW ISSN 0347-2035
BILSPORT. (Includes Fyndboersextra) 1962. fortn. SEK 695 (foreign SEK 839); newsstand price: SEK 34.50. Albinsson & Sjoeberg Foerlags AB, P.O. Box 529, 371 23 Karlskrona, Sweden. TEL 46-455-3353-25. FAX 46-455-311715. TELEX 431 65 FABAS. Ed. Torbjorn Lundgren. adv.; circ. 53,700 (controlled). **Document type:** consumer publication.

388.3 US ISSN 0897-9421
THE BLUE SEAL. 1984. s-a. free. National Institute for Automotive Service Excellence, 13505 Dulles Technology Dr., Herndon, VA 22071-3415. TEL 703-713-3800. FAX 703-713-0727. Ed. Martin Lawson. stat. circ. 425,000.
    Description: For automotive technicians who have passed ASE certification exams, and their employers.

388.33 629.2 UK ISSN 0006-5501
BODY. 1914. m. £30 (Europe £46). Vehicle Builders and Repairers Association Ltd., Belmont House, 102 Finkle In., Gildersome, Leeds LS27 7TW, England. TEL 01532-538333. FAX 01532-381892. Ed. Stephen Briers. adv. contact: Karen Metcalf. illus.; stat. circ. 9,700. **Document type:** trade publication.
—BLDSC (2117.204500).

629.286 US
BODY ENGINEERING. s-a. American Society of Body Engineers, 25875 Jefferson, St. Clair Shores, MI 48081. TEL 313-774-8180. Ed. Robert Szefi. adv.; tr.lit. circ. 5,225. (reprint service avail.) **Indexed:** Met.Abstr., World Alum.Abstr.

629.286 US
BODY LANGUAGE. 1982. m. $75 (foreign $85) (subscr. includes Collision Parts Journal). (Automotive Body Parts Association) Sarco Management and Publications, 2900 Wilcrest Dr., Ste.122, Houston, TX 77042-2752. TEL 800-323-5832. Ed. Stanley A. Rodman; Pub. Stanley A. Rodman. circ. 400. **Document type:** newsletter.
    Description: Covers automobile repair industry including updates on legislation, regulation and legal activities as they affect the state of collision repair and the use of aftermarket (non-OEM) replacement body parts.

388.3 CN ISSN 0045-2319
BODYSHOP. 1970. bi-m. Can.$13.91($21) (foreign $21). Southam Magazine Group, 1450 Don Mills Rd., Don Mills, ON M3B 2X7, Canada. TEL 416-445-6641. FAX 416-442-2261. Ed. Brian Harper. adv. circ. 13,500.
    Description: Contains industry news, technical and business management, shop profiles, new products as well as features of interest to the trade.

629.286 US ISSN 0730-7241
BODYSHOP BUSINESS; the Babcox magazine for the body repair industry. (Includes LiftGuide published in Feb. & Collision Repair Market Profile published in June) 1982. 12/yr. $49 (foreign $98) (effective 1995). Babcox Publications, 11 S. Forge St., Box 1810, Akron, OH 44309-1810. TEL 216-535-6117. FAX 216-535-0874. adv.: B&W page $5085. tr.lit.; circ. 486 (paid); 58,035 (controlled). (reprint service avail.) **Document type:** trade publication.
    Description: Edited for the owners and managers of collision repair shops. Features management and technical articles to help run a better business.

380 UK
BODYSHOP MAGAZINE. 1987. 10/yr. £45 (overseas £60). Juniper Court, Boxwell Rd., Berkhamsted, Herts. HP4 3ET, England. TEL 01442-876686. FAX 01442-870740. Ed. Rod Herman; Pub. Christopher Mann. adv.; circ. 14,000 (controlled). **Document type:** trade publication.
    Description: Directed to proprietors, directors, and managers of bodyshops, factories, and distributors.

629.286 US
BODYSHOP TOOL & EQUIPMENT NEWS. 1992. bi-m. $22. Professional Tool & Equipment News, Inc., 23121 Plaza Pointe Dr., No. 130, Laguna Hills, CA 92653-1425. TEL 714-830-7520. FAX 714-830-7523. Ed. Tom Carruthers; Pub. Rudy Wolf. adv.: B&W page $2985, color page $4410; trim 7 7/8 x 10 7/8. circ. 40,200. **Document type:** trade publication.

388.3 NE
BOVAGKRANT. 1938. 20/yr. (Bond van Garagehouders (BOVAG) Misset (Subsidiary of: Reed Elsevier plc), Postbus 4, 7000 BA Doetinchem, Netherlands. TEL 31-8340-49911. FAX 31-8340-63638. adv.: B&W page fl.3792, color page fl.6230; trim 310 x 465; adv. contact: Cor van Nek. bk.rev. circ. 18,180. **Document type:** newspaper, trade publication.
    Formerly: Bovagblad (ISSN 0006-839X)
    Description: For managers in automobile service and leasing companies, repair shops and tire shops, motoring schools, and related firms.

629.286 AT
BOYCE'S SERVICE STATION MANUAL. 1985. a. Aus.$60($70) David Boyce Publishing and Associates, 44 Regent St., Redfern, N.S.W. 2016, Australia. circ. 2,500.
    Description: For mechanics servicing the auto industry.

388.3 US ISSN 1056-6686
BRACKET RACING, U S A. 1989. 8/yr. $17.95. C S K Publishing Co., Inc., 299 Market St., Saddle Brook, NJ 07662. TEL 201-712-9300. FAX 201-712-9899. (Subscr. to: Box 1010, Denville, NJ 07834) Ed. Dale Wilson. adv.; bk.rev. circ. 24,500. (back issues avail.) **Document type:** consumer publication.
    Description: Geared toward bracket racers, with information on staging, reaction time, rollout, finish line strategies, vehicle preparation, safety equipment, and coverage of all major events.

388.33 US ISSN 0193-726X
TL275.A1
BRAKE & FRONT END; the complete undercar service magazine. (Includes LiftGuide published in Feb. & Aftermarket Training Guide published in July) 1931. 13/yr. $59 (foreign $115) (effective 1995). Babcox Publications, 11 S. Forge St., Box 1810, Akron, OH 44309-1810. TEL 216-535-6117. FAX 216-535-0874. Ed. Douglas Kaufman. adv.: B&W page $4395. bk.rev.; illus.; charts; index; circ. 40,000. circ. 1,128 (paid). **Document type:** trade publication.
    Formerly: Brake and Front End Service (ISSN 0006-9019)
    Description: Directed to shop owners, managers and technicians who are merchandisers of break, front end, chassis - steering - suspension, front-wheel drive, wheel alignment and balancing, exhaust and driveline work.

388.3 US ISSN 1052-0929
BRITISH CAR. 1985. bi-m. $22.95 (foreign $34.95). Box 9099, Canoga Park, CA 91309. TEL 818-710-1234. FAX 818-710-1877. Ed. Dave Destler. adv.; bk.rev. circ. 35,000. **Document type:** consumer publication.
    Formerly: British Car and Bike.

BRITISH RACING NEWS. see SPORTS AND GAMES

796.72 CN ISSN 0045-3226
BROKEN SPOKE. 1958. bi-m. Can.$10. Calgary Sports Car Club, P.O. Box 61143 Kensington Postal Stn., Calgary, AB T2N 4S6, Canada. TEL 403-285-1177. FAX 403-289-7256. Eds. Akio Nagatomi, Steve Barry. adv.; circ. 200 (controlled). **Document type:** newsletter.
    Description: Covers club, regional and national motorsport news, coming events in the western Canada area and technical articles pertaining to racing automobiles.

388 GW ISSN 0724-5955
BRUDERHILFE JOURNAL. 1976. q. DM.2.20. Publikom Z Verlagsgesellschaft mbH, Frankfurterstr. 168, 34121 Kassel, Germany. TEL 0561-2031787. FAX 0561-2032745. Ed. Armin Noll. adv. contact: Ute Behrens. circ. 311,174. **Document type:** bulletin.
    Formerly (until 1982): Bruderhilfe - Nachrichten (ISSN 0172-7508)

388 910.09 US ISSN 0162-9689
TL232
BUS WORLD; magazine of buses and bus systems. 1978. q. $14 (Canada $16; elsewhere $24). Stauss Publications, Box 39, Woodland Hills, CA 91365. TEL 818-710-0208. Ed. Julian Wolinsky; Pub. Ed Stauss. adv. contact: Barbara Buck. bk.rev.; charts; illus. circ. 5,000. **Document type:** trade publication.

796.77 AT ISSN 0155-0535
BUSHDRIVER. 1977. bi-m. Aus.$26($29.10) Ric Williams and Associates Pty. Ltd., 25 Valley Park Cres., Turramurra, N.S.W. 2074, Australia. FAX 61-2-488-8550. Ed. Ric Williams. adv.; charts; illus.; tr.lit. circ. 2,000. (back issues avail.) **Description:** Contains articles on travel and vehicle tests. Provides a historical background and tips on four-wheel drive.

BUSINESS DRIVER. see BUSINESS AND ECONOMICS — Marketing And Purchasing

388 658.8 UK ISSN 0954-2159
BUSINESS RATIO REPORT: CAR DEALERS.
INTERMEDIATE; an industry sector analysis. 1974. a. I C C Business Ratios Ltd., Freepost, Field House, Hampton, Mddx. TW12 1BR, England. TEL 081-783-0977. FAX 081-783-1940. charts; stat. **Document type:** trade publication.
    Superseded in part (in 1988): Business Ratio Report: Car Dealers (ISSN 0261-7544)

388 658.8   UK   ISSN 0954-2140
BUSINESS RATIO REPORT: CAR DEALERS. MAJOR; an industry sector analysis. 1974. a. I C C Business Ratios Ltd., Freepost, Field House, Hampton, Mddx. TW12 1BR, England. TEL 081-783-0977. FAX 081-783-1940. charts; stat. **Document type:** trade publication.
    Supersedes in part (in 1988): Business Ratio Report: Car Dealers (ISSN 0261-7544)

388 658.8   UK   ISSN 0261-765X
BUSINESS RATIO REPORT: COMMERCIAL VEHICLES; an industry sector analysis. 1979. a. I C C Business Ratios Ltd., Freepost, Field House, Hampton, Mddx. TW12 1BR, England. TEL 081-783-0977. FAX 081-783-1940. charts; stat. **Document type:** trade publication.
    —BLDSC (3337.301500).

388 658.8   UK   ISSN 0261-815X
BUSINESS RATIO REPORT: FOREIGN VEHICLE DISTRIBUTORS; an industry sector analysis. 1975. a. I C C Business Ratios Ltd., Freepost, Field House, Hampton, Mddx. TW12 1BR, England. TEL 081-783-0977. FAX 081-783-1940. charts; stat. **Document type:** trade publication.
    —BLDSC (3987.575000).

388.3   SW   ISSN 0282-7654
BUSS - SVENSK OMNIBUSTIDNING/SWEDISH BUS & COACH MAGAZINE. (Supplement avail.: Resor & Turism) 1929. m. SEK 315 (effective 1991). Bussfoerlaget AB, Gammelgaardsvaegen 21, 112 64 Stockholm, Sweden. TEL 08-130105. FAX 08-137600. Ed. Bjarne Wilmarsgaard. adv.; charts; illus.; stat.; index. circ. 4,122.
    Formerly (until vol.9, 1982): Svensk Omnibustidning (ISSN 0039-6672)

C A M S REPORT. (Confederation of Australian Motor Sport) see SPORTS AND GAMES

388.3   UK
CAB DRIVER. 1921. fortn. £12. London Publishing Company, 15 Harewood Ave., London NW1 GLX, England. Ed. David Allen. adv.; bk.rev.; illus. circ. 20,000. **Document type:** trade publication.
    Incorporates: Steering Wheel (ISSN 0039-0984)

388   GW
CABRIO UND SPORTCOUPE. q. Vereinigte Fachverlage GmbH, Lise-Meitner-Str. 2, 55129 Mainz, Germany. TEL 06131-99202. FAX 06131-992103. Ed. Otto Walenta. adv. contact: Peter Hart. circ. 60,000. **Document type:** consumer publication.

388   GW
CABRIOLET TOTAL. 1992. m. DM.48 (foreign DM.68). A M F Verlags GmbH, Sattlerstr. 7, 23556 Luebeck, Germany. TEL 0451-898814. FAX 0451-8966211. Ed. J. Koslowski. adv. circ. 50,000.

796.77 910.09   US
CALIFORNIA EVENTS ANNUAL. a. $7.95. Camaro Publishing Co., 90430 World Way Center, Los Angeles, CA 90009. TEL 213-837-7500.

796.77   US   ISSN 0747-0223
CALIFORNIA SPORTS CAR. 1980. m. Pfanner Communications, Inc., 1371 E. Warner Ave., Ste. E, Tustin, CA 92680-6442. TEL 714-259-8240. FAX 714-259-9377. Ed. Jane Shaw. adv. circ. 3,787.
    Formerly (until 1984): Finish Line (ISSN 0199-5936)

CAMARO ENTHUSIAST. see *ANTIQUES*

629.224   SP   ISSN 0211-2930
CAMBUS; actualidad tecnica del vehiculo industrial. 1970. 10/yr. 4000 ptas. Pedeca Sociedad Cooperativa, Ltda, Maria Auxiliadora 5, 28040 Madrid, Spain. TEL 1-459-60-00. FAX 1-450-94-29. TELEX 43056 PDEK E. Ed. Paco Perez. circ. 7,500.
    —CCC.

388.3   CN   ISSN 1192-2745
CANADIAN AUTO WORLD. 1992. m. Can.$18. World of Wheels Publishing Inc., 1200 Markham Rd., Ste. 220, Scarborough, ON M1H 3C3, Canada. TEL 416-438-7777. FAX 416-438-5333. Ed. Joe Duarte; Pub. Lynn R. Helpard. adv.: B&W page Can.$2625, color page Can.$3825; trim 9 3/4 x 13 1/4; adv. contact: Lise Ann Parker. circ. 10,000. (tabloid format) **Document type:** trade publication.

388.3   CN   ISSN 0707-624X
CANADIAN AUTOMOBILE ASSOCIATION. ANNUAL REPORT. (Text in English, French) 1959. a. free. Canadian Automobile Association, 1775 Courtwood Cres., Ottawa, ON K2C 3J2, Canada. TEL 613-226-7631. FAX 613-225-7383. **Document type:** corporate report.

388   CN   ISSN 0702-2441
CANADIAN AUTOMOBILE ASSOCIATION. STATEMENT OF POLICY. 1975. a. Canadian Automobile Association, 1775 Courtwood Cresc., Ottawa, ON K2C 3J2, Canada. TEL 613-226-7631. FAX 613-225-7383. Ed. David Leonhardt. circ. 4,000. **Document type:** bulletin.
    Formerly: Canadian Automobile Association. Policies and Resolutions.

629.286   CN   ISSN 0828-2161
CANADIAN AUTOMOTIVE FLEET. (Supplement avail.) 1984. bi-m. Bobit Publishing (Canada) Ltd., 152 Parliament St., Toronto, ON M5A 2Z1, Canada. TEL 416-864-1700. FAX 416-864-1498. Ed. Michael Goetz. adv. circ. 12,200.

629.286   CN   ISSN 1180-2065
CANADIAN AUTOMOTIVE TECHNICIAN. 1989. q. Can.$18($26) Southam Business Information & Communications Group Inc., 1450 Don Mills Rd., Don Mills, Ont. M3B 2X7, Canada. TEL 416-442-2000. FAX 416-442-2077. Ed. David Booth. circ. 30,600.
    Description: Discusses technological advances of interest to automotive service professionals.

388.3   CN   ISSN 0045-527X
CANADIAN RED BOOK; official used car valuations. (Text in English, French) 1959. m. Can.$60. Maclean-Hunter Ltd., Business Publication Division, Maclean-Hunter Bldg., 777 Bay St., Toronto, ON M5W 1A7, Canada. TEL 416-596-5082. Pub. I. Grotans. adv. circ. 16,000. (back issues avail.)

388.3   SA   ISSN 0008-5995
CAR; the motoring journal of Southern Africa. 1957. m. (foreign R.78). Ramsay, Son & Parker (Pty) Ltd., P.O. Box 180, Howard Place 7450, Cape Town, South Africa. TEL 27-21-5311391. FAX 27-21-5313333. Ed. David Trebett. adv.; charts; illus.; mkt.; stat. circ. 157,300. **Document type:** consumer publication.
    Incorporates: Technicar (ISSN 0040-1013)
    Description: Publishes articles on new cars, motor sport, exotic cars, do-it-yourself repairs, technical articles and car prices.

388.3   UK   ISSN 0008-5987
CAR. 1962. m. £31.20 (foreign £43.20) (effective 1995-1996). E M A P - Consumer, 30-32 Farringdon Ln., London EC1R 3AU, England. TEL 0171-972-6700. FAX 0171-972-6710. (Subscr. to: Tower Publishing Services Ltd., Tower House, Sovereign Park, Lathkill St., Market Harborough, Leics. LE16 9EF. TEL 01858-468811. FAX 01858-432164) adv.; illus.; mkt. circ. 581. **Document type:** consumer publication.
    —SWETS.
    Supersedes (in 1965): Small Car.

629.222 658.8   UK
CAR AFTERMARKET: THE INTERNATIONAL MARKET. (Subseries of: Market Direction reports) a. £1595($3190) (effective 1996). Euromonitor, 60-61 Britton St., London EC1M 5NA, England. TEL 0171-251-8024. FAX 0171-608-3149. (Addr. in N. America: Euromonitor International, 122 S. Michigan Ave., Ste., 1200, Chicago, IL 60603. TEL 312-922-1115. FAX 312-922-1157) (looseleaf format) **Document type:** trade publication.
    ●Also available online. Vendor(s): Data-Star, Knight-Ridder, Inc.
    Description: Analyzes the automotive accessories market for France, Germany, Italy, Spain, the U.K., the U.S., and Japan.

388.3   UK
CAR & ACCESSORY TRADER. Short title: C A T. 1979. m. £24 (foreign £35). Haymarket Specialist Motoring Publications, Ltd., 60 Waldegrave Rd., Teddington, Middx. TW11 8LG, England. TEL 081-943-5000. FAX 081-943-5927. TELEX 895 2440 HAYMART G. Ed. David Jenkinson. adv. circ. 17,458.
    Description: Contains news, features on trends, and information about cars and car accessories.

388.3   US   ISSN 0008-6002
TL236
CAR AND DRIVER. 1955. m. $19.95. Hachette Filipacchi Magazines, Inc., 1633 Broadway, New York, NY 10019. TEL 212-767-6000. FAX 212-767-5619. Ed. Csaba Csere. adv.: B&W page $52575. bk.rev. circ. 1,055,403. (also avail. in microform from UMI) **Indexed:** Acad.Ind., Consum.Ind., HRIS, Mag.Ind., PMR, R.G., Sports Per.Ind., TOM.
    ●Also available online. Vendor(s): Knight-Ridder, Inc., University Microfilms International.
    —SWETS; UMI; UnCover.

629.28 388.3   HK   ISSN 1017-3323
CAR AND DRIVER. 1986. m. HK.$378 (foreign HK.$1458). Hachette Filipacchi Asia - Pacific, Shop A8-9, 18 Hong On St., Quarry Bay, Kornhill, Hong Kong. TEL 852-2567-8707. FAX 852-2568-4650. Ed. Kenneth Leung. adv.: color page HK.$33350; trim 277 x 217; adv. contact: Tony Lo. circ. 34,500. **Document type:** consumer publication.

629.2   US   ISSN 1060-8141
CAR AND DRIVER BUYERS GUIDE. 1957. a. $4.95. Hachette Magazines, Inc., 1633 Broadway, New York, NY 10009. TEL 212-767-6000. Ed. Don Coulter. adv. circ. 155,000.
    Formerly: Car and Driver Yearbook (ISSN 0069-0260)

629.222   US   ISSN 8755-626X
TL1
CAR AND DRIVER ROAD TEST ANNUAL. a. $4.95. Hachette Magazines, Inc., 1633 Broadway, 45th Fl., New York, NY 10009. TEL 800-289-9464. (Subscr. to: Box 51133, Boulder, CO 80321-1133) Ed. William Jeanes. adv.; bk.rev.; illus.; stat. circ. 250,000.
    Description: Compiles road test evaluations of the preceding year, with comparisons of the most popular models.

629.286   GW   ISSN 0940-9157
CAR & HIFI. 1990. bi-m. DM.7.80. Michael E. Brieden Verlag GmbH, Ruhrorterstr. 9, 46049 Oberhausen, Germany. TEL 0208-85976-0. FAX 0208-8597649. Ed. Roland Katterwe; Pub. Michael Brieden. adv. contact: Jutta Brandt. **Document type:** consumer publication.

CAR & TRAVEL. see *TRAVEL AND TOURISM*

388   US   ISSN 1080-2231
CAR & TRAVEL (CENTRAL WEST JERSEY EDITION). bi-m. membership. A A A Central West Jersey, 3 AAA Drive, Robbinsville, NJ 08691-1898. TEL 609-890-2220. Ed. Sulvia Veitia.
    Formerly: Spotlight (Robbinsville) (ISSN 0887-3453)

388.3   US   ISSN 1080-2290
CAR & TRAVEL (NEW YORK METRO EDITION). 1926. m. $8. Automobile Club of New York, Inc., 1415 Kellum Pl., Garden City, NY 11530. TEL 516-873-2238. FAX 516-873-2355. Ed. Peter Crescenti. adv. contact: Matt Hamill. illus. circ. 680,000. (also avail. in microform) **Document type:** consumer publication.
    Formerly (until Mar. 1995): New York Motorist (ISSN 0028-7385)
    Description: Features legislative, governmental and traffic safety developments of significance to motorists, and information on travel and vacation opportunities.

CAR & TRAVEL (SOUTHERN PENNSYLVANIA). see *TRAVEL AND TOURISM*

CAR & TRAVEL (WISCONSIN EDITION). see *TRAVEL AND TOURISM*

CAR AUDIO & ELECTRONICS. see *SOUND RECORDING AND REPRODUCTION*

CAR AUDIO & FM; la prima rivista di musica in auto. see *MUSIC*

CAR AUDIO ANNUARIO; la guida mercato del car stereo. see *ENGINEERING — Electrical Engineering*

388.3   AT   ISSN 0818-8343
CAR AUSTRALIA. 1946. m. Aus.$0.70 per no. David Syme & Co. Limited, 250 Spencer St., Melbourne, Vic. 3000, Australia. TEL 03-601-2903. FAX 03-642-0852. Ed. Paul Harrington. circ. 31,662. **Indexed:** GdIns.
    Formerly: Motor Manual (ISSN 0047-8210)

TRANSPORTATION — AUTOMOBILES

CAR BOOK (YEAR); an indispensable guide to the safest, most economical new cars. see *CONSUMER EDUCATION AND PROTECTION*

388   UK   ISSN 0308-9460
CAR BUYER. 1976. w. £54.64. Shaw's Car Buyer Ltd., 182 Pentonville Rd., London N1 9LB, England. TEL 071-278-4393. FAX 071-837-6286. adv. circ. 35,000.
Description: Concerns new and second hand cars sold in London and the southeast counties.

629.286   US
CAR CARE NEWS. 1983. m. $24. 4010 Airline Dr., Houston, TX 77022. Ed. Jay Hagins. adv.; illus.
Description: For do-it-yourself enthusiasts and those who are mechanically inclined.

629.222   US   ISSN 0164-5552
TL1
CAR COLLECTOR AND CAR CLASSICS. 1966. m. $32 (foreign $42). Classic Publishing, Inc., Box 28571, Atlanta, GA 30328. TEL 404-449-1952. Ed. Westley D. Peterson. adv.; bk.rev.; illus. circ. 40,000.
Incorporates (1979-1988): Nostalgic Cars; Which was formerly (until 1987): Car Exchange (ISSN 0164-0836); Formed by the 1979 merger of: Car Classics (ISSN 0095-0556); Car Collector.
Description: Features factual articles on car history, opinion articles on current trends.

614.86   CN   ISSN 0705-1298
CAR COSTS. (Text in English) 1972. a. Canadian Automobile Association, 1775 Courtwood Cres., Ottawa, ON K2C 3J2, Canada. TEL 613-226-7631. FAX 613-225-7383. **Document type:** bulletin.
Description: Describes how to calculate costs of owning and operating an automobile in Canada.

796.72   US   ISSN 0008-6010
CAR CRAFT; the complete performance magazine. 1953. m. $19.94; newsstand price: 2.95. Petersen Publishing Co., 6420 Wilshire Blvd., Los Angeles, CA 90048. TEL 213-782-2000. FAX 213-782-2263. Ed. Charles Schifsky. adv.: B&W page $12420, color page $21325. illus.; circ. 375,000 (paid). (also avail. in microform from UMI) **Document type:** consumer publication.
—UMI.
Description: Covers automobile racing.

388.3   US   ISSN 1052-407X
CAR DEALER INSIDER (BRONX).* 1965. w. $235. Atcom, Inc., 1541 Morris Ave., Bronx, NY 10457-8702. TEL 212-873-5900. FAX 212-799-1728. Ed. James Koscs. bk.rev.; charts; tr.lit. circ. 3,000. (back issues avail.; reprint service avail. from UMI)
—CCC.
Former titles (until 1990): Car Dealer Insider Newsletter (ISSN 1043-6456); Car Dealer Insider (ISSN 0148-6721); **Incorporates (1965-1989):** Truck Insider Newsletter (ISSN 0041-3399)
Description: For automobile dealers in the new car retailing business.

629.222   US
CAR DEALER INSIDER (ROCKVILLE). w. $275. United Communications Group, 11300 Rockville Pike. Ste. 1100, Rockville, MD 20852-3030.
Former titles: Motor News Analysis Auto Retail Report; Car and Truck Rental Leasing Insider Newsletter.
Description: Features information about automobiles, small business, marketing, and advertising.

629.2   UK   ISSN 0961-9372
CAR DESIGN & TECHNOLOGY. m. Brackland House, Church St., Saffron Waldon, Essex CB10 1LB, England. TEL 0799-513213. FAX 0799-22118. Ed. Anthony Curtis. bk.rev. circ. 30,000.
Description: Examines car design and technology for the technically-minded motoring enthusiast, as well as the professional engineer.

380   UK
CAR FLEET ADMINISTRATION & FINANCE. q. Wentworth House, Wentworth St., Peterborough PE1 1DS, England. TEL 0733-63100. Ed. P Cooke.

629.22   JA   ISSN 0915-1702
CAR GRAPHIC. Key Title: C.G. Car Graphic. (Text in Japanese) 1962. m. 18300 Yen. Nigensha Publishing Co., Ltd., 2-2 Kanda-Jimbocho, Chiyoda-ku, Tokyo 101, Japan. TEL 81-3-5210-4706. FAX 81-3-5210-4726. Ed. S. Kumakura. adv.: B&W page 440000 Yen, color page 800000 Yen; trim 222 x 295; adv. contact: R Ohkoshi. bk.rev. circ. 200,000. **Indexed:** JTA.
Description: Provides graphic and professional information to new and classic car enthusiasts.

629.286   UK   ISSN 0953-0924
CAR HI FI. 1986. m. (11/yr.). £32.45. Quest Magazines Ltd., Publishing House, 652 Victoria Rd., South Ruislip, Mddx. HA4 0SX, England. TEL 0181-842-1010. FAX 0181-841-2557. Ed. Martyn Williams; Pub. Damian Riley-Smith. adv. contact: Rupert Heseltine. circ. 27,000 (paid). (back issues avail.) **Document type:** consumer publication.
Description: Reviews the latest radio, cassette and compact-disc players for cars, along with amplifiers, speakers, and security equipment.

629.2   UK   ISSN 0008-6037
CAR MECHANICS. 1958. m. £24.50 (Europe £27; rest of world £32). Kelsey Publishing Ltd., Kelsey House, 77 High St., Beckenham, Kent BR3 1AN, England. TEL 0181-658-3531. FAX 0181-650-8035. adv.; bk.rev.; illus. circ. 55,051. **Document type:** consumer publication.
—CCC.
Description: Targeted at the do-it-yourself enthusiast and the secondhand car buyer.

388.3   US   ISSN 0008-6053
CAR RENTAL & LEASING INSIDER NEWSLETTER.* 1963. bi-w. $235. Atcom, Inc., 1541 Morris Ave., Bronx, NY 10457-8702. TEL 212-873-5900. FAX 212-799-1728. Ed. John Kirk. circ. 1,000. (reprint service avail. from UMI) **Document type:** newsletter.
Formerly: Car and Truck Rental and Leasing Insider Newsletter.
Description: For professionals in the automobile rental and leasing industry.

388 658.8   UK
CAR RENTAL: THE INTERNATIONAL MARKET. (Subseries of: Market Direction reports) a. £1595($3190) (effective 1996). Euromonitor, 60-61 Britton St., London EC1M 5NA, England. TEL 0171-251-8024. FAX 0171-608-3149. (Addr. in N. America: Euromonitor International, 122 S. Michigan Ave., Ste. 1200, Chicago, IL 60603. TEL 312-922-1115. FAX 312-922-1157) (looseleaf format) **Document type:** trade publication.
●Also available online. Vendor(s): Data-Star, Knight-Ridder, Inc.
Description: Analyzes the car rental market in France, Germany, Italy, Spain, the U.K., the U.S., and Japan.

388   JA
CAR ROAD. (Text in Japanese) 1978. m. 2640 Yen. Kotsu Times Co. Ltd., 4-3 Uchi-kanda 2-chome, Chiyoda-ku, Tokyo 101, Japan. Ed. Takayoshi Yamada.

CAR STEREO E F M. see *MUSIC*

629.296   JA
CAR STYLING. (Text in English, Japanese) 1973. bi-m. $216. San'ei Shobo Publishing Co., 4-8-16, Kita-Shinjuku, Shinjuku-ku, Tokyo 169, Japan. TEL 03-364-4819. FAX 03-364-4819. (Dist. by: Intercontinental Marketing Corp., I.P.O. Box 5056, Tokyo 100-30, Japan. TEL 81-3-3661-7458. FAX 81-3-3667-9646) Ed. Akira Fujimoto. adv.; bk.rev. circ. 30,000. (back issues avail.) **Indexed:** DAAI, JTA.
Description: Primarily features automobile design, but also includes other design fields.

388   JA
CAR TOP. (Text in Japanese) 1968. m. 2640 Yen. Kotsu Times Co. Ltd., 4-3 Uchi-kanda 2-chome, Chiyoda-ku, Tokyo 101, Japan. Ed. Shuichi Miyasaka.

CARAVAN & CHALET PARKS GUIDE. see *TRAVEL AND TOURISM*

629.286 665.5   SP   ISSN 1130-8907
CARBUROL. 1991. 10/yr. Oilgas, S.A., P. de la Habana 48, 28036 Madrid, Spain. TEL 34-1-5632893. FAX 34-1-5635234. Ed. Carlos Alvarez; Pub. Carlos Martin. adv. contact: Alfonso Villanueva. circ. 72,000. **Document type:** trade publication.
Description: Covers service stations.

796.77   CN   ISSN 0384-9309
CARGUIDE. French edition: Magazine Carguide (ISSN 1187-9475) (Supplement avail.: Toronto International Auto Show Program (ISSN 0704-7339)) 1971. 6/yr. Can.$12.99 (foreign Can.$20.99). Formula Publications Ltd., 447 Speers Rd., Ste. 4, Oakville, ON L6K 3S7, Canada. TEL 905-842-6591. FAX 905-842-6843. Ed. Alan E. McPhee. adv.: B&W page Can.$4250, color page Can.$5000; trim 8 1/8 x 10 7/8. circ. 315,000 (220,000 Eng.ed., 95,000 Fr.ed.). **Document type:** consumer publication.
Incorporates: Light Truck Guide.
Description: Official program for Toronto International Auto Show and Ottawa-Hull Auto Show. Lists complete mechanical specifications, photos, suggested retail price and fuel consumption of every new car available in Canada.

388.3   NE   ISSN 0008-6940
CARROSSERIE. 1936. m. fl.92 (effective 1995). Nederlandse Vereniging van Ondernemers in het Carrosseriebedrijf, Postbus 299, 2170 AG Sassenheim, Netherlands. TEL 31-2522-65222. FAX 31-2522-65255. Ed. Henk Barnhoorn. adv.: B&W page fl.1225, color page fl.3675; trim 210 x 297. bk.rev.; circ. 3,000 (controlled). **Indexed:** Key to Econ.Sci. **Document type:** trade publication.
Description: Magazine for car bodyshops and car body builders.

629.286   FR   ISSN 0750-8131
CARROSSERIE. 1945. 8/yr. 280 F. Federation Francaise de la Carrosserie - French Body Work Federation, 8 cours Louis Lumiere, 94306 Vincennes Cedex, France. TEL 1-41-74-35-50. FAX 1-41-74-36-38. Ed. P. Stich; Pub. Catherine Moreau. adv. circ. 4,500. **Document type:** catalog.

388.3   UK   ISSN 0008-6967
CARS & CAR CONVERSIONS. 1965. m. £37.20. Link House Magazines Ltd., Link House, Dingwall Ave., Croydon, Surrey CR9 2TA, England. TEL 0181-686-2599. FAX 0181-760-0973. (Subscr. to: R F S, 120-126 Lavender Ave., Mitcham, Surrey CR4 3HP, England) Ed. Steve Bennett. adv.; bk.rev.; charts; illus.; tr.lit. circ. 43,620. **Document type:** consumer publication.
Incorporates: Autoperformance.
Description: Profiles rallies, racing, road automobiles, drivers, and competitions with extensively detailed features on technical developments in "ion" equipment.

629.288   US   ISSN 0008-6975
TL7.A1
CARS & PARTS; the magazine serving the car hobbyist. (Supplement avail.: Collector Car Annual (ISSN 1063-6315)) 1957. m. $24 (foreign $34). Amos Press Inc., 911 Vandemark Rd., Box 482, Sidney, OH 45365. TEL 513-498-0803. FAX 513-498-0808. Ed. Robert Jay Stevens. adv.; bk.rev.; illus.; index. circ. 105,000. **Document type:** consumer publication.
—UnCover.
Description: For car collectors and hobbyists.

388.3   US   ISSN 0008-7092
CARWASH JOURNAL.* vol.6, 1967. m. $10. Automatic Car Wash Association, 401 N. Michigan Ave., Chicago, IL 60611-4212. Ed. Robin King. adv.; illus.

629.286 380   IT
CATALOGO MOTORISTICO. (Text in English, French, German, Italian, Spanish) 1962. a. L.50000. Azienda Cataloghi Italiani s.a.s., Via B. Crespi, 30-2, 20159 Milan, Italy. TEL 39-2-606052. FAX 39-2-606487. Ed. Lucio Torella. adv.: B&W page $1200; trim 168 x 242. circ. 35,000 (controlled).
Description: Contains information on Italian production of parts, accessories, equipment and machinery for cars, motorcycles, trucks, agricultural machines, carts, boats, and more.

629 SP
CATALOGO RECAMBIOS Y ACCESORIOS. a. 4850 ptas. Tecnipublicaciones, S.A., C. Albacete 5, 28027 Madrid, Spain. TEL 34-1-3261440. FAX 34-1-3262539.

338.8 SP
CATALOGO TRANSPORTE MUNDIAL. 1988. a. 850 ptas. Luike - Motorpress, C. Ancora 40, 28045 Madrid, Spain. TEL 34-1-3470100. FAX 34-1-3470204. Ed. Javier Pedroche; Pub. Jose Luis Samaranch. adv.: B&W page 260000 ptas., color page 375000 ptas.; adv. contact: Agustin Valero. circ. 19,000. **Document type:** consumer publication.

388.3 SP
▼**CATALOGO 4 X 4.** 1994. a. 800 ptas. Luike - Motorpress, C. Ancora 40, 28045 Madrid, Spain. TEL 34-1-3470100. FAX 34-1-3470204. Ed. Carlos Hernandez. adv.: B&W page 325000 ptas., color page 460000 ptas.; adv. contact: Agustin Valero. **Document type:** consumer publication.
Description: Presents information on 4x4 vehicle models.

388.3 BE
CATALOGUE GENERAL DE L'INDUSTRIE ET DU COMMERCE AUTOMOBILE DE BELGIQUE. (Text in Dutch, French) 1950. a. 2600 BEF. Federauto a.s.b.l., Bd. de la Woluwe 46, Bte 9, B-1200 Brussels, Belgium. TEL 32-2-7786200. FAX 32-2-7786222. adv.

388.3 US ISSN 0889-2504
CAVALLINO MAGAZINE; the magazine of Ferrari. 1978. s-m. $30. Cavallino Inc., Box 810819, Boca Raton, FL 33481-0819. TEL 407-994-1345. FAX 407-994-9473. Ed. John Barnes. adv.; bk.rev. circ. 16,500. **Document type:** consumer publication.

388.3 918.904 UY
CENTUR. 1977. a. free. Centro Automovilista del Uruguay, Artigas 1773, Montevideo, Uruguay. Ed. Ever Cabrera Tornielli. adv. circ. 10,000.

CHAMBRE SYNDICALE NATIONALE DES ELECTRICIENS ET SPECIALISTES DE L'AUTOMOBILE. ANNUAIRE. see ENGINEERING — Electrical Engineering

388 DK ISSN 0901-3946
CHAUFFOEREN.* 1911. m. free. Cauffoerernes Fagforening, Vibevej 31, 2400 Copenhagen, Denmark. adv.; bk.rev.; illus. circ. 11,000.

388.3 SA ISSN 1016-5312
CHEQUERED FLAG. fortn. R.50. Titan Publications (Pty) Ltd., Rodland House, 382 Jan Smuts Av., Craighall 2196, South Africa. Ed. Justin Haler. adv. circ. 25,000.
Formerly: S A Motorscene (ISSN 0256-0550)

796.77 US
CHEVY - CORVETTE BUYER'S GUIDE.* 1984. m. $21.95. Buyer's Guide National Magazines, 14549 62nd St., N., Clearwater, FL 34620-2328. TEL 309-829-5214. FAX 309-827-7595. (Subscr. to: Box 1953, Mt. Morris, IL 61054) adv. circ. 40,000. **Document type:** consumer publication.
Formerly: Corvette - Chevy Buyer's Guide.
Description: Marketplace and news for car enthusiasts and restorers, includes new products, tech and club articles.

388.3 US ISSN 1062-192X
CHEVY HIGH PERFORMANCE. bi-m. $13.95. Petersen Publishing Co., 6420 Wilshire Blvd., Los Angeles, CA 90048. TEL 213-782-2000. Ed. Mike Magda. adv.; illus. circ. 100,000. **Document type:** consumer publication.
Formerly: Chevrolet High Performance (ISSN 1052-5491)

388 US
CHEVY TRUCKIN'. q. newsstand price: $3.50. McMullen & Yee Publishing, 744 S. Placentia Av., Placentia, CA 92670-6846. TEL 714-572-2255. FAX 714-572-1864. **Document type:** consumer publication.

629.222 US ISSN 1050-1207
TL214.C64
CHILTON MOTOR - AGE PROFESSIONAL ELECTRONIC ENGINE CONTROLS MANUAL. ASIAN. biennial. Chilton Book Co., 1 Chilton Way, Radnor, PA 19089.

629.28 US ISSN 0069-2631
TL152
CHILTON'S AUTO REPAIR MANUAL; American cars from 1990 to 1994. 1968. a. $26.95. Chilton Co., Automotive Editorial Department, Chilton Way, Radnor, PA 19089. **Document type:** trade publication.
—CCC.

388.3 US ISSN 0193-3264
CHILTON'S AUTOMOTIVE MARKETING; a monthly publication for the retail jobber & distributor automotive aftermarket. 1971. m. $48. Chilton Co. (Subsidiary of: Capital Cities - A B C Publishing), Chilton Way, Radnor, PA 19089. TEL 610-964-4000. FAX 610-964-4981. Ed. Ted Arnold. adv. 40,200. (also avail. in microform from UMI; reprint service avail. from UMI) **Indexed:** Bus.Ind., SRI, Tr.& Indus.Ind.
●Also available online. Vendor(s): Knight-Ridder, Inc., Lexis-Nexis.
—UMI. **CCC.**
Incorporates (1955-1991, May): Automotive Aftermarket News (ISSN 0192-0987); Former titles (until 1978): Chilton's A M. Automotive Marketing; (until 1976): Automotive Marketing (ISSN 0045-107X); (until 1972): Chilton's A M Automotive Marketing.

629.222 US ISSN 1053-220X
TL214.C64
CHILTON'S ELECTRONIC ENGINE CONTROLS MANUAL. GENERAL MOTORS CARS AND LIGHT TRUCKS. 1990. biennial. Chilton Professional Automotive (Subsidiary of: Capital Cities - A B C, Inc.), Chilton Way, Radnor, PA 19089. TEL 215-964-4000; 800-695-1214. FAX 215-964-4745. **Document type:** trade publication.
Description: Professional automotive service manual detailing complete electronic engine control information for GM cars and light trucks from 1991-1993. Focuses on EEC diagnostics.

629.2 US ISSN 0271-3608
TL152
CHILTON'S IMPORT CAR REPAIR MANUAL; from 1990-1994. 1971. a. $26.95. Chilton Co., Automotive Editorial Department, Chilton Way, Radnor, PA 19089. Ed.Bd. **Document type:** trade publication.
Former titles: Chilton's Import Automotive Repair Manual; Chilton's Import Car Repair Manual (ISSN 0084-8743); Chilton's Foreign Car Repair Manual.

338.4 US ISSN 0749-5579
TL152
CHILTON'S LABOR GUIDE AND PARTS MANUAL. MOTOR AGE PROFESSIONAL MECHANICS EDITION. 1927. a. $95. Chilton Co., Chilton Way, Radnor, PA 19089. TEL 215-964-4723. illus.
—CCC.
Former titles: Chilton's Motor-Age Professional Labor Guide and Parts Manual (ISSN 0361-9397); Chilton's Motor Age Labor Guide and Parts Manual.

388.3 US ISSN 0193-7022
CHILTON'S MOTOR AGE; for the professional automotive import & domestic service industry. 1899. m. $44. Chilton Co., One Chilton Way, Radnor, PA 19089. TEL 610-964-4390. FAX 610-964-4251. Ed. Tony Molla. adv.: B&W page $9680, color page $11010. illus.; mkt.; stat.; tr.lit.; index. circ. 146,400. (also avail. in microform from UMI; microfiche from UMI; reprint service avail. from UMI) **Indexed:** Bus.Ind., Tr.& Indus.Ind.
●Also available online. Vendor(s): Knight-Ridder, Inc., Lexis-Nexis.
—UMI. **CCC.**
Formerly: Motor Age (ISSN 0027-1772)

629.28 US ISSN 0363-2393
TL152
CHILTON'S MOTOR-AGE PROFESSIONAL AUTOMOTIVE SERVICE MANUAL. 1927. a. $100. Chilton Co., Chilton Way, Radnor, PA 19089. TEL 215-964-4000. FAX 215-964-4745. Ed. Kerry A. Freeman. illus.
—CCC.
Former titles: Chilton's Motor-Age Service Handbook (ISSN 0097-4773); Chilton's Automotive Service Manual.

629.224 US ISSN 0742-0315
TL230.2
CHILTON'S TRUCK AND VAN REPAIR MANUAL; gasoline and diesel engines, from 1988-1992. 1971. biennial. price varies. Chilton Co., Automotive Editorial Department, Chilton Way, Radnor, PA 19089. **Document type:** trade publication.
Formerly: Chilton's Truck Repair Manual (ISSN 0045-6721)

CHINA AUTO/ZHONGGUO QICHE. see TRANSPORTATION — Abstracting, Bibliographies, Statistics

388.3 HK ISSN 1021-1322
CHINA AUTOMOTIVE JOURNAL/XIANDAI QICHE; an automotive journal for P.R. China. (Text in Chinese; table of contents in Chinese, English) 1985. 4/yr. HK.$194($45) for Asia; elsewhere $50. (China Automotive Technology and Research Center, CC) Adsale Publishing Company, 14F, Devon House, Taikoo Place, 979 King's Rd., Quarry Bay, Hong Kong. TEL 852-2811-8897. FAX 852-2516-5119. (Co-sponsor: China National Automotive Industry Corporation) Ed. Alfred Wong. adv. circ. 16,500. (back issues avail.)
Description: Information on advanced technology development and market trends of the automotive industry for readers in the PRC.

388.3 GW ISSN 0777-8473
CHROM UND FLAMMEN. m. Kroom Verlag GmbH, Scheideweg 120, 45966 Gladbeck, Germany. TEL 02043-64774. FAX 02366-800378. Ed. Karlheinz Schnelzer. adv. contact: Guenther Zaluskowski. circ. 42,221. **Document type:** consumer publication.

796.77 US ISSN 0885-663X
CHRYSLER POWER. 1983. bi-m. $19.75. C P O Publishing, Box 1210, Azusa, CA 90702. TEL 818-303-6220. FAX 818-303-2481. Pub. Roland Osborne. adv. circ. 78,861. **Document type:** consumer publication.
Description: Attempts to serve the needs of Chrysler car owners, with emphasis on high performance, restoration and technical information.

796.77 US
CITROEN. 1987. q. $20 (foreign $25). Citroen Concours of America, 8180 Miramar Rd., San Diego, CA 92126. TEL 619-566-2860. FAX 619-566-2432. Ed. Rudy A. Heilig. adv. (back issues avail.) **Document type:** newsletter.
Description: For owners and aficionados of Citroen automobiles from 1919 to the present.

629.222 UK ISSN 0263-3183
CLASSIC & SPORTSCAR. 1963. m. £39.50. Haymarket Magazines Ltd., 60 Waldegrave Rd., Teddington, Middx. TW11 8LG, England. TEL 081-943-5000. FAX 081-943-5927. TELEX 895-2440-HAYMRT-G. Ed. Mick Walsh. circ. 101,054.
—BLDSC (3274.503200).
Formerly: Old Motor (Teddington).
Description: Devoted to classic cars, aimed at collectors and car enthusiasts.

CLASSIC CAR WEEKLY. see ANTIQUES

629.222 UK
CLASSIC CARS. 1973. m. $42.80. I P C Magazines, Specialist Magazine Group (Subsidiary of: Reed Elsevier group), King's Reach Tower, Stamford St., London SE1 9LS, England. TEL 0171-261-5858. FAX 01444-440619. TELEX 892084 REEDBP G. (Dist. by: Quadrant Subscription Services, Oakfield House, Perrymount Rd., Haywards Heath, W. Sussex RH16 3DH, England. TEL 01444-440421) Ed. Tony Dron. adv. contact: John Wilson. bibl.; charts; illus.; tr.lit. circ. 113,127. (also avail. in microform from UMI) **Document type:** consumer publication.
Formerly: Thoroughbred and Classic Cars (ISSN 0143-7267); Incorporates: Collector's Car (ISSN 0143-7259); Which was formerly: Veteran and Vintage (ISSN 0042-4773)
Description: Covers classic cars past and present with an emphasis on those built 1950-1975.

TRANSPORTATION — AUTOMOBILES

796.77 US
CLASSIC CARS NATIONAL BUYER'S GUIDE.* 1990. m. $34.95. Buyer's Guide National Magazines, 14549 62nd St., N., Clearwater, FL 34620-2328. TEL 309-829-5214. FAX 309-827-7595. (Subscr. to: Box 335, Mt. Morris, IL 61054) adv. **Document type:** consumer publication.
Description: Marketplace, price guide and show coverage for car enthusiasts and restorers.

629.283 GW ISSN 0933-7075
CLUB MAGAZIN; Aktuelle Informationen des ADAC Nordbaden. 1988. q. D W S Werbeagentur und Verlag GmbH, Kriegsstr. 160, 76133 Karlshue, Germany.

388 US
COBRAS. q. newsstand price: $3.50. McMullen & Yee Publishing, 744 S. Placentia, Placentia, CA 92670-6846. TEL 714-572-2255. FAX 714-572-1864. **Document type:** consumer publication.

388.3 SP
COCHE ACTUAL. w. 9360 ptas. (Europe 19860 ptas.; elsewhere 27860 ptas.); newsstand price: 225 ptas. Luike - Motorpress, C. Ancora 40, 28045 Madrid, Spain. TEL 34-1-3470100. FAX 34-1-3470204. TELEX 42022 LUIK E. Ed. Alberto Mayo. adv.: B&W page 470000 ptas., color page 675000 ptas.; adv. contact: Antonino Berges. circ. 150,000. **Document type:** consumer publication.

629.222 US ISSN 0742-812X
COLLECTIBLE AUTOMOBILE. 1984. bi-m. $28.50 (foreign $37.50). Publications International, Ltd., 7373 N. Cicero Ave., Lincolnwood, IL 60646. TEL 708-676-3470. FAX 708-676-3671. adv.; bk.rev.; charts; illus. circ. 100,000. (back issues avail.)
Formerly: Consumer Guide Elite Cars.

329.222 US ISSN 1073-869X
▼**COLLECTOR CAR & TRUCK PRICES.** 1994. a. $14.95 (Canada and Mexico $20.95; elsewhere $33). V M R International, Inc., 41 N. Main St., N. Grafton, MA 01536. TEL 508-839-6707. FAX 508-839-6266. (Dist. by: I C D - Hearst, 250 W. 55th St., New York, NY 10019. TEL 212-649-4443) Ed. John Iafolla; Pub. John Iafolla. adv. contact: Kelly Hulitzky. circ. 16,000. (paid). (back issues avail.) **Document type:** consumer publication.
—CCC.
Description: Lists prices for collectible automobiles built between 1946 and 1974.

629.288 US ISSN 1063-6315
TL7
COLLECTOR CAR ANNUAL. Variant title: Cars and Parts Annual. (Supplement to: Cars & Parts (ISSN 0008-6975)) 1983. a. $4.95. Amos Press Inc., 911 Vandemark Rd., Box 482, Sidney, OH 45365. TEL 513-498-0803. FAX 513-498-0808. Ed. Robert Stevens. **Document type:** consumer publication.
Description: Covers various aspects of automobile maintenance and collection for collectors and restorers of antique automobiles.

388 629.222 US ISSN 0888-1944
TL7.A1
COLLECTOR CAR NEWS. 1960. m. $18.75. Box 2210, Palm Springs, CA 92263-2210. TEL 619-778-1370. FAX 619-864-4175. adv.; bk.rev.; charts; illus.; tr.lit. circ. 20,000.
Former titles (until 1986): Collectors Motor News (ISSN 0746-8687); Antique Motor News; Antique Motor News and Atlantic Auto Advertiser (ISSN 0003-5890)
Description: For the collector car enthusiast focusing on all collectable cars from a Ford Model T to a Ferrari Testarossa. Provides information on events, personalities, museums, and books.

624.286 US ISSN 0739-7437
COLLISION; dedicated to the improvement of the auto body trade. 1960. 9/yr. $28. Kruza Kaleidoscopix, Inc., Box M, Franklin, MA 02038. TEL 508-528-6211. Ed. Jay Kruza. adv.; bk.rev.; charts; illus.; stat.; tr.lit. circ. 12,000. **Document type:** trade publication.
Formerly (until 1974): Shop Talk.

388 US
COLLISION PARTS JOURNAL. 1983. q. $20. (Automotive Body Parts Association) Sarco Management and Publications, 2900 Wilcrest Dr., Ste. 122, Houston, TX 77042-2752. TEL 800-323-5832; 800-323-5832. FAX 713-531-9411. Ed. Stanley A. Rodman; Pub. Stanley A. Rodman. circ. 2,300. (tabloid format) **Document type:** newspaper.
Formerly: A B P D A Journal.
Description: Covers happenings in the collision parts industry as they pertain to members of the Automotive Body Parts Association, and the manufacturer and distributor of replacement collision parts.

388.3 FR
COMMERCE-REPARATION AUTOMOBILE. 1949. 22/yr. 320 F. 89 rue Carnot, 92300 Levallois-Perret Cedex, France. TEL 47-48-09-00. FAX 47-48-13-16. Ed. Bertrand Tarisien. adv. circ. 24,800.
Description: Professional journal of information for automobile traders and service engineers.

388.3 678.2 FR ISSN 0993-9903
COMMUNICATION PNEU. 1988. 10/yr. Francese Editions, 11 rue d'Orleans, 92210 Saint-Cloud, France. TEL 47-71-14-68. FAX 46-02-71-26. Ed. Francois Francese. circ. 10,000.

338 UK ISSN 0267-8519
COMPANY CAR (REDHILL). (Supplement avail.: Company Van (ISSN 0955-5196)) 1971. m. £76($140) (effective 1994). Argus Business Media Ltd., International Trade Publications (Subsidiary of: Argus Press Group), Queensway House, 2 Queensway, Redhill, Surrey RH1 1QS, England. TEL 01737-768611. FAX 01737-761989. TELEX 948669 TOPJNL G. Ed. John Blauth. adv.; bk.rev. circ. 20,500. (back issues avail.) **Document type:** trade publication.
Formerly (until 1984): Car Fleet Management.

338.476 336 UK
COMPANY CAR TAX. 1993. q. £100 for print edition; diskette £215. Glass's Information Services Ltd., Elgin House, St. George's Ave., Weybridge, Surrey KT13 OBX, England. TEL 01932-823823. FAX 01932-546564. (Subscr. to: Sales and Marketing, St. Martins Ct., 37 Queens Rd., Weybridge, Surrey KT13 9TU, England) (also avail. in diskette format) **Document type:** trade publication.
Description: Provides price information for new company cars and their options.

338 UK ISSN 0955-5196
COMPANY VAN. (Supplement to: Company Car (ISSN 0267-8519)) 1988. m. Argus Business Media Ltd., International Trade Publications (Subsidiary of: Argus Press Group), Queensway House, 2 Queensway, Redhill, Surrey RH1 1QS, England. TEL 01737-768611. FAX 01737-760510. TELEX 948669 TOPJNL G. **Document type:** trade publication.

796.77 UK
COMPLETE CAR. 1984. m. $48. Perry-Motor Press Ltd., 2 Redan Pl., London W2 5SZ, England. TEL 0171-229-7799. FAX 0171-221-7846. Ed. David Raeside. adv.; B&W page £1000. bk.rev. circ. 51,073. **Document type:** consumer publication. —UMI.
Formerly (until 1994): Fast Lane (ISSN 0266-5182)
Description: Covers supercars and performance varieties of production cars.

629.22 US ISSN 0097-8337
TL5
CONSUMER GUIDE MAGAZINE. (Each issue is on a specific subject) 1966. irreg. (32-44/yr.). $99 for 34 nos. (effective 1992). Publications International, Ltd., 7373 N. Cicero Ave., Lincolnwood, IL 60646. TEL 708-676-3470. FAX 708-676-3671. Ed. Richard Popely. illus. circ. 220,000. **Indexed:** Hlth.Ind., Mag.Ind.

629.222 US
▼**CONSUMER REPORTS NEW CAR YEARBOOK.** 1994. a. $4.95 (Canada $5.95). Consumers Union of the United States, Inc., 101 Truman Ave., Yonkers, NY 10703-1057. TEL 914-378-2000. FAX 914-378-2906. **Document type:** consumer publication.
Description: Contains objective information on more than 150 new cars.

CONTINENTAL MOTORING HOLIDAYS. see TRAVEL AND TOURISM

629.286 US ISSN 0895-1047
CONVENIENT AUTOMOTIVE SERVICES RETAILER. 1987. bi-m. Graphic Concepts, Inc., 1801 Rockville Pike, Ste. 330, Rockville, MD 20852. TEL 301-984-4000. FAX 301-984-7340. Ed. Robert Silverstein. adv. contact: Martie Barley. circ. 15,000 (controlled). **Document type:** trade publication.
Description: For investors, franchise owners, and managers in the car care service industry.

629.2 621.38 US
CONVERGENCE: INTERNATIONAL CONGRESS ON TRANSPORTATION ELECTRONICS. PROCEEDINGS. biennial. Society of Automotive Engineers, 400 Commonwealth Dr., Warrendale, PA 15096-0001. TEL 412-776-4841. FAX 412-776-3036. (Co-sponsor: Institute of Electrical and Electronics Engineers) **Document type:** proceedings.
●Also available online. Vendor(s): European Space Agency, FIZ Technik, Orbit Search Service.
Formerly: Convergence: International Colloquium on Automotive Electronic Technology. Proceedings.

CORMORANT NEWS BULLETIN. see ANTIQUES

CORPORATE FLEET MANAGEMENT. see BUSINESS AND ECONOMICS — Management

629.286 IT
CORRERE DELL'AUTORIPARATORE. 1980. m. L.18000. Omicron, Via Susa 42, 10138 Turin, Italy. Ed. Gian Paolo Pecoraro. adv. circ. 12,000.

388.3 AG
CORSA. 1966. w. Editorial Abril S.A., Leandro N. Alem 896, Buenos Aires, Argentina. adv.; illus.; tr.lit. circ. 75,000.

388.3 US ISSN 0897-4179
CORVETTE QUARTERLY. 1988. q. $10. Aegis Group - Publishers (Subsidiary of: Lintas - Ceco Communications), 30400 Van Dyke Ave., Warren, MI 48093. TEL 810-574-9100. (Subscr. to: Box 40278, Redford, MI 48240) Ed. Jerry Burton. circ. 250,000. (back issues avail.) **Document type:** consumer publication.
Description: Covers the current and past model years of Corvettes. Geared towards the Corvette enthusiast for the purpose of selling new Corvettes.

658.8 US ISSN 0739-3695
COUNTERMAN; the magazine for the jobber sales team. (Includes Management Training Supplement published in Feb.; Technical Sales Seminars published in April; Tech-Forum published in Aug.) 1983. 17/yr. $49 (foreign $98) (effective 1995). Babcox Publications, 11 S. Forge St., Box 1810, Akron, OH 44309-1810. TEL 216-535-6617. FAX 216-535-0874. Ed. Gary Molinaro. adv.: B&W page $6425. tr.lit.; circ. 68 (paid); 53,820 (controlled). **Document type:** trade publication.
Description: Written for men and women responsible for sales in the nation's automotive wholesale - retail parts stores.

388 UK ISSN 0591-2334
CUSTOM CAR. 1970. m. £25 (Europe £28; rest of world £34). Kelsey Publishing Ltd., Kelsey House, 77 High St., Beckenham, Kent BR3 1AN, England. TEL 0181-658-3531. FAX 0181-650-8035. Ed. Tim Baggeley. adv. contact: Mike Stanton. bk.rev. circ. 34,079. **Document type:** consumer publication.
Incorporates: Hot Rod and Custom U.K.
Description: Contains feature articles and photography on automobile customizing, with profiles of models, owners, and customizers, technical advice, and announcements of events and competitions.

388.3 US
CYLINDER HEAD & BLOCK IDENTIFICATION GUIDE. biennial. $60 to non-members; members $30. Automotive Engine Rebuilders Association, 330 Lexington Dr., Buffalo Grove, IL 60089-6998. TEL 708-541-6550. FAX 708-541-5808. circ. 4,300.

D A C. (Digital Audio Club) see ENGINEERING — Electrical Engineering

D A R. (Deutsches Autorecht) see LAW

TRANSPORTATION — AUTOMOBILES

796.5   GW
D C C - CARAVAN UND MOTORCARAVAN MODELLFUEHRER. a. DM.25.80. (Deutscher Camping Club e.V.) D C C-Wirtschaftsdienst und Verlag GmbH, Postfach 400428, 80704 Munich, Germany. TEL 089-380142-0. FAX 089-334737. adv. circ. 15,000. **Document type:** consumer publication.
Formerly: D C C - Caravan Modellfuehrer.

388.3   US   ISSN 1051-9211
D R I - MCGRAW-HILL AUTOMOTIVE REVIEW. Key Title: Automotive Review. 1989. m. D R I - McGraw-Hill, 24 Hartwell Ave., Lexington, MA 02173. TEL 617-863-5100. FAX 617-860-6332. TELEX 200 284.

678   SW   ISSN 1103-3665
DAECK-PROFIL. 1991. q. SEK 80. Svenska Pro Motor AB, P.O. Box 22148, S-250 23 Helsingborg, Sweden. TEL 46-42-12-62-60. FAX 46-42-11-47-34. Ed. Olle Holm; Pub. Britt-Marie Andren. adv.: B&W page SEK 20000, color page SEK 23900; trim 280 x 400. circ. 7,700. **Document type:** trade publication.

629.2   UK   ISSN 0142-3282
DAILY EXPRESS GUIDE TO WORLD CARS. 1954. a. Express Newspapers plc., Ludgate House, 245 Blackfriars Rd., London SE1 9U4X, England. TEL 44-171-928-8000. adv.; illus. circ. 200,000. **Document type:** consumer publication.
Formerly (until 1978): Daily Express Review of the Motor Show.
Description: Provides pictures and details of the latest automobiles from manufacturing companies around the world.

796.77   UK   ISSN 0966-4327
DAILY MAIL MOTOR REVIEW. 1954. a. £2.10. Mail Newspapers plc., Carmelite House, c/o Dir. Sally Cartwright, Carmelite House, England. TEL 01-353-6000. FAX 01-353-1866.
Description: Guide to new cars available in the U.K.

629.286   US
DAMAGE REPORT. m. $48 (free to qualified personnel). (Massachusetts Auto Body Society) Maxco Publications, Inc., 1275 Bloomfield Ave., No. 6-36, Farfield, NJ 07004-2708. TEL 201-785-0764. FAX 201-785-0447. Ed. Pat McCarthy. adv.; circ. 3,500. (paid). **Document type:** trade publication.

629.1 629.2   FR   ISSN 1251-8719
DE L'AUTOMOBILE ET DE L'AERONAUTIQUE.* 1951. q. (Association des Anciens Eleves de l'Ecole Technique d'Aeronautique et de Construction Automobile) E.T.A.C.A., 3 rue Pablo Neruda, 92300 Levallois-Perret, France. (Orders to: J. Argoud, 61 bis av. J.B. Clement, 92140 Clamart, France) Ed. Jacques Argoud.
Formerly: E S T A C A: Ecole Superieure des Techniques Aeronautiques et de Construction Automobile (ISSN 0245-1379)

388.32   AT
DE LUXE & RED CAB NEWS. 1959. m. Aus.$0.02 per no. De Luxe & Red Cabs Co-Operative Trading Society Ltd., 357 Glenmore Road, Paddington, N.S.W. 2021, Australia. Ed. N.S. Lake. adv. circ. 1,250.

388.3   US   ISSN 1070-8294
DEALER BUSINESS.* 1966. m. $36. M H West, Inc. (Subsidiary of: Maclean Hunter Publishing Co.), 5743 Corsa Ave., Ste. 220, Westlake Village, CA 91362-4027. TEL 818-997-0644. FAX 818-997-1058. (Subscr. to: 29 N. Wacker Dr., Chicago, IL 60606) Ed. C.D. Bohon. adv.; illus.; circ. 33,501 (controlled). Indexed: PROMT. **Document type:** trade publication.
—UMI. CCC.
Former titles (until 1992): Auto Age (ISSN 0894-1270); (until 1986): Automotive Age (ISSN 0005-1470)
Description: Serves the new car and truck dealership industry, including manufacturers, distributors, finance and leasing companies, and repair and body shops.

388.3   US
DEALERS' CHOICE. 1961. q. avail. only to franchised Texas dealers of new cars and trucks. Texas Automobile Dealers Association, 1108 Lavaca St., Box 1028, Austin, TX 78767-1028. TEL 512-476-2686. FAX 512-476-2179. Ed. John T. Devenport. adv.; bk.rev.; index; circ. 1,800 (controlled). (back issues avail.) **Document type:** trade publication.
Description: Provides automotive and business information for franchised new car and truck dealers in Texas.

629.222   US
DELOREAN WORLD. 1983. q. $60. DeLorean Owners Association, 10831 Roycroft St., Ste. 32, Sun Valley, CA 91352. TEL 818-768-1364. FAX 818-768-6044. (Subscr. to: DeLorean Owners Association, Membership Data Center, 879 Randolph Rd., Santa Barbara, CA 93111) Ed. Kay L. Myhre. adv. circ. 2,000. (back issues avail.)
Description: Provides DeLorean maintenance, how-to, parts, suppliers, services and more.

343.489   DK   ISSN 0108-1306
DETAILFORSKRIFTER FOR KOERETOEJER/DETAILED REGULATIONS FOR VEHICLES. 1977. a. DKK 100. Faerdselsstyrelsen, Adelgade 13, P.O. Box 9039, DK-1304 Copenhagen K, Denmark. FAX 33-93-22-92. (Subscr. to: Schultz Boghandel, Vognmagergade 7, DK-1120, Copenhagen K, Denmark: FAX 33-15-57-72) **Document type:** government publication.

DIASPORA - M I V A; Verkehrshilfe des Bonifatiuswerkes. see RELIGIONS AND THEOLOGY — Roman Catholic

388   UK   ISSN 0956-3806
DIESEL CAR. 1988. m. £26.40 (Europe £37; elsewhere £59). Merricks Publishing Ltd., Wessex Bldgs., Somerton Business Park, Somerton, Somerset TA11 6SB, England. TEL 01458-274447. FAX 01458-274059. (Dist. by: MMC Ltd., White Hart Meadows, Ripley, Surrey GU23 6HR, England. TEL 01483-211222) Ed. John Kerswill. adv.: B&W page £700, color page £1300; adv. contact: Lisa Doerr. bk.rev.; charts; illus.; stat.; index. circ. 30,000. (back issues avail.) **Document type:** consumer publication.
Description: Consumer and technical information on diesel cars.

629.22   US   ISSN 0160-7065
TL229.D5
DIESEL CAR DIGEST; the quarterly journal of the light-duty diesel. 1976. q. $8.50. Diesel Car Journals, Box 160253, Sacramento, CA 95816. Ed. Robert E. Flock. adv.; bk.rev. circ. 10,000.

DIESEL - LEHTI. see ENGINEERING — Mechanical Engineering

388 362.4   UK
DISABLED DRIVER. 1948. bi-m. membership. 45 Castleton Ave., Bexleyheath, Kent, England. Ed. Ben H. Tinton. adv.; bk.rev. circ. 13,000.

DISCOVERY (CHICAGO). see TRAVEL AND TOURISM

388.3   FR   ISSN 0153-3142
DISTRIBUTEUR AUTOMOBILE. 1977. 10/yr. 194 rue Marcadet, 75018 Paris, France. TEL 42-55-02-57. FAX 42-54-11-19. TELEX PUBEXPER 281 433. Ed. Ph. Navarre. circ. 3,500.

629.28   US   ISSN 1041-4290
TL152
DOMESTIC CARS SERVICE & REPAIR; engine performance, electrical, mechanical. (In 2 vols.) 1967. a. $129. Mitchell International, Inc., 9889 Willow Creek Rd., Box 26260, San Diego, CA 92196-0260. TEL 800-648-8010. FAX 619-578-4752. illus. circ. 27,000.
●Also available on CD-ROM.
Formerly (until 1971): National Service Data: Domestic (ISSN 0272-8745)
Description: Auto service and repair manual for professional auto technicians.

629.28   US
DOMESTIC LIGHT TRUCKS & VANS SERVICE & REPAIR. 1917. a. $109. Mitchell International, Inc., 9889 Willow Creek Rd., Box 26260, San Diego, CA 92196-0260. TEL 800-648-8010. FAX 619-578-4752. illus. circ. 27,000. (also avail. in microform)
●Also available on CD-ROM.
Formerly (until 1967): Domestic Cars. Tune-up, Mechanical Transmission Service & Repair.
Description: Auto service and repair manual for professional auto technicians.

614.86 340   US   ISSN 0730-2568
KF2231.A15
DRINKING DRIVING LAW LETTER. 1982. 26/yr. $225. Clark - Boardman - Callaghan Company, Inc., 155 Pfingsten Rd., Deerfield, IL 60015. TEL 800-323-1336. Ed. Bob Bouchard. bk.rev.; index. circ. 2,000. (looseleaf format; back issues avail.) **Document type:** newsletter.
Description: Contains the latest legal, technical and procedural information on the latest issues in drunk driving cases.

629.222   US
DRIVE! (PLEASANT HILL); California's car magazine. 1986. m. $18. Bam Publications, Inc., 3470 Buskirk Ave., Pleasant Hill, CA 94523. TEL 510-934-3700. FAX 510-934-3958. Ed. Pete Biro. adv. circ. 86,000. **Document type:** consumer publication.
Formerly (until 1990): Swap Talk.
Description: For California car and truck enthusiasts.

629.283   UK
DRIVING. 1980. bi-m. £15($50) (Driving Instructors Association (D.I.A.)) D I A (International) Ltd., Safety House, Beddington Farm Rd., Croydon CR0 4XZ, England. TEL 081-665-5151. FAX 081-665-5565. Ed. Graham R.J. Fryer. adv.; bk./rev. circ. 16,000. (back issues avail.) **Document type:** trade publication.
Description: Informs careful drivers on safety matters and assists driving instructors.

388 374   UK
DRIVING INSTRUCTOR'S MANUAL. 1984. a. D I A International Ltd., Safety House, Beddington Farm Rd., Croydon, CR0 4XZ, England. TEL 081-665-5151. FAX 081-665-5565. Ed. Graham R.J. Fryer. stat. (looseleaf format) **Document type:** trade publication.
Description: Discusses various aspects of driving instruction.

388.3   US   ISSN 0012-7132
TL236.7
DUNE BUGGIES & HOT VWS; the fun car journal. 1967. m. $21.97. Wright Publishing Co., 2950 Airway A7, Box 2260, Costa Mesa, CA 92628. TEL 714-979-2560. FAX 714-979-3998. Ed. Michael Sommer; Pub. Judy/Wright. adv. contact: Linda Dill. bk.rev.; charts; illus.; stat.; index. circ. 100,000. **Document type:** consumer publication.

388.3   US   ISSN 0890-362X
DUPONT REGISTRY. 1985. 12/yr. $39.95 (Canada $54.95; elsewhere $99.95). DuPont Publishing, Inc., 2325 Ulmerton Rd., Ste. 16, Clearwater, FL 34622-3371. TEL 813-573-9339; 800-233-1731. FAX 813-572-5523. Dir. Clinton W. Babcock. adv. **Document type:** consumer publication.
Description: A gallery of exotic, luxury and classic automobiles for sale.

629.222   US
E I U AUTOMOTIVE. (Includes International Motor Business, Japanese Motor Business, European Motor Business, European Automotive Components, and Rubber Trends) base vol. (plus bi-m. updates). Economist Intelligence Unit, 111 W. 57th St., New York, NY 10019-2211. TEL 212-554-0600; 800-938-4685. FAX 212-586-1182. TELEX 175567. (UK addr.: Economist Intelligence Unit Ltd., Subscriptions Dept., P.O. Box 200, Harold Hill, Romford, Essex RM3 8UX, England. TEL 44-1708-381-444. FAX 44-1708-371-850)
Description: Provides EIU's latest research into global automotive trends, passenger car distribution and global car components.

TRANSPORTATION — AUTOMOBILES

338.476 UK
EAST LONDON & ESSEX AUTO TRADER; cars - bikes - boats - caravans - commercials - accessories. 1984. w. £104; newsstand price: £1. Hurst Publishing, 43-45 High Rd., Bushy Heath, Watford, Herts. WD2 1EE, England. TEL 0181-950-9900. FAX 0181-950-7581. Pub. Kate Stearman-Smith. adv. contact: Mary Ann Lambertucci. illus.; circ. 31,000 (paid). **Document type:** consumer publication.
Description: Lists all types of cars, light-duty commercial vehicles, motorcycles, and recreational vehicles for interested buyers and sellers.

388.3 US ISSN 0192-3595
EASTERN AFTERMARKET JOURNAL. 1957. bi-m. $36 for 3 yrs. Stan Hubsher, Ed. & Pub., Box 373, Cedarhurst, NY 11516. TEL 516-295-3680. FAX 516-569-5296. adv.; circ. 9,517 (controlled). **Document type:** trade publication.
Formerly: Eastern Automotive Journal.

629.2 IT ISSN 0422-2628
ECO MOTORI. 1958. m. (10/yr.). L.30000 (foreign L.40000). Editrice Cicerone s.r.l., Piazza A. Moro 33-A, 70122 Bari, Italy. TEL 39-80-5242204. Ed. Sebastiano Pugliese. adv.: B&W page L.2900000. illus.; stat. circ. 36,000.

796.77 GW
EDITION WEISS-BLAU; das Magazin der BMW-Freunde. 1985. m. DM.120. Krumdal 12, 22587 Hamburg, Germany. TEL 040-860400. FAX 040-860647. Ed. Thomas Mueller. (back issues avail.)
Formerly: Nullzwei.
Description: Geared towards BMW collectors worldwide.

388 US
EDMUND'S NEW CAR PRICES - DOMESTIC AND IMPORT. 1969. 3/yr. $15. Edmund Publications Corp., 300 N. Sepulveda Blvd., Ste. 2050, El Segundo, CA 90245-4469. TEL 310-640-7840. FAX 310-640-2456. (Dist. by: Curtis, 433 Hackensack Ave., Hackensack, NJ 07601; Subscr. to: NexTech, Box 338, Shrub Oak, NY 10588) Ed. Peter Steinlauf. illus.; stat. circ. 47,000. (back issues avail.) **Document type:** consumer publication.
Formerly: Edmund's New Car Prices (ISSN 1047-0751)
Description: Consumer guide to help consumers purchase new cars, detailing options, specifications, gas mileage and standard equipments.

629.2 US ISSN 1079-1477
TL162
EDMUND'S PICKUP, VAN AND SPORT UTILITY PRICES. 1978. 3/yr. $15. Edmund Publications Corp., 300 N. Sepulveda Blvd, Ste. 2050, El Segundo, CA 90245-4469. TEL 310-640-7840. circ. 38,000. **Document type:** consumer publication.
Former titles: Edmund's Van, Pickup, Sport Utility Buyer's Guide (ISSN 1043-8270); Edmund's Van, Pickup, Off Road Vehicles.
Description: Includes dealer cost and suggested retail price, specs, gas mileage and photos of over 65 models with factory installed option prices.

388 US ISSN 0424-5059
EDMUND'S USED CAR PRICES. 1968. 4/yr. $20. Edmund Publications Corp., 300 N. Sepulveda Blvd., Ste. 2050, El Segundo, CA 90245-4469. TEL 310-640-7840. FAX 310-640-2456. (Dist. by: Curts, 433 Hackensack Ave., Hackensack, NJ 07601; Sbuscr. to: NetTech, Box 338, Shrub Oak, NY 10588) Ed. Peter Steinlauf. circ. 75,000. (back issues avail.) **Document type:** consumer publication.
Description: Lists all American and popular foreign makes for the past 10 years. Includes price of each model and their current wholesale and retail evaluation.

796.7 US ISSN 0046-1326
EDSELETTER. 1969. m. $15 (membership). International Edsel Club, 3240 Sitterly Rd. N.W., Canal Winchester, OH 43110. (Subscr. to: Box 371, Sully, IA 50251) Ed. Paula S. Perrault. adv.; bk.rev. circ. 1,000. (processed) **Document type:** newsletter, directory.
Description: Contains information on the repair and preservation of the Edsel, folklore, club events, and cars and parts for sale.

629.286 AT ISSN 0818-8491
ELECTRIC VEHICLE NEWS. Short title: E V News. 1974. m. Aus.$30. Australian Electric Vehicle Association Inc., G.P.O. Box 4622, Melbourne, Vic. 3001, Australia. TEL 03-691-4094. FAX 03-691-1362. Ed. Phil Happ. adv.; bk.rev. circ. 430. (back issues avail.) **Document type:** newsletter.
Description: Covers electric road vehicle developments, solar and electric car racing news.

629.222 US ISSN 0190-4175
CODEN: EVEPEO
ELECTRIC VEHICLE PROGRESS. 1979. s-m. $387. Alexander Research & Communications, Inc., 215 Park Ave., S., Ste. 1301, New York, NY 10003. TEL 212-228-0246. FAX 212-228-0376. Ed. Paul Braus. bk.rev.; charts; illus. **Indexed:** Cadscan, Lead Abstr., Zincscan. **Document type:** newsletter.
Description: Provides in-depth news, data and information on worldwide electric vehicle commercialization with articles on new vehicles, research and development, demonstration projects, business and government and project developments.

629.286 US ISSN 0743-6076
TL272
ELECTRICAL COMPONENT LOCATOR - DOMESTIC CARS, LIGHT TRUCKS & VANS. 1980. a. $39. Mitchell International, Inc., 9889 Willow Creek Rd., Box 26260, San Diego, CA 92196-0260. TEL 619-578-6550; 800-648-8010. FAX 619-578-4752. illus. circ. 20,000.
●Also available on CD-ROM.
Description: Auto service and repair manual for professional auto technicians.

629.286 US
ELECTRICAL COMPONENT LOCATOR - IMPORTED CARS, LIGHT TRUCKS & VANS. 1980. a. $39. Mitchell International, Inc., 9889 Willow Creek Rd., Box 26260, San Diego, CA 92196-0260. TEL 800-648-8010. FAX 619-578-4752. circ. 15,000.
●Also available on CD-ROM.
Description: Auto service and repair manual for professional auto technicians.

ELECTRICITE AUTOMOBILE. see ENGINEERING — Electrical Engineering

629.222 US
ELECTRONIC CAR & ALTERNATIVE FUELS. q. newsstand price: $3.95. Argus Publishers Corporation, Box 49659, Los Angeles, CA 90049. TEL 310-820-3601. FAX 310-207-9388. (Subscr. to: Box 454, Nt. Morris, IL 61054) **Document type:** consumer publication.

EMERGENCY RESPONSE GUIDEBOOK. see PUBLIC HEALTH AND SAFETY

629.222 SA
EMERGENCY ROAD SERVICES GUIDE/NOODPADDIENSGIDS. (Editions in Afrikaans, English) a. membership only. Automobile Association of South Africa - Automobiel-Assosiasie van Suid-Afrika, P.O. Box 596, Johannesburg 2000, South Africa. illus. **Document type:** directory.
Formerly (until 1992): Emergency Road Services Directory.

629.286 FR ISSN 0984-3922
EQUIPEMENTS; pour vehicules automobiles. 5/yr. 450 F. (foreign 530 F.). (Federation des Industries des Equipement pour Vehicules) V B Promotion, 15 rue du 19 Janvier, 92380 Garches, France. TEL 47-01-44-74. FAX 47-01-48-25. TELEX V B PROMO 631 191. Ed. Jean Pierre Gosselin. circ. 7,000.

796.5 910.09 US
ESCAPEES. 1978. bi-m. $60. (Escapees Club) RoVing Press, 100 Rainbow Dr., Livingston, TX 77351. TEL 409-327-8873. FAX 409-327-4388. Ed. Kay Peterson. adv.; bk.rev. circ. 30,000. (back issues avail.)
Description: Information on travel as it applies to extended travel in recreational vehicles.

388.3 US
ESCAPEES CLUB. ANNUAL DIRECTORY. a. membership only. RoVing Press, 100 Rainbow Dr., Livingston, TX 77351. TEL 409-327-8873. FAX 409-327-4388. Ed. Kay Peterson. adv. **Document type:** directory.

629.286 SP
ESTACION DE SERVICIO. 12/yr. 6500 ptas. (foreign 10300 ptas.). Tecnipublicaciones, S.A., C. Albacete 5, 28027 Madrid, Spain. TEL 34-1-3261440. FAX 34-1-3262539.

388 UK
ESTATE CAR AND MULTI-PURPOSE VEHICLE. 1991. bi-m. £9.95. U.K. and International Press, 120 South St., Dorking, Surrey RH4 2EU, England. TEL 0306-743744. FAX 0306-742525. (Dist. by: Seymour, Windsor House, 1270 London Rd., London SW16 4DH, England. TEL 081-679-1899) Ed. Tony Robinson. adv. contact: Joy Robinson. circ. 11,000 (paid). (back issues avail.) **Document type:** consumer publication.
Formerly (until 1992): Estate Car and M P V (ISSN 0963-6498)

338.3 FR ISSN 0153-906X
ETUDES ET DOCUMENTATION DE LA R T A. (Revue Technique Automobile) 1946. irreg. 102 F. Editions pour l'Automobile et l'Industrie, 20-22 rue de la Saussiere, 92100 Boulogne-Billancourt, France. TEL 46-04-81-13. FAX 48-25-56-92. TELEX 204850F. Ed. Pascal Cromback. adv.; charts; illus. circ. 2,500.

388 US
EURO SPORT CAR. q. newsstand price: $3.25. McMullen & Yee Publishing, 774 S. Placentia Ave., Placentia, CA 92670-6846. TEL 714-572-2255. FAX 714-572-1864. **Document type:** consumer publication.

658
EUROPEAN AUTOMOTIVE COMPONENTS BUSINESS. q. £425($810) Economist Intelligence Unit, 111 W. 57th St., New York, NY 10019. TEL 212-554-0600; 800-938-4685. FAX 212-586-1182. TELEX 175567. (UK addr.: Economist Intelligence Unit Ltd., Subscriptions Dept., P.O. Box 200, Harold Hill, Romford, Essex RM3 8UX, England. TEL 44-1708-381-444. FAX 44-1708-371-850)
Description: Provides regular analysis of the issues and prospects facing the sector.

388.3 US ISSN 1056-8476
TL55
EUROPEAN CAR. 1971. 12/yr. $18.80. Argus Publishers Corporation, Box 49659, Los Angeles, CA 90049. TEL 310-820-3601. FAX 310-207-9388. (Subscr. to: Box 454, Mt. Morris, IL 61054) Ed. Greg Brown. circ. 59,374.
Former titles (until 1991): V W and Porsche Etc (ISSN 0273-6748); V W and Porsche; Volkswagen Greats (ISSN 0049-6723)
Description: Covers European marques, aftermarket products, replacement parts, restorations, and how-to-do-it, where-to-get-it articles.

388 658.8 UK
EUROPEAN MOTOR AND ALLIED TRADES MARKETING DIRECTORY. 1993. irreg. £175($350) (effective 1996). Euromonitor, 60-61 Britton St., London EC1M 5QU, England. TEL 0171-251-8024. FAX 0171-608-3149. (Addr. in N. America: Euromonitor International, 122 S. Michigan Ave., Ste. 1200, Chicago, IL 60603. TEL 312-922-1115. FAX 312-922-1157) **Document type:** directory.
Description: Contains extensive details on more than 2,000 manufacturers, retailers, and wholesalers of motor vehicles and reviews industry market trends.

TRANSPORTATION — AUTOMOBILES

388 US ISSN 0267-8233
HD9710.E8
EUROPEAN MOTOR BUSINESS. (Part of Automotive Intelligence Service consisting of: International Motor Business (ISSN 0267-8225); Japanese Motor Business (ISSN 0266-898X); European Motor Business (ISSN 0267-8233) 4/yr. £450($855) Economist Intelligence Unit, 111 W. 57th St., New York, NY 10019. TEL 212-554-0600; 800-938-4685. FAX 212-586-1182. TELEX 175567. (UK addr.: Economist Intelligence Unit Ltd., Subscriptions Dept., P.O. Box 200, Harold Hill, Romford, Essex RM3 8UX, England. TEL 44-1708-381-444. FAX 44-1708-371-850) (also avail. in microform from UMI.) **Indexed**: Cont.Pg.Manage.
● Also available online.
— BLDSC (3829.764520); UMI.
   Description: Analyzes the activity of the automotive industries of Western Europe and their national and international markets.

338 UK ISSN 1352-2027
EUROPEAN VEHICLE LEASING. 1989. a. Euromoney Publications plc., Nestor House, Playhouse Yard, London EC4V 5EX, England. TEL 0171-779-8935. FAX 0171-779-8541. (Orders to: Plymbridge Distributors Ltd., Estover, Plymouth PL6 7PZ, England. TEL 0171-779-8610. FAX 01752-695668) Ed. Adrian Hornbrook. **Document type**: trade publication.
   Formerly (until 1993): European Vehicle Leasing Annual (ISSN 0957-1701)

388 SZ
EUROTAX. (Text in French, German) 11/yr. Eurotax Inseratenverwaltung. Nauenstr. 30, CH-8630 Tann Rueti, Switzerland. TEL 055-318565. FAX 055-321202. Ed. B. Gubser. circ. 21,400.

388 AU
EUROTAX - AUTO - INFORMATION. w. Albertgasse 33, A-1080 Vienna, Austria. TEL 0222-427546. FAX 0222-4085420. TELEX 132872. Ed. Georg Auer.

629.222 US
AN EXAMINATION OF THE AUTOMOTIVE PARTS INDUSTRY. 1992. a. $395. Dun & Bradstreet Information Services (Murray Hill) (Subsidiary of: Dun & Bradstreet, Inc.), One Diamond Hill Rd., Murray Hill, NJ 07974. TEL 908-665-5224. FAX 908-771-7599. Ed. Mike Farinella.
   Description: Examines the original equipment manufacturers and the aftermarket to determine performance.

388.3 US ISSN 0896-0798
EXCELLENCE (NOVATO). 8/yr. $20 (effective Jan. 1992). Ross Periodicals, 42 Digital Dr., No. 5, Novato, CA 94949. TEL 415-382-0580. Ed. Tom Toldrian; Pub. Tom Toldrian. adv. contact: Stan Michelman. circ. 38,000. **Document type**: consumer publication.
   Description: Provides current news and information about the Porsche and the people who drive it.

659.1 UK ISSN 0014-4460
EXCHANGE AND MART. 1868. w. £300. Link House Advertising Periodicals Ltd., 25 West St., Poole, Dorset BH15 1LL, England. TEL 01202-445000. FAX 01202-445189. adv. circ. 148,048. **Document type**: trade publication.
   Description: Advertisements of various products, special focus on automobiles.

796.77 US ISSN 1054-8084
TL236
EXOTIC CARS QUARTERLY. q. Diamandis Communications, 1499 Monrovia Ave., Newport Beach, CA 92663-2752. TEL 714-720-5300. FAX 714-631-2374. Ed. Ron Sessions. circ. 100,000.

388.3 FR ISSN 0755-110X
L'EXPERT AUTOMOBILE. (Supplements avail.) 1965. m. 1100 F. Societe d'Edition de l'Expertise Automobile et Materiel Industriel, 19 rue des Filles du Calvaire, 75140 Paris Cedex 03, France. TEL 16-1-42-77-32-50. FAX 16-1-40-27-02-63. Ed. J. Barataud. adv.; illus.; stat. circ. 25,000.
● Also available on CD-ROM.

796.77 FR
F I A YEAR BOOK OF AUTOMOBILE SPORT. a. Editions V.M., 116 bd. Malesherbes, 75017 Paris, France. TEL 42-27-25-44. FAX 47-66-57-74. circ. 6,500.

388.3 GW ISSN 0014-6838
FAHRSCHULE; Zeitschrift fuer die Kraftfahrlehrer. 1949. m. DM.115.20 (foreign DM.125.80). Heinrich Vogel Fachzeitschriften GmbH, Neumarkter Str. 18, 81673 Munich, Germany. TEL 089-43180-0. (Subscr. to: Postfach 802020, 81620 Munich, Germany) Ed. Heinzmartin Nitsche. adv.; bk.rev.; circ. 16,500 (controlled). **Document type**: trade publication.
— CCC.

629.2 GW ISSN 0014-6862
FAHRZEUG UND KAROSSERIE. 1947. m. DM.172.20 (foreign DM.201.60) (effective 1995). (Zentralverband Karosserie und Fahrzeugtechnik) Verlagsgemeinschaft Gentner Verlag - Strobel Verlag, Forststr. 131, 70193 Stuttgart, Germany. TEL 0711-63672-0. FAX 0711-63672-11. Eds. Ingo Roever, E. Reisch. circ. 6,400. **Document type**: trade publication.

388.3 NO
FALKEN NYTT. q. NOK 12. Falken Redningskorps A-S, Stabburveien 1, 0873 Oslo 8, Norway. Ed. Arve Andreson. adv. circ. 105,000.

FAMILY SITES GUIDE. see SPORTS AND GAMES — Outdoor Life

796.77 UK ISSN 0951-7499
FAST CAR. 1987. m. £38.40 (foreign £73.68). Security Publications Ltd., Argosy House, 161a-163a High St., Orpington, Kent BR6 0LW, England. TEL 01689-74025. Ed. Greg Emmerson. circ. 60,000. (back issues avail.) **Document type**: consumer publication.
   Description: Covers engine modifications, body styling, and engine building.

629.22 UK ISSN 0958-0522
FAST FORD; the independent magazine for Ford enthusiasts. 1985. m. £22 (rest of Europe £38; elsewhere £58) (effective 1995). A & S Publishing Co. Ltd., Messenger House, 33-35 St. Michael's Sq., Gloucester GL1 1HX, England. TEL 01452-307181. FAX 01452-307170. Ed. Monty Watkins. adv. contact: Neil Stephens. bk.rev. circ. 25,000. (back issues avail.) **Document type**: consumer publication.
   Description: Devoted to Ford motor cars. Contains technical advice and motorsport reports.

338.3 US ISSN 1070-3926
FAST TRACK NEWS. 1989. 60/yr. $448. Integrated Automotive Resources, Inc., Box 7896, Newark, DE 19714-7896. TEL 302-368-2700. FAX 302-368-6099. Ed. Thomas O'Grady. circ. 1,500. **Document type**: newsletter.
   Description: Contains industry news, analysis and forecasting as well as sales, production and inventory data for the industry.

388.3 US ISSN 1057-0330
FAT FENDERED STREET RODS. bi-m. $13.95. Challenge Publications, Inc., 7950 Deering Ave., Canoga Park, CA 91304. TEL 818-887-0550. FAX 818-883-1343. **Document type**: consumer publication.

338 363.6 US ISSN 0093-0180
JK1677.M7
FEDERAL MOTOR VEHICLE FLEET REPORT. a. U.S. General Services Administration, Motor Equipment Management Division, G S A Bldg., 18th and F Sts., N.W., Washington, DC 20405. **Document type**: government publication.
   Formerly (until 1972): Annual Motor Vehicle Report (ISSN 0566-8166)

629.283 US ISSN 0364-6858
FEDERAL MOTOR VEHICLE SAFETY STANDARDS AND REGULATIONS; with amendments and interpretations. (Comprises 3 parts: Procedural Rules and Regulations; Standards; Rulings and Additional Regulations) 1972. base vol. (plus irreg. updates). $149 (foreign $186.25) (effective 1994). U.S. National Highway Traffic Safety Administration, Department of Transportation, 400 7th St., S.W., Washington, DC 20590. (Subscr. to: Superintendent of Documents, U.S. Government Printing Office, Box 371954, Pittsburgh, PA 15250-7954. TEL 202-512-1800. FAX 202-512-2250) (looseleaf format) **Document type**: government publication.

629.222 SZ
FEDERATION DES CARROSSIERS ROMANDS. JOURNAL. q. Route de Glane 16, CH-1700 Fribourg, Switzerland. TEL 037-243048. Ed. O. Maradan. circ. 500.

629.2 BE
FEDERAUTO MAGAZINE; la revue du professionnel de l'automobile. (Former name of issuing body: Chambre Syndicale du Commerce Automobile de Belgique) (Editions in Dutch, French) 1981. m. 3040 BEF. Federauto a.s.b.l., Bd. de la Woluwe 46, Bte 9, B-1200 Brussels, Belgium. TEL 32-2-7786200. FAX 32-2-7786222. **Document type**: trade publication.
   Former titles (until 1995): Autotechnica (ISSN 0771-4912); Chambre Syndicale du Commerce Automobile de Belgique. Bulletin Mensuel.

796.77 IT
FERRARI FORMULA 1 ANNUAL. (Text in English, French, Italian) 1989. a. L.90000. Automobilia s.r.l., Via Ponte Seveso, 25, 20125 Milan, Italy. TEL 39-2-67074391. FAX 39-2-67075000. Ed. Enrico Benzing.

796.72 914 IT
FERRARI ITALIAN STYLE; periodico internazionale d'immagine, automobilismo e cultura. (Text in English, Italian) bi-m. L.35000 (foreign L.60000). Esseffe Editrice S.r.l., Via Dogana, 3, Milan, Italy. TEL 02-867141. TELEX 323827 ABSERV. Ed. Sergio Massaro.

796.77 GW ISSN 0939-723X
FERRARI WORLD. 1991. q. DM.76.80. Heel-Verlag GmbH, Hauptstr. 354, 53639 Koenigswinter, Germany. TEL 02223-23026. FAX 02223-23028. (Dist. by: Inland Presse Vertrieb GmbH, Wendenstr. 27, 20097 Hamburg, Germany. TEL 040-23711110. FAX 040-23711235) Ed. Peter Braun. adv.: page DM.8900; trim 174 x 245; adv. contact: Elizabeth Doerr. bk.rev.; bibl.; illus. circ. 17,000. (back issues avail.) **Document type**: consumer publication.

796.77 UK ISSN 0958-7462
FERRARI WORLD MAGAZINE. bi-m. $40. International Publishers Corp., 242 West Ave., Darien, CT 06820-4111. TEL 203-656-3913. FAX 203-656-2774.

629 IT ISSN 0393-3318
FERRARISSIMA. (Text in English, French, Italian) 1984. s-a. L.80000 (for complete set). Automobilia s.r.l., Via Ponte Seveso, 25, 20125 Milan, Italy. TEL 39-2-67074391. FAX 39-2-67075000. Eds. Bruno Alfieri, Piero Casucci. circ. 5,000. (back issues avail.)

338.3 FR ISSN 0153-9108
FICHES TECHNIQUES R T C. (Revue Technique Carrosserie) irreg. 410 F. Editions Techniques pour l'Automobile et l'Industrie (ETAI), 20-22 rue de la Saussiere, 92100 Boulogne-Billancourt, France. charts; illus. (looseleaf format)

338.3 FR ISSN 0153-9094
FICHES TECHNIQUES R T D. (Revue Technique Diesel) irreg. 405 F. Editions Techniques pour l'Automobile et l'Industrie (ETAI), 20-22 rue de la Saussiere, 92100 Boulogne-Billancourt, France.

796.77 US ISSN 1066-6265
FIERO OWNER.* 1984. q. $29 (foreign $45). Fiero Owners Club of America, 2165 S. Dupont Dr., Ste. I, Anaheim, CA 92806-6103. TEL 714-978-3132. FAX 714-978-3059. Ed. Phil Huff. adv. circ. 3,000. (back issues avail.) **Description**: Provides information on performance and trouble-shooting expertise for hands-on corrective maintenance. Covers club activities. Includes want-ads.

629.2 NO ISSN 0800-5869
FIRMABIL. 1984. q. NOK 220. Fagbladforlaget AS, Urtegaten 9, P.O. Box 9247 Groenland, N-0134 Oslo, Norway. TEL 47-22-68-03-13. FAX 47-22-68-20-85. Ed. Knut Skallerud.

FLEET ASSOCIATION DIRECTORY. see BUSINESS AND ECONOMICS — Marketing And Purchasing

TRANSPORTATION — AUTOMOBILES

388   UK
FLEET CAR. £50($100) E M A P - Response Publishing, Wentworth House, Wentworth St., Peterborough, Cambs. PE1 1DS, England. TEL 01733-63100. FAX 01733-66437. Ed. Dave Calderwood. adv. contact: Jenny Nash. index. circ. 20,000. **Document type:** trade publication.
    Formerly (until 1993): Fleet Facts.

338.476   UK
▼**FLEET CAR RUNNING COSTS**. 1995. q. £75. Glass's Information Services Ltd., Elgin House, St. Georges Ave., Weybridge, Surrey KT13 0BX, England. TEL 01932-823823. FAX 01932-846564. (Subscr. to: Sales and Marketing, St. Martins Ct., 37 Queens Rd., Weybridge, Surrey KT13 9TU, England) **Document type:** trade publication.
    Description: Documents running costs for various models of cars for annual mileages over a 1- to 4-year period.

FLEET FINANCIALS. see BUSINESS AND ECONOMICS — Marketing And Purchasing

614.86   US
FLEET MAINTENANCE & SAFETY. 1987. m. $196 (effective 1995-1996). Skyline Publishing Co., Box 599, Brookfield, IL 60513-0599. TEL 708-485-6015. FAX 708-485-4237. Ed. Ralph McDarmont. (looseleaf format) **Document type:** newsletter.
    —CCC.
    Formerly: Runzheimer Reports on Fleet Maintenance & Safety (ISSN 0894-492X)

388 658.7   CN
FLEET MANAGEMENT JOURNAL. 1993. 4/yr. Can.$20 (foreign Can.$36). Powershift Communications Inc., 245 Fairview Mall Dr., Ste. 308, North York, ON M2J 4T1, Canada. TEL 416-494-2960. FAX 905-946-8931. Ed. Tony Whitney. adv.: B&W page Can.$3295, color page Can.$4390; trim 8 x 10 3/4; adv. contact: Dan Radulescu. circ. 13,000 (controlled). **Document type:** trade publication.
    Description: For auto, can and light truck fleet administrators in Canadian companies.

388   UK
FLEET NORTH. 1986. 8/yr. £19 (foreign £35). Tweedprint Ltd., 97 Heaton St., Standish, Wigan, Lancashire WN6 0DA, England. TEL 0257-427332. FAX 0257-422054. Ed. Alan Fawcett. circ. 17,100 (controlled). (back issues avail.) **Document type:** trade publication.

388.3   UK   ISSN 0953-9085
FLEET OPERATORS HANDBOOK. 1980. a. £30. E M A P - Response Publishing Ltd., Wentworth House, Wentworth St., Peterborough, Cambs. PE1 1DS, England. TEL 01733-63100. FAX 01733-67367. Ed. Rob Barrowman. adv.: B&W page £1713, color page £2273; trim 210 x 147. stat.; index; circ. 10,000 (controlled). (back issues avail.) **Document type:** trade publication.

FLORIDA MOTOR VEHICLE LIABILITY LAW. see LAW

388.3   US   ISSN 0015-4830
FLYING LADY. 1951. bi-m. membership. Rolls-Royce Owners' Club, Inc., Box 707, Exton, PA 19341-0707. Eds. Ken and Mermie Karger. adv.; bk.rev.; charts; illus.; index; circ. 6,500 (paid).
    Description: Includes historical and technical articles.

796.77   US
FOR VETTES ONLY. 1975. m. $18 to non-members; members $12. National Corvette Owners Association, 900 S. Washington St., Ste. G-13, Falls Church, VA 22046. TEL 703-533-7222. FAX 703-533-1153. (Subscr. to: Box 777A, Falls Church, VA 22056) Ed. Joseph R. Salta. adv. contact: circ. 11,000. (looseleaf format) **Document type:** newsletter.

796.77   US
FORD BUYER'S GUIDE.* 1986. m. $19.95. Buyer's Guide National Magazines, 14549 62nd St., N., Clearwater, FL 34620-2328. TEL 309-829-5214. FAX 309-827-7595. (Subscr. to: Box 1953, Mt. Morris, IL 61054) adv. circ. 30,000. **Document type:** consumer publication.
    Former titles: Ford, Mustang Buyer's Guide; Ford, Mustang and Classic Thunderbird Buyer's Guide.
    Description: Marketplace and news for the car enthusiasts and restorers, includes new products, tech and club articles.

796.77 790.13   US
FORD ENTHUSIAST MAGAZINE. 1980. bi-m. $22 (Canada $30; foreign $47). Performance Ford Club of America Inc., 13155 U S R 23, Ashville, OH 43103. TEL 614-983-2273. Ed. Wanda Nelson. adv.; bk.rev. circ. 6,000. (back issues avail.)
    Description: For those interested in Ford powered vehicles, especially models of the 1950's and later. Includes a sale-wanted section.

FORD HERITAGE. see ANTIQUES

388.3   GW   ISSN 0015-7007
FORD-NACHRICHTEN;* Zeitschrift fuer die Mitarbeiter der Ford-Werke AG. (Text in German, Italian, Turkish) 1958. m. free. Ford-Werke AG, Ottoplatz 2, Postfach 210369, 5000 Cologne, Germany. Ed. Heribert Schwinges. charts; illus.; stat.; tr.lit. circ. 50,000. (tabloid format)

FORD WORLD. see BUSINESS AND ECONOMICS — Labor And Industrial Relations

629.286   UK   ISSN 0957-9117
FORECOURT TRADER. m. £35 (Europe £55; worldwide 90). William Reed Publishing Ltd., Broadfield Park, Crawley, W. Sussex RH11 9RT, England. TEL 01293-613400. FAX 01293-613206. Ed. Merril Boulton. **Document type:** trade publication.
    Description: Covers the latest news and views in the industry, with product features and an independent look into market areas.

629.22 388.3   UK
FOUR WHEEL ALIGNMENT MANUAL. 1989. a. £45 for 3 yr. Glass's Information Services Ltd., Elgin House, St. Georges Ave., Weybridge, Surrey KT13 0BX, England. TEL 01932-823823. FAX 01932-846564. (Subscr. to: Sales and Marketing, St. Martins Ct., 37 Queens Rd., Weybridge, Surrey KT13 9TU, England) (looseleaf format) **Document type:** trade publication.

388.3   US   ISSN 0015-9123
FOUR WHEELER MAGAZINE; world's leading four wheel drive magazine. 1962. m. $17.87. Four Wheeler Publishing, Ltd. (Subsidiary of: General Media Publishing Group), 6728 Eton Ave., Canoga Park, CA 91303. TEL 818-992-4777. FAX 818-992-4979. (Subscr. to: Box 420235, Palm Coast, FL 32142-0235) Ed. John Stewart. adv. contact: Christopher Ballard. bk.rev.; charts; illus.; mkt.; tr.lit. circ. 313,716. **Document type:** consumer publication.

388 796.6   AU
FREIE FAHRT. m. membership. Auto-, Motor- und Radfahrerbund Oesterreichs, Mariahilferstr. 180, A-1150 Vienna, Austria. TEL 0222-89121257. FAX 0222-89121227. adv.: B&W page S.80000; trim 210 x 280; adv. contact: Peter Burger. circ. 400,000. **Document type:** newsletter.

388.3   GW
FREIZEITMOBILE. 1992. bi-m. newsstand price: DM.4.80. Vereinigte Motor-Verlage GmbH und Co. KG, Leuschnerstr. 1, 70162 Stuttgart, Germany. TEL 0711-1821226. FAX 0711-1821349. Ed. Adi Kemmer; Pub. M. Kleinjohann. adv. contact: M. Kleinjohann. circ. 35,000. **Document type:** consumer publication.

388.3 350.6   US   ISSN 0016-1810
FROM THE STATE CAPITALS. MOTOR VEHICLE REGULATION. Variant title: Motor Vehicle Regulation - From the State Capitals. 1946. w. $235 (effective 1994). Wakeman-Walworth, Inc., 300 N. Washington St., Alexandria, VA 22314. TEL 703-549-8606. FAX 703-549-1372. (processed; back issues avail.) **Document type:** newsletter.
    —CCC.
    Description: Covers highway safety, vehicle inspection and equipment requirements, driver licensing and education in the US.

629.2 796.77   GW   ISSN 0171-5046
G V A MITGLIEDERVERZEICHNIS. 1969. a. DM.70. Gesamtverband Autoteile-Handel e.V., Postfach 101256, 40832 Ratingen, Germany. TEL 02102-473037. FAX 02102-475663. adv.; stat. circ. 1,500. (back issues avail.) **Document type:** trade publication.

388.8   US   ISSN 1056-4330
TL162
GALE'S AUTO SOURCEBOOK. 1991. a. $93. Gale Research Inc., 835 Penobscot Bldg., Detroit, MI 48266. TEL 313-961-2242. FAX 313-961-6083. Ed. Karen Hill.
    Description: Profiles over 320 vehicle models sold in the past 6 years. Lists information sources.

388.33   UK   ISSN 0264-0163
GARAGE AND AUTOMOTIVE RETAILER. 1955. m. £30. Nexus Media Ltd., Nexus House, Azalea Dr., Swanley, Kent BR8 8HY, England. TEL 01322-660070. FAX 01322-337633. adv.; bk.rev. circ. 36,000. **Document type:** trade publication.
    —CCC.
    Former titles: Garage and Transport Group; Garage and Transport (ISSN 0307-1154); Garage and Transport Equipment (ISSN 0046-5429)

388.33   IT   ISSN 0016-4542
GARAGE & OFFICINA. 1953. m. L.100000 (foreign L.200000). (Associazione Nazionale Autoriparatori e Autoricambisti) Mediana s.r.l., Via Leon Battista Alberti 12, 20149 Milan, Italy. TEL 39-2-3315890. Ed. Marco Marone. adv.: B&W page L.5200000, color page L.7200000. circ. 30,000.

629.286   CN
GARAGE & SERVICE STATION NEWS. 1934. m. $7. Garage & Service Station News Publishing Co., No. 204, 260 Raymur Ave., Vancouver 6, B.C., Canada. Ed. Theodore L. Coates. adv.; illus.; tr.lit.; circ. controlled.

380   UK
GARAGE NEWS. m. Haymarket Specialist Motoring Publications Ltd., 60 Waldegrave Rd., Teddington, Middx. TW11 8LG, England. TEL 081-943-5875. FAX 081-943-5927. Ed. D. Jenkinson. circ. 37,000. **Document type:** trade publication.
    Description: Provides news and views about cars, garage equipment, motor components, accessories, and other aspects of the motor trade.

629.2   UK
GARAGE TRADER; the magazine for Ireland's automotive market. bi-m. £15. Main Stream Publications, 139 Thomas St., Portadown, Co. Armagh BT62 3BE, N. Ireland, England. TEL 01762-334272. FAX 01762-351046. Ed. Lorna Brown. adv.: B&W page £880; color page £980; trim 297 x 210; adv. contact: Karen Neill. circ. 10,214 (controlled). **Document type:** trade publication.
    Description: Contains material of interest to new and used car dealers, managers of service stations, fleet operators, body repair shop owners, electrical system specialists, and engine and component reconditioners.

388   GW   ISSN 0941-6080
GEFAHRGUT-PROFI. 1991. bi-m. DM.116 (foreign DM.134). Verlag T Ue V Rheinland GmbH, Viktoriastr. 26, 51149 Cologne, Germany. TEL 02203-170960. FAX 02203-15411. adv. contact: Gudrun Karafiol. **Document type:** consumer publication.
    —SWETS.

GENERAL MOTORS PUBLIC INTEREST REPORT. see BUSINESS AND ECONOMICS — Production Of Goods And Services

388 629.2 US
GENERAL MOTORS SYMPOSIA SERIES. 1971. irreg., latest 1988. price varies. Plenum Publishing Corp., 233 Spring St., New York, NY 10013-1578. TEL 212-620-8000. FAX 212-463-0742. TELEX 23-421139. **Document type:** proceedings.
Refereed Serial

388.3 IT ISSN 0393-7860
GENTE MOTORI. 1972. m. L.67200 (foreign L.110000). Rusconi Editori S.p.A., Servizio Abbonamenti, Viale Sarca 235, 20126 Milan, Italy. TEL 02-66191. FAX 02-6619-2737. Ed. Daniele Buzzonetti. adv.: page L.40000000. bk.rev. circ. 308,233.

388.3 IT
GENTLEMAN AUTOMOBILI. m. P.C. Boggio 38, 10138 Turin, Italy. Ed. Giorgio Bellia.

629.286 US ISSN 1067-0599
GEORGIA AUTOMOTIVE BUSINESS. m. 1395 S. Marietta Pkwy., Ste. 114, Marietta, GA 30067. TEL 404-499-2128. FAX 404-421-1649. Ed. Keisha L. McCray; Pub. James Tucker. adv. contact: Dan Keiser. circ. 10,000. **Document type:** trade publication.

629.2 GW ISSN 0072-145X
GERMAN MOTOR TRIBUNE. 1951. a. DM.35. Broenner Katalogverlag Breidenstein GmbH, Stuttgarter Str. 18-24, 60329 Frankfurt a.M., Germany. FAX 069-2600509. TELEX 411964. Ed. Klaus Breidenstein. adv. contact: Christiane Vey. circ. 10,000. **Document type:** catalog.
Description: Available free of charge to firms abroad interested in importing automotive goods from Germany.

GHANA. STATISTICAL SERVICE. MOTOR VEHICLE REGISTRATION. see *TRANSPORTATION — Abstracting, Bibliographies, Statistics*

629.286 IT ISSN 1120-8287
GIORNALE DEL MECCANICO. 9/yr. L.65000 (foreign L.130000) (effective 1995). Stammer S.p.A., Via della Liberazione 1, 20068 Peschiera Borromeo (MI), Italy. TEL 39-2-55302606. FAX 39-2-55302700. Ed. Pierpaolo Bellina. adv.: B&W page L.1750000. circ. 20,000.

388 UK
GLASS'S CAR CHECK BOOK. a. £26. Glass's Information Services Ltd., Elgin House, St. George's Ave., Weybridge, Surrey KT13 0BX, England. TEL 01932-823823. FAX 01932-846564. (Orders to: Sales and Marketing, St. Martins Ct., 37 Queens Rd., Weybridge, Surrey KT13 9TU, England) adv. **Document type:** trade publication.

338.476 629.286 UK
▼**GLASS'S GUIDE CAR CHOICE.** 1995. a. £250. Glass's Information Services Ltd., Elgin House, St. Georges Ave., Weybridge, Surrey KT13 0BX, England. TEL 01932-823823. FAX 01932-846564. (Orders to: Sales and Marketing, St. Martins Ct., 37 Queens Rd., Weybridge, Surrey KT13 9TU, England) (diskette format) **Document type:** trade publication.
Description: Enables users to select the most suitable car according to the criteria they set.

338.476 UK
GLASS'S GUIDE TO CAR VALUES. 1933. m. £145 (diskette £250). Glass's Information Services Ltd., Elgin House, St. George's Ave., Weybridge, Surrey KT13 0BX, England. TEL 01932-823823. FAX 01932-846564. (Subscr. to: Sales and Marketing, St. Martins Ct., 37 Queens Rd., Weybridge, Surrey KT13 9TU, England) Ed. Leslie Allen. adv. contact: Keith Mackenzie. circ. 48,714 (paid). (also avail. in diskette format) **Document type:** trade publication.
Formerly: Glass's Guide to Used Car Values.
Description: Offers dealers information on new and used cars.

338.476 UK
GLASS'S GUIDE TO COMMERCIAL VEHICLE VALUES. 1951. m. £130 (diskette £250). Glass's Information Services Ltd., Elgin House, St. George's Ave., Weybridge, Surrey KT13 0BX, England. TEL 01932-823823. FAX 01932-846564. (Subscr. to: Sales and Marketing, St. Martins Ct., 37 Queens St., Weybridge, Surrey KT13 9TU, England) adv. (also avail. in diskette format) **Document type:** trade publication.
Formerly: Glass's Guide to Used Commercial Vehicle Values.

338.476 UK
▼**GLASS'S GUIDE TO OLDER CAR VALUES.** 1994. q. £80. Glass's Information Services Ltd., Elgin House, St. Georges Ave., Weybridge, Surrey KT13 0BX, England. TEL 01932-823823. FAX 01932-846564. **Document type:** trade publication.
Description: Offers dealers valuation information for cars between 10 and 15 years old.

388 UK
GLASS'S INDEX OF REGISTRATION MARKS. a. £17. Glass's Information Services Ltd., Elgin House, St. George's Ave., Weybridge, Surrey KT13 0BX, England. TEL 01932-823823. FAX 01932-846564. (Orders to: Sales and Marketing, St. Martins Ct., 37 Queens Rd., Weybridge, Surrey KT13 9TU, England) **Document type:** trade publication.

629.286 UK
▼**GLASSTECH I C M E SERVICE SYSTEM.** 1995. a. £75. Glass's Information Services Ltd., Elgin House, St. Georges Ave., Weybridge, Surrey KT13 0BX, England. TEL 01932-823823. FAX 01932-846564. (Orders to: Sales and Marketing, St. Martins Ct., 37 Queens Rd., Weybridge, Surrey KT13 9TU, England) **Document type:** trade publication.
Description: Provides all the information to carry out and validate a service, according to the manufacturer's service schedules.

388.3 SA
GO!. (Text in English) 1963. 3/yr. free. (Public Affairs Department) Shell South Africa (Pty) Ltd., P.O. Box 2231, Cape Town 8000, South Africa. TEL 021-408-4911. FAX 021-253807. circ. 1,500 (controlled).
Formerly (until 1985): Shell Dealer News (ISSN 0037-3532)

388 371.3 AU
GO. m. S.110. Elektro und Wirtschaft Verlagsgesellschaft mbH, Wilhelminenstr. 91-IIC, A-1160 Vienna, Austria. TEL 0222-4531490. FAX 0222-46903230. Ed. Ronald Rockenbauer. circ. 75,000. **Document type:** newsletter.

GO (CHARLOTTE). see *TRAVEL AND TOURISM*

614.86 CN ISSN 0831-1560
GOING PLACES MAGAZINE. 1975. 6/yr. Can.$3($6) Canada Wide Magazines Ltd., 4180 Lougheed Hwy., No. 401, Burnaby, BC V5C 6A7, Canada. TEL 604-299-7311. FAX 604-299-9188. Ed. Robin Roberts. adv. contact: Tim Nast. bk.rev.; illus.; index. circ. 90,000. **Document type:** consumer publication.
Formerly: Westworld Magazine; *Supersedes:* B.C. Motorist (ISSN 0005-2884)
Description: Features automotive-related tips, club news and national and international travel.

629.222 US
GOLD BOOK CLASSICS & ANTIQUES. s-a. $35. Gold Book, Inc., 1400 Lake Hearn Dr., 2nd Fl., Atlanta, GA 30319. TEL 800-842-6848. FAX 404-847-6507. Ed. Patrick Keating. (looseleaf format) **Document type:** consumer publication.
Description: Provides values in four condition categories for more than 6,000 antique vehicles manufactured between 1897 and 1942.

629.2 US ISSN 1057-0535
GOLD BOOK CONTEMPORARY VEHICLES. 6/yr. $66. Gold Book, Inc., 1400 Lake Hearn Dr., Atlanta, GA 30319. TEL 800-842-6848. FAX 404-847-6507. Ed. Patrick Keating. (looseleaf format) **Document type:** consumer publication.
Supersedes in part: Gold Book Used Car Value Guide.
Description: Provides values in three condition categories plus wholesale and loan values for more than 10,000 domestic and imported cars and trucks manufactured since 1976.

629.2 US ISSN 1057-0136
GOLD BOOK OLDER VEHICLES. q. $46. Gold Book, Inc., 1400 Lake Hearn Dr., Atlanta, GA 30319. TEL 800-842-6848. FAX 404-847-6507. Ed. Patrick Keating. (looseleaf format) **Document type:** consumer publication.
Supersedes in part: Gold Book Used Car Value Guide.
Description: Provides values in three condition categories plus loan value for more than 10,000 domestic and imported cars and truck manufactured between 1945 and 1975.

388.3 UK ISSN 0017-2111
GOOD MOTORING. 1935. q. membership. Good Motoring (Publishers) Ltd., c/o Guild of Experienced Motorists, Station Rd., Forest Row, E. Sussex, RH18 5EN, England. TEL 01342-825676. FAX 01342-824847. Ed. Derek Hainge; Pub. John Newman. adv. contact: John Taylor. bk.rev.; illus.; circ. 53,000 (controlled). **Document type:** consumer publication.
Description: General motoring journal published for the members of the Guild of Experienced Motorists.

GOODGUYS GOODTIMES GAZETTE. see *SPORTS AND GAMES*

388.3 UK
GOODS VEHICLE COSTING AND PRICING HANDBOOK. irreg. £22.50. Kogan Page Ltd., 120 Pentonville Rd., London N1 9JN, England. TEL 071-278-0433. FAX 071-837-6348. TELEX 263088 KOGAN G. Ed. David Lowe. **Document type:** trade publication.
Description: Practical ways to cost vehicles and calculate profitable haulage rates.

338.3 SP
GRAN GUIA COCHE ACTUAL. a. 600 ptas. Luike - Motorpress, C. Ancora 40, 28045 Madrid, Spain. TEL 34-1-3470100. FAX 34-1-3470204. Ed. Alberto Mayo. adv.: B&W page 470000 ptas., color page 675000 ptas.; adv. contact: Agustin Valero. **Document type:** consumer publication.

629 IT ISSN 0392-6796
LE GRANDI AUTOMOBILI/GREAT CARS. (Text in English, Italian) 1983. q. L.50000($60) Automobilia s.r.l., Via Ponte Seveso, 25, 20125 Milan, Italy. TEL 39-2-67074391. FAX 39-2-67075000. Ed. Bruno Alfieri. circ. 9,000. (back issues avail.)

388.3 US ISSN 1047-0298
GRASSROOTS MOTORSPORTS. Key Title: Auto-X and Grassroots Motorsports. 1984. bi-m. $14.97. Motorsport Marketing, Inc., 425 Parque Dr., Ormond Beach, FL 32174. TEL 904-673-4148. FAX 904-673-6040. Ed. Marjorie Suddard. adv.; bk.rev. circ. 15,000.
Formerly: Auto-X (ISSN 1043-1748)

GREATER WASHINGTON - MARYLAND SERVICE STATION AND AUTOMOTIVE REPAIR ASSOCIATION. MEMBERSHIP DIRECTORY & BUYER'S GUIDE. see *BUSINESS AND ECONOMICS — Trade And Industrial Directories*

GREEN CAR JOURNAL. see *ENERGY*

GUERIN SPORTIVO MESE. see *SPORTS AND GAMES — Bicycles And Motorcycles*

629.286 VE
GUIA AUTOMOTRIZ DE VENEZUELA/VENEZUELAN AUTOMOTIVE GUIDE. 1970. a. $25. Promotrix, S.R.L., Av. Caurimare, Qta. Expo., Colinas de Bello Monte, Caracas, Venezuela. TEL 7511355. FAX 582-7511122. Ed. Armando Ortiz P. adv. contact: Maria Ortiz. circ. 8,000 (controlled). **Document type:** directory.

GUIA DE UTILLAJE Y EQUIPOS. see *TRAVEL AND TOURISM*

6376 TRANSPORTATION — AUTOMOBILES

388 PO
GUIA DO AUTOMOVEL. 1985. m. newsstand price: Esc. 330. Motorpress Lisboa, Av. Afonso III, Lote 2, Loja B, 1900 Lisbon, Portugal. TEL 351-1-8151134. FAX 351-1-8151542. Ed. Joao Ferreira; Pub. Luis Penha e Costa. adv. contact: Rita Vidreiro. circ. 46,000. Document type: consumer publication.

388.3 SP
GUIA UTIL COCHE ACTUAL. m. newsstand price: 175 ptas. Luike - Motorpress, C. Ancora 40, 28045 Madrid, Spain. TEL 34-1-3470100. FAX 34-1-3470204. Ed. Jose Luis Sarralde. adv.: B&W page 190000 ptas., color page 225000 ptas.; adv. contact: Antonino Berges. Document type: consumer publication.
Description: Price guide for new and used cars.

629.286 FR ISSN 1157-1888
GUIDE DE L'EQUIPEMENT ET DE L'OUTILLAGE. 1989. a. 350 F. Editions Techniques pour l'Automobile et l'Industrie (ETAI), 20-22 rue de la Saussiere, 92100 Boulogne-Billancourt, France. TEL 46-04-81-13. FAX 48-25-56-92. TELEX ETAIRTA 204850F. Ed. Jean Graudens. adv. circ. 55,000.
Description: Supplies jobber store owners and managers with names of products and locations of suppliers of all equipment related to cars, vans and trucks.

388 US
GUIDE TO AFTERMARKET PRODUCTS. biennial. $55. Automotive Service Industry Association, 25 Northwest Pt. Blvd., Ste. 425, Elk Grove Village, IL 60007-1035. TEL 708-228-1310. FAX 708-228-1510. Ed. Skip Potter. adv. contact: Gary McCoy. Document type: directory.
Description: Includes contact info of motor vehicle aftermarket product manufacturers.

388 US
GUIDE TO MANUFACTURERS' REPRESENTATIVE SERVICES. biennial. $120. Automotive Service Industry Association, 25 Northwest Pt. Blvd., Ste. 425, Elk Grove Village, IL 60007-1035. TEL 708-228-1310. FAX 708-228-1510. Ed. Skip Potter. adv. contact: Gary McCoy. Document type: directory.
Description: Includes contact info, size and market info for sales agencies representing motor vehicle aftermarket products.

388.3 UK
GUIDE TO THE LARGE GOODS VEHICLE DRIVING TEST AND LICENCES. 1976. a. £8.95. Kogan Page Ltd., 120 Pentonville Rd., London N1 9JN, England. TEL 071-278-0433. FAX 071-837-6348. TELEX 263088 KOGAN G. Ed. David P. Soye. Document type: bulletin.
Formerly: Guide to Heavy Goods Vehicle Test and Licences.
Description: Complete instruction on qualifying for the LGV license, including sample questions and useful addresses.

338.476 JA
GUIDE TO THE MOTOR INDUSTRY OF JAPAN. (Text in English) 1960. q. 4000 Yen per no. Japan Motor Industrial Federation, Otemachi Bldg., 6-1 Otemachi 1-chome, Chiyoda-ku, Tokyo 100, Japan. TEL 81-3-3211-8731. FAX 81-3-3211-5798. Ed. Kohki Fujimori. adv.; stat. circ. 20,000. (back issues avail.) Document type: catalog.
Description: Lists the export-version of Japanese cars, company information of 13 car manufacturers, car parts, machine and body manufacturers, and the main automobile organizations.

388.3 GW ISSN 0017-5765
GUTE FAHRT; das AutoSpecial fuer Volkswagen and Audi. 1950. m. DM.55 (foreign DM.65). Verlag Delius, Klasing und Co., Postfach 101671, 33516 Bielefeld, Germany. TEL 0521-559-280. FAX 0521-559-113. TELEX 932934-DEKLA. Ed. Wolfgang Hoffmann. adv.; illus. circ. 240,000. Document type: consumer publication.
—CCC.

614.85 US
H L D I INJURY AND COLLISION LOSS EXPERIENCE; cars by make and model. a. free. Highway Loss Data Institute, c/o Stephen L. Oesch, General Counsel, Sec.-Treas., 1005 N. Glebe Rd., Ste. 800, Arlington, VA 22201. TEL 703-247-1600. FAX 703-247-1678.

388.3 GW
HALLO! TAXI; Das Magazin fuer Taxifahrer. 1982. m. DM.36. Hallo! Taxi Fachverlag, Ostertorsteinweg 42-43, 28203 Bremen, Germany. TEL 0421-321681. FAX 0421-324883. Ed. Raimund Cassalette. adv. Document type: trade publication.

629.286 US
HEADLINER. m. $48 (free to qualified personnel). (Auto Body Association of Connecticut) Maxco Publications, 1275 Bloomfield Ave., No. 6-36, Fairfield, NJ 07004-2708. TEL 201-785-0764. FAX 201-785-0447. Ed. Pat McCarthy. adv. contact: Lynn Sands. circ. 2,300 (controlled). Document type: trade publication.

629.222 US
HEMMINGS MOTOR NEWS. 1954. m. $24.95 (Canada $58; Mexico $88; Central America $110; South America and Europe $165; elsewhere $215). Watering, Inc., Box 256, Bennington, VT 05201. TEL 802-442-3101; 800-227-4373. FAX 802-447-1561. (Subscr. address: Box 100, Bennington, VT 05201. FAX 802-447-1561) adv. circ. 267.904. Document type: consumer publication.
Description: Addresses antique automobiles.

629.286 US ISSN 1040-0044
HIGH-PERFORMANCE MOPAR. 1986. 7/yr. $16.95. C S K Publishing Co., Inc., 299 Market St., Saddle Brook, NJ 07662. TEL 201-712-9300. FAX 201-712-9899. (Subscr. to: Box 1010, Denville, NJ 07834) Ed. Jeff Bauer. adv.; bk.rev. circ. 57,500. (back issues avail.) Document type: consumer publication.
Description: Edited for the Chrysler activist who's into modifying, racing, collecting and restoring. New Chryslers featured and old Mopar retrospectives also covered.

796.77 US ISSN 0745-5941
HIGH-PERFORMANCE PONTIAC. 1979. bi-m. $16. C S K Publishing Co., Inc., 299 Market St., Saddle Brook, NJ 07662. TEL 201-712-9300. FAX 201-712-9899. Ed. Richard Lentinello. adv. circ. 44,250. (back issues avail.) Document type: consumer publication.
Description: For the dyed-in-the-wool Pontiac enthusiast covering all models from mid-'50s, with emphasis on stock musclecars.

HIGHWAY LOSS DATA INSTITUTE. VEHICLE DESCRIPTIONS. see *INSURANCE*

388.3 US
HILDY'S FORD BLUE BOOK.* 1926. a. Cummins Publishing Co., 6557 Forest Park Dr., Troy, MI 48098-1954. TEL 313-358-4900.

HOME & AWAY. see *TRAVEL AND TOURISM*

HORSELESS CARRIAGE GAZETTE. see *ANTIQUES*

388 GW
HOT CAR MAGAZIN. m. H C M Verlags GmbH, Hauptstr. 88, 65817 Eppstein, Germany. TEL 06198-32798. FAX 06198-32763. Ed. Helmut Redecker; Pub. Helmut Redecker. adv. contact: Sigrun Karow. circ. 12,984. Document type: consumer publication.

796.72 US ISSN 0018-6031
TL236
HOT ROD. 1948. m. $19.94. Petersen Publishing Co., 6420 Wilshire Blvd., Los Angeles, CA 90048. TEL 213-782-2000; 800-800-4681. FAX 213-782-2865. Ed. Drew Hardin. adv.; bk.rev.; charts; illus. circ. 800,000. (also avail. in microform from UMI; reprint service avail. from UMI) Indexed: Abr.R.G., Access (1980-1987), Consum.Ind., Jun.High.Mag.Abstr., Mag.Ind., PMR, R.G., Sports Per.Ind., TOM. Document type: consumer publication.
●Also available online. Vendor(s): Knight-Ridder, Inc. —Faxon; UMI; UnCover.
Description: Covers racing events.

I A D A SERVICE DIRECTORY. (Independent Automotive Damage Appraisers Association) see *INSURANCE*

614.86 388 JA ISSN 0386-1104
I A T S S RESEARCH. (Text in English) 1977. s-a. 10000 Yen($66) International Association of Traffic and Safety Sciences, 6-20, 2-chome, Yaesu, Chuo-ku, Tokyo 104, Japan. TEL 03-3273-7884. FAX 03-3272-7054. Ed. Katsutoshi Ohta. stat.; tr.lit. circ. 1,700. (back issues avail.) Indexed: HRIS, JTA. Document type: academic/scholarly publication.
Description: For administrators, policy-makers, and scientists on traffic and its safety.

338 629.2 UK
I B C A M JOURNAL. 1974. m. membership only. Institute of British Carriage and Automobile Manufacturers, 31 Redstone Farm Rd., Hall Green, Birmingham B28 9NU, England. TEL 0121-778-4354. FAX 1021-702-2615. Ed. Loraine Clarke. adv.; bk.rev.; illus. circ. 2,500. Document type: newsletter.
Former titles: News from I B C A M; I B C A M Journal (ISSN 0306-2910); Supersedes: Institute of British Carriage and Automobile Manufacturers. Institute Bulletin.

629.286 330 US
I C A LETTER.* m. International Carwash Association, 401 N. Michigan Ave., Chicago, IL 60611-4212. TEL 708-495-0144.

388.3 UK
I C M E (CARS). 1932. a. £49. Glass's Information Services Ltd., Elgin House, St. Georges Ave, Weybridge, Surrey KT13 0BX, England. TEL 01932-823823. FAX 01932-846564. (Orders to: Sales and Marketing, St. Martins Ct., 37 Queens Rd., Weybridge, Surrey KT13 9TU, England) Document type: trade publication.

388 UK
I C M E (HEAVY COMMERCIAL VEHICLES). 1989. a. £49. Glass's Information Services Ltd., Elgin House, St. Georges Ave., Weybridge, Surrey KT13 0BX, England. TEL 01932-823823. FAX 01932-846564. (Orders to: Sales and Marketing, St. Martins Ct., 37 Queens Rd., Weybridge, Surrey KT13 9TU, England) Document type: trade publication.

388 UK
I C M E (LIGHT COMMERCIAL VEHICLES). 1989. a. £32. Glass's Information Services Ltd., Elgin House, St. Georges Ave., Weybridge, Surrey KT13 0BX, England. TEL 01932-823823. FAX 01932-846564. (Orders to: Sales and Marketing, St. Martins Ct., 37 Queens Rd., Weybridge, Surrey KT13 9TU, England) Document type: trade publication.

629.2 US ISSN 0098-3551
TK6570.M6
I E E E VEHICULAR TECHNOLOGY CONFERENCE. RECORD. Key Title: Record - Vehicular Technology Conference. Title varies: Vehicular Technology Group Conference. Record; I E E E Vehicular Technology Group. Proceedings of the Annual Conference. a. Institute of Electrical and Electronics Engineers, Inc., 345 E. 47th St, New York, NY 10017-2394. TEL 908-981-1393. FAX 908-981-9667. (Subscr. to: Box 1331, 445 Hoes Ln., Piscataway, NJ 08855-1331) illus.
—BLDSC (4363.236000). **CCC.**

388.3 IT
ILLUSTRATOFIAT. 1952. m. Fiat, Corso Marconi 10, Turin, Italy. TEL 011-531009. adv.: B&W page L.22500000, color page L.29500000. bk.rev.; illus. circ. 245,000.

346 614.86 US ISSN 0162-4989
KF1297.A8
IMPACT (WASHINGTON). 1975. bi-m. $75 (foreign $90). Center for Auto Safety, 2001 S St., N.W., Ste. 410, Washington, DC 20009. TEL 202-328-7700. Ed. Debra Barclay. bk.rev.; index; circ. 1,000 (paid). (back issues avail.) Document type: consumer publication, newsletter.
Description: Reports on the auto safety work of CAS. Covers safety legislation, auto defects, lemon laws, recalls and federal and state investigations.

629.286 US ISSN 0199-4468
IMPORT AUTOMOTIVE PARTS & ACCESORIES. 1979. m. $34 (effective Jan. 1995). Meyers Publishing Corp., 6211 Van Nuys Blvd., Van Nuys, CA 91401. TEL 818-785-3900. FAX 818-785-4397. Ed. Steve Releya. adv. contact: Lana Meyers. circ. 35,000 (controlled). Document type: trade publication.

TRANSPORTATION — AUTOMOBILES

388.3   US   ISSN 1069-3238
HD9710.A1
IMPORT CAR PRICES. 1973. 4/yr. newsstand price: $5.99. Pace Publications (Milwaukee), 1020 N. Broadway, Ste. 111, Milwaukee, WI 53202. TEL 414-272-9977. FAX 414-272-9973.
    Former titles: New and Used Foreign and Japanese Car Prices (ISSN 1050-5423); (until 1992): Foreign Car Prices.
    Description: Lists dealer's cost and manufacturer's suggested list price for every foreign automobile and every single option available for each, with previous ten year listings for used foreign cars.

388.3   US   ISSN 0896-5722
IMPORT SERVICE. 1987. m. Gemini Communications, 306 N. Cleveland Massillon Rd., Akron, OH 44333-9302. TEL 216-666-9553. adv. circ. 66,000.

629.28   US   ISSN 1069-4714
TL159
IMPORTCAR; the complete import service magazine. (Includes Automotive Aftermarket Training Guide published in July) 1979. 13/yr. $59 (foreign $115) (effective 1995). Babcox Publications, 11 S. Forge St., Box 1810, Akron, OH 44309-1810. TEL 216-535-6117. FAX 216-535-0874. Ed. Mary Della Valle. adv.: B&W page $3955. charts; illus.; stat.; tr.lit.; circ. 28,000. circ. 63 (paid). (back issues avail.) **Document type:** trade publication.
    Former titles (until 1993): Importcar and Truck (ISSN 1040-5267); (until 1988): ImportCar (ISSN 0735-7877); (until 1982): Babcox's ImportCar (ISSN 0278-6532); (until 1980): Importcar (ISSN 0271-6712); Babcox's Importcar (ISSN 0194-2492)
    Description: Delivers current information relating to the import aftermarket. Reports on marketing trends, makes and models, accessories, technical updates, legislative issues and new products.

629.286   US
IMPORTED CARS, LIGHT TRUCKS & VANS SERVICE & REPAIR. (In 3 vols.: Engine Performance, Electrical, Mechanical) 1967. a. $149. Mitchell International, Inc., 9889 Willow Creek Rd., Box 26260, San Diego, CA 92196-0260. TEL 800-648-8010. FAX 619-578-4752. circ. 20,000. (also avail. in microform)
    •Also available on CD-ROM.
    Description: Auto service and repair manual for professional auto technicians.

629.2   CN   ISSN 0702-5785
IN THE DRIVER'S SEAT.* m. free. Ontario Safety League, 21 Four Seasons Place, Etobicoke, Ont. M9B 6J8, Canada. TEL 416-593-2670. circ. controlled.

388   II   ISSN 0971-1317
INDIAN AUTO. (Text in English) 1986. m. Rs.700($23) Business Press Private Ltd., Transmission House, Compartment No. 82, Plot No. 6-19, Marol Co-op Industrial Estate, M.V. Rd., Andheri East, Bombay 400059, India. TEL 8351871. FAX 91-22-8379070. TELEX 011-78455 BPPL IN. Ed. R.V. Pandit. adv.; bk.rev.; abstr.; charts; illus. circ. 35,000.
    Description: Covers road tests and news briefs.

388   II
INDIAN AUTO JOURNAL. (Text in English) 1986. m. Rs.90. Business Press Pvt. Ltd., Surya Mahal, Burjorji Bharucha Marg, Bombay 400 001, India. Ed. Gautam Sen; Pub. R.V. Pandit. adv. contact: Sanjay Thakur.

388   MX   ISSN 0187-4861
INDUSTRIA AUTOMOTRIZ EN MEXICO. 1981. a. Instituto Nacional de Estadistica, Geografia e Informatica, Secretaria de Programacion y Presupuesto, Av. Prol. Heroe de Nacozari 2301 Sur, Puerta 10, planta baja, 20290 Aguascalientes Ags., Mexico. TEL 91-49-18-14-77. FAX 91-491-80739. circ. 2,000.

629.2   FR   ISSN 0073-7747
INDUSTRIE FRANCAISE DES MOTEURS A COMBUSTION INTERNE; repertoire alphabetique des constructeurs. 1953. irreg. free. Syndicat des Constructeurs de Moteurs a Combustion Interne, 39-41 rue Louis Blanc, 92400 Courbevoie, France. TEL 47-17-62-81. FAX 47-17-62-82. (Subscr. to: Cedex 72, 92038 Paris la Defense, France)

INDY CAR RACING MAGAZINE. see SPORTS AND GAMES

629.2   FR   ISSN 0020-1200
INGENIEURS DE L'AUTOMOBILE. 1927. 8/yr. 690 F. (foreign 780 F.). (Societe des Ingenieurs de l'Automobile) V B Promotion, 15 rue de 19 janvier, 92380 Garches, France. TEL 47-01-44-74. FAX 47-01-48-25. TELEX 631 191 F. Ed. Paul Bardez. adv.; bk.rev.; abstr.; illus. circ. 5,500.
    Indexed: C.I.S. Abstr., Eng.Ind., Excerp.Med., World Alum.Abstr.
    —Ei.

INSTALLATION NEWS. see COMMUNICATIONS

621   UK   ISSN 0954-4070
TJ1   CODEN: PMDEEA
INSTITUTION OF MECHANICAL ENGINEERS. PROCEEDINGS. PART D: JOURNAL OF AUTOMOBILE ENGINEERING. 1984. q. £143($289) (rest of world £153) for Part D; £1191($2329) for parts A-J (effective 1995). Mechanical Engineering Publications Ltd., Northgate Ave., Bury St. Edmunds, Suffolk IP32 6BW, England. TEL 01284-763277. FAX 01284-704006. TELEX 817376. (Subscr. in N. & S. America to: Box 361, Birmingham, AL 35201-1964. TEL 205-991-1177. FAX 205-995-1588) Ed. D. Tidmarsh. bibl.; illus.; index, cum.index. circ. 1,294. **Indexed:** A.S.& T.Ind., Appl.Mech.Rev., B.C.I.R.A., BMT, Br.Rail.Bd., Br.Tech.Ind., Chem.Abstr., Curr.Cont., Eng.Ind., HRIS, INSPEC, Math.R., Met.Abstr. **Document type:** academic/scholarly publication, proceedings.
    —BLDSC (6724.900770); Ei; Faxon; SWETS; UMI. CCC.
    Formerly: Institution of Mechanical Engineers. Proceedings. Part D: Transport Engineering (ISSN 0265-1904); Supersedes in part: Institution of Mechanical Engineers. Proceedings (ISSN 0020-3483)
    Description: Concerned with research, design, development, production, operation, servicing and repair of cars, commercial vehicles, public service vehicles, off-highway vehicles and industrial agricultural tractors.

INSURANCE COLLISION REPORT PASSENGER CARS, CARGO VANS, PICKUPS, AND UTILITY VEHICLES. see INSURANCE

INSURANCE INJURY REPORT PASSENGER CARS, CARGO VANS, PICKUPS, AND UTILITY VEHICLES. see INSURANCE

INSURANCE SPECIAL REPORT: VARIOUS TOPICS. see INSURANCE

INSURANCE THEFT REPORT PASSENGER CARS, CARGO VANS, PICKUPS, AND UTILITY VEHICLES. see INSURANCE

INTER AUTO ECOLES DE FRANCE - INTER AUTO ROUTE. see EDUCATION

629.2   GW   ISSN 0946-9230
INTERNATIONAL AUTO STATISTICS. (Text in English) 1981. a. DM.126. Verband der Automobilindustrie e.V., Westendstr. 61, 60325 Frankfurt a.M., Germany. TEL 069-7570-0. FAX 069-7570-261. (back issues avail.) **Document type:** trade publication.
    Formerly: Auto-International in Zahlen (ISSN 0175-9531)

629.286   UK   ISSN 0261-2267
HD9710..A1
INTERNATIONAL AUTOMOTIVE REVIEW. q. $1276. E M A P - Response Publishing Ltd., Wentworth House, Wentworth St., Petersborough, Cambs. PE1 1DS, England. TEL 01274-499821. FAX 01274-547143. TELEX 51317 MCBUNI G. Ed. Mike Woodmansey. adv.; charts; stat. (back issues avail.; reprint service avail. from SWZ) **Document type:** trade publication.
    —BLDSC (4536.521000).
    Description: Aims to provide international, in-depth coverage of topics of current and incoming strategic interest to the automotive industry worldwide. Presents specialist articles and country surveys.

388 690   UK   ISSN 0966-4947
INTERNATIONAL CAR PARK DESIGN AND CONSTRUCTION TRENDS. s.a. £16 (foreign £24). Landor Publishing Ltd., Quadrant House, 250 Kennington Ln., London SE11 5RD, England. TEL 0171-582-6626. FAX 0171-735-1299. E-mail: 100570,73@compuserve.com. **Document type:** trade publication.
    Description: Examines the changing approaches to designing, building, equipping and refurbishing car parks.

629.286   US
INTERNATIONAL CONFERENCE ON VEHICLE STRUCTURAL MECHANICS. PROCEEDINGS. 1975. biennial. Society of Automotive Engineers, 400 Commonwealth Dr., Warrendale, PA 15096-0001. TEL 412-776-4841. FAX 412-776-3036. **Document type:** proceedings.

388   US   ISSN 0267-8225
HD9710.A1
INTERNATIONAL MOTOR BUSINESS. (Part of Automotive Intelligence Service consisting: International Motor Business (ISSN 0267-8225); Japanese Motor Business (ISSN 0266-898X); European Motor Business (ISSN 0267-8233)) q. £515($810) Economist Intelligence Unit, 111 W. 57th St., New York, NY 10019. TEL 212-554-0600; 800-938-4685. FAX 212-586-1182. TELEX 175567. (UK addr.: Economist Intelligence Unit Ltd., Subscriptions Dept., P.O. Box 200, Harold Hill, Romford, Essex RM3 8UX, England. TEL 44-1708-381-444. FAX 44-1708-371-850) (also avail. in microform from UMI) **Indexed:** Cont.Pg.Manage.
    •Also available online.
    —BLDSC (4544.361000); Faxon; UMI.
    Description: Provides an analysis of trends and forecasts of international automotive industries and markets.

INTERSTANDOX; information for the world of the car repair painter. see PAINTS AND PROTECTIVE COATINGS

INTERSTANDOX EXTRA. see PAINTS AND PROTECTIVE COATINGS

388.3   IE   ISSN 0376-7221
IRISH MOTOR INDUSTRY. 1968. m. £20 (foreign £35). (Society of the Irish Motor Industry) Jude Publications Ltd., Jude House, Tara St., Dublin 2, Ireland. TEL 01-6713500. FAX 01-6713074. Ed. Kate Tammemagi. adv.; bk.rev.; circ. 2,500 (controlled). **Document type:** trade publication.

388.3   US   ISSN 1350-1364
ITALIAN CARS AND BIKES.* bi-m. $30. International Publishers Corp., 26 Sixth St., Ste. 514, Stamford, CT 06905-4606. TEL 203-656-3913. FAX 203-656-2774.
    Formerly: Italian Cars - Classic and Sport.

388.3   US   ISSN 1050-0243
J.L QUINN'S MIDGETS & MOTORSPORTS ILLUSTRATED.* bi-m. Victory Lane Publishing, Inc., 19766 State Rd. 279, Oak Hill, OH 45656-9735. Ed. Marlon R. Atkins.
    Formerly: Midgets and Mini-Sprints Racing News (ISSN 0889-5279)

629.2   NE   ISSN 0389-4304
TL240   CODEN: JREVDY
J S A E REVIEW. (Text in English) 1978. q. fl.366($223) (effective 1996). (Society of Automotive Engineers of Japan, JA - Jidosha Gijutsukai) Elsevier Science B.V., P.O. Box 211, 1000 AE Amsterdam, Netherlands. TEL 31-20-4853911. FAX 31-20-4853598. TELEX 18582 ESPA NL. E-mail: nlinfo-f@elsevier.nl; usinfo-f@elsevier.com; forinfo-kyf04035@niftyserve.or.jp; Site addr.: http://www.elsevier.nl/. (Subscr. in U.S. and Canada to: Elsevier Science Inc., Box 882, Madison Sq. Sta., New York, NY 10159-0882. TEL 212-989-5800. FAX 212-633-3990) Ed. Y. Inatsugi. (also avail. in microform from UMI) **Indexed:** Chem.Abstr., Fluidex, HRIS, JTA, Met.Abstr., PROMT, World Alum.Abstr.
    —BLDSC (5073.725000); CASDDS; Ei; UnCover. CCC.
    Description: Disseminates advanced technical information on subjects such as fuel economy, automotive safety, emission and noise controls, electronics and production technology.
    Refereed Serial

TRANSPORTATION — AUTOMOBILES

629.222   UK
JAGUAR WORLD. 1988. bi-m. £20 (Europe £24; rest of world £29). Kelsey Publishing Ltd., Kelsey House, 77 High St., Beckenham, Kent BR3 1AN, England. TEL 0181-658-3531. FAX 0181-650-8035. **Document type:** consumer publication.
Formerly: Jaguar Quarterly (ISSN 0957-0608)

796.72   AT
JAGUARS WEST. m. Aus.$40 (typically set in July). Jaguar Car Club of Western Australia, P.O. Box 6027, East Perth, W.A. 6004, Australia. circ. 400.
Formerly (until 1990): Jaguar Torque.

338.476   JA
JAN CORPORATION. FACTS & INFO; annual guide to Japan's auto industry. (Text in English) 1981. a. 10960 Yen. Jan Corporation, DIK Shinbashi, No. 415, Shinbashi 6-5-4, Minato-ku, Tokyo 105, Japan. TEL 03-3438-0361. FAX 03-3438-0362. Ed. Shin Sato. circ. 8,000. **Document type:** trade publication.
Formerly (until 1991): Automotive Herald. Facts and Info.

JAPAN AUTO ABSTRACTS; real time database. see *TRANSPORTATION — Abstracting, Bibliographies, Statistics*

388.3   JA   ISSN 0021-4329
JAPAN AUTOMOTIVE NEWS. (Text in English) 1959. m. 14000 Yen. Jan Corporation, DIK Shinbashi No. 415, Shinbashi 6-5-4, Minato-ku, Tokyo 105, Japan. TEL 03-3438-0361. FAX 03-3438-0362. Ed. Shin Sato. adv.; bk.rev.; charts; illus.; stat. circ. 21,000. (tabloid format) **Indexed:** JCT, JTA. **Document type:** trade publication.

388.3   IT
JAPAN CAR MAGAZINE. 1990. m. L.50000 (foreign L.100000). Edizioni Oriente s.r.l., Via A. Ressi 12, 20125 Milan, Italy. TEL 39-2-66711711. FAX 39-2-66710170. Ed. Marcello Pirovano. adv.: B&W page L.11000000, color page L.14500000. circ. 40,000. **Document type:** consumer publication.

629.286   JA   ISSN 0289-6087
JAPAN MOTOR INDUSTRY. 6/yr. $115. Intercontinental Marketing Corp., P.O. Box 5056, Tokyo 100-31, Japan. FAX 81-3-3667-9646.

388   US   ISSN 0266-898X
JAPANESE MOTOR BUSINESS. (Part of Automotive Intelligence Service consisting of: International Motor Business (ISSN 9267-8225); Japanese Motor Business (ISSN 0266-898X); European Motor Business (ISSN 0267-8233) 4/yr. £540($810) Economist Intelligence Unit, 111 W. 57th St., New York, NY 10019. TEL 212-554-0600; 800-938-4685. FAX 212-586-1182. TELEX 175567. (UK addr.: Economist Intelligence Unit Ltd., Subscriptions Dept., P.O. Box 200, Harold Hill, Romford, Essex RM3 8UX, England. TEL 44-1708-381-444. FAX 44-1708-371-850) (also avail. in microform from UMI)
●Also available online.
—BLDSC (4659.660000).
Description: Examines the impact of the Japanese market on the international automotive markets.

629.286   CC
JIASHI YUAN/DRIVERS. (Text in Chinese) m. (Tianjin Qiche Zhizao Chang - Tianjin Automobile Manufacturing Company) Jiashi Yuan Bianjibu, 201 Hongqi Nanlu, Tianjin 300191, People's Republic of China. TEL 341918. Ed. Zhao Pengwan.

**629.286   JA   ISSN 0385-7298
                    CODEN: JDGJA9**
JIDOSHA GIJUTSU/SOCIETY OF AUTOMOTIVE ENGINEERS OF JAPAN. JOURNAL. (Text in Japanese) 1947. m. 21600 Yen. Society of Automotive Engineers of Japan, Inc. - Jidosha Gijutsukai, 10-2, Goban-cho, Chiyoda-ku, Tokyo 102, Japan. **Indexed:** JCT.
—BLDSC (4880.910000); CASDDS. **CCC.**
Formerly: Jidosha Gijutsu Kyokai Kaiho.

**629.286   JA   ISSN 0287-8321
                    CODEN: JGRODZ**
JIDOSHA GIJUTSUKAI RONBUNSHU/SOCIETY OF AUTOMOTIVE ENGINEERS OF JAPAN. TRANSACTIONS. (Text in Japanese; summaries in English) 1970. q. price varies. Society of Automotive Engineers of Japan, Inc. - Jidosha Gijutsukai, 10-2, Goban-cho, Chiyoda-ku, Tokyo 102, Japan. **Indexed:** JCT.
—BLDSC (9005.600000); CASDDS.

629.286 621   JA   ISSN 0388-3841
JIDOSHA KOGAKU/AUTOMOBILE ENGINEERING. 1952. m. 590 Yen. Tetsudo Nihon-sha, 1-4, 2-chome, Nishi-kanda, Chiyoda-ku, Tokyo, Japan. Ed. M. Okasawa. adv. circ. 98,000. **Indexed:** A.S.& T.Ind., JCT, JTA.

388.3   CN   ISSN 0021-7050
JOBBER NEWS; for Canadian automotive wholesalers and salesmen warehouse distributors and automotive rebuilders. 1931. m. Can.$51.36 (foreign $72). Southam Magazine Group, 1450 Don Mills Rd., Don Mills, ON M3B 2X7, Canada. TEL 416-445-6641. FAX 416-442-2261. Ed. Bob Blans. adv.; charts; illus.; tr.lit. circ. 11,900.
Description: Provides business management and product technology information to enhance the professionalism and overall profitability of warehouse distributors and jobbers nationally. Also provides shop management and technical rebuilding information for the engine rebuilder and machine shop trade across Canada.

388.3   US
JOBBER TOPICS REPORTS.* 1922. m. $50 (foreign $60). Irving-Cloud Publishing Co., 417 N. Hough St., Barrington, IL 60010-3028. TEL 708-674-7300. FAX 708-674-7015. Ed. Martin Schultz. bk.rev.; illus.; index. circ. 58,294. (also avail. in microfiche from CIS) **Indexed:** Bus.Ind., SRI (until 1992), Tr.& Indus.Ind.
Formerly (until 1992): Jobber Topics (ISSN 0021-7069); Incorporates: Automotive Distribution; Automotive Wholesaler.
Description: For wholesale distributors in the automotive aftermarket industry.

388.3   FR   ISSN 0242-0805
JOURNAL DE L'AUTOMOBILE. 1979. 26/yr. 27-28 quai Carnot, 92210 Saint-Cloud, France. TEL 46-02-70-90. FAX 47-71-22-12. TELEX 205 197. Ed. Jacques Farenc. circ. 8,074.

629.286   FR   ISSN 0991-0298
JOURNAL DU CONTROLE TECHNIQUE. 7/yr. 27-28 quai Carnot, 92210 Saint-Cloud, France. TEL 46-02-70-90. FAX 47-71-22-12. TELEX 205 197. Ed. Yves Guittat. circ. 12,000.

**629.283 614.8   US   ISSN 0164-1344
HE5614.3.C3**
JOURNAL OF TRAFFIC SAFETY EDUCATION. 1953. q. $8. California Association for Safety Education, 5151 State University Dr., Los Angeles, CA 90032. TEL 213-343-4622. Ed. William Cole. adv.; bk.rev. circ. 2,800. **Indexed:** Educ.Ind., HRIS.

629.28   GW
JURID-TIP. 1956. 3/yr. free. Jurid Werke GmbH, Postfach 1249, 21452 Reinbek, Germany. circ. 60,000.

388.3   BE   ISSN 0022-7242
K.A.C.B. AUTO REVUE/ROYAL AUTO. (Editions in Dutch, French) 1905. 4/yr. membership. (Koninklijke Automobiel Club van Belgie - Royal Automobile Club of Belgium) Eclips Promotion, 53 rue d'Arlon, B-1040 Brussels, Belgium. TEL 32-1-287094. FAX 32-2-2307584. Ed. Raoul Tuyttens. adv. contact: Mrs. Janssens. bk.rev.; charts; illus.; index; circ. 40,000 (controlled). **Document type:** consumer publication.

388.3   GW
K F Z BETRIEB AKTUELLE WOCHENZEITUNG. w. DM.294. (Zentralverband des Kraftfahrzeughandwerks) Vogel Verlag und Druck GmbH & Co. KG, Max-Planck-Str. 7-9, 97082 Wuerzburg, Germany. TEL 0931-4182145. FAX 0931-4182640. (Subscr. to: Vogel Verlag, 97064 Wuerzburg, Germany; Dist. in U.S. by: Vogel Europublishing, Inc., 19927 Villa Dr., Sonora, CA 95370. TEL 209-533-3555. FAX 209-533-9555) adv.: B&W page DM.12495, color page DM.15675; trim 382 x 288; adv. contact: Eberhard Boer. circ. 34,000 (controlled). **Document type:** trade publication.

388.3   GW
K F Z BETRIEB UNTERNEHMERMAGAZIN. 1910. m. DM.244. (Zentralverband des Kraftfahrzeughandwerks) Vogel Verlag und Druck GmbH & Co. KG, Max-Planck-Str. 7-9, 97082 Wuerzburg, Germany. TEL 0931-4182145. FAX 0931-4182640. (Subscr. to: Vogel Verlag, 97064 Wuerzburg, Germany; Dist. in U.S. by: Vogel Europublishing, Inc., 19927 Villa Dr., Sonora, CA 95370. TEL 209-533-3555. FAX 209-533-9555) Ed. E. Haack. adv.: B&W page DM.8997, color page DM.12057; trim 270 x 190; adv. contact: Eberhard Boer. illus.; circ. 33,940 (controlled). **Document type:** trade publication.
—**CCC.**
Former titles: K F Z Betrieb (ISSN 0722-7841); K F Z Betrieb und Automarkt (ISSN 0047-3049)

388.3   AU
K F Z PERFEKT. m. Oesterreichischer Wirtschaftsverlag, Nikolsdorfergasse 7-11, A-1051 Vienna, Austria. TEL 01-555585265. FAX 01-555585347. TELEX 111669. Ed. Guenther Greul. circ. 5,000.

388.3   AU
K F Z WIRTSCHAFT. 1948. m. S.684. (Bundesinnung der Kraftfahrzeugmechaniker) Oesterreichischer Wirtschaftsverlag, Nikolsdorfer Gasse 7-11, 1051 Vienna 5, Austria. Ed. Fritz Wagenleiter. adv.; bk.rev.; charts; illus. circ. 9,700.
Former titles: K F Z Werkstaette (ISSN 0022-7323); Kraftfahrzeug.

629.286   GW   ISSN 0343-9011
K F Z ZEITSCHRIFT FUER DEN NACHWUCHS DES KRAFTFAHRZEUHANDWERKS. 1957. m. DM.70.80. Frankfurter Fachverlag, Emil-Sulzbach-Str. 12, 60486 Frankfurt a.M., Germany. FAX 069-702003. Ed. Siegfried Rauch. adv.; bk.rev. circ. 20,000. **Document type:** trade publication.
—**CCC.**

614.86   JA   ISSN 0451-2006
KAGAKU KEISATSU KENKYUJO HOKOKU KOTSU KEN/NATIONAL RESEARCH INSTITUTE OF POLICE SCIENCE. REPORT. RESEARCH ON TRAFFIC SAFETY AND REGULATION. (Text in Japanese; summaries in English) 1960. s-a. Kagaku Keisatsu Kenkyujo - National Research Institute of Police Science, 6 Sanban-cho, Chiyoda-ku, Tokyo 102, Japan. circ. 900. **Indexed:** Abstr.Crim.& Pen., Psychol.Abstr.

629.228 380.1   US   ISSN 1070-2059
KART MARKETING INTERNATIONAL; the monthly trade magazine for the karting industry. 1993. m. $21.95 in U.S.; Canada and Mexico $29.95; elsewhere $59.95. Kart Marketing Group, 26 W. 237 Grand Ave., Wheaton, IL 60189. TEL 708-620-6347. FAX 708-653-2637. Ed. Robert A. Cycon. adv. contact: Darrell Sitraz. bk.rev.; index. circ. 5,000. (tabloid format; back issues avail.) **Document type:** trade publication.

796.77   US   ISSN 0744-5962
KART SPORT. 1982. m. 5510 Ashborn Rd., Baltimore, MD 21227. Ed. Joe Xavier. adv.; illus.

**796.7   US   ISSN 0096-3216
GV1029.5**
KARTER NEWS. 1957. m. $18. International Kart Federation, 4650 Arrow Hwy., Ste. B-4, Montclair, CA 91763. TEL 714-625-5497. FAX 714-621-6019. adv. circ. 5,000.

388.3   UK   ISSN 0022-913X
KARTING. 1960. m. £23 (foreign £25). Lodgemark Press, Bank House, Summerhill, Chislehurst, Kent BR7 5RD, England. TEL 081-467-6533. FAX 081-468-7999. Ed. M.C. Burgess. adv.; bk.rev.; charts; illus.; mkt.; tr.lit.; index. circ. 12,000. **Indexed:** Sportsearch. **Document type:** consumer publication.

388.3   NE   ISSN 0022-9881
KEMPHAAN.* 1956. m. free. Automobiel Sport Club "de Kempenrijders", Helmerslaan 27, Eindhoven, Netherlands. adv.; bk.rev.; illus.

388   UK
KEY NOTE MARKET REVIEW: U K MOTOR INDUSTRY. Variant title: U K Motor Industry. irreg. £375. Key Note Publications Ltd., Field House, 72 Field Rd., Hampton, Middlesex TW12 2HQ, England. TEL 0181-783-0755. FAX 0181-783-1720. **Document type:** trade publication.
●Also available online.
Also available on CD-ROM.

TRANSPORTATION — AUTOMOBILES

629.222   UK
KEY NOTE REPORT: AUTOPARTS. Variant title: Autoparts. irreg., no.10, 1995. £185. Key Note Publications Ltd., Field House, 72 Oldfield Rd., Hampton, Middlesex TW12 2HQ, England. TEL 0181-783-0755. FAX 0181-783-1720. Ed. Richard Caines. **Document type:** trade publication.
●Also available online.
Also available on CD-ROM.
—BLDSC (1835.064500).

388   UK   ISSN 1352-6529
KEY NOTE REPORT: CAR DEALER. Variant title: Car Dealer. irreg. £185. Key Note Publications Ltd., Field House, 72 Oldfield Rd., Hampton, Middlesex TW12 2HQ, England. TEL 0181-783-0755. FAX 0181-783-1720. **Document type:** trade publication.
●Also available online.
Also available on CD-ROM.
—BLDSC (3050.774300).

388   UK   ISSN 0951-6727
KEY NOTE REPORT: COMMERCIAL VEHICLES. Variant title: Commercial Vehicles. 1981. irreg. £185. Key Note Publications Ltd., Field House, 72 Oldfield Rd., Hampton, Middlesex TW12 2HQ, England. TEL 0181-783-0755. FAX 0181-783-1720. **Document type:** trade publication.
●Also available online.
Also available on CD-ROM.
—BLDSC (3337.302500).

388   UK
KEY NOTE REPORT: VEHICLE LEASING & HIRE. Variant title: Vehicle Leasing & Hire. irreg. £185. Key Note Publications Ltd., Field House, 72 Oldfield Rd., Hampton, Middlesex TW12 2HQ, England. TEL 0181-783-0755. FAX 0181-783-1720. **Document type:** trade publication.
●Also available online.
Also available on CD-ROM.

388   UK
KEY NOTE REPORT: VEHICLE SECURITY. Variant title: Vehicle Security. irreg. £185. Key Note Publications Ltd., Field House, 72 Oldfield Rd., Hampton, Middlesex TW12 2HQ, England. TEL 0181-783-0755. FAX 0181-783-1720. **Document type:** trade publication.
●Also available online.
Also available on CD-ROM.

388.3   US   ISSN 1055-1093
KEYSTONE A A A MOTORIST. 1911. bi-m. $2. A A A Mid-Atlantic, 2040 Market St., Philadelphia, PA 19103. TEL 215-864-5000. FAX 215-568-1153. Ed. John C. Moyer. adv.; illus. circ. 310,000. (tabloid format)
Formerly: Keystone Motorist (ISSN 0023-0995)
Description: Covers automotive subjects, foreign and domestic travel.

388   US
KIPLINGER'S NEW CAR BUYER'S GUIDE (YEAR). 1991. a. Kiplinger Washington Editors, Inc., 1729 H St., N.W., Washington, DC 20006. TEL 202-887-6400. FAX 202-223-8990.
Formerly: Kiplinger's Cars (Year).

KIT CAR. see *HOBBIES*

388.3   US   ISSN 1062-9610
KIT CAR ILLUSTRATED. bi-m. $2.50 per no. McMullen & Yee Publishing, 774 S. Placentia Ave., Placentia, CA 92670-6846. TEL 714-572-2255. FAX 714-572-1864.

388   UK
KIT CAR MAGAZINE. m. £26. Mailergraphic Ltd., Old Run Rd., Leeds LS10 2AA, England. TEL 0532-777711. FAX 0532-774009. Ed. Ewan Scott. adv. contact: Sarah Dunkley. **Document type:** consumer publication.
Former titles (until 1993): Street Rod & Sport Truck; 4 x 4 Driver.

629.283   DK   ISSN 0902-9818
KOERELAEREREN. m. (11/yr.). Dansk Koerelaerer Union, Ellested, 5853 Oerbaek, Denmark. adv. circ. 2,500.

388 678.2   US
KOVACH TIRE REPORT. 1984. m. $125 (foreign $250). Bill Communications, Inc., 355 Park Ave. S., New York, NY 10010. TEL 212-592-6263. FAX 212-592-6499. **Document type:** trade publication.
Description: For executives of tire manufacturers and tire dealers in North America.

629.2   GW   ISSN 0943-7118
KRAFTFAHRT-BUNDESAMT. MITTEILUNGEN. ERGAENZUNGSHEFTE. s.-a. DM.23 per no. Metzler - Poeschel Verlag, Postfach 1152, 72125 Kusterdingen, Germany. TEL 07071-935355. FAX 07071-935393. **Document type:** government publication.

629.2   GW   ISSN 0341-468X
HE5669
KRAFTFAHRT-BUNDESAMT. STATISTISCHE MITTEILUNGEN. 1954. m. DM.231.12. Foerderstr. 16, 24944 Flensburg, Germany. charts; stat. circ. 400.

388.3   GW   ISSN 0023-4419
TL4
KRAFTFAHRZEUGTECHNIK; technische Zeitschrift des Kraftfahrwesens. Short title: K F T. 1951. m. Heinrich Bauer Spezialzeitschriftenverlag, Industriestr. 16, 50735 Cologne, Germany. TEL 0221-7709157. FAX 0221-714153. Ed. Knut Boettcher. adv. contact: Sven Schrader. bk.rev.; charts; illus. circ. 103,850. Indexed: Excerp.Med., INIS Atomind. **Document type:** trade publication.
—SWETS.
Description: Covers all aspects of automotive engineering.

796.77   IT   ISSN 0394-7122
LAMBORGHINI REVIEW/RIVISTA LAMBORGHINI. (Text in English, Italian) 1988. s.-a. L.70000 (for complete set). Automobilia s.r.l., Via Ponte Seveso, 25, 20125 Milan, Italy. TEL 39-2-67074391. FAX 39-2-67075000. Ed. Stefano Pasini. circ. 2,000.

796.77   US
LANCIA ENTHUSIAST. 1983. m. membership. American Lancia Club, c/o Armand Giglio, Turk Hill Rd., Brewster, NY 10509. (Subscr. to: Keith Goring, Rt. 1, Box 136, Norfolk, CT 06058) Ed. Neil Pering. adv. circ. 1,000.

388.3   US   ISSN 0023-7515
LANCIANA. 1954. q. membership. American Lancia Club, c/o Armand Giglio, Turk Hill Rd., Brewster, NY 10509. (Subscr. to: Keith Coring, Rt. 1, Box 136, Norfolk, CT 06058) Ed. Paul Feine. adv.; bk.rev. circ. 1,000.

629.222   UK   ISSN 0954-1403
LAND ROVER OWNER INTERNATIONAL; Britain's biggest 4 x 4 magazine. 1987. m. £31. Diamond Europress Ltd., Unit 1, Burgess Rd., Ivyhouse Ln., Hastings, E. Sussex TN35 4NR, England. TEL 01424-430422. Ed. Carl Rogerson. adv. contact: Alan Morrison. bk.rev. circ. 60,000. (back issues avail.) **Document type:** consumer publication.
Description: Covers off-road and four-wheel vehicles for sale, technical tips, travel features, club news, and competitions.

629.2222   UK
LAND ROVER WORLD. 1993. m. £26.40 in Europe; rest of world £37.20. Link House Magazines Ltd., Link House, Dingwall Ave., Croydon, Surrey CR9 2TA, England. TEL 0181-686-2599. FAX 0181-781-6042. Ed. Alan Kidd. circ. 30,000. (back issues avail.) **Document type:** academic/scholarly publication.

388   GW   ISSN 0023-866X
LASTAUTO OMNIBUS. 1924. m. DM.78. EuroTransportMedia Verlagsund Veranstaltungs GmbH, Handwerkstr. 15, 70565 Stuttgart, Germany. TEL 0711-7849861. FAX 0711-7849889. Ed. Rainer Rex; Pub. Frank Neumann. adv.: B&W page DM.6550, color page DM.12118; trim 185 x 248; adv. contact: Bernd Rostock. charts; illus.; mkt.; pat.; tr.lit.; index. circ. 21,262. **Document type:** consumer publication.
—SWETS.
Incorporates: Kraftverkehr.
Description: Technical data and supply sources, company portraits and cost tables on cars and their manufacture.

388   GW
LASTAUTO OMNIBUS TESTJAHRBUCH. 1993. a. DM.12.80. EuroTransportMedia Verlags- und Veranstaltungs GmbH, Handwerkstr. 15, 70565 Stuttgart, Germany. TEL 0711-78498-0. FAX 0711-7849859. Ed. Rainer Rex; Pub. Frank Neumann. adv.: B&W page DM.7150, color page DM.13228; adv. contact: Bernd Rostock. circ. 30,000. **Document type:** consumer publication.

629.222   TS
LEGEND. (Text in Arabic, English) 1987. q. free. Motivate Publishing, P.O. Box 2331, Dubai, United Arab Emirates. TEL 246060. FAX 245270. TELEX 48366 MAM EM. Ed. Chuck Grieve. circ. 18,000.
Description: Lifestyle magazine for Jaguar owners in the Middle East.

LEISURE WORLD. see *LEISURE AND RECREATION*

629.22   CN   ISSN 0834-2423
LEMON AID MAGAZINE. French Edition: Roulez Sans Vous Faire Roulez (ISSN 0840-8475) (Editions in English, French) 1972. 4/yr. Can.$12.84. Automobile Protection Association Consumer Publications Co. Inc. - Association pour la Protection Automobile, 292 Ouest, bd. St. Joseph, Montreal, PQ H2V 2N7, Canada. TEL 514-273-5555. FAX 514-273-0797. Ed. Antoinette Greco. circ. 25,000. Indexed: Can.B.P.I. **Document type:** consumer publication.
Former titles: Lemon Aid Bulletin - Auto Conseils (ISSN 0821-3747); Consumer Bulletin - Bulletin aux Consommateurs (ISSN 0708-3963)

614.86 640.73   US
LEMON TIMES. 1979. q. $15. Center For Auto Safety, 2001 S St., N.W., Ste. 410, Washington, DC 20009. TEL 202-328-7700. Ed. Debra Barclay. circ. 13,000.
Description: Highlights important actions and findings, including such topics as airbags, tips for using small claims court and car defect.

338.3   SA
LEYKOR GUIDE TO BRIGHTER MOTORING. (Text in Afrikaans, English) 2/yr. Union Trades Directories (Pty) Ltd., 22-24 North Block, Mutual Square, Davenport Rd., P.O. Box 687, Durban 4000, South Africa. adv.

388.3   US   ISSN 8750-7374
TL232.7
LIMOUSINE & CHAUFFEUR. 1983. m. (plus Factbook in July). $28 (Canada $38; elsewhere $50). Bobit Publishing Company, 2512 Artesia Blvd., Redondo Beach, CA 90278-3210. TEL 310-376-8788. FAX 310-376-9043. circ. 10,000. **Document type:** trade publication.
Description: Serves the information needs of the limousine service industry.

338.3   FR   ISSN 0994-2750
LINEAIRE AUTO. 1988. 10/yr. 450 F. 96 rue de Paris, 92100 Boulogne, France. TEL 46-04-81-13. FAX 48-25-69-67. Ed. Pierre Besomi. adv. circ. 6,000.
Description: Covers economics, wholesalers, auto-parts, manufacturing, retail and repair networks.

388.3   US
LION OF BELFORT. 1970. bi-m. $12. Peugeot Owners' Club, 6649 E. 65th St., Indianapolis, IN 46220-4301. TEL 317-845-5050. Ed. Marvin A. Needler. adv.; bk.rev. circ. 650. (back issues avail.) **Document type:** newsletter.

388.33   US
LOCATOR (WHITING). 1955. m. $49. John F. Holmes Publishing Co., Inc., Whiting, IA 51063. TEL 800-457-0660. FAX 712-458-2687. Ed. John F. Holmes. adv.
Formerly: Salvage Locator (ISSN 0048-9050)
Description: Magazine of used auto and truck parts.

796.77   US
LOWRIDER. 1978. m. $35. Park Avenue Publishing, Box 648, Walnut, CA 91788-0648. TEL 909-598-2300. FAX 909-598-3551. Ed. David Cohen. adv. contact: Caroline Gray. circ. 142,707 (paid). **Document type:** consumer publication.
Description: Focuses on customizing, lowering, hydraulics and accessories for cars and trucks.

TRANSPORTATION — AUTOMOBILES

LUXEMBOURG. SERVICE CENTRAL DE LA STATISTIQUE ET DES ETUDES ECONOMIQUES. INDICATEURS RAPIDES. SERIE D. IMMATRICULATIONS DE VEHICULES AUTOMOTEURS. see
TRANSPORTATION — Abstracting, Bibliographies, Statistics

697 388   US
M A C S ACTION!. 1991. bi-m. membership. Mobile Air Conditioning Society Worldwide, Box 100, East Greenville, PA 18073. TEL 215-679-2220. FAX 215-679-4977. Eds. Elvis Hoffpauir, Amy Kline. circ. 850. **Document type:** newsletter, trade publication.
    Description: Provides industry news and information for members of the automotive air conditioning service and repair industry.

629.286   US
M A C S SERVICE REPORTS. 1987. m. $100 to non-members. Mobile Air Conditioning Society Worldwide, Box 97, East Greenville, PA 18041. TEL 215-679-2220. FAX 215-541-4635. Eds. Elvis Hoffpauir, Amy Kline. circ. 850. **Document type:** newsletter, trade publication.
    Formerly: R - 12.
    Description: Technical information for members of the automobile air conditioning service and repair industry.

629.288   US   ISSN 0888-4641
M AND M RAPPER.* 1986. q. $15. Microcar and Minicar Club, Box 1948, Vashon, WA 98070-1948. TEL 213-439-4148. Ed. Allan G.Y. Meyer. adv.; illus. circ. 250. (back issues avail.)

388   GW   ISSN 0027-1462
M O T; Autos Test & Technik. (Supplement avail.: Mot Spezial (ISSN 0941-7249) 1960. fortn. DM.110 (foreign DM.166.40); newsstand price: DM.5. Vereinigte Motor-Verlage GmbH und Co. KG, Leuschnerstr. 1, 70174 Stuttgart, Germany. TEL 0711-1821299. FAX 0711-1821691. Eds. Engelbert Maenner, Jochen Kruse; Pub. M. Kleinjohann. adv.: B&W page DM.10150, color page DM.18778; trim 185 x 248; adv. contact: Jochen Bechtle. circ. 122,109.
    —SWETS.
    Incorporates (in 1970): M R Motor-Rundschau & Kritik (ISSN 0941-9217); Which was previously (until 1969): Motor-Rundschau (ISSN 0724-925X); (until 1956): Motor-Rundschau mit NKZ (0724-9268); (1947-1951): Motor Rundschau (0724-9276).

388.3   GW   ISSN 0941-7249
M O T SPEZIAL. Issued with: M O T - Auto Technik Zukunft. 1988. a. DM.9.80. Vereinigte Motor-Verlage GmbH und Co. KG, Leuschnerstr. 1, 70174 Stuttgart, Germany. TEL 0711-1821299. FAX 0711-1821691. (Subscr. to: Postfach 106036, 70049 Stuttgart, Germany) Eds. J. Kruse, E. Maenner; Pub. M. Kleinjohann. adv. contact: Jochen Bechtle. illus. circ. 40,000. **Document type:** consumer publication.

629.283   UK
M S A NEWS JOURNAL. 1935. q. free to libraries. (Motor Schools Association of G.B.) Integral Publishing Co. Ltd., Castlefield Ho., Liverpool Rd., Castlefield, Manchester M60 9BF, England. Ed. John R. Lepine. adv.; bk.rev. circ. 28,000. (back issues avail.)

388.3   AT   ISSN 0047-5297
M T A JOURNAL. 1919. 10/yr. Aus.$54($41) (effective 1995 & 1996). Motor Traders' Association of New South Wales, Locked Bag 5012, Darlinghurst, N.S.W. 2010, Australia. TEL 61-2-211-4955. FAX 61-2-211-6889. Ed. Phil Keeffe. adv.: B&W page Aus.$1195, color page Aus.$1684; adv. contact: Keith Sandell. bk.rev. circ. 5,400. **Indexed:** Aus.Rd.Ind., Chem.Abstr. **Document type:** trade publication.
    Description: Provides news and information of interest to proprietors in the raitail motor vehicle industry and trades.

388.3 629.2   GW   ISSN 0024-8525
TJ751   CODEN: MOTZAS
M T Z. (Motortechnische Zeitschrift); Verbrennungsmotor und Gasturbine. 1939. m. DM.276 (effective 1996). Friedr. Vieweg und Sohn Verlagsgesellschaft mbH, Postfach 1546, 65005 Wiesbaden, Germany. TEL 0611-534389. FAX 0611-534430. Ed. Richard van Basshuysen. adv.: B&W page DM.4800, color page DM.8400; trim 185 x 256; adv. contact: Eva-Maria Lesch. bk.rev.; abstr.; bibl.; charts; illus.; stat.; index, cum.index every 20 yrs. circ. 3,667. **Indexed:** Appl.Mech.Rev., BMT, Eng.Ind., Excerp.Med., Fluidex, Sh.& Vib.Dig. **Document type:** trade publication.
    —BLDSC (5980.890000); Ei; SWETS. **CCC**.
    Description: For the engine and turbine industry. Features research and development, product engineering, tests and measurement. Also includes events, news, and new products.

338.476   US   ISSN 0146-9932
HD9710.U5
M V M A MOTOR VEHICLE FACTS AND FIGURES. Key Title: Motor Vehicle Facts & Figures. 1976. a. $7.50. Motor Vehicle Manufacturers Association of the U.S. Inc., 7430 Second Ave., Suite 300, Detroit, MI 48202. TEL 313-872-4311. **Indexed:** SRI.
    Formed by the merger of: Automobile Facts and Figures (ISSN 0067-253X); Motor Truck Facts (ISSN 0077-1643)

629.286   UK
MAINTENANCE MANUAL. 1993. a. £80 for 2 yrs. Glass's Information Services Ltd., Elgin House, St. Georges Ave., Weybridge, Surrey KT13 0BX, England. TEL 01932-853211. FAX 01932-846564. (Subscr. to: Sales and Marketing, St. Martins Ct., 37 Queens Rd., Weybridge, Surrey KT13 9TU, England) (looseleaf format) **Document type:** trade publication.

MANOVELLA; e route a raggi. see *HOBBIES*

388.3   US
MARKETPLACE. bi-m. membership. Nash Car Club of America, 4151 220 St., Clinton, IA 52732-8943. (Subscr. to: c/o Jim & Dorothy Bracewell, 1 N 274 Prairie, Glen Ellyn, IL 60137) **Document type:** consumer publication.
    Description: For car enthusiasts dedicated to promoting the history, preservation and restoration of the Nash and related automobiles.

MARYLAND MOTORIST. see *TRAVEL AND TOURISM*

629.222   UK
MAX POWER. m. £31.20 (foreign £46) (effective 1995-1996). E M A P - Consumer, Priory Ct., 30-32 Farringdon Ln., London EC1R 2AU, England. TEL 0171-972-6700. FAX 0171-972-6710. (Subscr. to: Tower Publishing Services Ltd., Tower House, Sovereign Park, Lathkill St., Market Harborough, Leics. LE16 9EF, England. TEL 01858-468811. FAX 01858-432164) adv. **Document type:** consumer publication.

388.3   SP
MEJORES AUTOMOVILES DEL MUNDO. a. 900 ptas. Luike - Motorpress, C. Ancora 40, 28045 Madrid, Spain. TEL 34-1-3470100. FAX 34-1-3470204. Ed. Carlos Hernandez. adv.: B&W page 430000 ptas., color page 600000 ptas.; adv. contact: Agustin Valero. **Document type:** consumer publication.

388.3   IS
MICHERON RECHEV VEACHZAKATO. 1987. 10/yr. Cheshev Ltd., P.O. Box 40021, Tel Aviv 61 400, Israel. TEL (03)216291.

MICHIGAN LIVING. see *TRAVEL AND TOURISM*

629   UK
MIDLANDS & EASTERN INSTRUCTOR. q. (Motor Schools Association of Great Britain) Integral Publishing Co. Ltd., Castlefield Ho., Liverpool Rd., Castlefield, Manchester M60 9BF, England. Ed. John Lepine. bk.rev. circ. 2,500. **Document type:** trade publication.

388.3
MIDWEST AUTOMOTIVE & AUTOBODY NEWS. 1928. m. $10. Automotive Publishing Co., 2900 W. Peterson Ave., Chicago, IL 60659. TEL 312-764-1640. Ed. Warren B. Daemicke. circ. 11,562 (controlled). **Document type:** trade publication.
    Formerly: Midwest Automotive News (ISSN 0026-3338)

388.3   US   ISSN 0026-3435
MIDWEST MOTORIST. 1915. bi-m. $3. Automobile Club of Missouri, 12901 North Forty Dr., St. Louis, MO 63141. TEL 314-523-7350. Ed. Michael J. Right. adv.; bk.rev.; charts; illus.; stat.; circ. 370,000 (controlled). **Document type:** consumer publication.
    Formerly: Auto Club News.

MIDWEST RACING NEWS. see *SPORTS AND GAMES*

388.3   US
MIDWESTERN STATE SALVAGE GUIDE; used auto and truck parts locator magazine. 1968. m. $12. Midwestern Salvage Guide Magazine Inc., 3700 Decker, Moore, OK 73160. TEL 405-787-0795. FAX 405-787-0795. (Subscr. to: Box 1864, Bethany, OK 73008) Ed. Louanne Duckworth. adv. circ. 9,000. (tabloid format) **Document type:** trade publication.
    Description: For bodyshop workers, adjusters, and auto salvagers. Covers used auto parts availability.

388.3   US
MID-WESTERN 4-WHEELER. 1979. 6/yr. $8. Midwest 4-Wheel Drive Association, 25624 Eaton Ave., Fairbault, MN 55021-8283. TEL 414-898-4598. Eds. Jim Schrot, Mel Schrot. adv. circ. 1,600.
    Description: Covers events and issues of special interest to owners of four-wheel drive vehicles.

MILE POST. see *HOBBIES*

388.3   UK   ISSN 0026-380X
MILESTONES. 1946. 3/yr. £0.30 per no. (Institute of Advanced Motorists) Advanced Mile-Posts Publications Ltd., I A M House, 359-365 Chiswick High Rd., London W4 4HS, England. TEL 081-994-4403. FAX 081-994-9249. Ed. Ian Webb. adv.; bk.rev.; charts; illus. circ. 102,000.

MILITARY VEHICLES. see *MILITARY*

388   UK   ISSN 0965-3937
MILLER'S COLLECTORS CARS PRICE GUIDE. 1991. a. Reed International, Michelin House, 81 Fulham Rd., London SW3 6RB, England. **Document type:** directory.

MISS INFORMATION'S AUTOMOTIVE CALENDAR OF EVENTS. see *ANTIQUES*

796.7   US
MODEL A NEWS. 1953. bi-m. $20 (foreign $24). Model A Restorer's Club, 24800 Michigan Ave., Dearborn, MI 48124-1713. TEL 313-278-1455. Ed. Kenneth Keeley. adv.; index. circ. 9,000. (back issues avail.)

388.3   FR   ISSN 0047-7648
MODELISME;* automobile internationel. (Text in English, French) bi-m. 26 F.($6.25) 94 bd. de Sebastopol, 75003 Paris, France. circ. 12,000.

MODERN TIRE DEALER; covering tire sales and car service. see *RUBBER*

388.3   CN   ISSN 0831-2958
LE MONDE DE L'AUTO. 1985. 6/yr. Can.$12. World of Wheels Publishing, Inc. (St. Laurent), 7575 Rte. Transcanadienne, Bur. 401, St. Laurent, PQ H4T 1V6, Canada. TEL 514-956-1361. FAX 514-956-1461. Ed. Luc Gagne; Pub. Lynn R. Helpard. adv. contact: Lise-Anne Parker. bk.rev. circ. 42,000. **Document type:** consumer publication.
    Description: Includes articles of general interest to car owners and operators such as information and prices on new cars, maintenance information and tips.

388   FR   ISSN 1145-8941
MONDE DE L'AUTOMOBILE. 1989. 10/yr. 46 rue de Troyon, 92310 Sevres, France. TEL 45-07-02-00. Ed. Esther Slama. circ. 40,000.
    Description: Of interest to those working in the car industry.

629.2   BE
LE MONITEUR DE L'AUTOMOBILE. Dutch edition: Auto Gids. (Text in French) 1979. s-m. 1740 Fr. Editions Auto-Magazine S.A., Chaussee de la Hulpe 181, bte. 2, 1170 Brussels, Belgium. TEL 02-660-1920. FAX 02-643-2200. TELEX 26379. Ed. Etienne Visart. circ. 390,000.

TRANSPORTATION — AUTOMOBILES

796.7   FI   ISSN 0359-7636
MOOTTORI (YEAR). (Text in Finnish; summaries in Swedish) 1925. 12/yr. FIM 180. Autoliitto r.y. - Automobile and Touring Club of Finland, Kansakoulukatu 10, 00100 Helsinki 10, Finland. FAX 90-5662360. Ed. Juha Partanen. adv.; bk.rev.; charts; illus. circ. 55,000.
    Former titles (until 1982): Auto ja Liikenne (ISSN 0356-4827); (until 1978): Moottori (ISSN 0027-0970).

629.222   GW
MOT AUTOS TEST UND TECHNIK. fortn. newsstand price: DM.5. Vereinigte Motor-Verlage GmbH und Co. KG, Leuschnerstr. 1, 70162 Stuttgart, Germany. TEL 0711-1821226. FAX 0711-1821349. adv.: B&W page DM.10150, color page DM.18778; trim 185 x 248. circ. 122,109 (paid). **Document type:** consumer publication.
    Description: In-depth testing of vehicles and accessories.

388   CN
MOTEUR QUEBEC.* (Text in French) m. Editions J D L Inc., 2202 rue Marcil, Montreal, PQ H4A 2Z1, Canada. TEL 514-369-6659. FAX 514-369-9048. Ed. Pierre Luc. adv.
    Formerly: Derriere le Volant.

338.3   FR
MOTEURS DIESEL. irreg. Editions Techniques pour l'Automobile et l'Industrie (ETAI), 20-22 rue de la Saussiere, 92100 Boulogne-Billancourt, France. charts; illus.

338.3   FR   ISSN 0766-0847
MOTO CRAMPONS. (Supplements avail.) 1985. m. 240 F. (foreign 300 F.); newsstand price: 25 F. Societe des Editions Techniques et Touristiques de France, 60-62 rue Danjou, 92100 Boulogne, France. TEL 46-09-95-96. FAX 46-09-99-85. TELEX 633 055 F. Ed. Jacques Bussillet; Pub. Monique Helfenberger. adv. contact: Bernard Potut. circ. 58,000. **Document type:** consumer publication.

388.3   FR   ISSN 0336-6596
MOTO FLASH. 1975. bi-m. Societe Europeene d'Editions, 4 rue du Progres, 13005 Marseille, France. Ed. Serge Klutchinikoff.

388.3   FR   ISSN 0751-591X
MOTO JOURNAL. (Supplements avail.) 1971. w. 558 F. (foreign 798 F.); newsstand price: 18 F. Societe des Editions Techniques et Touristiques de France, 60-62 rue Danjou, 92100 Boulogne, France. TEL 46-09-95-96. FAX 46-09-99-85. TELEX 633 055 F. Ed. Jacques Bussillet; Pub. Monique Helfenberger. adv. contact: Bernard Potut. circ. 74,000. **Document type:** consumer publication.

388.3 796.72   AT
MOTOR. 1954. m. Aus.$68.40. A C P Publishing Pty. Ltd., 54-58 Park St., Sydney, N.S.W. 2000, Australia. TEL 02-282-8356. FAX 02-267-9436. Ed. Graham Smith; Pub. Richard Walsh. adv. contact: Max Hyde. bk.rev.; illus.; pat.; index. circ. 40,602. (processed) **Indexed:** Gdlns. **Document type:** consumer publication.
    Formerly: Modern Motor (ISSN 0026-8143)
    Description: Contains latest industry trends, corrective computer car testing, comprehensive coverage of international racing events.

388.321 796.7   DK   ISSN 0047-8199
MOTOR. 1906. m. DKK 395 membership. (Forenede Danske Motorejere - Federation of Danish Motorists) Forlaget Motor ApS, Firskovvej 32, P.O. Box 500, DK-2800, Lyngby. TEL 45-930800. FAX 45-933242. TELEX 15857. Ed. Bo Christian Koch. adv.; bk.rev.; charts; illus.; pat.; stat.; tr.lit.; index; circ. 205,000 (controlled).

388.3   II   ISSN 0027-1713
MOTOR; Tamil auto-two wheeler publication. (Text in Tamil) 1959. m. Rs.50. V. Krishnan, Ed. & Pub., 9 State Bank St., First Lane, Mount Road, Madras 600 002, India. TEL 849305. adv.; bk.rev. circ. 18,000.

388.3   NO   ISSN 0027-173X
MOTOR. 1933. m. NOK 250 per no. Norges Automobil-Forbund - Norwegian Automobile Federation, P.O. Box 494, N-0105 Oslo, Norway. TEL 47-22-34-14-00. FAX 47-22-33-21-76. Ed. Svein Ola Hope. adv. contact: Anne Schwarz. bk.rev.; illus. circ. 394,782. **Document type:** trade publication, consumer publication.
    —CCC.
    Formerly (until 1965): Motortidende (ISSN 0332-897X)

388.3   SW   ISSN 0027-1764
MOTOR. Variant title: Nya Motor. 1943. m. SEK 325 (effective 1991). Motormaennens Riksfoerbund, Sturegatan 32, P.O. Box 5855, 102 48 Stockholm, Sweden. FAX 8-666-01-29. Ed. Erik Friberg. adv.; bk.rev.; illus. circ. 210,000.

388.3   US   ISSN 0027-1748
TL1
MOTOR; covering the world of automotive service. 1903. m. $24. Hearst Business Publishing, 645 Stewart Ave., Garden City, NY 11530. TEL 516-227-1370. FAX 516-227-1405. Ed. Tom Wilkinson. adv. contact: Michael S. Bernstein. bk.rev.; illus.; mkt.; stat.; tr.lit.; index; circ. 140,000 (controlled). (also avail. in microform from UMI) **Document type:** trade publication.
    —Faxon; UnCover.

388.3   BE
MOTOR; le magazine du moteur et des loisirs. (Text in French) 1922. 11/yr. 750 BEF membership. (Royal Motor Union) Miro Communication, 3 rue Raikem, 4000 Liege, Belgium. TEL 32-41-527684. FAX 32-41-525705. Ed. Michel Ernotte. adv.: B&W page 25000 BEF, color page 39500 BEF; bleed 295 x 208; adv. contact: Jacques Karablin. circ. 30,000.

629.2   US   ISSN 0098-1745
TL152
MOTOR AUTO REPAIR MANUAL. (In 2 vols.) 1938. a. $176. Hearst Corporation, Motor Manuals Department, 5600 Crooks Rd., Troy, MI 48098. TEL 800-426-6867. index. **Document type:** trade publication.
    Formerly: Motor's Auto Repair Manual.
    Description: Mechanical repair procedures for American-made cars.

338.3   SP
MOTOR CLASICO; magazin actual para los amigos de los automoviles clasicos. 1986. m. 7000 ptas. (Europe 11400 ptas., elsewhere 15000 ptas.); newsstand price: 700 ptas. Luike - Motorpress, C. Ancora 40, 28045 Madrid, Spain. TEL 34-1-3470100. FAX 34-1-3470204. Ed. Carlos Hernandez; Pub. Jose Luis Samaranch. adv.: B&W page 270000 ptas., color page 415000 ptas.; adv. contact: Antonino Berges. circ. 10,000. **Document type:** consumer publication.
    Description: For classic car enthusiasts.

MOTOR CLUB NEWS. see *TRAVEL AND TOURISM*

629.28   US   ISSN 0194-9411
MOTOR CRASH ESTIMATING GUIDE. 1955. 16/yr. $195. Hearst Corporation, Crash Books Department, 5600 Crooks Rd., Ste. 200, Troy, MI 48098. TEL 800-426-6867. (Subscr. to: Box 10115, Des Moines, IA 50350) Ed. Philip Cunningham. adv. circ. 25,000.
    Description: Provides information necessary for assessing vehicle collision damage.

614.86   US   ISSN 0160-1644
TL152
MOTOR EARLY MODEL CRASH ESTIMATING GUIDE. q. $152. Hearst Corporation, Crash Books Department, 5600 Crooks Rd., Ste. 200, Troy, MI 48098. TEL 800-426-6867. (Subscr. to: Box 10115, Des Moines, IA 50350) Ed. Philip C. Cunningham.

388.3   AT   ISSN 0129-1483
MOTOR EQUIPMENT NEWS. Short title: M.E.N. 1982. m. Aus.$40 (effective 1995). Trade Press Australia, 54 Kellett St., Kings Cross, N.S.W. 2011, Australia. TEL 61-2-3581155. FAX 61-2-3563834. Ed. Neil Thomas. adv.: B&W page Aus.$2600, color page Aus.$3536; trim 260 x 170; adv. contact: David Newton-Ross. bk.rev. circ. 23,377. **Document type:** trade publication.
    Description: Covers all aspects of the automotive industry trade including service and repair and parts and accessories.

338.4   US   ISSN 0164-6346
TL152
MOTOR IMPORTED CAR CRASH ESTIMATING GUIDE. m. $240. Motor Publications, Crash Books Department, 5600 Crooks Rd., Ste. 102, Troy, MI 48098. Ed. Philip C. Cunningham. illus.
    Description: Provides information necessary for assessing vehicle collision damage.

388.3   NZ
MOTOR INDUSTRY NEWS. 1951. bi-m. NZ.$39. Automotive Institute of New Zealand Inc., P.O. Box 1503, Wellington, New Zealand. TEL 04-847-289. FAX 04-828-201. Ed. M.K.S Sutherland. adv.; bk.rev.; illus.; stat.; index. circ. 2,000.
    Formerly: Service Side.

629.222   UK
MOTOR INDUSTRY OF GREAT BRITAIN (YEAR) WORLD AUTOMOTIVE STATISTICS. 1926. a. £95. Society of Motor Manufacturers and Traders Ltd., Forbes House, Halkin St., London SW1X 7DS, England. TEL 0171-235-7000. FAX 0171-235-7112. circ. 1,000. **Document type:** trade publication.
    —BLDSC (5975.010000).
    Formerly: Motor Industry of Great Britain (ISSN 0077-1597)

388.3   IT   ISSN 0027-1926
MOTOR ITALIA. 1926. a. $20. Motor Italia S.r.l., c/o Stamperia Artistica Nazionale, Corso Siracusa 37, 10136 Turin, Italy. TEL 0039-11-365593. TELEX 214134 SANTO I. Ed. G. Rogliatti. adv.; bk.rev.; bibl.; charts; illus.; pat.; index. circ. 5,000.

388   SZ
MOTOR JOURNAL. 18/yr. Villa Mueslischreck, CH-6042 Dietwil, Switzerland. TEL 041-912950. Ed. Alfred Wepf. circ. 8,000.

388   GW   ISSN 0177-8862
MOTOR KLASSIK. (Supplement avail.: Motor-Klassik Spezial (ISSN 0938-5746)) 1984. m. DM.75.60; newsstand price: DM.7. Vereinigte Motor-Verlage GmbH und Co. KG, Leuschnerstr. 1, 70174 Stuttgart, Germany. TEL 0711-18201. FAX 0711-1821156. Ed. Mike Riedner; Pub. Michael Kleinjohann. adv.: B&W page DM.7330, color page DM.13561; trim 185 x 248; adv. contact: Gerhard Merkel. circ. 65,437. **Document type:** consumer publication.
    Description: Information for sports car fans.

629.28   US
MOTOR LIGHT TRUCK & VAN REPAIR MANUAL. a. $100. Hearst Corporation, Motor Manuals Department, 5600 Crooks Rd., Troy, MI 48098. TEL 800-426-6867. Ed. John Lypen. **Document type:** trade publication.
    Former titles: Motor Light Truck and Van Tuneup and Repair Manual; Motor Light Truck and Van Repair Manual; Motor Truck Repair Manual (ISSN 0098-3624); Motor Truck and Diesel Repair Manual (ISSN 0077-1724)

629.286 388   DK   ISSN 0109-7490
MOTOR - MAGASINET. (Supplements avail.: Bremser & Kobling; Daek Profil; Karosseri & Autolak) 1969. 44/yr. DKK 417. Dansk Auto Media A-S, Hoejvangen 23, P.O. Box 159, DK-3480 Fredensborg, Denmark. TEL 45-42-28-51-00. FAX 45-42-28-20-15. Ed. Niels Verner Nielsen. adv.: B&W page DKK 12780, color page DKK 16380; trim 370 x 255; adv. contact: Aksel G. Johansen. bk.rev.; circ. 15,200 (controlled). (tabloid format) **Document type:** trade publication.

629.222   HK
MOTOR MAGAZINE. (Text in Chinese) 1990. m. HK.$280. Press Mark Media Ltd., Flat D, 1-F Prospect Mansion, 66-72 Paterson St., Causeway Bay, Hong Kong. TEL 852-8822-230. FAX 852-8823-949. TELEX 49505 EMART HX. Ed. Kenneth Li Kam Man. adv.: color page HK$13800; adv. contact: Jackie Ho. circ. 32,000. **Document type:** consumer publication.
    Description: Features the latest information on car industry, test reports and technical reports.

MOTOR MUNDIAL. see *TRANSPORTATION*

TRANSPORTATION — AUTOMOBILES

388.3   AT   ISSN 0818-5549
MOTOR NEWS. 1956. bi-m. membership. Royal Automobile Club of Tasmania, Murray & Patrick Sts., Hobart, Tas. 7001, Australia. TEL 002-326300. FAX 002-348784. Ed. D.J. Rose. adv.; bk.rev. circ. 100,000. **Document type:** consumer publication, newsletter.
    Formerly: Tasmanian Motor News (ISSN 0039-9841)

629.2   US   ISSN 0077-1716
MOTOR PARTS & TIME GUIDE. 1910. a. $118. Hearst Corporation, Motor Manuals Department, 5600 Crooks Rd., Troy, MI 48098. TEL 800-426-6867. Ed. Philip Cunningham. **Document type:** trade publication.
    Formerly: Motor's Flat Rate and Parts Manual.

388.3   UK   ISSN 0306-6274
MOTOR REPORT INTERNATIONAL. 1971. fortn. $350 (effective 1992). Circlemartin Ltd., Box 87, Dorking, Surrey RH4 2YS, England. TEL 0306-740042. Ed. A. Carding. circ. 500. **Indexed:** PROMT. **Document type:** newsletter.
    Description: News and statistical data of the automotive industry worldwide.

388.3   UK
MOTOR RETAILER. 1960. m. £35 to non-members. Retail Motor Industry Federation, 201 Great Portland St., London W1N 6AB, England. TEL 071-580-9122. FAX 071-580-6376. Ed. Beverly Hicks. adv.; bk.rev.; tr.lit.; index. circ. 16,500.
    Formerly: Motor Trade Executive (ISSN 0027-2027)

629.286   GW   ISSN 0027-1969
MOTOR REVUE. 1951. a. DM.10. Vereinigte Motor-Verlage GmbH und Co. KG, Leuschnerstr. 1, 70174 Stuttgart, Germany. TEL 0711-18201. FAX 0711-1821669. (Subscr. to: Postfach 106036, 70049 Stuttgart, Germany) Ed.Bd; Pub. Richard Stolz. adv. contact: Wolfgang Pietschmann. illus. circ. 60,000. **Document type:** consumer publication.

388.3   US   ISSN 0027-1977
TL1
MOTOR SERVICE; the journal for professional automotive repairmen. 1921. m. $36 (Canada and Mexico $45; elsewhere $86) (free to qualified personnel). Hunter Publishing Limited Partnership, 25 N.W. Point Blvd., Ste. 800, Elk Grove Village, IL 60007-1030. TEL 708-427-9512. FAX 708-427-2006. Ed. James J. Halloran. adv. circ. 175,374.
—CCC.

388.3   UK   ISSN 0027-2019
MOTOR SPORT. 1924. m. £21. Teesdale Publishing Company Ltd., Standard House, Bonhill St., London EC2A 4DA, England. TEL 071-628-4741. FAX 071-638-8497. TELEX 888602-MONEWS-G. Ed. Simon Arron. adv. contact: John Deverell. bk.rev.; charts; illus.; index. circ. 60,000. **Document type:** consumer publication.

338   AT
MOTOR TRADE ASSOCIATION OF WESTERN AUSTRALIA. JOURNAL. 1935. m. Aus.$50. Motor Trade Association of Western Australia, M T A House, 224 Balcatta Rd., Balcatta, W.A. 6021, Australia. TEL 61-9-345-3466. FAX 61-9-345-3465. Ed. Bob Draper. adv.: B&W page Aus.$640, color page Aus.$1175; trim 240 x 185. illus.; mkt. circ. 1,400. **Document type:** trade publication.
    Former titles: W A A C C S Motor Industry (Western Australian Automobile Chamber of Commerce) (ISSN 0042-9430); Service Station and Motor Trader.
    Description: Provides information on industrial and trade matters.

388.3   AT   ISSN 0027-2035
MOTOR TRADE JOURNAL. 1930. m. Aus.$48 plus postage. Motor Trade Association of S.A., Inc., 50-51 Greenhill Rd., Wayville, S.A. 5034, Australia. FAX 61-8-373-1724. Ed. Richard Flashman. adv.; bk.rev. circ. 2,300. (tabloid format) **Document type:** trade publication.

388.3   AT
MOTOR TRADER. 1933. m. Aus.$55. Motor Trades Association of Queensland, P.O. Box 359, South Brisbane, Brisbane, Qld. 4101, Australia. TEL 61-7-8447555. FAX 61-7-8444488. Ed. C.R. Jackson. adv.: B&W page $975, color page $1450. illus. circ. 2,900.
    Former titles: Q A C C Motor Trader; Queensland Motor Industry (ISSN 0033-6203)

388.3   UK   ISSN 0027-2043
MOTOR TRADER. 1905. w. £90($221) Reed Business Publishing Group (Subsidiary of: Reed Elsevier group), Quadrant House, The Quadrant, Sutton, Surrey SM2 5AS, England. TEL 0181-652-3276. FAX 0181-652-8982. (Subscr. to: Oakfield House, Perrymount Rd., Haywards Heath, W. Sussex RH16 3DH, England. TEL 01444-445566) Ed. Leon Clifford. adv.; charts; illus.; index; circ. 25,070 (controlled). **Document type:** trade publication.

388.3   RH   ISSN 0027-2051
MOTOR TRADER AND FLEET OPERATOR. 1956. m. Z.$64.80 (foreign Z.$82.20). (Motor Trade Association) Thomson Publications Zimbabwe (Pvt) Ltd., Thomson House, P.O. Box 1683, Harare, Zimbabwe. TEL 263-4-736835. FAX 263-4-752390. TELEX 24705 ZW. (Co-sponsor: Motor Industry Employers' Association) **Document type:** trade publication.

388.3   SW   ISSN 0077-1619
HE5680
MOTOR TRAFFIC IN SWEDEN. Swedish edition: Bilismen i Sverige (ISSN 0282-0536) 1948. a. SEK 72. (Bilindustri Foereningen - Association of Swedish Automobile Maufacturers and Wholesalers) AB Bilstatistik, P.O. Box 26173, S-100 41 Stockholm, Sweden. TEL 46-8-701-63-60. FAX 46-8-791-23-11. TELEX 119 23 BIL S. circ. 1,500. **Document type:** consumer publication.
    Description: Contains statistics on vehicles in use, production, export, import and other useful information.

388.3   US   ISSN 0027-2094
TL1
MOTOR TREND. 1949. m. $19.94. Petersen Publishing Co., 6420 Wilshire Blvd., Los Angeles, CA 90048. TEL 213-782-2000; 800-800-6848. FAX 213-782-2866. Ed. Jeff Karr. adv.; bk.rev.; charts; illus.; index. circ. 900,000. (also avail. in microfilm from UMI) **Indexed:** B.P.I., Consum.Ind., Jun.High.Mag.Abstr., Mag.Ind., PMR, R.G., Sports Per.Ind., TOM. **Document type:** consumer publication. ●Also available online. Vendor(s): Knight-Ridder, Inc.. Also available on CD-ROM. Producer(s): University Microfilms International.
—Faxon; SWETS; UMI; UnCover.
    Incorporates: Car Life; Sports Car Graphic (ISSN 0038-8165); Wheels Afield (ISSN 0043-4787)

629.28   US   ISSN 0160-8886
TL5
MOTOR TREND'S NEW CAR BUYERS' GUIDE. 1976. a. newsstand price: $5.95. Petersen Publishing Co., 6420 Wilshire Blvd., Los Angeles, CA 90048. TEL 213-782-2000. FAX 213-782-2866. adv. circ. 250,000. **Document type:** consumer publication.
    Description: Highlights cars from the US, Japan and Europe.

388.3   US   ISSN 1059-261X
MOTOR TREND'S ROAD TESTS. Key Title: Road Tests (Los Angeles). 1986. a. newsstand price: $4.95. Petersen Publishing Co., 6420 Wilshire Blvd., Los Angeles, CA 90048. TEL 213-782-2000. FAX 213-782-2866. adv. circ. 639.3. **Document type:** consumer publication.
    Description: Highlights domestic and imported vehicle road tests with subjective driving impressions, technical information, and comprehensive test results.

796.77   US   ISSN 0081-380X
MOTOR TREND'S SPORTS CARS OF THE WORLD. Key Title: Sports Cars of the World. 1985. a. newsstand price: $3.95. Petersen Publishing Co., 6420 Wilshire Blvd., Los Angeles, CA 90048. TEL 213-782-2000. FAX 213-782-2866. adv. circ. 200,000. **Document type:** consumer publication.
    Description: Showcases sports car classics. Analyzes current models.

629.22   US   ISSN 0190-3101
TL230.A1
MOTOR TREND'S TRUCK & VAN BUYER'S GUIDE. Key Title: Truck & Van Buyer's Guide (Los Angeles). a. newsstand price: $4.50. Petersen Publishing Co., 6420 Wilshire Blvd., Los Angeles, CA 90048. TEL 213-782-2000. FAX 213-782-2866. adv. circ. 200,000. **Document type:** consumer publication.
    Description: Contains descriptions and fact sheets for the buyer of a new truck or van.

388.3   AU
MOTOR UND ERDOEL. 1950. w. S.370 per month. Austria Presse Agentur (APA), Gunoldstr. 14, A-1199 Vienna, Austria. Ed. H. Jaros. (processed)
    Formerly: Motor - Dienst und Erdoel - Nachrichten (ISSN 0027-1888)

388 910.202   GW
MOTOR UND REISEN. 10/yr. (Automobilclub von Deutschland e.V.) A v D Verlag GmbH, Lyonerstr. 16, 60528 Frankfurt a.M., Germany. TEL 069-6606270. FAX 069-6606260. Ed. Gerhard Windpassinger. adv. contact: Christian Wolf. circ. 464,209. **Document type:** consumer publication.

629.2   CN   ISSN 0316-6198
MOTOR VEHICLE DATA BOOK. 1947. a. Can.$39. Sanford Evans Communications Ltd., 1700 Church Ave., Box 6900, Winnipeg, MB R3C 3B1, Canada. TEL 204-694-2022. FAX 204-694-3040. Ed. G.B. Henry; Pub. Gary Henry.
    Description: Identification and registration guide, listing 9 years of statistics including: curb weight, wheelbase, vehicle identification number, engine statistics and M.S. retail price.

629.286   JA
MOTOR VEHICLE ENGINEERING SPECIFICATIONS - JAPAN. (Text in Japanese) a. 12800 Yen. Society of Automotive Engineers of Japan, Inc. - Jidosha Gijutsukai, 10-2, Goban-cho, Chiyoda-ku, Tokyo 102, Japan.

629.287   US   ISSN 0565-7717
TL242
MOTOR VEHICLE SAFETY DEFECT RECALL CAMPAIGNS. Continues a publication with the same title issued by the administration under an earlier name: National Highway Safety Bureau. 1970. q. U.S. National Highway Traffic Safety Administration, 400 Seventh St., S.W., Washington, DC 20590. (Subscr. to: Superintendent of Documents, U.S. Government Printing Office, Box 371954, Pittsburgh, PA 15250-7954. TEL 202-783-3238. FAX 202-512-2233) (also avail. in microfiche from CIS; reprint service avail. from CIS) **Indexed:** Amer.Stat.Ind. (1976-). **Document type:** government publication.

388.34 310   JA   ISSN 0463-6635
MOTOR VEHICLE STATISTICS OF JAPAN. 1958. a. free. Japan Automobile Manufacturers Association, Otemachi Bldg., 1-6-1 Otemachi, Chiyoda-ku, Tokyo 100, Japan. FAX 03-287-2072. stat. circ. 7,500. **Document type:** trade publication.

629.222   US   ISSN 1055-8233
MOTOR WORLD.* (Supplement avail.) 1991. q. $29.99. Publishing & Business Consultants, 101 W. 64th St., Unit 3, Inglewood, CA 90302-1255. TEL 213-732-3477. FAX 213-732-9123. (Subscr. to: Box 75392, Los Angeles, CA 90075) Ed. Andeson Napoleon Atia. adv. circ. 120,000. **Document type:** consumer publication.
    Previously announced as: Car Owners.
    Description: Covers automotive maintenance with news of industry trends.

796.77   US
MOTORACING. 1956. m. $18. (Sports Car Club of America, San Francisco Region) Kelly Communications (Pleasanton), 3609 Virgin Islands Ct., Pleasanton, CA 94588. TEL 510-846-7728. FAX 510-846-0118. (Subscr. to: MotoRacing, Box 1203, Pleasanton, CA 94566-0120) Ed. John F. Kelly, Jr. adv. contact: Patricia J. Kelly. bk.rev. circ. 5,000. (tabloid format) **Document type:** newspaper.
    Formerly (until 1984): Wheel (ISSN 0888-1103)
    Description: Reports on Sports Car Club of America activities in Northern California.

388   AU
MOTORBOERSE OESTERREICH. m. Fernkorngasse 12-20, A-1100 Vienna, Austria. TEL 01-6048410. FAX 01-604841021. Ed. Amandeus Charamsa.

TRANSPORTATION — AUTOMOBILES

388.3   SW   ISSN 0027-2140
MOTORBRANSCHEN; official journal of the motor trade and repair organization in Sweden. 1940. m. SEK 179 (effective 1990). (Motorbranschens Riksfoerbund - Swedish National Association for Motor Trades; National Association of Tire Dealers and Repairers) Motorbranschens Foerlag, Karlavaegen 14 A, P.O. Box 5611, S-114 86 Stockholm, Sweden. FAX 08-206747. Ed. Hans Bister. adv.; charts; illus. circ. 6,380.
    Former titles (until vol.18, 1970): Motorbranschen med Laeckeraren; Formed by the 1961 merger of: Laeckeraren; Motorbranschen; Formed by the 1948 merger of: Tidskrift foer Motor- och Automobilbranschen; Bilverkstaederna.

629.2   NO   ISSN 0332-8864
MOTORBRANSJEN. 1976. 10/yr. NOK 375. Fagbladforlaget AS, Urtegaten 9, P.O. Box 9247 Groenland, N-0134 Oslo, Norway. TEL 47-22-68-03-13. FAX 47-22-68-20-85. Ed. Jon Winding-Sorensen. adv.; bk.rev. circ. 12,427.
    Formerly (until 1978): Bilreparatoeren (ISSN 0333-4287)

388   TH   ISSN 0125-1732
MOTORCYCLE MAGAZINE. (Text in Thai) 1974. m. B.300. Grand Prix International Co., Ltd., 129-133 Rim Klong Prapar, Prachachuen Rd., Bangsue, Bangkok 10800, Thailand. TEL 662-02-587-0101. FAX 662-02-587-6567. Dir. Prachin Eamlumnow. circ. 40,000. **Document type:** consumer publication.

388.3   SW   ISSN 0463-6678
MOTORFOERAREN. 1927. 10/yr. SEK 150; newsstand price: SEK 29. M H F, S-106 84 Stockholm, Sweden. TEL 46-8-454-43-50. FAX 46-8-454-43-97. Ed. Kenneth Hagberg. adv.: B&W page SEK 16500, color page SEK 23000; trim 194 x 270. circ. 99,000. cols./p.: 4; pp./issue: 48.

388.3   NO   ISSN 0027-2213
MOTORFOEREREN.* 1939. m. NOK 100. Motorfoerernes Avholdsforbund, Esko Nor, Boks 144, 2001 Lillestroem, Norway. Ed. Per Wangen. adv.; bk.rev.; illus. circ. 39,000.
    —CCC.

388   UK   ISSN 0963-7338
MOTORHOME MAGAZINE. q. £10 (foreign £15). Stone Leisure Group, Andrew House, 2a Granville Rd., Sidcup, Kent DA14 4BN, England. TEL 081-302-6150. FAX 081-300-2315. Ed. Dave Randle. circ. 18,000.

388   IT   ISSN 0393-7666
MOTORI. 1950. bi-m. L.30000 (foreign L.93000) (effective 1994). Torino Motori s.r.l., Corso Galileo Ferraris 155, Casella Postale 336, 10134 Turin, Italy. TEL 011-3181138. FAX 011-3181610. Ed. Raffaele Sanguineti. adv.: B&W page L.5700000, color page L.9000000. circ. 30,000. **Document type:** consumer publication.
    Formerly (until 1986): Torino Motori (ISSN 0493-5306)
    Description: Forum featuring articles on automobiles and trucks in their technical and commercial aspects. Includes articles on hi-fi in cars.

388.3   II   ISSN 0027-223X
MOTORINDIA. (Text in English) 1956. m. Rs.150. (Auto Dealers' & Fleet Operators' Associations) Gopali & Co., 407-408 Mount Rd., Madras 600 035, India. Ed. R. Kalidasan. adv.; bk.rev. circ. 25,000.

388.3   II   ISSN 0027-2248
MOTORING. (Text in English) 1964. m. rs.6 to non-members. Western India Automobile Association, 76 Veer Nariman Rd., Churchgate, Bombay 20, India. Ed. Lt.Col. L.C. Fonseca. adv.; circ. 30,000. (controlled). (tabloid format)

910.202 796.77   UK
MOTORING & LEISURE. 1924. m. £12. Civil Service Motoring Association Ltd., Britannia House, 95 Queens Rd., Brighton BN1 3WY, England. TEL 01273-321921. FAX 01273-323990. Ed. David Arnold. adv.; bk.rev.; circ. 320,000. (controlled). **Document type:** consumer publication.
    Formerly: Civil Service Motoring.

388.3   UK   ISSN 0027-2264
MOTORING NEWS. 1955. w. £53. News Publications Ltd., Standard House, Bonhill St., London EC2A 4DA, England. FAX 071-638-8497. TELEX 888602-MONEWS-G. Ed. Mark Skewis. adv.; bk.rev.; charts; illus. circ. 80,000. (tabloid format)

MOTORIST (SEATTLE). see *TRAVEL AND TOURISM*

388.3   CN
MOTORIST'S ADVOCATE. (Editions in English and French) 1991. bi-m. Canadian Automobile Association, 1775 Courtwood Cres., Ottawa, ON K2C 3J2, Canada. TEL 613-226-7631. FAX 613-225-7383. TELEX 053-4440. Ed. David Leonhardt. circ. 1,200. **Document type:** bulletin.
    Formerly: C A A News and Views.

388.3   UK   ISSN 0027-2302
MOTORISTS GUIDE TO NEW & USED CAR PRICES. 1962. m. £23.40. Foxpride Ltd., 67 Tyrrell St., Leicester LE3 5SB, England. TEL 0533-511393. FAX 0533-511335. Ed. L.J. Shoebridge. adv.; illus.; stat. circ. 50,000. **Document type:** consumer publication.
    Description: Valuation guide for the general public when purchasing or selling a car, light commercial vehicle, or recreational vehicle.

388.3   IT
MOTORNOVITA INTERNATIONAL. 1952. s-m. L.50000 (foreign L.100000). Multispe s.r.l., Piazza Conciliazione 2, 20123 Milan, Italy. TEL 39-2-48777589. FAX 39-2-4984494. Ed. Luigi Spezia. adv.: B&W page L.5850000, color page L.9000000. circ. 15,000.

MOTORSCOT. see *SPORTS AND GAMES*

629.286   CC   ISSN 1001-7666
MOTUOCHE JISHU/JOURNAL OF MOTORCYCLE TECHNOLOGY. (Text in Chinese) 1988. bi-m. $15 per no. Zhongguo Qiche Jishu Yanjiu Zhongxin - China Automative Technology & Research Center, P.O. Box 59, Tianjin 300162, People's Republic of China. TEL 86-22-473100. FAX 86-22-470843. Ed. Zhang Wencan. **Document type:** trade publication.

388.3   SP
MUNDO RECAMBIO Y TALLER; revista tecnica de la automocion. 1980. 11/yr. 5500 ptas. (Europe 9100 ptas.; elsewhere 10300 ptas.). C E I Arsis, S.L., Paris 150, 4o 3a, 08036 Barcelona, Spain. TEL 39-3-4395564. FAX 39-3-4306853. Ed. Yvonne Rubio; Pub. Pilar Grau. adv.: B&W page 101000 ptas., color page 155000 ptas.; 215 x 295; adv. contact: Gloria Vinals. circ. 12,000. **Document type:** trade publication.
    Description: For professionals in the automotive repair and spare parts industry, and its distribution, after-market.

MURRAY WALKER'S GRAND PRIX YEAR. see *SPORTS AND GAMES*

388.3   US   ISSN 1054-8912
MUSCLE MUSTANGS & FAST FORDS. 1988. 9/yr. $18.95. C S K Publishing Co., Inc., 299 Market St., Saddle Brook, NJ 07662. TEL 201-712-9300. FAX 201-712-9899. (Subscr. to: Box 1010, Danville, NJ 07834) Ed. Steve Collison. adv.; bk.rev. circ. 41,000. (back issues avail.) **Document type:** consumer publication.
    Description: For the late model Ford enthusiast, featuring only late-model hop-ups, performance tips and guides, straight line and circle track coverage, tech features and how-tos to make 'Stang faster.

629.286   US   ISSN 0897-0963
MUSCLECARS. 1983. bi-m. $15. C S K Publishing Co., Inc., 299 Market St., Saddle Brook, NJ 07662. TEL 201-712-9300. FAX 201-712-9899. (Subscr. to: Box 1010, Denville, NJ 07834) Ed. Jim Campisano. adv. circ. 40,000. (back issues avail.) **Document type:** consumer publication.
    Description: Edited for car lovers of the late Fifties, Sixties and early Seventies (1958-1972) featuring all the musclecars such as GTO, Hemi, Mustang, Chevelle, Camaro.

MUSTANG & FORDS. see *ANTIQUES*

796.77   US   ISSN 0898-8994
MUSTANG ILLUSTRATED. q. McMullen & Yee Publishing, 744 S. Placentia Ave., Placentia, CA 92670-6846. TEL 714-572-2255. FAX 714-572-1864.

388.3   US   ISSN 0027-5794
N A D A OFFICIAL USED CAR GUIDE. Eastern Edition (ISSN 0193-2780) (Avail. in 9 Regional Editions) 1933. m. $47. National Automobile Dealers Association, Used Car Guide Co., 8400 Westpark Dr., McLean, VA 22102. TEL 703-821-7000. circ. 370,000. **Document type:** directory.

388.3   US
N A D A OFFICIAL WHOLESALE USED CAR TRADE-IN GUIDE. fortn. $49. National Automobile Dealers Association, Used Car Guide Co., 8400 Westpark Dr., McLean, VA 22102. TEL 703-821-7000. **Document type:** directory.
    Former titles: Official Used Car Trade-In Guide; N A D A Dealers Wholesale Auto Auction Report; N A D A Official Car and Truck Appraisal Guide; N A D A Auto Auction True Values Guide (ISSN 0027-5786)

388.3   US
N A D A OLDER USED CAR GUIDE. 3/yr. $40. (National Automobile Dealers Association) N.A.D.A. Appraisal Guides, Box 7800, Costa Mesa, CA 92628-7800.

381   US   ISSN 0092-4601
HD9715.7.U6
N A D A RECREATION VEHICLE APPRAISAL GUIDE. 3/yr. $85. (National Automobile Dealers Association) N.A.D.A. Appraisal Guides, Box 7800, Costa Mesa, CA 92628-7800.

388.3   US
N A F A ANNUAL REFERENCE BOOK. 1960. a. $45. National Association of Fleet Administrators, Inc., 120 Wood Ave., S., Ste. 615, Iselin, NJ 08830-2709. TEL 908-494-8100. FAX 908-494-6789. Ed. Denise M. Rucci. adv.; stat. circ. 4,000.
    Formerly: N A F A Conference Brochure and Reference Book (ISSN 0550-8843)

796.77   US
N H R A SOUVENIR PROGRAM. a. $5. National Hot Rod Association, 2035 Financial Way, Glendora, CA 91741. TEL 818-963-7695. FAX 818-335-6651. circ. 100,000 (paid).
    Formerly: N H R A Souvenir Yearbook.
    Description: Drag racing year in review.

629.286   US
NASH TIMES. 1970. bi-m. $23 (foreign $24). Nash Car Club of America, 4151 220 St., Clinton, IA 52732-8943. TEL 319-242-5490. (Subscr. to: c/o Jim & Dorothy Bracewell, 1 N 274 Prairie, Glen Ellyn, IL 60137) Eds. Charlie and Maggie Wilson. circ. 2,000. (back issues avail.) **Document type:** consumer publication.
    Description: For car enthusiasts dedicated to promoting the history, preservation, and restoration of the Nash and related automobiles.

388.3   US
NATIONAL AUTOMOTIVE PARTS ASSOCIATION. OUTLOOK. 1967. 10/yr. National Automotive Parts Association, 2999 Circle 75 Parkway, Atlanta, GA 30339. TEL 404-956-2200. FAX 404-956-2211. Ed. Kathy Randall. adv. circ. 16,500.
    Description: For owners and managers of NAPA auto parts stores only.

796.72   US   ISSN 0466-2199
NATIONAL DRAGSTER. 1960. 48/yr. $52. National Hot Rod Association, 2035 Financial Way, Glendora, CA 91741. TEL 818-963-7695. Ed. Phil Burgess; Pub. Neil Britt. adv. contact: Sandy Wasserbeck. stat. circ. 80,000. (tabloid format) **Document type:** newspaper.
    Description: Covers drag racing and NHRA events. Features technical articles, new product data, performance standards, race previews, interviews and official rule changes.

629.22 288.3   US
NATIONAL FOUR WHEEL DRIVE ASSOCIATION NEWS.* m. National Four Wheel Drive Association, c/o Houser, 5051 E. Summerset Cir., Cave Creek, AZ 85331-5123. TEL 602-996-1124. bk.rev.; bibl.

6384 TRANSPORTATION — AUTOMOBILES

629.222 UK
NATIONAL MOTOR MUSEUM PICTORIAL GUIDE. 1959. a. £2. (National Motor Museum Trust) Montagu Ventures Ltd., Beaulieu, Hampshire SO42 7ZN, England. TEL 0590-612345. FAX 0590-612624. Ed. M.E. Ware. adv.; illus.; stat. circ. 120,000.

NATIONAL MOTORIST. see *TRAVEL AND TOURISM*

388.3 665.7 US
NATURAL GAS VEHICLE. 6/yr. $192 to non-members (foreign $240); members $96 (foreign $144). American Gas Association, 1515 Wilson Blvd., Arlington, VA 22209. TEL 703-841-8400. FAX 703-841-8406. (Subscr. to: Dept. 0765, McLean, VA 22109-0765)

629.22 JA ISSN 0289-6079
NAVI. (Text in Japanese) 1984. m. 12600 Yen. Nigensha Publishing Co., Ltd., 2-2, Kanda-Jimbocho, Chiyoda-ku, Tokyo 101, Japan. TEL 81-3-5210-4706. FAX 81-3-5210-4726. Ed. M. Suzuki. adv.: color page 650000 Yen; trim 222 x 295; adv. contact: R. Ohkoshi. circ. 220,000.
  Description: Covers social and economic aspects of cars and motoring for car enthusiasts and car buyers.

388 US ISSN 1069-322X
TL162
NEW CAR & TRUCK BUYING GUIDE. 1993. 4/yr. newsstand price: $5.99. Pace Publications (Milwaukee), 1020 N. Broadway, Ste. 111, Milwaukee, WI 53202. TEL 414-272-9977. FAX 414-272-9973. **Document type:** consumer publication.

629.222 US ISSN 1071-6106
TL162
NEW CAR PRICE GUIDE. 1991. 7/yr. $4.99 per no. Pace Publications (Milwaukee), 1020 N. Broadway, Ste. 111, Milwaukee, WI 53202. TEL 414-272-9977. FAX 414-272-9973.

388.3 US ISSN 1049-8583
HD9710.U5
NEW CAR PRICES - BUYER'S GUIDE REPORTS. 7/yr. $26.95. Pace Publications (Milwaukee), 1020 N. Broadway, Ste. 111, Milwaukee, WI 53202. TEL 414-272-9977. FAX 414-272-9973.
  Description: Lists dealer's cost and manufacturer's suggested list price for every American automobile and every option available for each model.

629.286 JA
NEW DEVELOPMENTS IN AUTOMOBILE MATERIALS FOR THE 90'S. 1988. w. $3200. Toray Research Center, Inc., (Subsidiary of: Toray Industries, Ltd.), 3-1-8, Nihonbashi - Muromachi, Chuo-ku, Tokyo 103, Japan. TEL 81-3-3245-5895. FAX 81-3-3245-5789. TELEX J22623 TRC.

NEW HAMPSHIRE MOTOR VEHICLE AND BOATING LAWS. see *LAW — Judicial Systems*

388.33 US ISSN 0028-713X
NEW YORK AUTO REPAIR NEWS. 1948. m. $12 (free to qualified personnel). Van Allen Publishing Co., Box 354, Hicksville, NY 11802. TEL 516-422-5521. Ed. Richard Van Allen. adv.; bk.rev.; circ. 11,300 (controlled).

629.286 796.72 NZ ISSN 0113-0196
NEW ZEALAND CAR. 1986. m. NZ.$49.50 (foreign NZ.$114.50). New Zealand Magazines Ltd., Cnr. Halsey & Madden Streets, Freemans Bay, Auckland, New Zealand. TEL 09-3098-292. FAX 09-3096-361. Ed. Donn Anderson. circ. 18,000. (back issues avail.)
  Description: Covers all automobile interests, new car tests, new car and product releases, and motor sports.

388 AU
NISSAN AKTUELL; das aktuelle Magazin fuer Auto, Reise und Freizeit. 3/yr. Nissan Oesterreich GmbH, Hainburger Bundesstr. 1, A-2320 Schwechat, Austria. TEL 01-70180640. FAX 01-70180639. adv.: B&W page S.47000, color page S.65000; trim 205 x 282; adv. contact: Christine Winkler. **Document type:** consumer publication.
  Description: General interest publication for the owners of Nissan automobiles in Austria.

388.3 JA ISSN 0029-0734
NISSAN DIESEL TECHNICAL REVIEW. (Text in Japanese; summaries in English, Japanese) 1950. a. free. Nissan Diesel Motor Co. Ltd. - Nihon Nissan Jizeru Kogyo K.K., 1-1 Ageoshi, Saitama-ken 362, Japan. bk.rev.; abstr.; bibl.; charts; illus. circ. 4,000.

388 GW
NISSAN LIFE. 1977. bi-m. DM.18. Nissan Motor Deutschland GmbH, Nissanstr. 1, 41456 Neuss, Germany. TEL 02131-388255. FAX 02131-37880. adv. circ. 400,000. **Document type:** consumer publication.
  Description: Cars, motor sports, new product information.

629.222 JA
NISSHA GIHO/NIPPON SHARYO TECHNICAL REVIEW. (Text in Japanese) s-a. Nippon Sharyo Seizo K.K., Kaihatsu Honbu, 1-1, Sanbonmatsu-cho, Atsuta-ku, Nagoya-shi, Aichi-ken 456, Japan.

388 FR
NORD-AUTOMOBILE. 10/yr. 150 F. Automobile-Club, B.P. 635, 59061 Roubaix Cedex, France. TEL 20-65-95-93. FAX 20-65-95-99. Ed. B. Morel. circ. 20,000.

796.72 US ISSN 1053-4881
NORTH AMERICAN PYLON; dedicated to sports car autocrossing. 1990. m. $24 (effective 1993). Kelly Communications, Box 1203, Pleasanton, CA 94566-0120. TEL 510-846-7728. Ed. John F. Kelly Jr. adv. contact: John F. Kelly Jr. bk.rev. circ. 3,200. (tabloid format; back issues avail.) **Document type:** newspaper.
  Description: Reports on autocross time trial events throughout the U.S. and Canada, with road tests of new cars and interviews of prominent drivers and personalities in the sport.

338.476 UK
NORTH LONDON AUTO TRADER; cars - bikes - boats - caravans - commercials - accessories. 1984. w. £104; newsstand price: £1. Hurst Publishing (Watford), 43-45 High Rd., Bushey Heath, Watford, Herts. WD2 1EE, England. TEL 0181-950-9900. FAX 0181-950-7581. Pub. Kate Stearman-Smith. adv. contact: Mary Ann Lambertucci. illus. **Document type:** consumer publication.
  Formerly: North Thames Auto Trader; **Supersedes:** North London, Herts and Beds Auto Trader.
  Description: Lists all types of cars, bikes, recreation vehicles and light-duty trucks for those interested in buying or selling.

629 US ISSN 0274-5348
NORTHERN AUTOMOTIVE NEWS. 1980. m. free to qualified personnel. 13304 Stone Rd., Minnetonka, MN 55305. TEL 612-544-6805. Pub. Bonnie M. McClard. adv. contact: Bonnie M. McClard. illus.; circ. 7,000 (controlled). **Document type:** trade publication.
  Description: For automotive aftermarket businesses in the upper Midwest.

629 UK
THE NORTHERN INSTRUCTOR. q. (Motor Schools Association of Great Britain) Integral Publishing Co. Ltd., Castlefield Ho., Liverpool Rd., Castlefield, Manchester M60 9BF, England. Ed. John Lepine. **Document type:** trade publication.
  Description: Distributed to driving instructors.

388.3 US ISSN 0029-3148
NORTHERN LIGHTS (MINNEAPOLIS). 1954. 8/yr. membership. Antique Automobile Club of America, Minnesota Region, 621 E. 61st St., Minneapolis, MN 55417. TEL 612-869-1710. Ed. Paul M. Remfer. adv. circ. 550.

338.476 UK ISSN 0958-4277
NORTH WEST AUTO TRADER. 1981. w. £2.65 per no. Maracomp Ltd., Unit 1, Catherine St., Bewsey Industrial Estate, Warrington, Cheshire WA5 5LH, England. TEL 01925-637000. FAX 01925-411181. Ed. Christine Jackson. adv. contact: Marie Hurdsfield. circ. 59,249. (back issues avail.) **Document type:** consumer publication.
  Formerly: North West Automart.
  Description: Advertising medium for buying and selling vehicles and motor related products.

388.3 US ISSN 0029-3393
NORTHWEST MOTOR; journal for the automotive industry. 1909. m. $15. Automotive Publishing Company, Box 46937, Seattle, WA 98126-0937. TEL 206-935-3336. FAX 206-937-9732. Ed. Jerry Smith. adv.; illus.; stat.; tr.lit. circ. 5,800. (also avail. in microform from UMI) **Document type:** trade publication.

NOSTALGIA MOTOR MAGAZINE. see *ANTIQUES*

388 388.324 IT
NOTIZIARIO MOTORISTICO/MOTOR NEWS/MOTOR - NACHRICHTEN/NOUVELLES DE L'AUTOMOBILE; autoattrezzature-impiantistica. (Text in English, French, German, Italian) 1966. m. L.50000. Azienda Cataloghi Italiani s.a.s., Via B. Crespi, 30-2, 20159 Milan, Italy. TEL 39-2-606052. FAX 39-2-606487. adv.: B&W page $1300; 210 x 297. bk.rev.; circ. 16,799 (controlled).
  Description: Covers technical, financial, and commercial news for the automotive industry, with special issues during international exhibitions.

388.3 SP
NOVOCAR. 1991. 12/yr. 6000 ptas. Caspe 54, 5o, 08010 Barcelona, Spain. TEL 3-301-28-89. FAX 3-412-53-75. Ed. Ma. Jose Mayor. adv.; bk.rev. circ. 5,000.

388.3 US ISSN 0029-5434
NOZZLE. 1970. m. Greater Washington - Maryland Service Station & Automotive Repair Association, 9420 Annapolis Rd., Ste. 307, Lanham, MD 20706-3021. TEL 301-577-2875. Ed. Roy Littlefield, III. adv.; charts; illus. circ. 3,500.

629.286 SP ISSN 0212-8330
NUESTROS TALLERES; revista profesional de la reparacion, mantenimiento, venta y postventa de vehiculos. 1980. m. (14/yr.). 7600 ptas. (foreign 11400 ptas.). Tecnipublicaciones, S.A., C. Albacete 5, 28027 Madrid, Spain. TEL 34-1-3261440. FAX 34-1-3262539. **Document type:** trade publication.
  Description: Covers the auto repair industry. Includes new equipment, legal articles and interviews.

629.222 US ISSN 1076-514X
NUTZ & BOLTZ. 1988. m. $26 (effective 1995). Nutz & Boltz, Inc., Box 123, Butler, MD 21023. TEL 410-584-7574; 800-888-0091. FAX 410-584-1054. Ed. David R. Solomon. circ. 4,500 (paid). **Document type:** newsletter.
  Formerly: Nutz and Boltz Newsletter (ISSN 1056-1714)
  Description: Covers all things automotive. Provides information and advice for the do-it-yourselfer and consumers interested in avoiding rip-offs.

797.77 GW
O N S - MITTEILUNGEN. m. DM.52. Obersten Nationalen Sportkommission fuer den Automobil in Deutschland GmbH, Haus des Motorsports, Waidmannstr. 47, 60596 Frankfurt, Germany. TEL 069-633007-0. TELEX 04-13149.

388 AU
OESTERREICHISCHE MOTORISTEN MAGAZIN. 1992. q. Verlag Lorenz, Ebendorferstr. 10, A-1010 Vienna, Austria. TEL 01-426695. FAX 01-438693. adv.: B&W page S.17100, color page S.30900; trim 167 x 254. **Document type:** consumer publication.

621.9 US ISSN 1074-6919
TA725
OFF-HIGHWAY ENGINEERING. 1991. q. Society of Automotive Engineers, 400 Commonwealth Dr., Warrendale, PA 15096. TEL 412-776-4841. FAX 412-776-4026. Ed. Daniel J. Holt. adv. contact: Larry Schneider. (also avail. in microfiche; microfilm; back issues avail.) **Document type:** trade publication. ●Also available online. Vendor(s): Orbit Search Service.
  Description: For U.S. and overseas automotive engineers and manufacturers of off-highway vehicle systems and components. Covers technological advances that can be applied to the development of new or enhanced systems.

TRANSPORTATION — AUTOMOBILES

796.7   US
OFF ROAD. 1969. m. $14.98. Argus Publishers Corporation, Box 49659, Los Angeles, CA 90049. TEL 310-820-3601. FAX 310-207-9388. (Subscr. to: Box 451, Mt. Morris, IL 61054) Ed. Duane Elliott. adv. circ. 84,213. (also avail. in microform from UMI; reprint service avail. from UMI) **Indexed:** Mag.Ind.
   Former titles: Off Road Vehicles and Adventure; Off Road Vehicles.
   Description: Four-wheel vehicle adventure and mechanics.

796.77   GW   ISSN 0172-4185
OFF ROAD. 1978. m. A C Verlag GmbH, Prof.-Messerschmitt-Str. 3, 85579 Neubiberg, Germany. TEL 089-60821-01. FAX 089-60821-200. Ed. Bernhard Weinbacher; Pub. Alfons Czerny. adv. contact: Alexander Muehlberger. circ. 133,952. **Document type:** consumer publication.

388.3 621.9   UK   ISSN 0953-203X
OFF ROAD AND 4 WHEEL DRIVE. 1984. m. £27.60 (foreign £35.40). Link House Magazines Ltd., Link House, Dingwall Ave., Croydon, Surrey CR9 2TA, England. TEL 0181-686-2599. FAX 0181-781-6042. Ed. Graham Scott. adv.; bk.rev.; charts; illus. circ. 40,000. (back issues avail.) **Document type:** consumer publication.

629   US   ISSN 0891-4648
GV1029.9.S74
OFFICIAL N A S C A R YEARBOOK AND PRESS GUIDE. 1986. a. $8. U M I Publications, Inc., Box 30036, Charlotte, NC 28230. TEL 704-374-0420. FAX 704-374-0729. Ed. Ivan Mothershead; Pub. Ivan Mothershead. adv. circ. 180,000. (back issues avail.)

629.286 330
OHIO & NORTHERN KENTUCKY GASOLINE DEALERS & GARAGE NEWS. bi-m. Greater Cincinnati Gasoline Dealers Association, 3410 Glenway Ave., Cincinnati, OH 45205-2902. TEL 513-921-3182. Ed. John Mike Kunnen. circ. 1,800. **Document type:** trade publication.

OHIO MOTORIST. see TRAVEL AND TOURISM

629.2   CN   ISSN 0841-775X
OLD AUTOS. 1987. s-m. Can.$25 (foreign Can.$45). Old Autos, 348 Main St., Box 419, Bothwell, Ont. N0P 1C0, Canada. TEL 519-695-2303. FAX 519-695-3716. Ed. Murray McEwan. adv. circ. 11,400. (tabloid format)

629.222   US   ISSN 0048-1637
OLD CARS; weekly news and marketplace. Variant title: Old Cars Weekly. 1973. w. $32.95. Krause Publications, Inc., 700 E. State St., Iola, WI 54990. TEL 715-445-2214; 800-258-0929. FAX 715-445-4087. TELEX 55 6461 KRAUSE PUB UD. Ed. Brad Bowling. adv.; bk.rev.; charts; illus.; tr.lit. circ. 70,363. (tabloid format; also avail. in microform from UMI,PMC)
   Description: Directed to collectors of antique and collectible cars of the last 100 years. Contains news and features on collector cars, restoration tips, auction results, and car show information.

796.77   GW   ISSN 0932-0075
OLDTIMER ADRESSEN LEXIKON; in- und auslaendische Adressen rund um den Oldtimer. 1984. a. DM.19.80. Heel-Verlag GmbH, Hauptstr. 354, 53639 Koenigswinter, Germany. TEL 02223-23026. FAX 02223-23028. (Dist. by: I P V, Wendenstr. 27, 20097 Hamburg, Germany. TEL 040-237110. FAX 040-23711235) Ed. Luis Fernandes. adv.: page DM.2200; trim 185 x 266; adv. contact: Sabine Tschiersch. circ. 5,000 (paid). (back issues avail.) **Document type:** directory.

796.77   GW
OLDTIMER KATALOG. 1983. a. DM.29.80. Heel-Verlag GmbH, Hauptstr. 354, 53639 Koenigswinter, Germany. TEL 02223-23026. FAX 02223-23028. (Dist. by: I P V, Wendenstr. 27, 20097 Hamburg, Germany) Ed. Joachim Hack. adv.: page DM.2200; trim 185 x 266; adv. contact: Sabine Tschiersch. circ. 5,000 (paid). (back issues avail.) **Document type:** catalog.

388   GW
OLDTIMER MAGAZIN. q. DM.33 (foreign DM.39.20). A C Verlagsgesellschaft mbH, Prof.-Messerschmitt-Str. 3, 85579 Neubiberg, Germany. TEL 089-6082101. FAX 089-60821200. Ed. Egbert Schwartz; Pub. Alfons Czerny. adv. contact: Alexander Muehlberger. circ. 57,878. **Document type:** consumer publication.

796.77   GW   ISSN 0943-7320
OLDTIMER-MARKT. 1980. m. DM.58 (foreign DM.80). V F Verlagsgesellschaft mbH, Lise-Meitner-Str. 2, 55129 Mainz, Germany. TEL 06131-992-0. FAX 06131-992103. Ed. Peter Steinfurth. adv.: B&W page DM.12200, color page DM.20800; trim 260 x 185; adv. contact: Peter Hart. bk.rev. circ. 266,150. **Document type:** consumer publication.
   Former titles (until 1993): Markt (ISSN 0939-9704); (until 1990): Markt fuer Klassische Automobile und Motorraeder (ISSN 0175-9698)
   Description: For classic automobile and motorcycle enthusiasts. Includes new products, readers' comments, and large classified listings for automobiles and parts for sale.

388   GW   ISSN 0937-6291
OLDTIMER PRAXIS. 1990. m. DM.32 (foreign DM.50). V F Verlagsgesellschaft mbH, Lise-Meitner-Str. 2, 55129 Mainz, Germany. TEL 06131-99202. FAX 06131-992100. (Subscr. to: Postfach 1147, 65001 Wiesbaden, Germany. TEL 0611-266106) Ed. Peter Steinfurth; Pub. Ulf Mommertz. adv.: B&W page DM.6050, color page DM.10500; trim 260 x 185; adv. contact: Peter Hart. circ. 85,279. **Document type:** consumer publication.

388.3   GW
OMNIBUS-REVUE UND BUS AKTUELL. 1950. m. DM.169.50 (foreign DM.190). Heinrich Vogel Fachzeitschriften GmbH, Neumarkter Str. 18, 81673 Munich, Germany. TEL 089-43180-0. FAX 089-43180398. (Subscr. to: Postfach 802020, 81620 Munich, Germany) Ed. Heinzmartin Nitsche. adv.; charts; illus.; tr.lit.; index; circ. 6,300 (controlled). **Document type:** trade publication.
—CCC.
   Formerly: Omnibus-Revue (ISSN 0030-2279)

ON THE LINE (PENSACOLA). see LEISURE AND RECREATION

796.77   US   ISSN 0279-2737
ON TRACK (LAS VEGAS).* 1981. fortn. $29.97. O T Publishing, Inc., Box 94618, Las VEgas, NV 89193-4618. Ed. Andrew Crask. adv.; bk.rev. circ. 39,000. (back issues avail.)
—CCC.

338.3   CN   ISSN 0832-8269
ONTARIO. MINISTRY OF TRANSPORTATION. ONTARIO ROAD SAFETY ANNUAL REPORT. 1957. a. free. Ministry of Transportation, 1201 Wilson Ave., Downsview, ON M3M 1J8, Canada. TEL 416-248-3585. FAX 416-235-3633. (Subscr. to: Publications Services Section, 5th Fl., 880 Bay St., Toronto, ON M7A 1N8, Canada. TEL 800-668-9938) illus.; stat.
   Former titles: Ontario. Ministry of Transportation and Communications. Ontario Road Safety Annual Report; (until 1985): Ontario. Ministry of Transportation and Communications. Motor Vehicle Accident Facts; Ontario. Ministry of Transportation and Communications. Highway Traffic Collisions.

388   AT   ISSN 0048-1947
OPEN ROAD. 1921. bi-m. membership. (National Roads and Motorists Association) Open Road Publishing Co., 151 Clarence St., Sydney, N.S.W. 2000, Australia. TEL 02-260-9222. FAX 02-260-9069. Ed. W. McKinnon. adv.; bk.rev. circ. 1,445,000. **Indexed:** Aus.Rd.Ind.
   Description: Feature articles and news on motoring and leisure with reports on new and used cars.

388.3   US   ISSN 0279-0254
GV1029.9.S74
OPEN WHEEL. 1980. m. $21.95. Open Wheel Publishing, Ltd. (Subsidiary of: General Media Publishing Group), 47 S. Main St., Ipswich, MA 01938. TEL 508-356-7030. FAX 508-356-2492. (Subscr. to: Box 420235, Palm Coast, FL 32142-0235) Ed. Dick Berggren. adv. contact: Christopher Ballard. circ. 64,875. (back issues avail.) **Document type:** consumer publication.
   Description: Covers sprint car, midget, supermodified and Indy car racing. Includes technical features, personality profiles, columns and race reports.

388.3 629.2   CN
OPPORTUNITIES UNLIMITED. biennial. free. Automotive Industries Association of Canada, 1272 Wellington St., Ottawa, ON K1Y 3A7, Canada. TEL 613-728-5821. FAX 613-728-6021. Ed. Mireille Schippers. circ. 40,000.

388.3   US   ISSN 0274-5844
OREGON MOTORIST. 1920. m. $1. American Automobile Association - Oregon, 600 S.W. Market St., Portland, OR 97201. TEL 503-222-6729. FAX 503-222-6756. Ed. Anne O'Ryan. circ. 290,000. **Document type:** consumer publication, newspaper.

629.286   US   ISSN 1059-0943
TL154
P B E SPECTRUM.* (Paint, Body, & Equipment) 1989. bi-m. Irving-Cloud Publishing Co., 410 N. Hough St., Barrington, IL 60010-3028. TEL 708-674-7300. FAX 708-674-7015. Ed. Martin Schultz.
   Description: Informs body shop personnel on procedures, products and trends.

388   GW
P S DIE MOTORRAD-ZEITUNG. 1976. m. DM.59.40; newsstand price: DM.5.50. Vereinigte Motor-Verlage GmbH und Co. KG, Leuschnerstr. 1, 70714 Stuttgart, Germany. TEL 0711-18201. FAX 0711-1821669. Ed. Volker Koerdt; Pub. Peter-Paul Pietsch. adv.: B&W page DM.7360, color page DM.13616; trim 185 x 248; adv. contact: Claus Schlosser. circ. 75,259. **Document type:** consumer publication.

388.3   US   ISSN 1064-4628
IN PROCESS
PACE BUYER'S GUIDES. DOMESTIC & FOREIGN TRUCK, VAN, 4 X 4 PRICES, NEW & USED. Short title: Truck, Van, 4 x 4 Prices. 1973. 7/yr. $26.95. Pace Publications (Milwaukee), 1020 N. Broadway, Ste. 111, Milwaukee, WI 53202. TEL 414-272-9977. FAX 414-272-9973.
   Formerly: Truck and Van Prices - Buyer's Guide Reports (ISSN 1050-7272)
   Description: Lists dealer's cost and manufacturer's suggested list price for every American small truck or van, with all options available, and prices for the preceding ten years.

629.2   US   ISSN 0744-8155
PACIFIC AUTOMOTIVE NEWS. 1973. bi-m. $15. Autoword Automotive Communications, Box 25, Port Gamble, WA 98364-0025. TEL 206-697-6200. FAX 206-697-4040. Ed. Peter D. duPre. adv. circ. 17,000. **Document type:** trade publication.
   Description: Independent publication serving the automotive trade of the Pacific Coast.

PACKARD CORMORANT. see ANTIQUES

796.77   US   ISSN 0887-9613
PANTERA INTERNATIONAL NEWS. Short title: P I News. 1975. q. $50 (foreign $60) (effective 1992). Pantera International, 18586 Main St., Ste. 100, Huntington Beach, CA 92648. Ed. David Adler. adv.; charts; illus.; index. circ. 500. (back issues avail.)
   Description: Features technical "how to" information on the repair, service and modification of the Pantera automobile. Includes reprints of out-of-print articles and want ads.

388   UK   ISSN 0958-0662
PARKERS CAR PRICE GUIDE. 1972. m. £55. Parkers Price Guides Ltd., 45 St. Mary's Rd., Ealing, London W5 5RQ, England. Ed. Nicholas Barfield. adv.

TRANSPORTATION — AUTOMOBILES

388.3   US   ISSN 0031-2193
HE371.A2
PARKING; the magazine of the parking industry. 1952. 10/yr. $95 include Products & Services Directory. National Parking Association, 1112 16th St. N.W., Ste. 300, Washington, DC 20036. TEL 202-296-4336. FAX 202-331-8523. Ed. Rich Parker. adv.: B&W page $1045, color page $1545; adv. contact: Dawn Newman. bk.rev.; charts; illus.; circ. 5,000 (controlled). Indexed: P.A.I.S. **Document type:** trade publication.
—BLDSC (6406.780000); Faxon.
    Incorporates (1973-1990): N P A Government Affairs Report; (1972-1990): Parking World; Which was formerly (1963-1971): National Parking Association Newsletter (ISSN 0277-0970); Newsletter - National Parking Association (ISSN 0027-9862)
    Description: Contains feature articles relating to the parking industry and governmental, legal, regional and association news.

388.3   US   ISSN 0896-2324
PARKING PROFESSIONAL. 1984. m. $60 (foreign $72). Institutional and Municipal Parking Congress, 701 Kenmore Ave., Ste. 200, Fredericksburg, VA 22404. TEL 703-371-7535. FAX 703-371-8022. E-mail: 75244.70atCompuserve.com. Ed. Marie E. Witmer; Pub. David L. Ivey. adv.: B&W page $965, color page $1715; trim 8 1/2 x 11; adv. contact: Lynne Chiara. bibl.; charts; illus.; stat.; tr.lit.; index. circ. 1,800. (back issues avail.) **Document type:** trade publication.
    Description: Focuses on the parking industry: construction, operation, enforcement, maintenance.

388   UK   ISSN 0962-3566
PARKING REVIEW. 1989. 10/yr. £36 (Europe £46; rest of world £56); newsstand price: £2.50. Landor Publishing Ltd., Quadrant House, 250 Kennington Ln., London SE11 5RD, England. TEL 0171-582-6626. FAX 0171-735-1299. E-mail: 100570,73@compuserve.com. Ed. Mark Moran; Pub. Peter Stonham. adv. contact: John French. circ. 5,000 (paid). (back issues avail.) **Document type:** trade publication.
    Description: Covers on- and off-street parking policy and equipment and services used by public and private car park operators.

629.24   IT   ISSN 1120-1789
PARTS. 1979. m. L.80000 (foreign L.160000) (effective 1995). Stammer S.p.A., Via della Liberazione 1, 20068 Peschiera Borromeo (MI), Italy. TEL 02-55302606. FAX 02-55302700. Ed. Girolamo Bellina. adv.: B&W page L.1880000, color page L.2500000; trim 185 x 267. circ. 8,000.
    Formerly: Tutto Ricambi.

629.283   US
PARTS & PEOPLE. (In 2 eds.: Midwest, Mountain) 1986. m. $20 (free to qualified personnel). Automotive Counseling & Publishing Co., Inc., 837 Sherman St., Ste. 2B, Denver, CO 80203-2913. TEL 303-860-0545; 800-530-8557. FAX 303-860-0532. Ed. Dave Lucia. adv.: B&W page $1568.84; 10 1/2 x 13 1/2; adv. contact: Lance R. Buchner. circ. 26,000. **Document type:** newspaper, trade publication.
    Description: For automotive parts and service specialists. The Mountain Edition serves Colorado, Wyoming, northern New Mexico and western Kansas and Nebraska. The Midwest Edition serves Kansas, Nebraska, and western Missouri, and Iowa. Focuses on business practices, industry issues, and education and training.

PEOPLE 'N PRIDE. see ENGINEERING — Mechanical Engineering

629.283   UK
PERFORMANCE & STYLE INTERNATIONAL. 1985. m. £15.80 (foreign £41) (1995). Security Publications Ltd., Argosy House, 161a-163a High St., Orpington, Kent BR6 0LW, England. TEL 01689-74025. Ed. Chris Wright. adv.; bk.rev. circ. 60,000. (back issues avail.) **Document type:** trade publication.
    Former titles (until 1994): Top Car Magazine (ISSN 0960-2429); (until 1990): Your Car Magazine (ISSN 0267-2952)

629.222   UK   ISSN 0265-6183
PERFORMANCE CAR. 1968. m. £33 (foreign £47.40) (effective 1995-1996). E M A P - Consumer, Priory Ct., 30-32 Farringdon Ln., London EC1R 3AU, England. TEL 0171-972-6700. FAX 0171-972-6710. (Subscr. to: Tower Publishing Services Ltd., Tower House, Sovereign Park, Lathkill St., Market Harborough, Leics. LE16 9EF, England. TEL 01858-468811. FAX 01858-432164) adv.; bk.rev.; charts; illus.; tr.mk. circ. 66,400. **Document type:** consumer publication.
—CCC.
    Formerly: Hot Car (ISSN 0018-6007)

388.3   US   ISSN 1068-4131
PERFORMANCE FOR THE CHRYSLER CAR ENTHUSIAST. 1984. bi-m. $15. R H O Publications, 1580 Hampton Rd., Bensalem, PA 19020-4610. TEL 215-639-4456. Ed. Robert Oskiera; Pub. Robert Oskiera. adv. contact: Robert Henry. circ. 60,000 (controlled). (back issues avail.) **Document type:** consumer publication.
    Formerly (until 1991): Morperformance.
    Description: Covers Chrysler cars from the '50s through current models, with particular emphasis on the muscle car period.

PETERSEN'S 4 WHEEL & OFF-ROAD. see SPORTS AND GAMES — Bicycles And Motorcycles

388.3   US
PIERCE-ARROW SERVICE BULLETIN. 1968. 6/yr. $25 membership. Pierce-Arrow Society, Inc., 135 Edgerton Ln., Rochester, NY 14607. Ed. Bernard J. Weis. circ. 1,100. (processed) **Document type:** bulletin.

388   JA
PIT INN. (Text in Japanese) 1972. m. 2400 Yen. Geibunsha, 5, 3-chome, Kanda-Surugadai, Chiyoda-ku, Tokyo, Japan. Ed. Keizo Takanashi.
    Formerly: Pit Stop.

PLYMOUTH BULLETIN. see ANTIQUES

PNEUMATIQUE; industrie - distribution - rechapage. see RUBBER

796.77   US   ISSN 0746-7591
POPULAR CARS. 1981. m. McMullen & Yee Publishing, 774 S. Placentia Ave., Placentia, CA 92670-6846. TEL 714-572-2255. FAX 714-572-1864. Ed. Bruce Hampson. adv.
    Formerly (until 1984): Custom Rodder (ISSN 0746-7583)

POPULAR CLASSICS. see ANTIQUES

388.3   US   ISSN 0032-4523
TL236
POPULAR HOT RODDING. 1962. m. $16.94. Argus Publishers Corporation, Box 49659, Los Angeles, CA 90049. TEL 310-820-3601. FAX 310-207-9388. (Subscr. to: Box 452, Mt. Morris, IL 61054. TEL 815-734-4151) Ed. Matt Hardesty. adv. contact: William Lloyd. illus. circ. 210,429.
    Description: Presents latest trends, technical developments, event coverage, performance car test, product evaluations, detailed how-to-articles and features on reader-modified vehicles.

388.7   US
▼**POPULAR MECHANICS, CAR SMART**. 1994. irreg. newsstand price: $2.95. Hearst Magazines, Popular Mechanics, 224 W. 57th St., New York, NY 10019. TEL 212-649-3076. adv. **Document type:** consumer publication.
    Description: Examines and compares the performance, handling, ride, and economy of cars, grouped by segment to help prospective buyers make informed decisions.

388.7   US   ISSN 1071-4731
TL162
POPULAR MECHANICS NEW CAR & TRUCK GUIDE. a. $3.95. Hearst Magazines, Popular Mechanics, 224 W. 57th St., New York, NY 10019. TEL 212-649-3076. adv. **Document type:** consumer publication.
    Description: Advises prospective purchasers of a new car or light truck.

388.3   UK   ISSN 0032-4574
POPULAR MOTORING; and practical car maintenance. 1962. m. £12. Frontline Ltd. (Subsidiary of: E M A P - Haymarket Ltd.), Park House, 117 Park Rd., Peterborough PE1 2TR, England. Ed. Dave Stirling. adv.; charts; illus.; mkt. circ. 66,389.
—CCC.

796.77   US   ISSN 0147-3565
TL215.P75
PORSCHE PANORAMA. 1955. m. $36 membership. Porsche Club of America, Inc., Box 30100, Alexandria, VA 22310. TEL 703-922-9300. FAX 404-377-7041. (Subscr. to: 912 Lullwater Rd., Atlanta, GA 30307. TEL 404-378-9823) Ed. Betty Jo Turner. adv.; bk.rev.; charts; illus.; stat. circ. 31,000. (also avail. in microfilm; back issues avail.; reprint service avail. from UMI)
—UMI.

796.77   US   ISSN 0192-8481
PORSCHE UEBER ALLES. 10/yr. $5. Porsche Club of America, Western Michigan Region, 1503 43rd St., Wyoming, MI 49509. Ed. Charlie Richardson.

POWER BUILDERS. see ENGINEERING — Mechanical Engineering

629.222   UK   ISSN 0260-2911
PRACTICAL CLASSICS. 1980. m. £31.20 (foreign £41) (effective 1995-1996). E M A P - National Publications Ltd., Bushfield House, Orton Centre, Peterborough, Cambs. PE2 5UW, England. TEL 01733-237111. FAX 01733-390171. (Subscr. to: Tower Publishing Services Ltd., Tower House, Sovereign Park, Lathkill St., Market Harborough, Leics. LE16 9EF, England. TEL 01858-468811. FAX 01858-432164) Ed. Peter Simpson. adv.; bk.rev.; illus.; circ. 82,006 (paid). (back issues avail.) **Document type:** consumer publication.
—BLDSC (6593.974300).

388.3   UK   ISSN 0960-2828
PRACTICAL MOTORIST. 1934. m. £24. P W Publishing Ltd., Arrowsmith Ct., Sta. Approach, Broadstone, Dorset BH18 8PW, England. TEL 01202-657480. FAX 01202-659950. E-mail: pwpub.demon.co.uk. Ed. Rodney Jaques. adv.: B&W page £385. bk.rev.; illus.; tr.lit. circ. 15,000. Indexed: Pinpointer. **Document type:** consumer publication.
    Former titles (until 1987): Motorist (ISSN 0266-3902); (until 1959): Practical Motorist (ISSN 0032-6437); Practical Motorist and Motor Cyclist.

388.3   IT
PRESA DIRETTA; quadrimestrale di automobilismo. 3/yr. Via Tiburtina 1159, 00156 Rome, Italy. Ed. Antonio Ghini. adv.: B&W page L.5865000, color page L.10557000; 190 x 270. circ. 460,000.

PREVENTION ROUTIERE. see PUBLIC HEALTH AND SAFETY

PREVISIONS GLISSANTES DETAILLEES EN PERSPECTIVES SECTORIELLES (VOL.15): CONSTRUCTION AUTOMOBILE. see BUSINESS AND ECONOMICS — Economic Situation And Conditions

388.3   IT
PRIMA RIDOTTA. bi-m. L.50000 (foreign L.80000). Giovanni Cassini Editore s.r.l., Viale Matteotti 14, 13051 Biella (VC), Italy. TEL 39-15-352766. FAX 39-15-352766. Ed. Giorgio Ursicino. adv.: B&W page L.5900000, color page L.7900000. **Document type:** consumer publication.

629.286   US
PROFESSIONAL CAR WASHING & DETAILING. 1976. m. $42. National Trade Publications, Inc., 13 Century Hill, Latham, NY 12110-2197. TEL 518-783-1281. FAX 518-783-1386. Ed. Marty Heck. adv.: B&W page $2090; trim 8 1/8 x 10 7/8; adv. contact: Lynn Granato. circ. 17,590 (controlled). **Document type:** trade publication.
—CCC.
    Formerly: Professional Car Washing (ISSN 0191-6823)
    Description: Provides technical, sales and marketing information to investors, owners, operators and managers of professional car washing facilities.

629.286 US
PROFESSIONAL TOOL AND EQUIPMENT NEWS. 1991. 6/yr. $22 (foreign $49). Professional Tool and Equipment News, Inc., 23121 Plaza Pointe Dr., No. 130, Laguna Hills, CA 92653-1425. TEL 714-830-7520. FAX 714-830-7523. Ed. Tom Carruthers; Pub. Rudy Wolf. adv. circ. 110,512. **Document type:** trade publication.
   Description: Reports on new tools and equipment available for diagnosing and repairing vehicles properly and profitably.

388.3 910.202 GW ISSN 0935-834X
PROMOBIL. 1982. m. DM.59.40; newsstand price: DM.5.80. Vereinigte Motor-Verlage GmbH und Co. KG, Leuschnerstr. 1, 70714 Stuttgart, Germany. TEL 0711-18201. FAX 0711-1821156. Ed. Adi Kemmer; Pub. Michael Kleinjohann. adv.: B&W page DM.7150, color page DM.12513; trim 185 x 248; adv. contact: Margarete Mueller. circ. 69,190. (back issues avail.) **Document type:** consumer publication.
   Description: Travel, touring and outfitting information for drivers of recreational vehicles.

388.3 910.202 GW
PROMOBIL KATALOG. 1989. a. DM.12. Vereinigte Motor-Verlage GmbH und Co. KG, Leuschnerstr. 1, 70162 Stuttgart, Germany. TEL 0711-1821226. FAX 0711-1821349. Ed. Adi Kemmer; Pub. M. Kleinjohann. adv. contact: M. Kleinjohann. circ. 50,000. **Document type:** consumer publication.

629.222 796.77 BE ISSN 0774-1391
PROMOTOR. (Text in French) 1983. m. 800 BEF (foreign 1100 BEF). Louyetron s.c., 42, rue Vanderstichelen, B-1210 Brussels, Belgium. TEL 32-2-4201060. FAX 32-2-4204570. Ed. Philippe Willain. adv.: B&W page 38000 BEF, color page 45000 BEF; adv. contact: Raymond Euchamps. illus. circ. 16,500. **Document type:** consumer publication.
   Description: Covers local, regional and international motor sports.

629.286 CC ISSN 1000-680X
QICHE GONGCHENG/AUTOMOTIVE ENGINEERING. (Text in Chinese; abstracts in English) 1979. q. Y21 (foreign Y90). Zhongguo Qiche Gongcheng Xuehui - Society of Automotive Engineers of China, 16 Fuxingmenwai St., Beijing 100860, People's Republic of China. TEL 86-1-860262. FAX 86-1-3263605. TELEX 22656 CNAIC CN. (Dist. outside China by: Guoji Shudian - International Book Trading Corp., P.O. Box 399, Beijing, P.R.C.) Ed. Wu Huile. adv. contact: Zhenmin Zhong. circ. 4,000. **Document type:** trade publication.

629.283 CC ISSN 1000-6796
QICHE ZHI YOU/AUTO FAN. (Text in Chinese) 1986. m. Zhongguo Qiche Gongcheng Xuehui - Society of Automotive Engineers of China, 16 Fuxingmenwai St., Beijing 100860, People's Republic of China. TEL 86-1-860262. FAX 86-1-3263605. Ed. Jin Ruting. **Document type:** consumer publication.

388.3 IT
QUADRIFOGLIO. bi-m. L.6000 per no. Ufficio Stampa Alfa Romeo, Viale Alfa Romeo, 20020 Arese (MI), Italy. TEL 39-2-93392474. FAX 39-2-93501222. Ed. Vittorio Meloni. adv.: B&W or color page L.10000000. circ. 140,000. **Document type:** consumer publication.

QUATRO RODAS. see TRAVEL AND TOURISM

388.3 IT ISSN 0033-5916
QUATTRORUOTE. 1956. m. L.70000($97) Editoriale Domus, Via Achille Grandi 5-7, 20089 Rozzano (MI), Italy. TEL 02-824721. FAX 02-26863093. Ed. Raffaele Mastrostefano. adv.: B&W page L.25500000, color page L.45900000. bk.rev.; illus.; index. circ. 700,000.
   —SWETS.

796.77 UK
QUESTE. 1986. q. (Rolls-Royce Motor Cars Ltd.) Premier Magazines Ltd., Haymarket House, 1 Oxendon St., London SW1Y 4EE, England. TEL 0171-925-2544. FAX 0171-839-4491. (Subscr. to: Rolls-Royce Motor Cars, Crewe, Cheshire CW1 3PL, England. TEL 01270-255155) Ed. David Taylor. adv. contact: Timothy Clark. circ. 25,000. (back issues avail.) **Document type:** consumer publication.
   Description: Contains information and news for purchasers of new Rolls-Royces worldwide.

R A C EUROPEAN HOTEL GUIDE. (Royal Automobile Club) see TRAVEL AND TOURISM

R A C HOTEL GUIDE GREAT BRITAIN & IRELAND. (Royal Automobile Club) see TRAVEL AND TOURISM

R A C MOTOR SPORTS YEAR BOOK. see SPORTS AND GAMES

388.3 NE ISSN 0166-1922
R A I ACTUEEL. 1945. w. fl.95($50) Nederlandse Vereniging "de Rijwiel- en Automobiel Industrie", Europaplein 2, 1078 GZ Amsterdam, Netherlands. TEL 020-5491212. FAX 020-463857. Ed. M.F. Timmer. bk.rev.; stat.; tr.mk. circ. 2,500. **Indexed:** Key to Econ.Sci.
   Formerly: R A I Orgaan (ISSN 0030-7785)

R V WEST. see TRAVEL AND TOURISM

629.228 UK ISSN 0961-1096
RACECAR ENGINEERING. 1990. bi-m. £21 (Europe £27; N. & S. America £35($57)). Q Editions Ltd., 33 Banstead Rd., Caterham, Surrey CR3 5QG, England. TEL 01883-341551. FAX 01883-344397. (Dist. by: COMAG Magazine Marketing, Mercury Centre, Central Way, Feltham, Middlesex TW14 0RX, England. TEL 0181-844-1000. FAX 0181-751-2666; Dist. in U.S. by: Eric Waiter Associates, 369 Springfield Ave., Berkeley Heights, NJ 07922. TEL 908-665-7811. FAX 908-665-1814) Ed. Quentin Spurring. circ. 16,000. **Document type:** trade publication.
   —BLDSC (7225.963900).
   Description: Focuses on technology of motorsports.

RACING WHEELS. see SPORTS AND GAMES

629.286 US ISSN 0739-2060
RADIATOR REPORTER. 1973. m. $140 (effective 1995-1996). Skyline Publishing Co., Box 599, Brookfield, IL 60513-0599. TEL 708-485-6015. FAX 708-485-4237. Ed. Ralph McDarmont. (looseleaf format) **Document type:** trade publication.

RADIO CONTROL MODEL CARS. see HOBBIES

RALLY SPORT. see SPORTS AND GAMES

RALLYCOURSE; the world's leading rally annual. see SPORTS AND GAMES

388.3 796.72 GW ISSN 0033-9148
RALLYE RACING. 1966. m. Top Special Verlag GmbH, Nebendahlstr. 16, 22041 Hamburg, Germany. TEL 040-3470-0. FAX 040-34725588. Ed. Guenther Frauenkron; Pub. Hans-Gerhard Dobler. adv.: B&W page DM.7920, color page DM.14469; trim 180 x 250; adv. contact: Beate Asmus-Fuegert. bk.rev.; charts; illus.; index. circ. 89,056. **Document type:** consumer publication.
   Incorporates (in 1987): Sportfahrer (ISSN 0176-8808); **Formerly:** Automobil Sport-Zeitschrift.

RANCHERO COURIER. see HOBBIES

790.13 US ISSN 0733-4745
TL298
RECREATIONAL VEHICLE BLUE BOOK. 3/yr. $110. Maclean Hunter Market Reports, Inc., 29 N. Wacker Dr., Chicago, IL 60606-3297. TEL 312-726-2802. FAX 312-726-2574. (back issues avail.)

388.3 US ISSN 0736-7953
HD9710.U5
RED BOOK USED CAR GUIDE. 8/yr. $49.50. Maclean Hunter Market Reports, Inc., 29 N. Wacker Dr., Chicago, IL 60606-3297. TEL 312-726-2802. FAX 312-726-2574. (back issues avail.)
   —CCC.

629.288 AT
REFINISHER. 1958. 4/yr. free. Dulux Australia, Box 60, Clayton, Vic. 3168, Australia. TEL 61-2-4763199. FAX 61-2-4765739. Ed. Ken Virtue. adv. contact: Ray Berghouse. circ. 17,000 (controlled). **Document type:** trade publication.

388.3 NE ISSN 0926-8537
REFLECTOR (DOETINCHEM). 1973. m. (Centraal Bureau Rijvaardigheidsbewijzen) Misset (Subsidiary of: Reed Elsevier plc), Postbus 4, 7000 BA Doetinchem, Netherlands. TEL 31-8340-49911. FAX 31-8340-63638. (Co-sponsor: Bond van Garagehouders (BOVAG)) adv.: B&W page fl.1694, color page fl.3371; trim 210 x 297; adv. contact: Cor van Nek. **Document type:** trade publication.
   Former titles (until 1991): C B R Reflector (ISSN 0922-0607); (until 1987): C B R Informatie (ISSN 0166-736X)
   Description: News and information for driving schools, instructors and examiners.

388 GW
REISEMOBIL INTERNATIONAL. m. DM.51 (foreign DM.60). C D S Verlag, Postwiesenstr. 5A, 70327 Stuttgart, Germany. TEL 0711-337355. FAX 0711-339944. Ed. Franz-Peter Strohbuecker. adv. contact: Hansjorg Schwab. circ. 35,807. **Document type:** consumer publication.

388.3 UK
RENAULT CONTACT. 1975. m. Renault U.K. Ltd., Western Ave., London W3 0RZ, England. Ed. Marguerite Nudd. circ. 9,500. **Document type:** trade publication.
   Description: Information magazine for Renault dealers in the U.K.

629.286 658 US
REPORTS ON FLEET MANAGEMENT. 1981. m. $247 (effective 1995-1996). Skyline Publishing Co., Box 599, Brookfield, IL 60513-0599. TEL 708-485-6015. FAX 708-485-4237. Ed. Ralph McDarmont. (looseleaf format; back issues avail.) **Document type:** trade publication.
   —CCC.
   Former titles: Runzheimer Reports on Fleet Management; Runzheimer Reports on Transportation (ISSN 0730-8655)

629.286 AT ISSN 0311-4163
RESTORED CARS. 1973. bi-m. Aus.$33. Eddie Ford Publications Pty. Ltd., P.O. Box Q277, Sydney, N.S.W. 2000, Australia. TEL 61-54-762212. FAX 61-54-762592. Ed. Eddie Ford. (back issues avail.)
   Description: Devoted to the restored or original car. Includes veteran, vintage, classic and post-war period cars to cars of the 50's, 60's, and 70's, and muscle cars.

629.28 796.77 PO ISSN 0870-273X
REVISTA A C P. 1929. m. Esc.300. Automovel Club de Portugal, R. Rosa Araujo, 24, 1200 Lisbon, Portugal. TEL 3563931. FAX 574732. adv. contact: Leopoldo Ludovice. illus. circ. 188,000.

388.3 PO
REVISTA TECNICA AUTOMOVEL. 11/yr. Rua Anibel Pereira Fernandes 10A, Barreiro, Portugal. TEL 205-87-22. Ed. Gregorio Loucao. circ. 10,000.
   Description: Contains mechanical and technical news.

REVUE AUTOMOBILE; journal suisse de l'automobile. see TRANSPORTATION

REVUE AUTOMOBILE MEDICALE. see MEDICAL SCIENCES

388.3 629.2 FR ISSN 0017-307X
REVUE TECHNIQUE AUTOMOBILE. 1946. m. 810 F. (foreign 985 F.). Editions Techniques pour l'Automobile et l'Industrie (ETAI), 22 rue de la Saussiere, 92100 Boulogne Billancourt, France. TEL 46-04-81-13. FAX 48-25-56-92. TELEX ETAIRTA 204 850 F. Ed. Benoit Perot. circ. 26,708. **Document type:** trade publication.
   —SWETS. CCC.
   Description: Technical review for professionals in the car repair field.

338.476 FR ISSN 0150-7206
REVUE TECHNIQUE CARROSSERIE. 1963. bi-m. 510 F. (foreign 585 F.). Editions Techniques pour l'Automobile et l'Industrie (ETAI), 20-22 rue de la Saussiere, 92100 Boulogne Billancourt, France. TEL 46-04-81-13. FAX 48-25-56-92. TELEX ETAIRTA 204 850 F. Ed. Jean-Pierre Nicolas. charts; illus. circ. 6,035. **Document type:** trade publication.
   —CCC.
   Description: Aimed at car body-builders, steel-workers and painters, details how to repair the car body and describes the tools to be used.

TRANSPORTATION — AUTOMOBILES

629.2   FR   ISSN 0037-2579
REVUE TECHNIQUE DIESEL. 1963. bi-m. 545 F. (foreign 640 F.). Editions Techniques pour l'Automobile et l'Industrie (ETAI), 22 rue de la Saussiere, 92100 Boulogne Billancourt, France. TEL 46-04-81-13. FAX 48-25-56-92. TELEX ETAIRTA 204 850 F. Ed. Bernard Adam. circ. 6,659. **Document type:** trade publication.
—CCC.
  Formerly: Service Diesel.
  Description: Deals with trucks, public works material and industrial engines. Describes a particular diesel oil truck and explains how to repair it.

388.3   AT   ISSN 0035-7170
ROAD AHEAD. 1914. bi-m. free to members. (Royal Automobile Club of Queensland, Brisbane) Road Ahead Publishing Co. Pty Ltd., G.P.O. Box 1403, Brisbane, Qld. 4001, Australia. FAX 257-1863. Ed. J.W. Mathers. adv.; B&W page Aus.$4950, color page Aus.$6450; trim 274 x 206; adv. contact: N.A. Willemsen. bk.rev.; charts; illus.; circ. 616,033 (controlled). **Document type:** consumer publication.

388.3   US   ISSN 0035-7189
TL1
ROAD & TRACK. 1947. m. $19.94. Hachette - Filipacchi Magazines, Inc., Road & Track, 1499 Monrovia Ave., Newport Beach, CA 92663. TEL 714-720-5300. FAX 714-631-2757. Ed. Tom Bryant. adv.; bk.rev.; rec.rev.; charts; illus.; index. circ. 700,000. (also avail. in microform from UMI; reprint service avail. from UMI) **Indexed:** Acad.Ind., Access, Consum.Ind., Mag.Ind., PMR, R.G., Sports Per.Ind., TOM. **Document type:** consumer publication.
●Also available online. Vendor(s): University Microfilms International.
—Faxon; SWETS; UMI; UnCover.

796.77   US   ISSN 1060-8656
ROAD & TRACK SPORTS & G T CARS. 1965. a. $4.95. Hachette Magazines, Inc. (Newport Beach), Road & Track Specials, 1499 Monrovia Ave., Newport Beach, CA 92663. TEL 714-720-5300. Ed. Ron Sessions. adv. circ. 250,000. (also avail. in microform from UMI; back issues avail.) **Indexed:** R.G. **Document type:** consumer publication.

629.286   US
ROAD SERVICE NEWS.* 1991. m. $24. Road Service News Corp., 75 N. Maple Ave., Ridgewood, NJ 07450-3247. TEL 908-738-5905. FAX 908-738-6116. adv.; B&W page $2250, color page $3250; trim 11 x 15; adv. contact: Mickey Kaplan. circ. 40,000.
  Description: Includes news, marketing, business trends, new products, service tips and education.

614.8   SA   ISSN 0035-7391
ROBOT. (Text in Afrikaans and English) 1962. 4/yr. free. National Road Safety Council - Nasionale Verkeersveiligheidsraad, N R S C Bldg., Beatrix St., Private Bag X147, Pretoria 0001, South Africa. TEL 27-12-328-5929. FAX 27-12-3232215. TELEX 320828. Ed. Ivor van Rensburg. adv.; bk.rev.; illus.; stat.; film rev. circ. 50,000. **Indexed:** Robomat. (until 1992). **Document type:** government publication, trade publication.
  Description: General interest road and traffic safety information.

ROCKY MOUNTAIN MOTORIST. see *TRAVEL AND TOURISM*

629.28   US   ISSN 1053-2064
TL236
ROD & CUSTOM. 1977. m. $21.95. Petersen Publishing Co., 6420 Wilshire Blvd., Los Angeles, CA 90048. TEL 213-782-2000. Ed. Jeff Tan. adv. circ. 100,000. **Document type:** consumer publication.
  Formerly (until 1989): Petersen's Rod and Custom (ISSN 1045-120X); Rod and Custom (ISSN 0161-150X)
  Description: Focuses on aspects of contemporary street rodding, including trends, racing and techniques.

796.77   US   ISSN 0745-5739
RODDER'S DIGEST. 1981. bi-m. $15.95. Target Publications Inc., Box 651118, Vero Beach, FL 32965. TEL 919-777-3619. FAX 919-724-0539. Ed. Steve Hendrickson; Pub. Gerry Burger. adv. contact: Garry McWhirter. **Document type:** consumer publication.

388.3   UK   ISSN 0035-7952
ROLLS ROYCE OWNER.* 1963. m. 42s.($6.25) Owner Publication, 6 The Lawn, St. Leonards on Sea, Sussex, England. Ed. Jeremy Bacon. adv.; bk.rev.; charts; illus.; index. circ. 500. **Document type:** consumer publication.

629.222   US   ISSN 0273-9453
ROUGH RIDER. 1965. 8/yr. membership. Morgan Car Club, Washington D.C., Inc., 616 Gist Ave., Silver Spring, MD 20910. TEL 301-858-0121. Ed. Ed Zielinski. **Document type:** newsletter.
  Description: News, features, technical information and other items of interest to Morgan car owners.

388.3   FR   ISSN 0035-8568
ROUTE. no.33, 1970. q. 40 F. Comite National du Secours Routiers Francais, 50 quai Bleriot, 75016 Paris, France. Ed. Pierre Merard. adv.; charts; illus.; stat. circ. 7,000.

388.3   AT   ISSN 0035-9300
ROYALAUTO. 1925. m. (except Jan.). membership. (Royal Automobile Club of Victoria) Automobile Publishing Co., 550 Princes Highway, Noble Park, Vic. 3174, Australia. FAX 613-790-2628. Ed. George Wilson. adv.; bk.rev. circ. 1,030,000. **Indexed:** Aus.Rd.Ind. **Document type:** newsletter.

629.221   CN   ISSN 0048-8771
THE RUNNING BOARD. 1961. 11/yr. Edmonton Antique Car Club, P.O. Box 102, Edmonton AB T5J 2G9, Canada. Ed. Dave Jeffares. adv. contact: Murray Walkemeyer. circ. 95. **Document type:** newsletter.
  Formerly: Edmonton Antique Car Club. Bulletin.
  Description: Review of club events, tours and events coming up.

388 330.9   US   ISSN 0730-8647
RUNZHEIMER ON CARS & LIVING COSTS. 1963. q. Runzheimer International, Runzheimer Park, Rochester, WI 53167. TEL 800-558-1702. Ed. Peter D. Packer. circ. 25,000. (tabloid format; back issues avail.) **Document type:** newsletter.

RUOTECLASSICHE. see *ANTIQUES*

629.283 628.5   US   ISSN 1043-1896
TL273
S A E GROUND VEHICLE LIGHTING MANUAL. a. Society of Automotive Engineers, 400 Commonwealth Dr., Warrendale, PA 15096-0001. TEL 412-776-4841. FAX 412-776-3036. **Document type:** trade publication.

629.28   US   ISSN 0362-8205
TL151
S A E HANDBOOK. 1905. a. $350 3-vol. set. Society of Automotive Engineers, 400 Commonwealth Dr., Warrendale, PA 15096-0001. TEL 412-776-4841. FAX 412-776-3036. **Document type:** trade publication.
●Also available online. Vendor(s): Orbit Search Service.
—CCC.

388   US   ISSN 0148-7191
CODEN: STPSDN
S A E TECHNICAL PAPERS. irreg. $10 to non-members; members $5. Society of Automotive Engineers, 400 Commonwealth Dr., Warrendale, PA 15096-0001. TEL 412-776-4841. FAX 412-776-3036. index, cum.index: 1906-1964, 1965-1993. (back issues avail.) **Indexed:** Pollut.Abstr., Soils & Fert. **Document type:** monographic series.
●Also available online. Vendor(s): European Space Agency, FIZ Technik, Orbit Search Service.
—CASDDS. CCC.

629.28   US   ISSN 0096-736X
TL1
S A E TRANSACTIONS. a. $975. Society of Automotive Engineers, 400 Commonwealth Dr., Warrendale, PA 15096. TEL 412-776-4970. FAX 412-776-0790. index. (also avail. in microform from PMC) **Indexed:** Geotech.Abstr., Noise Pollut.Publ.Abstr. **Document type:** academic/scholarly publication.
—BLDSC (8062.950000). CCC.

388.3   AT   ISSN 1030-8253
S A MOTOR. 1913. bi-m. membership. Royal Automobile Association of South Australia Inc., 41 Hindmarsh Square, Adelaide, S.A. 5000, Australia. TEL 08-2024500. FAX 08-2024520. Ed. Martin Chipperfield. circ. 335,517. **Indexed:** Aus.Rd.Ind., Pinpointer.
  Formerly (until 1986): South Australian Motor (ISSN 1030-8245)

629.286   US   ISSN 0279-5051
S E M A NEWS. 1968. m. membership. Specialty Equipment Market Association, PO Box 4910, Diamond Bar, CA 91765-0910. TEL 909-860-2961. FAX 909-860-1709. Ed. William Groak. adv. circ. 50,000. (tabloid format) **Document type:** trade publication.
  Incorporated (1988-1992): Performance and Specialty Aftermarket News (ISSN 1060-4839); Which was formerly: Performance Aftermarket Magazine (ISSN 1043-7991)
  Description: Covers specialty automotive product news.

629.222   UK
S M M T BUYERS GUIDE. a. £25 to non-members; members £15. Society of Motor Manufacturers and Traders Ltd., Forbes House, Halkin St., London SW1X 7DS, England. TEL 071-235-7000. FAX 071-235-7112. circ. 10,000.
  Former titles: Buyers' Guide to the Automotive Industry of Great Britain for International Buyers; Buyers' Guide to the Motor Industry of Great Britain.

SACRED OCTAGON. see *ANTIQUES*

614.8 629.28   UK   ISSN 0036-2387
SAFE DRIVER. 1929. 3/yr. £12 membership. Order of the Road, P.O. Box 227, Forest Row, E. Sussex RH18 5YS, England. TEL 01342-826536. FAX 01342-824847. Ed. John Taylor. adv.; bk.rev.; circ. 1,800 (controlled). **Document type:** newsletter.
  Description: News about road safety, members' services, motoring and travel.

796.77   UK
SAFETY FAST. m. £25. M G Car Club Ltd., P.O. Box 251, Abingdon, Oxfordshire OX14 1FF, England. TEL 01235-555552. FAX 01235-533755. Ed. A.P. Willmer. adv. contact: L. Jeffrey. bk.rev.; charts; illus.; stat. circ. 12,000. (back issues avail.) **Document type:** bulletin.
  Incorporates: M G Magazine & Sports Car.
  Description: Contains news and activities of MG car users and enthusiasts.

388
ST. PAUL, MINNESOTA. TWIN CITIES AREA METROPOLITAN TRANSIT COMMISSION. ANNUAL REPORT. 1969. a. free. Twin Cities Area Metropolitan Transit Commission, 560 N. 6th St., Minneapolis, MN 55411-4398. TEL 612-349-7696. FAX 612-349-7612. Ed. Steve Beseke. circ. 7,000.
  Formerly: St. Paul, Minnesota. Metropolitan Transit Commission. Annual Report (ISSN 0082-710X)
  Description: Examines the activities of the organizations' previous year.

388   CN   ISSN 0381-8179
SANFORD EVANS GOLD BOOK OF USED CAR PRICES. 1952. m. Can.$74. Sanford Evans Communications Ltd., 1700 Church Ave., Box 6900, Winnipeg, MB R3C 3B1, Canada. TEL 204-694-2022. FAX 204-694-3040. Ed. Gary Henry; Pub. Gary Henry.
  Description: Lists previous eight models of cars and light duty trucks. Valuations for three major Canadian markets, factory suggested price, and current wholesale and retail values.

629.224   JA   ISSN 0036-4398
SANGYO SHARYO/INDUSTRIAL VEHICLES. (Text in Japanese) 1964. m. 3600 Yen($12) Japan Industrial Vehicles Association - Nihon Sangyo Sharyo Kyokai, Tobu Bldg., 5-26, 1-chome, Moto-Akasaka, Minato-ku, Tokyo 107, Japan. TEL 03-403-5556. FAX 03-403-5057. Ed. Masaru Terada. circ. 1,000. **Indexed:** JTA.

388.3 380.5   YU   ISSN 0352-7026
SAVREMENI VOZAC. (Text in Serbo-Croatian) 1975. bi-m. 600 din. Savez Vozaca Srbije, Pop Lukina 1, 11000 Belgrade, Yugoslavia. TEL 636-515. Ed. Zdravko Ilic. circ. 20,000. (back issues avail.)

TRANSPORTATION — AUTOMOBILES

629.222   TS
AL-SAYYARAH AL-ARABIYYAH. (Text in Arabic) 1989. m. Muhammad Rashid Amiri, Prop., P.O. Box 8790, Dubai, United Arab Emirates. TEL 211123. FAX 213080. TELEX 48906. Ed. Abu Bakr Amiri. circ. 2,000.
Description: Provides news and information on cars for enthusiasts in the Gulf region, including road tests and safety topics.

SCALE MODELS INTERNATIONAL. see *HOBBIES*

388   SZ
SCHWEIZER AUTO GEWERBE. (Text in French, German, Italian) 21/yr. Mittelstr. 32, CH-3001 Bern, Switzerland. TEL 031-238494. FAX 031-455463. TELEX 912641-BURI-CH. Ed. Rudolf Baldinger. circ. 7,300.

388   UK   ISSN 0958-7969
SCOTTISH AUTO TRADER. 1986. w. £87. Scottish Auto Trader, 29 Fern St., Motherwell ML1 2AJ, Scotland. TEL 0698-258811. FAX 0698-27521. adv. circ. 27,163. **Document type:** consumer publication.

692.2   US
SECRETARY OF ENERGY ANNUAL REPORT TO CONGRESS. a. U.S. Department of Energy, Secretary of Energy, 1000 Independence Ave., S.W., Washington, DC 20585. **Document type:** government publication.

629.286   US   ISSN 1043-7053
SERVICE QUARTERLY. 1929. q. $40. Service Station Dealers Association of Michigan, 200 N. Capitol, Ste. 420, Lansing, MI 48933. TEL 517-484-4096. Ed. Melanie Disa. adv. circ. 3,500. (back issues avail.) **Document type:** trade publication.
Formerly: Service Station Dealers News.

388.33   CN   ISSN 0037-2668
SERVICE STATION & GARAGE MANAGEMENT. 1934. m. Can.$35.31($47) (foreign $47). Southam Magazine Group, 1450 Don Mills Rd., Don Mills, ON M3B 2X7, Canada. TEL 416-445-6641. FAX 416-442-2261. Ed. Gary Kenez. adv. circ. 31,100. **Indexed:** Can.B.P.I.
Incorporates (in 1991): Canadian Automotive Training (ISSN 1180-1093); **Formerly:** Service Station Management and Merchandising (ISSN 0037-2676); Canadian Automotive Training was formerly (until 1989): C A T: Canadian Automotive Trade (ISSN 0319-1990); (until 1969): Canadian Automotive Trade (ISSN 0008-2945).
Description: For the mechanical repair trade.

338.476 658.8   UK
SERVICE STATIONS: THE INTERNATIONAL MARKET. (Subseries of: Market Direction reports) a. £1595($3190) (effective 1996). Euromonitor, 60-61 Britton St., London EC1M 5NA, England. TEL 0171-251-8024. FAX 0171-608-3149. (Addr. in N. America: Euromonitor International, 122 S. Michigan Ave., Ste. 1200, Chicago, IL 60603. TEL 312-922-1115. FAX 312-5922-115) (looseleaf format) **Document type:** trade publication.
●Also available online. Vendor(s): Data-Star, Knight-Ridder, Inc.
Description: Analyzes the market for automobile repair and body shops for France, Germany, Italy, Spain, the U.K., the U.S., and Japan.

388.3   SP
SERVICIO. 6/yr. Montesa 31, 28006 Madrid, Spain. TEL 1-401-56-66. FAX 1-402-97-07. Ed. J.M. Garcia Guerrero.

614.86   IT
SETTESTRADE; mensile automobile Club Roma. m. (10/yr.). Settestrade S.r.l., Via C. Colombo 261, Palazzo ACI, Rome, Italy. TEL 06-5106. Ed. Attilio Baglioni.

380   UK   ISSN 0963-2506
SEWELLS CAR DIGEST. 1971. w. £155. Sewells International Ltd., Dart Business Centre, Dartington, Totnes, Devon TQ9 6JE, England. TEL 01803-867070. FAX 01803-866507. Ed. Stephen Hamilton. bk.rev.; abstr.; stat. circ. 2,500. **Document type:** trade publication.
Description: Digest of key developments in the international motor industry.

SHOP MANAGEMENT HANDBOOK. see *BUSINESS AND ECONOMICS — Management*

629.286   IT
SICILIA MOTORI. 1982. m. (11/yr.). L.35000. RODA Informazione & Immagine S.r.l., Via L. Ariosto 16-C, 90144 Palermo, Italy. TEL 91-6254302. FAX 91-6259751. TELEX P.P. PA 911153. Ed. Dario Pennica. adv.: B&W page L.1100000, color page L.198000; trim 184 x 270. circ. 5,000.

388.3   XR   ISSN 0322-7154
SILNICNI OBZOR; mesicnik pro otazky vystavby a udrzby silnic, dalnic, nistnich kominikaci, letsi, mostu, tunelu a silnicniho a mestskeho dopravniho inzynyrstvi. (Text in Czech or Slovak; summaries in English, French, German, Russian) 1922. m. 48 Kc.($57.90) (Federalni Ministerstvo Vnitra) Nakladatelstvi Silnicni Spolecnosti, Novotneho Lavaka 5, 110 00 Prague 1, Czech Republic. (Dist. by: Artia, Ve Smeckach 30, 111 27 Prague 1, Czech Republic) Ed. A.V. Novotny. adv. **Indexed:** Geotech.Abstr.
Formerly: Silnicni Doprava (ISSN 0037-5292)

SKOZI T A M. (Towarne Avtomobilov in Motorjev) see *ENGINEERING — Mechanical Engineering*

388.3   US
SKYLINER. 1971. m. $30. International Ford Retractable Club Inc., Box 389, Marlborough, MA 01752-0389. TEL 508-460-5101. adv.; charts; illus.; tr.lit. circ. 1,350. **Document type:** newsletter.
Description: Social and educational information on 1957-59 Ford Retractable cars.

629.222   US
SLANT 6 NEWS. 1980. q. $25 (effective 1995). Slant 6 Club of America, Box 4414, Salem, OR 97302. TEL 503-581-2230. Ed. Jackson A. Poehler. adv. contact: Jackson A. Poehler. charts; stat. circ. 2,000. (back issues avail.) **Document type:** newsletter.
Description: Offers technical advice on the preservation, restoration, and upgrading of Chrysler Corporation vehicles powered by the Slant 6 engine.

SOCIEDAD ESPANOLA DE AUTOMOVILES DE TURISMO. MEMORIA Y BALANCE. see *TRAVEL AND TOURISM*

796.72   SA
SOUTH AFRICAN 4 X 4. (Text in English) 1992. bi-m. Caravan Publications (Pty) Ltd., P.O. Box 15939, Vlaeberg 8018, South Africa. Ed. Godfrey Castle. adv.: B&W page $657, color page $1114; trim 210 x 276; adv. contact: Allan Caddick. illus.; circ. 15,000 (paid). **Document type:** consumer publication.
Description: Covers the South African 4 wheel drive vehicle market. Includes road tests, information on off-road driving, maintenance and tips.

629   UK
THE SOUTHERN INSTRUCTOR. q. (Motor Schools Association of Great Britain) Integral Publishing Co. Ltd., Hulton House, Chester Rd., Stockport SK7 5NU, England. TEL 061-456-1000. FAX 061-456-3709. Ed. John Lepine. circ. 2,500. **Document type:** trade publication.
Description: Distributed to driving instructors.

SOUTHERN MOTORACING. see *SPORTS AND GAMES*

796.77   UK
SOVEREIGN. (Text in English, German, Spanish) 1991. 3/yr. Sovereign Magazine Ltd., 45 Blondvil St., Coventry CV3 5QX, England. TEL 01203-505339. FAX 01203-503135. Ed. John Lowe. adv. contact: Debbie Boulton. circ. 187,000. (back issues avail.) **Document type:** consumer publication.

388.3   US   ISSN 0049-1845
SPECIAL INTEREST AUTOS. 1970. bi-m. $19.95. Watering, Inc., Special Interest Publications, Box 904, Bennington, VT 05201. TEL 802-442-3101. FAX 802-447-1561. (Subscr. to: Box 196, Bennington, VT 05201) Ed. David Brownell; Pub. Terry Ehrich. adv. contact: Lesley McFadden. charts; cum.index: 1970-1994; circ. 33,600 (paid). (back issues avail.) **Document type:** consumer publication.
Description: Covers cars built from 1925-1980.

796.77   US   ISSN 0894-7414
SPECIALTY AUTOMOTIVE. 1983. q. $18. Meyers Publishing Corp., 6211 Van Nuys Blvd., Van Nuys, CA 91401. TEL 818-785-3900. FAX 818-785-4397. Ed. Steve Relyea. adv. contact: Lana Meyers. tr.lit. circ. 25,000. (reprint service avail.) **Document type:** trade publication.

388   US
SPECIALTY CAR MARKETPLACE. m. newsstand price: $1.95. Deals on Wheels Publications, Box 205, Sioux Falls, SD 57101. TEL 605-338-7666. FAX 605-338-5337. **Document type:** consumer publication.

SPEEDWAY. see *HOBBIES*

388   GW
SPORT AND TUNING MARKT. 1991. m. DM.54; newsstand price: DM.4.50. A M F Verlag GmbH, Sattlerstr. 7, 23556 Luebeck, Germany. TEL 0451-898814. FAX 0451-8966211. Ed. Juergen Koslowski. adv. circ. 80,000. **Document type:** consumer publication.

SPORT-AUTO; le magazine du sport automobile et de l'automobile sportive. see *SPORTS AND GAMES*

796   GW
SPORT AUTO. 1971. m. DM.66; newsstand price: DM.6. Vereinigte Motor-Verlage GmbH und Co. KG, Leuschnerstr. 1, 70174 Stuttgart, Germany. TEL 0711-1821226. FAX 0711-1821349. (Subscr. to: Postfach 106036, 70049 Stuttgart, Germany) Ed. Juergen Schwartz; Pub. Richard Stolz. adv.: B&W page DM.8950, color page DM.16558; trim 185 x 248; adv. contact: A. Grzegorzewski. bk.rev.; index. circ. 71,342. (back issues avail.) **Document type:** consumer publication.
Description: Popular magazine for sportscar enthusiasts. Covers the latest trends and styles, technology, tests, racing, and events. Includes letters from readers.

SPORT AUTO. see *SPORTS AND GAMES*

796.77   LE
SPORT AUTO MAGAZINE. (Text in Arabic; summaries in Arabic and English) 1973. m. $40. Barson Publications, Ltd., P.O. Box 113-5358, Beirut, Lebanon. TEL 01-868608. TELEX 23388 BARSON LE. Ed. Ibrahim M. Fakhri. adv.; charts; illus.; stat. circ. 105,031. (back issues avail.) **Document type:** consumer publication.
Description: Includes new model reviews, road testing and evaluation, international and regional motor sports coverage.

388.3   US   ISSN 1062-9629
SPORT COMPACT CAR. bi-m. $3.25 per no. McMullen & Yee Publishing, 774 S. Placentia Ave., Placentia, CA 92670-6846. TEL 714-572-2255. FAX 714-572-1864.

388.3   US   ISSN 1042-9662
TL236
SPORTS CAR INTERNATIONAL. 1985. m. $17.95. S C I Publishing, Inc., 42 Digital Dr., No. 5, Novato, CA 94949. TEL 415-382-0580. Ed. Jay Lamm; Pub. Tom Toldrian. adv. contact: Stan Michelman. bk.rev.; charts; illus.; circ. 90,000 (paid). (back issues avail.) **Document type:** consumer publication.
Formerly (until Jul. 1989): Sports Car Illustrated.
Description: For performance car enthusiasts and those traditionalists who define cars as entertainment.

796.77   US
SPORTSCARS OF THE WORLD. a. newsstand price: $3.95. Petersen Publishing Co., 6420 Wilshire Blvd., Los Angeles, CA 90048. TEL 213-782-2000. **Document type:** consumer publication.

629.28   US   ISSN 0585-086X
TL6   CODEN: SCCCBR
STAPP CAR CRASH CONFERENCE. PROCEEDINGS. 10th, 1967. a. Society of Automotive Engineers, 400 Commonwealth Dr., Warrendale, PA 15096-0001. TEL 412-776-4841. FAX 412-776-3036. **Indexed:** Biol.Abstr. **Document type:** proceedings.
●Also available online. Vendor(s): European Space Agency, FIZ Technik, Orbit Search Service.
—CCC.
Former titles: Stapp Car Crash and Field Demonstration Conference (ISSN 0883-2161); Stapp Car Crash Conference. Proceedings (ISSN 0883-2153)

TRANSPORTATION — AUTOMOBILES

629.222 US ISSN 0744-155X
THE STAR (LAKEWOOD). Variant title: Mercedes-Benz Star. 1956. bi-m. $35 (overseas $40). (Mercedes-Benz Club of America) Toad Hall Motorbooks, Inc., 1235 Pierce St., Lakewood, CO 80214-1936. TEL 303-235-0116. FAX 303-237-6080. (Subscr. to: M B C A, 1907 Lelaray St., Colorado Springs, CO 80909. TEL 800-637-2360. FAX 719-633-9283; Membership addr.: Mercedes-Benz Club of America, 1907 Lelaray St., Colorado Springs, CO 80909. TEL 719-633-6427) Ed. Frank Barrett; Pub. Frank Barrett. adv. contact: Norm Martin. bk.rev.; circ. 26,000 (paid). (back issues avail.) **Document type:** consumer publication.
   Description: Contains features and articles on new and classic Mercedes-Benz cars from 1886 to present.

629.286 IT
STARTER. 1984. m. L.54000 (foreign L.91000). Casa Editrice Universo S.p.A., Via Margherita De Vizzi, 35, 20092 Cinisello Balsamo (MI), Italy. TEL 02-618331. Ed. Raffaele D'Argenzio. adv.: color page L.11900000. circ. 34,200.

STARTLINE. see *SPORTS AND GAMES*

388 665.5 FR ISSN 1249-7037
STATIONS - SERVICES ACTUALITES. bi-m. 200 F. Compagnie Francaise de Presse, 8 cours Louis Lumiere, 94036 Vincennes Cedex, France. TEL 41-74-35-50. FAX 41-74-36-32. Ed. Benoit Barbedette; Pub. Gilles Barissat. adv. contact: Jean Yves Kerbrat. circ. 30,000.
   Formerly: Reseaux Services Actualite (ISSN 1151-1486)
   Description: Provides topical news for those in the automobile and petroleum fields.

STATISTIK OVER REGISTRERING AF NYE AUTOMOBILER I DANMARK. see *TRANSPORTATION — Abstracting, Bibliographies, Statistics*

338.475 US ISSN 0561-9726
TL200
STEAM AUTOMOBILE. 1958. q. $20. Steam Automobile Club of America, Inc., Box 285, Niles, MI 49120. TEL 616-683-4269. (Subscr. to: 1227 W. Voorhees, Danville, IL 61832) Ed. Karl A. Petersen. adv.; bk.rev.; illus.; pat. circ. 915. (back issues avail.)

STEREO DRIVE; onafhankelijk tijdschrift voor caraudio, mobiele communication en autobeveiling. see *SOUND RECORDING AND REPRODUCTION*

STOCK CAR. see *SPORTS AND GAMES*

796.77
STOCK CAR & MOTORSPORTS.* m. $2.95 per no. 4639 Apricot Rd., Simi Valley, CA 93063.

STOCK CAR RACING. see *SPORTS AND GAMES*

629.222 388 US
STOCK CAR SPECTACULAR. q. newsstand price: $3.95. Starlog Group, Inc., 475 Park Ave. S., 8th Fl., New York, NY 10016. TEL 212-689-2830. FAX 212-899-7933. **Document type:** consumer publication.

388.3 XO ISSN 0139-6501
TL4
STOP; motoristicky magazin. 1971. fortn. $21. Exnarova 17, 820 13 Bratislava 12, Slovakia. (Subscr. to: Slovart, Gottwaldovo nam. 48, 805 32 Bratislava, Slovakia) Ed. Jan Korecky. adv.; illus. circ. 115,000.
   Description: Technical and sports motoring information.

STRASSENATLAS DEUTSCHLAND UND EUROPA. see *TRAVEL AND TOURISM*

629.222 UK ISSN 0143-5949
TL236.3
STREET MACHINE. 1979. m. £30.40 (foreign £35.10) (effective 1995-1996). E M A P - Consumer, Priory Ct., 30-32 Farringdon Ln., London EC1R 3AU, England, England. TEL 0171-972-6700. FAX 0171-972-5987. (Subscr. in to: Tower Publishing Services Ltd., Tower House, Sovereign Park, Lathkill St., Market Harborough, Leics. LE16 9EF, England. TEL 01858-468811. FAX 01858-432164) circ. 78,000. (back issues avail.) **Document type:** consumer publication.
   —CCC.

388.3 US ISSN 1046-5367
TL236.3
STREET ROD ACTION. 1972. m. $19.95. Challenge Publications, Inc., 7950 Deering Ave., Canoga Park, CA 91304. TEL 818-887-0550. FAX 818-883-1343. Ed. Eric Pierce. adv.; bk.rev.; charts; illus. circ. 95,000. **Document type:** consumer publication.
   Formerly: Rod Action.
   Description: Covers auto rebuild and restoration.

STREET RODDER. see *SPORTS AND GAMES*

796.77 US ISSN 8750-3298
STREET RODDING ILLUSTRATED. bi-m. McMullen & Yee Publishing, 774 S. Placentia Ave., Placentia, CA 92670-6846. TEL 714-572-2255. FAX 714-572-1864.

STRUCTURE OF THE JAPANESE AUTO PARTS INDUSTRY. see *BUSINESS AND ECONOMICS — Economic Situation And Conditions*

388 GW
SUCH & FIND KRAFTFAHRZEUG. 1983. w. DM.176. Kempen Verlag GmbH, Wilhelm-Stoppler-Platz 3, 56070 Koblenz, Germany. TEL 0261-89920. Ed. A. Kempen.

388.476 GW
SUEDHESSISCHES AUTO MAGAZIN. 1986. 10/yr. DM.60. Biber Druck und Satz, Justus-von-Liebig-Str. 7a, 64401 Gross-Bieberau, Germany. Ed. Guenter Zander; Pub. Bernd Ruths. adv. contact: Bernd Ruths. bk.rev. circ. 35,000. (back issues avail.) **Document type:** consumer publication.
   Former titles: Auto Magazin; Auto Anzeiger.

388.3 FI ISSN 0355-2691
SUOMEN AUTOLEHTI; the automotive magazine of Finland. 1933. m. FIM 350. Kustannusliike Autotieto Oy, Koydenpunojankatu 8, SF-00180 Helsinki, Finland. FAX 358-0-6944027. Ed. Heikki Haapaniemi. adv.; bk.rev. circ. 8,100. **Document type:** trade publication.

388.33 US ISSN 0896-0437
TL153.A1
SUPER AUTOMOTIVE SERVICE.* 1929. m. $79. Irving-Cloud Publishing Co., 417 N. Hough St., Barrington, IL 60010-3028. TEL 708-674-7300. FAX 708-674-7015. Ed. Martin Schultz. adv.; illus.; mkt.; stat.; index. (processed) Indexed: Bus.Ind., Tr.& Indus.Ind. **Document type:** trade publication.
   Formerly: Super Service Station (ISSN 0039-5676)
   Description: For service stations, independent repair shops and tire dealerships.

629.22 JA ISSN 0915-4116
SUPER C G. (Text in Japanese) 1989. bi-m. 15000 Yen. Nigensha Publishing Co. Ltd., 2-2 Kanda-Jimbocho, Chiyoda-ku, Tokyo 101, Japan. TEL 81-3-5210-4706. FAX 81-3-5210-4706. Ed. K. Itoh. adv.: B&W page 250000 Yen, color page 500000 Yen; trim 235 x 295; adv. contact: R. Ohkoshi. bk.rev. circ. 80,000.
   Description: Covers classic and "super" cars for enthusiasts and connoisseurs.

388.3 US ISSN 0146-2628
TL215.C5
SUPER CHEVY. 1973. m. $16.94. Argus Publishers Corporation, Box 49659, Los Angeles, CA 90049. TEL 310-820-3601. FAX 310-207-9388. (Subscr. to: Box 453, Nt. Morris, IL 61054) Ed. Bruce Hampson. adv.; illus. circ. 183,236.
   Formerly: Chevy Hi-Performance.
   Description: Contains hands-on and restoration articles, new product information, project cars and coverage of Chevy-powered events.

SUPER STOCK & DRAG ILLUSTRATED. see *SPORTS AND GAMES — Outdoor Life*

629.286 US
SUPERCHARGER. 1928. 8/yr. (Oct.-May). membership only. Society of Automotive Engineers, Detroit Section, 21000 W. Ten Mile Rd., Southfield, MI 48075. TEL 313-357-3340. Ed. Sandra Bouckley. adv. circ. 9,819.

388.3 380.1 US
SUPPLIER'S SOURCE DIRECTORY.* 1966. a. $10. M H West, Inc. (Subsidiary of: Maclean Hunter Publishing Co.), 5743 Corsa Ave., Ste. 220, Westlake Village, CA 91362-4027. TEL 818-997-0644. FAX 818-997-1058. (Subscr. to: 29 N. Wacker Dr., Chicago, IL 60606) adv. circ. 35,000. **Document type:** directory.
   Former title: Auto Age Buyer's Guide.

SUPPLY LINE. see *HOBBIES*

629.286 US
SURGEONS OF STEEL. 1982. m. $40 (effective Sep. 1992). (Nebraska Autobody Association, Inc.) Anderson Management Services, Inc., 1111 Lincoln Mall, Ste. 308, Lincoln, NE 68508-2882. TEL 402-476-1528. FAX 402-476-1259. Ed. Robert L. Anderson. adv. contact: Rebecca Barker. circ. 1,300. **Document type:** trade publication.
   Description: Covers automotive collision-repair.

629.286 SW ISSN 0348-3304
SVENSKA MOTOR-MAGASINET. 1978. fortn. SEK 250. Pro Motor AB, Florettgatan 5, P.O. Box 22148, S-250 22 Helsingborg, Sweden. FAX 42-114734. Ed. Olle Holm. adv.; illus. circ. 22,000. (tabloid format)

388.3 XR ISSN 0039-7016
SVET MOTORU. 1947. w. 156 Kc.($44) Vydavatelstvi Automedia, a.s., Strelnicna 1680, 182 00 Prague 8, Czech Republic. (Subscr. to: Artia, Ve Smeckach 30, 111 27 Prague 1, Czech Republic) Ed. Otakar Gregora. adv.; charts; illus.; index. circ. 100,000.

388 SZ ISSN 0258-7904
SWITZERLAND. BUNDESAMT FUER STATISTIK. STRASSENVERKEHRSUNFAELLE IN DER SCHWEIZ/ACCIDENTS DE LA CIRCULATION ROUTIERE EN SUISSE. (Text in French, German) 1963. a. 9 SFr. Bundesamt fuer Statistik, Schwarztorstr. 96, CH-3003 Bern, Switzerland. TEL 031-3236011. FAX 031-3236061. stat. **Document type:** government publication.

388 GW
T UE V AUTOREPORT; Sicherheitsanalyse, 78 Modelle des In- und Auslandes. 1976. a. DM.9.80. (Vereinigung der Technischen Ueberwachungs-Vereine e.V.) Verlag T Ue V Rheinland GmbH, Am Grauen Stein, 51105 Cologne, Germany. TEL 02203-170971. FAX 02203-15411. circ. 220,000. **Document type:** consumer publication.

629.286 GW ISSN 0342-622X
TANKSTELLE. 1954. m. DM.118.80. (National Association of the German Service Station and Garage Industry) Verlag Kirchheim und Co. GmbH, Kaiserstr. 41, 55116 Mainz, Germany. TEL 06131-96070-0. FAX 06131-9607070. circ. 15,000. **Document type:** trade publication.
   —CCC.

629.2 GW ISSN 0171-4686
TASCHENFACHBUCH FUER INSPEKTION UND REPARATUR. 1953. a. DM.13.50. Krafthand-Verlag Walter Schulz, St.-Anna-Str. 26, 86825 Bad Woerishofen, Germany. Ed. Walter Schulz.
   Formerly: Taschenfachbuch der Kraftfahrzeugbetriebe (ISSN 0171-4678)

338 629.2 GW ISSN 0083-548X
TATSACHEN UND ZAHLEN AUS DER KRAFTVERKEHRSWIRTSCHAFT. 1927. a. DM.115. Verband der Automobilindustrie e.V., Westendstr. 61, 60325 Frankfurt a.M., Germany. TEL 069-7570-0. FAX 069-7570-261. (back issues avail.) **Document type:** trade publication.

796.77 CN ISSN 0318-3467
TAYLOR'S LEISURE WHEELS. 1969. m. Tall Taylor Publishing Ltd., Box 40, Irricana, Alta. TOM 1B0, Canada. TEL 403-935-4688. illus.

388 US
TECH CENTER NEWS. 1975. w. free. Springer Publishing Inc., 31201 Chicago Rd. S., Warren, MI 48093. TEL 313-939-6800. FAX 313-939-5850. Ed. Peter Salinas. adv.; play rev.; circ. 17,500 (controlled). (tabloid format)
   Description: Reports on company and local community news affecting the employers of General Motors, Chrysler and Ford.

TRANSPORTATION — AUTOMOBILES

629.222 388.31 US ISSN 1069-3904
TECHLINK: AUTOMOTIVE AND ROAD TRANSPORTATION. (Yearbook avail.) 1993. m. $200 (outside N. America $280). U.S. National Technical Information Service, 5285 Port Royal Rd., Springfield, VA 22161. TEL 703-487-4630. FAX 703-321-8547. (Co-sponsor: Engineering Information, Inc.) bibl.
Document type: newsletter, government publication.
Description: Draws upon the scientific, technical and engineering data on automobile and road transportation contained in the Compendex Plus and N.T.I.S. Bibliographic databases.

600 UK
TECHNICAL SERVICE DATA (CARS). 1935. a. £38. Glass's Information Services Ltd., Elgin House, St. George's Ave., Weybridge, Surrey KT13 OBX, England. TEL 01932-823823. FAX 01932-846564. (Orders to: Sales and Marketing, St. Martins Ct., 37 Queens Rd., Weybridge, Surrey KT13 9TU, England) **Document type:** trade publication.
Formerly: Technical Service Data (Automotive) (ISSN 0082-2329)

388 UK
TECHNICAL SERVICE DATA (HEAVY COMMERCIAL VEHICLES). 1989. a. £38. Glass's Information Services Ltd., Elgin House, St. Georges Ave., Weybridge, Surrey KT13 OBX, England. TEL 01932-853211. FAX 01932-846564. (Orders to: Sales and Marketing, St. Martins Ct., 37 Queens St., Weybridge, Surrey KT13 9TU, England) **Document type:** trade publication.

388 UK
TECHNICAL SERVICE DATA (LIGHT COMMERCIAL VEHICLES). 1989. a. £36. Glass's Information Services Ltd., Elgin House, St. Georges Ave., Weybridge, Surrey KT13 OBX, England. TEL 01932-823823. FAX 01932-846564. (Orders to: Sales and Marketing, St. Martins Ct., 37 Queens Rd., Weybridge, Surrey KT13 9TU, England) **Document type:** trade publication.

629.286 IT
TECNICA DELL'AUTOMOBILE.* 1948. m. (11/yr.). L.30000($50) Associazione Tecnica dell'Automobile, Via Pettinati 20, 10126 Torino, Italy. adv. circ. 2,800.

629.13 SW ISSN 0346-5373
TEKNIKENS VAERLD; allt om bilen. (Supplement avail.: Bilboersen) 1920. fortn. SEK 648 (effective 1991). Bonniers Specialtidningar AB, P.O. Box 70452, 107 26 Stockholm, Sweden. (Subscr. to: Pressdata AB, P.O. Box 3217, S-103 64 Stockholm, Sweden) Ed. Christer Gerlach. adv.: B&W page SEK 25400, color page SEK 29900. circ. 96,000.
Formerly: Teknikens Varld Med Flying (ISSN 0040-2281) (until 1935): Flygning.

388 US
▼**TEX SMITH'S HOT ROD MECHANIX.** 1994. bi-m. $15.95. C S K Publishing Co., Inc., 299 Market St., Saddle Brook, NJ 07662. TEL 201-712-9300. FAX 201-712-9899. Ed. Tex Smith. adv.: B&W page $1805. circ. 60,000 (paid). **Document type:** consumer publication.

388.3 JA ISSN 0916-6408
THANKS. (Text in Japanese) 1947. m. Nissan Motor Co. Ltd., Advertising Department - Nissan Jidosha Kabushiki Gaisha, 6-17-2 Ginza, Chuo-ku, Tokyo 104, Japan. Ed. M. Uchida. adv.; bk.rev.; illus. circ. 500,000.
Formed by the merger of (1949-1990): Kuruma no Techo (ISSN 0286-4312); (1947-1990): Nissan Graphic (ISSN 0029-0742) & Prince.

288.3 CN
THUNDER BAY CAR & TRUCK NEWS. m. Can.$25. North Superior Publishing Inc., 115 Barton St., Thunder Bay, ON P7B 5N3, Canada. TEL 807-623-2348. FAX 807-623-7515. circ. 30,000.

388 629.222 US ISSN 1062-5755
THUNDERBIRD SCOOP. 1972. bi-m. $26 (foreign $45) (typically set in Jan.). Vintage Thunderbird Club International, P.O. Box 2250, Dearborn, MI 48123-2250. TEL 402-397-7462. Ed. Alan H. Tast; Pub. Robert J. Gadra. adv.: B&W page $75; 4 9/16 x 7 3/4; adv. contact: Rick Slots. bk.rev.; charts; illus. circ. 3,200 (paid). **Document type:** consumer publication.
Description: Informs, educates, and entertains owners of the 1958 to today's Ford Motor Company's Thunderbird series with articles about restoration, maintenance, and collecting. Also contains the current agenda, activities, events, and conventions of the club.

629.286 SP ISSN 0212-0526
TIENDA DE RECAMBIOS Y ACCESORIOS. Variant title: Recambios y Accesorios. 1982. m. (13/yr.). 7600 ptas. (foreign 11400 ptas.). Tecnipublicaciones, S.A., C. Albacete 5, 28027 Madrid, Spain. TEL 34-1-3261440. FAX 34-1-3262539. Ed. Miguel Angel F. Prieto. circ. 10,000.

388.3 US
TIGER TALES. 1969. m. $25 includes membership. California Association of Tiger Owners, 18321 Vista Del Lago, Yorba Linda, CA 92686. TEL 714-777-3744. Ed. Bob Norton. adv. circ. 980. **Document type:** newsletter.
Description: Provides a medium through which Sunbeam Tiger owners may pool ideas and resources on the care and maintenance of their vehicles.

TIRE BUSINESS. see *RUBBER*

678.32 US ISSN 0040-8085
TS1870
TIRE REVIEW; the authority on tire dealer profitability. (Includes C E O Report published in Jan.; LiftGuide published in Feb.; Custom Wheel & Tire Style Guide published in May; Sourcebook and Purchasing Directory published in Sept.; NTDRA Show Issues published in Sept.) 1901. 13/yr. $52 (foreign $104) (effective 1995). Babcox Publications, 11 S. Forge St., Box 1810, Akron, OH 44309-1810. TEL 216-535-6117. FAX 216-535-0874. Ed. Jim Davis. adv.: B&W page $5950. circ. 33,114. circ. 843 (paid). **Indexed:** Chem.Abstr., RAPRA. **Document type:** trade publication.
—BLDSC (8858.401000).
Formerly: Tire and T B A Review.
Description: Serves tire and automotive service dealers, distributors and retreaders.

340 US
TITLE AND REGISTRATION BOOK; summary of motor vehicle laws and regulations. 1977. a. $40. National Automobile Dealers Association (Costa Mesa), Box 7800, Costa Mesa, CA 92628. TEL 800-966-6232. Ed. Pat Phillips.

629.222 US
TODAY'S TRUCK & SPORT UTILITY PERFORMANCE. bi-m. newsstand price: $3.95. Mag-Tec Productions, 9582 Hamilton Ave., Huntington Beach, CA 92646. TEL 962-932-7795. FAX 714-965-2268. Ed. Eva Griffey. **Document type:** consumer publication.

388.3 FR ISSN 0984-9068
TOP'S CARS. (Supplement avail.: Top's Cars. Hors Serie (ISSN 1155-2891)) 1987. bi-m. 455 F. (foreign 685 F.). Societe des Publications Modernes Specialisees, 60-62 rue Danjou, 92100 Boulogne, France. TEL 46-09-95-96. FAX 46-09-99-85. (Subscr. to: 24 bd. Vauban, B.P. 137, 80103 Abbeville Cedex, France. TEL 22-31-31-12) Ed. Gilles Stievenart; Pub. Monique Helfenberger. adv. contact: Eric Brame. circ. 35,000. **Document type:** consumer publication.

796.77 CN ISSN 0704-7339
TORONTO INTERNATIONAL AUTO SHOW PROGRAM. Issued with: Carguide. 1974. a. Can.$4. Formula Publications Ltd., 447 Speers Rd., Ste. 4, Oakville, ON L6K 3S7, Canada. TEL 905-842-6591. FAX 905-842-6843. Ed. Alan McPhee. adv. circ. 50,000. **Document type:** consumer publication.

TOURING; auto et loisirs - auto en vrije tijd. see *TRAVEL AND TOURISM*

388.3 CN
TOURING. (Editions in English and French) 1922. 4/yr. Can.$10. Consultants C G E I Inc., 3281 Jean-Beraud Ave., Chomedey, Laval, PQ H7T 2L2, Canada. TEL 514-334-5912. FAX 514-688-6969. Ed. Andre Ducharme. adv.: B&W page Can.$6695, color page Can.$8340; trim 8 1/8 x 10 3/4; adv. contact: Christiane Parant. bk.rev.; film rev.; illus.; stat. circ. 474,000. **Document type:** consumer publication.
Formerly: Autoclub (ISSN 0005-0954)

TOURING. see *TRAVEL AND TOURISM*

388.3 FR
TOUT TERRAIN MAGAZINE. 1989. m. (includes a. supplement). 310 F. (foreign 406 F.) (effective 1994-1995). Ediregie, B.P. 86, 94420 Le Plessis Trevise, France. TEL 45-93-72-72. FAX 45-93-25-93. TELEX EDIGIE 262 572 F. Ed. Jean-Jacques Deverly. circ. 55,000. **Document type:** consumer publication.

629.222 US
TOWING NEWS. 1982. m. $24. Towing and Recovery Association of America, Inc., 2200 Mill Rd., Alexandria, VA 22314-4686. TEL 703-838-1897. FAX 703-684-6720. Ed. Anne Grant. adv. contact: Jeff Morrison. charts; tr.lit. (back issues avail.) **Document type:** newsletter, directory.
Formerly: National Towing News.
Description: Information on the automobile towing industry.

614.7 JA
TOYOTA; environmental programs and activities. (Text in English) 1991. irreg. free. Toyota Motor Corporation, International Public Affairs Division, 4-18, Koraku 1-chome, Bunkyo-ku, Tokyo 112, Japan. TEL 03-3817-9930. FAX 03-3817-9017. circ. 30,000 (controlled).
Formerly: Toyota and the Environment.
Description: Introduces Toyota's stance on environment protection and its current and future technology development.

629.286 JA
TOYOTA AND AUTOMOTIVE ELECTRONICS. (Text in English) 1987. irreg. free. Toyota Motor Corporation, International Public Affairs Division, 1-4-18, Koraku, Bunkyo-ku, Tokyo 112, Japan. TEL 03-3817-9930. FAX 03-3817-9017. circ. 10,000.
Formerly (until 1991): Toyota and Automotive Electronic.

629.286 JA
TOYOTA AND AUTOMOTIVE SAFETY. (Text in English) 1991. irreg. free. Toyota Motor Corporation, International Public Affairs Division, 1-4-18, Koraku, Bunkyo-ku, Tokyo 112, Japan. TEL 03-3817-9930. FAX 03-3817-9017. circ. 12,000.

629.286 JA
TOYOTA ENGINE TECHNOLOGY. (Text in English) 1989. irreg. free. Toyota Motor Corporation, International Public Affairs Division, 4-18, Koraku 1-chome, Bunkyo-ku, Tokyo 112, Japan. TEL 03-3817-9930. FAX 03-3817-9017. circ. 20,000 (controlled).
Description: Introduces Toyota's current engine technology and the future direction of its development.

629.222 JA ISSN 0916-7501
TOYOTA GIJUTSU. English edition: Toyota Technical Review (ISSN 0917-3706) (Text in Japanese) 1953. s-a. Toyota Motor Corporation, International Public Affairs Division, 1-4-18, Koraku, Bunkyo-ku, Tokyo 112, Japan. FAX 03-3817-9017.
Formerly (until 1991): Toyota Engineering (ISSN 0385-8898)
Description: Introduces Toyota's technical properties to engineers in automotive industries.

629.286 JA
TOYOTA MOTOR CORPORATION. ANNUAL REPORT. (Text in English) 1969. a. free. Toyota Motor Corporation, International Public Affairs Division, 1-4-18, Koraku, Bunkyo-ku, Tokyo 112, Japan. TEL 03-3817-9930. FAX 03-3817-9017. circ. 40,000. **Document type:** corporate report.

TRANSPORTATION — AUTOMOBILES

629.222　　　　JA　ISSN 0917-3706
TL1　　　　　　CODEN: TTEREB
TOYOTA TECHNICAL REVIEW. Japanese edition: Toyota Gijutsu (ISSN 0916-7501) (Text in English) 1991. s-a. Toyota Motor Corporation, International Public Affairs Division, 1-4-18, Koraku, Bunkyo-ku, Tokyo 112, Japan. FAX 03-3817-9017. Ed. Hideo Hattori. —BLDSC (8873.265000).
Description: Introduces Toyota's technical properties to engineers in automotive industries.

388.3　　　　SW
TRAFIK OCH MOTOR. 1960. 6/yr. SEK 80 membership. Foersvarets Motorklubb (F M K), P.O. Box 323, S-184 24 Aakersberga, Sweden. TEL 46-8-540-640-20. FAX 46-8-540-635-36. Ed. Johnny Hansson; Pub. Bo Stenson. adv.: B&W page SEK 14500, color page SEK 19500; trim 185 x 265; adv. contact: Patrik Irmer. circ. 65,800. cols./p.: 3; pp./issue: 44. **Document type:** consumer publication.

388.3　　　　SW　ISSN 0349-9790
TRAILER. 1980. 11/yr. SEK 350 (foreign SEK 416); newsstand price: SEK 36. Foerlags AB Albinsson & Sjoeberg, P.O. Box 529, S-371 23 Karlskrona, Sweden. TEL 46-455-335325. FAX 46-455-311715. Ed. Sture Bergendahl. adv.: B&W page SEK 16300, color page SEK 24900; trim 190 x 275; adv. contact: Martin Lindstroem. circ. 24,900 (controlled). cols./p.: 4; pp./issue: 84.

629.286　　　　US　ISSN 0277-8300
TRANSMISSION DIGEST. 1981. m. $34 in the U.S.; Canada and Mexico $60; elsewhere $86. M D Publications, Inc. (Springfield), 3057 E. Cairo, Box 2210, Springfield, MO 65801-2210. TEL 417-866-3917. FAX 417-866-2781. Ed. Lola Miller. adv. circ. 23,000. **Document type:** trade publication.
Description: Covers the automatic and standard transmission rerebuilding, repair and service aftermarket.

TRANSPORT-NYTT. see *TRANSPORTATION — Ships And Shipping*

388.3　　　　UY
TRANSPORTE AUTOMOTOR. 1977. m. Confederacion Uruguay del Transporte Automotor, Lima 1423, Montevideo, Uruguay. Ed. Jose M. Camano Abal.

338　　　　US　ISSN 1069-2274
TREND SETTER. m. $25. Kustom Kemps of Wichita, RR 1, Box 1521A, Cassville, MO 62625-9724. Ed. Geoff Carter007. **Document type:** trade publication.

629.283　　　　UK
TRUCK DRIVER'S HANDBOOK. irreg. £7.99. Kogan Page Ltd., 120 Pentonville Rd., London N1 9JN, England. TEL 0171-278-0433. FAX 0171-837-6348. TELEX 263088 KOGAN G. Ed. David P. Soye. **Document type:** monographic series.
Formerly: H G V Driver's Handbook.
Description: For truck drivers, with sections on the law and the road.

TRUCK ENGINEERING. see *TRANSPORTATION — Trucks And Trucking*

388　　　　US
TRUCK, RACE, AND RECREATIONAL MARKETPLACE. m. newsstand price: $1.95. Deals on Wheels Publications, Box 205, Sioux Falls, SD 57101. TEL 605-338-7666. FAX 605-338-5337. **Document type:** consumer publication.

388　　　　US
TRUCKIN' CLASSIC TRUCKS. bi-m. newsstand price: $3.50. McMullen & Yee Publishing, 774 S. Placentia Ave., Placentia, CA 92670-6846. TEL 714-572-2255. FAX 714-572-1864. **Document type:** consumer publication.

629.222 367　　　　US
TUCKER TOPICS. 1948. m. $25. (Tucker Automobile Club of America) P A F Associates, 9509 Hinton Dr., Santee, CA 92071-2760. TEL 619-576-3227. FAX 619-573-0196. Eds. William E. Pommering, Patricia A. Fortin. adv. contact: William E. Pommering. circ. 350 (paid). (back issues avail.) **Document type:** newsletter.
Description: Presents articles (original, reprints) relating to Preston Tucker, Tucker Corporation and Tucker automobiles.

388.3　　　　US
TURBO & HIGH TECH PERFORMANCE. 1985. bi-m. $19.97. Mag-Tec Productions, 9582 Hamilton Ave., Huntington Beach, CA 92646. TEL 714-962-7795. FAX 714-965-2268. Ed. Kipp Kington. adv.
Formerly: Turbo.
Description: Covers late-model, high-performance vehicles.

388　　　　DK　ISSN 0901-3032
TURIST- OG RUTEBILBLADET. 1941. 6/yr. DKK 78. Skolegade 19 A, DK-8000 Aarhus C, Denmark. TEL 86-118680. FAX 86-14-4452. Ed. Rene Wittendorff. adv.; circ. 4,000 (controlled). **Document type:** trade publication.
Formerly: Rutebil-Bladet.

388 388.324　　　　US　ISSN 1052-3251
TURNING WHEELS. 1968. m. $25. Studebaker Drivers Club, Inc., Box 1040, Oswego, IL 60543. TEL 800-527-3452. FAX 209-634-2163. Ed. Linda Fox; Pub. Laurence Swanson. adv. contact: Linda Fox. bk.rev.; cum.index; circ. 12,800 (paid). (back issues avail.)
Description: Provides articles on the history, restoration, maintenance, and current happenings concerning Studebaker cars, trucks and buggies manufactured from 1852 to 1966.

388.3　　　　IT
TUTTOFOURISTRADA OSSERVATORE MOTORISTICO. 1977. m. (11/yr.). L.45000. Free Wheels s.r.l., Via XXV Aprile 99, 20068 Peschiera Borromeo (MI), Italy. TEL 02-55-300837. Ed. Loriano Martinoli. adv.: B&W page L.2500000, color page L.4500000; adv. contact: Loriano Martinoli. circ. 55,000.
Formerly: Osservatore Motoristico.

TUTTOPISTA. see *SPORTS AND GAMES*

380.5　　　　FI　ISSN 0041-4468
TUULILASI. 1963. m. FIM 471. A-Lehdet Oy, Hitsaajankatu 7, FIN-00081 A-Lehdet, Finland. FAX 358-0-787-311. Ed. Matti Saario. adv.; bk.rev.; illus. circ. 83,311. **Document type:** consumer publication.
Incorporates (in 1973): Moottoriviesti (ISSN 0027-0962)
Description: Motoring magazine for Finland.

TYRE AND RIM ASSOCIATION OF AUSTRALIA STANDARDS MANUAL. see *RUBBER*

388　　　　II　ISSN 0970-8898
TYRE SAMACHAR. 1973. m. Rs.50. S. Swaminthan, Ed. & Pub., No. 9, State Bank St., First Lane, Mount Road, Madras 600 002, India. TEL 849305. adv.; bk.rev. circ. 17,000.

UIT: het V T B - V A B magazine. see *TRAVEL AND TOURISM*

388.3　　　　UK　ISSN 0041-6207
ULSTER MOTORIST. m. £1. c/o Ulster Bank Ltd., Waring St., Belfast 1, N. Ireland. adv.; illus.
Incorporates: Drive.

629.286　　　　US　ISSN 0893-6943
UNDERCAR DIGEST; the management journal for exhaust, brake and chassis specialists. 1976. m. $34 in the U.S.; Canada and Mexico $60; elsewhere $86. M D Publications, Inc. (Springfield), 3057 E. Cairo, Box 2210, Springfield, MO 65801. TEL 417-866-3917. FAX 417-866-2781. Ed. James R. Wilder. adv.; bk.rev.; charts; illus.; tr.lit. circ. 30,000. (back issues avail.) **Document type:** trade publication.
Formerly (until 1987): Muffler Digest (ISSN 0164-6044)
Description: Covers the undercar repair and service aftermarket including exhaust, ride control, chassis alignment and brakes.

338　　　　US　ISSN 1058-3602
UNDERCAR DIGEST SHORT LINE NEWSLETTER. 1978. m. $39 in the U.S.; Canada $44. M D Publications, Inc. (Springfield), 3057 E. Cairo, Box 2210, Springfield, MO 65801-2210. TEL 417-866-3917. FAX 417-866-2781. Ed. James R. Wilder. circ. 100. **Document type:** newsletter.
Description: Publishes industry news and updates for suppliers and service establishments in the undercare aftermarket.

629.286　　　　US　ISSN 1079-6177
▼**UNDERHOOD SERVICE**. (Includes Aftermarket Training Guide published in July) 1995. m. (13/yr.). $59 (foreign $115) (effective 1995). Babcox Publications, 11 S. Forge St., Akron, OH 44304. TEL 216-536-6117. FAX 216-535-0874. circ. 40,000 (controlled). **Document type:** trade publication.
Description: Each issue contains technical features, industry news and legislative updates, in-depth technical information on servicing various underhood systems, diagnostic and repair tips, shop management, and new products.

629.2　　　　US　ISSN 0270-756X
TL1
U.S. DEPARTMENT OF ENERGY. ANNUAL REPORT TO CONGRESS ON THE AUTOMOTIVE TECHNOLOGY DEVELOPMENT PROGRAM. Key Title: Annual Report to Congress on the Automotive Technology Development Program. 1979. a. free. U.S. Department of Energy, Advanced Propulsion Division, Transportation Technologies, EE-322, Washington, DC 20585. TEL 202-586-8012. Ed. Thomas M. Sebestyen. circ. 200. **Document type:** government publication.

388.3　　　　IT
UOMINI & MOTORI. 6/yr. Via Roma 26 C, 10023 Chieri (TO), Italy. TEL 11-94-22-194. FAX 11-94-23-477. Ed. Enzio Fonzo. circ. 35,000.

388.3　　　　II　ISSN 0500-6813
UPPER INDIA MOTORIST. 1954. m. $25 (free to members). Automobile Association of Upper India, C-8, Institutional Area, South of IIT, New Delhi 110 016, India. TEL 3312323. FAX 6866302. Ed. T.K. Malhotra. adv. circ. 20,000.
Refereed Serial

388　　　　US　ISSN 0895-3899
TL162
USED CAR BOOK (YEAR). biennial. $12.50. Harper Collins Publishers, 10 E. 53rd St., New York, NY 10022. TEL 212-207-7500. FAX 212-207-7936. Ed. Jack Gillis.

388.3　　　　US　ISSN 0279-425X
USED CAR DEALER. 1981. m. $36. National Independent Automobile Dealers Association, 2521 Brown Blvd., Ste. 100, Arlington, TX 76006-5203. TEL 817-640-3838. FAX 817-649-5866. Ed. Don A. Harris. adv.; charts; illus.; stat. circ. 16,033. **Document type:** trade publication.
Description: Covers items of interest to the used car dealer industry, including profit centers and legislative issues.

388.3　　　　US
TL162
USED CAR PRICE GUIDE. 1991. 7/yr. $4.99 per no. Pace Publications (Milwaukee), 1020 N. Broadway, Ste. 111, Milwaukee, WI 53202. TEL 414-272-9977. FAX 414-272-9973.
Formerly: Car Facts (ISSN 1056-1889)

388.3　　　　US
HD9710.A1
USED CAR PRICES. 1973. 7/yr. $26.95. Pace Publications (Milwaukee), 1020 N. Broadway, Ste. 111, Milwaukee, WI 53202. TEL 414-272-9977. FAX 414-272-9973.
Formerly: Used Car Prices - Buyer's Guide Reports (ISSN 1050-5415)
Description: Lists average wholesale and retail prices for all American and foreign cars for the past ten years.

629 658　　　　US　ISSN 1053-2552
USED CARS INSIDER.* 1983. bi-w. $175. Atcom, Inc., 1541 Morris Ave., Bronx, NY 10457-8702. TEL 212-873-5900. FAX 212-799-1728. Ed. Steve Byers. circ. 1,500. (reprint service avail. from UMI) —CCC.
Former titles: Used Cars Today (ISSN 0890-2291) & Used Cars Today Newsletter (ISSN 0740-0055)
Description: Newsletter for professionals in the used car business.

TRANSPORTATION — AUTOMOBILES

629.222 US ISSN 1069-8779
V M R STANDARD USED CAR PRICES. 1993. q. $18. V M R International, Inc., 41 N. Main St., N. Grafton, MA 01536. TEL 508-839-6707. FAX 508-839-6266. (Dist. by: I C D - Hearst, 250 W. 55th St., New York, NY 10019. TEL 212-649-4465) Ed. John Iafolla. circ. 26,000 (paid). (back issues avail.) Document type: consumer publication.
●Also available on CD-ROM.
—CCC.
Description: Lists U.S. prices of cars, vans, and light trucks for the past 10 years.

796.7 US
THE V W AUTOIST. (Volkswagen) 1955. bi-m. $16 ($10 for renewal). Volkswagen Club of America, Box 154, N. Aurora, IL 60542-0154. TEL 708-896-2803. E-mail: vwclub@aol.com. Ed. Fred Ortlip. adv. contact: Sneil Tomlin. illus.; stat.; circ. 2,000 (controlled). (back issues avail.)
Description: For owners and enthusiasts of Volkswagen and Audi automobiles.

338.476 UK ISSN 0953-6167
V W MOTORING. (Volkswagen) 1961. m. £26.40 (rest of Europe £33; elsewhere £43). R F W W Publications Ltd., P.O. Box 283, Cheltenham, Glos. GL52 3BT, England. TEL 01242-262723. FAX 01242-253273. (Subscr. to: Warners Distribution, The Maltings, Bourne, Lincs. PE10 9PH, England. TEL 01778-393652) Ed. Robin Wager; Pub. Robin Wager. adv. contact: Bev Cunnington. bk.rev.; charts; illus.; tr.lit. circ. 25,000. Indexed: Ergon.Abstr. Document type: consumer publication.
Formerly (until 1985): Safer (Volkswagen) Motoring (ISSN 0036-2417)

796.77 US ISSN 8750-3301
TL215.V6
V W TRENDS. (Volkswagen) 1983. m. McMullen & Yee Publishing, 774 S. Placentia Ave., Placentia, CA 92670-6846. TEL 714-572-2255. FAX 714-572-1864. Ed. Robin Hartfiel. adv. circ. 95,000. Document type: consumer publication.

796.72 FI ISSN 0782-4033
V 8 - MAGAZINE. 1978. 8/yr. FIM 235. Helsinki Media Company Oy, Sport, P.O. Box 16, SF-00381 Helsinki, Finland. TEL 358-0-120-5911. FAX 358-0-120-5959. Ed. Jarmo Markkanen. adv. contact: Esa Sairio. circ. 30,540.
Formerly: Street & Race (ISSN 0780-2102)

796.72 917
VALLEY MOTORIST. 1936. bi-m. $1. Valley Automobile Club, 100 Hazle St., Wilkes-Barre, PA 18702. TEL 717-824-2444. FAX 717-824-9855. Ed. Richard J. Myers. circ. 57,113. (tabloid format) Document type: newspaper.
Formerly: Wyoming Valley Motorist (ISSN 0049-822X)

388.3 790.13 US ISSN 0884-7231
VAN CONVERSION BLUE BOOK. 4/yr. $60. Maclean Hunter Market Reports, Inc., 29 N. Wacker Dr., Chicago, IL 60606-3297. TEL 312-726-2802. FAX 312-726-2574. (back issues avail.)

388 UK ISSN 0269-1825
VAN USER. 1985. m. £17.50. T E C Publications Ltd., Chesterfield House, 133 Victoria Rd., Diss, Norfolk IP22 3JN, England. TEL 01379-652126. FAX 01379-650116. Ed. M.C. Pegg. adv.: page £1000; trim 297 x 210; adv. contact: Joannah Pegg. circ. 15,000 (paid). (back issues avail.) Document type: trade publication.

388.3 FI ISSN 0355-4295
VAUHDIN MAAILMA. m. FIM 275. Yhtyneet Kuvalehdet Oy, Maistraatinportti 1, FIN-00240 Helsinki, Finland. TEL 358-0-156-6524. FAX 358-0-156-6505. TELEX 121364. Ed. Peter Geitel. adv.: B&W page FIM 8800, color page FIM 13000. circ. 36,192.

388.3 330 US
VEHICLE LEASING TODAY. 1981. bi-m. $29 (foreign $40). National Vehicle Leasing Association, Box 281230, San Francisco, CA 94128-1230. TEL 415-548-9135. FAX 415-548-9155. Ed. Rod Couts. adv. circ. 4,500. Document type: trade publication.
Description: Covers issues affecting the leasing of consumer and commercial vehicles.

388.1 DK ISSN 0083-5358
VEJTRANSPORTEN I TAL OG TEKST. (Text in Danish; notes in English) 1959. a. DKK 144 (effective 1992). Automobil-Importoerernes Sammenslutning, Ryvangs Alle 68, DK-2900 Hellerup, Denmark. Ed. Kai Noerrung. index, cum.index every 7 yrs.
Description: Covers import and new registration of vehicles, vehicles in use, motor traffic and taxation, road expenditure and traffic accidents.

796.72 AG ISSN 0049-5913
VELOCIDAD. 1950. bi-m. Av. Belgrano 1735, Buenos Aires, Argentina. Ed. Gilberto Julian Riega.

629.2 338 GW ISSN 0506-6573
VERBAND DER AUTOMOBILINDUSTRIE. JAHRESBERICHT. (Editions in English, German) a. free. Verband der Automobilindustrie e.V., Westendstr. 61, 60325 Frankfurt a.M., Germany. TEL 069-7570-0. FAX 069-7570-261. Indexed: Dok.Str. Document type: corporate report.
Formerly: Verband der Automobilindustrie. Taetigkeitsbericht (ISSN 0083-5471)

629.286 GW ISSN 0724-2050
VERKEHRSUNFALL UND FAHRZEUGTECHNIK; Verkehrsunfall Fachblatt fuer Kraftfahrzeugsachverstaendige. 1961. m. DM.350.50. Verlag Information Ambs GmbH, Postfach 208, 77968 Kippenheim, Germany. TEL 07825-7114. FAX 07825-9376. Ed.Bd. illus.; charts. Document type: bulletin.
Formerly: Verkehrsunfall (ISSN 0341-2210)

629.286 XV
VESTNIK A C; galsilo delavnihljudi W.O. A C. (Text and summaries in Serbo-Croatian, Slovenian) 1962. bi-m. free. W.O. Autocomerce, Trinova 4, Ljubljana, Slovenia. TEL 61 323-046. FAX 061-317-196. TELEX 31299 YUAC. Ed. Miran Juvancic. (back issues avail.)

VETERAN. see ANTIQUES

388.3 UK ISSN 0042-4781
VETERAN CAR. 1938. bi-m. membership. Veteran Car Club of Great Britain, Jessamine House, High St., Ashwell, Herts. SG7 5NL, England. Ed. Michael Brisby. adv.; bk.rev.; charts; illus.; index. circ. 1,500. Document type: consumer publication.

796.77 US ISSN 0199-7890
VETTE. 1976. m. $23.97. C S K Publishing Co., Inc., 299 Market St., Saddle Brook, NJ 07662. TEL 201-712-9300. FAX 201-712-9899. (Subscr. to: Box 1010, Denville, NJ 07834) Ed. D. Randy Riggs. adv.; bk.rev. circ. 55,000. (back issues avail.) Document type: consumer publication.
Description: For enthusiasts who eat and sleep Corvette. Covers legends and meets, the old and new, stock and modified, show and strip, personalities, road tests, and shootouts.

388.3 790.1 SW ISSN 0346-4210
VI BILAEGARE. Variant title: Nya Vi Bilaegare. 1929. 22/yr. SEK 224. O K Foerlaget AB, Huvudstagatan 1, S-171 58 Solna, Sweden. TEL 46-8-735-83-55. FAX 46-8-735-22-19. Ed. Nils-Eric Frendin. adv.: B&W page SEK 45800, color page SEK 59800; trim 235 x 325. bk.rev.; charts; illus. circ. 260,000. Document type: consumer publication.
Former titles (until 1975): Vi Bilaegare med Hem och Hobby; (until vol.19, 1970): Vi Bilaegare (ISSN 0042-4943); (until vol.7, 1949): Meddelanden fraan Bilaegarnas Inkoepsfoerening, Stockholm.
Description: Directed to car owners. Extends to homes, gardening, traveling and leisure, hunting, boats and fishing.

388.3 IT
VIA!. 1948. m. membership. Automobile Club di Milano, Corso Venezia 43, 20121 Milan, Italy. TEL 39-2-7745239. FAX 39-2-2781844. TELEX 312047 ACI MI I. Ed. Paolo Montagna. adv.: B&W page L.4780000, color page L.6900000. bk.rev.; abstr.; illus.; stat. circ. 180,000.
Formerly: Autoclub and Via (ISSN 0005-0962)

796.77 US
VIALE CIRO MENOTTI; a magazine for Maserati enthusiasts. 1976. q. $60. M I E Corporation, Box 772, Mercer Island, WA 98040. TEL 206-455-4449. FAX 206-646-5458. Ed. Francis G. Mandarano. adv.; bk.rev.; index. circ. 3,500. (back issues avail.)

VIE DE L'AUTO. see ANTIQUES

629.222 US ISSN 0147-9695
TL215.T7
VINTAGE TRIUMPH. 1975. q. $25 (foreign $38). Vintage Triumph Register, 15218 W. Larren Ave., Dearborn, MI 48126. TEL 609-758-8749. Ed. Chris Hansel. adv.; bk.rev. circ. 4,500. (back issues avail.) Document type: newsletter.
Description: Contains articles and information which fosters the ownership, operation and preservation of Triumph automobiles.

388.3 FR ISSN 1150-4919
VIRAGES. 1952. 6/yr. free. Renault Vehicules Industriels, 129 rue Servient, 69003 Lyon, France. TEL 78-63-71-20. FAX 78-63-72-40. Ed. Madette Odier. charts, illus.; stat. circ. 45,000.
Former titles (until 1989): Info Renault Vehicules Industriels; Magazine R V I - Info R V I (ISSN 0005-9218)

388.3 796.72 GW
VOILA - RENAULT REVUE; Autos zum Leben. 1956. q. DM.8. Deutsche Renault AG, Koelner Weg 6-10, 50321 Bruehl, Germany. TEL 0228-351111. Ed. Werner P. Roeser. circ. 100,000. (back issues avail.)

VOLANTE. see TRAVEL AND TOURISM

388 AU
VOLKSBLATT MOTOR JOURNAL. s-a. Hafenstr. 1-3, Postfach 63, A-4020 Linz, Austria. TEL 0732-281901. FAX 0732-279242. Ed. Hans Gilbert Mueller. circ. 150,000.

796.7 UK ISSN 0956-9294
VOLKSWAGEN AUDI CAR. 1953. m. £30 (effective May 1995). (AutoMetrix Publications) T - A Autometrix Publications, 10a High St., Toddington, Dunstable, Beds. LU5 6BY, England. TEL 01525-874019. FAX 01525-875582. Ed. Paul Harris; Pub. Paul Harris. adv. contact: Mary Sutherland. bk.rev.; illus.; cum.index. circ. 18,000. Document type: consumer publication.
Formerly (until Aug. 1982): Beetling.
Description: For Volkswagen and Audi enthusiasts supplying information on products and services.

388.3 US ISSN 0043-0315
HD9710.U5
WARD'S AUTO WORLD. 1964. m. $48.50. Ward's Communications (Subsidiary of: Intertec Publishing Corp.), 3000 Town Center, Ste. 2750, Southfield, MI 48075-1212. TEL 810-357-0800. FAX 810-357-0810. Ed. David Smith. adv.; bk.rev.; charts; illus.; stat.; index. circ. 100,543. Indexed: Bus.Ind., Mich.Mag.Ind., PROMT, Tr.& Indus.Ind. Document type: trade publication.
●Also available online. Vendor(s): University Microfilms International.
—Faxon; UMI; UnCover. CCC.
Formerly: Ward's Quarterly.
Description: Covers the automotive manufacturing industry. Provides in-depth reporting and analysis on every facet of the manufacturer's business, from components to finished vehicles, design to marketing, people to companies.

629.286 US ISSN 0895-2191
HD9710.A1
WARD'S AUTOMOTIVE INTERNATIONAL. 1986. s-m. $475. Ward's Communications (Subsidiary of: Intertec Publishing Corp.), 3000 Town Center, Ste. 2750, Southfield, MI 48075-1212. TEL 810-357-0800. FAX 810-357-0810. Ed. David E. Zoia. Document type: trade publication.
—CCC.
Description: News and analysis of auto industry internationally.

388.286 US ISSN 0886-5175
HD9710.U5
WARD'S AUTOMOTIVE REPORTS. 1924. w. $1045 (includes Ward's Automotive Yearbook). Ward's Communications (Subsidiary of: Intertec Publishing Corp.), 3000 Town Center, Ste. 2750, Southfield, MI 48075-1212. TEL 810-357-0800. FAX 810-357-0810. q. index. Indexed: PROMT.
Description: Provides statistics and news on the automotive industry, including production numbers, sales figures, and marketing trends.

WARD'S AUTOMOTIVE YEARBOOK. see TRANSPORTATION — Abstracting, Bibliographies, Statistics

TRANSPORTATION — AUTOMOBILES

629.286 US
WARD'S ENGINE UPDATE AND VEHICLE TECHNOLOGY. 1975. s-m. $730. Ward's Communications (Subsidiary of: Intertec Publishing Corp.), 3000 Town Center, Ste. 2750, Southfield, MI 48075-1212. TEL 810-375-0800. FAX 810-375-0810. Ed. Joel Pietrangelo. **Document type:** trade publication.
Former titles: Ward's Engine Update; Ward's Wankel Report.
Description: Provides technical information on the world of automotive technology. Covers the latest developments in engine design, drive trains, materials and components.

388 US
▼**WARD'S FOCUS ON CHINA.** 1994. m. $250. Ward's Communications (Subsidiary of: Intertec Publishing Corp.), 3000 Town Center, Ste. 2750, Southfield, MI 48075-1212. TEL 810-375-0800. FAX 810-375-0810. Ed. David E. Zoia. stat. **Document type:** trade publication.
Description: Provides news, analysis, and statistics of the world's fastest-growing industrial market for automobiles.

338.33 629 CN ISSN 1188-7222
WESTERN AUTOMOTIVE REPAIR. 1992. 6/yr. Can.$25.68($35) New Horizons West Ltd., 59 Deering Close, Winnipeg, MB R3K 4K6, Canada. TEL 204-654-3573. FAX 204-667-8422. Ed. Dan Proudly. adv.: B&W page Can.$2246, color page Can.$3234; trim 8 1/8 x 10 7/8. bk.rev. circ. 11,048. (back issues avail.)

338.33 629 CN ISSN 1188-7230
WESTERN COLLISION REPAIR. 1992. 5/yr. Can.$16.05($25) New Horizons West Ltd., 59 Deering Close, Winnipeg, MB R2K 4K6W2, Canada. TEL 204-654-3573. FAX 204-667-8922. Ed. Dan Proudly; Pub. Ilan Moyle. adv.: B&W page Can.$1636, color page Can.$2594; trim 8 1/8 x 10 7/8. bk.rev. circ. 5,915. (back issues avail.) **Document type:** trade publication.

388.3 US ISSN 0043-3977
TL1
WESTERN NEW YORK MOTORIST. 1909. m. $1.50. Automobile Club of Western New York, 100 International Dr., Buffalo, NY 14221. Ed. Earle V. Charles III. abstr.; charts; illus.; stat. circ. 250,000.
Formerly: Buffalo Motorist.

WESTWAYS. see TRAVEL AND TOURISM

614.86 790.01 CN ISSN 0831-1579
WESTWORLD ALBERTA MAGAZINE. 1926. 6/yr. membership. (Alberta Motor Association) Canada Wide Magazines Ltd., 4180 Lougheed Highway, Ste. 401, Burnaby, BC V5C 6A7, Canada. Ed. Robon Roberts. adv.: B&W page Can.$6650, color page Can.$8300; trim 8 1/8 x 10 7/8; adv. contact: Tim Nast. bk.rev.; charts; illus.; stat. circ. 305,000. **Document type:** consumer publication.
Former titles (until 1985): Alberta Motorist (ISSN 0826-4937); (until 1980): Alberta Magazine (ISSN 0228-1082); Alberta Motorist (ISSN 0002-4856).
Description: Features automotive-related tips; club news; and general interest, national and international travel articles.

388.3 CN ISSN 0831-1552
WESTWORLD SASKATCHEWAN. 1951. q. membership. (C A A Saskatchewan) Canada Wide Magazines Ltd., 401-4180 Lougheed Hwy., Burnaby, BC V5C 6A7, Canada. TEL 604-299-9188. FAX 604-949-4461. Ed. Robin Roberts. adv. contact: Tim Nast. bk.rev.; illus. circ. 112,000. **Document type:** consumer publication.
Formerly: Saskatchewan Motorist (ISSN 0036-4940)

388.3 US
WHALES ON WHEELS. 1981. q. $6. Group Ultra Van, 5537 Pioneer Rd., Boulder, CO 80301. TEL 303-530-1288. Ed. W. Christy Barden. circ. 250. **Document type:** newsletter.
Description: Technical information on the ongoing care and maintenance of an ultra van.

629.22 UK ISSN 0307-2991
WHAT CAR?. m. $81. Haymarket Magazines Ltd., 38-42 Hampton Rd., Teddington, Middx. TW11 OJE, England. TEL 081-943-5000. TELEX 895-2440-HAYMRT-G. Ed. Howard Walker. illus. circ. 142,086. **Document type:** consumer publication.
—BLDSC (9309.660000).
Description: Road tests and evaluations of new cars.

388.3 JA ISSN 0049-755X
THE WHEEL EXTENDED; a Toyota quarterly review. (Text in English) 1971. q. free. Toyota Motor Corporation, International Public Affairs Division, 1-4-18, Koraku, Bunkyo-ku, Tokyo 112, Japan. TEL 03-3817-9930. FAX 03-3817-9017. Ed.Bd. charts; illus.; circ. 11,000 (controlled). **Indexed:** Fuel & Energy Abstr. **Document type:** monographic series.
—BLDSC (9310.650000); UnCover.
Description: Covers issues relating to the automobile and transportation fields.

388.3 II ISSN 0970-8138
WHEEL FARE. 1976. 6/yr. Rs.20. V. Krishnan, Ed. & Pub., 9 State Bank St., 1st Lane, Mount Rd., Madras 600 002, India. TEL 849305. Ed. V. Krishnan. bk.rev. circ. 15,500.

388.3 AT ISSN 0043-4779
WHEELS (SYDNEY). 1953. m. Aus.$68.40. A C P Publishing Pty. Ltd., 54-58 Park St., Sydney, N.S.W. 2001, Australia. TEL 02-282-8641. FAX 02-267-9439. Ed. Angus MacKenzie; Pub. Richard Walsh. adv. contact: Peter Miller. bk.rev.; charts; illus.; index. circ. 56,470. **Indexed:** Aus.Rd.Ind., Pinpointer. **Document type:** consumer publication.

388.3 UK ISSN 0263-7081
WHEELS & TRACKS; international historical review of military vehicles. q. $26. Battle of Britain Prints International Ltd., Church House, Church St., Stratford, London E15 3JA, England. (Distr. in U.S. by: Sky Books International Inc., 48 East 50th St., New York, NY 10022) Ed. Bart Vanderveen.

388.3 SW
WHEELS MAGAZINE. 1977. m. SEK 329. Wheels Magazine AB, P.O. Box 6040, S-183 06 Taaby, Sweden. TEL 46-8-732-70-96. FAX 46-8-732-70-96. Eds. Olof Svenningsson, Sture Tomgren; Pub. Sture Tomgren. adv.: B&W page SEK 8600, color page SEK 11900; trim 190 x 260. circ. 28,100. cols./p.: 3; pp./issue: 100. **Document type:** consumer publication.

388.3 US
WILLYS OVERLAND JEEPSTER CLUB. NEWSLETTER. 1964. m. $15 membership. Willys Overland Jeepster Club, Box 12042, Coronado Sta., El Paso, TX 79913. TEL 915-581-2671. Ed. Jay Sherwin; Pub. Jay Sherwin. charts; illus.; stat.; tr.lit.; index. circ. 500. (looseleaf format; back issues avail.) **Document type:** newsletter.
Description: For owners of 1949-1951 Willys Overland Jeepster convertibles. Provides information on restoration and attempts to promote an understanding and appreciation of this particular vehicle.

388.3 US ISSN 0736-7988
WISCONSIN AUTO VALUATION GUIDE. 8/yr. $49.50. Maclean Hunter Market Reports, Inc., 29 N. Wacker Dr., Chicago, IL 60606-3297. TEL 312-726-2802. FAX 312-726-2574.

380.5 US ISSN 1043-979X
WOMEN WITH WHEELS; the newsletter on automobiles for women. 1989. q. $20 (effective 1995). Susan Frissell, Ed. & Pub., 1718 Northfield Sq., Ste. A, Northfield, IL 60093. TEL 708-501-3519. adv. contact: Patricia Stringer. bk.rev.; bibl, charts; illus.; stat.; tr.lit.; index. circ. 300. (back issues avail.) **Document type:** consumer publication, newsletter.
Description: Provides information on cars and their maintenance. Features articles on subjects such as: safety, leasing vs. buying, talking with auto salespeople, and choosing a mechanic.
Refereed Serial

WOODALL'S SOUTHERN R V. see SPORTS AND GAMES — Outdoor Life

388 US
WORLD AUTO FORECAST REPORT. q. D R I - McGraw-Hill, 24 Hartwell Ave., Lexington, MA 02173. TEL 617-863-5100. FAX 617-860-6332. TELEX 200 284. (back issues avail.)

629.2 US ISSN 0085-8307
HD9710.A1
WORLD MOTOR VEHICLE DATA. a. $35. Motor Vehicle Manufacturers Association of the U.S., Inc., 7430 Second Ave., Ste. 300, Detroit, MI 48202. TEL 313-872-4311. (also avail. in microfiche from CIS) **Indexed:** SRI.
—BLDSC (9356.720000).

629 CN ISSN 0824-5487
WORLD OF WHEELS. 1983. 6/yr. Can.$8.50. World of Wheels Publishing Inc., 1200 Markham Rd., Ste. 220, Scarborough, ON M1H 3C3, Canada. TEL 416-438-7777. FAX 416-438-5333. Ed. Joe Duarte. adv. circ. 119,000. **Document type:** consumer publication.

388.3 UK ISSN 0954-8742
WORLD SPORTS CARS. bi-m. Hyde Park Group, Mansford Rd., London SW15 2RS, England. FAX 203-348-3555. (Dist. in US by: Hyde Park Group, 2001 W. Main St., Stamford, CT 06902. TEL 203-969-2533) Ed. Daryn Styles.

338.476 UK ISSN 0958-4013
YORKSHIRE AUTO TRADER. 1982. w. per no.; newsstand price: 180. Hurst Publishing (Leeds), Munro House, Duke St., Leeds LS9 8AL, England. FAX 0113-242-5417. adv. contact: Chris Wright. circ. 45,897 (paid). **Document type:** consumer publication.
Formerly: Yorkshire Motor Trade.
Description: Contains trade and private advertisements of cars, motor bikes, caravans, buying and selling.

629.288 UK ISSN 0957-6525
YOUR CLASSIC. 1989. m. £21. Haymarket Magazines Ltd., 60 Waldegrave Road, Teddington, Mddx. TW11 8LG, England. TEL 081-943-5000. TELEX 8952440. Ed. Ian Bond. circ. 49,059. (back issues avail.)
Incorporates: Restoring Classic Cars & Classic Car Mechanics.
Description: Covers less expensive classic cars and first-time buying and owning, including renovation.

388 NE ISSN 0169-4723
ZAKENAUTO; Misset select. 1985. s-a. free to qualified personnel. Misset (Subsidiary of: Reed Elsevier plc), Postbus 4, 7000 BA Doetinchem, Netherlands. TEL 31-8340-49911. FAX 31-8340-43839. TELEX 45481. Ed. A.N. Cupedo. adv.: B&W page fl.14780; unit 187 x 257; adv. contact: Cor van Nek. circ. 174,000 (controlled). **Document type:** trade publication.
Description: Covers all aspects of purchase, operation and use of passenger cars used for business.

388.3 US
3 & 4 WHEEL ACTION. m. $18.98. Hi-Torque Publications, Inc., Box 957, Valencia, CA 91380-9057. TEL 818-365-6831.

380.5 GR ISSN 1105-1329
4 TROCHI TEST/4 WHEELS TEST. (Text in Greek) 1979. a. Technical Press, S.A., 31 Praxitelous St., 167 77 Athens, Greece. TEL 30-1-9961-861. FAX 30-1-9961-864. Ed. Costas Cavvathas; Pub. Sophie Cavvatha. circ. 18,000. **Document type:** consumer publication.
Description: Discusses new car models and driving tests.

629.286 GR ISSN 1105-1280
4 TROHI/4 WHEELS. Variant title: Tesseris Trohi. (Text in Greek) 1970. m. Dr.7500($36) (foreign Dr.12000). Technical Press S.A., 31-Praxitelous St., 167 77 Athens, Greece. TEL 30-1-9961-861. FAX 30-1-9961-864. Ed. Costas Cavvathas; Pub. Sophie Cavvatha. adv. contact: George Melitsiotis. circ. 95,000. **Document type:** consumer publication.
Description: Presents new car models, new technologies, environmental issues, and driving tests.

388.3 US
4-W D SPORT UTILITY. bi-m. $2.75 per no. McMullen & Yee Publishing, 744 S. Placentia Ave., Placentia, CA 92670-6846. TEL 714-572-2255. FAX 714-572-1864.
Formerly: 4-W D Action.

629.22 388.3 SW ISSN 0281-3580
4 WHEEL DRIVE. 1983. bi-m. SEK 195 (foreign SEK 231); newsstand price: SEK 38. Foerlags AB Albinsson & Sjoeberg, P.O. Box 529, S-371 23 Karlskrona, Sweden. TEL 46-455-335325. FAX 46-455-311715. Ed. Peter Oejeskog; Pub. Stig L. Sjoeberg. adv.: B&W page SEK 10500, color page SEK 17000; trim 190 x 275. circ. 23,000 (controlled). cols./p.: 4; pp./issue: 70. **Document type:** consumer publication.

796.7 UK ISSN 0306-6312
750 BULLETIN. 1939. m. £22.50 membership. Seven Fifty Motor Club Ltd., Courthouse, St. Winifreds Rd., Biggin Hill, Kent TN16 3HR, England. TEL 0959-575812. FAX 0959-540094. Ed. David Edroff. adv. contact: Mike Peck. bk.rev. circ. 2,500. **Document type:** newsletter.

TRANSPORTATION — Computer Applications

625.7 651.8 US ISSN 0091-5122
TE5
AMERICAN ASSOCIATION OF STATE HIGHWAY AND TRANSPORTATION OFFICIALS. SUB-COMMITTEE ON COMPUTER TECHNOLOGY. NATIONAL CONFERENCE. PROCEEDINGS. Key Title: Proceedings - Committee on Computer Technology. 1983. a. $19.25. American Association of State Highway and Transportation Officials, U.S. Department of Transportation, 444 N. Capitol St. N.W., Ste. 225, Washington, DC 20001. TEL 202-624-5800. FAX 202-624-5806. Ed. Keith F. Kohler. circ. controlled. **Document type:** proceedings.

385 RU ISSN 0005-2329
TF615 CODEN: ATSVAG
AVTOMATIKA, TELEMEKHANIKA I SVYAZ.* 1957. m. $61 (effective 1996). Izdatel'stvo Transport, Basmanny tupik 6A, 107174 Moscow, Russia. TEL 095-262-6773. (Co-sponsor: Ministerstvo Putei Soobshcheniya) charts; illus.; index. **Indexed:** Chem.Abstr, INSPEC (1968-1983).
—CASDDS.

380.5 US ISSN 1057-5618
EN ROUTE TECHNOLOGY; the newsletter of mobile systems integration. 1991. bi-w. Telecom Publishing Group, 1011 King St., Box 1455, VA 22313-2055. TEL 800-327-7205. FAX 703-739-6940. **Document type:** trade publication.
●Also available online. Vendor(s): NewsNet (TE33).
—CCC.

380.5 US
I E E E WORKSHOP ON AUTOMOTIVE APPLICATIONS OF ELECTRONICS (PUBLICATION). 1982. biennial. price varies. (I E E E, Industrial Electronics Society) Institute of Electrical and Electronics Engineers, Inc., 345 E. 47th St., New York, NY 10017-2394. TEL 212-705-7900. FAX 212-705-7682. (Subscr. to: Box 1331, 445 Hoes Ln., Piscataway, NJ 08855-1331)
Formerly (until 1986): Automotive Applications on Microprocessors.

352.7 624 UK
P T R C SUMMER ANNUAL MEETING. PROCEEDINGS. (Planning and Transport Research and Computation) 1968. a. (approx. 20 vols./yr.) price varies. P T R C Education and Research Services Ltd., Glenthorne House, Hammersmith Grove, London W6 0LG, England. TEL 0181-741-1516. FAX 0181-741-5993. TELEX 335269-COMET-G. circ. 350. (back issues avail.) **Indexed:** HRIS. **Document type:** proceedings.

SIGNAL UND DRAHT; Zeitschrift fuer Informationstechnik im Eisenbahnwesen. see *TRANSPORTATION — Railroads*

625 001.642 SA
SOUTH AFRICA. DIVISION OF ROADS AND TRANSPORT TECHNOLOGY. USER MANUALS AND COMPUTER PROGRAMS/DIVISIE VIR PAD- EN VERVOERTEGNOLOGIE. GEBRUIKERSHANDBOEKE EN REKENAARPROGRAMME. 1976. irreg., latest 1990. price varies. Division of Roads and Transport Technology, Computer Information Centre for Transportation, Box 395, Pretoria 0001, South Africa. (Co-sponsor: Department of Transport) **Document type:** government publication.
Formerly: National Institute for Transport and Road Research. User Manuals for Computer Programs.

TETSUDO NI OKERU SAIBANETIKKUSU RIYO KOKUNAI SHINPOJUMU RONBUNSHU/SYMPOSIUM ON THE USE OF CYBERNETICS ON THE RAILWAY. PAPERS. see *COMPUTERS — Cybernetics*

TRANSPORTATION — Railroads

385.2 UK ISSN 0001-0472
A B C RAIL GUIDE. 1853. m. £87.50. Reed Travel Group, Part of Reed Telepublishing (Subsidiary of: Reed Elsevier group), Church St., Dunstable, Beds. LU5 4HB, England. TEL 01582-600111. FAX 01582-695230. TELEX 82168 AIRABC G. Ed. C. Hopper. circ. 8,800. **Document type:** directory.
—BLDSC (0537.757700).
Formerly: A B C or Alphabetical Railway Guide.
Description: Contains rail schedules and full details of fares from London to all major U.K. cities.

A M R A JOURNAL. (Australian Model Railway Association) see *HOBBIES*

385 UK
A R P S INFORMATION PAPERS. irreg. Association of Railway Preservation Societies Ltd., c/o John M. Crane, Ed., 7 Robert Close, Potters Bar, Herts. EN6 2DH, England. TEL 01707-643568. **Document type:** monographic series.

625.1 US ISSN 1054-0253
TF858.A2
A S M E - I E E E JOINT RAILROAD CONFERENCE. I E E E TECHNICAL PAPERS. Key Title: I E E E Technical Papers Presented at the A S M E - I E E E Joint Railroad Conference (1989). a. price varies. Institute of Electrical and Electronics Engineers, Inc, 345 E. 47th St., New York, NY 10017-2394. TEL 212-705-7366. FAX 212-705-7682. (Subscr. to: Box 1331, 445 Hoes Ln., Piscataway, NJ 08855-1331. TEL 908-562-3871)
—UMI.
Former titles (until 1986): Joint A S M E - I E E E Railroad Conference. I E E E Technical Papers (ISSN 0885-3800); (1977-1981): Joint A S M E - I E E E - A A R Railroad Conference. I E E E Technical Papers (ISSN 0885-3819); Joint A S M E - I E E E Railroad Technical Conference. I E E E Papers; (until 1975): Joint Railroad Conference. I E E E Papers; Joint Railroad Conference Record; Which supersedes: Joint Railroad Technical Conference. Preprint (ISSN 0075-3998).
Description: Design and technical characteristics of current hardware used to improve the operation of systems in the railroad or transit industries.

385.264 II
AIR CARGO AGENTS ASSOCIATION OF INDIA. NEWS. bi-m. Air Cargo Agents Association of India, 28-B Nariman Bhavan, Nariman Point, 400 021 Bombay, India.

625.1 US
AMERICAN RAILWAY ENGINEERING ASSOCIATION. PROCEEDINGS. a. $78. American Railway Engineering Association, 50 F St., N.W., Ste. 7702, Washington, DC 20001. TEL 202-639-2190. Ed. Louis Cerny. (reprint service avail. from UMI) **Indexed:** Geotech.Abstr. **Document type:** proceedings.
Former titles: American Railway Engineering Association. Proceedings, Technical Conference (ISSN 0271-4450); American Railway Engineering Association. Proceedings of the Annual Convention.
Description: Reports of technical committees, proposed changes to AREA Manual for Railway Engineering and Portfolio of Trackwork Plans, results of research, papers on various phases of railway engineering construction and maintenance.

625.1 US ISSN 0003-0694
AMERICAN RAILWAY ENGINEERING ASSOCIATION BULLETIN. Short title: A R E A Bulletin. 1900. 5/yr. $78. American Railway Engineering Association, 50 F St., N.W., Ste. 7702, Washington, DC 20001. TEL 202-639-2190. Ed. Anne B. Hazell. adv.: B&W page $525, color page $1275. bibl.; charts; stat.; index, cum.index. circ. 4,000. (also avail. in microform from UMI; reprint service avail. from UMI) **Indexed:** Br.Rail.Bd., Chem.Abstr., Eng.Ind., Geotech.Abstr. **Document type:** bulletin.
—Ei; Faxon; SWETS; UMI; UnCover.

385 US ISSN 0097-7039
HE2791
AMTRAK ANNUAL REPORT. Cover title: National Railroad Passenger Corporation Annual Report. 1971. a. National Railroad Passenger Corporation, 60 Massachusetts Ave., N.E., Washington, DC 20002. TEL 202-906-3000. circ. 15,000. **Document type:** corporate report.

AMTRAK EXPRESS. see *TRAVEL AND TOURISM — Airline Inflight And Hotel Inroom*

385 BL ISSN 0102-4965
ANUARIO ESTATISTICO DAS FERROVIAS DO BRASIL. 1951. a. free. Rede Ferroviaria Federal, S.A., Gerencia de Estatistica, Pca. Procopio Ferreira 86 s - 1014, 20224 Rio de Janeiro, RJ, Brazil. adv. circ. 1,200.
Formerly (until 1977): Estatistico des Estradas de Ferro do Brasil (ISSN 0102-6232)

625.1 GW ISSN 0341-0463
ARCHIV FUER EISENBAHNTECHNIK. 1952. a. DM.89. Hestra-Verlag, Holzhofallee 33, 64295 Darmstadt, Germany. TEL 06151-3907-0. FAX 06151-390777. adv. **Indexed:** B.C.I.R.A., Fuel & Energy Abstr., INSPEC (1968-1987).
—CCC.

385 AG
ASOCIACION DEL CONGRESO PANAMERICANO DE FERROCARRILES. BOLETIN. 1916. bi-m. membership. Asociacion del Congreso Panamericano de Ferrocarriles - Pan-American Railway Congress Association, Av. 9 de Julio 1925, Piso 13, 1332 Buenos Aires, Argentina. TEL 814-1823. FAX 54-1-814-1823. Ed. Juan Carlos de Marchi. adv.; bk.rev.; charts; stat. circ. 800.

ASSOCIATION OF PRIVATE POSTAL SYSTEMS. DIRECTORY. see *COMMUNICATIONS — Postal Affairs*

ASSOCIATION OF PRIVATE POSTAL SYSTEMS. UPDATE. see *COMMUNICATIONS — Postal Affairs*

625.1 US
ASSOCIATION OF RAILROAD EDITORS. PROOF. 1922. m. Association of Railroad Editors, c/o Paula Newbaker, Association of American Railroads, 50 F St., N.W., Washington, DC 20001. TEL 202-639-2562. FAX 202-639-2559. **Document type:** newsletter.

385 UK
ASSOCIATION OF RAILWAY PRESERVATION SOCIETIES. JOURNAL. 1979. q. c/o John M. Crane, 7 Robert Close, Potters Bar, Herts. EN6 2DH, England. TEL 01707-643568. Eds. M. & J. Cope. adv. circ. 1,000. **Document type:** newsletter.
Description: Provides news, comment and articles on subjects of special interest to the railway preservation movement and details of society meetings and seminars.

385.264 IT
ASSOCIAZIONE ITALIANA INGEGNERI DEL TRAFFICO. BOLLETTINO. q. Associazione Italiana Ingegneri del Traffico, c/o Facolta di Ingegneria, Via Marzola 9, 35100 Padova, Italy. TEL 049-831510.

385.264 IT
ASSOCIAZIONE NAZIONALE AUTOSERVIZI IN CONCESSIONE. INFORMA. Short title: A N A C Informa. m. Associazione Nazionale Autoservizi in Concessione, Piazza dell'Esquilino 29, 00185 Rome, Italy. TEL 06-4820531. FAX 06-4821204.

TRANSPORTATION — RAILROADS

385   CN   ISSN 0004-7376
AU FIL DU RAIL. English edition: Keeping Track (ISSN 0453-4441) 1966. 10/yr. Canadian National Railways, P.O. Box 8100, Montreal, PQ H3C 3N4, Canada. TEL 514-399-8041. FAX 514-399-5344. Ed. Louise Cardella. circ. 15,400. (tabloid format)
Description: Covers news and events of interest to active and retired employees of Canadian National Railways.

AUSTRALIAN MODEL RAILWAY MAGAZINE. see *HOBBIES*

385   AT   ISSN 0005-0105
AUSTRALIAN RAILWAY HISTORICAL SOCIETY. BULLETIN. 1937. m. Aus.$20. Australian Railway Historical Society, P.O. Box E129, St. James, N.S.W., 2000, Australia. Ed. A. Bisits. bk.rev.; film rev.; charts; illus.; stat.; index. circ. 3,000. (also avail. in microfiche) **Document type:** bulletin.

AUSTRALIAN RAILWAYS UNION. FEDERAL OFFICE NEWS. see *LABOR UNIONS*

385.264   IT   ISSN 0393-5825
AUTOBUS OGGI. m. Associazione Nazionale Autoservizi in Concessione, Piazza dell'Esquilino 29, 00185 Rome, Italy. TEL 06-4820531. FAX 06-4821204.

385   US   ISSN 0362-2711
TF25.B8
B & M BULLETIN. 1971. irreg. $25 membership. Boston & Maine Railroad Historical Society, Inc., Box 2936, Woburn, MA 01888. TEL 617-628-4053. Ed. John Alan Roderick. bk.rev.; charts; illus. circ. 2,000. **Document type:** newsletter.
Description: Historical record of the B&M and its predecessor railroads.

385   GW
B D E F - JAHRBUCH. 1982. a. DM.15. (Bund Deutscher Eisenbahn-Freunde) Verlag Uhle und Kleimann, Pettenpohlstr. 17, 32312 Luebbecke, Germany. TEL 05741-7209. FAX 05741-90224. circ. 3,000. (back issues avail.) **Document type:** bulletin.

B M W E RAILWAY JOURNAL. (Brotherhood of Maintenance of Way Employes) see *LABOR UNIONS*

385   SZ
BAHNHOFBLATT. q. Schweizerischer Bundesbahnen SBB, Kreisdirektion 111, CH-8021 Zurich, Switzerland. TEL 01-8093111. FAX 01-8106002. circ. 220,000.

385   GW
BEKANNTGABEN DEUTSCHE BAHN. 1946. w. DM.265. Deutsche Bahn AG, Zentralbereich Konzernorganisation, Ruschestr. 59, 10365 Berlin, Germany. TEL 030-29751254. FAX 030-29751123. Ed. Elke Herbig. adv.; bk.rev. circ. 35,100. **Document type:** newsletter.
Formerly (until 1994): Bekanntgaben der Deutschen Bahnen - Amtsblatt; Which was formed by the 1993 merger of: Amtsblatt der Deutschen Bundesbahn (ISSN 0179-7824) & Amtsblatt der Deutschen Reichsbahn.

385   NE   ISSN 0282-888X
BENELUX RAIL. (Text in Dutch and French) 1981. biennial. $39 (effective 1995). Het Nijvere Lezerke, Postbus 233, 6400 AE Heerlen, Netherlands. TEL 31-4451-2152. FAX 31-4451-1949. Ed. Marcel Vleugels. illus. (back issues avail.) **Document type:** academic/scholarly publication.
Description: Provides information on events and devlopments affecting all railroads (including urban transport, industrial and museum railways) in the Benelux countries during the preceding two years. Includes network maps and list of all railways stations and depots.

385   UK   ISSN 0263-0125
BLASTPIPE. 1981. irreg. £0.10 per no. Fakenham and Dereham Railway Society, c/o I Jowett, Market Place, East Harling, Norfolk NOR 12X, England. illus.

385   IT
BOLLETTINO UFFICIALE DELLE FERROVIE DELLO STATO. PARTE PRIMA E SECONDA. b-w. L.20700. Azienda Autonoma delle Ferrovie dello Stato, Centro di Documentazione, Piazza Croce Rossa, 00100 Rome, Italy.

385   IT
BOLLETTINO UFFICIALE DELLE FERROVIE DELLO STATO. PARTE TERZA. m. L.11500. Azienda Autonoma delle Ferrovie dello Stato, Centro di Documentazione, Piazza Croce Rossa, 00100 Rome, Italy.

385   UK   ISSN 1354-0947
BRANCH LINE NEWS. 1955. s-m. £17 (effective 1995). Branch Line Society, Hon. General Secretary J.J.J Holmes, 40 Mede Way, Colchester, Essex CO7 9HW, England. TEL 01206-825019. Ed. A.M. Jervits. adv.; bk.rev.; index; circ. 1,200. (paid). **Document type:** newsletter.
Description: Provides general information on British and overseas railroad branch lines, openings and closings, local developments, and visits to interesting and unusual visits to interesting and unusual railroad sites.

385.2   CN   ISSN 0824-233X
BRANCHLINE; Canada's rail newsmagazine. 1965. m. Can.$32($26) Bytown Railway Society, Box 141, Sta. A, Ottawa, ON K1N 8V1, Canada. TEL 613-745-1201. Ed. Earl Roberts. adv. contact: Leslie Goodwin. bk.rev.; circ. 1,700 (paid); 70 (controlled). (back issues avail.)
Description: Promotes an interest in railways and railway history. Provides current news.

BRITAIN BY BRITRAIL; how to tour Britain by train. see *TRAVEL AND TOURISM*

385.264   UK
BRITISH INTERNATIONAL FREIGHT ASSOCIATION. YEARBOOK. 1944. a. £28.50. British International Freight Association, Redfern House, Browells Lane, Feltham, Middx. TW13 7EP, England. FAX 081-890-5546. adv. circ. 6,000. **Document type:** trade publication.
Formerly: Institute of Freight Forwarders. Yearbook.

385.1   UK   ISSN 0305-1420
BRITISH RAILWAYS BOARD. ANNUAL REPORT AND ACCOUNTS. 1963. a. price varies. British Railways Board, Euston House, P.O. Box 100, London NW1 1DZ, England. TELEX 299431-BRHQLN-G. (Dist. by: H.M.S.O., c/o Liason Officer, Atlantic House, London EC1P 1BW, England) **Document type:** government publication, corporate report.
Formerly: British Railways Board. Report and Statement of Accounts (ISSN 0068-242X)
Description: Annual statement of accounts and business report.

BULLETIN DES TRANSPORTS; et de la logistique. see *LAW*

385.2   CN   ISSN 1189-363X
C P RAIL SYSTEM NEWS. (Text in English, French) 1971. 16/yr. free. C P Trucks, Public Relations, 2255 Sheppard Ave. E., Ste. 335, Willowdale, Ont. N2J 4Y1, Canada. TEL 514-395-7596. Ed. Tim Humphreys. circ. 50,000.
Formerly (until 1992): C P Rail News (ISSN 0229-8694)

385.1   CM
CAMEROON. REGIE NATIONALE DES CHEMINS DE FER. COMPTE RENDU DE GESTION. a. Regie Nationale des Chemins de Fer, Douala, Cameroon. **Document type:** government publication.

385   CM
CAMEROON. REGIE NATIONALE DES CHEMINS DE FER. STATISTIQUES. irreg. Regie Nationale des Chemins de Fer, Douala, Cameroon. illus. **Document type:** government publication.

385   CN   ISSN 0008-4875
CANADIAN RAIL/RAIL CANADIEN. (Text in English, French) 1949. bi-m. Can.$31($28.50) Canadian Railroad Historical Association, Box 22, Sta. B, Montreal, PQ H3B 3J5, Canada. Eds. Frederick F. Angus, Douglas N.W. Smith. bk.rev.; illus.; index; circ. 1,300 (controlled). **Document type:** bulletin.

385   CN   ISSN 0226-157X
CANADIAN RAILWAY CLUB. NEWSLETTER. 1908. 3/yr. Can.$120 membership. Canadian Railway Club, Inc., Box 162, Sta. A, Montreal, Que. H3C 1C5, Canada. TEL 514-634-4515. FAX 514-631-2280. Ed. J.H. Glatzmayer. adv. contact: J.H. Glatzmayer. circ. 1,500. **Document type:** newsletter.
Formerly (until 1978): Canadian Railway Club. Official Proceedings (ISSN 0008-4883)
Description: Concerned with the construction, operation and maintenance of railroads and railroad equipment.

385.2   CN   ISSN 0829-3023
CANADIAN TRACKSIDE GUIDE. 1982. a. Can.$17.50. Bytown Railway Society, Box 141, Sta. A, Ottawa, ON K1N 8V1, Canada. TEL 613-745-1201. Ed. Earl Roberts. adv. contact: Les Goodwin. **Document type:** directory.
Description: Lists mainline, shortline and industrial locomotives, passenger cars, preserved equipment, urban rail transit equipment, cabooses, cranes, spreaders, plows, work service equipment, former passenger equipment now in non-revenue service and detailed listings for every mainline railway subdivision in Canada.

625.2   US
CAR AND LOCOMOTIVE CYCLOPEDIA. 1879. irreg.; latest 1984. $69.95. Simmons-Boardman Publishing Corporation (Omaha), 1809 Capitol Ave., Omaha, NE 10014. TEL 402-346-4300. Ed. K. Ellsworth. adv. contact: Pat Kentner. bibl.; charts; illus. circ. 6,500. **Document type:** trade publication.

385   US
CAR & LOCOMOTIVE YEARBOOK. 1988. a. $50. Trade Press Publishing Co., 230 W. Monroe, Ste. 2210, Chicago, IL 60606. circ. 6,000. **Document type:** trade publication.

385   SP
CARRIL; revista de divulgacion ferroviaria. 1978. 4/yr. 4000 ptas. Estacion Barcelona Termino, Escalera de la Aduana, 2o piso, Apdo. 1923, 08003 Barcelona, Spain. TEL 3-310-52-97. FAX 3-268-02-22. adv.: B&W page 45000 ptas., color page 70000 ptas.; adv. contact: Marta Balletbo-Coll. bk.rev.

625   US   ISSN 0069-1623
TF701
CENTRAL ELECTRIC RAILFANS' ASSOCIATION. BULLETIN. 1938. irreg., no.130, 1993. membership. Central Electric Railfans' Association, Box 503, Chicago, IL 60690. TEL 312-346-3723. Ed.Bd. circ. 2,000. **Document type:** bulletin.
Description: List of books and publications pertaining to the history of electric-powered trolleys, streetcars, and railroad systems.

385   US   ISSN 0008-9532
CENTRAL RAILWAY CHRONICLE. 1890. 4/yr. $3. Central Railway Club of Buffalo, 960 French St., Buffalo, NY 14227-3632. TEL 716-825-0248. Ed. Clarence Michael Voll. adv.; circ. 295 (controlled).

CHEMINOT. see *LABOR UNIONS*

CHEMINOT DE FRANCE. see *LABOR UNIONS*

CHEMINOT RETRAITE. see *LABOR UNIONS*

385   FR   ISSN 0009-2924
CHEMINS DE FER. 1937. bi-m. 310 F. Association Francaise des Amis des Chemins de Fer, Gare de l'Est, 75475 Paris Cedex 10, France. TEL 40-38-20-92. Ed. Bernard Porcher. adv.; bk.rev.; charts; illus. circ. 5,000.
Description: Discusses worldwide railways of yesterday, today and the future.

385   US   ISSN 0886-6287
CHESAPEAKE AND OHIO HISTORICAL MAGAZINE. 1969. m. $17. Chesapeake and Ohio Historical Society, Inc., Box 79, Clifton Forge, VA 24422. TEL 703-862-2210. Ed. Donald R. Traser. bk.rev.; charts; illus. circ. 2,500. (also avail. in microfilm from UMI; reprint service avail. from UMI) —UMI.
Formerly (until 1986): Chesapeake and Ohio Historical Newsletter (ISSN 0883-587X)

TRANSPORTATION — RAILROADS

385 531.64 US ISSN 0732-8397
COAL TRANSPORTATION REPORT. 1982. s-m. $595 (foreign $660) (effective Jan. 1995). Fieldston Publications, Inc., 1920 N St., N.W., Ste. 210, Washington, DC 20036-1613. TEL 202-775-0240. FAX 202-872-8045. Ed. John Gallagher; Pub. Jaime Heller. adv. contact: Laura Dowe. bk.rev. circ. 225. **Document type:** newsletter, trade publication.
Description: Studies all aspects of coal transportation and railroad legislation and regulation.

385.264 US
COMMON, CARRIER CONFERENCE-IRREGULAR ROUTE. NEWSLETTER. 1941. bi-m. Common, Carrier Conference-Irregular Route, 2200 Mill Rd., Ste.600, Alexandria, VA 22314. TEL 703-838-1950.

385 FR ISSN 0222-4844
CONNAISSANCE DU RAIL. 1979. m. 395 F. (Europe 442 F.; elsewhere 491 F.). Editions de l'Ormet, 03330 Valignat, France. TEL 70-58-53-19. FAX 70-58-54-36. Ed. Pierre Laederich. adv. contact: Patricia Laederich. bk.rev.; bibl.; cum.index. circ. 10,000. (back issues avail.)

385 CN ISSN 0319-8332
COUPLER. 1957. bi-m. free. B C Rail Ltd., P.O. Box 8770, Vancouver, B.C. V6B 4X6, Canada. TEL 604-984-5248. FAX 604-984-5090. Ed. K. Korbin. circ. 4,000.

625.143 US ISSN 0097-4536
CROSSTIES. 1919. bi-m. $35. (Railway Tie Association) Covey Communications Corp., Box 2267, Gulf Shores, AL 36547. TEL 334-968-5300. FAX 334-968-4532. adv.; charts; illus.; stat.; index. circ. 2,500. **Indexed:** Chem.Abstr.
Formerly: Cross Tie Bulletin (ISSN 0011-197X)
Description: Covers all aspects of the railroad crosstie industry, including forest management, timber processing, worker safety, legislative and engineering issues.

385 GW ISSN 0172-4479
D B. (Deine Bahn); Zeitschrift fuer das Bildungswesen der deutschen Bundesbahn. 1948. m. DM.57.60. (Deutsche Bahn AG) Eisenbahn-Fachverlag GmbH, Postfach 2330, 55013 Mainz, Germany. TEL 06131-222871. FAX 06131-227969. (Co-sponsor: Verband Deutscher Eisenbahn-Fachschulen) Ed. Hermann Geyer; Pub. Holger Huethig. adv. contact: Monika Trautwein. bk.rev.; charts; illus. **Document type:** academic/scholarly publication.
Formed by the 1973 merger of: Eisenbahner. Ausgabe A (ISSN 0172-2808); Eisenbahner. Ausgabe B (ISSN 0172-2816); Which superseded (in 1949): Eisenbahner (ISSN 0172-2824); Incorporates (1950-1973): Eisenbahnfachmann.

385 GW ISSN 0011-4758
D B - KUNDENBRIEF.* 1955. m. free. Deutsche Bundesbahn, Presse und Oeffentlichkeits Arbeit, Rhabanusstr. 3, 55118 Mainz, Germany. Ed. Hans Herrmann Waitz. adv.; bk.rev.; charts; illus.; stat.; index. circ. 60,000.

625.1 GW ISSN 0072-1549
HE3071
D B REPORT. 1965. a. DM.33.60. (Deutsche Bundesbahn) Hestra-Verlag, Holzhofallee 33, 64295 Darmstadt, Germany. TEL 06151-3907-0. FAX 06151-390777. adv.

385 GW ISSN 0722-0170
D G E G-NACHRICHTEN. 1969. bi-m. DM.24. Deutsche Gesellschaft fuer Eisenbahngeschichte e.V., Postfach 1111, 59369 Selm, Germany. TEL 02592-62040. (Subscr. to: DGEG- Schriftenversand, c/o Deutsche Gesellschaft fuer Industriekultur, Emseherstr. 71, 47137 Duisburg, Germany) Ed. K.-L. Lehmann. adv.; bk.rev.; charts; illus. circ. 2,500. (back issues avail.) **Document type:** newsletter.

385 GW ISSN 0933-7598
TF3
DAMPF UND REISE; Bahnerlebnisse rund um die Welt - Ueberseeische Bahnen. 1986. 4/yr. DM.80. Roehr-Verlag GmbH, Brandenburgerstr. 10, 47809 Krefeld, Germany. TEL 02151-58890. FAX 02151-588999. Ed. K.W. Koch. adv.; bk.rev. **Document type:** bulletin.
Incorporates: Verkehr in Afrika.

385 US ISSN 1073-6859
DELAWARE VALLEY RAIL PASSENGER. 1983. m. $16. Delaware Valley Association of Railroad Passengers, Box 7505, Philadelphia, PA 19010-7505. TEL 215-673-6445. Ed. Matthew D. Mitchell. adv.; bk.rev.; index. circ. 1,200. (also avail. in diskette format; back issues avail.) **Document type:** newsletter.
●Also available online.
Description: Published in the interest of continued, improved, and expanded rail service for the present and potential railroad and rail transit passengers.

385 GW ISSN 0942-5691
DIE DEUTSCHE BAHN. 1924. m. DM.218.40 (foreign DM.226.80). (Deutsche Bundesbahn) Hestra-Verlag, Holzhofallee 33, 64295 Darmstadt, Germany. TEL 06151-3907-0. FAX 06151-390777. adv.; bibl.; charts; illus.; index. circ. 10,000. (back issues avail.) **Indexed:** Excerp.Med., HRIS.
—CCC.
Formerly: Bundesbalm (ISSN 0007-5876)

385.5 UK ISSN 0268-5590
DEVELOPING METROS. 1985. a. £15. Reed Business Publishing (Subsidiary of: Reed Elsevier group), Quadrant House, The Quadrant, Sutton, Surrey SM2 5AS, England. TEL 0181-652-3739. FAX 0181-652-3738. (Dist. by: Esco Business Svcs., P.O. Box 935, Graintree, Essex CM7 4LN, England. TEL 01371-810433. FAX 01371-811065) Ed. Chris Jackson. adv. contact: S. Rennie. (back issues avail.) **Document type:** trade publication.
—SWETS.

621.2 US ISSN 0070-4830
DIESEL LOCOMOTIVE QUESTION & ANSWER MANUAL.* 1950. irreg. $8. International Association of Railway Operating Officers, 621 Peacock Cir., Granite City, IL 62040-6459.
Formerly: Diesel Electric Locomotive Examination Book.

385.264 US
DIRECTORY OF FREIGHT ACCOUNTING OFFICES AND OVERCHARGE CLAIMS. a. $10. Association of American Railroads, Economics Policy and Statistics Department, 50 F St., N.W., Washington, DC 20001. TEL 202-639-2325. (looseleaf format) **Document type:** trade publication, directory.

385 GW ISSN 0934-2230
DREHSCHEIBE. 1983. 8/yr. DM.44. ArGe Drehscheibe e.V., Gadelanderstr. 159, 24539 Neumuenster, Germany. adv.; bk.rev. (back issues avail.) **Document type:** bulletin.

385 GW ISSN 0936-3475
Z723.3
DUMJAHN'S JAHRBUCH FUER EISENBAHNLITERATUR; ein kritischer Wegweiser zu lieferbaren, angezeigten und empfehlenswerten Buechern "rund um die Eisenbahn". 1984. a. DM.15. Horst-Werner Dumjahn Verlag, Immenhof 12, 55128 Mainz, Germany. TEL 06131-35600. FAX 06131-35659. Ed. Horst-Werner Dumjahn. (back issues avail.) **Document type:** bibliography.
Formerly: Jahrbuch fuer Eisenbahnliteratur.

DYNAMIC. see LABOR UNIONS

385 II ISSN 0012-8880
EASTERN RAILWAY MAGAZINE. 1952. bi-m. Rs.12. 14-16 Govt. Place East, Calcutta 1, India. Eds. S.K. Basu, S. Sen. adv.; illus. circ. 5,000.

EISENBAHN-AMATEUR; Schweizerische Zeitschrift fuer Eisenbahn- und Modellbaufreunde. see HOBBIES

625.1 GW ISSN 0934-5930
EISENBAHN INGENIEUR KALENDER (YEAR). (In two parts: A & B) a. DM.42. Tetzlaff Verlag GmbH, Nordkanalstr. 36, 20097 Hamburg, Germany. TEL 040-2371401. Ed.Bd. adv. circ. 9,000. (back issues avail.) **Document type:** trade publication.
Formerly: Elsners Taschenbuch der Eisenbahntechnik (ISSN 0071-0075)
Description: Part A covers material required by railway engineers in their daily work; Part B covers building, machine engineering, electrical engineering, signalling and telecommunications.

385 GW ISSN 0720-051X
EISENBAHN-JOURNAL. 1975. m. DM.146. Hermann Merker Verlag GmbH, Postfach 1453, 82244 Fuerstenfeldbruck, Germany. TEL 08141-512048. FAX 08141-44689. Ed. Hermann Merker. adv. contact: Elke Albrecht. bk.rev.; bibl.; charts; illus.; stat.; index. circ. 48,000. (back issues avail.) **Document type:** consumer publication.

385 625.19 GW ISSN 0342-1902
EISENBAHN MODELLBAHN MAGAZIN. 1963. m. DM.120. Alba Publikationen Alf Teloeken, Roemerstr. 9, 40476 Duesseldorf, Germany. TEL 0211-469010. FAX 0211-484382. Ed. J. Werner. adv.; bk.rev.; circ. 61,556 (controlled). (back issues avail.) **Document type:** consumer publication.
—CCC.
Description: Covers all aspects of rail transport and model railroading.

385 SZ
EISENBAHN OESTERREICH. m. 93.80 SFr.; newsstand price: 9.80 SFr. Minirex AG, Maihofstr. 63, Postfach 3720, CH-6002 Luzern, Switzerland. TEL 041-368666. FAX 041-368806. **Document type:** consumer publication.

385 SZ
▼**EISENBAHN REVUE INTERNATIONAL.** 1994. 9/yr. 83.70 SFr. (foreign 93.70 SFr.). Minirex AG, Maihofstr. 63, Postfach 3720, CH-6002 Luzern, Switzerland. TEL 041-368666. FAX 041-368806. Ed. Walter von Andrian. adv.; B&W page 1975 SFr., color page 2955 SFr.; 188 x 257; adv. contact: C. Egli. circ. 12,000. **Document type:** bulletin.

385 AU ISSN 0013-2799
EISENBAHNER. 1892. m. S.24 to non-members. Oesterreichischer Gewerkschaftsbund, Gewerkschaft der Eisenbahner, Margaretenstr. 166, A-1050 Vienna, Austria. Ed. Adalbert Koranda. bk.rev.; play rev.; abstr.; charts; illus. circ. 118,000. **Document type:** newsletter.

625.1 GW ISSN 0013-2810
CODEN: ESBGAP
DER EISENBAHNINGENIEUR; Fachzeitschrift fuer Eisenbahntechnik. 1949. m. DM.155. (Verband Deutscher Eisenbahningenieure) Tetzlaff Verlag GmbH, Nordkanalstr. 36, 20097 Hamburg, Germany. TEL 040-2371401. Ed. Dieter Stuewe. adv.; bk.rev.; bibl.; charts; illus.; pat.; index. circ. 11,500. (back issues avail.) **Indexed:** Excerp.Med., INSPEC. **Document type:** trade publication.
—Ei. CCC.
Incorporates: Schienenfahrzeuge (ISSN 0036-6021) & Eisenbahnpraxis.
Description: Complete railway engineering including specialized branches such as building, building construction, surveying, signalling, telecommunications, machines, and electrical engineering.

385 625.1 GW ISSN 0013-2845
EISENBAHNTECHNISCHE RUNDSCHAU; Zeitschrift fuer die gesamte Eisenbahntechnik. (Text in German; summaries in English, French, Spanish) 1952. m. DM.242.40 (foreign DM.250.80). Hestra-Verlag, Holzhofallee 33, 64295 Darmstadt, Germany. TEL 06151-3907-0. FAX 06151-390777. Ed.Bd. adv.; bk.rev.; abstr.; bibl.; charts; illus.; index. circ. 6,050. **Indexed:** Excerp.Med., Geotech.Abstr., HRIS, INIS Atomind.
—Ei; SWETS. CCC.

385 UK ISSN 0013-4147
ELECTRIC RAILWAY SOCIETY. JOURNAL. 1956. bi-m. £6.75 (effective 1995). Electric Railway Society, 14 Askerfield Ave., Allestree, Derby DE3 2ST, England. TEL 01332-550786. Ed. J.A. Rosser. adv. contact: J.A. Rosser. bk.rev.; index; circ. 400 (paid).
Description: Presents both topical and historical articles on electric railways worldwide.

TRANSPORTATION — RAILROADS

385 621.38   GW   ISSN 0013-5437
TF701   CODEN: ELBAAQ
ELEKTRISCHE BAHNEN; Zeitschrift fuer Elektrotechnik im Verkehrswesen. 1903. m. DM.316 (effective 1996). R. Oldenbourg Verlag GmbH, Rosenheimerstr. 145, 81671 Munich, Germany. TEL 089-45051-0. FAX 089-45051207. (Subscr. to: Postfach 801360, 81613 Munich, Germany) adv.; abstr.; bibl.; charts; illus.; index. circ. 2,000. (also avail. in microform from UMI; reprint service avail. from UMI) Indexed: Br.Rail.Bd., Eng.Ind., INIS Atomind., INSPEC. Document type: trade publication. —BLDSC (3711.000000); Ei. **CCC**.
  Description: Latest developments of the use of electronics in railroads and tramways. Focus on high speed engineering, efficiency and automatic controls.

385   BE   ISSN 0777-933X
EN LIGNES. Dutch edition: Op de Baan (ISSN 0777-9321) (Text in French) 1989. q. 700 BEF. Patrimoine Ferroviaire Touristique (FPT) - Toeristisch Spoor Patrimonium (TSP), Av. des Eglantines 15, 1000 Brussels, Belgium. TEL 32-65-782922. FAX 32-65-664541. **Document type**: consumer publication.

625.1   US   ISSN 0013-8142
ENGINEERS AND ENGINES MAGAZINE. 1955. bi-m. $15 (foreign $18). Donald D. Knowles, Ed. & Pub., 2240 Oak Leaf St., Box 2757, Joliet, IL 60434-2757. TEL 815-741-2240. FAX 815-741-2243. adv.; charts; illus. circ. 9,500.

EURAIL GUIDE; how to travel Europe and all the world by train. see *TRAVEL AND TOURISM*

385   SP
EUROFER. 4/yr. Calle 1, Apdo. 2273, Barcelona, Spain. TEL 3-209-17-35. Ed. Antonio Ballara Roca. circ. 6,000.

EUROPE BY EURAIL; how to tour Europe by train. see *TRAVEL AND TOURISM*

385.1   SZ   ISSN 0071-2264
EUROPEAN COMPANY FOR THE FINANCING OF RAILWAY ROLLING STOCK. ANNUAL REPORT. Short title: EUROFIMA Annual Report. (Text in English, French and German) 1957. a. free. European Company for the Financing of Railway Rolling Stock (EUROFIMA), Rittergasse 20, CH-4001 Basel, Switzerland. FAX 061-2724105. circ. 4,000. **Document type**: corporate report.
  Description: For the business year of Eurofima.

EXPRESS. see *TRAVEL AND TOURISM — Airline Inflight And Hotel Inroom*

385 790.13   US   ISSN 0014-1380
EXTRA 2200 SOUTH; locomotive news magazine. vol.6, 1968. q. $15. Doug Cummings, Ed. & Pub., Box 8110-820, Blaine, WA 98231-8110. TEL 604-294-0175. FAX 604-294-0302. bk.rev.; charts; illus.; stat.; tr.lit.; cum.index. circ. 10,000. (back issues avail.) **Document type**: newsletter.

F E L A REPORTER & RAILROAD LIABILITY MONITOR. (Federal Employees Liability Act) see *LAW*

385.264   GW
FACHVEREINIGUNG GUTERFERNVERKEHR SCHLESWIG-HOLSTEIN. NACHRICHTENDIENST. m. Fachvereinigung Guterfernverkehr Schleswig-Holstein, Ilsahl 1-3, 24539 Neumunster, Germany. TEL 04321-31081. TELEX 299637.

385   AG   ISSN 0046-3698
FERROCARRILES ARGENTINOS.* 1971. m. Avda. Ramos Mejia 1302, Buenos Aires, Argentina. Ed.Bd. adv.; charts; illus.; stat.

FERROVIERE. see *LABOR UNIONS*

385   UK   ISSN 0015-0355
FESTINIOG RAILWAY MAGAZINE. 1958. q. £12 to non-members. Festiniog Railway Society Ltd., c/o P. Johnson, Ed., 12 Maplewell Dr., Leicester LE4 1BD, England. TEL 0116-235-7268. FAX 0116-235-7268. E-mail: 100330,3031@compuserve.com. Ed. Peter Johnson. adv.; bk.rev.; charts; illus.; circ. 6,000 (paid).

385   GW   ISSN 0945-6732
FISCHERS GUETERTRANSPORT NACHRICHTEN INFORMATIONEN FUER DEN GUETERVERKEHR. 1941. m. DM.33.85; newssprint price: DM.3. Verkehrs-Verlag J. Fischer, Paulusstr. 1, 40237 Duesseldorf, Germany. TEL 0211-991930. FAX 0211-6801544. Ed. Paul Urban. adv.: B&W page DM.720, color page DM.1347; trim 260 x 180. bk.rev.; charts; illus. circ. 3,000. **Document type**: trade publication.
  Formerly (until 1994): Fischers Tarif Nachrichten fuer Eisenbahn und Kraftwagen (ISSN 0015-2862)

385   UK
FIVE FOOT THREE. 1966. a. £2. Railway Preservation Society of Ireland, Whitehead Excursion Station, Whitehead, Co. Antrim, N. Ireland. Ed. N. Poots. adv.; bk.rev.; illus. circ. 1,500.

FOOTPLATE/VOETPLAAT. see *LABOR UNIONS*

FRACHT - DIENST. see *TRANSPORTATION — Ships And Shipping*

385   US   ISSN 0742-9355
TF470.A1
FREIGHT CARS JOURNAL; history, modeling, news. 1983. q. $20 (foreign $35). Society of Freight Car Historians, Box 2480, Monrovia, CA 91017. Ed. David G. Casdorph; Pub. David G. Casdorph. bk.rev. circ. 1,000. (back issues avail.) **Document type**: academic/scholarly publication.
  Description: Contains original articles on the history and development of American railway freight cars and related subjects.

385   GW   ISSN 0016-8866
GERMANA ESPERANTO FERVOJISTA ASOCIO. BULTENO. (Text in Esperanto; summaries in German) 1952. bi-m. An der Nikolaischule 3, 37412 Herzberg, Germany. TEL 05521-4586. FAX 05521-73313. Ed. Joachim Giessner. bk.rev.; illus. circ. 700. **Document type**: bulletin.

THE GOLDEN AGE OF MIDLANDS STEAM RAILWAYS. see *HISTORY — History Of Europe*

385   UK
GREAT WESTERN ECHO. 1963. q. £10. Great Western Society Ltd., Didcot, Oxfordshire, England. Ed. Michael Baker. adv.; bk.rev.; bibl.; charts; illus.; tr.lit. circ. 5,000.

315   US
GREEN BLOCK. 1965. m. $3 to non-members. National Railway Historical Society, Inc., Central New York Chapter, Box 229, Marcellus, NY 13108. Ed. Charles Abbott. bk.rev.

385.5   RU
GUDOK. d. Railway Transport Worker's Union - Gewerkschaft der Arbeiter des Eisenbahnwesens und Transportwegebaus, 21 Sadova - Spasskaya Ul., 107217 Moscow, Russia. (also avail. in microfilm from UMI) **Indexed**: Curr.Dig.Sov.Press.

625.1   US
GUNDERSON NEWS. 1987. q. free. Gunderson Inc., 4350 N.W. Front Ave., Portland, OR 97210. TEL 503-228-9281. FAX 503-242-0683. Ed. Julie Ward. adv. contact: Bruce Harmon. circ. 2,000. (back issues avail.)
  Description: Covers general happenings in the railroad car manufacturing shop, informs of upcoming company events.

385   SW   ISSN 0281-7411
GURKLISTEN. 1975. q. SEK 100 membership. Wadstena-Faagelsta Jaernvaeg, Jaernvaegsstationen, S-592 30 Vadstena, Sweden. TEL 0143-11145. FAX 013-136140. Ed. Christer Brimalm. adv. circ. 400.
  Description: Contains news about the museum railway and publishes articles on railway history, particularly Swedish narrow-gauge railways.

385.264   BE
HAVEN. 1913. s-a. Belgische Transportarbeidersbond, Paardenmarkt 66, B-2000 Antwerpen, Belgium. TEL 27-3-224-34-11. FAX 27-3-234-01-49.

385.264   GW
HESSISCHER VERKEHRSSPIEGEL. m. Fachverband Guterfernverkehr der Vereinigung des Verkehrsgewerbes in Hessen, Konigsberger Str 1-3, 60487 Frankfurt, Germany. TEL 774935. TELEX 12175.

385   US
HIGH SPEED RAIL - MAGLEV ASSOCIATION. YEARBOOK. 1984. a. $25. High Speed Rail Maglev Association, 206 Valley Court, Ste. 800, Pittsburgh, PA 15237. TEL 412-366-8698. FAX 412-369-6887. Ed. Robert J. Casey. circ. 5,000. **Document type**: proceedings.
  Formerly: High Speed Rail Yearbook (ISSN 0898-4611)
  Description: Covers proceedings of the convention, High Speed Rail directory and information about new transportation mode and industry of high speed rail.

385   SW   ISSN 1100-5165
HJULET. 1968. 10/yr. SEK 120 (effective 1991). Hjulet, P.O. Box 19039, S-104 32 Stockholm, Sweden.
  Formerly (until 1987): Tidningen Hjulet; **Supersedes**: Spaarvaegsmaennens Tidning.

385.22 790   US   ISSN 1055-3967
HOBO TIMES.* 6/yr. $18. National Hobo Association, World Way Center, Box 90430, Los Angeles, CA 90009.

HORSE BRASS. see *HOBBIES*

HOTBOX; the magazine of model railroaders. see *HOBBIES*

385   AU   ISSN 0005-0504
I F E F, AUSTRIA SEKCIO. BULTENO. (Federacio Esperantista Fervojista) (Text in Esperanto, German) 1956. 4/yr. free. Oesterreichischer Eisenbahner Esperant Verband, Postfach 117, A-1103 Vienna, Austria. Ed. Leopold Patek. illus.

385 387.7   II
INDIAN BRADSHAW. (Text in English) 1866. m. Rs.590. W. Newman & Co., Ltd., G.P.O. Box 76, 3 Old Court House St., Calcutta 700 069, India. TEL 248-9436. Ed. Milan Chandra Paul. adv. circ. 80,000.
  Description: Guide for rail and air travel in India.

625.1   II   ISSN 0019-6266
INDIAN RAILWAY TECHNICAL BULLETIN.* (Text in English) 1964. q. Rs.5. Research Designs and Standards Organization, Alambagh, Lucknow 5, India. abstr.; charts; illus.; stat. circ. 1,500. **Indexed**: Br.Rail.Bd. **Document type**: bulletin.

385   II   ISSN 0019-6274
INDIAN RAILWAYS; devoted to railway affairs in India and abroad. (Text in English) 1956. m. Rs.100($7.62) Ministry of Railways (Railway Board), c/o Railway Board, Box 467, New Delhi 110 001, India. TEL 11-383522. TELEX 031-66061. Ed. M.D. Banerjee. adv.; bk.rev.; charts; illus.; stat.; tr.lit. circ. 10,000.

385   II
INDIAN RAILWAYS SAFETY PERFORMANCE - A REVIEW. (Text in English) 1957. a. Railway Board, Directorate of Safety, New Delhi 110001, India.
  Formerly: Review of Accidents on Indian Government Railways (ISSN 0080-1933)

385 625.1   UK
INDUSTRIAL LOCOMOTIVE. 1947. q. £8 (effective 1995). Industrial Locomotive Society, Byfield, Wreford's Ln., Exeter, Devon EX4 5BR, England. TEL 01793-692588. Ed. R. Wear. adv.; bk.rev.; bibl.; illus.; circ. 350 (controlled). **Document type**: academic/scholarly publication.
  Formerly: Industrial Locomotive Society Journal.

385   US
INFO MAGAZINE. 1968. m. Union Pacific Railroad, Employee Communications Department, 1416 Dodge St., Omaha, NE 68179. Ed. J.H. Beck. circ. 78,000 (controlled).
  Formerly: Infonews.

INFORMATION EISENBAHN; Dokumentation des Fachschrifttums. see *TRANSPORTATION — Abstracting, Bibliographies, Statistics*

385 625.1   IT   ISSN 0020-0956
                         CODEN: INFEAE
INGEGNERIA FERROVIARIA; rivista di tecnica ed economia dei trasporti. (Text in Italian; summaries in English, French, German) 1904. m. $100 (effective 1994). Collegio Ingegneri Ferroviari Italiani, Via Giolitti 34, 00185 Rome, Italy. TEL 06-4827116. FAX 06-4742987. Dir. Giuseppe R. Corazza. adv.; bk.rev.; abstr.; bibl.; charts; illus.; index. **Indexed:** C.I.S. Abstr., Chem.Abstr., Eng.Ind., Geotech.Abstr. —Ei.

385   US
INSIDE B N. 1970. bi-m. free. Burlington Northern Railroad, 2900 Continental Plaza, 777 Main St., Ft. Worth, TX 76102. TEL 817-333-3042. FAX 817-333-7997. Ed. Robin Russell McCasland. cum.index: 1970-1990, 1990-1994. circ. 38,000. (back issues avail.)
   Formerly (until **1991**): B N News.
   Description: Covers news pertaining to Burlington Northern, industry and related subjects.

385   UK   ISSN 0954-4097
TF1   CODEN: PMFTEV
INSTITUTION OF MECHANICAL ENGINEERS. PROCEEDINGS. PART F: JOURNAL OF RAIL AND RAPID TRANSIT. s-a. £83($169) for Part F; £1191($2329) for parts A-J (effective 1995). Mechanical Engineering Publications Ltd., Northgate Ave., Bury St. Edmunds, Suffolk IP32 6BW, England. TEL 01284-763277. FAX 01284-704006. TELEX 817376. Ed. R. Gostling. circ. 888. **Indexed:** Br.Tech.Ind., INSPEC (1989-). **Document type:** academic/scholarly publication, proceedings.
   —BLDSC (6724.900850); Ei; Faxon; SWETS; UMI. **CCC**.
   Description: Covers railway and rapid transit systems and rolling stock.

625.1 385   UK   ISSN 0073-9839
                        CODEN: PRWEAY
INSTITUTION OF RAILWAY SIGNAL ENGINEERS. PROCEEDINGS. 1912. a. £14. Institution of Railway Signal Engineers, 1 Badlake Close, Badlake Hill, Dawlish, Devon EX7 9JA, England. TEL 01626-888096. FAX 01626-888571. Ed. J. Tilly. adv. circ. 2,500. **Indexed:** INSPEC (1968-). **Document type:** proceedings.
   —BLDSC (6726.000000).
   Description: Contains papers on modern railway signaling and telecommunications developments.

385.264   SZ   ISSN 1012-4020
INTERCONTAINER. 3/yr. International Company for the Transport by Transcontainers, Margarethenstr 38, CH-4008 Basel, Switzerland. TEL 061-452525. TELEX 62298.

385.264   US
INTERNATIONAL AIRFORWARDER AND AGENTS ASSOCIATION. UPDATE.* 1958. m. International Airforwarder and Agents Association, Box 788, Huntington, NY 11743-0788. TEL 516-536-6229. Dir. Stephen R. Morgan.

INTERNATIONAL BULK JOURNAL. see *TRANSPORTATION — Ships And Shipping*

385.204   XR
INTERNATIONAL GUETERKURSBUCH. a. European Goods Trains Timetable Conference, c/o Ustredni Reditelstvi CSD, Nabrezi L. Svobody 12, 110 15 Prague, Czech Republic.

385   US
TE1
INTERNATIONAL RAILWAY JOURNAL; the first international railway and rapid transit journal. (Text in English; summaries in French, German, Spanish) 1960. m. $35. Simmons-Boardman Publishing Corporation, 345 Hudson St., New York, NY 10014. TEL 212-620-7200. FAX 212-633-1165. (Addr. in Netherlands: Nijverheidsweg 46, 3340 Henrik Ido Ambacht, Netherlands) Ed. Luther S. Miller; Pub. A.J. McGinnis, Jr. adv.; charts; illus.; stat.; tr.lit.; index. circ. 9,101. (also avail. in microform from UMI; reprint service avail. from UMI) **Indexed:** Br.Rail.Bd., Excerp.Med. (until 19??). **Document type:** trade publication.
   —BLDSC (4545.605000); SWETS; UMI. **CCC**.
   Former titles (until **1993**): International Railway Journal and Rapid Transit Review (ISSN 0744-5326); (until **1979**): International Railway Journal (ISSN 0020-8470)

INTERNATIONAL RAILWAY STATISTICS. STATISTICS OF INDIVIDUAL RAILWAYS. see *TRANSPORTATION — Abstracting, Bibliographies, Statistics*

INTERNATIONAL RAILWAY TRAVELER. see *TRAVEL AND TOURISM*

INTERNATIONALES VERKEHRSWESEN; Fachzeitschrift fuer Information und Kommunikation im Verkehr. see *TRANSPORTATION — Roads And Traffic*

385   IT   ISSN 0021-3128
ITALY. AZIENDA AUTONOMA DELLE FERROVIE DELLO STATO. INFORMAZIONI DOC. 1961. bi-m. L.8000. Azienda Autonoma delle Ferrovie Dello Stato, Centro di Documentazione, Piazza Croce Rossa, 00100 Rome, Italy. abstr.; bibl.; index. circ. 2,500.

625.1   GW   ISSN 0075-2479
HE3071
JAHRBUCH DES EISENBAHNWESENS. 1950. a. DM.42. (Deutsche Bundesbahn) Hestra-Verlag, Holzhofallee 33, 64295 Darmstadt, Germany. TEL 06151-3907-0. FAX 06151-390777. adv.

385.264   GW
JAHRBUCH FUER DAS BAYERISCHE TRANSPORTGEWERBE. a. Fachvereinigung Guterfernverkehr im Landesverband Bayerischer Transportunternehmen, Leonrodstr. 48, Postfach 184, 80636 Munich, Germany. TEL 089-1292096. TELEX 22461.

385   UK
JANE'S INFORMATION UPDATE. WORLD RAILWAYS. 1993. 11/yr. Jane's Information Group, Sentinel House, 163 Brighton Rd., Coulsdon, Surrey CR5 2NH, England. TEL 0181-763-1030. FAX 0181-763-1006. E-mail: http://www.janes.com/janes.html. Ed. James Abbott; Pub. Simon Kay. **Document type:** bulletin.

385.1   UK
TA1215
JANE'S INTERMODAL TRANSPORTATION. 1968. a. £190. Jane's Information Group, Sentinel House, 163 Brighton Rd., Coulsdon, Surrey CR5 2NH, England. TEL 0181-763-1030. FAX 0181-763-1006. TELEX 916907-JANES-G. E-mail: http://www.janes.com/janes.html. (U.S. & Can. order from: Dept. DSM, 1340 Braddock Pl., Ste. 300, Box 1436, Alexandria, VA 22314-1651) Ed. John Reed. adv.; index. **Document type:** directory.
   —BLDSC (4646.720000).
   Former titles: Jane's Containerisation Directory (ISSN 0954-3813); Jane's Freight Containers (ISSN 0075-3033)
   Description: Overview of all aspects of the containerisation market worldwide; covers ports and terminals and their facilities, containers operators, handling systems, leasing services, computer systems and containers, and components manufacturers.

385.1 625.1   UK   ISSN 0075-3084
TF1
JANE'S WORLD RAILWAYS. 1950. a. (plus m. updates). £195. Jane's Information Group, Sentinel House, 163 Brighton Rd., Coulsdon, Surrey CR5 2NH, England. TEL 0181-763-1030. FAX 0181-763-1005. TELEX 916907 JANES G. E-mail: http://www.janes.com/janes.html. (U.S. & Can. order from: Dept. DSM, 1340 Braddock Pl., Ste. 300, Box 1436, Alexandria, VA 22314-1651) Ed. James Abbott; Pub. Robert Hutchinson. adv. contact: Richard West. index. **Document type:** trade publication.
   ●Also available on CD-ROM.
   —CCC.
   Description: Covers trends and dvelopments of the rail industry worldwide; includes a country-by-country survey of railway systems and equipment manufacturers.

385   DK   ISSN 0107-3702
JERNBANEN.* 1961. bi-m. DKK 175. Dansk Jernbane-Klub - Danish Railway Club, Kalvebod Brygge 40, DK-1560 Copenhagen V, Denmark. TEL 02-308222. Eds. Jan Koed, Jens Koefoed. adv.; bk.rev. circ. 2,500.

385   SW   ISSN 0347-1845
JERNVAEGSNYTT. 1966. q. SEK 60 (effective 1990). Museifoereningen Anten-Graefsnaes Jaernvaeg, P.O. Box 300, S-441 26 Alingsaas, Sweden.

385   CN   ISSN 0453-4441
KEEPING TRACK. French edition: Au Fil du Rail (ISSN 0004-7376) 1966. 10/yr. Canadian National Railways, P.O. Box 8100, Montreal, PQ H3C 3N4, Canada. TEL 514-399-8041. FAX 514-399-5344. Ed. Louise Cardella. circ. 73,400. (tabloid format)
   Former titles (until **1958**): Canadian National Magazine (ISSN 0703-5306); (until **1938**): Canadian National Railways Magazine (ISSN 0703-5128)
   Description: For active and retired employees of CN. Covers news and events about the company.

385   KE
KENRAIL. (Text in English and Swahili) 1955. q. free. Kenya Railways Corporation, Box 30121, Nairobi, Kenya. TEL 254-2-221211. FAX 254-2-340049. TELEX 22254-RAIL-KE. Ed. J.N. Luseno. adv.; bk.rev.; illus. circ. 10,000. cols./p.: 2. (tabloid format) **Document type:** newspaper.
   Supersedes in part: Sikio (ISSN 0037-5136)
   Description: Contains railway information geared primarily toward employees of Kenya Railways.

385   MY   ISSN 0047-3375
KERETAPI. (Text in English, Malay) 1957. q. M.$0.60 per no. Malaya Railway Administration - Pertadbiran Keretapi Tawah Malaya, Box 1, Kuala Lumpur, Malaysia. Ed.Bd. charts; illus.; stat. circ. 2,400.

KEY, LOCK AND LANTERN. see *ANTIQUES*

385   NE   ISSN 0023-3870
DE KOPPELING. 1962. w. fl.57 (effective 1995). N.V. Nederlandse Spoorwegen - Netherlands Railways Ltd., Postbus 19143, 3501 DC Utrecht, Netherlands. TEL 31-30-354719. FAX 31-30-355187. Ed. Jan Stellingwerff. bk.rev.; illus. circ. 50,000. (tabloid format) **Document type:** trade publication.

385   GW
KURSBUCH DER DEUTSCHEN MUSEUMS-EISENBAHNEN. 1978. a. DM.5. Verlag Uhle und Kleimann, Pettenpohlstr. 17, 32312 Luebbecke, Germany. TEL 05741-7209. FAX 05741-90224. Ed. Bernhard Uhle. circ. 15,000. (back issues avail.) **Document type:** bulletin.

385   GW   ISSN 0344-7146
L O K REPORT; Nachrichtenmagazin fuer Eisenbahnfreunde. 1972. 12/yr. DM.105. Arbeitsgruppe L O K Report e.V., Postfach 1280, 48002 Muenster, Germany. Ed.Bd. adv.; bk.rev.; illus.; stat. circ. 8,600. (back issues avail.) **Document type:** newsletter.

385   GW   ISSN 0170-4621
L O K REPORT REISEFUEHRER; Europa-Reisefuehrer fuer Eisenbahnfreunde. 1978. a. DM.28. Arbeitsgruppe L O K Report e.V., Postfach 1280, 48002 Muenster, Germany. adv.; illus.; stat.; index. circ. 3,800. (back issues avail.) **Document type:** newsletter.

LETTRE CONFIDENTIELLE DES TRANSPORTS. see *TRANSPORTATION — Air Transport*

385.9   US   ISSN 0888-7837
LEXINGTON QUARTERLY. 1942. q. $15. Lexington Group in Transportation History, St. Cloud State University, Department of History, St. Cloud, MN 56301. TEL 612-255-4906. FAX 612-654-5198. Ed. Don L. Hofsommer. bk.rev. circ. 450. (looseleaf format; back issues avail.) **Document type:** academic/scholarly publication, bibliography.

385.264   US
THE LIGHT (ARLINGTON). 1918. w. 225. Southern Transportation Logistics Association, Inc., 3426 N. Washington Blvd., Arlington, VA 22201. TEL 703-525-4050. **Document type:** trade publication.
   Formerly: Southern Traffic Light.

385 622   AT   ISSN 0155-2260
LIGHT RAILWAY NEWS. 1977. bi-m. Aus.$31 (foreign Aus.$38). Light Railway Research Society of Australia Inc., P.O. Box 21, Surrey Hills, Vic. 3127, Australia. TEL 61-3-888-7346. Ed. John Browning. circ. 600. (back issues avail.) **Document type:** newsletter.
   Description: News and research on operating light railways.

6400   TRANSPORTATION — RAILROADS

385 622   AT   ISSN 0727-8101
LIGHT RAILWAYS. 1962. q. Aus.$31 (foreign Aus.$38). Light Railway Research Society of Australia Inc., P.O. Box 21, Surrey Hills, Vic. 3127, Australia. TEL 61-3-888-7346. Ed. Norm Houghton. circ. 700. (back issues avail.) Document type: newsletter.
  Description: History of light railways in Australasia.

385   IT
LINEA TRENO. 1955. m. L.10000 (foreign L.20000). Linea Treno - State Railway, Piazza Croce Rossa, 1, 00161 Rome, Italy. TEL 06-8415667. FAX 06-8831108. index. circ. 150,000.
  Formerly: Voci della Rotaia.
  Description: Features articles on the Italian railway system. Includes articles on innovations in technology and transportation.

385   GW   ISSN 0720-8456
DIE LINIE (HANNOVER). 1930. 6/yr. Uestra Hannoversche Verkehrsbetriebe AG, Postfach 2540, 30025 Hannover, Germany. TEL 0511-1668519. FAX 0511-1668666. circ. 5,000. Document type: trade publication.
  Former titles (until 1980): Linien (ISSN 0344-5232); (until 1977): Linie (ISSN 0344-5240)

385   UK   ISSN 0142-7326
LIVE RAIL. 1970. bi-m. £8.50. Southern Electric Group, 67 Denham Crescent, Mitcham, Surrey CR4 4LZ, England. (Subscr. to: 12 Dorchester Gardens, Grand Ave., Worthing, W. Sussex BN11 5Ay, England) Ed. S. Kesterton. adv.; bk.rev.; index; circ. controlled.
  Description: History and developments in the southern region of British Railways.

LOCO-REVUE; pour les modelistes et amateurs de chemins de fer. see HOBBIES

385   US   ISSN 0891-7647
LOCOMOTIVE & RAILWAY PRESERVATION. 1986. bi-m. $21.50. Locomotive & Railway Preservation, Box 246, Richmond, VT 05477. TEL 802-434-2351. Ed. Mark Smith. adv.; bk.rev. circ. 16,000.
  Description: Articles and photographs depicting the history and preservation of railroads. Covers the history and restoration of railroads, locomotives, streetcars and more.

331.88   US   ISSN 0024-5747
HD6350.R32
LOCOMOTIVE ENGINEER NEWSLETTER. 1987. m. membership only. International Brotherhood of Locomotive Engineers, 1370 Ontario St., Mezzanine, Cleveland, OH 44113-1702. TEL 216-241-2630. FAX 216-861-0932. Ed. S.W. FitzGerald. circ. 51,000. Document type: newsletter.

331.8 385   US   ISSN 0894-3605
LOCOMOTIVE ENGINEERS JOURNAL. 1867. q. $9 to non-members. International Brotherhood of Locomotive Engineers, 1370 Ontario St., Mezzanine, Cleveland, OH 44113-1702. TEL 216-241-2630. FAX 216-861-0932. Ed. S.W. FitzGerald. circ. 52,000. Document type: trade publication.

385   UK
LOCOMOTIVE JOURNAL. 1888. m. membership. Associated Society of Locomotive Engineers and Firemen, 9 Arkwright Rd., Hampstead, London NW3 6AB, England. Ed. L.D. Adams. adv.; bk.rev.; illus. circ. 17,000.

625.26   US   ISSN 0076-0285
LOCOMOTIVE MAINTENANCE OFFICERS ASSOCIATION. ANNUAL PROCEEDINGS.* 1940. a. $6 (or $10 for both preconvention report and the annual proceedings). Locomotive Maintenance Officers Association, c/o Ron Pondel, Sec.-Tres., 6047 S. Mobile Ave., Chicago, IL 60638-4226. index. Document type: proceedings.

625.26   US   ISSN 0076-0293
TJ675
LOCOMOTIVE MAINTENANCE OFFICERS ASSOCIATION. PRECONVENTION REPORT;* full text of all seven technical committee reports on diesel locomotive and M.U. train maintenance. a. $10 for both preconvention report and the annual proceedings. Locomotive Maintenance Officers Association, 6047 S. Mobile Ave., Chicago, IL 60638-4226. Ed. C.M. Lipcomb. index.

385   UK   ISSN 0307-1804
LOCOMOTIVES ILLUSTRATED; their life and time. 1974. bi-m. £14.50. Ian Allan Ltd., Coombelands House, Coombelands Ln., Addlestone, Surrey KT15 1HY, England. TEL 01932-855909. Ed. Brian Stephenson. adv.; bk.rev.; charts; illus. circ. 15,000. (reprint service avail. from UMI) Document type: consumer publication.
  —BLDSC (5292.070000).
  Description: Publishes illustrated histories of the most important steam locomotive classes to have operated on Britain's railways.

385   GW   ISSN 0458-1822
LOK MAGAZIN; Eisenbahn gestern, heute, morgen. 1962. bi-m. DM.89.70. Franckh-Kosmos Verlags-GmbH und Co., Postfach 106011, 70049 Stuttgart, Germany. TEL 0711-2191-332. FAX 0711-2191-350. Ed. Horst J. Obermayer. adv.: B&W page DM.1440; trim 140 x 217. circ. 5,900. Document type: consumer publication.
  —CCC.
  Description: Magazine for railroad enthusiasts. Features the history, the present state and future development of steam engines. Includes national and international news, list of exhibitions, and special trips.

LOKOMOTIVET; tidsskrift om jernbaner i virkelighed og model. see HOBBIES

385   GW   ISSN 0170-379X
DIE LOKRUNDSCHAU. 1969. bi-m. DM.46.50. Arbeitsgemeinschaft Lokrundschau e.V., Postfach 800107, 21001 Hamburg, Germany. TEL 04151-82889. FAX 04151-82889. adv.; bk.rev. circ. 4,000. (back issues avail.) Document type: bulletin.

LUPTA C F R. see LABOR UNIONS

M A R T A RIDER'S DIGEST. (Metropolitan Atlanta Rapid Transit Authority) see GENERAL INTEREST PERIODICALS — United States

MAERKLIN-MAGAZIN; Zeitschrift fuer grosse und kleine Modell-Eisenbahner. see HOBBIES

385   UK   ISSN 0264-7028
MAIN LINE. 1969. q. £10. Great Central Railway, Main Line Steam Trust, Great Central Rd., Loughborough, Leics. LE11 1RW, England. TEL 01733-270977. Ed. Melville T. Holley. adv.; bk.rev. circ. 5,500. (back issues avail.) Document type: newsletter.
  Description: Explores historical concerns of this preserved steam railway, covering news and developments.

385   MW   ISSN 0076-3330
MALAWI RAILWAYS. ANNUAL REPORTS AND ACCOUNTS. Title varies: Malawi Railways. Directors' Reports and Accounts. 1932. a. free. Malawi Railways, Ltd., P.O. Box 5144, Limbe, Malawi. circ. 500. Document type: government publication, corporate report.

385   II
MAZDOOR NEWS. (Text in Telugu) m. Rs.20. South Central Railway Mazdoor Union, 7-C Railway Bldg., Accounts Office Compound, Secunderabad A.P. 500 025, India. TEL 821351. TELEX 6994-CA-RAILWAYMEN. Ed. S.N.C. Ramakrishnama Charyulu.
  Formerly: Rail Mazdoor.

385   US   ISSN 1082-5584
▼**THE MIDLANDER.** 1994. q. $20. New Jersey Midland Railroad Historical Society, Box 6125, Parsippany, NJ 07054. TEL 201-331-2739. Ed. Timothy O. Stuy. illus.; stat.; circ. 300 (paid). (back issues avail.) Document type: newsletter.
  Description: Publishes historical articles on railroads in northern New Jersey, southern New York, and eastern Pennsylvania.

MINIATURBAHNEN M I B A. see HOBBIES

MODEL RAILWAYS. see HOBBIES

621.2   US
MODERN LOCOMOTIVE HANDBOOK.* 1950. irreg. $8. International Association of Railway Operating Officers, 621 Peacock Cir., Granite City, IL 62040-6459.

385 625.2   UK   ISSN 0026-8356
CODEN: MORABC
MODERN RAILWAYS. 1946. m. £25.20. Ian Allan Ltd., Coombelands House, Coombelands Ln., Addlestone, Surrey KT15 1HY, England. TEL 01932-855909. Ed. James Abbott. adv.; bk.rev.; charts; illus. circ. 25,000 (paid). (also avail. in microform from UMI; reprint service avail. from UMI) Indexed: Br.Rail.Bd.; Br.Tech.Ind., HRIS. Document type: consumer publication.
  —BLDSC (5894.900000); SWETS; UMI. CCC.
  Incorporates: Locomotive, Railway Carriage & Wagon Review.
  Description: Publishes news and features covering railways worldwide.

388.4 625   UK   ISSN 0144-1655
TF701
MODERN TRAMWAY AND LIGHT RAIL TRANSIT. 1938. m. £26. (Light Rail Transit Association) Ian Allan Ltd., Coombelands House, Coombelands Ln., Addlestone, Surrey TW17 8AS, England. TEL 01932-855909. Ed. Howard Johnston. adv.; bk.rev.; charts; illus.; index. circ. 7,250. (reprint service avail. from UMI) Indexed: Br.Tech.Ind. Document type: trade publication, consumer publication.
  —Faxon.
  Former titles: Modern Tramway and Rapid Transit Review; Modern Tramway and Light Railway Review (ISSN 0026-850X)
  Description: Follows the development of tramways and rapid systems worldwide.

385   CN   ISSN 0704-1500
MOVIN'. French edition: En Voie (ISSN 0704-1519) 1968. 6/yr. Canadian National Railways, P.O. Box 8100, Montreal, PQ H3C 3N4, Canada. TEL 514-399-5822. FAX 514-399-5344. Ed. Patricia Tokai. circ. 28,500.
  Description: Keeps customers informed about Canadian National's new services and equipment and the results of the latest developments in technology.

385 625.19   SP   ISSN 1133-1437
MUNDO FERROVIARIO. 1992. m. 5600 ptas. Editorial A G B, S.L., Po. de la Castellana 212, 4o Izda., 28046 Madrid, Spain. TEL 34-1-3502533. FAX 34-1-3502623. adv.: B&W page 100000 ptas., color page 150000 ptas.; trim 180 x 230; adv. contact: Maria Martin. circ. 10,000. Document type: consumer publication.

385   GW   ISSN 0936-4609
MUSEUMS - EISENBAHN; Zeitschrift fuer Kleinbahn Geschichte. 1966. q. DM.30. Deutscher Eisenbahn-Verein e.V., Postfach 1106, 27300 Bruchhausen-Vilsen, Germany. TEL 04252-9300-0. FAX 04252-930012. Ed. Wolfram Baeumer. adv.; bk.rev. Document type: newsletter.

385   US   ISSN 0740-672X
HE2791
MUTUAL MAGAZINE. 1915. m. $1.20. Mutual Beneficial Association of Rail Transportation Employees, Inc., 1617 JFK Blvd., Ste. 366, Philadelphia, PA 19103-1822. Ed. Stephen M. Santarlasci. adv. circ. 9,000.
  Description: Serves as a railroad fraternal monitor. Also covers insurance-related news.

NARROW GAUGE & SHORT LINE GAZETTE. see HOBBIES

385   UK   ISSN 0142-5595
NARROW GAUGE NEWS. 1953. bi-m. £14.50 (foreign £19.50) membership. Narrow Gauge Railway Society, c/o Brian Gent, 38 Stone Chat Close, Petersfield, Hampshire GU31 4RE, England. adv.; bk.rev.; illus.; tr.lit. (back issues avail.) Document type: consumer publication.
  Description: News items and articles on current developments in narrow gauge rail transportation, focusing on old, present and operational systems, contractors and builders of locomotives and other stock, and miniature and model construction.

385   US   ISSN 0739-3490
NATIONAL ASSOCIATION OF RAILROAD PASSENGERS NEWS. 1969. 11/yr. $24 membership. National Association of Railroad Passengers, 900 Second St., N.E., Ste. 308, Washington, DC 20002-3557. TEL 202-408-8362. FAX 202-408-8287. Ed. Ross Capon. circ. 11,500 (paid); 2,300 (controlled). (back issues avail.) Document type: newsletter.
  Description: News and advocacy articles on rail passenger and transit service.

TRANSPORTATION — RAILROADS 6401

NATIONAL MODEL RAILROAD ASSOCIATION. BULLETIN.
see HOBBIES

385 970   US   ISSN 0885-5099
HE2715
NATIONAL RAILWAY BULLETIN. 1935. bi-m. $15. National Railway Historical Society, Box 58153, Philadelphia, PA 19102. Ed. Frank G. Tatnall. bk.rev.; illus. circ. 17,000.
—UnCover.
Description: Covers US railroads in the early to mid-twentieth century.

385   RH
NATIONAL RAILWAYS OF ZIMBABWE. ANNUAL REPORT. no.42, 1991. a. National Railways of Zimbabwe, P.O. Box 596, Bulawayo, Zimbabwe. TEL 322934. TELEX 33173. **Document type:** corporate report.

NATIONALE MAATSCHAPPIJ VAN BELGISCHE SPOORWEGEN. DOCUMENTATIEBULLETIN. see TRANSPORTATION — Abstracting, Bibliographies, Statistics

385   AT   ISSN 0159-7302
TF121
NETWORK (MELBOURNE); the railways of Australia quarterly. 1964. q. Aus.$20 (foreign Aus.$35). Star Media Services, 392 Belmore Rd., Box Hill N., Vic.3129, Australia. TEL 61-3-9875-8818. FAX 61-3-9816-3441. Ed. Maurice Reeves. adv.; bk.rev. circ. 10,000. (back issues avail.) **Document type:** trade publication.

385 625.1   AU
NEUE BAHN; oesterreichische Fachzeitschrift fuer modernen Eisenbahntechnik und umweltbewusste Verkehrspolitik. 1966. q. S.310. Bohmann Druck und Verlag GmbH & Co. KG, Leberstr. 122, A-1110 Vienna, Austria. TEL 0222-74095-0. FAX 0222-74095-183. TELEX 132312. Ed. Josef Mueller. adv.; abstr.; illus.; index. circ. 2,500.
Indexed: Br.Rail.Bd. **Document type:** trade publication.
Formerly: Eisenbahntechnik (ISSN 0013-2829)

385   US   ISSN 1048-3845
TF701
NEW ELECTRIC RAILWAY JOURNAL. 1988. q. $25 (Canada $31; elsewhere $43) (effective 1995). Free Congress Foundation, 717 Second St., N.E., Washington, DC 20002. TEL 202-546-3000; 800-546-4490. FAX 202-544-2819. E-mail: 70550.1775@compuserve.com. (Edit. addr.: 6305 N. Kenmore, No. 1, Chicago, IL 60660. TEL 312-764-5785. FAX 312-764-9551) Ed. Richard Kunz; Pub. Paul Weyrich. adv. contact: Barbara Buck. bk.rev. circ. 5,000. **Document type:** consumer publication.
Description: Includes scholarly articles, color photos and current railway information.

385   NZ   ISSN 1171-266X
NEW ZEALAND RAIL. ANNUAL REPORT. 188? a. free. New Zealand Rail Ltd., Private Bag, Wellington, New Zealand. TEL 04-498-2000. FAX 04-498-3259. illus./ stat. circ. 750. **Document type:** corporate report.
Former titles (until 1991): New Zealand Railways Corporation. Annual Report (ISSN 0114-0434); (until 1988): New Zealand Railways Corporation. Report (ISSN 0112-2215); (until 1982): New Zealand. Railways Department. Annual Report (ISSN 0110-2974); (until 1958): Railways Statement.

385   NZ   ISSN 0028-8624
NEW ZEALAND RAILWAY OBSERVER. 1944. q. NZ.$45 (effective 1994). New Zealand Railway & Locomotive Society, Inc., P.O. Box 5134, Wellington, New Zealand. TEL 4-566-2248. Ed. T.A. McGavin. adv.; bk.rev.; charts; illus.; maps; index; circ. 1,200 (paid). **Document type:** academic/scholarly publication.
—CCC.
Description: Provides information on the design, construction, operation, development and history of railways in New Zealand.

385   ZR
NJANJA. m. Societe Nationale des Chemins de Fer Zairois, Lubumbashi, P.O.B. 297, BP 10597, Kinshasa, Zaire.

385   SW
NORDENS JAERNVAEGAR. (Text in English and Swedish) 1966. a. SEK 146($27) Frank Stenvalls Foerlag, Foereningsgatan 67, S-211 52 Malmoe, Sweden. FAX 040-127700. Ed. Frank Stenvall. illus. circ. 250. (back issues avail.) **Document type:** consumer publication.
Description: Pictorial survey of current railways in the Nordic countries.

385   SW   ISSN 0029-1382
NORDISK JAERNBANETIDSKRIFT. Short title: N J T. (From 1972-1982 published in Norway) (Text in Danish, Finnish, Norwegian and Swedish; occasionally in English and German) 1874. bi-m. SEK 60. Nordiska Jaernvaegsmannasaellskapet, Affaersomraade SJ expressgods, Klarabergsviadukten 82, S-105 50 Stockholm, Sweden. adv.; bk.rev.; charts; illus.; index. circ. 2,200.
Formerly (until 1925): Jernbanebladet.

385.264   GW   ISSN 0171-2012
NORDRHEIN VERKEHR. m. Fachvereinigung Guternahverkehr Nordrhein, Engelbertstr 11, 40233 Dusseldorf, Germany. TEL 0211-7335491.

385   US
NORFOLK SOUTHERN WORLD. 1982. m. free to qualified personnel. Norfolk Southern Corporation, Public Relations Department, 3 Commercial Pl., Norfolk, VA 23510. TEL 804-629-2707. FAX 804-629-2822. Ed. Susan M. Terpay. bk.rev.; illus.; circ. 47,000 (controlled). **Document type:** newspaper.
Formed by the merger of: Norfolk and Western (ISSN 0029-1633); Southern Railway System.
Description: For employees and retirees of Norfolk Southern and its subsidiaries.

385   II   ISSN 0029-3210
NORTHERN RAILWAY NEWSLETTER. (Text in English, Hindi) vol.17, 1968. m. free to qualified personnel. Northern Railway, Public Relations Office Bldg., State Entry Rd., New Delhi, India. Ed. O.P. Chopra. adv.; charts; illus. circ. 2,000. **Document type:** newsletter.

385   US
NORTHWEST ELECTRIC RAILWAY REVIEW. 1958. bi-m. $25 includes membership. Oregon Electric Railway Historical Society, 1836 N. Emerson St., Portland, OR 97217-3855. TEL 503-285-7936. (Society addr.: Box 1891, Portland, OR 97207. TEL 503-357-3574) Ed. Richard Thompson. circ. 200. **Document type:** newsletter.
Formerly: Trolley Park News.
Description: Discusses the history, preservation and operation of electric railway vehicles, with particular emphasis on streetcar and trolley operations in the Northwest. Includes news of the Trolley Park Museum.

385   US   ISSN 0894-0800
NORTHWESTERNER. 1987. s-a. membership. Northwestern Pacific Railroad Historical Society, Box 667, Santa Rosa, CA 95402-0667. TEL 415-459-7082. Ed. Frederick P. Codoni. adv.; bk.rev. circ. 1,000. (back issues avail.) **Description:** Information on the history of the Redwood Empire Route.

385.2 331.8   AG   ISSN 0029-7658
OBRERO FERROVIARIO.* (Technical supplement) 1912. m. free. Union Ferroviaria, c/o Adolfo Medina, Independencia 2880, Buenos Aires, Argentina. Ed. Hugo Leguizamon. illus. circ. 140,000.
Description: Covers various topics on the Argentinian railway system. Includes the operators rights, present and future plans to make it more efficient and the railway's faults.

385 340   SZ
OFFICE CENTRAL DES TRANSPORTS INTERNATIONAUX FERROVIAIRES. BULLETIN. (Text in French and German) 1893. q. 40 SFr. Office Central des Transports Internationaux Ferroviaires - Zentralamt fuer den Internationalen Eisenbahnverkehr, Gryphenhuebelieweg 37, CH-3006 Bern, Switzerland. TEL 031-3511762. FAX 031-3511164. TELEX 912063-OCTI-CH. circ. 800. **Document type:** bulletin.

385   US   ISSN 0030-0373
OFFICIAL RAILWAY EQUIPMENT REGISTER. 1886. q. $159. K - III Directory Corp., 424 W. 33rd St., New York, NY 10001. TEL 800-221-5488. FAX 212-695-5025. circ. 7,000. (also avail. in magnetic tape)
Description: Contains complete descriptions of freight cars operated by railroads and private companies in N.A. including series numbers, dimensions and capacities.

380.5   US   ISSN 0190-6704
OFFICIAL RAILWAY GUIDE. NORTH AMERICAN FREIGHT SERVICE EDITION. 1868. bi-m. $139. K - III Directory Corp., 424 W. 33rd St., New York, NY 10001. TEL 800-221-5488. FAX 212-695-5025. Ed. Richard Parolisi. adv. circ. 6,000.
Formerly: Official Guide of the Railways and Steam Navigation Lines of the United States, Puerto Rico, Canada, Mexico and Cuba, Airline Schedules (ISSN 0030-0322)
Description: Contains maps, contact personnel, intermodal terminal locations, freight schedules and route profiles for all railroads.

385   US   ISSN 0273-9658
HE2727
OFFICIAL RAILWAY GUIDE. NORTH AMERICAN TRAVEL EDITION. 4/yr. $172. K - III Directory Corp., 424 W. 33rd St., New York, NY 10001. TEL 800-221-5488. FAX 212-695-5025. Ed. Frank Coyle. adv. circ. 8,500. (also avail. in magnetic tape)
Formerly: Official Railway Guide. North American Passenger Travel Edition (ISSN 0094-5218)

385   US
ON TRACK (WASHINGTON); railroad construction letter. 1977. 24/yr. free to members. National Railroad Construction and Maintenance Association, Inc., 122 C St., NW., Ste. 850, Washington, DC 20001-2109. FAX 202-638-1045. Ed. Steven Held. adv.; bk.rev.; stat.; tr.lit.; index; circ. 1,500 (controlled). (back issues avail.) **Document type:** newsletter.
Formerly: Clear Track (ISSN 0193-3477)

ORANGE EMPIRE RAILWAY MUSEUM GAZETTE. see MUSEUMS AND ART GALLERIES

051   US
P A T H WAYS. 1968. m. free. (Port Authority of New York and New Jersey) Port Authority Trans-Hudson Corporation, 1 PATH Plaza, Jersey City, NJ 07306. TEL 800-234-PATH. FAX 201-216-6266. Ed. Donald B. Roberts. **Document type:** newspaper.
Description: News of the PATH rail transit system and its services.

385   US   ISSN 8750-8486
TF23.6
PACIFIC RAIL NEWS;* your Western news source. 1964. m. $30. Interurban Press, Box 94911, Pasadena, CA 91109-4911. TEL 818-240-4777. Ed. Don Gulbrandsen. adv.: B&W page $600, color page $870. bk.rev.; charts; illus.; stat. circ. 11,500. (back issues avail.)
—UnCover.
Formerly: Pacific News (ISSN 0030-879X)

385   NZ   ISSN 1170-4810
PANTOGRAPH. 1956. bi-m. NZ.$45 (foreign NZ.$65) membership. Silver Stream Railway Inc., P.O. Box 30-786, Lower Hutt, New Zealand. TEL 637-348. Ed. A. Collins. bk.rev. circ. 120.
Former titles (until 1990): Smokebox (ISSN 0114-1104); (until 1988): Pantograph (ISSN 1170-5140); (until 1977): Pantograph News (ISSN 1170-5132); (until 1972): Pantograph (ISSN 0031-1014)

385.262   UK   ISSN 0969-1464
PASSENGER RAIL MANAGEMENT. 1993. bi-m. $140. Baltic Publishing Ltd., Great West Rd., Brentford, Mddx. TW8 9BU, England. TEL 0181-847-2446. FAX 0181-569-8688. Ed. Ken Harris; Pub. Patrick Hicks. adv. contact: Stephen Catchpole. **Document type:** trade publication.

385   US   ISSN 1042-7937
TF570
PASSENGER TRAIN ANNUAL.* 1987. a. $8.95. Interurban Press, Box 94911, Pasadena, CA 91109-4911. TEL 818-240-9130. FAX 818-240-5436. Ed. Carl Swanson. illus.
Description: Reviews events relating to railroad passenger trains, urban rail and rail transit.

6402 TRANSPORTATION — RAILROADS

385 US ISSN 0160-6913
HE2583
PASSENGER TRAIN JOURNAL.* Short title: P T J. 1968. m. $30 (foreign $36). Interurban Press, Box 94911, Pasadena, CA 91109-4911. Ed. Carl Swanson. adv.; B&W page $600, color page $870. bk.rev.; illus. circ. 11,500. (back issues avail.)
Formerly: P T J. Passenger Train Journal (ISSN 0160-6352)
Description: Covers inter-urban and mainline railroading in the United States.

385 UK ISSN 0031-5524
PERMANENT WAY INSTITUTION. JOURNAL AND REPORT OF PROCEEDINGS. 1884. 3/yr. £12. Permanent Way Institution, 4 Reginald Rd., Wombwell, Barnsley, S. Yorks S73 0HP, England. TEL 01226-752605. FAX 01226-754287. Ed. A. Blower. bk.rev.; abstr.; charts; illus.; stat.; index. circ. 8,000. **Indexed:** Br.Rail.Bd., Br.Tech.Ind. **Document type:** proceedings.
—BLDSC (4934.000000).

385 UK ISSN 0143-8875
PLATFORM (WEST RIDING). 1978. a. £12. Lancashire & Yorkshire Railway Society, 10 Magna Grove, Sandal, Wakefield, W. Riding, Yorkshire WF2 7NG, England. TEL 01924-256907. Ed. Jeff Wells. circ. 450. **Document type:** academic/scholarly publication.
Description: Devoted to the history of the Lancashire and Yorkshire Railway, including articles, photos, and scale drawings (mainly pre-1923).

385 US ISSN 0032-1826
HE2723
POCKET LIST OF RAILROAD OFFICIALS. (Includes Buyer's Guide) 1895. q. $64. K - III Press, Inc., 424 W. 33rd St., New York, NY 10001. TEL 800-221-5488. FAX 212-695-5025. adv. circ. 5,600.
Description: Lists over 30,000 officials in the freight railroad, rail transit and rail supply industries in North America.

385 US ISSN 1044-4688
HE1009
POCKET LIST OF RAILROAD OFFICIALS INTERNATIONAL EDITION. (Includes Buyer's Guide) a. $99 (foreign $140). K - III Directory Corp., 424 W. 33rd St., New York, NY 10001. TEL 800-221-5488. FAX 212-695-5025.
Description: Provides detailed corporate listings for freight and passenger railroads, rail transit, rail supply companies and related organizations outside N. America.

385 US ISSN 1047-9473
TF455
PRIVATE VARNISH.* 1985. bi-m. $22 (foreign $25). (American Association of Private Car Owners, Inc.) Interurban Press, Box 94911, Pasadena, CA 91109-4911. TEL 818-240-9130. Ed. John Kuehl. adv.; B&W page $460, color page $667. circ. 3,200.

385 US ISSN 0033-0817
PROGRESSIVE RAILROADING. 1958. m. $55 (free to qualified personnel). Trade Press Publishing Co., 230 W. Monroe, Ste. 2210, Chicago, IL 60606. TEL 312-629-1200. Ed. Tom Judge. adv.; illus.; tr.lit. circ. 18,000. **Indexed:** Br.Rail.Bd. **Document type:** trade publication.
—BLDSC (6924.665500); SWETS.

385 UK
PUSH AND PULL. 1965. q. £10. Keighley & Worth Valley Railway, Haworth Sta., Keighley, W. Yorks. BD22 8NJ, England. TEL 01535-645214. FAX 01535-647317. Ed. John Sagar. adv.; bk.rev.; circ. 5,200 (paid). **Document type:** consumer publication.
Refereed Serial

385 RU ISSN 0033-4715
PUT I PUTEVOE KHOZYAISTVO. 1957. m. $78 (effective 1996). Ministerstvo Putei Soobshcheniya, Krasnoprudnaya 22-24, 107140 Moscow, Russia. (Subscr. to: Mezhdunarodnaya Kniga, Moscow, G-200, Russia) Ed. L.F. Troitskii. bk.rev. circ. 25,000. **Indexed:** Ref.Zh.
—BLDSC (0135.421000).

R F F S A ANUARIO ESTATISTICO. (Rede Ferroviaria Federal, S.A.) see TRANSPORTATION — *Abstracting, Bibliographies, Statistics*

385.314 BL ISSN 0102-4957
R F F S A SISTEMA FERROVIATIO. Variant title: Sistema Ferroviario do Brasil. 1962. irreg. free. Rede Ferroviaria Federal, S.A., Departamento Geral de Estatistica, Rio de Janeiro, Brazil. adv.; illus. circ. 1,200. (also avail. in microfiche)

385 UK
R M T NEWS. 1880. m. £25. Rail, Maritime & Transport Union, 205 Euston Rd., London NW1, England. TEL 071-387-4771. FAX 071-387-4123. Ed. J. Finney. adv.; bk.rev.; illus.; stat. circ. 35,000. **Document type:** newsletter.
Former titles (until 1993): Transport Review; Railway Review (ISSN 0033-8974)

385 GW ISSN 0342-8761
R T F. (Revista Tecnica de los Ferrocarriles) 1952. a. DM.24.20. Hestra-Verlag, Holzhofallee 33, 64295 Darmstadt, Germany. TEL 06151-3907-0. FAX 06151-390777. Ed. Willy Wassmuth. adv.; bk.rev. circ. 4,787. **Document type:** trade publication.

385 FR
LE RAIL. (Text in French; summaries in English) 1954. bi-m. (plus 2 special issues) 355 F. I.A. Diffusion, 3 Ave. Hoche, 75008 Paris, France. TEL 46-22-53-71. FAX 40-54-98-93. Ed. Christian Scasso. adv.; bk.rev. circ. 18,000.
Former titles (until 1988): Rail et Le Monde (ISSN 0181-1878); (until no.286, 1979): Vie du Rail Outremer (ISSN 0049-6278)

385 UK ISSN 0953-4563
RAIL. 1981. fortn. £48.10 (foreign £64.30) (effective 1995-1996). E M A P - Apex, Tower House, Sovereign Park, Lathkill St., Market Harborough, Leics. LE16 9EF, England. TEL 01858-468811. FAX 01858-432164. adv.; bk.rev. circ. 44,000. **Document type:** consumer publication.
Formerly (until 1988): Rail Enthusiast.

385 US
RAIL AND WIRE. 1957. bi-m. $30 membership. Illinois Railway Museum, Inc., Box 427, Union, IL 60180. TEL 815-923-4391. FAX 815-923-2006. Ed. Walter Weart. bk.rev.; circ. 2,500 (paid). (looseleaf format) **Document type:** newsletter.
Description: Contains news and articles about restoration and history of railroad equipment at IRM.

385 US
RAIL CARRIER DIGEST SERVICE. 1927. 10 base vols. (plus m. suppl.). $375. Hawkins Publishing Co., Inc., Box 480, Mayo, MD 21106. TEL 301-798-1677. Ed. Carl R. Eyler. cum.index. circ. 500. (looseleaf format; back issues avail.) **Document type:** abstracting/indexing.

385 US ISSN 0743-9075
TF1
RAIL CLASSICS AND RAILWAY QUARTERLY. 1984. bi-m. $18. Challenge Publications, Inc., 7950 Deering Ave., Canoga Park, CA 91304. TEL 818-887-0550. FAX 818-883-1343. Ed. Ed Stauss. **Document type:** consumer publication.
Formed by the 1984 merger of: Rail Classics (ISSN 0194-9187); Railway Quarterly (ISSN 0191-1805)

625.1 UK ISSN 0141-4615
TF1 CODEN: REGIAX
RAIL ENGINEERING INTERNATIONAL. 1971. q. £7.50. Broadwick (Technical Publishers) Ltd., Little Leighs, Chelmsford, Essex CM3 1PF, England. Ed.Bd. adv.; bk.rev.; charts; illus. circ. 2,550. **Indexed:** Br.Rail.Bd., Eng.Ind., Excerp.Med., ISMEC.
—BLDSC (7242.827000); SWETS.

385 BE ISSN 0020-8442
TF1 CODEN: RAIIAF
RAIL INTERNATIONAL/SCHIENEN DER WELT. (Editions in English, French, German) 1970. m. 3200 BEF. International Railway Congress Association, 85 rue de France, Sect. 10, B-1070 Brussels, Belgium. TEL 32-2-5207831. FAX 32-2-5254084. adv.; bk.rev.; bibl.; charts; illus.; stat.; index. circ. 3,400. **Indexed:** Br.Rail.Bd., C.I.S. Abstr., Eng.Ind., INSPEC (1970-). **Document type:** bulletin.
—BLDSC (7242.840000); Ei; SWETS; UnCover.
Formerly: International Railway Congress Association. Monthly Bulletin.
Description: Covers technical and managerial information related to the railway business.

385 UK ISSN 1353-2502
RAIL PRIVATISATIONS; facts, issues and opportunities. irreg. £195. O X E R A Press, Blue Boar Ct., Alfred St., Oxford OX1 4EH, England. TEL 01865-251142. FAX 01865-201080. **Document type:** bulletin.
Description: Analysis of rail privatization and detailed information for companies and individuals interested in the future of the U.K. rail industry.

RAIL SYNDICALISTE. see *LABOR UNIONS*

385 II
HE3291
RAIL TRANSPORT JOURNAL. (Text in English) 1965. q. Rs.50 (foreign Rs.350). Institute of Rail Transport, Rm. 17, Rail Bhavan, Raisina Rd., New Delhi 110001, India. TEL 011-91-3384171. FAX 011-91-3384005. Ed. N.M. Balasubrahmanyam. adv.; page Rs.3000. bk.rev.; charts. circ. 6,000.
Formerly (until 1991): Institute of Rail Transport. Journal (ISSN 0020-3114)
Description: Covers the production and track of railway and ancillary equipments like locomotives, coaches, wagons, signaling and telecommunication equipments, electrical appliances and allied products.

385 US ISSN 0896-4440
RAIL TRAVEL NEWS. 1970. s-m. $26. Message Media, Box 9007, Berkeley, CA 94709. TEL 415-540-0809. Ed. James Russell. adv.; bk.rev.; illus. circ. 2,000.

385 US ISSN 0163-7266
TF
RAILFAN & RAILROAD. 1974. m. $25. Carstens Publications, Inc., Box 700, Newton, NJ 07860. TEL 201-383-3355. FAX 201-383-4064. Ed. James Boyd. adv.; B&W page $875, color page $1365. bk.rev. circ. 52,000. (back issues avail.)
Formerly: Railfan (Newton) (ISSN 0098-0714); Incorporates (in 1979): Railroad Magazine (ISSN 0033-8761); Which was formerly: Railroad Man's Magazine; And (beginning 1906): Railroad Stories.

385 UK ISSN 0033-8745
RAILNEWS. (One National Edition) 1963. m. price varies. British Railways Board, Euston House, P.O. Box 100, London NW1 1DZ, England. Ed. S. Knight. adv.; bk.rev.; charts; illus. circ. 175,000. **Indexed:** Br.Tech.Ind.
Description: Newspaper of the British Railways Board.

385 US ISSN 0745-5267
RAILPACE NEWSMAGAZINE. m. 210 Perrine Ave., Piscataway, NJ 08854-4628. TEL 908-463-1091. Ed. Thomas Nemeth. adv. circ. 8,500.

385 UK ISSN 0262-8805
RAILPOWER. 1963. 4/yr. free to qualified personnel. Railway Industry Association of Great Britain, 6 Buckingham Gate, London SW1E 6JP, England. FAX 01-821-1640. TELEX 297304-RIA-G. Ed. Roger Ford. circ. 2,500.

385 US
RAILROAD ENTHUSIASTS. NEW YORK DIVISION. BULLETIN.* 1957. m. $8. Railroad Enthusiasts, New York Division, Inc., Box 1318 Grand Central Sta., New York, NY 10017. Ed. W.S. Webber. bk.rev.; illus. circ. 500.

385 US ISSN 0090-7847
TF1
RAILROAD HISTORY. 1921. s-a. $35 to libraries; free to members. Railway & Locomotive Historical Society (Akron), c/o H. Roger Grant, Ed., Dept. of History, Univ. of Akron, Akron, OH 44325-1902. TEL 216-972-6199. adv.; bk.rev.; bibl.; charts; illus.; cum.index 1921-1984; then every 2 yrs. circ. 4,100. (also avail. in microform from UMI; reprint service avail. from UMI) **Indexed:** Amer.Hist.& Life, Hist.Abstr. **Document type:** academic/scholarly publication.
—UMI; UnCover.
Formerly: Railway and Locomotive Historical Society. Bulletin (ISSN 0033-8842)

RAILROAD MODEL CRAFTSMAN. see *HOBBIES*

RAILROAD NEWSLETTER. see *OCCUPATIONAL HEALTH AND SAFETY*

TRANSPORTATION — RAILROADS 6403

385 US
RAILROAD STATION HISTORICAL SOCIETY. BULLETIN. 1968. bi-m. $9 (foreign $12). J - B Publishing Co., 430 Ivy Ave., Crete, NE 68333. TEL 402-826-3356. Ed. Kent Hannah. adv.; bk.rev.; abstr.; charts; illus.; stat.; index. circ. 500. **Indexed:** Avery Ind.Archit.Per. **Document type:** bulletin.

385.26 US ISSN 0887-347X
RAILROAD STATION HISTORICAL SOCIETY. RAILROAD STATION MONOGRAPH. 1970. a. free to members. J - B Publishing Co., 430 Ivy Ave., Crete, NE 68333. TEL 402-826-3356. Ed.Bd. bibl.; illus. circ. 500. **Document type:** monographic series.

RAILS. see TRAVEL AND TOURISM

385 NZ ISSN 0110-6155
RAILS. 1971. m. NZ.$39.60 (foreign NZ.$50). Southern Press Ltd., R.D.I., Porirua, Wellington, New Zealand. TEL 04-239-9063. FAX 04-239-9063. Ed. Robert Stott. adv.; bk.rev.; bibl.; illus.; circ. 4,600 (paid). **Document type:** trade publication.
—CCC.

385 UK ISSN 0267-5943
RAILWATCH. 1978. q. £10 to non-members. Railway Development Society, 4 Christchurch Sq., London E9 7HU, England. TEL 0181-985-8548. FAX 0181-985-8212. E-mail: ray.king@mcri.seonet.de. Ed. Ray King. adv.; bk.rev. circ. 4,000. (processed) **Document type:** newsletter.
Former titles: Railway Development News; Railway Invigoration Society. Progress Reports.
Description: Contains reports on railways and rail user groups.

657 385
RAILWAY ACCOUNTING RULES. base vol. (plus s-a. updates). $15 base vol. Association of American Railroads, Economics Policy and Statistics Department, 50 F St., N.W., No. 311, Washington, DC 20001. TEL 202-639-2325. Ed. K. Eric Wolfe. **Document type:** trade publication.

385 625.1 US ISSN 0033-8826
TF1 CODEN: RAAGA3
RAILWAY AGE. 1856. m. $35 (free to railroad personnel). Simmons-Boardman Publishing Corporation, 345 Hudson St., New York, NY 10014. TEL 212-620-7200. (Addr. in Netherlands: Nijverheidsweg 46, 3340 Henrik Ido Ambacht, Netherlands) Ed. Robert E. Tuzik; Pub. Arthur J. McGinnis, Jr. adv. circ. 18,153. (also avail. in microform from UMI; microfiche from CIS; reprint service avail. from UMI) **Indexed:** B.P.I., Br.Rail.Bd., Bus.Ind., Energy Info.Abstr., Environ.Abstr., Fluidex, INSPEC, Key to Econ.Sci., Mag.Ind., P.A.I.S., PROMT, SRI, Tr.& Indus.Ind. **Document type:** trade publication.
●Also available online. Vendor(s): University Microfilms International.
—CIS; Ei; Faxon; SWETS; UMI; UnCover. **CCC.**
Incorporates (1947-1991, June): Modern Railroads (ISSN 0736-2064); Which was formerly (until 1982): Modern Railroads - Rail Transit (ISSN 0193-3272); (until 1971): Modern Railroads (ISSN 0026-8348); **Incorporates:** Railway Control Systems; Railway Locomotives and Cars (ISSN 0033-7102).

385 UK ISSN 0033-8834
RAILWAY AND CANAL HISTORICAL SOCIETY JOURNAL. 1954. 3/yr. membership. Railway and Canal Historical Society, 12 St. Quentin Rise, Sheffield S17 4PR, England. Ed. J.C. Cutler. adv.; bk.rev.; bibl.; charts; index. circ. 800. (also avail. in microform from UMI) **Document type:** academic/scholarly publication.
—BLDSC (4845.400000).
Refereed Serial

385 US
RAILWAY & LOCOMOTIVE HISTORICAL SOCIETY NEWSLETTER. 1981. s-a. membership. Railway & Locomotive Historical Society, Box 215, East Irvine, CA 92650. Ed. C. Zlatkovich. circ. 3,000. **Document type:** newsletter.

385 UK
RAILWAY BUSINESS REPORT. 1934. a. £20. Reed Business Publishing Group (Subsidiary of: Reed Elsevier group), Quadrant House, The Quadrant, Sutton, Surrey SM2 5AS, England. TEL 0181-652-3739. FAX 0181-652-3738. Ed. Andrew Hellawell. circ. 7,500. (reprint service avail. from UMI) **Document type:** trade publication.
—BLDSC (3578.553700).
Former titles: Developing Railways (ISSN 0309-1465); International Railway Progress (ISSN 0074-7572); Overseas Railways.

385 AT ISSN 0157-2431
RAILWAY DIGEST. 1963. m. Aus.$13. Australian Railway Historical Society, New South Wales Division, Box E129, St. James, N.S.W., Australia. Ed. I. Fathers. circ. 2,200. (also avail. in microfiche)

385 UK ISSN 0048-6647
RAILWAY DIGEST INTERNATIONAL. 1971. bi-m. £2.50. Maple Cottage, Ashburnum Ave., Harrow-on-the-Hill, Middlesex HA1 2JO, England. Ed. J.H. Court. adv.; bk.rev.; bibl.; charts; illus.

385 UK
HE1009
RAILWAY DIRECTORY. a. $160. Reed Business Publishing Group (Subsidiary of: Reed Elsevier group), Quadrant House, The Quadrant, Sutton, Surrey SM2 5AS, England. TEL 0181-652-3740. FAX 0181-652-3738. (Subscr. to: P.O. Box 935, Finchingfield, Essex CM7 4LN, England. TEL 01371-810433) Ed. Chris Bushell. **Document type:** directory.
Formerly: Railway Directory and Yearbook (ISSN 0079-9513)

385 US ISSN 0079-9521
TF501
RAILWAY FUEL AND OPERATING OFFICERS ASSOCIATION. PROCEEDINGS. a. $15. International Association of Railway Operating Officers, 621 Peacock Cir., Granite City, IL 62040-6459.

625.1 UK ISSN 0373-5346
TF1 CODEN: RWGIAN
RAILWAY GAZETTE INTERNATIONAL; a journal of management, engineering and operation. (Supplements avail.) 1835. m. $119. Reed Business Publishing Group (Subsidiary of: Reed Elsevier group), Quadrant House, The Quadrant, Sutton, Surrey SM2 5AS, England. TEL 0181-652-3739. FAX 0181-652-3738. (Subscr. to: Oakfield House, Perrymount Rd., Haywards Heath, W. Sussex RH16 3DH, England. TEL 01444-445434) Ed. Murray Hughes. adv.: B&W page $2400, color page $3960. bk.rev.; charts; illus.; stat.; tr.lit.; index. circ. 9,270. **Indexed:** Br.Rail.Bd., Br.Tech.Ind., C.I.S.Abstr., Eng.Ind., HRIS, INSPEC, Intl.Civil Eng.Abstr., Met.Abstr., Soft.Abstr.Eng., World Alum.Abstr. **Document type:** trade publication.
—BLDSC (7247.500000); Ei; Faxon; SWETS; UnCover. **CCC.**
Formerly: Railway Gazette (ISSN 0033-8907)

385 US ISSN 0093-8505
TF15
RAILWAY HISTORY MONOGRAPH. 1972. irreg. J - B Publishing Co., 430 Ivy Ave., Crete, NE 68333. TEL 402-826-3356. Ed. William F. Rapp. illus.; index. circ. 100.
—UnCover.

385 US ISSN 0190-6763
TF22
RAILWAY LINE CLEARANCES. 1897. a. $105 (foreign $110). K - III Directory Corp., 424 W. 33rd St., New York, NY 10001. TEL 800-221-5488. FAX 212-695-5025. Ed. Peter Coleman. adv. circ. 900.
Description: Contains vertical and horizontal clearances and weight limitations for nearly 300 North American railroad lines.

385 UK ISSN 0033-8923
TF1
RAILWAY MAGAZINE. 1897. m. $32. I P C Magazines, Specialist Magazine Group (Subsidiary of: Reed Elsevier group), King's Reach Tower, Stamford St., London SE1 9LS, England. TEL 071-261-5821. FAX 071-261-7851. Ed. Peter Kelly. adv.; bk.rev.; charts; illus.; index. circ. 35,972. (also avail. in microform from UMI; reprint service avail. from UMI) **Indexed:** Br.Hum.Ind., Br.Tech.Ind.
—BLDSC (7248.150000); UMI. **CCC.**
Description: Present information on all facets of steam, diesel and electric locomotives.

385 US ISSN 0094-2278
TF455
RAILWAY PASSENGER CAR ANNUAL. 1974. a. price varies. R P C Publications, Box 296, Godfrey, IL 62035. Ed. W. David Randall. circ. 1,500.
Description: Compilation of photographs of passenger cars taken when they were built. Shows exteriors, interiors, and mechanical details.

625.1 JA ISSN 0033-9008
TF1 CODEN: QRTIA8
RAILWAY TECHNICAL RESEARCH INSTITUTE. QUARTERLY REPORT. Key Title: Quarterly Report of R T R I. (Text in English) 1960. q. $134. Ken-yusha, Inc., 2-8-38, Hikari-cho, Kokubunji-shi, Tokyo 185, Japan. FAX 81-425-73-7255. Ed. Toshiaki Sasaki. charts; illus.; index. circ. 700. (back issues avail.) **Indexed:** Appl.Mech.Rev., Br.Rail.Bd., Eng.Ind., HRIS, INSPEC, JTA. **Document type:** academic/scholarly publication.
—BLDSC (7201.855000); Ei; SWETS.

625.1 GW ISSN 0079-9548
RAILWAY TECHNICAL REVIEW. (Text in English) 1952. a. DM.24. Hestra-Verlag, Holzhofallee 33, 64295 Darmstadt, Germany. TEL 06151-3907-0. FAX 06151-390777. adv. **Indexed:** Br.Rail.Bd.

625.1 US ISSN 0033-9016
CODEN: RTSTAR
RAILWAY TRACK & STRUCTURES. 1885. m. $28 ($14 to qualified railroad personnel). Simmons-Boardman Publishing Corporation, 345 Hudson St., New York, NY 10014. TEL 212-620-7200. (Addr. in Netherlands: Nijverheidsweg 46, 3340 Henrick Ido Ambacht, Netherlands) Ed. Robert E. Tuzik; Pub. Arthur J. McGinnis, Jr. adv.; illus.; index. circ. 7,629. (also avail. in microform from UMI; reprint service avail. from UMI) **Indexed:** Br.Rail.Bd., Chem.Abstr., Eng.Ind., HRIS. **Document type:** trade publication.
—BLDSC (7250.000000); Faxon; UMI; UnCover. **CCC.**
Formerly: Railway Engineering and Maintenance (ISSN 0097-6687)

385 UK ISSN 0033-9032
RAILWAY WORLD. 1939. m. £25.20. Ian Allan Ltd., Coombelands House, Coombelands Ln., Addlestone, Surrey KT15 1HY, England. TEL 01932-855909. Ed. Handel Kardas. adv.; bk.rev.; film rev.; rec.rev.; charts; illus. circ. 20,000. (reprint service avail. from UMI) **Indexed:** Br.Tech.Ind.
—BLDSC (7250.142000). **CCC.**
Description: Contains features and preservation articles relating to British railways.

RAILWAYS. see TRAVEL AND TOURISM

625.1 SA ISSN 0254-2218
TF1
RAILWAYS AFRICA. Key Title: Railways. (Text in English) 1957. bi-m. R.50 (foreign R.105) (effective 1995). Rail-Link C C, P.O. Box 4794, 2125 Randburg, Transvaal, South Africa. TEL 27-11-463-4330. FAX 27-11-463-4224. Ed. Barbara Sheat. adv. contact: Phillippa Tait. bk.rev.; charts; illus.; tr.lit.; circ. 2,500 (controlled). (back issues avail.) **Indexed:** Ind.S.A.Per., INSPEC. **Document type:** trade publication.
Former titles (until 1992): Railways in Southern Africa; S.A. Railway Engineering (ISSN 0033-8885)
Description: Covers developments, opinions, and news on the railroad industry in Africa.
Refereed Serial

385 AT ISSN 0033-9040
RAILWAYS INSTITUTE MAGAZINE. 1897. m. Aus.$5.60. Railways Institute Council, P.O. Box 8436, Perth Business Centre, Perth, W.A. 6849, Australia. TEL 61-9-3262461. FAX 61-9-3262754. Ed. Neil Clancy. adv.; bk.rev.; illus.; circ. 4,000 (controlled). **Document type:** newsletter.

ULRICH'S INTERNATIONAL PERIODICALS DIRECTORY 1996

TRANSPORTATION — RAILROADS

385   SA
RAILWAYS OF SOUTHERN AFRICA: LOCOMOTIVE GUIDE. a. R.20. Beyer-Garratt Publications, P.O. Box 91175, Auckland Park 2006, South Africa. (Dist. by: Transnet Museum, P.O. Box 3753, Johannesburg 2000, South Africa) Ed. J.N. Middleton.
Formerly (until 1990): South African Railways Locomotive Allocations.

385   UK   ISSN 0269-0608
RAILWAYS RESTORED. 1980. a. £6.95. Association of Railway Preservation Societies Ltd., c/o John M. Crane, 7 Robert Close, Potters Bar, Herts. EN6 2DH, England. TEL 01707-643658. (And: Ian Allan Ltd., Coombelands House, Coombelands Ln., Addlestone, Weybridge, Surrey KT15 1HY, England. TEL 01932-228959. FAX 01932-232366) Ed. Allan Butcher. circ. 6,000. **Document type:** directory.
Description: Gives details of more than 100 railways, museums and steam centers, including locomotives, rolling stock and associated organizations.

385   UK   ISSN 0265-0231
RAILWAYS TODAY. 1983. q. Goodhead Publications Ltd., 27 Murdock Rd., Bicester, Oxon. OX6 7RG, England. adv.

385   FI   ISSN 0048-6833
RAUTATIELIIKENNE. 1943. m. (11/yr.) Fmk.30. Rautatievirkamiesliitto - Union of Railway Officials, Rautatiehallitus, Vilhonkatu 13, 00100 Helsinki 10, Finland. Ed. T.P. Elomaa. adv.; bk.rev.; bibl.; charts; illus.; stat.; index. circ. 3,800.

385   CK
REIL. 1961. m. Calle 13, No. 18-24, Bogota, Colombia. adv. circ. 13,500.

385   US
RENMIN TIEDAO/PEOPLE'S RAILWAY. (Text in Chinese) 3/w. $152. China Books & Periodicals, Inc., 2929 24th St., San Francisco, CA 94110. TEL 415-282-2994. FAX 415-282-0994. **Document type:** newspaper.

385   BL   ISSN 0034-950X
REVISTA FERROVIARIA. (Yearbook avail.) 1939. m. Cr.$340000($50) Empresa Jornalistica dos Transportes, Rua Mexico 41-S-904, 20031-144 Rio de Janeiro, Brazil. TEL 021-532-0260. FAX 021-240-0139. Ed. Gerson Toller Gomes. adv.; bk.rev.; charts; illus.; stat. circ. 10,000.
Description: Covers the economics, politics and technology of the railway world in Brazil and abroad.

385   FR   ISSN 0035-3183
CODEN: RGCFAI
REVUE GENERALE DES CHEMINS DE FER. (Supplements avail.: Le Rail; Le Monde) 1885. 11/yr. 950 F. (Societe Nationale des Chemins de Fer Francais) Dunod, 15 rue Gossin, 92543 Montrouge Cedex, France. TEL 33-1-40-92-65-00. FAX 33-1-40-92-65-97. TELEX 634 916 F. (Subscr. to: Centrale des Revues, 11 rue Gossin, 92543 Montrouge Cedex, France. TEL 33-1-46-56-52-66) Ed. J.P. Bernard. adv.; bk.rev.; abstr.; bibl.; charts; illus.; stat.; index. circ. 4,200. (also avail. in microfilm from UMI) **Indexed:** Br.Rail.Bd., Eng.Ind., Excerp.Med., HRIS, INSPEC (1968-).
—Ei; SWETS. **CCC.**
Description: Covers technical aspects of railway transportation -- materials, trains and underground systems, networks, impact studies, technical difficulties, and new technologies.

385.262   GW
RHEINBAHN EXTRA. 1980. irreg. Rheinische Bahngesellschaft AG, Postfach 104263, 40033 Duesseldorf, Germany. TEL 0211-58201. FAX 0211-5821966. Ed. Hermann-Josef Vetten. circ. 75,000. **Document type:** consumer publication.
Formerly (until 1993): Steig Ein.

385   US   ISSN 0035-7898
ROLL SIGN. 1964. 6/yr. $8. Boston Street Railway Association, Inc., Box 181037, Boston, MA 02118-1037. Ed. Daniel T. Lenihan. bk.rev.; illus.; index; circ. 1,200 (paid). (reprint service avail. from UMI) **Document type:** newsletter.

385   US
ROSTER OF NORTH AMERICAN RAPID TRANSIT CARS (YEAR). a.? $100 to non-members; members $45. American Public Transit Association, Rolling Stock Equipment Committee, 1201 New York Ave., N.W., Washington, DC 20005. TEL 202-898-4089. FAX 202-989-4049. **Document type:** trade publication.
Description: Lists the cost, performance, dimensions, weights, H.V.A.C. systems, propulsion equipment, and trucks and suspensions for transit cars in North America.

385   SW   ISSN 0037-5985
S J - NYTT. 1943. m. free. Statens Jaernvaegars Huvudkontor - State Railways Head Office, S-105 50 Stockholm, Sweden. TEL 46-8-762-30-05. Ed. Gunnel Sundbom. bk.rev.; illus.

385   SZ   ISSN 1022-7113
SCHWEIZER EISENBAHN REVUE. 1978. 10/yr. 99.80 SFr. (foreign 105 SFr.). Minrex AG, Maihofstr. 63, Postfach 3720, CH-6002 Luzern, Switzerland. TEL 041-368666. FAX 041-368806. Ed. W. von Andrian. adv. circ. 12,300. **Document type:** bulletin.

SEASHORE TROLLEY MUSEUM DISPATCH. see *MUSEUMS AND ART GALLERIES*

385   CC   ISSN 1000-1913
SHANGHAI TIEDAO XUEYUAN XUEBAO/SHANGHAI RAILROAD INSTITUTE. JOURNAL. (Text in Chinese) q. Shanghai Tiedao Xueyuan, 1 Zhennan Lu, Shanghai 200333, People's Republic of China. TEL 2506344. Ed. Xia Jianxin.

385   US   ISSN 0199-4050
THE SHORT LINE; the journal of short line railroads. 1973. bi-m. $21. Garreth M. McDonald, Ed. & Pub., Box 607, Pleasant Garden, NC 27313. TEL 910-674-2168. bk.rev.; index, cum.index: nos.1-60, nos.61-120. circ. 1,600. (back issues avail.) **Document type:** consumer publication.
Description: Reviews short line railroad activity from historic to current lines; emphasizes newly created short lines, their management, operations, and equipment.

614.8   AU   ISSN 0037-4539
SICHERHEIT ZUERST. 1958. q. free. Versicherungsanstalt der Oesterreichischen Eisenbahnen, Unfallverhuetungsdienst, Linke Wienzeile 48-52, A-1060 Vienna, Austria. TEL 01-58848237. FAX 01-58848332. Ed. Anton Schifter. circ. 20,000. **Indexed:** C.I.S. Abstr. **Document type:** trade publication.

385   GW   ISSN 0037-4997
CODEN: SIGDAD
SIGNAL UND DRAHT;* Zeitschrift fuer Informationstechnik im Eisenbahnwesen. 1906. m. DM.153.60. Deutsche Verkehrs Verlag GmbH, Nordkanalstr. 36, Postfach 101609, 2000 Hamburg 1, Germany. Ed. L. Wehner. adv.; bk.rev.; abstr.; bibl.; charts; illus.; pat.; tr.lit.; tr.mk.; index. circ. 3,000. **Indexed:** HRIS, INSPEC (1969-).
—BLDSC (8276.000000). **CCC.**
Incorporates: Signal und Schiene (ISSN 0037-5004)
Description: Computer technology used in railway engineering including signalling and telecommunications, data processing, and data processing equipment for office use and selling.

385   BL   ISSN 0102-5694
SINTESE FERROVIARIA BRASILEIRA. 1981. irreg. free. Rede Ferroviaria Federal, S.A., Departamento Geral de Estatistica, Rio de Janeiro, Brazil.

385   SW   ISSN 0281-109X
SKENBLADET. 1978. s-a. SEK 100 membership only (effective 1994). Ostkustbanans Vaenner (OKBv), P.O. Box 458, S-851 06 Sundsvall, Sweden. Ed. Rolf Sten. **Document type:** bulletin.

625.1 385   SW   ISSN 1101-9727
SMALSPAARSINFORM. 1989. q. SEK 125 membership (effective 1995). Foereningen Smalspaaret Vaexjoe-Vaestervik, c/o Claes Swendsen, Hoehhult, S-57022 Landsbro, Sweden. TEL 46-495-100-61. FAX 46-495-141-42. Ed. Claes Swendsen. adv.; bk.rev. **Document type:** newsletter.

385   US
SMOKE AND CINDERS. 1961. q. $25. Tennessee Valley Railroad Museum, Inc., 4119 Cromwell Rd., Chattanooga, TN 37421. TEL 615-894-8028. FAX 615-894-8029. Ed. Steven R. Freer. bk.rev. circ. 850. **Document type:** newsletter.

385   BE   ISSN 0081-119X
SOCIETE NATIONALE DES CHEMINS DE FER BELGES. RAPPORT ANNUEL. (Editions in Dutch, French) 1926. a. Societe Nationale des Chemins de Fer Belges - Nationale Maatschappij de Belgischen Spoorwegen, Fonsnylaan 47B, Bureau 40-231, B-1060 Brussels, Belgium. circ. 4,000 (2,000 Dutch ed.; 2,000 French ed.). circ. controlled. **Document type:** corporate report.

385   UK
SOMERSET AND DORSET RAILWAY TRUST BULLETIN. 1966. bi-m. £12 membership. Somerset and Dorset Railway Trust, The Railway Station, Washford, Near Watchet, Somerset, England. TEL 01984-40869. FAX 01622-693531. Ed. David Grimwood. adv. contact: Hugh Rainbird. bk.rev. circ. 1,000. **Document type:** bulletin.

385   US   ISSN 0038-3805
SOUTHERN AND SOUTHWESTERN RAILWAY CLUB. PROCEEDINGS.* 1890. q. $3. Southern & Southwestern Railway Club, 717 Pinecliffe Dr., Chesapeake, VA 23320. adv.; charts; illus. circ. 500.

385   US
SOUTHERN PACIFIC BULLETIN. 1913. q. free to libraries; single copies avail. upon request. Southern Pacific Lines, Southern Pacific Bldg., One Market Plaza, San Francisco, CA 94105. TEL 415-541-1656. Ed. Jack Martin. bk.rev.; illus.; circ. 45,000 (controlled). **Document type:** bulletin.

385   II   ISSN 0038-450X
SOUTHERN RAILWAYS. (Text in English) 1949. m. $0.25. c/o T.S. Rao, 2235 Bhut Gosami Vattaram, Manojiappa St., Tanjore S., India. Ed. Tanjore Swamirao Krisnakao. circ. 9,000.

385   US
SPEEDLINES. 1984. m. membership. High Speed Rail Maglev Association, 206 Valley Court, Ste. 800, Pittsburgh, PA 15237. TEL 412-366-6887. FAX 412-369-8698. Ed. Robert J. Casey. adv. circ. 20,000. **Document type:** trade publication.
Description: News about new transportation mode and industry of high speed rail and magnetic levitation transportation.

385   BE   ISSN 0773-5901
HET SPOOR. French edition: Rail (ISSN 0033-8729) (Text in Dutch) 1956. m. 450 BEF. Nationale Maatschappij der Belgische Spoorwegen - Societe Nationale des Chemins de Fer Belges, 85 rue de France, Bureau 05-322, B-1070 Brussels, Belgium. FAX 32-2-5253516. Ed. M. Bouquiaux. bk.rev.; charts; illus.; tr.lit. circ. 107,000.

385 069.9   DK   ISSN 0106-6927
SPORVEJSMUSEET SKJOLDENAESHOLM. AARSBERETNING. 1979. a. DKK 28. Sporvejshistorisk Selskab, Valloevej 24, 2700 Broenshoej, Denmark. Ed. Per Soegaard. illus. circ. 1,500.

385   AU   ISSN 0038-870X
DER SPURKRANZ; Unabhaengige Zeitschrift fuer Verkehrspolitik. 1967. m. S.108. Verein zur Foerderung des Schienenverkehrs, Oldenburggasse 73, A-1232 Vienna, Austria. Ed. Friedrich Rodt. circ. 1,100. (processed)

385 790.13   UK   ISSN 0958-7373
STEAM CLASSIC. m. Argus Specialist Publications Ltd. (Subsidiary of: Argus Press Group), Argus House, Boundary Way, Hemel Hempstead, Herts. HP2 7ST, England. TEL 01442-665515. FAX 01442-66746. (Subscr. to: Argus Subscription Services, Queensway House, 2 Queensway, Redhill, Surrey RH1 1QS, England. TEL 01737-768611) **Document type:** consumer publication.
Description: Allows steam train enthusiasts to explore all types of engines and tells them where they can see, photograph, and travel on their favorite railways.

385   UK   ISSN 0269-0020
STEAM DAYS. 1971. m. £14. Ian Allan Ltd., Coombelands House, Coombelands Ln., Addlestone, Surrey KT15 1HY, England. TEL 01932-855909. Ed. Rex Kennedy. bk.rev.; charts; illus. circ. 18,000. (reprint service avail. from UMI) **Document type:** consumer publication.
  Former titles: Steam Train; Trains Illustrated - Railway Heritage; Trains Illustrated - Railway Preservation; Trains Illustrated - Express Trains (ISSN 0141-9935)
  Description: Illustrated feature articles on steam railways.

385.1   US   ISSN 0081-542X
TF6.U5
STEAM PASSENGER SERVICE DIRECTORY. 1966. a. $11.95 (effective Mar. 1995). (Empire State Railway Museum) Great Eastern Publishing, Box 246, Richmond, VT 05477-0246. TEL 802-434-2351. FAX 802-434-2364. Ed. Michelle Giroux; Pub. Mark Smith. adv. contact: Kathleen Truax. circ. 14,000. (back issues avail.) **Document type:** directory.

385   UK   ISSN 0143-7232
STEAM RAILWAY. m. £26.40 (foreign £35.80) (effective 1995-1996). E M A P - Apex, Tower House, Sovereign Park, Lathkill St., Market Harborough, Leics. LE16 9EF, England. TEL 01858-468811. FAX 01858-432164. adv.; bk.rev.; illus.; tr.lit. circ. 39,295. **Document type:** consumer publication.

385   UK   ISSN 0959-0897
STEAM WORLD. 1990. m. £26.40 (foreign £37.95) (effective 1995-1996). E M A P - Apex, Tower House, Sovereign Park, Lathkill St., Market Harborough, Leics. LE16 9EF, England. TEL 01858-468811. FAX 01858-432164. adv. **Document type:** consumer publication.

385   UK   ISSN 0039-1190
STEPHENSON LOCOMOTIVE SOCIETY JOURNAL. 1924. bi-m. £13. Stephenson Locomotive Society, 7 Salamanca, Crowthorne, Berkshire RG11 6AP, England. TEL 01344-776656. Ed. Bruce I. Nathan. adv.; bk.rev.; charts; illus.; stat. circ. 1,100. **Document type:** newsletter.

385   GW   ISSN 0340-7071
STRASSENBAHN MAGAZIN; Elektrischer Nahverkehr - gestern, heute, morgen. 1970. 4/yr. DM.85.80. Franckh-Kosmos Verlags-GmbH und Co., Postfach 106011, 70049 Stuttgart, Germany. TEL 0711-2191-332. FAX 0711-2191-350. Ed. Martin Pabst. adv.: B&W page DM.980; trim 140 x 221. bk.rev.; illus.; maps. circ. 3,000. **Document type:** bulletin.
  —CCC.
  Description: Publication devoted to the history and the present state of the tramway in Germany and other European countries.

385.264   SZ
STRASSENTRANSPORT. fortn. 76 SFr. (foreign 97 SFr.). (Schweizerischer Nutzfahrzeugverband) Huber and Co. AG, Promenadestr. 16, CH-8501 Frauenfeld, Switzerland. TEL 054-271111. **Document type:** trade publication.

385.264   GW
SUEDDEUTSCHER VERKEHRSKURIER. m. Fachvereinigung Guterfernverkehr im Landesverband Bayerischer Transportunternehmen, Leonrodstr 48, 80636 Munich, Germany. TEL 089-1292096. TELEX 215102.

SUVREMENI PROMET. see *TRANSPORTATION — Air Transport*

385 350.1   SW   ISSN 0346-2323
SVENSKA JAERNVAEGSTIDNINGEN. m. Jaernvaeg Statstjaenstemannafoerbundet, Box 5308, 102 46 Stockholm, Sweden. adv. circ. 2,923.

385   SW   ISSN 0081-9964
SVERIGES JAERNVAEGAR/RAILWAYS OF SWEDEN. (Subseries of: Sveriges Officiella Statistik: Transport- och Kommunikationsvaesen) 1953. a. free. Statens Jaernvaegars Huvudkontor - State Railways Head Office, S-105 50 Stockholm, Sweden. TEL 46-8-762-40-25. circ. 1,000.
  Supersedes: Allmaen Jaernvaegsstatistik; Statens Jaernvaegar.

385.264   SZ
SWISS CAMION. 1959. m. 60 SFr. Routiers Suisses, Rue de la Chocolatiere 26, CH-1026 Echandens, Switzerland. TEL 021-7014224. FAX 021-7010037. Ed. Daniel Waelti. adv. contact: R. Dieboldswyler. **Document type:** bulletin.

625.1   GW
T UND U. (Transport und Umschlagetechnik) a. DM.22. Hestra-Verlag, Holzhofallee 33, 64295 Darmstadt, Germany. TEL 06151-3907-0. FAX 06151-390777.
  Formerly: R T und G T.

385   SW   ISSN 0039-8683
TAAG/TRAINS. 1966. m. (10/yr.). SEK 200. Svenska Jaernvaegsklubben - Swedish Railway Club, P.O. Box 124, S-101 22 Stockholm, Sweden. Ed. Lars Tornqvist. adv.; bk.rev.; charts; illus.; cum.index. circ. 5,400.
  Formed by the merger of: Svenska Jaernvaegsklubbens Medlemsblad; Meddelanden fraan Svenska Jaernvaegsklubben.

TABI TO TETSUDO. see *TRAVEL AND TOURISM*

385.3   US
TACOMA TRAINSHEET. (Contains occasional supplements) 1965. m. (except Jul. & Aug.). $5 to libraries. National Railway Historical Society, Tacoma Chapter, Box 340, Tacoma, WA 98401. TEL 206-752-0047. Ed. Rick Bacon. bk.rev.; illus. circ. 275. (processed; also avail. in microform from UMI) **Document type:** newsletter.
  —UMI.
  Formerly (until 1994): Trainsheet (ISSN 0041-0845)

385   CH   ISSN 1011-6850
TAIWAN RAILWAY. (Text in Chinese and English) 1963. irreg. Taiwan Railway Administration, Taipei, Taiwan, Republic of China. Ed. J. Fan. illus. circ. 2,000.

385   UK   ISSN 0300-3272
TALYLLYN NEWS. 1953. q. £16. Talyllyn Railway Preservation Society, Flat One, 25 Gwendolen Ave., London SW15 6ET, England. Ed. John Slater. adv. contact: John Slater. bk.rev.; illus. circ. 2,300. **Document type:** newsletter.

385   TZ
TANZANIA RAILWAYS CORPORATION. HABARI ZA RELI. (Text in Kiswahili) 1977. m. Sh.12 per no. Tanzania Railways Corporation, Box 468, Dar es Salaam, Tanzania. TELEX 41308 TRC DSM. Ed. Winston Makamba. adv.; bk.rev. circ. 10,000.
  Supersedes in part: Sikio (ISSN 0037-5136)

625.1   AU
TECHNISCHE UNIVERSITAET WIEN. INSTITUT FUER EISENBAHNWESEN. ARBEITEN. 1971. irreg. Technische Universitaet Wien, Institut fuer Eisenbahnwesen, Karlsplatz 13, A-1040 Vienna, Austria. FAX 01-5055415. Ed. Edwin Engel. **Document type:** monographic series.
  Formerly (until 1991): Technische Universitaet Wien. Institut fuer Eisenbahnwesen, Spezialbahnen und Verkehrswirtschaft. Arbeiten.

625.1   IT
TECNICA PROFESSIONALE. 1933. m. $65 (effective 1994). Collegio Ingegneri Ferroviari Italiani, Via Giolitti 34, 00185 Rome, Italy. TEL 06-47307724. FAX 06-4742987. Dir. Antonio Lagana. adv.; bk.rev.; bibl.; charts; illus.

385 331.8   US
TELLING IT LIKE IT IS. bi-m. Transportation Communications International Union, 3 Research Pl., Rockville, MD 20850. TEL 301-948-4910. FAX 301-948-1369. Ed. R.A. Scardelletti. circ. 2,300 (controlled). (looseleaf format)
  Formerly (until 1991): Leadership Action Lines.
  Description: Examines economic trends and collective bargaining agreements affecting members employed in the transportation industry, especially railroads.

385   JA   ISSN 0040-4047
TETSUDO PIKUTORIARU/RAILWAY PICTORIAL. (Text in Japanese) 1951. m. 3480 Yen($9.70) Tetsudo Toshokankai, New Kokusai Bldg., 3-4-1 Marunouchi, Chiyoda-ku, Tokyo 100, Japan. Ed. Ryuzo Tanaka. adv.; charts; illus.; stat.

385   JA   ISSN 0915-9231
TETSUDO TO DENKI GIJUTSU/RAILWAY AND ELECTRICAL ENGINEERING. 1990. m. Nihon Tetsudo Denki Gijutsu Kyokai - Railway Electrical Engineering Association of Japan, 23-go 19-banchi, 1-chome, Ebisu, Shibuya-ku, Tokyo 150, Japan. TEL 03-432-7551.
  —BLDSC (7245.018350).
  Formed by the merger of (1946-1990): Shingo Hoan - Signal Engineering of Japan (ISSN 0286-3006); (1950-1990): Tetsudo Tsushin - Railway Telecommunications and Electronics (ISSN 0495-2197); (1987-1990): Tetsudo to Denki - Railway and Electricity (ISSN 0914-3076)

385   UK   ISSN 0144-2708
TIDDLY DYKE. 1978. q. Swindon & Cricklade Railway Society, 36 Parklands Rd., Swindon, Wiltshire, England.

625.1   CC
TIEDAO JIANZHU/RAILWAY CONSTRUCTION. (Text in Chinese) m. Tiedao-bu, Keji Qingbao-suo - Ministry of Railway, Science and Technology Information Institute, Daliushu Beizhan, Xizhimenwai, Beijing 100081, People's Republic of China. TEL 8996445. Ed. Shao Genda.

385   CC   ISSN 1001-8360
TIEDAO XUEBAO/CHINA RAILWAY SOCIETY. JOURNAL. (Text in Chinese) 1979. q. $12 per no. (effective 1996). Zhongguo Tiedao Xuehui - China Railway Society, 10 Fuxing Lu, Beijing 100844, People's Republic of China. TEL 8645861. (Dist. overseas by: China International Book Trading Corp., P.O. Box 399, Beijing, P.R.C.) Ed. Qing Jingxian. bk.rev.; circ. 1,200. (paid). **Document type:** academic/scholarly publication.
  Description: Contains academic research papers on the latest development and theories of management of Chinese railways.

385   CC   ISSN 1003-1421
TIEDAO YUNSHU YU JINGJI/RAILWAY TRANSPORTATION AND ECONOMICS. (Text in Chinese; abstracts in English) m. $60. Tiedaobu Kexue Yanjiuyuan, Yunshu yu Jingji Yanjiusuo - China Academy of Railway Sciences, Railway Transportation and Economics Research Institute, No.2 Daliushu Beicun, Xizhimenwai, Beijing 100081, People's Republic of China. TEL 3249452. Ed. Wu Jiahao. adv.: page $4000. circ. 6,000 (paid). **Document type:** academic/scholarly publication.

385   CC   ISSN 1000-0372
TIEDAO ZHISHI/RAILWAY KNOWLEDGE. 1980. bi-m. Y10.80($8) China Railway Society - Zhongguo Tiedao Xuehui, 10 Fuxing Lu, Beijing 100844, People's Republic of China. TEL 8645811. (Dist. overseas by: China International Book Trading Corp., P.O. Box 339, Beijing, P.R.C.) Ed. Ni Hannong. adv. contact: Wei Zhongyan. circ. 80,000.
  Description: News about China railway construction and international railroad developments.

385   UK   ISSN 1354-2753
▼**TODAY'S RAILWAYS.** 1994. bi-m. £15.90 (Europe £18.90). Platform 5 Publishing Ltd., 3 Wyvern House, Sark Rd., Sheffield, S. Yorks S2 4HG, England. TEL 0114-255-2625. FAX 0114-255-2471. (Dist. by: SM Magazine Distribution, 6 Leigham Court Rd., Streatham, London SW16 2PG, England. TEL 0181-677-8111. FAX 0181-769-9529) Ed. David Haydock; Pub. Peter Fox. adv.: B&W page £400, color page £600; trim 297 x 210; adv. contact: Peter Fox. bk.rev.; charts; illus.; video rev.; index; circ. 10,000 (paid). (back issues avail.) **Document type:** consumer publication.

385.2   UK
TOP RAIL. 1990. q. (S.N.C.F. (Societe Nationale des Chemins de Fer Francais)) B L A Group Ltd., 5-8 Hardwick St., London EC1R 4RB, England. TEL 0171-278-7711. FAX 0171-278-6246. Ed. Andrew Sanger. adv. contact: Tina Huggett. bk.rev.; circ. 200,000 (controlled). **Document type:** consumer publication.
  Description: Discusses various aspects of the French national railway for dedicated U.K. Francophiles.

385.264 388.324   JA
TORAKKU YUSO JOHO. 1948. 3/mo. Japan Trucking Association, Torakku Kaikan 2, Yotsuya 3-chome, Shinjuku-ku, Tokyo, Japan. TEL 03-357-6271.

TRANSPORTATION — RAILROADS

385   CN   ISSN 0040-9553
TORONTO RAILWAY CLUB. OFFICIAL PROCEEDINGS. 1931. 3/yr. membership only. Toronto Railway Club, Box 114, Union Station, Toronto, ON M5J 1E6, Canada. Ed. V.J. Macciocchi. adv.; charts; illus. circ. 1,200. **Document type:** proceedings.

625.1   US
TRACK YEARBOOK. 1982. a. $50. Trade Press Publishing Co., 230 W. Monroe, Ste. 2210, Chicago, IL 60606. TEL 312-629-1200. Ed. Tom Morgan. adv. circ. 6,000. **Document type:** trade publication.

TRAIN COLLECTORS QUARTERLY. see *HOBBIES*

TRAIN DISPATCHER. see *LABOR UNIONS*

385.22   US   ISSN 0896-4424
TRAIN RIDER MAGAZINE. 1986. bi-m. $6.50. Message Media, Box 9007, Berkeley, CA 94709. TEL 415-540-0809. Ed. James Russell. illus. circ. 750.
    Formerly: Train Rider Monthly.

385   US   ISSN 0041-0926
TRAINMASTER. 1956. m. $27 membership. National Railway Historical Society, Pacific Northwest Chapter, Rm. 1, Union Sta., 800 N.W. Sixth Ave., Portland, OR 97209-3715. TEL 503-226-6747. Ed. Jim Loomis. bk.rev. circ. 600. (processed) **Document type:** newsletter.
    Description: Contains information on chapter business and activities, original material by members pertaining to railroad history and preservation.

385   US   ISSN 0041-0934
TF1
TRAINS; the magazine of railroading. 1940. m. $34.95 (foreign $45). Kalmbach Publishing Co., Box 1612, Waukesha, WI 53187-1612. TEL 414-796-8776. FAX 414-796-0126. Ed. Kevin Keefe. charts; illus.; stat.; index. circ. 136,000. **Indexed:** Mag.Ind. **Document type:** consumer publication.
    —Faxon; UMI; UnCover.
    Description: Recalls the romance and glory of railroading's past, and explores the railroads of today. Emphasis on North American railroading, but coverage is worldwide.

385   UK   ISSN 0041-1019
TRAMWAY REVIEW. 1950. q. £7. Light Rail Transit Association, 23 Shrublands Close, Chigwell, Essex IG7 5EA, England. TEL 0181-500-2648. FAX 0171-538-9689. Ed. R.J.S. Wiseman. adv. contact: J.A. Cadish. bk.rev.; index; circ. 2,000 (paid). (back issues avail.) **Document type:** academic/scholarly publication.
    —BLDSC (8884.530000).
    Description: Provides information about the history of British and Irish tramway systems.

385 625.1   AT   ISSN 0818-5204
TRANSIT AUSTRALIA; the Australian urban transit magazine. 1946. m. Aus.$59 to individuals; institutions Aus.$75. Transit Australia Publishing, G.P.O. Box 1017, Sydney, N.S.W. 2001, Australia. TEL 61-2-99494424. FAX 61-2-99493282. Ed. Ian R. Hammond. adv.; bk.rev.; charts; illus.; stat.; index; circ. 1,000 (paid). (back issues avail.) **Indexed:** Aus.Rd.Ind.
    Formerly: Electric Traction (ISSN 0013-4163)

385   US
TRANSIT TIMES (ATLANTA). 1949. m. free. Metropolitan Atlanta Rapid Transit Authority, Public Information Division, 2424 Peidmont Rd., N.E., Atlanta, GA 30324. TEL 404-848-5157. Ed. Judith Weisberg. adv.; bk.rev.; illus. circ. 5,000.

385   SW   ISSN 0348-3118
TRANSPORT-JOURNALEN. 1955. 4/yr. free. Statens Jaernvaegars Huvudkontor, Godstransportdivisionen - State Railways Head Office, S-105 50 Stockholm, Sweden. TEL 46-8-762-43-72. Ed. Christer Beijbom. bk.rev.; charts; illus. circ. 40,000.

385   RU   ISSN 0131-4300
TA3
TRANSPORTNOE STROITEL'STVO.* 1951. m. $79 (effective 1996). Izdatel'stvo Transport, Basmanny tupik 6A, 107174 Moscow, Russia. (Dist. by: Mezhdunarodnaya Kniga, Moscow, G-200, Russia) bk.rev.; bibl.; charts; illus.; index. **Indexed:** Geotech.Abstr.
    —BLDSC (0182.000000).

388   NO
TRANSPORTOEKONOMISK INSTITUTT. AARSBERETNING. 1965. a. free. Transportoekonomisk Institutt - Institute of Transport Economics, P.O. Box 6110 Etterstad, 0602 Oslo 6, Norway. Ed. Harald Aas.
    Formerly: Norges Teknisk-Naturvitenskapelige Forskningsraad. Transportoekonomisk Institutt. Aarsberetning (ISSN 0078-124X)

385.264   BE
TRANSPORTROUTIER. every 3 wks. Federation Nationale Belge des Transportateurs Routiers, Rue Picard 69, B-1020 Brussels, Belgium. TEL 428-1160.

385   SP
TRENET. 4/yr. Amadeu Vies s-n, Apdo. 86, 08940 Cornella de Llobragat (Barcelona), Spain. circ. 10,000.

385 790.13 900   IT
TRENI. 1980. m. (11/yr.). L.78000 (foreign L.94000). Editrice Trasporti su Rotaie soc.coop.r.l., Piazza Vittorio Emanuele II, 42, 25087 Salo (Brescia), Italy. FAX 0365-41092. Ed. Erminio Mascherpa. adv.; bk.rev.; illus. circ. 14,000. (back issues avail.)
    Formerly (until 1993): Treni Oggi (ISSN 0392-4602)
    Description: Covers railroads, railroad history and railway modelling.

TROLLEY FARE. see *MUSEUMS AND ART GALLERIES*

625.1   US
U S COURT AND TRACK BUILDERS ASSOCIATION NEWSLINE. q. membership. U S Court and Track Builders Association, 720 Light St., Baltimore, MD 21230-3816. TEL 410-752-3500. FAX 410-752-8295. Ed. Carol T. Shaner. bk.rev. **Document type:** newsletter.

385   US   ISSN 0275-3758
U S RAIL NEWS. 1978. bi-w. $390 (effective Sep. 1992). Business Publishers, Inc., 951 Pershing Dr., Silver Spring, MD 20910-4464. TEL 301-587-6300. FAX 301-585-9075. Ed. Steve Lash. (looseleaf format) **Document type:** newsletter.
    ●Also available online. Vendor(s): NewsNet (TS11).
    —CCC.
    Description: Provides objective views of laws and new technologies affecting rail transport business, both passenger and goods transport.

331.88 385   MX
UNIFICACION.* vol.4, 1974. m. Sindicato de Trabajadores Ferrocarrileros de la Republica Mexicana, Calzada de Nonolco No. 206, Mexico D.F., Mexico. Ed.Bd. charts; illus. circ. 60,000.

385   US   ISSN 0163-4674
HE1780
U.S. FEDERAL RAILROAD ADMINISTRATION. OFFICE OF SAFETY. ACCIDENT - INCIDENT BULLETIN. Key Title: Accident - Incident Bulletin. no.144, 1975. a. $33.50. U.S. Federal Railroad Administration, Office of Safety, Washington, DC 20590. TEL 202-366-0881. (Orders to: Bernan, 4611-F Assembly Dr., Lanham, MD 20706. TEL 800-274-4447. FAX 301-459-0056) **Document type:** bulletin, government publication.
    Formerly: U.S. Federal Railroad Administration. Office of Safety. Accident Bulletin (ISSN 0092-1645)

V R - EXPRESS. (Valtionrautatiet) see *TRAVEL AND TOURISM*

385   HU   ISSN 0133-0314
VAROSI KOZLEKEDES/URBAN TRANSPORT. (Text in Hungarian; summaries in English (in special issues)) 1968. bi-m. 360 Ft.($25.50) (effective 1993). Petofi Lap- es Konyvkiado Kft., Szabadsag ter la, 6001 Kecskemet, Hungary. TEL 36-76-27611. Ed. Rudolf Nagy. adv.; bk.rev.; charts; illus.; maps; stat.; index. circ. 1,200.
    Description: Covers urban public and individual transport; includes national and international information.

385.264   GW
VERBAND DES WURTTEMBERGISCHEN VERKEHRSGEWERBES. SUEDDEUTSCHER VERKEHRSURIER. m. Verband des Wurttembergischen Verkehrsgewerbes, Hedelfinger Str. 25, 70327 Stuttgart, Germany. TEL 0711-423066. TELEX 22846.

385.204   GW
VERBUNDFAHRPLAN U - S. 1986. a. DM.2. Muenchner Verkehrs- und Tarifverbund GmbH, Thierschstr. 2, 80538 Munich, Germany. TEL 089-23803-0. FAX 089-238083-282. circ. 70,000. (back issues avail.) **Document type:** directory.

385   GW   ISSN 0232-9042
VERKEHRSGESCHICHTLICHE BLAETTER. 1974. bi-m. DM.26. Verkehrsgeschichtliche Blaetter e.V., Postfach 104, 10122 Berlin, Germany. TEL 030-2912502. Ed. Michael Guenther. bk.rev.; index. circ. 1,400. **Document type:** newsletter.

385.264   GW
VERKEHRSGEWERBE.* m. Hahn Verlag, Im Moore 17, Postfach 2427, 3000 Hannover 1, Germany.

385.264   GW
VERKEHRSGEWERBE FUER NIEDERSACHSEN UND BREMEN. m. Fachvereinigung Guterfernverkehr im Gesamtverband Verkehrsgewerbe Niedersachsen, Lortzingstr. 1, 30177 Hannover, Germany. TEL 6262273. TELEX 22461. (Subscr. to: Postfach 6160, 30061 Hannover, Germany)

385   FR
VIE DU RAIL ET DES TRANSPORTS. 1946. w. 650 F. 11 rue de Milan, 75440 Paris Cedex 09, France. TEL 49-70-12-00. (U.S. addr.: French National Railroads, 610 Fifth Ave., New York, NY 10020) Ed. Christian Fauvet. adv.; bk.rev.; film rev. circ. 220,000.
    —SWETS.
    Formerly: Vie du Rail (ISSN 0042-5478)
    Description: Technical and general railroad and transport information including tourism and travel by rail.

385   US
VIEWS AND NEWS. 1933. w. membership only. American Short Line Railroad Association, 1120 G St., N.W., No. 520, Washington, DC 20005-3889. TEL 202-628-4500. FAX 202-628-4500. Ed. A.C. Salor. circ. 1,400.

385   GW   ISSN 0171-8290
VORAUS. 1919. m. DM.20. Gewerkschaft Deutscher Lokomotivfuehrer, Baumweg 45, 60316 Frankfurt a.M., Germany. TEL 069-405709-0. FAX 069-40570940. Ed. Bernhard Ochs. adv.; bk.rev. circ. 45,000. **Document type:** trade publication.

385   RU
CODEN: VVNZAA
VSEROSSIISKII NAUCHNO-ISSLEDOVATEL'SKII INSTITUT ZHELEZNODOROZHNOGO TRANSPORTA. VESTNIK. 1942. 8/yr. $101. Moscow, Russia. TEL 287-73-36. FAX 287-72-36. (Dist. by: Mezhdunarodnaya Kniga, ul. Dimitrova D.39, 113096 Moscow, Russia) adv.; bk.rev.; index. **Indexed:** Chem.Abstr.
    —CASDDS.
    Formerly: Vsesoyuznyi Naucho-Issledovatel'skii Institut Zheleznodorozhnogo Transporta. Vestnik (ISSN 0042-4749)
    Description: For engineers, technicians and researchers of railway transport, research institutes.

380.3   XR   ISSN 0231-6951
VYZKUMNY USTAV SPOJU. SBORNIK PRACI. (Text in Czech; summaries in English, French, German, Russian) 1974. irreg. (2-3/yr.) 10 Kc. per no. Nakladatelstvi Dopravy a Spoju, Hybernska 5, 115 78 Prague 1, Czech Republic. (Dist. by: Artia, Ve Smeckach 30, 111 27 Prague 1, Czech Republic) Ed. Milos Matura. charts; illus.

385   CN
W C R A NEWS. 1961. m. Can.$30. West Coast Railway Association, Box 2790, Vancouver, BC V6B 3X2, Canada. TEL 604-524-1011. FAX 604-520-3088. Ed. Don Evans. bk.rev. circ. 500. **Document type:** newsletter.
    Description: Provides updates on Association activities, rail stories of interest, rail travel and tours.

385   US   ISSN 0897-7577
WAYBILL. 1970. q. $4. Mystic Valley Railway Society, Box 486, Hyde Park, MA 02136-0486. TEL 617-361-4445. Ed. W. Russell Rylko. adv. circ. 14,000. (tabloid format) **Document type:** newsletter.
    Description: Provides education in the field of railroad transportation.

385.264 BE
WEGWIJS - U B O T EN ROUTE. bi-m. Belgische Transportarbeidersbond, Pardenmarkt 66, B-2000 Antwerpen, Belgium. TEL 32-3-224-34-11. FAX 32-3-234-01-49.

385.264 GW ISSN 0175-3061
WERKVERKEHR UND VERLADER. 1955. q. Bundesverband Werkverkehr und Verlader, Lengsdorfer Hauptstr. 73, 53127 Bonn, Germany. TEL 0228-253034. TELEX 8869366.

385 CN ISSN 0085-8188
WESTERN CANADIAN STEAM LOCOMOTIVE DIRECTORY. 1969. biennial. $1. Richard L. Coulton, Ed. & Pub., Bentley, Alta. TOC 0J0, Canada. circ. 100. **Document type:** directory.

385 US
TF23.6
WESTERN RAILROADER. 1937. m. $31. Railway & Locomotive Historical Society, Pacific Coast Chapter, Milepost 1, Sutter St. No. 16, Folsom, CA 95680. bk.rev.; charts; illus.; maps. circ. 1,000. (also avail. in microform from UMI)
—UMI.
Former titles: Western Railroader and Western Railfan (ISSN 0149-4996); Western Railroader (ISSN 0043-4108)

385 US ISSN 0043-4744
WHEEL CLICKS. 1938. m. $20. Pacific Railroad Society, Inc., Box 80726, San Marino, CA 91118-8726. TEL 213-283-0087. Ed. Dick Finley. bk.rev.; charts; illus.; index. circ. 1,000. **Document type:** newsletter. **Description:** Details railway construction and operation. Covers Amtrak, SPT & ATSF, Peninsula CalTrain and West Coast rail transit, commuter and tourist lines.

385 JA ISSN 0386-1716
WHITE PAPER ON TRANSPORTATION SAFETY IN JAPAN. (Text in English) 1978. a. $22. (Management and Coordination Agency, Traffic Safety Policy Office) International Association of Traffic and Safety Sciences, 6-20, 2-chome, Yaesu, Chuo-ku, Tokyo 104, Japan. TEL 03-3273-7884. FAX 03-3272-7054. **Document type:** academic/scholarly publication.

385.264 GW
WIENER FUHRWERKERZEITUNG. m. Fachgruppe Guterbeforderungsgewerbe fuer Wien, Collorodogasse 24, A-1180 Wien, Germany. TEL 345121.

385 NZ ISSN 0044-023X
Y A R N. (Your Auckland Railway News) 1952. 11/yr. NZ.$48 membership. Auckland Railway Enthusiasts Society, Inc., P.O. Box 2429, Auckland, New Zealand. TEL 64-9-479-4299. FAX 64-9-832-4065. Ed. M. Ross. adv.; bk.rev. circ. 680.
—CCC.

385.264 BE
ZEE. s-a. Belgische Transportarbeidersbond, Paardenmarkt 66, B-2000 Antwerpen, Belgium. TEL 32-3-224-34-11. FAX 32-3-234-01-49.

385 SZ
ZEITSCHRIFT FUER DEN INTERNATIONALEN EISENBAHNVERKEHR. 1893. q. Office Central des Transports Internationaux Ferroviaires - Zentralamt fuer den Internationalen Eisenbahnverkehr, Gryphenhubeliweg 30, CH-3006 Bern, Switzerland. TEL 031-3511762. FAX 031-3511164. TELEX 912063-OCTI-CH. bk.rev. **Document type:** bulletin.

385 RU ISSN 0044-4448
HE7
ZHELEZNODOROZHNYI TRANSPORT.* 1919. m. $97 (effective 1996). Izdatel'stvo Transport, Basmanny tupik 6A, 107174 Moscow, Russia. TEL 095-262-6773. (Co-sponsor: Ministerstvo Putei Soobshcheniya) Ed. G.E. Sorokin. adv.; bk.rev.; abstr.; bibl.; charts; illus.; stat.; index. circ. 14,325. **Indexed:** C.I.S. Abstr., Chem.Abstr.
—BLDSC (0057.550000).

625.1 CC ISSN 1001-4632
ZHONGGUO TIEDAO KEXUE/CHINA RAILWAY SCIENCE. (Text in Chinese) s-a. (Tiedao-bu, Kexue Yanjiuyuan - Ministry of Railway, Science Academy) Zhongguo Tiedao Kexue Bianjibu, Daliushu Beizhan, Xizhimenwai, Beijing 100081, People's Republic of China. TEL 8996577. Ed. Tan Licheng.

625.1 CC ISSN 1001-683X
ZHONGGUO TIELU/CHINA RAILROAD. (Text in Chinese) bi-m. Tiedao-bu, Keji Qingbao-suo - Ministry of Railway, Science and Technology Information Institute, Daliushu Beizhan, Xizhimenwai, Beijing 100081, People's Republic of China. TEL 8317379. Ed. Xie Wenbin.

TRANSPORTATION — Roads And Traffic

see also Engineering–Civil Engineering

388.31 613.1 US
A A S H T O ENVIRONMENTAL BULLETIN. 1992. bi-m. American Association of State Highway and Transportation Officials, 444 N. Capitol St., N.W., Ste. 249, Washington, DC 20001. TEL 202-624-5800. FAX 202-624-5806. Ed. David Clowson. **Document type:** bulletin. **Description:** Informs state DOTs and federal agencies about environmental legislation and regulation affecting transportation programs.

338.31 624 US
A A S H T O JOURNAL; weekly transportation report. w. $225 (foreign $245). American Association of State Highway and Transportation Officials, 444 N. Capitol St., N.W., Ste. 249, Washington, DC 20001. TEL 202-624-5800. FAX 202-624-5806. Ed. Sunny Mays Schust. cum.index: 1988-1991. circ. 1,500. (back issues avail.) **Document type:** bulletin. **Description:** Covers current transportation events.

388.31 US
A A S H T O PLANNING BULLETIN. 1992. m. American Association of State Highway and Transportation Officials, 444 N. Capitol St., N.W., Ste. 249, Washington, DC 20001. TEL 202-624-5800. FAX 202-624-5806. **Document type:** bulletin. **Description:** Covers issues related to the increased role of planning resulting from the Intermodal Surface Transportation Efficiency Act (ISTEA) as well as the Clean Air Act Amendments of 1990. Provides information on transportation planning for the state DOTs and other organizations interested in transportation planning issues.

A A S H T O QUARTERLY. (American Association of State Highway and Transportation Officials) see ENGINEERING — Civil Engineering

A D A C ATLAS DEUTSCHLAND - EUROPA. (Allgemeiner Deutscher Automobil Club e.V.) see TRAVEL AND TOURISM

388.1 IT ISSN 0044-975X
A I S C A T INFORMAZIONI. 1966. q. free. Associazione Italiana Societa Concessionarie Autostrade e Trafori, Via Sardegna 40, 00187 Rome, Italy. FAX 6-4746968. Ed. Vito Rocco. bk.rev.; charts; stat. circ. 4,500. **Indexed:** Dok.Str.
—BLDSC (0785.450000).

A P T S PROJECT SUMMARIES. (Advanced Public Transportation Systems) see TRANSPORTATION — Abstracting, Bibliographies, Statistics

388.31 US
A R T B A NEWSLETTER. 1902. 22/yr. $50 to non-members. American Road & Transportation Builders Association, 1010 Massachusetts Ave., N.W., Washington, DC 20001. TEL 202-289-4434. FAX 202-289-4435. Ed. Gail M. Schell. circ. 4,800. **Document type:** newsletter.

624 690 US
A R T B A TRANSPORTATION OFFICIALS AND ENGINEERS DIRECTORY, STATE AND FEDERAL TRANSPORTATION AGENCY PERSONNEL. a. $35. American Road and Transportation Builders Association, 1010 Massachusetts Ave., N.W., Washington, DC 20001. TEL 202-289-4434. FAX 202-289-4435. **Document type:** directory.
Formerly: A R B A Officials and Engineers Directory, Transportation Agency Personnel (ISSN 0360-6996)

ABERDEEN'S PAVEMENT MAINTENANCE. see ENGINEERING — Civil Engineering

ADVANCED PUBLIC TRANSPORTATION SYSTEMS: STATE OF THE ART UPDATE (YEAR). see TRANSPORTATION — Abstracting, Bibliographies, Statistics

388.312 US
AMERICAN ASSOCIATION OF STATE HIGHWAY AND TRANSPORTATION OFFICIALS. PROCEEDINGS. a. $29.25. American Association of State Highway and Transportation Officials, 444 N. Capitol St. N.W., Ste. 249, Washington, DC 20001. TEL 202-624-5800. FAX 202-624-5806. **Indexed:** HRIS. **Document type:** proceedings.

388.312 GW
DIE ANTWORT. 1985. q. DM.6. Rettungsstiftung Juergen Pegler e.V., Schellengasse 8, 74072 Heilbronn, Germany. TEL 07131-80080. FAX 07131-81219. circ. 50,000. (back issues avail.)

ARCHIVIO DELLA CIRCOLAZIONE E DEI SINISTRI STRADALI. see LAW

388.1 US ISSN 0403-1792
ARKANSAS HIGHWAYS. 1953. q. free. State Highway and Transportation Department, Public Affairs Office, Box 2261, Little Rock, AR 72203. TEL 501-569-2000. FAX 501-569-2698. Ed. Randy Ort. charts; illus. circ. 5,000. **Document type:** government publication.

388.1 US ISSN 0004-4954
TN853
ASPHALT. 1949. 3/yr. free. Asphalt Institute, Box 14052, Lexington, KY 40512-4052. FAX 606-288-4999. Ed. John Davis. illus.; circ. 16,000 (controlled).
—Ei.
Formerly (until 1986): Asphaltnews; Supersedes (in 1976): Asphalt Institute. Newsletter.

665.5 US
ASPHALT EMULSION MANUFACTURERS ASSOCIATION. NEWSLETTER. 1973. q. membership. Asphalt Emulsion Manufacturers Association, 3 Church Circle, Ste. 250, Annapolis, MD 21401. TEL 410-267-0023. Ed. Michael R. Krissoff. adv. circ. 1,200. **Document type:** newsletter.

388.31 AT
AUSTRALIAN ROAD RESEARCH BOARD. BRIEFING. 1989. m. free. Australian Road Research Board, 500 Burwood Hwy., Vermont S, Vic. 3133, Australia. TEL 61-3-881-1555. FAX 61-3-887-8104. TELEX AA33113. circ. 2,200. (back issues avail.)

388 625.7 AT ISSN 0572-1431
AUSTRALIAN ROAD RESEARCH BOARD. PROCEEDINGS. 1962. biennial. Australian Road Research Board, 500 Burwood Hwy., Vermont S., Vic. 3133, Australia. TEL 03-881-1555. FAX 03-887-8104. TELEX AA33113. **Indexed:** Dok.Str., Eng.Ind., Geotech.Abstr., HRIS, Noise Pollut.Publ.Abstr. **Document type:** proceedings.
—BLDSC (6656.200000); Ei.

388.411 388.3 AT ISSN 0158-0728
AUSTRALIAN ROAD RESEARCH BOARD. RESEARCH REPORT. 1975. irreg. Aus.$30 per no. Australian Road Research Board, 500 Burwood Rd., Vermont S., Vic. 3133, Australia. TEL 03-881-1555. FAX 03-887-8104. TELEX AA33113. circ. 350. (back issues avail.) **Indexed:** Dok.Str.
—BLDSC (7760.260000).

380.5 388.3 AT ISSN 0572-144X
AUSTRALIAN ROAD RESEARCH BOARD. SPECIAL REPORT. 1966. irreg. Aus.$50 per no. Australian Road Research Board, 500 Burwood Highway, Vermont S., Vic. 3133, Australia. TEL 03-881-1555. FAX 03-887-8104. TELEX AA33113. circ. 350. (back issues avail.)
—BLDSC (8386.550000); Ei.

AUSTROPACK; Zeitschrift fuer alle Gebiete des Verpackungswesens fuer Transport und Verkehr. see PACKAGING

388.31 US ISSN 1063-0899
AUTO FREE PRESS. 1989. bi-m. $25 membership (includes City Cyclist). Transportation Alternatives, 92 St. Marks Pl., New York, NY 10012. TEL 212-475-4600. FAX 212-475-4551. E-mail: Transalt@echonyc.com. Ed. Mark Garbowski. adv. contact: John Kaehny. bk.rev. circ. 10,000. (back issues avail.) **Document type:** newsletter. **Description:** Promotes the use of alternative means of transportation, such as bicycling, walking, or using public transportation instead of driving.

TRANSPORTATION — ROADS AND TRAFFIC

388.31   **GW**
AUTO - STRASSENVERKEHR. 1952. fortn. newsstand price: DM.1.70. T und M Verlagsgesellschaft mbH, Borkumstr. 2, 13189 Berlin, Germany. TEL 030-47805-133. FAX 030-47805131. Ed. Oskar Weber. adv.: B&W page DM.18400, color page DM.31280; trim 195 x 265; adv. contact: Jochen Bechtle. bk.rev.; abstr.; charts; illus.; stat. circ. 348,365. **Document type:** consumer publication.
    Formerly: Deutsche Strassenverkehr (ISSN 0012-0804)

AUTOKAMPIOEN. see *TRANSPORTATION — Automobiles*

AUTOREVUU. see *TRANSPORTATION — Automobiles*

BETTER ROADS. see *ENGINEERING — Civil Engineering*

BIL. see *TRANSPORTATION — Automobiles*

388.31   **US**
BOHMAN TRAFFIC NEWS SUMMARY. m. $29.95. Bohman Industrial Traffic Consultants, Inc., 32 Pleasant St., Box 889, Gardner, MA 01440. TEL 617-632-1913. Ed. Raynard R. Bohman, Jr.

388   **BL**
BRASILIA. DEPARTAMENTO DE ESTRADAS DE RODAGEM DO DISTRITO FEDERAL. DIRETORIA GERAL. RELATORIO DE ATIVIDADES. 1978. a. free. Departamento de Estradas de Rodagem do Distrito Federal, Divisao de Programacao, 70000 Brasilia, DF, Brazil. circ. 300.
    Formerly: Brasilia. Departamento de Estradas de Rodagem do Distrito Federal. Diretoria Geral. Relatorio Anual.

BUTTERWORTHS ROAD TRAFFIC SERVICE. see *LAW*

388.411   **CN**
C U T A - A C T U FORUM. (Text in English and French) 1977. m. membership. Canadian Urban Transit Association - Association Canadienne de Transit Urbain, 55 York St., Ste. 901, Toronto, ON M5J 1R7, Canada. TEL 416-365-9800. FAX 416-365-1295. Ed. David Onodera. adv. contact: K. Kaus. illus. circ. 600. **Document type:** trade publication.
    Formerly: Transit Topics.
    Description: Serves urban transit service providers, suppliers and related organizations.

388   **FR**   **ISSN 1162-6925**
CAHIERS DE L'OBSERVATOIRE; les informations du C N R. 1987. m. (11/yr.). 330 F. (foreign 355 F.). Comite National Routier, 8 Villa Bosquet, 75007 Paris, France. TEL 45-55-95-94. FAX 47-53-02-42. Pub. Jean-Paul Philippon. adv.: B&W page 1160 F., color page 21000 F.

388.1   **FR**   **ISSN 0244-6316**
CAISSE NATIONALE DES AUTOROUTES. RAPPORT ANNUEL. 1963. a. free. Caisse Nationale des Autoroutes, 11 rue Saint-Dominique, 75356 Paris 07 SP, France. TEL 47-53-85-11. FAX 47-53-98-61. circ. 2,000. **Document type:** corporate report.
    Description: Report by the board of directors on the activities for the year of the Caisse Nationale des Autoroutes.

388.31 387   **CN**   **ISSN 0826-8770**
CANADIAN INDUSTRIAL TRANSPORTATION LEAGUE. TRANSPORT INFO. 1926. 20/yr. Can.$300 to non-members; free to members. Canadian Industrial Transportation League, Ste. 602, 1090 Don Mills Rd., Don Mills, ON M3C 3R6, Canada. TEL 416-447-7766. FAX 416-447-7312. Ed. Emily Atkins. adv.; bk.rev. circ. 1,000. **Document type:** newsletter.
    Formerly: Canadian Industrial Traffic League. Traffic Notes (ISSN 0045-4974)
    Description: Purpose is to bring Canadian shippers the most useful and timely information available on the transportation industry. Informs members of both legislative and policy changes as they relate to transportation.

388.31   **US**   **ISSN 0008-6789**
HE356.S5
CAROLINA HIGHWAYS. 1949. bi-m. free to qualified personnel. Department of Highways and Public Transportation, Box 191, Columbia, SC 29202. TEL 803-758-2102. Ed. James L. Walker, Jr. illus. circ. 9,000.

388   **UN**   **ISSN 0255-5263**
CENSUS OF MOTOR TRAFFIC ON MAIN INTERNATIONAL TRAFFIC ARTERIES. (Text in English and French) quinquennial; latest 1995. price varies. Economic Commission for Europe (ECE), Palais des Nations, 1211 Geneva 10, Switzerland. TEL 022-917-2542. FAX 022-917-0036. TELEX 412962. (Or: United Nations Publications, Room DC2-853, New York, NY 10017. TEL 212-963-8302. FAX 212-963-6489) (also avail. in microfiche) **Document type:** government publication, bulletin.
    Formerly: Census of Traffic on Main International Traffic Arteries (ISSN 0566-7631)

388.411   **II**   **ISSN 0069-1690**
CENTRAL ROAD RESEARCH INSTITUTE, NEW DELHI. ROAD RESEARCH PAPER. (Text in English) 1956. irreg., no.223, 1989. free. Central Road Research Institute, P.O. Central Road Research Institute, New Delhi 110020, India. TEL 6832274. TELEX 31-75369-CRRI-IN. (Affiliate: Council of Scientific and Industrial Research) circ. controlled. **Indexed:** Chem.Abstr., Eng.Ind.
—BLDSC (7995.900000).

CESTE I MOSTOVI/ROADS AND BRIDGES. see *ENGINEERING — Civil Engineering*

388.31   **UK**   **ISSN 0009-8698**
CLEARWAY; traffic magazine of the metropolitan police. 1967. s-a. free. Metropolitan Police, Traffic Division, c/o The Editor, 1 Area Traffic H.Q., 11 Grove Rd., Chadwell Heath, Essex RM6 4AG, England. TEL 0708-29338. FAX 01-599-7856. Ed.Bd. adv.; bk.rev.; charts; illus. circ. 3,000.

388.1   **II**
COMMERCE YEARBOOK OF ROAD TRANSPORT. (Text in English) a. Rs.35. Commerce Publications Ltd., NKM International House, 178 Backbay Reclamation, Bombay 400020, India.

CONCIENCIA VIAL. see *PUBLIC HEALTH AND SAFETY*

CONSTRUCTION INDUSTRIES OF MASSACHUSETTS DIRECTORY; a directory and catalog of highway and heavy construction in New England. see *BUSINESS AND ECONOMICS — Trade And Industrial Directories*

CONSTRUCTION PRODUCTS. see *ENGINEERING — Civil Engineering*

THE CONTROLLER; journal of air traffic control. see *AERONAUTICS AND SPACE FLIGHT*

388.1   **CR**
COSTA RICA. MINISTERIO DE OBRAS PUBLICAS Y TRANSPORTES. MEMORIAS.* irreg. Ministerio de Obras Publicas y Transportes, Apdo. 10.176, San Jose 1000, Costa Rica. TEL 26-7311.
    Formerly: Costa Rica. Ministerio de Transportes. Memoria (ISSN 0589-8617)

388.31   **US**
COUNTRY ROADS AND CITY STREETS. 1985. q. West Virginia Transportation Technology Transfer Center, Box 6103, Department of Civil Engineering, Engineering Sciences Bldg., West Virginia University, Morgantown, WV 26506. TEL 304-293-3031. FAX 304-293-7109. E-mail: Blanken@faculty.coe.wvu.edu. Ed. Michael Blankenship. circ. 1,300. (back issues avail.) **Document type:** newsletter.
    Description: Contains articles about road and bridge problem solving, regulations, maintenance techniques, safety issues, and design features.

COVJEK I PROMET. see *PUBLIC HEALTH AND SAFETY*

388 624   **UK**
CURRENT TOPICS IN TRANSPORT. irreg. price varies. Transport Research Laboratory, Library Services, Old Wokingham Rd., Crowthorne, Berks. RG11 6AU, England. TEL 01334-770203. FAX 01344-770193. TELEX 848272-TRLCR-G. E-mail: lib@lib.trl.co.uk. (Subscr. to: Transport Research Laboratory, P.O. Box 303, Wokingham, Berks. RG11 6YX, England) **Document type:** monographic series, government publication.

CYCLING WORLD; the Australian bicycling magazine. see *SPORTS AND GAMES — Bicycles And Motorcycles*

624 388.1   **AG**   **ISSN 0011-5177**
D.V.B.A. PUBLICACIONES TECNICAS. 1957. 10/yr. free. Direccion de Vialidad, Calle 7 No. 1175, 1900 la Plata, Argentina. charts; illus.; stat. circ. 1,500. (tabloid format)

388.31   **GW**   **ISSN 0940-9025**
D V R REPORT. 1969. 4/yr. Deutscher Verkehrssicherheitsrat e.V., Beueler Bahnhofsplatz 16, 53222 Bonn, Germany. TEL 0228-4000172. FAX 0228-4000167. Ed. Bernd Kulow. circ. 11,500. **Document type:** corporate report.
    Formerly: Partner Report.

338.31   **GW**   **ISSN 0012-0901**
D V Z. (Deutsche Verkehrs - Zeitung) 1947. 3/wk. DM.372. Deutscher Verkehrs Verlag GmbH, Nordkanalstr. 36, 20097 Hamburg, Germany. TEL 040-23714165. FAX 040-23714-123. Ed. Frank Schnell. adv. contact: Werner Holders. bk.rev.; charts; illus. circ. 18,250. **Document type:** trade publication.
    Description: International trade journal for transport and logistics, transport policy, forwarding, warehousing and transhipment.

388.1 352.7   **DK**   **ISSN 0107-0134**
DANMARKS TEKNISKE HOEJSKOLE. INSTITUTET FOR VEJE, TRAFIK OG BYPLAN. NOTAT/TECHNICAL UNIVERSITY OF DENMARK. INSTITUTE OF ROADS, TRANSPORT AND TOWN PLANNING. PAPER. 1976. irreg. price varies. Danmarks Tekniske Hoejskole, Institutet for Veje, Trafik og Byplan, Bygning 115, 2800 Lyngby, Denmark. illus. circ. 100.

388   **US**   **ISSN 0070-329X**
DELAWARE. DEPARTMENT OF HIGHWAYS AND TRANSPORTATION. TRAFFIC SUMMARY. 1957. a. $10. Department of Transportation, Bureau of Traffic, Box 778, Dover, DE 19901. TEL 302-739-3304. Ed. James Ho. circ. 400. **Document type:** government publication.

388.31   **DK**   **ISSN 0109-2405**
DENMARK. VEJDIREKTORATET. AARSBERETNING. 1983. a. free. Vejdirektoratet, Copenhagen, Denmark. illus.
    Formerly: Denmark. Vejdirektoratet. Aarsrapport.

388.31   **DK**
DENMARK. VEJDIREKTORATET. OEKONOMISK-STATISTISK AFDELING. TRAFIKRAPPORT. 1975. a. Vejdirektoratet, Oekonomisk Statistisk Afdeling, Copenhagen, Denmark. illus.
    Formerly: Denmark. Vejdirektoratet. Trafikrapport (ISSN 0106-7389)

DIRITTO E TECNICA DELLA CIRCOLAZIONE STRADALE E ASSICURAZIONE OBBLIGATORIA DI R C A. see *LAW*

388.314   **SP**   **ISSN 0211-2957**
DISMODA; lineas y tendencias del caldoza. 1980. 2/yr. 4000 ptas. Pedeca Sociedad Cooperativa, Ltda., Maria Auxiliadora 5, 28040 Madrid, Spain. TEL 1-450-88-37. FAX 1-450-94-29. Ed. Carlos Miguel Sanz. circ. 4,000.

DIXON'S ROAD TRAFFIC LAW. see *LAW*

DOROKYO NENPO/ANNUAL REPORT OF ROAD BRIDGES. see *ENGINEERING — Civil Engineering*

ESTADISTICA PANAMENA. SITUACION SOCIAL. SECCION 451. ACCIDENTES DE TRANSITO. see *TRANSPORTATION — Abstracting, Bibliographies, Statistics*

388.31   **GW**   **ISSN 0014-6803**
FAHR MIT UNS; Hamburger illustrierte Nahverkehrszeitschrift. 1954. q. DM.10. Hamburger Hochbahn AG, Steinstr. 20, 20095 Hamburg, Germany. TEL 040-32882824. FAX 040-326406. TELEX 2161858. (Subscr. to: Postfach 102720, 20019 Hamburg, Germany) Ed. Joachim Haeger. illus.; stat. circ. 16,000. (also avail. in microform; back issues avail.) **Document type:** consumer publication.

388.1
HE5614.2 — US — ISSN 0732-9792
FATAL ACCIDENT REPORTING SYSTEM. 1975. a. U.S. Department of Transportation, National Highway and Traffic Safety Administration, National Center for Statistics and Analysis, 400 Seventh St., S.W., Washington, DC 20590. TEL 202-366-5820. FAX 202-366-7078. (Subscr. to: 400 7th St., S.W., Washington, DC 20590) circ. 8,000. (also avail. in microfiche)
   Formerly (until 1979): Fatal Accident Reporting System. Annual Report (ISSN 0147-6939)
   Description: Presents descriptions of all fatal accidents reported within the 50 states, the District of Columbia, and Puerto Rico, with coded data elements that characterize the accident, the vehicles, and the persons involved.

388.413 — US
FLORIDA TRAFFIC & D U I PRACTICE. 2 base vols. (plus suppl. 4-5/yr.). $160. Butterworth Legal Publishers (Salem) (Subsidiary of: Reed Elsevier plc), 8 Industrial Way, Bldg. C, Salem, NH 03079. TEL 800-548-4001. FAX 603-898-9858. Ed. Marcia MacConnell. (looseleaf format)
   Description: Covers all applicable law and procedure, including recent legislative changes regarding drunk driving.

DER FLUGLEITER. see *TRANSPORTATION — Air Transport*

388 — GW
FORSCHUNGSGESELLSCHAFT FUER STRASSEN- UND VERKEHRSWESEN. ARBEITSGRUPPE MINERALSTOFFE IM STRASSENBAU. 1977. irreg. price varies. (Forschungsgesellschaft fuer Strassen- und Verkehrswesen) Kirschbaum Verlag GmbH, Siegfriedstr. 28, 53179 Bonn, Germany. TEL 0228-95453-0. FAX 0228-9545327. (Subscr. to: Postfach 210209, 53157 Bonn, Germany)
   Document type: monographic series.

388.3 — US
GARDEN STATE PARKWAY TRAFFIC REPORT. 1972. m. free. Highway Authority, Garden State Parkway, Traffic Division, Woodbridge, NJ 07095. TEL 201-442-8600. Ed. Jude T. Depko. charts; illus. circ. 750. (also avail. in microfilm)
   Formerly: Garden State Parkway Quarterly Report.

388 — GW
GERMANY. BUNDESMINISTERIUM FUER VERKEHR. STRASSENBAUBERICHT. 1971. a. DM.15. (Bundesministerium fuer Verkehr) Verlag Ed. Hans Heger, Herderstr. 56, 53173 Bonn, Germany. (Subscr. to: Postfach 200821, 53138 Bonn, Germany) illus. circ. 1,500. *Document type:* government publication.

388 — CC — ISSN 0451-0712
GONG LU/ROADS. (Text in Chinese) m. Jiaotong-bu, Gonglu Guihua Shejiyuan - Ministry of Communications and Transportation, Road Planning and Designing Institute, 33 Qianchaomian Hutong, Dongsi, Beijing 100010, People's Republic of China. TEL 5125565. Ed. He Xiumei.

388.31 — US
H E R P I C C POTHOLE GAZETTE. 1982. bi-m. free. (Highway Extension and Research Program, Indiana Counties and Cities) Purdue University, 1284 Civil Eng. Bldg., W. Lafayette, IN 47907-1284. TEL 317-226-7475. Ed. William B. McDermott. circ. 3,500. (back issues avail.) *Document type:* newsletter.
   Description: Covers maintenance techniques, management, engineering and design for local roads and streets.

388.312 — US
H M A T. (Hot Mix Asphalt Technology) 1964. q. free to qualified personnel. National Asphalt Pavement Association, N.A.P.A. Bldg. 5100 Forbes Blvd., Lanham, MD 20706-4413. TEL 301-731-4748. FAX 301-731-4621. Ed. George C. Goggin. adv.; bk.rev.; circ. 25,000 (controlled).
   Supersedes (in 1986): National Asphalt Pavement Association. Paving Forum (ISSN 0048-3079)

388.31 — IT — ISSN 0391-2019
H P TRASPORTI. 1974. m. L.50000($50) (Automobile Club d'Italia) Editrice dell' Automobile s.r.l., Viale Regina Margherita 290, 00198 Rome, Italy. TEL 39-6-4402061. FAX 39-6-44231160. Ed. Fabio Montanaro. adv.: B&W page L.3300000, color page L.5500000. bk.rev.; bibl.; charts; illus.; stat. circ. 25,000.
   Formerly: H P Energia Trasporti; *Supersedes:* Segnalazioni Stradali (ISSN 0037-0959)

264 — UK
HIGHWAY CODE. irreg. H.M.S.O., P.O. Box 276, London SW8 5DT, England. *Document type:* government publication.

HIGHWAY RESEARCH RECORD; general report on road research work done in India during (year). see *ENGINEERING — Civil Engineering*

388 — US
HIGHWAY SAFETY DIRECTIONS. 1970. q. free. University of North Carolina at Chapel Hill, Highway Safety Research Center, 134 1-2 E. Franklin St., CB 3430, Chapel Hill, NC 27599-3430. TEL 919-962-2202. FAX 919-962-8710. Ed. Jeffrey C. Lowrance. circ. 4,500. *Document type:* academic/scholarly publication.
   Formed by the 1987 merger of: Totline (Chapel Hill); Highway Safety Highlights (ISSN 0162-6205)
   Description: Reports on research being conducted by the university on alcohol and highway safety, roadway alignment and engineering, accident investigation and analysis, driver behavior, education and licensing, adult and child passenger safety, seat belts and child car seats. Looks at passenger protection laws, injury prevention, and North Carolina passenger and highway safety efforts.

HIGHWAYS AND TRANSPORTATION. see *ENGINEERING — Civil Engineering*

HUNGARY. KOZPONTI STATISZTIKAI HIVATAL. KOZLEKEDESI EVKONYV. see *TRANSPORTATION — Abstracting, Bibliographies, Statistics*

I A T S S RESEARCH. (International Association of Traffic and Safety Sciences) see *TRANSPORTATION — Automobiles*

388.31 — US — ISSN 1064-2560
I M S A JOURNAL. 1965. bi-m. $59. International Municipal Signal Association, 165 E. Union St., Box 539, Newark, NY 14513. TEL 315-331-2182; 800-723-4672. FAX 315-331-8205. Ed. Harold Glerum. adv. contact: Sharon Earl. charts; illus. circ. 5,100. adv.: B&W page $874; trim 8 1/2 x 11; cols./p.: 3. *Document type:* trade publication.
   Former titles: Municipal Signals; I M S A Signal Magazine (ISSN 0019-0055)
   Description: For those responsible directly in some manner for the installation, maintenance, specification writing or purchasing of equipment.

388.1 — II
I R C SPECIAL PUBLICATION. 1966. irreg. Indian Roads Congress, Jamnagar House, Shahjahan Rd., New Delhi 110 011, India. TEL 381649. bibl.; charts.

388.31 — US — ISSN 0162-8178
HE331 — CODEN: ITEJDZ
I T E JOURNAL. 1930. m. $50. Institute of Transportation Engineers, 525 School St., S.W., Ste. 410, Washington, DC 20024. TEL 202-554-8050. Ed. Kathy Harrington-Hughes. adv.; bk.rev. circ. 11,200. (also avail. in microfilm from UMI; reprint service avail. from UMI) Indexed: A.S.& T.Ind., CAD CAM Abstr., Cadscan, Curr.Cont., Dok.Str., Energy Info.Abstr., Eng.Ind., Environ.Abstr., Environ.Per.Bibl., Excerp.Med., Fluidex, Geo.Abstr., Geotech.Abstr., HRIS, INIS Atomind., Intl.Civil Eng.Abstr., Lead Abstr., P.A.I.S, Petrol.Abstr., Risk Abstr., Sage.Urb.Stud.Abstr., Soft.Abstr.Eng., Zincscan. —BLDSC (4588.550000); CIS; Ei; Faxon; Genuine Article; SWETS; UMI; UnCover.
   Former titles: Transportation Engineering (ISSN 0148-0170); (1933-1977): Traffic Engineering (ISSN 0041-0675)

625.7 — US — ISSN 0019-1175
IDAHO TRANSPORTATION DEPARTMENT. HIGHWAY INFORMATION. 1920. bi-m. free. Transportation Department, Box 7129, Boise, ID 83707-1129. TEL 208-334-8000. TELEX 334-3858. Ed. Barbara Babic. charts; illus.; stat. circ. 1,500.
   Formerly: Idaho Department of Highways. Highway Information.

INDIAN AUTO. see *TRANSPORTATION — Automobiles*

388 — II — ISSN 0376-4788
CODEN: HREBDK
INDIAN ROADS CONGRESS. HIGHWAY RESEARCH BOARD BULLETIN. (Text in English) 3/yr. Rs.16 per no. Indian Roads Congress, Jamnagar House, Shahjahan Rd., New Delhi 110 011, India. TEL 381649. circ. 6,600. Indexed: HRIS. *Document type:* bulletin. —Faxon.
   Supersedes (1975): Indian Roads Congress. Road Research Bulletin.

624 — II — ISSN 0258-0500
CODEN: JIRCAA
INDIAN ROADS CONGRESS. JOURNAL. (Text in English) 1934. q. $20. Indian Roads Congress, Jamnagar House, Shahjahan Rd., New Delhi 110 011, India. TEL 381649. circ. 6,500. Indexed: C.R.I.Abstr., C.R.I.Curr.Cont., Eng.Ind., Geotech.Abstr., HRIS. *Document type:* academic/scholarly publication. —BLDSC (4429.370000).

388.413 — GW
INSTITUT FUER VERKEHR UND STADTBAUWESEN. VEROEFFENTLICHUNGEN. 1967. irreg. (approx. 2/yr.). Institut fuer Verkehr und Stadtbauwesen, T U Braunschweig, Postfach 3329, 38023 Braunschweig, Germany. TEL 0531-391-7920. cum.index. circ. 250. *Document type:* academic/scholarly publication.
   Formerly: Institut fuer Stadtbauwesen. Veroeffentlichungen (ISSN 0341-5805)

INSTYTUT BADAWCZY DROG I MOSTOW. PRACE. see *ENGINEERING*

INSURANCE INSTITUTE FOR HIGHWAY SAFETY. STATUS REPORT. see *PUBLIC HEALTH AND SAFETY*

388.3 — US
INTERMODAL SURFACE TRANSPORTATION ACT: FLEXIBLE FUNDING OPPORTUNITIES FOR TRANSIT (YEAR). (Short title: I S T E A: Flexible Funding Opportunities for Transit (Year)) a. U.S. Federal Transit Administration, Office of Planning, U.S. Department of Transportation, TGM-20, 400 Seventh St., S.W., Rm. 9301, Washington, DC 20590. TEL 202-366-2360. FAX 202-366-7951. *Document type:* government publication.
   Description: Informs state, county, and local officials on the flexible funding opportunities the Surface Transportation Efficiency Act of 1991 offers each year.

388.31 — US
INTERNATIONAL BRIDGE, TUNNEL AND TURNPIKE ASSOCIATION. ANNUAL MEETING PROCEEDINGS. 1962. a. price varies. International Bridge, Tunnel and Turnpike Association, 2120 L St., N.W., Ste. 305, Washington, DC 20037. TEL 202-659-4620. FAX 202-6590500. TELEX 275445 TSI UR. Dir. Neil D. Schuster. circ. 2,500. *Document type:* proceedings.
   Formerly: International Bridge, Tunnel and Turnpike Association. Report of the Annual Meeting.

625.7 — US
INTERNATIONAL CONFERENCE ON ASPHALT PAVEMENTS. PROCEEDINGS. 1963. quinquennial. $100. International Society for Asphalt Pavements, 2602 Dellana La., Austin, TX 78746. TEL 512-327-4211. FAX 512-328-7246. Ed. Morris C. Reinhardt. *Document type:* proceedings.
   Formerly: International Conference on the Structural Design of Asphalt Pavements. Proceedings (ISSN 0074-3348)

388.31 — US
INTERNATIONAL FORUM ON TRAFFIC RECORDS SYSTEMS PROCEEDINGS. 1976. a. $25. National Safety Council, Traffic Safety Department, 1121 Spring Lake Dr., Itasca, IL 60143. TEL 708-285-1121. Ed. Clay Hatch. circ. 600. *Document type:* proceedings.
   Description: Covers all highway traffic records.

388.1 625.7 — FR — ISSN 0074-7815
INTERNATIONAL ROAD CONGRESSES. PROCEEDINGS. (Editions in English, French) quadrennial since 1964; 19th 1991, Marrakesh. Permanent International Association of Road Congresses, 27 rue Guenegaud, 75006 Paris, France. TEL 46-33-71-90. FAX 46-33-84-60. Ed. Patrice Retour. *Document type:* proceedings.

TRANSPORTATION — ROADS AND TRAFFIC

388.3   GW   ISSN 0020-9511
HE5
INTERNATIONALES VERKEHRSWESEN; Fachzeitschrift fuer Information und Kommunikation im Verkehr. (Supplement avail.: Internationales Verkehrswesen) 1949. m. DM.128. (Deutsche Verkehrswissenschaftliche Gesellschaft) Deutscher Verkehrs Verlag GmbH, Nordkanalstr. 36, 20097 Hamburg, Germany. TEL 06151-380-313. FAX 040-23714-236. (Subscr. to: Postfach 101609, 20010 Hamburg, Germany) adv.: B&W page DM.3800; trim 252 x 180; adv. contact: Werner Holders. bk.rev.; abstr.; bibl.; charts; illus.; index. circ. 5,715. **Indexed:** Dok.Str., Excerp.Med., HRIS, Key to Econ.Sci., SCIMP (1991-). —SWETS. **CCC.**
   Incorporates: DDR Verkehr (ISSN 0011-4820); **Formerly:** Internationales Archiv fuer Verkehrswesen.
   Description: Technical and scientific publication covering all fields of traffic and transport, including traffic policy, transport, traffic legislation, and traffic related technology.

ITOGI NAUKI I TEKHNIKI: AVTOMOBIL'NYI I GORODSKOI TRANSPORT. see *ENGINEERING — Civil Engineering*

388   RU   ISSN 0234-4742
HE5614
ITOGI NAUKI I TEKHNIKI: ORGANIZATSIYA I BEZOPASNOST' DOROZHNOGO DVIZHENIYA; avuomatiairovannye sistemy upravleniya dorozhnym dvizheniem. 1978. a. 0.75 Rub. Vsesoyuznyi Institut Nauchno-Tekhnicheskoi Informatsii (VINITI), Baltiiskaya ul. 14, Moscow A-219, Russia. TEL 238-46-00. (Subscr. to: Mezhdunarodnaya Kniga, Dimitrova ul. 39, 113095 Moscow, Russia) Ed. A.G. Romanov.
   —BLDSC (0128.184000).

625.7   JA   ISSN 0075-3319
JAPAN ROAD ASSOCIATION. ANNUAL REPORT OF ROADS.* (Text in English; summaries in French) 1961. a. free. Japan Road Association - Nihon Doro Kyokai, 3-1, Kasumigaseki 3-chome, Chiyoda-ku, Tokyo 100, Japan.

JOURNAL OF TRAFFIC MEDICINE; an international journal of traffic safety. see *MEDICAL SCIENCES — Orthopedics And Traumatology*

388.1   AU   ISSN 0075-7306
KURATORIUM FUER VERKEHRSSICHERHEIT. KLEINE FACHBUCHREIHE. (Text in German; summaries in English, French) 1959. irreg., no.20, 1984. price varies. (Kuratorium fuer Verkehrssicherheit) Literas Universitaetsverlag, Berggasse 4, A-1030 Vienna, Austria. Ed.Bd. cum.index: 1959-1971. circ. 1,300. **Indexed:** Dok.Str., Hwy.Res.Abstr., Psychol.Abstr., Psychopharmacol.Abstr.

388.1   DK   ISSN 0109-6044
LAENGDEN AF OFFENTLIGE VEJE. 1983. a. free. Vejdirektoratet - Ministry of Public Works, Transport Dept., Frederiksholm Kanal 27, 1220 Copenhagen K, Denmark.

388.31   GW   ISSN 0942-4849
LEHRSTUHL FUER VERKEHRS- UND STADTPLANUNG. SCHRIFTENREIHE. (Text in German; summaries in English, German) 1991. irreg. DM.30 per no. Technische Universitaet Muenchen, Lehrstuhl fuer Verkehrs- und Stadtplanung, Arcisstr. 21, 80333 Munich, Germany. TEL 089-21052438. FAX 089-285577. Ed. Dr. P. Kirchhoff. (back issues avail.) **Document type:** academic/scholarly publication.

LINKS UND RECHTS DER AUTOBAHN. see *HOTELS AND RESTAURANTS*

388.31   UK
LONDON CYCLIST. bi-m. £15 (free to members). London Cycling Campaign, 3 Stamford St., London SE1 9NT, England. TEL 0171-928-6112. FAX 0171-928-2318. Ed. Christine Morley. adv.: B&W page £300, color page £650; trim 180 x 260; adv. contact: Pippa Curtis. circ. 9,000. **Document type:** consumer publication.
   Formerly (until 1990): Daily Cyclist.
   Description: Contains information about campaigning for cycle facilities, research on traffic conditions, plus new proposal innovations for future transport policies.

388.312 692.8   US   ISSN 0024-7030
LOW BIDDER. 1928. bi-m. $25. Associated General Contractors of America, N.Y. State Chapter, 1900 Western Ave., Albany, NY 12203. TEL 518-456-1134. FAX 518-456-1198. Ed. Lois A. Mignano. adv.; illus.; mkt.; circ. 1,600 (controlled). **Document type:** trade publication.
   Description: Provides highway contracting technical and news information.

MARTIN AND MORLEY MOTOR VEHICLE LAW (QUEENSLAND). see *LAW*

388.3   US   ISSN 0094-6265
MARYLAND. STATE HIGHWAY ADMINISTRATION. TRAFFIC TRENDS. Key Title: Traffic Trends. 1963. a. free. State Highway Administration, Department of Transportation, 707 Calvert St., Baltimore, MD 21203. TEL 410-787-4050. FAX 301-553-6399. Ed. Peggy Eidman. stat.; circ. 200 (controlled). **Document type:** government publication.

MASKINKONTAKT. see *MACHINERY*

MELYEPITESTUDOMANYI SZEMLE. see *ENGINEERING — Civil Engineering*

388.4   NE   ISSN 0166-4654
MENSEN OP STRAAT. 1963. 5/yr. fl.15. Voetgangersvereniging, Emmapark 9, 2595 ES The Hague, Netherlands. TEL 31-70-3471501. FAX 31-70-3819654. Ed. Gerard J. van den Broek. bk.rev.; illus. **Document type:** consumer publication. **Former titles** (until 1977): Voetganger; Feiten, Cijfers, Meningen (ISSN 0014-9721).
   Description: Discusses all aspects of pedestrian safety, including government road safety policies, society initiatives to improve road safety, with particular emphasis on urban areas.

388   US
MISSOURI. DIVISION OF HIGHWAY SAFETY (YEAR). HIGHWAY SAFETY PLAN. 1971. triennial. Division of Highway Safety, Box 104808, Jefferson City, MO 65110-4808. TEL 314-751-4161. FAX 314-634-5977. Ed. Vicky S. Williams. circ. 50 (controlled). **Document type:** government publication.
   Former titles: Missouri's Annual Highway Safety Program; Missouri Annual Highway Safety Work Program (ISSN 0091-1097)
   Refereed Serial

MOT - BAU; Fachzeitschrift fuer Tiefbau, Strassenbau, Recycling, Entsorgung. see *ENGINEERING — Civil Engineering*

MOTOR & TRAFFIC LAW SERVICE - VICTORIA. see *LAW — Civil Law*

MOTOR VEHICLE LAW S.A. see *LAW — Civil Law*

N S W MOTOR ACCIDENTS PRACTITIONERS HANDBOOK. (New South Wales) see *LAW*

625.7 388.31   US   ISSN 0077-5614
TE7   CODEN: NCHRDA
NATIONAL COOPERATIVE HIGHWAY RESEARCH PROGRAM REPORTS. 1964. irreg., no.335, 1990. price varies. U.S. National Research Council, Transportation Research Board, 2101 Constitution Ave., N.W., Washington, DC 20418. TEL 202-334-3214. FAX 202-334-2519. TELEX 248664 NASWUR. circ. 3,000. (also avail. in microfiche) **Indexed:** Dok.Str. **Document type:** monographic series, government publication.
   —BLDSC (6021.863000).
   Description: Formal reports issued at the conclusion of N.C.H.R.P. research projects.

625.7   US   ISSN 0547-5570
   CODEN: NCHSBB
NATIONAL COOPERATIVE HIGHWAY RESEARCH PROGRAM SYNTHESIS OF HIGHWAY PRACTICE. 1969. irreg., no.170, 1990. price varies. U.S. National Research Council, Transportation Research Board, 2101 Constitution Ave., N.W., Washington, DC 20418. TEL 202-334-3214. FAX 202-334-2519. (Co-produced: American Association of State Highway & Transportation Officials) circ. 2,500. (also avail. in microfiche) **Indexed:** Dok.Str. **Document type:** monographic series, government publication.
   —BLDSC (6021.866000).
   Description: Studies current practices in the field.

388.3   UK   ISSN 0260-7735
NATIONAL COUNCIL ON INLAND TRANSPORTATION. NEWSLETTER. 1978. 2/yr. membership. National Council on Inland Transportation, 7 Barnsley Rd., Scawsby, South Yorks, Doncaster DN5 8QJ, England. Ed. R.S.S. Luffman. circ. 200. **Document type:** newsletter.
   Formerly: Civilised Transport.

625.7   US
TE192
NATIONALLY COORDINATED PROGRAM OF HIGHWAY RESEARCH, DEVELOPMENT, AND TECHNOLOGY. 1974. a. U.S. Federal Highway Administration, Office of Highway Information Management, Department of Transportation, 400 Seventh St., S.W., Washington, DC 20590. TEL 703-285-2101. FAX 703-285-2379. E-mail: bfalk@intergate.dot.gov. (Orders to: Superintendent of Documents, U.S. Government Printing Office, Box 371954, Pittsburgh, PA 15250-9754. TEL 202-512-1800. FAX 202-512-2250) Ed. Bonny Falk; Pub. Anne Barsanti. circ. 1,500 (controlled). **Document type:** government publication.
   Former titles (until 1983): Federally Coordinated Program of Highway Research and Development (ISSN 0361-4204); (until 1975): U.S. Federal Highway Administration. Research and Development Program (ISSN 0098-0234).

NEBRASKA. DEPARTMENT OF ROADS. NEBRASKA SELECTED STATISTICS. see *TRANSPORTATION — Abstracting, Bibliographies, Statistics*

388   US   ISSN 0091-844X
HE371.N25
NEBRASKA. DEPARTMENT OF ROADS. TRAFFIC ANALYSIS UNIT. CONTINUOUS TRAFFIC COUNT DATA AND TRAFFIC CHARACTERISTICS ON NEBRASKA STREETS AND HIGHWAYS. 1968. a. free. Department of Roads, Transportation Planning Division, 1500 Nebraska Hwy. 2, Box 94759, Lincoln, NE 68509-4759. TEL 402-471-4567. FAX 402-479-4325. circ. controlled.
   Description: Contains traffic data from permanent counter, organized by day, hour, and vehicle type.

388.31   US
NEBRASKA HIGHWAY PROGRAM. 1970. a. free. Nebraska Department of Roads, 1500 NE Hwy. 2, Box 94759, Lincoln, NE 68509-4759. TEL 402-479-4512. FAX 402-479-4325. charts; illus.; stat.; circ. 3,850 (controlled). (processed) **Document type:** government publication.
   Former titles: Challenge of the 80's; Focus on Nebraska Highways.

388.31   GW
NETZ WERK MAGAZIN. 1985. q. free. Versorgungs und Verkehrgesellschaft Saabruecken mbH, Hohenzollernstr. 104-106, 60117 Saarbruecken, Germany. TEL 0681-5870. FAX 0681-587-2203. TELEX 4428623-VVS. Ed. Siggi Petto. circ. 3,000.

625.7 388.31   US   ISSN 0028-5242
NEW HAMPSHIRE HIGHWAYS. vol.25, 1970. n. $25. New Hampshire Good Roads Association, Inc., Box 331, Concord, NH 03302-0331. TEL 603-224-1823. FAX 603-224-9399. adv.; bk.rev.; bibl.; charts; illus.; stat.; tr.lit. circ. 1,500.

NEW YORK CITY TRAFFIC RULES AND REGULATIONS. see *LAW*

338.413   BE
NIEUWSBRIEF VERKEERSPECIALIST. (Supplement avail.) (Text in Flemish) s-m. free. 3948 BEF. C E D Samsom (Subsidiary of: Wolters Samsom Belgie n.v.), Kouterveld 14, B-1831 Diegem, Belgium. TEL 32-2-7231111.
   Description: Provides information on traffic legislation and technical aspects of traffic control.

388 614   US
NORTH DAKOTA'S HIGHWAY SAFETY PLAN. 1967. a. free to qualified personnel. Department of Transportation, Driver's License and Traffic Safety, Traffic Safety Programs Section, 608 E. Blvd. Ave., Bismarck, ND 58505-0700. TEL 701-224-2600. FAX 701-224-4545. circ. 150 (controlled). (looseleaf format) **Document type:** government publication.
   Formerly: North Dakota's Highway Safety Work Programs.

TRANSPORTATION — ROADS AND TRAFFIC 6411

388.3 AU
OESTERREICHISCHE VERKEHRSWISSENSCHAFTLICHE GESELLSCHAFT. MITTEILUNGEN.* (Text in German; summaries in French, English) 1951. Oesterreichische Verkehrswissenschaftliche Gesellschaft, Gauermanngasse 4, Vienna, Austria. Ed. Otto Seidelmann. adv.; bk.rev.; bibl.; charts.

388.31 624 US ISSN 0030-0861
OHIO CONTRACTOR. 1961. bi-m. $20. (Ohio Contractors Association) Triad, Inc., 6525 Busch Blvd., Columbus, OH 43229. TEL 614-846-8761. FAX 614-846-8763. Ed. C. Clark Street. adv. contact: Carrie Silverstein. bk.rev.; charts; illus.; circ. 5,500 (controlled). **Document type:** trade publication.

388.1 US
OKLAHOMA. DEPARTMENT OF TRANSPORTATION. SUFFICIENCY RATING REPORT AND NEEDS STUDY: OKLAHOMA STATE TRANSPORTATION. 1966. biennial. free. Department of Transportation, Planning Division, 200 N.E. 21st., Oklahoma City, OK 73105. TEL 405-521-2579. FAX 405-521-2524. illus. circ. 200. **Document type:** government publication.
Formerly: Oklahoma. Department of Highways. Sufficiency Rating Report and Needs Study: Oklahoma State Highways (ISSN 0094-6230)

388.31 US
OKLAHOMA TURNPIKE AUTHORITY. ANNUAL REPORT TO THE GOVERNOR. 1954. a. free. Turnpike Authority, 3500 Martin Luther King Blvd., Box 11357, Oklahoma City, OK 73136-0357. TEL 405-425-3600. FAX 405-427-8246. charts; stat. circ. 1,000.

388.31 US
OKLAHOMA TURNPIKE AUTHORITY. REPORT TO BONDHOLDERS. a. Turnpike Authority, 3500 Martin Luther King Blvd., Box 11357, Oklahoma City, OK 73136-0357. TEL 405-425-3600. FAX 405-427-8246.

388.1 US
ORISSA STATE ROAD TRANSPORTATION CORPORATION. ANNUAL ADMINISTRATION REPORT. (Text in English) 1974. a. State Road Transportation Corporation, Cuttack 753001, India. stat.

P C M - LE PONT. see *ENGINEERING — Civil Engineering*

388.41 350 UK
P T R C TRAFFEX CONFERENCE REPORTS. (Planning and Transport Research and Computation) irreg. (1-3/yr.) price varies. P T R C Education and Research Services Ltd., Glenthorne House, Hammersmith Grove, London W6 OLG, England. TEL 0181-741-1516. FAX 0181-741-5993. TELEX 335269-COMET-G. (back issues avail.) **Document type:** proceedings.

PAVING AND TRANSPORTATION CONFERENCE. PROCEEDINGS.. see *ENGINEERING — Civil Engineering*

388.411 US
PEDESTRIAN RESEARCH.* 1966. q. $5 (foreign $8). American Pedestrian Association, 10 Dorchester, West Palm Beach, FL 33417-1422. Ed. L. Wilensky. charts. circ. 275.
Description: Advocates increased penalties, taxes, and tolls on motorists. Works to defend the pedestrian environment and interests against vehicular encroachments.

625.7 US ISSN 0079-8142
PURDUE UNIVERSITY. ROAD SCHOOL. PROCEEDINGS OF ANNUAL ROAD SCHOOL. (Subseries of: Engineering Bulletin. Engineering Extension Series) 1924. a. Purdue University, School of Civil Engineering, West Lafayette, IN 47907. TEL 317-494-2211. FAX 317-496-1105. Ed. K.C. Sinha. circ. 2,500. **Document type:** proceedings.

625.7 388.1 BU ISSN 0204-6350
PUTISHTA/ROADS. (Text in Bulgarian; summaries in English and Russian) 1961. m. 15 lv.($10) Ministerstvo na Transporta, Glavno Upravlenie na Putishchata, 3, Macedonia Bvrd., 1606 Sofia, Bulgaria. TEL 521354. TELEX 22679 GUP BG. (Dist. by: Hemus, 6, Rouski Blvd., 1000 Sofia, Bulgaria) (Co-sponsor: Nauchno-Tekhnicheski Saiuz po Transporta i Stroitelsvoto) Ed. Tanya Kremencka. adv.; bk.rev. circ. 1,200. **Indexed:** BSL Geo. **Document type:** bulletin.
Description: Scientific and technical magazine highlighting problems in the field of research, design, construction, repair, maintenance and operation of roads, bridges and tunnels, as well as of road construction equipment.

R C: REVISTA DE RESPONSIBILIDAD CIVIL, CIRCULACION Y SEGURO. see *LAW*

388.1 DK ISSN 0105-6956
RAPPORT FRA S T I K K; trafikuheld i Storkoebenhavn. 1977. a. free. Samarbejdsgruppen for Trafiksikkerhed i Kommuneerne i Koebenhavns-Omraadet, Gentofte Kommunes Tekniske Forvaltning, Sekretariat, Raadhuset, 2920 Charlottenlund, Denmark. illus. circ. 3,000.

388.31 AU
DAS RECHT DES KRAFTFAHRERS. 1980. m. Verlag Herta Ranner, Zeismannsbrunngasse 1, A-1070 Vienna, Austria. TEL 01-935387. FAX 01-9353874. **Document type:** bulletin.

388 SW ISSN 0284-0707
REFLEXEN. 1983. 7/yr. SEK 75 membership (effective 1994). T F - Trafiktekniska Foereningen, c/o Bjoern Abelsson, Ed., Scandiaconsult, P.O. Box 4205, S-10265 Stockholm, Sweden. TEL 46-8-615-6000. adv.; bk.rev. circ. 1,000. **Document type:** newsletter.

388.1 BL
REVISTA RODOVIARIA. 1972. m. Departamento Autonomo del Estradas de Rodagem, Divisao de Servicos Especiais, Av. Borges de Medeiros No 1555, Porto Alegre, Brazil. illus.

387.73 FR ISSN 0035-3191
REVUE GENERALE DES ROUTES ET DES AERODROMES. (Text in French; summaries in English, French, and Spanish) 1926. 11/yr. 1010 F. 9 rue Magellan, 75008 Paris, France. TEL 40-73-80-00. FAX 49-52-01-80. Ed. Bernard Dollon; Pub. Francois Bonis-Charancle. adv.; bk.rev.; abstr.; charts; illus.; index. circ. 3,250. **Indexed:** Dok.Str., Excerp.Med., Geotech.Abstr., Int.Aerosp.Abstr., Intl.Civil Eng.Abstr., Soft.Abstr.Eng. **Document type:** bibliography, monographic series, newspaper.
—SWETS.

385.1 388 UK ISSN 0307-6822
ROAD ACCIDENTS IN GREAT BRITAIN. (Joint publication with Scottish Development Department and the Welsh Office) 1969. a. price varies. H.M.S.O., P.O. Box 276, London SW8 5DT, England. **Document type:** government publication.
—BLDSC (7994.220000). CCC.

ROAD LAW AND ROAD LAW REPORTS. see *LAW*

388.1 UK ISSN 0306-5286
ROAD TRAFFIC REPORTS. 1970. 10/yr. £99. Kenneth Mason Publications Ltd., 12 North St., Emsworth, Hants. PO10 7DQ, England. TEL 0243-377977. FAX 0243-379136. Ed. L.N. Williams. cum.index. **Document type:** bulletin.
●Also available online. Vendor(s): Lexis-Nexis.
—BLDSC (7997.130000). CCC.

388 FR ISSN 1156-4865
ROUTE ACTUALITE. (Text in English, French) 10/yr. 230 F. (Europe 350 F., elsewhere 600 F.). Groupe Chantiers de France, Bords de Seine, 202 quai de Clichy, 92110 Clichy, France. TEL 47-56-17-23. FAX 47-56-14-32. Ed. Marc Montagnon; Pub. Arlette Surchamp. adv.; B&W page 16500 F., color page 30200 F.; trim 210 x 290; adv. contact: Sophie Roux. tr.lit./cum. 10,000. **Document type:** trade publication.
Description: Covers topical methods and equipment for road construction, activities or regional road constructors and reference sites.

388.1 CN ISSN 0319-3780
ROUTES ET TRANSPORTS. (Text in French) 1971. 4/yr. Can.$50($10) Association Quebecoise du Transport et des Routes Inc., 6455 Christophe-Colomb, Montreal, PQ H2S 2G5, Canada. FAX 514-274-9608. Ed. Catherine Hirou. adv.; bk.rev. circ. 2,000. (back issues avail.) **Indexed:** Pt.de Rep. (1983-). **Document type:** academic/scholarly publication.
Formerly: Routes du Quebec.

ROUTES - ROADS. see *ENGINEERING — Civil Engineering*

LES ROUTIERS. see *TRANSPORTATION — Trucks And Trucking*

388 624 SP ISSN 1130-7102
RUTAS. 1983? 6/yr. 6500 ptas. (Europe $90; elsewhere $120). Asociacion Tecnica de Carreteras, Monte Esquinza 24 4o dcha., 28010 Madrid, Spain. TEL 1-308-23-18. FAX 1-308-23-19. Ed. V. Barbera. adv.; bk.rev. circ. 5,000.

388.31 SA
S A R F NEWSLETTER. (Text in Afrikaans, English) 1955. q. membership. Southern Africa Road Federation, P.O. Box 8189, Johannesburg 2000, South Africa. FAX 27-11-337-5713. Ed. S.O. Eklund. adv. circ. 1,200. **Document type:** newsletter.
Description: Discusses transport economic issues in South Africa.

388.3 CN
S G I - AUTO FUND. ANNUAL REPORT. 1946. a. free. Saskatchewan Government Insurance, 2260 11th Ave., Regina, Sask. S4P OJ9, Canada. TEL 306-565-1200. FAX 306-757-7477. TELEX 306-071-2417. circ. 2,500.
Former titles: SaskAuto Annual Report; Saskatchewan. Government Insurance Office. Province of Saskatchewan Motor Vehicle Traffic Accidents. Annual Report.

388 553.6 US
SALT AND HIGHWAY DEICING NEWSLETTER. s-a. free. Salt Institute, 700 N. Fairfax, Ste. 600, Fairfax, VA 22314-2040. TEL 703-549-4648. FAX 703-548-2194. circ. 9,000. **Document type:** newsletter.
Formerly: Salt and Highway Digest.

388.31 NO ISSN 0332-8988
SAMFERDSEL. 1925. 10/yr. NOK 475. Transportoekonomisk Institutt - Institute of Transport Economics, P.O. Box 6110 Etterstad, 0602 Oslo, Norway. TEL 47-2-57-38-00. FAX 47-2-57-02-90. Ed. Harald Aas. adv.; bk.rev.; charts; illus.; tr.lit.; index. circ. 3,400. **Indexed:** Dok.Str.
Formerly: Norsk Veitidsskrift.

388.31 YU ISSN 0558-6208
SAOBRACAJ. (Issued also as part of Tehnika (ISSN 0350-2597)) (Text in Serbo-Croatian; summaries in English, Russian) vol.28, 1981. m. $50. Savez Inzenjera i Tehnicara Jugoslavije, Kneza Milosa 9, Box 187, 11000 Belgrade, Yugoslavia. Ed. Jovan Rados. adv.; bk.rev. circ. 3,000.

SAVREMENI VOZAC. see *TRANSPORTATION — Automobiles*

SECURITE ROUTIERE. see *TRANSPORTATION — Abstracting, Bibliographies, Statistics*

388.413 DK ISSN 0107-5179
SIKKERHEDSMAESSIG VURDERING OG PRIORITERING AF MINDRE ANLAEGSARBEJDER PAA HOVEDLANDEVEJE. 1975. a. free. Vejdirektoratet - Ministry of Public Works, Transport Dept., Frederiksholm Kanal 27, 1220 Copenhagen K, Denmark. illus.
Formerly: Denmark. Vejdirektoratet. Black-Spotundersoegelse paa Hovedlandeveje.

SILNICNI OBZOR; mesicnik pro otazky vystavby a udrzby silnic, dalnic, nistnich kominikaci, letsi, mostu, tunelu a silnicniho a mestskeho dopravniho inzynyrstvi. see *TRANSPORTATION — Automobiles*

TRANSPORTATION — ROADS AND TRAFFIC

625   SA
SOUTH AFRICA. DEPARTMENT OF TRANSPORT. TECHNICAL METHODS FOR HIGHWAYS. (Text in Afrikaans or English) 1978. irreg., no.3, 1988. price varies. Department of Transport, Private Bag X193, Pretoria 0001, South Africa.
    Former titles: South Africa. Division of Road and Transport Technology. Technical Methods for Highways; South Africa. National Institute for Transport and Road Research. Technical Methods for Highways.

388.312   SA
SOUTH AFRICA. DEPARTMENT OF TRANSPORT. TECHNICAL RECOMMENDATIONS FOR HIGHWAYS. (Text in Afrikaans or English) 1970. irreg., no.17, 1984. price varies. Department of Transport, Private Bag X193, Pretoria 0001, South Africa. **Indexed:** Dok.Str.
    Former titles: South Africa. Division of Roads and Transport Technology. Technical Recommendations for Highways; South Africa. National Institute for Transport and Road Research. Technical Recommendations for Highways.

388.1   SA
SOUTH AFRICA. DIVISION OF ROADS AND TRANSPORT TECHNOLOGY. P A D SERIES. Alternate title: C S I R Special Reports. (Text in Afrikaans or English) irreg., no.70, 1989. Division of Roads and Transport Technology, Box 395, Pretoria 0001, South Africa. FAX 8413232. TELEX 3-213125A.
    Formerly: National Institute for Transport and Road Research. P A D Series.

388.314   DK   ISSN 0106-7540
STOPINTERVIEWANALYSE. irreg. Vejdirektoratet - Ministry of Public Works, Transport Dept., Frederiksholm Kanal 27, DK-1220 Copenhagen K, Denmark. illus.
    Formerly: Trafikanalyse.

388.31   GW   ISSN 0039-2219
HE363.G29   CODEN: SVKTAC
STRASSENVERKEHRSTECHNIK. (Summaries in English, French and German) 1965. m. DM.132. (Forschungsgesellschaft fuer Strassen- und Verkehrswesen) Kirschbaum Verlag GmbH, Siegfriedstr. 28, 53179 Bonn, Germany. TEL 0228-95453-0. FAX 0228-9545327. (Subscr. to: Postfach 210209, 53157 Bonn, Germany) Ed. Klaus Kirschbaum. adv.; bk.rev.; charts; illus.; tr.lit.; index. circ. 2,500. **Indexed:** Dok.Str., Eng.Ind., Excerp.Med., Intl.Civil Eng.Abstr., Soft.Abstr.Eng. **Document type:** trade publication.
    —SWETS. **CCC.**

388.411   GW
STRASSENWAERTER. m. Verband Deutscher Strassenwaerter, Roesrather Str. 569, 51107 Cologne, Germany. TEL 864224. (Subscr. to: Postfach 950167, 51086 Cologne, Germany)

354.485   SW
SWEDEN. STATENS VAEG- OCH TRANSPORTFORSKNINGSINSTITUT. VERKSAMHETSBERAETTELSE. English edition: Swedish Road and Transport Research Institute. Annual Report. a. Statens Vaeg- och Transportforskningsinstitut, S-581 01 Linkoeping, Sweden. **Document type:** monographic series.
    Formerly: Sweden. Statens Vaeg- och Trafikinstitut. Verksamhetsberaettelse (ISSN 0282-5996)

690   FR   ISSN 0397-6513
T E C. (Transport Environnement Circulation) 1973. bi-m. 660 F. (foreign 750 F.). Association pour le Developpement des Techniques de Transport, d'Environnement et de Circulation (ATEC), 38 av. Emile Zola, 75015 Paris, France. TEL 45-79-56-11. FAX 45-79-52-86. Eds. Andre Imbert, Sylvie Blesson. adv.; bk.rev.; index. circ. 3,000. **Indexed:** Dok.Str., Excerp.Med.
    —BLDSC (9025.602000).

388.31   UK
T R L NEWS. q. Transport Research Laboratory, Press and Public Relations Section, Old Wokingham Rd., Crowthorne, Berks RG11 6AU, England. TEL 01344-773131. FAX 01344-770356. E-mail: lib@lib.trl.co.uk. **Document type:** newsletter.

388 625.7   UK   ISSN 0968-4107
T R L REPORTS. 1985. irreg. price varies. Transport Research Laboratory, Old Wokingham Rd., Crowthorne, Berks. RG1 6AU, England. TEL 01334-773131. FAX 01344-770356. E-mail: annet@lib.trl.co.uk. (Subscr. to: Transport Research Laboratory, Library Services, P.O. Box 304, Crowthorne, Berks. RG45 6YU, England) **Indexed:** Dok.Str. **Document type:** monographic series.
    —BLDSC (9050.782390).
    Formerly (until 1995): Transport Research Laboratory. Research Reports; Supersedes (in 1985): Road Notes (ISSN 0080-3294); Transport and Road Research; Which was formerly: Road Research (ISSN 0080-3308).
    Description: Covers a wide range of road transportation topics, including urban planning, traffic and vehicle safety, environmental issues, and highway, bridge and tunnel engineering.

388.31   UK
T R L STATE OF THE ART REVIEW. irreg. (Transport Research Laboratory) H.M.S.O., P.O. Box 276, London SW8 5DT, England. **Document type:** government publication.

TECHLINK: AUTOMOTIVE AND ROAD TRANSPORTATION. see *TRANSPORTATION — Automobiles*

388.411   DK   ISSN 0105-5119
TECHNICAL UNIVERSITY OF DENMARK. INSTITUTE OF ROADS, TRANSPORT AND TOWN PLANNING. PAPERS AND REPORTS. (Text in Danish and English; summaries in English) 1937. irreg. Technical University of Denmark, Institute of Roads, Transport and Town Planning, Building 115, DK-2800 Lyngby, Denmark. circ. 50. (back issues avail.)

388.314 333.77   DK
TECHNICAL UNIVERSITY OF DENMARK. INSTITUTE OF ROADS, TRANSPORT AND TOWN PLANNING. REPORT. 1976. irreg., no. 19, 1978. Polytekniske Laereanstalt, Danmarks Tekniske Hoejskole, Instituttet for Vejbygning, Trafikteknik og Byplanlaegning, Bygning 115, DK-2800 Lyngby, Denmark. circ. 250.

353.9   US   ISSN 0095-1994
HE5614.3.T2
TENNESSEE. DEPARTMENT OF SAFETY. ANNUAL REPORT. Key Title: Annual Report - Department of Safety. 1971. a. free to qualified personnel. Department of Safety, 1150 Foster Ave., Nashville, TN 37210. TEL 615-251-5313. FAX 615-251-5242. circ. 500. **Document type:** government publication.
    Description: Covers statewide patrol activity in relation to traffic enforcement data.

TIE JA LIIKENNE. see *ENGINEERING — Civil Engineering*

TIJDSCHRIFT LANDINRICHTING. see *AGRICULTURE — Crop Production And Soil*

388 382.7   US
TOLLWAYS. m. membership. International Bridge, Tunnel & Turnpike Association, 2120 L St. N.W., Ste. 305, Washington, DC 20037. TEL 202-659-4620. FAX 202-659-0500. TELEX 275-445 TSI UR. Ed. Janet M. Chaikin. circ. 2,500. **Document type:** newsletter.
    Description: Provides toll industry news, listings of events and other items of interest to members.

TOW TIMES; the international communications medium for the towing and recovery industry. see *TRANSPORTATION — Trucks And Trucking*

388.31   US
TRAFFIC AUDIT BUREAU. ANNUAL REPORT. a. Traffic Audit Bureau, 114 E. 32nd St., New York, NY 10016. TEL 212-213-9640.
    Description: For outdoor advertisers.

388.31   US
TRAFFIC AUDIT BUREAU. NEWSLETTER. irreg. Traffic Audit Bureau, 114 E. 32nd St., New York, NY 10016. TEL 212-213-9640. **Document type:** newsletter.
    Description: For outdoor advertising industry.

388.31   UK   ISSN 0041-0683
HE331   CODEN: TENCA4
TRAFFIC ENGINEERING & CONTROL. 1960. m. £58($110) Printerhall Ltd., 29 Newman St., London W1P 3PE, England. TEL 0171-636-3956. FAX 0171-436-7016. Ed. Keith Lumley. adv. contact: M. Stoneham. bk.rev.; charts; illus.; index. circ. 5,400. (also avail. in microform from UMI) **Indexed:** Br.Rail.Bd., Br.Tech.Ind., Dok.Str., Eng.Ind., Ergon.Abstr., Excerp.Med., Geo.Abstr., HRIS, IDA, INSPEC, Intl.Civil Eng.Abstr., Mid.East: Abstr.& Ind., Soft.Abstr.Eng. **Document type:** trade publication.
    —BLDSC (8882.100000); Ei; Faxon; SWETS; UMI; UnCover.

388   US   ISSN 0082-5859
TRAFFIC LAWS COMMENTARY. 1963. irreg., latest 1982. price varies. National Committee on Uniform Traffic Laws and Ordinances, 405 Church St., Box 1409, Evanston, IL 60204.

380.5   US   ISSN 0041-0705
TRAFFIC MANAGER. 1925. bi-m. $6. Daily Journal of Commerce, Box 10127, Portland, OR 97210. TEL 503-226-1311. Ed. Victor Graf. adv.; charts; illus.; stat. circ. 7,112. (also avail. in microform from UMI)
    —UMI.

614.86   US   ISSN 0041-0721
HV675.A1
TRAFFIC SAFETY (ITASCA). 1927. bi-m. $30 to non-members; members $24. National Safety Council, Periodicals Department, 1121 Spring Lake Dr., Itasca, IL 60143. TEL 708-775-2284. FAX 708-775-2285. Ed. Carrie Fearn; Pub. Kevin H. Axe. adv.; bibl.; illus.; stat.; tr.lit.; index. circ. 20,000. (also avail. in microfiche from UMI,CIS) **Indexed:** ASCA, C.I.S. Abstr., CJPI. **Document type:** trade publication.
    —BLDSC (8882.190000); Faxon; UMI; UnCover.
    Description: For traffic engineers, trainers, law enforcement officers, fleet managers and government personnel.

388.1   US   ISSN 0193-8908
HE5614.2
TRAFFIC SAFETY (WASHINGTON); a report on activities under the Highway Safety Act of 1966. 1966. a. U.S. National Highway Traffic Safety Administration, 400 Seventh St., N.W., Washington, DC 20590. (Co-sponsor: U.S. Federal Highway Administration) **Indexed:** CJPI. **Document type:** government publication.

388.31   US
TRAFFIC SAFETY SERIES. irreg., latest 1993. $19.95. Transaction Publishers, Transaction Periodicals Consortium, Department 3092, Rutgers University, New Brunswick, NJ 08903. TEL 908-445-2280. FAX 908-445-3138. Eds. Peter J. Cooper, J. Peter Rothe. (back issues avail.) **Document type:** monographic series.
    Description: Deals with issues ranging from drunk driving to seat belt use.

TRAFFIC TECH. see *TECHNOLOGY: COMPREHENSIVE WORKS*

338.41   SP
TRAFIKO-ISTRIPUAK E.A.E.KO ERREPIDEETAN/ACCIDENTES DE TRAFICO EN CARRETERAS DE LA C.A.V. (Text in Basque and Spanish) 1991. a. (Herrizaingo Saila, Bidezaingo Zuzendaritza - Departmento de Interior, Direccion de Trafico) Eusko Jaurlaritzaren Argitalpen-Zerbitzu Nagusia - Servicio Central de Publicaciones del Gobierno Vasco, Duque de Wellington, 2, 01011 Vitoria-Gasteiz, Spain. circ. 1,500. **Document type:** government publication.
    Description: Statistical tables of road traffic accidents in the Basque region for the year.

388.1 330   DK   ISSN 0106-1852
TRAFIKOEKONOMISKE ENHEDSPRISER. 1977. a. free. Vejdirektoratet, Oekonomisk-Statistik Afdelning, Copenhagen, Denmark.

388.1   NZ   ISSN 1170-7321
TRANSEARCH. 1991. irreg. (3-4/yr.). free. Transit New Zealand, Research and Development Section, P.O. Box 5084, Wellington, New Zealand. TEL 04-4996600. FAX 04-4966666. Ed. Jeanette Conland. circ. 1,800. **Document type:** newsletter.
    —BLDSC (9020.582900).
    Description: Provides information on road, traffic, safety, and land transport studies.

TRANSPORTATION — ROADS AND TRAFFIC

388.31 355　　US　　ISSN 0041-1639
UC270
TRANSLOG; journal of military transportation management. 1970. m. $24. U.S. Military Traffic Management Command, Washington, DC 20315. TEL 202-545-6700. FAX 202-289-2040. (Orders to: Supt. of Documents, Washington, DC 20402) charts; illus. circ. 29,000. (also avail. in microform from MIM,UMI) **Indexed:** Air Un.Lib.Ind., Ind.U.S.Gov.Per.
—UMI.
Formerly: Transportation Proceedings.

TRANSPORT EN LOGISTIEK; weekblad voor het goedenvervoer. see *TRANSPORTATION*

TRANSPORT STATISTICS GREAT BRITAIN. see *TRANSPORTATION — Abstracting, Bibliographies, Statistics*

625.7 690　　US　　ISSN 1043-4054
TE1
TRANSPORTATION BUILDER. 1923. 12/yr. $50. American Road & Transportation Builders Association, 1010 Massachusetts Ave., N.W., Washington, DC 20001. TEL 202-289-4434. FAX 202-289-4435. Ed. Gail Schell. adv.; bk.rev.; charts; illus.; index. circ. 10,000. **Indexed:** HRIS. **Document type:** trade publication.
Former titles: American Transportation Builder (ISSN 0149-4511); American Road Builder (ISSN 0003-0856)
Description: For transportation construction professionals.

388.413　　US
TRANSPORTATION IMPROVEMENT PROGRAM. a. $15. Omaha - Council Bluffs Metropolitan Area Planning Agency, 2222 Cuming St., Omaha, NE 68102-4328. TEL 402-444-6866. FAX 402-342-0949. circ. 500. **Document type:** government publication.
Description: Identifies all transportation capital and service improvement projects scheduled for the following 3 years in Douglas, Sarpy, and Washington counties in Nebraska, and Mills and Pottawatamie counties in Iowa.

TRANSPORTATION JOURNAL. see *TRANSPORTATION*

625.7 388　　US　　ISSN 0360-859X
　　　　　　　　　CODEN: SRTBDC
TRANSPORTATION RESEARCH BOARD SPECIAL REPORT. 1952. irreg., no.229, 1990. price varies. U.S. National Research Council, Transportation Research Board, 2101 Constitution Ave., N.W., Washington, DC 20418. TEL 202-334-3214. FAX 202-334-2519. circ. 3,250. (also avail. in microfiche; microfilm from BHP) **Indexed:** Concr.Abstr., Dok.Str., GeoRef., Geotech.Abstr., HRIS. **Document type:** monographic series, government publication.
—BLDSC (8401.007800); CASDDS; UnCover.
Formerly (until no.144, 1974): Highway Research Board Special Publication (ISSN 0077-5622)
Description: Addresses transportation policy issues of national significance.

625.7 388　　US　　ISSN 0361-1981
TE7　　　　　　　CODEN: TRREDM
TRANSPORTATION RESEARCH RECORD. (Subseries of: National Research Council. Transportation Research Board. Report) 1963. irreg., no.1413, 1993. $865 to N. America; elsewhere $900. U.S. National Research Council, Transportation Research Board, 2101 Constitution Ave., N.W., Washington, DC 20418. TEL 202-334-3213. FAX 202-334-2519. circ. 3,250. (also avail. in microfiche) **Indexed:** Chem.Abstr., Dok.Str., GeoRef., Geotech.Abstr., Intl.Civil Eng.Abstr., Noise Pollut.Publ.Abstr., Ocean.Abstr., Pollut.Abstr., Sel.Water Res.Abstr., Soft.Abstr.Eng., Sport Fish.Abstr., W.R.C.Inf., Wild.Rev. **Document type:** government publication.
—BLDSC (9026.275000); CASDDS; Ei; Faxon; SWETS; UnCover.
Formerly (until 1974): Highway Research Record (ISSN 0073-2206)
Description: Presents technical research papers. *Refereed Serial*

388.31　　US
TRANSPORTATION TOPICS. 1960. m. free. Department of Transportation, Public Affairs Office, Box 1708, Cheyenne, WY 82003-1708. TEL 307-777-4439. FAX 307-777-4289. Ed. Bruce Burrows; Pub. Bruce Burrows. circ. 2,000. **Document type:** government publication, newsletter.
Formerly: Road Construction News.
Description: Provides information on a variety of subjects related to transportation in Wyoming, ranging from road construction to systems planning to law enforcement.

388　　CN　　ISSN 0581-8079
TRAVEL ON SASKATCHEWAN HIGHWAYS. 1958. biennial. free. Department of Highways and Transportation, Planning and Coordination, 1855 Victoria Ave., Regina, SK S4P 3V5, Canada. TEL 306-787-8334. FAX 306-787-1007. Ed. Tom Anderson. circ. 1,000 (controlled). **Document type:** government publication.

388.41　　GW　　ISSN 0172-858X
TUMULT: SCHRIFTEN ZUR VERKEHRSWISSENSCHAFT. 1979. s-a. DM.32. c/o Frank Boeckelmann, Lilienstr. 51, 81669 Munich, Germany. (Alt. addr.: c/o Walter Seitter, Hoher Markt 4, A-1010 Vienna, Austria) Ed.Bd. **Document type:** bulletin.

388.3　　US　　ISSN 0277-2310
HE5614.2
U.S. DEPARTMENT OF TRANSPORTATION. HIGHWAY SAFETY STEWARDSHIP REPORT. 1974. a. U.S. Department of Transportation, 400 Seventh St. N.W., Washington, DC 20590. TEL 202-655-4000. (Order from: Supt. of Documents, Washington, DC 20402) stat. **Document type:** government publication.
Former titles: Highway Safety Improvement Programs & Annual Report on Highway Safety Improvement Programs (ISSN 0098-3209)

388.3 621.382　　US
U.S. DEPARTMENT OF TRANSPORTATION. INTELLIGENT VEHICLE HIGHWAY SYSTEMS PROJECTS. irreg. U.S. Federal Highway Administration, Office of Traffic Management and I V H S, U.S. Department of Transportation, 400 Seventh St., S.W., Rm. 3401, Washington, DC 20590. TEL 202-366-2196. (Co-sponsors: Federal Transit Administration, National Highway Traffic Safety Administration) **Document type:** monographic series, government publication.
Description: Profiles research into the application of emerging computer and information-management technologies to improve the efficiency and reduce the negative effects of ground transportation.

388.3　　US
U.S. FEDERAL TRANSIT ADMINISTRATION. NATIONAL PLANNING AND RESEARCH PROGRAM. BROCHURES. irreg. free. U.S. Federal Transit Administration, Office of Technical Assistance and Planning, National Planning and Research Program, U.S. Department of Transportation, 400 Seventh St., S.W., Rm. 6100, Washington, DC 20590. TEL 202-366-0207. FAX 202-366-3765. **Document type:** monographic series, government publication.
Description: Provides the transit community and general public with information on current F.T.A. National Planning and Research Program activities.

388.3　　US
U.S. FEDERAL TRANSIT ADMINISTRATION. NATIONAL PLANNING AND RESEARCH PROGRAM. TECHNICAL ASSISTANCE BRIEFS. irreg. free. U.S. Federal Transit Administration, Office of Technical Assistance and Safety, National Planning and Resaerch Program, U.S. Department of Transportation, 400 Seventh St., S.W., Rm. 6100, Washington, DC 20590. TEL 202-366-0207. FAX 202-366-3765. **Document type:** monographic series, government publication.
Description: Covers various topics in F.T.A. transit research and planning programs.

388.3　　US
U.S. FEDERAL TRANSIT ADMINISTRATION. TECHNICAL BROCHURE. irreg. U.S. Federal Transit Administration, Office of Technical Assistance and Safety, Advanced Public Transportation Division, U.S. Department of Transportation, 400 Seventh St., S.W., Rm. 6107, Washington, DC 20590. TEL 202-366-0264. FAX 202-366-3765. **Document type:** government publication, monographic series.

U.S. FEDERAL TRANSIT ADMINISTRATION. TECHNOLOGY SHARING PROGRAM. REPORT. see *TRANSPORTATION — Abstracting, Bibliographies, Statistics*

388.3　　US
U.S. FEDERAL TRANSIT ADMINISTRATION. UNIVERSITY RESEARCH AND TRAINING PROGRAM. ANNOUNCEMENT FOR FISCAL YEAR (YEAR). a. U.S. Federal Transit Administration, University Research and Training Program, U.S. Department of Transportation, 400 Seventh St., S.W., Washington, DC 20590. TEL 202-366-0242. FAX 202-366-3765. **Document type:** proceedings, government publication.

380.5　　US　　ISSN 0547-5554
TE1
U.S. NATIONAL COOPERATIVE HIGHWAY RESEARCH PROGRAM. RESEARCH RESULTS DIGEST. 1969. irreg., no.357, 1993. price varies. U.S. National Research Council, Transportation Research Board, 2101 Constitution Ave., N.W., Washington, DC 20418. TEL 202-334-3213. FAX 202-334-2519. circ. 4,200. **Indexed:** Dok.Str. **Document type:** monographic series, government publication.
—BLDSC (7769.587500).
Description: Publishes informal reports providing early awareness of results of N.C.H.R.P. research projects.

388.413　　GW
UNIVERSITAET MUENSTER. INSTITUT FUER VERKEHRSWISSENSCHAFT. BEITRAEGE. 1954. irreg. price varies. (Universitaet Muenster, Institut fuer Verkehrswissenschaft) Vandenhoeck und Ruprecht, Robert-Bosch-Breite 6, 37079 Goettingen, Germany. TEL 0551-695926. FAX 0551-695917. Ed. Helmut Seidenfuess. (back issues avail.) **Document type:** proceedings.

388.31　　UK　　ISSN 0966-1743
URBAN STREET ENVIRONMENT. bi-m. £24 (rest of Europe £32; elsewhere £42). Landor Publishing Ltd., Quadrant House, 250 Kennington Ln., London SE11 5RD, England. TEL 0171-582-6626. FAX 0171-735-1299. E-mail: 100570,73@compuserve.com. **Document type:** bulletin.
Description: Provides a forum for all areas that relate to the total design, management and maintenance of roads and open spaces in public areas.

388.1　　DK　　ISSN 0108-0385
V D L NYT. 1982. q. free. Vejdatalaboratoriet, Stationsalleen 42, 2730 Herlev, Denmark. illus.
Formed by the merger of: T P S Nyt & Terminal-Nyt.

388.31　　SW　　ISSN 0283-7021
V T I ANNUAL REPORT. 1971. a. free. Statens Vaeg- och Trafikinstitut - Swedish Road and Traffic Research Institute, S-581 01 Linkoeping, Sweden. TEL 13204000. FAX 13141436. TELEX 50125-VTISGI-S. Ed. Thomas Lange. charts. circ. 2,000. **Indexed:** Dok.Str. **Document type:** monographic series.
—BLDSC (9258.903000).

338.1　　SW　　ISSN 0347-6049
TE89
V T I MEDDELANDE. (Text in Swedish; summaries in English) 1976. irreg. (50-60/yr.). free. Statens Vaeg- och Transportforskningsinstitut - Swedish Road and Transport Research Institute, S-581 01 Linkoeping, Sweden. Ed. Thomas Lange. **Indexed:** Dok.Str., HRIS. **Document type:** academic/scholarly publication, bulletin.

338.1　　SW　　ISSN 0347-6030
V T I RAPPORT. (Text in English and Swedish; summaries in English) 1971. irreg. (15-20/yr.). free. Statens Vaeg- och Transportforskningsinstitut - Swedish Road and Transport Research Institute, S-581 01 Linkoeping, Sweden. Ed. Thomas Lange. circ. 800. **Document type:** academic/scholarly publication, bulletin.
—BLDSC (9258.905000); Ei.

V W-AUTOGRAMM. (Volkswagen AG) see *BUSINESS AND ECONOMICS — Labor And Industrial Relations*

388 310 GW ISSN 0083-5021
V W Z. (Verkehrswirtschaftliche Zahlen) 1954. a. DM.9.35. Bundesverband des Deutschen Gueterfernverkehrs e.V., Breitenbachstr. 1, 60457 Frankfurt a.M., Germany. TEL 069-7919273. FAX 069-7919227. circ. 6,500. **Indexed:** Dok.Str. **Document type:** bulletin.

VAROSI KOZLEKEDES/URBAN TRANSPORT. see TRANSPORTATION — Railroads

388.1 DK ISSN 0107-0614
VEJDATALABORATORIET. RAPPORT. 1965. irreg. free. Vejdatalaboratoriet, Stationsalleen 42, 2730 Herlev, Denmark. illus.

388.312 SZ
VEREINIGUNG SCHWEIZERISCHER STRASSENFACHLEUTE. FORSCHUNGSBERICHTE. vol.5, 1974. irreg. price varies. Vereinigung Schweizerischer Strassenfachleute, Seefeldstr. 9, CH-8008 Zurich, Switzerland. TEL 01-2516914. FAX 01-2523130. charts; stat. circ. 140. **Document type:** academic/scholarly publication.
  Former titles: Vereinigung Schweizerischer Strassenfachleute. Versuchsberichte; Vereinigung Schweizerischer Strassenfachmaenner. Versuchsbericht.

388 364 NE ISSN 0920-3834
VERKEERSKNOOPPUNT; tijdschrift voor verkeersvraagstukken. 1973. 6/yr. fl.40. (Politie Verkeersinsituut) Vuga Uitgeverij B.V., P.O. Box 16400, 2500 BK The Hague, Netherlands. TEL 31-70-3614011. FAX 31-70-3625468. Ed. F.H. Lenting. adv.; B&W page fl.1495, color page fl.3450; trim 210 x 297. bk.rev.; illus. **Indexed:** Abstr.Crim.& Pen. **Document type:** trade publication. —SWETS.
  Formerly (until 1980): Verkeersinformatie (ISSN 0920-7279)
  Description: Covers all aspects of traffic, including commentary on recent laws, law enforcement, safety issues, and related topics.

388.31 NE ISSN 0377-8495
VERKEERSKUNDE; maandelijks tijdschrift over verkeer en vervoer. 1949. 11/yr. fl.145 to non-members (foreign fl.166). Koninklijke Nederlandse Toeristenbond ANWB, Afdeling Verkeer en Vervoer, Postbus 93200, 2509 BA The Hague, Netherlands. TEL 31-70-3146533. FAX 31-70-3147207. (Subscr. to: Infolio B.V., Postbus 16500, 2500 BM The Hague, Netherlands. TEL 31-70-3338333. FAX 31-70-3338399) Ed. R. Hendriks. adv.; B&W page fl. 1675, color page fl.3515; trim 210 x 297. bk.rev.; illus.; circ. 2,200 (paid). **Indexed:** Dok.Str., Excerp.Med., Key to Econ.Sci. **Document type:** trade publication. —SWETS.
  Formerly (until 1975): Verkeerstechniek (ISSN 0042-3998)
  Description: Covers technical, social and political developments affecting all phases of the transport and traffic sector, from pedestrians to high-speed trains.

VERKEERSRECHT. see LAW

VERKEERSVEILIGHEID. see TRANSPORTATION — Abstracting, Bibliographies, Statistics

388 AU ISSN 0254-5314
VERKEHR; internationale Fachzeitung fuer Verkehrswirtschaft. 1945. w. S.3671. Bohmann Druck und Verlag GmbH & Co. KG, Leberstr. 122, A-1110 Vienna, Austria. TEL 0222-74095-0. FAX 0222-74095-183. adv. circ. 4,900. **Indexed:** Dok.Str. **Document type:** trade publication.

388 GW ISSN 0340-4536
TF3
VERKEHR UND TECHNIK; Zeitschrift fuer Verkehrstechnik, Verkehrspolitik, Verkehrswirtschaft. 1948. m. DM.184.80. Erich Schmidt Verlag GmbH & Co. (Bielefeld), Viktoriastr. 44A, 33602 Bielefeld, Germany. TEL 0521-583080. (Subscr. to: Postfach 102453, 33524 Bielefeld, Germany) adv.; bk.rev.; charts; illus.; pat.; stat.; index. circ. 2,100. **Indexed:** Dok.Str., Excerp.Med. **Document type:** trade publication. —SWETS.

VERKEHRS RUNDSCHAU. see TRANSPORTATION

388.31 GW ISSN 0042-4013
VERKEHRSBLATT. 1947. bi-m. DM.149.80 (Europe DM.168.40; elsewhere DM.179.80. (Bundesministerium fuer Verkehr) Verkehrsblatt Verlag Borgmann GmbH, Hohe Str. 39, 44139 Dortmund, Germany. TEL 0231-128047. FAX 0231-125640. adv.; bk.rev.; bibl.; illus.; index, cum.index; circ. 10,000 (controlled). **Indexed:** Dok.Str. **Document type:** government publication. —SWETS.

388.413 GW ISSN 0341-4388
VERKEHRSDIENST. m. DM.164.40 (foreign DM.169.90). Heinrich Vogel Fachzeitschriften GmbH, Neumarkterstr. 18, 81673 Munich, Germany. TEL 089-43180-0. FAX 089-4312837. (Subscr. to: Postfach 802020, 81620 Munich, Germany) **Document type:** trade publication. —CCC.

VERKEHRSGESCHICHTLICHE BLAETTER. see TRANSPORTATION — Railroads

388.31 AU ISSN 0042-4048
VERKEHRSPSYCHOLOGISCHER INFORMATIONSDIENST. 1962. a. free. Kuratorium fuer Verkehrssicherheit, Verkehrspsychologisches Institut, Oelzeltgasse 3, A-1031 Vienna, Austria. TEL 0222-71770171. FAX 0222-717709. TELEX 3222195. Ed. Werner Klemenjak. circ. 1,500. **Indexed:** Dok.Str. **Document type:** corporate report.

388.31 SZ
VERKEHRSVERBAND OBERAARGAU. OFFIZIELLES BULLETIN. 10/yr. Orell Fuessli Werbe AG, Aarwangenstr. 4, Postfach 338, CH-4900 Langenthal, Switzerland. TEL 063-231812. circ. 5,500.

388 BE ISSN 0775-9002
VIA SECURA. Dutch edition (ISSN 0775-9010) (Text in French) 1953; N.S. 1987. q. 250 BEF. Institut Belge pour la Securite Routiere - Belgisch Instituut voor de Verkeersveiligheid, Chaussee de Haecht 1405, 1130 Brussels, Belgium. TEL 32-2-2441511. FAX 32-2-2164342. Pub. C. van den Meerschaut. adv.: B&W page 15000 BEF, color page 30000 BEF. bk.rev. circ. 7,300 (4,200 Dutch ed.; 3,100 French ed.). **Document type:** trade publication.
  Description: Publishes news and information on road safety, including pedestrian and cycling related issues, and European initiatives.

377.411 BL
VIA URBANA; politica, negocios e sistemas de transporte urbano. 1991. m. Cr.$430000($50) (effective 1993). Empresa Jornalistica dos Transportes, Rua Mexico 41, salas 904-5, 20031-144 Rio de Janeiro RJ, Brazil. TEL 021-532-0260. FAX 021-240-0139. illus.
  Description: Covers problems and issues in city transportation.

388.411 UK ISSN 0266-8947
VINTAGE ROADSCENE. 1984. q. £9. Ian Allan Ltd., Coombelands House, Coombelands Ln., Addlestone, Surrey KT15 1HY, England. TEL 01932-855909. Ed. S.W. Stevens-Stratten. bk.rev.; charts; illus. circ. 18,000. (reprint service avail. from UMI) **Document type:** consumer publication.
  Description: Publishes news and features from the field of historic road transport.

388.1 US
VIRGINIA DEPARTMENT OF TRANSPORTATION BULLETIN. 1934. m. free to qualified personnel and libraries. Department of Transportation, 1401 E. Broad St., Richmond, VA 23219. TEL 804-786-4243. FAX 804-786-6250. Ed. Charles M. Armstrong. illus. circ. 16,000. **Document type:** newsletter.
  Former titles: Virginia Department of Highways and Transportation Bulletin; (until 1974): Virginia Highway Bulletin (ISSN 0042-6547)

614.86 UK ISSN 0144-2694
WALK. 1950. 3/yr. $13.50. Pedestrians Association, 1-5 Wandsworth Rd., London SW8 2XX, England. TEL 01-735 3270. Ed. Ronald Binns. adv.; bk.rev.; abstr.; charts; illus.; index. circ. 1,200. —BLDSC (9261,474400).
  Former titles (until Nov. 1979): Arrive (ISSN 0031-3874); Pedestrian.

WEGEN; maandblad voor verkeer, grond-, water- en wegenbouw. see ENGINEERING — Civil Engineering

WISCONSIN. DEPARTMENT OF TRANSPORTATION. DIVISION OF PLANNING AND BUDGET. HIGHWAY MILEAGE DATA. see TRANSPORTATION — Abstracting, Bibliographies, Statistics

388.1 UK ISSN 0043-8529
WORLD HIGHWAYS/ROUTES DU MONDE. 1950. 9/yr. $75. (International Road Federation, US) Route One Publishing Ltd., Huntingdon House, 278-280 Huntingdon St., Nottingham NG1 3LY, England. TEL 0115-9508098. FAX 0115-9508120. Ed. Russ Swan. adv. contact: John Williamson. bk.rev.; charts; illus.; stat. circ. 18,000. **Indexed:** Dok.Str., HRIS. **Document type:** trade publication. —UMI.

388.413 US ISSN 0511-0440
WYOMING TRUCKER. 1952. q. free. Wyoming Trucking Association, Inc., Box 1909, Casper, WY 82602. TEL 307-234-1579. Sheila D. Foertsch. adv. contact: Kathy Cundall. circ. 4,200. (back issues avail.) **Document type:** trade publication.

Z F K - ZEITUNG FUER KOMMUNALE WIRTSCHAFT; das Fachblatt fuer Energie, Wasser, Entsorgung, Stadtverkehr und Umweltschutz. see HOUSING AND URBAN PLANNING

388.1 GW ISSN 0341-2334
ZEITSCHRIFT FUER VERKEHRSERZIEHUNG. 1955. 4/yr. DM.25. Rot-Gelb-Gruen Lehrmittel GmbH, Theodor-Heuss-Str. 3, 38122 Braunschweig, Germany. TEL 0531-809070. FAX 0531-8090721. TELEX 952357. Ed. D. Hohenadel. adv.; bk.rev.; circ. 5,000 (controlled).
  Formerly: Schulverkehrswacht.
  Description: Features traffic safety and education for children. Deals with risks, bicycles, traffic rules, and accidents. Includes statistics and charts.

388.31 GW ISSN 0044-3654
HE331
ZEITSCHRIFT FUER VERKEHRSSICHERHEIT. (Occasional articles in English) 1955. q. DM.150 (foreign DM.156). Verlag T Ue V Rheinland GmbH, Viktoriastr. 26, 51149 Cologne, Germany. TEL 02203-1709-02. FAX 02203-15411. Ed. Walter Schneider. adv.; bk.rev.; abstr.; bibl.; charts; illus.; index. circ. 1,400. **Indexed:** Dok.Str., Ergon.Abstr., Ger.J.Psych. **Document type:** bulletin. —Faxon; SWETS.

380.5 GW ISSN 0044-3670
HE5
ZEITSCHRIFT FUER VERKEHRSWISSENSCHAFT. 1921. q. DM.82.05. Verkehrs-Verlag J. Fischer, Paulusstr. 1, 40237 Duesseldorf, Germany. TEL 0211-991930. FAX 0211-6801544. (Subscr. to: Postfach 140265, 40072 Duesseldorf, Germany) Ed. Rainer Willeke. adv.; bk.rev. circ. 800. **Indexed:** Dok.Str., Key to Econ.Sci., P.A.I.S.For.Lang.Ind. **Document type:** trade publication. —SWETS.

338.31 CC ISSN 1001-7372
ZHONGGUO GONGLU XUEBAO/CHINA JOURNAL OF HIGHWAY AND TRANSPORT. (Text in Chinese; abstracts in Chinese, English) 1988. q. Y14. Zhongguo Gonglu Xuehui - China Highway and Transportation Society, 48 Beisanhuan Zhonglu, Beijing 100088, People's Republic of China. TEL 2013399. FAX 86-1-2014130. TELEX 22462 COMCTCN. Ed. Chen Bingling. (reprint service avail.) **Document type:** academic/scholarly publication. —BLDSC (3180.182000).
  Description: Covers traffic engineering, road construction machinery, automobile, trailer, and transportation.

TRANSPORTATION — Ships And Shipping

387.4   UK   ISSN 1357-1214
A B C CRUISE AND FERRY GUIDE. 1952. q. £120. Reed Travel Group, Part of Reed Telepublishing (Subsidiary of: Reed Elsevier group), Church St., Dunstable, Beds. LU5 4HB, England. TEL 01582-600111. FAX 01582-695230. TELEX 82168 AIRABC G. Ed. Denise Eyre. circ. 5,100. **Document type:** directory.
   Former titles: A B C Passenger Shipping Guide (ISSN 0957-0810); A B C Shipping Guide (ISSN 0001-0480)
   Description: Provides a comprehensive guide to passenger shipping and cruises throughout the world, including independent reviews of cruise ships, port maps and information, cruise area maps and ferry rate maps.

387   AT
A B ORGANISATION MARINE PORTFOLIO. a. A.B. Organisation Pty. Ltd., P.O. Box 319, Avalon Beach, N.S.W. 2107, Australia. TEL 02-918-8322. FAX 02-918-8884.
   Description: Deals with Australian Marine industry with details of related magazines published by the A.B. Organisation.

387   US   ISSN 0517-5828
A W O LETTER. 1944. bi-w. $75. American Waterways Operators, 1600 Wilson Blvd., Ste. 1000, Arlington, VA 22209. TEL 703-841-9300. FAX 703-841-0389. Ed. Tia Gibbs. circ. 1,500. **Document type:** newsletter, trade publication.
   Formerly: A W O Weekly Letter.

A W T A O ANNUAL REPORT. (Association of Water Transportation Accounting Officers) see *BUSINESS AND ECONOMICS — Accounting*

A W T A O BULLETIN. (Association of Water Transportation Accounting Officers) see *BUSINESS AND ECONOMICS — Accounting*

DE AAN- EN AFVOER VAN GOEDEREN OVER ZEE IN DE NEDERLANDSE ZEEHAVENS. see *TRANSPORTATION — Abstracting, Bibliographies, Statistics*

ABERDEEN PORT HANDBOOK. see *BUSINESS AND ECONOMICS — Trade And Industrial Directories*

387.109   BE   ISSN 0776-3468
ACADEMIE ROYALE DE MARINE DE BELGIQUE. COMMUNICATIONS/KONINKLIJKE BELGISCHE MARINE ACADEMIE. MEDEDELINGEN. (Text in Dutch, French; summaries in English, French) 1936. irreg. (approx. a.) 720 BEF to individuals; institutions on exchange basis. Nationaal Scheepvaartmuseum, Steinplein 1, B-2000 Antwerp, Belgium. TEL 32-3-232-08-50. Ed. G. Asaert. adv.; bibl.; illus. (back issues avail.) **Document type:** proceedings.
   Formerly (until 1986): Academie de Marine. Communications - Marine Academie. Mededelingen (ISSN 0776-345X)
   Description: Dedicated to the study of shipping and maritime history, including shipbuilding, navigation, and maritime economics, mainly in Belgium and Zaire (the former Belgian Congo).

387   PO
ADMINISTRACAO DO PORTO DE LISBOA. RELATORIO E CONTAS. 1935. a. free. Administracao do Porto de Lisboa, Divisao de Relacoes Publicas e Marketing, Rua da Junqueira, 94, 1300 Lisbon, Portugal. TEL 1-3637151. FAX 1-3643114. TELEX 18529-PORLI. circ. 1,000.
   Former titles: Administracao do Porto de Lisboa. Relatorio; Administracao Geral do Porto de Lisboa. Relatorio.

387   IT   ISSN 0870-3892
AGENDA NAUTICA. 1955. a. L.24000 (effective 1996). Istituto Idrografico della Marina, Passo Osservatorio, 4, 16134 Genoa, Italy. TEL 10-2443-274. FAX 10-261400. TELEX 270435 MARIDR I. Ed.Bd. circ. 22,000. **Document type:** consumer publication.
   Description: Provides seaman and navigation information.

387   TS
AL-MAJALLAH AL-BAHRIYYAH/MARITIME MAGAZINE. (Text in Arabic) 1981. q. exchange basis. Arab Maritime Transport Academy, P.O. Box 1552, Sharjah, United Arab Emirates. TEL 358866. FAX 372869. TELEX 68167 ACAD EM. Ed. Abd al-Wahhab al-Diwani. circ. 500.
   Description: News and activities of the academy.

387   IT
ALMANACCO NAVALE. 1963. biennial. L.120000. Istituto Idrografico della Marina, Passo Osservatorio, 4, 16134 Genoa, Italy. TEL 10-2443-274. FAX 10-261400. TELEX 270435 MARIDR I. Ed.Bd. circ. 2,500. **Document type:** catalog.
   Description: Provides a detailed description of military ships and analyzes the characteristics of the world's navies.

387   US
AMERICAN BUREAU OF SHIPPING. RECORD. 1869. a. $520. American Bureau of Shipping, 2 World Trade Center, 106th Fl., New York, NY 10048. TEL 212-839-5100. FAX 212-839-5130. TELEX 232099 ABNY UR. Ed. William R. Hartman. circ. 209. **Indexed:** BMT.

387   US   ISSN 0740-588X
AMERICAN CANALS. 1972. q. $15. American Canal Society, 809 Rathton Rd., York, PA 17403-3349. TEL 717-843-4035. Ed. Denver L. Walton. bk.rev.; circ. 850 (paid). **Document type:** newsletter.
   Description: For canal buffs, professional planners, historians and archeologists. Covers canal news, history, activities and practical information from the US and around the world.

387   US
AMERICAN INSTITUTE FOR SHIPPERS ASSOCIATIONS. NEWS. m. American Institute for Shippers Associations, Box 33457, Washington, DC 20033. TEL 202-628-0933. **Document type:** newsletter, trade publication.

623.87   US   ISSN 0002-9866
VM1
AMERICAN MARINE ENGINEER.* 1906. m. National Marine Engineers Beneficial Association, 444 N. Capitol, Ste. 800, Washington, DC 20001. Ed. Victor Rollo. charts; illus.

AMERICAN MARITIME OFFICER. see *LABOR UNIONS*

387.5   US   ISSN 0364-7374
HE745
AMERICAN MERCHANT MARINE CONFERENCE. PROCEEDINGS. 1935. a. $20. Propeller Club of the United States, 3927 Old Lee Hwy., No. 101A, Fairfax, VA 22030. TEL 703-691-2777. FAX 703-691-4173. **Document type:** proceedings.

AMERICAN NEPTUNE; a quarterly journal of maritime history & arts. see *HISTORY — History Of North And South America*

380.5   US   ISSN 0160-225X
HF1
AMERICAN SHIPPER; ports, transportation and industry. 1959. m. $48. Howard Publications, Inc., 33 S. Hogan St., Ste. 230, Box 4728, Jacksonville, FL 32201-4728. TEL 904-355-2601. FAX 904-791-8836. Ed. David A. Howard. adv. contact: Hayes H. Howard. charts; illus.; mkt.; stat. circ. 14,884. (also avail. in microform from UMI; reprint service avail. from UMI) **Indexed:** B.P.I., Bus.Ind., P.A.I.S., Tr.& Indus.Ind.
   —BLDSC (0857.100000); Faxon; SWETS; UMI. CCC.
   Former titles (until 1976): Florida Journal of Commerce - American Shipper (ISSN 0097-6237); (until 1974): Florida Journal of Commerce (ISSN 0015-413X)

387   US
ANCHOR NEWS. 1969. q. $25. Wisconsin Maritime Museum, 75 Maritime Dr., Manitowoc, WI 54220. TEL 414-684-0218. FAX 414-684-0219. Ed. Isacco A. Valli. adv. contact: Jan Pukita. bk.rev. circ. 2,400. **Indexed:** Amer.Hist.& Life, Hist.Abstr. **Document type:** academic/scholarly publication.
   Description: Includes articles on the history of the Upper Great Lakes, primarily Lake Superior and Lake Michigan.

623.89 387.5   FR   ISSN 0373-3629
VK798   **CODEN:** AHDGAG
ANNALES HYDROGRAPHIQUES. 1848. irreg., vol.10, 1992. price varies. Service Hydrographique et Oceanographique de la Marine, 3 av. Octave Greard, 00300 Armees, France. TEL 98-03-09-17. FAX 98-47-11-42. TELEX HYDRO 940568 F. (Subscr. to: EPSHOM, B.P. 426, 29275 Brest Cedex, France) charts; illus.; index, cum.index. circ. 400. **Indexed:** Chem.Abstr., Deep Sea Res.& Oceanogr.Abstr., Meteor.& Geoastrophys.Abstr. **Document type:** government publication.
   —BLDSC (0980.000000); CASDDS.

623.89 387.1   FR   ISSN 0180-989X
ANNUAIRE DES MAREES POUR L'AN. TOME 1. PORTS DE FRANCE. 1839. a. 45 F. (effective 1995-1996). Service Hydrographique et Oceanographique de la Marine, 3 av. Octave Greard, 00300 Armees, France. TEL 98-03-09-17. FAX 98-47-11-42. TELEX HYDRO 940568 F. (Subscr. to: EPSHOM, B.P. 426, 29275 Brest Cedex, France) index. circ. 10,000. (tabloid format) **Document type:** government publication.
   Description: Furnishes predictions on the tides and depths at 22 major French ports, along with amendments for 228 smaller harbors.

623.89 387.1   FR   ISSN 0180-9962
ANNUAIRE DES MAREES POUR L'AN. TOME 2. PORTS D'OUTRE MER. 1885. a. 74 F. (effective 1995). Service Hydrographique et Oceanographique de la Marine, 3 av. Octave Greard, 00300 Armees, France. TEL 98-03-09-17. FAX 98-47-11-42. TELEX HYDRO 940568 F. (Subscr. to: EPSHOM, B.P. 426, 29275 Brest Cedex, France) **Document type:** government publication.
   Description: Furnishes predictions on the tides and depths at major non-French harbors.

623.89   AT   ISSN 1035-6878
VK927
ANNUAL AUSTRALIAN NOTICES TO MARINERS. 1933. a. free. Hydrographic Office R A N, Locked Bag 8801, Wollongong, N.S.W. 2521. FAX 61-42-218599. Ed. Mark Bolger. illus.; index; circ. 3,200 (controlled). **Document type:** government publication.
   Formerly: Annual Summary of Australian Notices to Mariners (ISSN 0727-2405)

623.82   JA   ISSN 0448-3294
ANNUAL STATISTICS OF MARITIME SAFETY. (Text in Japanese) 1950. a. Kaijo Hoancho, Suirobu - Maritime Safety Agency, Hydrographic Department, 3-1, Tsukiji 5-chome, Chuo-ku, Tokyo 104, Japan. stat.

ANNUAL SUMMARY OF MERCHANT SHIPS COMPLETED IN THE WORLD. see *TRANSPORTATION — Abstracting, Bibliographies, Statistics*

387.164 381   FR   ISSN 0395-8582
L'ANTENNE; seul quotidien francais des transports. 1828. d. (5/wk.) 2460 F.($720) Smei l'Antenne, 17 rue Venture, P.O. Box 1811, 13221 Marseille Cedex 1, France. TEL 91-33-25-81. FAX 91-55-58-97. TELEX 400 865. Ed. Edmond Oliva. adv. contact: Eric Fleury. circ. 8,000. pp./issue: 20. (tabloid format; back issues avail.) **Document type:** newspaper.
   Former titles (until 1947): Antenne de Marseille (ISSN 1153-8473); (until 1946): Marseille Maritime (ISSN 1153-8465)

387 623.8   GW   ISSN 0003-6080
ANTRIEB; Fachzeitschrift fuer Schiffstechnik und Seeverkehrswirtschaft. 1955. bi-m. DM.42 (foreign DM.48). Verein der Schiffsingenieure in Bremen e.V., Senator-Boemers-Str. 4, 28197 Bremen, Germany. TEL 0421-851552. Ed. Herwig Pollem. adv.: B&W page DM.1500, color page DM.2400; trim 246 x 170; adv. contact: Wilhelm Groeneveld. bk.rev.; stat.; tr.lit. circ. 4,000. **Document type:** trade publication.

ANTWERP PORT ANNUAL. see *BUSINESS AND ECONOMICS — Trade And Industrial Directories*

386   BL   ISSN 0101-5710
ANUARIO DE PORTOS E NAVIOS. a. $30. Revista Tecnica e Informativa Ltda., Av. Rio Branco, 185, 1914, Caixa Postal 2791, 20040-007 Rio de Janeiro, Brazil. Ed. Rosangela Vieira. adv. contact: Marcos Godoy. charts; stat. **Document type:** academic/scholarly publication.

TRANSPORTATION — SHIPS AND SHIPPING

621.8 658   HU   ISSN 0003-6242
ANYAGMOZGATAS-CSOMAGOLAS. (Text in Hungarian; summaries in English, German, Russian) 1956. m. $28. (Muszaki es Termeszettudomanyi Egyesuletek Szovetsege) Lapkiado Vallalat, Lenin korut 9-11, 1073 Budapest 7, Hungary. TEL 1-222-408. (Subscr. to: Kultura, Box 149, H-1389 Budapest, Hungary) (Co-sponsor: Anyagmozgatasi es Csomagolasi Intezet) Ed. Laszlo Felfoldi. adv.; bk.rev.; bibl.; charts; illus. circ. 1,600. **Indexed:** Food Sci.& Tech.Abstr., Hung.Build.Bull, Packag.Sci.Tech.

387   UA   ISSN 0304-2855
ARAB MARITIME TRANSPORT ACADEMY. JOURNAL/AL-AKADEMIYYAH AL-ARABIYYAH LIL-NAQL AL-BAHRI. MAJALLAH. (Text in Arabic, English) 1975. s-a. $40. Arab Maritime Transport Academy, P.O. Box 1029, Alexandria, Egypt. FAX 5602144. Ed. Alfonse Habib Sadek. **Document type:** academic/scholarly publication.
— BLDSC (4698.630000).

387   US
ARBITRATOR. q. free. Society of Maritime Arbitrators, 61 Broadway, Ste. 1650, New York, NY 10006-2701. TEL 212-483-0616. FAX 212-480-3320. circ. 500. **Document type:** trade publication.

387 971   CN   ISSN 0842-0866
V1
ARGONAUTA. (Text in English, French) 1984. Can.$30 to individuals; institutions Can.$55. Memorial University of Newfoundland, Maritime Studies Research Unit, St. John's, NF A1C 5S7, Canada. TEL 709-737-8424. FAX 709-737-8427. TELEX 016-4677. (Subscr. to: Canadian Nautical Research Society, P.O. Box 21076, Sta. J, Ottawa, ON K2A 3Z6, Canada) Eds. Lewis R. Fischer, Olf U. Janzen. adv.; bk.rev. circ. 325. **Document type:** academic/scholarly publication.
    Formerly (until 1986): Canadian Nautical Research Society. Newslettter (ISSN 0842-0858)
    Description: Publishes articles, news and information on publications and conferences of interest to Canadian maritime historians.

387.54   UK   ISSN 1352-8033
ARROWSMITH'S BRISTOL CHANNEL TIDE TABLE. 1835. a. £2.50. J.W. Arrowsmith Ltd., Winterstoke Rd., Bristol BS3 2NT, England. TEL 0117-966-7545. FAX 0117-9637829. adv. contact: Diane Reeman. circ. 5,000. **Document type:** directory.

L'ART ET LA MER. see *ART*

387   HK
ASIAN SHIPPING. (Text in English) 1978. m. HK.$350. Asia Trade Journals Ltd., Box 20014, Hennessy Rd., Hong Kong. TEL 852-2527-8532. FAX 852-2527-8753. Ed. A.G. Barnett. adv. contact: Karen Dodd. charts; illus. circ. 6,700. **Document type:** trade publication.

387   UK
ASSOCIATED BRITISH PORTS HOLDINGS. ANNUAL REPORT AND ACCOUNTS. 1983. a. free. Associated British Ports Holdings plc., 150 Holborn, London EC1N 2LR, England. TEL 0171-430-1177. FAX 0171-430-1384. Ed. M. Collins. **Document type:** corporate report.
    Formerly: British Transport Docks Board. Annual Report and Accounts (ISSN 0068-2659)

359.97   FR   ISSN 0373-9090
VK1000
ASSOCIATION INTERNATIONALE DE SIGNALISATION MARITIME. BULLETIN/I A L A BULLETIN. Key Title: Bulletin de l'A.I.S.M. (Text in English, French) 1958. q. 400 F. (effective 1996). Association Internationale de Signalisation Maritime - International Association of Lighthouse Authorities, 20 ter, rue Schnapper, 78100 Saint Germain en Laye, France. TEL 33-1-34-51-70-01. FAX 33-1-34-51-82-05. TELEX 695 499 F. Ed. Paul Ridgway. adv. contact: M.H. Grillet. bk.rev. circ. 600. **Document type:** bulletin.
    Description: Technical papers and general information articles on aids to navigation technique and history.

387 623.8 629.1   FR   ISSN 0066-9814
    CODEN: BATMA8
ASSOCIATION TECHNIQUE MARITIME ET AERONAUTIQUE, PARIS. BULLETIN. (Text in French; summaries in English and French) 1890. a. 450 F. to non-members. Association Technique Maritime et Aeronautique, 47 rue de Monceau, 75008 Paris, France. Ed.Bd. index. circ. 1,000. (back issues avail.) **Indexed:** Appl.Mech.Rev.
—UMI.

387   CN   ISSN 1192-0203
ATLANTIC BUSINESS REPORT. 1990. m. Can.$32.10. A B J Publishing Inc., 599 Main St., Ste. 203, Moncton, NB E1C 1C8, Canada. TEL 506-857-9696. FAX 506-859-7395. Ed. Suzanne McDonald Boyce. adv. contact: Dalton Jenson. illus.; circ. 14,000. (controlled). (tabloid format; also avail. in microform from UMI) **Indexed:** Can.B.P.I. **Document type:** newspaper.
    Formerly (until 1990): Maritime Report.
    Description: Focuses on trends and issues that affect business people in the Atlantic Province.

387   AT   ISSN 0314-0377
AUSTRALASIAN SHIPPING RECORD. 1970. bi-m. Aus.$18 (foreign Aus.$20). Australasian Maritime Historical Society, P.O. Box 89, Lobethal, S.A. 5241, Australia. TEL 389-4292. Ed. Ronald H. Parsons. bk.rev.; index. (back issues avail.)
    Description: Contains news of current nautical events in Australia and New Zealand plus historial material touching on nautical matters concerning Australia and New Zealand.

AUSTRALIA. BUREAU OF STATISTICS. FREIGHT MOVEMENTS, AUSTRALIA. see *TRANSPORTATION — Abstracting, Bibliographies, Statistics*

387   AT   ISSN 1031-3516
AUSTRALIA AND THE SEA. 1988. a. free to qualified personnel. Baird Publications Pty. Ltd., 10 Oxford St., South Yarra, Vic. 3141, Australia. TEL 61-3-98268741. FAX 61-3-98270704. Ed. Neil Baird. adv. circ. 8,000. **Document type:** trade publication.
    Description: For overseas companies, individuals and government agencies who are likely to purchase marine products.

387 639.2   AT
AUSTRALIAN CENTRE FOR MARITIME STUDIES. OCCASIONAL PAPERS IN MARITIME AFFAIRS. 1982. a. Aus.$50 to individuals (foreign Aus.$70); institutions Aus.$100 (foreign Aus.$120); corporates Aus.$300 (foreign Aus.$320) (includes Maritime Studies) (effective 1995). Australian Centre for Maritime Studies, P.O. Box E20, Queen Victoria Terrace, Canberra, A.C.T. 2600, Australia. Eds. M. Ward, W.S. Bateman. circ. 500. (back issues avail.) **Document type:** monographic series, academic/scholarly publication.

AUSTRALIAN SEA HERITAGE. see *MUSEUMS AND ART GALLERIES*

623.89   FR   ISSN 0180-9938
VK798
AVIS AUX NAVIGATEURS. 1886. w. 851 F. (effective 1995). Service Hydrographique et Oceanographique de la Marine, 3 av. Octave Greard, 00300 Armees, France. TEL 98-03-09-17. FAX 98-47-11-42. TELEX HYDRO 940568 F. (Subscr. to: EPSHOM, B.P. 426, 29275 Brest Cedex, France) illus. **Document type:** government publication.
    Description: Provides mariners with special notices and changes to charts, regulations, and radio signals.

387   IT
AVVISATORE MARITTIMO. d. Via S. Vincenzo 42, 16121 Genoa, Italy. TEL 10-589-513. circ. 15,000.

387   DK   ISSN 0901-814X
HE381.A2
B I M C O BULLETIN. 1969. bi-m. DKK 2070 (typically set in Jan.). Baltic and International Maritime Council, Bagsvaerdvej 161, DK 2880 Bagsvaerd, Denmark. TEL 4544-444500. FAX 4544-444450. TELEX 19086. Ed. Peter Thornton; Pub. Finn Frandsen. adv. contact: Peter Rygaard Andersen. bk.rev.; index. circ. 3,000. **Document type:** bulletin, trade publication.
    Formerly (until 1970): Baltic and International Maritime Conference. Bulletin (ISSN 0903-4242)
    Description: Articles on developments affecting the shipping industry at large.

B M T ABSTRACTS. (British Maritime Technology Ltd.) see *TRANSPORTATION — Abstracting, Bibliographies, Statistics*

387   UK
B M T NEWS. 1980. 3/yr. free. British Maritime Technology Ltd., Orlando House, 1 Waldegrove Rd., Teddington, Mddx. TW11 8LZ, England. Ed. David R. Owen. charts; illus.; circ. 7,000. (controlled). **Document type:** corporate report.
    Formerly: N M I News (ISSN 0260-4817)

B P SHIPPING REVIEW. see *PETROLEUM AND GAS*

387   TH
B S A A (YEAR) THAILAND SHIPPING HANDBOOK; official BSAA (year) handbook of shipping, transportation and services for industry, trade and commerce in Thailand and worldwide. (Text in English) 1989. biennial. $24. (Bangkok Shipowners and Agents Association) Cosmic Group of Companies, 4th Fl., Phyathai Bldg., 31 Phyathai Rd., Rajthevi, Bangkok 10400, Thailand. TEL 245-3850. FAX 246-4737. adv.: color page $1200. circ. 5,000. (controlled). **Document type:** directory.

387   BF
BAHAMAS. MINISTRY OF TRANSPORT. PORT AND MARINE DEPARTMENT. ANNUAL REPORT. a. Ministry of Transport, Port and Marine Department, P.O. Box N-8175, Nassau N.P., Bahamas. FAX 809-322-5545.

387   SP
BARCELONA PORT; guia de servicios del puerto de Barcelona. 1978. a. 1300 ptas. Publicaciones Men-Car, S.A., Paseo de Colon 24, 08002 Barcelona, Spain. TEL 93-301-5516. FAX 93-318-6645. Eds. Juan Cardona, Manuel Cardona. adv. circ. 15,000.
    Formerly: Port (Year).

387   UK
BARROW AND SILLOTH DOCKS TIDAL PREDICTIONS. a. £1. Associated British Ports (Barrow in Furness), Port Office, Ramsden Dock Rd., Barrow in Furness, Cumbria LA14 2TW, England. TEL 01229-822911. FAX 10229-835822.

BASIC PORT STATISTICS OF INDIA. see *TRANSPORTATION — Abstracting, Bibliographies, Statistics*

387   BE
BELGIUM. ADMINISTRATION DES AFFAIRES MARITIMES ET DE LA NAVIGATION. RAPPORT ANNUEL SUR L'EVOLUTION DE LA FLOTTE DE PECHE. a. Administration des Affaires Maritimes et de la Navigation, 104 rue d'Arlon, 1040 Brussels, Belgium. TEL 32-2-233-12-11. FAX 32-2-230-30-02. TELEX 61880 VERTRA B. **Document type:** government publication.
    Former titles: Belgium. Administration de la Marine et de la Navigation Interieure. Rapport Annuel sur l'Evolution de la Flotte de Peche; Belgium. Administration de la Marine. Rapport Annuel sur l'Evolution de la Flotte de Peche.

BENEDICT ON ADMIRALTY. see *LAW — Maritime Law*

387 623.8   NE   ISSN 0006-4661
BLAUWE WIMPEL; maandblad voor scheepvaart en scheepsbouw in de lage landen. 1946. m. fl.105.50. Roto Smeets de Boer n.v., Postbus 507, 1200 AM Hilversum, Netherlands. TEL 31-35-258611. FAX 31-35-238978. Ed. Ineke van Haga. adv.; bk.rev.; charts; illus.; index. circ. 8,000.

BOATBUILDER'S INTERNATIONAL DIRECTORY; the boatbuilder's source book of designers, kit makers and suppliers. see *SPORTS AND GAMES — Boats And Boating*

BOATING INDUSTRY MARINE BUYERS' GUIDE. see *BUSINESS AND ECONOMICS — Trade And Industrial Directories*

387   US
BOHMAN OCEAN SHIPPING NEWS SUMMARY. 1982. m. $29.95. Bohman Industrial Traffic Consultants, Inc., 32 Pleasant St., Box 889, Gardner, MA 01440. TEL 617-632-1913. Ed. Raynard F. Bohman, Jr.

TRANSPORTATION — SHIPS AND SHIPPING

387   AG
BOLETIN MARITIMO DE LA EXPORTACION ARGENTINA. 1918. s-w. $744. Editorial Boletin Maritimo S.C.A., Aguero 892, 1171 Buenos Aires, Argentina. Ed. Luis Kramer. adv. circ. 3,500. **Document type:** bulletin.

387   UK
THE BRISTOL PORT COMPANY. 1886. a. free to qualified personnel. The Bristol Port Company, St. Andrews Rd., Avonmouth, Bristol BS11 9DQ, England. TEL 01272-820000. FAX 01272-820698. TELEX 44240. Ed. Julie Gough. adv. circ. 3,000.
   Former titles: Port of Bristol Authority; Port of Bristol. Handbook.

387   UK   ISSN 0265-8178
BRITISH COLUMBIA PORTS HANDBOOK (YEAR). 1984. biennial. £50. Compass Publications Ltd., Macron House, Castle Acre, King's Lynn, Norfolk PE32 2BQ, England. TEL 01760-755783. FAX 01760-755782. Ed. James P. Moriarty. adv. circ. 7,000. **Document type:** directory.

623.82
BRITISH MARINE INDUSTRIES FEDERATION YEARBOOK. 1947. a. £12. (British Marine Industries Federation) Charles Smith Publications, Meadlake Pl., Thorpe Lee Rd., Egham, Surrey TW20 8HE, England. TEL 0784-473377. FAX 0784-439678. Ed. Susan Grant. adv. circ. 1,500. **Document type:** directory.
   Formerly: Ship and Boat Builders National Federation Handbook.

386   UK   ISSN 0068-2683
HE663
BRITISH WATERWAYS BOARD. ANNUAL REPORT AND ACCOUNTS. 1963. a. free. British Waterways Board, Willow Grange, Church Rd., Watford, Herts. WD1 3QA, England. TEL 01923-226422. FAX 01923-226081. **Document type:** corporate report.

623.8   CI   ISSN 0007-215X
BRODOGRADNJA. (Text in Croatian, English; summaries in English) 1950. q. $50. (Ministry of Science of the Republic of Croatia) Brodarski Institut, Av. V. Holjevca 20, 41020 Zagreb, Croatia. TEL 385-41-651022. FAX 385-41-650946. Ed. Dragan Stulhofer. adv.: B&W page $800, color page $115; adv. contact: Zdenko Barisic. bk.rev.; abstr.; bibl.; illus.; index. circ. 800. **Indexed:** BMT.
—BLDSC (2349.200000); Ei.
   Description: Publishes scientific and professional articles in the field of shipbuilding and suporting industry.

623.8   PL   ISSN 1230-7718
BUDOWNICTWO OKRETOWE I GOSPODARKA MORSKA. (Text in various languages) 1956. m. $51. (Stowarzyszenie Inzynierow i Technikow Mechanikow Polskich) Oficyna Wydawnicza SIMP Press, Ltd., Ul. Swietokrzyska 14A, 00-950 Warsaw, Poland. TEL 48-22-271637. Ed. Zbigniew Grzywaczewski. adv.: page $1000. bk.rev.; illus.; index. circ. 1,000. **Indexed:** ISMEC.
   Formerly: Budownictwo Okretowe (ISSN 0007-2990)
   Description: Covers safety of ships, builidng of ships, boarding platforms, protection of sea environment.

627   UK   ISSN 0305-0122
BULK CARRIER REGISTER. (Monthly and quarterly updates avail.) 1969. a. £150 ($240) (outside Europe £175 ($280)); m. updates £96 ($155) (outside Europe £120 ($190)); q. diskettes £300 ($480) (effective 1995). Clarkson Research Studies, 12 Camomile St., London EC3A 7BP, England. TEL 0171-283-8955. FAX 0171-623-0539. TELEX 881 2927 CLTNK G. adv.; charts; stat. (also avail. in diskette format) **Document type:** bulletin.
   Description: Lists bulk carrier ships by name, along with their technical characteristics; includes ship size and weight, type, age, and capacity and a separate listing of the companies that own or manage them.

623.89   FR   ISSN 0298-7104
BULLETIN DIFRAP. Key Title: Bulletin de Diffusion Rapide d'Informations l'Usage des Navigateurs. w. 225 F. (effective 1995). Service Hydrographique et Oceanographique de la Marine, 3 av. Octave Greard, 00300 Armees, France. TEL 98-03-09-17. FAX 98-47-11-42. TELEX HYDRO 940568 F. (Subscr. to: EPSHOM, B.P. 426, 29275 Brest Cedex, France) **Document type:** bulletin, government publication.

BULLETIN FROM JOHNNY CAKE HILL. see HISTORY — History Of North And South America

BULLINGER'S POSTAL AND SHIPPERS GUIDE FOR THE UNITED STATES AND CANADA. see COMMUNICATIONS — Postal Affairs

623.8   FR   ISSN 0007-5752
TJ2
BUREAU VERITAS. BULLETIN TECHNIQUE. (Text in English and French) 1919. 4/yr. 245 F. (foreign 290 F.). Bureau Veritas, Cedex 44, 92077 Paris la Defense, France. TEL 42-91-52-71. FAX 42-91-54-47. Ed. Philippe Boisson. bk.rev.; bibl.; illus.; stat.; index. circ. 2,500. **Indexed:** Excerp.Med., INIS Atomind. **Document type:** bulletin.
—BLDSC (2911.000000); Faxon; SWETS.

387 658.8   UK   ISSN 0268-0793
BUSINESS RATIO REPORT: THE BOAT BUILDING INDUSTRY; an industry sector analysis. 1980-1981; resumed 1985. a. I C C Business Ratios Ltd., Freepost, Field House, Hampton, Mddx. TW12 1BR, England. TEL 081-783-0977. FAX 081-783-1940. charts; stat. **Document type:** trade publication.
—BLDSC (2116.687750).
   Formerly (until 1981): Business Ratio Report: Boatbuilders (ISSN 0261-7455)

387.4 658.8   UK   ISSN 0953-5454
BUSINESS RATIO REPORT: PASSENGER SHIPPING; an industry sector analysis. 1988. a. I C C Business Ratios Ltd., Freepost, Field House, Hampton, Mddx. TW12 1BR, England. TEL 081-783-0977. FAX 081-783-1940. charts; stat. **Document type:** trade publication.
—BLDSC (6407.996000).

387 343.09   US   ISSN 1062-6506
C I B DAILY MARITIME NEWSLETTER. 1897. d. (230/yr.). $1260 (foreign $1440). Congressional Information Bureau, Inc., 3030 Clarendon Blvd., Ste. 202, Arlington, VA 22201. TEL 703-516-4801. FAX 703-561-4804. Ed. R. Cazalas. cum.index. circ. 1,000. (looseleaf format; back issues avail.) **Document type:** newsletter.
—CCC.
   Description: Maritime news, including regulation, promotion, congressional activities, courts, steamship lines, legal matters, conventions and seminars.

387 343.09   US
C I B DAILY MARITIME NEWSLETTER INDEX. 4/yr. $225 (foreign $240). Congressional Information Bureau, Inc., 1325 G St., N.W., Ste. 1005, Washington, DC 20005. TEL 202-347-2275. FAX 202-347-2278. Ed. Robert P. Cazalas. index. (back issues avail.) **Document type:** abstracting/indexing.

387   NO   ISSN 0778-9882
C M I NEWS LETTER. (Text in English, French) 1975. q. NOK 590 in Nordic countries; elsewhere $100 (includes yearbook) (effective 1996). (International Maritime Committee - Comite Maritime International) Scandinavian University Press, P.O. Box 2959 Toeyen, N-0608 Oslo, Norway. TEL 47-22-57-54-00. FAX 47-22-57-53-53. (U.S. addr.: Scandinavian University Press, 200 Meacham Ave., Elmont, NY 11002. TEL 516-352-7300) Ed. Francesco Berlingieri. circ. 2,500.
   Supersedes in part (in 1978): International Maritime Committee. Documentation (ISSN 0538-8643)

387   NO
C M I YEAR BOOK. 1978. a. NOK 590 in Nordic countries; elsewhere $100 (included with newsletter) (effective 1996). (International Maritime Committee - Comite Maritime International) Scandinavian University Press, P.O. Box 2925 Toeyen, N-0608 Oslo, Norway. TEL 47-22-57-54-00. FAX 47-22-57-53-53. (U.S. addr.: Scandinavian University Press, 200 Meacham Ave., Elmont, NY 11002. TEL 516-351-7300) circ. 2,500.
   Supersedes in part (in 1978): International Maritime Committee. Documentation (ISSN 0538-8643)

CANADIAN INDUSTRIAL TRANSPORTATION LEAGUE. TRANSPORT INFO. see TRANSPORTATION — Roads And Traffic

387   CN   ISSN 0821-5944
HE561
CANADIAN SAILINGS. 1937. w. Can.$90. K-III Directories, 4634 St. Catherine St. W., Montreal, PQ H3Z 1S3, Canada. TEL 514-934-0373. FAX 514-934-4708. Ed. Brian Gallery. adv. contact: Brian Gallery. illus.; stat.; tr.lit. circ. 11,000. **Indexed:** Can.B.P.I., Can.B.P.I. **Document type:** trade publication.
   Incorporates: Seaports and the Shipping World. Annual Issue (ISSN 0080-8423); **Incorporates:** Seaports and the Shipping World (ISSN 0037-0150)
   Description: Covers seaway tolls, pilotage, pollution, productivity shipbuilding subsidies, sailing dates.

623.89   AT
CAPE HORNER JOURNAL. 1960. q. Aus.$2. Cape Horners - Australia Inc., c/o James Hopton, 63 Hurtle Sq., Adelaide, SA 5000, Australia. TEL 81 232-1110. Ed. Jason Hopton. adv.; bk.rev. circ. 250.
   Formerly: Cape Horners - Australia. Newsletter.

387 380   CN   ISSN 0822-9481
CAPTAIN LILLIE'S BRITISH COLUMBIA COAST GUIDE AND RADIOTELEPHONE DIRECTORY. 1936. biennial. Can.$19.95. Progress Publishing Co. Ltd., 1765 Bellevue Ave., West Vancouver, BC V7V 1A8, Canada. TEL 604-922-6717. FAX 604-922-1739. **Document type:** directory, trade publication.
   Formerly (until 1984): Captain Lillie's Coast Guide and Radiotelephone Directory (ISSN 0318-3742)

387.164   IT
CARGO. 6/yr. Via A. Nota 6, 10122 Turin, Italy. TEL 11-436-63-00. FAX 11-436-65-00. Ed. Renzo Druetto. circ. 9,800.

387.164   HK
CARGO CLAN. (Text in English) 1976. q. free. Emphasis HK Ltd., 505-508 Westlands Centre, 20 Westlands Rd., Quarry Bay, Hong Kong, Hong Kong. TEL 25161000. FAX 25613306. Ed. Geoff Burpee. adv.: B&W page $550, color page $850; trim 305 x 223; adv. contact: Cecilia Clinch. circ. 10,000 (controlled). (back issues avail.)
   Description: Features cargo news of the Cathay Pacific Airways and topics of general interest to the airfreight industry.

387   HK   ISSN 0252-9610
CARGONEWS ASIA. (Text in English) 1977. s-m. HK.$198.90 (Asia $25.50; elsewhere $59.50). Far East Trade Press Ltd., 2-F Kai Tak Commercial Bldg., 317 Des Voeux Rd., Central, Hong Kong. TEL 5453028. FAX 5446979. (Subscr. to: Times Publishing Group, Block C, 10th Fl. Seaview Estate, 2-8 Watson Rd., North Point, Hong Kong. TEL 852-566-8381. FAX 852-508-0255) Ed. Martin Savery. adv. circ. 12,840.
—CCC.
   Description: Provides the region's freight professionals with news and future coverage about the freighting business.

387   HK
CARGONEWS CHINA. q. HK.$65 (Asia $15.50; elsewhere $19.50). Far East Trade Press Ltd., 2-F Kai Tak Commercial Bldg., 317 Des Voeux Rd., Central, Hong Kong. TEL 852-5453028. FAX 852-5446979. (Subscr. to: Times Publishing Group, Block C, 10th Fl. Seaview Estate, 2-8 Watson Rd., North Point, Hong Kong. TEL 852-566-8381. FAX 852-508-0255) **Document type:** trade publication.

6418 TRANSPORTATION — SHIPS AND SHIPPING

387.164 UK ISSN 0958-5230
CARGOWARE INTERNATIONAL. 1989. m. E M A P - Business Publishing Ltd., 33-39 Bowling Green Ln., London EC1R ODA, England. TEL 0171-837-1212. FAX 0171-278-9509. Ed. Andrew Foxcroft. adv. circ. 8,674. **Document type:** trade publication.
Description: Contains information on container box and handling equipment and hardware.

387 GW ISSN 0172-9314
VM1
CARGOWORLD; Europe's transport newsletter. (Text in English) 1956. w. DM.564 (foreign DM.612). Deutscher Verkehrs Verlag GmbH, Nordkanalstr. 36, 20097 Hamburg, Germany. TEL 040-23714165. FAX 040-23714-123. Ed. Alison Bailey. adv.; B&W page DM.3050; trim 260 x 170. bk.rev. circ. 18,000. **Document type:** newsletter.
Description: Covers developments in all fields of the international transportation industry.

CASUALTY RETURN. see TRANSPORTATION — Abstracting, Bibliographies, Statistics

623.89 387.1 FR ISSN 0989-5973
CATALOGUE DES CARTES MARINES ET DES OUVRAGES NAUTIQUES. 1983. a. free. Service Hydrographique et Oceanographique de la Marine, 3 av. Octave Greard, 00300 Armees, France. TEL 98-03-09-17. FAX 98-47-11-42. TELEX HYDRO 940568 F. (Subscr. to: EPSHOM, B.P. 426, 29275 Brest Cedex, France) **Document type:** catalog, government publication.
Description: Lists and describes marine charts and nautical publications.

CENTER FOR NAVAL ANALYSES. BIENNIAL REPORT. see MILITARY

387 AG
CENTRO DE NAVEGACION. HANDBOOK. RIVER PLATE HANDBOOK FOR SHIPOWNERS AND AGENTS. Cover title: River Plate Shipping Guide; Ship Owners', Masters' and Agents' Handbook, River Plate Ports. (Text in English) 1972. triennial. $100. Centro de Navegacion, Maipu 521, 1006 Buenos Aires, Argentina. TEL 322-1423. FAX 325-0042. TELEX 25572 CNT AR. adv.; B&W page $1050; 130 x 200. circ. 2,500. **Document type:** directory.
Formerly: Centro de Navegacion Transatlantica. C.N.T. Handbook. River Plate Handbook for Shipowners and Agents; Supersedes a similar publication issued 1933-1966 as: M A R Year Book.

387 CE
CEYLON SHIPPING CORPORATION. ANNUAL REPORT & STATEMENT OF ACCOUNTS. (Text in English) a. Ceylon Shipping Corporation, Box 1718, Colombo, Sri Lanka.

387 US
CHARTERING ANNUAL. 1954. a. $95. Maritime Research, Inc., 499 Ernston Rd., Box 805, Parlin, NJ 08855. TEL 201-727-8040. adv.; abstr.; charts; index.
Description: Offers the shipping industry a yearly listing of charter fixture information.

387 UK ISSN 0969-9139
CHEMICAL TANKER REGISTER. (Monthly and quarterly updates avail.) 1993. a. £130($210) (outside Europe £142 ($230)); m. updates £96 ($155) (outside Europe £120 ($190)) (effective 1995). Clarkson Research Studies, 12 Camomile St., London EC3A 7BP, England. TEL 0171-283-8955. FAX 0171-623-0539. TELEX 881 2927 CLTNK G. charts; stat. **Document type:** directory.
Description: Lists chemical tankers by name and type; includes ship size and weight, age, capacity, and other technical characteristics.

387 CH
CHINESE SEAMEN'S NEWS. m. National Chinese Seamen's Union, 2nd Fl., No. 115, Changchow S. Rd. Sec.1, Taipei, Taiwan, Republic of China.

387.54 BG
CHITTAGONG PORT AUTHORITY. PORT FOLIO, PORT OF CHITTAGONG. (Text in English) m. Chittagong Port Authority, Box 2013, Chittagong, Bangladesh.
Supersedes: Chittagong Port Authority. Monthly Bulletin.

387 BG
CHITTAGONG PORT AUTHORITY. YEARBOOK. (Text in English) a. Chittagong Port Authority, Box 2013, Chittagong, Bangladesh.
Formerly: Chittagong Port Trust. Yearbook of Information (ISSN 0069-3723)

623.82 CC ISSN 1000-6982
CHUANBO GONGCHENG/SHIP ENGINEERING. (Text in Chinese; abstracts in English) 1979. bi-m. $2 per no. Zhongguo Zaochuan Gongcheng Xuehui - Chinese Society of Naval Architecture and Marine Engineering, 71 Sipailou Lu, P.O. Box 040-002, Shanghai 200010, People's Republic of China. TEL 3203055. FAX 86-21-3290929. (Dist. overseas by: Guoji Shudian - China International Book Trading Corporation, P.O. Box 399, Beijing, P.R.C.) Ed. Yu Fengchang. adv.; bk.rev. circ. 5,000. —BLDSC (8258.600000).

387 CC ISSN 1001-4624
CHUANBO SHEJI TONGXUN. (Text in Chinese) 1072. q. $3. Shanghai Chuanbo Yanjiu Shejiyuan - Shanghai Merchant Ship Design & Research Institute, 221 Zhaojiabang Lu, P.O. Box 020-017, Shanghai 200032, People's Republic of China. TEL 021-4313600. FAX 021-4334213. Ed. Zhang Jingliang. bk.rev. circ. 3,000. **Document type:** academic/scholarly publication.

387 UK
CLARKSON RESEARCH STUDY REPORTS. irreg. price varies. Clarkson Research Studies, 12 Camomile St., London EC3A 7BP, England. TEL 0171-283-8955. FAX 0171-623-0539. TELEX 881 2927 CLTNK G. charts; stat. **Document type:** trade publication, monographic series.
Description: Each monograph covers an issue of current importance to the shipping industry.

387.164 UK ISSN 0269-381X
COALTRANS. vol.3, 1981. bi-m. $110. CoalTrans Publishing Ltd., 42 Rutherwyke, Epsom, Surrey KT17 2NB, England. FAX 44-81-786-8175. Ed. Norman Penwarden. adv.; bk.rev. circ. 4,728. **Indexed:** Fluidex.
—BLDSC (3292.214000).
Formerly (until 1986): Bulk Systems International (ISSN 0143-7852)
Description: Information on the international coal market: mined product trading, transportation, end-user technology.

359.97 UK
COASTGUARD. 1946. q. free. Department of Transport, H.M. Coastguard, Rm. S13-03 2, Marsham St., London SW1P 3EB, England. TEL 0171-276-5082. FAX 0171-276-6080. Ed. Ian Fraser. adv. contact: Peter Barnes. bk.rev.; film rev.; illus.; stat.; circ. 16,000 (controlled). **Document type:** government publication.
Description: Features training, equipment and good practice for mariners and carries news of activities of organizations.

387.5 FR ISSN 0069-5815
COLLOQUES INTERNATIONAUX D'HISTOIRE MARITIME. TRAVAUX. 1957. irreg., 9th, 1967. price varies. Ecole Pratique des Hautes Etudes, 45-47 rue des Ecoles, 75005 Paris, France.

387 II
COMMERCE YEARBOOK OF PORTS, SHIPPING AND SHIPBUILDING. (Text in English) 1974. a. Rs.50. Commerce Publications Ltd., NKM International House, 178 Backbay Reclamation, Bombay 40020, India. Ed. Subhash Chandra Sarker. illus.; stat.
Continues: Commerce Yearbook of Shipping and Shipbuilding.

COMMERCIAL TRANSPORT AND TRANSPORT MANAGERS JOURNAL. see TRANSPORTATION — Trucks And Trucking

387 US
CONNECTIONS (TOLEDO, 1956). 1956. q. free. Toledo-Lucas County Port Authority, One Maritime Plaza, 7th Fl., Toledo, OH 43604-1866. TEL 419-243-8251. FAX 419-243-1835. Ed. T. Mark Sweeney. charts; illus. circ. 7,000. **Document type:** newsletter.
Formerly (until 1989): Port of Toledo News (ISSN 0032-4868)
Description: Contains news and information on the Port of Toledo area airports and economic development.

354.44 623.8 FR
CONSTRUCTION NAVALE. 1919. a. free. Chambre Syndicale des Constructeurs de Navires, 47 rue de Monceau, 75008 Paris, France. FAX 42-89-25-32. Ed. P. Castanie. circ. 1,500.
Former titles: Evolution de la Construction Navale; Construction Navale.
Description: Surveys the French shipbuilding industry

387.164 UK ISSN 0269-7726
CONTAINER MANAGEMENT. 1984. m. $240. Baltic Publishing Ltd., Great West Rd., Brentford, Mddx. TW8 9BU, England. TEL 0181-847-2446. FAX 0181-569-8688. Ed. Dylan Griffiths; Pub. Patrick Hicks. adv. contact: Andrew Kingsley. circ. 8,000. (back issues avail.) **Document type:** trade publication.
Description: Addresses cargo-handling issues.

387.5 US ISSN 1073-5321
CORPUS CHRISTI MARINER NEWS. 1988. irreg. (4-8/yr.). $10. Box 1960, Corpus, TX 78403. TEL 512-882-7262. Ed. David C. Holiman. adv. circ. 60. **Document type:** newsletter.

387 IT ISSN 0010-9193
CORRIERE DEI TRASPORTI; settimanale indipendente di informazioni. 1958. w. L.90000 (foreign L.200000). I N D A s.r.l., Piazza Dante, 9, 16121 Genoa, Italy. TEL 39-10-566678. FAX 39-10-564962. Ed. Virgilio Dardani. adv.; illus.; stat. circ. 7,500. (tabloid format)

COSTRUIRE CANTIERE. see BUSINESS AND ECONOMICS

COSTRUZIONI; tecnica ed organizzazione dei cantieri. see ENGINEERING — Civil Engineering

387 BE
COURTIER NAUTIQUE. (Text in Flemish and French) 1970. m. 8 rue du Sceptre, B-1040 Brussels, Belgium. adv. circ. 13,400.

387 UK ISSN 0070-1629
CRONER'S WORLD DIRECTORY OF FREIGHT CONFERENCES. 1954. m. £115.55 (effective 1993). Croner Publications Ltd. (Subsidiary of: Wolters Kluwer N.V.), Croner House, London Rd., Kingston, Surrey KT2 6SR, England. TEL 081-547-3333. FAX 081-547-2637. TELEX 267778. Ed. Colin Clark. (looseleaf format) **Document type:** directory.
Description: Contains current information on the world's freight conferences and agreements.

CRUISE INDUSTRY NEWS. see TRAVEL AND TOURISM

CRUISE INDUSTRY NEWS ANNUAL. see TRAVEL AND TOURISM

CRUISE INDUSTRY NEWS QUARTERLY. see TRAVEL AND TOURISM

387 GW ISSN 0172-9519
D A G - SCHIFFAHRT; Zeitschrift fuer Seeleute. 1947. 6/yr. DM.55 (free to members). Deutsche Angestellten-Gewerkschaft, Karl-Muck-Platz 1, 20355 Hamburg, Germany. TEL 040-34915238. FAX 040-349-15-400. TELEX 211642-AGHV-D. Ed. Klaus-Dieter Schwettscher-Fink. bk.rev. circ. 7,000. **Document type:** trade publication.

387 551.3 DK ISSN 0905-3549
D M I NEWS. 1979. irreg. free. Danish Maritime Institute, Hjortekaersvej 99, 2800 Lyngby, Denmark. TEL 45-45-87-93-25. FAX 45-45-87-93-33. TELEX 37223-SHILAB-DK. Ed. Arne Hasle Nielsen. bk.rev.; illus. circ. 1,200. **Document type:** newsletter.
Former titles: D M I Update (ISSN 0903-112X) & Vind - Nyt (ISSN 0109-2049)

387 BL
DADOS ESTATISTICOS DA MOVIMENTACAO DE CARGA E PASSAGEIROS. Cover title: Dados Estatisticos da Navegacao. a. Empresa de Navegacao de Amazonia, S.A., Setor de Processamento de Dados Estatisticos, Av. Presidente Vargas 41, Belem, Para, Brazil. stat.

387.164 US
DAILY SHIPPING NEWS. 1920. d. (5/w.). $150. 7831 S.E. Stark St., Ste. 200, Portland, OR 97215-2357. TEL 503-255-2142. FAX 503-255-2735. Ed. James Eggar. bk.rev. circ. 1,000. (tabloid format) **Document type:** newspaper.

TRANSPORTATION — SHIPS AND SHIPPING

387   DK   ISSN 0107-8011
DANSK ILLUSTRERET SKIBSLISTE. 1980. a. DKK 280. Seapress, Postboks 288, 8100 Aarhus C, Denmark. Eds. Per Rungholm, Bent Mikkelsen. adv.; illus. circ. 3,500.

387   US
DEEPWATER. 1956. q. free. Greater Baton Rouge Port Commission, Box 380, Pt. Allen, LA 70767. TEL 504-342-1660. FAX 504-342-1660. adv. contact: Karen St.Cyr. circ. 1,000 (controlled). **Document type:** newsletter.

387.54409489   DK   ISSN 0901-781X
DEN BLAA BESEJLINGSLISTE (YEAR). 1958. a. Teknisk Forlag AS, Skelbaekgade 4, DK-1780 Copenhagen V, Denmark. TEL 45-31-21-68-01. FAX 45-31-21-04-01. adv.; B&W page DKK 13000, color page DKK 17900. circ. 2,500.
     Former titles (until 1975): Besejlingslisten for Koebenhavn og vigtigste danske provinshavne (ISSN 0901-7828); (until 1967): Besejlingslisten for Koebenhavn (ISSN 0525-5899); (until 1962): Besejlingsliste.

623.89 621.38   JA   ISSN 0287-6346
DENPA KOHO/ELECTRONIC NAVIGATION REVIEW. (Text in Japanese) 1960. m. Japanese Committee for Radio Aids to Navigation - Denpa Koho Kenkyukai, c/o Kaijo Hoan-cho Todai-bu, 2-1-3 Kasumigaseki, Chiyoda-ku, Tokyo 100, Japan. adv.; charts; illus.; stat. **Indexed:** JTA.

DETROIT NEWSPAPER AGENCY. TRAVEL DIRECTORY. see TRANSPORTATION — Air Transport

387   GW
DEUTSCHE SEESCHIFFAHRT. 1902. m. DM.75 (students DM.35). (Verband Deutscher Reeder e.V.) Verlag Paul-Gerhard Kuhls, Maria-Louisen-Stieg 29, 22299 Hamburg, Germany. TEL 040-462623. FAX 040-462623. (Co-sponsor: Verband Deutscher Kuestenschiffseigner) Eds. Ralf Schneider, Klaus Koester. adv.; B&W page DM.3300, color page DM.5400; trim 210 x 297. bk.rev. circ. 10,500. **Document type:** trade publication.
     Formed by the 1995 merger of: Deutsche Kuestenschiffahrt & Kehrwieder (ISSN 0176-473X)

387   GW   ISSN 0343-3668
DEUTSCHES SCHIFFAHRTSARCHIV. 1975. a. DM.38. (Deutsches Schiffahrtsmuseum Bremerhaven) Ernst Kabel Verlag GmbH, Sportallee 54B, 22335 Hamburg, Germany. TEL 040-500567-0. FAX 040-50056711. Ed. Uwe Schnall. adv. contact: Detlef Lerch. circ. 250. **Document type:** academic/scholarly publication.

DIRECTORY OF SINGAPORE SHIPBUILDING & OFFSHORE INDUSTRIES (YEAR). see BUSINESS AND ECONOMICS — Trade And Industrial Directories

DIRITTO MARITTIMO; rivista trimestrale di dottrina giurisprudenza legislazione italiana e straniera. see LAW

387   UK   ISSN 0012-4419
TC1   CODEN: DHBAAL
THE DOCK & HARBOUR AUTHORITY. 1921. 10/yr. £58($140) (rest of Europe £65; overseas £75) (effective 1996). Foxlow Publications Ltd., 20 Harcourt St., London W1H 2AX, England. TEL 0171-724-6547. FAX 0171-724-3442. Ed. Bill Reid. adv.; B&W page $720, color page $1170; 262 x 188; adv. contact: Alfred Schnackenberg. bk.rev.; charts; illus.; index; circ. 2,176 (paid). (also avail. in microform from UMI; back issues avail.; reprint service avail.) **Indexed:** BMT, Br.Tech.Ind., Eng.Ind., Excerp.Med., Fluidex, Geo.Abstr., Geotech.Abstr., J.of Ferroc., Key to Econ.Sci., Ocean.Abstr., P.A.I.S., Pollut.Abstr., Soft.Abstr.Eng., 037805700I Eng.Abstr. **Document type:** directory, trade publication.
     —BLDSC (3606.000000); Ei; Faxon; SWETS; UMI.
     Description: Presents details of port facilities worldwide and alerts readers to site and infrastructure improvements.

387.1   AT
DOG WATCH. 1943. a. Aus.$9. (Shiplovers' Society of Victoria) Research Publications Pty., G.P.O. Box 1169K, Melbourne, VIC 3001, Australia. Ed. T.E. Goldfinch. adv.; bk.rev. circ. 1,000. **Document type:** consumer publication.
     Formerly: Annual Dog Watch (ISSN 0066-3921)

387   JA   ISSN 0910-6197
DOKKUMASUTA. (Text in Japanese) 1960. 3/yr. membership. Nihon Senkyocho Kyokai - Japan Dockmasters Association, 1, Yamashita-cho, Naka-ku, Yokohama-shi, Kanagawa-ken 231, Japan. Ed. B. Togure. **Document type:** corporate report.

387   US
DOMESTIC WATERBORNE TRADE OF THE UNITED STATES. a. U.S. Maritime Administration, Office of Domestic Shipping, MAR-810, Rm. 7301, Washington, DC 20590. TEL 202-366-4374. (Subscr. to: Superintendent of Documents, U.S. Government Printing Office, Box 371954, Pittsburgh, PA 15250-7954. TEL 202-783-3238. FAX 202-512-2233) **Document type:** government publication.
     Supersedes: Domestic Oceanborne and Great Lakes Commerce of the United States (ISSN 0070-7058)
     Description: Shows the flow of domestic waterborne commerce in the U.S., with the purpose of promoting awareness of the scale, diversity, and vitality of that commerce.

387 380   UK   ISSN 0265-1165
DOVER PORT HANDBOOK.* 1983. a. £10. Charter Publications Ltd., Downham Market, Bank Chambers, Norfolk PE38 9BU, England. Ed. James P. Moriarty. adv. circ. 6,000.

387 910.202   UK   ISSN 1351-640X
DREAM WORLD CRUISE DESTINATIONS. 1993. q. Contract Communications Ltd., Nestor House, Playhouse Yard, London EC4V 5EX, England. TEL 071-779-8714. FAX 071-779-8760. (back issues avail.) **Document type:** trade publication.

387 623.8   UK   ISSN 0264-4835
DREDGING & PORT CONSTRUCTION. m. £104($208) (overseas £113) (effective Sep. 1995). Argus Business Media Ltd., International Trade Publications (Subsidiary of: Argus Press Group), Queensway House, 2 Queensway, Redhill, Surrey RH1 1QS, England. TEL 01737-768611. FAX 01737-761989. TELEX 948669 TOPJNL G. Ed. Jim Hanson; Pub. Roy Greenslade. adv. contact: Richard Harris. circ. 3,396. **Indexed:** BMT, Fluidex, Key to Econ.Sci. **Document type:** trade publication.
     —Ei; SWETS.
     Formerly: International Dredging and Port Construction (ISSN 0579-546X)

387.5   UK
DRY BULK MARKET. QUARTERLY REPORT. 1982. q. £880. Drewry Shipping Consultants (Subsidiary of: Drewry International Ltd.), 11 Heron Quay, London E14 4JF, England. TEL 0171-538-0191. FAX 0171-987-9396. TELEX 21167 HPDLDN G. Ed. Peter Rowbotham. charts; stat. (back issues avail.) **Document type:** trade publication.
     Description: Gives a thorough overview of the fast-moving world of bulk shipping. Comments on the developments and trades in the market, monitors the economics, and records fleet changes.

623.82   UK   ISSN 0143-5000
DRYDOCK; international journal of ship repair & maintenance. 1979. q. £25 (foreign £30). Marine Publications International Ltd., 4 Hubbard Rd., Houndmills, Basingstoke, Hampshire RG21 2UH, England. TEL 01256-840444. FAX 01256-817877. Ed. Derek Deere. adv.; illus. circ. 8,502. **Indexed:** Biodet.Abstr., BMT, Br.Tech.Ind., Excerp.Med., Fluidex, World Surf.Coat. **Document type:** trade publication.
     —BLDSC (3630.225000); SWETS.

387   IE
DUBLIN PORT AND DOCKS YEARBOOK. a. Tara Publishing Co. Ltd., Poolbeg House, 1-2 Poolbeg St., Dublin 2, Ireland. TEL 01-6719244. FAX 01-6719263. Ed. Fergus Farrell. adv.; B&W page I£945, color page I£1175; trim 297 x 210; adv. contact: Tony Murphy. **Document type:** trade publication.

387.5   IO   ISSN 0126-1819
DUNIA MARITIM.* vol.22, 1972. m. rps. 800. Directorate General of Sea Communication - Direktorat Jenderal Perhubungan Laut, Jl. Merdeka Timur 5, Jakarta, Indonesia. Ed.Bd. adv.; charts; illus.

E P E. see ENGINEERING — Electrical Engineering

387   CC   ISSN 1006-1088
     CODEN: HCHGEE
EAST CHINA SHIPBUILDING INSTITUTE. JOURNAL. (Text in Chinese) 1986. q. $50. East China Shipbuilding Institute, 2 Huancheng Rd., Zhenjiang, Jiangsu 212003, People's Republic of China. TEL 86-511-4422290. FAX 86-511-4421823. Ed. Cheng Huading. adv.: page $600; adv. contact: Ma Guangxiong. **Document type:** academic/scholarly publication.
     Formerly (until vol.7, no.2, 1993): Zhenjiang Shipbuilding Institute. Journal (ISSN 1000-5765)
     Description: Publishes research results in such areas as shipbuilding engineering, power engineering, mechanical engineering, civil engineering, automation, computer science and fundamental science.

387 330.9   IO
ECONOMIC & SHIPPING REVIEW. 1979. m. Rps.7500. Indonesian Shipowners Association, Jalan Bungur Besar 54, Jakarta, Indonesia.

386   UA
EGYPT. SUEZ CANAL AUTHORITY. MONTHLY REPORT. m. Suez Canal Authority, Information Center, Ismailia 41515, Egypt. FAX 64-320784. TELEX 63543 SUCAN UN.

ELECTRONAUT. see COMMUNICATIONS

387   BL
EMPRESA DE NAVEGACAO DA AMAZONIA. ESTATISTICA DA NAVEGACAO. a. Empresa de Navegacao da Amazonia, Av. Presidente Vargas 41, Belem, Para, Brazil. Dir. Eugenio Marques Frazao. charts.

623.89 520   FR   ISSN 0240-8376
EPIDECIDES LUNAIRES/LUNAR EPIDECIS. 1981. a. 20 F. Service Hydrographique et Oceanographique de la Marine, 3 av. Octave Greard, 00300 Armees, France. TEL 98-03-09-17. FAX 98-47-11-42. TELEX HYDRO 940568 F. (Subscr. to: EPSHOM, B.P. 426, 29275 Brest Cedex, France) **Document type:** government publication.
     Description: Lists lunar phases to aid in marine navigation.

623.89 520   FR   ISSN 0240-8368
EPIMENIDES/EPIMENIS. 1980. base vol. plus a. updates. 54 F. for base vol.; updates 20 F. Service Hydrographique et Oceanographique de la Marine, 3 av. Octave Greard, 00300 Armees, France. TEL 98-03-09-17. FAX 98-47-11-42. TELEX HYDRO 940568 F. (Subscr. to: EPSHOM, B.P. 426, 29275 Brest Cedex, France) **Document type:** government publication.
     Description: Tracks celestial phenomena to aid in marine navigation.

387   FR
ESCALE; revue de personnel du Port Autonome du Havre. 1949. q. free. Port Autonome du Havre, B.P. 1413, Terre-Plein de la Barre, 76067 Le Havre Cedex, France. Ed. Michel Langlet. charts; illus.; stat. circ. 4,200.
     Formerly: Havre (ISSN 0023-9534)

387   BE
EUROPEAN COMMUNITY SHIPOWNERS' ASSOCIATION. ANNUAL REPORT. a. European Community Shipowners' Association, 45 rue Ducale, B-1000 Brussels, Belgium. TEL 32-2-5113949. FAX 32-2-5118092. **Document type:** corporate report.
     Supersedes: Comite des Associations d'Armateurs des Communautes Europeens. Annual Report.

387   UK
F I D I FOCUS. (Text in English, French, German) 1982. 8/yr. £40. (Federation Internationale des Demenageurs Internationaux - International Federation of International Furniture Removals) Quarrington-Curtis Ltd., 1517 Canute Rd., Southampton SO1 1FJ, England. TEL 0703-635438. FAX 0703-632198. Ed. Colin Quarrington. circ. 2,200.
     Description: News items, feature articles, photography, and classified advertisements pertaining to the activities of this organization for overseas furniture moving and storage facilities.

6420 TRANSPORTATION — SHIPS AND SHIPPING

623.82 639.2   JA   ISSN 0385-552X
F R P GYOSEN/F R P FISHING BOAT. (Text in Japanese) 1967. bi-m. F R P Gyosen Kenkyukai - F R P Fishing Boat Research Association of Japan, 10-7-201, Higashishinbashi 2-chome, Minato-ku, Tokyo 105, Japan.

387   NE   ISSN 0929-4678
F W Z MARITIEM MAGAZINE. 1966. m. FL125 (foreign fl.32.50). (Algemeene Vereniging van Zeevaarenden) Federatie van Werknemersorganisaties in de Zeevaart, Postbox 25131, 3001 HC Rotterdam, Netherlands. FAX 31-10-4773846. Ed.Bd. adv.; bk.rev.; charts; illus.; stat.; index. circ. 8,000.
—SWETS.
Formerly: Peiling (ISSN 0031-4099)

387.54   UK
▼**FAIRPLAY CONTAINER OPERATORS DIRECTORY (YEAR).** 1994 (Nov.). a. £95($170) Fairway Publications Ltd., P.O. Box 96, Coulsdon, Surrey CR5 2TE, England. TEL 0181-645-2800. FAX 0181-660-2824. TELEX 884595 FRPLAY G. (N. American subscr. to: Fairplay Publications Ltd., Box 354, Germantown, NY 12526. TEL 518-537-6682. FAX 518-537-6667) charts. **Document type:** directory.
Description: Profiles more than 120 container operator companies, including their commerce, fleet registry and profiles, and business alliances.

387   UK   ISSN 0960-6165
HE561
FAIRPLAY INTERNATIONAL SHIPPING WEEKLY. (Includes: q. Newbuildings (Formerly: World Ships on Order)) 1883. w. $265. Fairplay Publications Ltd. (Subsidiary of: The Prime Group), P.O. Box 96, Coulsdon, Surrey CR5 2TE, England. TEL 0181-660-2800. FAX 0181-660-2824. TELEX 884595 FRPLAY G. (N. American subscr. to: Fairplay Publications Ltd., Box 354, Germantown, NY 12526. TEL 518-537-6682. FAX 518-537-6667) Ed. Christopher Hewer. adv.; bk.rev.; charts; illus.; mkt.; pat.; tr.lit.; stat. circ. 5,660. **Indexed:** Euro.LJI, Fluidex, Key to Econ.Sci., LJI. **Document type:** trade publication.
—BLDSC (3865.505500); Faxon; SWETS; UnCover.
Former titles (until 1989): Fairplay International Shipping Weekly (ISSN 0307-0220); Fairplay International Shipping Journal.

387 338   UK   ISSN 0267-0879
FAIRPLAY MARINE COMPUTING GUIDE. 1984. a. £45($89) Fairplay Publications Ltd. (Subsidiary of: The Prime Group), P.O. Box 96, Coulsdon, Surrey CR5 2TE, England. TEL 081-645-2800. FAX 081-660-2824. (N. American subscr. to: Fairplay Publications Ltd., Box 354, Germantown, NY 12526. TEL 518-537-6682. FAX 518-537-6667) Ed. P. Malpas. **Document type:** trade publication.
—BLDSC (3865.507700).
Description: Provides a complete list of all commercially available computer systems, software packages, and services for the maritime industry. Describes each software package in detail.

387   UK   ISSN 0961-2181
HE552
FAIRPLAY WORLD PORTS DIRECTORY (YEAR). 1869. a. £130($228) for print version; diskette £295 ($515) (effective 1995). Fairplay Publications Ltd., P.O. Box 96, Coulsdon, Surrey CR5 2TE, England. TEL 0181-645-2800. FAX 0181-660-2824. TELEX 884895 FRPLAY G. (N. American subscr. to: Fairplay Publications Ltd., Box 354, Germantown, NY 12526. TEL 518-537-6682. FAX 518-537-6667) maps. (also avail. in diskette format) **Document type:** directory.
Formed by the 1989 merger of: Fairplay World Ports Directory. Vol. 1: North European Ports (ISSN 0952-9659); Fairplay World Ports Directory. Vol. 2: The Americas (ISSN 0952-9667); Fairplay World Ports Directory. Vol 3. The Mediterranean, Africa and the Middle East (ISSN 0952-9675); Fairplay World Ports Directory. Vol. 4: Indian and Pacific Ocean Ports (ISSN 0952-9683); All of which supersede (in 1988): Fairplay World Ports Directory. Vol. 1: Port Information (ISSN 0261-2356) and Fairplay World Ports Directory (ISSN 0264-2840).
Description: Lists the latest port prices from around 600 ports. Includes vessel and harbor dues, berthing and mooring dues, wharfage and commodity dues, and pilotage, towage and water charges. Also contains update details on port facilities and accommodations for nearly 2,500 ports and waterways, along with more than 9,000 addresses of port services and authorities.

387   UK   ISSN 0959-3101
HE561
FAIRPLAY WORLD SHIPPING DIRECTORY. a. £99($179) (effective 1995). Fairplay Publications Ltd. (Subsidiary of: The Prime Group), P.O. Box 96, Coulsdon, Surrey CR5 2TE, England. TEL 0181-645-2800. FAX 0181-660-2824. TELEX 884595 FRPLAY G. (N. American subscr. to: Fairplay Publications Ltd., Box 354, Germantown, NY 12526. TEL 518-537-6682. FAX 518-537-6667) Ed. P. Malpas. **Document type:** directory.
—BLDSC (3865.508250).
Former titles (until 1978): Fairway World Shipping Year Book (ISSN 0142-6974); (until 1977): Fairplay International World Shipping Year Book (ISSN 0140-5047); Financial Times World Shipping Year Book (ISSN 0141-8629)
Description: Lists more than 20,000 companies in the maritime industry and more than 3,600 shipowners with fleets totaling some 25,000 vessels.

387 380   UK   ISSN 0260-9282
FALMOUTH PORT AND INDUSTRY HANDBOOK 1984.*
1981. a. Charter Publications Ltd., Downham Market, Bank Chambers, Norfolk PE38 9BU, England. Ed. James P. Moriarty. adv. circ. 6,000.

629.3   UK   ISSN 0954-3988
VM362   CODEN: FFINE5
FAST FERRY INTERNATIONAL. 1961. 10/yr. £65($100) 24 Leaf Close, Northwood, Middsx. HA6 2YY, England. TEL 09274-27262. FAX 0923-835278. Ed. Alan Blunden. adv. contact: David Woodgate. bk.rev.; charts; illus.; pat. circ. 1,200. **Indexed:** Appl.Mech.Rev., BMT, Br.Rail.Bd., Br.Tech.Ind., Met.Abstr., Ocean.Abstr., Pollut.Abstr., World Alum.Abstr. **Document type:** trade publication.
—BLDSC (3897.170000); SWETS; UMI; UnCover.
Formerly (until 1989): High-Speed Surface Craft (ISSN 0144-7823); *Incorporates:* Hovering Craft and Hydrofoil (ISSN 0018-6775)
Description: Contains news of worldwide developments involving catamarans, hovercraft, hydrofoils, surface-effect ships and other marine designs. Also features details of powerplants and other equipment in the fast ferry industry.

387   NO
FEARNLEYS MID-WEEK REPORT. (Issued with: Fearnleys Monthly Report, Fearnleys Review, World Bulk Fleet, World Bulk Trade) w. $320. Fearnleys A-S, Grev Wedelsplass 9, P.O. Box 1158 Sentrum, N-0107 Oslo, Norway. TEL 47-22-93-60-00. FAX 47-22-9361-10. **Document type:** trade publication.
Description: Provides updated information on world economy, chartering markets, sale and purchase, contracting, demolition and more.

387   NO
FEARNLEYS MONTHLY REPORT. m. $300. Fearnleys A-S, Grev Wedelsplass 9, P.O. Box 1158 Sentrum, N-0107 Oslo 1, Norway. TEL 47-22-93-60-00. FAX 47-22-93-61-10. TELEX 74607 FADM. (back issues avail.)
Description: Provides updated information on world economy, chartering markets, sale and purchase, contracting, demolition, etc.

387   NO   ISSN 0801-5589
FEARNLEYS REVIEW. a. $195. Fearnleys A-S, Grev Wedelsplass 9, Box 1158-Sentrum, 0107 Oslo 1, Norway. TEL 47-22-93-60-00. FAX 47-22-93-61-10. (back issues avail.)
Formerly: Fearnly and Egers Chartering Co. Review.
Description: Provides a comprehensive survey of freight markets, sale and purchase, contracting, etc. during the preceeding year.

387   US
FEDERAL MARITIME COMMISSION DIGEST SERVICE. m. $315. Hawkins Publishing Co., Inc., 1270B Central Ave., Box 480, Mayo, MD 21106. **Document type:** abstracting/indexing.

623.89   FR   ISSN 0223-5358
FEUX ET SIGNAUX DE BRUME. 1950. irreg. price varies. Service Hydrographique et Oceanographique de la Marine, 3 av. Octave Greard, 00300 Armees, France. TEL 98-03-09-17. FAX 98-47-11-42. TELEX HYDRO 940568 F. (Subscr. to: EPSHOM, BP 426, 29275 Brest Cedex, France) **Document type:** government publication.
Description: List the light and sound properties of navigation aides for various regions worldwide. Includes the positions of lighthouses, beacons, and buoys.

FINANCIAL SURVEY. COMPANY DATA FOR SUCCESS: BOAT BUILDERS & MARINE ENGINEERS. *see* SPORTS AND GAMES — Boats And Boating

FISKERI OG SKIBSFART. *see* FISH AND FISHERIES

387   BE
FLANDRIA MAGAZINE. (Text in Dutch, French, German) 1986. q. Looman Marine nv, Grote Singel 6, 2900 Schoten, Belgium. TEL 32-3-6580006. FAX 32-3-6580006. Ed. Willem Manteleers. adv.: B&W page 6200 BEF; trim 420 x 300. circ. 60,000. (tabloid format) **Document type:** newsletter.

387   US   ISSN 0884-8548
FLORIDA SHIPPER. 1975. w. $38 (Canada $40; overseas $85). Journal of Commerce, Inc., Box 371305, Miami, FL 33137-1305. TEL 305-579-1040. FAX 305-579-1052. Ed. Alinda Montfort; Pub. Brian Neuhart. adv. contact: Kim Davis. circ. 2,150. **Document type:** trade publication.

FORD'S DECK PLAN GUIDE. *see* TRAVEL AND TOURISM

FORD'S FREIGHTER TRAVEL GUIDE AND WATERWAYS OF THE WORLD. *see* TRAVEL AND TOURISM

FORD'S INTERNATIONAL CRUISE GUIDE. *see* TRAVEL AND TOURISM

387   GW   ISSN 0939-7965
FRACHT - DIENST. 1945. m. DM.48 (foreign DM.78). Postfach 3240, 38022 Braunschweig, Germany. TEL 0531-340954. FAX 0531-340950. Ed. Andreas Klose. adv.; bk.rev. circ. 8,000. (back issues avail.)

387   NO   ISSN 0015-9352
FRAKTEMANN. 1935. 5/yr. NOK 60.($3.50) Fraktefartoyenes Rederiforening, P.O. Box 2020 Nordnes, N-5024 Bergen, Norway. Ed. Einar Haakon Kirkefjord. adv. circ. 1,000.
—CCC.

387   FR
FRANCE. COMMISSION CENTRALE POUR LA NAVIGATION DU RHIN. RAPPORT ANNUEL. (Text in French, German) 1835. a. 70 F. Commission Centrale pour la Navigation du Rhin, Palais du Rhin, 67082 Strasbourg Cedex, France. TEL 88-52-20-10. FAX 88-32-10-72. Ed. Hans van der Werf. charts; stat.; circ. 500 (controlled). **Document type:** government publication.
Description: Contains reviews and statistical information about the Rhine river for each year as well as statistics about the preceeding decades.

TRANSPORTATION — SHIPS AND SHIPPING

387.5 FR ISSN 0988-4386
FRANCE. MINISTERE DE LA MER. BULLETIN OFFICIEL.
Key Title: Bulletin Officiel du Ministere de la Mer (1988). 1920. irreg. 500 F. (Ministere de la Mer) Imprimerie Nationale, B.P. 514, 59505 Douai Cedex, France. TEL 27-93-70-70. FAX 27-93-70-96. TELEX 120 389 F. **Document type:** government publication.
Former titles (until 1988): France. Secretariat d'Etat a la Mer. Bulletin Officiel (ISSN 0980-3440); Which was formerly (until 1986): France. Secretariat d'Etat aupres du Ministere de l'Urbanisme, du Logement et des Transports Charge de la Mer. Bulletin Officiel (ISSN 0767-1288); (until 1984): France. Secretariat d'Etat aupres du Ministere des Transports Charge de la Mer. Bulletin Officiel (ISSN 0755-7841); (until 1983): France. Ministere de la Mer. Bulletin Officiel (ISSN 0292-3548); (until 1981): France. Ministere des Transports Marine Marchand. Bulletin Officiel (ISSN 0221-0681); (until 1979): Bulletin Officiel de la Marine Marchande (ISSN 0221-0673).

FREIGHT WORLD. see TRANSPORTATION — Trucks And Trucking

387.1 AT
FREMANTLE PORT NEWS. 1961. q. free. Fremantle Port Authority, P.O. Box 95, Fremantle, W.A. 6160, Australia. TEL 61-9-430-3438. FAX 61-9-430-4112. Ed. Carolyn Walker. adv.; bk.rev.; illus.; circ. 3,000 (controlled). **Document type:** newsletter.
Formerly: Port of Fremantle.
Description: Explores port development, export trade and shipping lines. Includes staff appointments and port activities.

623.82 JA ISSN 0387-0863
FUNE NO KAGAKU. (Text in Japanese) 1948. m. 1400 Yen per no. Senpaku Gijutsu Kyokai - Association of Shipbuilding Technology, 23-17, Shinkawa 1-chome, Chuo-ku, Tokyo 104, Japan. TEL 81-3-3552-8798. Ed. Hirotaro Ohsawa; Pub. Kenji Hamamura. adv. contact: Kenji Hamamura. bk.rev. **Document type:** academic/scholarly publication.

FUNE TO KAIJO KISHO/SHIP AND MARITIME METEOROLOGY. see METEOROLOGY

FUNE TO KISHO/VESSELS AND WEATHER. see METEOROLOGY

387.54 UK
GARSTON DOCKS TIDE TABLE. a. free. Associated British Ports (Liverpool), Port Office, Garston, Liverpool L19 2JW, England. TEL 0151-427-5971. FAX 0151-494-3232.

387 US ISSN 0016-8149
HE554.A3
GEORGIA ANCHORAGE. 1955. q. free. Georgia Ports Authority, Box 2406, Savannah, GA 31402. TEL 912-964-3811. FAX 912-964-3921. Ed. Amy Rhodes. adv.; charts; illus.; circ. 12,500 (controlled). **Document type:** trade publication.
Description: News articles on the export and import trade and shipping industry in the state, as well as news on the activities of the State's Ports Authority.

387 GW ISSN 0178-2495
GERMAN MARITIME INDUSTRY JOURNAL. (Text in English) 1985. bi-m. DM.48. Seehafen Verlag GmbH, Nordkanalstr. 36, 20097 Hamburg, Germany. TEL 040-2371402. FAX 040-23714154. Ed. Hans Juergen Witthoeft. adv. circ. 3,500. (back issues avail.)

387 GW ISSN 0070-4148
GERMAN MERCHANT FLEET; die Deutsche Handelsflotte. 1954. a. DM.549. Seehafen Verlag GmbH, Nordkanalstr. 36, 20097 Hamburg, Germany. (Subscr. to: Postfach 105605, 20038 Hamburg, Germany) adv. **Document type:** trade publication.

THE GREAT CIRCLE. see HISTORY

387 US ISSN 1067-4144
GREAT LAKES LOG. 1972. bi-w. $28. Harbor House Publishers, Inc., 221 Water St., Boyne City, MI 49712. TEL 616-582-2814. FAX 616-582-3392. Ed. David Knight; Pub. Michelle Cortright. bk.rev. circ. 1,200. (back issues avail.) **Document type:** newsletter.
Formerly: Lake Log Chips (ISSN 0270-5680)
Description: Contains informations on the boats, the cargoes and the people that make up the maritime tradition of the Great Lakes.

387 CN ISSN 0824-8583
HE554.A5
GREAT LAKES NAVIGATION.* 1917. a. Canadian Marine Publications Ltd., Ste. 512, 1434 St. Catherine St. W., Montreal, PQ H3G 1R4, Canada. TEL 514-861-6715. FAX 514-861-0966. Ed. O.J. Silva. adv.

386 US ISSN 0072-7318
GREAT LAKES RED BOOK. 1901. a. $8.50. Freshwater Press, Inc., 1700 E 13th St., Ste. 3R-E, Cleveland, OH 44114. TEL 216-241-0373. Ed. John O. Greenwood. adv.; index. circ. 1,300.

387 UK ISSN 0260-9517
GREAT YARMOUTH PORT AND INDUSTRY HANDBOOK. 1980. a. £50. Compass Publications Ltd., Aboot House, Castle Acre, King's Lynn, Norfolk PE32 2BQ, England. TEL 01760-755783. FAX 01760-755782. Ed. James P. Moriarty. adv.; illus. circ. 6,000. **Document type:** directory.

386 US
GREATER CHICAGO OCEAN FREIGHT DIRECTORY. 1991. a. $11. Fourth Seacoast Publishing Co., Inc., Box 145, St. Clair Shores, MI 48080. TEL 810-779-5570. FAX 810-779-5547. Ed. Thomas Buysse. circ. 15,000. **Document type:** directory.
Description: Guide to the industry centered around the port of Chicago and neighboring rail and barge facilities.

386 US ISSN 0072-7490
HE630.G7
GREENWOOD'S GUIDE TO GREAT LAKES SHIPPING. 1958. a. $66.42. Freshwater Press, Inc., 1700 E. 13th St., Ste. 3R-E, Cleveland, OH 44114. TEL 216-241-0373. Ed. John O. Greenwood. adv. circ. 3,000.

387 GD
GRENADA PORTS AUTHORITY ANNUAL REPORT & ACCOUNTS. a. Grenada Ports Authority, Carenage, St. George's, Grenada, W.I. **Document type:** corporate report.

387 GW
GUETERTRANSPORT IN SEEVERKEHR. 1954. a. DM.59.81. K.O. Storck Verlag, Stahltwiete 7, 22761 Hamburg, Germany. TEL 040-853292-0. FAX 040-8507758. Ed. H. Meder. **Document type:** trade publication.
Formerly: Fracht-Schiffahrts-Konferenzen.

387 SP
GUIA DEL TRANSPORTE MARITIMO. 52/yr. Santa Maria de la Cabeza 11 T, Apdo. 210, 11007 Cadiz, Spain. TEL 56-25-04-98. Ed. Antonio Conde Burgos. **Document type:** bulletin.

387 PO
GUIA DO PORTO DE LISBOA. 1965. a. free. Administracao do Porto de Lisboa, Divisao de Relacoes Publicas e Marketing, Rua da Junqueira, 94, 1300 Lisbon, Portugal. circ. 3,000.

GUIA MARITIMA, PORTUARIA Y DE LA INDUSTRIA NAVAL DE VENEZUELA/MARITIME, PORT AND NAVAL INDUSTRY GUIDE OF VENEZUELA. see BUSINESS AND ECONOMICS — Trade And Industrial Directories

623.89 FR
GUIDE DU NAVIGATEUR. (In 3 vols.: Documentation et Information Nautiques; Methodes et Instruments de Navigation; Reglementation Nautique) 1992. irreg., no.2, 1994. 139 F. per vol. (all 3 vols. 397 F.) (effective 1995). Service Hydrographique et Oceanographique de la Marine, 3 av. Octave Greard, 00300 Armees, France. TEL 98-03-09-17. FAX 98-47-11-42. (Subscr. to: EPSHOM, B.P. 426, 29275 Brest Cedex, France) **Document type:** government publication.
Description: Informs mariners about new nautical publications, navigation instruments and methods, and maritime law.

387 UK
GUIDE TO PORT ENTRY (YEAR). 1971. biennial. £205 (foreign £215). Shipping Guides Ltd., 75 Bell St., Reigate, Surrey RH2 7AN, England. TEL 01737-242255. FAX 01737-222449. TELEX 917070-SHIPG-G. Ed. Robert Pedlow. **Document type:** trade publication.
Description: Detailed port information including port plans, mooring diagrams, regulations, maximum size, port restrictions, port access, required documentation, customs allowances, berthing times and availability for masters and owners.

387.1 UK
GUIDE TO TANKER PORTS. base vol. (plus bi-m. updates). Shipping Guides Ltd., Shipping Guides House, 75 Bell St., Reigate RH2 7AN, England. TEL 01737-242255. FAX 01737-222449. maps. (looseleaf format) **Document type:** directory.

387 JA
GUIDE TO THE PORT OF YOKOHAMA. (Includes Map) (Text in English and Japanese) a. free. Port and Harbor Bureau, Industry and Trade Center Bldg., 2 Yamashita-cho, Naka-ku, Yokohama, Japan. FAX 45-671-7158.

387 620 JA ISSN 0385-7093
GYOSEN KIKAN/FISHING BOAT ENGINEERING. (Text in Japanese) 1924. m. 700 Yen. Gyosen Kikan Gijutsu Kyokai - Fishing Boat Engineering Association, 10-13, Misuji 2-chome, Taito-ku, Tokyo 108, Japan.

387 GW
H B DEUTSCHE SCHIFFAHRSZEITUNG. (Hafen Bericht) 1947. d. DM.170.50 per mo. Seehafen Verlag GmbH, Nordkanalstr. 36, 20097 Hamburg, Germany. Ed. Jens Meyer. adv.; bk.rev.; charts; illus.; stat. circ. 1,000. **Document type:** newspaper.
Former titles: T H B. Taeglicher Hafenbericht (ISSN 0933-0984); (until 1979): T H B. Taeglicher Hafenbericht (Ausgabe A) (ISSN 0933-0976); (until 1976): T H B. Taeglicher Hafenbericht, Ausgabe A (ISSN 0341-0870).

387 GW
H B JAHRESAUSGABE. (Hafen Bericht) a. DM.39.80. Seehafen Verlag GmbH, Nordkanalstr. 36, 20097 Hamburg, Germany. charts; stat. **Document type:** bulletin.
Formerly: Taeglicher Hafenbericht. Jahresausgabe.

387 GW
H H L A REPORT. 1974. q. free. Hamburger Hafen- und Lagerhaus-Aktiengesellschaft, Bei St. Annen 1, 20457 Hamburg, Germany. TEL 040-30883355. FAX 040-30883355. TELEX 2161209. Ed. Gerhard Angerer. circ. 4,500. **Document type:** consumer publication.

623.82 NE ISSN 0923-666X
VM77
H S B INTERNATIONAL. 1951. m. fl.97.50 (foreign fl. 145). Uitgeverij Radius B.V., P.O. Box 277, 3300 AG Dordrecht, Netherlands. TEL 31-78-166844. FAX 31-78-214975. Ed. D.A. Vinkoert; Pub. A.L. Coomans. adv.; B&W page fl.2090, color page fl.3710; trim 292 x 212. bk.rev.; charts; illus.; mkt.; pat.; tr.lit. circ. 7,308. Indexed: BMT, Eng.Ind., Fluidex, Key to Econ.Sci., Ocean.Abstr., Pollut.Abstr. **Document type:** trade publication.
—Ei; SWETS.
Former titles: Holland Shipbuilding; Holland Shipbuilding, Marine Engineering and Shipping Herald (ISSN 0018-3571)
Description: Covers shipbuilding, dredging, engineering, oil and gas industry, ports and shipping, industry, maintenance and corrosion prevention.

TRANSPORTATION — SHIPS AND SHIPPING

387   IS
HADASHOT SAPANUT VETEUFAH - YIDION; shipping and aviation news. (Text in Hebrew) m. Wydra Shipping & Aviation Research Institute, University of Haifa, Eshkol Tower, Haifa 31905, Israel. TEL 972-4-240186. FAX 972-4-348908. Ed. M. Ofek. **Document type:** trade publication.
    Formerly: Israel Shipping and Aviation Research Institute. Yidion.
    Description: News and statistics on shipping and aviation.

387   GW
HAMBURG THE QUICK PORT. (Text in English) 1958. a. DM.34.58. K.O. Storck Verlag, Stahltwiete 7, 22761 Hamburg, Germany. TEL 040-853292-0. FAX 040-8507758. Ed. H. Meder. **Document type:** trade publication.

387.54   GW   ISSN 0341-0862
HAMBURGER HAFEN - NACHRICHTEN. 1947. w. DM.230.40. Seehafen Verlag GmbH, Nordkanalstr. 36, 20097 Hamburg, Germany. Ed. Klaus Heims. adv.; charts; illus. circ. 7,000. **Document type:** bulletin.
    Formerly: Hamburger Hafen-Nachrichten und Schiffsabfahrten (ISSN 0017-694X)
    Description: Contains timetables.

387.009489   DK   ISSN 0085-1418
HF61
HANDELS- OG SOEFARTSMUSEET PAA KRONBORG. AARBOG. (Text in Danish; summaries in English) 1942. a. DKK 200 for non-members; members DKK 160. Handels- og Soefartsmuseet paa Kronborg, DK-3000 Helsingoer, Denmark. TEL 45-49-21-06-85. FAX 45-49-21-34-40. Ed. Hans Jeppesen. adv.; illus.; cum.index. circ. 2,000. **Document type:** academic/scholarly publication.

387   CC   ISSN 1000-0356
HANG HAI. (Text in Chinese) bi-m. Shanghai Hanghai Xuehui, No.2, Rm.1001, Yuanping Nanlu, Alley 590, Shanghai 200030, People's Republic of China. TEL 4385774. Ed. Zhou Yiheng.

387   CC   ISSN 1006-1738
HANGHAI JISHU/OCEAN SHIPPING TECHNOLOGY. (Text in Chinese) 1979. bi-m. $24. Zhongguo Hanghai Xuehui, No.2, Rm. 1005, Aijian Dasha, Yuanping Nanlu, Alley 590, Shanghai 200030, People's Republic of China. TEL 021-4385457. Ed. Jin Zhongming. circ. 15,000 (paid).

387   CC   ISSN 1000-4688
HANGHAI KEJI DONGTAI. (Text in Chinese) m. Jiaotong-bu, Shanghai Chuanbo Yunshu Kexue Yanjiusuo - Ministry of Transportation, Shanghai Institute of Shipping Transportation Science, 200 Minsheng Lu, Shanghai 200135, People's Republic of China. TEL 8840438. (Co-sponsor: Zhongguo Hanghai Xuehui) Ed. Lu Wenbiao.

623.8   GW   ISSN 0017-7504
VK3
HANSA; Zeitschrift fuer Schiffahrt, Schiffbau, Hafen. (Text in German; summaries in English) 1864. m. DM.297.80. Wirtschafts- und Verkehrsverlag Hansa GmbH, Elbchaussee 277, 22605 Hamburg, Germany. TEL 040-822807-0. FAX 040-82280752. (Subscr. to: Verlagsgruppe Koehler - Mittler, Postfach 2352, 32045 Herford, Germany. TEL 05221-599146) adv.; bk.rev.; abstr.; bibl.; charts; illus.; stat.; index. circ. 6,100. **Indexed:** BMT, C.I.S. Abstr., Excerp.Med., INIS Atomind., Key to Econ.Sci., Met.Abstr., World Alum.Abstr. **Document type:** trade publication.
    —BLDSC (4262.250000); Faxon; SWETS.

HARBIN CHUANBO GONGCHENG XUEYUAN XUEBAO/HARBIN INSTITUTE OF SHIPPING ENGINEERING. JOURNAL. see *ENGINEERING*

387   CN   ISSN 0017-7636
HARBOUR AND SHIPPING. 1918. m. Can.$42.80($52) Progress Publishing Co. Ltd., 1765 Bellevue Ave., West Vancouver BC V7V 1A8, Canada. TEL 604-922-6717. FAX 604-922-1739. adv.; illus.; tr.lit. circ. 2,000. **Indexed:** BMT, Fluidex. **Document type:** trade publication.

387   NE   ISSN 0920-3753
HAVEN AMSTERDAM. 1970. bi-m. free outside the Netherlands. Amsterdam Ports Association, Het Havengebouw, 13e etage, De Ruyterkade 7, 1013 AA Amsterdam, Netherlands. TEL 31-20-6273706. Ed. Karl O. Kolb.
    Formerly (until 1980): Haven Bulletin (ISSN 0920-4466)

387   NE   ISSN 1381-0162
HAVENNIEUWS. 1931. 8/yr. fl.45 (effective 1995). Scheepvaart Vereniging Zuid Rotterdam - Port Industries Association, Postbus 4222, 3006 AE Rotterdam, Netherlands. TEL 31-10-4020399. FAX 31-10-4120687. Ed. H.J.H. Donia. adv. circ. 3,500. **Document type:** newspaper.

623.82   JA
HINKAN JIHO. (Text in Japanese) m. Nihon Senpaku Hinshitsu Kanri Kyokai - Japan Ship Machinery Quality Control Association, 1-9, Kanda Sakumacho, Chiyoda-ku, Tokyo 101, Japan.

387   BE   ISSN 0773-1922
HINTERLAND (ENGLISH EDITION); periodical of the port of Antwerp. Hinterland (Nederlandse Editie) (ISSN 0773-1906); Hinterland (Edition Francaise) (ISSN 0773-1914); Hinterland (Deutsche Ausgabe) (ISSN 0773-1930) 1950. q. 360 BEF. (Port of Antwerp Promotion Association) Publitra, Brouwersvliet 33, Box 4, B-2000 Antwerp, Belgium. FAX 32-3-231-27-52. adv.; charts; illus.; stat. circ. 12,000. **Indexed:** Avery Ind.Archit.Per., Geo.Abstr.
    Superseded (in 1976): Hinterland (Edition Quadrilingue) (ISSN 0018-1978)

HONG KONG. CENSUS AND STATISTICS DEPARTMENT. SHIPPING STATISTICS. see *TRANSPORTATION — Abstracting, Bibliographies, Statistics*

387   UK   ISSN 0018-4675
HONOURABLE COMPANY OF MASTER MARINERS. JOURNAL. 1933. q. £7.50 per no. Honourable Company of Master Mariners, c/o H.Q.S. Wellington, Temple Stairs, Victoria Embankment, London WC2R 2PN, England. TEL 071-836-8179. FAX 071-240-3082. Ed.Bd. adv.; bk.rev.; illus.; cum.index every 3 yrs.; circ. 1,200 (paid).

623.8   JA   ISSN 0018-9820
TA1   CODEN: IHERA6
I H I ENGINEERING REVIEW. Japanese edition: Ishikawajima-Harima Giho (ISSN 0578-7904) (Text in English) 1968. q. membership. Ishikawajima-Harima Heavy Industries Co., Ltd. - Ishikawajima Harima Jukogyo K.K., 2-16, Toyosu 3-chome, Koto-ku, Tokyo 135, Japan. Ed. Akira Tsutsui. bk.rev. (also avail. in microfilm from UMI; reprint service avail. from UMI) **Indexed:** BMT, Chem.Abstr., INIS Atomind., INSPEC, Int.Aerosp.Abstr., JCT, JTA, Met.Abstr., World Alum.Abstr.
    —BLDSC (4363.570000); CASDDS; UMI.

387.2   UN   ISSN 0253-8199
I M O NEWS. French edition: Organisation Maritime Internationale. Nouvelles (ISSN 1010-6197) 1977. 4/yr. free. International Maritime Organization - Organisation Maritime Internationale, 4 Albert Embankment, London SE1 7SR, England. TEL 071-735-7611. FAX 071-587-3210. TELEX 23588. Ed. Roger Kohn. adv.; bk.rev.; illus. circ. 10,000. **Indexed:** Deep Sea Res.& Oceanogr.Abstr.
    —BLDSC (4369.790000).
    Former titles: I M C O News (ISSN 0140-6434); I M C O Bulletin (ISSN 0047-0422)

I N A QUARTERLY. (Institute of Nautical Archaeology) see *ARCHAEOLOGY*

387   II   ISSN 0970-4299
INDIAN SHIPPING. (Text in English) 1949. m. Rs.250($28) (effective 1993). Indian National Shipowners' Association, 22 Maker Tower F, Cuffe Parade, Bombay 400 005, India. TEL 2182103. FAX 2182104. TELEX 011-4611-INSA-IN. Ed. B.V. Nilkund. adv.; bk.rev. circ. 1,000. **Indexed:** BMT. **Document type:** trade publication.
    —BLDSC (4429.600000).

387 623.82   II
INDIAN SHIPPING AND SHIPBUILDING. (Text in English) m. Rs.100. V.S. Chhabra, 5 B Bakhtavar, Nariman Point, Bombay 400021, India.

387.1   FR   ISSN 0073-7720
INDUSTRIE DE LA MANUTENTION DANS LES PORTS FRANCAIS. 1964. a. Union Nationale des Industries de la Manutention dans les Ports Francais, 76 Av. Marceau, 75008 Paris, France.

387.5   IT
INFORMARE. 1984. 10/yr. Media Angle S.r.l., Via G. Pacini 36, 30131 Milan, Italy. TEL 39-2-70638283. FAX 39-2-70638298. Ed. Paolo Trimigno. adv.: B&W page L.2500000, color page L.3100000; adv. contact: Tiziana Negri.

623.8   SP   ISSN 0020-1073
INGENIERIA NAVAL. 1929. m. 7200 ptas. Asociacion de Ingenieros Navales de Espana, Castello 66, 28001 Madrid, Spain. TEL 575-10-24. FAX 577167975. TELEX 43582 INAV E. Dir. Juan A. Alcaraz Infante. adv.; bk.rev.; abstr.; illus.; index. circ. 2,300. **Indexed:** BMT, Chem.Abstr., Ind.SST. —Faxon.

386   US   ISSN 0198-859X
HE627
INLAND RIVER GUIDE. 1972. a. $50. Waterways Journal, Inc., 319 N. Fourth St., 650 Security Bldg., St. Louis, MO 63102. TEL 314-241-7354. FAX 314-241-4207. Ed. Dan Owen. adv. circ. 4,500.

386   US
INLAND RIVER RECORD. 1945. a. $32. Waterways Journal, Inc., 319 N. Fourth St., 650 Security Bldg., St. Louis, MO 63102. TEL 314-241-7354. FAX 314-241-4207. Ed. Dan Owen. adv. circ. 3,800.

INLAND SEAS. see *HISTORY — History Of North And South America*

386   UK   ISSN 0264-4789
INLAND WATERWAYS GUIDE.* 1972. a. £1.45. (Inland Waterways Association) Britain Publications Ltd., 137 George Lane, London E18 1AJ, England. Ed. Michael Faulkner.

387   JA   ISSN 0386-1198
INSTITUTE FOR SEA TRAINING. JOURNAL. (Text in Japanese, summaries in English) 1951. irreg. free. Ministry of Transport, Institute for Sea Training, 2-1-3 Kasumigaseki, Chiyoda-ku, Tokyo 100, Japan. TEL 81-3-3580-4190. FAX 81-3-3580-4492. Ed.Bd. circ. 300.
    Description: Covers navigation, equipment and outfit of ships, marine engineering, and education for seafarers.

387   UK   ISSN 0267-2006
INSTITUTE OF CHARTERED SHIPBROKERS. REFERENCE BOOK AND LIST OF MEMBERS (YEAR). 1983. a. £25. Millbank Publications Ltd., 25 Catherine St., London WC2B 5JW, England. TEL 071-379-3036. FAX 071-240-6840. adv. circ. 4,000. **Document type:** directory.

623.87   UK
INSTITUTE OF MARINE ENGINEERS. CONFERENCE PROCEEDINGS. 3/yr. £180. (Institute of Marine Engineers) Marine Management Holdings Ltd., The Memorial Bldg., 76 Mark Ln., London EC3R 7JN, England. TEL 44-71-481-8493. FAX 44-71-488-1854. (Subscr. in N. America to: Learned Information, Inc., 143 Old Marlton Pike, Medford, NJ 08055. TEL 609-654-6266. FAX 609-654-4309) (back issues avail.) **Document type:** proceedings.
    Description: Publishes papers presented at conferences dealing with such topics as fire safety, maritime defense, and offshore oil platform design and development.

TRANSPORTATION — SHIPS AND SHIPPING

623.87 UK ISSN 0268-4152
CODEN: TIMTDD
INSTITUTE OF MARINE ENGINEERS. TRANSACTIONS. 1889. 6/yr. £115 to non-members. (Institute of Marine Engineers) Marine Management Holdings Ltd., Memorial Bldg., 76 Mark Ln., London EC3R 7JN, England. TEL 44-71-481-8493. FAX 44-71-488-1854. (Subscr. in N. America to: Learned Information Inc, 143 Old Marlton Pike, Medford, NJ 08055. TEL 609-654-6266. FAX 609-654-4309) Ed. Peter Yakimuik. adv.; abstr.; charts; illus.; index. circ. 5,000. (also avail. in microform from WMP.) **Indexed:** API Catal., API Hlth.& Environ., API Oil., API Pet.Ref., API Pet.Subst., API Transport., BMT, Br.Tech.Ind., Chem.Abstr., Eng.Ind., Fluidex, ISMEC, Met.Abstr., Ocean.Abstr., Pollut.Abstr., Sh.& Vib.Dig., World Alum.Abstr. **Document type:** proceedings.
—BLDSC (8940.000000); SWETS. **CCC.**
Former titles: Institute of Marine Engineers. Technical Reports (ISSN 0309-3948); Institute of Marine Engineers. Transactions (ISSN 0020-2924)
Description: Publishes papers contributed by leading authorities from the maritime industry.

623.89 US
INSTITUTE OF NAVIGATION. PROCEEDINGS OF THE ANNUAL MEETING. a. $85 to non-members. Institute of Navigation, 1800 Diagonal Rd., Ste. 480, Alexandria, VA 22314-2840. **Document type:** proceedings.

623.8 II ISSN 0020-3475
INSTITUTION OF MARINE TECHNOLOGISTS. JOURNAL. (Text in English) 1956. s-a. Rs.7.50($1) Institution of Marine Technologists, c/o Ericson & Richards, 32 Nicol Rd., Ballard Estate, Bombay 400038, India. Ed. J.S. Bhatti. adv.; bk.rev. circ. 700.

363.12 FR ISSN 0223-534X
INSTRUCTIONS NAUTIQUES. (Avail. for specific areas worldwide) 1902. irreg. price varies. Service Hydrographique et Oceanographique de la Marine, 3 av. Octave Greard, 00300 Armees, France. TEL 98-03-09-17. FAX 98-47-11-42. TELEX HYDRO 940568 F. (Subscr. to: EPSHOM, BP 426, 29275 Brest Cedex, France) **Document type:** government publication.
Description: Provides mariners with all the information not provided on charts to ensure a safe journey.

387 UK ISSN 0260-1087
INTERNATIONAL BULK JOURNAL. 1981. m. £160($310) I B J Associates, Ranmore House, Ranmore Rd., Dorking, Surrey RH4 1HE, England. TEL 01306-740447. FAX 01306-883650. TELEX 859 597 1BJASS. Ed. Richard G. Peckham. adv.; bk.rev. circ. 6,000. **Indexed:** Fluidex. **Document type:** trade publication.
—BLDSC (4537.678000); SWETS.

387 UK
INTERNATIONAL CARGO HANDLING - BUYERS GUIDE TO MANUFACTURERS. 1984. a. International Cargo Handling Coordination Association, 71 Bondway, London SW8 1SH, England. TEL 0171-793-1022. FAX 0171-820-1703. **Document type:** trade publication.
Description: Lists services and equipment suppliers in the cargo handling industry.

385 FR
INTERNATIONAL COMMISSION OF MARITIME HISTORY. COLLOQUES. ACTES. 1957. irreg. Service d'Edition et de Vente des Publications de l'Education Nationale, 13 rue du Four, 75006 Paris, France. **Document type:** proceedings.

623.89 FR ISSN 0538-6128
INTERNATIONAL CONFERENCE ON LIGHTHOUSES AND OTHER AIDS TO NAVIGATION. REPORTS. (Includes: "Discussion Reports" which are in English; occasionally in French) 1929. every 4 yrs. Association Internationale de Signalisation Maritime - International Association of Lighthouse Authorities, 20 ter, rue Schnapper, 78100 Saint Germain en Laye, France. TEL 33-1-34-51-70-01. FAX 33-1-34-51-82-05. TELEX 695 499 F. Ed. Paul Ridgway. **Document type:** proceedings.
Description: Technical reports, some with photographs and-or drawings covering the conferences.

387 UK
INTERNATIONAL CONTAINER REVIEW. q. Contract Communications Ltd., Nestor House, Playhouse Yard, London EC4V 5EX, England. TEL 071-779-8714. FAX 071-779-8760. (back issues avail.) **Document type:** trade publication.

387 910.09 UK ISSN 0957-7696
INTERNATIONAL CRUISE AND FERRY REVIEW. 1989. q. £60. Contract Communications Ltd., Nestor House, Playhouse Yard, London EC4V 5EX, England. TEL 071-779-8714. FAX 071-779-8670. TELEX 927828-CONTCO-G. circ. 7,000. (back issues avail.) **Document type:** trade publication.
Description: Reviews developments affecting the international cruise and ferry industry.

387 UK
INTERNATIONAL FEDERATION OF SHIPMASTERS ASSOCIATIONS. ANNUAL REPORT. a. free. International Federation of Shipmasters Associations, 202 Lambeth Rd., London SE1 7JY, England. TEL 0171-261-0450. FAX 0171-401-3537. TELEX 934089 MARSOC G. Ed. Capt. Roger Clipsham. **Document type:** corporate report.

387 UK
INTERNATIONAL FEDERATION OF SHIPMASTERS ASSOCIATIONS. NEWSLETTER. q. International Federation of Shipmasters Associations, 202 Lambeth Rd., London SE1 7JY, England. TEL 0171-261-0450. FAX 0171-401-2537. TELEX 934089 MARSOC G. Ed. Capt. Roger Clipsham. **Document type:** newsletter.

387 971 CN ISSN 0843-8714
INTERNATIONAL JOURNAL OF MARITIME HISTORY. 1989. $45. Maritime Economic History Association, c/o Memorial University of Newfoundland, Maritime Studies Research Unit, St. John's, NF A1C 5S7, Canada. TEL 709-737-8424. FAX 709-737-8427. TELEX 016-4677. Eds. Lewis R. Fischer, Helge W. Nordvik. adv.; bk.rev. circ. 400. (also avail. in microform) **Document type:** academic/scholarly publication.
—BLDSC (4542.329500); Faxon.
Description: Publishes scholarly articles, notes, and reviews on maritime economic and social history.
Refereed Serial

623.8 387.2 UN
INTERNATIONAL MARITIME ORGANIZATION. INTERNATIONAL CODE FOR THE CONSTRUCTION AND EQUIPMENT OF SHIPS CARRYING LIQUEFIED GASES IN BULK. Abbreviated title: I G C Code. (Also avail. in Arabic, Chinese, French, Russian, and Spanish.) a. £14. International Maritime Organization, 4 Albert Embankment, London SE1 7SR, England. TEL 071-735-7611. FAX 071-587-3210. TELEX 23588.

623.8 387.2 UN
INTERNATIONAL MARITIME ORGANIZATION. TESTING AND EVALUATION OF LIFE-SAVING APPLIANCES. a. £8. International Maritime Organization, 4 Albert Embankment, London SE1 7SR, England. TEL 071-735-7611. FAX 071-587-3210. TELEX 23588.

INTERNATIONAL NAVIGATION ASSOCIATION. PROCEEDINGS OF ANNUAL MEETING. see *AERONAUTICS AND SPACE FLIGHT*

INTERNATIONAL NAVIGATION ASSOCIATION NEWSLETTER. see *TRANSPORTATION — Air Transport*

623.89 BE ISSN 1015-9568
INTERNATIONAL NAVIGATION CONGRESS. PAPERS. (Text in English or French; summaries in English or French) 1901. quadrennial, 28th, 1994, Seville. 13000 BEF. Permanent International Association of Navigation Congresses, WTC - Tour 3, Bld. Simon Bolivar 30, B-1210 Brussels, Belgium. TEL 32-2-2085216. FAX 32-2-2085215. **Document type:** proceedings.
Description: Publishes papers presented at the international congress.

388 623.89 BE
INTERNATIONAL NAVIGATION CONGRESS. PROCEEDINGS. (Text in English or French) 1961, 20th, Baltimore. quadrennial, 28th, 1994, Seville. Permanent International Association of Navigation Congresses, WTC - Tour 3, Bld. Simon Bolivar 30, B-1210 Brussels, Belgium. TEL 32-2-2085216. FAX 32-2-2085216. circ. 4,000. **Document type:** proceedings.

387 UK
INTERNATIONAL OFFSHORE CRAFT CONFERENCE. PROCEEDINGS.* irreg., 2nd 1977; 3rd 1979. $50. Thomas Reed Publications Ltd., 38 S. John St., London EC1M 4AY, England. Ed. Kenneth D. Troup. **Document type:** proceedings.

INTERNATIONAL SAFETYNET MANUAL. see *COMMUNICATIONS*

623.82 NE ISSN 0020-868X
CODEN: ISBPAS
INTERNATIONAL SHIPBUILDING PROGRESS. q. fl.260. Delft University Press, Stevinweg 1, 2628 CN Delft, Netherlands. TEL 31-15-2783254. FAX 31-15-2781661. **Document type:** academic/scholarly publication.
—BLDSC (4549.300000); Ei; SWETS; UnCover.

387 UK ISSN 0967-1056
INTERNATIONAL SHIPPING REVIEW; quarterly review of ship technology & services. 1989. q. £65 (overseas £75). Contract Communications Ltd., Nestor House, Playhouse Yard, London EC4V 5EX, England. TEL 071-779-8714. FAX 071-779-8760. Ed. Paul Richardson. adv. contact: Alex Karnaos. circ. 10,000. (back issues avail.) **Document type:** trade publication.
Formerly: Scandinavian and European Shipping Review (ISSN 0955-4408)

387 UK
INTERNATIONAL TUG CONVENTION PROCEEDINGS.* 1969. biennial. $85. Thomas Reed Publications Ltd., 38 S. John St., London EC1M 4AY, England. Ed. Ken Troup. adv. circ. 1,000. **Document type:** proceedings.

387.5 UK
INTERNATIONAL WHEAT COUNCIL. OCEAN FREIGHT RATES. a. £200($325) to non-members; members and subscribers to Grain Market Report £100 ($165) (effective Jun. 1995). International Wheat Council, One Canary Wharf, London E14 5AE, England. TEL 0171-513-1122. FAX 0171-712-0071. TELEX 8823241. charts; stat. **Document type:** directory.

INTERNATIONALE TRANSPORT ZEITSCHRIFT/JOURNAL POUR LE TRANSPORT INTERNATIONAL/INTERNATIONAL TRANSPORT JOURNAL-OVERSEAS DIGEST. see *TRANSPORTATION*

387 PL ISSN 0867-4299
INZYNIERIA MORSKA I GEOTECHNIKA. (Text in Polish; summaries and contents page in English) 1951. 6/yr. (Politechnika Gdanska, Wydzial Hydrotechniki) Wydawnictwo Czasopism i Ksiazek Technicznych SIGMA - NOT, Ul. Ratuszowa 11, P.O. Box 1004, 00-950 Warsaw, Poland. Ed. Eugeniusz Dembicki. adv.; bk.rev.; stat.; index. circ. 400. **Indexed:** Packag.Sci.Tech.
Former titles: Inzynieria Morska (ISSN 0138-0540); (until 1980): Technika i Gospodarka Morska (ISSN 0040-1137); Which was formed by the merger of (1948-1951): Gospodarka Morska (ISSN 0860-6129); (1946-1951): Technika Morza i Wybrzeza (ISSN 0860-6110)

IRISH SKIPPER. see *FISH AND FISHERIES*

623.89 DK ISSN 0106-5076
IS- OG BESEJLINGSFORHOLDENE I DE DANSKE FARVANDE I VINTEREN/ICE AND NAVIGATIONAL CONDITIONS IN THE DANISH WATERS DURING THE WINTER. 1932. a. DKK 42.70. Soefartsstyrelsen, Istjenesten, Vermundsgade 38 C, DK-2100 Copenhagen Oe, Denmark. illus.
—BLDSC (4582.300000).

TRANSPORTATION — SHIPS AND SHIPPING

623.89 550   IT   ISSN 0368-0649
CODEN: IUNNAS
ISTITUTO UNIVERSITARIO NAVALE, NAPOLI. ANNALI. (Text in English and Italian) 1932. a. free. Istituto Universitario Navale, Facolta di Scienze Nautiche, Via Ammiraglio Acton 38, 80133 Naples, Italy. TEL 81-5524342. FAX 81-5527126. Ed. Antonio Pugliano. circ. 600. (back issues avail.) **Document type:** academic/scholarly publication.
—BLDSC (1008.080000).
Description: Covers a wide variety of disciplines related to modern navigation and earth sciences.

ITALY. ISTITUTO NAZIONALE DI STATISTICA. STATISTICHE DEI TRASPORTI MARITTIMI. see *TRANSPORTATION — Abstracting, Bibliographies, Statistics*

386   RU   ISSN 0202-7879
TC1
ITOGI NAUKI I TEKHNIKI: VODNYI TRANSPORT. 1966. irreg., latest vol.14-15, 1989. 5.40 Rub. Vsesoyuznyi Institut Nauchno-Tekhnicheskoi Informatsii (VINITI), Baltiiskaya ul. 14, Moscow A-219, Russia. (Subscr. to: Mezhdunarodnaya Kniga, Dimitrova ul. 39, 113095 Moscow, Russia)
—BLDSC (0040.920000).

387   JA   ISSN 0913-5480
J A M R I REPORT. (Text in English) 1984. irreg. free. Japan Maritime Research Institute - Kaiji Sangyo Kenkyusho, Kaiun Bldg., 2-6-4 Hirakawa-cho, Chiyoda-ku, Tokyo 102, Japan. TEL 03-3265-5231. FAX 03-3265-5035. Ed. Kazuhiko Nomura. circ. 700. (back issues avail.) **Document type:** academic/scholarly publication.

387   JM
JAMAICA PORT NEWS. 1968. q. Port Authority, 15-17 Duke St., Kingston, Jamaica, W.I. TEL 809-922-0290. FAX 809-924-9437. TELEX 2386-PORTOPS. Ed. Jennifer McDonald. circ. 700.
Description: Highlights shipping and cruise line innovations. Lists promotions and appointments.

JANE'S FIGHTING SHIPS. see *MILITARY*

387   UK   ISSN 0960-7994
JANE'S HIGH-SPEED MARINE CRAFT. hydrofoils, builders of air-cushion vehicles and other civil and military vessels, civil operators, engineering components, associations. 1967. a. £190. Jane's Information Group, Sentinel House, 163 Brighton Rd., Coulsdon, Surrey CR5 2NH, England. TEL 0181-763-1030. FAX 0181-763-1006. TELEX 916907-JANES-G. E-mail: http://www.janes.com/janes.html. (U.S. & Can. order from: Dept. DSM, 1340 Braddock Pl., Ste. 300, Box 1436, Alexandria, VA 22314-1651) Ed. Stephen Phillips. adv.; index. **Document type:** directory.
●Also available on CD-ROM.
—BLDSC (4647.059000).
Former titles (until 1989): Jane's High-Speed Marine Craft and Air Cushion Vehicles (ISSN 0951-3124); (until 1986): Jane's Surface Skimmers (ISSN 0075-305X)

JANE'S INFORMATION UPDATE. FIGHTING SHIPS. see *MILITARY*

387   JA   ISSN 0447-3728
JAPAN. MARITIME SAFETY AGENCY. HYDROGRAPHIC DEPARTMENT. NOTICES TO MARINERS/SUIRO TSUHO. (Text in English) 1889. w. exchange basis. Kaijo Hoancho, Suirobu - Maritime Safety Agency, Hydrographic Department, 3-1, Tsukiji 5-chome, Chuo-ku, Tokyo 104, Japan. FAX 03-545-2885. TELEX 2522452 HDJODC J. Ed. Takahiro Sato. stat.

387 551.46 629.1   JA   ISSN 0388-7405
CODEN: NKGRDR
JAPAN INSTITUTE OF NAVIGATION. JOURNAL/NIHON KOKAI GAKKAI RONBUNSHU. (Text in English, Japanese; summaries in English) 1949. s-a. 3000 Yen($21) per no. Japan Institute of Navigation - Nihon Kokai Gakkai, c/o Tokyo University of Mercantile Marine, 2-1-6 Echujima, Koto-ku, Tokyo 135, Japan. Ed. H. Imazu. circ. 1,700. (back issues avail.) **Indexed:** INSPEC (1983-), JTA.
—BLDSC (4805.300000).

387   JA
JAPAN PORT INFORMATION. (Text in English) 1969. biennial. 20000 Yen. (Japan Association of Foreign Ship Agencies) Japan Press Ltd., C.P.O. Box 6, Tokyo 100-91, Japan. TEL 03-3404-5161. FAX 03-3423-2358. TELEX 242-5374 JPRESS J. (Subscr. to: 2-12-8 Kita Aoyama, Minato-ku, Tokyo 107, Japan) Ed. Yoshio Wada.

623.82 359   CC   ISSN 1000-7148
JIANCHUAN ZHISHI. (Text in Chinese) 1979. m. $0.40 per no. (Zhongguo Zaochuan Gongcheng Xuehui - Chinese Ship Engineering Society) Jianchuan Zhishi Bianjibu, 70 Xueyuan Nanlu, Beijing 100081, People's Republic of China. TEL 8315522. Ed. Yang Pu.

387   CC   ISSN 1001-5388
JIANGSU CHUANBO/JIANGSU SHIP. (Text in Chinese) 1980. q. Y8 (HK, Macao & Taiwan HK.$30; elsewhere $20). Jiangsu Sheng Chuanbo Sheji Yanjiusuo - Ship Design & Research Institute of Jiangsu Province, 37 Zhengdong Road, Zhenjiang, Jiangsu 212003, People's Republic of China. TEL 0511-4422493. FAX 0511-4424389. (Co-sponsor: Jiangsu Provincial Society of Naval Architecture and Marine Engineering) Ed. Zhu Minhu. adv.: B&W page Y2000, color page Y4000. circ. 3,000. **Document type:** academic/scholarly publication.
Refereed Serial

387   CC   ISSN 1000-4696
JIAOTONGBU SHANGHAI CHUANBO YUNSHU KEXUE YANJIUSUO XUEBAO. (Text in Chinese) s-a. Jiaotong-bu, Shanghai Chuanbo Yunshu Kexue Yanjiusuo - Ministry of Transportation. Shanghai Institute of Shipping Transportation Science, 200 Minsheng Lu, Shanghai 200135, People's Republic of China. TEL 8840438. Ed. Lu Fusheng.

JIB GEMS. see *SPORTS AND GAMES — Boats And Boating*

387.5   FR   ISSN 0983-0537
VK2   CODEN: JMMMED
JOURNAL DE LA MARINE MARCHANDE ET DU TRANSPORT MULTIMODAL. 1919. w. 3260 F. (foreign 3940 F.). Moreux, 190 bd. Haussmann, 75008 Paris, France. TEL 44-95-99-50. FAX 1-42-89-08-72. TELEX 290 131. adv.; bk.rev.; abstr.; charts; illus.; stat. circ. 14,500. **Indexed:** BMT, Excerp.Med., Key to Econ.Sci.
Incorporates: Marine Marchande (ISSN 0294-8508); **Former titles** (until 1986): Journal de la Marine Marchande (ISSN 0762-3151); (until 1982): Journal de la Marine Marchande et de la Navigation Aerienne (ISSN 0397-6467); (until 1938): Journal de la Marine Marchande (ISSN 0021-7786)

JOURNAL OF MARITIME LAW AND COMMERCE. see *LAW — Maritime Law*

623.8   UK   ISSN 0373-4633
VK1   CODEN: JONVAL
JOURNAL OF NAVIGATION. 1947. 3/yr. £112($198) (effective 1996). (Royal Institute of Navigation) Cambridge University Press, Edinburgh Bldg., Shaftesbury Rd., Cambridge CB2 2RU, England. TEL 01223-312393. FAX 01223-315052. (N. American addr.: Cambridge University Press, Journals Dept., 40 W. 20th St., New York, NY 10011. TEL 212-924-3900. FAX 212-691-3239) Ed. J.F. Kemp. adv.; bk.rev.; charts; illus.; maps; index, cum.index every 15 yrs. (back issues avail.) **Indexed:** BMT, Br.Tech.Ind., Curr.Cont., Deep Sea Res.& Oceanogr.Abstr., Ergon.Abstr., Excerp.Med., Fluidex, Geo.Abstr., INSPEC, Int.Aerosp.Abstr., Ocean.Abstr., Pollut.Abstr. **Document type:** academic/scholarly publication.
—BLDSC (5021.320000); Ei; Faxon; Genuine Article; SWETS; UMI; UnCover. **CCC.**
Formerly: Institute of Navigation. Journal (ISSN 0020-3009)
Description: Presents papers on every aspect of navigation - air, land, sea, and space - and papers on every type - scientific, historical, and narrative.

623.87   UK
JOURNAL OF OFFSHORE TECHNOLOGY. 4/yr. £40 to non-members. (Institute of Marine Engineers) Marine Management Holdings Ltd., The Memorial Bldg., 76 Mark Ln., London EC3R 7JN, England. TEL 44-71-481-8493. FAX 44-71-488-1854. (Subscr. in N. America to: Learned Information Inc., 143 Old Marlton Pike, Medford, NJ 08055-8750. TEL 609-654-6266. FAX 609-654-4309) **Document type:** trade publication.
—PADDS.
Description: Informs senior offshore marine engineers of the latest technological developments in the industry and of the international context in which they increasingly have to plan and operate.

623.8   US   ISSN 8756-1417
JOURNAL OF SHIP PRODUCTION. 1985. q. $65 (foreign $75). Society of Naval Architects and Marine Engineers, 601 Pavonia Ave., Jersey City, NJ 07306-2907. TEL 201-798-4800. FAX 201-798-4975. illus.; index. circ. 1,750. **Document type:** academic/scholarly publication.
—BLDSC (5064.350000); Ei; Faxon; UnCover.
Description: Contains technical papers addressing the problems of shipyard techniques and production of merchant and naval ships.

623.8   US   ISSN 0022-4502
VM1   CODEN: JSRHAR
JOURNAL OF SHIP RESEARCH. 1957. q. $80 (foreign $90). Society of Naval Architects and Marine Engineers, 601 Pavonia Ave., Jersey City, NJ 07306-2907. TEL 201-798-4800. FAX 201-798-4975. charts; illus.; stat.; index. circ. 2,800. **Indexed:** Appl.Mech.Rev., BMT, Curr.Cont., Eng.Ind., Fluidex, Ocean.Abstr., Pollut.Abstr., Sh.& Vib.Dig. **Document type:** academic/scholarly publication.
—BLDSC (5064.400000); Ei; Faxon; SWETS; UnCover. **CCC.**
Description: Presents techical papers on applied research in hydrodynamics, propulsion, ship motions, structures and vibrations.

387   PK
K P T NEWS BULLETIN. (Text in English) 1966. fortn. Rs.2.40 per no. Karachi Port Trust, Post Box 4725, Pakistan. TEL 201305. FAX 2415567. TELEX 2739 KPT PK. Ed. Kafil Ahmed Khan. charts; illus.; stat. circ. 2,000.

387   JA   ISSN 0286-9152
KAIJI SANGYO KENKYUSHOHO/JAPAN MARITIME RESEARCH INSTITUTE. BULLETIN. (Text in Japanese) 1966. m. 10500 Yen. Japan Maritime Research Institute - Kaiji Sangyo Kenkyujo, Kaiun Bldg., 2-6-4 Hirakawa-cho, Chiyoda-ku, Tokyo 102, Japan. TEL 03-3265-5231. FAX 03-3265-5035. Ed. Kazuhiko Nomura. bk.rev.; index. circ. 1,300. (back issues avail.) **Document type:** bulletin.
Description: Journal of shipping, shipbuilding and port research.

KAIJO HOANCHO. SUIROBU KANSOKU HOKOKU. EISEI SOKUCHI HEN/DATA REPORT OF HYDROGRAPHIC OBSERVATIONS. SERIES OF SATELLITE GEODESY. see *EARTH SCIENCES — Geophysics*

623.82 629.1   JA
KAIJO JIEITAI KANTEI TO KOKUKISHU/J.M.S.D.F. SHIPS AND AIRCRAFT. (Text in Japanese) 1967. a. 800 Yen. Kaijo Jiei Shinbunsha, 11-4, Roppongi 4-chome, Minato-ku, Tokyo 106, Japan.

387   JA   ISSN 0022-7803
KAIUN/SHIPPING. (Text in Japanese) 1922. m. 14,400 Yen. Japan Shipping Exchange, Inc. - Nihon Kaiun Shukaijo, Mitsuirokugokan 3-16 Muromachi 2-chome, Nihonbashi, Chuo-ku, Tokyo, Japan. FAX 81-3-3279-2785. TELEX 02222140 SHIPEX. Ed. Tadashi Inoue. adv.; bk.rev.; stat.; index. circ. 8,000. **Document type:** trade publication.

KAIYO KOGAKU SHINPOJUMU/OCEAN ENGINEERING SYMPOSIUM. see *EARTH SCIENCES — Oceanography*

623.82   JA
KAKI KOZA ATARASHII ZOZENGAKU/SUMMER SEMINAR ON NEW TOPICS IN NAVAL ARCHITECTURE. (Text in Japanese) a. Nihon Zosen Gakkai - Society of Naval Architects of Japan, 15-16, Toranomon 1-chome, Minato-ku, Tokyo 105, Japan.

TRANSPORTATION — SHIPS AND SHIPPING

623.82　　　JA　　ISSN 0919-7591
KANSAI ZOSEN KYOKAI KOEN RONBUNSHU/KANSAI SOCIETY OF NAVAL ARCHITECTS. PREPRINTS OF MEETING. (Text in English, Japanese; summaries in English) 2/yr. Kansai Zosen Kyokai - Kansai Society of Naval Architects, c/o Osaka Daigaku Kogakubu Senpaku-Kaiyou Kyoshitsu, 2-1, Yamadaoka, Suita-shi, Osaka 565, Japan. TEL 06-879-7593. FAX 06-878-5364. E-mail: KSNAJ@naoe.eng.os ka-u.ac.jp.
Formerly (until 1993): Kansai Zosen Kyokai Koenkai Ronbun Maezuri.

623.82　　　JA　　ISSN 0389-9101
VM298.5
KANSAI ZOSEN KYOKAISHI/KANSAI SOCIETY OF NAVAL ARCHITECTS. JOURNAL. (Text in English, Japanese; summaries in English) 1912. 2/yr. 5000 Yen. Kansai Zosen Kyokai, c/o Osaka Daigaku Kogakubu Senpaku-Kaiyou Kyoshitsu, 2-1, Yamadaoka, Suita-shi, Osaka 565, Japan. TEL 06-879-7593. FAX 06-878-5364. E-mail: KSNAJ@naoe.eng.os ka-u.ac.jp.
—BLDSC (4810.300000).

387.164　　　BG
KARNAPHULI SHIPPING NEWS. (Text in English) 1977. s-w. 88 Ghat Farhadbag, Kazem Ali Rd., Chittagong 4000, Bangladesh. TEL 31-220366. FAX 880-31-225204. TELEX 66483 RAS BJ. Ed. F. Karim. circ. 10,000.

387.5　　　UK
KEY NOTE REPORT: PASSENGER SHIPPING. Variant title: Passenger Shipping. irreg. £185. Key Note Publications Ltd., Field House, 72 Oldfield Rd., Hampton, Middlesex TW12 2HQ, England. TEL 0181-783-0755. FAX 0181-783-1720.
Document type: trade publication.
●Also available online.
Also available on CD-ROM.

387　　　DK　　ISSN 0023-2629
KOEBENHAVNS HAVNEBLAD/PORT OF COPENHAGEN REVIEW. (Text in Danish; summaries in English) 1948. 10/yr. free. Faellesrepraesentationen for Funktionaerer ved Koebenhavns Havnevaesen, Nordre Toldbod 7, Postboks 2083, 1013 Copenhagen K, Denmark. TEL 33 14 43 40, local 310. FAX 33-93-23-40. Eds. John Pri, Per Hagelund. adv.; bk.rev.; illus.; circ. 4,400 (controlled).
Description: Features articles and news items related to the Port of Copenhagen and its role in international commerce. Includes timetables of scheduled departures from the port.

387　　　GW　　ISSN 0075-6474
KOEHLERS FLOTTENKALENDER. JAHRBUCH FUER SCHIFFAHRT UND HAEFEN. 1901. a. DM.22.50. Koehlers Verlagsgesellschaft mbH, Striepenweg 31, 21147 Hamburg, Germany. TEL 040-79713322. FAX 040-79713324. adv.; bk.rev.; abstr.; charts; illus.; stat. circ. 20,000. Document type: trade publication.

387　　　JA　　ISSN 0450-660X
KOKAI/NAVIGATION. (Text in Japanese; titles, authors in English) 1954. q. 2000 Yen($14) per no. Japan Institute of Navigation - Nihon Kokai Gakkai, c/o Tokyo Institute of Mercantile Marine, 2-1-6 Echujima, Koto-ku, Tokyo 135, Japan. Ed. K. Ohtus. circ. 1,900. (back issues avail.) Indexed: INSPEC (1984-), JTA.
—BLDSC (6067.100000).

KONKYLIEN. see WOMEN'S INTERESTS

387　　　DK　　ISSN 0107-3109
KONTAKTUDVALGET FOR DANSK MARITIM HISTORIE- OG SAMFUNDSFORSKNING. AARSBIBLIOGRAFI.* 1979. a. DKK 25. Kontaktudvalget for Dansk Maritim Historie- og Samfundsforskning, Copenhagen, Denmark.
Formerly (until 1980): Aarsbibliografi for Kontaktudvalget for Dansk Maritim Historie- og Samfundsforskning (ISSN 0903-5230)

623.8 386　　　BU
KORABOSTROENE I KORABOPLAVANE/SHIPBUILDING AND SHIPPING. (Text in Bulgarian; summaries in English) 1956. m. $11. Ministerstvo na Transporta, Sofia, Bulgaria. (Dist. by: Hemus, 6, Rouski Blvd., 1000 Sofia, Bulgaria) (Co-sponsor: Bulgaria. Ministerstvo na Mashinostroeneto i Metalurgiiata) Ed. S. Popov. circ. 2,017. Indexed: BMT.

387　　　KO
KOREA SHIPPING GAZETTE. (Text in English, Korean) 1971. w. 34000 Won($550) (Korea Maritime Research Institute) Korea Shipping Gazette Co., Ltd., 43-1 Tongeni-dong, Jongro-ku, C.P.O. Box 3198, Seoul, S. Korea. Ed. Jong Ok Lee. adv.; bk.rev.; illus. circ. 5,000.

627.2　　　JA
KOWAN GIJUTSU KENKYUJO. GAIDO/PORT AND HARBOUR RESEARCH INSTITUTE. GUIDE. irreg. exchange basis. Un'yu-sho, Kowan Gijutsu Kenkyujo - Ministry of Transportation, Port and Harbour Research Institute, 1-1, 3-chome, Nagase, Yokosuka, Kanagawa 239, Japan. illus. Indexed: Geotech.Abstr.
Formerly: Port and Harbour Technical Research Institute. Guide.

387　　　US
LAKE BOATS. 1965. a. $8.50. Freshwater Press, Inc., 1700 E. 13th St., Ste. 3R-E, Cleveland, OH 44114. TEL 216-241-0373.

386.5　　　US　　ISSN 0075-7748
HE564.A4
LAKE CARRIERS' ASSOCIATION. ANNUAL REPORT. 1885. a. $20. Lake Carriers' Association, 915 Rockefeller Bldg., Cleveland, OH 44113-1383. TEL 216-621-1107. FAX 216-241-8262. Ed. Glen G. Nekvasil. index. circ. 1,500. Document type: corporate report.

387.5　　　IT　　ISSN 0024-032X
LEGA NAVALE. 1897. 9/yr. L.27000 to non-members; foreign L.48000. Lega Navale Italiana, Via 24 Maggio 11, 00187 Rome, Italy. TEL 39-6-6780017. FAX 39-6-6784471. Ed. Claudio Ressmann. adv.; B&W page L.500000. bk.rev.; illus.; stat. circ. 35,000.
Description: Covers the merchant marine.

LETTRE CONFIDENTIELLE DES TRANSPORTS. see TRANSPORTATION — Air Transport

287　　　UK
LIBERIAN SHIPPING JOURNAL. 1957. m. Arthur H. Thrower Ltd., 44-46 S. Ealing Rd., London W5, England. Ed. A. Thrower. adv.

623.8　　　UK　　ISSN 0308-7441
LIFEBOAT INTERNATIONAL. 1975. a. Royal National Lifeboat Institution, West Quay Rd., Poole, Dorset BH15 1HZ, England. (Co-sponsor: International Lifeboat Federation) Ed. Edward Wake-Walker.
Document type: bulletin.
—BLDSC (5208.965600).

387 662　　　UK　　ISSN 0305-1803
HE566.T3
LIQUID GAS CARRIER REGISTER. (Monthly and quarterly updates avail.) 1966. a. £99($160) (outside Europe £106 ($170)); q. diskettes £300 ($480) (effective 1995). Clarkson Research Studies, 12 Camomile St., London EC3A 7BP, England. TEL 0171-283-8955. FAX 0171-623-0539. TELEX 881 2927 CLTNK G. charts; stat. (also avail. in diskette format) Document type: directory.
Description: Lists liquid gas carrier ships by name; also includes ship size and weight, age, capacity, and other technical characteristics.

387　　　UK　　ISSN 0260-7387
HE565.A3
LIST OF SHIPOWNERS. 1955. a. $214. Lloyd's Register of Shipping, 71 Fenchurch St., London EC3M 4BS, England. TEL 0171-709-9166. (Subscr. in the U.S. to: Lloyd's Register of Shipping, 17 Battery Pl., New York, NY 10004) Document type: directory.
Description: Lists approximately 40,000 shipowners, managers and managing agents: addresses, telephone, telex and fax numbers, and fleet lists.

363.12　　　FR
LISTE DES SIGNAUX DISTINCTIFS ET INDICATIFS INTERNATIONAUX DES STATIONS FRANCAISES (NAVIRES, STATIONS TERRESTRES). 1941. a. 278 F. (effective 1995). Service Hydrographique et Oceanographique de la Marine, 3 av. Octave Greard, 00300 Armees, France. TEL 98-03-09-17. FAX 98-47-11-42. TELEX HYDRO 940568 F. (Subscr. to: EPSHOM, B.P. 426, 29275 Brest Cedex, France) Ed.Bd. circ. 1,500. (also avail. in magnetic tape) Document type: government publication.
Description: Informs sea captains of standard marine signals.

387.2　　　BE
LISTE OFFICIELLE DES NAVIRES DE MER BELGES ET DE LA FLOTTE DE LA FORCE NAVALE. a. Administration des Affaires Maritimes et de la Navigation, 104 rue d'Arlon, 1040 Brussels, Belgium. TEL 32-2-233-12-11. FAX 32-2-230-30-02. TELEX 61880 VERTRA B. illus. Document type: government publication.

387　　　UK
LLOYD'S A S E A N SHIPPING DIRECTORY. (Association of South East Asian Nations) a. $70. Lloyd's of London Press Ltd., Sheepen Pl., Colchester, Essex CO3 3LP, England. TEL 01206-772277. FAX 01206-46273. TELEX 987321 LLOYDS G. (U.S. addr.: Lloyd's of London Press Inc., 611 Broadway, Ste. 523, New York, NY 10012. TEL 212-529-9500) adv.; tr.lit. (back issues avail.) Document type: directory.

387　　　UK
LLOYD'S INTERNATIONAL MARINE EQUIPMENT GUIDE (YEAR). a. $160. Lloyd's of London Press Ltd., Sheepen Pl., Colchester, Essex CO3 3LP, England. TEL 01206-772277. FAX 01206-46273. TELEX 987321 LLOYDS G. (U.S. subscr. to: Lloyd's of London Press Inc., 611 Broadway, Ste. 308, New York, NY 10012. TEL 212-529-9500) Ed. Suzanne Hooke. adv. Document type: directory.
Formerly (until 1988): Lloyd's Marine Equipment Guide (ISSN 0268-3253)
Description: For international buyers and sellers of marine and offshore equipment and services. Provides worldwide list of marine equipment manufacturers available. Contains more than 40,000 product entries and 6,300 company listings.

387 368.2　　　UK　　ISSN 0144-820X
LLOYD'S LIST INTERNATIONAL. Key Title: Lloyd's List. 1734. 6/w. (Mon.-Sat.). $1395. Lloyd's of London Press Ltd., Sheepen Pl., Colchester, Essex CO3 3LP, England. TEL 01206-772277. FAX 01206-46273. (U.S. subscr. to: 611 Broadway, Ste. 308, New York, NY 10012. TEL 212-529-9500) Ed. David Gilbertson. adv.; bk.rev. circ. 14,650. (also avail. in microfilm from RPI,WMP) Document type: newspaper.
Description: Covers shipping, insurance, energy, transportation and finance, with special reports on selected business topics.

387　　　HK
HE873
LLOYD'S LIST MARITIME ASIA. (Text in English) 1979. m. $130. Lloyd's of London Press (Far East) Ltd., 1101 Hollywood Centre, 233 Hollywood Rd., Hong Kong. TEL 854-3222. FAX 854-1538. (Subscr. in the U.K.: One Singer St., London EC2A 4LQ, England. TEL 0171-250-1500) Ed. Kevin Chinnery. adv. contact: Jonathan Hughes. adv.; charts; illus.; stat.; tr.lit. circ. 8,260. (back issues avail.) Document type: trade publication.
—BLDSC (5287.261300).
Incorporates: Intermodal Asia (ISSN 1015-2253);
Formerly: Lloyd's Maritime Asia (ISSN 1015-227X)

387　　　UK　　ISSN 0144-6681
LLOYD'S LOADING LIST. (Free supplements avail.) w. $995. Lloyd's of London Press Ltd., Sheepen Pl., Colchester, Essex CO3 3LP, England. TEL 01206-77227. FAX 01206-46273. TELEX 987321. (U.S. subscr. to: 611 Broadway, Ste. 308, New York, NY 10012. TEL 212-529-9500)
Description: Provides coverage of freighting services by sea, road, rail and air from the U.K. to more than 1,000 destinations in all parts of the world.

LLOYD'S MARITIME & COMMERCIAL LAW QUARTERLY. see LAW — Maritime Law

387　　　UK　　ISSN 0076-020X
G1060
LLOYD'S MARITIME ATLAS. 1951. biennial. $90. Lloyd's of London Press Ltd., Sheepen Pl., Colchester, Essex CO3 3LP, England. TEL 01206-772277. FAX 01206-46273. TELEX 987321 LLOYDS G. (U.S. subscr. to: 611 Broadway, Ste. 308, New York, NY 10012. TEL 212-529-9500) maps; index. circ. 14,000. Document type: trade publication, directory.
Description: Gives reference to more than 10,000 ports and shipping places around the world. Includes maps, economic information, distance tables, text and other shipping information.

TRANSPORTATION — SHIPS AND SHIPPING

387   UK   ISSN 0268-327X
HE951
LLOYD'S MARITIME DIRECTORY (YEAR); international shipping & shipbuilding directory. 1982. a. $265. Lloyd's of London Press Ltd., Sheepen Pl., Colchester, Essex CO3 3LP, England. TEL 01206-772277. FAX 01206-46273. TELEX 987321 LLOYDS G. (U.S. subscr. to: 611 Broadway, Ste. 308, New York, NY 10012. TEL 212-529-9500) Ed. Chris Emery. adv. **Document type:** directory.
—BLDSC (5287.275000).
Description: Provides names and addresses of more than 5,500 shipowners, managers and agents arranged in alphabetical order under countries, details of the 34,000 vessels under their control, with listings of maritime service industry firms, from shipbuilding to salvage.

LLOYD'S MARITIME LAW NEWSLETTER. see *LAW — Maritime Law*

387   UK   ISSN 0266-6189
LLOYD'S MONTHLY LIST OF LAID UP VESSELS. m. £550. Lloyd's of London Press Ltd., Sheepen Pl., Colchester, Essex CO3 3LP, England. TEL 01206-772277. FAX 01206-46273. TELEX 987321. (U.S. subscr. to: 611 Broadway, Ste. 308, New York, NY 10012. TEL 212-529-9500) Ed. C.J. Fairweather. circ. 260.
Description: Report the constantly changing record of vessels laid up, with analyses of the listed vessels by type, flag and age.

387   UK   ISSN 0952-5394
LLOYD'S NAUTICAL YEAR BOOK. 1892. a. $65. Lloyd's of London Press Ltd., Sheepen Pl., Colchester, Essex CO3 3LP, England. TEL 01206-772277. FAX 01206-46273. TELEX 987321 LLOYDS G. (U.S. subscr. to: 611 Broadway, Ste. 308, New York, NY 10012. TEL 212-529-9500) Ed. Paul Cuny. adv. circ. 10,000.
—BLDSC (5287.280000).
Former titles: Lloyd's Nautical Yearbook and Calendar; Lloyd's Calendar and Nautical Yearbook (ISSN 0076-0196).
Description: Presents information on shipping regulations, legislation, and statistics, for companies and individuals involved with shipping ashore or afloat.

387   US
LLOYD'S PASSENGER SHIPPING INTERNATIONAL. 1989. m. $395. Lloyd's of London Press, Inc., 611 Broadway, Ste. 308, New York, NY 10012-2608. TEL 212-529-9500. FAX 212-529-9826. Ed. Marilyn Green.
Description: Covers all practical aspects of the dynamic shipping industry. Combines worldwide cruise and ferry news with data on passenger shipping demand and supply, international rules and regulations, port developments, vessel sale and purchase.

387   UK   ISSN 0266-6197
LLOYD'S PORTS OF THE WORLD (YEAR). 1982. a. $260. Lloyd's of London Press Ltd., Sheepen Pl., Colchester, Essex CO9 3LP, England. TEL 01206-772277. FAX 01206-46273. TELEX 987321 LLOYDS G. (U.S. subscr. to: 611 Broadway, Ste. 308, New York, NY 10012. TEL 212-529-9500) Ed. Brian Pinchin. **Document type:** directory.
—BLDSC (5287.283000).
Description: Lists 2,700 ports worldwide, with name and address of the relevant port authority, approach hazards, and facilities for anyone involved in international trade.

387   UK   ISSN 0261-6688
LLOYD'S REGISTER OF CLASSED YACHTS. 1981. a. $50. Lloyd's Register of Shipping, 71 Fenchurch St., London EC3M 4BS, England. TEL 0171-709-9166. FAX 0171-488-4796. (Subscr. in the U.S. to: Lloyd's Register of Shipping, 17 Battery Pl., New York, NY 10004)
Supersedes: Lloyd's Register of Yachts.
Description: Provides details of all yachts classed with Lloyd's Register of Shipping.

LLOYD'S REGISTER OF SHIPPING. STATISTICAL TABLES. see *TRANSPORTATION — Abstracting, Bibliographies, Statistics*

387   UK   ISSN 0141-4909
HE565.A3
LLOYD'S REGISTER OF SHIPS. (In three volumes) 1764. a. (with m. supplements). $925. Lloyd's Register of Shipping, 71 Fenchurch St., London EC3M 4BS, England. TEL 0171-709-9166. (Subscr. in U.S. to: Lloyd's Register of Shipping, 17 Battery Pl., New York, NY 10004) **Document type:** directory.
Description: Provides information on more than 78,000 merchant ships, listed in alphabetical order by ship name.

387   UK   ISSN 0265-2455
VM12
LLOYD'S SHIP MANAGER. 1977. m. $275. Lloyd's of London Press Ltd., Sheepen Pl., Colchester, Essex CO3 3LP, England. TEL 01206-772277. FAX 01206-46273. TELEX 987321. (U.S. subscr. to: 611 Broadway, Ste. 308, New York, NY 10012. TEL 212-529-9500) Ed. Paul Gunton. adv.; bk.rev.; illus. circ. 8,500. **Indexed:** BMT, Fluidex. **Document type:** trade publication.
—BLDSC (5287.735000); SWETS; UMI.
Incorporates (in 1987): Shipping News International (ISSN 0800-9163); Which was formerly (1945-1984): Norwegian Shipping News (ISSN 0029-3709); Incorporates (1972-1984): Shipbuilding and Marine Engineering International (ISSN 0262-463X); Formerly: Nautical Review (ISSN 0309-6254).
Description: Provides monthly information service on all management, technical and operational aspects relating to the safe and profitable operation of ocean-going tonnage.

LLOYD'S SHIPPING CONNECTIONS. see *BUSINESS AND ECONOMICS — Trade And Industrial Directories*

387   UK   ISSN 0144-6673
LLOYD'S SHIPPING ECONOMIST. 1979. m. $995. Lloyd's of London Press Ltd., Sheepen Place, Colchester, Essex CO3 3LP, England. TEL 01206-772277. FAX 01206-46273. TELEX 987321 LLOYDS G. (U.S. subscr. to: 611 Broadway, Ste. 308, New York, NY 10012. TEL 212-529-9500) Ed. Deborah Seyman. **Document type:** trade publication.
—BLDSC (5287.743000); SWETS.
Description: Provides information, analysis and commentary on supply-and-demand factors in the international shipping markets.

387   UK   ISSN 0144-4549
LLOYD'S SHIPPING INDEX. 1882. d. $2095. Lloyd's of London Press Ltd., Sheepen Pl., Colchester, Essex CO3 3LP, England. TEL 01206-772277. FAX 01206-46273. TELEX 987321 LLOYDS G. (U.S. subscr. to: 611 Broadway, Ste. 308, New York, NY 10012. TEL 212-529-9500) Ed. T.C. Bird. circ. 5,500.
Description: Presents the current voyages, latest reported movements and vital particulars of 23,000 merchant ships, together with any casualty or other information reported.

387   UK
LLOYD'S SURVEY HANDBOOK. a. $85. Lloyd's of London Press Ltd., Sheepen Pl., Colchester, Essex CO3 3LP, England. TEL 01206-77227. FAX 01206-46273. TELEX 987321 LLOYDS G. (US subscr. to: 611 Broadway, Ste. 308, New York, NY 10012. TEL 212-529-9500) tr.lit. (back issues avail.) **Document type:** trade publication.
Description: References packing stowage, transportation, and commodity storage for cargo surveyors, loss adjusters, and insurers; also covers general causes of damage and problems associated with transporting goods, along with information about handling hazardous cargoes.

387   UK   ISSN 0144-4557
HE730
LLOYD'S VOYAGE RECORD. 1946. w. $2435. Lloyd's of London Press Ltd., Sheepen Pl., Colchester, Essex CO3 3LP, England. TEL 01206-772277. FAX 01206-46273. TELEX 987321 LLOYDS G. (U.S. subscr. to: 611 Broadway, Ste. 308, New York, NY 10012. TEL 212-529-9500) Ed. M.D.S. Rodger. adv. circ. 1,000. (also avail. in microfiche) **Document type:** trade publication.
Description: Records vessels' movements chronologically, providing details of the last four ports of call for tankers, six for bulk carriers and eight for dry cargo vessels.

LLOYD'S WEEKLY CASUALTY REPORTS. see *INSURANCE*

387   AT   ISSN 0815-0052
LOG. 1954. q. Aus.$20 (foreign Aus.$25). Nautical Association of Australia, G.P.O. Box 4114, Melbourne, Vic. 3001, Australia. TEL 03-609-3629. FAX 03-609-3318. Ed. W.G. Volum. adv.; bk.rev.; illus.; index. circ. 600. (back issues avail.)

LOG (CAMP SPRINGS). see *LABOR UNIONS*

387   SW
LOGGEN MAGAZINE. (Text in English and Swedish) 1981. 10/yr. SEK 150($7) Saellskapet foer Bogser och Passagerarfartyg, P.O. Box 7036, S-250 07 Helsingborg, Sweden. TEL 042-153648. FAX 153648. Ed. Lennart Hellstroem. adv.; bk.rev.; charts; illus. circ. 2,500.
Formerly: Loggen (ISSN 0280-8234).

387   UK   ISSN 0260-8839
LONDON PORT HANDBOOK (YEAR). 1981. a. £25. Compass Publications Ltd., Abbot House, Castle Acre, King's Lynn, Norfolk PE32 2BQ, England. TEL 01760-755783. FAX 01760-755782. Ed. James P. Moriarty. adv. circ. 6,000. **Document type:** directory.

387   SW   ISSN 0024-6328
LONGITUDE; tidskrift fraan de sju haven/magazine of the seven seas. (Text in Swedish) 1966. a. SEK 195. Carlstedt Foerlag AB, Artillerigatan 2, 114 51 Stockholm, Sweden. Ed. J.E. Carlstedt. charts; illus.

387   US   ISSN 0882-9004
HE745
M A R A D (YEAR). 1950. a. U.S. Maritime Administration, Washington, DC 20590. TEL 202-426-5812. (Subscr. to: Superintendent of Documents, U.S. Government Printing Office, Box 371954, Pittsburgh, PA 15250-7954. TEL 202-783-3238. FAX 202-512-2233) **Document type:** government publication.
Formerly: U.S. Maritime Administration. Annual Report (ISSN 0083-1670)
Description: Incorporates reports by the Congress on the following topics: acquisition of obsolete vessels in exchange for vessel trade-in credit; war-risk insurance activities; scrapping or removal of obsolete vessels owned by the U.S.; and U.S.-flag carriage of government-sponsored cargoes. Includes information on the state of the maritime industry, as well as other MARAD activities.

M A S T; for mailing and shipping professionals. (Mailing and Shipping Technology) see *COMMUNICATIONS — Postal Affairs*

387   SP
MADRID TRANS-PORT. 1983. a. 650 ptas. Publicaciones Men-Car, S.A., Paseo de Colon 24, 08002 Barcelona, Spain. TEL 93-301-5516. FAX 93-318-6645. Eds. Juan Cardona, Manuel Cardona. adv. circ. 15,000.

MALTA. CENTRAL OFFICE OF STATISTICS. SHIPPING AND AVIATION STATISTICS. see *TRANSPORTATION — Abstracting, Bibliographies, Statistics*

387   CL   ISSN 0047-5866
MAR. 1914. a. Liga Maritima de Chile, Errazurriz 471, Casilla 117-V, Valparaiso, Chile. TEL 255179. Dir. Alejandro Navarette Torres. adv.; charts; illus.; circ. 2,000. (controlled).

MARCOM; a business guide to the application of advanced electronics, information systems and computers in shipping. see *ENGINEERING — Computer Applications*

LE MARIN. see *FISH AND FISHERIES*

387   IT   ISSN 0025-309X
MARINA ITALIANA; rassegna delle industrie del mare. 1902. bi-m. L.80000 (foreign L.140000). (Associazione Italiana di Tecnica Navale) Silvio Basile Editore, Lungo Bisagno Istria, 34c, 16141 Genoa, Italy. TEL 852151. FAX 010-8355055. TELEX 272372. (Co-sponsor: Centro Studi Tecnica Navale) adv.: B&W page L.1200000, color page L.1800000; trim 190 x 257. bibl.; illus.; stat.; index. circ. 4,750. **Indexed:** BMT, C.I.S. Abstr.
—BLDSC (5373.600000).

387.5 IT ISSN 0025-3103
HE839
MARINA MERCANTILE. (Text in Italian; summaries in English and Italian) 1947. m. L.12000. Silvio Basile Editore, Lungo Bisagno Istria, 34c, 16141 Genoa, Italy. TEL 10-852-151. FAX 10-835-50-55. Ed. Ugo Marchese. adv.; bk.rev.; abstr.; bibl.; charts; illus.; pat.; stat.; tr.lit.; index. circ. 6,000. **Indexed:** BMT.

387 AT
MARINE BOARD OF HOBART. ANNUAL REPORT. 1858. a. free. Marine Board of Hobart, Franklin Wharf, Tas. 7000, Australia. TEL 61-02-351000. FAX 61-02-310693. TELEX MARHOB AA58319. Ed. H.C. Knoop. circ. 600. **Document type:** corporate report.

387 US ISSN 1059-2970
HE561
MARINE DIGEST AND TRANSPORTATION NEWS. 1922. m. $28 (foreign $70). Marine Publishing Inc., 1201 1st Ave. S., No. 200, Box 3905, Seattle, WA 98124. TEL 206-682-3607. FAX 206-682-4023. Ed. Alec Fisher. adv. contact: Jim Lengell. bk.rev. circ. 4,500. **Document type:** trade publication.
Formerly: Marine Digest (ISSN 0025-3197)
Description: Serves the maritime and shipping community primarily along the West Coast.

623.82 JA ISSN 0287-203X
MARINE ENGINEER. (Text in Japanese) 1962. m. 600 Yen per no. Japan Marine Engineers' Association - Nihon Senpaku Kikanshi Kyokai, 4-5, Kojimachi, Chiyoda-ku, Tokyo 102, Japan.

623.87 UK ISSN 0047-5955
VM1 CODEN: MRERBJ
MARINE ENGINEERS REVIEW. (Supplement avail.: Directory of Marine Diesel Engines (ISSN 0954-2604)) 1967. m. £55. (Institute of Marine Engineers) Marine Management Holdings Ltd., The Memorial Bldg., 76 Mark Ln., London EC3R 7JN, England. TEL 0171-481-8493. FAX 0171-488-1854. (Subscr. in N. America to: Learned Information, Inc., 143 Old Marlton Pike, Medford, NJ 08055-8750. TEL 609-654-6266. FAX 609-654-4309) Ed. John Butchers. adv.; bk.rev.; abstr.; charts; illus.; tr.lit.; index. circ. 15,504. **Indexed:** API Abstr., API Catal., API Hlth.& Environ., API Oil., API Pet.Ref., API Pet.Subst., API Transport., BMT, Br.Tech.Ind., Chem.Abstr., Energy Info.Abstr. (until 1994), Eng.Ind., Excerp.Med., Fluidex, ISMEC, Met.Abstr., Ocean.Abstr., Pollut.Abstr., World Alum.Abstr. **Document type:** trade publication.
—BLDSC (5375.260000); Ei; SWETS; UnCover. CCC.
Formerly (until 1971): Marine Engineers Journal (ISSN 0368-8364)
Description: Covers a wide variety of topics pertaining developments in ship design, shipping, world markets, and maritime banking.

623.87 UK ISSN 0954-2604
MARINE ENGINEERS REVIEW. DIRECTORY OF MARINE DIESEL ENGINES. Key Title: Directory of Marine Diesel Engines. (Supplement to: Marine Engineers Review (ISSN 0047-5955)) 1988. a. (Institute of Marine Engineers) Marine Management (Holdings) Ltd., The Memorial Bldg., 76 Mark Ln., London EC3R 7JN, England. TEL 44-71-481-8493. FAX 44-71-488-1854. TELEX 886841. (Subscr. in N. America to: Learned Information Inc., 143 Old Marlton Pike, Medford, NJ 08055. TEL 609-654-6266. FAX 609-654-4309) **Document type:** directory.

623.81 US ISSN 0882-1984
MARINE EQUIPMENT CATALOG. 1984. a. $65. Maritime Activity Reports Inc., 118 E. 25th St., New York, NY 10010. TEL 212-477-6700. Ed. Laura Ann Sciame. adv. circ. 12,000. **Document type:** catalog.

387 CN ISSN 0824-8729
VM470
MARINE EQUIPMENT DIRECTORY.* 1917. a. Can.$10. Canadian Marine Publications Ltd., 1434 St. Catherine St. W., Ste. 504, Montreal, PQ H3G 1R6, Canada. TEL 514-861-6715. FAX 514-861-0966. Ed. O. J. Silva. adv. **Document type:** directory.

387 AT ISSN 1320-5889
MARINE INDUSTRY NEWS; Australia's boating business magazine. m. Aus.$42 (foreign Aus.$115) (effective Feb. 1995). Yaffa Publishing Group, 17-21 Bellevue St., Surry Hills, N.S.W. 2010, Australia. TEL 61-2-271-2333. FAX 61-2-281-2750. Ed. Bob Wonders. adv.; B&W page Aus.$1360, color page Aus.$1830; trim 273 x 210. circ. 2,976. **Document type:** trade publication.
Description: For manufacturers, suppliers, distributors and retailers of pleasure boats, boating equipment and components and for marina operators throughout Australia.

MARINE INDUSTRY RETAILER. see BUSINESS AND ECONOMICS — Marketing And Purchasing

623.87 US ISSN 0897-0491
VM1
MARINE LOG. 1878. m. $35 (foreign $60). Simmons-Boardman Publishing Corporation, 345 Hudson St., New York, NY 10014. TEL 212-620-7200. (Addr. in Netherlands: Nijverheidsweg 46, 3340 Henrik Ido Ambacht, Netherlands) Ed. Nicholas Blenkey; Pub. Arthur J. McGinnis, Jr. adv.; bk.rev.; charts; illus.; stat.; tr.lit.; index. circ. 19,041. (also avail. in microform from UMI) **Indexed:** A.S.& T.Ind., Corros.Abstr., Curr.Cont., DM & T, Energy Info.Abstr., Eng.Ind, Environ.Abstr., Excerp.Med., Ocean.Abstr., Pollut.Abstr., PROMT, Risk Abstr. **Document type:** trade publication.
●Also available online. Vendor(s): Lexis-Nexis.
—BLDSC (5376.030000); CIS; Ei; Faxon; SWETS; UMI; UnCover. CCC.
Formerly (until 1987): Marine Engineering - Log (ISSN 0025-3219)
Description: Highlights shipbuilding and ship operations.

387 UK ISSN 0025-3243
MARINE NEWS. 1947. m. £20. World Ship Society, 28 Natland Rd., Kendal LA9 7LT, England. Ed. Michael Crowdy. adv.; bk.rev.; charts; illus.; index. circ. 4,200. (also avail. in microfiche; back issues avail.) **Document type:** newsletter.

623.8 UK ISSN 0143-3709
CODEN: MPRIEC
MARINE PROPULSION INTERNATIONAL. 1981. bi-m. £90($187) (overseas £101) (effective Sep. 1995). Argus Business Media Ltd., International Trade Publications (Subsidiary of: Argus Press Group), Queensway House, 2 Queensway, Redhill, Surrey RH1 1QS, England. TEL 01737-768611. FAX 01737-761989. TELEX 948669 TOPJNL G. Ed. Bill Thomson; Pub. Roy Greenslade. adv. contact: Richard Harris. illus. circ. 4,437. **Document type:** trade publication.
—SWETS.

387 355 GW ISSN 0025-3294
V3
MARINE-RUNDSCHAU.* 1890. m. DM.90. (Arbeitskreis fuer Wehrforschung) Bernard und Graefe Verlag, Karl-Mand-Str. 2, Postfach 2060, 5400 Koblenz, Germany. Ed. Juergen Friese. adv.; bk.rev.; charts; illus.; stat.; index. circ. 2,500. **Indexed:** Abstr.Mil.Bibl., Amer.Hist.& Life, Hist.Abstr.

387 623.82 US
MARINE SERVICE CENTER.* 1993. bi-m. Van Zevern Publications, Inc., 7800 N. Merrimac Ave., Niles, IL 60714-3426. adv.; B&W page $1500, color page $1250; trim 8 1/8 x 11 1/8. circ. 17,500. **Document type:** trade publication.

623.8 JA
MARINE STANDARDIZATION IN JAPAN.* (Text in Japanese) a. 1500 Yen. Nihon Senpaku Hyojun Kyokai, Nihon Zosen Gijutsu Senta Biru, 3-8, Mejiro 1-chome, Toshima-ku, Tokyo 105, Japan.
Formerly: Marine Standardization.

623.8 US ISSN 0025-3316
VM1 CODEN: MARTA4
MARINE TECHNOLOGY. 1964. q. $70 to non-members (foreign $80). Society of Naval Architects and Marine Engineers, 601 Pavonia Ave., Jersey City, NJ 07306-2907. TEL 201-798-4800. FAX 201-798-4975. charts; illus.; index. circ. 10,350. **Indexed:** A.S.& T.Ind., API Abstr., API Catal., API Hlth.& Environ., API Oil., API Pet.Ref., API Pet.Subst., API Transport., BMT, Chem.Abstr., Curr.Cont., Eng.Ind., Excerp.Med., Geo.Abstr., Ocean.Abstr., Pollut.Abstr., Risk Abstr. **Document type:** academic/scholarly publication.
—BLDSC (5378.500000); Ei; Faxon; Genuine Article; SWETS; UnCover. CCC.
Description: Includes selected meeting papers and news about the society.
Refereed Serial

387 GW ISSN 0172-8539
MARINEFORUM. 1925. 10/yr. DM.97. Verlag E.S. Mittler und Sohn GmbH, Striepenweg 31, 21147 Hamburg, Germany. TEL 040-79713322. FAX 040-79713324. Eds. Capt. Z. See, Erhard Rosenkranz. adv.; bk.rev.; abstr.; charts; illus.; stat. circ. 7,000. **Document type:** trade publication.

387 623.8 NE
MARITIEM NEDERLAND; scheepvaart - techniek - marine - havens - offshore. 1911. 9/yr. fl.55 to members; non-members fl.62.50. (Koninklijke Nederlandse Vereniging Onze Vloot) Ten Brink Meppel B.V., Postbus 1064, 7940 KB Meppel, Netherlands. TEL 31-5220-54646. FAX 31-5220-55517. (Editorial addr.: Prins Mauritslaan 2, flat 46, 2012 SP Haarlem, Netherlands. TEL 31-23-286799. FAX 31-23-341801) Eds. W. de Bruin, W.C. Mabesoone. adv. contact: H. Zevenberg. bk.rev.; illus. circ. 6,500.
Formed by the 1994 merger of: Maritiem (ISSN 0927-6637); Which was formerly (1984-1991): Maritiem Gezien (ISSN 0927-6645) & Zeewezen (ISSN 0165-8182); Which was formerly: Ons Zeewezen (ISSN 0030-2791)
Description: Examines the Navy, the Merchant Navy, shipbuilding, national and international harbor services and offshore activities.

387 SP
MARITIMAS INFORMACION COMERCIAL. 1948. d. 28500 ptas. Diario Maritimas, S.A., Paseo de Colon 24, 08002 Barcelona, Spain. TEL 34-93-301-5646. FAX 34-93-318-6645. Eds. Juan Cardona, Manuel Cardona. adv.; illus. circ. 8,700. (back issues avail.) **Document type:** newspaper.

387 343.09 US ISSN 0894-6698
KF1097
MARITIME ADVISOR ARBITRATION AWARD DIGEST. 1981. m. $295. Maritime Advisory Services Inc., 10 Signal Rd., Stamford, CT 06902. TEL 203-975-7070. FAX 203-975-7002. Ed. George Tsagaris. circ. 250. (back issues avail.)
Description: North American arbitration decisions affecting the shipping industry.

387 343.09 US
MARITIME ADVISOR MARINE OPERATIONS REPORTER. 1981. m. $250. Maritime Advisory Services Inc., 10 Signal Rd., Stamford, CT 06902-7909. TEL 203-975-7070. FAX 203-975-7002. Ed. Sherry Stossel. circ. 200. (back issues avail.)
Description: Professional guide to U.S. state and federal regulations affecting ship operations and navigation.

387.5 US
MARITIME ASSOCIATION OF THE PORT OF NEW YORK - NEW JERSEY. MARITIME NEWSLETTER. 1973. fortn. membership. Maritime Association of the Port of New York - New Jersey, 17 Battery Place, Ste. 1115, New York, NY 10004. adv.; bk.rev.; charts; illus.; stat. circ. 1,500. **Document type:** newsletter.
Formerly: Maritime Association of the Port of New York. Newsletter; Supersedes: Maritime Exchange Bulletin (ISSN 0025-3421)

623 US
MARITIME DIRECTORY AND MARINE INDUSTRY CENSUS. a. $145. Maritime Directory Reports Inc., 118 E. 25th St., New York, NY 10010. TEL 212-477-6700. FAX 212-254-6271. **Document type:** directory.

6428 TRANSPORTATION — SHIPS AND SHIPPING

387   **UK**   **ISSN 0264-6420**
HE561
MARITIME GUIDE. 1984. a. $220. Lloyd's Register of Shipping, 71 Fenchurch St., London EC3M 4BS, England. TEL 0171-709-9166. (U.S. subscr. to: Lloyd's Register of Shipping, 17 Battery Pl., New York, NY 10004) Document type: directory.
—BLDSC (5381.352950).
    Formerly: Appendix (ISSN 0261-1821)
    Description: Covers port facilities (wet and dry docks) worldwide.

MARITIME HANDBOOK OF SOUTHERN AFRICA. see ENGINEERING — Industrial Engineering

MARITIME INFORMATION REVIEW. see TRANSPORTATION — Abstracting, Bibliographies, Statistics

387   **UK**   **ISSN 0957-7009**
MARITIME JOURNAL. 1987. m. £47 (Europe £55; rest of world £60). Maritime Journal Ltd., The Old Mill, Lower Quay, Fareham, Hants. PO16 0RA, England. TEL 01329-825335. FAX 01329-825330. Ed. Peter Moth; Pub. Peter Moth. adv.: B&W page £795, color page £1050; adv. contact: Ian Caldwell. circ. 6,017. Document type: trade publication.
    Description: Trade guide to inshore, ports and harbors as well as short sea operations across Europe.

387   **GR**
MARITIME MONITOR; international shipping & trade weekly. 1993. w. $150 throughout Europe (U.K. £100) (N. America $150; S. America and S. Africa $170; Asia $180; Australia and New Zealand $200) (effective 1996). Rigas Publishing Co. S.A., P.O. Box 80076, 185 10 Piraeus, Greece. circ. 2,468. Document type: trade publication.
    Description: Contains shipping news of interest to shipowners, shipping managers, and executives in banking, insurance, shipbuilding, and engineering.

MARITIME NEWSLETTER. see LABOR UNIONS

MARITIME PERSONAL INJURY REPORT. see LAW — Maritime Law

387   **UK**   **ISSN 0308-8839**
HC92
MARITIME POLICY AND MANAGEMENT. 1973. q. £242($399) (effective 1996). Taylor & Francis Ltd., Rankine Rd., Basingstoke, Hants. RG24 8PR, England. TEL 44-1256-840366. FAX 44-1256-479438. TELEX 858540. E-mail: info@tandf.co.uk. (Subscr. in N. America to: Taylor & Francis Inc., 1900 Frost Rd., Ste. 101, Bristol, PA 19007-1598. TEL 800-821-8312. FAX 215-785-5515) Eds. J. Evans, R. Goss. adv.; bk.rev. (back issues avail.) **Indexed:** Asian-Pac.Econ.Lit., BMT, C.I.S. Abstr., C.R.E.J., Deep Sea Res.& Oceanogr.Abstr., Fluidex, Geo.Abstr., IDA, Mar.Aff.Bibl., Ocean.Abstr., Pollut.Abstr. Document type: trade publication.
—BLDSC (5381.358000); SWETS; UnCover. CCC.
    Formerly: Maritime Studies and Management.
    Description: Emphasizes organizational, economic, sociolegal, and management topics at port, community, shipping company, and shipboard levels. Refereed Serial

623.8 387   **US**   **ISSN 0025-3448**
VM1
MARITIME REPORTER AND ENGINEERING NEWS. 1939. m. $44. Maritime Activity Reports Inc., 118 E. 25th St., New York, NY 10010. TEL 212-477-6700. Ed. Charles O'Malley. adv.; bk.rev.; illus. circ. 25,000. **Indexed:** Tr.& Indus.Ind.

387   **US**
MARITIME RESEARCH CHARTER NEWSLETTER. 1953. w. $250 (foreign $270). Maritime Research, Inc., Box 805, Parlin, NJ 08859. TEL 908-727-8040. FAX 908-727-0243. TELEX 4993951. Ed. Jay Lillianthal. adv.; index. circ. 5,000. (back issues avail.) Document type: newsletter.
    Description: Contains a listing of all charter fixtures reported worldwide in the tramp charter market.

387 639.2   **AT**   **ISSN 0726-6472**
MARITIME STUDIES. 1983. bi-m. Aus.$50 to individuals (foreign Aus.$70); institutions Aus.$100 (foreign Aus.$120); corporates Aus.$300 (foreign Aus.$320) (includes Occasional Papers in Maritime Affairs) (effective 1994). Australian Centre for Maritime Studies, P.O. Box E20, Queen Victoria Terrace, Canberra, A.C.T. 2600, Australia. TEL 61-6-295-0056. FAX 61-6-295-3367. Ed. R.J. Sherwood. bk.rev. circ. 350. (back issues avail.) **Indexed:** Aus.P.A.I.S.
    Description: Covers all aspects of marine affairs relevant to Australia and its region.

387   **AT**   **ISSN 0025-3464**
MARITIME WORKER. 1938. 11/yr. Aus.$16. Waterside Workers Federation of Australia, 2nd Floor, 365-375 Sussex St., Sydney, N.S.W. 200, Australia. TEL 02-267-9134. FAX 02-261-3481. Ed. T. Bull. adv.; bk.rev.; play rev.; illus.; stat. circ. 7,000. (tabloid format)
    Description: Union magazine covering stevedoring and industrial issues.

MARPOL 73 - 78 AMENDMENTS. see CONSERVATION

623.8   **SW**   **ISSN 0025-4622**
MASKINBEFAELET. 1891. 8/yr. SEK 190. Svenska Maskinbefaelsfoerbundet - Swedish Engineer Officers' Association, P.O. Box 12100, S-102 23 Stockholm, Sweden. TEL 46-8-693-56-21. FAX 46-8-693-55-50. TELEX 14364. Ed. Benkt Lundgren. adv.; charts; illus.; index; circ. 4,283 (controlled).
    Former titles (until 1944): Maskinbefaelsfoerbundets Tidskrift; (until 1928): Tidskrift foer Maskinister.
    Description: Technical and trade magazine for Swedish marine engineers.

MASTER, MATE & PILOT. see LABOR UNIONS

387.2   **US**   **ISSN 0025-6129**
MAY DAY PICTORIAL NEWS;* the west coast's best monthly maritime magazine. 1961. m. $11. (May Day Pictorial News) Wion Publications, 3846 Mountcliffe Ct., San Jose, CA 95136-1429. TEL 415-947-2138. Ed. Helen Wion. adv.; tr.lit.; circ. 5,298 (controlled).
    Description: News, articles, and announcements on issues that affect maritime activities on the West Coast.

387 340   **UK**   **ISSN 0957-5855**
MEDITERRANEAN SHIPPING DIRECTORY. 1989. biennial. £55. Lloyd's of London Press Ltd., Sheepen Pl., Colchester, Essex CO3 3LP, England. TEL 01206-772115. FAX 01206-772888. Ed. Chris Emery. adv. contact: Jacqueline Raven. Document type: directory.

MELBOURNE PORT AND SHIPPING HANDBOOK. see BUSINESS AND ECONOMICS — Trade And Industrial Directories

MERCHANT SHIPBUILDING RETURN. see TRANSPORTATION — Abstracting, Bibliographies, Statistics

623.82   **JA**   **ISSN 0911-5234**
MESSAGE. (Text in Japanese) 1985. q. Mitsui Zosen K.K. - Mitsui Engineering and Shipbuilding Co., Ltd., 6-4, Tsukiji 5-chome, Chuo-ku, Tokyo 102, Japan.

623.8   **JA**   **ISSN 0026-6825**
CODEN: MIZGAR
MITSUI ZOSEN TECHNICAL REVIEW/MITSUI ZOSEN GIHO. (Text in Japanese; summaries in English, Japanese) 1952. q. free to qualified organizations or personnel. Mitsui Engineering & Shipbuilding Co., Ltd., Corporate Technical Research & Development Headquarters - Mitsui Zosen K.K. Gijutsu Soukatsu Honbu, 6-4, Tsukiji 5-chome, Chuo-ku, Tokyo 104, Japan. Ed. T. Ohi. bk.rev.; abstr.; bibl.; charts; illus.; cum.index. circ. 1,900. (also avail. in microfilm) **Indexed:** BMT, Chem.Abstr., INSPEC.
—BLDSC (5829.833000); CASDDS.
    Description: Examines the computer applications as well as latest developments and research in engineering and shipbuilding.

MODELE REDUIT DE BATEAU. see HOBBIES

387   **CN**   **ISSN 0229-2408**
MONTREAL PORT GUIDE & TRANSPORTATION REGISTER.* a. Canadian Marine Publications Ltd., Ste. 512, 1434 St. Catherine St. W., Montreal, PQ H3G 1R4, Canada. TEL 514-861-6715. FAX 514-861-0966. adv.
    Formerly (until 1979): Montreal Repertoire du Transport (ISSN 0225-4603); Incoporated (in 1979): Guide du Port de Montreal (ISSN 0225-4727); Which was formerly (until 1978): Montreal Guide du Port et Annuaire Commercial (ISSN 0225-4735); (until 1975): Montreal Port Guide and Directory (ISSN 0225-4743)

387   **MJ**
MONTSERRAT. PORT AUTHORITY. ANNUAL REPORT. a. Port Authority, Plymouth, Montserrat, W. Indies.

387   **RU**   **ISSN 0369-1276**
VM4   **CODEN: MORFAQ**
MORSKOI FLOT;* journal of U.S.S.R. merchant marine. (Text in Russian; summaries in English) 1886. bi-m. $102 (effective 1996). (Ministerstvo Kommercheskogo Flota) Izdatel'stvo Transport, Basmanny tupik 6A, 107174 Moscow, Russia. FAX 095-262-6773. (Dist. by: Mezhdunarodnaya Kniga, Moscow, G-200, Russia) Ed. A.V. Klementiev. adv.; bk.rev.; abstr.; bibl.; charts; illus.; stat.; index. circ. 70,550. (also avail. in microform) **Indexed:** BMT, Chem.Abstr., Ref.Zh.
—BLDSC (0118.000000).

387   **PL**
MORZE. 1924. m. Ul. Widok 10, 00-024 Warsaw, Poland. TEL 48-22-273551. Ed. Janusz Wolniewicz. illus. circ. 60,000.
    Description: Covers maritime affairs.

623.82   **UK**   **ISSN 0027-2000**
VM1   **CODEN: MOSHA3**
MOTOR SHIP. 1920. m. £74($127) Reed Business Publishing Group (Subsidiary of: Reed Elsevier group), Quadrant House, The Quadrant, Sutton, Surrey SM2 5AS, England. TEL 0181-652-3369. FAX 0181-652-8180. (Subscr. to: Oakfield House, Perrymount Rd., Haywards, Heath, W. Sussex RH16 3DH, England. TEL 01444-445410) Ed. Paul Doughty; Pub. Jerry Gosney. adv. contact: Mark Janaway. bk.rev.; charts; illus.; tr.lit.; index. circ. 8,080. **Indexed:** BMT, Br.Tech.Ind., Bus.Ind., Eng.Ind., Excerp.Med., INSPEC, Tr.& Indus.Ind. Document type: trade publication.
—BLDSC (5975.540000); Ei; Faxon; SWETS; UnCover.
    Description: Focuses on technical shipping.

387   **UK**   **ISSN 0963-8466**
MOTOR SHIP DIRECTORY. Key Title: Motor Ship Directory of Shipowners & Shipbuilding. 1902. a. $150. Reed Business Publishing Group (Subsidiary of: Reed Elsevier group), Quadrant House, The Quadrant, Sutton, Surrey SM2 5AS, England. TEL 0181-652-3369. FAX 0181-652-8180. (Subscr. to: Robjohns Farm, Vicarage Rd., Finchingfield, Essex CM7 4L3, England. TEL 01371-810433) Ed. Paul Doughty; Pub. Jerry Gosney. adv. contact: Mark Janaway. index. Document type: directory.
    Former titles (until 1989): Directory of Shipowners and Shipbuilding; (until 1988): Directory of Shipowners, Shipbuilders and Marine Engineers (ISSN 0070-6310).

MULTIHULLS WORLD. see SPORTS AND GAMES — Boats And Boating

N K K NEWS; steelmaking, engineering, construction & shipbuilding, advanced materials, electronics, urban development, biotechnology. see ENGINEERING — Mechanical Engineering

387   **NR**
N P A ANNUAL REPORT. a. Nigerian Ports Authority, Public Relations Department, 26-28 Marina, PMB 12588, Lagos, Nigeria.

387   **NR**   **ISSN 0794-3008**
N P A BULLETIN. q. free. Nigerian Ports Authority, Public Relations Department, 26-28 Marina, P.M.B. 12588, Lagos, Nigeria. TELEX 21500 ONPNPA NG.

387   **NR**   **ISSN 0547-0730**
N P A NEWS. 1973. q. free. Institute of Transport, Nigerian Ports Authority, Headquarters, 26-28 Marina, Lagos, Nigeria. Ed. Agidi Ovurevu. illus.

TRANSPORTATION — SHIPS AND SHIPPING

387 GW ISSN 0027-7444
NACHRICHTEN FUER SEEFAHRER. 1849. w. DM.208.80. Bundesamt fuer Seeschiffahrt und Hydrographie, Bernhard-Nocht-Str. 78, 20359 Hamburg, Germany. TEL 040-3190-0. FAX 040-3190-5000. TELEX 211138-BSHHH-D. index. circ. 3,100. **Document type:** trade publication.

387 GR ISSN 0047-861X
NAFTIKA CHRONIKA. (Text in English and Greek) 1931. s-m. $100. Naftika Chronika Ltd., P.O. Box 80076, 185 10 Piraeus, Greece. FAX 417-2268. TELEX 212845. Ed. D. Rigas-Cottakis. adv.; bk.rev.; charts; illus.; stat. circ. 4,000. **Document type:** trade publication.
  Description: Presents information about shipping.

387 GR
NAFTILIAKI; Greek shipping review. (Supplement avail.; Index to Greek Shipping avail.) (Text in English, Greek) 1957. q. $40 (subscr. includes supplements plus a. index. Diorama Publishers Ltd., 4-6 Efplias St., P.O. Box 80-162, 185 37 Piraeus, Greece. TEL 30-1-428 2788. FAX 30-1-428-3193. TELEX 212310 NAFT GR. Ed. David Glass; Pub. Themistocles Vokos. adv. contact: Natassa Vassilaki. bk.rev.; index. circ. 3,400. (back issues avail.) **Document type:** trade publication.
  Description: Provides news and analysis of Greek merchant shipping and shipping-related business worldwide.

387.5 PK
NATIONAL SHIPPING CORPORATION. REPORT AND ACCOUNTS. (Text in English) a. free. National Shipping Corporation, N S C Bldg., Moulvi Tamizuddin Khan Rd., Karachi, Pakistan. **Document type:** corporate report.

387 NE
NATIONALE HAVENRAAD. JAARVERSLAG (YEAR). 1970. a. free. Nationale Havenraad, Koninginnegracht 19, 2514 AB The Hague, Netherlands. TEL 31-70-3517615. FAX 31-70-3517600. (back issues avail.) **Document type:** government publication. **Supersedes:** Netherlands. Provisional National Ports Council. Jaarverslag; **Formerly:** Netherlands. Commissie Zeehavenoverleg. Jaarverslag (ISSN 0077-7552)
  Description: Reports on the activities of the Dutch National Seaports Council, developments in Dutch seaports, including infrastructure, industry, labor and environmental issues. Provides statistical data concerning seaborne traffic, employment and land use.

623.89 528 UK ISSN 0077-619X
THE NAUTICAL ALMANAC. 1960. a. $20 price varies. U.S. Naval Observatory, Department of the Navy, Washington, DC 20392. (Dist. by: Bernan, 4611-F Assembly Dr., Lanham, MD 20706. TEL 800-274-4447. FAX 301-459-0056; Subscr. also to: Superintendent of Documents, U.S. Government Printing Office, Box 371954, Pittsburgh, PA 15250-7954. TEL 202-512-1800. FAX 202-512-2250; Subscr. in the U.K. to: H.M.S.O. Publications Centre, P.O. Box 273, London SW8 5DT, England. TEL 0171-873-9090. FAX 0171-873-8200) (Co-sponsors: H.M. Nautical Almanac Office (UK); Royal Greenwich Observatory (UK)) (back issues avail.) **Document type:** government publication.
  —CCC.
  Description: Contains the astronomical data required for marine navigation.

387.2 UK ISSN 0028-1336
NAUTICAL MAGAZINE; for those interested in ships and the sea. 1832. m. £31.80 (effective 1996). Brown, Son and Ferguson, Ltd., 4-10 Darnley St., Glasgow G41 2SD, Scotland. TEL 0141-429-5922. FAX 0141-420-1694. Ed. L. Ingram-Brown. adv. contact: David H. Provan. bk.rev.; s-a. index. circ. 1,200. (also avail. in microfiche from BHP) **Document type:** consumer publication.
  Description: Discusses nautical arts and science.

387 623.82 US ISSN 0738-7245
V1
NAUTICAL RESEARCH JOURNAL. 1949. q. $25 (effective 1992). Nautical Research Guild, Inc., 19 Pleasant Ln., Everett, MA 02149-2810. TEL 617-389-2505. adv.; bk.rev.; illus.; index. circ. 1,600. (also avail. in microfilm; microform from UMI; reprint service avail. from UMI) **Indexed:** Amer.Hist.& Life, Hist.Abstr.
  —BLDSC (6063.000000).
  Description: For marine artists, model builders, and those interested in marine history. Provides information on maritime lore and model building.

387 SW ISSN 0028-1379
VK4
NAUTISK TIDSKRIFT. 1908. 8/yr. SEK 110 (effective 1991). Sveriges Fartygsbefaelsfoerening (SFBF) - Swedish Ship Officers' Association, P.O. Box 12100, S-102 23 Stockholm, Sweden. FAX 8-503493. Ed. Manfred Spanner. adv.; bk.rev.; charts; illus.; tr.lit.; index. circ. 8,079.

623.81 UK ISSN 0306-0209
CODEN: NVARA3
NAVAL ARCHITECT. 1971. 10/yr. £60 (Europe £70; elsewhere £75). Royal Institution of Naval Architects, 10 Upper Belgrave St., London SW1X 8BQ, England. TEL 0171-235-4622. FAX 0171-245-6959. TELEX 265844-SINAI-G. Ed. Tim Knaggs. adv.; B&W page £1255, color page £1680; trim 297 x 210; adv. contact: Debbi Bonner. bk.rev.; bibl.; charts; illus. circ. 7,661. **Indexed:** Appl.Mech.Rev., BMT, Br.Tech.Ind., Curr.Cont., Eng.Ind., Excerp.Med., Ocean.Abstr., Pollut.Abstr. **Document type:** trade publication.
  —BLDSC (6063.850000); Ei; SWETS.
  Description: News items and research articles on legislation, architectural and technological developments, and products and services pertaining to the construction and operation of ocean-going vessels.

623.89 FR ISSN 0028-1530
VK2 CODEN: NVGNAL
NAVIGATION; revue technique de navigation maritime, aerienne, terrestre et spatiale. (Text in French, summaries in English) 1953. q. 400 F. (effective 1996). Institut Francais de Navigation, 3 av. Octave Greard, 75007 Paris, France. TEL 33-1-42-92-10-43. FAX 33-1-40-61-93-19. Ed. C. Ville. adv.: page 5000 F. bk.rev.; abstr.; illus.; index, cum.index every 5 yrs. circ. 1,500. **Indexed:** Bibl.Cart., Deep Sea Res.& Oceanogr.Abstr., INSPEC, Int.Aerosp.Abstr. **Document type:** monographic series.
  —BLDSC (6067.000000); Ei.
  Description: Dedicated to scientific and technical problems arising from positioning and routing of ships, aircraft and land vehicles.

387 UK ISSN 0268-6317
NAVIGATION NEWS. 1986. bi-m. £30. Waterline Communications Ltd., The Old Mill, Lower Quay, Fareham, Hants. PO16 0RA, England. TEL 01329-825335. FAX 01329-825330. Ed. Rebecca Dudley. adv.: B&W page £445, color page £595; trim 297 x 210; adv. contact: Philip Parkin. bk.rev.; circ. 4,000 (paid). (back issues avail.) **Document type:** trade publication.

NAVIGATIONAL RADIO AIDS. see COMMUNICATIONS — Radio

387 623.89 DK ISSN 0107-4806
NAVIGATOER. (Text in Danish; summaries in English) 1907. 10/yr. DKK 270($45) Navigatoerenes Faellesforening - Danish Navigators Association, Navigatoerenes Hus, 55 Havnegade, DK-1058 Copenhagen K, Denmark 45-33-129385. TELEX 21025 HAVHUS. Ed. Capt. K. Mols Soerensen. adv.; bk.rev.; index. circ. 5,800.
  Former titles: Navigatoer Nyt; Navigatoer (ISSN 0028-1565) Dansk Havneblad; Dansk Lodstidende.

387 IT ISSN 0390-2927
NAVIGAZIONE INTERNA. 1974. q. L.25000 (effective 1993). Unione di Navigazione Interna Italiana, Comunita Padana delle Camere di Commercio, Via Baldesio, 8, 26100 Cremona, Italy. TEL 0372-32281. FAX 0372-21396. Ed. Giorgio Michieli. adv.

387 FR ISSN 0077-6270
NAVIS; annuaire de la marine marchande, de la construction navale et des ports. 1942. a. 500 F. Moreux, 190 bd. Haussmann, 75008 Paris, France. TEL 44-95-99-50. TELEX NAVIMAR 290131F. index.

623.8 AG
NAVITECNIA Y COMERCIO MARITIMO. 1947. m. $25. Navitecnia S.A.P.E.C.I.M.F., Alsina 1170, 1088 Buenos Aires, Argentina. TEL 1-37-2795. Ed. Ernest Potthoff. adv.; bk.rev.; illus.; index. circ. 2,500.
  Formerly: Navitecnia (ISSN 0028-1611)

NAVTEX MANUAL. see COMMUNICATIONS

387 PO
NEPTUNO. 12/yr. Pc. D. Luis 9 1o D., Lisbon, Portugal.

387 BE ISSN 0028-2790
NEPTUNUS; info marine. (Text in Dutch and French) 1952. bi-m. 200 Fr. Force Navale - Belgische Zeemacht, Postbus 17, Oostende 1, Belgium. Ed. J.C. Lienart. adv.; bk.rev.; charts; illus. circ. 2,500.

NETHERLANDS. CENTRAAL BUREAU VOOR DE STATISTIEK. STATISTIEK VAN DE ZEEVAART/NETHERLANDS. CENTRAL BUREAU OF STATISTICS. STATISTICS OF SEABORNE SHIPPING. see TRANSPORTATION — Abstracting, Bibliographies, Statistics

NETHERLANDS. CENTRAAL BUREAU VOOR DE STATISTIEK. STATISTIEK VAN DE INTERNATIONALE BINNENVAART/NETHERLANDS. CENTRAL BUREAU OF STATISTICS. STATISTICS OF THE INTERNATIONAL INLAND SHIPPING. see TRANSPORTATION — Abstracting, Bibliographies, Statistics

NETHERLANDS. CENTRAAL BUREAU VOOR DE STATISTIEK. STATISTIEK VAN DE KOOPVAARDIJVLOOT/NETHERLANDS. CENTRAL BUREAU OF STATISTICS. STATISTICS OF THE MERCHANT MARINE. see TRANSPORTATION — Abstracting, Bibliographies, Statistics

NETHERLANDS. CENTRAAL BUREAU VOOR DE STATISTIEK. STATISTIEK VAN HET BINNENLANDS GOEDERENVERVOER. STATISTICS OF INTERNAL GOODS TRANSPORT IN THE NETHERLANDS. see TRANSPORTATION — Abstracting, Bibliographies, Statistics

NEW SOUTH WALES PORTS HANDBOOK. see BUSINESS AND ECONOMICS — Trade And Industrial Directories

387 665.5 US ISSN 0953-9336
NEW WORLDWIDE TANKER NOMINAL FREIGHT SCALE; code name Worldscale. 1969. a. $1425 (typically set in Sep.). Worldscale Association (NYC), Inc., 17 Battery Pl., New York, NY 10004. TEL 212-422-2786. FAX 212-344-4169. TELEX 62351 WSCALE UW. (U.K. addr.: 64 Queen St., London EC4R 1AD, England. TEL 44-71-248-4747) Eds. Sara Bierman, Robert Porter. circ. 1,200. (back issues avail.) **Document type:** trade publication.
  Formerly (until Jul. 1988): Worldwide Tanker Nominal Freight Scale (ISSN 0267-1913)

387 NZ ISSN 0549-0502
NEW ZEALAND MARINE NEWS. 1949. q. NZ.$28. New Zealand Ship and Marine Society Inc., P.O. Box 5104, Wellington, New Zealand. TEL 64-04-4377-0362. FAX 64-04-471-1373. bk.rev. circ. 600. (back issues avail.)
  —CCC.
  Description: For laypersons interested in historical and general aspects of shipping and nautical matters, particularly in reference to New Zealand.

387 NZ ISSN 0545-7866
HE932.5
NEW ZEALAND SHIPPING DIRECTORY. 1962. a. NZ.$19. Mercantile Gazette Marketing, P.O. Box 20-034, Christchurch 5, New Zealand. FAX 64-3-3584490. Ed. G. Everts. adv.; illus. **Document type:** directory.

387 NZ ISSN 0027-724X
NEW ZEALAND SHIPPING GAZETTE. w. NZ.$106.95. Mercantile Gazette Marketing, P.O. Box 20-034, Christchurch 5, New Zealand. FAX 64-9-3584490. **Document type:** newspaper.
  —CCC.

TRANSPORTATION — SHIPS AND SHIPPING

387　　UK
NEWBUILDINGS. (Supplement to: Fairplay International Shipping Weekly) 1964. q. included with subscr. to Fairplay International. Fairplay Publications Ltd., P.O. Box 96, Coulsdon, Surrey CR5 2TE, England. TEL 0181-645-2800. FAX 0181-660-2824. TELEX 884595 FRPLAY G. (N. American subscr. to: Fairplay Publications Ltd., Box 354, Germantown, NY 12526. TEL 518-537-6682. FAX 518-537-6667) Ed. C. Hewer. stat. circ. 5,666.
Document type: directory.
　　Formerly: World Ships on Order (ISSN 0043-9010)

387　　JA
NIHON KAIJI SHIMBUN/JAPAN MARITIME DAILY. 1942. d. (Mon.-Fri.). 6000 Yen per mo.; newsstand price: 310 Yen. Nihon Kaiji Shimbunsha, 13-4, Shimbashi 5-chome, Minato-ku, Tokyo, Japan. TEL 03-3436-3221. FAX 03-3436-6553. Ed. Minoru Takashimizu; Pub. Takaaki Ohyama. adv.: page 1600000 Yen; adv. contact: Hideo Sakon.
Document type: newspaper.

387　　JA
NIHON SENPAKU MEISAISHO/JAPAN SHIPPING REGISTER. (Text in Japanese) 1930. a. 19000. Nihon Kaiun Shukaijo - Japan Shipping Exchange Inc., Mitsuirokugokan 3-16 Muromachi 2-chome, Nihonba-shi, Chuo-ku, Tokyo 103, Japan.

NIHON SHOSEN SENPUKU TOKEI. see *TRANSPORTATION — Abstracting, Bibliographies, Statistics*

387　　JA　　ISSN 0514-8499
CODEN: NZGRDU
NIHON ZOSEN GAKKAI RONBUNSHU/SOCIETY OF NAVAL ARCHITECTS OF JAPAN. JOURNAL. (Text in English, Japanese; summaries in English) 1897. s-a. $248. Nihon Zosen Gakkai - Society of Naval Architects of Japan, 15-16, Toranomon 1-chome, Minato-ku, Tokyo 105, Japan. (Dist. overseas by: Intercontinental Marketing Corp., I.P.O. Box 5056, Tokyo 100-31, Japan. TEL 81-3-3661-7458. FAX 81-3-3667-9646) **Indexed:** INIS Atomind., Jap.Per.Ind.
　—BLDSC (4894.000000); CASDDS; Ei.

387　　JA
NIPPON YUSEN. ANNUAL REPORT. a. Nippon Yusen Kaisha, Corporate Communication Chamber, 2-3-2 Marunouchi, Chiyoda-ku, Tokyo 100, Japan. TEL 03-3284-5193. FAX 03-3284-6382.

NOR'EASTER (DULUTH). see *HISTORY — History Of North And South America*

623.82　　NO
NORSK BAATINDUSTRI. bi-m. Norsk Baatinformasjon, Postboks 317, 1601 Fredrikstad, Norway. adv. circ. 4,000.

623.87　　NO　　ISSN 0333-0192
VM4
NORSK MASKIN TIDENDE/NORWEGIAN MARINE ENGINEERS' MAGAZINE. 1895. 10/yr. NOK 220. Norske Maskinistforbund - Norwegian Union of Marine Engineers, P.O. Box 7153 Majorstua, N-0307 Oslo, Norway. TEL 47-22-56-73-10. FAX 47-22-56-86-10. TELEX 72 832 FENSO N. Ed. Frode Gross. adv.: B&W page NOK 5800, color page NOK 13200; trim 210 x 297. charts; illus.; tr.lit. circ. 7,000. **Document type:** consumer publication.
　　Description: For marine personnel at sea, onshore and in the offshore industry. Contains trade information, technical news and topics of general interest.

387 331.8　　NO　　ISSN 0029-2079
NORSK SJOEMANNSFORBUND. MEDLEMSBLAD. 1910. m. (11/yr.). free to qualified personnel. Norsk Sjoemannsforbund, Grev Wedels Plass 7, Oslo 1, Norway. Ed. Henrik Aasaroed. adv.; bk.rev.; charts; illus. circ. 17,000.
　—CCC.

387　　NO　　ISSN 0048-0606
NORSK SKIBSFOERERTIDENDE. 1898. m. NOK 120($20) Norges Skibsfoererforbund - Norwegian Shipmasters' Association, Hafrsfjordgate 11, Oslo 2, Norway. Ed. Gudmund Aasheim. adv.; bk.rev.; charts; illus.; stat.; index. circ. 4,000.

NORTH AMERICAN SOCIETY FOR OCEANIC HISTORY. NEWSLETTER. see *HISTORY — History Of North And South America*

NORTHERN MARINER. see *HISTORY*

O A G CRUISE & SHIPLINE GUIDE - WORLDWIDE EDITION. (Official Airline Guides) see *TRAVEL AND TOURISM*

387　　FR　　ISSN 0474-5884
HE821
O E C D MARITIME TRANSPORT COMMITTEE. MARITIME TRANSPORT. 1954. a. price varies. Organization for Economic Cooperation and Development, 2 rue Andre-Pascal, 75775 Paris Cedex 16, France. (U.S. orders to: O.E.C.D. Publications and Information Center, 2001 L St., N.W., Ste. 700, Washington, D.C. 20036-4910. TEL 202-785-6323) (also avail. in microfiche from OEC,CIS) **Indexed:** IIS.
　—BLDSC (5381.370000).

387 910.09　　US
OCEAN & CRUISE NEWS. 1980. m. $28. World Ocean & Cruise Liner Society, Box 92, Stamford, CT 06904. TEL 203-329-2787. FAX 203-329-2787. Ed. George C. Devol, III; Pub. George C. Devol, III. circ. 6,000. (back issues avail.) **Document type:** newsletter.
　　Description: Covers the latest news about cruises and cruise ships.

387 301.6　　UK　　ISSN 0261-6777
VK562
OCEAN VOICE; maritime information technology and electronics. 1981. q. free. International Maritime Satellite Organization, 99 City Rd., London EC1Y 4AX, England. TEL 0171-728-1000. FAX 0171-728-1044. TELEX 297201 INMSAT G. Ed. Lee Adamson. adv.: B&W page £1700; color page £2410; adv. contact: Peter Honeywell. bk.rev.; illus.; charts; circ. 18,684 (controlled). **Document type:** trade publication.
　—BLDSC (6231.396000); UnCover.
　　Description: Covers all aspects of maritime information technology and electronics.

387　　II　　ISSN 0029-8123
OCEANITE; the maritime magazine of India. (Text in English) 1945. m. Rs.12($2.50) Maritime Union of India, Udyog Bhavan, 4th Fl., 29 Walchand Hirachand Marg, Ballard Estate, Bombay 400 038, India. TEL 2613052. FAX 91-22-2615507. Ed. K.E. Sukhia. adv. contact: Blaise R. Fernandes. bk.rev.; illus. circ. 15,000. **Document type:** trade publication.
　　Description: Includes information for the International Transportworkers' Federation. Covers fuels, repairs, provisions, and job opportunities in the Indian shipping industry.

OFFICIAL SHIPPERS GUIDE - ST. LOUIS MOTOR FREIGHT DIRECTORY. see *TRANSPORTATION — Trucks And Trucking*

387.1　　US　　ISSN 0094-8454
HE554.A6
OFFICIAL SOUTHERN CALIFORNIA PORTS MARITIME DIRECTORY AND GUIDE.* 1974. a. $10. Civic - Data Corp., 941 W. Bay Ave., Balboa Island, CA 92661-1012. illus.

387　　UK　　ISSN 0309-040X
OFFSHORE SERVICE VESSEL REGISTER. (Quarterly updates avail.) 1977. a. £150($240) (outside Europe £170 ($275)); diskette £150 ($240); quarterly updates on diskette £540 ($870). Clarkson Research Studies, 12 Camomile St., London EC3A 7BP, England. TEL 0171-283 8955. FAX 0171-623-0539. TELEX 081 2927 CLTNK G. adv. (also avail. in diskette format)
　　Description: Contains full details of the more than 3,000 offshore service ships and the 1,200 companies that own or manage them; statistics of each ship are compiled in regard to size, age, capacity, and registry.

387　　CI　　ISSN 0030-0713
OGLAS ZA POMORCE/NOTICES TO MARINERS. (Text in Serbo-Croatian) 1924. m. $15. Hidrografski Institut Jugoslavenske Ratne Mornarice, 58000 Split, Croatia. FAX 058-47045. TELEX 26270. bk.rev.

387　　US　　ISSN 0093-2124
VK1323
ON SCENE. 1969. q. U.S. Coast Guard, Office of Navigation Safety and Waterway Services, 2100 Second St., S.W., Washington, DC 20593-0001. TEL 202-267-1876. E-mail: j.opiel/gnrs@cgsmtp.comdt.uscg.mil. Ed. Lt.J.G. Jerome Popiel. bibl.; charts; illus. (also avail. in microform from UMI; reprint service avail. from UMI) **Document type:** government publication.
　—UMI; UnCover.
　　Formerly (until 1971): National Maritime S A R Review (ISSN 0047-8946)
　　Description: Provides a forum for information on maritime search and rescue.

387　　NE
ONTWIKKELINGSPLANNEN VAN DE HAVENS IN DE HAMBURG - LE HAVRE RANGE; infrastructurele projecten in de belangrijkste Duitse, Nederlandse, Belgische en Franse Havens. 1989. a. free. Nationale Havenraad, Koninginnegracht 19, 2514 AB The Hague, Netherlands. TEL 31-70-3517615. FAX 31-70-3517600. **Document type:** government publication.
　　Description: Describes infrastructure development projects at the main German, Dutch, Belgian and French seaports.

623.89 384　　FR
LES OUVRAGES DE RADIOSIGNAUX. (Includes several subseries) irreg., no.99, 1995. price varies. Service Hydrographique et Oceanographique de la Marine, 3 av. Octave Greard, 00300 Armees, France. TEL 98-03-09-17. FAX 98-47-11-42. TELEX HYDRO 940568 F. (Subscr. to: EPSHOM, B.P. 426, 29275, Brest Cedex, France) **Document type:** government publication.
　　Description: Offers mariners up-to-date information on radiocommunications.

P & I INTERNATIONAL; monthly review of mutual insurance. (Protection & Indemnity) see *INSURANCE*

387　　US　　ISSN 1062-6484
P M A UPDATE. 1989. m. membership. (Pacific Maritime Association) P M A Research, Box 7861, San Francisco, CA 94120-7861. stat. (looseleaf format) **Document type:** newsletter.
　　Description: Covers issues related to longshore labor relations and port traffic along the US Pacific coast.

387　　US　　ISSN 0741-7586
PACIFIC MARITIME MAGAZINE. 1983. m. $12. R.H. Philips Co., 1818 Westlake Ave. N., No.430, Seattle, WA 98109-2707. TEL 206-284-8285. FAX 206-284-0391. Ed. Richard H. Philips. adv.; bk.rev. circ. 6,112. (back issues avail.) **Document type:** trade publication.
　　Formerly (until 1984): Port Reporter.
　　Description: Geared toward owner-operators of steamship lines, their agents and representatives, tug and barge lines, terminal operators, stevedores and port and harbor operations executives in the Pacific.

387　　US　　ISSN 0030-8900
PACIFIC SHIPPER. 1926. w. $111 (foreign $145). K - III Press, Inc., 424 W. 33rd St., New York, NY 10001. TEL 800-221-5488. FAX 212-695-5025. adv. circ. 6,300.

387　　UK
PADDLE WHEELS. 1959. q. membership. Paddle Steamer Preservation Society, 26 Wood St., Mitcham Junction, Surrey CR4 4JS, England. TEL 0181-640-0838. Ed. M. Allen. adv.; bk.rev.; illus. circ. 3,500. **Document type:** newsletter.

623.89　　BE　　ISSN 0480-0516
PERMANENT INTERNATIONAL ASSOCIATION OF NAVIGATION CONGRESSES. BULLETIN. 1926; N.S. 1961; N.S. 1968. 4/yr. 2500 BEF. Permanent International Association of Navigation Congresses, WTC - Tour 3, Bld. Simon Bolivar 30, B-1210 Brussels. TEL 32-2-2085216. FAX 32-2-2085215. (back issues avail.) **Indexed:** BMT. **Document type:** bulletin.

387　　UK
PETERHEAD PORT HANDBOOK. 1985. irreg. £25. Compass Publications Ltd., Macron House, Castle Acre, King's Lynn, Norfolk PE32 2AG, England. TEL 0176-755783. FAX 01760-755782. Ed. James P. Moriarty. adv.; illus. circ. 6,000. **Document type:** directory.

623.89 UK
PILOT (WESTMINSTER). 1887. q. £5 membership. United Kingdom Pilots' Association (Marine), Transport House, Smith Square, Westminster, London SW1P 3JB, England. TEL 01-828-7788. Ed. J.D. Godden. bk.rev.; index. circ. 1,300. **Document type:** bulletin.

387.5 NO ISSN 0802-0213
PLATOU REPORT. 1947. a. free. R. S. Platou A-S, Fjordveien 1, P.O. Box 10, N-1322 Hoevik, Norway. Ed. Johan Aabyholm. illus. circ. 3,000.

387 SP ISSN 0210-9956
PLAYAMAR; revista tecnica de actualidad nautica. m. 2200 ptas. Editorial Borrmart, S.A., Ramon de la Cruz 68, Madrid 1, Spain. adv.; bk.rev.; play rev.; bibl.; illus.; tr.lit.; index. circ. 19,500.

623.8 PL ISSN 0373-868X
POLITECHNIKA GDANSKA. ZESZYTY NAUKOWE. BUDOWNICTWO OKRETOWE. (Text in English, Polish; summaries in Russian and one West-European language) 1957. irreg. price varies. Politechnika Gdanska, Ul. G. Narutowicza 11-12, 80-952 Gdansk 6, Poland. (Dist. by: Osrodek Rozpowszechniania Wydawnictw Naukowych PAN, Palac Kultury i Nauki, 00-901 Warsaw, Poland) bibl.; charts; illus. **Document type:** academic/scholarly publication.
  Description: Reasearch on ship design and equipment, steam and gas turbines, mechanics and hydromechanics of structures and power installations.

387 UK ISSN 0032-4809
PORT. 1967. m. £5. Port Publishing Co. Ltd., Focal House, 18-19 Sheds, Tilbury Dock, Tilbury, Essex RM18 7ND, England. Ed. Michael Guy. adv.; bk.rev.; illus. circ. 10,000. (tabloid format)

387 FR ISSN 0396-4388
PORT AUTONOME DU HAVRE. BULLETIN ANALYTIQUE DE DOCUMENTATION GENERALE. 1971. m. free on exchange basis. Port Autonome du Havre, Centre de Documentation, B.P. 1413, 76067 Le Havre Cedex, France. Ed. E. Berthoud. circ. 150.

387 FR ISSN 0396-4396
PORT AUTONOME DU HAVRE. BULLETIN ANALYTIQUE DE DOCUMENTATION TECHNIQUE. 1966. m. free on exchange basis. Port Autonome du Havre, Centre de Documentation, B.P. 1413, 76067 Le Havre Cedex, France. Ed. E. Berthoud. circ. 150.

387 JM
PORT BUSTAMANTE HANDBOOK. 1972. a. free. Shipping Association of Jamaica, Confederation Life Building, 5-7 King Street, P.O. Box 40, Kingston 15, Jamaica, W.I. (Co-sponsor: Port Authority of Jamaica) Ed. T.A. Gambrill. circ. 1,700.
  Formerly (until 1977): Port of Kingston Handbook.

623.89 UK ISSN 0267-4823
PORT DEVELOPMENT INTERNATIONAL. 1985. m. £119 (Europe £135; elsewhere $282). Mundy Perry Ltd., 102-108 Clerkenwell Rd., London EC1M 5SA, England. TEL 0171-417-0073. FAX 0171-417-0075. Ed. Chris Orr. adv. contact: Rosemary Little. bk.rev. circ. 7,900. **Document type:** trade publication.
  —BLDSC (6555.260000); SWETS.
  Description: Covers all critical aspects of port development: port planning, infrastructure development, cargo handling, computerization.

387 UK ISSN 0965-8203
PORT ENGINEERING MANAGEMENT. bi-m. Lands Services, c/o Eldon Publications Ltd., 292-294 Walton Rd., E. Molesey, Surrey KT8 0HY, England. TEL 081-941-7510. FAX 081-941-7449. Ed. David Foxwell.
  —BLDSC (6555.301000); SWETS.
  Former title: World Port Construction and Ocean Technology.

387 US
PORT OF BALTIMORE MAGAZINE. 1946. m. free. Maryland Port Administration, World Trade Center Baltimore, Baltimore, MD 21202. TEL 410-385-4480. FAX 410-385-4485. Ed. Sara Moriarty. adv.; circ. 11,000 (controlled). **Document type:** government publication.
  Formerly: Port of Baltimore Handbook (ISSN 0079-3981)

386.8 US
HE550
PORT OF DETROIT WORLD HANDBOOK. 1973. a. $11. Fourth Seacoast Publishing Co., Inc., Box 145, St. Clair Shores, MI 48080. TEL 810-779-5570. FAX 810-779-5547. Ed. Thomas J. Buysse; Pub. Roger J. Buyssw. adv. contact: Thomas Buysse. illus. circ. 10,000. **Document type:** directory.
  Formerly: Official Port of Detroit World Handbook (ISSN 0093-1799)
  Description: Analysis of facilities and services for international commerce at the port. Includes photos, articles and statistical info.

380 US ISSN 0032-4825
HE554.H65
PORT OF HOUSTON MAGAZINE. 1959. m. free. Port of Houston Authority, Box 2562, Houston, TX 77252. TEL 713-670-2594. FAX 713-670-2498. Ed. Ann Bordelon. adv.; charts; illus. circ. 14,000. **Document type:** government publication.

387 FR ISSN 0338-1927
PORT OF LE HAVRE FLASHES. 1972. m. free. Port Autonome du Havre - Port of Le Havre Authority, Terre Plein de la Barre, 76067 Le Havre, France. TEL 35-21-74-00. FAX 35-21-74-29. TELEX PAHAVRE 190 663 F. (U.S. orders to: Port of Le Havre Authority, One World Trade Center, Ste. 2551, New York, N.Y. 10048) Ed. Patrick Cornet. circ. 7,200.
  Description: Covers news of interest concerning the Port of le Havre Authority.

387 UK ISSN 0030-8064
HE558.L8
PORT OF LONDON. 1925. q. £9 (foreign £12). Port of London Authority, Devon House, 58-60 St. Katharine's Way, London E1 9LB, England. TEL 0171-265-2656. FAX 0171-265-2699. Ed. Roger Mutton. adv.; bk.rev.; illus.; index. circ. 5,000. **Indexed:** Fluidex, Geo.Abstr., W.R.C.Inf. **Document type:** trade publication.
  —BLDSC (6555.330000); SWETS.
  Formerly: P L A Monthly.

387.2 AT
PORT OF MELBOURNE AUTHORITY. ANNUAL REPORT. a. Port of Melbourne Authority, P.O. Box 4721, Melbourne, Vic. 3001, Australia. TEL 61-3-611-1777. FAX 61-3-611-1905. **Document type:** corporate report.

387 JA
PORT OF OSAKA/OSAKA-KO. (Text in English and Japanese) 1955. a. free. Port and Harbour Bureau - Osaka-shi Kowan-Kyoku, 2-8-24 Chikko, Minato-ku, Osaka 552, Japan. FAX 06-572-0554. TELEX 525-6320. stat.

387 GR
PORT OF PIRAEUS AUTHORITY. ANNUAL REPORT. a. Port of Piraeus Authority, Akti Miaouli II, Merarchias Corner, Piraeus, Greece. **Document type:** corporate report.

387 GR
PORT OF PIRAEUS AUTHORITY. QUARTERLY REPORT. q. Port of Piraeus Authority, Akti Miaouli II, Merarchias Corner, Piraeus, Greece.

387 GR
PORT OF PIRAEUS AUTHORITY. STATISTICAL REPORT. (Text in English and Greek) 1913. m. Port of Piraeus Authority, Akti Miaouli II, Merarchias Corner, Piraeus, Greece. adv. circ. 4,000.
  Supersedes: Port of Piraeus Authority. Statistical Bulletin (ISSN 0079-399X)

387 NE ISSN 0922-7148
HE558.R75
PORT OF ROTTERDAM MAGAZINE. (Editions in Dutch, English and German) 1962. bi-m. fl.59. (Port of Rotterdam, Municipal Port Management) Wyt Publishing Group B.V., Postbus 6438, 3002 AK Rotterdam, Netherlands. TEL 31-10-4255944. FAX 31-10-4780904. Ed. Willem C.N. van Horssen. adv.; bk.rev.; charts; illus.; stat.; circ. 16,000 (controlled). **Indexed:** Excerpt.Med., Fluidex, Key to Econ.Sci.
  —BLDSC (6555.382000); SWETS.
  Formerly (until 1988): Rotterdam Europoort Delta (ISSN 0035-8487)
  Description: Magazine for port, transport and logistics.

387.1 JA
PORT OF TOKYO; a hand book. 1951. a. free. Tokyo Metropolitan Government, Port and Harbor Bureau, 8-1 Marunouchi 3-chome, Chiyoda-ku, Tokyo 100-81, Japan. TEL 03-3211-7949. TELEX 33346 PORTOKYO J. illus. circ. 7,000.

315.2 JA
PORT OF YOKOHAMA. ANNUAL REPORT. (Text in Chinese, English and Japanese) a. free. Port and Harbor Bureau, Industry and Trade Center Bldg., 2 Yamashita-cho, Naka-ku, Yokohama, Japan. FAX 45-671-7158. stat. **Document type:** corporate report.

387 US
PORT PROGRESS NEWS AND EVENTS. 1964. q. free. Port of Oakland, 530 Water St., Oakland, CA 94607. TEL 510-272-1100. FAX 510-231-1172. Ed. Robert Middleton. circ. 15,000 (controlled). **Document type:** newsletter.
  Description: Covers personnel, facilities and transport service developments at the Oakland seaport and airport.

387 380 UK ISSN 0266-3848
PORT RASHID: DUBAI SHIPPING HANDBOOK.* (Text in Arabic and English) 1984. a. Charter Publications Ltd., Downham Market, Bank Chambers, Norfolk PE38 9BU, England. Ed. James P. Moriarty. adv. circ. 6,000.

PORTHOLE; the intelligent cruise magazine. see TRAVEL AND TOURISM

387 IT ISSN 0032-4957
IL PORTO DI SAVONA. (Includes English supplement) 1956. m. L.25000 (foreign L.50000). Ente Autonomo del Porto di Savona, Via Gramsci 14, 17100 Savona, Italy. TEL 019-85541. FAX 19827399. TELEX 271462 EAP SV. Dir. Sergio Ravera. adv.; bk.rev.; charts; illus.; stat.; index. circ. 4,500.
  Description: Covers shipping activities and statistics in the port of Savona.

387 BL ISSN 0101-5664
VM41
PORTOS E NAVIOS; revista tecnica e informativa. 1958. m. Revista Tecnica e Informativa Ltda., Av. Rio Branco 185, 1914, 20040-007 Rio de Janiero, Brazil. Eds. Rosangela Vieira, Marcos Godoy. adv. contact: Marcos Godoy. abstr.; bibl.; charts; illus.; stat.; index, cum.index. circ. 20,000. **Indexed:** BMT. **Document type:** trade publication.
  —BLDSC (6555.850000).

623.89 387.1 FR ISSN 1167-5381
PORTS & MOUILLAGES. irreg. 186 F. Service Hydrographique et Oceanographique de la Marine, 3 av. Greard, 00300 Armees, France. TEL 98-03-09-17. FAX 98-47-11-42. TELEX HYDRO 940568 F. (Subscr. to: EPSHOM, B.P. 426, 29275 Brest Cedex, France) illus.; maps. **Document type:** government publication.
  Description: Describes and evaluates ports and anchorages.

387.1 CN ISSN 0225-5456
PORTS ANNUAL.* 1972. a. Canadian Marine Publications Ltd., Ste. 512, 1434 St. Catherine St. W., Montreal, PQ H3E 1R4, Canada. TEL 514-861-6715. FAX 514-861-0966. illus.

387 NE
PORTS MAGAZINE. bi-m. fl.48. Internationale Publiciteits Diensten, Postbus 317, 4530 AH Terneuzen, Netherlands. adv. circ. 25,000.

387 US ISSN 0048-489X
PORTSIDE. 1971. q. free. Port of Portland, Box 3529, Portland, OR 97208. TEL 503-231-5000. Ed. R.G. Montgomery. circ. 9,000 (controlled).
  Description: News of the Port of Portland marine cargo, aviation, land development and ship repair activities.

387 SP
PROA A LA MAR. 4/yr. Spanish Naval League, Mayor 16, 28013 Madrid, Spain. TEL 1-266-44-94.

TRANSPORTATION — SHIPS AND SHIPPING

387 US ISSN 1066-2774
PROFESSIONAL MARINER; the journal of professional seamanship. 1993. bi-m. $25. Navigator Publishing Corp., Box 569, 18 Danforth St., Portland, ME 04101. TEL 207-772-2466. Ed. Greg Walsh; Pub. Alex Agnew. adv.: B&W page $1547, color page $2321; trim 8 1/4 x 10 7/8; adv. contact: Alex Agnew. circ. 18,500 (paid). **Document type:** trade publication.

387 US ISSN 0048-5551
PROPELLER CLUB QUARTERLY. 1972. 4/yr. membership. Propeller Club of the United States, 3927 Old Lee Hwy, Ste. 101A, Fairfax, VA 22030. TEL 703-691-2777. FAX 703-691-4173. Ed. J. Daniel Smith. illus. circ. 14,000.

387.5 PO
PROPULSOR. 1971. bi-m. free. Centro Cultural dos Oficiais e Engenheiros Maquinistas da Marinha Mercante, Avda. D. Carlos I No. 10, 1 Esq., 1200 Lisbon, Portugal. TEL 39-61775. Ed.Bd. adv.; bk.rev.; charts; illus. circ. 1,750.
 Description: Contains scientific and technical news on shipping, marine engineering and marine pollution.

PUERTO RICO. PORTS AUTHORITY. OFFICE OF ECONOMIC RESEARCH. STATISTICAL REPORT. see
TRANSPORTATION — Air Transport

QUARTERDECK. see MUSEUMS AND ART GALLERIES

RADIO AIDS TO MARINE NAVIGATION. see
COMMUNICATIONS — Radio

623.89 384 FR
RADIOCOMMUNICATIONS MARITIMES. (Subseries of: Ouvrages de Radiosignaux) 1991. irreg., latest 1992. 437 F. (effective 1995). Service Hydrographique et Oceanographique de la Marine, 3 av. Octave Greard, 00300 Armees, France. TEL 98-03-09-47. FAX 98-47-11-42. TELEX HYDRO 940568 F. (Subscr. to: EPSHOM, B.P. 426, 29275 Brest Cedex, France) **Document type:** government publication.
 Description: Covers communications between ships and land-based radio stations.

623.89 384 FR
RADIONAVIGATION. (Subseries of: Ouvrages de Radiosignaux) 1988. biennial. 397 F. (effective 1995). Service Hydrographique et Oceanographique de la Marine, 3 av. Octave Greard, 00300 Armees, France. TEL 98-03-09-17. FAX 98-47-11-42. TELEX HYDRO 940568 F. (Subscr. to: EPSHOM, B.P. 426, 29275 Brest Cedex, France) **Document type:** government publication.
 Description: Gives the position of all radionavigation signals, beacons, satellites, and lighthouses and describes each one.

RAILWAY AND CANAL HISTORICAL SOCIETY JOURNAL. see TRANSPORTATION — Railroads

623.82 JA ISSN 0916-0981
VM4
RAN/KANSAI SOCIETY OF NAVAL ARCHITECTS. BULLETIN. (Text in Japanese) 1988. 4. 9000 Yen. Kansai Zosen Kyokai - Kansai Society of Naval Architects, Japan, c/o Osaka Daigaku Kogakubu Senpaku-Kaiyou Kyoshitsu, 2-1, Yamadaoka, Suita-shi, Osaka 565, Japan. TEL 06-879-7593. FAX 06-878-5364. E-mail: KSNAJ@naoe.eng.oska-u.ac.jp.

387 SP
REAL CLUB NAUTICO DE VALENCIA. REVISTA. 4/yr. Real Club Nautico de Valencia, Avda. Primado Reig. 96, 46010 Valencia, Spain. TEL 6-369-66-01. Ed. J.M. Lajara.

387 RU ISSN 0034-1290
CODEN: RETRAN
RECHNOI TRANSPORT.* 1941. q. $55 (effective 1996). Izdatel'stvo Transport, Basmanny tupik 6A, 107174 Moscow, Russia. TEL 095-262-6773. (Co-sponsor: Ministerstvo Rechnogo Flota) Ed. M.S. Nazarov. bk.rev.; bibl.; charts; illus.; stat.; index. circ. 15,490. **Indexed:** Chem.Abstr.
 —BLDSC (0154.000000).

RECOMMENDATIONS ON THE SAFE USE OF PESTICIDES IN SHIPS. see ENVIRONMENTAL STUDIES — Toxicology And Environmental Safety

623.89 FR
RECUEIL A L'USAGE DES PLAISANCIERS. a. free. Service Hydrographique et Oceanographique de la Marine, 3 av. Octave Greard, 00300 Armees, France. TEL 98-03-09-17. FAX 98-47-11-42. TELEX HYDRO 940568 F. (Avail. from: EPSHOM, B.P. 426, 29275 Brest Cedex, France) **Document type:** catalog, government publication.
 Description: Lists charts, bulletins, and other publications to aid mariners in navigating the seas worldwide.

623.89 FR ISSN 0180-9970
RECUEIL DES CORRECTIONS DE CARTES (YEAR). 1978. a. 117 F. (effective 1995). Service Hydrographique et Oceanographique de la Marine, 3 av. Octave Gerard, 00300 Armees, France. TEL 98-03-09-17. FAX 98-47-11-42. TELEX HYDRO 940568 F. (Subscr. to: EPSHOM, B.P. 426, 29275 Brest Cedex, France) **Document type:** government publication.

623.89 UK
REED'S COMMERCIAL SALVAGE PRACTICE.* (In 2 vols. plus 3 annual supplements) 1987. every 5 yrs. £700 includes 3 annual reviews. Thomas Reed Publications Ltd., 38 S. John St., London EC1M 4AY, England. Ed. David Hancox. circ. 700.

623.89 UK ISSN 0263-3620
REED'S MEDITERRANEAN NAVIGATOR.* 1983. a. $21. Thomas Reed Publications Ltd., 38 S. John St., London EC1M 4AY, England. Ed. Jean Fowler. adv. circ. 5,000.

623.89 UK
REED'S OCEAN NAVIGATOR.* 1969. irreg. Thomas Reed Publications Ltd., 38 S. John St., London EC1M 4AY, England. circ. 5,000.

387 UK
REGISTER OF OFFSHORE UNITS, SUBMERSIBLES AND UNDERWATER SYSTEMS. 1976. a. $198. Lloyd's Register of Shipping, 71 Fenchurch St., London EC3M 4BS, England. TEL 0171-709-9166. (U.S. subscr. to: Lloyd's Register of Shipping, 17 Battery Pl., New York, NY 10004) **Document type:** directory.
 Formerly: Register of Offshore Units, Submersibles and Diving Systems (ISSN 0141-4143)
 Description: Supplies technical information on mobile drilling rigs, submersibles, diving systems and work units. Includes owners' names and addresses.

387 FR ISSN 0152-9994
REGISTRE MARITIME. 1829. a. (with q. supplements). 1000 F. Bureau Veritas, Service Maritime, 17 bis, Place des Reflets, La Defense 2, 92400 Courbevoie, France. FAX 42-91-52-98. TELEX 612440F BVDSM. Ed. Berger Levrault. circ. 800. (also avail. in microfilm)
 Supersedes in part: Registre International de Classification de Navires et d'Aeronefs (ISSN 0080-0678)

RENENG DONGLI GONGCHENG/JOURNAL OF ENGINEERING FOR THERMAL ENERGY AND POWER. see ENGINEERING — Mechanical Engineering

623.89 380 FR ISSN 0989-5981
REPERTOIRE DES RADIOSIGNAUX. (Subseries of: Ouvrages de Radiosignaux) 1977. a. 60 F. Service Hydrographique et Oceanographique de la Marine, 3 av. Octave Greard, 00300 Armees, France. TEL 98-03-09-17. FAX 98-47-11-42. TELEX HYDRO 940568 F. (Subscr. to: EPSHOM, B.P. 426, 29275 Brest Cedex, France) **Document type:** government publication.
 Description: Lists the major radio signals, beacons, and stations giving navigation information.

387.2 UN ISSN 0085-560X
REVIEW OF MARITIME TRANSPORT. Arabic edition (ISSN 0252-5437); Chinese edition (ISSN 0252-5445); French edition (ISSN 0252-5429); Russian edition (ISSN 0252-5453); Spanish edition (ISSN 0252-5410) 1968. a. price varies. (United Nations Conference on Trade and Development (UNCTAD)) United Nations Publications, Room DC2-853, New York, NY 10017. TEL 212-963-8302; 800-253-9646. FAX 212-963-3489. (Or: Palais des Nations, 1211 Geneva, Switzerland) (also avail. in microfiche from CIS) **Indexed:** IIS.

387 PO ISSN 0034-8546
REVISTA DE MARINHA. 1937. m. Esc.3780. Editora Nautica Nacional, Apdo. 3115, 1303 Lisbon Codex, Portugal. TEL 351-1-4390424. FAX 351-1-4391485. Ed. Gabriel Lobo Fialho. adv.; bk.rev. circ. 5,000.

623.8 FR ISSN 0767-094X
HE387.R5
REVUE DE LA NAVIGATION FLUVIALE EUROPEENNE, PORTS ET INDUSTRIES. Short title: Navigation, Ports and Industries. 1922. fortn. $200. Editions de la Navigation du Rhin, 7 Quai du General Koenig, 67085 Strasbourg Cedex, France. FAX 88-37-04-82. Ed. Maurice Ruscher. adv. contact: Jean-Marie Lochert. bk.rev.; charts; illus.; bibl.; index. circ. 2,500. **Indexed:** Excerp.Med. —SWETS.
 Description: Covers current events in navigation such as productivity, port traffic as well as various projects and developments taking place in ports world-wide.

387 NE
RHINE SHIPS REGISTER. 1879. a. fl.600. Internationale Vereniging het Rijnschepenregister (IVR) - International Association for the Rhine Ships Register, Vasteland 12E, Postbus 23210, 3001 KE Rotterdam, Netherlands. TEL 31-10-4116070. FAX 31-10-4129091. (also avail. in diskette format) **Document type:** trade publication.
 Description: Contains data on ships from Switzerland, France, Germany, Holland, Belgium, and Luxembourg, that sail on the Rhine River.

387 FR
RIVAGES. irreg. Universite de Montpellier (Universite Paul Valery), Laboratoire Amenagement des Littoraux et Organisation de l'Espace, B.P. 5043, 43032 Montpellier Cedex 1, France. TEL 67-14-20-00. Eds. Christian Verlaque, Jean-Marie Miossec.

359.97 US ISSN 0145-0689
VG53
RIVER CURRENTS. 1947. q. free. U.S. Coast Guard, Public Affairs Office, 1222 Spruce St., St. Louis, MO 63103. TEL 314-539-2627. FAX 314-539-2630. Ed. R. Roskiewicz. charts; illus. circ. 1,800. (also avail. in microform from UMI; reprint service avail. from UMI)
 —UMI.

387 IT ISSN 0035-5925
RIVISTA DEL PORTO DI NAPOLI. 1965. bi-m. L.18000 (foreign L.36000). Consorzio Autonomo del Porto, Molo Pisacane, 80133 Naples, Italy. TEL 266566. TELEX 721271 CAPNA I. Ed. Ernesto Mazzetti. adv.; bk.rev.; charts; illus.; stat.; index. circ. 2,000. —BLDSC (7992.730500).
 Description: Features articles on the Port of Naples. Includes information on tourism, import-export and the shipping industry.

ROLL ON ROLL OFF IN EUROPE; international guide for roll-on-roll-off shipping. see BUSINESS AND ECONOMICS — International Commerce

623.82 SP ISSN 0211-2892
ROTACION; actualidad tecnica de maquinaria y equipos para buques. 1968. m. (13/yr.). 6996 ptas. Pedeca Sociedad Cooperativa, Ltda., Maria Auxiliadora 5, 28040 Madrid, Spain. TEL 1-450-88-37. FAX 1-450-94-29. Ed. Antonio Alarcon Sanchez. adv.; bk.rev.; illus.; tr.lit. circ. 7,500. **Indexed:** Ind.SST.

387 JA ISSN 0286-8474
RYOKAKUSEN/PASSENGERBOAT. (Text in Japanese) 1955. q. 400 Yen per no. Nihon Ryokakusen Kyokai - Japan Passengerboat Association, 1-1, Uchisaiwa-cho 2-chome, Chiyoda-ku, Tokyo 100, Japan.

S A R STATISTICS. (Search and Rescue) see
TRANSPORTATION — Abstracting, Bibliographies, Statistics

623.82 JA
S R C NEWS. (Text in Japanese) 1987. q. Shipbuilding Research Center of Japan - Nihon Zosen Gijyutsu Senta, 3-8, Mejiro 1-chome, Toshima-ku, Tokyo 171, Japan.

TRANSPORTATION — SHIPS AND SHIPPING

387   MY   ISSN 0080-522X
HE884.6.S22
SABAH. MARINE DEPARTMENT. ANNUAL REPORT. (Text in English) 1961. a. M.$2. Marine Department, Jabatan Laut Sabah, Peti Surat 5, 87008 Labuan, Malaysia. TEL 087-412597. FAX 087-413515. TELEX MARKIN MA 80314. **Document type:** government publication.

387   623.888   UK   ISSN 0142-0666
VK200
SAFETY AT SEA INTERNATIONAL. 1967. m. £100($209) (overseas £114) (effective Sep. 1995). Argus Business Media Ltd., International Trade Publications (Subsidiary of: Argus Press Group), Queensway House, 2 Queensway, Redhill, Surrey RH1 1QS, England. TEL 01737-768611. FAX 01737-761989. TELEX 948669 TOPJNL G. Ed. Bill Evett; Pub. Roy Greenslade. adv. contact: Richard Harris. bk.rev.; abstr.; illus. circ. 5,400. **Indexed:** BMT. **Document type:** trade publication.
—BLDSC (8069.130000); SWETS.
    Formerly (until 1978): Safety at Sea International (ISSN 0036-2441)

387   JA   ISSN 0287-590X
SAGYOSEN/WORKVESSEL. (Text in Japanese) 1959. bi-m. Nihon Sagyosen Kyokai - Japan Workvessel Association, 9-7, Yaesu 2-chome, Chuo-ku, Tokyo 104, Japan.

387   CN   ISSN 0581-3298
HD1694
ST. LAWRENCE SEAWAY AUTHORITY. ANNUAL REPORT. (Text in English and French) 1955. a. free. St. Lawrence Seaway Authority, Constitution Sq., 360 Albert St., Ottawa, ON K1R 7X7, Canada. TEL 613-598-4614. FAX 613-598-4620. circ. 3,000. **Document type:** corporate report.

387   IS
HASAPANUT HAYISRAELIT/ISRAEL SHIPPING. (Text in Hebrew; summaries in English) a. free. Wydra Shipping & Aviation Research Institute, University of Haifa, Eshkol Tower, Haifa 31905, Israel. TEL 972-4-240186. FAX 972-4-348908. Ed. M. Ofek. **Document type:** monographic series.
    Description: Description and analysis of world developments in shipping and ports; with a detailed survey of Israeli developments; comprehensive statistical appendix.

623.8   627.2   GW   ISSN 0938-1643
VM3   CODEN: SHASEZ
SCHIFF UND HAFEN. (Text in English and German) 1948. m. DM.298. (Schiffbautechnische Gesellschaft e.V.) Seehafen Verlag, Postfach 105605, 20038 Hamburg, Germany. TEL 040-2371402. FAX 040-23714154. adv.; bk.rev.; charts; illus.; index. circ. 5,500. **Indexed:** BMT, C.I.S. Abstr., Chem.Abstr., Excerp.Med., Fluidex, Met.Abstr., World Alum.Abstr. **Document type:** trade publication.
—BLDSC (8088.700000); SWETS.
    Formerly: Schiff und Hafen - Kommandobruecke; Which was formed by the merger of: Schiff und Hafen (ISSN 0036-603X); Kommandobruecke.

387.2   GW
SCHIFF UND ZEIT. 1973. irreg., vol.41, 1995. DM.49.60. (Deutsche Gesellschaft fuer Schiffahrts-und Marinegeschichte e. V.) Koehlers Verlagsgesellschaft mbH, Striepenweg 31, 21147 Hamburg, Germany. TEL 040-79713322. FAX 040-79713324. illus. **Document type:** trade publication.

623.8   GW   ISSN 0342-491X
SCHIFFAHRT INTERNATIONAL. 1949. m. DM.110.40. Wirtschafts- und Verkehrsverlag Hansa GmbH, Elbchaussee 277, 22605 Hamburg, Germany. TEL 040-822807-0. FAX 040-82280752. (Subscr. to: Verlagsgruppe Koehler - Mittler, Postfach 2352, 32045 Herford, Germany. TEL 05221-599146) Ed. Garrit Leemreijze. adv.; bk.rev.; abstr.; charts; illus.; stat.; index. circ. 9,000. **Indexed:** BMT. **Document type:** trade publication.
    Former titles: Schiffahrt International mit Seekiste und Nautilus; Schiffahrt International - Seekiste (ISSN 0037-0843)

387   AU
SCHIFFAHRT UND STROM. bi-m. S.300. Oesterreichischer Wasserstrassen- und Schiffahrtsverein - Austrian Navigation and Waterways Association, Leberstr. 122, A-1110 Vienna, Austria. FAX 01-74095-430. adv.; bk.rev. **Document type:** trade publication.

623.8   GW   ISSN 0036-6056
VM156
SCHIFFBAUFORSCHUNG; Schriftenreihe fuer Ingenieurwissenschaften. (Text in German; contents page and summaries in English, German, Russian, and Spanish) 1962. q. DM.140. Universitaet Rostock, Fachbereich Maschinenbau und Schiffstechnik, Albert-Einstein-Str. 2, 18059 Rostock, Germany. TEL 0381-4405322. FAX 0381-4405253. Ed. Mathias Paschen. bk.rev.; charts; illus. circ. 450. **Indexed:** BMT. **Document type:** academic/scholarly publication.
—BLDSC (8088.740000); Faxon.

623.82   US   ISSN 0374-1222
VM3
SCHIFFBAUTECHNISCHEN GESELLSCHAFT. JAHRBUCH. a. price varies. Springer-Verlag, 175 Fifth Ave, New York, NY 10010. TEL 212-460-1500. FAX 212-473-6272. (Also Berlin, Heidelberg, Tokyo and Vienna) (reprint service avail. from ISI) **Document type:** academic/scholarly publication.

387   GW
SCHIFFS-INGENIEUR JOURNAL. bi-m. Verein der Schiffs-Ingenieur zu Hamburg, Gurlittstr. 32, 20099 Hamburg, Germany. TEL 040-2803883.

387   621.9   GW   ISSN 0177-1116
SCHIFFSBETRIEBSTECHNIK FLENSBURG. 1954. q. DM.25 membership; newsstand price: DM.5.50. Schiffsbetriebstechnische Gesellschaft Flensburg e.V., Kanzleistr. 91-93, 24943 Flensburg, Germany. TEL 0461-29222. Ed. H. Meier-Peter. adv.; bk.rev. circ. 1,500. (back issues avail.) **Document type:** trade publication.
    Description: Trade publication for the shipbuilding industry. Features the latest technology, marketing, industry and trade school information. Includes list of events and exhibitions.

387   GW
SCHIFFSLISTE; Verzeichnis der deutschen Reedereien & ihre Schiffe. 1902. a. DM.56. Eckardt & Messtorff GmbH, Roedingsmarkt 16, 20459 Hamburg, Germany. FAX 040-373028. Ed. G.U. Detlefsen. adv. circ. 3,000. **Document type:** trade publication.

623.8   GW   ISSN 0036-6064
    CODEN: SCFTAO
SCHIFFSTECHNIK; Forschungshefte fuer Schiffbau und Schiffsmaschinenbau. 1952. 4/yr. DM.192.20. Wirtschafts- und Verkehrsverlag Hansa GmbH, Elbchaussee 277, 22605 Hamburg, Germany. TEL 040-822807-0. FAX 040-82280752. (Subscr. to: Verlagsgruppe Koehler - Mittler, Postfach 2352, 32045 Herford, Germany. TEL 05221-599146) adv.; charts. circ. 1,000. **Indexed:** Appl.Mech.Rev., BMT, Deep Sea Res.& Oceanogr.Abstr., Eng.Ind. **Document type:** trade publication.

387   340   NE   ISSN 0165-103X
SCHIP EN SCHADE; beslissingen op het gebied van zee- en binnenvaartrecht, transport en brandverzekeringsrecht. (Supplement avail. (ISSN 0165-1080)) 1957. 10/yr. fl.317.55. W.E.J. Tjeenk Willink B.V. (Subsidiary of: Wolters Kluwer N.V.), Postbus 25, 8000 AA Zwolle, Netherlands. TEL 31-38-211444. FAX 31-38-216500. adv.; circ. 900 (paid). **Document type:** trade publication.

387   340   NE   ISSN 0165-1080
SCHIP EN SCHADE, KAARTEN. 1957. 10/yr. W.E.J. Tjeenk Willink B.V. (Subsidiary of: Wolters Kluwer N.V.), Postbus 25, 8000 AA Zwolle, Netherlands. TEL 31-38-211444. FAX 31-38-216500. adv. **Document type:** trade publication.

623.8   NE   ISSN 0926-4213
VM4
SCHIP EN WERF DE ZEE. 1934. m. fl.97.50 (foreign fl.149.50). (Nederlandsche Vereniging van Technici op Scheepvaartgebied - Dutch Association of Marine Engineers) Wyt Uitgeefgroep B.V., P.O. Box 6438, 3002 AK Rotterdam, Netherlands. TEL 31-10-4255944. FAX 31-10-4780904. (Co-sponsors: Centrale Bond van Scheepsbouwmeesters in Nederland; National Instituut voor Scheepvaart en Scheepsbouw; Nederlandsch Scheepsbouwkundig Proefstation) adv.; index. circ. 4,500. **Indexed:** BMT, C.I.S. Abstr., Excerp.Med., Key to Econ.Sci. **Document type:** trade publication.
—BLDSC (8089.030000); SWETS.
    Formed by the 1991 merger of: Schip en Werf (ISSN 0036-6099) & N T T De Zee (ISSN 0921-2450); Which was formerly (until 1985): Nautisch Technisch Tijdschrift de Zee (ISSN 0165-6236)

387   NE   ISSN 0166-5111
SCHIPPERSWEEKBLAD. 1919. bi-w. fl.59.50. (Federatie van Samenwerkende Schippesbonden) Numij B.V., Postbus 4, 2300 AA Leiden, Netherlands. adv.; bk.rev. circ. 2,000. **Document type:** trade publication.
    Formed by the 1976 merger of: Shippersblad (ISSN 0926-1869) & Ons Kompas (ISSN 0926-1842) & Getij (ISSN 0926-1850)

387   UK   ISSN 0308-2253
SEA. 1974. bi-m. £1.50. Missions to Seamen, St. Michael Paternoster Royal, College Hill, London EC4R 2RL, England. TEL 0171-248-5202. FAX 0171-248-4761. Ed. Gillian Ennis. circ. 13,000. (tabloid format)

387   UK   ISSN 0036-9977
HE753.P32
SEA BREEZES; the magazine of ships and the sea. 1919. m. $45. Jocast Ltd., 202 Cotton Exchange Bldg., Old Hall St., Liverpool L3 9LA, England. Ed. C.H. Milsom. adv.; bk.rev.; charts; illus.; index. **Document type:** trade publication.
—BLDSC (8213.560000).
    Description: Contains authoritative articles on ships, seamen and the sea written from first-hand experience or after long and careful research.

387   970   US   ISSN 0582-3471
SEA CHEST. 1967. q. $35. Puget Sound Maritime Historical Society, 1216 Broadway, Bremerton, WA 98337. Ed. Michael Jay Mjelde. bk.rev.; illus.; index. circ. 750. (back issues avail.) **Indexed:** Amer.Hist.& Life, Hist.Abstr. **Document type:** academic/scholarly publication.

387   US   ISSN 0146-9312
VK23
SEA HISTORY; the art, literature, adventure, lore & learning of the sea. 1972. q. $30 (foreign $40). (National Maritime Historical Society) Sea History Press, 5 John Walsh Blvd., Box 68, Peekskill, NY 10566-5324. TEL 914-737-7878. Ed. Peter Stanford; Pub. Peter Stanford. adv. contact: Norma Stanford. bk.rev.; circ. 15,000 (paid); 15,000 (controlled). (back issues avail.) **Indexed:** Amer.Hist.& Life, Bk.Rev.Ind. (1990-), Child.Bk.Rev.Ind. (1990-), Hist.Abstr. **Document type:** consumer publication.
—UnCover.
    Description: Features articles on maritime history and related subjects.

387   US   ISSN 0896-1646
VK23
SEA HISTORY GAZETTE. 1987. m. $18.75 (foreign $28.75). National Maritime Historical Society, 5 John Walsh Blvd., Charles Point, Peekskill, NY 10566-5324. TEL 914-271-2177. Ed. Kevin F. Haydon. circ. 1,000.
    Description: Digest of maritime heritage news.

SEA HISTORY'S GUIDE TO AMERICAN & CANADIAN MARITIME MUSEUMS. see *MUSEUMS AND ART GALLERIES*

387   US   ISSN 0732-6882
SEA LETTER. 1961. s-a. membership. National Maritime Museum Association, Presidio of San Francisco Bldg. 275, Crissy Field, San Francisco, CA 94129. TEL 415-929-0202. Ed. Russell Booth. bk.rev.; illus. circ. 2,000. **Document type:** academic/scholarly publication.
    Formerly: San Francisco Maritime Museum. Sea Letter (ISSN 0037-0010)

TRANSPORTATION — SHIPS AND SHIPPING

SEA POWER. see *MILITARY*

370 UK ISSN 0037-007X
VK1
THE SEAFARER. 1934. q. £8($15.20) to individuals; institutions £9.50($18.05). Marine Society, 202 Lambeth Rd., London SE1 7JW, England. TEL 0171-261-9535. FAX 0171-401-2537. TELEX 934089-MARSOC-G. Ed. Michael Moore. adv.; bk.rev.; illus. circ. 2,500. (back issues avail.) **Document type:** newsletter.
Description: Short fiction, poetry, historical vignettes, and informational articles pertaining to British seafaring, with news and announcements about the Society, a maritime charity.

387 UK ISSN 0964-8895
HE561
SEATRADE REVIEW. (Includes special supplement with each issue) 1970. m. £96 (foreign $192). Seatrade Publications Ltd., Seatrade House, 42 North Station Rd., Colchester, Essex CO1 1RB, England. TEL 01206-45121. FAX 01206-45190. N. America subscr. to: 125 Village Blvd., Ste.220, Princeton Forrestal Village, Princeton, NJ 08540-5703. TEL 609-452-9414. FAX 609-452-9374) Ed. Mary Bond; Pub. Christopher Hayman. adv.; B&W page £1620, color page £2295; adv. contact: Anthony Nash. bk.rev. circ. 10,436. **Indexed:** BMT, Fuel & Energy Abstr., Key to Econ.Sci., P.A.I.S. **Document type:** trade publication.
—BLDSC (8216.055070); SWETS.
Former titles (until 1992): Seatrade Business Review (ISSN 0951-6832); Seatrade (ISSN 0037-0428).

387 HK
SEATRADE WEEK NEWSFRONT. 1982. w. $695 includes Seatrade Review. Seatrade Information Services Ltd., China Resources Bldg., 44th Fl., 28 Harbour Rd., Hong Kong. TEL 0852-827-9128. FAX 0852-827-7831. TELEX 98517-DISOP-G. (Dist. by: Seatrade Publications Ltd., Seatrade House, 42 North Station Rd., Colchester CO1 1RB, England. TEL 044-206-45121. FAX 044-206-45190; N. American subscr. to: 125 Village Blvd., Ste. 220, Princeton Forrestal Village, Princeton, NJ 08540-5703. TEL 609-452-9414. FAX 609-452-9374) Ed. Ian Middleton. adv.; bk.rev. circ. 3,500. **Document type:** trade publication.
Formerly: Seatrade Week Information Service.
Description: Shipping news and market data.

387 US ISSN 0037-0487
HE381.A2
SEAWAY REVIEW; the magazine of North America's freshwater transportation system. 1970. q. $20. Harbor House Publishers, Inc., 221 Water St., Boyne City, MI 49712. TEL 616-582-2814. FAX 616-582-3392. David L. Knight; Pub. Michelle Cortright. adv.; bk.rev.; charts; illus.; stat. circ. 7,500. (also avail. in microfilm from UMI; back issues avail.) **Indexed:** BMT, Mich.Mag.Ind. **Document type:** trade publication.
—Faxon; UMI. **CCC.**
Incorporates (as of vol.6, 1977): Limnos (ISSN 0024-3604).
Description: Edited for the bi-national transportation industry and infrastructure in the Great Lakes - St. Lawrence transportation system. Articles concern international trade, port development, shipbuilding, shipping, economics, maritime technology and hardware, ship maintenance, foreign and U.S. liner services and cargo handling.

387 UK ISSN 0144-1019
SEAWAYS. 1980. m. £50($72) Nautical Institute, 202 Lambeth Rd., London SE1 7LQ, England. TEL 0171-928-1351. FAX 0171-401-2817. Ed. Claire Walsh; Pub. Julian Parker. adv. contact: Tina Scott. bk.rev.; charts; illus.; index. circ. 6,389. (back issues avail.) **Document type:** trade publication.
—BLDSC (8216.055600).

THE SEAWAYS; journal of maritime history and research. see *HOBBIES*

SEFUNIM. see *ARCHAEOLOGY*

623.81 JA ISSN 0389-911X
SEIBU ZOSENKAI KAIHO/WEST JAPAN SOCIETY OF NAVAL ARCHITECTS. TRANSACTIONS. (Text in English, Japanese; summaries in English) 1949. s-a. Seibu Zosenkai, c/o Kyushu Daigaku Kogakubu Zosengaku Kyoshitsu, 10-1, Hakozaki 6-chome, Higashi-ku, Fukuoka-shi, Fukuoka-ken 812, Japan.
—BLDSC (9012.890000).

SEIBU ZOSENKAI RONBUN KOGAI/WEST JAPAN SOCIETY OF NAVAL ARCHITECTS. ABSTRACTS FROM RESEARCH REPORT. see *TRANSPORTATION — Abstracting, Bibliographies, Statistics*

SEKAI NO KANSEN/SHIPS OF THE WORLD. see *MILITARY*

623.81 JA
SENPAKU GIJUTSU KENKYUJO HAPPYO RONBUN HYODAISHU/SHIP RESEARCH INSTITUTE. LIST OF PAPERS. (Text in Japanese) 1966. every 5 yrs. Un'yusho, Senpaku Gijutsu Kenkyujo - Ministry of Transport, Ship Research Institute, 38-1, Shinkawa 6-chome, Mitaka-shi, Tokyo 181, Japan. **Document type:** government publication.

623.81 JA ISSN 0285-7332
SENPAKU GIJUTSU KENKYUJO KENKYU HAPPYOKAI KOENSHU/SHIP RESEARCH INSTITUTE. REPORTS OF MEETING. (Text in English, Japanese) 1974. s-a. Un'yusho, Senpaku Gijutsu Kenkyujo - Ministry of Transport, Ship Research Institute, 38-1, Shinkawa 6-chome, Mitaka-shi, Tokyo 181, Japan. **Document type:** government publication.

623.8 JA
SENPAKU GIJUTSU KENKYUJO KIKAN DORYOKUBU KIYO/SHIP RESEARCH INSTITUTE. POWER AND ENERGY ENGINEERING DIVISION. MEMOIRS. (Text in English, Japanese; summaries in English) 1991. irreg. Un'yusho, Senpaku Gijutsu Kenkyujo - Ministry of Transport, Ship Research Institute, 38-1, Shinkawa 6-chome, Mitaka-shi, Tokyo 181, Japan.

623.81 JA
SENPAKU GIJUTSU KENKYUJO NENPO/SHIP RESEARCH INSTITUTE. ANNUAL REPORT. (Text in Japanese) 1950. a. Un'yusho, Senpaku Gijutsu Kenkyujo - Ministry of Transport, Ship Research Institute, 38-1, Shinkawa 6-chome, Mitaka-shi, Tokyo 181, Japan. **Document type:** government publication.

623.8 JA ISSN 0288-1233
SENPAKU HYOJUNKA GIHO/TECHNICAL JOURNAL OF MARINE STANDARDIZATION. (Text in Japanese) 1969. s-a. Nihon Senpaku Hyojun Kyokai - Japan Marine Standards Association, Nihon Zosen Gijutsu Senta Biru, 3-8, Mejiro 1-chome, Toshima-ku, Tokyo 105, Japan. TEL 03-3984-9051. FAX 03-3984-8994. Ed. Ryohei Kume. circ. 850 (controlled). **Document type:** monographic series.

623.8 JA ISSN 0916-8672
SENPAKU KAIHATSU GIHO/SHIP RESEARCH REPORT. (Text in Japanese) 1975. a. Kaijo Hoancho, Sobi Gijutsubu - Maritime Safety Agency, Equipment and Technology Department, 1-3, Kasumigaseki 2-chome, Chiyoda-ku, Tokyo 100, Japan.
Formerly (until 1986): Kaihatsu Giho (ISSN 0911-6702)

387 SP ISSN 0211-304X
SERNAVAL. (Servicio Informacion Naval); informe mensual sobre la actividad naval y maritima. (Text in English and Spanish) 1972. m. 40000 ptas. Pedeca Sociedad Cooperativa, Ltda., Maria Auxiliadora 5, 28040 Madrid, Spain. TEL 459 60 00. Ed. Bernardo Moll. stat. circ. 1,000. (back issues avail.)

387 SZ
SEXTANT. (Text in French and German) 1974. q. Schweizerischer Bootbauer-Verband, Gemeindehaus, Postfach 74, CH-8117 Faellanden, Switzerland. TEL 01-825-0388. FAX 01-825-2256. adv.

387 CC ISSN 1000-5188
SHANGHAI HAIYUN XUEYUAN XUEBAO. (Text in Chinese) 1979. q. Shanghai Haiyun Xueyuan, 1550 Pudong Dadao, Shanghai 200135, People's Republic of China. TEL 8848911. Ed. Fu Xianghao. **Document type:** academic/scholarly publication.

SHI PAWA/SEA POWER. see *MILITARY*

387 UK ISSN 0037-3834
VM320
SHIP & BOAT INTERNATIONAL. 1937. 10/yr. £50 (Europe £55; elsewhere £60). Royal Institution of Naval Architects, 10 Upper Belgrave St., London SW1X 8BQ, England. TEL 0171-235-4622. FAX 0171-245-6959. Ed. Richard White. adv.: B&W page £990, color page £1415; trim 297 x 210; adv. contact: Sheila Smale. bk.rev.; charts; illus.; mkt.; pat.; stat.; tr.lit.; tr.mk. circ. 7,352. **Indexed:** BMT, Br.Tech.Ind., Excerp.Med., Fluidex, Ocean.Abstr., Pollut.Abstr., So.Pac.Per.Ind. **Document type:** trade publication.
—BLDSC (8258.550000); SWETS.
Incorporating: International Tug and Workboat.
Description: Covers all aspects of the workboat, small craft and small ship industry worldwide.

387 UK ISSN 0969-9635
SHIP FINANCE ANNUAL (YEAR). 1993. a. £95($170) Euromoney Publications plc., Books, Nestor House, Playhouse Yard, London EC4V 5EX, England. TEL 0171-779-8935. FAX 0171-779-8541. (Orders to: Plymbridge Distributors Ltd., Estover, Plymouth, Devon PL6 7PZ, England. TEL 0171-779-8610. FAX 01752-695668) Ed. Adrian Hornbook. **Document type:** directory.
Description: Covers all financial aspects of ships and shipping, profiling more than 650 companies in 28 countries.

623.81 UK
SHIP REPAIR AND CONVERSION TECHNOLOGY. 1989. q. £15 (Europe £20; elsewhere £25). Royal Institution of Naval Architects, 10 Upper Belgrave St., London SW1X 8BQ, England. TEL 0171-235-4622. FAX 0171-245-6959. Ed. Tim Knaggs. adv.: B&W page £1130, color page £1555; trim 297 x 210; adv. contact: Debbi Bonner. circ. 6,038. **Document type:** trade publication.
Description: Covers all aspects of repair and conversion work ranging from fishing vessels and workboats to cruise liners, ferries, container ships and supertankers.

SHIP SAFETY AND POLLUTION PREVENTION - SHIP MANAGEMENT AND PORT STATE CONTROL. see *ENVIRONMENTAL STUDIES — Toxicology And Environmental Safety*

623.8 UK ISSN 0263-7944
SHIPCARE & MARITIME MANAGEMENT. 1968. bi-m. £86($165) (overseas £89) (effective Sep. 1995). Argus Business Media Ltd., International Trade Publications (Subsidiary of: Argus Press Group), Queensway House, 2 Queensway, Redhill, Surrey RH1 1QS, England. TEL 01737-768611. FAX 01737-761989. TELEX 948669 TOPJNL G. Ed. Bill Evett; Pub. Roy Greenslade. adv. contact: Richard Harris. abstr.; illus.; stat. circ. 1,740. **Indexed:** API Abstr., API Catal., API Hlth.& Environ., API Oil., API Pet.Ref., API Pet.Subst., API Transport., BMT, Br.Tech.Ind., Excerp.Med., Ocean.Abstr. **Document type:** trade publication.
—BLDSC (8261.200000); Faxon.
Formed by the 1979 merger of: Shipcare International; Which was previously (until 1976): Ship Repair and Maintenance International (ISSN 0049-0369); And: Maritime Management (ISSN 0263-5585); Which was previously (until 1978): Tanker and Bulker International (ISSN 0306-946X); (until 1975): Tanker and Bulk Carrier (ISSN 0039-9426)

387 HK
SHIPPERS TODAY. (Text in Chinese, English) 1978. bi-m. HK.$100 (foreign HK.$250). Hong Kong Shippers Council, 31F, Wu Chung House, 213 Queen's Rd. E., Hong Kong. TEL 852-824-1228. FAX 852-824-0394. Ed. David Clarke. adv. circ. 6,000. **Document type:** trade publication.
Description: Covers international trade and transportation topics of interest to shippers in Hong Kong.

387.5 639.2 551.46 II ISSN 0970-0285
HE561
SHIPPING AND MARINE INDUSTRIES JOURNAL; devoted to shipping and shipbuilding industries, fisheries and oceanography. (Text in English) 1972. q. Rs.110($25) V.J. Joseph, Ed. & Pub., C-4 Rishikesh II, Evershine Nagar, Malad West, Bombay 400 064, India. TEL 8826614. adv.; charts, illus, stat. (reprint service avail.) **Indexed:** BMT.

TRANSPORTATION — SHIPS AND SHIPPING

387 910.09 GR
SHIPPING AND TOURISM. (Supplement to: Epilogi) 1991. a. Dr.1000. Electra Press, 4 Stadiou, 105 64 Athens, Greece. TEL 30-1-3233-303. FAX 30-1-3255-160. TELEX 210564. Ed. Christos Papaioannou. adv. circ. 9,000. **Document type:** trade publication.

387 382 JA
SHIPPING AND TRADE NEWS. (Text in English) 1949. d. (plus m. special issues). 42900 Yen. Tokyo News Service Ltd., Tsukiji Hamarikyu Bldg., 3-3 Tsukiji, 5-chome, Chuo-ku, Tokyo 104, Japan. TEL 03-3542-8521. Ed. Chiaki Sakurai. circ. 15,000. **Document type:** newspaper.

387 BA ISSN 0958-8485
SHIPPING & TRANSPORT NEWS INTERNATIONAL. (Text in English) bi-m. $25. Al Hilal Publishing & Marketing Group, P.O. Box 224, Manama, Bahrain. TEL 973-293131. FAX 973-293400. TELEX 8981 HILAL BN. (In the U.K.: Hilal International (UK) Ltd., Crescent Ct., 102 Victor Rd., Teddington, Middx. TW11 8SS, England. TEL 44-181-943-3630) Ed. Fermin D'Souza. adv.: B&W page $2800, color page $3920; 400 x 275. circ. 5,600. (tabloid format) **Document type:** trade publication.
Formerly: Shipping and Transport News; Incorporates: Middle East Shipping and Transport (ISSN 0958-8477); Gulf Shipping and Transport.
Description: For senior management personnel in the shipping and transport industries of the Middle East and Far East, including air cargo, marine transport, airlines, import-export, and shipping agencies.

387 BA ISSN 1352-2051
SHIPPING & TRANSPORT NEWS INTERNATIONAL YEARBOOK AND DIRECTORY. (Text in English) 1989. a. Al Hilal Publishing & Marketing Group, P.O. Box 224, Manama, Bahrain. TEL 973-293131. FAX 973-293400. TELEX 8981 HUKAK BN. (In the U.K.: Hilal International (UK) Ltd., Crescent Ct., 102 Victor Rd., Teddington, Mddx. TW11 8SS, England. TEL 44-181-943-3630) adv. **Document type:** trade publication, directory.

387 US ISSN 0037-3893
HE561
SHIPPING DIGEST; for export and transportation executives. 1923. w. $46. Geyer-McAllister Publications, Inc., 51 Madison Ave., New York, NY 10010. TEL 212-689-4411. (Subscr. to: Box 1129, Dover, NJ 07801) adv. circ. 4,900. (back issues avail.) **Document type:** trade publication.
—CCC.

387 US
SHIPPING DIGEST'S HANDBOOK FOR INTERNATIONAL TRADE. 2/yr. Geyer-McAllister Publications, Inc., 51 Madison Ave., New York, NY 10010. TEL 212-689-4411. FAX 212-683-7929. adv. circ. 4,884.
Description: Shipping industry reference guide containing export documentation requirements for well over 100 countries, a glossary of shipping terms, port cross-references, pier information, intermodal schedules and trade routes.

387 JA ISSN 0037-3915
SHIPPING GAZETTE; weekly of shipping schedules and news digest. (Text in English and Japanese) 1951. w. 24000 Yen. Japan Press, Ltd., C.P.O. Box 6, Tokyo 100-91, Japan. TEL 03-3404-5151. FAX 03-3423-2358. TELEX 242-5374 JPRESS J. (Subscr. to: 2-12-8 Kita Aoyama, Minato-ku, Tokyo 107, Japan) Ed. Yoshio Wada. adv. circ. 23,000.

387 II
SHIPPING INFORMATION SERVICES. m. South-Western India Shippers Association, Cochin Chamber Bldg., Bristow Road, Willingdon Island, Cochin 682 003, India. TEL 0484-6349.

387 UK
SHIPPING INTELLIGENCE WEEKLY. w. £322 (outside Europe £380. Clarkson Research Studies, 12 Camomile St., London EC3A 7BP, England. TEL 0171-283-8955. FAX 0171-623-0539. TELEX 881 2927 CLTNK G. adv.; charts; stat. **Document type:** trade publication.
Description: Reports on developments accross the range of shipping markets.

623.8 CN ISSN 0037-3923
SHIPPING REGISTER AND SHIPBUILDER.* (Annual Number) 1917. bi-m. Can.$10. Canadian Marine Publications Ltd., Ste. 512, 1434 St. Catherine St. W., Montreal, PQ H3G 1R4, Canada. TEL 514-861-6715. FAX 514-861-0966. Ed. O.J. Silva. adv.; illus. circ. 5,000.

387 UK
SHIPPING REVIEW & OUTLOOK. s-a. £180 (outside Europe £190); diskette £120 ($195). Clarkson Research Studies, 12 Camomile St., London EC3A 7BP, England. TEL 0171-283-8955. FAX 0171-623-0539. TELEX 881 2927 CLTNK G. stat. (also avail. in diskette format) **Document type:** trade publication.
Description: Analyzes developments in 17 shipping industry market segments. Includes a comprehensive time-series statistical section.

623.82 UK ISSN 0037-3931
CODEN: SWSBA5
SHIPPING WORLD & SHIPBUILDER. 1883. 10/yr. £45 (foreign £55). Marine Publications International Ltd., 4 Hubbard Rd., Houndmills, Basingstoke, Hampshire RG21 2UH, England. TEL 01256-840444. FAX 01256-817877. Ed. Derek Deere. adv.; bk.rev.; illus. circ. 4,621. (also avail. in microform from UMI; reprint service avail.) **Indexed:** Appl.Mech.Rev.; BMT, Br.Tech.Ind., C.I.S. Abstr., Eng.Ind., Fluidex, Key to Econ.Sci., Ocean.Abstr., Pollut.Abstr., World Surf.Coat. **Document type:** trade publication.
—BLDSC (8263.300000); SWETS; UMI.
Incorporates: Syren and Shipping.

387 AT ISSN 1032-3449
SHIPS & PORTS. 1988. m. Aus.$70. Baird Publications Pty. Ltd., 10 Oxford St., South Yarra, Vic. 3141, Australia. TEL 61-3-98268741. FAX 61-3-98270704. Ed. Neil Baird. adv.: B&W page Aus.$1700, color page Aus.$2200. circ. 3,000.
Description: Newsmagazine of the ports and shipping industry in Australia and the South West Pacific.

387 US ISSN 1052-6862
G521
SHIPS & SHIPWRECKS. 1990. bi-m. $24. Riderwood Publishing Co., 5049 Smith Rd., Rohrersville, MD 21779-1039. TEL 301-432-4815. Ed. Lynn K. Sibley. bk.rev. **Document type:** newsletter.

387 UK
SHIPS ATLAS. 5th edition, 1994. irreg. £40 (foreign £45). Shipping Guides Ltd., Shipping Guides House, 75 Bell St., Reigate RH2 7AN, England. TEL 01737-242255. FAX 01737-722449. Ed. Robert Pedlow. maps. **Document type:** directory.
Description: Lists ports worldwide and gives coordinates, draft, and information on facilities.

387 UK ISSN 0037-394X
VM1
SHIPS MONTHLY. 1966. m. £23.40 (foreign £32); newsstand price: £1.95. Waterway Productions Ltd., Kottingham House, Dale St., Burton-on-Trent, Staffs DE14 3TD, England. TEL 01283-564290. FAX 01283-561077. Ed. Robert Shopland. adv.; bk.rev.; charts; illus.; stat.; index. circ. 21,663. **Document type:** trade publication.
—BLDSC (8266.150000); Ei.

623.82 US
SHIPYARD BULLETIN. 1927. m. free. Newport News Shipbuilding, Newport News, VA 23607. TEL 804-380-2342. FAX 804-380-3867. Ed. Pam Curley. circ. 30,000 (controlled). (tabloid format)
Description: Includes news on company business as well as employee features.

387 US ISSN 1061-9244
SHIPYARD CHRONICLE. 1975. bi-m. $175 (foreign $250). Shipbuilders Council of America, 901 N. Washington St., Ste. 204, Alexandria, VA 22314-1535. TEL 703-548-7447. FAX 703-518-0276. Ed. Franklin W. Losey. bk.rev.; stat. circ. 1,200. **Document type:** newsletter.
Formerly: Shipyard Weekly.
Description: Contains news and opinions related to shipbuilding and repair.

SHIPYARD LOG. see MILITARY

387 UK ISSN 0265-8291
SHIPYARD ORDERS. WEEKLY REPORT. 1984. w. £780. Lloyd's Register of Shipping, 71 Fenchurch St., London EC3M 4BS, England. TEL 0171-709-9166. (U.S. subscr. to: Lloyd's Register of Shipping, 17 Battery Pl., New York, NY 10004) **Document type:** newsletter.
Description: Reports shipyard orders and cancellations worldwide for ships of 100 gross tons and above.

623.8 II ISSN 0037-3958
SHIPYARD REVIEW. (Text in English and Telugu) 1959. q. Rs.4. Hindustan Shipyard Ltd., Visakhapatnam 5, India. Ed. K.M. Reddy. adv.; bk.rev.; illus. circ. 5,000.

386 CC ISSN 1001-3962
TC160 CODEN: SSKYEA
SHUILI SHUIYUN KEXUE YANJIU. (Text in Chinese) q. Nanjing Shuili Kexue Yanjiuyuan, 34 Hujuguan, Nanjing, Jiangsu 210024, People's Republic of China. TEL 637430. Ed. Liu Jinpei.

387 658 CC ISSN 1000-8799
SHUIYUN GUANLI/WATER TRANSPORTATION MANAGEMENT. (Text in Chinese) bi-m. Shanghai Haiyun Xueyuan, 1550 Pudong Dadao, Shanghai 200135, People's Republic of China. TEL 8840911. Ed. Su Peiji.

SIGNALS. see MUSEUMS AND ART GALLERIES

387 SI
SINGAPORE. NATIONAL MARITIME BOARD. REPORT. (Text in English) 1974. q. National Maritime Board, Singapore, Singapore. TEL 2227311. FAX 2251176. circ. 800. **Document type:** corporate report.

387 SI
SINGAPORE MARITIME DIRECTORY (YEAR). (Text in English) a. $50. Times Trade Directories Pte. Ltd., Times Centre, 1 New Industrial Rd., Singapore 1953, Singapore. TEL 2848844. FAX 2881186. TELEX RS 25713 TIMES. **Document type:** directory.
Description: Shipping directory contains in-depth editorial coverage of the dynamic port of Singapore and a comprehensive listing of companies concerned with shipping and maritime as well as those in the supporting industries.

SINGAPORE PORT STATISTICS. see TRANSPORTATION — Abstracting, Bibliographies, Statistics

387 SP
SINGULADURAS. 1969. w. 12000 ptas. (elsewhere L.15000). Bilbao Maritimo, S.A., Ercilla 24, 4o piso, 48011 Bilbao, Spain. TEL 4-416-23-56. FAX 4-4163797. TELEX 31027 AROS E. Ed. Mercedes Obrego. adv.; bk.rev. circ. 1,500.
Formerly: Bilbao Maritimo.

387.9 070.5 NO ISSN 0080-9888
SJOEFARTSHISTORISK AARBOK/NORWEGIAN YEARBOOK OF MARITIME HISTORY. (Text in Norwegian; summaries in English) 1928. a. NOK 90 to non-members; members NOK 75. Foreningen "Bergens Sjoefartsmuseum" - Bergen Maritime Museum, P.O. Box 2736, Moehlenpris, 5026 Bergen, Norway. TEL 47-532-7980. FAX 32-91-37. Ed. Atle Thowsen. adv. circ. 1,100. **Indexed:** Amer.Hist.& Life, Hist.Abstr. **Document type:** academic/scholarly publication.
Formerly (until 1965): Foreningen "Bergens Sjoefartsmuseum". Aarshefte (ISSN 0802-5843)

387.509 362.6 IC
SJOMANNADAGSBLADID. 1938. a. ISK 450 (effective 1992). (Sjomannadagsrad) Seamen's Welfare Organization, Hrafnista D A S, 104 Reykjavik, Iceland. TEL 354-553-8465. circ. 4,500. (back issues avail.)
Description: Devoted to the interests of seamen, their life and work.

387 NO ISSN 0800-1235
HE563.N8
SKANDINAVISKE SKIPSREDERIER/YEARBOOK OF SCANDINAVIAN SHIPOWNERS. (Text in English) 1936. a. NOK 300. Maritime Year Books AS, P.O. Box 9156 Vaterland, N-0134 Oslo 1, Norway. adv. **Document type:** directory.

6436 TRANSPORTATION — SHIPS AND SHIPPING

387　　　　　　　DK　　ISSN 0900-9132
SKIPPEREN. 1910. m. DKK 100. Rederiforeningen for Mindre Skibe, Valmuevej 4, 9380 Vestbjerg, Denmark. Ed. A. Traumholm. adv. circ. 1,000.

623.8 387　　　　UK　　ISSN 0262-480X
SMALL SHIPS. 1976. bi-m. $191 (effective 1995). Argus Business Media Ltd., International Trade Publications (Subsidiary of: Argus Press Group), Queensway House, 2 Queensway, Redhill, Surrey RH1 1QS, England. TEL 017337-768611. FAX 01737-760564. Ed. Bill Thomson. adv. contact: Glen Day. circ. 5,210 (paid). Indexed: BMT. Document type: trade publication.
  Description: Discusses the management, operation, and building of workboats and commercial and military vessels up to 100 meters in length.

387　　　　　　　US
SOCIETY OF MARITIME ARBITRATORS. AWARD SERVICE. 1965. a. $495. Society of Maritime Arbitrators, 61 Broadway, Ste. 1650, New York, NY 10006-2701. TEL 212-483-0616. FAX 212-480-3320. circ. 300. Document type: trade publication.

623.8　　　　　　US　　ISSN 0081-1661
VM1　　　　　　　CODEN: SNAMAL
SOCIETY OF NAVAL ARCHITECTS AND MARINE ENGINEERS. TRANSACTIONS. 1893. a. $67.50 (foreign $80). Society of Naval Architects and Marine Engineers, 601 Pavonia Ave., Jersey City, NJ 07306-2907. TEL 201-798-4800. FAX 201-798-4975. index. circ. 9,950. Indexed: BMT, Deep Sea Res.& Oceanogr.Abstr., Ocean.Abstr., Petrol.Abstr., Pollut.Abstr. Document type: academic/scholarly publication, proceedings.
  —BLDSC (9008.000000); Ei; UnCover.
  Description: Includes papers and annual reports presented at the Society's Annual Meeting, including certain award-winning techincal papers.

387　　　　　　　DK　　ISSN 0038-0520
SOEFART. 1950. w. membership. Foreningen til Soefartens Fremme - Association for the Promotion of the Danish Merchant Marine, Box 288, DK-8100 Aarhus C, Denmark. Ed. P. Rungholm. adv.; bk.rev.; charts; illus. circ. 9,500.

SOLAS - INTERNATIONAL CONVENTION FOR THE SAFETY OF LIFE AT SEA. AMENDMENTS. see ENVIRONMENTAL STUDIES — Toxicology And Environmental Safety

387　　　　　　　US
SOUNDINGS (LONG BEACH). 1983. m. $125. Professional Mariners Alliance, Inc., 370 W. Park Ave., Long Beach, NY 11561-3292. TEL 516-431-4441. FAX 516-889-5111. Ed. Thomas J. O'Hara III. adv.; bk.rev.; cum.index: 1983-1984. circ. 5,000. (back issues avail.)
  Formerly (until 1986): Professional Mariner.

SOUNDINGS (MILWAUKEE). see HISTORY — History Of North And South America

387　　　　　　　SA　　ISSN 0038-2671
HE561
SOUTH AFRICAN SHIPPING NEWS AND FISHING INDUSTRY REVIEW. Variant title: S.A. Shipping News and Fishing Industry Review. (Text in English) 1946-1983; resumed. bi-m. R.80. George Warman Publications (Pty.) Ltd., P.O. Box 3847, Cape Town 8000, South Africa. TEL 27-21-245320. FAX 27-21-261332. Ed. Tessa O'Hara. adv.; bk.rev.; charts; illus.; tr.lit. circ. 1,250. Indexed: BMT, Ind.S.A.Per., Ocean.Abstr., Pollut.Abstr. Document type: trade publication.

387　　　　　　　AG
SOUTH AMERICAN PORTS HANDBOOK. (Text in English) 1974. biennial. $80. Agencia Maritima Internacional S.A., 25 de Mayo 555, piso 20, 1002 Buenos Aires, Argentina. FAX 313-1996. TELEX 21115. illus. circ. 1,500.
  Formerly (until 1976): Owners, Masters, Brokers and Agents Handbook on South American Caribbean and Pacific Ports in Venezuela, Colombia, Panama, Ecuador, Peru, Bolivia and Chile.

387 382　　　　US　　ISSN 0896-2278
WMCL 82/61
SOUTH CAROLINA PORT NEWS. 1947. m. free to qualified personnel. Ports Authority, Box 817, Charleston, SC 29402. TEL 803-577-8622. FAX 803-577-8710. TELEX 810-881-1860 SCPORTSAUTH. Ed. L. Marion Bull; Pub. L. Duane Grantham. adv. contact: L. Marion Bull. charts; illus.; stat. circ. 11,200. Document type: trade publication.
  Description: Covers news relevant to the Port of Charleston. Features customers and stories of general interest to the community.

SOUTHAMPTON PORT HANDBOOK. see BUSINESS AND ECONOMICS — Trade And Industrial Directories

623.82　　　　　UK
SOVIET MARITIME NEWSLETTER. m. £185. Marine Publications International Ltd., 4 Hubbard Rd., Houndmills, Basingstoke, Hants. RG21 2UH, England. TEL 01256-840444.
FAX 01256-817877. Document type: newsletter, trade publication.

387　　　　　　　RU　　ISSN 0203-3933
　　　　　　　　　　　　　CODEN: SOVSEJ
SOVIET SHIPPING. (Text in English) 1981. q. free. Association of Soviet Shipowners, 4 Rakhmanovsky, Moscow, GSP-4 101412, Russia. Ed. K.A. Ivanov.

SPINDRIFT (PHILADELPHIA). see MUSEUMS AND ART GALLERIES

623.89 384 551.5　　FR
STATIONS RADIOMETEOROLOGIQUES. (Subseries of: Ouvrages de Radiosignaux) 1990. irreg., latest 1993. 397 F. (effective 1995). Service Hydrographique et Oceanographique de la Marine, 3 av. Octave Greard, 00300 Armees, France. TEL 98-03-09-17. FAX 98-47-11-42. TELEX HYDRO 940568 F. (Subscr. to: EPSHOM, B.P. 426, 29275 Brest Cedex, France) Document type: government publication.
  Description: Enables mariners to understand and transmit meteorological observations.

387　　　　　　　US　　ISSN 0039-0844
VM1
STEAMBOAT BILL; relating primarily to steam and other power vessels, past and present. 1940. q. $25. Steamship Historical Society of America, Inc., 300 Ray Dr., Ste. 4, Providence, RI 02906. Ed. William M. Rau. adv.; charts; illus.; cum.index: 1940-1974, 1975-1989. circ. 3,400. (also avail. in microform from UMI; reprint service avail. from UMI)
  —UMI.

STEAMBOATING; steamboater's handbook. see SPORTS AND GAMES — Boats And Boating

387.164　　　　GW　　ISSN 0934-6260
STOWAGE AND SEGREGATION GUIDE TO I M D G CODE. 1973. a. DM.117.76. K.O. Storck Verlag, Stahltwiete 7, 22761 Hamburg, Germany. TEL 040-853292-0. FAX 040-8507758. Ed. H. Meder, Document type: trade publication.
  Formerly: Stowage and Segregation to I M D G Code (ISSN 0172-8660)

387　　　　　　　SZ　　ISSN 0039-2510
STROM & SEE; Zeitschrift fuer Schiffahrt und Weltverkehr. 1906. 7/yr. membership. Schweizerische Schiffahrtsvereinigung - Swiss Shipping Association, Suedquaistr. 14, CH-4019 Basel, Switzerland. Ed. Joerg Meier. adv.; bk.rev.; charts; illus.; tr.lit.; index. circ. 2,500. Document type: trade publication.

387 343.09　　　　IT　　ISSN 0392-5021
STUDI MARITTIMI; economia, diritto e tecnica della navigazione dei porti. 1978. q. L.30000. Consorzio Autonomo del Porto, Piazzale Pisacane, 80133 Naples, Italy. TEL 081-266566. TELEX 721271 CAPNA I. Ed. Ernesto Mazzetti. stat.; charts.
  Description: Features maritime and naval studies. Includes navigation, economics, law and technology.

623.8　　　　　　RU　　ISSN 0039-4580
　　　　　　　　　　　　　CODEN: SUDOAN
SUDOSTROENIE. 1898. m. $105 (effective 1996). (Nauchno-tekhnicheskoe Obshchestvo Sudostroietel'noi Promyshlennosti im. A.N. Krylova) Izdatel'stvo Sudostroenie, Ul. Gogolya, 8, St. Petersburg 190000, Russia. (Co-sponsor: Ministerstvo Sudostroeniya) Ed. G.G. Pulyaevskii. bibl.; charts; illus.; tr.lit. circ. 12,000. (also avail. in microform) Indexed: Appl.Mech.Rev., C.I.S. Abstr., Chem.Abstr. —CASDDS.

SUISAN KOGAKU KENKYUJO GIHO. GYOSEN KOGAKU/NATIONAL RESEARCH INSTITUTE OF FISHERIES ENGINEERING. TECHNICAL REPORT. FISHING BOAT AND INSTRUMENT. see FISH AND FISHERIES

SUVREMENI PROMET. see TRANSPORTATION — Air Transport

387　　　　　　　SW　　ISSN 0039-6702
VK4
SVENSK SJOEFARTS TIDNING/SCANDINAVIAN SHIPPING GAZETTE. (Text in English and Swedish) 1905. w. SEK 685($95) Sveriges Redareforening - Swedish Shipowners' Association, Box 53090, S-400 14 Goeteborg, Sweden. TEL 31-178540. FAX 46-31-711-5418. TELEX 20746 SWESHIP S. Ed. Thorsten Rinman. adv. contact: Lennart Fougelberg. bk.rev.; illus.; index. circ. 7,300. Indexed: BMT. Document type: trade publication.

SVEUCILISTE U ZAGREBU. FAKULTET STROJARSTVA I BRODOGRADNJE. ZBORNIK RADOVA. see ENGINEERING — Mechanical Engineering

387　　　　　　　TH
T I F F A FREIGHT FORWARDING HANDBOOK. 1991. biennial. $24 per no. (Thai International Freight Forwarders Association) Cosmic Group of Companies, 4th Fl., Phyathai Bldg., 31 Phyathai Rd., Rajthevi, Bangkok 10400, Thailand. TEL 245-3850. FAX 246-4737. adv.: color page $1200. circ. 5,000 (controlled). Document type: directory.
  Description: Covers multimodal transport, scope of freight forwarding services, container types, and seaports of Thailand.

387　　　　　　　UK
TANK WORLD I B CS TODAY. 1990. 10/yr. $220. Baltic Publishing Ltd., Great West Rd., Brentford, Mddx. TW8 9BU, England. TEL 0181-847-2446. FAX 0181-569-8688. Ed. Rachael White; Pub. Patrick Hicks. adv. contact: Andrew Kingsley. Document type: trade publication.
  Formerly: Tank Container World (ISSN 0959-6089)

387.5　　　　　　UK
TANKER QUARTERLY REPORT. 1980. q. £990. Drewry Shipping Consultants (Subsidiary of: Drewry International Ltd.), 11 Heron Quay, London E14 4JF, England. TEL 0171-538-0191. FAX 0171-987-9396. TELEX 21167 HPDLDN G. Eds. John Harris, Nigel Gardiner. (back issues avail.) Document type: trade publication.
  Description: Forecasts and updates market trends, interpreting supply-and-demand developments and suggesting how freight rates may develop in the medium-term.

387　　　　　　　UK　　ISSN 0305-179X
TANKER REGISTER. (Monthly and quarterly updates avail.) 1960. a. £150($240) (outside Europe £170 ($275)); q. diskette £300 ($480); m. updates £96 ($155) (outside Europe £120 ($190) (effective 1995). Clarkson Research Studies, 12 Camomile St., London EC3A 7BP, England. TEL 0171-623-0539. FAX 0171-623-0539. TELEX 881 2927 CLTNK G. charts; stat. (also avail. in diskette format)
  —BLDSC (8602.517000).
  Description: Lists oil tankers by name with technical characteristics, including ship size, capacity, weight, age, and registry.

623.81　　　　　JA　　ISSN 0916-8699
TECHNO MARINE. (Text in Japanese) 1915. m. 1000 Yen per no. Nihon Zosen Gakkai - Society of Naval Architects of Japan, 15-16, Toranomon 1-chome, Minato-ku, Tokyo 105, Japan. Indexed: INIS Atomind.
  —BLDSC (8755.460850).

TRANSPORTATION — SHIPS AND SHIPPING

387 551.46 IT
TECNOLOGIE E TRASPORTI PER IL MARE. (Includes English translation) 1969. m. (except Aug.). L.120000 (effective 1995). Via O. Ganduccio 7, Casella Postale 7463, 16167 Genoa Nervi, Italy. TEL 39-10-3724340. FAX 39-10-3726447. Ed. Decio Lucano. adv.: B&W page L.2300000, color page L.3300000; trim 170 x 253. bk.rev. circ. 8,500. (back issues avail.) **Document type:** trade publication.
Formerly (until 1995): Automazione Navale (ISSN 0392-2294)
Description: Deals with ships, ports, shipyards, maritime communication, transportation, environment activities and marine operators. Includes informative articles on development and progress in boating technology.

387 UK ISSN 0040-2575
TELEGRAPH. 1969. m. £12 (foreign £24) to non-members. National Union of Marine Aviation and Shipping Transport Officers (NUMAST), Oceanair House, 750-760 High Rd., Leytonstone, London E11 3BB, England. TEL 0181-989-6677. FAX 0181-530-1051. TELEX 892648-NUMAST-G. Ed. Andrew Linington. adv.; bk.rev.; charts; illus.; stat. circ. 20,500. (tabloid format) **Indexed:** BMT. **Document type:** newspaper.
Supersedes: Merchant Navy Journal; Ships' Telegraph.
Description: Provides information for ship masters and officers.

387.1 NE ISSN 0376-6411
TC187 CODEN: TEAQEJ
TERRA ET AQUA. 1972. 3/yr. free. International Association of Dredging Companies, P.O. Box 80521, 2508 GM The Hague, Netherlands. TEL 31-70-3523334. FAX 31-70-3512654. TELEX 31102 DUNE NL. Ed. Marsha R. Cohen. charts; illus.; stat. circ. 3,200. **Indexed:** BMT, Curr.Tit.Ocean.; Fluidex, Geo.Abstr., Geol.Abstr., Sport Fish.Abstr., Wild.Rev.
—UnCover.
Formerly (until 1972): Terra.
Description: Aimed at individuals and organizations with a professional interest in development of ports and waterways; particularly dredging work.

387 NE ISSN 0167-9988
TIJDSCHRIFT VOOR ZEEGESCHIEDENIS. (Text in Dutch, English, German) 1961. s-a. fl.55 to members (foreign members fl.70). Instituut voor Maritieme Historie, Jan van Nassaustraat 112, 2596 BW The Hague, Netherlands. Ed. P.C. van Royen. adv.; bk.rev.; abstr.; bibl.; cum.index. 700. **Indexed:** E.I. **Document type:** academic/scholarly publication.
—SWETS.
Formerly: Nederlandse Vereniging voor Zeegeschiedenis. Mededelingen (ISSN 0028-2340)

387 UK
TIME CHARTERS. 1987. irreg. latest 3rd ed. Lloyd's of London Press Ltd., Sheepen Pl., Colchester, Essex CO3 3LP, England. TEL 01206-772277. FAX 01206-46273. TELEX 987321 LLOYDS G. (U.S. subscr. to: 611 Broadway, Ste. 523, New York, NY 10012. TEL 212-529-9500) **Document type:** trade publication.
Description: Provides current reference to law and arbitration on the chartering and operation of ships on both sides of the Atlantic.

387 US ISSN 0040-8182
TITANIC COMMUTATOR. 1963. q. $25 U.S. and Canadian membership (U.K. and rest of Europe $30; elsewhere $35). Titanic Historical Society, Inc., Box 51053, Indian Orchard, MA 01151-0053. Ed.Bd. adv.; bk.rev.; charts; illus. circ. 5,000.
Description: Contains rticles on the Titanic and other White Star and North Star Atlantic liners. Includes biographies from survivors and others, maritime art, photographs and deck plans. Many accounts contain the results of original research about the liners of the past, the people who built and sailed in them as well as contemporary issues on the subject.

387 621.39 JA ISSN 0387-9283
TOBA SHOSEN KOTO SENMON GAKKO KIYO/TOBA NATIONAL COLLEGE OF MARITIME TECHNOLOGY BULLETIN. (Text in English, Japanese; summaries in English) 1979. a. Toba Shosen Koto Senmon Gakko, 1-1, Ikegami-cho, Toba-shi, Mie-ken 517, Japan. TEL 0599-25-8015. FAX 0599-25-8016. circ. 250. **Document type:** bulletin, academic/scholarly publication.
Description: Covers ships and shipping, computers and engineering.

TOKYO SHOSEN DAIGAKU KENKYU HOKOKU. SHIZEN KAGAKU/TOKYO UNIVERSITY OF MERCANTILE MARINE. JOURNAL. NATURAL SCIENCES. see SCIENCES: COMPREHENSIVE WORKS

387.5 JA
TOYAMA SHOSEN KOTO SENMON GAKKO KENKYU SHUROKU/TOYAMA NATIONAL COLLEGE OF MARITIME TECHNOLOGY. RESEARCH STUDIES. (Text in Japanese; summaries in English) 1968. a. Toyama Shosen Koto Senmon Gakko, 1-2 Ebie Neriya, Shinminato-shi, Toyama-ken 933-02, Japan. Ed. Henshu linkai. illus. circ. 140.

387 AT
TRADE-A-BOAT. 1977. m. Aus.$50. A C P Publishing Pty. Ltd., Trade Division, 122 Ormond Rd., Elwood, Vic. 3184, Australia. TEL 03-525-6033. FAX 03-531-5788. (Or: P.O. Box 86, Elwood, Vic. 3184, Australia) adv. circ. 26,334. **Document type:** consumer publication.

387 NO ISSN 0803-9364
TRADEWINDS; international shipping gazette. 1990. w. NOK 3315 in Europe; elsewhere NOK 3525. TradeWinds A-S, P.O. Box 1182, Sentrum, N-0107 Oslo, Norway. TEL 47-22-00-12-00. FAX 47-22-00-12-60. Eds. Kaare Valebrokk, Trond Lillestolen. adv.; B&W page NOK 38750, color page NOK 61250; trim 9 1/2 x 14 1/4. circ. 6,500. **Document type:** newspaper.

TRAFALGAR HOUSE TODAY. see ENGINEERING

387 US ISSN 0082-5867
TRAFFIC REPORT OF THE ST. LAWRENCE SEAWAY. a. U.S. Saint Lawrence Seaway Development Corporation, 400 7th St., S.W., Rm. 5424, Box 44090, Washington, DC 20026-4090. TEL 202-366-0091. **Document type:** government publication.

387 SZ
TRANSHELVETIQUE. q. Rue des Amis 5, CH-1018 Lausanne, Switzerland. TEL 021-363661. Ed. Daniel Jaquinet. circ. 3,000.

387 SW ISSN 0041-1523
TRANSPORT-NYTT. (Text in Scandinavian languages) 1958. 10/yr. SEK 440. Transport-Nytt Foerlags AB, Box 3044, S-122 03 Enskede, Sweden. TEL 46-8-81-12-80. FAX 46-8-81-16-75. Ed. Christer Hillerstroem. adv. contact: Ingrid Olow. bk.rev.; charts; illus. circ. 6,000. **Document type:** trade publication.
Description: Directed to: users of trucks, lifters, warehouse equipment, as well as persons involved in shipping and air cargo.

TRANSPORTATION & DISTRIBUTION. see TRANSPORTATION

387 US
TRANSPORTATION SERVICES DIRECTORY. a. $74 (foreign $94). K - III Press, Inc, 424 W. 33rd St., New York, NY 10001. TEL 800-221-5488. FAX 212-695-5025. **Document type:** directory.
Formerly: Coast Marine and Transportation Directory.

387 DK ISSN 0109-128X
TRANSPORTNYT; orientering for transportkoebere om transport og Kommunikation. 1982. m. DKK 610 (effective 1996). Danish Shippers' Council - Erhvervenes Transportudvalg, H.C. Andersens Boulevard 18, DK-1553 Copenhagen V, Denmark. FAX 45-33155928. Ed. Palle Egebjerg. circ. 600. **Document type:** newsletter.
Formerly: Fragtnyt.

TRAVLTIPS. see TRAVEL AND TOURISM

623.8 UK ISSN 0049-4690
TRIDENT; Portsmouth Naval Base newspaper. 1969. m. 60p. Ministry of Defence, Business Information Centre, Rm. 110, Somerset House, Somerset St., Bath, Avon BA1 5AB, England. Ed. D. Moore. adv.; bk.rev.; charts; illus. circ. 2,500. (tabloid format) **Document type:** newspaper.
—CCC.

387 351.46 JA
TSUKUBA INSTITUTE. TECHNICAL REPORT/TSUKUBA KENKYUJO GIHO. (Text in English, Japanese; summaries in English) 1981. a. Ship and Ocean Foundation, Tsukuba Institute, 2, Minamihara, Tsukuba-shi, Ibaraki-ken 305, Japan.

387 UK ISSN 0267-9485
TUG WORLD NEWSLETTER.* (Includes annual supplement: Reed's Tugworld Annual Review) 1984. q. (with a. supplement). $60. Thomas Reed Publications Ltd., 38 S. John St., London EC1M 4AY, England. Ed. Kenneth D. Troup. bk.rev.; circ. 2,500 (controlled). **Document type:** newsletter.
Description: Covers the design, construction, operation and economics of the vessels employed in the international towage and marine salvage industry.

TUNISIA. OFFICE DES PORTS NATIONAUX. BULLETIN ANNUEL DES STATISTIQUES. see TRANSPORTATION — Abstracting, Bibliographies, Statistics

387.1 TI
TUNISIA. OFFICE DES PORTS NATIONAUX. BULLETIN TRIMESTRIEL. q. Office des Ports Nationaux, Tunis, Tunisia. charts; stat. **Document type:** government publication, bulletin.

387 347.75 US
U S MARITIME ALERT. w. $435. Lloyd's of London Press, 611 Broadway, Ste. 308, New York, NY 10012. TEL 212-529-9500. FAX 212-529-9826.
Description: Covers events in Washington, as they relate to the maritime industry. Provides news and commentary on legislation and regulatory developments that affect the maritime industry.

387.5 US
U S S REPORTS. 1942. s-a. free. United Seamen's Service, One World Trade Center, Ste. 2161, New York, NY 10048. FAX 212-432-5492. TELEX 222146 UNS UR. Ed. C. Elizabeth Leach. circ. 5,000. **Document type:** newsletter.
Description: Reports on USS and AMMLA's activities.

U S S ST. LOUIS HUBBLE BUBBLE. see MILITARY

387 NE ISSN 0041-588X
UIT EUROPOORTKRINGEN; euregionaal management magazine voor het bedrijfsleven van Amsterdam tot en met Vlanderen. 1962. 20/yr. fl.110. Uitgeversmaatschappij L.A. van Beek B.V., Postbus 33050, 3005 EB Rotterdam, Netherlands. TEL 31-10-4613000. FAX 31-10-4612401. Ed.Bd. adv.; B&W page fl.2130; color page fl.3830. bk.rev.; charts; illus.; stat. circ. 5,425. **Document type:** trade publication.
—SWETS.

623.81 SW ISSN 0282-7999
UNDER SVENSK FLAGG; sjoefart, sjoefoersvar, sjoeintressen. (Text in Swedish) 1905. 10/yr. SEK 300 (foreign SEK 360). Foereningen Sveriges Sjoefart och Sjoefoersvar - Swedish Maritime League, Kastellet, Kastellholmen, S-111 49 Stockholm, Sweden. TEL 08-611-76-60. FAX 08-611-74-76. Ed. Ulf Samuelson. adv.; bk.rev.; illus.; index. circ. 4,000.
Former titles (until vol.4, 1985): Sveriges Flotta (ISSN 0039-6966); (until 1939): Vaar Flotta.
Description: Features news and stories of historical interest to the Swedish Navy and merchant marine.

UNDERWATER MAGAZINE. see BUSINESS AND ECONOMICS — Marketing And Purchasing

623.81 JA
UNDO SEINO KENKYU IINKAI SHINPOJUMU/MARINE DYNAMICS SYMPOSIUM. (Text in Japanese) a. Nihon Zosen Gakkai - Society of Naval Architects of Japan, 15-16, Toranomon 1-chome, Minato-ku, Tokyo 105, Japan.

TRANSPORTATION — SHIPS AND SHIPPING

387.1   US   ISSN 0083-0305
U.S. ARMY. CORPS OF ENGINEERS. PORT SERIES.* 1921. irreg. U.S. Army Corps of Engineers, Waterways Experiment Sta., 3909 Halls Ferry Rd., Vicksburg, MS 39180-6199. TEL 202-272-6001. (Orders to: National Technical Information Service, 5285 Port Royal Rd., Springfield, VA 22161. TEL 703-487-4630. FAX 703-321-5847) **Document type:** government publication, monographic series.

387   623.888   US   ISSN 0364-0981
VK23
U.S. COAST GUARD MARINE SAFETY COUNCIL. PROCEEDINGS. Key Title: Proceedings of the Marine Safety Council. 1944. bi-m. free. U.S. Coast Guard, Commandant G-MP-4, 2100 Second St., S.W., Washington, DC 20593-0001. TEL 202-267-1408. Ed. Betty Murphy. circ. 7,000. **Indexed:** BMT, Ind.U.S.Gov.Per. **Document type:** government publication, proceedings.
—SWETS; UnCover.
Formerly: U.S. Coast Guard. Merchant Marine Council. Proceedings (ISSN 0041-7564)

287   US   ISSN 0083-0755
U.S. FEDERAL MARITIME COMMISSION. ANNUAL REPORT. 1962. a. free. U.S. Federal Maritime Commission, 800 N. Capital St., N.W., Washington, DC 20573. TEL 202-523-5725. **Document type:** government publication.

387   US   ISSN 0083-3207
U.S. SAINT LAWRENCE SEAWAY DEVELOPMENT CORPORATION. ANNUAL REPORT. 1954. a. U.S. Saint Lawrence Seaway Development Corporation, 400 7th St., S.W., Rm. 5424, Box 44090, Washington, DC 20026-4090. TEL 202-366-0091. FAX 202-366-7147. TELEX EASYLINK 510-100-4787. **Document type:** government publication, corporate report.

387   UK   ISSN 0967-5566
UNIVERSITY OF WALES. DEPARTMENT OF MARITIME STUDIES AND INTERNATIONAL TRANSPORT. OCCASIONAL PAPERS. 1992. irreg., no.9, 1993. University of Wales, Department of Maritime Studies and International Transport, P.O. Box 907, Cardiff CF1 3YP, Wales. **Document type:** monographic series.
—BLDSC (6217.162700).

387   PL   ISSN 0208-483X
UNIWERSYTET GDANSKI. WYDZIAL EKONOMIKI TRANSPORTU. ZESZYTY NAUKOWE. EKONOMIKA TRANSPORTU MORSKIEGO. (Text in Polish; summaries in English and Russian) 1971. irreg., latest no.18. price varies. Uniwersytet Gdanski, Wydzial Ekonomiki Transportu, c/o Biblioteka Glowna, Ul. Armii Krajowej 110, 81-824 Sopot, Poland. TEL 51-0061. TELEX 051-2247 BMOR PL. (Dist. by: Ars Polona-Ruch, Krakowskie Przedmiescie 7, 00-680 Warsaw, Poland) circ. 300. **Document type:** academic/scholarly publication.
Description: Covers shipping and seaport policy, the role of shipping and seaports in national economy, economic and financial system of the maritime transport enterprises, international freight market, etc.

386   333.91   SP
VALENCIA PORT; guia del servicios del puerto de Valencia. 1978. a. 1300 ptas. Publicaciones Men-Car, S.A., Paseo de Colon 24, 08002 Barcelona, Spain. TEL 93-301-5516. FAX 93-318-6645. Eds. Juan Cardona, Manuel Cardona. adv. circ. 15,000.

387   UK   ISSN 0264-5661
VANCOUVER PORT HANDBOOK. 1983. biennial. £50. Compass Publications Ltd., Abbot House, Castle Acre, King's Lynn, Norfolk PE32 2BQ, England. TEL 01760-755783. FAX 01760-755782. Ed. James P. Moriarty. adv. circ. 7,000. **Document type:** directory.

387   623.82   GW
VERBAND FUER SCHIFFBAU UND MEERESTECHNIK. JAHRESBERICHT. 1962. a. free. Verband fuer Schiffbau und Meerestechnik e.V., An der Alster 1, 20099 Hamburg, Germany. TEL 040-246205. FAX 040-246287. bk.rev.; stat. circ. 1,750. **Document type:** trade publication.
Formerly (until 1987): Deutscher Shiffbau.
Description: Comprehensive report covering current situation, development, industry, political and technical questions.

387.09   NE
VEREENIGING NEDERLANDSCH HISTORISCH SCHEEPVAART MUSEUM TE AMSTERDAM. JAARBOEK. 1991. a., latest 1995. fl.50. Vereeniging Nederlandsch Historisch Scheepvaart Museum te Amsterdam, Kattenburgerplein 1, 1018 KK Amsterdam, Netherlands. TEL 31-20-5232222. FAX 31-20-5232213.
Description: Describes important objects in the museum's collections, and reports on significant projects.

387   US   ISSN 0735-2220
HE565.U5
VESSEL INVENTORY REPORT. 1938. s-a. free. U.S. General Services Administration, Publications, 18th and F Sts., N.W., Washington, DC 20405. TEL 202-501-4281. FAX 202-501-4281. (Avail. from: Supt. of Documents, U.S. Government Printing Office, Washington, DC 20402. TEL 202-783-3238) Ed. R. Brown. stat. circ. 500. (processed) **Document type:** government publication.

387.164   IT
VIA DELLE MERCI. 12/yr. Ikon s.r.l., Corso Sempione 9, 20145 Milan, Italy. TEL 2-33-19-861. FAX 2-66-800-537. Ed. Arturo Chiurazzi.

387   US   ISSN 1065-7096
HE554.N7
VIA INTERNATIONAL PORT OF NEW YORK - NEW JERSEY. 1949. m. $36 (free to export-import shippers). Port Authority of New York and New Jersey, One World Trade Ctr., Rm. 34E, New York, NY 10048. TEL 212-435-6614. FAX 212-435-6032. Ed. Shirley Fraenkel. adv. contact: Dorothy Roscoszewski. bk.rev.; illus.; circ. 30,000 (controlled). **Indexed:** P.A.I.S. **Document type:** trade publication.
Former titles: Via Port of New York - New Jersey (ISSN 0193-6565); Via Port of New York (ISSN 0042-5001)

387   VI
VIRGIN ISLANDS PORT AUTHORITY. ANNUAL REPORT. 1968. a. Virgin Islands Port Authority, Box 1707, St. Thomas, VI 00803-1707. TEL 809-774-3140. FAX 809-774-0025. Ed. Jean M. Bozzuto. circ. 500. (reprint service avail.)

387   VI
VIRGIN ISLANDS PORT AUTHORITY DIRECTORY. 1988. irreg. (every 2-3 yrs.), latest 1991. free. Virgin Islands Port Authority, Box 1707, St. Thomas, VI 00803-1707. TEL 809-774-3140. FAX 809-774-0025. **Document type:** directory.
Description: Provides complete description of cruise shipping, marine cargo and airport facilities and the companies that provide various services to their operations throughout the territory.

387   US
VIRGINIA MARITIMER. 4/yr. free. Port Authority, 600 World Trade Center, Norfolk, VA 23510. TEL 804-683-8000. FAX 804-683-8500. Ed. Tina Dulong. adv.; illus.; circ. 9,500 (controlled). **Document type:** government publication, trade publication.
Former titles: Ports of Virginia; Port of Hampton Roads Monthly Log; (until Oct. 1981): Virginia Ports.
Description: International trade development news and information about Virginia's ports, public and private sector.

387   US   ISSN 1060-7900
HE561   CODEN: WWSHE3
W W S - WORLD WIDE SHIPPING.* 1914. 8/yr. $30. World Wide Shipping Guide, Inc., 20 S. Delaware Dr., Nyack, NY 10960. TEL 914-358-3813. FAX 914-358-3854. Ed. Lee di Paci. adv.; illus. circ. 15,000. **Indexed:** Ocean.Abstr., Pollut.Abstr.
Former titles (until 1985): W W S - World Shipping (ISSN 0278-6664); (until 1981): American Seaport (ISSN 0161-6323); (until 1978): World Ports - American Seaport; World Ports (ISSN 0043-888X); World Ports and Marine News.

WARSHIP INTERNATIONAL. see *MILITARY*

WATER TRANSPORT STATISTICS OF INDIA. see *TRANSPORTATION* — *Abstracting, Bibliographies, Statistics*

387   US   ISSN 0083-7725
HE563.U5
WATERBORNE COMMERCE OF THE UNITED STATES. (In 5 parts: Atlantic Coast; Gulf Coast, Mississippi River System & Antilles (Puerto Rico & Virgin Islands); The Great Lakes; Pacific Coast, Alaska & Hawaii; National Summary of Data from vols. 1-4) 1952. a. price varies. U.S. Army Corps of Engineers, Water Resources Support Center, Box 61280, New Orleans, LA 70161-1280. TEL 504-862-1424. FAX 504-862-1423. (Subscr. to: U.S. Army Engineer District, New Orleans, Attn.: CELMN-ED-SX, Box 60267, New Orleans, LA 70160-0267. TEL 504-862-2715. FAX 504-862-1091) Ed. Thomas Mire. stat. circ. 1,100. **Document type:** government publication.

387   US   ISSN 0043-1524
HE623
WATERWAYS JOURNAL; devoted to the marine profession and commercial interest of all inland waterways. (Annual Review Number) 1887. w. $28. Waterways Journal, Inc., 319 N. Fourth St., 650 Security Bldg., St. Louis, MO 63102. TEL 314-241-7354. FAX 314-241-4207. Ed. Jack R. Simpson. adv.; bk.rev.; charts; illus.; tr.lit. circ. 5,500.

387   UK   ISSN 0309-1422
WATERWAYS WORLD. 1972. m. £23.40 (foreign £39). Waterway Productions Ltd., Kottingham House, Dale St., Burton-on-Trent, Staffs DE14 3TD, England. TEL 01283-564290. FAX 01283-561077. Ed. Hugh Potter. adv.; bk.rev.; charts; illus.; stat.; index. circ. 18,905. **Document type:** trade publication.

387   NE   ISSN 0165-490X
WEEEKBLAD SCHUTTEVAER; vakblad voor de Rijn- en binnenvaart, kustvaart, visserij, offshore, scheepsbouw. 1888. w. fl.209 (foreign fl.299). (Koninklijke Schippersvereniging Schuttevaer) Kluwer Bedrijfsinformatie B.V. (Subsidiary of: Wolters Kluwer N.V.), Postbus 23, 7400 GA Deventer, Netherlands. TEL 31-5700-48810. FAX 31-5700-17873. Ed. H.S. Klos; Pub. J.M. Salverda. adv. contact: B. Veninga. circ. 16,000 (paid). **Document type:** newspaper, trade publication.
—SWETS.

387   US   ISSN 1057-5863
HF1
WEEKLY COMMERCIAL NEWS AND SHIPPING GUIDE.* w. C.A. Page Publishing Co., Box 530, Redondo Beach, CA 90277-0530. TEL 213-568-4560. FAX 213-568-4567. Ed. Andres Moura. circ. 2,000.
Formerly (until 1991): Daily Commercial News and Shipping Guide (ISSN 1053-9042)

WERKGELEGENHEID IN DE NEDERLANDSE ZEEHAVENS. see *TRANSPORTATION* — *Abstracting, Bibliographies, Statistics*

DIE WESER. see *ENVIRONMENTAL STUDIES*

387   GW   ISSN 0043-2857
WESERLOTSE; Bremer Wirtschafts- und Hafendienst. 1948. m. DM.30. (Bremische Hafenvertretung e.V.) W. Waechter GmbH, Elsasserstr. 41, 28211 Bremen, Germany. FAX 0421-344009. Ed. Werner Sauermilch. adv.; bk.rev.; illus. circ. 6,000. **Document type:** bulletin.

387   796.95   CN   ISSN 0844-5567
WESTCOAST MARINER. 1986. m. Can.$32.10 (foreign $40). Westcoast Publishing Ltd., 1496 W. 72nd Ave., Vancouver, BC V6P 3C8, Canada. TEL 604-266-7433. FAX 604-263-8620. Ed. Rob Morris. adv. circ. 11,000.
Description: For skippers and crews who work the Pacific Coast.

387.5   AT
WESTERN AUSTRALIAN COASTAL SHIPPING COMMISSION. ANNUAL REPORT. a. free. Coastal Shipping Commission, P.O. Box 394, Fremantle, Australia. stat.; circ. controlled.

387   NO   ISSN 0800-1200
WHERE TO BUILD - WHERE TO REPAIR. (Text in English) 1952. a. NOK 300. Maritime Year Books AS, P.O. Box 9156 Vaterland, 0134 Oslo 1, Norway. adv. **Document type:** directory.

387 UK ISSN 1015-1532
WHO'S WHO IN CARGO HANDLING. 1960. a. membership only. International Cargo Handling Coordination Association, 71 Bondway, London SW8 1SH, England. TEL 0171-793-1022. FAX 0171-820-1703. circ. (controlled). **Document type:** directory.
Description: Lists I.C.H.C.A. members.

387 380.1 GW ISSN 0172-990X
WIE ERREICHE ICH WEN?. 1958. a. DM.27.10. K.O. Storck Verlag, Stahltwiete 7, 22761 Hamburg, Germany. TEL 040-853292-0. FAX 040-8507758. Ed. H. Meder.

387 AT
WORK BOAT WORLD. 1982. m. Aus.$95($65) Baird Publications Pty. Ltd., 10 Oxford St., South Yarra, Vic. 3141, Australia. TEL 61-3-98268741. FAX 61-3-98270704. (U.K. addr.: Baird Publications, 4A Carmelite St., London EC4Y 0BN, England. TEL 0171-353-1085. FAX 0171-353-1084) Ed. Neil Baird. adv.; B&W page Aus.$1720, color page Aus.$2450. illus. circ. 4,500. (back issues avail.)
Former titles: Work and Patrol Boat World (ISSN 0812-1648); (until 1983): Asia - Pacific Work and Patrol Boat (ISSN 0726-3724)
Description: Covers ferries and other commercial vessels up to 100 m. in length, military patrol boats, oil-spill boats, pilot boats, and other utility craft.

387 US ISSN 0043-8014
VK1 CODEN: WOBOAF
WORKBOAT. 1943. bi-m. $26 (foreign $35). Journal Publications (Rockland), Box 908, Rockland, ME 04841-0908. TEL 207-594-6222. FAX 207-594-8978. Ed. Don Nelson. adv.; bk.rev.; charts; illus.; stat. circ. 12,500. (back issues avail.)
Indexed: Ocean.Abstr., Pollut.Abstr.
—Ei.
Description: For owners, operators, builders and designers of U.S. commercial shallow-draft vessels under 400 feet. Contains trade-related news, waterway development, economic trends and new legislation.

387 US
WORKBOAT DIRECTORY. 1992. a. $45. Journal Publications, 120 Tillson Ave., Rockland, ME 04841. TEL 207-594-6222. FAX 207-594-8978. Ed. Don Nelson; Pub. Scott Allmendinger. adv.: B&W & color, B&W page $1790; trim 8 1/8 x 10 7/8; adv. contact: John Allen. circ. 2,000. **Document type:** directory.
Description: Documents, indexes and cross-references every business component of the coastal and inland marine industry.

387 UK ISSN 0268-733X
WORKBOAT INTERNATIONAL. 1985. 10/yr. Rushton Marine Press Ltd., Woodside, Burnhams Rd., Little Bookham, Leatherhead, Surrey KT23 3BA, England. TEL 01372-453316. FAX 01372-459974. Ed. Iain Sutherland; Pub. Robert Hall. adv. contact: Marilyn Stansell. circ. 6,500. (controlled). **Document type:** trade publication.
Description: News items on legislation, technological developments, products and services, and contracts pertaining to the marine trade industry worldwide, oriented toward builders and architects, equipment manufacturers, repairers, owners and operators, and governmental authorities.

387 NO ISSN 0801-5007
WORLD BULK FLEET. 1960. s-a. $310 (includes World Bulk Trades). Fearnleys A-S, Grev Wedelsplass 9, P.O. Box 1158 Sentrum, N-0107 Oslo 1, Norway. TEL 47-22-93-60-00. FAX 47-22-93-61-10. TELEX 74607 FADM. stat.
Description: Provides details on the total world fleet of tankers, bulk carriers and combined carriers, existing and on order as well as estimated future fleet.

387 NO ISSN 0801-4086
WORLD BULK TRADES. a. $310 (includes World Bulk Fleet). Fearnleys A-S, Grev Wedelsplass 9, P.O. Box 1158 Sentrum, N-0107 Oslo 1, Norway. TEL 47-22-93-60-00. FAX 47-22-93-61-10. charts; stat.
Description: Provides a comprehensive review of the total seaborne trade and cargo movements by tankers, combined carriers and bulk carriers.

WORLD METEOROLOGICAL ORGANIZATION. COMMISSION FOR MARINE METEOROLOGY. ABRIDGED FINAL REPORT OF THE (NO.) SESSION. see *METEOROLOGY*

WORLD METEOROLOGICAL ORGANIZATION. WEATHER REPORTING. VOLUME D: INFORMATION FOR SHIPPING. see *METEOROLOGY*

387 UK
▼**WORLD SHIPYARD MONITOR.** 1994. m. Clarkson Research Studies, 12 Camomile St., London EC1Y 4XX, England. TEL 0171-283-8955. FAX 0171-623-0539. TELEX 881 2927 CLTNK G. (also avail. in diskette format)
Description: Provides coverage of supply-demand trends in the ship-building market.

387 UK ISSN 0049-8157
WORLD TANKER FLEET REVIEW. 1921. s-a. £350($520) (effective 1995). Jacobs Holdings PLC, 9 Mandeville Pl., London W1M 5LB, England. TEL 0171-486-3000. FAX 0171-486-1937. Ed. David G. Barker-Benfield. charts; stat. circ. 600. **Document type:** trade publication.
—BLDSC (9360.068000).

387.164 US ISSN 0162-0088
HE561
WORLD WIDE SHIPPING GUIDE. 1976. a. $85. World Wide Shipping Guide, Inc., 20 S. Delaware Dr., Nyack, NY 10960. TEL 914-358-3813. FAX 914-358-3854. adv. circ. 12,500.

387.5 PL
WYZSZA SZKOLA MORSKA. ZESZYTY NAUKOWE. irreg. 103 Zl. Wyzsza Szkola Morska w Gdyni - Merchant Marine Academy, Czerwonych Kosynierow 83, 81-225 Gdynia, Poland. (Dist. by: Ars Polona-Ruch, Krakowskie Przedmiescie 7, Warsaw, Poland) Ed. Bozena Sobolewska.

387 JA ISSN 0388-449X
YOKOHAMA PORT NEWS. (Text in English) s-a. Port and Harbor Bureau, Industry & Trade Center Bldg., 2 Yamashita-cho, Nakaku, Yokohama, Japan. FAX 45-671-6158.
Description: Covers current activities as well as future plans of the port of Yokohama.

387 CC ISSN 1000-3878
ZAOCHUAN JISHU/MARINE TECHNOLOGY. (Text in Chinese) 1973. m. $4. Zhongguo Chuanbo Gongye Zong Gongsi, Chuanbo Gongyi Yanjiusuo, P.O. Box 032-201, Shanghai 200032, People's Republic of China. TEL 4399626. FAX 4390908. Ed. Li Yilu. adv. contact: Liang Huajun. circ. 2,500.
Description: Covers the application of new technology into shipbuilding and offshore engineering.
Refereed Serial

387 US
ZHONGGUO CHUANBO BAO/CHINA'S SHIPS. (Text in Chinese) w. $35. China Books & Periodicals, Inc., 2929 24th St., San Francisco, CA 94110. TEL 415-282-2994. FAX 415-282-0994. **Document type:** newspaper.
Formerly: Chuanbo Shijie.

387 CC ISSN 1006-124X
ZHONGGUO GANGKOU/CHINA PORTS. (Text in Chinese) 1986. bi-m. $12 (effective 1995). Zhongguo Gangkou Zashishe, 12 Zhongshan 2 Lu, Room 415, Shanghai 200002, People's Republic of China. TEL 021-3280010. FAX 021-3742473. TELEX 33023 SHACO CN. Ed. Tang Shaowu; Pub. Liu Lizhu. adv. contact: Mao Boke. circ. 20,000. **Document type:** trade publication.
Description: Covers the exchanges between domestic and foreign harbours, management and administration, and the construction of Chinese ports and harbours.

387 CC
ZHONGGUO HAIYUAN/CHINESE SEAMEN. (Text in Chinese) bi-m. Zhongguo Haiyuan Gonghui - China Seamen's Union, 1441 Changyang Lu, Shanghai 200090, People's Republic of China. TEL 5462878. Ed. Tong Menghou.

387 HK ISSN 0258-3240
ZHONGGUO HAIYUN/MARITIME CHINA. (Text in Chinese and English) 1983. q. HK.$190($55) (China Ocean Shipping Co., CC - Zhongguo Yuanyang Yunshu Gongsi) Maritime China Ltd. - Zhongguo Haiyun Youxian Gongsi, 4306 China Resources Bldg., 26 Harbour Rd., Hong Kong. TEL 5-8913831. TELEX 68444-HKTF-HX. (Co-sponsor: Seatrade - Haimao Chuban Gongsi) Ed. Oliver Wong. adv.; bk.rev.; illus. circ. 6,000.

387 CC ISSN 1000-4653
ZHONGGUO HANGHAI/CHINESE NAVIGATION. (Text in Chinese) s-a. Jiaotong-bu, Shanghai Chuanbo Yunshu Kexue Yanjiusuo - Ministry of Transportation, Shanghai Institute of Shipping Transportation Science, 200 Minsheng Lu, Shanghai 200135, People's Republic of China. TEL 8840348. (Co-sponsor: Zhongguo Hanghai Xuehui) Ed. Qiu Min.

387 CC ISSN 1001-8328
ZHONGGUO XIUCHUAN/CHINA SHIPREPAIR. (Text in Chinese) 1987. bi-m. Y2.80 per no. Zhongguo Chuanbo Zonggongsi, Tianjin Xiuchuan Jishu Yianjiusuo - Shiprepairing Technology Research Institute of Tianjin, CSSC, P.O. Box 562, Tanggu, Tianjin 300456, People's Republic of China. TEL 022-5792835. FAX 022-5794559. TELEX 23166 TJSIC CN. Ed. Wang Ying. adv.; index.
Description: Provides news and technical developments in the Chinese ship repairing industry.

623.82 JA ISSN 0387-2203
VM4
ZOSEN GIJUTSU/SHIPBUILDING AND ENGINEERING. (Text in Japanese) 1968. m. 1400 Yen per no. Japan Industrial Publishing Co., Ltd., P.O. Box 9, Shirai Yubinkyo-ku, Chiba-ken 270-14, Japan. **Document type:** trade publication.

623.82 JA
ZOSEN GIJUTSU KENKYU KAIHATSU KADAI CHOSHO/REPORTS OF DEVELOPMENT OF SHIPBUILDING TECHNIQUE. (Text in Japanese) a. Zosen Gijutsu Kaihatsu Kyogi Kiko - Organization for Development of Shipbuilding Techniques, Nihon Zosen Kenkyu Kyokai, 15-16, Toranmon 1-chome, Minato-ku, Tokyo 105, Japan. **Document type:** trade publication.

623.82 JA
ZOSEN GIJUTSU KENKYU KAIHATSU KADAISHU/RESEARCH SUBJECT FOR DEVELOPMENT SHIPBUILDING TECHNIQUES. (Text in Japanese) 1969. a. Zosen Gijutsu Kaihatsu Kyogi Kiko - Organization for Development of Shipbuilding Techniques, Nihon Zosen Kenkyu Kyokai, 15-16, Toranomon 1-chome, Minato-ku, Tokyo 105, Japan. **Document type:** trade publication.

623.82 JA
ZOSEN GIJUTSU, KIKAN. (Text in Japanese) 1988. q. 2000 Yen per no. Japan Industrial Publishing Co., Ltd., P.O. Box 9, Shirai Yubinkyo-ku, Chiba-ken 270-14, Japan.

623.82 JA ISSN 0514-7999
ZOSEN KENKYU/SHIPBUILDING RESEARCH. (Text in Japanese) 1960. q. Nihon Zosen Kenkyu Kyokai - Shipbuilding Research Association of Japan, 15-16, Toranomon 1-chome, Minato-ku, Tokyo 105, Japan. **Document type:** trade publication.

623.82 JA
ZOSEN ZOKI TOKEI GEPPO/MONTHLY REPORT OF SHIPBUILDING AND MACHINE MAKING. (Text in Japanese) 1950. m. Un'yusho, Un'yu Seisakukyoku, Joho Kanribu - Ministry of Transport, Transport Policy Bureau, Research and Data Processing Department, 1-3, Kasumigaseki 2-chome, Chiyoda-ku, Tokyo 100, Japan. **Document type:** government publication.

623.82 JA
ZOSENGYO DAYORI/SHIPBUILDING NEWS. (Text in Japanese) 1963. m. 200 Yen per no. Nihon Kogata Senpaku Kogyokai - Japan Ship and Boat Manufacturers' Association, 9-2, Nihonbashi Kayaba-cho 1-chome, Chuo-ku, Tokyo 103, Japan. **Document type:** trade publication.

TRANSPORTATION — TRUCKS AND TRUCKING

387
VM1
100A1. UK ISSN 0266-8971
1962. q. free. Lloyd's Register of Shipping, 71 Fenchurch St., London EC3M 4BS, England. TEL 0171-709-9166. illus. circ. 28,000. **Indexed:** Met.Abstr.
Formerly: Lloyds Register World.
Description: Contains articles of general and technical interest to those involved in marine, industrial and offshore activities, likely to use LR services.

TRANSPORTATION — Trucks And Trucking

388.324 UK ISSN 0308-9304
A B C FREIGHT GUIDE. 1953. a. £29.50. Centaur Communications Ltd., 50 Poland St., London W1V 4AX, England. adv. circ. 8,000.
Incorporates: A B C Truck Breakdown Guide; A B C Guide to Recovery Services; **Formerly:** A B C Goods Transport Guide (ISSN 0001-0421)
Description: Reference source covering road haulage, storage and distribution, driver agencies, international services, heavy haulage and tankers.

A M C SCALE DIRECTORY (YEARS); United States and Canada. (American Movers Conference) see *BUSINESS AND ECONOMICS — Trade And Industrial Directories*

388.324 SW ISSN 0348-0356
AAKERI & TRANSPORT. Abbreviated title: Aa T. 1941. m. (9/yr.). SEK 220 (effective 1990). Aakeriaegarnas Centralfoerbund, 598 10 Vimmerby, Sweden. Ed. Alf Wesik. adv.; bk.rev.; charts; illus. circ. 26,000.
Former titles (until 1987): Aakeri on Transport; (until 1977): Aakerifoeretagaren - Transportoeren; Which was formed by the 1942 merger of: Transportoeren; Aakerifoeretagaren (ISSN 0001-298X)

AIR CONDITIONING & HEATING SERVICE & REPAIR - DOMESTIC CARS, LIGHT TRUCKS & VANS. see *TRANSPORTATION — Automobiles*

AIR CONDITIONING & HEATING SERVICE & REPAIR - IMPORTED CARS & TRUCKS. see *TRANSPORTATION — Automobiles*

388.3 US
ALLEGHENY - CAROLINA TRUCKER EXCHANGE; merchandising everything for the trucking industry. 1978. m. $18. Allied Publications, 7355 N. Woodland, Box 603, Indianapolis, IN 46206-0603. TEL 317-297-5500. FAX 317-299-1356. adv. circ. 39,405. **Document type:** trade publication.
Formerly: Allegheny Trucker (ISSN 1048-9673)

388.324 US ISSN 0897-0807
AMERICAN MOTOR CARRIER DIRECTORY: NORTH AMERICAN EDITION. s-a. $275 (foreign $350). K - III Press, Inc., 424 W. 33rd St., New York, NY 10001. TEL 800-221-5488. FAX 212-695-5025. **Document type:** directory.
Incorporates: American Motor Carrier Directory: Specialized Services Edition (ISSN 0569-6364); **Formerly:** American Motor Carrier Directory: National Edition (ISSN 0569-6356)

388.324 US ISSN 0886-9707
AMERICAN MOVER. 1936. m. $50 (Canada and Mexico $60; elsewhere $85). American Movers Conference, 1611 Duke St., Alexandria, VA 22314. TEL 703-683-7410. FAX 703-683-7527. Ed. Mike Hayes. adv. contact: Karen B. Climo. circ. 3,100 (paid).
Former titles: Movers Journal; In the Van.
Description: Provides in-depth articles on subject of interest to executives of member moving companies.

AMERICAN TRUCKING ASSOCIATIONS. CURRENT ECONOMIC BULLETIN. see *TRANSPORTATION — Abstracting, Bibliographies, Statistics*

388.4 US
AMERICAN TRUCKING TRENDS (YEAR). 1942. a. $50. (American Trucking Associations) Trucking Information Services, Inc., 2200 Mill Rd., Alexandria, VA 22314. TEL 703-838-1792. FAX 703-683-9751. illus, stat.; index. circ. 1,500. **Indexed:** SRI. **Document type:** trade publication.
Former titles (until 1986): American Trucking Trends. Statistical Report; American Trucking Associations Report (ISSN 0066-0892)
Description: Profiles the industry for past 10 years; equipment and employment, financial state of industry, and taxes.

388.324 US
ANTIQUE TRUCK REGISTRY. 1985. biennial. $5. American Truck Historical Society, Box 531168, Birmingham, AL 35253. TEL 205-870-0566. FAX 205-870-3069.
Description: Lists nearly 6,000 trucks, tractors and trailers, representing nearly 300 manufacturers, owned by over 1,752 members of the society.

388.324 US
ARKANSAS MOTOR CARRIER.* q. Arkansas Motor Carriers Association, Box 2798, Little Rock, AR 72203. TEL 501-372-3462. FAX 501-376-1810. Ed. Mary Gwin. circ. 475.

388.324 CN ISSN 0830-1808
ATLANTIC TRUCKING. 1956. 4/yr. Can.$18. Atlantic Provinces Trucking Association, 1 Trites Rd., Ste. 14, Riverview, NB E1B 2V5, Canada. TEL 506-387-4413. FAX 506-387-7424. Ed. Dale Elliott. adv.; illus. circ. 2,000. **Document type:** trade publication.
Former titles: Atlantic Truck Transport Review (ISSN 0004-6868); Maritime Truck Transport Review.
Description: Features people in the industry, new product news and industry updates.

388.324 AT
AUSTRALASIAN TRANSPORT NEWS. 1985. m. (except Dec.). Aus.$40($70) Publishing Services (Australia) Pty. Ltd., 244 St. Paul's Terrace, Spring Hill, Brisbane, Qld. 4000, Australia. TEL 617-854-1286. Ed. Andrew Stewart. adv.: B&W page Aus.$1985, color page Aus.$3150; trim 25 x 45; adv. contact: Dave Rigby. circ. 17,232. (back issues avail.) **Document type:** trade publication.
Formerly: Queensland Transport News.
Description: Covers up-to-date news, management and fleet issues for owners and senior managers of transport and distribution companies.

AUSTRALIAN FLEET MAGAZINE. see *TRANSPORTATION — Automobiles*

AUTO TREND. see *TRANSPORTATION — Automobiles*

AUTOSPARK. see *TRANSPORTATION — Automobiles*

B C I NEWS. (Battery Council International) see *TRANSPORTATION — Automobiles*

388.324 GW
B D F INFODIENST. 1992. s-m. free. Bundesverband des Deutschen Gueterfernverkehrs e.V., Breitenbachstr. 1, 60457 Frankfurt a.M., Germany. TEL 069-7919273. FAX 069-7919227. circ. 1,280. **Document type:** bulletin.

388.324 US ISSN 1048-9819
BADGER TRUCKER; merchandising everything for the trucking industry. 1980. m. $18. Allied Publications, 7355 N. Woodland, Box 603, Indianapolis, IN 46206-0603. TEL 317-297-5500. FAX 317-299-1356. adv. circ. 20,000. **Document type:** trade publication.
Formerly: Badger Truck Exchange.

388.322 DK ISSN 0901-3229
BILRUTEN. 1925. m. DKK 210. Landsforeningen Danmarks Bilruter, P.O. Box 17, DK-7100 Vejle, Denmark. FAX 45-75834610. Ed. Henning Korshoej Nielsen. adv.; bk.rev. circ. 2,500.
Formerly: Danmarks Bilruter.

388.324 CN ISSN 0707-5014
BRITISH COLUMBIA MOTOR TRANSPORT DIRECTORY. 1978. a. Can.$49.95. British Columbia Trucking Association, 1610 Kebet Way, No. 1, Port Coquitlam, BC V3C 5W9, Canada. TEL 604-942-3200. FAX 604-942-3191. adv. contact: Randy Ellis. circ. 850. **Document type:** directory.
Description: Directory of trucking services in B.C.

388.3 US ISSN 1048-9665
BUCKEYE TRUCKER; merchandising everything for the trucking industry. 1976. m. $18. Allied Publications, 7355 N. Woodland, Box 603, Indianapolis, IN 46206-0603. TEL 317-297-5500. FAX 317-299-1356. adv. circ. 22,000. **Document type:** trade publication.

388.324 658.8 UK ISSN 0956-7380
BUSINESS RATIO REPORT: DELIVERY AND DESPATCH SERVICES; an industry sector analysis. 1989. a. I C C Business Ratios Ltd., Freepost, Field House, Hampton, Mddx. TW12 1BR, England. TEL 081-783-0977. FAX 081-783-1940. charts; stat. **Document type:** trade publication.
—BLDSC (3547.840900).

388.324 UK ISSN 0968-1493
C V MANAGER. (Commercial Vehicle) 1979. m. £140. Sewells International Ltd., Dart Business Centre, Dartington, Totnes, Devon TQ9 6JE, England. TEL 01803-867070. FAX 01803-866507. Ed. Toby Proctor. bk.rev.; stat.; circ. 500 (paid). **Document type:** newsletter.
Formerly: Commercial Vehicle Digest (ISSN 0963-1992)
Description: Management guide to earning profit from selling and servicing commercial vehicles.

388.3 US ISSN 1049-1023
CALIFORNIA TRUCKER; merchandising everything for the trucking industry. 1979. m. $18. Allied Publications, 7355 N. Woodland, Box 603, Indianapolis, IN 46206-0603. TEL 317-297-5500. FAX 317-299-1356. adv. circ. 25,000. **Document type:** trade publication.

388.324 US ISSN 1040-2705
CALTRUX. Represents: California Trucking Association. Newsletter. 1949. w. membership. California Trucking Association, 1251 Beacon Blvd., West Sacramento, CA 95691. TEL 916-329-3554. Ed. Deborah B. Smith. adv.; charts; illus. circ. 4,500. **Document type:** newsletter.

388.324 IT ISSN 0008-2252
CAMION;* la voce degli autotrasportatori professionali. vol.25, 1970. m. L.1000. Assistenza Sindacale per gli Auto Trasportatori, Via Rocco Santoliquido 23, 00123 Rome, Italy. Ed. Maurizio Caldan. adv.; illus.

388.324 US
CAR AND DRIVER TRUCK GUIDE. 1993. a. $4.95. Hachette Magazines, Inc., 1633 Broadway, New York, NY 10019. TEL 212-767-6095. FAX 212-767-6019. adv.: B&W page $4780, color page $7450; trim 7 7/8 x 10 1/2. circ. 180,000. **Document type:** consumer publication.

388.324 US
CARGO TANK HAZARDOUS MATERIAL REGULATIONS. a. $65 to non-members; members $45. National Tank Truck Carriers, Inc., 2200 Mill Rd., Alexandria, VA 22314-4677. TEL 703-838-1960. FAX 703-684-5753. circ. 3,000.

388.324 SZ
CARROSSIER. vol.4, 1976. bi-m. 46 SFr. (foreign 54 SFr.). (Verband der Schweizerischen Carrosserie-Industrie) Huber und Co. AG, Promenadenstr. 16, CH-8501 Frauenfeld, Switzerland. TEL 054-271111. Ed.Bd. adv.; charts; illus. **Document type:** trade publication.

388.423 US ISSN 1049-1031
CASCADE TRUCKER; merchandising everything for the trucking industry. 1980. m. $18. Allied Publications, 7355 N. Woodland, Box 603, Indianapolis, IN 46206-0603. TEL 317-297-5500. FAX 317-299-1356. adv. circ. 20,000. **Document type:** trade publication.

CATALOGO MOTORISTICO. see *TRANSPORTATION — Automobiles*

TRANSPORTATION — TRUCKS AND TRUCKING

388.324   US   ISSN 1049-006X
CENTRAL STATES TRUCKER; merchandising everything for the trucking industry. 1980. m. $18. Allied Publications, 7355 N. Woodland, Box 603, Indianapolis, IN 46206-0603. TEL 317-297-5500. FAX 317-299-1356. adv. circ. 20,000. **Document type:** trade publication.

CHEVY TRUCKIN'. see *TRANSPORTATION — Automobiles*

388.324   US   ISSN 0734-1423
TL1
CHILTON'S COMMERCIAL CARRIER JOURNAL; for fleet management. 1911. m. $45. Chilton Co., One Chilton Way, Radnor, PA 19089. TEL 610-964-4000. FAX 610-964-4512. (Subscr. to: Box 2045, Radnor, PA 19089) Ed. Jerry Standley. adv.: B&W page $7860; adv. contact: Haig Dagdigian. bk.rev.; charts; illus.; stat.; tr.lit.; index. circ. 86,000. (also avail. in microfilm from UMI; microfiche from CIS; reprint service avail. from UMI) **Indexed:** P.A.I.S., SRI. **Document type:** trade publication.
—Faxon; UMI. **CCC.**
Former titles (until 1982): Chilton's C C J (ISSN 0193-628X); Commercial Car Journal (ISSN 0010-292X)
Description: For heavy duty transportation fleet managers with 10 or more vehicles.

CHINA AUTOMOTIVE JOURNAL/XIANDAI QICHE; an automotive journal for P.R. China. see *TRANSPORTATION — Automobiles*

388.324   PO
CLUBE DO CAMIONISTA. 12/yr. Av. Gomes Pereira, 41-1o Esq., 1500 Lisbon, Portugal. TEL 1-7153264. FAX 7154257.

388.324   UK   ISSN 0010-3063
COMMERCIAL MOTOR. 1905. w. £95($247) Reed Business Publishing Group (Subsidiary of: Reed Elsevier group), Quadrant House, The Quadrant, Sutton, Surrey SM2 5AS, England. TEL 0181-652-3302. FAX 0181-652-8960. (Subscr. to: Oakfield House, Perrymount Rd., Haywards Heath, W. Sussex, RH16 3DH, England. TEL 01444-445566) Ed. Brian Weatherley. adv.; bk.rev.; charts; illus.; mkt.; stat.; s-a. index. circ. 28,600. (also avail. in microform from PMC,UMI) **Indexed:** Br.Tech.Ind., C.I.S.Abstr., HRIS. **Document type:** trade publication.
—UMI. **CCC.**

388   SA
COMMERCIAL TRANSPORT. 1945. m. R.88.92 (foreign R.118) (effective 1994). Thomson Publications (Subsidiary of: Times Media Ltd.), P.O. Box 56182, Pinegowrie 2123, South Africa. TEL 27-11-789-2144. FAX 27-11-789-3196. Ed. Ivan Philip. adv.; bk.rev.; charts; illus.; mkt.; tr.lit. circ. 7,309. **Indexed:** Ind.S.A.Per. **Document type:** trade publication.
Supersedes in part: Commercial Transport and Freight (ISSN 0376-5849); Which was formed by the merger of: Commercial Transport (ISSN 0036-2107); Freight (ISSN 0016-0857)

388.324 387   IE
COMMERCIAL TRANSPORT AND TRANSPORT MANAGERS JOURNAL. 1971. m. £35. Media 2000, 24 Thomas St., Dublin 8, Ireland. TEL 01-535335. FAX 01-535401. Ed. Catriona Gavin. adv.; bk.rev. circ. 17,760.
Formerly (until 1976): Commercial Transport.

388.324   SA   ISSN 1019-0899
COMMERCIAL VEHICLE DATA DIGEST. 1982. a. R.37. Mead & McGrouther (Pty) Ltd., P.O. Box 1240, Randburg 2125, South Africa. adv. circ. 4,667. **Document type:** trade publication.

388.324   SA
COMMERCIAL VEHICLE DEALERS' GUIDE. 1978. bi-m. R.57.90. Mead & McGrouther (Pty) Ltd., P.O. Box 1240, Randburg 2125, South Africa. Ed. O. Peruch. circ. 3,412. **Document type:** trade publication.
Formerly: Commercial Vehicle Dealers' Digest.

388.3   UK   ISSN 0070-1610
CRONER'S ROAD TRANSPORT OPERATION. 1977. m. £136.80 (effective 1992). Croner Publications Ltd. (Subsidiary of: Wolters Kluwer N.V.), Croner House, London Rd., Kingston, Surrey KT2 6SR, England. TEL 081-547-3333. FAX 081-547-2637. TELEX 267778. Ed. Colin Clark. (looseleaf format) —BLDSC (3487.835000).
Description: Provides information on United Kingdom and European legislation affecting operators of commercial vehicles.

388.324 621.436   US   ISSN 0884-6324
TJ795.A1
D E S. (Diesel Equipment Superintendent); the information source for truck fleet equipment managers. 1923. m. $35. Business Journals, 50 Day St., Box 5550, Norwalk, CT 06856. TEL 203-853-6015. FAX 203-852-8175. Ed. James E. Jones. adv.; charts; illus.; stat.; tr.lit. circ. 25,000. (also avail. in microfilm from UMI; reprint service avail. from UMI) **Indexed:** A.S.& T.Ind., ISMEC. **Document type:** trade publication.
—Ei; UMI; UnCover.
Former titles (until 1984): Diesel Equipment Superinendent (ISSN 0731-0803); (until 1980): D.E.S. (ISSN 0012-2610); (until 1962): Equipment Superintendent (ISSN 0741-8744); (until 1961): Diesel Power (ISSN 0096-1612); (until 1954): Diesel Power and Diesel Transportation (ISSN 0096-0071)

388.324   US   ISSN 1049-0566
DAKOTA TRUCK MERCHANDISER; merchandising everything for the trucking industry. Alternate edition: Minnesota Truck Merchandiser (ISSN 1049-0558) 1975. Allied Publications, 7355 N. Woodland, Box 603, Indianapolis, IN 46206-0603. TEL 317-297-5599. FAX 317-299-1356. **Document type:** trade publication.

388.324   DK   ISSN 0011-6629
DANSKE VOGNMAEND. 1948. m. DKK 375. Danske Vognmaend Hovedorganisationen, Gammeltorv 18, 1457 Copenhagen K, Denmark. TEL 33-13-88-00. FAX 33-32-57-07. adv.; charts; illus.; mkt.; stat.; index; circ. 6,900 (controlled).

388.324   AT
DEALS ON WHEELS. 1983. m. Aus.$65. A C P Publishing Pty. Ltd., Trade Division, 122 Ormond Rd., Elwood, Vic. 3184, Australia. TEL 03 525 6033. FAX 03-531-5788. (Or: P.O. Box 86, Elwood, Vic. 3184, Australia) adv. circ. 26,334. **Document type:** consumer publication.
Description: Listing of used trucks for sale.

388.324   IT
DELIVERY TRASPORTI COMMERCIALI. 1981. bi-m. L.35000. Edizioni Andrea Latorre s.a.s., Via Giovanni Rotondi 3, 20145 Milan, Italy. TEL 02-462538. FAX 02-4697561. Ed. Carlo Latorre. adv.; bk.rev. circ. 25,000. **Document type:** trade publication.

388.324   US   ISSN 0092-7449
HF5487
DIRECTION (ALEXANDRIA);* for the moving and storage industry. 1920. m. $50 to non-members; members $30. National Moving & Storage Association, 11150 Main St., Ste. 402, Fairfax, VA 22030-5066. TEL 703-671-8813. FAX 703-671-6712. Ed. Joyce McDowell. adv.; bk.rev.; charts; illus.; tr.lit.; index, cum.index. circ. 3,100.
Formerly: Furniture Warehouseman (ISSN 0016-3082)
Description: Articles relating to all aspects of the moving and storage industry, labor relations, equipment and warehousing. Also features management and diversification issues.

388.324   US
DIRECTORY OF MOVERS. 1936. a. membership. American Movers Conference, 1611 Duke St., Alexandria, VA 22314. TEL 703-683-7410. FAX 703-683-7527. **Document type:** directory.

388.324   CN   ISSN 0705-7040
L'ECHO DU TRANSPORT. (Text in French) 1976. 10/yr. Can.$35($45) Editions Bomart Ltee., 7493 TransCanada Hwy., Ste. 103, St. Laurent, PQ H4T 1T3, Canada. TEL 514-337-9043. FAX 514-337-1862. Ed. Jean Roch Savard. adv. contact: Claude Boutin. bk.rev.; circ. 18,709 (controlled). **Document type:** trade publication.
Description: Covers all areas of local, national and international road transportation industry.

ELECTRICAL COMPONENT LOCATOR - DOMESTIC CARS, LIGHT TRUCKS & VANS. see *TRANSPORTATION — Automobiles*

ELECTRICAL COMPONENT LOCATOR - IMPORTED CARS, LIGHT TRUCKS & VANS. see *TRANSPORTATION — Automobiles*

388.324   US
EUROPEAN TRUCKS FORECAST REPORT. s-a. D R I - McGraw-Hill, 24 Hartwell Ave., Lexington, MA 02173. TEL 617-863-5100. FAX 617-860-6332. TELEX 200 284. (back issues avail.)

388.324   US
EXCISE TAX QUARTERLY. 1979. q. $6 to non-members; members $3. National Truck Equipment Association, 37400 Hills Tech Dr., Farmington Hills, MI 48331-3414. TEL 810-489-7090. FAX 810-489-8590. Ed. Joan Christophersen. circ. 1,600. (looseleaf format; back issues avail.) **Document type:** newsletter.
Description: Review of I.R.S. releases and court cases concerning federal excise tax on motor vehicles.

385.324   IT
F A I. 1964. m. Federazione Autotraportatori Italiani, Via Panama 62, 00198 Rome, Italy. Ed. Renato Bertacchi. adv. circ. 34,000.

388.324   GW
FACHVEREINIGUNG GUETERFERNVERKEHR HAMBURG. MITTEILUNGEN. 1948. m. Fachvereinigung Gueterfernverkehr Hamburg e.V., Bullerdeich 36, 20537 Hamburg, Germany. TEL 040-25450-0. FAX 040-2512983. **Document type:** newsletter.

388.324   GW
FAHRERPOST. bi-m. Iveco Magirus AG, Robert-Schuman-Str. 1, 85716 Munich, Germany. TEL 089-31771120. FAX 089-31771452. circ. 50,000. **Document type:** trade publication.

388.324 659.1   US
FASTLINE FOR DIXIE TRUCKERS. 1981. m. $8. Fastline Publications, Inc., 4900 Fox Run Rd., Buckner, KY 40010. TEL 502-222-0146. FAX 502-222-9874. circ. 22,000. **Document type:** catalog.
Former titles: Dixie Trucker; Dixie Truck Trader.

388.324   US
FASTLINE FOR FLORIDA TRUCKERS. 1980. m. $8. Fastline Publications, Inc., 4900 Fox Run Rd., Buckner, KY 40010. TEL 502-222-0146. FAX 502-222-9874. Ed. William G. Howard. circ. 22,000. **Document type:** catalog.
Formerly: Florida Trucker.

388.324   US
FASTLINE FOR GEORGIA TRUCKERS. 1979. m. $8. Fastline Publications, Inc., 4900 Fox Run Rd., Buckner, KY 40010. TEL 502-222-0146. FAX 502-222-9874. Ed. William G. Howard. circ. 22,000. **Document type:** catalog.
Formerly: Georgia Trucker.

388.324   US
FASTLINE FOR KENTUCKY TRUCKERS. 1978. m. $8. Fastline Publications, Inc., 4900 Fox Run Rd., Buckner, KY 40010. TEL 502-222-0146. FAX 502-222-9874. Ed. William G. Howard. adv. circ. 16,968. **Document type:** catalog.
Formerly: Bluegrass Trucker.

388.324 659.1   US
FASTLINE FOR TENNESSEE TRUCKERS. 1979. m. $82. Fastline Publications, Inc., 4900 Fox Run Rd., Buckner, KY 40010. TEL 502-222-0146. FAX 502-222-9874. circ. 17,121. **Document type:** catalog.
Formerly: Tennessee Trucker.

388.324   GW   ISSN 0257-3180
FERNFAHRER; Magazin fuer L K W-Fahrer im Nah- und Fernverkehr. 1983. m. Vereinigte Fachverlage GmbH, Lise-Meitner-Str. 2, 55129 Mainz, Germany. TEL 06131-992-0. FAX 06131-992100. Ed. Udo Wuest. adv. contact: Peter Hart. bk.rev. circ. 40,980. **Document type:** trade publication.
Description: Publication of interest to truckers. Features travel reports, technical information, new truck designs, road testing, traffic and transportation, new product information. Includes reports and calendar of events, readers' letters, classified adds.

TRANSPORTATION — TRUCKS AND TRUCKING

388.324 US ISSN 0015-0819
FIFTH WHEEL.* 1945. q. $9 to non-members. (Indiana Motor Truck Association, Inc.) Naylor Publications, Inc., P.O. Box 1167, Cockeysville Hunt Valley, MD 21030-6167. TEL 410-785-2445. Ed. Judith K. Spencer. adv. circ. 2,000. **Document type:** trade publication.

388.324 US ISSN 0747-2544
TL230.2
FLEET EQUIPMENT. 1974. 12/yr. $80. Maple Publishing, 134 W. Slade St., Palatine, IL 60067. TEL 708-359-6100. FAX 708-359-6420. Ed. Thomas A. Gelinas. adv.; circ. 61,923 (controlled). **Indexed:** ABI Inform. **Document type:** trade publication. ●Also available online. Vendor(s): University Microfilms International.
—BLDSC (3950.321800); UMI. **CCC.**
Formerly (until 1984): Fleet Maintenance and Specifying (ISSN 0095-3245)

388.324 US
FLEET OWNER. 1928. m. $45. Intertec Publishing Corp. (White Plains), 707 Westchester Ave., Ste. 101, White Plains, NY 10604-3102. TEL 914-949-8500. FAX 914-287-6752. (Subscr. to: Fulfillment Manager, Box 512, Winchester, MA 01890. TEL 617-729-4200) Ed. Tom Duncan. adv.: B&W page &8665, color page $11290. bk.rev.; illus.; tr.lit.; circ. 100,150 (controlled). (also avail. in microform from UMI; reprint service avail. from UMI) **Indexed:** ABI Inform., B.P.I., Bus.Ind., Chem.Abstr., Tr.& Indus.Ind. **Document type:** trade publication.
—BLDSC (3950.350000); UMI; UnCover. **CCC.**
Formerly: Fleet Owner: Big Fleet Edition; Superseded in part: Fleet Owner (ISSN 0731-9622)

388.324 US ISSN 0015-4334
FLORIDA TRUCK NEWS. 1946. m. $14. Florida Trucking Association, Inc., 350 E. College Ave., Tallahassee, FL 32301. TEL 904-222-9900. FAX 904-222-9363. Ed. Joseph A. Bono. adv. contact: Ed Pooser. bk.rev.; illus.; circ. 2,300 (controlled). **Document type:** trade publication.

388.324 AT ISSN 0727-9752
FREIGHT CARRIERS. m. Aus.$1.20. (New South Wales Road Transport Association) Percival Publishing Co. Pty. Ltd., 862-870 Elizabeth St., Waterloo, N.S.W. 2017, Australia. adv.; charts; illus. circ. 1,500.
Formerly (until 1973): Master Carriers Journal (ISSN 0025-5009)

388 SA ISSN 0259-4773
FREIGHT WORLD. 1977. fortn. Bowford Publications, P.O. Box 835, Kempton Park 1620, South Africa. circ. 3,688. **Document type:** trade publication.
Supersedes: S.A. Freight News; Which supersedes in part: Commercial Transport and Freight (ISSN 0376-5849); Which was formed by the merger of: Commercial Transport (ISSN 0036-2107); Freight (ISSN 0016-0857)

388.324 US
FURNITURE TRANSPORTER.* 1965. s-m. $49. Bohman Industrial Traffic Consultants, Inc., Box 889, Gardner, MA 01440. TEL 617-632-1913. Ed. Raynard F. Bohman Jr.

388.324 US ISSN 0738-5935
TL230.A1
GO WEST. 1941. m. $30. Motor Transport Publishers Inc., 11344 Coloma Rd., Ste. 445, Gold River, CA 95670. TEL 916-852-5700. FAX 916-852-5707. Ed. James Beach. adv.; charts; illus.; mkt.; stat.; tr.lit.; circ. 46,238 (controlled). **Document type:** trade publication.
Formerly: Go (Burlingame) (ISSN 0017-1433)
Description: Focuses on serving the managerial needs of operators of diesel trucks with routes in or through the fastest growing regions of the United States--the Pacific, Mountain, Southwestern and Central states.

388.324 US ISSN 0738-3096
GOVERNMENT TENDER REPORT. w. $350 (with Government Traffic Bulletin $450). (American Trucking Associations) Trucking Information Services, Inc., 2200 Mill Rd., Alexandria, VA 22314. TEL 703-838-1792. FAX 703-683-9751. Ed. Emry Williams. **Document type:** trade publication.
Description: Summary of tenders submitted to the I.C.C. by motor carriers.

388.324 US ISSN 0738-310X
GOVERNMENT TRAFFIC BULLETIN. w. $150 (including Government Tender Report $450). (American Trucking Associations) Trucking Information Service, Inc., 2200 Mill Rd., Alexandria, VA 22314. TEL 703-838-1792. FAX 703-683-9751. Ed. Susan Stowell. **Document type:** bulletin.
Description: Reports on the transportation needs of major US government shippers, with emphasis on motor carrier traffic information.

388.324 GW ISSN 0017-5137
GUETERVERKEHR. 1951. m. DM.42. Kirschbaum Verlag GmbH, Siegfriedstr. 28, 53179 Bonn, Germany. TEL 0228-95453-0. FAX 0228-9545327. (Subscr. to: Postfach 210209, 53157 Bonn, Germany) adv.; bk.rev.; charts; illus.; index. circ. 25,000. (back issues avail.) **Document type:** trade publication.
—SWETS. **CCC.**

388.324 UK
HAULAGE MANUAL. 1970. biennial. Road Haulage Association, 35 Monument Hill, Weybridge KT13 8RN, England. TEL 01932-841515. Ed. Sydney Balgarnie. adv.; stat.; index. circ. 12,000. **Document type:** trade publication.

388.24 604.7 US
HAZARDOUS COMMODITY HANDBOOK. 9th ed., 1989. a. $75 to non-members; members $55. National Tank Truck Carriers, Inc., 2200 Mill Rd., Alexandria, VA 22314-4677. TEL 703-838-1960. FAX 703-684-5763.

388.324 US
HEAVY DUTY NEWSLETTER. 1989. bi-m. members only. Heavy Duty Manufacturers Association, Box 13966, Research Triangle Park, NC 27709-3966. TEL 919-549-4800. Ed. J.J. Conner. circ. 250. **Document type:** newsletter.
Description: Keeps top executives of truck component manufacturers informed of industry trends and government regulations.

388.324 US ISSN 0017-9434
HE5601
HEAVY DUTY TRUCKING. 1922. m. $54 (foreign $108). Newport Communications (Subsidiary of: H.I.C. Corporation), Box W, Newport Beach, CA 92658. TEL 714-261-1636. Ed. Doug Condra. adv.; illus. circ. 100,812.
—UnCover. **CCC.**

388.324 US ISSN 0018-1706
HIGHWAY COMMON CARRIER NEWSLETTER. 1948. fortn. $26. Regular Common Carrier Conference, 2200 Mill Rd., Ste. 350, Alexandria, VA 22314-4677. TEL 703-898-1970. Ed. Shawn Fields. bk.rev. circ. 1,500. (looseleaf format; back issues avail.) **Document type:** newsletter.
Description: Summarizes the legislative and regulatory developments affecting the general freight trucking industry.

629.2 SZ
I N U F A KATALOG; internationaler Nutzfahrzeugkatalog. 1958. a. 45 SFr. Vogt-Schild AG, Zuchwilerstr. 21, CH-4501 Solothurn, Switzerland. TEL 065-247247. FAX 065-247235. Ed. Andre Vollmar. adv.: B&W page 3320 SFr., color page 4520 SFr.; trim 185 x 260; adv. contact: Andreas Benz. bk.rev. circ. 5,000. **Document type:** catalog.
—**CCC.**
Formerly: I N U F A: Internationaler Nutzfahrzeug-Katalog - International Catalogue for Commercial Vehicles (ISSN 0073-4292)

388.324 AU ISSN 0019-0845
I T R. (International Transport Revue) 1962. 14/yr. S.560. Technopress Fachzeitschriften Verlagsgesellschaft mbH, Felix-Mottl-Str. 12, A-1190 Vienna, Austria. TEL 0222-322551. Ed. Dr. Helmut Tober. adv.; bk.rev.; illus.; circ. 14,000 (controlled). (tabloid format) **Indexed:** C.I.S. Abstr.

388.324 US ISSN 0019-2309
ILLINOIS TRUCK NEWS. 1935. q. Illinois Trucking Association, 2000 N. 5th Ave., River Grove, IL 60171-1907. FAX 708-452-3508. Ed. Julie McGowen. adv.; bk.rev.; circ. 5,326 (controlled). **Description:** Includes items on election issues, safety and maintenance, legislation and management.

388.3 US ISSN 1049-0051
ILLINOIS TRUCKER; merchandising everything for the trucking industry. 1977. m. $18. Allied Publications, 7355 N. Woodland, Box 603, Indianapolis, IN 46206-0603. TEL 317-297-5500. FAX 317-299-1356. adv. circ. 20,000. **Document type:** trade publication.

IMPORTED CARS, LIGHT TRUCKS & VANS SERVICE & REPAIR. see TRANSPORTATION — Automobiles

388.3 US ISSN 1048-9657
INDIANA TRUCKER; merchandising everything for the trucking industry. 1975. m. $18. Allied Publications, 7355 N. Woodland, Box 603, Indianapolis, IN 46206-0603. TEL 317-297-5500. FAX 317-299-1356. adv. circ. 20,000. **Document type:** trade publication.
Formerly: Indiana Truck Exchange.

388 FR
INFORMATION ROUTIERE ET TOURISTIQUE. 1946. m. 48 F. S E D I T, 48 rue de la Bienfaisance, 75008 Paris, France. Ed. Jean Charrier. adv. circ. 3,000.

388.324 UK ISSN 0960-0035
HF5415.7 CODEN: IPDMEC
INTERNATIONAL JOURNAL OF PHYSICAL DISTRIBUTION & LOGISTICS MANAGEMENT. 1970. 10/yr. £2399($3999) (effective 1996). M C B University Press Ltd., 60-62 Toller Ln., Bradford, W. Yorks BD8 9BY, England. TEL 01274-499821. FAX 01274-547143. TELEX 51317-MCBUNI-G. Ed. James Stock. bk.rev.; index. (reprint service avail. from SWZ) **Indexed:** ABI Inform., Account.& Data Proc.Abstr., BPIA, Bus.Ind., Cont.Pg.Manage., Curr.Cont., Excerp.Med., INSPEC (1990-), Int.Abstr.Oper.Res., Key to Econ.Sci., Manage.Cont., SCIMP, SSCI. **Document type:** academic/scholarly publication.
—BLDSC (4542.461500); SWETS; UMI; UnCover. **CCC.**
Formerly: International Journal of Physical Distribution and Materials Management; Supersedes (with vol.8, 1977): International Journal of Physical Distribution (ISSN 0020-7527)
Description: Covers transport and inventory management, materials purchasing management, distribution planning and costs, customer service policy and order processing systems.

388.324 UK ISSN 0262-6195
INTERNATIONAL ROAD HAULAGE BY UNITED KINGDOM REGISTERED VEHICLES. 1979. a. £16.50. H.M.S.O., P.O. Box 276, London SW8 5DT, England. Ed. A.K. Pepper. circ. 180. **Document type:** government publication.
●Also available online.
—BLDSC (4548.460000). **CCC.**
Formerly (until 1980): International Road Haulage by British Registered Vehicles (ISSN 0262-4508)

388.324 340 US ISSN 0884-8394
INTERSTATE INFORMATION REPORT; a monthly bulletin for motor carrier licensing managers. 1977. m. $60. American Trucking Associations, State Laws Department, 2200 Mill Rd., Alexandria, VA 22314-4677. TEL 703-838-1797; 800-ATA-LINE. FAX 703-838-1992. Ed. Renee Griest. circ. 900. **Document type:** newsletter.
Description: Compilation of currently enacted state legislation, regulations and court decisions having direct impact on vehicle operations, fuel taxes, sizes and weights and other areas of interest to the interstate trucking industry.

388.324 US
IOWA TRUCKING LIFELINER. 1943. m. $4. Iowa Motor Truck Association, Capital Center One, 600 E. Court, Ste. D, Des Moines, IA 50309-2020. TEL 515-244-5193. FAX 515-244-2204. Ed. Brenda Neville. adv.; illus.; circ. 3,187 (controlled). **Former titles:** Lifeliner (Des Moines); Motor Truck News (ISSN 0027-2116)

ITRAFIK - MED BUSS I TRAFIK. see TRANSPORTATION

388.324 GW ISSN 0341-9681
K F Z ANZEIGER; Truck und Transport in Europa. 1947. fortn. DM.124 (foreign DM.147). Stuenings Verlagsgesellschaft mbH, Luisenstr. 100-104, 47799 Krefeld, Germany. TEL 02151-853-0. FAX 02151-853103. Ed.Bd. adv.: B&W page DM.6880, color page DM.11320; trim 185 x 255; adv. contact: Manfred Schenk. bk.rev. circ. 37,492. **Document type:** trade publication.
Formerly: Kraftfahrzeug Anzeiger.

388.324 US
KEEP ON TRUCKIN' NEWS. 1974. m. membership only. Mid-West Truckers Association, Inc., 2727 N. Dirksen Parkway, Springfield, IL 62702. TEL 217-525-0310. FAX 217-525-0342. Ed. Robert Jasmon. adv. circ. 3,500.
   Description: Information on activities in the trucking industry.

388.324 UK ISSN 0954-5174
KEY NOTE REPORT: ROAD HAULAGE. Variant title: Road Haulage. irreg. £185. Key Note Publications Ltd., Field House, 72 Oldfield Rd., Hampton, Middlesex TW12 2HQ, England. TEL 0181-783-0755. FAX 0181-783-1720. **Document type:** trade publication.
● Also available online.
Also available on CD-ROM.
—BLDSC (7994.648100).

388.324 US ISSN 1049-0582
KEYSTONE - JERSEY TRUCK EXCHANGE; merchandising everything for the trucking industry. 1980. m. $18. Allied Publications, 7355 N. Woodland, Box 603, Indianapolis, IN 46206-0603. TEL 317-297-5500. FAX 317-299-1356. adv. circ. 21,000. **Document type:** trade publication.
   Formerly: Keystone - Jersey Trucker.

KIT CAR MAGAZINE. see TRANSPORTATION — Automobiles

388.324 FI
KULJETUSYRITTAJA. (Text in Finnish and Swedish) 1945. m. FIM 450. Suomen Kuorma-autoliitto r.y., Nuijamiestentie 7, 00400 Helsinki, Finland. TEL 90-578-500. FAX 358-0-578520. TELEX 19100648 VDX SF. Ed. Juha Norppa-Rahkola. adv. circ. 15,500. **Document type:** trade publication.
   Formerly: Ammattiautoilija (ISSN 0355-7286)

388.324 SW ISSN 1101-0010
LAETTA LASTBILAR. 1990. 10/yr. SEK 120. Cobra Foerlag AB, P.O. Box 82, S-533 04 Haellekis, Sweden. TEL 46-510-407-97. Ed. Roland Goetblad. adv.: B&W page SEK 10400, color page SEK 14900; trim 192 x 275; adv. contact: Ove Johansson. circ. 800. cols./p.: 4; pp./issue: 40.

388.324 US ISSN 0279-6503
LAND LINE MAGAZINE; the business magazine of owner-operator truckers. 1975. bi-m. $14. Owner-Operator Independent Drivers Association of America, Box L, Grain Valley, MO 64029. TEL 816-229-5791. FAX 816-229-0518. Ed. Todd Spencer. adv. contact: Ray Gurney. bk.rev.; circ. 110,000. (controlled). **Document type:** trade publication.
   Incorporates: Owner Operator News.
   Description: For the small business men and women of commercial trucking. Provides news for the serious decision-makers in this segment of the industry.

388.324 GW ISSN 0941-6285
LASTAUTO OMNIBUS KATALOG. 1970. a. DM.22. Vereinigte Motor-Verlage GmbH und Co. KG, Leuschnerstr. 1, 70174 Stuttgart, Germany. TEL 0711-18201. FAX 0711-1821669. (Subscr. to: Postfach 106036, 70049 Stuttgart, Germany) Ed. Rainer Rex; Pub. Frank Neumann. adv.: B&W page DM.7450, color page DM.13783; adv. contact: Bernd Rostock. charts; illus. circ. 30,000. **Document type:** catalog.

388.324 SW ISSN 0023-8678
LASTBILEN; svensk aakeritidning. 1932. 15/yr. SEK 470. Aakerifoerlaget AB, P.O. Box 508, 182 15 Danderyd, Sweden. TEL 46-08-753-54-40. FAX 46-08-755-88-95. TELEX 13653. Ed. Eric Bjoerklund. adv. contact: Inger Kalin. bk.rev.; illus.; stat.; circ. 16,900. **Document type:** trade publication.
   Incorporates (in 1984): Transportveteranen;
   Formerly (until 1944): Lasttrafikbilaegaren.

388.324 NO ISSN 0023-8686
LASTEBILEN. m. (11/yr.). NOK 320 (foreign NOK 400). Norges Lastebileier-Forbund - Norwegian Truck-Owners' Association, Th. Meyersgt. 72, P.O. Box 4658 Sofienberg, N-0506 Oslo, Norway. TEL 47-22-11-01-55. FAX 47-22-20-56-15. Ed. Kaare Samuelsen. adv. contact: Arild Holm. charts; circ. 13,000 (controlled). **Document type:** trade publication.
   —CCC.

388.324 690 US ISSN 1045-442X
HE5623.A1
LIFTING & TRANSPORTATION INTERNATIONAL. 1953. m. $65 (foreign $145). Douglas Publications, Inc., 9609 Gayton Rd., Ste. 100, Richmond, VA 23233. TEL 804-741-6704. FAX 804-750-2399. Ed. Dennis Melamed. adv. contact: Carolyn Ward. bk.rev. circ. 22,108. **Document type:** trade publication.
   Formerly: Transportation Engineer (ISSN 0041-1604)
   Description: Contains the latest news from the crane, rigging and specialized transportation industries worldwide.

THE LIGHT (ARLINGTON). see TRANSPORTATION — Railroads

388.324 US
M M C A NEWS. 1990. m. $12.50. (Montana Motor Carriers Association, Inc.) Motor Carrier Service Inc., Box 1714, Helena, MT 59624. TEL 406-442-6600. Ed. B.G. Havdahl. circ. 850.

388.324 US
MAINE MOTOR TRANSPORT NEWS. 1946. 10/yr. $25. Maine Motor Transport Association, Inc., 142 Whitten Rd., Augusta, ME 04330. TEL 207-623-4128. FAX 207-623-4096. Ed. Dale E. Hannington. adv. contact: Gayle Baber. (reprint service avail.) **Document type:** trade publication.
   Description: Covers the trucking industry.

388.324 US
MAINTENANCE. m. $75. American Trucking Associations, 2200 Mill Rd., Alexandria, VA 22314. TEL 800-ATA-LINE. FAX 703-684-5720. **Document type:** newsletter.
   Formed by the 1988 merger of: Maintenance (Newsletter for Professional Truck Equipment Managers) (ISSN 0890-1775); Maintenance (Newsletter for Professional Truck Equipment Supervisors) (ISSN 0890-1783); Maintenance (Newsletter for Professional Truck Equipment Executives) (ISSN 0890-1767); Maintenance (Newsletter for Professional Truck Driver-Owner) (ISSN 0890-1791)

388.324 US
MAINTENANCE MANAGER MAGAZINE. 1988. q. membership. American Trucking Associations, Maintenance Council, 2200 Mill Rd., Alexandria, VA 22314. TEL 703-838-1700; 800-ATA-LINE. FAX 703-684-4328. Ed. Rob Braswell.
   Formerly: Maintenance: Managers.
   Description: Focuses on current equipment management issues, new equipment and products, and management training, and internal matters pertaining to the Maintenance Council of the ATA.

388.324 US
MAYFLOWER WAREHOUSEMAN. 1955. 6/yr.. $12. 9247 N. Meridian St., Ste. 120, Indianapolis, IN 46260. TEL 317-844-6226. FAX 317-848-3744. Ed. Julie McLaughlin Foster. adv. circ. 2,000. **Document type:** trade publication.
   Description: Magazine for moving and storage industry.

388.324 US ISSN 1048-969X
MICHIGAN TRUCK EXCHANGE; merchandising everything for the trucking industry. 1989. bi-w. $18. Allied Publications, 7355 N. Woodland, Box 603, Indianapolis, IN 46206-0603. TEL 317-297-5500. FAX 317-299-1356. adv. circ. 25,000. **Document type:** trade publication.

388.324 US
MID-AMERICA TRANSPORTER. 1946. 11/yr. $12. Kansas Motor Carriers Association, 2900 S. Topeka Blvd., Box 1673, Topeka, KS 66601. TEL 913-267-1641. FAX 913-266-6551. Ed. Carl Hill. adv.; illus.; tr.lit. circ. 4,500. **Document type:** trade publication.
   Formerly (until 1984): Kansas Transporter (ISSN 0022-8842)

388.324 US
MID-SOUTH TRUCKING NEWS. fortn. $28. 9 Lucy Lane, Sherwood, AR 72120. TEL 501-834-8600. FAX 501-834-8120. Ed. Gene Williams. **Document type:** newspaper, trade publication.

TRANSPORTATION — TRUCKS AND TRUCKING   6443

388.324 US ISSN 0026-3427
MIDWEST MOTOR TRANSPORT NEWS. 1935. 12/yr. membership only. Minnesota Trucking Association, Box 14417, St. Paul, MN 55114-0417. TEL 612-646-7351. FAX 612-641-8995. Ed. Andy Piilola. adv.; stat.; tr.lit. circ. 850. **Document type:** newsletter.
   Description: Provides members of the Minnesota Trucking Association with information regarding rules, regulations, laws and events that affect the trucking industry.

388.324 US
MILEAGE GUIDE (NO.). 1993. every 3 yrs. $110 per no. American Movers Conference, 1611 Duke St., Alexandria, VA 22314. TEL 703-683-7410. FAX 703-683-7527. **Document type:** trade publication.
   Description: Serves as governing tariff publication to establish distances between all points in the U.S., Canada and Mexico.

388.324 US ISSN 0199-2317
MILK AND LIQUID FOOD TRANSPORTER. 1960. m. $12. Brady Co., Inc., N80 W12878 Fond du Lac Ave., Box 878, Menomonee Falls, WI 53052-0878. TEL 414-255-0108. Ed. Linda Mittag. adv. circ. 2,500. (back issues avail.)

388.324 US ISSN 1052-0961
MINI TRUCKIN'. q. $2.95 per no. McMullen & Yee Publishing, 774 S. Placentia Ave., Placentia, CA 92670-6846. TEL 714-572-2255. FAX 714-572-1864.

388.324 US ISSN 0031-6431
TN860
MODERN BULK TRANSPORTER. 1937. m. $25 (foreign $40) (free to qualified personnel). Tunnell Publications, Inc., Box 66010, Houston, TX 77266. TEL 713-523-8124. FAX 713-523-8384. Ed. Charles Wilson. adv.; charts; illus.; stat.; tr.lit. circ. 16,000.
—BLDSC (5883.760000).
   Formerly: Petroleum and Chemical Transporter.
   Description: Serves the tank truck industry which transports petroleum and petroleum products, chemicals, milk, other food products, and other types of liquid and dry commodities in bulk form.

338.324 330 US ISSN 0199-0373
MODERN TRUCKSTOP NEWS. 1979. bi-m. free. G C I Publishing Co., Inc., 1801 Rockville Pike, No. 330, Rockville, MD 20852-1633. TEL 301-984-7333. FAX 301-984-7340. Ed. Louise Classon. adv. circ. 10,500. **Document type:** trade publication.
   Description: For owners and managers.

388.3 US ISSN 0738-3088
MONTHLY TRUCK TONNAGE REPORT. m. $35. (American Trucking Associations) Trucking Information Services, Inc., 2200 Mill Rd., Alexandria, VA 22314. TEL 703-838-1792. FAX 703-683-9751. Indexed: SRI. **Document type:** trade publication.
   Description: Publishes tonnage reports from ongoing survey of Class I and II general freight carriers; comparisons with other economic indicators.

388.324 US
MOTOR CARRIER - FREIGHT FORWARDER SERVICE. 1940. 4 base vols. (plus m. suppl.). $365. Hawkins Publishing Co., Inc., Box 480, Mayo, MD 21106-0480. TEL 301-798-1677. Ed. Carl R. Eyler. circ. 500. (back issues avail.) **Document type:** abstracting/indexing.

388.324 US
MOTOR CARRIER SAFETY REPORT. m. $90. J.J. Keller & Associates, Inc., 3003 W. Breezewood Lane, Box 368, Neenah, WI 54957-0368. TEL 414-722-2848. FAX 414-727-7516. Ed.Bd.
   Description: Reports on motor carrier safety and trucking safety.

MOTOR FLEET SUPERVISION; principles and practices. see BUSINESS AND ECONOMICS — Personnel Management

388.324 US ISSN 0886-8778
NOT IN LC
MOTOR FREIGHT CONTROLLER. bi-m. members only. American Trucking Associations, 2200 Mill Rd., Alexandria, VA 22304. TEL 703-838-1700. FAX 703-836-6070. Ed. Cynthia Zuckerman. adv.

TRANSPORTATION — TRUCKS AND TRUCKING

388.324   UK   ISSN 0027-206X
MOTOR TRANSPORT. 1905. w. £90. Reed Business Publishing Group (Subsidiary of: Reed Elsevier group), Quadrant House, The Quadrant, Sutton, Surrey SM2 5AS, England. TEL 0181-652-3284. FAX 0181-652-8957. (Subscr. to: c/o Computer Action Ltd., 27 Park St., Croydon, Surrey CR0 1YO, England. TEL 0181-681-8416) Ed. Geoff Hadwick. adv.; bk.rev.; illus.; circ. 28,766 (controlled). **Indexed:** C.I.S.Abstr. **Document type:** trade publication. —BLDSC (5975.610000).

MOTOR TREND'S TRUCK & VAN BUYER'S GUIDE. see *TRANSPORTATION — Automobiles*

388.324   CN   ISSN 0027-2108
MOTOR TRUCK. 1934. m. Can.$32.10 (foreign $47). Southam Magazine Group, 1450 Don Mills Rd., Don Mills, ON M3B 2X7, Canada. TEL 416-445-6641. FAX 416-442-2261. Ed. Barry Holmes. adv.; illus.; stat.; tr.lit. circ. 29,800. **Indexed:** Can.B.P.I. —UMI. **CCC**.
Description: Published specifically for heavy duty truck fleet managers and fleet operators.

388.324   US   ISSN 1049-1007
MOUNTAIN AMERICA TRUCK TRADER; merchandising everything for the trucking industry. 1978. m. $18. Allied Publications, 7355 N. Woodland, Box 603, Indianapolis, IN 46206-0603. TEL 317-297-5500. FAX 317-299-1356. adv. circ. 18,000. **Document type:** trade publication.

338.324   US   ISSN 8750-1155
MOVERS NEWS. 1937. m. $39. N Y S Movers & Warehousemen's Association, 132 State St., Albany, NY 12207-1610. TEL 518-449-8786. FAX 518-449-8981. Ed. Donald J. Boyle. adv. circ. 600.

MOVERS STATISTICAL PROFILE (YEAR); demographic, economic and financial data of the moving industry. see *TRANSPORTATION — Abstracting, Bibliographies, Statistics*

MOVICARGA. see *BUSINESS AND ECONOMICS — Production Of Goods And Services*

388.324   US
MOVIN' OUT. 1975. m. $12. Pollock Enterprises, Ltd., 118 1-2 Franklin St., Box 97, Slippery Rock, PA 16057. TEL 412-794-6857. FAX 412-794-1314. Ed. Pamela S. Pollock; Pub. Steven M. Pollock. adv.; circ. 42,000 (controlled). **Document type:** trade publication, newspaper.
Description: Contains trucking news on a national and local level. Includes new product information.

388.324   US
MOVING INDUSTRY FINANCIAL ANNUAL (YEAR); household goods carriers' (year) I C C annual report data. a. $30. American Movers Conference, 1611 Duke St., Alexandria, VA 22314. TEL 703-683-7410. FAX 703-683-7527. **Document type:** trade publication.
Formerly (until 1993): Digest of Household Goods Carriers.
Description: Provides operating data of household goods carriers that file annual reports with the I.C.C. Aimed at persons dealing with the moving business.

388.324   US
THE MOVING INDUSTRY PROFESSIONAL SOURCEBOOK. a. $195. American Movers Conference, 1611 Duke St., Alexandria, VA 22314. TEL 703-683-7410. FAX 703-683-7527. circ. 3,000. **Document type:** directory.
Formerly: A M C - H G C B Joint Membership Directory.
Description: Lists AMC's 3000 members, domestic and international moving companies, state and local moving associations and supplier companies.

388.324   US   ISSN 1064-4253
MOVING WORLD. 1992. s-m. $50 (Canada & Mexico $60; elsewhere $85). American Movers Conference, 1611 Duke St., Alexandria, VA 22314. TEL 703-683-7410. FAX 703-683-7527. adv. contact: Karen B. Climo. circ. 3,100 (paid). (tabloid format) **Document type:** newspaper.
Description: Provides news and information for moving company members.

380.14   US   ISSN 0192-7027
MY LITTLE SALESMAN TRUCK CATALOG. (In two editions: Central and Western U.S.) 1958. m. $18; newsstand price: $2.50. Industrial Publishing Co., Box 70208, Eugene, OR 97401. TEL 503-342-1201. FAX 503-342-3307. adv.: B&W page $895; adv. contact: Rod Womack. circ. 60,000.
Description: Provides information to those buying or selling trucks and trucking equipment.

388.324   US   ISSN 1040-2284
N A T S O TRUCKERS NEWS. Variant title: Truckers News. 1977. m. $20. (National Association of Truck Stop Operators) Newport Communications (Irvine), 38 Executive Park, Ste. 300, Irvine, CA 92714. TEL 714-261-1636. FAX 714-261-2904. (Subscr. to: N A T S O Subscription Dept., 1199 N. Fairfax St., Alexandria, VA 22314. TEL 703-549-2100) adv. circ. 175,000. **Document type:** trade publication. —CCC.
Description: Features news and articles of interest to professional truck drivers.

388.324   US
N T E A TECHNICAL REPORT. irreg., 8-10/yr. membership. National Truck Equipment Association, 37400 Hills Tech Dr., Farmington Hills, MI 48331-3414. TEL 810-489-7090. FAX 810-489-8590. **Document type:** trade publication.

388.324   US   ISSN 0077-586X
NATIONAL TANK TRUCK CARRIER DIRECTORY. 1954. a. $67 to non-members; members $44. National Tank Truck Carriers, Inc., 2200 Mill Rd., Alexandria, VA 22314-4677. TEL 703-838-1960. FAX 703-684-5753. Ed. Patricia Whiting. adv. circ. 2,000. **Document type:** directory.

388.324   US
NATIONAL TRUCK EQUIPMENT ASSOCIATION. WASHINGTON UPDATE. 1979. m. $4 to non-members; members $2. National Truck Equipment Association, 37400 Hills Tech Dr., Farmington Hills, MI 48331-3414. TEL 810-489-7090. FAX 810-489-8590. Ed. Joan Christophersen. circ. 1,600. (looseleaf format; back issues avail.) **Document type:** newsletter.
Formerly: National Truck Equipment Association. Legislative Report; **Incorporates:** National Truck Equipment Association. Regulations Report.
Description: Discussion of legislative and current federal and state regulatory activities, includes updates on congressional committee action and pending congressional bills.

388.324   US
NEBRASKA TRUCKER. 1940. m. $16. Nebraska Motor Carriers' Association, Inc., 1701 K St., Box 81010, Lincoln, NE 68501. TEL 402-476-7822. FAX 402-476-0579. E-mail: 75613.1316@compuserve.com. Ed. Nance Kirk. adv. contact: Sue Wilson. circ. 2,600 (paid). (also avail. in diskette format) **Document type:** trade publication.
Formerly: Midwestern Trucker and Shipper.

388.324   GW   ISSN 0431-6444
NEUZULASSUNGEN BESITZUMSCHREIBUNGEN LOESCHUNGEN VON KRAFTFAHRZEUGEN UND KRAFTFAHRZEUGANHAENGERN. a. DM.47. Kraftfahr-Bundesamt, Foerdestr. 16, 24944 Flensburg, Germany.
Former titles (until 1959): Bestand an Kraftfahrzeugen und Kraftfahrzeuganhaengern und Seine Veraenderungen im Gebiet der Bundesrepublik Deutschland in Berlin (West) (ISSN 0341-6453); (until 1955): Bestand an Kraftfahrzeugen und Kraftfahrzeuganhaengern im Gebiet der Bundesrepublik Deutschland (ISSN 0433-7735)

388.324   US   ISSN 1048-9681
NEW ENGLAND TRUCK EXCHANGE; merchandising everything for the trucking industry. 1981. m. $18. Allied Publications, 7355 N. Woodland, Box 603, Indianapolis, IN 46206-0603. TEL 317-297-5500. FAX 317-299-1356. adv. circ. 21,000. **Document type:** trade publication.

388.324   US   ISSN 0028-5838
NEW JERSEY MOTOR TRUCK ASSOCIATION. BULLETIN. 1964. m. $45. New Jersey Motor Truck Association, 160 Tices Ln., E. Brunswick, NJ 08816. TEL 908-254-5000. FAX 908-613-1745. Ed. Anthony Buccino. adv.; bk.rev.; illus.; circ. 2,100 (controlled). **Document type:** trade publication.

388.324   US   ISSN 1049-0612
NEW YORK TRUCK EXCHANGE; merchandising everything for the trucking industry. 1977. m. $18. Allied Publications, 7355 N. Woodland, Box 603, Indianapolis, IN 46206-0603. TEL 317-297-5500. FAX 317-299-1356. Ed. Robert W. Poorman, Jr. adv. circ. 20,000. **Document type:** trade publication.

NISSAN DIESEL TECHNICAL REVIEW. see *TRANSPORTATION — Automobiles*

NOTIZIARIO MOTORISTICO/MOTOR NEWS/MOTOR-NACHRICHTEN/NOUVELLES DE L'AUTOMOBILE; autoattrezzature-impiantistica. see *TRANSPORTATION — Automobiles*

388.324   CN
OFFICIAL MANITOBA SHIP BY TRUCK DIRECTORY. 1958. a. Can.$27. Manitoba Trucking Association, 25 Bunting St., Winnipeg, MB R2X 2P5, Canada. Ed. Dianne Milton. adv. circ. 1,000. **Document type:** directory.
Former titles: Manitoba Ship by Truck Directory (ISSN 0713-8776); M T A Ship by Truck Directory.

388.324   US   ISSN 0472-6243
HE5623.A45
OFFICIAL MOTOR CARRIER DIRECTORY. 1958. s-a. $49.50. Official Motor Freight Guide, Inc., 1700 W. Cortland St., Chicago, IL 60622-1150. TEL 312-278-2454. FAX 312-489-0482. Ed. Edward K. Koch. adv.; charts. circ. 5,200. **Document type:** directory.

388.324   US   ISSN 0030-0357
OFFICIAL MOTOR FREIGHT GUIDE. (Published in 17 Regional Editions) 1932. s-a. $49.50. Official Motor Freight Guide, Inc., 1700 W. Cortland St., Chicago, IL 60622-1150. TEL 312-278-2454. FAX 312-489-0482. Ed. E. Eric J. Robison. adv. contact: Hugh Morgan. circ. 11,590 (paid); 1,767 (controlled). **Document type:** directory.

388.324   US
OFFICIAL SHIPPERS GUIDE - NEW YORK MOTOR EXPRESS GUIDE. 1872. s-a. $49.50. Official Motor Freight Guide, Inc., 1700 W. Cortland St., Chicago, IL 60622-1150. TEL 312-278-2454. Ed. E. Eric Robison. adv.; charts.

388.324   US
OFFICIAL SHIPPERS GUIDE - ST. LOUIS MOTOR FREIGHT DIRECTORY. 1872. s-a. $45. Official Motor Freight Guide, Inc., 1700 W. Cortland St., Chicago, IL 60622-1150. TEL 312-278-2454. Ed. Eric Robison.

629.2 380.5   FR   ISSN 1163-0736
OFFICIEL DES TRANSPORTEURS; l'hebdomadaire du transport routier. 1925. w. 890 F. (foreign 837.25 F.) (effective 1994-95). Groupe Liaisons, 92856 Reuil-Malmaison Cedex, France. TEL 41-29-99-99. FAX 41-29-97-90. Ed. Jean Pierre Lagarde. adv. circ. 25,841.
Formerly (until 1991): Officiel des Transports (ISSN 1156-3133)

OHIO GOVERNMENT DIRECTORY - OHIO TRUCKING TIMES. see *PUBLIC ADMINISTRATION*

388.324   US
OKLAHOMA MOTOR CARRIER. 1937. q. $4. Associated Motor Carriers of Oklahoma, Inc., Box 14620, Oklahoma City, OK 73113. TEL 405-843-9488. FAX 405-843-7310. Ed. Jalynn Marsee. adv. contact: Jalynn Marsee. charts; illus.; stat. circ. 3,300 (controlled). **Document type:** trade publication.
Former titles: Truck and Commerce; Oklahoma Motor Carrier.
Description: For the Oklahoma trucking industry.

388.324   US   ISSN 0736-6124
OLDER CAR RED BOOK. 4/yr. $69. Maclean Hunter Market Reports, Inc., 29 N. Wacker Dr., Chicago, IL 60606-3297. TEL 312-726-2802. FAX 312-726-2574. (back issues avail.)

388.324   US
OVER THE ROAD. m. Ramp Publishing Group, 610 Colonial Park Dr., Roswell, GA 30075-3746. TEL 404-587-0311. FAX 404-642-8874. Ed. Ken Kent. circ. 125,000. **Document type:** trade publication.

TRANSPORTATION — TRUCKS AND TRUCKING

388.324   US
OWNER AND OPERATOR DIRECTORY.* 1977. bi-m. Ramp Enterprises, Inc., 610 Colonial Park Dr., Roswell, GA 30075-3746. TEL 404-587-0338. Ed. Penny Shefsky. adv. **Document type:** directory.

388.324   US   ISSN 0475-2112
HE5601
OWNER OPERATOR. 1970. 9/yr. $18. Chilton Co., Chilton Way, Radnor, PA 19089. TEL 215-964-4264. FAX 215-964-4512. Ed. Leon Witconis. adv.; bk.rev.; charts; illus.; tr.lit. circ. 93,000. (also avail. in microfilm from UMI; microfiche from UMI; back issues avail.; reprint service avail. from UMI)
—UMI. **CCC.**

388.324   US   ISSN 1042-2641
P & D MAGAZINE. (Pickup & Delivery) 10/yr. Motor Transport Publishers Inc., 11344 Coloma Rd., Ste. 445, Gold River, CA 95670. TEL 916-852-5700. FAX 916-852-5707. Ed. James Beach. adv. circ. 40,000. **Document type:** trade publication.

388.324   US
PENNTRUX. 1933. m. membership only. Pennsylvania Motor Truck Association, 910 Linda Ln, Camp Hill, PA 17011-6401. TEL 717-761-7122. FAX 717-761-8434. Ed. Charles A. Schulz. adv.; index; circ. 2,500 (controlled). **Document type:** trade publication.
Description: Covers state and federal developments affecting the trucking industry, and chapter relations, member news.

388.324   US   ISSN 0032-8871
HE5623.A1
PRIVATE CARRIER. 1964. m. free to qualified personnel. National Private Truck Council, Private Carrier Conference, 66 Canal Center Plaza, Ste. 600, Alexandria, VA 22314. TEL 703-683-1300. FAX 703-683-1217. Ed. James M. Galligan. adv.; bk.rev.; charts; illus.; stat.; tr.lit.; circ. 10,000 (controlled). (back issues avail.) **Document type:** trade publication.

388.324   US
PRIVATE LINE (ALEXANDRIA). 1983. m. membership only. National Private Truck Council, 66 Canal Center Plaza, Ste. 600, Alexandria, VA 22314. TEL 703-683-1300. FAX 703-683-1217. Ed. James M. Galligan. adv.; bk.rev.; circ. 2,500 (controlled). **Document type:** trade publication.

388.324   US
PRO TRUCKER.* 1988. m. Ramp Enterprises, Inc., 610 Colonial Park Dr., Roswell, GA 30075-3746. TEL 404-587-0338. FAX 404-462-8874. Ed. Ryan Rees. adv. circ. 50,000.
Formerly (until 1988): Pro Driver.
Description: For professional truck drivers, owner operators, fleet owners and drivers in the trucking industry. Covers industry news, and new products.

QUARTERLY OPERATING STATISTICS; of major household goods carriers. see TRANSPORTATION — Abstracting, Bibliographies, Statistics

QUICK CALLER: BOSTON AREA AIR CARGO DIRECTORY. see TRANSPORTATION — Air Transport

QUICK CALLER: CHICAGO AREA AIR CARGO DIRECTORY. see TRANSPORTATION — Air Transport

QUICK CALLER: DETROIT AREA AIR CARGO DIRECTORY. see TRANSPORTATION — Air Transport

QUICK CALLER: LOS ANGELES AREA AIR CARGO DIRECTORY. see TRANSPORTATION — Air Transport

QUICK CALLER: MIAMI - ORLANDO - FLORIDA AIR CARGO DIRECTORY. see TRANSPORTATION — Air Transport

QUICK CALLER: NEW YORK METRO AREA AIR CARGO DIRECTORY. see TRANSPORTATION — Air Transport

QUICK CALLER: SAN FRANCISCO BAY AREA AIR CARGO DIRECTORY. see TRANSPORTATION — Air Transport

388.324   US   ISSN 0745-0389
R V TRADE DIGEST. m. $36 (Canada and Mexico $55; elsewhere $72). Continental Publishing Company of Indiana, Inc., 58025 C.R. No.9 S., Box 1805, Elkhart, IN 46517. TEL 219-295-1962. FAX 219-295-7574. Ed. Thomas A. Russell. circ. 16,500. **Document type:** trade publication.
Description: For business professionals actively engaged in the manufacture, distribution, or sales of RV's and accessories with emphasis on sales, marketing, and business-oriented features.

388.324   US
RAND MCNALLY MOTOR CARRIERS' ROAD ATLAS. a. $18.95. Rand McNally & Co., 8255 N. Central Pk. Ave., Skokie, IL 60076. TEL 708-673-9100. (Subscr. to: Box 7600, Chicago, IL 60680) Ed. Virginia O'Neill.

388.324   US   ISSN 0034-3129
REFRIGERATED TRANSPORTER. 1964. m. $25 (foreign $40) (free to qualified personnnel). Tunnell Publications, Inc., Box 66010, Houston, TX 77266. TEL 713-523-8124. FAX 713-523-8384. Ed. Gary Macklin. adv.; illus. circ. 15,000. **Indexed:** Tr.& Indus.Ind.
Description: Serves the operators and shippers of transportation and distribution services concerned with the handling of temperature-controlled commodities.

388.324   US
ROAD KING; the magazine for the professional driver. 1963. bi-m. $12. (National Auto - Truck Stop, Inc.) Hammock Publishers, 3100 West End Ave., Ste. 200, Box 76, Nashville, TN 37202-0076. TEL 615-783-2600. adv.; bk.rev.; circ. 219,000. **Document type:** trade publication.

388.324   UK   ISSN 0035-7316
ROAD WAY. 1935. m. £28. Road Haulage Association, 35 Monument Hill, Weybridge KT13 8RN, England. TEL 01932-841515. Ed. Steve Gray. adv.; bk.rev.; illus.; stat. circ. 14,000. **Document type:** bulletin.

388.324   US
ROADWISE. 1949. s-a. $12.50. (Montana Motor Carriers Association, Inc.) Motor Carrier Service Inc., Box 1714, Helena, MT 59624. TEL 406-442-6600. Ed. B.G. Havdahl. adv. circ. 1,000.

388.324   388.312   FR   ISSN 0243-6795
LES ROUTIERS. 1934. m. 260 F. (foreign 320 F.). S E J T, 6 rue d'Isly, 75008 Paris, France. TEL 43-87-61-68. FAX 45-22-74-61. Ed. Patrice de Saulieu. adv.; bk.rev. circ. 45,000.

388.324   US
RYDER RESOURCE. 3/yr. free. Ryder System, Inc., c/o Dave Dawson, Public Relations Department, Box 020816, Miami, FL 33102-0816. TEL 305-593-3668. FAX 305-593-3203. **Document type:** newsletter.
Description: Informs consumers and customers of Ryder truck rental services.

388.324   US
S C & R A NEWSLETTER.* w. membership. Specialized Carriers & Rigging Association, 2750 Prosperity Ave., No.620, Fairfax, VA 22031-4312. TEL 703-838-1980. circ. 775.
Description: Industry news on legislation, industrial relations, management and safety.

388.324   US
S C T A HI-LIGHTS. 1937. m. $5. South Carolina Trucking Association, Inc., 2425 Devine St., Box 50166, Columbia, SC 29250-0166. TEL 803-799-4306. FAX 803-254-7148. Ed. J. Richards Todd. adv. contact: Harriette G. Derrick. bk.rev.; illus. circ. 2,504. **Document type:** trade publication.
Formerly: Motor Transportation Hi-Lights (ISSN 0027-2078)

388.324   US
SAFETY & COMPLIANCE NEWS. 1993. m. membership only. National Private Truck Council, 66 Canal Center Plaza, Ste. 600, Alexandria, VA 22314. TEL 703-683-1300. FAX 703-683-1217. Ed. James M. Galligan. adv.; bk.rev.; circ. 2,500 (controlled). **Document type:** trade publication.

388.324   US
SAFETY, INDUSTRIAL RELATIONS, AND GOVERNMENT AFFAIRS SPECIAL REPORT.* m. membership. Specialized Carriers & Rigging Association, 2750 Prosperity Ave., No.620, Fairfax, VA 22031-4312. TEL 703-838-1890. circ. 775.
Description: For transportation, crane, millwrighting and rigging professionals.

388.324   CN   ISSN 0229-9666
SASKATCHEWAN TRUCKING. 1980. q. ProWest Publications, No. 208, 438 Victoria Ave. E., Regina, SK S4N 0N7, Canada. TEL 306-352-3400. FAX 306-525-0960. adv. circ. 4,795.

388.324   CN
SASKATCHEWAN TRUCKING - SHIP BY TRUCK DIRECTORY. 1973. a. Can.$11. Saskatchewan Trucking Association, 1335 Wallace St., Regina, Sask. S4N 3Z5, Canada. TEL 306-569-9696. adv. circ. 2,000. **Document type:** directory.
Formerly: Saskatchewan Motor Transport Guide (ISSN 0707-0365)

SAVREMENI VOZAC. see TRANSPORTATION — Automobiles

388.324   SP
SOLO CAMION; industrial ligero y derivados de turismo. 1989. 11/yr. 4000 ptas. (Europe 6000 ptas.). Alesport, S.A., Gran Via 8-10, 7a planta, 08980 Hospitalet (Barcelona), Spain. TEL 34-3-4315533. FAX 34-3-4313250. Ed. Juan Montenegro; Pub. Jaime Alguersuari. adv. contact: Maite Vinals. circ. 39,000. **Document type:** trade publication.
Description: Provides news from truck and components manufacturers, information on special transports and fleets, and truck tests.

388.324   US
SOUTH DAKOTA TRUCKING NEWS. m. South Dakota Trucking Association, Box 89008, Sioux Falls, SD 57105. TEL 605-334-8871.

388.324   US   ISSN 0038-4372
TL230.A1
SOUTHERN MOTOR CARGO; truck equipment magazine of the South. 1945. m. $30. Southern Motor Cargo, Inc., Box 40169, Memphis, TN 38174. FAX 901-276-5400. Ed. Randy Duke. adv.; illus. circ. 58,000. (also avail. in microform from UMI; reprint service avail. from UMI)
—UMI.

796   US   ISSN 1044-7903
SPORT TRUCK. 1988. m. $19.94. Petersen Publishing Co., 6420 Wilshire Blvd., Los Angeles, CA 90048. TEL 213-782-2000. Ed. Hoyt Vandenberg. adv. circ. 150,000. **Document type:** consumer publication.
Incorporates (in 1991): Hot Truck.
Description: Puts trucks in a social context, providing evaluations of the latest trucks and truck products, addresses the truck owners for whom the truck represents a lifestyle.

388.324   US
STANDARD METROPOLITAN WAGE ANALYSIS. a. $50. American Movers Conference, 1611 Duke St., Alexandria, VA 22314. TEL 703-683-7410. FAX 703-683-7527. **Document type:** trade publication.
Description: Provides wage information in the moving industry; contains regional analysis. For anyone who deals with the moving business.

629.22   US   ISSN 0161-6080
SUCCESSFUL DEALER. 1978. bi-m. $50 (foreign $60). Kona Communications, Inc., 707 Lake Cook Rd., Ste. 300, Deerfield, IL 60015. TEL 708-498-3180. FAX 708-498-3197. Ed. Denise L. Rondini. adv. contact: John S. Dickson. charts; illus.; stat. circ. 19,000. **Document type:** trade publication.
—CCC.
Description: For dealer organizations selling medium- and heavy-duty trucks, construction equipment, industrial trucks, trailers and diesel engines.

388.324   US
T A R A NEWS & TOPICS. 1966. m. free. Truck-Frame & Axle Repair Association, 915 E. 99th St., Brooklyn, NY 11236. TEL 718-257-6133. FAX 718-272-9198. circ. 1,000. **Document type:** trade publication.
Description: Contains information about truck repairs.

TRANSPORTATION — TRUCKS AND TRUCKING

388.324 US
T E NEWS. (Truck Equipment) m. $48 to non-members; members $24. National Truck Equipment Association, 37400 Hills Tech Dr., Farmington Hills, MI 48331-3414. TEL 810-489-7090. FAX 810-489-8590. Ed. Joan Christophersen. circ. 1,600. (back issues avail.) **Document type:** newsletter.
Description: Truck body and equipment industry newsletter.

388.324 NE ISSN 1380-2852
T T M. (Truck en Transport Management) 1976. m. fl.169.50. Misset (Subsidiary of: Reed Elsevier plc), Postbus 4 1, 7000 BA Doetinchem, Netherlands. TEL 31-8340-49527. FAX 31-8340-43991. TELEX 45481 NL. Ed. P.C. Wieman. adv.: B&W page fl.3550; trim 215 x 285; adv. contact: Cor van Nek. bk.rev. circ. 11,800. **Document type:** trade publication.
Formerly (until 1985): Eigen Vervoer (ISSN 0165-2796)
Description: For executives and managers responsible for the management of road haulage companies and, in conjunction, for the purchase, operation and control of road transport vehicles in the road haulage industry as well as in industrial enterprises with their own vehicle fleets.

388.324 US ISSN 0039-968X
TARHEEL WHEELS. 1944. 4/yr. $3.14. North Carolina Trucking Association, Inc., Box 2977, Raleigh, NC 27602. TEL 919-834-0387. FAX 919-832-0390. Ed. Elbert L. Peters. adv.; illus. circ. 4,500. **Document type:** trade publication.
Description: Information on trucking operations and personalities involved in trucking. Includes announcements of meetings of interest to truckers.

TEAMSTER CONVOY DISPATCH; voice of the teamster rank and file since 1975. see *LABOR UNIONS*

388.324 US
TENNESSEE TRUCKING NEWS. bi-m. $25. Tennessee Trucking Association, 1415 Murgreesboro Rd., Ste. 672, Nashville, TN 37217. TEL 615-360-9200. FAX 615-361-3137. adv.; illus. 1,000 (controlled).
Formerly: Transport News of Tennessee.
Description: Covers various topics in transportation.

388.3 US ISSN 1049-104X
TEXAS - LOUISIANA TRUCKER; merchandising everything for the trucking industry. 1975. m. $18. Allied Publications, 7355 N. Woodland, Box 603, Indianapolis, IN 46206-0603. TEL 317-297-5500. FAX 317-299-1356. adv. circ. 25,000. **Document type:** trade publication.
Former titles: Texas Truck Trader - Louisiana Trucker - Oklahoma Trucker; Texas Truck Trader - Louisiana Trucker; Texas Truck Trader.

388.324 US ISSN 1068-1744
THIS OLD TRUCK. 1981. bi-m. $20 (Canada $28; elsewhere $34). Antique Power Inc., Box 838, Yellow Springs, OH 45387. TEL 513-767-1344. FAX 513-767-2726. E-mail: auntpow@aol.com. (Subscr. addr.: Box 562, Yellow Springs, OH 45387) Ed. Tom Brownell; Pub. Patrick W. Ertel. adv.: page $290. bk.rev.; index; circ. 4,500 (paid). (tabloid format; back issues avail.) **Document type:** consumer publication.
Former titles (until 1993): Classic Trucks; Plugs 'n Points.
Description: Devoted to the interests of antique light truck entyusiasts. Contains recollections of their use, restoration tips, show information, color photographs, historica research.

TORAKKU YUSO JOHO. see *TRANSPORTATION — Railroads*

388.324 US
TOW-AGE. 1974. 6/yr. Kruza Kaleidoscopix, Inc., Box 389, Franklin, MA 02038. TEL 508-528-6211. Ed. J.A. Kruza. adv.; bk.rev.; illus.; stat.; tr.lit. circ. 12,000. **Document type:** trade publication.
Formerly: Tow-Line.
Description: For towing and road service personnel who recover vehicles.

388 US
TOW TIMES; the international communications medium for the towing and recovery industry. 1983. m. $34. T T Publications, Inc., 398 Freeman St., Longwood, FL 32750. TEL 407-260-0712. FAX 407-260-1486. (Subscr. to: Box 522020, Longwood, FL 32752-2020) Ed. Tim Jackson; Pub. Clarissa Powell. adv. contact: Eleanor Joyce. tr.lit.; circ. 30,000 (controlled). (back issues avail.) **Document type:** trade publication.
Description: Covers all aspects of the towing industry: economics and law, new products, technical data, recovery reviews, and company profiles.

388.324 US
TOWING AND RECOVERY PHOOTNOTES. 1990. m. $45. Phootnote Publishing Co., 11520 N. Princeville Jubilee Rd., Princeville, IL 61559. TEL 309-243-7900. FAX 309-243-7801. Pub. Jon Lehman. adv.: B&W page $2540; trim 10 1/4 x 15. circ. 45,686. **Document type:** trade publication.
Description: Provide towing and road service company owners and managers with business management ideas to improve profitability and quality of service.

TRACK AND TIRE. see *BUILDING AND CONSTRUCTION*

388.324 US ISSN 0041-0772
TRAILER-BODY BUILDERS. 1959. m. $25 (foreign $40) (free to qualified personnel). Tunnell Publications, Inc., Box 66010, Houston, TX 77266. TEL 713-523-8124. FAX 713-523-8384. Ed. Paul Schenck. adv.; illus.; circ. 14,000 (controlled).
Description: Serves the truck body and trailer manufacturing industry, including tank, van containers, school buses, mobile homes and truck equipment.

388.324 US
TRANSPORT FLEET NEWS. 1980. m. $20. Transport Publishing Co., 1962 N. Bissell St., Suite 3, Chicago, IL 60614-5015. TEL 312-880-0086. FAX 312-880-5125. Ed. Phillip Scopelite; Pub. Liliana Rogala. adv. contact: Liliana Rogala. bk.rev.; film rev.; play rev. circ. 10,500. (back issues avail.) **Document type:** trade publication.
Description: Covers industry news and offers product information for the industry for fleet supervisors.

388.324 FR ISSN 1162-387X
TRANSPORT MAGAZINE. 1983. m. 315 F. (foreign 450 F.). 8 cours Louis Lumiere, 94306 Vincennes Cedex, France. TEL 41-74-36-11. FAX 41-74-36-38. Ed. Pascal Stich. circ. 40,000. **Document type:** trade publication.
Formerly (until 1991): Camions Magazine (ISSN 0756-4643)

388.3 SA ISSN 1015-5287
TRANSPORT MANAGER'S HANDBOOK AND TRUCKER'S GUIDE. 1978. a. R.228. Thomson Publications (Subsidiary of: Times Media Ltd.), P.O. Box 56182, Pinegowrie 2123, South Africa. TEL 27-11-789-2144. FAX 27-11-789-3196. adv. circ. 1,000. **Document type:** trade publication.
Formerly (until 1989): Transport Manager's Handbook; Incorporates: Commercial Transport Equipment Index; Supersedes (1964-1978): Commercial Transport Handbook and Buyer's Guide for S A (ISSN 0069-6676)

388.324 UK ISSN 0954-2647
TRANSPORT OF GOODS BY ROAD IN GREAT BRITAIN. 1972. a. price varies. (Department of Transport, Statistics Transport Division) H.M.S.O., P.O. Box 276, London SW8 5DT, England. FAX 0171-276-8690. Ed. R. Garland. charts; stat. circ. 250. (looseleaf format; back issues avail.) **Document type:** government publication.
Description: Presents data on goods carried, mileages, and output per vehicle for trucks in the U.K.

388.324 UK ISSN 0267-4335
TRANSPORT OPERATOR. 1955. m. £30 (foreign £40). A.G.B. Hulton Ltd., Warwick House, Azalea Dr., Swanley, Kent BR8 8JR, England. TEL 01322-660070. FAX 01322-667633. Ed. Mark Robinson. circ. 20,000. **Document type:** trade publication.
Formerly (until 1984): Garage and Transport (ISSN 0264-0171)
Description: Management information supplied to individuals responsible for H.G.V. fleets and workshops.

629.2 SZ ISSN 0255-6871
TRANSPORT RUNDSCHAU; Unabhaengige Zeitschrift fuer Nutzfahrzeuge, Strassentransport, Logistik, und Werkstatt und Betrieb. 1980. m. 85 SFr. (foreign 105 SFr.). Vogt-Schild AG, Zuchwilerstr. 21, CH-4501 Solothurn, Switzerland. TEL 065-247247. FAX 065-247235. Ed. Andre Vollmar. adv.: B&W page 2170 SFr., color page 3270 SFr.; trim 185 x 260; adv. contact: Barbara Staugassinger. illus. circ. 12,290. **Document type:** trade publication.
—CCC.
Formerly: I N U F A Rundschau.

388.324 US ISSN 0041-1558
HE5601
TRANSPORT TOPICS; national newspaper of the trucking industry. 1935. w. $69. American Trucking Associations, 2200 Mill Rd., Alexandria, VA 22314. TEL 703-838-1770. FAX 703-548-3662. Ed. Oliver Patton. adv.; charts; illus.; stat. circ. 30,768. (processed; also avail. in microform from UMI)
—UMI; UnCover. **CCC.**
Description: Emphasizes trucking industry business, regulation, economics, maintenance, equipment, data processing. Covers all segments of for-hire and private trucking.

388.324 658 US ISSN 0897-8077
TRANSPORTATION EXECUTIVE UPDATE. 1987. bi-m. $48. Regular Common Carrier Conference, 2200 Mill Rd., Ste. 350, Alexandria, VA 22314-4654. TEL 703-838-1970. Ed. Shawn Fields. circ. 2,000.
Description: For upper level management of the general freight trucking industry.

(YEAR) TRANSPORTATION FACT BOOK. see *TRANSPORTATION — Abstracting, Bibliographies, Statistics*

TRANSPORTATION LAW INSTITUTE PAPERS AND PROCEEDINGS. see *LAW*

388.324 GW ISSN 0943-9366
TRANSPORTING. 1948. m. DM.102.80 (foreign DM 114.20). Heinrich Vogel Fachzeitschriften GmbH, Neumarkter Str. 18, 81673 Munich, Germany. TEL 089-43180-0. FAX 089-43180398. (Subscr. to: Postfach 802020, 81620 Munich, Germany) Ed. Graf von Sauring-Jeltsch. adv.: B&W page DM.5350, color page DM.8950; trim 185 x 253. bk.rev.; bibl.; illus.; pat.; stat.; index; circ. 42,000 (controlled). **Document type:** trade publication.
—CCC.
Formerly: Nutzfahrzeug (ISSN 0029-6686)

388.324 UK ISSN 0308-0641
TRUCK. 1974. m. £24 (foreign £29). Village Publishing Ltd., 24A Brook Mews North, Paddington, London W2 3BW, England. TEL 0171-224-9242. FAX 0171-402-3994. Ed. George Bennett. circ. 39,686 (paid). **Document type:** trade publication.
Incorporates: Truck and Driver.

388.324 US ISSN 1075-8178
▼**TRUCK ACCESSORY NEWS;** products and trends for retailers. Abbreviated title: T A N. 1994. m. $30. Shore Communications, Inc., 6255 Barfield Rd., Ste. 200, Atlanta, GA 30328-4300. TEL 404-252-8831. FAX 404-252-4436. Ed. Alfreda D. Vaughn; Pubs. Gary Fong, Randy Easton. adv.: page $2065; trim 8 1/8 x 10 7/8; adv. contact: Randy Easton. tr.lit. circ. 8,000. (back issues avail.) **Document type:** trade publication.
Description: Covers trends and new products for aftermarket retailers tapping into today's truck accessories market.

388.324 SA ISSN 0258-9281
TRUCK & BUS, SOUTH AFRICA. 1980. m. R.40. Titan Publications (Pty) Ltd., Rodland House, 382 Jan Smuts Av., Craighall 2196, South Africa. Ed. John Marsh. adv. contact: R. Considine. illus. circ. 4,000. **Indexed:** Ind.S.A.Per. **Document type:** trade publication.

TRANSPORTATION — TRUCKS AND TRUCKING

388.324   AT   ISSN 0041-3380
TRUCK AND BUS TRANSPORTATION; Australia's leading national road transport fleetowner monthly. 1936. m. Aus.$30 (New Zealand Aus.$66; elsewhere Aus.$72) (effective 1994). Shennen Publishing & Publicity Co. Pty. Ltd., 64 Kippax St., Surry Hills, N.S.W. 2010, Australia. TEL 61-2-211-3411. FAX 61-2-281-1691. Ed. G.L. Johnson. adv.: B&W page Aus.$1997, color page Aus.$2930; adv. contact: Gary Chant. bk.rev.; illus.; tr.lit.; index; circ. 17,569 (paid). (back issues avail.) **Indexed:** Aus.Rd.Ind., HRIS. **Document type:** trade publication.
—UnCover.
   Description: Covers Australian commercial vehicle industries (trucks & buses) with exclusive news, features, specifications sections, road tests, product news and presentations, technical articles and dealer listings.

388.324   BE   ISSN 0778-838X
TRUCK & BUSINESS. Dutch edition (ISSN 0772-5000) (Text in French) 8/yr. Multi Media Management, Rue des Pres 2-001, 4802 Verviers Heusy, Belgium. adv.: B&W page 71000 BEF, color page 99400 BEF; trim 297 x 210.
   Formerly (until 1992): Mini-Maxi-Truck (ISSN 0770-5441)

338.324   UK   ISSN 0966-3533
TRUCK & DRIVER MAGAZINE. m. £24 (foreign £29). Village Publishing Ltd., 24A Brook Mews North, Paddington, London W2 3BW, England. TEL 0171-224-9242. FAX 0171-402-3994. Ed. Dave Young. adv. contact: Nick Payne. circ. 30,000 (paid). **Document type:** trade publication.

388.324   CN   ISSN 0319-7492
TRUCK & TRAILER. 1987. m. Can.$28. New Communications Group, 452 Attwell Dr., Ste. 100, Etobicoke, ON M9W 5C3, Canada. TEL 416-798-2977. FAX 416-798-3017. Pub. A. Hohenadel. adv. contact: A. Hohenadel. circ. 34,000. **Document type:** trade publication.
   Description: Catalog of new and used trucks, trailers, parts for sale; services available; owner-operator recruitment section.

388.324   US   ISSN 8756-4041
TRUCK BLUE BOOK LEASE GUIDE. q. $65 includes Truck Identification Book. Maclean Hunter Market Reports, Inc., 29 N. Wacker Dr., Chicago, IL 60606-3297. TEL 312-726-2802. FAX 312-726-2574. (back issues avail.)

388.324   CN   ISSN 0564-3392
TRUCK DATA BOOK; identification data for all makes and models of trucks found in Canada. 1949. a. Can.$39. Sanford Evans Communications Ltd., 1700 Church Ave., Box 6900, Winnipeg, MB R3C 3B1, Canada. TEL 204-694-2022. FAX 204-694-3040. Ed. Gary Henry.
   Description: Nine model years listed. Identification and registration data includes, GVW and curb weight, wheelbase, engine stats and vehicle identification number for light, medium and heavy duty trucks. MSR price for light trucks featured.

621.9   US   ISSN 1048-2571
TRUCK ENGINEERING. (Supplement to: Automotive Engineering Magazine (ISSN 0098-2571)) 1990. s-a. Society of Automotive Engineers, 400 Commonwealth Dr., Warrendale, PA 15096. TEL 412-776-4841. FAX 412-776-4026. Ed. Daniel J. Holt. adv. contact: Larry Schneider. circ. 30,000 (controlled). (also avail. in microfiche; microfilm; back issues avail.) **Document type:** trade publication.
   ●Also available online. Vendor(s): Orbit Search Service.
   Description: Covers advances in truck and bus technology that can be applied to the development of new or enhanced vehicle systems in the U.S. and overseas.

388.324   US   ISSN 0889-3888
TL230.A1
TRUCK IDENTIFICATION BOOK. a. $15. Maclean Hunter Market Reports, Inc., 29 N. Wacker Dr., Chicago, IL 60606-3297. TEL 312-726-2802. FAX 312-726-2574.

388   US
TRUCK NEWS.* m. $7. New York State Motor Truck Association, c/o Motor Carrier NY Welfare Trust, 300 Winston Dr., No. 914, Cliffside Park, NJ 07010-3215. circ. 1,800.

388.324   CN   ISSN 0712-2683
TRUCK NEWS. 1981. m. Can.$25.68 (foreign $48). Southam Magazine Group, 1450 Don Mills Rd., Don Mills, ON M3B 2X7, Canada. TEL 416-445-6641. FAX 416-442-2042. Ed. Brenda Yarrow. circ. 40,000.
—CCC.
   Incorporates: Eastern Trucker; Which was formerly: Eastern Western Trucker.
   Description: Covers Canadian truck operators' concerns: regulations, products, events.

388.324   US
TRUCK PAPER. 1981. w. $59. Peed Corporation, Box 85010, Lincoln, NE 68501. TEL 402-477-8900. Ed. Lee Chapin. circ. 485,000. (tabloid format)

629.224 388.3   US   ISSN 0895-3856
TRUCK PARTS & SERVICE. 1966. m. $50 (foreign $60). Kona Communications, Inc., 707 Lake Cook Rd., Ste. 300, Deerfield, IL 60015. TEL 708-498-3180. FAX 708-498-3197. Ed. David Zaritz. adv. contact: John S. Dickson. circ. controlled. **Document type:** trade publication.
   Former titles (until Aug. 1987): Heavy-Duty Distribution (ISSN 0191-6777) & Fleet Distribution.
   Description: Covers the truck parts and service market.

388.324   US
TL230.A1
TRUCK PRICE GUIDE. bi-m. (7/yr.). $4.99 per no. Pace Publications (Milwaukee), 1020 N. Broadway, Ste. 111, Milwaukee, WI 53202. TEL 414-272-8877. FAX 414-272-9973.
   Formerly: Truck Facts (ISSN 1056-1870)

338.3 658.8   US   ISSN 1053-5942
HD9710.35.U6
TRUCK SALES & LEASING MAGAZINE. 1983. bi-m. $30 (free to qualified personnel) Newport Communications East, Inc., 600 Reisterstown Rd., Ste. 404, Baltimore, MD 21208-5107. TEL 410-486-7430. FAX 410-786-7478. Ed. David A. Kolman; Pub. David A. Kolman. adv. contact: David A. Kolman. bk.rev.; tr.lit. circ. 22,000. **Document type:** trade publication.
—CCC.
   Formerly (until 1990): Heavy Truck Salesman (ISSN 0740-3541).
   Description: Intended for truck dealer salespersons and leasing company specialists.

388.324   US   ISSN 0049-478X
TRUCK TRENDS.* 1963. m. $15. c/o Paul, 5115 N. First St., DeKalb, IL 60115. adv.; stat. circ. 9,500 (controlled).

388.324   CN   ISSN 1185-3409
TRUCK WEST. 1990. m. Can.$25.68 (foreign Can.$40). Southam Business Communications Inc. (Winnipeg) (Subsidiary of: Southam Inc.), 1555 Dublin Ave., No.9, Winnipeg, MB R3E 3M8, Canada. Ed. Patricia Cancilla; Pub. Patrick Munro. adv. circ. 22,000. (tabloid format) **Document type:** trade publication.
   Description: For the trucking industry in western Canada.

388.324   CN   ISSN 0836-5156
TRUCK WORLD. 1984. 9/yr. Global Trade Publications Ltd., 11 - 106 E. 14th St., North Vancouver, BC V7L 2N3, Canada. TEL 604-984-2002. FAX 604-984-2820. adv.: B&W & color, B&W page Can.$2468; trim 8 1/8 x 10 7/8. circ. 19,703. **Document type:** trade publication.
   Formerly (until 1987): Transport Electronic News (ISSN 0829-2566)

388.324   CN
TRUCK WORLD & WESTERN TRUCKING NEWS. 1984. m. Can.$24. Global Trade Publications Ltd., 11-106 E. 14th St., North Vancouver, B.C. V7L 2N3, Canada. TEL 604-984-2002. FAX 604-984-2820. Ed. Rob Robertson. circ. 30,000. (tabloid format; back issues avail.)
   Formed by the merger of: Truck World; Western Trucking News.

388.324   US
TRUCKER.* 1987. bi-w. $21.50. Belmont Publishing, Inc., Box 3412, Little Rock, AR 72203-3413. TEL 800-666-2770. FAX 501-375-8317. adv.: B&W page $604, color page $799; trim 11 1/4 x 13 3/4. circ. 16,500.
   Description: Covers industry news for professional drivers.

388.324   US
TRUCKER'S CONNECTION. 1987. m. $26.95. 5960 Crooked Creek Rd., Ste. 15, Norcross, GA 30092. TEL 404-416-0927. FAX 404-416-1734. Ed. Dan Gleason; Pub. Jim Deal. adv.: B&W page $3895, color page $5495; trim 5 3/8 x 8 3/8. circ. 170,081 (controlled). **Document type:** trade publication.
   Description: Includes industry and carrier news, information on new and used trucks, vehicle operation, and safety. Contains current events, employment opportunities, and product news.

388.324   US   ISSN 0897-9219
TRUCKERS - U S A. 1984. m. $29. B P S Inc., Box 3168, Tuscaloosa, AL 35403-3168. TEL 205-758-3070. Ed. Dave Adams; Pub. Bobby Seale. adv. contact: Linda Seale. circ. 75,000. **Document type:** trade publication.
   Description: Covers manufacturing and industry news and new products.

388.324   US   ISSN 0277-5743
TRUCKIN'. m. $23.95. McMullen & Yee Publishing, 774 S. Placentia Ave., Placentia, CA 92670-6846. TEL 714-572-2255. FAX 714-572-1864. Ed. Steve Stillwell. adv.; bk.rev.; charts; illus. circ. 79,312. **Document type:** consumer publication.

388.324   AT   ISSN 0155-9648
TRUCKIN' LIFE; the voice of the Australian truck driver. 1976. m. Aus.$47. Federal Publishing Company, 180 Bourke Rd., Alexandria, N.S.W. 2015, Australia. TEL 07-854-1119. FAX 07-252-3692. Ed. Paul Sattler. adv. contact: Paul Sattler. bk.rev. circ. 21,000. (back issues avail.)
   Description: Highlights innovations in the trucking industry, freight rates and new motor truck models.

388.324   UK   ISSN 0950-1738
TRUCKING INTERNATIONAL. 1983. m. £19 (rest of Europe £30; elsewhere £55) (effective 1995). A & S Publishing Co. Ltd., Messenger House, 33-35 St. Michael's Sq., Gloucester GL1 1HX, England. TEL 01452-307181. FAX 01452-307170. Ed. Stewart Brown. adv.: page £830; trim 297 x 210; adv. contact: Donuta Hornsby. circ. 34,324. (back issues avail.) **Document type:** trade publication.
   Description: Offers road transport professionals news and articles on the U.K. trucking industry, with emphasis on topics of interest to small fleet owners and independent truckers.

388.3   US
TRUCKING PERMIT & TAX BULLETIN. m. $90. J.J. Keller & Associates, Inc., 3003 W. Breezewood Lane, Box 368, Neenah, WI 54957-0368. TEL 414-722-2848. FAX 414-727-7516. Ed.Bd.
   Description: Covers operating authority, vehicle registration and taxes.

388.324   US
TRUCKING PERMIT GUIDE. 1974. irreg., no.78, 1987. $155. J.J. Keller and Associates, Inc., 3003 W. Breezewood Lane, Box 368, Neenah, WI 54957-0368. TEL 800-558-5011. FAX 414-727-7516. Ed. George B. McDowell.
   Description: Descriptions of the Federal Heavy Vehicle Use Tax.

388.324   US
TRUCKING SAFETY GUIDE. 1974. irreg., no.54, 1986. $155. J.J. Keller and Associates, Inc., 3003 W. Breezewood Lane, Box 368, Neenah, WI 54957-0368. TEL 800-558-5011. Ed. George B. McDowell.
   Description: Reference to federal and state safety requirements.

388.324   US   ISSN 0884-8947
TRUCKS.* 1986. 6/yr. $17.50. Trucks Magazine Inc., 25 Oak Forest Dr., Ronkonkoma, NY 00779. Ed. John Stevens. circ. 100,000.
   Description: Dedicated to those who make a living driving long-haul trucks or own fleets of these trucks. Articles focus on health, safety, profitability, government regulations, image, new products and technology.

TRUCKSTOP WORLD. see *BUSINESS AND ECONOMICS — Small Business*

6448 TRAVEL AND TOURISM

388.324   **US**
TRUX. 1949. q. membership only. Georgia Motor Trucking Association, 500 Piedmont Ave., N.E., Atlanta, GA 30308. TEL 404-876-4313. FAX 404-874-9765. Ed. Diane B. Emrick; Pub. Edward Crowell. adv.; illus. circ. 4,000. **Document type:** trade publication.

388   **CN**   **ISSN 0820-5655**
TRUXBOOK. 1947. a. Can.$50. Alberta Trucking Association, Box 5520, Sta. A, Calgary, AB T2H 1X9, Canada. TEL 403-253-8401. adv.; bk.rev. circ. 400.
   Former titles: Alberta Motor Transport Directory; Alberta Shippers Guide.

388.324   **CN**   **ISSN 0834-3624**
TRUXPRESS. 1978. 6/yr. membership. Alberta Trucking Association, Box 5520, Sta. "A", Calgary, AB T2H 1X9, Canada. TEL 403-253-8401. adv.; circ. 600 (controlled).
   Former titles: Pyramid (ISSN 0709-4272); A T A News Bulletin (ISSN 0380-8920); A M T A News Bulletin (ISSN 0044-7161).

TURNING WHEELS. see *TRANSPORTATION — Automobiles*

388.324   **IT**   **ISSN 1121-5585**
TUTTOTRASPORTI. 11/yr. L.72000($90) Editoriale Domus, Via Achille Grandi 5-7, 20089 Rozzano (MI), Italy. TEL 39-2-824721. FAX 39-2-26863093. TELEX 316822 EDIDOM I. Ed. Lorenzo Raffo. adv.: B&W page L.6250000, color page L.11250000. circ. 70,000.

388.324   **CN**   **ISSN 0841-2472**
UPDATE (ETOBICOKE). 1957. bi-w. Can.$400 to non-members. Ontario Trucking Association, 555 Dixon Rd., Etobicoke, ON M9W 1H8, Canada. TEL 416-249-7401. FAX 416-245-6152. Ed. Rebecka Torn. adv.; bk.rev.; stat.; tr.lit. circ. 1,100. (processed) **Document type:** trade publication.
   Formerly: O T A News Round-up.
   Description: Provides Ontario Trucking Association members, government and industry with information on the Ontario truck transport industry.

388.324   **US**   **ISSN 1053-4903**
UTILITY FLEET MANAGEMENT. 1982. 9/yr. $15 (free to qualified utility personnel). American Trucking Associations, 2200 Mill Rd., Alexandria, VA 22314. TEL 703-838-1770. FAX 703-838-1777. Ed. Nancy Coe Bailey. adv.: B&W page $3345. bk.rev. circ. 13,219. **Document type:** trade publication.
   Formerly: Electric Utility Fleet Management (ISSN 0744-3501)
   Description: Provides information for specifying, purchasing, operating and maintaining cars, trucks, construction and maintenance equipment and tools for the electric, gas, telephone and water utilities.

388.324   **IT**   **ISSN 0042-2096**
VADO E TORNO; magazine for lorry-drivers. 1962. 10/yr. L.67000 (foreign L.75000). Vado e Torno Edizioni S.r.l., Via Lattanzio 77, 20137 Milan, Italy. TEL 39-2-55193629. FAX 39-2-55193660. Ed. Paolo Scarpat. adv.; B&W page L.5900000, color page L.10500000. bk.rev.; illus. circ. 64,820. **Document type:** trade publication.

388.324   **US**
VEHICLE SIZES AND WEIGHTS MANUAL. 1974. irreg., no.26, 1987. $95. J.J. Keller and Associates, Inc., 3003 W. Breezewood Lane, Box 368, Neenah, WI 54957-0368. TEL 800-558-5011. Ed. George B. McDowell.
   Description: Federal, state and Canadian requirements for overdimensional movements.

388.324   **CN**   **ISSN 0843-6207**
VOIX DU VRAC. 1972. 6/yr. Association Nationale des Camionneurs Artisans Inc., 710 Bouvier St., Ste. 215, Quebec, PQ G2J 1C2, Canada. TEL 418-623-7923. FAX 418-623-0448. Ed. Andre Lavoie. adv.; B&W page Can.$1095, color page Can.$1825. circ. 10,000.

388.3   **US**   **ISSN 1075-0282**
HF5415.6
WAREHOUSING - DISTRIBUTION DIRECTORY. 1963. a. $52. K-III Directory Corp., 424 W. 33rd St., New York, NY 10001. TEL 212-714-3100. Ed. David Wise. adv. circ. 20,000. **Document type:** directory.
   Former titles (until 1992): M C D's Warehousing Distribution Directory (ISSN 1075-0517); National Distribution Directory of Local Cartage - Short-Haul Carriers Warehousing (ISSN 0364-9539); National Distribution Directory (ISSN 0077-4219)

388.324   **US**
WEST VIRGINIA TRANSPORTER. vol.29, 1972. m. membership. West Virginia Motor Truck Association, Box 5187, Charleston, WV 25311. TEL 304-345-2800. Ed. Robert E. Stanley. adv. circ. 1,450.

388.324   **CN**
WESTERN CANADA HIGHWAY NEWS MAGAZINE. 1971. 4/yr. (Manitoba Trucking Association) Craig Kelman & Associates Ltd., 3C - 2020 Portage Ave., Winnipeg, MB R3J 0K4, Canada. TEL 204-885-7798. FAX 204-889-3576. (Co-sponsors: Saskatchewan Trucking Association; Alberta Trucking Association; B.C. Trucking Association) Ed. Terry Ross. adv. contact: John Vollrath. circ. 4,500 (controlled). (back issues avail.) **Document type:** trade publication.
   Formerly (until 1995): Manitoba Highway News (ISSN 0380-4852)

388.324   **UK**
WHAT VAN?. 1986. 10/yr. £29.50. Quest Magazines Ltd., Publishing House, 652 Victoria Rd., South Ruislip, Mddx. HA4 0SX, England. TEL 0181-842-1010. FAX 0181-841-2554. Ed. Neil McIntee; Pub. Damian Riley-Smith. adv. contact: Nick Johnstone. circ. 25,000 (paid). (back issues avail.) **Document type:** trade publication.
   Formerly: Good Van Guide.
   Description: Includes road test reports, a full data section, news, and features.

388.324 629.222   **US**   **ISSN 0738-565X**
TL230.A1
WHEELS OF TIME. 1980. bi-m. $25 membership (foreign $35). American Truck Historical Society, Box 531168, Birmingham, AL 35253. TEL 205-870-0566. FAX 205-870-3069. adv.; bk.rev. circ. 18,000.
   Description: Covers the history of trucks, the trucking industry, and its pioneers.

388.324 621   **NO**   **ISSN 0333-1911**
YRKESBIL. 1980. 15/yr. NOK 320. Fagbladforlaget AS, Urtgaten 9, P.O. Box 9247, Vaterland, N-0134 Oslo, Norway. TEL 47-22-68-03-13. FAX 47-22-68-20-85. Ed. Jorgen Seemann Berg. circ. 32,000. **Document type:** consumer publication, trade publication.

388.324   **PL**   **ISSN 0514-809X**
Z M P D. KWARTALNY BIULETYN INFORMACYJNY. 1965. q. free. Zrzeszenie Miedzynarodowych Przewoznikow Drogowych, Grojecka 17, 02-021 Warsaw, Poland. Ed. Boleslaw Rajkowski. circ. controlled. (processed) **Document type:** bulletin.

TRAVEL AND TOURISM

see also *Travel and Tourism–Airline Inflight and Hotel Inroom*

910.09   **US**
A A A - CHICAGO MOTOR CLUB HOME & AWAY. bi-m. $6 or membership. American Automobile Association, Chicago Motor Club, 999 E. Touhy, Des Plains, IL 60018-2798. TEL 708-390-9000. FAX 708-390-9112. Ed. G. Lionel Kramer. adv. circ. 381,000.

910   **US**
A A A GOING PLACES. 1982. bi-m. membership. Automobile Association of America, A A A Auto Club South, 1515 N. Westshore Blvd., Box 31087, Tampa, FL 33631. TEL 813-289-5923. FAX 813-289-1318. Ed. Phyllis W. Zeno. adv.; bk.rev. circ. 910,000. (back issues avail.) **Document type:** consumer publication.
   Description: Directed to AAA members, with AAA news, legislation affecting motorists and travel articles.

910.09   **US**
A A A MOTORIST OF NORTHEASTERN PENNSYLVANIA. bi-m. American Automobile Association of Northeastern Pennsylvania, 1035 N. Washington Ave., Scranton, PA 18509-2917. TEL 717-348-2513. Ed. Craig H. Smith. circ. 92,000.

A A A READING - BERKS. bi-m. (American Automobile Association, Reading-Berks Auto Club) Roberts & Company, P.O. Box 716, Reading, PA 19603. TEL 215-375-4525. Ed. Bob Gerhart. adv. circ. 75,500.
   Formerly: Reading - Berks Auto Club Magazine (ISSN 0744-7043)

910.202 388.3   **US**   **ISSN 1051-3701**
A A A TODAY (CINCINNATI). 1923. bi-m. membership. American Automobile Association, Cincinnati Division, 15 W. Central Parkway, Cincinnati, OH 45202. FAX 513-762-8741. Ed. Merrilee Campbell. circ. 170,000.
   Formerly: Motour.

910.09   **US**   **ISSN 1049-8133**
A A A TODAY (POTTSTOWN). bi-m. American Automobile Association, East Penn Motor Club, 95 S. Hanover St., Pottstown, PA 19464. TEL 215-323-6300. FAX 215-323-6684. Ed. Franklin Mann. circ. 32,500.

A A A TODAY MAGAZINE. (American Automobile Association) see *TRANSPORTATION — Automobiles*

910.09   **US**
A A A TRAVEL TOPICS. 5/yr. American Automobile Association, Central Pennsylvania Automobile Club, 2023 Market St., Harrisburg, PA 17103-2531. TEL 717-236-4021. Ed. Thomas G. Miller. circ. 80,000.

629.286   **US**
A A A TRAVELER (FLORHAM PARK). 1924. bi-m. $4. (American Automobile Association) New Jersey Automobile Club, 1 Hanover Rd., Florham Park, NJ 07932. TEL 201-377-7200. FAX 201-377-2979. Ed. Pamela S. Fischer. adv. contact: Pamela S. Fischer. circ. 171,000 (controlled). (tabloid format; back issues avail.) **Document type:** newspaper.
   Former titles (until 1994): Driving; (until 1969): New Jersey Autoist.
   Description: Features travel advice, car care and buying information, safety, legislation and insurance information for motorists and travelers.

910.202   **UK**   **ISSN 1357-1222**
A B C AGENTS' GAZETTEER. (In 6 vols.) 1968. a. £225. Reed Travel Group, Part of Reed Telepublishing (Subsidiary of: Reed Elsevier group), Church St., Dunstable, Beds. LU5 4HB, England. TEL 01582-600111. FAX 01582-695230. TELEX 82168 AIRABC G. Ed. Graham Johnson. circ. 21,000. **Document type:** directory.
   Formerly (until 1994): A B C Agents' Hotel and Apartments Gazetteers.
   Description: Contains detailed independent appraisals of thousands of hotels, apartments and resorts worldwide. Covers Mediterranean hotels and apartments, European cities, America, ski lakes and mountains.

910   **UK**   **ISSN 0263-2748**
A B C AIR TRAVEL ATLAS. 1979. s-a. £27.50. Reed Travel Group, Part of Reed Telepublishing (Subsidiary of: Reed Elsevier group), Church St., Dunstable, Beds. LU5 4HB, England. TEL 01582-600111. FAX 01582-695230. TELEX 82168 AIRABC G. Ed. Mary Marchant. circ. 10,800. **Document type:** directory.
—BLDSC (0537.756250).
   Description: Contains maps of major domestic and international flights, time zones, country, city and state codes, and airline designators.

910   **UK**   **ISSN 0141-6278**
A B C GUIDE TO INTERNATIONAL TRAVEL. q. £46. Reed Travel Group, Part of Reed Telepublishing (Subsidiary of: Reed Elsevier group), Church St., Dunstable, Beds. LU5 4HB, England. TEL 01582-600111. FAX 01582-695230. TELEX 82168 AIRABC G. Ed. Ken Smith. adv. circ. 7,500. **Document type:** directory.
   Description: Provides a guide to passport controls, visa regulations, vaccination requirements, currency regulation, and import allowances on more than 200 countries.

TRAVEL AND TOURISM

910   UK   ISSN 1357-1184
A B C HOLIDAY GUIDE. 1970. q. £72.50 for summer ed.; winter ed. $64. Reed Travel Group, Part of Reed Telepublishing (Subsidiary of: Reed Elsevier group), Church St., Dunstable, Beds. LU5 4HB, England. TEL 01582-600111. FAX 01582-695230. TELEX 82168 AIRABC G. Ed. Bozena Briggs. circ. 4,000. **Document type:** directory.
    Formerly (until 1972): Holiday Guide.
    Description: Covers all commission-paying A.B.T.A. tour operators by country.

910   UK   ISSN 1357-1192
A B C SELF CATERING GUIDE. 1993. a. £38.50. Reed Travel Group, Part of Reed Telepublishing (Subsidiary of: Reed Elsevier group), Church St., Dunstable, Beds. LU5 4HB, England. TEL 01582-600111. FAX 01582-695230. TELEX 82168 AIRABC G. Ed. Bozena Griggs. circ. 4,200. **Document type:** directory.
    Description: Provides details of self-catering holidays all over the world. Includes reference information on ferry routes and services to the continent, European motorail services, European mileage chart and a cost of living guide.

910.09   UK   ISSN 1357-1176
A B C TRAVEL DIRECTORY. a. £72. Reed Travel Group, Part of Reed Telepublishing (Subsidiary of: Reed Elsevier group), Church St., Dunstable, Beds. LU5 4HB, England. TEL 01582-600111. FAX 01582-695230. TELEX 82168 AIRABC G. Ed. Alison Barker. circ. 4,800. **Document type:** directory.
    Formerly: Travel Directory.
    Description: Provides a comprehensive reference guide to the travel trade, covering more than 18,000 companies from over 40 travel industry sectors, including A.B.T.A. tour operators, retail travel agents, airlines and airports, tourist offices, and hotel groups.

910   UK   ISSN 1357-1206
A B C U.K. HOLIDAY GUIDE. 1986. a. £36.50. Reed Travel Group, Part of Reed Telepublishing (Subsidiary of: Reed Elsevier group), Church St., Dunstable, Beds. LU5 4HB, England. TEL 01582-600111. FAX 01582-695230. TELEX 82168 AIRABC G. Ed. Bozena Briggs. circ. 4,000.
    Description: Covers all commission-paying A.B.T.A. tour operators by country.

A B C WORLD AIRWAYS GUIDE. see *TRANSPORTATION — Air Transport*

A C E LENKRAD. (Auto Club Europa e.V.) see *TRANSPORTATION — Automobiles*

910.202   GW   ISSN 0936-6326
A D A C ATLAS DEUTSCHLAND - EUROPA. a. DM.52. (Allgemeiner Deutscher Automobil Club e.V.) A D A C Verlag GmbH, Am Westpark 8, 81373 Munich, Germany. TEL 089-7676-0. **Document type:** bulletin.

A D A C CAMPINGFUEHRER. BAND 1: SUEDEUROPA. (Allgemeiner Deutscher Automobil-Club e.V.) see *SPORTS AND GAMES — Outdoor Life*

A D A C CAMPINGFUEHRER. BAND 2: DEUTSCHLAND, MITTEL- UND NORDEUROPA. (Allgemeiner Deutscher Automobil-Club e.V.) see *SPORTS AND GAMES — Outdoor Life*

A D A C HANDBUCH: REISERECHT ENTSCHEIDUNGEN. (Allgemeiner Deutscher Automobil-Club e.V.) see *LAW*

A D A C HANDBUCH: UNFALL IM AUSLAND - SCHADENSREGULIERUNG. (Allgemeiner Deutscher Automobil-Club e.V.) see *LAW*

A D A C HANDBUCH: UNFALL RATGEBER. (Allgemeiner Deutscher Automobil-Club e.V.) see *LAW*

A D A C MOTORWELT. (Allgemeiner Deutscher Automobil-Club e.V.) see *TRANSPORTATION — Automobiles*

A D A C SKI-ATLAS ALPEN. (Allgemeiner Deutscher Automobil-Club e.V.) see *SPORTS AND GAMES — Outdoor Life*

910.202   GW   ISSN 0939-4206
A D A C SPECIAL REISE. bi-m. DM.88.80. (Allgemeiner Deutscher Automobil-Club e.V.) A D A C Verlag GmbH, Am Westpark 8, 81373 Munich, Germany. TEL 089-7676-0. FAX 089-76762500. Ed. Michael Dultz. adv. contact: Michael Behrend. circ. 169,548. **Document type:** consumer publication.

910.202   GW   ISSN 0937-9096
A D A C SPECIAL SKI. a. DM.14.80. (Allgemeiner Deutscher Automobil-Club e.V.) A D A C Verlag GmbH, Am Westpark 8, 81373 Munich, Germany. TEL 089-7676-0. FAX 089-76762500. **Document type:** consumer publication.

910.4   MX
A I M. (Adventures in Mexico Newsletter); a newsletter on retirement and travel in Mexico. (Text in English) 1974. bi-m. $16 (Canada $22). AIM, S.A., Apdo. Postal 31-70, Guadalajara, Jalisco, Mexico. Ed. J.W. Wilkins. circ. 2,400. **Document type:** newsletter.

387.7   US
A P A HOLIDAY.* 1970. 6/yr. $1. (Airline Passengers Association) Curtis Publishing Co., 1000 Waterway Blvd., Indianapolis, IA 46202-2191. Ed. Carole Story. adv.; charts; illus. circ. 75,000.
    Former titles (until Fall 1976): APAce; (until Spring 1976): Airline Passengers Association News (ISSN 0044-7013)

910   US
A S U TRAVEL GUIDE. (Airline Services Unlimited); the airline employee's discount directory. 1970. q. $32.95. A S U Travel Guide, Inc., 1525 Francisco Blvd., E., San Rafael, CA 94901. TEL 415-459-0300. FAX 415-459-0494. Ed. Christopher Gil. adv. contact: Hank Sousa. circ. 60,000. **Document type:** trade publication.
    Formerly: Interline Tour Guide.

910.4   AU
A T P; Branchen und Presseinformationsdienst. 1975. bi-w. S.390. (Austrian Travel Press) A T P Zeitungsverlags GmbH, Seidengasse 32-1-17, A-1070 Vienna, Austria. TEL 01-5236386. FAX 01-5266116. Ed. Heidrun Farag. adv. contact: Leo Froehlich. circ. 2,200. **Document type:** trade publication.

A V D AUTO BORD UND SPORT BUCH. see *TRANSPORTATION — Automobiles*

910.09   GW   ISSN 0935-0454
A Z U R CAMPING MAGAZIN. 1987. s-a. free. A Z U R Freizeit GmbH, Kesselstr. 36, 70327 Stuttgart, Germany. TEL 0711-4093500. FAX 0711-4093580. Ed. Joerg Eisenach. adv. contact: Joerg Eisenach. bk.rev.; index. circ. 50,000. (back issues avail.) **Document type:** consumer publication.
    Description: News about camping in Europe, about campers and caravans.

910.09   GW   ISSN 0176-5388
ABENTEUER & REISEN; Das Erlebnis-Magazin. 1981. m. DM.79.60 (foreign DM.96). W D V Wirtschaftsdienst, Lange Str. 13, 60311 Frankfurt a.M., Germany. TEL 069-29907-0. Ed. Wolfgang C. Ehrnsperger. circ. 100,000. **Document type:** consumer publication.

914.204   UK
ABOUT LONDON. 1976. m. free. About London Publications, 60-62 Westbourne Terrace, London W2 3UJ, England. Ed. Vass Anderson. adv.

910.09   US
ABSTRACT OF INTERNATIONAL TRAVEL TO AND FROM THE UNITED STATES. a. free. U.S. Travel and Tourism Administration, Office of Research, U.S. Department of Commerce, Main Commerce Bldg., Rm. 1868, Washington, DC 20230. TEL 202-482-4028. FAX 202-482-2887. charts; stat. **Document type:** government publication.
    Formerly: Recap.
    Description: Summarizes U.S. inbound and outbound tourist statistics.

915.6   TS
ABU DHABI NEWS. (Text in English) w. Department of Information and Tourism, Abu Dhabi, United Arab Emirates.

917.204   US   ISSN 1055-5633
F1391.A15
ACAPULCO (YEAR). a. $11. Harper Collins Publishers, Birnbaum Travel Guides, 10 E. 53rd St., New York, NY 10022-5299. TEL 212-207-7542. illus.; index.

910.09   US   ISSN 0740-0365
ACCENT WEST AMARILLO; chronicle of the Southwestern lifestyle. m. $14.98. Accent West, Inc., Box 1504, Amarillo, TX 79105. TEL 806-359-6801. Ed. Don Cantrell. **Document type:** consumer publication.
    Description: Covers city and regional issues for greater Amarillo, focusing on the life-styles of middle- to upper-income adults.

647   AT
ACCOMMODATION AUSTRALIA. 1984. s-a. Aus.$10 to non members; members Aus.$4. R A C V, 550 Princes Highway, Noble Park, Vic. 3174, Australia. TEL 61-3-790-2646. FAX 61-3-790-2844. Ed. A. Bowes. circ. 200,000.
    Formerly: Australian National Tourguide.

919.4   AT
ACCOMMODATION AUSTRALIA GUIDE. 1963. s-a. $10 to non-members; members $4. Royal Automobile Association of South Australia Inc., 41 Hindmarsh Sq., Adelaide, S.A. 5000, Australia. (Co-sponsor: Royal Automobile Club of Victoria) adv. circ. 220,000.
    Former titles: Australian Accommodation Guide; Royal Automobile Association of South Australia. Accommodation Guide (ISSN 0085-5782)

919.4   AT   ISSN 1030-0406
ACCOMMODATION DIRECTORY. 1957. s-a. membership. (National Roads and Motorists Association) N R M A Ltd., 151 Clarence St., Sydney, N.S.W. 2000, Australia. TEL 64-2-260-2631. FAX 64-2-260-2639. **Document type:** directory.
    Former titles (until 1987): Accommodation Guide (ISSN 0817-1726); (until 1985): Accommodation Directory (ISSN 0817-1718)

ACCOMMODATOR; the magazine of Ontario's hospitality industry. see *HOTELS AND RESTAURANTS*

910.09   PL   ISSN 0860-1119
ACTA UNIVERSITATIS LODZIENSIS: TURYZM. (Text in Polish; summaries in English, French) 1985; N.S. 1988. irreg. Wydawnictwo Uniwersytetu Lodzkiego, Ul. Jaracza 34, Lodz, Poland. TEL 331671. (Dist. by: Ars Polona-Ruch, Krakowskie Przedmiescie 7, Warsaw, Poland) **Document type:** academic/scholarly publication.

910.09   UK   ISSN 0962-1865
ACTION HOLIDAYS. 1991. a. £2.50. Activity Associates Ltd., 27 Belsize Ln., London NW3 5AS, England. TEL 0171-435-5472. FAX 0171-431-3742. TELEX 295441 BUSYB G. Ed. Chrsitopher Thomas. adv.: B&W page £850, color page £1300; trim 298 x 210; adv. contact: Cathy Fourie. circ. 27,000. **Document type:** consumer publication.
    Description: Covers activity holidays in the U.K. and abroad.

ACTUALIDAD HOSTELERA Y TURISTICA. see *HOTELS AND RESTAURANTS*

910.09   SP
ACTUALIDAD TURISTICA. 12/yr. Corcega 434 8o, 08037 Barcelona, Spain. TEL 3-258-07-55. FAX 3-459-10-94. Ed. L.G. Domingo Masmitja.

ADIRONDACK LIFE. see *SPORTS AND GAMES — Outdoor Life*

914.204   UK
ADVANTAGE. 1992. q. (British Rail Network) B M I Publications, Suffolk House, George St., Croydon, Surrey CR9 1SR, England. TEL 0181-649-7233. FAX 0181-649-7234. Ed. Alan Orbell; Pub. Alan Orbel. adv.: B&W page £2350, color page £2950; trim 8 1/4 x 11 7/10; adv. contact: Melanie Walker. circ. 160,000 (controlled). **Document type:** consumer publication.

910.202   US
ADVENTURE ANNUAL. 1970. a. Mountain Travel - Sobek, 6420 Fairmount Ave., El Cerrito, CA 94530. TEL 510-527-8100. FAX 510-525-7710. Ed. Dena Bartolome. circ. 100,000 (controlled). **Document type:** catalog.

TRAVEL AND TOURISM

910.202 UK ISSN 0143-389X
GV191.35
ADVENTURE HOLIDAYS. 1978. a. $12.95. Vacation - Work, 9 Park End St., Oxford OX1 1HJ, England. (Dist. in U.S. by: Peterson's Guides, 202 Carnegie Ctr., Princeton, NJ 08543-2123. TEL 800-338-3282) Ed. Victoria Pybus. circ. 10,000. **Document type:** directory.

910.09 US ISSN 1041-9314
ADVENTURE TRAVEL. 1987. s-a. $3.95 per no. Rodale Press, Inc., 33 E. Minor St., Emmaus, PA 18098. TEL 610-967-5171. Ed. Bob Woodward. circ. 160,000. **Document type:** consumer publication.

910 US
ADVENTURE TRAVEL NORTH AMERICA. 1972. biennial. $19.95. Adventure Guides, Inc., 7550 E. McDonald Dr., Ste. M, Scottsdale, AZ 85250. TEL 602-596-0226. FAX 602-596-1722. Ed. Pat Dickerman. illus. **Indexed:** Access. **Document type:** directory.
 Former titles: Adventure Travel (New York) (ISSN 0195-8445); (until 1976): Adventure Trip Guide (ISSN 0084-5965)
 Description: Provides specific information for vacationers wanting to arrange guided adventure trips on foot, by horse, on wheels, on water, in wilderness, in snow and in the air.

917.904 796 US ISSN 1072-4370
GV191.42.W47
ADVENTURE WEST. 1992. bi-m. $13.50. Ski West Publications, Box 3210, Incline Village, NV 89450-3210. TEL 702-832-3700. FAX 702-832-3775. Ed. Marianne Mullins Porter; Pub. Tom Hill. adv.; B&W page $8075, color page $11230; trim 8 3/8 x 10 7/8; adv. contact: Dan Nourse. circ. 165,000. **Document type:** consumer publication.
 Description: Explores the diverse pursuits available in the West.

910.202 US
ADVISOR (MITCHELL). w. W. M. Johnson, Ed. & Pub., Box 343, Mitchell, SD 57301. TEL 605-996-8916.

AERZTLICHES REISE & MEDIZIN JOURNAL. see *MEDICAL SCIENCES*

918.04 US ISSN 1062-9084
AFFORDABLE CARIBBEAN; the newsletter for the value-conscious traveler. 1992. m. $49. Caribbean Travel and Life, Inc., 8403 Colesville Rd., Ste. 830, Silver Spring, MD 20910. TEL 301-588-2300. FAX 301-588-2256. (Subscr. to: Box 3000, Denville, NJ 07834-9498) Ed. Laura Randall; Pub. Patricia B. Fox. circ. 4,000 (paid). (back issues avail.) **Document type:** newsletter.
 Description: Features travel in the Caribbean, Bahamas and Bermuda, with emphasis on economic lodging, restaurants, activities and shopping.

968.9 916 RH
AFRICA CALLS WORLDWIDE. 1961. bi-m. Z.$20. Argosy Press, P.O. Box 2677, Harare, Zimbabwe. TEL 263-4-755084. FAX 263-4-752162. TELEX 26334 MODUS ZW. Ed. Mike Hamilton. adv.; bk.rev.; illus. circ. 5,000.
 Former titles: Africa Calls from Zimbabwe; Africa Calls; Rhodesia Calls (ISSN 0035-4708)

910 US ISSN 0194-4584
AFRICA UPDATE; annual newsletter with congress program. 1978. s-a. $10. c/o Africa Travel Association, 347 Fifth Ave., Ste. 610, New York, NY 10016. TEL 212-447-1926. FAX 212-725-8253. Dir. Mira Berman. **Document type:** newsletter.

917.304 973 US ISSN 1072-4052
910.03
AFRICAN-AMERICAN SITES & INSIGHTS;* a guide to places to go and people to know. 1993. biennial. $7.95 (effective 1993). Grace Communications Group, 1204 Old Hammond Chase, Atlanta, GA 30350-4937. TEL 516-997-5251. FAX 516-997-4125. **Document type:** consumer publication.
 Description: Provides historical, cultural and practical travel information for people interested in knowing about and experiencing the US from the African-American perspective. Lists restaurants, entertainment, historical sites, shops and churches.

AFRIKAGRUPPERNAS AARSKROENIKA. see *HISTORY — History Of Africa*

AGENT'S HOTEL GAZETTEER: AMERICA. see *HOTELS AND RESTAURANTS*

AGENT'S HOTEL GAZETTEER: RESORTS OF EUROPE. see *HOTELS AND RESTAURANTS*

910 SP
AGENTTRAVEL. (Monthly supplement avail.: Empresas y Empresarios) 1987. m. 10000 ptas.($130) (effective 1991). Ediciones Jaguar, C. Olimpo, 42, 28043 Madrid, Spain. TEL 91-388-01-62. FAX 91-759-94-84. adv.; B&W page 145000 ptas.; color page 200000 ptas.; 280 x 380. index. circ. 10,000. **Document type:** trade publication.
 Description: For travel agents, tour operators, hotel and restaurant managers, airline workers, and government tourism agency personnel.

910.2 IT ISSN 0002-0869
AGENZIA DI VIAGGI; quotidiano di notizie di interesse professionale. 1965. 6/w. L.50000($33) Editrice Turistica s.r.l., Via Rasella, 155, 00187 Rome, Italy. TEL 4821539. FAX 4826721. TELEX 621684 ADUGAU. Ed. Alberto Garlanda. adv.; illus. circ. 12,000. (tabloid format)

910.09 US
AIR TRAVEL JOURNAL. 1971. s-m. $40. Air Travel Publications, 120 Boylston St., Boston, MA 02116-4611. TEL 617-423-0900. FAX 617-423-1040. Ed. Robert H. Weiss. adv. circ. 15,000. **Document type:** consumer publication.
 Description: Covers news of Logan International Airport in Boston. Includes news of the Massachusetts port authority, airlines and regional events.

917.904 US ISSN 0733-1711
AIRCAL.* 1967. m. $36. (Air California) Halsey Publishing Co., 600 Corporate Dr., Ste. 300, Fort Lauderdale, FL 33334-3604. TEL 305-893-1520. Ed. Steve Winston. adv.; bk.rev.; illus. circ. 60,000.
 Former titles: AirCal Magazine (ISSN 0733-4567) & Air California Magazine (ISSN 0195-8062)

387.7 US
AIRFAIR. 1970. q. $10. Airfair Publishing Corp., 6401 Congress Ave., Ste. 100, Boca Raton, FL 33487. TEL 407-994-4509. Ed. Debra Fredel; Pub. Robert A. Barrett. adv.; B&W page $2065, color page $2995; trim 8 3/8 x 10 7/8; adv. contact: Dawn Silverberg. circ. 27,000. **Document type:** trade publication.
 Formerly: Airfair Interline (ISSN 0044-7005)

910.202 GW
DAS AKTUELLE MONATSMAGAZIN. m. DM.24. (Arbeitsgemeinschaft der Verkehrsvereine der Staedte Nuernberg, Fuerth, Erlangen und Schwabach) Omnia Druck und Verlag, Pretzfelderstr. 7-11, 90425 Nuernberg, Germany. TEL 0911-3409-100. FAX 0911-382530. Ed. Herbert Walchshoefer. adv. contact: Elvira Hirsing. circ. 30,000. **Document type:** consumer publication.

338 US
AL DIA; travel agent update. (Text mainly in Spanish; occasionally in English, Portuguese) 1991. bi-m. $15 (foreign $40). Pepperdine Enterprises, 1367 Tadsworth Terr., Heathrow, FL 32746. TEL 407-333-3393. FAX 407-333-3533. Pub. Noemi Pepperdine. adv.; B&W page $2500, color page $3200; trim 8 1/4 x 11. circ. 6,156. **Document type:** trade publication.

910.202 US
ALABAMA BOOK OF SURPRISES. q. free. Bureau of Tourism and Travel, 401 Adam Ave., Box 4927, Montgomery, AL 36103-4927. TEL 334-242-4169. FAX 334-242-4554.

910.202 US
ALABAMA TOURIST GUIDE. q. Bureau of Tourism and Travel, 401 Adam Ave., Box 4927, Montgomery, AL 36103-4927. TEL 334-242-4169. FAX 334-242-4554.
 Formerly: Travel in Alabama.

910.202 UK ISSN 0969-9708
ALAN ROGERS DIRECTORY OF CAMPING AND CARAVANNING, ALL YEAR ROUND. 1993. biennial. £5.99. Deneway Guides and Travel Ltd. (Subsidiary of: Response Marketing Initiatives Ltd.), Chesil Lodge, W. Bexington, Dorset DT2 9DG, England. TEL 03108-879809. FAX 01308-898017. Ed. Clive Edwards. adv. contact: Sue Smart. **Document type:** consumer publication, directory.
 Description: Provides full details on selected sites in the U.K. and rest of Europe that are open at least ten months of the year.

ALASKA ALMANAC: FACTS ABOUT ALASKA. see *ENCYCLOPEDIAS AND GENERAL ALMANACS*

917.9 US
ALL ABOUT ARIZONA, THE HEALTHFUL STATE. biennial. $5.95. Harian Publications, One Vernon Ave., Floral Park, NY 11001. TEL 516-437-3440. Ed. Thomas B. Lesure.

910.202 HK ISSN 0072-4939
DS504
ALL-ASIA GUIDE. 1961. biennial. latest 17th ed. Review Publishing Co. Ltd., G.P.O. Box 160, Hong Kong. TEL 852-508-4300. FAX 852-503-1549. TELEX 66452 REVCD HX. Ed. Michael Malik. adv. **Document type:** consumer publication.
 Formerly: Golden Guide to South and East Asia.
 Description: Covers custom and visa procedures, hotels, restaurants, and history and culture of all Asian countries.

910.09 917 US ISSN 0533-0653
ALL OF MEXICO AT LOW COST. biennial. $3.45. Harian Publications, One Vernon Ave., Floral Park, NY 11001. TEL 516-437-3440. Ed. Norman D. Ford. charts.

919.4 AT
ALL STATES TOURIST PARK GUIDE. 1948. a. Aus.$3.25. David Syme & Co. Limited, 250 Spencer St., Melbourne, Vic. 3000, Australia. TEL 03-601-2903. FAX 03-642-0852.

910.202 UK ISSN 1351-4636
ALL U.K. AGENTS HANDBOOK (YEAR). 1992. a. £14.95. (English Tourist Board) Kogan Page Ltd., 120 Pentonville Rd., London N1 9JN, England. TEL 0171-278-0433. FAX 0171-837-6348. TELEX 263088-KOGAN-G. **Document type:** directory.

ALLES UEBER WEIN. see *FOOD AND FOOD INDUSTRIES*

914 GW
ALLGAUER MAGAZIN. 1986. m. DM.33.60. Thomas Dreyer Verlag, Salzstr. 5, 87700 Memmingen, Germany. TEL 08331-4062. FAX 08331-4064. Ed. R. Dreyer. adv.; bk.rev.; film rev.; illus.; tr.lit. circ. 15,000. (back issues avail.)

914.404 FR
ALLIER MAGAZINE; magazines de France. 1967. m. 280 F. Editions Rene Dessagne, 11 rue Pierre Leroux, B.P. 90, 87000 Limoges cedex, France. TEL 55-77-25-97. Ed. Rene Dessagne. adv.

ALLSTATE MOTOR CLUB FISHING HOTSPOTS. WISCONSIN. see *FISH AND FISHERIES*

915 US ISSN 0147-5436
DU620
ALOHA; the magazine of Hawaii and the Pacific. 1977. bi-m. $17.97. Davick Publications, Inc., Box 3260, Honolulu, HI 96801. TEL 808-593-1191. FAX 808-593-1327. Ed. Cheryl C. Tsutsumi; Pub. Rick Davis. adv. contact: Dale Horning. bk.rev. circ. 65,000. (also avail. in microform from UMI) **Document type:** consumer publication.
 Formerly: Pacific.

388 FR ISSN 0767-8444
ALSACE AUTOMOBILE. 1927. m. 65 F. to non-members; members 45 F. Automobile-Club d'Alsace, 5 av. de la Paix, 67000 Strasbourg, France. TEL 88-360-434. FAX 88-36-00-63. Ed. Roger Braun. adv.; color page 11350 F.; 230 x 297. bk.rev. circ. 54,000. **Document type:** consumer publication.
 Description: Covers all aspects of vehicular transportation, including profiles of cars, car insurance, recreational driving, etc.

TRAVEL AND TOURISM

910.09 572   SP   ISSN 1131-7817
ALTAIR. 1991. bi-m. 2750 ptas. (foreign 4625 ptas.). Oasis, S.L., Taquigraf Garrifa 10, 08014 Barcelona, Spain. TEL 34-3-4193888. FAX 34-3-4197588. circ. 35,000.

AM-CAN REPORT; marketing & trade journal. see *BUSINESS AND ECONOMICS — Marketing And Purchasing*

917   US   ISSN 0569-1966
AMERICA BY CAR. 1958. biennial. $4.95. Harian Publications, One Vernon Ave., Floral Park, NY 11001. TEL 516-437-3440. Ed. Norman D. Ford.

917.304   US   ISSN 1055-9191
E169.04
AMERICAN HOLIDAY AND LIFE. bi-m. A T L Publishing, Inc., 237 E. 39th St., New York, NY 10016. TEL 212-983-6100. Ed. Louis Montesano. adv.: B&W page $4400; color page $5650; trim 8 3/4 x 11 1/2. circ. 100,000.

910.09   UK   ISSN 0957-0667
AMERICAN IN LONDON. 1985. bi-m. £15($36) (effective 1992). American in Europe Publications Ltd., 93-97 Bushey Mill Lane, Watford, Herts WD2 4JG, England. TEL 0923-234141. FAX 0923-223555. Ed. Martha Mader. adv.: B&W page £1045, color page £1350. bk.rev. circ. 19,000. (back issues avail.)
Description: Examines all areas of expatriate life for Americans living and working in the United Kingdom.

910.09   US   ISSN 0098-4981
DP501
AMERICAN PORTUGUESE SOCIETY. JOURNAL. Key Title: Journal of the American Portuguese Society. 1966. 2/yr. free. American Portuguese Society, Inc., 555 Madison Ave., New York, NY 10022. Ed.Bd. adv.; bk.rev. circ. 1,000.
Formerly: American Portuguese Cultural Society. Journal (ISSN 0003-0570)

910.202   US
AMERICAN URBAN GUIDENOTES; the newsletter of guidebooks. 1979. q. $10. American Urban Guides, Box 186, Washington, DC 20044. TEL 202-667-1357. Ed. John Fondersmith. bk.rev. circ. 200. (back issues avail.) **Indexed:** Avery Ind.Archit.Per. **Document type:** newsletter.

910.202   US   ISSN 1070-3365
▼**AMERICANS TRAVELING ABROAD: WHAT YOU SHOULD KNOW BEFORE YOU GO**; an international traveler's resource guide. 1994. biennial. $39.99. World Travel Institute Press, Inc., 8268 Streamwood Dr., Box 32674, Baltimore, MD 21208. TEL 410-922-4903. FAX 410-922-8115. Ed. Gladson I. Nwanna; Pub. Gladson I. Nwanna. **Document type:** directory.

910.09 917.206
790.1   MX
AMISTAD. (Text in English) 1942. m. $42. American Society of Mexico, A.C., Apdo. 555, 06000 Mexico, D.F., Mexico. TEL 525-202-4600. FAX 525-208-9675. Ed. Carlos Marban; Pub. James S. Wright. adv.; circ. 4,000 (paid) **Document type:** bulletin.
Formerly: American Society of Mexico. Bulletin.

910.09   US   ISSN 0275-5564
AMOCO TRAVELER. 1981. q. membership. (Amoco Travel Club) Amoco Enterprises, Inc., 200 E. Randolph Dr., Chicago, IL 60601. TEL 212-303-6987. FAX 312-856-2379. circ. 75,000 (controlled).

910   US   ISSN 0884-7622
ANDREW HARPER'S HIDEAWAY REPORT; a connoisseur's worldwide guide to peaceful and unspoiled places. 1979. m. $100. Harper Associates, Inc., Box 50, Sun Valley, ID 83353. TEL 208-622-3183. (Subscr. to: Box 300, Whitefish, MT 59937. TEL 406-862-3480. FAX 406-862-3486) Ed. Andrew Harper. bk.rev.; illus.; index; circ. 18,000 (paid) (back issues avail.) **Document type:** newsletter.
Description: Covers the world's most exclusive and stylish resorts.

915.9   PH
ANG PHILIPINAS: YOUR TOURIST MAGAZINE.* 4/yr. Bureau of Tourism Promotion, Ministry of Tourism, Tourism Bldg. 3F, TM Kalaw St. Ermita, Manila, Philippines.

914.2   IE
ANGLING HOLIDAYS IN IRELAND. (Text in English and French) 1986. a. $5. Libra House Ltd., 4 St. Kevin's Terrace, Dublin 8, Ireland. TEL 01-4542717. FAX 01-4546371. Ed. Cathal Tyrrell. illus. circ. 15,780. **Document type:** directory.
Description: Details of facilities and species of fish available at locations throughout Ireland.

910.91   UK   ISSN 0160-7383
G155.A1
ANNALS OF TOURISM RESEARCH; a social sciences journal. (Text in English; summaries in French) 1982. q. £207($330) (effective 1996). Elsevier Science Ltd., Pergamon, P.O. Box 800, Kidlington, Oxford OX5 1DX, England. TEL 44-1865-843000. FAX 44-1865-843010. E-mail: nlinfo-f@elsevier.nl; usinfo-f@elsevier.com; forinfo-kyf04035@niftyserve.or.jp; Site addr.: http://www.elsevier.nl/. (Subscr. in U.S. and Canada to: Elsevier Science, 660 White Plains Rd., Tarrytown, NY 10591-5153. TEL 914-524-9200. FAX 914-333-2444) Ed. Jafar Jafari. adv.; bk.rev.; film rev.; index. circ. 1,200. (also avail. in microfilm from UMI; back issues avail.) **Indexed:** Abstr.Anthropol., Anthropol.Lit., Art.Hosp.& Tour., Asian-Pac.Econ.Lit., Commun.Abstr., Curr.Cont., E.I., Geo.Abstr., IDA, P.A.I.S., Rural Recreat.Tour.Abstr., Sociol.Abstr., Sportsearch (1979-), SSCI, World Agri.Econ.& Rural Sociol.Abstr. **Document type:** academic/scholarly publication.
—BLDSC (1044.800000); Faxon; Genuine Article; SWETS; UMI; UnCover. **CCC.**
Description: Provides a forum for academic perspectives on tourism.
Refereed Serial

ANTARCTIC; a news bulletin. see *GEOGRAPHY*

914   UK
APARTMENT GAZETTEER (EUROPE). a. £17. C.H.G. Travel Publications, Waterside House, West Common, Gerrards Cross, Bucks, England.

APPALACHIAN HERITAGE; a magazine of southern Appalachian life and culture. see *GENERAL INTEREST PERIODICALS — United States*

917.204   HO
AQUI Y AHORA. 1976. q. Secretaria de Cultura, Turismo e Informacion, Oficina Central de Informacion, Tegucigalpa, Honduras. illus. (tabloid format)

914.604   SP
ARAGON TURISTICO Y MONUMENTAL. 4/yr. Sindicato de Iniciativa y Propaganda de Aragon, Pl. de Sas 7, Zaragoza, Spain. TEL 76-22-11-17. Ed. S. Parra de Mas.

ARCHEOLOGISCHE ROUTES IN NEDERLAND; op zoek naar de geschiedenis in het landschap. see *ARCHAEOLOGY*

910 959.9   PH   ISSN 0303-8564
DS651
ARCHIPELAGO. 1974. m. P.100($12.50) Department of Public Information, c/o Bureau of National and Foreign Information, U P L Building, Box 3396, Intramuros, Manila, Philippines. Ed. Lorenzo J. Cruz. adv.; illus. circ. 5,000.

910   CU
ARENATURIST. 1972. a. free. Arenaturist, Pula, Croatia. Ed. Marijan Fistrovic.

388.3   US
ARIZONA A A A HIGHROADS. 1968. bi-m. $2 to non-members. Arizona Automobile Association, Box 33119, 3144 N. 7th Ave., Phoenix, AZ 85013. TEL 602-274-1116. FAX 602-277-1194. Ed. Pamela Heck. adv.; circ. 260,000 (controlled). **Document type:** trade publication.
Description: Covers Arizona and foreign travel; automotive, civic and legislative activities; club seminars and benefits.

917.904 979   US
ARIZONA COAST. 1988. bi-m. free. Hale Communications, Box 5054, 1212 Fourth St., Parker, AZ 85344. TEL 602-669-6464. FAX 602-669-6464. Ed. Jerry Hale. adv.; bk.rev. circ. 15,000. (back issues avail.) **Document type:** consumer publication.
Description: Covers tourism along the Colorado River in Western Arizona and Old West history.

917   US   ISSN 0004-1521
TE24.A6   CODEN: AZHIAW
ARIZONA HIGHWAYS. 1925. m. $19 (foreign $29). Department of Transportation, 2039 W. Lewis Ave., Phoenix, AZ 85009. TEL 602-258-6641. FAX 602-254-4505. Ed. Robert J. Early. bk.rev.; circ. 420,000 (paid). **Indexed:** Access (1975-), Chic.Per.Ind., GeoRef., Mag.Ind., PMR.
—Faxon; UnCover.
Description: Encourages tourist travel throughout Arizona. Contains articles on Southwest history, nature, travel, personalities, Native American art and archeology.

338.4   US
ARKANSAS TRAVEL AND TOURISM REPORT. 1972. a. free. Department of Parks and Tourism, Tourism Division, One Capitol Mall, Little Rock, AR 72201. TEL 501-682-7777. Ed. Charles McLemore. illus. circ. 900. **Document type:** government publication.
Formerly: Tourism in Arkansas. Activity Report.

910   US   ISSN 1060-2569
ARTISTIC TRAVELER; architecture & travel with art & photography. 1991. bi-m. $29. S & R Research, 2500 E. Fourth Plain Blvd., Ste. 104, Vancouver, WA 98661-3965. TEL 360-737-0632. Pub. Richard Hovey. bk.rev. (back issues avail.) **Document type:** newsletter.
Description: Aims to guide people interested in the artistic aspect of architecture to exciting visual experiences. Included is a calendar of museum exhibits and news about architectural attractions, awards and important new buildings.

915.04   TH
ASIA MAGAZINE. (Text in English) fortn. Post Publishing Co., Ltd., 136 Na Ranong Rd., Off Sunthorn Kosa Rd., Bangkok 10110, Thailand. TEL 662-240-3700. FAX 662-240-3790.

910.09   US   ISSN 1045-3881
DS10
ASIA PACIFIC TRAVEL;* your guide to Asia & the Pacific Rim. 1990. q. $12 (foreign $30). Publishing Today (Subsidiary of: Health World Magazine, Inc., 1675 Rollins Rd., Ste. B-3, Burlingame, CA 94010-2320. TEL 415-697-8038. FAX 415-697-7937. Ed. Don Douglas. adv.

338.4   PK
ASIA TRAVEL NEWS. vol.5, 1993. fortn. Rs.100 (foreign $20) (effective 1993). 101 Muhammadi House, Chundrigar Rd., Karachi, Pakistan. TEL 92-21-2412591. FAX 92-21-2420797. TELEX 21101 WINGS PK. Ed. Javed Mushtaq; Pub. M. Anwar Mushtaq. adv. contact: Mahboob M. Alam. illus. (tabloid format) **Document type:** newspaper.
Description: Publishes international and Pakistani news affecting the travel industry, including financial issues, reports on changes in airline services, new hotels, and other items of interest.

915.04   SI   ISSN 0255-7320
ASIA TRAVEL TRADE. 1969. m. $40. Interasia Publications, Ltd., 190 Middle Rd., No.11-01 Fortune Centre, Singapore 0718, Singapore. TEL 339-7622. FAX 339-8521. TELEX RS 36252 RSASIA. (H.K. addr.: 200 Lockhart Rd., 14th Fl., Hong Kong. TEL 852-74-9317) Ed. Hwu Chen Ju. adv.; bk.rev.; illus.; circ. 14,300 (controlled).
Description: Covers the economics and politics of tourism in the Asia-Pacific region.

914.9 410   GR   ISSN 1011-8993
THE ATHENIAN; Greece's English language monthly. (Text in English) 1974. m. $48 throughout Europe; elsewhere $50; newsstand price: Dr.600. Athenian Press Ltd., 4 K. Tsatsou, Plaka, 105 58 Athens, Greece. TEL 30-1-322-2802. FAX 30-1-322-3052. Ed. Sloane Elliott; Pub. D.V. Elliott. adv.; bk.rev.; film rev.; play rev.; bibl.; illus. circ. 13,200. (back issues avail.) **Document type:** consumer publication.
Description: Provides coverage of cultural and political events, as well as information of interest to tourists.

ATLANTE. see *GEOGRAPHY*

ATLANTIC CITY MAGAZINE. see *GENERAL INTEREST PERIODICALS — United States*

TRAVEL AND TOURISM

910   FR   ISSN 0767-5240
ATLAS - AIR FRANCE; geographie physique et humaine - decouverte de l'homme et de la nature. (Text in English, French) 1982? m. 99 F. Editions Atlas, 89 rue de Boetie, 75008 Paris, France. TEL 45-63-04-14. Ed. Guy Gouezel. adv. circ. 730,000.
Former titles: Atlas (Paris, 1960) (ISSN 0004-6922); Atlas Histoire (ISSN 0519-3273)

663.2   US   ISSN 0739-3733
ATTERBURY LETTER - WINE, DINING & TRAVEL. 1964. irreg. Atterbury Letter, Box 1197, Bethel Is., CA 94511. TEL 415-684-3142. Ed. Kirby Atterbury. bk.rev. circ. 1,500. (looseleaf format) **Document type:** consumer publication.
Description: Recommendations, reviews and anecdotes on food, wine and travel.

647   AT
ATTRACTIONS AUSTRALIA. 1988. a. Aus.$10 to non-members; members Aus.$5. R A C V, 550 Princess Highway, Noble Park, Vic. 3174, Australia. TEL 61-3-790-2646. FAX 61-3-790-2844. TELEX AA 30788. Ed. A. Bowes. adv. circ. 80,000. **Document type:** directory.
Formerly: R A C V's Out and About.

910   IT   ISSN 0394-414X
ATTRAVERSO IL MONDO. 1986. q. L.14000. Fouring Periodici s.r.l., Corso Italia 10, Milan, Italy. TEL 02-852673. FAX 02-58300315. TELEX 312476 TCIADM1. Ed. Raffaella Fiory Ceccopieri.

910.2   FR   ISSN 0004-7392
AUBERGE DE LA JEUNESSE. 1932. m. 2.50 F. Ligue Francaise pour les Auberges de la Jeunesse, 38 Bd. Raspail, 75007 Paris, France. TEL 1-45-48-69-84.

914   GW   ISSN 0004-7961
AUGSBURGER KULTURNACHRICHTEN. 1948. m. DM.40. Stadt Augsburg, Kulturbuero, Maximilianstr. 36, 86150 Augsburg, Germany. FAX 0821-324-2765. adv.; illus. circ. 15,000. (also avail. in microform) **Document type:** bulletin, government publication.

AUSTRALASIAN BUS AND COACH; the management magazine for bus and coach operators. see *TRANSPORTATION*

AUSTRALIAN-AMERICAN NEWS N.S.W. ANNUAL EDITION. see *POLITICAL SCIENCE — International Relations*

910.09   US   ISSN 1064-010X
AUSTRALIAN EXPATRIATE.* 1989. bi-m. $13.50. Box 184, APO, AP 96555. TEL 619-793-3694. FAX 619-793-7736. Ed. Elizabeth Kemmis. adv.; bk.rev.; film rev.; illus. circ. 8,000.
Description: Covers subjects about Australia relating to current events, travel, immigration, economics, art, theatre, music and sports.

910.202   AT   ISSN 1034-9006
AUSTRALIAN GOURMET TRAVELLER. 1967. m. Aus.$65. A C P Publishing Pty. Ltd., 54-58 Park St., Sydney, N.S.W. 2000, Australia. TEL 02-282-8758. FAX 02-267-8037. Ed. Nick Cham; Pub. Richard Walsh. adv. contact: Peter Miller. bk.rev. circ. 47,345. **Document type:** consumer publication. —UnCover.
Formerly: Australian Gourmet (ISSN 0155-3380)

AUSTRALIAN HOTELIER. see *HOTELS AND RESTAURANTS*

919.4   AT   ISSN 0728-7143
AUSTRALIAN TOURIST COMMISSION. ANNUAL REPORT. 1968. a. free. Australian Tourist Commission, Level 3, 80 William St., Woolloomooloo, Sydney, N.S.W. 2011, Australia. TEL 02-360-1111. FAX 02-331-4809. TELEX 22322. adv.; bk.rev.; illus.; stat.

919   AT
AUSTRALIAN WAY (MELBOURNE). 1935. m. Aus.$60($55) (Qantas Airways Ltd.) David Syme & Co. Limited, 250 Spencer St., Melbourne, Vic. 3000, Australia. TEL 03-601-2903. FAX 03-642-0852. (Subscr. addr.: P.O. Box 257C, Melbourne, Vic. 3001, Australia) adv.: B&W page $3850, color page $5000; trim 8 1/4 x 10 7/8; adv. contact: Guy Moore. circ. 1,070,000. **Document type:** consumer publication.
Former titles (until 1993): Airways Inflight (ISSN 0314-4003); (until 1976): Airways (ISSN 0002-2896)
Description: Covers sport, arts, travel, lifestyle for Australian domestic and international Qantas Airways passengers.

910.202   AU
AUSTRIA NACHRICHTEN. 6/yr. Rotenturmstr. 14, A-1010 Vienna, Austria. TEL 01-5131003. FAX 01-513100317. Ed. Hans Wallner. circ. 15,000. **Document type:** bulletin.

796.5 910.202   IT
AUTO CARAVAN NOTIZIE. 1975. m. L.32000 (foreign L.60000). Crisalide Editrice, Via Brusuglio 66, 20161 Milan, Italy. TEL 6464663. Ed. Bianca Carretto. adv.; bk.rev. circ. 60,000.
Formerly: Caravan Notizie.

AUTO-JOURNAL. see *TRANSPORTATION — Automobiles*

AUTO TOURING; die Oesterreichische Kraftfahrzeug-Zeitung. see *TRANSPORTATION — Automobiles*

910.2   GW   ISSN 0045-1010
AUTO UND REISE. 1953. 10/yr. DM.30. Auto und Reise GmbH Verlag und Wirtschaftsdienst, Postfach 440, 91427 Bad Windsheim, Germany. TEL 09841-409-0. FAX 09841-7033. TELEX 61876-KVDB-D. Ed. Joseph Harrer; Pub. Bernd Opolka. adv. contact: Walter Dippell. bk.rev.; illus.; stat.; tr.lit. circ. 125,000. **Document type:** consumer publication.
Formerly: Kraftfahrervereinigung Deutscher Beamter E.V. K V D B Mitteilungen.

910   FI   ISSN 0355-2896
AUTOLLA ULKOMAILLE. 1965. a. FIM 30. Autoliitto - Automobile and Touring Club of Finland, Kansakoulukatu 10, 00100 Helsinki, Finland. Ed. Reijo Kaukinen. adv. circ. 10,000.
Formerly: Kansainvalinen Automatkailu (ISSN 0075-4900)

910.09   UK
AUTOMOBILE ASSOCIATION MEMBERS HANDBOOK. biennial. free to AA members. (Automobile Association) A A Publishing, Norfolk House, Priestly Rd., Basingstoke, Hants. RG24 9NY, England. TEL 01256-20123. FAX 01256-22575. circ. 4,000,000. **Document type:** consumer publication.
Description: Covers services offered by the association, lists hotels, and includes road maps for members.

910.09 614.86   FR   ISSN 0758-6957
AUTOMOBILE MAGAZINE. (Supplements avail.) 1945. m. 200 F.; newsstand price: 22 F. Societe des Editions Techniques et Touristiques de France, 60-62 rue Danjou, 92100 Boulogne, France. TEL 46-09-95-96. FAX 46-09-99-85. TELEX 633 055 F. Eds. Jean-Luc Martin, Marc Schliklin; Pub. Monique Helfenberger. adv. contact: Eric Brame. illus. circ. 205,000. **Document type:** consumer publication.

914.4   FR   ISSN 1140-7352
AUTOMOBILISME ARDENNAIS. 1901. q. 45 Fr. Automobile Club Ardennais, 10 Cours A. Briand, 08107 Charleville Mezieres, France. FAX 24-56-29-66. adv.

917.104   CN
AUTOROUTE. (Text in English, French) 1989. 4/yr. Can.$9.99. Morris Marketing and Media Services, Inc., 366 Adelaide St. W., No. 606, Toronto, ON M5V 1R9, Canada. TEL 416-599-9900. FAX 416-599-9700. Ed. John Terrauds; Pub. Rod Morris. adv.: B&W page Can.$5190, color page Can.$6990; trim 8 1/8 x 10 3/4. circ. 285,000 (paid). **Document type:** consumer publication.

AUTOSPORT. see *SPORTS AND GAMES*

AUVERGNE MAGAZINE; magazines de France. see *GENERAL INTEREST PERIODICALS — France*

910.09   SP   ISSN 0211-2361
AVIACION Y TURISMO. 1980. 12/yr. Aviacion y Turismo, S.A., German Perez Carrasco 81 bajo, 28027 Madrid, Spain. TEL 1-377-46-40. FAX 1-377-42-86. Ed. Hipolito Navarro. circ. 4,286.

AVIATION & SPACE JOURNAL. see *TRANSPORTATION — Air Transport*

910.202   IE
AVIS - PERSONALLY YOURS. (Text in English) 1984. a. free to qualified personnel. International Fairs & Exhibitions Ltd., Belgrave House, 15 Belgrave Rd., Rathmines, Dublin 6, Ireland. TEL 965711. FAX 964142. Ed. Michael Flood. circ. 50,000.

910.202   IT   ISSN 0394-719X
AVVENTURA. 4/yr. Marco Manicini Editore, Via San Simpliciano, 20121 Milan, Italy. adv. circ. 86,000.

910.09   IT
AVVENTURE NEL MONDO. 1972. bi-m. L.10000($15) (foreign L.20000). Viaggi nel Mondo, Via Cino da Pistoia, 7, 00152 Rome, Italy. TEL 39-6-5816365. FAX 39-6-5809540. Ed. Vittorio Kulczycki. adv.: color page L.9900000. circ. 100,000.
Description: Reports on adventure trips internationally.

910.202   UK
AWAY FROM IT ALL; a guide to retreat houses. 1976. irreg., vol.4, 1991. The Lutterworth Press, P.O. Box 60, Cambridge CB1 2NT, England. TEL 01223-350865. FAX 01223-66951. Ed. Colin Lester. **Document type:** directory.

910.202   US
B & B SHOPTALK. (Bed & Breakfast) 1981. bi-m. $65. American Bed & Breakfast Association, Box 1387, Midlothian, VA 23113-8387. TEL 804-379-2222. circ. 3,000. (looseleaf format; back issues avail.)
Description: For operators of bed and breakfast guesthouses and inns.

790.1   UK   ISSN 0965-2434
B B C HOLIDAYS MAGAZINE; the magazine for all your leisure time. 1992. m. £19.20 (rest of Europe £37; elsewhere £56.40); newsstand price: £1.60. B B C Magazines, 101 Bayham St., London NW1 0AG, England. TEL 0171-331-8079. FAX 0171-331-8030. (Subscr. to: Fulham House, Goldsworth Rd., Woking, Surrey GU21 1LY, England. TEL 01483-73345) Ed. Alison Rice. adv.; illus.; tr.lit. circ. 431,000. (back issues avail.) **Document type:** consumer publication.
Description: Describes noteworthy tourist destinations worldwide and how to get the most for your money. Also offers general travel advice.

910.09   UK
B H & P A JOURNAL. 1958. bi-m. membership. British Holiday & Home Parks Association Ltd., 6 Pullman Ct., Great Western Rd., Gloucester GL1 3ND, England. TEL 01452-526911. FAX 01452-307226. Ed. R.A. Pritchard. adv. contact: A.J. Pritchard. stat.; tr.lit. circ. 3,000. **Document type:** trade publication.
Formerly: N F S O Journal (National Federation of Site Operations).
Description: Provides information on the holiday and home park industry, including reports on legislation and regulations affecting parks. Geared toward commercial operators of trailer parks in the U.K.

B INTERNATIONAL. see *GENERAL INTEREST PERIODICALS — Hong Kong*

647.94   GW
BAD ABBACHER KUR- UND GESCHAEFTSANZEIGER. 1974. m. DM.66. Roter Brachweg 72a, 93049 Regensburg, Germany. Ed. Annelore Olbrich. index. circ. 3,000. (back issues avail.)

943   GW
BAD TOELZ AKTUELL. 1950. m. DM.36. Staedtische Kurverwaltung, Ludwigstr. 11, 83646 Bad Toelz, Germany. TEL 08041-70071. FAX 08041-70075. Ed. Stefan Kirsch. adv.; play rev. circ. 4,500. **Document type:** bulletin, government publication.
Formerly: Kurjournal - Bad Toelz.
Description: Information for visitors to Bad Toelz, including local events and health treatments.

917.2 BF
BAHAMA OUT ISLANDS TRAVEL GUIDE. 1972. a. $1. (Bahamas Out Islands Promotion Board) Star Publishers Ltd, P.O. Box 4855, Nassau, Bahamas. TEL 809-322-4528. FAX 809-322-4827. Ed. Bobby Bower. adv.; illus. circ. 150,000. **Document type:** trade publication.
   Former titles (until 1993): Bahamas Family Islands Travel Guide; (until 1977): Bahamas Out Islands Travel Guide; Bahama Out Islands Tourist News.

917.204 US ISSN 1055-5625
F1652
BAHAMAS (YEAR) INCLUDING TURKS & CAICOS. a. $12. Harper Collins Publishers, Birnbaum Travel Guides, 10 E. 53rd St., New York, NY 10022-5299. TEL 212-207-7542. Ed. Alexandra Mayes Birnbaum. illus.; index.
   Supersedes in part: Caribbean, Bermuda, and the Bahamas (Year).

BAHAMAS DATELINE. see BUSINESS AND ECONOMICS — Investments

910.202 790.1 US
BALTIMORE QUICK GUIDE. 3/yr. free. (Baltimore Area Convention and Visitors Association) Guest Informant, 21200 Erwin St., Woodland Hills, CA 91367. TEL 818-716-7484. (Dist. by: B A C V A, 400 E. Pratt St., Ste. 818, Baltimore, MD 21202. TEL 410-783-7520. FAX 410-783-1763) Ed. Jeremy Lyon. adv. contact: Karen Slicher. circ. 550,000. **Document type:** consumer publication.
   Description: Informs visitors to Baltimore of activities, attractions, hotels, and restaurants.

910 FR ISSN 0764-3578
BANCS D'ESSAI DU TOURISME. 6/yr. M E C C, 13 rue Gutenberg, Z I Mauniere de Bondoufle, 91037 Evry Cedex, France. TEL 60-86-82-40. FAX 60-86-44-54. TELEX 601 917 BDE. Ed. Leo Pietri. circ. 100,000.

919.704 BB
BARBADOS TOURIST BOARD. ANNUAL REPORT. no.14, 1972. a. $3. Barbados Tourist Board, Bridgewater, Barbados, W.I. charts; illus.

914.604 US ISSN 1056-4381
DP402.B24
BARCELONA (YEAR). a. $11. Harper Collins Publishers, Birnbaum Travel Guides, 10 E. 53rd St., New York, NY 10022-5299. TEL 212-207-7542. illus.; index.

BARCOS. see SPORTS AND GAMES — Boats And Boating

910.202 SZ
BASEL AKTUELL. 26/yr. Petersgasse 34, CH-4001 Basel, Switzerland. TEL 061-258166. circ. 10,000.

910.202 GW
BAYERN ZEITUNG; Nachrichten, Tips und Information aus dem Urlaubsland Bayern. 1983. q. free. M T M Muenchen, Poccistr. 7, 80336 Munich, Germany. TEL 089-776019. FAX 089-7250981. Eds. Karl Stankiewitz, W.E. Matthaeus. adv. circ. 100,000. (back issues avail.)
   Description: Information about tourism in Bavaria.

914.6 IS ISSN 0302-6221
DP14
BAZAK GUIDE TO SPAIN.* (Text in English) irreg. $4.95. Bazak Israel Guidebook Publishers Ltd., P.O. Box 4471, Jerusalem, Israel. (Dist. in U.S. by: Harper & Row, 60 E. 42nd St., Ste. 411, New York, NY 10017) illus.

917 CN ISSN 0005-7460
BEAUTIFUL BRITISH COLUMBIA MAGAZINE. 1959. q. Can.$15.95. Beautiful British Columbia Magazine Ltd., 929 Ellery St., Victoria, BC V9A 7B4, Canada. TEL 604-384-5456. FAX 604-384-2812. Ed. Bryan McGill; Pub. John Thomson. adv. contact: Debbie MacLean. illus.; index. circ. 252,000. **Indexed:** Can.B.P.I., CMI.
   —UnCover.
   Description: Devoted to travel and geography of BC.

910.3 UK ISSN 0267-3436
BED AND BREAKFAST IN BRITAIN. 1955. a. £2.90. F H G Publications Ltd., Abbey Mill Centre, Seedhill, Paisley PA1 1JN, Scotland. TEL 0141-887-0428. FAX 0141-889-7204. Ed. Peter Clark. **Document type:** consumer publication.
   Formed by the merger of: Bed and Breakfast in South and Southwest England (ISSN 0067-4761); Bed and Breakfast in Wales, Northern England and Scotland (ISSN 0067-477X)

910.22 US
BED & BREAKFAST NORTH AMERICA; a national directory for B & B travel. irreg., latest 8th ed. $15.95. Betsy Ross Publications, 24406 S. Ribbonwood Dr., Sun Lakes, AZ 85248. TEL 602-895-2795. Pub. Norma Buzan. illus. **Document type:** directory.
   Description: Features historic Victorian Inns, intimate urban hotels, country inns, guesthouses and reservation services with details on prices, amenities, facilities, and attractions.

914.2 UK ISSN 0267-3363
BED & BREAKFAST STOPS. 1975. a. £3.60. F H G Publications Ltd., Abbey Mill Business Centre, Seedhill, Paisley PA1 1JN, Scotland. TEL 0141-887-0428. FAX 0141-889-7204. **Document type:** consumer publication.

910.202 US
BED AND BREAKFAST U S A; guide to tourist homes and guest houses. 1977. a. $14 (typically set in Jan.). Penguin Books U S A, Inc., 375 Hudson St., New York, NY 10014. TEL 800-526-0275. FAX 800-227-9604. (Editorial addr.: RR1, Box 12A, Greentwon, PA 18426) Ed. Peggy Ackerman. circ. 43,000.
   Formerly: Guide to Tourist Homes and Guest Houses.

914.2 UK ISSN 0084-7755
BED, BREAKFAST & EVENING MEAL. 1963. a. £3.95. Pastime Publications Ltd., 6 York Pl., Edinburgh EH1 3EP, Scotland. TEL 0131-556-1105. FAX 0131-556-1129. adv. contact: Diane Gibson. circ. 60,000. **Document type:** consumer publication.

910.09 055.1 IT ISSN 0394-7203
BELL'ITALIA; alla scoperta del paese piu bello del mondo. 1986. m. L.60000 (foreign L.140000). Editoriale Giorgio Mondadori S.p.A., Via A. Ponti, 10, 20143 Milan, Italy. TEL 02-8916611. FAX 02-89125888. Ed. Ettore Mocchetti. adv.: B&W page L.13900000, color page L.16700000. circ. 140,000.

910.202 US
BERKSHIRE RESTAURANT & ENTERTAINMENT GUIDE.* 1970. s-a. $1. Ski America Enterprises, Inc., Box 1140, Pittsfield, MA 01202-1140. TEL 413-637-9810. Ed. Barry Hollister. adv. circ. 30,000.

914 GW ISSN 0005-9250
BERLIN PROGRAMM. 1951. m. DM.33.60; newsstand price: DM.2.80. Rimbach Verlag GmbH, Postfach 370144, 14131 Berlin, Germany. TEL 030-8021071. FAX 030-8029988. Ed.Bd. adv. contact: Rainer Rimbach. illus. circ. 60,150. **Document type:** consumer publication.

BERLIN UND BRANDENBURG, SACHSEN-ANHALT, SACHSEN VON HINTEN; das Schwule Reisebuch. see HOMOSEXUALITY

919.404 US ISSN 1057-4689
DU95
BERLITZ TRAVELLERS GUIDE TO AUSTRALIA. 1989. a. $14.95. Berlitz Publishing, Inc., 257 Park Ave. S., 17th Fl., New York, NY 10010. TEL 212-777-7878. FAX 212-353-9786.
   Formerly (until 1992): Penguin Guide to Australia (ISSN 0897-6880)

914.304 US ISSN 1065-6294
DD859
BERLITZ TRAVELLERS GUIDE TO BERLIN. 1993. a. $11.95. Berlitz Publishing, Inc., 257 Park Ave. S., 17th Fl., New York, NY 10010. TEL 212-777-7878. FAX 212-353-9786.

917.104 US ISSN 1057-4778
F1009
BERLITZ TRAVELLERS GUIDE TO CANADA. 1989. a. $16.95. Berlitz Publishing, Inc., 257 Park Ave. S., New York, NY 10010. TEL 212-598-2990. FAX 212-353-9786.
   Formerly (until 1992): Penguin Guide to Canada (ISSN 0897-6872)

917.204 US ISSN 1067-7135
▼**BERLITZ TRAVELLERS GUIDE TO COSTA RICA.** 1994. a. $11.95. Berlitz Publishing, Inc., 257 Park Ave. S., 17th Fl., New York, NY 10010. TEL 212-777-7878. FAX 212-353-9786.

914.204 US ISSN 1057-4735
DA650
BERLITZ TRAVELLERS GUIDE TO ENGLAND & WALES. 1989. a. $16.95. Berlitz Publishing, Inc., 257 Park Ave. S., 17th Fl., New York, NY 10010. TEL 212-777-7878. FAX 212-353-9786.
   Formerly (until 1992): Penguin Guide to England and Wales (ISSN 0897-6864)

914.404 US ISSN 1057-476X
DC16
BERLITZ TRAVELLERS GUIDE TO FRANCE. 1989. a. $17.95. Berlitz Publishing, Inc., 257 Park Ave. S., 17th Fl., New York, NY 10010. TEL 212-598-2490. FAX 212-777-7878. FAX 212-353-9786. Ed. Alan Tucker. **Document type:** directory.
   Formerly (until 1992): Penguin Guide to France (ISSN 0897-683X)

914.304 US ISSN 1057-462X
DD258.25
BERLITZ TRAVELLERS GUIDE TO GERMANY. 1990. a. $17.95. Berlitz Publishing, Inc., 257 Park Ave. S., 17th Fl., New York, NY 10010. TEL 212-777-7878. FAX 212-353-9786.
   Formerly (until 1992): Penguin Guide to Germany (ISSN 1043-4615)

914.9504 US ISSN 1057-4670
DF716
BERLITZ TRAVELLERS GUIDE TO GREECE. 1990. a. $17.95. Berlitz Publishing, Inc., 257 Park Ave. S., 17th Fl., New York, NY 10010. TEL 212-777-7878. FAX 212-353-9786.
   Formerly (until 1992): Penguin Guide to Greece (ISSN 1043-4607)

917.904 US ISSN 1057-4700
DU622
BERLITZ TRAVELLERS GUIDE TO HAWAII. 1990. a. $13.95. Berlitz Publishing, Inc., 257 Park Ave. S., New York, NY 10010. TEL 212-598-2990. FAX 212-353-9786. Ed. Alan Tucker.
   Formerly (until 1992): Penguin Guide to Hawaii (ISSN 1043-4569)

914.104 US ISSN 1057-4719
DA980
BERLITZ TRAVELLERS GUIDE TO IRELAND. 1989. a. $13.95. Berlitz Publishing, Inc., 257 Park Ave. S., 17th Fl., New York, NY 10010. TEL 212-777-7878. FAX 212-353-9786.
   Formerly (until 1992): Penguin Guide to Ireland (ISSN 0897-6856)

914.204 US ISSN 1057-4751
DA679
BERLITZ TRAVELLERS GUIDE TO LONDON. 1991. a. $14.95. Berlitz Publishing, Inc., 257 Park Ave. S., 17th Fl., New York, NY 10010. TEL 212-777-7878. FAX 212-353-9786. Ed. Alan Tucker.
   Formerly (until 1992): Penguin Guide to London (ISSN 1049-1457)
   Description: Guidebook to London and surrounding area.

917.204 US ISSN 1057-4786
F1209
BERLITZ TRAVELLERS GUIDE TO MEXICO. 1990. a. $16.95. Berlitz Publishing, Inc., 257 Park Ave. S., 17th Fl., New York, NY 10010. TEL 212-777-7878. FAX 212-353-9786.
   Formerly (until 1992): Penguin Guide to Mexico (ISSN 1043-4577)

917.404 US ISSN 1062-3655
F2.3
BERLITZ TRAVELLERS GUIDE TO NEW ENGLAND. 1993. a. $18.95. Berlitz Publishing, Inc., 257 Park Ave. S., 17th Fl., New York, NY 10010. TEL 212-777-7878. FAX 212-353-9786.

TRAVEL AND TOURISM

917.404 US ISSN 1057-4743
F128.18
BERLITZ TRAVELLERS GUIDE TO NEW YORK CITY. 1989. a. $14.95. Berlitz Publishing, Inc., 257 Park Ave. S., 17th Fl., New York, NY 10010. TEL 212-777-7878. FAX 212-353-9786.
Formerly (until 1992): Penguin Guide to New York City (ISSN 0898-8072)

914.504 US ISSN 1057-4654
DG416
BERLITZ TRAVELLERS GUIDE TO NORTHERN ITALY AND ROME. 1989. a. $16.95. Berlitz Publishing, Inc., 257 Park Ave. S., 17th Fl., New York, NY 10010. TEL 212-777-7878. FAX 212-353-9786.
Supersedes in part (in 1992): Penguin Guide to Italy (ISSN 0897-6848)

914.604 US ISSN 1057-4646
DP516
BERLITZ TRAVELLERS GUIDE TO PORTUGAL. 1990. a. $16.95. Berlitz Publishing, Inc., 257 Park Ave. S., 17th Fl., New York, NY 10010. TEL 212-777-7878. FAX 212-353-9786.
Formerly (until 1992): Penguin Guide to Portugal (ISSN 1043-4585)

917.904 US ISSN 1057-4727
F869.S33
BERLITZ TRAVELLERS GUIDE TO SAN FRANCISCO AND NORTHERN CALIFORNIA. 1991. a. $14.95. Berlitz Publishing, Inc., 257 Park Ave. S., 17th Fl., New York, NY 10010. TEL 212-598-2990. FAX 212-353-9786. Ed. Alan Tucker.
Formerly (until 1992): Penguin Guide to San Francisco and Northern California (ISSN 1049-1449)

914.504 US ISSN 1057-4662
DG416
BERLITZ TRAVELLERS GUIDE TO SOUTHERN ITALY AND ROME. 1989. a. $14.95. Berlitz Publishing, Inc., 157 Park Ave. S., 17th Fl., New York, NY 10010. TEL 212-777-7878. FAX 212-353-9786.
Supersedes in part (in 1992): Penguin Guide to Italy (ISSN 0897-6848)

914.604 US ISSN 1057-4638
DP14
BERLITZ TRAVELLERS GUIDE TO SPAIN. 1990. a. $17.95. Berlitz Publishing, Inc., 257 Park Ave. S., 17th Fl., New York, NY 10010. TEL 212-777-7878. FAX 212-353-9786.
Formerly (until 1992): Penguin Guide to Spain (ISSN 1043-4593)

917.804 US ISSN 1071-2704
F787
BERLITZ TRAVELLERS GUIDE TO THE AMERICAN SOUTHWEST. 1993. a. $15.95. Berlitz Publishing, Inc., 257 Park Ave. S., 17th Fl., New York, NY 10010. TEL 212-777-7878. FAX 212-353-9786.

917.204 US ISSN 1057-4697
F1609
BERLITZ TRAVELLERS GUIDE TO THE CARIBBEAN. 1989. a. $14.95. Berlitz Publishing, Inc., 257 Park Ave. S., 17th Fl., New York, NY 10010. TEL 212-777-7878. FAX 212-353-9786.
Formerly (until 1992): Penguin Guide to the Caribbean (ISSN 0897-6821)

915.6104 US ISSN 1049-1465
DR416
BERLITZ TRAVELLERS GUIDE TO TURKEY. 1992. a. Berlitz Publishing, Inc., 257 Park Ave. S., 17th Fl., New York, NY 10010. TEL 212-777-7878. FAX 212-353-9786.

914.204 US ISSN 1055-5684
F1632
BERMUDA (YEAR). a. $12. Harper Collins Publishers, Birnbaum Travel Guides, 10 E. 53rd St., New York, NY 10022-5299. TEL 212-207-7542. Ed. Alexandra Mayes Birnbaum. illus.; index.
Supersedes in part: Caribbean, Bermuda, and the Bahamas (Year).
Description: Covers hidden coves, dream beaches and great golf courses.

910.09 US
BERMUDA SHORTS. 1986. q. Bermuda Department of Tourism, 310 Madison Ave., Ste. 201, New York, NY 10017. TEL 212-818-9800. (Bermuda addr.: P.O. Box HM 465, Hamilton HM BX, Bermuda. TEL 800-223-6106) Ed. Mario Almonte. circ. 6,000 (controlled). (back issues avail.) **Document type:** government publication, newsletter.
Description: Relates to Bermuda and the travel industry.

919 US
BERMUDA, THE BAHAMAS & ISLANDS OF THE CARIBBEAN TRAVELBOOK. a. $7.95. American Automobile Association, 1000 AAA Dr., Heathrow, FL 32746-5063. TEL 407-444-8200. FAX 407-444-8204. adv.; illus. circ. 284,000. **Document type:** consumer publication.
Former titles: Caribbean TravelBook & Travel Guide to the Caribbean.

914 SZ ISSN 0005-9412
BERNER WOCHEN BULLETIN/THIS WEEK IN BERNE/SEMAINE A BERNE. (Text in English, French, German) 1943. w. 51 SFr. (Verkehrsverein Bern) Buri Druck AG, Eigerstr. 71, CH-3001 Bern, Switzerland. TEL 031-462323. FAX 031-455463. adv.: B&W page 156 SFr., color page 311 SFr.; trim 94 x 180. illus. circ. 7,200. **Document type:** bulletin.

BERTRAND VACANCES. see *REAL ESTATE*

912 US ISSN 1054-4089
TX907.5.G7
BEST BED & BREAKFAST IN ENGLAND, SCOTLAND & WALES. a. $18.95. Globe Pequot Press, Box 833, Old Saybrook, CT 06475-0833. TEL 203-395-0440. FAX 203-395-1418.
Formerly (until 1992): Best Bed and Breakfast in the World (ISSN 1057-5472)
Description: Profiles over 1000 B&Bs along with information on rates, amenities and sights of local interest.

387.7 US ISSN 8750-2410
BEST FARES. 1983. m. $58 to individuals; institutions $78. Box 171212, Arlington, TX 76003. TEL 817-261-6114; 800-576-1234. circ. 10,000.
Description: Lists over 10,000 airfares, hidden cities, split fares, hotel and car rental discounts, travel tips and frequent flyer news.

BEST GUIDE TO AMSTERDAM & THE BENELUX; for gay men and lesbians, with country and city maps. see *HOMOSEXUALITY*

BEST GUIDE TO ASIA, AUSTRALASIA, AND SOUTH PACIFIC ISLANDS; for gay men, with country and city maps. see *HOMOSEXUALITY*

BEST GUIDE TO THE NORTH PACIFIC AND ORIENT; for gay men, with country and city maps. see *HOMOSEXUALITY*

917.504 UK
THE BEST OF FLORIDA. (Text in English, German) a. Phoenix Publishing & Media Ltd., 18-20 Scrutton St., London EC2A 4RJ, England. TEL 0171-247-0537. FAX 0171-377-2741. Ed. Mary Moore Mason; Pub. Maureen Miller. adv. contact: Kathryn McGowan. circ. 135,000 (paid). **Document type:** consumer publication.
Description: Regional travel information aimed at consumers in the United Kingdom.

910.202 US
BEST OF LAUDERDALE AND THE GOLD COAST. 1980. q. $7.95. Best of Broward, Inc., 11 N. E. 12th Ave., Fort Lauderdale, FL 33301. TEL 305-523-2378. Ed. Yolanda Maurer. adv. circ. 14,739.

910.09 US
BEST OF MAUI; best of Maui sports, recreation, dining and shopping. 1988. a. $12. Sandwich Islands Publishing Co., Box 10669, Lahaina, Maui, HI 96761. TEL 808-661-5844. FAX 808-661-9878. Ed. Joe Harabin. adv.; bk.rev. circ. 20,000. (back issues avail.) **Document type:** consumer publication.

917.504 US
BEST OF THE BEACH.* 1991. a. First Publishing Inc., Box 380545, Birmingham, AL 35238-0545. TEL 205-733-1970. FAX 205-733-1974.
Description: Profiles the Alabama - Florida Gulf Coast tourism industry.

910.202 US ISSN 1048-5422
TX907.3.C2
BEST PLACES TO STAY IN CALIFORNIA. 1990. biennial. Houghton Mifflin Co., 215 Park Ave. S., New York, NY 10003. TEL 212-420-5800. (Orders to: Houghton Mifflin Co., Wayside Rd., Burlington, MA 01803. TEL 800-225-3362)

917 US ISSN 1055-0879
TX907.5.M6
BEST PLACES TO STAY IN MEXICO. 1991. biennial. Houghton Mifflin Co., 215 Park Ave. S., New York, NY 10003. TEL 212-420-5800. (Orders to: Houghton Mifflin Co., Wayside Rd, Burlington, MA 01803. TEL 800-225-3362)

910 US ISSN 1048-5465
TX907.3.N96
BEST PLACES TO STAY IN THE PACIFIC NORTHWEST. 1988. biennial. Houghton Mifflin Co., 215 Park Ave. S., New York, NY 10003. TEL 212-420-5800. (Orders to: Houghton Mifflin Co., Wayside Rd., Burlington, MA 01803. TEL 800-225-3362)

910.202 US ISSN 1048-549X
TX907.3.S69
BEST PLACES TO STAY IN THE SOUTHWEST. 1988. biennial. Houghton Mifflin Co., 215 Park Ave. S., New York, NY 10003. TEL 212-420-5800. (Orders to: Houghton Mifflin Co., Wayside Rd., Burlington, MA 01803. TEL 800-225-3362)

917.404 US
BEST READ GUIDE. 1988. m. $18. Box 1958, 77 Finlay Rd., Orleans, MA 02653. TEL 508-240-1212. FAX 508-240-2912. Ed. Walter Brooks. adv. contact: Pat Brooks. bk.rev.; maps; circ. controlled. **Document type:** consumer publication.
Description: Contains a calendar of events, listings of attractions and restaurants, and ideas for vacationers and travelers.

643 US ISSN 1054-9757
TX907.5.C27
BEST VACATION RENTALS. CARIBBEAN. 1991. biennial. Prentice Hall, 15 Columbus Cir., New York, NY 10023. TEL 212-373-8500.

910.202 IT
BIBIONE VACANZE. (Text in German, Italian) 1968. w. during summer. L.12000($5.50) Pubblistudio de Zorzi Casa Editrice s.a.s., Via Marinoni 53, Udine, Italy. TEL 0432-508243. FAX 0432-508243. adv. circ. 10,000. (back issues avail.)
Description: Guide for tourists in Bibione.

914.304 US
▼**BIRNBAUM'S BERLIN.** 1994. a. $12. Harper Collins Publishers, Birnbaum Travel Guides, 10 E. 53rd St., New York, NY 10022-5299. TEL 212-207-7000. (Subscr. to: Order Dept., 1000 Keystone Industrial Park, Scranton, PA 18512-4621. TEL 800-242-7737. FAX 800-822-4090) Ed. Alexandra Mayes Birnbaum. illus.; maps; index.

914.304 US
▼**BIRNBAUM'S GERMANY.** 1994. a. $18. Harper Collins Publishers, Birnbaum Travel Guides, 10 E. 53rd St., New York, NY 10022-5299. TEL 212-207-7000. (Subscr. to: Order Dept., 1000 Keystone Industrial Park, Scranton, PA 18512-4621. TEL 800-242-7737. FAX 800-822-4090) Ed. Alexandra Mayes Birnbaum. illus.; maps; index. **Document type:** directory.

917.904 US ISSN 1060-3875
DU629.H7
BIRNBAUM'S HONOLULU. 1993. a. $11. Harper Collins Publishers, Birnbaum Travel Guides, 10 E. 53rd St., New York, NY 10022-5299. TEL 212-270-7542. Ed. Alexandra Mayes Birnbaum. **Document type:** consumer publication.

917.504 US ISSN 1056-4454
F319.M6
BIRNBAUM'S MIAMI & FT. LAUDERDALE. a. $12. Harper Collins Publishers, Birnbaum Travel Guides, 10 E. 53rd St., New York, NY 10022-5299. TEL 212-207-7542. Ed. Alexandra Mayes Birnbaum. illus.; index.
Formerly: Miami (Year).
Description: Lists 9 walking and driving tours including the Everglades and the Florida Keys.

917.104 US ISSN 1061-5415
F1054.5.M83
BIRNBAUM'S MONTREAL & QUEBEC CITY. a. $12. Harper Collins Publishers, Birnbaum Travel Guides, 10 E. 53rd St., New York, NY 10022-5299. TEL 212-207-7000. (Subscr. to: Order Dept., 1000 Keystone Industrial Park, Scranton, PA 18512-4621. TEL 800-242-7737. FAX 800-822-4090) Ed. Alexandra Mayes Birnbaum. illus.; maps; index.

917.204 US ISSN 1060-3883
BIRNBAUM'S PUERTO VALLARTA. 1993. a. $11. Harper Collins Publishers, Birnbaum Travel Guides, 10 E. 53rd St., New York, NY 10022-5299. TEL 212-270-7542. Ed. Alexandra Mayes Birnbaum.

917.904 US ISSN 1068-722X
F804.S23
▼**BIRNBAUM'S SANTE FE & TAOS.** 1994. a. $12. Harper Collins Publishers, Birnbaum Travel Guides, 10 E. 53rd St., New York, NY 10022-5299. TEL 212-207-7000. (Subscr. to: Order Dept., 1000 Keystone Industrial Park, Scranton, PA 18512-4621. TEL 800-242-7737. FAX 800-822-4090) Ed. Alexandra Mayes Birnbaum. illus.; maps; index. **Document type:** directory.

918 US ISSN 0883-2463
F2211
BIRNBAUM'S SOUTH AMERICA. 1980. a. $18. Harper Collins Publishers, Birnbaum Travel Guides, 10 E. 53rd St., New York, NY 10022-5299. TEL 212-207-7500. FAX 212-207-7936. Ed. Alexandra Mayes Birnbaum. circ. 10,000.
Formerly: South America (New York) (ISSN 0193-7944)
Description: Includes detailed driving routes covering the entire continent.

917.504 US ISSN 1061-544X
F192.3
BIRNBAUM'S WASHINGTON DC. a. $12. Harper Collins Publishers, Birnbaum Travel Guides, 10 E. 53rd St., New York, NY 10022-5299. TEL 212-207-7000. (Subscr. to: Order Dept., 1000 Keystone Industrial Park, Scranton, PA 18512-4621. TEL 800-242-7737. FAX 800-822-4090) Ed. Alexandra Mayes Birnbaum. illus.; maps; index. **Document type:** directory.

796.95 914.2 UK
BLAKES HOLIDAY BOATING IN BRITAIN AND ABROAD. 1974. a. free. Blakes Holidays Ltd., Wroxham, Norwich NR12 8DH, England. TEL 01603-782141. FAX 01603-782871. TELEX 97114. Ed. T.E. Howes. circ. 400,000. **Document type:** consumer publication.
Former titles: Blakes Boating in Britain; Which supersedes in part: Blakes Holiday Boating; Which superseded: Blakes Boating in Britain; Blakes Boating in Europe; Blakes Boating in Britain & Blakes Boating in Europe superseded in part: Blakes Holidays Afloat; Which was formed by the merger of: Blakes International Holidays Afloat & Norfolk Broads Holidays Afloat (ISSN 0078-1142).

910.202 AU
BLICK. m. Postfach 4, A-8962 Groebming, Austria. TEL 3685-22191. FAX 3685-22476. Ed. Winfried Halasz. circ. 30,600.

BLUE BOOK OF EUROPEAN SKI RESORTS. see SPORTS AND GAMES — Outdoor Life

BLUE BOOK: THE DIRECTORY OF GEOGRAPHIC, TRAVEL & DESTINATION STOCK PHOTOGRAPHY. see PHOTOGRAPHY

910.91 CN
BOATING EAST CRUISING & VACATION GUIDE. 1982. a. free. Marble Rock Publishing, R.R. 2, Gananoque, ON K7G 2V4, Canada. TEL 613-382-5735. FAX 613-382-5735. Ed. Morison Bock; Pub. Kathrine Christensen. adv. contact: Kathrine Christensen. bk.rev.; play rev. circ. 25,000. **Document type:** consumer publication.

BOATING IN THE SAN JUAN ISLANDS. see SPORTS AND GAMES — Boats And Boating

BOCA RATON MAGAZINE. see GENERAL INTEREST PERIODICALS — United States

BOLERO; mode beaute cinema travel. see CLOTHING TRADE — Fashions

918 BO ISSN 0006-6540
BOLIVIA. * 1969. bi-m. Bol.$6. Ministerio de Cultura, Informacion y Turismo, Av. Camacho 1394, La Paz, Bolivia. Ed. Juan Siles Guevaro. bk.rev.; film rev.; bibl.; charts; illus.

910.09 663.2 US
BON VIVANT. 1975. 6/yr. $10. 138 Lake View Dr. N., Macon, GA 31210-8638. TEL 416-741-3057. Ed. J.D. Shortt. bk.rev.

BONNE TABLE ET TOURISME; revue de la gastronomie et du tourisme dans le monde. see FOOD AND FOOD INDUSTRIES

917.404 US ISSN 1056-4357
BOSTON (YEAR). a. $12. Harper Collins Publishers, Birnbaum Travel Guides, 10 E. 53rd St., New York, NY 10022-5299. TEL 212-207-7542. Ed. Alexandra Mayes Birnbaum. illus.; index.

914.2 BE
BRABANT WALLON TOURISME. (Editions in Dutch and French) 1938. 4/yr. 500 BEF. Federation Touristique du Brabant Wallon, CHaussee de Bruxelles, 218, 1410 Brussels, Belgium. TEL 32-2-3511200. FAX 32-2-3511300. Dir. Gilbert Menne. adv.; bk.rev.; bibl.; illus. circ. 450.
Former title (until 1995): Brabant Tourisme; (until 1984): Brabant (ISSN 0006-8616); Brabant-Tourisme (ISSN 0772-2214)

BRASILIANS JOURNAL. see ETHNIC INTERESTS

910.09 BL
BRASILTURIS JOURNAL. bi-w. Av. Pacaembi 1400, CEP 01234 Sao Paulo SP, Brazil. TEL 11-825-6811. TELEX 011-37124 SETL BR. Ed. Horacio Neves. circ. 10,000.

918.1 UK ISSN 1351-4520
BRAZIL BUSINESS BRIEF. 1942. bi-m. £25. Brazilian Chamber of Commerce, 32 Green St., London W1Y 3FD, England. TEL 071-499-0186. TELEX 25814-BRASTC-G. Ed. Dionisio A. de Castro Cerqueira. adv. contact: Emi Swan. bk.rev. circ. 400. **Document type:** newsletter.
Former titles (until Apr. 1993): Brazil News Update (ISSN 0968-1035); (until 1988): Brazil Journal.

942 US
BRITAIN BY BRITRAIL; how to tour Britain by train. 1980. biennial. $13.95. Globe Pequot Press, Box 833, Old Saybrook, CT 06475-0833. TEL 203-395-0440. FAX 203-395-1418.
Description: Covers every facet of rail travel in Britain. Provides routes from London, Glasgow and Edinburgh with suggested side trips.

914.2 UK ISSN 0267-1468
BRITAIN'S BEST HOLIDAYS - A QUICK REFERENCE GUIDE. 1968. a. £2.90. F H G Publications Ltd., Abbey Mill Business Centre, Seedhill, Paisley PA1 1JN, Scotland. TEL 0141-887-0428. FAX 0141-889-7204. **Document type:** consumer publication.
Formerly: Guide to Britain's Best Holidays.

BRITISH AIRWAYS EXECUTIVE. see TRANSPORTATION — Air Transport

BRITISH HERITAGE. see HISTORY — History Of Europe

914.2 UK ISSN 0953-3540
BRITISH TOURIST AUTHORITY. ANNUAL REPORT. 1969. a. £10. British Tourist Authority, Department D, Thames Rd., Black's Rd., Hammersmith, London W6 9EL, England. circ. 8,500. **Document type:** corporate report.
—BLDSC (1128.150000).
Formerly (until 1977): British Travel Association. Annual Report.
Description: Reports on the Authority's activities during the year, ending March 31; provides an outlook for British tourism for the coming year.

910.202 VB
BRITISH VIRGIN ISLANDS WELCOME TOURIST GUIDE; the welcome. 1971. bi-m. $25 (foreign $38). Island Publishing Co., P.O. Box 133, Road Town - Tortola, British Virgin Islands, W.I. TEL 809-494-2413. FAX 809-494-4413. Ed. Claudia Colli. adv. contact: Claudia Colli. circ. 135,000. **Document type:** consumer publication.
Description: Contains articles on the history, people, and locales of B.V.I., as well as information on accomodations, charterboats, dining and shopping.

BRITISH WATERWAYS BOARD. ANNUAL REPORT AND ACCOUNTS. see TRANSPORTATION — Ships And Shipping

647.94 UK
BUDGET ACCOMMODATION. Variant title: Hostelling International Budget Accommodation. a. International Youth Hostel Federation, 9 Guessens Rd., Welwyn Garden City, Hertfordshire AL8 6QW, England. TEL 44-707-332487.

917.204 MX
BUEN VIAJEI; convenciones - viajes de incentivo - sunshine - grupos. (Text in English, Spanish) 1990. bi-m. Mex.$10($29.95) Grupo Editoriale Aviare, Queretaro 229, Desp. 407, Apdo. 71339, 06700 Mexico D.F., Mexico. TEL 2-584-31-94. FAX 2-584-48-21. (In U.S.: c/o Alfredo Villagran Arnaud, Fruitland Ste. 40, Los Angeles CA 10937. TEL 818-769-4298) Ed. Alfredo Villagran Arevalo. adv.: B&W page Mex.$3000, color page Mex.$4000. circ. 25,000.
Description: Contains travel information for business travelers.

BUITENSPOOR. see SPORTS AND GAMES — Outdoor Life

916.8 778.5 RH
BULAWAYO THIS MONTH. 1972. m. free. Modern Publications, P.O. Box 1183, Bulawayo, Zimbabwe. Ed. Les Broughton. adv.; illus. circ. 2,500.

BULLETIN EKONOMI INDONESIA. see BUSINESS AND ECONOMICS — Domestic Commerce

910 CN ISSN 0706-215X
BULLETIN VOYAGES. (Text in French) 1978. w. Can.$52.92 (US Can.$65.88, elsewhere Can.$78.84). Editions Acra Ltee., 78 bd. St. Jospeh West, Montreal, PQ H2T 2P4, Canada. TEL 514-287-9773. FAX 514-842-6180. Ed. Andre Desiront; Pub. Etienne Olan-Groulx. adv.: B&W page Can.$1380, color page Can.$2170; adv. contact: Isabelle Honnorat. circ. 7,371. (back issues avail.) **Document type:** trade publication.
Incorporates in 1987: Tour Hebdo (ISSN 0835-1503)

910.09 IT ISSN 1121-2969
BUON VIAGGIO. 1991. m. L.5000 per no. Editrice Portoria s.r.l., Via Chissetto 1, 20122 Milan, Italy. TEL 39-2-760711. FAX 39-2-782601. Ed. Cesare Pillon. adv.; B&W page L.8560000, color page L.12840000. circ. 142,000.

910.202 UK
BURKE'S GUIDE TO COUNTRY HOUSES. 1977. irreg. £27.50. Burke's Peerage, 205 St. John's Hill, Battersea, London SW11 1TH, England. TEL 071-924-5132. FAX 071-978-5732.

388.3 GW ISSN 0341-5244
BUS-FAHRT; internationale Fachzeitschrift fuer Omnibusverkehr. 1952. m. DM.105 (foreign DM.124); newsstand price: DM.10. Stuenings Verlagsgesellschaft mbH, Luisenstr. 100-104, 47799 Krefeld, Germany. TEL 02151-853-0. FAX 02151-853103. Ed.Bd. adv.: B&W page DM.3160, color page DM.5320; trim 185 x 255; adv. contact: Karin Voigt. bk.rev.; charts; illus.; stat. circ. 7,871. **Document type:** trade publication.
Description: Focuses on bus travel and tourism.

910.202 388.3 GW
BUS-FAHRT ZIELE. (Supplement to: Bus-Fahrt (ISSN 0341-5244)) a. DM.7.50. Stuenings Verlagsgesellschaft mbH, Luisenstr. 100-104, 47799 Krefeld, Germany. TEL 02151-853-0. FAX 02151-853103. circ. 50,000. **Document type:** consumer publication.

TRAVEL AND TOURISM

910.09   GW
BUS TOURIST; international Fachmagazin fuer die international Bustouristik. 1981. bi-m. DM.8. Suedwestdeutsche Verlagsanstalt, Postfach 121863, 68161 Mannheim, Germany. TEL 0621-3922860. FAX 0621-3922800. circ. 8,500. **Document type:** trade publication.

BUS TOURS MAGAZINE. see TRANSPORTATION

910.202   AU
BUS- UND HOTELREPORT. q. Loquaiplatz 12, A-1060 Vienna, Austria. TEL 01-59960-0. FAX 01-59960-220. Ed. Harald Binder. circ. 10,800.

BUS WORLD; magazine of buses and bus systems. see TRANSPORTATION — Automobiles

914.704   PL
BUSINESS FOUNDATION. BUSINESS & PLEASURE. A GENERAL GUIDE TO POLAND. (Text in English) 1993. a. free. Business Foundation Co. Ltd., Ul. Krucza 38-42, 00-512 Warsaw, Poland. TEL 48-22-219993. FAX 48-22-219761. Eds. Monika Chojna, Hanna Zalewska. adv. contact: Monika Lechowska. circ. 20,000. (controlled). **Document type:** directory.
    Description: A businessperson's guide to important facts and recommendations to the world of business and pleasure throughout Poland. Offers necessary information for businesspeople and visitors, as well as an array of recommendations to ensure one's visit to Poland is productive and pleasurable.

THE BUSINESS OF TOURISM. see HOTELS AND RESTAURANTS

BUSINESS TRAVEL MANAGEMENT. see BUSINESS AND ECONOMICS — Management

910.202   US   ISSN 8750-3670
BUSINESS TRAVEL NEWS;* the newspaper of the business travel industry. 1984. 27/yr. C M P Publications, Inc., 600 Community Dr., Manhasset, NY 11030. TEL 516-562-5000. FAX 516-365-4601. TELEX 647035 CMP PUB MAHA. adv.: B&W page $8995; trim 10 1/2 x 13 11/16. circ. 54,000. **Indexed:** Hospit.Ind. **Document type:** newspaper.
    ●Also available online. Vendor(s): Data-Star, Knight-Ridder, Inc., NewsNet (TR08). —UMI. **CCC.**

910.09   NE   ISSN 0923-4470
BUSINESS TRAVEL NIEUWS; vakblad voor de travel secretary, travel manager en zakenreiziger. 8/yr. fl.75 (1550 BEF). Misset (Subsidiary of: Reed Elsevier plc), Postbus 4, 7000 BA Doetinchem, Netherlands. TEL 31-8340-49911. FAX 31-8340-43839. adv.; B&W page fl.2093; trim 215 x 285; adv. contact: Cor van Nek. illus. circ. 10,230. **Document type:** trade publication.
    Description: Covers the business travel industry in the Netherlands.

910.2   US
BUSINESS TRAVELER MAGAZINE. 1980. q. $24. National Association of Business Travel Agents, 3255 Wilshire Blvd., Ste. 1514, Los Angeles, CA 90010. TEL 213-382-3335. Ed. Stuart J. Faber. circ. 34,000.
    Description: Informs business travelers on the best hotels, cities, airlines and auto rental centers.

330   UK   ISSN 0309-9334
BUSINESS TRAVELLER. 1976. m. £37.80($41) Perry Publications (Holdings) PLC, 22 Redan Pl., London W2 4SZ, England. TEL 0171-229-7799. FAX 0171-229-9441. (U.S. addr: 51 E. 42nd St., Ste. 1806, New York, NY 10017. TEL 212-697-1700) Ed. Gillian Upton; Pub. David Hammond. adv. contact: David Hammond. illus.; index. circ. 47,500. **Indexed:** BMT. **Document type:** consumer publication.
    —SWETS.
    Description: Provides information for the regular traveller on every aspect of service provided by the travel industry.

910.202   HK   ISSN 0255-7312
BUSINESS TRAVELLER ASIA - PACIFIC. 1982. m. $80. Interasia Publications Ltd., 13th Fl., 200 Lockhart Rd., Hong Kong. TEL 511-9317. FAX 519-6846. TELEX 62107. Ed. Vijay Verghese. circ. 22,355. **Document type:** consumer publication.
    —BLDSC (2934.901000).

910.09   330   US
BUSINESS TRAVELLER INTERNATIONAL. 1988. m. $36. Perry Publications Ltd. (Subsidiary of: Perry Publications PLC), 51 E. 42nd St., Ste. 1806, New York, NY 10017-5404. TEL 212-697-1700. FAX 212-697-1005. (In UK: Compass House, 22 Redan Pl., London W2 4SZ, England) Ed. Kate Rice. adv.; bk.rev.; illus. circ. 42,000. (back issues avail.) **Document type:** consumer publication.
    Description: Provides travel tips, feature articles for the international business traveller.

910.09   US
BYWAYS (FAIRFAX). 1984. 6/yr. $17.95. National Motorcoach Network, Inc., Patriot Sq., 10527-C Braddock Rd., Fairfax, VA 22032. TEL 703-250-7897. FAX 703-250-1477. adv.; circ. 37,000.(controlled).
    Description: Features travel destinations in U.S. and Canada.

910.09   IE
C I E TRAVEL EXPRESS. 1972. m. free. (Covas Iompair Eireann) Marine and General Publicity Ltd., 127 Lower Baggot St., Dublin 2, Ireland. Ed. Cyril Ferris. adv. circ. 110,000.

914.504   IT   ISSN 0394-1434
C I R V I BOLLETTINO. (Text in English, French and Italian) 1980. s.a. L.30000 (foreign L.38000) (effective 1992). Centro Interuniversitario di Ricerche sul Viaggio in Italia, Str. Rivigliasco 6, 10024 Moncalieri, Italy. TEL 011-6407488. bk.rev.

918   AG   ISSN 0007-8859
C O T A L; la revista del turismo total. (Supplement avail.) (Text in English, Spanish; occasionally in Portuguese.) 1961. m. membership. (Confederacion de Organizaciones Turisticas de la America Latina) M. Seoane y Cia., S.A., Lavalle 357, 12th Fl., Ste. 124, Buenos Aires, 1047, Argentina. TEL 541-393-5598. FAX 541-111253. TELEX 23385 COTAL AR. Ed. Mario Seoane. adv.; abstr.; bibl.; illus.; stat.; index, cum.index. circ. 10,000.

910.202   US
C T P A NEWS. 1975. m. membership. California Travel Parks Association, Inc., Box 5648, Auburn, CA 95604. TEL 916-885-1624. FAX 916-823-6331. Ed. Judy Miller. adv. circ. 900. (back issues avail.) **Document type:** newsletter.
    Description: News of California, Nevada and Oregon RV park and campground industry.

914   FR   ISSN 0068-5151
CAHIERS DU TOURISME. SERIE A: FRANCE. 1963. irreg., no.38, 1991. price varies. Universite d'Aix-Marseille III (Universite de Droit, d'Economie et des Sciences), Centre des Hautes Etudes Touristiques, Immeuble Euroffice, 38 av. de l'Europe, B.P. 661, 13094 Aix-en-Provence Cedex 2, France. TEL 42-20-09-73. FAX 42-20-50-98. circ. 140. (back issues avail.) **Indexed:** World Agri.Econ.& Rural Sociol.Abstr. **Document type:** monographic series, academic/scholarly publication.

910.09   FR   ISSN 0768-3162
CAHIERS DU TOURISME. SERIE B: ETRANGER. 1966. irreg., no.76, 1994. price varies. Universite d'Aix-Marseille III (Universite de Droit, d'Economie et des Sciences), Centre des Hautes Etudes Touristiques, Immeuble Euroffice, 38 av. de l'Europe, B.P. 661, 13094 Aix-en-Provence Cedex 2, France. TEL 42-20-09-73. FAX 42-20-50-98. (back issues avail.) **Document type:** monographic series.

910.09   FR   ISSN 0768-0279
CAHIERS DU TOURISME. SERIE C: RECHERCHE FONDAMENTALE ET APPLIQUEE - METHODOLOGIE. 1963. irreg., no.188, 1994. price varies. Universite d'Aix-Marseille III (Universite de Droit, d'Economie et des Sciences), Centre des Hautes Etudes Touristiques, Immeuble Euroffice, 38 av. de l'Europe, B.P. 661, 13094 Aix-en-Provence Cedex 2, France. TEL 42-20-09-73. FAX 42-20-50-98. (back issues avail.) **Document type:** monographic series. —BLDSC (9101.579000).

910.09   340   FR   ISSN 0767-2667
CAHIERS DU TOURISME. SERIE E: LEGISLATION. irreg., no.18, 1982. price varies. Universite d'Aix-Marseille III (Universite de Droit, d'Economie et des Sciences), Centre des Hautes Etudes Touristiques, Immeuble Euroffice, 38 av. de l'Europe, B.P. 661, 13094 Aix-en-Provence Cedex 2, France. TEL 42-20-09-73. FAX 42-20-50-98. (back issues avail.) **Document type:** monographic series.

CALIFORNIA EVENTS ANNUAL. see TRANSPORTATION — Automobiles

917.904   US   ISSN 1052-5467
F866.2
CALIFORNIA HIGHWAYS. 1988. bi-m. $16.50. S & K Marketing, Inc., 8306 Wilshire Blvd., Ste. 7002, Beverly Hills, CA 90211. TEL 213-935-3107. adv.: B&W page $2675, color page $3680; trim 9 x 12. circ. 30,000.
    Description: Focuses on the beauty and splendor of the state through pictorials and journalism. Includes history, architecture, culture and travel.

CALIFORNIA INNTOUCH. see HOTELS AND RESTAURANTS

910.202   US
CALIFORNIA R V & CAMPING GUIDE. 1975. a. free. (California Travel Parks Association) Executive Services Group, Box 5578, Auburn, CA 95604. TEL 916-823-1076. FAX 916-823-6331. Ed. Judy Miller. adv. circ. 250,000. **Document type:** directory.

979.4 641.2   US
CALIFORNIA VISITORS REVIEW. 1981. w. $36. Box 92, E. Verano, CA 95433. TEL 707-938-3494. FAX 707-938-3673. Ed. Elsie Groves. adv. contact: Greg Martin. **Document type:** newspaper.
    Description: Visitors guide to Northern California wine country.

917 796.5   US
CAMPBOOK: CALIFORNIA - NEVADA. Cover title: R V and Tent Sites in California, Nevada. a. membership. American Automobile Association, 1000 AAA Dr., Heathrow, FL 32746-5063. TEL 407-444-8200. FAX 407-444-8204. circ. 455,000. **Document type:** consumer publication.
    Formerly (until 1980): California - Nevada Camping.

917 796.5   US
GV191.46.M4
CAMPBOOK: EASTERN CANADA. Cover title: R V and Tent Sites in New Brunswick, Newfoundland, Nova Scotia, Ontario, Prince Edward Island, Quebec. a. membership. American Automobile Association, 1000 AAA Dr., Heathrow, FL 32746-5063. TEL 407-444-8200. FAX 407-444-8204. adv.; illus. circ. 210,000. **Document type:** consumer publication.
    Formerly (until 1980): Eastern Canada Camping (ISSN 0363-2091)

910.202   US   ISSN 0734-8517
GV198.65.G7
CAMPBOOK: GREAT LAKES. Cover title: R V and Tent Sites in Illinois, Indiana, Michigan, Ohio, Wisconsin. a. membership. American Automobile Association, 1000 AAA Dr., Heathrow, FL 32746-5063. TEL 407-444-8200. FAX 407-444-8204. adv.; illus. circ. 254,000. **Document type:** consumer publication.
    Formerly (until 1981): Great Lakes Camping (ISSN 0363-5171)

917 796.5   US   ISSN 0734-2705
GV191.42.A84
CAMPBOOK: MIDEASTERN. Cover title: R V and Tent Sites in Delaware, District of Columbia, Maryland, New Jersey, Pennsylvania, Virginia, West Virginia. a. membership. American Automobile Association, 1000 AAA Dr., Heathrow, FL 32746-5063. TEL 407-444-8200. FAX 407-444-8204. adv.; illus. circ. 263,800. **Document type:** consumer publication.
    Formerly (until 1980): Mideastern Camping (ISSN 0147-7285)

917 796.5   US   ISSN 0732-2585
GV198.65.N67
CAMPBOOK: NORTH CENTRAL. Cover title: R V and Tent Sites in Iowa, Minnesota, Nebraska, North Dakota, South Dakota. a. membership. American Automobile Association, 1000 AAA Dr., Heathrow, FL 32746-5063. TEL 407-444-8200. FAX 407-444-8204. adv.; illus. circ. 214,400. **Document type:** consumer publication.
    Formerly (until 1980): North Central Camping (ISSN 0147-8613)

647.94   US   ISSN 0732-7315
GV191.42.N74
CAMPBOOK: NORTHEASTERN. Cover title: R V and Tent Sites in Connecticut, Maine, Massachusetts, New Hampshire, New York, Rhode Island, Vermont. a. American Automobile Association, 1000 AAA Dr., Heathrow, FL 32746-5063. TEL 407-444-8200. FAX 407-444-8204. adv.; illus. circ. 249,300. **Document type:** consumer publication.
  Former titles (until 1980): Northeastern Camping (ISSN 0196-6456); Northeastern Camping and Trailering.

917.8   US   ISSN 0732-2577
GV191.35
CAMPBOOK: NORTHWESTERN. Cover title: R V and Tent Sites in Idaho, Montana, Oregon, Washington, Wyoming. a. membership. American Automobile Association, 1000 AAA Dr., Heathrow, FL 32746-5063. TEL 407-444-8200. FAX 407-444-8204. adv.; illus. circ. 342,400. **Document type:** consumer publication.
  Former titles (until 1980): Northwestern Camping (ISSN 0095-4411); Northwestern Camping and Trailering.

917 796.5   US   ISSN 0731-535X
GV198.65.S68
CAMPBOOK: SOUTH CENTRAL. Cover title: R V and Tent Sites in Arkansas, Kansas, Missouri, Oklahoma, Texas. a. membership. American Automobile Association, 1000 AAA Dr., Heathrow, FL 32746-5063. TEL 407-444-8200. FAX 407-444-8204. adv.; illus. circ. 209,500. **Document type:** consumer publication.
  Formerly (until 1980): South Central Camping (ISSN 0364-7161)

917 796.5   US   ISSN 0731-5112
GV191.42.S83
CAMPBOOK: SOUTHEASTERN. Cover title: R V and Tent Sites in Alabama, Florida, Georgia, Kentucky, Louisiana, Mississippi, North Carolina, South Carolina, Tennessee. a. membership. American Automobile Association, 1000 AAA Dr., Heathrow, FL 32746-5063. TEL 407-444-8200. FAX 407-444-8204. adv.; illus. circ. 306,500. **Document type:** consumer publication.
  Formerly (until 1980): Southeastern Camping (ISSN 0162-9166)

917 796.5   US   ISSN 0731-8103
GV191.42.A165
CAMPBOOK: SOUTHWESTERN. Cover title: R V and Tent Sites in Arizona, Colorado, New Mexico, Utah. a. membership. American Automobile Association, 1000 AAA Dr., Heathrow, FL 32746-5063. TEL 407-444-8200. FAX 407-444-8204. adv.; illus. circ. 338,000. **Document type:** consumer publication.
  Formerly (until 1980): Southwestern Camping (ISSN 0094-2855)

917.12   US   ISSN 0732-5347
GV198.67.C2
CAMPBOOK: WESTERN CANADA AND ALASKA. Cover title: R V and Tent Sites in Alberta, British Columbia, Manitoba, Northwest Territories, Saskatchewan, Yukon Territory and Alaska. a. membership. American Automobile Association, 1000 AAA Dr., Heathrow, FL 32746-5063. TEL 407-444-8200. FAX 407-444-8204. adv.; illus. circ. 227,000. **Document type:** consumer publication.
  Formerly (until 1980): Western Canada. Alaska Camping.

910.09   UK   ISSN 0266-4437
CAMPING AND CARAVAN SITE SELECTOR. 1965. a. £2. Stone Leisure Ltd., 2a Granville Rd., Sidcup, Kent DA14 4BN, England. TEL 0181-302-6150. FAX 0181-300-2315. Ed. Bob Griffiths. adv. circ. 10,000. **Document type:** directory.

CAMPING DANMARK; godkendte campingpladser i Danmark. see SPORTS AND GAMES — Outdoor Life

910.202   IT
CAMPING IN ITALY. (Text in English, French, German, Spanish) 1985. q. free. Editoriale Eurocamp s.r.l., Via Durini n.3, 20122 Milan, Italy. TEL 02-76022377. FAX 02-76022430. Ed. Maria Paola Canegrati. adv.; bk.rev.; charts; illus. circ. 60,000. **Document type:** catalog.

CAMPING MAGAZINE. see SPORTS AND GAMES — Outdoor Life

CAMPING REVUE; Magazin des Oesterreichischen Camping Clubs. see SPORTS AND GAMES — Outdoor Life

917.104   US   ISSN 0884-1039
F1009
CANADA (YEAR). a. $18. Harper Collins Publishers, Birnbaum Travel Guides, 10 E 53rd St., New York, NY 10022-5299. TEL 212-207-7542. Ed. Alexandra Mayes Birnbaum.

917.104   UK
CANADA HOLIDAY GUIDE. a. (Canada Tourist Office) Phoenix Publishing & Media Ltd., 18-20 Scrutton St., London EC2A 4RJ, England. TEL 0171-247-0537. FAX 0171-377-2741. Ed. Mary Moore Mason; Pub. Maureen Miller. adv. contact: Kathryn McGowan. circ. 165,000 (paid). **Document type:** consumer publication.

916   UK   ISSN 0951-5267
CANADA NEWS. 1986. m. £15 (foreign £26.50). Outbound Newspapers, 1 Commercial Rd., Eastbourne, E. Sussex BN21 3XQ, England. TEL 01323-412001. FAX 01323-649249. Ed. Stephen Hartridge. adv.; bk.rev. circ. 25,000. (tabloid format) **Document type:** newspaper.
  Description: Gives potential migrants and travelers to Canada information about real estate, employment, education, investing and lifestyle.

917   CN   ISSN 1199-1615
CANADIAN TRAVEL PRESS. 1968. w. Can.$53.50. Baxter Publishing Co., 310 Dupont St., Toronto, ON M5R 1V9, Canada. TEL 416-968-7252. FAX 416-968-2377. Ed. Edith Baxter. adv. contact: Earl Lince. bk.rev.; circ. 13,000 (controlled). **Document type:** trade publication.
  Former titles (until 1994): Canadian Travel Press Weekly (ISSN 0831-9138); (until 1986): Canadian Travel Press (ISSN 0045-5490)
  Description: Provides timely coverage of events of concern to the travel industry and carries in-depth destination reports from around the world.

910.09   US
CANADIAN TRAVEL TO THE UNITED STATES. 1980. a. free. U.S. Travel and Tourism Administration, Office of Research, U.S. Department of Commerce, Main Commerce Bldg., Rm. 1868, Washington, DC 20230. TEL 202-482-4026. FAX 202-482-2887. stat. **Document type:** government publication.
  Description: Summarizes data on tourism to the U.S., nationally and by state.

917.1   CN   ISSN 1185-216X
CANADIAN TRAVELLER; an Altracs publication for the travel industry. 1983. m. Can.$40 (U.S. Can.$54, elsewhere Can.$72). Canadian Traveller, 115-5200 Miller Rd., Richmond, BC V7B 1K5, Canada. TEL 604-276-0818. FAX 604-276-0843. Ed. Doreen Ormiston; Pub. J. Frazer. adv.: B&W page Can.$2120, color page Can.$2820; trim 8 1/8 x 10 7/8; adv. contact: Doug Deyagher. circ. 12,782 (paid). **Document type:** trade publication.
  Former titles (until 1991): TravelTrade Canada (ISSN 0841-9191); (until 1988): TravelTrade, Travelexchange (ISSN 0841-9183); (until 1988): Travelexchange (ISSN 0841-9175)

917.204   US   ISSN 1055-5641
F1333
CANCUN, COZUMEL, AND ISLA MUJERES. a. $12. Harper Collins Publishers, Birnbaum Travel Guides, 10 E. 53rd St., New York, NY 10022-5299. TEL 212-207-7542. Ed. Alexandra Mayes Birnbaum. illus.; index.
  Description: Includes beaches, scuba and snorkeling spots.

917.204   MX
CANCUN TIPS. (Text in English) 1987. q. $12. Cancun Tips S.A., Av. Tulum no.29 S.M. 5, Ste. 102, Cancun, Q. Roo, Mexico C.P. 77500, Mexico. TEL 988-4-40-44. (US addr.: 12403 Nacogdoches St., Ste. 110, San Antonio, TX 78217) Ed. Victor Vera. circ. 90,000. (tabloid format; back issues avail.)
  Formerly: Cancun Scene.
  Description: Tourist information and tips on vacationing in Cancun and surrounding areas.

910.4   US
CAPE COD & ISLANDS ATLAS AND GUIDE BOOK. a. $14.95. Butterworth Company of Cape Cod, 38 Rt. 134, S. Dennis, MA 02660. TEL 508-432-8200. FAX 508-760-2003. Ed. Rod Schou. adv. contact: Christopher Schou. circ. 30,000. **Document type:** consumer publication.
  Description: Complete detailed maps and guide information for all Cape Cod towns and the islands of Martha's Vineyard and Nantucket, plus sections on Cape Cod living, the national seashore, outdoor activities and 80 fresh water fishing maps.

917.4   US
CAPE COD GUIDE. 1946. 3/yr. $5. M P G Specialty Publications, Box 1416, Plymouth, MA 02362-1416. TEL 508-760-2027. FAX 508-747-2148. Pub. Sheryl Woodford. adv. circ. 900,000.

974   US
CAPE COD RESORT DIRECTORY. 1921. a. free. Cape Cod Chamber of Commerce Inc., Routes 6 and 132, Hyannis, MA 02601. TEL 508-362-3225. adv. circ. 250,000. **Document type:** directory.

917.504   US
CAPITAL MAGAZINE. 1974. m. $12. Cappub, Inc., 300 Mill St., Vienna, VA 22180-4524. FAX 703-938-4562. adv.; circ. 70,000 (controlled).

917.504   UK
CAPITAL REGION U S A. a. Phoenix Publishing & Media Ltd., 18-20 Scrutton St., London EC2A 4RJ, England. TEL 0171-247-0537. FAX 0171-377-2741. (Dist. in US by: Northeast Media Group, 273 Post Rd. W., Westport, CT 06880. TEL 203-226-8151. FAX 203-227-1106) Ed. Mary Moore Mason; Pub. Maureen Miller. adv. contact: Kathryn McGowan. circ. 95,000. **Document type:** consumer publication.
  Description: Holiday and travel planner aimed at consumers in Scandinavia and the United Kingdom.

914.504   IT
▼**CAPRI REVIEW.** 1994. s-a. P R C s.r.l., Via Germanico 197, 00192 Rome, Italy. TEL 39-6-3243010. FAX 39-6-3242857. Ed. Antonio Di Raimondo. adv.: color page L.7000000. **Document type:** consumer publication.

388.3   US
CAR & TRAVEL. 1947. bi-m. $4 to non-members; members $2. American Automobile Association, 1000 A A A Dr., Heathrow, FL 32746-5063. TEL 407-444-8544. FAX 407-444-8030. Ed. Douglas H. Damerst. adv.; charts; illus. circ. 3,400,000.
  Formerly (until Mar. 1995): A A A World (Heathrow); Supersedes (in 1981): American Motorist (ISSN 0199-0268)
  Description: Devoted to travel and automotive concerns.

CAR & TRAVEL (CENTRAL WEST JERSEY EDITION). see TRANSPORTATION — Automobiles

CAR & TRAVEL (NEW YORK METRO EDITION). see TRANSPORTATION — Automobiles

614.86 388.3   US   ISSN 1080-2339
G149
CAR & TRAVEL (SOUTHERN PENNSYLVANIA). 1930. bi-m. $4. American Automobile Association, 1000 AAA Drive, Heathrow, FL 32746-5063. TEL 407-444-7900. FAX 407-444-7380. Ed. Donna Sizemore. adv.; illus. circ. 124,000. **Document type:** newsletter.
  Former titles (until Mar. 1995): A A A World (Southern Pennsylvania) (ISSN 1063-3847); (until 1992): A A A Traveler (York) (ISSN 0746-0007); Motorist; Johnstown Motorist (ISSN 0047-2042); White Rose Motorist (ISSN 0043-4981); South Penn Traveler (US 0273-8147); South Penn Motorist (US 0038-3503).

TRAVEL AND TOURISM

796.7 US ISSN 1080-2355
CAR & TRAVEL (WISCONSIN EDITION). 1937. bi-m. $4 to non-members (foreign $7). American Automobile Association, A A A Wisconsin, Box 33, Madison, WI 53701-0033. TEL 608-828-2486. FAX 608-828-2443. Ed. Ernest Stetenfeld. adv.; bk.rev.; charts; illus. circ. 263,535. **Document type:** consumer publication.
  Former titles (until 1995): A A A World: Wisconsin Edition (ISSN 0277-1411); (until 1981): A A A Traveler (Madison) (ISSN 0162-3591); Wisconsin A A A Motor News (ISSN 0043-6348)

910.2 UK ISSN 0269-8730
CARAVAN & CHALET PARKS GUIDE. a. £3. Haymarket Magazines Ltd., 38-42 Hampton Rd., Teddington, Middx. TW11 0JE, England. TEL 081-943-5000. TELEX 895-2440-HAYMRT-G. circ. 30,000.
  Formerly: Caravan and Chalet Sites Guide (ISSN 0069-0317).
  Description: Lists over 3,000 caravan and chalet sites.

796 SA ISSN 0379-4636
CARAVAN AND OUTDOOR LIFE. 1960. m. R.40 (foreign $25). Caravan Publications (Pty) Ltd., P.O. Box 15939, Vlaeberg 8018, South Africa. TEL 27-21-241457. FAX 27-21-261809. Ed. Godfrey Castle; Pub. Godfrey Castle. adv.: B&W page $800, color page $1383; trim 210 x 276; adv. contact: Allan Caddick. bk.rev. circ. 23,000. **Document type:** consumer publication.
  Formerly: Caravan.
  Description: Articles on travel and tourism for caravans(trailers), motorhomes, camping and backpacking. Includes vehicle tests, tips and hints for readers.

910.202 AT
CARAVAN BUYERS MANUAL. 1946. a. Aus.$3.25. Syme Magazines (Subsidiary of: Syme Media Pty. Ltd.), G.P.O. Box 628E, Melbourne, Vic. 3000, Australia.

914 388.3 UK
CARAVAN HOLIDAYS. 1980. q. £5. Gildea & Co. Ltd., Ste. 14D, Monkscoole House, Rathcoole, Co. Antrim BT37 9DA, N. Ireland. Ed. Andrew Gildea.

914 UK
CARAVAN INDUSTRY. 1969. m. £15.50 includes Directory (foreign £19.50) (effective 1996). A.E. Morgan Publications Ltd., Stanley House, 9 West St., Epsom, Surrey KT18 7RL, England. TEL 01372-741411. FAX 01372-744493. Ed. G.D. Ritchie; Pub. Terence Morgan. adv. contact: Doreen Reed. bk.rev. **Document type:** trade publication.
  Formerly: Caravan Business Plus Caravan Industry (ISSN 0268-5558); Formed by the 1985 merger of: Caravan Business; Caravan Industry and Park Operator (ISSN 0045-5725)
  Description: Trade magazine for the caravan market, developments, advice and special features for park operators, dealers and manufacturers.

910.202 UK ISSN 0957-6282
CARAVAN LIFE. 1987. m. £24 (foreign £42). Sanglier Publications Ltd., The Maltings, West St., Bourne, Lincs. PE10 9PH, England. TEL 01778-393313. FAX 01778-425437. Ed. Stuart Craig. adv. circ. 18,147. (back issues avail.) **Document type:** consumer publication.

914.2 UK ISSN 0268-0440
CARAVAN MAGAZINE. 1933. m. £36.10. Link House Magazines Ltd., Link House, Dingwall Ave., Croydon, Surrey CR9 2TA, England. TEL 0181-686-2599. FAX 0181-760-0973. Ed. Barry Williams. adv.; bk.rev.; charts; illus. circ. 25,778. **Document type:** consumer publication.
  Formerly: Caravan (ISSN 0008-6142); Which incorporated: Caravanning Monthly; Which incorporated (in Feb. 1978): Modern Caravanning; Which was formerly: Modern Caravan (ISSN 0026-7554)
  Description: Informational and feature articles pertaining to touring trailer and motorized caravans, with reviews of products and equipment, technical advice, and ratings of sites.

910.2 914 UK
CARAVAN SITES. 1955. a. Link House Magazines Ltd., Link House, Dingwall Ave., Croydon, Surrey CR9 2TA, England. TEL 0181-686-2599. FAX 0181-760-0973. Ed. B. Williams. **Document type:** consumer publication.
  Formerly: Caravan Sites and Mobile Home Parks (ISSN 0069-0309).
  Description: Lists caravan sites in Great Britain for trailer caravans, motor caravans, caravan holiday homes, and mobile homes.

910.202 AT ISSN 0313-1823
CARAVAN TEST. 1970. s-a. Aus.$2.75. David Syme & Co. Limited, 250 Spencer St., Melbourne, Vic. 3000, Australia.

388.346 AT ISSN 1320-2111
CARAVAN WORLD AND OUTDOOR LIFE. 1970. m. Aus.$34. David Syme & Co. Limited, 250 Spencer St., Melbourne, Vic. 3000, Australia. TEL 03-601-2903. FAX 03-642-0852. Ed. John Green. adv.; charts; illus. circ. 20,000.
  Former titles: Australian Caravan World and Camper Trailering; Australian Caravan World.
  Description: News about driving and camping in Australia.

796.5 910.202 IT ISSN 1121-7227
CARAVANING. CARAVAN & CAMPER; vacanze turismo auto. Key Title: Caravan e Camper. 1975. m. L.80000. Edimedia s.r.l., Via Sant'Erasmo 11, 00184 Rome, Italy. TEL 39-6-70000718. FAX 39-6-7000648. Ed. Maurizio Testa. adv.: B&W page L.4620000, color page L.8250000. circ. 56,000.
  Formerly (until 1987): Caravanning. Vacanze Turismo (ISSN 1121-7219).

388.3 US ISSN 0008-6193
CARAVANNER. 1954. q. free to qualified personnel. Airstream, Inc., 419 W. Pike St., Jackson Center, OH 45334. TEL 513-596-6111. FAX 614-596-6092. illus.; circ. 350,000 (controlled).

919.704 US ISSN 1065-9714
F2165
CARIBBEAN (YEAR). Key Title: Birnbaum's Caribbean. a. $18. Harper Collins Publishers, Birnbaum Travel Guides, 10 E. 53rd St., New York, NY 10022-5299. TEL 212-207-7542. Ed. Alexandra Mayes Birnbaum.
  Supersedes in part: Caribbean, Bermuda, and the Bahamas (Year) (ISSN 0883-248X)
  Description: Includes 40 idyllic island destinations.

CARIBBEAN AVIATION AND TOURISM NEWS/NOTICIERO AERONAUTICO Y TURISMO CARIBENSE. see AERONAUTICS AND SPACE FLIGHT

CARIBBEAN DATELINE. see BUSINESS AND ECONOMICS — Investments

910.202 UK ISSN 0967-4748
CARIBBEAN ISLANDS HANDBOOK. 1990. a. £14.95. Trade & Travel Publications Ltd., 6 Riverside Ct., Lower Bristol Rd., Bath BA2 3DZ, England. TEL 01225-469141. FAX 01225-469461. (Dist. in N. America by: Passport Books, NTC Publishing Group, 4255 W. Touhy Ave., Lincolnwood, IL 60646-1975. TEL 708-679-5500. FAX 708-679-6375) Eds. Ben Box, Sarah Cameron. **Document type:** directory.

910.09 US ISSN 0891-9496
F2171.3
CARIBBEAN TRAVEL AND LIFE. 1986. bi-m. $19.95. Caribbean Travel and Life, Inc., 8403 Colesville Rd., Ste. 830, Silver Spring, MD 20910. TEL 301-588-2300. FAX 301-588-2256. Ed. Veronica Gould Stoddart. adv.; bk.rev.; circ. 118,000 (paid).
  Description: Targeted toward a sophisticated, up-scale audience. Articles and photographs devoted to the unique vacation, recreational, cultural opportunities available throughout the island chain of the Caribbean, the Bahamas, and Bermuda.

910.09 640 CN
CARIBOO CHILCOTIN COAST ADVENTURE PLANNER. (Graeme/Drew) 1963. a. free. (Cariboo Tourism Association) Altracs Publishing, P.O. Box 4900, Williams Lake, BC V2G 2V8, Canada. TEL 604-392-2226. FAX 604-392-2838. Ed. Marilynne Prupas. circ. 70,000. **Document type:** directory.
  Formerly (until 1995): Cariboo Chilcotin Coast Travel Guide.

910.09 US
CARNIVAL CURRENTS. 3/yr. International Voyager Media, 29C E. St., S. Salem, NY 10590. TEL 914-533-6830. Ed. Barbara Coats. adv. circ. 619,133.

914 PO
CARTAZ; revista mensal de cultura e informacao e turismo. vol. 6, 1970. m. Avenida de Roma 72, 1 Esq. Frente, Lisbon, Portugal. Ed. A. Borges Pires. adv.; charts; illus.

CASINO DIGEST. see SPORTS AND GAMES

CATALOGUE OF CANADIAN RECREATION AND LEISURE RESEARCH. see LEISURE AND RECREATION

910.09 US
CAVES AND CAVERNS; national caves association directory. 1973. a. free. National Caves Association, 4138 Dark Hollow Rd., McMinnville, TN 37110. TEL 615-668-3925. FAX 615-668-3988. Ed. Barbara Munson. circ. 600,000. **Document type:** directory.
  Description: Includes name, address and phone number of current NCA members. Supplies locator map and many pictures.

910.202 UY
CENTAUR. 1977. a. Centro Automovilista del Uruguay, Artigas 1773, Montevideo, Uruguay. Ed. Ever Cabrera Tornielli. adv. Indexed: Anim.Breed.Abstr.

914.704 US
CENTRAL WISCONSIN RESORTER. 1965. w. $30 out of county. Box 838, Wautoma, WI 54982. TEL 414-787-3334. Ed. Mary Kunasch. adv. circ. 11,000.

CENTUR. see TRANSPORTATION — Automobiles

910.202 US
CHANGING PLACES.* m. newsstand price: $4.95. International Publishers Group, 26 Sixth St., Ste. 514, Stamford, CT 06905-4606. TEL 203-656-3913; 800-935-6171. FAX 203-656-2774. adv. **Document type:** consumer publication.

910.04 GW ISSN 0934-5140
CHECK-IN; das Magazin fuer Geschaeftsreisende Business & Pleasure. 1988. bi-m. DM.42 (foreign DM.48). Verlag Moderne Industrie AG, Ingolstaedter Str. 20, 80807 Munich, Germany. TEL 089-35093160. FAX 089-35093187. TELEX 5215777. Ed. Gerd Otto-Rieke. adv.; bk.rev. circ. 80,000. (back issues avail.) **Document type:** consumer publication.
  Formerly (until March, 1988): Fliegen.
  Description: Magazine for business travelers.

914.2 UK
CHERWELL OXFORD INTRODUCTION. 1948. a. Oxford Student Publications Ltd., 7 St. Aldates, Oxford OX1 1BS, England. TEL 01865-246461. FAX 01865-200321. Ed. Lucy Manning; Pub. Rob Crothers. adv. contact: Adrienne Lam. circ. 6,000.
  Formerly: Cherwell Guide to Oxford (ISSN 0955-4165)

CHESAPEAKE BAY MAGAZINE. see SPORTS AND GAMES — Boats And Boating

917.704 US ISSN 1056-4365
CHICAGO (YEAR). a. $12. Harper Collins Publishers, Birnbaum Travel Guides, 10 E. 53rd St., New York, NY 10022-5299. TEL 212-207-7542. Ed. Alexandra Mayes Birnbaum. illus.; index.

CHICAGO ARCHITECTURE FOUNDATION NEWS. see ARCHITECTURE

TRAVEL AND TOURISM 6459

917 US ISSN 0362-4595
F548.1
CHICAGO MAGAZINE. 1952. m. $19.90. K-III Magazine Corporation, 414 N. Orleans, Chicago, IL 60610. TEL 312-222-8999; 800-999-0879. Ed. Richard Babcock. adv.; bk.rev.; illus. circ. 165,000. (also avail. in microfiche from UMI) **Indexed:** Access (1975-), Art & Archaeol.Tech.Abstr., Mag.Ind. —UMI.
Former titles (until 1976): Chicago Guide (ISSN 0042-9651); (until 1970): W F M T Guide.

910 917.7 US
CHICAGOLAND DINING GUIDE. 1981. a. P B Communications, Inc., 874 Green Bay Rd., Winnetka, IL 60093. TEL 708-441-7892. Ed. Asher J. Birnbaum. adv.; illus. circ. 60,000. **Document type:** consumer publication.
Former titles: Chicagoland Dining and Nightlife Guide; North Shore Dining Guide.
Description: Guide to Chicago area nightlife and dining.

910.2 914 UK
CHILDREN WELCOME! FAMILY HOLIDAY GUIDE. 1952. a. £3.80. F H G Publications Ltd., Abbey Mill Business Centre, Seedhill, Paisley PA1 1JN, Scotland. TEL 0141-887-0428. FAX 0141-889-7204. Ed. Peter Clark. adv.
Formerly: Family Holiday Guide (ISSN 0071-3740); Formed by merger of: Children Welcome (ISSN 0069-3456); Holiday Guide.
Description: Holiday guidebook covering hotels and guesthouses where children are welcome.

CHINA GUIDEBOOK. see *GENERAL INTEREST PERIODICALS — China*

951.04 HK
CHINA TOURISM. French Edition: Voyage en Chine. Chinese edition: Zhongguo Luyou. (Editions in Chinese, English) 1980. m. $38 for English ed.; Chinese ed. $29. Hong Kong China Tourism Press, 24F Westlands Centre, 20 Westlands Rd., Quarry Bay, Hong Kong, Hong Kong. TEL 852-2560-8001. FAX 852-2561-8196. TELEX 822225-HKCTP-HX. (US subscr. to: China Books & Periodicals, 2929 24th St, San Francisco, CA 94110) adv.; illus.; cum.index. circ. 80,000. (back issues avail.)
Former titles: Culture, Arts and Crafts; China Tourism Pictorial.
Description: Contains feature articles on sights, scenery, customs, travel experiences, recent archeological discoveries, and places of historical interest. Also contains regular articles on hotels and shopping.

910.202 HK
CHINA TRAVEL PRESS. (Text in English) 1986. m. $15. Ismay Publications Co., C.C. Wu Bldg., Rm. 2204, 302-308 Hennessy Rd., Wanchai, Hong Kong. TEL 5752270. FAX 8345647. Ed. Shann Davies. adv. circ. 7,000.

910.4 US
CHINCOTEAGUE BEACHCOMBER. 1959. 20/yr. free. Box 249, Onley, VA 23418-0249. TEL 804-787-1200. FAX 804-787-9567. Ed. Bill Sterling. circ. 10,000.

639.950968 SA
CHRIS AND TILDE STUART'S GUIDE TO SOUTHERN AFRICAN GAME & NATURE RESERVES. 3rd ed., 1994. irreg. R.79.99. Struik Publishers, P.O. Box 1144, Cape Town 8000, South Africa. TEL 27-21-4624360. FAX 27-21-4624379. Eds. Chris & Tilde Stuart. illus.

CICLOTURISMO. see *SPORTS AND GAMES — Bicycles And Motorcycles*

910.4 IT
CIOCIARIA; ieri, oggi, domani. (Special editions avail.) vol.7, 1987. bi-m? Ente Provinciale per il Turismo di Frosinone, Piazzale de Matthaeis, Grattacielo L'Edera, Frosinone, Italy. TEL (0775)872525. Ed. Mario Grieco. adv.; charts; illus.
Description: Features information on tourism, art and culture.

CITY LINE NEWS. see *BUSINESS AND ECONOMICS — Economic Situation And Conditions*

CLUB DE GOURMETS; gastronomy & travel magazine - gastronomia y viajes. see *HOTELS AND RESTAURANTS*

917 US
CLUBMEX; Baja California, Sea of Cortez, Mexico's west coast, interior Mexico. 1976. m. $35 membership. Clubmex, Box 1646, Bonita, CA 91908-1646. TEL 619-585-3033. FAX 619-420-8133. Ed. Chuck Stein. adv. circ. 7,000. (back issues avail.) **Document type:** newsletter.
Formerly: Mexico West (ISSN 0889-7107)
Description: Contains articles, news, and announcements on vacations and travel to Mexico.

910.2 UK ISSN 0260-7573
COACHES & PARTIES WELCOME. 1977. a. free to qualified personnel. Lewis Productions Ltd., Unit 3, River Gardens Bus. Centre, Spur Rd., Feltham, Middx TW14 0SN, England. Ed. Jonathan Lewis. adv. circ. 40,000.

COASTAL CRUISING. see *SPORTS AND GAMES — Boats And Boating*

910.4 GW
COLOGNE. TRAVEL-REPORT; information for travel agents. (Text in English, French, German, Italian and Spanish) a. free. Verkehrsamt der Stadt Koeln, Unter Fettenhennen 19, 50667 Cologne, Germany. TEL 0221-221-3345. FAX 0221-221-3320. TELEX 8883421-TOC-D. Ed.Bd. circ. 50,000. **Document type:** trade publication.

910 CK
COLOMBIA. CORPORACION NACIONAL DE TURISMO. BOLETIN INFORMATIVO C E N T U R. 1978. q. free. Corporacion Nacional de Turismo, Centro de Informacion Turistico, Calle 28, 13A-15, Piso 17, Apdo. Aereo 8400, Bogota, Colombia. TEL 2843049. TELEX 441350 COTUR. circ. 700.

910 CK ISSN 0121-1870
COLOMBIA. CORPORACION NACIONAL DE TURISMO. CATALOGO NACIONAL DE TESIS DE TURISMO Y HOTELERIA. 1988. a. free. Corporacion Nacional de Turismo, Centro de Informacion y Turistica, Calle 28, 13A-15, Piso 17, Apdo. Aereo 8400, Bogota, Colombia. TEL 2843049. TELEX 441350 COTUR. bibl. circ. 500. **Document type:** bibliography.
Description: Bibliography of graduate study works done by hotel and tourism students in Colombia.

910 CK ISSN 0121-1889
COLOMBIA. CORPORACION NACIONAL DE TURISMO. CATALOGO TURISTICO. 1987. a. free. Corporacion Nacional de Turismo, Centro de Informacion Turistica, Calle 28, 13A-15, Piso 17, Apdo. Aereo 8400, Bogota, Colombia. TEL 2843049. TELEX 441350 COTUR. bibl. circ. 500. **Document type:** government publication, catalog.

910 CK
COLOMBIA. CORPORACION NACIONAL DE TURISMO. CRONICA TURISTICA. 1988. q. free. Corporacion Nacional de Turismo, Centro de Informacion Turistica, Calle 28, 13A-15, Piso 17, Apdo. Aereo 8400, Bogota, Colombia. TEL 2843049. TELEX 441350 COTUR. circ. 700.

910.09 US
COLORADO DIRECTORY OF CAMPING, CABINS, LODGES, FUN THINGS TO DO. 1980. a. free. (Colorado Association of Campground, Cabins & Lodges) Colorado Agency for Campgrounds, Cabins & Lodges, Inc., 5101 Pennsylvania Ave., Boulder, CO 80303. TEL 303-499-9343. FAX 303-499-9333. Ed. Hilton Fitt-Peaster; Pub. Jenny Fitt-Peaster. adv. circ. 400,000. (back issues avail.) **Document type:** directory.
Former titles: Colorado Directory of Camping, R Vs, Cabins, Fun Things to Do; Colorado Directory of Camping, Cabins, Rafting, Fun Things to Do.

917.88 US ISSN 0146-9991
COLORADO EXPRESS. 1972. s-a. $20 for 2 yrs. Box 18214, Capitol Hill Station, Denver, CO 80218. TEL 303-320-6976. Ed. Karl Kocivar. adv.; bk.rev.; bibl.; charts; illus.; cum.index for vols. 1-13 in vol. 13. circ. 18,000. (back issues avail.)
Description: Explores alternative cultures.

917.904 US ISSN 1063-763X
COLUMBIA GORGE MAGAZINE. 1990. q. $7.95. Gorge Publishing, Inc., 500 Morton Rd., Box 918, Hood River, OR 97031. TEL 503-386-7440. FAX 503-386-7480. Ed. Carol York; Pub. Pete Fotheringham. adv.: B&W page $1575, color page $2555; trim 8 3/8 X 10 7/8. circ. 60,000. **Document type:** consumer publication.
Description: Visitor and recreation guide to the Columbia River Gorge.

COMMERCIO E TURISMO ROMAGNOLO. see *BUSINESS AND ECONOMICS — Domestic Commerce*

COMMERCIO TURISMO SERVIZI. see *BUSINESS AND ECONOMICS — Domestic Commerce*

910.09 US ISSN 0893-9683
AP2
CONDE NAST'S TRAVELER; the truth in travel. 1954. m. $18 (Canada $32; elsewhere $33). Conde Nast Publications Inc., Conde Nast Traveler Magazine, 360 Madison Ave., New York, NY 10017. TEL 212-880-8800. FAX 212-880-2190. (Subscr. to: Box 57018, Boulder, CO 80322. TEL 800-777-0700) Ed. Thomas J. Wallace. adv. contact: Cara Ferragamo. bk.rev.; illus. circ. 909,092. (also avail. in microform from UMI) **Indexed:** Access (1988-1991), R.G. —UMI.
Formerly (until 1987): Signature (ISSN 0037-5039)

910.09 UK ISSN 0965-125X
CONFERENCE AND INCENTIVE TRAVEL. 1990. m. £45 (foreign £55). Haymarket Business Publications, 22 Lancaster Gate, London W2 3LP, England. TEL 0171-413-4307. FAX 0171-413-4509. (Subscr. to: P.O. Box 219, Woking, Surrey GU21 1ZW, England. TEL 01483-733880) Ed. Sara White; Pub. Andrew O'Kelly. adv. contact: Tim Waldron. bk.rev.; illus. circ. 15,107. **Indexed:** Art.Hosp.& Tour., Build.Manage.Abstr., Intl.Polym.Sci.& Tech., RAPRA. **Document type:** trade publication.
—BLDSC (3408.777500).
Formed by the merger of (1979-1990): Conference Britain (ISSN 0142-7474); (1985-1990): Incentive Travel World (ISSN 0950-0758); Incorporates (in 1993): C E I International (ISSN 0967-6279); Which was formerly (until 1990): Conference and Exhibitions International (ISSN 0260-8316); (until 1980): Conferences and Exhibitions (ISSN 0306-9397); (until 1974): Conferences, Exhibitions and Executive Travel (ISSN 0010-5597); Conference News.
Description: Reports on destinations and venues for the conference and incentive travel market.

CONGRESS TODAY E INCENTIVE TRAVEL. see *MEETINGS AND CONGRESSES*

914.406 FR ISSN 0336-9455
CONNAISSANCE DU PAYS D'OC. (Text in French and Occitan) 1973-1983; N.S. 1984. bi-m. 110 F. Editions de la Source, B.P. 1034, 34006 Montpellier Cedex, France. Ed. Jean Boekholt. adv.; bk.rev.; illus.

917.404 US ISSN 0746-8636
CONNECTICUT TRAVELER. 1983. m. membership. Connecticut Motor Club, Inc., 2276 Whitney Ave., Hamden, CT 06518. TEL 203-288-7441. Ed. Annette Cormany; Pub. Gerald L. Terwilliger. adv. circ. 184,000. (tabloid format) **Document type:** newspaper.
Description: Covers vacationing, weekending, recreation and entertainment.

974 US
CONNECTICUT VACATION GUIDE. 1950. a. free. Department of Economic Development, 865 Brook St., Rocky Hill, CT 06067. TEL 203-258-4355. circ. 450,000.

917 US
CONNECTICUT WEST. 1970. a. $2. Foothills Trader, Inc., 85 River Rd., Collinsville, CT 06022-1226. TEL 203-693-2990. FAX 203-693-2875. Ed. James Timpano. adv.; bibl. circ. 30,000.

910.202 UK
CONSTABULARY. 1980. bi-m. (Constabulary Travel Club) National Press Publishers, Peel House, 5 Balfour Rd., Weybridge, Surrey KT13 8HE, England. TEL 0932-859155. FAX 0932-859661. Ed. Chris Locke. adv.; bk.rev.; play rev. circ. 70,000.

TRAVEL AND TOURISM

658.8 NE ISSN 0165-6821
CONSUMENTEN REISGIDS. 1973. q. fl.27. Consumentenbond, Leeghwaterplein 26, 2521 CV The Hague, Netherlands. FAX 31-70-3847413. TELEX 33713. charts; illus. circ. 61,000. **Indexed:** Rural Recreat.Tour.Abstr., World Agri.Econ.& Rural Sociol.Abstr.
—SWETS.
  Description: Evaluation of trips and tourist attractions in all parts of the world. Covers hotel accomodation, transportation, sights, prices, and organized trips. Includes travel guide evaluation and maps.

910.202 640.73 US ISSN 0887-8439
CODEN: CRTLE3
CONSUMER REPORTS TRAVEL LETTER. 1985. m. $37 (foreign $43). Consumers Union of the United States, Inc., 101 Truman Ave., Yonkers, NY 10703-1057. TEL 914-378-2000. FAX 914-378-2906. (Subscr. to: Box 53629, Boulder, CO 80322-3629) Ed. Ed Perkins. circ. 60,000. (back issues avail.)
●Also available online. Vendor(s): Knight-Ridder, Inc. (File no.646).
—CASDDS.

914.7 388 UK
CONTINENTAL MOTORING HOLIDAYS. 1972. a. £50. Contemporary Press Ltd., 21A Alma Square, London NW8 9QA, England. Ed. Brian Hedges.

914 UK
CONTINENTAL MOTORING NEWS. m. £50. Travel Publications Ltd., 23 Elizabeth St., London SW1W 9RW, England. Ed. David Wickers. adv. circ. 45,000. **Document type:** bulletin.

COOL TRAVELER; literary publication about "place". see LITERATURE

914 DK
COPENHAGEN - THIS WEEK. m. Politikens Service Selskab A-S, Vestergade 4, DK-1456 Copenhagen K, Denmark. FAX 45-33-328674. Ed. John Jensen. adv. circ. 110,000.

914.2 UK
CORNWALL BLUE BOOK GUIDE AND COUNTY HANDBOOK. 1927. a. E.J. Hubber, Ed. & Pub., Carnmellyn, Newquay, Cornwall, Trenhaile TR8 5JL, England. adv. circ. 30,000.

910.9 US ISSN 0739-1587
CORPORATE & INCENTIVE TRAVEL. 1983. m. $55. Coastal Communications Corporation, 488 Madison Ave., New York, NY 10022. TEL 212-888-1500. FAX 212-888-8008. Ed. Harvey Grotsky. adv. circ. 60,069. **Document type:** trade publication.
  Description: Covers corporate meetings and incentive travel planners.

910.09 US
CORPORATE CRUISE NEWS. bi-m. free to qualified personnel. Landry & Kling, Inc., 1390 S. Dixie Hwy., Ste. 1207, Coral Gables, FL 33146-2943. TEL 305-661-1880. Ed. Josephine King. circ. controlled.

CORPORATE MEETINGS & INCENTIVES. see MEETINGS AND CONGRESSES

910 US ISSN 0882-8709
CORPORATE TRAVEL; news and ideas for business travel management. 1985. m. $65 (Canada & Mexico $67; elsewhere $125). Miller Freeman Inc. (New York) (Subsidiary of: United Newspapers Group), 1515 Broadway, New York, NY 10036. TEL 212-869-1300. FAX 212-302-6273. Ed. Julie Moline. adv. circ. 45,000. (tabloid format; back issues avail.)
—UnCover. CCC.

COREZE MAGAZINE; magazines de France. see GENERAL INTEREST PERIODICALS — France

CORRIERE DEL MEZZOGIORNO; il tridente. see POLITICAL SCIENCE

914.504 IT
CORTINA MAGAZINE. 1987. 3/yr. (Consorzio per lo Sviluppo Turistico si Cortina d'Ampezzo) Renografica s.r.l., Via Ca dell'Orbo 25, 40050 Villanova di Castenaso (BO), Italy. TEL 39-436-866488. FAX 39-436-866588. Ed. Gianni Milani. adv.: page L.7500000. **Document type:** consumer publication.

914 IT ISSN 0045-8716
COSMORAMA; viaggi e turismo. 1960. q. L.3000. Compagnia Italiana Turismo, Piazza della Repubblica 68, Rome, Italy. adv.; bk.rev.; illus.

COSTA RICA ADVENTURE & BUSINESS. see GENERAL INTEREST PERIODICALS — Costa Rica

914.502 IT
COSTA SMERALDA MAGAZINE. (Text and summaries in English and Italian) 1975. q. L.50000. (Consorzio Costa Smeralda) Servizi Consortili Costa Smeralda, 07020 Porto Cervo, Sardinia, Italy. Ed. Claudio Miorelli. adv.: page L.8000000; adv. contact: Maurizio Cinquanta. bk.rev. circ. 40,000. (back issues avail.)

COUNTRY HOMES & INTERIORS. see INTERIOR DESIGN AND DECORATION

330 US ISSN 0898-560X
TX901
COUNTRY INNS, BED & BREAKFAST. 1986. bi-m. $19.95. Country Inns Publications, Inc., Box 182, S. Orange, NJ 07079-0182. TEL 201-762-7090. FAX 201-762-1491. Ed. Gail Rudder Kent. adv.; bk.rev. circ. 257,000. **Document type:** consumer publication.
  Description: Covers country inns and bed and breakfast across the United States, international features, interior design, and gourmet dining.

910.202 US
COUNTRY LIVING HOLIDAYS. a. $2.95. Hearst Magazines, 250 W. 55th St., New York, NY 10019. TEL 212-649-4184. FAX 212-262-1238. **Document type:** consumer publication.

910.202 US
COUNTRY LIVING TRAVELS. a. $2.95. Hearst Magazines, 250 W. 55th St., New York, NY 10019. TEL 212-694-4184. FAX 212-262-1238. **Document type:** consumer publication.

910.202 UK
COUNTRYSIDE CONFERENCE VENUES IN BRITAIN (YEAR). a. £6.99. (English National Tourist Board) Kogan Page Ltd., 120 Pentonville Rd., London N1 9JN, England. TEL 071-278-0433. FAX 071-837-6348. TELEX 263088-KOGAN-G. **Document type:** directory.

910.202 CN ISSN 0709-2679
COUP D'OEIL SUR LE SAGUENAY-LAC-SAINT-JEAN.* 1978. q. Can.$5. Promotions Gaston Maziade Enr., 1048 d'Avaugour, Chicoutimi, Que. G7H 2T1, Canada. TEL 418-696-4805. Ed. Gaston Maziade. circ. 22,500.

910.09 US ISSN 0279-4489
COURIER (LEXINGTON). 1974. m. $36. National Tour Association, Inc., 546 E. Main St., Lexington, KY 40508-2342. TEL 606-253-1036. FAX 606-231-9837. Ed. William A. Bowden. adv.; circ. 5,200 (controlled).

910.09 382 US
CRAIGHEAD'S COUNTRY REPORTS. 1988. m. $95 per no. Craighead Publications Inc., Box 1253, Darien, CT 06820-1253. **Document type:** trade publication.
  Formerly: Craighead's International Executive Travel and Relocation Service.
  Description: Seventy-seven country reports discussing what it's like to live and do business overseas.

910.09 US ISSN 1058-3904
HF5549.5.E45
CRAIGHEAD'S INTERNATIONAL BUSINESS, TRAVEL AND RELOCATION GUIDE. biennial. $460. Gale Research Inc., 835 Penobscot Bldg., Detroit, MI 48226. TEL 313-961-2242. FAX 313-961-6637. **Document type:** directory.
  Description: Contains business, travel and cultural information on over 80 countries for individuals who do business overseas.

910.202 US ISSN 0210-3532
CRASH. 1992. q. $5 (foreign $9). Scribble Unlimited Productions, 519 Castro St., Ste. 7, San Francisco, CA 94114. TEL 415-206-1822. Eds. Miles Poindexter, John Labovitz. adv.: B&W page $35; trim 4 7/8 x 7 7/8. bk.rev.; circ. 1,000 (paid). (back issues avail.) **Document type:** newsletter.
  Formerly: Crash Update.
  Description: Includes descriptions of places to visit, advise on traveling cheaply, tales of successful crashes, alternative travel information, and letters from around the world.

910.09 AT
CRESCENT CHATTER. 1973. w. Crescent Head Country Club Ltd., 1 Rankine St., Crescent Head, N.S.W. 2440, Australia. Ed. Brian Bowyer. bk.rev. circ. 500.

910.09 US ISSN 0898-4867
CRUISE AND VACATION VIEWS; leisure travel sales and marketing. 1987. bi-m $20 (free to qualified personnel). Orban Communications, Inc., 60 E. 42nd St., Ste. 905, New York, NY 10165-0905. TEL 212-867-7470. FAX 212-682-4437. Ed. Michael Brown. adv.; circ. 35,000 (controlled). **Document type:** trade publication.
  Formerly (until 1991): Cruise Views.

917.14 US ISSN 0893-1240
CRUISE INDUSTRY NEWS. Key Title: Cruise Industry News (Newsletter). 1985. s-m. $485. Nissen-Lie Communications, Inc., 441 Lexington Ave., Ste. 1209 A, New York, NY 10017. TEL 212-986-1025. FAX 212-986-1033. Ed. Oivind Mathisen. circ. 2,000. **Document type:** trade publication.
  Description: Inside news report of the cruise shipping industry in North America.

917.04 US ISSN 1047-3378
CRUISE INDUSTRY NEWS ANNUAL. 1988. a. $445. Nissen-Lie Communications, Inc., 441 Lexington Ave., Ste. 1209 A, New York, NY 10017. TEL 212-986-1025. FAX 212-986-1033. Ed. Oivind Mathisen. circ. 1,100. **Document type:** trade publication.
  Former titles: Cruise Industry Annual (Year); North American Cruise Industry (Year).
  Description: Covers the cruise shipping industry worldwide.

917.14 US
CRUISE INDUSTRY NEWS QUARTERLY. 1985. q. $20. Nissen-Lie Communications, Inc., 441 Lexington Ave., Ste. 1209 A, New York, NY 10017. TEL 212-986-1025. FAX 212-986-1033. circ. 10,000. **Document type:** trade publication.
  Description: For cruise industry professionals.

910.09 US
CRUISE TRADE. m. Travel Trade Publications, 15 W. 44th St., New York, NY 10036. TEL 212-730-6600. FAX 212-730-7137. Ed. Joel M. Abels. adv. circ. 36,983.
  Description: Provides cruise sellers with news and marketing tools.

910.09 US ISSN 0199-5111
CRUISE TRAVEL; ships, ports, schedules, prices. 1979. bi-m. $18. World Publishing Co. (Subsidiary of: Century Publishing Company), 990 Grove St., Evanston, IL 60201. TEL 708-491-6440. FAX 718-491-0459. (Subscr. to: Box 342, Mt. Morris, IL 61054-0342) Ed. Robert Meyers. adv.; charts; illus.; stat. circ. 225,000. (also avail. in microfiche; microfilm; reprint service avail. from UMI) **Document type:** consumer publication.
—UMI.

910.91 US
CRUISELETTER. 1992. m. $24. Seaspray Publishing, Inc., R.D. 2, Box 736, Sussex, NJ 07461. TEL 201-827-1435. Ed. Janet Gregory. adv.; bk.rev.; index. (looseleaf format; back issues avail.) **Document type:** consumer publication, newsletter.
  Description: Publishes articles written for and by cruise-ship passengers. Reviews cruise ships, ports, and special-interest cruises for families, gays, singles, and handicapped persons.

910.09 US ISSN 1060-0086
CRUISES AND TOURS. 1992. q. $15.80. Vacation Publications, Inc., 1502 Augusta Dr., Ste. 415, Houston, TX 77057. TEL 713-974-6903. FAX 713-974-0445. adv. circ. 50,000. **Document type:** consumer publication.
  Incorporates: Cruise Vacations.

TRAVEL AND TOURISM

910.09 US
CRUISING WITH CHILDREN. a. $22 (Canada Can.$33; overseas $27) (effective 1995-1996). Travel With Your Children (TWYCH), 45 W. 18th St., 7th Fl., New York, NY 10011. TEL 212-206-0688. FAX 212-645-5942. Pub. Dorothy Jordon.
   Description: Provides detailed information on more than 100 cruise ships and their ammenities for children.

910.202 CU
CUBA NOTICIAS TURISTICAS. m. Instituto Nacional del Turismo, Malecon y G, Vedado, Havana, Cuba. TEL 7-32-9881. TELEX 511955.

910.4 382 CY
CYPRUS. TOURISM ORGANISATION. ANNUAL REPORT. (Editions in Greek and English) 1972. a. Tourism Organisation, 19 Leoforos Lemesou, P.O. Box 4535, Nicosia, Cyprus. TEL 357-2-315715. FAX 357-2-313022. TELEX CYTOUR CY. charts; stat. circ. 2,600. **Document type:** corporate report, government publication.

910.4 338 CY ISSN 0256-1069
CYPRUS TIME OUT; tourist and business guide. (Text in English) 1978. m. $48. Comarts, Pygmalionos Sts., Christophides Bldg., 2nd Fl., A.P. 9, P.O. Box 3697, Nicosia, Cyprus. TEL 357-2-452079. FAX 357-2-360668. Ed. Lyn Haviland; Pub. Ellada Sophocleous. adv.: B&W page £C80; adv. contact: Myria Oleovoulou. bk.rev.: circ. 8,000. (back issues avail.) **Document type:** directory.

910.2 GW ISSN 0078-3943
D C C - CAMPING FUEHRER EUROPA. 1950. a. DM.29.80. (Deutscher Camping Club e.V.) D C C-Wirtschaftsdienst und Verlag GmbH, Postfach 400428, 80704 Munich, Germany. TEL 089-380142-0. FAX 089-334737. adv. circ. 100,000. **Document type:** consumer publication.

647.94 GW
D J H; Informationen Meinungen Berichte. 1951. bi-m. DM.18. Deutsches Jugendherbergswerk, Postfach 1455, 32704 Detmold, Germany. TEL 05231-74010. FAX 05231-740167. Ed. Gabriele Greenlee; Pub. Andreas Geiger. bk.rev.; illus. circ. 4,000. **Document type:** bulletin.
   Description: Provides news and information for the staff of the German Youth Hostel Association.

910.09 GW ISSN 0931-1807
D L T FLUGZEIT. (Text in English and German) 4/yr. free on board Lufthansa flights. (D L T Luftverkehrsgesellschaft mbH) Koesler Verlag GmbH, Von-Werth-Str. 44, 50670 Cologne, Germany. TEL 0221-131366. FAX 0221-137541. TELEX 889990-RSB-D. circ. 40,000.

910.202 UK
DAILY TELEGRAPH SEASONS. 1991. q. National Press Publishers, Peel House, 5 Balfour Rd., Weybridge, Surrey KT13 8HE, England. TEL 0932-859155. FAX 0932-859661. Ed. Chris Locke. adv. circ. 12,000.

DAMPF UND REISE; Bahnerlebnisse rund um die Welt - Ueberseeische Bahnen. see *TRANSPORTATION — Railroads*

910.09 301.415 US
DAMRON ADDRESS BOOK. 1964. a. $13.95. Damron Company, Inc., P.O. Box 42-2458, San Francisco, CA 94142-2458. TEL 415-255-0404. FAX 415-703-9049. Eds. Rovert Ian Philips, Gina M. Gatta. adv. circ. 100,000.
   Formerly: Bob Damron's Address Book.
   Description: Gay pocket guide for U.S., Canada, Mexico and the Caribbean.

910.202 US
DAMRON ROAD ATLAS. 1989. biennial. $13.95. Damron Company, Inc., P.O. Box 42-2458, San Francisco, CA 94142-2458. TEL 415-255-0404. FAX 415-703-9049. Ed. Gina M. Gatta. adv.; illus. circ. 50,000.
   Description: Atlas for gay and lesbians highlighting gay locations and tourist attractions in major North American metropolitan areas.

914.8 DK ISSN 0109-6125
DANMARKS TURIST VEJVISER. (Text in Danish, English and German) 1984. a. DKK 40.10. Glumsoe Bogtrykkeri, Noeddevej 10, 4171 Glumsoe, Denmark. illus.

914.8 DK ISSN 0109-6486
DANSK FAELLESREJSE FORENING. MEDLEMSBLAD. 1982. 3/yr. Dansk Faellerejse Forening, c/o Knud Noerr, Sct. Jullerilavej 114, 9990 Skagen, Denmark. illus.

914 DK ISSN 0904-1796
DANSK TURISME. 1982. 10/yr. DKK 300. Danmarks Turistraad - Danish Tourist Board, Vesterbrogade 6 D, 1620 Copenhagen V, Denmark. FAX 33-931416. TELEX 27586. Ed. Lone Zilstorff. adv.; bk.rev.; illus. circ. 10,000.
   Formerly: D T Forum (ISSN 0108-190X)

919.4 AT ISSN 0812-3640
DAWSONS GUIDE TO AUSTRALIAN & WORLDWIDE HOTELS. (In two editions: Australian and International) 1951. s-a. Aus.$79.50. Dawson Magazines Pty. Ltd., Tramore Place, Killarney Heights, Sydney, N.S.W. 2087, Australia. TEL 452-1777. FAX 451-5251. adv. circ. 4,000.
   Formerly (until 1968): Dawsons Guide to Hotels, Motels and Resorts.

910.202 AT ISSN 0815-6794
DAWSONS VENUE DIRECTORY. 1984. s-a. Aus.$45. Dawson Magazines Pty. Ltd., Tramore Place, Killarney Heights, Sydney, N.S.W. 2087, Australia. TEL 452 1777. FAX 451-5251. (Subscr. to: P.O. Box 173, 2086 Frenchs Forest, Australia) adv.; index. circ. 5,500. **Document type:** directory.
   Formerly: Dawsons Venues and Meeting Places (ISSN 0815-5151)
   Description: Directory of convention venues and incentive resorts throughout Australasia.

914.2 UK
DAYS OUT IN BRITAIN. a. £6.99. (Automobile Association) A A Publishing, Norfolk House, Priestly Rd., Basingstoke, Hants. RG24 9NY, England. TEL 01256-20123. FAX 01256-22575. adv. **Document type:** consumer publication.
   Former titles: 2000 Days Out in Britain; 2000 Places to Visit in Britain; Stately Homes, Museums, Castles and Gardens in Britain; Stately Homes, Museums, Castles and Gardens; Britain's Heritage.

DECCAN GEOGRAPHER. see *GEOGRAPHY*

917.4 US ISSN 1052-4592
DELAWARE VALLEY; magazine of suburban living. 1981. m. $19. Pleasure Hunt Magazine Inc., 345 N. York Rd., Hatboro, PA 19040-2045. TEL 215-750-7840. FAX 215-750-7992. Ed. Jodie Green. adv.; bk.rev. circ. 185,000.
   Formerly: Pleasure Hunt Magazine (ISSN 0883-2382)

914 US
DEPARTURES. (Editions avail. for the United Kingdom, Europe, Australia, and Japan) 1984. bi-m. free to members. American Express Publishing Corp. (New York), 1120 Ave. of the Americas, New York, NY 10036. TEL 212-382-5600. Ed. Gary Walther. circ. 250,000.
   Description: Provides information about gourmet food, hotels and culture necessary for a luxury and up-scale travel experience.

917.104 CN
DESTINATION CALGARY. 1987. bi-m. membership. Calgary Convention & Visitors Bureau, 237 Eighth Ave., S.E., Calgary, AB T2E 0K8, Canada. TEL 403-263-8510. FAX 403-262-3809. Ed. W.A. (Pat) Bell. circ. 1,100 (controlled). (tabloid format; back issues avail.) **Document type:** newsletter.
   Description: Includes news stories, features and reports about visitor industry events, activities and issues including marketing, industry trends and business in Calgary and the area.
   Refereed Serial

917.1 CN
DESTINATION CANADA. (Text in German) 1993. 4/yr. Ruland Communications Inc., 12 Lawton Blvd., Toronto, ON M4V 1Z4, Canada. TEL 416-927-9129. FAX 416-927-9118. adv.; B&W page Can.$1800, color page Can.$2690; trim 8 1/8 x 10 7/8. circ. 3,000.

993.1 919.304 UK
▼**DESTINATION NEW ZEALAND.** 1994. m. £15 (foreign £26.50). Outbound Newspapers, 1 Commercial Rd., Eastbourne, E. Sussex BN21 3XQ, England. TEL 01323-412001. FAX 01323-649249. Ed. Magnus Cohen. circ. 17,000. (tabloid format; back issues avail.) **Document type:** newspaper.
   Description: Gives potential migrants and travelers to New Zealand information about real estate, employment, education, investing and lifestyle.

915.404 II
DESTINATION TRAVELLER. (Text in English) 1976. m. Cross Section Publications Pvt. Ltd., F-74, Bhagat Singh Market, New Delhi 110 001, India. TEL 3732471. Pub. Navin Berry. adv.: B&W page Rs.22000, color page 32000; 240 x 170.

910.202 US
▼**DESTINATION: VIETNAM.** 1994. bi-m. $20. Global Directions, Inc., 58 Genebern Way, San Francisco, CA 94112. adv.; illus.; maps; circ. 25,000 (paid). **Document type:** consumer publication.
   Description: Covers the art, cuisine, culture, and history of Vietnam and its many tourist destinations. Includes travel essays and tips on shopping.

910.4 US ISSN 0279-8468
DESTINATIONS (WASHINGTON). 1979. m. membership. American Bus Association, 1100 New York Ave., N.W., Ste. 1050, Washington, DC 20005. TEL 202-842-1645. FAX 202-842-0850. Ed. Mark Beavers. adv.; illus.; tr.lit. circ. 6,000. (back issues avail.)

910.202 US
▼**DESTINATIONS WEST.** 1994. q. Destinations West, 159 E. D St., Benicia, CA 94510-9222. TEL 707-747-0650. Ed. Phil Barber; Pub. Mary Hand. adv.: B&W page $3871. circ. 200,000. **Document type:** consumer publication.
   Description: Travel and leisure guide to the cities of Las Vegas, Los Angeles and San Francisco.

914.406 FR ISSN 1148-0858
DETOURS EN FRANCE. 6/yr. 210 F. B 270, 60732 Sainte-Genevieve Cedex 9, France. maps.

DETROIT NEWSPAPER AGENCY. TRAVEL DIRECTORY. see *TRANSPORTATION — Air Transport*

382 GW
DEUTSCHES WIRTSCHAFTSWISSENSCHAFTLICHES INSTITUT FUER FREMDENVERKEHR. SCHRIFTENREIHE. irreg., no.46, 1995. DM.54. Deutsches Wirtschaftswissenschaftliches Institut fuer Fremdenverkehr, Hermann-Sack-Str. 2, 80331 Munich, Germany. TEL 089-267091. FAX 089-267613. Ed.Bd. **Document type:** monographic series.

382 GW
DEUTSCHES WIRTSCHAFTSWISSENSCHAFTLICHES INSTITUT FUER FREMDENVERKEHR. SONDERREIHE. irreg., vol.60, 1993. DM.90. Deutsches Wirtschaftswissenschaftliches Institut fuer Fremdenverkehr, Hermann-Sack-Str. 2, 80331 Munich, Germany. TEL 089-267091. FAX 089-267613. Ed. J. Maschke. **Document type:** monographic series.

910.4 UK ISSN 0269-0551
DEVON TOURISM REVIEW. 1981. a. £10. Devon County Council, Engineering & Planning Department, County Hall, Topsham Rd., Exeter EX2 4QQ, England. FAX 0392-382135. Ed. Carol Sandys. illus.; charts. circ. 1,000.
   Former titles (until 1985): Devon. Property Department. Tourism and Recreation. Topic Report; Devon County Planning Department. Tourism and Recreation. Topic Report (ISSN 0261-2445)
   Description: Reports on the characteristics and trends of the county's tourist industry. Includes details of recent developments in investment, marketing and other related visitor services.

THE DIABETIC TRAVELER. see *MEDICAL SCIENCES — Endocrinology*

914.504 IT ISSN 1122-3456
DIMORE E GIARDINI STORICI VISITABILI IN ITALIA. 1990. a. L.15000. Elemond Periodici s.r.l., Via D. Trentacoste 7, 20134 Milan, Italy. TEL 39-2-215631. FAX 39-2-26413603. Ed. Nani Prina. adv.: B&W page L.6000000, color page L.8500000. circ. 60,000. **Document type:** consumer publication.

TRAVEL AND TOURISM

910.202   AG
DINERS CLUB. m. (Diners Club (Argentina)) Editorial Alton Nivel, S.A.L., Carlos Pellegrini 1023, 9 No. Piso, Buenos Aires, Argentina. adv. circ. 100,000.

910.202   GW
DINERS CLUB MAGAZINE. (Text in German) 1968. m. DM.8. Gong Verlag, Postfach 400549, 80705 Munich, Germany. FAX 089-27270485. Ed. Karin Felix. adv.; bk.rev. circ. 135,000. **Document type:** consumer publication.

790   US
DIRECTORY OF FUNPARKS & ATTRACTIONS; international guide to amusement parks, family entertainment centers, waterparks, and attractions. Variant title: Amusement Business's Funparks Directory. 1961. a. $50. B P I Communications, Amusement Business Division, Box 24970, Nashville, TN 37202. TEL 615-321-4250. FAX 615-327-1575. adv. circ. 6,250. (also avail. in microfilm) **Document type:** directory.
    Former titles: Funparks Directory; Funspots Directory (ISSN 0071-9951)
    Description: Complete guide to over 2,500 amusement and theme parks, water parks, tourist attractions, zoos and family entertainment centers in the US, Canada and overseas.

910.09   HK
DIRECTORY OF HONG KONG TOURISM.* a. HK.$200. Hong Kong Trade and Industry Promotion Centre, c/o Hong Kong Trade Development Council, 36th-39th Fl., Office Tower, Convention Plaza, 1 Harbor Rd., Wanchai, Hong Kong. TEL 3-882708. FAX 3-7716438. **Document type:** directory.

910.09   US   ISSN 0732-6572
HD5260
DIRECTORY OF INCENTIVE TRAVEL INTERNATIONAL. 1977. a. $50. Advanstar Communications, Inc., 7500 Old Oak Blvd., Cleveland, OH 44130. TEL 216-826-2839. FAX 216-891-2726. (Subscr. to: 1 E. First Ave., Duluth, MN 55802. TEL 800-346-0085) Ed. Connie Goldstein. adv.; bk.rev. circ. 40,061. **Document type:** directory, trade publication.
    Former titles: Incentive Travel International; Directory of Incentive Travel International.
    Description: Annual guide to incentive destinations and suppliers worldwide.

910   US
DIRECTORY OF LOW COST VACATIONS WITH A DIFFERENCE. 1986. irreg., latest 1992. $5.95. Pilot Books, 103 Cooper St., Babylon, NY 11702. TEL 516-422-2225. FAX 516-422-2227. Ed. J. Crawford. **Document type:** directory.
    Description: Guide to alternatives to the ordinary vacation such as student exchange, bed and breakfast and work-study programs.

910.202   US
DIRECTORY OF THEME & AMUSEMENT PARKS. 1978. irreg., latest 1992. $5.95. Pilot Books, 103 Cooper St., Babylon, NY 11702. TEL 516-422-2225. FAX 516-422-2227. Ed. Eleanor Popelka. **Document type:** directory.
    Formerly (until 1992): National Directory of Theme Parks and Amusement Areas.
    Description: State by state listing of parks, kiddielands, amusement areas and zoos. Entries include major attractions, address and telephone number.

973   US   ISSN 0898-6231
THE DISCERNING TRAVELER. 1987. 6/yr. $50 in the U.S.; Canada $60; elsewhere $65. Lida Limited, 504 W. Mermaid Lane, Philadelphia, PA 19118. TEL 215-247-5578. Ed. Linda Glickstein. bk.rev. **Document type:** newsletter.
    Description: Covers the east coast of the United States and Canada; includes what to do, where to stay and where to dine for each location covered.

910.09   US
DISCOVER COSTA RICA. (Text in English, Spanish) 1989. a. North-South Net, Inc., 100 Almeria Ave., Ste. 220, Coral Gables, FL 33134. TEL 305-441-9744. FAX 305-441-9739. charts; illus.
    Description: Informs travelers about Costa Rica and supplies useful information.

918.04   US
DISCOVER ECUADOR. (Text in English, Spanish) 1990. a. North-South Net, Inc., 100 Almeria Ave., Ste. 220, Coral Gables, FL 33134. TEL 305-441-9744. FAX 305-441-9739. charts; illus.
    Description: Provides useful information for travellers to Ecuador.

910.09   US
DISCOVER GUATEMALA. (Text in English, Spanish) 1989. a. North-South Net, Inc., 100 Almeria Ave., Ste. 200, Coral Gables, FL 33134. TEL 305-441-9744. FAX 305-441-9739. charts; illus.
    Description: Informs travelers about Guatemala, and supplies useful information.

910.09   US
DISCOVER HAWAII SALES PLANNER; the travel professional's guide to the island. 1975. s-a. $15. Hawaii Business Publishing Corp., Box 913, Honolulu, HI 96814. TEL 808-946-3978. Ed. Jody Mishan. circ. 30,000.
    Formerly: Discover Hawaii (ISSN 0191-8230)

918.04   US
DISCOVER HONDURAS. (Text in English, Spanish) 1990. a. North-South Net, Inc., 100 Almeria Ave., Ste. 220, Coral Gables, FL 33134. TEL 305-441-9744. FAX 305-441-9739.
    Description: Provides useful information for travellers to Honduras.

917   UK   ISSN 0951-8134
DISCOVER NORTH AMERICA TRAVEL TRADE DIRECTORY. 1981. a. Phoenix Publishing & Media Ltd., 18-20 Scrutton St., London EC2A 4RJ, England. TEL 0171-247-0537. FAX 0171-377-2741. Ed. Mary Moore Mason; Pub. Maureen Miller. adv. contact: Kathryn McGowan. tr.lit.; circ. 15,000 (controlled). **Document type:** directory.

910.09   US
DISCOVER THE PLATINUM COAST.* 1986. bi-m. Pacetta Enterprises, Inc., c/o Reeves Actg., 501 Goodlette Rd., N., Ste.B204, Naples, FL 33940-5664. TEL 813-263-1633. Ed. B. Jane Pinel. circ. 150,000.

910.03   US
DISCOVER YOURSELF AT A BED & BREAKFAST. 1993. a. $8.95. Pudding House Publications, c/o Pudding House Writers Resource Center, 60 N. Main St., Johnstown, OH 43031. Ed. Jennifer Bosveld. **Document type:** consumer publication.
    Description: Covers "the personal journey in the midst of tourism," travel tips, and history, with personal accounts of visits to area bed & breakfasts.

910.2   US   ISSN 0012-3641
GV1024
DISCOVERY (CHICAGO). 1961. q. $8 to non-members. (Allstate Motor Club) Aegis Group - Publishers (Subsidiary of: Lintas - Ceco Communications), 30400 Van Dyke Ave., Warren, MI 48093. TEL 810-558-3105. FAX 810-558-4683. Ed. Steve Wilke. adv.; bk.rev.; illus. circ. 1,650,000. (also avail. in microform from UMI; back issues avail.; reprint service avail. from UMI)
    —UMI.
    Description: Explores the world by emphasizing sightseeing by car.

916.2   UK
DISCOVERY GUIDE TO CAIRO. 1985. irreg. £7.95. Immel Publishing Ltd., 20 Berkeley St., Berkeley Sq., London N1X 5AE, England. TEL 0403-710971. FAX 0403-711143. TELEX 265871. (Subscr. to: Biblios PDS Ltd., Star Road, Partridge Green, West Sussex RH13 8LD, England)
    Description: Serves the historically-minded traveler and the demanding egyptologist alike.

916.2   UK
DISCOVERY GUIDE TO EGYPT. 1981. irreg. £12.95. Immel Publishing Ltd., 20 Berkeley St., Berkeley Sq., London N1X 5AE, England. TEL 0403-710971. FAX 0403-711143. TELEX 265-871. (Subscr. to: Biblios PDS Ltd., Star Road, Partridge Green, West Sussex, West Sussex RH13 8LD, England)
    Formerly: Travelaid Guide to Egypt.

910.4   JA
DISNEY FAN. (Text in Japanese) 1990. bi-m. Kodansha Ltd., 12-2 Otowa 2-chome, Bunkyo-ku, Tokyo 112, Japan. TEL 03-3945-1673. FAX 03-3942-8043. TELEX J34509 KODANSHA. Ed. Masataka Ono. circ. 70,000. **Document type:** consumer publication.
    Description: Provides Disneyland information for the Disney fan.

917.904   US
DISNEYLAND (YEAR). a. $9.95. Harper Collins Publishers, Birnbaum Travel Guides, 10 E. 53rd St., New York, NY 10022-5299. TEL 212-270-7542. FAX 212-227-5409. Ed. Alexandra Mayes Birnbaum.

DIVER MAGAZINE. see *SPORTS AND GAMES*

DIVERSION (NEW YORK); for physicians at leisure. see *LEISURE AND RECREATION*

910.09   US
DIVERSION (TAPPAN). 1986. m. $36. Corporacion Editorial, S.A., Box 70, c/o Gretta Alison Int'l, Inc., Tappan, NY 10983. TEL 914-359-6928. FAX 914-359-3986. adv.: B&W page $1621, color page $2586; trim 8 1/4 x 10 7/8. circ. 15,723.
    Description: Directed to Mexican physicians.

910.2   AE   ISSN 0012-4311
DJEZAIR. 1965. s-a. free. Ministere du Tourisme, Office National de l'Animation, de la Promotion et de l'Information Touristique, 27 rue Khelifa Boukhalfa, Algiers, Algeria. Ed. Hafida Chaouch. bk.rev.; charts; illus.

910.09   CN   ISSN 0821-5758
DOCTOR'S REVIEW; leisure-time journal for physicians. 1983. m. Can.$40. Parkhurst Publishing, 400 McGill St., 3rd Fl., Montreal, PQ H2Y 2G1, Canada. FAX 514-397-0228. Ed. Madeleine Partous; Pub. David Elkins. circ. 36,950.

DOMOVA POKLADNICA. see *LITERATURE*

914.504   IT   ISSN 1121-1792
DOVE. 1991. m. L.67200. De Agostini - Rizzoli Periodici s.r.l., Via Gaspare Gozzi 1-A, 20129 Milan, Italy. TEL 39-2-700231. FAX 39-2-70100336. Ed. Luca Grandori. adv.: page L.30800000; adv. contact: Flavio Biondi. circ. 123,326. **Document type:** consumer publication.

910.09   IT
DOV'E - DOV'E. 1992. a. L.80000 (foreign L.100000). A. Dam. Editoriale s.r.l., Via Riboty 23, 00195 Rome, Italy. TEL 39-6-3720040. FAX 39-6-3723355. Ed. Andrea Lovelock. adv. contact: Roberta D'Amato. circ. 11,000. **Document type:** directory, trade publication.
    Formerly: Dati Turismo.

DREAM WORLD CRUISE DESTINATIONS. see *TRANSPORTATION — Ships And Shipping*

910   US
DREAMTRIPS!. q. c/o Plunkett, Box 670466, Dallas, TX 75367-0466. Pub. Jack W. Plunkett. circ. 25,000. **Document type:** newsletter.

910.4   US   ISSN 1073-8533
DUDE RANCHER MAGAZINE - DIRECTORY. 1930. a. $5. Dude Ranchers Association, Box 471, LaPorte, CO 80535. TEL 303-223-8440. Ed. Bobbi Futterer. adv. contact: Jim Futterer. bk.rev.; illus.; circ. 18,000. (paid). (back issues avail.) **Document type:** consumer publication.
    Formed by the merger of: Dude Rancher & Dude Rancher Directory.
    Description: Provides descriptions of the association's members and activities.

914   GW   ISSN 0012-7027
DUESSELDORFER HEFTE. 1955. s-m. DM.50. Triltsch Druck und Verlag GmbH und Co. KG, Herzogstr. 53, 40215 Duesseldorf, Germany. adv.; bk.rev.

917.204   MX
DURANGO. m. (Durango Hotel Association) Editorial Bonanza, S. de R.L., Dr. Velasco 95, Ed. 5, Of. 203, Col. Doctores, Del. Cuauhtemoc, 07620 Mexico DF, Mexico. TEL 525-5938720. FAX 525-7052492.

963 UK ISSN 1352-7886
▼EAST AFRICAN HANDBOOK. 1994. a. £14.95. Trade & Travel Publications Ltd., 6 Riverside Ct., Lower Bristol Rd., Bath BA2 3DZ, England. TEL 01255-469141. FAX 01255-469461. (Dist. in N. America by: Passport Books, NTC Publishing Group, 4255 W. Touhy Ave., Lincolnwood, IL 60646-1975. TEL 708-679-5500. FAX 708-679-6375) Ed. Michael Hodd. **Document type:** directory.

914.2 UK
EAST ANGLIA GUIDE. 1973. a. £3.50 (effective 1995). East Anglia Tourist Board, Toppesfield Hall, Hadleigh, Suffolk, England. FAX 01473-823063. TELEX 987447 EATB G. Ed. Michael Penn. adv. contact: Michael Penn. circ. 37,000 (paid). **Document type:** government publication, directory.
 Description: Lists tourist attractions, restaurants, boat rentals, beaches, and historic towns in East Anglia.

914.704 US ISSN 1056-439X
DJK8
EASTERN EUROPE (YEAR). a. $18. Harper Collins Publishers, Birnbaum Travel Guides, 10 E. 53rd St., New York, NY 10022-5299. TEL 212-207-7542. Ed. Alexandra Mayes Birnbaum. illus.; index.

051 US
EASTERN MASSACHUSETTS INCLUDING BOSTON ATLAS. 1989. quadrennial. $15.95. Butterworth Company of Cape Cod, 39 Rt. 134, S. Dennis, MA 02660. TEL 508-760-2000. FAX 508-760-2003. Ed. Rodney Schou. adv. contact: Christopher Schou. circ. 50,000. **Document type:** consumer publication.
 Description: Complete detailed maps and town information for 173 cities and towns in eastern Massachusetts including Boston Metro maps. Maps cover from the New Hampshire border to the Cape Cod Canal and west to Worcester County.

910.09 IT
EASY WORLD. 1992. q. free to cardholders. De Agostini - Rizzoli Periodici s.r.l., Via G. Gozzi 1-A, 20129 Milan, Italy. Ed. Luca Grandori. adv.: color page L.4000000; adv. contact: Flavio Biondi. **Document type:** consumer publication.

910.09 FR
ECHO TOURISTIQUE. 1933. w. 490 F. (foreign 723 F.)(effective Jan. 1991). (Editions Touristiques Internationales) Groupe L S A, 6 rue Marius Aufan, 92300 Levallois Perret, France. TEL 47-58-20-00. FAX 47-58-77-00. Ed. Anne Gillet. adv. circ. 9,200.

914 IT ISSN 0012-9488
ECO DELLA RIVIERA. 1915. s-w. L.14000. Giacomo Gandolfi S.p.A., Corso Mombello 54, 18038 San Remo, Italy. adv. circ. 8,600. (looseleaf format; also avail. in cards)

910.202 910.03 US
ECONOMIC IMPACT OF THE NEGRO TRAVELER. 1963. biennial. $102.50. Travelers' Research Publishing Co., Inc., 11717 S. Vincennes Ave., Chicago, IL 60643. TEL 312-881-3712. Ed. Clarence M. Markham, Jr. stat. circ. 10,000. (tabloid format; back issues avail.) Indexed: World Bank.Abstr.
 Formerly: Impact of the Negro Traveler.

910.09 US ISSN 0733-642X
G155.U6
ECONOMIC REVIEW OF TRAVEL IN AMERICA (YEAR). a. $70. Travel Industry Association of America, 1100 New York Ave., N.W., Ste. 450, Washington, DC 20005-3934. TEL 202-408-8422. (reprint service avail.) Indexed: SRI. **Document type:** trade publication.
 Description: Analysis of travel data presented in tables and charts.

910.09 US
ECOSPHERE. 1965. q. $12. (International Ecosystems University) Forum International, Inc., 91 Gregory Lane, Ste. 21, Pleasant Hill, CA 94523. TEL 510-671-2900. FAX 510-946-1500. Ed. Nicolas D. Hetzer. adv. contact: Franco Battaglia. bk.rev.; abstr.; bibl.; illus. circ. 6,000. (tabloid format) **Document type:** consumer publication, academic/scholarly publication.

910.202 EC
ECUADOR GUIA TURISTICA. (Text in English and Spanish) 1969. irreg. Prensa Informative Turistica, Edificio Brauer, Meja 438, Ofc. 43, Quito, Ecuador. Ed. Jorge Vaca O. adv. circ. 30,000.

914.6 SP ISSN 0422-6186
EDITUR; semanario de informacion y documentacion turisticas. 1960. w. 24500 ptas. Ediciones Turisticas, S.A., Gran Via Carlos III 86, 7o, Barcelona 28, Spain. TEL 3-330-70-52. FAX 3-330-74-96. TELEX 52220 ARTRA E. Ed. Jaime Arias Zimmermann; Pub. Luisa Vila. adv. contact: Cecilia Vila. circ. 12,000. **Document type:** trade publication.

910.09 SP
EDITUR INTERNATIONAL. 11/yr. Gran Via Carlos III, 86 7o, 08028 Barcelona, Spain. TEL 3-330-70-52. FAX 3-330-74-96. TELEX 52220 ARTRA E. Ed. Jorge Vila Fradera. circ. 12,800.

910.09 US ISSN 1052-0597
THE EDUCATED TRAVELER. 1990. 6/yr. $45 (foreign $54) includes a. Directory of Museum-Sponsored Tours. Box 220822, Chantilly, VA 22022. TEL 703-471-1063; 800-648-5168. FAX 703-471-4807. Ed. Ann H. Waigand; Pub. Ann H. Waigand. adv.; bk.rev.; circ. 1,500 (paid). **Document type:** newsletter.
 Description: Examines the area of international speciality travel including tourism, educational travel, special interest tours, ecotourism, museum travel, activity holidays, intercultural and socially responsible travel.

910.202 371.8 CN ISSN 1196-3700
EDUCATIONAL TRAVEL; the original guide to adult learning vacations around the world. 1986. a. Can.$8.95 (effective Jan. 1994). Athabasca University, P.O. Box 10,000, Athabasca, AB T0G 2R0, Canada. TEL 403-675-5864. FAX 403-675-6467. Ed. Vicky Busch. adv. circ. 3,500. (back issues avail.) Indexed: Can.B.P.I. **Document type:** directory.
 Former titles (until 1993): Educational Travel Planner (ISSN 1183-1308); (until 1989): International Educational Travel Planner (ISSN 1187-385X)
 Description: Features descriptions of study tours, language schools, eco tours and alternative vacation ideas around the world.

EDUCATIONAL TRAVEL RESOURCE GUIDE. see EDUCATION — International Education Programs

910.2 UA ISSN 0013-2381
EGYPT TRAVEL MAGAZINE.* no.156, 1971. q. Ministry of Tourism, 5 Sh. Adly, Cairo, Egypt.

910.202 US
EMBASSY'S COASTAL CRUISING GUIDE: ATLANTIC COAST. 1993. a. $19.95. Embassy Imprint Inc., 142 Ferry Rd., Ste. 16, Old Saybrook, CT 06475. TEL 203-395-0188. FAX 203-395-0410. E-mail: MBC MarPub@aol.com. adv. circ. 10,000. **Document type:** trade publication.
 Description: Covers the entire eastern seaboard from Maine to Florida and serves as an overview and introduction to the cruising opportunities to be found in these waters.

EMPLOYEE SERVICES MANAGEMENT; the journal of employee services, recreation, health and education. see BUSINESS AND ECONOMICS — Management

918.1 BL
EMPRESA BRASILEIRA DE TURISMO. ANUARIO ESTATISTICO. 1970. a. (with supplement). price varies. Empresa Brasileira de Turismo, Rua Mariz e Barros 13, 20270-000 Rio de Janeiro, Brazil. stat.
 Description: Details balance of payments, domestic tourism, international, national and EMBRATUR statistics.

918.104 BL
EMPRESA BRASILEIRA DE TURISMO. CALENDARIO TURISTICO. English edition: Empresa Brasileira de Turismo. Tourist Calendar. a. free. Empresa Brasileira de Turismo, Rua Mariz e Barros 13, 20270-000 Rio de Janeiro, Brazil. TEL 55-21-273-2212. FAX 55-21-273-9290. TELEX 38-21-21066 ETUR.

917.704 US
ENCOUNTER INDIANAPOLIS. 1989. m. $20. Encounter Publications Inc., 2105 N. Meridian, Ste. 202, Indianapolis, IN 46202. TEL 317-923-8868. FAX 317-923-8571. Ed. Richard L. Schillen. adv. circ. 20,000.
 Description: Provides tourists, business professionals, and relocators with greater access to the city by offering a calendar of events, restaurants, reviews and sporting events.

910.09 US ISSN 0279-4853
TX907
ENDLESS VACATION. 1975. bi-m. $65. Endless Vacation Publications, Box 80260, Indianapolis, IN 46280-0260. TEL 317-871-9504. FAX 317-871-9507. adv.; bk.rev. circ. 949,604. **Document type:** consumer publication.
 Description: Gives vacation ideas for avid travelers.

914.2 US ISSN 1042-8399
DA650
ENGLAND ON FIFTY DOLLARS A DAY. 1980. a. $14.95. Frommer Books (Subsidiary of: Simon & Schuster, Inc.), 15 Columbus Circle, New York, NY 10023. TEL 212-373-8125. Eds. S. Haggart, D. Porter.
 Former titles: England on Forty Dollars a Day; England and Scotland on Twenty-Five Dollars a Day; England and Scotland on Twenty Dollars a Day (ISSN 0271-3977); **Supersedes:** England on Fifteen Dollars a Day.

914.2 UK ISSN 0260-0420
ENGLISH HERITAGE MONITOR. 1977. a. £15. English Tourist Board, Planning and Research Services, Black's Rd., Hammersmith, London W6 9EL, England. TEL 0181-846-9000. FAX 0181-563-0302.
 —BLDSC (3774.690000).
 Description: Takes a detailed look at ancient monuments, churches, and historic buildings from a conservation and tourism viewpoint, listing those that are open to the public.

910.09 UK
ENGLISH TOURIST BOARD. ANNUAL REPORT. 1971. a. £10. English Tourist Board, Black's Rd., Hammersmith, London W6 9EL, England. TEL 0181-846-9000. FAX 0181-563-0302. Ed. Sandie Dawe. **Document type:** corporate report.
 Description: Reports on the Board's activities for the year ended March 31 and examines the prospects for the future.

910.09 330 CN ISSN 0703-0312
ENROUTE; your complementary in-flight magazine. (Text in English, French) 1973. m. free to Air Canada passengers. (Air Canada) Publicor (Subsidiary of: Groupe Quebecor Inc.), 7 chemin Bates, Outremont, PQ H2V 1A6, Canada. Ed. Lise Ravary. adv. contact: Pauline Fortier. bibl.; illus. circ. 120,000. (back issues avail.) Indexed: Can.Per.Ind. **Document type:** consumer publication.

910.09 US
ENTREE; an uncompromising and confidential traveler's newsletter. 1982. m. $59. Entree Travel, 695 Olive Rd., Santa Barbara, CA 93108. TEL 805-969-5848. FAX 805-966-7095. (Subscr. to: Box 5148, Santa Barbara, CA 93150) Ed. William Tomicki. bk.rev.; film rev.; play rev. circ. 6,000. (back issues avail.) **Document type:** newsletter.
 Description: Hotel and restaurant critiques; an insider's look at travel and eating; books spas, cruises, shopping reviews.

EPICUREAN REVUE; a confidential gastronomical & tourism letter. see HOTELS AND RESTAURANTS

910.09 US ISSN 0046-2462
ERIE MOTORIST. bi-m. American Automobile Association, Erie County Motor Club, 420 W. Sixth St., Erie, PA 16507-1216. TEL 814-454-0123. FAX 814-455-5688. Ed. Jim Brown. circ. 29,000.

910.91 US
▼**ESCAPE**; the global guide for the adventurous traveler. 1994. q. $18. P.O. Box 5159, Santa Monica, CA 90409-5159. Ed. Joe Robinson.

ESCAPEES. see TRANSPORTATION — Automobiles

910 647.9 SP
ESPANA HOSTELERA Y TURISTICA. 1950. m. 3000 ptas.($85) Padre Jesus Ordeonez, 10 bajo, 28002 Madrid, Spain. TEL 262-95-49. FAX 262-00-35. Ed. Juan Romero Calvillo. adv. circ. 17,000.

TRAVEL AND TOURISM

917   UK   ISSN 1352-2825
ESSENTIALLY AMERICA. 1981. q. £7.80 (Europe £20; rest of world £36.40). Phoenix Publishing & Media Ltd., 18-20 Scrutton St., London EC2A 4RJ, England. TEL 0171-247-0537. FAX 0171-377-2741. (Subscr. to: Warners Distribution, The Maltings, Manor Ln., Bourne, Lincs. PE10 9PH, England. TEL 0778-393652; Dist. in US by: Northeast Media Group, 273 Post Rd. W., Box 2414, Westport, CT 06880. TEL 203-226-8151. FAX 203-227-1106) Ed. Mary Moore Mason; Pub. Maureen Miller. adv.: color page $4700; adv. contact: Kathryn McGowan. circ. 50,000. (back issues avail.) **Document type:** consumer publication.
    Former titles (until 1994): Discover North America (ISSN 0951-8126); (until 1986): Holiday U.S.A. and Canada Magazine; Holiday U.S.A.

914.604   SP   ISSN 0423-5037
ESTUDIOS TURISTICOS. (Text in Spanish; summaries in English, Spanish) 1963. q. 3200 ptas. (foreign 3900 ptas. ($40) (effective 1995). Ministerio de Comercio y Turismo, Instituto de Estudios Turisticos, C. Almagro, 36, 3o, 28010 Madrid, Spain. TEL 34-1-3082349. FAX 34-1-3082658. Dir. Miguel Gongora. bk.rev.; stat. circ. 2,000. **Indexed:** Rural Recreat.Tour.Abstr., World Agri.Econ.& Rural Sociol.Abstr. **Document type:** government publication.
—BLDSC (3812.816550).
    Description: Contains economic, geographic and sociological studies about tourism, travel, leisure and recreation. Includes a calendar of fairs, congresses and seminars and a review of tourism legislation.

ESTUDOS DE GEOGRAFIA HUMANA E REGIONAL. see *GEOGRAPHY*

914 385   US   ISSN 0085-0330
HE3004
EURAIL GUIDE; how to travel Europe and all the world by train. 1971. a. $14.95. Houghton Mifflin Co., 215 Park Ave., S., New York, NY 10003. TEL 212-420-5800. Eds. Kathryn S. Turpin, Marvin L. Saltzman. **Document type:** consumer publication.
—BLDSC (3828.087000).
    Description: Contains information about every train ride in the world a tourist might want to take. Includes departure and arrival times, as well as on-board services (eating, sleeping and air-conditioning facilities).

914   AU
EURO-CITY; das Reisemagazin der neuen Bahn. 1928. 6/yr. S.259. Bohmann Druck und Verlag GmbH & Co. KG, Leberstr. 122, A-1110 Vienna, Austria. TEL 0222-74095-0. FAX 0222-74095-183. TELEX 132312. circ. 70,000. **Document type:** trade publication.
    Former titles (until 1991): Reiseland Oesterreich (ISSN 0254-5292); Fremdenverkehr-Reiseland-Oesterreich (ISSN 0016-0954)

910   AU
EUROGAST. q. Rottweg 17, A-5020 Salzburg, Austria. TEL 0662-32395. FAX 0662-32396. Ed. H. Kriechhammer. circ. 46,500.

910.09   GW
EUROKUNST: BESSER REISEN & MEHR ERLEBEN; Magazin fuer Urlaub und Freiheit. (Text in English, German) 1968. q. DM.18. Eurokunstverlag A.R. Purtauf, Postfach 2332, 65013 Wiesbaden, Germany. Ed.Bd. circ. 15,100.
    Former titles: Eurokunst; Eurokunst Magazin Reisen (ISSN 0177-4557)

EUROPA CAMPING UND CARAVANING. INTERNATIONALER FUEHRER. see *SPORTS AND GAMES — Outdoor Life*

914   US   ISSN 0883-2498
D909
EUROPE (YEAR). a. $18. Harper Collins Publishers, Birnbaum Travel Guides, 10 E. 53rd St., New York, NY 10022-5299. TEL 212-270-7542. Ed. Alexandra Mayes Birnbaum. **Indexed:** ABI Inform, INIS Atomind., P.A.I.S., Tel.Abstr.

910   US
EUROPE BY EURAIL; how to tour Europe by train. 1976. biennial. $14.95. Globe Pequot Press, Box 833, Old Saybrook, CT 06475-0833. TEL 203-395-0440. FAX 203-395-1418.
    Description: Covers more than 20 base cities in 17 countries, with 92 day excursions to surrounding destinations.

914   US   ISSN 0749-4815
D909
EUROPE FOR BUSINESS TRAVELERS. a. $14. Harper Collins Publishers, Birnbaum Travel Guides, 10 E. 53rd St., New York, NY 10022-5299. TEL 212-270-7542. Ed. Alexandra Mayes Birnbaum.

910.202   US
D909
EUROPE ON FORTY DOLLARS A DAY. a. $15.95. Frommer Books (Subsidiary of: Simon & Schuster, Inc.), 15 Columbus Circle, New York, NY 10023. TEL 212-373-8125.
    Former titles: Europe on Thirty Dollars a Day (ISSN 0730-1510); Europe on Twenty-Five Dollars a Day; Europe on Fifteen Dollars a Day.

914.1   US   ISSN 1074-7516
D909
EUROPE TRAVELBOOK. a. $9.95. American Automobile Association, 1000 AAA Dr., Heathrow, FL 32746-5063. TEL 407-444-8200. FAX 407-444-8204. adv.; illus. circ. 317,600. **Document type:** consumer publication.
    Formerly: Travel Guide to Europe; Which was formed by the merger of: British Isles and Ireland Travel Guide (ISSN 0095-1579); Central Europe and Scandinavia Travel Guide (ISSN 0094-3657); Eastern Europe Travel Guide (ISSN 0094-8632); Southern Europe Travel Guide (ISSN 0094-3614)

914.04 917.904   US
EUROPEAN TRAVEL AND ENTERTAINMENT MAGAZINE. 1969. m. Box 14545, Phoenix, AZ 85063. TEL 602-233-2342. circ. 5,000.

380 910.202   UK
EUROPEAN TRAVEL AND TOURISM MARKETING DIRECTORY. 1992. irreg. £160($335) Euromonitor, 60-61 Britton St., London EC1M 5NA, England. TEL 0171-251-8024. FAX 0171-608-3149. (Addr. in N. America: Euromonitor International, 122 S. Michigan Ave., Ste. 1200, Chicago, IL 60603. TEL 312-922-1115. FAX 312-922-1157) charts; stat. **Document type:** directory.
    Description: Details all the major important sources of marketing information and covers the major tour operators in Europe.

EUROS. see *HOMOSEXUALITY*

910.202   TO
EVA, YOUR HOLIDAY GUIDE TO TONGA. (Text and summaries in English) 1989. bi-m. free. Vava'u Press Ltd., P.O. Box 427, Nuku'alofa, Tonga. TEL 676-23101. FAX 676-23101. Ed. Pesi S. Fonua. circ. 3,500. (back issues avail.) **Document type:** newspaper.

910.09   US   ISSN 0890-9911
EXCHANGE BOOK;* home exchange directory. 1960. s-a. $50. (Directory Group Association) Vacation Exchange Club, Inc., Box 650, Key West, FL 33041-0650. TEL 800-638-3841. FAX 808-638-5184. Ed. D.J. Costabel. adv.; illus. circ. 15,000. **Document type:** directory.
    Formerly: Home Exchange Directory.

914.2   UK
EXCLUSIVE LONDON. 1978. q. Exclusive Publications Ltd., 11 Dalmore Rd., London SE21 8HD, England. Ed. Robert Redman. adv.

910.09   CN   ISSN 0847-933X
EXCURSIONS EN AUTOCAR. English edition: Tours on Motorcoach (ISSN 0847-9348) 1988. m. Can.$40 (effective Jan. 1991). (Bus Owners Association) Publicom Inc., C.P. 365, Place d'Armes, Montreal, PQ H2Y 3H1, Canada. TEL 514-274-0004. FAX 514-274-5884. Ed. Francois Marquis. adv.; circ. 6,447 (controlled). **Document type:** trade publication.
    Description: Trade publication for group tour organizers.

910.202   UK   ISSN 0263-7685
EXECUTIVE TRAVEL. 1979. m. £32.50 (foreign £50). Reed Travel Group (London), Part of the Reed Elsevier Group (Subsidiary of: Reed Telepublishing), 6 Chesterfield Gardens, London W1Y 8DN, England. TEL 0171-355-1600. FAX 0171-355-9630. Ed. Mike Toynbee. adv. contact: Bridget McCarney. bk.rev.; circ. 41,444 (controlled). **Document type:** trade publication.
—BLDSC (3836.223900).
    Formerly: Executive Travel and Leisure.
    Description: Covers industry news and developments for corporate travelers and company travel planners.

EXHIBITION BULLETIN. see *MEETINGS AND CONGRESSES*

910.202   FR   ISSN 0247-8684
EXPANSION VOYAGES. 1981. q. Groupe Expansion, Le Ponant, 25 rue Leblanc, 75842 Paris, France. TEL 40-60-43-37. FAX 40-60-41-25. adv.: B&W page 65000 F., color page 93000 F. illus. circ. 140,000.
    Description: Appeals to senior executives, business men and professionals.

EXPLORE; Canada's outdoor adventure magazine. see *SPORTS AND GAMES — Outdoor Life*

917.704
EXPLORE MINNESOTA BED AND BREAKFAST - HISTORIC INNS. a. free. Office of Tourism, 100 Metro Square, 121 7th Pl. E., St. Paul, MN 55101. TEL 800-657-3700. circ. 35,000. **Document type:** directory.

EXPLORE MINNESOTA BIKING. see *SPORTS AND GAMES — Bicycles And Motorcycles*

917 796.5   US
EXPLORE MINNESOTA CAMPGROUND GUIDE. 1984. a. free. Minnesota Association of Campground Operators, 245 Sixth St. E., Ste. 817, St. Paul, MN 55101-1940. TEL 612-227-0851. FAX 612-227-0851. Ed. Carol Lovro. circ. 200,000. **Document type:** directory, consumer publication.
    Former titles: Explore Minnesota Campgrounds; Camping Guide.

EXPLORE MINNESOTA CROSS-COUNTRY SKIING. see *SPORTS AND GAMES — Outdoor Life*

EXPLORE MINNESOTA DOWNHILL SKIING. see *SPORTS AND GAMES — Outdoor Life*

917.704 796   US
EXPLORE MINNESOTA HIKING. irreg. (every 2-3 yrs.) free. Office of Tourism, 100 Metro Square, 121 7th Pl. E., St. Paul, MN 55101. TEL 800-657-3700. circ. 20,000.
    Formerly: Explore Minnesota Canoeing, Backpacking and Hiking.

910.09   AT   ISSN 0895-8521
EXPLORER NEWS. 1982. q. Aus.$8. Barossa News Pty. Ltd., 27 Murray St., Tanunda, S.A. 5352, Australia. TEL 61-85-632041. FAX 61-85-633655. (Subscr. to: Box 43, Tanunda, S.A. 5453, Australia) Ed. Tim Jednes. adv.; circ. 30,000 (controlled). (tabloid format)
    Description: Covers Barossa and Clare Valleys.

917.104   CN
EXPLORER'S GUIDE. Cover title: Manitoba Explorer's Guide. a. free. Department of Industry, Trade and Tourism, 155 Carlton St., 7th Fl., Department SS6, Winnipeg, MB R3C 3H8, Canada. TEL 800-665-0040. FAX 204-945-2302. Ed. Colette Fontaine; Pub. Colette Fontaine. adv.; illus. **Document type:** government publication, consumer publication.
    Former titles (until 1994): Manitoba Vacation Planner (ISSN 1185-4391); (until 1987): Manitoba Vacation Guide (ISSN 0703-6248); (until 1975): Manitoba, Canada, Vacation Guide (ISSN 0703-6256); (until 1972): Manitoba Vacation Handbook (ISSN 0542-5638); (until 196?): Manitoba Family Accommodation and Vacation Guide.
    Description: Describes the many cultural, historic, and scenic tourist attractions in Winnipeg and throughout the rest of Manitoba.

TRAVEL AND TOURISM

914.4 UK
EXPLORING FRANCE. 1981. irreg. £7.95. Jarrold Publishing, Whitefriars St., Norwich, NR3 1TR, England. TEL 01603-763300. FAX 01603-662748. Ed. Peter Titchmarsh. **Document type:** directory.
Description: Includes 30 maps and over 1,000 illustrations for a comprehensive guide for the English speaking visitor.

914.15 US ISSN 1066-5358
EXPLORING IRELAND. 1990. 6/yr. $39. 318 Pershing Ave., Roselle Park, NJ 07204. TEL 908-298-0315. Eds. Charlene Komar Storey, Gregory D. Storey. bk.rev.; circ. 900 (paid). **Document type:** newsletter.
Description: Contains travel tips and articles that introduce towns, cities, hotels and restaurants in Ireland.

910.09 SP
EXPO TURISMO. 6/yr. Publicaciones Internacionales S.A., Po. de la Castellana 210, 28046 Madrid, Spain. TEL 1-563-43-11. FAX 1-457-29-38. Ed. Fernando Escribano.

EXPRESS. see TRAVEL AND TOURISM — Airline Inflight And Hotel Inroom

910.2 GW
EXTRATOUR. 1920; N.S. 1951. bi-m. membership only. Hauptverband fuer Jugendwandern und Jugendherbergen e.V., Postfach 1455, 32704 Detmold, Germany. TEL 05231-7401-0. Ed. Gabriele Greenlee. adv.; bk.rev.; illus. circ. 900,000. **Document type:** bulletin.
Formerly: Jugendherberge (ISSN 0022-5932)

910.09 GW ISSN 0939-6039
F V W INTERNATIONAL. 1967. bi-w. DM.102 (foreign DM.150). Verlag Dieter Niedecken GmbH, Jungfrauenthal 47, 20149 Hamburg, Germany. TEL 040-44187381. FAX 040-44187349. Ed. Ines Niedecken. adv. contact: M. Rosteck. circ. 22,018. **Document type:** trade publication.

910.09 US ISSN 0429-9639
FABULOUS MEXICO; where everything costs less. biennial. $2.50. Harian Publications, One Vernon Ave., Floral Park, NY 11001. TEL 516-437-3440.

FACTS AND ADVICE FOR AIRLINE PASSENGERS. see TRANSPORTATION — Air Transport

914.806 GW ISSN 0724-8342
FAHREN IN EUROPA. (Editions avail.: Germany, Switzerland, Austria, Netherlands-Belgium, France, U.K.) 1983. a. DM.20. Fie Verlag GmbH, Spaldingstr. 210, 20097 Hamburg, Germany. TEL 040-230696. FAX 040-234613. Ed. Gerd Achilles. adv. contact: Anja Barenscher. circ. 52,700. **Document type:** consumer publication.

919.7 UK ISSN 0256-1824
F3031
FALKLAND ISLANDS JOURNAL. (Text in English) 1967. a. £8($15) Queen's University of Belfast, Department of Applied Plant Science, Newforge Ln., Belfast BT9 5PX, N. Ireland. TEL 0232-661166. FAX 0232-669551. E-mail: aihe1875@uk.ac.qub.agv1. Ed. J.H. McAdam. bk.rev.; illus. circ. 400. **Document type:** academic/scholarly publication.
Description: Includes general material on all aspects of the history, geography and natural history of the Falkland Islands.

FAMILY MOTOR COACHING. see TRANSPORTATION

910.09 US
FAMILY TRAVEL TIMES. 1984. q. $40 (effective 1995-1996). Travel With Your Children (TWYCH) (Subsidiary of: Dorthy Jordon & Associates), 45 W. 18th St., 7th Fl., New York, NY 10011. TEL 212-206-0688. FAX 212-645-5942. Ed. Joy Anderson; Pub. Dorothy Jordon. bk.rev. circ. 2,500. (back issues avail.) **Document type:** newsletter.
Description: Contains news and features about family travel around the U.S. and around the world.

910.09 US ISSN 1068-736X
FAMILY TRAVELERS.* 1993. q. free. 4709 Cumberland Ave., Chevy Chase, MD 20815-5457. TEL 301-986-1227. Ed. Rebecca R. Kahlenberg. adv.; B&W page $1600; trim 8 1/2 x 11. circ. 10,000. (controlled) **Document type:** consumer publication.

915.204 JA
FAR EAST TRAVELER. (Text in English) vol.4, 1972. m. $132. Far East Reporters Inc., 1F Palace Nishi-Azabu, 3-17-40 Nishi-Azabu, Minato-ku, Tokyo 106, Japan. TELEX 242-4972 FETMAG. Ed. David M. Umeda; Pub. George Pokrovsky. adv.; bk.rev.; charts; illus. circ. 35,000.
Incorporates (in 1968): Far East Reporter (ISSN 0425-7170)

914.2 UK
FARM & COUNTRY HOLIDAYS. 1969. a. £3.95. Pastime Publications Ltd., 6 York Pl., Edinburgh EH1 3EP, Scotland. TEL 0131-556-1105. FAX 0131-556-1129. adv. contact: Diane Gibson. circ. 40,000. **Document type:** consumer publication.

914.2 UK
FARM HOLIDAY GUIDE (ENGLAND, WALES & IRELAND). 1946. a. £3.99. F H G Publications Ltd., Abbey Mill Business Centre, Seedhill, Paisley PA1 1JN, Scotland. TEL 0141-887-0428. FAX 0141-889-7204. **Document type:** consumer publication.
Formed by the merger of: Farm Holiday Guide (England Edition) (ISSN 0267-2871); Farm Holiday Guide (Wales Edition) (ISSN 0267-2898)

914.1 UK ISSN 0267-288X
FARM HOLIDAY GUIDE (SCOTLAND EDITION). a. £2.80. F H G Publications Ltd., Abbey Mill Business Centre, Seedhill, Paisley PA1 1JN, Scotland. TEL 0141-887-0428. FAX 0141-559-7204. **Document type:** consumer publication.

914.2 IE
FARM HOLIDAYS IN IRELAND. 1970. a. $10. Libra House Ltd., 4 St. Kevin's Terrace, Dublin 8, Ireland. TEL 01-4542717. FAX 01-4546371. Ed. Cathal Tyrrell. illus. circ. 85,775. **Document type:** directory.
Description: List about 460 houses providing meals and accomodation in the countryside and coastal areas.

796 US ISSN 0195-8437
TX907
FARM, RANCH AND COUNTRY VACATIONS. 1949. irreg. (every 2 or 3 years), latest ed. 1995. $19.95. Adventure Guides, Inc., 7550 E. McDonald Dr., Ste. M, Scottsdale, AZ 85250. Ed. Pat Dickerman. **Document type:** directory.
Former titles: Country Vacations USA (ISSN 0147-3867); Farm, Ranch and Country Vacations; Farm, Ranch and Countryside Guide; Farm and Ranch Vacation Guide (ISSN 0085-0438)

FARVIS - AFANGAR; timarit um ferdamal. see SPORTS AND GAMES — Outdoor Life

910.09 338 US
FAX TRAVEL BULLETIN. 48/yr. $95. Nationwide Intelligence, Box 1922, Saginaw, MI 48605. TEL 517-752-6123; 800-333-4130. FAX 517-752-1605.
Description: Provides the latest information on developments affecting travel.

910.4 CC ISSN 1003-5516
FENGJING MINGSHENG/SCENIC SPOTS AND HISTORICAL SITES. (Text in Chinese) 1984. m. Y36. Hangzhou Yuanlin Wenwu Guanliju - Hangzhou Municipa Administration of Gardens and Cultural Relics. 12 Jiangyuan Nong, Xiaoying Xiang, Hangzhou, Zhejiang 310003, People's Republic of China. TEL 0571-711944. FAX 0571-7027890. Ed. Chen Dawei; Pub. Zhang Jun. adv. contact: Zhu Jiaji. circ. 40,000.
Description: Covers the construction, protection and management of senic spots and historical sites in China. Reports the latest development in gardening, archaeology, tourism and urban design.
Refereed Serial

914.604 IC ISSN 0256-8470
FERDAFELAG ISLANDS. ARBOK. 1928. a. ISK 3100. Ferdafelag Islands, Moerkin 6, IS-108 Reykjavik, Iceland. TEL 354-568-2533. FAX 354-568-2535. Ed. Hjalti Kristgeirsson. circ. 9,500.

910.202 NO ISSN 0801-5880
FERIEFORUM; magasin for reiseliv og turisme. (Text in Norwegian) 1983. q. NOK 80($16) Skogveien 85A, N-1320 Stabekk, Norway. TEL 02-534773. Ed. Reidar Nordheim. circ. 20,000.

914.34 GW
FERIEN MAGAZIN ST. PETER - ORDING. a. (Fremdenverkehrsgemeinschaft Eiderstedt e.V.) Westholsteinische Verlagsanstalt Boyens und Co., Wulf-Isebrand-Platz, 25746 Heide, Germany. TEL 0481-691-0.

910.202 GW
FERNREISEN. 1982. m. DM.48. S-P Verlag, Westendstr. 52, 60325 Frankfurt, Germany. TEL 069-723145. Ed. Hansjoerg Schoen. circ. 13,300.
Description: Travel and tourism in non-European regions.

FERRARI'S PLACES FOR MEN (YEAR). see HOMOSEXUALITY

FERRARI'S PLACES FOR WOMEN: USA AND WORLDWIDE. see HOMOSEXUALITY

FERRARI'S PLACES OF INTEREST (YEAR); worldwide gay and lesbian guide. see HOMOSEXUALITY

917.904 US
FERRY TRAVEL GUIDE. 1984. 3/yr. $7. Olympic Publishing, Inc., 7450 Oak Bay Rd., Port Ludlow, WA 98365-9411. TEL 206-437-2277. FAX 206-437-9503. Ed. Dan Youra. adv. circ. 100,000. (back issues avail.) **Document type:** consumer publication.
Former titles: Olympic Travel Guide (ISSN 0897-9618); Olympic Magazine.
Description: Travel information for Washington State and British Columbia with maps, ferry schedules, resorts, cities and attractions.

338 658 US ISSN 1065-2701
FESTIVAL MANAGEMENT & EVENT TOURISM. 1993. q. $95 (foreign $115) (effective 1996). Cognizant Communication Corporation, 3 Hartsdale Rd., Elmsford, NY 10523-3701. TEL 914-592-7720. FAX 914-592-8981. Eds. Dr. Bruce Wicks, Dr. Donals Getz. Indexed: Hosp.Abstr.
—BLDSC (3910.819000); Faxon; UnCover. CCC.
Description: Publishes articles to meet the need of an evoloving profession intentionally. Dealing with the business of special events for non-profit and public organizations to carry out the missions and as a catalyst for community development.
Refereed Serial

FETES ET FESTIVALS. see BUSINESS AND ECONOMICS — Marketing And Purchasing

910.4 FJ
FIJI MAGIC. (Text in English) m. George Rubine Ltd., P.O. Box 12511, Suva, Fiji. TEL 313944. Ed. Gabriel Singh. circ. 10,000.

FINANCIAL TIMES INTERNATIONAL YEAR BOOKS: WORLD HOTEL DIRECTORY. see HOTELS AND RESTAURANTS

FINE WINE FOLIO; an appreciation of vineyards and vintages. see BEVERAGES

910.09 GW
FLIEGEN UND SPAREN; das Magazin fuer clevere Urlauber. 1986. 4/yr. DM.20($20) Markt Control, Postfach 110431, 47144 Duisburg, Germany. TEL 0203-554248. FAX 0203-547970. Eds. Juergen Zupancic, Wolfgang Grahl. adv.; bk.rev. circ. 70,000. **Document type:** consumer publication.

910.202 GW
FLIEGENDE BLAETTER. 1971. q. free. (Condor Airlines) Koesler Verlag GmbH, Von-Werth Strasse 44, 50670 Cologne, Germany. TEL 0221-131366. FAX 0221-137541. TELEX 889990-RSB-D. adv. circ. 300,000.

629.132 US ISSN 0194-9039
FLIGHT REPORTS. 1978. N. $36. Peter Katz Productions, Inc., Box 831, 9 Romar Ave., White Plains, NY 10605-0831. TEL 914-949-7443. Ed. Peter Katz. bk.rev.

914.504 US ISSN 1056-4489
DG732
FLORENCE (YEAR). a. $12. Harper Collins Publishers, Birnbaum Travel Guides, 10 E. 53rd St., New York, NY 10022-5299. TEL 212-207-7542. Ed. Alexander Mayes Birnbaum. illus.; index.

TRAVEL AND TOURISM

914.504 US
FLORIDA INTERNATIONAL PLANNER. a. Worth International Communications Corp., 5979 N.W. 151st St., Ste. 120, Miami Lakes, FL 33014. TEL 305-828-0123. FAX 305-826-6950. Ed. Hal Herman; Pub. Laural A. Herman. adv. contact: Terry Murphy. circ. 60,000. **Document type:** trade publication.

917.5 US
FLORIDA QUARTERLY. 1992. q. $15. Cotton Publishing Inc., Box 6026, Sarasota, FL 34278. TEL 813-953-8956. Ed. Michelle D. Cotton; Pub. Donald Cotton. **Document type:** consumer publication.

338.4 US
FLORIDA'S VISITORS. 1973? a. Department of Commerce, Division of Tourism, 107 W. Gaines St., Tallahassee, FL 32304. TEL 904-488-7300.
Formerly: Florida Tourist Study (ISSN 0430-6953)

FLYER INTERNATIONAL; aviation and tourism. see TRANSPORTATION — Air Transport

910.09 CN
FOCUS ON FESTIVALS. 1980. q. Can.$20 membership. Associated Manitoba Arts Festivals, Inc., 424 - 100 Arthur St., Winnipeg, MB R3B 1H3, Canada. TEL 204-945-4578. FAX 204-948-2073. Ed. Karen Oliver. adv. contact: Tanya Gregory. circ. 500. (back issues avail.) **Document type:** newsletter.
Description: News about Manitoba's 38 local community arts festivals, the Manitoba Community Arts Development, and provincial festival events.

915.47 PK
FOCUS ON PAKISTAN. (Text in English) 1971-1973; resumed 1976. s-a. Rs.125($10) per no. Pakistan Tourism Development Corporation Ltd., House No. 2, Street 61, F-7-4, P.O. Box 1465, Islambad 44000, Pakistan. TEL 92-51-811001. FAX 92-51-824173. TELEX 54356 PTDC PK. Ed. Ashab Naqvi. adv. contact: Abdul Ghafoor Khan Qaisrani. circ. 5,000 (controlled). **Document type:** consumer publication.
Description: Articles on the culture, customs, heritage and tourist attractions of Pakistan.

918.6 PN
FOCUS ON PANAMA. (Editions in English and Spanish) 1971. s-a. $5 per no. (free in Panama). Focus Publications (Int.) S.A., Apdo. 6-3287, El Dorado, Panama, Panama. TEL 507-225-6638. FAX 507-225-0466. Ed. Kenneth J. Jones. adv. circ. 70,000. **Document type:** consumer publication.
Description: Full color guide for visitors emphasizing both tourist attractions, business facilities and culture.

917.204 US ISSN 1070-8642
F1391.A15
FODOR'S ACAPULCO, IXTAPA, ZIHUATANIJO. irreg. $9. Fodor's Travel Publications, Inc. (Subsidiary of: Random House, Inc.), 201 E. 50th St., New York, NY 10022. TEL 800-733-3000. (Dist. by: Random House, Inc., 400 Hahn Dr., Westminster, MD 21157) Ed. Craig Seligman.
Formerly: Fodor's Fun in Acapulco.

914.04 US
D909
FODOR'S AFFORDABLE EUROPE. 1972. biennial. $12.95. Fodor's Travel Publications, Inc. (Subsidiary of: Random House, Inc.), 201 E. 50th St., New York, NY 10022. TEL 800-533-6478. (Dist. by: Random House, Inc., 400 Hahn Rd., Westminster, MD 21157) Ed. Paula Rackow.
Former titles: Fodor's Budget Europe (ISSN 0197-4998); (until 1979): Fodor's Europe on a Budget (ISSN 0276-0738)

914.404 US ISSN 1068-3593
DC16
FODOR'S AFFORDABLE FRANCE. 1980. biennial. $14. Fodor's Travel Publications, Inc. (Subsidiary of: Random House, Inc.), 201 E. 50th St., New York, NY 10022. TEL 800-533-6478. (Dist. by: Random House, Inc., 400 Hahn Rd., Westminster, MD 21157) Ed. Jillian Magalaner.
Former titles: Fodor's Great Travel Values: France; Fodor's Budget Travel France; Fodor's Budget France (ISSN 0194-4150)

914.304 US
FODOR'S AFFORDABLE GERMANY. 1979. biennial. $15. Fodor's Travel Publications, Inc. (Subsidiary of: Random House, Inc.), 201 E. 50th St., New York, NY 10022. TEL 800-533-6478. (Dist. by: Random House, Inc., 400 Hahn Rd., Westminster, MD 21157) Ed. Carolyn Price.
Former titles: Fodor's Great Travel Values: Germany; Fodor's Budget Travel Germany; Fodor's Budget Germany (ISSN 0193-9033)

914.204 US
FODOR'S AFFORDABLE GREAT BRITAIN. 1979. biennial. $14. Fodor's Travel Publications, Inc. (Subsidiary of: Random House, Inc.), 201 E. 50th St., New York, NY 10022. TEL 800-533-6478. (Dist. by: Random House, Inc., 400 Hahn Rd., Westminster, MD 21157) Ed. Alison Hoffman.
Former titles: Fodor's Great Travel Values: Britain; Fodor's Budget Travel Britain; Fodor's Budget Britain (ISSN 0193-2381)

914.504 US
FODOR'S AFFORDABLE ITALY. biennial. $15. Fodor's Travel Publications, Inc. (Subsidiary of: Random House, Inc.), 201 E. 50th St., New York, NY 10022. TEL 800-533-6478. (Dist. by: Random House, Inc., 400 Hahn Rd., Westminster, MD 21157) Ed. Paula Consolo.
Former titles: Fodor's Great Travel Values: Italy; Fodor's Budget Travel Italy; Fodor's Budget Italy (ISSN 0270-787X)

917.9804 US ISSN 0271-2776
F902.3
FODOR'S ALASKA. 1979. a. $14. Fodor's Travel Publications, Inc. (Subsidiary of: Random House, Inc.), 201 E. 50th St., New York, NY 10022. TEL 800-733-3000. (Dist. by: Random House, Inc., 400 Hahn Rd., Westminster, MD 21157) Ed. Suzanne DeGalan.

917.904 US
FODOR'S ARIZONA. a. $13. Fodor's Travel Publications, Inc. (Subsidiary of: Random House, Inc.), 201 E. 50th St., New York, NY 10022. TEL 800-733-3000. (Dist. by: Random House, Inc., 400 Hahn Rd., Westminster, MD 21157) Ed. Jillian Magalaner.

919.04 US
DU95
FODOR'S AUSTRALIA AND NEW ZEALAND. a. $18. Fodor's Travel Publications, Inc. (Subsidiary of: Random House, Inc.), 201 E. 50th St., New York, NY 10022. TEL 800-733-3000. (Dist. by: Random House, Inc., 400 Hahn Rd., Westminster, MD 21157) Ed. Craig Seligman. illus.
Formerly: Fodor's Australia, New Zealand and the South Pacific (ISSN 0191-2321)

914.3604 US ISSN 0071-6340
DB16
FODOR'S AUSTRIA. 1951. a. $16. Fodor's Travel Publications, Inc. (Subsidiary of: Random House, Inc.), 201 E. 50th St., New York, NY 10022. TEL 800-733-3000. (Dist. by: Random House, Inc., 400 Hahn Rd., Westminster, MD 21157) Ed. Craig Seligman.

919.704 US
FODOR'S BAHAMAS. a. $11. Fodor's Travel Publications, Inc. (Subsidiary of: Random House, Inc.), 201 E. 50th St., New York, NY 10022. TEL 800-733-3000. (Dist. by: Random House, Inc., 400 Hahn Rd., Westminster, MD 21157) Ed. Julie Tomasz.
Supersedes in part: Fodor's Caribbean and Bahamas (ISSN 0271-4760)

917.204 US
FODOR'S BAJA AND MEXICO'S PACIFIC COAST RESORTS. irreg. $11. Fodor's Travel Publications, Inc. (Subsidiary of: Random House, Inc.), 201 E. 50th St., New York, NY 10022. TEL 800-733-3000. (Dist. by: Random House, Inc., 400 Hahn Rd., Westminster, MD 21157) Ed. Carolyn Price.
Formerly: Fodor's Mexico's Baja.

917.2904 US ISSN 1050-9771
F2041
FODOR'S BARBADOS. irreg. $8. Fodor's Travel Publications, Inc. (Subsidiary of: Random House, Inc.), 201 E. 50th St., New York, NY 10022. TEL 800-733-3000. (Dist. by: Random House, Inc., 400 Hahn Rd., Westminster, MD 21157) Ed. Caroline Haberfeld.
Formerly: Fodor's Fun in Barbados.

917.404 US
FODOR'S BED AND BREAKFASTS AND COUNTRY INNS AND OTHER WEEKEND PLEASURES: NEW ENGLAND. irreg. $14. Fodor's Travel Publications, Inc. (Subsidiary of: Random House, Inc.), 201 E. 50th St., New York, NY 10022. TEL 800-733-3000. (Dist. by: Random House, Inc., 400 Hahn Rd., Westminster, MD 21157) Ed. Conrad Paulus.

917.04 US
FODOR'S BED AND BREAKFASTS AND COUNTRY INNS AND OTHER WEEKEND PLEASURES: THE MID-ATLANTIC REGION. irreg. $14. Fodor's Travel Publications, Inc. (Subsidiary of: Random House, Inc.), 201 E. 50th St., New York, NY 10022. TEL 800-733-3000. (Dist. by: Random House, Inc., 400 Hahn Rd., Westminster, MD 21157) Ed. Conrad Paulus.

917.04 US ISSN 1069-899X
TX907.3.S68
FODOR'S BED AND BREAKFASTS AND COUNTRY INNS AND OTHER WEEKEND PLEASURES: THE SOUTH. irreg. $15. Fodor's Travel Publications, Inc. (Subsidiary of: Random House, Inc.), 201 E. 50th St., New York, NY 10022. TEL 800-733-3000. (Dist. by: Random House, Inc., 400 Hahn Rd., Westminster, MD 21157) Ed. Conrad Paulus.

917.904 US ISSN 1069-9007
TX907.3.P33
FODOR'S BED AND BREAKFASTS AND COUNTRY INNS AND OTHER WEEKEND PLEASURES: THE WEST COAST. irreg. $15. Fodor's Travel Publications, Inc. (Subsidiary of: Random House, Inc.), 201 E. 50th St., New York, NY 10022. TEL 800-733-3000. (Dist. by: Random House, Inc., 400 Hahn Rd., Westminster, MD 21157) Ed. Paula Rackow.

914.9304 US ISSN 0071-6359
FODOR'S BELGIUM AND LUXEMBOURG. 1951. biennial. $16. Fodor's Travel Publications, Inc. (Subsidiary of: Random House, Inc.), 201 E. 50th St., New York, NY 10022. TEL 800-733-3000. (Dist. by: Random House, Inc., 400 Hahn Rd., Westminster, MD 21157) Ed. Nancy van Itallie.

914.304 US ISSN 1065-4593
DD859
FODOR'S BERLIN. 1992. a. $10. Fodor's Travel Publications, Inc. (Subsidiary of: Random House, Inc.), 201 E. 50th St., New York, NY 10022. TEL 800-733-3000. (Dist. by: Random House, Inc., 400 Hahn Rd., Westminster, MD 21157) Ed. Julie Tomasz.

919.704 US ISSN 0192-3765
F1632
FODOR'S BERMUDA. 1979. a. $11. Fodor's Travel Publications, Inc. (Subsidiary of: Random House, Inc.), 201 E. 50th St., New York, NY 10022. TEL 800-733-3000. (Dist. by: Random House, Inc., 400 Hahn Rd., Westminster, MD 21157) Ed. Julie Tomasz.

917.404 US ISSN 0882-0074
F73.18
FODOR'S BOSTON. 1984. a. $10. Fodor's Travel Publications, Inc. (Subsidiary of: Random House, Inc.), 2 Park Ave., New York, NY 10016. TEL 800-733-3000. (Dist. by: Random House, Inc., 400 Hahn Rd., Westminster, MD 21157) Ed. Jillian Magalaner.

918.104 US ISSN 0163-0628
F2509.5
FODOR'S BRAZIL. 1978. irreg. $11. Fodor's Travel Publications, Inc. (Subsidiary of: Random House, Inc.), 201 E. 50th St., New York, NY 10022. TEL 800-733-3000. (Dist. by: Random House, Inc., 400 Hahn Rd., Westminster, MD 21157) Ed. Paula Consolo.

TRAVEL AND TOURISM

910.09
DB983.5 US ISSN 1065-4607
FODOR'S BUDAPEST. irreg. $11. Fodor's Travel Publications, Inc. (Subsidiary of: Random House, Inc.), 201 E. 50th St., New York, NY 10022. TEL 800-733-3000. (Dist. by: Random House, Inc., 400 Hahn Rd., Westminster, MD 21157) Ed. Christopher Billy.
 Supersedes: Fodor's Hungary.

917.904
F859.3 US ISSN 0192-9925
FODOR'S CALIFORNIA. a. $16. Fodor's Travel Publications, Inc. (Subsidiary of: Random House, Inc.), 201 E. 50th St., New York, NY 10022. TEL 800-733-3000. (Dist. by: Random House, Inc., 400 Hahn Rd., Westminster, MD 21157) Ed. Larry Peterson.

917.104
F1009 US ISSN 0160-3906
FODOR'S CANADA. 1978. a. $16. Fodor's Travel Publications, Inc. (Subsidiary of: Random House, Inc.), 201 E. 50th St., New York, NY 10022. TEL 800-733-3000. (Dist. by: Random House, Inc., 400 Hahn Rd., Westminster, MD 21157) Ed. Conrad Paulus.

917.104 US
FODOR'S CANADA'S GREAT COUNTRY INNS BY ANITA STEWART. irreg. $13. Fodor's Travel Publications, Inc. (Subsidiary of: Random House, Inc.), 201 E. 50th St., New York, NY 10022. TEL 800-733-3000. (Dist. by: Random House, Inc., 400 Hahn Rd., Westminster, MD 21157) Ed. Michael Spring.

917.204
F1376 US ISSN 1051-6336
FODOR'S CANCUN, COZUMEL & THE YUCATAN PENINSULA. a. $11. Fodor's Travel Publications, Inc. (Subsidiary of: Random House, Inc.), 201 E. 50th St., New York, NY 10022. TEL 800-733-3000. (Dist. by: Random House, Inc., 400 Hahn Rd., Westminster, MD 21157) Ed. Carolyn Price.
 Formerly: Fodor's Cancun, Cozumel, Merida and the Yucatan.

917.404
F72.C3 US ISSN 1047-6768
FODOR'S CAPE COD. 1982. a. $12. Fodor's Travel Publications, Inc. (Subsidiary of: Random House, Inc.), 201 E. 50th St., New York, NY 10022. TEL 800-733-3000. (Dist. by: Random House, Inc., 400 Hahn Rd., Westminster, MD 21157) Ed. Jillian Magalaner.

917.2904 US
FODOR'S CARIBBEAN. 1962. a. $16. Fodor's Travel Publications, Inc. (Subsidiary of: Random House, Inc.), 201 E. 50th St., New York, NY 10022. TEL 800-733-3000. (Dist. by: Random House, Inc., 400 Hahn Rd., Westminster, MD 21157) Ed. Caroline Haberfield.
 Supersedes in part: Fodor's Caribbean and Bahamas (ISSN 0271-4760); Former titles: Fodor's Caribbean, Bahamas and Bermuda (ISSN 0098-2547); Fodor's Guide to the Caribbean, Bahamas and Bermuda (ISSN 0071-6561).

917.504 US
FODOR'S CAROLINAS & THE GEORGIA COAST. a. $11. Fodor's Travel Publications, Inc. (Subsidiary of: Random House, Inc.), 201 E. 50th St., New York, NY 10022. TEL 800-733-3000. (Dist. by: Random House, Inc., 400 Hahn Rd., Westminster, MD 21157) Ed. Andrew Collins.

917.204
F1429 US ISSN 0270-8183
FODOR'S CENTRAL AMERICA; Belize, Costa Rica, El Salvador, Guatemala, Honduras, Nicaragua, Panama. irreg., latest 1993 ed. $15. Fodor's Travel Publications, Inc. (Subsidiary of: Random House, Inc.), 201 E. 50th St., New York, NY 10022. TEL 800-733-3000. (Dist. by: Random House, Inc., 400 Hahn Rd., Westminster, MD 21157) Ed. Carolyn Price.

917.704
F548.18 US ISSN 0743-9326
FODOR'S CHICAGO. 1982. a. $11. Fodor's Travel Publications, Inc. (Subsidiary of: Random House, Inc.), 201 E. 50th St., New York, NY 10022. TEL 800-733-3000. (Dist. by: Random House, Inc., 400 Hahn Rd., Westminster, MD 21157) Ed. Suzanne DeGalan.
 Formerly: Fodor's Chicago and the Great Lakes.

915.104
DS705 US ISSN 1070-6895
FODOR'S CHINA. 1979. a. $19. Fodor's Travel Publications, Inc. (Subsidiary of: Random House, Inc.), 201 E. 50th St., New York, NY 10022. TEL 800-733-3000. (Dist. by: Random House, Inc., 400 Hahn Rd., Westminster, MD 21157) Ed. Craig Seligman.
 Formerly: Fodor's People's Republic of China (ISSN 0192-2378).

915.104 US
FODOR'S CHINA'S GREAT CITIES. irreg. $9.95. Fodor's Travel Publications, Inc. (Subsidiary of: Random House, Inc.), 201 E. 50th St., New York, NY 10022. TEL 800-733-3000. (Dist. by: Random House, Inc., 400 Hahn Rd., Westminster, MD 21157) Ed. Vernon Nahrgang.
 Formerly: Fodor's Beijing, Guangzhou and Shanghai.

914.704
DK16 US
FODOR'S COMMONWEALTH OF INDEPENDENT STATES AND THE BALTIC COUNTRIES. 1975. a. $18. Fodor's Travel Publications, Inc. (Subsidiary of: Random House, Inc.), 201 E. 50th St., New York, NY 10022. TEL 800-733-3000. (Dist. by: Random House, Inc., 400 Hahn Rd., Westminster, MD 21157) Ed. Christopher Billy. illus.
 Formerly: Fodor's Soviet Union (ISSN 0095-1358).

914.204 US
FODOR'S COTTAGES, BED AND BREAKFASTS AND COUNTRY INNS OF ENGLAND AND WALES BY ELIZABETH GUNDRY. irreg. $15. Fodor's Travel Publications, Inc. (Subsidiary of: Random House, Inc.), 201 E. 50th St., New York, NY 10022. TEL 800-733-3000. (Dist. by: Random House, Inc., 400 Hahn Rd., Westminster, MD 21157) Ed. Michael Spring.

910.202
G550 US ISSN 1070-4477
FODOR'S CRUISES AND PORTS OF CALL. a. $17. Fodor's Travel Publications, Inc. (Subsidiary of: Random House, Inc.), 201 E. 50th St., New York, NY 10022. TEL 800-733-3000. (Dist. by: Random House, Inc., 400 Hahn Rd., Westminster, MD 21157) Ed. Andrew Collins.

917.504
F319.07 US ISSN 1070-6402
FODOR'S DISNEY WORLD & THE ORLANDO AREA. Cover title: Fodor's (Year) Walt Disney World and the Orlando Area. a. $10. Fodor's Travel Publications, Inc. (Subsidiary of: Random House, Inc.), 201 E. 50th St., New York, NY 10022. TEL 800-733-3000. (Dist. by: Random House, Inc., 400 Hahn Rd., Westminster, MD 21157) Ed. Karen Cure.
 Formerly (until **1989**): Fodor's Fun in Disney World and the Orlando Area.

914.704
DJK8 US ISSN 0734-8010
FODOR'S EASTERN EUROPE. 1980. a. $17. Fodor's Travel Publications, Inc. (Subsidiary of: Random House, Inc.), 201 E. 50th St., New York, NY 10022. TEL 800-733-3000. (Dist. by: Random House, Inc., 400 Hahn Rd., Westminster, MD 21157) Ed. Christopher Billy.

916.204
DT45 US ISSN 0147-8176
FODOR'S EGYPT. 1977. biennial. $14. Fodor's Travel Publications, Inc. (Subsidiary of: Random House, Inc.), 201 E. 50th St., New York, NY 10022. TEL 800-733-3000. (Dist. by: Random House, Inc., 400 Hahn Rd., Westminster, MD 21157) Ed. Edie Jarolim. illus.

914.404
GV1853.4.F82 US ISSN 1074-4142
FODOR'S EURO DISNEY. 1993. a. $10. Fodor's Travel Publications, Inc. (Subsidiary of: Random House, Inc.), 201 E. 50th St., New York, NY 10022. TEL 800-733-3000. (Dist. by: Random House, Inc., 400 Hahn Rd., Westminster, MD 21157) Ed. Paula Consolo.

914.04
D909 US ISSN 0362-0204
FODOR'S EUROPE. 1959. a. $18. Fodor's Travel Publications, Inc. (Subsidiary of: Random House, Inc.), 201 E. 50th St., New York, NY 10022. TEL 800-733-3000. (Dist. by: Random House, Inc., 400 Hahn Rd., Westminster, MD 21157) Ed. Paulu Rackow.
 Formerly: Fodor's Guide to Europe (ISSN 0071-6375).

914.04
D909 US ISSN 1074-1216
FODOR'S EUROPE'S GREAT CITIES. a. $14. Fodor's Travel Publications, Inc. (Subsidiary of: Random House, Inc.), 201 E. 50th St., New York, NY 10022. TEL 800-733-3000. (Dist. by: Random House, Inc., 400 Hahn Rd., Westminster, MD 21157) Ed. Paula Rackow.

917.504
F309.3 US ISSN 0193-9556
FODOR'S FLORIDA. a. $15. Fodor's Travel Publications, Inc. (Subsidiary of: Random House, Inc.), 201 E. 50th St., New York, NY 10022. TEL 800-733-3000. (Dist. by: Random House, Inc., 400 Hahn Rd., Westminster, MD 21157) Ed. Alison Hoffman.

914.404 US ISSN 0071-6383
FODOR'S FRANCE. 1951. a. $16. Fodor's Travel Publications, Inc. (Subsidiary of: Random House, Inc.), 201 E. 50th St., New York, NY 10022. TEL 800-733-3000. (Dist. by: Random House, Inc., 400 Hahn Rd., Westminster, MD 21157) Ed. Jillian Magalaner.

914.304 US
FODOR'S GERMANY. 1951. a. $17. Fodor's Travel Publications, Inc. (Subsidiary of: Random House, Inc.), 201 E. 50th St., New York, NY 10022. TEL 800-733-3000. (Dist. by: Random House, Inc., 400 Hahn Rd., Westminster, MD 21157) Ed. Christopher Billy.
 Former titles: Fodor's Germany: West and East (ISSN 0192-0952); Fodor's Germany (ISSN 0071-6391).

914.304 US
FODOR'S GREAT AMERICAN VACATIONS. irreg. $14. Fodor's Travel Publications, Inc. (Subsidiary of: Random House, Inc.), 201 E. 50th St., New York, NY 10022. TEL 800-733-3000. (Dist. by: Random House, Inc., 400 Hahn Rd., Westminster, MD 21157) Ed. Jillian Magalaner.

914.104
DA650 US ISSN 0071-6405
FODOR'S GREAT BRITAIN. 1951. a. $16. Fodor's Travel Publications, Inc. (Subsidiary of: Random House, Inc.), 201 E. 50th St., New York, NY 10022. TEL 800-733-3000. (Dist. by: Random House, Inc., 400 Hahn Rd., Westminster, MD 21157) Ed. Caroline Haberfield.

914.9504
DF716 US ISSN 0071-6413
FODOR'S GREECE. 1951. biennial. $16. Fodor's Travel Publications, Inc. (Subsidiary of: Random House, Inc.), 201 E. 50th St., New York, NY 10022. TEL 800-733-3000. (Dist. by: Random House, Inc., 400 Hahn Rd., Westminster, MD 21157) Ed. Conrad Paulus.

919.6904
DU622 US ISSN 0071-6421
FODOR'S HAWAII. 1961. a. $15. Fodor's Travel Publications, Inc. (Subsidiary of: Random House, Inc.), 201 E. 50th St., New York, NY 10022. TEL 800-733-3000. (Dist. by: Random House, Inc., 400 Hahn Rd., Westminster, MD 21157) Ed. Larry Peterson.

TRAVEL AND TOURISM

910.202 613.7   US   ISSN 1057-8048
RA802
FODOR'S HEALTHY ESCAPES. 1989. irreg. $15. Fodor's Travel Publications, Inc. (Subsidiary of: Random House, Inc.), 201 E. 50th St., New York, NY 10022. TEL 800-733-3000. (Dist. by: Random House, Inc., 400 Hahn Rd., Westminster, MD 21157) Ed. Carolyn Price.
   Formerly (until 1990): Fodor's Health and Fitness Vacations (ISSN 1047-5052)

914.9204   US   ISSN 0071-643X
DJ16
FODOR'S HOLLAND. 1951. biennial. $14. Fodor's Travel Publications, Inc. (Subsidiary of: Random House, Inc.), 201 E. 50th St., New York, NY 10022. TEL 800-733-3000. (Dist. by: Random House, Inc., 400 Hahn Rd., Westminster, MD 21157) Ed. Nancy van Itallie.

915.1204   US   ISSN 1070-6887
DS796.H74
FODOR'S HONG KONG. 1984. a. $12. Fodor's Travel Publications, Inc. (Subsidiary of: Random House, Inc.), 201 E. 50th St., New York, NY 10022. TEL 800-733-3000. (Dist. by: Random House, Inc., 400 Hahn Rd., Westminster, MD 21157) Ed. Caroline Haberfeld.
   Formerly: Fodor's Hong Kong and Macau (ISSN 0882-0066)

915.404   US
DS406
FODOR'S INDIA. 1963. biennial. $19. Fodor's Travel Publications, Inc. (Subsidiary of: Random House, Inc.), 201 E. 50th St., New York, NY 10022. TEL 800-733-3000. (Dist. by: Random House, Inc., 400 Hahn Rd., Westminster, MD 21157) Ed. Paula Consolo.
   Former titles: Fodor's India and Nepal (ISSN 0276-5500); Fodor's India (ISSN 0362-0212); Which supersedes: Fodor's Guide to India (ISSN 0071-6456)

914.1504   US   ISSN 0071-6464
FODOR'S IRELAND. 1968. a. $16. Fodor's Travel Publications, Inc. (Subsidiary of: Random House, Inc.), 201 E. 50th St., New York, NY 10022. TEL 800-733-3000. (Dist. by: Random House, Inc., 400 Hahn Rd., Westminster, MD 21157) Ed. Andrew Collins.

915.6904   US   ISSN 0071-6588
DS103
FODOR'S ISRAEL. 1967. a. $16. Fodor's Travel Publications, Inc. (Subsidiary of: Random House, Inc.), 201 E. 50th St., New York, NY 10022. TEL 800-733-3000. (Dist. by: Random House, Inc., 400 Hahn Rd., Westminster, MD 21157) Ed. Paula Rackow.

914.504   US   ISSN 0071-6472
FODOR'S ITALY. 1951. a. $17. Fodor's Travel Publications, Inc. (Subsidiary of: Random House, Inc.), 201 E. 50th St., New York, NY 10022. TEL 800-733-3000. (Dist. by: Random House, Inc., 400 Hahn Rd., Westminster, MD 21157) Ed. Holly Hughes.

914.504   US
FODOR'S ITALY'S GREAT CITIES. a. $11. Fodor's Travel Publications, Inc. (Subsidiary of: Random House, Inc.), 201 E. 50th St., New York, NY 10022. TEL 800-733-3000. (Dist. by: Random House, Inc., 400 Hahn Rd., Westminster, MD 21157) Ed. Holly Hughes.
   Formerly: Fodor's Florence and Venice.

915.204   US   ISSN 0736-9956
DS811
FODOR'S JAPAN. 1962. a. $19. Fodor's Travel Publications, Inc. (Subsidiary of: Random House, Inc.), 201 E. 50th St., New York, NY 10022. TEL 800-733-3000. (Dist. by: Random House, Inc., 400 Hahn Rd., Westminster, MD 21157) Ed. Paula Consolo.
   Supersedes in part: Fodor's Japan and Korea (ISSN 0098-1613); Which supersedes in part: Fodor's Japan and East Asia (ISSN 0071-6480)

916.7604   US
FODOR'S KENYA & TANZANIA. irreg. $16. Fodor's Travel Publications, Inc. (Subsidiary of: Random House, Inc.), 201 E. 50th St., New York, NY 10022. TEL 800-733-3000. (Dist. by: Random House, Inc., 400 Hahn Rd., Westminster, MD 21157) Ed. Conrad Paulus.
   Formerly: Fodor's Kenya.

915.104   US
FODOR'S KOREA. a. $14. Fodor's Travel Publications, Inc. (Subsidiary of: Random House, Inc.), 201 E. 50th St., New York, NY 10022. TEL 800-733-3000. (Dist. by: Random House, Inc., 400 Hahn Rd., Westminster, MD 21157) Ed. Julie Tomasz.
   Supersedes in part: Fodor's Japan and Korea (ISSN 0098-1613); Which supersedes in part: Fodor's Japan and East Asia (ISSN 0071-6480)

917.904   US
FODOR'S LAS VEGAS, RENO, TAHOE. a. $12. Fodor's Travel Publications, Inc. (Subsidiary of: Random House, Inc.), 201 E. 50th St., New York, NY 10022. TEL 800-733-3000. (Dist. by: Random House, Inc., 400 Hahn Rd., Westminster, MD 21157) Ed. Jillian Magalaner.
   Formerly: Fodor's Fun in Las Vegas.

914.2104   US   ISSN 0071-6596
FODOR'S LONDON. 1971. a. $11. Fodor's Travel Publications, Inc. (Subsidiary of: Random House, Inc.), 201 E. 50th St., New York, NY 10022. TEL 800-733-3000. (Dist. by: Random House, Inc., 400 Hahn Rd., Westminster, MD 21157) Ed. Craig Seligman.

917.904   US   ISSN 0743-3336
F869.L83
FODOR'S LOS ANGELES. a. $12. Fodor's Travel Publications, Inc. (Subsidiary of: Random House, Inc.), 201 E. 50th St., New York, NY 10022. TEL 800-733-3000. (Dist. by: Random House, Inc., 400 Hahn Rd., Westminster, MD 21157) Ed. Larry Peterson.

914.604   US
FODOR'S MADRID AND BARCELONA. a. $11. Fodor's Travel Publications, Inc. (Subsidiary of: Random House, Inc.), 201 E. 50th St., New York, NY 10022. TEL 800-733-3000. (Dist. by: Random House, Inc., 400 Hahn Rd., Westminster, MD 21157) Ed. Suzanne DeGalan.
   Formerly: Fodor's Madrid (ISSN 0884-0393)

917.404   US   ISSN 1073-6581
F17.3
FODOR'S MAINE, VERMONT, NEW HAMPSHIRE. 1991. irreg. $10. Fodor's Travel Publications, Inc. (Subsidiary of: Random House, Inc.), 201 E. 50th St., New York, NY 10022. TEL 800-733-3000. (Dist. by: Random House, Inc., 400 Hahn Rd., Westminster, MD 21157) Ed. Jillian Magalaner.

917.2904   US
FODOR'S MAUI. a. $9. Fodor's Travel Publications, Inc. (Subsidiary of: Random House, Inc.), 201 E. 50th St., New York, NY 10022. TEL 800-733-3000. (Dist. by: Random House, Inc., 400 Hahn Rd., Westminster, MD 21157) Ed. Larry Peterson.
   Formerly: Fodor's Fun in Maui.

917.204   US   ISSN 0071-6499
FODOR'S MEXICO. 1972. a. $16. Fodor's Travel Publications, Inc. (Subsidiary of: Random House, Inc.), 201 E. 50th St., New York, NY 10022. TEL 800-733-3000. (Dist. by: Random House, Inc., 400 Hahn Rd., Westminster, MD 21157) Ed. Carolyn Price.

917.504   US   ISSN 1070-6399
F319.M6
FODOR'S MIAMI & THE KEYS. a. $10. Fodor's Travel Publications, Inc. (Subsidiary of: Random House, Inc.), 201 E. 50th St., New York, NY 10022. TEL 800-733-3000. (Dist. by: Random House, Inc., 400 Hahn Rd., Westminster, MD 21157) Ed. Alison Hoffman.
   Formerly: Fodor's Greater Miami and the Gold Coast.

917.104   US
FODOR'S MONTREAL & QUEBEC CITY. a. $12. Fodor's Travel Publications, Inc. (Subsidiary of: Random House, Inc.), 201 E. 50th St., New York, NY 10022. TEL 800-733-3000. (Dist. by: Random House, Inc., 400 Hahn Rd., Westminster, MD 21157) Ed. Conrad Paulus.
   Formerly: Fodor's Fun in Montreal.

916.104   US   ISSN 0190-1508
DT309
FODOR'S MOROCCO. 1980. irreg. $16.95. Fodor's Travel Publications, Inc. (Subsidiary of: Random House, Inc.), 201 E. 50th St., New York, NY 10022. TEL 800-733-3000. (Dist. by: Random House, Inc., 400 Hahn Rd., Westminster, MD 21157) Ed. Paula Consolo.
   Formerly: Fodor's North Africa.

914.304   US
FODOR'S MUNICH. 1984. irreg. $11. Fodor's Travel Publications, Inc. (Subsidiary of: Random House, Inc.), 201 E. 50th St., New York, NY 10022. TEL 800-733-3000. (Dist. by: Random House, Inc., 400 Hahn Rd., Westminster, MD 21157) Ed. Larry Peterson.

917.804   US
FODOR'S NATIONAL PARKS OF THE WEST. irreg. $17. Fodor's Travel Publications, Inc. (Subsidiary of: Random House, Inc.), 201 E. 50th St., New York, NY 10022. TEL 800-733-3000. (Dist. by: Random House, Inc., 400 Hahn Rd., Westminster, MD 21157) Ed. Paula Consolo.

917.404   US   ISSN 0192-3412
F2.3
FODOR'S NEW ENGLAND. 1975. a. $16. Fodor's Travel Publications, Inc. (Subsidiary of: Random House, Inc.), 201 E. 50th St., New York, NY 10022. TEL 800-733-3000. (Dist. by: Random House, Inc., 400 Hahn Rd., Westminster, MD 21157) Ed. Jillian Magalaner. illus.

917.604   US   ISSN 0743-9385
F379.N53
FODOR'S NEW ORLEANS. a. $11. Fodor's Travel Publications, Inc. (Subsidiary of: Random House, Inc.), 201 E. 50th St., New York, NY 10022. TEL 800-733-3000. (Dist. by: Random House, Inc., 400 Hahn Rd., Westminster, MD 21157) Ed. Nancy van Itallie.

917.404   US   ISSN 0736-9395
F128.18
FODOR'S NEW YORK CITY. 1975. a. $13. Fodor's Travel Publications, Inc. (Subsidiary of: Random House, Inc.), 201 E. 50th St., New York, NY 10022. TEL 800-733-3000. (Dist. by: Random House, Inc., 400 Hahn Rd., Westminster, MD 21157) Ed. Suzanne DeGalan. illus.
   Former titles: Fodor's New York; Fodor's New York and New Jersey.

919.304   US
FODOR'S NEW ZEALAND. a. $9. Fodor's Travel Publications, Inc. (Subsidiary of: Random House, Inc.), 201 E. 50th St., New York, NY 10022. TEL 800-733-3000. (Dist. by: Random House, Inc., 400 Hahn Rd., Westminster, MD 21157) Ed. Craig Seligman.

917.404   US   ISSN 1073-6603
DL407
FODOR'S NORWAY. 1992. irreg. $10. Fodor's Travel Publications, Inc. (Subsidiary of: Random House, Inc.), 201 E. 50th St., New York, NY 10022. TEL 800-733-3000. (Dist. by: Random House, Inc., 400 Hahn Rd., Westminster, MD 21157) Ed. Nancy van Itallie.

917.104   US   ISSN 1064-7643
F1035.8
FODOR'S NOVA SCOTIA, PRINCE EDWARD ISLAND AND NEW BRUNSWICK. irreg. $9. Fodor's Travel Publications, Inc. (Subsidiary of: Random House, Inc.), 201 E. 50th St., New York, NY 10022. TEL 800-733-3000. (Dist. by: Random House, Inc., 400 Hahn Rd. Westminster, MD 21157) Ed. Edie Jarolim.
   Formerly: Fodor's Canada's Maritime Provinces.

TRAVEL AND TOURISM

917.904　　　　US　　ISSN 1072-0391
F852.3
FODOR'S PACIFIC NORTH COAST. 1984. a. $16. Fodor's Travel Publications, Inc. (Subsidiary of: Random House, Inc.), 201 E. 50th St., New York, NY 10022. TEL 800-733-3000. (Dist. by: Random House, Inc., 400 Hahn Rd., Westminster, MD 21157) Ed. Larry Peterson.

914.404　　　　US　　ISSN 0149-1288
DC708
FODOR'S PARIS. 1973. a. $12. Fodor's Travel Publications, Inc. (Subsidiary of: Random House, Inc.), 201 E. 50th St., New York, NY 10022. TEL 800-733-3000. (Dist. by: Random House, Inc., 400 Hahn Rd., Westminster, MD 21157) Ed. Paula Consolo.

917.404
FODOR'S PHILADELPHIA & THE PENNSYLVANIA DUTCH COUNTRY. irreg. $11. Fodor's Travel Publications, Inc. (Subsidiary of: Random House, Inc.), 201 E. 50th St., New York, NY 10022. TEL 800-733-3000. (Dist. by: Random House, Inc., 400 Hahn St., Westminster, MD 21157) Ed. Caroline Haberfeld.
　Formerly: Fodor's Philadelphia.

917.2904　　　US　　ISSN 1074-1208
F1869
FODOR'S POCKET JAMAICA. a. $7. Fodor's Travel Publications, Inc. (Subsidiary of: Random House, Inc.), 201 E. 50th St., New York, NY 10022. TEL 800-733-3000. (Dist. by: Random House, Inc., 400 Hahn Rd., Westminster, MD 21157) Ed. Caroline Haberfeld.
　Formerly: Fodor's Fun in Jamaica.

914.2104　　　US
FODOR'S POCKET LONDON. a. $8. Fodor's Travel Publications, Inc. (Subsidiary of: Random House, Inc.), 201 E. 50th St., New York, NY 10022. TEL 800-733-3000. (Dist. by: Random House, Inc., 400 Hahn Rd., Westminster, MD 21157) Ed. Craig Seligman.
　Formerly: Fodor's Fun in London.

917.404　　　　US　　ISSN 1056-7712
F128.18
FODOR'S POCKET NEW YORK CITY. a. $8. Fodor's Travel Publications, Inc. (Subsidiary of: Random House, Inc.), 201 E. 50th St., New York, NY 10022. TEL 800-733-3000. (Dist. by: Random House, Inc., 400 Hahn Rd., Westminster, MD 21157) Ed. Suzanne DeGalan.
　Formerly: Fodor's Fun in New York City.

914.404　　　　US
FODOR'S POCKET PARIS. a. $8. Fodor's Travel Publications, Inc. (Subsidiary of: Random House, Inc.), 201 E. 50th St., New York, NY 10022. TEL 800-733-3000. (Dist. by: Random House, Inc., 400 Hahn Rd., Westminster, MD 21157) Ed. Paula Consolo.
　Formerly: Fodor's Fun in Paris.

917.204　　　　US
FODOR'S POCKET PUERTO RICO. a. $7. Fodor's Travel Publications, Inc. (Subsidiary of: Random House, Inc.), 201 E. 50th St., New York, NY 10022. TEL 800-733-3000. (Dist. by: Random House Inc., 400 Hahn Rd., Westminster, MD 21157) Ed. Andrew Collins.

917.904　　　　US　　ISSN 1046-8978
FODOR'S POCKET SAN FRANCISCO. a. $8. Fodor's Travel Publications, Inc. (Subsidiary of: Random House, Inc.), 201 E. 50th St., New York, NY 10022. TEL 800-733-3000. (Dist. by: Random House, Inc., 400 Hahn Rd., Westminster, MD 21157) Ed. Larry Peterson.
　Formerly: Fodor's Fun in San Francisco.

917.504　　　　US
FODOR'S POCKET WASHINGTON. a. $8. Fodor's Travel Publications, Inc. (Subsidiary of: Random House, Inc.), 201 E. 50th St., New York, NY 10022. TEL 800-733-3000. (Dist. by: Random House, Inc., 400 Hahn Rd., Westminster, MD 21157) Ed. Suzanne DeGalan.

914.6904　　　US　　ISSN 0071-6510
DP516
FODOR'S PORTUGAL. 1951. a. $17. Fodor's Travel Publications, Inc. (Subsidiary of: Random House, Inc.), 201 E. 50th St., New York, NY 10022. TEL 800-733-3000. (Dist. by: Random House, Inc., 400 Hahn Rd., Westminster, MD 21157) Ed. Alison Hoffman.

914.504　　　　US　　ISSN 0276-2560
DG804
FODOR'S ROME. 1979. a. $13. Fodor's Travel Publications, Inc. (Subsidiary of: Random House, Inc.), 201 E. 50th St., New York, NY 10022. TEL 800-733-3000. (Dist. by: Random House, Inc., 400 Hahn Rd., Westminster, MD 21157) Ed. Julie Tomasz.

917.904　　　　US　　ISSN 1053-5950
F869.S22
FODOR'S SAN DIEGO. a. $11. Fodor's Travel Publications, Inc. (Subsidiary of: Random House, Inc.), 201 E. 50th St., New York, NY 10022. TEL 800-733-3000. (Dist. by: Random House, Inc., 400 Hahn Rd., Westminster, MD 21157) Ed. Larry Peterson.

917.904　　　　US　　ISSN 0743-9334
F869.S33
FODOR'S SAN FRANCISCO. 1982. a. $11. Fodor's Travel Publications, Inc. (Subsidiary of: Random House, Inc.), 201 E. 50th St., New York, NY 10022. TEL 800-733-3000. (Dist. by: Random House, Inc., 400 Hahn Rd., Westminster, MD 21157) Ed. Larry Peterson.

917.804　　　　US
FODOR'S SANTA FE, TAOS, ALBUQUERQUE. a. $12. Fodor's Travel Publications, Inc. (Subsidiary of: Random House, Inc.), 201 E. 50th St., New York, NY 10022. TEL 800-733-3000. (Dist. by: Random House, Inc., 400 Hahn Rd., Westminster, MD 21157) Ed. Julie Tomasz.
　Formerly: Fodor's New Mexico.

914.804　　　　US　　ISSN 0071-6529
FODOR'S SCANDINAVIA. 1951. a. $19. Fodor's Travel Publications, Inc. (Subsidiary of: Random House, Inc.), 201 E. 50th St., New York, NY 10022. TEL 800-733-3000. (Dist. by: Random House, Inc., 400 Hahn Rd., Westminster, MD 21157) Ed. Nancy van Itallie.

914.804　　　　US
FODOR'S SCANDINAVIAN CITIES. irreg. $9. Fodor's Travel Publications, Inc. (Subsidiary of: Random House, Inc.), 201 E. 50th St., New York, NY 10022. TEL 800-733-3000. (Dist. by: Random House, Inc., 400 Hahn Rd., Westminster, MD 21157) Ed. Nancy van Itallie.
　Formerly: Fodor's Stockholm, Copenhagen, Oslo, Helsinki and Reykjavik.

914.104　　　　US　　ISSN 0743-0973
DA870
FODOR'S SCOTLAND. a. $16. Fodor's Travel Publications, Inc. (Subsidiary of: Random House, Inc.), 201 E. 50th St., New York, NY 10022. TEL 800-733-3000. (Dist. by: Random House, Inc., 400 Hahn Rd., Westminster, MD 21157) Ed. Caroline Haberfeld.

917.904　　　　US
FODOR'S SEATTLE AND VANCOUVER. irreg. $10. Fodor's Travel Publications, Inc. (Subsidiary of: Random House, Inc.), 201 E. 50th St., New York, NY 10022. TEL 800-733-3000. (Dist. by: Random House, Inc., 400 Hahn Rd., Westminster, MD 21157) Ed. Alison Hoffman.

915.9504　　　US
FODOR'S SINGAPORE. irreg. $13. Fodor's Travel Publications, Inc. (Subsidiary of: Random House, Inc.), 201 E. 50th St., New York, NY 10022. TEL 800-733-3000. (Dist. by: Random House, Inc., 400 Hahn Rd., Westminster, MD 21157) Ed. Craig Seligman.

917.04 796.93　　US
FODOR'S SKIING IN THE U S A & CANADA. irreg. $15. Fodor's Travel Publications, Inc. (Subsidiary of: Random House, Inc.), 201 E. 50th St., New York, NY 10022. TEL 800-733-3000. (Dist. by: Random House, Inc., 400 Hahn Rd., Westminster, MD 21157)
　Formerly: Fodor's Ski Resorts of North America.

918.04　　　　US　　ISSN 0071-6537
F2211
FODOR'S SOUTH AMERICA. 1966. a. $17. Fodor's Travel Publications, Inc. (Subsidiary of: Random House, Inc.), 201 E. 50th St., New York, NY 10022. TEL 800-733-3000. (Dist. by: Random House, Inc., 400 Hahn Rd., Westminster, MD 21157) Ed. Julie Tomasz.

919.604　　　　US
FODOR'S SOUTH PACIFIC. irreg. $12. Fodor's Travel Publications, Inc. (Subsidiary of: Random House, Inc.), 201 E. 50th St., New York, NY 10022. TEL 800-733-3000. (Dist. by: Random House, Inc., 400 Hahn Rd., Westminster, MD 21157) Ed. Craig Seligman.

915.904　　　　US　　ISSN 0160-8991
DS504
FODOR'S SOUTHEAST ASIA. 1975. a. $18. Fodor's Travel Publications, Inc. (Subsidiary of: Random House, Inc.), 201 E. 50th St., New York, NY 10022. TEL 800-733-3000. (Dist. by: Random House, Inc., 400 Hahn Rd., Westminster, MD 21157) Ed. Craig Seligman.
　Supersedes in part: Fodor's Japan and East Asia (ISSN 0071-6480)

914.604　　　　US　　ISSN 0071-6545
FODOR'S SPAIN. 1955. a. $16. Fodor's Travel Publications, Inc. (Subsidiary of: Random House, Inc.), 201 E. 50th St., New York, NY 10022. TEL 800-733-3000. (Dist. by: Random House, Inc., 400 Hahn Rd., Westminster, MD 21157) Ed. Suzanne DeGalan.

FODOR'S SPORTS: CYCLING. see SPORTS AND GAMES — Bicycles And Motorcycles

FODOR'S SPORTS: HIKING. see SPORTS AND GAMES — Outdoor Life

FODOR'S SPORTS: RUNNING. see SPORTS AND GAMES — Outdoor Life

FODOR'S SPORTS: SAILING. see SPORTS AND GAMES — Boats And Boating

917.404　　　　US
FODOR'S SUNDAY IN NEW YORK. irreg. $11. Fodor's Travel Publications, Inc. (Subsidiary of: Random House, Inc.), 201 E. 50th St., New York, NY 10022. TEL 800-733-3000. (Dist. by: Random House, Inc., 400 Hahn Rd., Westminster, MD 21157) Eds. David Low, Andrew Anspach.

914.8504　　　US
FODOR'S SWEDEN. irreg. $9. Fodor's Travel Publications, Inc. (Subsidiary of: Random House, Inc.), 201 E. 50th St., New York, NY 10022. TEL 800-733-3000. (Dist. by: Random House, Inc., 400 Hahn Rd., Westminster, MD 21157) Ed. Nancy van Itallie.

914.9404　　　US　　ISSN 0071-6553
DQ16
FODOR'S SWITZERLAND. 1951. a. $17. Fodor's Travel Publications, Inc. (Subsidiary of: Random House, Inc.), 201 E. 50th St., New York, NY 10022. TEL 800-733-3000. (Dist. by: Random House, Inc., 400 Hahn Rd., Westminster, MD 21157) Ed. Karen Cure.

915.9304　　　US　　ISSN 1064-0983
DS563
FODOR'S THAILAND. irreg. $12. Fodor's Travel Publications, Inc. (Subsidiary of: Random House, Inc.), 201 E. 50th St., New York, NY 10022. TEL 800-733-3000. (Dist. by: Random House, Inc., 400 Hahn Rd., Westminster, MD 21157) Ed. Conrad Paulus.

917.504　　　　US
FODOR'S THE CHESAPEAKE REGION. irreg. $8.95. Fodor's Travel Publications, Inc. (Subsidiary of: Random House, Inc.), 201 E. 50th St., New York, NY 10022. TEL 800-733-3000. (Dist. by: Random House, Inc., 400 Hahn Rd., Westminster, MD 21157) Ed. Vernon Nahrgang.
　Formerly: Fodor's Chesapeake.

TRAVEL AND TOURISM

917.04 US ISSN 0147-8680
F207.3
FODOR'S THE SOUTH. 1975. a. $15. Fodor's Travel Publications, Inc. (Subsidiary of: Random House, Inc.), 201 E. 50th St., New York, NY 10022. TEL 800-733-3000. (Dist. by: Random House, Inc., 400 Hahn Rd., Westminster, MD 21157) Ed. Andrew Collins. illus.

914.404 440 US
FODOR'S THREE-IN-ONE: FRANCE; guidebook, language cassette and phrase book. irreg. $27.50. Fodor's Travel Publications, Inc. (Subsidiary of: Random House, Inc.), 201 E. 50th St., New York, NY 10022. TEL 800-733-3000. (Dist. by: Random House, Inc., 400 Hahn Rd., Westminster, MD 21157)

914.304 430 US
FODOR'S THREE-IN-ONE: GERMANY; guidebook, language cassette and phrase book. irreg. $27.50. Fodor's Travel Publications, Inc. (Subsidiary of: Random House, Inc.), 201 E. 50th St., New York, NY 10022. TEL 800-733-3000. (Dist. by: Random House, Inc., 400 Hahn Rd., Westminster, MD 21157)

914.504 450 US
FODOR'S THREE-IN-ONE: ITALY; guidebook, language cassette and phrase book. irreg. $27.50. Fodor's Travel Publications, Inc. (Subsidiary of: Random House, Inc.), 201 E. 50th St., New York, NY 10022. TEL 800-733-3000. (Dist. by: Random House, Inc., 400 Hahn Rd., Westminster, MD 21157)

917.204 460 US
FODOR'S THREE-IN-ONE: MEXICO; guidebook, language cassette and phrase book. irreg. $27.50. Fodor's Travel Publications, Inc. (Subsidiary of: Random House, Inc.), 201 E. 50th St., New York, NY 10022. TEL 800-733-3000. (Dist. by: Random House, Inc., 400 Hahn Rd., Westminster, MD 21157)

914.604 460 US
FODOR'S THREE-IN-ONE: SPAIN; guidebook, language cassette and phrase book. irreg. $27.50. Fodor's Travel Publications, Inc. (Subsidiary of: Random House, Inc.), 201 E. 50th St., New York, NY 10022. TEL 800-733-3000. (Dist. by: Random House, Inc., 400 Hahn Rd., Westminster, MD 21157)

915.204 US
FODOR'S TOKYO. irreg. $12. Fodor's Travel Publications, Inc. (Subsidiary of: Random House, Inc.), 201 E. 50th St., New York, NY 10022. TEL 800-733-3000. (Dist. by: Random House, Inc., 400 Hahn Rd., Westminster, MD 21157) Ed. Paula Consolo.

917.104 US ISSN 1044-6133
F1059.5.T683
FODOR'S TORONTO. 1984. a. $12. Fodor's Travel Publications, Inc. (Subsidiary of: Random House, Inc.), 201 E. 50th St., New York, NY 10022. TEL 800-733-3000. (Dist. by: Random House, Inc., 400 Hahn Rd., Westminster, MD 21157) Ed. Jillian Magalaner.
 Formerly (until 1989): Fodor's Toronto and Nearby Attractions (ISSN 1066-6141)

914.04 US
FODOR'S TOURING EUROPE. irreg. $14. Fodor's Travel Publications, Inc. (Subsidiary of: Random House, Inc.), 201 E. 50th St., New York, NY 10022. TEL 800-733-3000. (Dist. by: Random House, Inc., 400 Hahn Rd., Westminster, MD 21157) Ed. Nancy van Itallie.

917.304 US
FODOR'S TOURING U S A: EASTERN EDITION. irreg. $16. Fodor's Travel Publications, Inc. (Subsidiary of: Random House, Inc.), 201 E. 50th St., New York, NY 10022. TEL 800-733-3000. (Dist. by: Random House, Inc., 400 Hahn Rd., Westminster, MD 21157) Ed. Holly Hughes.

917.804 US
FODOR'S TOURING U S A: WESTERN EDITION. irreg. $16. Fodor's Travel Publications, Inc. (Subsidiary of: Random House, Inc.), 201 E. 50th St., New York, NY 10022. TEL 800-733-3000. (Dist. by: Random House, Inc., 400 Hahn Rd., Westminster, MD 21157) Ed. Craig Seligman.

915.6104 US ISSN 0071-6618
DR416
FODOR'S TURKEY. 1969. a. $17. Fodor's Travel Publications, Inc. (Subsidiary of: Random House, Inc.), 201 E. 50th St., New York, NY 10022. TEL 800-733-3000. (Dist. by: Random House, Inc., 400 Hahn Rd., Westminster, MD 21157) Ed. Karen Cure.

917.304 US ISSN 0147-8745
E158
FODOR'S U S A. 1976. a. $18. Fodor's Travel Publications, Inc. (Subsidiary of: Random House, Inc.), 201 E. 50th St., New York, NY 10022. TEL 800-733-3000. (Dist. by: Random House, Inc., 400 Hahn Rd., Westminster, MD 21157) Ed. Nancy van Itallie. illus.

919.704 US ISSN 1070-6380
F2136.2
FODOR'S U S & BRITISH VIRGIN ISLANDS. 1990. a. $12. Fodor's Travel Publications, Inc. (Subsidiary of: Random House, Inc.), 201 E. 50th St., New York, NY 10022. TEL 800-733-3000. (Dist. by: Random House, Inc., 400 Hahn St., Westminster, MD 21157) Ed. Suzanne DeGalan.
 Formerly: Fodor's Virgin Islands (ISSN 1048-1060)

917.404 US
FODOR'S VACATIONS IN NEW YORK STATE. irreg. $14.95. Fodor's Travel Publications, Inc. (Subsidiary of: Random House, Inc.), 201 E. 50th St., New York, NY 10022. TEL 800-733-3000. (Dist. by: Random House, Inc., 400 Hahn Rd., Westminster, MD 21157)
 Formerly: Fodor's New York State.

917.404 US
FODOR'S VACATIONS ON THE NEW JERSEY SHORE. irreg. $11. Fodor's Travel Publications, Inc. (Subsidiary of: Random House, Inc.), 201 E. 50th St., New York, NY 10022. TEL 800-733-3000. (Dist. by: Random House, Inc., 400 Hahn Rd., Westminster, MD 21157)
 Formerly: Fodor's Atlantic City and the New Jersey Shore.

914.304 US
FODOR'S VIENNA AND THE DANUBE VALLEY. 1984. irreg. $10. Fodor's Travel Publications, Inc. (Subsidiary of: Random House, Inc.), 201 E. 50th St., New York, NY 10022. TEL 800-733-3000. (Dist. by: Random House, Inc., 400 Hahn Rd., Westminster, MD 21157) Ed. Jillian Magalaner.
 Formerly: Fodor's Vienna.

917.504 US ISSN 1075-0711
F224.3
FODOR'S VIRGINIA & MARYLAND. irreg. $12. Fodor's Travel Publications, Inc. (Subsidiary of: Random House, Inc.), 201 E. 50th St., New York, NY 10022. TEL 800-733-3000. (Dist. by: Random House, Inc., 400 Hahn Rd., Westminster, MD 21157) Ed. Alison Hoffman.
 Formerly: Fodor's Virginia.

919.6904 US ISSN 1044-923X
DU629.H7
FODOR'S WAIKIKI. irreg. $9. Fodor's Travel Publications, Inc. (Subsidiary of: Random House, Inc.), 201 E. 50th St., New York, NY 10022. TEL 800-733-3000. (Dist. by: Random House, Inc., 400 Hahn Rd., Westminster, MD 21157) Ed. Jillian Magalaner.
 Formerly: Fodor's Fun in Waikiki.

917.504 US ISSN 0743-9741
F192.3
FODOR'S WASHINGTON, D.C.. a. $11. Fodor's Travel Publications, Inc. (Subsidiary of: Random House, Inc.), 201 E. 50th St., New York, NY 10022. TEL 800-733-3000. (Dist. by: Random House, Inc., 400 Hahn Rd., Westminster, MD 21157) Ed. Suzanne DeGalan.

914.9704 US ISSN 0071-657X
DR304.5
FODOR'S YUGOSLAVIA. 1951. irreg. $16. Fodor's Travel Publications, Inc. (Subsidiary of: Random House, Inc.), 201 E. 50th St., New York, NY 10022. TEL 800-733-3000. (Dist. by: Random House, Inc., 400 Hahn Rd., Westminster, MD 21157) Ed. Nancy van Itallie.

910.09 IT
FOLLOW ME. 1989. m. L.35000($22) Lancio S.p.A., Via Roccagiovine 267, 00156 Rome, Italy. TEL 39-6-4112651. FAX 39-6-6748185. Ed. Fernando Mercurio. adv.: color page L.44000000; trim 210 x 280. circ. 405,440. (back issues avail.) **Document type:** consumer publication.
 Description: Contains information and articles on airport life, flying, tourism, art, culture and science. For frequent flyers, distributed free in Italian airports.

387.2 US ISSN 0096-1353
VM381
FORD'S DECK PLAN GUIDE. Short title: Deck Plan Guide. 1974. a. $75. Ford's Travel Guides, 19448 Londelius St., Northridge, CA 91324. TEL 818-701-7414. Ed. Judith A. Howard; Pub. Ron Howard. illus. circ. 5,000. **Document type:** directory.

910.2 US
FORD'S FREIGHTER TRAVEL GUIDE AND WATERWAYS OF THE WORLD. 1952. s-a. $20. Ford's Travel Guides, 19448 Londelius St., Northridge, CA 91324. TEL 818-701-7414. Ed. Judith A. Howard; Pub. Ron Howard. adv.; illus. circ. 12,408. **Document type:** directory.
 Formerly: Ford's Freighter Travel Guide (ISSN 0015-7058)

910.2 US ISSN 0015-7066
HE568
FORD'S INTERNATIONAL CRUISE GUIDE. 1970. q. $40. Ford's Travel Guides, 19448 Londelius St., Northridge, CA 91324. TEL 818-701-7414. Ed. Judith A. Howard; Pub. Ron Howard. adv.; illus. circ. 12,000. **Document type:** directory.

914.404 US ISSN 0749-2553
DC16
FRANCE (YEAR). a. $18. Harper Collins Publishers, Birnbaum Travel Guides, 10 E. 53rd St., New York, NY 10022-5299. TEL 212-207-7542. Ed. Alexandra Mayes Birnbaum.

910.202 US
FRANCE TRAVEL NEWS. vol.2, 1989. m. free. French Government Tourist Office, 610 Fifth Ave., New York, NY 10020. TEL 212-757-1125.
 Description: Provides travel news and information to various destinations in France.

FRANKFURT - RHEIN MAIN NECKAR SAAR VON HINTEN. see HOMOSEXUALITY

914 GW ISSN 0177-4883
FRANKFURTER WOCHE. 1935. s-m. Verlag Bodet & Partner, Speyererstr. 2-4, 60327 Frankfurt a.M., Germany. TEL 069-730536. FAX 069-735536. film rev.; play rev.; tr.lit. circ. 20,000.
 Formerly (until 1984): Frankfurter Wochenschau (ISSN 0016-0024)

910.2 US ISSN 0016-089X
FREIGHTER TRAVEL NEWS. 1958. m. $20 (foreign $24). Freighter Travel Club of America, 3524 Harts Lake Rd., Roy, WA 98580. Ed. Leland J. Pledger. adv.; bk.rev.; illus.; index. circ. 3,000. **Document type:** newsletter.
 Description: Contains first-hand reports of recent freighter or unusual water transportation. Features news bulletins about changes in freighter opportunities, answers specific questions and general information about freighter travel.

FREIZEIT - CARAVAN - CAMPING MAGAZIN. see SPORTS AND GAMES — Outdoor Life

910.202 GW
FREIZEIT UND REISEN. m. E R Medien GmbH, Falkstr. 45-47, 47058 Duisburg, Germany. TEL 0203-3051111. Ed. Jochen Bleckmann. adv. contact: Uwe Wuertenberger. circ. 84,000. **Document type:** consumer publication.

910 AU
FREMDENVERKEHR. m. Zieglergasse 1-3, Postfach 35, A-1072 Vienna, Austria. TEL 01-52131-0. FAX 01-939217. TELEX 112378-MUCHA-A. Ed. Christian Mucha. circ. 18,200.

910 AU ISSN 0071-948X
FREMDENVERKEHR IN OESTERREICH. (Subseries of: Beitraege zur Oesterreichischen Statistik) 1956. a. S.320. Oesterreichisches Statistisches Zentralamt, Hintere Zollamtsstr. 2b, A-1033 Vienna, Austria. TEL 0222-71128. FAX 0222-7156828. circ. 600. **Document type:** government publication.

TRAVEL AND TOURISM

914.404　　　　FR　　ISSN 1162-2490
FRENCH TIME; the independent travel trade magazine covering France. (Text in English) 1990. bi-m. 220 F.($38) Cadran Solaire, 61 rue de Vaugirard, 75006 Paris, France. TEL 33-1-45-44-94-95. FAX 33-1-42-22-14-81. Ed. Carole Dany. adv.: page 24000 F.; adv. contact: Patricia Reboulleau. circ. 19,000. (back issues avail.) **Document type**: trade publication.
 Description: Circulated to foreign tourism organizers in 20 countries who program French tourism. Each issue includes a regional report plus articles on transport, hotels, luxury and business tourism.

914.6　　　　US　　ISSN 1045-9324
DP402.B24
FROMMER'S BARCELONA, PLUS MAJORCA, IBIZA, AND MINORCA. 1990. biennial. Frommer Books (Subsidiary of: Simon & Schuster), Prentice Hall Trade Division, 15 Columbus Circle, New York, NY 10023.

647.9　　　　US　　ISSN 1051-6824
TX907.2
FROMMER'S BED & BREAKFAST, NORTH AMERICA. 1985. biennial. Frommer Books (Subsidiary of: Simon & Schuster, Inc.), Prentice Hall Trade Division, 15 Columbus Circle, New York, NY 10023.
 Formerly (until 1987): Bed and Breakfast, North America (ISSN 1051-7812).

917.004　　　　US　　ISSN 1044-2383
F1632
FROMMER'S BERMUDA AND THE BAHAMAS, PLUS TURKS AND CAICOS. biennial. Frommer Books (Subsidiary of: Simon & Schuster, Inc.), 15 Columbus Cir., New York, NY 10023. TEL 212-373-8125.
 Formerly (until 1991): Frommer's Dollarwise Guide to Bermuda and the Bahamas (ISSN 1042-8305).

914　　　　US　　ISSN 1055-5331
DA679
FROMMER'S BUDGET TRAVEL GUIDE. LONDON ON ...DOLLARS A DAY. 1993. biennial. Frommer Books (Subsidiary of: Simon & Schuster), 15 Columbus Circle, New York, NY 10023. TEL 212-373-8125.

914　　　　US　　ISSN 1055-5323
DP355
FROMMER'S BUDGET TRAVEL GUIDE. MADRID ON ...DOLLARS A DAY. 1993. biennial. Frommer Books (Subsidiary of: Simon & Schuster), 15 Columbus Circle, New York, NY 10023. TEL 212-373-8125.

917.94　　　　US　　ISSN 1044-2146
F859.3
FROMMER'S CALIFORNIA AND LAS VEGAS. a. Frommer Books (Subsidiary of: Simon & Schuster), Prentice Hall Trade Division, 15 Columbus Circle, New York, NY 10023.
 Former titles (until 1990): Frommer's Dollarwise California and Las Vegas (ISSN 0899-3319); Frommer's Dollarwise Guide to California and Las Vegas (ISSN 0277-187X).

917.104　　　　US　　ISSN 1044-2251
F1009
FROMMER'S CANADA. 1983. biennial. Frommer Books (Subsidiary of: Simon & Schuster), 15 Columbus Circle, New York, NY 10023. TEL 212-373-8125.
 Formerly: Frommer's Dollarwise Guide to Canada (ISSN 1042-8313).

915　　　　US　　ISSN 1055-5374
DS589.B2
FROMMER'S COMPREHENSIVE TRAVEL GUIDE. BANGKOK. 1993. biennial. Frommer Books (Subsidiary of: Simon & Schuster), 15 Columbus Circle, New York, NY 10023. TEL 212-373-8125.

917.304　　　　US　　ISSN 1048-2660
FROMMER'S COMPREHENSIVE TRAVEL GUIDE. BERLIN. 1992. biennial. Frommer Books (Subsidiary of: Simon & Schuster, Inc.), Prentice Hall Travel, 15 Columbus Circle, New York, NY 10023.

914　　　　US　　ISSN 1057-4026
DA650
FROMMER'S COMPREHENSIVE TRAVEL GUIDE. ENGLAND & SCOTLAND. a. Frommer Books (Subsidiary of: Simon & Schuster, Inc.), 15 Columbus Circle, New York, NY 10023. TEL 212-373-8125. Ed. D. Porter.
 Former titles (until 1991): Frommer's England and Scotland (ISSN 1044-2359) & Frommer's Dollarwise Guide to England and Scotland (ISSN 0276-8674)

916　　　　US　　ISSN 1053-2447
DT304
FROMMER'S COMPREHENSIVE TRAVEL GUIDE. MOROCCO. 1993. biennial. Frommer Books (Subsidiary of: Simon & Schuster, Inc.), 15 Columbus Circle, New York, NY 10023. TEL 212-373-8125.

917.404　　　　US　　ISSN 1056-5787
F2.3
FROMMER'S COMPREHENSIVE TRAVEL GUIDE. NEW ENGLAND. 1978. a. $14.95. Frommer Books (Subsidiary of: Simon & Schuster, Inc.), 15 Columbus Circle, New York, NY 10023.
 Former titles (until 1991): Frommer's New England (ISSN 1044-2286); Frommer's Dollarwise Guide to New England.

917.94　　　　US　　ISSN 1057-7645
F379.N53
FROMMER'S COMPREHENSIVE TRAVEL GUIDE. NEW ORLEANS. 1982. biennial. Frommer Books (Subsidiary of: Simon & Schuster), Prentice Hall Trade Division, 15 Columbus Circle, New York, NY 10023.
 Former titles (until 1991): Frommer's New Orleans (ISSN 0899-2908); (until 1990): Frommer's Guide to New Orleans (ISSN 0277-4410)

917.404　　　　US　　ISSN 1064-5276
F117.3
FROMMER'S COMPREHENSIVE TRAVEL GUIDE. NEW YORK STATE. biennial. Frommer Books (Subsidiary of: Simon & Schuster), Prentice Hall Trade Division, 15 Columbus Circle, New York, NY 10023. TEL 212-373-8125.

917.94　　　　US　　ISSN 1057-3399
F869.S33
FROMMER'S COMPREHENSIVE TRAVEL GUIDE. SAN FRANCISCO. 1982. biennial. Frommer Books (Subsidiary of: Simon & Schuster), Prentice Hall Trade Division, 15 Columbus Circle, New York, NY 10023.
 Former titles (until 1991): Frommer's San Francisco (ISSN 0899-3254); (until 1990): Frommer's Guide to San Francisco (ISSN 0277-4429)

919.704　　　　US　　ISSN 1055-5447
F2136.2
FROMMER'S COMPREHENSIVE TRAVEL GUIDE. THE VIRGIN ISLANDS. 1993. biennial. Frommer Books (Subsidiary of: Simon & Schuster, Inc.), 15 Columbus Circle, New York, NY 10023. Ed. Darwin Porter.

916.204　　　　US　　ISSN 1044-226X
DT45
FROMMER'S EGYPT. 1980. biennial. $14.95. Frommer Books (Subsidiary of: Simon & Schuster), 15 Columbus Circle, New York, NY 10023. TEL 212-373-8125.
 Formerly: Frommer's Dollarwise Guide to Egypt.

914.3　　　　US　　ISSN 1044-2405
DD16
FROMMER'S GERMANY. a. $14.95. Frommer Books (Subsidiary of: Simon & Schuster, Inc.), 15 Columbus Circle, New York, NY 10023. TEL 212-373-8125. Ed. D. Porter.
 Former titles: Frommer's Dollarwise Guide to Germany (ISSN 0731-4442); Arthur Frommer's Dollarwise Guide to Germany (ISSN 0272-0035)

914.509　　　　US　　ISSN 1044-2170
DG416
FROMMER'S ITALY. 1969. a. $14.95. Frommer Books (Subsidiary of: Simon & Schuster, Inc.), 15 Columbus Circle, New York, NY 10023. TEL 212-373-8125.
 Formerly: Frommer's Dollarwise Guide to Italy (ISSN 0899-336X)

917.404　　　　US　　ISSN 1050-2939
F106
FROMMER'S MID-ATLANTIC STATES. 1989. biennial. Frommer Books (Subsidiary of: Simon & Schuster), 15 Columbus Circle, New York, NY 10023. TEL 212-373-8125.
 Formerly (until 1989): Frommer's Dollarwise Guide to the Mid-Atlantic States, Including Pennsylvania, New Jersey, Delaware, Maryland, and Washington, D.C. (ISSN 1042-8348)

944　　　　US　　ISSN 0899-3203
DC708
FROMMER'S PARIS. 1982. a. Frommer Books (Subsidiary of: Simon & Schuster), Prentice Hall Trade Division, 15 Columbus Circle, New York, NY 10023. **Document type**: consumer publication.
 Formerly (until 1990): Frommer's Guide to Paris (ISSN 0277-3309)
 Description: Informs readers of attractions, lodging and restaurants in the French capital.

917.504　　　　US　　ISSN 1044-2316
F207.3
FROMMER'S SOUTHERN ATLANTIC STATES. biennial. Frommer Books (Subsidiary of: Simon & Schuster), 15 Columbus Circle, New York, NY 10023. TEL 212-373-8125.
 Former titles (until 1991): Frommer's Dollarwise Guide to the Southeast and New Orleans (ISSN 0731-8588); Arthur Frommer's Dollarwise Guide to the Southeast and New Orleans (ISSN 0731-857X)

914.904　　　　US　　ISSN 1042-8712
DJ411.A53
FROMMER'S TOURING GUIDES. AMSTERDAM. 1990. biennial. Frommer Books (Subsidiary of: Simon & Schuster, Inc.), Prentice Hall Trade Division, 15 Columbus Circle, New York, NY 10023. TEL 212-373-8125.

917.104　　　　US　　ISSN 1045-9316
F1089.5.V22
FROMMER'S VANCOUVER AND VICTORIA. 1990. biennial. Frommer Books (Subsidiary of: Simon & Schuster, Inc.), Prentice Hall Trade Division, 15 Columbus Circle, New York, NY 10023. TEL 212-373-8125.

910.4　　　　SA
THE G S A TRAVEL AGENTS' SALES GUIDE. (Text in English) 1980. m. R.15 per no. (effective 1994). G S A Marketing Pty. Ltd., P.O. Box 3239, Capetown 8000, South Africa. TEL 27-21-419-1671. FAX 27-21-419-4851. Ed. Jeff Hawthorne. adv. circ. 3,800. (back issues avail.) **Document type**: trade publication.
 Former titles (until vol.14, no.10, 1993): G S A Travel Marketing Magazine; (until 1983): G S A.
 Description: Provides comprehensive coverage of the South African travel industry.

910.09　　　　SP
GACETA ESPANOLA DE TURISMO PROFESIONAL. 12/yr. General Moscardon 7, 4o Ag., Madrid, Spain. TEL 1-234-25-03. FAX 1-2540457.

910.09　　　　GW
GAESTE JOURNAL. 1979. 7/yr. free. (Turistik Zentrale) Wilhelm Bing Verlag, Lengefelderstr. 6, 34497 Korbach, Germany. TEL 05631-56000. FAX 05631-6994. Ed. Arthur Cromm. adv.; bk.rev. circ. 25,000. **Document type**: consumer publication.
 Formerly (until 1990): Ferienpost.

910.4　　　　MP
GAL/FIRE. (Text in Mongolian) 1991. bi-m. Mongolian Cultural Foundation, P.O. Box 527, Ulan Bator, Mongolia. TEL 210611. Ed. Y. Baatar.
 Description: Covers non-political, cultural affairs.

910.09　　　　US　　ISSN 1049-9431
GARDENS AND COUNTRYSIDES.* 10/yr. Travel Publications, Inc. (San Antonio), Box 69807, San Antonio, TX 78209-0907. TEL 512-826-5222. FAX 512-826-8996. Ed. Peter C. Selig.

910.202 664 641.5　　　　SZ
GASTRONOMIE & TOURISME. (Text and summaries in French, German, Italian) 1973. bi-m. 42 SFr. (foreign 60 SFr.). Gastronomie & Tourisme SA, Case Postale 2507, CH-6901 Lugano, Switzerland. TEL 091-528548. FAX 091-524920. Ed. Alberto Dell'Acqua. circ. 20,000. **Document type**: trade publication.
 Description: Covers international tourism and gastronomy.

TRAVEL AND TOURISM

GASTROTOUR. see *HOME ECONOMICS*

910.202 FR ISSN 0753-986X
GAULT - MILLAU MAGAZINE. 1969. m. 250 F.($55) Jour-Azur S.A., 22 bis, rue de Volontaires, 75015 Paris, France. FAX 42-73-04-50. TELEX 203561. Ed. Yves Bridault. adv.; bk.rev.; illus.; charts. circ. 160,000. (back issues avail.)
    Formerly: Nouveau Guide Gault-Millau (ISSN 0399-8223)

917 MX ISSN 0016-5379
GAZER/MIRON. 1950. w. $30. Editorial Monex S. de R.L. y C.V., Ave. Insurgentes Centro 132-204, Mexico 06030, D.F., Mexico. Ed. Raul Esquivel. adv.; charts; illus.; stat. circ. 25,000.
    Description: Description and travel information on Mexico.

914 FR ISSN 0016-5573
GAZETTE OFFICIELLE DU TOURISME; bulletin d'information et de documentation sur le tourisme. w. 1400 F. (foreign 1500 F.) (effective 1995). Office des Nouvelles Internationales, 18 rue de Folin, 64200 Biarritz, France. TEL 59-43-80-45. FAX 59-43-80-41. TELEX 570061 F. Ed. Dominique Laporte. adv. contact: Jacques Darrigrand. **Document type:** newspaper.

910.09 IT ISSN 0393-7895
GENTE VIAGGI. 1979. m. L.67200 (foreign L.118000). Rusconi Editori S.p.a, Servizio Abbonamento, Viale Sarca 235, 20126 Milan, Italy. TEL 39-2-66191. FAX 39-2-6619-2737. Ed. Giuseppe Alberto Orefice. adv.: page L.33000000. circ. 151,033.

GEO. see *ENVIRONMENTAL STUDIES*

918.304 CL ISSN 0431-1930
F3064 CODEN: GCHLAE
GEOCHILE. 1951. irreg. (Sociedad Geografica de Chile) Lord Cochrane S.A., Providencia 711, Santiago, Chile. illus. **Indexed:** GeoRef.

910.9 IT
GEODES;* la terra che vive. 1978. m. L.52000. Europress s.r.l., Via del Salviantino 1, Fiesole, 50016 Florence, Italy. TEL 02-29404473. FAX 02-2948031. Ed. Riccardo Venchiarutti. adv.; bk.rev. circ. 44,000. (also avail. in microform)

910.202 GW
GEOSAISON. 1989. 10/yr. DM.65 (Europe DM.98.50; elsewhere DM.171). Gruner und Jahr AG & Co., Am Baumwall 11, 20459 Hamburg, Germany. TEL 040-3703-0. FAX 040-37035617. Ed. Peter-Matthias Gaede. circ. 142,474. **Document type:** consumer publication.
    Formerly: Saison.

910.202 US ISSN 1067-4527
GEOTRAVELER. 1993. q. $18. Geotravel Research Center, Inc., 160 Fiesta Dr., Ste. 259, Kissimmee, FL 34743. TEL 407-348-7330; 800-654-0403. E-mail: 75040,761@compuserve.com. Ed. Bob Martin. adv. contact: Beverly Martin. **Document type:** newsletter.
    Description: Provides its readers with unique information that will help them understand the places they travel to, the things they see and the people they meet.

910.09 GW ISSN 0723-6875
TI GESCHAEFTSREISE. 1981. s-m. DM.93. Deutscher Verkehrs Verlag GmbH, Nordkanalstr. 36, 20097 Hamburg, Germany. TEL 040-23714125. FAX 040-23714123. Ed. Hans-Juergen Klesse. adv. contact: Werner Holders. circ. 10,300.
    Formerly: Touristik Information (ISSN 0342-717X)
    Description: Provides information for travel agencies and business travel departments.

910.202 UK ISSN 0954-0369
GETTING ABOUT BRITAIN; for the independent traveller. 1988. 3/yr. £9 rest of Europe £11; elsewhere £13 (effective 1994). (British Tourist Authority) Drumport Ltd., 21 Church Walk, Thames Ditton, Surrey KT7 0NP, England. TEL 44-81-398-8332. FAX 44-81-398-8322. Ed. Clive Lewis. adv.; circ. 47,000. (controlled). **Document type:** consumer publication.
    —BLDSC (4165.228000).
    Description: Color features and service listings guide to UK destinations served by bus, train, plane and ferry.

GIORNALE DEI GELATIERI. see *BUSINESS AND ECONOMICS — Chamber Of Commerce Publications*

914 UK ISSN 1352-8807
GITES GUIDE; French farm and village holiday guide. 1976. a. £8.50($13.95) F H G Publications Ltd., Abbey Mill Business Centre, Seedhill, Paisley PA1 1JN, Scotland. TEL 0141-887-0428. FAX 0141-889-7204. adv.; illus. circ. 12,000. **Document type:** consumer publication.
    Formerly (until 1994): French Farm and Village Holiday Guide (ISSN 0140-0177)

GLOBE (LONDON). see *CLUBS*

910.202 SZ
GLOBO; das Reisemagazin. (Text in German) 12/yr. 7.80 Fr. Verlag C.J. Bucher AG, Zurichstr. 5, 6002 Lucerne, Switzerland. circ. 35,000.
    Formerly (until 1989): Diners Club Magazine.

910.202 GW ISSN 0942-5284
GLOBO; das Reisemagazin. 1989. m. DM.84 (foreign DM.93.60). Ringier Verlag GmbH, Gustav-Heinemann-Ring 212, 81739 Munich, Germany. TEL 089-63818134. FAX 089-63818169. (Subscr. to: DSB Abo-Betreuung GmbH, 74168 Neckarsulm, Germany. TEL 07132-959222. FAX 07132-959105) Ed. Peter Telle. adv.: color page DM.20780; adv. contact: Raimund Arntzen. index. circ. 102,372. (back issues avail.) **Document type:** consumer publication.
    Refereed Serial

796.7 US ISSN 0017-1441
GO (CHARLOTTE). 1923. bi-m. membership only. American Automobile Association, Carolina Motor Club, Box 30008, 720 E. Morehead St., Charlotte, NC 28230. TEL 704-377-3600. FAX 704-358-1585. Ed. Tom Crosby. adv. contact: Donna Emmary. bk.rev.; charts; illus.; stat. circ. 420,000. (tabloid format) **Document type:** newspaper.
    Description: Provides domestic and international travel and tourism information; includes automotive and insurance news and legislative issues.

914.2 UK ISSN 0309-507X
GOFF'S GUIDE TO CATER YOURSELF HOLIDAYS.* 1977. a. 50p. Eastern Counties Newspaper Group, Prospect House, Rouen Rd., Norwich, Norfolk NR1 1RE, England. TEL 44-1603-628311. FAX 44-1603-612930. TELEX 975276 ECNNCH G. Ed. R. De Young.

910.09 US
GOING PLACES (MINOT). 1990. m. $14.97 (effective 1995). Box 1427, Minot, ND 58702-1427. TEL 701-839-0809. FAX 701-852-0408. Ed. Cindy Kittelson; Pub. Debbie Schmidt. adv. contact: Marilou VonGunden. circ. 40,000 (controlled). **Document type:** consumer publication.
    Description: Promotes North Dakota's people, places and events.

910.09 UK ISSN 0955-629X
GOING PLACES INTERNATIONAL; Britain's premier travel magazine. 1984. q. £2($5.25) Pericles Press, 38 Buckingham Palace Rd., London SW1 W0RE, England. TEL 071-486-5353. FAX 071-486-2094. TELEX 27659. Ed. Daphne Aldis. adv.; bk.rev. circ. 40,000.
    Formerly (until 1988): Going Places (ISSN 0956-9626)

GOING PLACES MAGAZINE. see *TRANSPORTATION — Automobiles*

916 UK ISSN 0965-3732
GOING U S A. 1991. m. £15 (foreign £26.50). Outbound Newspapers, 1 Commercial Rd., Eastbourne, E. Sussex BN21 3XQ, England. TEL 01323-412001. FAX 01323-649249. Ed. Stephen Hartridge. adv.; bk.rev. (tabloid format) **Document type:** newspaper.
    Description: Gives potential migrants and travelers to the United States information about real estate, employment, education, investing and lifestyle.

910.202 US
GOLDEN CALIFORNIA. 1984. q. $12. (R H L-Golden State) Meredith Corp., 801 K St., Ste. 1600, Sacramento, CA 95814. TEL 916-322-2881. FAX 916-322-3402. Ed. Sharon Smith-Hansgen. adv.; circ. 3,125,000 (controlled).
    Formerly: Golden State (ISSN 0743-6742)
    Description: Distributed to out-of-state motorists at agricultural checkpoints in the state, with articles on site and events, as well as auto-travel tips.

917.9 US
GOLDEN CALIFORNIA.* 1993. q. M H West, Inc. (Subsidiary of: Maclean Hunter Publishing Co.), 5743 Corsa Ave., Ste. 220, Westlake, CA 91362-4027. TEL 818-997-0644. FAX 818-997-1058. adv.; B&W page $1950; trim 8 1/4 x 10 7/8. circ. 500,000. **Document type:** consumer publication.

917.9 US
GOLDEN CALIFORNIA VISITOR'S GUIDE.* 1993. a. M H West, Inc. (Subsidiary of: Maclean Hunter Publishing Co.), 5743 Corsa Ave., Ste. 220, Westlake Village, CA 91362-4027. TEL 818-997-0644. FAX 818-997-1058. adv.; color page $21450; trim 8 1/4 x 10 7/8. circ. 50,000. **Document type:** consumer publication.

910.202 UK
GOLDEN FALCON. (Text in Arabic and English) m. (Gulf Air) Bryan Richardson & Associates, Parkway House, Sheen Lane, London SW14 8LS, England. Ed. Joanna Donaldson. adv. circ. 20,000.

GOLF & TURISMO. see *SPORTS AND GAMES — Ball Games*

GOLF GUIDE - WHERE TO PLAY AND WHERE TO STAY. see *SPORTS AND GAMES — Ball Games*

GOLF JOURNAL. see *SPORTS AND GAMES — Ball Games*

GOLF MAGAZINE. see *SPORTS AND GAMES — Ball Games*

796.5 UK ISSN 0963-1135
GOOD CAMPS GUIDE BRITAIN (YEAR). (Subseries of: Alan Rogers Good Camps Guide) 1968. a. £5.99. Deneway Guides and Travel Ltd. (Subsidiary of: Response Marketing Initiatives Limited), Chesil Lodge, W. Bexington, Dorset DT2 9DG, England. TEL 01308-897809. FAX 01308-898017. Eds. Clive Edwards. adv. contact: Sue Smart. circ. 25,000. **Document type:** consumer publication, directory.
    Formerly: Alan Rogers' Good Camps Guide Britain (ISSN 0142-5978)

796.54 UK ISSN 0955-9183
GOOD CAMPS GUIDE EUROPE (YEAR). (Subseries of: Alan Rogers Good Camps Guide) 1968. a. £8.99. Deneway Guides and Travel Ltd. (Subsidiary of: Response Marketing Initiatives Limited), Chesil Lodge, W. Bexington, Dorset DT2 9DG, England. TEL 01308-897809. FAX 01308-898017. Ed. Clive Edwards. adv. contact: Sue Smart. illus. circ. 20,000. **Document type:** consumer publication, directory.
    Former titles: Selected Sites for Caravanning and Camping in Europe (ISSN 0065-5686); Alan Rogers' Selected Sites for Caravanning and Camping in Europe (ISSN 0000-6556)
    Description: Provides information for campers, caravaners and motor caravaners regarding location, sanitary facilities, amenities, costs, cleanliness, and maintenance.

796.5 UK ISSN 0955-9205
GOOD CAMPS GUIDE FRANCE (YEAR). (Subseries of: Alan Rogers Good Camps Guide) 1985. a. £6.99. Deneway Guides and Travel Ltd. (Subsidiary of: Response Marketing Initiatives Ltd.), Chesil Lodge, W. Bexington, Dorset DT2 9DG, England. TEL 01308-879809. FAX 01308-898017. Ed. Lois Broughton Edwards. adv. contact: Sue Smart. illus. circ. 20,000. **Document type:** consumer publication, directory.
    Formerly: Alan Rogers' Good Camps Guide for France (ISSN 0267-8934)
    Description: Covers specially selected camping sites in France for the discerning camper.

TRAVEL AND TOURISM

910.202　　UK　　ISSN 0955-5994
GOOD HOLIDAY MAGAZINE. 1980. q. £9.95. Hill Publications, 1-2 Dawes Court, 93 High St., Esher, Surrey KT10 8QA, England. TEL 0372-69799. Ed. John Hill. circ. 250,000. (back issues avail.)

910　　　　GW
GOSTELOW REPORT. 1992. m. £95($150) Mary Gostelow, Ed. & Pub., Clyffe House, Tincleton, Dorset DT2 8QP, England. TEL 01305-848193. FAX 01305-848138. **Document type:** newsletter. **Description:** Reports developments in air travel and the hotel and restaurant industry.

GOURMED; magazine for doctors. see *MEDICAL SCIENCES*

GOURMET; the magazine of good living. see *FOOD AND FOOD INDUSTRIES*

910.09　　　　US
GRACIOUS STAYS AND SPECIAL PLACES. 1991. q. Person to Person Travel Prod., Inc., 2856 Hundred Oaks, Baton Rouge, LA 70808-1533. TEL 504-343-0672. FAX 504-343-0672. Ed. Helen Heath. bk.rev. circ. 2,500. **Document type:** consumer publication. **Description:** Covers historically and architecturally significant accomodations, including bed & breakfasts, country inns and guest houses.

910.202　　　　GW
DER GRAUE. 1967. 60/yr. DM.480. R B Reisebuero Marketing, Schraemelstr. 126, 81247 Munich, Germany. TEL 089-88888888. FAX 089-8110655. Ed. Hans Nechleba; Pub. Hans Nechleba. adv.: B&W page DM.720, color page DM.2800. circ. 1,100 (paid). **Document type:** newsletter.

914.204　　US　　ISSN 0896-8683
DA650
GREAT BRITAIN (YEAR). a. $18. Harper Collins Publishers, Birnbaum Travel Guides, 10 E 53rd St., New York, NY 10022-5299. TEL 212-207-7542. Ed. Alexandra Mayes Birnbaum.
　Supersedes (in 1990): Great Britain and Ireland (Year).

910.5　　US　　ISSN 0706-7682
GREAT EXPEDITIONS. 1978. 4/yr. $11.95. Great Expeditions, Inc., Box 18036, Raleigh, NC 27619. TEL 919-846-3600. FAX 919-847-0780. Ed. George W. Kane. adv.; bk.rev. circ. 27,000. (back issues avail.) **Document type:** consumer publication. **Description:** Emphasizes independent, socially responsible travel outside the usual tourist areas.

917.704　　　　US
GREAT LAKES GETAWAY. 1985. 12/yr. $18. Camden Publications, 331 E. Bell St., Box 8, Camden, MI 49232-0008. TEL 517-368-5265. FAX 517-368-5131. Ed. John Snyder; Pub. Kurt Greenhoe. adv contact: Kurt Greenhoe. circ. 130,000 (controlled). **Document type:** newsletter. **Description:** Travel and tourism guide to the Great Lakes area.

917.7　　US　　ISSN 0887-6223
GREAT LAKES TRAVEL & LIVING. 1986. 8/yr. $17.90. Great Lakes Publishing Co. (Port Clinton), 108 W. Perry St., Port Clinton, OH 43452. TEL 419-734-5774. (Subscr. to: Box 423, Mt. Morris, IL 61054) Ed. David G. Brown. adv. circ. 40,000. (back issues avail.) **Description:** General interest magazine covering Minnesota, Wisconsin, Illinois, Michigan, Indiana, Ohio, Pennsylvania and New York.

914.95　　GR　　ISSN 0432-6105
DF727
GREECE. (Text in English) 1950. a. National Tourist Organisation of Greece, General Direction of Promotion, Odos Amerikis 2, Athens, Greece. illus.

910.202　　　　GR
GREEK TRAVEL PAGES; Greede's monthly travel guide - magazine. 1975. m. Dr.38000 in Greece (rest of Europe $200; elsewhere $250). International Publications Ltd., 6 Psylla & Filellinon Sts., 105 57 Athens, Greece. TEL 30-1-3247-511. FAX 30-1-3249-996. TELEX 21-6253. Pub. Eleftherios Theofanopoulos. adv. contact: Maria Theofanopoulou. bk.rev. circ. 10,000. **Document type:** directory.
　Description: Covers information and news concerning the Greek tourism sector.

GREENSCENE; the only magazine for young vegetarians. see *NUTRITION AND DIETETICS*

338.4　　　　GD
GRENADA. BOARD OF TOURISM. QUARTERLY; overview of the tourism sector. q. Board of Tourism, Carenage, St. George's, Grenada, W.I.

910.09 601.435　　US
GROUP TRAVEL LEADER.* 1991. m. $39. Group Travel Leader, Inc., 130 N. Broadway St., Lexington, KY 40507-1227. TEL 606-253-0455. FAX 606-253-0499. adv.; circ. 30,000. (controlled). **Description:** Contains industry news, destination features, and educational articles and information on group travel for seniors.

910.202　　UK　　ISSN 0962-8266
GROUP TRAVEL ORGANISER. 10/yr. £24 (foreign £36). Group Travel Organiser Ltd. (Subsidiary of: Landor Publishing Ltd.), Quadrant House, 250 Kennington Ln., London SE11 5RD, England. TEL 0171-735-5058. FAX 0171-735-1299. E-mail: 100570,73@compuserve.com. **Document type:** trade publication. **Description:** Provides news and information for the group travel organizer.

380.5　　　　PE
GUIA AEREA Y MARITIMA. 1962. m. $60 (S. America $130; N. America $160; elsewhere $215). Lima Editora, S.A., Av. Canaval y Moreyra, 340, p. 12, Lima 27, Peru. TEL 4069930. FAX 407543. Ed. Jose Luis Arrarte. adv. circ. 2,200. (back issues avail.)
　Description: Covers the travel and airline industries.

GUIA AEREA Y MARITIMA DE VENEZUELA C.A.; Aruba, Curacao y Bonaire. see *TRANSPORTATION*

GUIA AERONAUTICO. see *TRANSPORTATION — Air Transport*

918　　　　BL
GUIA BRASIL. (Text in Portuguese; summaries in English, Spanish) 1966. a. price varies. Editora Abril, S.A., Rua do Curtume 769, 110 andar, 05066-900 Sao Paulo, Brazil. TEL 011-8716168. FAX 011-8716270. Ed. Regner Camilo. charts; illus. circ. 230,000.
　Description: Details information on 744 cities, as well as various hotels, restaurants, and tourist attractions.

338.4　　　　MX
GUIA DE TURISMO Y DE SERVICIOS. 1992. s-a. Editorial del Norte Mexicano, Allende 980-1 pte., Torreon, Coahiula, Mexico. TEL 169470.

910　　　　SP
GUIA DE UTILLAJE Y EQUIPOS. a. 1350 ptas. Tecnipublicaciones, S.A., C. Albacete 5, 28027 Madrid, Spain. TEL 34-1-3261440. FAX 34-1-3262539.
　Formerly: Catalogo Automoviles Turismos.

917.204　　　　MX
GUIA DE VIAJES. m. free. Editorial This Is Mexico, Calle Londres 166, Apdo. 6-728, 06600 Mexico, D.F., Mexico. FAX 915-208-38. TELEX 017-71-881. illus. circ. 20,000.
　Former titles: Visitors' Guide to Mexico; Now in Mexico.

910.202　　　　CU
GUIA DEL SOL. s-a. Instituto Nacional del Turismo, Malecon y G, Vededo, Havana, Cuba. TEL 7-32-9881. TELEX 511955.

918.104　　BL　　ISSN 0104-5024
GUIA ESTRADAS - QUATRO RODAS. 1988. a. Editora Abril, S.A., Rua do Curtume 769, Bl. G, 11o, 05066-900 Sao Paulo, Brazil. TEL 011-8716168. Ed. Regner Camilo. circ. 70,000. **Document type:** consumer publication.
　Description: Includes detailed maps of Brazil with cities ande highways in small format.

910.202　　　　AG
GUIA INTERNACIONAL DE TRAFICO. 1963. m. $230 in America; elsewhere $300. Suipacha 207, Piso 3, Ofc. 316, 1008 Buenos Aires, Argentina. TEL 541-394-9008. FAX 541-394-9034. (U.S. adress: c/o Ms. Patricia Carman, Market Links, Dupont Plaza Center 723, 300 Biscayne Blvd. Way, Miami, FL 33131. TEL 305-374-1634) Ed. Alan Rodrigue. adv.; circ. 10,000 (paid). **Document type:** directory.
　Formerly: Guia Internacional de Trafico - Division Viajes.
　Description: Airline guide providing international travel information and news.

917.204　　　　HO
GUIA OFICIAL DE CENTRO-AMERICA. 1922. irreg. Apartado 494, Tegucigalpa, Honduras.

910.09　　BL　　ISSN 0102-3225
GUIA PANROTAS. 1972. m. $180. Panrotas Editora Ltda., Av. Jabaquara, 1761, CEP 04045-901 Sao Paulo, SP, Brazil. TEL 011-584-0211. FAX 011-276-1602. TELEX (11) 56693. Ed. Jose Guillermo Condomi Alcorta. adv. circ. 11,000.

918.104　　BL　　ISSN 0104-5067
GUIA PRAIAS - QUATRO RODAS. 1991. a. Editora Abril, S.A., Rua do Curtume 769, Bl. G, 11o, 05066-900 Sao Paulo SP, Brazil. TEL 011-8716168. Ed. Regner Camilo. circ. 75,000. **Document type:** consumer publication.

910.202　　　　BL
GUIA QUATRO RODAS. SUL. 1975. a. Editora Abril, S.A., R. do Curtume 769, Bl. G, 11o andar, 05066-900 Sao Paulo, Brazil. FAX 011-871-6270. Ed. Victor Civita. adv.; charts; illus.; stat. circ. 38,000.

910.202　　BL　　ISSN 0104-4982
F2509.5
GUIA QUATRO RODAS BRASIL. 1966. a. Editora Abril, S.A., Rua do Curtume 769, Bl. G, 11o andar, 05066-900 Sao Paulo SP, Brazil. TEL 011-8716168. FAX 011-8716270. Ed. Regner Camilo. adv.; charts. circ. 250,000. **Document type:** consumer publication.
　Description: Details information on 820 cities, including various hotels, restaurants and tourist attractions.

910.202　　　　BL
GUIA RODOVIARIO - QUATRO RODAS. Variant title: Guia Quatro Rodas. Rodoviario. 1976. a. Editora Abril, S.A., R. fo Curtume 769, Bl. G 11o andar, 05066-900 Sao Paulo SP, Brazil. TEL 011-8716168. FAX 011-871-6270. Ed. Regner Camilo. adv.; charts. circ. 113,000. **Document type:** consumer publication.
　Description: Includes detailed maps of Brazil with cities and highways in large format.

910.202　　BL　　ISSN 0104-4990
GUIA SAO PAULO - QUATRO RODAS. Variant title: Guia Quatro Rodas. Sao Paulo. 1973. a. Editora Abril, S.A., Rua do Curtume 769, Bl. G 11o andar, 05066-900 Sao Paulo, Brazil. TEL 011-8716168. Ed. Regner Camilo. adv.; charts; illus. circ. 75,000. **Document type:** consumer publication.
　Description: Contains hotel, restaurant, service, tourist attraction, bus line and city information for the greater Sao Paulo region.

918.104　　　　AG
GUIA TURISTICA DE ROSARIO Y SANTE FE. vol.13, 1975. irreg. Talleres Graficos Amalevi, Calle Mendoza 1851, Rosario, Santa Fe, Argentina. Ed. Rafael Vinas Paris. adv.; illus.

910.202　　　　IT
GUIDA EUROCAMPING EUROPA. q. L.25000. Editoriale Eurocamp s.r.l., Via Durini, n.3, 20122 Milan, Italy. TEL 02-76022377. FAX 02-76022430. Ed. Maria Paola Canegrati. adv.; charts; illus. circ. 40,000. **Document type:** catalog.

910.202　　　　IT
GUIDA EUROCAMPING ITALIA E CORSICA. q. L.25000. Editoriale Eurocamp s.r.l., Via Durini, n.3, 20122 Milan, Italy. TEL 02-76022377. FAX 02-76022430. Ed. Maria Paola Canegrati. adv.; charts; illus. circ. 60,000. **Document type:** catalog.

TRAVEL AND TOURISM

914.504   IT
GUIDA PIRELLI - VIAGGARE IN ITALIA. a. L.35000. (Societa Pneumatici Pirelli) Editoriale Giorgio Mondadori S.p.A., Via A. Ponti, 10, 20143 Milan, Italy. TEL 02-891661. (Co-sponsor: Ministerio del Turismo e dello Spettacolo) Ed. Paolo Altieri.

910.202   IT
GUIDA VIAGGI. 1973. s-m. L.120000. G I V I, s.r.l., Via Larga, 2, 20122 Milan, Italy. TEL 876936. FAX 02-866561. Ed. P. Barni. circ. 7,000.

910.202   IT
GUIDE A P A. 18/yr. L.54000. Zanfi Editori s.r.l., Via Emilia Ovest 954, 41100 Modena, Italy. TEL 39-59-891700. FAX 39-59-891701. TELEX 522272 ZANFI I. adv.: color page L.3000000. circ. 10,000.

910.202   CN   ISSN 0838-0023
GUIDE DE LA ROUTE: L'ONTARIO. French translation of: American Automobile Association. Ontario TourBook. (Text in French) 1988. a. membership. Canadian Automobile Association, 1775 Courtwood Cres., Ottawa, ON K2C 3J2, Canada. TEL 613-226-7631. FAX 613-225-7383. **Document type:** bulletin.
Description: Lists accomodations, sites to see in the province of Ontario.

910.202   CN
GUIDE DE LA ROUTE: LA CAROLINE DU NORD, LA CAROLINE DU SUD ET LA GEORGIE. 1993. a. membership. Canadian Automobile Association, 1775 Courtwood Cres., Ottawa, ON K2C 3J2, Canada. TEL 613-226-7631. FAX 613-225-7383. **Document type:** bulletin.

910.202   CN   ISSN 0838-0015
GUIDE DE LA ROUTE: LA FLORIDE. French translation of: American Automobile Association, Florida TourBook. (Text in French) 1987. a. membership. Canadian Automobile Association, 1775 Courtwood Cres., Ottawa, ON K2C 3J2, Canada. TEL 613-226-7631. FAX 613-225-7383. adv. **Document type:** bulletin.
Description: Listing accommodation, sites to see, things to do in the state of Florida.

917.504   CN
GUIDE DE LA ROUTE: LE CENTRE DE LA COTE ATLANTIQUE. French translation of: American Automobile Association. Mid-Atlantic TourBook. (Text in French) 1992. a. Canadian Automobile Association, 1775 Courtwood Cres., Ottawa, ON K2C 3J2, Canada. TEL 613-226-7631. FAX 613-225-7383. **Document type:** bulletin.
Description: Lists accomodations, sites to see in the states of Delaware, Maryland, Virginia, West Virginia and the District of Columbia.

910.202   CN
GUIDE DE LA ROUTE: LE MAINE, LE NEW HAMPSHIRE, ET LE VERMONT. French translation of: American Automobile Association. Maine, New Hampshire, Vermont TourBook. (Text in French) 1991. a. membership. Canadian Automobile Association, 1775 Courtwood Cres., Ottawa, ON K2C 3J2, Canada. TEL 613-226-7631. FAX 613-225-7383. **Document type:** bulletin.
Description: Tourbook listing accommodations, sites to see, and things to do in Maine, New Hampshire and Vermont.

910.202   CN
GUIDE DE LA ROUTE: LES PROVINCES DE L'ATLANTIQUE ET LE QUEBEC. French translation of: American Automobile Association. Atlantic Provinces and Quebec TourBook. (Text in French) 1978. a. membership. Canadian Automobile Association, 1775 Courtwood Cres., Ottawa, ON K2C 3J2, Canada. TEL 613-226-7631. FAX 613-225-7383. adv.
Description: Tourbook listing accommodations, sites to see, things to do in the province of Quebec and the maritime provinces.

914.92   BE
GUIDE DELTA DES HOTELS DU BENELUX. (Text in French) 1992. biennial. 695 BEF. Editions Delta, Rue Scailquin 55, B-1030 Brussels, Belgium. TEL 32-2-217-55-55. FAX 32-2-217-93-93. Ed. Pol Walheer. adv. **Document type:** directory.
Description: Reviews and rates the 400 best hotels and their restaurants in Belgium, Luxembourg and the Netherlands (in all price categories).

914.92   BE
GUIDE DELTA DES HOTELS ET RESTAURANTS DE BRUXELLES. (Text in French) 1978. a. 695 BEF (effective 1995). Editions Delta, Rue Scailquin 55, B-1030 Brussels, Belgium. TEL 32-2-217-55-55. FAX 32-2-217-93-93. Ed. Georges-Francis Seingry. adv. **Document type:** directory.
Formerly: Guide Delta des Hotels de Bruxelles (ISSN 0771-7768)
Description: Guide to more than 1800 restaurants and hotels in Brussels, in all price ranges.

910.4   FR   ISSN 0991-4781
GUIDE DES AUBERGES DE CAMPAGNE ET HOTELS DE CHARME EN FRANCE. 1988. irreg. Rivages, 106 bd. Saint-Germain, 75006 Paris, France. Ed. Michelle Gastaut.

910.202   DK   ISSN 0106-3022
GUIDE I JYLLAND. 1979. a. DKK 28.50. Bureau Vildmosen, Solvej 5, 9293 Kongerslev, Denmark. illus.

917.504   US
GUIDE MAGAZINE (ST. PETERSBURG). m. $8.50 (free to hotel guests). Guide Publishing Co. (St. Petersburg), 3651 Central Ave., St. Petersburg, FL 33713. Ed. Brian R. Cummins. adv.: color page $600. circ. 21,000.
Description: Covers entertainment, dining and shopping for Pinellas County.

910.202   MG
GUIDE ROUTIER ET TOURISTIQUE: MADAGASCAR, REUNION, MAURICE, COMORES ET SEYCHELLES. a. Automobile Club de Madagascar, Service du Guide Routier, B.P. 571, Antananarivo, Madagascar. illus.
Formerly: Guide Routier (ISSN 0572-2330)

916.8 647.94   SA
▼**GUIDE TO BED AND BREAKFAST AND GUEST HOUSES.** Cover title: Guide to Bed and Breakfast and Guest Houses in South Africa. (Text in English) 1994. biennial. R.44.99 (effective 1996). Struik Publishers, P.O. Box 1144, Cape Town 8000, South Africa. TEL 27-21-4624360. FAX 27-21-4624379. **Document type:** consumer publication.

796.5   UK   ISSN 0267-3355
GUIDE TO CARAVAN AND CAMPING HOLIDAYS. 1975. a. £2.90. F H G Publications Ltd., Abbey Mill Business Centre, Seedhill, Paisley PA1 1JN, Scotland. TEL 0141-887-0428. FAX 0141-889-7204. **Document type:** consumer publication.

910.09   US
GUIDE TO CHARLESTON'S ISLANDS MAGAZINE. 1987. a. free. Sea Islands Publishing, Inc., 2 Revenel Center, Kiawah Island, SC 29455. TEL 803-768-2304. FAX 803-768-8016. Ed. Robert H. Moore. adv. contact: Shelley Gibson. tr.lit. circ. 100,000. (back issues avail.) **Document type:** consumer publication.
Formerly: Islands Magazine.

GUIDE TO CRUISING THE CHESAPEAKE BAY. see SPORTS AND GAMES — Boats And Boating

916.8 647.94   SA
▼**GUIDE TO GUEST FARMS AND COUNTRY LODGES IN SOUTHERN AFRICA.** (Text in English) 1994. biennial. R.44.99 (effective 1996). Struik Publishers, P.O. Box 1144, Cape Town 8000, South Africa. TEL 27-21-4624360. FAX 27-21-4624379. maps. **Document type:** consumer publication.
Description: Covers South Africa, Lesotho, Namibia and Swaziland.

917.9   US   ISSN 0191-8303
GUIDE TO MAUI. 1981. q. Guide Magazines, 1833 Kalakaua Ave., Ste. 900, Honolulu, HI 96815. TEL 808-949-9988. FAX 808-947-1252. adv.: B&W page $2961; trim 7 7/8 x 10 3/4. circ. 50,000. **Document type:** consumer publication.

917.9   US   ISSN 0191-829X
GUIDE TO OAHU. 1981. m. Guide Magazines, 1833 Kalakaua Ave., Ste. 900, Honolulu, HI 96815. TEL 808-949-9988. FAX 808-947-1252. adv.: B&W page $5131; trim 7 7/8 x 10 3/4. circ. 100,000. **Document type:** consumer publication.

910.202 051   US
GUIDE TO PEACHTREE CITY. 1988. a. free. Print Graphics Services, Inc., Box 2752, Peachtree City, GA 30269. TEL 404-631-9159. FAX 404-631-8852. Ed. Tray Baggerly; Pub. Charles Nelson. adv.: B&W page $1850, color page $2380; trim 8 3/8 x 10 7/8; adv. contact: Neal Dupre. circ. 30,000 (controlled). **Document type:** consumer publication.
Description: Covers local government, education, healthcare, recreation, retail, industry, Peachtree City milestones, civic organizations, home buyer information. Includes articles highlighting people and events of the city.

917.9   US
GUIDE TO THE BIG ISLAND. 1981. q. Guide Magazines, 1833 Kalakaua Ave., Ste. 900, Honolulu, HI 96815. TEL 808-949-9988. FAX 808-947-1252. adv.: B&W page $2417; trim 7 7/8 x 10 3/4. circ. 40,000. **Document type:** consumer publication.

910.09   US
GUIDE TO THE QUEEN CHARLOTTES. biennial. $10.95. Raincoast Books in Vancouver, 8680 Cambie St., Vancouver, B.C. V6P 6M9, Canada. TEL 604-323-7100.

641.2209687   SA
GUIDE TO THE WINELANDS OF THE CAPE. irreg., latest 1994. R.35.95. C G R Wine Enterprises, P.O. Box 435, Stellenbosch 7599, South Africa. Ed. Christine Rudman. illus.; maps.

910.09   SP   ISSN 0432-9791
GUIDEPOST. 1959. 52/yr. Edif. Espana, grupo 2, planta 5, 28003 Madrid, Spain. TEL 1-248-01-07. Ed. Daniel H. Lowell.

910.09   BA
GULF TOURISM DIRECTORY. (Text in English) 1990. a? P.O. Box 859, Manama, Bahrain. TEL 731224. FAX 731067. Ed. Rashid Bin Muhammad al-Khalifa. **Document type:** directory.

910.09   IT   ISSN 1122-0627
GULLIVER. 1992. m. L.62400. De Agostini - Rizzoli Periodici s.r.l., Via Gaspare Gozzi 1-A, 20129 Milan, Italy. TEL 39-2-700231. FAX 39-2-70023260. Ed. Luca Grandori. adv.: color page L.23000000; adv. contact: Flavio Biondi. circ. 136,000. **Document type:** consumer publication.

910.202   US
H I A Y H DISCOVERY TOURS. 1984. a. free. Hostelling International - American Youth Hostels, Box 37613, Washington, DC 20013-7613. TEL 202-783-6161. FAX 202-783-6171. circ. 100,000. **Document type:** catalog.
Formerly: World Adventure Trip Catalogue.
Description: Provides complete information (price, itineraries, departures) of 30 different cycling, hiking, backpacking and canoeing tours offered by HI-AYH.

HORESCA - INFORMATIONS. (Federation Nationale des Hoteliers, Restaurateurs et Cafetiers du Grand-Duche de Luxembourg) see HOTELS AND RESTAURANTS

526 910   US
HAGSTROM MAP AND TRAVEL NEWSLETTER. 1986. q. free. Hagstrom Map and Travel, 57 W. 43rd St., New York, NY 10036. TEL 212-398-1222. Ed. Douglas B. Rose. bk.rev. circ. 15,780. **Document type:** newsletter.
Formerly: Hagstrom Map and Travel Center Newsletter.

914.04   GW
HAMBURGER TOP INFO FOR VISITORS. (Text in English) 1984. m. DM.66. Hamburg Fuehrer Verlag GmbH, Rothenbaumchaussee 195, 20149 Hamburg, Germany. TEL 040-448185. FAX 040-452368. Ed. Susan Kunst-Elliot. adv. contact: Sabine Mackprang. illus. (back issues avail.) **Document type:** consumer publication.

915.1   KO
HANDBOOK OF KOREA. 1978. a. Korean Overseas Information Service, Ministry of Culture and Information, Sejongno 1, Seoul, S. Korea.

TRAVEL AND TOURISM

910.09   GW
HANSESTADT LUEBECK TRAVEMUENDE AKTUELL; das offizielle Programm der Hansestadt Luebeck. 1951. m. DM.12. Schmidt-Roemhild Verlag, Mengstr. 16, 23552 Luebeck, Germany. TEL 0451-1605-0. FAX 0451-1605280. adv. circ. 9,000. **Document type:** bulletin.

919.604   US   ISSN 0883-2471
DU622
HAWAII (YEAR). a. $18. Harper Collins Publishers, Birnbaum Travel Guides, 10 E 53rd St., New York, NY 10022-5244. TEL 212-270-7542. Ed. Alexandra Mayes Birnbaum.

910.202   US
HAWAII DRIVE GUIDES. 1974. 3/yr. Honolulu Publishing Company, Ltd., 36 Merchant St., Honolulu, HI 96813. TEL 808-524-7400. FAX 808-531-2306. Ed. Brett Uprichard. circ. 67,500.
Description: Touring guides for Oahu, Maui, Hawaii and Kauai, with detailed maps and descriptions of scenic and historical sites, visitor attractions, selected restaurants, shops and centers, things to do, sports and other information for the independent traveller.

919.69   US
HAWAII HOTEL NETWORK. (In 7 editions for 45 hotels) 1973. 3/yr. free in Waikiki and neighbor island hotels of Hawaii. Spotlight Hawaii Publishing, 532 Cummins St., Honolulu, HI 96814. TEL 808-524-8404. FAX 808-537-2121. Ed. Camie Foster. adv. circ. 580,000.
Formerly: Here's Hawaii.
Description: Presents feature articles on a range of subjects for the first-time and repeat visitor. Includes calendar, and directory information.

910.09   US   ISSN 0892-0990
HAWAII MAGAZINE; gateway to the Pacific. 1982. bi-m. $11.99; newsstand price: $3.50. Fancy Publications, 2401 Beverly Blvd., Los Angeles, CA 90057. TEL 213-385-2222. FAX 714-855-8822. (Subscr. to: Box 485, Mt. Morris, IL 61054-0485) Ed. Dennis Shattuck. adv.; bk.rev.; index. circ. 63,000. (also avail. in microfilm) **Document type:** consumer publication.

919   US
HAWAII ON 60 DOLLARS A DAY. a. $14.95. Frommer Books (Subsidiary of: Simon & Schuster, Inc.), 15 Columbus Circle, New York, NY 10023. TEL 212-373-8125.
Former titles: Hawaii on 35 Dollars a Day (ISSN 8755-9250); Hawaii on 30 Dollars a Day; Hawaii on 25 Dollars a Day (ISSN 0197-8527); Hawaii on 20 Dollars a Day.

917.904   US
HAWAII: THE BIG ISLAND, A PARADISE GUIDE. (Supplement avail.: Hawaii: The Big Island Update) biennial. Paradise Publications, 8110 S.W. Wareham, Portland, OR 97223. TEL 503-246-1555.
Description: Guide to beaches, restaurants, budget travel, and resorts.

917.904   US   ISSN 1042-8046
HAWAII: THE BIG ISLAND UPDATE. (Supplement to: Hawaii: The Big Island, a Paradise Guide) 1989. q. $10 (Canada $12). Paradise Publications, 8110 S.W. Wareham, Portland, OR 97223. TEL 503-246-1555. Ed. John Penisten. circ. 2,000.
Description: Information for tourists and island residents on restaurants, tourist attractions, airlines and hotels.

HEALTH SPA AND RESORT NEWSLETTER. see HOTELS AND RESTAURANTS

910.202   IS   ISSN 0333-712X
HELLO ISRAEL. 1972. w. Tourguide Ltd., P.O. Box 3656, Tel Aviv 61036, Israel. TEL 972-3-490930. FAX 972-3-497640. Ed. I. Tamir. adv.; circ. 15,000 (controlled).

HERALD CARAVANNING GUIDE. see SPORTS AND GAMES — Outdoor Life

210.202   US   ISSN 0741-1952
HIDEAWAYS GUIDE. 1981. 2/yr. $99 includes membership. Hideaways International, 767 Islington St., Portsmouth, NH 03801-4236. TEL 603-430-4433. FAX 603-430-4444. Ed. Michael F. Thiel. adv.; bk.rev. circ. 12,000. (back issues avail.)
Description: Lists villa rentals worldwide, especially Caribbean, Mexico, Hawaii, and Europe. Includes articles about out-of-the-ordinary vacations.

910.202   US
HIDEAWAYS NEWSLETTER. 1983. 4/yr. membership. Hideaways International, 767 Islington St., Portsmouth, NH 03801-4236. TEL 603-430-4433. FAX 603-430-4444. Ed. Michael F. Thiel. adv. contact: Gail D. Richard. circ. 12,000. (back issues avail.) **Document type:** newsletter.
Description: Lists villa rentals worldwide, especially Caribbean, Mexico, Hawaii, and Europe. Includes travel tips, features on less-traveled destinations, members' ratings on small resorts.

HILTON INTERNATIONAL (U.K.) MAGAZINE. see HOTELS AND RESTAURANTS

HOERZU. see GENERAL INTEREST PERIODICALS — Germany

910.202   GW
HOLIDAY. 1988. bi-m. DM.39. Burda Verlag GmbH, Postfach 1230, 77602 Offenburg, Germany. TEL 089-9250-0. FAX 089-92503519. Ed. Lothar Strobach. (back issues avail.) **Document type:** consumer publication.

910   AU
HOLIDAY & BUSINESS IN AUSTRIA. s-a. Redaktionsbuero fuer Touristik, Am See 89, A-2443 Deutsch Brodersdorf, Austria. TEL 01-932745. FAX 01-5266116. Ed. Leo Froehlich. circ. 50,000.

916.8 362.4   SA
▼**HOLIDAY GUIDE O F S/VAKANSIEGIDS O V S.** (Text in English, Afrikaans) 1994. a. free. Satour, Private Bag X164, Pretoria 0001, South Africa. **Document type:** government publication, consumer publication.
Description: Covers vacationing in the Orange Free State for disabled people.

914.204   UK
HOLIDAY ISLANDER. 1976. a. free. Portsmouth Publishing, Box 1, Hayling Island PO11 9RL, England. Ed. Pat Holt. adv.; bk.rev. circ. 10,000.
Former titles: Hayling Islander; (until 1984): Hayling Island Magazine.

914.2   UK
HOLIDAY SCOTLAND. 1972. a. free. Scottish Tourist Board, 23 Ravelston Terrace, Edinburgh EH4 3EU, Scotland. TEL 0131-332-2433. FAX 0131-343-1513. TELEX 72272. charts; illus. circ. 750,000. **Document type:** directory.
Former titles: Scotland; Scotland's for Me; Enjoy Scotland; Scotland: A World of Difference.

910.202   UK
HOLIDAY WEST HIGHLAND. 1980. a. £0.75. Oban Times Ltd., P.O. Box 1, Oban, Argyll PA34 5PY, Scotland. TEL 0631-63058. FAX 0631-65470. Ed. Hazel Clowes. adv. circ. 38,000. (tabloid format; back issues avail.) **Document type:** newspaper.
Formerly (until 1992): Holiday West.

919   AT
HOLIDAY WESTERN AUSTRALIA. TRAVEL NEWS. 1980. bi-m. free. Western Australia Tourism Commission, P.O. Box X2261, Perth, W.A. 6000, Australia. FAX 09-2201702. Ed. Graeme Cocks. circ. 2,500.
Supersedes: Travel News from Western Australia.

910.202   UK
HOLIDAY WHICH?. q. £16. Consumers' Association, 2 Marylebone Rd., London NW1 4DF, England. TEL 071-830-6000. (Subscr. addr.: Consumers' Association, Castlemead, Gascoyne Way, Hertford. SG14 1LH, England) Ed. Patricia Yates. circ. 131,000. **Indexed:** Art.Hosp.& Tour.

914   RM   ISSN 0018-3555
HOLIDAYS IN ROMANIA. Rumanian edition: Romania Pitoreasca. (Editions in English, French, German, Rumanian) 1958. m. $27. Ministerul Turismului - Ministry of Tourism, Gabriel Peri Str. 8, 70148 Bucharest, Rumania. TEL 597893. (Subscr. to: ROMPRESFILATELIA Sectorul Export-Import Presa, POB.12-201, Calea Grvitei nr. 64-66, Rumania) Ed. Simion Pop. adv.; bk.rev.; illus. circ. 22,000.
Formerly: Romania for Tourists.

HOLY PLACES OF PALESTINE. see RELIGIONS AND THEOLOGY

910.202   US   ISSN 8750-5649
HOME & AWAY. 1913. bi-m. $6. Automobile Association of America, Hoosier Motor Club, Box 88505, Indianapolis, IN 46208-0505. TEL 317-923-1500. FAX 317-924-4669. Ed. Hugh F. Orr. adv. circ. 185,000.
Formerly: Hoosier Motorist (ISSN 0199-6975)
Description: Travel, finance and safety oriented magazine for AAA members in Central Indiana; promotes member services.

910.09   US   ISSN 0889-4078
HOME & AWAY (OHIO EDITION). bi-m. $6 (effective 1993). (American Automobile Association) A A A - Ohio Auto Club, 90 E. Wilson Bridge Rd., Worthington, OH 43085-2325. TEL 614-431-7919. Ed. William J. Purpura. adv.: B&W page $31055, color page $35055; trim 8 x 10 7/8; adv. contact: Vera Cornish. circ. 460,000. **Document type:** consumer publication.

910.202   US   ISSN 0199-5383
HOME & AWAY MINNESOTA. bi-m. $6. American Automobile Association, Minnesota State Automobile Association, Seven Travelers Trail, Burnsville, MN 55337. TEL 612-890-2500. FAX 612-894-4079. Ed. Ronald R. Siegmund. adv.; circ. 212,000 (controlled). **Document type:** trade publication.

919.404   AT
HOMESTAY EASTERN AUSTRALIA; a guide to accommodation & travel - cities - farms - outback. 1989. a. Aus.$22($18) Sydney's Good Accommodation & Travel Guide Pty. Ltd., P.O. Box 1222, Bathurst, N.S.W. 2795, Australia. FAX 063-37-3558. Ed. W. L. Ogilvie.
Formerly (until 1991): Homestay Australia.

910.09   HO
HONDURAS. CONSEJO SUPERIOR DE PLANIFICACION ECONOMICA. PLAN OPERATIVO ANUAL SECTOR TURISMO. a. Consejo Superior de Planificacion Economica, Secretaria Tecnica, Tegucigalpa, Honduras.

915   HK
HONG KONG GUIDE - STREETS AND PLACES. (Text in Chinese and English) 1978. irreg. (approx. 3/yr.). HK.$65 (effective Aug. 1994). Principal Government Land Surveyor, Survey and Mapping Office, Lands Department, Murray Bldg., Garden Rd., Hong Kong. TEL 852-2848-2480. FAX 852-2521-8726. Ed. Cheung Chung Tong. circ. 40,000. **Document type:** government publication.
Formerly (until 1988): Hong Kong Streets and Places.
Description: Comprehensive directory with maps for the Territory of Hong Kong.

915   HK   ISSN 0018-4616
HONG KONG TRAVEL BULLETIN. (Text in English) 1959. m. free. Hong Kong Tourist Association, Box 2597, Hong Kong. TEL 28076543. FAX 28060303. Ed. Penelope Byrne. adv.; charts; illus. circ. 22,200. **Document type:** bulletin.

910.202 052   HK
HONG KONG VISITOR. (Text in English, Japanese) 1984. m. South China Morning Post Publishers Ltd., 6-F, South China Morning Post Bldg., Tong Chong Street 57, Quarry Bay, Hong Kong. TEL 5652430. FAX 5658961. Ed. Deirbhile O'Grady. circ. 50,000 (controlled).
Formerly: Hong Kong and Guangzhou Visitor.
Description: Guide and social calender for tourists.

TRAVEL AND TOURISM

914.2 647.94 UK ISSN 0260-2539
HORWATH - E T B ENGLISH HOTEL OCCUPANCY SURVEY (YEAR). Key Title: English Hotel Occupancy Survey. 1971. m. (plus a. survey). £300. English Tourist Board, Black's Rd., Hammersmith, London W6 9EL, England. TEL 0181-846-9000. FAX 0181-563-0302.
  Description: Provides data on hotel occupancy and the proportion of guests from overseas.

HOSEASONS BOATING HOLIDAYS. see *SPORTS AND GAMES — Boats And Boating*

910.202 UK
HOSEASONS HOLIDAY-HOMES IN U.K.. 1946. a. free. (Hoseasons Holidays) Sunway House, Lowestoft, Suffolk NR32 2LW, England. TEL 01502-500-505. FAX 01502-514298. Ed. James Hoseason. circ. 1,400,000. **Document type:** catalog.
  Formerly (until 1970): Hoseasons Holiday-Homes.

HOSPITALITY & TOURISM EDUCATOR. see *EDUCATION — Adult Education*

910.4 AT ISSN 1030-0384
HOSTEL TRAVEL. 1949. q. Aus.$12. Youth Hostels Association of N.S.W Inc., G.P.O. Box 5276, Sydney, N.S.W. 2001, Australia. FAX 02-2611969. Ed. Paul Page. adv.; bk.rev. circ. 40,000.
  Former titles: Y H A Hostel Yarn; Hostel Yarn (ISSN 0156-0115); Y H A Hostel Yarn.

910.09 SP
HOSTELERIA Y TURISMO. 12/yr. Balmes 6, 08007 Barcelona, Spain. TEL 3-318-78-36. FAX 3-317-57-55. circ. 30,000.

919 AT ISSN 0157-3977
HOSTELLER. 1949. 3/yr. Aus.$9 to non-members. Youth Hostels Association of Victoria, 357 Barkly St., Elwood, Vic. 3184, Australia. TEL 03-670-7991. FAX 03-670-9840. Ed. Michele Tardini. adv.; bk.rev. circ. 31,000. **Document type:** consumer publication.

919 AT ISSN 0725-8968
HOSTELLING. 1969. q. Aus.$8. Youth Hostels Association of South Australia, Inc., 38 Sturt St., Adelaide, S.A. 5000, Australia. FAX 61-8-231-4219. Ed. D. Brauington. adv.; bk.rev. circ. 6,500. **Document type:** newsletter.

910.1 647.94 US
HOSTELLING NORTH AMERICA/AUBERGES DE JEUNESSE EN AMERIQUE DU NORD; a directory of hostels in the Canada and the United States. 1934. a. $5 to non-members (Canada Can.$6.95). Hostelling International - American Youth Hostels, Box 37613, Washington, DC 20013-7613. TEL 202-783-6161. FAX 202-783-6171. (Addr. in Canada: Hostelling International - Canada, 400 - 205 Catherine St., Ottawa, ON K2P 1C3, Canada. TEL 613-237-7884) (Co-sponsor: Hostelling International - Canada) adv. contact: Justin J. Cline. circ. 200,000. **Document type:** directory.
  Former titles: North American Hostels Handbook; American Youth Hostels Handbook; American Youth Hostels Guide and Handbook (ISSN 0066-1201)
  Description: Lists nearly 250 hostels in the U.S. and Canada, including location maps and travel information.

915.204 JA
HOTEL. (Text in Japanese) m. 6000 Yen($100) Ohta Publications Co., Ltd., Dame Ginza Bldg., 7-18 Ginza, 6-chome, Chuo-ku, Tokyo 104, Japan. TEL 03-3571-1181. FAX 03-3574-1650. Ed. Minoru Murakami. adv. circ. 160,000.
  Description: Offers information on luxury hotels worldwide, and includes detailed coverage of special events, fairs, conventions, seminars, entertainment, arts, and fashion.

910.4 II
HOTEL & TOURISM DEVELOPMENT REPORT. 1979. w. $85. International Press Cutting Service, Box 63, Allahabad 211001, India. Ed. Nandi Khanna. (looseleaf format)

HOTEL AND TRAVEL INDEX; the world wide hotel directory. see *HOTELS AND RESTAURANTS*

910 AU
HOTEL REVUE. w. Kettenbrueckengasse 22, Postfach 57, A-1040 Vienna, Austria. TEL 01-5888150. FAX 01-5888166. Ed. Walter Norden. circ. 12,400.

HOTEL UND TOURISMUS REVUE. see *HOTELS AND RESTAURANTS*

HOTEL & TOURISTIK. see *HOTELS AND RESTAURANTS*

910.09 SP
HOTEL VILLA MAGNA. (Text in English, Spanish) q. Editorial J.S. Publicaciones Especiales, Santa Susana 55, 5o, 1 y 2, 28033 Madrid, Spain. TEL 1-763-34-01. adv.: color page 130000; trim 258 x 185.

914 NO ISSN 0803-7019
HOTELL - RESTAURANT & REISELIV. 1991. m. (9/yr.). NOK 70. (Landslaget for Reiselivet i Norge, Hotell - Restaurant & Reiseliv - Norway Travel Association) Nortra Produkjon A-S, Oevre Slottsgate 12, N-0157 Oslo, Norway. (Co-sponsor: Norske Reisebyraaforening) Ed. Oddvar Hegge. adv.; bk.rev.; charts; illus. circ. 3,300.
  Formed by the merger of (1973-1991): Reiseliv (ISSN 0333-2373); (1989-1991): Hotell og Restaurant (ISSN 0802-6203); Which was formerly (until 1989): Norsk Hotell og Restaurantblad (ISSN 0332-7760); Which was formed by the merger of (1923-1943): Tidsskrift for Norsk Hotell og Restaurantforbund (ISSN 0802-6262); Which was formerly (until 1923): Norssk Tidsskrift for Hotel og Turistvaesen (ISSN 0802-6297); Oslo Hotell og Restaurantblad (ISSN 0802-6270); Which was formerly (until 1932): Norsk Hotell og Restaurantblad (ISSN 0802-6289); Reiseliv was formerly (until 1973): Reiseliv i Norge (ISSN 0034-3676); (until 1937): Turist og Reiseliv (ISSN 0333-2381); (until 1934): Medlemsblad - Landslaget for Reiselivet i Norge (ISSN 0333-239X); (until 1929): Reiseforeningens Medlemsblad (ISSN 0333-2403).

647 US
HOTELS & TOURISM: LATIN AMERICAN INDUSTRIAL REPORT. (Avail. for each of 22 Latin American countries) 1985. a. $435 per country report. Aquino Productions, Box 15760, Stamford, CT 06901. TEL 203-325-3138. Ed. Andres C. Aquino.

919 BF
HOTELS, MOTELS AND GUESTHOUSES AND RESTAURANTS: NEW PROVIDENCE, PARADISE ISLAND AND GRAND BAHAMA. 1980. a. B.$2. Ministry of Finance, Department of Statistics, Box N 3904, Nassau, Bahamas. Ed.Bd.
  Formerly: Hotels, Motels and Guest Houses in New Providence and Paradise Island.

914.04 GW ISSN 0343-5555
HUSUMER MONATSHEFTE; Informationen, Fahrplaene, Veranstaltungen. m. DM.28. Husum Druck- und Verlagsgesellschaft mbH, Postfach 1480, 25804 Husum, Germany. TEL 04841-6081. FAX 04841-61397. Ed. Alfred Lorenzen. adv. circ. 8,000. **Document type:** bulletin.

374 910.202 US
I C T A UPDATE. bi-m. free to members. Institute of Certified Travel Agents, 148 Linden St., Box 812059, Wellesley, MA 02181-0012. TEL 617-237-0280. FAX 617-237-3860. Ed. Dawn Ringel. circ. 28,000. (back issues avail.)
  Formerly: I C T A News.
  Description: Focuses on ICTA activities and programs, including members' accomplishments and management ideas.

I F L NIEUWS. (International Friendship League) see *CLUBS*

917.04 US
I LOVE NEW YORK: THE FINGER LAKES TRAVEL GUIDE. 1951. a. free. Finger Lakes Association, Inc., 309 Lake Street, Penn Yan, NY 14527. TEL 315-536-7488. FAX 315-536-1237. Ed. Jack Kidd. adv.; circ. 65,000 (controlled). **Document type:** directory.
  Formerly: Finger Lakes Travel Guide.

910.03 US
I LOVE NEW YORK TRAVEL GUIDE. a. free. Department of Economic Development, 1 Commerce Plaza, Albany, NY 12245. TEL 518-474-4116. FAX 518-474-6416. Ed. Mary Ellen Walsh. **Document type:** government publication.
  Description: Lists tourist attractions and events in New York State.

910.09 US ISSN 1055-8314
IDEAL TRAVELLER.* (Supplement avail.) 1991. q. $26.99. Publishing & Business Consultants, 101 W. 64th St., Unit 3, Inglewood, CA 90302-1255. TEL 213-732-3477. FAX 213-732-9123. (Subscr. to: Box 75392, Los Angeles, CA 90075) Ed. Andeson Napoleon Atia. adv. circ. 120,000. **Document type:** consumer publication.
  Previously announced as: Vacation Overseas.
  Description: Provides information on popular vacation destinations, and advice for travelers.

910.09 GW
IHRE FERIENWOHNUNG; das ganzjaehrige Urlaubsmagazin. 1984. a. DM.14.50($8) Touristikverlag H.U.B. GmbH und Co. KG, Stepahienstr. 6, 79100 Freiburg, Germany. TEL 0761-709693. Eds. W. Bachelle, W. Schwoerer. circ. 40,000. (back issues avail.)

ILLINOIS GOLFER'S TRAVEL GUIDE. see *SPORTS AND GAMES — Ball Games*

IMPRESA ITALIA. see *BUSINESS AND ECONOMICS — Domestic Commerce*

941.3 GW ISSN 0404-6307
IN BADEN - WUERTTEMBERG. 1961. 4/yr. DM.34. Verlag G. Braun GmbH, Karl-Friedrich-Str. 14-18, 76133 Karlsruhe, Germany. TEL 0721-165-0. FAX 0721-1657345. circ. 13,000. **Indexed:** GeoRef. **Document type:** bulletin.
  Formerly: Welt am Oberrhein.

914 UK ISSN 0019-3143
DA650
IN BRITAIN. 1930. m. $39.95. British Tourist Authority, Thames Tower, Blacks Rd., London W6 9EL, England. TEL 0181-846-9000. (Subscr. to: Premier Magazines, Haymarket House, 1 Oxendon St., London SW1Y 4EE, England) Ed. Andrea Spain; Pub. Kathy Green. **Document type:** consumer publication.

IN CORNWALL MAGAZINE. see *GENERAL INTEREST PERIODICALS — Great Britain*

910.09 US
IN-FLIGHT SURVEY OF INTERNATIONAL AIR TRAVELERS: INBOUND COUNTRY REPORTS. (Avail. for Australia, Brazil, Canada, France, Germany, Italy, Japan, Mexico, South Korea, the U.K., Venezuela) 1988. a. $250 for each country. U.S. Travel and Tourism Administration, Office of Research, U.S. Department of Commerce, Main Commerce Bldg., Rm. 1868, Washington, DC 20230. TEL 202-482-4028. FAX 202-293-3155. (Subscr. to: U.S. Travel Data Center, 2 Lafayette Centre, 1123 21st St., N.W., Washington, DC 20036. TEL 202-293-1040. FAX 202-293-3155) stat.; charts. (back issues avail.) **Document type:** government publication.
  Description: Provides statistics and summaries of data of tourists from specific countries.

910.09 US
IN-FLIGHT SURVEY OF INTERNATIONAL AIR TRAVELERS: INBOUND NATIONAL REPORT. a. $250. U.S. Travel and Tourism Administration, Office of Research, U.S. Department of Commerce, Main Commerce Bldg., Rm. 1868, Washington, DC 20230. TEL 202-482-4028. FAX 202-482-2887. (Subscr. to: U.S. Travel Data Center, 2 Lafayette Centre, 1123 21st St., N.W., Washington, D.C. 20036. TEL 202-293-1040 577. FAX 202-482-2887) stat. (back issues avail.) **Document type:** government publication.
  Description: Provides a comprehensive comparative analysis of overseas travelers to the U.S. from nine world regions and 20 countries.

TRAVEL AND TOURISM

910.09   US
IN-FLIGHT SURVEY OF INTERNATIONAL AIR TRAVELERS: OUTBOUND COUNTRY REPORTS. (Avail. in two reports: U.S. Air Travelers to Mexico, U.S. Air Travelers to Canada) 1983. a. $250. U.S. Travel and Tourism Administration, Office of Research, U.S. Department of Commerce, Main Commerce Bldg., Rm. 1868, Washington, DC 20230. TEL 202-482-4028. FAX 202-482-2887. (Subscr. for Mexico Report to: U.S. Travel Data Center, 2 Lafayette Centre, 1133 21st St., N.W., Washington, DC 20036. TEL 202-293-1040. FAX 202-293-3155; Subscr. for Canada Report to: Canadian Tourism Research Institute, 255 Smyth Rd., Ottawa, ON K1H 8M7, Canada. TEL 613-526-3280. FAX 613-526-4306) charts; stat. **Document type:** government publication.
     Description: Reports on statistics of U.S. residents traveling abroad.

910.09   US
IN-FLIGHT SURVEY OF INTERNATIONAL AIR TRAVELERS: OUTBOUND NATIONAL REPORT. a. $250. U.S. Travel and Tourism Administration, Office of Research, U.S. Department of Commerce, Main Commerce Bldg., Rm. 1868, Washington, DC 20230. TEL 202-482-4028. FAX 202-482-2887. (Subscr. to: U.S. Travel Data Center, 2 Lafayette Centre, 1133 21st St., N.W., Washington, DC 20036. TEL 202-293-1040. FAX 202-293-3155) (back issues avail.) **Document type:** government publication.
     Description: Compiles data on U.S. residents traveling overseas.

910.202   UK
IN FOCUS (LONDON, 1990). Cover title: Tourism in Focus. 1990. q. £12 (Europe £16; elsewhere £20) to individuals; institutions £16 (Europe £20; elsewhere £25). Tourism Concern, Southlands College, Roehampton Institute, Wimbledon Parkside, London SW19 5NN, England. TEL 0181-944-0464. Ed. Tricia Barnett. (back issues avail.) **Document type:** bulletin.
     Description: Discusses the impact of tourism on host communities and the environment, promotes awareness of development issues relating to tourism, and encourages responsible and sustainable tourism.

IN MOTION (EUREKA). see SPORTS AND GAMES

910.09   US
IN - S I T E MAGAZINE. 1987. bi-m. membership. Society of Incentive Travel Executives, 21 W. 38th St., 10th Fl., New York, NY 10018. TEL 212-575-0910. FAX 212-575-1838. Ed. Maureen P. Mangan. adv. circ. 2,500. **Document type:** newsletter.
     Description: Covers incentive travel as a tool to increase productivity in business.

910.09   IT
INCENTIVARE. 1984. 8/yr. Ediman s.r.l., Corso San Gottardo 39, 20136 Milan, Italy. TEL 39-2-58103791. FAX 39-2-58103789. Ed. Rosella Giovannini. adv.: B&W page L.4100000, color page L.6200000. circ. 11,000.

INDEPENDENT NATIONAL EDITION; a monthly journal for thoughtful Canadians. see ENVIRONMENTAL STUDIES

910.202   UK   ISSN 1352-7851
INDIA HANDBOOK; India and Bhutan. 1992. a. £16.95. Trade & Travel Publications Ltd., 6 Riverside Ct., Lower Bristol Rd., Bath BA2 3DZ, England. TEL 01225-469141. FAX 01225-469461. (Dist. in N. America by: Passport Books, NTC Publishing Group, 4255 W. Touhy Ave., Lincolnwood, IL 60646-1975. TEL 708-679-5500. FAX 708-679-6375) Ed. Robert Bradnock. **Document type:** directory.
     Formerly (until 1994): South Asian Handbook (ISSN 0968-0934)

INDIANA GOLFER'S TRAVEL GUIDE. see SPORTS AND GAMES — Ball Games

910.202   UK   ISSN 0968-0942
INDONESIA, MALAYSIA AND SINGAPORE HANDBOOK. 1993. a. £15.95. Trade & Travel Publications Ltd., 6 Riverside Ct., Lower Bristol Rd., Bath BA2 3DZ, England. TEL 01225-469141. FAX 01225-469461. (Dist. in N. America by: Passport Books, N T C Publishing Group, 4255 W. Touhy Ave., Lincolnwood, IL 60646-1975. TEL 708-679-5500. FAX 708-679-6375) Ed. Joshua Eliot. **Document type:** directory.

917   US   ISSN 0019-7777
INDUSTRIA TURISTICA. (Text in Spanish) 1957. m. $25. Charles Francis Publications, Inc., Box 52-1898, Miami, FL 33152-1898. TEL 305-592-3168. Eds. Charles Francis, Lucky Francis. adv.; bk.rev.; stat.; tr.lit.; circ. 6,000 (controlled). **Document type:** trade publication.
     Former titles: Industria and Mundo Turistico; Industria Turistica.

910.09   GW
INFO-HEFT. 1993. a. DM.7. Deutsche Zentrale fuer Globetrotter e.V., c/o Hans Michael Buer, Suhlenkamp 6, 24558 Henstedt-Ulzburg, Germany. TEL 04193-92138. circ. 3,000. **Document type:** directory.

INFORMATION ROUTIERE ET TOURISTIQUE. see TRANSPORTATION — Trucks And Trucking

INFORMATORE DEI COMMERCIANTI. see BUSINESS AND ECONOMICS — Chamber Of Commerce Publications

910.09 340   IT
INFORMATORE GIURIDICO DELL'OPERATORE TURISTICO. 3/yr. Via Emilia Ovest 21A, 42048 Rubiera, Italy. TEL 522-62-229. Ed. Giancarlo Bellei.

INN MARKETING NEWSLETTER; country inns, small hotels and bed & breakfasts. see HOTELS AND RESTAURANTS

INN PLACES (YEAR). see HOMOSEXUALITY

641.9   US   ISSN 1052-794X
TX907.2
THE INNKEEPERS' REGISTER. 1990. a. $12.95. Independent Innkeepers' Association, Box 150, Marshall, MI 49068. TEL 616-789-0393; 800-344-5244. FAX 616-789-0970. Ed. Kathryn Kinney. adv. contact: Norman Kinney. circ. 250,000. **Document type:** directory.

910.4   US
INSIDE TRAVEL NEWS. 1971. m. $9. 6229 Bristol Pkwy., Culver City, CA 90230. TEL 213-296-8858. Ed. Lozetta Slaton. adv. circ. 6,000.

910.202   SZ
INSIDER INNERSCHWEIZ. w. Actualis Verlag AG, Ruopigenplatz 8, Postfach 70, CH-6015 Reussbuehl, Switzerland. TEL 041-570288. FAX 041-574784. Ed. Clemens Rimoldi. circ. 15,000.

914.604   SP
INSPAIN. (Text in English) 1985. m. 2500 ptas.($21) InSpain Magazine, Dr. Esquerdo 35, 1F, 28028 Madrid, Spain. TEL 256-1779. FAX 256-1779. Ed. George C. Hall. adv.; bk.rev.; circ. 15,000 (controlled).
     Description: For native English speakers living in Spain. Covers culture, travel, and sports.

914.2   UK
INSPECTED BED & BREAKFAST IN BRITAIN. a. £7.99. A Publishing (Subsidiary of: Automobile Publishing), Norfolk House, Priestly Rd., Basingstoke, Hants. RG24 9NY, England. TEL 0256-20123. FAX 0256-22575. adv. **Document type:** consumer publication.
     Former titles: Guesthouses, Farmhouses and Inns in Britain; Automobile Association. Budget Guide.

910.202   UK
INSTITUTE OF TRAVEL & TOURISM. JOURNAL. 1955. q. Institute of Travel & Tourism, 113 Victoria St., St. Albans, Herts. AL1 3TJ, England. TEL 0727-854395. FAX 0727-847415. Ed. Roger Edwards. charts; stat.; tr.lit. circ. 5,000. (back issues avail.) **Document type:** trade publication.

917.204   CR
INSTITUTO COSTARRICENSE DE TURISMO. MEMORIA ANUAL. 1955. a. free. Instituto Costarricense de Turismo, San Jose, Costa Rica. TEL 506-33-21-64. FAX 223-54-52. illus. circ. 100. **Document type:** government publication.

910.09   IT
INTERLINE AND TRAVEL NEWS ITALIA. 1971. 11/yr. L.22000. Via Bissolati 54, 00187 Rome, Italy. TEL 39-6-4740227. FAX 39-6-48903681. Ed. Alberto Marani. adv.; bk.rev.; circ. 10,000 (paid). **Document type:** trade publication.

910   US   ISSN 1012-8042
INTERNATIONAL ACADEMY FOR THE STUDY OF TOURISM. NEWSLETTER. 1986. q. 60. Tourism Center, 116 Classroom Office Bldg., University of Minnesota, St. Paul, MN 55108. TEL 612-624-4947. FAX 612-625-6245. E-mail: wgartner@mes.umn.edu. (Co-sponsor: World Tourism Organization (Organizacion Mundial del Turismo)) Ed. Bill Gartner; Pub. Bill Gartner. abstr. circ. 150. (back issues avail.) **Document type:** newsletter.
     Description: Covers important events of the organization, as well as conferences and events.

INTERNATIONAL ASSOCIATION OF CONVENTION AND VISITOR BUREAUS. NEWSLETTER. see MEETINGS AND CONGRESSES

917.29   BF
INTERNATIONAL BAHAMA LIFE. m. $16. Johnson Publications, P.O. Box N-1505, Nassau, Bahamas.

INTERNATIONAL CRUISE AND FERRY REVIEW. see TRANSPORTATION — Ships And Shipping

INTERNATIONAL EMPLOYMENT HOTLINE. see OCCUPATIONS AND CAREERS

910.2   BE   ISSN 0074-5979
INTERNATIONAL FEDERATION OF JOURNALISTS AND TRAVEL WRITERS. OFFICIAL LIST/REPERTOIRE OFFICIEL. (Text in English and French) 1965. q. 75 Fr. International Federation of Journalists and Travel Writers, Zavelstraat 62, B-3071 Kortenberg, Belgium. adv.; bk.rev. circ. 2,500.

917 642.5   CN
INTERNATIONAL GUIDE. 1977. a. Can.$9.95. I G Publications Ltd., 999 8th St., S.W., Ste. 222, Calgary, AB T2R 1J5, Canada. FAX 403-229-2470. Ed. S.K. Bell. adv. circ. 148,000.

INTERNATIONAL JOURNAL OF HOSPITALITY MANAGEMENT. see HOTELS AND RESTAURANTS

910.4   US   ISSN 0277-2442
INTERNATIONAL LIVING. 1981. m. $58. Agora, Inc., 824 E. Baltimore St., Baltimore, MD 21202-4799. TEL 410-223-2611. FAX 410-223-2619. TELEX 910250 6212. Ed. Siri Lise Doub; Pub. William Bonner. adv. contact: Janet Wisner. bk.rev.; index. circ. 50,000. (back issues avail.)

910.202   UK   ISSN 0268-5671
INTERNATIONAL MEETING PLACE; a guide to international conference & exhibition locations. 1986. a. £25. Millbank Publications Ltd., 25 Catherine St., London WC2B 5JW, England. TEL 071-379-3036. FAX 071-240-6840. adv.; charts; illus. circ. 5,000. **Document type:** directory.

385 910.09   US   ISSN 0891-7655
INTERNATIONAL RAILWAY TRAVELER. 1983. bi-m. $39.95 (Canada $41.45, elsewhere $45.95). Hardy Publishing Co., Inc., The Belknap Bldg., 1810 Sils Ave., Ste. 306B, Louisville, KY 40205. TEL 502-454-0277. FAX 502-458-8901. (Subscr. to: Fulco, 30 Broad St., Denville, NJ 07834) Ed. Gena Holle; Pub. Owen Hardy. adv. contact: Richard Vaughan. bk.rev.; charts; illus.; tr.lit. circ. 5,000. (back issues avail.) **Document type:** newsletter.
     Description: For all who love to travel by trains, whether by Amtrak or the East African Railway.

6478 TRAVEL AND TOURISM

910.202 US ISSN 0269-3747
G155.A1
INTERNATIONAL TOURISM REPORTS. 1971. q. £325($535) Economist Intelligence Unit, 111 W. 57th St., New York, NY 10019. TEL 212-554-0600; 800-938-4685. FAX 212-586-1182. TELEX 175567. (UK addr.: Economist Intelligence Unit Ltd., Subscriptions Dept., P.O. Box 200, Harold Hill, Romford, Essex RM3 8UX, England. TEL 44-1708-381-444. FAX 44-1708-371-850) charts; stat. (also avail. in microform from WMP) **Indexed:** Art.Hosp.& Tour., Cont.Pg.Manage., Hospit.Ind., Key to Econ.Sci., Rural Recreat.Tour.Abstr., World Agri.Econ.& Rural Sociol.Abstr.
• Also available online.
—BLDSC (4551.222000).
Formerly: International Tourism Quarterly (ISSN 0306-4336)
Description: Explores national tourism markets worldwide. Includes country reports with forecasts.

910.09 IT
INTERNATIONAL TOURIST PRESS. 12/yr. C T A Bonelli S.a.s., Viale Tito Livo 166, 00136 Rome, Italy. TEL 6-34-51-670. FAX 6-34-20-978. TELEX 620553 BONELLI I. Ed. Antonio Bonelli.

910.202 CN
INTERNATIONAL TRAVEL GUIDE/GUIDE INTERNATIONAL DU VOYAGE.* (Text in English, French) 1992. a. Can.$15. Editions Guide Annuel, 714 Chemin du Golfe, Nun's Island, Quebec, H3E 1A8, Canada. TEL 514-766-1000. FAX 514-766-7667. adv. circ. 40,000.

INTERNATIONAL TRAVEL HEALTH GUIDE. see *MEDICAL SCIENCES*

910 US ISSN 0191-8761
INTERNATIONAL TRAVEL NEWS. Abbreviated title: I T N. 1976. m. $16 (foreign $26). Martin Publications Inc., 2120 28th St., Sacramento, CA 95818. TEL 916-457-3643. (Subscr. to: 520 Calvados Ave., Sacramento, CA 95815) Ed. David Tykol; Pub. Armond Noble. adv. contact: Helen Noble. bk.rev.; illus.; tr.lit. **Document type:** consumer publication.
Description: Contains reader-written, consumer-oriented information for overseas travelers, including appraisals of tours, cruises and airlines, plus travel warnings and inside tips.

914.94 796.552 SZ
INTERNATIONAL UNION OF ALPINE ASSOCIATIONS. BULLETIN/UNION INTERNATIONALE DES ASSOCIATIONS D'ALPINISME. BULLETIN. (Text in English, French or German) 1934. q. 25 Fr. International Union of Alpine Associations, Case Postale 237, 1211 Geneva 11, Switzerland. Ed. Adalbert Fontana. adv.; bk.rev. circ. 700.

910.91 US ISSN 1058-5575
INTERNATIONAL VISITOR; a newsletter about America's fastest growing travel market. 1990. 10/yr. $78 (foreign $85). International Visitor Publishing, Inc., 799 Broadway, Ste. 309, New York, NY 10003-6811. TEL 212-533-9405. FAX 212-533-9295. Ed. Scott Wogendorf; Pub. Walter Matthews. bk.rev. circ. 10,000. (looseleaf format; back issues avail.) **Document type:** newsletter.
Description: Helps travel companies world-wide to send travelers to the US and US companies to attract and better serve international visitors.

INTERP CENTRAL CLEARINGHOUSE NEWSLETTER. see *ENVIRONMENTAL STUDIES*

910 US
INTERVAC U S; international holiday. 1953. 3/yr. $62. Intervac US - International and USA Home Exchange, 30 San Fernando Ct., Tiburon, CA 94920. TEL 415-435-3497. FAX 415-386-6853. (Subscr. to: Box 590504, San Francisco, CA 94159) Ed. Paula Jaffe. adv. circ. 9,100. **Document type:** catalog.

910.09 US
INTERVAL INTERNATIONAL TRAVELER. q. Interval International, Inc., 6262 Sunset Dr., Miami, FL 33143-8800. TEL 305-666-1861. FAX 305-665-2546. Ed. Edrea Kaiser. adv. circ. 282,000.

910.202 US
IRELAND (YEAR) (BOSTON). 1990. a. $14.95. Houghton Mifflin Co., 215 Park Ave. S., New York, NY 10003. TEL 212-420-5800. (Orders to: Houghton Mifflin Co., Wayside Rd., Burlington, MA 01803. TEL 800-225-3362)

914.104 US ISSN 0896-8691
DA980
IRELAND (YEAR) (NEW YORK). a. $18. Harper Collins Publishers, Birnbaum Travel Guides, 10 E. 53rd St., New York, NY 10022-5299. TEL 212-207-7542. illus.; index.
Description: Includes 12 countryside driving tours.

914 IE ISSN 0021-0943
IRELAND OF THE WELCOMES. 1952. bi-m. I£11 (Europe, U.S. & Canada £13; New Zealand & Australia £17; rest of world £25). Bord Failte - Irish Tourist Board, Baggot St. Bridge, Dublin 2, Ireland. TEL 01-6024000. FAX 01-6024100. (Subscr. to: P.O. Box 84. Limerick, Ireland; Subscr. in US to: Box 2745, Boulder, CO 80322. TEL 800-726-7207) Ed. Peter Harbison; Pub. Bob Bowman. adv. contact: Bob Bowman. bk.rev.; illus.; circ. 93,000 (paid). **Document type:** consumer publication.
—UMI.
Description: Contains articles on the culture, history, people, places and events of Ireland.

914 IE ISSN 0021-1419
IRISH TRAVEL TRADE NEWS. 1965-1980; resumed. $40. 9 Western Parkway Business Centre, Ballymount Rd., Dublin 12, Ireland. TEL 01-4502422. FAX 01-4502954. Ed. Michael Flood. adv. contact: Fan Bloomfield. bk.rev. circ. 1,800. **Document type:** trade publication.

910.09 IT
ISCHIA MONDO. 1972. fortn. L.25000. Lubranopublicitas, Via Roma, 139 T, Ischia, Italy. Ed. Vittorio A. Caravaglios. adv.; bk.rev. circ. 15,000. (also avail. in microfilm)

910.09 US ISSN 1056-392X
ISLAND ESCAPES. m. $39. Islands Publishing Company, 3886 State St., Santa Barbara, CA 93105-3112. TEL 805-682-7177. FAX 805-569-0349. Ed. Tony Gibbs; Pub. Bill Kasch. circ. 4,000. **Document type:** newsletter.
Description: Provides ratings and evaluations of where to go, how to get there, where to stay, where and what to eat and what to do.

975 US
ISLAND LIFE; featuring the enchanting islands of Florida's Gulf Coast. (Former name of issuing body: West Coast Publications, Inc.) 1982. s-a. $12 for 4 nos. Hooper Publishing Co., Box 929, Sanibel Island, FL 33957. TEL 813-337-0010. Ed. Joan Hooper; Pub. Van B. Hooper. adv. contact: W.H. Farnsworth III. bk.rev. circ. 20,000. **Document type:** consumer publication.

910.202 US ISSN 0745-7847
G500
ISLANDS; an international magazine. 1981. bi-m. $19.95. Islands Publishing Company, 3886 State St., Santa Barbara, CA 93105-3112. TEL 805-682-7177. FAX 805-569-0349. E-mail: islands@islandsmag.com. Ed. Joan Tapper; Pub. Bill Kasch. adv. contact: Alan Rack. bk.rev.; circ. 185,000 (paid). (back issues avail.) **Document type:** consumer publication.
—UnCover.
Description: Focuses on islands all over the world - tropical and temperate, undeveloped and urban, famous or virtually undiscovered.

051 US
ISLANDS' SOUNDER; serving all of San Juan County. 1964. 52/yr. $22 for county residents; state residents $30; elswhere in U.S. $35. Box 758, Eastsound, WA 98245. bk.rev.; illus. circ. 5,400.
Formerly: Orcas Island Booster.

790 IS
ISRAEL INFORMATION LETTER. (Text in English) 1962. m. free. Ministry of Tourism, Communications and Information Department, Information Centre, P.O. Box 1018, Jerusalem 91009, Israel. TEL 972-2-754811. FAX 972-2-250890. Ed. Ruth Eilat. adv. circ. 3,000. (processed) **Document type:** government publication.
Former titles: Israel. Tourism News. Information Letter; Tourism Administration. Information Letter; Israel. Ministry of Tourism. Tourist Promotion Department. Information Letter.

914 IT
ITALIA TURISTICA; rivista di cultura e turismo delle regioni italiane. (Text in English, German, Italian) 1962. bi-m. L.40000 (foreign L.100000). (Italia Turistica) Editrice Ituri s.r.l., Via C. Anti, 9, Casella Postale 1060-8, 35124 Padua, Italy. TEL 39-49-8011180. FAX 39-49-8011182. Dir. Antonio Ravazzolo. adv.: page L.6000000. bk.rev.; film rev.; illus. circ. 150,000. (back issues avail.)
Formerly: Venezie e l'Italia; **Incorporates:** Turismo in Italia (ISSN 0042-336X)
Description: Features articles on the various regions of Italy. Includes the "hot spots", culture and food of Italy.

914 US
THE ITALIAN TRAVELER. 1988. 11/yr. $59. Box 32, Livingston, NJ 07039. TEL 201-535-6572. FAX 201-994-3847. TELEX 139114. Ed. Howard M. Isaacs. **Document type:** newsletter.
Description: Reviews hotels and restaurants, provides travel itineraries, travel tips.

910.09 IT
ITALIEN REISE AKTUELL. 26/yr. Editrice Turistica s.r.l., Via Rasella 155, 00187 Rome, Italy. TEL 6-48-21-539. FAX 6-48-26-721. Ed. Holger Lenz.

914.504 US ISSN 0890-1139
DG416
ITALY (YEAR). a. $18. Harper Collins Publishers, Birnbaum Travel Guides, 10 E. 53rd St., New York, NY 10022-5299. TEL 212-207-7542. Ed. Alexandra Mayes Birnbaum. illus.; index.

914.504 US ISSN 0393-3725
ITALY ITALY. (Text in English) 1983. bi-m. L.30000($30) (effective 1995). Italy Italy Corp. s.r.l., Via Michele Mercati 51, 00197 Rome, Italy. TEL 39-6-3221150. FAX 39-6-3223869. (US office: 138 Wooster St., New York, NY 10012. TEL 212-674-4132. FAX 212-674-4933) Ed. Joseph Lapalombara; Pub. Francesco Nicotra. adv. contact: Cristiana Cuomo. **Document type:** consumer publication.
Description: Guide to Italian people, places, and things.

910.09 IT
ITINERARI E LUOGHI. 1992. m. L.35000. Fioratti s.r.l., Via Manuzio 15, 20124 Milan, Italy. TEL 39-2-6570414. FAX 39-2-6570414. Ed. Delia Junod. adv.: color page L.8000000. **Document type:** consumer publication.

910.09 362.4 US ISSN 0743-5223
ITINERARY (BAYONNE); the magazine for travelers with physical disabilities. 1981. 6/yr. $10. Box 2012, Bayonne, NJ 07002-7012. TEL 201-858-3400. Eds. Robert Zywicki, Elizabeth Zywicki. adv.; bk.rev. circ. 10,400.

917.204 US ISSN 1055-5676
F1391.I88
IXTAPA & ZIHUATANEJO (YEAR). a. $11. Harper Collins Publishers, Birnbaum Travel Guides, 10 E. 53rd St., New York, NY 10022-5299. TEL 212-207-7542. illus.; index.

914 SP ISSN 0021-3810
JACETANIA. 1966. bi-m. 600 ptas. Centro de Iniciativa y Turismo, Aptdo. 110, Jaca (Huesca), Spain. adv.; illus.

THE JAGUAR; the First Coast's business guide and historical review. see *BUSINESS AND ECONOMICS — Trade And Industrial Directories*

TRAVEL AND TOURISM

382 GW ISSN 0075-2649
JAHRBUCH FUER FREMDENVERKEHR. 1950. a. DM.45. Deutsches Wirtschaftswissenschaftliches Institut fuer Fremdenverkehr, Hermann-Sack-Str. 2, 80331 Munich, Germany. TEL 089-267091. FAX 089-267613. Ed. Manfred Zeiner. bk.rev. circ. 500. Document type: bulletin.
—BLDSC (4631.462000).

910.09 US
JAPANESE CITY GUIDE. (Text in Japanese) 1988. bi-m. $24 (foreign $44). Bill of Fare Inc., 853 Seventh Ave., Ste. 1-A, New York, NY 10019-5215. TEL 212-315-0800. FAX 212-397-9513. adv. circ. 40,000.
 Description: Articles cover what is and what will be going on in New York over a two month period.

910.202 US
JAPANESE GUIDE TO HAWAII. (Text in Japanese) 1980. bi-m. free. Stone Publishing Company, 425 South, Ste. 1101, Honolulu, HI 96813. Ed. Yukie Anthony; Pub. Marjorie Stone. adv.: B&W page $1675, color page $1800; trim 7 7/8 x 10 13/16; adv. contact: Isabel Figel. circ. 45,000 (controlled). Document type: consumer publication.
 Description: Serves as the island's Japanese-language visitor publication.

910 US ISSN 0279-7984
JAX FAX TRAVEL MARKETING MAGAZINE; the official leisure travel booking magazine. 1973. m. $12. Jet Airtransport Exchange, Inc. (JAX), 397 Post Rd., Ste. 102, Darien, CT 06820-1413. TEL 203-655-8746. FAX 203-655-6257. (Subscr. to: Box 4013, Darien, CT 06820) Ed. Donna Attra; Pub. Clifton Cooke. adv. contact: Joan Brennan. bk.rev. circ. 28,000. (back issues avail.) Document type: trade publication.
 Formerly: Jax Fax (ISSN 0148-9542)
 Description: For travel agents.

910.09 UI
JERSEY HOLIDAY POST. 1975. w. (30/yr.). Michael Stanley Publishers, 1 Britannia Pl., Bath St., St. Helier, Jersey, Channel Islands, England. TEL 0534-25517. Ed. Rob Shipley.
 Description: Holiday information for people in Jersey.

JETSTREAM AIR NEWS; Swiss aviation magazine. see TRANSPORTATION — Air Transport

910.2 FR ISSN 0021-616X
JEUNES DES AUBERGES. 1956. q. $2.60 to non-members. Federation Unie des Auberges de Jeunesse, 10 rue N-D de Lorette, 75009 Paris, France. charts; illus.; play rev.; stat.; index.

910.2 UK ISSN 0075-3750
G153
JEWISH TRAVEL GUIDE. 1950. a. $7.95. Jewish Chronicle Publications Ltd., 25 Furnival St., London EC4A 1JT, England. FAX 071-405-9040. TELEX 940-11415. (N. American dist. addr.: Sepher Hermon Press, Inc., 1265 46th St., Brooklyn, New York, NY 11219) Ed. S.W. Massil. adv.; index. circ. 10,000.

910.09 IT
JONATHAN DIMENSIONE AVVENTURA. 1984. m. L.75000. Systems Comunicazioni, Via Olanda 6, 20083 Vigano di Gaggiano (MI), Italy. TEL 39-2-90841814. FAX 39-2-90841682. Ed. Ambrogio Fogar. adv.: B&W page L.4000000, color page L.7000000. circ. 54,000. Document type: consumer publication.

JOURNAL OF APPLIED RECREATION RESEARCH. see LEISURE AND RECREATION

910.202 613.1 UK ISSN 0966-9582
JOURNAL OF SUSTAINABLE TOURISM. 1993. 4/yr. £26($56) to individuals; institutions £79($169). Multilingual Matters Ltd., Frankfurt Lodge, Clevedon Hall, Victoria Rd., Clevedon, Avon BS21 7SJ, England. TEL 01275-876519. FAX 01275-343096. Eds. Bill Bramwell, Bernard Lane. Document type: academic/scholarly publication.
—BLDSC (5067.735000).
 Description: Provides information and research on helping to reduce tensions between tourism, the environment and host communities.

910.202 AT ISSN 1035-4662
THE JOURNAL OF TOURISM STUDIES. m. Aus.$35 (foreign Aus.$45) (effective 1995 & 1996). James Cook University of North Queensland, Department of Tourism, Townsville, Qld. 4811, Australia. TEL 61-77-815133. FAX 61-77-251116. Ed. P.L. Pearce. (back issues avail.) Indexed: Art.Hosp.& Tour., Hospit.Ind.
—BLDSC (5069.710000); UnCover.

338 658 US ISSN 1054-8408
G155.A1 CODEN: JTTMET
JOURNAL OF TRAVEL & TOURISM MARKETING. 1992. q. $80 (foreign $112) (effective 1996). Haworth Press, Inc., 10 Alice St., Binghamton, NY 13904-1580. TEL 607-722-5857; 800-342-9678. FAX 607-722-1424. TELEX 4932599. Ed. Kaye S. Chon. (also avail. in microform from UMI; reprint service avail. from HAW) Indexed: Hospit.Ind., Mgmt.& Market.Abstr., Sage Urb.Stud.Abstr., Sociol.Abstr., SOPODA, Urb.Aff.Abstr.
—BLDSC (5070.542000); Faxon; Haworth.
 Description: Includes travel services, tourism management organizations, meetings and convention services, and transportation services.
 Refereed Serial

JOURNAL OF TRAVEL MEDICINE. see MEDICAL SCIENCES

910.2 US ISSN 0047-2875
G155.A1
JOURNAL OF TRAVEL RESEARCH. 1962. q. $85 to non-members (Canada $90; elsewhere $100). University of Colorado, Business Research Division, Campus Box 420, Boulder, CO 80309-0420. TEL 303-492-8227; 303-492-3620. (Co-sponsor: Travel and Tourism Research Association) Ed. Charles R. Goeldner. bk.rev. circ. 1,600. Indexed: ABI Inform., Art.Hosp.& Tour., B.P.I., Geo.Abstr., Hospit.Ind., Rural Recreat.Tour.Abstr., World Agri.Econ.& Rural Sociol.Abstr. Document type: academic/scholarly publication.
●Also available online. Vendor(s): University Microfilms International.
—BLDSC (5070.550000); Faxon; SWETS; UMI; UnCover.
 Formerly: Travel Research Bulletin (ISSN 0147-2399)

910 658 UK ISSN 1355-6355
▼**JOURNAL OF VACATION MARKETING.** 1995. q. £45($210) (foreign £140) (effective 1996). Henry Stewart Publications, Russell House, 28-30 Little Russell St., London WC1A 2HN, England. TEL 0171-404-3040. FAX 0171-404-2081. Ed.Bd. (back issues avail.) Document type: academic/scholarly publication.
 Description: Covers the latest practice and thought in the marketing of vacation services.
 Refereed Serial

910.2 YU ISSN 0022-605X
JUGOSLAWISCHE TOURISTENZEITUNG/YUGOSLAV TOURIST NEWS. (Editions in English, French and German) 1963. m. $10. Turisticka Stampa, Knez Mihailova 21, Belgrade, Yugoslavia. Ed. Dobrivoje Djokovic.

919 II ISSN 0047-2999
JUNGLE; a journal for promotion of tourism and nature study. (Text in English) 1971. bi-m. Rs.12. Wild Life Camp, A-268 Defence Colony, New Delhi 3, India. Ed. Priti Debnath. adv.; bibl.; charts; illus.

K.A.C.B. AUTO REVUE/ROYAL AUTO. (Koninklijke Automobiel Club van Belgie) see TRANSPORTATION — Automobiles

KAKTUSBLUETE. see CHILDREN AND YOUTH — About

910 NE ISSN 0165-4128
KAMPEER EN CARAVANKAMPIOEN. 1941. m. fl.102 to non-members. Koninklijke Nederlandse Toeristenbond ANWB - Royal Dutch Touring Club, Wassenaarseweg 220, Postbus 93200, 2509 BA The Hague, Netherlands. TEL 31-70-3146119. FAX 31-70-3242500. Ed. F. Voorbergen. adv.: B&W page fl.5424, color page fl.9763; trim 25 x 285; adv. contact: J.W. Boersen. illus. circ. 146,700. Indexed: Key to Econ.Sci. Document type: consumer publication.

910.2 NE ISSN 0022-8265
DJ1
KAMPIOEN; A N W B club magazine. 1885. m. fl.31 to non-members. Koninklijke Nederlandse Toeristenbond ANWB - Royal Dutch Touring Club, Postbus 93200, Wassenaarseweg 220, 2509 BA the Hague, Netherlands. TEL 31-70-3146119. FAX 31-70-3242509. Ed. J. Karsemeijer. adv.: B&W page fl.46000, color page fl.69000; trim 223 x 270; adv. contact: J.W. Boersen. bk.rev.; charts; illus.; index. circ. 3,100,000. Indexed: Key to Econ.Sci. Document type: consumer publication.
—SWETS.

KANSAS CITY MAGAZINE. see GENERAL INTEREST PERIODICALS — United States

KARATE AND ORIENTAL ARTS. see SPORTS AND GAMES

960 KE
KARIBU. (Text in English) 1977. m. Oryx Publications Ltd., P.O. Box 40106, Nairobi, Kenya. adv.; illus. circ. 5,000.

910.202 II
KARNATAKA. DEPARTMENT OF TOURISM. ANNUAL REPORT. (Text in English) 1975. a. Department of Information and Tourism, 5 Infantry Rd., Bangalore, India.

917.904 US
KAUAI, A PARADISE FAMILY GUIDE. (Supplement avail.: Kauai Update) biennial. Paradise Publications, 8110 S.W. Wareham, Portland, OR 97223. TEL 503-246-1555.
 Formerly: Kauai, a Paradise Guide.
 Description: Guide to beaches, restaurants, and accomodations.

917.904 US ISSN 0898-1418
KAUAI UPDATE. (Supplement to: Kauai, a Paradise Family Guide) 1988. q. $10 (Canada $12). Paradise Publications, 8110 S.W. Wareham, Portland, OR 97223. TEL 503-246-1555. Ed. Christie Stilson. circ. 2,000.
 Description: Provides an overview of island events and happenings for tourists and island residents.

914.304 GW
KAUPERTS DEUTSCHLAND REISEFUEHRER. 1950. a. DM.19.50. Adressbuch-Gesellschaft Berlin mbH, Friedrichstr. 210, 1000 Berlin 61, Germany. Eds. E. Spitzing-Pistorius, C. Georgi-Polotzek. adv. circ. 8,500.
 Formerly: Kauperts Deutschland Staedte-, Hotel-, und Reisefuehrer.

KENTUCKY EXPLORER; featuring things about Kentucky and its history. see HISTORY — History Of North And South America

917.6 US ISSN 0453-5812
KENTUCKY TRAVEL GUIDE. 1967. a. Editorial Services Company, 451 Baxter Ave., Louisville, KY 40204-1145. TEL 502-584-2720. FAX 502-584-2722. adv.: B&W page $4560, color page $5395; trim 5 1/2 x 8 1/2; adv. contact: Stacey Brinkop. maps. circ. 300,000. Document type: consumer publication.

916.04 KE
KENYA TOURIST DEVELOPMENT CORPORATION. REPORT AND ACCOUNTS. (Text in English) a. free. Kenya Tourist Development Corporation, Box 42013, Nairobi, Kenya. TEL 330820. FAX 227815. TELEX 23009.

917.904 US
KEY MAGAZINE. CARMEL & MONTEREY PENINSULA. 1969. m. $15. Tri-County Publications, Box 223859, Carmel, CA 93922-3859. adv. circ. 37,000.

917 US ISSN 0040-6279
KEY MAGAZINE. THIS WEEK IN CHICAGO. 1920. w. $55. This Week in Chicago, Inc., 904 W. Blackhawk, 2nd Fl., Chicago, IL 60622-2518. FAX 312-664-6113. Ed. Lynn Gilman; Pub. Walter L. West, Jr. adv. contact: Walter L. West III. circ. 20,000. Document type: consumer publication.
 Formerly: This Week in Chicago.

TRAVEL AND TOURISM

917 US
KEY MAGAZINE. THIS WEEK IN LOS ANGELES AND SOUTHERN CALIFORNIA; the leading weekly magazine of Southern entertainment & dining. 1936. w. $22. Falcon Publications, 8432 Steller Dr., Culver City, CA 90232. TEL 310-559-3700. Ed. George Falcon. adv.: B&W page $392; 4 13/16 x 7 1/2. bk.rev.; charts; illus. circ. 19,500.
  Formerly: Key (Los Angeles); Incorporates: Information Los Angeles (ISSN 0020-0131)

917 US
KEY MAGAZINE. THIS WEEK IN SAN FRANCISCO. 1933. w. $84. L. Publishing Co., Inc., 1164 Bryant St., San Francisco, CA 94103-4335. TEL 415-865-2300. FAX 415-252-1308. Ed. Brian Stott. adv. contact: Dennis R. Perry. circ. 22,000. (back issues avail.)
  Description: Visitor's guide to San Francisco and Bay Area activities. Also available at hotels, shops, galleries and tourist oriented points of interest.

910.202 UK
KEY NOTE MARKET REVIEW: PASSENGER TRAVEL IN U K. Variant title: Passenger Travel in U K. irreg. £375. Key Note Publications Ltd., Field House, 72 Oldfield Rd., Hampton, Middlesex TW12 2HQ, England. TEL 0181-783-0755. FAX 0181-783-1720.
  Document type: trade publication.
  •Also available online.
  Also available on CD-ROM.

910.202 UK ISSN 1357-6895
KEY NOTE MARKET REVIEW: U K TOURISM & TRAVEL. Variant title: U K Tourism & Travel. 1991. irreg. £375. Key Note Publications Ltd., Field House, 72 Oldfield Rd., Hampton, Middlesex TW12 2HQ, England. TEL 0181-783-0755. FAX 0181-783-1720. **Document type:** trade publication.
  •Also available online.
  Also available on CD-ROM.

910.202 330 UK ISSN 0268-4896
KEY NOTE REPORT: BUSINESS TRAVEL. Variant title: Business Travel. irreg. £185. Key Note Publications Ltd., Field House, 72 Oldfield Rd., Hampton, Middlesex TW12 2HQ, England. TEL 0181-783-0755. FAX 0181-783-1720.
  Document type: trade publication.
  •Also available online.
  Also available on CD-ROM.
  —BLDSC (2934.897300).

910.202 UK ISSN 1354-232X
KEY NOTE REPORT: TOURIST ATTRACTIONS. Variant title: Tourist Attractions. irreg. £185. Key Note Publications Ltd., Field House, 72 Oldfield Rd., Hampton, Middlesex TW12 2HQ, England. TEL 0181-783-0755. FAX 0181-783-1720.
  Document type: trade publication.
  •Also available online.
  Also available on CD-ROM.
  —BLDSC (8870.922690).

910.202 UK
KEY NOTE REPORT: TRAVEL AGENTS & OVERSEAS TOUR OPERATORS. Variant title: Travel Agents & Overseas Tour Operators. irreg. £185. Key Note Publications Ltd., Field House, 72 Oldfield Rd., Hampton, Middlesex TW12 2HQ, England. TEL 0181-783-0755. FAX 0181-783-1720.
  Document type: trade publication.
  •Also available online.
  Also available on CD-ROM.

919 CJ
KEY TO CAYMAN. 1978. s-a. free. Cayman Free Press Ltd., Box 1365, Grand Cayman, Cayman Islands, British W.I. TEL 809-949-5111. FAX 809-949-7033. adv. circ. 130,000.
  Formerly (until Dec. 1989): Tourist Weekly.

910.09 CN ISSN 0710-9628
KEY TO KINGSTON. 1980. m. Can.$15($8) Kingston Publications, P.O. Box 1352, 6 Princess St., Kingston, Ont. K7L 5C6, Canada. Ed. K. Wright. adv.; charts; illus.; play rev. circ. 16,000. (back issues avail)

KEYSTONE A A A MOTORIST. see *TRANSPORTATION — Automobiles*

910.202 GW
KOELN. VERKEHRSAMT. MONATSVORSCHAU. (Text in German; summaries in English, French) 1958. m. DM.30. Stadt Koeln, Verkehrsamt, Unter Fettenhennen 19, 50667 Cologne, Germany. TEL 0221-221-3343. FAX 0221-221-3320. Ed. Erhard Schlieter. adv. contact: Gabriele Pilath. circ. 12,500. **Document type:** government publication.

KOELN, DUESSELDORF, NORDRHEIN-WESTFALEN VON HINTEN; das schwule Reisebuch. see *HOMOSEXUALITY*

910.09 GW
KOELN - REISE - REPORT. (Text in English, French, German, Italian) a. Verkehrsamt der Stadt Koeln, Unter Fettenhennen 19, 50667 Cologne, Germany. TEL 0221-2213345. FAX 0221-2213320. TELEX 8883421-TOC-D.

KOELNER KONGRESS REPORT. see *MEETINGS AND CONGRESSES*

KONCIZE. see *MEETINGS AND CONGRESSES*

910.4 KN
KOREA. (Editions in Chinese, English, French, Korean, Russian, Spanish) 1956. m. Pyongyang, N. Korea. illus.

914 GW
KREFELD LIFE. a. Stuenings Verlagsgesellschaft mbH, Luisenstr. 100-104, 47799 Krefeld, Germany. TEL 02151-853-0. FAX 02151-853103. circ. 35,000. **Document type:** directory.

910.202 BE ISSN 0778-7871
KREO. (Text in Dutch) 1965. m. 1295 BEF (foreign 1395 BEF). Vakantiegenoegens v.z.w., Wetstraat 121, B-1040 Brussels, Belgium. TEL 32-2-2373635. FAX 32-2-2373758. Ed. Ludo Van Lint. circ. 45,000 (paid). **Document type:** consumer publication.
  Formerly (until 1992): Info Vakantiegenoegens.
  Description: Publishes practical articles on tourism in Belgium and other countries, covering nature, folklore and cultural topics.

KULTURNOPOLITICKY KALENDAR. see *MEETINGS AND CONGRESSES*

910.09 GW
KURZEITUNG GRONENBACH. 1976. m. DM.12. Kurverwaltung Gronenbach, Marktplatz, Postfach 1110, 87728 Gronenbach, Germany. TEL 08334-7711. circ. 850.

L S A NEWSLETTER. (Leisure Studies Association) see *LEISURE AND RECREATION*

LAKE SUPERIOR MAGAZINE. see *HISTORY — History Of North And South America*

910.09 US
LAKESHORE LIFE AND PRODUCT NEWS. 1992. bi-m. $2.25 per no. Recreational Publications, Inc., Box 25182, 7582 Currell Blvd., Ste. 212, St. Paul, MN 55125. TEL 612-738-1953. FAX 612-738-2302. adv.: B&W page $1295, color page $1995; trim 4 x 13. circ. 25,000. (tabloid format)
  Description: Focuses on the unique style of the vacation property homeowner.

910.4 LS
LAOS. (Editions in English and Lao) q. 80 rue Sethathirath, BP 310, Vientiane, Laos. TEL 2405. Eds. V. Phomchanheuang, O. Phrakhamsay. illus.

917.904 793 ISSN 1064-167X
LAS VEGAS ADVISOR. 1983. m. $45 (Canada & Mexico $50, elsewhere $60). Huntington Press, 5280 S. Valley View Blvd., Ste. B, Las Vegas, NV 89118. TEL 702-597-1884. FAX 702-597-5208. E-mail: Na@infi.net. Ed Deke Castleman. bk.rev.; circ. 7,200 (paid). (back issues avail.) **Document type:** consumer publication, newsletter.
  Description: For Las Vegas visitors. Covers dining, gambling, entertainment and accommodations, with an emphasis on bargain and value.

910.202 790.1 US ISSN 0271-0145
LAS VEGAS INSIDER. 1973. m. $45. Lucky Publishing Co., Box 29274, La Vegas, NV 89126. TEL 602-636-1649. FAX 602-636-1649. Ed. Donald Currier; Pub. Donald Currier. adv.; cum.index: 1973-1988. circ. 5,100. (back issues avail.)
  Document type: newsletter.
  Description: Contains the latest gaming, tournament and travel information. Includes tourist tips, freebies, and discounts.

910.202 CN
LAST MINUTE TRAVEL REPORT. 1991. 5/yr. Can.$55. 1300 Don Mills Rd., Don Mills, ON M3B 2W6, Canada. TEL 416-449-9440. FAX 416-441-9754. Ed. William Maki. adv.; bk.rev. circ. 100,000. (tabloid format) **Document type:** consumer publication.
  Formerly: Travelsavelife.
  Description: Travel destinations and activities aimed primarily at travelers on a budget.

918.04 EC ISSN 1390-0161
▼**LATIN AMERICAN TRAVEL ADVISOR.** (Text in English) 1994. q. $39. Latin American Travel Consultants, Box 17-17-908, Quito, Ecuador. FAX 593-2-562-566. E-mail: rku@pi.pro.ec. Eds. Robert & Daisy Kunstaetter. charts; maps. (fax deliv. avail.) **Document type:** newsletter.
  •Also available online.
  Description: News bulletin for business, vacation and long term travellers to South and Central America. Updated information on 17 countries featuring: public safety, health, weather, travel costs, the economy and politics.

910.91 CN ISSN 1195-7158
LATITUDES. French edition (ISSN 1195-714X) (Text in English) 1993. 4/yr. Plan B Strategies Inc., 252 Ave. des Pins E., Montreal, PQ H2W 1P3, Canada. TEL 514-281-0905. FAX 514-281-0682. Ed. Louis Gauthier; Pub. Eve Howse. adv.: B&W page Can.$13000, color page Can.$14500; trim 8 1/8 x 10 7/8. circ. 250,000. **Document type:** consumer publication.

917.104 CN ISSN 0829-8033
LAURENTIDES/LAURENTIANS; montagnes de plaisir au nord de Montreal. (Text in English and French) 1976. 2/yr. free. Association Touristique des Laurentides, 14142 rue de Lachapelle, R.R. 1, St. Jerome, PQ J7Z 5T4, Canada. TEL 514-436-8532. FAX 514-436-5309. Ed. Andre Goyer. adv. circ. 150,000. **Document type:** consumer publication.
  Formerly (until 1985): Image des Laurentides (ISSN 0704-6383)

914 700 IT ISSN 0047-4231
LAZIO IERI E OGGI; rivista mensile di cultura, arte, turismo. 1965. m. L.40000. Via Taranto 178, 00182 Rome, Italy. TEL 06-7020663. Dir. Willy Pocino. bk.rev.; illus.; index.

LEISURE WORLD. see *LEISURE AND RECREATION*

910.2 914 US ISSN 0163-4585
D909
LET'S GO: THE BUDGET GUIDE TO EUROPE. 1960. a. $9.95. St. Martin's Press, 175 Fifth Ave., New York, NY 10010. TEL 212-674-5151. adv. circ. 60,000.
  Formerly: Let's Go: The Student Guide to Europe (ISSN 0075-8868)

956 US ISSN 0749-0569
DF716
LET'S GO: THE BUDGET GUIDE TO GREECE. a. (Harvard Student Agencies, Inc.) St. Martin's Press, 175 Fifth Ave., New York, NY 10010. TEL 212-674-5151.
  Supersedes in part (in 1984): Let's Go: The Budget Guide to Greece, Israel and Egypt (ISSN 0276-6779)

938 956 US ISSN 0882-9535
DS103
LET'S GO: THE BUDGET GUIDE TO ISRAEL & EGYPT; including Jordan and the West Bank. a. $8.95. (Harvard Student Agencies, Inc.) St. Martin's Press, 175 Fifth Ave., New York, NY 10010. TEL 212-674-5151. Ed. Joanne Dushay.
  Supersedes in part (in 1984): Let's Go: The Budget Guide to Greece, Israel and Egypt (ISSN 0276-6779)

TRAVEL AND TOURISM

917.04 US ISSN 0192-2920
DG416
LET'S GO: THE BUDGET GUIDE TO ITALY. 1981. a. $8.95. St. Martin's Press, 175 Fifth Ave., New York, NY 10010. TEL 212-674-5151. Ed. Jeremy Metz.

917.504 US
LET'S GO: THE BUDGET GUIDE TO WASHINGTON, D.C.. a. (Harvard Student Agencies, Inc.) St. Martin's Press, 175 Fifth Ave., New York, NY 10010. TEL 212-674-5151.

917.04 US ISSN 0275-9837
E158
LET'S GO: U S A. 1973. a. $9.95. St. Martin's Press, 175 Fifth Ave., New York, NY 10010. TEL 212-674-5151. illus.
Formerly: Let's Go: The Student Guide to the United States and Canada (ISSN 0090-788X)

LETTRE TOURISTIQUE. see OCCUPATIONS AND CAREERS

354 LB
LIBERIA. MINISTRY OF INFORMATION, CULTURAL AFFAIRS & TOURISM. ANNUAL REPORT TO THE SESSION OF THE LEGISLATURE.* (Text in English) a. Ministry of Information, Cultural Affairs and Tourism, Monrovia, Liberia.

910.2 960 UK
LIBYA PAST AND PRESENT SERIES. 1970. irreg. price varies. Oleander Press, 17 Stansgate Ave., Cambridge CB2 2QZ, England. (U.S. addr.: 80 Eighth Ave., Ste. 303, New York, NY 10011) Ed. Philip Ward. Document type: monographic series.
Formerly: Libyan Travel Series (ISSN 0075-9309)

LIMOUSIN MAGAZINE; magazines de France. see GENERAL INTEREST PERIODICALS — France

LINKS; The Best of Golf. see SPORTS AND GAMES — Ball Games

LINKS UND RECHTS DER AUTOBAHN. see HOTELS AND RESTAURANTS

914 AU ISSN 0024-4147
LINZER WOCHE. 1963. m. S.42. (Magistrat) Rudolf Trauner Verlag, Koeglstr. 14, A-4020 Linz-Donau, Austria. Ed. Dr. Walter Knoglinger. circ. 45,000.

910.202 640.73 UK
LIVING ABROAD; the Daily Telegraph guide. irreg. £8.99. Kogan Page Ltd., 120 Pentonville Rd., London N1 9JN, England. TEL 0171-278-0483. FAX 0171-837-6348. Document type: bulletin.
Formerly (until 1993): Living and Retiring Abroad.

910.202 333.33 UK ISSN 0960-5444
LIVING FRANCE. 1989. 10/yr. £23 (foreign £44). Brilliant Blue Co., Gairnside House, Gate End, Northwood, Mddx. HA6 3QG, England. TEL 01923-828100. FAX 01923-836572. (Dist. by.: 6 Leigham Court Rd., London SW16 2PG, England. TEL 0181-677-6060) Ed. Trevor Yorke. adv.: color page £1500; adv. contact: Jim Vickers. bk.rev.; illus.; circ. 15,000 (paid). (back issues avail.) Document type: consumer publication.
Formerly (until 1990): French Living (ISSN 0958-3092)
Description: Provides U.K. Francophiles living in or visiting France with information on the country's various regions. Also covers French culture and history. Features real-estate advertisements on properties in each region.

910.09 VE
LIVING IN VENEZUELA. (Text in English) 1980. a. $45. Venezuelan-American Chamber of Commerce and Industry - Camara Venezolano Americana de Comercio e Industria, Apdo. 5181, Caracas 1010A, Venezuela. TEL 58-2-2630833. FAX 58-2-2631629. TELEX 28399. adv.; index. circ. 5,000. (back issues avail.)
Formerly: VenAmCham's Executive Newcomers Guide.
Description: Contains detailed information on all aspects of Venezuelan life.

LOAN-A-HOME DIRECTORY. see REAL ESTATE

LODGING AND RESTAURANT INDEX. see HOTELS AND RESTAURANTS — Abstracting, Bibliographies, Statistics

914.204 US ISSN 1056-4470
DA679
LONDON (YEAR). a. $12. Harper Collins Publishers, Birnbaum Travel Guides, 20 E. 53rd St., New York, NY 10022-5299. TEL 212-207-7542. Ed. Alexandra Mayes Birnbaum. illus.; index.

952 UK
LONDON DAYORI; the Japanese journal of London. 1974. m. £15. Dayori of London Publishing Ltd., 7 Wind Mill St., London W1P 1HF, England. FAX 0171-580-4844. Ed. Yuriko Akishima. adv.; film rev.; play rev.; illus. circ. 20,000. (back issues avail.)

910.202 CN ISSN 1189-637X
LONDON GUIDEBOOK. 1989. a. Can.$6. Blackburn Group, 231 Dundas St., Ste. 203, London, ON N6A 1H1, Canada. TEL 519-679-4901. FAX 519-434-7842. Ed. Judy Jarosch. circ. 45,000.
Formerly: London Guide.

915 TH ISSN 0857-1139
LOOKEAST. (Text in English) 1969. m. Advertising and Media Consultants Ltd., Silom Condominium, 12th Fl., 52-38 Soi Saladaeng 2, Bangkok, Thailand. TEL 2333401. FAX 2366764. TELEX 82463 LOOKEAS TH. Ed. Satish Sehgal. adv.; bk.rev.; charts; illus. circ. 15,000. Document type: trade publication.

917.904 US ISSN 1056-4462
LOS ANGELES (YEAR). a. $12. Harper Collins Publishers, Birnbaum Travel Guides, 10 E. 53rd St., New York, NY 10022-5299. TEL 212-270-7542. Ed. Alexandra Mayes Birnbaum. illus.; index.

LOUISIANA LIFE. see GENERAL INTEREST PERIODICALS — United States

910.202 GW
LUFTVERKEHR. 1950. q. free. Flughafen Hannover-Langenhagen GmbH, Postfach 420280, 30662 Hannover, Germany. TEL 0511-977-1755. FAX 0511-977-1855. Ed. Reinhard Wille. adv. circ. 20,000. (back issues avail.) Document type: consumer publication.

910.202 CC ISSN 1000-7253
LUYOU/TOURISM. (Text in Chinese) 1979. m. $60; newsstand price: Y2.30. (Beijing Luyou Shiye Guanliju - Beijing Tourism Management Bureau) Luyou Zazhishe, 13 Xia Gongfu Jie, Dongcheng-qu, Beijing, People's Republic of China. TEL 5134102. (Dist. outside China by: China International Book Trading Corp., P.O. Box 399, Beijing, P.R.C.. TEL 8413063; Dist. in US by: China Books & Periodicals, Inc., 2929 24th St., San Francisco, CA 94110. TEL 415-282-2994) Ed. Guotian Jiang. adv. contact: Laiyun Yang. Document type: consumer publication.

915.1 CC
LUYOU TIANDI/TRAVELLING SCOPE. (Text in Chinese) bi-m. $24.30. Shanghai Wenhua Chubanshe - Shanghai Culture Press, 74 Shaoxing Lu, Shanghai 200020, People's Republic of China. TEL 4372608. (Dist. in US by: China Books & Periodicals, Inc., 2929 24th St., San Francisco, CA 94110. TEL 415-282-2994)

910.4 CC ISSN 1002-5006
LUYOU XUEKAN/JOURNAL OF TOURISM. (Text in Chinese) 1987. q. Beijing Lianhe Daxue, Luyou Xueyuan, 1, Panjiapo, Chaowai, Beijing 100020, People's Republic of China. TEL 5024956. Ed. Zhao Kefei.

M & C. (Meeting & Congressi) see MEETINGS AND CONGRESSES

910.4 GW ISSN 0178-1529
M I S - MOTOR IM SCHNEE. 1970. 8/yr. DM.120 (effective 1995). Stein-Verlag Baden-Baden GmbH, Josef-Herrmann-Str. 1-3, 76473 Iffezheim, Germany. TEL 07229-606-0. FAX 07229-60610. Ed. Wilhelm Joesch. circ. 4,000. (back issues avail.) Document type: trade publication.

MACAO. DIRECCAO DOS SERVICOS DE ESTATISTICA E CENSOS. ESTATISTICAS DO TURISMO/MACAO. CENSUS AND STATISTICS DEPARTMENT. TOURISM STATISTICS. see TRAVEL AND TOURISM — Abstracting, Bibliographies, Statistics

MACAO. DIRECCAO DOS SERVICOS DE ESTATISTICA E CENSOS. INDICADORES DO TURISMO/MACAO. CENSUS AND STATISTICS DEPARTMENT. TOURISM INDICATORS. see TRAVEL AND TOURISM — Abstracting, Bibliographies, Statistics

MAENNER AKTUELL. see HOMOSEXUALITY

917.404 US
MAINE INVITES YOU. 1930. a. free. Maine Publicity Bureau, Inc., 325B Water St., Box 2300, Hallowell, ME 04347. TEL 207-623-0363. FAX 207-623-0388. Ed. Lynn Verrill. adv. contact: Diane Hopkins. circ. 135,000. Document type: directory.

791 YU ISSN 0025-1178
MALA UKRSTENICA. 1956. m. 240 din.($3.15) Enigmatski Klub, Bulevar Vojvode Misica 67, Box 219, Belgrade, Yugoslavia. Ed. Vlasta Pavlovic.

916 MW
MALAWI: A GUIDE FOR THE VISITOR. (Text in English) 1983. a. free. Department of Tourism, P.O. Box 402, Blantyre, Malawi. FAX 620947. TELEX 44645.

MALTA YEARBOOK. see POLITICAL SCIENCE

MAN TO MAN GUIDE; gay-lesbian guide to Holland. see HOMOSEXUALITY

917.204 MX
MAR DE CORTES. m. (Circuito Ecological del Mar de Cortes y Copper Canyon) Editorial Bonanza, S. de R.L., Dr. Velasco 95, Ed. 5, Of. 203, Col. Doctores, Del. Cuauhtemoc, 06720 Mexico DF, Mexico. TEL 525-5938720. FAX 525-7052492.

910.202 HK
MARCO POLO NEWS.* (Text in English) 6/yr. Hong Kong Standard, 4-F Sing Tao Bldg., 1 Wang Kwong Rd., Kowloon Bay, Hong Kong. FAX 810-6738. TELEX 74523-EMPAS-HX. Ed. Derek Davies. adv. circ. 32,500.
Formerly: Marco Polo.

910.4 FI ISSN 0784-5480
MARINA. (Text in Finnish, Swedish, has a supplement in German) 3/yr. Erikoislehdet Oy Business Publications, P.O. Box 16, SF-00381 Helsinki, Finland. Ed. Marketta Rentola. circ. 10,000.

MARINEFACTS; topical directory of marine information. see SPORTS AND GAMES — Boats And Boating

910.202 US ISSN 1062-516X
MARYLAND MOTORIST. 1920. every 45 days. $1. Automobile Club of Maryland, 1401 Mt. Royal Ave., Baltimore, MD 21217. TEL 301-462-4000. FAX 301-523-0380. Ed. William F. Zorzi. bk.rev. circ. 230,000.

910.09 IS
MASA ACHER. (Text in Hebrew) 1987. bi-m. $45. Masa Acher Inc., P.O. Box 20493, Tel Aviv 61204, Israel. TEL 03-383898. FAX 03-379-455. TELEX 381528-GILAD. Eds. Gil El-Ami, Moshe Gilad. circ. 32,000.
Description: Dedicated to the topics of geography and travel.

910.09 IT
MASTERCLUB MEMBERS' MAGAZINE. 1991. 3/yr. membership. Masterclub s.r.l., Viale G. Di Vittorio 307-1, 20099 Sesto G. Giovanni (MI), Italy. TEL 39-2-2405759. FAX 39-2-22470780. Ed. Sergio Media. adv.: page L.7000000. circ. 50,000. Document type: consumer publication.

916.8 RH
MASVINGO DIARY. (Text in English) 1963. m. free. Masvingo Great Zimbabwe Publicity Association, P.O. Box 340, Masvingo, Zimbabwe. Ed. Mrs. B. Kanjanga. adv.; illus. circ. 2,500. Document type: consumer publication.
Formerly: Fort Victoria Diary.

910.09 TS
MATAR DUBAI AL-DAWLI/DUBAI INTERNATIONAL AIRPORT. (Text in Arabic, English) 1987. q. free. Motivate Publishing, P.O. Box 2331, Dubai, United Arab Emirates. TEL 246060. FAX 245270. TELEX 48366 MAM EM. Ed. Obaid Humaid al-Tayer. circ. 4,000.
Description: For airline passengers using Dubai airport.

TRAVEL AND TOURISM

914 796.5   FI   ISSN 0789-1393
MATKAILU/TOURISM. (Text in Finnish; summaries in Swedish) 1936. 6/yr. Fmk.120. Suomen Matkailuliitto - Finnish Travel Association, Mikonkatu 25, 00100 Helsinki 10, Finland. FAX 0-654358. TELEX 122619-FTATA-ST. Ed. Jussi Yrjola. adv. contact: Seija Ahtola. bk.rev.; bibl.; illus. circ. 30,000. (also avail. in microfilm)
    Formerly (until 1990): Suomen Matkailu - Tourism of Finland (ISSN 0359-0607); Formed by the merger of: Leirinta ja Retkeily (ISSN 0356-0805) & Matkailumaailma (ISSN 0025-5963); Which were originally titled: Leirintasanomat; Matkailu ja Retkeily.

910.09   US   ISSN 1043-2280
MATURE TRAVELER; travel bonanzas for 49-ers-plus. 1984. m. $29.95. G E M Publishing Group, 250 E. Riverview Circle, Reno, NV 89509. TEL 702-786-7419. (Subscr. to: Box 50400, Reno, NV 89513) Ed. Gene E. Malott. adv.; bk.rev.; index. circ. 2,500. (back issues avail.) **Document type:** newsletter.
    Description: News about discounts and trips for mature adults, travel tips, cruise news and senior-friendly destinations.

917.904   US   ISSN 0895-9609
DU628.M3
MAUI, A PARADISE FAMILY GUIDE. Key Title: Maui. (Supplement avail.: Maui Update) 1986. biennial. Paradise Publications, 8110 S.W. Wareham, Portland, OR 97223. TEL 503-246-1555.
    Formerly: Maui, a Paradise Guide.
    Description: Guide to beaches, restaurants, accomodations, and attractions.

917.904   US   ISSN 0895-9390
MAUI UPDATE. (Supplement to: Maui, a Paradise Family Guide) 1987. q. $10 (Canada $12). Paradise Publications, 8110 S.W. Wareham, Portland, OR 97223. TEL 503-246-1555. Ed. Christie Stilson. adv.; bk.rev. circ. 2,000. (back issues avail.)
    Description: Provides an overview of current island events of particular interest to the vacationer traveling to Maui, Hawaii.

M'BOLO. *see* HISTORY — History Of Africa

910.09   IT
MED INTERNATIONAL. 1992. m. free to qualified personnel; newsstand price: L.5000. (Club Mediterranee) Edizioni del Tridente s.r.l., Largo Corsia dei Servi 11, 20122 Milan, Italy. TEL 39-2-7786291. Ed. Andreina Vanni. adv.: B&W page L.1200000, color page L.16000000. circ. 365,000. **Document type:** consumer publication.

MEETING AND INCENTIVE TRAVEL. *see* MEETINGS AND CONGRESSES

MEETING COMMUNICATIONS. *see* MEETINGS AND CONGRESSES

914.204   UK
MEETING IN LONDON. q. World Trade Magazines Ltd., World Trade House, 49 Dartford Rd., Sevenoaks, Kent TN13 3TE, England. TEL 01732-458144. FAX 01732-456295. adv. (reprint service avail. from UMI) **Document type:** consumer publication.
    Formerly: Destination London.

614.86   GW
MEINE GESUNDHEIT "REISEAPOTHEKE". 1981. a. Otto Hoffmanns Verlag GmbH, Possartstr. 9, 81679 Munich, Germany. TEL 089-4702041. circ. 2,550,000. **Document type:** consumer publication.

910.02   NE   ISSN 0926-9525
MERIDIAN INTERNATIONAL. (Text in Dutch) 1991. q. fl.41. B.V. Hollandse Pers Unie, Herengracht 105-107, 1015 BE Amsterdam, Netherlands. TEL 31-20-5235111. FAX 31-20-5235198. Ed. Rene Boers. adv.: color page fl.7995; trim 215 x 285; adv. contact: Jeanine Tissink. circ. 50,000. **Document type:** consumer publication.

647.94   IT   ISSN 1120-804X
MERIDIANI. 1988. bi-m. L.60000($82) Editoriale Domus, Via Achille Grandi 5-7, 20089 Rozzano (MI), Italy. TEL 39-2-824721. FAX 39-2-8255033. Andreina Vanni. adv.: color page L.17000000. circ. 70,000.

910.09   IT
METROQUADRO VACANZE. 1993. 3/yr. L.10000. Edizioni Living International, Via Anton Giulio Bragaglia 33, 00123 Rome, Italy. TEL 39-6-3789282. FAX 39-6-3789944. Ed. Enrico Morelli. adv.: B&W page L.2400000, color page L.4000000; adv. contact: Carla Dall'Oglio. **Document type:** consumer publication.

910.202   US   ISSN 1073-6786
F1216.5
MEXICAN MEANDERINGS. 1991. bi-m. $18. Box 33057, Austin, TX 78764. TEL 512-441-1815. FAX 512-441-2330. Ed. Carla Felsted; Pub. Herb Felsted. bk.rev. circ. 500. **Document type:** newsletter.
    Description: Describes unusual places in Mexico you can reach by automobile, bus or train. Includes archaeology, folk art, cuisine and special events.

917.204   US   ISSN 0884-1209
F1209
MEXICO (YEAR). a. $18. Harper Collins Publishers, Birnbaum Travel Guides, 10 E. 53rd St., New York, NY 10022-5299. TEL 212-270-7542. Ed. Alexandra Mayes Birnbaum.

910.202   UK   ISSN 0965-5492
MEXICO AND CENTRAL AMERICAN HANDBOOK. 1990. a. £14.95($21.95) Trade & Travel Publications Ltd., 6 Riverside Ct., Lower Bristol Rd., Bath BA2 3DZ, England. TEL 01225-469141. FAX 01225-469461. (Dist. in N. America by: Passport Books, NTC Publishing Group, 4255 W. Touhy Ave., Lincolnwood, IL 60646-1975. TEL 708-679-5500. FAX 708-679-6375) Ed. Ben Box. **Document type:** directory.

917.204 647   MX
MEXICO CITY DAILY BULLETIN. (Text in English) 1936. d. free. Edit, S.A., Gomez Farias 41, Col. San Rafael, 06470 Mexico, D.F. Mexico. TEL 905-546-5115. FAX 905-535-6060. Ed. Klaus Rener y Mejia. adv. contact: Raul Paredes Parra. film rev.; music rev.; play rev.; circ. 10,000. (controlled. cols./p.: 2; pp./issue: 25. (back issues avail.) **Document type:** bulletin, newspaper.
    Description: Provides English-speaking visitors information of major international happenings as well as information on sites of interest in their own language. Includes local news.

917.204   US
MEXICO EVENTS AND DESTINATIONS. 1992. q. $11. Travel Mexico Magazine Group, Box 188037, Carlsbad, CA 92009. TEL 619-929-0707. FAX 619-929-0714. Ed. Gabriela Flores; Pub. Kirk Whisler. adv.: B&W page $4200, color page $5600; trim 8 3/8 x 10 7/8; adv. contact: Jim Sullivan. bk.rev. circ. 100,000. **Document type:** consumer publication.
    Formerly (until 1993): Mexico Events (ISSN 1048-5139)
    Description: Covers cultural, community, and entertainment events occurring throughout various regions of Mexico.

917.204   MX   ISSN 0462-1069
THE MEXICO NEWS. 1962. m. $60. (Mexican Journalist Association) Editorial Bonanza, S. de R.L., Dr. Velasco 95, Edif. 5, Of. 203, Col. Doctores, Del. Cuauhtemoc, 06720 Mexico D.F., Mexico. TEL 525-5938720. FAX 525-7052492. Ed. Mario Perez Morales. adv.; bk.rev. circ. 10,000. **Document type:** trade publication.

914.404   FR
MICHELIN GREEN GUIDE SERIES: ALPES DU NORD. 1978. irreg., latest 1992. $15 per no. Michelin, Services de Tourisme, 46 av. de Breteuil, 75341 Paris Cedex 7, France. (Dist. in U.S. by: Michelin Travel Publications, Box 19008, Greenville, SC 29602-9008. TEL 800-423-0485)
    Supersedes in part: Michelin Green Guide Series: Alpes.

914.404   FR
MICHELIN GREEN GUIDE SERIES: ALPES DU SUD. irreg., latest 1994. $18 per no. Michelin, Services de Tourisme, 46 av. de Breteuil, 75341 Paris Cedex 7, France. (Dist. in U.S by: Michelin Travel Publications, Box 19008, Greenville, SC 29602-9008. TEL 800-423-0485)
    Supersedes in part: Michelin Green Guide Series: Alpes.

914.404   FR
MICHELIN GREEN GUIDE SERIES: ALSACE ET LORRAINE (VOSGES). irreg., latest 1992. $15. Michelin, Services de Tourisme, 46 av. de Breteuil, 75341 Paris Cedex 7, France. (Dist. in U.S. by: Michelin Travel Publications, Box 19008, Greenville, SC 29602-9008. TEL 800-423-0485)
    Formerly: Michelin Green Guide Series: Vosges.

914.36   FR
MICHELIN GREEN GUIDE SERIES: AUSTRIA. (Text in English) irreg., latest 1992. $17 per no. Michelin, Services de Tourisme, 46 av. de Breteuil, 75341 Paris Cedex 7, France. (Dist. in U.S. by: Michelin Travel Publications, Box 19008, Greenville, SC 29602-9008. TEL 800-423-0485)

914.404   FR
MICHELIN GREEN GUIDE SERIES: AUVERGNE. 1977. irreg., latest 1991. $15. Michelin, Services de Tourisme, 46 av. de Breteuil, 75341 Paris Cedex 7, France. (Dist. in U.S. by: Michelin Travel Publications, Box 19008, Greenville, SC 29602-9008. TEL 800-423-0485)

914.404   FR
MICHELIN GREEN GUIDE SERIES: BELGIQUE - LUXEMBOURG. (Text in French) irreg., latest 1988. $17 per no. Michelin, Services de Tourisme, 46 av. de Breteuil, 75341 Paris Cedex 7, France. (Dist. in U.S. by: Michelin Travel Publications, Box 19008, Greenville, SC 29602-9008. TEL 800-423-0485)

914.404   FR
MICHELIN GREEN GUIDE SERIES: BERRY-LIMOUSIN. (Text in French) irreg., latest 1994. $18. Michelin, Services de Tourisme, 46 av. de Breteuil, 75346 Paris Cedex 7, France. (Dist. in U.S. by: Michelin Travel Publications, Box 19008, Greenville, SC 29304-9008. TEL 800-423-0485)

914.404   FR
MICHELIN GREEN GUIDE SERIES: BOURGOGNE. (Text in French) irreg., latest 1990. $15. Michelin, Services de Tourisme, 46 av. de Breteuil, 75341 Paris Cedex 7, France. (Dist. in U.S. by: Michelin Travel Publications, Box 19008, Greenville, SC 29602-9008. TEL 800-423-0485)

914.4   FR
MICHELIN GREEN GUIDE SERIES: BRITTANY. (Editions in English, French) irreg., latest 1991. $15 per no. Michelin, Services de Tourisme, 46 av. de Breteuil, 75341 Paris Cedex 7, France. (Dist. in U.S. by: Michelin Travel Publications, Box 19008, Greenville, SC 29602-9008. TEL 800-423-0485)

914.404   FR
MICHELIN GREEN GUIDE SERIES: BURGUNDY. (Text in English) irreg., latest 1992. $15. Michelin, Services de Tourisme, 46 av. de Breteuil, 75346 Paris Cedex 7, France. (Dist. in U.S. by: Michelin Travel Publications, Box 19008, Greenville, SC 29602-9008. TEL 800-423-0485)

917.104   FR
MICHELIN GREEN GUIDE SERIES: CANADA. (Editions in English, French) irreg., latest 1993. $17. Michelin, Services de Tourisme, 46 av. de Breteuil, 75346 Paris Cedex 7, France. (Dist. in U.S. by: Michelin Travel Publications, Box 19008, Greenville, SC 29602-9008. TEL 800-423-0485)

914.404   FR
MICHELIN GREEN GUIDE SERIES: CHAMPAGNE-ARDENNES. (Text in French) irreg., latest 1994. $18. Michelin, Services de Tourisme, 46 av. de Breteuil, 75346 Paris Cedex 7, France. (Dist. in U.S. by: Michelin Travel Publications, Box 19008, Greenville, SC 29602-9008. TEL 800-423-0485)

914.4   FR
MICHELIN GREEN GUIDE SERIES: CHATEAUX OF THE LOIRE. (Editions in English, French) irreg., latest 1991. $15 per no. Michelin, Services de Tourisme, 46 av. de Breteuil, 75341 Paris Cedex 7, France. (Dist. in U.S. by: Michelin Travel Publications, Box 19008, Greenville, SC 29602-9008. TEL 800-423-0485)

914.404   FR
MICHELIN GREEN GUIDE SERIES: CORSE. irreg., latest 1989. $15. Michelin, Services de Tourisme, 46 av. de Breteuil, 75341 Paris Cedex 7, France. (Dist. in U.S. by: Michelin Travel Publications, Box 19008, Greenville, SC 29602-9008. TEL 800-423-0485)

914.4 FR
MICHELIN GREEN GUIDE SERIES: COTE D'AZUR. irreg., latest 1998. $18. Michelin, Services de Tourisme, 46 av. de Breteuil, 75341 Paris Cedex 7, France. (Dist. in U.S. by: Michelin Travel Publications, Box 19008, Spartanburg, SC 29602-9008. TEL 800-432-0485)

914.4 FR
MICHELIN GREEN GUIDE SERIES: DORDOGNE. English edition: Michelin Green Guide Series: Perigord. (Editions in English, French) irreg., latest 1991. $15. Michelin, Services de Tourisme, 46 av. de Breteuil, 75346 Paris Cedex 7, France. (Dist. in U.S. by: Michelin Travel Publications, Box 19008, Greenville, SC 29602-9008. TEL 800-423-9001)

914.204 FR
MICHELIN GREEN GUIDE SERIES: ENGLAND, THE WEST COUNTRY. irreg., latest 1990. $15. Michelin, Services de Tourisme, 46 av. de Breteuil, 75346 Paris Cedex 7, France. (Dist. in U.S. by: Michelin Travel Publications, P.O. Box 19008, Greenville, SC 29602-9008. TEL 800-423-0485)

914.4 FR
MICHELIN GREEN GUIDE SERIES: EURO-DISNEY. irreg., latest 1992. $15. Michelin, Services de Tourisme, 46 av. de Breteuil, 75346 Paris Cedex 7, France. (Dist. in U.S. by: Michelin Travel Publications, Box 19008, Spartansburg, SC 29602-9008. TEL 800-423-0485)

914.404 FR
MICHELIN GREEN GUIDE SERIES: FLANDRES, ARTOIS, PICARDIE. (Text in French) irreg., latest 1994. $18. Michelin, Services de Tourisme, 46 av. de Breteuil, 75346 Paris Cedex 7, France. (Dist. in U.S. by: Michelin Travel Publications, Box 19008, Greenville, SC 29602-9008. TEL 800-423-0485) **Document type:** trade publication.
Formerly: Michelin Green Guide Series: Nord de la France; **Supersedes:** Michelin Green Guide Series: Ile de France; Michelin Green Guide Series: Nord de la France.

914.4 FR
MICHELIN GREEN GUIDE SERIES: FRANCE. (Editions in English, French) irreg., latest 1994. $18. Michelin, Services de Tourisme, 46 av. de Breteuil, 75341 Paris Cedex 7, France. (Dist. in U.S. by: Michelin Travel Publications, Box 19008, Spartansburg, SC 29602-9008. TEL 800-423-0485)

914.4 FR
MICHELIN GREEN GUIDE SERIES: FRENCH RIVIERA. (Text in English) irreg., latest 1991. $15 per no. Michelin, Services de Tourisme, 46 av. de Breteuil, 75346 Paris Cedex 7, France. (Dist. in U.S. by: Michelin Travel Publications, Box 19008, Greenville, SC 29602-9008. TEL 800-423-0485)

914.3 FR
MICHELIN GREEN GUIDE SERIES: GERMANY. (Text in English) irreg., latest 1993. $17 per no. Michelin, Services de Tourisme, 46 av. de Breteuil, 75341 Paris Cedex 7, France. (Dist. in U.S. by: Michelin Travel Publications, Box 19008, Greenville, SC 29602-9008. TEL 800-423-0485)

914.4 FR
MICHELIN GREEN GUIDE SERIES: GORGES DU TARN. irreg., latest 1989. $15. Michelin, Services de Tourisme, 46 av. de Breteuil, 75341 Paris Cedex 7, France. (Dist. in U.S. by: Michelin Travel Publications, Box 19008, Spartansburg, SC 29602-9008. TEL 800-423-0485)

914.2 FR
MICHELIN GREEN GUIDE SERIES: GREAT BRITAIN. irreg., latest 1994. $18. Michelin, Services de Tourisme, 46 av. de Breteuil, 75341 Paris Cedex 7, France. (Dist. in U.S. by: Michelin Travel Publications, Box 19008, Spartansburg, SC 29602-9008. TEL 800-423-0485)

914.9 FR
MICHELIN GREEN GUIDE SERIES: GREECE. irreg., latest 1994. $18. Michelin, Services de Tourisme, 46 av. de Breteuil, 75341 Paris Cedex 7, France. (Dist. in U.S. by: Michelin Travel Publications, Box 19008, Spartansburg, SC 29602-9008. TEL 800-423-0485)

914.904 FR
MICHELIN GREEN GUIDE SERIES: HOLLAND. irreg., latest 1988. $17. Michelin, Services de Tourisme, 46 av. de Breteuil, 75341 Paris Cedex 7, France. (Dist. in U.S. by: Michelin Travel Publications, Box 19008, Greenville, SC 29602-9008. TEL 800-423-0485)

914.1 FR
MICHELIN GREEN GUIDE SERIES: IRELAND. (Text in English) irreg., latest 1992. $17. Michelin, Services de Tourisme, 46 av. de Breteuil, 75346 Paris Cedex 7, France. (Dist. in U.S. by: Michelin Travel Publications, Box 19008, Spartansburg, SC 29602-9008. TEL 800-423-0485)

914.5 FR
MICHELIN GREEN GUIDE SERIES: ITALY. (Text in English) irreg., latest 1992. $17 per no. Michelin, Services de Tourisme, 46 av. de Breteuil, 75346 Paris Cedex 7, France. (Dist. in U.S. by: Michelin Travel Publications, Box 19008, Greenville, SC 29602-9008. TEL 800-423-0485)

914.404 FR
MICHELIN GREEN GUIDE SERIES: JURA - FRANCHE COMTE. irreg., latest 1992. $15. Michelin, Services de Tourisme, 46 av. de Breteuil, 75341 Paris Cedex 7, France. (Dist. in U.S. by: Michelin Travel Publications, Box 19008, Greenville, SC 29602-9008. TEL 800-423-0485)
Formerly: Michelin Green Guide Series: Jura (ISSN 0293-9436)

914.204 FR
MICHELIN GREEN GUIDE SERIES: LONDON. (Text in English) irreg., latest 1990. $15. Michelin, Services de Tourisme, 46 av. de Breteuil, 75346 Paris Cedex 7, France. (Dist. in U.S. by: Michelin Travel Publications, Box 19008, Greenville, SC 29602-9008. TEL 800-423-0485)

916.4 FR
MICHELIN GREEN GUIDE SERIES: MAROC. (Text in French) irreg., latest 1988. $17 per no. Michelin, Services de Tourisme, 46 av. de Breteuil, 75346 Paris Cedex 7, France. (Dist. in U.S. by: Michelin Travel Publications, Box 19008, Greenville, SC 29602-9008. TEL 800-423-0485)

917.204 FR
MICHELIN GREEN GUIDE SERIES: MEXICO. (Editions in English, Spanish) irreg., latest 1990. $17. Michelin, Services de Tourisme, 46 av. de Breteuil, 75346 Paris Cedex 7, France. (Dist. in U.S. by: Michelin Travel Publications, Box 19008, Greenville, SC 29602-9008. TEL 800-423-0485)

914.9 FR
MICHELIN GREEN GUIDE SERIES: NETHERLANDS. 1990. irreg., latest 1994. $18. Michelin, Services de Tourisme, 46 av. de Breteuil, 75341 Paris Cedex 7, France. (Dist. in U.S. by: Michelin Travel Publications, Box 19008, Spartansburg, SC 29602-9008. TEL 800-423-0485)

917.404 FR
MICHELIN GREEN GUIDE SERIES: NEW ENGLAND. (Editions in English, French) irreg., latest 1993. $15. Michelin, Services de Tourisme, 46 av. de Breteuil, 73546 Paris Cedex 7, France. (Dist. in U.S. by: Michelin Travel Publications, Box 19008, Greenville, SC 29602-9008. TEL 800-423-0485)

917.4 FR
MICHELIN GREEN GUIDE SERIES: NEW YORK (CITY). (Text in English, French) irreg., latest 1991. $15 per no. Michelin, Services de Tourisme, 46 av. de Breteuil, 75346 Paris Cedex 7, France. (Dist. in U.S. by: Michelin Travel Publications, Box 19008 Greenville, SC 29602-9008. TEL 800-423-0485)

914.404 FR
MICHELIN GREEN GUIDE SERIES: NORMANDY, COTENTIN. (Editions in English, French) irreg., latest 1994. $18. Michelin, Services de Tourisme, 46 av. de Breteuil, 75346 Paris Cedex 7, France. (Dist in U.S. by: Michelin Travel Publications, Box 3305, Spartanburg SC 19008, Greenville, SC 29602-9008. TEL 800-423-0485)

914.404 FR
MICHELIN GREEN GUIDE SERIES: NORMANDY, VALLEY SEINE. (Editions in English, French) irreg., latest 1994. $18. Michelin, Services de Tourisme, 46 av. de Breteuil, 75346 Paris Cedex 7, France. (Dist. in U.S. by: Michelin Travel Publications, Box 19008, Greenville, SC 29602-9008. TEL 800-423-0485)

914.4 FR
MICHELIN GREEN GUIDE SERIES: PARIS. (Editions in English, French) irreg., latest 1992. $15 per no. Michelin, Services de Tourisme, 46 av. de Breteuil, 75341 Paris Cedex 7, France. (Dist. in U.S. by: Michelin Travel Publications, Box 19008, Greenville, SC 29602-9008. TEL 800-423-0485)

914.404 FR
MICHELIN GREEN GUIDE SERIES: PERIGORD-QUERCY. (Text in French) irreg., latest 1994. $18. Michelin, Services de Tourisme, 46 av. de Breteuil, 75346 Paris Cedex 7, France. (Dist. in U.S. by: Michelin Travel Publications, Box 19008, Greenville, SC 29602-9008. TEL 800-423-0485)

914.404 FR
MICHELIN GREEN GUIDE SERIES: POITOU-VENDEE-CHARENTES. (Text in French) irreg., latest 1994. $18. Michelin, Services de Tourisme, 46 av. de Breteuil, 75346 Paris Cedex 7, France. (Dist. in U.S. by: Michelin Travel Publications, Box 19008, Greenville, SC 29602-9008. TEL 800-423-0485)

914.69 FR
MICHELIN GREEN GUIDE SERIES: PORTUGAL. (Editions in English and Spanish) irreg., latest 1989. $17 per no. Michelin, Services de Tourisme, 46 av. de Breteuil, 75346 Paris Cedex 7, France. (Dist. in U.S. by: Michelin Travel Publications, Box 19001, Greenville, SC 29602-9001. TEL 800-423-0485)

914.404 FR
MICHELIN GREEN GUIDE SERIES: PROVENCE. (Editions in English, French) 1980. irreg., latest 1991. $15. Michelin, Services de Tourisme, 46 av. de Breteuil, 75346 Paris Cedex 7, France. (Dist. in U.S. by: Michelin Travel Publications, Box 19008, Greenville, SC 29602-9008. TEL 800-423-0485)

914.404 FR
MICHELIN GREEN GUIDE SERIES: PYRENEES AQUITAINE. irreg., latest 1992. $15. Michelin, Services de Tourisme, 46 av. de Breteuil, 75341 Paris Cedex 7, France. (Dist. in U.S. by: Michelin Travel Publications, Box 19008, Greenville, SC 29602-9008. TEL 800-423-0485)
Supersedes: Michelin Green Guide Series: Pyrenees.

914.404 FR
MICHELIN GREEN GUIDE SERIES: PYRENEES ROUSSILLON. irreg., latest 1994. $15. Michelin, Services de Tourisme, 46 av. de Breteuil, 75346 Paris Cedex 7, France. (Dist. in U.S. by: Michelin Travel Publications, Box 19008, Greenville, SC 29602-9008. TEL 800-423-0485)

917.1 FR
MICHELIN GREEN GUIDE SERIES: QUEBEC PROVINCE. (Editions in English, French) irreg., latest 1992. $15. Michelin, Services de Tourisme, 46 av. de Breteuil, 75346 Paris, France. (Dist. in U.S. by: Michelin Travel Publications, Box 3305, Spartansburg, SC 29304-3305. TEL 800-423-0485)

914.404 FR
MICHELIN GREEN GUIDE SERIES: ROME. (Text in English, French) 1985. irreg., latest 1992. $15. Michelin, Services de Tourisme, 46 de Breteuil, 75341 Paris Cedex 7, France. (Dist. in U.S. by: Michelin Travel Publications, Box 19008, Greenville, SC 29602-9008. TEL 800-423-0485)

914.104 FR
MICHELIN GREEN GUIDE SERIES: SCOTLAND. irreg., latest 1990. $17. Michelin, Services de Tourisme, 46 av. de Breteuil, 75341 Paris Cedex 7, France. (Dist. in U.S. by: Michelin Travel Publications, P.O. Box 19008, Greenville, SC 29602-9008. TEL 800-423-0485)

TRAVEL AND TOURISM

914.6   FR
MICHELIN GREEN GUIDE SERIES: SPAIN. (Editions in English, Spanish) irreg., latest 1993. $17 per no. Michelin, Services de Tourisme, 46 av. de Breteuil, 75341 Paris Cedex 7, France. (Dist. in U.S. by: Michelin Travel Publications, Box 19008, Greenville, SC 29602-9008. TEL 800-423-0485)

914.94   FR
MICHELIN GREEN GUIDE SERIES: SWITZERLAND. (Editions in English, French) 1988. irreg., latest 1992. $17 per no. Michelin, Services de Tourisme, 46 av. de Breteuil, 75346 Paris Cedex 7, France. (Dist. in U.S. by: Michelin Travel Publications, Box 19008, Greenville, SC 29602-9008. TEL 800-423-0485)

914.404   FR
MICHELIN GREEN GUIDE SERIES: VALLEE DU RHONE. 1989. irreg., latest 1991. $15. Michelin, Services de Tourisme, 46 av. de Breteuil, 75346 Paris Cedex 7, France. (Dist. in U.S. by: Michelin Travel Publications, Box 19008, Greenville, SC 29602-9008. TEL 800-423-0485)

917.4   FR
MICHELIN GREEN GUIDE SERIES: WASHINGTON, DC. irreg., latest 1994. $15. Michelin, Services de Tourisme, 46 av. de Breteuil, 75341 Paris Cedex 7, France. (Dist. in US by: Michelin Travel Publications, Box 3305, Spartansburg, SC 29304-3305. TEL 800-423-0485)

910.2 914   FR   ISSN 0076-7743
MICHELIN RED GUIDE SERIES: BENELUX. Key Title: Michelin (Guides Rouges). a. $24. Michelin, Services de Tourisme, 46 av. de Breteuil, 75346 Paris Cedex 7, France. (Dist. in U.S. by: Michelin Travel Publications, P.O. Box 19008, Greenville, SC 29602-9008. TEL 800-423-0485)

910.2 914   FR
MICHELIN RED GUIDE SERIES: CAMPING, FRANCE. (Text in Dutch, English, French, German) a. $15. Michelin, Services de Tourisme, 46 av. de Breteuil, 75346 Paris Cedex 7, France. (Dist. in U.S. by: Michelin Travel Publications, Box 19008, Greenville, SC 29602-9008. TEL 800-423-0485)
  Formerly: Camping, Caravaning in France (ISSN 0076-7735)

910.2 914   FR
MICHELIN RED GUIDE SERIES: DEUTSCHLAND. (Text in German) a. $26. Michelin, Services de Tourisme, 46 av. de Breteuil, 75346 Paris Cedex 7, France. (Dist. in U.S. by: Michelin Travel Publications, Box 19001, Greenville, SC 29602-9001. TEL 800-423-0485)
  Formerly: Michelin Red Guide Series: Germany (ISSN 0076-7751)

910.2 914   FR   ISSN 0076-776X
MICHELIN RED GUIDE SERIES: ESPANA & PORTUGAL. a. $24. Michelin, Services de Tourisme, 46 av. de Breteuil, 75346 Paris Cedex 7, France. (Dist. in U.S. by: Michelin Travel Publications, P.O. Box 19008, Greenville, SC 29602-9008. TEL 800-423-0485)

914.04   FR
MICHELIN RED GUIDE SERIES: EUROPE, MAIN CITIES. (Text in English) a. $25. Michelin, Services de Tourisme, 46 av. de Breteuil, 75346 Paris Cedex 7, France. (Dist. in U.S. by: Michelin Travel Publications, P.O. Box 19008, Greenville, SC 29602-9008. TEL 800-423-0485)

910.2 914   FR   ISSN 0076-7778
MICHELIN RED GUIDE SERIES: FRANCE. a. $25. Michelin, Services de Tourisme, 46 av. de Breteuil, 75346 Paris Cedex 7, France. (Dist. in U.S. by: Michelin Travel Publications, P.O. Box 19008, Greenville, SC 29602-9008. TEL 800-423-0485)

914.204   FR
MICHELIN RED GUIDE SERIES: GREAT BRITAIN AND IRELAND. a. $24. Michelin, Services de Tourisme, 46 av. de Breteuil, 75346 Paris Cedex 7, France. (Dist. in U.S. by: Michelin Travel Publications, P.O. Box 19008, Greenville, SC 29602-9008. TEL 800-423-0485) illus.

914.21   FR
MICHELIN RED GUIDE SERIES: GREATER LONDON. (Text in English) a. $10. Michelin, Services de Tourisme, 46 av. de Breteuil, 75346 Paris Cedex 7, France. (Dist. in U.S. by: Michelin Travel Publications, P.O. Box 19008, Greenville, SC 29602-9008. TEL 800-423-0485) illus.

914.1   FR
MICHELIN RED GUIDE SERIES: IRELAND. 1992. a. $10. Michelin, Services de Tourisme, 46 av. de Breteuil, 75346 Paris, France. (Dist. in U.S. by: Michelin Travel Publications, Box 3305, Spartansburg, SC 29304-3305. TEL 800-423-0485)

914   FR   ISSN 0076-7786
MICHELIN RED GUIDE SERIES: ITALIA. (Text in English, French, German, Italian) a. $24. Michelin, Services de Tourisme, 46 av. de Breteuil, 75341 Paris Cedex 7, France. (Dist. in U.S. by: Michelin Travel Publications, P.O. Box 19008, Spartanburg, SC 29602-9008. TEL 800-423-0485)

910.2 914   FR
MICHELIN RED GUIDE SERIES: PARIS ET ENVIRONS. (Text in French) a. $10. Michelin, Services de Tourisme, 46 av. de Breteuil, 75346 Paris Cedex 7, France. (Dist. in U.S. by: Michelin Travel Publications, P.O. Box 19008, Greenville, SC 29602-9008. TEL 800-423-0485)
  Formerly: Michelin Red Guide Series: Paris (ISSN 0076-7794)

MICHIGAN GOLFER'S MAP & GUIDE. see SPORTS AND GAMES — Ball Games

MICHIGAN GOLFER'S TRAVEL GUIDE. see SPORTS AND GAMES — Ball Games

796.7   US   ISSN 0735-1798
TL1
MICHIGAN LIVING. 1918. m. $9. Automobile Club of Michigan, One Auto Club Dr., Dearborn, MI 48126. TEL 313-336-1506. Ed. Leonard R. Barnes. adv.: B&W page $12765, color page $15500. bk.rev.; illus. circ. 1,2,205,190. **Indexed:** Mich.Mag.Ind.
  Former titles: Michigan Living - A A A Motor News; Motor News (ISSN 0027-1934)
  Description: Includes description and travel information.

MIDWEST MOTORIST. see TRANSPORTATION — Automobiles

MILITARY LIVING'S R & R REPORT; the voice of the military traveler. see MILITARY

910.202 355   US   ISSN 1056-3989
MILITARY TRAVEL GUIDE. m. $6.95. J F H Publishing Inc., Box 17572, Arlington, VA 22216. TEL 703-528-3727. adv. circ. 40,000. **Document type:** directory.
  Description: Helps military personnel and their families save money per day on billeting, recreation and Space-A-Flights at US and overseas military facilities.

910.09 353   US
MILITARY TRAVEL NEWS. 1970. bi-m. $6.95. Box 3050, Oakton, VA 22124. TEL 703-491-2419. Ed. Ed Wojtas. adv. circ. 7,500.
  Description: Contains travel bargains and space "A" information for the military traveler, both active duty and retired.

977   US
MINNESOTA EXPLORER; newspaper. 3/yr. free. Office of Tourism, 100 Metro Square, 121 7th Pl. E., St. Paul, MN 55101. TEL 800-657-3700. Ed. Joan Hummel. adv. contact: Steve Markuson. circ. 550,000. **Document type:** newspaper.
  Former titles: Explore Minnesota; Incorporating: Minnesota Fall Color Guide and Calendar of Events; Minnesota Spring-Summer Calendar of Events; Minnesota Winter Sports Guide and Calendar of Events.

MINNESOTA - WISCONSIN GOLFER'S TRAVEL GUIDE. see SPORTS AND GAMES — Ball Games

915   RU   ISSN 0868-9547
MIR PUTESHESTVII. 1929. m. $74 (effective 1996). B. Khariton'evskii per. 14, 107078 Moscow, Russia. TEL 095-9211390. FAX 095-9752329. Ed. Boris V. Moskvin. adv.; illus. circ. 15,000.
  Formerly (until 1991): Turist (ISSN 0041-4182)

910.09   US
MOBIL MOTORIST. 1981. q. $2. (Mobil Auto Club) Signature Group, 200 N. Martingale Rd., Schaumburg, IL 60173-2096. TEL 708-605-7418. Ed. Bruce Gorman. adv. **Document type:** consumer publication.

910.09 388.3   FR   ISSN 0993-1996
MONDE DU CAMPING CAR. 10/yr. 210 F. (foreign 250 F.). Editions Lariviere, 15-17 Quai de l'Oise, 75166 Paris Cedex 19, France. TEL 1-40-34-22-07. FAX 1-40-35-84-41. TELEX 211 678 F.

910.202   GW   ISSN 0945-8107
MONDO; der ungewoehnliche Reisefuehrer. 1993. bi-m. newsstand price: DM.14.80. Vereinigte Motor-Verlage GmbH und Co. KG, Leuschnerstr. 1, 70162 Stuttgart, Germany. TEL 0711-1821226. FAX 0711-1821349. Ed. Michael Tafelmaier; Pub. Uwe Hagen. adv. contact: Peter Michael Heyde. circ. 40,000. **Document type:** consumer publication.

916.004   FR   ISSN 0767-3795
MONITEUR DU TOURISME AFRICAIN. 1986. m. 15 bd. de Picpus, 75012 Paris, France. TEL 43-45-65-99. FAX 45-88-28-10. Ed. Isabelle Mercier. circ. 6,000.

910.09   US   ISSN 0899-6059
MONK. 1986. q. $10 (foreign $15). Michael Lane and Jim Crotty, Eds. & Pubs., 175 Fifth Ave., Ste. 2322, New York, NY 10010. TEL 212-465-3231. adv.; bk.rev. circ. 29,000. (also avail. in microfilm)
  Description: Irreverent and humorous look at the odd and notorious in all corners of the U.S.A.

917.94   US
MONTEREY PENINSULA VISITORS GUIDE AND TRAVEL AND MEETING PLANNER.* a. Latimer Publications, 617 Veterans Blvd., Redwood City, CA 94063. TEL 415-324-1570. FAX 415-324-4420. Ed. Merlyn Holmes; Pub. Douglas H. Latimer. circ. 125,000. **Document type:** directory.
  Description: Official visitors guide to the Monterey Peninsula. Includes maps, shops, sights, dining, lodging and events.

MONTHLY REPORT ON TOURISM - REPUBLIC OF CHINA/KUAN KUANG TZU LIAO. see TRAVEL AND TOURISM — Abstracting, Bibliographies, Statistics

910.202   KO
MORNING CALM. 1977. m. Korean Air, c/o Choong Hoon Cho, Chairman, 41-3 Seosomun-dong, Chung-ku, Seoul, S. Korea. Ed. Choong Kun Cho. adv. circ. 120,000.

964   UK   ISSN 1358-3301
▼**MOROCCO AND TUNISIA;** including Mauritania, Libya and Algeria. 1995. a. £14.95. Trade & Travel Publications Ltd., 6 Riverside Ct., Lower Bristol Rd., Bath BA2 3DZ, England. TEL 01225-469141. FAX 01225-469461. (Dist. in N. America by: Passport Books, NTC Publishing Group, 4255 W. Touhy Ave., Lincolnwood, IL 60646-1975. TEL 708-679-5500. FAX 708-679-6375) Eds. Anne McLachlan, Keith MacLachlan. **Document type:** directory.

916   MR   ISSN 0027-1160
MOROCCO TOURISM.* (Editions in English, French and German) no.49, 1968. q. DH.20($4) Office National Marocain du Tourisme - Al-Maktab al-Watani al-Maghrebi lil-Siyahah, 31 angle ave. al-Abtal, Rue Oved Fas, Agdal, Rabat, Morocco. Dir. Abdelkader Lyagoubi. adv.; charts; illus.; stat. circ. 35,000.

388.3   US   ISSN 0463-6457
MOTOR CLUB NEWS. vol.30, 1974. q. membership. Motor Club of America, c/o Marlene Timm, Ed., 484 Central Ave., Newark, NJ 07107. adv.; bk.rev.; charts; illus.; stat.; circ. 130,000 (controlled). (tabloid format; back issues avail.)

MOTOR UND REISEN. see TRANSPORTATION — Automobiles

MOTORCARAVAN & MOTORHOME MONTHLY. see SPORTS AND GAMES — Outdoor Life

MOTORCYCLE TOUR & TRAVEL; adventure in style. see SPORTS AND GAMES — Bicycles And Motorcycles

MOTORCYCLIST. see SPORTS AND GAMES — Bicycles And Motorcycles

MOTORING & LEISURE. see TRANSPORTATION — Automobiles

TRAVEL AND TOURISM

796.7 US ISSN 0899-7578
MOTORIST (SEATTLE). 1915. m. $3. Automobile Club of Washington, 330 6th Ave. N., Seattle, WA 98109. TEL 206-448-5353. FAX 206-448-8627. Ed. Janet Ray. adv. contact: Brian Rounds. bk.rev.; illus. circ. 250,000. (tabloid format)
Formerly: Washington Motorist (ISSN 0043-0641)

388.3 US ISSN 0027-2310
MOTORLAND. 1917. bi-m. $3.50. California State Automobile Association, 150 Van Ness Ave., San Francisco, CA 94101. TEL 415-565-2451. FAX 415-863-4726. Ed. Lynn L. Ferrin; Pub. Don Patton. adv. contact: Keith Radcliff. bk.rev.; charts; illus.; circ. 2,300,000 (paid). Document type: consumer publication.
Description: For AAA members in Northern California, Nevada & Utah; features travel (regional, Western, and worldwide), motoring, cars and car care, insurance issues, food, and safety.

915 796.93 AT
MOUNT BULLER NEWS. 1983. w. free. Mansfield Newspapers Pty. Ltd., 96 High St., Mansfield, Vic. 3722, Australia. TEL 057-752115. FAX 057-751580. adv.; bk.rev. circ. 8,000.
Incorporates: This Week in Mount Buller; Formerly: Mount Buller Guide.

910.202 US
MOUNTAIN TRAVEL - SOBEK, THE ADVENTURE COMPANY. 1970. a. membership. Mountain Travel - Sobek, 6420 Fairmount Ave., El Cerrito, CA 94530. Ed. Dena Bartolome. adv.; illus.; index; circ. 160,000 (controlled). (back issues avail.)
Former titles: Sobek's Exceptional Adventures; Sobek's Adventure Annual; Sobek's Adventure Vacation.
Description: Descriptive listing of adventure travel vacations with dates and costs.

917 796 US ISSN 0027-2612
MOUNTAIN VISITOR. 1964. w. free. Mountain Press (Sevierville), Box 4810, Sevierville, TN 37864. TEL 615-428-0746. FAX 615-453-4913. adv.; charts; illus.; maps. circ. 25,000. (tabloid format; also avail. in microfilm)

MOVING TO & AROUND ALBERTA. see REAL ESTATE

MOVING TO & AROUND MARITIMES & NEWFOUNDLAND. see REAL ESTATE

MOVING TO & AROUND SASKATCHEWAN. see REAL ESTATE

MOVING TO & AROUND TORONTO & AREA. see REAL ESTATE

MOVING TO & AROUND VANCOUVER & B.C.. see REAL ESTATE

MOVING TO & AROUND WINNIPEG & MANITOBA. see REAL ESTATE

MOVING TO METRO OTTAWA - HULL. see REAL ESTATE

MPLS. - ST. PAUL MAGAZINE. see GENERAL INTEREST PERIODICALS — United States

910.202 KE ISSN 0251-0340
MSAFIRI.* 1980. q. (Kenya Airways) Transportation Displays International (Africa) Ltd., P.O. Box 47188, Nairobi, Kenya. Ed. Eric Hanna. adv. circ. 30,000.

MUENCHEN & BAYERN VON HINTEN; das schwule Reisebuch. see HOMOSEXUALITY

MULTIHULLS WORLD. see SPORTS AND GAMES — Boats And Boating

915.3 QA
AL-MURSHID/GUIDE. (Text in Arabic, English) 1983. bi-m. Dallah Advertising Agency, P.O. Box 8545, Doha, Qatar. TEL 429920. FAX 447793. TELEX 4420. Ed. Rashid Muhammad al-Noaimi. circ. 15,000.
Description: Information for business visitors and tourists.

059.9204 BA
AL-MUSAFIR AL-ARABI/ARAB TRAVELLER. 1984. bi-m. Falcon Publishing, P.O. Box 5028, Manama, Bahrain. TEL 253162. FAX 259694. TELEX 8917 FALPUB BN. Ed. Muhammad as-Said.

MUSEUMS IN MANITOBA (YEAR)/MUSEES DU MANITOBA (YEAR); preserving Manitoba's heritage. see MUSEUMS AND ART GALLERIES

917.604 US
MUSIC CITY VACATION GUIDE.* 1992. a. (Nashville Convention & Visitors Bureau) Tom Jackson & Associates, Inc., 3100 W. End Ave., Ste. 1210, Nashville, TN 37203-1348. TEL 615-242-7747. FAX 615-259-2042. Ed. Suzanne Boggs. adv.: B&W page $3520, color page $4195; trim 5 3/8 x 8 5/8. circ. 500,000. Document type: consumer publication, trade publication.
Description: Lists lodging, dining, attractions, tours, shopping and airline services for Nashville area.

N A D A MOBILE - MANUFACTURED HOUSING APPRAISAL GUIDE. see BUILDING AND CONSTRUCTION

910.09 658 US
N C A CAVE TALK. 1972. bi-m. membership. National Caves Association, 4138 Dark Hollow Rd., McMinnville, TN 37110. TEL 615-668-3925. FAX 615-668-3988. Ed. Barbara Munson. circ. 115. Document type: trade publication.
Description: For show cave industry personnel on tourism events and ideas.

791 NE ISSN 0027-6766
N K B. 1923. s-m. fl.35($10) Nederlandse Kermisbond, Oudegracht 186, Alkmaar, Netherlands. Indexed: Key to Econ.Sci.
Formerly: Komeet.

910.09 SI ISSN 0129-1467
N T U C LIFESTYLE. (Text in Chinese, English) 1987. bi-m. S.$1.50 per no. 1 New Industrial Rd., Times Centre, Singapore 1953, Singapore. TEL 2848844. FAX 2881186. TELEX 25713. Ed. Diana Tan. adv. circ. 244,000.
Description: Covers travel and leisure.

919.304 NZ
N Z T B COMMITTEE - DEPARTMENTAL REPORT SERIES. 1982. irreg., latest 1989. price varies. New Zealand Tourism Board, Market Research, P.O. Box 95, Wellington, New Zealand. TEL 04-4728-860. FAX 04-4781-736. stat.
Formerly: N Z T P Committee - Departmental Report Series (ISSN 0112-9821)

919.304 NZ
N Z T B DOMESTIC RESEARCH SERIES. 1981. irreg., latest 1991. price varies. New Zealand Tourism Board, Market Research, P.O. Box 95, Wellington, New Zealand. TEL 04-4728-860. FAX 04-4781-736.
Former titles (until 1991): N Z T D Domestic Research Series (ISSN 1170-5469); N Z T P Domestic Research Series (ISSN 0112-9767)

N Z T B ECONOMIC RESEARCH SERIES. (New Zealand Tourism Board) see BUSINESS AND ECONOMICS

919.304 NZ
N Z T B IMPLICATIONS OF TOURISM GROWTH SERIES. 1988. irreg. price varies. New Zealand Tourism Board, Market Research, P.O. Box 95, Wellington, New Zealand. TEL 04-4728-860. FAX 04-4781-736.
Former titles: N Z T D Implications of Tourism Growth Series; N Z T P Implications of Tourism Growth Series (ISSN 0114-0353)

910.4 NZ
N Z T B OVERSEAS MARKET RESEARCH SERIES. 1980. irreg., latest 1992. price varies. New Zealand Tourism Board, Market Research, P.O. Box 95, Wellington, New Zealand. TEL 04-728-860. TELEX 3941. (U.S. addr.: Ste. 1206, 432 Park Ave. South, New York, NY 10111. TEL 212-447-0550) stat.
Formerly: N Z T P Overseas Market Research Series (ISSN 0112-9724)

919.304 NZ
N Z T B REGIONAL RESEARCH SERIES. 1988. irreg., latest 1991. price varies. New Zealand Tourism Board, Market Research, P.O. Box 95, Wellington, New Zealand. TEL 04-4728-860. FAX 04-4781-736.
Former titles: N Z T D Regional Research Series (ISSN 1170-831X); (until 1991): N Z T P Regional Research Series (ISSN 0112-9783)

N Z T B SOCIAL RESEARCH SERIES. (New Zealand Tourism Board) see SOCIOLOGY

919.304 NZ
N Z T B TOURISM INCENTIVES SERIES. 1982. irreg., latest 1988. price varies. New Zealand Tourism Board, Market Research, P.O. Box 95, Wellington, New Zealand. TEL 04-4728-860. FAX 04-4781-736. TELEX 3941.
Formerly: N Z T P Tourism Incentives Series (ISSN 0112-9686)

916 KE ISSN 0047-8636
NAIROBI HANDBOOK.* 1958. m. English Press, Accra Rd., POB 30127, Nairobi, Kenya. Ed. R. Ouma. adv.; charts; illus. circ. 20,000.

917.604 US
NASHVILLE TRAVEL GUIDE.* 1986. a. (Nashville Convention & Visitors Bureau) Tom Jackson & Associates, Inc., 3100 W. End Ave., Ste. 1210, Nashville, TN 37203-1348. TEL 615-242-7747. FAX 615-259-2042. Ed. Suzanne Boggs. adv. circ. 20,000. Document type: trade publication, consumer publication.
Description: Lists regional cultural and recreational attractions, annual events, lodging, dining, nightlife, shopping, leisure opportunities, convention services and tours for professional tour planners and charter tour companies.

917 BF
NASSAU CABLE BEACH AND PARADISE ISLAND TOURIST NEWS. 1962. s-a. $6. (Nassau Cable Beach and Paradise Island Promotion Board) Star Publishers Ltd., Box 4855, Nassau, Bahamas. TEL 809-322-4528. FAX 809-322-4827. Ed. Bobby Bower. adv.; illus. circ. 80,000. (tabloid format) Document type: trade publication.
Former titles: Nassau and Paradise Island Tourist News; (until 1971): Bahamas Weekly and Nassau Tourist News (ISSN 0005-3961); (until 1968): Bahamas Weekly.

NATIONAL DIRECTORY OF BUDGET MOTELS; a nation-wide guide to low-cost chain motel accommodations. see HOTELS AND RESTAURANTS

910.202 US
NATIONAL DIRECTORY OF FREE TOURIST ATTRACTIONS. 1976. irreg., latest 1991. $4.95. Pilot Books, 103 Cooper St., Babylon, NY 11702. TEL 516-422-2225. FAX 516-422-2227. Document type: directory.
Description: Locates free attractions in all 50 states.

910.202 US ISSN 0747-0932
G1
NATIONAL GEOGRAPHIC TRAVELER. 1984. bi-m. $17.95. National Geographic Society, 17th & M Sts., N.W., Washington, DC 20036. TEL 202-857-7000. Ed. Richard Busch. adv.; maps. circ. 700,000. Indexed: Access (1983-). Document type: consumer publication.
—Faxon; SWETS; UnCover.
Description: Offers articles on vacation places in the US and Canada, plus popular spots abroad. Includes columns on photography, weekend destinations, and learning vacations, as well as a regional calendar of events in the US, Canada, Mexico, and the Caribbean.

910.09 388.3 US ISSN 0279-3083
NATIONAL MOTORIST. 1924. q. $2 in California. National Automobile Club, 188 The Embarcadero, San Francisco, CA 94105. TEL 415-777-4000. FAX 415-882-2141. Ed. Jane M. Offers. adv.; bk.rev.; circ. 100,000 (paid). Document type: consumer publication.
Description: Covers domestic and international travel and transportation plus automotive topics.

NATIONWIDE OVERNIGHT STABLING DIRECTORY & EQUESTRIAN VACATION GUIDE. see SPORTS AND GAMES — Horses And Horsemanship

910.2 SZ ISSN 0028-0925
NATURFREUND/AMI DE LA NATURE. (Text in French and German) 1962. bi-m. 30 SFr. Naturfreunde Schweiz - Federation Suisse des Amis de la Nature, Pavillonweg 3, P.O. Box 7364, CH-3001 Bern, Switzerland. TEL 031-3016088. adv.; bk.rev.; abstr.; charts; illus.; stat. Document type: bulletin.

TRAVEL AND TOURISM

910.202   BE
NATURISM; world handbook - guide mondiale - f.k.k. weltfuerer. (Text in Dutch, English, French, German) 1952. biennial. $32 (effective 1994). International Naturist Federation, St. Hubertusstr. 3, B-2600 Berchem-Antwerp, Belgium. TEL 32-3-2300572. FAX 32-3-2812607. Ed. Bertus Boivin. adv.; charts; illus. circ. 30,000.
   Description: Lists vacation centers and club grounds as well as activies, clubs and guides for the naturist.

915.4 320   II
NAVE PARVA. (Text in English, Konkani or Marathi) 1965. q. Rs.10. Department of Information and Publicity, Panaji, Goa, India. Ed. N. Rajasekhar. bk.rev.; illus. circ. 2,500.
   Formerly: New Era (ISSN 0548-4537)

910.202   US
NETWORK BED & BREAKFAST DIRECTORY. 1985. a. $29.95. Kib Communications, Box 1676, Humble, TX 77396-1676. TEL 713-590-1139. Ed. Veal Johnson. adv. circ. 200. **Document type:** directory.
   Former titles: Network Bed and Breakfast Registry; Bare Texan.
   Description: Travel accommodations for the nudist.

917   US   ISSN 0199-1248
F836
NEVADA. 1936. 6/yr. $14.95. State of Nevada, 1800 Hwy. 50 E., Ste. 200, Carson City, NV 89710. TEL 702-687-5416. FAX 702-687-6159. Ed. Dave Moore. adv. contact: Patty Noll. bk.rev.; illus. circ. 110,000. (also avail. in microform from UMI; reprint service avail. from UMI) **Indexed:** Access (1975-), Amer.Hist.& Life, Hist.Abstr. **Document type:** government publication.
   —UMI; UnCover.
   Incorporates: Nevada Events; **Formerly:** Nevada Highways and Parks (ISSN 0028-405X)

NEW JERSEY AND NATIONAL REGISTERS OF HISTORIC PLACES. see *ARCHITECTURE*

910.202 790.1   US
NEW JERSEY CALENDAR OF EVENTS. s-a. free. Department of Commerce and Economic Development, Division of Tourism, CN 826, Trenton, NJ 08625. TEL 609-292-2470; 800-537-7397. **Document type:** consumer publication, government publication.
   Description: Lists cultural, sports, and recreational activities in New Jersey.

917   US   ISSN 0028-6249
F791
NEW MEXICO MAGAZINE. 1923. m. $21.95. Tourism Department, 495 Old Santa Fe Trail, Santa Fe, NM 87503. TEL 505-827-7447. Ed. Emily Drabanski. adv.; bk.rev.; illus.; circ. 125,000 (paid). **Indexed:** Access (1975-), Chic.Per.Ind.
   —Faxon; UnCover.
   Description: Focuses on travel, history, art and culture.

910.2 915.2   JA   ISSN 0077-8591
DS805.2
NEW OFFICIAL GUIDE: JAPAN. (Text in English) 1952. irreg., 1991. 12000 Yen. (Japan National Tourist Organization) Japan Travel Bureau Inc., Publishing Division, Shibuya Nomura Bldg., 7F, 1-10-8, Dogenzaka, Shibuya-ku, Tokyo 150, Japan. TEL 03-3477-9529. FAX 03-3477-9587. Ed. Ryouji Fujishima. index.
   Formerly: Japan: the Official Guide.

917.53   US   ISSN 0097-8213
F192.3
NEW SETTLER'S GUIDE FOR WASHINGTON, D.C. AND COMMUNITIES IN NEARBY MARYLAND AND VIRGINIA. 1972. a. $8.50 (effective 1993). Robco, Inc., 8824 Tuckerman Lane, Potomac, MD 20854. TEL 301-299-7507. Ed. Robert B. Minogue. adv.; illus. circ. 15,000. **Document type:** consumer publication, directory.
   Description: Contains comprehensive information on relocating to metropolitan Washington, including community profiles, a real estate agency directory, public and private school and day care listings, and information for newcomers on shopping, recreation, dining, and cultural attractions in the region.

917.404   US   ISSN 1056-4446
F128.18
NEW YORK (YEAR). a. $12. Harper Collins Publishers, Birnbaum Travel Guides, 10 E. 53rd St., New York, NY 10022-5299. TEL 212-207-7542. Ed. Alexandra Mayes Birnbaum. illus.; index.

917   US   ISSN 0028-7288
NEW YORK CONVENTION & VISITORS BUREAU. QUARTERLY CALENDAR OF EVENTS. 1947. 4/yr. free. New York Convention & Visitors Bureau, Inc., 2 Columbus Circle, New York, NY 10019. Ed. Kathryn Diminnie. circ. 300,000.

900
NEW YORK JOURNAL JAPAN.* 1973. m. $10. c/o Waldorf Astoria, Ste. 1852, 301 Park Ave., New York, NY 10022-6897. Ed. J. Benjamin. adv.; bk.rev. circ. 201,000.

974   US
NEW YORK STATE FAIR MAGAZINE. 1955. a. $2. New York State Fair, State Fairgrounds, Syracuse, NY 13209. FAX 315-487-9260. Ed. Joseph J. LaGuardia. adv. circ. 32,500. **Document type:** consumer publication.
   Formerly: New York State FairGround.

917.4   US
NEW YORK'S NIGHTLIFE.* 1979. m. $15. M.J.C. Publishers, Inc., c/o New York Update, 990 Motor Pky., Central Islip, NY 11722-1001. TEL 516-242-7722. Ed. Bill Ervolini. adv.; bk.rev. circ. 175,062.
   Former titles: New York's and Long Island's Nightlife; Long Island's Nightlife (ISSN 0744-7590)

919.304   NZ   ISSN 1172-2304
NEW ZEALAND TOURISM NEWS. 1990. irreg. New Zealand Tourism Board, 256 Lambton Quay, P.O. Box 95, Wellington, New Zealand. TEL 64-4-4728860. FAX 64-4-4781736. **Document type:** newsletter.
   Former titles (until 1992): New Zealand. Ministry of Tourism. Newsletter (ISSN 1171-1760); (until 1991): New Zealand Tourism Department Newsletter (ISSN 1170-5078)

NEWCOMER; an introduction to life in Belgium. see *GENERAL INTEREST PERIODICALS* — Belgium

910.202   US
NEWPORT DINING GUIDE. 1974. q. free. Newport This Week, Box 159, Newport, RI 02840-0002. FAX 401-846-4974.

917.404   US
NEWPORT TRAVELER. m. Traveler Publications, 172 Bellevue Ave., Ste. 319, Newport, RI 02840. TEL 401-847-0089. FAX 401-847-5267. Ed. Joanne Blake; Pub. Jeffrey Hall. adv.; B&W page $1872; trim 11 x 17; adv. contact: Monica Grady. circ. 40,000. (tabloid format) **Document type:** newspaper, consumer publication.
   Formerly: Ocean State Traveler.
   Description: Focuses on places of interest to travelers visiting Rhode Island and on events taking place there.

NIAGARA PARKS COMMISSION. ANNUAL REPORT. see *CONSERVATION*

916.69   NR
NIGERIA TOURIST BOARD. OFFICIAL TOURIST GUIDE. Variant title: Welcome to Nigeria ...The Land of Hospitality, Cultural Diversity and Scenic Beauty. 1969. irreg. free. Nigerian Tourism Development Corporation, Block 2, Sefadu St., P.M.B. 167, Zone 4, Wuse-Abuja, Nigeria. TEL 234-9-5230418. FAX 234-9-5230962. adv.; illus. **Document type:** government publication, consumer publication.
   Formerly: Nigeria Tourist Guide.
   Description: Fosters an awareness of everything Nigeria has to offer to tourists, including scenic and cultural attractions, conference and hotel facilities, and international and domestic travel.

NIKKEI EVENTS. see *MEETINGS AND CONGRESSES*

NIX WIE WEG; Mitfahrzentralen in Deutschland und uller Welt. see *TRANSPORTATION*

NORDDEUTSCHLAND, HAMBURG VON HINTEN; das schwule Reisebuch. see *HOMOSEXUALITY*

NORDIC NETWORK. see *SPORTS AND GAMES* — Outdoor Life

917.5   US   ISSN 0546-3432
F306
NORMAN FORD'S FLORIDA. biennial. $4.95. Harian Publications, One Vernon Ave., Floral Park, NY 11001. TEL 516-437-3440. Ed. Norman D. Ford. charts; illus.

917.04   US
NORTH AMERICAN GUIDE TO NUDE RECREATION. 1966. a. $26.95. American Association for Nude Recreation, 1703 N. Main St., Kissimmee, FL 34744. TEL 800-879-6833. FAX 407-933-7577. Eds. Arne Eriksen, Julie Bagby. illus. circ. 30,000.
   Formerly: Nudist Park Guide.

NORTH ATLANTIC REPORT. see *TRANSPORTATION* — Air Transport

974 910.09   US   ISSN 8756-9256
F291.7
NORTH GEORGIA JOURNAL. 1984. 4/yr. $17.95. Legacy Communications, Inc., P.O. Box 127, Roswell, GA 30077-0127. TEL 404-642-5569. FAX 404-642-6598. Ed. R. Olin Jackson; Pub. R. Olin Jackson. adv.: B&W page $1195, color page $1695; adv. contact: Kathy Hodge. bk.rev.; circ. 16,701 (paid); 2,451 (controlled). (back issues avail.) **Document type:** consumer publication.
   Description: Provides a captivating source of information on travel opportunities, lifestyles, history, and historic real estate throughout the North Georgia region.

917.7   US
NORTH SHORE NEW RESIDENTS' GUIDE. 1983. a. P B Communications, Inc., 874 Green Bay Rd., Winnetka, IL 60093. TEL 708-441-7892. Ed. Asher J. Birnbaum. adv.; illus. circ. 60,000. **Document type:** consumer publication.
   Formerly: North Shore Newcomers' Guide.
   Description: For new residents of Chicago's North Shore area.

910.202   US   ISSN 0892-8363
NORTHWEST PALATE; wine, food, & lifestyles of the Pacific Northwest. 1983. bi-m. $21. Box 10860, Portland, OR 97210. TEL 503-224-6039. FAX 503-222-5312. Ed. Cameron Nagel. adv. contact: Bruce Watkins. bk.rev. circ. 15,000. **Document type:** consumer publication.
   Formerly (until 1987): Oregon Wine Review (ISSN 0736-8496)
   Description: Includes wine reviews in the form of rated tasting notes of new releases, food and wine feature articles, recipes, restaurant and lodging information, wine-maker and chef profiles.

910.202   US   ISSN 1059-9681
NORTHWEST TRAVEL. 1991. bi-m. $14.95. Spooner Industries, Box 18000, Florence, OR 97439. TEL 503-997-8401. FAX 503-997-1124. Ed. Rob Spooner. adv.; illus. circ. 40,000. **Document type:** consumer publication.
   Description: Devoted to active as well as armchair travelers with travel tips on Washington State, Oregon and Idaho.

914   FR   ISSN 0048-0843
NOS MAISONS FAMILIALES DE VACANCES. 1954. q. 27.50 F. Federation des Maisons Familiales de Vacances, 28 place St-Georges, 75442 Paris 9, France. circ. controlled.

NOUVELLE FIPREGAZETTE. see *FOOD AND FOOD INDUSTRIES*

914.3   GW
NUERNBERG HEUTE. 1964. s-a. free. Stadt Nuernberg, Presse- und Informationsamt, Rathaus, 90317 Nuernberg, Germany. TEL 0911-2312372. FAX 0911-2313660. Ed. Norbert Schuergers. adv.; bk.rev.; charts; illus. circ. 35,000. **Document type:** government publication.
   Description: News about the city of Nuernberg.

917   US   ISSN 1053-0002
TX907   CODEN: OBTEE2
O A G BUSINESS TRAVEL PLANNER. NORTH AMERICAN EDITION. 1958. q. $130. Reed Travel Group, Part of the Reed Elsevier group (Subsidiary of: Reed Telepublishing), 500 Plaza Dr., Secaucus, NY 07096. TEL 201-902-1600. FAX 201-902-1914. Ed. Margaret Pritt. adv. circ. 60,352. **Document type:** directory.
—BLDSC (6196.360000).
   Formerly (until 1990): O A G Travel Planner Hotel and Motel Guide Redbook. North American Edition (ISSN 0894-1726); Which was formed by the 1987 merger of: O A G Travel Planner and Hotel Motel Guide. North American Edition (ISSN 0193-3299); Which was formerly: O A G Travel Planner and Hotel - Motel Guide (ISSN 0090-0869); part of: Red Book (Walnut Creek) (ISSN 0896-1565); Which was formerly: Hotel and Motel Red Book (ISSN 0073-3490)
   Description: Reference guide for business travelers and those planning travel within North America. Includes listings for over 32,000 hotels, data for over 14,760 destinations, ground and air transportation, and more than 242 maps and airport diagrams.

910 387   US   ISSN 0097-8779
HE568
O A G CRUISE & SHIPLINE GUIDE - WORLDWIDE EDITION. 1975. 6/yr. $102. Official Airline Guides, Part of Reed Travel Group (Subsidiary of: Reed Elsevier plc), 2000 Clearwater Dr., Oak Brook, IL 60521. TEL 708-574-6000. FAX 708-574-6091. TELEX 210144. circ. 5,500. **Document type:** directory.
   Description: Includes individual cruise listings, organized by geographical area and departure date, as well as worldwide ferry schedules, which are displayed on a to-from basis. Also features listings of cruise and ferry operations, port diagrams, and ship profiles.

O A G HOTEL GAZETTEER. see *HOTELS AND RESTAURANTS*

910.09 350   US
O A G OFFICIAL TRAVELER FLIGHT GUIDE. 1992. m. Reed Travel Group, Airline Division (Subsidiary of: Reed Elsevier plc), 2000 Clearwater Dr., Oak Brook, IL 60521-9953. TEL 708-574-6000. FAX 708-574-6091. adv.; circ. 26,000 (paid). **Document type:** trade publication.

910.09 350   US   ISSN 1073-0338
TX907.2
O A G OFFICIAL TRAVELER TRAVEL GUIDE. 1992. q. Reed Travel Group, Airline Division (Subsidiary of: Reed Elsevier plc), 2000 Clearwater Dr., Oak Brook, IL 60521-9953. TEL 708-574-6000. FAX 708-574-6091. Ed. Barbara J. Comiskey; Pub. Curt Reilly. adv.; circ. 26,000 (paid). **Document type:** trade publication.

910   US   ISSN 1069-2150
TX907.5.P33   CODEN: OPAEE5
O A G TRAVEL PLANNER. ASIA PACIFIC EDITION. 1985. q. $130. Reed Travel Group, Part of the Reed Elsevier group (Subsidiary of: Reed Telepublishing), 500 Plaza Dr., Secaucus, NJ 07096. TEL 201-902-1600. FAX 201-902-1914. Ed. Margaret Pritt. adv. circ. 104,190. **Document type:** directory.
   Formerly (until 1992): O A G Travel Planner Hotel and Motel Redbook. Pacific Asia Edition (ISSN 0894-1734); Which was formed by the 1987 merger of: O A G Travel Planner and Hotel - Motel Guide. Pacific Area Edition (ISSN 8750-8672); part of: Red Book (Walnut Creek) (ISSN 0896-1565); Which was formerly: Hotel and Motel Red Book (ISSN 0073-3490)
   Description: Reference guide for those planning travel within the Pacific Asia area. Includes over 4,700 hotel listings, destination data for more than 3,100 cities, ground and air transportation information, country travel "basics," maps and airport diagrams.

914.04   US
TX907.5.E85   CODEN: OTHEEY
O A G TRAVEL PLANNER. EUROPEAN EDITION. 1978. q. $130. Reed Travel Group, Part of the Reed Elsevier group (Subsidiary of: Reed Telepublishing), 500 Plaza Dr., Secaucus, NJ 07096. TEL 201-902-1600. FAX 201-902-1914. Ed. Margaret Pritt. adv. circ. 14,155. **Document type:** directory.
   Formerly (until 1992): O A G Travel Planner Hotel and Motel Redbook. European Edition (ISSN 0894-1718); Which was formed by the 1987 merger of: O A G Travel Planner and Hotel - Motel Guide. European Edition (ISSN 0162-735X); part of: Red Book (Walnut Creek) (ISSN 0896-1565); Which was formerly: Hotel and Motel Red Book (ISSN 0073-3490)
   Description: Reference guide for those planning travel within Europe. Includes about 10,000 hotel listings, destination data for more than 14,100 cities, ground and air transportation information, country travel "basics", with additional information for travel to the Middle East and Africa.

O A G WORLD AIRWAYS GUIDE. see *TRANSPORTATION — Air Transport*

917.1   CN   ISSN 1187-4198
O M C A RESOURCE GUIDE. 1986. a. (Ontario Motor Coach Association) Naylor Communications Ltd., 920 Yonge St., 6th Fl., Toronto, ON M4W 3C7, Canada. TEL 416-961-1028. FAX 416-924-4408. adv. **Document type:** trade publication.
   Formerly (until 1991): Ontario Motor Coach Association Resource Guide (ISSN 0836-4214)

910.202   US   ISSN 0191-8478
OAHU DRIVE GUIDE. 1974. 3/yr. free. Honolulu Publishing Company, Ltd., 36 Merchant St., Honolulu, HI 96813. TEL 808-524-7400. FAX 808-531-2306. Ed. Brett Uprichard.
   Description: For visitors; includes road maps of the island, restaurant guide, places of interest, travel information, and history.

917.94
OAKLAND VISITORS GUIDE AND TRAVEL & MEETING PLANNER.* a. Latimer Publications, 617 Veterans Blvd., Redwood City, CA 94063-1404. TEL 415-324-1570. FAX 415-324-4420. Ed. Merlyn Holmes. circ. 210,000.
   Description: Includes maps, shops, sights, dining, lodging and events.

915.404   II
THE OBEROI GROUP MAGAZINE. (Text in English) 1971. q. $25. East India Hotels Ltd., Oberoi Towers, Nariman Point, Bombay 400 021, India. TEL 2025757. FAX 2043282. TELEX 84153-OBBY-IN. Ed. Gouri Umashankar. adv.; bk.rev.; illus. circ. 15,000.
   Formerly: Soma.

OCEAN & CRUISE NEWS. see *TRANSPORTATION — Ships And Shipping*

917.504   US
OCEANA MAGAZINE. 1978. w. free. Independent Publishers Group, Inc., Box 1943, Ocean City, MD 21842. TEL 302-539-6313. FAX 302-539-6815. Ed. Elizabeth Brownell. adv. (tabloid format; back issues avail.)
   Description: Contains general information on resorts, beaches, tourism, and sports.

301.4157 910   US   ISSN 0883-3664
E158
ODYSSEUS; an accommodations & travel guide for the gay community, USA & international. 1985. a. $25 (effective 1994). Odysseus Enterprises Ltd., Box 1548, Port Washington, NY 11050. TEL 516-944-5330. FAX 516-944-7540. TELEX 6719473 BDIT UW. Ed. Eli Angelo; Pub. Joseph H. Bain. adv. contact: Tim Nugent. bk.rev. circ. 350,000. **Document type:** directory.
   Description: International gay travel planner, including information on hotels, bed and breakfasts, and resorts catering to the gay community in the USA, Canada and worldwide.

910.202   US   ISSN 1073-5259
E158
ODYSSEY (SANTA ROSA); the magazine of the Chevron Travel Club. 1969. q. membership. (Chevron Travel Club) Dunham Bergquist & Associates, Inc., 131 Stony Circle, Ste. 500, Santa Rosa, CA 95401. TEL 707-526-3222. FAX 707-526-9815. Ed. Jean Pierce. bk.rev. circ. 500,000. **Document type:** consumer publication.
   Formerly (until 1993): Chevron U S A Odyssey (ISSN 0886-5418); Which was formed by the merger of: Chevron U S A (ISSN 0199-5707); Odyssey (San Jose) (ISSN 0164-8063)

OESTERREICHISCHE GASTGEWERBE- UND HOTELZEITUNG. see *HOTELS AND RESTAURANTS*

910.2   AU   ISSN 0048-1483
OESTERREICHISCHE TOURISTENZEITUNG. 1888. m. membership. Oesterreichischer Touristenklub, Baeckerstr. 16, A-1010 Vienna, Austria. Ed. Guenther J. Wolf. bk.rev.; film rev.; illus. circ. 20,000.

051 792   US   ISSN 1055-1778
OFFICIAL CITY GUIDE. 1982. w. $29. Bill of Fare Inc., 853 7th Ave., Ste. 1-A, New York, NY 10019-5215. FAX 212-397-9513. Ed. Peter Insalaco. adv. circ. 50,000. **Document type:** consumer publication.
   Former titles: City Guide (ISSN 1043-3937); City Guide, Broadway Magazine (ISSN 0892-2446)

910.09   US   ISSN 1065-2450
G550
OFFICIAL CRUISE GUIDE. 1992. a. Reed Travel Group, Part of the Reed Elsevier group (Subsidiary of: Reed Telepublishing), 500 Plaza Dr., Secaucus, NJ 07096. TEL 201-902-2000. FAX 201-319-1755. (Subscr. to: Box 7653, Riverton, NJ 08077-8953) adv.: B&W page $10450, color page $11675; trim 9 x 10 7/8; adv. contact: Marie Mason. circ. 18,400. **Document type:** directory.
   Description: Provides data on cruises and ships worldwide.

910.2   US   ISSN 1043-1195
TX907.2
OFFICIAL GUIDE TO AMERICAN HISTORIC INNS; 1,100 bed & breakfast and country inns. 1987. a. $19.95. Association of American Historic Inns, Box 336, Dana Point, CA 92629. TEL 800-397-INNS. FAX 714-499-4022. Eds. Timothy J. Sakach, Deborah Edwards Sakach. circ. 1,200,000. **Document type:** directory.
   Former titles: Official Guide to American Historic Bed and Breakfast Inns and Guesthouses; (until 1988): Official Guide to American Bed and Breakfast Inns and Guesthouses.
   Description: Offers travellers a complete listing of historic inns, bed and breakfasts, and guesthouses built prior to 1940. Includes a coupon for one free night at any inn with one night paid.

910.202   US
▼**OFFICIAL GUIDE TO HOUSTON.** 1994. q. free. Desert Publications, Inc., 303 N. Indian Canyon Dr., Palm Springs, CA 92262. TEL 619-325-2333. FAX 619-325-7008. (Dist. by: 1936 W. Gray Dr., Ste. 216, Houston, TX 77019) Ed. Kate Loggins; Pub. Milton W. Jones. adv.: B&W page $4450, color page $5650; trim 8 3/8 x 10 7/8. circ. 600,000 (controlled). **Document type:** consumer publication.

910.202   HK
OFFICIAL HONG KONG GUIDE. (Text in English) 1982. m. (Hong Kong Tourist Association) Off Duty Publications, 1605 Pacific Plaza, 410 Des Voeux Rd., W., Hong Kong. TEL 852-2517-2063. FAX 852-2540-4063. TELEX 74720 HX. Ed. Robert Bonds. adv.: B&W page HK$18340, color page HK$20450; trim 138 x 208. circ. 60,000.
   Description: Provides information on sightseeing, shopping, dining and other activities for visitors.

OFFICIAL HOTEL GUIDE. see *HOTELS AND RESTAURANTS*

OFFICIAL RAILWAY GUIDE. NORTH AMERICAN TRAVEL EDITION. see *TRANSPORTATION — Railroads*

6488 TRAVEL AND TOURISM

917.604   US
OFFICIAL TENNESSEE VACATION GUIDE. 1992. a. (Department of Tourist Development) Journal Communications, Inc., 1749 Mallory Ln., Ste. 110, Brentwood, TN 37027. TEL 615-371-0010. FAX 615-371-0258. Ed. Mark Forester; Pub. Bob Schwartzman. adv.: B&W page $12995, color page $14995; trim 7 3/4 x 10 3/4; adv. contact: Sharon Butler. circ. 700,000. **Document type:** consumer publication.

917.504   US
OFFICIAL VISITORS GUIDE TO CENTRAL FLORIDA. 1985. s-a. free. Orlando - Orange County Convention and Visitors Bureau, Inc., 7208 Sandlake Rd., Ste. 300, Orlando, FL 32819. TEL 407-363-5800. FAX 407-363-5899. adv.: B&W page $6625, color page $7270; trim 5 3/8 x 8 3/8. circ. 1,000,000 (controlled).
  Description: Lists accommodations, attractions, restaurants and other categories.

910.202   FR   ISSN 0755-1460
OFFICIEL DES CONGRES ET DU TOURISME D'AFFAIRES.* m. 270 F. E D I T A, 167 av. Victor Hugo, 75116 Paris, France. TEL 45-53-01-97. FAX 45-53-17-99. Ed. Jane Bezlade. circ. 10,000.

914   FR   ISSN 0030-0500
OFFICIEL DES SPECTACLES. cette semaine. 1946. w. 550 F. 100 Champs-Elysees, 75008 Paris, France. TEL 42-25-57-84. FAX 45-61-04-00. Ed. J. P. Richemond. adv.; film rev.; play rev.; illus.; circ. 188,986 (paid). **Document type:** consumer publication.
  Description: Paris entertainment guide.

914   SZ
OFFIZIELLES BERNER WOCHEN BULLETIN. w. Verkehrs Verein, Hauptbahnhof, CH-3001 Bern, Switzerland. TEL 031-462323. FAX 031-210820. TELEX 912641. circ. 7,200.

OHIO GOLFER'S TRAVEL GUIDE. see *SPORTS AND GAMES — Ball Games*

796.7   US   ISSN 0030-0985
OHIO MOTORIST. 1909. m. $1.50. American Automobile Association, Ohio Motorists Association, 6000 S. Marginal Rd., Cleveland, OH 44103. TEL 216-361-6216. FAX 216-361-6109. (Subscr. to: Box 6150, Cleveland, OH 44101) Ed. F. Jerome Turk. adv.; bk.rev.; illus. circ. 390,000. (tabloid format)

387.7   PL   ISSN 1230-3925
OKECIE; airport magazine. 1992. m. Warsaw Voice S.A., Ksiecia Janusza 64, 01-452 Warsaw, Poland. TEL 48-22-366377. FAX 48-22-371995. adv.: page 4375 Zl. illus. **Document type:** newspaper.
  Description: Provides information for businessmen and tourists on Warsaw and Poland.

910   UK
OLEANDER TRAVEL BOOKS SERIES. a. Oleander Press, 17 Stansgate Ave., Cambridge CB2 2QZ, England. (U.S. address: 80 Eighth Ave., Ste. 303, New York, NY 10011) **Document type:** bulletin.

647.94   AT
ON THE GO; YHA's budget travel magazine. 1963. q. membership. Youth Hostels Association of Queensland, G.P.O. Box 1128, Brisbane, Qld. 4001, Australia. TEL 61-7-236-1680. FAX 61-7-236-1702. Ed.Bd. adv.: B&W page Aus.$530, color pate Aus.$675; trim 297 x 420. bk.rev. circ. 20,000. (back issues avail.) **Document type:** trade publication.
  Formerly: Queensland Hosteller (ISSN 0818-4380)

ON THE LINE (PENSACOLA). see *LEISURE AND RECREATION*

914.704   US
ON THE LOOSE IN EASTERN EUROPE. 1993. a. Fodor's Travel Publications, Inc. (Subsidiary of: Random House, Inc.), 201 E. 50th St., New York, NY 10022. TEL 800-733-3000. Ed. Katie Clark. illus.; maps.

917.204   US
ON THE LOOSE IN MEXICO. 1993. a. Fodor's Travel Publications, Inc. (Subsidiary of: Random House, Inc.), 210 E. 50th St., New York, NY 10022. TEL 800-733-3000. Ed. Deborah Meacham. maps.

917.904   US
ON THE LOOSE IN THE PACIFIC NORTHWEST & ALASKA. 1993. a. Fodor's Travel Publications, Inc. (Subsidiary of: Random House, Inc.), 210 E. 50th St., New York, NY 10022. TEL 800-733-3000. maps.

917.504   UK
ONE FLORIDA MANY FACES. a. Phoenix Publishing & Media Ltd., 18-20 Scrutton St., London EC2A 4RJ, England. TEL 0171-247-0537. FAX 0171-377-2741. Ed. Mary Moore Mason; Pub. Maureen Miller. adv. contact: Kathryn McGowan. circ. 115,000. **Document type:** consumer publication.
  Description: Holiday and travel planner for United Kingdom consumers.

ONTARIO BED & BREAKFAST GUIDE. see *HOTELS AND RESTAURANTS*

917.104 796   US
ONTARIO FARM & COUNTRY ACCOMMODATIONS DIRECTORY. a. Ontario Farm & Country Accommodations, R.R. No.2, Alma, ON N0B 1A0, Canada. TEL 519-846-9788. FAX 519-846-9378. adv. **Document type:** directory, consumer publication.
  Description: Lists and describes each of the association's bed and breakfast and farm vacation establishments, with rates, farm activities, maps, and surrounding attractions.

917.1   CN   ISSN 0824-9776
ONTARIO MOTOR COACH ASSOCIATION REVIEW. 1981. a. Naylor Communications Ltd., 920 Yonge St., 6th Fl., Toronto, ON M4W 3C7, Canada. TEL 416-961-1028. FAX 416-924-4408. Ed. Lori Knowles. adv. **Document type:** trade publication.
  Formerly: Ontario Motor Coach Association Yearbook.

910.202   CN   ISSN 0707-1442
ONTARIO TOURISM NEWS. 1978. q. Ministry of Tourism and Recreation, 77 Bloor St. W., 7th Fl., Toronto, Ont. M7A 2R9, Canada. TEL 416-965-7680.

OP PAD. see *SPORTS AND GAMES — Outdoor Life*

910   IT
OPERATORE TURISTICO.* 1973. 22/yr. L.50000. Federazione Italiana Agenzia Viaggi e Turismo, Via Livenza 8, 00198 Rome, Italy. TEL 6-38-49-45. Ed. Sergio Piscitello. adv.: B&W page L.2000000, color page L.2400000; adv. contact: Claudio Galli. circ. 8,000.

OREGON MOTORIST. see *TRANSPORTATION — Automobiles*

917.5   US   ISSN 0279-1323
ORLANDO MAGAZINE.* 1946. m. $19.95. Abarta Metro Publishing, 260 Maitland Ave., Ste. 2000, Altamonte Springs, FL 32701-5501. TEL 609-272-7900. FAX 609-272-7910. Ed. John Kiely. adv.; illus.; tr.lit. circ. 35,000. **Document type:** consumer publication.
  Incorporates: Central Florida Magazine; (1986-1988): Orbus (ISSN 0890-6432); Which was formerly: Orlando-Land (ISSN 0145-6431)

910.09 647.9   SP
ORO VERDE. 6/yr. German Perez Carrasco 63, Edif. Ofice, 28027 Madrid, Spain. TEL 1-267-24-03. Ed. Pilar Pardo. circ. 30,000.

910.09 296   US
OSCAR ISRAELOWITZ'S GUIDE TO JEWISH NEW YORK CITY. 1987. a. $11.95. Box 228, Brooklyn, NY 11229. TEL 718-951-7072. Ed. Oscar Israelowitz; Pub. Oscar Israelowitz. adv.; bibl. circ. 5,000. **Document type:** consumer publication.

914   NO
OSLO CITY GUIDE. m. Per Sletholt og Co., Boks 57, Tveita, Oslo 6, Norway. adv.

OUR WORLD; the international gay travel magazine. see *HOMOSEXUALITY*

917.504   US
OUT AND ABOUT SMITH MOUNTAIN LAKE. 1989. 3/yr. Rte. 1, Box 437, Moneta, VA 24121. TEL 703-297-6444. Eds. Anne Kidd, Barbie White. adv.; circ. 40,000 (controlled).
  Description: Provides information on accommodations, restaurant locations and shopping centers.

918   US   ISSN 0899-1413
OUT WEST. 1988. q. $11.95. Out West Publishing (Nevada City), 408 Broad St., Ste. 11, Nevada City, CA 95959. TEL 916-478-9080. FAX 916-478-9082. E-mail: outwestcw@aol.com. Ed. Chuck Woodbury; Pub. Chuck Woodbury. bk.rev.; circ. 11,000 (paid). (tabloid format; back issues avail.) **Document type:** consumer publication.
  Description: Covers travel and the "back roads" of Americas West, includes reports on the various findings.

OUTDOOR; das andere Reisemagazin. see *SPORTS AND GAMES — Outdoor Life*

OUTDOOR & TRAVEL PHOTOGRAPHY. see *PHOTOGRAPHY*

OUTDOOR CANADA. see *SPORTS AND GAMES — Outdoor Life*

917.504   US   ISSN 1069-9627
GV191.42.M52
OUTDOOR TRAVELER. MID-ATLANTIC. 1993. q. $12. W M S Publications Inc., Box 1788, Charlottesville, VA 22902. TEL 804-973-3952. FAX 804-978-7449. Ed. Marianne Marks. adv.: B&W page $1495, color page $2025; trim 8 1/4 x 10 7/8. bk.rev. circ. 30,000. **Document type:** consumer publication.
  Description: Covers activities in the Mid Atlantic region, including outdoor recreation, travel adventure, and nature.

910.09   US
OUTLOOK FOR INTERNATIONAL TRAVEL TO AND FROM THE UNITED STATES. 3/yr. free. U.S. Travel and Tourism Administration, Office of Research, U.S. Department of Commerce, Main Commerce Bldg., Rm. 1860, Washington, DC 20230. TEL 202-482-1048. FAX 202-482-2887. stat. **Document type:** government publication.
  Description: Provides one-year forecasts of international travel to and from the U.S. and evaluates economic and social conditions that influence tourist activity.

910.09   US   ISSN 0737-8815
G155.U6
OUTLOOK FOR TRAVEL AND TOURISM. a. $135. Travel Industry Association of America, 1100 New York Ave., N.W., Ste. 450, Washington, DC 20005-3934. TEL 202-408-8422. charts. (reprint service avail.) **Document type:** trade publication.
—BLDSC (6314.575000).
  Formerly: Travel Outlook Forum Proceedings (ISSN 0160-4651)
  Description: Contains verbatim accounts of travel industry experts forecasts on economic developments, demographic life-style changes, market segmentation developments, and other issues affecting U.S. travel and tourism.

OVER THE RAINBOW. see *HANDICAPPED*

910.2   UK   ISSN 0030-7424
OVERSEAS. 1915. q. membership. Royal Over-Seas League, Over-Seas House, Park Place, St. James's St., London SW1A 1LP, England. TEL 071-408-0214. FAX 071-499-6738. TELEX 268995-ROSL-G. Ed. Pat Treasure. adv.; illus. circ. 25,000. (tabloid format) **Document type:** bulletin.

914.2 312   UK
OVERSEAS VISITOR SURVEY (YEAR). a. £59. British Tourist Authority, Department D, Thames Tower, Black's Rd., Hammersmith, London W6 9EL, England.
  Description: Surveys the behavior of foreign visitors to Britain to collect and publish data not currently available from the International Passenger Survey.

OWNER - DRIVER; dedicated to the success of the person behind the wheel. see *TRANSPORTATION*

917   US   ISSN 0030-7769
F417.09
OZARKS MOUNTAINEER; the Ozarkswide bi-monthly periodical. 1952. bi-m. $11.50. Box 20, Kirbyville, MO 65679. TEL 417-336-2665. FAX 417-336-2679. Ed. Gerald Dupy; Pub. Barbara Wehrman. adv.; bk.rev.; charts; illus.; tr.lit. circ. 28,000.

919   IO   ISSN 0048-2625
P A T A INDONESIA.* 1971. bi-m. free. Pacific Area Travel Association, Indonesia Chapter, Jalan Kramat Raya 81, Jakarta, Indonesia. Ed. J.W. Adnan. adv.; charts; illus.

910.09   US
P A T A TASK FORCE REPORTS. 1979. irreg., no. T32, 1991. $150 to non-members; members $50. Pacific Asia Travel Association, Telesis Tower, Ste. 1750, 1 Montgomery St., San Francisco, CA 94104. TEL 415-986-4646. FAX 415-986-3458. (back issues avail.) **Document type:** proceedings.
Description: Case studies of tourism development in the Pacific Asia region.

P A T H WAYS. (Port Authority Trans-Hudson Corporation) see *TRANSPORTATION — Railroads*

PACIFIC BOATING ALMANAC. NORTHERN CALIFORNIA & NEVADA. see *SPORTS AND GAMES — Boats And Boating*

PACIFIC BOATING ALMANAC. PACIFIC NORTHWEST EDITION. see *SPORTS AND GAMES — Boats And Boating*

PACIFIC BOATING ALMANAC. SOUTHERN CALIFORNIA & MEXICO. see *SPORTS AND GAMES — Boats And Boating*

917   CN   ISSN 0030-8692
PACIFIC HOSTELLER. 1964. q. membership. Canadian Hostelling Association, B.C. Region, 1515 Discovery St., Vancouver, B.C. V6R 4K5, Canada. TEL 604-224-7177. FAX 604-224-4852. adv.; bk.rev.; illus.; circ. 10,000 (controlled).

919   FJ   ISSN 0030-8722
DU1
PACIFIC ISLANDS MONTHLY. 1930. m. F.$2.50 per issue. Fiji Times Ltd., P.O. Box 1167, Suva, Fiji. TEL 679-304111. FAX 679-303809. Ed. Rory Gibson; Pub. Brian O'Flaherty. adv.; bk.rev.; charts; illus.; mkt.; stat.; index; circ. 9,500 (paid). **Indexed:** So.Pac.Per.Ind.
—BLDSC (6329.840000); Faxon; SWETS; UnCover.

PACIFIC TRAVEL DIRECTORY. see *BUSINESS AND ECONOMICS — Trade And Industrial Directories*

919.6   HK
PACIFIC TRAVELLER. 6/yr. $30. Sky Trend Development Ltd., Mezzanine Fl., 20-22 Old Bailey St., Central, Hong Kong. TEL 5220037. FAX 5267488. Ed. Derek Maitland.
Description: Covers hotel news and prices. Aims at the frequent business traveller.

943.04   GW
PADERBORN JOURNAL. 1973. m. DM.60. Verkehrsverein Paderborn e.V., Marienplatz 2a, 33098 Paderhorn, Germany. TEL 05251-26461. FAX 05251-22884. Ed. Gerhard Ortner. adv. contact: Wolfgang Geese. bk.rev. circ. 40,000. **Document type:** consumer publication.
Formerly (until 1992): Kump - Paderborn von Tag zu Tag.

910.09 647.9   PK   ISSN 0250-3662
PAKISTAN HOTEL AND TRAVEL REVIEW. (Text in English) 1978. m. Rs.500($42) Maulai Enterprise, J-6-2, al-Naseer, Federal B Area, Blk. No. 1, Karachi 75950, Pakistan. TEL 92-21-6322764. Ed. Syed Wali Ahmad Maulai. adv.; stat. circ. 5,000. (back issues avail.) **Document type:** trade publication.

910.202   PK
PAKISTAN HOTELS & TOURISM. 1975. a. Rs.5. Bhatti Publications, 103-B Gulberg, Lahore, Pakistan. Ed. Mukhtar Bhatti. adv.

910.202 642.5   US   ISSN 1061-7701
TX661
PALATE AND SPIRIT; the travel magazine for food lovers. 1992. q. $36 (Canada $42; elsewhere $49) (effective 1993). David Roth, Ed. & Pub., 245 Eighth Ave., Ste. 336, New York, NY 10011. TEL 212-969-0950. FAX 212-675-8395. adv. contact: David Roth. illus. circ. 50,000. **Document type:** consumer publication.
Description: Comprehensive international coverage of culinary travel programs and food festivals, with articles focusing on people and their relationship to fine food, and extensive listings of events, tours and cooking schools.

917.8   US   ISSN 0031-0425
PALM SPRINGS LIFE. 1947. m. $38. Desert Publications, Inc., 303 N. Indian Canyon Dr., Box 2724, Palm Springs, CA 92262. TEL 619-325-2333. FAX 619-325-7008. Ed. Stuart Weiner. adv.; bk.rev.; film rev.
Description: Covers events in and around Palm Springs.

917.904   US
PALM SPRINGS LIFE DESERT GUIDE. 1967. m. Desert Publications, Inc., 303 N. Indian Canyon Dr., Box 2724, Palm Springs, CA 92263. TEL 619-325-2333. FAX 619-325-7008. Ed. Donna Curran. circ. 76,325.

910.4   US   ISSN 0553-0601
PAN AM WORLD GUIDE;* encyclopedia of travel. a. $9.95. Pan American World Airways, c/o East-West Network, Inc., 419 N. Larchmont Blvd. 12, Los Angeles, CA 90004-3000. adv.; charts; illus. circ. 50,000.

PANAMA NOW. see *BUSINESS AND ECONOMICS — Domestic Commerce*

917   US   ISSN 0048-282X
PANORAMA (BOSTON); Boston's official bi-weekly visitor guide. 1951. fortn. $50. Jerome Press, 332 Congress St., Boston, MA 02210. TEL 617-423-3400. FAX 617-423-7108. Ed. Rita A. Fucillo. adv.; film rev.; play rev.; charts; illus. circ. 64,940. **Indexed:** Int.Packag.Abstr.
Incorporates: Cityguide.

910.09   SP
PANORAMA MELIA. 12/yr. Dr. Esquerdo 155-B, 28007 Madrid, Spain. TEL 409-02-47.

PAPERS IN LEISURE AND TOURISM STUDIES. see *LEISURE AND RECREATION*

914.404   US   ISSN 1056-4438
DC708
PARIS (YEAR). a. $12. Harper Collins Publishers, Birnbaum Travel Guides, 10 E. 53rd St., New York, NY 10022-5299. TEL 212-207-7542. Ed. Alexandra Mayes Birnbaum. illus.; index.
Description: Includes 8 walking tours of the city's sights.

910.202   US
PARTNERS-IN-TRAVEL. 1981. 2/yr. $25. 11660 Chenault St., Ste. 119, Los Angeles, CA 90049-4527. Ed. Miriam E. Tobolowsky. circ. 500. (tabloid format)
Description: Offers cost-cutting tips and information relating to the needs and interests of the single traveler.

914.504   IT
PASSEGGIATE NEL LAZIO. 1977. irreg. price varies. (Regione Lazio, Assessorato al Turismo) Bulzoni Editore, Via dei Liburni, 00185 Rome, Italy.

910.2   US   ISSN 0031-272X
PASSPORT; the newsletter for the discriminating international traveler. 1965. m. $65. Remy Publishing Co., 350 W. Hubbard St., No. 440, Chicago, IL 60610-4011. TEL 312-464-0300. **Document type:** newsletter.

910.202   JA
PASSPORT.* 1958. m. Japan Tourist Bureau Inc., c/o Kokusai Kanko Kaikan, 8-3 Marunouchi 1-chome, Chiyoda-ku, Tokyo 100, Japan. Ed. Herbert Slew Sai. adv. circ. 100,000.

947   US
PASSPORT TO THE NEW WORLD. 1991. bi-m. Zigzag Venture Group, Attn.: John Small, 645 Fifth Ave., 7th Fl., New York, NY 10022. TEL 212-725-6700. FAX 212-725-6915. **Document type:** consumer publication.
Description: Covers travel, culture, art, and interesting places in Russia, the Baltic republics, and other parts of the former Soviet Union.

910.09   HK
PATA TRAVEL NEWS AMERICAS. Short title: P T N Americas. 1990. bi-m. Americas Publishing Co., 4636 E. Elmwood St., Ste. 5, Phoenix, AZ 85040-1963. TEL 602-997-7200. FAX 602-997-9875. adv.; B&W page $4720; color page $5895; trim 8 x 10 7/8. circ. 25,000.

910.09   HK
PATA TRAVEL NEWS ASIA - PACIFIC. Short title: P T N Asia - Pacific. (Text in English) 1987. m. $60 in Asia; elsewhere $70. Miller Freeman Pte. Ltd. (Hong Kong) (Subsidiary of: United News & Media), 738 Kings Rd., 102-5 Stanhope House, Quarry Bay, Hong Kong, Hong Kong. TEL 8335022. FAX 65-298-5534. TELEX HX-63393-ABPHK. (Alt. addr.: 100 Beech Rd., 26-00 Shaw Towers, Singapore 0718, Singapore. TEL 65-294-3366) Ed. Yeoh Siew Hoon. adv. circ. 13,848.
Description: Trade information for Asia's travel and tourism industries.

910.4   HK
PATA TRAVEL NEWS EUROPE. Short title: P T N Europe. (Text in English) 1990. m. Miller Freeman Pte. Ltd. (Hong Kong) (Subsidiary of: United News & Media), 738 Kings Rd., 102-5 Stanhope House, Quarry Bay, Hong Kong, Hong Kong. (Alt. addr.: Morgan Grampian House, Calderwood St., London SE18 6QH. TEL 44-181-855-7777. FAX 44-181-316-3119) adv. **Document type:** trade publication.

910.09   US   ISSN 1056-0025
PAUL EDWARDS' TRAVEL CONFIDENTIAL. 1991. m. $95. Lowell Communications, Inc., 88 Bleecker St., New York, NY 10012. TEL 212-254-1069. Ed. Paul L. Edwards.
Formerly (until 1991): Travel Smarter (ISSN 1055-0488)
Description: Covers low-cost travel for individuals and groups.

915.94   HK
PENINSULA GROUP MAGAZINE. 1974. 3/yr. free to qualified personnel. Peninsula Group, St. George's Bldg., 6th Fl., 2 Ice House St., Central, Hong Kong. TEL 840-7619. FAX 845-5512. TELEX 74509-KREM-HX. Ed. Liam Fitzpatrick. adv. contact: Margaret Tan. circ. 53,000. **Document type:** consumer publication.
Description: Covers travel, leisure and art in Asia and the United States.

941.04   UK   ISSN 0261-2836
PENNINE MAGAZINE. 1979. bi-m. £9 (foreign £10). Pennine Heritage Ltd., Birchcliffe Centre, Hebden Bridge, W. Yorks. HX7 8DG, England. Ed. Hilary Darby. adv.; bk.rev. circ. 8,000. (back issues avail.)

PENNSYLVANIA MAGAZINE. see *GENERAL INTEREST PERIODICALS — United States*

910.09   US
PENTON EXECUTIVE NETWORK. (Includes supplement: Executives on the Go) 1969. m. (avail. only with subscr. to selected Penton magazines). Penton Publishing (Subsidiary of: Pittway Company), 1100 Superior Ave., Cleveland, OH 44114-2543. TEL 216-696-7000. FAX 216-696-8765. (Subscr. to: Box 95759, Cleveland, OH 44101) adv.; illus. circ. 1,600,000. (reprint service avail. from UMI)
Former titles: Management Personal Time Network; Management Personal Time; Management Leisure Time; Management Time and Leisure.
Description: Provides a channel of communication to upscale managers and professionals.

910.09 338   US
PERSONAL TRAVEL REPORT. m. $25. Nationwide Intelligence, Box 1922, Saginaw, MI 48605. TEL 517-752-6123; 800-333-4130. FAX 517-752-1605.
Description: Helps the individual business or leisure traveler get the best value and avoid rip-offs and inferior products and services.

917   CN   ISSN 0048-3451
PERSONNEL GUIDE TO CANADA'S TRAVEL INDUSTRY. 1969. s-a. Can.$47.08 (U.S. $50, elsewhere $55). Baxter Publishing Co., 310 Dupont St., Toronto, ON M5R 1V9, Canada. TEL 416-968-7252. FAX 416-968-2377. Ed. Wendy Baxter-McClung. adv. contact: Clare Earle. circ. 5,000. **Document type:** directory.
Description: Provides complete listings of all travel agencies, tour operators, wholesalers, airlines, car rentals, hotel representatives, tourist boards, travel insurance firms and cruise lines operating in Canada.

TRAVEL AND TOURISM

371.42 US ISSN 0894-9417
GV186
PETERSON'S SUMMER OPPORTUNITIES FOR KIDS AND TEENAGERS (YEAR). 1983. a. $21.95. Peterson's Guides, Inc., 202 Carnegie Center, Box 2123, Princeton, NJ 08543-2123. TEL 609-243-9111. FAX 609-243-9150.
  Description: Covers more than 1200 summer programs for young people, including those offered by private schools, colleges, camps, religious organizations and travel and sports groups.

910.2 914 UK ISSN 0079-130X
PETS WELCOME; animal lovers' holiday guide. 1961. a. £3.99. F H G Publications Ltd., Abbey Mill Business Centre, Seedhill, Paisley PA1 1JN, Scotland. TEL 0141-887-0428. FAX 0141-889-7204. Ed. Peter Clark. **Document type:** consumer publication.

910.202 915.9 PH
PHILIPPINE TRAVELER; a pocket guide to the Philippine experience. (Text in English) 1991. s-a. (Duty Free Philippines) Eastgate Publishing Corporation, Rms. 603-604, Emerald Bldg., Emerald Ave., Pasig, 1600 Metro Manila, Philippines. TEL 632-6312921. FAX 632-6312992. Ed. Cecile G. Mauricio. adv. contact: Gina C. Sanchez. circ. 75,000. **Document type:** catalog.
  Description: Travel guide covers the essential points a traveler needs to know about the Philippines.

PHILIPPINES TRANSPORTATION. see *TRANSPORTATION*

910.202 US ISSN 0745-4554
PHYSICIANS' TRAVEL & MEETING GUIDE. 1982. m. $158 to institutions outside the Americas; $100 to institutions in U.S (effective 1996). Excerpta Medica, Inc. (Subsidiary of: Reed Elsevier Medical group), 105 Raider Blvd., Belle Meade, NJ 08502. TEL 908-874-8550. FAX 908-874-5611. (Subscr. to: Box 3085, Princeton, NJ 08543-3085) Ed. Bea Riemschneider. adv.; tr.lit. circ. 113,335. **Document type:** trade publication.
  —UMI. CCC.
  Description: For physicians to help them plan their attendance at medical meetings and their personal and business travel.

PIACERE ITALIA. see *HOTELS AND RESTAURANTS*

791 YU ISSN 0031-9880
PINGRIN;* nedeljni ilustrovani zabavnik. 1966. w. 50 din. Napred, Valjevo, Vuka Karadzica 26, Fah 62, Valjevo, Yugoslavia. Ed. Bronislav Nikolic.

PINK PAGES; Scotland's premier guide to food and drink. see *HOTELS AND RESTAURANTS*

910.4 US
PINKERTON EYE ON TRAVEL.* 1987. m. $199. Pinkerton Risk Assessment Services, 200 N. Glebe Rd., No. 1011, Arlington, VA 22203-3728. TEL 703-525-6111. FAX 703-525-2454. Ed. Frank Johns. circ. 1,000. (diskette format)
  ●Also available on CD-ROM.
  Formerly: International Travel Briefing Service.
  Description: Publishes travel warnings and advisories, information on currency exchnage, weather, passport & visa requirements, and health issues.

614.86
PINKERTON WORLD STATUS MAP.* 1983. bi-m. $69.99. Pinkerton Risk Assessment Services, 200 N. Glebe Rd., No. 1011, Arlington, VA 22203-3728. TEL 703-525-6111. FAX 703-525-2454. Ed. Frank Johns. circ. 1,700.
  Formerly: World Status Map (ISSN 0887-9559)
  Description: Provides danger-medical warnings for international travelers.

PLAISIRS. see *HOTELS AND RESTAURANTS*

910.09 US
PLEASURE TRAVEL MARKETS TO NORTH AMERICA. a. price varies. U.S. Travel and Tourism Administration, Office of Research, U.S. Department of Commerce, Main Commerce Bldg., Rm. 1868, Washington, DC 20230. TEL 202-482-4028. FAX 202-482-2887. (Subscr. to: U.S. Travel Data Center, 2 Lafayette Centre, 1133 21st St., N.W., Washington, DC 20036. TEL 202-293-1040. FAX 202-293-3155) **Document type:** government publication.
  Description: Explores the perception overseas of specific travel destinations in the U.S. and Canada.

910.09 US
PLYMOUTH GUIDE. 1980. s-a. $5. M P G Specialty Publications, Box 1416, 9 Long Pond Rd., Plymouth, MA 02362-1416. TEL 508-830-0350. FAX 508-747-2148. Ed. Polly McGrory; Pub Sheryl Woodford. adv.: B&W page $1117; trim 5 1/4 x 7 1/2. circ. 340,000.
  Description: Covers historical attractions, waterfront activities, whale watching, pilgrim history, museums, arts and crafts.

918 BF
POCKET GUIDE TO THE BAHAMAS. 1947. s-a. Cartwright Publications, Box N494, Nassau, Bahamas. Ed. Kevin B. Cartwright. circ. 150,000.

338.4 FR ISSN 1017-0685
POLITIQUE DU TOURISME ET TOURISME INTERNATIONAL DANS LES PAYS MEMBRES DE L'O C D E. English edition: Tourism Policy and International Tourism in O E C D Member Countries (ISSN 0256-7598) 1961. a. price varies. Organization for Economic Cooperation and Development, 2 rue Andre-Pascal, 75775 Paris Cedex 16, France. (Dist. in US by: O.E.C.D. Publications and Information Center, 2001 L St., N.W., Ste. 700, Washington, DC 20036-4910. TEL 202-785-6323) (also avail. in microfiche from OEC,CIS) Indexed: IIS.
  Former titles (until 1970): Tourisme dans les Pays de l'O C D E (ISSN 1021-1659); (until 1962): Tourisme en Europe (ISSN 1021-1640)

910.202 US ISSN 1070-9479
PORTHOLE; the intelligent cruise magazine. 1982. bi-m. $35 (foreign $45). Panoff Publishing, Inc., 10 Fairway Dr., Ste. 200, Deerfield Beach, FL 33441-9805. TEL 305-426-0046. FAX 305-427-0037. Ed. Douglas Ward. adv.; bk.rev. circ. 30,000. **Document type:** consumer publication.
  Formerly: Cruise Digest Reports (ISSN 0886-5604)
  Description: Presents in-depth reports and reviews on cruise ships, cruise industry news and U.S.P.H. scores.

910.202 790.1 US ISSN 1073-1857
PORTLAND; Maine's city magazine. 1986. 10/yr. $20; newsstand price: $2.95 (Canada Can.$3.95). Sargent Publishing Inc., 578 Congress St., Portland, ME 04101. TEL 207-775-4339. FAX 207-775-2334. E-mail: 75363,1716@CompuServe.com. Ed. Colin W. Sargent; Pub. Colin W. Sargent. adv.; bk.rev. circ. 10,000. (back issues avail.) **Document type:** consumer publication.
  Description: Covers the arts and business in the Portland area and the rest of Maine.

914.2 UK
PORTLAND SOUVENIR MAGAZINE. 1971. a. £0.25. Royal Naval Association, Portland Branch, 2 Clarence Rd., Portland, Dorset, England. Ed. John Barnes.

914.904 US ISSN 1055-5668
DP516
PORTUGAL (YEAR). a. $18. Harper Collins Publishers, Birnbaum Travel Guides, 10 E. 53rd St., New York, NY 10022-5299. TEL 212-207-7542. Ed. Alexandra Mayes Birnbaum. illus.; index.
  Supersedes in part: Birnbaum's Spain - Portugal (ISSN 1042-6353)
  Description: Includes 9 detailed driving routes.

914.604 PO
PORTUGAL TURISMO ACTUALIDADE. 1980. m. Rua Joaquim Antonio de Aguiar 45-5o, Esq., 1000 Lisbon, Portugal. TEL 01-557175. FAX 01-557667. circ. 40,000.

914 PL ISSN 0032-6151
POZNAJ SWOJ KRAJ;* miesiecznik krajoznawczo-turystyczny. 1958. m. 2400 Zl.($9) Instytut Wydawniczy "Nasza Ksiegarnia", c/o Ars-Polona Ruch, Krakowskie Przedmiescie 7, Warsaw, Poland. TEL 48 22 26-24-31. Ed. Andrzej Gordon. adv.; bk.rev.; illus.; index. circ. 25,000.

910.202 US
PRAIRIE PROFILE. w. 312 Fifth St., Box 177, Brookings, SD 57006. TEL 605-692-6271. Ed. Kristin Anderson.

PRESIDENTS' JOURNAL. see *HISTORY — History Of North And South America*

917 BM ISSN 0048-5268
PREVIEW BERMUDA. 1959. m. $30. Preview of Bermuda, Ltd., P.O. Box HM 266, Hamilton HMAX, Bermuda. TEL 809-292-4155. FAX 809-295-4724. Eds. Ann Brown, Roxana Kaufmann. adv.; charts; illus.
  Description: Complete guide for the Bermuda visitor.

PREVISIONS GLISSANTES DETAILLEES EN PERSPECTIVES SECTORIELLES (VOL.37): TOURISME, HOTELLERIE, RESTAURATION, LOISIRS. see *BUSINESS AND ECONOMICS — Economic Situation And Conditions*

PRIMI PIANI; mensile d'arte, costume, cultura, scienza, spettacolo e turismo. see *MUSIC*

910.09 GW ISSN 0932-4631
PROFITRAVEL; das internationale Geschaeftsreise-Magazin. 1987. bi-m. DM.36. Gesellschaft fuer Wirtschaftspublizistik (GWP) mbH, Kasernenstr. 67, 40213 Dusseldorf, Germany. TEL 0211-887-2501. FAX 0211-326943. TELEX 17211308-HBL. Ed. Thomas Michael Schweizer. adv. circ. 181,000. (back issues avail.)

914 AU
PROGRAMM WIEN; events-manifestations. (Text in English, French, German, Italian) 1957. m. S.180. Vienna Tourist Board, Obere Augartenstr. 40, A-1025 Vienna, Austria. TEL 01-21114-0. FAX 01-2168492. Ed.Bd. adv. circ. 120,000. **Document type:** bulletin.
  Formerly: Wien-Veranstaltungen.

338.4 647.94 UK
▼**PROGRESS IN TOURISM AND HOSPITALITY.** 1995. s-a. $95 to institutions worldwide. John Wiley & Sons Ltd., Journals, Baffins Ln., Chichester, W. Sussex PO19 1UD, England. TEL 01243-779777. FAX 01243-776128. TELEX 86290 WIBOOK G. (Subscr. in the Americas to: John Wiley & Sons, Inc., 605 Third Ave., New York, NY 10158. TEL 212-850-6645. FAX 212-850-6021) (also avail. in microform from UMI; back issues avail.)

301 US ISSN 1077-3509
▼**PROGRESS IN TOURISM AND HOSPITALITY PRACTICE.** 1995. q. $195 (effective 1996). (Consortium of Hospitality Research Information Services) John Wiley & Sons, Inc., Journals, 605 Third Ave., New York, NY 10158-0012. TEL 212-850-6645. FAX 212-850-6021. E-mail: subinfo@jwiley.com. (Subscr. outside the Americas to: John Wiley & Sons Ltd., Baffins Ln., Chichester, W. Sussex PO19 1UD, England. TEL 44-1243-779777. FAX 44-1243-776128) (back issues avail.) **Document type:** academic/scholarly publication.

910.09 UK ISSN 0952-5424
G155.A1
PROGRESS IN TOURISM, RECREATION AND HOSPITALITY MANAGEMENT. 1989. a. £39 (typically set in June). John Wiley & Sons Ltd., Journals, Baffin's Ln., Chichester, W. Sussex PO19 1UD, England. TEL 01243-779777. FAX 01243-776128. TELEX 86290-WIBOOK-G. Ed. C.I. Stevenson. bk.rev.; bibl.; index. circ. 1,200. Indexed: Art.Hosp.& Tour. **Document type:** academic/scholarly publication.
  —BLDSC (6924.608300).
  Description: Reviews research in tourism and related fields, with emphasis on the fields rapidly advancing and of international importance.

PROMENADE. see *GENERAL INTEREST PERIODICALS — United States*

PROMOBIL. see *TRANSPORTATION — Automobiles*

PROMOBIL KATALOG. see *TRANSPORTATION — Automobiles*

910.4 PO
PUBLITURIS; jornal da industria do turismo. 1968. s-m. Esc.2000($35) Publiotel Ltd, Rua Marechal Sandanha, 4-1, 1200 Lisbon, Portugal. TEL 3475201. FAX 327718. TELEX 64440 NEWS P. Ed. Joao Constantino. adv. circ. 8,000.
  Description: Covers various areas of travel and tourism, includes air transport, hotels, meetings and incentives.

PUERTO RICO LIVING. see *GENERAL INTEREST PERIODICALS — Puerto Rico*

TRAVEL AND TOURISM 6491

910.09 US ISSN 1053-3842
PUNCH IN INTERNATIONAL TRAVEL AND ENTERTAINMENT MAGAZINE. 1970. m. $100 (typically set in Nov.). Enterprises Publishing, 400 E. 59th St., Ste.9F, New York, NY 10022. TEL 212-755-4363. FAX 212-755-4365. Ed. Jerome Walman. circ. 650,000. (back issues avail.) **Document type:** consumer publication.
●Also available online.
Also available on CD-ROM.

PUNGOLO DEL SUD; periodico di cronache mediterranee. see *GENERAL INTEREST PERIODICALS — Italy*

Q T DIRECTORY. (Quality Travel) see *BUSINESS AND ECONOMICS — Trade And Industrial Directories*

QUADERNI DE "LA TERRA SANTA". see *RELIGIONS AND THEOLOGY*

910.9 IT
QUALITYTRAVEL MAGAZINE; rivista di congressi - viaggi - incentive per l'uomo d'affari. (Text in Italian; summaries in English) 1986. bi-m. (8/yr.). L.180000 (effective 1995). Promos Edizioni s.r.l., Corso di Porta Romana 122, 20122 Milan, Italy. TEL 39-2-58314981. FAX 39-2-58314993. Ed. Luciano Ferrari; Pub. Roberto Angri. adv.: B&W page L.3500000, color page L.5000000; adv. contact: Claudia Fossati. bk.rev. circ. 9,000. **Document type:** trade publication.
Description: Deals with congresses, incentive travel and business travel. Distributed to Italian PCO and corporate meeting planners and event organizers.

916.8 SA
QUARTERLY REVIEW. Variant title: Satour Quarterly Review. 1992. q. Satour, Private Bag X164, Pretoria 0001, South Africa. **Document type:** government publication.
Description: Covers topics relating to domestic and international tourism, Satour activities and other developments of interest.

388.3 796.7 BL ISSN 0033-5908
QUATRO RODAS. 1960. m. $130. Editora Abril, S.A., R. Geraldo Flausino Gomes, 61, 04573-900 Sao Paulo SP, Brazil. TEL 011-534-5347. FAX 011-5051700. (Subscr. to: Rua do Curtume, 769, 05065-900 Sao Paulo SP, Brazil. TEL 011-823-9100) Ed. Jorge Tarquini. adv.; charts; illus.; stat.; index. circ. 250,000. **Document type:** consumer publication.
Description: For the auto enthusiast, contains exclusive tests, technological advances, price tables for new and used cars, insurance information, competition news, and travel.

917 PR
QUE PASA; official visitors guide to Puerto Rico. 1948. q. free. Tourism Company of Puerto Rico, Box 4435, Old San Juan Sta., San Juan, PR 00905. FAX 809-721-3878. Ed. Mary Anne Hopgood. adv. contact: Linda Anne Stockton. charts; illus. circ. 320,000. **Document type:** consumer publication.
Formerly: Que Pasa in Puerto Rico (ISSN 0048-623X)

QUE SAVOIR; industrie-commerce-tourisme. see *BUSINESS AND ECONOMICS*

910.2 AT ISSN 0725-6264
QUEENSLAND TOURIST AND TRAVEL CORPORATION. ANNUAL REPORT. 1980. a. free. Queensland Tourist and Travel Corporation, 123 Eagle St., G.P.O. Box 328, Brisbane, Qld. 4001, Australia. illus. circ. 400.

QUERCY MAGAZINE; magazines de France. see *GENERAL INTEREST PERIODICALS — France*

910.2 FR ISSN 0048-6450
QUEYRAS. 1971. 3/yr. 24 F. Courier du Queyras, Rt. de la Gare, 05600 Guillestre, France. FAX 92-45-27-20. Ed. Alain Bayrou. adv.; bk.rev.; charts; illus. circ. 2,000.

910.2 IT ISSN 0042-546X
QUI TOURING. 1971. m. L.3800 to non-members; membership. (Touring Club Italiano) Touring Periodici s.r.l., Corso Italia 10, 20122 Milan, Italy. TEL 02-85261. TELEX 321160. Ed. Giuseppe Bozzini. adv.: B&W page L.22000000, color page L.27500000. bk.rev. circ. 510,000.
Supersedes: Vie d'Italia.

910 FR ISSN 1152-8729
QUOTIDIEN DU TOURISME. 180/yr. 40-42 bd. Jean Jaures, 92110 Clichy, France. TEL 47-37-53-86. FAX 47-37-23-83. Ed. Pierre Doulcet. circ. 10,000.

910.202 UK
R A C EUROPEAN HOTEL GUIDE. 1932. a. £9.99. (Royal Automobile Club) R A C Publishing, R A C House, P.O. Box 100, South Croydon, Surrey CR2 6XW, England. TEL 081-686-0088. FAX 081-688-2882. adv. **Document type:** directory.
Former titles: R A C Continental Hotel Guide; (until 1986): R A C Continental Handbook and Hotel Guide; R A C Continental Motoring Guide; (until 1982): R A C Continental Handbook.

796.77 UK
R A C HOTEL GUIDE GREAT BRITAIN & IRELAND. 1904. a. £12.99. (Royal Automobile Club) R A C Publishing, R A C House, P.O. Box 100, South Croydon, Surrey CR2 6XW, England. TEL 081-686-0088. FAX 081-688-2882.
Former titles: R A C Hotel Guide; (until 1986): R A C Handbook and Hotel Guide; (until 1985): R A C Guide and Handbook.

R A C MOTOR SPORTS YEAR BOOK. see *SPORTS AND GAMES*

910.4 GW
R B LUFTFAHRT MARKETING. 1967. 60/yr. DM.480($390) R B Redaktions Buero, Schraemelstr. 126, 81247 Munich, Germany. TEL 089-88888888. FAX 089-882686. Ed. Hans Nechleba. adv. contact: Erika Nechleba. circ. 1,150. (looseleaf format; back issues avail.) **Document type:** trade publication.

910.09 GW
R B MARKETING; der Graue Newsletter. 1967. 60/yr. DM.480($300) R B Marketing, Schraemelstr. 126, 81247 Munich, Germany. TEL 089-88888888. FAX 089-882686. Ed. Hans N. Nechleba. adv.: B&W page DM.720; trim 275 x 188; adv. contact: E. Waldmann. bk.rev. circ. 1,100. **Document type:** newsletter.

910.4 GW
R B REISEBUERO-MARKETING & HOTEL-MARKETING. (Supplement avail.: R B Congress Marketing) 1967. 60/yr. DM.480. R B Redaktions Buero, Schraemelstr. 126, 81247 Munich, Germany. TEL 089-88888888. FAX 089-882686. Ed. Hans Nechleba. **Document type:** trade publication.
Formerly: R B Hotel Marketing.

796.6 CN
R V TIMES. (Recreational Vehicle) 6/yr. Can.$15. Sheila Jones Publishing Ltd., 33154 7th Ave., Mission, BC V2V 2E1, Canada. TEL 604-826-4249. FAX 604-826-1999. Ed. Sheila Jones. adv.; bk.rev.; circ. 45,000 (controlled).
Description: Includes events of interest in BC and Washington state, camping stories, repair tips and general RV and camping information.

910.202 388.2 US ISSN 1041-9772
R V WEST. 1976. m. $13.99. Vernon Publications Inc., 3000 Northrup Way, Ste. 200, Bellevue, WA 98004. TEL 800-700-6962. FAX 206-827-9900. Ed. Michele Andrus Dill. adv. circ. 25,000. (back issues avail.) **Document type:** consumer publication.
Former titles (until Nov. **1988**): Western R V Traveler; (until 1985): California Traveler.
Description: Dedicated to the recreational vehicle lifestyle.

385 NE ISSN 0923-7690
RAILS. 1951. m. fl.62.50. (Nederlandse Spoorwegen) Multi Magazines bv, Prinsengracht 659, 1016 HV Amsterdam, Netherlands. Ed. C. Bauer. adv.; rec.rev.; illus.; tr.lit.
Formerly (until 1989): Tussen de Rails (ISSN 0041-4379)

910.09 385.26 US ISSN 1048-9076
RAILWAYS. q. Parlor Car Press, Box 10396, Glendale, CA 91209-3396. TEL 818-500-0542. FAX 818-247-9671. Ed. Vincent Prest. circ. 1,100.

910.09 IO
RAJAWALI.* m. Jalan Pelepah Hijan IVTN, V14-15 Kelapa Gading Permai, Jakarte 14240, Indonesia. Ed. Karyono Adhy.

910.202 330 US
RAND MCNALLY BUSINESS TRAVELER'S ROAD ATLAS; and trip planner. a. $9.95. Rand McNally & Co., 8255 N. Central Park, Skokie, IL 60076. TEL 708-673-9100. (Subscr. to: Box 7600, Chicago, IL 60680) Ed. Virginia O'Neill.

910.202 US
RAND MCNALLY ROAD ATLAS. 1924. a. $8.95. Rand McNally & Co., 8255 N. Central Park Ave., Skokie, IL 60076. TEL 708-329-8100; 800-284-6565. (Subscr. to: Box 32, Skokie, IL 60075) adv.

910.202 US
RAND MCNALLY ROAD ATLAS & VACATION GUIDE; United States, Canada, Mexico. a. $18.95. Rand McNally & Co., 8255 N. Central Park, Skokie, IL 60076. TEL 708-673-9100. (Subscr. to: Box 7600, Chicago, IL 60680) Ed. Virginia O'Neill.

910.202 914.04 US
RAND MCNALLY ROAD ATLAS OF EUROPE. a. $11.95. Rand McNally & Co., 8255 N. Central Park, Skokie, IL 60076. TEL 708-673-9100. (Subscr. to: Box 7600, Chicago, IL 60680) Ed. Virginia O'Neill. illus.

917 US ISSN 1058-448X
RECOMMEND: MAGAZINE. 1967. m. $48. Worth International Communications Corp., 5979 N.W. 151st St., Ste. 120, Miami Lakes, FL 33014. TEL 800-447-0123. FAX 305-826-6950. Pub. Laural A. Herman. adv. contact: Terry Murphy. circ. 60,000. (processed) **Document type:** trade publication.
Formerly: Recommend: Florida (ISSN 0034-1452)

910.2 914 UK ISSN 0267-3428
RECOMMENDED COUNTRY HOTELS OF BRITAIN. 1973. a. £3.60. F H G Publications Ltd., Abbey Mill Business Centre, Seedhill, Paisley PA1 1JN, Scotland. TEL 0141-887-0428. FAX 0141-889-7204. Ed. Peter Clark. **Document type:** consumer publication.

917.504 647 US ISSN 1078-5523
RECOMMENDED COUNTRY INNS: MID-ATLANTIC AND CHESAPEAKE REGION. 1989. biennial. $14.95. Globe Pequot Press, Box 833, Old Saybrook, CT 06475. TEL 203-395-0440. FAX 203-395-1418. Ed. Brenda Boelts Chapin.
Formerly: Guide to the Recommended Country Inns of the Mid-Atlantic States.
Description: Presents more than 200 of the finest inn residences of the region.

917.404 647 US ISSN 1047-4668
TX907
RECOMMENDED COUNTRY INNS: NEW ENGLAND. 1974. biennial. $14.95. Globe Pequot Press, Box 833, Old Saybrook, CT 06475. TEL 203-395-0440. FAX 203-395-1418. Ed. Elizabeth Squier.
Formerly (until 1987): Guide to the Recommended Country Inns of New England (ISSN 0093-4585)
Description: Provides more than 220 descriptive entries of only the very finest inns.

917.804 647 US ISSN 1078-5485
RECOMMENDED COUNTRY INNS: ROCKY MOUNTAIN REGION. 1989. biennial. $14.95. Globe Pequot Press, Box 833, Old Saybrook, CT 06475. TEL 203-395-0440. FAX 203-395-1418. Ed. Doris Kennedy.
Formerly: Guide to the Recommended Country Inns of the Rocky Mountain Region.
Description: Reviews more than 170 getaways in the region. Includes information on recreational activities in the area.

917.704 647 US ISSN 1078-5507
RECOMMENDED COUNTRY INNS: THE MIDWEST. 1989. biennial. $14.95. Globe Pequot Press, Box 833, Old Saybrook, CT 06475. TEL 203-395-0440. FAX 203-395-1418. Ed. Bob Puhala.
Formerly: Guide to the Recommended Country Inns of the Midwest.
Description: Profiles 210 inns in the nation's heartland.

917.604 647 US ISSN 1078-5493
RECOMMENDED COUNTRY INNS: THE SOUTH. biennial. $14.95. Globe Pequot Press, Box 833, Old Saybrook, CT 06475. TEL 203-395-0440. FAX 203-395-1418. Ed. Sara Pitzer.
Formerly: Guide to the Recommended Country Inns of the South.
Description: Profiles 165 gracious lodgings, from rustic cottages to sprawling country estates.

6492   TRAVEL AND TOURISM

917.904 647 US ISSN 1078-5515
RECOMMENDED COUNTRY INNS: THE SOUTHWEST. 1991. biennial. $14.95. Globe Pequot Press, Box 833, Old Saybrook, CT 06475. TEL 203-395-0440. FAX 203-395-1418. Ed. Eleanor S. Morris.
 Formerly: Guide to the Recommended Country Inns of Arizona, New Mexico, and Texas.
 Description: Profiles 190 country inns in Arizona, New Mexico and Texas.

917.904 647 US ISSN 1078-5531
RECOMMENDED COUNTRY INNS: THE WEST COAST. biennial. $14.95. Globe Pequot Press, Box 833, Old Saybrook, CT 06475. TEL 203-395-0440. FAX 203-395-1418. Ed. Julianne Belote.
 Formerly: Guide to the Recommended Country Inns of the West Coast.
 Description: Provides more than 210 detailed descriptions of great lodgings in the Pacific states.

917.04 US ISSN 1078-554X
RECOMMENDED ROMANTIC INNS OF AMERICA. 1992. biennial. $14.95. Globe Pequot Press, Box 833, Old Saybrook, CT 06475-0833. TEL 203-395-0440. FAX 203-395-1418.
 Description: Profiles delightful inns selected for their romantic settings.

914 UK
RECOMMENDED SHORT BREAK HOLIDAYS. a. £3.60. F H G Publications Ltd., Abbey Mill Business Centre, Seedhill, Paisley PA1 1JN, Scotland. TEL 0141-887-0428. FAX 0141-889-7204. Ed. Peter Clark. Document type: consumer publication.
 Formerly: Mini-Break Holidays in Britain (ISSN 0267-341X)

910.2 914 UK ISSN 0080-0252
RECOMMENDED WAYSIDE INNS OF BRITAIN. 1962. a. £3.60. F H G Publications Ltd., Abbey Mill Business Centre, Seedhill, Paisley PA1 1JN, Scotland. TEL 0141-887-0428. FAX 0141-889-7204. Ed. Peter Clark. Document type: consumer publication.

RECREATION ADVISOR. see *LEISURE AND RECREATION*

910 796 US ISSN 1056-9294
RECREATION NEWS. m. $12. Icarus Publishers, Inc., Box 32335, Washington, DC 20007-0635. TEL 202-965-6960. Ed. M.M. Ghannam. adv. circ. 104,000. (tabloid format) Document type: newspaper.

914 SZ
REGION DU LEMAN. 34/yr. Agence Neumann, CH-1113 St. Saphorin-sur-Morges, Switzerland. TEL 021-8011120. circ. 9,917.

910.202 GW
REISE-DIENST. a. DM.5. Stuenings Verlagsgesellschaft mbH, Luisenstr. 100-104, 47799 Krefeld, Germany. TEL 02151-853-0. FAX 02151-853103. circ. 1,000. Document type: consumer publication.

910.202 AU
REISE UND CAMPING. 4/yr. W. Rothmueller, Lerchenfelderquertel 25, 1160 Vienna, Austria. adv. circ. 25,000.

910.202 GW ISSN 0932-4186
REISE UND PREISE; magazine of air travel and vacation planning. 1987. q. DM.24 (foreign DM.32). Reise und Preise Verlags GmbH, Rudolf-Diesel-Str. 4, 21614 Buxtehude, Germany. TEL 04161-7169-0. FAX 04161-716915. Ed. Oliver Kuehn. adv.: B&W page DM.4150, color page DM.8350; trim 270 x 186. bk.rev. circ. 46,500. (back issues avail.) Document type: consumer publication.

910.09 GW
REISEBUERO BULLETIN; weekly news for the German travel trade. 1967. w. DM.32. Bulletin Verlag GmbH, Roentgenstr. 80, 64291 Darmstadt, Germany. TEL 06151-374066. FAX 06151-370114. Ed. Michael Knuth. adv. circ. 15,085. (back issues avail.) Document type: trade publication.
 Description: Features all aspects of travel such as hotels, tourism, airline information, travel agency news and events.

910.09 GW ISSN 0177-4050
REISEFIEBER; das nuetzliche Reisemagazin. 1985. bi-m. DM.29.40. Hayit Verlag GmbH, Hansaring 82, 50670 Cologne, Germany. TEL 0221-912846-0. FAX 0221-132967. Ed. Ertay Hayit. adv.: bk.rev. circ. 47,000. (back issues avail.) Document type: consumer publication.
 Description: Provides practical and useful information on travel to destinations throughout the world.

910.202 GW
REISEFUHRER - WOHIN IN BERLIN; internationaler Fremdenverkehr. 1950. a. Commerzia Verlag GmbH, Oxfordstr. 9, 53111 Bonn, Germany. Ed. Horst Borchardt.

910 AU
REISEMAGAZIN. 10/yr. Einsiedlerplatz 4, A-1050 Vienna, Austria. TEL 01-547516. FAX 01-547245. Ed. Peter Nemeskal. circ. 50,000.

910.202 GW ISSN 0177-2953
REISEN IN DEUTSCHLAND: REISEFUEHRER. 1949. a. DM.36.80. Jaeger Verlag GmbH, Arhellger Weg 17, 64380 Rossdorf, Germany. TEL 06154-6995-01. FAX 06154-6995490. TELEX 4191324-DAV-D. Ed. Guenter Hulwa. circ. 15,000. Document type: directory.

910.2 GW
REISEN IN DEUTSCHLAND: ZIMMERKATALOG. 1925. a. DM.34.80. Jaeger Verlag GmbH, Arhellger Weg 17, 64380 Rossdorf, Germany. TEL 06154-6995-01. FAX 06154-6995490. TELEX 4191324-DAV-D. adv. Document type: directory.
 Former titles: Zimmerkatalog; Reisen in Deutschland; Deutsches Handbuch fuer Fremdenverkehr: Volume 2 (ISSN 0177-2961)

910.202 GW ISSN 0936-627X
REISEN UND LEBEN. 1980. s-a. DM.18. Verlag Ursula Hinrichsen, Postfach 1451, 37594 Holzminden, Germany. Ed. Alex W. Hinrichsen. adv.; bk.rev. circ. 500.
 Description: Looks at the history of tourism and of tour guides.

910.202 340.5 GW ISSN 0944-7490
REISERECHT AKTUELL. 1993. m. DM.128. Luchterhand Verlag, Heddesdorferstr. 31, 56564 Neuwied, Germany. TEL 02631-801-0. FAX 02631-801210. Ed. Christiane Bachmann. adv.: page DM.500; adv. contact: Christiane Bachmann. cum.index. (back issues avail.) Document type: trade publication.

914.806 GW
REISEWEG ISLAND - GROENLAND - FAEROEER. a. DM.9.80. Fie Verlag GmbH, Spaldingstr. 210, 20097 Hamburg, Germany. TEL 040-230696. FAX 040-234613. Ed. Gerd Achilles. adv. contact: Anja Barenscher. circ. 30,000. Document type: consumer publication.
 Formerly: Reiseweg nach Island.

914.806 GW
REISEWEGE SKANDINAVIEN. 1954. a. DM.9.80. Fie Verlag GmbH, Spaldingstr. 210, 20097 Hamburg, Germany. TEL 040-230696. FAX 040-234613. Ed. Gerd Achilles. adv. contact: Anja Barenscher. circ. 60,000. Document type: consumer publication.
 Former titles: Reiseweg nach Skandinavien; Fahren nach Skandinavien.

910.09 GW
REISEZIELE; Landkarten, Reisefuehrer, Bildbaende, mit vielen touristischen Tips. 1970. a. GeoCenter Verlagsvertrieb GmbH, Neumarkterstr. 18, 81673 Munich, Germany. TEL 089-43189-505. FAX 089-43189555. Document type: consumer publication.

338 BE
REISKRANT. (Text in Dutch) 1981. bi-m. 750 BEF (effective 1995 & 1996). Wegwijzer v.z.w., Beenhouwersstraat 24, 8000 Brugge, Belgium. TEL 32-50-332178. FAX 32-50-345983. Ed. Joris Verbeure. adv.: B&W page 20000 BEF; adv. contact: Randi Roose. illus. circ. 15,000. Document type: consumer publication.

910.09 NE
REISREVUE; het toeristisch vakblad. 17/yr. fl.75 (1550 BEF). Misset (Subsidiary of: Reed Elsevier plc), Postbus 4, 7000 BA Doetinchem, Netherlands. TEL 31-8340-49911. FAX 31-8340-43839. adv.: B&W page fl.2855; trim 215 x 285; adv. contact: Cor van Nek. illus. circ. 14,500. Document type: trade publication.
 Description: Covers all aspects of the travel industry in the Netherlands.

910.2 NE
REISVAKADRESBOEK. a. fl.49.50 (free with subscr. to Reisvakmagazine DIT). Nijgh Periodieken B.V., Postbus 122, 3100 AC Schiedam, Netherlands. TEL 31-10-4274100. FAX 31-10-4739911. adv.; B&W page fl.1730, color page fl.3242; trim 148 x 210; adv. contact: Bert Niewold. circ. 4,000. Document type: directory.

910.2 NE
REISVAKMAGAZINE D I T. (Documentatie en Informatie over Toerisme) 1959. fortn. fl.130. Nijgh Periodieken B.V., Postbus 122, 3100 AC Schiedam, Netherlands. TEL 31-10-4271400. FAX 31-10-4739911. adv.: B&W page fl.1765, color page fl.3115; trim 210 x 297; adv. contact: Bert Niewold. bk.rev.; illus.; stat. circ. 3,800. Indexed: Key to Econ.Sci. Document type: trade publication.
 —SWETS.
 Formerly: D I T (ISSN 0012-4109)

910 NE ISSN 0921-0032
REIZEN. 1937. m. fl.102 to non-members. Koninklijke Nederlandse Toeristenbond ANWB - Royal Dutch Touring Club, Wassenaarseweg 220, Postbus 93200, 2509 BA The Hague, Netherlands. TEL 31-70-3146119. FAX 31-70-3242509. Ed. M. Bisschops. adv.: B&W page fl.3504, color page fl.6307; trim 215 x 285; adv. contact: J.W. Boersen. illus. circ. 55,100. Indexed: Key to Econ.Sci. Document type: consumer publication.
 —SWETS.
 Formerly (until 1986): Toeristenkampioen (ISSN 0165-4225)
 Description: For adventurous and well-to-do tourists

910.09 DK ISSN 0108-6812
REJSEBOGEN (YEAR); muligheder for ophold i udlandet af kortere eller laengere varighed. 1983. a. DKK 97. Forlaget Nuna, Fasanvej 3, 9670 Loegstoer, Denmark. Ed. Georg Harmsen. adv.; bk.rev. circ. 8,000.

915.1 JA
REKISHI TO TABI/HISTORY AND TRAVEL. (Text in Japanese) 1974. m. 5400 Yen. Akita Shoten Publishing Co. Ltd., 10-8, 2-chome, Iidabashi, Tokyo 102, Japan. Ed. Toru Suzuki.

910.202 FR
RELAIS ROUTIERS. 1934. m. 85 Fr. Societe d'Exploitation de Journeaux Techniques, 6 rue de l'Isly, 75008 Paris, France. TEL 43-87-61-68. FAX 43-87-50-46. Ed. Patrice de Saulieu. adv.; bk.rev. circ. 4,500.

910.09 US
RELAX; the travel magazine for practicing physicians. 1984. m. $60 (effective 1993). Advanstar Communications, Inc., 7500 Old Oak Blvd., Cleveland, OH 44130. TEL 216-826-2839. FAX 216-891-2726. (Subscr. to: 1 E. First St., Duluth, MN 55802. TEL 800-346-0085) Ed. Mary Kay Stray. index. circ. 115,174. (back issues avail.) Document type: trade publication.
 Description: Travel and recreation news for physicians.

RELEVE. see *POLITICAL SCIENCE*

917.1 CN
RENDEZ-VOUS CANADA. 1981. a. Baxter Publishing Co., 310 Dupont St., Toronto, ON M5R 1V9, Canada. TEL 416-968-7252. FAX 416-968-2377. Ed. Edith Baxter. adv. Document type: trade publication.

910.2 FR ISSN 0034-4575
REPERTOIRE DES VOYAGES/TRAVEL TRADE REPERTORY; international travel trade magazine. (Text in French) 1948. Editions Touristiques Internationales, 1 cite Bergere, 75009 Paris, France. adv. circ. 8,300.

TRAVEL AND TOURISM

910 II ISSN 0378-7478
RESEARCH IN TOURISM. q. Rs.400($80) K.K. Roy (Private) Ltd., 55 Gariahat Rd., P.O. Box 10210, Calcutta 700 019, India. Ed. Kuldip Kumar Roy. —BLDSC (7773.721000).

910 647.9 SW ISSN 0284-6853
RESETIDNINGEN VAGABOND. Variant title: Vagabond. 1987. 10/yr. SEK 295; newsstand price: SEK 43. Vagabond, Resetidningen, P.O. Box 201 23, S-104 60 Stockholm, Sweden. TEL 46-8-462-93-19. FAX 46-8-462-02-19. Ed. Christian Nyreroed. adv.: B&W page SEK 18800, color page SEK 25400; Trim 190 x 250; adv. contact: Kerstin Wilson. circ. 45,000. cols./p.: 4; pp./issue: 108. **Document type:** consumer publication.

910.202 CN
RESORT WEEKLY. 1989. 13/yr. (w. May-Aug.) Can.$25. South East Press Ltd., 521 Main St., P.O. Box 329, Kipling, SK S0G 2S0, Canada. TEL 306-736-2535. FAX 306-736-8445. Ed. G. Scott. adv. contact: G. Scott Kearns. circ. 3,000. **Document type:** newspaper.
 Description: Reports on weekly happenings and serves as an entertainment and shopping guide.

338 US ISSN 0897-5833
RESORTS & GREAT HOTELS. 1987. a. $15. R & R Publishing Co., 123 W. Padre St., Santa Barbara, CA 93105. TEL 805-687-1422. FAX 805-682-8634. Ed. Annette Burden. adv.; illus. circ. 120,000. (back issues avail.) **Document type:** consumer publication.
 Description: Profiles luxury hotels and resorts around the world.

910.09 US ISSN 0193-4341
G153
RETIREMENT PARADISES OF THE WORLD. biennial. $4.95. Harian Publications, One Vernon Ave, Floral Park, NY 11001. TEL 516-437-3440. Ed. Norman D. Ford. illus.
 Superseded: Bargain Paradises of the World (ISSN 0408-568X)

918 EC
REVISTA DINERS. 1979. m. $40. (Ecuadorian Diners Club) Dinediciones S.A., Av. Gonzalez Suarez 335 y San Ignacio, Quito, Ecuador. TEL 505525. Ed. Jorge Ortiz. adv. contact: Yolanda Arroyo. bk.rev. circ. 45,000.

791.4 LU ISSN 0035-0729
REVUE; Letzeburger illustreiert (Luxembourg's weekly magazine). (Incl. supplement Tele Revue) (Text in German) 1945. w. 2600 Fr. Editions Revue S.A., B.P. 2755, 1027 Luxembourg, Luxembourg. TEL 45-41-51. FAX 45-88-74. Ed. Yolande Kieffer; Pub. Guy Ludig. adv.; bk.rev.; film rev.; abstr.; illus.; stat. circ. 29,000. **Document type:** newspaper.

REVUE GENERALE DE L'HOTELLERIE, DE LA GASTRONOMIE ET DU TOURISME. see *HOTELS AND RESTAURANTS*

971 CN
RICE LAKE VACATION GUIDE. 1956. a. Can.$3. Clay Publishing Co. Ltd., One Oak St., Bewdley, Ont. K0L 1E0, Canada. TEL 416-797-2281. Ed. Charlotte Clay. adv. (back issues avail.)

RIDER; motorcycle touring & sport touring. see *SPORTS AND GAMES — Bicycles And Motorcycles*

910 IT
RIVIERA ECO. 1962. w. free. Viale dei Mille 14, Riccione, Italy. Ed. Costantino Zangheri. adv. circ. 100,000.

ROAD AHEAD. see *TRANSPORTATION — Automobiles*

ROAD RIDER; America's first motorcycle touring magazine. see *SPORTS AND GAMES — Bicycles And Motorcycles*

333.78 US
ROAD SMART. 1964. q. $5 to non-members. Amoco Enterprises, Inc., Amoco Motor Club, 200 E. Randolph Dr., Chicago, IL 60601-0607. TEL 810-558-7275. FAX 810-558-5897. Ed. Michael Brudenell. adv.; bk.rev.; illus.; tr.lit.; circ. 1,500,000 (controlled).
 Formerly: Adventure Road (ISSN 0001-8805)

ROBERT NOAH'S PARIS EN CUISINE NEWSLETTER; the insider's guide to gastronomic news of France. see *FOOD AND FOOD INDUSTRIES*

910 US ISSN 0273-6772
ROCKY MOUNTAIN MOTORIST. 1926. m. membership. (American Automobile Association) Rocky Mountain Motorists, Inc., 4100 E. Arkansas Ave., Denver, CO 80222. TEL 303-753-8800. FAX 303-758-8515. Ed. Barbara Bauerle. adv. circ. 224,000. **Document type:** consumer publication.
 —UnCover.

RODALE'S SCUBA DIVING. see *SPORTS AND GAMES — Outdoor Life*

790.13 US ISSN 0896-7261
ROLLER COASTER!. 1978. q. $50. American Coaster Enthusiasts, Box 352, Penfield, NY 14526. TEL 716-381-1012. Ed. Paul L. Ruben. adv.; bk.rev.; charts; illus.; cum.index: 1978-1988; circ. 4,000 (paid). (back issues avail.) **Document type:** consumer publication.
 Description: Contains roller coaster-related articles, pictures, history, and news.

914.7 RM ISSN 1221-0692
ROMANIA PITOREASCA; revista de supravietuire prin turism si inteligenta. English edition: Holidays in Romania. (Supplement avail.: Montana (ISSN 1221-0684)) (Editions in English, French, German, Rumanian) 1958. m. 60 lei ($20) Ministerul Turismului - Ministry of Tourism, Gabriel Peri Str. 8, 70148 Bucharest, Rumania. TEL 6597893. (Subscr. to: Rodipet S.A., Piata Presei Libere nr. 1, Bucharest Sector 1, Rumania) Ed. Pop Simion. adv.; bk.rev.; charts; illus. circ. 32,000.

910.09 US ISSN 1053-0177
ROMANTIC TRAVELING. 1989. q. $20 (effective 1995-1996). Moonlight Partners, 448 Ignacio Blvd., No. 225, Novato, CA 94949. TEL 415-883-5198. FAX 415-883-5199. Ed. Carolyn Koening; Pub. Diane Brady. bk.rev.; circ. 1,000 (paid). (back issues avail.) **Document type:** newsletter.
 Formerly (until 1990): Travel Publishing News (ISSN 1043-6138)
 Description: Helps couples intensify their relationship through travel destinations covered throughout the world.

914.504 US ISSN 1056-442X
ROME (YEAR). a. $12. Harper Collins Publishers, Birnbaum Travel Guides, 10 E. 53rd St., New York, NY 10022-5299. TEL 212-207-7542. Ed. Alexandra Mayes Birnbaum. illus.; index.

ROUERGUE MAGAZINE; magazines de France. see *GENERAL INTEREST PERIODICALS — France*

ROYAL TEHRAN HILTON. see *HOTELS AND RESTAURANTS*

ROYALAUTO. see *TRANSPORTATION — Automobiles*

910.09 US
RUNAWAY. 1971. q. Travel Publications, Inc., Box 610, Alta Loma, CA 91701. FAX 714-944-9274. Ed. Robert R. Hill. adv.; bk.rev.; circ. 267,000 (controlled).

RUNZHEIMER ON CARS & LIVING COSTS. see *TRANSPORTATION — Automobiles*

RUNZHEIMER REPORTS ON RELOCATION. see *BUSINESS AND ECONOMICS — Personnel Management*

RUNZHEIMER REPORTS ON TRAVEL MANAGEMENT. see *BUSINESS AND ECONOMICS — Personnel Management*

388.3 US ISSN 0036-0171
HE5623.A1
RUSSELL'S OFFICIAL NATIONAL MOTOR COACH GUIDE; official publications of bus lines for United States and Canada. Title varies: Official Bus Guide. 1908. m. $97 (Canada $117.17; elsewhere $110.80) (effective 1995-1996). Russell's Guides, Inc., 834 Third Ave., S.E., Box 278, Cedar Rapids, IA 52403. TEL 319-364-6138. FAX 319-364-4853. Ed. Gary Widel. adv.; charts; maps; circ. 14,000 (paid). **Document type:** trade publication.

914.7 658 US
RUSSIA AND CHINA NEWS. 1979. w. $62. International Intertrade Index, Box 636 Federal Sq., Newark, NJ 07101. TEL 908-686-2382. Ed. John E. Felber. bk.rev.; pat.; stat.; tr.lit. (looseleaf format; back issues avail.) **Document type:** newsletter.
 Former titles: Russia and East Travel News; (until 1993): C I S Soviet Travel Newsletter (ISSN 1059-4957)
 Description: News on travel, transportation, hotels, restaurants, marketing and media.

915.04 AT ISSN 1321-2923
RUSSIA, SIBERIA, MONGOLIA AND NORTH KOREA TRAVEL NEWS. 1992. q. $15. Red Bear Tours, 320B Glenferrie Rd., Malvern, Vic. 3144, Australia. TEL 61-3-824-7183. FAX 61-3-822-3956. Ed. Athol Yates. adv. circ. 1,800.
 Formerly (until 1993): Russian Travel News (ISSN 1320-1670)
 Description: Provides travel news, tips and options for independent travellers, students and special interest groups.

S A MOTOR. see *TRANSPORTATION — Automobiles*

910.202 US
S A T H NEWS. 1978. q. membership. Society for the Advancement of Travel for the Handicapped, 347 Fifth Ave., Ste.610, New York, NY 10016. TEL 212-447-7284. FAX 212-725-8253. Ed. Laura Van Horn. bk.rev.; circ. 1,000 (controlled). (tabloid format; back issues avail.) **Document type:** newsletter.
 Description: Contains travel and tourism information as it relates to the handicapped population.

S J - NYTT. (Statens Jaernvaegars Huvudkontor) see *TRANSPORTATION — Railroads*

910.202 VI
ST. CROIX THIS WEEK. 1960. m. This Week Publishing, Inc., P.O. Box 1627, St. Thomas, VI 00804. TEL 809-774-2500.
 Description: For the tourist market.

914 SZ ISSN 0036-2832
ST. GALLEN; St. Gallen Aktuell - Tourist Information. (Text in English, French, German) 1946. w. 30 SFr.($2) Tourist Information St. Gallen, Postfach 2242, Bahnhofplatz 1a, CH-9001 St. Gallen, Switzerland. TEL 071-226262. FAX 071-234304. adv. circ. 5,500 (controlled). **Document type:** bulletin.

917.704 US
ST. LOUIS POCKET GUIDE. 1991. q. Pocket Guide Publications, Inc., 9650 Clayton Rd., St. Louis, MO 63124. TEL 314-991-5222. Ed. Jackson D. Waterbury. adv.: B&W page $1400, color page $2000; trim 5 x 7 3/8. circ. 250,000 (controlled). **Document type:** consumer publication.
 Formerly: Visitor's Pocket Guide to St. Louis.
 Description: Lists places to go, things to do, history and significant information about the area.

910.202 VI
ST. THOMAS THIS WEEK. 1960. w. This Week Publishing, Inc., P.O. Box 1627, St. Thomas, VI 00804. TEL 809-774-2500. Ed. Margot Macdonald Bachman.
 Description: For the tourist market.

914.04 GW
SALES GUIDE TO GERMANY. (Editions in English and Japanese) 1971. a. (German National Tourist Office) Redaktion fuer Wirtschaftspublizistik, Heidelbergerstr. 33, 64285 Darmstadt, Germany. TEL 06151-3990-0. FAX 06151-399022. **Document type:** catalog.

910.4 GW
SAMMLUNG DENKWUERDIGER REISEN. 1988. a. DM.29.80. Edition Temmen, Hohenlohestr. 21, 28209 Bremen, Germany. TEL 0421-344280. FAX 0421-348094. **Document type:** bulletin.

917.904 US
SAN DIEGAN. 1969. a. $1.95. San Diego Guide, Inc., 6370 Lusk Blvd., No.F-202, San Diego, CA 92121-2754. TEL 619-453-1633. FAX 619-453-2332. Ed. Deborah Craig. adv.; cum.index. circ. 175,000. **Document type:** consumer publication.
 Description: Covers San Diego, Baja California, Mexico, Arizona, and Orange County.

6494 TRAVEL AND TOURISM

917.904 US ISSN 1056-4403
IN PROCESS
SAN FRANCISCO (YEAR). a. $12. Harper Collins Publishers, Birnbaum Travel Guides, 10 E. 53rd St., New York, NY 10022-5299. TEL 212-207-7542. Ed. Alexandra Mayes Birnbaum. illus.; index.

917.904 US
SAN FRANCISCO BOOK. 1984. q. San Francisco Convention & Visitors Bureau, 201 Third St., Ste. 900, San Francisco, CA 94103. TEL 415-974-6900. FAX 415-227-2602. Ed. Cynthia W. Hu; Pub. John Marks. adv. contact: Linda Chase. circ. 600,000. **Document type:** consumer publication.
 Description: Provides information on the San Francisco Bay area: sightseeing, restaurants, retail and events.

917.94 US
SAN JOSE TRAVEL AND MEETING PLANNER.* a. Latimer Publications, 617 Veterans Blvd., Ste. 213, Redwood City, CA 94063-1404. TEL 415-324-1570. FAX 415-324-4420. Ed. Merlyn Holmes; Pub. Douglas H. Latimer. circ. 20,000.
 Description: Travel and meeting planner for San Jose, California. Includes accomodations, meeting and convention facilities, convention suppliers, transportation and recreation.

917.94 US
SAN JOSE VISITORS GUIDE.* a. Latimer Publications, 617 Veterans Blvd., Ste. 213, Redwood City, CA 94063-1404. TEL 415-324-1570. FAX 415-324-4420. Ed. Merlyn Holmes; Pub. Douglas H. Latimer. circ. 100,400.
 Description: Includes maps, shops, sights, dining, lodging and events.

910.09 US
SAN JUANS BECKON; San Juan Islands, Fidalgo Islands, Sidney, B.C. 1964. 2/yr. $5. Islanders' Sounder, Box 758, Eastsound, WA 98245. FAX 206-376-4501. circ. 95,000.

THE SAND PAPER. see *HOBBIES*

910.09 US
SANDWICH ISLANDS MAGAZINE. 1986-199? q. $16. Resort Publications, Inc., Box 748, Kilauea, Kauai, HI 96754. TEL 808-828-1125. FAX 808-828-1266. Ed. Patricia Ewing. adv.; circ. 20,000 (controlled).
 Incorporates (in 1990): North Shore; Which was formerly: Hawaiian North Shore.
 Description: Regional magazine covering the history and ecology of Kauai Island.

916.8 SA
SATOUR NEWS. 1992. irreg. Satour, Division: Corporate Communications, Private Bag X164, Pretoria 0001, South Africa. illus. **Document type:** newsletter.

910.09 387.7 SP ISSN 0214-8951
SAVIA. 6/yr. S.L. Grupo Editorial Incafo, Castello 59, 28001 Madrid, Spain. TEL 1-431-34-60. FAX 1-431-35-89. Ed. Manuel L. Colmenarejo.
 Description: Reviews reservation distribution systems for tourism professionals.

791 FR ISSN 0036-5793
SCENES ET PISTES. 1954. 8/yr. 85 F. Manita Carrington, Pub., 127 rue Saint-Germain, 27400 Louviers, France. Ed. Pierre Balancia. adv.; illus. circ. 4,000.

SCHOOL VISITS GUIDE. see *EDUCATION*

914.904 SZ
SCHWEIZER TOURISTIK; Switzerland's leading travel trade magazine. (Text in German) 1983. w. 151 SFr. (foreign 165 SFr.). Schweizer Touristik AG, Forchstr. 60, CH-8008 Zurich, Switzerland. TEL 01-3822380. FAX 01-3822388. TELEX 812105. Ed. Hans Stocker. adv. circ. 6,400.
 Document type: trade publication.
 Description: Each issue focuses on a specific area.

SCI; rivista degli sport invernali. see *SPORTS AND GAMES — Outdoor Life*

910.202 UK
SCOTLAND ACTIVITY HOLIDAYS. a. £4.50. (Scottish Tourist Board) Pastime Publications Ltd., 6 York Pl., Edinburgh EH1 3EP, Scotland. TEL 0131-556-1105. FAX 0131-556-1129. adv. **Document type:** directory.

914.1 UK
SCOTLAND: BED AND BREAKFAST. a. £4.99. Scottish Tourist Board, 23 Ravelston Terrace, Edinburgh EH4 3EU, Scotland. TEL 0131-332-2433. FAX 0131-343-1513. TELEX 72272. circ. 45,000. **Document type:** directory.
 Former titles: Scotland: Where to Stay, Bed and Breakfast; Where to Stay in Scotland. Bed and Breakfast; Supersedes in part: Where to Stay in Scotland (ISSN 0083-9221)

914.1 UK
SCOTLAND: CAMPING AND CARAVAN PARKS. 1960. a. £3.99. Scottish Tourist Board, 23 Ravelston Terrace, Edinburgh EH4 3EU, Scotland. TEL 0131-332-2433. FAX 0131-343-1513. adv. circ. 35,000. **Document type:** directory.
 Former titles: Scotland: Camping and Caravan Sites; Scotland for Touring Caravans; Scotland for Caravan Holidays.

914.104 UK
SCOTLAND FOR OUTDOOR ACTIVITIES. 1992. a. £3.95. Pastime Publications Ltd., 6 York Pl., Edinburgh EH1 3EP, Scotland. TEL 0131-556-1105. FAX 0131-556-1129. adv. contact: Diane Gibson. circ. 30,000. **Document type:** consumer publication.

914.1 UK
SCOTLAND FOR THE MOTORIST. 1970. a. £3.95. Pastime Publications Ltd., 6 York Pl., Edinburgh EH1 3EP, Scotland. TEL 0131-556-1105. FAX 0131-556-1129. adv. contact: Diane Gibson. circ. 30,000. **Document type:** consumer publication.

914.1 UK
SCOTLAND: HOTELS AND GUEST HOUSES. 1947. a. £6.99. Scottish Tourist Board, 23 Ravelston Terrace, Edinburgh EH4 3EU, Scotland. TEL 0131-332-2433. FAX 0131-343-1513. circ. 30,000. **Document type:** directory.
 Former titles: Scotland: Where to Stay, Hotels and Guest Houses; Where to Stay in Scotland. Hotels and Guest Houses; Supersedes in part: Where to Stay in Scotland (ISSN 0083-9221)

914.2 UK
SCOTLAND: SELF-CATERING ACCOMMODATION. 1971. a. £5.50. Scottish Tourist Board, 23 Ravelston Terrace, Edinburgh EH4 3EU, Scotland. TEL 0131-332-2433. FAX 0131-343-1513. charts. circ. 20,000. **Document type:** directory.

910.2 UK
SCOTLAND: 1001 THINGS TO SEE. 1970. irreg. £3.95. Scottish Tourist Board, 23 Ravelston Terrace, Edinburgh EH4 3EU, Scotland. TEL 0131-332-2433. FAX 0131-343-1513. **Document type:** directory.
 Former titles: Scotland: 600 Things to See; Scottish Castles and Historic Houses (ISSN 0080-7931); Scotlands Castles.

910.09 381 UK
SCOTTISH COMMERCIAL TRAVELLERS' ASSOCIATION. NEWSCALL. 1903. a. £20. Scottish Commercial Travellers' Association, 20 Anderson St., Airdrie ML6 OAA, Scotland. TEL 01236-756161. FAX 01236-66149. Ed. P. Neal. circ. 450. **Document type:** newsletter.

914.1 UK
SCOTTISH TRAVEL AGENTS NEWS. 1990. w. £32. S & G Publishing (Scotland) Ltd., 71 Henderson St., Bridge of Allan, Stirling FK9 4NG, Scotland. TEL 01786-834238. FAX 01786-834295. Ed. Susan Harris; Pub. George Bell. adv.: B&W page £580, color page £950; trim 300 x 210; adv. contact: George Bell. circ. 1,000. (back issues avail.) **Document type:** trade publication.
 Description: All matters relating to the travel trade that affect Scotland.

910.202 US
SEA BREEZE. 1977. bi-m. $10. Wachters' Organic Sea Products Corporation, 360 Shaw Rd., South San Francisco, CA 94080. FAX 415-875-1626. Ed. Joseph Wachter. bk.rev.; circ. 50,000 (controlled).

917.904 US
SEATTLE COMPASS. (Text in Japanese) 1983. q. free. Japan Pacific Publications, Inc., 419 Occidental Ave., Ste. 509, Seattle, WA 98104. TEL 206-622-7443. FAX 206-621-1786. Ed. Junko Yajima. adv. contact: Richard Crabill. circ. 15,000.
 Formerly: Pacific Companion.
 Description: Provides local information and events for tourists and visitors.

910.202 AT
SEE AUSTRALIA REGIONAL INFORMATION SERIES. 1980. 2/yr. Aus.$24. Research Publications Pty. Ltd., 27A Boronia Rd., Vermont, Vic. 3133, Australia. TEL 03-873-1450. Ed. Ted Colville. adv. circ. 3,500.
 Former titles: See Australia (ISSN 0810-2236) & Regional Information Series (ISSN 0159-7485)

919 II ISSN 0037-0762
SEE INDIA; quarterly journal on travel, tourism & hotel. (Text in English) 1967. q. Rs.60($15) A-47-D, DDA Flats, Munirka, New Delhi 110067, India. TEL 91-11-661414. Ed. J.M.L. Bhatnagar. adv.; illus. circ. 5,000.

917.504 US
SEE MAGAZINES. 1935. 6/yr. free. Miles Media Group, Inc., 3675 Clark Rd., Sarasota, FL 34233-2358. TEL 813-922-3575. FAX 813-923-6309. Ed. Janet Fusco. adv. circ. 500,000.
 •Also available online.
 Description: Contains information on tourist attractions, shopping, dining, recreation and real estate.

914.2 UK ISSN 0267-4599
SELF-CATERING AND FURNISHED HOLIDAYS. 1968. a. £3.60. F H G Publications Ltd., Abbey Mill Business Centre, Seedhill, Paisley PA1 1JN, Scotland. TEL 0141-887-0428. FAX 0141-889-7204. **Document type:** consumer publication.
 Formed by the merger of: Self-Catering Holiday Homes, Caravans & Boats; Furnished Holidays in Britain.

916.8 SA
SELF-CATERING GETAWAYS; the holiday home guide. Running title: A A Self-Catering Getaways. 1992. a. R.19.50 (effective 1995). (Automobile Association) R & V Business Services, P.O. Box 802, Highlands North 2037, South Africa. TEL 27-11-8838770. FAX 27-11-883-2087. E-mail: aatravel@iaccess.za. Eds. Sue Briggs; Pub. V.E. Sand. adv. contact: V.E. Sand. illus.; maps. **Document type:** directory.
 Description: Detailed guide to all types of self-catering accomodation in Southern Africa, including South Africa, Namibia and Zimbabwe.

910.4 UK ISSN 0080-8679
SELF CATERING HOLIDAYS. 1959. a. £3.95. Pastime Publications Ltd., 6 York Pl., Edinburgh EH1 3EP, Scotland. TEL 0131-556-1105. FAX 0131-556-1129. adv. contact: Diane Gibson. circ. 45,000. **Document type:** consumer publication.

910.202 UK ISSN 0959-6496
SELLING LONG-HAUL. 1990. m. B M I Publications Ltd., Suffolk House, George St., Croydon, Surrey CR9 1SR, England. TEL 0181-649-7233. FAX 0181-649-7234. Ed. Alan Orbell. adv.: color page $5330. circ. 19,000 (controlled). (back issues avail.) **Document type:** trade publication.
 Description: Covers the selling of long-distance travel from the U.K. (i.e., beyond Europe) for travel agents.

910.202 UK
SELLING SHORT BREAKS. q. B M I Publications Ltd., Suffolk House, George St., Croydon, Surrey CR9 1SR, England. TEL 0181-649-7233. FAX 0181-649-7234. Ed. Alan Orbell. adv.: color page $4200; adv. contact: Gareth Davies.
 Description: Covers the selling of short vacations from the U.K.

910 US
SENIOR CITIZEN'S GUIDE TO BUDGET TRAVEL IN THE UNITED STATES AND CANADA. 1983. irreg. $5.95. Pilot Books, 103 Cooper St., Babylon, NY 11702. TEL 516-422-2225. FAX 516-422-2227. Ed. Paige Palmer. **Document type:** consumer publication.
 Description: How to find low cost transportation, accommodations, restaurants, and tours all over the U.S. and Canada.

910.09 US ISSN 1081-907X
SENIOR GROUP TRAVELER; the reference source for senior group leaders. 1991. q. $15. Senior Travel Publications, Inc., 750 Old Hickory Blvd., Ste. 150-Bldg. 2, Brentwood, TN 37027-4502. TEL 615-371-6181. FAX 615-221-8825. Ed. George Lowden. adv.: B&W page $1695, color page $2565; trim 8 1/4 x 11; adv. contact: George Lowden. circ. 11,740 (controlled). **Document type:** trade publication.
  Formerly: Mature Group Traveler (ISSN 1062-2772)
  Description: Includes feature articles and relevant information about destinations, attractions, entertainment, tours and other travel services of interest to the senior-group travel market.

910.09 301.435 US
SENIOR TRAVEL TIPS (SAN RAFAEL). 1990. bi-m. $12 (effective 1995-1996). Senior Marketing Associates, 710 C St., Ste. 200, San Rafael, CA 94901. TEL 415-453-8481. FAX 415-453-8540. Ed. Linnea Jessup; Pub. Elana Anderson. adv.: B&W page $1045; trim 8 1/4 x 11; adv. contact: Gene Watts. circ. 11,000. **Document type:** trade publication.
  Description: Contains articles of interest to travel planners and tour operators with a clientele over 50. Describes domestic and international destinations, attractions, events, festivals, cruises, motorcoach tours, and other services that cater to this age group.

910.09 US
SENIOR TRAVEL TIPS (SCOTTS VALLEY); serving group travel & activity planners for the mature market from the West. 1987. bi-m. free to qualified personnel. 5281 Scotts Valley Dr., Scotts Valley, CA 95066-3514. TEL 408-438-6085. FAX 408-438-4705. Ed. Linnea Smith Jessup; Pub. Elana Andersen. adv.: B&W page $1045; 7 x 10; adv. contact: Gene Watts. bk.rev./ tr.lit.; circ. 11,500 (controlled). **Document type:** trade publication.
  Formerly (until 1993): Travel Tips.
  Description: Informs tour planners of new and interesting destinations of interest to senior travelers in the U.S. western states and western Canadian provinces.

910.202 CC
SHANDONG LUYOU/TRAVEL IN SHANDONG. (Text in Chinese) bi-m. Shandong Sheng Luyou Ju - Shandong Provincial Bureau of Tourism, No. 26, Jing 10 Lu, Jinan, Shandong 250014, People's Republic of China. TEL 615858. Ed. Sun Chuanyuan.

916.8 SA
SHELL TOURIST GUIDE TO SOUTH AFRICA. a. R.4.40. Chris van Rensburg Publications (Pty) Ltd., P.O. Box 29159, Melville 2109, South Africa. adv.

SHIPPING AND TOURISM. see *TRANSPORTATION — Ships And Shipping*

910.202 US
SHOESTRING TRAVELER. 1990. bi-m. $29. International Features, Inc., 8 S. J St., Box 1349, Lake Worth, FL 33460. TEL 407-582-8320. Ed. Byron Lutz. adv. contact: Lachelle Granholm. bk.rev. circ. 12,560. **Document type:** newsletter.
  Description: Budget travel news for the international traveler with an emphasis on air courier travel.

910.202 688 SZ
SHOPPING GUIDE ZURICH. (Text in English, French, German) 1981. m. 86 SFr. Promotion Verlag AG, Mainaustr. 35, Postfach 10, CH-8034 Zurich, Switzerland. TEL 01-3835252. FAX 01-3839233. Ed. Roberto Bretscher. adv.: page 1720 SFr.; trim 148 x 210; adv. contact: Michael Hrabe. circ. 28,000. (back issues avail.) **Document type:** consumer publication.

914.1 UK ISSN 0261-5517
SHOPPING IN EDINBURGH. a. £1. Pastime Publications Ltd., 6 York Pl., Edinburgh EH1 3EP, Scotland. TEL 0131-556-1105. FAX 0131-556-1129. adv. contact: Diane Gibson. circ. 50,000. **Document type:** consumer publication.
  Formerly (until 1981): Edinburgh Chamber of Commerce. Shopping Guide.

915.7704 AT
▼**SIBERIAN B A M RAILWAY GUIDE**; a handbook to the second trans-siberian railway for rail enthusiasts and travellers. 1994. a. $25. Red Bear Tours, 320B Glenferrie Rd., Malvern, Vic. 3144, Australia. TEL 61-3-824-7183. FAX 61-3-822-3956. E-mail: bmccunn@werple.mira.net.au. Ed.Bd.

914.2 UK
SIGHTSEEING IN THE U K (YEAR). a. £20. English Tourist Board, Black's Rd., Hammersmith, London W6 9EL, England. TEL 0181-846-9000. FAX 0181-563-0302. **Document type:** trade publication.
  Description: Analyzes the use and capacity of attractions. Includes data on the number of visitors to the sites, new attractions, periods open and admission charges, employment, capital expenditure, and revenue trends.

910.4 SA
SIGNATURE. (Text in Afrikaans, English) 1968. 6/yr. R.12. Diners Club S.A. (Pty) Ltd., Box 10727, Johannesburg 2000, South Africa. Ed. Jack Fisch. adv.; bk.rev. circ. 41,000.

910.202 II
SIGNATURE. 1977. 12/yr. membership. Business India Group of Publications, Wadia Bldg., 17-19 Dalal St., Fort, Bombay 400 023, India. Ed. Jehangir R. Patel. adv.; bk.rev. circ. 40,000.
  Description: Citibank Diner Club magazine focussing primarily on travel.

910.202 JA
SIGNATURE. (Text in Japanese) 1961. m. 4800 Yen. Diners Club of Japan, Senshu Bldg., 13-7 Shibuya 1-chome, Shibuya-ku, Tokyo, Japan. TEL 03-3499-1311. FAX 03-3352-6415. TELEX 2423066 DCTRVLJ. Ed. Yoichiro Akashi. adv.; bk.rev. circ. 350,000.

910.202 SI
SIGNATURE. (Text in English) m. Signature Publishing Pty. Ltd., 2-201 Merlin Place, Beach Rd., Singapore 7, Singapore. Ed. Filipina Elizabeth Reyes. adv. circ. 32,000.

916 KE
SIGNATURE. (Text in English) 1982. bi-m. EAs.55. Signature, Diners Club Africa, Box 30403, Nairobi, Kenya. TEL 727-2438. FAX 723747. TELEX 22554. Ed. Carole McNab. adv.; bk.rev.; illus.; cum.index. circ. 8,000.

910.202 GR
SIGNATURE EXCLUSIVE. (Text in Greek) bi-m. membership. Diners Club of Greece, S.A., P.O. Box 10, Athens, Greece. adv. circ. 100,000 (controlled).
  Formerly (until 1989): Signature.

SIGNPOST FOR NORTHWEST TRAILS. see *SPORTS AND GAMES — Outdoor Life*

910.09 IT ISSN 1123-7058
SIKANIA. (Text in English, Italian) 1985. m. L.45000 (foreign L.80000($50)) (effective 1995). Krea s.r.l., Piazza Don Bosco 6, 90142 Palermo, Italy. TEL 39-91-543506. FAX 39-91-6373378. TELEX 912163. Ed. Giovanni Castellucci; Pub. Hanne Carstensen. adv.: B&W page L.1500000, color page L.2000000; adv. contact: Lidia Varisco. circ. 12,000. (back issues avail.) **Document type:** consumer publication.
  Description: For tourists in Sicily and Sicilian emigrants all over the world. Covers travel, geography and history of the region.

SILENCE COURIER; Gaestezeitschrift der Silencehotels Deutschland. see *GENERAL INTEREST PERIODICALS — Germany*

SINGAPORE SURVEY OF OVERSEAS VISITORS. see *TRAVEL AND TOURISM — Abstracting, Bibliographies, Statistics*

919 SI ISSN 0129-5020
SINGAPORE TRAVEL. 1964. bi-m. free. Singapore Tourist Promotion Board, Raffles City Tower No. 36-04, 250 North Bridge Road, Singapore 0617, Singapore. TEL 65-3396622. FAX 65-3399423. TELEX STBSIN RS 33375. Ed. Margaret Teo. adv.; illus. circ. 30,000. **Document type:** newsletter, trade publication.
  Formerly (until 1978): Singapore Travel News (ISSN 0037-5713)

910.202 SI ISSN 0129-9980
SINGAPORE VISITOR. Japanese edition: Japanese Singapore Visitor. (Text in English) English edition 1970; Japanese edition 1981. w. free. Creations and Communications Pte. Ltd., 38 Duxton Hill, Singapore 0208, Singapore. FAX 221-3530. Ed. Susan A. Gallagher. adv. circ. English ed. 23,000; Japanese ed. 14,000. **Document type:** consumer publication.
  Description: Contains information on places of interest, nightlife, shopping, and restaurants for tourists visiting Singapore.

SKI MAGAZINE. see *SPORTS AND GAMES — Outdoor Life*

910.09 US
SKIING WITH CHILDREN. biennial. $29 (Canada Can.$40; overseas $32) (effective 1995-1996). Travel With Your Children (TWYCH), 45 W. 18th St., 7th Fl., New York, NY 10011. TEL 212-206-0688. FAX 212-645-5942. Pub. Dorothy Jordon.
  Description: Contains information parents need to select a ski resort that meets the needs of their families.

SLOAN'S GREEN GUIDE TO ANTIQUING IN NEW ENGLAND. see *ANTIQUES*

914.6 388.3 SP
SOCIEDAD ESPANOLA DE AUTOMOVILES DE TURISMO. MEMORIA Y BALANCE. 1953. a. free. Sociedad Espanola de Automoviles de Turismo, S.A., Paseo Castellana, 278, Madrid 16, Spain. charts; stat. circ. 1,000.

SOFIA NEWS; weekly for politics, economics, culture, tourism and sport. see *POLITICAL SCIENCE*

910.09 US
SOJOURNS. s-a. free to qualified personnel. Journal Communications, Inc., 1749 Mallory Ln., Ste.110, Brentwood, TN 37027. TEL 615-371-0010. FAX 615-371-0258. Ed. Barry Parket; Pub. Bob Schwartzman. circ. 2,500,000. **Document type:** consumer publication.

910.09 CU
SOL DE CUBA. (Editions in English, French, Spanish) 1983. q. Instituto Nacional del Turismo, Malecon y G, Vedado, Havana, Cuba. TEL 7-32-9881. TELEX 511955. Ed. Aurelio Pedraso. circ. 200,000.

916 UK ISSN 0265-6787
SOUTH AFRICA NEWS. 1982. m. £15 (foreign £26.50). Outbound Newspapers, 1 Commercial Rd., Eastbourne, E. Sussex BN21 3XQ, England. TEL 01323-412001. FAX 01323-649249. Ed. Stephen Hartridge. circ. 18,000. (tabloid format; back issues avail.) **Document type:** newspaper.
  Description: Gives potential migrants and travelers to South Africa information about real estate, employment, education, investing and lifestyle.

918 F2224 US ISSN 0889-7891
SOUTH AMERICAN EXPLORER. (Text in English) 1977. q. $30 membership. South American Explorers Club, 126 Indian Creek Rd., Ithaca, NY 14850. TEL 607-277-0488. Ed. Don Montague. adv. contact: Sorise McClory. bk.rev.; illus.; circ. 8,000 (paid). (back issues avail.)
  Description: Explores various field sciences in Latin America.

910.202 F1401 UK ISSN 0309-4529
SOUTH AMERICAN HANDBOOK. 1924. a. £21.95. Trade & Travel Publications Ltd., 6 Riverside Ct., Lower Bristol Rd., Bath BA2 3DZ, England. TEL 01225-469141. FAX 01225-469461. (Dist. in N. America by: Passport Books, NTC Publishing Group, 4255 W. Touhy Ave., Lincolnwood, IL 60646-1975. TEL 708-679-5500. FAX 708-679-6375) Ed. Ben Box. **Document type:** directory.

910.202 SI ISSN 0218-0553
SOUTH EAST ASIA TRAVELLER;* the complete ASEAN travel magazine. (Text in English) 1985. bi-m. S.$113 for 18 nos. Compass Publishing Private Ltd., 1090 Lower Delta Rd. 01-06, Singapore 0316, Singapore. TEL 2211111. FAX 222-5251. Ed. Julia Goh. adv. circ. 21,000. (back issues avail.)
  Description: Travel news and information for South East Asia.

6496 TRAVEL AND TOURISM

910.09 US
SOUTHEAST TRAVEL PROFESSIONAL. 1988. m. $12 (free to travel agents) (effective 1995-96). Florida Travel Professional, 1200 N.W. 78th Ave., No. 216, Miami, FL 33126-1817. TEL 305-592-6133. FAX 305-592-9741. Ed. Lawrence Cafiero; Pub. John Devereaux. adv. contact: Roz Kornblum. bk.rev.; circ. 10,000 (controlled). (tabloid format) **Document type:** trade publication, newspaper.
  Description: Sent to travel agents in Southeastern US and US Virgin Islands and Puerto Rico.

910 SA
SOUTHERN AFRICAN TRAVEL GUIDE. 1971. a. R.24.90. Promco (Pty) Ltd., 12 Annerley Rd., Rosebank 7700, South Africa. TEL 27-21-6866341. FAX 27-21-6866332. Ed. L.D. Solomon. adv.; bk.rev.
  Formerly: Travel Guide, S.A.

910 SA
SOUTHERN AFRICA'S TRAVEL NEWS WEEKLY. (Text in English) 1970. w. R.215. Travel and Trade Publishing (Pty) Ltd., P.O. Box 662, Auckland Park 2006, South Africa. TEL 27-11-7263036. FAX 27-11-7263994. Ed. Leona Marsh. adv.: B&W page R.8100, color page R.10530; trim 320 x 225; adv. contact: Leona Marsh. circ. 5,670 (controlled). **Document type:** trace publication.
  Formerly: Southern Africa's Travel News.
  Description: Provides timely news and information of relevance to the Southern African travel industry.

917 US ISSN 0038-3902
SOUTHERN CALIFORNIA GUIDE; the current directory of restaurants, art galleries, hotels, motels, entertainment, shopping, sightseeing, tourist attractions. (Text in English and Japanese) 1919. m. (avail. only by single no.). Westworld Publishing Corp., 11385 Exposition Bl., No. 102, Los Angeles, CA 90064. TEL 310-391-8255. Ed. Valerie Summers; Pub. Valerie Summers. adv.; bk.rev.; circ. 34,000 (controlled). **Document type:** directory, consumer publication.

910.09 051 US ISSN 1041-3642
SOUTHERN LIVING TRAVEL SOUTH. 1984. q. $12 (effective Jan. 1992). Southern Progress Corp. (Subsidiary of: Time, Inc. Magazine Co.), c/o H. Johnson, V.P. Circulation, 2100 Lakeshore Dr., Birmingham, AL 35209. TEL 205-877-6000. (Subscr. to: P.O Box 830611, Birmingham, AL 35201) adv.; charts; illus.; tr.lit. circ. 200,000. (back issues avail.)
  —UMI.
  Formerly (until 1988): Southern Travel; **Supersedes (in 1986):** Travel South (ISSN 0743-6629)
  Description: Travel magazine for tourists visiting the Southern United States.

910.09 AG ISSN 0327-6597
SOUTHERN SOUTH AMERICA. q. Zagier & Urruty Publicaciones, P.O. Box 94, Sucursal 19, 1419 Buenos Aires, Argentina. TEL 541-572-1050. FAX 541-572-5766. (U.S. addr.: Box 526806, Miami, FL 33152-6086) **Document type:** bulletin, catalog.

910.202 AT
SOUTHERN SUN. 1985. m. Aus.$10. Southern Publishers, 34 Auckland St., Bega, N.S.W., Australia. TEL 044-725-342. (Subscr. to: P.O. Box 411, Batemans Bay, N.S.W. 2536, Australia) circ. 30,000. (back issues avail.)

SOUVENIR. see *GIFTWARE AND TOYS*

910.09 CN ISSN 1186-8848
SPA DESTINATIONS. French edition: Destinations Spa (ISSN 1186-883X) (Text in English) 1989. q. $32 (overseas $52). Publicom Inc., C.P. 365, Place d'Armes, Montreal, PQ H2Y 3H1, Canada. TEL 514-274-0004. FAX 514-274-5884. (Dist. by: Publicom Inc., Box 2699, Champlain, NY 12919, USA) Ed. Ann Bolduc. adv.; circ. 12,923. **Document type:** trade publication.

SPA FINDER. see *PHYSICAL FITNESS AND HYGIENE*

914.604 US ISSN 1055-565X
DP14
SPAIN (YEAR). a. $18. Harper Collins Publishers, Birnbaum Travel Guides, 10 E. 53rd St., New York, NY 10022-5299. TEL 212-207-7542. Ed. Alexandra Mayes Birnbaum. illus.; index.
  Supersedes in part: Birnbaum's Spain - Portugal (ISSN 1042-6353)
  Description: Includes itineraries for the Balearic and Canary Islands.

SPAIN GOURMETOUR; food, wine, and travel quarterly magazine. see *HOTELS AND RESTAURANTS*

SPARTACUS INTERNATIONAL GAY GUIDE. see *HOMOSEXUALITY*

910.202 US ISSN 0889-7085
SPECIALTY TRAVEL INDEX; directory of special interest travel. 1980. s-a. $10 (effective 1996). Alpine Hansen Publishers, 305 San Anselmo Ave., Ste. 313, San Anselmo, CA 94960. TEL 415-459-4900. FAX 415-459-4974. Ed. C. Steen Hansen. adv. contact: Paige Brooks. bk.rev. circ. 45,000. (back issues avail.) **Document type:** directory, trade publication.
  Description: Directory of adventure and special interest travel listing 600 tour operators. Range from expeditions to cultural and sports tours.

SPELEO. see *EARTH SCIENCES*

914.604 387.7 SP ISSN 0036-1852
SPIC; revista de turismo. 1966. fortn. (21/yr.). 10000 ptas. europe $245; America $305, Asia $490 (effective 1995). S P I C Ediciones S.A., Sanchez Barcaiztegui 38, 1r Jardin, 4, 28007 Madrid, Spain. TEL 34-1-5510126. FAX 34-1-4338354. TELEX 46322 SPIC E. Ed. Lorenzo Herranz Garcia. adv.: B&W page 1725 ECU, color page 2400 ECU; bleed 215 x 290; adv. contact: Josefina Carrasco. bk.rev.; illus. circ. 11,500.

915.404 CE
SPICY ISLE.* (Text in English) 1971. q. 23 Rajamalwatte Rd., Colombo 15, Sri Lanka. Ed.Bd. adv.; illus.

SPORTACCOM; magazine voor realisatie, beheer en onderhoud van sportaccomodaties. see *SPORTS AND GAMES*

SPORTS LOISIRS TOURISME; la lettre de l'economie des equipements. see *LEISURE AND RECREATION*

915.04 CE
SRI LANKA ACCOMMODATION GUIDE. (Text in English, French, German) s-a. free. Ceylon Tourist Board, P.O. Box 1504, Colombo 3, Sri Lanka. adv.; charts. circ. 10,000. **Document type:** catalog.
  Formerly: Welcome to Sri Lanka.

910.202 CE
SRI LANKA OFFICIAL TOURIST HANDBOOK. (Text in English, French, German) s-a. Ceylon Tourist Board, P.O. Box 1504, Colombo 3, Sri Lanka. Ed. Florence Ratwalte. circ. 100,000.
  Formerly: Sri Lanka Tourist Information.

910.4 CE
SRI LANKA TODAY. (Text in English) q. Government Department of Information, 7 Sir Baron Jayatilaka Mawatha, Colombo 1, Sri Lanka. TEL 1-28376. Ed. Manel Abhayaratne. circ. 80,000.

914 DK
STADTFUEHRER KOPENHAGEN. (Text in German) a. Politikens Service Selskab A-S, Versergade 4, DK-1456 Copenhagen K, Denmark. FAX 45-33-328674. adv. circ. 200,000.

910.202 US
STAR SERVICE. 1960. base vol. (plus q. supplements). $395. Reed Travel Group, Part of Reed Elsevier group (Subsidiary of: Reed Telepublishing), 500 Plaza Dr., Secaucus, NJ 07096. TEL 201-902-2000. FAX 201-319-1797. Ed. Steven R. Gordon. circ. 6,600. (looseleaf format) **Document type:** directory.
  Former titles: A B C Star Service; S T A R Service.
  Description: Provides critical reviews of hotel properties and cruise ships throughout the world written by free-lance travel writers.

914 IT ISSN 0039-1131
STELUTIS ALPINIS. 1955. m. L.12000 membership. Unione Operaia Escursionisti Italiani, Sezione di Udine, Viale Europa Unita 117, 33100 Udine, Italy. TEL 0432-678292. Dir. Enzo Driussi. adv.; abstr.; illus.; stat. circ. 4,000. (tabloid format)
  Description: For hikers and travelers.

STI OG VARDE. see *SPORTS AND GAMES — Outdoor Life*

910.09 IT
STRALIGNANO. (Text in German, Italian) 1956. w. during summer. L.12000($6) Pubblistudio de Zorzi Casa Editrice s.a.s., Via Marinoni 53, 33100 Udine, Italy. TEL 0432-508243. FAX 0432-508243. Ed.Bd. adv. circ. 10,000. (back issues avail.)

917.504 US
STRAND MAGAZINE. 1986. a. 1359 21st Ave. N., No. 106, Myrtle Beach, SC 29577. TEL 803-626-8911. FAX 803-626-6452. adv. circ. 1,000,000. **Document type:** consumer publication.

910.202 GW
STRASSENATLAS DEUTSCHLAND UND EUROPA. 1962. a. DM.14.80. Ravenstein Verlag GmbH, Auf der Krautweide 24, 65812 Bad Soden, Germany. TEL 06196-609630. FAX 06196-63619. TELEX 4072538-HACO-D. Pub. Ruediger Bosse. **Document type:** directory.

910.202 CN
STUDENT TRAVELLER. 1978. s-a. free. Canadian Federation of Sudents, 171 College St., 2nd Fl., Toronto, Ont. M5T 1P7, Canada. TEL 416-977-5228. FAX 416-977-7112. Ed. Ann Klug; Pub. Mike Fuller. adv.; bk.rev. circ. 150,000.
  Formerly (until 1991): Canadian Student Traveller (ISSN 0706-9758)

STUDENT TRAVELS. see *EDUCATION — International Education Programs*

910.09 IT
SUITE; tecnhotel magazine. (Text in English, Italian) 1988. 7/yr. BE-MA Editore s.r.l., Via Teocrito 50, 20128 Milan, Italy. TEL 39-2-2552451. FAX 39-2-27000692. Ed. Giuseppe Biondo. adv.: B&W page L.4200000, color page L.5700000; trim 230 x 300. circ. 15,348.
  Description: covers the design and improvement of hotel and catering facilities.

910.09 US ISSN 0095-3482
G155.U6
SUMMARY AND ANALYSIS OF INTERNATIONAL TRAVEL TO THE UNITED STATES. 1983. m. $315. U.S. Travel and Tourism Administration, Office of Research, U.S. Department of Commerce, Main Commerce Bldg., Rm. 1868, Washington, DC 20230. TEL 202-482-1904. FAX 202-482-2887. (Subscr. to: U.S. Travel Data Center, 2 Lafayette Centre, 1133 21st St., N.W., Washington, DC 20230. TEL 202-293-1040. FAX 202-293-3155) Ed. Ron Erdmann. stat. (also avail. in diskette format) **Indexed:** Amer.Stat.Ind. (1973-). **Document type:** government publication.
  Description: Provides statistics of international visitor arrivals to the U.S. by world region and each of 90 individual countries.

910.09 US
SUMMER POCKET GUIDE. (18 regional editions avail.) a. Pocket Guide Publications, Inc., 9650 Clayton Rd., St. Louis, MO 63124. TEL 314-991-5222. FAX 314-991-8911. Ed. Jackson D. Waterbury. adv.: color page $9000. circ. 400,000. **Document type:** consumer publication.

SUMMER WEEK. see *LEISURE AND RECREATION*

919 CJ
SUN LIVING. q. free. Cayman News, Ltd., Box 764, Grand Cayman, British W.I. Ed. Mike Cross. adv.

910.202 GW
SUN'N FUN; junge Reiseideen. s-a. Unterwegsverlag Manfred Klemann, Dr.-Andler-Str. 28, 78224 Singen, Germany. TEL 07731-63544. FAX 07731-62401. Ed. Manfred Klemann. adv. contact: Anette Hildebrandt. circ. 60,000. **Document type:** consumer publication.

910.09　　　US　　ISSN 1047-8965
HD38
SURVEY OF BUSINESS TRAVELERS. 1987. a. $150. Travel Industry Association of America, 1100 New York Ave., N.W., Ste. 450, Washington, DC 20005-3934. FAX 202-408-8422. **Document type:** trade publication.

910.09　　　US　　ISSN 0361-8307
G155.U6
SURVEY OF STATE TRAVEL OFFICES. 1973. a. $475. Travel Industry Association of America, 1100 New York Ave., N.W., Ste. 450, Washington, DC 20005-3934. TEL 202-408-8422. (also avail. in microfiche from CIS; reprint service avail.) **Indexed:** SRI. **Document type:** trade publication.
　　Description: Provides a state-by-state analysis of official government agencies responsible for travel promotion.

914　　　SZ　　ISSN 1420-1151
SWISS NEWS. 10/yr. 84 SFr. Swiss Scene Verlags AG, Postfach 4341, CH-8052 Zurich, Switzerland. TEL 01-3027606. FAX 01-3022022. Ed. R. Kuhn. circ. 21,000. **Document type:** consumer publication.

910.09　　　GW
T I D TOURISTIK KONTAKT. 1965. a. DM.70. TourCon Hannelore Niedecken GmbH, Postfach 323462, 20119 Hamburg, Germany. TEL 040-44187381. FAX 040-44187349. Pub. Hannelore Niedecken. adv. contact: M. Rosteck. circ. 13,600. **Document type:** trade publication.

910.09　　　JA
T M. (Travel Management) (Text in English, Japanese) 1978. s-m. 8000 Yen. Travel Consultants of Japan, Ltd., Dai-ichi Akiyama Bldg., 7F, 2-3-22 Toranomon, Minato-ku, Tokyo 105, Japan. TEL 03-3506-8311. FAX 03-3506-8326. Ed. Hisao Ohta. circ. 10,282. (back issues avail.)

910.09　　　US　　ISSN 0893-1259
T M S - LETTER. (Travel Marketing and Sales Newsletter) 1987. s-m. $120. Nissen-Lie Communications, Inc., 441 Lexington Ave., Ste. 1209 A, New York, NY 10017. TEL 212-986-1025. FAX 212-986-1033. Ed. Angela Reale Mathisen. adv.; bk.rev. circ. 1,500.
　　Description: News report and digest on travel marketing, sales, advertising and public relations.

647.945 915　　　SI
T T G ASIA HOTEL GUIDE. (Text in English) 1985. s-a. Miller Freeman Pte. Ltd., 100 Beach Rd., 26-00 Shaw Towers, Singapore 0718, Singapore. TEL 65-2943366. FAX 65-2985534. Ed. Yeoh Siew Hoon. adv.: color page $4450; adv. contact: Michael Chow. circ. 60,608 (controlled). **Document type:** trade publication.

910.09　　　US
T T N - T T G NORTH AMERICA. 1985. 48/yr. free to qualified personnel. Miller Freeman, Inc. (New York), 1515 Broadway, New York, NY 10036. TEL 212-869-1300. FAX 212-944-7350. TELEX 647035-CMP-PUB-MAHA. Ed. Mary Pat Fulliban. adv.: B&W page $9075, color page 11150; trim 10 3/4 x 14 3/8. circ. 54,217. **Document type:** trade publication, newspaper.
　●Also available online. Vendor(s): Data-Star, Knight-Ridder, Inc., NewsNet (TR09).
　—UMI. **CCC.**
　　Formerly (until Jan. 1994): Tour and Travel News (ISSN 0889-3349)

910.09　　　US　　ISSN 1080-837X
T T R A NEWS. bi-m. membership. (Travel and Tourism Research Association) University of Utah, 10200 W. 44th Ave., No. 304, Wheat Ridge, CO 80033. TEL 303-422-6557. FAX 303-422-8894. Ed. J.P. Smith. adv. circ. 900 (controlled). (back issues avail.) **Document type:** newsletter.

910　　　JA
TABI NI DEYO. 1973. bi-m. 2700 Yen. Mainichi Newspapers, 1-1-1, Hitotsubashi, Chiyoda-ku, Tokyo 100-51, Japan. TEL 03-3212-0321. FAX 03-3211-0895. TELEX 22324. Ed. Reimi Yamazaki. circ. 130,000.

910.202 385　　　JA
TABI TO TETSUDO. 1971. 4/yr. 880 Yen. Tetsudo Journal Sha, Iidabashi 4-8-6, Chiyoda-ku, Tokyo, Japan. TEL 03-3264-1891. FAX 03-3265-3597. Ed. Toshimoto Takeshima. adv.; bk.rev. circ. 120,000.

910.202　　　FP　　ISSN 1157-349X
TAHITI BEACH PRESS. 1980. w. Tahiti Publications Touristiques, P.O. Box 887, Papeete, Tahiti. TEL 689-426850. FAX 689-435184. Ed. Alan Prince; Pub. Gerard Warti. circ. 2,700 (controlled). cols./p.: 4; pp./issue: 16. **Document type:** newspaper.

915.4　　　II
TAJ MAGAZINE. (Text in English) 1972. q. Rs.440($24) (Taj Group of Hotels) Indian Hotels Company Ltd., Apollo Bunder, Bombay 400 039, India. TEL 22-2023366. FAX 022-2872711. TELEX 11-82442 TAJB IN. Ed. Camellia Panjabi. adv. contact: Sunita Nair. charts; illus. circ. 25,000.
　　Description: News about India for tourists.

338.4791 910.2　　　DK　　ISSN 0107-1270
TAKE OFF; travel trade magazine for Scandinavian agents, tourist offices, airlines, hotels. (Supplement avail.: Aussie News) 1957. m. DKK 420 (foreign DKK 525). Skandinavisk Bladforlag A-S, Frederiksberg Alle 3, DK-1621 Copenhagen V, Denmark. TEL 45-31-23-80-99. FAX 45-31-23-70-42. Ed. Erik Ryge. adv.; bk.rev.; illus.; stat.; circ. 6,000 (controlled). **Document type:** trade publication.

338.7　　　II
TAMIL NADU TOURISM DEVELOPMENT CORPORATION. ANNUAL REPORT.* (Text in English) a. Tamil Nadu Tourism Development Corporation, V.S.T. Motor Bldgs., 34 Mount Rd., Madras 600008, India.

910.09　　　AT
TASMANIAN TRAVELWAYS. 1960. bi-m. free. (Department of Tourism) Creative Publications Pty., Ltd., 71-75 Paterson St., Launceston, Tas. 7250, Australia. Ed.Bd. adv.; charts; illus.; stat. circ. 78,000.

914.2　　　UK
TASTE OF SCOTLAND GUIDE (YEAR); selected places to eat and stay in scotland. 1972. a. £4.50($20) Taste of Scotland Scheme Ltd., 33 Melville St., Edinburgh EH3 7JF, Scotland. TEL 0131-220-1900. FAX 0131-220-6102. Ed. Nancy K. Campbell. adv. contact: Amanda Clark. illus. circ. 50,000. **Document type:** directory.
　　Formerly: Taste of Scotland.

TEACHERS' GUIDE TO OVERSEAS TEACHING; a complete and comprehensive guide of English-language schools and colleges overseas. see EDUCATION — International Education Programs

910.202　　　US
TEACHERS TRAVEL GAZETTE. q? Teachers Travel, Box 5513, Santa Monica, CA 90405.

910.09　　　SP
TECTUR. 1988. 12/yr. free. Apdo. 592, 29080 Malaga, Spain. TEL 52-212-635. Ed. Pablo Chaurit. adv. circ. 3,000. **Document type:** bulletin.

TEMA VERDE. see CONSERVATION

910.4　　　AT
TEMPO AUSTRALIA. 1983. bi-m. Aus.$30. Unimedia Publications Pty. Ltd., 272 Elgin St., Carlton, Vic. 3053, Australia. TEL 03-347-3422. FAX 03-347-5769. Ed. Ettore Flacco. circ. 35,000. (back issues avail.)
　　Formerly: Australian Tempo Libero.

910.202　　　CN　　ISSN 0823-5708
TEMPS LIBRE. 1983. 4/yr. Can.$11.50 (foreign Can.$20). Regroupement Tourisme Jeunesse, 4545 Pierre de Coubertin Av., Montreal, PQ H1V 3R2, Canada. TEL 514-252-3117. FAX 514-252-3119. TELEX 05-829647. adv. circ. 50,000. **Document type:** consumer publication.
　　Description: Covers youth tourism, foreign exchange programs, travel tips, youth hostels.

917.604　　　US
TENNESSEE TRAVEL GUIDE.* 1983. a. Tom Jackson & Associates, Inc., 3100 W. End Ave., Ste. 1210, Nashville, TN 37203-1348. TEL 615-242-7747. FAX 615-259-2042. Ed. Suzanne Boggs. adv. circ. 40,000. **Document type:** consumer publication.
　　Description: Lists lodging, dining, attractions, tours, shopping and airline services statewide.

910　　　CN　　ISSN 0712-8657
TEOROS. 1982. q. Can.$15 (foreign Can.$18). Universite du Quebec a Montreal, Service des Publications, C.P. 8888, Succ. "A", Montreal, Que. H3C 3P8, Canada. TEL 514-987-7747. Ed. Jean Stafford. (back issues avail.) **Indexed:** Pt.de Rep. (1991-).

TERRA (BARCELONA, 1993); revista catalana de geografia, cartografia, ciencias de la terra. see GEOGRAPHY

TERRA GRISCHUNA - GRAUBUENDEN; Zeitschrift fuer buendner Natur, Kultur und Freizeit. see ENVIRONMENTAL STUDIES

917　　　SZ　　ISSN 0257-6686
TERRA PLANA.* no.6, 1972. s-a. 6 Fr. Sarganserlaendische Buchdruckerei AG, 8887 Mels, Switzerland. Ed. A. Stucky.

914　　　SZ
TERRA TICINESE. 6/yr. Via alla Chiesa 7, CH-6962 Viganello, Switzerland. TEL 091-513568. Ed. G.M. Fontana. circ. 6,000.

625.7　　　US　　ISSN 0040-4349
TE24.T4
TEXAS HIGHWAYS. 1974. m. $12.50 (foreign $20). Department of Transportation, Travel and Information Division, Box 141009, Austin, TX 78714-1009. TEL 512-483-3675. FAX 512-483-3672. Ed. Jack Lowry. bk.rev.; illus. circ. 430,000. (back issues avail.) **Document type:** government publication.

917.604　　　US
TEXAS PEOPLE AND PLACES. 1991. m. $18. Maverick Media Group, Box 810, Joshua, TX 76058. TEL 817-556-3605. FAX 817-645-3497. Ed. Billy J. Huckaby. adv.; bk.rev. circ. 30,000. **Document type:** consumer publication.
　　Description: Covers travel, lifestyle, history and people of Texas, with listings of upcoming festivals and celebrations.

917.604　　　US
TEXAS TOUR AND MEETING GUIDE. 1990. a. $4 (free to qualified personnel). Publishing Partnership (Subsidiary of: Texas Monthly, Inc.), Box 1569, Austin, TX 78767. TEL 512-320-6900. FAX 512-476-9007. Ed. Cathy S. Casey. adv. contact: Jim Stone. circ. 52,355 (controlled). **Document type:** trade publication.
　　Description: Provides travel information on the seven regions of Texas. Covers cities, attractions, events, weather, ranches, wineries, and golf courses, shopping, suggested travel itineraries. Lists useful addresses and phone numbers.

949.21　　　NE
TEXELTOERIST MAGAZINE. (Text in Dutch, English, German) 1969. a. fl.4.95. Uitgeverij Langeveld & de Rooy BV, Postbus 11, 1790 AA Den Burg, Texel, Netherlands. TEL 31-2220-62600. FAX 31-2220-14111. Ed. Joop Rommets. adv.; illus. **Document type:** consumer publication.
　　Description: Provides a comprehensive guide to tourism on the Frisian island of Texel, including information on accommodations, museums, tourist activities, natural areas, and beaches.

910.202　　　UK　　ISSN 1352-786X
THAILAND AND BURMA HANDBOOK. 1993. a. £12.95. Trade & Travel Publications Ltd., 6 Riverside Ct., Lower Bristol Rd., Bath BA2 3DZ, England. TEL 01225-469141. FAX 01225-469461. (Dist. in N. America by: Passport Books, NTC Publishing Group, 4255 W. Touhy Ave., Lincolnwood, IL 60646-1975. TEL 708-679-5500. FAX 708-679-6375) Ed. Joshua Eliot. **Document type:** directory.
　　Formerly (until 1994): Thailand, Indochina and Burma Handbook (ISSN 0968-0926)

914　　　UK　　ISSN 0040-6171
THIS ENGLAND. 1968. q. £15($30) This England Ltd., Box 52, Cheltenham, Gloucestershire, England. TEL 01242-577775. FAX 01242-222034. Ed. Roy Faiers. adv.; bk.rev.; illus. circ. 165,000. **Indexed:** Child.Lit.Abstr. **Document type:** consumer publication.

TRAVEL AND TOURISM

916.7   BS
THIS IS BOTSWANA. 1983. irreg. free. Information and Broadcasting, Private Bag 0060, Gaborone, Botswana. Ed. Itumeleng Sabone. circ. 20,000. **Document type:** government publication.
Description: Presents travel and tourism features for travelers and business people. Highlights the natural wonders and potential for development in tourism and related industries.

918.604   EC
THIS IS ECUADOR. (Text in English) 1968. m. La Nina 55 y Avda. Amazonas, Quito, Ecuador. Dir. Gustavo Vallejo.

917.704   US
THIS IS INDIANAPOLIS. 1990. s-a. free. Indianapolis Convention and Visitors Association, One RCA Dome, Ste. 100, Indianapolis, IN 46325. TEL 317-639-4282. FAX 317-639-5273. Ed. William Hendrickson. adv. contact: Mary Huggard. circ. 150,000. **Document type:** consumer publication.
Description: For business and pleasure travelers and convention delegates staying at ICVA member hotels. Covers area leisure interests, travel-related services and city information.

914   UK   ISSN 0040-6198
THIS IS LONDON; the weekly magazine for visitors. 1956. w. £50. This Is London Magazine Ltd., 3 Heddon St., London W1R 7LE, England. TEL 0171-434-1281. FAX 0171-287-0592. Ed. Sue Webster. adv.: B&W page £364, color page £495. bk.rev.; film rev.; play rev.; illus. circ. 10,250. **Document type:** consumer publication.

910.09   MX
THIS IS MEXICO; Mexico's weekly visitor's pocket guide. 1960. w. free. Editorial This Is Mexico, Calle Londres 166, Apdo 6-728, 06600 Mexico, D.F., Mexico. TEL 533-15-40. FAX 915-208-28-38. TELEX 017-71-881. Ed. Jesus Maldonado. adv.; charts; illus. circ. 20,000.

915.3   QA
THIS IS QATAR. (Text in English) 1978. q. Gulf Publica Relations (Qatar), P.O. Box 4015, Doha, Qatar. TEL 413813. FAX 413814. TELEX 4787. Ed. Yousuf Qassim Darwish. adv. circ. 5,000.

330 910.9   HK
THIS IS VIETNAM. (Text in English) 1990. s-a. $10. Beca Investments Ltd., Bank of America Bldg., No.606, Harcourt Rd., Central, Hong Kong. TEL 8122614. FAX 8126046. Ed. Peter Witton. adv. circ. 6,000.
Description: Includes travel and business tips, a business directory, and maps of Hanoi and Ho Chi Minh City.

910.202   US   ISSN 0191-8354
THIS WEEK BIG ISLAND. 1966. w. free. Hagadone Hawaii, Inc., This Week Magazines, 715 S. King St., Ste. 325, Honolulu, HI 96813. TEL 808-526-1702. FAX 808-533-0471. Ed. Simone Grandmain; Pub. Ron Cruger. adv. contact: Diane Rivas. circ. 18,500. **Document type:** consumer publication.
Description: Includes information, maps and coupons for the visitor.

919 910.202   AT   ISSN 0817-6167
THIS WEEK IN ADELAIDE. 1963. m. Peter Isaacson Publications Pty. Ltd., 45-50 Porter St., Prahran, Vic. 3181, Australia. TEL 03-245-7777. FAX 03-245-7606. Ed. Robert Gibson. circ. 14,785. **Document type:** consumer publication.
Description: General information for travel in Adelaide.

910.202   GR
THIS WEEK IN ATHENS/SEMAINE A ATHENES/EBDOMADA STIN ATHINA. 1947. w. free. National Tourist Organization, c/o Yannis Horn, Pub., 26 Tim. Vassou, Athens, Greece. TEL 30-1-3224253.
Description: Informs visitors to Athens of hotels, restaurants, activities, and travel in and around the city.

919 910.202   AT   ISSN 0817-6159
THIS WEEK IN BRISBANE. 1963. m. Peter Isaacson Publications Pty. Ltd., 45-50 Porter St., Prahran, Vic. 3181, Australia. TEL 03-245-7777. FAX 03-245-7606. Ed. Robert Gibson. circ. 15,278. **Document type:** consumer publication.
Description: General information for travel in Brisbane.

919 910.202   AT   ISSN 0817-6140
THIS WEEK IN CANBERRA. 1960. m. Peter Isaacson Publications Pty. Ltd., 45-50 Porter St., Prahran, Vic. 3181, Australia. TEL 03-245-7777. FAX 03-245-7606. Ed. Robert Gibson. circ. 10,457. **Document type:** consumer publication.
Description: Travel information on sightseeing, shopping, entertainment, and dining out in Canberra.

919 910.202   AT
THIS WEEK IN DARWIN. m. Peter Isaacson Publications Pty. Ltd., 45-50 Porter St., Prahran, Vic. 3181, Australia. TEL 03-245-7777. FAX 03-245-7606. Ed. Robert Gibson. circ. 6,319. **Document type:** consumer publication.
Description: Travel information on sightseeing, shopping, entertainment, accommodations and dining out in Darwin.

919 910.202   AT   ISSN 0817-6124
THIS WEEK IN MELBOURNE. 1958? m. Peter Isaacson Publications Pty. Ltd., 45-50 Porter St., Prahran, Vic. 3181, Australia. TEL 03-245-7777. FAX 03-245-7606. Ed. Robert Gibson. circ. 10,665. **Document type:** consumer publication.
Description: Travel information on sightseeing, shopping, entertainment, accommodations, and dining out in Melbourne.

919 910.202   AT
THIS WEEK IN PERTH. m. Peter Isaacson Publications Pty. Ltd., 45-50 Porter St., Prahran, Vic. 3181, Australia. TEL 03-245-7777. FAX 03-245-7606. Ed. Robert Gibson. circ. 12,004.
Description: Tourist information on accommodations, sightseeing, shopping, entertainment, and dining out in Perth.

914   IT   ISSN 0040-6295
THIS WEEK IN ROME/SETTIMANA A ROMA. (Editions in English, French and Italian) 1948. m. L.4000 per no. Standard Media s.r.l., Via Madonna del Riposo 89, 00165 Rome, Italy. TEL 39-6-6228315. adv.: B&W page L.800000. illus. circ. 30,000.

919 910.202   AT   ISSN 0817-6175
THIS WEEK IN SYDNEY. 1964. m. Peter Isaacson Publications Pty. Ltd., 45-50 Porter St., Prahran, Vic. 3181, Australia. TEL 03-245-7777. FAX 03-245-7606. Ed. Robert Gibson. circ. 26,000. **Document type:** consumer publication.
—CCC.
Description: Tourist information on sightseeing, shopping, entertainment, dining out and accommodations in Sydney.

919 910.202   AT   ISSN 0817-6132
THIS WEEK IN TASMANIA. 1966. m. Peter Isaacson Publications Pty. Ltd., 45-50 Porter St., Prahran, Vic. 3181, Australia. TEL 03-245-7777. FAX 03-245-7606. Ed. Robert Gibson. circ. 9,063. **Document type:** consumer publication.
—CCC.

910.09   US   ISSN 0194-3596
THIS WEEK IN THE PIEDMONT TRIAD.* 1960. w. $24. 1703 Wembly Ct., Greensboro, NC 27410-3040. TEL 919-854-3033. Ed. Richard Crotners. adv. circ. 7,000.

917.4   US
THIS WEEK IN THE POCONOS. 1932. 29/yr. $52. Printing Craftsmen, Inc., Box 48, Pocono Pines, PA 18350. TEL 717-839-7103. FAX 717-646-4528. Ed. Iris E. Matucha. adv. circ. 248,000. **Document type:** consumer publication, bulletin.

910.2   US
THIS WEEK IN WESTERN NORTH CAROLINA. 1930. w. $26. Priceless Group Inc., 959 Merrimon Ave., Box 1513, Asheville, NC 28802. TEL 704-253-9299. Ed. Cindy Tunnell; Pub. Bobby Cannon. adv.; charts; illus. circ. 8,000. **Document type:** directory.
Formerly: This Week (ISSN 0040-6309)
Description: Informs the local resident, newcomer and tourist about things to do and see in western North Carolina.

910.202   US   ISSN 0191-8362
THIS WEEK KAUAI. 1966. w. free. Hagadone Hawaii, Inc., This Week Magazines, 715 S. King St., Ste. 325, Honolulu, HI 96813. TEL 808-526-1702. FAX 808-533-0471. Ed. Simone Grandmain; Pub. Ron Cruger. adv. contact: Erica Franklin. circ. 17,500. **Document type:** consumer publication.
Description: Provides information, maps and coupons for the visitor.

919.404   AT
THIS WEEK MAGAZINE. 1989. w. Aus.$26. Regional Publishers (N.S.W.) Pty. Ltd., 41 Helen St., Forster, N.S.W. 2423, Australia. TEL 065-546688. FAX 065-556399.
Formerly: Great Lakes Entertainer.
Description: Features tourist information, fishing, entertainment, and leisure.

910.202   US   ISSN 0191-8370
THIS WEEK MAUI. 1966. w. free. Hagadone Hawaii, Inc., This Week Magazines, 715 S. King St., Ste. 325, Honolulu, HI 96813. TEL 808-526-1702. FAX 808-879-1846. Ed. Simone Grandmain; Pub. Ron Cruger. adv. contact: Stan Mulkey. circ. 25,500. **Document type:** consumer publication.
Description: Provides information, maps and coupons for the visitor.

910.202   US
THIS WEEK OAHU. 1966. w. free. Hagadone Hawaii, Inc., This Week Magazines, 715 S. King St., Ste. 325, Honolulu, HI 96813. TEL 808-526-1702. FAX 808-533-0471. Ed. Simone Grandmain; Pub. Ron Cruger. adv. contact: Terri Pike. circ. 42,000. **Document type:** consumer publication.
Description: Provides information, maps and coupons for the visitor.

910.202   SI   ISSN 0129-6930
THIS WEEK SINGAPORE; tourist guide to Singapore. 1975. w. Miller Freeman Pte. Ltd., 100 Beach Rd., 26-00 Shaw Towers, Singapore 0718, Singapore. TEL 294-3366. FAX 298-5534. Ed. Gaynor Thomas. adv. circ. 25,000.
Formerly (until 1989): Lion City (ISSN 0129-4822)

910.2 919   US
THRUM'S ALL ABOUT HAWAII. 1970. a. $3.50. S B Printers, Inc., Box 100, Honolulu, HI 96810-0100. TEL 808-537-5353. Ed. Arlene King Duncan. adv. circ. 25,000.
Former titles: Almanac of the Pacific (ISSN 0065-6461); All About Hawaii.

917.1   CN
THUNDER BAY GUEST; visitor's magazine. 1963. m. free. Algoma Publishers Ltd., 1126 Roland St., Thunder Bay, ON P7B 5M4, Canada. TEL 807-623-4424. FAX 807-622-3140. Ed. Lorraine Deck. adv. contact: Laury Rae Alexander. circ. 160,000.

910.202   CN   ISSN 0846-5363
THUNDER BAY LIFE. 1985. m. Can.$15($15) North Superior Publishing Inc., 1145 Barton St., Thunder Bay, ON P7B 5N3, Canada. TEL 807-623-2348. FAX 807-623-7515. Ed. Scott A. Sumner. circ. 5,000. (back issues avail.)
Formerly: Thunder Bay Destinations.

TIBET SOCIETY BULLETIN. see *ETHNIC INTERESTS*

910.2   SZ
TICKET. (Editions in French and German) 1930. 5/yr. membership. Schweizer Jugendherbergen - Swiss Youth Hostel Association, Schaffhauserstr. 14, Postfach 161, CH-8042 Zurich, Switzerland. TEL 01-3601414. FAX 01-3601460. adv.; bk.rev.; illus. circ. 80,000. **Document type:** bulletin.
Formerly: Jugi - Ajiste (ISSN 0022-6009)

910.202 355   GW
TICKET; tips and travel. 1985. m. $12 (outside Europe $22). Wheels Verlag, Fuertherstr. 171, 90429 Nuernberg, Germany. TEL 0911-315831. FAX 0911-316349. Ed. Thomas Derra. adv. circ. 32,000.
Formerly: Monthly Ticket for More Information.

910.09   SP
TIEMPO DE VIAJAR. m. Ediciones Mensuales, O'Donnell 12, 28009 Madrid, Spain. TEL 34-1-5863300. Dir. Carlos Carnicero.

917.204   MX
TIJUANA. m. (Tijuana Hotel Association) Editorial Bonanza, S. de R.L., Dr. Velasco 95, Ed. 5, Of. 203, 06720 Mexico DF, Mexico. TEL 525-5938720. FAX 525-7052492.

TRAVEL AND TOURISM

910.2 917   US   ISSN 1054-5034
F902.3
TIM BELL'S ALASKA TRAVEL GUIDE. 1960. a. $8.95. Timothy J. Bell, Ed. & Pub., 413B 19th St., Ste. 170, Lynden, WA 98264. TEL 604-769-3073. adv.; bk.rev.; illus.; maps. circ. 60,000. **Document type:** consumer publication.
    Formerly: Alaska Travel Guide (ISSN 0065-5848)
    Description: Contains mile-by-mile information for Alaska, the Yukon, and northwestern British Columbia.

914   UK   ISSN 0049-3910
TIME OUT;* London's biggest selling magazine listing London's events plus news & reviews. 1968. w. £1.20. Time Out Magazine Ltd., Universal House, 251 Tottenham Court Rd., London W1P 0AB, England. (Subscr. to: Unit 8, Grove Ash, Bletchley, Milton Keynes MK1 1BZ, England) Ed. John Morrish. adv.; bk.rev.; film rev.; play rev.; illus. circ. 88,000. **Indexed:** Int.Ind.Film Per.
    —BLDSC (8852.150000).

910.03   US   ISSN 1075-3613
TODAY'S TRAVELER. 1992. bi-m. $14 (effective 1994). Bluestone Group, Inc., 68 E. Wacker Pl., Ste. 800, Chicago, IL 60601. TEL 312-853-4775. FAX 312-782-7367. (Subscr. to: Today's Traveler, Subscription Services, Box 641691, Chicago, IL 60664-9972. TEL 800-814-0380) Ed. Donna Kishbaugh; Pub. Earl Smith. adv.: B&W page $1500, color page L.2100; adv. contact: Sharon Reid. bk.rev.; illus. **Document type:** consumer publication.
    ●Also available online.
    Description: Provides in-depth articles about different cultures, peoples and events for a sophisticated audience. Covers art, architecture, food, people, countries and celebrities of interest to travelers.

914.39   NE   ISSN 0169-5738
TOERISMEE. 1967. m. Streek - V.V.V. West Brabant, Postbus 7000, 4800 GA Breda, Netherlands. TEL 31-76-222444. FAX 31-76-218530. adv.; charts; illus. circ. 10,500.
    Former titles (until 1981): Uit in West-Brabant (ISSN 0006-9558); (until 1976): Breda; Baronie.

915.204   JA
TOKYO CITY GUIDE TOUR COMPANION. 24/yr. Tokyo News Service Ltd., Tsukiji Hamarikyu Bldg., 5-3-3 Tsukiji, Chuo-ku, Tokyo 104, Japan. TEL 03-3542-6511.

915.2   JA   ISSN 0289-811X
TOKYO JOURNAL. 1981. m. $67 in Asia; U.S. $118; Europe $133. Intercontinental Marketing Corp., I.P.O. Box 5056, Tokyo 100-31, Japan. TEL 81-3-3661-7458. FAX 81-3-3667-9646.
    Description: Provides useful news for the foreign resident or traveler.

919.04   AT   ISSN 0725-5365
TOOWOOMBA AND GOLDEN WEST VISITORS' GUIDE. a. free. Toowoomba and Golden West Regional Tourist Association Ltd., P.O. Box 3090, Toowoomba, Qld. 4350, Australia. TEL 61-76-321988. FAX 61-76-324404. adv.; circ. 100,000 (paid); controlled. **Document type:** consumer publication, trade publication.
    Description: Regional information for tourists and travellers to this area.

TOOWOOMBA - QUEENSLAND'S GROWTH CENTRE. see BUSINESS AND ECONOMICS — Production Of Goods And Services

914.504   IT
TOP SHOP. (Text in English, Italian) 1982. q. Ideatour s.r.l., Via Mario Pagano 39, 20145 Milan, Italy. TEL 39-2-4982763. FAX 39-2-4817755. Ed. Mario Zanzi. adv.: page L.1500000. **Document type:** consumer publication.

914   IT
TOSCANA QUI. 1981. m. L.60000 (foreign L.120000). Casa Editrice Bonechi, Via Cairoli, 18-A, Florence, Italy. TEL 39-55-576841. FAX 39-55-5000766. adv.: B&W page L.2500000, color page L.3500000. **Document type:** consumer publication.

910.202   US
TOUR & TRAVEL MARKETPLACE.* 6/yr. C M P Publications, Inc., 600 Community Dr., Manhasset, NY 11030. TEL 516-562-5000. FAX 516-365-4601. TELEX 647035-CMP-PUB-MAHA. adv. circ. 51,000.

910   JA
TOUR COMPANION. (Text in English) 1973. fortn. free. Tokyo News Service Ltd. - Tokyo Nyusu Tsushinsha, Tsukiji Hamarikyu Bldg., 10th Fl., 3-3 Tsukiji 5-chome, Chuo-ku, Tokyo 104, Japan. TEL 03-3542-6511. Ed. Takashi Takeda. adv.; bk.rev.; charts; illus. circ. 80,000.
    Description: Provides all foreigners in the Tokyo vicinity, whether tourists or residents, with the most up-to-date information concerning events, shopping, dining, night-life and other topics of interest.

910.09   US
TOUR TRADE. m. Travel Trade Publications, 15 W. 44th St., New York, NY 10036. TEL 212-730-6600. FAX 212-730-7137. adv. circ. 69,983.
    Description: Provides travel agency personnel with news and features on the North American tour and travel market.

917.6   US   ISSN 0361-4948
F324.3
TOURBOOK: ALABAMA, LOUISIANA, MISSISSIPPI. Cover title: Alabama, Louisiana, Mississippi TourBook. a. membership. American Automobile Association, 1000 AAA Dr., Heathrow, FL 32746-5063. TEL 407-444-8200. FAX 407-444-8204. adv.; illus. circ. 955,800. **Document type:** consumer publication.

917.89   US   ISSN 0362-3599
F809.3
TOURBOOK: ARIZONA, NEW MEXICO. Cover title: Arizona, New Mexico TourBook. a. membership. American Automobile Association, 1000 AAA Dr., Heathrow, FL 32746-5063. TEL 407-444-8200. FAX 407-444-8204. adv.; illus. circ. 1,578,800. **Document type:** consumer publication.

917.6   US   ISSN 0363-1486
F409.3
TOURBOOK: ARKANSAS, KANSAS, MISSOURI, OKLAHOMA. Cover title: Arkansas, Kansas, Missouri, Oklahoma TourBook. a. membership. American Automobile Association, 1000 AAA Dr., Heathrow, FL 32746-5063. TEL 407-444-8200. FAX 407-444-8204. adv.; illus. circ. 1,260,500. **Document type:** consumer publication.

917.15   US   ISSN 0363-1788
F1035.8
TOURBOOK: ATLANTIC PROVINCES AND QUEBEC. Cover title: Atlantic Provinces and Quebec; New Brunswick, Newfoundland, Nova Scotia, Prince Edward Island, Quebec TourBook. a. membership. American Automobile Association, 1000 AAA Dr., Heathrow, FL 32746-5063. TEL 407-444-8200. FAX 407-444-8204. (Co-sponsor: Canadian Automobile Association) adv.; illus. circ. 566,600. **Document type:** consumer publication.
    Formerly: Eastern Canada Tour Book (ISSN 0569-2857)

917.9   US
TOURBOOK: CALIFORNIA, NEVADA; including Baja California, Mexico. Cover title: California, Nevada TourBook. a. membership. American Automobile Association, 1000 AAA Dr., Heathrow, FL 32746-5053. TEL 407-444-8200. FAX 407-444-8204. adv.; illus. circ. 3,076,100. **Document type:** consumer publication.

917.8   US   ISSN 0362-9821
F774.3
TOURBOOK: COLORADO, UTAH. Cover title: Colorado, Utah TourBook. a. membership. American Automobile Association, 1000 AAA Dr., Heathrow, FL 32746-5063. TEL 407-444-8200. FAX 407-444-8204. adv.; illus. circ. 1,178,700. **Document type:** consumer publication.

917.4   US   ISSN 0363-1494
F92.3
TOURBOOK: CONNECTICUT, MASSACHUSETTS, RHODE ISLAND. Cover title: Connecticut, Massachusetts, Rhode Island TourBook. a. membership. American Automobile Association, 1000 AAA Dr., Heathrow, FL 32746-5063. TEL 407-444-8200. FAX 407-444-8204. adv.; illus. circ. 1,293,800. **Document type:** consumer publication.
    Supersedes in part: Northeastern Tour Book (ISSN 0468-6853)

917.59   US   ISSN 0516-9674
GV1024
TOURBOOK: FLORIDA. Cover title: Florida TourBook. 1965. a. membership. American Automobile Association, 1000 AAA Dr., Heathrow, FL 32746-5063. TEL 407-444-8200. FAX 407-444-8204. adv.; illus. circ. 2,528,300. **Document type:** consumer publication.

917.5   US   ISSN 0361-4956
F284.3
TOURBOOK: GEORGIA, NORTH CAROLINA, SOUTH CAROLINA. Cover title: Georgia, North Carolina, South Carolina TourBook. a. membership. American Automobile Association, 1000 AAA Dr., Heathrow, FL 32746-5063. TEL 407-444-8200. FAX 407-444-8204. adv.; illus. circ. 2,526,400. **Document type:** consumer publication.

917   US   ISSN 0160-6921
DU622
TOURBOOK: HAWAII. Cover title: Hawaii TourBook. a. membership. American Automobile Association, 1000 AAA Dr., Heathrow, FL 32746-5063. TEL 407-444-8200. FAX 407-444-8204. adv.; illus. circ. 417,300. **Document type:** consumer publication.

917.9   US   ISSN 0363-2695
F744.3
TOURBOOK: IDAHO, MONTANA, WYOMING. Cover title: Idaho, Montana, Wyoming TourBook. a. membership. American Automobile Association, 1000 AAA Dr., Heathrow, FL 32746-5063. TEL 407-444-8200. FAX 407-444-8204. adv.; illus. circ. 937,300. **Document type:** consumer publication.
    Supersedes in part: Northwestern Tour Book (ISSN 0094-078X); Formerly: Northwestern States.

917   US   ISSN 0363-1508
F539.3
TOURBOOK: ILLINOIS, INDIANA, OHIO. Cover title: Illinois, Indiana, Ohio TourBook. a. membership. American Automobile Association, 1000 AAA Dr., Heathrow, FL 32746-5063. TEL 407-444-8200. FAX 407-444-8204. adv.; illus. circ. 2,067,500. **Document type:** consumer publication.

917.68   US   ISSN 0361-4964
F449.3
TOURBOOK: KENTUCKY, TENNESSEE. Cover title: Kentucky, Tennessee TourBook. a. membership. American Automobile Association, 1000 AAA Dr., Heathrow, FL 32746-5063. TEL 407-444-8200. FAX 407-444-8204. adv.; illus. circ. 1,632,700. **Document type:** consumer publication.

917.4   US   ISSN 0363-1516
F17.3
TOURBOOK: MAINE, NEW HAMPSHIRE, VERMONT. Cover title: Maine, New Hampshire, Vermont TourBook. a. membership. American Automobile Association, 1000 AAA Dr., Heathrow, FL 32746-5063. TEL 407-444-8200. FAX 407-444-8204. adv.; illus. circ. 1,059,500. **Document type:** consumer publication.
    Supersedes in part: Northeastern Tour Book (ISSN 0468-6853)

917   US   ISSN 0363-1524
F564.3
TOURBOOK: MICHIGAN, WISCONSIN. Cover title: Michigan, Wisconsin TourBook. a. membership. American Automobile Association, 1000 AAA Dr., Heathrow, FL 32746-5063. TEL 407-444-8200. FAX 407-444-8204. adv.; illus. circ. 1,046,400. **Document type:** consumer publication.

917   US   ISSN 0364-0086
F106
TOURBOOK: MID-ATLANTIC. Cover title: Mid-Atlantic-Delaware, District of Columbia, Maryland, Virginia, West Virginia TourBook. a. membership. American Automobile Association, 1000 AAA Dr., Heathrow, FL 32746-5063. TEL 407-444-8200. FAX 407-444-8204. adv.; illus. circ. 2,527,700. **Document type:** consumer publication.

917   US   ISSN 0363-1532
F132.3
TOURBOOK: NEW JERSEY, PENNSYLVANIA. Cover title: New Jersey, Pennsylvania TourBook. a. membership. American Automobile Association, 1000 AAA Dr., Heathrow, FL 32746-5063. TEL 407-444-8200. FAX 407-444-8204. adv.; illus. circ. 2,040,200. **Document type:** consumer publication.

TRAVEL AND TOURISM

917   US   ISSN 0363-1540
F117.3
TOURBOOK: NEW YORK; including Niagara Falls, Ontario, Canada. Cover title: New York TourBook. a. membership. American Automobile Association, 1000 AAA Dr., Heathrow, FL 32746-5063. TEL 407-444-8200. FAX 407-444-8204. adv.; illus. circ. 1,574,600. **Document type:** consumer publication.

917   US   ISSN 0733-8368
GV1024
TOURBOOK: NORTH CENTRAL. Cover title: North Central TourBook - Iowa, Minnesota, Nebraska, North Dakota, South Dakota. a. membership. American Automobile Association, 1000 AAA Dr., Heathrow, FL 32746-5063. TEL 407-444-8200. FAX 407-444-8204. adv.; illus. circ. 1,018,100. **Document type:** consumer publication.
   Formerly: North Central Tour Book (ISSN 0733-835X).

917   US   ISSN 0363-1559
F1057
TOURBOOK: ONTARIO; including Niagara Falls, New York, USA. Cover title: Ontario TourBook. a. membership. American Automobile Association, 1000 AAA Dr., Heathrow, FL 32746-5063. TEL 407-444-8200. FAX 407-444-8204. (Co-sponsor: Canadian Automobile Association) adv.; illus. circ. 798,900. **Document type:** consumer publication.

918   US   ISSN 0363-1567
F874.3
TOURBOOK: OREGON, WASHINGTON. Cover title: Oregon, Washington TourBook. a. membership. American Automobile Association, 1000 AAA Dr., Heathrow, FL 32746-5063. TEL 407-444-8200. FAX 407-444-8204. adv.; illus. circ. 1,195,800. **Document type:** consumer publication.

917   US   ISSN 0363-1575
F384.3
TOURBOOK: TEXAS. Cover title: Texas TourBook. a. membership. American Automobile Association, 1000 AAA Dr., Heathrow, FL 32746-5063. TEL 407-444-8200. FAX 407-444-8204. adv.; illus. circ. 1,021,000. **Document type:** consumer publication.

917.12   US   ISSN 0362-3602
F1060.4
TOURBOOK: WESTERN CANADA AND ALASKA. Cover title: Western Canada and Alaska - Alberta, British Columbia, Manitoba, Northwest Territories, Saskatchewan, Yukon Territory and Alaska TourBook. a. American Automobile Association, 1000 AAA Dr., Heathrow, FL 32746-5063. TEL 407-444-8200. FAX 407-444-8204. (Co-sponsor: Canadian Automobile Association) adv.; illus. circ. 873,700. **Document type:** consumer publication.

910   FR   ISSN 0222-061X
TOURHEBDO. 1979. 43/yr. 175 F. 14 rue Chaptal, 92300 Levallois, France. TEL 47-57-31-66. FAX 47-59-09-56. Ed. Pierre Amalou. circ. 12,500.

388.3 796.7   BE
TOURING; auto et loisirs - auto en vrije tijd. (Editions in Dutch, French) 1895. m. 1055 BEF membership (effective 1994). Touring Club of Belgium, Rue de la Loi 44, 1040 Brussels, Belgium. TEL 32-2-2332211. FAX 32-2-2332205. adv.; B&W page 288000 BEF, color page 410000 BEF; trim 280 x 203; adv. contact: Lieve Sonck. bk.rev.; bibl.; illus.; index. circ. 760,000 (342,000 Dutch ed.; 418,000 French ed.). **Document type:** consumer publication.
   Formed by the July 1993 merger of: Touring Secours & Touring Club Magazine (ISSN 0772-2540); Which was formerly (until 1984): Autotouring (ISSN 0045-1126)
   Description: Publishes articles on automobile safety, reviews of new car models, ideas for travel in Belgium and throughout Europe, listings of local and regional events of interest, and other topics of interest to car owners.

TOURING. see *TRANSPORTATION* — *Automobiles*

914   SZ   ISSN 0040-9758
TOURING. (Editions in French, German and Italian) 1936. fortn. 35 SFr. Druck- und Verlags Konsortium Touring, c/o Zollikofer AG, Fuerstenlandstr. 122, CH-9001 St. Gallen, Switzerland. FAX 031-250226. Ed. Bernhard Bickel. adv.; bk.rev.; illus.; stat. circ. 1,200,000. **Document type:** newspaper.

TOURING GIOVANI. see *CHILDREN AND YOUTH — For*

910.09   UK   ISSN 0261-3700
TOURISM. 1978. q. £25 (foreign £30). The Tourism Society, 26 Chapter St., London SW1P 4ND, England. TEL 0171-834-0461. FAX 0171-932-0238. Ed. Kate Davidson. adv.; B&W page £250; trim 277 x 188. bk.rev. circ. 1,800. **Document type:** bulletin.
   —BLDSC (8870.920560).

910.09   II
TOURISM AND WILDLIFE. (Text in English) 1972. q. Rs.32($16) G.C. Verma, Ed. & Pub., 24 Gola Market, Netaji Subash Marg, New Delhi 110 002, India. adv.; bk.rev.; charts; illus. circ. 20,000.
   Description: For the tourist industry as well as educational institutions. Covers various tourist and wildlife attractions, in addition to art and cultural events.

338.4   UK   ISSN 1354-8166
▼**TOURISM ECONOMICS.** 1995. q. £125($195) (effective 1996). In Print Publishing Ltd., c/o Mr. A. Dingwall, Dir., 9 Beaufort Terrace, Brighton BN2 2SU, England. TEL 01273-682836. FAX 01273-620958. (Subscr. to: Turpin Distribution Services, Blackhorse Rd., Letchworth, Herts. SG6 1HN, England. TEL 01462-672555. FAX 01462-480947) Ed. Stephen Wanhill; Pub. John Edmondson. **Document type:** academic/scholarly publication.
   Description: Contains original research papers on the business and economics of tourism and recreation.
   Refereed Serial

TOURISM EDUCATION DIRECTORY. see *EDUCATION*

914.2   UK   ISSN 0309-8958
TOURISM INTELLIGENCE QUARTERLY. 1977. q. £80. British Tourist Authority, Thames Tower, Black's Rd., Hammersmith, London W6 9EL, England. (Co-sponsor: English Tourist Board) stat.
   —BLDSC (8870.920850).
   Description: Collates and interprets current statistical data relating to international tourism and tourism into, within, and out of the U.K.

910.02 647.068   UK   ISSN 0261-5177
G155.A1
TOURISM MANAGEMENT. 1980. 8/yr. £333($530) (effective 1996). Butterworth - Heinemann, Part of the Reed Elsevier group, Linacre House, Jordan Hill, Oxford OX2 8DP, England. TEL 0865-310366. FAX 0865-310898. TELEX 83111 BHPOXF G. (Subscr. to: Elsevier Science Ltd., P.O. Box 800, Kidlington, Oxford OX5 1DX, England. TEL 44-865-843000. FAX 44-865-843010; Subscr. in U.S. and Canada to: Elsevier Science, 660 White Plains Rd., Tarrytown, NY 10591-5153. TEL 914-524-9200. FAX 914-333-2444) Ed. Frances Brown. abstr.; charts; illus. (also avail. in microform from UMI; back issues avail.) Indexed: Art.Hosp.& Tour., Cont.Pg.Manage., Geo.Abstr., IDA. **Document type:** academic/scholarly publication.
   —BLDSC (8870.920970); Faxon; Genuine Article; SWETS; UMI; UnCover. **CCC.**
   Description: Publishes original research in tourism, analysis of trends, and information on the planning and management of all aspects of travel and tourism.
   Refereed Serial

382   FR   ISSN 0256-7598
TOURISM POLICY AND INTERNATIONAL TOURISM IN O E C D MEMBER COUNTRIES. French edition: Politique du Tourisme et Tourisme International dans les Pays Membres de l'OCDE (ISSN 1017-0685) 1961. a. price varies. Organization for Economic Cooperation and Development, 2 rue Andre-Pascal, 75775 Paris Cedex 16, France. (Dist. in U.S. by: O.E.C.D. Publications and Information Center, 2001 L St., N.W., Ste. 700, Washington, DC 20036-4910. TEL 202-785-6323) (also avail. in microfiche from OEC,CIS; back issues avail.) Indexed: IIS.
   —BLDSC (8870.922300).
   Former titles (until 1970): Tourism in O E C D Member Countries (ISSN 0474-604X); (until 1962): Tourism in Europe (ISSN 1021-1632)

915.4   II   ISSN 0250-8281
TOURISM RECREATION RESEARCH. (Special issues avail.) (Text in English) 1976. s-a. Rs.500($100) (effective 1994). Centre for Tourism Research and Development, A 965-6 Indira Nagar, Lucknow 226 016, India. TEL 0522-381586. FAX 091-0522-234023. Ed. Tej Vir Singh. adv. contact: Shalini Singh. bk.rev.; bibl.; illus. circ. 600. (back issues avail.) Indexed: Rural Recreat.Tour.Abstr., Sportsearch (1981-), World Agri.Econ.& Rural Sociol.Abstr.
   —BLDSC (8870.922350).
   Description: Multidisciplinary research journal focusing on problems in various recreational environments of ecology, economy and culture. Attempts to seek possible answers for sustainable development of tourism.

914   SZ   ISSN 0251-3102
TOURISM REVIEW. q. 57 SFr. (foreign 64 SFr.) A I E S T, Varnbuelstr. 19, CH-9000 St. Gallen, Switzerland. TEL 071-302525. FAX 071-302536. Ed. C. Kaspar. circ. 1,250. **Document type:** trade publication.
   —SWETS.

338.4 910.2   CN
TOURISM TODAY. 1946. bi-m. free. Tourism Industry Association of Canada, 130 Albert St., Ste. 1016, Ottawa, ON K1P 5G4, Canada. TEL 613-238-3883. FAX 613-238-3878. Ed. Debra Berk. circ. 2,000. **Document type:** newsletter.
   Former titles (until 1992): T I A C Newsletter (ISSN 1184-7255); (until 1990): T I A C Tourism Industry Association (ISSN 0845-4744); (until 1988): Tourism Association of Canada Newsletter (ISSN 0827-5505)

TOURISME ET GASTRONOMIE. see *HOTELS AND RESTAURANTS*

910   FR   ISSN 1147-9604
TOURISME MARKETING ET COMMUNICATION. 25/yr. Evenement - Tourisme - Communication, 29 rue du Faubourg-Poissoniere, 75009 Paris, France. TEL 48-24-08-97. FAX 42-47-00-76. Ed. Josette Sicsic. circ. 10,000. **Document type:** trade publication.

910.202   CN   ISSN 0836-205X
TOURISME PLUS, LE JOURNAL DES VOYAGES. (Text in French) 1980. w. (46/yr.). Can.$48. Publications Transcontinental Inc., 1100 boul. Rene Levesque W., 24th Fl., Montreal, PQ H3B 4X9, Canada. TEL 514-392-9000. FAX 514-392-4726. TELEX 055-61971. Ed. Michel Villeneuve. circ. 6,500. (back issues avail.)
   Formed by the 1986 merger of: Tourisme Plus (ISSN 0226-6601); Journal des Voyages (ISSN 0225-0462)
   Description: Trade information for travel agents, wholesalers, airlines, cruises, and hotels.

910.4   AU
TOURIST AKTUELL. 1982. fortn. Media Emap Verlag GmbH, Loquaiplatz 12, A-1061 Vienna, Austria. TEL 01-59960-0. FAX 01-5996021. Ed. Otto Komarek. circ. 7,000. **Document type:** trade publication.

910.09   GW   ISSN 0936-3637
TOURIST AUF REISEN; Tourist-Information fuer Gruppen- und Einzelreisen. 1989. a. DM.7.50. Stuenings Verlag, Postfach 2980, 47729 Krefeld, Germany. TEL 021521-8530. circ. 50,000. (back issues avail.)

TRAVEL AND TOURISM

910 AU
TOURIST AUSTRIA INTERNATIONAL. w. Dr.-Walter-Norden-Platz 1, A-7061 Trausdorf, Austria. TEL 2682-4888. Ed. Walter Norden. circ. 12,400.

971.04 CN ISSN 0319-0439
TOURIST GUIDE BOOK OF ONTARIO. 1921. a. free. Ontario Motorist Publishing Co. Ltd., 1253 Ouellette Ave., Windsor, ON N8X 1J3, Canada. TEL 519-971-3209. FAX 519-977-1197. Ed. Douglas O'Neil. adv. circ. 150,000. **Document type:** consumer publication.
Description: Details the sights, sounds and activities in Ontario and the U.S.

910.202 AU
TOURIST INTERN. w. Media Emap Verlag GmbH, Loquaiplatz 12, A-1061 Vienna, Austria. TEL 01-59960-0. FAX 01-5996021. circ. 200. **Document type:** trade publication.

910.4 790.1 IT
TOURIST MAGAZINE. 1988. q. L.2000 per no. Editoriale Eurocamp s.r.l, Via Durini, No.3, 20122 Milan, Italy. TEL 39-2-76022377. FAX 39-2-76022430. Ed. Maria Paola Canegrati. adv. contact: Claudio Benaglia. circ. 5,000. **Document type:** newspaper.

910.202 UK
TOURIST NEWS. q. Northern Ireland Tourist Board, St. Anne's Ct., 59 North St., Belfast BT1 1NB, N. Ireland. TEL 01232-231221. FAX 01232-310933. circ. 1,500. **Document type:** newsletter.

910.202 AT
TOURIST PARK GUIDE. 1946. a. Aus.$4.75. David Syme & Co. Limited, 250 Spencer St., Melbourne, Vic. 3000, Australia. TEL 03-601-2903. FAX 03-642-0852. Ed. Gwen Haslar. adv.: B&W page $770, color page $1670; trim 182 x 241; adv. contact: Kate Shaw.
Description: Contains details of caravan and camping parks throughout the country.

910.2 GW ISSN 0049-4283
TOURISTIK AKTUELL; the Travel Trade Report. 1970. w. DM.150. Jaeger Verlag GmbH, Arhellger Weg 17, 64380 Rossdorf, Germany. TEL 06154-6995-01. FAX 06154-6995490. TELEX 4191324-DAV-D. adv.; bk.rev.; abstr.; illus.; stat. circ. 15,000. **Document type:** trade publication.

910.09 GW ISSN 0173-606X
TOURISTIK R.E.P.O.R.T.. 1980. fortn. DM.72($36) W D V Wirtschaftsdienst, Lange Str. 13, 60311 Frankfurt a.M., Germany. TEL 069-29907-0. FAX 069-29907-499. Ed. Heiner Berninger. circ. 16,128. **Document type:** consumer publication.

910.202 CY ISSN 0259-3580
TOURISTIKA CHRONIKA/TOURISM CHRONICLE. 1986. bi-m. P.O. Box 7083, Nicosia, Cyprus. TEL 357-2-443240. Ed. A. Karouzis. circ. 2,000.

910.202 GW ISSN 0173-3877
TOURS; das Abenteuer Magazin. bi-m. DM.46.20. Allpress Verlag GmbH, Kleine Schuetzenstr. 7, 56203 Hoehr-Grenzhausen, Germany. TEL 02624-10645. FAX 02624-4662. Ed. Christian Pehlemann. adv. contact: Peter Schachtl. circ. 72,693. **Document type:** consumer publication.

910.202 US ISSN 0278-467X
T49.5
TOURS AND VISITS DIRECTORY. irreg., 2nd ed., 1981. $120. Gale Research Inc., 835 Penobscot Bldg., Detroit, MI 48226. TEL 313-961-2242. FAX 313-961-6083. TELEX 810-221-7086. **Document type:** directory.
Formerly: Behind the Scenes (ISSN 0270-3416)

917.1 CN ISSN 0847-9348
TOURS ON MOTORCOACH. French edition: Excurions en Autocar (ISSN 0847-933X) 1988. m. (Bus Owners Association) Publicom Inc., C.P. 365, Place d'Armes, Montreal, PQ H2Y 3H1, Canada. TEL 514-274-0004. FAX 514-274-5884. Ed. Ray Dulude. adv.; circ. 13,302 (controlled). **Document type:** trade publication.
Description: Travel trade publication for group tour organizers.

TOUTES LES NOUVELLES DE L'HOTELLERIE ET DU TOURISME. see HOTELS AND RESTAURANTS

330 060 US ISSN 0743-9709
T394
TRADESHOW & CONVENTION GUIDE. 1964. a. $85. B P I Communications, Amusement Business Division, Box 24970, Nashville, TN 37202. TEL 615-321-4250. FAX 615-327-1575. adv. circ. 4,000. **Document type:** directory.
Description: Sourcebook for those planning trade shows and conventions, corporate or association meetings and exhibits. Includes dates and data for conventions and trade shows for up to the next 5 years. Also lists hotels, auditoriums, convention centers and facilities serving the industry.

TRADESHOW DIRECTORY. see BUSINESS AND ECONOMICS — Trade And Industrial Directories

910.09 US ISSN 0276-4873
TL298
TRAILBLAZER.* 1978. m. $24. Thousand Trails, Inc. (Subsidiary of: Southmark Corp.), 2711 L.B.J. Frwy. No. 254, Dallas, TX 75234-7317. FAX 206-644-1100. Ed. Gregg Olsen. adv.: B&W page $2982, color page $4377; 8 1/4 x 10 3/4. tr.lit. circ. 150,000. **Document type:** consumer publication.
Description: For R.V. travelers and resort camping enthusiasts.

TRAILER LIFE CAMPGROUND AND R V SERVICES DIRECTORY. see BUSINESS AND ECONOMICS — Trade And Industrial Directories

910.202 UK
TRAILFINDER. 1970. 3/yr. £8 (foreign £12). Trailfinders Ltd., 42-50 Earls Court Rd., London W8 6FT, England. TEL 0171-937-8499. FAX 0171-938-1868. Ed. Heie Sanders. adv. circ. 250,000. **Document type:** consumer publication.
Description: Travel articles on non-European destinations, especially Australia, Asia and North America. Section on latest flight prices worldwide.

TRANSITIONS ABROAD; the guide to learning, living, and working overseas. see EDUCATION — International Education Programs

TRANSPORT; guia ecuatoriana de transporte y turismo. see TRANSPORTATION

TRANSPORT AND TOURISM JOURNAL. see TRANSPORTATION

914 BE ISSN 0041-1442
TRANSPORT ET TOURISME/TRANSPORT EN TOERISME. (Editions in Dutch, French) 1928. m. 2300 BEF. Federation Belge des Exploitants d'Autobus et d'Autocars, Chaussee de Haecht 1803 B, B-1130 Brussels, Belgium. TEL 32-2-245-3570. FAX 32-2-245-2050. Ed. Luc Glorieux. adv. contact: Conny Desmet. illus. circ. 2,000 (French ed. 800; Dutch ed. 1,200).

910.09 SP ISSN 0211-9633
TRANSPORTE AEREO Y TURISMO. 1982. 10/yr. 3500 ptas.($45) Apdo. de Correos 14027, Mejico 31, 28028 Madrid, Spain. TEL 34-1-725-64-54. FAX 34-1-361-07-01. Ed. Antonio Florez. adv. contact: M. Fernanda Fernandez. bk.rev. circ. 7,000. **Document type:** trade publication.

910.09 CN ISSN 0836-7353
TRAVEL A LA CARTE. 1988. 6/yr. Can.$11.97($18) (foreign $22). Interpress, Inc., 136 Walton St., Port Hope, ON L1A 1N5, Canada. TEL 905-885-7948. FAX 905-885-7202. Ed. Donna Carter. adv. circ. 145,000. **Indexed:** Can.B.P.I. **Document type:** consumer publication.
Description: Gloval travel and leisure magazine. Features articles focusing on domestic and international travel.

910.2 UK ISSN 0041-1981
TRAVEL AGENCY; Britain's monthly business, marketing and sales publication for the travel trade. 1925. m. £60. Maclean Hunter Ltd., Maclean Hunter House, Chalk Ln., Cockfosters Rd., Barnet, Herts. EN4 0BU, England. TEL 0181-242-3000. FAX 0181-242-3185. TELEX 299072 MACHUN G. Ed. Andrew McGeehan. adv.; charts; illus.; mkt.; stat.; tr.lit.; index. circ. 10,280. **Indexed:** Art.Hosp.& Tour. **Document type:** trade publication.
—BLDSC (9045.425000).

910.09 MY
TRAVEL AGENCY.* vol.5, 1978. m. Aus.$20. Phoenix Enterprise, KTM Godown No. 2A, Jalan Tun Sambanthan, 50470 Kuala Lumpur, Malaysia. adv.; illus.

910.09 US ISSN 1068-2279
G154
TRAVEL AGENCY REFERENCE & PROFILE DIRECTORY. 1991. a. $80. World Travel Communications Inc., 7380 S. Eastern Ave., No. 124-142, Las Vegas, NV 89123. TEL 702-795-2411. FAX 702-361-0371. Ed. J.A. Cabell. **Document type:** directory.
Formed by the merger of (1983-1991): Travel Agency Communications Reports - Eastern Edition; Which was formerly: Eastern Travel Sales Guide & Travel Agency Communications Reports - North American Edition; (1970-1991): Travel Agency Communications Reports - Western Edition; Which was formerly: Western Travel Sales Guide.

338 US ISSN 1053-9360
TRAVEL AGENT; the national newsweekly magazine of the travel industry. 1930. w. $250. Universal Media, Inc., 801 Second Ave., New York, NY 10017. TEL 212-370-5050. FAX 212-370-4491. Ed. Eric Friedbeim; Pub. Richard P. Friese. adv.: B&W page $9010, color page $11725; trim 8 3/8 x 10 7/8. bk.rev.; film rev.; charts; illus.; mkt.; circ. 53,503 (controlled). **Indexed:** P.A.I.S., Tr.& Indus.Ind. **Document type:** trade publication.
Former titles (until 1990): Travel Agent Magazine (ISSN 1041-0783); (until 1988): Travel Agent (ISSN 0041-199X); Incorporates: Travel Agent Domestic Tour Manual; Official Sales Guide Motorcoach Tours of North America; Motorcoach Tour Mart.

914 CN ISSN 0842-425X
TRAVEL AGENTS GUIDE TO EUROPE. (Text English, French) 1988. a. Motivations International Inc., 14 Ronan Ave., Toronto, ON M4N 2X9, Canada. TEL 416-481-6384. Ed. John Stephenson. adv. circ. 10,000. **Document type:** trade publication.

910.91 387.7 CN
TRAVEL AGENT'S HANDBOOK. a. price varies. International Air Transport Association, 2000 Peel St., Montreal, PQ H3A 2R4, Canada. TEL 514-844-6311. FAX 514-844-5286.
Description: Sets out the resolutions and other provisions of interest to IATA passenger sales agents in the exercise of their rights and obligations as approved agents and contains information of a practical value in their day-to-day work.

910.09 338 US ISSN 1068-7416
CODEN: TALBEZ
TRAVEL ALERT BULLETIN. 1987. s-m. $95. Nationwide Intelligence, Box 1922, Saginaw, MI 48605. TEL 517-752-6123; 800-333-4130. FAX 517-752-1605. Ed. David W. Oppermann. bk.rev. (looseleaf format) **Document type:** newsletter.
●Also available online.
Description: Covers developments affecting corporate travel.

TRAVEL AND HOSPITALITY CAREER DIRECTORY. see OCCUPATIONS AND CAREERS

910.2 US ISSN 0041-2007
G149
TRAVEL & LEISURE. (In 3 regional eds., and 1 demographic ed.) 1971. m. $32. American Express Publishing Corp. (New York), 1120 Ave. of the Americas, New York, NY 10036. TEL 212-382-5600. FAX 212-768-1568. Ed. Nancy Novogrod; Pub. Richard B. Barthelmes. adv.; bk.rev.; illus.; tr.lit. circ. 900,000. (also avail. in microform from UMI) **Indexed:** Access (1975-), Mag.Ind., PMR. **Document type:** consumer publication.
●Also available online.
—Faxon; UMI; UnCover.
Formerly: Travel and Camera (ISSN 0049-4542)

910.202 UK
TRAVEL AND LEISURE MAGAZINE. 1990. bi-m. £2.99. Travel and Leisure Magazines Ltd., 301 Channel Sea Centre, Abbey Ln., Stratford, London E15 3ND, England. TEL 0181-519-8488. FAX 0181-555-0061. Ed. Simon Deane. adv. contact: Terry Stafford. bk.rev.; tr.lit. circ. 26,000. **Document type:** consumer publication.
Description: Provides hints and advice to aid in obtaining the best holiday for the least money.

TRAVEL AND TOURISM

TRAVEL AND TOURISM - ABSTRACTING, BIBLIOGRAPHIES, STATISTICS. see *TRAVEL AND TOURISM — Abstracting, Bibliographies, Statistics*

910.202   US   ISSN 0269-3755
G155.A1
TRAVEL & TOURISM ANALYST. bi-m. £495($945) Economist Intelligence Unit, 111 W. 57th St., New York, NY 10019. TEL 212-554-0600; 800-938-4685. FAX 212-586-1182. TELEX 175567. (UK addr.: Economist Intelligence Unit Ltd., Subscriptions Dept., P.O. Box 200, Harold Hill, Romford, Essex RM3 8UX, England. TEL 44-1708-381-444. FAX 44-1708-371-850) (also avail. in microform from UMI) **Indexed:** Art.Hosp.& Tour., Hospit.Ind.
•Also available online. Vendor(s): Lexis-Nexis.
—BLDSC (9045.450900); UMI. **CCC.**
Description: News and forecasts for all sectors of the industry: airlines, travel agents, hotels and accommodations.

350   US   ISSN 1070-8855
TRAVEL & TOURISM EXECUTIVE REPORT. 1979. m. $65 to non-members. (Association of Travel Marketing Executives) Leisure Industry - Recreation News, Box 43563, Washington, DC 20010. TEL 202-232-7107. Ed. Marj Jensen. adv.; charts; stat. circ. 4,000. **Document type:** newsletter.
Formerly (until 1981): Travel and Tourism Newsletter; **Supersedes:** Travel Marketing News.
Description: Focuses on the marketing and promotion of travel destination products. Presents information and data on trends and demographics.

910.202   BA
TRAVEL & TOURISM NEWS MIDDLE EAST. (Text in English) m. $68. Al Hilal Publishing & Marketing Group, P.O. Box 224, Manama, Bahrain. TEL 973-293131. FAX 973-293400. TELEX 8981 HILAL BN. (In U.K.: Hilal International (UK) Ltd., Crescent Ct., 102 Victor Rd., Teddington, Middx TW11 8SS, England. TEL 44-81-943-3630. FAX 44-81-943-3701) Ed. Frederick Rocque. adv.: B&W page £2800, color page £3920; 400 x 275. circ. 5,130. (tabloid format) **Document type:** trade publication.
Formerly: Travel and Tourism News International; **Incorporates:** Arab Travel Magazine.
Description: For travel industry professionals, including travel and tour agents, airline and airport personnel, government tourist offices.

910.09   US
G149.5
TRAVEL AND TOURISM RESEARCH ASSOCIATION. PROCEEDINGS OF THE ANNUAL MEETING. 1970. a. $75 to non-members; members $35. Travel and Tourism Research Association, 10200 W. 44th Ave., Ste. 304, Wheat Ridge, CO 80033. TEL 303-940-6557. FAX 303-422-8894. Ed. Francine Butler. charts; illus. circ. 750. **Document type:** proceedings.
Formerly: Travel and Tourism Research Association. Proceedings of the Annual Conference (ISSN 0276-8968)

910 658.8   UK
TRAVEL AND TOURISM: THE INTERNATIONAL MARKET. (Subseries of: Market Direction reports) a. £1595($3190) (effective 1996). Euromonitor, 60-61 Britton St., London EC1M 5NA, England. TEL 0171-251-8024. FAX 0171-608-3149. (Addr. in N. America: Euromonitor International, 122 S. Michigan Ave., Ste. 1200, Chicago, IL 60603. TEL 312-922-1115. FAX 312-922-1157) (looseleaf format) **Document type:** trade publication.
•Also available online. Vendor(s): Data-Star, Knight-Ridder, Inc.
Description: Analyzes the market for travel and tourism for France, Germany, Italy, Spain, the U.K., the U.S., and Japan.

990   AT   SSN 0817-2935
TRAVEL AUSTRALIA. 1986. s-a. Aus.$55. Australian Tourism Magazine, G.P.O. Box 7039, Sydney, N.S.W. 2000, Australia. TEL 61-2-2621333. FAX 61-2-2676784. Ed. Shamoli Dutt; Pub. Shamoli Dutt. adv.; bk.rev. circ. 5,300. **Document type:** trade publication.
Description: Promotes Australia as a destination and Australian tourist products.

910.202 070.5   US   ISSN 1058-7098
TRAVEL BOOKS WORLDWIDE; 'he travel book review. 1991. 10/yr. $36 (overseas $72). Travel Keys, Box 162266, Sacramento, CA 95816-2266. TEL 916-452-5200. Ed. Peter B. Manston; Pub. Peter B. Manston. bk.rev.; video rev.; circ. 1,500 (paid). (back issues avail.) **Document type:** newsletter, bibliography.
•Also available online.
Description: Reviews travel guides, maps, atlases, and trade books with a travel angle. Also reviews gift books, cookbooks, and books on outdoor sports.

910.202   UK
TRAVEL BRITAIN. 1989. bi-m. £20($32) Travelscope Publications, Foundation House, 3rd Fl., Perserverance Works, 38 Kingsland Rd., London E2 8DD, England. TEL 0171-729-4337. FAX 0171-729-1716. Ed. Stuart Bowden; Pub. Bob MacBeth-Seath. adv.: page £2100; trim 398 x 285; adv. contact: Gary Kaye. stat.; tr.lit. circ. 22,800. (tabloid format; back issues avail.) **Document type:** trade publication.
Description: Informs and assists the U.S. travel trade in selling the U.K. as a travel and tourism destination.

910.09   UK
TRAVEL BULLETIN; the weekly for retail staff. 1976. w. Alain Charles Publishing Ltd., Alain Charles House, 27 Wilfred St., London SW1E 6PR, England. TEL 0171-834-7676. FAX 0171-973-0076. TELEX 297165 ACPLTD G. Ed. Valery Hary. adv. contact: Patricia Fairfield. circ. 8,700. **Document type:** trade publication, bulletin.
Description: Aimed at U.K. travel agents; lists jobs, travel incentives, and competitions. Also contains industry news and training and marketing features.

910.22 330.9   HK   ISSN 1011-7768
TRAVEL BUSINESS ANALYST. European edition (ISSN 0256-419X) 1981. 6/yr. $100. Travel Business Analyst, G.P.O. Box 12761, Hong Kong. TEL 2507-2310. FAX 2507-4620. TELEX 62107-HX. Ed. Murray Bailey. bk.rev.; charts; stat. (back issues avail.)
Description: Provides travel business information, statistics and analysis for senior management and investors in the travel business.

910.22 330.9   FR   ISSN 0256-419X
TRAVEL BUSINESS ANALYST (EUROPEAN EDITION). Asia Pacific edition (ISSN 1011-7768) 1991. 10/yr. 250 ECU. Travel Business Analyst (Paris), 10 rue Auguste Vitu, 75015 Paris, France. TEL 45-78-64-22. FAX 45-79-50-19. (Hong Kong addr.: 200 Lockhart Rd., 14th Fl., P.O. Box 12761, Hong Kong) Ed. Nancy Cockerell.
Description: Provides business information, statistics and analysis for senior management and investors in travel business.

914   BE
TRAVEL CHECK; the Benelux buyer's guide to business & incentive travel. (Text in English) 1982. m. Travel Check, Keesinglaan 19, 2100 Antwerp, Belgium. TEL 323-325-2235. circ. 13,850. (back issues avail.)

915.104   CN   ISSN 0834-258X
TRAVEL CHINA NEWSLETTER. 1986. m. $87. Blendon Information Services, 126 Willowdale Ave., No. 1, Willowdale, ON M2N 4Y2, Canada. TEL 416-223-5397. FAX 416-223-5397. Ed. Ruth Lor Malloy; Pub. R.V. Orchard. (back issues avail.) **Document type:** newsletter.

910.202   US   ISSN 1076-5719
TRAVEL COMPANIONS; North America's foremost newsletter for solo travelers. 1982. bi-m. $48. (Travel Companion Exchange, Inc.) Jens Jurgen, Ed. & Pub., Box 833, Amityville, NY 11701. TEL 516-454-0880. FAX 516-454-0170. bk.rev.; circ. 5,000 (paid). (back issues avail.) **Document type:** newsletter.
Description: Provides travel news and tips for single travelers and listings from singles seeking travel companions.

910.09   US   ISSN 1071-3867
TRAVEL COUNSELOR MAGAZINE. 1991. bi-m. free to qualified persons. (Institute of Certified Travel Agents) Miller Freeman Inc. (New York) (Subsidiary of: United Newspapers Group), 1515 Broadway, New York, NY 11031. TEL 212-626-2505. Ed. Diane Merlino; Pub. Bob Sullivan. adv. contact: Joanne Nelson. bk.rev.; circ. 28,000 (controlled). (also avail. in microform from UMI) **Document type:** trade publication.
—UMI.
Formerly (until 1993): Travel Counselor (ISSN 1069-6245)
Description: Presents cutting-edge information for certified travel counselors and career travel agents.

917   CN   ISSN 1182-9699
TRAVEL COURIER. 1965. w. Can.$42.80 (foreign Can.$110). Baxter Publishing Co., 310 Dupont St., Toronto, ON M5R 1V9, Canada. TEL 416-968-7252. FAX 416-968-2377. Ed. Edith Baxter. adv.; charts; illus.; stat.; circ. 7,290 (controlled). **Indexed:** Can.B.P.I. **Document type:** trade publication, newsletter.
Formerly (until 1982): Canadian Travel Courier (ISSN 0008-5219)
Description: Profiles, surveys and articles in the tourist trade.

914.04   GW
TRAVEL DIARY. 1977. a. DM.34. Bulletin Verlag GmbH, Roentgenstr. 80, 64291 Darmstadt, Germany. TEL 06151-374066. FAX 06151-370114. Ed. Michael Knuth. circ. 7,500. **Document type:** directory.

910.202   HK   ISSN 0256-4203
TRAVEL DIRECTORY. 1977. a. $50. Interasia Publications Ltd., 13th Fl., 200 Lockhart Rd., Hong Kong. TEL 511-9317. FAX 519-6846. Ed. Murray Bailey. adv.; bk.rev.; illus. circ. 6,000. **Document type:** trade publication.
Formerly: Asia Travel Trade Directory.

910.202   SI   ISSN 0218-236X
TRAVEL DIRECTORY (YEAR). (Text in English) 1977. a. $50. Interasia Publications Ltd., Fortune Centre 11-01, 190 Middle Rd., Singapore 0718, Singapore. TEL 3397622. FAX 3398521. adv.; circ. 3,700 (controlled). **Document type:** trade publication.
Description: Reference for Asian and Pacific's travel industry professionals and business travellers.

914   CN   ISSN 0843-0799
TRAVEL EUROPE. 1988. s-a. Motivations International Inc., 14 Ronan Ave., Toronto, ON M4N 2X9, Canada. TEL 416-481-6384. Ed. John Stephenson. adv. circ. 5,000.

910 664   US
TRAVEL, FOOD & WINE. 1970. m. $100. Punch In Syndicate, 400 E. 59th St., Ste. 9F, New York, NY 10022. TEL 212-755-9363. E-mail: punchin@gcomm.com. Ed. Tom Weston. bk.rev. circ. 10,000. **Document type:** newspaper.
Description: Review articles on travel, airlines, hotels, restaurants, food and wine.

914.2   UK   ISSN 1355-462X
TRAVEL G.B.I.; the trade journal of British Isles tourism, transport services and business travel. 1978. m. £25. Travelscope Publications, Foundation House, 3rd Fl., Perserverance Works, 38 Kingsland Rd., London E2 8DD, England. TEL 0171-729-5171. FAX 0171-729-1716. Ed. Stuart Bowden; Pub. Bob MacBeth-Seath. adv. contact: Gary Kaye. bk.rev.; illus. circ. 18,000. **Document type:** trade publication.
Description: Covers tourism and travel exclusively in the British Isles. Contains color photographs.

TRAVEL AND TOURISM

917 US ISSN 0199-025X
G149
TRAVEL HOLIDAY. 1901. 10/yr. $12.97. Travel Publications, Inc. (Subsidiary of: Reader's Digest Association, Inc.), 28 W. 23rd St., New York, NY 10010. TEL 212-366-8700; 800-937-9241. FAX 212-366-8798. (Subscr. to: Box 2036, Marion OH 43305) Ed. Margaret Staats Simmons. adv. contact: Sara Davis Greenwood. bk.rev.; dance rev.; film rev.; play rev.; rec.rev.; s.a. index. circ. 575,000. (also avail. in microform from UMI; reprint service avail. from UMI) **Indexed:** Acad.Ind., Bk.Rev.Ind. (1965-), Child.Bk.Rev.Ind. (1965-), Mag.Ind., PMR, R.G., TOM.
—SWETS.
Incorporates (in Jan. 1979): Travel Advisor; Formerly (until 1979): Travel Incorporating Holiday (ISSN 0161-7184); Formed by the Nov. 1977 merger of: Travel (ISSN 0041-1965); Holiday (ISSN 0018-3520)

914.95 GR
TRAVEL IN GREECE. (Text in Greek) 1970. a. Hellenews Ltd., 39 Amaroussiou-Halandriou, Amaroussion, Athens, Greece.

658 US ISSN 0959-6186
G155.A1
TRAVEL INDUSTRY MONITOR. 1990. m. £325($595) Economist Intelligence Unit, 111 W. 57th St., New York, NY 10019. TEL 212-554-0600; 800-938-4685. FAX 212-586-1182. TELEX 175567. (UK addr.: Economist Intelligence Unit Ltd., Subscriptions Dept., P.O. Box 200, Harold Hill, Romford, Essex RM3 8UX, England. TEL 44-1708-381-444. FAX 44-1708-371-850) charts; stat. (also avail. in microform from UMI) **Indexed:** Hospit.Ind. **Document type:** trade publication.
—UMI.
Description: Provides an assessment of the present and of future trends in the travel and tourist industry.

TRAVEL INDUSTRY PERSONNEL DIRECTORY. see *BUSINESS AND ECONOMICS — Trade And Industrial Directories*

910 AU
TRAVEL INDUSTRY PROFESSIONAL. w. Profi Reisen Verlagsgesellschaft mbH, Gaertnergasse 15-1-22, A-1030 Vienna, Austria. TEL 01-7142414. FAX 01-71424144. Ed. Rainer Pilcik. adv. circ. 7,300. **Document type:** trade publication.
Formerly: Traveller.

TRAVEL INDUSTRY WORLD YEARBOOK; the big picture. see *TRAVEL AND TOURISM — Abstracting, Bibliographies, Statistics*

914 SZ
TRAVEL INSIDE. 1986. w. 48 SFr. (foreign 63 SFr.). Primus Verlag AG, Weinbergstr. 43, CH-8023 Zurich, Switzerland. TEL 01-2620707. FAX 01-2620704. Ed. Angelo Heuberger. adv.: B&W page 3904 SFrs., color page 5054 SFr.; trim 210 x 290; adv. contact: Muriel Bassin. circ. 6,864. **Document type:** trade publication.
Description: Contains information, commentary and analysis about the travel industry.

910.202 BE ISSN 0771-937X
TRAVEL JOURNALIST/JOURNALISTE DE TOURISME. (Text in English and French) 1977. q. 320 Fr. Centre International de Documentation Touristique, Avenue Brugmann 29-23, B-1060 Brussels, Belgium. TEL 2-5387599. FAX 2-539-40-57. (Co-sponsor: Federation Internationale des Journalistes et Ecrivains du Tourisme) Ed. Marton Payrits. adv.; stat. circ. 3,200. (back issues avail.) **Description:** Studies made by experts in tourism worldwide.

910.202 LE
TRAVEL MAGAZINE. m. Picot St., Nassau Bldg., P.O. Box 2323, Beirut, Lebanon. adv. circ. 4,000.

910.2 US ISSN 0041-2015
TRAVEL MANAGEMENT DAILY. 1969. 5/w. $735. Reed Travel Group, Part of the Reed Elsevier group (Subsidiary of: Reed Telepublishing), 500 Plaza Dr., Secaucus, NJ 07096. TEL 201-902-2000. FAX 201-902-1967. Ed. Alan Fredericks. adv. contact: Ann Findlay. **Document type:** newsletter.
●Also available online.

910.09 US
TRAVEL MARKET REPORT (YEAR). 1979. a. $250. Travel Industry Association of America, 1100 New York Ave., N.W., Ste. 450, Washington, DC 20005-3934. TEL 202-408-5422. (also avail. in microfiche from CIS; reprint service avail.) **Indexed:** SRI. **Document type:** trade publication.
Formerly (until 1993): National Travel Survey (ISSN 0737-2620)

TRAVEL MEDICINE ADVISOR. see *MEDICAL SCIENCES*

TRAVEL MEDICINE INTERNATIONAL. see *MEDICAL SCIENCES*

910.09 US
TRAVEL NATIONAL. 1985. w. $40. E W A Publications, 275 Bay 37th St., Brooklyn, NY 11214. TEL 718-996-5406. FAX 718-373-1352. Ed. Kevin Browne. adv. contact: Adrienne Knoll. bk.rev. circ. 248,000. (tabloid format) **Document type:** newspaper.
Description: Covers travel destinations, hotels, airlines, and towns and local people.

917.404 US
TRAVEL NEW ENGLAND.* m. Robert Weiss Associates, 120 Boylston St., Boston, MA 02116-4611. TEL 617-561-4000. Ed. Robert H. Weiss. circ. 5,500. **Document type:** consumer publication.

915 HK ISSN 0252-9629
TRAVEL NEWS ASIA. 1974. fortn. HK.$156 (Asia $20; elsewhere $30). Far East Trade Press Ltd., 2-F Hi Tak Commercial Bldg., 317 Des Voeux Rd., Central, Hong Kong. TEL 5453028. FAX 544-6979. (Subscr. to: Times Publishing Group, Block C, 10th Fl. Seaview Estate, 2-8 Watson Rd., North Point, Hong Kong. TEL 852-566-8381. FAX 852-508-0255) Ed. Mike Sullivan. adv. circ. 17,843.
—CCC.
Description: News magazine covering developments in Southeast Asia's travel industry.

910.09 IT
TRAVEL NEWS ITALIA. 52/yr. Michele de Cesare Editore, 80014 Lago Patria, Italy. TEL 81-775-41-42. Ed. Antonio de Cesare. circ. 10,000.

910.202 362.4 US ISSN 1076-6405
TRAVEL NOTES. 1986. q. $15 (effective 1995). Accessible Journeys, 35 W. Sellers Ave., Ridley Park, PA 19078. TEL 610-521-0339. FAX 610-521-6959. Ed. Howard J. Mcloy. adv. contact: Howard J. McCoy. bk.rev. circ. 5,000. (tabloid format; back issues avail.) **Document type:** newsletter.
Description: Covers recreational travel for disabled travelers.

910.202 US
TRAVEL PEOPLE.* 1988. m. C M P Publications, Inc., 600 Community Dr., Manhasset, NY 11030. TEL 516-562-5000. FAX 516-365-4601. TELEX 647035-CMP-PUB-MAHA. Ed. Linda Ball. adv.
Description: Profiles influential people in the travel industry, provides information on travel discounts, travel directories and other publications. Includes a calendar of events.

910.202 US ISSN 1059-8251
TRAVEL PUBLICITY LEADS; Global Travel Media Placement Opportunities. 1985. bi-m. $147 worldwide (includes a supplement) (effective 1995). Scott American Corp., Box 88, W. Redding, CT 06896-0088. TEL 203-938-2955. Ed. Frank Scott; Pub. Frank Scott. (looseleaf format; back issues avail.) **Document type:** newsletter.

910.09 CN ISSN 0822-9228
TRAVEL SCOOP. 1983. 10/yr. Can.$44. 1110 Yonge St., Ste. 200, Toronto, ON M4W 2L6, Canada. TEL 416-926-0111. FAX 416-926-0222. Ed. Ann Wallace; Pub. Nigel Raincock. adv. contact: Nigel Raincock. bk.rev. circ. 12,500. **Document type:** consumer publication.
Description: Information to help Canadians make informed decisions about travel.

910.09 US ISSN 0741-5826
TRAVEL SMART. 1976. m. $37 (renewal $44) (effective 1995 & 1996). Communications House Inc., 40 Beechdale Rd., Dobbs Ferry, NY 10522. TEL 914-693-8300. Ed. H.J. Teison. tr.lit.; index. circ. 16,000. (back issues avail.) **Document type:** consumer publication, newsletter.
Incorporates (in 1983): Joy of Travel (ISSN 0277-7738); Which was formerly (1969-1983): Joyer Travel Report (ISSN 0145-9473)
Description: Provides "inside" info on current travel deals and value destinations, thus allowing one to travel better for less.

917.504 UK
TRAVEL SOUTH U S A. a. Phoenix Publishing & Media Ltd., 18-20 Scrutton St., London EC2A 4RJ, England. TEL 0171-247-0537. FAX 0171-377-2741. Ed. Mary Moore Mason; Pub. Maureen Miller. adv. contact: Kathryn McGowan. circ. 85,000. **Document type:** consumer publication.
Description: Travel and holiday planner for United Kingdom consumers.

910.09 JA
TRAVEL TIMES. (Text in Japanese) s-m. 16000 Yen($195) Ohta Publications Co., Ltd., Dame Ginza Bldg., 7-18 Ginza, 6-chome, Chuo-ku, Tokyo 104, Japan. TEL 03-3571-1181. FAX 03-3574-1650. Ed. Hiroyuki Takagishi. stat. circ. 8,300. **Document type:** trade publication.
Description: Travel and tourism marketing magazine. Offers market analyses and surveys, practical tips on how to cope with emerging trends and consumer preferences, new tour possibilities, profitable auxiliary services, and information on industry activities and events.

910.09 US
TRAVEL TIMES. (Supplements avail.) 1986. w. $26. E W A Publications, 275 Bay 37th St., Brooklyn, NY 11214. TEL 718-996-5406. FAX 718-373-1352. Ed. Kevin Browne. adv. contact: Adrienne Knoll. bk.rev. circ. 312,000. (tabloid format) **Document type:** newspaper.
Description: Features comprehensive coverage of all consumer travel industry: hotels, destinations, car rentals, cruises, and airlines.

910.2 US ISSN 0041-2066
CODEN: TRTRD3
TRAVEL TRADE;* the business paper of the travel industry. 1929. w. $10. Travel Trade Publications, 15 W. 44th St., 6th Fl., New York, NY 10036. TEL 212-730-6600. FAX 212-730-7020. Ed. Joel M. Abels. adv.; illus. circ. 35,053. **Document type:** trade publication.
—CASDDS.

910.09 AT
TRAVEL TRADE. 1964. fortn. Aus.$45. Reed Business Publishing Pty. Ltd. (Subsidiary of: Reed International PLC), 1-5 Railway St., Chatswood, N.S.W. 2067, Australia. TEL 02-372-5222. FAX 02-419-7533. Ed. Michael Woolley. adv.; illus. circ. 8,048. (tabloid format) **Document type:** trade publication.

901.09 SI
TRAVEL TRADE GAZETTE ASIA. Short title: T T G Asia. (Text in English) 1974. w. $180 in Asia; elsewhere $199. Miller Freeman Pte. Ltd., 100 Beach Rd., 26-00 Shaw Towers, Singapore 0718, Singapore. TEL 294-3366. FAX 298-5534. Ed. Yeoh Siew Hoon. adv. circ. 16,130. (tabloid format; back issues avail.) **Document type:** trade publication.

380 910.2 UK ISSN 0966-4297
TRAVEL TRADE GAZETTE DIRECTORY. (In ten sections: Tour Operators; Special Interest Holidays; Hotels; Car Travel; Coach Travel; Sea Travel; Air Travel; Travel Agents; Travel Trade Information; Travel Trade Services) 1958. s-a. £67 (rest of Europe £84; elsewhere £92-£97). Miller Freeman Information Services (Subsidiary of: United News & Media), Riverbank House, Angel Ln., Tonbridge, Kent TN9 1SE, England. TEL 01732-362666. FAX 01732-767301. TELEX 957892. Ed. Gwen Young. adv. contact: Elaine Soni. bk.rev.; charts; illus.; mkt.; tr.lit. circ. 5,500. **Document type:** directory.
—BLDSC (9045.470200).
Former titles: Travel Trade Directory (ISSN 0268-120X); (until 1970): United Kingdom and Eire Travel Trade and Directory (ISSN 0082-7932)
Description: Provides a comprehensive guide to the U.K. travel market.

TRAVEL AND TOURISM

914 UK
TRAVEL TRADE GAZETTE EUROPA. Short title: T T G Europa. 1968. fortn. $140. Miller Freeman Technical Ltd. (Subsidiary of: Miller Freeman plc), Miller Freeman House, 30 Calderwood St., London SE18 6QH, England. TEL 0181-855-7777. FAX 0181-316-3354. Ed. Stewart Cruttenden. adv. contact: Jason Sayward. circ. 16,267. (tabloid format) **Document type:** trade publication.
Formerly: T T G International (ISSN 0039-8500)

914 UK
TRAVEL TRADE GAZETTE U K & IRELAND. Short title: T T G - U K & Ireland. w. $175. Miller Freeman Technical Ltd. (Subsidiary of: Miller Freeman plc), Miller Freeman House, 30 Calderwood St., London SE18 6QH, England. TEL 0181-855-7777. FAX 0181-316-3354. Ed. Nigel Coombs. adv. contact: Chris Lewis. circ. 25,157. **Indexed:** Art.Hosp.& Tour. **Document type:** trade publication.

910.09 US
TRAVEL TRADE NEWS EDITION. w. Travel Trade Publications, 15 W. 44th St., New York, NY 10036. TEL 212-730-6600. FAX 212-730-7020. Ed. Joel M. Abels. **Document type:** trade publication.

910.202 TH
TRAVEL TRADE REPORTER - ASIA. 1978. w. $70 (effective through 1994). Orient Pacific Enterprises Ltd., Asia Bldg., 6th Fl., 294-1 Phya Thai Rd., Bangkok 10400, Thailand. TEL 2-216-7252. FAX 2-216-7253. Ed. Don Ross. adv.; circ. 8,500(controlled). **Document type:** trade publication.
Description: Covers travel industry, with product news on destinations marketed in Asia.

910 AT
TRAVEL TRADE YEARBOOK. 1965. s-a. Aus.$30. Reed Business Publishing Pty. Ltd. (Subsidiary of: Reed International PLC), 1-5 Railway St., Chatswood, N.S.W 2067, Australia. TEL 02-372-5222. FAX 02-419-7533. Ed. Kaye Tanner. circ. 4,200. **Document type:** trade publication.

910.09 CN
TRAVEL TRENDS MAGAZINE. 1993. 4/yr. Can.$7.50. K T G Publishing, 112 Fairholme Ave., Ste. 101, Toronto, ON M6B 2W9, Canada. TEL 416-256-0974. FAX 416-256-9354. Ed. Ted Kosoy. adv.; B&W page Can.$995, color page Can.$1585; trim 8 1/8 x 10 11/16. circ. 10,000. **Document type:** consumer publication.

910.202 GW
TRAVEL TRIBUNE. 1982. w. DM.456. M. Schweizer, Ed. & Pub., Schweizerstr. 14, 60594 Frankfurt a.M., Germany. TEL 069-625024. FAX 069-625026. circ. 1,500. **Document type:** trade publication.

910.202 SA
TRAVEL VALUE REPORT. 1982. m. $70 (effective through Oct. 1996). Prescon Publishing Corporation (Pty) Ltd, P.O. Box 84004, Greenside 2034, Johannesburg 2001, South Africa. TEL 27-11-646-9750. FAX 27-11-646-4617. Ed. Marjorie Dean. adv.; bk.rev. circ. 4,500. (back issues avail.) **Document type:** newsletter.
Formerly: Travel World.
Description: Covers Southern African and international travel.

910.2 AT
TRAVEL WEEK; fortnightly newspaper of the travel industry. 1961. fortn. $45. Peter Isaacson Publications Pty. Ltd., 45-50 Porter St., Prahran, Vic. 3181, Australia. TEL 03-245-7777. FAX 03-245-7606. Ed. Ian McMahon. adv.; bk.rev.; illus.; stat. circ. 8,913. (tabloid format)
Former titles: International Travelweek; International Travel (ISSN 0020-9015)

910.2 US ISSN 0041-2082
G155.A1
TRAVEL WEEKLY. 1958. s-w. $26 to individuals; travel agents $19.50. Reed Travel Group, Part of the Reed Elsevier group (Subsidiary of: Reed Telepublishing), 500 Plaza Dr., Secaucus, NJ 07096. TEL 201-902-2000. FAX 201-317-1755. (Subscr. to: Box 7661, Riverton, NJ 08077-7661; U.K. addr.: 6 Chesterfield Gardens, London W1Y 8BN, England. TEL 0144-71-355-9606) adv.; bk.rev.; charts; illus.; mkt.; stat. circ. 51,000. (tabloid format) **Indexed:** Bus.Ind., Tr.& Indus.Ind.
—UMI.
Incorporates (1969-1991): Travel News (ISSN 0049-4577)

910.09 US ISSN 1044-4602
TRAVEL WORLD NEWS.* m. Travel Industry Network, 50 Washington St., Norwalk, CT 06854-2710. TEL 203-853-4955. FAX 203-866-1153. Ed. Sara Southworth. circ. 35,706.

TRAVEL WRITER. see *JOURNALISM*

910.202 301.435 US ISSN 1049-6211
TRAVEL 50 & BEYOND. 1990. q. $15.80. Vacation Publications, Inc., 1502 Augusta Dr., Ste. 415, Houston, TX 77057. TEL 713-974-6903. FAX 713-974-0445. Ed. Alan Fox. adv. circ. 50,000. **Document type:** consumer publication.
Description: Aimed at travelers 50 and older. Offers practial tips and recommendations for finding the best values.

917.204 US
TRAVELAGE CARIBBEAN.* m. free to qualified personnel. Official Airline Guides (New York), Part of Reed Travel Group (Subsidiary of: Reed Elsevier plc), 500 Plaza Dr., Fl. 6, Secaucus, NJ 07094-3619. TEL 212-237-3000. FAX 212-237-3667. Ed. Ed Sullivan.

910.2 US ISSN 0041-2104
TRAVELAGE EAST. 1967. w. $63 (free to qualified personnel). Reed Travel Group, Part of the Reed Elsevier group (Subsidiary of: Reed Telepublishing), 500 Plaza Dr., Secaucus, NJ 07096. TEL 201-902-2000. FAX 201-902-1967. Ed. Tim Simmons. adv. contact: Tom Hayden. illus.; circ. 23,224 (controlled). (back issues avail.) **Document type:** trade publication.
Incorporates (1976-1987): TravelAge Southeast (ISSN 0744-1592)
Description: Contains travel industry news and features for front line sales counselors, managers and owners of travel agencies.

914.04 US
TRAVELAGE EUROPE.* m. free to qialified personnel. Official Airline Guides (New York), Part of Reed Travel Group (Subsidiary of: Reed Elsevier plc), 500 Plaza Dr., Fl. 6, Secaucus, NJ 07094-3619. TEL 212-237-3000. FAX 212-237-3667. Ed. Ed Sullivan.

910.09 US ISSN 0744-1606
TRAVELAGE MID-AMERICA. 1974. w. $63 (free to qualified personnel). Reed Travel Group, Part of the Reed Elsevier group (Subsidiary of: Reed Telepublishing), 500 Plaza Dr., Secaucus, NJ 07096. TEL 201-902-2000. FAX 201-902-1967. Ed. Tim Simmons. adv. contact: Tom Hayden. circ. 17,053 (controlled). (also avail. in microfiche; back issues avail.) **Document type:** trade publication.
Description: Contains travel industry news and features for front line sales counselors, managers and owners of travel agencies.

917 US ISSN 0041-1973
TRAVELAGE WEST; the weekly newspaper for the travel agency sales forces in the West. 1969. w. $63 (free to qualified personnel). Reed Travel Group, Part of the Reed Elsevier group (Subsidiary of: Reed Telepublishing), 500 Plaza Dr., Secaucus, NJ 07096. TEL 201-902-1200. FAX 201-902-1967. Ed. Tim Simmons. adv. contact: Dick Neal. bk.rev.; illus.; tr.lit.; circ. 33,044 (controlled). **Document type:** trade publication.
Description: Contains industry news and features for front line sales counselors, managers, and owners of travel agencies.

910.202 US ISSN 1068-2554
TRAVELAMERICA. 1985. bi-m. $22 (effective 1994); newsstand price: $3.75. World Publishing Co. (Subsidiary of: Century Publishing Co.), 990 Grove St., Evanston, IL 60201. TEL 708-491-6440. FAX 708-491-0459. (Subscr. to: Box 400, Mt. Morris, IL 61054-0400) Ed. Robert Meyers; Pub. Norman Jacobs. adv.; illus.; tr.lit.; circ. 416,776 (paid). (also avail. in microform) **Document type:** consumer publication.
Formerly (until Jun. 1993): Tours and Resorts (ISSN 0890-2852)
Description: Covers tours and travel destinations throughout the U.S.

910.09 SP
TRAVELDATA. 12/yr. Gran Via Carlos III 86, 7o, 08028 Barcelona, Spain. TEL 3-330-70-52. FAX 3-330-74-96. Ed. Pablo Morata.

919.404 AT ISSN 1034-5043
TRAVELEISURE. 1986. q. Aus.$10. Australasian Holiday Passport Pty. Ltd., P.O. Box 6495, Gold Coast Mail Centre, Surfers Paradise, Qld. 4217, Australia. TEL 075-911-466. Ed. Ray Bolwell. adv.; bk.rev. circ. 50,000. (back issues avail.)
Formerly (until Mar. 1989): Australian Holiday.

910.09 US
TRAVELER; business and travel magazine for international traders. 1991. m. $29.95. Trade Sources, Inc., 1020 Church St., Evanston, IL 60201-3062. TEL 708-475-1900. FAX 708-475-2794. adv.; B&W page $4370, color page $6720; trim 8 1/8 x 10 11/16. circ. 69,928. **Document type:** trade publication.

915 HK ISSN 1019-7664
TRAVELER; business and travel magazine for international traders. (Text in English) 1991. m. $28.95. Asian Sources Media Group, 22-F Vita Tower, 29 Wong Chuk Hang Rd., Aberdeen, Hong Kong. TEL 852-2555-4777. FAX 852-2873-0488. E-mail: asmgroup@signet.com.sg. (Subscr. to: Asiamag Ltd., G.P.O. Box 12367, Hong Kong; US subscr. to: Wordright Enterprises Inc., Box 3062, Evanston, IL 60204-3062. TEL 708-475-1900) Ed.Michael Hay. adv.; color page $7730; adv. contact: Don Rider. bk.rev. circ. 45,000. (back issues avail.) **Document type:** trade publication.
Description: Provides tips on travel and trade in Asia.

917 US
TRAVELER & CONVENTIONEER. 1942. bi-m. $7.50. Travelers' Research Publishing Co., Inc., 11717 S. Vincennes Ave., Chicago, IL 60643. TEL 312-881-3712. Ed. C. M. Markham, Jr. adv.; bk.rev.; stat. circ. 72,000. (also avail. in microform from UMI)
Former titles: Negro Traveler and Conventioneer (ISSN 0028-2537); Negro Travel.

910.09 US
TRAVELER NIHONGOBAN. 1991. m. Trade Sources Inc., 1020 Church St., Evanston, IL 60201-3062. TEL 708-475-1900. FAX 708-475-2794. adv.; B&W page $2180, color page $3415; trim 205 x 270. circ. 20,000. **Document type:** trade publication.

TRAVELER'S GUIDE TO ART MUSEUM EXHIBITIONS. see *MUSEUMS AND ART GALLERIES*

910.09 US ISSN 1051-9335
TRAVELIN' MAGAZINE. 1990. bi-m. $14.95. Russ Heggen, Ed. & Pub., Box 23005, Eugene, OR 97402-0424. TEL 503-485-8533. FAX 503-485-8528. adv.; B&W page $840, color page $1360; trim 8 3/8 x 10 7/8. circ. 10,000. **Document type:** consumer publication.
Description: Covers recreational travel in the Western U.S. and Canada. Features little known and out-of-the-way places.

910.20 US ISSN 1052-1615
THE TRAVELIN' TALK NEWSLETTER. 1989. q. $15 to $20 (contribution). 130 Hillcrest, Ste.102, Box 3534, Clarksville, TN 37043. TEL 615-552-6670. FAX 615-552-1182. Ed. Rick Crowder; Pub. Rick Crowder. bk.rev. circ. 2,000. (looseleaf format; also avail. in audio cassette) **Document type:** newsletter, directory.
Description: Updates the Travelin' Talk Network by providing resources, travel tips, and success stories of assistance provided to travelers with disabilities.

910 610 US ISSN 0899-2169
TRAVELING HEALTHY. 1988. bi-m. $32 (foreign $38). Mercury Marketing, 108-48 70th Rd., Forest Hills, NY 11375. TEL 718-268-7290. Ed. Karl Neumann. circ. 1,000 (paid). (also avail. in diskette format; back issues avail.) **Document type:** newsletter.
Description: Alerts travelers about health and medical issues.

910.09 UK ISSN 0262-2726
TRAVELLER. 1970. q. £39.58 (foreign £50.42). Wexas Ltd., 45 Brompton Rd., London SW3 1DE, England. TEL 0171-581-4130. FAX 0171-581-1357. TELEX 297155-WEXAS-G. Ed. Caroline Brandenburger. adv.; bk.rev.; charts; illus. circ. 35,359. **Document type:** consumer publication.
Formerly: Expedition.
Description: Travel-related articles and letters.

910.4   HK
TRAVELLING MAGAZINE/LU HSING TSA CHIH; the first Chinese language travel magazine. (Text in Chinese; captions in English) m. HK.$10 per no. Rm.903, Yat Fat Bldg., 44 Des Voeux Rd., Central, Hong Kong. TEL 5-247738. FAX 5-218390. Ed. Tien-Pei Hsu. adv.; illus.
  Description: Covers travel to all parts of the world.

910.202 636   CN   ISSN 1194-3165
TRAVELLING WITH YOUR PET.* 1992. a. Can.$4.95. Patrick Communications, Ltd., 89 Skyway Ave. Unit 200, Etobicoke ON NYW 604, Canada. TEL 416-441-3228. FAX 416-798-9778. Ed. Susan Pearce. adv.: B&W page Can.$1490, color page Can.$2290; trim 5 3/8 x 7 3/8. circ. 30,000.

910.09   AT   ISSN 1034-2370
TRAVELNEWS AUSTRALIA; Australia's magazine for travel consultants. 1988. bi-m. $22. McIntosh Publications, 22 Alexandra St., Hunters Hill, N.S.W. 2110, Sydney, Australia. TEL 61-2-8170261. FAX 61-2-816556. Pub. Ian McIntosh. adv.: B&W page Aus.$1416, color page Aus.$2295; trim 8 1/4 x 10 3/4; adv. contact: Graham Richards. circ. 7,200. **Document type:** trade publication.

TRAVELODGE NORTH AMERICAN - INTERNATIONAL TRAVEL DIRECTORY. see *BUSINESS AND ECONOMICS — Trade And Industrial Directories*

917   US
TRAVELOG. 1960. a. $2. Meridian Publishing, Inc., Box 10010, Ogden, UT 84409. TEL 801-394-9446. Ed. Marjorie Rice. adv.; illus. circ. 125,000.

910.202   CN
TRAVELWEEK BULLETIN. 1973. s-w. Can.$48.15($85) (typically set in Jul.). Concepts Travel Media, Ltd., 282 Richmond St. E., Toronto, ON M5A 1P4, Canada. FAX 416-365-1504. Ed. Patrick Dineen; Pub. Elga Mannik. adv. contact: Tina Cancilla. circ. 9,000. **Document type:** trade publication.
  Formerly: C T M Weekly Bulletin (ISSN 0380-2019)

TRAVELWRITER MARKETLETTER. see *JOURNALISM*

910.2   US   ISSN 0162-9816
TRAVLTIPS. 1967. bi-m. $15. TravLtips Inc., Box 188, Flushing, NY 11358. TEL 718-939-2400; 800-872-8584. Ed. Edmund M. Kirk. adv.; illus. circ. 26,000. (tabloid format) **Document type:** consumer publication.
  Formerly: TravLtips Freighter Bulletin (ISSN 0049-4585)
  Description: Accounts of freighter and other unusual cruises.

914   BE
TREKKERSKRANT. 1945. bi-m. 200 Fr. to non-members. Vlaamse Jeugdherbergcentrale, Van Stralenstraat 40, B-2000 Antwerp, Belgium. Ed. E. De Roover. adv. circ. 20,000.
  Formerly: Trekker (ISSN 0041-2260)
  Description: News concerning hostels.

910.09   IT
TREKKING. m. L.60000 (Europe L.85000; elsewhere L.120000). Piero Amighetti Editore s.r.l., Via Maiatico 10, Sala Baganza (PR), Italy. TEL 39-521-833140. FAX 39-521-834754. adv.: B&W page L.3520000, color page L.5250000. circ. 30,000. **Document type:** consumer publication.

TRENDS IN THE HOTEL INDUSTRY. see *HOTELS AND RESTAURANTS*

910.2   UK   ISSN 0264-1763
TRIANGLE. 1972. 3/yr. £6. Youth Hostels Association (England and Wales), Trevelyan House, St. Albans, Herts. AL1 2DY, England. TEL 01727-855215. FAX 01727-844126. Ed. Hellen Barnes. adv.; bk.rev.; illus. circ. 300,000. Indexed: INSPEC. **Document type:** bulletin.
  Former titles: Hostelling News (ISSN 0267-9353); Hostelling News (ISSN 0306-8927); Supersedes: Youth Hosteller (ISSN 0044-1268)

917   US   ISSN 0041-2619
TRIANGLE POINTER. 1961. m. $27. Village Companies, Inc., Box 2777, Chapel Hill, NC 27515. TEL 919-968-4801. FAX 919-942-2826. Ed. Randy Bullock; Pub. Sue Chen Reeder. adv. contact: Shelly Sheppick. charts. circ. 40,000.

910.09   UK
TRIP OUT; directory passenger boat services in British Isles. 1977. biennial. £4.25. G.P. Hamer, Ed. & Pub., 77 St. Mary's Grove, London W4 3LW, England. (back issues avail.) **Document type:** directory.

917.204   PR   ISSN 1078-1404
TROPICAL AMERICAN CRUISING. 1992. m. $17. Sailaway Cruising Club, Box 473, Puerto Real, PR 00740-0473. Ed. J.A. Rogers. bk.rev. circ. 1,000. **Document type:** newsletter.
  Formerly (until 1993): Sailaway Cruising Report.
  Description: Contains information for boaters on all aspects of planning a small boat cruise to Central America and the Caribbean.

910.09   GW
DER TROTTER. 1975. q. DM.50 membership. Deutsche Zentrale fuer Globetrotter e.V., c/o Hans Michael Buer, Suhlenkamp 6, 24558 Henstedt-Ulzburg, Germany. TEL 04193-92138. bk.rev.; abstr.; charts; illus.; stat.; index. circ. 1,400. (back issues avail.) **Document type:** consumer publication.
  Formerly: Globetrotter.
  Description: Magazine for world travellers with travel accounts, information, tips, personal stories, and reader's letters.

TUEBINGER BLAETTER. see *COLLEGE AND ALUMNI*

917   PN
TURISGUIA. (Text in English, Spanish) 1964. m. $36. Apdo. Postal 9525, Panama 4, Panama. TEL 25-8486. Ed. Roy Tasco Wesley. adv. circ. 10,000.

910.09   IT
TURISMO ATTUALITA INTERNATIONAL. 1977. m. L.80000 (foreign L.100000). A. Dam Editore s.r.l., Via Riboty 23, 00195 Rome, Italy. TEL 39-6-3720040. FAX 39-6-3723355. Ed. Andrea Lovelock. adv.: B&W page L.2700000, color page L.3600000; trim 220 x 310; adv. contact: Cornecia Viazzi. circ. 16,100. **Document type:** trade publication.

917   IT
TURISMO D'AFFARI. m. L.55000. Ediman s.r.l., Corso San Gottardo, 39, 20136 Milan, Italy. TEL 02-58103791. FAX 02-58103789. Ed. Aldo LoRe. adv.: B&W page L.4900000, color page L.7000000. circ. 30,000.

910.202   IT
TURISMO D'ITALIA. 1988. m. L.120000 to non-members; members L.90000. (Federazione delle Associazioni Italiane Alberghi e Turismo) Ediman, Corso San Gottardo, 39, 20136 Milan, Italy. TEL 02-58103875. FAX 02-58103789. adv.: B&W page L.3100000, color page L.4500000.

910.09   IT
TURISMO DOMANI; uomini avvenimenti idee. m. L.60000. Turismo Domani s.r.l., Via Timavo 12, 00195 Rome, Italy. TEL 06-3720645. FAX 06-32-50-566. Ed. Osvaldo Bevilacqua. **Document type:** consumer publication.

910.09   BL   ISSN 0103-5541
   G155.B7
TURISMO EM ANALISE. 1990. s-a. exchange basis. Universidade de Sao Paulo, Departamento de Relacoes Publicas, Propaganda e Turismo, Av. Prof. L. Martins Rodrigues 443, Bloco B, S. 13, 05011 Sao Paulo SP, Brazil. TEL 011-813-3222 ext. 2122. FAX 011-815-4272. TELEX 011-80629 UVSI BR. Ed. Mirian Rejowski de Carvalho. **Document type:** academic/scholarly publication.
  Description: Publishes the department's studies and research in the areas of tourism and leisure.

910.91   SP   ISSN 1130-1627
TURISMO EN NAVARRA. 1985. s-a. 1000 ptas. (Departamento de Industria, Comercio y Turismo) Gobierno de Navarra, Fondo de Publicaciones, Navas de Tolosa, 21, 31002 Pamplona, Spain. TEL 34-48-107121. FAX 34-48-227673.

910.202   IT
TURISMO GRADESE. (Text in German, Italian) 1960. w. during summer. L.12000($5.50) Pubblistudio de Zorzi Casa Editrice s.a.s., Via Marinoni 53, Udine, Italy. TEL 0432-508243. FAX 0432-508243. adv. circ. 7,000. (back issues avail.)
  Description: Guide for tourists to Grado.

914.504   IT
TURISMO VENETO. 1980. m. (8/yr.). L.40000 (foreign L.100000). Editrice Turismo Triveneto, Via D. Manin 33, 30174 Mestre (VE), Italy. TEL 39-41-940258. FAX 39-41-951486. Ed. Anna Renda. adv.: page L.2400000; adv. contact: Luigi Rigutto. circ. 20,000.

910.09   SP
TURISMO Y OCIO. 4/yr. Plaza Lesseps, 4 y 5, 08023 Barcelona, Spain. TEL 3-218-29-61. Ed. Silvia Bazzufet. circ. 21,000.

910.09 647.94   PO
TURISMOHOTEL. 12/yr. Rua de Entreparedes 6-1 e 2o, 4000 Porto, Portugal. TEL 2-23875. FAX 2-318426. TELEX 23809. Ed. Silva Tavares. circ. 30,000.

910.09   BL
TURISPRESS. 1961. m. $300. Hotelnews Edicoes e Promocoes Ltda., Rua Camuiramo 96, 22270-020 Rio de Janeiro RJ, Brazil. TEL 55-21-286-2218. FAX 55-21-286-2179. TELEX 21-34148. Ed. Mariam Hauch; Pub. Magdala Castro. adv. contact: Katia Castro. **Document type:** trade publication.

914   SW   ISSN 0041-4190
TURIST; Svenska Turistfoereningens tidning. 1933. 6/yr. SEK 190 membership. Svenska Turistfoereningen - Swedish Touring Club, Drottninggatan 33, P.O. Box 25, 101 20 Stockholm, Sweden. TEL 08-790-31-00. FAX 08-2430-78. Eds. Thelma Kimsjo, Cenneth Sparby. adv.; bk.rev.; illus.; index. circ. 280,000. **Document type:** trade publication.
  Formerly (until 1962): S T F - Svenska Turistfoereningens Tidning.

TURIST- OG RUTEBILBLADET. see *TRANSPORTATION — Automobiles*

914.891   DK   ISSN 0108-8734
TURISTFOERER. Variant title: Turistfoererforeningen. Medlemliste. 1975. a. free. (Turistfoererforeningen) Scan-ide Publishing ApS, Gersonsvej 33, DK-2900 Hellerup, Denmark. TEL 31-62-73-10. Ed. Robert Bachmann. adv. circ. 3,500. **Document type:** trade publication, directory.

914   YU   ISSN 0041-4204
TURISTICKE NOVINE. 1952. w. 300 din. Turisticka Stampa, Knez Mihailova 21, Belgrade, Yugoslavia. Ed. Dobrivoje Djokovic. adv.; bk.rev.; abstr.; bibl.; charts; illus.; index.

910.09   PO
TURISVER. 52/yr. Rua da Esperanca 16-2o, 1200 Lisbon, Portugal. TEL 342-1580. FAX 3960787. TELEX 61628. Ed. Silva Rosa.

TURIZM DUNYASI & USTA ASCI; turk turizm ekonomisi ve turizm yatir imlari. see *HOTELS AND RESTAURANTS*

910.09   HU   ISSN 0237-5249
TURIZMUS. m. $21. Muzeum u. 11, 1088 Budapest, Hungary. TEL 138-4638. TELEX 22-5297. Ed. Zsolt Szebeni. circ. 8,000.

TURKISH TREASURES; culture-art-tourism magazine. see *ART*

910   TU
TURKIYE TURING VE OTOMOBIL KURUMU BELLETENI. 1930. q. membership. Turk Turing ve Otomobil Kurumu - Touring and Automobile Club of Turkey, Halaskargazi Cad. 364, Sisli 80222, Istanbul, Turkey. TEL 90-212-2314631. FAX 90-212-2489661. TELEX 27800 TR RING. Dir. Celik Gulersoy. **Document type:** bulletin.

910.09   IT   ISSN 0392-8020
TUTTOTURISMO. 12/yr. $102. Editorale Domus, Via Grandi 5-7, 20089 Rozzano (MI), Italy. TEL 39-2-824721. FAX 39-2-8255033. Ed. Giuliano Albani. adv.: B&W page L.13500000, color page L.20250000. circ. 120,300.

917.704   US
TWIN CITIES VISITOR. m. $15. Skyway Publications, 15 S. Fifth St., Ste. 800, Minneapolis, MN 55402. TEL 512-375-9222. FAX 512-375-9208. Pub. Mari Adamson-Bray. adv.; play rev.; circ. 30,000 (controlled). (back issues avail.)
  Formerly (until 1991): Where Twin Cities.

6506   TRAVEL AND TOURISM

U J Q. (Uncle Jam Quarterly) see *LITERARY AND POLITICAL REVIEWS*

917   US   ISSN 0883-251X
E158
U S A FOR BUSINESS TRAVELERS. a. $14. Harper Collins Publishers, Birnbaum Travel Guides, 10 E. 53rd St., New York, NY 10022-5299. TEL 212-270-7542. Ed. Alexandra Mayes Birnbaum.

910.09   US
U S T T A RESOURCES AND OPPORTUNITIES MANUAL. a. $75. U.S. Travel and Tourism Administration, Office of Research, U.S. Department of Commerce, Main Commerce Bldg., Rm. 1868, Washington, DC 20230. TEL 202-482-4028. FAX 202-482-2887. (Subscr. to: U.S. Travel and Tourism Administration, Office of Tourism and Marketing, Main Commerce Bldg., Rm. 1860, Washington, DC 20230. TEL 202-782-1904) **Document type:** government publication.
Description: Describes U.S.T.T.A. international marketing activities.

914   CI   ISSN 0041-557X
U T; revija za ugostiteljstvo i turizam. (Text in Croatian) 1952. m. $60. Ugostiteyski i Turisticki Marketing, d.o.o., Trg Mazuravica 5-2, Zabreg, Croatia. TEL 041-440-049. Ed. Drago Ferencic. index. circ. 20,000.
Formerly: Ugostiteljstvo i Turizam.
Description: Covers the catering and tourist trade.

914.9   BE   ISSN 0774-1324
UIT; het V T B - V A B magazine. (Text in Dutch) 1985. m. 1100 BEF. Vlaamse Toeristenbond, Vlaamse Automobilistenbond, Sint-Jakobsmarkt 45, B-2000 Antwerp, Belgium. TEL 32-3-2203400. FAX 32-3-2340598. Ed. Gerrit De Clercq; Pub. Henri Meiresonne. adv. contact: Ann Lenaerts. bk.rev. circ. 200,000. (back issues avail.) **Document type:** consumer publication.
Description: Travel reports, tips for weekend traveling, consumers' information, tests of food products, restaurant reports and road tests.
Refereed Serial

UITKRANT. see *LEISURE AND RECREATION*

910.91   FR   ISSN 0990-7068
ULYSSE; la culture du voyage. 1988. bi-m. 130 F. Publications Historiques, 12 rue Ampere, 75017 Paris, France. TEL 48-88-45-35. FAX 48-88-45-50. (Subscr. to: 163 bd Malesherbes, 75017 Paris, France. TEL 48-88-85-82) Ed. Daniel Elouard; Pub. Philippe Boitel. adv.: page 20000 F.; adv. contact: Martine Gil. bk.rev. circ. 45,000. (back issues avail.)

914   FR   ISSN 0049-5190
UNE SEMAINE DE PARIS-PARISCOPE. Variant title: Pariscope. 1923. w. 390 F. (foreign 680 F.) (effective 1995). Publications Filipacchi, 65 av. des Champs-Elysees, 75008 Paris, France. TEL 40-74-70-00. TELEX 651 294. (Subscr. to: 99 rue d'Amsterdam, 75008 Paris, France. TEL 42-80-68-55) film rev.; play rev. **Document type:** consumer publication.

910.202   US   ISSN 1073-1873
UNIQUE & EXOTIC TRAVEL REPORTER. 1982. m. $45. 6716 Eastside Dr. N.E., No.12, Tacoma, WA 98422-1114. TEL 206-927-1688. Ed. Patricia Chesebro; Pub. L.K. Chesebro. adv.; bk.rev. (back issues avail.) **Document type:** newsletter.
Description: Provides information about unique and special interest travel opportunities throughout the world.

719.32   US   ISSN 0083-2316
U.S. NATIONAL PARK SERVICE. HISTORICAL HANDBOOK SERIES. 1950. irreg. U.S. National Park Service, Interior Bldg., Washington, DC 20240. TEL 202-343-1100. (Orders to: Supt. of Doc., Washington, DC 20402)

917   US   ISSN 0883-2501
E158
UNITED STATES (YEAR). a. $18. Harper Collins Publishers, Birnbaum Travel Guides, 10 E 53rd St., New York, NY 10022-5299. TEL 212-207-7542. Ed. Alexandra Mayes Birnbaum.

914   FR   ISSN 0395-8086
UNIVERSITE D'AIX-MARSEILLE 3. CENTRE DES HAUTES ETUDES TOURISTIQUES. COLLECTION "ESSAIS". 1976. irreg., no.765, 1995. 50 F. Universite d'Aix-Marseille III (Universite de Droit, d'Economie et des Sciences), Centre des Hautes Etudes Touristiques, Immeuble Euroffice, 38 av. de l'Europe, B.P. 661, 13094 Aix-en-Provence, Cedex 2, France. TEL 42-20-09-73. FAX 42-20-50-98. (back issues avail.) **Indexed:** Rural Recreat.Tour.Abstr., World Agri.Econ.& Rural Sociol.Abstr. **Document type:** monographic series.

914   FR   ISSN 0065-4965
UNIVERSITE D'AIX-MARSEILLE 3. CENTRE DES HAUTES ETUDES TOURISTIQUES. ETUDES ET MEMOIRES. 1963. irreg., no.259, 1995. price varies. Universite d'Aix-Marseille III (Universite de Droit, d'Economie et des Sciences), Centre des Hautes Etudes Touristiques, Immeuble Euroffice, 38 av. de l'Europe, B.P. 661, 13094 Aix-en-Provence, Cedex 2, France. TEL 42-20-09-73. FAX 42-20-50-98. (back issues avail.) **Document type:** monographic series.

919.09 338   PL   ISSN 0239-9067
UNIWERSYTET GDANSKI. WYDZIAL EKONOMIKI PRODUKCJI. ZESZYTY NAUKOWE. EKONOMIKA I ORGANIZACJA TURYSTYKI I USLUG. (Text in Polish; summaries in English, Russian) 1985. irreg., latest no.4. price varies. Uniwersytet Gdanski, Wydzial Ekonomiki Produkcji, c/o Biblioteka Glowna, Ul. Armii Krajowej 110, 81-824 Sopot, Poland. TEL 51-0061. TELEX 051 2247 BMOR PL. Ed. Wladyslaw Gaworecki. circ. 250. **Document type:** academic/scholarly publication.
Description: Covers the economics of consumption, services, trade, small manufacturers, and organization of tourism and tourist enterprises.

UPSTATE MAGAZINE. see *GENERAL INTEREST PERIODICALS — United States*

910.4 385.23   FI   ISSN 0358-7711
V R - EXPRESS. q. (Valtionrautatiet) Erikoislehdet Oy Business Publications, P.O. Box 16, SF-00381 Helsinki, Finland. Ed. Marketta Rentola. circ. 100,000.

910.202   CN   ISSN 0831-3067
VACANCES POUR TOUS. 1971. 7/yr. Can.$14. Editions Vacances pour Tous, 1291 Charest Blvd. W., Ste. 120, Quebec, PQ G1N 2C9, Canada. TEL 418-682-5464. FAX 418-682-0746. Ed. Eric Chasse. adv.: B&W page Can.$2445, color page Can.$2895; trim 7 1/8 x 9 3/4. circ. 55,000. (tabloid format) **Document type:** consumer publication.
Former titles (until 1985): Journal Vacances - Familles (ISSN 0831-3059); (until 1984): Vacances - Familles - Information (ISSN 0700-821X)
Description: Offers literature on many destinations and attractions, and articles on travel insurance, guide books, event calendars, museums, restaurants and maps.

910.09 790.1   US   ISSN 1052-0848
HD7289.2
VACATION INDUSTRY REVIEW. (Text mainly in English; some material published in a Spanish edition) 1984. q. Interval International, 6262 Sunset Dr., Penthouse 1, S. Miami, FL 33143. TEL 305-666-1861. FAX 305-667-4495. Ed. George Leposky. adv.: B&W page $1010, color page $1390; trim 8 1/2 x 11; adv. contact: Cheryl Clarke. circ. 15,000. (controlled) **Document type:** trade publication.
Description: Covers development, finance, marketing and management of timeshare resorts and mixed-use projects such as hotels, resorts and second-home communities with a vacation-ownership component.

910.202   US
VACATION WEEK. 1953. 12/yr. 330 W. Division St., Box 1929, Eagle River, WI 54521. TEL 715-479-4421. Ed. Kurt Krueger; Pub. Byron McNutt. adv. circ. 16,000. **Document type:** newspaper.

917.204   JM
VACATIONER; Jamaica resort guide. 1987. s-m. J.$380($12.50) (effective 1994). Holjam Enterprises Ltd., P.O. Box 614, Montego Bay, Jamaica. TEL 809-952-0997. Ed. Evelyn Robinson. adv.; circ. 8,000 (paid). (tabloid format; back issues avail.) **Document type:** newspaper.
Description: Provides information on attractions, accommodations, dining, entertainment and tourism news from hotels and the government.

910.09   US   ISSN 0894-9093
VACATIONS. 1987. q. $15.80. Vacation Publications, Inc., 1502 Augusta Dr. Ste. 415, Houston, TX 77057. TEL 713-974-6903. FAX 713-974-0445. Ed. R. Alan Fox. adv. circ. 260,000. **Document type:** consumer publication.

VANUATU IN FACTS AND FIGURES. see *TRAVEL AND TOURISM — Abstracting, Bibliographies, Statistics*

VARTA - FUEHRER; ausgewaehlte Hotels und Restaurants in der Bundesrepublik Deutschland. see *HOTELS AND RESTAURANTS*

918   VE
VE VENEZUELA CARIBBEAN CONNEXION. (Text in English and Spanish) 1965. a. $1.50. Elaboraciones Venezuela, Apdo. del Este 60182, Caracas, Venezuela. TEL 582-2835237. Ed. Hilary Brauch. adv. contact: Alesandra Sosnowski. bk.rev. circ. 10,000. **Document type:** consumer publication.
Incorporates: Ve Venezuela (ISSN 0042-2932); Which was formerly: Caribbean Connexion.
Description: Covers Venezuela, St. Lucia, St. Vincent and Grenada.

910.09   CU
VEA. s-a. Instituto Nacional del Turismo, Malecon y G, Vedado, Havana, Cuba. TEL 7-32-9881. TELEX 511955.

VEGETARIAN HANDBOOK. see *NUTRITION AND DIETETICS*

914.504   US   ISSN 1056-4411
DG672
VENICE (YEAR). a. $11. Harper Collins Publishers, Birnbaum Travel Guides, 10 E. 53rd St., New York, NY 10022-5299. TEL 212-207-7542. Ed. Alexandra Mayes Birnbaum. illus.; index.

910.4   US
VERMONT VACATION. 1972. 3/yr. $1 per no. Travel Routes, Inc., 86 Canal St., Brattleboro, VT 05301. FAX 802-257-0848. adv.; maps; circ. 150,000 (controlled). **Document type:** consumer publication.
Description: Provides tourist information. Includes calendar of events.

VERMONT YEAR BOOK. see *BUSINESS AND ECONOMICS — Trade And Industrial Directories*

VIA! see *TRANSPORTATION — Automobiles*

910.09 642.5   IT   ISSN 1122-3499
VIAGGI DI GRAND GOURMET. 1992. s-a. L.14000 per no. Elemond Periodici s.r.l., Via D. Trentacoste 7, 20134 Milan, Italy. TEL 39-2-215631. FAX 39-2-26410847. Ed. Enrico Guagnini. adv.: B&W page L.9000000, color page L.11000000. **Document type:** consumer publication.

910   IT
VIAGGI VACANZE.* 1971. bi-m. L.5000 per no. (Centro de Turismo) Alfa Centauri s.r.l., Viale Tunisia 36, 20121 Milan, Italy. Ed. Gino Baglio. adv.: B&W page L.5000000, color page L.7000000. circ. 40,000. **Document type:** consumer publication.

910   IT
VIAGGIANDO IN AUTOSTRADE. m. L.27500 (foreign L.55000). Autostrade - Concessioni e Costruzioni Autostrade S.p.A., Via A. Bergammi, 50, 00159 Rome, Italy. TEL 0643631. Ed. Giuseppe Fedi. (back issues avail.)

910.09   IT
VIAGGIARE. 1988. m. L.30800 (foreign L.61600). Editrice Portoria S.r.l., Via Chiossetto, 1, 20122 Milan, Italy. TEL 39-2-760711. FAX 39-2-782601. Ed. Mario Oriani. adv.: B&W page L.5000000, color page L.8000000. bk.rev. circ. 120,000. **Document type:** consumer publication.
Former titles: Italia Viaggia Viaggiare; (until 1994): Italia Viaggia (ISSN 1122-3162)

TRAVEL AND TOURISM

910.09   IT
VIAGGIO IN ITALIA. (Text in English, Italian) 1983. 4/yr. L.35000 (foreign L.58000). Edizioni Scientifiche Tecniche Europee s.r.l., Via G. Vasari 15, 20135 Milan, Italy. TEL 39-2-55018039. FAX 39-2-5455644. Ed. Franco Paloscia; Pub. Gianni Ceriani. adv.: color page L.6800000. bk.rev. circ. 50,000.

910.09   US
VIAJANDO/TRAVELING. (Text in English, Spanish) 1989. m. Global Magazines, Inc., 6355 N.W. 36th St., Virginia Gardens, FL 33166. TEL 305-871-6400. TELEX 441094. Ed. Cristina J. Arencibia. adv. circ. 20,000.
    Description: Contains general interest for frequent airline travelers.

910.09   PO
VIAJAR. 11/yr. Rua Cecilio de Sousa 20-2o Esq., 1200 Lisbon, Portugal. TEL 1-365701. FAX 346-90-73. TELEX 18375. Ed. Joao Rosa. circ. 15,000.

910.09   BL
VIAJAR BEM E BARATO. 1992. a. Editora Abril, S.A., Rua do Curtume 769, Bl. G, 11o, 05066-900 Sao Paulo SP, Brazil. TEL 011-8716168. FAX 011-871-6270. Ed. Regner Camilo. adv.; charts; illus. circ. 80,000. **Document type:** consumer publication.
    Description: Contains tips for places, food and lodging in Brazil for the budget traveler.

910.202   BL
VIAJE BEM. 1961. 6/yr. Grupo Editorial Spagat Ltda., Rua Prof. Artur Ramos 183, Andar 10, CEP 01454 Sao Paulo, SP, Brazil. TEL 0110-813-4455. Ed. Carlos Andre Spagat. adv. circ. 100,000.

917.104   CN
VICTORIA CLIPPER. s-a. Smart Publishing Group Ltd., 1368 Hampshire Rd., Victoria, B.C V8V 3L1, Canada. TEL 604-386-1433. FAX 604-386-3664.

910.09   IT
VIE DEL MONDO. 1987. m. L.58000; newsstand price: L.6500. Touring Periodici s.r.l., Via Adamello 10, 20139 Milan, Italy. TEL 39-2-55213036. FAX 39-2-55213036. TELEX 312476 TCIADM 1. Ed. Adriano Agnati. adv.: B&W page L.9600000, color page L.12000000. circ. 64,945.

614.7   FR
VIE MANCELLE; revue mensuelle de l'Association Culturelle et Touristique du Maine. 1959. m. 120 F. Association Culturelle et Touristique du Mans et de la Sarthe, 64, rue de la Pelouse, 72000 Le Mans, France. Ed. J.P. Martin. bk.rev.

910.202   MR
VIE TOURISTIQUE. (Text in French) w. 142 bd. Mohamed V, Casablanca, Morocco. Ed. Mohamed Zghari. adv.

959   UK   ISSN 1352-7878
▼**VIETNAM, LAOS AND CAMBODIA HANDBOOK.** 1994. a. £11.95. Trade & Travel Publications Ltd., 6 Riverside Ct., Lower Bristol Rd., Bath BA2 3DZ, England. TEL 01225-469141. FAX 01225-469461. (Dist. in N. America by: Passport Books, NTC Publishing Group, 4255 W. Touhy Ave., Lincolnwood, IL 60646-1975. TEL 708-679-5500. FAX 708-679-6375) Ed. Joshua Eliot. **Document type:** directory.

910.09   IT
VILLE, CASTELLI E PALAZZI. 1991. a. L.10000. Convegni s.r.l., Viale Lombardia 20, 20131 Milan, Italy. TEL 39-2-70600058. FAX 39-2-70601411. Ed. Vittore Castellazzi. adv.: color page L.5000000. circ. 10,000. **Document type:** consumer publication.

910.202   VI
VIRGIN ISLANDS PLAYGROUND. a. free. Island Media, Inc., P.O. Box 10563, St. Thomas, VI 00801. TEL 809-776-3646. Ed. Frances E. Newbold.
    Description: Includes restaurant directory, shopping guide, island map.

917   US   ISSN 0195-2420
VISIT U S A GUIDE.* 1979. m. Travel Trade Publishing Co., 15 West 44th St., New York, NY 10036. TEL 212-883-1110. Eds. Nanette Lind, Lewis Abels. adv. circ. 16,000.

VISITOR BEHAVIOR. see *PSYCHOLOGY*

917.1   CN   ISSN 0839-1265
VISITOR MAGAZINE. 1978. 5/yr. Can.$10. Fairway Group Inc., 215 Barnett St., Kitchener, ON N2G 4E5, Canada. TEL 519-886-2831. FAX 519-886-9383. adv.: B&W page Can.$1125, color page Can.$1640; trim 5 3/8 x 8 1/8. circ. 50,000 (controlled). (back issues avail.) **Document type:** consumer publication.
    Formerly: Waterloo Region Visitor's Guide.
    Description: Lists dining, accommodations, shopping and tourist information in the Kitchener, Waterloo, Cambridge, Guelph and Stratford areas.

910.202   JM
VISITOR VACATION GUIDE. 1980. w. free. Western Publishers Ltd., 82 Barnett St., P.O. Box 1258, Montego Bay, Jamaica, W.I. TEL 809-952-5253. FAX 809-952-6513. Ed. Lloyd B. Smith. adv. circ. 10,000. (tabloid format; back issues avail.)
    Formerly: Visitor.
    Description: Contains travel and tourist news, tips on where to shop, what to buy, what to see, villas, restaurants, hotels, and tours.

917   CN
VISITORS CHOICE. 1992. s-a. free. I G Publications Ltd., 999 8th St., S.W., Ste. 222, Calgary, AB T2R 1J5, Canada. FAX 403-229-2470.

914.2   UK   ISSN 0963-6226
VISITORS TO TOURIST ATTRACTIONS (YEAR). a. £16. British Tourist Authority, Department D, Thames Tower, Black's Rd., Hammersmith, London W6 9EL, England. (Co-sponsor: English Tourist Board)
    Description: Details the attendances at U.K. tourist attractions, along with opening hours and admission fees.

917.504   US
VISTA MAGAZINE; the magazine for all Hispanics. 1980. m. Horizon, 999 Ponce de Leon Blvd., Ste. 600, Coral Gables, FL 33134. TEL 305-442-2462. FAX 305-443-7650. adv.: B&W page $25900, color page $31900; trim 9 1/8 x 11. bk.rev.; circ. 1,100,000 (controlled). (back issues avail.) **Document type:** consumer publication.
    Formerly: Vista Magazine Miami Metro Guide (ISSN 0743-5738)
    Description: Information and entertainment for Hispanic Americans from different countries of origin and geographic locations.

917 790.13 051   US
VISTA U S A. 1965. q. $3. (Exxon Travel Club, Inc.) Aegis Group - Publishers, 30400 Van Dyke Ave., Warren, MI 48093. TEL 810-574-9100. (Alt. addr.: 3550 Dacoma, Houston, TX 77092) Ed. Jerry Burton. adv.; bk.rev. circ. 875,000. **Document type:** bulletin.
    Formerly: Vista (ISSN 0507-1577)

914   DK   ISSN 0108-2167
VOGNMANDEN. 1951. m. DKK 270. Turistvognmaendenes Landsorganisation - Danish Coach Owners Association, Carit Etlars Vej 3, DK-1814 Frederiksberg C, Denmark. TEL 31-211888. FAX 31-211901. Ed. Michael Brandt-Nielsen. adv. circ. 1,500. **Document type:** trade publication.

910.09 388.3   PO
VOLANTE.* w. Ediauto Publicacoes S.A., Rua Ruben A Leitao 2-1o, 1200 Lisbon, Portugal. TEL 01-521653. Dir. Fernando Petroninho.

910.202   II   ISSN 0971-3794
VOYAGE. (Text in English) 1992. m. Rs.250. Parsiana Publications Pvt. Ltd., c/o H.L. Rochat & Co, 39 Navsari Chambers, Amrit, Keshav Nayak Marg., Bombay 400001, India. TEL 2042624. FAX 2042922. TELEX 011-85710 RABO IN. (Subscr. to: c/o Kaiser-E-Hind Pvt. Ltd., 300 Perin Nariman St. (Behind RBI), Fort, Bombay 400001, India) Ed. Jehangir R. Patel. bk.rev. circ. 12,000. (back issues avail.) **Document type:** consumer publication.
    Description: Covers places of tourist interest, facilities available, tariffs, restaurants and special cuisines.

910.09   CN   ISSN 0711-6136
VOYAGE EN GROUPE; votre kiosque d'information touristique a domicile. (Text in French) 1981. bi-m. Can.$8. Voyage en Groupe, 425 Harris St., St-Laurent, Que. H4N 2G8, Canada. TEL 514-744-3867. FAX 514-744-9209. Ed. Andre Quesnel; Pub. Andre Quesnel. adv.: B&W page Can.$1185, color page Can.$1500. bk.rev. circ. 10,000. (back issues avail.) **Document type:** trade publication, directory.

910.09   US   ISSN 1040-8541
VOYAGER INTERNATIONAL. 1984. m. $38. Argonaut Enterprises, Inc., 7 Northgate, Box 2777, Westport, CT 06880. TEL 203-226-1647. FAX 203-846-2796. Ed. Jason N. Fisher. bk.rev.; film rev.; cum.index: 1987-1991. circ. 20,000. (back issues avail.) **Document type:** newsletter.
    Description: Evaluates the world for the discerning traveller.

910   FR   ISSN 0337-0402
VOYAGES CONTACT. 20/yr. 12 cite Falguiere, 75015 Paris, France. TEL 45-38-51-52. FAX 43-22-98-00. Ed. F. Guedes da Costa. circ. 10,400.

910   FR   ISSN 0995-4228
VOYAGES D'AFFAIRES. 1988. 10/yr. (France 600 F; elsewhere 750 F). Varenne Entreprises, 39 rue Saint-Dominique, 75007 Paris, France. TEL 47-83-89-80. FAX 47-83-89-37. Pub. Jean-Arnaud Dyens. adv.: B&W page 26000 F., color page 32000 F.; trim 280 x 205. circ. 40,000. **Document type:** trade publication.

910 011   FR   ISSN 0989-1080
VOYAGES ET STRATEGIE; le magazine de la stimulation et du tourisme d'affaires. 9/yr. Editions Re, 13 rue de l'Abbe Groult, 75015 Paris, France. TEL 48-42-06-60. FAX 48-42-30-72. Eds. Francois Perruche, Michel Foraud. adv.: B&W page 26000 F., color page 32000 F.; trim 280 x 205. circ. 16,000.

914   CV   ISSN 0258-0691
VOZ DI POVO. 1962. 3/wk. Direccao Nacional de Informacao, Caixa Postal 118, Praia, Sao Tiago, Cape Verde Islands. Ed. Alfredo Simao Carvalho Santos. circ. 3,000. **Indexed:** Bio-Contr.News & Info. **Supersedes:** Arquipelago (ISSN 0004-2668)

059.918   XO   ISSN 0139-7168
VYSOKE TATRY. (Text in Czech or Slovak; summaries in German, Russian) 1962. bi-m. $20. (Administration of Tatra National Park) Obzor, Spitalska ul. 35, 815 85 Bratislava, Slovakia.

052   ZA
W T G TOURISM NEWS. (Where to Go) 1991. m. K.100 per no. P A M Communications Ltd., P.O. Box 35637, Lusaka, Zambia. **Document type:** consumer publication.

910.09   SP   ISSN 1014-7276
W T O NEWS. French edition: Organisation Mondiale du Tourisme. Nouvelles (ISSN 1014-7292); Spanish edition: Organizacion Mundial del Turismo. Noticias (ISSN 1014-7284) (Text in English) 1989. bi-m. $55 to non-members (effective 1993). World Tourism Organization - Organizacion Mundial del Turismo, Capitan Haya 42, 28020 Madrid, Spain. TEL 571-06-28. FAX 5713733.
    Description: Contains articles and news about key tourism trends and issues around the world.

910 613.1   UK
W T T E R C TRAVEL & TOURISM. a. World Travel & Tourism Environment Research Centre, Oxford Brookes University, Headington, Oxford OX3 0BP, England. TEL 01865-484830. FAX 01865-484838. **Document type:** bulletin.
—BLDSC (9360.154205).

919.6   US
WAIKIKI NEWS. 1971. m. $16. Fred C. Pugarelli, Ed. & Pub., Box 89133, Honolulu, HI 96830-9133. adv.; bk.rev.; illus. circ. 1,000.

914.04   US
WALL STREET JOURNAL GUIDE TO BUSINESS TRAVEL: EUROPE. irreg. $50. Fodor's Travel Publications, Inc. (Subsidiary of: Random House, Inc.), 201 E. 50th St., New York, NY 10022. TEL 800-733-3000. (Dist. by: Random House, Inc., 400 Hahn Rd., Westminster, MD 21157) Ed. Edie Jarolim.

TRAVEL AND TOURISM

915.04   US
WALL STREET JOURNAL GUIDE TO BUSINESS TRAVEL: PACIFIC RIM. irreg. $20. Fodor's Travel Publications, Inc. (Subsidiary of: Random House, Inc.), 201 E. 50th St., New York, NY 10022. TEL 800-733-3000. (Dist. by: Random House, Inc., 400 Hahn Rd., Westminster, MD 21157) Ed. Edie Jarolim.

917.04   US
WALL STREET JOURNAL GUIDE TO BUSINESS TRAVEL: U S A & CANADA. irreg. $20. Fodor's Travel Publications, Inc.), 201 E. 50th St., New York, NY 10022. TEL 800-733-3000. (Dist. by: Random House, Inc., 400 Hahn Rd., Westminster, MD 21157) Ed. Edie Jarolim.

910.202   SZ
WALLIS. 1980. 6/yr. price varies. (Vereinigung Oberwalliser Verkehrsinteressenten) Rotten-Verlags AG, Leser-Dienst, Terbinerstr. 2, CH-3930 Visp, Switzerland. Ed. Armin Karlen. adv.

917.504   US   ISSN 8756-9779
GV1853.3.F62
WALT DISNEY WORLD (YEAR). Key Title: Steve Birnbaum Brings You the Best of Walt Disney World. a. Hearst Corporation, Walt Disney World, 250 W. 55th St., 11th Fl., New York, NY 10019. TEL 212-903-5190. Ed. Stephen Birnbaum.
●Also available online.

915.4   II
WARRIOR. (Text in English) 1971. m. free. Director of Information and Public Relations, Kohima, Nagaland, India. Ed. Chipeni Merry. stat. circ. 6,000. **Document type:** government publication.

917.504   US
WASHINGTON, D.C. VISITOR'S GUIDE. a. Bell Atlantic Specialty Guides, 6701 Democracy Blvd., 9th Fl., Bethesda, MD 20817. TEL 301-493-3258. circ. 315,000.
Description: Lists business and leisure services and facilities in and around D.C. Features articles on transportation services, sightseeing, performing arts and special events.

917.504   US   ISSN 1046-3089
WASHINGTON FLYER MAGAZINE.* 1989. bi-m. $15 (Canada $29, elsewhere $48). Ackerly Airport Advertising, Inc., 1707 L St., N.W. Ste. 350, Washington, DC 20036-4201. TEL 703-739-9292. FAX 703-683-2848. adv.; bk.rev. (reprint service avail.) **Document type:** consumer publication.
Description: Focuses on travel, transportation, trade and communication, hospitality and business. Contains information for travelers on the nation's capital.

910.09   US   ISSN 1051-0257
WASHINGTON INTERNATIONAL; building bridges in the international community. 1986. bi-m. $12. 1090 Vermont Ave. N.W., Ste. 700, Washington, DC 20005. TEL 202-223-3180. FAX 301-946-0779. (Subscr. to: Box 18031, Washington, DC 20036) Ed. Patricia Keegan. adv.; bk.rev. circ. 25,000. (tabloid format; back issues avail.) **Document type:** newsletter, consumer publication.
Description: Contains diplomatic news and travel articles directed toward the international, travel, and cultural community of Washington DC. Includes interviews with personalities, and features international hotel spotlights and a calendar of cultural events.
Refereed Serial

917.904   US   ISSN 1073-2578
F899.3
WASHINGTON STATE LODGING & TRAVEL GUIDE. 1987. a. $4.95. (Washington (State) Tourism Development Division) T S I - Technigraphic System Inc., 111 James St., Edmonds, WA 98020. TEL 800-324-4938. FAX 206-775-5727. (Co-sponsor: Washington State Hotel and Motel Association) Ed. Becky Tilbury. adv. contact: Becky Tilbury. circ. 350,000. **Document type:** consumer publication.
Formerly (until 1994): Destination Washington.
Description: Features outdoor recreation information, and a city-by-city listing of lodging and activities.

WASSERSKI MAGAZIN. see SPORTS AND GAMES — Boats And Boating

WATERFRONT NEWS; South Florida's nautical newspaper. see SPORTS AND GAMES — Boats And Boating

914.5   IT   ISSN 1121-1520
WEEKEND VIAGGI; il mensile dei sogni possibili. 1973. m. L.66000 (foreign L.135000). Arianna S.p.A., Piazza Aspromonte 13-A, 20131 Milan, Italy. TEL 39-2-706421. FAX 39-2-70638544. Ed. Enrico Mayer. adv.: B&W page L.10900000, color page L.15000000. (back issues avail.)

914.37   XR
DB2021
WELCOME; tourist revue. 1965. q. 48 Kc.($8.80) (Ministerstvo Obchodu a Cestovniho Ruchu) Orbis, Vinohradska 46, 120 00 Prague 2, Czech Republic. Ed. Vit Suchy. illus. circ. 36,000.
Formerly (until 1993): Welcome to Czechoslovakia (ISSN 0043-2210)

914   CY   ISSN 0044-0698
WELCOME TO CYPRUS. 1959. m. £C20. PAN Publishing House, Makarios & Xenopoullos Sts., Box 1209, Nicosia, Cyprus. Ed. P. Kokkinos. adv. circ. 4,500.
Formerly: You Are Welcome Sir, to Cyprus.

917.6
WELCOME TO GREATER LOUISVILLE. 1951. bi-w. $30. Editorial Services Company, 451 Baxter Ave., Louisville, KY 40204-1145. TEL 502-584-2720. FAX 502-584-2722. Ed. Sara N. Reisz. adv.: B&W page $740, color page $775; trim 5 1/2 x 8 1/2; adv. contact: Stacey Brinkop. circ. 17,500. **Document type:** consumer publication.

910.202   LE
WELCOME TO LEBANON & THE MIDDLE EAST. 1959. m. Tourist Information and Advertising Bureau, Starco Centre, N. Block 711, P.O. Box 4204, Beirut, Lebanon. Ed. Souhaji Toufik Abou-Jamra. adv. circ. 6,000.

914.2   UK
WELCOME TO SALISBURY DISTRICT. 1983. a. free. Salisbury District Council, Leisure and Tourism Services, Bourne Hill, Salisbury SP1 3UZ, England. TEL 01722-334956. FAX 01722-335855. (Subscr. to: Tourist Information Centre, Fish Row, Salisbury SP1 1EJ, England) adv.; maps. circ. 80,000. **Document type:** bulletin.
Former titles (until 1992): Salisbury; (until 1989): Touring from Salisbury; (until 1987): Touring in Historic Wessex.
Description: Promotional brochure for prospective visitors to Salisbury area.

917.504   US
WEST VIRGINIA - IT'S YOU. 1989. a. $3.95. Bell Atlantic Specialty Guides, 6701 Democracy Blvd., 9th Fl., Bethesda, MD 20817. TEL 301-493-3258. FAX 301-493-3833. Ed. Debra Auerback-Deutsch. adv. circ. 265,000.

916.87   SA   ISSN 1021-5530
▼**WESTERN CAPE TRAVEL GUIDE;** official guide, with accomodation directory. (Text in English) 1994. a. (Western Cape Tourism Association) G S A Marketing Pty. Ltd., P.O. Box 3239, Cape Town 8000, South Africa. TEL 27-21-419-1671. FAX 27-21-419-4851. (Co-sponsor: SA Tourism Board) illus.; maps. **Document type:** consumer publication.

914.004   US   ISSN 1056-4373
D909
WESTERN EUROPE (YEAR). a. $18. Harper Collins Publishers, Birnbaum Travel Guides, 10 E. 53rd St., New York, NY 10022-5299. TEL 212-207-7542. Ed. Alexandra Mayes Birnbaum. illus.; index.

796.7   US   ISSN 0043-4434
WESTWAYS. 1909. m. $12.95. Automobile Club of Southern California, Box 2890, Los Angeles, CA 90051. TEL 213-741-4760. FAX 213-741-3033. Ed.Eric Seyfarth. bk.rev.; illus. circ. 430,000.
Indexed: Access (1975-), Amer.Hist.& Life, Cal.Per.Ind. (1978-), Hist.Abstr.
—UnCover.

917.104   CN   ISSN 0843-3356
WESTWORLD BRITISH COLUMBIA. q. Can.$2($6). Canada Wide Magazines, 4180 Lougheed Hwy., Ste. 401, Burnaby, BC V5C 6A7, Canada. TEL 604-299-7311. FAX 604-299-9188. Ed. Robin Roberts; Pub. Peter Legge. adv. contact: Tim Nast. circ. 450,000. **Document type:** consumer publication.

WESTWORLD SASKATCHEWAN. see TRANSPORTATION — Automobiles

914.2   UK
WHAT TO DO IN THE NORFOLK BROADS. 1927. a. £3.95. Jarrold Publishing, Whitefriars St., Norwich NR3 1TR, England. TEL 01603-763300. FAX 01603-662748. maps; illus.; charts. **Document type:** directory.
Description: Includes 20 maps and over 25 illustrations, tide tables and distance charts.

914   UK
WHAT'S ON IN ABERDEEN. 1945. m. £5. Aberdeen Tourist Board, St. Nicholas House, Broad St., Aberdeen AB9 1DE, Scotland. TEL 01224-632727. FAX 01224-620415. Ed. Neil Paterson. adv. contact: Maureen Gorshkov. circ. 162,500. **Document type:** consumer publication.
Former titles: What's on and Where to Shop in Aberdeen; What's on in Aberdeen (ISSN 0043-4639)

914.204   UK
WHAT'S ON IN AND AROUND MANCHESTER. 1971. m. free. Intercity Publications (N.W.) Ltd., 21 Roebuck Lane, Sale, Cheshire M33 1SY, England. Ed. Dennis Haines. adv.; bk.rev. circ. 16,000.

914.204   UK
WHAT'S ON IN AVON. 1976. m. £0.20 per no. Newswest International, Foxlark, Smitham Hill, E. Harptree, Bristol BS18 6BZ, England. Ed. Tony Ferrand. adv.

919   II   ISSN 0043-4647
WHAT'S ON IN CALCUTTA; city's entertainment & tourist guide. 1965. fortn. Rs.300($100) India-International News Service, 12 India Exchange Place, Calcutta 700 001, India. Ed. H. Kothari. adv.; film rev.; mkt.; play rev.

914.2   UK
WHAT'S ON IN EAST ANGLIA. 1969. m. £7.50. Profile Publishing, 101 Thunder Lane, Norwich NR7 0JG, England. Ed. Stephen Ford. adv.; bk.rev. circ. 26,000.
Description: Leisure guide for East Anglia.

910.202 790.1   US
WHAT'S ON IN LAS VEGAS MAGAZINE. 1953. s-m. $56 (effective 1995). 4425 S. Industrial, Las Vegas, NV 89103. TEL 702-891-8811; 800-494-2876. FAX 702-891-8804. E-mail: haley@wizard.com. Ed. Stacey Hertz; Pub. Murray Hertz. adv. contact: Pamela Hertz-Garcell. circ. 130,000. (back issues avail.) **Document type:** consumer publication.
Description: Informs visitors on local entertainment, including gambling, shows, sightseeing, shopping, and dining.

914 792
WHAT'S ON IN LONDON. 1982. w. £60.84. Where to Go Ltd., 182 Pentonville Rd., London N1 9LB, England. TEL 0171-278-4393. FAX 0171-837-5838. Ed. Michael Darvell; Pub. E.G. Shaw. adv. contact: Dave Pierce. bk.rev.; film rev.; play rev. circ. 40,000. **Document type:** consumer publication.
Former titles: What's on and Where to Go in London (ISSN 0264-3227); Which was formed by merger of (1937-1982): What's on in London (ISSN 0043-4671); Where to Go in London and Around (ISSN 0043-4817)
Description: Guide to London's mainstream and fringe theatre, cinema, opera, ballet, classical, jazz and popular music, art galleries, museums, restaurants, pageantry, entertainment and leisure.

915.9   PH
WHAT'S ON IN MANILA. 26/yr. Western Communications, Inc., Pacific Bldg., no.403, Ayala Ave., Makati MM, Philippines. TEL 8150659.

914   IT
WHAT'S ON IN MILAN. m. Garp - Spd, Piazza San Simpliciano, 7, 20121 Milan, Italy. TEL 02-870078. Ed. Marina Saccheri Borri. circ. 10,000.

TRAVEL AND TOURISM

910.09   AT   ISSN 0812-2040
WHAT'S ON IN VICTORIA. 1983. q. Aus.$12($14.80) Life Be In It Australia, Batmar Ave., Melbourne, Vic. 3004, Australia. FAX 03-654-4973. Eds. Wilma Bedford, Jenny Robinson. adv. circ. 20,000. (back issues avail.)

914.204   UK
WHAT'S ON NORTH WEST. a. free. Intercity Publications (N.W.) Ltd., 21 Roebuck Lane, Sale, Cheshire M33 1SY, England. adv.; illus. circ. 100,000.

796   US   ISSN 0194-0384
GV198.56
WHEELERS R V RESORT AND CAMPGROUND GUIDE: NORTH AMERICAN EDITION. 1972. a. $12.95. Print Media Services, Ltd., 1310 Jarvis Ave., Elk Grove Village, IL 60007. TEL 708-981-0100. FAX 708-981-0106. adv. circ. 180,000. **Document type:** consumer publication, directory.
    Supersedes regional editions of: Wheelers Recreational Vehicle Resort and Campground Guide; Which superseded: Wheelers Trailer Resort and Campground Guide (ISSN 0090-600X)

910.202   TH
WHERE. m. B.20($0.85) per no. Media Transasia (Thailand) Ltd., 14th Fl., Orakarn Bldg., 26 Chidlom Rd., Bangkok 10330, Thailand. FAX 2535335. TELEX 84003-MEDTRAN-TH. Ed. Kelvin Rugg. adv. circ. 25,940.
    Description: Tourist guide to Thailand aimed at affluent travelers.

917.502   US
▼**WHERE BALTIMORE.** 1994. m. Where Magazines International (Baltimore), 516 N. Charles St., Ste. 300, Baltimore, MD 21201. TEL 410-539-4373. FAX 410-539-4381. Ed. Laura Reiley; Pub. Anthony Ondrusek. adv.: B&W page $1650, color page $2090; trim 8 1/8 x 10 7/8. circ. 30,000 (controlled). **Document type:** consumer publication.

917.102   US
WHERE EDMONTON. q. Where Magazines International (Edmonton), 9343-50th St., Unit 4, Edmonton, AB T6B 2L5, Canada. TEL 403-465-3362. FAX 403-448-0424. adv.: B&W page Can.$2260, color page Can.$2825; trim 8 1/8 x 10 7/8. circ. 40,000 (controlled).

910.202   CN   ISSN 0849-309X
WHERE ROCKY MOUNTAINS. 1978. s-a. Can.$4($4) R M V Publications Ltd., Ste. 250, One Palliser Sq., 125 Ninth Ave. S.E., Calgary, AB T2G 0P6, Canada. TEL 403-299-1888. FAX 403-299-1899. Ed. Jack Newton. adv.; circ. 180,000 (controlled). **Document type:** consumer publication.
    Formerly: Rocky Mountain Visitor (ISSN 0821-5146)
    Description: Information for visitors to the Canadian Rocky Mountains.

910.202   US
WHERE SEATTLE; the city magazine for visitors. 1992. m. free to hotel patrons. Where Magazines International (Seattle), 2505 Third Ave., Ste. 305, Seattle, WA 98121. TEL 206-728-2624. FAX 206-728-1423. Ed. Trish Picknell; Pub. Wendy Vos. adv.: B&W page $1905, color page $2190; trim 8 1/8 x 10 7/8; adv. contact: Wendy Vos. illus.; circ. 30,000 (controlled). **Document type:** consumer publication.
    Description: Visitor's guide to Seattle sights, dining, entertainment, and cultural events.

WHERE TO EAT IN CANADA. see HOTELS AND RESTAURANTS

WHERE TO EAT IN NORTH WEST ENGLAND. see HOTELS AND RESTAURANTS

WHERE TO EAT IN SOUTH AND SOUTHEAST ENGLAND. see HOTELS AND RESTAURANTS

WHERE TO EAT IN THE CHANNEL ISLANDS. see HOTELS AND RESTAURANTS

WHERE TO EAT IN THE WEST COUNTRY AND WALES. see HOTELS AND RESTAURANTS

914.2   UK
WHERE TO GO IN THE THAMES AND CHILTERNS.*
1980. a. £1.95. Automobile Association, Fanum House, Basingstoke RG21 2EA, England. Ed. Stan Bowes. adv. circ. 25,000.
    Description: Guide to tourist attractions and accommodation in the five-county region: Buckinghamshire, Berkshire, Oxfordshire, Bedfordshire and Hertfordshire.

914.2   UK
WHERE TO GO, WHAT TO DO IN THE SOUTH. a. £1.50. Michael Brewer Publishing, Kestrel House, Alma Rd., Romsey, Hants. SO51 8EB, England. TEL 0794-518151. FAX 0794-518015. Ed. M. Brewer. adv. circ. 25,000. **Document type:** consumer publication.
    Description: Details over 1000 places to visit in Hampshire, Wiltshire, Dorset, Sussex and the Isle of Wight.

918   PE
WHERE, WHEN, HOW... m. Peruvian Times, S.A., Apartado 2484, Lima, Peru. Ed. Anne Arrarte. circ. 25,000.

914.204   UK
WHICH AIRLINE? AND BUSINESS TRAVEL UPDATE. 1990. s-a. B M I Publications Ltd., Suffolk House, George St., Croydon, Surrey CR9 1SR, England. TEL 0181-649-7233. FAX 0181-649-7234. Ed. Alan Orbell. adv.: B&W page £1000, color page £1400; trim 148 x 210; adv. contact: Sherida Haley. circ. 45,000 (controlled). (back issues avail.) **Document type:** consumer publication.
    Description: Caters to frequent flyers.

WHITE BOOK OF SKI AREAS. U S AND CANADA. see SPORTS AND GAMES — Outdoor Life

WHO'S WHO IN AMERICA'S RESTAURANTS; encyclopedia of America's dining establishments. see ENCYCLOPEDIAS AND GENERAL ALMANACS

WHO'S WHO IN RECREATION. see BIOGRAPHY

WIESBADENER LEBEN. see GENERAL INTEREST PERIODICALS — Germany

WINESTATE. see BEVERAGES

WINGS OF ALOHA. see TRANSPORTATION — Air Transport

WINGS WEST; the Western aviation magazine. see TRANSPORTATION — Air Transport

914.04   GW
WIR; in Nieder-Erlenbach. 1970. m. Sozialdemokratische Partei Deutschlands, Ortsverein Nieder - Erlenbach, Bornweg 30, 60437 Frankfurt, Germany. TEL 06101-43434. circ. 1,500.

WISCONSIN WEST MAGAZINE. see HISTORY — History Of North And South America

910.09 053.931   NE   ISSN 0043-7212
WOLKENRIDDER. English edition: Wolkenridder International. 1946. m. fl.40. K L M Royal Dutch Airlines, Public Relations Bureau, Postbus 7700, 1117 ZR Schiphol Airport, Netherlands. TEL 31-20-6491126. FAX 31-20-6488200. Ed. Nicholas S. Gale. adv.: B&W page fl.2800, color page fl.4000; trim 210 x 285. bk.rev.; illus. circ. 39,000 (Dutch ed. 32,000; English ed. 7,000).
    Description: Covers news of KLM and general aviation topics for KLM staff.

910.09   US   ISSN 1055-1905
E158
WOMEN'S TRAVELLER. 1989. a. $10.95. Damron Company, Inc., Box 42-2458, San Francisco, CA 94142-2458. TEL 415-255-0404. FAX 415-703-9049. Ed. Gina M. Gatta. circ. 50,000.
    Description: Complete travel guide and atlas for women. Provides information on women's accommodations.

796.5   US   ISSN 0744-8120
WOODALL'S CAMPERWAYS; the Middle Atlantic campers' newspaper. 1978. m. $15. Woodall Publishing Co., 13975 W. Polo Trail Dr., Lake Forest, IL 60045-9952. TEL 708-362-6700; 800-323-9076. FAX 708-362-8776. Pub. Deborah A. Spriggs. adv.: B&W page $740, color page $1079; 10 x 13; adv. contact: Mary Sgaraglino. circ. 40,000. **Document type:** newspaper, consumer publication.

WOODALL'S TRAILS-A-WAY. see SPORTS AND GAMES — Outdoor Life

910.222 790.1   US
WORCESTER MAGAZINE. 1972. w. $26. Worcester Publishing Ltd., 172 Shrewsbury St., Worcester, MA 01604. TEL 508-755-8004. FAX 508-755-8860. Ed. Walter Crockett. adv. contact: Kathy Real. bk.rev.; film rev.; play rev.; illus.; circ. 40,000 (paid). (tabloid format; back issues avail.) **Document type:** newspaper.
    Description: Covers and reviews people, places, and events in the Worcester, MA, area.

WORKAMPER NEWS; America's guide to working while camping. see OCCUPATIONS AND CAREERS

WORKING ABROAD (LONDON). see BUSINESS AND ECONOMICS — Labor And Industrial Relations

WORKING HOLIDAYS (YEAR). see OCCUPATIONS AND CAREERS

910.202 551.46   US   ISSN 1063-3448
WORLD AQUATIC NEWS & TRAVEL. 1983. q. $7 (Canada $8; elsewhere $10). 1117 Concepts Publishing, Box 1415, Duarte, CA 91009-4415. TEL 818-793-2582. FAX 818-792-7947. Ed. Margaret Samson. bk.rev. circ. 500. (back issues avail.) **Document type:** newsletter.
    Formerly: M S I News.
    Description: Features news from around the world, international calendar, directory of aquatics, and tours to international swimming events.

910 709   US
WORLD CULTURAL GUIDES.* irreg. Holt, Rinehart and Winston, Inc., c/o Harcourt Brace Jovanovich, 6277 Sea Harbor Dr., Orlando, FL 32887. TEL 407-345-2500.

910.202   US
WORLD HOLIDAY AND TIME GUIDE. 1982. a. Morgan Guaranty Trust Company of New York, 23 Wall St., New York, NY 10015. TEL 212-483-2323.

WORLD HOTEL AND CONVENTION DIRECTORY. see HOTELS AND RESTAURANTS

WORLD LEISURE AND RECREATION. see LEISURE AND RECREATION

910.09 639.9   UK   ISSN 0951-2195
GF1
WORLD MAGAZINE; the magazine of mankind. 1987. m. £24 (Europe £38; rest of world £48). World Publications Ltd., B B C Enterprises, Rm. A1040, 80 Wood Ln., Woodlands, London W1Z 0TT, England. TEL 081-576-2000. FAX 081-576-2931. (Subscr. to: Punch Subscriptions, Stephenson Hse., Brunel Ctr., Bletcheley, Milton Keynes, London MK2 2EW, England) Ed. Peter Crookston. adv.; bk.rev. circ. 35,000. (also avail. in microfilm from UMI) **Indexed:** Mag.Ind. **Document type:** consumer publication.
    Description: Combines photography with writing to tell stories of the Earth's people, places and the marvels of its geography.

910.09   US   ISSN 0163-1780
WORLD TRAVELING. 1978. bi-m. $12. Midwest News Service, Inc., 30943 Club House Lane, Farmington Hills, MI 48018. Ed. Theresa Mitan. adv.; bk.rev. circ. 60,000.

910.09   US   ISSN 1051-6247
G149
WORLDWIDE TRAVEL INFORMATION CONTACT BOOK. 1991. biennial. $175. Gale Research Inc., 835 Penobscot Bldg., Detroit, MI 48226. TEL 313-961-2242. FAX 313-961-6083. Ed. Burkhard Herbote.
    Description: Lists over 45000 travel information sources.

6510 TRAVEL AND TOURISM — ABSTRACTING, BIBLIOGRAPHIES, STATISTICS

915.13   CC
XINAN LUYOU/TOURING SOUTHWEST CHINA. (Text in Chinese) 1980. bi-m. $20.70. Sichuan Renmin Chubanshe, 3, Yandao Jie, Chengdu, Sichuan 610016, People's Republic of China. TEL 6670439. (Dist. in US by: China Books & Periodicals, Inc., 2929 24th St., San Francisco, CA 94110. TEL 415-282-2994) Ed. Deng Hongping. circ. 30,000.
Document type: consumer publication.
Formerly: Sichuan Luyou - Touring Sichuan.
Description: Covers tourism in southwestern China.

XTRA!; your gay & lesbian guide to Toronto. see HOMOSEXUALITY

649.94   AT
Y H A HOSTELS IN AUSTRALIA. 1957. a. Aus.$1.50. (Australian Youth Hostels Association Inc.) Kingsgrove Press Pty. Ltd., 43 Kingsway, Kingsgrove NSW 2208, Australia. Ed. P. Carter. adv. circ. 150,000.
Formerly: Australian Youth Hostels Handbook (ISSN 0156-0107)
Description: Hostel information, addresses, maps of locations state by state, booking information, regional descriptions, holidays, festival dates, concessions.

YACHTSMAN'S GUIDE TO THE BAHAMAS. see SPORTS AND GAMES — Boats And Boating

917.4   US   ISSN 1055-226X
F2.3
YANKEE MAGAZINE'S TRAVEL GUIDE TO NEW ENGLAND, NEW YORK & EASTERN CANADA. 1972. a. $4.95. Yankee Publishing, Inc., Box 520, Dublin, NH 03444-0520. TEL 617-723-4309. Ed. Janice Brand. adv. circ. 210,000. (reprint service avail. from UMI)
Former titles: Yankee Magazine's Travel Guide to New England and Its Neighbors (ISSN 1055-2251); Yankee Magazine's Travel Guide to New England (ISSN 0740-6215); Yankee Magazine's Guide to New England; Yankee Guide to the New England Countryside.

917.404   US   ISSN 1061-4699
YANKEE TRAVELER. 9/yr. $36 (foreign $42). Yankee Publishing, Inc., Box 523, Dublin, NH 03444. (Subscr. to: Box 10008, Des Moines, IA 50347-0008) Ed. Janice Brand; Pub. Judson D. Hale Jr. (looseleaf format; back issues avail.)
Document type: newsletter.

919   II   ISSN 0049-8289
YATRI; a bimonthly newsletter of Indian tourism. (Text in English) no. 27, 1971. bi-m. free. India Tourism Development Corporation, Himalaya House, 6th Fl., 23 Kasturba Gandhi Marg, New Delhi 110001, India. Ed. Chandni Luthra. illus. circ. 10,000.

YELLOW PAGES OF GOLF; for North America. see SPORTS AND GAMES — Ball Games

YELLOW PAGES OF SKIING; (year) North American planner & directory. see SPORTS AND GAMES — Outdoor Life

647.94   UK
YOUTH HOSTELS ASSOCIATION (ENGLAND AND WALES) ACCOMMODATION GUIDE. 1931. a. £5.99. Youth Hostels Association (England and Wales), Trevelyan House, St. Albans, Herts AL1 2DY, England. TEL 01727-855215. FAX 01727-844126. Ed. Hellen Barnes. adv. circ. 370,000. **Document type:** bulletin.
Former titles: Youth Hostels Association (England and Wales) Guide; Youth Hostels Association (England and Wales) Handbook.

910.09   NE
ZAKENREIS/BUSINESS TRAVEL. 1969. m. fl.25. Esdoornhof 20, 3831 XX Leusden, Netherlands. TEL 31-33-941368. FAX 31-33-943366. TELEX 43776. Ed. C.G. Hundenpool. adv.; bk.rev. circ. 12,000.

914   SZ   ISSN 0044-2755
ZEITSCHRIFT FUER FREMDENVERKEHR/REVUE DE TOURISME/TOURIST REVIEW. (Text in English, French, German, Italian and Spanish) 1946. q. 52 SFr.($37) International Association of Scientific Experts in Tourism, Varnbuelstr. 19, CH-9000 St. Gallen, Switzerland. (Co-sponsors: University of Berne, Tourist Research Institute; University of St. Gallen, Institute for Tourism and Transport Economy) Ed. C. Kaspar. adv.; bk.rev.; bibl.; stat. Indexed: Key to Econ.Sci., P.A.I.S.For.Lang.Ind., Rural Recreat.Tour.Abstr., World Agri.Econ.& Rural Sociol.Abstr.
—BLDSC (8870.925000). **CCC.**

614.86 387.742   CC   ISSN 1001-2079
ZHONGGUO MINHANG BAO/CIVIL AVIATION ADMINISTRATION OF CHINA. JOURNAL. (Text in Chinese) 1989. bi-m. Y62.40. Zhongguo Minhang Baoshe, 155 Dongsi Xidajie, Beijing 100710, People's Republic of China. TEL 86-10-4031776. FAX 86-10-4031776. Ed. Zhang Shusheng. adv. contact: Ren Joan. circ. 100,000. **Document type:** newspaper.
Description: In-house publication of CAAC.

968   RH
ZIMBABWE: A TOURIST PARADISE. bi-m. Z.$40.80 (foreign Z.$45.90). Thomson Publications Zimbabwe (Pvt) Ltd., Thomson House, P.O. Box 1683, Harare, Zimbabwe. TEL 263-4-736835. FAX 263-4-752390. TELEX 24705 ZW. adv.; illus.
Document type: consumer publication.

2 C PLEIN AIR; cultura e strumenti del turismo all'aria aperta. see SPORTS AND GAMES — Outdoor Life

917.704   US   ISSN 1058-6113
F551
2 TO 22 DAYS AROUND THE GREAT LAKES. 1991. a. John Muir Publications, Box 613, Santa Fe, NM 87504.

914.04   US   ISSN 1059-2946
D909
2 TO 22 DAYS IN EUROPE. a. John Muir Publications, Box 613, Santa Fe, NM 87504.
Formerly (until 1992): 22 Days in Europe (ISSN 1059-3004)

914.804   US   ISSN 1058-6091
DL4
2 TO 22 DAYS IN NORWAY, SWEDEN, AND DENMARK. 1991. a. John Muir Publications, Box 613, Santa Fe, NM 87504.

4 TAXIS. see ART

910.09   US
800 & FAX TRAVEL DIRECTORY. 1972. a. $25. World Travel Communications Inc., 7380 S. Eastern Ave., No. 124-142, Las Vegas, NV 89123. TEL 702-795-2411. FAX 702-361-0371. Ed. J.A. Cabell. **Document type:** directory.
Formerly (until 1991): Travel 800.
Description: Toll-free and fax reference for professional travel planners.

TRAVEL AND TOURISM — Abstracting, Bibliographies, Statistics

914.2 312   UK
AGE AND SEX PROFILE OF OVERSEAS VISITORS TO THE U K (YEAR). irreg., latest 1993. £10. British Tourist Authority, Department D, Thames Tower, Black's Rd., Hammersmith, London W6 9EL, England.
Description: Provides the basic facts about the age and sex of overseas visitors to the U.K.

ARTICLES IN HOSPITALITY AND TOURISM. see HOTELS AND RESTAURANTS — Abstracting, Bibliographies, Statistics

310   AT   ISSN 1036-2606
AUSTRALIA. BUREAU OF STATISTICS. DIRECTORY OF TOURISM STATISTICS. 1991. a. Aus.$38. Australian Bureau of Statistics, P.O. Box 10, Belconnen, A.C.T. 2616, Australia. **Document type:** government publication, directory.
Description: Contains comprehensive information on sources of tourism statistics.

AUSTRALIA. BUREAU OF STATISTICS. NEW SOUTH WALES OFFICE. TOURIST ACCOMMODATION, NEW SOUTH WALES. see HOTELS AND RESTAURANTS — Abstracting, Bibliographies, Statistics

AUSTRALIA. BUREAU OF STATISTICS. NORTHERN TERRITORY OFFICE. TOURIST ACCOMMODATION, NORTHERN TERRITORY. see HOTELS AND RESTAURANTS — Abstracting, Bibliographies, Statistics

310   AT   ISSN 0157-3578
AUSTRALIA. BUREAU OF STATISTICS. SOUTH AUSTRALIAN OFFICE. TOURIST ACCOMMODATION, SOUTH AUSTRALIA. 1975. q. Aus.$25 per no. Australian Bureau of Statistics, South Australian Office, G.P.O. Box 2272, Adelaide, S.A. 5001, Australia. **Document type:** government publication.
Description: Contains information about hotels, motels, caravan parks, holiday flats and units, and visitor hostels, occupancy rates and takings from accommodation for each month by type of establishment.

AUSTRALIA. BUREAU OF STATISTICS. TASMANIAN OFFICE. TOURIST ACCOMMODATION, TASMANIA. see HOTELS AND RESTAURANTS — Abstracting, Bibliographies, Statistics

910 310   AT   ISSN 1321-4144
AUSTRALIA. BUREAU OF STATISTICS. TOURISM INDICATORS, AUSTRALIA. 1993. q. Aus.$30 per no. Australian Bureau of Statistics, P.O. Box 10, Belconnen, A.C.T. 2616, Australia. **Document type:** government publication.

AUSTRALIA. BUREAU OF STATISTICS. TOURIST ACCOMMODATION, AUSTRALIA. see HOTELS AND RESTAURANTS — Abstracting, Bibliographies, Statistics

AUSTRALIA. BUREAU OF STATISTICS. TOURIST ACCOMMODATION, AUSTRALIAN CAPITAL TERRITORY. see HOTELS AND RESTAURANTS — Abstracting, Bibliographies, Statistics

AUSTRALIA. BUREAU OF STATISTICS. TOURIST ACCOMMODATION, WESTERN AUSTRALIA. see HOTELS AND RESTAURANTS — Abstracting, Bibliographies, Statistics

AUSTRALIA. BUREAU OF STATISTICS. VICTORIAN OFFICE. TOURIST ACCOMMODATION, VICTORIA. see HOTELS AND RESTAURANTS — Abstracting, Bibliographies, Statistics

914   AU
AUSTRIA. WIRTSCHAFTSKAMMER OESTERREICH. TOURISMUS IN ZAHLEN; Oesterreichische und internationale Fremdenverkehrs- und Wirtschaftsdaten. 1965. a. free. Wirtschaftskammer Oesterreich, Sektion Tourismus, Wiedner Hauptstr. 63, A-1045 Vienna, Austria. illus.; stat. circ. 350. **Document type:** government publication.
Former titles: Austria. Bundeskammer der Gewerblichen Wirtschaft. Fremdenverkehr in Zahlen; Austria. Bundeskammer der Gewerblichen Wirtschaft. Statistik und Dokumentation. Information (ISSN 0039-0585)

319   BB
BARBADOS. STATISTICAL SERVICE. DIGEST OF TOURISM STATISTICS. a. Statistical Service, National Insurance Building, 3rd Fl., Fairchild St., Bridgetown, Barbados, W.I.

910.202   BB
BARBADOS. TOURISM AUTHORITY. ANNUAL REPORT. 1972. a. Tourism Authority, Harbour Rd., P.O. Box 242, Bridgetown, Barbados, W.I. TEL 809-427-2623. FAX 809-426-4080. TELEX WB 2420. **Document type:** government publication.
Formerly: Barbados. Board of Tourism. Annual Report.
Description: Records the Board's function, structure, achievements and undertakings.

910.2   BE   ISSN 0067-5547
BELGIUM. INSTITUT NATIONAL DE STATISTIQUE. STATISTIQUE DU TOURISME ET DE L'HOTELLERIE. (Subseries of: Statistiques du Commerce Interieur et des Transports (ISSN 0773-4255)) (Text in Dutch, French) a. 52 BEF (foreign 95 BEF). Institut National de Statistique, 44 rue de Louva'n, B-1000 Brussels, Belgium. **Document type:** government publication.

TRAVEL AND TOURISM — ABSTRACTING, BIBLIOGRAPHIES, STATISTICS

959 016   SI   ISSN 0068-0176
Z3248.S5
BOOKS ABOUT SINGAPORE. (Text in English) 1963. irreg. free. National Library, Stamford Rd., Singapore 0617, Singapore. TEL 3323660. FAX 3371470. circ. 1,500.
    Formerly: Books About Malaysia.

916.8 316   BS   ISSN 1013-5715
BOTSWANA. CENTRAL STATISTICS OFFICE. TOURIST STATISTICS. 1974. a. P.5. Central Statistics Office, Ministry of Finance and Development Planning, Private Bag 0024, Gaborone, Botswana. TEL 267-352200. (Orders to: Government Printer, P.O. Box 87, Gaborone, Botswana) Ed. G.M. Charumbira; Pub. J.G. Segwe. charts; stat. **Document type:** government publication.
    Description: Provides information on travelers, length of stay and residence permit issues.

914.2   UK
THE BRITISH ON HOLIDAY (YEAR). a. £20. British Tourist Authority, Department D, Thames Tower, Black's Rd., Hammersmith, London W6 9EL, England.
    Description: Summarizes the results from the British National Travel Survey of holidays taken by the British.

914.2   UK   ISSN 0068-2616
BRITISH TOURIST AUTHORITY. DIGEST OF TOURIST STATISTICS. 1969. irreg., no.17, 1993. £50. British Tourist Authority, Department D, Thames Tower, Black's Rd., Hammersmith, London W6 9EL, England. **Document type:** consumer publication.
—BLDSC (3588.325500).
    Description: Provides a wealth of facts and figures relating to tourism to, within, and from the U.K., including data on international tourism, tourism and the economy, sightseeing, and hotel numbers and occupancy rates.

790.1 332.6   UK   ISSN 0956-683X
BUSINESS MONITOR: OVERSEAS TRAVEL AND TOURISM. (Part of the Miscellaneous Monitors series) 1969. a. Central Statistical Office, C.S.O. Library, Government Bldgs., Cardiff Rd., Newport, Gwent NP9 1XG, Wales. TEL 01633-812973. FAX 01633-812599. TELEX 497121 ALBBSONPT G. (Subscr. to: H.M.S.O. Publications Centre, P.O. Box 276, London SW8 5DT, England. TEL 0171-873-9090. FAX 0171-873-8200) charts. (back issues avail.) **Document type:** government publication.
—BLDSC (2934.325000).

910.09   FR   ISSN 0294-6831
CAHIERS DU TOURISME. SERIE D: STATISTIQUES. 1981. irreg., no.35, 1993. price varies. Universite d'Aix-Marseille III (Universite de Droit, d'Economie et des Sciences), Centre des Hautes Etudes Touristiques, Immeuble Euroffice, 38 av. de l'Europe, B.P. 661, 13094 Aix-en-Provence, Cedex 2, France. TEL 42-20-09-73. FAX 42-20-50-98. (back issues avail.) **Document type:** monographic series.

910.09   FR
CAHIERS DU TOURISME. SERIE F: BANQUE DE DONNEES STATISTIQUES. 1990. irreg., no.32, 1994. 750 F. per no. Universite d'Aix-Marseille III (Universite de Droit, d'Economie et des Sciences), Centre des Hautes Etudes Touristiques, Immeuble Euroffice, 38 av. de l'Europe, B.P. 661, 13094 Aix-en-Provence Cedex 2, France. TEL 42-20-09-73. FAX 42-20-50-98. (back issues avail.) **Document type:** monographic series.

338.4   CN   ISSN 0838-3952
G155.C3
CANADA. STATISTICS CANADA. INTERNATIONAL TRAVEL. (Catalogue 66-001) (Text in English and French) 1931. q. Can.$154($185) (foreign $216). Statistics Canada, Publications Sales and Services, Ottawa, Ont. K1A 0T6, Canada. TEL 613-951-7277. FAX 613-951-1584. (also avail. in microform from MML)
    Formerly: Canada. Statistics Canada. Travel Between Canada and Other Countries (ISSN 0317-6738)
    Description: Shows province of entry, transportation and country of residence of visitors as well as estimates of the travel account for the balance of payments both seasonally and not seasonally adjusted.

917.2   BB
CARIBBEAN TOURISM ORGANIZATION. STATISTICAL NEWS. 1977. q. $60. Caribbean Tourism Organization, Sir F. Walcott Bldg., 2nd Fl., Culloden Farm, St. Michael, Barbados, W.I. TEL 809-427-5242. FAX 809-429-3065. circ. 2,000.
    Formerly: Caribbean Tourism; Which superseded (in 1981): Caribbean Tourism Research Centre. Newsletter.

919.704   BB
CARIBBEAN TOURISM STATISTICAL REPORT. 1978. a. $200. Caribbean Tourism Organization, Sir F. Walcott Bldg., 2nd Fl., Culloden Farm, St. Michael, Barbados, W.I. TEL 809-427-5242. FAX 809-429-3065. circ. 1,000.
    Formerly: Caribbean Tourism Statistics.
    Description: Source of key statistics and overview of tourism trends in the Caribbean.

910.09   CE
CEYLON TOURIST BOARD. ANNUAL STATISTICAL REPORT. 1968. a. $10. Ceylon Tourist Board, Research & Planning Division, P.O. Box 1504, Colombo 3, Sri Lanka. circ. 1,000.

910.09   CE
CEYLON TOURIST BOARD. MONTHLY BULLETIN ON THE PERFORMANCE OF THE TOURISM SECTOR. m. $10. Ceylon Tourist Board, Research & Planning Division, P.O. Box 1504, Colombo 3, Sri Lanka.

915.1   CH
CHINA, REPUBLIC. MINISTRY OF COMMUNICATION. TOURISM BUREAU. ANNUAL REPORT. (Text in English) 1972. a. free. Ministry of Communications, Tourism Bureau, Box 1490, Taipei, Taiwan, Republic of China. FAX 02-7735487. TELEX 26408. Ed. Mao Chi-Kuo. illus. circ. 2,500. **Document type:** government publication.
    Formerly: Annual Report on Tourism Statistics, Republic of China.

915 310   CH
CHINA, REPUBLIC. TOURISM BUREAU. REPORT ON TOURISM STATISTICS (YEAR). a. Tourism Bureau, 9-F, 280 Chunghsiao E. Rd, Sec. 4, P.O. Box 1490, Taipei, Taiwan, Republic of China. TEL 02-721-8541. FAX 02-781-5399. TELEX 26408 ROCTB. **Document type:** government publication.

910.202   CK
COLOMBIA. CORPORACION NACIONAL DE TURISMO. BOLETIN DE ESTADISTICA TURISTICA. (YEAR). 1970. irreg., latest no.22, 1989. free. Corporacion Nacional de Turismo, Oficina de Planeacion, Calle 28 No. 13A-15, Piso 1, Local 3, Apdo. Aereo 8400, Bogota, Colombia. TEL 2839466. FAX 2843818. TELEX 441350 COTUR. (Co-sponsor: Ministerio de Desarrollo Economico) bk.rev.; charts; stat. circ. 2,500.
    Formerly: Colombia. Corporacion Nacional de Turismo. Boletin de Investigaciones e Informacion Turistica.
    Description: Presents general information on Colombian tourism. Provides details on airlines, makes various distinctions between towns and regions and looks at Colombia's role in the evolution of world travel.

910 016   SP   ISSN 1013-1744
COMPENDIUM OF TOURISM STATISTICS. French edition: Compendium de Statistiques du Tourisme (ISSN 1014-7241); Spanish edition: Compendio de Estadisticas del Tourismo (ISSN 1014-7233) (Text in English) 1959. a. $50 (effective 1993). World Tourism Organization - Organizacion Mundial del Turismo, Capitan Haya 42, 28020 Madrid, Spain. TEL 5710628. FAX 5713733. TELEX 42188 OMT E.
—BLDSC (3363.981500).
    Former titles: Tourism Compendium; (until 1976): Tourist Bibliography (ISSN 0082-5468)
    Description: Provides tourism statistical information on 171 countries and territories.

301.32 312   CY   ISSN 0253-8709
CYPRUS. DEPARTMENT OF STATISTICS AND RESEARCH. TOURISM, MIGRATION AND TRAVEL STATISTICS. (Text in English, Greek) 1973. a. £C4. Ministry of Finance, Department of Statistics and Research, 13 Lord Byron Ave., Nicosia, Cyprus. TEL 357-2-302349. FAX 357-2-456712. **Document type:** government publication.
    Description: Tracks the movements of travelers, departures and returns of permanent residents, and emigrants and immigrants.

997 330   DQ
DOMINICA. MINISTRY OF FINANCE. CENTRAL STATISTICAL OFFICE. ANNUAL TOURISM STATISTICS. a. $3.70. Ministry of Finance, Central Statistical Office, Kennedy Ave., Roseau, Dominica, W.I. **Document type:** government publication.

997   DQ
DOMINICA. MINISTRY OF FINANCE. CENTRAL STATISTICAL OFFICE. QUARTERLY TRAVEL REPORT. 1978. q. $5. Ministry of Finance, Central Statistical Office, Kennedy Ave., Roseau, Dominica, W.I. **Document type:** government publication.
    Formerly: Dominica. Ministry of Finance. Statistical Division. Quarterly Bulletin of Tourism Statistics.

916   UA   ISSN 0041-4948
EGYPT. MINISTRY OF TOURISM. STATISTICAL BULLETIN.* q. free. Ministry of Tourism, Under-Secretariat for Planning and Follow-up, General Directorate for Research and Statistics, 5 Adly St., Cairo, Egypt. (processed) **Document type:** government publication.

914.2 370   UK
ENGLISH LANGUAGE COURSE VISITORS TO THE U K. irreg., latest 1992. £15. British Tourist Authority, Department D, Thames Tower, Black's Rd., Hammersmith, London W6 9EL, England.
    Description: Surveys persons visiting the U.K. to attend an English-language course.

319   FJ
FIJI. BUREAU OF STATISTICS. TOURISM AND MIGRATION STATISTICS. 1973. a., latest 1990. $5. Bureau of Statistics, Box 2221, Suva, Fiji. **Document type:** government publication.
    Supersedes: Statistical Report on Tourism in Fiji.

914.94   SZ
FREMDENVERKEHRSBILANZ DER SCHWEIZ/BALANCE TOURISTIQUE DE LA SUISSE. (Text in French and German) 1967. a. 4 SFr. Bundesamt fuer Statistik, Schwarztorstr. 96, CH-3003 Bern, Switzerland. TEL 031-3236011. FAX 031-3236061. **Document type:** government publication.

339   GM
GAMBIA. CENTRAL STATISTICS DEPARTMENT. SUMMARY OF TOURIST STATISTICS. (Formerly issued by Central Statistics Division) m. D.12. Central Statistics Department, Wellington St., Banjul, Gambia. **Document type:** government publication.

312.8 910   GM
GAMBIA. CENTRAL STATISTICS DEPARTMENT. TOURIST STATISTICS. a. D.12. Central Statistics Department, Wellington St., Banjul, Gambia. **Document type:** government publication.

GEO KATALOG (YEAR). VOLUME 1. TOURISTISCHE VEROEFFENTLICHUNGEN. see GEOGRAPHY

910 314   GW   ISSN 0072-1999
GERMANY. STATISTISCHES BUNDESAMT. FACHSERIE 6, HANDEL, GASTGEWERBE, REISEVERKEHR; REIHE 7: REISEVERKEHR. irreg. price varies. Statistisches Bundesamt, 65180 Wiesbaden, Germany. TEL 0611-75-1. FAX 0611-724000. TELEX 61186-STBA-D. **Document type:** government publication.

338.4   IC   ISSN 1024-0012
TX910.I2
▼**GISTISKYRSLUR/TOURIST ACCOMMODATION.** (Text in Icelandic; table headings in English) 1994. a. $15. Hagstofa Islands - Statistics Iceland, TEL 354-560-9800. FAX 354-562-8865. E-mail: hagstofa@hag.stjr.is. Dir. Hallgrimur Snorrason. (back issues avail.) **Document type:** government publication.

TRAVEL AND TOURISM — ABSTRACTING, BIBLIOGRAPHIES, STATISTICS

910.2   GR
GREECE. NATIONAL STATISTICAL SERVICE. TOURIST STATISTICS. (Text in English, Greek) 1981. irreg. $10. National Statistical Service of Greece, Statistical Information and Publications Division - Ethniki Statistiki Yperesia tes Ellados, 14-16 Lykourgou, 101 66 Athens, Greece. TEL 30-1-3244-748. FAX 30-1-3222-205. TELEX 216734 ESYE GR. (back issues avail.) **Document type:** government publication.
   Description: Monitors tourism activity in Greece.

338.4   GD
GRENADA. BOARD OF TOURISM. ANNUAL STATISTICAL REPORT. a. Board of Tourism, Carenage, St. George's, Grenada, W.I.

338.4   GD
GRENADA. BOARD OF TOURISM. MONTHLY STATISTICAL REPORT. m. Board of Tourism, Carenage, St. George's, Grenada, W.I.

338.4   GD
GRENADA. BOARD OF TOURISM. SEMI-ANNUAL STATISTICAL REVIEW. s-a. Board of Tourism, Carenage, St. George's, Grenada, W.I.

HOSPITALITY INDEX; an index for the hotel, foodservice and travel industries. see *HOTELS AND RESTAURANTS — Abstracting, Bibliographies, Statistics*

914.704 314   HU   ISSN 0230-4414
G155.H9
HUNGARY. KOZPONTI STATISZTIKAI HIVATAL. IDEGENFORGALMI EVKONYV. a. 408 Ft. Statisztikai Kiado Vallalat, Kaszasdulo u. 2, P.O.Box 99, 1300 Budapest 3, Hungary. TEL 1-688-635. TELEX 22-6699. (Subscr. to: Kultura, Box 149, H-1389 Budapest, Hungary) circ. 800.
   Supersedes: Idegenforgalmi Statisztika (ISSN 0209-4819)

INTERNATIONAL RARE BOOK PRICES - VOYAGES, TRAVEL & EXPLORATION. see *PUBLISHING AND BOOK TRADE — Abstracting, Bibliographies, Statistics*

915.69   IS   ISSN 0075-1405
ISRAEL TOURIST STATISTICS/TAYARUT BE-YISRAEL. (Subseries of the Bureau's Special Series) (Text in English and Hebrew) irreg., latest no. 732, 1982. $8 price varies. Central Bureau of Statistics, Box 13015, Jerusalem, Israel. **Document type:** government publication.

914.5   IT
ITALY. ISTITUTO NAZIONALE DI STATISTICA. STATISTICHE DEL TURISMO. 1957. a. L.13000 (effective 1992). Istituto Nazionale di Statistica, Via Cesare Balbo 16, 00100 Rome, Italy. FAX 06-46735198. **Document type:** government publication.
   Supersedes in part: Italy. Istituto Centrale di Statistica. Annuario Statistico del Commercio Interno e del Turismo; Which was formerly: Italy. Istituto Centrale di Statistica. Annuario Statistico del Commercio Interno (ISSN 0075-1782).

338.4   KE   ISSN 0377-1385
G155.K4
KENYA. CENTRAL BUREAU OF STATISTICS. MIGRATION AND TOURISM STATISTICS. (Former name of issuing body: Kenya. Ministry of Planning and National Development) 1971. irreg., latest 1978. Ministry of Finance and Planning, Central Bureau of Statistics, P.O. Box 30266, Nairobi, Kenya. (Subscr. to: Government Press, Haile Selaissie Ave., P.O. Box 30128, Nairobi, Kenya. TEL 254-2-334075) stat. **Document type:** government publication.

910 016   UK   ISSN 0261-1392
GV191.6
LEISURE, RECREATION AND TOURISM ABSTRACTS. 1976. q. £160($290) (effective 1996). CAB International, Wallingford, Oxon. OX10 8DE, England. TEL 01491-832111. FAX 01491-833508. TELEX 847964 COMAGG G. E-mail: cabi@cabi.org. (U.S. subscr. to: C.A.B. International, North American Office, 845 N. Park Ave., Tucson, AZ 85719. TEL 800-528-4841) circ. 350. (also avail. in diskette format; back issues avail.) **Document type:** abstracting/indexing.
   ●Also available online. Vendor(s): CISTI, DIMDI, European Space Agency (File nos.16 & 124/CAB), Knight-Ridder, Inc., Ovid Technologies (TOUR). —BLDSC (5182.267000).
   Formerly: Rural Recreation and Tourism Abstracts (ISSN 0308-0137)
   Description: Presents information on the many aspects of leisure for those interested in research and strategic development of leisure, recreation, sport, and tourism and hospitality activities, facilities, products, and services.

910.4   MH
MACAO. DIRECCAO DOS SERVICOS DE ESTATISTICA E CENSOS. ESTATISTICAS DO TURISMO/MACAO. CENSUS AND STATISTICS DEPARTMENT. TOURISM STATISTICS. (Text in English, Chinese, Portuguese) 1986. m. plus a. review. free. Direccao dos Servicos de Estatistica e Censos, Rua Inacio Baptista, No.4-6, P.O. Box 3022, Macao. TEL 853-3995311. FAX 853-607825. **Document type:** government publication.
   Description: Presents data on visitors arrivals, number of hotels and other accommodation establishments, room occupancy rates.

910.4   MH
MACAO. DIRECCAO DOS SERVICOS DE ESTATISTICA E CENSOS. INDICADORES DO TURISMO/MACAO. CENSUS AND STATISTICS DEPARTMENT. TOURISM INDICATORS. (Text in Chinese, English, Portuguese) 1988. m. free. Direccao dos Servicos de Estatistica e Censos, Rua Inacio Baptista, No.4-6, P.O. Box 3022, Macao. TEL 853-3995311. FAX 853-307825. **Document type:** government publication.
   Formerly: Macao. Direccao dos Servicos de Estatistica e Censos. Estatisticas do Turismo - Tourism Statistics.
   Description: Presents monthly data on visitor arrivals and occupancy rates among hotels and other establishments of accomodation.

910.09   MH
MACAO. DIRECCAO DOS SERVICOS DE ESTATISTICA E CENSOS. INQUERITO AS DESPESAS DOS VISITANTES/MACAO. CENSUS AND STATISTICS DEPARTMENT. VISITOR EXPENDITURE SURVEY ANNUAL REPORT. (Text in Chinese, English, Portuguese) 1988. a. free. Direccao dos Servicos de Estatistica e Censos, Rua Inacio Baptista, No. 4-6, P.O. Box 3022, Macao. TEL 853-3995311. FAX 853-307825. circ. 300. **Document type:** government publication.

916   MW
MALAWI TOURISM REPORT. 1970. a. K.25. National Statistical Office, Commissioner for Census and Statistics, P.O. Box 333, Zomba, Malawi. TEL 265-50-522-377. FAX 265-50-523-130. TELEX 44015 CENSUS MI. stat. (processed) **Document type:** government publication.
   Formerly: Malawi. National Statistical Office. Tourist Report (ISSN 0085-302X)

338.4   MF
MAURITIUS. CENTRAL STATISTICAL OFFICE. INTERNATIONAL TRAVEL AND TOURISM STATISTICS. 1974. a. Rs.75 (effective June 1995). Central Statistical Office, Toorawa Centre, Cr. S.S. R & J. Mosque Sts., Port Louis, Mauritius. (Subscr. to: Government Printing Office, Ramtoolah Bldg., Sir S. Ramgoolam St., Port Louis, Mauritius. TEL 230-234-5294. FAX 230-208-4011) **Document type:** government publication.
   Formerly (until 1984): Mauritius. Central Statistical Office. International Travel and Tourism.

915   CH   ISSN 1021-4534
MONTHLY REPORT ON TOURISM - REPUBLIC OF CHINA/KUAN KUANG TZU LIAO. (Text in Chinese and English) 1968. m. free. Ministry of Communications, Tourism Bureau - Chiao T'ung Pu, Kuan Kuang Chu, Ta Lu Bldg., 9th Fl., 280 Chung Hsiao E. Rd. Sec. 4, Taipei, Taiwan, Republic of China. TEL 02-721-8541. FAX 02-7815399. TELEX 26408 ROTCB. (Subscr. to: P.O. Box 1490, Taipei, Taiwan, R.O.C.) Ed. Lin Ch'ing-Shih. charts; stat. circ. 3,500. (looseleaf format) **Document type:** government publication.
   Description: Presents statistics of tourism in Taiwan, broken down by country of origin, nationality, sex, age.

997   MJ
MONTSERRAT. STATISTICS OFFICE. TOURISM REPORT. irreg. Statistics Office, Government Headquarters, Plymouth, Montserrat. **Document type:** government publication.

910.4   NZ   ISSN 1171-2937
N Z T B INTERNATIONAL VISITORS RESEARCH SERIES. 1982. irreg., latest 1992. price varies. New Zealand Tourism Board, Market Research, P.O. Box 95, Wellington, New Zealand. TEL 04-4728-860. FAX 04-4781-736. **Document type:** government publication.
   Former titles (until 1992): N Z T D International Visitors Research Series (ISSN 1170-4713); (until 1990): N Z T P International Visitors Research Series (ISSN 0112-983X)

647.94   NZ
N Z T B PRODUCT RESEARCH SERIES. 1980. irreg., latest 1989. price varies. New Zealand Tourism Board, Market Research, P.O. Box 95, Wellington, New Zealand. TEL 04-4728-860. FAX 04-4781-736.
   Former titles: N Z T D Product Research Series; N Z T P Product Research Series (ISSN 0112-9589)

919.3   NZ   ISSN 1171-1418
N Z T B VISITOR STATISTICS RESEARCH SERIES. 1973. a. price varies. New Zealand Tourism Board, Market Research, P.O. Box 95, Wellington, New Zealand. TEL 04-728-860. FAX 04-781-736. adv.
   Former titles: N Z T D Visitor Statistics Research Series (ISSN 1171-333X); N Z T P Visitor Statistics Research Series (ISSN 0112-9732)
   Description: Provides information on visitor arrivals in New Zealand; statistical tables including summary data, historical series, ccuntry profiles and department information.

910 310   NE   ISSN 0168-5538
NETHERLANDS. CENTRAAL BUREAU VOOR DE STATISTIEK. STATISTIEK VREEMDELINGENVERKEER. (Text in Dutch and English) 1952. a. Centraal Bureau voor de Statistiek, Prinses Beatrixlaan 428, Voorburg, Netherlands. (Orders to: SDU - Publishers, Christoffel Plantijnstraat, The Hague, Netherlands) **Document type:** government publication.

910.2   NE   ISSN 0168-3411
G155.N2
NETHERLANDS. CENTRAAL BUREAU VOOR DE STATISTIEK. VAKANTIEONDERZOEK. (Text in Dutch and English) 1954. a. Centraal Bureau voor de Statistiek, Prinses Beatrixlaan 428, Voorburg, Netherlands. (Orders to: SDU - Publishers, Christoffel Plantijnstraat, The Hague, Netherlands) **Document type:** government publication.
   Formerly: Vakantiebesteding van de Nederlandse Bevolking (ISSN 0077-7501)

338.4791 314   NO   ISSN 0333-208X
NORWAY. STATISTISK SENTRALBYRAA. REISELIVSTATISTIKK/STATISTICS ON TRAVEL. (Subseries of its Norges Offisielle Statistikk) (Text in Norwegian and English) 1977. a. NOK 80. Statistisk Sentralbyraa, P.O. Box 8131 Dep., N-0033 Oslo, Norway. TEL 47-22-864500. FAX 47-22-864976. stat. circ. 800. **Document type:** government publication.

914.2   UK
OVERSEAS CONFERENCE VISITORS TO THE U K (YEAR). irreg., latest 1992. £15. British Tourist Authority, Department D, Thames Tower, Black's Rd., Hammersmith, London W6 9EL, England.
   Description: Presents figures on visitors to the U.K. attending a conference.

TRAVEL AND TOURISM — ABSTRACTING, BIBLIOGRAPHIES, STATISTICS

914.2   UK
OVERSEAS TRADE FAIR - EXHIBITION VISITORS TO THE UK (YEAR). irreg., latest 1992. £12. British Tourist Authority, Department D, Thames Tower, Black's Rd., Hammersmith, London W6 9EL, England.
Description: Profiles visitors to the U.K. attending trade shows and exhibitions.

910.09   US
PACIFIC ASIA TRAVEL ASSOCIATION. ANNUAL STATISTICAL REPORT. Variant title: P A T A Annual Statistical Report. 1967. a. $500 to non-members; members $200. Pacific Asia Travel Association, Telesis Tower, Ste. 1750, 1 Montgomery St., San Francisco, CA 94104. TEL 415-986-4646. FAX 415-986-3458. Ed. Low Poh Gek. circ. 500. **Indexed:** Hospit.Ind., SRI.
Description: Report that includes data on visitor arrivals in PATA destinations, outbound travel statistics from PATA countries, and other tourism-related statistics.

910.09   US   ISSN 1066-0356
PACIFIC ASIA TRAVEL ASSOCIATION. QUARTERLY STATISTICAL REPORT. Variant title: P A T A Quarterly Statistical Report. q. $800 to non-members; members $200. Pacific Asia Travel Association, Telesis Tower, Ste. 1750, 1 Montgomery St., San Francisco, CA 94104. TEL 415-986-4646. FAX 415-986-3458. **Indexed:** Hospit.Ind.

910 314   PL   ISSN 0494-3171
POLAND. GLOWNY URZAD STATYSTYCZNY. TURYSTYKA. (Subseries of: Statystyka Polski) 1950. irreg., latest 1988. 10 Zl. Zaklad Wydawnictw Statystycznych, Al. Niepodleglosci 208, 00-925 Warsaw, Poland. TEL 22-25-03-45. **Document type:** government publication.
Formerly (until 1969): Poland. Glowny Urzad Statystyczny. Statystyka Turystyki (ISSN 1230-5774)

914.69   PO   ISSN 0377-2306
G155.P75
PORTUGAL. INSTITUTO NACIONAL DE ESTATISTICA. ESTATISTICAS DO TURISMO. CONTINENTE, ACORES E MADEIRA. 1969. a. Esc.5200. Instituto Nacional de Estatistica, Av. Antonio Jose de Almeida, 1078 Lisbon Codex, Portugal. (Orders to: Imprensa Nacional, Casa da Moeda, Direccao Comercial, rua D. Francisco Manuel de Melo 5, 1000 Lisbon, Portugal)
Formerly: Portugal. Instituto Nacional de Estatistica. Estatisticas do Turismo.

914.2   UK   ISSN 1350-6633
REGIONAL TOURISM FACTS. CUMBRIA. a.? £10 (set of 11 reports £90). English Tourist Board, Thames Tower, Black's Rd., Hammersmith, London W6 9EL, England. TEL 0181-846-9000. FAX 0181-563-0302. (Co-sponsor: British Tourist Authority) charts.
Former titles (until 1991): Tourism Fact Sheets. Cumbria (ISSN 0264-0023); (until 1982): Research - English Tourist Board. Cumbria (ISSN 0262-6209); (until 1978): Tourism Regional Fact Sheet. Cumbria.
Description: Reports on tourism activity in Cumbria.

914.2   UK   ISSN 1350-6811
REGIONAL TOURISM FACTS. EAST ANGLIA. a.? £10 (set of 11 reports £90). English Tourist Board, Department D, Thames Tower, Black's Rd., Hammersmith, London W6 9EL, England. TEL 0181-846-9000. FAX 0181-563-0302. (Co-sponsor: British Tourist Authority) charts.
Former titles (until 1991): Tourism Fact Sheets. East Anglia (ISSN 0264-0031); (until 1982): Research - English Tourist Board. East Anglia (ISSN 0262-6217); (until 1978): Tourism Regional Fact Sheet. East Anglia.
Description: Examines tourism activity in East Anglia.

914.2   UK   ISSN 1350-6749
REGIONAL TOURISM FACTS. EAST MIDLANDS. a.? £10 (set of 11 reports £90). English Tourist Board, Department D, Thames Tower, Black's Rd., Hammersmith, London W6 9EL, England. TEL 0181-846-9000. FAX 0181-563-0302. (Co-sponsor: British Tourist Authority) charts.
Former titles (until 1991): Tourism Fact Sheets. East Midlands (ISSN 0264-004X); (until 1982): Research - English Tourist Board. East Midlands (ISSN 0262-6225); (until 1978): Tourism Regional Fact Sheets. East Midlands.
Description: Reports on tourist activities in the East Midlands region.

914.2   UK   ISSN 1350-6358
REGIONAL TOURISM FACTS. HEART OF ENGLAND. a.? £10 (set of 11 reports £90). English Tourism Board, Department D, Thames Tower, Black's Rd., Hammersmith, London W6 9EL, England. TEL 0181-846-9000. FAX 0181-563-0302. (Co-sponsor: British Tourist Authority) charts.
Former titles (until 1991): Tourism Fact Sheets. Heart of England (ISSN 0264-0058); (until 1982): Research - English Tourist Board. Heart of England (ISSN 0262-6233); (until 1978): Tourism Regional Fact Sheet. Heart of England.
Description: Analyzes the tourism activity for central England.

914.2   UK   ISSN 1350-634X
REGIONAL TOURISM FACTS. LONDON. a.? £10 (set of 11 reports £90). English Tourist Board, Department D, Thames Tower, Black's Rd., Hammersmith, London W6 9EL, England. TEL 0181-846-9000. FAX 0181-563-0302. (Co-sponsor: British Tourist Authority) charts.
Former titles: Tourism Fact Sheets. London (ISSN 0264-0066); (until 1982): Research - English Tourist Board (ISSN 0262-6241); (until 1978): Tourism Regional Fact Sheet. London.
Description: Examines the tourist activity in and around London.

914.2   UK   ISSN 1350-6382
REGIONAL TOURISM FACTS. NORTH WEST. a.? £10 (set of 11 reports £90). British Tourist Authority, Department D, Thames Tower, Black's Rd., Hammersmith, London W6 9EL, England. TEL 0181-846-9000. FAX 0181-563-0302. (Co-sponsor: British Tourist Authority) charts.
Former titles (until 1991): Tourism Fact Sheets. North West (ISSN 0264-0074); (until 1982): Research - English Tourist Board. North West (ISSN 0262-625X); (until 1978): Tourism Regional Fact Sheets. North West.
Description: Analyzes tourism activities in northwestern England.

914.2   UK   ISSN 1350-6641
REGIONAL TOURISM FACTS. NORTHUMBRIA. a.? £10 (set of 11 reports £90). English Tourist Board, Department D, Thames Tower, Black's Rd., Hammersmith, London W6 9EL, England. TEL 0181-846-9000. FAX 0181-563-0302. (Co-sponsor: British Tourist Authority) charts.
Former titles (until 1991): Tourism Fact Sheets. Northumbria (ISSN 0264-0082); (until 1982): Research - English Tourist Board. Northumbria (ISSN 0262-6268); (until 1978): Tourism Regional Fact Sheets. Northumbria.
Description: Examines the data for tourist activity in Northumbria.

914.2   UK   ISSN 1350-6374
REGIONAL TOURISM FACTS. THAMES & CHILTERNS. a. £10 (set of 11 reports £90). English Tourist Board, Department D, Thames Tower, Black's Rd., Hammersmith, London W6 9EL, England. TEL 0181-846-9000. FAX 0181-563-0302. (Co-sponsor: British Tourist Authority) charts.
Former titles (until 1991): Tourism Fact Sheets. Thames and Chilterns (ISSN 0264-0112); (until 1982): Research - English Tourist Board. Thames and Chilterns (ISSN 0262-6284); (until 1978): Tourism Regional Fact Sheets. Thames and Chilterns.
Description: Analyzes the tourist activity in this region of southeastern England.

914.2   UK   ISSN 1350-6668
REGIONAL TOURISM FACTS. WEST COUNTRY. a.? £10 (set of 11 reports £90). English Tourist Board, Department D, Thames Tower, Black's Rd., Hammersmith, London W6 9EL, England. TEL 0181-846-9000. FAX 0181-563-0302. (Co-sponsor: British Tourist Authority) charts.
Former titles (until 1991): Tourism Fact Sheets. West Country (ISSN 0264-0120); (until 1982): Research - English Tourist Board. West Country (ISSN 0262-6292); (until 1978): Tourism Regional Fact Sheet. West Country.
Description: Evaluates tourist activity in Cornwall, Devon, Dorset, Avon, and elsewhere in southwestern England.

914.2   UK   ISSN 1350-665X
REGIONAL TOURISM FACTS. YORKSHIRE & HUMBERSIDE. a.? £10 (set of 11 reports £90). English Tourist Board, Department D, Thames Tower, Black's Rd., Hammersmith, London W6 9EL, England. TEL 0181-846-9000. FAX 0181-563-0302. (Co-sponsor: British Tourist Authority) charts.
Former titles (until 1991): Tourism Fact Sheets. Yorkshire and Humberside. (ISSN 0264-0139); (until 1981): Research - English Tourist Board. Yorkshire and Humberside (ISSN 0262-6306); (until 1978): Tourism Regional Fact Sheets. Yorkshire and Humberside.
Description: Reports on tourist activity in Yorkshire and elsewhere in northeastern England.

914.2   UK   ISSN 1350-6676
REGIONAL TOURISM FACTS. SOUTHERN. Key Title: Regional Tourism Facts. South of England. a.? £10 (set of 11 reports £90). English Tourist Board, Department D, Thames Tower, Black's Rd., Hammersmith, London W6 9EL, England. TEL 0181-546-9000. FAX 0181-563-0302. (Co-sponsor: British Tourist Authority) charts.
Former titles (until 1991): Tourism Fact Sheets. Southern (ISSN 0264-0104); (until 1982): Research - English Tourist Board. Southern (ISSN 0262-6314); (until 1978): Tourism Regional Fact Sheets. Southern.
Description: Reports on tourist activity in southern England.

914.94   SZ
DER REISEVERKEHR DER SCHWEIZER IM AUSLAND/TOURISTES SUISSES A L'ETRANGER. (Text in French and German) 1984. a. 6.50 SFr. Bundesamt fuer Statistik, Schwarztorstr. 96, CH-3003 Bern, Switzerland. TEL 031-3236011. FAX 031-3236061. **Document type:** government publication.

910.09   TZ   ISSN 0564-836X
REPORT ON TOURISM STATISTICS IN TANZANIA. 1968. irreg. Bureau of Statistics, Box 796, Dar es Salaam, Tanzania. (Orders to: Government Publications Agency, Box 1801, Dar es Salaam, Tanzania) **Document type:** government publication.

ST. LUCIA. STATISTICAL DEPARTMENT. ANNUAL MIGRATION AND TOURISM STATISTICS. see *POPULATION STUDIES — Abstracting, Bibliographies, Statistics*

ST. LUCIA. STATISTICAL DEPARTMENT. QUARTERLY MIGRATION & TOURISM STATISTICS. see *POPULATION STUDIES — Abstracting, Bibliographies, Statistics*

914.94   SZ
SCHWEIZER TOURISMUS IN ZAHLEN/TOURISME SUISSE EN CHIFFRES. (Text in French and German) 1988. a. Bundesamt fuer Statistik, Schwarztorstr. 96, CH-3003 Bern, Switzerland. TEL 031-3236011. FAX 031-3236061. **Document type:** government publication.

960 316   SE
SEYCHELLES. MANAGEMENT AND INFORMATION SYSTEMS DIVISION. TOURISM AND MIGRATION STATISTICS. a. Rs.15. Department of Finance, Management and Information Systems Division, P.O. Box 26, Mahe, Seychelles. **Document type:** government publication.
Former titles (until 1987): Seychelles. President's Office. Statistics Division. Migration and Tourism Statistics; Seychelles. President's Office. Statistics Division. Tourism and Migration Report.

TRAVEL AND TOURISM — ABSTRACTING, BIBLIOGRAPHIES, STATISTICS

910.4 310 — SE
SEYCHELLES. STATISTICS DIVISION. STATISTICAL BULLETIN. TOURISM. m. Rs.5.00. Department of Finance, Statistics Division, P.O. Box 313, Victoria, Seychelles.
Formerly (until 1982): Seychelles. President's Office. Statistics Division. Tourism.

310 — SE
SEYCHELLES. STATISTICS DIVISION. STATISTICAL BULLETIN. VISITOR SURVEY. a. R.5. Department of Finance, Statistics Division, P.O. Box 313, Victoria, Seychelles. **Document type:** government publication.
Formerly: Seychelles. Department of Finance. Visitor Survey.

915.95 — SI — ISSN 0218-4567
SINGAPORE ANNUAL REPORT ON TOURISM STATISTICS. 1969. a. S.$60. Singapore Tourist Promotion Board, Planning Department, Raffles City Tower No. 36-04, 250 North Bridge Rd., Singapore 0617, Singapore. TEL 3396622. FAX 3399423. TELEX STBSIN-RS-33375. charts; stat. circ. 1,000. (tabloid format)
Formerly: Singapore Tourist Promotion Board. Annual Statistical Report on Visitor Arrivals.

915.9 — SI — ISSN 0218-4575
SINGAPORE MONTHLY REPORT ON TOURISM STATISTICS. (Supplement avail.) 1972. m. S.$130 (foreign S.$145). Singapore Tourist Promotion Board, Planning Department, Raffles City Tower No. 36-04, 250 N. Bridge Rd., Singapore 0617, Singapore. TEL 3396622. FAX 3399423. TELEX STBSIN RS 33375. charts; stat. circ. 1,000.
Formerly: Singapore Tourist Promotion Board. Monthly Statistical Report on Visitor Arrivals.
Description: Brings out statistical information on visitor arrivals by country of residence, nationality and travel characteristics.

919 — SI — ISSN 0218-4583
SINGAPORE SURVEY OF OVERSEAS VISITORS. (Text in English) 1975. a. S.$100 (foreign S.$110). Singapore Tourist Promotion Board, Planning Department, Raffles City Tower No. 36-04, 250 N. Bridge Rd., Singapore 0617, Singapore. TEL 3396622. FAX 3399423. TELEX STBSIN RS 33375. charts.
Formerly: Survey of Overseas Visitors to Singapore.
Description: Visitor expenditure data, lead times, visit impressions, ratings of facilities and activities during visit.

316.8 — SA
SOUTH AFRICA. CENTRAL STATISTICAL SERVICE. STATISTICAL RELEASE. TOURISM - JAN SMUTS, D F MALAN AND LOUIS BOTHA AIRPORTS. (No. P0351.1) 1993. m. free. Central Statistical Service - Sentrale Statistiekdiens, Private Bag X44, Pretoria 0001, South Africa. TEL 27-12-310-8911. FAX 27-12-310-8500. **Document type:** government publication.

SOUTH AFRICA. CENTRAL STATISTICAL SERVICE. TOURISM AND MIGRATION. see *POPULATION STUDIES — Abstracting, Bibliographies, Statistics*

STATISTICAL OFFICE OF THE EUROPEAN COMMUNITIES. TRANSPORT, COMMUNICATIONS, TOURISME - ANNUAIRE STATISTIQUE. see *TRANSPORTATION — Abstracting, Bibliographies, Statistics*

338.4 — IO
STATISTICAL REPORT ON VISITOR ARRIVALS TO INDONESIA. (Text in English) 1975. a. free. Department of Tourism, Post, and Telecommunications, Research and Development Centre, Jalan Kebon Sirih, No.36, Jakarta, Indonesia. TEL 021-347611. FAX 021-375409. TELEX 45157. bk.rev.; circ. 500 (controlled). **Document type:** government publication.
Former titles (until 1983): Statistics of Incoming Visitors; (until 1978): Indonesia Tourist Statistics.

915.1 — HK — ISSN 0377-5704
STATISTICAL REVIEW OF TOURISM IN HONG KONG. (Text in English) 1974. a. HK.$120($15) Hong Kong Tourist Association, Research Department, G.P.O. Box 2597, Hong Kong. TEL 28076543. FAX 28060303. Ed.Bd. circ. 5,500.
Supersedes: Hong Kong Tourist Association. Digest of Annual Statistics.

310 — IS — ISSN 0334-2476
STATISTICS OF TRAVEL AND TOURISM/TAYARUT V'SHERUTEI HA-ARAHA. (Text in English and Hebrew) q. $30. Central Bureau of Statistics, Box 13015, Jerusalem, Israel. TEL 02-533400. **Document type:** government publication.
Description: Data on tourists and tourism services in Israel.

910.202 — US — ISSN 0895-6065
TAOS MAGAZINE. 1984. 8/yr. $25. Whitney Publishing Co., Inc., Box 1380, Taos, NM 87571. TEL 505-758-5404. Pub. John K. Whitney. adv.: B&W page $930; adv. contact: Merle Kout. bk.rev. circ. 8,500. (back issues avail.) **Document type:** consumer publication.
Description: Covers the arts, culture, dining, personalities, and crafts in Taos, New Mexico.

338.4 — VB
TOURISM IN THE BRITISH VIRGIN ISLANDS. 1973. a. $3. Statistics Office, Finance Department, Road Town, Tortola, British Virgin Islands, W.I. stat. **Document type:** government publication.

917.29 — PR
TOURISM INDUSTRY OF PUERTO RICO. SELECTED STATISTICS. 1970. a. free. Tourism Company of Puerto Rico, Office of Statistics and Economic Studies, P.O. Box 4435, Old San Juan Sta., San Juan, PR 00905. FAX 809-722-6352. Ed. Margie Arroyo. stat. circ. 1,250. (processed)

917 — CN
TOURISM ROOM REVENUES. 12/yr. Can.$60. Ministry of Government Services, B C Stats, 553 Superior St., Victoria, BC V8V 1X4, Canada. TEL 604-387-1502. FAX 604-387-0329. **Document type:** government publication.
Description: Details revenues received from room rentals by type of accomodation, with a geographic breakdown by development region.

910.202 — US — ISSN 1050-6152
TOURISM'S TOP TWENTY. 1980. quadrennial. $50. (University of Colorado, Business Research Division) U.S. Travel Data Center, 1133 21st St., N.W., Washington, DC 20036. (Alt. addr.: Campus Box 420, Boulder, CO 80309-0420. TEL 303-492-4267. FAX 303-792-3620) circ. 600 (paid). **Document type:** consumer publication.
Description: Contains fast facts on the travel and tourism industry. Lists top ski areas, airlines, hotels, national parks, and more.

914.94 — SZ — ISSN 0258-8684
TOURISMUS IN DER SCHWEIZ/TOURISME EN SUISSE. (Text in French and German) 1974. a. 18 SFr. Bundesamt fuer Statistik, Schwarztorstr. 96, CH-3003 Bern, Switzerland. TEL 031-3236011. FAX 031-3236061. **Document type:** government publication.

TRANSPORTE, COMUNICACIONES, TURISMO. see *TRANSPORTATION — Abstracting, Bibliographies, Statistics*

310 — IS
TRAVEL AND TOURISM - ABSTRACTING, BIBLIOGRAPHIES, STATISTICS. (Text in English and Hebrew) q. $30. Central Bureau of Statistics, Box 13015, Jerusalem 91 130, Israel. TEL 02-553400. **Document type:** government publication.

910.09 — SP — ISSN 1019-3707
TRAVEL AND TOURISM BAROMETER. French edition: Barometre des Voyages et du Tourisme (ISSN 1014-7322); Spanish edition: Barometro de los Viajes y del Turismo (ISSN 1014-7314) (Text in English) q. $300 (effective 1993). World Tourism Organization - Organizacion Mundial del Turismo, Capitan Haya 42, 28020 Madrid, Spain. TEL 341-571-06-28. FAX 341-571-37-33. TELEX 42188 OMT E. **Document type:** trade publication.
Formerly (until 1990): Current Travel and Tourism Indicators (ISSN 1014-7306)
Description: Contains marketing, promotion strategies and planning in tourism.

910 Z6004.T6 — US — ISSN 1040-8142
TRAVEL & TOURISM INDEX. 1984. q. (plus a. cum.). $50. Brigham Young University, Hawaii Campus, Business Division, Box 1773, Laie, HI 96762. FAX 808-293-3645. Ed. Gerald V. Bohnet. circ. 500. **Document type:** abstracting/indexing.
Description: Indexes articles by subject/title from periodicals in the travel and tourism field.

910.09 G155.A1 — US — ISSN 0738-9515
TRAVEL INDUSTRY WORLD YEARBOOK; the big picture. 1956. a. $79 (foreign $90). Child & Waters, Inc., Box 610, Rye, NY 10580-0811. TEL 914-921-0988. Ed. Somerset Waters. (back issues avail.) **Indexed:** SRI. **Document type:** academic/scholarly publication, trade publication. —BLDSC (2057.271000); UnCover.
Description: Information and statistics pertaining to trends in and prospects for the international and national tourism industry, with industry trends for motels-hotels, airlines, travel agents, cruise lines, food services, and supplemental amenities.
Refereed Serial

917.1 — CN — ISSN 0713-2840
TRAVEL-LOG. 1982. q. Can.$42($50) (foreign $59). Statistics Canada, Publications Division, Ottawa, Ont. K1A 0T6, Canada. TEL 613-951-7277. FAX 613-951-1584. **Document type:** government publication.
Description: Presents a diverse range of tourism topics in an easy-to-read format drawing together data from several tourism-related surveys conducted by Statistics Canada.

910 310 — TR — ISSN 0082-6537
TRINIDAD AND TOBAGO. CENTRAL STATISTICAL OFFICE. INTERNATIONAL TRAVEL REPORT. 1955. a. T.T.$5. Central Statistical Office, 35-41 Queen St., P.O. Box 98, Port-of-Spain, Trinidad & Tobago, W.I. TEL 809-625-3705. (Dist. by: Government Printing Office, 2-4 Victoria Ave., Port-of-Spain, Trinidad & Tobago, W.I.) **Document type:** government publication.

910.09 — TR
TRINIDAD AND TOBAGO. CENTRAL STATISTICAL OFFICE. QUARTERLY TRAVEL. 1955; N.S. 1965. q. T.T.$3 per no. Central Statistical Office, 35-41 Queen St., P.O. Box 98, Port-of-Spain, Trinidad & Tobago, W.I. TEL 809-625-3705. (Dist. by: Government Printing Office, 2-4 Victoria Ave., Port-of-Spain, Trinidad & Tobago, W.I.) stat. **Document type:** government publication.
Formerly: Trinidad and Tobago. Central Statistical Office. Monthly Travel.

918.3 318 — CL
TURISMO; estadisticas de turismo y movimiento internacional de viajeros. 1965-1971; resumed. a. Esc.1050 (US $7.30; elsewhere $8.40) (effective 1994). Instituto Nacional de Estadisticas, Casilla 498, 3 Santiago, Chile. stat. (processed) **Document type:** government publication.

338.4 — RM — ISSN 1223-7515
TURISMUL IN ROMANIA/TOURISM IN ROMANIA. (Text in English, Rumanian) a. $10 (effective 1995 & 1996). Comisia Nationala pentru Statistica - National Commission for Statistics, Bd. Liberatii 16, Sector 5, 70542 Bucharest, Rumania. TEL 40-1-6143371. FAX 40-1-3124873. **Document type:** government publication.
Description: Contains data regarding the tourist accommodation capacity structured by tourism regions, unit types, comfort categories, Rumanian and foreign citizens.

315.61 — TJ — ISSN 1013-6150
TURKEY. DEVLET ISTATISTIK ENSTITUSU. TURIZM ISTATISTIKLERI/TURKEY. STATE INSTITUTE OF STATISTICS. TOURISM STATISTICS. Key Title: Turizm Istatistikleri. (Text in English, Turkish) 1959. a., latest 1991. $25. Devlet Istatistik Enstitusu - State Institute of Statistics, Necatibey Caddesi No. 114, 06100 Ankara, Turkey. TEL 90-312-4180527. FAX 90-312-4170432. circ. 1,300. **Document type:** government publication.
Description: Provides statistical information on numbers of tourists, arrival and departure information, duration of stay and other related information.

TRAVEL AND TOURISM — AIRLINE INFLIGHT AND HOTEL INROOM

914.2   UK   ISSN 1351-5535
THE U K TOURIST: STATISTICS (YEAR). a. £60. English Tourist Board, Black's Rd., Hammersmith, London W6 9EL, England. TEL 0181-846-9000. FAX 0181-563-0302. (Co-sponsors: Northern Ireland Tourist Board; Scottish Tourist Board; Wales Tourist Board (Bwrdd Croesco Cymru))
—BLDSC (9082.668795).
Description: Surveys tourists to the U.K. as to the purpose of their trip, destination, mode of transport, accommodations, leisure activities, and level of spending.

910.09   US
U.S. INTERNATIONAL AIR TRAVEL STATISTICS. m., with q. and a. updates. $500 (single m., q., or a. nos. also avail.). U.S. Department of Transportation, Center for Transportation Information, c/o Pat Harrington, DTS-44, Volpe National Transportation Systems Center, Kendall Sq., Cambridge, MA 02142. TEL 617-494-2450. FAX 617-494-2633. **Document type:** government publication.
Description: Supplies gateway data on passenger travel between the U.S. and other countries, as reported by the U.S. Immigration and Naturalization Service.

919.604   NN
VANUATU IN FACTS AND FIGURES. (Text in English, French) 1975. a. free. Statistics Office, Private Mail Bag 19, Port-vila, Vanuatu. TEL 678-22110. FAX 678-24583. stat. circ. 500. **Document type:** government publication.
Former titles: Vanuatu in Figures; New Hebrides. Bureau of Statistics. Some Facts and Figures about the New Hebrides.
Description: A compact digest containing the key statistical data about Vanuatu.

910.2   SP   ISSN 1011-8977
YEARBOOK OF TOURISM STATISTICS. (Text in English, French and Spanish) 1953. a. $125 (effective 1993). World Tourism Organization, Capitan Haya 42, 28020 Madrid, Spain. TEL 571-06-28. FAX 5713733. TELEX 42188 OMT E. (looseleaf format)
—BLDSC (9416.810000).
Former titles: World Tourism Statistics; International Travel Statistics (ISSN 0074-9184)
Description: Contains data on tourism trends from over 150 countries and territories.

910.09   YU
YUGOSLAVIA. SAVEZNI ZAVOD ZA STATISTIKU. TURIZAM. (Subseries of its Statisticki Bilten) a. 30 din.($1.67) Savezni Zavod za Statistiku, Kneza Milosa 20, Belgrade, Yugoslavia. TEL 38-11-681999. stat. **Document type:** government publication.

910.09 316   RH   ISSN 0259-7519
ZIMBABWE. CENTRAL STATISTICAL OFFICE. MONTHLY MIGRATION AND TOURIST STATISTICS. m. Z.$0.45. Central Statistical Office, P.O. Box 8063, Causeway, Harare, Zimbabwe. circ. 220. **Document type:** government publication.

TRAVEL AND TOURISM — Airline Inflight And Hotel Inroom

051   US
ABOARD AEROPERU. (Text in English and Spanish) 1978. q. (Aeroperu) North-South Net, Inc., 100 Almeria Ave., Ste. 220, Coral Gables, FL 33134. TEL 305-441-9744. FAX 305-441-9739. Ed. Roberto Casin. adv. circ. 10,000. **Document type:** consumer publication.

056.1 051   US
ABOARD AVIATECA. (Text in English, Spanish) 1987. bi-m. free to airline passengers. North-South Net, Inc., 100 Almeria Ave., Ste. 220, Coral Gables, FL 33134. TEL 305-441-9744. FAX 305-441-9739. Ed. Roberto Casin. bk.rev.; illus. circ. 10,000.
Description: General interest articles for travelers into and out of Latin America. Includes information on tourist attractions.

056.1 051   US
ABOARD DOMINICANA. (Text in English, Spanish) 1983. bi-m. free to airline passengers. North-South Net, Inc., 100 Almeria Ave., Ste. 220, Coral Gables, FL 33134. TEL 305-441-9744. FAX 305-441-9739. Ed. Gloria Shanahan. bk.rev.; illus. circ. 6,000.
Description: General interest articles for travelers into and out of Latin America. Includes information on tourist attractions.

056.1 051   US
ABOARD ECUATORIANA. (Text in English, Spanish) 1983. bi-m. free to airline passengers. North-South Net, Inc., 100 Almeria Ave., Ste. 220, Coral Gables, FL 33134. TEL 305-441-9744. FAX 305-441-9739. Ed. Gloria Shanahan. bk.rev.; illus. circ. 10,000.
Description: General interest articles for travellers to and from Latin America, with information on tourist attractions.

056.1 051   US
ABOARD L A B AIRLINES. (Lloyd Aero Boliviano) (Text in English, Spanish) 1977. bi-m. free to airline passengers. North-South Net, Inc., 100 Almeria Ave., Ste. 220, Coral Gables, FL 33134. TEL 305-441-9744. FAX 305-441-9739. Ed. Gloria Shanahan. bk.rev.; illus. circ. 14,000.
Description: Features general interest articles for travelers into and out of Latin America. Includes information on tourist attractions.

056.1 051   US
ABOARD LAN-CHILE. (Text in English, Spanish) 1976. bi-m. free to airline passengers. North-South Net, Inc., 100 Almeria Ave., Ste. 220, Coral Gables, FL 33134. TEL 305-441-9744. FAX 305-441-9739. Ed. Gloria Shanahan. bk.rev.; illus. circ. 23,000.
Description: Features general interest articles for travelers into and out of Latin America. Includes information on tourist attractions.

051   US
ABOARD LAPSA. (Text in English, Spanish) 1979. bi-m. free to airline passengers. (Air Paraguay) North-South Net, Inc., 100 Almeria Ave., Ste. 220, Coral Gables, FL 33134. TEL 305-441-9744. FAX 305-441-9739. Ed. Roberto Casin. adv.; bk.rev.; illus. circ. 10,000. (back issues avail.) **Document type:** consumer publication.
Former titles (until 1994)**:** Aboard Air Paraguay; Dimension (Pembroke Lakes); Which superseded (in 1985): Aboard Lineas Aereas Paraguayas.
Description: General interest articles for travelers into and out of Latin America. Includes information on tourist attractions.

051   US
ABOARD TACA; international airlines. (Text in English, Spanish) 1981. bi-m. free to airline passengers. North-South Net, Inc., 100 Almeria Ave., Ste. 220, Coral Gables, FL 33134. TEL 305-441-9744. FAX 305-441-9739. Ed. Gloria Shanahan. bk.rev.; illus. circ. 14,000.
Description: Features general-interest articles for travelers into and out of Latin America. Includes information on tourist attractions.

056.1 051   US
ABOARD TAN SAHSA; the international airlines of Honduras. (Text in English, Spanish) 1986. bi-m. free to airline passengers. North-South Net, Inc., 100 Almeria Ave., Ste. 220, Coral Gables, FL 33134. TEL 305-441-9744. FAX 305-441-9739. Ed. Gloria Shanahan. bk.rev.; illus. circ. 10,000.
Description: Features general-interest articles for travelers into and out of Latin America. Includes information on tourist attractions.

056.1 051   US
ABOARD VIASA; la linea aerea de Venezuela. (Text in English, Spanish) 1977. bi-m. free to airline passengers. North-South Net, Inc., 100 Almeria Ave., Ste. 220, Coral Gables, FL 33134. TEL 305-441-9744. FAX 305-441-9739. Ed. Cristina Juri Arencibia. circ. 18,000.
Description: Features general interest articles for travelers into and out of Latin America. Includes information on tourist attractions.

387.742   US
ACCENT (OGDEN). 1981. m. Meridian Publishing, Inc., Box 10010, Ogden, UT 84409. TEL 801-394-9446. Ed. Robyn C. Walker. adv.; tr.lit. circ. 150,842.
Formerly: Inflight.

910.09   GW
AERO LLOYD; Bord Magazin. 1984. q. (Aero Lloyd Airlines) F U V Flugurlaub Verlag GmbH, Lessingstr. 7-9, 61440 Oberursel, Germany. TEL 06171-6404. FAX 06171-641049. Ed. Eduard Wolczak. adv. contact: Bogomir Gradisnik. circ. 100,000. (back issues avail.) **Document type:** consumer publication.
Formerly: Flugurlaub.

056.1 051   MX
AEROMEXICO ESCALA. (Text in English and Spanish) 1990. m. (AeroMexico) Impresiones Aereas, S.A. de C.V., Arquimedes, 5, Col. Polanco C.P., 11560 Mexico D.F., Mexico. TEL 250-58-79. adv. circ. 100,000.

910.09
AEROMEXICO PREMIER. (Text in English, Spanish) 3/yr. Impresiones Aereas, S.A. de C.V., Arquimedes 5, Col. Polanco, 11560 Mexico DF, Mexico. adv.: color page $6100; trim 8 13/16 x 10 13/16. circ. 32,000. (controlled). **Document type:** consumer publication.

052   UK
AFRICA LIFE; the Block Hotels magazine. 1988. s-a. Camerapix Magazines Ltd., 8 Reston Mews, London W11 1RB, England. TEL 071-221-0077. FAX 071-792-8105. Ed. D. Gaiger. bk.rev.; charts; maps; stat. circ. 30,000. **Document type:** consumer publication.
Description: Includes articles about African culture and life in general.

059.927   SU   ISSN 1319-1543
AHLAN WA SAHLAN/WELCOME. (Text in Arabic) 1977. 12/yr. Saudi Arabian Airlines, P.O. Box 8013, Jeddah 21482, Saudi Arabia. TEL 966-2-6842000. FAX 966-2-6842000. Ed. Yarub A. Balkhair. adv. circ. 150,000. **Document type:** consumer publication.
Description: In-flight magazine.

910.09   UK   ISSN 1003-3823
AIR CHINA/ZHONGGUO GUOJI HANGKONG GONGSI JINEI ZAZHI. 1988. bi-m. Regie Club International, Cromwell House, 136 Cromwell Rd., London SW7 4HA, England. TEL 44-71-244-6565. adv.: color page $6000; trim 8 1/4 x 11 1/4. circ. 60,000. (controlled). **Document type:** consumer publication.

059.956   FR
AIR FRANCE BON VOYAGE. (Text in Japanese) q. Regie Club International, 31 Rue du Collsee, 75008 Paris, France. TEL 40-75-50-50. FAX 42-89-14-66. adv.: color page 27500 F. illus. circ. 100,000.

051 054   FR   ISSN 0980-7519
AIR FRANCE MADAME. (Text in English, French) 6/yr. Air France, 71 rue Desnouettes, Paris 75015, France. TEL 44-19-90-33. FAX 48-28-39-50. Ed. Francis Rousseau. adv. contact: Michel Devos.
Description: Covers personalities, culture, fashion, and travel.

054.1   FR
AIR INTER PARCOURS. 1992. 11/yr. B C Regie, 53 Ave. Victor Hugo, 75116 Paris, France. TEL 33144175500. FAX 33145001256. Ed. Bernard Chevry. adv.: B&W page $14202, color page $20514; trim 7 1/8 x 9 7/8. circ. 200,000.

051   US
AIR WISCONSIN - AIR DESTINATIONS.* m. (United Express System) Stout Publishing Corp., 6006 S. Holly St., Ste. 123, Englewood, CO 80111-4200. TEL 303-399-3000. Ed. Rod Manuel. adv.
Description: In-flight magazine.

051   US
ALASKA AIRLINES MAGAZINE. 1977. m. $45. Paradigm Press, 2701 1st Ave., Ste. 250, Seattle, WA 98121. TEL 206-441-5871. FAX 206-448-6939. Ed. Paul Frichtl. adv. contact: Michael Quin. bk.rev.; circ. 45,000. (controlled).
Formerly: Alaskafest (ISSN 0199-0586)
Description: General interest publication for business and leisure travellers.

055.1   IT
ALITALIA ARRIVEDERCI. 1987. m. Alitalia Linee Aeree Italiane, Via A. Marchetti 111, 00148 Rome, Italy. TEL 39-6-65622526. Ed. Marco Zanichelli. adv.: B&W page $9400, color page $10700; trim 8 1/8 x 10 7/8. circ. 500,000.

TRAVEL AND TOURISM — AIRLINE INFLIGHT AND HOTEL INROOM

055.1   IT
ALITALIA FASCINO. q. Alitalia Linee Aeree Italiane S.p.A., Via Della Magliana 886, 00148 Rome, Italy. Ed. Marco Zanichelli. adv.: color page $13200; trim 9 1/16 x 11 1/16. circ. 150,000. **Document type:** consumer publication.
Description: For first class passengers.

051   US   ISSN 1073-0745
AMERICA WEST AIRLINES MAGAZINE. 1986. m. $31. Skyword Marketing, Inc., 4636 E. Elwood St., No. 5, Phoenix, AZ 85040-1963. TEL 602-997-7200. Ed. Michael Derr. adv.; bk.rev.; bibl.; charts; illus. **Document type:** consumer publication.

051   US   ISSN 0003-1518
AMERICAN WAY. 1966. s-m. $72 (free to American Airlines and American Eagle passengers). (American Airlines) A A Magazine Publications, Box 619640, Dallas-Ft. Worth Airport, TX 75261-9640. TEL 817-967-1804. FAX 817-967-1571. Ed. John H. Ostdick. adv.: B&W page $13910; adv. contact: Terrie Hadnely Lonergan. bk.rev.; illus. circ. 300,000. (also avail. in microform from UMI) **Document type:** consumer publication.

056.1 051   US
AMIGOS VOLANDO.* (Text in English, Spanish) 1983. m. (Avianca Airlines) Carvajal International, Inc., 901 Ponce de Leon Blvd., Ste. 901, Coral Gables, FL 33134-3073. TEL 305-448-6875. FAX 305-448-9942. Ed. Gustavo M. Garcia Arena. circ. 90,000.
Description: For passengers of Avianca Airlines to read during flights.

385.23 051   US   ISSN 1040-1776
AMTRAK EXPRESS. 1981. bi-m. $18. (National Railroad Passenger Corporation) Pace Communications Inc., 1301 Carolina St., Greensboro, NC 27401. TEL 910-378-6065. FAX 910-275-2864. Ed. Melinda L. Stovall; Pub. Edward Calfo. adv. contact: William Shea. circ. 253,000 (controlled). **Document type:** consumer publication.
Description: General interest articles on life in the U.S., with travel and railroad-related features.

051   US
ARRIVED. q. Russ Moore & Associates Inc., 4151 Knob Dr., Ste. 200, Eagan, MN 55122. TEL 612-452-0571. Ed. Diane Steen. circ. 200,000 (controlled).
Description: In-room magazine distributed to guests at Carlson Hospitality Group hotels located in the United States, Mexico, Canada and the Caribbean. Covers exotic locations, tips for business travelers, personality profiles, and the hospitality industry.

051   KO
ASIANA. m. Asiana Airlines, Asiana Bldg., 10-1 Hoehyon-dong 2 ga, Chung-gu, Seoul, Korea. TEL 82-2-758-8452. FAX 82-2-758-8008. Ed. Sam-Koo Park. adv. circ. 100,000.
Description: Airline inflight magazine on Korea, Japan, Hong Kong, Tapei, Bangkok and Singapore.

051   US
ASPEN AIRWAYS - AIR DESTINATIONS.* 1984. m. $9.95. (United Express System) Stout Publishing Corp., 6006 S. Holly St., Ste. 123, Englewood, CO 80111-4200. TEL 303-399-3000. Ed. Kristi Theis.
Description: In-flight magazine for Aspen Airways, focusing on Colorado, Wyoming and New Mexico.

052   IC
ATLANTICA. (Text in English) 1976. 5/yr. free. (Icelandair) Iceland Review, Hoefdabakki 9, P.O. Box 12122, IS-112 Reykjavik, Iceland. TEL 354-567-4067. Ed. Haraldur J. Hamar. adv. circ. 55,000. Indexed: Deep Sea Res.& Oceanogr.Abstr.
Description: Icelandair in-flight magazine.

056.9   PO   ISSN 0870-8924
ATLANTIS; inflight magazine. 1981. 6/yr. free. T A P Air Portugal, Bldg. 27, 7th fl., Lisbon Airport, 1704 Lisbon, Portugal. TEL 351-1-841-6463. FAX 351-1-841-5772. TELEX 12231 TAPLIS P. Ed. A. Campos Batista. adv.: color page $6070; trim 200 x 290. circ. 100,000. **Document type:** consumer publication.

052   AU
AUSTRIAN AIRLINES SKYLINES. bi-m. Osterreichischer Luftverkehrs, A.G., Vienna A1107, Austria. TEL 43-222-68-35-11. Ed. Nicole Schmidt. adv.: B&W page S.7254; color page S.11606; trim 7 1/8 x 9 1/8. circ. 150,000.
Description: Airline inflight magazine.

910.09   SZ
BALAIR - C T A YELLOW WINGS. (Text in French, German) 3/yr. Airpage AG, Haldenstr. 65, CH-8045 Zurich, Switzerland. TEL 01-451-2920. FAX 01-451-2961. Ed. Elisabeth Dennler. adv.: B&W page $6477, color page $7860; 7 5/16 x 10 1/8; adv. contact: Peter Furrer. circ. 150,000 (controlled). **Document type:** consumer publication.

917.04   US   ISSN 0192-4249
BIENVENIDOS A MIAMI. (Text in Spanish) 1975. bi-w. free to visitors in hotels & motels. Welcome Publications, Inc., Box 630518, Miami, FL 33163. TEL 305-944-9444. Ed. Mona K. Levine; Pub. Mona K. Levine. adv. contact: Alan Levine. circ. 13,000. **Document type:** consumer publication.
Formerly: Bienvenidos a Miami y a la Florida.

052   FI   ISSN 0358-7703
BLUE WINGS; Finnair's in-flight magazine. (Text in English) 1980. bi-m. Erikoislehdet Oy Business Publications, Box 16, SF-00381 Helsinki, Finland. Ed. Marketta Rentola. adv. circ. 92,000.

052   UK
BRITANNIA AIRWAYS SKYSCENE. s-a. free Britannia Airways passengers. John Brown Publishing, Ltd., The Boat House, Crabtree Ln., Fulham, London SW6 8NJ, England. TEL 44-71-381-6007. FAX 44-71-381-6903. Ed. Sean Carvill. adv.: color page $12163; trim 8 x 10 13/16. circ. 1,150,000. **Document type:** consumer publication.
Description: Contains articles and information of interest to passengers aboard Britannia Airways flights.

052   UK
BRITISH AIRWAYS CONCORDE. m. Premier Magazines Ltd., Haymarket House, 1 Oxendon St., London SW1Y 4EE, England. TEL 0171-925-2544. FAX 0171-839-4491. Ed. William Davis. adv.: B&W page $3427; trim 7 x 10. circ. 19,000. **Document type:** consumer publication.
Description: For passengers on Concorde flights.

059.956   UK
BRITISH AIRWAYS DREAM JOURNEYS. (Text in Japanese) q. Premier Magazines Ltd., Haymarket House, 1 Oxendon St., London SW1Y 4EE, England. TEL 0171-925-2544. FAX 0171-839-4491. Ed. William Davis. adv.: B&W or color page $4790; trim 8 1/4 x 11 3/8. circ. 100,000. **Document type:** consumer publication.

052   UK
CALEDONIAN AIRWAYS SKY LIFE. s-a. Premier Magazines Ltd., Haymarket House, 1 Oxendon St., London SW1Y 4EE, England. TEL 0171-925-2544. FAX 0171-839-4491. Ed. Caroline Cook. adv.: color page $1064. circ. 600,000. **Document type:** consumer publication.

051   CN   ISSN 0836-3196
CANADIAN (VERNON). 1978. m. (Canadian Airlines International) Synergism Marketing & Communications Inc., 199 Avenue Rd., 3rd Fl., Toronto, ON M5R 2J3, Canada. TEL 416-962-9184. FAX 416-962-2380. Ed. Kathleen Hurd. adv.: bk.rev. circ. 125,000. Indexed: Can.Per.Ind.
Description: In-flight magazine.

052   IE   ISSN 0008-6088
CARA; inflight magazine of Aer Lingus. 1968. 6/yr. £12($30) Aer Lingus, Publicity Department, Box 180, Dublin Airport PA7, Dublin, Ireland. FAX 01-426-998. Ed. Bernard Share. adv.; bk.rev. circ. 330,000.
Description: Publication for passengers on all Aer Lingus flights: scheduled, charter, and commuter.

051   US
CONTINENTAL PROFILES. 1968. m. (Continental Airlines) Cadmus Custom Publishing, 376 Boylston St., Boston, MA 02116-3812. TEL 617-424-7700. FAX 617-437-7714. adv. circ. 397,549. **Document type:** consumer publication.
Description: In-flight magazine for the business traveler.

052   SZ
CROSSTALK. (Text in English, French, German, Italian) 1984. m. (11/yr.). 40 SFr. (foreign 52 SFr.). (Crossair) Zuerichsee Zeitschriftenverlag, Seestr. 86, CH-8712 Staefa, Switzerland. TEL 01-9285611. FAX 01-9285600. adv.: B&W page 7900 SFr., color page 9900 SFr.; trim 197 x 267; adv. contact: Elisabeth Godelman. circ. 70,000. **Document type:** consumer publication.

052   FR
CZECHOSLOVAK AIRLINES REVIEW. 4/yr. (Czechoslovak Airlines) Regie Club International, 31 Rue de Colisee, 75008 Paris, France. TEL 33140755050. FAX 33142891466. adv.: B&W page $5880; 8 7/16 x 11. circ. 60,000 (controlled). **Document type:** consumer publication.

910.202   HK
DISCOVERY. (Text in English) 1973. m. (Cathay Pacific Airways) Emphasis HK Ltd., 505-508 Westlands Centre, 20 Westlands Rd., Quarry Bay, Hong Kong, Hong Kong. TEL 25161000. FAX 25613306. Ed. Stuart Lawrence. circ. 250,000.

910.09   HK
DISCOVERY (JAPANESE EDITION). (Text in Japanese) 1992. bi-m. (Cathay Pacific Airways) Emphasis HK Ltd., 505-508 Westlands Centre, 20 Westlands Rd., Quarry Bay, Hong Kong, Hong Kong. TEL 25161000. FAX 25613306. adv.: B&W or color page $6500; trim 210 x 285. circ. 45,000.

658.8   UK
DUTY FREE NEWS INTERNATIONAL. s-m. Park Pl., 10 Lawn Ln., London SW8 1UD, England. TEL 0171-735-0811. FAX 0171-582-8072. Ed. Martin Moodie; Pub. Vivien Raven. adv. contact: Roy Downes. circ. 2,200. **Document type:** trade publication.
Description: General information about the duty free industry.

052   CH
DYNASTY. (Text in Chinese and English) 1969. 6/yr. free. China Airlines Ltd. - Chung Hua Hang K'ung Kung Ssu, 131 Nanking E. Rd. Sec. 3, Taipei, Taiwan, Republic of China. Ed. Wu I-Shou. adv. circ. 60,000.

052   UK
EASTERN AIR EASTERN. (Text in Chinese, English) bi-m. (Eastern Air) Regie Club International, Cromwell House, 136 Cromwell Rc., London SW7 4HA, England. TEL 44-71-244-6565. FAX 44-71-3670-3727. adv.: color page $5500; trim 8 1/4 x 11 1/4. circ. 60,000 (controlled). **Document type:** consumer publication.

910.09   FR
ELYSSA. (Text in Arabic, English, French) 4/yr. (Tunisair) Regie Club International, 31 Rue de Colisee, 75008 Paris, France. TEL 33-1-40-75-50-50. adv.: B&W page $4675, color page $5844; 8 1/4 x 11 1/4. circ. 135,000 (controlled). **Document type:** consumer publication.

910.09   CH
EVA AIRWAYS VERVE. m. Eva Airways Corp., 7-F, 330 Minsheng East Rd., Taipei, Taiwan, Republic of China. TEL 02-505-7766. adv. circ. 17,000.

051 910.4   US
EXPRESS.* 1981. bi-m. $12 (free to qualified personnel). Amtrak, 53 Belknap Dr., Northport, NY 11768-3401. TEL 516-385-9299. Ed. Christopher Podgus. adv.; bk.rev. circ. 160,000. Indexed: Avery Ind.Architt.Per.
Description: For Amtrak riders. Covers a broad spectrum of topics, including places of interest, interviews, and current events.

028.5
FANTASTIC FLYER MAGAZINE. 1988. q. free. Delta Air Lines, Inc., 1030 Delta Blvd., Dept. 790, Atlanta, GA 30320. TEL 404-765-4813. adv. circ. 1,100,000.
Description: Includes information on cities, profiles of exceptional children, news, fiction, cartoons and games for child passengers.

052   UK
FLIGHTPATH; in-flight magazine for Logan Air. 1988. q. Kingsclere Contract Publishing, Furlongs House, Peasemore, Newbury, Berkshire RG16 OJE, England. TEL 0635-247770. FAX 0635-247272. Ed. Diana Breadmure. adv.; bk.rev.; circ. 10,000 (controlled). **Document type:** consumer publication.

TRAVEL AND TOURISM — AIRLINE INFLIGHT AND HOTEL INROOM

051 054   **LU**
FLYDOSCOPE; magazine de bord de Luxair. (Text in English, French, German) 1975. 3/yr. free to passengers. Luxair, L-2987 Luxembourg, Luxembourg. TEL 4798-2221. FAX 43-63-44. TELEX 2372 LGDDAP LU. Ed. Nicole Eastwood. adv.: Color page 150000 Fr.; trim 210 x 270. circ. 40,000 (controlled). **Document type:** consumer publication.
  Description: Consists of feature articles on aviation, art, culture travel and places of interest to those who fly Luxair.

051   **NE**   **ISSN 0925-7802**
FLYING DUTCHMAN. (Regional edition avail.: Far East & South Pacific) (Text in English) 1981. 6/yr. free to qualified personnel. (K L M Royal Dutch Airlines) Media Partners, P.O. Box 2215, 1180 EE Amstelveen, Netherlands. TEL 31-20-5473600. FAX 31-20-6475121. Ed. Rob Ligtelijn. adv.: color page fl.10096; 285 x 215; adv. contact: Henk Kamstra. illus.; circ. 100,000 (controlled). **Indexed:** Key to Econ.Sci. **Document type:** consumer publication.
  Formerly: Flying Dutchman Directions; Which superseded: Flying Dutchman International (ISSN 0925-7810)
  Description: Short informative articles for KLM frequent flyers.

910.202   **SA**   **ISSN 0302-7163**
FLYING SPRINGBOK/VLIEENDE SPRINGBOK. 1961. q. (South African Airways) A B B M Printing and Pub. Co., P.O. Box 3734, Randburg 2125, South Africa. Ed. Ernest Webb-Stock. adv.; bk.rev. circ. 50,000. (also avail. in microfiche)

051 059.992   **SI**
GARUDA MAGAZINE; the official in-flight magazine of Garuda Indonesia. (Text in English and Indonesian) 1971. m. free. (Garuda Indonesia, IO) Aerospace Communications Pte. Ltd., 14 Shaw Rd., No. 04-03, BTC Bldg., Singapore 1336, Singapore. TEL 65-344-6465. FAX 65-345-9919. Ed. Gerald Dick. adv.: page 6500; trim 190 x 265; adv. contact: Hoo Siew Sai. charts; illus.; circ. 75,000 (controlled).
  Formerly (until 1981): Garuda Indonesia Airways Magazine (ISSN 0046-5453)

917.304   **US**
GUEST INFORMANT. (In 36 U.S. city editions.) 1937. a. Guest Informant, 21200 Erwin St., Woodland Hills, CA 91367. TEL 818-716-7484. FAX 818-716-7583. adv.
  Description: Hotel inroom publication providing travelers with information on shopping, dining, history, culture, sights and recreational opportunities in specific cities.

910.4   **US**
GUEST INFORMANT - ATLANTA. 1982. a. L I N Cellular Communications Corp., 21200 Irwin St., Woodland Hills, CA 91367. TEL 818-716-7484. Ed. Andrea Zwerdling. circ. 2,730,000.
  Formerly: Leisureguide - Atlanta.

917.4   **US**
GUEST INFORMANT - BOSTON. 1978. a. L I N Cellular Communications Corp., 21200 Irwin St., Woodland hills, CA 91367. TEL 818-716-7484. Ed. Andrea Zwerdling. adv. circ. 2,979,000.
  Formerly: Leisureguide - Boston.

917   **US**
GUEST INFORMANT - CHICAGO. 1971. a. L I N Cellular Communications Corp., 21200 Irwin St., Woodland Hills, CA 91367. TEL 818-716-7484. Ed. Andrea Zwerdling. adv. circ. 3,800,000.
  Formerly: Leisureguide - Chicago.

917   **US**
GUEST INFORMANT - HOUSTON. 1978. a. L I N Cellular Communications Corp., 21200 Irwin St., Woodland Hills, CA 91367. TEL 818-716-7484. Ed. Andrea Zwerdling. adv. circ. 3,186,000.
  Formerly: Leisureguide - Houston.

910.4   **US**
GUEST INFORMANT - KANSAS CITY. 1982. a. L I N Cellular Communications Corp., 21200 Irwin St., Woodland Hills, CA 91367. TEL 818-716-7484. Ed. Andrea Zwerdling. circ. 1,740,000.
  Formerly: Leisureguide - Kansas City.

910.4   **US**
GUEST INFORMANT - NEW ORLEANS. 1982. a. L I N Cellular Communications Corp., 21200 Irwin St., Woodland Hills, CA 91367. TEL 818-716-7484. Ed. Andrea Zwerdling. circ. 1,980,000.
  Formerly: Leisureguide - New Orleans.

917.5   **US**
GUEST INFORMANT - ORLANDO. 1980. a. L I N Cellular Communications Corp., 21200 Irwin St., Woodland Hills, CA 91367. TEL 818-716-7484. Ed. Andrea Zwerdling. adv. circ. 3,100,000.
  Formerly: Leisureguide - Orlando.

917.2   **US**
GUEST INFORMANT - PUERTO RICO. 1980. a. L I N Cellular Communications Corp., 21200 Irwin St., Woodland Hills, CA 91367. TEL 818-716-7484. Ed. Andrea Zwerdling. adv. circ. 3,045,000.
  Formerly: Leisureguide - Puerto Rico.

917   **US**
GUEST INFORMANT - THE FLORIDA GOLD COAST. 1974. a. L I N Cellular Communications Corp., 21200 Irwin St., Woodland Hills, CA 91367. TEL 818-716-7484. Ed. Andrea Zwerdling. adv. circ. 5,590,000.
  Formerly: Leisureguide - The Florida Gold Coast.

910.4   **US**
GUEST INFORMANT - TWIN CITIES. 1982. a. L I N Cellular Communications Corp., 21200 Irwin St., Woodland Hills, CA 91367. TEL 818-716-7484. Ed. Andrea Zwerdling. circ. 1,800,000.
  Formerly: Leisureguide - Twin Cities.

051   **US**
HEMISPHERES. 1957. m. $50 (free to qualified personnel). (United Airlines) Pace Communications Inc., 1301 Carolina St., Greensboro, NC 27401. TEL 910-378-6065. Ed. Kate Greer; Pub. Bonnie McElveen-Hunter. adv. contact: John Ballantyne. bk.rev.; illus. circ. 500,000. **Document type:** consumer publication.
  Former titles (until Oct. 1992): Vis a Vis; United; United Mainliner; Mainliner (ISSN 0025-083X)

052   **UK**   **ISSN 1350-1631**
HIGH LIFE. 1973. m. (British Airways) Premier Magazines Ltd., Haymarket House, 1 Oxendon St., London SW1Y 4EE, England. TEL 0171-925-2544. FAX 0171-839-4491. Ed. William Davis. adv.; charts; illus.; tr.lit. circ. 275,000. **Document type:** consumer publication.
  Description: Inflight magazine featuring current travel news and information.

052   **NE**   **ISSN 0018-3563**
HOLLAND HERALD; magazine of the Netherlands. (Text in English) 1966. m. Media Partners International, P.O. Box 469, 1180 AL Amstelveen, Netherlands. TEL 31-20-5473550. FAX 31-20-6438581. Ed. Ken Wilkie. adv.: color page fl.28300; adv. contact: Jopie Baijings. bk.rev.; illus.; circ. 170,000 (controlled). **Document type:** consumer publication.
  Description: Includes regular international travel features.

051   **US**   **ISSN 1050-2440**
HORIZON AIR MAGAZINE. 1979. m. $30. Paradigm Press, 2701 First Ave., Ste. 250, Seattle, WA 98121. TEL 206-441-5871. FAX 206-448-6939. Ed. Paul Frichtl. adv. contact: Michael Quin. tr.lit.; circ. 20,000 (controlled).
  Description: Aimed at business travelers in the Northwest and includes regional business, travel and general interest topics.

052   **UK**   **ISSN 0952-7974**
HOT AIR; Virgin Atlantic Airways in-flight magazine. (Text in English, Japanese) 1983. q. free to Virgin Atlantic passengers. John Brown Publishing Ltd., The Boat House, Crabtree Ln., Fulham, London SW6 8NJ, England. TEL 44-71-381-6007. FAX 44-71-381-6903. Ed. Alex Finer. adv.: B&W page $8039, color page $9694; trim 8 1/4 x 11 11/16. bk.rev. circ. 150,000. **Document type:** consumer publication.
  Description: Contains articles and information of interest to passengers aboard Virgin Atlantic flights.

910.202   **TH**
HUMSAFAR. 1980. 6/yr. $29. (Pakistan International Airlines) Media Transasia (Thailand) Ltd., 14th Fl., Orakarn Bldg., 26 Chidlom Rd., Ploenchit, Bangkok 10330, Thailand. FAX 2535335. TELEX 84003-MEDTRAN-TH. Ed. X. Colaco. adv. circ. 70,000.
  Description: Inflight publication of Pakistan International Airlines. Focuses on travel and tourism.

051   **BL**
ICARO; revista de bordo Varig. (Text in English, Portuguese) 1983. m. (Varig Airlines) Icaro Editora Ltd., Rua Jundiai 50, 4th Fl., CEP 04001-140 Sao Paulo SP, Brazil. TEL 55-011-8874233. FAX 55-011-8853717. Ed. Carlos Drumond; Pub. Carlos Alberto de Almeida. adv.: B&W page $6150, color page $9180; 210 x 275; adv. contact: Nelson Amorin. circ. 130,000. **Document type:** consumer publication.
  Description: Inflight magazine covering business, cultural and international topics on Brazil and on Varig's destinations.

051 059.927   **TS**
AL-IMARAT FIL-AJWA/EMIRATES IN FLIGHT. (Text in Arabic, English) 1987. m. free. (Emirates Airlines) Motivate Publishing, P.O. Box 2331, Dubai, United Arab Emirates. TEL 246060. FAX 214820. TELEX 48366 MAM EM. Ed. Obaid Humaid al-Tayer. circ. 1,000.
  Description: In-flight magazine.

910.202   **US**
INN ROOM MAGAZINE. 1977. m. free. 210 S. Juniper, Ste. 215, Escondido, CA 92025. TEL 619-489-5252. FAX 619-489-6752. (Subscr. to: Box 3395, Escondido, CA 92033) Ed. Donna Abate; Pub. Jerry Barash. adv. contact: Suzanne Wilkinson. bk.rev. circ. 91,850. **Document type:** consumer publication.

054.1 387.74   **CN**   **ISSN 0848-9793**
INTER-CANADIEN. (Avail. to subscribers as: Globe Magazine (ISSN 1195-21) 1978. 6/yr. Globe Magazine Inc., 422 chemin du Roy, Saint-Augustin-de-Desmaures, PQ G3A 1W8, Canada. TEL 418-878-1800. FAX 418-878-4506. Ed. Florian Chasse; Pub. Florian Chasse. adv.; bk.rev. circ. 43,000.
  Former titles (until 1989): Altitude (ISSN 0832-5812); (until 1987): Envol (ISSN 0823-1141); Auberge.

910.202   **IS**
ISRAELAL. (Text in English, Hebrew) 1981. bi-m. (El Al (Israel Airlines)) Fraser Communications Ltd., 11 Harugei Malchut St., Tel Aviv, Israel. TEL 972-3-6478982. FAX 972-3-6478980. Pub. Orna Fraser. adv.: B&W page $4000, color page $5000; 7 7/8 x 10 1/4. circ. 750,000. **Document type:** consumer publication.
  Formerly: Welcome Abroad.

055.956   **JA**
JAPAN AIRLINES AGORA. m. J A L Cultural Development Co. Ltd., Fujiya Ginza Bldg., 9-3 Ginza 6-chrome, Cho-Ku, Tokyo 104, Japan. adv.: color page $11300; trim 8 1/4 x 10 3/4. circ. 160,000.

052   **UK**
JERSEY EUROPEAN FLYING COLOURS. q. free to passengers aboard Jersey European Airways flights. (Jersey European Airways) B M I Publications Ltd., Suffolk House, George St., Croydon, Surrey CR9 1SR. TEL 0181-649-7233. FAX 0181-649-7234. Ed. Alan Orbell. adv.: color page $4000; adv. contact: Sally Cresswell. circ. 25,000. (back issues avail.) **Document type:** consumer publication.
  Description: Contains articles on various topics of interest to passengers aboard Jersey European Airways flights.

910.03 059.957   **NE**
K L M AMSTERDAM. (Text in Korean) 2/yr. (K L M Royal Dutch Airlines) Media Partners International, P.O. Box 469, 1180 AL Amstelveen, Netherlands. TEL 31-20-5473550. FAX 31-20-6438581. Ed. Cho Eun Kyung. adv.: color page $2800; trim 280 x 210. **Document type:** consumer publication.
  Description: For passengers on KLM flights to and from Korea.

TRAVEL AND TOURISM — AIRLINE INFLIGHT AND HOTEL INROOM

910.09   NE
K L M BLUEBIRD. (Text in Chinese) bi-m. (K L M Royal Dutch Airlines) Media Partners International, P.O. Box 469, 1180 AL Amstelveen, Netherlands. TEL 31-20-547-3550. FAX 31-20-643-8581. adv.: color page fl.4000; trim 285 x 215; adv. contact: Karin Amende. circ. 40,000. **Document type:** consumer publication.

059.956   US
K L M WINDMILL. (Text in Japanese) bi-m. (K L M Royal Dutch Airlines) Media Partners International, P.O. Box 469, 1180 Amstelveen, Netherlands. TEL 31-20-5473550. FAX 31-20-6438581. Ed. Ken Wilkie. adv.: color page fl.8500; trim 280 x 210. circ. 90,000.

057.85   PL
KALEIDOSCOPE. 1979. q. (L O T Polish Airlines) A G P O L, Ul. Sienkiewicza 12, P.O. Box 136, 00-950 Warsaw, Poland. adv. circ. 80,000.

051   US
KIWI IN FLIGHT. bi-m. $24. (Kiwi International Air Lines) M & A Publishing, Ltd., 122 E. 25th St., 2nd Fl., New York, NY 10010. TEL 212-673-8930. Ed. Marilyn Holstein. adv.; illus. **Document type:** consumer publication.

053.1   GW
L T U MAGAZIN. (Luft Transport Unternehmung) 1986. q. DM.18. (L T U International Airways) Westend GmbH, Westendstr. 1, 45143 Essen, Germany. TEL 0201-1882269. FAX 0201-1882235. Ed. Wolfgang Osinski. adv. contact: F. Zanetti. bk.rev.; circ. 400,000 (controlled). (back issues avail.) **Document type:** consumer publication.

056.1   CL   ISSN 0716-9140
LADECO AMERICA. (Text in English, Spanish) bi-m. Ladeco Chilean Airlines, Casilla 333-22, Santiago, Chile. Ed. Ana Francisca Aldunate. adv.: B&W or color page $4910. circ. 75,000.

051 056.1   US
LASCA'S WORLD. (Text in English, Spanish) 1985. bi-m. $25. E R Publishing, 1911 N.W. 114th St., Pembroke Lakes, FL 33026. TEL 305-431-0161. FAX 305-431-4661. Ed. Manja Rippen. circ. 20,000. (back issues avail.) **Description:** Covers leisure activities, business trends, travel and dining, and travel destinations in the United States, Caribbean, Central and South America.

910.09   US   ISSN 1052-1011
LATITUDES SOUTH. (Text in English, Spanish) 1991. q. (American Eagle Airlines) Caribbean Travel and Life, Inc., 8403 Colesville Rd., Ste. 830, Silver Spring, MD 20910. TEL 301-588-2300. FAX 301-588-2256. Ed. Laura Randall; Pub. Josepa N. DiMarino. adv. **Description:** Inflight magazine.

053.1 052   AU
LAUDA AIR MAGAZINE. (Text in English and German) 1989. 4/yr. Orac Zeitschriftenverlag GmbH, Schoenbrunnerstr. 59-61, A-1050 Vienna, Austria. TEL 01-54621-0. FAX 01-5462178. Ed. Herbert Voelker. adv.: B&W page S.74280, color page S.111420; trim 185 x 250. circ. 140,000. (back issues avail.) **Document type:** consumer publication.

051   UK
LEISUREJET; the inflight magazine of Air UK leisure. 1989. s-a. free to passengers aboard Air UK flights. (Air UK) B B B Publishing Ltd., 34 Hereford Rd., London W2 5AJ, England. TEL 0171-229-6632. FAX 0171-727-0986. Ed. Peter R.A. Fryd; Pub. Philip O'Donnell. adv. contact: Philip O'Donnell. circ. 200,000. **Document type:** consumer publication. **Description:** Contains articles on air travel, tourism, and holidays of interest to passengers aboard Air UK flights.

387.7 051   AQ
LIAT ISLANDER. 1979. 3/yr. F T Caribbean, P.O. Box 1037, St. John's, Antigua, W.I. FAX 462-3492. Ed.Bd. circ. 50,000. (back issues avail.)

053.1   GW
LUFTHANSA BORDBUCH. (Text in English, German) 1972. bi-m. Deutsche Lufthansa AG, Von-Gablenz-Str. 2-6, 50679 Cologne, Germany. TEL 0221-8262392. FAX 0221-8262306. Ed. Thomas Quinn. adv. circ. 630,000. **Document type:** bulletin.

053.1   GW
LUFTHANSA EXPRESS. bi-w. (Deutsche Lufthansa AG) Commpra Inflight Media Group, Emserstr. 1, 65191 Wiesbaden, Germany. adv.: color page $13697. circ. 150,000 (controlled). **Document type:** consumer publication.

051   PH   ISSN 0217-6998
MABUHAY; the inflight magazine of Philippine Airlines. (Text in English) 1988. m. $60. (Philippine Airlines) Eastgate Publishing Corporation, Attn: Ms. Jing Sanchez-Lagandaon, Rms.603-604 Emerald Bldg., Emerald Ave., Pasig, 1600 Metro Manila, Philippines. TEL 632-6312921. FAX 632-6312992. TELEX 43162 VAFOC PM. Ed. Cecile G. Mauricio. adv. contact: Gina C. Sanchez. circ. 103,000. (back issues avail.) **Indexed:** Ind.Phil.Per.

910.09   TS
MATAR ABU DHABI AL-DAWLI/SHOPTALK - ABU DHABI DUTY FREE GUIDE. (Text in Arabic, English) 1988. q. free. (Abu Dhabi Department of Civil Aviation) Abu Dhabi Duty Free, Marketing Department, P.O. Box 3167, Abu Dhabi, United Arab Emirates. TEL 757350. FAX 757172. Ed. Bassam el-Khazen. circ. 20,000. **Document type:** consumer publication. **Description:** Tourist and duty free information regarding Abu Dhabi and its airport, and other features of interest to international travellers.

052   CN   ISSN 0848-0877
MEMO (MONTREAL); le gout des regions. (Text in French) 1989. bi-m. Can.$15($25); newsstand price: Can.$3. Editions du Rineva, 3715 av. Lacombe, Ste. 200, Montreal, PQ H3T 1M3, Canada. TEL 514-341-7916. FAX 514-341-2644. Ed. Michel Guenard; Pub. Marie-Claire Dupre. adv.: B&W page Can.$2090, color page Can.$2940; trim 8 1/8 x 10 7/8; adv. contact: Marie-Claire Dupre. circ. 22,000. **Document type:** consumer publication. **Description:** Covers issues of interest to persons visiting the region of Quebec that Air Alliance serves, including the tourist destinations, the economy, administrative regions, aspects of management, leading-edge technology, conditions in the workplace and applied research.

055.1   IT
MERIDIANA AIRLINES ATMOSPHERE. (Text in English, Italian) 1988. 5/yr. free to qualified personnel. Meridiana S.p.A., San Marco 2236, Calle del Teatro 2245-A, 30124 Venice, Italy. Ed. Ettore Della Giovanna. adv.: page L.10000000; adv. contact: Maurizio Cinquanta. circ. 500,000.

051   US
MESA CONNECTION.* 1987. bi-m. (Mesa Airlines) Stout Publishing Corp., 6006 S. Holly St., Ste. 123, Englewood, CO 80111-4200. TEL 303-399-3000. Ed. Kristi Theis. adv. circ. 10,000.

051   US   ISSN 1068-3135
MIDWEST EXPRESS MAGAZINE. 1990. bi-m. Paradigm Press, 2701 First Ave., Ste. 250. 30 93081, Seattle, WA 98121. TEL 206-441-5871. FAX 206-448-6939. Ed. Eric Lucas. adv.: B&W page $2710, color page $3580; trim 8 3/8 x 10 7/8. circ. 32,000. **Document type:** consumer publication.

910.202   GR
MOTION/KINISI. (Text in English, Greek) 1969. q. free. Olympic Airways S.A., 120 Syngrou Ave., 3rd Fl., 117 41 Athens, Greece. TEL 30-1-9267-628. FAX 30-1-9267-818. TELEX 215823 OA GR. Ed. Maria ven Sourmelis. adv.: color page $6450; adv. contact: Marie Sourmelis. circ. 180,000. **Formerly:** Your Air Companion.

051 056.1   CK
EL MUNDO AL VUELO - INFLIGHT NOTES. (Text in English and Spanish) 1972. 12/y. $40. (Avianca) Caravajal S.A., Apdo. 53550, Bogota, Colombia. Ed. Maria Christina Lamus. adv.; bk.rev. circ. 90,000. **Formerly:** Apuntes de Abordo - Inflight Notes. **Description:** For passengers on Avianca's domestic and international flights, also sent to important commercial and tourist organizations.

051   US
N P A - AIR DESTINATIONS.* bi-m. (United Express System) Stout Publishing Corp., 6006 S. Holly St., Ste. 123, Englewood, CO 80111-4200. TEL 303-399-3000. Ed. Kristi Theis. adv. **Description:** In-flight magazine.

052   II
NAMASKAAR. (Text in English) 1980. 6/yr. (Air India) Asia Publishing House, Bhogilal Hargobindas Bldg., 18-20 K Dubash Marg, Bombay 400 023, India. TEL 225353. FAX 010-9122-225685. Ed. Homi J. Vakeel. adv. circ. 45,000.

051   US   ISSN 0029-327X
NORTHLINER MAGAZINE;* news and features for passengers of North Central Airlines. 1969. q. free to airline passengers. (North Central Airlines) Dorn Communications, Inc., 15 5th St. S., Ste. 900, Minneapolis, MN 55402. Ed. James Carney. adv.; bk.rev.; charts; illus. circ. 80,000.

051   US
NORTHWEST AIRLINES WORLD TRAVELER. 1989. m. $50. (Northwest Airlines) Meredith Publishing Co., 1912 Grand Ave., Des Moines, IA 50309. TEL 515-284-2906. FAX 515-284-2479. Ed. Doug Holtajus. adv.: B&W page $17000, color page $21850; trim 8 1/8 x 10 7/8. circ. 350,000. **Document type:** consumer publication. **Formerly:** Compass Readings (ISSN 1051-7383)

059.957   KO
NORTHWEST AIRLINES WORLD TRAVELER (KOREAN EDITION). (Text in Korean) 1990. q. Sharp Travel Service Co., Ltd., Northwest Bldg., 8th Fl., 111-1 Seoulin, Dong, Chongro-Ku, Seoul 110-110, S. Korea. TEL 82-2-735-8500. FAX 82-2-734-2813. Ed. Chongkeun Paik. adv.: color page $4200; trim 180 x 260. circ. 100,000. **Document type:** consumer publication.

052   PP
PARADISE. 1976. 6/yr. $24 (typically set in Jan). Air Nuigini, P.O. Box 7186, Boroko, Papua New Guinea. FAX 273-416. Ed. Geoff McLaughlin. adv. circ. 50,000.

052   BE
PASSPORT; SABENA's inflight monthly. (Text in English) m. (Sabena Belgian World Airlines) Ackroyd Publications, 329 Av. Mcliere, B-1060 Brussels, Belgium. TEL 32-2-34339909. adv. circ. 78,000. **Document type:** consumer publication. **Formerly:** Sabena Sphere.

056.1   US
PLUNA. (Text in Spanish) bi-m. North-South Net, Inc., 100 Almeria Ave., Ste. 220, Coral Gables, FL 33134. TEL 305-441-9744. FAX 305-441-9739. adv.: B&W page $960; trim 8 3/8 x 10 7/8. **Document type:** consumer publication.

**917.04   **
PORTLAND AND THE PACIFIC NORTHWEST. 1975. a. $12. Fox Publishing Co., 320 S.W. Stark, Ste. 519, Portland, OR 97204. TEL 503-223-0051. FAX 503-225-1245. Ed. Susan Monti. adv. contact: Patrick Casciato. circ. 18,500. **Document type:** consumer publication. **Description:** In-room guidebook.

051   US
PRESIDENTIAL - AIR DESTINATIONS.* bi-m. (United Express System) Stout Publishing Corp., 6006 S. Holly St., Ste. 123, Englewood, CO 80111-4200. TEL 303-399-3000. Ed. Rod Manuel. adv. **Description:** In-flight magazine.

051 056.1   SP
RONDA IBERIA. (Text in English, Spanish) 1974. m. free. (Iberia Airlines) Ediciones Reunidas, S.A., O'Donnell, 12, 28009 Madrid, Spain. TEL 91-522-0072. FAX 91-564-03-75. TELEX 41969 EDIT E. bk.rev. circ. 220. **Description:** Provides useful information for Iberia passengers and reports on various national and international destinations. Includes articles on nature and sports activities.

910.09   BX
ROYAL BRUNEI AIRLINES MUHIBAH. 1991. 6/yr. Royal Brunei Airlines Sdn. Bhd., P.O. Box 737, Bandar Seri Begawan 1907, Negara, Brunei Darussalam. TEL 673-2-237779. FAX 673-2-237778. Ed. Douglas Kelly. adv.: color page $4500; adv. contact: Christina Chin. bk.rev. circ. 20,000.

TRAVEL AND TOURISM — AIRLINE INFLIGHT AND HOTEL INROOM

914.604 SW ISSN 1102-9722
ST. PETERSBURG NEWS. (Text in English; summaries in Russian) 1990. q. $35. (Aeroflot) Florman Marketing, Nybrogatan 21, S-114 39 Stockholm, Sweden. TEL 4686631970. FAX 4686610480. TELEX 12350. adv. contact: Petra Eurenius. circ. 70,000.
Formerly: Leningrad News.
Description: Focuses on Russian foreign trade and international business. Covers hotels, restaurants, recreation and culture in St. Petersburg.

052 HK ISSN 0251-7418
SAWASDEE. 1971. m. $70. (Thai Air International) Travel & Trade Publishing (Asia) Ltd., 16-F, Capitol Centre, 5-19 Jardine's Bazaar, Causeway Bay, Hong Kong. TEL 890-3067. FAX 895-2375. TELEX 76591-TPAL-HX. Ed. Julia Birch. adv. circ. 100,000.
Description: In-flight magazine.

052 SW ISSN 0346-7775
SCANORAMA. (Text in English) 1972. 10/yr. free. Media Partner, Gaevlegatan 18B, S-11330 Stockholm, Sweden. TEL 46-8-7297575. FAX 46-8-7288524. Ed. Lars Bringert. illus. circ. 140,000.
Formerly (until 1972): Scandinavian Times (ISSN 0105-0664)
Description: In-flight magazine.

052 UK
SELAMTA/GREETINGS; the in-flight magazine of Ethiopian Airlines. (Text in English) 1983. q. £12($30) (Ethiopian Airlines) Camerapix Publishers International, P.O. Box 45048, Nairobi, Kenya. TEL 254-2-223511. FAX 254-2-217244. TELEX 22576 KE. (Subscr. to: Camerapix, 8 Ruxton Mews, London W11 1RB, England. TEL 0171-221-0077. FAX 0171-792-8105; Alt. addr.: Ethiopian Airlines, Foxglove House, 166 Piccadilly, London W1, England. TEL 0171-491-9119) Ed. D. Gaiger. adv. contact: Mohamed Amin. bk.rev.; maps; stat. circ. 50,000. (back issues avail.) **Document type:** consumer publication.
Description: Includes articles relating to Ethiopian or African travel and culture with in-flight, duty-free listings and crossword puzzles.

052 HK
SERENDIB. (Text in English) 1982. 6/yr. free. (Air Lanka) Emphasis HK Ltd., 505-508 Westlands Centre, 20 Westlands Rd., Quarry Bay, Hong Kong. TEL 25161000. FAX 25613306. Ed. Geoff Burpee. adv. circ. 25,000.
Description: In-flight magazine on travel in Sri Lanka.

051 US
SHUTTLE QUARTERLY. 1988. q. Shuttle Quarterly, Inc., 50 Freedom Hollow, Ste. 401, Salem, MA 01970. TEL 508-745-1874. adv. circ. 30,000.
Description: In-flight magazine for passengers of the Pan-Am and Trump shuttles between Boston, New York and Washington D.C.

052 UK
SILHOUETTE; the in-flight magazine for Air Seychelles. (Text in English, French) 1990. s-a. Camerapix Magazines Ltd., 8 Ruston Mews, London W11 1RB, England. TEL 071-221-0077. FAX 071-792-8105. charts; maps; stat. circ. 40,000. **Document type:** consumer publication.
Description: Includes articles about travel and culture in the Seychelles; with in-flight, duty-free listings.

052 HK
SILKROAD. 1991. bi-m. (Dragon Airlines Ltd.) Emphasis (HK) Ltd., Ste. 5-8, 5F, Westlands Ctr., 20 Westlands Rd., Quarry Bay, Hong Kong. TEL 590-1328. FAX 590-1333. Ed. Tom/Chapman. adv.; circ. 46,425 (controlled).
Description: Inflight magazine.

052 SI ISSN 0129-606X
SILVER KRIS; Singapore Airlines inflight magazine. (Text in English) 1976. m. (Singapore International Airlines) M P H Magazines Pty. Ltd., Pan-I Warehouse Complex 03-21, 601 Sims Drive, Singapore 1438, Singapore. FAX 7440620. TELEX 35853 MPHMAG. Ed. Arthur Hullett. adv. circ. 250,000.

051 US ISSN 0734-8967
SKY. 1972. m. $36. (Delta Airlines) Halsey Publishing Co., 600 Corporate Dr., Ste. 300, Ft. Lauderdale, FL 33334. TEL 305-776-0066. FAX 305-493-8969. Ed. Lidia DeLeon. adv. circ. 500,000. **Document type:** consumer publication.
Description: Provides articles that entertain and inform on such subjects as business, sports, the arts, personalities, foreign and domestic travel and human interest topics.

052 JM
SKYWRITINGS. 1973. q. (Air Jamaica) Creative Communications, Inc., Ltd., P.O. Box 105, Kingston 10, Jamaica, W.I. TEL 809-968-7281. FAX 809-926-2217. Ed. Ashley Gambrill. adv. circ. 30,000. **Document type:** consumer publication.

051 US
SOUTHWEST SPIRIT. 1972. m. $36. (SouthWest Airlines) A A Magazine Publications, 4333 Amon Carter Blvd., Fort Worth, TX 76155. TEL 817-967-1804. Ed. John Clark. adv.: B&W page $9551, color page $12403; trim 8 x 10 7/8; adv. contact: Terrie Handley Lonergan. bk.rev. circ. 210,254.
Formerly: Southwest Airlines Spirit.

051 US ISSN 0199-7092
SPIRIT OF ALOHA. 1976. m. (Aloha Airlines) Honolulu Publishing Company, Ltd., 36 Merchant St., Honolulu, HI 96813. TEL 808-524-7400. FAX 808-531-2306. Ed. Pat Pitzer. adv. circ. 65,000.
Description: Inflight magazine of Aloha Airlines and Aloha Island Air.

055.1 IT
SULLE NUVOLE. 1992. q. Air Europe S.p.A., Corso Sempione 15-A, 21023 Gallarte (VA), Italy. Ed. Isabella Antonello. adv.: B&W page L.8000000, color page L.12000000; adv. contact: Antonio Carriero. circ. 100,000. **Document type:** consumer publication.

052 CY ISSN 1011-1727
SUNJET; Cyprus Airways in-flight magazine. (Text in English) 1973. q. $30. Action Publications Ltd., P.O. Box 4676, Nicosia, Cyprus. TEL 444104. FAX 450048. Ed. Tony Christodoulou. adv.; bk.rev. circ. 75,000.

052 053 054 SZ
SWISSAIR GAZETTE. (Text in English, French and German) m. 55 SFr. (Swissair AG) Airpage AG, Haldenstr. 65, CH-8045 Zurich, Switzerland. TEL 01-451-2920. FAX 01-451-2961. Ed. Viviane Egli. adv.: B&W page 25500 SFr., color page 30600 SFr.; trim 210 x 275; adv. contact: Peter Furrer. circ. 470,000. **Document type:** consumer publication.
Description: Airline publication devoted to news and features about Switzerland and other parts of the world. Also includes Swiss culture, travel, education, products, and hotel guide.

051 US ISSN 0039-8632
T W A AMBASSADOR. 1968. m. $36. (Trans World Airlines) T W A Ambassador Magazine, 274 Madison Ave., New York, NY 10016. TEL 212-532-3318. Ed. Joseph Manghise. adv.; bk.rev.; illus.; tr.lit. circ. 223,000. **Document type:** consumer publication.
Description: In-flight magazine for passengers on T.W.A., with articles on a variety of topics of interest to travelers.

917.204 MX
TRAVELERS GUIDE TO MEXICO. (Text in English) 1969. a. $17.95. Promociones de Mercados Turisticos, S.A. de C.V., Apdo. 6-1007, 06600 Mexico, D.F., Mexico. TEL 905-271-4736. FAX 905-272-5942. Ed. Wendy Luft; Pub. Chris Luhnow. adv. contact: Laily Ko. circ. 3,600,000.
Description: Guide book to Mexico placed in first class hotel rooms in major resorts and sold in the gift shops of these hotels. Contains color photos of Mexico's resorts, detailed city maps, and the latest information on traveling, vacationing and living in Mexico.

910.20 US
TRAVELHOST. 1968. m. Travelhost, Inc., 10701 N. Stemmons, Dallas, TX 75220. TEL 214-556-0541. Ed. Brenda Ondich; Pub. James E. Buerger. adv.: B&W page $29422, color page $36779; trim 8 x 10 3/4; adv. contact: Brad Calley. illus.; maps. circ. 761,674. **Document type:** consumer publication.
Description: Contains news features and general interest on travel, leisure, recreation, and business. Each of the 100 regional edition contains dining and entertainment guides and T.V. listings.

051 US ISSN 1055-5064
U S AIR MAGAZINE. 1973. m. $50. New York Times Custom Publishing, 590 Madison Ave., 32nd Fl., New York, NY 10022. TEL 212-745-6414. Ed. Terri Barnes. adv.: B&W page $20370, color page $28100; trim 8 x 10 7/8. bk.rev.; tr.lit. circ. 434,800. **Document type:** consumer publication.
Formerly (until 1979): Pace.

055.1 IT
ULISSE 2000; viaggi, costume, attualita. 1978. m. Alitalia Linee Aeree Italiane S.p.A., Via della Magliana 886, 00148 Rome, Italy. Ed. Marco Zanichelli. adv.: B&W page $9900. color page $11300; trim 8 1/8 x 10 3/4. illus. circ. 180,000.

917.1 CN ISSN 0228-698X
VOILA QUEBEC. (Text in English, French) 1975. q. single copies free. (Association Hoteliere de la Region de Quebec) Publications Vacances Quebec Inc., 185 St-Paul St., Quebec, PQ G1K 3W2, Canada. TEL 418-694-1272. FAX 418-694-0083. Ed. Jo Ouellet; Pub. Curtis J. Sommerville. adv.: B&W page Can.$3275, color page Can.$4095; trim 4 5/8 x 7 5/16; adv. contact: Curtis J. Sommerville. circ. 56,250. **Document type:** consumer publication.
Description: Informs visitors to Quebec of local historic and cultural sites of interest and provides a guide to the city's fine restaurants and shops.

052 US ISSN 1358-8907
VOYAGER; British Midland inflight magazine. 1990. bi-m. £20. (British Midland) Mediamark Publishing International Ltd., 35 Gresse St., Rathbone Pl., London W1P 1PN, England. TEL 0171-580-3105. FAX 0171-580-1695. Ed. Michael North; Pub. Peter Moore. **Document type:** consumer publication.

910.09 US
WEEKENDS (SOUTHPORT). 1992. bi-m. $10 per no. Weekends, Inc., 481 Bronson Rd., Southport, CT 06490. TEL 203-255-0064. Ed. Patricia Morgan; Pub. Douglas Chouteau. adv.: B&W page $1995, color page $2795; trim 8 3/8 x 10 7/8; adv. contact: Douglas Chouteau. bk.rev. circ. 250,000. **Document type:** consumer publication.
Formerly: Best Weekends.
Description: Discusses where to go and what to do for short vacations in eastern Canada and New England.

917.04 US ISSN 0192-4257
WELCOME TO MIAMI AND THE BEACHES. 1970. w. $35. Welcome Publications, Inc., Box 630518, Miami, FL 33163. TEL 305-944-9444. Ed. Mona K. Levine; Pub. Mona K. Levine. adv. contact: Alan Levine. circ. 25,500. **Document type:** consumer publication.
Description: Describes area shopping, dining, beaches, attractions, and points of interest.

051 US
WHERE ATLANTA. m. Where Magazines International (Atlanta), 180 Allen Rd., N. Bldg., Atlanta, GA 30328. TEL 404-843-9800. FAX 404-843-9070. Ed. Kathy Roberts; Pub. Tom Casey. adv.: B&W page $2310, color page $2760; trim 8 1/8 x 10 7/8; adv. contact: Carol Campbell. illus.; circ. 50,000 (controlled). **Document type:** consumer publication.
Description: Visitor's guide to Atlanta's dining, nightlife, entertainment and cultural attractions.

051 US
WHERE BOSTON.* m. Where Magazines International (Boston), 120 Boylston St., Fl. 3, Boston, MA 02116-4611. TEL 617-482-6777. FAX 617-482-3337. adv.: B&W page $3750, color page $4480; trim 8 1/8 x 10 7/8. illus.; circ. 60,000 (controlled). **Document type:** consumer publication.
Description: Guide to Boston's dining, entertainment, nightlife and other activities of interest to visitors.

TRAVEL AND TOURISM — AIRLINE INFLIGHT AND HOTEL INROOM

059.945 HU ISSN 1217-5714
WHERE BUDAPEST. 1993. m. (11/yr.) 1056 Budapest, Molnar u. 13 LL.11, Hungary. TEL 361-137-8758. (Canada addr.: 70 The Esplanade, Toronto, ON M5E 1R2, Canada) Ed. Charles Hebbert. adv.: B&W page $1694. circ. 30,000. **Document type:** consumer publication.
Description: Focuses on cultural events, festivals, folk dancing, restaurants, galleries, sightseeing and entertainment.

910.202 CN ISSN 1182-1981
WHERE CALGARY; visitors' magazine. 1981. m. Can.$20 (foreign Can.$25). Key West Publishers Ltd. (Subsidiary of: Where Magazines International), 125 Ninth Ave. S.E., Ste. 250, Calgary, AB T2G 0P6, Canada. TEL 403-299-1888. FAX 403-299-1899. Ed. Jennifer Mac Leod; Pub. Thomas Tait. adv.: B&W page Can.$1660, color page Can.$2010; trim 8 1/8 x 10 7/8; adv. contact: Kathryn Dixon. circ. 18,900 (controlled). **Document type:** consumer publication.
Formerly (until 1990): Key to Calgary (ISSN 0711-4400)
Description: Information and maps about things to see and do in Calgary.

051 US
WHERE CHICAGO. m. $30. Where Magazines International (Chicago), 1165 N. Clark St., Chicago, IL 60610-2845. TEL 312-642-1896. FAX 312-642-5467. Ed. Margaret Doyle; Pub. Christine Salmon. adv.; circ. 100,000 (controlled). **Document type:** consumer publication.
Description: Informs persons visiting Chicago of historic and cultural attractions and pprovides a guide to the city's restaurants and shops. Contains city maps.

051 CN
WHERE HALIFAX - DARTMOUTH. 1948. 10/yr. Can.$20 (foreign $22). Metro-Guide Publishing (Subsidiary of: Where Magazines International), Box 14, 5475 Spring Garden Rd., Halifax, NS B3J 3T2, Canada. TEL 902-420-9943. FAX 902-429-9058. Ed. Karen Janik; Pub. Bob LeBlanc. adv.: B&W page Can.$1305, color page Can.$1555; trim 5 1/2 x 8 3/8; adv. contact: Sheila Pottie. circ. 24,000 (controlled). **Document type:** consumer publication.
Description: Guide to shopping, sightseeing, dining and cultural events and activities for visitors to the Halifax Dartmouth area.

051 US
WHERE LOS ANGELES. m. Where Magazines International, 3733 Motor Ave., Ste. 301, Los Angeles, CA 90034-6403. TEL 310-280-2880. FAX 310-836-1803. adv.: B&W page $3480, color page $4095; trim 8 1/8 x 10 7/8. illus.; circ. 50,000 (controlled). **Document type:** consumer publication.
Description: Covers dining, entertainment, tourist and cultural activities for visitors to LA.

052 UK ISSN 0951-323X
WHERE MAGAZINE; your best guide to: shopping, dining, sightseeing and entertainment. 1975. m. £12 (foreign £24). Where Publications (Subsidiary of: Where Magazines International), 26-27 Market Place, London W1N 7AL, England. TEL 0171-436-5553. FAX 0171-436-4507. Ed. Mary Anne Evans; Pub. James Weymouth. adv. contact: Odeyne McGowan. circ. 60,000. **Document type:** consumer publication.
Formerly (until 1983): Where in London (ISSN 0143-2478)
Description: Guide to London for high-earning and free-spending visitors.

051 US
WHERE MINNEAPOLIS - ST. PAUL. 1962. m. $20. Where Magazines International (Minneapolis), 511 11th Ave. S., Ste. 261, Box 87, Minneapolis, MN 55415. TEL 612-339-1619. FAX 612-339-1848. Ed. Astrid Sandell; Pub. Brad Hughes. adv.: B&W page Can.$1440, color page $1800; trim 8 1/8 x 10 7/8; adv. contact: M. Kathryn Cashman. circ. 30,000 (controlled). **Document type:** consumer publication.

051 US
WHERE NEW ORLEANS. (Text in English, Spanish) 1968. m. $15 (free to hotel patrons). V.I.P. (Subsidiary of: Where Magazines International), 621 Decatur St., 2nd Fl., New Orleans, LA 70130. TEL 504-522-6468. FAX 504-522-0018. Ed. Linda Bays Powers. adv.: B&W page $2800, color page $3450; trim 8 1/8 x 10 7/8. circ. 70,000 (controlled). (back issues avail.) **Document type:** consumer publication.
Description: Contains information for visitors: maps, dining, shopping, special events, nightlife, arts and antiques, and points of interest.

051 US
WHERE NEW YORK. 1934. m. $39. Where Magazines International (New York), 600 Third Ave., 15th Fl., New York, NY 10016. TEL 212-687-4646. FAX 212-687-4661. Ed. Lois Anzelowitz-Tanner; Pub. Merrie Davis. adv.: B&W page $8835, color page $9455; trim 8 1/8 x 10 7/8. circ. 119,000 (controlled). **Document type:** consumer publication.
Description: Distributed to hotels, airline clubs, and university clubs for out-of-town visitors.

917 CN ISSN 1187-1350
WHERE OTTAWA - HULL. (Text in English, French) 1958. m. Can.$25. Capital Publishers (Subsidiary of: Where Magazines International), 400 Cumberland St., Ottawa, ON K1N 8X3, Canada. TEL 613-241-7888. FAX 613-241-3112. Ed. Marc Choma. adv.: B&W page Can.$2660, color page Can.$3275; trim 8 1/8 x 10 7/8. bk rev.; play rev.; circ. 32,000 (controlled). **Document type:** consumer publication.
Formerly: What's On - Voici Ottawa, Hull; What's On in Ottawa - Voici Ottawa (ISSN 0043-468X)
Description: For visitors to Canada's capital. Includes information on sightseeing, events, shopping and dining.

052 FR ISSN 1241-8625
WHERE PARIS. (Text in English) 1992. m. 175 F. (Europe 225 F., elsewhere 500 F.). (Subsidiary of: Where Magazines International), 5 rue La Boetie, 75008 Paris, France. TEL 44-56-31-96. FAX 42-66-49-11. Ed. Elisabeth Cherdel; pub. Kay Rolland. adv. contact: Kay Rolland. illus.; circ. 40,000 (controlled). **Document type:** consumer publication.

051 US
WHERE PHILADELPHIA. 1992. m. $19.95. South Jersey Publishing (Subsidiary of: Where Magazines International), 1000 W. Washington Ave., Box 2100, Pleasantville, NJ 08232. TEL 609-272-7918. FAX 609-272-7910. adv.: B&W page $1405, color page $1755; trim 8 1/8 x 10 7/8. circ. 25,000. **Document type:** consumer publication.

051 US
WHERE ST. LOUIS. m. free to hotel patrons. Where Magazines International (St. Louis), 1750 S. Brentwood Blvd., Ste. 311, St. Louis, MO 63144. TEL 314-968-4940. FAX 314-968-0813. adv.: B&W page $1930, color page $2310; trim 8 1/8 x 10 7/8. illus.; circ. 32,000 (controlled). **Document type:** consumer publication.
Description: Visitor's guide to dining, entertainment, tourist and cultural attractions of the St. Louis area.

051 US
WHERE SAN FRANCISCO. 1992. m. $30. Where Magazines International (San Francisco), 74 New Montgomery St., Ste. 320, San Francisco, CA 94105. TEL 415-546-6101. FAX 415-546-6108. Ed. Bonnie Wach. adv.: B&W page $2875; color page $3470; trim 8 1/8 x 10 7/8. circ. 57,000 (controlled). **Document type:** consumer publication.
Description: Highlights restaurants, shopping, entertainment, nightlife, and cultural attractions in the city and its environs for visitors to San Francisco and the Bay Area.

052 CN ISSN 0849-1135
WHERE TORONTO. 1954. m. Can.$30. Key Publishers Co. Ltd. (Subsidiary of: Where Magazines International), 6 Church St., Toronto, ON M5E 1M1, Canada. TEL 416-364-3333. FAX 416-594-3375. Ed. Jacquelyn Waller-Vintar; Pub. Giorgina Bigioni. adv.: B&W page Can.$4320, color page Can.$5250; trim 8 1/8 x 10 7/8; adv. contact: June Dickenson. illus.; circ. 79,000 (controlled). **Document type:** consumer publication.
Formerly: Key to Toronto (ISSN 0023-0863)

052 CN ISSN 1180-9671
WHERE VANCOUVER. 1969. m. Where Canada, Inc. (Subsidiary of: Where Magazines International), The Sixth Estate, 2208 Spruce St., Vancouver, BC V6H 2P3, Canada. TEL 604-736-5586. FAX 604-736-3465. E-mail: 766312,716@compuserve.com. Ed. Louise Whitney; Pub. Peggie Terry. adv.: B&W page Can.$1880, color page Can.$2235; trim 8 1/8 x 10 7/8; adv. contact: Penny Christie. circ. 38,938 (controlled). **Document type:** consumer publication.
Former titles (until 1990): Key to Vancouver (ISSN 0829-0601); (until 1983): Vancouver Guideline (ISSN 0715-6715)

052 CN ISSN 1182-0705
WHERE VICTORIA. 1977. m. Key Pacific Publishers Co. Ltd. (Subsidiary of: Where Magazines International), 1001 Wharf St., 3rd Fl., Victoria, BC V8W 1T6, Canada. TEL 604-388-4324. FAX 604-388-6166. Ed. Kirsten Meincke. adv.: B&W page Can.$1920, color page Can.$2140; trim 8 1/8 x 10 7/8; adv. contact: Debbie McLean. circ. 22,000 (controlled). **Document type:** consumer publication.
Former titles (until 1990): Key to Victoria (ISSN 0829-7150); (until 1984): Victoria Guideline (ISSN 0715-6723)
Description: Current events, shopping and dining information for visitors.

051 US
WHERE WASHINGTON, DC. 1965. m. $36 (foreign $72). Where Magazines International (Washington, DC), 1625 K St., N.W., Ste. 1290, Washington, DC 20006. TEL 202-463-4550. FAX 202-463-4553. (Addr. in Canada: Where Magazines International, 70 The Esplanade, 4th Fl., Toronto, ON M5E 1R2, Canada) Ed. Colleen Grewing; Pub. Christine Allegro. adv.: B&W page $4180, color page $5020; trim 8 1/8 x 10 7/8; adv. contact: Christine Allegro. illus.; circ. 90,000 (controlled). **Document type:** consumer publication.
Description: Covers dining, entertainment, tourist and cultural attractions of interest to visitors to Washington, DC. Provides maps.

917.1 CN ISSN 0847-8511
WHERE WINNIPEG. 1985. 6/yr. Can.$16.05 (foreign Can.$21.05). Where Magazines International (Winnipeg), 128 James Ave., Ste. 300, Winnipeg, MB R3B 0N8, Canada. TEL 204-943-4439. FAX 204-947-5463. Ed. Alison Kirkland. adv.: B&W page Can.$2033, color page Can.$2541.25; trim 8 1/8 x 10 7/8. illus.; circ. 32,000 controlled. **Document type:** consumer publication.
Formerly (until 1989): Key to Winnipeg (ISSN 0834-3314)

052 059.956 JA ISSN 0387-8406
WINDS. (Text in English, Japanese) 1979. m. 6000 Yen($31) (Japan Air Lines Co. Ltd.) Emphasis, Inc., Central Roppongi Bldg., 1-4-27 Roppongi, Minato-ku, Tokyo 106, Japan. FAX 03-3585-1596. Ed. Tom Chapman. adv. circ. 490,000. **Document type:** consumer publication.
Description: Inflight magazine of Japan Air Lines.

052 MY ISSN 0126-5393
WINGS OF GOLD. 1975. m. $48. Malaysia Airlines, Corporate Communications Department, 32nd Fl., MAS Bldg., Jalan Sultan Ismail, 50250 Kuala Lumpur, Malaysia. TEL 6-03-265-5038. FAX 6-03-263-3178. Ed. Khalilah Talha. adv.; bk.rev. circ. 600,000.
Description: Contains general interest articles on travel business in Malaysia.

910.202 NP
YETI. 2/yr. Royal Nepal Airlines, Public Relations & Publicity Service, Kanti Path, Kathmandu, Nepal. Ed. I.K. Pradhan. adv. circ. 20,000.

387.7 CC
ZHONGGUO MINHANG/C A A C INFLIGHT MAGAZINE. (Text in Chinese, English, Japanese) 1982. bi-m. free. Zhongguo Minhang Xuanchuan Guanggao Gongsi - Civil Aviation and Administration of China, Publicity and Advertising Corp., No. 4, Bldg. 47, Tongfu Jiadao, Dengshi Dongkou, Beijing 100006, People's Republic of China. Ed. An Shiqin. adv. circ. 150,000. **Document type:** consumer publication.

TRUCKS AND TRUCKING

see Transportation–Trucks and Trucking

UROLOGY AND NEPHROLOGY

see Medical Sciences–Urology and Nephrology

VETERINARY SCIENCE

636.089   AT   ISSN 1034-9219
A A H L BIENNIAL REPORT. biennial. Australian Animal Health Laboratory, P.O. Bag 24, Geelong, Vic. 3220, Australia. TEL 61-52-275000. FAX 61-52-275555. E-mail: aahl@aahl.dah.csiro.au. Ed. Niall Byrne.

636.089   AT
A A H L NEWSLETTER. irreg. Australian Animal Health Laboratory, P.O. Bag 24, Geelong, Vic. 3220, Australia. TEL 61-52-275000. FAX 61-52-275555. E-mail: aahl@aahl.dah.csiro.au. Ed. Niall Byrne. Document type: newsletter.

636.089   AT   ISSN 0811-6997
A V A NEWS. 1977. m. Aus.$160. Australian Veterinary Association, 134-136 Hampden Rd., Artarmon, N.S.W. 2064, Australia. TEL 61-2-422-2733. FAX 61-2-411-5089. Ed. S. Andrew. circ. 4,000. Document type: newsletter.
Formerly (until 1982): A V A Newsletter (ISSN 0155-7173)

636.089   US
A V E A NEWSLETTER.* 1936. q. membership. American Veterinary Exhibitors Association, 106 W. 11th St., Ste. 1600, Kansas City, MO 64105-1806. TEL 805-683-0489. Ed. Fred Hamlin. circ. 200. (tabloid format) Document type: newsletter.
Description: Concerns exhibiting at veterinary conventions.

636.089   FR   ISSN 0001-4192
CODEN: BAVFAV
ACADEMIE VETERINAIRE DE FRANCE. BULLETIN. 1844. 4/yr. 660 F. (effective 1994). Academie Veterinaire de France, 60, blvd. Latour-Maubourg, 75007 Paris, France. FAX 20-87-79-06. TELEX 820 187 F. Ed. Marc V. Catsaras. adv.; bk.rev.; abstr.; bibl.; charts; illus.stat.; index. circ. 800. Indexed: Anim.Breed.Abstr., Biol.Abstr., Biotech.Abstr., Chem.Abstr., Curr.Adv.Ecol.Sci., Curr.Cont., Dairy Sci.Abstr., Food Sci.& Tech.Abstr., Helminthol.Abstr., Ind.Vet., Nutr.Abstr., Poult.Abstr., Rev.Plant Path., Vet.Bull. Document type: bulletin.
—BLDSC (2378.000000); CASDDS; Faxon; SWETS.

636.089   PL   ISSN 0860-2840
CODEN: AAAVEZ
ACTA ACADEMIAE AGRICULTURAE AC TECHNICAE OLSTENENSIS. VETERINARIA/AGRICULTURAL AND TECHNICAL ACADEMY IN OLSZTYN. VETERINARY MEDICINE. (Supplement avail.: Veterinary Science) (Text in Polish; summaries in English, Polish) 1972. irreg. price varies. (Akademia Rolniczo-Techniczna im. M. Oczapowskiego) Wydawnictwo A R T Olsztyn, Blok 12, 10-957 Olsztyn-Kortowo, Poland. TEL 48-89-273310. TELEX 0526419. E-mail: artbib@mrowka.art.olsztyn.pl. (Dist. by: Ars Polona-Ruch, Krakowskie Przedmiescie 7, 00-901 Warsaw, Poland. TEL 48-22-265334) illus.; charts; bibl.; illus.; circ. 130 (controlled). Indexed: Chem.Abstr., Curr.Cont., Dairy Sci.Abstr., Ind.Vet., Pig News & Info., Ref.Zh., Vet.Bull. Document type: academic/scholarly publication.
—CASDDS.
Formerly: Akademia Rolniczo-Techniczna. Zeszyty Naukowe. Weterynaria (ISSN 0324-9220)

636.089   IT   ISSN 0001-6136
CODEN: AMVEAX
ACTA MEDICA VETERINARIA. (Text in Italian; summaries in English, French, German and Spanish) 1955. bi-m. $10. Facolta di Medicina Veterinaria, Via Veterinaria 1, 80137 Naples, Italy. bk.rev.; charts; illus.; tr.lit.; index. Indexed: Anim.Breed.Abstr., Biol.Abstr., Chem.Abstr., Dairy Sci.Abstr., Excerp.Med., Food Sci.& Tech.Abstr., Herb.Abstr., Ind.Med., Ind.Vet., Nutr.Abstr., Pig News & Info., Protozool.Abstr., Rev.Med.& Vet.Mycol., Small Anim.Abstr., Vet.Bull.
—BLDSC (0635.500000); CASDDS.

636.08   SP   ISSN 0214-039X
ACTA VETERINARIA. 1987. a. 2000 ptas. Universidad de Extremadura, Servicio de Publicaciones, Ctra. de Trujillo, s-n, 10071 Caceres, Spain.

636.089   XR   ISSN 0001-7213
CODEN: ACVTB9
ACTA VETERINARIA BRNO. (Text in English; summaries in Czech, English, Russian) 1922. q. $80. Vysoka Skola Veterinarni, Brno, Palackiho 1-3, 612 42 Brno, Czech Republic. TEL 42-5-41321107. FAX 42-5-4121151. Ed. Ed. Baranyiova. bk.rev.; bibl.; charts; illus.; index. cum.index. circ. 500. Indexed: Anim.Breed.Abstr., Apic.Abstr., Biol.Abstr., Chem.Abstr., Curr.Adv.Ecol.Sci., Curr.Cont., Dairy Sci.Abstr., Excerp.Med., Food Sci.& Tech.Abstr., Helminthol.Abstr., Ind.Vet., Nutr.Abstr., Pig News & Info., Poult.Abstr., Protozool.Abstr., Sci.Cit.Ind, Sport Fish.Abstr., Vet.Bull., Wild.Rev., Zoo.Rec. Document type: academic/scholarly publication.
—BLDSC (0670.890000); CASDDS; Genuine Article; UnCover.
Formerly: Acta Universitatis Agriculturae. Facultas Veterinaria: Rada B.
Description: Publishes original research articles in basic and applied veterinary sciences and medicine, including food hygiene.
Refereed Serial

636.089   HU   ISSN 0236-6290
CODEN: AVHUEA
ACTA VETERINARIA HUNGARICA. (Text in English) 1951. q. $84 (effective 1992). (Magyar Tudomanyos Akademia) Akademiai Kiado, Publishing House of the Hungarian Academy of Sciences, P.O. Box 245, H-1519 Budapest, Hungary. TEL 181-2134. FAX 166-6466. TELEX 22-6228 AKNYO H. Eds. J. Meszaros, A. Szekely. adv.; bk.rev.; bibl.; charts; illus.; index. Indexed: Anim.Breed.Abstr., ASCA, Biol.Abstr., Biotech.Abstr., Chem.Abstr., Curr.Adv.Ecol.Sci., Curr.Cont., Dairy Sci.Abstr., Excerp.Med., Helminthol.Abstr., Ind.Med., Ind.Vet., INIS Atomind., Nutr.Abstr., Pig News & Info., Poult.Abstr., Protozool.Abstr., Rev.Plant Path., Sci.Cit.Ind., Soils & Fert., Vet.Bull. Document type: academic/scholarly publication.
—BLDSC (0670.980000); CASDDS; Faxon; Genuine Article. CCC.
Formerly (until 1982): Academiae Scientiarum Hungaricae. Acta Veterinaria (ISSN 0001-7205)
Description: Publishes studies concerned with research on morphology, physiology, biochemistry, microbiology, immunology, reproduction biology and clinical veterinary medicine, etiology, pathogenesis, diagnostics and control of infectious, parasitic and metabolic diseases.

636.089   DK   ISSN 0044-605X
CODEN: AVSCA7
ACTA VETERINARIA SCANDINAVICA. (Supplement avail. (ISSN 0065-1699) (Text in English; summaries in Danish and English) 1959. q. DKK 950 (incl. supplements). (Societatum Veteranariarum Scandanivacarum) Danske Dyrlaegeforening, Rosenlunds Alle 8, DK 2720 Vanloese, Denmark. TEL 45-38-71-08-88. FAX 45-38-71-03-22. Ed. Dr. J.F. Agger. bibl.; charts; illus. Indexed: Anim.Breed.Abstr., Biol.Abstr., Biotech.Abstr., Chem.Abstr., Curr.Adv.Ecol.Sci., Curr.Cont., Dairy Sci.Abstr., Excerp.Med., Food Sci.& Tech.Abstr., Helminthol.Abstr., Ind.Med., Ind.Sci.Rev., Ind.Vet., INIS Atomind., Nutr.Abstr., Pig News & Info., Poult.Abstr., Protozool.Abstr., Rev.Plant Path., Sci.Cit.Ind., Small Anim.Abstr., Soils & Fert., Sport Fish.Abstr., Triticale Abstr., Vet.Bull., Wild.Rev., Zoo.Rec. Document type: academic/scholarly publication.
—BLDSC (0671.300000); CASDDS; Faxon; SWETS; UnCover.

636.089   DK   ISSN 0065-1699
SF604   CODEN: AVSPAC
ACTA VETERINARIA SCANDINAVICA. SUPPLEMENTUM. (Text in English, French or German; summaries in English and German) 1961. irreg. DKK 950 (incl. main vols.). (Societatum Veteranariarum Scandanivacarum) Danske Dyrlaegeforening, Rosenlunds Alle 8, DK-2720 Vanloese, Denmark. TEL 45-38-71-08-88. FAX 45-38-71-03-22. Ed. Dr. J.F. Agger. Indexed: Biol.Abstr., Dairy Sci.Abstr., Food Sci.& Tech.Abstr., Ind.Vet., INIS Atomind., Nutr.Abstr., Zoo.Rec. Document type: academic/scholarly publication.
—BLDSC (0671.301000); SWETS; UnCover.

ACTA ZOOLOGICA ET PATHOLOGICA ANTVERPIENSIA.
see BIOLOGY — Zoology

636.089   MX
ACTUALIDAD VETERINARIA. 1976. 6/yr. Via Gustavo Baz No. 118, Bosques de Echegaray, Naucalpan, Edo. de Mexico, Mexico. Ed. Alfonso Ortega Said. circ. 5,000.

ADELAIDE. INSTITUTE OF MEDICAL AND VETERINARY SCIENCE. ANNUAL REPORT OF THE COUNCIL. see MEDICAL SCIENCES

636.089   US   ISSN 1041-7826
ADVANCES IN SMALL ANIMAL MEDICINE AND SURGERY; a monthly review of current developments in veterinary medicine. 1988. m. $90 (foreign $125) (effective 1996). W.B. Saunders Co. (Subsidiary of: Harcourt Brace & Company), Curtis Center, 3rd Fl., Indepencence Sq. W., Philadelphia, PA 19106-3399. TEL 215-238-7800. FAX 215-238-6445. (Subscr. to: Periodicals Fulfillment, W.B. Saunders Co., 6277 Sea Harbor Dr., 4th Fl., Orlando, FL 32891-4800. TEL 800-654-2452. FAX 800-874-6418) Ed. Dr. Rhea V. Morgan. Document type: newsletter, abstracting/indexing.
—UMI. CCC.
Description: Provides insight into specific topics and allows veterinarians and veterinary technicians apply new tests and treatments in their practices. Abstracts material from recent publications and presentations.
Refereed Serial

636.089   UK
ADVANCES IN VETERINARY DERMATOLOGY. irreg., vol.2, 1993. price varies. Elsevier Science Ltd., Books Division, P.O. Box 800, Kidlington, Oxford OX5 1DX, England. TEL 44-1865-843000. FAX 44-1865-843010. E-mail: nlinfo-f@elsevier.nl; usinfo-f@elsevier.com; forinfo-kyf04035@niftyserve.or.jp; Site addr.: http://www.elsevier.nl/. (Subscr. in U.S. and Canada to: Elsevier Science, 660 White Plains Rd., Tarrytown, NY 10591-5153. TEL 914-524-9200. FAX 914-333-2444) Document type: proceedings.
Refereed Serial

636.089   GW   ISSN 0301-2794
CODEN: AVYMAX
ADVANCES IN VETERINARY MEDICINE/FORTSCHRITTE DER VETERINAERMEDIZIN. (Supplement to: Advances in Veterinary Medicine, Series A, Anatomia; Serie B, Histologia; and Series C, Embryologia) 1958. irreg. price varies. Verlag Paul Parey (Berlin), Seelbuschring 9-17, 12105 Berlin, Germany. TEL 030-70784-0. FAX 030-70784199. bibl.; illus.; index. Indexed: Biol.Abstr., Chem.Abstr., Excerp.Med., Food Sci.& Tech.Abstr., Ind.Sci.Rev., Ind.Vet., Sci.Cit.Ind., Small Anim.Abstr., Vet.Bull. Document type: academic/scholarly publication.
—CASDDS.

636.089   US   ISSN 0065-3519
SF745   CODEN: AVSCB8
ADVANCES IN VETERINARY SCIENCE AND COMPARATIVE MEDICINE. 1953. irreg., vol.36, 1991. Academic Press, Inc., 525 B St., Ste. 1900, San Diego, CA 92101-4495. TEL 619-231-0926. FAX 619-699-6715. (Subscr. to: Order Dept., 6277 Sea Harbor Dr., 4th Fl., Orlando, FL 32887. TEL 800-321-5068) Eds. Charles E. Cornelius, Charles F. Simpson. index. (reprint service avail. from ISI) Indexed: Anim.Breed.Abstr., Biol.Abstr., Biotech.Abstr., Dairy Sci.Abstr., Dent.Ind., Excerp.Med., Helminthol.Abstr., Ind.Med., Ind.Sci.Rev., Ind.Vet., Nutr.Abstr., Pig News & Info., Protozool.Abstr., Sci.Cit.Ind., Vet.Bull. Document type: monographic series.
—BLDSC (0711.820000); CASDDS; Faxon; UnCover. CCC.
Refereed Serial

VETERINARY SCIENCE

636.089 US ISSN 0745-452X
AGRI-PRACTICE; the journal of medicine and surgery for the food animal practitioner. 1980. 10/yr. $38 (Canada and Mexico $45; elsewhere $50) (effective 1996). Veterinary Practice Publishing Co., 7 Ashley Ave. S., Santa Barbara, CA 93103-9989. TEL 805-965-1028. FAX 805-965-0722. (Subscr. addr.: Box 4457, Santa Barbara, CA 93140-4457) Ed.Bd. adv.; bk.rev.; abstr.; charts; illus.; stat.; tr.lit.; index. circ. 5,500. (also avail. in microform from UMI; reprint service avail. from UMI) **Indexed:** Anim.Breed.Abstr., Curr.Adv.Ecol.Sci., Dairy Sci.Abstr., Ind.Vet., Pig News & Info., Rev.Med.& Vet.Mycol., Vet.Bull. **Document type:** academic/scholarly publication.
—BLDSC (0764.155000); Faxon; Genuine Article; SWETS; UMI; UnCover.
Formerly (until 1982): Bovine Practice (ISSN 0199-5456)
Description: Devoted to food animals, including cattle and swine, with topics important to the food animal practitioner.
Refereed Serial

AGROTROPICA. see *AGRICULTURE*

636.089 PL ISSN 0137-1975
CODEN: ZNRWA9
AKADEMIA ROLNICZA WE WROCLAWIU. ZESZYTY NAUKOWE. WETERYNARIA. (Subseries of: Akademia Rolnicza we Wroclawiu. Zeszyty Naukowe (ISSN 0867-7964)) 1955. irreg. price varies. Akademia Rolnicza we Wroclawiu, Ul. Norwida 25, 50-375 Wroclaw, Poland. FAX 48-71-229576. (Subscr. to: Dzial Wydawnictw i Poligrafii Akademii Rolniczej, ul. Sopocka 23, 50-344 Wroclaw, Poland. TEL 48-71-211277) circ. 350. **Document type:** academic/scholarly publication.
—CASDDS.
Formerly (until 1973): Wyzsza Szkola Rolnicza we Wroclawiu. Zeszyty Naukowe. Weterynaria (ISSN 0520-9315)

590 636.089 IT
ALLEVATORE. 1945. w. L.40000. Associazione Italiana Allevatori - Italian Breeders' Association, Via A. Torlonia 15 A, 00161 Rome, Italy. TEL 39-6-8550207. Ed. Fortunato Tirelli. adv.: color page L.2400000. circ. 76,000.

636.089 US ISSN 0164-1999
SF605 CODEN: SPAHDN
AMERICAN ANIMAL HOSPITAL ASSOCIATION. ANNUAL MEETING SCIENTIFIC PROCEEDINGS. a. $42 to non-members. American Animal Hospital Association, Box 150899, Denver, CO 80215-0899. TEL 303-986-2800. FAX 303-986-1700. **Document type:** proceedings.
—CASDDS.

636.089 US ISSN 0587-2871
SF601 CODEN: JAAHBL
AMERICAN ANIMAL HOSPITAL ASSOCIATION JOURNAL.
Key Title: Journal of the American Animal Hospital Association. 1965. bi-m. $97 (foreign $110). American Animal Hospital Association, Box 150899, Denver, CO 80215-0899. TEL 303-986-2800. FAX 303-986-1700. Ed. Dr. Janis Cleland. adv.; bk.rev.; abstr.; charts; illus.; tr.lit. circ. 12,500. (also avail. in microform from UMI; reprint service avail. from UMI) **Indexed:** Anim.Breed.Abstr., Biol.Abstr., Biol.& Agr.Ind., Chem.Abstr, Curr.Cont., Excerpt.Med., Helminthol.Abstr., Ind.Sci.Rev., Ind.Vet., Protozool.Abstr., Rev.Med.& Vet.Mycol., Rev.Plant Path., Small Anim.Abstr., Vet.Bull.
—BLDSC (4683.790000); CASDDS; Faxon; Genuine Article; SWETS; UMI; UnCover.
Formerly: American Animal Hospital Association Bulletin (ISSN 0002-7251)
Description: Clinical manuscripts relating to animal care.
Refereed Serial

636.089 US ISSN 0065-7182
AMERICAN ASSOCIATION OF EQUINE PRACTITIONERS. PROCEEDINGS OF THE ANNUAL CONVENTION. 2nd convention, 1956. a. $35 for members; non-members $70. American Association of Equine Practitioners, 4075 Iron Works Rd., Lexington, KY 40511-8434. TEL 606-233-0147. FAX 606-233-1968. Ed. Linda Caddel. circ. 6,000. (also avail. in microform from UMI; back issues avail.) **Indexed:** Helminthol.Abstr., Ind.Vet., Vet.Bull. **Document type:** proceedings.
—BLDSC (6840.585000); UMI.

636.08 US
AMERICAN ASSOCIATION OF ZOO VETERINARIANS. ANNUAL PROCEEDINGS. 1968. a. $45 per issue (typically set in Oct.). American Association of Zoo Veterinarians, 3400 W. Girard Ave., Philadelphia, PA 19104-1196. TEL 215-387-9094. FAX 215-387-2165. circ. 1,250. (back issues avail.) **Indexed:** Sport Fish.Abstr., Wild.Rev., Zoo.Rec. **Document type:** proceedings.
Description: Covers zoo and wildlife veterinary medicine.

636.089 US ISSN 0894-7708
CODEN: PAVME6
AMERICAN COLLEGE OF VETERINARY INTERNAL MEDICINE. PROCEEDINGS. 1983. a. $45 (foreign $50). American College of Veterinary Internal Medicine, 7175 W. Jefferson Ave., Ste. 2125, Lakewood, CA 80235-2320. TEL 303-980-7136. FAX 303-980-7137. Ed. Robert DeNovo. adv. contact: June Johnson. (back issues avail.) **Document type:** proceedings.
—BLDSC (6842.444000).
Description: Covers topics in internal medicine, cardiology, oncology, neurology, nutrition, clinical pathology, comparative endocrinology, comparative gastroenterology, urology and nephrology, and liver study.

636.089 US
AMERICAN FUND FOR ALTERNATIVES TO ANIMAL RESEARCH. NEWS ABSTRACTS. 1977. 3/yr. $15 to individuals; students and seniors $10 (effective 1995). American Fund for Alternatives to Animal Research, 175 W. 12th St., Apt. 16G, New York, NY 10011-8275. TEL 212-989-8073. Ed. Ethel Thurston. adv.; bk.rev. circ. 7,000. (back issues avail.) **Document type:** bulletin, newsletter.
Description: Provides finance for scientific programs to develop or teach alternatives to animals in research, testing, validation and education.

636.7 US
AMERICAN HEARTWORM SOCIETY. BULLETIN. 1974. q. $30. American Heartworm Society, 161 S. Lincolnway, Ste. 302, N. Aurora, IL 60542. TEL 708-844-9676. Ed. Dr. Mark D. Soll. adv. circ. 1,200. **Document type:** bulletin.
Description: Keeping up on current research and commercial development on the prevention and treatment of heartworm disease in dogs.

636.089 US ISSN 1053-5608
SF992.H4
AMERICAN HEARTWORM SOCIETY. SYMPOSIUM PROCEEDINGS. 1977. triennial. price varies. American Heartworm Society, 161 S. Lincolnway, Ste. 302, N. Aurora, IL 60542. TEL 708-844-9676. **Document type:** proceedings.

636.087 US
AMERICAN HOLISTIC VETERINARY MEDICAL ASSOCIATION. JOURNAL. 1982. q. $50 membership. American Holistic Veterinary Medical Association, 2214 Old Emmorton Rd., Bel Air, MD 21015. TEL 410-569-0695. FAX 410-515-7774. Ed. Carvel G. Tiekert. adv.: page $165. bk.rev. circ. 800.
Formerly (until Sep. 1989): American Holistic Veterinary Medical Association. Newsletter.
Description: Promotes natural healing, preventive health care, nutrition and avoidance of drugs and medication.

636.089 US ISSN 0002-9645
SF601 CODEN: AJVRAH
AMERICAN JOURNAL OF VETERINARY RESEARCH. 1940. m. $165 (foreign $175). American Veterinary Medical Association, 1931 N. Meacham Rd., Ste. 100, Schaumburg, IL 60173-4360. TEL 708-925-8070. FAX 708-925-1329. Ed. Dr. Albert Koltveit. adv.; bk.rev.; charts; illus.; stat.; index. circ. 7,000. (also avail. in microform from UMI,PMC) **Indexed:** Anim.Breed.Abstr., Biol.Abstr., Biol.& Agr.Ind, Biotech.Abstr., Chem.Abstr., Curr.Adv.Cancer Res., Curr.Adv.Ecol.Sci., Curr.Cont., Dairy Sci.Abstr., Dent.Ind., Diar.Dis.Res., Excerpt.Med., Food Sci.& Tech.Abstr., Helminthol.Abstr., Herb.Abstr., Ind.Med., Ind.Sci.Rev., Ind.Vet., INIS Atomind., Maize Abstr., Nutr.Abstr., Pig News & Info., Poult.Abstr., Protozool.Abstr., Rev.Appl.Entomol., Rev.Med.& Vet.Mycol., Sci.Cit.Ind, Small Anim.Abstr., Sport Fish.Abstr., Vet.Bull., Weed Abstr., Wild.Rev., Zoo.Rec. **Document type:** academic/scholarly publication.
—BLDSC (0840.000000); CASDDS; Faxon; Genuine Article; SWETS; UMI; UnCover.
Refereed Serial

AMERICAN LARYNGOLOGICAL ASSOCIATION. TRANSACTIONS. see *MEDICAL SCIENCES — Otorhinolaryngology*

636.089 US ISSN 0066-1147
SF611
AMERICAN VETERINARY MEDICAL ASSOCIATION. DIRECTORY. 1920. a. $90 (foreign $105). American Veterinary Medical Association, 1931 N. Meacham Rd., Ste. 100, Schaumburg, IL 60173-4360. TEL 708-925-8070. FAX 708-925-1329. Ed. Mrs. J. La Frana. adv. circ. 57,000. **Indexed:** Curr.Adv.Ecol.Sci., SRI. **Document type:** directory.

636.089 US ISSN 0003-1488
SF601 CODEN: JAVMA4
AMERICAN VETERINARY MEDICAL ASSOCIATION. JOURNAL. 1877. s-m. $120 (foreign $140). American Veterinary Medical Association, 1931 N. Meacham Rd., Ste. 100, Schaumburg, IL 60173-4360. TEL 708-925-8070. FAX 708-925-1329. Ed. Dr. Albert J. Koltveit. adv.; bk.rev.; charts; illus.; s-a. index. circ. 57,000. (also avail. in microform from UMI; microfiche from BHP) **Indexed:** Anim.Breed.Abstr., Biol.Abstr., Biol.& Agr.Ind., Biotech.Abstr., Chem.Abstr., Curr.Adv.Cancer Res., Curr.Cont., Dairy Sci.Abstr., Dent.Ind., Excerpt.Med., Food Sci.& Tech.Abstr., Helminthol.Abstr., Herb.Abstr., Ind.Med., Ind.Vet., INIS Atomind., Nutr.Abstr., Pig News & Info., Poult.Abstr., Protozool.Abstr., Rev.Appl.Entomol., Rev.Med.& Vet.Mycol., Rev.Plant Path., Small Anim.Abstr., Soils & Fert., Sport Fish.Abstr., SRI, Vet.Bull., Wild.Rev., World Agri.Econ.& Rural Sociol.Abstr., Zoo.Rec. **Document type:** academic/scholarly publication.
—BLDSC (4695.000000); CASDDS; Faxon; Genuine Article; SWETS; UMI; UnCover.
Refereed Serial

636.089 AG ISSN 0365-5148
CODEN: ANVTAH
ANALECTA VETERINARIA. (Text in Spanish; summaries in English, French or German) 1969. 3/yr. $21. Universidad Nacional de la Plata, Facultad de Ciencias Veterinarias, Calle 60 y 118, 1900 La Plata, Argentina. circ. 800. (back issues avail.) **Indexed:** Biol.Abstr., Chem.Abstr., Food Sci.& Tech.Abstr., Ind.Vet., Vet.Bull.
—CASDDS.

636.089 SP ISSN 0213-5434
CODEN: AVMAE9
ANALES DE VETERINARIA DE MURCIA. (Text in Spanish and English) 1985. a. 1500 ptas. Universidad de Murcia, Secretariado de Publicaciones e Intercambio Cientifico, Santo Cristo, 1, 30001 Murcia, Spain. TEL 3468-363012. FAX 3468-363414. Ed. Antonio Martinez. bk.rev.; abstr. circ. 300. **Document type:** academic/scholarly publication.
Description: Contains original research and advances in all fields of veterinary science.

VETERINARY SCIENCE

636.089   GW   ISSN 0340-2096
CODEN: AHEMA5
ANATOMIA, HISTOLOGIA, EMBRYOLOGIA. (Supplement avail.: Advances in Veterinary Medicine) (Text in English and German) 1972. q. DM.412($305) to individuals in Europe (rest of world DM.435($322)); institutions in Europe DM.808($599) (rest of world DM.831($616)) (effective 1996). (World Association of Veterinary Anatomists) Blackwell Wissenschaft, Kurfuerstendamm 57, 10707 Berlin, Germany. TEL 030-32790623.
FAX 030-32790610. Eds. J. Breazile, F. Sinowatz. adv.: B&W page DM.560; trim 202 x 122. bk.rev.; illus.; stat. (back issues avail.) **Indexed:** Biol.Abstr., Biotech.Abstr., Curr.Adv.Ecol.Sci., Curr.Cont., Dairy Sci.Abstr., Dent.Ind., Excerp.Med., Helminthol.Abstr., Ind.Med., Ind.Vet., Nutr.Abstr., Sci.Cit.Ind., Sport Fish.Abstr., Vet.Bull., Zoo.Rec. **Document type:** academic/scholarly publication.
—BLDSC (0897.960000); Faxon; Genuine Article; SWETS. **CCC.**
  Formerly (until 1973): Zentralblatt fuer Veterinaermedizin. Reihe C: Anatomia, Histologia, Embryologica (ISSN 0300-8649)
  Description: Anatomical, histological and embryological investigations involving human, veterinary and zoological studies.

ANIMAL BEHAVIOUR. see BIOLOGY — Zoology

ANIMAL FEED SCIENCE AND TECHNOLOGY; an international scientific journal. see AGRICULTURE — Feed, Flour And Grain

636.089   US
ANIMAL FEEDING AND NUTRITION. 1977. irreg., vol.11, 1990. Academic Press, Inc., 525 B St., Ste. 1900, San Diego,CA 92101-4495. TEL 619-231-6616. FAX 619-699-6715. (Subscr. to: Order Dept., 6277 Sea Harbor Dr., 4th Fl., Orlando, FL 32887. TEL 800-321-5068) Ed. Tony J. Cunha. (back issues avail.) **Document type:** monographic series.
  Refereed Serial

636.089   UG
ANIMAL HEALTH RESEARCH CENTRE. ANNUAL REPORT. (Text in English) a. Animal Health Research Centre, Box 24, Entebbe, Uganda. **Indexed:** Rev.Appl.Entomol.

636.089   UK   ISSN 0142-6591
ANIMAL HEALTH TRUST. ANNUAL REPORT. 1963. a. £4.50. Animal Health Trust, P.O. Box 5, Newmarket, Suffolk CB8 7DW, England. TEL 01638-66111. FAX 01638-665789. TELEX 818418 ANHLTH G. (And: 122 E. 55th St., New York, NY 10022) Ed. Phil Spiby. adv.; bk.rev.; charts; illus.; index. circ. 3,500. **Indexed:** Biol.Abstr. **Document type:** corporate report.
  Formerly: Animal Health (ISSN 0003-3502)

636.089   UN   ISSN 0066-1872
ANIMAL HEALTH YEARBOOK. (Text in English, French and Spanish) 1957. a. $55. Food and Agriculture Organization of the United Nations, c/o UNIPUB, 4611-F Assembly Dr., Lanham, MD 20706-4391. TEL 301-459-7666. FAX 301-459-0056. (also avail. in microfiche from CIS) **Indexed:** Dairy Sci.Abstr., Helminthol.Abstr., IIS, Nutr.Abstr.
—BLDSC (0904.010000).

ANIMAL HUSBANDRY AND BREEDING. see AGRICULTURE — Poultry And Livestock

636.089   UK   ISSN 0262-2238
ANIMAL PHARM; world animal health and nutrition news. 1982. 2/m. £330 (foreign $650). P J B Publications Ltd., 18-20 Hill Rise, Richmond, Surrey TW10 6UA, England. TEL 0181-948-3262. FAX 0181-332-8998. Ed. Ashley Yeo. adv. contact: Maria Ryback. bk.rev. circ. 12,000. **Indexed:** ABC, PROMT. **Document type:** newsletter.
●Also available online. Vendor(s): Ovid Technologies (PJIN,PHIC,PHID), Data-Star, Knight-Ridder, Inc.
—BLDSC (0905.030000); SWETS. **CCC.**
  Description: Includes regulations, companies, livestock and market trends, product news (introductions, R&D) and environmental issues for the international animal health and nutrition industry.

ANIMAL REPRODUCTION SCIENCE. see AGRICULTURE — Poultry And Livestock

636.089   UK   ISSN 0264-4754
ANIMAL TECHNOLOGY. 1950. 3/yr. £25. Institute of Animal Technology of Great Britain, c/o Geoffrey E. Ward, Ed., Department of Biochemistry, University College, Box 78, Cathays Park, Cardiff, Wales. (Subscr. addr.: c/o John A. Gregory, Zoology Department, Royal Postgraduate Medical School, Ducane Rd., London W12 OHS, England) adv.; bk.rev.; charts; illus. circ. 1,500. **Indexed:** Anim.Breed.Abstr., Bio-Contr.News & Info., Biol.Abstr., Ind.Vet., Nutr.Abstr., Protozool.Abstr., Rev.Med.& Vet.Mycol., Vet.Bull.
—BLDSC (0905.125000); SWETS.
  Formerly: Institute of Animal Technicians. Journal (ISSN 0020-2711)

636.089   TU   ISSN 1300-0861
CODEN: VTFDAQ
ANKARA UNIVERSITESI VETERINER FAKULTESI DERGISI/UNIVERSITY OF ANKARA. FACULTY OF VETERINARY MEDICINE. JOURNAL. (Text in Turkish; summaries in English, French or German) 1954. q. $10. University of Ankara, Faculty of Veterinary Medicine, Ankara, Turkey. Ed.Bd. bk.rev.; bibl.; charts; illus. circ. 750. **Indexed:** Anim.Breed.Abstr., Bio-Contr.News & Info., Biol.Abstr., Chem.Abstr., Dairy Sci.Abstr., Helminthol.Abstr., Ind.Vet., INIS Atomind., Int.Polit.Sci.Abstr., Nutr.Abstr., Poult.Abstr., Protozool.Abstr., Small Anim.Abstr., Soyabean Abstr., Triticale Abstr., Vet.Bull. **Document type:** academic/scholarly publication.

636.089   BE   ISSN 0003-4118
CODEN: AMVRA4
ANNALES DE MEDECINE VETERINAIRE. 1849. 6/yr. 1500 BEF. Imprimerie Bietlot, 20 Bd. de Colonster, B42, B-4000 Sart Tilman, Liege, Belgium. TEL 32-41-664020. FAX 32-41-662938. Ed. F. Lomba. adv.; bk.rev.; charts; illus.; index. circ. 1,500. **Indexed:** Agri.Eng.Abstr., Anim.Breed.Abstr., Biol.Abstr., Biotech.Abstr., Chem.Abstr., Curr.Adv.Ecol.Sci., Curr.Adv.Genetics & Molec.Biol., Curr.Cont., Dairy Sci.Abstr., Helminthol.Abstr., Ind.Med., Ind.Sci.Rev., Ind.Vet., Key Word Ind.Wildl.Res., Pig News & Info., Poult.Abstr., Protozool.Abstr., Rev.Plant Path., Sci.Cit.Ind, Small Anim.Abstr., Vet.Bull. **Document type:** academic/scholarly publication.
—BLDSC (0982.000000); CASDDS; Genuine Article; SWETS.

636.089   PL   ISSN 0301-7737
CODEN: ACDDA6
ANNALES UNIVERSITATIS MARIAE CURIE-SKLODOWSKA. SECTIO DD. MEDICINA VETERINARIA. (Text in Polish or English; summaries in English) 1949. a. price varies. Uniwersytet Marii Curie-Sklodowskiej, Wydawnictwo, Pl. M. Curie-Sklodowskiej 5, 20-031 Lublin, Poland. Ed. Zdzislaw Glinski. circ. 500. **Indexed:** Anim.Breed.Abstr., Biol.Abstr., Chem.Abstr., Ind.Vet., Landwirt.Zentralbl., Rev.Med.& Vet.Mycol., Sport Fish.Abstr., Vet.Bull., Wild.Rev., Zoo.Rec. **Document type:** academic/scholarly publication.
—BLDSC (0959.000000); CASDDS.

636.089   PL   ISSN 0239-4243
SF84   CODEN: AUEZE3
ANNALES UNIVERSITATIS MARIAE CURIE-SKLODOWSKA. SECTIO EE. ZOOTECHNIKA. (Text in English or Polish; summaries in English) 1983. a. price varies. Uniwersytet Marii Curie-Sklodowskiej, Wydawnictwo, Pl. M. Curie-Sklodowskiej 5, 20-031 Lublin, Poland. TEL 48-81-375304. FAX 48-81-336699. TELEX 0643223. Ed. Marian Budzynski. circ. 650. **Indexed:** Sport Fish.Abstr., Wild.Rev., Zoo.Rec. **Document type:** academic/scholarly publication.
—BLDSC (0961.010000).

636.089   US   ISSN 0887-7386
CODEN: AHPDE3
APIS; the international journal bulletin for specialty livestock and pet-animal product development. 1989. 4/yr. $165. C I T A International (USA), Industrial Journals Division, Box 70, Phoenix, AZ 85001. TEL 602-447-0480. FAX 602-447-0305. Ed. E.M. Morsy. adv.; bibl.; charts; illus.; index. circ. 2,000. (back issues avail.) **Document type:** trade publication.
—**CCC.**
  Description: Covers research and development, manufacture, chemistry formulation and raw materials for veterinary products, animal health and allied industries.

636.089   UA   ISSN 0003-746X
ARAB VETERINARY MEDICAL ASSOCIATION. JOURNAL. (Text in Arabic and English) vol.14, 1964. q. $10. Arab Veterinary Medical Association, 8 Sh 26 July, Cairo, Egypt. Ed. K.N. Soliman. bk.rev.; charts; illus.

ARANETA RESEARCH JOURNAL. see AGRICULTURE

636.089   US   ISSN 0003-942X
CODEN: ARTIA2
ARCHIVES OF ANIMAL NUTRITION/ARCHIV FUER TIERERNAEHRUNG. (Text and summaries in English, German) 1951. m. (in 3 vols.). 98 ECU per vol. (effective 1996). Harwood Academic Publishers, c/o International Publishers Distributor, 820 Town Center Dr., Langhorne, PA 19047.
TEL 215-750-2642. FAX 215-750-6343. (Subscr. to: International Publishers Distribbutor PO Box 90, Reading, Berkshire, RG1 8JL, England. TEL 44-173-456-8316) Ed. H. Bergner. bk.rev.; charts; illus.; index. **Indexed:** Anim.Breed.Abstr., Biodet.Abstr., Biol.Abstr., Biotech.Abstr., Chem.Abstr., Curr.Adv.Ecol.Sci., Curr.Cont., Excerp.Med., Food Sci.& Tech.Abstr., Helminthol.Abstr., Ind.Med., Ind.Vet., INIS Atomind., Maize Abstr., Nutr.Abstr., Pig News & Info., Poult.Abstr., Protozool.Abstr., Rice Abstr., Sci.Cit.Ind., Soils & Fert., Soyabean Abstr., Sugar Ind.Abstr., Triticale Abstr., Vet.Bull.
—BLDSC (1631.227000); CASDDS; Genuine Article; SWETS. **CCC.**

636.089   IT   ISSN 0004-0479
CODEN: AVEIAN
ARCHIVIO VETERINARIO ITALIANO. (Text in English, Italian; summaries in English, French, German) 1950. bi-m. L.50000 (foreign L.70000). (Universita degli Studi di Milano, Facolta di Veterinaria) Edizioni Citta Studi, P. Leonardo da Vinci 7, 20133 Milan, Italy. TEL 02-70634844. FAX 02-2367642. TELEX 326593 CLUP I. (Co-sponsor: Istituto di Ispezione degli Alimenti di Origine Animale, Facolta Medica Veterinaria) Dir. Carlo Cantoni. adv.; bk.rev.; abstr.; charts; illus.; index. circ. 1,000. (also avail. in microfilm from PMC) **Indexed:** Agri.Eng.Abstr., Anim.Breed.Abstr., Biol.Abstr., Biotech.Abstr., Curr.Adv.Ecol.Sci., Curr.Cont., Dairy Sci.Abstr., Food Sci.& Tech.Abstr., Helminthol.Abstr., Ind.Sci.Rev., Ind.Vet., Nutr.Abstr., Sport Fish.Abstr., Vet.Bull., Wild.Rev., Zoo.Rec. **Document type:** academic/scholarly publication.
—BLDSC (1648.900000); CASDDS.

636.08   SP   ISSN 0210-5799
ARCHIVOS DE ANATOMIA Y EMBRIOLOGIA. 1966. a. 2000 ptas. Universidad Complutense de Madrid, Facultad de Veterinaria, Ciudad Universitaria, 28040 Madrid, Spain.

636.08   CL   ISSN 0301-732X
CODEN: AMVED2
ARCHIVOS DE MEDICINA VETERINARIA. 1969. s-a. Universidad Austral de Chile, Facultad de Ciencias Veterinarias, Casilla 567, Valdivia, Chile. **Indexed:** Sport Fish.Abstr., Wild.Rev., Zoo.Rec. **Document type:** academic/scholarly publication.
—BLDSC (1655.410000); CASDDS; Genuine Article.

ARCHIVOS DE ZOOTECNIA. see AGRICULTURE — Poultry And Livestock

636.089   PL   ISSN 1230-5359
CODEN: AVPOEW
ARCHIVUM VETERINARIUM POLONICUM. (Text in English; summaries in Polish) 1951. irreg., vol.33, 1994. price varies. (Polska Akademia Nauk, Komitet Nauk Weterynaryjnych) Wydawnictwo Naukowe P W N, Miodowa 10, 00-251 Warsaw, Poland. (Dist. by: Osrodek Rozpowszechniania Wydawnictw Naukowych PAN ORPAN, Palac Kultury i Nauki, 00-901 Warsaw, Poland) Ed. Piotr Wyrost. abstr.; charts; illus. circ. 400. **Indexed:** Anim.Breed.Abstr., Biol.Abstr., Chem.Abstr., Dairy Sci.Abstr., Excerp.Med. (until 19??), Field Crop Abstr., Food Sci.& Tech.Abstr., Herb.Abstr., Ind.Med., Ind.Vet., Nutr.Abstr., Pig News & Info., Rev.Med.& Vet.Mycol., Rev.Plant Path., Vet.Bull.
—BLDSC (1659.568600); CASDDS.
  Formerly (until 1992): Polskie Archiwum Weterynaryjne (ISSN 0079-3647)

VETERINARY SCIENCE

636.089   BL   ISSN 0102-0935
CODEN: ABMZDB
ARQUIVO BRASILEIRO DE MEDICINA VETERINARIA E ZOOTECNIA. (Text and summaries in Portuguese or English) 1943. bi-m. $100. Universidade Federal de Minas Gerais, Escola de Veterinaria, Av. Antonio Carlos, 6627, C.P. 567, 30161-970 Belo Horizonte, Minas Gerais, Brazil. TEL 55-31-441-8364. FAX 55-31-441-2996. TELEX 0312308 UFMG. Ed. Ilto Jose Nunes. adv. contact: Lygia Maria Friche Passos. circ. 1,000. (also avail. in microform; reprint service avail. from ISI) **Indexed:** Agrindex, Anim.Breed.Abstr., Bibl.Agri., Biodet.Abstr., Biol.Abstr., Chem.Abstr., Dairy Sci.Abstr., Food Sci.& Tech.Abstr., Helminthol.Abstr., Herb.Abstr., Ind.Med., Ind.Vet., Nutr.Abstr., Pig News & Info., Poult.Abstr., Poult.Abstr., Protozool.Abstr., Ref.Zh., Soyabean Abstr., Sport Fish.Abstr., Sugar Ind.Abstr., Vet.Bull., Wild.Rev., Zoo.Rec. **Document type:** academic/scholarly publication.
—BLDSC (1695.100000); Genuine Article; UnCover.
Formerly (until vol.35, 1983): Universidade Federal de Minas Gerais. Escola de Veterinaria. Arquivos (ISSN 0076-8863)
Description: Contains articles on veterinary medicine, animal science, technology and inspection of products of animal origin.
Refereed Serial

636.089   BL   ISSN 0102-6380
CODEN: ARSVE6
ARS VETERINARIA. (Text in Portuguese; summaries in English) 1985-1988; resumed 1992. s-a. $30 or exchange basis. (Universidade Estadual Paulista, Departamento de Patologia Veterinaria) Editora U N E S P, Rodovia Carlos Tonanni, km 5, 14870-000 Jaboticabal SP, Brazil. TEL 55-163-224000. TELEX 111-9016 UJMF. Ed.Bd. charts; illus.; stat. **Indexed:** Anim.Breed.Abstr., Biodet.Abstr., Biol.Abstr., Dairy Sci.Abstr., Ind.Vet., Vet.Bull.
—BLDSC (1697.885000).

636.089   UA   ISSN 1012-5973
ASSIUT VETERINARY MEDICAL JOURNAL. (Text and summaries in Arabic and English) 1974. 4/yr. £E20($45) Assiut University, Faculty of Veterinary Medicine, Assiut, Egypt. FAX 088-333938. TELEX 92863 ASUNV UN. Ed. A.A. Ismail. charts; illus.; stat. circ. 30. **Indexed:** Agri.Eng.Abstr., Anim.Breed.Abstr., Biodet.Abstr., Dairy Sci.Abstr., Helminthol.Abstr., Ind.Vet., Nutr.Abstr., Poult.Abstr., Protozool.Abstr., Rev.Med.& Vet.Mycol., Rice Abstr., Small Anim.Abstr., Vet.Bull. **Document type:** academic/scholarly publication.
—BLDSC (1746.672100).
Refereed Serial

636.087   US   ISSN 0892-9904
CODEN: AAVTEW
ASSOCIATION OF AVIAN VETERINARIANS. JOURNAL. (Text in English; summaries in Dutch, French, German, Italian, Spanish) 1980. q. $70 ($75 to Canada & Mexico; Europe $80; elsewhere $90). Association of Avian Veterinarians, Box 618372, Orlando, FL 32861-8372. TEL 407-521-6101. FAX 407-521-6401. Ed. Kathy Lyon. bk.rev.; abstr.; illus. circ. 3,500. **Indexed:** Bibl.Agri., Helminthol.Abstr., Ind.Vet., Protozool.Abstr., Small Anim.Abstr., Sport Fish.Abstr., Wild.Rev., Zoo.Rec. **Document type:** bulletin.
—UnCover.
Former titles (until 1989): A A V Today; (until 1987): A A V Newsletter.
Description: Addresses avian research, pet bird medicine and surgery, conservation, aviculture, pharmaceuticals and biologicals and veterinary medical education.

636.089   IT   ISSN 0004-5977
ASSOCIAZIONE ITALIANA VETERINARI PER PICCOLI ANIMALI. BOLLETTINO. 1961. q. membership. Cartografica Artigiana, Via Bela Bartok 21-23, 44100 Ferrara I-AIVPA, Italy. FAX 0532-92668. Ed. Cesare Pareschi. adv.; bk.rev.; abstr.; bibl.; charts; illus.; stat.; tr.lit.; index. circ. 300. **Indexed:** Anim.Breed.Abstr., Ind.Vet., Rev.Med.& Vet.Mycol., Small Anim.Abstr., Vet.Bull.

636.089   AT   ISSN 1032-6626
AUSTRALIAN EQUINE VETERINARIAN. 1983. q. Aus.$135. Australian Equine Veterinary Association, P.O. Box 371, Artarmon, N.S.W. 2064, Australia. TEL 02-411 5342. FAX 02-413-3765. Ed. C. Pummer. adv. contact: D. Johnson. bk.rev.
—BLDSC (1798.868000).

AUSTRALIAN JOURNAL OF EXPERIMENTAL AGRICULTURE. see *AGRICULTURE — Crop Production And Soil*

636.089   AT   ISSN 1320-9582
AUSTRALIAN VETERINARY ASSOCIATION. ANNUAL REPORT. 1981. a. Aus.$30 (effective 1994). Australian Veterinary Association, 134-136 Hampden Rd., Artarmon, N.S.W. 2064, Australia. TEL 61-2-411-2733. FAX 61-2-411-5089.
Formerly (until 1990): Australian Veterinary Association. Year Book (ISSN 0812-9169)

636.089   AT
AUSTRALIAN VETERINARY ASSOCIATION CONFERENCE HANDBOOK. 1981. a. Aus.$30 to non-members (effective 1994). Australian Veterinary Association, 134-136 Hampden Rd., Artarmon, N.S.W. 2064, Australia. TEL 612-411-2733. FAX 612-411-5089. adv. circ. 6,000.
Formerly (until 1991): Australian Advances in Veterinary Science (ISSN 0728-8425)

636.089   AT   ISSN 0005-0423
CODEN: AUVJA2
AUSTRALIAN VETERINARY JOURNAL. 1925. m. Aus.$270. Australian Veterinary Association, 272 Brunswick Rd., Brunswick, Vic. 3056, Australia. TEL 61-2-411-2733. FAX 61-2-411-5089. Ed. J.T. Faragher. adv.; bk.rev.; index. circ. 4,500. (back issues avail.) **Indexed:** Abstr.Hyg., Agroforest.Abstr., Anim.Breed.Abstr., Bio-Contr.News & Info., Biol.Abstr., Biol.& Agr.Ind., Biotech.Abstr., Cadscan., Chem.Abstr., Curr.Adv.Ecol.Sci., Curr.Cont., Dairy Sci.Abstr., Dent.Ind., Excerp.Med., Field Crop Abstr., Helminthol.Abstr., Herb.Abstr., Ind.Med., Ind.Sci.Rev., Ind.Vet., Key Word Ind.Wildl.Res., Lead Abstr., Nutr.Abstr., Ornam.Hort., Pig News & Info., Poult.Abstr., Protozool.Abstr., Rev.Appl.Entomol., Rev.Med.& Vet.Mycol., Rev.Plant Path., Risk Abstr., Sci.Cit.Ind, Small Anim.Abstr., So.Pac.Per.Ind., Soils & Fert., Soyabean Abstr., Sport Fish.Abstr., Triticale Abstr., Trop.Dis.Bull., Vet.Bull., Weed Abstr., Wild.Rev., Zincscan, Zoo.Rec.
—BLDSC (1824.000000); CASDDS; Faxon; Genuine Article; SWETS; UnCover. CCC.

636   AT   ISSN 0310-138X
AUSTRALIAN VETERINARY PRACTITIONER. 1971. q. Aus.$70 (foreign Aus.$75). Australian Small Animal Veterinary Association, P.O. Box 243, Bondi, N.S.W. 2026, Australia. TEL 02-360-7189. FAX 02-360-7184. Ed. R.E. Atwell. adv.: B&W page Aus.$450, color page Aus.$900; trim 27.5 x 21; adv. contact: Jenny Wade. bk.rev. circ. 1,200. **Indexed:** Anim.Breed.Abstr., Biol.Abstr., Curr.Adv.Ecol.Sci., Curr.Cont., Helminthol.Abstr., Ind.Sci.Rev., Ind.Vet., Protozool.Abstr., Sci.Cit.Ind, Small Anim.Abstr., Vet.Bull.
—BLDSC (1824.100000); Genuine Article; UnCover.

636.089   US   ISSN 0005-2086
CODEN: AVDIAI
AVIAN DISEASES. 1957. q. $100 (foreign $110) (effective 1996). American Association of Avian Pathologists, Inc., University of Pennsylvania, New Bolton Center, Kennett Sq., PA 19348-1692. TEL 215-444-4282. FAX 215-444-5387. Ed. Dr. L. van der Heide. adv.; bibl.; charts; illus.; index. circ. 1,900. (also avail. in microform from UMI; microfilm from WSH,PMC; back issues avail.) **Indexed:** Anim.Breed.Abstr., Biol.Abstr., Biotech.Abstr., Chem.Abstr., Curr.Adv.Cancer Res., Curr.Adv.Ecol.Sci., Curr.Cont., Helminthol.Abstr., Ind.Med., Ind.Sci.Rev., Ind.Vet., Poult.Abstr., Protozool.Abstr., Rev.Med.& Vet.Mycol., Rev.Plant Path., Sci.Cit.Ind, Small Anim.Abstr., Sport Fish.Abstr., Vet.Bull., Wild.Rev., Zoo.Rec. **Document type:** academic/scholarly publication.
—BLDSC (1837.890000); CASDDS; Faxon; Genuine Article; SWETS; UMI; UnCover.
Refereed Serial

636.089   UK   ISSN 0307-9457
CODEN: AVPADN
AVIAN PATHOLOGY. (Text in English; summaries in French, German, Spanish) 1972. q. £54 to individuals; institutions £144 (effective 1996). (World Veterinary Poultry Association) Carfax Publishing Co., P.O. Box 25, Abingdon, Oxon. OX14 3UE, England. TEL 01235-555335. FAX 01235-553559. (Subscr. in N. America to: Carfax Publishing Co., 875-81 Massachusetts Ave., Cambridge, MA 02139) Ed. B.M. Freeman. adv.; bk.rev. circ. 700. (back issues avail.) **Indexed:** Anim.Breed.Abstr., Biol.Abstr., Biotech.Abstr., Curr.Adv.Ecol.Sci., Helminthol.Abstr., Ind.Sci.Rev., Ind.Vet., Poult.Abstr., Protozool.Abstr., Rev.Med.& Vet.Mycol., Sci.Cit.Ind, Small Anim.Abstr., Sport Fish.Abstr., Vet.Bull., Wild.Rev., Zoo.Rec. **Document type:** academic/scholarly publication.
—BLDSC (1837.891000); CASDDS; Faxon; Genuine Article; SWETS; UMI; UnCover. CCC.
Refereed Serial

636.089 591   JA   ISSN 0389-1836
CODEN: ADJHDO
AZABU DAIGAKU JUIGAKUBU KENKYU HOKOKU/AZABU UNIVERSITY. VETERINARY MEDICINE. BULLETIN. (Text in English or Japanese; summaries in English) 1954-1986; resumed 1988. s-a. exchange basis. Azabu University, School of Veterinary Medicine - Azabu Daigaku Juigakubu, 1-17-71 Fuchinobe, Sagamihara-shi, Kanagawa-ken 229, Japan. TEL 81-427-54-7111. FAX 81-427-54-7661. Ed. Kiyoshi Tabuchi. circ. 800. **Indexed:** Biol.Abstr., Dairy Sci.Abstr., Rev.Med.& Vet.Mycol., Rev.Plant Path., Small Anim.Abstr., Vet.Bull. **Document type:** academic/scholarly publication, bulletin.
—BLDSC (2409.440000); CASDDS.
Formerly: Azabu Veterinary College. Bulletin.

B T I A; la revue francaise de la genetique et de la reproduction. (Bulletin Technique de l'Insemination Artificielle) see *AGRICULTURE — Poultry And Livestock*

BANGLADESH JOURNAL OF ANIMAL SCIENCE. see *AGRICULTURE — Poultry And Livestock*

636.089   BG   ISSN 0378-8113
CODEN: BVJODC
BANGLADESH VETERINARY JOURNAL. 1967. q. $10. Bangladesh Veterinary Association, Bangladesh Agricultural University, Mymensingh, Bangladesh. Ed. M.L. Dewan. adv.; bk.rev.; charts; illus. circ. 1,000. **Indexed:** Anim.Breed.Abstr., Ind.Vet., Vet.Bull.
Formerly (until 1969): Pakistan Journal of Veterinary Science (ISSN 0030-9915)

BEITRAEGE ZUR TROPISCHEN LANDWIRTSCHAFT UND VETERINAERMEDIZIN. see *AGRICULTURE*

636.089   GW   ISSN 0005-9366
CODEN: BEMTAM
BERLINER UND MUENCHENER TIERAERZTLICHE WOCHENSCHRIFT. (Text in German; summaries in English and German) 1888. m. DM.437($324) to individuals in Europe (rest of world DM.468($347)); institutions in Europe DM.537($398) (rest of world DM.568($421)) (effective 1996). Blackwell Wissenschaft, Kurfuerstendamm 57, 10707 Berlin, Germany. TEL 030-32790623. FAX 030-32790610. Ed. H.-J. Sinell. adv.; bk.rev.; abstr.; illus.; stat.; index. (back issues avail.) **Indexed:** Anim.Breed.Abstr., Biodet.Abstr., Biol.Abstr., Biotech.Abstr., Chem.Abstr., Curr.Adv.Ecol.Sci., Curr.Cont., Dairy Sci.Abstr., Dent.Ind., Field Crop Abstr., Food Sci.& Tech.Abstr., Helminthol.Abstr., Herb.Abstr., Ind.Med., Ind.Sci.Rev., Ind.Vet., INIS Atomind., Key Word.Ind.Wildl.Res., Nutr.Abstr., Pig News & Info., Poult.Abstr., Protozool.Abstr., Rev.Plant Path., Sci.Cit.Ind., Small Anim.Abstr., Soils & Fert., Vet.Bull. **Document type:** academic/scholarly publication.
—BLDSC (1941.360000); CASDDS; Faxon; Genuine Article; SWETS. CCC.

636.089   BL   ISSN 0029-6953
BIOLOGICO. (Text in Portuguese; summaries in English) 1935. s-a. Cr.$1260($12) Instituto Biologico, Av. Rodrigues Alves 1252, C.P. 4185, Sao Paulo, Brazil. TEL 572-9822. Ed.Bd. bibl.; illus.; index. cum.index. circ. 2,000. **Indexed:** Bio-Contr.News & Info., Biol.Abstr., Biotech.Abstr., Chem.Abstr., Field Crop Abstr., Forest.Abstr., Helminthol.Abstr., Herb.Abstr., Hort.Abstr., Ind.Vet., Plant Breed.Abstr., Rev.Appl.Entomol., Rev.Plant Path., Seed Abstr., Triticale Abstr., Trop.Oil Seeds Abstr., Vet.Bull., Weed Abstr.

VETERINARY SCIENCE 6525

636.089 GW ISSN 0723-6212
BIOLOGISCHE TIERMEDIZIN. (Text in German, Spanish) 1984. q. DM.25. Aurelia Verlag GmbH, Dr.-Reckeweg-Str. 2-4, 76532 Baden-Baden, Germany. TEL 07221-50102. FAX 07221-501420. Ed. Dr. Peter Hamlcik. adv.: B&W page DM.3000; trim 204 x 140. circ. 13,500. Document type: academic/scholarly publication.

636 615.1 XR
CODEN: BCZVDE
BIOPHARM. (Text in Czech, Slovak or English) 1964. bi-m. 54 Kc.($26.20) (Spojene Podniky pro Zdravotnickou Vyrobu, Vyzkumny Ustav pro Biofaktory a Veterinarni Leciva, Odbor Vedeckych Informaci) Vetpres, Pohori-Chatoun, 254 49 Jilove v. Prague, Czech Republic. TEL 26 59 51. (Subscr. to: Artia, ve Smeckach 30, 11127 Prague 1, Czech Republic) Ed. Bohumil Sevcik. adv.; bk.rev.; bibl.; charts; illus.; stat. (reprint service avail. from ISI) Indexed: Anim.Breed.Abstr., Cadscan, Chem.Abstr., Curr.Adv.Ecol.Sci., Curr.Cont., Dairy Sci.Abstr., Excerp.Med. (until 19??), Helminthol.Abstr., Ind.Sci.Rev., Ind.Vet., Lead Abstr., Nutr.Abstr., Pig News & Info., Poult.Abstr., Protozool.Abstr., Rev.Med.& Vet.Mycol., Sci.Cit.Ind, Vet.Bull., Zincscan.
—BLDSC (2089.353600); CASDDS; Genuine Article.
Formerly (until 1991): Biologizace a Chemizace Zivocisne Vyroby - Veterinaria (ISSN 0139-8571)

BIOTECH REPORTER; agricultural research - business. see BIOLOGY — Biotechnology

BLAA STJAERNAN; djurvaard inom totalfoersvaret. see PETS

636.089 UK
BLACK'S VETERINARY DICTIONARY. 1928. irreg., (every 2-3 yrs.). £19.99 (effective 1996). A & C Black (Publishers) Ltd., Howard Rd., Eaton Socon, Huntingdon, Cambs. PE19 3EZ, England. TEL 01480-212666. FAX 01480-405014. Ed. Geoffrey P. West. Document type: academic/scholarly publication.
Description: Comprehensive veterinary dictionary for veterinary and agricultural students, veterinarians, and farmers. Covers related fields.

636.089 SW ISSN 0282-3926
BLADMAGEN. 1967. 5/yr. SEK 120 membership (effective 1990). Veterinaermedicinska Foereningen, P.O. Box 7074, S-750 07 Uppsala, Sweden.

636.089 US ISSN 0524-1685
CODEN: BOVPBO
BOVINE PRACTITIONER. 1969. a. $20 (foreign $28). American Association of Bovine Practitioners, c/o Dr. Eric I. Williams, Ed., 1226 N. Lincoln, Stillwater, OK 74075. TEL 405-372-3693. FAX 405-372-0939. adv. contact: James Jarrett. bk.rev.; index. circ. 5,000. Indexed: Dairy Sci.Abstr., Protozool.Abstr. Document type: academic/scholarly publication.
—BLDSC (2264.630000).
Description: Publishes manuscripts of interest to veterinarians engaged in cattle practice and research.

636.08 US
BOVINE VETERINARIAN. 1993. bi-m. $25. Vance Publishing Corporation (Lenexa), Livestock Division, 10901 W. 84th Terr., Lenexa, KS 66214-1631. TEL 913-438-8700. FAX 913-438-0695. Ed. Geni Wren; Pub. Bill Newham. adv. contact: Cliff Becker. circ. 7,500. Document type: trade publication.
Description: Focuses on business management information for bovine veterinarians so they can better assist their beef and dairy clients.

636.089 SP ISSN 1130-4804
BOVIS. 1984. 6/yr. 4770 ptas. Luzan 5 S.A. de Ediciones, Pasaje Virgen de la Alegria 14, 28027 Madrid, Spain. TEL 1-4051595. FAX 1-4034907. Ed. Oliva Nunez. circ. 30,000.

636.089 615 UK
BRITISH PHARMACOPOEIA: VETERINARY EDITION. 1977. irreg., 1993. £70 (includes annual supplement) (effective 1994). (British Pharmacopoeia Commission) H.M.S.O., Market Towers, 51 Nine Elms Ln., London SW8 5DR, England. TEL 071-873-0011. FAX 071-873-8463. (Subscr. to: H.M.S.O. Publications Centre, P.O. Box 276, London SW8 5DT, England. TEL 071-873-9090. FAX 071-873-8200) Document type: government publication.
• Also available on CD-ROM.
Description: Updates existing monographs on U.K. standards in veterinary medicine.

636.089 UK ISSN 0007-1935
CODEN: BVJOA9
BRITISH VETERINARY JOURNAL. 1875. bi-m. £95 to individuals (outside Europe $175); institutions £136 (outside Europe $245). Bailliere Tindall - W.B. Saunders Co. Ltd. (Subsidiary of: Harcourt Brace & Company Ltd.), 24-28 Oval Rd., London NW1 7DX, England. TEL 0171-267-4466. FAX 0171-482-2293. TELEX 25775 ACPRES G. (Subscr. to: Harcourt Brace & Company Ltd., Foots Cray High St., Sidcup, Kent DA14 5HP, England. TEL 0181-300-3322. FAX 0181-309-0807; Subscr. in N. America to: W.B. Saunders Co., Journal Subscription Fulfillment, 6277 Sea Harbor Dr., 4th Fl., Orlando, FL 32887-4800. TEL 800-654-2452. FAX 800-874-6418) Ed. A.J. Higgins. adv.; bk.rev.; abstr.; charts; illus.; stat.; index. (also avail. in microform from UMI,PMC; reprint service avail. from UMI) Indexed: Anim.Breed.Abstr., Biol.Abstr., Biotech.Abstr., C.I.S. Abstr., Chem.Abstr., Curr.Adv.Ecol.Sci., Curr.Cont., Dairy Sci.Abstr., Diar.Dis.Res., Excerp.Med., Food Sci.& Tech.Abstr., Helminthol.Abstr., Ind.Med., Ind.Sci.Rev., Ind.Vet., Nutr.Abstr., Pig News & Info., Poult.Abstr., Protozool.Abstr., Rev.Appl.Entomol., Rev.Plant Path., Risk Abstr., Sci.Cit.Ind, Small Anim.Abstr., Sport Fish.Abstr., Vet.Bull., Wild.Rev., Zoo.Rec. Document type: academic/scholarly publication.
—BLDSC (2347.000000); CASDDS; Faxon; Genuine Article; SWETS; UMI; UnCover. CCC.
Formerly (until 1949): Veterinary Journal (ISSN 0372-5545); (until 1900): Veterinary Journal and Annals of Comparative Pathology.
Description: Publishes worldwide contributions on all aspects of veterinary science and its related subjects.
Refereed Serial

BUFFALO JOURNAL; an international journal of buffalo science. see AGRICULTURE — Poultry And Livestock

BULLETIN OF ANIMAL HEALTH AND PRODUCTION IN AFRICA/BULLETIN DES SANTE ET PRODUCTION ANIMALES EN AFRIQUE. see AGRICULTURE — Poultry And Livestock

636.08 SZ
BUNDESAMT FUER VETERINAERWESEN. MITTEILUNGEN. 1900. 26/yr. 26 SFr. Bundesamt fuer Veterinaerwesen, Schwarzenburgstr. 161, CH-3097 Liebefeld, Switzerland. TEL 031-9708568. FAX 031-9708570. Ed. Heinz Mueller. circ. 13,000. Document type: government publication, newsletter.
Description: Provides statistics and data concerning outbreaks of animal diseases. Also covers regulation of the exportation and importation of animals, meat and meat products to and from Switzerland.

636.089 US
C V M QUARTERLY. 1945. q. $5. Auburn University, College of Veterinary Medicine, 104 J E Greene Hall, Auburn, AL 36849. TEL 205-844-3698. FAX 334-844-3697. E-mail: hendrji@vetmed.auburn.edu. Ed. Gary Beard. adv.; bk.rev.; bibl.; illus. circ. 1,200. Indexed: Ind.Vet., Rev.Plant Path., Sport Fish.Abstr., Vet.Bull., Wild.Rev., Zoo.Rec. (until 19??). Document type: newsletter.
Formerly: Auburn Veterinarian.

636.089 US ISSN 0008-1612
CALIFORNIA VETERINARIAN. 1947. bi-m. $35 (Canada $45; elsewhere $55). California Veterinary Medical Association, 5231 Madison Ave., Sacramento, CA 95841. TEL 916-344-4985. FAX 916-344-6147. Ed. Rosanne VanCleve. adv.: B&W page $800. illus.; index. circ. 3,800. (also avail. in microform from UMI; back issues avail.) Indexed: Biotech.Abstr., Chem.Abstr., Ind.Vet., Rev.Med.& Vet.Mycol., Small Anim.Abstr., Sport Fish.Abstr., Vet.Bull., Wild.Rev., Zoo.Rec. Document type: trade publication.
—BLDSC (3015.350000); UMI; UnCover.
Description: Includes business, legislative and regulatory information of interest to the veterinary profession; and association and allied organization news.
Refereed Serial

CANADIAN HORSEMAN. see SPORTS AND GAMES — Horses And Horsemanship

636.089 610 CN ISSN 0830-9000
CODEN: CJVRE9
CANADIAN JOURNAL OF VETERINARY RESEARCH/REVUE CANADIENNE DE RECHERCHE VETERINAIRE. (Text in English and French) 1937. q. Can.$75 (foreign $90). Canadian Veterinary Medical Association, 339 Booth St., Ottawa, ON K1R 7K1, Canada. TEL 613-236-1162. FAX 613-236-9681. Ed. Dr. Peter Conlon. adv. contact: Laima Laffitte. bibl.; charts; illus.; index; circ. 2,000 (paid). Indexed: Anim.Breed.Abstr., Biol.Abstr., Biotech.Abstr., Chem.Abstr., Curr.Adv.Ecol.Sci., Curr.Cont., Dairy Sci.Abstr., Dent.Ind., Excerp.Med., Food Sci.& Tech.Abstr., Helminthol.Abstr., Ind.Med., Ind.Sci.Rev., Ind.Vet., Med.Care Rev., Nutr.Abstr., Pig News & Info., Poult.Abstr., Protozool.Abstr., Rev.Med.& Vet.Mycol., Sci.Cit.Ind., Small Anim.Abstr., Sport Fish.Abstr., Vet.Bull., Wild.Rev., Zoo.Rec. Document type: academic/scholarly publication.
—BLDSC (3036.700000); CASDDS; Faxon; Genuine Article; SWETS; UnCover. CCC.
Former titles: Canadian Journal of Comparative Medicine (ISSN 0008-4050); Canadian Journal of Comparative Medicine and Veterinary Science.
Refereed Serial

636.089 CN ISSN 0008-5286
CODEN: CNVJA9
CANADIAN VETERINARY JOURNAL/REVUE VETERINAIRE CANADIENNE. (Text in English and French) 1960. m. Can.$100 (foreign $110). Canadian Veterinary Medical Association, 339 Booth St., Ottawa, ON K1R 7K1, Canada. TEL 613-236-1162. FAX 613-236-9681. Ed. Dr. Doug Hare. adv. contact: Laima Laffitte. bk.rev.; abstr.; charts; illus.; index; circ. 5,000 (paid). (also avail. in microform from UMI,PMC) Indexed: Agri.Eng.Abstr., Anim.Breed.Abstr., Biol.Abstr., Biotech.Abstr., Chem.Abstr., Curr.Adv.Ecol.Sci., Curr.Cont., Dairy Sci.Abstr., Excerp.Med., Helminthol.Abstr., Ind.Med. (1994-), Ind.Sci.Rev., Ind.Vet., INIS Atomind., Nutr.Abstr., Pig News & Info., Poult.Abstr., Protozool.Abstr., Rev.Appl.Entomol., Rev.Med.& Vet.Mycol., Sci.Cit.Ind., Small Anim.Abstr., Sport Fish.Abstr., Vet.Bull., Wild.Rev., Zoo.Rec. Document type: academic/scholarly publication.
—BLDSC (3046.100000); CASDDS; Faxon; Genuine Article; SWETS; UnCover. CCC.
Refereed Serial

636.089 IT
CANI, GATTI E COMPAGNIA. 1987. q. L.20000 (foreign L.40000) (free to qualified personnel). Editore S.C.I.V.A.C., Via Pallavicino, 26, 26100 Cremona, Italy. TEL 0372-23501. Ed. Antonio Manfredi. adv.: B&W or color page L.3500000. circ. 90,000.

VETERINARY SCIENCE

636.089   US   ISSN 1057-6622
SF991   CODEN: CPRAEE
CANINE PRACTICE; the journal of canine medicine & surgery for the practitioner. 1974. bi-m. $28 (Canada and Mexico $35; elsewhere $45) (effective 1996). Veterinary Practice Publishing Co., 7 Ashley Ave. S., Santa Barbara, CA 93103-9989. TEL 805-965-1028. FAX 805-965-0722. (Subscr. to: Box 4457, Santa Barbara, CA 93140-4457) Ed. Dr. Joseph Alexander. adv.; bk.rev.; illus.; index. circ. 6,500. (also avail. in microform from UMI) **Indexed:** Curr.Adv.Ecol.Sci., Ind.Vet., Small Anim.Abstr., Soyabean Abstr., Vet.Bull. **Document type:** academic/scholarly publication.
—UMI.
    Supersedes in part (in 1987): Companion Animal Practice (ISSN 0894-9794); Which was formed by the merger of (1971-1987): Feline Practice (ISSN 0046-3639), Canine Practice (ISSN 0094-4904), Avian-Exotic Practice (ISSN 8750-037X).
    Description: Aimed at practitioners of vetinary medicine and surgery for dogs.
    Refereed Serial

636.089   II   ISSN 0379-542X
CODEN: CHRNAR
CHEIRON; Tamil Nadu journal of veterinary science and animal husbandry. (Text in English) 1972. bi-m. Rs.40($20) Tamil Nadu Veterinary & Animal Science University, Madras-600007, India. TEL 581-506. FAX 044-560114. Ed. M. Mohamed Habibulla Khan. adv.: B&W page Rs.1000. index. circ. 750. (back issues avail.) **Indexed:** Agri.Eng.Abstr., Anim.Breed.Abstr., Biodet.Abstr., Biol.Abstr., Chem.Abstr., Curr.Adv.Ecol.Sci., Dairy Sci.Abstr., Food Sci.& Tech.Abstr., Helminthol.Abstr., Herb.Abstr., Ind.Vet., Nutr.Abstr., Poult.Abstr., Protozool.Abstr., Rev.Appl.Entomol., Rev.Med.& Vet.Mycol., Trop.Oil Seeds Abstr., Vet.Bull., World Agri.Econ.& Rural Sociol.Abstr.
—BLDSC (3133.430000); CASDDS.

CIENCIA RURAL. see *AGRICULTURE*

636.089   CU   ISSN 0253-5750
CODEN: CASVDA
CIENCIA Y TECNICA EN LA AGRICULTURA. SERIE: VETERINARIA. (Table of contents and abstracts in English) 1978. 2/yr. $14 in N. and S. America; Europe $16; others $17; or exchange basis. Centro de Informacion y Documentacion Agropecuario, Gaveta Postal 4149, Havana 4, Cuba. (Dist. by: Ediciones Cubanas, Obispo No. 527, Apdo. 605, Havana, Cuba) **Indexed:** Agrindex, Ind.Vet., Vet.Bull.
—CASDDS.

636.089   CR   ISSN 0250-5649
CODEN: CIVEEV
CIENCIAS VETERINARIAS. 3/yr. Escuela de Medicina Veterinaria, Biblioteca, Apdo. 86, Heredia, Costa Rica. **Indexed:** Sport Fish.Abstr., Wild.Rev., Zoo.Rec. **Document type:** academic/scholarly publication.

636.089   IT   ISSN 1120-7957
CINOLOGIA. 1990. 4/yr. L.60000 (foreign L.80000). Via Pallavicino 26, 26100 Cremona, Italy. TEL 372-23-501. FAX 372-45-7091. Ed. Mauriz Cornelli. adv.: color page L.2000000. circ. 14,000.

636.089   IT   ISSN 0009-9082
CODEN: CLVEAE
CLINICA VETERINARIA. (Text in Italian; summaries in English) 1878. m. L.20000. Istituto Sieroterapico Milanese, Via Darwin 20, Milan, Italy. adv.; bk.rev.; bibl.; illus.; index. circ. 2,800. **Indexed:** Anim.Breed.Abstr., Biol.Abstr., Biotech.Abstr., Chem.Abstr., Dairy Sci.Abstr., Excerp.Med., Food Sci.& Tech.Abstr., Helminthol.Abstr., Ind.Vet., Nutr.Abstr., Pig News & Info., Poult.Abstr., Protozool.Abstr., Small Anim.Abstr., Vet.Bull.
—CASDDS.

636.089   CN
COLLEGE OF VETERINARIANS OF ONTARIO. UPDATE. 1983. 8/yr. $35. College of Veterinarians of Ontario, 2106 Gordon St., Guelph, ON N1L 1G6, Canada. FAX 519-824-6497. Ed. Dr. Robert Hayes. circ. 3,000.
    Formerly: Ontario Veterinary Association. Update (ISSN 0821-6320)

636   JA   ISSN 0913-5316
COMPANION ANIMAL PRACTICE. Key Title: C A P. Companion Animal Practice. 1986. m. 2000 Yen per no. Chikusan Publishing Co., Ltd. (Subsidiary of: Midori Group), Ikebukuro Nishiguchi Sky Bldg., 2-14-4 Ikebukuro, Toshima-ku, Tokyo 171, Japan. TEL 03-3590-9454. circ. 5,000.
    Description: Contains articles on small, companion animals.

COMPARATIVE IMMUNOLOGY, MICROBIOLOGY AND INFECTIOUS DISEASES; the international journal for medical and veterinary researchers and practitioners. see *BIOLOGY — Microbiology*

COMPARATIVE PATHOLOGY BULLETIN. see *MEDICAL SCIENCES*

636.089   US   ISSN 0193-1903
COMPENDIUM ON CONTINUING EDUCATION FOR THE PRACTICING VETERINARIAN. 1979. m. $56 to individuals (Canada and Mexico $68; elsewhere $92); institutions $75 (Canada and Mexico $98; elsewhere $104) (effective 1996). Veterinary Learning Systems, 425 Phillips Blvd., Ste. 100, Trenton, NJ 08618. TEL 609-882-5600; 800-426-9119. FAX 609-882-6357. Ed.Bd. adv.; index. circ. 33,857. (also avail. in microform from UMI; back issues avail.) **Indexed:** Agri.Eng.Abstr., Anim.Breed.Abstr., Curr.Cont., Dairy Sci.Abstr., Herb.Abstr., Pig News & Info., Protozool.Abstr., Rev.Med.& Vet.Mycol., Small Anim.Abstr., Vet.Bull. **Document type:** trade publication.
—BLDSC (3363.967520); Faxon; Genuine Article; SWETS; UMI; UnCover.
    Formerly: Compendium on Continuing Education for the Small Animal Practitioner (ISSN 0164-5455)

COMPLETING THE INTERNAL MARKET OF THE EUROPEAN COMMUNITY: 1992 LEGISLATION - VETERINARY & PHYTOSANITARY CONTROLS. see *LAW — International Law*

636.089   CN   ISSN 0843-5634
CREST.* 1989. q. Ontario Veterinary College, Alumni Association, Dean's Office, U. of Guelph, Guelph, ON N1G 2W1, Canada. TEL 519-823-8800. FAX 519-837-3230. Ed. Martha Leibbrandt. illus. circ. 5,000.
    Description: News of OVC's people, events and programs.

636.089   CU   ISSN 0138-8134
CUBA. CENTRO DE INFORMACION Y DOCUMENTACION AGROPECUARIO. BOLETIN DE RESENAS. SERIE: VETERINARIA. (Abstracts in English) 1974. irreg. exchange basis. Centro de Informacion y Documentacion Agropecuario, Gaveta Postal 4149, Havana 4, Cuba. TEL 292227. (Dist. by: Ediciones Cubana, Obispo No. 461, Apdo. 605, Havana, Cuba) stat. **Indexed:** Agrindex.
    Formerly: Cuba. Centro de Informacion y Divulgacion Agropecuario. Boletin de Resenas. Serie: Veterinaria.

636.089   NE   ISSN 0166-2333
CODEN: CTVSDD
CURRENT TOPICS IN VETERINARY MEDICINE AND ANIMAL SCIENCE. (Text in English) 1978. irreg. price varies. (Commission of the European Communities) Kluwer Academic Publishers, Postbus 17, 3300 AA Dordrecht, Netherlands. TEL 31-78-392392. FAX 31-78-392254. TELEX 29245 KAPG NL. (Dist. by: Kluwer Academic Publishers Group, P.O. Box 322, 3300 AH Dordrecht, Netherlands. TEL 31-78-392392. FAX 31-78-546474; N. America dist. addr.: Box 358, Accord Sta., Hingham, MA 02018-0358. TEL 617-871-6600. FAX 617-871-6528) **Document type:** monographic series.
—CASDDS; Faxon.
    Formerly (until 1979): Current Topics in Veterinary Medicine (ISSN 0165-4586)
    Refereed Serial

636.089   GW   ISSN 0341-6593
CODEN: DDTWDG
D T W - DEUTSCHE TIERAERZTLICHE WOCHENSCHRIFT. (Text in German; summaries in English) 1893. 12/yr. DM.310. Verlag M. und H. Schaper GmbH, Kalandstr. 4, 31061 Alfeld, Germany. TEL 05181-8009-0. FAX 05181-800933. (Subscr. to: Postfach 1642, 31046 Alfeld, Germany) adv.; bk.rev.; abstr.; bibl.; charts; illus.; index. circ. 1,500. **Indexed:** Agri.Eng.Abstr., Anim.Breed.Abstr., Biol.Abstr., Biotech.Abstr., Chem.Abstr., Curr.Adv.Ecol.Sci., Curr.Cont., Dairy Sci.Abstr., Dent.Ind., Excerpt.Med., Field Crop Abstr., Food Sci.& Tech.Abstr., Helminthol.Abstr., Herb.Abstr., Ind.Med., Ind.Sci.Rev., Ind.Vet., Ind.Vet., INIS Atomind., Key Word Ind.Wildl.Res., Key Word Ind.Wildl.Res., Maize Abstr., Nutr.Abstr., Pig News & Info., Potato Abstr., Poult.Abstr., Protozool.Abstr., Rev.Plant Path., Sci.Cit.Ind, Soils & Fert., Soyabean Abstr., Triticale Abstr., Vet.Bull. **Document type:** trade publication.
—BLDSC (3574.000000); CASDDS; Faxon; Genuine Article; SWETS. **CCC.**
    Former title: Deutsche Tieraerztliche Wochenschrift (ISSN 0012-0847)

636.089 658   US
D V M MANAGEMENT CONSULTANTS REPORTS. (Doctor of Veterinary Medicine); the business newsletter for the practicing veterinarian. 10/yr. $92 (foreign $102) (effective 1993). American Veterinary Publications, Inc., 5782 Thornwood Dr., Goleta, CA 93117-3896. TEL 805-967-5988. (looseleaf format)
    Formerly: D V M Management.

636.089   US   ISSN 0012-7337
D V M NEWSMAGAZINE. 1970. m. $28. Advanstar Communications, Inc., 7500 Old Oak Blvd., Cleveland, OH 44130. TEL 216-826-2839. FAX 216-891-2726. (Subscr. to: 131 W. First St., Duluth, MN 55802. TEL 800-346-0085) Ed. Maureen Hrehocik. adv.; bk.rev.; abstr.; illus.; tr.lit. circ. 40,014. (tabloid format; also avail. in microform from UMI) **Document type:** academic/scholarly publication, trade publication.
—UMI. **CCC.**
    Description: Covers news and trends for veterinarians.

DAIRY INDIA YEARBOOK. see *AGRICULTURE — Dairying And Dairy Products*

636.089   DK   ISSN 0106-6854
DANSK VETERINAERTIDSSKRIFT/DANISH VETERINARY JOURNAL. 1918. 24/yr. DKK 850. Danske Dyrlaegeforening - Danish Veterinary Association, Rosenlunds Alle 8, DK-2720 Vanloese, Denmark. TEL 45-38-71-08-88. FAX 45-38-71-03-22. Ed. Lars Petersen. adv.; bk.rev. circ. 4,000. **Indexed:** Agri.Eng.Abstr., Anim.Breed.Abstr., Biodet.Abstr., Biol.Abstr., Dairy Sci.Abstr., Food Sci.& Tech.Abstr., Ind.Vet., Nutr.Abstr., Pig News & Info., Protozool.Abstr., Rev.Med.& Vet.Mycol., Small Anim.Abstr., Vet.Bull., World Agri.Econ.& Rural Sociol.Abstr.
—BLDSC (3533.035000).
    Formerly: Danske Dyrlaegeforening. Medlemsblad (ISSN 0011-6564)

636.089   FR   ISSN 0180-3573
DEPECHE VETERINAIRE. 1977. 44/yr. 670 F. to non-members; members 550 F. (foreign 720 F.) Syndicat National des Veterinaires de France, 10 Place Leon Blum, 75011 Paris, France. TEL 43-79-11-52. FAX 43-79-76-96. Ed. Daniel Delmotte. adv. contact: Didier Menet. bk.rev.

636.089   GW   ISSN 0340-1898
DEUTSCHES TIERAERZTEBLATT. 1949. m. DM.190 (foreign DM.220). (Deutsche Tieraerzteschaft e.V.) Schluetersche Verlagsanstalt GmbH und Co., Hans-Boeckler-Allee 7, 30173 Hannover, Germany. TEL 0511-8550-0. FAX 0511-8550-100. (Subscr. to: Postfach 5440, 30054 Hannover, Germany) Ed. Dr. Margund Mrozek. adv.; bk.rev.; stat. circ. 25,342. **Indexed:** Ind.Vet., Vet.Bull. **Document type:** academic/scholarly publication.
—BLDSC (3578.160000). **CCC.**

VETERINARY SCIENCE

636.089 NE ISSN 0167-5168
CODEN: DAVSDR
DEVELOPMENTS IN ANIMAL AND VETERINARY SCIENCES. (Text in English) 1976. irreg., vol.25, 1991. price varies. Elsevier Science B.V., Books Division, P.O. Box 211, 1000 AE Amsterdam, Netherlands. TEL 31-20-4853911. FAX 31-20-4853705. TELEX 18582 ESPA NL. E-mail: nlinfo-f@elsevier.nl; usinfo-f@elsevier.com; forinfo-kyf04035@niftyserve.or.jp; Site addr.: http://www.elsevier.nl/. (Subscr. in U.S. and Canada to: Elsevier Science Inc., Box 882, Madison Sq. Sta., New York, NY 10159. TEL 212-989-5800) (back issues avail.) **Document type:** monographic series.
—BLDSC (3579.062000); CASDDS; Faxon.
Refereed Serial

636.089 NE
DEVELOPMENTS IN VETERINARY MEDICINE. (Text in English) irreg. price varies. Kluwer Academic Publishers, Postbus 17, 3300 AA Dordrecht, Netherlands. TEL 31-78-392392. FAX 31-78-392254. TELEX 29245 KAPG NL. (Dist. by: Kluwer Academic Publishers Group, P.O. Box 322, 3300 AH Dordrecht, Netherlands. TEL 31-78-392392. FAX 31-78-546474; N. America dist. addr.: Box 358, Accord Sta., Hingham, MA 02018-0358. TEL 617-871-6600. FAX 617-871-6528) **Document type:** monographic series.
Refereed Serial

636.089 NE ISSN 0920-2412
DIER - EN - ARTS; wetenschappelijke praktijkgerichte informatie. 1986. 9/yr. fl.90 (students fl.47.50) (foreign fl.125) (free to qualified personnel). Transmondial B.V., Baron van Nagellstr. 27, 3781 AP Voorthuizen, Netherlands. TEL 31-342-4373137. FAX 31-342-437154. Ed.Bd. adv.: B&W page fl.1950, color page fl.3650; trim 210 x 297. bk.rev.; abstr.; bibl.; charts; illus.; stat.; circ. 3,200 (controlled). (back issues avail.) **Document type:** trade publication.
●Also available online.
—BLDSC (3580.557000).
Description: Provides information for practicing veterinary surgeons and includes examples of practical solutions to problems encountered in daily practice.

636.089 FR ISSN 1012-5329
DISEASE INFORMATION. (Text in English, French, Spanish) 1988. w. 550 F.($102) (effective 1995). Office International des Epizooties, 12, rue de Prony, 75017 Paris, France. TEL 44-15-18-88. FAX 42-67-09-87. TELEX EPIZOTI 642 285 F. (U.S. Subscr. to: Scientific, Medical Publications of France, 100 East 42nd St., Ste 1002, New York, NY 10017. TEL 212-983-6278) Ed. J. Blancou. adv. contact: G.S. Dilmitis. (back issues avail.) **Document type:** newsletter.
Description: Weekly reports on status and outbreaks of emergency animal diseases and their status.

636.089 616.4 US ISSN 0739-7240
CODEN: DANEEE
DOMESTIC ANIMAL ENDOCRINOLOGY. 1984. bi-m. $210 to institutions (effective 1996). (Auburn University, College of Veterinary Medicine) Butterworth - Heinemann, Part of the Reed Elsevier group, 313 Washington St., Newton, MA 02158. TEL 617-928-2500; 800-366-2665. FAX 617-928-2610. TELEX 880052. (Subscr. to: Elsevier Science Inc., Box 882, Madison Sq. Sta., New York, NY 10159-0882. TEL 212-989-5800. FAX 212-633-3990) adv.; charts; illus.; stat.; index. **Indexed:** Anim.Breed.Abstr., Biol.Abstr., Chem.Abstr., Curr.Cont., Dairy Sci.Abstr., Ind.Vet., INSPEC, Pig News & Info., Poult.Abstr., Rev.Med.& Vet.Mycol., Small Anim.Abstr., Vet.Bull. **Document type:** academic/scholarly publication.
—BLDSC (3616.884000); CASDDS; Faxon; Genuine Article; SWETS; UMI; UnCover. CCC.
Refereed Serial

636.08 591 JA ISSN 0912-1129
DOSEI KYOKAI KAIHO/JAPANESE ASSOCIATION OF VETERINARY BIOLOGISTS. BULLETIN. (Text in Japanese) 1968. q. Dobutsuyo Seibutsugakuteki Seizai Kyokai, 11, Kanda Mikuracho, Chiyoda-ku, Tokyo 101, Japan.

636.089 IC
DYRALAEKNARITID. 1981. s-a. membership. Dyralaeknafelag Islands, Lagmula 7, 108 Reykjavik, Iceland. TEL 354-568-9545. Eds. Konrad Konardsson, Olafur Jonsson.
Description: Features articles on veterinary medicine, hygiene, and the environment.

636.089 DK ISSN 0906-1290
DYRENES RET - VOR PLIGT. 1975. q. Landsforeningen Komiteen mod Dyreforsoeg, Valdemarsgade 67, 5.tv., P.O. Box 228, DK-1502 Copenhagen V, Denmark. TEL 31-22-41-15. Ed. Poul Erik Buch. adv.: B&W page DKK 2300. bk.rev. circ. 2,000. **Document type:** consumer publication.
Formerly (until 1990): Komiteen mod Dyreforsoeg, Fonden til Sygdomsbekaempelse uden Dyreforsoeg (ISSN 0109-3878)

636 UA ISSN 1110-0222
EGYPTIAN JOURNAL OF VETERINARY SCIENCE. (Text in English; summaries in Arabic and English) 1964. a. $32 (effective 1996). (Arabic Veterinary Medical Association) National Information and Documentation Centre (NIDOC), Tahrir St., Dokki, Awqaf P.O., Cairo, Egypt. TEL 20-2-701696. Ed. M.R. Shalash. circ. 1,500. (reprint service avail. from IRC) **Indexed:** Anim.Breed.Abstr., Biol.Abstr., Chem.Abstr., Curr.Adv.Ecol.Sci., Diar.Dis.Res., Excerp.Med. (until 19??), ExtraMED, Ind.Vet., Vet.Bull. **Document type:** academic/scholarly publication.
●Also available on CD-ROM.
Former titles (until vol.9, 1972): United Arab Republic Journal of Veterinary Science (ISSN 0041-7165); (until 1970): Journal of Veterinary Science of the United Arab Republic (ISSN 0368-4709)

EMBRYO TRANSFER NEWSLETTER. see *BIOLOGY — Biotechnology*

636.089 UN
EPIDEMIOLOGICAL SURVEILLANCE OF RABIES FOR THE AMERICAS. Spanish Edition: Vigilancia Epidemiologica de la Rabia para las Americas. 1969. s-a. Instituto Panamericano de Proteccion de Alimentos y Zoonosis - Panamerican Institute for Food Protection and Zoonoses, Casilla 44, 1640 Martinez Buenos Aires, Argentina. TEL 792-4047. FAX 112328. TELEX 24577 AR PAZ. (Affiliate: World Health Organization) Ed. Eduardo Guarnera. circ. 1,400 (Spanish ed. 950; English ed. 450).

636.089 GR ISSN 0374-7417
CODEN: EEKSA
EPISTIMONIKI EPITERIS KTENIATRIKIS SCHOLIS. (Text in Greek; summaries in English) 1952. irreg. Aristotelian University of Thessaloniki, School of Veterinary Science, Thessaloniki 54006, Greece. Ed. A.G. Spais. circ. 500. **Indexed:** Biol.Abstr. **Document type:** academic/scholarly publication.

636 US ISSN 1047-8620
EQUINE ATHLETE; the equine sports medicine newsjournal. 1988. bi-m. $36 (Canada and Mexico $60; elsewhere $75) (effective 1996). Veterinary Practice Publishing Co., 7 Ashley Ave. S., Santa Barbara, CA 93103-9989. TEL 805-965-1028. FAX 805-965-0722. (Subscr. to: Box 4457, Santa Barbara, CA 93140-4457) Ed. Dr. Jerry R. Gillespie. adv.; charts; illus. circ. 6,500. **Document type:** academic/scholarly publication.
—Genuine Article.
Refereed Serial

636.089 US ISSN 0162-8941
SF951 CODEN: EQPRDF
EQUINE PRACTICE; journal of equine medicine and surgery for the practitioner. 1979. 10/yr. $36 to individuals; students $20 (Canada and Mexico $45; elsewhere $50) (effective 1996). Veterinary Practice Publishing Co., 7 Ashley Ave. S., Santa Barbara, CA 93103-9989. TEL 805-965-1028. FAX 805-965-0722. (Subscr. to: Box 4457, Santa Barbara, CA 93140-4457) Ed. Dr. Charles Vail; Pub. Nancy A. Bull. adv.; bk.rev.; illus.; index. circ. 5,000. (also avail. in microform from UMI; reprint service avail. from UMI) **Indexed:** Anim.Breed.Abstr., Curr.Adv.Ecol.Sci., Dairy Sci.Abstr., Ind.Vet., Protozool.Abstr., Rev.Med.& Vet.Mycol., Rice Abstr., Vet.Bull. **Document type:** academic/scholarly publication.
—BLDSC (3794.518000); CASDDS; Genuine Article; SWETS; UMI; UnCover.
Incorporates: Journal of Equine Medicine and Surgery (ISSN 0147-0833)
Description: Directed to the equine segment of the veterinary clinical market.
Refereed Serial

636.089 US ISSN 0739-9065
EQUINE VETERINARY DATA. 1980. m. $95 to individuals; institutions $120 (Canada and Mexico $105; elsewhere $120) (effective 1995). Veterinary Data, Box 1209, Wildomar, CA 92595. TEL 909-678-1889. FAX 909-678-1885. Ed. Dr. William E. Jones; Pub. Dr. William E. Jones. index. (back issues avail.) **Indexed:** Ind.Vet. **Document type:** newsletter.
—BLDSC (3794.519000).
Description: Professional newsletter for DVM equine practitioners.

636.087 375 UK ISSN 0957-7734
SF955
EQUINE VETERINARY EDUCATION. 1989. 6/yr. £72 (foreign £84). R & W Publications (Newmarket) Ltd., Goodwin House, Willie Snaith Rd., Newmarket, Suffolk CB8 7SQ, England. TEL 0638-667600. FAX 0638-667229. Ed. I.G. Mayhew. illus. circ. 1,400. **Document type:** academic/scholarly publication.
—BLDSC (3794.519400); UnCover.
Description: Covers continuing education for equine veterinarians.

636.089 UK ISSN 0425-1644
CODEN: EQVJAI
EQUINE VETERINARY JOURNAL. 1968. bi-m. £60 (foreign £80). (British Equine Veterinary Association) R & W Publications (Newmarket) Ltd., Goodwin House, Willie Snaith Rd., Newmarket, Suffolk CB8 7SQ, England. TEL 0638-667600. FAX 0638-667229. Ed. P.D. Rossdale. adv.; bk.rev.; abstr.; charts; illus.; stat.; index. circ. 2,300. (reprint service avail. from UMI) **Indexed:** Agri.Eng.Abstr., Anim.Breed.Abstr., Biol.Abstr., Curr.Adv.Ecol.Sci., Curr.Cont., Dent.Ind., Helminthol.Abstr, Ind.Med., Ind.Sci.Rev., Ind.Vet., Nutr.Abstr., Protozool.Abstr., Rev.Med.& Vet.Mycol, Rev.Plant Path., Sci.Cit.Ind, Vet.Bull. **Document type:** trade publication.
—BLDSC (3794.520000); Faxon; Genuine Article; SWETS; UMI; UnCover.

EQUINEWS; serving the horse industry - all breeds, all disciplines. see *SPORTS AND GAMES — Horses And Horsemanship*

EQUUS. see *SPORTS AND GAMES — Horses And Horsemanship*

636.089 UK
F A B JOURNAL. 1958. q. £12.50p. membership. Feline Advisory Bureau, 235 Upper Richmond Rd., London SW15 6SN, England. TEL 0181-789-9553. Ed. Claire Bessant. adv. contact: Claire Bessant. bk.rev.; charts; illus.; stat.; circ. 550 (paid). (processed; back issues avail.) **Document type:** academic/scholarly publication.
Formerly: F A B Bulletin.
Description: Contains items of interest to veterinarians and breeders specializing in cats, as well as general-interest articles for cat lovers and owners.

F A S S VET; foeretackning oever laekemedel foer veterinaermedicinsk bruk. (Farmacevtiska Specialiteter i Sverige) see *PHARMACY AND PHARMACOLOGY*

VETERINARY SCIENCE

636.089 US ISSN 1057-6223
F D A VETERINARIAN. 1979-1984; resumed. bi-m. $8.50 (foreign $10.65) (effective 1995). U.S. Food & Drug Administration, Center for Veterinary Medicine, 7500 Standish Pl., Rockville, MD 20855. TEL 301-594-5909. FAX 301-594-1831. (Subscr. to: Superintendent of Documents, U.S. Government Printing Office, Box 371954, Pittsburgh, PA 15250-7954. TEL 202-512-1800. FAX 202-512-2250) Ed. Linda A. Grassie. charts; index. circ. 3,600. (also avail. in microfiche; back issues avail.) **Document type:** trade publication, government publication.

636.08 SP ISSN 0373-1170
CODEN: AFVLA5
FACULTAD DE VETERINARIA DE LEON. ANALES. 1955. a. 1000 ptas. Universidad de Leon, Facultad de Veterinaria, Campus de Vegazana, 24071 Leon, Spain.
—CASDDS.

636.08 PK
FARM SCIENTIST. (Text in English, Urdu) 1990. m. $3 per no. Press Corporation of Pakistan, P.O. Box 3138, Karachi 754000, Pakistan. TEL 21-455-3703. FAX 21-7736198. Ed. Dr. M.S. Jaffery. circ. 5,000.

636.039 614 US ISSN 0164-6257
FEDERAL VETERINARIAN. 1922. m. $35 (foreign $50) (effective 1996). National Association of Federal Veterinarians, 1101 Vermont Ave., N.W., Ste. 710, Washington, DC 20005-3521. TEL 202-289-6334. Ed. Dr. Edward L. Menning. adv.; bk.rev. circ. 2,000. (tabloid format; back issues avail.) **Document type:** newsletter.
Description: Federal regulatory news, meat inspection, animal disease control, human disease from animals and federal personnel issues.

636.089 US
FELINE HEALTH TOPICS. 1981. q. $25. Cornell Feline Health Center, Cornell University, College of Veterinary Medicine, Ithaca, NY 14853-6401. TEL 607-253-3414. FAX 607-253-3419. Ed. June Tuttle. circ. 5,000. (back issues avail.) **Document type:** newsletter.
Description: For veterinary professionals.

636.8 US ISSN 1057-6614
SF985 CODEN: FELPEJ
FELINE PRACTICE; the journal of feline medicine & surgery for the practitioner. 1971. bi-m. $28 (Canada and Mexico $35; elsewhere $45) (effective 1996). (American Association of Feline Practitioners) Veterinary Practice Publishing Co., 7 Ashley Ave. S., Santa Barbara, CA 93103-9989. TEL 805-965-1028. FAX 805-965-0722. (Subscr. to: Box 4457, Santa Barbara, CA 93140-4457) Ed. Dr. Fred Scott. adv.; bk.rev.; illus.; index. circ. 6,500. (also avail. in microform from UMI; reprint service avail. from UMI) **Indexed:** Curr.Adv.Ecol.Sci., Ind.Vet., Rev.Med.& Vet.Mycol., Small Anim.Abstr. **Document type:** academic/scholarly publication.
—BLDSC (3047.100000); Genuine Article; SWETS; UMI; UnCover.
Incorporates (1983-1992): A A F P Journal; **Supersedes in part (in 1987):** Companion Animal Practice (ISSN 0894-9794); **Which was formed by the merger of (1971-1987):** Feline Practice (ISSN 0046-3639); (1971-1987): Canine Practice (ISSN 0094-4904); Avian-Exotic Practice (ISSN 8750-037X)
Description: Focuses on the veterinary medicine and surgery of cats.
Refereed Serial

636.089 634.9 XO
FOLIA VENATORIA; pol'ovnicky zbornik. (Text in Czech, Slovak; summaries in English, German, Russian) 1971. a. price varies. (Forest Research Institute, Federal Committee of Hunting Associations in the CSSR) Priroda, Krizkova 9, 815 34 Bratislava, Slovakia. TEL 472-41-45. Ed. Pavel Hell. bk.rev.; charts; illus.; cum.index. **Indexed:** Biol.Abstr.

636.089 XO ISSN 0015-5748
FOLIA VETERINARIA. (200 Sk.) (Text and summaries in English) 1955. q. 200 Sk. Univerzita Veterinarskeho Lekarstva v Kosiciach - University of Veterinary Medicine, c/o Dir. Marta Prosbova, Library and Institute of Scientific Information, Komenskeho 73, 041-81 Kosice, Slovakia. TEL 42-95-6330127. FAX 42-95-767675. TELEX 77322. Ed. Rudolf Cagadaj. adv.; bk.rev.; abstr.; bibl.; index.; cum.index. circ. 550. **Indexed:** Agri.Eng.Abstr., Biol.Abstr., Chem.Abstr., Dairy Sci.Abstr., Ind.Vet., Nutr.Abstr., Pig News & Info., Poult.Abstr., Protozool.Abstr., Small Anim.Abstr., Soyabean Abstr., Vet.Bull. **Document type:** academic/scholarly publication.
—CASDDS.

636.089 CC ISSN 1003-4331
FUJIAN XUMU SHOUYI/FUJIAN JOURNAL OF ANIMAL HUSBANDRY AND VETERINARY. (Text in Chinese; abstracts and table of contents in English) 1979. q. newsstand price: Y1.50. Fujina Xumu Shouyi Bianjibu, Pudang, Fuzhou Shijiao (Suburb), Fuzhou, Fujian 350013, People's Republic of China. TEL 0591-7593074. FAX 0591-7840650. (Dist. overseas by: Jiangsu Publications Import & Export Corp., 56 Gao Yun Ling, Nanjing, Jiangsu, P.R.C.) Ed. Youquan Cheng. adv.: page Y1000.
Description: Publishes investigative report, monographs, clinical information and productive experiences in the field of animal husbandry and veterinary sciences.

636.089 FR
G T V BULLETIN. 1974. 5/yr. 700 F. (foreign 918.90 F.) (effective 1995). Groupements Techniques Veterinaires, Syndicat National des Groupements Techniques Veterinaires (SNGTV), 10 pl. Leon Blum, 75011 Paris, France. TEL 43-79-11-52. FAX 43-72-07-00. Ed. Dr. G. Gauthey. adv.; bk.rev. circ. 2,800. **Indexed:** Agri.Eng.Abstr., Anim.Breed.Abstr., Biodet.Abstr., Chem.Abstr., Dairy Sci.Abstr., Ind.Vet., Protozool.Abstr., Vet.Bull. **Document type:** bulletin.

GANAGRINCO; ganaderia - agricultura - industria - comercio. see *AGRICULTURE*

636.08 US
GEORGIA EXTENSION NEWSLETTER. m. University of Georgia at Statesboro, Georgia Extension, Landrum Box 8112-G.S.U., Statesboro, GA 30460. TEL 912-681-5639. FAX 912-681-0376. **Document type:** newsletter.

636.089 US
GRAYSON GRAM. 1984. q. free. Grayson Foundation, Inc., 1718 Alexandria Dr., Box 4158, Lexington, KY 40544. TEL 606-278-5243. Ed. Edward S. Ford. circ. 3,500.

636.089 IT ISSN 0391-1918
GUIDA DI VETERINARIA E ZOOTECNIA; guida italiana dei prodotti e delle industrie veterinarie e zootecniche. 1966. biennial. L.110000 (foreign L.126000). Organizzazione Editoriale Medico-Farmaceutica, Via Edolo 42, Box 10434, 20125 Milan, Italy. TEL 02-675051. FAX 02-67505223. TELEX 323598. (U.S. dist.: Drug Intelligence & Clinical Pharmacy, Box 42435, Cincinnati, OH 45242) Ed. Carlo Marini. adv.: B&W page L.2500000, color page L.3000000; trim 210 x 290.

GUOWAI XUMU KEJI/FOREIGN ANIMAL HUSBANDRY SCIENCE AND TECHNOLOGY. see *AGRICULTURE* — *Poultry And Livestock*

HARYANA AGRICULTURAL UNIVERSITY. JOURNAL OF RESEARCH. see *AGRICULTURE*

636.089 II ISSN 0033-4359
HARYANA VETERINARIAN. (Text in English) vol.10, 1971. s-a. Rs.20($12) Haryana Agricultural University, Haryana Agricultural University, College of Veterinary Sciences, Hissar 125 004, Haryana, India. Ed. Dr. A.R. Rao. adv.; bk.rev.; abstr.; charts; illus.; stat. circ. 500. **Indexed:** Dairy Sci.Abstr., Ind.Vet., Poult.Abstr., Rev.Med.& Vet.Mycol., Vet.Bull. **Document type:** academic/scholarly publication.
—BLDSC (4271.150000).
Formerly: Punjab Veterinarian.

636.089 GR ISSN 0257-2354
HELLENIC VETERINARY MEDICAL SOCIETY. BULLETIN/ELLINIKIS KTINIATRIKIS ETERIAS. DELTIO. Key Title: Deltion tes Ellenikes Ktiniatrikes Eterias. (Text in Greek; summaries in English) 1924. q. Dr.5000($120) Hellenic Veterinary Medical Society, P.O. Box 18281, 116 10 Athens, Greece. (Subscr. to: Olga Sabatakou, P.O. Box 3546, 102 10 Athens, Greece) Ed. Dr. Agesilaus Tsagarakis. adv.; bk.rev.; circ. 1,000 (controlled). **Indexed:** Biodet.Abstr., Biol.Abstr., Ind.Vet., Vet.Bull. **Document type:** bulletin.
—BLDSC (2554.500000).

636.089 UK ISSN 0268-4276
HENSTON VETERINARY VADE MECUM (LARGE ANIMALS). 1984. a. £30 (foreign £33). The Chequers, 2 Church St., High Wycombe HP11 2DE, England. TEL 01494-474433. Ed. Dr. J.M. Evans. adv.; index. circ. 5,000. (back issues avail.) **Document type:** trade publication.
Description: For veterinary surgeons or similarly qualified personnel. Covers diseases, conditions, and symptoms of large animals, as well as therapeutic products.

636.089 UK ISSN 0268-4268
HENSTON VETERINARY VADE MECUM (SMALL ANIMALS). 1982. a. £30 (foreign £33). The Chequers, 2 Church St., High Wycombe HP11 2DE, England. TEL 01494-474433. Ed. Allan J. Henderson. adv. contact: John O'Hara. index. circ. 5,000. (back issues avail.) **Document type:** trade publication.
Description: For veterinary surgeons or similarly qualified personnel. Covers diseases, conditions, and symptoms of small animals, as well as therapeutic products.

HIMACHAL JOURNAL OF AGRICULTURAL RESEARCH. see *AGRICULTURE*

636.089 DK ISSN 0105-1423
SF615
HISTORIA MEDICINAE VETERINARIAE. (Text and summaries in English, French and German) 1976. q. DKK 366($66) (typically set in Jan.). Historia Medicinae Veterinariae, Soendergade 39, 4130 Viby Sjaelland, Denmark. Ed. Vibeke Dantzer. adv.; bk.rev.; illus.; index, cum.index. circ. 250. **Indexed:** Ind.Vet., Vet.Bull. **Document type:** academic/scholarly publication.
—BLDSC (4316.056500).

636.089 JA ISSN 0018-3385
HOKKAIDO VETERINARY MEDICAL ASSOCIATION. JOURNAL/HOKKAIDO JUISHIKAI ZASSHI. (Text in Japanese) 1957. m. newsstand price: 250Yen. Hokkaido Veterinary Medical Association, 9-3, 5-chome, Nijuyonken 4-jo, Nishi-ku, Sapporo-shi, Hokkaido 063, Japan. adv.; abstr.; bibl.; charts; illus.; tr.lit. circ. 2,000. **Indexed:** Agrindex, Vet.Bull.

636.1 US
THE HORSE REPORT. q. University of California at Davis, Equine Research Laboratory, School of Veterinary Medicine, Davis, CA 95616-8589. TEL 916-752-6433. FAX 916-752-6433. Ed. Lauric Fio. circ. 26,000. (looseleaf format; back issues avail.) **Document type:** newsletter.
Description: Covers recent researches in equine health for horse owners, breeders, and veterinarians.

636.089 615 SA ISSN 0019-0918
I V S. (Index of Veterinary Specialists) 1962. q. M I M S, Division of Times Media Limited, P.O. Box 2059, Pretoria 0001, South Africa. TEL 27-12-3485010. FAX 27-12-477716. Ed. Dr. A. Immelman. adv. circ. 2,439. (back issues avail.)
Description: Indexes veterinary medicines available in South Africa in pharmacological order, alphabetically.

636.089 SA
I V S DESK REFERENCE. 1991. biennial. M I M S, Division of Times Media Limited, P.O. Box 2059, Pretoria 0001, South Africa. TEL 27-12-3485010. FAX 27-12-477716. Ed. Dr. A. Immelman. adv.; circ. 1,300 (paid).
Description: Provides details of veterinary medicines, including a generic-trade name index and a reference section.

636.089　　　　　UK　　ISSN 0263-841X
　　　　　　　　　　　CODEN: IPRCDH
IN PRACTICE (LONDON). bi-m. £29.50. British Veterinary Association, 7 Mansfield St., London W1M OAT, England. TEL 0171-636-6541. FAX 0171-637-0620. Ed. Edward Boden. adv. circ. 10,000. Indexed: Anim.Breed.Abstr., Biol.Abstr., Biol.& Agr.Ind., Dairy Sci.Abstr., Dent.Ind., Excerp.Med., Food Sci.& Tech.Abstr., Ind.Med., Ind.Vet., Pig News & Info., Small Anim.Abstr., Vet.Bull. **Document type:** trade publication.
—BLDSC (4372.411000); Faxon; Genuine Article; SWETS; UnCover. **CCC**.

636.089　　　　　II　　ISSN 0019-5057
　　　　　　　　　　　CODEN: IJAHA4
INDIAN JOURNAL OF ANIMAL HEALTH. (Text in English) 1960. s-a. $35. 68 Belgachia Rd., Calcutta 700037, India. TEL 556-5304. Ed. M.S. Das. adv.; bk.rev.; abstr.; bibl.; charts; illus.; stat. circ. 2,000. Indexed: Anim.Breed.Abstr., Biol.Abstr., Chem.Abstr., Curr.Cont., Dairy Sci.Abstr., Food Sci.& Tech.Abstr., Helminthol.Abstr., Hort.Abstr., Ind.Vet., Nutr.Abstr., Protozool.Abstr., Rev.Med.& Vet.Mycol., Rev.Plant Path., Vet.Bull.
—BLDSC (4410.190000); CASDDS.

INDIAN JOURNAL OF ANIMAL NUTRITION. see AGRICULTURE — Poultry And Livestock

INDIAN JOURNAL OF ANIMAL RESEARCH; half-yearly research journal of animal, food and zoological sciences. see AGRICULTURE — Poultry And Livestock

636.089　　　　　II　　ISSN 0367-8318
SF601　　　　　　　　CODEN: IJLAA4
INDIAN JOURNAL OF ANIMAL SCIENCES. (Text in English) 1931. m. Rs.420($80) Indian Council of Agricultural Research, Krishi Anusandian, Pusa, New Delhi 110012, India. Ed. R.R. Lokeshwar. adv.; bk.rev.; charts; illus.; index. circ. 2,000. (also avail. in microform from UMI; reprint service avail. from UMI) Indexed: Agrindex, Agroforest.Abstr., Anim.Breed.Abstr., Biol.Abstr., Biotech.Abstr., Chem.Abstr., Curr.Adv.Ecol.Sci., Curr.Adv.Genetics & Molec.Biol., Curr.Cont., Dairy Sci.Abstr., Diar.Dis.Res., Excerp.Med., Field Crop Abstr., Food Sci.& Tech.Abstr., Forest.Abstr., Helminthol.Abstr., Herb.Abstr., Ind.Sci.Rev., Ind.Vet., INIS Atomind., Nutr.Abstr., Pig News & Info., Poult.Abstr., Protozool.Abstr., Rev.Appl.Entomol., Rev.Med.& Vet.Mycol., Rev.Plant Path., Rice Abstr., Rural Recreat.Tour.Abstr., Sci.Cit.Ind., Small Anim.Abstr., Sorghum & Millets Abstr., Soyabean Abstr., Sport Fish.Abstr., Sugar Ind.Abstr., Triticale Abstr., Vet.Bull., Weed Abstr., Wild.Rev., World Agri.Econ.& Rural Sociol.Abstr., Zoo.Rec.
—BLDSC (4410.195000); CASDDS; Faxon; Genuine Article; SWETS; UMI; UnCover.
Formerly: Indian Journal of Veterinary Science and Animal Husbandry (ISSN 0019-5715)
Description: Covers all aspects of animal sciences.

636.089 611　　　　II　　ISSN 0971-1937
INDIAN JOURNAL OF VETERINARY ANATOMY. (Text and summaries in English) 1989. s-a. Rs.150($30) (effective 1992). Indian Association of Veterinary Anatomists (IAVA), c/o D.N. Sharma, Secr., Dept. of Veterinary Anatomy and Histology, H.P. Agricultural University, Palampur 176062, India. TEL 01894-30306. (Affiliate: World Association of Veterinary Anatomists) adv.; bk.rev. circ. 225.
Description: Publishes the original research articles, short communications, reviews and comments on experimental and applied anatomy.

639.089　　　　　II　　ISSN 0970-051X
　　　　　　　　　　　CODEN: IJVMDP
INDIAN JOURNAL OF VETERINARY MEDICINE. (Text in English) 1981. s-a. Indian Society for Veterinary Medicine, c/o Dr. S.K. Dwivedi, Div. of Experimental Medicine & Surgery, Indian Veterinary Research Institute, Izatnagar 243122, Uttar Pradesh, India. Indexed: Sport Fish.Abstr., Wild.Rev., Zoo.Rec.
—BLDSC (4421.880000); UnCover.

636.089　　　　　II　　ISSN 0254-4105
　　　　　　　　　　　CODEN: IJVSD9
INDIAN JOURNAL OF VETERINARY SURGERY. (Text in English) 1980. s-a. Rs.150($50) Indian Society for Veterinary Surgery, Division of Surgery, Indian Veterinary Research Institute, Izatnagar 243122, India. TEL 0581-71587. TELEX 577 205 IVRI IN. Ed. Dr. Gaj Raj Singh. adv.; bk.rev. circ. 600. Indexed: Biol.Abstr., Ind.Vet., Indian Sci.Abstr., Sport Fish.Abstr., Vet.Bull., Wild.Rev. **Document type:** academic/scholarly publication.
Description: Publishes research results, clinical and review articles in Indian and foreign veterinary surgery and related subjects.

INDIAN POULTRY INDUSTRY YEARBOOK. see AGRICULTURE — Poultry And Livestock

INDIAN POULTRY REVIEW. see AGRICULTURE — Poultry And Livestock

636.089　　　　　II　　ISSN 0019-6479
SF604　　　　　　　　CODEN: IVEJAC
INDIAN VETERINARY JOURNAL; a monthly record of veterinary science. (Text in English) 1924. m. $45 (effective 1995). Indian Veterinary Association, 7, Chamiers Rd., Madras 600 035, India. TEL 451006. Ed. Dr. V.S. Alwar. adv.; bk.rev.; abstr.; illus.; stat.; index. circ. 4,700. (reprint service avail. from ISI) Indexed: Anim.Breed.Abstr., Biol.Abstr., Biotech.Abstr., Chem.Abstr., Curr.Adv.Cancer Res., Curr.Adv.Ecol.Sci., Curr.Adv.Genetics & Molec.Biol., Curr.Cont., Dairy Sci.Abstr., Field Crop Abstr., Food Sci.& Tech.Abstr., Helminthol.Abstr., Herb.Abstr., Hort.Abstr., Ind.Med., Ind.Sci.Rev., Ind.Vet., Maize Abstr., Nutr.Abstr., Pig News & Info., Poult.Abstr., Protozool.Abstr., Rev.Appl.Entomol., Rev.Med.& Vet.Mycol., Rev.Plant Path., Sci.Cit.Ind, Small Anim.Abstr., Soyabean Abstr., Sport Fish.Abstr., Trop.Oil Seeds Abstr., Vet.Bull., Wild.Rev., Zoo.Rec. **Document type:** academic/scholarly publication.
—BLDSC (4431.000000); CASDDS; Genuine Article; SWETS; UnCover.

590　　　　　　　II　　ISSN 0250-5266
　　　　　　　　　　　CODEN: IVMJDL
INDIAN VETERINARY MEDICAL JOURNAL. (Text in English; association news in English and Hindi) 1977. q. (foreign $79). Uttar Pradesh Veterinary Association, c/o Institute of Veterinary Biologicals, Badshahbagh, Lucknow 226007, India. TEL 387353. Ed. J.N.S. Yadava. adv.: page $120. bk.rev.; bibl. circ. 2,500. Indexed: Anim.Breed.Abstr., Biol.Abstr., Chem.Abstr., Dairy Sci.Abstr., Helminthol.Abstr., Hort.Abstr., Ind.Vet., Poult.Abstr., Protozool.Abstr., Rev.Med.& Vet.Mycol., Sport Fish.Abstr., Vet.Bull., Wild.Rev., Zoo.Rec. **Document type:** academic/scholarly publication.
—CASDDS; UnCover.
Supersedes: U P Veterinary Journal.

636.089　　　　　II　　ISSN 0304-7067
SF779.M78
INDIAN VETERINARY RESEARCH INSTITUTE. ANNUAL REPORT. (Text in English) 1947. a. exchange basis. Indian Veterinary Research Institute, Mukteswar-Kumaon, Izatnagar 243122, Uttar Pradesh, India. circ. 1,500. Indexed: Anim.Breed.Abstr.
Formerly: Muktesar, India. Imperial Veterinary Research Institute. Report.

636.089　　　　　CU　　ISSN 0138-7235
INFORMACION EXPRESS. SERIE: VETERINARIA. 1977. 4/yr. $9 in N. America; S. America $11; Europe $13; others $18; or exchange basis. Centro de Informacion y Documentacion Agropecuario, Gaveta Postal 4149, Havana 4, Cuba. (Dist. by: Ediciones Cubanas, Obispo No. 527, Apdo. 605, Havana, Cuba) Indexed: Agrindex.

636.089　　　　　SP　　ISSN 1130-5436
INFORMACION VETERINARIA. 1962. 12/yr. Colegio Veterinario Espanol, Joaquim M. Lopez 23, 4oD, 28015 Madrid, Spain. TEL 1-543-61-48. FAX 1-544-75-70.

636.089　　　　　IT
INFORMATORE DI VETERINARIA E ZOOTECNIA. 1966. a. Organizzazione Editoriale Medico Farmaceutica, Via Edolo 42, 20125 Milan, Italy. TEL 39-2-6691344. FAX 39-2-6690213. adv.: B&W page L.2500000. circ. 45,000.

636.08 664　　　　UN
▼**INPAZ EN LAS AMERICAS.** (Editions in English, Spanish) 1994. irreg. Instituto Panamericano de Proteccion de Alimentos y Zoonosis - Panamerican Institute for Food Protection and Zoonoses, Casilla 44, 1640 Martinez Buenos Aires, Argentina. TEL 792-4047. FAX 112328. TELEX 24577 AT PAZ. (Affiliate: World Health Organization) **Document type:** newsletter.

636.089　　　　　CN
INSIDE EQUINE; news from the Equine Research Centre. 1986. s-a. free. Equine Research Centre, University of Guelph, Guelph, ON N1G 2W1, Canada. TEL 519-837-0061. FAX 519-767-1081. E-mail: kcounsel@uoguelph.ca. Ed. Kelly Counsell. bk.rev.; cum.index 1986-1991. circ. 15,000. (back issues avail.) **Document type:** newsletter.
●Also available online.
Former titles (until 1995): Equine Research Centre Newsletter (ISSN 0835-5509); (until 1987): Guelph Centre for Equine Research. Newsletter (ISSN 0837-1156)
Description: Contains articles on equine research and health written for the horse owner, educator and equine veterinary practitioner. Discusses practical applications of research being conducted at the center, as well as news of initiatives and achievements.

636.089　　　　　IR　　ISSN 0365-3439
INSTITUT RAZI. ARCHIVES. Key Title: Arshiv-i Mu'assasah-i Razi. (Text and summaries in English and French) 1940. a. free. Institut Razi, P.O. Box 11365-1588, Tehran, Iran. Indexed: Biol.Abstr., Dairy Sci.Abstr., Ind.Vet., Vet.Bull., Zoo.Rec. **Document type:** academic/scholarly publication.
—BLDSC (1628.300000).
Formerly (until 1963): Institut d'Hessarek. Archives (ISSN 0365-3196)

636.089　　　　　NP　　ISSN 1018-6182
　　　　　　　　　　　CODEN: JOISEP
INSTITUTE OF AGRICULTURE AND ANIMAL SCIENCE. JOURNAL. (Text in English) 1980. a. Institute of Agriculture and Animal Science, Rampur, Chitwan, Nepal. Indexed: Sport Fish.Abstr., Wild.Rev., Zoo.Rec. **Document type:** academic/scholarly publication.
—BLDSC (4769.935000).

636.089　　　　　BL　　ISSN 0020-3653
　　　　　　　　　　　CODEN: AIBOA3
INSTITUTO BIOLOGICO. ARQUIVOS. (Text in Portuguese; summaries in English) 1928. s-a. Cr.$1890($18) Instituto Biologico, Av. Rodrigues Alves 1252, C.P. 4185, Sao Paulo, Brazil. TEL 572-98-22. Ed. Manuel A.S.C. Portugal. illus.; index. (also avail. in microfilm) Indexed: Biol.Abstr., Chem.Abstr., Curr.Adv.Ecol.Sci., Dairy Sci.Abstr., Excerp.Med., Helminthol.Abstr., Hort.Abstr., Ind.Med., Ind.Vet., Rev.Appl.Entomol., Seed Abstr., Sorghum & Millets Abstr., Trop.Oil Seeds Abstr., Vet.Bull.
—BLDSC (1687.000000); CASDDS.

INSTITUTO COLOMBIANO AGROPECUARIO. REVISTA I C A. see AGRICULTURE

636.089　　　　　BL
INSTITUTO DE PESQUISAS VETERINARIAS DESIDERIO FINAMOR. BOLETIM. (Text in Portuguese; summaries in English) 1972. a. exchange basis only. Instituto de Pesquisas Veterinarias Desiderio Finamor, Caixa Postal 2076, 90000 Porto Alegre, RS, Brazil. adv. circ. 1,000. Indexed: Biol.Abstr., Dairy Sci.Abstr., Pig News & Info., Protozool.Abstr., Vet.Bull.

636.089　　　　　PE　　ISSN 0020-3963
INSTITUTO DE ZOONOSIS E INVESTIGACION PECUARIA REVISTA. (Text in Spanish; summaries in English) 1950. s-a. donations. Ministerio de Salud, Instituto de Zoonosis e Investigacion Pecuaria, Bibliotecaria, Apartado 1128, Lima, Peru. bk.rev.; abstr. circ. 1,000.
Formerly: Instituto de Investigaciones Pecuarias Revista.

636.08 664　　　　UN
INSTITUTO PANAMERICANO DE PROTECCION DE ALIMENTOS Y ZOONOSIS. PUBLICACION TECNICA. 1993. irreg., no.3, 1994. Instituto Panamericano de Proteccion de Alimentos y Zoonosis - Panamerican Institute for Food Protection and Zoonoses, Casilla 44, 1064 Martinez Buenos Aires, Argentina. TEL 792-4047. FAX 112328. TELEX 24577 AR PAZ. **Document type:** monographic series.

VETERINARY SCIENCE

INSTITUTUL AGRONOMIC ION IONESCU DE LA BRAD. LUCRARI STIINTIFICE, SERIA ZOOTEHNIE - MEDICINA VETERINARIA. see AGRICULTURE — Poultry And Livestock

636.089　　　　　　SW
INTERNATIONAL CONGRESS ON ANIMAL REPRODUCTION. PROCEEDINGS. 1948. quadrennial, 11th, 1988, Dublin. $60. International Standing Committee on International Congress on Animal Reproduction, c/o Prof. Stig Einarsson, Dept. of Obstetrics and Gynaecology, Swedish University of Agricultural Sciences, P.O. Box 7039, S-750 07 Uppsala, Sweden. circ. 2,000. **Indexed:** Biol.Abstr.
　Formerly: International Congress on Animal Reproduction and Artificial Insemination. Proceedings (ISSN 0074-4026)

636.089　　　　　　KE
INTERNATIONAL SCIENTIFIC COUNCIL FOR TRYPANOSOMIASIS RESEARCH AND CONTROL. (Text in English or French) 1951. biennial. price varies. (Interafrican Bureau for Animal Resources) Eleza Services Ltd., P.O. Box 30786, Nairobi, Kenya. Ed. K.M. Katondo. circ. 1,000. (back issues avail.) **Indexed:** Biol.Abstr.

636.7　　　　　　　US
INTERNATIONAL SYMPOSIUM ON CANINE HEARTWORM DISEASE. PROCEEDINGS. 1969. irreg., 2d, Jacksonville, 1971. $12. University of Florida, Institute of Food and Agricultural Sciences, Department of Veterinary Science, Gainesville, FL 32611-0620. TEL 904-392-1733. Ed. Richard E. Bradley. bibl.; illus. **Document type:** proceedings.

636.089　　　US　ISSN 0099-5851
　　　　　　　　　CODEN: ISUVA5
IOWA STATE UNIVERSITY VETERINARIAN. 1938. s-a. $12 to non-members. (American Veterinary Medical Association, Iowa State University Chapter) Iowa State University, College of Veterinary Medicine, Ames, IA 50011. TEL 515-294-0867. Ed. J.H. Greve. adv.; bk.rev.; index. circ. 2,500. (also avail. in microfiche from UMI; reprint service avail. from UMI) **Indexed:** Dairy Sci.Abstr., Ind.Vet., Pig News & Info., Small Anim.Abstr., Sport Fish.Abstr., Vet.Bull., Wild.Rev., Zoo.Rec. **Document type:** academic/scholarly publication.
　—Faxon; UMI.

636.089 798　　IT　ISSN 1120-5776
IPPOLOGIA. 1990. 4/yr. L.150000 (foreign L.170000). Societa Culturale Italiana Veterinaria per Piccoli Animali, Via Pallavicino 26, 26100 Cremona, Italy. TEL 39-372-235-01. FAX 39-372-45-70-91. Ed. Claudio Peruccio. adv.: B&W or color page L.1500000. circ. 6,800.
　—BLDSC (4567.462200).

636.089　　　　IE　ISSN 0368-0762
　　　　　　　　　CODEN: IVTJAJ
IRISH VETERINARY JOURNAL. vol.34, 1980. m. I£6. Irish Veterinary Association, 53 Lansdowne Rd., Ballsbridge, Dublin, Ireland. TEL 01-6685263. FAX 01-6604345. Ed. Dr. P.J. Hartigan. adv.; bk.rev.; abstr. circ. 1,300. **Indexed:** Agri.Eng.Abstr., Anim.Breed.Abstr., Chem.Abstr., Curr.Cont., Dairy Sci.Abstr., Excerp.Med., Helminthol.Abstr., Ind.Sci.Rev., Ind.Vet., INIS Atomind., Pig News & Info., Poult.Abstr., Protozool.Abstr., Rev.Med.& Vet.Mycol., Rev.Plant Path., Sci.Cit.Ind., Small Anim.Abstr., Sport Fish.Abstr., Vet.Bull., Wild.Rev., Zoo.Rec. **Document type:** academic/scholarly publication.
　—BLDSC (4575.000000); CASDDS; Genuine Article; UnCover.

ISRAEL INSTITUTE OF ANIMAL SCIENCE. SCIENTIFIC ACTIVITIES. see MEDICAL SCIENCES — Experimental Medicine, Laboratory Technique

636.089　　　IS　ISSN 0334-9152
　　　　　　　　　CODEN: RVETA5
ISRAEL JOURNAL OF VETERINARY MEDICINE. (Text in English and Hebrew) 1943. q. $75 (effective 1993). Israel Veterinary Medical Association, P.O. Box 3076, Rishon Le-Zion 75130, Israel. FAX 972-3-9681753. Ed. A. Hadani. adv.; bk.rev.; charts; illus. circ. 1,200. **Indexed:** Biol.Abstr., Biotech.Abstr., Chem.Abstr., Curr.Cont., Dairy Sci.Abstr., Excerp.Med., Food Sci.& Tech.Abstr., Helminthol.Abstr., Ind.Vet., Pig News & Info., Poult.Abstr., Protozool.Abstr., Rev.Appl.Entomol., Rev.Med.& Vet.Mycol., Small Anim.Abstr., Soyabean Abstr., Sport Fish.Abstr., Vet.Bull., Wild.Rev., Zoo.Rec.
　—BLDSC (4583.816000); CASDDS; SWETS; UnCover.
　Formerly (until 1986): Refuah Veterinarith (ISSN 0034-3153)

636.089　　　TU　ISSN 0378-2352
　　　　　　　　　CODEN: IUVDD7
ISTANBUL UNIVERSITESI. VETERINER FAKULTESI DERGISI/UNIVERSITY OF ISTANBUL. FACULTY OF VETERINARY MEDICINE. JOURNAL. Key Title: Veteriner Fakultesi Dergisi. (Text in Turkish; summaries in English, French and German) 1975. 2/yr. $6. Istanbul Universitesi, Veteriner Fakultesi - University of Istanbul, Faculty of Veterinary Medicine, Avcilar Campus, 34851 Avcilar - Istanbul, Turkey. TEL 90-212-5912193. FAX 90-212-5916991. Ed. Dr. M. Ercan Artan. circ. 750. **Indexed:** Biol.Abstr., Ind.Vet. **Document type:** academic/scholarly publication.

ISTITUTO SUPERIORE DI SANITA. ANNALI. see PUBLIC HEALTH AND SAFETY

636.08　　　　　JA
J A H A SHOREI HAPPYOKAI/JAPANESE ANIMAL HOSPITAL ASSOCIATION. PROCEEDINGS. (Text in Japanese) a. Nihon Dobutsu Byoin Fukushi Kyokai - Japanese Animal Hospital Association, 1-15 Shinogawa-cho, Ikeda Bldg. 201, Shinjuku-ku, Tokyo 162, Japan. TEL 03-3235-3251. FAX 03-3235-3277. **Document type:** proceedings.

J N K V V NEWS. (Jawaharlal Nehru Krishi Vishwa Vidyalaya) see AGRICULTURE

636.089　　　AU　ISSN 0075-2606
JAHRBUCH FUER DEN OESTERREICHISCHEN TIERARZT. 1950. a. S.378. Alois Goeschl and Co., Trummelhofgasse 12, A-1190 Vienna, Austria. Ed. Hiltraud Lechner. adv.

636.089　　　JA　ISSN 0388-7421
SF917　　　　　　CODEN: DIKNAA
JAPAN. MINISTRY OF AGRICULTURE, FORESTRY AND FISHERIES. NATIONAL VETERINARY ASSAY LABORATORY. ANNUAL REPORT. (Text and summaries in English, Japanese) 1960. a. free. Ministry of Agriculture, Forestry and Fisheries, National Veterinary Assay Laboratory, 1-15-1, Tokura, Kokubunji, Tokyo 185, Japan. TEL 423-21-1841. FAX 423-21-1769. Ed.Bd. circ. 800. (back issues avail.) **Indexed:** Ind.Vet., Poult.Abstr., Vet.Bull.
　—BLDSC (1369.500000); CASDDS.

636　　　　　JA　ISSN 0388-2403
　　　　　　　　　CODEN: NSKHD5
JAPAN. NATIONAL INSTITUTE OF ANIMAL HEALTH. BULLETIN/NORIN SUISANSHO KACHIKU EISEI SHIKENJO KENKYU HOKOKU. (Text in Japanese; summaries in European languages) 1918. s-a. exchange basis. Norin Suisansho, Kachiku Eisei Shikenjo - Ministry of Agriculture, Forestry and Fisheries, National Institute of Animal Health, 1-1 Kannondai 3-chome, Tsukuba-shi, Ibaraki-ken 305, Japan. FAX 0298-38-7907. Ed. Shinichi Terui. circ. 2,050. **Indexed:** Ind.Vet. **Document type:** government publication.
　—BLDSC (2640.030000); CASDDS.

JAPANESE JOURNAL OF SANITARY ZOOLOGY/EISEI DOBUTSU. see BIOLOGY — Zoology

636.089　　　JA　ISSN 0047-1917
　　　　　　　　　CODEN: JJVRAE
JAPANESE JOURNAL OF VETERINARY RESEARCH. (Text in English and European languages) 1954. q. exchange basis. Hokkaido University, Faculty of Veterinary Medicine - Hokkaido Daigaku Juigakubu, Nishi-9-chome, Kita-18-jo, Sapporo 060, Japan. FAX 011-717-7569. Ed. Masao Kamiga. bk.rev.; illus. circ. 650. (also avail. in microfilm; microfiche) **Indexed:** Anim.Breed.Abstr., Biol.Abstr., Chem.Abstr., Curr.Cont., Dairy Sci.Abstr., Excerp.Med., Helminthol.Abstr., Ind.Med., Ind.Sci.Rev., Ind.Vet., Nutr.Abstr., Pig News & Info., Protozool.Abstr., Sci.Cit.Ind., Sport Fish.Abstr., Vet.Bull., Wild.Rev., Wild.Rev. **Document type:** academic/scholarly publication.
　—BLDSC (4659.090000); EMDOCS; Genuine Article; UnCover.
　Formerly: Juigaku Kenkyu.

636.089　　　　JA
JOURNAL OF CLINICAL VETERINARY MEDICINE. m. 1200 Yen per no. Chikusan Publishing Co., Ltd. (Subsidiary of: Midori Group), Ikebukuro Nishiguchi Sky Bldg., 2-14-4 Ikebukuro, Toshima-ku, Tokyo 171, Japan. TEL 03-3590-9454. circ. 36,000. **Document type:** trade publication.
　Description: Designed for large animal veterinarians. Covers clinical medicine for large animals.

636.089　　　UK　ISSN 0021-9975
　　　　　　　　　CODEN: JCVPAR
JOURNAL OF COMPARATIVE PATHOLOGY. 1888. 8/yr. (in 2 vols.). £153 in Europe (rest of world $282) to individuals; institutions £218 in Europe (rest of world $392). W.B. Saunders Ltd. (Subsidiary of: Harcourt Brace & Company Ltd.), 24-28 Oval Rd., London NW1 7DX, England. TEL 0171-267-4466. FAX 0171-482-2293. TELEX 25775-ACPRES-G. (Subscr. to: Harcourt Brace & Company Ltd., Foots Cray High St., Sidcup, Kent DA14 5HP, England. TEL 0181-300-3322. FAX 0181-309-0807; US, Canadian, and Mexican subscr. to: W.B. Saunders Co., Journal Subscription Fulfilment, 6277 Sea Harbor Dr., 4th Fl., Orlando, FL 32887-4800. TEL 800-654-2452. FAX 800-874-6418) Ed. E.J.H. Ford. adv.; bibl.; charts; illus.; index. (reprint service avail. from KTO) **Indexed:** Anim.Breed.Abstr., Biol.Abstr., Biotech.Abstr., Chem.Abstr., Curr.Cont., Curr.Ref.Fish Res., Dairy Sci.Abstr., Dent.Ind., Excerp.Med., Helminthol.Abstr., Ind.Med., Ind.Sci.Rev., Ind.Vet., Nutr.Abstr., Pig News & Info., Poult.Abstr., Protozool.Abstr., Rev.Med.& Vet.Mycol., Rev.Plant Path., Sci.Cit.Ind., Small Anim.Abstr., Soyabean Abstr., Sport Fish.Abstr., Vet.Bull., Wild.Rev., Zoo.Rec. **Document type:** academic/scholarly publication.
　—BLDSC (4962.800000); CASDDS; EMDOCS; Faxon; Genuine Article; SWETS; UnCover. CCC.
　Description: Directed to workers in veterinary and medical science who investigate diseases of all vertebrate animals, including domesticated zoo, wild and marine species, and man.

636.089　　　US　ISSN 0737-0806
JOURNAL OF EQUINE VETERINARY SCIENCE. 1981. m. $60 to individuals; institutions $85 (Canada and Mexico $70; elsewhere $85) (effective 1994). Veterinary Data, Box 1209, Wildomar, CA 92595. TEL 909-678-1889. FAX 909-678-1885. Ed. Dr. William E. Jones; Pub. Dr. William E. Jones. adv.; bk.rev. circ. 3,175. **Indexed:** Anim.Breed.Abstr., Dairy Sci.Abstr., Ind.Vet., Vet.Bull. **Document type:** academic/scholarly publication.
　—BLDSC (4979.492000); Genuine Article; SWETS; UnCover.
　Incorporates: Equine Sportsmedicine News.

636.089　　　UK　ISSN 0022-4510
　　　　　　　　　CODEN: JAPRAN
JOURNAL OF SMALL ANIMAL PRACTICE. 1960. m. £88($220) British Veterinary Association, 7 Mansfield St., London W1M 0AT, England. TEL 0171-636-6541. FAX 0171-637-0620. Ed. W.D Tavernor. adv.; bk.rev.; bibl.; charts; illus.; index. circ. 3,500. (back issues avail.; reprint service avail. from ISI) **Indexed:** Anim.Breed.Abstr., Biotech.Abstr., Chem.Abstr, Curr.Adv.Ecol.Sci., Curr.Cont., Dairy Sci.Abstr., Excerp.Med., Helminthol.Abstr., Ind.Med., Ind.Sci.Rev., Ind.Vet., Protozool.Abstr., Rev.Med.& Vet.Mycol., Rev.Plant Path., Rice Abstr., Small Anim.Abstr., Sport Fish.Abstr., Vet.Bull., Wild.Rev., Zoo.Rec. **Document type:** academic/scholarly publication.
　—BLDSC (5064.700000); Faxon; Genuine Article; SWETS; UnCover. CCC.

VETERINARY SCIENCE

636.08 616.97 US ISSN 1082-2046
THE JOURNAL OF VETERINARY AND CLINICAL IMMUNOLOGY. 1993. q. $50 (Canada and Mexico $60; elsewhere $65) (effective 1996). (Academy of Veterinary Allergy & Clinical Immunology) Veterinary Practice Publishing Co., 7 Ashley Ave., S., Santa Barbara, CA 93103-3307. TEL 805-965-1028. FAX 805-965-0722. (Subscr. to: Box 4457, Santa Barbara, CA 93140-4457) **Document type:** academic/scholarly publication.

636.089 II ISSN 0971-0701
CODEN: KJVSAS
JOURNAL OF VETERINARY AND ANIMAL SCIENCES. 1970. s-a. Rs.40($25) (effective 1990). Kerala Agricultural University, Faculty of Veterinary and Animal Sciences, Trichur, Kerala, India. TEL 0487-23877. TELEX 887-268 KAU IN. Ed. C.P.N. Iyer. circ. 1,000. **Indexed:** Anim.Breed.Abstr., Biol.Abstr., Chem.Abstr., Dairy Sci.Abstr., Helminthol.Abstr., Ind.Vet., Nutr.Abstr., Rural Ext.Educ.& Tr.Abstr., Rural Recreat.Tour.Abstr., Sport Fish.Abstr., Vet.Bull., Wild.Rev., World Agri.Econ.& Rural Sociol.Abstr., Zoo.Rec. **Document type:** academic/scholarly publication.
—CASDDS.
Formerly (until vol.20, 1991): Kerala Journal of Veterinary Science (ISSN 0374-8774)

636.089 US ISSN 1040-6387
JOURNAL OF VETERINARY DIAGNOSTIC INVESTIGATION. 1989. q. $50 (foreign $60). American Association of Veterinary Laboratory Diagnosticians, c/o H.S. Gosser, Sec.-Treas., Box 6023, Columbia, MO 65205. TEL 314-882-6811. FAX 314-882-1411. Ed. Lenn R. Harrison. adv. **Indexed:** Sport Fish.Abstr., Wild.Rev.
—BLDSC (5072.360000); Genuine Article; SWETS; UnCover.
Description: Covers molecular biology, immunology, microbiology, clinical pathology, parasitology, anatomical pathology, toxicology, computer science and public health.

636.089 617.1 US ISSN 1056-6392
JOURNAL OF VETERINARY EMERGENCY AND CRITICAL CARE. 1991. 2/yr. $30 to individuals (Canada and Mexico $35; overseas $50); institutions $35 (Canada and Mexico $40; overseas $50). V.E.C.C.S. Administration Office, 15729 San Pedro, TX 78232. TEL 210-826-1488. Ed. Dr. Gary L. Stamp. adv.: B&W page $600; color page $1045; adv. contact: Mickey Debner. circ. 1,400. **Document type:** academic/scholarly publication.
Description: Covers clinical and nonclinical problems and solutions, case reports, and guest editorials.
Refereed Serial

636.089 US ISSN 0891-6640
CODEN: JVIMEM
JOURNAL OF VETERINARY INTERNAL MEDICINE. 1987. bi-m. $52 to individuals; institutions $73 (foreign $84); students and residents $27 (effective 1995). (American College of Veterinary Internal Medicine) W.B. Saunders Co. (Subsidiary of: Harcourt Brace & Company), Curtis Center, 3rd Fl., Independence Sq. W., Philadelphia, PA 19106-3399. TEL 215-238-7800. FAX 215-238-6445. (Subscr. to: Periodicals Fulfillment, W.B. Saunders Co., 6277 Sea Harbor Dr., 4th Fl., Orlando, FL 32891-4800. TEL 800-654-2452. FAX 800-874-6418) Ed. Dr. C. Guillermo Couto; Pub. Joan W. Blumberg. adv.: B&W page $625, color page $1450; 7 x 10; adv. contact: Steve Gray. illus.; index. circ. 3,924. (also avail. in microform from UMI) **Indexed:** Curr.Cont., Ind.Med., Ind.Vet., Rev.Med.& Vet.Mycol., Small Anim.Abstr., Vet.Bull. **Document type:** academic/scholarly publication.
—BLDSC (5072.365000); CASDDS; Faxon; Genuine Article; SWETS; UMI; UnCover. CCC.
Description: Covers small- and large-animal internal medicine, cardiology, neurology, pathophysiology, and the disease process.
Refereed Serial

636.089 378 US ISSN 0748-321X
JOURNAL OF VETERINARY MEDICAL EDUCATION. 1974. irreg. (2-4/yr.). $20 to individuals; institutions and foreign $30 (effective 1993). Association of American Veterinary Medical Colleges, c/o Richard B. Talbot, Ed., Virginia-Maryland Regional College of Veterinary Medicine, Virginia Polytechnic Institute and State University, Blacksburg, VA 24061. TEL 703-552-4701. FAX 703-552-8143. E-mail: Rtalbrt@Vt.edu. adv.; bk.rev. circ. 3,400. (also avail. in microform from UMI; reprint service avail. from UMI) **Indexed:** C.I.J.E., Cont.Pg.Educ. **Document type:** academic/scholarly publication.
—BLDSC (5072.370000); Faxon; Genuine Article; SWETS; UMI; UnCover.

636.089 JA ISSN 0916-7250
CODEN: JVMSEQ
JOURNAL OF VETERINARY MEDICAL SCIENCE. (Text in English) 1939. 6/yr. 25000 Yen (effective 1994). (Japanese Society of Veterinary Science - Nihon Juigakkai) Maruzen Co., Ltd., Maruzen Bldg., 3-10 Nihonbashi 2-chome, Chuo-ku, Tokyo 103, Japan. Ed. Hideaki Karaki. adv.; bk.rev. circ. 5,000. **Indexed:** Anim.Breed.Abstr., Biol.Abstr., Biotech.Abstr., Chem.Abstr., Curr.Cont., Dairy Sci.Abstr., Dent.Ind., Diar.Dis.Res., Helminthol.Abstr., Ind.Med., Ind.Vet., Nutr.Abstr., Pig News & Info., Poult.Abstr., Protozool.Abstr., Rev.Med.& Vet.Mycol., Sci.Cit.Ind., Small Anim.Abstr., Soils & Fert., Sport Fish.Abstr., Vet.Bull., Weed Abstr., Wild.Rev., Zoo.Rec. **Document type:** academic/scholarly publication.
—BLDSC (5072.375000); CASDDS; Faxon; Genuine Article; SWETS; UnCover. CCC.
Formerly (until 1991): Japanese Journal of Veterinary Science (ISSN 0021-5295)
Description: International journal on basic and applied veterinary medical sciences

636.089 GW ISSN 0931-184X
CODEN: JVMAE6
JOURNAL OF VETERINARY MEDICINE. SERIES A; animal physiology, pathology, and clinical veterinary medicine. (Supplement avail.: Advances in Veterinary Medicine - Fortschritte der Veterinaermedizin) (Text in English, German) 1953. 10/yr. DM.1401($1038) in Europe; rest of world DM.1437($1064) (effective 1996). Blackwell Wissenschaft, Kurfuerstendamm 57, 10707 Berlin, Germany. TEL 030-32790623. FAX 030-32790610. Ed.Bd. adv.: B&W page DM.560; trim 202 x 122. bk.rev.; illus.; index, cum.index. circ. 400. (back issues avail.) **Indexed:** Anim.Breed.Abstr., Biol.Abstr., Biotech.Abstr., Chem.Abstr., Curr.Adv.Biochem., Curr.Adv.Ecol.Sci., Curr.Cont., Dairy Sci.Abstr., Excerpt.Med. (until 1993), Food Sci.& Tech.Abstr., Helminthol.Abstr., Ind.Med., Ind.Vet., Nutr.Abstr., Pig News & Info., Poult.Abstr., Sci.Cit.Ind., Small Anim.Abstr., Sport Fish.Abstr., Triticale Abstr., Vet.Bull., Wild.Rev., Zoo.Rec. **Document type:** academic/scholarly publication.
—BLDSC (5072.385000); CASDDS; Faxon; Genuine Article; SWETS; UnCover. CCC.
Formerly: Zentralblatt fuer Veterinaermedizin. Reihe A (ISSN 0300-8711); Supersedes in part (1953-1969): Zentralblatt fuer Veterinaermedizin (ISSN 0044-4294)

636.089 GW ISSN 0931-1793
CODEN: JVMBE9
JOURNAL OF VETERINARY MEDICINE. SERIES B; infectious diseases and veterinary public health. (Supplement: Advances in Veterinary Medicine) (Text in English, German; summaries in English) 1953. 10/yr. DM.1401($1048) in Europe; rest of world DM.1437($1064) (effective 1996). Blackwell Wissenschaft, Kurfuerstendamm 57, 10707 Berlin, Germany. TEL 030-32790623. FAX 030-32790610. Ed.Bd. adv.: B&W page DM.560; trim 190 x 122. bk.rev.; illus.; stat.; index; cum.index. circ. 450. (back issues avail.) **Indexed:** Biol.Abstr., Biotech.Abstr., Chem.Abstr., Curr.Adv.Ecol.Sci., Curr.Cont., Dairy Sci.Abstr., Food Sci.& Tech.Abstr., Helminthol.Abstr., Ind.Med., Nutr.Abstr., Pig News & Info., Poult.Abstr., Protozool.Abstr., Rev.Med.& Vet.Mycol., Rev.Plant Path., Sci.Cit.Ind., Sport Fish.Abstr., Vet.Bull., Wild.Rev., Zoo.Rec. **Document type:** academic/scholarly publication.
—BLDSC (5072.386000); CASDDS; Faxon; SWETS; UnCover. CCC.
Formerly: Zentralblatt fuer Veterinaermedizin. Reihe B (ISSN 0514-7166); Supersedes in part (1953-1963): Zentralblatt fuer Veterinaermedizin (ISSN 0044-4294)
Description: Covers all aspects of veterinary microbiology and parasitology.

JOURNAL OF VETERINARY PHARMACOLOGY AND THERAPEUTICS. see PHARMACY AND PHARMACOLOGY

636.089 US ISSN 0090-3558
CODEN: JWIDAW
JOURNAL OF WILDLIFE DISEASES. 1965. q. $89 to institutions. Wildlife Disease Association, Inc., Box 1897, Lawrence, KS 66044-8897. TEL 913-843-1221. FAX 913-843-1221. adv.; bk.rev.; abstr.; charts; illus.; index; circ. 1,350 (paid). (back issues avail.) **Indexed:** Bio-Contr.News & Info., Biol.Abstr., Biol.Dig., Chem.Abstr., Curr.Adv.Ecol.Sci., Curr.Cont., Curr.Ref.Fish Res., Dairy Sci.Abstr., Dent.Ind., Environ.Per.Bibl., Helminthol.Abstr., Ind.Med., Ind.Sci.Rev., Ind.Vet., INIS Atomind., Key Word Ind.Wildl.Res., Ocean.Abstr., Pig News & Info., Pollut.Abstr., Poult.Abstr., Protozool.Abstr., Rev.Appl.Entomol., Rev.Med.& Vet.Mycol., Rev.Plant Path., Small Anim.Abstr., Soils & Fert., Sport Fish.Abstr., Vet.Bull., Wild Life Rev., Wild.Rev., Zoo.Rec. **Document type:** academic/scholarly publication.
—BLDSC (5072.620000); CASDDS; Faxon; UnCover.
Former titles: Wildlife Disease Association. Journal (ISSN 0043-5473); Wildlife Disease Association. Bulletin.
Refereed Serial

JOURNAL OF WILDLIFE REHABILITATION. see BIOLOGY

636 US ISSN 1042-7260
CODEN: JZWMEI
JOURNAL OF ZOO AND WILDLIFE MEDICINE. 1971. q. $140 (Canada & Mexico $140; elsewhere $155) (effective 1996). American Association of Zoo Veterinarians, 3400 Girard Ave., Philadelphia, PA 19104-1196. TEL 215-387-9094. FAX 215-387-2165. Ed. Wilbur B. Amond. adv.; bk.rev.; charts; illus.; stat.; cum.index: 1970-1987. circ. 1,200. (processed; back issues avail.) **Indexed:** Curr.Adv.Ecol.Sci., Curr.Cont., Dairy Sci.Abstr., Environ.Abstr., Helminthol.Abstr., Ind.Sci.Rev., Ind.Vet., Small Anim.Abstr., Sport Fish.Abstr., Vet.Bull., Wild.Rev., Zoo.Rec. **Document type:** academic/scholarly publication.
—BLDSC (5072.765000); Faxon; Genuine Article; UnCover.
Formerly: Journal of Zoo Animal Medicine (ISSN 0093-4526)
Description: Publishes original research findings and clinical observations as well as case reports in the field of veterinary medicine dealing with captive and free-ranging wild animals.
Refereed Serial

VETERINARY SCIENCE

636.089   MY   ISSN 0128-2506
CODEN: JVEME2
JURNAL VETERINAR MALAYSIA. (Text in English; summaries in English and Malay) 1967; N.S. 1989. s-a. Veterinary Association of Malaysia (VAM), Universiti Pertanian Malaysia, Faculty of Veterinary Medicine & Animal Science, 43400 UPM, Serdang, Selangor, Malaysia. TEL 03-9486101. FAX 03-9482507. TELEX UNIPER-MA-37454. Ed. Dr. Tan Hock Seng. adv.; bk.rev.; abstr.; charts; illus.; index. circ. 500. **Indexed:** Anim.Breed.Abstr., Helminthol.Abstr., Ind.Vet., Nutr.Abstr., Pig News & Info., Poult.Abstr., Small Anim.Abstr., Sport Fish.Abstr., Vet.Bull., Virol.Abstr., Wild.Rev., Zoo.Rec. **Document type:** academic/scholarly publication.
     Supersedes (in 1989): Kajian Veterinar Malaysia (ISSN 0126-9437); Which was formerly (until 1978): Kajian Veterinar (ISSN 0047-309X)
     Description: Publishes research papers, articles and short communications on various apects of veterinary medicine and animal science.

636.089   KE
KENYA AGRICULTURAL RESEARCH INSTITUTE. VETERINARY RESEARCH DEPARTMENT. ANNUAL REPORT. (Text in English) 1977. a. Kenya Agricultural Research Institute, Box 30148, Nairobi, Kenya. **Indexed:** Field Crop Abstr., Herb.Abstr., Rev.Appl.Entomol., Weed Abstr.

636.089   KE   ISSN 0256-5161
KENYA VETERINARIAN. (Text in English) 1977. s-a. $10. Kenya Veterinary Association, Box 29089, Nairobi, Kenya. Ed. Dr. Thomas T. Dolan. adv. circ. 500. **Indexed:** Ind.Vet., Soils & Fert., Vet.Bull.

636.089   GW   ISSN 0023-2076
KLEINTIER-PRAXIS; Archiv fuer kleine Haus- und Nutztiere sowie Laboratoriums- und Zoo-Tiere. (Text in German; summaries in English) 1956. 12/yr. DM.195. (World Small Animal Veterinary Association, Deutsche Gruppe) Verlag M. und H. Schaper GmbH, Kalandstr. 4, 31061 Alfeld, Germany. TEL 05181-8009-0. FAX 05181-800933. (Subscr. to: Postfach 1642, 31046 Alfeld, Germany) adv.; bk.rev.; bibl.; charts; illus.; index. circ. 3,500. **Indexed:** Anim.Breed.Abstr., Biol.Abstr., Biotech.Abstr., Chem.Abstr., Curr.Adv.Ecol.Sci., Curr.Cont., Dairy Sci.Abstr., Helminthol.Abstr., Ind.Sci.Rev., Ind.Vet., Nutr.Abstr., Rev.Plant Path., Small Anim.Abstr., Soils & Fert., Vet.Bull. **Document type:** trade publication.
—BLDSC (5099.121000); Genuine Article; SWETS. CCC.

KONGELIGE VETERINAER- OG LANDBOHOEJSKOLE. HAANDBOG. see *AGRICULTURE*

LARGE ANIMAL VETERINARIAN; covering health & nutrition. see *AGRICULTURE — Poultry And Livestock*

636.089   US   ISSN 1069-1774
LARGE ANIMAL VETERINARY REPORT. 1990. m. $50 to individuals; institutions $75 (Canada and Mexico $60; elsewhere $75) (effective 1994). Veterinary Data, Box 1209, Wildomar, CA 92595. TEL 909-678-1889. FAX 909-678-1885. Ed. Dr. William E. Jones; Pub. Dr. William E. Jones. **Document type:** newsletter.

LIVESTOCK ADVISER; an English monthly dedicated to improve the animal wealth of India. see *AGRICULTURE — Poultry And Livestock*

LLAMAS MAGAZINE; information for Camelid lovers everywhere. see *BIOLOGY — Zoology*

636.089   HU   ISSN 0025-004X
CODEN: MGALA5
MAGYAR ALLATORVOSOK LAPJA/JOURNAL OF HUNGARIAN VETERINARY SCIENCE. (Text in Hungarian; table of contents and summaries in English, German and Russian) 1946. m. 1680 Ft.($42) (Ministry of Agriculture) Springer Hungarica Kiado Ltd., Wesselenyi u. 28, 1075 Budapest, Hungary. TEL 141-3023. FAX 142-6518. TELEX 61-2294391 AAOE H. Ed. Hollo Ferenc. adv.; bk.rev.; abstr.; bibl.; charts; illus.; index. circ. 4,300. **Indexed:** Agri.Eng.Abstr., Anim.Breed.Abstr., Biol.Abstr., Biotech.Abstr., Chem.Abstr., Curr.Adv.Ecol.Sci., Curr.Cont., Dairy Sci.Abstr., Food Sci.& Tech.Abstr., Helminthol.Abstr., Ind.Sci.Rev., Ind.Vet., INIS Atomind., Maize Abstr., Nutr.Abstr., Pig News & Info., Poult.Abstr., Protozool.Abstr., Rev.Med.& Vet.Mycol., Rev.Plant Path., Small Anim.Abstr., Soyabean Abstr., Vet.Bull.
—BLDSC (5340.300000); CASDDS; Genuine Article; SWETS.

636.089   IR   ISSN 1022-646X
CODEN: JVFTDR
MAJALLAH-I DANISHKADAH-I DAMPIZISHKI/JOURNAL OF THE FACULTY OF VETERINARY MEDICINE. (Text in Persian; contents page in English) 1937. q. Rs.1000($10) University of Teheran, Faculty of Veterinary Medicine - Danishgah-i Tehran, Danishkadah-i Dampizishki, Azadi Ave., P.O. Box 14155-6453, Tehran, Iran. Ed. I. Pousty. adv.; bk.rev.; abstr.; bibl.; illus. circ. 700. **Indexed:** Anim.Breed.Abstr., Dairy Sci.Abstr., ExtraMED, Ind.Vet., Nutr.Abstr., Poult.Abstr., Protozool.Abstr., Vet.Bull., Zoo.Rec. **Document type:** academic/scholarly publication.
●Also available on CD-ROM.
—BLDSC (4912.243000); CASDDS.
     Formerly (until 1993): Namah-i Danishkadah-i Dampizishki (ISSN 0042-0123)
     Description: Publishes original research results in all branches of veterinary medicine.

636.089   MW   ISSN 0076-3365
MALAWI. DEPARTMENT OF VETERINARY SERVICES AND ANIMAL INDUSTRY. ANNUAL REPORT. a. K.1.50. Government Printer, P.O. Box 37, Zomba, Malawi. **Indexed:** Anim.Breed.Abstr., Field Crop Abstr., Herb.Abstr. **Document type:** government publication.

636.089   CN   ISSN 0225-9591
CODEN: MVEQDC
MEDECIN VETERINAIRE DU QUEBEC. (Text in French) 1971. q. Can.$30($40) Corporation Professionnelle des Medecins Veterinaires du Quebec - Corporation of Veterinarians of Quebec, 795, av. du Palais, Ste. 200, Saint Hyacinte, PQ J2S 5C6, Canada. TEL 514-774-1423. FAX 514-774-7635. Ed. Guy-Pierre Martineau. adv. circ. 2,050. **Indexed:** Biol.Abstr., Dairy Sci.Abstr., Helminthol.Abstr., Ind.Vet., Pt.de Rep. (1983-), Small Anim.Abstr., Sport Fish.Abstr., Vet.Bull., Wild.Rev.
—BLDSC (5487.670000).

636.08   SP   ISSN 0212-8292
SF604   CODEN: MEVEEB
MEDICINA VETERINARIA. 1984. m. Pulso Ediciones S.A., Rambla del Celler, 117-119, 08190 Sant Cugat del Vallei (Barcelona), Spain. TEL 34-3-5896264. **Indexed:** Apic.Abstr., Excerp.Med. (1993-), Rev.Med.& Vet.Mycol., Sport Fish.Abstr., Wild.Rev., Zoo.Rec.
—BLDSC (5533.845000).

636.08   PO   ISSN 0870-4295
MEDICO VETERINARIO. 1986. q. Esc.7300 in Europe; elsewhere Esc.8500 (effective 1995). Edicoes Vade-mecum, Lda., Calcada do Tijolo 45, 1200 Lisbon, Portugal. TEL 351-1-3420518. FAX 351-1-3420682. Ed. Dr. Jose Paulo Sales Luis. adv. contact: Joaquim Azevedo. circ. 3,000.
     Description: Publishes veterinary articles. Includes information on new products and services, meetings and congresses.

636.089   PL   ISSN 0025-8628
CODEN: MDWTAG
MEDYCYNA WETERYNARYJNA. (Text in Polish; summaries in English) 1945. m. $84. (Polskie Towarzystwo Nauk Weterynaryjnych - Polish Society of Veterinary Sciences) Medycyna Weterynaryjna, Ul. Akademicka 12, 20-033 Lublin, Poland. TEL 48-81-329-12. TELEX 643176 ARPL. Ed. Prof. Dr. Edmund Prost. adv.; bk.rev.; abstr.; bibl.; charts; illus.; mkt.; index, cum.index. circ. 3,300. **Indexed:** Agri.Eng.Abstr., Anim.Breed.Abstr., Biol.Abstr., Chem.Abstr., Dairy Sci.Abstr., Excerp.Med., Food Sci.& Tech.Abstr., Helminthol.Abstr., Ind.Vet., INIS Atomind., Nutr.Abstr., Pig News & Info., Poult.Abstr., Protozool.Abstr., Rev.Appl.Entomol., Rev.Med.& Vet.Mycol., Rev.Plant Path., Small Anim.Abstr., Vet.Bull. **Document type:** academic/scholarly publication.
—BLDSC (5536.050000); CASDDS; Genuine Article.
     Description: Devoted to the problems of veterinary science and practice.

636.089   US   ISSN 0076-6542
SF748
MERCK VETERINARY MANUAL: A HANDBOOK OF DIAGNOSIS AND THERAPY FOR THE VETERINARIAN. 1955. irreg., 7th ed., 1992. $24. Merck and Co., Inc., Attn: Merck Publishing, Box 2000, WBS-435, Rahway, NJ 07065. TEL 908-855-4558. Ed. Clarence Fraser.

636.089 616.01   DK
MIKROBIOLOGI-NYT. 1983. q. $10. Mikrobiologisk Gruppe-Levnedsmiddelselskabet, Ingenioerhuset, Vester Farimagsgade 29, DK-1606 Copenhagen V, Denmark. TEL 45-42-88-33-22. FAX 45-42-88-47-74. TELEX 37529 DTHDIA. Ed. Lone Gram. adv.; bk.rev. (looseleaf format) **Document type:** newsletter.
     Formerly: Hurtigmetode-nyt (ISSN 0109-0763)

636.089   US   ISSN 0362-8140
CODEN: MVPRAX
MODERN VETERINARY PRACTICE. 1920. 12/yr. $42 (Canada $49; foreign $65) (effective 1993). American Veterinary Publications, Inc., 5782 Thornwood Dr., Goleta, CA 93117-3896. TEL 805-967-5988. Ed. Dr. P.W. Pratt. adv.; bk.rev.; bibl.; charts; illus. circ. 3,000. **Indexed:** Anim.Breed.Abstr., Biol.Abstr., Biotech.Abstr., Chem.Abstr., Curr.Adv.Ecol.Sci., Curr.Cont., Dairy Sci.Abstr., Dent.Ind., Helminthol.Abstr., Ind.Med., Ind.Sci.Rev., Ind.Vet., Poult.Abstr., Protozool.Abstr., Rev.Med.& Vet.Mycol., Rev.Plant Path., Small Anim.Abstr., Vet.Bull.
—UMI. CCC.
     Incorporates (1983-1986): Veterinary Computing (ISSN 8755-0946)
     Description: Abstracts of clinically oriented articles from worldwide veterinary literature.

636.089 574.524   PL   ISSN 0540-6722
MONOGRAFIE PARAZYTOLOGICZNE. 1959. irreg., vol.10, 1985. price varies. Polskie Towarzystwo Parazytologiczne (Wroclaw), Norwida 29, 50-375 Wroclaw, Poland. (Dist. by: Ars Polona, Krakowskie Przedmiescie 7, 00-068 Warsaw, Poland) Ed. Leszek Grzywinski. bibl.; illus. circ. 400. (back issues avail.) **Indexed:** Biol.Abstr. **Document type:** monographic series.

NAUKA U PRAKSI. see *AGRICULTURE*

636.089   US   ISSN 0277-3015
NEW METHODS; the journal of animal health technology. 1977-1984 (Jan.); resumed Nov. 1984. irreg. $29. New Methods Co., Box 22605, San Francisco, CA 94122-0605. TEL 415-664-3469; 800-435-3218. Ed. Ronald S. Lippert. adv.; bk.rev.; bibl.; charts; illus.; index; circ. 5,600. (controlled). (back issues avail.) **Document type:** trade publication, newsletter.
—CCC.
     Formerly: Methods: The Journal of Animal Health Technology.
     Description: Information source that represents basic interests in the animal health profession.

VETERINARY SCIENCE 6533

636.089   NZ   ISSN 0048-0169
CODEN: NEZTAF
NEW ZEALAND VETERINARY JOURNAL. 1952. 6/yr. NZ.$70 to individuals; institutions NZ.$140. New Zealand Veterinary Association, P.O. Box 27-499, Wellington, New Zealand. TEL 64-4-471-0484. FAX 64-4-471-0494. Ed. A. W. Keber. bk.rev.; illus. circ. 1,750. **Indexed:** Anim.Breed.Abstr., Biol.Abstr., Biotech.Abstr., Cadscan, Chem.Abstr., Curr.Adv.Ecol.Sci., Curr.Cont., Dairy Sci.Abstr., Excerp.Med., Field Crop Abstr., Helminthol.Abstr., Herb.Abstr., Ind.Med., Ind.Sci.Rev., Ind.Vet., Lead Abstr., Maize Abstr., Nutr.Abstr., Pig News & Info., Poult.Abstr., Protozool.Abstr., Rev.Appl.Entomol., Rev.Med.& Vet.Mycol., Rev.Plant Path., Small Anim.Abstr., Soils & Fert., Sport Fish.Abstr., Vet.Bull., Wild.Rev., Zincscan, Zoo.Rec. **Document type:** academic/scholarly publication.
—BLDSC (6099.900000); CASDDS; Faxon; Genuine Article; SWETS; UnCover. **CCC.**
Description: Publishes original research and clinical observations in all aspects of veterinary science.
Refereed Serial

NIGERIA. NATIONAL ANIMAL PRODUCTION RESEARCH INSTITUTE. JOURNAL. see *AGRICULTURE — Poultry And Livestock*

630 636.089   JA   ISSN 0373-8361
CODEN: NJDKAF
NIPPON JUI CHIKUSAN DAIGAKU KENKYU HOKOKU/NIPPON VETERINARY AND ANIMAL SCIENCE UNIVERSITY. BULLETIN. (Text in English or Japanese; summaries in English) 1953. a. 2000 Yen (effective 1993). Nippon Jui Chikusan Daigaku, 1-7-1 Kyonan-cho, Musashino-shi, Tokyo 180, Japan. TEL 422-31-4151. FAX 422-33-2035. Ed.Bd. circ. 500 (controlled). (reprint service avail.) **Indexed:** Anim.Breed.Abstr., Biol.Abstr., Dairy Sci.Abstr., Helminthol.Abstr., Ind.Vet., Protozool.Abstr., Rev.Med.& Vet.Mycol., Vet.Bull. **Document type:** academic/scholarly publication.
●Also available online.
—BLDSC (2446.875000); CASDDS.
Formerly: Nippon Jui Chikusan Daigaku Kiyo (ISSN 0078-0839)

636.089   NO   ISSN 0078-6721
NORGES VETERINAERHOEGSKOLE. PUBLIKASJONER/NORWEGIAN COLLEGE OF VETERINARY MEDICINE. PUBLICATIONS. 1981. a. free or on exchange basis. Norges Veterinaerhoegskole - Norwegian College of Veterinary Medicine, P.O. Box 8146 Dep., 0033 Oslo 1, Norway. TEL 47-22-96-45-55. FAX 47-22-96-45-31. circ. 1,500. **Document type:** academic/scholarly publication.

636.089   NO   ISSN 0029-2273
CODEN: NOVDAH
NORSK VETERINAERTIDSSKRIFT. 1888. m. NOK 650 (free to qualified personnel). Norske Veterinaerforening, General Birchs Gate 16, N-0454 Oslo, Norway. TEL 47-22-567650. FAX 47-22-690450. Ed. Ulf Erik Gustavsen. adv.; bk.rev.; charts; illus.; index. circ. 2,300. (reprint service avail.) **Indexed:** Anim.Breed.Abstr., Biol.Abstr., Biotech.Abstr., Dairy Sci.Abstr., Food Sci.& Tech.Abstr., Helminthol.Abstr., Ind.Vet., Landwirt.Zentralbl., Pig News & Info., Protozool.Abstr., Ref.Zh., Small Anim.Abstr., Vet.Bull. **Document type:** academic/scholarly publication.
Description: Prints information of interest to veterinarians and others with interest in public health, hygiene and meat control.

NOVOSTI VETERINARNOI FARMATSII I MEDITSINY. see *PHARMACY AND PHARMACOLOGY*

636.089 578   FR   ISSN 0300-9823
SF781   CODEN: OTEBA6
O I E BULLETIN. (Text in English, French, Spanish) m. 800 F.($148) (effective 1995). Office International des Epizooties, 12 rue de Prony, 75017 Paris, France. TEL 44-15-18-88. FAX 42-67-09-87. TELEX EPIZOTI 642 285 F. (U.S. Subscr. to: Scientific, Medical Publications of France, 100 E. 42nd St., Ste 1002, New York, NY 10017. TEL 212-983-6278) Ed. J. Blancou. adv. contact: Gill Dilmitis. **Indexed:** Ind.Vet., Vet.Bull. **Document type:** bulletin.
—BLDSC (2663.000000).
Description: Presents monthly evolution of the major epizootic diseases throughout the world.

636.089 578   FR   ISSN 0253-1933
SF781   CODEN: RTOEDX
O I E REVUE SCIENTIFIQUE ET TECHNIQUE/O I E SCIENTIFIC AND TECHNICAL REVIEW. (Text in English, French or Spanish; summaries in English, French, Spanish) 1982. q. 735 F.($136) (effective 1995). Office International des Epizooties, 12 rue de Prony, 75017 Paris, France. TEL 44-15-18-88. FAX 42-67-09-87. TELEX EPIZOTI 642 285 F. (U.S. Subscr. to: Scientific, Medical Publications of France, 100 E. 42nd St., Ste. 1002, New York, NY 10017. TEL 212-983-6278) Ed. J. Blancou. adv. contact: Gill Dilmitis. **Indexed:** Bio-Contr.News & Info., Dairy Sci.Abstr., Ind.Vet., Pig News & Info., Protozool.Abstr., Small Anim.Abstr., Vet.Bull. **Document type:** academic/scholarly publication.
—BLDSC (7950.029000); Genuine Article; SWETS; UnCover.
Description: Promotes experimental or other research work on diagnosis and control of contagious diseases of livestock. Also includes documents of importance to Chief Veterinary Officers of 143 member countries and to the world medical and veterinary scientific communities.
Refereed Serial

636.089   IT   ISSN 0392-1913
OBIETTIVI E DOCUMENTI VETERINARI. Short title: O D V. 1980. m. (11/yr.) L.73000 (effective 1996). Edagricole S.p.A., Via Emilia Levante 31, 40139 Bologna, Italy. TEL 39-51-492211. FAX 39-51-493660. Ed. Giovanni Ballarini. adv.: B&W page L.1250000, color page L.1950000; 185 x 247. circ. 16,900. **Indexed:** Dairy Sci.Abstr., Ind.Vet., Protozool.Abstr., Small Anim.Abstr., Vet.Bull. —BLDSC (6196.955000).
Description: Covers the veterinary sciences. Provides professional training information.

636.08   AU
OESTERREICHISCHE FREIBERUFS TIERARZT. q. S.250; newsstand price: S.75. (Berufverband Freiberuflich Taetiger Tieraerzte Oesterreichs) Ostag Werbung und Verlag, Wickenburggasse 17, A-1082 Vienna, Austria. TEL 01-4027573. FAX 01-4088292. adv.: B&W page S.7490, color page S.16040; trim 250 x 165. circ. 2,750. **Document type:** trade publication.

636.089   AU   ISSN 0048-1475
OESTERREICHISCHE TIERAERZTEZEITUNG. 1949. m. S.400 (foreign S.450) (effective 1995). (Bundeskammer der Tieraerzte Oesterreichs) Ostag Werbung und Verlag, Wickenburggasse 17, A-1082 Vienna, Austria. TEL 01-4027573. FAX 01-4088292. Ed. Dr. Richard Elhenicky. adv.: B&W page S.7950, color page S.16500; trim 250 x 180. bk.rev. circ. 2,450. **Indexed:** Ind.Vet., Pig News & Info., Vet.Bull. **Document type:** trade publication.

636.089   AU   ISSN 0029-9766
OESTERREICHISCHER KLEINTIERZUECHTER, Fachblatt fuer die gesamte Kleintierzucht. 1946. m. S.250. Rassezuchtverband Oesterreichischer Kleintierzuechter, Postfach 14, A-4910 Ried im Innkreis, Austria. Ed. Karl Rudinger. adv.; bk.rev.; illus. circ. 6,000.

636.089   US
OHIO VETERINARY MEDICAL ASSOCIATION. NEWSLETTER. 1952. m. $2 membership. Ohio Veterinary Medical Association, 3168 Riverside Dr., Columbus, OH 43221. TEL 614-486-7253. FAX 614-486-1325. Ed. George Kukor. adv.; illus. circ. 1,930. **Document type:** newsletter.
Formerly (until 1970): Ohio Veterinarian (ISSN 0030-1213)

636.089   JA   ISSN 0911-5137
OKINAWA-KEN KACHIKU EISEI SHIKENJO NENPO/OKINAWA PREFECTURAL INSTITUTE OF ANIMAL HEALTH. ANNUAL REPORT. (Text in Japanese; summaries in English) 1958. a. free. Okinawa-ken Kachiku Eisei Shikenjo - Okinawa Prefectural Institute of Animal Health, 112 Kohagura, Naha-shi, Okinawa-ken 900, Japan. TEL 0988-32-1515. circ. 300. (back issues avail.)
Description: Covers research on animal diseases.

636.089   SA   ISSN 0030-2465
SF601   CODEN: OJVRAZ
ONDERSTEPOORT JOURNAL OF VETERINARY RESEARCH. 1933. q. R.120 (effective 1995). Agricultural Research Council, Onderstepoort Veterinary Institute, Private Bag X05, Onderstepoort 0110, South Africa. TEL 27-12-5299101. FAX 27-12-5299318. TELEX 322088 SA. E-mail: library@moon.ovi.ac.za. (Subscr. to: M. Hechter, Technical Ed., Directorate of Agricultural Information, Private Bag X144, Pretoria 0001, South Africa) Ed. D.W. Verwoerd. bk.rev.; bibl.; charts; illus.; index, cum.index: 1933-1968, 1969-1973; circ. 600 (controlled). (also avail. in microform from UMI,PMC; reprint service avail. from UMI) **Indexed:** Abstr.Hyg., Agri.Eng.Abstr., Anim.Breed.Abstr., Biol.Abstr., Biol.& Agr.Ind., Biotech.Abstr., Chem.Abstr., Curr.Adv.Ecol.Sci., Curr.Cont., Dairy Sci.Abstr., Field Crop Abstr., Food Sci.& Tech.Abstr., Helminthol.Abstr., Herb.Abstr., Ind.Med., Ind.S.A.Per., Ind.Vet., Nutr.Abstr., Pig News & Info., Poult.Abstr., Protozool.Abstr., Rev.Appl.Entomol., Rev.Med.& Vet.Mycol., Rev.Plant Path., Sport Fish.Abstr., Trop.Dis.Bull., Vet.Bull., Wild.Rev., Zoo.Rec. **Document type:** academic/scholarly publication.
—BLDSC (6258.000000); CASDDS; Faxon; Genuine Article; SWETS; UMI; UnCover.
Description: Publishes papers reporting on original research covering all aspects of veterinary science, with particular emphasis on diseases and disease vectors of livestock and wildlife on the African continent of more than local interest.
Refereed Serial

ONS VEE; maandblad voor de veehouderij. see *AGRICULTURE — Poultry And Livestock*

636.08   FR
ORDRE DES VETERINAIRES. REVUE. 4/yr. 34 rue Breguet, 75011 Paris, France. TEL 47-00-12-27. FAX 47-00-09-25. Ed. Christine Santoni. circ. 8,500.

PAKISTAN JOURNAL OF AGRICULTURE, AGRICULTURAL ENGINEERING AND VETERINARY SCIENCES. see *AGRICULTURE*

PAKISTAN JOURNAL OF ANIMAL SCIENCES. see *AGRICULTURE — Poultry And Livestock*

636.089   PK
PAKISTAN VETERINARIAN; animal sciences. (Text in English) 1988. m. $5 per no. Press Corporation of Pakistan, P.O. Box 3138, Karachi 75400, Pakistan. TEL 21-455-3703. FAX 21-7736198. Ed. Saeed Hafeez. circ. 5,000.

636.089   PK   ISSN 0253-8318
CODEN: PVJODU
PAKISTAN VETERINARY JOURNAL. (Text in English) 1981. q. Rs.200($50) (effective 1994). University of Agriculture, Faculty of Veterinary Science, Faisalabad, Pakistan. TEL 92-411-618161. FAX 92-411-60200. Ed. Mohammed Nawaz. adv.; bk.rev. circ. 600. **Indexed:** Anim.Breed.Abstr., Biol.Abstr., Chem.Abstr., Dairy Sci.Abstr., Ind.Vet., Poult.Abstr., Protozool.Abstr., Small Anim.Abstr., Sport Fish.Abstr., Vet.Bull., Wild.Rev., Zoo.Rec. **Document type:** academic/scholarly publication.
—BLDSC (6343.170000); CASDDS.

PARASITOLOGY TODAY; international review journal in the field of medical and veterinary parasites. see *MEDICAL SCIENCES — Communicable Diseases*

PARASITOLOGY TODAY (REFERENCE EDITION). see *MEDICAL SCIENCES — Communicable Diseases*

636.089   IE
PEGASUS. 1954. a. £1. Veterinary Students Union of Ireland, Veterinary College of Ireland, Ballsbridge, Dublin, 4, Ireland. Eds. Donal Sammin, Brendan Fee. adv.; bk.rev. circ. 1,500.
Formerly: A V S Journal (ISSN 0066-9768)
Description: Concerned with up-to-date developments and opportunities for recent graduates in Ireland and the world.

VETERINARY SCIENCE

636.08   US
▼PERSPECTIVES: A RESOURCE FOR WOMEN IN VETERINARY MEDICINE. 1994. bi-m. $34 to individuals (Canada and Mexico $42; elsewhere $49); institutions £48 (Canada and Mexico $63; elsewhere $95) (effective 1996). Veterinary Learning Systems, 425 Phillips Blvd., Ste. 100, Trenton, NJ 08618. TEL 609-882-5600; 800-426-9119. FAX 609-882-6357. Ed. Yvonne Claire Stecher. adv. contact: Beth Green. bk.rev. circ. 20,000. (back issues avail.) **Document type:** academic/scholarly publication.
    Description: Contains a mix of clinical, business, and personal life-style articles geared toward serving the needs and interests of women in veterinary medicine.

PERSPECTIVES IN ETHOLOGY. see BIOLOGY — Zoology

PERSPECTIVES ON CATS. see PETS

PET CARE REPORT. see PETS

PET FOCUS; the magazine for people who love pets. see PETS

636.089   GW   ISSN 0177-7726
PFERDEHEILKUNDE; zeitschrift fuer wissenschaft und praxis. (Text in English, German; summaries in English) 1985. bi-m. DM.260 (foreign DM.272). Hippiatrika Verlag GmbH, Buehlstr. 5, 75387 Neubulach, Germany. TEL 07053-3261. FAX 07053-39168. Eds. H.D. Lauk, K.A. von Plocki. (back issues avail.) **Document type:** academic/scholarly publication.
    —BLDSC (6437.519000).

636.089   PH   ISSN 0115-2173
    CODEN: PJVSDI
PHILIPPINE JOURNAL OF VETERINARY AND ANIMAL SCIENCES. (Text and summaries in English) 1975. q. $90. Philippine Society of Animal Sciences, c/o Institute of Animal Science, University of the Philippines, College of Agriculture, Los Banos, Laguna 4031, Philippines. Ed. Dr. Salcedo L. Eduardo. adv.; bk.rev. circ. 1,100. **Indexed:** Biol.Abstr., Chem.Abstr., Dairy Sci.Abstr., Food Sci.& Tech.Abstr., Nutr.Abstr.
    —CASDDS.
    Formerly: Philippine Journal of Animal Science.

636.089   PH   ISSN 0031-7705
    CODEN: PJVMAV
PHILIPPINE JOURNAL OF VETERINARY MEDICINE. Abbreviated title: P J V M. 1962. 2/yr. $30. University of the Philippines, College of Veterinary Medicine, Los Banos, Laguna 4031, Philippines. TEL 094-2727. Ed. Joseph. S. Masangkay. adv.; bk.rev.; bibl.; charts; illus. circ. 500. **Indexed:** Biol.Abstr., Chem.Abstr., Curr.Cont., Helminthol.Abstr., Ind.Vet., Vet.Bull. **Document type:** academic/scholarly publication.
    —BLDSC (6456.050000); CASDDS.

636.089   UK   ISSN 1352-9749
THE PIG JOURNAL. 1976. s-a. £20 (overseas £22). (Pig Veterinary Society) Grove International, The Grove Centre, Corston, Malmesbury, Wilts. SN16 0HL, England. TEL 01666-822967. FAX 01666-822009. (Subscr. to: The Grove Centre, Corston, Malmesbury, Wilts. SN16 OHL, England) Ed. D. Basinger. bk.rev. circ. 900. (back issues avail.) **Indexed:** Agri.Eng.Abstr., Anim.Breed.Abstr., Ind.Vet., Rev.Med.& Vet.Mycol., Vet.Bull. **Document type:** proceedings.
    Former titles (until 1994): Pig Veterinary Journal (ISSN 0956-0939); (until 1989): Pig Veterinary Society. Proceedings (ISSN 0141-3074)
    Description: Discussses topics on pig diseases and treatment presented at international meetings or submitted to the editor.

PLACENTA. see BIOLOGY — Physiology

636.089   FR   ISSN 0335-4997
    CODEN: POVTEN
POINT VETERINAIRE. 1973. 8/yr. 810 F. Editions du Point Veterinaire S.A., 9 rue Alexandre, 94700 Maisons-Alfort, France. TEL 45-17-02-25. FAX 45-17-02-74. Ed. Maryvonne Barbaray. adv.; bk.rev. circ. 6,000. **Indexed:** Agri.Eng.Abstr., Bio-Contr.News & Info., Dairy Sci.Abstr., Ind.Vet., Pig News & Info., Poult.Abstr., Protozool.Abstr., Rev.Med.& Vet.Mycol., Small Anim.Abstr., Vet.Bull., Weed Abstr.
    —BLDSC (6541.862000); Genuine Article. **CCC.**

636.089   SP   ISSN 1130-8451
PORCI. 1991. 6/yr. Virgen de la Alegria 9, 28027 Madrid, Spain. TEL 1-405-15-05. FAX 1-403-49-07.

POULTRY ADVISER; English monthly dedicated to poultry development. see AGRICULTURE — Poultry And Livestock

636.089   GW   ISSN 0032-681X
    CODEN: PRTIAV
DER PRAKTISCHE TIERARZT. 1921. 13/yr. DM.194 (foreign DM.224). (Bundesverbandes praktischer Tieraerzte e.V.) Schluetersche Verlagsanstalt GmbH und Co., Hans-Boeckler-Allee 7, 30173 Hannover, Germany. TEL 0511-8550-0. FAX 0511-8550-100. (Subscr. to: Postfach 5440, 30054 Hannover, Germany) Ed. Dr. H. Hagenlocher. adv.; bk.rev.; charts; illus.; index. circ. 8,980. **Indexed:** Agri.Eng.Abstr., Anim.Breed.Abstr., Biotech.Abstr., Chem.Abstr., Curr.Adv.Cancer Res., Curr.Adv.Ecol.Sci., Curr.Cont., Dairy Sci.Abstr., Helminthol.Abstr., INIS Atomind., Key Word Ind.Wildl.Res., Pig News & Info., Protozool.Abstr., Small Anim.Abstr., Vet.Bull. **Document type:** academic/scholarly publication.
    —BLDSC (6601.200000); CASDDS; Genuine Article; SWETS. **CCC.**

636.089   FR   ISSN 0758-1882
PRATIQUE MEDICALE ET CHIRURGICALE DE L'ANIMAL DE COMPAGNIE. 1966. 7/yr. 1200 F. Conference Nationale des Veterinaires Specialises en Petits Animaux, 82, av. de Villiers, 75017 Paris, France. TEL 42-67-72-96. FAX 42-67-51-76. Ed. Dr. J.P. Pages. adv.; bk.rev. circ. 3,000.
    —BLDSC (6602.160000); Genuine Article.
    Formerly (until 1983): Animal de Compagnie (ISSN 0245-9302)

636.089   NE   ISSN 0167-5877
PREVENTIVE VETERINARY MEDICINE; an international journal on research and development in veterinary epidemiology, animal disease prevention and control, and animal health economics. (Text in English) 1982. 16/yr. fl.1568($956) (effective 1996). Elsevier Science B.V., P.O. Box 211, 1000 AE Amsterdam, Netherlands. TEL 31-20-4853911. FAX 31-20-4853598. TELEX 18582 ESPA NL. E-mail: nlinfo-f@elsevier.nl; usinfo-f@elsevier.com; forinfo-kyf04035@niftyserve.or.jp; Site addr.: http://www.elsevier.nl/. (Subscr. in U.S. and Canada to: Elsevier Science Inc., Box 882, Madison Sq. Sta., New York, NY 10159-0882. TEL 212-989-5800. FAX 212-633-3990) Eds. H.N. Erb, I.R. Dohoo. bk.rev.; illus.; index. circ. 800. (also avail. in microform from UMI; back issues avail.) **Indexed:** Anim.Breed.Abstr., Biol.Abstr., Curr.Adv.Ecol.Sci., Curr.Cont., Dairy Sci.Abstr., Ind.Vet., Pig News & Info., Poult.Abstr., Protozool.Abstr., Rev.Appl.Entomol., Small Anim.Abstr., Sport Fish.Abstr., Vet.Bull., Wild.Rev., Zoo.Rec. **Document type:** academic/scholarly publication.
    —BLDSC (6612.795000); Faxon; Genuine Article; SWETS; UnCover. **CCC.**
    Description: Aims to disseminate, on a worldwide basis, information and reports of significance in the field of animal (mammalian, aquatic and avian) health programs and preventive veterinary medicine.
    Refereed Serial

PRIMATES; journal of primatology. see BIOLOGY — Zoology

636.08   IT   ISSN 1121-1547
PROFESSIONE VETERINARIA. 1991. q. L.60000 (foreign L.80000). Societa Culturale Italiana Veterinaria per Piccoli Animali, Via Pallavicino 26, 26100 Cremona, Italy. TEL 39-372-23501. FAX 39-372-457091. Ed. Carlo Scotti. adv.: color page L.1000000; adv. contact: Antonio Manfredi. circ. 11,800.

636.087   US   ISSN 1061-575X
    CODEN: PVNEEL
PROGRESS IN VETERINARY NEUROLOGY; an international journal of veterinary neurology and neurosurgery. 1990. q. $50 (Canada and Mexico $60; elsewhere $65) (effective 1996). Veterinary Practice Publishing Co., 7 Ashley Ave., S, Santa Barbara, CA 93103-9989. TEL 805-965-1028. FAX 805-965-0722. (Subscr. to: Box 4457, Santa Barbara, CA 93140-4457) Ed. Dr. Alan J. Parker. bk.rev. circ. 2,500. **Document type:** academic/scholarly publication.
    —Genuine Article; UnCover.
    Refereed Serial

636.089   MX
PRONTUARIO DE ESPECIALIDADES VETERINARIAS. 1971. a. Ediciones P L M, S.A. de C.V., San Bernadino 17, Col. del Valle, 03100 Mexico D.F., Mexico. TEL 687-1766. FAX 536-5027. Ed. Luis Hochenstein. circ. 5,000.

636.08   US
PULSE (PICO RIVERA). 1959? m. membership. Southern California Veterinary Medical Association, 8338 Rosemead Blvd., Pico Rivera, CA 90660. TEL 310-948-4979. Ed. Richard L. Holden. adv. contact: Marilyn Jensen. illus.; circ. 1,100 (controlled). **Document type:** trade publication.
    Description: Publishes case studies and other scientific and medical news of interest to doctors of veterinary medicine.

R F L. (Rundschau Fleischhygiene und Lebensmittelueberwachung) see FOOD AND FOOD INDUSTRIES

RASSEGNA DI DIRITTO, LEGISLAZIONE E MEDICINA LEGALE VETERINARIA. see LAW

636.089   IT
RAZZA BRUNA. 1961. 6/yr. L.20000 (foreign L.45000). Associazione Nazionale Razza Bruna, Localita Ferlina 204, 37012 Bussolengo VR, Italy. TEL 39-45-6701990. FAX 39-45-7156655. Ed. Giuseppe Perotti. adv.: B&W page L.70000, color page L.1000000; adv. contact: Claudio Pietraforte.

636.089   FR   ISSN 0034-1843
    CODEN: RMVEAG
RECUEIL DE MEDECINE VETERINAIRE D'ALFORT. (Text in French, summaries in English, Spanish) 1824. 9/yr. 1050 F. Association pour la Publication du Recueil de Medecine Veterinaire, Ecole Nationale Veterinaire, 7 av. du General de Gaulle, 94704 Maisons Alfort Cedex, France. TEL 1-43-96-71-76. FAX 1-43-75-12-10. Ed. M. Paragon. adv.: bk.rev.; abstr.; illus.; index. circ. 25,000. (reprint service avail. from UMI) **Indexed:** Anim.Breed.Abstr., Biol.Abstr., Chem.Abstr., Curr.Adv.Ecol.Sci., Curr.Cont., Excerp.Med., Food Sci.& Tech.Abstr., Helminthol.Abstr., Ind.Vet. Key Word Ind.Wildl.Res., Maize Abstr., Nutr.Abstr., Poult.Abstr., Protozool.Abstr., Rev.Med.& Vet.Mycol., Sport Fish.Abstr., Vet.Bull., Wild.Rev., Zoo.Rec.
    —BLDSC (7329.000000); CASDDS; Genuine Article; SWETS; UMI.

636.089   UK
REGISTERS & DIRECTORY OF VETERINARY SURGEONS. 1870. a. £18. Royal College of Veterinary Surgeons, 32 Belgrave Sq., London SW1X 8QP, England. TEL 0171-235-4971. FAX 0171-245-6100. Ed. B. Needham. adv. circ. 15,500. **Document type:** directory.

636.089   GW   ISSN 0936-6768
S494   CODEN: RDANEF
REPRODUCTION IN DOMESTIC ANIMALS; Physiology, Pathology, Biotechnology. (Text in English; summaries in English and German) 1966. 6/yr. DM.622($461) in Europe; rest of world DM.653($484) (effective 1996). Blackwell Wissenschaft, Kurfuerstendamm 57, 10707 Berlin, Germany. TEL 030-32790623. FAX 030-32790610. Ed. D. Rath. adv.: B&W page DM.540; trim 200 x 125. bk.rev.; illus.; stat.; index. circ. 500. (back issues avail.) **Indexed:** Anim.Breed.Abstr., Biol.Abstr., Biotech.Abstr., Chem.Abstr., Curr.Adv.Cell & Devel.Biol., Curr.Adv.Ecol.Sci., Curr.Adv.Genetics & Molec.Biol., Curr.Cont., Dairy Sci.Abstr., Ind.Vet., Pig News & Info., Rev.Med.& Vet.Mycol., Vet.Bull. **Document type:** academic/scholarly publication.
    —BLDSC (7713.599600); CASDDS; Faxon; Genuine Article; SWETS; UnCover. **CCC.**
    Formerly: Zuchthygiene (ISSN 0044-5371)
    Description: Offers comprehensive information concerning physiology, pathology, and biotechnology of reproduction.

VETERINARY SCIENCE

636.089   UK   ISSN 0034-5288
SF601   CODEN: RVTSA9
RESEARCH IN VETERINARY SCIENCE. 1960. bi-m. £103.50 (foreign £166). British Veterinary Association, 7 Mansfield St, London W1M 0AT, England. TEL 44-171-636-6541. FAX 44-171-637-0620. Ed. E.N. Boden. adv.; bibl.; charts; illus.; index. circ. 945. (also avail. in microform from UMI,PMC; reprint service avail. from UMI) **Indexed:** Anim.Breed.Abstr., Biol.Abstr., Biotech.Abstr., Chem.Abstr., Curr.Adv.Ecol.Sci., Curr.Cont., Dairy Sci.Abstr., Dent.Ind., Excerp.Med., Food Sci.& Tech.Abstr., Helminthol.Abstr., Ind.Med., Ind.Vet., Nutr.Abstr., Pig News & Info., Protozool.Abstr., Rev.Appl.Entomol., Rev.Med.& Vet.Mycol., Rev.Plant Path., Risk Abstr., Soils & Fert., Soyabean Abstr., Sport Fish.Abstr., Vet.Bull., Wild.Rev., Zoo.Rec. **Document type:** academic/scholarly publication.
—BLDSC (7774.100000); CASDDS; EMDOCS; Faxon; Genuine Article; SWETS; UMI; UnCover. **CCC.**

REVISTA CERES; orgao de divulgacao tecnico-cientifica em ciencias agrarias. see *AGRICULTURE*

636.089   CU   ISSN 0048-7678
REVISTA CUBANA DE CIENCIAS VETERINARIAS. (Text in Spanish; summaries in Spanish and English) 1970. 3/yr. $28 in S. America; N. America $30; elsewhere $34 or exchange basis. (Consejo Cientifico Veterinario) Ediciones Cubanas, Obispo No. 527, Apto. 605, Havana, Cuba. bk.rev.; bibl.; charts; illus. circ. 3,000. (also avail. in microfilm) **Indexed:** Anim.Breed.Abstr., Apic.Abstr., Biol.Abstr., Dairy Sci.Abstr., Helminthol.Abstr., Ind.Vet., Maize Abstr., Nutr.Abstr., Pig News & Info., Poult.Abstr., Protozool.Abstr., Rev.Med.& Vet.Mycol., Vet.Bull.
—BLDSC (7852.098000).

636.08   SP   ISSN 1130-2739
REVISTA DE EXPERIMENTACION ANIMAL. 1990. s-a. 3000 ptas. Universidad de Leon, Facultad de Veterinaria, Departamento de Medicina Animal, Campus de Vegazana, s-n, 24007 Leon, Spain. Ed. Dr. Carlos Cesar Perez Garcia.

636.089   PE   ISSN 0376-4370
SF604   CODEN: RIPEDT
REVISTA DE INVESTIGACIONES PECUARIAS. (Text in English; summaries in English) 1972. 3/yr. $40. Universidad Nacional Mayor de San Marcos, Instituto Veterinario de Investigaciones Tropicales y de Altura, Apto. 41-0068, Lima 41, Peru. TEL 51-14-353059. FAX 51-14-353064. Ed. C. Novoa. circ. 1,500. **Indexed:** Vet.Bull.

636.089   CU   ISSN 0253-570X
CODEN: RSANDH
REVISTA DE SALUD ANIMAL. (Text in Spanish; summaries in English) 1979. 4/yr. $21 in N. and S. America; Europe $26. (Centro Nacional de Sanidad Agropecuaria) Ediciones Cubanas, Obispo No. 527, Apdo. 605, Havana, Cuba. charts; bibl. **Indexed:** Agri.Abstr., Anim.Breed.Abstr., Biol.Abstr., Bull.Signal., Chem.Abstr., Dairy Sci.Abstr., Food Sci.& Tech.Abstr., Helminthol.Abstr., Herb.Abstr., Ind.Vet., Pig News & Info., Poult.Abstr., Protozool.Abstr., Ref.Zh., Rev.Med.& Vet.Mycol., Soyabean Abstr., Sugar Ind.Abstr., Vet.Bull.
—BLDSC (7870.518000); CASDDS.

636.089   PO   ISSN 0035-0389
REVISTA PORTUGUESA DE CIENCIAS VETERINARIAS. 1902. q. Esc.4500 (typically set in Jan.). Sociedade Portuguesa de Ciencias Veterinarias, Rua D. Dinis 2-A, 1200 Lisbon, Portugal. Ed. Maria C. Peleteiro. adv.; bk.rev.; abstr.; bibl.; index. circ. 1,100. **Indexed:** Anim.Breed.Abstr., Biol.Abstr., Dairy Sci.Abstr., Helminthol.Abstr., Ind.Vet., Nutr.Abstr., Vet.Bull.
—BLDSC (7869.880000).
Description: Papers from Portuguese researchers on all areas of veterinary science.

636.089   VE   ISSN 0484-8284
REVISTA VETERINARIA VENEZOLANA. m. Federacion de Colegios de Medicos Veterinarios de Venezuela, Qta. Marilina, Av. Paez, Calle Stolk, El Paraiso, Apdo. 2921, Caracas 102, Venezuela. Ed. Dr. C. Ruiz Martinez.
Formerly (until 1956): Revista Grancolombiana de Zootecnia Higiene y Medicina Veterinaria.

591 636.089   CK   ISSN 0120-4114
REVISTA VETERINARIA Y ZOOTECNICA DE CALDAS. 1982. 2/yr. Col.2000($5) University of Caldas, School of Veterinary Medicine & Animal Husbandry, Apdo. Aereo 275, Manizales, Colombia. TEL 968-852139. Ed. Rodrigo Hoyos. adv. circ. 600. (back issues avail.)
Description: Contains research articles on animal medicine and husbandry.

636.089   ISSN 0035-1865
REVUE D'ELEVAGE ET DE MEDECINE VETERINAIRE DES PAYS TROPICAUX. (Text in English, French; summaries in English, French, Spanish) 1947. q. 290 F. (foreign 480 F.) (effective 1992). (Institut d'Elevage et de Medecine Veterinaire des Pays Tropicaux) Expansion Scientifique, 31 bd. de la Tour Maubourg, 75007 Paris, France. TEL 40-62-64-00. FAX 45-55-69-20. Ed. A.H. Robinet. adv.; bk.rev.; abstr.; bibl.; charts; index. cum.index: 1947-1977; circ. controlled. (also avail. in microfiche) **Indexed:** Anim.Breed.Abstr., Biol.Abstr., Biotech.Abstr., Curr.Adv.Ecol.Sci., Curr.Cont., Dairy Sci.Abstr., Excerp.Med., Field Crop Abstr., Helminthol.Abstr., Herb.Abstr., Ind.Med., Ind.Vet., Irr.& Drain.Abstr., Nutr.Abstr., Pig News & Info., Poult.Abstr., Protozool.Abstr., Rev.Appl.Entomol., Rev.Med.& Vet.Mycol., Rev.Plant Path., So.Pac.Per.Ind., Trop.Oil Seeds Abstr., Vet.Bull.
—BLDSC (7900.000000); Faxon; SWETS; UMI.

636.089   FR   ISSN 0035-1555
CODEN: RVMVAH
REVUE DE MEDECINE VETERINAIRE. (Text and summaries in French, English) 1838. m. 850 F. Ecole Nationale Veterinaire, 23 chemin des Capelles, 31076 Toulouse Cedex, France. TEL 61-19-38-39. FAX 61-19-39-75. Ed. J.P. Euzeby. adv.; bk.rev.; abstr.; illus.; index. circ. 3,300. (reprint service avail. from ISI, UMI) **Indexed:** Anim.Breed.Abstr., Biol.Abstr., Biotech.Abstr., Bull.Signal., Chem.Abstr., Curr.Adv.Ecol.Sci., Curr.Cont., Dairy Sci.Abstr., Excerp.Med., Helminthol.Abstr., Ind.Vet., Nutr.Abstr., Pig News & Info., Poult.Abstr., Protozool.Abstr., Psychol.Abstr., Rev.Med.& Vet.Mycol., Rev.Plant Path., Small Anim.Abstr., Sport Fish.Abstr., Vet.Bull., Wild.Rev., Zoo.Rec. **Document type:** academic/scholarly publication.
—BLDSC (7932.000000); CASDDS; Genuine Article; SWETS; UMI.
Description: Provides reviews, original reports, clinical reports.

636.089   UK   ISSN 0952-7222
ROWETT RESEARCH INSTITUTE ANNUAL REPORT. a. free. Rowett Research Institute, Greenburn Rd., Bucksburn, Aberdeen AB2 9SB, Scotland. TEL 01224-712751. FAX 01224-715349. Ed. Ian Bremner. circ. 2,000. **Document type:** academic/scholarly publication.

SANS LAISSE. see *PETS*

636.089   SZ   ISSN 0036-7281
SATHAA
SCHWEIZER ARCHIV FUER TIERHEILKUNDE. 12/yr. 199 SFr. (foreign 235 SFr.). (Gesellschaft Schweizerischer Tieraerzte) Verlag Hans Huber, Laengassstr. 76, CH-3000 Bern 9, Switzerland. TEL 031-3004500. FAX 031-3004592. adv. circ. 2,500. **Indexed:** Anim.Breed.Abstr., ASCA, Biol.Abstr., Biotech.Abstr., Chem.Abstr., Curr.Adv.Ecol.Sci., Curr.Cont., Dairy Sci.Abstr., Excerp.Med., Food Sci.& Tech.Abstr., Helminthol.Abstr., Ind.Med., Ind.Vet., Key Word Ind.Wildl.Res., Nutr.Abstr., Pig News & Info., Poult.Abstr., Protozool.Abstr., Rev.Plant Path., Small Anim.Abstr., Soils & Fert., Vet.Bull. **Document type:** academic/scholarly publication.
—BLDSC (8110.000000); CASDDS; Faxon; Genuine Article; SWETS. **CCC.**

636.089   FR   ISSN 0750-7682
CODEN: SVMCD8
SCIENCES VETERINAIRES - MEDECINE COMPAREE. 1898. 3/yr. 285 F. (foreign 355 F.). Societe des Sciences Veterinaires et de Medecine Comparee de Lyon, Ecole Nationale Veterinaire de Lyon, B.P. 83, 69280 Marcy l'Etoile, France. TEL 78-87-25-25. FAX 78-87-82-62. adv.; bk.rev. **Indexed:** Biol.Abstr., Chem.Abstr., Ind.Vet., Nutr.Abstr., Poult.Abstr., Vet.Bull.
—BLDSC (8167.600000); CASDDS.
Formerly (until 1982): Societe des Sciences Veterinaires et de Medecine Comparee de Lyon. Bulletin (ISSN 0301-1194)

636.089   IT   ISSN 0037-1521
CODEN: SVETDJ
SELEZIONE VETERINARIA. 1960. m. L.80000($80) (effective Jan. 1993). Istituto Zooprofilattico Sperimentale della Lombardia e dell'Emilia, Via A. Bianchi 7, 25100 Brescia, Italy. FAX 030-225613. Eds. G.L. Gualandi, G.F. Panina. bk.rev. circ. 3,000. (reprint service avail.) **Indexed:** Anim.Breed.Abstr., Dairy Sci.Abstr., Ind.Vet., Key Word Ind.Wildl.Res., Pig News & Info., Poult.Abstr., Protozool.Abstr., Rev.Med.& Vet.Mycol., Sugar Ind.Abstr., Vet.Bull.
—BLDSC (8235.340000); CASDDS.
Description: Articles on veterinary sciences with emphasis on infectious diseases, microbiology, parasitology, reproduction and breeding.

636.089   FR   ISSN 0396-5015
SEMAINE VETERINAIRE. 1976. 40/yr. 1200 F. Editions du Point Veterinaire S.A., 9 rue Alexandre, B.P. 233, 94702 Maisons-Alfort Cedex, France. TEL 45-17-02-25. FAX 45-17-02-74. Ed. Laurent Jessenne. adv. circ. 5,000.
—CCC.
Incorporates: Eurovet.

636.089   US   ISSN 1055-937X
SF994.2.A1
SEMINARS IN AVIAN AND EXOTIC PET MEDICINE. 1992. q. $108 (foreign $134) (effective 1996). W.B. Saunders Co. (Subsidiary of: Harcourt Brace & Company), Curtis Bldg., 3rd Fl., Independence Sq. W., Philadelphia, PA 19106-3399. TEL 215-238-7800. FAX 215-238-6445. (Subscr. to: Periodicals Fulfillment, W.B. Saunders Co., 6277 Sea Harbor Dr., 4th Fl., Orlando, FL 32891-4800. TEL 800-654-2452. FAX 800-874-6418) Ed. Dr. Alan M. Fudge; Pub. Joan W. Blumberg. adv.: B&W page $565, color page $1340; 7 x 10; adv. contact: Cindy Gray. circ. 2,628. **Document type:** academic/scholarly publication.
—BLDSC (8239.448200); Genuine Article; UMI; UnCover. **CCC.**
Description: Covers a single topic in avian and exotic-pet medicine in each issue.

636.089   US   ISSN 0882-0511
CODEN: SVMSEN
SEMINARS IN VETERINARY MEDICINE AND SURGERY: SMALL ANIMAL. (Spanish translation avail.) 1986. q. $115 (foreign $139) (effective 1996). W.B. Saunders Co. (Subsidiary of: Harcourt Brace & Company), Curtis Center, 3rd Fl., Independence Sq. W., Philadelphia, PA 19106-3399. TEL 215-238-7800. FAX 215-238-6445. (Subscr. to: Periodicals Fulfillment, W.B. Saunders Co., 6277 Sea Harbor Dr., 4th Fl., Orlando, FL 32891-4800. TEL 800-654-2452. FAX 800-874-6418) Ed. Dr. Robert J. Murtaugh; Pub. Joan W. Blumberg. adv.: B&W page $565, color page $1415; 7 x 10; adv. contact: Steve Gray. bibl.; charts; illus.; index. circ. 1,133. **Indexed:** Curr.Cont., Ind.Med., Ind.Vet., Small Anim.Abstr., Vet.Bull. **Document type:** academic/scholarly publication.
—BLDSC (8239.487000); Genuine Article; SWETS; UMI; UnCover. **CCC.**
Description: Covers a specific theme of interest to small-animal veterinarians in each issue. *Refereed Serial*

636.089   CC   ISSN 1000-7725
SHANGHAI XUMU SHOUYI TONGXUN/SHANGHAI BULLETIN OF VETERINARY SCIENCE. (Text in Chinese) 1956. bi-m. Y4.80. Shanghai Nongye Kexueyuan, Xumu Shouyi Yanjiusuo - Shanghai Academy of Agricultural Science, Institute of Veterinary Science, 2451 Xietu Lu, Shanghai 200030, People's Republic of China. TEL 4383161. Ed. Liu Ruisan. adv.; bk.rev.

636.089   JA   ISSN 0912-2494
SHODOBUTSU HIFUKA RINSHO/JAPANESE JOURNAL OF SMALL ANIMAL DERMATOLOGY. (Text in English, Japanese) 1973. irreg. Shodobutsu Hifuka Kenkyukai - Japanese Society for Small Animal Dermatology, c/o Tokyo Daigaku Nogakubu Kachiku, Naikagaku Kyoshitsu, 1-1 Yayoi 1-chome, Bunkyo-ku, Tokyo 113, Japan.

SINGAPORE JOURNAL OF PRIMARY INDUSTRIES. see *AGRICULTURE*

VETERINARY SCIENCE

636.089 US
SMALL ANIMAL PRACTICE. 1976. m. $108. Audio Veterinary Medicine, 810 S. Myrtle Ave., Monrovia, CA 91016. TEL 818-303-2531. FAX 818-303-2534. (Subscr. to: Box 1729, Monrovia, CA 91017-5729) Ed. Gregory P. Stavish. circ. 100. (also avail. in audio cassette; back issues avail.) **Document type:** bulletin.

SMALL RUMINANT RESEARCH. see *AGRICULTURE — Poultry And Livestock*

636.089 637 BL ISSN 0100-4859
CODEN: RSBZBM
SOCIEDADE BRASILEIRA DE ZOOTECNIA. REVISTA. (Text in Portuguese; summaries in English) 1972. bi-m. $100. Sociedade Brasileira de Zootecnia, Departamento de Zootecnia, Universidade Federal de Vicosa, 36570 Vicosa MG, Brazil. TEL 031-899-2260. FAX 031-899-2270. TELEX 031-1587. Ed. Jose Brandao Fonseca. circ. 2,000. (back issues avail.) **Indexed:** Anim.Breed.Abstr., Biol.Abstr., Dairy Sci.Abstr., Field Crop Abstr., Maize Abstr., Poult.Abstr., Sorghum & Millets Abstr., Soyabean Abstr., Sport Fish.Abstr., Wild.Rev., Zoo.Rec. **Document type:** academic/scholarly publication.
—BLDSC (7834.455000); CASDDS; Genuine Article.

SODOBNO KMETIJSTVO. see *AGRICULTURE*

SOUTH AFRICAN JOURNAL OF ANIMAL SCIENCE. see *AGRICULTURE — Poultry And Livestock*

636.089 SA
CODEN: JAVTAP
SOUTH AFRICAN VETERINARY ASSOCIATION. SCIENTIFIC JOURNAL. 1929. q. $250. South African Veterinary Association, P.O. Box 25033, Monument Park, 0105 Pretoria, South Africa. TEL 27-12-3461150. FAX 27-12-3462929. Ed. J. van Heerden. adv.; bk.rev.; abstr.; charts; illus.; index. circ. 1,600. (back issues avail.) **Indexed:** Anim.Breed.Abstr., Bio-Contr.News & Info., Biotech.Abstr., Chem.Abstr., Curr.Adv.Ecol.Sci., Curr.Cont., Dairy Sci.Abstr., Dent.Ind., Excerp.Med., Field Crop Abstr., Helminthol.Abstr., Herb.Abstr., Ind.Med., Ind.S.A.Per., Ind.Vet., INIS Atomind., Nutr.Abstr., Protozool.Abstr., Rev.Appl.Entomol., Rev.Med.& Vet.Mycol., Small Anim.Abstr., Vet.Bull., Weed Abstr. **Document type:** academic/scholarly publication.
—BLDSC (4901.950000); CASDDS; EMDOCS; Genuine Article; SWETS; UnCover. **CCC.**
Former titles: South African Veterinary Association. Journal (ISSN 1019-9128); (until 1972): South African Veterinary Medical Association. Journal (ISSN 0038-2809)
Refereed Serial

SPAIN. INSTITUTO NACIONAL DE INVESTIGACIONES AGRARIAS. COMUNICACIONES. SERIE: HIGIENE Y SANIDAD. see *AGRICULTURE — Poultry And Livestock*

636.089 CE
SRI LANKA VETERINARY JOURNAL. (Text in English) 1953. s-a. $10. Veterinary Research Institute, Peradeniya, Sri Lanka. Ed. Prof. S.T. Fernando. adv.; bk.rev.; abstr.; charts; illus.; index. circ. 1,000. (tabloid format) **Indexed:** Anim.Breed.Abstr., Biol.Abstr., Chem.Abstr., Dairy Sci.Abstr., Field Crop Abstr., Helminthol.Abstr., Herb.Abstr., Ind.Vet., Nutr.Abstr., Pig News & Info., Poult.Abstr., Protozool.Abstr., Rev.Appl.Entomol., Small Anim.Abstr., Soils & Fert., Sri Lanka Sci.Ind., Vet.Bull.
—BLDSC (8425.138000).
Formerly (until 1982): Ceylon Veterinary Journal (ISSN 0009-0891)

636.089 FI ISSN 0039-5501
SUOMEN ELAINLAAKARILEHTI/FINSK VETERINAERTIDSKRIFT. (Text in Finnish and Swedish; summaries in English) 1893. m. FIM 450. Suomen Elainlaakariliitto - Finnish Veterinary Association, Akavatalo, Makelankatu 2 C, FIN- 00500 Helsinki, Finland. Ed. Marjut Haemaelainen. adv. contact: Pirkko Nousiainen. bk.rev.; bibl.; charts; illus. circ. 1,550. **Indexed:** Anim.Breed.Abstr., Apic.Abstr., Biol.Abstr., Dairy Sci.Abstr., Food Sci.& Tech.Abstr., Helminthol.Abstr., Ind.Vet., Nutr.Abstr., Pig News & Info., Poult.Abstr., Protozool.Abstr., Rev.Med.& Vet.Mycol., Small Anim.Abstr., Vet.Bull.
—BLDSC (8541.800000).

636.089 SW ISSN 0346-2250
SVENSK VETERINAERTIDNING. (Supplement avail.) 1949. 16/yr. SEK 890 within Scandinavia; elsewhere SEK 1000. Sveriges Veterinaerfoerbund - Swedish Veterinary Association, P.O. Box 12 709, S-112 94 Stockholm, Sweden. TEL 08-654-2480. FAX 08-6517082. Eds. Johan Beck-Friis, Aase Tronstad. adv. contact: Birgitta Ahlkvist. bk.rev.; circ. 2,600 (controlled). **Indexed:** Anim.Breed.Abstr., Dairy Sci.Abstr., Food Sci.& Tech.Abstr., Helminthol.Abstr., Ind.Vet., Nutr.Abstr., Pig News & Info., Protozool.Abstr., Rev.Med.& Vet.Mycol., Vet.Bull., World Agri.Econ.& Rural Sociol.Abstr. **Document type:** academic/scholarly publication.
—BLDSC (8562.598000).
Former titles (until 1964): Medlemsblad foer Sveriges Veterinaerfoerbund; (until 1950): Svenska Veterinaerlaekarefoereningens Medlemsblad.
Description: Articles of interest to veterinarians and news about the association.
Refereed Serial

636.089 US
SWINE PRACTITIONER. 1988. q. $12. Vance Publishing Corporation (Lenexa), 10901 W. 84th Terr., Ste. 200, Lenexa, KS 66214-1631. TEL 913-438-8700. FAX 913-438-0695. Ed. Jim Carlton. circ. 4,000. **Document type:** trade publication.

636.089 US ISSN 1071-0566
TEXAS VETERINARIAN. 1939. bi-m. $50 to individuals; institutions $30 (Canada & Mexico $40; elsewhere $55). Texas Veterinary Medical Association, 6633 Hwy., 290 E., No. 201, Austin, TX 78723-1134. TEL 512-452-4224. FAX 512-452-6633. Ed. Donald M. Ward. adv. contact: Ellen Smith. bk.rev.; charts; illus.; stat. circ. 3,000. **Document type:** trade publication.
Formerly (until Apr. 1993): Texas Veterinary Medical Journal (ISSN 0040-4756)

636.089 US ISSN 0093-691X
CODEN: THGNBO
THERIOGENOLOGY; an international journal of animal reproduction. 1974. 16/yr. $595 to institutions (effective 1996). Butterworth - Heinemann, Part of the Reed Elsevier group, 313 Washington St., Newton, MA 02158. TEL 617-928-2500; 800-366-2665. FAX 617-928-2610. TELEX 880052. (Subscr. to: Elsevier Science Inc., Box 882, Madison Sq. Sta., New York, NY 10159-0882. TEL 212-989-5800. FAX 212-633-3990) Ed. Victor Shille. (also avail. in microfiche from UMI; back issues avail.) **Indexed:** Anim.Breed.Abstr., ASCA, Bibl.Repro., Biol.Abstr., Chem.Abstr., Curr.Adv.Cell & Devel.Biol., Curr.Adv.Ecol.Sci., Curr.Adv.Genetics & Molec.Biol., Curr.Cont., Dairy Sci.Abstr., Helminthol.Abstr., Ind.Vet., Nutr.Abstr., Pig News & Info., Poult.Abstr., Small Anim.Abstr., Sport Fish.Abstr., Vet.Bull., Wild.Rev., Zoo.Rec. **Document type:** academic/scholarly publication.
—BLDSC (8814.773000); CASDDS; Faxon; Genuine Article; SWETS; UMI; UnCover. **CCC.**
Description: Forum for information on the reproduction of domestic and wild animals.
Refereed Serial

636.08 GW ISSN 0720-2237
TI HO - ANZEIGER. 1972. 8/yr. DM.24. Tieraerztliche Hochschule Hannover, Buenteweg 2, 30559 Hannover, Germany. TEL 0511-9538002. FAX 0511-953828002. E-mail: daltva@vw.tiho-hannover.de. Ed. Dr. Doris Altvater. **Document type:** academic/scholarly publication.

636.08 GW ISSN 0947-0956
▼**TI HO - FORSCHUNG FUERS LEBEN.** 1994. a. DM.8. Tieraerztliche Hochschule Hannover, Bunteweg 2, 30559 Hannover, Germany. TEL 0511-9538002. FAX 0511-9538050. E-mail: daltra@vw.tiho-hannover.de. Ed. Dr. Doris Altvater. **Document type:** academic/scholarly publication.

636.089 GW ISSN 0303-6286
CODEN: TAZPB8
TIERAERZTLICHE PRAXIS. 6/yr. DM.308($254) to individuals; institutions DM.392($306). F.K. Schattauer Verlagsgesellschaft mbH, Postfach 104545, 70040 Stuttgart, Germany. TEL 0711-22987-0. FAX 0711-22987-50. circ. 5,300. **Indexed:** Anim.Breed.Abstr., Ind.Vet., Key Word Ind.Wildl.Res., Poult.Abstr., Protozool.Abstr., Rev.Med.& Vet.Mycol., Small Anim.Abstr., Vet.Bull. **Document type:** academic/scholarly publication.
—BLDSC (8831.800000); Genuine Article; SWETS. **CCC.**

636.089 GW ISSN 0049-3864
TIERAERZTLICHE UMSCHAU; Zeitschrift fuer alle Gebiete der Veterinaermedizin. 1946. m. DM.168 (foreign DM.191). Terra Verlag GmbH, Postfach 102144, 78421 Konstanz, Germany. TEL 07531-8122-0. FAX 07531-812299. Ed. Prof. O.C. Straub. adv.; bk.rev. circ. 9,000. **Indexed:** Agri.Eng.Abstr., Anim.Breed.Abstr., Apic.Abstr., ASCA, Biol.Abstr., Biotech.Abstr., Chem.Abstr., Curr.Adv.Ecol.Sci., Curr.Cont., Dairy Sci.Abstr., Food Sci.& Tech.Abstr., Helminthol.Abstr., Ind.Vet., Key Word Ind.Wildl.Res., Nutr.Abstr., Poult.Abstr., Protozool.Abstr., Rev.Med.& Vet.Mycol., Rev.Plant Path., Small Anim.Abstr., Soils & Fert., Vet.Bull. **Document type:** academic/scholarly publication.
—BLDSC (8832.000000); Genuine Article; SWETS; UMI. **CCC.**
Incorporates (1946-1994): Monatshefte fuer Veterinaermedizin (ISSN 0026-9263)

636.089 NE ISSN 0040-7453
CODEN: TIDIAY
TIJDSCHRIFT VOOR DIERGENEESKUNDE/NETHERLANDS JOURNAL OF VETERINARY SCIENCE. (Text in Dutch, titles and summaries in Dutch and English) 1863. 24/yr. fl.275 (foreign fl.295) (effective 1996). Koninklijke Nederlandse Maatschappij voor Diergeneeskunde - Royal Netherlands Veterinary Association, Julianalaan 10, Box 14031, 3508 SB Utrecht, Netherlands. TEL 31-30-510111. FAX 31-30-511787. Ed. W.S. Sybesma. adv.: B&W page fl.1775; 210 x 297. adv. contact: R.G.J.M. Haring. bk.rev.; abstr.; bibl.; charts; illus.; index. circ. 4,750. **Indexed:** Abstr.Hyg., Agri.Eng.Abstr., Anim.Breed.Abstr., ASCA, Bibl.Agri., Biol.Abstr., Chem.Abstr., Curr.Adv.Cancer Res., Curr.Adv.Ecol.Sci., Curr.Cont., Dairy Sci.Abstr., Dairy Sci.Abstr., Food Sci.& Tech.Abstr., Helminthol.Abstr., Ind.Med., Ind.Vet., Landwirt.Zentralbl., Nutr.Abstr., Pig News & Info., Poult.Abstr., Protozool.Abstr., Rev.Med.& Vet.Mycol., Rev.Plant Path., Rural Recreat.Tour.Abstr., Small Anim.Abstr., Sport Fish.Abstr., Trop.Dis.Bull., Vet.Bull., Wild.Rev., World Agri.Econ.& Rural Sociol.Abstr., Zoo.Rec. **Document type:** academic/scholarly publication.
—BLDSC (8838.000000); CASDDS; Genuine Article; SWETS.

636.089 US ISSN 1064-5101
TOPICS IN VETERINARY MEDICINE. 1926. 3/yr. free to qualified personnel. Pfizer Animal Health, 812 Springdale Dr., Exton, PA 19341-2803. TEL 610-363-3100. FAX 610-363-3783. Ed. Kathleen M. Etchison. adv. circ. 45,000. **Indexed:** Ind.Vet., Sport Fish.Abstr., Vet.Bull., Wild.Rev.
Formerly (until 1990): Norden News (ISSN 0890-3727)

636.089 US ISSN 1062-8266
TRENDS MAGAZINE. 1985. bi-m. $60 (foreign $70). American Animal Hospital Association, Box 150899, Denver, CO 80215-0899. TEL 303-986-2800. FAX 303-986-1700. Ed. Marilyn Bergquist. circ. 11,969.

636.089 UK ISSN 0049-4747
SF601 CODEN: TAHPAJ
TROPICAL ANIMAL HEALTH AND PRODUCTION. 1969. q. £72($136) to individuals and institutions (outside the E.U. £79) (effective 1996). Edinburgh University Press, 22 George Sq., Edinburgh EH8 9LF, Scotland. TEL 44-131-650-6207. FAX 44-131-662-0053. TELEX 727442 UNIVED G. Ed. A.G. Hunter; Pub. Vivian C. Bone. adv. contact: Kathryn MacLean. bk.rev.; charts; illus.; stat. circ. 500. **Indexed:** Abstr.Hyg., Anim.Breed.Abstr., Biol.Abstr., Biotech.Abstr., Chem.Abstr., Curr.Adv.Ecol.Sci., Curr.Cont., Dairy Sci.Abstr., Excerp.Med., Field Crop Abstr., Helminthol.Abstr., Herb.Abstr., Ind.Med., Ind.Vet., Nutr.Abstr., Poult.Abstr., Protozool.Abstr., Rev.Appl.Entomol., Rev.Med.& Vet.Mycol., Small Anim.Abstr., So.Pac.Per.Ind., Sugar Ind.Abstr., Trop.Dis.Bull., Vet.Bull.
—BLDSC (9054.300000); CASDDS; Faxon; SWETS; UnCover. **CCC.**
Description: Publishes research, investigation, and observation in all fields of animal health and production that may lead to improved health and productivity of livestock, as well as better use of animal resources in developing nations.
Refereed Serial

VETERINARY SCIENCE

636.089 NR ISSN 0794-4845
CODEN: TRVTDJ
TROPICAL VETERINARIAN. 1983. 4/yr. University of Ibadan, Faculty of Veterinary Medicine, Ibadan, Nigeria. Indexed: Curr.Cont., Ind.Vet., Pig News & Info., Poult.Abstr., Protozool.Abstr., Sport Fish.Abstr., Wild.Rev., Zoo.Rec. Document type: academic/scholarly publication.

636 TU ISSN 1300-0128
CODEN: DVHSE3
TURK VETERINERLIK VE HAYVANCILIK DERGISI/TURKISH JOURNAL OF VETERINARY AND ANIMAL SCIENCES. (Text in English, Turkish) 1976. bi-m. $100 (effective 1995 & 1996). Scientific and Technical Research Council of Turkey - TUBITAK - Turkiye Bilimsel ve Teknik Arastirma Kurumu, Ataturk Bulvari, No. 221, Kavaklidere, 06100 Ankara, Turkey. TEL 90-312-4685300. FAX 90-312-4271336. TELEX 43186 BTAK TR. Ed. Sevinc Turker. Indexed: Anim.Breed.Abstr., Biol.Abstr., Chem.Abstr., Dairy Sci.Abstr., INIS Atomind., Maize Abstr. Document type: academic/scholarly publication.
—CASDDS; Genuine Article.
Former titles (until 1994): Doga Turkish Journal of Veterinary and Animal Sciences - Doga Turk Veterinerlik ve Hayvancilik Dergisi (ISSN 1010-7592); Formerly: Doga Bilim Dergisi. Series D: Veterinary and Animal Sciences.
Refereed Serial

636.089 US
U.S. DEPARTMENT OF AGRICULTURE. ANIMAL AND PLANT HEALTH INSPECTION SERVICE. REPORTED ARTHROPOD-BORNE ENCEPHALITIDES IN HORSES AND OTHER EQUIDAE. 1966. a. free. U.S. Animal and Plant Health Inspection Service, Federal Building, Hyattsville, MD 20782. TEL 301-436-8645. illus.; stat. Indexed: Bibl.Agri.

636.089 US ISSN 0082-8750
SF601
UNITED STATES ANIMAL HEALTH ASSOCIATION. PROCEEDINGS OF THE ANNUAL MEETING. no.73, 1969. a. $30. United States Animal Health Association, 8100 3 Chopt Rd., Ste. 203, Box K227, Richmond, VA 23288-0001. TEL 804-285-3210. FAX 804-285-3367. circ. 1,400. (back issues avail.) Indexed: Ind.Med., Ind.Vet., Pig News & Info., Vet.Bull. Document type: proceedings.
—BLDSC (6841.958000).
Supersedes: United States Livestock Sanitary Association. Proceedings.

636.089 VE ISSN 0258-6576
UNIVERSIDAD CENTRAL DE VENEZUELA. FACULTAD DE CIENCIAS VETERINARIAS. REVISTA. (Text in Spanish; summaries mainly in English and Spanish) 1939. 4/yr. free to qualified personnel. Universidad Central de Venezuela, Facultad de Ciencias Veterinarias, Apdo. de Correos 4563, Maracay-Edo. Aragua, Venezuela. Eds. Dr. Haroldo Mayaudon Tarbes, Dr. Arnaldo Leon D'Alessandro. circ. 1,800. Indexed: Biol.Abstr., Chem.Abstr., Ind.Vet., Protozool.Abstr., Rev.Appl.Entomol., Vet.Bull.
Formerly: Revista de Medicina Veterinaria y Parasitologia (ISSN 0048-7724)

636.089 GT ISSN 0375-0884
UNIVERSIDAD DE SAN CARLOS DE GUATEMALA. FACULTAD DE MEDICINA VETERINARIA Y ZOOTECNIA REVISTA. (Text in Spanish; summaries in English and Spanish) 1962. irreg. exchange basis. Universidad de San Carlos de Guatemala, Facultad de Medicina Veterinaria y Zootecnia, Ciudad Universitaria, Zona 12, Guatemala. TEL 760790. Indexed: Biol.Abstr.

636.089 VE ISSN 0798-2259
UNIVERSIDAD DE ZULIA. FACULTAD DE CIENCIAS VETERINARIAS. REVISTA CIENTIFICA. (Text in Spanish; abstracts in English, Spanish) 1991. q. Bs.1000($20) (effective 1994). Universidad de Zulia, Facultad de Ciencias Veterinarias, Apdo. 526, Maracaibo, Zulia, Venezuela. TEL 58-61-413302. FAX 58-61-519338. TELEX 64287 LUZ. Ed. Dr. Mario Perez. bk.rev.; bibl.; charts; illus. circ. 1,000. Document type: academic/scholarly publication.
—Genuine Article.
Description: Contains scientific papers and reviews in veterinary science.

636.089 IT ISSN 0365-4729
SF604 CODEN: AMVPAW
UNIVERSITA DEGLI STUDI DI PISA. FACOLTA DI MEDICINA VETERINARIA DI PISA. ANNALI. Key Title: Annali della Facolta di Medicina Veterinaria di Pisa. 1947. a. exchange basis only. Universita degli Studi di Pisa, Facolta di Medicina Veterinaria di Pisa, Biblioteca Centrale, Viale delle Piagge 2, 56100 Pisa, Italy. TEL 39-50-570270. Ed. Tito Livio Frateschi. Indexed: Sport Fish.Abstr., Wild.Rev., Zoo.Rec. Document type: academic/scholarly publication.
—CASDDS.
Description: Publishes original research articles in areas of veterinary medicine and animal production. Reports on faculty members.

UNIVERSITATEA DE STIINTE AGRICOLE CLUJ-NAPOCA. BULETINUL. SERIA ZOOTEHNIE SI MEDICINA VETERINARA. see *AGRICULTURE — Poultry And Livestock*

636.08 RM
UNIVERSITATEA DE STIINTE AGRONOMICE. LUCRARI STIINTIFICE. SERIA C, MEDICINA VETERINARA. 1960. a. Universitatea de Stiinte Agronomice, Bdul. Marasti, 59, Bucharest, Sec. 1, Rumania.
Formerly (until 1992): Institutul Agronomic Nicolae Balcescu. Lucrari Stiintifice. Seria C, Medicina Veterinara (ISSN 0254-0509); Which supersedes in part (in 1970): Institutul Agronomic Nicolae Balcescu. Lucrari Stiintifice. Seria C, Zootehnie si Medicina Veterinara (ISSN 0524-8108); Which supersedes in part: Institutul Agronomic Nicolae Balcescu. Anuarul Lucrarilor Stiintifice (ISSN 1220-1987).

636 CN ISSN 0383-8455
UNIVERSITE DE MONTREAL. FACULTE DE MEDECINE VETERINAIRE. ANNUAIRE. 1968. a. free. Universite de Montreal, Faculte de Medecine Veterinaire, C.P. 6128, succ. A, Montreal, PQ H3C 3J7, Canada. TEL 514-343-6111. FAX 514-773-2161.
Formerly: Ecole de Medecine Veterinaire, Saint-Hyacinthe, Quebec. Annuaire (ISSN 0383-8447)

UNIVERSITY OF DAR ES SALAAM. FACULTY OF AGRICULTURE, FORESTRY AND VETERINARY SCIENCE. ANNUAL RECORD OF RESEARCH. see *AGRICULTURE*

636 US ISSN 0076-9711
UNIVERSITY OF MISSOURI AT COLUMBIA. VETERINARY MEDICAL DIAGNOSTIC LABORATORY. ANNUAL REPORT. 1967. a. $5. University of Missouri at Columbia, Veterinary Medical Diagnostic Laboratory, Box 6023, Columbia, MO 65205. TEL 314-882-6811. FAX 314-882-1411. Ed. H.S. Gosser. circ. 800. Document type: corporate report.

636.089 XV
UNIVERZA V LJUBLJANI. VETERINARSKA FAKULTETA. ZBORNIK. 1960. s-a. 800 din.($15) Univerza v Ljubljani, Veterinarska Fakulteta, Gerbiceva 60, 61115 Ljubljana, Slovenia. FAX 061-218-005. circ. 500. Indexed: Biol.Abstr., Hort.Abstr., Maize Abstr., Nutr.Abstr., Pig News & Info., Soyabean Abstr., Sport Fish.Abstr., Triticale Abstr., Wild.Rev., Zoo.Rec.
Formerly (until 1990): Univerza E. Kardelja v Ljubljani. Biotehnicki Fakultet. Zbornik.

636.089 UK ISSN 0268-2877
V.C.F. NEWSLETTER. 1963. q. free. Veterinary Christian Fellowship, 112 Lenthay Rd., Sherborne, Dorset DT9 6AG, England. TEL 01935-812872. Ed. David Forster. bk.rev.; circ. 420 (controlled). Document type: newsletter.
Description: General interest veterinary material for Christians.

VACCINE. see *MEDICAL SCIENCES — Allergology And Immunology*

636.08 AT
VET BUSINESS. 1992. bi-m. Aus.$36. Richard Milne Pty. Ltd., 409 Henry Lawson Business Centre, Birkenhead Point, N.S.W. 2047, Australia. TEL 61-2-819-7322. FAX 61-2-819-7650. Ed. Rex Holyoake. circ. 3,435. (back issues avail.)
Description: Provides business and product news for practising veterinarians.

636.08 US ISSN 1074-7796
VET INDUSTRY NEWSLETTER. 1993. m. $295. Good Communications, Inc., Box 31292, Charleston, SC 29417. TEL 803-795-9555; 800-968-1738. FAX 803-795-2930. Ed. Heather Siegel; Pub. Ross Becker. Document type: newsletter.
Description: For executives at veterinary pharmaceuticals, pet product and pet food companies. Provides sensitive information about new products, strategies, and promotions to the veterinary market.

636.08 GW
VETERINAER SPIEGEL. q. DM.36 (foreign DM.48). Beta Verlag GmbH, Postfach 140121, 53056 Bonn, Germany. TEL 0228-91937-0. FAX 0228-252067. TELEX 8869536-BETA-D. Ed. Thomas Steidl. circ. 9,843. Document type: academic/scholarly publication.

636.089 SP
VETERINARIA;* revista tecnica. (Text mainly in Spanish; occasionally in English or French) bi-m. 750 ptas.($15) Editorial Veterinaria, S.A., Maria Auxiliadora 19, Salamanca, Spain.

636.089 BN ISSN 0372-6827
CODEN: VTRNAE
VETERINARIA. (Text in Serbo-Croatian; summaries in English) 1951. q. $40. University of Sarajevo, Veterinary Faculty, V. Putnika 134, 71000 Sarajevo, Bosnia Hercegovina. TEL 071 655-922. adv.; bk.rev.; index. (back issues avail.) Indexed: Ind.Vet., Maize Abstr., Pig News & Info., Rev.Med.& Vet.Mycol., Small Anim.Abstr., SPort Fish.Abstr., Vet.Bull., Wild.Rev., Zoo.Rec. Document type: academic/scholarly publication.
—BLDSC (9223.000000); CASDDS.
Description: Covers the field of animal production.

636.089 IT ISSN 0394-3151
VETERINARIA. 4/yr. Via Pallavicino 26, 26100 Cremona, Italy. TEL 372-235-01. FAX 372-457091. Ed. Claudio Peruccio. circ. 7,500.

636.089 AG ISSN 0326-4629
VETERINARIA ARGENTINA. (Text in Spanish; summaries in English) 1984. m. (10/yr.). $66 (America $80; elsewhere $90) (effective 1995). Veterinaria Argentina S.R.L., Viamonte 494, 1053 Buenos Aires, Argentina. TEL 54-1-3128339. FAX 54-1-3119997. Dir. Emilio G. Morini; Pub. Norberto Speroni. adv.: B&W page $435; 150 x 210; adv. contact: Norberto A. Speroni. bk.rev.; abstr.; bibl.; illus.; pat.; index, cum.index. circ. 4,500. Indexed: Agri.Eng.Abstr., Anim.Breed.Abstr., Biol.Abstr., Chem.Abstr., Dairy Sci.Abstr., Helminthol.Abstr., Ind.Vet., Protozool.Abstr., Rev.Med.& Vet.Mycol., Rev.Plant Path., Small Anim.Abstr., Vet.Bull. Document type: trade publication.
—BLDSC (9223.350000).
Supersedes (1939-1984): Gaceta Veterinaria (ISSN 0367-3812)

636 BL ISSN 0102-5716
CODEN: VEZOEO
VETERINARIA E ZOOTECNIA. (Text in Portuguese; summaries in English, Portuguese) 1985; ceased same yr.; resumed (vol.2). a. $30 or exchange basis. Universidade Estadual Paulista, Av. Vicente Ferreira 1278, Caixa Postal 603, 17515-901 Marilla SP, Brazil. TEL 0144-33-1844. FAX 0144-22-2504. TELEX 1119016 UJME BR. Ed.Bd. Document type: academic/scholarly publication.
Description: Original papers in veterinary medicine and zoological research.
Refereed Serial

VETERINARY SCIENCE

636.089   MX   CODEN: VTERBU
VETERINARIA MEXICO. (Text in Spanish; summaries in English, Spanish) 1970. q. Mex.$60($50) (effective 1994). Universidad Nacional Autonoma de Mexico, Facultad de Medicina Veterinaria y Zootecnia, Ciudad Universitaria, Deleg. Coyoacan, 04510 Mexico, D.F., Mexico. TEL 622-58-75. FAX 550-86-97. Ed. Dr. Raymundo Martinez Pena. adv. contact: Renate Marie Thummler Blum. bk.rev.; charts; illus.; stat.; index. circ. 2,000. (back issues avail.) **Indexed:** Anim.Breed.Abstr., Biol.Abstr., Chem.Abstr., Dairy Sci.Abstr., Helminthol.Abstr., Herb.Abstr., Ind.Vet., Nutr.Abstr., Pig News & Info., Poult.Abstr., Protozool.Abstr., Rural Recreat.Tour.Abstr., Small Anim.Abstr., Sport Fish.Abstr., Vet.Bull., Wild.Rev., World Agri.Econ. & Rural Sociol.Abstr., Zoo.Rec.
—BLDSC (9225.040000); CASDDS; **Genuine Article.**
    Formerly (until 1975): Veterinaria (ISSN 0301-5092)
    Description: Original research articles and clinical case reports in the general field of veterinary and animal science, with emphasis on local and national events.

636.089   VE   ISSN 0379-8275
CODEN: VETRE3
VETERINARIA TROPICAL. (Text in Spanish; summaries in English and Spanish) 1976. a. Bs.40($8) or exchange basis. Fondo Nacional de Investigaciones Agropecuarias, Apdo. 2103, Maracay 2105, Venezuela. Ed.Bd. bibl.; charts; illus. circ. 800. **Indexed:** Helminthol.Abstr., Ind.Vet., Pig News & Info., Poult.Abstr., Protozool.Abstr., Vet.Bull.
    Formerly (until 1976): Instituto de Investigaciones Veterinarias. Boletin.

636.089   CN   ISSN 0849-5009
VETERINARIAN MAGAZINE. 1989. 6/yr. Can.$30 (US $48, elsewhere $64). H G K Communications, Inc., 248 Mary St., Rockwood, ON N0B 2K0, Canada. TEL 519-856-4050. FAX 519-856-4146. Ed. Maggie Clark. adv. contact: S. Lynn Hewitt. circ. 4,600. (back issues avail.) **Document type:** trade publication.
    Description: Professional information for veterinarians across Canada about companion animals, food animals, research, nutrition, new procedures and clinical management.

636.089   IT
VETERINARIO D'ITALIA. m. Medici Veterinari Italiani di Medicina Pubblica, Via del Tritone 125, 00187 Rome, Italy. Ed. Roberto Cicala. circ. 9,000.

636.089   CN   ISSN 0830-1743
VETERINARIUS. (Text in French) 1984. 6/yr. $20. Corporation Professionnelle des Medecins Veterinaires du Quebec, 795 Av. du Palais, Ste. 200, St. Hyacinthe, PQ J2S 5C6, Canada. TEL 514-774-1427. FAX 514-774-7635. adv. circ. 1,900.

636.089   RU   ISSN 0042-4846
CODEN: VETNAL
VETERINARIYA. 1924. m. $97 (effective 1996). Izdatel'stvo Kolos, Sadovo-Spasskaya, 18, 107807 Moscow, Russia. (Co-sponsor: Ministerstvo Sel'skogo Khozyaistva S.S.S.R.) Ed. Vladimir A. Gar'kavtsev. bk.rev.; bibl.; illus.; index. circ. 20,000. **Indexed:** Agri.Eng.Abstr., Anim.Breed.Abstr., Apic.Abstr., Biol.Abstr., Chem.Abstr., Dairy Sci.Abstr., Food Sci.& Tech.Abstr., Helminthol.Abstr., Ind.Med., Ind.Vet., Maize Abstr., Nutr.Abstr., Pig News & Info., Poult.Abstr., Protozool.Abstr., Rev.Appl.Entomol., Rev.Med.& Vet.Mycol., Small Anim.Abstr., Soyabean Abstr., Triticale Abstr., Vet.Bull., Weed Abstr. **Document type:** academic/scholarly publication.
—BLDSC (0038.000000); CASDDS.

636   XR   ISSN 0375-8427
CODEN: VTMDAR
VETERINARNI MEDICINA/VETERINARY MEDICINE; vedecky casopis. (Text and summaries in Czech or Slovak and English) 1956. m. $92. Ustav Zemedelskych a Potravinarskych Informaci, Slezska 7, 120 56 Prague 2, Czech Republic. TEL 257541. FAX 257090. Ed. Z. Radosova. adv.; bibl.; charts; illus.; stat. circ. 500. **Indexed:** Anim.Breed.Abstr., Apic.Abstr., Biol.Abstr., Chem.Abstr., Curr.Adv.Ecol.Sci., Curr.Cont., Dairy Sci.Abstr., Excerp.Med., Field Crop Abstr., Food Sci.& Tech.Abstr., Helminthol.Abstr., Herb.Abstr., Ind.Med., Ind.Vet., Maize Abstr., Nutr.Abstr., Pig News & Info., Poult.Abstr., Protozool.Abstr., Rev.Med.& Vet.Mycol., Rev.Plant Path., Rice Abstr., Small Anim.Abstr., Triticale Abstr., Vet.Bull. **Document type:** academic/scholarly publication.
—BLDSC (9225.550000); CASDDS; **Genuine Article.**

636.089 597   CI   ISSN 0372-5480
CODEN: VEARA6
VETERINARSKI ARHIV. (Text in Croatian, English) 1931. bi-m. DM.40 (foreign $50). Sveuciliste u Zagrebu, Veterinarski Fakultet - University of Zagreb, Veterinary Faculty, Heinzelova 55, P.O. Box 190, 41001 Zagreb, Croatia. TEL 385-41-290111. Ed. Dubravko Timet. index, cum.index. circ. 900. (back issues avail.) **Indexed:** Anim.Breed.Abstr., Biol.Abstr., Biotech.Abstr., Chem.Abstr., Helminthol.Abstr., Herb.Abstr., Ind.Vet., Nutr.Abstr., Pig News & Info., Poult.Abstr., Protozool.Abstr., Ref.Zh., Rev.Med.& Vet.Mycol., Small Anim.Abstr., Soyabean Abstr., Vet.Bull.
—BLDSC (9226.100000); CASDDS; **Genuine Article.**
    Description: Scientific journal of veterinary and related sciences: microbiology, immunology, parasitology, clinical sciences, animal science, physiology, anatomy.

636.089   YU   ISSN 0350-2457
VETERINARSKI GLASNIK. (Text in Serbo-Croatian; summaries in English, Russian) 1947. m. 900 din.($100) (effective Jan. 1990). Savez Veterinara i Veterinarskih Tehnicara, Bulevar JNA 18, 11000 Belgrade, Yugoslavia. TEL 011 684-597. (Dist. by: Jugoslovenska Knjiga, Trg. Republike 5-5, 11000 Belgrade, Yugoslavia) Ed. Dr. Bozidar Markovic. adv.; bk.rev.; index. circ. 2,500. (back issues avail.) **Indexed:** Anim.Breed.Abstr., Apic.Abstr., Dairy Sci.Abstr., Forest Prod.Abstr., Herb.Abstr., Ind.Vet., Maize Abstr., Pig News & Info., Poult.Abstr., Protozool.Abstr., Rev.Med.& Vet.Mycol., Small Anim.Abstr., Triticale Abstr., Vet.Bull.
—BLDSC (9226.400000).

636.089 617.7   US   ISSN 1076-4607
SF891
VETERINARY & COMPARATIVE OPHTHALMOLOGY; an international journal of clinical and investigational ophthalmology. 1991. q. $50 (Canada and Mexico $60; elsewhere $65) (effective 1996). (International Society of Veterinary Ophthalmology) Veterinary Practice Publishing Co., 7 Ashley Ave. S., Santa Barbara, CA 93103-9989. TEL 805-965-1028. FAX 805-965-0722. (Subscr. to: Box 4457, Santa Barbara, CA 93140-4457) Ed. Dr. Robert L. Peiffer; Pub. Nancy Bull. abstr.; bibl.; charts; illus.; stat. circ. 2,500. (reprint service avail. from ISI) **Document type:** academic/scholarly publication.
—Genuine Article.; UnCover.
    Formerly (until 1994): Progress in Veterinary and Comparative Ophthalmology (ISSN 1061-5768)
    Description: Publishes original ophthalmologic research and case studies.
    Refereed Serial

636.089   GW   ISSN 0932-0814
SF910.5
VETERINARY AND COMPARATIVE ORTHOPAEDICS AND TRAUMATOLOGY. Short title: V.C.O.T. (Text in English) 1988. q. DM.248($185) to individuals; institutions DM.310($228). F.K. Schattauer Verlagsgesellschaft mbH, Postfach 104545, 70040 Stuttgart, Germany. TEL 0711-22987-0. FAX 0711-22987-50. (Co-sponsors: Veterinary Orthopedic Society (North America), European Society of Veterinary Orthopaedics and Traumatology, British Veterinary Orthopaedic Association) Ed. G. Sumner-Smith. bk.rev.; abstr. circ. 1,000. **Indexed:** Bibl.Agri., Ind.Vet., Small Anim.Abstr., Vet.Bull. **Document type:** academic/scholarly publication.
—BLDSC (9226.600000); Genuine Article; SWETS; UnCover. **CCC.**
    Refereed Serial

VETERINARY AND HUMAN TOXICOLOGY. see ENVIRONMENTAL STUDIES — Toxicology And Environmental Safety

636.089   UK   ISSN 0083-5870
SF601   CODEN: VEANAS
VETERINARY ANNUAL. 1959. a. £60. Blackwell Science Ltd., Osney Mead, Oxford, England. TEL 01865-240201. FAX 01865-721205. TELEX 83355 MEDBOK G. (also avail. in microform from UMI; back issues avail.) **Indexed:** Anim.Breed.Abstr., Biol.Abstr., Dairy Sci.Abstr., Ind.Vet., Nutr.Abstr., Pig News & Info., Sport Fish.Abstr., Vet.Bull., Wild.Rev. **Document type:** monographic series.
—BLDSC (9226.850000); Faxon. **CCC.**

636 660   FR   ISSN 1018-533X
VETERINARY BIOTECHNOLOGY NEWSLETTER. (Text in English, French, Spanish) 1991. a. 400 F.($74) (effective 1995). Office International des Epizooties, 12 rue de Prony, 75017 Paris, France. TEL 44-15-18-88. (U.S. subscr. to: Scientific, Medical Publications of France, 100 East 42nd St., Ste. 1002, New York, NY 10017. TEL 212-983-6278) Ed. J. Blancou. adv. contact: Gill Dilmitis. **Document type:** newsletter.
    Description: Inventories the major developments in biotechnology applicable to animal health and production: monoclonal antibodies, nucleic acid probes, genetically-engineered vaccines, resistance marker genes.

636.08   US
▼**VETERINARY CLINICAL NUTRITION.** 1994. q. $50 (Canada and Mexico $60; elsewhere $65) (effective 1996); newsstand price: $15. Veterinary Practice Publishing Co., 7 Ashley Ave. S., Santa Barbara, CA 93103-3397. TEL 805-965-1028. FAX 805-965-0722. Ed. Francis Kallfelz; Pub. Nancy Bull. adv.: B&W page $648. circ. 6,000 (paid). **Document type:** trade publication.
    Refereed Serial

636.089   US   ISSN 0275-6382
CODEN: VCPADJ
VETERINARY CLINICAL PATHOLOGY. 1972. q. $50 (Canada and Mexico $60; elsewhere $65) (effective 1996). (American Society for Veterinary Clinical Pathology) Veterinary Practice Publishing Co., 7 Ashley Ave. S., Santa Barbara, CA 93103-9989. TEL 805-965-1028. FAX 805-965-0722. (Subscr. to: Box 4457, Santa Barbara, CA 93140-4457) Ed. Dr. Alan Rebar. bk.rev.; abstr. circ. 1,500. (also avail. in microfilm from UMI; reprint service avail. from UMI) **Indexed:** Chem.Abstr., Ind.Vet., Small Anim.Abstr., Vet.Bull. **Document type:** academic/scholarly publication.
—BLDSC (9227.015500); CASDDS; Genuine Article.; SWETS; UnCover.
    Former titles: American Society for Veterinary Clinical Pathology. Journal; (until 1977): American Society of Veterinary Clinical Pathologists. Bulletin (ISSN 0147-0701)
    Refereed Serial

VETERINARY SCIENCE 6539

636.089   US   ISSN 0749-0739
VETERINARY CLINICS OF NORTH AMERICA: EQUINE PRACTICE. 1985. 3/yr. $105 (foreign $130) (effective 1996). W.B. Saunders Co. (Subsidiary of: Harcourt Brace & Company), Curtis Center, 3rd Fl., Independence Sq. W., Philadelphia, PA 19106-3399. TEL 215-238-7800. FAX 215-238-6445. (Subscr. to: Periodicals Fulfillment, W.B. Saunders Co., 6277 Sea Harbor Dr., 4th Fl., Orlando, FL 32891-4800. TEL 800-654-2542. FAX 800-874-6418) Ed. A. Simon Turner. (also avail. in microfilm; back issues avail.) **Indexed:** Curr.Adv.Ecol.Sci., Ind.Vet., Protozool.Abstr. **Document type:** academic/scholarly publication.
—BLDSC (9227.017800); Genuine Article; SWETS; UMI. **CCC.**
Description: Each issue covers a single topic relating to the treatment of conditions and diseases of horses.

636.089   US   ISSN 0749-0720
VETERINARY CLINICS OF NORTH AMERICA: FOOD ANIMAL PRACTICE. 1985. 3/yr. $85 (foreign $110) (effective 1996). W.B. Saunders Co. (Subsidiary of: Harcourt Brace & Company), Curtis Center, 3rd Fl., Independence Sq. W., Philadelphia, PA 19106-3399. TEL 215-238-7800. FAX 215-238-6445. (Subscr. to: Periodicals Fulfillment, W.B. Saunders Co., 6277 Sea Harbor Dr., 4th Fl., Orlando, FL 32891-4800. TEL 800-654-2452. FAX 800-874-6418) Ed. Elaine Hunt. (also avail. in microfilm; back issues avail.) **Indexed:** Agri.Eng.Abstr., Anim.Breed.Abstr., Curr.Adv.Ecol.Sci., Ind.Vet., Pig News & Info., Poult.Abstr., Vet.Bull. **Document type:** academic/scholarly publication.
—BLDSC (9227.017900); Genuine Article; SWETS; UMI. **CCC.**
Description: Each issue discusses an aspect of the treatment of conditions in cows, pigs, and sheep.

636.089   US   ISSN 0195-5616
                       CODEN: VNAPDW
VETERINARY CLINICS OF NORTH AMERICA: SMALL ANIMAL PRACTICE. 1971. bi-m. $120 (foreign $152) (effective 1996). W.B. Saunders Co. (Subsidiary of: Harcourt Brace & Company), Curtis Center, 3rd Fl., Independence Sq. W., Philadelphia, PA 19106-3399. TEL 215-238-7800. FAX 215-238-6445. (Subscr. to: Periodicals Fulfillment, W.B. Saunders Co., 6277 Sea Harbor Dr., 4th Fl., Orlando, FL 32891-4800. TEL 800-654-2452. FAX 800-874-6418) Ed. Ruth Savitz. illus.; index. (also avail. in microform from MIM,UMI; reprint service avail. from UMI, ISI) **Indexed:** Anim.Breed.Abstr., Biol.Abstr., Curr.Adv.Ecol.Sci., Curr.Cont., Dent.Ind., Excerp.Med., Helminthol.Abstr., Ind.Med., Ind.Vet., Poult.Abstr., Protozool.Abstr., Small Anim.Abstr., Vet.Bull. **Document type:** academic/scholarly publication.
—BLDSC (9227.020000); Faxon; Genuine Article; SWETS; UMI; UnCover. **CCC.**
Supersedes in part (in 1979): Veterinary Clinics of North America (ISSN 0091-0279)

636.089   UK   ISSN 0959-4493
                       CODEN: VEDEEK
VETERINARY DERMATOLOGY; an international journal. 1990. 4/yr. £155 to institutions in Europe; elsewhere £170.50($270) (effective 1996). Balckwell Science Ltd., Osney Mead, Oxford OX2 OEL, England. TEL 44-1865-206206. FAX 44-1865-206219. (Co-sponsors: European Society of Veterinary Dermatology; American College of Veterinary Dermatology) Eds. Ian Mason, David Lloyd. (also avail. in microfilm from UMI; back issues avail.) **Document type:** academic/scholarly publication.
—BLDSC (9227.026000); UMI; UnCover. **CCC.**
Description: Research papers on all aspects of the skin of mammals, birds, reptiles, amphibians and fish.
Refereed Serial

636.089   FR   ISSN 1010-3538
VETERINARY DRUG REGISTRATION NEWSLETTER. (Text in English, French, Spanish) 1987. s-a. 350 F.($65) (effective 1995). Office International des Epizooties, 12, rue de Prony, 75017 Paris, France. TEL 44-15-18-88. FAX 42-67-09-87. TELEX EPIZOTI 642 285 F. (U.S. Subscr. to: Scientific, Medical Publications of France, 100 E. 42nd St., Ste. 1002, New York, NY 10017. TEL 212-983-6278) Ed. J. Blancou. adv. contact: Gill Dilmitis. **Document type:** newsletter.
—BLDSC (9227.060000).
Description: Features information on international meetings, procedures for registering veterinary drugs, registration of new veterinary drugs, quality of pharmaceutical products, industry news and recent developments.

636.089   US   ISSN 0042-4862
VETERINARY ECONOMICS; the veterinarian's business magazine. 1960. m. $35 (Canada and Mexico $50; elsewhere $70). Veterinary Medicine Publishing Co. (Subsidiary of: Medical Economics), 9073 Lenexa Dr., Lenexa, KS 66215. TEL 913-492-4300. FAX 913-492-4157. Ed. Renee Anderson; Pub. Dr. Ray Glick. adv. contact: Doug Catt. bk.rev.; charts; illus.; stat.; tr.lit.; index. circ. 45,572. (also avail. in microform from UMI) **Indexed:** Account.Ind. (1974-), Helminthol.Abstr., Ind.Vet., SRI, Vet.Bull. **Document type:** trade publication.
—BLDSC (9227.070000); UMI; UnCover.
Description: Covers all aspects of veterinary practice management and finance.

636.089   US   ISSN 1047-6326
VETERINARY FORUM. 1982. m. $35 (free to qualified personnel). Forum Publications, Inc., 1610-A Frederica Rd., St. Simons Island, GA 31522-2509. TEL 912-638-4848. FAX 912-634-0768. Ed. Michael D. Sollars. adv.; bk.rev.; tr.lit.; circ. 45,000 (controlled). **Document type:** trade publication.
—UnCover.
Formerly: Veterinary Classified.
Description: Created to educate readers on the various ways they can offer more services and products to their clients. Provides a ready reference in medical and practical management.

636.089   UK   ISSN 0301-6943
VETERINARY HISTORY. 1978. s-a. £4 (foreign £6) individuals; £6(foreign £8) institutions. Veterinary History Society, c/o E. Barbour-Hill, Tan-Y-Coed, High St., Penlon, Bangor, Gwynedd LL57 1PX, Wales. Ed. A.W. Johnson. adv.; bk.rev. circ. 200. **Indexed:** Ind.Vet. **Document type:** academic/scholarly publication.

636.089   NE   ISSN 0165-2427
                       CODEN: VIIMDS
VETERINARY IMMUNOLOGY AND IMMUNOPATHOLOGY; an international journal of comparative immunology. (Text in English) 1980. 24/yr. fl.2184($1332) (effective 1996). Elsevier Science B.V., P.O. Box 211, 1000 AE Amsterdam, Netherlands. TEL 31-20-4853911. FAX 31-20-4853598. TELEX 18582 ESPA NL. E-mail: nlinfo-f@elsevier.nl; usinfo-f@elsevier.com; forinfo-kyf04035@niftyserve.or.jp; Site addr.: http://www.elsevier.nl/. (Subscr. in U.S. and Canada to: Elsevier Science Inc., Box 882, Madison Sq. Sta., New York, NY 10159-0882. TEL 212-989-5800. FAX 212-633-3990) Eds. J. Goudswaard, S. Krakowka. adv.; bk.rev.; illus.; index. (also avail. in microform from UMI; back issues avail.) **Indexed:** Anim.Breed.Abstr., Biol.Abstr., Chem.Abstr., Curr.Adv.Ecol.Sci., Curr.Cont., Dairy Sci.Abstr., Excerp.Med., Helminthol.Abstr., Ind.Med., Ind.Vet., Pig News & Info., Poult.Abstr., Protozool.Abstr., Rev.Med.& Vet.Mycol., Small Anim.Abstr., Sport Fish.Abstr., Vet.Bull., Wild.Rev., Zoo.Rec. **Document type:** academic/scholarly publication.
—BLDSC (9228.200000); CASDDS; Faxon; Genuine Article; SWETS; UnCover. **CCC.**
Description: Deals with the study of veterinary immunology and immunopathology as applied to domestic animals, laboratory animals and other species that are useful to man.
Refereed Serial

636.089   PL   ISSN 0042-4870
                       CODEN: BVIPA7
VETERINARY INSTITUTE, PULAWY. BULLETIN. (Text and summaries in English) 1957. s-a. $50 or exchange basis. Instytut Weterynarii, c/o Krystyna Ciemiega-Wilczynska, Sec., Al. Partyzantow 57, 24-100 Pulawy, Poland. TEL 48-831-30-51. FAX 48-831-25-95. TELEX 642401 IWET PL. Ed. Marian Grundboeck. circ. 500. **Indexed:** Anim.Breed.Abstr., Biol.Abstr., Chem.Abstr., Curr.Adv.Ecol.Sci., Dairy Sci.Abstr., Food Sci.& Tech.Abstr., Helminthol.Abstr., Ind.Vet., Landwirt.Zentralbl., Nutr.Abstr., Pig News & Info., Poult.Abstr., Ref.Zh., Rev.Med.& Vet.Mycol., Small Anim.Abstr., Vet.Bull. **Document type:** bulletin.
—BLDSC (2805.300000); CASDDS; Genuine Article; UnCover.
Description: Publishes original scientific papers of research performed in the institute.
Refereed Serial

636.08   UA
                       CODEN: VMJGEA
VETERINARY MEDICAL JOURNAL GIZA. (Text in English) 1953. q. Cairo University, Faculty of Veterinary Medicine, Giza, Cairo, Egypt. Ed. M. Refai. **Indexed:** Rev.Med.& Vet.Mycol., Sport Fish.Abstr., Wild.Rev., Zoo.Rec. **Document type:** academic/scholarly publication.
—BLDSC (9228.974000); CASDDS.
Formerly (until 1988): Veterinary Medical Journal (ISSN 0506-8266)
Refereed Serial

636.089   US   ISSN 1059-0994
VETERINARY MEDICAL REVIEW. 1971; N.S. 1980. s-a. free. University of Missouri at Columbia, College of Veterinary Medicine, Veterinary Medical Library, W218 Veterinary Medicine, Columbia, MO 65211. TEL 314-882-2461. Ed. Deborah Beroset Diamond. charts; illus.; stat. circ. 3,000. (back issues avail.) **Indexed:** Anim.Breed.Abstr., Biotech.Abstr., Chem.Abstr., Dairy Sci.Abstr., Helminthol.Abstr., Ind.Vet., Protozool.Abstr., Vet.Bull.
Incorporates (1950-1979): Missouri Veterinarian (ISSN 0540-4517); Which was formerly: Veterinary Scope.
Description: For alumni, faculty and students, as well as other practicing veterinarians in Missouri.

636.089   US   ISSN 8750-7943
                       CODEN: VEMEEV
VETERINARY MEDICINE. 1905. m. $54 (Canada and Mexico $64; elsewhere $87) (effective 1996). Veterinary Medicine Publishing Co. (Subsidiary of: Medical Economics), 9073 Lenexa Dr., Lenexa, KS 66215. TEL 913-492-4300. FAX 913-492-4157. Ed. Dr. Tracy Revoir; Pub. Dr. Ray Glick. adv. contact: Doug Catt. bk.rev.; abstr.; bibl.; charts; illus.; stat.; tr.lit.; index. circ. 26,020. (also avail. in microform from UMI) **Indexed:** Anim.Breed.Abstr., Biol.Abstr., Biol.& Agr.Ind., Biotech.Abstr., Curr.Adv.Ecol.Sci., Curr.Cont., Dairy Sci.Abstr., Helminthol.Abstr., Herb.Abstr., Ind.Med., Ind.Vet., Nutr.Abstr., Pig News & Info., Protozool.Abstr., Rev.Med.& Vet.Mycol., Rev.Plant Path., Risk Abstr., Small Anim.Abstr., Sport Fish.Abstr., Vet.Bull., Wild.Rev., Zoo.Rec. **Document type:** trade publication.
—BLDSC (9229.000000); Faxon; Genuine Article; SWETS; UMI; UnCover. **CCC.**
Formerly (until 1985): Veterinary Medicine - Small Animal Clinician (ISSN 0042-4889)
Description: Provides practicing veterinarians with practical solutions to common diagnostic and therapeutic problems.
Refereed Serial

VETERINARY MEDICINE GUIDANCE MANUAL. see *PUBLIC HEALTH AND SAFETY*

VETERINARY SCIENCE

636 593 578   NE   ISSN 0378-1135
CODEN: VMICDQ
VETERINARY MICROBIOLOGY; an international journal. (Text in English) 1976. 24/yr. fl.2208($1346) (effective 1996). Elsevier Science B.V., P.O. Box 211, 1000 AE Amsterdam, Netherlands. TEL 31-20-4853911. FAX 31-20-4853598. TELEX 18582 ESPA NL. E-mail: nlinfo-f@elsevier.nl; usinfo-f@elsevier.com; forinfo-kyf04035@niftyserve.or.jp; Site addr.: http://www.elsevier.nl/. (Subscr. in U.S. and Canada to: Elsevier Science Inc., Box 882, Madison Sq. Sta., New York, NY 10159. TEL 212-989-5800. FAX 212-633-3990) Eds. P.B. Spradbrow, A.J. Frost. adv.; bk.rev.; bibl.; illus.; index. (also avail. in microform from UMI) **Indexed:** Abstr.Hyg., Biol.Abstr., Chem.Abstr., Curr.Adv.Ecol.Sci., Curr.Cont., Dairy Sci.Abstr., Dent.Ind., Excerp.Med., Helminthol.Abstr., Ind.Med., Ind.Vet., Microbiol.Abstr., Pig News & Info., Poult.Abstr., Ref.Zh., Rev.Med.& Vet.Mycol., Small Anim.Abstr., Sport Fish.Abstr., Trop.Dis.Bull., Vet.Bull., Wild.Rev., Zoo.Rec. **Document type:** academic/scholarly publication.
—BLDSC (9229.120000); ADONIS; CASDDS; Faxon; Genuine Article; SWETS; UnCover. **CCC**.
Description: Concerned with microbiological diseases of all animals that are useful to man. Publishes information on pathogenesis, host responses, immunology, epidemiology, disease prevention, treatment, control and comparative studies of diseases affecting man and animals, as well as laboratory studies of the causal agents of diseases of animals.
Refereed Serial

636.089   NE   ISSN 0304-4017
CODEN: VPARDI
VETERINARY PARASITOLOGY; an international scientific journal. (Text in English) 1975. 24/yr. fl.2280($1390) (effective 1996). Elsevier Science B.V., P.O. Box 211, 1000 AE Amsterdam, Netherlands. TEL 31-20-4853911. FAX 31-20-4853598. TELEX 18582 ESPA NL. E-mail: nlinfo-f@elsevier.nl; usinfo-f@elsevier.com; forinfo-kyf04035@niftyserve.or.jp; Site addr.: http://www.elsevier.nl/. (Subscr. in U.S. and Canada to: Elsevier Science Inc., Box 882, Madison Sq. Sta., New York, NY 10159. TEL 212-989-5800. FAX 212-633-3990) Ed. S.M. Gaafar. (also avail. in microform from UMI) **Indexed:** Abstr.Hyg., Biol.Abstr., Chem.Abstr, Curr.Adv.Ecol.Sci., Curr.Cont., Dairy Sci.Abstr., Dent.Ind., Excerp.Med., Helminthol.Abstr., Ind.Med., Ind.Vet., Pig News & Info., Poult.Abstr., Protozool.Abstr., Ref.Zh., Rev.Appl.Entomol., Small Anim.Abstr., Sport Fish.Abstr., Trop.Dis.Bull., Vet.Bull., Wild.Rev., Zoo.Rec. **Document type:** academic/scholarly publication.
—BLDSC (9229.163000); ADONIS; CASDDS; Faxon; Genuine Article; SWETS; UnCover. **CCC**.
Description: Publishes papers dealing with all aspects of disease prevention, pathology, treatment, epidemiology, and control of parasites in all animals which can be regarded as being useful to man.
Refereed Serial

636.089   US   ISSN 0300-9858
SF769   CODEN: VTPHAK
VETERINARY PATHOLOGY. (Text in English and German) 1964. bi-m. $107 (Canada & mexico $116; elsewhere $128) (effective 1996). (American College of Veterinary Pathologists) Waverly Press, Inc. (Subsidiary of: Williams & Wilkins), 428 E. Preston St., Box 64025, Baltimore, MD 21202. TEL 410-528-4000. FAX 410-528-4412. Ed.Bd. adv.; bk.rev.; bibl.; charts; illus.; index. circ. 1,200. **Indexed:** Biol.Abstr., Biotech.Abstr., Chem.Abstr., Curr.Adv.Cancer Res., Curr.Adv.Ecol.Sci., Curr.Cont., Dairy Sci.Abstr., Dent.Ind., Excerp.Med., Helminthol.Abstr., Herb.Abstr., Ind.Med., Ind.Vet., Nutr.Abstr., Pig News & Info., Poult.Abstr., Protozool.Abstr., Rev.Med.& Vet.Mycol., Rev.Plant Path., Small Anim.Abstr., So.Pac.Per.Ind., Sport Fish.Abstr., Vet.Bull., Wild.Rev., Zoo.Rec.
—BLDSC (9229.165000); CASDDS; Faxon; SWETS; UnCover.
Formerly: Pathologia Veterinaria (ISSN 0031-2975)
Refereed Serial

636.089   US   ISSN 0272-4669
SF917
VETERINARY PHARMACEUTICALS AND BIOLOGICALS. biennial. $81 (Canada $83; elsewhere $85) (effective 1996). Veterinary Medicine Publishing Co. (Subsidiary of: Medical Economics), 9073 Lenexa Dr., Lenexa, KS 66215. TEL 913-492-4300. FAX 913-492-4157. Kim K. Holt, Man.Ed; Pub. Dr Ray Glick. (also avail. in microform from UMI) **Document type:** directory, monographic series.
—BLDSC (9229.167000); UMI.
Description: Covers veterinary products, including pharmaceuticals, biologicals, parasiticides, diets, nutritional supplements, and diagnostic aids and supplies for the veterinary professional.

636.089   UK   ISSN 0042-4897
VETERINARY PRACTICE. 1966. m. £18 (foreign £21) (effective 1996). A.E. Morgan Publications Ltd., Stanley House, 9 West St., Epsom, Surrey KT18 7RL, England. TEL 01372-741411. FAX 01372-744493. Ed. C. Cattrall; Pub. Terence Morgan. adv. contact: Bill Sherry. bk.rev.; abstr.; charts; illus. (tabloid format; also avail. in microform from UMI) **Indexed:** Ind.Vet., Small Anim.Abstr., Vet.Bull. **Document type:** trade publication.
—UMI.
Formerly: Veterinary News.
Description: News and articles on products and developments in the veterinary profession.

636.089   US   ISSN 1047-8639
VETERINARY PRACTICE STAFF; current ideas and new information. 1989. bi-m. $28 (Canada and Mexico $35; elsewhere $45) (effective 1996). Veterinary Practice Publishing Co., 7 Ashley Ave. S., Santa Barbara, CA 93103-9989. TEL 805-965-1028. FAX 805-965-0722. (Subscr. to: Box 4457, Santa Barbara, CA 93140-4457) Ed. Dr. Donald Applegate. circ. 16,000. **Document type:** academic/scholarly publication.
—Genuine Article.
Description: For employees of the veterinary clinic, including technicians, assistants, office personnel, and receptionists.
Refereed Serial

636.089   US
VETERINARY PRODUCT NEWS.* Short title: V P N. 1987. 8/yr. $30 ($62 in N. America; elsewhere $98)(effective 1992). Fancy Publications, 2401 Beverly Blvd., Los Angeles, CA 90057. TEL 714-855-8822. FAX 714-855-3045. Ed. Lynn E. Densford. adv. circ. 41,500.

636.089   NE   ISSN 0165-2176
CODEN: VEQUDU
VETERINARY QUARTERLY. (Text in English) 1979. 4/yr. fl.221($127) (effective 1995). (Koninklijke Nederlandse Maatschappij voor Diergeneeskunde - Royal Netherlands Veterinary Association) Kluwer Academic Publishers, Postbus 17, 3300 AA Dordrecht, Netherlands. TEL 31-78-392392. FAX 31-78-392254. TELEX 29245 KAPG NL. E-mail: SERVICES@WKAP.NL. (Dist. by: Kluwer Academic Publishers Group, P.O. Box 322, 3300 AH Dordrecht, Netherlands. TEL 31-78-392392. FAX 31-78-546474; N. America dist. addr.: Box 358, Accord Sta., Hingham, MA 02018-0358. TEL 617-871-6600. FAX 617-871-6528) Ed E. W Sybesma. adv. (also avail. in microform from UMI; back issues avail.; reprint service avail. from SWZ) **Indexed:** Anim.Breed.Abstr., ASCA, Bibl.Agri., Biol.Abstr., Biotech.Abstr., Chem.Abstr., Curr.Adv.Ecol.Sci., Curr.Cont., Dairy Sci.Abstr., Excerp.Med., Food Sci.& Tech.Abstr., Helminthol.Abstr., Ind.Med., Ind.Vet., Pig News & Info., Poult.Abstr., Protozool.Abstr., Rev.Med.& Vet.Mycol., Sci.Cit.Ind., Small Anim.Abstr., Sport Fish.Abstr., Vet.Bull., Wild.Rev., Zoo.Rec. **Document type:** academic/scholarly publication.
—BLDSC (9229.270000); CASDDS; Faxon; Genuine Article; SWETS; UMI; UnCover. **CCC**.
Description: Publishes the results of applied veterinary research in a variety of specialties.

636.089   US   ISSN 1058-8183
SF757.8   CODEN: VRULED
VETERINARY RADIOLOGY & ULTRASOUND. 1960. bi-m. $72 to individuals (foreign $82); institutions $92 (foreign $102). American College of Veterinary Radiology, c/o Lucinda Ayres, 2520 Beechridge Rd., Raleigh, NC 27608. TEL 919-881-4165. FAX 919-821-9578. (Co-sponsors: International Veterinary Radiological Association; European Veterinary Radiology Association) Ed. Dr. Donald E. Thrall. adv. contact: Lucinda Ayres. illus.; index. circ. 1,000. (also avail. in microform from UMI) **Indexed:** Biol.Abstr., Helminthol.Abstr., Ind.Vet., Small Anim.Abstr., Sport Fish.Abstr., Vet.Bull., Wild.Rev., Zoo.Rec. **Document type:** academic/scholarly publication.
—BLDSC (9229.281000); Genuine Article; SWETS; UMI; UnCover.
Former titles (until 1992): Veterinary Radiology (ISSN 0196-3627); (until 1980): American Veterinary Radiology Society. Journal (ISSN 0066-1155)
Description: Presents articles of interest to the practicing veterinarian. Covers radiologic and ultrasound techniques, diagnostic interpretation, radiologic therapy and current advances in the field.
Refereed Serial

636.089   UK   ISSN 0042-4900
CODEN: VETRAX
VETERINARY RECORD. 1888. w. £100 (foreign £138.50). British Veterinary Association, 7 Mansfield St., London W1M 0AT, England. TEL 0171-636-6541. FAX 0171-637-0620. Ed. Edward Boden. circ. 10,000. (also avail. in microform from UMI; reprint service avail. from UMI) **Indexed:** Anim.Breed.Abstr., Biol.Abstr., Biol.& Agr.Ind., Biotech.Abstr., Chem.Abstr., Curr.Adv.Biochem., Curr.Adv.Cancer Res., Curr.Adv.Ecol.Sci., Curr.Cont., Dairy Sci.Abstr., Dent.Ind., Excerp.Med., Food Sci.& Tech.Abstr., Helminthol.Abstr., Herb.Abstr., Ind.Med., Ind.Vet., Nutr.Abstr., Pig News & Info., Poult.Abstr., Protozool.Abstr., Rev.Appl.Entomol., Rev.Med.& Vet.Mycol., Rev.Plant Path., Risk Abstr., Rural Recreat.Tour.Abstr., Small Anim.Abstr., Sport Fish.Abstr., Vet.Bull., W.R.C.Inf., Weed Abstr., Wild.Rev., World Agri.Econ. & Rural Sociol.Abstr., Zoo.Rec. **Document type:** academic/scholarly publication.
—BLDSC (9230.000000); CASDDS; EMDOCS; Faxon; Genuine Article; SWETS; UMI; UnCover. **CCC**.

636.089   FR   ISSN 0928-4249
CODEN: VEREEM
VETERINARY RESEARCH. (Text mainly in English; summaries in English, French) 1968. bi-m. 1335 F. in France; foreign 1625 F.($317) (effective 1996). (Institut National de la Recherche Agronomique) Editions Scientifiques Elsevier, 141 rue de Javel, 75747 Paris, France. TEL 33-1-45589063. (Subscr. in U.S. and Canada to: Elsevier Science Inc., Box 882, Madison Sq. Sta., New York, NY 10159. TEL 212-989-5800. FAX 212-633-3990) Eds. J. Charley-Poulain, J. Laporte. adv. circ. 2,000. (also avail. in microform; reprint service avail. from ISI) **Indexed:** Anim.Breed.Abstr., Bibl.Agri., Biol.Abstr., Biotech.Abstr., Chem.Abstr., Curr.Adv.Ecol.Sci., Curr.Cont., Dairy Sci.Abstr., Dent.Ind., Diar.Dis.Res., Excerp.Med., Field Crop Abstr., Helminthol.Abstr., Herb.Abstr., Ind.Med., Ind.Sci.Rev., Ind.Vet., Nutr.Abstr., Pig News & Info., Poult.Abstr., Protozool.Abstr., Rev.Plant Path, Sci.Cit.Ind., Sport Fish.Abstr., Vet.Bull., Wild.Rev. **Document type:** academic/scholarly publication.
—BLDSC (9230.090000); CASDDS; Faxon; Genuine Article; SWETS; UnCover. **CCC**.
Former titles (until 1993): Annales de Recherches Veterinaires (ISSN 0003-4193); (until 1969): Recherches Veterinaires (ISSN 0486-1418)
Description: Covers all scientific aspects of veterinary and comparative medicine and related subjects. The principal areas of interest are: immunology, virology, parasitology, physiology and biochemistry.
Refereed Serial

636.089 NE ISSN 0165-7380
CODEN: VRCODX
VETERINARY RESEARCH COMMUNICATIONS; an international journal publishing topical reviews and research articles on all aspects of the veterinary sciences. 1977. bi-m. fl.472 to institutions; $303 to institutions in U.S. (effective 1996). Kluwer Academic Publishers, Postbus 17, 3300 AA Dordrecht, Netherlands. TEL 31-78-392392. FAX 31-78-392254. TELEX 29245 KAPG NL. E-mail: SERVICES@WKAP.NL. (Dist. by: Kluwer Academic Publishers Group, P.O. Box 322, 3300 AH Dordrecht, Netherlands. TEL 31-78-392392. FAX 31-78-546474; N. America dist. addr.: Box 358, Accord Sta., Hingham, MA 02018-0358. TEL 617-871-6600. FAX 617-871-6528) Ed. M.M.H. Sewell. adv.; bk.rev.; abstr.; bibl.; charts; illus.; index, cum.index. (also avail. in microform from UMI; back issues avail.; reprint service avail. from SWZ) **Indexed:** Anim.Breed.Abstr., ASCA, Biol.Abstr., Chem.Abstr., Curr.Adv.Ecol.Sci., Curr.Cont., Dairy Sci.Abstr., Excerp.Med., Helminthol.Abstr., Ind.Med., Ind.Vet., Nutr.Abstr., Pig News & Info., Poult.Abstr., Protozool.Abstr., Rev.Med.& Vet.Mycol., Small Anim.Abstr., Soyabean Abstr., Sport Fish.Abstr., Vet.Bull., Wild.Rev., Zoo.Rec. **Document type:** academic/scholarly publication.
—BLDSC (9230.200000); CASDDS; Faxon; Genuine Article; SWETS; UMI; UnCover. **CCC.**
Formerly: Veterinary Science Communications (ISSN 0378-4312)
Description: Forum for current research in all disciplines of veterinary sciences.
Refereed Serial

636.089 IE
VETERINARY SURGEON. 1979. m. I£25. Jude Publications Ltd., Jude House, Tara St., Dublin 2, Ireland. TEL 01-6713500. FAX 01-6713074. Ed. Austin Shinnors. illus. circ. 1,700. **Indexed:** Dairy Sci.Abstr., Ind.Vet., Pig News & Info., Protozool.Abstr., Small Anim.Abstr., Vet.Bull. **Document type:** trade publication.
Formerly (until 1993): Irish Veterinary News (ISSN 0332-236X)

636 NZ
VETERINARY SURGEONS IN NEW ZEALAND; registered under the Veterinary Surgeons Act 1956 & persons entitled to use the title or description of veterinary practitioner. 1957. a. price varies. Government Printing Office, Private Bag, Wellington, New Zealand. circ. 1,000.

636.089 US ISSN 0161-3499
SF911 CODEN: VESUD6
VETERINARY SURGERY. 1978. bi-m. $135 (foreign $169) (effective 1996). (American College of Veterinary Surgeons) W.B. Saunders Co. (Subsidiary of: Harcourt Brace & Company), Curtis Center, 3rd Fl., Independence Sq. W., Philadelphia, PA 19106-3399. TEL 215-238-7800. FAX 215-238-6445. (Subscr. to: Periodicals Fulfillment, W.B. Saunders Co., 6277 Sea Harbor Dr., 4th Fl., Orlando, FL 32891-4800. TEL 800-654-2452. FAX 800-874-6418) (Co-sponsors: American College of Veterinary Anesthesiologists; European College of Veterinary Surgeons) Ed. Dr. Philip B. Vasseur; Pub. Joan W. Blumberg. adv.; B&W page $540, color page $1415; 7 x 10; adv. contact: Steve Gray. illus.; index. circ. 1,527. (reprint service avail. from UMI) **Indexed:** Biol.Abstr., Ind.Vet., Pig News & Info., Small.Anim.Abstr., Sport Fish.Abstr., Vet.Bull., Wild.Rev. **Document type:** academic/scholarly publication.
—BLDSC (9231.037000); CASDDS; Genuine Article; SWETS; UMI; UnCover. **CCC.**
Incorporates: Veterinary Anesthesia (ISSN 0149-3949); **Formerly:** Journal of Veterinary Surgery.
Description: Covers clinical and research topics of interest to veterinary surgeons and anesthesiologists.
Refereed Serial

636.089 US ISSN 8750-8990
VETERINARY TECHNICIAN. 1980. m. (11/yr.). $35 to individuals (Canada and Mexico $42; elsewhere $49); insititutions $48 (Canada and Mexico $58; elsewhere $63) (effective 1996). Veterinary Learning Systems, 425 Phillips Blvd., Ste. 100, Trenton, NJ 08618. TEL 609-882-5600; 800-426-9119. FAX 609-882-6357. Ed. Richard B. Ford, DVM. adv.; index. circ. 17,104. **Indexed:** Dairy Sci.Abstr., Ind.Vet., Protozool.Abstr., Small Anim.Abstr. **Document type:** trade publication.
—BLDSC (9231.038000); SWETS.

636.089 UK ISSN 1352-9374
VETERINARY TIMES. 1970. m. £49 (foreign £64) (free to qualified personnel). Veterinary Business Development Ltd., Olympus House, Werrington Centre, Peterborough, Cambs. PE4 6NA, England. TEL 01733-325522. FAX 01733-325512. E-mail: 100303,1416@compuserve.com. Ed. David Ritchie; Pub. Douglas Hutchison. adv. contact: Pippa Hutchison. bk.rev. circ. 8,800. (tabloid format) **Indexed:** Agri.Eng.Abstr., Ind.Vet., Pig News & Info., Small Anim.Abstr. **Document type:** trade publication.
Formerly (until 1984): Veterinary Drug.
Description: Covers new products, new techniques and news.

636.089 IE ISSN 0790-1682
VETERINARY UPDATE. 1984. bi-m. Jude Publications Ltd., Jude House, Tara St., Dublin 2, Ireland. TEL 01-6713500. FAX 01-6713074. Ed. Maria Farren. **Indexed:** Ind.Vet. **Document type:** bulletin.

636.089 TU ISSN 0377-6395
VETERINER HEKIMLERI DERNEGI DERGISI. 1930. 4/yr. Turk Veteriner Hekimleri Dernegi - Turkish Veterinary Medical Association, Saglik Sok. 21-3, Yenisehir, Ankara, Turkey. Ed. Dr. Huseyin Pulat. adv.; bk.rev. **Document type:** bulletin.
—BLDSC (9231.050000).
Formerly: Turk Veteriner Hekimleri Dernegi Dergisi (ISSN 0376-8104)
Refereed Serial

636.089 UN ISSN 0379-0045
VIGILANCIA EPIDEMIOLOGICA DE LA RABIA PARA LAS AMERICAS. English edition: Epidemiological Surveillance of Rabies for the Americas. 1969. m. free. Instituto Panamericano de Proteccion de Alimentos y Zoonosis - Panamerican Institute for Food Protection and Zoonoses, Casilla 44, 1064 Martinez Buenos Aires, Argentina. TEL 792-4047. FAX 112328. TELEX 24577 AR PAZ. (Affiliate: World Health Organization) Ed. Eduardo Guarnera. circ. 1,400 (Spanish ed. 950; English ed. 450).
Supersedes in part (since vol.7, no.4, 1978): Vigilancia Epidemiologica.

636.08 NE
VIRUS INFECTIONS OF VERTEBRATES. (Text in English) 1987. irreg., vol.4, 1993. price varies. Elsevier Science B.V., Books Division, P.O. Box 211, 1000 AE Amsterdam, Netherlands. TEL 31-20-4853911. FAX 31-20-4853705. TELEX 18582 ESPA NL. E-mail: nlinfo-f@elsevier.nl; usinfo-f@elsevier.com; forinfo-kyf04035@niftyserve.or.jp; Site addr.: http://www.elsevier.nl/. (Subscr. in U.S. and Canada to: Elsevier Science Inc., Box 882, Madison Sq. Sta., New York, NY 10159. TEL 212-989-5800) (back issues avail.) **Document type:** monographic series.
Refereed Serial

636.089 BE ISSN 0303-9021
CODEN: VDTIAX
VLAAMS DIERGENEESKUNDIG TIJDSCHRIFT/FLEMISH VETERINARY JOURNAL. (Text in Dutch and English; summaries in English) 1932. bi-m. 1000 BEF. Natuur- en Geneeskundige Vennootschap, Krijgslaan 281 S.8, B-9000 Ghent, Belgium. Ed. P. Simoens. adv.; bk.rev.; abstr.; charts; illus.; index. circ. 1,550. **Indexed:** Anim.Breed.Abstr., Biol.Abstr., Biotech.Abstr., Chem.Abstr., Curr.Adv.Ecol.Sci., Curr.Cont., Dairy Sci.Abstr., Helminthol.Abstr., Ind.Vet., Pig News & Info., Protozool.Abstr., Rev.Med.& Vet.Mycol., Rev.Plant Path., Small Anim.Abstr., Vet.Bull. **Document type:** academic/scholarly publication.
—BLDSC (9246.000000); CASDDS; Genuine Article.

VORTRAEGE ZUM THEMA MENSCH UND TIER. see *ANIMAL WELFARE*

636.089 PL
CODEN: AWAMDP
WARSAW AGRICULTURAL UNIVERSITY. S G G W. ANNALS. VETERINARY MEDICINE. (Text mainly in English; occasionally in French, German or Russian; summaries in Polish) 1957. irreg. $10 per no. Szkola Glowna Gospodarstwa Wiejskiego (SGGW) - Warsaw Agricultural University, Ul. Nowoursynowska 166, 02-766 Warsaw, Poland. Ed. T. Roskosz. **Indexed:** Chem.Abstr., Food Sci.& Tech.Abstr., Ind.Vet., Vet.Bull. **Document type:** academic/scholarly publication.
—BLDSC (1035.050000); CASDDS.
Former titles: Warsaw Agricultural University. S G G W - A R. Annals. Veterinary Medicine (ISSN 0208-5763); (until 1980): Akademia Rolnicza, Warsaw. Zeszyty Naukowe. Weterynaria (ISSN 0324-9085)

636.089 AU ISSN 0253-9411
CODEN: WTMOA3
WIENER TIERAERZTLICHE MONATSSCHRIFT. (Text in German; summaries in English) 1913. m. S.1250 (effective 1995); newsstand price: S.140. (Oesterreichische Tieraerzteschaft) Ostag Werbung und Verlag, Wickenburggasse 17, A-1082 Vienna, Austria. TEL 01-4027573. FAX 01-4088292. (Co-sponsor: Oesterreichische Gesellschaft der Tieraerzte) Ed.Bd. adv.; B&W page S.7150, color page S.15700; trim 245 x 170. bk.rev.; abstr.; bibl.; charts; illus.; index. circ. 1,600. **Indexed:** Anim.Breed.Abstr., Biol.Abstr., Biotech.Abstr., Chem.Abstr., Curr.Adv.Ecol.Sci., Curr.Cont., Dairy Sci.Abstr., Excerp.Med., Food Sci.& Tech.Abstr., Helminthol.Abstr., Ind.Vet., Key Word Ind.Wildl.Res., Nutr.Abstr., Pig News & Info., Poult.Abstr., Protozool.Abstr., Rev.Plant Path., Soils & Fert., Soyabean Abstr., Vet.Bull. **Document type:** trade publication.
—BLDSC (9316.000000); CASDDS; SWETS.
Supersedes: Berliner und Muenchener Tieraerztliche Wochenschrift and Wiener Tieraerztliche Monatschrift (ISSN 0723-6956); Which supersedes (in 1943): Wiener Tieraerztliche Monatschrift (ISSN 0043-535X)

WILDLIFE DISEASE REVIEW. see *MEDICAL SCIENCES*

636.089 639.9 US ISSN 1044-2618
WILDLIFE REHABILITATION TODAY. 1989. q. $15 (Canada $18; elsewhere $27). Coconut Creek Publishing Co., 2201 N.W. 40th Terr., Coconut Creek, FL 33066-2032. TEL 305-972-6092. FAX 305-977-5158. adv.; bk.rev. circ. 7,509. (back issues avail.) **Indexed:** Environ.Abstr. **Document type:** consumer publication, trade publication.
—CIS.
Description: Contains technical and non-technical veterinary, wildlife rescue, reintroduction care and rehab education articles.

636.089 FR ISSN 1017-3102
WORLD ANIMAL HEALTH. (Text in English, French, Spanish) a. 400 F.($74) (effective 1995). Office International des Epizooties, 12, rue de Prony, 75017 Paris, France. TEL 44-15-18-88. FAX 42-67-09-87. TELEX EPIZOTI 642 285 F. (U.S. Subscr. to: Scientific, Medical Publications of France, 100 E. 42nd St., Ste. 1002, New York, NY 10017. TEL 212-983-6278) Ed. J. Blancou. adv. contact: Gill Dilmitis. (back issues avail.) **Document type:** bulletin, government publication.
—BLDSC (9352.912250).
Description: Disease status of over 100 countries for 108 diseases of animals and fish.

WORLD ANIMAL SCIENCE. see *BIOLOGY — Zoology*

636.089 BE
WORLD BUIATRICS CONGRESS. (Each report published in the host country) (Text in English, French, German and Spanish) 1960. biennial. World Association for Buiatrics, c/o P. Lekeux, Sec., Faculte de Medecine Veterinaire, Bat B42, Sart Tilman, B-4000 Liege, Belgium. TEL 32-41-564030. FAX 32-41-562935. **Document type:** proceedings.
Formerly: International Meeting on Cattle Diseases. Reports. (ISSN 0074-6975)

VETERINARY SCIENCE — ABSTRACTING, BIBLIOGRAPHIES, STATISTICS

636.089 636   CC   ISSN 0366-6964
XUMU SHOUYI XUEBAO/ACTA VETERINARIA ET ZOOTECHNICA SINICA. (Text in Chinese) q. $1.80 per no. Zhongguo Nongye Kexueyuan, Xumu Yanjiusuo - Chinese Academy of Agriculture, Institute of Animal Husbandry, Ma Lian Wa, Haidian Qu, Beijing 100094, People's Republic of China. TEL 2581177. Ed. Dong Wei. **Indexed:** Anim.Breed.Abstr., Biol.Abstr., Curr.Leather Lit., Ind.Vet., Nutr.Abstr., Pig News & Info., Poult.Abstr., Protozool.Abstr., Rev.Med.& Vet.Mycol., Vet.Bull. —BLDSC (0670.900000); Genuine Article.

YOU & YOUR VET. see *PETS*

636.089   ZA
ZAMBIA. DEPARTMENT OF VETERINARY AND TSETSE CONTROL SERVICES. ANNUAL REPORT. (Text in English) a. K.200. Zambia Government Printing Department, P.O. Box 30136, Lusaka, Zambia. **Document type:** government publication.
Description: Reports on the year's veterinary research and diagnostic work in the identification of disease in Zambia.

636.089   NR
ZARIYA VETERINARIAN. (Text in English) s-a. £N40 (foreign $50). Ahmadu Bello University, Faculty of Veterinary Medicine, Zaria, Kaduna State, Nigeria. Ed. J.B. Adeyanju. circ. 1,000. (back issues avail.)

636.089   GW   ISSN 0939-7868
ZEITSCHRIFT FUER GANZHEITLICHE TIERMEDIZIN. q. DM.56 (students DM.36). (Deutsche Gesellschaft fuer Biologische Veterinaer-Medizin e.V.) Karl F. Haug Verlag GmbH, Fritz-Frey-Str. 21, 69121 Heidelberg, Germany. TEL 06221-4062-0. FAX 06221-400727. TELEX 461683-HVVFMD. (Subscr. to: Postfach 102840, 69018 Heidelberg, Germany) Ed. Dr. H. Krueger. **Document type:** academic/scholarly publication.
Formerly: Deutsche Zeitschrift fuer Biologische Veterinaermedizin (ISSN 0179-714X)

ZHONGGUO RENSHOU GONGHUANBING ZAZHI/CHINESE JOURNAL OF ZOONOSES. see *BIOLOGY — Microbiology*

636.089   CC
ZHONGGUO SHOUYI ZAZHI/CHINESE JOURNAL OF VETERINARY MEDICINE. (Text in Chinese) m. $0.80 per no. Guoji Shudian, Qikan Bu - China International Book Trading Corp., Chegongzhuang Xilu 21, P.O. Box 399, Beijing 100044, People's Republic of China. **Indexed:** Anim.Breed.Abstr., Ind.Vet., Pig News & Info., Poult.Abstr., Protozool.Abstr., Rev.Med.& Vet.Mycol., Vet.Bull.

636.089   CC   ISSN 0258-7033
CODEN: ZXZADM
ZHONGGUO XUMU ZAZHI/CHINESE JOURNAL OF ANIMAL SCIENCE. (Text in Chinese) 1963. bi-m. $0.70 per no. Zhongguo Xumu Shouyi Xuehui - Chinese Society of Animal Husbandry and Veterinary Science, 33 Nong Feng Li, Dongdaqiao, Chaoyangqu, Beijing 100020, People's Republic of China. TEL 5002288. Ed. Feng Yanglian. **Indexed:** Chem.Abstr., Ind.Vet., Maize Abstr., Pig News & Info., Poult.Abstr., Soyabean Abstr., Trop.Oil Seeds Abstr.
—CASDDS.

636.089   CH   ISSN 0253-9179
CODEN: CKSCDN
ZHONGHUA MINGUO SHOUYI XUEHUI ZAZHI/CHINESE SOCIETY OF VETERINARY SCIENCE. JOURNAL. (Text in Chinese, English) 1975. q. Zhonghua Minguo Shouyi Xuehui - Chinese Society of Veterinary Science, 142 Chou San Rd., Taipei 107, Taiwan, Republic of China. **Indexed:** Sport Fish.Abstr., Wild.Rev., Zoo.Rec. —BLDSC (4729.330500); CASDDS.

636.089   RH   ISSN 1016-1511
CODEN: ZVJOD4
ZIMBABWE VETERINARY JOURNAL. (Text and summaries in English) 1970. q. $50 (effective 1995 & 1996). (Zimbabwe Veterinary Association) Zimbabwe Veterinary Journal, P.O. Box CY168, Causeway, Harare, Zimbabwe. TEL 263-4-495859. Ed. G. Hill. adv.; bk.rev.; abstr.; index. circ. 350 (back issues avail.) **Indexed:** Field Crop Abstr., Ind.Vet., Rev.Appl.Entomol., Sport Fish.Abstr., Vet.Bull., Wild.Rev., Zoo.Rec. **Document type:** academic/scholarly publication.
Formerly (until 1980): Rhodesian Veterinary Journal (ISSN 0253-3278)
Description: Contains original and review papers on all aspects of animal health in Zimbabwe and SADCC countries, including articles by non-veterinarians.
Refereed Serial

636.089   SP   ISSN 0044-5312
CODEN: ZOTCAY
ZOOTECHNIA; acta societatis internationalis veterinariorum zootechnicorum. (Text in Spanish; summaries in English and French) 1950. q. 2500 ptas.($40) Sociedad Veterinaria de Zootecnia, Isabel La Catolica 12, 28013 Madrid, Spain. Ed. Prof. Dr. Carlos Luisde Cuenca. adv.; bk.rev.; abstr.; bibl.; charts; illus.; index. circ. 3,000. **Indexed:** Anim.Breed.Abstr., Biol.Abstr., Biotech.Abstr., Chem.Abstr., Curr.Adv.Ecol.Sci., Dairy Sci.Abstr., Helminthol.Abstr., Ind.SST, Ind.Vet., Rural Recreat.Tour.Abstr., Soils & Fert., Vet.Bull., World Agri.Econ. & Rural Sociol.Abstr.
—CASDDS.

VETERINARY SCIENCE — Abstracting, Bibliographies, Statistics

636.097 016   JA   ISSN 0001-7221
ACTA VETERINARIA JAPONICA.* (Text in English and European languages) 1956. q. exchange basis. Nihon University, Research Institute for Veterinary Science - Nihon Daigaku Juigaku Kenkyujo, c/o Japanese Society of Veterinary Science, Rokuno-Kaikan Bldg., 1-37-20 Yoyogi, Shibuya-ku, Tokyo 151, Japan. Ed. Ushio Tanaka. bk.rev.; index. circ. 650.

AGRICULTURAL AND VETERINARY PRODUCT INDEX. see *AGRICULTURE — Abstracting, Bibliographies, Statistics*

636.089   UK   ISSN 0144-3879
ANIMAL DISEASE OCCURRENCE. Abbreviated title: A D O. (Not avail. in printed format) 1980-1989; resumed 1991. a. £35($60) (effective 1996). CAB International, Wallingford, Oxon. OX10 8DE, England. TEL 01491-832111. FAX 01491-833508. TELEX 847964 COMAGG G. E-mail: cabi@cabi.org. (U.S. subscr. to: CAB International, North American Office, 845 N. Park Ave., Tucson, AZ 85719. TEL 800-528-4841) Ed. G.D. Phillips. circ. 1,000. (diskette format) **Indexed:** Sport Fish.Abstr., Vet.Bull., Wild.Rev. **Document type:** bibliography.
●Also available online. Vendor(s): CISTI, DIMDI, European Space Agency (File nos.16 & 124/CAB), Knight-Ridder, Inc., Ovid Technologies (VETR).
Description: Covers the world literature on bacterial, viral, fungal, and protozoal diseases, as well as nutritional and metabolic disorders.

636.08   US   ISSN 1067-8964
FOCUS ON: VETERINARY SCIENCE AND MEDICINE. m. $215. Institute for Scientific Information, 3501 Market St., Philadelphia, PA 19104. TEL 215-386-0100. FAX 215-386-2991. (U.K. addr.: Brunel Science Park, Brunel University, Uxbridge UB6 3PQ, England) (diskette format) **Document type:** academic/scholarly publication bibliography.
Description: Provides bibliographic data and English-language author abstracts from international scholarly research journals and conference proceedings.

636.089 016   UK   ISSN 0019-3941
INDEX OF VETERINARY SPECIALITIES. 1961. bi-m. £19 (foreign £19.50) (effective 1996). A.E. Morgan Publications Ltd., Stanley House, 9 West St., Epsom, Surrey KT18 7RL, England. TEL 01372-741411. FAX 01372-744493. Ed. C. Cattrall; Pub. Terence Morgan. adv. contact: Peter Louatt. circ. 3,700. (also avail. in microform from UMI; reprint service avail. from UMI) **Document type:** abstracting/indexing.
—UMI.
Description: Articles and news of products and developments in the veterinary field.

636.089   AT   ISSN 1033-2863
INDEX OF VETERINARY SPECIALTIES. 1980. a. Aus.$72. M I M S Australia, 48 Albany St., Crows Nest, N.S.W. 2065, Australia. TEL 02-438-3588. Ed. Linda H. Badewitz-Dodd. circ. 3,500.
Description: Classified listing of all veterinary drugs available in Australia.

636 016   UK   ISSN 0019-4123
Z6674
INDEX VETERINARIUS; a classified subject and author index produced by computer processes of current literature on veterinary science with approximately 23,000 titles. 1933. m. (with a. cumulation). £590($1065) (effective 1996). CAB International, Wallingford, Oxon. OX10 8DE, England. TEL 01491-832111. FAX 01491-833508. TELEX 847964 COMAGG G. E-mail: cabi@cabi.org. (U.S. subscr. to: CAB International, North American Office, 845 N. Park Ave., Tucson, AZ 85719. TEL 800-528-4841) bibl. circ. 750. (also avail. in diskette format; back issues avail.) **Indexed:** Dairy Sci.Abstr., Helminthol.Abstr., Nutr.Abstr., Rev.Appl.Entomol., Rev.Plant Path. **Document type:** abstracting/indexing.
●Also available online. Vendor(s): CISTI, DIMDI, European Space Agency (File nos.16 & 124/CAB), Knight-Ridder, Inc., Ovid Technologies (VETR).
—BLDSC (4390.000000).

636.089   PK
PAKISTAN VETERINARY INDEX. (Text in English) 1985. a. $15. Press Corporation of Pakistan, P.O. Box 3138, Karachi 75400, Pakistan. TEL 21-455-3703. FAX 21-7736198. Ed. Saeed Hafeez. circ. 5,000.

595.7 016   UK   ISSN 0957-6770
REVIEW OF MEDICAL AND VETERINARY ENTOMOLOGY. 1913. m. £230($410) (effective 1996). CAB International, Wallingford, Oxon. OX10 8DE, England. TEL 01491-832111. FAX 01491-833508. TELEX 847964 COMAGG G. (U.S. subscr. to: CAB International, North American Office, 845 N. Park Ave., Tucson, AZ 85719. TEL 800-528-4841) Ed.Bd. adv.; bk.rev.; abstr.; index. circ. 1,250. (also avail. in diskette format; back issues avail.) **Indexed:** Abstr.Hyg., Chem.Abstr., Helminthol.Abstr., Poult.Abstr., Rev.Appl.Entomol., Sport Fish.Abstr., Trop.Dis.Bull., Vet.Bull., Wild.Rev. **Document type:** abstracting/indexing, academic/scholarly publication.
●Also available online. Vendor(s): CISTI, DIMDI, European Space Agency (File nos.16 & 124/CAB), Knight-Ridder, Inc., Ovid Technologies (VETR).
Formerly: Review of Applied Entomology. Series B: Medical and Veterinary (ISSN 0305-0084)
Description: Deals with insects and other arthropods that transmit diseases or are otherwise injurious to man and animals of significance to man.

REVIEW OF MEDICAL AND VETERINARY MYCOLOGY. see *BIOLOGY — Abstracting, Bibliographies, Statistics*

636 016   UK
SMALL ANIMALS. (Not avail. in printed format) 1975. a. £55($93) (effective 1996). CAB International, Wallingford, Oxon. OX10 8DE, England. TEL 01491-832111. FAX 01491-833508. TELEX 847964 COMAGG G. E-mail: cabi@cabi.org. (U.S. subscr. to: CAB International, North American Office, 845 N. Park Ave., Tucson, AZ 85719. TEL 800-528-4841) circ. 250. (diskette format; back issues avail.) **Indexed:** Rev.Appl.Entomol. **Document type:** bibliography.
●Also available online. Vendor(s): CISTI, DIMDI, European Space Agency (File nos.16 & 124/CAB), Knight-Ridder, Inc., Ovid Technologies (VETR).
Formerly (until 1991): Small Animal Abstracts (ISSN 0306-7580)
Description: Covers the research literature on diseases, physiology, reproduction, nutrition, and behavior of dogs, cats, and other pets.

636.08 316.8   SA
SOUTH AFRICA. CENTRAL STATISTICAL SERVICE. CENSUS OF VETERINARY SERVICES, ANIMAL HOSPITALS AND CARE CENTRES. (Report No. 06-05-02) irreg., latest 1984. R.2.31 (foreign R.2.89). Central Statistical Service - Sentrale Statistiekdiens, Private Bag X44, Pretoria 0001, South Africa. TEL 27-12-310-8911. FAX 27-12-310-8500. (Orders to: Government Printing Works, Private Bag X85, Pretoria 0001, South Africa) **Document type:** government publication.

636.089   UK   ISSN 0042-4854
SF601
VETERINARY BULLETIN; a monthly abstract journal on veterinary science. 1931. m. £475($860) (effective 1996). CAB International, Wallingford, Oxon. OX10 8DE, England. TEL 01491-832111. FAX 01491-833508. TELEX 847964 COMAGG G. (U.S. subscr. to: CAB International, North American Office, 845 N. Park Ave., Tucson, AZ 85719. TEL 800-528-4841) Ed. R. Mack. adv.; bk.rev. circ. 1,900. (also avail. in diskette format; back issues avail.) **Indexed:** Abstr.Hyg., Anim.Breed.Abstr., Biotech.Abstr., Chem.Abstr., Dairy Sci.Abstr., Field Crop Abstr., Helminthol.Abstr., Herb.Abstr., Ind.Vet., Nutr.Abstr., Rev.Appl.Entomol., Trop.Dis.Bull. **Document type:** abstracting/indexing.
●Also available online. Vendor(s): CISTI, DIMDI, European Space Agency (File nos.16 & 124/CAB), Knight-Ridder, Inc., Ovid Technologies (VETR).
—BLDSC (9227.000000).
   Description: Presents abstracts of the core literature in the whole field of animal health.

636.089   US   ISSN 1059-8456
VETERINARY UPDATE CLINICAL ABSTRACT SERVICE: LARGE ANIMAL. (Avail. in 2 editions: Small Animal, Large Animal) 1960. q. $112 (foreign $138); combined editions $189 (foreign $232). American Veterinary Publications, Inc., 5782 Thornwood Dr., Goleta, CA 93117. TEL 805-967-5988. FAX 805-967-6682. (also avail. in diskette format; back issues avail.) **Document type:** abstracting/indexing.
—CCC.
   Description: Provides summaries of clinically oriented articles published in worldwide veterinary journals. Covers articles on horses, cattle, pigs, sheep and goats.

636.089   US   ISSN 1059-8448
VETERINARY UPDATE CLINICAL ABSTRACT SERVICE: SMALL ANIMAL. (In 2 editions: Small Animal, Large Animal) 1960. q. $112 (foreign $138); combined eds. $189 (foreign $232) (effective 1993). American Veterinary Publications, Inc., 5782 Thornwood Dr., Goleta, CA 93117-3896. TEL 805-967-5988. FAX 805-967-6682. Ed. Dr. P.W. Pratt. circ. 3,000. (also avail. in diskette format) **Indexed:** Biol.Abstr., Chem.Abstr. **Document type:** abstracting/indexing.
—CCC.
   Formerly: Update Veterinary Reference Service.
   Description: Provides summaries of clinically oriented articles published in worldwide veterinary journals. Covers articles on dogs, cats and caged birds.

VIDEO

see Communications—Video

VISUALLY IMPAIRED

see Handicapped—Visually Impaired

WASTE MANAGEMENT

see Environmental Studies—Waste Management

WATER RESOURCES

see also Environmental Studies

333.91   US
A S D W A UPDATE. 1986. bi-m. $40 to non-members. Association of State Drinking Water Administrators, 1120 Connecticut Ave., N.W., Ste. 1060, Washington, DC 20036. TEL 202-293-7655. FAX 202-293-7656. Ed. Vanessa M. Leiby. bk.rev. circ. 400. **Document type:** newsletter.
   Description: Examines issues related to the protection of public health through the assurance of high quality drinking water.

A W T; Abfalltechnik und Recycling. (Abwassertechnik) *see ENVIRONMENTAL STUDIES — Waste Management*

333.91   US   ISSN 0273-3218
A W W A MAINSTREAM. 1955. m. $13 to non-members (foreign $18.50). American Water Works Association, 6666 W. Quincy Ave., Denver, CO 80235. TEL 303-794-7711. Ed. Mary Parmelee. charts; illus.; tr.lit. circ. 40,000. **Document type:** newspaper.
   Incorporates: Willing Water (Denver) (ISSN 0149-8037).
   Description: Reports current association news; includes features on noteworthy utilities, safety, education and community relations.

ACQUISITIONS AND DIVERSIFICATIONS; the record of the privatised utilities. *see ENERGY — Electrical Energy*

333.19 639.2   PL   ISSN 0860-2611
                             CODEN: ATOPEG
ACTA ACADEMIAE AGRICULTURAE AC TECHNICAE OLSTENENSIS. PROTECTIO AQUARUM ET PISCATORIA/AGRICULTURAL AND TECHNICAL ACADEMY IN OLSZTYN. WATER CONSERVATION AND INLAND FISHERIES. (Supplement avail.: Protectio Aquarum et Piscatoria) (Text in Polish; summaries in English, Polish) 1956. irreg. price varies. (Akademia Rolniczo-Techniczna im. M. Oczapowskiego) Wydawnictwo A R T Olsztyn, Blok 12, 10-957 Olsztyn-Kortowo, Poland. TEL 48-89-273310. TELEX 0526419. E-mail: artbib@morwka.art. (Dist. by: Ars Polona-Ruch, Krakowskie Przedmiescie 7, 00-901 Warsaw, Poland. TEL 48-22-265334) bibl.; charts; illus.; circ. 130 (controlled). **Indexed:** Chem.Abstr., Potato Abstr., Ref.Zh. **Document type:** academic/scholarly publication.
—CASDDS.
   Formerly: Akademia Rolniczo-Techniczna. Zeszyty Naukowe. Ochrona Wod i Rybactwo Srodladowe (ISSN 0324-9190)

628   GW   ISSN 0323-4320
TD430   CODEN: AHCBAU
ACTA HYDROCHIMICA ET HYDROBIOLOGICA; jpurnal for water and wastewater research. (Text in German and English) 1967. bi-m. DM.592($420) (effective 1996). (Gesellschaft Deutscher Chemiker, Fachgruppe Wasserchemie) V C H Verlagsgesellschaft mbH, Postfach 101161, 69451 Weinheim, Germany. TEL 06201-606-147. FAX 06201-606117. TELEX 465516-VCHWH-D. (U.S. addr.: V C H Publishers Inc., 220 E. 23rd St., New York, NY 10010-4606. TEL 212-683-8333) Ed. F. Frimmel. adv.; bk.rev.; abstr.; charts; illus.; stat.; index. circ. 1,100. (reprint service avail. from ISI) **Indexed:** Chem.Abstr., Curr.Adv.Ecol.Sci., Curr.Cont., Curr.Ref.Fish Res., Risk Abstr., Sel.Water Res.Abstr., Soils & Fert., Weed Abstr. **Document type:** academic/scholarly publication.
—BLDSC (0624.520000); CASDDS; Faxon; Genuine Article; SWETS. **CCC.**
   Formerly (until 1992): Zeitschrift fuer Wasser- und Abwasserforschung (ISSN 0044-3727)

333.7 628   US
ADVANCED WATER CONFERENCE. PROCEEDINGS. irreg., 3rd, 1971. price varies. Oklahoma State University, College of Engineering, Engineering Extension, 512 Engineering North, Stillwater, OK 74078. TEL 405-624-5033. **Document type:** proceedings.

ADVANCES IN SOIL AND WATER RESEARCH IN ALEXANDRIA. *see EARTH SCIENCES*

551.4 333.91   UK   ISSN 0309-1708
TC1   CODEN: AWREDI
ADVANCES IN WATER RESOURCES. 1978. bi-m. £275($438) (effective 1996). Elsevier Science Ltd., P.O. Box 800, Kidlington, Oxford OX5 1DX, England. TEL 44-1865-843000. FAX 44-1865-843010. E-mail: nlinfo-f@elsevier.nl; usinfo-f@elsevier.com; forinfo-kyf04035@niftyserve.or.jp; Site addr.: http://www.elsevier.nl/. (Subscr. in U.S. and Canada to: Elsevier Science, 660 White Plains Rd., Tarrytown, NY 10591-5153. TEL 914-524-9200. FAX 914-333-2444) Eds. W.G. Gray, M.A. Celia. (also avail. in microform from UMI; back issues avail.) **Indexed:** Appl.Mech.Rev., Curr.Tit.Ocean, Eng.Ind., Environ.Abstr., Environ.Per.Bibl. (1986-), Excerp.Med., Fluidex, Geo.Abstr., Geol.Abstr., GeoRef., INSPEC (1985-), Intl.Civil Eng.Abstr., Irr.& Drain.Abstr., Sel.Water Res.Abstr., Soft.Abstr.Eng., Soils & Fert., Sport Fish.Abstr., W.R.C.Inf., Wild.Rev. **Document type:** academic/scholarly publication.
—BLDSC (0712.120000); Ei; Faxon; Genuine Article; SWETS; UnCover. **CCC.**
   Incorporates (in 1991): Hydrosoft (ISSN 0268-6856)
   Description: For engineers or scientists interested in theoretical and computational aspects of water resources engineering: groundwater hydrology, water quality, surface water hydrology and stochastic hydrology.
   Refereed Serial

333.91   FR
AGENCES DE L'EAU. irreg. 330 F. (foreign 314.36 F.). Pierre Johanet et ses Fils, 7 av. Franklin Roosevelt, 75008 Paris, France. TEL 43-59-08-91. FAX 42-25-59-47.

AGRICULTURAL RESEARCH DEPARTMENT. WINAND STARING CENTRE FOR INTEGRATED LAND, SOIL AND WATER RESEARCH. REPORTS. *see AGRICULTURE — Crop Production And Soil*

AGRICULTURAL WATER MANAGEMENT; an international journal. *see AGRICULTURE — Crop Production And Soil*

WATER RESOURCES

333.91   US
ALASKA SNOW SURVEY REPORT. 1962. q. free. U.S. Natural Resources Conservation Service (Anchorage), 949 E. 36th Ave., Ste. 400, Anchorage, AK 99508-4362. TEL 907-271-2424. FAX 907-271-3951. Ed. Rick McClure. charts; illus.; stat.; index. circ. 500. (tabloid format; also avail. in microfiche from CIS; back issues avail.; reprint service avail. from CIS) **Indexed:** Amer.Stat.Ind. (1974-). **Document type:** government publication, bulletin.
●Also available online.
   Former titles (until 1992): Alaska Snow Surveys - Basin Outlook Reports; Alaska Snow Surveys; (until 1985): Snow Surveys and Water Supply Outlook for Alaska (ISSN 0731-8499); (until 1981): Federal-State-Private Snow Surveys and Water Supply Outlook for Alaska.
   Description: Focuses on seasonal snow depth, snow-water content, accumulated water-year precipitation statistics from a network of 200 data sites and selected streamflow facts.

133.3   US   ISSN 0093-089X
BF1628
AMERICAN DOWSER. 1961. q. $25 membership. American Society of Dowsers, Inc., Box 24, Danville, VT 05828. TEL 802-684-3417. FAX 802-684-2565. Ed.Bd. bk.rev.; cum.index every 5 yrs. circ. 4,000.
   Supersedes: American Society of Dowsers. Quarterly Digest.

627 551.4   US
AMERICAN INSTITUTE OF HYDROLOGY. BULLETIN. 1983. q. $16. American Institute of Hydrology, 3416 University Ave., S.E., Minneapolis, MN 55414-3328. TEL 612-379-1030. FAX 612-379-0169. adv.; bk.rev. circ. 1,000. (tabloid format; back issues avail.) **Document type:** bulletin.
   Description: Newsletter regarding activities and members of institute.

AMERICAN SHORE AND BEACH PRESERVATION ASSOCIATION. NEWSLETTER. see *ENVIRONMENTAL STUDIES*

333.91   US   ISSN 0894-847X
AMERICAN WATER RESOURCES ASSOCIATION. MONOGRAPHS. irreg., no.19, 1993. price varies. American Water Resources Association, 950 Herndon Pky., Ste. 300, Herndon, VA 22070-5531. TEL 703-904-1225. FAX 703-904-1228. **Document type:** monographic series.

333.91   US
AMERICAN WATER RESOURCES SYMPOSIA. ANNUAL PROCEEDINGS. 1965. a. price varies. American Water Resources Association, 950 Herndon Pky., Ste. 300, Herndon, VA 22070-5531. TEL 703-904-1225. FAX 703-904-1228. **Indexed:** GeoRef. **Document type:** proceedings.
   Formerly: American Water Resources Conferences. Annual Proceedings (ISSN 0066-1171)

628   US   ISSN 0003-150X
TD201   **CODEN:** JAWWA5
AMERICAN WATER WORKS ASSOCIATION. JOURNAL. 1914. m. $85 to libraries and governmental agencies only. American Water Works Association, 6666 W. Quincy Ave., Denver, CO 80235. TEL 303-794-7711. Ed. Nancy M. Zeilig. adv.; bk.rev.; abstr.; bibl.; charts; illus.; stat.; tr.lit.; index, cum.index: 1946-1980 in 5 vols. circ. 45,000. (also avail. in microfilm from UMI,PMC; microfiche from UMI; back issues avail., reprint service avail. from UMI) **Indexed:** A.I.Abstr., A.S.& T.Ind., Abstr.Bull.Inst.Pap.Chem., Acid Pre.Dig., Acid Rain Abstr., Acid Rain Ind., AESIS, Anal.Abstr., Biol.Abstr., Cadscan, Chem.Abstr., Copper Abstr., Corros.Abstr., Curr.Cont., Deep Sea Res.& Oceanogr.Abstr., Dok.Arbeitsmed., Eng.Ind., Environ.Abstr., Environ.Per.Bibl. (1973-), Excerp.Med., Food Sci.& Tech.Abstr., Geo.Abstr., GeoRef., INIS Atomind., Intl.Civil Eng.Abstr., Lead Abstr., Met.Abstr., Ocean.Abstr., Pollut.Abstr., Repindex, Sci.Cit.Ind., Sel.J.Water, Sel.Water Res.Abstr., Soft.Eng.Abstr., Zincscan. **Document type:** academic/scholarly publication.
   —BLDSC (4696.000000); CASDDS; CIS; Ei; Faxon; Genuine Article; SWETS; UMI; UnCover. **CCC.**
   Description: Contains technical papers, discussions, news, and reports of water treatment technology.

628   US   ISSN 0360-814X
TD201   **CODEN:** PWACDC
AMERICAN WATER WORKS ASSOCIATION. PROCEEDINGS, A W W A ANNUAL CONFERENCE. Key Title: Proceedings, A W W A Annual Conference. a. American Water Works Association, 6666 W. Quincy Ave., Denver, CO 80235. TEL 303-794-7711. illus. **Indexed:** GeoRef. **Document type:** proceedings.
   —BLDSC (1082.452000); CASDDS.

627   BL   ISSN 0373-9260
ANAIS HIDROGRAFICOS. 1933. a. free. Ministerio da Marinha, Diretoria de Hidrografia e Navegacao, Rio de Janeiro, Brazil. charts; illus.; stat.; circ. controlled.

333.91   UK
ANGLIAN WATER. ANNUAL REPORT. a. Anglian Water plc., Anglian House, Ambury Rd., Huntingdon, Cambs. PE18 6NZ, England. **Document type:** corporate report.
   Formerly (until 1994): Anglian Water. Annual Review.
   Description: Discusses various economic and environmental issues affecting water utilities.

333.91   US   ISSN 0161-4924
GB705.N6
ANNUAL NEW MEXICO WATER CONFERENCE. PROCEEDINGS. 1956. a. $5.25. New Mexico Water Resources Research Institute, Box 30001, Dept. 3167, New Mexico State University, Las Cruces, NM 88003-0001. TEL 505-646-4337. FAX 505-646-6418. Ed. Cathy Ortega Klett. circ. 500 (controlled). **Document type:** proceedings.

333.91   UK   ISSN 0003-7214
TD201   **CODEN:** AQUAAA
AQUA; journal of water supply research & technology. (Text in English and French) 1951. bi-m. £148.50($239) (effective 1996). (International Water Supply Association) Blackwell Science Ltd., Osney Mead, Oxford OX2 0EL, England. TEL 44-1865-206206. FAX 44-1865-721205. TELEX 83355 MEDBOK G. Ed. M. Bernhardt. adv. contact: Maura O'Bherty. bk.rev.; abstr.; charts; illus. circ. 3,000. (also avail. in microform from UMI; back issues avail.) **Indexed:** Chem.Abstr., Curr.Adv.Ecol.Sci., Environ.Per.Bibl. (1989-), Fluidex, Geo.Abstr., GeoRef., IDA, Repindex, Sel.Water Res.Abstr., W.R.C.Inf. **Document type:** academic/scholarly publication.
   —BLDSC (1581.860000); CASDDS; SWETS; UMI; UnCover. **CCC.**
   Description: Concerned with water supply for domestic, agricultural and industrial purposes and the safeguarding, control and provision of the necessary water resources.
   Refereed Serial

331.91   FI   ISSN 0356-7133
GB727.4   **CODEN:** AQFEDI
AQUA FENNICA. (Text in English; summaries in Finnish) 1971. s-a. FIM 120($40) Aqua Fennica Publishing Board, P.O. Box 436, 00101 Helsinki 10, Finland. TEL 358-0-73144184. FAX 358-0-73144188. Ed. Pertti Seuna. adv.; bk.rev.; charts; illus. circ. 350. (back issues avail.) **Indexed:** Chem.Abstr., Curr.Adv.Ecol.Sci., Curr.Cont., Deep Sea Res.& Oceanogr.Abstr., Ecol.Abstr., Geo.Abstr., Geol.Abstr., Pollut.Abstr., Sel.Water Res.Abstr., Sport Fish.Abstr., W.R.C.Inf., Wild.Rev., Zoo.Rec. **Document type:** academic/scholarly publication.
   —BLDSC (1581.863000); CASDDS; Ei; UnCover.

333.91   US   ISSN 1048-8111
AQUA TERRA; water concepts for the ecological society. 1985. s-a. $9.95. (National Water Center) Waterworks Publishing, Rte. 7, Box 716, Eureka Springs, AR 72632. TEL 501-253-9431. FAX 501-253-8280. Ed. Jacqueline Froelich. adv. contact: Barbara Harmony. bk.rev. circ. 2,000. (back issues avail.) **Document type:** academic/scholarly publication.
   Formerly (until 1991): Water Center News.
   Description: Information on technical and metaphysical ways of keeping waste out of water. Also features poetry and interviews.

AQUACULTURAL ENGINEERING. see *FISH AND FISHERIES*

AQUACULTURE; an international journal devoted to fundamental aquatic food resources. see *FISH AND FISHERIES*

AQUACULTURE MAGAZINE. see *FISH AND FISHERIES*

AQUACULTURE RESEARCH. see *FISH AND FISHERIES*

627   UK   ISSN 0261-5355
AQUATECHNIC INTERNATIONAL. 1981. 10/yr. £75. D.J.L. Marketing Ltd., 47 Burney St., Greenwich, London SE10 8EX, England. FAX 081-853-4079. Ed. David Longhurst. adv.; bk.rev. circ. 13,000. (back issues avail.) **Indexed:** Fluidex.

AQUATIC CONSERVATION: MARINE AND FRESHWATER ECOSYSTEMS. see *CONSERVATION*

AQUATIC GEOCHEMISTRY. see *EARTH SCIENCES*

AQUATIC LIVING RESOURCES; international journal devoted to aquatic resources. see *FISH AND FISHERIES*

333.91   US
AQUEDUCT 2000. 1934. 6/yr. free to qualified personnel. Metropolitan Water District of Southern California, Box 54153, Los Angeles, CA 90054. TEL 213-250-6000. Ed. Jim Parsons. illus. circ. 40,000. **Document type:** trade publication.
   Incorporates: Focus on Water; Which superseded (1974-1979): Meter; Former titles: Aqueduct (ISSN 0092-0622); Aqueduct News (ISSN 0003-7338); Colorado River Aqueduct News.

333.91   LE   ISSN 0255-8580
ARAB WATER WORLD/ALAM AL-MIYAH AL-ARABI. (Text in Arabic, English) 1977. 6/yr. $60. Chatila Publishing House, P.O. Box 135121, Chouran, Beirut, Lebanon. TEL 961-1-352413. FAX 961-1-352419. Ed. Fathi Chatila. adv.; bk.rev. circ. 9,167. **Indexed:** Fluidex, W.R.C.Inf. **Document type:** trade publication.
   —BLDSC (1583.298000).
   Formerly (until 1991): Arab Water World International.

627   PL   ISSN 1231-3726
TC1   **CODEN:** AHDRAF
ARCHIVES OF HYDRO-ENGINEERING AND ENVIRONMENTAL MECHANICS. (Text and summaries in English) q. $44. Polska Akademia Nauk, Instytut Budownictwa Wodnego - Polish Academy of Sciences, Institute of Hydroengineering, Ul. Koscierska 7, 80-952 Gdansk-Oliwa, Poland. TEL 48-58-522011. FAX 48-58-524211. TELEX 0512845. (Dist. by: Ars Polona, Krakowskie Przedmiescie 7, 00-068 Warsaw, Poland) Ed. Andrzej Sawicki. illus.; charts; index. circ. 500. **Indexed:** Appl.Mech.Rev., Fluidex, Geotech.Abstr., Sel.Water Res.Abstr. **Document type:** academic/scholarly publication, monographic series.
   Former titles (until 1993): Archives of Hydrotechnics (ISSN 1230-235X); (until no.3-4, 1990): Archiwum Hydrotechniki (ISSN 0004-0789)
   Description: Covers computer applications in civil and environmental engineering, hydrology, civil engineering, environmental studies.

331.91   US
ARIZONA. DEPARTMENT OF WATER RESOURCES. OPEN-FILE REPORT. 1986. irreg. $3. Department of Water Resources, Basic Data Section, 2810 S. 24th St., Ste. 122, Phoenix, AZ 85034. TEL 602-255-1543.
   Description: Covers water resources of Arizona.

333.91   US   ISSN 0571-0278
ARKANSAS. GEOLOGICAL COMMISSION. WATER RESOURCES CIRCULARS. 1955. irreg., no.16, 1987. price varies. Geological Commission, Vardelle Parham Geology Center, 3815 West Roosevelt Rd., Little Rock, AR 72204. TEL 501-663-9714. (back issues avail.) **Indexed:** GeoRef. **Document type:** monographic series.

ASIAN ENVIRONMENT; journal of environmental science and technology for balanced development. see *ENVIRONMENTAL STUDIES*

ASIAN WATER & SEWAGE; Asia's journal of environmental technology. see *ENVIRONMENTAL STUDIES*

333.7   MY   ISSN 0128-0538
                       CODEN: ASWNE9
ASIAN WETLAND NEWS. biennial. Asian Wetland Bureau, Institute of Advanced Sciences (IPT), University of Malaya, Lembah Pantai, 59100 Kuala Lumpur, Malaysia. **Indexed:** Sport Fish.Abstr., Wild.Rev., Zoo.Rec.

WATER RESOURCES 6545

ATTENDERINGSBULLETIN BIBLIOTHEEK STARING-GEBOUW: LAND, BODEM, WATER. see ENVIRONMENTAL STUDIES — Abstracting, Bibliographies, Statistics

333.9 US ISSN 0067-043X
TD224.A2
AUBURN UNIVERSITY. WATER RESOURCES RESEARCH INSTITUTE. ANNUAL REPORT. 1965. a. free. Auburn University, Water Resources Research Institute, 202 Hargis Hall, Auburn, AL 36849. TEL 205-826-5075. Eds. Joseph F. Judkins, Jr., Dennis H. Block. circ. 600.

627 AT
AUSTRALASIAN DRILLING. 1972. bi-m. Aus.$100. Australian Drilling Industry Association, P.O. Box 269, Mentone, Vic. 3194, Australia. TEL 613-580-6222. FAX 613-580-6699. Ed. Graeme Wakeling. adv. contact: G.V. Dolder. bk.rev.; charts; illus. circ. 6,000. (back issues avail.) **Indexed:** AESIS. **Document type:** trade publication.
Former titles: Australian Drilling (ISSN 1037-3535); (until 1991): Water and Mineral Development (ISSN 0811-5931); (until 1982): National Water Well Association. Journal (ISSN 0310-3625)
Description: Provides information on technical advances, new equipment and product news.

614 AT
AUSTRALIAN FLUORIDATION NEWS. AQUA-PURA. 1963. bi-m. $15 membership. Anti-Fluoridation Association of Victoria, P.O. Box C9, Clarence St., Sydney, N.S.W. 2000, Australia. TEL 03-592-5088. Ed. G. Walker. bk.rev. circ. 2,000. **Document type:** newsletter.
Formerly: Aqua Pura.

333.91 AT ISSN 0811-5397
AUSTRALIAN WATER RESOURCES COUNCIL. WATER RESOURCES SERIES. irreg. Department of Primary Industries and Energy, Australian Water Resources Council, G.P.O. Box 858, Canberra, A.C.T. 2601, Australia. **Indexed:** AESIS.

627 GW ISSN 0937-3756
TN860 CODEN: BWROEQ
B B R; Wasser und Rohrbau. 1949. m. DM.187 (foreign DM.199). Verlagsgesellschaft Rudolf Mueller GmbH, Stolberger Str. 84, 50933 Cologne, Germany. TEL 0221-5497-0. FAX 0221-5497326. (Subscr. to: Postfach 410949, 50869 Cologne, Germany) Ed. Rudolf Bleser. adv.: B&W page DM.3450, color DM.6240; trim 188 x 267. bk.rev. circ. 3,400. **Indexed:** Chem.Abstr., INIS Atomind. **Document type:** trade publication.
—BLDSC (1871.366070); CASDDS; SWETS.
Former titles: Brunnenbau, Bau von Wasserwekr, Rohrleitungsbau (ISSN 0340-3874); B B R (ISSN 0006-5765)

628.1 UK ISSN 1358-3271
BATHING WATER QUALITY IN ENGLAND AND WALES. 1991. a. £8.95. National Rivers Authority, Rivers House, Waterside Dr., Aztec West, Almondsbury, Bristol BS12 4UD, England. TEL 01454-624400. FAX 01454-624409. **Document type:** bulletin.

551 GW ISSN 0176-4217
BAYERISCHES LANDESAMT FUER WASSERWIRTSCHAFT. INFORMATIONSBERICHTE. 1975. 5/yr. Bayerisches Landesamt fuer Wasserwirtschaft, Lazarettstr. 67, 80636 Munich, Germany. TEL 089-12101203. circ. 1,000 (controlled). **Document type:** government publication.

551 GW ISSN 0172-665X
GB651 CODEN: SBLWEQ
BAYERISCHES LANDESAMTES FUER WASSERWIRTSCHAFT. SCHRIFTENREIHE. 1975. irreg. (approx. 3/yr.). Bayerisches Landesamt fuer Wasserwirtschaft, Lazarettstr. 67, 80636 Munich, Germany. TEL 089-12101203. circ. 1,000. **Document type:** government publication.

BEITRAEGE ZUR HYDROLOGIE. see EARTH SCIENCES — Hydrology

628 II ISSN 0006-0461
TC903
BHAGIRATH; Indian water resources quarterly. (Editions in English and Hindi) 1954. q. Rs.6($5) Ministry of Water Resources, Central Water Commission, Sewa Bhawan, R.K. Puram, New Delhi 110066, India. TEL 601104. FAX 6875516. TELEX 31-7283 CWC IN. (Subscr. in U.S. to: M-S Inter Culture Associates, Thompson, CT 06277) Ed. M.S. Ramchander. adv.; bk.rev.; charts; illus.; index. circ. 5,000. **Indexed:** INIS Atomind. **Document type:** government publication.
Description: Contains information, research, news and views on water resources development in India.

628 MW ISSN 0084-7925
BLANTYRE WATER BOARD. ANNUAL REPORT AND STATEMENT OF ACCOUNTS. 1967. a. Blantyre Water Board, Box 30369, Chichiri, Blantyre 3, Malawi. stat. circ. 500.

333.91 SA ISSN 1011-128X
BOREHOLE WATER. (Text in English) 1984. bi-m. R.32. Borehole Water Association, P.O. Box 2178, Southdale 2135, South Africa. Ed. P.M. Mony. adv. circ. 5,000. **Indexed:** Ind.S.A.Per.
Formerly (until 1987): Borehole Water Journal (ISSN 1012-2923)
Description: Covers information on the newest developments and equipment used in the manipulation of water resources.

BRITISH COLUMBIA. MINISTRY OF ENVIRONMENT, LANDS AND PARKS. ANNUAL REPORT. see CONSERVATION

627 631 GR
BULLETIN G C I D. (Text in Greek; summaries in English) 1962. s-a. Dr.300. International Commission on Irrigation and Drainage, Greek National Committee, 13 Tsakona St., Psychico, Athens, Greece. Ed. George Papadopoulos. adv.; bk.rev.; bibl.; charts; illus.; stat.; tr.lit. circ. 4,000.
Former titles: G C I D Scientific Bulletin; G C I D Information Letter; International Committee on Irrigation and Drainage. Greek National Committee. Bulletin (ISSN 0011-8109)

354.66 631.7 UV
BURKINA FASO. DIRECTION DE L'HYDRAULIQUE ET DE L'EQUIPEMENT RURAL. SERVICE I.R.H. RAPPORT D'ACTIVITES. irreg. Direction de l'Hydraulique et de l'Equipement Rural, Service I.R.H., Ministere du Plan, du Developpement Rural, de l'Environnement et du Tourisme, Ouagadougou, Burkina Faso. **Document type:** government publication.
Formerly: Upper Volta. Direction de l'Hydraulique et de l'Equipement Rural. Service I.R.H. Rapport d'Activites.

627 UV
BURKINA FASO. MINISTERE DE L'EAU. ANNUAIRE HYDROLOGIQUE DU BURKINA. a. Ministere de l'Eau, Direction de l'Inventaire des Ressources Hydrauliques, B.P. 7025, Ouagadougou 03, Burkina Faso. TEL 30-80-35. **Document type:** government publication.

627 UV
BURKINA FASO. MINISTERE DE L'EAU. BULLETIN HYDROLOGIQUE DU BURKINA. m. Ministere de l'Eau, Direction de l'Inventaire des Ressources Hydrauliques, B.P. 7025, Ouagadougou 03, Burkina Faso. TEL 30-80-35. **Document type:** government publication.

333.91 US
C R A NEWSLETTER.* q. Colorado River Association, 900 S. Orange Grove Blvd., Ste. A, Pasadena, CA 91105-3515. FAX 213-628-4910. Ed. Pat Messigian. **Document type:** newsletter.

333.9 US ISSN 0084-8263
CODEN: CAWRAF
CALIFORNIA. DEPARTMENT OF WATER RESOURCES. BULLETIN. (Issued in several sub-series) a. price varies. Department of Water Resources, Box 924836, Sacramento, CA 94236-0001. TEL 916-445-9248. circ. controlled. **Indexed:** GeoRef. **Document type:** government publication.
—CASDDS.

333.91 US
CALIFORNIA DIRECTORY OF WATER RESOURCES EXPERTISE. 1975. biennial. free. University of California at Riverside, Centers for Water and Wildlife Resources, Rubidoux Hall, Riverside, CA 92521. TEL 909-787-4327. FAX 909-787-5295. Ed. Joe de Vries. circ. 1,750. **Document type:** directory.

614.772 US
CALIFORNIA WATER ENVIRONMENT ASSOCIATION. BULLETIN. 1964. q. $30 or membership. California Water Environment Association, 7677 Oakport St., Ste. 525, Oakland, CA 94621-1935. FAX 510-382-7810. Ed. Lindsay Roberts. adv.; bk.rev.; bibl.; charts; illus.; circ. 7,000 (controlled). **Indexed:** Biol.Abstr., Ocean.Abstr., Pollut.Abstr. **Document type:** trade publication.
Formerly: California Water Pollution Control Association. Bulletin (ISSN 0008-1620)

CALIFORNIA WATER LAW & POLICY REPORTER. see LAW

333.91 US ISSN 0575-4941
GB705.C2 CODEN: CUWCA8
CALIFORNIA WATER RESOURCES CENTER. CONTRIBUTION. irreg., no.203, 1993. Water Resources Center, University of California, Rubidoux Hall 094, 4501 Glenwood Dr., Riverside, CA 92521-0436. TEL 909-787-4327. FAX 909-787-5295. Ed.Bd. bibl.; charts. circ. 265. **Indexed:** GeoRef. **Document type:** academic/scholarly publication.

333.91 US
CALIFORNIA WATER RESOURCES DIRECTORY; a guide to organizations and information resources. 1984. irreg., 2nd ed. 1991. $25. California Institute of Public Affairs, Box 189040, Sacramento, CA 95818. TEL 916-442-CIPA. FAX 916-442-2478. (Affiliate: The Claremont Graduate School) Ed. Roberta Childers. circ. 750. **Document type:** directory.
Description: Comprehensive guide to the nearly 1,000 governmental and non-governmental organizations in the state that deal with water policy, development, supply, and conservation, as well as related health, environmental protection, energy, and economic aspects.

CANADA. AGRICULTURE CANADA. ANNUAL REPORT OF PRAIRIE FARM REHABILITATION ADMINISTRATION. see AGRICULTURE — Crop Production And Soil

333.91 CN ISSN 0836-0278
CANADIAN WATER AND WASTEWATER ASSOCIATION. BULLETIN/ASSOCIATION CANADIENNE DES EAUX POTABLES ET USEES. BULLETIN. (Text in English, French) 1987. 10/yr. membership. Canadian Water and Wastewater Association, 45 Rideau St., Ste. 402, Ottawa, ON K1N 5W8, Canada. TEL 613-241-5692. FAX 613-241-5193. Ed. Mr. S. Bonk. bk.rev. circ. 1,200. **Document type:** bulletin.
Formerly: Canadian Water and Wastewater Association. Newsletter.

333.91 CN ISSN 0701-1784
CANADIAN WATER RESOURCES JOURNAL/REVUE CANADIENNE DES RESOURCES EN EAU. (Text in English and French) 1976. q. Can.$70. Canadian Water Resources Association - Association Canadienne des Ressources Hydriques, c/o Dept. Geography, University of Waterloo, Waterloo, ON N2L 3G1, Canada. TEL 519-888-1211. FAX 579-746-2031. Ed. Marie Sanderson. adv.: page Can.$600; trim 5 x 7 1/2. bk.rev. circ. 900. **Document type:** academic/scholarly publication.
—BLDSC (3046.135000); Ei; Faxon; UnCover. CCC.
Formerly: Reclamation.
Refereed Serial

333.91 631 CN ISSN 1180-050X
CANADIAN WATER WELL. 1978. 4/yr. Can.$22. A I S Communications Ltd., 145 Thames Rd. W., Exeter, ON N0M 1S3, Canada. TEL 519-235-2400. FAX 519-235-0798. Ed. Craig Power. adv. contact: Bill Branderhorst. illus. circ. 3,878. (back issues avail.)

627 624 US
CENTER FOR DREDGING STUDIES NEWSLETTER. 1967. s-a. free. Center for Dredging Studies, Civil Engineering Department, Texas A & M University, College Station, TX 77843-3136. TEL 409-845-4516. FAX 409-845-6156. Ed. John B. Herbich. (looseleaf format; back issues avail.) **Document type:** newsletter.

WATER RESOURCES

628 SW ISSN 0280-4026
CODEN: PCTHET
CHALMERS UNIVERSITY OF TECHNOLOGY. DEPARTMENT OF SANITARY ENGINEERING. PUBLICATIONS; current reports on research in water supply and sewage disposal. (Text in Swedish; summaries in English) 1962. irreg. price varies. Chalmers University of Technology, Department of Sanitary Engineering - Chalmers Tekniska Hoegskolan, S-412 96 Goeteborg 5, Sweden. FAX 46-31-77-22-128. Ed. Torsten Hedberg. charts; illus. circ. 100. **Document type:** academic/scholarly publication.
—CASDDS.

333.91 614 UK ISSN 1360-4015
TD201 CODEN: JIWMEZ
CHARTERED INSTITUTION OF WATER AND ENVIRONMENTAL MANAGEMENT. JOURNAL. bi-m. £115 to non-members (effective 1996). Chartered Institution of Water and Environmental Management, 15 John St., London WC1N 2EB, England. TEL 0171-831-3110. FAX 0171-405-4967. Ed. S. Pressey; Pub. M.D.F. Haigh. adv. contact: A. Merson. bk.rev.; charts; illus.; index; cum. index vols. circ. 11,694. (back issues avail.) **Indexed:** Br.Tech.Ind., Energy Info.Abstr., Environ.Per.Bibl. (1972-), Geo.Abstr., Geol.Abstr., Repindex, Sel.Water Res.Abstr., Sport Fish.Abstr., Wild.Rev.
—BLDSC (9267.575000); CASDDS; Ei; Faxon; Genuine Article; SWETS; UMI; UnCover. **CCC.**
Formerly (until 1995): Institution of Water and Environmental Management. Journal (ISSN 0951-7359); Which was formed by the 1987 merger of: Public Health Engineer (ISSN 0300-5925); Water Pollution Control (ISSN 0043-129X); Institution of Water Engineers and Scientists. Journal (ISSN 0309-1600); Public Health Engineer superseded (in 1973): Institution of Public Health Engineers. Journal (ISSN 0020-3513); Which was formerly (until 1955): Institution of Sanitary Engineers. Journal (ISSN 0368-2765); (until 1943): Institution of Sanitary Engineers. Bulletin (ISSN 0366-4376); (1916-1939): Institution of Sanitary Engineers. Water Pollution Control superseded (in 1967): Institution of Sewage Purification. Journal and Proceedings (ISSN 0368-0215); Which was formerly (until 1933): Institution of Sewage Purification. Proceedings (ISSN 0370-0100); (1932-1933): Association of Managers of Sewage Disposal Works. Proceedings. Journal of the Institution of Water Engineers and Scientists superseded (in 1975): Instutitution of Water Engineers. Journal (ISSN 0020-3556); Which was formerly (1896-1947): Institution of Water Engineers. Transactions.
Description: Covers water, including water resources, river management, pollution control, fisheries, sewerage, navigation, and waste management.

333.91 UK ISSN 0964-4245
CHARTERED INSTITUTION OF WATER AND ENVIRONMENTAL MANAGEMENT. NEWSLETTER. 1967. m. £30 to non-members; Newsletter and Journal to non-members £123. Chartered Institution of Water and Environmental Management, 15 John St., London WC1N 2EB, England. TEL 0171-831-3110. FAX 0171-405-4967. Ed. Suzanne Pressey; P.A. Walters. circ. 11,694. (back issues avail.) **Document type:** newsletter.
Formerly (until 1987): I W P C Newsletter (ISSN 0143-960X)

333.91 US ISSN 0277-8467
CODEN: CWANEH
CLEAN WATER ACTION NEWS. 1976. 4/yr. $24 to members; institutions $40. Clean Water Action Project, 1320 18th St. N.W., 3rd fl., Washington, DC 20035-1811. TEL 202-547-1196. Ed. David Zwick. adv. circ. 60,000.
Description: News articles on the legislative, policy, and environmental efforts at the federal and state levels to control pollution and contamination.

CLEARWATERS. see *ENVIRONMENTAL STUDIES — Pollution*

333.91 US ISSN 0069-4657
HD1694.S6 CODEN: CUWRBK
CLEMSON UNIVERSITY. WATER RESOURCES RESEARCH INSTITUTE. REPORT. 1967. irreg., no.140, 1994. free in SC; out-of-state $10. Clemson University, Water Resources Research Institute, 310 Lowry Hall, Clemson, SC 29634-2900. TEL 803-656-3271. FAX 803-656-3273. E-mail: scwrri@eng.clemson.edu. circ. 200 (controlled). **Indexed:** Pollut.Abstr., Water Resour.Abstr. **Document type:** academic/scholarly publication.

333.9 US ISSN 0360-6864
TC425.C7
COLUMBIA RIVER WATER MANAGEMENT REPORT. 1971. a. free. U.S. Army Corps of Engineers, CENPD-PE-WM, Box 2870, Portland, OR 97208-2870. TEL 503-326-3762. FAX 503-326-4161. illus. **Document type:** government publication.
Description: Reviews the annual operation of the major dams and powerhouses in the Columbia Basin and the Northwest.

333.91 UN
CONFLUENCE. (Text in English) 1982. s-a. United Nations Economic and Social Commission for Asia and the Pacific (ESCAP), Natural Resources Division, Water Resources Section, United Nations Bldg., Rajadamnern Nok Ave., Bangkok 10200, Thailand. TEL 2-2829161-170. circ. 600. (back issues avail.)
Description: Aids information exchange between government programs and agencies engaged in water resources development in ESCAP member countries. Covers the range of technological, managerial, and conceptual information.

627 BL ISSN 0589-3305
CONGRESSO LATINOAMERICANO DE HIDRAULICA (PAPERS). irreg. Associacao Internacional de Pesquisas Hidraulicas, Av. Bento Goncalves 10600, Porto Allegre, Brazil.

551.48 628.168 US ISSN 0589-400X
TD201 CODEN: CWCBAL
CONNECTICUT WATER RESOURCES BULLETINS. irreg. Department of Environmental Protection, 165 Capitol Ave., Rm. 555, Hartford, CT 06106. TEL 203-566-7719. illus. **Indexed:** Biol.Abstr., GeoRef. **Document type:** bulletin.

CONSERVATION VOTER. see *ENVIRONMENTAL STUDIES*

333.91 FR ISSN 1146-5786
COURANTS. revue de l'eau et de l'amenagement. 1990. 7/yr. 465 F. (foreign 560 F.) P Y C Edition, B.P. 105, 5, av. de Verdun, 94208 Ivry sur Seine Cedex, France. TEL 1-49-60-86-36. FAX 1-46-72-41-85. Ed. Dominique Bomstein. adv.; bk.rev.; abstr.; charts; illus. circ. 5,000.

COVICRIER. see *ENVIRONMENTAL STUDIES*

627 AT
CROSSCURRENT. m. Australian Water & Wastewater Association, P.O. Box 388, Artarmon, N.S.W. 2064, Australia. TEL 02-4131288. FAX 02-4131047. Ed. Bill Rees. adv.
Description: Contains news updates, articles and papers about water and its use.

628.1 US
D W R NEWS. q. Department of Water Resources, Box 94236, Sacramento, CA 95814. Ed. Joyce Ito. **Document type:** government publication, newsletter.
Description: Discusses news of the California Department of Water Resources.

333.91 US
DELAWARE RIVER BASIN BIENNIAL WATER RESOURCES CONFERENCE. PROCEEDINGS. 1962. biennial. membership. Water Resources Association of the Delaware River Basin, Box 867, Davis Rd., Valley Forge, PA 19482. TEL 610-783-0634. FAX 610-783-0635. **Document type:** proceedings.
Formerly: Delaware River Basin Water Resources Conference. Proceedings.

333.8 NE ISSN 0927-3301
DELFT STUDIES IN INTEGRATED WATER MANAGEMENT. (Text in English) 1992. irreg., vol.5, 1994. (Working Group Integrated Water Management) Delft University Press, Stevinweg 1, 2628 CN Delft, Netherlands. TEL 31-15-2783254. FAX 31-15-2781661. **Document type:** monographic series.

628 NE ISSN 0011-9164
TD478 CODEN: DSLNAH
DESALINATION; the international journal on the science and technology of desalting and water purification. (Text in English, French, German) 1966. 18/yr. fl.3240($1976) (effective 1996). Elsevier Science B.V., P.O. Box 211, 1000 AE Amsterdam, Netherlands. TEL 31-20-4853911. FAX 31-20-4853598. TELEX 18582 ESPA NL. E-mail: nlinfo-f@elsevier.nl; usinfo-f@elsevier.com; forinfo-kyf04035@niftyserve.or.jp; Site addr.: http://www.elsevier.nl/. (Subscr. in U.S. and Canada to: Elsevier Science Inc., Box 882, Madison Sq. Sta., New York, NY 10159-0882. TEL 212-989-5800. FAX 212-633-3990) Ed. M. Balaban. adv.; bk.rev.; charts; illus.; pat.; stat.; tr.mk.; index. (also avail. in microform from UMI) **Indexed:** AESIS, Biol.Abstr., Chem.Abstr., Chem.Eng.Abstr., Curr.Cont., Energy Ind., Energy Info.Abstr., Energy Rev., Eng.Ind., Environ.Abstr., Environ.Per.Bibl. (1972-), Excerp.Med., Fluidex, Food Sci.& Tech.Abstr., Foul.Prev.Res.Dig., Geo.Abstr., Ind.Sci.Rev., INSPEC, Ocean.Abstr., Pollut.Abstr., Sel.Water Res.Abstr., T.C.E.A., W.R.C.Inf. **Document type:** academic/scholarly publication.
—BLDSC (3555.700000); CASDDS; Ei; Faxon; Genuine Article; SWETS; UnCover. **CCC.**
Description: Covers all desalting fields - distillation, membranes, reverse osmosis, electrodialysis, ion exchange, freezing and water purification.
Refereed Serial

628.167 IS
DESALINATION DIRECTORY; desalination and water reuse. (Text in English) 1981. a. $210 to non-members; members $140. Balaban Publishers, International Science Services, P.O. Box 2039, Rehovot 76120, Israel. TEL 972-8-476216. FAX 972-8-467632. (And: Mario Negri Sud Research Institute, School for Scientific Communication, 66030 S. Maria Imbara, Italy. TEL 39-872-570316. FAX 39-872-578240) Ed. Miriam Balaban; Pub. Miriam Balaban. **Document type:** directory.
Description: Guide to academic, government and private institutions, organizations, companies and individuals concerned with desalination and water reuse.

627 551.4 GW ISSN 0012-0235
GB651 CODEN: DGMTAO
DEUTSCHE GEWAESSERKUNDLICHE MITTEILUNGEN; Mitteilungsblatt der gewaesserkundlichen Dienststellen des Bundes und der Laender. (Text in German; summaries in English) 1957. bi-m. DM.50. Bundesanstalt fuer Gewaesserkunde, Postfach 309, 56003 Koblenz, Germany. TEL 0261-1306-0. FAX 0261-1306-302. Ed. Hans-Juergen Liebscher. bk.rev.; abstr.; bibl.; charts; illus.; maps; tr.lit.; index. circ. 1,600. **Indexed:** Biol.Abstr., Chem.Abstr., Excerp.Med., Geo.Abstr., GeoRef., INIS Atomind., Pollut.Abstr., Sel.Water Res.Abstr., W.R.C.Inf. **Document type:** government publication.
—CASDDS.
Description: Reports on quantitative and qualitative hydrology, water resources management and water protection.

551.4 627 GW ISSN 0340-5176
DEUTSCHES GEWAESSERKUNDLICHES JAHRBUCH. DONAUGEBIET. 1898. a. Bayerisches Landesamt fuer Wasserwirtschaft, Lazarettstr. 67, 80636 Munich, Germany. TEL 089-12101203. charts; stat. circ. 500. **Indexed:** GeoRef. **Document type:** government publication.

551.4 627 GW
DEUTSCHES GEWAESSERKUNDLICHES JAHRBUCH. KUESTENGEBIET DER NORDSEE. 1941. a. DM.40. Landesamt fuer Wasserhaushalt und Kuesten, Saarbrueckenstr. 38, 24114 Kiel, Germany. TEL 0431-6649-0. FAX 0431-6649101. Ed. Mr. Hoefer. stat.; index, cum.index. circ. controlled. **Document type:** government publication.
Formerly: Deutsches Gewaesserkundliches Jahrbuch. Kuestengebiet der Nord- und Ostsee (ISSN 0340-5184)
Description: Hydrological statistics of German North Sea coast.

551 627 GW ISSN 0173-7260
DEUTSCHES GEWAESSERKUNDLICHES JAHRBUCH. RHEINGEBIET TEIL 2: MAIN. 1898. a. Bayerisches Landesamt fuer Wasserwirtschaft, Lazarettstr. 67, 80636 Munich, Germany. TEL 089-12101203. charts; stat. circ. 500. **Document type:** government publication.

551.48 NE ISSN 0167-5648
DEVELOPMENTS IN WATER SCIENCE. 1974. irreg., vol.45, 1994. price varies. Elsevier Science B.V., Books Division, P.O. Box 211, 1000 AE Amsterdam, Netherlands. TEL 31-20-4853911. FAX 31-20-4853705. TELEX 18582 ESPA NL. E-mail: nlinfo-f@elsevier.nl; usinfo-f@elsevier.com; forinfo-kyf04035@niftyserve.or.jp; Site addr.: http://www.elsevier.nl/. (Subscr. in U.S. and Canada to: Elsevier Science Inc., Box 882, Madison Sq. Sta, New York, NY 10159. TEL 212-989-5800. FAX 212-633-3680) Indexed: Soils & Fert. **Document type:** monographic series.
—BLDSC (3579.096500); Ei.
Refereed Serial

DIENST LANDBOUWKUNDIG ONDERZOEK. STARING CENTRUM, INSTITUUT VOOR ONDERZOEK VAN HET LANDELIJK GEBIED. JAARVERSLAG. see *AGRICULTURE — Crop Production And Soil*

DIENST LANDBOUWKUNDIG ONDERZOEK. STARING CENTRUM, INSTITUUT VOOR ONDERZOEK VAN HET LANDELIJK GEBIED. RAPPORT. see *AGRICULTURE — Crop Production And Soil*

333.91 US ISSN 0736-5454
DIVINING ROD. 1977. q. free. New Mexico Water Resources Research Institute, Box 30001, Dept. 3167, New Mexico State University, Las Cruces, NM 88003-0001. TEL 505-646-1813. FAX 505-646-6418. Ed. Cathy Ortega Klett. circ. 2,500. (back issues avail.) **Document type:** newsletter.
Description: Covers current water research projects and water-related issues in New Mexico for researchers and employees of state and federal governmental agencies.

628 GW
Z7935
DOKUMENTATION WASSER - ABFALL. 1960. 9/yr. DM.268.20. (Umwelt Bundesamt, Dokumentationszentrale Wasser) Erich Schmidt Verlag GmbH & Co. (Bielefeld), Viktoriastr. 44a, 33602 Bielefeld, Germany. TEL 0521-583080. (Subscr. to: Postfach 102451, 33524 Bielefeld, Germany) (back issues avail.) **Document type:** academic/scholarly publication.
—CCC.
Formerly: Dokumentation Wasser (ISSN 0012-5156)

133.3 US
DOWSERS NETWORK. q. American Society of Dowsers, Inc., Box 24, Danville, VT 05828. TEL 802-684-3417. FAX 802-684-2565. **Document type:** newsletter.

627 620 US
DREDGING SEMINAR. PROCEEDINGS. 1968. a. price varies. Center for Dredging Studies, Civil Engineering Department, Texas A & M University, College Station, TX 77843-3136. TEL 409-845-4516. FAX 409-845-6156. Ed. Robert E. Randall. charts. circ. 800. **Document type:** proceedings.

333.91 US ISSN 1055-9140
TD353
DRINKING WATER RESEARCH. 1991. bi-m. $40. American Water Works Association, Research Foundation, 6666 W. Quincy Ave., Denver, CO 80235-3098. TEL 303-794-7711. Ed. Marianne Prekker.
Description: Describes the activities of the AWWA Research Foundation; reports on results of research programs.

333.91 CN ISSN 0843-8277
DRINKING WATER SURVEILLANCE PROGRAM ANNUAL REPORT. AJAX WATER SUPPLY PLANT. 1988. a. free to qualified personnel. Ministry of Environment and Energy, Water Resources Branch, 135 St. Clair Ave. W., Toronto, Ont. M4V 1P5, Canada. TEL 416-323-4321. FAX 416-323-4564. **Document type:** government publication.

333.91 CN ISSN 0839-8992
DRINKING WATER SURVEILLANCE PROGRAM ANNUAL REPORT. ALVINSTON WATER SYSTEM. 1986. a. free to qualified personnel. Ministry of Environment and Energy, Water Resources Branch, 135 St. Clair Ave. W., Toronto, Ont. M4V 1P5, Canada. TEL 416-323-4321. FAX 416-323-4564. **Document type:** government publication.

333.91 CN ISSN 0839-900X
DRINKING WATER SURVEILLANCE PROGRAM ANNUAL REPORT. AMHERSTBURG AREA WATER SYSTEM. 1986. a. free to qualified personnel. Ministry of Environment and Energy, Water Resources Branch, 135 St. Clair Ave. W., Toronto, Ont. M4V 1P5, Canada. TEL 416-323-4321. FAX 416-323-4564. **Document type:** government publication.

333.91 CN ISSN 0843-8331
DRINKING WATER SURVEILLANCE PROGRAM ANNUAL REPORT. ATIKOKAN WATER TREATMENT PLANT. 1988. a. free to qualified personnel. Ministry of Environment and Energy, Water Resources Branch, 135 St. Clair Ave. W., Toronto, Ont. M4V 1P5, Canada. TEL 416-323-4321. FAX 416-323-4564. **Document type:** government publication.

333.91 CN ISSN 0840-5603
DRINKING WATER SURVEILLANCE PROGRAM ANNUAL REPORT. BAYSIDE SCHOOL WATER TREATMENT PLANT. 1987. a. free to qualified personnel. Ministry of Environment and Energy, Water Resources Branch, 135 St. Clair Ave. W., Toronto, Ont. M4V 1P5, Canada. TEL 416-323-4321. FAX 416-323-4564. **Document type:** government publication.

333.91 CN ISSN 1183-6105
DRINKING WATER SURVEILLANCE PROGRAM ANNUAL REPORT. BELLE RIVER WATER TREATMENT PLANT. 1990. a. free to qualified personnel. Ministry of Environment and Energy, Water Resources Branch, 135 St. Clair Ave. W., Toronto, Ont. M4V 1P5, Canada. TEL 416-323-4321. FAX 416-323-4564. **Document type:** government publication.

333.91 CN ISSN 0840-5123
DRINKING WATER SURVEILLANCE PROGRAM ANNUAL REPORT. BELLEVILLE WATER TREATMENT PLANT. 1987. a. free to qualified personnel. Ministry of Environment and Energy, Water Resources Branch, 135 St. Clair Ave. W., Toronto, Ont. M4V 1P5, Canada. TEL 416-323-4321. FAX 416-323-4564. **Document type:** government publication.

333.91 CN ISSN 0840-5344
DRINKING WATER SURVEILLANCE PROGRAM ANNUAL REPORT. BRANTFORD WATER TREATMENT PLANT. 1987. a. free to qualified personnel. Ministry of Environment and Energy, Water Resources Branch, 135 St. Clair Ave. W., Toronto, Ont. M4V 1P5, Canada. TEL 416-323-4321. FAX 416-323-4564. **Document type:** government publication.

333.91 CN ISSN 0839-9026
DRINKING WATER SURVEILLANCE PROGRAM ANNUAL REPORT. BRITANNIA WATER TREATMENT PLANT, OTTAWA. 1986. a. free to qualified personnel. Ministry of Environment and Energy, Water Resources Branch, 135 St. Clair Ave. W., Toronto, Ont. M4V 1P5, Canada. TEL 416-323-4321. FAX 416-323-4564. **Document type:** government publication.

333.91 CN ISSN 0840-5247
DRINKING WATER SURVEILLANCE PROGRAM ANNUAL REPORT. BURLINGTON WATER TREATMENT PLANT. 1987. a. free to qualified personnel. Ministry of Environment and Energy, Water Resources Branch, 135 St. Clair Ave. W., Toronto, Ont. M4V 1P5, Canada. TEL 416-323-4321. FAX 416-323-4564. **Document type:** government publication.

333.91 CN ISSN 1180-2138
DRINKING WATER SURVEILLANCE PROGRAM ANNUAL REPORT. CASSELMAN WATER TREATMENT PLANT. 1989. a. free to qualified personnel. Ministry of Environment and Energy, Water Resources Branch, 135 St. Clair Ave. W., Toronto, Ont. M4V 1P5, Canada. TEL 416-323-4321. FAX 416-323-4564. **Document type:** government publication.

333.91 CN ISSN 0843-8323
DRINKING WATER SURVEILLANCE PROGRAM ANNUAL REPORT. CAYUGA WATER TREATMENT PLANT. 1988. a. free to qualified personnel. Ministry of Environment and Energy, Water Resources Branch, 135 St. Clair Ave. W., Toronto, Ont. M4V 1P5, Canada. TEL 416-323-4321. FAX 416-323-4564. **Document type:** government publication.

333.91 CN ISSN 1180-2162
DRINKING WATER SURVEILLANCE PROGRAM ANNUAL REPORT. CENTRAL HALDIMAND - NORFOLK WATER TREATMENT PLANT. 1989. a. free to qualified personnel. Ministry of Environment and Energy, Water Resources Branch, 135 St. Clair Ave. W., Toronto, Ont. M4V 1P5, Canada. TEL 416-323-4321. FAX 416-323-4564. **Document type:** government publication.

333.91 CN ISSN 0843-8315
DRINKING WATER SURVEILLANCE PROGRAM ANNUAL REPORT. CHATHAM WATER TREATMENT PLANT. 1989. a. free to qualified personnel. Ministry of Environment and Energy, Water Resources Branch, 135 St. Clair Ave. W., Toronto, Ont. M4V 1P5, Canada. TEL 416-323-4321. FAX 416-323-4564. **Document type:** government publication.

333.91 CN ISSN 0840-5298
DRINKING WATER SURVEILLANCE PROGRAM ANNUAL REPORT. CORNWALL WATER TREATMENT PLANT. 1987. a. free to qualified personnel. Ministry of Environment and Energy, Water Resources Branch, 135 St. Clair Ave. W., Toronto, Ont. M4V 1P5, Canada. TEL 416-323-4321. FAX 416-323-4564. **Document type:** government publication.

333.91 CN ISSN 1183-613X
DRINKING WATER SURVEILLANCE PROGRAM ANNUAL REPORT. DELHI WATER SUPPLY SYSTEM. 1990. a. free to qualified personnel. Ministry of Environment and Energy, Water Resources Branch, 135 St. Clair Ave. W., Toronto, Ont. M4V 1P5, Canada. TEL 416-323-4321. FAX 416-323-4564. **Document type:** government publication.

333.91 CN ISSN 0840-5131
DRINKING WATER SURVEILLANCE PROGRAM ANNUAL REPORT. DESERONTO WATER TREATMENT PLANT. 1987. a. free to qualified personnel. Ministry of Environment and Energy, Water Resources Branch, 135 St. Clair Ave. W., Toronto, Ont. M4V 1P5, Canada. TEL 416-323-4321. FAX 416-323-4564. **Document type:** government publication.

333.91 CN ISSN 0839-8984
DRINKING WATER SURVEILLANCE PROGRAM ANNUAL REPORT. DRESDEN WATER TREATMENT PLANT. 1986. a. free to qualified personnel. Ministry of Environment and Energy, Water Resources Branch, 135 St. Clair Ave. W., Toronto, Ont. M4V 1P5, Canada. TEL 416-323-4321. FAX 416-323-4564. **Document type:** government publication.

333.91 CN ISSN 0843-8293
DRINKING WATER SURVEILLANCE PROGRAM ANNUAL REPORT. DRYDEN WATER TREATMENT PLANT. 1988. a. free to qualified personnel. Ministry of Environment and Energy, Water Resources Branch, 135 St. Clair Ave. W., Toronto, Ont. M4V 1P5, Canada. TEL 416-323-4321. FAX 416-323-4564. **Document type:** government publication.

333.91 CN ISSN 1192-1196
DRINKING WATER SURVEILLANCE PROGRAM ANNUAL REPORT. DUNNVILLE WATER TREATMENT PLANT. 1990. a. free to qualified personnel. Ministry of Environment and Energy, Water Resources Branch, 135 St. Clair Ave. W., Toronto, Ont. M4V 1P5, Canada. TEL 416-323-4321. FAX 416-323-4564. **Document type:** government publication.

333.91 CN ISSN 0840-5166
DRINKING WATER SURVEILLANCE PROGRAM ANNUAL REPORT. EASTERLY WATER TREATMENT PLANT, TORONTO. 1986. a. free to qualified personnel. Ministry of Environment and Energy, Water Resources Branch, 135 St. Clair Ave. W., Toronto, Ont. M4V 1P5, Canada. TEL 416-323-4321. FAX 416-323-4564. **Document type:** government publication.

333.91 CN ISSN 0843-8382
DRINKING WATER SURVEILLANCE PROGRAM ANNUAL REPORT. ELMIRE WELL SUPPLY. 1988. a. free to qualified personnel. Ministry of Environment and Energy, Water Resources Branch, 135 St. Clair Ave. W., Toronto, Ont. M4V 1P5, Canada. TEL 416-323-4321. FAX 416-323-4564. **Document type:** government publication.

WATER RESOURCES

333.91 CN ISSN 0840-5182
DRINKING WATER SURVEILLANCE PROGRAM ANNUAL REPORT. FORT ERIE TREATMENT PLANT. 1987. a. free to qualified personnel. Ministry of Environment and Energy, Water Resources Branch, 135 St. Clair Ave. W., Toronto, Ont. M4V 1P5, Canada. TEL 416-323-4321. FAX 416-323-4564. **Document type:** government publication.

333.91 CN ISSN 0843-8358
DRINKING WATER SURVEILLANCE PROGRAM ANNUAL REPORT. FORT FRANCES WATER TREATMENT PLANT. 1989. a. free to qualified personnel. Ministry of Environment and Energy, Water Resources Branch, 135 St. Clair Ave. W., Toronto, Ont. M4V 1P5, Canada. TEL 416-323-4321. FAX 416-323-4564. **Document type:** government publication.

333.91 CN ISSN 0840-5174
DRINKING WATER SURVEILLANCE PROGRAM ANNUAL REPORT. GRIMSBY WATER TREATMENT PLANT. 1987. a. free to qualified personnel. Ministry of Environment and Energy, Water Resources Branch, 135 St. Clair Ave. W., Toronto, Ont. M4V 1P5, Canada. TEL 416-323-4321. FAX 416-323-4564. **Document type:** government publication.

333.91 CN ISSN 1192-120X
DRINKING WATER SURVEILLANCE PROGRAM ANNUAL REPORT. GUELPH WELL SUPPLY. 1990. a. free to qualified personnel. Ministry of Environment and Energy, Water Resources Branch, 135 St. Clair Ave. W., Toronto, Ont. M4V 1P5, Canada. TEL 416-323-4321. FAX 416-323-4564. **Document type:** government publication.

333.91 CN ISSN 0839-9034
DRINKING WATER SURVEILLANCE PROGRAM ANNUAL REPORT. HAMILTON WATER TREATMENT PLANT. 1986. a. free to qualified personnel. Ministry of Environment and Energy, Water Resources Branch, 135 St. Clair Ave. W., Toronto, Ont. M4V 1P5, Canada. TEL 416-323-4321. FAX 416-323-4564. **Document type:** government publication.

333.91 CN ISSN 0840-5239
DRINKING WATER SURVEILLANCE PROGRAM ANNUAL REPORT. HARROW - COLCHESTER SOUTH WATER SUPPLY SYSTEM. 1986. a. free to qualified personnel. Ministry of Environment and Energy, Water Resources Branch, 135 St. Clair Ave. W., Toronto, Ont. M4V 1P5, Canada. TEL 416-323-4321. FAX 416-323-4564. **Document type:** government publication.

333.91 CN ISSN 1180-2146
DRINKING WATER SURVEILLANCE PROGRAM ANNUAL REPORT. HAWKESBURY WATER TREATMENT PLANT. 1989. a. free to qualified personnel. Ministry of Environment and Energy, Water Resources Branch, 135 St. Clair Ave. W., Toronto, Ont. M4V 1P5, Canada. TEL 416-323-4321. FAX 416-323-4564. **Document type:** government publication.

333.91 CN ISSN 0843-8307
DRINKING WATER SURVEILLANCE PROGRAM ANNUAL REPORT. KENORA WATER TREATMENT PLANT. 1989. a. free to qualified personnel. Ministry of Environment and Energy, Water Resources Branch, 135 St. Clair Ave. W., Toronto, Ont. M4V 1P5, Canada. TEL 416-323-4321. FAX 416-323-4564. **Document type:** government publication.

333.91 CN ISSN 0839-9050
DRINKING WATER SURVEILLANCE PROGRAM ANNUAL REPORT. KINGSTON WATER TREATMENT PLANT. 1986. a. free to qualified personnel. Ministry of Environment and Energy, Water Resources Branch, 135 St. Clair Ave. W., Toronto, Ont. M4V 1P5, Canada. TEL 416-323-4321. FAX 416-323-4564. **Document type:** government publication.

333.91 CN ISSN 0840-5190
DRINKING WATER SURVEILLANCE PROGRAM ANNUAL REPORT. KITCHENER WATER SUPPLY SYSTEMS. 1987. a. free to qualified personnel. Ministry of Environment and Energy, Water Resources Branch, 135 St. Clair Ave. W., Toronto, Ont. M4V 1P5, Canada. TEL 416-323-4321. FAX 416-323-4564. **Document type:** government publication.

333.91 CN ISSN 0840-5271
DRINKING WATER SURVEILLANCE PROGRAM ANNUAL REPORT. LAKE HURON WATER SUPPLY SYSTEM. 1986. a. free to qualified personnel. Ministry of Environment and Energy, Water Resources Branch, 135 St. Clair Ave. W., Toronto, Ont. M4V 1P5, Canada. TEL 416-323-4321. FAX 416-323-4564. **Document type:** government publication.

333.91 CN ISSN 0840-5107
DRINKING WATER SURVEILLANCE PROGRAM ANNUAL REPORT. LAMBTON AREA SUPPLY, SARNIA. 1986. a. free to qualified personnel. Ministry of Environment and Energy, Water Resources Branch, 135 St. Clair Ave. W., Toronto, Ont. M4V 1P5, Canada. TEL 416-323-4321. FAX 416-323-4564. **Document type:** government publication.

333.91 CN ISSN 0840-5204
DRINKING WATER SURVEILLANCE PROGRAM ANNUAL REPORT. LEMIEUX ISLAND WATER TREATMENT PLANT, OTTAWA. 1986. a. free to qualified personnel. Ministry of Environment and Energy, Water Resources Branch, 135 St. Clair Ave. W., Toronto, Ont. M4V 1P5, Canada. TEL 416-323-4321. FAX 416-323-4564. **Document type:** government publication.

333.91 CN ISSN 0840-531X
DRINKING WATER SURVEILLANCE PROGRAM ANNUAL REPORT. MITCHELL'S BAY WATER TREATMENT PLANT. 1986. a. free to qualified personnel. Ministry of Environment and Energy, Water Resources Branch, 135 St. Clair Ave. W., Toronto, Ont. M4V 1P5, Canada. TEL 416-323-4321. FAX 416-323-4564. **Document type:** government publication.

333.91 CN ISSN 0839-8925
DRINKING WATER SURVEILLANCE PROGRAM ANNUAL REPORT. NIAGARA FALLS WATER TREATMENT PLANT. 1986. a. free to qualified personnel. Ministry of Environment and Energy, Water Resources Branch, 135 St. Clair Ave. W., Toronto, Ont. M4V 1P5, Canada. TEL 416-323-4321. FAX 416-323-4564. **Document type:** government publication.

333.91 CN ISSN 0840-5212
DRINKING WATER SURVEILLANCE PROGRAM ANNUAL REPORT. NORTH BAY WATER TREATMENT PLANT. 1987. a. free to qualified personnel. Ministry of Environment and Energy, Water Resources Branch, 135 St. Clair Ave. W., Toronto, Ont. M4V 1P5, Canada. TEL 416-323-4321. FAX 416-323-4564. **Document type:** government publication.

333.91 CN ISSN 0843-8366
DRINKING WATER SURVEILLANCE PROGRAM ANNUAL REPORT. ODESSA WATER TREATMENT PLANT. 1988. a. free to qualified personnel. Ministry of Environment and Energy, Water Resources Branch, 135 St. Clair Ave. W., Toronto, Ont. M4V 1P5, Canada. TEL 416-323-4321. FAX 416-323-4564. **Document type:** government publication.

333.91 CN ISSN 1183-6172
DRINKING WATER SURVEILLANCE PROGRAM ANNUAL REPORT. OWEN SOUND WATER SUPPLY SYSTEM. 1990. a. free to qualified personnel. Ministry of Environment and Energy, Water Resources Branch, 135 St. Clair Ave. W., Toronto, Ont. M4V 1P5, Canada. TEL 416-323-4321. FAX 416-323-4564. **Document type:** government publication.

333.91 CN ISSN 0840-514X
DRINKING WATER SURVEILLANCE PROGRAM ANNUAL REPORT. PETERBOROUGH WATER TREATMENT PLANT. 1987. a. free to qualified personnel. Ministry of Environment and Energy, Water Resources Branch, 135 St. Clair Ave. W., Toronto, Ont. M4V 1P5, Canada. TEL 416-323-4321. FAX 416-323-4564. **Document type:** government publication.

333.91 CN ISSN 1183-6180
DRINKING WATER SURVEILLANCE PROGRAM ANNUAL REPORT. PORT COLBORNE WATER TREATMENT PLANT. 1990. a. free to qualified personnel. Ministry of Environment and Energy, Water Resources Branch, 135 St. Clair Ave. W., Toronto, Ont. M4V 1P5, Canada. TEL 416-323-4321. FAX 416-323-4564. **Document type:** government publication.

333.91 CN ISSN 0840-5328
DRINKING WATER SURVEILLANCE PROGRAM ANNUAL REPORT. PORT DOVER - DOAN'S HOLLOW WATER TREATMENT PLANT. 1987. a. free to qualified personnel. Ministry of Environment and Energy, Water Resources Branch, 135 St. Clair Ave. W., Toronto, Ont. M4V 1P5, Canada. TEL 416-323-4321. FAX 416-323-4564. **Document type:** government publication.

333.91 CN ISSN 0839-8968
DRINKING WATER SURVEILLANCE PROGRAM ANNUAL REPORT. PORT STANLEY WATER TREATMENT PLANT. 1986. a. free to qualified personnel. Ministry of Environment and Energy, Water Resources Branch, 135 St. Clair Ave. W., Toronto, Ont. M4V 1P5, Canada. TEL 416-323-4321. FAX 416-323-4564. **Document type:** government publication.

333.91 CN ISSN 0839-8941
DRINKING WATER SURVEILLANCE PROGRAM ANNUAL REPORT. R.C. HARRIS WATER TREATMENT PLANT, TORONTO. 1986. a. free to qualified personnel. Ministry of Environment and Energy, Water Resources Branch, 135 St. Clair Ave. W., Toronto, Ont. M4V 1P5, Canada. TEL 416-323-4321. FAX 416-323-4564. **Document type:** government publication.

333.91 CN ISSN 0839-8976
DRINKING WATER SURVEILLANCE PROGRAM ANNUAL REPORT. R.L. CLARK WATER TREATMENT PLANT, TORONTO. 1986. a. free to qualified personnel. Ministry of Environment and Energy, Water Resources Branch, 135 St. Clair Ave. W., Toronto, Ont. M4V 1P5, Canada. TEL 416-323-4321. FAX 416-323-4564. **Document type:** government publication.

333.91 CN ISSN 1180-2111
DRINKING WATER SURVEILLANCE PROGRAM ANNUAL REPORT. RENFREW WATER TREATMENT PLANT. 1989. a. free to qualified personnel. Ministry of Environment and Energy, Water Resources Branch, 135 St. Clair Ave. W., Toronto, Ont. M4V 1P5, Canada. TEL 416-323-4321. FAX 416-323-4564. **Document type:** government publication.

333.91 CN ISSN 0840-528X
DRINKING WATER SURVEILLANCE PROGRAM ANNUAL REPORT. ST. CATHARINES WATER TREATMENT PLANT. 1987. a. free to qualified personnel. Ministry of Environment and Energy, Water Resources Branch, 135 St. Clair Ave. W., Toronto, Ont. M4V 1P5, Canada. TEL 416-323-4321. FAX 416-323-4564. **Document type:** government publication.

333.91 CN ISSN 0840-5255
DRINKING WATER SURVEILLANCE PROGRAM ANNUAL REPORT. ST. THOMAS (ELGIN) WATER SUPPLY SYSTEM. 1989. a. free to qualified personnel. Ministry of Environment and Energy, Water Resources Branch, 135 St. Clair Ave. W., Toronto, Ont. M4V 1P5, Canada. TEL 416-323-4321. FAX 416-323-4564. **Document type:** government publication.

333.91 CN ISSN 0840-5158
DRINKING WATER SURVEILLANCE PROGRAM ANNUAL REPORT. SAULT STE. MARIE WELLS AND WATER TREATMENT PLANT. 1987. a. free to qualified personnel. Ministry of Environment and Energy, Water Resources Branch, 135 St. Clair Ave. W., Toronto, Ont. M4V 1P5, Canada. TEL 416-323-4321. FAX 416-323-4564. **Document type:** government publication.

333.91 CN ISSN 1183-6202
DRINKING WATER SURVEILLANCE PROGRAM ANNUAL REPORT. SIMCOE WELL SUPPLY. 1990. a. free to qualified personnel. Ministry of Environment and Energy, Water Resources Branch, 135 St. Clair Ave. W., Toronto, Ont. M4V 1P5, Canada. TEL 416-323-4321. FAX 416-323-4564. **Document type:** government publication.

333.91 CN ISSN 0839-9069
DRINKING WATER SURVEILLANCE PROGRAM ANNUAL REPORT. SOUTH PEEL (LAKEVIEW) WATER TREATMENT PLANT. 1986. a. free to qualified personnel. Ministry of Environment and Energy, Water Resources Branch, 135 St. Clair Ave. W., Toronto, Ont. M4V 1P5, Canada. TEL 416-323-4321. FAX 416-323-4564. **Document type:** government publication.

333.91　　　　CN　ISSN 1187-6824
DRINKING WATER SURVEILLANCE PROGRAM ANNUAL REPORT. SOUTH PEEL (LORNE PARK) WATER SUPPLY SYSTEM. 1986. a. free to qualified personnel. Ministry of Environment and Energy, Water Resources Branch, 135 St. Clair Ave. W., Toronto, Ont. M4V 1P5, Canada. TEL 416-323-4321. FAX 416-323-4564. **Document type:** government publication.
　　Formerly (until 1988): Drinking Water Surveillance Program Annual Report. Lorne Park Water Treatment Plant, Mississauga (ISSN 0839-9042)

333.91　　　　CN　ISSN 0839-8933
DRINKING WATER SURVEILLANCE PROGRAM ANNUAL REPORT. STONEY POINT WATER TREATMENT PLANT. 1986. a. free to qualified personnel. Ministry of Environment and Energy, Water Resources Branch, 135 St. Clair Ave. W., Toronto, Ont. M4V 1P5, Canada. TEL 416-323-4321. FAX 416-323-4564. **Document type:** government publication.

333.91　　　　CN　ISSN 0840-5301
DRINKING WATER SURVEILLANCE PROGRAM ANNUAL REPORT. STOUFFVILLE WATER SUPPLY SYSTEM. 1987. a. free to qualified personnel. Ministry of Environment and Energy, Water Resources Branch, 135 St. Clair Ave. W., Toronto, Ont. M4V 1P5, Canada. TEL 416-323-4321. FAX 416-323-4564. **Document type:** government publication.

333.91　　　　CN　ISSN 0840-5336
DRINKING WATER SURVEILLANCE PROGRAM ANNUAL REPORT. SUDBURY (RAMSEY LAKE) WATER TREATMENT PLANT. 1987. a. free to qualified personnel. Ministry of Environment and Energy, Water Resources Branch, 135 St. Clair Ave. W., Toronto, Ont. M4V 1P5, Canada. TEL 416-323-4321. FAX 416-323-4564. **Document type:** government publication.

333.91　　　　CN　ISSN 0840-5220
DRINKING WATER SURVEILLANCE PROGRAM ANNUAL REPORT. SUDBURY (WANAPITEI) WATER TREATMENT PLANT. 1987. a. free to qualified personnel. Ministry of Environment and Energy, Water Resources Branch, 135 St. Clair Ave. W., Toronto, Ont. M4V 1P5, Canada. TEL 416-323-4321. FAX 416-323-4564. **Document type:** government publication.

333.91　　　　CN　ISSN 1183-6210
DRINKING WATER SURVEILLANCE PROGRAM ANNUAL REPORT. TECUMSEH WATER TREATMENT PLANT. 1990. a. free to qualified personnel. Ministry of Environment and Energy, Water Resources Branch, 135 St. Clair Ave. W., Toronto, Ont. M4V 1P5, Canada. TEL 416-323-4321. FAX 416-323-4564. **Document type:** government publication.

333.91　　　　CN　ISSN 0843-8374
DRINKING WATER SURVEILLANCE PROGRAM ANNUAL REPORT. THAMESVILLE WATER SUPPLY SYSTEM. 1988. a. free to qualified personnel. Ministry of Environment and Energy, Water Resources Branch, 135 St. Clair Ave. W., Toronto, Ont. M4V 1P5, Canada. TEL 416-323-4321. FAX 416-323-4564. **Document type:** government publication.

333.91　　　　CN　ISSN 0843-8285
DRINKING WATER SURVEILLANCE PROGRAM ANNUAL REPORT. THUNDER BAY (BARE POINT) WATER TREATMENT PLANT. 1988. a. free to qualified personnel. Ministry of Environment and Energy, Water Resources Branch, 135 St. Clair Ave. W., Toronto, Ont. M4V 1P5, Canada. TEL 416-323-4321. FAX 416-323-4564. **Document type:** government publication.

333.91　　　　CN　ISSN 0843-834X
DRINKING WATER SURVEILLANCE PROGRAM ANNUAL REPORT. THUNDER BAY (LOCH LOMOND) WATER TREATMENT PLANT. 1988. a. free to qualified personnel. Ministry of Environment and Energy, Water Resources Branch, 135 St. Clair Ave. W., Toronto, Ont. M4V 1P5, Canada. TEL 416-323-4321. FAX 416-323-4564. **Document type:** government publication.

333.91　　　　CN　ISSN 1180-212X
DRINKING WATER SURVEILLANCE PROGRAM ANNUAL REPORT. TRENTON WATER TREATMENT PLANT. 1989. a. free to qualified personnel. Ministry of Environment and Energy, Water Resources Branch, 135 St. Clair Ave. W., Toronto, Ont. M4V 1P5, Canada. TEL 416-323-4321. FAX 416-323-4564. **Document type:** government publication.

333.91　　　　CN　ISSN 0840-5115
DRINKING WATER SURVEILLANCE PROGRAM ANNUAL REPORT. UNION WATER TREATMENT PLANT. 1987. a. free to qualified personnel. Ministry of Environment and Energy, Water Resources Branch, 135 St. Clair Ave. W., Toronto, Ont. M4V 1P5, Canada. TEL 416-323-4321. FAX 416-323-4564. **Document type:** government publication.

333.91　　　　CN　ISSN 0839-9018
DRINKING WATER SURVEILLANCE PROGRAM ANNUAL REPORT. WALLACEBURG WATER TREATMENT PLANT. 1986. a. free to qualified personnel. Ministry of Environment and Energy, Water Resources Branch, 135 St. Clair Ave. W., Toronto, Ont. M4V 1P5, Canada. TEL 416-323-4321. FAX 416-323-4564. **Document type:** government publication.

333.91　　　　CN　ISSN 0839-8917
DRINKING WATER SURVEILLANCE PROGRAM ANNUAL REPORT. WALPOLE ISLAND WATER TREATMENT PLANT. 1986. a. free to qualified personnel. Ministry of Environment and Energy, Water Resources Branch, 135 St. Clair Ave. W., Toronto, Ont. M4V 1P5, Canada. TEL 416-323-4321. FAX 416-323-4564. **Document type:** government publication.

333.91　　　　CN　ISSN 1180-2103
DRINKING WATER SURVEILLANCE PROGRAM ANNUAL REPORT. WELLAND WATER SUPPLY SYSTEM. 1989. a. free to qualified personnel. Ministry of Environment and Energy, Water Resources Branch, 135 St. Clair Ave. W., Toronto, Ont. M4V 1P5, Canada. TEL 416-323-4321. FAX 416-323-4564. **Document type:** government publication.

333.91　　　　CN　ISSN 0839-895X
DRINKING WATER SURVEILLANCE PROGRAM ANNUAL REPORT. WINDSOR WATER TREATMENT PLANT. 1986. a. free to qualified personnel. Ministry of Environment and Energy, Water Resources Branch, 135 St. Clair Ave. W., Toronto, Ont. M4V 1P5, Canada. TEL 416-323-4321. FAX 416-323-4564. **Document type:** government publication.
　　Formerly (until 1987): Drinking Water Surveillance Program Annual Report. Windsor Utilities Commission Water Treatment Plant (ISSN 0848-3345)

333.91　　　　CN　ISSN 0846-7471
DRINKING WATER SURVEILLANCE PROGRAM ANNUAL REPORT (YEAR) PLANT SUMMARIES. a. free to qualified personnel. Ministry of Environment and Energy, Water Resources Branch, 135 St. Clair Ave. W., Toronto, Ont. M4V 1P5, Canada. TEL 416-323-4321. FAX 416-323-4564. **Document type:** government publication.

333.91 631.7　　　　US
DROUGHT NETWORK NEWS. 1989. 3/yr. free. International Drought Information Center, 241 L.W. Chase Hall, University of Nebraska, Box 830728, Lincoln, NE 68583-0728. TEL 402-472-6707. FAX 402-472-6614. TELEX UNL COMM LCN 484340. (Co-sponsor: National Oceanic and Atmospheric Administration) illus. circ. 1,248. (back issues avail.) **Document type:** newsletter.
　　Description: Provides information on current episodes of drought; drought response, mitigation and planning activities; new technologies relating to planning and management.

627 628.167　　　　II
DRYLAND RESOURCES AND TECHNOLOGY ANNUAL (YEAR). a. $50. Divyajyoti Prakashan, 5 Bhagat-ki-kothi, Jodhpur 342 003, India. (Co-sponsor: Geo-Environ Academia) Eds. Alam Singh, G.R. Chowdhary. **Document type:** academic/scholarly publication.
　　—BLDSC (3630.226700).
　　Former titles: Current Practices in Dryland Resources and Technology; Dryland Resources and Technology (ISSN 0254-8305); (until 1984): Desert Resources and Technology.

333.7 338　　　　FR　ISSN 0755-5016
　　　　　　　　　　　　　　CODEN: EINUDQ
L'EAU, L'INDUSTRIE, LES NUISANCES. 1975. m. 570 F. Pierre Johanet et ses Fils, 7 av. Franklin-D.-Roosevelt, 75008 Paris, France. TEL 43-59-08-91. FAX 42-25-59-47. adv.; illus. circ. 6,000. Indexed: Chem.Abstr., Excerp.Med., W.R.C.Inf.
　　—BLDSC (3647.003800); CASDDS.
　　Formerly (until 1982): Eau et l'Industrie (ISSN 0337-9329)

333.91　　　　FR　ISSN 0424-2033
EAU PURE.* 4/yr. 45 F. Association Nationale pour la Protection des Eaux, 4 rue Menard, 78000 Versailles, France. TEL 39-51-88-94. Ed. Jacques Vrignaud. **Indexed:** Pollut.Abstr.
　　Description: Provides technical documentation of the industrial, medical, legal and administrative areas of water purification.

ECOALERT. see *ENVIRONMENTAL STUDIES*

EFFLUENT AND WATER TREATMENT JOURNAL. see *ENVIRONMENTAL STUDIES — Pollution*

627　　　　US
ENGINEERING COMMITTEE ON OCEANIC RESOURCES. PROCEEDINGS OF THE GENERAL ASSEMBLY. irreg., 2nd, 1975, Tokyo. Engineering Committee on Oceanic Resources, 2101 Constitution Ave. N.W., Washington, DC 20418. TEL 202-334-2000. **Document type:** proceedings.

ENVIRONMENTAL TOXICOLOGY AND WATER QUALITY; an international journal. see *ENVIRONMENTAL STUDIES — Toxicology And Environmental Safety*

EUROPEAN WATER POLLUTION CONTROL. see *ENVIRONMENTAL STUDIES — Pollution*

627　　　　UN　ISSN 0254-5284
F A O IRRIGATION AND DRAINAGE PAPERS. Spanish edition: Estudio sobre Riego y Avenamiento (ISSN 1014-2924); French edition: Bulletin F A O d'Irrigation et de Drainage (ISSN 0253-4703) 1971. irreg., no.49, 1994. price varies. Food and Agriculture Organization of the United Nations, c/o UNIPUB, 4611-F Assembly Dr., Lanham, MD 20706-4391. TEL 301-459-7666. FAX 301-459-0056. **Indexed:** Excerp.Med. **Document type:** monographic series.
　　—BLDSC (3865.683500).

333.91　　　　US　ISSN 0046-306X
FACETS OF FRESHWATER. 1976. bi-m. $35 membership. Freshwater Foundation, 725 County Rd. 6, Wayzata, MN 55391. TEL 612-449-0092. FAX 617-449-0592. E-mail: frshwtr@freshwater.org. Ed. Stewart Crosby. bibl.; charts; illus.; circ. controlled. **Document type:** newsletter.

333.91　　　　US　ISSN 0896-1794
TD485
FLORIDA WATER RESOURCES JOURNAL; the overflow. 1949. m. $24. (Florida Water & Pollution Control Operator's Association, Inc.) Florida Water Resources Journal, Inc., 5200 N.W. 43rd St., Ste. 102-301, Gainesville, FL 32606. TEL 904-374-4946. FAX 904-372-6229. (Co-sponsors: American Water Works Association, Florida Section; Florida Pollution Control Association) Ed. John Crane. adv. contact: John Crane. circ. 8,000. **Document type:** trade publication.
　　Description: Covers water supply, treatment, and distribution; includes waste water collection, treatment and disposal.

333.91 614.7　　　　CN　ISSN 0832-6673
FOCUS ON INTERNATIONAL JOINT COMMISSION ACTIVITIES. 1974. 3/yr. free. International Joint Commission, Great Lakes Regional Office, 100 Ouellette Ave., 8th Fl., Windsor, Ont. N9A 6T3, Canada. TEL 519-256-7821. FAX 519-256-7791. (Or: Box 32869, Detroit, MI 48232) Ed. Sally Cole-Misch. bk.rev.; bibl.; illus. circ. 14,000. (also avail. in microform from UMI) **Indexed:** Energy Ind., Energy Info.Abstr., Environ.Abstr.
　　Former titles (until vol.11, no.2, 1986): Focus on Great Lakes Water Quality (ISSN 0711-0855); (until vol.7, 1981): Great Lakes Focus on Water Quality.

628.1　　　　UK　ISSN 0969-6237
▼**FOCUS ON WATER QUALITY.** 1994. m. The Royal Society of Chemistry, Thomas Graham House, Science Park, Milton Rd., Cambridge CB4 4WF, England. TEL 01223-420066. FAX 01223-423623. E-mail: rsc1@rsc.org. (Dist. by: Turpin Distribution Services Ltd., Blackhorse Rd., Letchworth, Herts. SG6 1HN, England. TEL 01462-480947. FAX 01462-480947) **Document type:** newsletter.
　　Description: Disseminates technical and commercial news in the water-treatment sector, emphasizing legislative and environmental issues.

FORCES. see *GENERAL INTEREST PERIODICALS — Canada*

WATER RESOURCES

G W A. (Gas - Wasser - Abwasser) see *PETROLEUM AND GAS*

GAS - ERDGAS - G W F; das Gas- und Wasserfach. see *PETROLEUM AND GAS*

333.7 333.7   GW   ISSN 0170-5156
TC473   CODEN: JBGEDH
GERMANY. BUNDESANSTALT FUER GEWAESSERKUNDE. JAHRESBERICHT. 1949-1962; resumed 1974. a. Bundesanstalt fuer Gewaesserkunde, Postfach 309, 56003 Koblenz, Germany. TEL 0261-1306-0. FAX 0261-1306-302. illus. **Document type:** government publication.
—BLDSC (4633.302000).
    Description: Working report on scientific and technical projects.

621.312   RU   ISSN 0016-9714
                       CODEN: GTSTA8
GIDROTEKHNICHESKOE STROITEL'STVO. English translation: Hydrotechnical Construction (US ISSN 0018-8220) 1930. m. $112 (effective 1996). Ministerstvo Goryuchego i Energetiki Rosii - Ministry of Fuel and Energetics of Russia, Bol'shoi Cherkasskii Per., 2-10, 103012 Moscow, Russia. Ed. V.A. Lukin. adv.; bk.rev.; abstr.; bibl.; charts; illus.; stat.; index. circ. 6,400. **Indexed:** Appl.Mech.Rev., Chem.Abstr., Eng.Ind., Fluidex, Geotech.Abstr., INSPEC, Intl.Civil Eng.Abstr., Soft.Abstr.Eng.

628 551.4   PL   ISSN 0017-2448
                       CODEN: GOWOAC
GOSPODARKA WODNA. (Text in Polish; contents page in English) 1935. m. $51. Wydawnictwo Czasopism i Ksiazek Technicznych SIGMA - NOT, Ul. Ratuszowa 11, P.O. Box 1004, 00-950 Warsaw, Poland. TEL 48-22-180918. FAX 48-22-192187. TELEX 814550 SIGMA PL. (Dist. by: SIGMA NOT Ltd., Ul. Bartycka 20, 00-716 Warsaw, Poland) Ed. Marian Chudzynski. adv.: page $1000. bk.rev.; charts; illus.; maps; stat.; index. circ. 2,000. **Indexed:** Chem.Abstr., Geotech.Abstr., W.R.C.Inf.
—CASDDS.

977 016   US   ISSN 0072-7326
GREAT LAKES RESEARCH CHECKLIST. 1959. s-a. free. Great Lakes Commission, 400 Fourth St., Ann Arbor, MI 48103. TEL 313-665-9135. FAX 313-665-4370. Ed. Albert G. Ballert. bk.rev. circ. 700. (also avail. in microfilm from UMI; reprint service avail. from UMI) **Document type:** bibliography.
—UMI.
    Description: Bibliography of current Great Lakes related journals, articles, books and documents. Includes news notes.

363.6   CN   ISSN 0710-8702
TD223.3
GREAT LAKES SCIENCE ADVISORY BOARD. REPORT. 1975. biennial. free. International Joint Commission, Great Lakes Regional Commission, 100 Ouellette Ave., 8th Fl., Windsor, ON N9A 6T3, Canada. TEL 519-257-6700. FAX 519-257-6740. Ed.Bd. charts; stat.; circ. 8,000 (controlled). (also avail. in microfilm from UMI; reprint service avail. from UMI) **Indexed:** Environ.Abstr., Sel.Water Res.Abstr.
    Formerly: Great Lakes Research Advisory Board. Annual Report.

333.91 614.7   US   ISSN 0882-6188
                       CODEN: GWMOEM
GROUND WATER MONITOR; legislation, regulation, litigation, technology. 1985. bi-w. $507 (effective Sep. 1992). Business Publishers, Inc., 951 Pershing Dr., Silver Spring, MD 20910-4464. TEL 301-587-6300. FAX 301-585-9075. Ed. Charles Anderson. (looseleaf format; back issues avail.) **Document type:** newsletter.
●Also available online. Vendor(s): Data-Star (PTBN), Knight-Ridder, Inc., NewsNet (EV18).
—CCC.
    Description: News from Congress, EPA and states on cleanup of ground water contamination across the U.S.

GROUND WATER MONITORING & REMEDIATION. see *EARTH SCIENCES — Hydrology*

333.91   FR
GUIDE DE L'EAU. a. 1100 F. (foreign 934.55 F.). Pierre Johanet et ses Fils, 7, av. Franklin Roosevelt, 75008 Paris, France. TEL 43-59-08-91. FAX 42-25-59-47. **Document type:** directory.

628.1   UK   ISSN 1350-6684
GUIDE TO THE ECONOMIC REGULATION OF THE WATER INDUSTRY (YEAR). biennial. £150. O X E R A Press, Blue Boar Ct., Alfred St., Oxford OX1 4EH, England. TEL 01865-2511342. FAX 01865-201080. **Document type:** bulletin.
    Description: The theoretical and legal framework of regulation in the U.K. water sector and analysis of its development since the privatization of the industry.

333.91   GW
HAMBURGER WASSERWERKE. FACHLICHE BERICHTE. 1982. s-a. free to qualified personnel. Hamburger Wasserwerke GmbH, Billhorner Deich 2, 20539 Hamburg, Germany. TEL 040-7888-2483. FAX 040-7888-2513. Ed. Peter Schreiber. circ. 1,000. **Document type:** monographic series.

551.49   HU   ISSN 0018-1323
                       CODEN: HIDRAV
HIDROLOGIAI KOZLONY. (Text in Hungarian; contents page and summaries in English) 1918. bi-m. 300 Ft.($27.50) Magyar Hidrologiai Tarsasag, H-1027 Budapest, Fo u.68, Hungary. (Subscr. to: Kultura, Box 149, H-1389 Budapest, Hungary) Ed. A. Szollosi-Nagy. adv.; bk.rev.; abstr.; bibl.; charts; illus.; index. cum.index. circ. 1,150. **Indexed:** Appl.Mech.Rev., Chem.Abstr., Fluidex, Geotech.Abstr., Meteor.& Geoastrophys.Abstr., Sel.Water Res.Abstr.
—CASDDS.

627   JA
HOKKAIDO NO CHUSHO KASEN/MEDIUM AND SMALL SCALE RIVER IN HOKKAIDO. (Text in Japanese) a. 1600 Yen. Hokkaido Doboku Kyokai - Hokkaido Civil Engineering Association, Nishi 4-chome, Kita 4-jo, Chuo-ku, Sapporo-shi, Hokkaido 060, Japan.

620 551.4 333.91 FR   ISSN 0018-6368
TC1   CODEN: HOBLAB
HOUILLE BLANCHE; revue internationale de l'eau. (Text in English or French; summaries in English, French, German, Spanish) 1946. 8/yr. 940 F. (Societe Hydrotechnique de France) Revue Generale de l'Electricite S.A., 48 rue de la Procession, 75724 Paris Cedex 15, France. FAX 44-49-60-35. TELEX SEE 200565F. Ed. J. Valembois. adv.; bk.rev.; abstr.; bibl.; charts; illus.; index. circ. 4,000. (back issues avail.) **Indexed:** Appl.Mech.Rev., Chem.Abstr., Deep Sea Res.& Oceanogr.Abstr., Eng.Ind., Excerp.Med., Fluidex, Fuel & Energy Abstr., Geotech.Abstr., INIS Atomind., INSPEC, Math.R., Meteor.& Geoastrophys.Abstr., Sel.Water Res.Abstr.
—BLDSC (4334.000000); SWETS. **CCC.**
    Description: Covers a range of preoccupations of engineers interested in water problems: fluid mechanics, hydraulic theory and its applications, river and maritime engineering works, water resources management, waters treatment.

HUNTER VALLEY RESEARCH FOUNDATION. WORKING PAPERS. see *STATISTICS*

333.91   US
HYDATA - NEWS AND VIEWS. 1988. bi-m. $23 (foreign $29). American Water Resources Association, 950 Herndon Pky., Ste. 300, Herndon, VA 22070-5531. TEL 703-904-1225. FAX 703-904-1228. **Document type:** newsletter.
    Description: Disseminates information relating to water resources science and monitors news affecting the water resources profession.

333.91 551.4 614.7
620   US   ISSN 0887-686X
GB651
HYDROLOGICAL SCIENCE AND TECHNOLOGY. 1985. q. $100. American Institute of Hydrology, 3416 University Ave., S.E., Minneapolis, MN 55414-3328. TEL 612-379-1030. FAX 612-379-0169. Ed.Bd. adv.; charts; illus.; stat. circ. 400. (back issues avail.) **Document type:** academic/scholarly publication.
—BLDSC (4347.627000).
    Description: Papers communicating new ideas, findings, methods and techniques in all aspects of hydrology, hydrogeology and water resources.
    Refereed Serial

551.4   FR   ISSN 0246-1528
GB651   CODEN: HYCOEV
HYDROLOGIE CONTINENTALE. (Text in French; summaries in English) 1964. s.a. 270 F. (Institut Francais de Recherche Scientifique pour le Developpement en Cooperation) O R S T O M Editions - Diffusion, 72 Route d'Aulnay, 93143 Bondy Cedex, France. TEL 48-02-55-00. FAX 48-47-30-88. circ. 800. (back issues avail.) **Indexed:** Biol.Abstr., Deep Sea Res.& Oceanogr.Abstr., Geo.Abstr., IDA, INIS Atomind. **Document type:** academic/scholarly publication.
—BLDSC (4347.880000).
    Supersedes: Cahiers O R S T O M Serie Hydrologie (ISSN 0008-0381)

331.91   FR   ISSN 1164-8783
HYDROPLUS; magazine international de l'eau - international water review. (Text in English, French) 1988. m. (10/yr.). 600 F. (foreign 740 F.). Hydrocom, 13 rue Saint-Florentin, 75008 Paris, France. TEL 47-03-33-13. FAX 40-15-05-79. Ed. Christian Chesnot; Pub. Jean Jacques Lemoigne. adv.: B&W page 12800 F., color page 17000 F.; trim 210 x 297; adv. contact: Georges Henri Laureau. circ. 7,500. **Document type:** trade publication.
    Description: Listens to and informs water industrial professionals and provides a forum for reflection in the international water market.

627   NE   ISSN 0166-8439
H2O; tijdschrift voor watervoorziening en afvalwaterbehandeling. (Supplement avail.: Jaarboek voor de Waterleiding in Nederland) 1968. s-m. fl.164 (effective 1995). Vereniging van Exploitanten van Waterleidingbedrijven in Nederland, Postbus 70, 2280 AB Rijswijk, Netherlands. FAX 31-70-3953420. Ed. G.B. Vinke. adv.: B&W page fl.1770, color page fl.3430; trim 210 x 297. bk.rev. circ. 4,700. **Indexed:** Excerp.Med. (until 1992). **Document type:** trade publication.
—BLDSC (4352.700000); SWETS.
    Description: Publishes news, official announcemnets and other items of concern to professionals in the waste water treatment field, as well as government officials and members of related industries.

I C A S A L S NEWSLETTER. (International Center for Arid and Semiarid Land Studies) see *AGRICULTURE*

I C I D JOURNAL. (International Commission on Irrigation and Drainage) see *AGRICULTURE*

628.167   US
I D A NEWSLETTER. m. International Desalination Association, Box 387, Topsfield, MA 01983-0387. TEL 508-356-2727. FAX 508-356-9964. Ed. Patricia Burke.

I G W M C GROUND WATER MODELING NEWSLETTER. (International Ground Water Modeling Center) see *EARTH SCIENCES — Hydrology*

333.91   IS   ISSN 0333-5194
I O L R COLLECTED REPORTS. (Text in English) 1971. a. free. Israel Oceanographic and Limnological Research Ltd., P.O. Box 8030, Haifa 31080, Israel. TEL 972-4-515202. FAX 972-4-511911.

333.91   UK   ISSN 0254-0592
I W S A YEAR BOOK. (Text in English and French) 1979. a. £37 to non-members. International Water Supply Association, c/o L.R. Bays, Sec. Gen., 1 Queen Anne's Gate, London SW1H 9BT, England. TEL 0171-957-4567. FAX 0171-222-7243. Ed. L.R. Bays. adv. circ. 5,000. **Document type:** directory.
    Formerly: International Who's Who in Water Supply (ISSN 0260-4604)
    Description: Provides general information about the association, a list of members, committees, and regional associations. Includes a buyer's guide and editorials.

IDAHO CURRENTS. see *ENVIRONMENTAL STUDIES — Pollution*

WATER RESOURCES

627   IT   ISSN 0390-6655
TC1   CODEN: IDTEDH
IDROTECNICA; l'acqua nell'agricoltura, nell'igiene, nell'industria. 1930. bi-m. L.130000 (effective 1994). (Associazione Idrotecnica Italiana) Maggioli Editore, Viale Vespucci 12-n, Casella Postale 290, 47037 Rimini, Italy. TEL 0541-626777. FAX 0541-622020. Ed. Umberto Messina. adv.: B&W page L.1300000, color page L.2000000; trim 170 x 270.

627   II   ISSN 0019-5537
TC1   CODEN: IJPRA7
INDIAN JOURNAL OF POWER AND RIVER VALLEY DEVELOPMENT. 1950. m. $55. Books & Journals Private Ltd., 6-2 Madan St., Calcutta 700 072, India. Ed. P.K. Menon. adv.; bk.rev.; abstr.; charts; illus. circ. 2,662. (also avail. in microform from UMI; reprint service avail. from UMI) Indexed: Eng.Ind., Fluidex, Geotech.Abstr., INSPEC (1969-), Rural Recreat.Tour.Abstr., Soils & Fert., Sport Fish.Abstr., Wild.Rev., World Agri.Econ.& Rural Sociol.Abstr.
—BLDSC (4420.200000); Ei; UMI; UnCover.

333.91   PK   ISSN 0537-4715
INDUS. (Text in English) 1960. q. Rs.150. Water and Power Development Authority, WAPDA House, Shara-e-Quaid-e-Azam, Lahore, Pakistan. TEL 212900. TELEX 44869 WAPDA PK. Ed. Raziuddin Shaikh. adv.; illus.
   Description: Articles on water and power resources of the country and technical information on completed and on-going projects.

333.91 628.4   US   ISSN 1067-5337
TD897.5
INDUSTRIAL WASTEWATER. 1993. bi-m. Water Environment Federation, 601 Wythe St., Alexandria, VA 22314. TEL 703-684-2400. FAX 703-684-2492. Ed. Kimberly Roy. adv.: B&W page $2100, color page $3150; trim 8 3/16 x 11. circ. 20,000. **Document type**: trade publication.

627   US   ISSN 1058-3645
INDUSTRIAL WATER TREATMENT. 1990. bi-m. $18 in N. America (overseas $63). Tall Oaks Publishing, Inc., Box 621669, Littleton, CO 80162. TEL 303-973-6700. adv. circ. 14,000. **Document type**: trade publication.
—UMI. **CCC**.
   Description: For operators of boilers, cooling systems, and industrial processes using chemically treated water.

333.91   FR   ISSN 0012-9003
INFORMATION EAUX. 1949. 11/yr. 1600 F. (foreign 1750 F.). Office International de l'Eau, Direction de la Documentation et des Donnees, Rue Edouard Chamberland, 87065 Limoges Cedex, France. TEL 55-11-47-80. FAX 55-77-71-15. TELEX 590 357 FONDEAU F. Ed. Jean Antoine Faby. bk.rev.; charts. Indexed: GeoRef., Repindex, W.R.C.Inf. **Document type**: academic/scholarly publication, bibliography.
●Also available online. Vendor(s): European Space Agency (File no.73/AFEE).
—BLDSC (4493.565000).
   Formerly: Eaux et Industries.

INGEGNERIA AMBIENTALE. see *PUBLIC HEALTH AND SAFETY*

INGEGNERIA AMBIENTALE QUADERNI. see *PUBLIC HEALTH AND SAFETY*

627   MX   ISSN 0186-4076
TC28   CODEN: IHMEEB
INGENIERIA HIDRAULICA EN MEXICO. (Supplement avail.) (Text in Spanish; summaries in English) 1930. 3/yr. Mex.$60($25) for 3 yrs. (effective 1995). Instituto Mexicano de Tecnologia del Agua, Apdo. Postal No. 202, C.P. 65500, CIVAC, Morelos, Mexico. TEL 52-73-194000 ext. 553. FAX 52-73-194341. Ed. Alvaro Alberto Aldama Rodriguez. bk.rev.; adv.; charts; illus. circ. 3,700. (back issues avail.) Indexed: GeoRef, Repindex, Soils & Fert.
—Ei.
   Former titles (until 1978): Recursos Hidraulicos (ISSN 0020-1057); (until 1972): Ingenieria Hidraulica en Mexico; (until 1947): Irrigacion en Mexico.
   Description: Covers all aspects of hydraulic engineering.
   Refereed Serial

333.91 551.4   GW   ISSN 0343-8090
INSTITUT FUER WASSERWIRTSCHAFT, HYDROLOGIE UND LANDWIRTSCHAFTLICHEN WASSERBAU. MITTEILUNGEN. 1958. irreg. DM.50 per no. Institut fuer Wasserwirtschaft, Hydrologie und landwirtschaftlichen Wasserbau, Universitaet Hannover, Appelstr. 9A, 30167 Hannover, Germany. TEL 0511-7623728. FAX 0511-762-3731. TELEX 0923868-UNIHN-D. E-mail: runde@mbox.iww.uni-hannover.de. (back issues avail.) **Document type**: monographic series.

INSTITUTION OF ENGINEERS (INDIA). ENVIRONMENTAL ENGINEERING DIVISION. JOURNAL. see *PUBLIC HEALTH AND SAFETY*

333.91   RM
INSTITUTUL DE STUDII CERCETARI SI PROIECTARI PENTRU GOSPODARIREA APELOR. STUDII DE ECONOMIA APELOR. Continues a publication with the same title issued by: Institutul de Studii si Cercetari Pentru Imbunatatiri Funciare si Gospodarirea Apelor. (Text in Rumanian; summaries in English, French and Russian.) 1972. irreg. Institutul de Studii Cercetari si Proiectari Pentru Gospodarirea Apelor, Splaiul Indepentei 294, Sector 6, Bucharest 17, Rumania. illus.

628.1   PL   ISSN 0239-6238
INSTYTUT METEOROLOGII I GOSPODARKI WODNEJ. MATERIALY BADAWCZE. SERIA: GOSPODARKA WODNA I OCHRONA WOD/INSTITUTE OF METEOROLOGY AND WATER MANAGEMENT. RESEARCH PAPERS SERIES: WATER MANAGEMENT AND WATER PROTECTION. (Text in Polish; summaries in English) 1973. irreg. $15. Instytut Meteorologii i Gospodarki Wodnej - Institute of Meteorology and Water Management, 61 Podlesna St., 01-673 Warsaw, Poland. FAX 48-22-345466. TELEX 814331. circ. 200.
   Description: Articles on water management, water quality, water pollution, hydraulics, sanitary engineering, sewage, research works.

INSTYTUT METEOROLOGII I GOSPODARKI WODNEJ. WIADOMOSCI/INSTITUTE OF METEOROLOGY AND WATER MANAGEMENT. REPORTS. see *METEOROLOGY*

333.91 551.4   UV
INTERAFRICAN COMMITTEE FOR HYDRAULIC STUDIES. LIAISON BULLETIN. French edition: Comite Interafricain d'Etudes Hydrauliques. Bulletin de Liaison. 1970. q. 7000 Fr.CFA. Interafrican Committee for Hydraulic Studies, B.P. 369, Ouagadougou 01, Burkina Faso. TEL 30-71-12. TELEX 5277 BF. adv.; bk.rev.; bibl. circ. 700.

631.6   II   ISSN 0538-5768
INTERNATIONAL COMMISSION ON IRRIGATION AND DRAINAGE. REPORT. (Text in English and French) 1951. a. avail. only to qualified personnel. International Commission on Irrigation and Drainage - Commission Internationale des Irrigations et du Drainage, 48 Nyaya Marg, Chanakyapuri, New Delhi 110021, India. TEL 3016837. circ. 1,000 (controlled).
   Description: Contains administrative matters of the council meeting.

628.167 333.91   US   ISSN 1022-5404
INTERNATIONAL DESALINATION AND WATER REUSE QUARTERLY. 1991. q. $30. (International Desalination Association) Green Global Publications Inc., 15 Old Mill Rd., Westport, CT 06880. TEL 203-227-6500. FAX 203-227-6500. Ed. Floyd H. Meller. adv.: B&W page $2590, color page $3490; trim 8 x 10 3/4. circ. 6,605. **Document type**: trade publication.
   Description: Publishes technical information, case studies, equipment and product development. Reviews research advances to promote a better understanding of the potential of the desalination process and advances in water treatment for re-use.

333.91   US
TD403
INTERNATIONAL GROUND WATER TECHNOLOGY. 1969. m. $90. National Trade Publications, Inc., 13 Century Hill, Latham, NY 12110-2197. TEL 518-783-1281. FAX 518-783-1386. Ed. Susan Wheeler. adv.: B&W page $2500; trim 8 1/8 x 10 7/8. bk.rev.; charts; illus.; pat.; tr.lit.; circ. 10,000 (controlled). (also avail. in microform from UMI; reprint service avail. from UMI) **Indexed**: Excerp.Med., W.R.C.Inf. **Document type**: trade publication.
—UMI. **CCC**.
   Supersedes (in 1995): Ground Water Age (ISSN 0046-645X)

INTERNATIONAL INSTITUTE FOR LAND RECLAMATION AND IMPROVEMENT. PUBLICATION. see *AGRICULTURE — Crop Production And Soil*

INTERNATIONAL JOURNAL OF CLIMATOLOGY. see *METEOROLOGY*

553.72   NE   ISSN 1037-0544
INTERNATIONAL JOURNAL OF SALT LAKE RESEARCH. (Text in English) 1992. q. fl.315 to institutions; $202 to institutions in U.S. (effective 1996). Kluwer Academic Publishers, Postbus 17, 3300 AA Dordrecht, Netherlands. TEL 31-78-392392. FAX 31-78-392254. E-mail: SERVICES@WKAP.NL. (Dist. by: Kluwer Academic Publishers Group, P.O. Box 322, 3300 AH Dordrecht, Netherlands. TEL 31-78-392392. FAX 31-78-546474; N. America dist. addr.: Box 358, Accord Sta., Hingham, MA 02018-0358. TEL 617-871-6600. FAX 617-871-6528) Ed. W.D. Williams. (back issues avail.) **Document type**: academic/scholarly publication.
—**CCC**.
   Description: Publishes original research on inland (non-marine) saline waters and environments, including topics of chemical, biological, geological, geochemical and hydrological interest, as well as conservation, management and economic issues.
   Refereed Serial

INTERNATIONAL JOURNAL OF WATER JET TECHNOLOGY. see *ENGINEERING — Hydraulic Engineering*

333.91   UK   ISSN 0790-0627
INTERNATIONAL JOURNAL OF WATER RESOURCES DEVELOPMENT. Online edition (ISSN 1360-0648) 1983. q. £44 to individuals; institutions £158 (effective 1996). Carfax Publishing Co., P.O. Box 25, Abingdon, Oxon. OX14 3UE, England. TEL 01235-555335. FAX 01235-553559. (Subscr. in N. America to: Carfax Publishing Co., 875-81 Massachusetts Ave., Cambridge, MA 02139) Ed. Asit K. Biswas. (also avail. in microform from UMI; back issues avail.) **Indexed**: Abstr.Rural Dev.Trop., Agri.Eng.Abstr., Energy Rev., Environ.Abstr., Environ.Per.Bibl. (1991-), Irr.& Drain.Abstr., Rice Abstr., Soils & Fert., Sport Fish.Abstr., Wild.Rev. **Document type**: academic/scholarly publication.
●Also available online.
—CIS; Ei; Faxon; SWETS; UMI; UnCover. **CCC**.
   Description: Covers all aspects of water development and management in both industrialized and developing nations.
   Refereed Serial

333.91 628.44   CN
INTERNATIONAL SYMPOSIUM ON WASTEWATER TREATMENT. (Text in English, French) a. free. Environment Canada, E P Publications, Ottawa, ON K1A 0H3, Canada. FAX 819-953-9029. circ. 1,000. **Document type**: government publication.

627   IS
INTERNATIONAL WATER & IRRIGATION REVIEW. (Text in English) 1981. q. $60 (effective 1994). Amir Cohen Advertising Co. Ltd., P.O. Box 21051, 55 Weizmann St., Tel Aviv 61210, Israel. TEL 972-3-6953192. FAX 972-3-6956116. Ed. Joshua Jacobson. adv. contact: Erika Cohen. circ. 14,215. **Indexed**: Irr.& Drain.Abstr. **Document type**: trade publication.
—BLDSC (4551.704000); Ei.
   Formerly (until 1993): Water and Irrigation Review (ISSN 0334-5807)
   Description: Articles on all aspects of water and irrigation technology.

6552 WATER RESOURCES

333.91 US ISSN 0074-9575
TD201 CODEN: PWWPAY
INTERNATIONAL WATER CONFERENCE. PROCEEDINGS. 1941. a. $55 (foreign $65). Engineers' Society of Western Pennsylvania, International Water Conference, 337 Fourth Ave., Pittsburgh, PA 15222-2097. TEL 412-261-0710. FAX 412-261-1606. adv.; cum.index: 1940-1974. circ. 500. Indexed: Chem.Abstr. **Document type:** proceedings.
—BLDSC (6847.040000); CASDDS; Ei.
Description: Provides current technological updates and case studies dealing with industrial water treatment, use and reuse for both industrial and engineering purposes.

627.8 UK ISSN 0306-400X
TK1081 CODEN: IWPCDM
INTERNATIONAL WATER POWER AND DAM CONSTRUCTION. 1949. m. £93($226) Reed Business Publishing Group (Subsidiary of: Reed Elsevier group), Quadrant House, The Quadrant, Sutton, Surrey SM2 5AS, England. TEL 0181-652-3111. FAX 0181-652-8904. (Subscr. to: Stuart House, 35 Perrymount Rd., Haywards Heath, W. Sussex RH19 3BN, England. TEL 01444-445566) Ed. Janet Dansie. adv.; bk.rev.; abstr.; charts; illus.; index. circ. 4,014. (also avail. in microform from UMI; reprint service avail. from UMI) **Indexed:** Abstr.J.Earthq.Eng., Br.Tech.Ind., Energy Info.Abstr., Eng.Ind., Environ.Abstr., Fluidex, Fuel & Energy Abstr., Geo.Abstr., Geol.Abstr., Geotech.Abstr., IDA, INSPEC, Intl.Civil Eng.Abstr., ISMEC, Sel.Water Res.Abstr., Soft.Abstr.Eng., W.R.C.Inf. **Document type:** trade publication.
—BLDSC (4551.705000); CIS; Ei; Faxon; SWETS; UnCover. CCC.
Formerly: Water Power (ISSN 0043-1338)
Description: Practical and theoretical articles and news concerning all aspects of hydro-electric developments and large dam construction throughout the world. Coverage of research into hydraulics, hydraulic machinery, wave and tidal power.

333.91 US ISSN 0893-8776
INTERNATIONAL WATER REPORT. 1978. q. $47 (foreign $57) (effective Jan. 1995) (free to subscribers of Water Newsletter). Water Information Center, Inc., 1099 18th St., Ste. 2150, Denver, CO 80202. TEL 303-391-8799. FAX 303-294-1239. Ed. Judith M. Schoeck. bk.rev. **Document type:** newsletter.
—CCC.

620 II ISSN 0021-1664
IRRIGATION AND POWER. (Text in English) 1943. q. $100. Central Board of Irrigation and Power, c/o Member Secretary, Malcha Marg, Chanakyapuri, New Delhi 110 021, India. TEL 11-3015984. FAX 91-11-3016347. TELEX CBIP@CBIPDEL.UUNET.IN. (Subscr. to: Department of Publication, Civil Lines, Delhi 110 054, India) Ed. C.V.J. Varma. adv.; bk.rev.; charts; illus.; index. circ. 4,500. (reprint service avail. from UMI) **Indexed:** Agri.Eng.Abstr., C.R.I.Abstr., C.R.I.Curr.Cont., Chem.Abstr., Eng.Ind., Fluidex, Geo.Abstr., Geotech.Abstr., Herb.Abstr., Rice Abstr. **Document type:** academic/scholarly publication.

IRRIGATION JOURNAL (VAN NUYS). see AGRICULTURE — Crop Production And Soil

627 630 UK ISSN 0265-5136
IRRIGATION NEWS. 1981. s-a. £10. U.K. Irrigation Association, c/o Silsoe College, Silsoe, Beds. MK45 4DT, England. TEL 01525-863290. FAX 01525-863001. TELEX 826838 SILCAM G. Ed. M.K.V. Carr. adv.; bk.rev.; cum.index: vols.1-10, 10-20. circ. 1,000. (back issues avail.) **Document type:** academic/scholarly publication.
—BLDSC (4580.969000).

627 PK
IRRIGATION RESEARCH INSTITUTE, LAHORE. REPORT. 1973. irreg. Irrigation Research Institute, The Mall, Lahore, Pakistan.

IRRIGATION SCIENCE. see AGRICULTURE

631 627 IT ISSN 0394-9338
IRRIGAZIONE E DRENAGGIO. (Text in Italian; summaries in English) 1954. q. L.69000 (effective 1996). (Centro Internazionale Studi sull'Irrigazione) Edagricole S.p.A., Via Emilia Levante 31, 40139 Bologna, Italy. TEL 39-51-492211. FAX 39-51-493660. Ed. Ariosto Degan. adv.: B&W page L.1000000, color page L.1450000; 185 x 247. bk.rev.; charts; illus.; index. circ. 8,600. **Indexed:** Agri.Eng.Abstr., Field Crop Abstr., Hort.Abstr., Irr.& Drain.Abstr., Rural Recreat.Tour.Abstr., Soils & Fert., Soyabean Abstr., World Agri.Econ.& Rural Sociol.Abstr.
Formerly: Irrigazione (ISSN 0021-1680)

ISRAEL. METEOROLOGICAL SERVICE. RAINFALL SEASON. see METEOROLOGY

JOURNAL OF AGRICULTURE AND WATER RESEARCH. PLANT PRODUCTION. see AGRICULTURE

JOURNAL OF AGRICULTURE AND WATER RESOURCES RESEARCH. ANIMAL PRODUCTION. see AGRICULTURE

JOURNAL OF AGRICULTURE AND WATER RESOURCES RESEARCH. SOIL AND WATER RESOURCES. see AGRICULTURE

JOURNAL OF AQUARICULTURE AND AQUATIC SCIENCES. see BIOLOGY

JOURNAL OF AQUATIC ECOSYSTEM HEALTH. see ENVIRONMENTAL STUDIES

JOURNAL OF HYDRAULIC RESEARCH. see ENGINEERING — Hydraulic Engineering

JOURNAL OF SOIL AND WATER CONSERVATION. see AGRICULTURE — Crop Production And Soil

JOURNAL OF SOIL AND WATER CONSERVATION IN INDIA. see CONSERVATION

627 US ISSN 1063-455X
TD204
JOURNAL OF WATER CHEMISTRY AND TECHNOLOGY. English translation of: Khimiya i Tekhnologiya Vody (RU ISSN 0204-3556) 1981. m. $1060 (effective 1996). (Russian Academy of Sciences, RU) Allerton Press, Inc., 150 Fifth Ave., New York, NY 10011. TEL 212-924-3950. FAX 212-463-9684. (Co-sponsor: Ukrainian Academy of Sciences, KR) Ed. V.V. Goncharuk. bk.rev.; charts; illus.; pat. **Indexed:** Sel.J.Water, W.R.C.Inf. **Document type:** academic/scholarly publication.
—BLDSC (0415.401000); Ei; SWETS; UnCover. CCC.
Formerly: Soviet Journal of Water Chemistry and Technology (ISSN 0734-1679)

JOURNAL OF WATER RESOURCES. see EARTH SCIENCES — Hydrology

333.91 US
KANSAS. WATER OFFICE. FACT SHEET. s-m. Water Office, 109 S.W. 9th St., Ste. 300, Topeka, KS 66612-1249. TEL 913-296-3185. FAX 913-296-0878. **Document type:** government publication.

333.91 US
KANSAS WATER PLAN. a. Water Office, 109 S.W. Ninth St., Ste. 300, Topeka, KS 66612-1249. TEL 913-296-3187. FAX 913-296-0878. Dir. Stephen A. Hurst. **Document type:** government publication.

333.91 US ISSN 0160-2659
TC424.K2
KANSAS WATER RESOURCES RESEARCH INSTITUTE. ANNUAL REPORT. 1964. a. free. Kansas Water Resources Research Institute, 144 Waters Hall, Kansas State Univ., Manhattan, KS 66506-4007. Ed. Hyde S. Jacobs. circ. 65. **Indexed:** GeoRef. **Document type:** corporate report.

627 JA ISSN 0287-9859
KASEN/RIVERS. (Text in Japanese) 1942. m. 720 Yen per no. Nihon Kasen Kyokai - Japan Rivers Association, 2-13, Hayabusa-cho, Chiyoda-ku, Tokyo 102, Japan.

551.48 JA ISSN 0914-7861
KASEN JOHO KENKYUJO HOKOKU/INSTITUTE OF RIVER AND BASIN INTEGRATED COMMUNICATIONS. REPORT. (Text in English, Japanese; summaries in English) 1987. a. Kasen Joho Senta - Foundation of River and Basin Integrated Communications, 1-3, Kojimachi, Chiyoda-ku, Tokyo 102, Japan.

624 JA
KASEN KANRI KENSHU TEKISUTO. (Text in Japanese) a. Nihon Kasen Kyokai - Japan Rivers Association, 2-13, Hayabusa-cho, Chiyoda-ku, Tokyo 102, Japan.

627 JA ISSN 0910-0938
KASEN REBYU/RIVERS REVIEW. (Text in Japanese) 1955. q. 1900 Yen. Shin Koronsha, 2-1-607, Ebisu Nishi 1-chome, Shibuya-ku, Tokyo 150, Japan.

628.1 UK ISSN 1352-7169
KEY NOTE REPORT: WATER UTILITIES. Variant title: Water Utilities. 1993. irreg. £185. Key Note Publications Ltd., Field House, 72 Oldfield Rd., Hampton, Middlesex TW12 2HQ, England. TEL 0181-783-0755. FAX 0181-783-1720. **Document type:** trade publication.
●Also available online.
Also available on CD-ROM.

KORRESPONDENZ ABWASSER; Wasser - Abwasser - Abfall. see ENVIRONMENTAL STUDIES

333.91 628 US ISSN 1040-2381
CODEN: LRMAEY
LAKE & RESERVOIR MANAGEMENT.* 2/yr. $55 to individuals in N. America (overseas $65); non-profits $65; libraries $75. North American Lake Management Society, 13649 Dornock Ct., Herndon, VA 22071-3376. Ed. Roger Bachmann. circ. 2,000. **Indexed:** Environ.Abstr., Sport Fish.Abstr., Wild.Rev., Zoo.Rec.
—BLDSC (5143.925000).
Formerly (until 1987): North American Lake Management Society Conference. Proceedings (ISSN 0743-8141)
Description: For professionals and scientists in the lake management field.

333.91 628 AT ISSN 1320-5331
▼**LAKE AND RESERVOIR MANAGEMENT.** 1994. 2/yr. Aus.$352($250) (24000 Yen) (effective 1996). Blackwell Science Pty Ltd, P.O. Box 378, Carlton South, Vic. 3053, Australia. TEL 61-3-93470300. FAX 61-3-93493016. (back issues avail.) **Document type:** academic/scholarly publication.
—BLDSC (5143.946330). CCC.

LAKE LINE. see CONSERVATION

LAND & WATER; magazine vook civiele en milieutechniek. see ENVIRONMENTAL STUDIES

LANDSCAPE & IRRIGATION. see AGRICULTURE — Crop Production And Soil

LEGAL TIDES. see ENVIRONMENTAL STUDIES

LES. see FORESTS AND FORESTRY

333.91 FR
LEXIQUE TRILINGUE DE L'EAU. a. 350 F. (foreign 333.27 F.). Pierre Johanet et ses Fils, 7, av. Franklin Roosevelt, 75008 Paris, France. TEL 43-59-08-91. FAX 42-25-59-47.

LITERATURBERICHTE UEBER WASSER, ABWASSER, LUFT UND FESTE ABFALLSTOFFE. see ENVIRONMENTAL STUDIES — Pollution

628 551.4 US
LOUISIANA WATER RESOURCES RESEARCH INSTITUTE. ANNUAL REPORT. 1965. a. $10 (typically set in Sep.). Louisiana Water Resources Research Institute, 3418 Ceba Bldg., Louisiana State University, Baton Rouge, LA 70803. FAX 504-388-5990. (Co-sponsor: U.S. Department of Interior) circ. controlled. (reprint service avail. from NTI) **Indexed:** GeoRef.

620 333.91 US ISSN 0025-0805
MAINE WATER UTILITIES ASSOCIATION. JOURNAL. 1924. 6/yr. membership. Maine Water Utilities Association, 225 Douglass St., Portland, ME 04104. Ed. J. Ronald Caron. adv. circ. 400.

MAJI REVIEW. see ENERGY

333.91 US ISSN 0090-5968
TC424.C2
MANAGEMENT OF THE CALIFORNIA STATE WATER PROJECT. (Subseries of California. Dept. of Water Resources. Bulletin) 1963. a. price varies. Department of Water Resources, Box 942836, Sacramento, CA 94236-0001. TEL 916-445-9248. illus.; stat.; circ. controlled. (back issues avail.)

354 CN ISSN 0318-3912
TD227.M3
MANITOBA. WATER SERVICES BOARD. ANNUAL REPORT. 1973. a. free. Water Services Board, 2022 Currie Blvd., Box 22080, Brandon, MB R7A 6Y9, Canada. FAX 204-726-6290. circ. 300. **Document type:** government publication.

MARINE AND FRESHWATER BEHAVIOUR AND PHYSIOLOGY. see BIOLOGY

333.91 US ISSN 0076-4817
MARYLAND. GEOLOGICAL SURVEY. WATER RESOURCES BASIC DATA REPORT. 1966. irreg., latest no.18. price varies. Maryland Geological Survey, 2300 St. Paul St., Baltimore, MD 21218. TEL 301-554-5500. FAX 301-554-5502. **Indexed:** GeoRef.

MARYLAND TOMORROW. see HOUSING AND URBAN PLANNING

333.91 IS
MAYIM VE HASHKAIYA. 1975. m. IS.36. Water Works Association, 8 King Saul Blvd., Tel Aviv, Israel. FAX 03-250530. Ed. Yoseff Gur-Arie. adv.

627 RU ISSN 0235-2524
TC1 CODEN: MVKHEG
MELIORATSIYA I VODNOE KHOZYAISTVO. (Text in Russian; summaries in English) 1949. bi-m. $71 (effective 1996). Izdatel'stvo Kolos, Sadovo-Sasskaya, 18, 107807 Moscow, Russia. (Dist. by: Mezhdunarodnaya Kniga, B. Yakimanka 39, 117049 Moscow, Russia; Dist. in U.S. by: Victor Kamkin Inc., 4956 Boiling Brook Pkwy., Rockville, MD 20852. TEL 301-881-5973. FAX 301-881-1637) (Co-sponsor: Ministerstvo Sel'skogo Khozjaistva) Ed. E.A. Nesterov. adv.; bk.rev.; bibl.; charts; illus.; maps; stat. circ. 36,500. **Indexed:** Chem.Abstr., Field Crop Abstr., Geotech.Abstr., Herb.Abstr., Soils & Fert.
—CASDDS.
Formerly (until 1988): Gidrotekhnika i Melioratsiya (ISSN 0016-9722)

628 US ISSN 0271-9606
MICHIGAN STATE UNIVERSITY. INSTITUTE OF WATER RESEARCH. ANNUAL REPORT. 1966. a. price varies. Michigan State University, Institute of Water Research, 334 Natural Resources Bldg., East Lansing, MI 48824. TEL 517-353-3744. Ed. Frank M. D'ltri. illus. circ. 150. (processed; reprint service avail. from UMI) **Indexed:** GeoRef.

628 US ISSN 0580-9746
MICHIGAN STATE UNIVERSITY. INSTITUTE OF WATER RESEARCH. TECHNICAL REPORTS. 1968. a. price varies. Michigan State University, Institute of Water Research, 334 Natural Resources Bldg., East Lansing, MI 48824. TEL 517-353-3742. (Dist. by: National Technical Information Service, 5285 Port Royal Rd., Springfield, VA 22151) (back issues avail.; reprint service avail. from UMI) **Indexed:** GeoRef. **Document type:** monographic series.

628 US
MICHIGAN WATER ENVIRONMENT MATTERS. vol.20, 1964. q. $30 membership. Michigan Water Environment Association, P.O. Box 82410, Rochester, MI 48308-2410. Ed. Kevin Donovan. adv. contact: Karen Flaherty. bk.rev.; illus. circ. 1,200. **Document type:** newsletter.
Formerly: Wastewater Works News (ISSN 0043-1028)
Description: Deals with water quality issues in Michigan for association members.
Refereed Serial

333.91 LE ISSN 0255-8564
MIDDLE EAST AND WORLD WATER DIRECTORY. (Text in English) 1980. biennial. $110. Chatila Publishing House, P.O. Box 135121, Chouran, Beirut, Lebanon. TEL 961-1-352413. FAX 961-1-352419. TELEX 23008 MIYAH LE. Ed. Fathi Chatila. adv. circ. 5,100. **Document type:** directory.
Description: Serves as a link between importers, manufacturers, wholesalers, contractors and consulting engineers engaged in the water and sewerage industry in the Middle East and Africa.

333.91 551.4 US ISSN 0076-9614
CODEN: MGWAAE
MISSOURI. DIVISION OF GEOLOGICAL SURVEY AND WATER RESOURCES. WATER RESOURCES REPORT. 1956. irreg., no.36, 1985. price varies. Department of Natural Resources, Division of Geology and Land Survey, Box 250, Rolla, MO 65401. TEL 314-368-2125. Ed. Dwight Weaver.

628.1 JA ISSN 0288-3112
MIZU SHIGEN KAIHATSU KODAN. SHIKENJO HOKOKU/WATER RESOURCES DEVELOPMENT PUBLIC CORP. LABORATORY REPORT. (Text in Japanese) 1983. a. Mizu Shigen Kaihatsu Kodan Shikenjo, 936, Jinde, Urawa-shi, Saitama-ken 338, Japan. **Indexed:** IDA.

628.1 JA
MIZU SHIGEN KANKYO GAKKAI KENKYU TAIKAI KOEN GAIYOSHU/PROCEEDINGS OF SYMPOSIUM ON WATER RESOURCES AND ENVIRONMENT. (Text in Japanese) 1984. a. Mizu Shigen Kankyo Gakkai - Japanese Association for Water Resources and Environment, 16-12-803 Nishishinjuku 6-chome, Shinjuku-ku, Tokyo 160, Japan. **Document type:** proceedings.

628.1 JA ISSN 0913-8277
MIZU SHIGEN KANKYO KENKYU/JOURNAL OF WATER AND ENVIRONMENTAL ISSUES. (Text in English, Japanese; summaries in English) 1987. a. 1500 Yen. Mizu Shigen Kankyo Gakkai - Japanese Association for Water Resources and Environment, 16-12-803 Nishishinjuku 6-chome, Shinjuku-ku, Tokyo 160, Japan.

628.1 363.3 JA ISSN 0285-4872
MIZU SHIGEN KENKYU SENTA KENKYU HOKOKU/WATER RESOURCES CENTER. RESEARCH REPORT. (Text in Japanese) 1981. a. Kyoto Daigaku, Bosai Kenkyujo, Fuzoku Mizu Shigen Kenkyu Senta - Kyoto University, Disaster Prevention Research Institute, Water Resources Research Center, Gokasho, Uji-shi, Kyoto 611, Japan. Ed. S. Ikebuchi. circ. 500. **Document type:** academic/scholarly publication.

628.1 JA
MIZU TO TOMONI. (Text in Japanese) 1971. m. 500 Yen per no. Mizu Shigen Kaihatsu Kodan - Water Resources Development Public Corp., 3-3, Akasaka 5-chome, Minato-ku, Tokyo 107, Japan.

629 333.91 US ISSN 0275-6633
MONO LAKE COMMITTEE NEWSLETTER. 1978. q. $25. Mono Lake Committee, P.O. Box 29, Lee Vining, CA 93541. TEL 619-647-6595. FAX 619-647-6377. Ed. Geoffrey McQuilkin. adv.; bk.rev.; charts; illus.; stat. circ. 22,000. **Document type:** newsletter.
Description: Covers the damaging effects of the excessive diversion of water from Mono Lake, and the struggle, legal and scientific, to protect a valuable and endangered ecosystem.

628 US
MONTANA WATER RESOURCES CENTER. ANNUAL REPORT. 1982. a. Montana Water Resources Center, Montana State University, 208 Cobleigh Hall, Bozeman, MT 59717. TEL 406-994-6690. abstr.
Formerly: Montana Water Resources Research Center. Annual Report.

628 US
MONTANA WATER RESOURCES CENTER. TECHNICAL REPORTS. 1966. 5/yr. Montana Water Resources Center, Montana State University, 208 Cobleigh Hall, Bozeman, MT 59717. TEL 406-994-6690. FAX 406-994-6105. circ. 125. (processed)
Formerly: Montana Water Resources Research Center. Technical Report.

628.1 UK ISSN 1358-3263
N R A ANNUAL R & D REVIEW. 1991. a. £22. National Rivers Authority, Rivers House, Waterside Dr., Aztec West, Almondsbury, Bristol BS12 4UD, England. TEL 01454-624400. FAX 01454-624409. **Document type:** bulletin.

628.1 UK
N R A ANNUAL REPORT. a. National Rivers Authority, Rivers House, Waterside Dr., Aztec West, Almondsbury, Bristol BS12 4UD, England. TEL 01454-624400. FAX 01454-624409. **Document type:** corporate report.

628.1 UK
N R A CORPORATE PLAN. a. National Rivers Authority, Rivers House, Waterside Dr., Aztec West, Almondsbury, Bristol BS12 4UD, England. TEL 01454-624400. FAX 01454-624409. **Document type:** corporate report.

N R A FISHERIES STATISTICS. (National Rivers Authority) see FISH AND FISHERIES — Abstracting, Bibliographies, Statistics

628.1 UK
N R A RESEARCH & DEVELOPMENT REPORT. irreg., no.18, 1995. £8. National Rivers Authority, Rivers House, Waterside Dr., Aztec West, Almondsbury, Bristol BS12 4UD, England. TEL 01454-624400. FAX 01454-624409. **Document type:** monographic series.

628.1 UK
N R A WATER QUALITY SERIES. 1991. irreg., no.20, 1994. £9.95. National Rivers Authority, Rivers House, Waterside Dr., Aztec West, Almondsbury, Bristol BS12 4UD, England. TEL 01454-624400. FAX 01454-624409. adv. **Document type:** monographic series.

627 JA
NAGOYA DAIGAKU SUIKEN KAGAKU KENKYUJO NENPO/NAGOYA UNIVERSITY. WATER RESEARCH INSTITUTE. ANNUAL REPORT. (Text in Japanese) 1974. a. Nagoya Daigaku, Suiken Kagaku Kenkyujo - Nagoya University, Water Research Institute, Furo-cho, Chikusaku, Nagoya-shi, Aichi-ken 464, Japan. illus.

627 665.5 622 US ISSN 0279-7739
NATIONAL DRILLERS BUYERS GUIDE. 1980. m. $80 (foreign £150). National Drillers Buyers Guide, Box 400, Hwy. 90 East, Bonifay, FL 32425. TEL 904-547-4244. FAX 904-547-5277. Ed. W.C. "Doc" Faison. adv. contact: Priscilla "Cissy" Adams. charts; illus.; tr.lit. circ. 39,200. (tabloid format) **Document type:** trade publication.
Description: Provides information for the water well drilling, monitoring, shallow oil and gas, mining and hydrology industries.

628.1 CN ISSN 0839-5950
TD226
NATIONAL WATER RESEARCH INSTITUTE. CURRENT RESEARCH. 1987. a. National Water Research Institute, P.O. Box 5050, Burlington, ON L7R 4L7, Canada. TEL 905-336-4884. FAX 905-336-6444. bibl. **Document type:** bulletin.

333.7 US
▼**NATIONAL WATER RIGHTS DIGEST**; covering water rights legislation, adjudication and transfer. 1995. m. $129. Ridenbaugh Press, Box 2276, Boise, ID 83701. TEL 208-338-9700. FAX 208-338-9769. E-mail: stapilus@cerfnet.com. Ed. Randy Stapilus. (back issues avail.) **Document type:** newsletter.
●Also available online.

333.9 US
NEBRASKA. NATURAL RESOURCES COMMISSION. STATE WATER PLANNING AND REVIEW PROCESS. irreg. Natural Resources Commission, 301 Centennial Mall South, Box 94876, Lincoln, NE 68509. TEL 402-471-2081. illus. **Document type:** government publication.
Formerly: Nebraska. Natural Resources Commission. State Water Plan Publication (Lincoln) (ISSN 0092-6442)
Description: Technical data on title subjects used in future planning of resources.

NEUE D E L I W A - ZEITSCHRIFT; Fachzeitschrift fuer die Energie- und Wasserversorgung. see ENERGY

WATER RESOURCES

628.1 US ISSN 0028-4939
TD201 CODEN: JNEWA6
NEW ENGLAND WATER WORKS ASSOCIATION. JOURNAL. 1882. q. $20 (foreign $28). New England Water Works Association, 64 Dilla St., Milford, MA 01757. TEL 508-478-6996. FAX 508-634-8643. Ed. Peter Karalekas, Jr. adv.; bk.rev.; charts; illus.; cum.index every 10 yrs.; circ. 2,700 (paid). (also avail. in microform from UMI,PMC; reprint service avail. from UMI) **Indexed:** Biol.Abstr., Chem.Abstr., Eng.Ind., Excerp.Med., Fluidex, GeoRef., Ocean.Abstr., Pollut.Abstr., Sel.Water Res.Abstr., W.R.C.Inf.
● Also available on CD-ROM. Producer(s): Knight-Ridder, Inc.
—BLDSC (4832.000000); CASDDS; Ei; Faxon; UMI; UnCover.

NEW JERSEY WASTEWATER TREATMENT TRUST. ANNUAL REPORT. see ENVIRONMENTAL STUDIES — Waste Management

333.91 551.94 US ISSN 0897-5094
NEW WAVE (COLLEGE STATION). 1988. q. free. Texas Water Resources Institute, c/o Texas A & M Univ., Texas Agricultural Experiment Sta., College Station, TX 77843-2118. TEL 409-845-8571. FAX 409-845-8554. E-mail: rjensen@tamu.edu. Ed. Ric Jensen. bk.rev. circ. 3,500. **Document type:** academic/scholarly publication, newsletter.
● Also available online.
Description: Covers water quality, water demand in communities, groundwater problems, and microscopic water plant and animal life. Focuses on water-related research at all universities in Texas.

628.1 JA ISSN 0288-9455
NIHON NO KAWA/RIVERS IN JAPAN. (Text in Japanese) 1973. q. Nihon Kasen Kaihatsu Chosakai - Japanese Research Association for River Development, 44-6-403, Sekiguchi 1-chome, Bunkyo-ku, Tokyo 112, Japan.

627 US
NORTHWATER; notes on water resources research in Alaska. 1974. s-a. free. University of Alaska, Institute of Northern Engineering, Water Research Center, Fairbanks, AK 99775-1760. TEL 907-474-7775. FAX 907-474-6087. circ. 1,800. (back issues avail.)

OCEAN SCIENCE, RESOURCES AND TECHNOLOGY. see EARTH SCIENCES — Oceanography

628 AU
CODEN: OSWAAI
OESTERREICHISCHE WASSER- UND ABFALLWIRTSCHAFT. (Text in German) 1949. m. DM.204($148) (effective 1996). Springer-Verlag, Sachsenplatz 4-6, Postfach 89, A-1201 Vienna, Austria. TEL 0222-3302415. FAX 0222-3302426. (N. American subscr. to: Journal Fulfillment Services, Box 2485, Secaucus, NJ 07096-2491. TEL 800-777-4643. FAX 201-348-4505; Elsewhere: Heidelberger Platz 3, 14197 Berlin, Germany. TEL 030-8207-1. FAX 030-821-4091) Ed.Bd. bk.rev.; bibl.; charts; illus.; index. (also avail. in microform from UMI; reprint service avail. from ISI) **Indexed:** Biol.Abstr., Chem.Abstr., Fluidex, Geo.Abstr., Geol.Abstr., Geotech.Abstr., Intl.Civil Eng.Abstr., Sel.Water Res.Abstr., Soft.Abstr.Eng. **Document type:** academic/scholarly publication.
—CCC.
Formerly (until 1994): Oesterreichische Wasserwirtschaft (ISSN 0029-9588)
Description: Discusses all technical, scientific and legal issues of common waterways.

628.1 UK
▼**OFWAT OCCASIONAL PAPER.** 1994. irreg. £3. Office of Water Services, Centre City Tower, 7 Hill St., Birmingham B5 4UA, England. TEL 0121-625-1300. **Document type:** corporate report.

333.9 US ISSN 0092-2528
TC424.O5
OKLAHOMA WATER RESOURCES RESEARCH INSTITUTE. ANNUAL REPORT. Key Title: Annual Report of the Oklahoma Water Resources Research Institute. 1966. a. free. Oklahoma Water Resources Research Institute, 003 Life Sciences E., Stillwater, OK 74078. TEL 405-744-9994. FAX 405-744-7673. Ed. Carol Engle. illus. circ. 200. **Document type:** academic/scholarly publication.

333.91 US ISSN 0887-2104
OPERATIONS FORUM; a W E F publication for wastewater professionals. 1984. m. $79 (foreign $99). Water Environment Federation, 601 Wythe St., Alexandria, VA 22314-1994. TEL 703-684-2400. FAX 703-684-2492. Ed. Lisa Preston. adv.; B&W page $1950, color page $3000; trim 8 3/16 x 10 7/8. tr.lit. circ. 20,000. (back issues avail.; reprint service avail.) **Indexed:** Excerp.Med., Repindex.
—BLDSC (6268.790000); Faxon.
Description: Features three plant profiles each month according to region, common process, or size.

OPFLOW. see ENGINEERING

333.91 JA
OSAKA MUNICIPAL WATER WORKS BUREAU. WATER EXAMINATION LABORATORY. ANNUAL REPORT. (Text in Japanese) 1949. a. free. Osaka Municipal Water Works Bureau, Water Examination Laboratory, 1-3-14 Kunijima, Higasiyodogawa-ku, Osaka-shi 533, Japan. FAX 06-320-3259. Ed. Masashi Kajino. circ. 500. **Document type:** bulletin.

OZONE: SCIENCE AND ENGINEERING. see ENGINEERING — Chemical Engineering

PASSAIC RIVER REVIEW. see CONSERVATION

PENNSYLVANIA STATE UNIVERSITY. ENVIRONMENTAL RESOURCES RESEARCH INSTITUTE. NEWSLETTER. see CONSERVATION

PIPES AND PIPELINES INTERNATIONAL; pipes, hoses, tubes, pumps, valves. see PETROLEUM AND GAS

POLIMERY V MELIORATSII I VODNOM KHOZYAISTVE. see ENGINEERING — Hydraulic Engineering

333.011 627 PL
POLITECHNIKA KRAKOWSKA. MONOGRAFIE. SERIA: INZYNIERIA SANITARNA I WODNA. (Subseries of: Politechnika Krakowska. Monografie (ISSN 0860-097X)) (Text in Polish; summaries in English, French, German, Russian) 1985. irreg. price varies. Politechnika Krakowska, Ul. Warszawska 24, 31-155 Krakow, Poland. TEL 48-12-374289. FAX 48-12-335773. TELEX 322468 PK PL. bibl.; charts; illus. circ. 200. **Document type:** academic/scholarly publication, monographic series.

333.91 627 PL
POLITECHNIKA KRAKOWSKA. ZESZYTY NAUKOWE. INZYNIERIA SRODOWISKA. (Text in Polish; summaries in English, French, German and Russian) 1957. irreg. price varies. Politechnika Krakowska, Ul. Warszawska 24, 31-155 Krakow, Poland. TEL 48-12-374289. FAX 48-12-335773. TELEX 322468 PK PL. bibl.; charts; illus. circ. 200. **Document type:** academic/scholarly publication.
Former titles (until no.45, 1994): Politechnika Krakowska. Zeszyty Naukowe. Inzynieria Sanitarna i Wodna (ISSN 0867-177X); Politechnika Krakowska. Zeszyty Naukowe. Budownictwo Wodne i Inzynieria Sanitarna (ISSN 0137-1363)

628 PL ISSN 0079-3477
POLSKA AKADEMIA NAUK. KOMITET GOSPODARKI WODNEJ. PRACE I STUDIA. 1956. irreg., vol.11, 1972. price varies. Polska Akademia Nauk, Komitet Gospodarki Wodnej, Palac Kultury i Nauki, Pietro XX, pok.20-21, 00-901 Warsaw, Poland. (Dist. by: Ars Polona, Krakowskie Przedmiescie 7, 00-068 Warsaw, Poland)

628.167 333.91 US ISSN 1072-8627
HD1695.P56
POTOMAC BASIN REPORTER. 6/yr. free. Interstate Commission on the Potomac River Basin; 6110 Executive Blvd., Ste. 300, Rockville, MD 20852. TEL 301-984-1908. Ed. Curtis M. Dalpra. **Document type:** government publication.
Incorporates (in 1994): In the Anacostia Watershed (ISSN 1061-2513)
Description: Current events on Potomac River water quality, supply, recreation.

354.712 CN ISSN 0704-8726
TC427.P7
PRAIRIE PROVINCES WATER BOARD ANNUAL REPORT. (First report covers period Oct. 30, 1969-Mar. 31, 1972) 1972. a. free. Prairie Provinces Water Board, Rm. 201, 2050 Cornwall St., Regina, SK S4P 2K5, Canada. TEL 306-522-6671. circ. 400. **Document type:** corporate report.

PROBLEMY OSVOENIYA PUSTYN'. see AGRICULTURE

333.91 US
PURDUE UNIVERSITY. INDIANA WATER RESOURCES RESEARCH CENTER. ANNUAL REPORT. 1966. a. free. Purdue University, Indiana Water Resources Research Center, 1284 School of Civil Engineering, W. Lafayette, IN 47907-1284. TEL 317-494-8041. FAX 317-494-0395. Ed. Jeff R. Wright. circ. 230. (also avail. in microfiche)

QUALITY OF SERVICE REGULATION. see ENERGY — Electrical Energy

333.91 BE
LA RADIOACTIVITE DES PRINCIPALES SOURCES D'EAU MINERALE EN BELGIQUE. ETUDE. (Editions in Flemish, French) a. Ministere de la Sante Publique et de la Famille, Institut d'Hygiene et d'Epidemiologie - Ministerie van Volksgezondheid en van het Gezin, 14 rue Juliette Wytsman, B-1050 Brussels, Belgium. Eds. Dr. P. Binaux, Dr. P. Le Jeune.

333.91 AG ISSN 0048-6981
RECURSOS HIDRICOS. 1971. q. free. Secretaria de Recursos Naturales y Ambiante Humano, Av. Santa Fe 1548, Buenos Aires 1060, Argentina. Ed.Bd. charts; illus.

333.9 UK ISSN 0886-9375
TC530 CODEN: RRRMEP
REGULATED RIVERS: RESEARCH AND MANAGEMENT; an international journal devoted to river research and management. 1986. bi-m. $495 (foreign $495) (effective 1996). John Wiley & Sons Ltd., Journals, Baffins Ln., Chichester, W. Sussex PO19 1UD, England. TEL 01243-779777. FAX 01243-776128. TELEX 86290 WIBOOK G. (Subscr. in the Americas to: John Wiley & Sons, Ltd., 605 Third Ave., New York, NY 10158. TEL 212-850-6645. FAX 212-850-6021) Ed. G. Petts. adv.; bk.rev.; illus.; maps. circ. 270. (also avail. in microform from UMI; back issues avail.; reprint service avail. from SWZ) **Indexed:** Ecol.Abstr., Energy Info.Abstr., Environ.Abstr., Environ.Per.Bibl. (1990-), Geo.Abstr., Geol.Abstr., IDA, Sel.Water Res.Abstr., Sport Fish.Abstr., Wild.Rev., Zoo.Rec. **Document type:** academic/scholarly publication.
—BLDSC (7345.650000); Ei; Genuine Article; SWETS; UMI; UnCover. CCC.
Description: Devoted to interdisciplinary research and covers activity from the effects of major dams, weirs, canalization and more; includes original papers.
Refereed Serial

REINWATER. see ENVIRONMENTAL STUDIES — Pollution

REPORT ON FINANCIAL PERFORMANCE AND CAPITAL INVESTMENT OF THE WATER COMPANIES IN ENGLAND AND WALES. see BUSINESS AND ECONOMICS — Investments

REPORT ON THE INDUSTRIAL DIRECT DISCHARGES IN ONTARIO. see ENVIRONMENTAL STUDIES

REVISTA DE DERECHO DE MINAS Y AGUAS. see MINES AND MINING INDUSTRY

REVUE DES SCIENCES DE L'EAU; journal of water science. see EARTH SCIENCES — Hydrology

333.91 II ISSN 0970-9258
TC503
RIVER BEHAVIOUR AND CONTROL. (Text in English) vol.9, 1976. a. Department of Irrigation & Waterways, River Research Institute, 11-A Mirza Ghalib St., Calcutta 700087, India. circ. 300.
Description: News for research workers and field engineers. Covers hydraulics, hydrology, sedimentation and soil mechanics.

333.91 US ISSN 0898-8048
GB1201 CODEN: RIVREV
RIVERS; studies in the science, environmental policy and law of instream flow. 1990. q. $115 (foreign $130) (effective 1996). S E L & Associates, 19 Old Town Sq., Ste. 238, Ft. Collins, CO 80524-2471. TEL 970-224-1220. FAX 970-482-0251. Ed. Susan Lamb. adv.; bk.rev. circ. 410. (back issues avail.; reprint service avail. from WSH) **Indexed**: ASCA, Biol.Abstr., Curr.Ref.Fish Res., Ecol.Abstr., Environ.Abstr., Geo.Abstr., Sport Fish.Abstr., Wild.Rev., Zoo.Rec. **Document type**: academic/scholarly publication.
—BLDSC (7977.145000); Genuine Article; UnCover.
Description: Addresses issues of North American, European and Australian instream flow. Covers multiagency actions, water resource planning, fisheries biology, water law, riparian corridor management, and regulations involved with flow usage.
Refereed Serial

620 PL ISSN 0035-9394
TC7 CODEN: RZHTAE
ROZPRAWY HYDROTECHNICZNE/HYDROTECHNICAL TRANSACTIONS. (Text in various languages; summaries in English) 1956. irreg., vol.54, 1991. price varies. Polska Akademia Nauk, Instytut Budownictwa Wodnego - Polish Academy of Sciences, Institute of Hydroengineering, Ul. Koscierska 7, 80-952 Gdansk-Oliwa, Poland. (Dist. by: Ars Polona, Krakowskie Przedmiescie 7, 00-068 Warsaw, Poland) Ed. Ryszrd Zeidler. circ. 280. **Indexed**: Chem.Abstr., Fluidex, Geotech.Abstr., INSPEC (1968-). **Document type**: academic/scholarly publication, monographic series.
—BLDSC (8035.900000).

614.8 627.5 US ISSN 0270-4447
T55.A1
SAFETY NEWS (DENVER). 1937. q. membership. Bureau of Reclamation, Safety Office, Box 25007, D-7600 Denver, CO 80225. TEL 303-236-6774. charts; illus.; stat. circ. 550. **Indexed**: Bibl.Agri., C.I.S. Abstr., Sel.Water Res.Abstr.
—BLDSC (8067.248000).
Former titles: Reclamation Safety News (ISSN 0034-1436); Reclamation Safety Record.

627 JA
SAKUSEI. (Text in Japanese) 1967. irreg. Zenkoku Sakusei Kyokai - National Water Well Association of Japan, 5-1, Hatchobbori 2-chome, Chuo-ku, Tokyo 104, Japan.

333.91 YU ISSN 0408-9936
SAOPSTENJA. 1954. q. 11000 din.($90) Institut za Vodoprivredu Jaroslav Cerni, Ulica Jaroslava Cernija 80, 11223 Belgrade - Beli Potok, Yugoslavia. circ. 500.

SASKATCHEWAN HORIZONTAL WELL PRODUCTION REPORT. see *PETROLEUM AND GAS*

SASKATCHEWAN HORIZONTAL WELL SUMMARY. see *PETROLEUM AND GAS*

SCAN. see *AGRICULTURE — Crop Production And Soil*

SCIENCE ET CHANGEMENT PLANETAIRES, SECHERESSE. see *ENVIRONMENTAL STUDIES*

SCOOP. see *ENVIRONMENTAL STUDIES — Abstracting, Bibliographies, Statistics*

628.167 US ISSN 0720-0773
TD478
SEAWATER AND DESALTING. 1980. irreg. price varies. Springer-Verlag, 175 Fifth Ave., New York, NY 10010. TEL 212-460-1500. FAX 212-473-6272. (Also Berlin, Heidelberg, Vienna) (reprint service avail. from ISI) **Document type**: academic/scholarly publication.

333.91 639.2 US ISSN 8755-4682
SEICHE. 1976. q. free. University of Minnesota at Duluth, Sea Grant Program, 2305 E. Fifth St., Duluth, MN 55812. TEL 218-726-8175. FAX 218-726-6556. Ed. Michael McLean. circ. 3,500. (back issues avail.) **Document type**: newsletter.
Description: Covers issues related to the Great Lakes: fisheries, policy, research and education.

628 US ISSN 0892-9548
SENSUS WATER JOURNAL; devoted to the operation and management of water works. Key Title: Water Journal. 1908. a. (with irreg. supplements). free. Sensus Technologies, Inc., 450 N. Gallatin Ave., Box 487, Uniontown, PA 15401. TEL 412-439-7700. FAX 412-430-3959. Ed. R.D. Neely; Pub. D. Harness. charts; illus.; circ. 15,000 (controlled). **Document type**: trade publication.
Formerly: Rockwell Water Journal.

628.1 UK
SEVERN TRENT PLC. ANNUAL REPORT AND ACCOUNTS (YEAR). 1989. a. free. Severn Trent Plc., 2308 Coventry Rd., Birmingham B26 3JZ, England. TEL 0121-722-6000. circ. 130,000. **Document type**: corporate report.

628.1 UK
SEVERN TRENT WATER. DRINKING WATER QUALITY (YEAR). 1990. a. Severn Trent Water Ltd., 2297 Coventry Rd., Birmingham B26 3PU, England. TEL 0121-722-4000. FAX 0121-722-4800. **Document type**: corporate report.

333.91 550 CC ISSN 0559-9342
SHUILI FADIAN/HYDROELECTRIC POWER. (Text in Chinese; abstracts in English) 1954. m. $35.52. (Shuili Shuidian Guihua Sheji Guanli-ju - Institute of Water Resources and Hydropower Planning) Shuili Fadian Bianjibu, 65 Ande Lu, Xicheng-qu, Beijing 100011, People's Republic of China. TEL 4011177. FAX 4014092. (Dist. by: China International Book Trading Corp., P.O. Box 399, P.R. China) Ed. Liu Fangchun. adv. contact: Guoqing Zhao. circ. 15,000.
—BLDSC (9271.960000).

SOCIETY AND NATURAL RESOURCES. see *ENVIRONMENTAL STUDIES*

333.91 SA
SOUTH AFRICA. WATER RESEARCH COMMISSION. ANNUAL REPORT. (Text in Afrikaans or English) 1971. a. free. Water Research Commission - Waternavorsingskommissie, P.O. Box 824, Pretoria 0001, South Africa. TEL 27-12-330-0340. FAX 27-12-331-2565. TELEX 32-0464-WATCO-SA. charts; illus.; stat. circ. 3,200. **Document type**: corporate report.
Description: Covers the research activities of the Commission. Also lists publications issued from research connected with the Commission.

SOUTHERN AFRICAN JOURNAL OF AQUATIC SCIENCES. see *BIOLOGY*

627 DK ISSN 0108-0466
SPILDEVANDSTEKNISK TIDSSKRIFT. 1973. 4/yr. membership. Spildevandsteknisk Forening, Teglmarken 69, DK-8800 Viborg, Denmark. TEL 45-86-61-05-32. FAX 45-86-62-66-20. Ed. Ole Poulsen. illus. circ. 1,800.

SPILL SCIENCE & TECHNOLOGY BULLETIN; oils - chemicals - land - marine. see *ENVIRONMENTAL STUDIES — Pollution*

333.91 UK ISSN 0307-9074
STREAM. 1974. 10/yr. £3. Severn-Trent Water Authority, Abelson House, 2297 Coventry Rd., Sheldon, Birmingham B26 3PU, England. Ed. Christine Mosley. adv. circ. 13,000. (tabloid format; back issues avail.)

627 RM
STUDII DE IRIGATII SI DESECARI. (Text in Rumanian; summaries in English and French) a. Academia de Stiinte Agricole si Silvice, Institutul de Cercetari Pentru Imbunatatiri Funciare, B-dul Marasti, 61, Bucharest, Rumania. (Subscr. to: ILEXIM, Str. 13 Decembrie Nr. 3, P.O. Box 136-137, Bucharest, Rumania)

SUIMON MIZU SHIGEN GAKKAI NYUSU/JAPAN SOCIETY OF HYDROLOGY AND WATER RESOURCES NEWS. see *EARTH SCIENCES — Hydrology*

SUIMON MIZU SHIGEN GAKKAISHI/JAPAN SOCIETY OF HYDROLOGY AND WATER RESOURCES. JOURNAL. see *EARTH SCIENCES — Hydrology*

333.91 JA ISSN 0039-4858
SUIRI KAGAKU/WATER SCIENCE. 1957. bi-m. 8800 Yen per no. Suiri Kagaku Kenkyujo - Water Utilization Institute, 7-12 Koraku 1-chome, Bunkyo-ku, Tokyo 112, Japan. Ed. Hirotada Muto. adv.; bk.rev. **Indexed**: Chem.Abstr.

WATER RESOURCES 6555

333.9 US ISSN 0094-6427
TC425.S8
SUSQUEHANNA RIVER BASIN COMMISSION. ANNUAL REPORT. Key Title: Annual Report - Susquehanna River Basin Commission. 1972. a. free. Susquehanna River Basin Commission, 1721 N. Front St., Harrisburg, PA 17102. TEL 717-238-0422. FAX 717-238-2436. illus. **Document type**: government publication.
Description: Describes the work of the commission for the fiscal year. Also contains featured articles about special subjects.

TECHNIQUES - SCIENCES - METHODES. GENIE URBAIN RURAL. see *PUBLIC ADMINISTRATION — Municipal Government*

333 SP ISSN 0211-8173
CODEN: TEAGEN
TECNOLOGIA DEL AGUA; revista tecnica de la captacion, distribucion, tratamiento, y depuracion del agua. 1980. 14/yr. 25100 ptas.($215) (effective 1995). Elsevier Prensa S.A., Avda Parallel, 180, Apdo. No. 350 F.D., 08015 Barcelona, Spain. TEL 34-3-3255350. FAX 34-3-4252880. Ed. Ramon Quevalt Torrell. adv. contact: Manuel Fernandez de Liencres. bk.rev.; charts; illus. circ. 6,000. **Indexed**: Fluidex, Ind.SST. **Document type**: trade publication.
—BLDSC (8762.800200).
Description: Covers all topics of water and hydrology, including techniques and application solutions for collection, distribution, water treatment, storage, control and monitoring, canalization, purification and industrial waste water.

333.91 US
TEXAS. WATER COMMISSION. LIBRARY. BULLETIN.. 1969. irreg. free. Water Commission, Library, Box 13087, Capitol Station, Austin, TX 78711. TEL 512-463-7834. Ed. Sylvia von Fange. circ. 130. **Document type**: bibliography.
Former titles (1977-1985): Texas. Department of Water Resources. Library. Bulletin (ISSN 0148-7876); Texas. Water Development Board. Library. Bulletin.
Description: Lists new holdings added to the libarary collection for the period between issues.

333.8 US ISSN 0197-2340
TEXAS NATURAL RESOURCES REPORTER.* 1977. s-m. $495. Research & Planning Consultants, Inc., 7600 Chevy Chase Dr., Ste. 500, Austin, TX 78752-1568. TEL 512-472-7765. FAX 512-472-2232. Ed. Gaylon Finklea. circ. 250. (looseleaf format; back issues avail.)

333.91 628.4 US
TEXAS ON-SITE INSIGHTS; information on on-site wastewater treatment systems in Texas. 1992. q. free. Texas Water Resources Institute, c/o Texas A & M Univ., College Station, TX 77843-2118. TEL 409-845-8571. FAX 409-845-8554. E-mail: rjensen@tamu.edu. Ed. Ric Jensen. **Document type**: newsletter.
●Also available online.
Formerly: On-Site Insights.

333.91 US ISSN 0744-1320
CODEN: TWREDN
TEXAS WATER RESOURCES. 1964. q. free. Texas Water Resources Institute, c/o Texas A & M University, College Station, TX 77843-2118. TEL 409-845-8571. FAX 409-845-8554. E-mail: rjensen@tamu.edu. Ed. Ric Jensen. circ. 3,000. **Document type**: newsletter.
●Also available online.
Description: Delves into specific water issues, such as the effect of chlorinated drinking water on human health, home water treatment systems, wetlands, and women in science and public policy.

333.91 US ISSN 0275-5483
TD224.T4 CODEN: TRTIDA
TEXAS WATER RESOURCES INSTITUTE. TECHNICAL REPORT. irreg. Texas Water Resources Institute, c/o Texas A & M University, College Station, TX 77843-2118. TEL 409-845-8571. FAX 409-845-8554. E-mail: rjensen@tamu.edu. illus. **Document type**: academic/scholarly publication.
●Also available online.

WATER RESOURCES

627 628   US   ISSN 1051-709X
TEXAS WATER UTILITIES JOURNAL. 1990. m. $20 (foreign $25) (typically set in June). Texas Water Utilities Association, 1106 Clayton Ave., Ste. 101 E., Austin, TX 78793-1033. TEL 512-459-3124. FAX 512-459-7124. Ed. Christine Loven. adv. contact: Christine Loven. circ. 9,800. (back issues avail.) **Document type:** trade publication.
—CIS.
Description: Covers essential information for all individuals working within the water utilities industry in Texas, including rules and regulations, certification, education, and communication.

THALASSIA SALENTINA. see BIOLOGY — Botany

TIJDSCHRIFT LANDINRICHTING. see AGRICULTURE — Crop Production And Soil

TIJDSCHRIFT VOOR WATERSTAATSGESCHIEDENIS. see HISTORY — History Of Europe

333.91   BE
TRIBUNE D'EAU; eau, environnement, pollution. 1947. 5/yr. 4600 Fr. (Centre Belge d'Etude et de Documentation de l'Environnement) C E B E D O C S.P.R.L., 2 rue Armand Stevart, 4000 Liege, Belgium. adv.; bk.rev.; abstr.; bibl.; charts; index. circ. 10,000. **Indexed:** Biol.Abstr., Excerp.Med., Sel.Water Res.Abstr., Sugar Ind.Abstr.
Formerly (until 1988): C E B E D E A U. Tribune (ISSN 0577-1056)

TRIBUTARY (TRENTON). see ENVIRONMENTAL STUDIES — Waste Management

628.1   UK
U.K. IRRIGATION ASSOCIATION QUARTERLY. 1981. q. £5 per no. U.K. Irrigation Association, c/o Silsoe College, Silsoe, Beds. MK45 4DT, England. TEL 01525-863290. FAX 01525-863001. TELEX 826838 SILCAM G. Ed. M.K.V. Carr. adv. contact: S.H. Anness. bk.rev. **Document type:** newsletter.
Description: Keeps members of the UKIA informed about developments in irrigation.

627   II   ISSN 0080-4045
U P IRRIGATION RESEARCH INSTITUTE. ANNUAL REPORT. (Issued in its Technical Memorandum Series) a. U P Irrigation Research Institute, Roorkee, Uttar Pradesh, India. **Document type:** government publication.

627   II   ISSN 0080-4053
U P IRRIGATION RESEARCH INSTITUTE. TECHNICAL MEMORANDUM. (Text in English) irreg. U P Irrigation Research Institute, Roorkee, Uttar Pradesh, India. **Document type:** government publication.

627   US
U S C I D NEWSLETTER. 1958. q. membership. United States Committee on Irrigation and Drainage, 1616 17th St., Ste. 483, Denver, CO 80202. TEL 303-628-5430. FAX 303-628-5431. Ed. Larry D. Stephens. bk.rev. circ. 750.
Formerly: I.C.I.D. Newsletter.

620   US   ISSN 0041-5480
U S C O L D NEWSLETTER. 1960. 3/yr. membership. U S Committee on Large Dams, (Subsidiary of: International Commission on Large Dams), 1616 17th St., Ste. 483, Denver, CO 80202. TEL 303-628-5430. FAX 303-628-5431. bk.rev. circ. 1,500. **Document type:** newsletter.

333.91   US   ISSN 0749-1980
CODEN: USWNEP
U S WATER NEWS. 1984. m. $49 (foreign $89). U S Water News, Inc., 230 Main St., Halstead, KS 67056. TEL 316-835-2222. FAX 316-835-2223. E-mail: uswaternews@aol.com. Ed. Steven D. Seibel; Pub. Thomas C. Bell. adv.; bk.rev. circ. 20,000. (tabloid format; back issues avail.) **Indexed:** Environ.Abstr.
Description: Provides wide range of national news about water resources.

333.91   US   ISSN 0747-8291
CODEN: ULWAE5
ULTRAPURE WATER. 1984. 9/yr. $18 in N. America (overseas $63). Tall Oaks Publishing, Inc., Box 621669, Littleton, CO 80162-1669. TEL 303-973-6700. adv.; bk.rev. circ. 14,000. **Indexed:** Chem.Abstr., Energy Info.Abstr., Environ.Abstr., INSPEC (1992-), Telegen. **Document type:** trade publication.
—BLDSC (9082.783500); CASDDS; Ei; Faxon; SWETS; UMI; UnCover. **CCC.**
Description: Addresses all aspects of high-purity water production in the high-pressure boiler industry, electric utilities, semiconductor manufacturing, pharmaceuticals and biotechnology.

UNION DES INDUSTRIES ET ENTREPRISES DE L'EAU ET DE L'ENVIRONNEMENT. ANNUAIRE. see ENVIRONMENTAL STUDIES

333.91   UN   ISSN 1010-397X
JX1977
UNITED NATIONS. ECONOMIC AND SOCIAL COMMISSION FOR ASIA AND THE PACIFIC. NATURAL RESOURCES - WATER SERIES. 1964. irreg., no.60, 1985. price varies. United Nations Economic and Social Commission for Asia and the Pacific (ESCAP), Rajademnern Ave., Bangkok 10200, Thailand.
Formerly: United Nations. Department of International Economic and Social Affairs. Natural Resources - Water Series.

333.91   UN   ISSN 0082-8130
UNITED NATIONS. ECONOMIC AND SOCIAL COMMISSION FOR ASIA AND THE PACIFIC. WATER RESOURCES SERIES. 1951. irreg., no.72, 1993. price varies. United Nations Economic and Social Commission for Asia and the Pacific (ESCAP), United Nations Bldg., Rajamnern Ave., Bangkok 10200, Thailand. (Dist. by: United Nations Publications, Rm. DC2-0853, New York, NY 10017; or Distribution and Sales Section, Palais des Nations, CH-1211 Geneva 10, Switzerland) (also avail. in microfiche from CIS; back issues avail.) **Indexed:** Abstr.Rural Dev.Trop., IIS. **Document type:** monographic series.
—BLDSC (9275.205000).
Former titles: United Nations. Economic and Social Commission for Asia and the Pacific. Water Resources Development Series; (until 1964): United Nations. Economic and Social Commission for Asia and the Pacific. Flood Control Series (ISSN 1010-5328)

U.S. BUREAU OF RECLAMATION. ANNUAL REPORT. see CONSERVATION

U.S. BUREAU OF RECLAMATION. ENGINEERING MONOGRAPH. see ENGINEERING — Hydraulic Engineering

333.91   US
U.S. SOIL CONSERVATION SERVICE. ANNUAL REPORT. a. free. U.S. Department of Agriculture, Natural Resources Conservation Service (Spokane), 316 W. Boone Ave., Ste. 450, Spokane, WA 99201-2348. TEL 509-353-2341. **Document type:** government publication, corporate report.

333.91   GW
UNIVERSITAET HANNOVER. INSTITUT FUER SIEDLUNGSWASSERWIRTSCHAFT. VEROEFFENTLICHUNGEN. 1957. irreg., no.83, 1992. DM.50. Universitaet Hannover, Institut fuer Siedlungswasserwirtschaft und Abfalltechnik, Welfengarten 1, 30167 Hannover, Germany. **Document type:** monographic series.
Formerly: Technische Universitaet Hannover. Institut fuer Siedlungswasserwirtschaft. Veroeffentlichungen (ISSN 0073-0319)

333.91   US
UNIVERSITY OF ALASKA. INSTITUTE OF NORTHERN ENGINEERING. 1975. biennial. free. University of Alaska, Institute of Northern Engineering, Water Research Center, Fairbanks, AK 99775-1760. TEL 907-474-7775. FAX 907-474-6087. circ. 1,800.
Former titles: University of Alaska. Institute of Water Resources-Engineering Experiment Station. Annual Report; University of Alaska. Institute of Water Resources. Annual Report (ISSN 0065-5953)

333.91   US   ISSN 0068-6301
UNIVERSITY OF CALIFORNIA, DAVIS. WATER RESOURCES CENTER. CONTRIBUTIONS. 1957. irreg. (5-7/yr.). free. University of California at Davis, Water Resources Center, Davis, CA 95616. TEL 916-752-8070. FAX 916-572-8086. E-mail: CWWA@udavis.edu. Ed. Jeff Woled. circ. 600. **Indexed:** Sel.Water Res.Abstr., Soils & Fert. **Document type:** academic/scholarly publication, monographic series.
Refereed Serial

333.9   US   ISSN 0069-9063
CODEN: CUWRAJ
UNIVERSITY OF CONNECTICUT. INSTITUTE OF WATER RESOURCES. REPORT SERIES. 1966. irreg., latest 1990. University of Connecticut, Institute of Water Resources, Storrs, CT 06269-4018. TEL 203-486-0335. **Indexed:** GeoRef.
Description: Includes chemical, biological, geological, legal, engineering and sociopolitical reports on resources.
Refereed Serial

333.7   US
UNIVERSITY OF CONNECTICUT. INSTITUTE OF WATER RESOURCES. WETLANDS CONFERENCE. PROCEEDINGS. (Subseries of its Report) 1973. irreg., 3rd, 1976. University of Connecticut, Institute of Water Resources, Box U-18, Storrs, CT 06296-4018. TEL 203-486-0335. charts; illus. (also avail. in microfiche from NTI) **Indexed:** Sel.Water Res.Abstr. **Document type:** proceedings.

333.91   US   ISSN 0440-5013
TD224.H3   CODEN: RHWRDS
UNIVERSITY OF HAWAII. WATER RESOURCES RESEARCH CENTER. ANNUAL REPORT. 1966; suspended 1984-1985. a. free. University of Hawaii, Water Resources Research Center, 2540 Dole St., Holmes Hall 283, Honolulu, HI 96822. TEL 808-956-7847. FAX 808-956-5044. E-mail: kytanoue@uhunix.uhcc.hawaii.edu. Ed. K. Tanoue. circ. 500. (back issues avail.) **Document type:** corporate report.

333.9 628   US   ISSN 0073-1307
TC1   CODEN: HUWTAC
UNIVERSITY OF HAWAII. WATER RESOURCES RESEARCH CENTER. TECHNICAL REPORT. 1967. irreg. price varies. University of Hawaii, Water Resources Research Center, 2540 Dole St., Honolulu, HI 96822. TEL 808-956-7847. FAX 808-956-5044. E-mail: kytanoue@uhunix.uhcc.hawaii.edu. Ed. K. Tanoue. circ. 300. (also avail. in microfiche from NTI) **Indexed:** Pollut.Abstr. **Document type:** academic/scholarly publication.
—CASDDS.
Refereed Serial

333.9 627   US   ISSN 0073-4616
TC424.I2
UNIVERSITY OF IDAHO. WATER RESOURCES RESEARCH INSTITUTE. ANNUAL REPORT. 1965. a. free. University of Idaho, Water Resources Research Institute, Morrill Hall 106, Moscow, ID 83844-3011. TEL 208-885-6429. Ed. Leland L. Mink. circ. 400. **Document type:** academic/scholarly publication.

333.91   US   ISSN 0073-5434
UNIVERSITY OF ILLINOIS AT URBANA-CHAMPAIGN. WATER RESOURCES CENTER. ANNUAL REPORT. 1965. a. $5. University of Illinois at Urbana-Champaign, Water Resources Center, 1101 W. Peabody Dr., Rm. 278, Urbana, IL 61801. TEL 217-333-0536. FAX 217-244-8583. E-mail: iwrc@uiuc.edu. Ed. John B. Braden. (also avail. in microform from NTI)

333.91   US   ISSN 0073-5442
HD1694   CODEN: IUWRAH
UNIVERSITY OF ILLINOIS AT URBANA-CHAMPAIGN. WATER RESOURCES CENTER. RESEARCH REPORT. 1966. irreg., no.219, 1994. price varies. University of Illinois at Urbana-Champaign, Water Resources Center, 1101 W. Peabody Dr., Rm. 278, Urbana, IL 61801. TEL 217-333-0536. FAX 217-244-8583. E-mail: iwrc@uiuc.edu. Ed. John B. Braden. (also avail. in microform from NTI) **Indexed:** Biol.Abstr., Pollut.Abstr. **Document type:** monographic series.
—CASDDS.
Refereed Serial

WATER RESOURCES 6557

333.91
UNIVERSITY OF ILLINOIS AT URBANA-CHAMPAIGN. WATER RESOURCES CENTER. SPECIAL REPORTS. 1968. irreg., no.20, 1993. price varies. University of Illinois at Urbana-Champaign, Water Resources Center, 1101 W. Peabody Dr., Rm. 278, Urbana, IL 61801. TEL 217-333-0536. FAX 217-244-8583. E-mail: iwrc@uiuc.edu. **Indexed:** Biol.Abstr., GeoRef., Pollut.Abstr. **Document type:** monographic series.

333.91 634.9
UNIVERSITY OF MINNESOTA. CENTER FOR NATURAL RESOURCE POLICY AND MANAGEMENT. WORKING PAPERS. 1984. irreg., latest no.5. University of Minnesota, Center for Natural Resource Policy & Management, 115 Green Hall, Dept. of Forest Resources, St. Paul, MN 55108. TEL 612-624-9796. FAX 612-625-5212. Ed. James Perry. circ. 150.
Description: Covers water quality, common property and economics of natural resources and forestry research.

333.9 US
UNIVERSITY OF NEBRASKA. WATER CENTER. ANNUAL REPORT OF ACTIVITIES. 1968. a. free. University of Nebraska, Water Center, 103 Natural Resources Hall, Lincoln, NE 68583-0844. TEL 402-472-3305. FAX 402-472-3574. circ. 1,500. **Document type:** corporate report.
Formerly: Nebraska Water Resources Research Institute. University of Nebraska. Annual Report of Activities (ISSN 0077-6394)

628.1 AT ISSN 1038-3859
UNIVERSITY OF NEW ENGLAND. CENTRE FOR WATER POLICY RESEARCH. DISCUSSION PAPERS (NO.). 1991. irreg., latest no.5. Aus.$5 per no. University of New England, Centre for Water Policy Research, Armidale, N.S.W. 2351, Australia. TEL 61-67-732420. FAX 61-67-733237. E-mail: cwpr@une.edu.au. **Document type:** monographic series.

333.91 AT ISSN 1030-4134
UNIVERSITY OF NEW ENGLAND. CENTRE FOR WATER POLICY RESEARCH. OCCASIONAL PAPERS (NO.). 1987. irreg., latest no.8. price varies. University of New England, Centre for Water Policy Research, Armidale, N.S.W. 2351, Australia. TEL 61-67-7-2420. FAX 61-67-733237. E-mail: cwpr@une.edu.au. **Document type:** monographic series, proceedings.

627 333.9 AT ISSN 0077-8818
UNIVERSITY OF NEW SOUTH WALES. WATER RESEARCH LABORATORY, MANLY VALE. LABORATORY RESEARCH REPORTS. 1959. irreg., latest no.173, 1988. price varies. University of New South Wales, Water Research Laboratory, King St., Manly Vale, N.S.W. 2093, Australia. **Indexed:** GeoRef., Sel.Water Res.Abstr.

333.9 628 US
UNIVERSITY OF RHODE ISLAND. WATER RESOURCES CENTER. ANNUAL REPORT. 1965. a. $10 (effective Sep. 1991). Rhode Island Water Resources Center, University of Rhode Island, Kingston, RI 02881. TEL 401-792-2680. FAX 401-792-2786. Ed. Calvin Poon. circ. 800. **Document type:** academic/scholarly publication.

**333.91 US ISSN 0147-2194
CODEN: TRURD8**
UNIVERSITY OF TEXAS AT AUSTIN. CENTER FOR RESEARCH IN WATER RESOURCES. TECHNICAL REPORT SERIES. 1964. irreg., latest CRWR-244. price varies. University of Texas at Austin, Center for Research in Water Resources, Balcones Research Center, Austin, TX 78712. TEL 512-471-3131. FAX 512-471-0072. **Indexed:** Chem.Abstr. **Document type:** academic/scholarly publication.
—BLDSC (8723.430000); CASDDS; Ei.
Description: Summary of research findings resulting from sponsored projects in the water resources area conducted by faculty members of the university.
Refereed Serial

**333.91 US ISSN 0083-7709
CODEN: WARSA9**
UNIVERSITY OF TEXAS AT AUSTIN. CENTER FOR RESEARCH IN WATER RESOURCES. WATER RESOURCES SYMPOSIUM SERIES. 1968. irreg. price varies. University of Texas at Austin, Center for Research in Water Resources, 10100 Burnet Rd., Austin, TX 78758-4497. TEL 512-471-3131. **Document type:** academic/scholarly publication, proceedings.
—CASDDS.
Former titles: University of Texas at Austin. Center for Research in Water Resources. Symposium Series; University of Texas at Austin. Center for Research in Water Resources. Resource Symposium Series.
Description: Compilation of papers presented at the latest Water Resources Symposium.

331.91 US
UPPER MISSISSIPPI RIVER CONSERVATION COMMITTEE. NEWSLETTER. Abbreviated title: U M R C C Newsletter. 1979. bi-m. free. Upper Mississippi River Conservation Commission, 4469 48th Ave. Ct., Rock Island, IL 61201. TEL 309-793-5800. Ed. Jon Duyvejonck. circ. 575. (looseleaf format; back issues avail.) **Document type:** newsletter.
Description: Contains information about the management of the the river's natural resources for professionals who live and work near it.

551 623 333.7 US ISSN 0886-2664
UPWELLINGS. 1977. q. free. Michigan Sea Grant College Program, 4113 I.S.T., 2200 Bonisteel Blvd., Ann Arbor, MI 48109-2099. TEL 313-764-1138. FAX 313-747-0768. (Co-sponsors: University of Michigan; Michigan State University) Eds. Martha L. Walter, Carol S. Allaire. bk.rev. circ. 5,000. (back issues avail.) **Document type:** newsletter.
Description: Contains news, articles, and information on issues related to the Great Lakes.

VALENCIA PORT; guia del servicios del puerto de Valencia. see TRANSPORTATION — Ships And Shipping

VANDERBILT UNIVERSITY. DEPARTMENT OF ENVIRONMENTAL AND WATER RESOURCES ENGINEERING. TECHNICAL REPORTS. see ENVIRONMENTAL STUDIES

627 DK ISSN 0106-3677
VANDTEKNIK. 1926. 10/yr. DKK 340 (foreign DKK 365). Danske Vandvaerkers Forening, Vilh. Becks Vej 60, 8260 Viby J, Denmark. TEL 86112333609. Eds. Anders Baekgaard, Eva Munck. adv. contact: Eva Munck. bk.rev.; circ. 1,555 (controlled). **Document type:** academic/scholarly publication.
Description: Focuses on water resources, groundwater protection, abstraction and administration, water quality, waterworks technique, water distribution, pipelines, domestic installations, consumption and consumer relations.

**629 333.91 SW ISSN 0042-2886
CODEN: VTTNAO**
VATTEN/WATER; tidskrift foer vattenvaard/periodical on water conservation. (Text mainly in Swedish, occasional papers in English or German; summaries in English, German) 1945. q. SEK 580. Foereningen foer Vattenhygien - Swedish Association for Water Hygiene, Avd. VA-teknik, P.O. Box 118, S-221 00 Lund, Sweden. Ed. Anders Hilmer. adv.; bk.rev.; bibl.; charts; illus.; index, cum.index. circ. 1,700. **Indexed:** Biol.Abstr., Chem.Abstr., Environ.Per.Bibl. (1972-), Excerp.Med., Ocean.Abstr., Pollut.Abstr., W.R.C.Inf. **Document type:** academic/scholarly publication.
—BLDSC (9149.680000); CASDDS.
Formerly (until 1967): Vattenhygien - Water Hygiene.

**333.91 CN
CODEN: STEADG**
VECTEUR ENVIRONNEMENT. (Text in French; abstracts in English and French) 1968. q. Can.$51.28 in Quebec; Canada Can.$53.50; U.S. Can.$55; elsewhere Can.$60. Association Quebecoise des Techniques de l'Environnement, 911 rue Jean-Talon Est, Montreal, PQ H2R 1V5, Canada. TEL 514-270-7110. FAX 514-270-7154. Ed. Guy Giasson; Pub. Christian Scott. adv. contact: Francine Perrault. bk.rev.; index. circ. 4,000. (back issues avail.) **Indexed:** Appl.Ecol.Abstr., Biol.Abstr., Bull.Signal., Chem.Abstr., Energy Ind., Energy Info.Abstr., Eng.Ind., Environ.Abstr., Environ.Per.Bibl., Excerp.Med., Microbiol.Abstr., Pollut.Abstr., Pt.de Rep. (1983-), RADAR, Repindex. **Document type:** trade publication.
—CASDDS.
Former titles: Sciences et Techniques de l'Eau (ISSN 0823-0269); (until 1985): Eau du Quebec (ISSN 0315-2081)

VERSORGUNGSWIRTSCHAFT. see ENGINEERING — Electrical Engineering

333.91 627 FI ISSN 0505-3838
VESITALOUS; Finnish journal of water economy, hydraulic and agricultural engineering. (Text in Finnish; summaries in English) 1960. bi-m. FIM 200. Maa- Ja Vesitekniikan Tuki, Tontunmaentie 33D, 02200 Espoo, Finland. TEL 358-0-425530. FAX 358-0-425207. Ed. Aimo Maasilta. adv. contact: Marja-Leena Jarvi. bk.rev.; charts; illus. circ. 2,000. **Indexed:** Chem.Abstr., Excerp.Med., W.R.C.Inf. —BLDSC (9218.460000).

353.9 US ISSN 1047-7438
VIRGINIA. STATE WATER CONTROL BOARD. BASIC DATA BULLETIN. 1930. irreg., no.44, 1975. State Water Control Board, 4900 Cox Road, Glen Allen, VA 23060. TEL 804-527-5215. FAX 804-527-5313. **Document type:** monographic series.

353.9 US
VIRGINIA. STATE WATER CONTROL BOARD. INFORMATION BULLETIN. no.527, 1977. irreg. State Water Control Board, 4900 Cox Road, Glen Allen, VA 23233. TEL 804-367-0056. FAX 804-367-0067.

353.9 US ISSN 0271-4922
VIRGINIA. STATE WATER CONTROL BOARD. PLANNING BULLETIN. no.304, 1976. irreg. State Water Control Board, 4900 Cox Rd., Glen Allen, VA 23233. TEL 804-367-0056. FAX 804-367-0067. **Indexed:** GeoRef.

**333.91 US ISSN 0097-2584
CODEN: BWRRAV**
VIRGINIA. WATER RESOURCES RESEARCH CENTER. BULLETIN. 1965. irreg., latest no. 184. free to Virginia residents; others $10. Water Resources Research Center, Virginia Polytechnic Institute and State University, 617 N. Main St., Blacksburg, VA 24060. TEL 703-231-8036. abstr.; bibl.; illus. circ. 250. (also avail. in microfilm from UMI; back issues avail.) **Indexed:** Geo.Abstr., GeoRef. **Document type:** academic/scholarly publication, bulletin.
—BLDSC (2808.100000); CASDDS; UMI.
Refereed Serial

VODNI HOSPODARSTVI A OCHRANA OVZDUSI. see ENGINEERING — Hydraulic Engineering

627 BU ISSN 0204-8248
VODNI PROBLEMI. 1975. irreg. 1.40 lv. per no. (Bulgarska Akademiia na Naukite, Institut po Vodni Problemi) Publishing House of the Bulgarian Academy of Sciences, Acad. G. Bonchev St., Bldg. 6, 1113 Sofia, Bulgaria. circ. 480. (reprint service avail. from IRC) **Indexed:** BSL Geo.
—BLDSC (0040.743000).
Supersedes: Bulgarska Akademiia na Naukite. Institut po Vodni Problemi. Izvestiia.

**333.7 RU ISSN 0321-0596
CODEN: VDRSBK**
VODNYE RESURSY. English translation: Water Resources (US ISSN 0097-8078) 1972. bi-m. $218 (effective 1996). (Rossiiskaya Akademiya Nauk, Institut Vodnykh Problem) Izdatel'stvo Nauka, 90 Profsoyuznaya ul., 117864 Moscow, Russia. TEL 234-05-84. (Dist. by: Mezhdunarodnaya Kniga, ul. Dimitrova D.39, 113095 Moscow, Russia) Ed. G.V. Voropaev. bk.rev.; abstr.; charts; illus.; index. circ. 1,575. **Indexed:** Chem.Abstr., GeoRef.
—BLDSC (0040.860000); CASDDS. CCC.

WATER RESOURCES

551.4 628   XO   ISSN 0042-790X
GB772.C95   CODEN: VOCAAZ
VODOHOSPODARSKY CASOPIS/WATER SYSTEM PERIODICAL. (Text in Czech or Slovak; summaries in English, French, German, Russian) 1953. bi-m. $38. Slovenska Akademia Vied, Ustav Hydrologie, Trnavska 32, 826 51 Bratislava, Slovakia. (Dist. by: Slovart, Nam. Slobody 6, 817 64 Bratislava, Slovakia) Ed. Jan Benetin. charts; illus.; index, cum.index: 1953-1968. circ. 1,200. **Indexed:** Chem.Abstr., Fluidex, Geo.Abstr., GeoRef., Geotech.Abstr., Ref.Zh., Soils & Fert.
—CASDDS.
Description: Presents news regarding research status in water system regions, information concering new measurement and computer methods, new devices coming out of congresses and symposia.

VODOSNABZHENIE I SANITARNAYA TEKHNIKA. see *PUBLIC HEALTH AND SAFETY*

VOLUNTAD HIDRAULICA. see *ENGINEERING — Hydraulic Engineering*

608 540   GW   ISSN 0083-6915
TD203   CODEN: VJWWAU
VOM WASSER; ein Fachbuch fuer Wasserchemie und Wasserreinigungstechnik. irreg., vol.81, 1993. price varies. (Gesellschaft Deutscher Chemiker, Fachgruppe Wasserchemie) V C H Verlagsgesellschaft mbH, Postfach 101161, 69451 Weinheim, Germany. TEL 06201-606-0. FAX 06201-606328. TELEX 465516-VCHWH-D. (U.S. addr.: V C H Publishers Inc., 220 E. 23rd St., New York, NY 10010-4606) adv. (reprint service avail. from ISI) **Indexed:** Biol.Abstr., Chem.Abstr., Excerp.Med., W.R.C.Inf. **Document type:** monographic series.
—BLDSC (9255.000000); CASDDS; Ei; SWETS. **CCC.**

333.91   PK
W A P D A NEWS. (Text in English) 1978. fortn. Rs.70. Water and Power Development Authority, Public Relations Division, WAPDA House, Shara-e-Quaid-e-Azam, Lahore, Pakistan. TEL 212900. TELEX 44869 WAPDA PK. Ed. Raziuddin Shaikh.
Description: News coverage of the activities of the authority.

628.1   US
W R C NEWS AND ANNOUNCEMENTS. 1973. irreg. (approx. 3-4/yr.) free. Water Resources Center, 278 Emv. and Agr. Sci. Bldg., 1101 W. Peabody Dr., Urbana, IL 61801. TEL 217-333-0536. FAX 217-244-8583. Ed. Harini Narayanan. circ. 800. **Document type:** newsletter.

333.9   US   ISSN 0549-799X
HD1694.N8   CODEN: RWRCDT
W R R I NEWS. 1966. bi-m. $10 outside N. Carolina. University of North Carolina, Water Resources Research Institute, Box 7912, Raleigh, NC 27695-7912. TEL 919-515-2815. FAX 919-515-7802. Ed. Jeri Gray. bk.rev.; bibl.; index. circ. 3,000. **Indexed:** Pollut.Abstr., Sel.Water Res.Abstr.
●Also available online. Vendor(s): VU/TEXT Information Services, Inc.
—BLDSC (7629.600000); CASDDS; Ei.
Formerly: North Carolina State University. Water Resources Research Institute. Report (ISSN 0078-1525)
Description: Directed to university faculty, government agencies, and the public concerning scientific, technical, legal, economic, and regulatory issues related to water.

333.91   US   ISSN 0044-9970
W R R I NEWS REPORT. 1971. q. free. Auburn University, Water Resources Research Institute, 202 Hargis Hall, Auburn, AL 36849. TEL 205-826-5075. Eds. Joseph F. Judkins, Jr., Dennis H. Block. circ. 1,100. (processed) **Indexed:** Environ.Abstr., GeoRef.

333.91   US
WASHINGTON BASIN OUTLOOK REPORT. 1954. bi-m. free. U.S. Department of Agriculture, Natural Resources Conservation Service (Spokane), 316 W. Boone Ave., Ste. 450, Spokane, WA 99201-2348. TEL 509-353-2341. circ. 870. (also avail. in microfiche from CIS; reprint service avail. from CIS) **Indexed:** Amer.Stat.Ind. (1974-). **Document type:** government publication.

333.91   GW
WASSER - ABWASSER - G W F; das gas- und wasserfach. 1858. m. DM.368 to non-members; members DM.258 (effective 1996). (Bundesverband der Deutscher Gas- und Wasserwirtschaft) R. Oldenbourg Verlag GmbH, Rosenheimerstr. 145, 81671 Munich, Germany. TEL 089-45051-0. FAX 089-45051207. (Subscr. to: Postfach 801360, 81613 Munich, Germany) (Co-sponsor: Abwassertechnische Vereinigung) **Indexed:** Chem.Abstr., Excerp.Med., INIS Atomind., Repindex, Sel.Water Res.Abstr., Sugar Ind.Abstr. **Document type:** trade publication.
—BLDSC (4085.100000); CASDDS; SWETS. **CCC.**
Former titles: G W F Gas- und Wasserfach (ISSN 0016-3651); Wasser - Abwasser.
Description: For the water and sewer industry. Publishes information and chemical research on water pollution, quality and treatment of drinking water.

620   SZ   ISSN 0377-905X
TC1
WASSER, ENERGIE, LUFT/EAU, ENERGIE, AIR. (Text mainly in German, partly in French) 1910. 7/yr. 140 SFr. Schweizerischer Wasserwirtschaftsverband, Ruetistr. 3A, CH-5401 Baden, Switzerland. TEL 056-225069. FAX 056-211083. Ed. Georg Weber. adv.; bk.rev.; charts; illus.; index, cum.index. circ. 3,000. **Indexed:** Eng.Ind., Excerp.Med., Geotech.Abstr., Intl.Civil Eng.Abstr., Sel.Water Res.Abstr., Soft.Abstr.Eng. **Document type:** trade publication.
Formerly: Wasser und Energiewirtschaft (ISSN 0043-096X)
Description: Trade publication covering water rights and supply, hydraulic construction, water power utilization, protection of waterways, irrigation, drainage, flood protection, and inland navigation. Includes reports and announcements of events.

628.1 333.7   GW   ISSN 0511-3520
TD203   CODEN: WAKADP
WASSER - KALENDER; Jahrbuch fuer das gesamte Wasserfach. 1966. a. price varies. Erich Schmidt Verlag GmbH & Co. (Berlin), Genthiner Str. 30G, 10785 Berlin, Germany. TEL 030-2500850. FAX 030-25008521. Ed. R. Wagner. charts; stat. circ. 3,000. **Document type:** academic/scholarly publication.
—CASDDS.

WASSER, LUFT UND BODEN; unabhaengige Zeitschrift fuer Wasserwirtschaft, Luftreinhaltung, Abfallverwertung und Umwelttechnik. see *ENVIRONMENTAL STUDIES — Pollution*

333.91   GW
WASSER MAGAZIN; Kundeninformation der Hamburger Wasserwerke. 1981. 2/yr. free. Hamburger Wasserwerke GmbH, Billhorner Deich 2, 20539 Hamburg, Germany. TEL 040-7888-2483. FAX 040-7888-2883. Ed. Hans-Werner Krueger. adv.: color page DM.15500. circ. 780,000. **Document type:** consumer publication.

333.7 628.1   GW   ISSN 0512-5030
        CODEN: WAFPDB
WASSER UND ABWASSER IN FORSCHUNG UND PRAXIS. (Text in German; summaries in English and French) 1969. irreg., vol.21, 1993. price varies. Erich Schmidt Verlag GmbH & Co. (Bielefeld), Viktoriastr. 44A, 33602 Bielefeld, Germany. TEL 0521-583080. (Subscr. to: Postfach 102451, 33524 Bielefeld, Germany) (back issues avail.) **Document type:** monographic series.
—CASDDS.

624   GW   ISSN 0043-0951
S605   CODEN: WUBOAN
WASSER UND BODEN; Zeitschrift fuer die gesamte Wasserwirtschaft. 1949. m. DM.170 ($113.50) Verlag Paul Parey (Hamburg), Spitalerstr. 12, 20095 Hamburg, Germany. TEL 040-33969-0. FAX 040-33969-199. TELEX 2161-391-PARV-D. adv.; bk.rev.; bibl.; charts; illus.; index. circ. 6,000. (reprint service avail. from ISI) **Indexed:** Biol.Abstr., Chem.Abstr., Excerp.Med., GeoRef., Sel.Water Res.Abstr. **Document type:** trade publication.
—SWETS. **CCC.**

628.1 628.4   GW   ISSN 0942-1327
WASSERABWASSERPRAXIS. 6/yr. Bertelsmann Fachzeitschriften GmbH, Postfach 120, 33111 Guetersloh, Germany. TEL 05241-802332. FAX 05241-73055. circ. 6,879. **Document type:** trade publication.

333.7 340 628.1   GW   ISSN 0508-1254
WASSERRECHT UND WASSERWIRTSCHAFT. 1960. irreg., vol.29, 1993. price varies. Erich Schmidt Verlag GmbH & Co. (Berlin), Genthiner Str. 30G, 10785 Berlin, Germany. TEL 030-2500850. FAX 030-25008521. bibl.; charts; illus.; stat. **Indexed:** W.R.C.Inf. **Document type:** monographic series.

WASSERTRIEBWERK. see *ENERGY — Hydroelectrical Energy*

628   GW   ISSN 0043-0978
        CODEN: WSWTAR
WASSERWIRTSCHAFT; Fachzeitschrift fuer Wasser und Umwelttechnik. 1905. m. DM.190.80 (students DM.99) (effective 1996). (Deutscher Verband fuer Wasserwirtschaft und Kulturbau e.V.) Friedr. Vieweg und Sohn Verlagsgesellschaft mbH, Postfach 1546, 65005 Wiesbaden, Germany. TEL 0611-534389. FAX 0611-534430. Ed. Guenter Marotz. adv.: B&W page DM.2928, color page DM.5124; trim 183 x 250. bk.rev.; abstr.; bibl.; charts; illus.; index. circ. 3,750. **Indexed:** Appl.Mech.Rev., Chem.Abstr., Excerp.Med., Geo.Abstr., GeoRef., Geotech.Abstr., Intl.Civil Eng.Abstr., Ocean.Abstr., Pollut.Abstr., Sel.Water Res.Abstr., Soft.Abstr.Eng. **Document type:** trade publication.
—CASDDS. **CCC.**
Description: Trade publication for the water and sewer industry. Features technology of water purification, ground-water protection, and sewage treatment. Includes industry news, list of events and suppliers.

620   GW   ISSN 0043-0986
TC1   CODEN: WSWSAO
WASSERWIRTSCHAFT - WASSERTECHNIK (W W T); Fachzeitschrift fuer oekologisches und umwelttechnisches Management. 1951. 8/yr. DM.142. Verlag fuer Bauwesen GmbH, Am Friedrichshain 22, 10407 Berlin, Germany. Ed. Petra Neumann. adv.; bk.rev.; abstr.; illus.; index. **Indexed:** Chem.Abstr., Excerp.Med., Fluidex, GeoRef., Geotech.Abstr., Intl.Civil Eng.Abstr., Ocean.Abstr., Pollut.Abstr., Sel.Water Res.Abstr., Soft.Abstr.Eng., W.R.C.Inf.
—BLDSC (9266.500000); CASDDS.

627   AU   ISSN 0043-0994
WASSERWIRTSCHAFTLICHE MITTEILUNGEN. 1964. m. membership. Oesterreichischer Wasserwirtschaftsverband, Marc-Aurel-Strasse 5, A-1010 Vienna, Austria. bk.rev. circ. 950.

WASTE DISPOSAL AND WATER MANAGEMENT IN AUSTRALIA. see *ENVIRONMENTAL STUDIES — Waste Management*

627   AT   ISSN 0310-0367
        CODEN: WTRMDP
WATER. 1973. bi-m. Aus.$35. Australian Water and Wastewater Association, P.O. Box 388, Artarmon, N.S.W. 2064, Australia. TEL 02-4131288. FAX 02-4131047. Ed. E.A. Swinton. adv.; bk.rev. circ. 3,500. **Indexed:** Chem.Abstr., W.R.C.Inf.
—BLDSC (9267.454000); CASDDS; Ei; UnCover.
Description: Studies water, water supply and sewerage; treatment, operation, management, administration and environmental aspects.

333.91   SA
WATER. 2/yr. Erudita Publications (Pty) Ltd., Cnr. 11th Ave. & Main Rd., P.O. Box 29159, Melville, Johannesburg 2109, South Africa. adv. **Indexed:** Excerp.Med.

333.91   US
WATER ACTIVITIES TRADE REPORT.* 1987. bi-w. $100. American Water Foundation, 7341 S. Quarry Mtn., Littleton, CO 80217-3230. TEL 303-628-5516. FAX 303-236-5151. Ed. Michael R. Vaughan. bk.rev. circ. 100. (back issues avail.)
Description: Provides current information on trade opportunities, bids, and tenders in developing countries in the water sector.

WATER RESOURCES

627 FI ISSN 0783-9472
GB772.F5 CODEN: PWEIET
WATER AND ENVIRONMENT RESEARCH INSTITUTE. PUBLICATIONS. (Text in Finnish; summaries in English) 1972. irreg. price varies. Painatuskeskus Oy, P.O. Box 516, FIN-00101 Helsinki, Finland. TEL 90-56-601. FAX 90-566-0374. TELEX 123458 VAPK SF. illus. **Indexed:** Environ.Abstr. **Document type:** government publication, catalog.
—BLDSC (7116.955000); CASDDS; Ei.
  Formerly (until 1988): Vestientutkimuslaitos. Julkaisuja (ISSN 0355-0982)

338.7 II
WATER AND POWER DEVELOPMENT CONSULTANCY SERVICES. ANNUAL REPORT AND STATEMENT OF ACCOUNTS. (Report year ends Mar. 31) (Text in English) a. Water and Power Development Consultancy Services (India) Ltd., Kailash, 26 K. G. Marg, New Delhi 110001, India.

628.1 AT
WATER AND THE ENVIRONMENT. 1959. bi-m. Aus.$100 (includes Research Report Series and Annual Report). Water Research Foundation of Australia, c/o Centre for Resource and Environmental Studies, Australian National University, Canberra, A.C.T. 0200, Australia. TEL 61-6-249-0651. FAX 61-6-249-0757. circ. 1,000. **Indexed:** AESIS. **Document type:** academic/scholarly publication, newsletter.
  Formerly: Water Research Foundation of Australia. Newsletter.

628 UK ISSN 0043-1133
WATER AND WASTE TREATMENT. 1950. m. £50($96) (foreign £60) (effective 1995). Faversham House Group Ltd., Faversham House, 232a Addington Rd., South Croydon, Surrey CR2 8LE, England. TEL 44-181-651-7100. FAX 44-181-651-7117. adv.; bk.rev.; bibl.; charts; illus.; tr.lit. circ. 8,644. (also avail. in microform from MIM,UMI) **Indexed:** Biol.Abstr., BMT, Br.Ceram.Abstr., Br.Tech.Ind., Chem.Abstr., Environ.Per.Bibl., Excerp.Med., Intl.Civil Eng.Abstr., Pollut.Abstr., Sel.Water Res.Abstr., Soft.Abstr.Eng., W.R.C.Inf., World Text.Abstr. **Document type:** trade publication, academic/scholarly publication.
—UMI.

WATER AND WASTES DIGEST. see ENVIRONMENTAL STUDIES — Waste Management

333.91 UK ISSN 0262-9909
TD257
WATER BULLETIN. 1982. w. £45 (foreign £65). Water Services Association of England and Wales, 1 Queen Anne's Gate, London SW1H 9BT, England. TEL 071-957-4567. FAX 071-222-1811. Ed. Paul Garrett. adv.; bk.rev.; charts; illus. circ. 8,000. **Indexed:** Br.Tech.Ind., Chem.Abstr., Curr.Adv.Ecol.Sci., Fluidex, Geo.Abstr., W.R.C.Inf.
—BLDSC (9269.250000).
  Supersedes: Water (ISSN 0305-3105)

628.1 US ISSN 0746-4029
CODEN: WCPUEN
WATER CONDITIONING AND PURIFICATION. 1959. m. $39 (effective 1995). Publicom Inc., 2800 E. Ft. Lowell Rd., Tucson, AZ 85716-1518. FAX 520-323-7412. E-mail: publicom@rtd.com. Ed. Michelle Williams; Pub. Sharon Peterson. adv. contact: Jon Fritz. bk.rev.; charts; illus.; index; circ. 17,737 (controlled). **Indexed:** Environ.Abstr. **Document type:** trade publication.
—BLDSC (9269.450000); CIS.
  Former titles: Water Conditioning (ISSN 0043-1184); Water Conditioning Sales.
  Description: Covers industry news, regulatory developments, new products, and technical, marketing, sales and business management issues relating to water conditioning and purification.

628 US ISSN 0043-1206
WATER DESALINATION REPORT. 1965. w. $300 (typically set in Dec.) Maria C. Smith, Ed. & Pub., Box 10, Tracey's Landing, MD 20779. TEL 301-261-5010. FAX 301-261-5010. bk.rev. **Document type:** newsletter.

628 US ISSN 0273-2238
TD1 CODEN: WENMD2
WATER ENGINEERING AND MANAGEMENT. 1882. m. $25 (foreign $45). Scranton Gillette Communications, Inc., 380 E. Northwest Hwy., Des Plaines, IL 60016. TEL 708-298-6622. FAX 708-390-0408. adv.; bk.rev.; abstr.; charts; illus.; stat.; index, cum.index. circ. 41,000. (also avail. in microform from UMI) **Indexed:** A.S.& T.Ind., Abstr.Bull.Inst.Pap.Chem., Acid Pre.Dig., Anal.Abstr., Biol.Abstr., Chem.Abstr., Chem.Eng.Abstr., Curr.Adv.Ecol.Sci., Curr.Cont., Energy Info.Abstr., Eng.Ind., Environ.Abstr., Environ.Per.Bibl., Excerp.Med., Fluidex, Geo.Abstr., GeoRef., Intl.Civil Eng.Abstr., Ocean.Abstr., Pollut.Abstr., PROMT, Repindex, Sel.J.Water, Sel.Water Res.Abstr., Soft.Abstr.Eng., T.C.E.A., W.R.C.Inf. **Document type:** trade publication.
● Also available online. Vendor(s): University Microfilms International.
—BLDSC (9269.780000); CASDDS; Ei; Faxon; Genuine Article; SWETS; UMI; UnCover. **CCC.**
  Formerly (until 1981): Water and Sewage Works (ISSN 0043-1125); Incorporates (1964-1981): Water and Wastes Engineering (ISSN 0043-115X); Which was formerly: Water Works and Wastes Engineering (ISSN 0096-6320)
  Description: Informational articles pertaining to research on and the application of applied water and wastewater technology, with product and legislative updates.

WATER ENVIRONMENT & TECHNOLOGY. see ENVIRONMENTAL STUDIES

WATER ENVIRONMENT LABORATORY SOLUTIONS. see ENVIRONMENTAL STUDIES — Pollution

WATER ENVIRONMENT RESEARCH. see ENVIRONMENTAL STUDIES — Pollution

333.91 630 US ISSN 1051-0583
WATER FARMING JOURNAL; America's aquaculture news monthly. 1986. m. $19 (foreign $40). Carroll Trosclair and Associates, Inc., 3400 Neyrey Dr., Metairie, LA 70002. TEL 504-454-8934. FAX 504-488-4135. Ed. Carroll Trosclair. adv.; bk.rev.; charts; illus.; stat.; tr.lit. circ. 6,000. (back issues avail.)
  Description: Covers production, marketing, legislation, new technology, research and equipment relating to aquaculture.

333.91 US
WATER IMPACTS. 1980. m. free. Michigan State University, Institute of Water Research, 334 Natural Resources Bldg., East Lansing, MI 48824-1222. TEL 517-353-3742. FAX 517-353-1812. Ed. Lois G. Wolfson. bk.rev.; index. circ. 2,800. (back issues avail.) **Indexed:** Environ.Abstr. **Document type:** newsletter.

333.91 US ISSN 0250-8060
GB651
WATER INTERNATIONAL. 1975. q. $75 (foreign $90). International Water Resources Association, University of Illinois, 1101 W. Peabody Dr., Urbana, IL 61801. TEL 217-333-6275. FAX 217-244-6633. E-mail: g-stout@uiuc.edu. Ed. Glenn E. Stout. adv.; bk.rev.; bibl.; illus. circ. 1,800. (back issues avail.) **Indexed:** Abstr.Hyg., AESIS, Energy Ind., Energy Info.Abstr., Environ.Abstr., Environ.Per.Bibl. (1981-), Geo.Abstr., GeoRef., IDA, Irr.& Drain.Abstr., Repindex, Rural Devel.Abstr., Sel.Water Res.Abstr. **Document type:** academic/scholarly publication.
—BLDSC (9270.400000); Faxon; Genuine Article; SWETS; UnCover.
  Description: Provides members with news about IWRA, their activities, events in the international water resources field, and reports on water related topics.
  Refereed Serial

WATER INVESTMENT NEWSLETTER. see BUSINESS AND ECONOMICS — Investments

628 JA
WATER JAPAN; Japan's water works yearbook. (Editions in English, Japanese) 1966. a. 1600 Yen. (Journal of Water Works Industry - Suido Sangyo Shinbunsha) Suido Sangyo Shinbun Ltd., Osaka Godo Bldg., 1-5, Doyama-cho, Kita-ku, Osaka-shi 530, Japan. (And: 15-16, Shinbaura 2-chome, Minato-ku, Tokyo 108, Japan) Ed. Hiroshi Ishimaru. **Document type:** trade publication, directory.
  Formerly: Japan Water Works Association. Journal.
  Description: Discusses supply systems, quality management, pollution control. Includes international activities and an industry directory.

628.1 340 UK ISSN 0959-9754
KD1070.A13
WATER LAW. bi-m. $395 (foreign $395) (effective 1996). John Wiley & Sons Ltd., Journals, Baffins Ln., Chichester, W. Sussex PO19 1UD, England. TEL 01243-779777. FAX 01243-776128. TELEX 86290 WIBOOK G. (Subscr. in the Americas to: John Wiley & Sons, Inc., 605 Third Ave., New York, NY 10158. TEL 212-850-6645. FAX 212-850-6021) Ed.Bd. adv.; bk.rev. (also avail. in microform from UMI; back issues avail.) **Indexed:** Euro.LJI, LJI. **Document type:** academic/scholarly publication.
—BLDSC (9270.655000); SWETS.
  Description: Deals with the legal aspects of aquatic - environmental issues.
  Refereed Serial

WATER LAW NEWSLETTER. see LAW

628.1 UK ISSN 0963-9403
WATER MANAGEMENT EUROPE (YEAR); annual review of the European water and wastewater industry. 1992. a. £55. Sterling Publications Ltd. (Subsidiary of: Sterling Publishing Group Plc.), Garfield House, 86-88 Edgware Rd., London W2 2YW, England. TEL 0171-258-0066. Ed. Robin Wiseman. **Document type:** directory.
—BLDSC (9270.905000).

628 GH ISSN 0043-1265
WATER NEWS. 1968. bi-m. free. Ghana Water & Sewerage Corporation, Box M194, Accra, Ghana. Ed. E.Y. Frempong-Mensah. adv.; bk.rev. circ. 8,000. **Indexed:** AESIS.
  Former titles: Sewerage News; Water.

333.91 CN ISSN 0821-0233
WATER NEWS/NOUVELLES DE L'EAU. 1982. q. Canadian Water Resources Association - Association Canadienne des Ressources Hydriques, c/o Membership Services Office, PO Box 1329, Cambridge, ON N1R 7G6, Canada. TEL 519-622-4764. FAX 519-621-4844. Ed. Marie Sanderson. adv. **Document type:** academic/scholarly publication.
  Description: Provides news and information on branch and membership activities and disseminates water resource related information of a regional and national character.

628 333.91 US ISSN 0043-1273
WATER NEWSLETTER; water supply, waste disposal, conservation, pollution. (Includes free supplement: News and International Water Report) 1958. s-m. $219 (foreign $249) (effective Jan. 1994). Water Information Center, Inc., 1099 18th St., Ste. 2150, Denver, CO 80202. TEL 303-391-8799. FAX 303-294-1239. Ed. Judith M. Schoeck. bk.rev. **Document type:** newsletter.
—CCC.
  Incorporates: Research and Development News.

628.1 US
WATER POLICY REPORT. bi-w. $495 (foreign $545). Inside Washington Publishers, Box 7176, Benjamin Franklin Sta., Washington, DC 20044. TEL 703-416-8500. FAX 703-416-8543. **Document type:** newsletter.

614.7 US
WATER POLLUTION: A SERIES OF MONOGRAPHS. 1974. irreg., no.7, 1984. Academic Press, Inc., 525 B St., Ste. 1900, San Diego, CA 92101-4495. TEL 619-231-0926. FAX 619-699-6715. (Subscr. to: Order Dept., 6277 Sea Harbor Dr., 4th Fl., Orlando, FL 32887. TEL 800-321-5068) Eds. K.S. Speigler, J. Bregman. (reprint service avail. from ISI) **Document type:** monographic series.
  Refereed Serial

WATER RESOURCES

WATER POLLUTION CONTROL; a biweekly summary of industrial practices, regulatory trends, and control techniques. see ENVIRONMENTAL STUDIES — Pollution

628.1   UK   ISSN 1358-328X
WATER POLLUTION INCIDENTS IN ENGLAND AND WALES. 1992. a. £5.50. National Rivers Authority, Rivers House, Waterside Dr., Aztec West, Almondsbury, Bristol BS12 4UD, England. TEL 01454-624400. FAX 01454-624409. **Document type:** bulletin.

628.1   US   ISSN 0745-1512
WATER QUALITY ASSOCIATION NEWSLETTER. bi-m. membership. Water Quality Association, 4151 Naperville Rd., Lisle, IL 60532. TEL 708-505-0160. FAX 708-505-9637. Ed. Keith Reid; Pub. Edward J. Fierko. circ. 3,000.

333.9   CN   ISSN 0843-5871
WATER QUALITY DATA FOR ONTARIO LAKES AND STREAMS. CENTRAL REGION. 1965. a. free. Ministry of Environment and Energy, Water Resources Branch, 135 St. Clair Ave. W., Toronto, Ont. M4V 1M2, Canada. TEL 416-323-4321. FAX 416-323-4564.
   Supersedes in part (in 1982): Water Quality Data for Ontario Lakes and Streams (ISSN 0383-5472)

333.9   CN   ISSN 0843-5820
WATER QUALITY DATA FOR ONTARIO LAKES AND STREAMS. NORTHEASTERN REGION. 1965. a. free. Ministry of Environment and Energy, Water Resources Branch, 135 St. Clair Ave. W., Toronto, Ont. M4V 1P5, Canada. TEL 416-323-4321. FAX 416-323-4564.
   Supersedes in part (in 1982): Water Quality Data for Ontario Lakes and Streams (ISSN 0383-5472)

333.91   CN   ISSN 0843-5863
TD227.05
WATER QUALITY DATA FOR ONTARIO LAKES AND STREAMS. NORTHWESTERN REGION. 1965. a. free. Ministry of Environment and Energy, Water Resources Branch, 135 St. Clair Ave. W., Toronto, Ont. M4V 1P5, Canada. TEL 416-323-4321. FAX 416-323-4564.
   Supersedes in part (in 1982): Water Quality Data for Ontario Lakes and Streams (ISSN 0383-5472)

333.9   CN   ISSN 0843-5839
WATER QUALITY DATA FOR ONTARIO LAKES AND STREAMS. SOUTHEASTERN REGION. 1965. a. free. Ministry of Environment and Energy, Water Resources Branch, 135 St. Clair Ave. W., Toronto, Ont. M4V 1P5, Canada. TEL 416-323-4321. FAX 416-323-4564.
   Supersedes in part (in 1982): Water Quality Data for Ontario Lakes and Streams (ISSN 0383-5472)

333.9   CN   ISSN 0843-5847
WATER QUALITY DATA FOR ONTARIO LAKES AND STREAMS. SOUTHWESTERN REGION. 1965. a. free. Ministry of Environment and Energy, Water Resources Branch, 135 St. Clair Ave. W., Toronto, Ont. M4V 1P5, Canada. TEL 416-323-4321. FAX 416-323-4564.
   Supersedes in part (in 1982): Water Quality Data for Ontario Lakes and Streams (ISSN 0383-5472)

333.9   CN   ISSN 0843-5855
WATER QUALITY DATA FOR ONTARIO LAKES AND STREAMS. WEST CENTRAL REGION. 1965. a. free. Ministry of Environment and Energy, Water Resources Branch, 135 St. Clair Ave. W., Toronto, Ont. M4V 1P5, Canada. TEL 416-323-4321. FAX 416-323-4564.
   Supersedes in part (in 1982): Water Quality Data for Ontario Lakes and Streams (ISSN 0383-5472)

WATER QUALITY INTERNATIONAL. see ENVIRONMENTAL STUDIES — Pollution

WATER QUALITY RESEARCH JOURNAL OF CANADA. see ENVIRONMENTAL STUDIES — Pollution

627   UK   ISSN 0043-1354
TD420   CODEN: WATRAG
WATER RESEARCH. (Former name of sponsoring body: International Association on Water Pollution Research and Control) 1967. m. £1426($2268) (effective 1996). (International Association on Water Quality) Elsevier Science Ltd., Pergamon, P.O. Box 800, Kidlington, Oxford OX5 1DX, England. TEL 44-1865-843000. FAX 44-1865-843010. E-mail: nlinfo-f@elsevier.nl; usinfo-f@elsevier.com; forinfo-kyf04035@niftyserve.or.jp; Site addr.: http://www.elsevier.nl/. (Subscr. in U.S. and Canada to: Elsevier Science, 660 White Plains Rd., Tarrytown, NY 10591-5153. TEL 914-524-9200. FAX 914-333-2444) Ed. K.J. Ives. adv.; bk.rev.; charts; illus.; stat.; index, cum.index. circ. 3,800. (also avail. in microfiche from MIM; microfilm from UMI) **Indexed:** A.S.& T.Ind., Abstr.Bull.Inst.Pap.Chem., Acid Pre.Dig., Acid Rain Abstr., Acid Rain Ind., Biol.Abstr., Biol.& Agr.Ind., Biotech.Abstr., Chem.Abstr., Curr.Adv.Ecol.Sci., Curr.Cont., Curr.Ref.Fish Res., Deep Sea Res.& Oceanogr.Abstr., Ecol.Abstr., Energy Rev., Eng.Ind., Environ.Abstr., Environ.Per.Bibl. (1972-), Excerpt.Med., Food Sci.& Tech.Abstr., Geo.Abstr., Geol.Abstr., GeoRef., Helminthol.Abstr., IDA, Ind.Vet., INSPEC, Int.Abstr.Biol.Sci., Intl.Civil Eng.Abstr., Irr.& Drain.Abstr., Ocean.Abstr., Pig News & Info., Pollut.Abstr., Potato Abstr., Protozool.Abstr., Repindex, Sel.Water Res.Abstr., Soft.Abstr.Eng., Soils & Fert., Sport Fish.Abstr., Vet.Bull., W.R.C.Inf., Weed Abstr., Wild.Rev., Zoo.Rec. **Document type:** academic/scholarly publication.
   —BLDSC (9273.400000); CASDDS; Ei; EMDOCS; Faxon; Genuine Article; SWETS; UMI; UnCover. CCC.
   Description: Covers all aspects of the pollution of ground water, marine and fresh water, and the management of water resources and water quality.
   Refereed Serial

628.168   UK   ISSN 0954-5638
WATER RESEARCH CENTRE. ANNUAL REVIEW. 1974. a. free. Water Research Centre plc, P.O. Box 16, Henley Rd., Medmenham, Marlow, Bucks SL7 2HD, England. circ. 5,000.
   Formerly: Water Research Centre. Annual Report (ISSN 0143-2443); Formed by the merger of: Water Research Association. Report; Water Pollution Research.

628.1   AT
WATER RESEARCH FOUNDATION OF AUSTRALIA. ANNUAL REPORT. a. Aus.$100 (includes Research Report Series, Water and the Environment - Newsletter). Water Research Foundation of Australia, c/o Centre for Resource and Environmental Studies, Australian National University, Canberra, A.C.T. 0200, Australia. TEL 61-6-249-0651. FAX 61-6-249-0757.

628.1   AT   ISSN 0085-8021
TC521   CODEN: WRARB7
WATER RESEARCH FOUNDATION OF AUSTRALIA. RESEARCH REPORT. 1959. bi-m. Aus.$100 (includes Water and the Environment - Newsletter, and Annual Report). Water Research Foundation of Australia, c/o Centre for Resource and Environmental Studies, Australian National University, Canberra, A.C.T. 0200, Australia. TEL 61-6-2490651. FAX 61-6-2490757. bk.rev.; circ. 1,000 (paid). **Indexed:** Aus.Sci.Ind., Biol.Abstr., GeoRef. **Document type:** academic/scholarly publication, newsletter.
   Incorporates: Water Research Foundation of Australia. Bulletin (ISSN 0085-8013)

333.91   AT
WATER RESEARCH IN AUSTRALIA: CURRENT PROJECTS. 1982. a. free. Department of Primary Industries and Energy, G.P.O. Box 858, Canberra, A.C.T. 2601, Australia. FAX 062-724526. circ. 1,604. **Indexed:** AESIS.
   ●Also available online.
   Former titles: Water Research in Australia (ISSN 0810-736X); Inventory of Water Resources Research.

553.7 333.9   RU   ISSN 0097-8078
GB746   CODEN: WARED4
WATER RESOURCES. English translation of: Vodnye Resursy (RU ISSN 0321-0596) 1974. bi-m. $975 (foreign $1140) (effective 1996). (Russian Academy of Sciences) Interperiodica, Ul. Profsoyuznaya 90, Moscow 11784, Russia. TEL 7-095-3360066. FAX 7-095-3360666. (Dist. by: Plenum Publishing Corp., 233 Spring St., New York, NY 10013-1578. TEL 212-620-8468. FAX 212-463-0742) (Co-publisher: Maik Nauka) Ed. G.V. Voropaev. (also avail. in microfilm from JSC; back issues avail.) **Indexed:** Eng.Ind., Geo.Abstr., Irr.& Drain.Abstr., Saf.Sci.Abstr., Sel.Water Res.Abstr. **Document type:** academic/scholarly publication.
   —BLDSC (0431.700000); CASDDS; Faxon; SWETS; UMI; UnCover. CCC.
   Refereed Serial

333.91   US
WATER RESOURCES ASSOCIATION OF THE DELAWARE RIVER BASIN. ALERTING BULLETIN. irreg., no.228, 1988. membership. Water Resources Association of the Delaware River Basin, Box 867, Davis Rd., Valley Forge, PA 19482. TEL 610-783-0634. FAX 610-783-0635.

333.91   US
WATER RESOURCES ASSOCIATION OF THE DELAWARE RIVER BASIN. NEWSLETTER. 1962. q., with m. supplements. membership. Water Resources Association of the Delaware River Basin, Box 867, Davis Rd., Valley Forge, PA 19482. TEL 610-783-0634. FAX 610-783-0635. Ed. William Palmer. circ. 1,500. **Document type:** newsletter.

628 333.91   US   ISSN 0043-1370
GB651   CODEN: WARBAQ
WATER RESOURCES BULLETIN; a journal of water resources research, planning, development and management. 1965. bi-m. $115 (foreign $135). American Water Resources Association, 950 Herndon Pky., Ste. 300, Herndon, VA 22070-5531. TEL 703-904-1225. FAX 703-904-1228. Ed. William Lord. bk.rev.; abstr.; charts; illus.; index. circ. 4,000. (also avail. in microform from UMI) **Indexed:** Acid Rain Abstr., Acid Rain Ind., Agri.Eng.Abstr., Biol.Abstr., Chem.Abstr., Crop Physiol.Abstr., Curr.Adv.Ecol.Sci., Curr.Cont., Energy Info.Abstr., Eng.Ind., Environ.Abstr., Environ.Ind., Environ.Per.Bibl. (1984-), Excerpt.Med., Field Crop Abstr., Forest.Abstr., Geo.Abstr., GeoRef., Intl.Civil Eng.Abstr., Irr.& Drain.Abstr., Meteor.& Geoastrophys.Abstr., Ocean.Abstr., Pollut.Abstr., Repindex, Rural Recreat.Tour.Abstr., Sel.J.Water, Sel.Water Res.Abstr., So.Pac.Per.Ind., Soft.Abstr.Eng., Soils & Fert., Soyabean Abstr., Sport Fish.Abstr., W.R.C.Inf., Wild.Rev., World Agri.Econ.& Rural Sociol.Abstr., Zoo.Rec. **Document type:** bulletin.
   —BLDSC (9273.750000); CASDDS; CIS; Ei; Faxon; Genuine Article; SWETS; UMI; UnCover.
   Description: Publishes original papers covering water resources issues. Includes litigation and legislation issues.
   Refereed Serial

333.91   US
WATER RESOURCES DEVELOPMENT IN NORTH CAROLINA (YEAR). biennial. free. U.S. Army Corps of Engineers, South Atlantic Division, 77 Forsyth St., S.W., Atlanta, GA 30335-6801. TEL 404-331-6698. FAX 404-331-6697. circ. 2,000. **Document type:** government publication.
   Description: Summarizes the status of all Corps of Engineers civil works studies and projects within the state of North Carolina.

333.91   UN   ISSN 0377-8053
JX1977
WATER RESOURCES JOURNAL. 1949. q. free. United Nations Economic and Social Commission for Asia and the Pacific (ESCAP), United Nations Bldg., Rajadamnern Ave, Bangkok 10200, Thailand. (also avail. in microfiche from CIS) **Indexed:** GeoRef., IIS, Rural Recreat.Tour.Abstr., Sel.Water Res.Abstr., World Agri.Econ. & Rural Sociol.Abstr.
   —BLDSC (9273.900000).
   Formerly: Flood Control Journal (ISSN 1010-531X)

333.91 NE ISSN 0920-4741
TC401 CODEN: WRMAEJ
WATER RESOURCES MANAGEMENT. (Text in English) 1987. bi-m. fl.543 to institutions; $348 to institutions in U.S. (effective 1996). (European Water Resources Association) Kluwer Academic Publishers, Postbus 17, 3300 AA Dordrecht, Netherlands. TEL 31-78-392392. FAX 31-78-392254. TELEX 29245 KAPG NL. E-mail: SERVICES@WKAP.NL. (Dist. by: Kluwer Academic Publishers Group, P.O. Box 322, 3300 AH Dordrecht, Netherlands. TEL 31-78-392392. FAX 31-78-546474; N. America dist. addr.: Box 358, Accord Sta., Hingham, MA 02018-0358. TEL 617-871-6600. FAX 617-871-6528) Ed. G. Tsakiris. (also avail. in microform from UMI; back issues avail.; reprint service avail. from SWZ) **Indexed:** Agri.Eng.Abstr., Bull.Signal., Ecol.Abstr., Environ.Abstr., Environ.Per.Bibl. (1992-), Field Crop Abstr., Geo.Abstr., Geol.Abstr., IDA, Irr.& Drain.Abstr., Soils & Fert. **Document type:** academic/scholarly publication.
—CIS; Ei; Faxon; SWETS; UMI; UnCover. **CCC.**
Description: Multidisciplinary forum for the presentation of original research in the management of water resources, including assessment, development, conservation and control, with an emphasis on policy and strategy, as well as the planning, operation, maintenance and administration of water resource systems.
Refereed Serial

333.91 620 US ISSN 0270-9600
CODEN: WRMSE5
WATER RESOURCES MONOGRAPHS. 1971. irreg. American Geophysical Union, 2000 Florida Ave., N.W., Washington, DC 20009. TEL 202-462-6900. FAX 202-328-0566. TELEX 710-822-9300. (reprint service avail. from ISI) **Indexed:** GeoRef., INSPEC. **Document type:** monographic series.
—**CCC.**

551.4 US ISSN 0043-1397
GB651 CODEN: WRERAQ
WATER RESOURCES RESEARCH. 1965. m. $675 to non-members (foreign $710); members $115 (foreign $150); students $58 (foreign $93). American Geophysical Union, 2000 Florida Ave., N.W., Washington, DC 20009. TEL 202-462-6900. FAX 202-328-0566. TELEX 710-822-9300. Ed. George Hornberger. abstr.; charts; illus.; index. circ. 4,000. (also avail. in microform from AGU; reprint service avail. from ISI) **Indexed:** Acid Pre.Dig., Acid Rain Abstr., Acid Rain Ind., AESIS, Agri.Eng.Abstr., Appl.Mech.Rev., Biol.Abstr., Chem.Abstr., Curr.Adv.Ecol.Sci., Curr.Cont., Deep Sea Res.& Oceanogr.Abstr., Ecol.Abstr., Energy Ind., Energy Info.Abstr., Environ.Abstr., Environ.Per.Bibl., Excerp.Med., Field Crop Abstr., Fluidex., Forest.Abstr., Forest Prod.Abstr., Geo.Abstr., Geol.Abstr., GeoRef., Geotech.Abstr., Herb.Abstr., IDA, INSPEC, Int.Abstr.Oper.Res., Int.Aerosp.Abstr., Intl.Civil Eng.Abstr., Irr.& Drain.Abstr., J.of Econ.Lit., Meteor.& Geoastrophys.Abstr., Ocean.Abstr., Petrol.Abstr., Pollut.Abstr., Repindex, Risk Abstr., Rural Recreat.Tour.Abstr., Sel.J.Water, Sel.Water Res.Abstr., Soft.Abstr.Eng., Soils & Fert., Sport Fish.Abstr., Triticale Abstr., W.R.C.Inf., Wild.Rev., World Agri.Econ.& Rural Sociol.Abstr.
—BLDSC (9275.150000); CASDDS; Faxon; Genuine Article; PADDS; SWETS; UnCover. **CCC.**
Description: Provides a comprehensive source for students, scientists, and engineers to obtain the latest ideas conserning hydrologic processes in the environment.

551.4 333.9 US ISSN 0518-6374
TC424.A8 CODEN: AGWAAI
WATER RESOURCES SUMMARY. (Former name of issuing body: Arkansas Geological and Conservation Commission) 1962. irreg., no.16, 1985. price varies. Geological Commission, Vardelle Parham Geology Center, 3815 W. Roosevelt Rd, Little Rock, AR 72204. TEL 501-663-9714. illus.

333.9 SA ISSN 0378-4738
TD201 CODEN: WASADV
WATER S.A.. (Text in Afrikaans, English; summaries in English) 1975. q. free. Water Research Commission - Waternavorsingskommissie, P.O. Box 824, Pretoria 0001, South Africa. Ed. Ingrid Buchan. abstr.; bibl.; charts. circ. 3,200. (back issues avail.; reprint service avail. from ISI) **Indexed:** Abstr.Bull.Inst.Pap.Chem., Acid Rain Abstr., Acid Rain Ind., Agri.Eng.Abstr., Biol.Abstr., Chem.Abstr., Curr.Adv.Ecol.Sci., Curr.Cont., Eng.Ind., Environ.Abstr., Ind.S.A.Per., Irr.& Drain.Abstr., J.of Ferroc., Maize Abstr., Ocean.Abstr., Pollut.Abstr., Sci.Cit.Ind., Sel.J.Water, Sel.Water Res.Abstr., Soils & Fert., Sport Fish.Abstr., W.R.C.Inf., Water Resour.Abstr., Wild.Rev., Zoo.Rec. **Document type:** academic/scholarly publication.
—BLDSC (9275.430000); CASDDS; CIS; Ei; Faxon; Genuine Article; UMI; UnCover.
Description: Contains original work in all branches of water science, technology, and engineering.
Refereed Serial

333.91 628.168 UK ISSN 0273-1223
TD419 CODEN: WSTED4
WATER SCIENCE AND TECHNOLOGY. (Former name of sponsoring body: International Association of Water Pollution Research and Control) 1972. 24/yr. £1690($2688) (effective 1996). (International Association on Water Quality) Elsevier Science Ltd., Pergamon, P.O. Box 800, Kidlington, Oxford OX5 1DX, England. TEL 44-1865-843000. FAX 44-1865-843010. E-mail: nlinfo-f@elsevier.nl; usinfo-f@elsevier.com; forinfo-kyf04035@niftyserve.or.jp; Site addr.: http://www.elsevier.nl/. (Subscr. in U.S. and Canada to: Elsevier Science, 660 White Plains Rd., Tarrytown, NY 10591-5153. TEL 914-524-9200. FAX 914-333-2444) Ed. Elizabeth Izod. adv.; index. (also avail. in microfilm from UMI; back issues avail.) **Indexed:** Acid Rain Abstr., Acid Rain Ind., Biol.Abstr., Biotech.Abstr., Chem.Abstr., Curr.Adv.Ecol.Sci., Curr.Ref.Fish Res., Dairy Sci.Abstr., Energy Rev., Environ.Abstr., Environ.Ind., Environ.Per.Bibl. (1992-), Excerp.Med., Fluidex, Food Sci.& Tech.Abstr., Geo.Abstr., Geol.Abstr., GeoRef., IDA, J.of Ferroc., Ocean.Abstr., Pollut.Abstr., Repindex, Risk Abstr., Sel.J.Water, Sel.Water Res.Abstr., Soils & Fert., Sport Fish.Abstr., Sugar Ind.Abstr., Wild.Rev., Zoo.Rec. **Document type:** academic/scholarly publication.
—BLDSC (9275.445000); CASDDS; Ei; Faxon; Genuine Article; SWETS; UMI; UnCover. **CCC.**
Supersedes: International Conference on Water Pollution Research. Proceedings; Which was formerly (until 1981): Progress in Water Technology (ISSN 0306-6746).
Refereed Serial

551.4 NE ISSN 0921-092X
WATER SCIENCE AND TECHNOLOGY LIBRARY. (Text in English) 1982. irreg., vol.12, 1994. price varies. Kluwer Academic Publishers, Postbus 17, 3300 AA Dordrecht, Netherlands. TEL 31-78-392392. FAX 31-78-392254. TELEX 29245 KAPG NL. (Dist. by: Kluwer Academic Publishers Group, P.O. Box 322, 3300 AH Dordrecht, Netherlands. TEL 31-78-392392. FAX 31-78-546474; N. America dist. addr.: Box 358, Accord Sta., Hingham, MA 02018-0358. TEL 617-871-6600. FAX 617-871-6528) **Indexed:** INSPEC. **Document type:** monographic series, proceedings.
Refereed Serial

628.1 SA ISSN 0257-8700
WATER SEWAGE AND EFFLUENT. 1980. q. R.45 (Southern Africa R.55; elsewhere R.95) (effective Aug. 1995). Brooke Pattrick (Pty) Ltd., P.O. Box 422, Bedfordview 2008, South Africa. TEL 27-11-6224666. FAX 27-11-6167196. Ed. Helen Gow. adv. contact: John Pattrick. bk.rev.; circ. 3,210. **Indexed:** Ind.S.A.Per., W.R.C.Inf. **Document type:** trade publication.
—BLDSC (9275.480000).
Description: Concerns itself with all aspects of water, agriculture and industry. Seeks to inform about issues regarding the collection, conveyance and storage of source water, and related topics.

628.1 UK ISSN 0735-1917
TD201 CODEN: WASUDN
WATER SUPPLY. (Text in English and French) 1983. q. £422($679) (effective 1996). (International Water Supply Association) Blackwell Science Ltd., Osney Mead, Oxford OX2 0EL, England. TEL 01865-206206. FAX 01865-206219. TELEX 83355 MEDBOK G. Ed. L.R. Bays. adv. circ. 2,800. (also avail. in microform from UMI; back issues avail.) **Indexed:** Biol.Abstr., Curr.Adv.Ecol.Sci., Curr.Cont., Environ.Abstr., Environ.Per.Bibl. (1989-), Geo.Abstr., Repindex, W.R.C.Inf. **Document type:** proceedings.
—BLDSC (9275.680000); CASDDS; Ei; Faxon; SWETS; UMI. **CCC.**
Incorporates (in 1983): International Water Supply Congress. Proceedings (ISSN 0074-9583)
Description: Publishes research presented at selected I.W.S.A. congresses, conferences, and workshops.

628 NE ISSN 0169-2577
WATER SUPPLY AND WASTEWATER DISPOSAL - INTERNATIONAL ALMANAC. (Text in English, French, German) 1976. a. $70. International Institute for Water Supply and Wastewater Disposal, Gooiland 11, 2716 BP Zoetermeer, Netherlands. TEL 31-79-210-126. Eds. A. Kepinski, W.A.S. Kepinski. bk.rev. circ. 750. **Document type:** monographic series, bibliography.
—BLDSC (9275.830000).

333.91 US
WATER SUPPLY OUTLOOK FOR THE WESTERN UNITED STATES.* 6/yr. free. U.S. Soil Conservation Service (Portland), West National Technical Service Center, 101 S.W. Main St., Ste. 1700, Portland, OR 97204-3225. TEL 503-326-2843. Eds. C. Pachecko, J. Matheson. circ. 1,500. (also avail. in microfiche from CIS; reprint service avail. from CIS) **Indexed:** Amer.Stat.Ind. (1973-).

614.7 US ISSN 0192-3633
CODEN: WATTEQ
WATER TECHNOLOGY; the magazine for the water treatment professional. 1978. m. $42. National Trade Publications, Inc., 13 Century Hill, Latham, NY 12110-2197. TEL 518-783-1281. FAX 518-783-1386. Ed. Mark Wilson. adv.: B&W page $2375; trim 8 1/8 x 10 7/8; adv. contact: Charlotte Prior. circ. 17,680 (controlled). **Indexed:** Corros.Abstr. **Document type:** trade publication.
—BLDSC (9277.750000); Faxon. **CCC.**

628.167 CC ISSN 0921-2639
TD430 CODEN: WTREE2
WATER TREATMENT. Chinese Edition: Shui Chuli. (Editions in Chinese, English) q. $152 or fl.580 (effective 1994). (Guojia Haiyang-ju, Hangzhou Shui Chuli Jishu Kaifa Zhongxin) China Ocean Press, International Cooperation Department, Haimao Dalou, 1 Fuxingmenwai Dajie, Beijing 100860, People's Republic of China. TEL 8032211. FAX 8033515. TELEX 22536 NBO CN. Ed. Shi Song. **Indexed:** Chem.Eng.Abstr., T.C.E.A. **Document type:** academic/scholarly publication.
—BLDSC (9278.250000); CASDDS; Ei; SWETS. **CCC.**
Description: Publishes scientific papers, monographs, research reports, and reviews on applied techniques of water treatment. Includes special topics such as membrane separation, desalination, and other treatment techniques using physical chemistry and biochemistry methods.
Refereed Serial

628.1 US ISSN 0043-1443
TD405 CODEN: WWJOA9
WATER WELL JOURNAL. 1946. m. $26 (foreign $52). Ground Water Publishing Co., 6375 Riverside Dr., Dublin, OH 43017. TEL 614-761-3222. Ed. Anita B. Stanley. adv.; tr.lit.; index. circ. 35,000. (reprint service avail. from UMI) **Indexed:** Eng.Ind., Environ.Abstr., Excerp.Med., Geo.Abstr., GeoRef., Repindex, Sel.Water Res.Abstr.
—BLDSC (9278.500000); Ei; Faxon; SWETS; UnCover. **CCC.**

333.91 US
WATER WRITES. 1993. m. Rutgers University, Water Resources Research Institute, Institute of Marine and Coastal Sciences, Doolittle Hall 105, Busch Campus, New Brunswick, NJ 08903. Ed. Aviva Zuller. illus. **Document type:** newsletter.

WATER RESOURCES

628.1 UK ISSN 0262-8104
WATERLINES; the journal of appropriate water supply and sanitation technologies. 1982. q. £15($28) to individuals; institutions £20 ($37) (effective 1996). Intermediate Technology Publications Ltd., 103-105 Southampton Row, London WC1B 4HH, England. TEL 0171-436-9761. FAX 0171-436-2013. TELEX 888 941 A/BLCCI G. E-mail: itpubs@gn.apc.org. Ed. Kimberly Clarke. adv.; bk.rev. **Indexed:** Abstr.Hyg., Abstr.Rural Dev.Trop., Fluidex, Geo.Abstr., IDA, Repindex, Rural Devel.Abstr., Rural Ext.Educ.& Tr.Abstr., W.R.C.Inf. **Document type:** academic/scholarly publication.
—BLDSC (9279.428000).
Description: Devoted entirely to low-cost water supply and sanitation.
Refereed Serial

333.91 US ISSN 0894-511X
CODEN: WATME5
WATERMARKS. 1965. irreg. (3-4/yr.). free. University of Texas at Austin, Center for Research in Water Resources, Balcones Research Center, 10100 Burnet Rd., Austin, TX 78712. TEL 512-471-3131. Ed. Michelle Gilson. bk.rev. circ. 3,000. **Document type:** academic/scholarly publication, newsletter.
Former titles: Center for Research in Water Resources Newsletter; C R W R News (ISSN 0049-3538)
Description: Details current work in progress at the center.

628 NE ISSN 1380-4251
HD1683.N2
HET WATERSCHAP; veertiendaags tijdschrift voor waterschapsbestuur en waterschapsbeheer. 1915. 24/yr. fl.120 (foreign fl.152; students fl.110). Unie van Waterschappen - Association of Water Boards, Johan van Oldenbarneveltlaan 5, P.O. Box 80 200, 2508 GE The Hague, Netherlands. TEL 31-70-3519751. FAX 31-70-3544642. Ed.Bd. adv.; bk.rev.; index. circ. 3,400. **Indexed:** Excerp.Med., Key to Econ.Sci. **Document type:** trade publication.
Formerly: Waterschapsbelangen (ISSN 0043-1486)
Description: Covers current news and information concerning the waterboards. Features studies, laws, safety, new projects, government, technical subjects, and environmental protection. Includes list of events and courses, positions available.

628.1 US
WATERWEEK; incorporating Washington Report. 1992. bi-w. $150 to non-members; members $100. American Water Works Association, 6666 W. Quincy Ave., Denver, CO 80235. TEL 303-794-7711. Ed. Mark Scharfenaker. **Document type:** trade publication.
Description: Contains news and analysis of the drinking water field.

627 US
TD430
WATERWORLD; serving municipal water and wastewater industries. 1984. 8/yr. $25. PennWell Publishing Co., Box 1260, Tulsa, OK 74101. TEL 918-835-3161. FAX 918-831-9476. Ed. James Laughlin; Pub. L. John Ford. adv.; tr.lit. circ. 100,000. (tabloid format; reprint service avail.) **Indexed:** Energy Rev., Environ.Abstr., Ind.Hyg.Dig. **Document type:** trade publication.
—Ei; UnCover. **CCC.**
Former titles (until 1995): Waterworld Review (ISSN 1068-5839); (until 1993): Waterworld News (ISSN 0747-9735)
Description: For engineers, managers, consultants and operations people in the municipal water and wastewater industries.

551.4 US ISSN 0271-230X
WELL LOG. 1967. m. $145 to non-members. National Ground Water Association, 6375 Riverside Dr., Dublin, OH 43017. TEL 614-761-1711. FAX 614-761-3446. circ. 6,000. **Document type:** newsletter.
Description: Association and industry news.

628.44 CN ISSN 0835-0698
WESTERN CANADA WATER AND WASTE WATER ASSOCIATION. BULLETIN. 1949; N.S. 1983. q. Can.$45. Western Canada Water and Waste Water Association, Ste. 130, 1209 59 Ave. S.E., Calgary, AB T2H 2P6, Canada. TEL 403-259-4041. FAX 403-258-1631. (Subscr. to: Box 6168, Sta. A, Calgary, AB T2H 2L4, Canada) Ed. M.M. Janice Taylor. adv. contact: M.M. Janice Taylor. bk.rev. circ. 3,000. **Indexed:** Environ.Abstr. **Document type:** bulletin, directory.
Former titles: Western Canada Water and Sewage Conference. Bulletin; Western Canada Water and Sewage Conference. Papers Presented at Annual Convention (ISSN 0083-8799)
Description: Presents regional news, technical articles, committee and president's reports.

333.9 627 US ISSN 0735-5424
WESTERN WATER. vol.25, 1973. bi-m. $25. Water Education Foundation, 717 K St., No. 517, Sacramento, CA 95814-3406. FAX 916-448-7699. Ed. Rita Schmidt Sudman. bk.rev.; illus.; tr.lit. circ. 15,000. (back issues avail.) **Indexed:** Environ.Per.Bibl. (1990-), P.A.I.S.
Description: Explores various aspects of water resources in California.

620.85 331.91 US ISSN 0277-5212
QH75.A1 CODEN: WETLEU
WETLANDS. 1981. q. $40 includes membership; libraries $100. Society of Wetlands Scientists, Box 1897, Lawrence, KS 66044. TEL 913-843-1235. FAX 913-843-1274. Ed. Douglas A. Wilcox. bk.rev.; abstr.; circ. 3,800 (paid). **Indexed:** Aqua.Sci.& Fish.Abstr., Biol.Abstr., Curr.Cont., Ecol.Abstr., Entomol.Abstr., Ocean.Abstr., SPort Fish.Abstr., Wild.Rev., Zoo.Rec. **Document type:** academic/scholarly publication.
—BLDSC (9306.630800); Faxon; Genuine Article.
Description: Publishes interdisciplinary research on all aspects of freshwater and estuarine wetlands biology, ecology, hydrology, soil and sediment characteristics, as well as management, legal, and regulatory issues.
Refereed Serial

620.85 628.1 NE ISSN 0923-4861
CODEN: WEMAEU
WETLANDS ECOLOGY AND MANAGEMENT. (Text in English) 1989. 4/yr. fl.255($145) (effective 1995). S P B Academic Publishing b.v., P.O. Box 11188, 1001 GD Amsterdam, Netherlands. Ed. Eugene Turner. **Indexed:** Ecol.Abstr., Geo.Abstr. **Document type:** academic/scholarly publication.
—BLDSC (9306.632000); UnCover.
Description: Publishes research and review papers on fundamental and applied aspects of wetlands of freshwater, brackish or marine origin, as well as contributions on integrated wetlands research and management, and topics including techno-cultural transformations, pollution impact, and environmental conservation.
Refereed Serial

333.91 UK
WHO'S WHO IN THE WATER INDUSTRY. 1975. a. £32. (Water Services Association) Turret Group Plc., Turret House, 171 High St., Rickmansworth, Herts WD3 1SN, England. TEL 01923-777000. FAX 01923-771297. Ed. Donna Burnell. adv. circ. 4,500. **Document type:** directory.

627 333.91 AU ISSN 0379-5349
TD203 CODEN: WMWAAU
WIENER MITTEILUNGEN: WASSER, ABWASSER, GEWAESSER. 1968. irreg. price varies. Technische Universitaet Wien, Institut fuer Wasserguete und Abfallwirtschaft, A-1040 Vienna, Austria. FAX 0222-5042234. (Co-sponsors: Institute for Hydraulik, Gewaesserkunde und Wasserwirtschaft; Universitaet fuer Bodenkultur) circ. 350. **Indexed:** Chem.Abstr.
—BLDSC (9315.928000); CASDDS.

628.168 US
TD224.W6
WISCONSIN. DEPARTMENT OF NATURAL RESOURCES. BIENNIAL WATER QUALITY REPORT TO CONGRESS. biennial. Department of Natural Resources, WR-2 Box 7921, Madison, WI 53707. TEL 608-266-0152. illus. **Document type:** government publication.
Former titles (until 1989): Wisconsin. Department of Natural Resources. Water Quality Report to Congress (Year) (ISSN 0740-4700); (until 1982): Wisconsin. Department of Natural Resources. Water Quality Inventory Report to Congress (ISSN 0191-3190); (until 1975): Wisconsin. Department of Natural Resources. Annual Water Quality Report to Congress (ISSN 0362-5354)

628.167 UK ISSN 1354-313X
TD201
WORLD WATER AND ENVIRONMENTAL ENGINEERING. 1978. 10/yr. £80($144) (foreign £90) (effective 1995). Faversham House Group Ltd., Faversham House, 232a Addington Rd., South Croydon, Surrey CR2 8LE, England. TEL 44-181-651-7100. FAX 44-181-651-7117. Ed. Andreas King. adv. contact: Sebastian Smith. circ. 10,333. (back issues avail.) **Indexed:** AESIS, Environ.Per.Bibl. (1991-), Excerp.Med., Fluidex, Geo.Abstr., GeoRef., J.of Ferroc., Key to Econ.Sci., Repindex, W.R.C.Inf. **Document type:** trade publication, academic/scholarly publication.
—BLDSC (9360.176400); SWETS; UnCover.
Former titles (until 1995): World Water and Environmental Engineer (ISSN 0963-584X); (until 1990): World Water (ISSN 0140-9050)
Description: Covers international water and wastewater industry. Oriented toward administrators, engineers, and government officials. Emphasizes European issues.

333.91 UK
WORLD WATER DEVELOPING WORLD BULLETIN. 1992. q. Thomas Telford Ltd., Thomas Telford House, 1 Heron Quay, London E14 4JD, England. TEL 44-71-987-6999. FAX 44-71-538-9849. Ed. Roy Opie. adv.: B&W page $1980; trim 8 1/4 x 11 1/4. circ. 7,560. **Indexed:** Environ.Per.Bibl. (1992-).
Description: Reports on all safe water and sanitation issues initiated by the UN Water Decade.

628.1 JA
WOTA SAIENSU KENKYUKAI SEMINA YOKOSHU/WATER SCIENCE INSTITUTE. SEMINAR PROCEEDINGS. (Text in Japanese) 1989. m. 5000 Yen per no. Wota Saiensu Kenkyukai, Tekuno Manejimento Kenkyukai, 9-11, Minamisenba 4-chome, Chuo-ku, Osaka-shi, Osaka 542, Japan. **Document type:** proceedings.

333.9 US
HC107.W93
WYOMING. WATER QUALITY DIVISION. STATE - E P A AGREEMENT. (Environmental Protection Agency) a. Department of Environmental Quality, Water Quality Division, Cheyenne, WY 82002. TEL 307-777-7781. FAX 307-777-5973.
Formerly: Wyoming. Water Quality Division. Wyoming State Plan (ISSN 0098-0846)

YEARS AHEAD. see *PUBLIC HEALTH AND SAFETY*

ZAHLENTAFELN DER PHYSIKALISCH-CHEMISCHEN UNTERSUCHUNGEN DES RHEINWASSERS/TABLEAUX NUMERIQUES DES ANALYSES PHYSICO-CHIMIQUES DES EAUX DU RHIN. see *ENVIRONMENTAL STUDIES — Pollution*

333.91 627 ZA ISSN 0084-4705
ZAMBIA. DEPARTMENT OF WATER AFFAIRS. REPORT. 1964. a. K.200. Zambia Government Printing Department, P.O. Box 30136, Lusaka, Zambia. **Document type:** government publication.
Description: Reviews hydrogeological concerns in Zambia.

ZAMBIA. MINISTRY OF AGRICULTURE AND WATER DEVELOPMENT. LAND USE BRANCH. SOIL SURVEY REPORT. see *AGRICULTURE — Crop Production And Soil*

628 340   GW   ISSN 0722-8910
ZEITSCHRIFT FUER WASSERRECHT. 1961. 4/yr. (plus 1 special no.). DM.198. Carl Heymanns Verlag KG, Luxemburgerstr. 449, 50939 Cologne, Germany. TEL 0221-94373-0. FAX 0221-94373901. Ed. Dr. Manfred Czychowski. adv.; bk.rev. circ. 500. **Document type:** bulletin.
—SWETS.

WATER RESOURCES — Abstracting, Bibliographies, Statistics

628.1 614.7 016   UK
AQUALERT; selective dissemination of information. 12/yr. £195 (effective 1993). Water Research Centre, P.O. Box 85, Frankland Rd., Blagrove, Swindon, Wilts SN5 8YF, England. **Document type:** abstracting/indexing.
Description: Provides a selection of current abstracts from the Aqualine database on topics of interest to the water industry according to subscriber's specific information needs.

628.1 614.7 016   UK   ISSN 0748-2531
AQUALINE ABSTRACTS. Variant title: Aqualine. 1927. 12/yr. £600 (effective 1995). Water Research Centre, P.O. Box 85, Frankland Rd., Blagrove, Swindon, Wilts SN5 8YF, England. Ed. Karen Hutcheson. bibl. circ. 3,600. **Indexed:** Abstr.Bull.Inst.Pap.Chem., Anal.Abstr., Fluidex, Ind.Vet., Vet.Bull., Weed Abstr., World Text.Abstr. **Document type:** abstracting/indexing.
●Also available online. Vendor(s): European Space Agency, Orbit Search Service (AQUA).
—CCC.
Formerly (until 1985): W R C Information (ISSN 0306-6649); **Supersedes:** Water Pollution Abstracts (ISSN 0043-1281)

551.46 639.3 016
333.7   US   ISSN 0140-5373
AQUATIC SCIENCES & FISHERIES ABSTRACTS. PART 1: BIOLOGICAL SCIENCES AND LIVING RESOURCES. 1971. m. $985 (foreign $995). (Food and Agriculture Organization of the U.N.) Cambridge Scientific Abstracts, 7200 Wisconsin Ave., 6th Fl., Bethesda, MD 20814. TEL 301-961-6750. FAX 301-961-6720. E-mail: market@csa.com. (Co-sponsors: U.N. Division for Ocean Affairs and the Law of the Sea; U.N. Environment Programme; Intergovernmental Oceanographic Commission) Ed. R. Pepe; Pub. Ted Caris. adv.; abstr.; bibl.; index. (also avail. in magnetic tape; back issues avail.) **Indexed:** Cal.Tiss.Abstr., Chemorec.Abstr., Oncol.Abstr., Pollut.Abstr., Sport Fish.Abstr., Weed Abstr., Wild.Rev. **Document type:** abstracting/indexing.
●Also available online. Vendor(s): CISTI, DIMDI, Knight-Ridder, Inc. (File no.44), European Space Agency, STN International.
Also available on CD-ROM. Producer(s): NISC, SilverPlatter Information, Inc.
—BLDSC (1582.460000).
Supersedes in part: Aquatic Sciences and Fisheries Abstracts (ISSN 0044-8516); Which was formed by the merger of: Aquatic Biology Abstracts (ISSN 0003-7311); Current Bibliography for Aquatic Sciences and Fisheries (ISSN 0011-3239)
Description: International network of aquatic science centers' studies on marine, freshwater and brackish water organisms.

551.46 639.3 016   US   ISSN 0140-5381
AQUATIC SCIENCES & FISHERIES ABSTRACTS. PART 2: OCEAN TECHNOLOGY, POLICY AND NON-LIVING RESOURCES. 1969. m. $735 (foreign $835). (Food and Agriculture Organization of the U.N.) Cambridge Scientific Abstracts, 7200 Wisconsin Ave., 6th Fl., Bethesda, MD 20814. TEL 301-961-6750. FAX 301-961-6720. E-mail: market@csa.com. (Co-sponsors: U.N. Division for Ocean Affairs and the Law of the Sea; U.N. Environment Programme; Intergovernmental Oceanographic Commission) Ed. R. Pepe; Pub. Ted Caris. adv.; abstr.; bibl.; index. (also avail. in magnetic tape; back issues avail.) **Indexed:** Cal.Tiss.Abstr., Chemorec.Abstr., Comput.& Info.Sys., Oncol.Abstr., Pollut.Abstr., Weed Abstr. **Document type:** abstracting/indexing.
●Also available online. Vendor(s): CISTI, DIMDI, Knight-Ridder, Inc. (File no.44), European Space Agency, STN International.
Also available on CD-ROM. Producer(s): NISC, SilverPlatter Information, Inc.
—BLDSC (1582.470000).
Supersedes in part: Aquatic Sciences and Fisheries Abstracts (ISSN 0044-8516); Which was formed by the merger of: Aquatic Biology Abstracts (ISSN 0003-7311); Current Bibliography for Aquatic Sciences and Fisheries (ISSN 0011-3239)
Description: International network of aquatic science centers' studies on ocean resources, offshore and coastal structures and oceanography.

333.91 620   PL   ISSN 0239-622X
BIBLIOGRAFIA GOSPODARKI I INZYNIERII WODNEJ/BIBLIOGRAPHY OF WATER MANAGEMENT AND ENGINEERING. (Text in English, French, German, Polish, Russian) 1977. irreg. $75. Instytut Meteorologii i Gospodarki Wodnej - Institute of Meteorology and Water Management, 61 Podlesna St., 01-673 Warsaw, Poland. FAX 48-22-345466. TELEX 814331. circ. 150. **Document type:** bibliography.
Description: Articles on water management, hydraulics, water engineering, water pollution, water resources, water quality, sanitary engineering, and sewage water treatment.

627 016   II   ISSN 0523-302X
BIBLIOGRAPHY ON IRRIGATION, DRAINAGE, RIVER TRAINING AND FLOOD CONTROL/BIBLIOGRAPHIE DE LA C I I D. IRRIGATION, DRAINAGE ET MAITRISE DES CRUES. (Text in English and French) 1954. a. $10 per copy. International Commission on Irrigation and Drainage - Commission Internationale des Irrigations et du Drainage, 48 Nyaya Marg, Chanakyapuri, New Delhi 110021, India. bk.rev. circ. 1,200. (back issues avail.)

628.1   US
DREDGING ABSTRACTS. 1969. m. $110. Center for Dredging Studies, Civil Engineering Department, Texas A & M University, College Station, TX 77843-3136. TEL 409-845-4516. FAX 409-845-6156. Ed. Robert E. Randall. **Document type:** abstracting/indexing.

ECOLOGY ABSTRACTS. see *ENVIRONMENTAL STUDIES — Abstracting, Bibliographies, Statistics*

628.1 314   GW
GERMANY. STATISTISCHES BUNDESAMT. FACHSERIE 19, UMWELTSCHUTZ, REIHE 2: WASSERVERSORGUNG UND ABWASSERBESEITIGUNG. (Consists of several subseries) irreg. price varies. Statistisches Bundesamt, 65180 Wiesbaden, Germany. TEL 0611-75-1. FAX 0611-724000. TELEX 61186-STBA-D. **Document type:** government publication.

620 016   YU   ISSN 0018-1358
HIDROTEHNICKA BIBLIOGRAFIJA. 1953. bi-m. 6000 din.($60) Institut za Vodoprivredu "Jaroslav Cerni", Bulevar vojvode Misica 43, Belgrade, Yugoslavia. Ed. M. Hajdukovic. bk.rev. circ. 600.

333.91 314   HU   ISSN 0209-7915
TD265.5
HUNGARY. KOZPONTI STATISZTIKAI HIVATAL. VIZGAZDALKODASI STATISZTIKAI ZSEBKONYV. quadrennial. 40 Ft. Statisztikai Kiado Vallalat, Kaszasdulo u. 2, P.O.B. 99, 1300 Budapest 3, Hungary. TEL 688-635. TELEX 22-6699. (Subscr. to: Kultura, Box 149, H-1389 Budapest, Hungary)

IRRIGATION AND DRAINAGE ABSTRACTS. see *AGRICULTURE — Abstracting, Bibliographies, Statistics*

630 016   II   ISSN 0021-1672
IRRIGATION AND POWER ABSTRACTS. (Text in English) 1943. q. $100. Central Board of Irrigation and Power, c/o Member Secretary, Malcha Marg, Chanakyapuri, New Delhi 110 021, India. TEL 11-3015984. FAX 91-11-3016347. E-mail: cbip@cbipdel.uunet.in. Ed. Shri C.V.J. Varma. adv.; bk.rev.; abstr.; bibl.; index, cum.index. circ. 2,150. (back issues avail.; reprint service avail. from UMI) **Indexed:** Field Crop Abstr., Fluidex, Herb.Abstr. **Document type:** abstracting/indexing.
Formerly: Abstracts of Current Technical Literature.

551.4 011   US   ISSN 0037-136X
TC1   CODEN: SWRABW
SELECTED WATER RESOURCES ABSTRACTS. (Not avail. in printed format as of 1992) 1968. m. $115 (with index $145). U.S. Geological Survey, Water Resources Scientific Information Center, 425 National Center, Reston, VA 22092. TEL 703-648-6820. (Dist. by: NTIS, Springfield, VA 22161) Ed. R.A. Jensen. index. cum. circ. 2,000. (also avail. in microfiche from BHP) **Indexed:** Petrol.Abstr. **Document type:** abstracting/indexing.
●Also available online. Vendor(s): Knight-Ridder, Inc. (File no.117).
Also available on CD-ROM. Producer(s): Cambridge Scientific Abstracts, NISC (Water Resources Abstracts Volume 1), SilverPlatter Information, Inc.
—UMI.

333.91 016   JA
SUIDO JIGYO NENPO/ANNUAL STATISTICS OF WATER WORKS. (Text in Japanese) 1971. a. free. Toyama City Water Works Bureau, 7-38 Shin-Sakura-machi, Toyama-shi 930, Japan. index. circ. 350. (back issues avail.)

TURKEY. DEVLET ISTATISTIK ENSTITUSU. GAZ VE SU ISTATISTIKLERI/TURKEY. STATE INSTITUTE OF STATISTICS. GAS AND WATER STATISTICS. see *ENERGY — Abstracting, Bibliographies, Statistics*

333.91 310 363.3   UK   ISSN 0968-0756
THE U K WATER INDUSTRY: CHARGES FOR WATER SERVICES (YEAR). (Subseries of: C R I Statistics Series) 1978. a. £10 to non-members, members £8 (effective 1994). Chartered Institute of Public Finance and Accountancy, Centre for the Study of Regulated Industries, 3 Robert St., London WC2N 6BH, England. TEL 0171-895-8823. FAX 0171-895-8825. (back issues avail.) **Document type:** trade publication.
Supersedes in part (in 1990): Chartered Institute of Public Finance and Accountancy. United Kingdom Water Industry (Books 1 & 2); Which was formerly (until 1985): Chartered Institute of Public Finance and Accountancy. Water Services Charges Statistics (ISSN 0141-7835)
Description: Disseminates financial statistics regarding water utilities in the U.K.

333.91 310 363.6   UK
THE U K WATER INDUSTRY: WATER SERVICES & COSTS (YEAR). (Subseries of: C R I Statistics Series) 1978. a. £15 to non-members, members £12 (effective 1994). Chartered Institute of Public Finance and Accountancy, Centre for the Study of Regulated Industries, 3 Robert St., London WC2N 6BH, England. TEL 0171-895-8823. FAX 0171-895-8825. (back issues avail.) **Document type:** trade publication.
Supersedes in part (in 1990): Chartered Institute of Public Finance and Accountancy. United Kingdom Water Industry (Books 1 & 2); Which was formerly (until 1985): Chartered Institute of Public Finance and Accountancy. Water Services Charges Statistics (ISSN 0141-7835)
Description: Disseminates financial statistics of the U.K. water utilities.

333.91 016   AT
UNIVERSITY OF NEW SOUTH WALES. WATER RESEARCH LIBRARY. WATER INFORMATION UPDATE. 1962. 6/yr. University of New South Wales, Water Research Laboratory, Water Reference Library, King St., Manly Vale, N.S.W. 2093, Australia. bibl. circ. 1,000.
Former titles: University of New South Wales. Water Reference Library. Current Awareness List; University of New South Wales. Water Reference Library. Accession List.

VA-NYTT; litteratur om miljoevaard. see *ENVIRONMENTAL STUDIES — Abstracting, Bibliographies, Statistics*

WELDING

333.91 016 US
WATER RESOURCES ABSTRACTS VOLUME 1. Running title: S W R A on C D - R O M. q. $685. National Information Services Corporation (NISC), Wyman Towers, Ste. 6, 3100 St. Paul St., Baltimore, MD 21218. TEL 410-243-0797. FAX 410-243-0982.
●Available only on CD-ROM. Producer(s): NISC.
Description: Publishes the contents of the Selected Water Resources Abstratcs database.

333.91 016 US
WATER RESOURCES ABSTRACTS VOLUME 2. s-a. $695. National Information Services Corporation (NISC), Wyman Towers, Ste. 6, 3100 St. Paul St., Baltimore, MD 21218. TEL 410-243-0797. FAX 410-243-0982. **Document type:** abstracting/indexing.
●Available only on CD-ROM. Producer(s): NISC.
Description: Publishes information from 3 water resource databases: South Africa's WATERLIT, Canada's AQUAREF, and DELFT HYDRO from the Netherlands.

WELDING

see Metallurgy–Welding

WIND ENERGY

see Energy–Wind Energy

WOMEN'S HEALTH

see also Medical Sciences–Obstetrics and Gynecology

A A - B A NEWSLETTER. (American Anorexia - Bulimia Association, Inc.) see PSYCHOLOGY

A L R A NEWSLETTER. (Abortion Law Reform Association) see BIRTH CONTROL

A N A D: WORKING TOGETHER. (National Association of Anorexia Nervosa and Associated Disorders) see PSYCHOLOGY

A N R E D ALERT. (Anorexia Nervosa & Related Eating Disorders, Inc.) see PSYCHOLOGY

A W H O N N NEWSLETTER. (Association of Women's Health, Obstetric, and Neonatal Nurses) see MEDICAL SCIENCES — Nurses And Nursing

613.9 UK ISSN 0262-7299
ABORTION REVIEW. 1981. q. £20 to individuals; institutions £30. Birth Control Trust, 16 Mortimer St., London W1N 7RJ, England. TEL 0171-580-9360. FAX 0171-637-1378. Ed. Ann Furedi. bk.rev.; stat. circ. 500. **Document type:** newsletter.
Incorporates (in 1995): Abortion Research Notes (ISSN 0361-1116)
Description: Round-up of the medical, legal and social aspects of abortion in the U.K., Europe, and the U.S.

AMERICAN INSTITUTE OF STRESS. NEWSLETTER. see MEDICAL SCIENCES

ARIZONA PARENTING FROM A TO Z. see CHILDREN AND YOUTH — About

610 II
ASSOCIATION OF MEDICAL WOMEN IN INDIA. JOURNAL. (Text in English) 1920. bi-m. Rs.15. Association of Medical Women in India, IMA Bldg., 16 Haji Ali Park, Keshavrao Khudye Marg, Bombay 400034, India. Ed. Dr. Tara Ramarao. adv. circ. 500.

BACK TO HEALTH MAGAZINE; your guide to relief recovery and well-being. see PHYSICAL FITNESS AND HYGIENE

BATTERED WOMEN'S DIRECTORY. see WOMEN'S INTERESTS

613.7 US ISSN 1055-3398
BEST OF HEALTH. 1987. q. $10. Wista Jeanne Johnson, Ed. & Pub., Box 40-1232, Brooklyn, NY 11240-1232. TEL 718-756-2245. adv.; bk.rev. circ. 1,000. (back issues avail.) **Document type:** newsletter.
Description: Health issues for African-American women.

BLAST. see BIOLOGY — Physiology

610 GW ISSN 0933-0747
CLIO; eine feministische Zeitschrift zur gesundheitlichen Selbsthilfe. 1976. s-a. DM.36($12) for 4 nos. Feministisches Frauen Gesundheitszentrum e.V., Bambergerstr. 51, 10777 Berlin, Germany. TEL 030-2139597. FAX 030-2141927. Ed. Cornelia Burgert. adv. contact: Petra Benz. bk.rev.; illus. circ. 5,000. (back issues avail.) **Indexed:** Abstr.Engl.Stud. **Document type:** consumer publication.
Description: Topics covered include women's health, gynecological diseases and feminist critiques of medical care, self-help and reproductive technology.

CONTRACEPTION - FERTILITE - SEXUALITE. see BIRTH CONTROL

CUADERNOS DE SALUD DE LA MUJER. see MEDICAL SCIENCES — Obstetrics And Gynecology

DONNA MODERNA. see WOMEN'S INTERESTS

EESTI NAINE; a magazine for women. see WOMEN'S INTERESTS

EUROPEAN EATING DISORDERS REVIEW. see PSYCHOLOGY

618.082 US ISSN 0888-2398
CODEN: FPPCE9
FEMALE PATIENT: PRACTICAL ADVICE FOR PRIMARY CARE; total health care for women. 1976. m. $100 to institutions outside the Americas; $79 to institutions in U.S (effective 1996). Excerpta Medica, Inc., Core Publishing Division (Subsidiary of: Reed Elsevier Medical group), 105 Raider Blvd., Belle Mead, NJ 08503. TEL 908-874-8550. FAX 908-874-0707. (Subscr. to: Box 3085, Princeton, NJ 08543-3085)
—BLDSC (3905.168200); UMI. **CCC.**
Supersedes in part (in 1981): Female Patient (ISSN 0364-1198)

FIELD ADVOCATE. see GERONTOLOGY AND GERIATRICS

FOCAL POINT. see MEDICAL SCIENCES — Obstetrics And Gynecology

A FRIEND INDEED; for women in the prime of life/pour les femmes dans la force de l'age. see WOMEN'S INTERESTS

618.082 AU
DAS GRUENE HAUS. 1981. m. S.30. Tuttenhofstr. 63, A-2103 Langenzersdorf, Austria. TEL 02244-292370. FAX 02244-292373. Ed. Dieter Altermiller. adv. contact: Gertraud Altermiller. (also avail. in diskette format) **Document type:** consumer publication.

H E R S NEWSLETTER. (Hysterectomy Educational Resources & Services) see MEDICAL SCIENCES — Obstetrics And Gynecology

HANDLING PREGNANCY AND BIRTH CASES. see LAW — Family And Matrimonial Law

618.082 US ISSN 1070-910X
HARVARD WOMEN'S HEALTH WATCH. 1993. m. $24 (Canada Can.$36; elsewhere $39). (Harvard Medical School) Harvard Health Publications Group, 164 Longwood Ave., Boston, MA 02115. FAX 617-432-1506. E-mail: jrudin@warren.med.edu. (Subscr. to: Box 420234, Palm Coast, FL 32142-0234) Ed. Celeste Robb-Nicholson. **Document type:** newsletter.
●Also available online. Vendor(s): Information Access Co.
Description: Addresses issues unique to women's health. Provides concise information to help readers make informed decisions.

THE HEALING WOMAN. see PSYCHOLOGY

HEALTH & FITNESS; magazine for healthy, sound living. see PHYSICAL FITNESS AND HYGIENE

618 US ISSN 0739-9332
CODEN: HCWIDQ
HEALTH CARE FOR WOMEN, INTERNATIONAL. 1979. bi-m. £115($190) (effective 1996). Taylor & Francis Inc., 1900 Frost Rd., Ste. 101, Bristol, PA 19007-1598. TEL 215-785-5800; 800-821-8312. FAX 215-785-5515. (Subscr. in Europe to: Taylor & Francis Ltd., Rankine Rd., Basingstoke, Hants. RG24 8PR, England. TEL 44-1256-840366. FAX 44-1256-479438) Ed. Phyllis Noerager Stern. adv.; bk.rev.; film rev.; bibl.; charts; illus.; index. circ. 400. (back issues avail.; reprint service avail. from UMI) **Indexed:** CINAHL, Int.Nurs.Ind., J.of Abstr.Int.Educ., Lang.& Lang.Behav.Abstr., Mult.Ed.Abstr., NRN, Nurs.Abstr., Psychol.Abstr. (1992-), Sage Fam.Stud.Abstr., Sociol.Abstr., Sp.Ed.Needs Abstr., Stud.Wom.Abstr. **Document type:** academic/scholarly publication.
—BLDSC (4274.950600); Faxon; UnCover. **CCC.**
Formerly (until 1983): Issues in Health Care of Women (ISSN 0161-5246)
Description: Takes an interdisciplinary approach to health care and related topics that concern women.

HEALTH EDUCATION JOURNAL. see PHYSICAL FITNESS AND HYGIENE

HEALTH NOW. see NUTRITION AND DIETETICS

HEARTBEAT (ORLANDO). see BIRTH CONTROL

HOT FLASH. see WOMEN'S INTERESTS

618.082 GW
IDEAL - GESUENDER LEBEN. 8/yr. Atlanticpresse Verlags GmbH, Im Neudeck 1, 67346 Speyer, Germany. TEL 06232-310-0. FAX 06232-310292. Ed. Norbert Pirzer. adv. contact: Andreas Werner. circ. 250,000. **Document type:** consumer publication.

INDUCED ABORTION: A WORLD REVIEW. see BIRTH CONTROL

INSTITUTE FOR POSITIVE WEIGHT MANAGEMENT NEWSLETTER. see NUTRITION AND DIETETICS

JOURNAL OF SPIRITUAL HEALTH. see ALTERNATIVE MEDICINE

618.082 US ISSN 1059-7115
RA564.85 CODEN: JWOHEA
JOURNAL OF WOMEN'S HEALTH. 1992. bi-m. $119 (foreign $159). (Society for the Advancement of Women's Health Research) Mary Ann Liebert, Inc. Publishers, 2 Madison Ave., Larchmont, NY 10538. TEL 914-834-3100. FAX 914-834-3688. E-mail: Liebert@pipeline.com. Ed. Dr. Anne Colston Wentz. adv. (back issues avail.) **Indexed:** Excerp.Med. (1993-). **Document type:** academic/scholarly publication.
—BLDSC (5072.634400); UnCover.
Description: Publishes papers on diseases or conditions that hold greater risk for, or are more prevalent among women.
Refereed Serial

L.E. BEACON. (Lupus Erythematosus) see MEDICAL SCIENCES — Rheumatology

LIFE GUARDIAN. see SOCIAL SERVICES AND WELFARE

613.7 US
LIVING FIT; a guide to fitness at any age. 1993. bi-m. $12.97; newsstand price: 2.95. Weider Publications, 21100 Erwin St., Woodland Hills. TEL 818-884-6800. FAX 818-704-5734. Ed. Barbara Harris. adv. contact: Peter L. Miller. illus. (back issues avail.) **Document type:** consumer publication.
Description: Focuses on issues of women's health and well-being in today's society. Discusses ways for women to stay in shape and good health and to look their best.

LONGEVITY; the art and science of staying young. see GERONTOLOGY AND GERIATRICS

LONGEVITY. see GERONTOLOGY AND GERIATRICS

M & M. see WOMEN'S INTERESTS

M I D S NEWSLETTER. (Miscarriage, Infant Death, and Stillbirth) see WOMEN'S STUDIES

WOMEN'S HEALTH

618 US
M O M MAGAZINE. 1984. q. $12. Mothers and Others for Midwives, Box 1068, Sugarloaf, CA 92386. TEL 714-585-4175. Ed. Jeriann Fairman. adv.; bk.rev. circ. 2,000.
  Description: Promotes women's choices in health care. Offers alternative birth and parenting information.

MASSAGE THERAPY JOURNAL. see *PHYSICAL FITNESS AND HYGIENE*

618.082 US
MEDICAL MISSION SISTERS NEWS. 1927. q. free. Society of Catholic Medical Missionaries, Inc., 8400 Pine Rd., Philadelphia, PA 19111. FAX 215-342-3948. Ed. Monica M. McGinley. illus.; index, cum.index. circ. 52,000. **Document type:** newsletter.
  Supersedes: Medical Missionary (ISSN 0025-7389)

613.7 US ISSN 1043-8734
RA564.85
MELPOMENE JOURNAL; a journal for women's health research. 1981. 3/yr. $32 to individuals; institutions $50. Melpomene Institute for Women's Health Research, 1010 University Ave. W., Saint Paul, MN 55104-4706. TEL 612-642-1951. FAX 612-642-1871. Ed. Judy Remington. illus. circ. 2,500. (reprint service avail.) **Indexed:** Sportsearch (1988-). **Document type:** academic/scholarly publication.
  —UnCover.
  Formerly: Melpomene Report.
  Description: Research articles with scientific bibliographies, personal profiles, news and updates, providing information about health and physically active women.

MENOPAUSE. see *MEDICAL SCIENCES — Obstetrics And Gynecology*

MENOPAUSE NEWS. see *GERONTOLOGY AND GERIATRICS*

MIDWIFERY TODAY AND CHILDBIRTH EDUCATION. see *MEDICAL SCIENCES — Obstetrics And Gynecology*

MOTHER AND CHILD. see *WOMEN'S INTERESTS*

618 362.7 US ISSN 0733-3013
MOTHERING. 1976. q. $18.95. Mothering Magazine, Box 1690, Santa Fe, NM 87504. TEL 800-984-8116. FAX 505-986-8335. (Subscr. addr.: Box 532, Mt. Morris, IL 61054. TEL 800-827-1061) Ed. Kathy Lamb. adv.: B&W page $2750, color page $3400; adv. contact: Heather Patrick. bk.rev.; circ. 70,000 (paid). (also avail. in microfiche from UMI; back issues avail.) **Indexed:** Alt.Press.Ind., Child.Lit.Abstr., Hlth.Ind. **Document type:** consumer publication.
  —UMI; UnCover.
  Description: Articles and departments pertaining to progressive childrearing in the areas of health, learning, and emotional and personal development.

MOTHER'S DAY REPORT. see *GERONTOLOGY AND GERIATRICS*

618.082 UK
N H S BREAST SCREENING PROGRAMME. a. National Health Service, Breast Screening Programme, Fulwood House, Old Fulwood Rd., Sheffield S10 3TH, England. Ed. Julietta Patnick. **Document type:** government publication.
  —BLDSC (7786.388000).

613.7 US
NATIONAL WOMEN'S HEALTH NETWORK. q. National Women's Health Network, 1325 G St., N.W., Washington, DC 20005.

610 US ISSN 0741-9147
NATIONAL WOMEN'S HEALTH REPORT. 1984. 6/yr. $25 to individuals; institutions and international $75. National Women's Health Resource Center, 2440 M St., N.W., Ste. 325, Washington, DC 20037. TEL 202-293-6045. FAX 202-293-7256. Ed. Heidi Rosvold-Brenholtz. bk.rev.; index. circ. 30,000. (back issues avail.) **Document type:** newsletter.
  —BLDSC (6033.412000).
  Description: Covers medical and public policy issues relating to women's health.

613.7 US ISSN 8755-867X
NETWORK NEWS (WASHINGTON, 1975). Key Title: Network News - National Women's Health Network. 1975. 6/yr. $25. National Women's Health Network, 1325 G St., N.W., Washington, DC 20005. bk.rev.
  —UMI.
  Former titles (until 1982): National Women's Health Network Newsletter (ISSN 0277-0385); Network News.
  Description: For women's health activists. The network is a consciousness-raising political watchdog organization. Covers controversial issues and includes product alerts and interviews.

618.08 JA ISSN 1340-8380
▼**NIKKEI WELLNESS.** 1994. m. 490 Yen per no. Nikkei Business Publications, Inc. (Subsidiary of: Nihon Keizai Shimbun, Inc.), 2-7-6 Hirakawacho, Chiyoda-ku, Tokyo 102, Japan. TEL 03-5210-8502. FAX 03-5210-8119. Ed. Osamu Hasuike. adv. contact: Masahiro Toda. circ. 200,000. **Document type:** consumer publication.
  Description: Covers a broad range of health-related matters from proper food and exercises to mental health and information on good medical institutions, doctors, and medicines.

NYUGAN NO RINSHO/JAPANESE JOURNAL OF BREAST CANCER. see *MEDICAL SCIENCES — Oncology*

O W L OBSERVER. (Older Women's League) see *GERONTOLOGY AND GERIATRICS*

ON THE ISSUES; the progressive woman's quarterly. see *WOMEN'S INTERESTS*

OUR SPECIAL; magazine devoted to matters of interest to blind women. see *HANDICAPPED — Visually Impaired*

OVULATION METHOD TEACHERS ASSOCIATION (PUBLICATION). see *BIRTH CONTROL*

PAIS E FILHOS; revista mensal da familia moderna. see *CHILDREN AND YOUTH — About*

PRIMARY CARE UPDATE FOR O B - GYNS. see *MEDICAL SCIENCES — Obstetrics And Gynecology*

PRO-CHOICE NEWS. see *BIRTH CONTROL*

PULSE (ORLANDO). see *BIRTH CONTROL*

RADIANCE; the magazine for large women. see *WOMEN'S INTERESTS*

618.082 CL
RED DE SALUD DE LAS MUJERES LATINOAMERICANAS Y DEL CARIBE. REVISTA. English edition: Women's Health Journal. q. $40. Isis Internacional, Casilla 2067, Correo Central, Santiago, Chile. TEL 56-2-6382219. FAX 56-2-6383142.
  Description: Network news, opinions, analysis and up-to-date information on women's health issues.

REDE NACIONAL FEMINISTA DE SAUDE E DIREITOS REPRODUTIVOS. JORNAL. see *WOMEN'S STUDIES*

618.082 US
REGARDING WOMEN AND HEALTHCARE. q. free. Robert Wood Johnson University Hospital, One Robert Wood Johnson Pl., New Brunswick, NJ 08901. TEL 908-828-3000.
  Description: Discusses the emotional and physical health and well-being of women.

051 US ISSN 1073-2713
RODALE'S HEALTHY WOMAN. 1993. 2/yr. $6. Rodale Press, Inc., 33 E. Minor St., Emmaus, PA 18098. TEL 610-967-5171. Ed. Catherine Cassidy. adv.; illus. **Document type:** consumer publication.
  Description: Covers issues pertaining to women's health.

SCARLET LETTER. see *WOMEN'S INTERESTS*

618.082 US
SEASONS (GARDEN CITY). bi-m. free. Wyeth-Ayerst Laboratories, Box 9251, Garden City, NY 11530-9836. Ed. Jane Townsend. **Document type:** consumer publication.
  Description: Contains articles on health, beauty, and life-style of interest to postmenopausal women.

SELF. see *WOMEN'S INTERESTS*

SHATTERED DREAMS. see *MEDICAL SCIENCES — Obstetrics And Gynecology*

SOBERING THOUGHTS. see *DRUG ABUSE AND ALCOHOLISM*

SPECIAL DELIVERY. see *MEDICAL SCIENCES — Obstetrics And Gynecology*

618.082 155.3 US ISSN 0272-202X
SPRINGER SERIES: FOCUS ON WOMEN. 1980. irreg., latest 1995. price varies. Springer Publishing Company, 536 Broadway, New York, NY 10012-3955. TEL 212-431-4370. FAX 212-941-7842. Ed. Violet Franks. **Document type:** monographic series.
  —BLDSC (8424.763300).
  Description: Explores women's issues from a psychological perspective.

THYROBULLETIN. see *MEDICAL SCIENCES — Endocrinology*

618.082 052 UK
TOP SANTE; health & beauty. 1993. m. £18 (foreign £35). Presse Publishing, 17 Radley Mews, Kensington, London W8 6JP, England. TEL 0171-938-3033. FAX 0171-938-5464. (Dist. by: Comag Ltd., Tavistock Rd., W. Drayton, Middx. UB7 7QE, England. TEL 01895-433600; Subscr. to: Galleon, Fulham House, Goldsworth Rd., Woking GU21 1LZ, England. TEL 01483-747008) Ed. Jane Garton; Pub. Elizabeth Rees-Jones. adv. contact: Jacqui Elliot. bk.rev.; circ. 148,064 (paid). (back issues avail.) **Document type:** consumer publication.

613.7 CN
TURNER'S SYNDROME NEWS. 1982. q. Can.$25 individual membership; institutions Can.$35; students Can.$15. Turner's Syndrome Society, 7777 Keele St., 2nd Fl., Concord, ON L4K 1Y7, Canada. TEL 905-660-7766; 800-465-6744. FAX 905-660-7450. Ed. Sandi Hofbauer. circ. 500. **Document type:** newsletter.

618.082 US ISSN 1069-742X
VIA (DENVILLE); a guide through menopause and beyond. 1993. q. $19.97. (National Coalition for Consumer Education, Inc.) Carrington Communicatios, Inc., 227 Rt. 206, Bldg. 1, Fl.2, Box 658, Flanders, NJ 07836. TEL 201-584-3040. FAX 201-584-8867. Ed. Dr. Karen Hutchinson; Pub. Pamela Boggs. adv.: B&W page $3500, color page $5600. bk.rev.; circ. 50,000 (paid). **Document type:** consumer publication.
  Description: Covers healthcare issues, particularly peri- and postmenopause for mature women.

618.082 US
W O R L D. (Women Organized to Respond to Life-Threatening Diseases); a newsletter by, for and about women facing HIV disease. (Editions in English, Spanish) 1991. m. (Spanish ed. q.) $20 to individuals; institutions $50 (donation). W O R L D, Box 11535, Oakland, CA 94611. TEL 510-658-6930. FAX 510-601-9746. Ed. Rebecca Denison. adv. contact: Diana Kuderna. **Document type:** newsletter.
  Description: Discusses social and medical issues women facing HIV disease encounter and lists important forthcoming conferences throughout the world.

618 US
WOMAN'S HEALTH ADVISER. m. Whittle Communications L.P., 333 Main Ave., Knoxville, TN 37902. TEL 615-595-5300. Ed. Margot Leske.
  Description: A guide to mind and body fitness for women. Topics vary from pregnancy to general health care.

WOMEN'S HEALTH — ABSTRACTING, BIBLIOGRAPHIES, STATISTICS

610 US ISSN 0363-0242
RG1 CODEN: WOHEDI
WOMEN & HEALTH; the journal of women's health care. 1976. q. (2 vols./yr.). $400 (foreign $560) (effective 1996). Haworth Press, Inc., 10 Alice St., Binghamton, NY 13904. TEL 607-722-5857; 800-342-9678. FAX 607-722-1424. TELEX 4932599. Ed. Jeanne Stellman. adv.; bk.rev. circ. 705. (also avail. in microfiche from HAW,ISI) back issues avail.; reprint service avail. from HAW,ISI) **Indexed:** Abstr.Crim.& Pen., Abstr.Health Care Manage.Stud., Abstr.Hyg., Adol.Ment.Hlth.Abstr., Alt.Press Ind., Biol.Abstr., Bull.Signal., CINAHL, Curr.Cont., Curr.Lit.Fam.Plan., Excerp.Med., Hlth.Ind., IMFL, Ind.Med., Lang.& Lang.Behav.Abstr., Med.Care Rev., Mult.Ed.Abstr., P.A.I.S., Psychol.Abstr. (1979-), Risk Abstr., Soc.Work Res.& Abstr., SSCI, Stud.Wom.Abstr., Viol.& Abuse Abstr., Wom.Stud.Abstr. (1976-).
—BLDSC (9343.260000); Faxon; Genuine Article; Haworth; SWETS; UnCover.
Description: Contains information that is useful for all women, consumers, and providers of health care. *Refereed Serial*

WOMEN & THERAPY; a feminist quarterly of research and opinion. see *PSYCHOLOGY*

610 US
WOMEN IN CONTEXT. 1978. irreg. latest 1990. price varies. Plenum Publishing Corp., 233 Spring St., New York, NY 10013-1578. TEL 212-620-8000. FAX 212-463-0742. TELEX 23-421139. Ed.Bd. (back issues avail.) **Document type:** monographic series.
Formerly: Women in Context: Development and Stresses.
Refereed Serial

WOMEN'S EXERCISE. see *PHYSICAL FITNESS AND HYGIENE*

618.082 US
WOMEN'S HEALTH CENTER MANAGEMENT. 1993. m. $219. American Health Consultants, Inc., Six Piedmont Center, Ste. 400, Atlanta, GA 30305. TEL 404-262-7436; 800-688-2421. FAX 800-284-3291. Ed. Yvonne Hiott. circ. 270. **Document type:** newsletter.
Description: Provides coverage on developing comprehensive women's health programs.

618 US ISSN 1049-3867
RG1
WOMEN'S HEALTH ISSUES. 1991. bi-m. $155 to institutions (effective 1996). (Jacobs Institute of Women's Health) Elsevier Science Inc., 655 Ave. of Americas, New York, NY 10010. TEL 212-989-5800. FAX 212-633-3990. TELEX 420643 AEP UI. (Subscr. to: Box 882, Madison Sq. Sta., New York, NY 10159-0882) Ed. Warren Pearse. (also avail. in microform from UMI; back issues avail.) **Indexed:** Excerp.Med. (1993-), Ind.Med (1992-). **Document type:** academic/scholarly publication.
—BLDSC (9343.379010); UnCover. **CCC.**
Description: For health professionals, social scientists, policy makers, and others concerned with developments affecting health care for women.
Refereed Serial

618.082 US ISSN 1062-4163
WOMEN'S HEALTH LETTER; the monthly review of women's health issues. 1992. m. $24 (foreign $30). Ballard Publishing Inc., 2245 E. Colorado Blvd., Ste. 104, Pasadena, CA 91107. TEL 818-798-0638. FAX 818-798-0639. (Subscr. to: Box 18902, Anaheim, CA 92817-8902. TEL 714-693-1866) Ed. Kerri Bodmer. bk.rev.; charts; illus. circ. 30,000. (looseleaf format; back issues avail.) **Document type:** newsletter.
Description: Covers information and issues concerning women's health, including research findings and viewpoints of leading experts from around the world.

618.082 UK ISSN 0954-6677
WOMEN'S HEALTH NEWSLETTER. 1984. q. £10 (Europe £12; elsewhere £14) to individuals; institutions £15 (Europe £20; elsewhere £25). Women's Health, 52 Featherstone St., London EC1Y 8RT, England. TEL 0171-251-6333. Ed. Bernadette Britain. bk.rev.; circ. 600. **Document type:** newsletter.

618.082 150 US ISSN 1077-2928
▼**WOMEN'S HEALTH: RESEARCH ON GENDER, BEHAVIOR, AND POLICY.** 1995. q. $35 to individuals (foreign $60); institutions $95 (foreign $120). Lawrence Erlbaum Associates, Inc., 10 Industrial Dr., Mahwah, NJ 07430-2262. TEL 201-236-9500. FAX 201-236-0072. Ed. Tracey A. Revenson. adv.: page $400; 5 x 8. **Document type:** academic/scholarly publication.
Description: Dedicated to advancing our knowledge of the psychological, social, cultural, and political processes that affect women's physical health, and how gender influences health-behavior relationships, illness and health care.

613.7 US ISSN 1069-4927
WOMEN'S PHYSIQUE WORLD. q. $3.95 per no. Women's Physique Magazine, Box 429, Midland Park, NJ 07432. TEL 201-825-7448. Ed. Steve Wennerstrom. **Document type:** consumer publication.
Description: Covers contests and features biographical articles on competitive women bodybuilders.

WOMEN'S SPORTS AND FITNESS. see *SPORTS AND GAMES*

613 305.4 US ISSN 0890-9695
WOMENWISE. 1978. q. $10 to individuals; institutions $20. Concord Feminist Health Center, 38 S. Main St., Concord, NH 03301. TEL 603-225-2739. FAX 603-668-6255. Ed. Luita D. Spangler. adv. contact: Susanne Hendrick. bk.rev. circ. 5,000. (tabloid format; back issues avail.) **Document type:** consumer publication.
Description: Covers women's health issues with a feminist perspective. Includes political analyses.
Refereed Serial

WOMEN'S HEALTH — Abstracting, Bibliographies, Statistics

618.082 310 AT
▼**AUSTRALIA. BUREAU OF STATISTICS. WOMEN'S HEALTH.** 1994. irreg. Aus.$30. Australian Bureau of Statistics, P.O. Box 10, Belconnen, A.C.T. 2616, Australia. **Document type:** government publication.
Description: Contains a selection of statistics describing the health status of women, their use of health services and health related aspects of their lifestyle.

WOMEN'S INTERESTS

A A R P - W I N. (American Association of Retired Persons, Women's Initiative) see *GERONTOLOGY AND GERIATRICS*

A A W C J C NEWSLETTER. (American Association of Women in Community and Junior Colleges) see *EDUCATION — Higher Education*

A L F NEWSLETTER. (Association of Libertarian Feminists) see *POLITICAL SCIENCE*

A M B A JOURNAL. (Australian Multiple Birth Association Inc.) see *MEDICAL SCIENCES — Obstetrics And Gynecology*

A M B A NEWS. (Australian Multiple Birth Association Inc.) see *CHILDREN AND YOUTH — About*

A S - SEKRETARKA. see *BUSINESS AND ECONOMICS — Office Equipment And Services*

A U L INSIGHTS. (Americans United for Life) see *LAW*

A U L STUDIES IN LAW, MEDICINE & SOCIETY. (Americans United for Life) see *LAW*

A U T WOMAN. see *EDUCATION — Higher Education*

500 600 US ISSN 1057-5839
Q149.U5
A W I S MAGAZINE. 1971. bi-m. $60 to libraries. Association for Women in Science, 1522 K St. N.W., Ste. 820, Washington, DC 20005. TEL 202-408-0742. FAX 202-408-8321. Ed. Tamare Maeda Wong. adv. contact: Annette Duplinsky. bk.rev. circ. 4,000. **Document type:** newsletter.
—UnCover.
Former titles (until 1991): A W I S Newsletter (ISSN 0160-256X); Association for Women in Science. Newsletter (ISSN 0098-6267)
Description: Features articles on the status of women in science and policy issues, listings of current grant and employment opportunities, and news of chapter activities.

A W N Y MATTERS. (Advertising Women of New York) see *ADVERTISING AND PUBLIC RELATIONS*

A W S C P A. NEWSLETTER. (American Women's Society of Certified Public Accountants) see *BUSINESS AND ECONOMICS — Accounting*

301.412 BG
AACHAL. (Text in Bengali) 1985. w. $4. 100B Malibagh Chowdhury Para, Dhaka 1219, Bangladesh. TEL 2-414043. Ed. Ferdousi Begum. adv.; bk.rev. circ. 25,000.

301.412 CR
ABANICO. (Supplement to: Prensa Libre) w. Calle 4, esq. Avda. 4, Apdo. 10121, San Jose, Costa Rica. TEL 23-6666. Ed. Guiselle Borrase. circ. 50,000.

ABOUT WOMEN ON CAMPUS. see *EDUCATION — Higher Education*

ACTION ALERT (WASHINGTON, 1980). see *LAW*

301.412 CN ISSN 1187-5305
ACTION NOW/A L'ACTION. (Text in English and French) 9/yr. National Action Committee on the Status of Women, 57 Mobile Dr., Toronto, ON M4A 1H5, Canada. TEL 416-759-5252. FAX 416-759-5370. **Document type:** newsletter.
Formerly (until 1990): Action (Toronto) (ISSN 0820-5728)
Description: Published to encourage action in response to legislative issues of concern to the committee.

301.412 UK ISSN 0953-9816
DA125.N4
AFRICAN WOMAN. 1990? s-a. £8 to individuals in the U.K. and Africa (elsewhere £10); institutions £20 in the U.K. and Africa (elsewhere £25). (Akina Mama wa Afrika) London Women's Centre, 4 Wild Ct., London WC2B 5AU, England. Ed.Bd. bk.rev.
—BLDSC (0735.050000).

301.412 SA ISSN 1013-0950
AGENDA; a journal about women and gender. 1987. 4/yr. R.38 to individuals (foreign £20 or $30); institutions R.75 (foreign £40 or $75) (effective 1994). Agenda, P.O. Box 37432, Overport 4067, South Africa. TEL 3054074. FAX 3010740. Ed.Bd. adv.; bk.rev.; illus. circ. 3,000. (back issues avail.) **Indexed:** Documentatieblad. **Document type:** academic/scholarly publication.
Description: Provides a forum for discussion and debate on all aspects of women's lives in South Africa.

AIR FRANCE MADAME. see *TRAVEL AND TOURISM — Airline Inflight And Hotel Inroom*

ALARM CLOCK; women in alternative music and female vocalists. see *MUSIC*

ALASKA WOMEN. see *LITERARY AND POLITICAL REVIEWS*

055.1 IT ISSN 0002-4627
ALBA; settimanale femminile di attualita, narrativa, cultura e moda. 1922. w. L.115000 (foreign L.185000). Editrice Nuova Alba, Via S. Sofia 9-1, 20122 Milan, Italy. TEL 39-2-58306167. FAX 39-2-58306219. Ed. Andrea Franchini. adv.: B&W page L.5700000, color page L.9000000. bk.rev.; film rev. circ. 80,000. **Indexed:** Artbibl.Mod.

WOMEN'S INTERESTS

301.42 CN ISSN 0712-5143
ALBERTA WOMEN.* 1993. 4/yr. Merrick Enterprises, 349 Claremont Cres., Oakville, ON L6J 6J9, Canada. Pub. John Merrick. adv.: B&W page Can.$600, color page Can.$1125; trim 8 1/8 x 10 7/8. circ. 82,000. **Document type:** consumer publication.

305.4 US
ALBUQUERQUE WOMAN. 1987. bi-m. $9.50. Duval Publications, Box 12955, Albuquerque, NM 87195-0955. TEL 505-247-9195. FAX 505-247-9129. Ed. Jill Duval. adv.: bk.rev. circ. 17,000. **Document type:** consumer publication.

301.412 US
ALERT (WASHINGTON, 1980).* 1980. bi-m. membership. Federation of Organizations for Professional Women, 1825 I St., N.W., Ste. 400, Washington, DC 20006. TEL 202-328-1415. FAX 202-462-5241. Ed. Viola M. Young-Horvath. adv.; bk.rev. circ. 250. (back issues avail.)
Description: Opportunity for organizations and individuals to use their collective power to influence policy and enhance status of professional women.

323.42 AT
ALIVE & W E L. 1972. m. Aus.$40. Women's Electoral Lobby (Vic.), Fl. 9, 10 Queen St., Melbourne, Vic. 3000, Australia. TEL 03-614-1128. FAX 03-629-2904. Ed. Valda Byth. **Document type:** newsletter.

396 PK
ALL PAKISTAN WOMEN'S ASSOCIATION. TRIENNIAL CONFERENCE REPORT. (Text in English) triennial. All Pakistan Women's Association, Information and Research Bureau, 67-B Garden Rd., Karachi 3, Pakistan.

305.42 SW ISSN 1103-291X
ALL VAERLDENS KVINNOR. 1989. q. Internationella Kvinnofoergundet, Vasavaegen 49, 3 tr., S-582 33 Linkoeping, Sweden. TEL 46-13-10-56-47.

053.1 GW
▼**ALLEGRA.** 1995. m. Axel Springer Verlag AG, Axel-Springer-Platz 1, 20355 Hamburg, Germany. TEL 040-3470-0. FAX 040-34722628. adv.: B&W page DM.14800, color page DM.19600; trim 183 x 249; adv. contact: Michael Bayer. circ. 150,000. (paid).

305.412 DK ISSN 0002-6506
ALT FOR DAMERNE. (Supplement avail.) 1946. w. DKK 832. Egmont Magasiner A-S, Vognmagergade 10, 1145 Copenhagen K, Denmark. Ed. Hanne Hoeiberg. adv.; illus. circ. 85,000.

AMERICAN ASSOCIATION OF WOMEN DENTISTS. CHRONICLE. see *MEDICAL SCIENCES — Dentistry*

AMERICAN BAPTIST WOMAN. see *RELIGIONS AND THEOLOGY — Protestant*

AMERICAN CATTLEWOMAN. see *AGRICULTURE — Poultry And Livestock*

AMERICAN FEMINIST. see *POLITICAL SCIENCE — Civil Rights*

AMERICAN MEDICAL WOMEN'S ASSOCIATION. JOURNAL. see *MEDICAL SCIENCES*

AMERICAN SENIOR. see *GERONTOLOGY AND GERIATRICS*

051 US ISSN 1054-9595
AMERICAN WOMAN (NEW YORK, 1991). 1991. q. $7.99. G C R Publishing Group, Inc., 1700 Broadway, 34th Fl., New York, NY 10019. TEL 212-541-7100. Ed. Lynn Varacalli. adv. contact: Laura Lapatin. circ. 130,000. (also avail. in microfilm from KTO)
Description: Covers relationships, careers and changing lifestyles.

THE AMERICAN WOMAN (YEAR); a status report. see *WOMEN'S STUDIES — Abstracting, Bibliographies, Statistics*

AMERICAN WOMAN MOTORSCENE. see *SPORTS AND GAMES*

055.1 IT ISSN 1120-432X
AMICA. 1962. w. L.124800. Rizzoli Editore-Corriere della Sera, Via A. Rizzoli 2, 20132 Milan, Italy. TEL 39-2-2588. Ed. Giovanna Mazzetti. adv.: page L.64920000; adv. contact: Flavio Biondi. circ. 201,740.

301.412 BL ISSN 0003-1755
AMIGA. 1970. w. $103. Bloch Editores S.A., Rua do Russell 766-804, 22210-010 Rio de Janeiro, RJ, Brazil. TEL 021-5554000. FAX 021-2059998. TELEX 2121525 BLOC. Ed. Eli Halfoun. adv. circ. 80,000. **Document type:** consumer publication.
Description: Contains news about television and movie stars.

059 FR ISSN 0244-0008
AMINA. 1972. m. 350 F. Amina International, 11 rue Teheran, 75008 Paris, France. Ed. Assiatou Diallo. adv. contact: Christiane Pierre. bk.rev. circ. 96,400. **Document type:** consumer publication.
Incorporates (in 1985): Wife.

AMIT WOMAN. see *ETHNIC INTERESTS*

ANCHORA. see *CLUBS*

305.412 PR ISSN 0279-3385
ANGELA LUISA. 1967. m. Publicaciones Torregrosa, Apdo. 1807, Hato Rey, PR 00919. Ed. Angela Luisa Torregrosa. adv.; illus. circ. 20,000.

059.94 FI ISSN 0355-3035
ANNA. 1963. w. FIM 618. Yhtyneet Kuvalehdet Oy, Maistraatinportti 1, FIN-00240 Helsinki, Finland. TEL 358-0-156-6524. FAX 358-0-156-6505. TELEX 121364. Ed. Riitta Tulonen. adv.: B&W page FIM 22200, color page FIM 32600. illus. circ. 152,180.

301.412 IT ISSN 1120-4346
ANNA. 1933. w. L.124800. Rizzoli Editore-Corriere della Sera, Via A. Rizzoli 2, 20132 Milan, Italy. TEL 39-2-2588. adv.: page L.61000000; adv. contact: Flavio Biondi. circ. 363,482.
Former titles (until 1984): Annabella (ISSN 1120-480X); (until 1938): Lei (ISSN 1120-4796).

053.1 GW ISSN 0937-3527
ANNA. English edition: Anna (ISSN 0937-3535) 1980. m. Verlag Aenne Burda, Am Kestendamm 2, 77652 Offenburg, Germany. TEL 0781-8402. FAX 0781-843508. Ed. Maria Blumrich; Pub. Aenne Burda. adv. contact: Bodo Schlimpen. circ. 201,166. **Document type:** consumer publication.

052 UK ISSN 0003-3758
ANNABEL; the magazine women really enjoy. 1966. m. D. C. Thomson & Co. Ltd., Albert Sq., Dundee DD1 9QJ, Scotland. adv.; bk.rev.; illus. **Document type:** consumer publication.

055.1 IT ISSN 0003-3766
ANNABELLA (ENGLISH EDITION). 1932. w. L.78000. Rizzoli Editore-Corriere della Sera, Via A. Rizzoli 2, 20132 Milan, Italy. TEL 02-25843213. Ed. M. Venturi. circ. 270,000.

053.1 SZ
ANNABELLE. 1938. fortn. 105 SFr.; newsstand price: 5.40 SFr. T A Media AG, Werdstr. 21, CH-8021 Zurich, Switzerland. TEL 01-2484111. FAX 01-2484191. adv.; bk.rev.; film rev.; play rev.; bibl.; illus. circ. 106,463. (tabloid format) **Document type:** consumer publication.
Former titles: Annabelle-Femina; Annabelle (ISSN 0003-3774)

346.013 US
ANTISEXISM NEWSLETTER. 1984. 4/yr. $15 to non-members. National Lawyers Guild, Anti-Sexism Task Force, c/o Carpenter & Mayfield, 131 George St., San Jose, CA 95110-2116. Eds. Constance Carpenter, Tony Prees. bk.rev. circ. 800.
Formerly: Women's Newsletter.

301.412 323.4 US
APROPOS.* 1984. m. $12. Pulse Publications, Inc. (Mt. Vernon), 1730 Continental Pl., Mt. Vernon, WA 98273-5640. TEL 206-671-3933. adv. circ. 6,000.
Description: Informs women of Whatcom County about people, news, trends, and opinions affecting their lives.

ARIADNE. see *INTERIOR DESIGN AND DECORATION*

301.412 GW ISSN 0178-1073
ARIADNE. 1985. s-a. DM.16. Archiv der Deutschen Frauenbewegung e.V., Sommerweg 1B, 34125 Kassel, Germany. TEL 0561-55600. FAX 0561-576012. adv.; bk.rev.; bibl.; illus. circ. 1,000. (back issues avail.) **Document type:** consumer publication.

338.91 UG
ARISE; a women's developmental magazine. (Text in English) 1989. q. $20. Action for Development (A C F O D E), P.O. Box 16729, Wandegeya, Uganda, Uganda. TEL 256-41-532311. FAX 256-41-532311. Ed. Rebecca Musoke. **Indexed:** P.L.E.S.A.
Formerly (until 1990): Acfode Newsletter.

ARIZONA TRENDS. see *CLOTHING TRADE — Fashions*

301.412 US
ARIZONA WOMEN'S VOICE. 1984. m. $12. 5515 N. 7th St., Ste. 5-173, Phoenix, AZ 85014. TEL 602-279-1347. Ed. Joanne Brickman. adv.; bk.rev. circ. 17,000. (tabloid format; back issues avail.)
Description: Purpose is to share information, issues and news items for and about women.

051 UK
ARMY WIVES JOURNAL. 1990. q. £6. Method Publishing Co. Ltd., Sutherland Press House, Golspie, Sutherland KW10 6RA, Scotland. TEL 01408-633871. FAX 01408-633876. Ed. Polly Christopherson. adv. contact: Diana Glasscock. circ. 68,000 (paid). **Document type:** consumer publication.
Description: Provides information on matters pertaining to the life-styles of British Army wives.

ARTEMIS - ARTISTS AND WRITERS; artists and writers from the Blue Ridge Mountains. see *LITERATURE — Poetry*

618 MY
ASIAN AND PACIFIC WOMEN'S RESOURCE AND ACTION SERIES. (Text in English) 1989. irreg. free. Asian and Pacific Development Centre, P.O. Box 12224, 50770 Kuala Lumpur, Malaysia. TEL 03-2548088. FAX 03-2550316. TELEX MA-30676-APDEC. Ed. Noeleen Heyzerc. **Indexed:** Abstr.Rural Dev.Trop. **Document type:** newsletter.
Description: Provides a forum for women's experiences and thoughts on issues critical to women's health, the environment, work and law from a Third World perspective.
Refereed Serial

510 376 US
ASSOCIATION FOR WOMEN IN MATHEMATICS. NEWSLETTER. 1971. 6/yr. $40 individual membership; institutions $80. Association of Women in Mathematics, 4114 Computer & Space Sciences Bldg., University of Maryland, College Park, MD 20742-2461. TEL 301-405-7892. Ed. Anne Leggett. adv. contact: Dawn Wheeler. bk.rev. circ. 4,000. **Document type:** newsletter.
Description: Serves and encourages women to study and have active careers in the mathematical sciences.

ASSOCIATION OF MEDICAL WOMEN IN INDIA. JOURNAL. see *WOMEN'S HEALTH*

305.412 RH
ASSOCIATION OF WOMEN'S CLUBS. NEWS. 1964. q. $0.50. Association of Women's Clubs, P.O. Box UA 339, Harare, Zimbabwe. TEL 790339. Ed. F. Samhungu. circ. 1,100.
Formerly: Federation of African Women's Clubs.

305.412 FI
ASTRA NOVA. 1919. m. FIM 170. Utgivarfoereningen foer Tidskriften Astra Nova, P.O. Box 354, FIN-65101 Vasa, Finland. TEL 961-3128-694. FAX 961-317-6530. Ed. Charlotta Oedman. adv.; bk.rev. circ. 3,000.
Formerly: Astra (ISSN 0004-6094)

053.1 GW
ATELIER 19 HEIM UND WELT. 1948. w. (Wed.). DM.192.40. Produktions- und Vertriebsgesellschaft mbH, Am Jungfernplan 2, 30171 Hannover, Germany. TEL 0511-28378-0. FAX 0511-854603. Ed. Jan Wuerger. adv.; illus. circ. 120,000. **Document type:** consumer publication.
Formerly: Neue Heim und Welt.

WOMEN'S INTERESTS

305.412   US
ATLANTA N O W NEWS.* vol.6, 1973. m. $15. 604, National Organization for Women, Atlanta Chapter, Box 8556, Atlanta, GA 30306-0556. TEL 404-523-1227. FAX 404-688-0869. Ed. Samantha Claar. adv.; bk.rev.; circ. 700 (controlled).
    Formerly: N O W Notes - Atlanta Chapter.

301.412 323.4   AU
AUF - EINE FRAUENZEITSCHRIFT. 1974. q. S.190 (foreign S.235). Verein zur Foerderung Feministischer Projekte, Kleeblattgasse 7, Postfach 817, A-1011 Vienna, Austria. TEL 0222-5339164. adv.; bk.rev. circ. 2,500. **Document type:** bulletin.

AURORA (MADISON); S F science fiction-speculative feminism. see *LITERATURE — Science Fiction, Fantasy, Horror*

378   AT   ISSN 0812-4345
AUSTRALIAN FEDERATION OF UNIVERSITY WOMEN. NEWSLETTER.* 1960. q. membership. Australian Federation of University Women, A.F.U.W. Federal Council, Dymocks Bldg., 428 George St., Sydney, N.S.W. 2000, Australia. Ed. M. Coatman. circ. 2,200. **Document type:** newsletter.

AUSTRALIAN WOMEN'S CHESS BULLETIN. see *SPORTS AND GAMES*

305.412   AT   ISSN 0005-0458
AUSTRALIAN WOMEN'S WEEKLY. 1933. m. Aus.$46. A C P Publishing Pty. Ltd., 54-58 Park St., Sydney, N.S.W. 2000, Australia. TEL 02-282-8258. FAX 02-267-8037. TELEX 120514. Dir. Nene King; Pub. Richard Walsh. adv. contact: David Malone. bk.rev.; tele.rev.; illus. circ. 1,016,781. **Document type:** consumer publication.

THE AUSTRALIAN WOMEN'S WEEKLY HANDMADE; craft, decorating, fashion. see *ARTS AND HANDICRAFTS*

305.412   NE
AVENUE BOX. 1965. m. fl.96 (effective 1994). Geillustreerde Pers B.V., Haaksbergweg 75, 1101 BR Amsterdam, Netherlands. TEL 31-20-4300300. FAX 31-20-4300316. Ed. Harriet Calo. adv.; bk.rev. circ. 50,000. **Document type:** consumer publication.
    Formerly: Avenue (ISSN 0005-1985); Incorporates (1980-1993): Intermagazine (ISSN 0927-1139)

B B W: BIG BEAUTIFUL WOMAN MAGAZINE. see *CLOTHING TRADE — Fashions*

051   CN   ISSN 0045-3080
B.C. VOICE. 1963. q. Can.$8 to individuals; institutions Can.$10. British Columbia Voice of Women, P.O. Box 235, Nanaimo, BC V9R 5K9, Canada. Ed. Marjorie Stewart. bk.rev. circ. 400. **Document type:** newsletter.
    Description: Women's interests, particularly as these relate to world peace and the environment.

301.4   ZR
B E A MAGAZINE DE LA FEMME. fortn. 2 ave Masimanimba, B.P. 113380, Kinshasa I, Zaire. Ed. Mutinga Mutwishayi.

B P W NEWS INTERNATIONAL. (Business and Professional Women) see *OCCUPATIONS AND CAREERS*

B W P A NEWSLETTER. (British Women Pilots Association) see *AERONAUTICS AND SPACE FLIGHT*

301.412   CN   ISSN 1193-3313
BABY AND CHILD CARE QUICK REFERENCE ENCYCLOPEDIA. 1990. s-a. Family Communications, Inc., 37 Hanna Ave., Toronto, ON M6K 1X1, Canada. TEL 416-537-2604. FAX 416-538-1794. Ed. Bettie Bradley. adv. circ. 100,000.

301.412   GW
BABY UND DIE ERSTEN LEBENSJAHRE; Magazin fuer Eltern. m. Wort und Bild Verlag Konradshoehe GmbH, Konradshoehe, 82065 Baierbrunn, Germany. TEL 089-74433-0. FAX 089-74433155. Ed. Dorothee Walzel. **Document type:** consumer publication.
    Formerly: Baby (ISSN 0930-2867)

BAD ATTITUDE; a lesbian sex magazine. see *HOMOSEXUALITY*

301.42   US
BATTERED WOMEN'S DIRECTORY.* 1975. irreg., latest 1985. $12. c/o Terry Mehlman, 2506 Hoot Owl Dr., Hillsborough, NC 27278-9511. adv.; bk.rev.; bibl.; stat. circ. 2,000. (also avail. in microform) **Document type:** directory.
    Formerly: Working on Wife Abuse.

305.4   IT
BEAUTIFUL. 1990. w. L.62000 (foreign L.127000). Casa Editrice Universo S.p.A., Via M. Vigano De Vizzi 35, 20092 Cinisello Balsamo (MI), Italy. TEL 39-2-618331. FAX 39-2-6128931. Ed. Attilio Malnati. adv.; B&W page L.16500000, color page L.19200000. circ. 147,575. **Document type:** consumer publication.

BEAUTY. see *BEAUTY CULTURE*

BEGINNINGS (RALEIGH). see *MEDICAL SCIENCES — Nurses And Nursing*

301.412   BG
BEGUM. (Text in Bengali) w. 66 Loyal St., Dhaka 1, Bangladesh. TEL 2-233789. Ed. Nurjahan Begum. circ. 25,000.

305.412   GW   ISSN 0935-6207
BELLA. 1978. w. (Thu.). DM.114.40 (foreign DM.248). Heinrich Bauer Verlag, Burchardstr. 11, 20095 Hamburg, Germany. TEL 040-3019-0. FAX 040-324879. Ed. Juergen Pietzker. adv. contact: Goesta Ahrweiler. illus. circ. 705,470. **Document type:** consumer publication.
    Description: Concentrates on fashion, cosmetics, home economics, nutrition, advice and entertainment.

055.1   IT   ISSN 0005-8602
BELLA (MILAN, 1947); settimanale di attualita e moda. 1947. w. L.67600. Rizzoli Editore-Corriere della Sera, Via Angelo Rizzoli 2, 20132 Milan, Italy. Ed. Mara Santini. adv.; bk.rev.; illus.
    Incorporates: Buona Tavola.

208   US   ISSN 1074-3634
THE BELTANE PAPERS; a journal of women's mysteries. 1984. 2/yr. $13 (foreign $18). (Brideswell Collective) The Beltane Papers, 1333 Lincoln St., No. 240, Bellingham, WA 98225. TEL 206-366-4571. Eds. Helen G. Farias, Waverly Fitzgerald. adv.: page $175; trim 7 x 9; adv. contact: Linda Ledbetter. bk.rev.; bibl.; illus. circ. 3,000.
    Former titles: T B P's Octava; Beltane Papers.
    Description: Covers all aspects of the women's spirituality movement.

BENISSIMO. see *CLOTHING TRADE — Fashions*

BERKELEY WOMEN'S LAW JOURNAL. see *LAW*

BI-LIFESTYLES; devoted to the sensual interests of bisexual gay males, females and couples. see *MEN'S INTERESTS*

BICENTENARY BROCHURE. see *RELIGIONS AND THEOLOGY — Protestant*

BIG APPLE PARENTS' PAPER. see *CHILDREN AND YOUTH — About*

BIMBOX. see *MEN'S INTERESTS*

BLISS. see *MATRIMONY*

BODY PLAY AND MODERN PRIMITIVES QUARTERLY. see *NEW AGE PUBLICATIONS*

305.412   FR   ISSN 0399-1628
BONNE SOIREE TELE.* 1922. w. 6.50 F. per no. Editions Mondiales, 2 rue des Italiens, 75440 Paris Cedex 09, France. FAX 1-40-70-98-93. TELEX 643 932. Ed. M.H. Adler. circ. 234,637.

BOOKWOMAN. see *PUBLISHING AND BOOK TRADE*

BRASIL VOGUE. see *CLOTHING TRADE — Fashions*

301.412   GW
BRAUT UND BRAEUTIGAM; wissenwertes ueber heiraten und wohnen. 1986. q. DM.40. Christiaan Publishing GmbH, Hoersterstr. 52, 48143 Muenster, Germany. TEL 0251-41853-0. FAX 0251-46764. Ed. Bert Klomp. adv.; bk.rev. circ. 53,000. (back issues avail.) **Document type:** consumer publication.
    Formerly: Braut und Braeutigam mit Trachtenmode.

305.4   IT
BRIC. q. L.5000 per no. Edizioni Internazionali Cioe s.r.l., Via G. Fabbroni 24, 00196 Rome, Italy. TEL 39-6-3295390. adv.; B&W page L.2300000, color page L.4000000. **Document type:** consumer publication.

305.412   GW   ISSN 0931-8763
BRIGITTE. 1957. fortn. DM.104 (Europe DM.187.20; elsewhere DM.193.18). Gruner und Jahr AG & Co., Am Baumwall 11, 20459 Hamburg, Germany. TEL 040-3703-0. FAX 040-37035617. Ed. Anne Volk. circ. 1,126,054. (also avail. in microfilm from UMI; reprint service avail. from UMI) **Document type:** consumer publication.
    Incorporates (1948-1969): Constanze (ISSN 0941-5742)

305.412   NZ   ISSN 0110-8603
HQ1101
BROADSHEET; New Zealand feminist magazine. 1972. 4/yr. NZ.$27.50 (foreign NZ.$40) (effective 1995). Womanfile Research and Information Centre Incorporated, P.O. Box 56-147, Auckland, New Zealand. TEL 09-8343472. adv.; bk.rev. circ. 4,500. (back issues avail.) **Indexed:** Bibl.Engl.Lang.& Lit., Wom.Stud.Abstr.
    —UnCover. **CCC.**

BUSINESS AND PROFESSIONAL WOMAN. see *OCCUPATIONS AND CAREERS*

051   US
BUST. 4/yr. $10; newsstand price: $2.50. Box 319, Ansonia Sta., New York, NY 10023. Ed. Marcelle Karp. music rev. **Document type:** bulletin.
    Description: Provides a wide range of experiences and outlooks from womens' perspectives.

323.4   CN   ISSN 1188-2654
C A C S W NEWS. 1986. s-a. free. Canadian Advisory Council on the Status of Women - Conseil Consultatif Canadien sur la Situation de la Femme, 110 O'Connor St., 9th Fl., P.O. Box 1541, Sta. B, Ottawa, ON K1P 5R5, Canada. TEL 613-992-4975. FAX 613-992-1715. Ed. James C. Young. bk.rev. circ. 7,000. **Document type:** newsletter.
    Former titles (until 1991): Fine Balances - Juste Equilibre; Inside Out.
    Description: Covers recent Council activities, publications, emerging issues for women of Canada.

C E D H U. (Centro de Estudios Humanitarios) see *LAW*

305.412 338.91   US
C E D P A NETWORK. 1984. q. free. Centre for Development and Population Activities, 1717 Massachusetts Ave., N.W., Ste. 200, Washington, DC 20036. TEL 202-667-1142. FAX 202-332-4496. TELEX 440384 CFPA. Ed. Majorie Brahms Signer. bk.rev. circ. 6,000. (back issues avail.) **Document type:** newsletter.
    Formerly: C E D P A World Wide.
    Description: News and announcements pertaining to the CEDPA's mission to empower women to be full partners in development at all levels of society and its work in health, population, development, and training in developing countries.

CADERNOS DE PESQUISA; revista de estudos e pesquisas em educacao. see *EDUCATION*

CALIFORNIA FAMILY LAW MONTHLY. see *LAW — Family And Matrimonial Law*

305.412   US   ISSN 0008-1663
CALIFORNIA WOMAN. vol.37, 1970. 3/yr. $6. California Federation of Business & Professional Women's Clubs, Inc., 3420 S. Half Moon Dr., Bakersfield, CA 93309-5659. TEL 805-837-8291. adv.; illus. circ. 6,000.

CALIFORNIA YOUTH AUTHORITY'S STATUS OF FEMALE EMPLOYEES. REPORT. see *BUSINESS AND ECONOMICS — Labor And Industrial Relations*

WOMEN'S INTERESTS

CANADA. LABOUR CANADA. WOMEN'S BUREAU. WOMEN IN THE LABOUR FORCE. see *BUSINESS AND ECONOMICS — Labor And Industrial Relations*

301.412   CN   ISSN 0705-6028
HQ1453
CANADIAN ADVISORY COUNCIL ON THE STATUS OF WOMEN. ANNUAL REPORT - RAPPORT ANNUEL. 1973. a. free. Canadian Advisory Council on the Status of Women - Conseil Consultatif Canadien sur la Situation de la Femme, 110 O'Connor St., 9th Fl., P.O. Box 1541, Sta. B, Ottawa, ON K1P 5R5, Canada. TEL 613-992-4975. FAX 613-992-1715. Ed. James C. Young. bk.rev. circ. 10,000. **Document type:** corporate report.
    Description: Analysis of women's issues plus news of the Council.

305.412   CN   ISSN 0229-7256
CANADIAN RESEARCH INSTITUTE FOR THE ADVANCEMENT OF WOMEN. NEWSLETTER/INSTITUT CANADIEN DE RECHERCHES SUR LES FEMMES. BULLETIN. Variant title: C R I A W Newsletter. (Text in English and French) 1981. q. membership. Canadian Research Institute for the Advancement of Women - Institut Canadien de Recherches sur les Femmes, 151 Slater St., Ste. 408, Ottawa, ON K1P 5H3, Canada. TEL 613-563-0681. FAX 613-563-0682. Ed. Linda Clippingdale. adv. circ. 1,000. **Document type:** newsletter.
    Description: Features the latest in research news, print, audiovisual and film resources, employment and funding opportunities.

305.4   UK
CANDICE. 1992. bi-m. £9.90. New Horizons Publishing, 111a Cricklewood Broadway, London NW2 4JG, England. TEL 081-208-2639. Ed. Rasheda Ashanti. circ. 40,000. (back issues avail.)

CAREERS FOR WOMEN GRADUATES. see *OCCUPATIONS AND CAREERS*

301.412   BL
CARINHO. 1978. m. $19. Bloch Editores S.A., Rua do Russell 766-804, 22210-000 Rio de Janeiro, RJ, Brazil. TEL 021-5554000. FAX 021-2059998. TELEX 2121525 BLOC. Ed. Dalce Souto L. circ. 65,000. **Document type:** consumer publication.
    Description: For middle and lower class teenage girls.

CENTER FOR SELF-SUFFICIENCY UPDATE. see *EDUCATION — Adult Education*

305.412 338.91   US
CENTRE FOR DEVELOPMENT AND POPULATION ACTIVITIES. WORKING PAPER. 1992. irreg. free. Centre for Development and Population Activities, 1717 Massachusetts Ave., N.W., Ste.200, Washington, DC 20036. TEL 202-667-1142. FAX 202-332-4496. Ed. Marjorie Brahms Signer. circ. 2,000.
    Description: Publishes research reports on family planning and women's health and development projects.

CENTRE INTERNATIONAL DE L'ENFANCE. PROGRAMME OF ACTIVITIES. see *CHILDREN AND YOUTH — About*

052   UK
CENTREPIECES. 1986. irreg. King's Cross Women's Centre, P.O. Box 287, London NW6 5QU, England. TEL 071-837-7509. FAX 071-833-4817. (U.S. addr.: Box 11795, Philadelphia, PA 19101. TEL 215-668-9886) Ed. Selma James. **Document type:** bulletin.

323.4   PY   ISSN 1017-6063
CENTRO DE DOCUMENTACION Y ESTUDIOS. INFORMATIVO MUJER. 1989. m. $30. Centro de Documentacion y Estudios, Pai Perez 737, Asuncion, Paraguay. (Dist. by: D.I.P.P., Box 2507, Asuncion, Paraguay) Ed. Dr. Line Bareiro. circ. 500.

305.4   PE
CENTRO DE LA MUJER PERUANA "FLORA TRISTAN". DOCUMENTO DE TRABAJO. 1990. irreg., no.3, 1990. Centro de la Mujer Peruana "Flora Tristan", Parque Hernan Velarde, 42, Lima 14, Peru. TEL 51-14-330694. FAX 51-14-339060.

301.412   UK
CHAT. 1985. w. I P C Magazines, Weeklies Group (Subsidiary of: Reed Elsevier group), King's Reach Tower, Stamford St., London SE1 9LS, England. TEL 071-261-6560. FAX 0444-440619. TELEX 892084 REEDBP G. (Quadrant Subscriptions Services, Oakfield House, Perrymount Rd., Haywards Heath, W. Sussex RH16 3DH, England. TEL 0444-440421) Ed. Terry Tavner. adv. contact: Jane Credland. circ. 568,095. **Document type:** consumer publication.
    Description: Entertainment magazine for women 25-34. Includes a weekly puzzle pull-out.

301.412   CN   ISSN 0009-1995
AP5
CHATELAINE (ENGLISH EDITION). French edition (ISSN 0317-2635) 1928. m. Can.$19.98 (us $42; elsewhere $46). Maclean Hunter Ltd., Maclean Hunter Bldg., 777 Bay St., Toronto, ON M5W 1A7, Canada. TEL 416-596-5425. FAX 416-593-3197. TELEX 062-19547. (Subscr. to: Box 4003, Sta. A, Toronto, ON M5W 1A7, Canada) Ed. Rona Maynard. adv.; bk.rev.; film rev.; illus. circ. 900,000. (also avail. in microform from MIM,UMI) **Indexed:** Can.B.P.I., Can.Lit.Ind., Can.Per.Ind., CMI, Mag.Ind., Pt.de Rep.
—UnCover. **CCC**.

301.412   CN   ISSN 0317-2635
CHATELAINE (FRENCH EDITION). English edition (ISSN 0009-1995) 1960. m. Can.$27.92 (in US Can.$38; elsewhere Can.$78). Magazines Maclean Hunter Quebec Inc., 1001 bvd. de Maisonneuve W., Montreal, PQ H3A 3E1, Canada. TEL 514-845-5141. FAX 514-845-4302. TELEX 055-60604. Ed. Catharine Elie. adv.: B&W page Can.$9528, color page Can.$11210; trim 8 x 10 3/4. bk.rev.; film rev.; illus. circ. 178,592. (also avail. in microform from MIM,UMI) **Indexed:** Can.B.P.I., Can.Wom.Per.Ind., Pt.de Rep. (1979-). **Document type:** consumer publication.

301.412   SI   ISSN 0217-5045
CHERIE MAGAZINE. (Text in English) 1983. bi-m. 12 Everton Road, Singapore 0208, Singapore. TEL 2229733. FAX 2843859. Ed. Josephine Ng. circ. 34,000.

301.412 640   US
CHERITH. (Suppl. to: Cottage Connections) 1981. q. $10 (Canada $12; elsewhere $17; includes m. Cottage Connections). Cottage Connections, 11113 Radisson Ct., Burnsville, MN 55337. Ed. Mary Morgan Bevis.
    Former titles: Cottage Cheese; Homemakers' Journal.
    Description: Provides encouragement for the many women in the home. Includes poetry, short stories, articles and essays; features their experiences in politics, education, Writers' clubs, penpaling and Christian ministries.

CHILD CARE ACTION NEWS. see *CHILDREN AND YOUTH — About*

CHRISTIAN MOTHER (PITTSBURGH). see *RELIGIONS AND THEOLOGY*

CHRISTIAN WOMAN. see *RELIGIONS AND THEOLOGY*

053.1   GW   ISSN 0009-5788
CHRISTLICHE FRAU. 1902. 6/yr. DM.20. Katholischer Deutscher Frauenbund e.V., Kaesenstr. 18, 50677 Cologne, Germany. TEL 0221-314930. FAX 0221-322954. Ed. Gabriele Kloeckner. bk.rev. circ. 28,000. (back issues avail.) **Document type:** bulletin.

305.4   SI
CITTA BELLA/DUHUI JIAREN. (Text in Chinese) 1993. m. newsstand price: S.$4.50. Singapore Press Holdings Ltd., Corporate Relations Department, 82 Genting Lane News Centre, Singapore 1334, Singapore. TEL 743-8800. FAX 748-0747. Ed.Chew Keng Juea. adv.: B&W page S.$2100, color page S.$2800; trim 300 x 225; adv. contact: David Tay. bk.rev.; film rev.; music rev.; play rev. circ. 15,000. pp./issue: 160. **Document type:** consumer publication.

305.4   US   ISSN 1077-3207
CITY FAMILY; ideas for better living. Spanish edition: Familia de la Ciudad (ISSN 1077-3215) 1992. q. $3.95. City Family, Inc., 44 W. 69th St., Ste. 4B, New York, NY 10023. TEL 212-362-3052. FAX 212-580-4833. (Subscr. to: Box 748, Ansonia Sta., New York, NY 10023) Ed. Ellen Frankel; Pub. Arthur Schiff. adv. circ. 210,000. **Document type:** consumer publication.
    Description: Covers health, law, food, fashion, furnishing and other topics of interest to women and families.

THE CIVIL WAR LADY; women studies, living history, historical information, research, clothing. see *MILITARY*

305.4   SP   ISSN 1132-3213
CLARA. 1986. m. $108.24. H U M S.A., Aribau, 28, 08011 Barcelona, Spain. TEL 3237063. FAX 4541322. Ed. Assumpta Soria Badia. adv.; bk.rev.; charts; illus. circ. 301,533.

305.4   US
▼**CLARITY.** 1994. bi-m. $18.97; newsstand price: $3.50. Navigators, Box 35004, Colorado Springs, CO 80935. TEL 719-548-9222. FAX 719-598-7128. Ed. Judith Couchman; Pub. Kent Wilson. adv.: B&W page $1017. circ. 100,000 (paid). **Document type:** consumer publication.

305.412   AG   ISSN 0009-8493
CLAUDIA. 1957. m. $44. Ryela, S.A., Av. Leandro N. Alem 896, Buenos Aires, 1001, Argentina. TEL 1-312-6010. TELEX 9229. Dir. Mercedes Marques. adv.; bk.rev.; abstr.; illus. circ. 17,100.

056.9   BL   ISSN 0009-8507
CLAUDIA. (Supplement avail.: Claudia Cozinha) 1961. m. $49.48. Editora Abril, S.A., R. Geraldo Flausino Gomes, 61, 04573-900 Sao Paulo SP, Brazil. TEL 011-534-5598. FAX 011-534-5779. (Subscr. to: Rua do Curtume, 769, 0506-900, Sao Paulo, Brazil. TEL 011-823-9100) Ed. Celia Pardi. adv.; bk.rev.; film rev.; music rev.; play rev.; rec.rev.; video rev.; illus. circ. 540,000. **Document type:** consumer publication.
    Description: For the woman of today, who has both career and home. Contains information on education for children, fashion, beauty, health, decorating, medicine and psychology.

301.412   MX   ISSN 0009-8515
CLAUDIA. 1965. m. $67. Editorial Mex-Ameris, S.A., Av. Morelos 16, 4o piso, 06040 Mexico D.F., Mexico. TEL 5-521-4690. Ed. Hilda O'Farrill de Compean. adv.; bk.rev.; bibl.; illus. circ. 181,170.

CLEAR BEGINNINGS. see *LITERATURE*

052   AT   ISSN 0310-1797
CLEO. 1972. m. Aus.$55.20. A C P Publishing Pty. Ltd., 54-58 Park St., Sydney, N.S.W. 2000, Australia. TEL 02-282-8617. FAX 02-267-4361. Ed. Lisa Wilkinson; Pub. Richard Walsh. adv. contact: Nick Cham. bk.rev.; film rev. circ. 328,329. **Document type:** consumer publication.

CLIN D'OEIL. see *CLOTHING TRADE — Fashions*

CLIO; eine feministische Zeitschrift zur gesundheitlichen Selbsthilfe. see *WOMEN'S HEALTH*

301.412   JA
CLIQUE. (Text in Japanese) 1989. bi-w. newsstand price: 390Yen. Magazine House, 3-13-10, Ginza, Chuo-ku, Tokyo 104, Japan. TEL 03-3545-7080. FAX 03-3542-6375. Ed. Takako Noguchi. circ. 176,000.

CLUBDATE MAGAZINE; magazine of the good life in Cleveland, U.S.A. see *CONSUMER EDUCATION AND PROTECTION*

CO-LABORER MAGAZINE. see *RELIGIONS AND THEOLOGY*

COMMON LIVES - LESBIAN LIVES. see *HOMOSEXUALITY*

288   US
COMMUNICATOR (BOSTON). 1976. 5/yr. price varies. Unitarian Universalist Women's Federation, 25 Beacon St., Boston, MA 02108. TEL 617-742-2100. Ed. Ellen Spencer. circ. 9,000. (back issues avail.) **Document type:** newsletter.
    Formerly: U U W F Federation Newsletter.

WOMEN'S INTERESTS

640   JA
COMO. (Text in Japanese) 1990. m. 10440 Yen. Shufunotomo Co., Ltd., 2-9 Kanda Surugadai, Chiyoda-ku, Tokyo 101, Japan. Ed. Yumiko Koma. circ. 300,000. **Document type:** consumer publication.

052   305.412   UK   ISSN 0141-1144
COMPANY. 1978. m. £20.40. National Magazine Co. Ltd., 72 Broadwick St., London W1V 2BP, England. TEL 0171-439-5000. FAX 0171-439-5117. Ed. Mandi Norwood. circ. 305,592. **Indexed:** DAAI. **Document type:** consumer publication.

301.412   US   ISSN 0278-0534
COMPLETE WOMAN. 1981. bi-m. $13. Associated Publications, 875 N. Michigan Ave., Ste. 3434, Chicago, IL 60611-1901. TEL 312-266-8680.

301.412   SP   ISSN 0213-2680
COMPLICE. 1985. m. Pedro Teixeira 8, 28020 Madrid, Spain. TEL 91-5560048. Dir. Martha Cardozo. circ. 80,991.

055.1   IT   ISSN 1120-4974
CONFIDENZE. 1946. w. L.93600 (foreign L.126800). Arnoldo Mondadori Editore S.p.A., Casella Postale 1833, 20101 Milan, Italy. TEL 39-2-3199345. Ed. Aldo Gustavo Cimarelli. adv.: page L.26800000. circ. 281,000.
     Formerly (until 1951): Confidenze di Liala (ISSN 1120-8279).

CONNECTION (NASHVILLE). see ENERGY — Electrical Energy

305.4   US   ISSN 1046-9559
THE CONNECTION (WASHINGTON). 1992. bi-m. $39.95. National Foundation for the National Order of Women Legislators, Inc., 3240 Prospect, N.W., Washington, DC 20007. TEL 202-337-3565. FAX 202-337-3566. adv.; bk.rev. circ. 3,600. **Document type:** newsletter.
     Description: Focuses on issues of importance to women state legislators.

305.412   US   ISSN 0886-7062
HQ1101
CONNEXIONS (OAKLAND); an international women's quarterly. 1981. 4/yr. $15 to individuals (foreign $17); institutions $24. Peoples Translation Service, Box 14431, Berkeley, CA 94701-5431. TEL 510-654-6725. Ed./Bd. adv.; bk.rev. circ. 3,000. (back issues avail.) **Indexed:** Alt.Press Ind., Can.Wom.Per.Ind., HR Rep., Left Ind. (1982-), Stud.Wom.Abstr.
     —BLDSC (3417.678000); Faxon; UnCover.
     Description: Thematic coverage of women's issues, with writings, translations and interviews focusing on women outside the U.S.

CONSCIENCE (WASHINGTON); a news journal of prochoice Catholic opinion. see RELIGIONS AND THEOLOGY — Roman Catholic

305.412   IT   ISSN 1121-1318
CONSIGLI PRATICI. 1968. m. L.20000. Industrie Grafiche Cino del Duca S.p.A., Via Borgogna 5, 20122 Milan, Italy. TEL 39-2-781051. Ed. Sandra Rudoni. adv.: B&W page L.5900000, color page L.10600000. circ. 87,102.

301.412   US
CONTRA COSTA WOMAN. q. Gretchen Weberling, Ed.& Pub., 1481 Yosemite Cir., Clayton, CA 94517-2124. TEL 415-672-7899. circ. 12,000.

COOKING CONTEST CHRONICLE. see FOOD AND FOOD INDUSTRIES

CORNERSTONE (ANN ARBOR). see EDUCATION — Higher Education

051   US   ISSN 0010-9541
AP2
COSMOPOLITAN. 1886. m. $24.97. Hearst Corporation, Cosmopolitan, 224 W. 57th St., New York, NY 10019. TEL 212-649-2000. FAX 212-956-3268. (Subscr. to: Box 7162, Red Oak, IA 51591. TEL 800-888-2676) Ed. Helen Gurley Brown. bk.rev.; film rev.; illus. circ. 2,528,280. (also avail. in microform from UMI) **Indexed:** Access (1975-1987), Biog.Ind., Mag.Ind., Media Rev.Dig., R.G. **Document type:** consumer publication.
     —UnCover.
     Description: For the contemporary woman. Features articles on beauty, health, fashion, career and social issues affecting today's woman.

054.1   FR   ISSN 1161-2258
COSMOPOLITAN; magazine de la femme moderne. 1973. m. 121 F.($150) Inter-Edi (Subsidiary of: Groupe Marie-Claire), 11 bis rue Boissy d'Anglas, 75008 Paris, France. (Subscr. in US to: International Subscription Inc., 30 Montgomery St., 7th Fl., Jersey City, NJ 07302. TEL 800-544-6748) Ed. Juliette Boisriveaud. adv.; bk.rev. circ. 300,000. **Indexed:** PMR.

052   AT   ISSN 0310-2076
COSMOPOLITAN. 1973. m. Aus.$55.20. A C P Publishing Pty. Ltd., 54-58 Park St., Sydney, N.S.W. 2000, Australia. TEL 02-267-8129. FAX 02-267-4457. Ed. Pat Ingram; Pub. Richard Walsh. adv. contact: Nick Cham. circ. 299,000. **Document type:** consumer publication.

055.1   IT   ISSN 1121-547X
COSMOPOLITAN. 1976. m. L.4500 per no. Dellaschiava Editore s.r.l., Viale Stelvio 57, 20159 Milan, Italy. TEL 39-2-6988. FAX 39-2-6988337. Ed. Patrizia Pontremoli. adv.: page L.22500000. circ. 210,000.

305.412   NE   ISSN 0923-6872
COSMOPOLITAN. 1981. m. fl.82.20. Geillustreerde Pers b.v., Haaksbergweg 75, 1101 BR Amsterdam, Netherlands. TEL 31-20-4300316. Ed. Rieja v.d. Aart. adv.; bk.rev.; illus. circ. 135,000. **Document type:** consumer publication.

301.412   746.96   JA
COSMOPOLITAN. (Text in Japanese) 1980. m. Shueisha, Inc., 2-5-10 Hitotsubashi, Chiyoda-ku, Tokyo, Japan. Ed. Hiroshi Ohtsuka. adv.; bk.rev. circ. 300,000.

301.412   746.96   GW
COSMOPOLITAN. 1980. m. DM.6.30 per no. M V G Medien Verlagsgesellschaft, Arabellastr. 33, 81925 Munich, Germany. TEL 089-9234-0. FAX 089-9234202. Eds. Christa Geissler, Angelika von Hatzfeld; Pub. Juerg Marquard. adv. contact: Waltraud von Mengden. bk.rev. circ. 375,080. **Document type:** consumer publication.
     Description: Magazine for modern young women dealing with self-improvement, careers, clothes, health, travel, and entertainment.

301.412   746.96   SA   ISSN 0256-0283
COSMOPOLITAN. 1984. m. R.93 (foreign R.100). Associated Magazines (Pty) Ltd., The Avalon, 2nd Fl., Corner Mill & Hope Sts., Gardens, Cape Town 8001, South Africa. TEL 27-21-462-3070. FAX 27-21-461-2500. Ed. Jane Raphaely. adv.; bk.rev. circ. 110,272. **Document type:** consumer publication.

305.412   GR
COSMOPOLITAN. 1987. m. P. Rokanas, Leoforos Marathonas 14, Pallini, 153 00 Athens, Greece. TEL 6665706. Ed. K. Kostoulias.
     Description: Covers fashion, beauty and health.

301.412   SP
COSMOPOLITAN. 1990. m. 4500 ptas. (Europe 10100 ptas., elsewhere 14500 ptas.). G y J Publicaciones Internacionales S.L. y Cia., Marques de Villamagna, 4, 28001 Madrid, Spain. TEL 34-1-435-00-18. FAX 34-1-435-87-01. Ed. Sarah Glattstein Franco. adv.: color page 1700000 ptas.; adv. contact: Elena Sanchez Fabres. circ. 183,457. **Document type:** consumer publication.
     Description: Covers life, fashion, beauty, love, sex, and health. Includes articles, columns, and interviews.

305.412   US   ISSN 0188-0616
COSMOPOLITAN EN ESPANOL. (Editions avail. for Central America, Chile, Colombia, Argentina, Ecuador, Mexico, Peru, Puerto Rico, U.S., Venezuela) (Text in Spanish) 1973. m. $19.50. Editorial America, S.A., Vanidades Continental Bldg., 6355 N.W. 36th St., Virginia Gardens, FL 33166. TEL 305-871-6400. FAX 305-871-8769. Ed. Sara M. Castany. circ. 287,000. (also avail. in microform from UMI) **Document type:** consumer publication.

305.412   BL
COSMOPOLITAN NOVA. 1973. m. $46.16. Editora Abril, S.A., Rua Geraldo Flausino Gomez, 61, 04573-900 Sao Paulo SP, Brazil. TEL 011-534-5598. FAX 011-534-5779. (Subscr. to: Rua do Curtume, 665, 05065-900 Sao Paulo Sp, Brazil. TEL 011-823-9100) Ed. Marcia Neder. adv.; bk.rev.; music rev.; play rev.; rec.rev.; video rev.; illus. circ. 360,000. **Document type:** consumer publication.
     Formerly: Nova.
     Description: For the contemporary woman.

051   US
COTTAGE CONNECTIONS (BURNSVILLE). (Supplement avail: Cherith) m. $10 (Canada $12; elsewhere $17; includes q. Cherith). Cottage Connections, 11113 Radisson Ct., Burnsville, MN 55337. circ. 1,000 (controlled).
     Description: Keeps networking of outreaches and ministries recommended by members current; features their active involvement in politics, education, writers' clubs, and Christian ministries.

305.412   630   US   ISSN 0892-8525
GT3470
COUNTRY WOMAN. 1971. bi-m. $16.98. Reiman Publications, Inc., 5400 S. 60th St., Greendale, WI 53129. TEL 414-423-0100. FAX 414-423-1143. (Subscr. to: Box 995, Greendale, WI 53129) Ed. Ann Kaiser. circ. 2,300,000 (paid). **Document type:** consumer publication.
     —UMI.
     Former titles: Farm Woman (ISSN 0888-1472); Farm Wife News.

305.412   UK   ISSN 0011-0302
COUNTRYWOMAN. 1933. q. £15. Associated Country Women of the World, Vincent House, Vincent Sq., London SW1P 2NB, England. TEL 071-834-8635. adv.; illus. circ. 5,000. **Indexed:** New Per.Ind.

301.412   JA
CREA; women's magazine for up-scale readers. 1989. 8400 Yen. Bungei Shunju Ltd., 3-23 Kioi-cho, Chiyoda-ku, Tokyo 102, Japan. TEL 03-3265-1211. FAX 03-3265-0046. Ed. Takahiro Hirao. circ. 250,000. **Document type:** consumer publication.

700   800   US   ISSN 0736-4733
CREATIVE WOMAN. 1977. q. $16 (foreign $42). T A P P, Inc., 126 E. Wing St., Ste. 288, Arlington Hts., IL 60004. TEL 708-255-1232. FAX 708-255-1243. Ed. Margaret Choudhury. adv. contact: Kristine Rynne. bk.rev.; film rev.; bibl.; illus.; cum.index every 2 yrs.; circ. 450 (paid). **Indexed:** Stud.Wom.Abstr. **Document type:** consumer publication.
     —BLDSC (3487.249000); UnCover.
     Description: Contains articles, poetry, verse, biographical sketches, essays and photographs pertaining to the artistic and scientific endeavors of women.

301.412   BL
CRIATIVA. (Supplements avail. a.: Natal de Criativa, Cozinha Criativa) 1989. m. $60. Editora Globo S.A., Rua do Curtume 665, 05065-001 Sao Paulo SP, Brazil. TEL 55-11-8612042. FAX 55-11-8612042. Dir. Oscar D. Neves. adv.: color page Cr.8650; trim 208 x 274; adv. contact: Geraldo Leite. circ. 183,300.
     Description: For the modern woman. Covers living together, sex, fashion, beauty, decor, children, education, work, fitness, cooking, gardening, knitting, sewign and more.

305.412   IT   ISSN 0574-475X
CRONACHE E OPINIONI. Title varies: Cronache. m. free for members. Centro Italiano Femminile, Via Carlo Zucchi 25, 00165 Rome, Italy. FAX 39-6-6621167. Ed. Lilliana Piccinini. adv.; bk.rev.

CROSS-TALK; transgender community news & information monthly. see SOCIOLOGY

WOMEN'S INTERESTS

261.8344 305.4   DK   ISSN 0109-1476
D K K F - NYT. 1981. bi-m. DKK 30. Dansk Katolsk Kvinde-Forbund, c/o Lillian Hinge, Banegaardsgade 27, 1., DK-8000 Aarhus C, Denmark. TEL 45-86-12-55-61. illus.

D M W B E ACTION NEWSLETTER. (Disadvantaged Minority and Women Business Enterprises) see TRANSPORTATION

DAUGHTERS OF NYX; a magazine of goddess stories, mythmaking and fairy tales. see NEW AGE PUBLICATIONS

305.412   US   ISSN 0739-1749
BV4527
DAUGHTERS OF SARAH. 1974. q. $18. 2121 Sheridan Rd., Evanston, IL 60201-3298. TEL 708-866-3882. Ed. Elizabeth Anderson. adv. contact: Cathi Falsani. bk.rev.; index; circ. 5,200 (paid). (also avail. in microfilm from UMI; back issues avail.) **Indexed:** Rel.Ind.One. **Document type:** consumer publication.
—UMI.
Description: Christian feminist magazine addressing issues of interest to women in the church: biblical interpretation, poverty, racism, women in ministry and sexuality. Includes personal stories.

305.412   US   ISSN 0745-6395
DAWN FOR THE ORANGE COUNTY WOMAN. 1975. m. $7.50. Jeanne and Gerry Parham, Pubs., 26412 Payaso, Mission Viejo, CA 92691. Ed. Maryann Easley. adv.; bk.rev. circ. 33,000.

DE TEXTOS. see SOCIOLOGY

DENEUVE. see HOMOSEXUALITY

640.73   NE   ISSN 0011-8370
DENKEN EN DOEN. 1913. 6/yr. fl.25 to non-members. Nederlandse Vereniging van Huisvrouwen (NVVH), Jan van Nassaustraat 89, 2596 BR The Hague, Netherlands. TEL 31-70-3241347. FAX 31-70-3244362. Ed. W. van de Ven. adv.; bk.rev.; illus. circ. 50,000. **Document type:** consumer publication.

051   US
DETROIT METROPOLITAN WOMAN. 1991. m. $15. Metropolitan Woman Inc., 17117 W. Nine Mile Rd., Ste. 1115, Southfield, MO 48075. TEL 313-443-6500. FAX 313-443-6501. Ed. Patricia Banker Peart. adv.: B&W page $2375, color page $3190; trim 8 x 10 3/4; adv. contact: Alice Sieloff. circ. 30,000. **Document type:** consumer publication.

DIARY. see CLOTHING TRADE — Fashions

A DIFFERENT LIGHT REVIEW; a catalog of gay and lesbian literature. see HOMOSEXUALITY

DINAH. see HOMOSEXUALITY

101   FR
DIPLOMEES. 1952. q. 120 F. Association Francaise des Femmes Diplomees des Universites, 4, rue de Chevreuse, 75006 Paris, France. Ed. Nicole Becaud. adv.; bk.rev. circ. 2,000.

301.412   US
DIRECTORY OF NEW YORK CITY WOMEN'S ORGANIZATIONS. 1982. irreg. $12. Commission on the Status of Women, 52 Chambers St., Rm. 317, New York, NY 10007. TEL 212-788-2738. FAX 212-788-3298. Ed. Mery Jones. circ. 5,000. (looseleaf format) **Document type:** directory.
Formerly: Women's Organizations: A New York City Directory.
Description: Annotated listing of over 400 women's business, professional, and advocacy groups in New York City.

DIRECTORY TO CANADIAN PAGAN RESOURCES. see RELIGIONS AND THEOLOGY

305.4   II   ISSN 0971-166X
DOCUMENTATION ON WOMEN'S CONCERNS. 1989. s-a. Rs.300 (foreign $80). All India Association for Christian Higher Education, Library and Documentation Centre, 39, Institutional Area, D-Block, Janakpuri, New Delhi-110058, India. TEL 5491033. Ed. Nisha Oairae; Pub. Mani Jacob. circ. 500.

301.412   RM
DOLGOZO NO. (Text in Hungarian) 1945. m. National Women's Council, Str. Napoca 16, Cluj-Napoca, Rumania. circ. 106,000.

DOMINANTLY YOURS. see SINGLES' INTERESTS AND LIFESTYLES

DOMINATRIX CROSS ROADS. see MEN'S INTERESTS

DONNA; international fashion magazine. see CLOTHING TRADE — Fashions

301.412   IT
DONNA E MAMMA. 1989. m. L.46900. Eurotrend S.p.A., Via Nino Bixio 6, 20129 Milan, Italy. TEL 39-2-29405653. FAX 39-2-29404868. Ed. Guido Colonna. adv.: B&W or color page L.14500000. circ. 90,078.

055   IT   ISSN 0046-0591
DONNA DI CASA; rivista mensile femminile. 1959. m. L.180000($360) Oscar Vona, Ed. & Pub., 44 Via Benedetto Marcello, 20124 Milan, Italy. TEL 02-2047940. adv.; bk.rev.; illus.

301.412   IT
DONNA E SOCIETA. 1968. q. L.15000. Corso Rinascimento 113, 00186 Rome, Italy. TEL 656-9166. Ed. Maria Paola Colombo Svevo. adv.; bk.rev.

301.412   IT   ISSN 1120-5024
DONNA MODERNA. 1988. w. L.78000 (foreign L.114400). Arnoldo Mondadori Editore S.p.A., Casella Postale 17135, 20170 Milan, Italy. TEL 39-2-3199345. Ed. Edvige Bernasconi. adv.: page L.64800000. circ. 634,000.

DONNE RURALI. see AGRICULTURE

301.412 746.92   SP   ISSN 1130-409X
DUNIA. 1976. m. 3000 ptas. (Europe 7200 ptas.; elsewhere 9200 ptas.). G y J Espana Ediciones, S.L. (Subsidiary of: Gruner & Jahr USA Publishing), Marques de Villamagna, 4, 28001 Madrid, Spain. TEL 431-6631. FAX 5767881. TELEX 43419 ORBOSA E. adv. contact: Elena Sanchez Fabres. bk.rev. circ. 112,863. **Document type:** consumer publication.

301.412   IO   ISSN 0852-5900
DUNIA WANITA. 1949. fortn. Rps.1500 (effective 1991). Jalan Brigjen, Katamso1, Medan, Indonesia. TEL 061-520858. FAX 061-510025. Ed. Rayati Syafrin. adv.: B&W page Rps.500000, color page Rps.650000. circ. 10,000.

DYKE DIANNIC WICCA SEPARATIST AMAZON MAGICK. see HOMOSEXUALITY

E K - BLADET. (Erhverskvinders Klub) see BUSINESS AND ECONOMICS

305.412   US   ISSN 0163-0989
PS508.W7
EARTH'S DAUGHTERS; a feminist arts periodical. 1971. 3/yr. $14 to individuals; institutions $22. Box 41, Central Park Sta., Buffalo, NY 14215. TEL 716-886-2410. Ed. B. Kastle Brill. bk.rev. circ. 1,000.

305.4   US
EAST BAY WOMEN FOR PEACE. NEWSLETTER. 1965. a. $10. East Bay Women for Peace, 2302 Ellsworth St., Berkeley, CA 94704. TEL 510-849-3020. Ed. June Naborsek. bk.rev. circ. 400. **Document type:** newsletter.

305.412   GW   ISSN 0342-1619
ECHO DER FRAU. 1973. w. (Wed.). Welt am Sonnabend GmbH, Adlerstr. 22, 40211 Duesseldorf, Germany. TEL 0211-3666-0. FAX 0211-3666329. Ed. Knut Ihne. adv. contact: Josef Wolter. bk.rev. circ. 458,091. **Document type:** consumer publication.

EDITH WHARTON REVIEW. see LITERATURE

301.412   CN
EDMONTON WOMAN. 1993. 10/yr. Alberta Business Research Ltd., 10179 105th St., Ste. 800, Edmonton, AB T5J 3N1, Canada. TEL 403-424-1221. FAX 403-421-7667. Ed. Colin Smith; Pub. Lorne Silverstein. adv.: B&W page Can.$1265, color page Can.$1660. circ. 30,000. (tabloid format) **Document type:** consumer publication.

376   ER   ISSN 0235-7488
EESTI NAINE; a magazine for women. (Text in Estonian) 1924. m. Estonian Press, Parnu mnt. 67a, 0007 Tallinn, Estonia. TEL 681-310. Ed. Aimi Paalandi. adv. contact: Leo Kikas. illus. circ. 50,000.
Formerly: Noukogude Naine.

305.412   FI   ISSN 0358-8351
EEVA. 1934. m. FIM 480. A-Lehdet Oy, Hitsaajankatu 7, FIN-00081 A-Lehdet, Finland. FAX 358-0-786-858. Heljae Laukkanen. adv.; bk.rev.; charts; illus. circ. 94,839. **Document type:** consumer publication.
Formerly (until 1977): Uusi Eeva (ISSN 0355-2985)
Description: For the refined adult woman.

305.412   JA
EF. (Text in Japanese) 1985. m. 11280 Yen. Shufunotomo Co., Ltd., 2-9 Kanda Surugadai, Chiyoda-ku, Tokyo 101, Japan. Ed. Kiyoju Endo. circ. 200,000. **Document type:** consumer publication.

305.4   GR
EGO; sychrone gunaika. m. Ekdoseon Lymperi A.E., Kifisias 64, 151025 Marousi, Athens, Greece. TEL 30-1-689-9550. FAX 30-1-389-9553. Ed. Antonis Lumperis. adv.; illus. **Document type:** consumer publication.
Description: Contains various items of interest to the contemporary Greek woman.

301   US   ISSN 0740-8307
HQ29
EIDOS; sexual freedom and erotic entertainment for women, men and couples. 1984. q. $55. Box 96, Boston, MA 02137-0096. TEL 617-262-0096. FAX 617-364-0096. Ed. Brenda Loew Tatelbaum. adv.: page $375; 10 x 14. bk.rev.; film rev. circ. 10,000. (tabloid format; back issues avail.) **Document type:** newspaper.
Formerly: Eidos. Erotica for Women.
Description: Advocates freely chosen mutually respectful consensual human sexual expression for all sexual orientations, preferences and lifestyles.

053.932   BE   ISSN 0775-4779
EIGEN AARD. 1909. m. (Katholiek Vormingswerk van Landelijke Vrouwen) Publicarto N.V., Langestraat 170, B-1150 Brussels 15, Belgium. TEL 32-2-7790000. FAX 32-2-7791616. adv.; bk.rev.; illus.; circ. 156,273 (controlled). **Document type:** consumer publication.
Former titles (until 1987): Bij de Haard (ISSN 0006-2227); (until 1949): Boerin (ISSN 0770-2361).
Description: Socio-cultural magazine addressed to members of the K.V.L.V. women's organization.

301.412 305.3   BL   ISSN 0531-9153
ELE E ELA; uma revista para ler a dois. 1969. m. $42. Bloch Editores S.A., Rua do Russell 766-804, 22210-000 Rio de Janeiro, RJ, Brazil. TEL 021-5554000. FAX 021-2059988. TELEX 2121525 BLOC. Ed. Leo Borges. adv.; charts; illus. circ. 150,000. **Document type:** consumer publication.

687   NE
ELEGANCE. 1943. m. fl.99.50 (foreign fl.237.50) (effective 1995). B.V. Uitgeversmaatschappij Bonaventura (Subsidiary of: Elsevier N.V.), Postbus 2158, 1000 CD Amsterdam, Netherlands. TEL 31-20-6914111. FAX 31-20-5674398. Ed. Rupert Van Woerkom. bk.rev.; illus. circ. 55,000. **Document type:** consumer publication.

301.412   BE   ISSN 0775-4205
ELGA. (Text in Dutch) 1987. m. 1000 BEF. Tijdschriften Vereniging Vlaanderen S.A., Rue de Jonckers 46, 1060 Brussels, Belgium. TEL 32-2-537-08-00. FAX 32-2-534-02-38. adv.: B&W page 96000 BEF, color page 145000 BEF; 203 x 265. circ. 79,040.

305.4 051   US   ISSN 1073-256X
▼**ELIGIBLE**; for the independent woman. 1994. q. $11.50; newsstand price: $2.95. L A's Eligible, Inc., Box 17625, Encino, CA 91416. TEL 818-344-1753. Ed. Sada Volkoff; Pub. Katherine Duliakis. adv.: B&W page $2900. circ. 50,000. **Document type:** consumer publication.
Formerly: L A's Eligible (ISSN 1079-7319)

WOMEN'S INTERESTS

054.1   FR   ISSN 0013-6298
ELLE. 1945. w. 540 F. (foreign 800 F.) Hachette Filipacchi Publications, 6 rue Ancelle, 92525 Neuilly-sur-Seine Cedex, France. TEL 1-40-88-72-59. FAX 1-40-88-72-62. TELEX 611 462. (Subscr. to: 90 rue Flandre, 75947 Paris Cedex 19, France. TEL 40-34-35-00; Subscr. in US to: Box 0007, Rouses Point, NY 12979. TEL 800-363-1310) Ed. Anne Marie Perier. adv.; illus. circ. 395,007. **Indexed:** DAAI. **Document type:** consumer publication.

301.412   US   ISSN 0888-0808 TT500
ELLE. (American Edition) 1985. m. $26. Elle Publishing (Subsidiary of: Hachette Filipacchi Magazines), 1633 Broadway, New York, NY 10019. TEL 212-767-5800. FAX 212-489-4210. (Subscr. to: Box 53581, Boulder, CO 80322. TEL 800-876-8775) adv.; bk.rev. circ. 875,000. **Indexed:** Access (1986-), DAAI. **Document type:** consumer publication.
—UnCover.
   Description: International style magazine for the sophisticated, affluent, well traveled woman. Reports on global ideas and trends in fashion, personalities and lifestyles.

301.412   BL   ISSN 0104-1703
ELLE. 1988. m. $160. Editora Abril, S.A., R. Geraldo Flausino Gomez, 61, 04573-900 Sao Paulo SP, Brazil. TEL 011-534-5598. FAX 011-534-5779. (Subscr. to: Rua do Curtume 769, 05065-900 Sao Paulo SP, Brazil. TEL 011-823-9100) Ed. Regina Guerreiro. adv.; illus. circ. 92,000. **Document type:** consumer publication.
   Description: International style magazine for the sophisticated, affluent, well-traveled woman.

301.412   HK   ISSN 1018-1148
ELLE; Hong Kong. (Text in Chinese; summaries in Chinese and English) 1987. m. HK.$378 (foreign HK.$1458). Hachette Filipacchi Asia - Pacific, Shop A8-9, 18 Hong On St., Quarry Bay Kornhill, Hong Kong. TEL 852-567-8707. FAX 852-568-4650. Ed. Mary Lui. adv.: color page $34000; trim 214 x 275; adv. contact: Rosana Wang. film rev. circ. 44,775. (back issues avail.) **Document type:** consumer publication.
   Description: Fashion and beauty magazine for the Chinese women.

301.412   PO
ELLE. 1988. m. Av. 5 de Outubro 204-2o A-B-C, 1200 Lisbon, Portugal. TEL 01-736878. Dir. Maria Teresa Coelho. circ. 40,000.

301.412   SP   ISSN 0214-3364
ELLE. 1987. m. 3840 ptas. (foreign 5360 ptas.) (effective Jan. 1992). Hachette Publicaciones, S.A., Santa Engracia 6, 1o, 28010 Madrid, Spain. TEL 91-593-84-62. FAX 91-446-09-06. (Subscr. to: Cempro, Plaza del Conde Valle Suchill 20, 28015 Madrid, Spain. TEL 593-34-11) Dir. Charo Izquierdo. adv. contact: Alvaro Gomez Acebo. circ. 200,000.

053.1   GW   ISSN 0935-462X
ELLE. 1988. m. DM.78. Burda GmbH and F.E.P., Arabellastr. 23, 81925 Munich, Germany. TEL 089-9250-3213. FAX 089-92503040. Ed. Renate Rosenthal; Pubs. Hubert Burda, Daniel Filipacchi. adv.: B&W page DM.23740, color page DM.35570; trim 230 x 285; adv. contact: Stephanie Albrecht. circ. 228,833 (paid). **Document type:** consumer publication.
   Description: Covers fashion, books, arts, cosmetics, cuisine, and films.

059.956   JA
ELLE. 1989. fortn. 6000 Yen. Time - Hachette, Daini Sakae Bldg., 11-14, Otawa 2-chome, Tokyo 112, Japan. TEL 81-3-5395-2602. FAX 81-3-5395-1086. adv.: B&W page 1140000 Yen, color page 1720000 Yen; trim 267 x 210. circ. 250,000.
   Description: Covers fashion, books, art, cuisine, and films.

052   UK   ISSN 0269-2597
ELLE. 1985. m. £1.60 per no. Hachette Magazines, Rex House, 5-12 Lower Regent St., London SW1Y 4PE. TEL 44-171-930-9050. FAX 44-171-839-2762. adv.: B&W page £4400, color page £5900; trim 222 x 300. circ. 183,178. **Indexed:** DAAI. **Document type:** consumer publication.
   Description: Covers fashion, books, art, cuisine and films.

301.412   CH   ISSN 1018-8649
ELLE. (Text in Chinese, English) 1991. m. NT$2000. Hachette Interculture Inc., 62 Jen-Ai Rd., Section 2, Taipei, Taiwan, Republic of China. TEL 88-62-397-9099. adv.; bk.rev.

301.412   AT
ELLE. 1990. m. Aus.$4.95 per no. Hachette Consolidated Press Pty. Ltd., G.P.O. Box 4088, 54 Park St., Sydney, N.S.W. 2001, Australia. TEL 61-2-2828000. FAX 61-2-674375. Ed. Deborah Thomas; Pub. Richard Walsh. adv.: B&W page Aus.$5045, color page Aus.$8135; trim 210 x 275; adv. contact: Lisa Poulos. bk.rev. circ. 72,000. **Document type:** consumer publication.

301.412   SW   ISSN 0284-6969
ELLE. 1988. m. SEK 390. Hachette Publicist Gruppen, Box 1717, Regeringsgaten 42, 111 87 Stockholm, Sweden. TEL 4687016970. FAX 468216520. adv.: B&W page SEK 33000, color page SEK 38500; trim 290 x 225. circ. 69,000. **Document type:** consumer publication.

301.412   KO
ELLE. 1992. m. 3800 Won per no. Hachette, 200 Naejn-dong, Seoul, S. Korea. TEL 822-723-1101. FAX 822-723-1180. adv.: B&W or color page 2000000 Won; trim 223 x 297. circ. 80,000 (paid). **Document type:** consumer publication.

301.412   NE   ISSN 0926-9398
ELLE. 1989. m. newsstand price: fl.8.25. Hachette, Singel 466-468, 1017 AW Amsterdam, Netherlands. TEL 31-20-6244961. FAX 31-20-6208149. Ed. Liesbeth Hendrikse; Pub. Maarten van den Bogelaar. adv.: B&W page fl.9950, color page fl.16250; 207 x 272; adv. contact: Jolanda Sier. circ. 65,000 (paid). **Document type:** consumer publication.

301.412   FR
ELLE (GREEK EDITION). 1988. m. Dr.6700. France Editions & Publications, 2-6 rue Ancelle, 92525 Neuilly-sur-Seine, France. TEL 33-1-40-88-60-00. adv.: B&W page Dr.850000, color page Dr.1000000; 200 x 277. circ. 48,000 (paid). **Document type:** consumer publication.

301.412   BE   ISSN 0779-9535
ELLE (VLAAMSE EDITIE). 1993. w. 13000 BEF. Hachette Filipacchi Press, 127 Bd. Emile Jacqmain, 1000 Brussels, Belgium. TEL 02-211-2929. FAX 02-2111-2914. adv.: B&W page 62000 BEF, color page 81000 BEF; trim 227 x 297. circ. 17,000 (paid). **Document type:** consumer publication.

301.412   HK   ISSN 1006-1169
ELLE, CHINA. (Text in Chinese) 1988. bi-m. Y72. Hachette Filipacchi Asia - Pacific, Shop A8-9, Hong On Street, Quarry Bay, Kornhill, Hong Kong. TEL 852-2567-8707. FAX 852-2568-4650. Ed. Ronnie Lee. adv.: color page $9000; trim 214 x 275; adv. contact: Rosanna Wong. circ. 200,000. **Document type:** consumer publication.

301.412   IT   ISSN 1120-4397
ELLE ITALIA. 1987. m. L.57600. Rizzoli Editore-Corriere della Sera, Via A. Vespucci 2, 20124 Milan, Italy. TEL 39-2-628-6183. Ed. Daniela Giussani. adv.: color page L.39900000; trim 230 x 287. circ. 145,295. **Indexed:** DAAI.

EMERGE!; a journal for Christian Scientists supporting lesbians, bisexuals, and gay men. *see* HOMOSEXUALITY

301.435   TS
EMIRATES WOMAN. (Text in English) 1981. m. Motivate Publishing, P.O. Box 2331, Dubai, United Arab Emirates. TEL 246060. FAX 245270. TELEX 48366 MAM EM. Ed. Fay Yendell. circ. 12,000.
   Description: Fashion, health, beauty and other topics of interest to women in the U.A.E.

323.4   GW   ISSN 0721-9741
EMMA; Magazin von Frauen fuer Menschen. 1977. bi-m. DM.70.80 (Europe DM.79.80). Emma Frauen Verlag GmbH, Alteburgerstr. 2, 50678 Cologne, Germany. TEL 0221-316071. FAX 0221-316075. (Subscr. to: Zenit Pressevertrieb, Postfach 810640, 70523 Stuttgart, Germany) Ed. Monika Gloecklhofer; Pub. Alice Schwarzer. adv.: B&W page DM.6600, color page DM.9800; trim 180 x 241; adv. contact: Christina Schmalfuss. bk.rev.; tr.lit.; index. circ. 60,000 (back issues avail.) **Document type:** consumer publication.

059.8   GR
ENA. 1983. w. A. Moatsos, Pub., 15 Voukourestiou, 106 71 Athens, Greece. TEL 30-1-364-4151. FAX 30-1-362-7524. adv. circ. 32,000. **Document type:** consumer publication.

051   US
ENCORE MAGAZINE; celebrating return of the crone. 1992. 5/yr. $20. Dynamic Communications, 604 Pringle Ave., Ste. 91, Galt, CA 95652. TEL 209-745-0915. (Subscr. addr.: P.O. Box 1599, Mariposa, CA 95338) Ed. Joyce Cupps. adv. contact: Joyce Cupps. bk.rev.; circ. 1,000 (paid). (back issues avail.) **Document type:** consumer publication.
   Description: Aimed at women of 45 and older. Includes articles, interviews, columns, stories, poetry, art on many subjects such as aging and ageism, menopause, spirituality, grandmothering.

ENDOMETRIOSIS ASSOCIATION NEWSLETTER. *see* MEDICAL SCIENCES — Obstetrics And Gynecology

301.412   CN
ENFANTS. 2/yr. Quebecor Inc., 2 Bates Chemin, Outremont, Que. H2V 1A7, Canada. TEL 514-270-1100. FAX 514-270-4810. Ed. Jean Lessard. circ. 40,000.

ENTREPRENEURIAL WOMAN. *see* BUSINESS AND ECONOMICS — Small Business

323.4   US
EQUAL RIGHTS. 1930. q. $15. National Women's Party, 144 Constitution Ave., N.E., Washington, DC 20002. TEL 202-546-1210. Ed. Helen Arnold. circ. 3,000. (also avail. in microfilm; back issues avail.) **Document type:** newsletter.

EQUAL RIGHTS ADVOCATE. *see* LAW

301.412   US   ISSN 1063-0589
EQUAL TIME.* 1992. 10/yr. $19 (effective Dec. 1992). Femality House, Inc., c/o Cynthia Scott, Pub., 121 S. 8th St., Ste. 1600, Minneapolis, MN 55402-2833. TEL 216-473-1020. FAX 216-473-0878. Ed. Donna M. McKee. adv.; bk.rev.; illus. circ. 15,000. (back issues avail.) **Document type:** newsletter.
   Description: Provides empowerment information for women to encourage achievement. Also inspires cooperation and unity among women, including increasing awareness about issues particularly important to women.

305.412 323.4   US
EQUALITY N O W!. 1972. m. $7. National Organization for Women, Madison Chapter, Box 2512, Madison, WI 53701. TEL 608-255-3911. Eds. Beth Brace, Lori Nelson. adv.; bk.rev. circ. 900. (processed) **Indexed:** Build.Manage.Abstr., High.Educ.Curr.Aware.Bull. **Document type:** newsletter.
   Formerly: Madison N O W Chapter Newsletter.

301.412 028.5   MX
ERES. 1988. bi-w. $42. Editorial Eres, S.A., Andres Bello, 45, piso 14, Polanco, 11560 Mexico D.F., Mexico. TEL 525-7097302. FAX 525-2813200. adv.: B&W page Mex.$8867, color page Mex.$13800; trim 8 1/8 x 10 3/4. circ. 20,157.

051   US
EROTIC EARTHBODY; sacred sexuality, eros and the life force - networking our way toward evolution. 1993. 2/yr. $15 (effective 1995). Nadir Publications, RR1, Box 4528 (U), Camden, ME 04843. Ed. Patrikyia de Wicce. adv.; bk.rev.; circ. 2,000 (paid). **Document type:** newsletter.
   Description: Discusses personal experiences and changing cultural behavior practices among adults.

EROTIC WRITER'S AND COLLECTOR'S MARKET. *see* PUBLISHING AND BOOK TRADE

376   BO
ESCOBA. 1986. 4/yr. Centro de Informacion y Desarrollo de la Mujer, Casilla 3961, La Paz, Bolivia.

ESPRESSO. *see* BUSINESS AND ECONOMICS

ESSEN UND TRINKEN. *see* FOOD AND FOOD INDUSTRIES

WOMEN'S INTERESTS

917.309   US   ISSN 0014-0880
E185.86
ESSENCE (NEW YORK); the magazine for today's black woman. 1970. m. $14.96. Essence Communications Inc., 1500 Broadway, New York, NY 10036. TEL 212-642-0600. FAX 212-921-5173. Ed. Susan L. Taylor. adv.; bk.rev.; film rev.; charts; illus. circ. 950,000. (also avail. in microfilm from UMI) **Indexed**: Bk.Rev.Ind. (1984-), Child.Bk.Rev.Ind. (1984-), Curr.Lit.Fam.Plan., Hlth.Ind., Ind.Per.Negroes, Mag.Ind., Media Rev.Dig., PMR, R.G., TOM.
—Faxon; UMI; UnCover.
Description: Black women's interests.

301.412 640   UK   ISSN 0953-6337
ESSENTIALS. 1988. m. £21.90 (foreign £24.40); newsstand price: £1.30. I P C Magazines, Southbank Publishing Group (Subsidiary of: Reed Elsevier group), King's Reach Tower, Stamford St., London SE1 9LS, England. TEL 071-836-0519. FAX 0444-440619. TELEX 892084 REEDBP G. (Dist. by: Quadrant Subscription Services, Oakfield House, Perrymount Rd., Haywards Heath, W. Sussex RH16 3DH, England. TEL 0444-440421; Subscr. to: P.O. Box 272, Oakfield House, 35 Perrymount Rd., Haywards Heath, W. Sussex H16 3FS, England. TEL 0444-445555) Ed. Gilly Cubitt; Pub. Jackie Newcombe. adv. contact: Louise Dickinson. circ. 543,000. (back issues avail.) **Document type**: consumer publication.
Description: Offers women culinary, health, beauuty and fashion advice.

301.412   CN
L'ESSENTIEL. m. Quebecor Inc., 7 Bates Chemin, Outrement, Que. H2V 1A6, Canada. TEL 514-270-1100. FAX 514-270-4810. Ed. Sylvie Bergeron. circ. 141,000.

305.412   US
▼**ETERNELLE**. 1994. q. $18; newsstand price: $3.50. Eternelle Magazine Co., Box 1646, Los Altos, CA 94023-1646. TEL 415-917-1557. Ed. Laura Dayton; Pub. Valerie Foster. adv.; B&W page $3750, color page $5000. circ. 50,000. **Document type**: consumer publication.

305.412   GW   ISSN 0174-3465
DIE EULE; Diskussionsforum fuer rationalitaetsgenealogische, insbesondere feministische Theorie. 1978. s-a. DM.1 per no. (Arbeitsgruppe fuer Anti-Psychoanalyse) Heide Heinz, Ed.& Pub., Augustastr. 123, 5600 Wuppertal 1, Germany. illus.

EUROPEAN SOCIETY OF WOMEN IN THEOLOGICAL RESEARCH. YEARBOOK/EUROPAEISCHE GESELLSCHAFT FUER DIE THEOLOGISCHE FORSCHUNG VON FRAUEN. JAHRBUCH. see RELIGIONS AND THEOLOGY

056.1   DR   ISSN 0014-3286
EVA. 1967. fortn. RD.$4($17) Publicaciones Ahora, Ave. San Martin 236, Apdo. Postal 1402, Santo Domingo, Dominican Republic. Ed. Magda Florencio.

EVA. see CLOTHING TRADE — Fashions

052   HK
EVE. (Text in Chinese and English) 1979. m. HK.$216. Communication Management Ltd., 1811 Hong Kong Plaza, 188 Connaught Rd. W., Hong Kong. TEL 2547-7117. FAX 2858-2671. Ed. Lina Ross; Pub. M. Mohindar. adv. contact: Michelle Lee. circ. 20,000. **Document type**: consumer publication.

052   II   ISSN 0014-3812
EVE'S WEEKLY. (Text in English) 1947. w. newsstand price: Rs.20. Maurya Publications Pvt. Ltd., Office No. 20-21, Centaur Hotel, Juhu Beach, Juhu Tara Rd., Bombay 400 049, India. TEL 6116631. Ed. Vanit Jain. adv.; B&W page Rs.15000, color page Rs.30000; trim 180 x 240. circ. 40,000.

305.4 150   US
▼**EVOLVING WOMAN**. 1994. m. $24. Borders Publishing Company, Box 73, Gardner, KS 66030. TEL 913-856-7491. Ed. Jill Borders; Pub. Jill Borders. adv.; B&W page $398. circ. 10,000. **Document type**: consumer publication.

EXEC-U-TARY. see BUSINESS AND ECONOMICS — Office Equipment And Services

301   US   ISSN 0199-2880
HF5500.3.U54
EXECUTIVE FEMALE. 1978. bi-m. $29 membership. National Association for Female Executives, 30 Irving Pl., 5th Fl., New York, NY 10003. TEL 212-477-2200; 800-634-6233. (Subscr. to: Box 469031, Escondido, CA 92046) Ed. Basia Hellwig. adv.; bk.rev.; circ. 190,000 (paid). **Indexed**: B.P.I., BPIA, Bus.Ind., Tr.& Indus.Ind.
●Also available online.
—BLDSC (3836.214300); Faxon; UnCover.
Formerly: Executive Female Digest (ISSN 0160-8134)
Description: Focuses on career and financial management topics for upwardly mobile executive women and entrepreneurs.

EXECUTIVE WOMEN INTERNATIONAL. PULSE. see BUSINESS AND ECONOMICS

301.412   UK   ISSN 0142-2170
EXPLORATIONS IN FEMINISM. no.7, 1981. irreg. Women's Research and Resources Centre, Explorations in Feminism Collective, c/o Silver Moon Women's Bookshop, 68 Charing Cross Rd., London WC2H 0BB, England.

323.4   US
EXPONENT II; a quarterly newspaper concerning Mormon women, published by Mormon women, and of interest to Mormon women and others. 1974. q. $10 (effective 1989). Exponent II, Inc., Box 37, Arlington, MA 02174. TEL 617-868-3464. FAX 617-862-1928. Ed. Susan L. Paxman. bk.rev.; illus.; index. circ. 4,000. (tabloid format) **Document type**: newspaper.

305.412 054   FR   ISSN 0014-5327
EXPRESSION; revue culturelle feminine internationale. (Text in English, French and German) 1964. a. membership. Editions Expression et Communication, 1 av. de Chatou, 92561 Reuil-Malmaison Cedex, France. Ed. Perigot De LaTour. adv.; illus. circ. 3,000. (tabloid format)

305.4   UK   ISSN 0264-7060
HQ1389
F A N.* (Feminist Arts News) 1988. irreg. £2 per no. Black Horse Press, 15 Wordsmith Ct., Shakespeare Rd., Bedford MK40 2EJ, England. (Dist. by: Central Books, 14 The Leathermarket, London SE1 3ER, England. TEL 071-407-5447) Ed.Bd. **Indexed**: DAAI.
—BLDSC (3905.197050); UnCover.

305.412   US   ISSN 0895-3619
F E W'S NEWS AND VIEWS. 1969. bi-m. $12. Federally Employed Women Inc., 1400 Eye St., N.W., Ste. 425, Washington, DC 20005. TEL 202-898-0994. FAX 202-898-0998. Ed. Michael J. Varhola. adv.; bk.rev.; bibl.; illus. circ. 10,000.
Former titles: News and Views from Federally Employed Women (ISSN 0162-2471); F E W's News and Views (ISSN 0046-3477)

FACETS (CHICAGO). see MEDICAL SCIENCES

052   SA   ISSN 0014-6927
FAIR LADY. 1965. fortn. R.165.15. National Magazines (Subsidiary of: National Media Ltd.), P.O. Box 1802, Cape Town 8000, South Africa. TEL 27-21-4062100. FAX 27-21-4062936. Ed. Roz Wrottesley. adv.; bk.rev.; film rev.; illus. circ. 162,200. **Indexed**: Ind.S.A.Per. **Document type**: consumer publication.

052   SA
FAIR LADY JUNIOR. (Text in English) 1990. fortn. National Magazines (Subsidiary of: National Media Ltd.), P.O. Box 1802, Cape Town 8000, South Africa. TEL 27-21-4062100. FAX 27-21-4062936. **Document type**: consumer publication.
Description: Intended for readers of Fair Lady who have children under six years of age.

305.312   US
FAIRFIELD COUNTY WOMAN. 1983. m. $15. F C W, Inc., 15 Bank St., Stamford, CT 06901. TEL 203-323-3105. Ed. Joan Honig. adv. contact: Connie Ilowitz. circ. 50,000. (tabloid format) back issues avail.) **Document type**: newspaper.

059.927   TS
FAJR AL-JADID/NEW DAWN. (Text in Arabic) 1973. m. Jam'iyyat al-Nisa'iyyah, Umm al-Quwain - Umm al-Quwain Women's Society, P.O. Box 43, Umm al-Quwain, United Arab Emirates. TEL 666455. Ed. Mariam Ali Rashid al-Muala. circ. 1,000.
Description: Covers the activities of the society, the state of the women's movement in the U.A.E., and women's health issues.

305.4   US   ISSN 1077-3215
LA FAMILIA DE LA CIUDAD; ideas para una vida mejor. English edition: City Family (ISSN 1077-3207) (Text in Spanish) 1992. q. $3.95. City Family, Inc., 44 W. 69th St., Ste. 4B, New York, NY 10023. TEL 212-362-3052. FAX 212-580-4833. (Subscr. to: Box 748, Ansonia Sta., New York, NY 10023) Ed. Ellen Frankel; Pub. Arthur Schiff. adv. **Document type**: consumer publication.
Description: Covers health, law, fashion, food, furnishing and other topics of interest to women.

FAMILY (NEW YORK); the magazine for military wives. see MILITARY

FAMILY AFFAIRS. see MEN'S INTERESTS

301.412 640   US
FASHION POETRY PATTERNS & RECITALS NEWS. 1986. biennial. $25. Patterns Etc., by Alfreda, c/o Prosperity & Profits Unlimited, Box 416, Denver, CO 80201-0416. TEL 303-575-5676. Ed. A.C. Doyle. circ. 1,500. (looseleaf format; also avail. in microfiche; back issues avail.) **Document type**: newsletter.
Description: Patterns in poetry form.

FEDERATION FEMININE FRANCO-AMERICAINE. BULLETIN. see ETHNIC INTERESTS

301.412   BE   ISSN 0777-3439
FEELING. (Text in Dutch) 1990. s-m. 4108 Fr. I U M, Jan Blockxtraat 7, Antwerp 2018, Belgium. TEL 32-3-247-4511. FAX 32-3-237-6136. adv. circ. 62,861.
Description: Covers beauty, home and environment, health, cooking, and culture and tourism.

305.412   MX   ISSN 0185-4666
HQ1104
FEM. 1976. m. $60. Difusion Cultural Feminista, A.C., Av. Insurgentes Sur 598-302, Col. Del Valle, C.P. 03100 Mexico, D.F., Mexico. TEL 536-92-61. FAX 523-46-57. Ed. Esperanza Brito de Marti. adv.; Rotmi/Enciso. bk.rev. circ. 15,000. **Indexed**: Chic.Per.Ind., Hisp.Amer.Per.Ind. (1977-).
Description: Focuses on the women's liberation movement.

FEMALE BODYBUILDING AND WEIGHT TRAINING. see PHYSICAL FITNESS AND HYGIENE

055.91   RM   ISSN 0046-3655
FEMEIA; revista social politica si culturala. 1948. m. 36 lei($8) (Consiliul National al Femeilor din Republica Socialista Romania) Editura Scinteia, Piata Presei Libere 1, 71341 Bucharest, Rumania. (Subscr. to: ILEXIM, Str. 13 Decembrie Nr. 3, P.O. Box 136-137, Bucharest, Rumania) Ed. Constanta Niculescu. adv.; bk.rev.; film rev.; charts; illus. circ. 475,000.

058.81   DK   ISSN 0014-9853
FEMINA. 1874. w. DKK 421; newsstand price: DKK 14.75. Aller Press A-S, Vigerslev Alle 18, DK-2500 Valby, Denmark. TEL 45-36-30-33-33. FAX 45-36-30-2440. Ed. Jutta Larsen. adv.; B&W page DKK 17700, color page DKK 22200; trim 185 x 252; adv. contact: Mogens Astinger. bk.rev. circ. 146,415. cols./p.: 4.
Formerly (until 1952): Moenster Tidende (ISSN 0908-262X)

311   II   ISSN 0430-2990
FEMINA. (Text in English, Gujarati) 1959. fortn. $29. Bennett, Coleman & Co., Ltd. (Bombay), Times of India Bldg., Dr. Dadabhai Naoroji Road, Bombay 400 001, India. TEL 22-2620271. TELEX 1182699. (U.S. subscr. addr.: Ms. Kalpana, 42-75 Main St., Flushing, NY 11355) Ed. Vimla Patil. adv.; bk.rev.; illus

WOMEN'S INTERESTS

305.412   SA   ISSN 0256-0313
FEMINA. 1982. m. R.76 (foreign R.88). Associated Magazines (Pty) Ltd., The Avalon, 2nd Fl., Corner Mill & Hope Sts., Gardens, Cape Town 8001, South Africa. TEL 27-21-462-3070. FAX 27-21-461-2500. Ed. Jane Raphaely. adv. contact: Volker Kuehnel. bk.rev. circ. 109,321. **Document type:** consumer publication.
    Formerly (until 1988): Darling.
    Description: Provides general information of interest to women in South Africa.

301.412   IO
FEMINA. 1972. w. Blok B, Jalan H.R. Rasuna Said, Kav. 32-33, Jakarta Selatan, Indonesia. TEL 021-513816. FAX 021-513-041. TELEX 62338. circ. 130,000.

301.412   SW
FEMINA. m. SEK 29 per no. Allerfoeretagen, S-251 85 Helsingborg, Sweden. TEL 46-08-667-9870. FAX 46-08-661-88-19. adv.: B&W page SEK 43000, color page SEK 43000; trim 190 x 265. bk.rev. circ. 144,734.
    Description: Covers food, fashion and the home. Includes beauty, gardening, art, health, sports, entertainment, furniture and travel.

058.7 746.9   SW   ISSN 0280-7807
FEMINA MAANADENS MAGASIN/FEMINA MONTHLY MAGAZINE. (Supplement avail.: Laestidningen) 1944. m. SEK 330; newsstand price: SEK 34. Aller Specialtidningar AB, Landskronavaegen 23, S-251 85 Helsingborg, Sweden. TEL 46-42-17-35-00. FAX 46-42-17-37-67. Ed. Stina Norling. adv.: B&W page SEK 43000; trim 190 x 265. circ. 117,900. cols./p.: 4; pp./issue: 216.
    Formed by the merger of: IdeFemina Hus Hem & Traegaard (ISSN 0349-8239) & IdeFemina Mat & Fest (ISSN 0349-7755) & IdeFemina Mode (ISSN 0349-7763)

FEMINALE. see *SPORTS AND GAMES*

FEMINIST BOOKSTORE NEWS. see *PUBLISHING AND BOOK TRADE*

FEMINIST ECONOMICS. see *BUSINESS AND ECONOMICS*

305.412   FR   ISSN 0764-4523
FEMME. 1978. m. 130 F. (foreign 186 F.). Hachette Filipacchi Publications, 6 rue Ancelle, 92525 Neuilly sur Seine Cedex, France. TEL 40-88-72-59. FAX 40-88-72-62. (Subscr. to: 9 rue de Flandre, 75947 Paris Cedex 19, France. TEL 40-34-35-00) Dir. Ms. Claude Servan-Schreiber. circ. 230,000.
    Former titles (until 1984): F (ISSN 0754-0612); (until 1983): Nouveau F (ISSN 0750-3121); F Magazine (ISSN 0180-3832)

054.1   FR   ISSN 0764-0021
FEMME ACTUELLE. 1984. w. Prisma Presse, 6 rue Daru, 75008 Paris, France. TEL 44-15-30-00. FAX 47-64-10-42. Ed. Maryse Bonnet. adv. circ. 1,768,000. **Document type:** consumer publication.

300   CN   ISSN 0838-9446
FEMME PLUS. m. (Quebecor Inc.) Publicor Inc., 7 Chemin Bates, Outremont, Que. H2V 1A6, Canada. TEL 514-270-1100. FAX 514-270-6900. Ed. Sylvie Bergeron. circ. 77,000. **Indexed:** Pt.de Rep. (1991-).

305.412   FR   ISSN 0014-9926
FEMME PRATIQUE.* (Text in Belgian and French) 1960. m. 110 F.($38.83) Editions Femme Pratique, Z.A.C. de Fregy, 77610 Fontenay Tresigny, France. TEL 43-72-61-02. Ed. Jannick Lichter. adv.; bk.rev.; film rev.; play rev.; bibl.; illus.; pat.; tr.lit. circ. 380,000. (tabloid format)

305.412   CN   ISSN 0226-9902
FEMMES D'ACTION. 1970. 5/yr. Can.$15 to individuals; institutions Can.$27 (foreign Can.$35). Federation Nationale des Femmes Canadiennes Francaises, 325 Dalhousie Piece 525, Ottawa, ON K1N 7G2, Canada. TEL 613-241-3500. Ed. Lucille Gaudet. adv.; bk.rev. circ. 2,400. **Indexed:** Can.B.P.I., Can.Per.Ind., Can.Wom.Per.Ind.

305.412   BE   ISSN 0014-9950
FEMMES D'AUJOURD'HUI. 1933. w. 290 Fr. (foreign 390 Fr.). Edibel, 9 av. Frans van Kalken, B-1070 Brussels, Belgium. adv.; bk.rev.; film rev.; play rev.; rec.rev.; bibl.; illus.; mkt.; pat.; tr.mk. circ. 160,000.

323.4   CN   ISSN 0705-3851
FEMMES D'ICI. 1977. 5/yr. Can.$15. Association Feminine d'Education et d'Action Sociale, 5999 De Marseille St., Montreal, PQ H1N 1K6, Canada. TEL 514-251-1636. Ed. Paula Provencher-Lambert. adv. contact: Hugette Dalpe. bk.rev. circ. 30,000. **Document type:** bulletin.
    Formerly: A.F.E.A.S. Bulletin (ISSN 0044-9458)
    Description: Covers news of the association, profiles of important feminists, reports of congresses and committee activities.

FEMMES EN LITTERATURE. see *LITERATURE*

053.936   SA
FEMNET. (Text in Afrikaans, English) 1991. q. R.60 membership. Femnet: Gemeenskapsgerigte Vroue-organisasie van Transnet - Community-Oriented Women's Organization of Transnet, Transnet Park Fase 2, Hillsideweg 8, Parktown 2193, South Africa. TEL 27-11-488-7134. FAX 27-11-4887031. Ed. Lisel Krige. illus. circ. 3,500. **Document type:** consumer publication.
    Supersedes: Sasvrou - Sarwoman.

051   CN
FEMZINE. irreg. $3 per issue. 2 Bloor St., W., Ste. 100, P.O. Box 120, Toronto, Ont. MAW 3E2, Canada.

FERRARI'S PLACES FOR WOMEN: USA AND WORLDWIDE. see *HOMOSEXUALITY*

FETISH & FANTASY MAGAZINE. see *MEN'S INTERESTS*

FIELD ADVOCATE. see *GERONTOLOGY AND GERIATRICS*

FIGHTING WOMAN NEWS. see *SPORTS AND GAMES*

301.412   FJ
FIJI WOMEN. (Text in English) m. George Rubine Ltd., P.O. Box 12511, Suva, Fiji. TEL 313944. Ed. George Matai.

301.412   PH
FINA MAGAZINE. 1972. m. P.55. Soller Press & Publishing House, Inc., 45 E. Jacinto St., Expana Extension, Box 121, Quezon City, Philippines. Ed. Franklin Roosevelt C. Cabaluna. adv.; bk.rev.; film rev.; charts; illus. circ. 30,000.

FINANCIAL WOMAN TODAY. see *BUSINESS AND ECONOMICS — Banking And Finance*

FINANCIAL WOMEN'S ASSOCIATION OF NEW YORK NEWSLETTER. see *BUSINESS AND ECONOMICS — Banking And Finance*

323   SG
FIPPU. 1987. q. Yewwu Yewwi Pour la Liberation des Femmes, Dakar, Senegal. Ed. Fatoumata Sow.

810.8 700   CN   ISSN 0706-3857
FIREWEED; a feminist quarterly. 1978. 4/yr. Can.$20 to individuals; institutions Can.$30 (effective 1996). Fireweed Inc., Box 279, Sta. B, Toronto, ON M5T 2W2, Canada. TEL 416-504-1339. adv.; bk.rev.; bibl.; film rev.; illus. circ. 1,500. (back issues avail.) **Indexed:** Can.Lit.Ind., Can.Wom.Per.Ind. **Document type:** consumer publication.
—CCC.
    Description: A feminist journal of writing, politics, art and culture.

305.412   BE   ISSN 0775-0021
FLAIR. (Text in Dutch) 1980. w. 3016 BEF. Tijdschriften Uitgevers Maatschappij N.V.I.U.M., Jan Blockxstraat 7, 2018 Antwerp, Belgium. Ed. Christena van Wackerbarth. adv.: Jan/Van De Wyngaerde. illus. circ. 153,342. **Document type:** consumer publication.

305.412   BE   ISSN 0774-9945
FLAIR (EDITION FRANCAISE); l'hebdo au feminin. (Text in French) 1987. w. 2600 BEF. L N P, Av. Brugmann 27 A, 1060 Brussels, Belgium. TEL 32-2-538-8020. FAX 32-2-5379626. Ed. Mireille Martens. adv.; bk.rev. circ. 85,000. **Document type:** consumer publication.

FLIGHTLOG. see *TRANSPORTATION — Air Transport*

305.4 338.91   UK   ISSN 0968-2864
HQ1870.9   CODEN: FOGEEV
FOCUS ON GENDER. 1993. 3/yr. £20 (foreign £25). Oxfam, 274 Banbury Rd., Oxford OX2 7DZ, England. TEL 0865-313196. FAX 0865-313117. Ed. Bridget Walker. bk.rev. circ. 100. (back issues avail.) **Document type:** bulletin.
—CCC.
    Description: Provides a forum for development practitioners, students and all concerned with the theory and practice of gender-oriented development to exchange views, record experience, and disseminate information about networks and resources.

301.412   CN   ISSN 1182-0012
FOCUS ON WOMEN. 1988. m. Can.$35. Campbell Communications Inc., 1218 Langley St., 3rd Fl., Victoria, BC V8W 1W2, Canada. TEL 604-388-7231. FAX 604-383-1140. Ed. Kerry Slavens. adv.; circ. 30,000 (controlled). **Document type:** consumer publication.

FOKUS; tidning foer centerpartiet och centerkvinnorna. see *POLITICAL SCIENCE*

052   UK   ISSN 0966-2790
FOR WOMEN. 1992. m. £62. Portland Publishing Ltd., 1 Tyburn Ln., Harrow-on-the-Hill, Middlesex HA1 3AG, England. TEL 071-538-8969. FAX 071-538-1170. Ed. Jonathan Richards. adv.: color page £3000; adv. contact: Danielle Fisher. circ. 250,000. **Document type:** consumer publication.

FORD FOUNDATION ANNUAL REPORT. see *SOCIAL SCIENCES: COMPREHENSIVE WORKS*

FORD FOUNDATION REPORT. see *SOCIAL SCIENCES: COMPREHENSIVE WORKS*

301.412 055.1   IT
FOTOROMANZA. m. Edizioni Tempi Moderni Coop, Via E.Q. Visconti 21, 00193 Rome, Italy. TEL 39-6-3219776. Ed. Salvatore Puzzo. adv.: B&W page L.1650000, color page L.2970000. circ. 47,000.

301.412   GW
FRANKFURTER FRAUENBLATT. 1978. bi-m. DM.35. Weibliche Erkenntnisse im Bundesland Hessen e.V., Hamburgerallee 45, 60486 Frankfurt a.M., Germany. TEL 069-7074157. index. (back issues avail.)

301.412   JA
FRAU. 1963. s-m. Kodansha Ltd., 12-21 Otowa 2-chome, Bunkyo-ku, Tokyo 112, Japan. TEL 03-5395-3542. FAX 03-3944-4308. TELEX J34509 KODANSHA. Ed. Michinori Ihara. circ. 200,000. (reprint service avail. from SCH) **Document type:** consumer publication.
    Formerly (until 1991): Young Lady.
    Description: Variety magazine for women 25 to 27 years old.

305.412   AU
FRAU AKTUELL. no.54, 1973. q. Oesterreichische Frauenbewegung, Landesleitung Wien, Falkestr. 3, A-1010 Vienna, Austria. Ed. Barbara Stigmayr. adv.; bk.rev.; charts; illus.
    Formerly (until 1980): Frau in Wien.

305.435   GW   ISSN 0174-0423
FRAU AKTUELL. 1965. w. (Wed.). Welt am Sonnabend GmbH, Adlerstr. 22, 40211 Duesseldorf, Germany. TEL 0211-3666-0. FAX 0211-3666329. Ed. Dieter Ulrich. adv. contact: Josef Wolter. illus. circ. 403,739. **Document type:** consumer publication.
    Formerly: Frau.

200   GW   ISSN 0016-0148
FRAU IM LEBEN. 1948. m. DM.36. Weltbild Verlag GmbH, Frauentorstr. 5, 86152 Augsburg, Germany. TEL 0821-3257-0. FAX 0821-3257201. Ed. Dagmar Kutscher. adv. contact: Kurt Telschig. bk.rev.; illus. circ. 280,895. **Document type:** consumer publication.
    Formerly: Katholische Frau.

053 GW ISSN 0046-497X
FRAU IM SPIEGEL. 1946. w. (Thu.). DM.130 (Europe DM.234; elsewhere DM.240.24). Verlag Ehrlich und Sohn KG, Griegstr. 75, 22763 Hamburg, Germany. TEL 040-883035. FAX 040-88303402. (Subscr. to: Postfach 500425, 22704 Hamburg, Germany) Ed. Klaus Freikamp. adv. contact: Christian Schlottau. illus. circ. 752,111. **Document type:** consumer publication.

396 GW ISSN 0723-9580
HQ1621
FRAU IN UNSERER ZEIT; Materialien zur freiheitlich sozialen Politik. 1971. q. DM.36 (foreign DM.42). (Konrad-Adenauer-Stiftung fuer Politische Bildung und Studienfoerderung e.V.) Verlag Leske und Budrich GmbH, Postfach 300551, 51334 Leverkusen, Germany. TEL 02171-2079. FAX 02171-41209. bk.rev.; bibl.; stat. **Document type:** bulletin.
 Formerly: Frau in der Offenen Gesellschaft (ISSN 0721-6971)

640 GW
FRAU MIT HERZ. 1948. w. (Thu.). Sonnenverlag GmbH, Lichtentaler Allee 10, 76530 Baden-Baden, Germany. TEL 07221-3501-0. FAX 07221-350142. Ed. Karin Karsten; Pub. Gerd Rose. adv. contact: Klaus Fortmann. circ. 207,409. **Document type:** consumer publication.

FRAU OHNE HERZ; feministische Lesbenzeitschrift. see HOMOSEXUALITY

FRAU UND FREIZEIT. see CLOTHING TRADE — Fashions

053.1 GW ISSN 0344-0745
FRAU UND KULTUR; Erleben & Gestalten. 1897. s-m. DM.20. Deutscher Verband Frau und Kultur e.V., Winterbergstr. 90, 32602 Vlotho, Germany. TEL 05733-4220. Ed. Irma Hildebrandt. adv.; bk.rev.; illus. circ. 5,000. **Document type:** bulletin.
 Formerly (until 1974): Frauenkultur (ISSN 0016-0245)

FRAUEN UND FILM. see MOTION PICTURES

376 GW
FRAUENBILDUNGS- UND FERIENHAUS OSTERESCH. 1981. s-a. Frauenbildungs- und Ferienhaus e.V. Osteresch, Zum Osteresch 1, 48496 Hopsten, Germany. TEL 05457-1513. (back issues avail.)

301.412 SZ ISSN 1015-2431
FRAUEZITG. Short title: FRAZ. 1982. q. 25 SFr. (Europe 37 SFr.; elsewhere 42 SFr.). Postfach 648, CH-8025 Zurich, Switzerland. TEL 01-2727371. adv.; bk.rev. circ. 4,000. **Document type:** newspaper.

FREE FOCUS. see LITERATURE — Poetry

329.81 US ISSN 0272-4367
FREEDOM SOCIALIST; voice of revolutionary feminism. 1966. q. $5 to individuals; institutions $10. Freedom Socialist Party, 5018 Rainier Ave. S., Seattle, WA 98118-1927. TEL 206-722-2453. FAX 206-723-7691. E-mail: hnoble@eskimo.com. Ed. Andrea Bauer. bk.rev. circ. 10,000. (also avail. in microform; back issues avail.) **Indexed:** Alt.Press Ind., Left Ind. (1984-).

FREUNDIN; Leben im jungen Stil. see HOME ECONOMICS

301.412 CN ISSN 0824-1961
A FRIEND INDEED; for women in the prime of life/pour les femmes dans la force de l'age. French edition: Veritable Amie (ISSN 0831-0866) (Text in English or French) 1984. m. (10/yr.). $30. A Friend Indeed Publications Inc., 3575 bd. Saint Laurent, Ste. 402, Montreal, PQ H2X 2T7, Canada. TEL 514-843-5730. FAX 514-843-5681. (US addr.: Box 1710, Champlain, NY 12919-1710) Eds. Janine O'Leary Cobb, Lucette Proulx-Sammut. bk.rev.; bibl.; cum.index: 1984-87. circ. 7,000. (looseleaf format; back issues avail.) **Indexed:** Can.Wom.Per.Ind. **Document type:** newsletter. —CCC.
 Description: Information, support and exchange for women in menopause or mid-life.

FRONT PAGE. see HOMOSEXUALITY

FUJIN NO TOMO/WOMEN'S FRIEND. see EDUCATION — Adult Education

FUJINKORON. see LITERATURE

305.412 US
FULL CIRCLE. 1979. m. $10. Box 235, Contoocook, NH 03229. Ed. Elizabeth Alexander. adv.; bk.rev. circ. 300.

FULL-TIME DADS; the magazine for caring fathers. see MEN'S INTERESTS

305.412 CC
FUNU/WOMEN. (Text in Chinese) m. $35.90. Funu Zazhishe, 25 Heping Dajie Erduan, Shenyang, Lianning 110002, People's Republic of China. (Dist. in US by: China Books & Periodicals, Inc., 2929 24th St., San Francisco, CA 94110. TEL 415-282-2994)

301.412 CC ISSN 1002-7904
FUNU SHENGHUO. (Text in Chinese) 1982. m. Y0.80 per no. Funu Shenghuo Zazhishe, 15, Jinshui Lu, Zhengzhou, Henan 450003, People's Republic of China. (Dist. outside China by: China Publications Foreign Trade Corp., P.O. Box 782, Beijing, P.R.C.) Eds. Liu Xuqian, Xu Chunting. adv.
 Description: Covers topics of interest to women. Includes personal ads.

301.412 CC
FUNU ZHI YOU/WOMEN'S FRIEND. (Text in Chinese) m. Heilongjiang Sheng Funu Lianhehui, 11, Ashihe Jie, Nangang-qu, Harbin, Heilongjiang 150001, People's Republic of China. TEL 34059. Ed. Liu Xiangyao.

G F W C CLUBWOMAN. (General Federation of Women's Clubs) see CLUBS

GAEA. see EARTH SCIENCES

301.412 BE ISSN 0776-3190
GAEL. (Text in French) 1988. m. 1000 BEF. Editions Francophones Belges S.A., Rue de Joncker 46, 1060 Brussels, Belgium. TEL 32-2-537-08-00. FAX 32-2-534-02-38. adv.; B&W page 96000 BEF; color page 145000 BEF; trim 203 x 265. circ. 53,839.

GAME SU. see EDUCATION — Adult Education

LA GAUCHE. see POLITICAL SCIENCE

305.412 CN ISSN 0704-4550
GAZETTE DES FEMMES. (Text in French) 1979. 6/yr. Can.$17 (US Can.$23.25; elsewhere Can.$26.50). Conseil du Statut de la Femme, 8 rue Cook, 3e Etage, Bur. 300, Quebec, PQ G1R 5J7, Canada. TEL 418-643-4326. FAX 418-643-8926. (Subscr. to: Informatique Rive-Sud, 25, boul. Taschereau, bureau 201, Greenfield Park, Quebec, J4V 3P1, Canada) Ed. Claire Minguy. adv.; film rev.; circ. 17,000 (controlled) (also avail. in diskette format) **Indexed:** Can.Wom.Per.Ind., Pt.de Rep. (1981-). **Document type:** government publication.
 Description: Contains women's issues (health, work, pay, equity, law, education, social policies, sexism in advertising, alimony, violence, etc.).

GENERAL COUNCIL OF THE ASSEMBLIES OF GOD. MEMOS; leadership magazine for Women's Ministries Auxiliary. see RELIGIONS AND THEOLOGY — Other Denominations And Sects

GEORGE SAND STUDIES. see LITERATURE

GET KINKY. see MEN'S INTERESTS

354 GH
GHANA. NATIONAL COUNCIL ON WOMEN AND DEVELOPMENT. ANNUAL REPORT. 1976. a. National Council on Women and Development, Box M.53, Accra, Ghana. TEL 229119. circ. 3,000 (controlled).
 Description: Reports on the activities of the council at all levels as it works to ensure the integration of women in society during the development of the country.

055.1 IT ISSN 0017-0062
GIOIA. 1938. w. L.124800 (foreign L.290000). Rusconi Editori S.p.A., Servizio Abbonamenti, Viale Sarca 235, 20126 Milan, Italy. TEL 39-2-66191. FAX 39-2-6619-2737. Ed. Silvana Giacobini. adv.: page L.71000000. bk.rev.; film rev.; play rev.; illus. circ. 552,836.

305.412 UK
GIRL ABOUT TOWN.* 1972. w. G A T Publishing Ltd., Grosvenor Hse., 141-143 Drury Lane, London WC2B 5TS, England. FAX 071-836-2618. Ed. Claire Gillman. adv.; bk.rev. circ. 125,000.

GIRLJOCK. see HOMOSEXUALITY

055.1 IT ISSN 1121-5348
GLAMOUR. 1976. m. L.38400 (foreign L.73800). Edizioni Conde Nast S.p.A., Piazza Castello 27, 20121 Milan, Italy. TEL 39-2-85611. FAX 39-2-8055716. Ed. Valeria Corbetta. adv.: page L.15000000. circ. 66,552. **Document type:** consumer publication.
 Formerly (until Feb. 1992): Lei (ISSN 1120-7736)

301.412 FI ISSN 0783-6856
GLORIA. (Supplement avail.: Gloria Sisustuslehti (ISSN 0789-5895)) 1986. 11/yr. FIM 369. Helsinki Media Magazines, P.O. Box 107, Hoylaametie 1A, 00381 Helsinki, Finland. TEL 358-0-1201. FAX 358-0-1205599. Ed. Riitta Lindegren. adv.: B&W page FIM 19500, color page FIM 26850; trim 194 x 248. circ. 53,000 (paid). **Document type:** consumer publication.

GLOS POLEK/POLISH WOMENS' VOICE. see ETHNIC INTERESTS

305.412 SI ISSN 0217-765X
GO. 1980. m. S.$73; newsstand price: S.$3. Singapore Press Holdings Ltd., Corporate Relations Department, 82 Genting Lane, News Centre, Singapore 1334, Singapore. TEL 743-8800. FAX 748-0747. (Subscr. to: Times Periodicals Pvt. Ltd., Times Industrial Bldg., 422 Thomson Rd., Singapore 1129, Singapore. TEL 255-0011. FAX 256-8016) Ed. Tan Wang Joo. adv.: B&W page S.$1950, color page S.$2590; 275 x 205; adv. contact: David Tay. bk.rev.; film rev.; music rev.; illus. circ. 27,000. **Document type:** consumer publication.
 Supersedes: Fanfare (ISSN 0046-3248)
 Description: For young, single and trendy girls, aged 18 to 24. Contains beauty and fashion features.

053 GW ISSN 0046-6093
DAS GOLDENE BLATT. 1971. w. (Wed.). Bastei-Verlag Gustav H. Luebbe GmbH und Co., Scheidtbachstr. 23-31, 51469 Bergisch Gladbach, Germany. TEL 02202-121-0. FAX 02202-121251. Ed. Heinz-Juergen Spors; Pub. Gustav Luebbe. adv. contact: Frank-Michael Mueller. bk.rev. circ. 446,249. **Document type:** consumer publication.

GOLF FOR WOMEN. see SPORTS AND GAMES — Ball Games

052 UK ISSN 0017-2081
GOOD HOUSEKEEPING. 1922. m. £22.80. National Magazine Co. Ltd., 72 Broadwick St., London W1V 2BP, England. TEL 0171-439-5000. FAX 0171-439-5138. Ed. Sally O'Sullivan. adv.; bk.rev.; illus. circ. 518,495. **Indexed:** Consum.Ind., DAAI, Ind.How To Do It. **Document type:** consumer publication.

GOOD HOUSEKEEPING. see HOME ECONOMICS

GRAPEVINE (CHICKASHA). see HOMOSEXUALITY

055.1 IT ISSN 1120-5113
GRAZIA. 1938. w. L.130000 (foreign L.232600). Arnoldo Mondadori Editore S.p.A., Casella Postale 1833, 20101 Milan, Italy. TEL 39-2-75421. Ed. Andreina Vanni. adv.: page L.70800000. illus. circ. 391,000. (back issues avail.) **Document type:** consumer publication.

GREAT EXPECTATIONS. see MEDICAL SCIENCES — Obstetrics And Gynecology

301.412 II ISSN 0971-152X
GRIH SHOBHA. (Editions in Gujarati, Hindi, Marathi) 1979. m. Rs.465($15) for Hindi ed.; Gujarati ed. or Marathi ed. Rs.258 ($8). Delhi Press Patra Prakashan Ltd., Delhi Press Bldg., E-3, Jhandewalan Estate, Rani Jhansi Rd., New Delhi 110 055, India. TEL 11-5261311. TELEX 31-63053. Ed. Vishwa Nath. circ. 673,000.
 Description: Includes fiction, recipes, fashion notes and other articles of interest to women of India.

WOMEN'S INTERESTS

305.4 — II
GRIHSHOBHA. (Editions in Hindi, Gujarati, Kannada, Marathi) 1979. m. Delhi Press Patra Prakashan Ltd., Delhi Press Bldg., E-3, Jhandewala Estate, Rani Jhansi Rd., New Delhi 110 055, India. Ed. Vishwa Nath. adv.: B&W page Rs.35000, color page Rs.70000; trim 198 x 265. circ. 314,310 Hindi ed.; 54,035 Gujarati ed.; 42,227 Marathi ed.

301.412 — GW
GRUENE BLAETTER. 1989. bi-m. Forstr. 93, 70176 Stuttgart, Germany. TEL 0711-638140. circ. 7,000.

GUIDE MAGAZINE (SEATTLE). see *HOMOSEXUALITY*

300 — GV
GUINEENNE. * m. c/o Agence Guineene de Presse, B.P. 1535, Conakry, Guinea.

GULLIVER; German-English Yearbook. see *LINGUISTICS*

305.412 — GR — ISSN 1105-1493
GYNAIKA/WOMAN. 1950. m. $82. E. Terzopoulos Publishing Enterprises S.A., 7 Odos Fragoklisias, GR-151 25 Marousi, Greece. TEL 30-1-689-9149. FAX 30-1-689-9162. Ed. Liana Elefteroudaki. adv. contact: Athina Seytanides. illus. circ. 70,000.
Document type: consumer publication.
Description: Covers fashion, beauty, handicrafts, cooking, social issues, and fiction.

301.412 — US
H A N O W HERALD. * 1970. m. $3. Houston Area National Organization for Women, Box 1256, Austin, TX 78767-1256. TEL 713-668-9008. bk.rev. bibl. circ. 500.
Formerly: Broadside (Houston).

301.412 — SP — ISSN 1133-8687
▼**HACER FAMILIA.** 1994. m. $68. Ediciones Palabra S.A., Castellana 210, 28046 Madrid, Spain. TEL 34-1-3501179. FAX 34-1-3590337. (Dist. in US by: DDL Books Inc., 6521 N.W. 87 Ave., Miami, FL 33166) Ed. Belen Martin G. Cabiedes. adv. contact: Arturo Hernansanz. circ. 25,000.

HADASSAH HEADLINES. see *ETHNIC INTERESTS*

HADASSAH MAGAZINE. see *ETHNIC INTERESTS*

305.412 — NR — ISSN 0331-1457
HAPPY HOME. 1971. m. £N6. Punch (Nigeria) Ltd., Kudeti Street, P. M. B. 1204, Ikeja, Lagos, Nigeria. Ed. Sam Amuka. adv.; bk.rev.; illus. circ. 50,000.
Formerly: Happy Home and Family Health.

305.412 — II
HAREEM. (Text in Urdu) 1931. m. Rs.24. Nasim Book Depot, 25, Latouche Rd., Lucknow 226018, India. Ed. Nasim Inhonvi. adv.; bk.rev. circ. 2,000.

052 — UK — ISSN 0141-0547
HARPERS & QUEEN. 1970. m. £32.40. National Magazine Co. Ltd., 72 Broadwick St., London W1V 2BP, England. TEL 0171-439-5000. FAX 0171-439-5506. Ed. Fiona Macpherson. adv.; bk.rev. circ. 85,451. (also avail. in microform from UMI; reprint service avail. from UMI) **Indexed:** DAAI. Document type: consumer publication.
—UMI.
Incorporates: Queen (ISSN 0033-6009)

HARPER'S BAZAAR EN ESPANOL. see *CLOTHING TRADE — Fashions*

059.92 — UA
HAWA'A/EVE. (Text in Arabic) w. Dar Al-Hilal, 12 Sharia Muhammad Ezz al-Arab, Cairo, Egypt. TELEX 92703. Ed. Suad Ahmad Hilmi. adv.; illus. circ. 160,837.

HE - SHE DIRECTORY. see *MEN'S INTERESTS*

HEARTLAND CRITIQUES. see *LITERARY AND POLITICAL REVIEWS*

305.412 — DK — ISSN 0907-4732
HENDES VERDEN. 1937. w. DKK 897. Egmont Magasiner, Hellerupvej 51, DK-2900 Hellerup, Denmark. TEL 45-33-15-15-95. FAX 45-33-15-65-05. Ed. Iben Nielsen. adv. circ. 60,000.

305.412 — SI — ISSN 0046-7278
HER WORLD. 1960. m. S.$132; newsstand price: S.$4.50. Singapore Press Holdings Ltd., Corporate Relations Department, 82 Genting Lane, News Centre, Singapore 1334, Singapore. TEL 743-8800. FAX 748-0747. (Subscr. to: Times Periodicals Pvt. Ltd., 422 Thomson Rd., Times Industrial Bldg., Singapore 1129, Singapore. TEL 255-0011. FAX 256-8016) Ed. Tan Wang Joo. adv.: B&W page S.$3220, color page S.$4290; 275 x 205. bk.rev.; illus. circ. 57,000. cols./p.: 3; pp./issue: 300.
Document type: consumer publication.
Description: Tackles issues of interest to women, such as relationships, work, money, fashion, beauty, travel and lifestyle.

301.412 — MY — ISSN 0127-0079
HER WORLD. (Text in English) 1961. m. Berita Publishing Snd. Bhd., 22 Jalan Liku, 59100 Kuuala Lumpur, Malaysia. TEL 03-2744322. FAX 03-2740605. Ed. Foong Peto. circ. 30,000.

052 — SI — ISSN 0217-1058
HER WORLD ANNUAL. 1976. a. S.$5. Singapore Press Holdings Ltd., Corporate Relations Department, 82 Genting Lane, News Centre, Singapore 1334, Singapore. TEL 743-8800. FAX 748-0747. (Subscr. to: Times Periodicals Pvt. Ltd., Times Industrial Bldg., 422 Thomson Rd., Singapore 1129, Singapore. TEL 255-0011. FAX 256-8016) adv.: B&W page S.$2200, color page S.$3600; 275 x 205. bk.rev.; illus. circ. 25,000.
Description: Takes a broad look at subjects and trends covered by the monthly Her World.

301.4157 613.7 — US
HERA; Binghamton's women's newspaper. 1981. 10/yr. $10 or donation. Women's Center, Box 354, Binghamton, NY 13902. TEL 607-724-3462. Ed. Peg Johnston. adv.; bk.rev. circ. 1,000. (tabloid format; back issues avail.) Document type: newspaper.
Description: Regional feminist news and analysis.

HERD. see *LITERARY AND POLITICAL REVIEWS*

305.412 — CN — ISSN 0711-7485
HERIZONS. (Text in English, French) 1979. 4/yr. Can.$23.50 (foreign Can.$32.50). Box 128, Winnipeg, MB R3C 2G1, Canada. TEL 204-774-6225. FAX 204-786-8038. Ed. Penni Mitchell. adv. contact: Penni Mitchell. bk.rev. circ. 4,500. (also avail. in microform; back issues avail.) **Indexed:** Alt.Press.Ind., Can.B.P.I., CMI. Document type: consumer publication.
Formerly: Manitoba Women's News Magazine.
Description: Feminist magazine stimulating lively debate on issues and events affecting women's daily lives.

305.412 — SW — ISSN 0018-0912
HERTHA. 1914. 4/yr. SEK 150. Fredrika-Bremer Foerbundet, Hornsgatan 52, S-118 21 Stockholm, Sweden. TEL 46-8-644-32-70. FAX 46-8-643-38-44. Ed. Maerta Fritz. adv.; bk.rev.; bibl.; illus. circ. 6,000.

HIGHER EDUCATION OPPORTUNITIES FOR MINORITIES AND WOMEN: ANNOTATED SELECTIONS. see *EDUCATION — Higher Education*

301.412 — II
HIGHLAND BOOKNEWS; book review magazine. (Text in English and Malayalam) 1990. q. Rs.20($5) Women's Alliance for Publishing, Cheeroth Building, Kodimatha, Kottayam 686 039, India. Ed. Nicyk Runnoose. circ. 2,000. (back issues avail.)

HIKANE; the capable womon. see *HOMOSEXUALITY*

301.435 — TS
HIYA. (Includes children's supplement: Qanadil) 1978. m. Dar al-Suhuf al-Wahda, Majallat Hiya, P.O. Box 26248, Abu Dhabi, United Arab Emirates. TEL 330115. FAX 211386. TELEX 22596. Ed. Mamduh Taha.
Formerly: Samra'a.
Description: Woman's magazine with a family focus.

059.927 — UK — ISSN 1319-0903
HIYA. (Text in Arabic) m. $154 (effective 1994). Saudi Research and Marketing, Arab Press House, 184 High Holborn, London WC1V 7AP, England. TEL 44-171-831-8181. FAX 44-171-404-6311. (And: P.O. Box 4556, Jeddah 21441, Saudi Arabia. TEL 966-2-6691888. FAX 966-2-6671650; Subscr. in U.S. to: Attache International, 3050 Broadway, Ste. 300, Boulder, CO 80304-3154. TEL 303-442-8900. FAX 303-442-7979) Ed. Mattar Al-Ahmadi. adv.: B&W page $2400, color page $4000; trim 220 x 285. circ. 26,190 (paid).
Document type: consumer publication.
Description: Covers beauty, fashion, jewelry and cosmetics for a sophisticated international audience.

056.1 — EC — ISSN 0018-3210
HOGAR; la revista de la familia ecuatoriana. 1964. m. $50. Editores Nacionales, Aguirre 724 y Boyaca, Apdo. 1239, Guayaquil, Ecuador. TEL 4-327-200. TELEX 3423. Ed. Rosa A. Alvarado. circ. 35,000 (controlled).

305.412 640 — UK — ISSN 1355-4735
HOME AND COUNTRY. 1919. m. £18. National Federation of Women's Institutes, 104 New Kings Rd., Fulham, London SW6 4LY, England. TEL 0171-371-5777. FAX 0171-736-4061. Ed. Penny Kitchen. adv. contact: Barbara Wickham. bk.rev. circ. 90,000. (back issues avail.) Document type: consumer publication.

640 — JA
HOMEMAKERS NETWORK NEWSLETTER. 1986. bi-m. $4.75. Homemakers Network, c/o Lois Altenkirch, Ed., 340 Caldwell Ave., Paterson, NJ 07501. adv.; bk.rev. circ. 175. Document type: newsletter.
Description: Offers tips on child care and homemaking to expectant mothers.

HOOKS AND LINES. see *SPORTS AND GAMES — Outdoor Life*

HOT FAMILY LETTERS. see *MEN'S INTERESTS*

305.412 — US — ISSN 1074-0848
HOT FLASH. 1981. q. $25. National Action Forum for Midlife and Older Women, Box 816, Stonybrook, NY 11790-0609. Ed. Jane Porcino. bk.rev. circ. 2,000. (back issues avail.) Document type: newsletter.

305.4 — US
▼**HOT FLASHES FROM THE GUERRILLA GIRLS.** 1994. q.? $9. Guerrilla Girls, 532 LaGuardia Pl., Ste. 237, New York, NY 10012. Document type: newsletter.
Description: Anti-sexism, anti-racism and anti-homophobia.

305.4 363.49 — US — ISSN 1069-5281
HOTHEAD PAISAN; homicidal lesbian terrorist. 1991. q. $14. Giant Ass Publishing, Box 214, New Haven, CT 06502. circ. 5,000.

HOUSEWIFE - WRITER'S FORUM. see *LITERATURE — Poetry*

640 — JA
HOUSEWIVES AND LIVING. (Text in Japanese) 1946. m. 8380 Yen. Shufu-to-Seikatsusha Ltd., 5-7, 3-chome, Kyobashi, Chuo-ku, Tokyo 104, Japan. Ed. Hiroaki Watari.

HOUSEWIVES' HANDY HINTS, SMALL BUSINESSWOMAN'S NEWSLETTER. see *NEEDLEWORK*

HUMAN SEXUALITY. see *BIOLOGY — Physiology*

305.412 — US — ISSN 0882-7907
HQ1101
HURRICANE ALICE; a feminist quarterly. 1983. 4/yr. $12. Hurricane Alice Foundation, 207 Lind Hall, 207 Church St., S.E., Minneapolis, MN 55455. TEL 612-625-1834. Ed. Marth Roth. adv. contact: Jennifer Gordon. bk.rev. circ. 1,000.
Description: Feminist review of culture.

058.69 — IC — ISSN 0018-7984
HUSFREYJAN. 1949. q. ISK 1500($12) Kvenfelagasamband Islands - Union of Women's Societies, Hallveigarstoedum, Tungotu 14, Reykjavik, Iceland. TEL 354-552-7430. FAX 354-562-5150. Ed. Greta E. Palsdottir. adv.; bk.rev.; cum.index. circ. 5,200.

640   NO   ISSN 0018-8034
HUSMORBLADET. 1886. m. NOK 20. Norges Husmorforbund, Oskarsgate 43, 0258 Oslo 2, Norway. TEL 02-55-79-07. Ed. Barbro Sveen. adv.; bk.rev.; film rev.; play rev.; illus. circ. 47,000. (back issues avail.)
—CCC.

053.1   GW
HYDRA NACHTEXPRESS; Zeitung fuer Bar, Bordell und Bordstein. 1980. irreg. DM.6. Hydra e.V., Rigaerstr. 3, 10247 Berlin, Germany. TEL 030-7074723. FAX 030-7074723. adv.: page DM.500. bk.rev.; circ. 2,000. (back issues avail.) **Document type:** newsletter.
Description: Seeks to promote the rights of prostitutes.

051   US   ISSN 1065-9633
PN6231.W6
HYSTERIA; women's humor magazine. 1993. q. $18. Box 8581, Brewster Sta., Bridgeport, CT 06605. TEL 203-333-9399. FAX 203-335-6777. Ed. Deborah Werksman. adv.; bk.rev. circ. 6,000.
Description: Humor, feminism and social commentary.

301.412   GW
I A F - INFORMATION. 1975. q. DM.25 (foreign DM.30). (Interessengemeinschaft der mit Auslaendern Verheirateten Frauen e.V.) Verband Bi-Nationaler Familien und Partnerschaften, Kasseler Str. 1A, 60486 Frankfurt a.M., Germany. TEL 069-7075087. FAX 069-7075092. bk.rev. circ. 3,500. (back issues avail.) **Document type:** consumer publication.

I A W M JOURNAL. see *MUSIC*

I C A E NEWS. (International Council for Adult Education) see *EDUCATION — Adult Education*

301   US
I C R W OCCASIONAL PAPER SERIES. 1984. irreg. price varies. International Center for Research on Women, 1717 Massachusetts Ave., N.W., Ste. 302., Washington, DC 20036. TEL 202-797-0007. FAX 202-797-0020. E-mail: ICRW@IGC.APC.ORG. (back issues avail.)
Description: Concerns economic policies, family and household structure, health and nutrition and agriculture and the environment as they pertain to women and development in Africa, Asia, Latin America and the Caribbean.

I L G A BULLETIN. (International Lesbian and Gay Association) see *HOMOSEXUALITY*

376   UN   ISSN 1014-4579
I N S T R A W NEWS. (Text in English, French and Spanish) 1984. s-a. $12 free to developing countries. International Research and Training Institute for the Advancement of Women, P.O. Box 21747, Santo Domingo, Dominican Republic. TEL 809-685-2111. FAX 809-685-2117. TELEX 326-4280 WRASD. bk.rev. circ. 14,500. **Document type:** newsletter.
Description: Presents trends, disseminates training materials, and promotes networking for women concerning development issues at a global level.

378 320   NE
I U S WOMENS NEWSLETTER. (Editions in English, French and Spanish) 1967. q. free. International Union of Students, 211 Laan Van Meerdevoort, The Hague, Netherlands. Ed. Allison Lewis. illus.
Formerly: D E (ISSN 0323-1429)
Description: Presents women student issues.

I W F A YEARBOOK. (International Women's Fishing Association) see *SPORTS AND GAMES — Outdoor Life*

052   GH   ISSN 0855-2010
IDEAL WOMAN/OBAA SIMA; the magazine for the woman who looks ahead. (Text in English) 1971. q. NC.9000($24) Teiba Publications Ltd., Box 5737, Accra, Ghana. TEL 233-21-221399. Ed. Kate Abbam. adv. contact: Efua Abokoma Abbam. bk.rev.; illus. circ. 10,000. **Document type:** consumer publication.

053.1   SZ
IDELLE. (Text in German) 1913. 11/yr. 29 SFr. (Schweizerischer Gemeinnuetziger Frauenverein) Vogt-Schild AG, Zuchwilerstr. 21, CH-4501 Solothurn, Switzerland. TEL 065-247247. FAX 065-247235. Ed. Karin Mercier-Zeltner. adv.: B&W page 1470 SFr., color page 2570 SFr.; trim 185 x 260; adv. contact: Elsi Spiri. circ. 8,000. **Document type:** bulletin.
Formerly: Schweizerischer Gemeinnuetziger Frauenverein. ZentralBlatt.

301.412   GW
IGITTE; Dortmunder Frauenzeitung. 1987. bi-m. DM.12. Igitte e.V., Adlerstr. 81, 44137 Dortmund, Germany. TEL 0231-162366. circ. 2,000.

IMPETUS. see *ART*

305.4 384.55   US
IN HER OWN IMAGE; films and videos empowering women for the future - a media network guide. biennial. (Alternative Media Information Center) Media Network, 39 W. 14th St., Ste. 403, New York, NY 10011. TEL 212-929-2663. FAX 212-929-2732. illus.
Description: Describes 82 films and videos listed by eight categories, indexed by subject, region, appropriate audience, and title. Each entry gives the title, producer, director, length, available language versions, year released, name of distributor, formats, and cost.

INCITING DESIRE; the zine of desire without boundaries. see *MEN'S INTERESTS*

INDEPENDENT WOMEN'S SPECIALTY STORES & BOUTIQUES. see *CLOTHING TRADE*

305.4   US
▼**INFORMATION PLEASE WOMEN'S SOURCEBOOK.** 1994. a. $12.95. Houghton Mifflin Co., 215 Park Ave. S., New York, NY 10003. TEL 212-420-5800. (Subscr to: Houghton Mifflin Co., Wayside Rd., Burlington, MA 01803. TEL 800-225-3362) Eds. Lisa Dimona, Constance Herndon.
Description: Provides handy up-to-date reference information of interest to women on careers, health and fitness, civil rights and activism, sexuality, and retirement. Also includes speeches and essays by prominent contemporary women.

305.412   GW   ISSN 0020-0352
INFORMATIONEN FUER DIE FRAU. 1952. 10/yr. DM.34($6) Deutscher Frauenrat - National Council of German Women's Organizations, Simrockstr. 5, 53113 Bonn, Germany. TEL 0228-223008. FAX 0228-218819. Ed. Hanne E. Pollmann. bk.rev.; index. circ. 3,000. (tabloid format) Indexed: Dok.Arbeitsmed. **Document type:** bulletin.

640   GW
INGRID. 1977. q. Sonnenverlag GmbH, Lichtentaler Allee 10, 76530 Baden-Baden, Germany. TEL 07221-3501-0. FAX 07221-350142. Ed. Erika Poese; Pub. Gerd Rose. adv. contact: Klaus Fortmann. circ. 180,000. **Document type:** consumer publication.

INITIATIVES. see *EDUCATION — School Organization And Administration*

320   AT   ISSN 1036-871X
INKWEL. 1978. bi-m. Aus.$25 to individuals; institutions Aus.$45. Women's Electoral Lobby Australia, P.O. Box 191, Civic Square, A.C.T. 2608, Australia. TEL 61-6-247-6679. FAX 61-6-247-4699. Ed. Ingrid McKenzie. adv.; bk.rev. circ. 450. **Document type:** newsletter.
Formerly (until 1990): Women's Electoral Lobby. National Bulletin (ISSN 0813-4529)
Description: Provides discussion of issues from a feminist perspective.

305.4   UK
INSIDE WAGES FOR HOUSEWORK. 1991. irreg. £0.35 per no. P.O. Box 287, London NW6 5QU, England. TEL 071-837-7509. FAX 071-833-4817. (U.S. addr.: Box 11795, Philadelphia, PA 19101. TEL 215-668-9886) Ed. Selma James. bk.rev. (back issues avail.) **Document type:** bulletin.
Description: Contains transcripts of speeches and internal meetings, showing how we organize as a campaign and are developing as individuals.

304.5   IT   ISSN 1120-4427
INSIEME (MILAN). 1979. m. L.57600. Rizzoli Editore - Corriere della Sera, Via A. Rizzoli 2, 20132 Milan, Italy. TEL 39-2-2588. Ed. Nessia Laniado. adv.: page L.26550000; adv. contact: Flavio Biondi. circ. 196,099. **Document type:** consumer publication.

323.4 362.7   US
INSIGHT (NEW YORK). 1940; N.S. 1991. q. membership. National Council of Jewish Women, 53 W. 23rd St., New York, NY 10010. TEL 212-645-4048. FAX 212-645-7466. Ed. Lauren Schwartz. adv.; bk.rev. circ. 100,000. **Document type:** newsletter.
Former titles (until 1991): N C J W Journal (ISSN 0161-2115); Council Woman (ISSN 0148-2106)

INTENSIVE CARING UNLIMITED. see *CHILDREN AND YOUTH — About*

396   US   ISSN 0538-2912
HQ1239
INTER-AMERICAN COMMISSION OF WOMEN. NEWS BULLETIN. Spanish edition: Inter-American Commission of Women. Noticiero (ISSN 0538-2920) 1953. irreg., latest no.33. Organization of American States, Department of Publications, 1889 F St., N.W., Washington, DC 20006. TEL 703-941-1617. **Document type:** bulletin.

396   US   ISSN 0538-2920
HQ1239
INTER-AMERICAN COMMISSION OF WOMEN. NOTICIERO. English edition: Inter-American Commission of Women. News Bulletin (ISSN 0538-2912) 1951. irreg., latest no. 33. Organization of American States, 1889 F St., N.W., Washington, DC 20006. TEL 703-941-1617.

INTERNATIONAL FASHION GROUP. ANNUAL REPORT. see *CLOTHING TRADE — Fashions*

INTERNATIONAL FASHION GROUP. BULLETIN. see *CLOTHING TRADE — Fashions*

INTERNATIONAL FASHION GROUP. NEWSLETTER. see *CLOTHING TRADE — Fashions*

INTERNATIONAL SOCIETY OF WOMEN AIRLINE PILOTS NEWSLETTER. see *AERONAUTICS AND SPACE FLIGHT*

301.412   GR   ISSN 0020-9120
INTERNATIONAL WOMEN'S NEWS. (Text in English, French) vol.58, 1963. 6/yr. membership. International Alliance of Women, 1 Lycavittou St., 10672 Athens, Greece. Dir. Alice Marangopoulos. bk.rev. circ. 1,200.

301   FR
INTIMITE. 1949. w. 2 rue des Italiens, 75009 Paris, France. Ed. Antoine de Clermont-Tonnerre. illus. circ. 509,622.

301.412   US
IOWA IMAGE.* 1989. q. Kay Baughman, Ed. & Pub., 506 Sharrell Ct., Nixa, MO 65714. TEL 515-437-1143. adv. circ. 7,000.
Description: Provides advice on the spiritual, social, mental, financial and physical beauty growth of women using the editor's five-point concept.

IOWA WOMAN. see *LITERATURE*

301.412 808.8   US   ISSN 0896-1301
HQ1101
IRIS: A JOURNAL ABOUT WOMEN. 1980. s-a. $17 to individuals; institutions $40. University of Virginia, Women's Center, Box 323 HSC, University of Virginia, Charlottesville, VA 22903. TEL 804-924-4500. Eds. Rebecca Hyman. adv.; bk.rev.; film rev.; play rev. circ. 3,500. (back issues avail.) Indexed: Wom.Stud.Abstr.
—Faxon; UnCover.
Description: Covers the following by and about women: fiction, poetry, humor and art; also includes information about social, ethnic, and international affairs as they pertain to women.

WOMEN'S INTERESTS

305.412 296 200   IS
ISHA L'ISHA NEWSLETTER. (Text in Arabic, English, Hebrew) 1973. bi-m. IS.50($10) Isha L'isha Haifa Feminist Center, 88 Arlozorov St., Haifa, Israel. TEL 972-4-664949. FAX 972-4-670780. Sharon BenYehuda. bk.rev. circ. 1,500. **Document type:** newsletter.
   Former titles: Isha I'isha - Woman to Woman; (until 1984): Haifa Feminist Circle. Newsletter; (until 1977): Haifa Feminist Movement. Journal; (until 1974): Nilham.
   Description: News of current and upcoming projects and activities, updates on women's issues, and news of the lesbian-feminist community.

ISHRAQAT JEEL. see *RELIGIONS AND THEOLOGY — Islamic*

305.4   US   ISSN 1072-1762
HQ1402
▼**ISSUES QUARTERLY;** an intelligent resource for research, policy and action affecting the lives of women and girls. Cover title: IQ. 1994. q. $35 to individuals; institutions $100. National Council for Research on Women, 530 Broadway, 10th Fl., New York, NY 10012-3920. TEL 212-274-0730. FAX 212-274-0821. E-mail: MECHC@CUNYVM.CUNY.EDU. Ed. Lorraine D. Kennt. circ. 2,000. **Document type:** academic/scholarly publication.

059.927 915.3   QA
AL-JAWHARA. 1977. m. Al-Ahd Establishment for Journalism, Printing and Publications Ltd., P.O. Box 2531, Doha, Qatar. TEL 671338. FAX 671338. Ed. Khalifa Yousuf al-Hussaini. adv. contact: Jamal M. Ahmed. circ. 8,000. **Document type:** consumer publication.

JENNY CRAIG'S YOUR BODY, YOUR HEALTH. see *PHYSICAL FITNESS AND HYGIENE*

JETZT; Frauen auf dem Weg des Evangeliums - Kirche - Ordensleben - Geistliche Gemeinschaften. see *RELIGIONS AND THEOLOGY — Roman Catholic*

JIATING/FAMILY. see *HOME ECONOMICS*

JOE WEIDER'S SHAPE; the best information available for your body, mind, spirit and beauty. see *PHYSICAL FITNESS AND HYGIENE*

JOURNAL OF COUPLES THERAPY; studies in the enhancement of intimacy and bonding for the clinical practitioner. see *PSYCHOLOGY*

305.412 340 331   US   ISSN 0362-062X
KF478.A45
JOURNAL OF REPRINTS OF DOCUMENTS AFFECTING WOMEN.* Variant title: Journal of Reprints Affecting Women's Rights & Opportunities. 1975. q. $40. M & O Publications, 120 E. 34th St., 7th Fl., New York, NY 10016. TEL 202-628-6663. Ed. Myra E. Barrer.

JOURNAL OF WOMEN AND MINORITIES IN SCIENCE AND ENGINEERING. see *ENGINEERING*

JOURNEY: A WOMAN'S GUIDE TO INTIMACY WITH GOD. see *RELIGIONS AND THEOLOGY — Protestant*

THE JOYFUL WOMAN. see *RELIGIONS AND THEOLOGY — Protestant*

305.412   JA
JUNON. (Text in Japanese) 1973. m. 6360 Yen. Shufu-to-Seikatsu Sha Ltd., 5-7, Kyobashi 3-chome, Chuo-ku, Tokyo 104, Japan. TEL 03-3563-5131. FAX 03-3567-7893. Ed. Junichi Hamamoto.
   Description: Covers television and entertainment.

JURISFEMME. see *LAW*

JUST SEVENTEEN. see *CHILDREN AND YOUTH — For*

331.4   CN   ISSN 1189-4024
JUST WAGES; a bulletin on wage discrimination and pay equity. 1991. q. Can.$10 to individuals; institutions Can.$15; foreign Can.$18. Trade Union Research Bureau, 111 Victoria Dr., No. 170, Vancouver, BC V5L 4C4, Canada. TEL 604-255-7346. FAX 604-255-0971. Ed. Ted Byrne. bk.rev.; illus.; stat.; circ. 370 (paid). **Document type:** bulletin.

301.412   IO   ISSN 0852-9744
K O W A N I NEWS. Indonesian edition: Warta K O W A N I (ISSN 0852-9736) (Text in English) 1986 (English ed.). irreg. Kongres Wanita Indonesia - Indonesian Women's Congress, Jl. Imam Bonjol 58, Jakarta Pusat, Jakarta 10310, Indonesia. TEL 62-21-3152787. FAX 62-21-3152784. Ed. Kuraisin Sunhadi (English ed.). **Document type:** bulletin.
   Formerly: Indonesian Women's Congress. Bulletin - Kongres Wanita Indonesia. Berita.

KALLIOPE; a journal of women's art. see *LITERATURE*

305.412   II
KALUVABALA; women's fortnightly. fortn. Andhra Patrika, 14-14-21 Mallikarjuna Rao St., Gandhinagar, Vijayawada 520 003, India. TEL 61247. adv.

305.4   II
KANYAKA. (Text in Malayalam) 1983. m. newsstand price: Rs.4. Claramma Varghese, Ed. & Pub., Mangalam Complex, P.B. No. 3, S.H. Mount, Kottayam 686 006, Kerala, India. TEL 563024. adv.: B&W page Rs.3000, color page Rs.6000; trim 260 x 195.
   Description: Feminine magazine.

KELUARGA. see *HOME ECONOMICS*

305.412   VE
KENA.* w. Plaza del Panteon, Torre de la Prensa, piso 11, Caracas, Venezuela. Ed. Maria E. Matheus. circ. 40,000.

052   UK   ISSN 0951-4414
KEY NOTE REPORT: WOMENS MAGAZINES. Variant title: Womens Magazines. irreg. £185. Key Note Publications Ltd., Field House, 72 Oldfield Rd., Hampton, Middlesex TW12 2HQ, England. TEL 0181-783-0755. FAX 0181-783-1720. **Document type:** trade publication.
●Also available online.
Also available on CD-ROM.

KICK IT OVER. see *POLITICAL SCIENCE*

KID NEWS; children's bargain guide. see *CHILDREN AND YOUTH — About*

346.013   CN   ISSN 0317-9095
KINESIS; news about women that's not in the dailies. 1972. 10/yr. Can.$20 to individuals (foreign Can.$28); institutions Can.$45 (foreign Can.$53). Vancouver Status of Women, 301-1720 Grant St., Vancouver, BC V5L 2Y6, Canada. TEL 604-255-5499. FAX 604-255-5511. Ed. Fatima Jaffer; Pub. Jennifer Johnstone. adv. contact: Yasmin Jiwani. bk.rev.; film rev.play rev. circ. 2,500. Indexed: Alt.Press Ind. **Document type:** newspaper.
   Description: Covers news from a feminist angle. Analyzes government policies, feminist theories and debates within the women's movement.

301.412   US
KINHEART CONNECTION. 1982. 5/yr. membership. Kinheart, 2214 Ridge Ave., Evanston, IL 60201. TEL 708-491-1103. Ed. Mary Jo Osterman. bk.rev. circ. 1,000.
   Formerly: Kinheart Quarterly.
   Description: Includes calendar of programs groups and special events; news items and an educational article about homophobia or heterosexism.

KNIP MODE. see *CLOTHING TRADE — Fashions*

057.85   PL   ISSN 0023-2548
KOBIETA I ZYCIE. (Supplement avail.: Wykroje i Wzory) 1946. w. $114. Dziennikarska Spolka Wydawnicza, Ul. Solec 22, 00-410 Warsaw, Poland. TEL 48-22-628-9030. (Subscr. to: C.H.S. Ars Polona, 00-950 Warsaw, Poland) Ed. Zofia Kaminska. adv.; bk.rev.; illus. circ. 471,000.

305.412   DK   ISSN 0900-2855
KONKYLIEN. 1977. 10/yr. DKK 80. Soemandskoneforeningen af 1976, c/o Jette Haugaard, Sandbjergvej 7, 3660 Stenloese, Denmark. Ed. Birgit Kjeldsen. adv.; bk.rev. circ. 1,200.

KOREAN WOMEN. see *POLITICAL SCIENCE*

KOTILIESI. see *HOME ECONOMICS*

KVINDER, KVINDER. see *HOMOSEXUALITY*

301.412   DK   ISSN 0108-3961
KVINDESTUDIER VED A U C. AARBOG. (Aalborg Universitetscenter) (Also forms part of: Serie om Kvindeforskning) 1982. a. DKK 132. (Institut for Samfundsudvikling og Planaegning) Aalborg Universitetsforlag, Aalborg, Denmark. illus.

058.82   NO   ISSN 0023-5857
KVINNER OG KLAER/WOMEN & CLOTHES. 1873. w. NOK 1722. A-S Allers Familie-Journal, Persveien 20, Box 250, Oslo 5, Norway. Ed. June Traenness Hansen. adv.; illus. circ. 97,006.
—CCC.

305.412   SW   ISSN 0345-5998
KVINNOBULLETINEN. 1971. q. SEK 150 (foreign SEK 200). Grupp 8, Stockholm, Snickarbacken 10, 111 39 Stockholm, Sweden. TEL 46-8-10-76-26. Ed. Inga-Lisa Sangregorio. bk.review. circ. 1,500.

305.42 230   SW   ISSN 1104-5035
KVINNOR OCH FUNDAMENTALISM. 1991. s-a. SEK 70. Defense Committee for Women in Iran, P.O. Box 26034, S-750 26 Uppsala, Sweden. FAX 46-8-760-44-01. Ed. Sholeh Irani. adv. contact: Maria Teherani. bk.rev. **Document type:** bulletin.
   Description: Contains news, debates, analyses, and interviews concerning women and their lives and struggle in various disparate countries, particularly Afghanistan, Algeria, Egypt, Iran, Turkey, U.S.A. and Sweden.

301.412   CY
KYPRIA/CYPRIOT WOMAN. (Text in Greek) 1984. bi-m. P.O. Box 8506, Nicosia, Cyprus. Ed. Maro Karayianni. circ. 7,000.
   Description: Greek-Cypriot woman's interest review.

L A PARENT; magazine for Southern California families. see *CHILDREN AND YOUTH — About*

L E A F LINES. (Women's Legal Education and Action Fund) see *LAW*

L F L REPORTS. (Libertarians for Life) see *BIRTH CONTROL*

301   US   ISSN 0895-7134
LABYRINTH; the Philadelphia Women's newspaper. 1983. m. $15. Labyrinth, Inc., 4722 Baltimore Ave., Philadelphia, PA 19143. TEL 215-724-6181. adv.; bk.rev.; film rev. circ. 10,000. (tabloid format; back issues avail.) **Document type:** newspaper.
   Description: Coverage of women's issues, news of feminist activities, monthly feminist movie reviews and creative writing by women.

051   US   ISSN 0023-7124
AP2
LADIES HOME JOURNAL (INKPRINT EDITION). 1883. m. $12. Meredith Corporation, 1716 Locust St., Des Moines, IA 50336. TEL 515-284-3000. (Or: 100 Park Ave., New York, NY 10017-5599) Ed. Myrna Blyth. adv.; illus.; tr.lit. circ. 5,000,000. (also avail. in microform from UMI) Indexed: Abr.R.G., CINAHL, Consum.Ind., Hlth.Ind., Mag.Ind., R.G., TOM.
●Also available online. Vendor(s): Knight-Ridder, Inc. —Faxon; UMI; UnCover.
   Description: Contains women's issues, cooking recipes, consumer tips, and features about family life.

051   US   ISSN 1060-9598
HQ755.8
LADIES' HOME JOURNAL PARENT'S DIGEST. Key Title: Parent's Digest. 1991. s-a. Meredith Corporation, 1716 Locust St., Des Moines, IA 50336. TEL 515-284-3000. **Document type:** consumer publication.

301.412   US
LADY; the international magazine for today's woman. q. Vivian Seton, Ed. & Pub., 3535 Olympic St., Silver Spring, MD 20906. TEL 301-949-6949. circ. 50,000.

051   US   ISSN 0023-7191
LADY'S CIRCLE.* 1963. bi-m. $11.97. Lopez Publications, Inc., 105 E. 35th St., New York, NY 10016-3877. TEL 212-689-3933. FAX 212-725-2239. Ed. Mary F. Bemis. adv.; bk.rev.; illus. circ. 200,000.

WOMEN'S INTERESTS

305 778   US
LADYSLIPPER CATALOG AND RESOURCE GUIDE OF RECORDS, TAPES, COMPACT DISCS AND VIDEOS BY WOMEN. 1976. a. free. Ladyslipper, Inc., Box 3124, Durham, NC 27715. TEL 919-683-1570. FAX 919-682-5601. Ed. Laurie Fuchs. adv.; bk.rev.; film rev.; index. circ. 250,000. (back issues avail.) **Document type:** catalog.
    Description: Comprehensive catalog of records, tapes, CDs, videos by women.

301.412   IS
LAISHA/FOR WOMEN. (Text in Hebrew) 1946. w. Nitzan Ltd., 35 Bnei Brak St., Tel Aviv 66021, Israel. TEL 03-371464. FAX 03-378071. Ed. Zvi Elgat.

301.412   UK   ISSN 0954-0342
LAVENDER LIST. 1985. bi-m. West & Wilde Bookshop, 25A Dundas St., Edinburgh EH3 6QQ, Scotland. TEL 031-556-0079. FAX 031-558-3717. Ed. Sigrid Nielsen. bk.rev. circ. 1,000. (back issues avail.) **Document type:** bibliography.

LAVENDER MORNING; a lesbian newsletter for lesbians. see *HOMOSEXUALITY*

LAVENDER PRAIRIE NEWS. see *HOMOSEXUALITY*

LAW & WOMEN SERIES. see *LAW*

305.4   PH   ISSN 0117-4134
LAYA; feminist quarterly. (Text in English) 1992. q. P.200($35) Laya Women's Collective, 35 Scout Delgado St., Quezon City, Philippines. TEL 99-80-34. (Subscr. to: P.O. Box 5396, Manila 1093, Philippines) Ed. Chit Balmaceda. adv. **Indexed:** Ind.Phil.Per.

305.412   IT
LEGGERE DONNA. 1980. bi-m. L.60000. Via Ticchioni 38-1, 44100 Ferrara, Italy. TEL 0532-53186. FAX 0532-53186. Ed. Luciana Tufani. adv.; bk.rev. circ. 5,000.

305.412   IS
LEISHA. w. Beit Yediot Acharanot, Derech Petach Tikva 138, Tel Aviv, Israel. TEL 03-378071.

LESBENRUNDBRIEF. see *HOMOSEXUALITY*

LESBENSTICH; das Lesbenmagazin fuer den aufrechten Gang. see *HOMOSEXUALITY*

LESBIAN CENTER NEWS. see *HOMOSEXUALITY*

LESBIAN CONNECTION. see *HOMOSEXUALITY*

305.42 301.4157   US   ISSN 1064-4776
LESBIAN CONTRADICTION; a journal of irreverent feminism. q. $8. 584 Castro St., No. 356, San Francisco, CA 94114. Ed.Bd. **Indexed:** Alt.Press Ind.

LESBIAN ETHICS. see *HOMOSEXUALITY*

LESBIAN NEWS. see *HOMOSEXUALITY*

LESBIANS RISING. see *HOMOSEXUALITY*

LETRAS FEMENINAS. see *LITERATURE*

LEX VITAE; the pro-life legislation and litigation summary. see *LAW*

305.4   UK   ISSN 0954-1411
LIBAS INTERNATIONAL. 1988. q. £10($30) Libas International Magazine Ltd., 10A Berkeley St., Mayfair, London W1X 5AD, England. TEL 071-493-2102. FAX 071-495-0908. Ed. Sehyr Saigol. adv. contact: Shugufta Anwar. bk.rev.; film rev.; play rev.; bibl.; illus. (back issues avail.) **Document type:** consumer publication.
    Description: Lifestyle and fashion magazine for women.

053.932 054.1   BE   ISSN 0024-175X
LIBELLE. (Text in Dutch) 1945. w. 2860 BEF. Tijdschriften Uitgevers Maatschappij N.V.I.U.M., Jan Blockstraat 7, 2018 Antwerp, Belgium. Ed. Christina von Wackerbarth. adv.; Jan/Van De Wyngaerde. illus. circ. 202,212. **Document type:** consumer publication.

053.931   NE   ISSN 0165-4926
LIBELLE. 1934. w. fl.135.20; newsstand price: fl.2.95. Uitgeverij Spaarnestad B.V., Postbus 1, 2000 MA Haarlem, Netherlands. TEL 31-23-304304. adv.; illus.; circ. 759,984 (paid). **Document type:** consumer publication.
    Incorporates (1982-1987): Libelle Medisch (ISSN 0168-115X)

305.4   NE
DE LIBERALE VROUW. 1980. q. membership. Vrouwen V V D, Postbus 30836, 2500 GV The Hague, Netherlands. TEL 31-70-3613040. FAX 31-70-3608276. Ed. Mrs L. Traas-van Vianen. circ. 3,000.
    Description: Covers political subjects, with particular attention to those affecting women.

LIFE DOCKET. see *LAW*

305.8 296.3   US   ISSN 0146-2334
BM729.W5
LILITH; the independent Jewish women's magazine. 1976. q. $18 to individuals; institutions $24. Lilith Publications, Inc., 250 W. 57th St., Ste. 2432, New York, NY 10107-0172. TEL 212-757-0818. (Subscr. to: LILITH Subscription Services, Dept. LIL, P.O. Box 3000, Denville, NJ 07834-3000) Ed. Susan Weidman Schneider. adv. contact: Leslie Hollis Margulies. bk.rev. circ. 10,000. (also avail. in microfilm from UMI) **Indexed:** Ind.Jew.Per., Mid.East: Abstr.& Ind., Wom.Stud.Abstr. (1976-). —UnCover.
    Description: Directed to Jewish women, featuring editorials, fiction, poetry, news.

301.412 284   CN   ISSN 0380-4100
LINK & VISITOR; a magazine for Baptist women. 1927. 9/yr. Can.$9 to groups, individuals $10; foreign $14. Baptist Women's Missionary Society of Ontario & Quebec, 30 Arlington Ave., Toronto, ON M6G 3K8, Canada. TEL 416-651-7192. FAX 416-651-0438. Ed. Esther Barnes. adv. contact: Esther Barnes. bk.rev.; index. circ. 5,000. (back issues avail.) **Document type:** consumer publication.
    Description: Encourages Christian women to create a difference in their world.

LINKX. see *POPULATION STUDIES*

051   US   ISSN 0893-8083
LISTEN REAL LOUD; news of women's liberation worldwide. 1979. q. donation. American Friends Service Committee, Inc., Nationwide Women's Program, 1501 Cherry St., Philadelphia, PA 19102. TEL 215-241-7051. FAX 215-864-0104. bk.rev. circ. 3,000. **Indexed:** HR Rep. (1986-1988).
    Description: Promotes communication and debate among regional, national, overseas staff, and committee members; expands dialogue with other movements involved with AFSC.

301.412   SA   ISSN 0256-0496
LIVING AND LOVING. 1973. m. R.46.78 (overseas R.92.24) (effective 1993). Republican Press (Pty) Ltd., P.O. Box 32083, Mobeni 4060, Natal, South Africa. TEL 27-31-422041. FAX 27-31-921231. Ed. Angela Still. circ. 135,000. **Document type:** consumer publication.
    Description: Successful parenting for first-time mothers.

LONG ISLAND PARENTING NEWS. see *CHILDREN AND YOUTH — About*

305.4   UK   ISSN 0268-4969
LOOKS. 1985. m. £20 (foreign £25) (effective 1995-1996). E M A P - New Woman, 20 Orange St., London WC2H 7ED, England. TEL 01858-468811. FAX 0171-930-5728. (Subscr. to: Tower Publishing Services Ltd., Tower House, Sovereign Park, Lathkill St., Market Harborough, Leics. LE16 9EF, England. TEL 01858-468811. FAX 01858-462164) **Document type:** consumer publication.

LOVER; literatuuroverzicht over feminisme, cultuur en wetenschap. see *WOMEN'S STUDIES*

LOVING MORE. see *SOCIOLOGY*

LOW FAT FOR LIFE. see *NUTRITION AND DIETETICS*

305.412   CN   ISSN 0704-7886
LUNDI. 1976. w. Can.$69. Quebecor Inc., 7 Chemin Bates, Outremont, Que. H2V 1A6, Canada. TEL 514-270-1100. FAX 514-270-6900. Ed. Michel Choiniere. adv.; illus. circ. 106,000.

LUST & GRATIE; lesbisch cultureel universeel tijdschrift. see *HOMOSEXUALITY*

LUTHERAN WOMAN TODAY. see *RELIGIONS AND THEOLOGY — Protestant*

LUTHERAN WOMAN'S QUARTERLY; knowing Christ and making Him known. see *RELIGIONS AND THEOLOGY — Protestant*

301.412   GW   ISSN 0939-138X
LYDIA; die christliche Zeitschrift fur die Frau. (Editions in German, Hungarian, Rumanian) 1986. q. DM.18. Lydia Verlag GmbH, Postfach 1222, 35608 Asslar, Germany. TEL 06443-3011. FAX 06443-1707. E-mail: 100442,3576@compuserve.com. Ed. Elizabeth Mittelstaedt. adv. contact: Reinhold Appel. (back issues avail.) **Document type:** consumer publication.
    Description: Themes covering the interest of Christian women.

M A N A. see *ETHNIC INTERESTS*

305.412 649   UK   ISSN 1353-7032
M & M. 1966. bi-m. £6.50 (U.K. only). Nexus Media Ltd., Warwick House, Azalea Dr., Swanley, Kent BR8 8HY, England. TEL 01322-660070. FAX 01322-667633. adv.; B&W page £2502, color page £3146; trim 187 x 268. circ. 140,000. **Document type:** consumer publication.
    Formerly: Maternity and Mothercraft.

305.412   US   ISSN 8756-9965
M O T C'S NOTEBOOK. 1960. q. $15 (foreign $25). National Organization of Mothers of Twins Clubs, Inc., Box 23188, Albuquerque, NM 87192-1188. TEL 505-275-0955. FAX 505-296-1863. Ed. Lisa Swift. adv.; bk.rev.; illus. circ. 17,000. (tabloid format) **Document type:** newspaper.
    Description: Articles and news to increase the understanding of child development and rearing, especially relating to multiple births.

M S U U NEWSLETTER: GLEANINGS. (Ministerial Sisterhood Unitarian Universalist) see *RELIGIONS AND THEOLOGY — Protestant*

051   US   ISSN 0024-8908
TT500   CODEN: MCCAEQ
MCCALL'S. 1876. m. $36.94. McCall's Magazine (Subsidiary of: Gruner & Jahr U S A Publishing), 110 Fifth Ave., New York, NY 10011. TEL 212-463-1000. (Subscr. to: Box 3194, Harlan, IA 51537. TEL 800-777-0333) Ed. Sally Koslow. adv.; film rev.; illus. circ. 4,600,000. (also avail. in microform from UMI) **Indexed:** CINAHL, Hlth.Ind., Mag.Ind., Media Rev.Dig., PMR, R.G., TOM. **Document type:** consumer publication.
    —BLDSC (5413.417000); Faxon; UMI; UnCover.
    Description: Emphasis on women's home interests: cooking, decorating, and parenting. Includes information and how-to-tips on beauty, health and fashion.

MCCALL'S SILVER. see *GERONTOLOGY AND GERIATRICS*

MADAM; lesbisch tijdschrift. see *HOMOSEXUALITY*

053.1   GW   ISSN 0024-936X
MADAME. 1950. m. $90. Magazinpresse Verlag GmbH, Elisenstr. 3, 80335 Munich, Germany. TEL 089-55135-0. FAX 089-55135299. TELEX 522745-MAPR-D. (Subscr. in US: GLP International, 153 S. Dean St., Englewood, NJ 07631. TEL 201-871-1010. FAX 201-871-0870) Ed. Irene Krawehl. adv.; B&W page DM.15038, color page DM.24059; adv. contact: Maritta Obytz-Nehry. bk.rev.; illus.; circ. 110,079. **Document type:** consumer publication.

MADAME (SWEDEN). see *GENERAL INTEREST PERIODICALS — Sweden*

WOMEN'S INTERESTS

640 US ISSN 0024-9394
AP2
MADEMOISELLE. 1935. m. $15 (Canada $30, elsewhere $34); newsstand price: $2.50. Conde Nast Publications Inc., Mademoiselle Magazine, 350 Madison Ave., 7th. Fl., New York, NY 10017-3704. TEL 212-880-8800. FAX 212-880-8289. (Subscr. to: Box 54348, Boulder, CO 80322. TEL 800-274-4750) Ed. Elizabeth Crow; Pub. Catherine Viscardi Johnston. adv. contact: Cathy Kruchko. bk.rev.; illus. circ. 1,219,159. (also avail. in microform from UMI; reprint service avail. from UMI) Indexed: Biog.Ind., Consum.Ind., Hlth.Ind., Mag.Ind., Media Rev.Dig., R.G., TOM. **Document type:** consumer publication.
—Faxon; UMI; UnCover.
   Description: Directed toward young women; includes articles on fashion, beauty, self-help, and how-to.

MADISON GAY LESBIAN RESOURCE CENTER. DIRECTORY; a guide to organizations serving Madison's gay/lesbian/bisexual community. see HOMOSEXUALITY

301.412 649 IT ISSN 1120-6101
MADRE. 1888. m. L.39000 (foreign L.70000). Societa Edizioni Madre, Bassiche 47-G, 25122 Brescia, Italy. TEL 39-30-290521. Ed. Angelo Onger. adv.: page L.12000000. bk.rev. circ. 100,000.

MADWOMAN. see LITERARY AND POLITICAL REVIEWS

059.94 HU ISSN 0029-0963
MAGYAR NOK LAPJA. 1949. w. $24. Vico Press R.T., Torokvesz u. 30-A, 1022 Budapest, Hungary. TEL 115-40-37. FAX 115-40-39. TELEX 22-5554. (Subscr. to: Kultura, Box 149, 1389 Budapest, Hungary) Ed. Lili Zetenyi. illus. circ. 550,000.

MAHJUBAH. see RELIGIONS AND THEOLOGY — Islamic

305.412 RH
MAHOGANY. (Text in English) bi-m. Z.$9 (rest of Africa $11; elsewhere $13). Munn Publishing (Pvt.) Ltd., Box UA 589, Union Ave., Harare, Zimbabwe. TEL 700475. FAX 705411. TELEX 24748 ZW. Ed. G. Beach. circ. 32,000. **Document type:** consumer publication.

MAINE LESBIAN FEMINIST NEWSLETTER. see HOMOSEXUALITY

MALCHUS; the nation's lesbian & gay Christian monthly. see HOMOSEXUALITY

301.4 ML
MALI MUSO. q. Union des Femmes du Mali, Bamako, Mali. circ. 5,000.

301 US
MAMA BEARS NEWS AND NOTES. 1983. bi-m. $6. Mama Bears Bookstore Coffeehouse, 6536 Telegraph Ave., Oakland, CA 94609. TEL 510-428-9684. Ed. Alice Molloy. adv.; bk.rev. circ. 10,000. (tabloid format; back issues avail.) **Document type:** newsletter.
   Description: Articles, features and announcements on feminist and lesbian issues.

305.4 II
MANGALAM WEEKLY. (Text in Malayalam) 1969. w. newsstand price: Rs.2. Mangalam Publications, Mangalam Complex, P.B. No. 3, S.H. Mount, Kottayam 686006, India. TEL 563024. Ed. M.C. Varghese. adv.: B&W page Rs.30000; trim 260 x 195. cols./p.: 4.

305.412 NE ISSN 0025-2956
MARGRIET. 1939. w. fl.122.20. Geillustreerde Pers B.V., Haaksbergweg 75, 1101 BR Amsterdam, Netherlands. TEL 31-20-4300300. FAX 31-20-4300316. Ed. Aty Luitze. adv.; illus. circ. 550,000. **Document type:** consumer publication.

301.412 PO
MARIA. 1978. w. Esc.4700 (effective 1992). Impala Sociedade Editorial, Lda., Av. Miguel Bombarda 33-35, 2745 Queluz, Portugal. TEL 1-436-43-88. FAX 1-436-50-01. TELEX 16088 CENDIP P. Dir. Jaques Rodriques. adv. circ. 369,000. **Document type:** consumer publication.

301.412 PO
MARIE CLAIRE. 1989. m. Rua Mouzinho da Silveira 27, 1200 Lisbon, Portugal. TEL 01-526553. Dir. Maria Elisa Domingues. circ. 45,000.

301.412 SP
MARIE CLAIRE. 1987. m. 3460 ptas. (Europe 10740 ptas.; elsewhere 16640 ptas.) (effective 1995). Informacion y Moda, S.A., Marques de Villamagna, 4, 28001 Madrid, Spain. TEL 34-1-5780375. FAX 34-1-5752617. Dir. Ana Rosa Semprun. circ. 115,000.

053.1 GW
MARIE CLAIRE. 1990. m. DM.78 (Europe DM.123; elsewhere DM.129). Gruner und Jahr AG & Co. (Munich), Neherstr. 9, 81675 Munich, Germany. TEL 089-4152-0. FAX 089-4152636. (Co-publisher: M.C. Verlagsgesellschaft mbH) Ed. Barbara Kraus. circ. 271,140. **Document type:** consumer publication.

052 UK ISSN 0955-0178
MARIE CLAIRE. 1988. m. $55.50; newsstand price: £2. I P C Magazines, European Magazines (Subsidiary of: Reed Elsevier group), King's Reach Tower, Stamford St., London SE1 9LS, England. TEL 0171-261-5240. FAX 01444-440619. TELEX 892084 REEDBP G. (Dist. by: Quadrant Subscription Services, Oakfield House, Perrymount Rd., Haywards Heath, W. Sussex RH16 3DH, England. TEL 01444-440421) Ed. Glenda Bailey; Pub. Heather Love. adv. contact: Claire Portis. Indexed: DAAI. **Document type:** consumer publication.

051 US
▼**MARIE CLAIRE.** 1994. bi-m. Hearst Magazines, 250 W. 55th St., New York, NY 10019. TEL 212-694-4184. FAX 212-262-1238. Ed. Bonnie Fuller. adv. circ. 350,000. **Document type:** consumer publication.

305.4 BL
MARIE CLAIRE. m. Editora Globo S.A., Rua do Curtume 665, 05065-001 Sao Paulo SP, Brazil. FAX 55-11-861-2042. adv.; illus.; circ. 184,790 (paid). **Document type:** consumer publication.
   Description: Covers fashion, beauty, health, cooking, behavior, sex, and social problems.

053.932 BE
MARIE CLAIRE (VLAAMSE EDITIE). French edition: Marie Claire Belgique. (Text in Dutch) 1960. m. Societe Belgo-Francaise de Presse et de Promotion S.A., 68 av. Winston Churchill, 1180 Brussels, Belgium. TEL 32-2-3490090. FAX 32-2-3942827. Ed. Claude Cuvelier. adv. contact: Dominique Van Der Heyden. illus. **Document type:** consumer publication.

055.1 IT
MARIE CLAIRE - DONNAPIU. 1984. m. L.54000 (foreign L.79800). Arnoldo Mondadori Editore S.p.A., Casella Postale 1833, 20101 Milan, Italy. TEL 39-2-3199345. Ed. Vera Montanari. adv.: page L.43800000. circ. 201,000.
   Formerly: Donnapiu.

305.412 JA
MARIE CLAIRE JAPON. (Text in Japanese) 1982. m. 6510 Yen. Chuokoron-Sha, Inc., No. 2-8-7 Kyobashi, Chuo-ku, Tokyo, Japan. Ed. Kazuo Matsumura.

059 NE ISSN 0926-8898
MARIE CLAIRE - NEDERLANDSE EDITIE. (Supplement avail.: Marie Claire. Wonen (ISSN 0926-8952)) 1990. m. fl.78. Geillustreerde Pers B.V., Haaksbergweg 75, 1101 BR Amsterdam, Netherlands. TEL 31-20-4300300. FAX 31-20-4300316. Ed. Renie van Wijk. adv.; illus. circ. 76,000. **Document type:** consumer publication.

054.1 FR ISSN 0025-3057
MARIE-FRANCE. 1944. m. 176 F. Editions Bauer, 13 rue Bleue, 75009 Paris, France. TEL 1-48-01-31-31. FAX 1-48-24-06-63. TELEX 281 100. (Ed. addr.: 31 rue Bergere, 75009 Paris, France) Ed. Charlotte Seeling. adv. circ. 315,058.

054 MU ISSN 0047-5920
HQ1804.M38
MARIEMOU; revue de la jeune fille et de la femme Mauritaniennes. (Editions in Arabic and French) 1969. q. B.P. 47, Nouakchott, Mauritania. Ed. Toure Aissata Kane. adv.; bk.rev.; illus.

301.412 CN ISSN 0836-7515
MATCH NEWS. (Text in English, French, Spanish) 1976. q. Can.$25 membership. Match International Centre, 1102-200 Elgin St., Ottawa, ON K2P 1L5, Canada. TEL 613-238-1312. FAX 613-238-6867. circ. 5,000. (back issues avail.) **Document type:** newsletter.
   Description: News about women and development.

MATH SCIENCE NETWORK BROADCAST. see MATHEMATICS

305.4157 808 US
MATRICES: A LESBIAN-FEMINIST RESEARCH NEWSLETTER. 1977. s-a. $12. University of Minnesota, 496 Ford Hall, Minneapolis, MN 55455. E-mail: matrices@gold.tc.umn.edu. Ed. Jacquelyn Zita. **Document type:** newsletter.

301.412 GW ISSN 0930-1224
MAXI. 1986. m. DM.45.60 (foreign DM.91.20). Heinrich Bauer Verlag, Burchardstr. 11, 20095 Hamburg, Germany. TEL 040-3019-0. FAX 040-337640. Ed. Andreas Danch. adv. contact: Goesta Ahrweiler. circ. 402,702. **Document type:** consumer publication.

301.412 UK ISSN 0956-2486
ME. 1989. w. I P C Magazines, Weeklies Group (Subsidiary of: Reed Elsevier group), King' Reach Tower, Stamford St., London SE1 9LS, England. TEL 071-836-0519. FAX 01444-440619. TELEX 892084 REEDBP G. (Dist. by: Quadrant Subscription Services, Oakfield House, Perrymount Rd., Haywards Heath, W. Sussex RH16 3DH, England. TEL 0444-440421) Ed. Kay Goddard. adv. contact: Suzanne Bull. film rev. circ. 500,000. **Document type:** consumer publication.
   Description: Directed to the 18- to 40-year-old woman with an emphasis on feats & practical information. Includes a free sewing pattern every week.

059.94 FI ISSN 0025-6277
AP80
ME NAISET. 1952. w. FIM 458. Helsinki Media Magazines, P.O. Box 107, SF-00381 Helsinki, Finland. TEL 358-0-1201. FAX 358-0-120-5599. Ed. Ulla-Maija Paavilainen. adv.: B&W page FIM 16600, color page FIM 23000; 194 x 248. circ. 103,474 (paid).

305.16 US ISSN 0145-9651
HQ1402
MEDIA REPORT TO WOMEN. 1972. q. $30 to individuals (foreign $40); institutions $50 (foreign $60). Communication Research Associates, Inc., 10606 Mantz Rd., Silver Spring, MD 20903-1228. TEL 301-445-3230. Ed. Sheila Gibbons; Ed. Sheila Gibhi. adv.; bk.rev.; cum.index: 1972-1985. circ. 650. (back issues avail.) Indexed: Chic.Per.Ind., Film Lit.Ind. (1985-), HR Rep., Wom.Stud.Abstr. **Document type:** newsletter.
—Faxon. CCC.
   Description: Devoted to women in media topics.

051 US ISSN 0191-9377
MEDICAL - MRS; the magazine for doctors' wives. 1977. bi-m. $9.95. Hillbart Publications, Inc., Kirby Lane, Rye, NY 10580. TEL 914-967-7173. Ed. Cynthia S. Smith. adv.; film rev. circ. 100,000.

301.4 IT ISSN 1121-2829
MEDITERRANEA; l'observatorio delle donne. 1990. q. L.40000. Editrice Pellegrini, Via Roma 74, Casella Postale 158, 87100 Cosenza, Italy. TEL 39-984-21472. FAX 39-984-25245.

301.412 GW ISSN 0179-8596
MEIN ERLEBNIS; Frauen von heute berichten. 1975. m. DM.31.20. Publica Verlag GmbH, Bismarckstr. 67, 10627 Berlin, Germany. TEL 030-3424000. FAX 030-3415722. Ed. Rolf Henke. adv. circ. 120,000. (back issues avail.) **Document type:** consumer publication.

301.412 GW
MEIN GEHEIMNIS; moderne Frauen sprechen sich aus. 1977. bi-m. Condor-Interpart Verlag GmbH und Co. Zeitschriften KG, Karlsruherstr. 31, 76437 Rastatt, Germany. TEL 07222-130. FAX 07222-13404. Ed. Wolfgang M. Biehler. **Document type:** consumer publication.

WOMEN'S INTERESTS

301.412   GW
MEIN SCHICKSAL; Frauen von heute sprechen sich aus. 1979. bi-m. Condor-Interpart Verlag GmbH und Co. Zeitschriften KG, Karlsruherstr. 31, 76437 Rastatt, Germany. TEL 07222-130. FAX 07222-13404. Ed. Wolfgang M. Biehler. **Document type:** consumer publication.

301.412   GW   ISSN 0935-8005
MEINE GESCHICHTE; erlebnis magazin fuer die moderne Frau. 1972. fortn. DM.62.40. Publica Verlag GmbH, Bismarckstr. 67, 10627 Berlin, Germany. TEL 030-3424000. FAX 030-3415722. Ed. Rolf Henke. adv. circ. 112,000. (back issues avail.) **Document type:** consumer publication.

640   UK   ISSN 0965-7738
MELA. 1978. 6/yr. £4. Stiwdio Mei, 32-36 Stryd y Wyddfa, Penygroes, Caernarfon, Gwynedd LL54 6NG, Wales. TEL 0286-880302. FAX 0286-880302. circ. 5,000. **Document type:** consumer publication.
    Formerly: Pais.

305.4   II
MENAKA. (Text in Marathi) 1960. m. newsstand price: Rs.12. Menaka Prakashan Pvt. Ltd., 2117, Sadashiv Peth, Pune 30, India. Ed. Purushottam Vishnu Beheray.

MEXICO VOGUE. see *CLOTHING TRADE — Fashions*

301.412   LS
MEYING LAO. (Text in Lao) 1980. m. Vientiane, Laos. Ed. Khamphon Phimmaseng. circ. 4,000.

301.412   SP
MIA. 1986. w. 6000 ptas. (Europe 16200 ptas.; elsewhere 24700 ptas.) G y J Espana Ediciones, S.L. (Subsidiary of: Gruner and Jahr USA Publishing), Marques de Villamagna 4, 28001 Madrid, Spain. TEL 91-4356032. FAX 91-5767881. adv. contact: Elena Sanchez Fabres. circ. 155,000. **Document type:** consumer publication.

301.412   US   ISSN 1055-856X
MICHIGAN FEMINIST STUDIES. 1974. a. $7 to individuals; institutions $11 (effective 1995). University of Michigan, Women's Studies Department, 230 W. Engineering, Ann Arbor, MI 48109-1902. TEL 313-763-2047. Ed. Louise Tilly. adv. circ. 500. **Indexed:** Wom.Stud.Abstr.
    Former titles (until 1987): New Occasional Papers in Women's Studies (ISSN 1050-4893); (until 1983): Michigan Occasional Paper (ISSN 0731-163X); Supersedes (in 1978): University of Michigan Papers in Women's Studies.

055.1   IT
MILLE IDEE PER LA DONNA. m. L.31680. Rizzoli Editore-Corriere della Sera, Via A. Rizzoli 2, 20132 Milan, Italy. TEL 39-2-2588. Ed. Anna Condemi. adv.: color page L.30800000; adv. contact: Flavio Biondi. circ. 168,871.

646.7   JA
MINE. (Text in Japanese) 1920. s-m. Kodansha Ltd., 12-21 Otowa 2-chome, Bunkyo-ku, Tokyo 112, Japan. TEL 03-5395-3540. FAX 03-3945-4821. TELEX J34509 KODANSHA. Ed. Katsumi Mochida. circ. 350,000. **Document type:** consumer publication.
    Formerly (until 1987): Fujin Club.
    Description: Fashion and variety magazine for young homemakers.

MINERVA; quarterly report on women and the military. see *MILITARY*

MINERVA. see *CLOTHING TRADE — Fashions*

MINERVA'S BULLETIN BOARD. see *MILITARY*

052   US
MINNESOTA WOMEN'S PRESS. 1985. fortn. $25. Minnesota Women's Press, Inc., 771 Raymond Ave., St. Paul, MN 55114. TEL 612-646-3968. FAX 612-646-2186. Ed Mollie Hoben. adv. contact: Kathy Magnuson. bk.rev.; film rev.; play rev. circ. 40,000. (tabloid format) **Document type:** newspaper.

301.412   RU   ISSN 0869-494X
AP50
MIR ZHENSHCHINY; illyustrirovannyi ezhemesyachnyi zhurnal. (Editions in Bengali, Chinese, English, Finnish, German, Hindi, Russian, Spanish, Vietnamese) 1945. m. $78. (Soyuz Zhenshchin Rossii) Izdatel'stvo Pressa, Ul. Pravdy, 24, Moscow 125047, Russia. TEL 095-221-0781. (Dist. in U.S. by: Victor Kamkin Inc., 4956 Boiling Brook Pkwy, MD 20852. TEL 301-881-5973) Ed. Valentina Fedotova. bk.rev.; illus. circ. 1,000,000.
    Formerly (until 1992): Sovetskaya Zhenshchina (ISSN 0038-5913)
    Description: Covers social and political issues as well as literature and art. Features include special reports on current events, interviews with national female leaders, health reports, news from world women's organizations, fashion reports, cooking, crafts and fiction.

051   US   ISSN 1044-5153
TT500
MIRABELLA. 1989. 6/yr. $15.94 (effective Sept. 1995). Hachette Publications, Inc. (Subsidiary of: Hachette Filipacchi Press), 1633 Broadway, 44th Fl., New York, NY 10019. TEL 212-767-6000; 800-283-0484. FAX 212-767-5631. (Subscr. to: Box 52249, Boulder, CO 80322. TEL 303-504-1464. FAX 303-504-7455) Ed. Amy Gross; Pub. Carl Portale. adv. contact: Helene Tricarico. (reprint service avail. from UMI) **Indexed:** Access (1990-). **Document type:** consumer publication.
    —UMI; UnCover.
    Description: Covers a variety of topics ranging from art and politics to beauty, travel, business and fashion, for the savvy woman.

MIRJAM; Monatszeitschrift der weltoffenen Frau. see *RELIGIONS AND THEOLOGY — Roman Catholic*

MISS MOM - MISTER MOM. see *CHILDREN AND YOUTH — About*

305.412   UK   ISSN 0955-0119
MIZZ. 1985. fortn. £26 (foreign £32.60); newsstand price: £0.75. I P C Magazines, Southbank Publishing Group (Subsidiary of: Reed Elsevier group), King's Reach Tower, Stamford St., London SE1 9LS, England. TEL 071-261-6318. FAX 0444-440619. TELEX 892084 REEDBP G. (Dist. by: Quadrant Subscription Services, Oakfield House, Perrymount Rd., Haywards Heath, W. Sussex RH16 3DH, England. TEL 0444-4404 21) Ed. Simon Geller. adv. contact: Bridget Morrison. circ. 180,328. **Document type:** consumer publication.
    Description: Covers fashion and beauty teenage life-styles

MODA. see *CLOTHING TRADE — Fashions*

MODE AUSTRALIA. see *CLOTHING TRADE — Fashions*

305.412   NR   ISSN 0047-7761
MODERN WOMAN. 1964. m. £N3.48. Modern Publications Co. Ltd., Box 2583, Lagos, Nigeria. Ed. Romke Bamisebi. adv. circ. 40,000.

301.412   IE   ISSN 0790-3855
MODERN WOMAN. 1984. m. I£10. Meath Chronicle Ltd., Market Square, Navan, Co. Meath, Ireland. TEL 046-21442. FAX 046-23565. Ed. Margot Davis. adv. circ. 30,000. (tabloid format; back issues avail.)

051   CN   ISSN 1194-7470
MODERN WOMAN. 1993. m. Maclean-Hunter Ltd., 777 Bay St., 8th Fl., Toronto, Ont. M5W 1A7, Canada. TEL 416-596-5425. FAX 416-593-3197. Ed. Charlotte Empy. adv. contact: Reg Finlayson. circ. 774,000.

053.1   GW   ISSN 0177-090X
MODERNE HAUSFRAU. 10/yr. DM.28. (Deutscher Hausfrauen Bund e.V.) Moderne Medien Verlagsgesellschaft mbH, Schefestr. 11, 21493 Schwarzenbek, Germany. TEL 04151-889064. FAX 04151-889044. Ed. Jens Robrahn. adv. contact: Ricardo Viebranz. circ. 52,500. **Document type:** consumer publication.

305.412   US
MOM'S APPLE PIE. 1974. q. $20 to non-members; members $15. Lavender Families Resource Network, Box 21567, Seattle, WA 98111. TEL 206-325-2643. Ed. Jenny Sayward. adv.; bk.rev.; bibl.; illus. circ. 500. (back issues avail.) **Document type:** newsletter.
    Description: Publishes information about lesbian-gay mothers' parenting issues: custody and visitation, donor insemination, adoption and foster parenting, co-parent roles and children's family experience.

MONEYTALK. see *HOBBIES*

305.412   GW   ISSN 0047-7885
MONIKA; Zeitschrift fuer die Frau. 1869. m. DM.38.40. (Paedagogische Stiftung Cassianeum) Verlag Ludwig Auer GmbH, Postfach 1152, 86601 Donauwoerth, Germany. TEL 0906-73-0. FAX 0906-73177. Ed. Gerda Roeder. adv. contact: Dagmar Reiter. bk.rev. circ. 59,000. **Document type:** consumer publication.

MONTREAL WOMEN'S DIRECTORY/ANNUAIRE DES FEMMES DE MONTREAL. see *BUSINESS AND ECONOMICS — Trade And Industrial Directories*

301.412 133   US
MOONCIRCLES. 1985. 8/yr. $12.50. Circles of Exchange, 9594 First Ave., N.E., Ste. 413, Seattle, WA 98115. E-mail: arrowatCOE@aol.co, Ed. Nan Hawthrone. adv.; bk.rev. circ. 225. (looseleaf format; also avail. in magnetic tape; back issues avail.) **Document type:** bulletin.
    Description: Newsletter of women's spiritual correspondence and creativity exchange. Includes announcements and members' comments on different themes.

640   JA
MORE. (Text in Japanese) 1977. m. Shueisha Inc., 5-10, 2-chome, Hitotsubashi, Chiyoda-ku, Tokyo 101-50, Japan. TEL 03-3230-6350. Ed. Kouzo Tsuruya.

376   NZ   ISSN 0112-0808
MORE. 1983. m. NZ.$62.40. Australian Consolidated Press (NZ) Ltd., Private Bag, Wellesley St., Auckland, New Zealand. TEL 09-373-5408. FAX 09-309-8718. adv. contact: Sandra Taua. bk.rev.; film rev.; music rev. circ. 47,000.
    Description: New Zealand's glossy for savvy women.

305.4   UK
MORE. m. £26.35 (foreign £33.98) (effective 1995-1996). E M A P - New Woman, 20 Orange St., London WC2H 7ED, England. TEL 0171-957-8383. FAX 0171-930-5728. (Subscr. to: Tower Publishing Services Ltd., Tower House, Sovereign Park, Lathkill St., Market Harborough, Leics. LE16 9EF, England. TEL 01858-468811. FAX 01858-432164) adv. **Document type:** consumer publication.

305.4   LI
MOTERIS. 1952. m. Maironio 1, Vilnius 232600, Lithuania. TEL (0122) 610-169. Ed. Regina Paulauskiene.

362   PK   ISSN 0379-2617
MOTHER AND CHILD. (Text in English) 1965-1972; resumed 1974. q. Rs.100($10) per no. Maternity & Child Welfare Association of Pakistan, MCH House, 30-F, Gulberg-II, Lahore 54666, Pakistan. TEL 92-42-874621. Ed. Akram Sheikh. adv.; bk.rev. circ. 1,000. **Indexed:** ExtraMED.
    ●Also available on CD-ROM.

MOTHER-TO-MOTHER. see *CHILDREN AND YOUTH — About*

MOTHER'S DAY REPORT. see *GERONTOLOGY AND GERIATRICS*

301.412   US   ISSN 0047-830X
MOVING OUT; a feminist literary & arts journal. 1971. irreg. $6 to individuals; libraries $9. Box 21249, Detroit, MI 48221. Ed.Bd. adv.; bk.rev.; illus. circ. 1,000. (also avail. in microform from UMI; back issues avail.) **Indexed:** A.I.P.P.; Wom.Stud.Abstr.

301.412   SP   ISSN 0213-134X
MUCHO MAS. 1985. w. Pedro Teixeira 8, 28020 Madrid, Spain. TEL 91-5560048. Dir. Alicia Otero.

WOMEN'S INTERESTS

301.412   MX
MUJER; casos de la vida real. Cover title: Silvia Pinal Presenta Mujer. vol.6, 1994. fortn. Editorial Divina, S.A. de C.V., Bucareli 128 Depto. 1-B, Col. Centro, 06040 Mexico DF, Mexico. TEL 510-29-24.

056.1   CU   ISSN 0581-2011
MUJERES. 1961. q. $22 in S. America; N. America $24; elsewhere $28. Federacion de Mujeres Cubanas, Editora de la Mujer, Galiano 264 esq. Neptuno, Apdo. 2545, Havana 2, Cuba. TEL 7-61-5919. (Dist. by: Ediciones Cubanas, Obispo No. 527, Apdo. 605, Havana, Cuba) Dir. Regla Zulueta. illus. circ. 270,000.

305.412   AG
MUJERES. 1981. m. Sarmiento 2210, 1 Piso, Buenos Aires, Argentina. Ed. Ana Maria Giacosa.

301.512   BL
MULHER DE HOJE. 1979. m. $40. Bloch Editores S.A., Rua do Russel 766-804, 22210-000 Rio de Janeiro, RJ, Brazil. TEL 021-5554000. FAX 021-2059998. TELEX 2121525 BLOC. Ed. Janir Hollanda. circ. 10,000. **Document type:** consumer publication.

301.412   PO
MULHER MODERNA. w. Impala Sociedade Editorial, Lda., Rua Cristino da Silva, 1 r-c, 2745 Queluz, Portugal. TEL 439-02-34. FAX 439-02-33. **Document type:** consumer publication.

MUSICAL WOMAN. see MUSIC

305.412   UK   ISSN 0141-6030
MY GUY. 1977. w. I P C Magazines, Southbank Publishing Group (Subsidiary of: Reed Elsevier group), King's Reach Tower, Stamford St., London SE1 9LS, England. TEL 071-261-6348. FAX 044-4440619. TELEX 892084 REEDBP G. (Dist. by) Quadrant Subscription Services, Oakfield House, Perrymount Rd., Haywards Heath, W. Sussex RH16 3DA, England. TEL 0444-440421) Ed. Frank Hopkinson. adv. contact: Nicole Marks. circ. 80,197. **Document type:** consumer publication.
    Incorporates (1981-1984): Girl (ISSN 0261-6726)

305.412   UK   ISSN 0955-0127
MY GUY MONTHLY. 1985. m. I P C Magazines, Southbank Publishing Group (Subsidiary of: Reed Elsevier group), King's Reach Tower, Stanford St., London SE1 9LS, England. TEL 071-261-6375. FAX 0444-440619. TELEX 892084 REEDBP G. (Dist. by) Quadrant Subscription Services, Oakfield House, Perrymount Rd., Haywards Heath, W. Sussex RH16 3DH, England. TEL 0444-440421) Ed. Lorna Read. adv. contact: Bridget Marrison. **Document type:** consumer publication.

305.412   UK   ISSN 0262-026X
MY WEEKLY. 1910. w. D.C. Thomson & Co. Ltd., Albert Square, Dundee DD1 9QJ, Scotland.

N A B A REVIEW. (North American Benefit Association) see CLUBS

N A W J COUNTERBALANCE. (National Association of Women Judges) see LAW — Judicial Systems

N C A W E NEWS. (National Council of Administrative Women in Education) see EDUCATION — School Organization And Administration

N C O M D R NEWS. (National Clearinghouse on Marital & Date Rape) see POLITICAL SCIENCE — Civil Rights

968   SA   ISSN 0027-6367
N C W NEWS. (Text in Afrikaans, English) 1936. 11/yr. R.5.50 per issue. National Council of Women of South Africa - Nasionale Vroueraad van Suid-Afrika, P.O. Box 72499, Parkview 2122, South Africa. TEL 27-11-4474407. FAX 27-11-4474407. Ed. Mrs. P.J. Lloyd. bk.rev. circ. 2,000. **Document type:** newsletter.

N F E - W I D EXCHANGE - ASIA. NEWSLETTER. see EDUCATION

323.42   US
N O W NEWS (BOSTON).* vol.4, 1973. m. membership. National Organization for Women, 1000 - 16th St. N.W., Ste.700, Washington, DC 20036. TEL 202-331-0066. Ed. Rosemary Dempsey. adv.; bk.rev. circ. 600.
    Former titles: Boston N O W; National Organization for Women. Eastern Massachusetts Chapter. Newsletter.

301.412   US
N O W SAN DIEGO NEWS. 1971. m. $20. National Organization for Women, San Diego County Chapter, Box 80292, San Diego, CA 92138. TEL 619-237-1824. Ed. Kris Anderson. adv.; bk.rev. circ. 900. (also avail. in microfilm)

305.412   UK   ISSN 0952-5335
N W R NATIONAL NEWSLETTER. 1965. 2/yr. membership. National Women's Register, National Office, 9 Bank Plain, Norwich, Norfolk NR2 4SL, England. TEL 0603-765392. Ed. Nikki Iles. adv.; bk.rev. circ. 18,000. Indexed: Hum.Ind., Soc.Sci.Ind. **Document type:** newsletter.
    Former titles (until 1987): N H R National Newsletter (ISSN 0142-2146); National Housewives Register. Newsletter.

N W S S NEWS. (Network of Women in Slavic Studies) see LINGUISTICS

NA'AMAT WOMAN. see POLITICAL SCIENCE

301.412 327   US
NAJDA NEWSLETTER. 1964. q. $5. Najda: Women Concerned About the Middle East, Box 7152, Berkeley, CA 94707. TEL 415-854-0535. Ed. Alice Kawash. bk.rev. circ. 600. **Document type:** newsletter.
    Description: Publishes cultural and historical articles and coverage of contemporary issues concerning women in the Arab World.

305.412   XV   ISSN 0350-9737
NASA ZENA. (Includes supplement: Krojne Pole) (Text in Slovenian) 1940. w. 1440 din.($32) T.O.Z.D. Delavska Enotnost, N.sol.o. Celovska 43, N.sub.o. CGP Delo, Box 313-VI, 61001 Ljubljana, Slovenia. Ed. Sonja Tramsek.

305.412   US
NASHVILLE WOMEN'S ALLIANCE. NEWSLETTER. 1977. 11/yr. $10 contribution. Nashville Women's Alliance, Box 120834, Nashville, TN 37212. TEL 615-793-7619. Ed. Nancy Bolen. adv.; film rev.; play rev.; illus.; tr.lit. circ. 525. Indexed: Lang.& Lang.Behav.Abstr., Rehabil.Lit. **Document type:** newsletter.
    Description: Publishes news about social, political and health issues for the Nashville area lesbian community.

051 650   US   ISSN 0027-8831
HD6050
NATIONAL BUSINESS WOMAN. 1919. 4/yr. $10. National Federation of Business and Professional Women's Clubs, Inc., 2012 Massachusetts Ave., N.W., Washington, DC 20036. TEL 202-293-1100. FAX 202-861-0298. Ed. Marcia Clemmitt. adv.; illus.; index; circ. 75,000 (paid). Indexed: Mag.Ind., Pers.Lit., Work Rel.Abstr. **Document type:** newsletter. —Faxon; UnCover.
    Description: Covers topics of interest to working women, such as economic equality, dependent care, reproductive freedom and women in business.

NATIONAL DIRECTORY OF WOMAN - OWNED BUSINESS FIRMS. see BUSINESS AND ECONOMICS — Trade And Industrial Directories

323.42   US   ISSN 0149-4740
NATIONAL N O W TIMES. 1968? 6/yr. $35 to non-members. National Organization for Women, Inc., 1000 16th St., N.W., Ste. 700, Washington, DC 20036-5705. TEL 202-347-2279. Ed. Rosemary Dempsey. adv.; illus. circ. 200,000. (tabloid format) Indexed: Alt.Press Ind., New Per.Ind., PMR. —UMI.
    Formerly: Do It N O W.

NATIONAL NEWSBYTES MAGAZINE. see COMPUTERS — Computer Industry

301.412   CC
NEI MENGGU FUNU/INNER MONGOLIAN WOMEN. (Text in Mongolian) m. Nei Menggu Zizhiqu Funu Lianhehui - Inner Mongolian Autonomous Region Women's Association, 9 Zhongshan Donglu, Huhhot, Nei Menggu 010020, People's Republic of China. TEL 662584. Ed. Xi Xingfang.

NEMESIS; tijdschrift voor vrouwen en recht. see LAW

NETWORK (NEW YORK); a network for the empowerment of women through writing. see JOURNALISM

301.412   US   ISSN 0890-3530
NETWORK (SALT LAKE CITY). 1978. m. $12. 155 E. 4905 South, Salt Lake City, UT 84107. TEL 801-262-8091. FAX 801-486-8120. Ed. Lynne Tempest; Pub. Peter Bernhard. adv. contact: Kate Olson. bk.rev. circ. 16,000. **Document type:** consumer publication.

NETWORK NEWS (WASHINGTON, 1985). see GERONTOLOGY AND GERIATRICS

301.412   IS
NETWORKING FOR WOMEN. (Text in English) 1986. q. $48 membership or exchange basis. Israel Women's Network, P.O. Box 3171, Jerusalem 91031, Israel. TEL 972-2-439966. FAX 972-2-435976. Dir. Linda Futterman. **Document type:** newsletter.
    Formerly: Israel Women's Network. Newsletter.
    Description: Covers women's issues in Israel.

305.412   GW   ISSN 0940-0583
NEUE POST. 1981? w. (Fri.) DM.114.40 (foreign DM.238). Heinrich Bauer Verlag, Burchardstr. 11, 20095 Hamburg, Germany. TEL 040-3019-0. FAX 040-326494. Ed. Hartmut Klemann. adv. contact: Sven Schrader. bk.rev.; film rev.; illus. circ. 1,774,907. (tabloid format) **Document type:** consumer publication.
    Description: Topical reports, background information, entertainment, relaxation, advice and support.

NEW BOOKS ON WOMEN & FEMINISM. see WOMEN'S STUDIES — Abstracting, Bibliographies, Statistics

NEW DAWN. see HOMOSEXUALITY

NEW FAMILY. see HOME ECONOMICS

301.412   US
NEW JERSEY WOMAN MAGAZINE. 1979. 7/yr. $17. Advantage Publication Services, Inc., 177 Main St., No. 232, Fort Lee, NJ 07024-6936. TEL 201-886-2185. Ed. Louise Hafesh. adv.; bk.rev. circ. 35,000. (back issues avail.)
    Formerly: Jersey Woman Magazine (ISSN 0197-4610)
    Description: Directed toward New Jersey woman of accomplishment and the upscale market.

NEW MOON; the magazine for girls and their dreams. see CHILDREN AND YOUTH — For

NEW MOON NETWORK; for adults who care about girls. see CHILDREN AND YOUTH — About

NEW PARENT. see MEDICAL SCIENCES — Obstetrics And Gynecology

052   AT
NEW WEEKLY. 1993. w. Aus.$124.80. A C P Publishing Pty. Ltd., 54-58 Park St., Sydney, N.S.W. 2000, Australia. TEL 02-282-8281. FAX 02-264-6005. Ed. Juliet Ashworth; Pub. Richard Walsh. adv. contact: David Malone. circ. 211,989. **Document type:** consumer publication.
    Description: Entertainment, news and features magazine for women.

WOMEN'S INTERESTS

305.412 US ISSN 0028-6974
HQ1101
NEW WOMAN. 1971. m. $16.97 in U.S.; Canada $20.97; elsewhere $26.97. K-III Magazines, 200 Madison Ave., New York, NY 10016. TEL 212-447-4700. FAX 212-447-4778. (Subscr. to: Box 56229, Boulder, CO 80322. TEL 800-627-2557) Ed. Betsy Carter. adv.; bk.rev.; film rev. circ. 1,300,000. (also avail. in microform from UMI; reprint service avail. from UMI) Indexed: PMR. Document type: consumer publication.
—Faxon; UMI; UnCover.
Description: Covers health, food and diet, fashion, beauty and decorating, love, sex and relationships, psychology, self-improvement and self discovery.

301.412 UK ISSN 0955-6907
NEW WOMAN. 1988. m. £1.50 new no. Hachette - E M A P, 20 Orange St., London WC2H 7ED, England. TEL 071-957-8383. FAX 071-957-8400. adv.: B&W page £4400, color page £5900; trim 222 x 300. circ. 261,708 (paid).

052 NZ ISSN 0028-8829
NEW ZEALAND WOMAN'S WEEKLY. 1932. w. NZ.$227.50. New Zealand Magazines Ltd., Cnr. Halsey & Madden Streets, Freemans Bay, Auckland, New Zealand. TEL 09-638-8105. FAX 09-630-9128. Ed. Jenny Lynch. adv. contact: Wendy Bloxham. bk.rev.; illus. circ. 150,000. Document type: consumer publication.
—CCC.

305.412 374 CN ISSN 1188-0910
NEWFOUNDLAND AND LABRADOR WOMEN'S INSTITUTES. NEWSLETTER. 1966. q. Can.$5. Newfoundland and Labrador Women's Institutes, P.O. Box 1854, St. John's, Nfld. A1C 5P9, Canada. Ed. Jennifer Perry. bk.rev. circ. 750. (back issues avail.) Document type: newsletter.

NIGHTINGALE. see *MEDICAL SCIENCES — Nurses And Nursing*

509.2 JA
NIHON FUJIN KAGAKUSHA NO KAI NYUSU/SOCIETY OF JAPANESE WOMEN SCIENTISTS. NEWS. (Text in Japanese) 1958. irreg., latest no.71. 3000 Yen($30) membership. Nihon Fujin Kagakusha no Kai - Society of Japanese Women Scientists, Toho Daigaku Rigakubu, 2-2-1, Miyama, Funabashi-shi, Chiba-ken 274, Japan. TEL 81-474-70-1335. E-mail: kazuno@jpnkekvx. Ed. Masako Sasaki. circ. 1,000 (controlled). Document type: newsletter.
Description: Contains reports of events, lectures and meetings held by the Society.

305.4 JA
NIKKEI WOMAN. (Text in Japanese) m. Nikkei Home Publishing, Inc. (Subsidiary of: Nihon Keizai Shimbun, Inc.), 2-2-7 Kanda Tsukasa-cho, Chiyoda-ku, Tokyo 101, Japan. TEL 03-3258-7818. Document type: consumer publication.
Description: An information magazine for working women.

376 360 369.4 XO
NO. (Text in Hungarian) 1951. w. (Slovak Women's Union) Zivena, Nalepkova 15, 812 64 Bratislava, Slovakia. TEL 33 04 20. (Subscr. to: Slovart, Gottwaldovo n. 6, 810 05 Bratislava, Slovakia) (back issues avail.)

301.412 IS ISSN 0333-6387
NOGA. 1980. 3/yr. IS.16($14) Lilit, P.O. Box 21376, Tel Aviv 61 213, Israel. TEL 03-227663. Ed. Rachel Ostrawitz. bk.rev. circ. 2,000. (back issues avail.)

055.1 IT ISSN 0029-0920
NOI DONNE. 1944. m. L.50000 (foreign L.76000). (Unione Donne Italiane) Cooperativa Libera Stampa, Via della Trinita dei Pellegrini 12, 00186 Rome, Italy. FAX 6-6545380. Ed. Mariella Gramaglia. adv.: B&W page L.6000000, color page L.9000000. bk.rev.; film rev.; play rev.; illus.; tr.lit.; index. circ. 180,000.

301 CN ISSN 1192-4543
NORTH ISLAND WOMAN. 1992. m. Can.$20($25) (foreign Can.$30). RR 1, Site 168, C-11, Comox, BC V9N 5N1, Canada. TEL 604-339-5313. FAX 604-339-6945. Ed. Mary Peppard. adv.: B&W page Can.$400, color page Can.$575; trim 8 1/4 x 10 1/2; adv. contact: Wendy Keating. circ. 6,500. Document type: consumer publication.

053.931 NE ISSN 0923-6864
NOUVEAU. 1986. m. fl.78. Uitgeverij Spaarnestad B.V., Postbus 1, 2000 MA Haarlem, Netherlands. TEL 31-23-304304. FAX 31-23-350621. adv.; circ. 150,000 (paid). Document type: consumer publication.

NOUVELLES PRATIQUES SOCIALES. see *SOCIAL SERVICES AND WELFARE*

305.412 FR ISSN 0248-4951
HQ1102
NOUVELLES QUESTIONS FEMINISTES. 1977. q. 400 F. to individuals; institutions 500 F. Nouvelles Questions Feministes - I R E S C O, c/o C. Delphy, 59-61 rue Pouchet, 75017 Paris, France. Ed.Bd. bk.rev. circ. 600.
Formerly (until 1980): Questions Feministes (ISSN 0154-9960)

301.412 IO ISSN 0853-0300
NOVA; mingguan berita wanita. 1988. w. Rps.33.80. Jl. Kebahagiaan No. 4-14, Jakarta 11140, Indonesia. TEL 021-6297809. FAX 021-5494035. TELEX 073-46327 KOMPAS IA. Ed. Evie Fadjari. adv. contact: Tommy Anwar. circ. 330,000.

301.412 PO
NOVA COSMOPOLITA. m. Impala Sociedade Editorial, Lda., Rua Cristino da Silva, 1 r-c, 2745 Queluz, Portugal. TEL 439-02-34. FAX 439-02-33. Document type: consumer publication.

055.1 IT ISSN 1120-4443
NOVELLA 2000. 1920. w. L.91500. Rizzoli Editore-Corriere della Sera, Via A. Rizzoli 2, 20132 Milan, Italy. TEL 39-2-2588. Ed. Guido Carretto. adv.: page L.23400000; adv. contact: Flavio Biondi. circ. 322,533.
Formerly (until 1966): Novella (ISSN 1120-6209)

301.412 CC
NUZI SHIJIE/WOMEN'S WORLD. (Text in Chinese) m. Hebei Sheng Funu Lianhehui - Hebei Provincial Women's Association, 244 Nanma Lu, Shijiazhuang, Hebei 050051, People's Republic of China. TEL 27871. Ed. Ding Cong.

058.82 NO ISSN 0048-122X
DET NYE. 1957. m. NOK 396. Hjemmet Mortensen Forlag AS, Kr. Augustsgt. 14, 0164 Oslo, Norway. TEL 22-94-10-00. Ed. Kristin Ma Berg. illus. circ. 71,588.
—CCC.

059.396 659.152 IC ISSN 1017-3595
NYTT LIF; fashion magazine. 1978. 10/yr. ISK 4632 (effective Jan. 1995). Frodi Ltd., Seljavegur 2, 101 Reykjavik, Iceland. TEL 354-515-5500. FAX 354-515-5599. Ed. Gullveig Saemundsdottir. adv.: B&W page ISK 75800, color page ISK 117300; trim 20.5 x 27.5; adv. contact: Erla Hardardottir. circ. 15,000.
Formerly: L I F.
Description: Focuses on fashion and social issues.

O W L OBSERVER. (Older Women's League) see *GERONTOLOGY AND GERIATRICS*

OF A LIKE MIND. see *RELIGIONS AND THEOLOGY — Other Denominations And Sects*

301.412 CN ISSN 1192-4047
OH. 1992. q. Box 41030, 5134 Cordova Bay Rd., Victoria, BC V8Y 2K0, Canada. FAX 604-658-2954.

305.412 IS
OLAM HA-EISHA. 1984. m. Bari Communications (1984) Ltd., P.O. Box 20530, Tel Aviv, Israel. TEL 03-5615677. FAX 03-5611644. TELEX 341759-WISCO. Ed. R. Keinan. adv.; bk.rev. circ. 50,000.

059.927 915.3 MK
AL-OMANIYYAH. m. P.O. Box 6303, Ruwi, Muscat, Sultanate of Oman. TEL 707849. TELEX 3758. Ed. Saida bint Khatir al-Farisi. circ. 11,500.

ON OUR BACKS; entertainment for the adventurous lesbian. see *HOMOSEXUALITY*

323.4 US ISSN 0895-6014
RA564.85
ON THE ISSUES; the progressive woman's quarterly. 1983. 4/yr. $14.95. Choices Women's Medical Center, 97-77 Queens Blvd., Flushing, NY 11374. TEL 718-275-6020. FAX 718-997-1206. (Subscr. to: Box 3000, Dept. OTI, Denville, NJ 07834) Ed. Merle Hoffman. adv. contact: Carolyn Handel. bk.rev. circ. 50,000. Indexed: Access (1993-), Alt.Press Ind.
—Faxon; UnCover.
Description: Feminist topics fostering global political consciousness, anti-racism, anti-sexism, anti-speciesism.

051 100 US
ON WINGS. 1983. m. $10. Women In Constant Creative Action (W I C C A), Box 5080, Eugene, OR 97405. TEL 503-942-0889. Ed. Norma Joyce. bk.review. Document type: newsletter.
Description: Deals with issues of women's spirituality and self-growth.

301.41 CN ISSN 0830-9442
HQ1457
ONTARIO ADVISORY COUNCIL ON WOMEN'S ISSUES. ANNUAL REPORT. 1974. a. free. Ontario Advisory Council on Women's Issues, 880 Bay St., 5th Fl., Toronto, ON M7A 1N3, Canada. TEL 416-326-1840. FAX 416-326-1836. Ed. Lydia Oleksyn. illus. circ. 9,000. Document type: government publication.
Former titles: Ontario. Advisory Council on Women's Issues. Annual Report on the Status of Women's Issues; Ontario. Status of Women Council. Annual Report.

301.412 CN
ONTARIO WOMAN. q. Can.$20. Merrick Enterprises, 349 Claremont Cres., Oakville, Ont. L6J 6J9, Canada. Ed. John Merrick.

OPEN DOOR INTERNATIONAL FOR THE EMANCIPATION OF THE WOMAN WORKER. REPORT OF CONGRESS. see *BUSINESS AND ECONOMICS — Labor And Industrial Relations*

053.1 UK ISSN 0263-2624
OPTIONS. 1982. m. $53.21; newsstand price: £1.70. I P C Magazines, Southbank Publishing Group (Subsidiary of: Reed Elsevier group), King's Reach Tower, Stamford St., London SE1 9LS, England. TEL 071-261-6601. FAX 0444-440619. TELEX 892084 REEDBP G. (Dist. by: Quadrant Subscription Services, Oakfield House, Perrymount Rd., Haywards Heath, W. Sussex RH16 3DH, England. TEL 0444-440421) Ed. Maureen Rice. adv. contact: Anne Marie Ffitch. Document type: consumer publication.

305.4 NE ISSN 0166-2007
OPZIJ; feministisch opiniemaandblad. 1972. 11/yr. fl.71.50. Weekbladpers B.V., Postbus 1050, 1000 BB Amsterdam, Netherlands. TEL 31-20-5518540. FAX 31-20-6278537. Ed. C. Dresselhuys; Pub. H. Vervoort. adv.; film rev.; play rev.; bibl.; illus. circ. 73,828. (back issues avail.) Indexed: Child.Lit.Abstr. Document type: consumer publication.
—SWETS.

ORAH. see *ETHNIC INTERESTS*

OSAKA KUKUSAI JOSHI DAIGAKU KIYO/OSAKA INTERNATIONAL UNIVERSITY FOR WOMEN. BULLETIN. see *WOMEN'S STUDIES*

OTHER BLACK WOMAN; an international magazine for women. see *ETHNIC INTERESTS*

OUR SPECIAL; magazine devoted to matters of interest to blind women. see *HANDICAPPED — Visually Impaired*

OUT. see *HOMOSEXUALITY*

OUTLOOK (SEATTLE); drug regulation and reproductive health. see *PUBLIC HEALTH AND SAFETY*

OUTRAGEOUS LETTERS. see *MEN'S INTERESTS*

305.412 323 UK ISSN 0265-8429
OUTWRITE WOMEN'S NEWSPAPER. 1982. m. £6. Feminist Newspaper Ltd., Oxford House, Derbyshire St., London E2 6HG, England. Ed.Bd. adv.; bk.rev.; film rev.; play rev. circ. 7,000. (tabloid format; back issues avail.) Document type: newspaper.

WOMEN'S INTERESTS

OVER 40. see *MEN'S INTERESTS*

353.9 US
P C S W ANNUAL REPORT. 1974. a. free. Permanent Commission on the Status of Women, 90 Washington St., Hartford, CT 06106. TEL 203-566-5702. FAX 203-566-6044. Ed. Leslie J. Brett.
  Description: Provides detailed explanation of the Commission's activities during the fiscal year, including analysis of special studies, and legislative work.

P S A C UNION UPDATE. (Public Service Alliance of Canada) see *LABOR UNIONS*

P W P NEWSLETTER. (Professional Women Photographers) see *PHOTOGRAPHY*

PAGANS FOR PEACE. see *RELIGIONS AND THEOLOGY*

305 646 VE
PAGINAS. 1948. w. Bs.3.50 per no. Editorial Elite, Torre de la Prensa, Plaza del Panteon, Apdo. Postal 2976, Caracas 101, Venezuela. TEL 2-81-4931. Ed. Miguel Angel Capriles. adv.; illus. circ. 80,025.

PALABRA DE MUJER; revista de poesia latinoamericana. see *LITERATURE — Poetry*

052 659.152 BB ISSN 1023-6384
▼**PANACHE.** 1994. q. Caribbean Communications Inc., Lefferts Pl., River Rd., St. Michael, Barbados, W.I. TEL 809-436-1902. **Document type:** consumer publication.
  Description: Contains fashion and life-style features for women.

059.8 GR
PANTHEON. (Text in Greek) m. Labrakis Press S.A., 1 Cornarou, 105 63 Athens, Greece. TEL 30-1-325-5058. FAX 30-1-324-1112. circ. 65,000 (paid). **Document type:** consumer publication.

305.412 AG
PARA TI. 1922. w. Editorial Atlantida, S.A., Azopardo 579, 1307 Buenos Aires, Argentina. TEL 33-4591. Ed. Anibal C. Vigil. adv.; illus. circ. 104,000.

PARENT CARE; your child care news-line. see *CHILDREN AND YOUTH — About*

PARENTING MAGAZINE OF ORANGE COUNTY. see *CHILDREN AND YOUTH — About*

PARENTS EXPRESS; the newspaper for Philadelphia area parents. see *EDUCATION — Teaching Methods And Curriculum*

305.412 SP ISSN 0214-3666
PATRONES. 1982. m. $132.21. H Y M S.A., Aribau 28, 08011 Barcelona, Spain. TEL 3-323-70-63. FAX 3-454-13-22. Ed. Anna Puges i Gibert. adv.; film rev. circ. 75,000.

301.412 CL
PAULA. fortn. Triana 851, Santiago, Chile. TEL 2-225-3447. Dir. Andrea Eluchans. circ. 20,000.

PEACE AND FREEDOM. see *POLITICAL SCIENCE — International Relations*

THE PEN WOMAN. see *LITERATURE*

PENTHOUSE FORUM; the international journal of human relations. see *MEN'S INTERESTS*

PENTHOUSE VARIATIONS; for liberated lovers. see *MEN'S INTERESTS*

305.412 UK ISSN 0262-2386
PEOPLE'S FRIEND. 1869. w. D.C. Thomson & Co. Ltd., Albert Sq., Dundee DD1 9QJ, Scotland. **Document type:** consumer publication.

PERCEPTIONS; women's poetry for a change. see *LITERATURE — Poetry*

301.412 CR
PERFIL. fortn. Llorente de Tibas, Apdo. 10138, San Jose, Costa Rica. TEL 35-1211. FAX 36-6485. TELEX 2358. Dir. Patricia de Liberman. circ. 24,500.

PERSPECTIVES (CHICAGO); a newsletter for and about women lawyers. see *LAW*

PERSPECTIVES: A RESOURCE FOR WOMEN IN VETERINARY MEDICINE. see *VETERINARY SCIENCE*

053.1 GW ISSN 0031-630X
PETRA. 1967. m. Jahreszeiten Verlag GmbH, Possmoorweg 5, 22301 Hamburg, Germany. TEL 040-27170. FAX 040-27172056. TELEX 213214-JAG-D. Ed. Andreas Millies. adv. contact: Helma Spieker. charts; illus.; tr.lit. circ. 408,485. **Document type:** consumer publication.
  Formerly: Moderne Frau (ISSN 0026-8593)

301.412 VN
PHU NU VIET-NAM/VIETNAMESE WOMEN. w. Vietnamese Women's Union, 47 Hang Chuoi, Hanoi, Socialist Republic of Vietnam. TEL 53500. Ed. Phyong Minh.

323.4 355 370 US ISSN 0556-0152
E839.5
PHYLLIS SCHLAFLY REPORT. 1967. m. $20. Eagle Trust Fund, Box 618, Alton, IL 62002. TEL 618-462-5415. Ed. Phyllis Schlafly. circ. 70,000. (back issues avail.)
  Description: Commentary on women's issues, education, national defense, legal issues, economics and foreign policy.

PILLOW TALK; adult erotica. see *MEN'S INTERESTS*

305.412 IT ISSN 1120-4451
PIU BELLA. 1944. w. L.83200 (effective 1994). Rizzoli Editore-Corriere della Sera, Via A. Rizzoli 2, 20132 Milan, Italy. TEL 39-2-25843213. Ed. Antonella Di Scovolo. adv.: color page L.44500000; 185 x 257; adv. contact: Flavio Biondi. circ. 325,389.
  Formerly (until 1988): Bella (ISSN 1120-7450)

051 US ISSN 0273-6918
AP2
PLAYGIRL; entertainment for women. 1973. 12/yr. $21.95 (foreign $46). Playgirl, Inc., 801 Second Ave., New York, NY 10017-4706. TEL 212-661-7878. FAX 212-697-6343. (Subscr. to: Box 533, Mt. Morris, IL 61054. TEL 800-877-6139) adv.; bk.rev. circ. 575,547.
  Description: Focuses on women's sexuality, with centerfolds and pictorials.

053.1 GW
PLAYGIRL. m. DM.91. Playgirl Deutschland GmbH, Schillerstr. 7, 80336 Munich, Germany. TEL 089-551904-0. FAX 089-598656. Ed. Bernhard Hausner. **Document type:** consumer publication.

301.412 SP ISSN 0212-3231
PODER Y LIBERTAD. 1976. irreg. 3375 ptas. Partido Feminista de Espana, Bailen 18, Barcelona, Spain. TEL 34-1-369-44-88. (Or. Magdalena 29, 1o A, 28012 Madrid, Spain) Ed. Lidia Falcon. adv.; bk.rev.; illus. circ. 1,000. **Document type:** monographic series.
  Formerly: Vindicacion Feminista (ISSN 0212-324X)

POLITICAL WOMAN HOTLINE; charting our progress towards equality. see *POLITICAL SCIENCE*

917.309 US ISSN 0032-3594
POLKA; Polish women's quarterly magazine. 1935. q. $2. National United Women's Societies of the Adoration of the Most Blessed Sacrament, Polish National Catholic Church of U.S. and Canada, 1004 Pittston Ave., Scranton, PA 18505. TEL 717-344-1513. Ed. Cecelia D. Lallo. adv. circ. 1,200. Indexed: CERDIC.

301 PO ISSN 0871-3316
PORTUGAL. COMISSAO PARA A IGUALDADE E DIREITOS DAS MULHERES. NOTICIAS. 1985. q. free. Comissao para a Igualdade e Direitos das Mulheres, Avda. da Republica 32-1, 1093 Lisbon Codex, Portugal. TEL 351-1-7976081. FAX 351-1-7937691.
  Formerly: Portugal. Comissao da Condicao Feminina. Noticias.

057.86 XR ISSN 0231-6471
PRAKTICKA ZENA. (Text in Czech) 1950. m. 144 Kc.($41.50) Mona spol. s.r.o., Zitna 18, 120 79 Prague 2, Czech Republic. TEL 42-2-298641. FAX 42-02-297335. Ed. Miroslava Lanska. circ. 270,000. **Document type:** consumer publication.
  Formerly (until 1967): Prirucka Casopisu Zena a Moda (ISSN 0032-8774)
  Description: Covers handworks, croacheting, embroidering, fashion, cooking, gardening, household advice.

057.8 YU ISSN 0032-6747
PRAKTICNA ZENA. 1956. fortn. $96. B I G Z, Bulevar vojvode Misica 17, Belgrade, Yugoslavia. Ed. Olivia Panic.

305.412 GR ISSN 1105-1477
PRAKTIKI - IDEES. 1981. m. $53 (effective 1994). E. Terzopoulos Publishing Enterprises S.A., 7 Odos Fragoklisias, GR-151 25 Marousi, Greece. TEL 30-1-689-9149. FAX 30-1-689-9162. Ed. Simoni Kafiri. adv. contact: Athina Seytanides. illus. circ. 50,000. **Document type:** consumer publication.
  Description: Covers handicrafts, including knitting and needlework, cooking, and decoration. Geared toward women.

301.412 IT ISSN 1120-4575
PRATICA. 1988. m. L.3800 per no. Fabbri Rizzoli Edizioni Periodiche, Via Mecenate 87-6, 20138 Milan, Italy. TEL 39-2-580801. FAX 39-2-5862865. Ed. Marisa Deimichei. adv.: page L.32000000. circ. 271,849. **Document type:** consumer publication.

301.412 PO
PRATICA E CRIATIVA. m. Impala Sociedade Editorial, Lda., Rua Cristino da Silva, 1 r-c, 2745 Queluz, Portugal. TEL 439-02-34. FAX 439-02-33. **Document type:** consumer publication.

323.4 US
PREPARE. 3/yr. membership. Interfaith Impact for Justice and Peace, 110 Maryland Ave., NE, Washington, DC 20002. TEL 202-543-2800.
  Description: Publishes information on Congress's voting record and justice issues.

053.1 GW ISSN 0931-1432
PRIMA. 1986. m. DM.48 (Europe DM.234; elsewhere DM.245.96). Gruner und Jahr AG & Co. (Munich), Neherstr. 9, 81675 Munich, Germany. TEL 089-4152-0. FAX 089-4152-650. Ed. Jutta Fritsch. circ. 639,767. **Document type:** consumer publication.

301.412 800 US ISSN 0364-7609
PS508.W7
PRIMAVERA (CHICAGO). 1975. a. $10. Box 37-7547, Chicago, IL 60637-7547. TEL 312-324-5920. Ed.Bd. illus. circ. 1,000. (also avail. in microfilm from UMI; reprint service avail. from UMI) **Indexed:** Amer.Hum.Ind., Ind.Amer.Per.Verse.
  Description: Publishes original fiction, poetry, illustrations, and photography that reflect the experiences of women.

PRIVATE LETTERS. see *MEN'S INTERESTS*

PRO-CHOICE NEWS. see *BIRTH CONTROL*

PROBE (CHICAGO); feminist religious women. see *RELIGIONS AND THEOLOGY — Roman Catholic*

301.412 659.152 US ISSN 1058-1081
PROFESSIONAL MODEL NEWSLETTER. 1990. m. Professional Model Publications, Inc., 201 N. Wells St., Ste. 410, Chicago, IL 60606-1305. TEL 312-263-3513. FAX 312-236-8870. Ed. Linda Balhorn. **Document type:** newsletter.

PROFESSIONAL WOMEN AND MINORITIES; a total human resources data compendium. see *OCCUPATIONS AND CAREERS*

305.4 SP
PRONTO. 1972. w. Publicaciones Heres, S.A., Gran Via de Carlos 3, 124-5o, 08034 Barcelona, Spain. TEL 93-2800088. FAX 93-2805555. Ed. Antonio G. Abad. circ. 867,145.

301.412 057.85 PL ISSN 0033-2534
PRZYJACIOLKA. 1948. w. $78. Oferta dla Kazdego, Spolka z o.o., Ul. Wiejska 12, 00-490 Warsaw, Poland. TEL 48-22-280583. (Dist. by: Ars Polona-Ruch, Krakowskie Przedmiescie 7, Warsaw, Poland) Ed. Ewa Luszczuk. adv.; illus. circ. 1,500,000.

PSYCHOLOGIE UND GESELLSCHAFTSKRITIK. see *PSYCHOLOGY*

346.013 PY ISSN 1017-2815
LA PUERTA. 1990. q. $10. Centro de Estudios Humanitarios, Azara 3267, Asuncion, Paraguay. Ed. Esther Prieto. circ. 500.

WOMEN'S INTERESTS

301.412 646.7 IT
PUI BELLA. w. Rizzoli Editore-Corriere della Sera, Via A. Rizzoli 2, 20132 Milan, Italy. TEL 02-2588. Ed. Mirella Pallotti.

305.412 IT ISSN 0048-6205
QUARTO MONDO. 1971. m. Fronte Italiano di Liberazione Femminile, Piazza Ss. Apostoli 49, 00187 Rome, Italy. Ed. Laura Lilli. bk.rev.; illus.

052 AT ISSN 0033-6092
QUEENSLAND COUNTRY WOMAN. 1930. m. Aus.$18. Queensland Country Women's Association, 1st Fl., Ruth Fairfax House, 89-95 Gregory Terrace, Brisbane, Qld. 4000, Australia. Ed. Mardi Land. adv.; bk.rev. circ. 10,000. (tabloid format) **Document type:** bulletin.

QUERIDA. see CHILDREN AND YOUTH — For

R N I B APHRA. (Royal National Institute for the Blind) see HANDICAPPED — Visually Impaired

RADCLIFFE QUARTERLY. see COLLEGE AND ALUMNI

305.412 613.7 US ISSN 0889-9495
RA778
RADIANCE; the magazine for large women. 1984. q. $20 (Canada $26; elsewhere $34). Alice Ansfield, Ed. & Pub., Box 30246, Oakland, CA 94604. TEL 510-482-0680. FAX 510-482-0680. adv.; bk.rev. circ. 30,000. (back issues avail.) **Document type:** consumer publication.
Description: Source of support, information and inspiration for women all sizes of large. Features dynamic large women from all walks of life, along with articles on health, media, fashion and politics.

055.1 IT ISSN 0033-9113
RAKAM; mensile di moda e lavori femminili. 1929. m. L.48000 (foreign L.85000). Rusconi Editori S.p.A., Servizio Abbonamenti, Viale Sarca 235, 20126 Milan, Italy. TEL 39-2-66191. FAX 39-2-6619-2737. Ed. Anna Gualteri. adv.: page L.27000000. illus. circ. 191,661.

646.7 305.42 GW ISSN 0344-5828
RATGEBER FRAU UND FAMILIE. m. DM.37.20. J. Weck Verlag GmbH, Wehratalstr. 3, 79664 Wehr, Germany. TEL 07761-3014. FAX 07761-57691. Ed. Eberhard Hackelsberger; Pub. Franzjosef Hackelsberger. adv. contact: Eva-Maria Federspiel. circ. 351,085. **Document type:** consumer publication.

305.412 JA
RAY. (Text in Japanese) 1988. m. 11280 Yen. Shufunotomo Co., Ltd., 2-9 Kanda Surugadai, Chiyoda-ku, Tokyo 101, Japan. Ed. Tatsuro Nakanishi. circ. 200,000. **Document type:** consumer publication.

READING WOMAN. see PUBLISHING AND BOOK TRADE

REBIRTH OF ARTEMIS. see LITERATURE — Poetry

051 US ISSN 0034-2106
AP2
REDBOOK. 1903. m. $15.97. Hearst Corporation, Redbook, 224 W. 57th St., New York, NY 10019. TEL 212-649-2000. (Subscr. to: C.D.S., 1901 Bell Ave., Des Moines, IA 50315. TEL 800-888-0008) Ed. Kate White. adv.; illus. circ. 3,200,000. (also avail. in microform from UMI) **Indexed:** Curr.Lit.Fam.Plan., Hlth.Ind., Mag.Ind., PMR, R.G., TOM. **Document type:** consumer publication.
—Faxon; UnCover.

305.412 FI ISSN 0355-841X
REGINA. s-m. FIM 410. Kolmiokirja Oy, P.O. Box 246, 90101 Oulu, Finland. TEL 358-81-537-0033. FAX 358-81-530-6118. Ed. Eeva Vainikainen. adv. circ. 26,000.

301.412 305.3 US
RELATIONSHIPS TODAY.* 1988. m. $24. Romantic Lifelines, c/o Jon Anderson, 1224 N.W. Ninth Ave., Gainesville, FL 32601-4942. Ed. Lyle Benjamin. circ. 160,000.

RESIST NEWSLETTER. see POLITICAL SCIENCE — Civil Rights

305.412 US ISSN 0894-7597
CODEN: RVWCEE
RESPONSE TO THE VICTIMIZATION OF WOMEN AND CHILDREN.* 1976. q. $27.50 to individuals; institutions $50. Response, Inc., 4938 Hampden Ln., No. 255, Bethesda, MD 20814-2962. TEL 301-951-0039. Ed. Jane Roberts Chapman. adv.; bk.rev.; play rev.; bibl.; stat.; tr.lit. circ. 3,000. (back issues avail.) **Indexed:** Psychol.Abstr., Stud.Wom.Abstr.
—UMI; UnCover.
Former titles: Response to Violence in the Family and Sexual Assault; Response (Washington); Response to Family Violence and Sexual Assault.
Description: Latest developments in the advocacy and the treatment and prevention of victims of interpersonal violence.
Refereed Serial

RESPONSIVE PHILANTHROPY. see SOCIAL SERVICES AND WELFARE

RETI - PRATICHE E SAPERI DI DONNE. see POLITICAL SCIENCE

RETIRED MILITARY FAMILY. see MILITARY

054.1 CN
REVUE FERMIERES AUJOURD'HUI. 1974. 5/yr. Can.$12.84. Editions Penelope, 3945 St. Martin Blvd. W., Laval, Que. H7T 1B7, Canada. TEL 514-688-6380. FAX 514-681-1682. Ed. Pierrette Pare Walsh. adv.; bk.rev.; illus. circ. 81,000.
Formerly: Revue des Fermieres (ISSN 0381-8225)

641.5 GW
REZEPTE MIT PFIFF. 1975. m. Sonnenverlag GmbH, Lichtentaler Allee 10, 76530 Baden-Baden, Germany. TEL 07221-3501-0. FAX 07221-350133. Ed. Erika Poese; Pub. Marie-Luise Rose. adv. contact: Klaus Fortmann. circ. 107,796. **Document type:** consumer publication.

RICHMOND LESBIAN FEMINIST FLYER. see HOMOSEXUALITY

305.412 BE ISSN 0035-5313
HET RIJK DER VROUW. (Text in Flemish) 1928. w. 2150 Fr. Edibel, 9 Av. Frans van Kalken, B-1070 Brussels, Belgium. adv.; bk.rev.; film rev.; play rev.; rec.rev.; bibl.; illus.; mkt.; pat.; tr.lit. circ. 160,000.

055 IT
RIVISTA DELLA DONNA. 1971. q. Istituto Publiaci, Corso Vittorio Emanuele 326, 00186 Rome, Italy. Ed. Marcello Vazio. adv. circ. 75,000.

ROCK AGAINST SEXISM. see MUSIC

057.87 XO
RODINA. m. 12 Sk. per issue. Euroskop, Inc., Pribinova 25, 810 11 Bratislava, Slovakia. TEL 42-7-2104027. Ed. M. Varos. adv. contact: J. Sokolova. circ. 145,000.

305.412 640 SA ISSN 0035-8207
ROOI ROSE. (Text in Afrikaans) 1944. fortn. R.91.22 (overseas R.181.80) (effective 1993). Republican Press (Pty) Ltd., P.O. Box 3208, Mobeni 4060, Natal, South Africa. TEL 27-31-422041. FAX 27-31-921231. Ed. Joan Kruger. adv.; bk.rev.; film rev.; illus. circ. 202,000. (tabloid format) **Indexed:** Ind.S.A.Per. **Document type:** consumer publication.
Description: Cookery and homecrafts, fashion and beauty, as well as general interest features.

305.4 II
ROSHNI. (Text in English) q. Rs.50($25) All India Women's Conference, Central Office, AIWC, 6, Bhagwan Das Rd., New Delhi 110001, India. Ed. Aparna Basu.
Description: Devoted to women problems in India.

305.412 US
S F N O W TIMES. Alternate title: N O W. 1971. m. $4.50. National Organization for Women, San Francisco Chapter, Box 422002, San Francisco CA 94142-2002. TEL 415-861-8880. Ed. Helen L. Grieco. adv.; bk.rev.; illus. circ. 750.
Formerly: N O W San Francisco.

S W E. (Society of Women Engineers) see ENGINEERING

301.412 US ISSN 1068-1698
SAGE WOMAN; a quarterly magazine of women's spirituality. 1983. q. $18 (foreign $28) (effective 1995). Box 641, Point Arena, CA 95468. TEL 707-882-2052. FAX 707-882-2793. Ed. Anne Newkirk Niven; Pub. Anne Newkirk Niven. adv. contact: Christina Alexander. bk.rev.; circ. 10,000 (paid). **Document type:** consumer publication.
—UnCover.

051 CN ISSN 0838-7397
SALLY ANN; a Christian magazine for women. 1953. m. Can.$6.95($9.50) Salvation Army, Canada Territorial Headquarters, Editorial Department, 455 N. Service Rd. E., Oakville, ON L6H 1A5, Canada. TEL 416-844-2561. Ed. Shirley Pavey. bk.rev.; illus. circ. 12,000. **Document type:** newspaper.
Former titles: Home Leaguer (ISSN 0822-5079); Canadian Home Leaguer (ISSN 0008-3771)

SAN DIEGO PARENT. see CHILDREN AND YOUTH — About

323.4 305.412 US
SAN JOAQUIN N O W NEWSLETTER. 1973. irreg. $10. National Organization for Women, San Joaquin Chapter, Box 4073, Stockton, CA 95204. Ed. Renee LaCouture-Tulloch. circ. 100. **Document type:** newsletter.

SANDMUTOPIA GUARDIAN & DUNGEON JOURNAL. see MEN'S INTERESTS

052 SA ISSN 0256-0399
SARIE. 1949. fortn. R.154.68. National Magazines (Subsidiary of: National Media Ltd.), P.O. Box 1802, Cape Town 8000, South Africa. TEL 27-21-4062100. FAX 27-21-4062936. Ed. L. Rabe. adv.; bk.rev.; film rev.; illus. circ. 227,335. **Indexed:** Ind.S.A.Per. **Document type:** consumer publication.

SASSY. see CHILDREN AND YOUTH — About

301.412 TH ISSN 0125-0698
SATRI SARN. (Text in Thai) 1948. w. 83-35 Arkarntrithosthep 2, Prachathipatai Rd., Bangkok, Thailand. TEL 02-281-9136. Ed. Nilawan Pintong.

SAVANTE. see WOMEN'S STUDIES

301.435 TS
SAWT AL-MAR'AH/WOMAN'S VOICE. (Text in Arabic) 1976. m. Women's Union Society, Cultural Section - Jam'iyyat al-Ittihad al-Nisa'iyyah, Al-Lajnah al-Thiqafiyyah, P.O. Box 142, Sharjah, United Arab Emirates. TEL 22646. Ed. Fatimah Muhammad Hadi. circ. 1,000.
Description: Covers women's issues in the U.A.E.

363 AT ISSN 0311-7057
SCARLET LETTER. 1969. bi-m. Aus.$2- Council for the Single Mothers and their Children, G.P.O. Box 1399 M, Melbourne, Vic. 3001, Australia. FAX 03-650-4755. Ed. Sharon Good. adv.; bk.rev. circ. 2,000.
Formerly (until May 1977): C S M C News.

053.1 200 GW ISSN 0036-696X
SCHRIFTENREIHE FUER DIE EVANGELISCHE FRAU.* 1938. 6/yr. DM.19.80. Burckhardthaus-Laetare Verlag GmbH, Schumannstr. 161, 6050 Offenbach, Germany. illus. circ. 8,000.

640 UK ISSN 0036-925X
SCOTTISH HOME AND COUNTRY. 1924. m. £10.80 (foreign £14.20). Scottish Women's Rural Institutes, 42a Heriot Row, Edinburgh EH3 6ES, Scotland. TEL 0131-225-1934. FAX 0131-225-8129. Ed. Stella Roberts. adv.; bk.rev.; circ. 15,000 (paid). **Document type:** consumer publication.
Description: Contains regular features on handicrafts, cookery, travel, fashion, gardening, floral art, consumer news and country customs. Includes patterns and information on competitions.

052 UK ISSN 1351-3591
SECOND SHIFT. 1993. q. £2.50 per no. 11 Petworth St., Cambridge, England. Ed. Nicola Upson. **Document type:** consumer publication.

SECRETARESSE; vakblad voor het dynamisch secretariaat. see BUSINESS AND ECONOMICS — Office Equipment And Services

WOMEN'S INTERESTS

305.412   US   ISSN 0149-0699
RA778.A1
SELF. 1979. m. $12. Conde Nast Publications Inc., Self Magazine, 350 Madison Ave., New York, NY 10017. TEL 212-880-8800; 800-274-6111. FAX 212-880-8110. (Subscr. to: Box 5267, Boulder, CO 80321) Ed. Alexandra Penney. circ. 1,408,975. (also avail. in microform from UMI; reprint service avail. from UMI) **Indexed:** PMR. —UMI.

SENSATIONS. see *LITERATURE*

SENSUOUS LETTERS. see *MEN'S INTERESTS*

056.1   US
SER PADRES/BEING PARENTS. (Text in Spanish) 1990. bi-m. $1.95 per no. Gruner & Jahr U.S.A. Publishing, 685 Third Ave., New York, NY 10017. TEL 212-878-8700. Ed. Elvia Delgado z. circ. 325,000 (controlled). **Document type:** consumer publication.
    Description: For young Hispanic mothers and mothers-to-be. Addresses the day-to-day needs and concerns of Hispanic parents living in the United States.

305.412   PE
SERIE MUJER. 1982. m. Asociacion Amauta, Apto. Postal 982, Cusco, Peru. circ. 2,000.

051   US   ISSN 0037-301X
SEVENTEEN. 1944. m. $16.95 in U.S.; Canada $27; elsewhere $28. K-III Magazines, 200 Madison Ave., New York, NY 10016. TEL 212-447-4700. FAX 212-447-4778. (Subscr. to: Box 55195, Boulder, CO 80322. TEL 800-388-1749) Ed. Caroline Miller. adv.; illus. circ. 1,950,000. (microform; also avail. in microform from UMI; reprint service avail. from UMI) **Indexed:** Abr.R.G., Can.B.P.I., Hlth.Ind., Jun.High.Mag.Abstr., Mag.Ind., Media Rev.Dig., PMR, R.G., TOM. **Document type:** consumer publication.
    ●Also available on CD-ROM. Producer(s): University Microfilms International.
    —Faxon; SWETS; UMI; UnCover.
    Description: Covers fashion and beauty ideas, health and fitness, career topics, and personal relationships as they pertain to young women.

059.927   SU
AL-SHARQIYYAH ELLE. m. P.O. Box 6, Riyadh, Saudi Arabia. TELEX 40112. Ed. Samira M. Khashaggi.

305.412   UK   ISSN 0037-3370
AP4
SHE. 1955. m. £21.60. National Magazine Co. Ltd., 72 Broadwick St., London W1V 2BP, England. TEL 0171-439-5000. FAX 0171-439-5350. Ed. Linda Kelsey. adv.; bk.rev.; illus. circ. 281,109. **Document type:** consumer publication.

301.412   CC   ISSN 1002-7459
SHIDAI JIEMEI/MODERN SISTERS. (Text in Chinese) 1984. m. Y1.20 per no. Jilin Sheng Funu Lianhehui - Jilin Women's Federation, 49, Stalin Street, Changchun, Jilin 130051, People's Republic of China. TEL 802316. Ed. Wang Yujie. adv. contact: Wang Yuzhang. bk.rev. circ. 120,000. **Document type:** consumer publication.
    Description: Covers the contemporary life style of modern women.

SHORT FICTION BY WOMEN. see *LITERATURE*

305.415   AA
SHQIPTARJA E RE. m. $7.40. Union des Femmes d'Albanie, Tirana, Albania.

640   JA
SHUFU NO TOMO/FRIEND OF HOUSEWIVES. (Text in Japanese) 1917. m. 15000 Yen. Shufunotomo Co. Ltd., 2-9 Kanda Surugadai, Chiyoda-ku, Tokyo 101, Japan. Ed. Koichi Murata. circ. 400,000. **Document type:** consumer publication.

301.412   JA
SHUFU-TO-SEIKATSU. (Text in Japanese) m. Shufu-To-Seikatsu Sha Ltd., 5-7, Kyobashi 3-chome, Chuo-ku, Tokyo 104, Japan. TEL 03-3563-5131. FAX 03-3567-7893. circ. 368,999.

301.412   JA
SHUKAN JOSEI. (Text in Japanese) 1957. w. Shufu-To-Seikatsu Sha Ltd., 507, Kyobashi 3-chome, Chuo-ku, Tokyo 104, Japan. TEL 03-3563-5131. FAX 03-3567-7893. circ. 800,000.

059.9193   LV   ISSN 0868-4715
SIEVIETE. 1952. m. Elizabetes iela 45-47, 408 ist., 226010 Riga, Latvia. Ed. Monika Zile. circ. 202,000.

305.4   IT
▼**SILHOUETTE DONNA.** 1994. m. L.25000 (foreign L.62000). Tre D Editoriale s.r.l., Via B. Eustachi 3, 20129 Milan, Italy. TEL 39-2-29515858. FAX 39-2-29511070. Ed. Gabriele Zappa. adv.: color page L.31000000. **Document type:** consumer publication.

305.412   FI   ISSN 0359-0267
SINAMINA. 1983. s-m. FIM 395. Kolmiokirja Oy, P.O. Box 246, 90101 Oulu, Finland. FAX 358-81-537-0033. Ed. Paivi Kangasniemi. adv. circ. 24,000.
    Formerly: Tarina.

SING HEAVENLY MUSE!; women's poetry and prose. see *LITERATURE*

SINGLE PARENT NEWS. see *SOCIAL SERVICES AND WELFARE*

306.874 649.12   US   ISSN 1074-0775
SINGLEMOTHER; a support group in your hands. 1991. bi-m. $15 to non-members; mebers $12.97 (effective 1995). National Association of Single Mothers, Box 68, Midland, NC 28107. TEL 704-888-2337. FAX 704-888-1752. E-mail: solomother@aol.com. Ed. Andrea Engber. adv. contact: Andrea Engber. bk.rev.; illus. circ. 4,000. (back issues avail.) **Document type:** newsletter.
    Description: Publishes advice, self-help tips, and articles relating to single mothers, including legal concerns, parenting issues, commentary and resources for networking.

305.412   US   ISSN 0196-1853
PS508.W7
SINISTER WISDOM; a journal for the lesbian imagination in the arts and politics. 1976. q. $17 to individuals (foreign $22); institutions $30. Box 3252, Berkeley, CA 94703. Ed. Caryatis Cardea. adv.; bk.rev.; illus. circ. 5,000. (back issues avail.) **Indexed:** Alt.Press Ind., Stud.Wom.Abstr.

051   US
▼**SISTERS IN STYLE.** 1994. q. $9.97 (foreign $14.97); newsstand price: $2.95. Sterling - Macfadden Partnership, 35 Wilbur St., Lynbrook, NY 11563. TEL 516-593-1220. FAX 516-593-0065. Ed. Cynthia Horner; Pub. John Plunkett. adv.: B&W page $4000. circ. 215,000 (paid). **Document type:** consumer publication.

SISTERS UNITED. see *HOMOSEXUALITY*

SKINFLINT NEWS. see *HOME ECONOMICS*

SLIPPERY WHEN WET; bisexual, penetration-positive, queer. see *MEN'S INTERESTS*

SOBERING THOUGHTS. see *DRUG ABUSE AND ALCOHOLISM*

SOCIAL ANARCHISM; a journal of practice & theory. see *LITERARY AND POLITICAL REVIEWS*

331.4   UK
SOCIETY FOR PROMOTING TRAINING OF WOMEN. ANNUAL REPORT. 1859. a. £5. Society for Promoting Training of Women, The Rectory, Great Casterton, Stamford, Lincs PE9 4AP, England. TEL 01780-64036. circ. 50. **Document type:** corporate report.

SOLIDAIRES (PARIS). see *SOCIAL SERVICES AND WELFARE*

305.412   NQ
SOMOS. 1982. 3/yr. Asociacion de Mujeres Nicaraguenses "Luisa Amanda Espinoza", Apdo. Postal A-238, Managua, Nicaragua. TEL 71661. Ed. Patricia Lindo. bk.rev. circ. 30,000.

SONOMA COUNTY WOMEN'S VOICES. see *WOMEN'S STUDIES*

646.7   JA
SOPHIA (TOKYO, 1984). (Text in Japanese) 1984. m. Kodansha Ltd., 12-21 Otowa 2-chome, Bunkyo-ku, Tokyo 112, Japan. TEL 03-5395-3449. FAX 03-3945-4821. TELEX J34509 KODANSHA. Ed. Hiroshi Ohhira. circ. 150,000. **Document type:** consumer publication.
    Description: Life-style magazine for women.

305   US
SOPHIA CIRCLE. 1985. s-a. 8319 Fulham Court, Richmond, VA 23227-1712. TEL 804-266-7400. Ed. Donna Gorman. circ. 313.
    Description: Advocates disestablishing patriarchy.

SOROPTIMIST; of the Americas. see *SOCIAL SERVICES AND WELFARE*

SOUTH AFRICAN BRIDE TO BE: FIRST HOME. see *MATRIMONY*

SOUTHERN ASSOCIATION FOR WOMEN HISTORIANS. NEWSLETTER. see *HISTORY*

SPARTACIST CANADA. see *POLITICAL SCIENCE — International Relations*

SPES NOSTRA - OUR HOPE; a marian missionary magazine for youth and families. see *RELIGIONS AND THEOLOGY — Roman Catholic*

821 820 305.412   NZ   ISSN 0110-1145
SPIRAL.* 1976. irreg. NZ.$25 per no. Women's Gallery Inc., P.O. Box 9600, Wellington, New Zealand. TEL 04-4710601. FAX 04-4710489. (Dist. by: Daphne Brasell Associates, P.O. Box 12214, Toradon, Wellington, New Zealand) Ed.Bd. adv.; bk.rev. circ. 1,500. (back issues avail.)

301.412   US
SPOKANE WOMAN. (Supplement to: Journal of Business (Spokane)) 1989. 3/yr. Northwest Business Press, Inc., 112 E. First St., Spokane, WA 99202. TEL 509-456-0203. Ed. Deborah Wilbert. adv. circ. 20,000. **Document type:** consumer publication.
    Description: For women in their mid-20s to mid-50s in the Spokane area.

SPORTSTALK; the Women's Sports Foundation newsletter for young female athletes. see *SPORTS AND GAMES*

301.412   CE
SRI. (Text in English) 1963. m. 5 Gunasena Mawatha, Colombo 12, Sri Lanka. TEL 1-23864.

STEPFAMILIES & BEYOND; America's first independent newsletter about remarriage for stepparents and professionals. see *CHILDREN AND YOUTH — About*

646.4   GW
STRICK UND HAEKELMODE. 1975. m. DM.2.80 per no. Sonnenverlag GmbH, Lichtentaler Allee 10, 76530 Baden-Baden, Germany. (Subscr. to: Postfach 720, 76484 Baden-Baden, Germany) Ed. G. Maenner. adv.

STUDIES IN WOMEN AND RELIGION. see *RELIGIONS AND THEOLOGY*

305.412   EI   ISSN 1012-1935
HQ1101
SUPPLEMENTS TO WOMEN OF EUROPE. 1977. irreg. free. Commission of the European Communities, Directorate General of Information, Culture, Communication, Audiovisual, 200 rue de la Loi, B-1049 Brussels, Belgium. TEL 32-2-299-94-11. FAX 32-2-299-92-83. TELEX COMEU B 21877. bk.rev.; index. circ. 30,000. **Indexed:** EC Ind., IIS. —BLDSC (9343.288000).
    Supersedes (in 1992): Women of Europe (ISSN 0258-6169)

058.7   SW   ISSN 0039-6486
SVENSK DAMTIDNING.* 1889. w. SEK 720 (effective 1991); newsstand price: SEK 20. Allers Foerlag AB, S-251 85 Helsingborg, Sweden. (Subscr. to: P.O. Box 21083, 100 31 Stockholm) Ed. Karin Lenmor; Pub. Karin Lenmor. adv.: page SEK 2600; trim 210 x 282. bk.rev.; film rev.; play rev.; charts; illus. circ. 136,600. cols./p.: 4; pp./issue: 85.

SWINGER'S TODAY. see *MEN'S INTERESTS*

SWINGERS UPDATE. see *MEN'S INTERESTS*

SWINGING TIMES. see *MEN'S INTERESTS*

AL-TAHIRAH. see *RELIGIONS AND THEOLOGY — Islamic*

TAS TOTS. see *CHILDREN AND YOUTH — For*

TASTE OF LATEX; entertainment for the sexually disenfranchised. see *LITERATURE*

305.4 028.5   US   ISSN 1074-7974
TEEN VOICES. 1991. q. $20; newsstand price: $2. Women Express, Inc., Box 6329, JFK, Boston, MA 02114. TEL 617-262-2434. Ed. Shannon Berning; Pub. Alison Amoroso. adv. contact: Alison Amoroso. bk.rev.; music rev. circ. 24,000. (back issues avail.) **Document type:** consumer publication.
  Description: Seeks to raise the self-esteem of teenage girls and women by providing a healthy alternative to fashion magazines and discussing the issues they feel are important.

TENPERCENT; UCLA's lesbian, gay, and bisexual newsmagazine. see *HOMOSEXUALITY*

305.4   FI   ISSN 0789-8789
TERVE ELAMA. (Oriented towards women's interests.) 1990. 8/yr. FIM 215. Helsinki Media Company OY, P.O. Box 16, SF-00381 Helsinki, Finland. TEL 358-0-120-5911. FAX 358-0-120-5959. Ed. Sinikka Raivio. circ. 17,230.

301.4   TG
TEV FEMA. (Text in Kabiye) 1977. m. Ministry of Social and Women's Affairs, 19 ave. de la Nouvelle Marche, B.P. 1247, Lome, Togo. TEL 21-37-18. circ. 3,000.

323   US
TEXAS WOMAN'S NEWS. 1984. m. $13. T W N Communications Inc., HCR 5, Box 574-46, Kerrville, TX 78028-9025. Ed. Lorraine Bruck. adv.; bk.rev.; play rev. circ. 50,000. (tabloid format; back issues avail.)

TEXTURES; Hadassah National Jewish studies bulletin. see *ETHNIC INTERESTS*

052   SA
THANDI. 1985. m. R.30.78 (overseas R.59.60) (effective 1993). Republican Press (Pty) Ltd., P.O. Box 32083, Mobeni 4060, South Africa. TEL 27-31-422041. FAX 27-31-921231. Ed. Lorna Nisbet. circ. 55,000. **Document type:** consumer publication.
  Description: Lifestyle and inspirational features for young black women.

301.412   CE
THARUNEE. (Text in Sinhala) 1969. w. Lake House, D.R. Wijewardene Mawatha, P.O. Box 248, Colombo 10, Sri Lanka. TEL 1-21181. Ed. Sumana Sapramadu. circ. 95,000.

THESMOPHORIA; voice of the new women's religion. see *RELIGIONS AND THEOLOGY — Other Denominations And Sects*

THIRD WORLD WOMAN'S GAY-ZETTE. see *HOMOSEXUALITY*

TIDEWATER PARENT. see *CHILDREN AND YOUTH — About*

TINA. see *HOME ECONOMICS*

301.412   US
TODAY'S ARIZONA WOMAN (SCOTTSDALE). 1986. m. $18. Publishers West, Inc., 4425 N. Saddlebag Trail, Scottsdale, AZ 85251-3419. TEL 602-945-5000. FAX 602-941-5196. Ed. Becky Kistler; Pub. Eleanore Klein. adv. contact: Deborah Gatzke. bk.rev.; circ. 50,000. **Document type:** newspaper, consumer publication.

301.412   US
TODAY'S ARIZONA WOMAN (TUCSON EDITION). m. Publishers West, Inc. (Tucson), 2840 N. Country Club, Ste. 102, Tucson, AZ 85716. TEL 602-795-6202. FAX 602-795-6305. Ed. Yolanda Montealegre. circ. 20,000 (controlled). **Document type:** newspaper, consumer publication.

TODAY'S ARIZONA WOMAN BUSINESS DIRECTORY; a directory of women's businesses and businesses interested in reaching the women's market. see *BUSINESS AND ECONOMICS — Trade And Industrial Directories*

301.412   US   ISSN 1071-3786
TODAY'S CHICAGO WOMAN. 1982. m. $12. Leigh Communications, Inc., 233 E. Ontario St., Ste. 1300, Chicago, IL 60611-3214. TEL 312-951-7600. FAX 312-951-9083. Ed. Sherren Leigh. adv. contact: Ann Rex. bk.rev. circ. 160,000. **Document type:** consumer publication.
  Description: Contains personality profiles, career strategies, business trends, health, finance, fitness, fashion and activities for professional women.

200 305.412   US   ISSN 0163-1799
BV4527
TODAY'S CHRISTIAN WOMAN. 1978. bi-m. $17.95. Christianity Today, Inc., 465 Gunderson Dr., Carol Stream, IL 60188. TEL 708-260-6200. FAX 708-260-0114. E-mail: tcwedit@aol.com. (Subscr. to: CDS, Box 11618, Des Moines, IA 50340. TEL 800-365-9484) Ed. Ramona Cramer Tucker. adv. contact: Linda Schambach. circ. 355,000. **Indexed:** CCR. **Document type:** consumer publication.
—UMI.
  Description: Encourages, inspires and enables Christian women to live out biblica values in their relationships.

TODAY'S INSURANCE WOMAN. see *INSURANCE*

051   US
TODAY'S LIFESTYLES. 1992. bi-m. Prestige Publications, Inc., 4151 Knob Dr., St. Paul, MN 55122. TEL 612-452-0571. FAX 612-454-5791. Ed. Carla Waldemar; Pub. Russ Moore. adv. contact: Don Beeson. circ. 160,000 (paid). **Document type:** consumer publication.

051   US   ISSN 1054-9587
TODAY'S WOMAN. 1991. m. G C R Publishing Group, Inc., 1700 Broadway, 34th Fl., New York, NY 10019. TEL 212-541-7100. adv. contact: Laura Lapatin.
  Description: Covers women's issues and concerns, for a Canadian audience.

TODAY'S WOMAN IN BUSINESS. see *BUSINESS AND ECONOMICS*

TOGETHER (LONDON, 1992). see *LABOR UNIONS*

TOP SANTE; health & beauty. see *WOMEN'S HEALTH*

052 330   UK
TOP WOMAN. bi-m. £10 (effective 1995); newsstand price: £1.95. Raconteur Publications Ltd., 44 Gray's Inn Rd., London WC1X 8LR, England. TEL 0171-242-3595. FAX 0171-242-3598. Ed. Liz Hodgkinson; Pub. John Jenkins. adv. contact: Mel Gregg. bk.rev.; circ. 75,000 (paid). **Document type:** consumer publication.
  Former titles: Career Woman (ISSN 1356-9376); Business Woman.

TOPICAL WOMAN. see *PHILATELY*

331.4 331   US
TRADE TRAX. 1983. bi-m. $15. Tradeswomen, Inc., Box 2622, Berkeley, CA 94702. TEL 510-649-6260. circ. 1,000. (back issues avail.) **Document type:** trade publication.

331.4   US   ISSN 0739-344X
TRADESWOMEN; for women in blue-collar work. 1981. q. $25. Tradeswomen, Inc., Box 2622, Berkeley, CA 94702. TEL 510-649-6260. Eds. J.S. Johnson, R. Murphy. adv.; bk.rev.; circ. 1,500. (back issues avail.) **Indexed:** Alt.Press Ind. **Document type:** trade publication.

305.412   UK   ISSN 0041-2244
TREFOIL. 1955. q. £5. Trefoil Guild, 17 Buckingham Palace Rd., London SW1W 0PT, England. TEL 071-834-6242. FAX 071-828-8317. Ed. Myra Street. adv.; bk.rev.; illus. circ. 22,000. **Document type:** consumer publication.

305.412   US   ISSN 0738-9779
THE TRIBUNE. Spanish edition: Tribuna (ISSN 0748-4607); French edition: Tribune (ISSN 0748-4593) (Text in English) 1976. 4/yr. $17 in N. America, Canada and Europe. International Women's Tribune Centre, 777 United Nations Plaza, New York, NY 10017. TEL 212-687-8633. FAX 212-661-2704. Ed. Anne S. Walker. circ. 20,000 (10,000 Eng. ed.; 7,000 Sp. ed.; 3,000 Fr. ed.). (back issues avail.) **Indexed:** HR Rep. **Document type:** newsletter.
  Formerly: International Women's Tribune Center. Newsletter.

TRIVIA; a journal of ideas. see *LITERARY AND POLITICAL REVIEWS*

301.432 910.3   SA   ISSN 0256-4696
TRUE LOVE AND FAMILY. (Text in English) 1970. m. R.27.16 (foreign R.32.76). Drum Publications, National Magazines (Subsidiary of: National Media Limited), 2nd Fl., Eaton Place, Norwich Park, Sandton 2199, South Africa. TEL 011-783-7227. FAX 011-783-8822. (Subscr. to: P.O. Box 1802, Cape Town 8000, South Africa) Ed. Barney Cohen. adv.; bk.rev. circ. 96,000. **Document type:** consumer publication.
  Description: For black women. Features news and views on fashion, beauty, and parenting.

TRUE ROMANCE. see *LITERATURE — Adventure And Romance*

301.412   US   ISSN 0746-9691
TU INTERNACIONAL. (Editions avail. for: Ecuador, Central America, Chile, Colombia, Mexico, Peru, Puerto Rico, U.S., Venezuela) (Text in Spanish) 1980. m. $22.50. Editorial America, S.A., 6355 N.W. 36th St., Virginia Gardens, FL 33166. TEL 305-871-6400. (Subscr. to: Box 10950, Des Moines, IA 50347-0950) Ed. Irene Carol. adv.; film rev.; music rev.; illus. circ. 190,000.
  Description: For teens; covers health, beauty, fashion, relationships, entertainment and psychology.

TUCSON PARENT. see *CHILDREN AND YOUTH — About*

TWINS. see *CHILDREN AND YOUTH — About*

TWOJ STYL. see *CLOTHING TRADE — Fashions*

649   PL
TWOJE DZIECKO. 1951. m. Res Publica Press International Ltd., Ul. Grazyny 13, 02-548 Warsaw, Poland. TEL 48-22-462602. FAX 48-22-454216. Ed. Ewa Szperlich. circ. 150,000.
  Description: Women's magazine concerning children's affairs.

301.412   UG
UGANDA ASSOCIATION OF UNIVERSITY WOMEN. BULLETIN. 1960; N.S. 1987. a. $5. Uganda Association of University Women, c/o Makerere University Library, P.O. Box 7062, Kampala, Uganda. TELEX 62104 MAKU. Ed. Maria G. Musoke. adv.; bk.rev. **Document type:** bulletin.
  Description: Includes articles on and by women, reports from committees, courses, seminars and conferences, research projects by association members, announcements and other items of interest to women in development.

ULSTER BRIDE. see *MATRIMONY*

UNCENSORED AMATEUR SWINGER. see *MEN'S INTERESTS*

305.4   US
UNFORGETTABLE FIRE; a newsletter by, for, and about women's voices. 1991. s-a. $10. Jordan O'Neill, Ed. & Pub., 530 Riverside Dr., No. 5G, New York, NY 10027. adv.: page $80; 9 1/2 x 7 1/4; adv. contact: Jordan O'Neill. bk.rev. circ. 4,000. (back issues avail.) **Document type:** newsletter.
  Description: Publishes poems, short stories and essays on issues affecting women from a feminist perspective.
  Refereed Serial

UNIQUE HAIR & BEAUTY. see *BEAUTY CULTURE*

UNTER UNS; Zeitschrift fuer Frauen und Maedchen. see *HANDICAPPED — Visually Impaired*

WOMEN'S INTERESTS

301.412   GW   ISSN 0939-5474
UNTERSCHIEDE. 1991. q. DM.49.60. (Neue Bildungswege fuer Frauen e.V.) Kleine Verlag GmbH, Postfach 4822, 4800 Bielefeld 1, Germany. TEL 0521-15811. adv. circ. 3,000.

URODA. see *BEAUTY CULTURE*

305.412   FI   ISSN 0500-8476
UUSI NAINEN. 1945. 10/yr. FIM 280. Palmikot ry, P.O. Box 314C27, FIN-33901 Tampere, Finland. TEL 931-2662148. FAX 931-2662148. Ed. Anneli Kanto. adv.; bk.rev. circ. 5,000. **Document type:** consumer publication.

V B MAGAZINE; voor vrouwen in business. see *BUSINESS AND ECONOMICS*

301.412   US
VALLEY WOMEN'S VOICE; a chronicle of feminist thought and action. 1979. m. $12. University of Massachusetts, 321 Student Union, Amherst, MA 01003. TEL 413-545-2436. Ed.Bd. adv. contact: Andrea Alexander. bk.rev.; film rev.; play rev.; circ. 6,000 (paid). (tabloid format; back issues avail.) **Document type:** newspaper.
Description: Contains radical feminist news and analysis plus fiction, poetry, graphic and photographic art; also includes an abuse survivor column.
Refereed Serial

301.412   US   ISSN 0505-0146
VANIDADES CONTINENTAL. (Editions avail. for Central America, Chile, Colombia, Dominican Republic, Ecuador, Peru, Puerto Rico, U.S., Venezuela) (Text in Spanish) 1961. bi-w. $46. Editorial America, S.A., Vanidades Continental Bldg., 6355 N.W. 36th St., Virginia Gardens, FL 33166. TEL 305-871-6400. FAX 305-871-8769. Ed. Sara Castany. adv. circ. 434,000.
—UMI.

301.412   MX   ISSN 0188-0640
VANIDADES DE MEXICO. 1960. fortn. Editorial Samra, S.A. de C.V., Lucio Blanco 435, Azcapotzalco, 02400, Mexico DF, Mexico. Dir. Sara Barcelo de Castany. adv.

301.412   II
VANITA JYOTI. (Text in Telugu) 1978. m. Rs.54. Labbipet, Vijayawada 520 010, India. TEL 866-474532. Ed. J. Satyanarayana. circ. 30,000.
Description: Provides information regarding women's problems and solutions. Also includes interviews of woman doctors, lawyers, ministers, social workers and world-famous women.

301.412   II
VANITHA. (Text in Malayalam) 1975. fortn. Rs.138; newsstand price: Rs.4.5. M.M. Publications Pvt. Ltd., P.O. Box 226, Erayilkadavu, Kottayam 686 001, India. TEL 481-563721. FAX 481-562479. TELEX 0888-201 MNR IN. Ed. Mrs. K.M. Mathew; Pub. K.I. George. adv.: B&W page Rs.18000; 240 x 175. circ. 317,748.

301.412   CE
VANITHA VITTI. (Text in Sinhala) 1957. m. Wijeya Publications, 8 Humiptiya Cross Rd., Colombo 2, Sri Lanka. TEL 1-435454. Ed. Anula De Silva. circ. 50,000.

301.412   VE
VARIEDADES. w. Edif. Bloque Dearmas, Final Avda. San Martin cruce con Mona. La Paz, Caracas 1020, Venezuela. TEL 2-572-0322. Ed. Armando de Armas. circ. 58,230.

THE VEGAS CONNECTION. see *MEN'S INTERESTS*

301.412   US
VENUS. 1993. bi-m. Prestige Publications, Inc., 4151 Knob Dr., St. Paul, MN 55122-1876. TEL 612-452-0571. FAX 612-454-5791. Ed. Carla Waldemar; Pub. Russ Moore. circ. 100,000. **Document type:** consumer publication.

301.412   IT   ISSN 1120-8198
VERA. 1990. m. L.3300 per no. Gruner und Jahr - Mondadori S.p.A., Corso Monforte 54, 20122 Milan, Italy. TEL 39-2-76009645. TELEX 76013439. Ed. Alida Militello. adv.: page L.39800000. circ. 396,389. **Document type:** consumer publication.

VIDEO RESERVED COLLECTION. see *COMMUNICATIONS — Video*

746.96   BE
VIE FEMININE. 1920. m. (Mouvement Chretien d'Action Culturelle et Sociale) Publicarto N.V., Langestraat 170, B-1150 Brussels, Belgium. TEL 32-2-7790000. FAX 32-2-7791616. circ. 81,291.
Description: Forum for members of the Mouvement Chretien d'Action Culturelle et Sociale.

305.412   MF
VIRGINIE; le magazine de la femme Mauricienne. (Text in French) bi-m. Ave. des Azalees, Quatre Bornes, Mauritius.

305.413 200   US   ISSN 0164-7288
BJ1610
VIRTUE.* 1977. 6/yr. $16.95 (effective Jan. 1992). (Virtue Ministries, Inc.) Good Family Magazine, Box 36630, Colorado Springs, CO 80936-3663. TEL 503-549-8261. FAX 503-549-0153. Ed. Marlee Alex. adv.: B&W page $4835, color page $5800; trim 8 1/8 x 10 7/8. bk.rev. circ. 150,000.
Description: For Christian homemakers. Offers articles on creative home management, self-improvement, spiritual enrichment and family relationships.

053.931   NE   ISSN 0165-4462
VIVA. 1925. w. fl.124.80. Geillustreerde Pers B.V., Haaksbergweg 75, 1101 BR Amsterdam, Netherlands. TEL 31-20-4300300. FAX 31-20-4300316. Ed. Tineke Verhoeven. adv.; bk.rev.; film rev.; play rev.; illus.; tr.lit.; index. circ. 135,000. **Document type:** consumer publication.
Formerly (until 1972): Eva (ISSN 0014-3294)

305.412   PE
VIVA (LIMA). 1984. q. $30 in Latin America; elsewhere $45 (typically set in Mar.). Centro de la Mujer Peruana "Flora Tristan", Parque Hernan Velarde, 42, Lima 14, Peru. TEL 51-14-330694. FAX 51-14-339060. Ed. Mariella Sala. adv. circ. 2,000.

VIVE LA DIFFERENCE. see *SOCIOLOGY*

646.7   JA
VIVI. (Text in Japanese) 1983. m. Kodansha Ltd., 12-21 Otowa 2-chome, Bunkyo-ku, Tokyo 112, Japan. TEL 03-5395-3448. FAX 03-3945-4821. TELEX J34509 KODANSHA. Ed. Masahiro Senda. circ. 550,000. **Document type:** consumer publication.
Description: Fashion and variety magazine for young women.

054.1   FR   ISSN 0750-3628
AP20
VOGUE. 1921. m. 350 F.($250) (in N. America 746 F.). Conde Nast S.A., 73 rue de Vaugirard, 75006 Paris, France. TEL 40-62-00-11. FAX 40-62-02-55. TELEX 260 752. (Subscr. to: 60732 Sainte-Genevieve Cedex, France. TEL 16-44-89-50-00; Subscr. in U.S. to: International Subscriptions Inc., 30 Montgomery St., 7th Fl., Jersey City, NJ 07302. TEL 201-451-9420) Ed. Gardner Bellanger. adv. circ. 80,020. **Indexed:** Consum.Ind., DAAI. **Document type:** consumer publication.
—SWETS.

VOICE OF WORKING WOMEN. see *BUSINESS AND ECONOMICS*

305.4 360   TH
VOICES OF THAI WOMEN. (Text in English) 2/yr. $10. Foundation for Women, P.O. Box 47, Bangkok 10700, Thailand. TEL 66-2-433-5149. FAX 66-2-434-6774. **Document type:** newsletter.
Description: Provides information and counselling for women victims of sexual violence.

301.412   FR   ISSN 0986-7481
VOICI. w. 360 F. (foreign 575 F.) Prisma Presse, 6 rue Daru, 75008 Paris, France. TEL 44-15-30-00. FAX 47-64-10-42. Ed. Patrick Marescaux. adv. circ. 797,000.
Description: Covers women's entertainment, leisure and news, as well as fitness, cooking, fashion and beauty.

301.412   AG
VOSOTRAS. (Includes monthly supplements: Labores, Modas) 1935. w. Avda. Leandro N. Alem 896, 3o, 1001 Buenos Aires, Argentina. TEL 32-6010. Dir. Abel Zanotto. circ. 33,000.

301.412   CN   ISSN 0842-0963
VOUS. 10/yr. Quebecor Inc., 7 Bates Chemin, Outrement, PQ H2V 1A6, Canada. TEL 514-270-1100. FAX 514-270-7079. circ. 50,000.

746.96   BE
VROUW EN WERELD. 1920. m. Publicarto N.V., Langestraat 170, B-1150 Brussels, Belgium. TEL 32-2-7790000. FAX 32-2-7791616. adv.; bk.rev. circ. 321,923.
Description: Addressed to members of the K.A.V. women's organization.

200   NE
VROUW EN WOORD; informatie en uitwisseling rond vrouw, geloot en samenleving. 1980. 6/yr. fl.39. Publivorm, P.O. Box 29, 2700 AA Zoetermeer, Netherlands. TEL 31-79-615481. FAX 31-79-615489. Ed. Joanne Seldenrath. bk.rev. **Document type:** bulletin.
Description: Covers issues relating to women and faith.

305.412   NE
VROUWENSTUDIES UTRECHT.* q. fl.2.50 per no. Studium Generale, Gen. Foulkesweg 1, 6703 BG Wageningen, Netherlands. bk.rev. circ. 500.

301.42   US
W A M M NEWSLETTER. 1982. m. $35 to individuals; families $40. Women Against Military Madness, 310 E. 38th St., Ste. 225, Minneapolis, MN 55409-1300. TEL 612-827-5364. FAX 612-827-6433. Eds. Juliana Pegues, Jackie Starbird. adv. circ. 2,500. (back issues avail.) **Document type:** newsletter.

333.7   US
W A N D BULLETIN. 1982. q. $35. Women's Action for Nuclear Disarmament, Box B, Arlington, MA 02174-0001. TEL 617-643-6740. Ed. Margaret Covert. bk.rev.; charts; illus. circ. 20,000. (tabloid format) **Document type:** bulletin.
Description: Attempts to educate women in political action so that they can work to eliminate weapons of mass destruction and redirect military spending to human and environmental needs.

W B. see *SPORTS AND GAMES — Ball Games*

W C P S QUARTERLY. (Women's Caucus for Political Science) see *POLITICAL SCIENCE*

W F S QUARTERLY. (Women in the Fire Service) see *FIRE PREVENTION*

W I D BULLETIN. (Women and International Development Program) see *POLITICAL SCIENCE — Civil Rights*

W I D FORUM. (Women and International Development Program) see *POLITICAL SCIENCE — Civil Rights*

W I S E WOMEN'S NEWS. (Women's International Studies Europe) see *WOMEN'S STUDIES*

301.412 940   IS   ISSN 0042-9732
W I Z O REVIEW. Spanish edition: Revista W I Z O. (Editions in English, German and Spanish) 1947. q. $5. Women's International Zionist Organization, 38 David Hamelech Blvd., Tel Aviv 64237, Israel. TEL 972-3-5421805. FAX 972-3-6958267. Ed. Hillel Schenker. adv.; bk.rev.; illus. circ. 20,000.

W L D F NEWS. (Women's Legal Defense Fund) see *LAW*

W M A 'NOUNCEMENTS. (Women Marine Association) see *MILITARY*

W O W MAGAZINE. (Women on Wheels) see *SPORTS AND GAMES — Bicycles And Motorcycles*

W R E E - VIEW OF WOMEN. (Women for Racial and Economic Equality) see *POLITICAL SCIENCE — Civil Rights*

WOMEN'S INTERESTS

301.412 323.4 US
WASHINGTON EQUAL TIMES. 1969. m. $25 to non-members. (National Organization for Women, Washington D.C. Metropolitan Chapter) Washington Equal Times, Box 7279, Washington, DC 20044. TEL 202-234-4558. Ed. Paula McKenzie. adv.; bk.rev. circ. 12,000. **Document type:** newsletter.
  Formerly: Vocal Majority.

305.4 363.49
155.67 US
WE ARE VISIBLE; a magazine for ageful lesbians and all women. 1979. 3/yr. $12. Box 1494, Mendocino, CA 95460. TEL 707-964-2756. Ed. Vashte Doublex. adv.; bk.rev. circ. 400. (also avail. in looseleaf format; back issues avail.) **Document type:** newsletter.
  Description: Raises women's issues on aging and ageism to network and inform, lists resources, and publishes the work of the older women and lesbians.

WEIGHT WATCHERS MAGAZINE. see *PHYSICAL FITNESS AND HYGIENE*

155 361.41 US ISSN 8750-9563
WELCOME HOME; a publication for support and encouragement as you nurture your children. 1984. m. $18 in U.S.; Canada $21; elsewhere $28. Mothers-at-Home, Inc., 8310A Old Courthouse Rd., Vienna, VA 22182. TEL 703-827-5903. FAX 703-790-8587. Eds. Laura Jones, Cheryl Hughes. bk.rev.; illus. circ. 15,000. **Document type:** newsletter.

053.1 GW
WELT DER FRAU. bi-m. Atlantikpresse Verlagsgesellschaft mbH, Im Neudeck 1, 67346 Speyer, Germany. TEL 06232-310266. FAX 06232-310273. Ed. Ulrich Metzner; Pub. Marie-Luise Rose. adv. contact: Klaus Fortmann. circ. 180,000.

305.412 US
WHAT SHE WANTS; Cleveland's only women's newspaper. 1973. m. Box 18465, Cleveland Heights, OH 44118. Ed.Bd. adv. circ. 1,000. **Document type:** newspaper.

WHOM NEWSLETTER. see *HISTORY*

301.412 US
WICHITA WOMEN MAGAZINE; to ease, enrich & celebrate the lives of busy women. 1986. m. $18. Watson Wordsmiths, Inc, Box 781001, Wichita, KS 67278-1001. TEL 316-684-3620. Ed. Kate Watson. adv.; film rev.; illus. circ. 5,000. (tabloid format; back issues avail.) **Document type:** consumer publication.

WIENERIN. see *GENERAL INTEREST PERIODICALS — Austria*

323.4 GW ISSN 0178-6083
WIR FRAUEN. 1982. q. DM.16 (foreign DM.25). Wir Frauen Verein zur Foerderung von Frauenpublizistik, Rochusstr. 43, 40479 Duesseldorf, Germany. TEL 0211-4912078. Ed. Florence Herve. adv.; bk.rev. circ. 4,000.

301.412 US
WISCONSIN WOMAN.* 1987. m. $14.95. E C K Lectic, Inc, Box 10, Menomonee Falls, WI 53052-0010. TEL 414-273-1234. adv.; bk.rev. circ. 25,000.
  Description: Covers business, law, finance, health, parenting, fashion and travel for professional women.

WISCONSIN WOMEN'S LAW JOURNAL. see *LAW*

305.412 133.4 US ISSN 0883-119X
THE WISE WOMAN. 1980. q. $15. Ann Forfreedom, Ed. & Pub., 2441 Cordova St., Oakland, CA 94602. TEL 510-536-3174. adv.; bk.rev.; illus. (also avail. in microform from UMI)
  Description: Focuses on feminist issues, Goddess lore, feminist spirituality, and feminist witchcraft. Includes history, news, analysis, art, poetry, interviews and original research about witch-hunts, women's heritage and women today.

WISHING WELL. see *HOMOSEXUALITY*

646.7 JA
WITH. 1981. m. Kodansha Ltd., 12-21 Otowa 2-chome, Bunkyo-ku, Tokyo 112, Japan. TEL 03-5395-3447. FAX 03-3945-4821. TELEX J34509 KODANSHA. Ed. Akiko Watarai. circ. 830,000. **Document type:** consumer publication.
  Description: Fashion and variety magazine for women.

052 UK ISSN 0043-7220
WOMAN. 1937. w. newsstand price: £0.50. I P C Magazines, Weeklies Group (Subsidiary of: Reed Elsevier group), King's Reach Tower, Stamford St., London SE1 9LS, England. TEL 071-261-6452. FAX 0444-440619. TELEX 892084 REEDBP G. (Dist. by: Quadrant Subscription Services, Oakfield House, Perrymount Rd., Haywards Heath, W. Sussex RH16 3DH, England. TEL 0444-440421) Ed. David Durman. adv. contact: Ian Scott. bk.rev.; film rev.; illus. circ. 928,170. **Document type:** consumer publication.
  —CCC.
  Description: Women's fashion magazine for the 20-40 age group with an emphasis on celebrities, as well as features and advice.

301.412 CH ISSN 1017-4435
THE WOMAN. (Text in Chinese) 1968. m. 3 Lane 52, Nanking E. Rd., Sec.4, Taipei, Taiwan, Republic of China. TEL 02-7524425. FAX 02-7814308. TELEX 11887. Ed. C.Y. Chang. circ. 80,000.

301.412 CH
WOMAN A B C MAGAZINE. (Text in Chinese) 1982. m. Apollo Bldg., 13th Floor, 218-4 Chung Hsiao E. Rd., Sec.4, Taipei, Taiwan, Republic of China. TEL 02-7314625. FAX 02-7314328. circ. 72,000.

WOMAN ACTIVIST; an action bulletin for women's rights from the courthouse to the White House. see *POLITICAL SCIENCE — Civil Rights*

WOMAN ALIVE. see *RELIGIONS AND THEOLOGY*

331.4 US
WOMAN & CO..* 1985. m. $18. City Business - LaCrosse, Inc., Box 83, New Albin, IA 52160-0083. Ed. Vickie Lyons. adv.; bk.rev. circ. 12,000.

331.4 UK
WOMAN AND HOME. 1926. m. I P C Magazines, Southbank Publishing Group (Subsidiary of: Reed Elsevier group), King's Reach Tower, Stamford St., London SE1 9LS, England. TEL 071-261-5423. FAX 0444-440619. TELEX 892084 REEDBP G. (Dist. by: Quadrant Subscription Services, Oakfield House, Perrymount Rd., Haywards Heath, W. Sussex RH16 3DH, England. TEL 0444-440421) Ed. Sue Dobson. adv. contact: Veronica Dower. circ. 600,100. **Document type:** consumer publication.
  —CCC.
  Incorporates (1928-1971): My Home and Family (ISSN 0027-5409)

THE WOMAN ENGINEER. see *ENGINEERING*

WOMAN ENGINEER. see *ENGINEERING*

331.4 US
WOMAN ENTREPRENEUR.* m. American Woman's Economic Development Corp., 71 Vanderbilt Ave., 3rd Fl., New York, NY 10169-0005.

301.412 US ISSN 0195-9743
WOMAN IN HISTORY. 1980. irreg., vol.169, 1993. price varies. Monument Press (Las Colinas), Box 160361, Las Colinas, TX 75016-9998. TEL 214-686-5332. (Co-publishers: Texas Independent Press; Liberal Press; Tanglewulf Press; Liberal Arts Press) Ed. Belinda Buxjom. adv. contact: Rick Donovan. circ. 300. **Document type:** academic/scholarly publication.

WOMAN OF POWER; a magazine of feminism, spirituality, and politics. see *WOMEN'S STUDIES*

WOMAN POET. see *LITERATURE — Poetry*

WOMAN'S ART JOURNAL. see *ART*

305.412 AT ISSN 1321-9839
WOMAN'S DAY. 1948. w. Aus.$124.80. A C P Publishing Pty. Ltd., 54-58 Park St., Sydney, N.S.W. 2000, Australia. TEL 02-282-8158. FAX 02-267-4360. Ed. Bob Cameron; Pub. Richard Walsh. adv. contact: David Malone. circ. 1,026,357. **Document type:** consumer publication.
  Formerly: Woman's Day and Woman's World (ISSN 0159-1916); Which was formed by the merger of (1953-1980): Woman's Day (ISSN 0043-7328); Woman's World.
  Description: Entertainment, news and features magazine for women.

301.412 US
WOMAN'S DAY BRIDE'S HANDBOOK.* 1979. 2/yr. newsstand sales only. Hachette Magazines, Inc., 1633 Broadway, 45th Fl., New York, NY 10009. TEL 212-767-6000. Ed. Ellene Saunders. adv. circ. 400,000. (back issues avail.)

305.412 640 II ISSN 0971-1503
WOMAN'S ERA. (Text in English) 1973. fortn. Rs.800($26); newsstand price: Rs.12. Delhi Press Patra Prakashan Ltd., Delhi Press Bldg., E-3 Jhandewala Estate, New Delhi 110 055, India. TEL 011-526311. FAX 011-7525020. TELEX 31-63053 DEPR IN. Ed. Vishwa Nath. adv.; B&W page Rs.25000, color page Rs.50000; 198 x 265. illus. circ. 115,000.
  Description: Includes fiction, recipes, fashion notes, and other articles of interest to the women of India.

305.412 UK ISSN 0043-7344
AP4
WOMAN'S JOURNAL. 1927. m. £22($63.41) I P C Magazines, Southbank Publishing Group (Subsidiary of: Reed Elsevier group), King's Reach Tower, Stamford St., London SE1 9LS, England. TEL 071-261-6622. FAX 0444-440619. TELEX 892084 REEDBP G. (Dist. by: Quadrant Subscription Services, Oakfield House, Perrymount Rd., Haywards Heath, W. Sussex RH16 3DH, England. TEL 0444-440421) Ed. Deirdre Vine. adv. contact: Yvonne O'Sullivan. bk.rev.; illus. circ. 193,003. **Indexed:** DAAI. **Document type:** consumer publication.
  —CCC.

305.412 KE
WOMAN'S MIRROR. (Text in English) 1982. m. $230. New Press Publications, P.O. Box 8454, Nairobi, Kenya. Ed. Muli wa Kyendo. adv.; bk.rev. circ. 17,320.

051 US
WOMAN'S NATIONAL FARM & GARDEN MAGAZINE. 1914. 3/yr. membership. Woman's National Farm & Garden Association, Inc., 531 Clinton Ct., Findlay, OH 45840. TEL 419-422-5972. Ed. Freda Rose. bk.rev.; illus. circ. 5,500.
  Formerly: Woman's National Magazine (ISSN 0043-7352)

305.412 US
WOMAN'S NEWSPAPER;* for the professional woman. no.56, 1986. m. Woman's Newspaper of Princeton, Inc., 330 Milltown Rd., East Brunswick, NJ 08816-2267. TEL 609-890-0999. (And: Middlesex Publications, Inc., 575 Cranbury Rd., Ste. B5, E. Brunswick, NJ 08816) Ed. Karen Bookmam. adv.; bk.rev. circ. 30,000.
  Description: Reports on business news, health, home improvements, education, and fashion for the business and professional woman.

052 UK ISSN 0043-7360
WOMAN'S OWN. 1932. w. newsstand price: £0.48. I P C Magazines, Weeklies Group (Subsidiary of: Reed Elsevier group), King's Reach Tower, Stamford St., London SE1 9LS, England. TEL 071-261-5500. FAX 0444-440619. TELEX 892084 REEDBP G. (Dist. by: Quadrant Subscription Services, Oakfield House, Perrymount Rd., Haywards Heath, W. Sussex RH16 3DH, England. TEL 0444-440421) Ed. Keith McNeill. adv. contact: Suzanne Bull. illus. circ. 783,000. **Document type:** consumer publication.
  —CCC.
  Formerly: Woman's Own and Woman's Day.

051 US
WOMAN'S OWN. 1992. 8/yr. $10.79. Harris Publications, Inc., 1115 Broadway, 8th Fl., New York, NY 10010. TEL 212-807-7100. Ed. Sherry Amatenstein. adv.; illus. **Document type:** consumer publication.

WOMEN'S INTERESTS

052   UK
WOMAN'S OWN HOLIDAY READING. a. £0.90. I P C Magazines, Weeklies Group (Subsidiary of: Reed Elsevier group), King's Reach Tower, Stamford St., London SE1 9LS, England. TEL 071-261-5849. FAX 071-261-7851. TELEX 892084 REEDBP G. (Dist. by: Quadrant Subscription Services, Oakfield House, Perrymount Rd., Haywards Heath, W. Sussex RH16 3DH, England. TEL 0444-440421) circ. 250,000. **Document type:** consumer publication.

052   UK   ISSN 0043-7387
WOMAN'S REALM. 1958. w. I P C Magazines, Weeklies Group (Subsidiary of: Reed Elsevier group), King's Reach Tower, Stamford St., London SE1 9LS, England. TEL 071-261-6033. FAX 0444-440619. TELEX 892084 REEDBP G. (Dist. by: Quadrant Subscription Services, Oakfield House, Perrymount Rd., Haywards Heath, W. Sussex RH16 3DH, England. TEL 0444-440421) Ed. Sue Reid. adv. contact: Bill Gash. illus. circ. 483,000. **Document type:** consumer publication.
—CCC.
Description: Directed to the 30- to 55-year-old woman emphasizing features, advice and family issues.

WOMAN'S TOUCH; an inspirational magazine for women. see *RELIGIONS AND THEOLOGY — Other Denominations And Sects*

052   SA   ISSN 0256-0658
WOMAN'S VALUE. 1977. m. R.72.48. National Magazines (Subsidiary of: National Media Ltd.), P.O. Box 1802, Cape Town 8000, South Africa. TEL 27-21-4062100. FAX 27-21-4062936. Ed. Rieta Burgers. adv.; bk.rev.; film rev.; illus. circ. 156,333. **Document type:** consumer publication.

305.412   BB
WOMAN'S VOICE. 1977. m. $12. (National Organization of Women) Impact Productions Ltd., Bridgetown, Barbados, W.I. Ed. Jeannette Layne-Clarke. adv.; bk.rev.; illus. circ. 5,000.

301.412   US
WOMAN'S VOICE. 1990. m. $12. Shelby J. Hoon, Ed. & Pub., Box 454, Kent, OH 44240-0454. TEL 216-673-2990. FAX 216-673-6141. adv.; bk.rev.; circ. 20,000 (controlled). **Document type:** newspaper.

305.412   IE
WOMAN'S WAY. 1963. w. £35. Smurfit Publications, 126 Lower Baggot St., Dublin 2, Ireland. TEL 01-6608264. FAX 01-6619486. Ed. Celine Naughton. adv. contact: Ciaran Havelin. bk.rev.; illus. circ. 66,260. **Document type:** bulletin.
Formerly: Woman's Way Weekly (ISSN 0043-7409)

052   UK   ISSN 0043-7417
WOMAN'S WEEKLY. 1911. w. newsstand price: £0.45. I P C Magazines, Weeklies Group (Subsidiary of: Reed Elsevier group), King's Reach Tower, Stamford St., London SE1 9LS, England. TEL 071-261-6131. FAX 0444-440619. TELEX 892084 REEDBP G. (Dist. by: Quadrant Subscription Services, Oakfield House, Perrymount Rd., Haywards Heath, W. Sussex RH16 3DH, England. TEL 0444-440421) Ed. Iris Burton. adv. contact: Tracy Dollimore. illus. circ. 993,986. **Document type:** consumer publication.
—CCC.

305.412   US   ISSN 0272-961X
WOMAN'S WORLD; the woman's weekly. 1981. w. $78 (Canada $110); newsstand price: $1.19. Heinrich Bauer North America, Inc., 270 Sylvan Ave., Box 1649, Englewood Cliffs, NJ 07632. TEL 201-569-6699; 800-457-4443. FAX 201-569-3584. (Subscr. to: GLP International, 153 S. Dean St., Englewood, NJ 07631) Ed. Stephenie Saible. adv.; illus. circ. 1,200,000. (back issues avail.)

301.412   NR   ISSN 0331-4162
WOMAN'S WORLD. 1965. m. £N36. Daily Times of Nigeria Ltd., Publications Division, New Isheri Rd., Agidingbi - Ikeja, P.M.B. 21340, Lagos, Nigeria. TEL 900850-9. Ed. Toyin Johnson.

305.412   KO
WOMEN/YEO SUNG. (Text in English and Korean) 1964. m. free. Korean National Council of Women, 40-427 3ka Hangangro, Yongsanku, Seoul, S. Korea. Ed. Yo-Shik Lee.

051   US
WOMEN AGAINST RAPE NEWSLETTER. 1984. a. $15. Women Against Rape, Box 02084, Columbus, OH 43202. TEL 614-291-9751. adv.; bk.rev. circ. 5,000. **Document type:** newsletter.
Description: Provides rape prevention information to women in the Greater Columbus, Ohio area.

WOMEN & GOLF. see *SPORTS AND GAMES — Ball Games*

WOMEN & GUNS MAGAZINE. see *SPORTS AND GAMES*

WOMEN AND INTERNATIONAL DEVELOPMENT ANNUAL. see *BUSINESS AND ECONOMICS — International Development And Assistance*

WOMEN AND MATHEMATICS EDUCATION NEWSLETTER. see *MATHEMATICS*

WOMEN & PERFORMANCE; a journal of feminist theory. see *THEATER*

WOMEN AND POLITICS (WESTPORT). see *POLITICAL SCIENCE*

305.4   157.6   US
WOMEN & RECOVERY; surviving, thriving, & reclaiming your body, mind & spirit. q. $24. Need to Know Press, Box 161775, Cupertino, CA 95016. Ed. Margaret J. Cole.
Description: Empowers women in the journey toward physical, mental and spiritual wellness.

323.4   US
WOMEN AND REVOLUTION. 1971. irreg. $1 per no. (free with subscr. to Workers Vanguard). (Spartacist League, Commission for Work Among Women) Spartacist Publishing Co., Box 1377, New York, NY 10116. TEL 212-732-7861. Ed.Bd. illus. **Indexed:** Alt.Press Ind., Left Ind. (1982-). **Document type:** newspaper.

WOMEN AND WORK (NEWBURY PARK). see *BUSINESS AND ECONOMICS — Labor And Industrial Relations*

WOMEN AND WORK (WASHINGTON); news from the Department of Labor. see *BUSINESS AND ECONOMICS — Labor And Industrial Relations*

WOMEN ARTISTS NEWS. see *ART*

WOMEN DIRECTORS OF THE TOP 1000 CORPORATIONS. see *BUSINESS AND ECONOMICS — Management*

WOMEN ENTREPRENEURS IN SOUTH AFRICA. see *BUSINESS AND ECONOMICS — Small Business*

301.412   PH
WOMEN IN ACTION. (Text in English) 3/yr. $40. Isis International, P.O. Box 1837, Quezon City, Philippines. TEL 632-967297. FAX 632-92410652. **Indexed:** Alt.Press Ind., Mult.Ed.Abstr., Wom.Stud.Abstr.
Description: Offers news and information about groups, conferences, events and resources. Keeps readers up-to-date on the women's movement worldwide.

WOMEN IN BUSINESS. see *BUSINESS AND ECONOMICS*

301.2   US
WOMEN IN CULTURE AND SOCIETY. 1984. irreg., latest 1986. price varies. University of Chicago Press, 5801 S. Ellis Ave., Chicago, IL 60637. TEL 312-702-7899. (Subscr. to: 11030 Langley Ave., Chicago, IL 60628) Ed. Catharine R. Stimpson. *Refereed Serial*

305.4   II
WOMEN IN DEVELOPMENT. 1990. irreg., vol.2, 1991. price varies. Hindustan Publishing Corp., 4805-24, Bharat Ram Rd., Flat Nos. 1&2, 1st Fl., Daryaganj, New Delhi 110002. TEL 9-11-3254401. FAX 9-11-6863511. Ed. T. Scarlett Epstein. **Document type:** academic/scholarly publication, monographic series.

301.412 320   US
WOMEN IN GOVERNMENT.* q. $25. National Order of Women Legislators, Inc., c/o Joy N. Stone, 1101 30th St., NW, Washington, DC 20006. TEL 202-347-0044. Ed. Annie Rhodes.
Formerly: National Order of Women Legislators News & Views.
Description: Promotes and reports on participation of women in public affairs.

WOMEN IN HIGHER EDUCATION. see *EDUCATION — Higher Education*

WOMEN IN LIBRARIES. see *LIBRARY AND INFORMATION SCIENCES*

WOMEN IN MANAGEMENT REVIEW & ABSTRACTS. see *BUSINESS AND ECONOMICS — Management*

WOMEN IN MINING NATIONAL QUARTERLY. see *MINES AND MINING INDUSTRY*

305.412 350   US
WOMEN IN PUBLIC SERVICE BULLETIN. 1978. s-a. Center for Women in Government, SUNY - Albany, Draper Hall 302, 135 Western Ave., Albany, NY 12222. TEL 518-442-3900. FAX 518-442-3877. Ed. Judith R. Saidel. circ. 20,000. **Document type:** academic/scholarly publication.
Formerly (until 1991): News on Women in Government.

WOMEN IN THE ARTS. see *ART*

WOMEN IN THE ARTS NEWSLETTER. see *ART*

305.412   VN   ISSN 0512-1825
HQ1750.5
WOMEN OF VIETNAM. (Editions in English and French) 1973. q. $8. Vietnam Women's Union, 39 Hang Chuoi Str., Hanoi, Socialist Republic of Vietnam. TEL 53143. Ed. Duong Thi Duyen. bk.rev.; illus. —UnCover.

301.412   II
WOMEN ON THE MARCH.* (Text in English) vol.16, 1972. m. All India Congress Committee, Women's Department, Dept. 7, Jantar Mantar Rd., Connaught Circus, New Delhi 1, India. Ed. Mukul Banerjee. adv.; illus.

052   UK   ISSN 0966-5390
WOMEN ON TOP. 1992. m. £62. Portland Publishing Ltd., 1 Tyburn Ln., Harrow-on-the-Hill, Middlesex HA1 3AG, England. TEL 071-538-8969. FAX 071-538-1170. Ed. Sharon Longford. adv.: color page £3000; adv. contact: Chris Payne. circ. 100,000. **Document type:** consumer publication.

WOMEN ON WINE CHAPTER FLYER. see *BEVERAGES*

WOMEN ON WINE NATIONAL NEWS. see *BEVERAGES*

052   UK
WOMEN ONLY. 1992. m. £62. Portland Publishing Ltd., 1 Tyburn Ln., Harrow-on-the-Hill, Middlesex HA1 3AG, England. TEL 071-538-8969. FAX 071-538-1170. Ed. Isabel Koprowski. adv.: color page £3000; adv. contact: Chris Payne. circ. 100,000. **Document type:** consumer publication.

305.4 796.5   US
WOMEN OUTDOORS. 1980. q. $25 membership (effective Oct. 1995). Women Outdoors, Inc., 55 Talbot Ave., Medford, MA 02155. Ed. Carol Harley. adv.; bk.rev. circ. 1,000. **Document type:** newsletter.
Description: Contains trip accounts, how-to articles, poetry, information about scholarships, and other women's outdoor activities.

WOMEN STRIKE FOR PEACE. LEGISLATIVE ALERT. see *POLITICAL SCIENCE — Civil Rights*

051   US   ISSN 0043-7506
WOMEN TODAY.* 1970. 26/yr. $40. M & O Communications, 120 E. 34th St., 7th Fl., New York, NY 10016. TEL 202-628-6999. Ed. Lester A. Barrer. bk.rev.; bibl.; stat.; index. (looseleaf format)
Formerly: Frontline News for Women.

301.412   US
WOMEN UNLIMITED. 1989. m. $21. Alice Stelzer, Ed. & Pub., 603 Sumner Ave., Springfield, MA 01108. TEL 413-733-1231. FAX 413-737-1008. adv. circ. 3,000. **Document type:** consumer publication.
Description: Written for women in western Massachusetts.

WOMEN WITH WHEELS; the newsletter on automobiles for women. see *TRANSPORTATION — Automobiles*

WOMEN'S INTERESTS

323.42 US
WOMENEWS. 1975. q. free upon request. Commission for Women, 209 Finance Bldg., Harrisburg, PA 17120-0018. TEL 717-787-8128. FAX 717-772-0653. Ed. Kelly Toth McCall. bk.rev.; bibl. circ. 20,000. (tabloid format; reprint service avail. from UMI) **Document type:** newsletter.
Formerly: Pennsylvania Commission for Women News.

WOMEN'S ART MAGAZINE. see *ART*

305.4 330 US ISSN 1068-9087
WOMEN'S BUSINESS EXCLUSIVE. 1993. 10/yr. $55. 3528 Torrance Blvd., Ste. 101, Torrance, CA 90503. TEL 310-540-9398. FAX 310-792-8263. Ed. Jeanie M. Barnett; Pubs. Jeanie M. Barnett, Ginger Conrad. index. (back issues avail.) **Document type:** newsletter.
Description: Advises women business owners on corporate and government procurement and offers tips on financing, marketing, negotiating, and more.

WOMEN'S CAUCUS FOR ART. HONOR AWARDS CATALOGUE. see *ART*

WOMEN'S CAUCUS FOR ART. NATIONAL UPDATE. see *ART*

305.412 US ISSN 0509-089X
WOMEN'S CIRCLE. bi-m. $9.95. House of White Birches Publishing, 306 E. Parr Rd., Berne, IN 46711. TEL 219-589-8741. Ed. Marjorie Pearl. illus. circ. 51,000. **Document type:** consumer publication.
Description: Contains decorating ideas, craft projects, recipes and advice. Readers share how to turn home hobbies into businesses.

367 IE ISSN 0332-446X
WOMEN'S CLUBS MAGAZINE. 1971. q. £1.70 per issue. (Irish Federation of Women's Clubs) Maxwell Publicity, 49 Wainsfort Park, Dublin 6W, Ireland. TEL 353-1-4924034. FAX 353-1-4924035. Ed. June Cooke. adv. contact: Terry Grogan. circ. 23,000. (processed) **Document type:** consumer publication.

301.412 US
WOMEN'S COLLECTION NEWSLETTER. 1974. irreg. free. Northwestern University Library, Special Collections Department, 1935 Sheridan Rd., Evanston, IL 60208. TEL 708-491-3635. FAX 708-491-5685. E-mail: s-perry.nwu.edu. Ed. Sigrid P. Perry. bk.rev.; abstr.; bibl. circ. 1,500. **Document type:** newsletter.
Description: Provides an overview of collection acquisitions and patrons' research topics.

301.412 200 US
WOMEN'S CONCERNS REPORT. 1973. bi-m. $20 for 2 yrs. Mennonite Central Committee, 21 S. 12th St., Box 500, Akron, PA 17501-0500. TEL 717-859-3889. FAX 717-859-3875. Ed. Tina Mast Burnett. bibl.; illus.; cum.index (1973-1986). circ. 2,700. (looseleaf format; back issues avail.) **Document type:** newsletter.
Description: Information on various women's issues ranging from religious concerns to women in the arts.

WOMEN'S CONTACT BULLETIN. see *LABOR UNIONS*

305.4 360 TH
WOMEN'S DIARY (YEAR). a. $6. Foundation for Women, P.O. Box 47, Bangkoknoi, Bangkok 10700, Thailand. TEL 66-2-433-5149. FAX 66-2-434-6774.
Description: Covers women's issues and lists Thai organizations of interest to women.

376 374 CN ISSN 0714-9786
WOMEN'S EDUCATION/EDUCATION DES FEMMES. (Text and summaries in English and French) 1982. q. Can.$18.19 to individuals; institutions Can.$30.70. Canadian Congress for Learning Opportunities for Women, 47 Main St., Toronto, ON M4E 2V6, Canada. TEL 416-699-1909. FAX 416-699-2145. Ed. Christina Starr. bk.rev.; index, cum.index vols.1-6. circ. 1,600. (also avail. in microform from MML; back issues avail.) **Indexed:** Alt.Press Ind., Can.B.P.I., Can.Wom.Per.Ind. **Document type:** consumer publication.
Description: Discusses women's access to education and provides a feminist analysis of education and learning.

WOMEN'S ELECTORAL LOBBY (SOUTH AUSTRALIAN) NEWSLETTER. see *SOCIAL SERVICES AND WELFARE*

WOMEN'S HEALTH LETTER; the monthly review of women's health issues. see *WOMEN'S HEALTH*

WOMEN'S HISTORY CATALOG. see *WOMEN'S STUDIES*

WOMEN'S HISTORY NETWORK NEWS. see *WOMEN'S STUDIES*

301.412 026 UG
WOMEN'S INFORMATION UPDATES. Variant title: W I C C E Newsletter. (Text in English, French, Spanish) 1976. s.a. Isis - Women's International Cross-Cultural Exchange, P.O. Box 4934, Kampala, Uganda. TEL 256-41-266007. FAX 256-41-268676. Ed. Gladys Siwela. adv.; bk.rev.; bibl.; stat. (also avail. in microfiche)
Description: Lists new documentation and books at the center as well as in-depth thematic listings of resources, information about new groups, activities, actions, and campaigns.

WOMEN'S LEAGUE OUTLOOK. see *RELIGIONS AND THEOLOGY — Judaic*

WOMEN'S MUSIC PLUS; directory of resources in women's music & culture. see *MUSIC*

301.4157 780 US
WOMEN'S NETWORK; national newsletter for women. 1977. s.a. donation. 2137 Quimby Ave., Bronx, NY 10473. TEL 212-597-7091. Ed. Dorothy Feola. adv.; bk.rev.; illus. **Document type:** newsletter.
Formerly: Women's Network - Women in Music.

310.412 NL ISSN 1017-3900
WOMEN'S NEWS. French edition: L'Actualite au Feminin (ISSN 1019-6811) (Text in English) 1982. q. South Pacific Commission, B.P. D5, Noumea, Cedex, New Caledonia. TEL 687-262000. FAX 687-263818. TELEX 3139 NM SOPACOM. **Document type:** newsletter.
Formerly: Women's Newsletter.

301.412 US
WOMEN'S NEWS. m. Popper - Strong Communications Inc., Box 829, Harrison, NY 10528. TEL 914-835-5400. Ed. Marjorie Roberts; Pub. Merna Popper. circ. 250,000. **Document type:** newspaper.

052 UK
WOMEN'S ORGANISATIONS IN THE UNITED KINGDOM. biennial. Women's National Commission, Caxton House, Tothill St., London SW1H 9NF, England. **Document type:** directory, government publication.

301.41 US ISSN 0092-6639
HQ1883
WOMEN'S ORGANIZATIONS & LEADERS DIRECTORY. 1973. biennial. $65. M & O Communications, 120 E. 34th St., 7th Fl., New York, NY 10016. TEL 202-638-0348. Ed. Lester A. Barrer.

WOMEN'S OUTDOOR JOURNAL. see *SPORTS AND GAMES — Outdoor Life*

WOMEN'S POLITICAL TIMES. see *POLITICAL SCIENCE*

305.412 JA
WOMEN'S PUBLIC OPINION/FUJIN KORON. (Text in Japanese) 1916. m. 8950 Yen. Chuokoron-Sha, Inc., No. 2-8-7 Kyobashi, Chuo-ku, Tokyo, Japan. Ed. Toshiaki Matsuda.

305.412 US ISSN 1079-6622
WOMEN'S QUARTERLY. q. $16.95. 2111 Wilson Blvd., Ste. 550, Arlington, VA 22201-3057. TEL 703-243-8989. Ed. Danielle Crittenden; Pub. Grace Paine Terzian. **Document type:** consumer publication.
Description: Covers cultural and public policy issues affecting women.

051 US
WOMEN'S RESOURCE & ACTION CENTER. NEWSLETTER. 1971. m. $5. (Women's Resource & Action Center) University of Iowa, 130 N. Madison, Iowa City, IA 52240. TEL 319-335-1486. bk.rev.; bibl. circ. 1,000. **Document type:** newsletter.
Description: Feminist newsletter covering activities and issues of interest to women.

WOMEN'S SPORTS AND FITNESS. see *SPORTS AND GAMES*

WOMEN'S SPORTS EXPERIENCE. see *SPORTS AND GAMES*

WOMEN'S TRAVELLER. see *TRAVEL AND TOURISM*

640 AT ISSN 1320-064X
WOMEN'S VIEW. 1962. q. Aus.$4 to non-members. (View Clubs of Australia) Smith Family, 16 Larkin St., Camperdown, N.S.W. 2050, Australia. TEL 61-2-550-4422. FAX 61-2-550-4235. Ed. Bridget Battersby. adv.: B&W page Aus.$1150, color page Aus.$3000; trim 275 x 200; adv. contact: Bridget Battersby. bk.rev.; circ. 27,000 (controlled). **Document type:** consumer publication.
—UnCover.
Formerly (until Sep. 1991): View World.
Description: For contemporary women with traditional values.

WOMEN'S WATCH; reporting on law and policy change in accordance with the principles of the Convention on the Elimination of All Forms of Discrimination Against Women. see *POLITICAL SCIENCE — Civil Rights*

301.412 KO
WOMEN'S WEEKLY. (Text in English) w. 14 Chunghak-dong, Chongno-ku, Seoul, S. Korea.

305.412 296 US ISSN 0043-759X
WOMEN'S WORLD. 1951. 4/yr. membership only. B'nai B'rith Women, Inc., 1828 L St., N.W., Ste. 250, Washington, DC 20036. TEL 202-857-1320. FAX 202-857-1380. Ed. Susan Tomchin. bk.rev.; charts; illus.; circ. 120,000 (controlled). (tabloid format) **Indexed:** Mag.Ind. **Document type:** newsletter.
Description: Feature articles of interest to women and jews.

WOMEN'S YELLOW PAGES. see *BUSINESS AND ECONOMICS — Trade And Industrial Directories*

301.412 US ISSN 0049-786X
WOMYN'S PRESS; a feminist news journal. 1970. bi-m. $11 to individuals; institutions $18 (effective 1995-1996). Womyn's Press Collective, Box 562, Eugene, OR 97440. TEL 503-389-3974. FAX 503-689-3974. Eds. J.R. David, Natascha Bruckner. adv. contact: J.R. David. bk.rev.; film rev.; play rev.; charts; illus.; circ. 2,000 (paid). (tabloid format; back issues avail.) **Document type:** newspaper.
Description: Explores women's issues, spirituality, and life from a feminist perspective. Also discusses surviving abuse.

WOOLF STUDIES ANNUAL. see *LITERATURE*

WORKING AT HOME. see *BUSINESS AND ECONOMICS — Small Business*

640 US ISSN 0278-193X
HQ759
WORKING MOTHER. 1978. m. $7.97. Lang Communications, 230 Park Ave., New York, NY 10169. TEL 212-551-9399; 800-627-0690. FAX 212-551-9757. Ed. Judson Culdreth. circ. 850,000. (also avail. in microform from UMI) **Indexed:** PMR.
—UMI; UnCover. **CCC.**
Incorporates (1986-1988): Baby; McCall's Working Mother (ISSN 0160-6131)

WORKING PAPERS ON WOMEN IN INTERNATIONAL DEVELOPMENT. see *BUSINESS AND ECONOMICS — International Development And Assistance*

305.412 US ISSN 0145-5761
HQ1101 CODEN: WOWODL
WORKING WOMAN. 1976. m. $11.97. Lang Communications, 230 Park Ave., New York, NY 10169. TEL 212-551-9500; 800-234-9675. (Subscr. to: Box 10132, Des Moines, IA 50340) Ed. Lynn Povich. adv.; bk.rev.; illus. circ. 900,000. (also avail. in microfiche from UMI; reprint service avail. from UMI) **Indexed:** ABI Inform, Acad.Ind., BPIA, Bus.Ind., Curr.Lit.Fam.Plan., Hlth.Ind., Mag.Ind., PMR, PSI, R.G.
●Also available online. Vendor(s): Knight-Ridder, Inc..
—BLDSC (9351.213000); CASDDS; Faxon; Genuine Article; UMI; UnCover. **CCC.**

051 US
WORLD CLASS ENTERTAINMENT. 1990. m. $17.95. Duncan Publications, 621 Renken Rd., Staunton, IL 62088. TEL 618-637-2202. Ed. Susan Duncan. circ. 100,000. (tabloid format)
Description: For upscale women between the ages of 25 and 54. Covers fashion, travel, celebrities and entertainment.

WOMEN'S INTERESTS — ABSTRACTING, BIBLIOGRAPHIES, STATISTICS

920.72   UK
WORLD WHO'S WHO OF WOMEN. 1973. every 18 mos. £105. Melrose Press Ltd., 3 Regal Ln., Soham, Ely, Cambridgeshire CB7 5BA, England. TEL 01353-721091. FAX 01353-721839. (Dist. in U.S. by: Taylor and Francis Inc., 1900 Frost Rd., Ste. 101, Bristol, PA 19007-1598) Ed. Jocelyn Timothy; Pub. Nicholas Law. adv. contact: Jean Pearson. illus. **Document type:** directory.

800   US   ISSN 1062-3434
WRITING FOR OUR LIVES. 1992. s-a. $11.50 to individuals; institutions $14. Running Deer Press, 647 N. Santa Cruz Ave., Annex, Los Gatos, CA 95030. TEL 408-354-8604. Ed. Janet M. McEwan. (back issues avail.)
     Description: Serves as a vessel for poems, short fiction, stories, autobiographies, letters and journal excerpts from the life stories, experiences and spiritual journeys of women.

X FAMILY LETTERS. see *MEN'S INTERESTS*

301.412   CC
XIANDAI FUNU/MODERN WOMEN. (Text in Chinese) m. Xiandai Funu Zazhishe, 213 Minjiaqiao, Lanzhou, Gansu 730000, People's Republic of China. TEL 465667. (Dist. overseas by: Jiangsu Publications Import & Export Corp., 56 Gao Yun Ling, Nanjing, Jiangsu, P.R.C.) Ed. Han Xiangjing.

301.412   CC   ISSN 1003-4196
XINGFU/HAPPINESS. (Text in Chinese) bi-m. Wuhan Shi Funu Lianhehui - Wuhan Municipal Women's Association, No. 22, Haomengling Lu, Hankou, Wuhan, Hubei 430010, People's Republic of China. TEL 512071. Ed. Yang Fuhua.

301.412   CC
YANBIAN FUNU/YANBIAN WOMEN. (Text in Korean) m. Yanbian Funu Lianhehui, 1 Youyi Lu, Guangming Jie, Yanji, Jilin 133000, People's Republic of China. TEL 518494. Ed. Jin Yangjin.

305.4   NE
YES. 1986. w. newsstand price: FL.2.50. Uitgeverij Sparnestad B.V. (Haarlem), P.O. Box 1, 2000 MA Haarlem, Netherlands. TEL 31-203-304304. FAX 31-23-350382. Ed. Margaret Hagdorn. adv.: color page fl.15476. bk.rev.; illus.; circ. 180,000 (paid). **Document type:** consumer publication.
     Description: For young women.

DI YIDDISHE HEIM/JEWISH HOME. see *ETHNIC INTERESTS*

301.412   AG
YO MUJER ACTUAL. (Supplement avail.: Yo Mama) fortn. Editores Asociados S.A., Maipu 942 2o piso, 1340 Buenos Aires, Argentina. TEL 312-6211. FAX 541-311-9504.

301.412   KO
YOSONG DONG-A. 1933. m. Dong-A Ilbo, 139 Sejongno, Chongno-gu, Seoul, S. Korea. TEL 02-721-7114. Ed. Kwon O-Kie. circ. 237,000.

305.412   SA   ISSN 0301-6137
YOUR FAMILY. m. R.46.78 (overseas R.92.24) (effective 1993). Republican Press (Pty) Ltd., P.O. Box 32083, Mobeni 4060, Natal, South Africa. TEL 27-31-422041. FAX 27-31-921231. Ed. Angela Waller-Paton. circ. 250,000. **Document type:** consumer publication.
     Description: Do-it-yourself information on cookery, garment-making, and homecrafts.

Z MAGAZINE. see *POLITICAL SCIENCE*

301.435   TS
ZAHRAT AL-KHALIJ. (Text in Arabic) 1979. w. Al-Ittihad Press, Publishing and Distribution Corp., Zahrat al-Khalij, P.O. Box 3342, Abu Dhabi, United Arab Emirates. TEL 451600. FAX 461801. TELEX 22984 ITTPRESS EM. Ed. Abla Al-Nuwais. circ. 709,900. **Document type:** consumer publication.
     Description: Covers issues of interest to Arab women throughout the Gulf and the Arab world.

301.435 915.5   IR
ZAN-E RUZ. (Text in Persian) 1964. w. $318 to N. America (effective 1994). Kayhan Publications, Ferdowsi Ave., P.O. Box 11365-9631, Teheran, Iran. TEL 98-21-3110251. TELEX 212467. circ. 100,000. **Document type:** consumer publication.

ZARJA/DAWN. see *ETHNIC INTERESTS*

059.927   SU
ZEINA. 6/yr. P.O. Box 157, Jeddah 21411, Saudi Arabia. TEL 682-7736. circ. 48,260.

305.4   GW   ISSN 0724-3626
ZEITSCHRIFT FUER FRAUENFORSCHUNG. 1983. 3/yr. DM.42. (Institut Frau und Gesellschaft) Kleine Verlag GmbH, Postfach 101668, 33416 Bielefeld, Germany. TEL 0521-15811. FAX 0521-140043. Ed. Robert Schreiber. **Document type:** academic/scholarly publication.

053.1   SZ
ZEITSPIEGEL FRAU.* (Text in German) 1918. s-m. Aemtlerstr. 201, CH-8040 Zurich, Switzerland. Ed. H. Oberholzer. adv.; bk.rev.; illus. circ. 9,500.
     Formerly (until 1989): Schweizer Frauenblatt (ISSN 0036-7346)

640   CI   ISSN 0513-9473
ZENA. 1943. bi-m. $18. Savjet za Pitanja Drustvenog Polozaja Zene PK SSRNH, Vlaska 70a-III, 41000 Zagreb, Croatia. Ed. Melita Singer. adv.; bk.rev. circ. 1,700.

323   RU
ZHENSHCHINA: VEK XX. 1991. m. 1 Rub. per issue. (Komitet Sovetskikh Zhentshchin) T.A.S.S., Tverskoi Bul'var, 10-12, 103009 Moscow, Russia. Ed. S.F. Bulantsev. circ. 1,700.

057.1   RU   ISSN 0044-4456
ZHENSHCHINY MIRA.* 1958. q. $8.50. (Mezhdunarodnaya Demokraticheskaya Federatsiya Zhenshchin) Izdatel'stvo Progress, Zubovsky blv. 17, 119847 Moscow, Russian. TEL 246-3308. FAX 95-230-2403. TELEX 411800-KEGL-SX. (Dist. in U.S. by: Victor Kamkin Inc., 4956 Boiling Brook Pkwy, Rockville, MD 20852. TEL 301-881-5973)

305   CN   ISSN 0513-9856
HQ1104
ZHINOCHYI SVIT/WOMAN'S WORLD. (Text in Ukrainian and English) 1950. m. Can.$25 (effective 1995). Ukrainian Women's Organization, 937 Main St., Winnipeg, MB R2W 3P2, Canada. TEL 416-943-8230. FAX 204-943-8230. Ed. Anne Wach. adv.; bk.rev.; illus. circ. 2,500. **Indexed:** Amer.Bibl.Slavic & E.Eur.Stud.

305.4   CC   ISSN 1000-4157
ZHIYIN/BOSOM FRIEND. (Text in Chinese) 1985. m. $36.10. Hubei Sheng Funu Lianhehui, Shuiguo Hu, Wuhan, Hubei 430071, People's Republic of China. TEL 711030. FAX 711223. (Dist. in US by: China Books & Periodicals, Inc., 2929 24th St., San Francisco, CA 94110. TEL 415-282-2994) Ed. Hu Xunbi. **Document type:** consumer publication.

301.412   CC
ZHONGGUO FUYUN/CHINESE WOMEN'S MOVEMENT. (Text in Chinese) 1951. m. Zhonghua Quanguo Funu Lianhehui - All-China Women's Federation, No. 50, Dengshikou, Beijing 100730, People's Republic of China. TEL 5134017. Ed. Wang Shubo. adv. contact: Munei Tang. bk.rev. circ. 100,000. **Document type:** government publication.
     Formerly: Funu Gongzuo - Women's Affairs.

301.412   CC
ZHONGWAI FUNU WENZHAI. (Text in Chinese) m. Neimenggu Zizhiqu Funu Lianhehui, 9, Zhongshan Donglu, Huhhot, Neimenggu (Inner Mongolia) 010020, People's Republic of China. Ed. Xi Xingfang.

ZIJ AAN ZIJ TIJDSCHRIFT; voor, door en over lesbische en biseksuele vrouwen. see *HOMOSEXUALITY*

057.87   XO   ISSN 0139-6323
ZIVOT; rodinny tezdennik. 1950. w. 12 Sk. per issue. Euroskop, Inc., Pribinova, Inc., 819 37 Bratislava, Slovakia. TEL 42-7-368121. FAX 42-7-363391. Ed. Milan Varos. adv. contact: J. Markova. illus. circ. 255,000.

301.412   US   ISSN 0279-3229
ZONTIAN. (Text in English; summaries in French, German, Italian, Japanese, Spanish) 1920. q. $7 (effective until June 1996). Zonta International, 557 W. Randolph St., Chicago, IL 60661-2206. TEL 312-930-5848. FAX 312-930-0951. TELEX 190200. Ed. Walidah G. Sherman. circ. 36,000 (controlled).
     Description: Presents articles regarding organization's programs and activities, particularly as they relate to the status of women.

323.4   GW
ZWEIWOCHENDIENST FRAUEN UND POLITIK. 1986. m. DM.108 to individuals; institutions DM.180; low income DM.84. Zweiwochendienst Verlag GmbH, Pressehaus I, Rm. 234, Heussallee 2-10, 53113 Bonn, Germany. TEL 0228-217375. FAX 0228-215226. Ed. Karin Dupp. bibl.; stat. circ. 2,500. **Document type:** newsletter.
     Description: Covers women in politics and provides suggestions on how to better women's chances in education and business. Includes information on equal rights for men and women.

9 TO 5 NEWSLETTER. see *BUSINESS AND ECONOMICS — Labor And Industrial Relations*

13TH MOON; a feminist literary magazine. see *LITERATURE*

054.1   FR
20 ANS. 1967. 12/yr. 176 F. (foreign 279 F.)(effective 1992). Excelsior Publications, 1 rue du Colonel Pierre Avia, 75503 Paris Cedex 15, France. TEL 46-48-48-48. FAX 46-48-48-09. TELEX 631 994 F. Ed. Yveline Dupuy. adv. contact: Gilles de Keranflech. circ. 106,000.

055.1   IT
100 COSE. 1978. m. L.71400. Arnoldo Mondadori Editore S.p.A., Casella Postale 1833, 20101 Milan, Italy. TEL 02-75421. Ed. Kicca Menoni. circ. 161,000.

305.412   FR
100 IDEES. m. 70 F. 11 bis rue Boissy d'Anglas, 75008 Paris, France. Ed. Collette Gouvion. circ. 346,978.

WOMEN'S INTERESTS — Abstracting, Bibliographies, Statistics

305.412 011   CN   ISSN 0847-2882
CANADIAN WOMEN'S PERIODICALS INDEX/INDEX DES PERIODIQUES POUR FEMMES CANADIENNES. (Text in English and French) 1984. 3/yr. Can.$40 to non-members; members Can.$30; libraries Can.$50. 11019-90 Avenue, University of Alberta, Edmonton, AB T6G 2E1, Canada. TEL 403-492-3093. FAX 403-492-1186. (back issues avail.) **Document type:** abstracting/indexing.
     Former titles: Canadian Women's Periodicals: Title Word Index (ISSN 0829-9552); Canadian Women's Periodicals: K W I C Index.

LESBIAN HERSTORY ARCHIVES NEWSLETTER. see *HOMOSEXUALITY*

LESBISCH ARCHIVARIA. see *HOMOSEXUALITY — Abstracting, Bibliographies, Statistics*

WOMEN'S STUDIES

ABOUT WOMEN ON CAMPUS. see *EDUCATION — Higher Education*

AFFILIA; journal of women and social work. see *SOCIAL SERVICES AND WELFARE*

WOMEN'S STUDIES

305.4 327   SJ   ISSN 0255-4070
HQ1793.5
AHFAD JOURNAL; women and change. (Text in English; summaries in Arabic) 1984. s-a. $40. Ahfad University for Women, P.O. Box 167, Omdurman, Sudan. TEL 53363. (Subscr. in U.S.: c/o Dr. Lee G. Burchinal, Ste. 1216, 4141 N. Henderson Rd., Ste. 1216, Arlington, VA 22203. TEL 703-525-9045) Ed. Amna El Sadik Badri. adv.; bk.rev. circ. 400. (also avail. in microform; back issues avail.; reprint service avail. from UMI) **Indexed:** Mult.Ed.Abstr., Wom.Stud.Abstr. (1989-). **Document type:** academic/scholarly publication.
—BLDSC (0772.281500); UMI; UnCover.
Description: Covers issues affecting women, families and children in developing countries, and role of women in national development.

305.4   US   ISSN 1042-5985
AMERICAN UNIVERSITY STUDIES. SERIES 27. FEMINIST STUDIES. 1990. irreg. Peter Lang Publishing, Inc., 62 W. 45th St., 4th Fl., New York, NY 10036. TEL 212-302-6740. Ed. Christopher Myers. **Document type:** academic/scholarly publication, monographic series.

THE AMERICAN WOMAN (YEAR); a status report. see WOMEN'S STUDIES — Abstracting, Bibliographies, Statistics

305.4 200   US   ISSN 1056-4578
BL458
ANNUAL REVIEW OF WOMEN IN WORLD RELIGIONS. 1991. a. price varies. State University of New York Press, State University Plaza, Albany, NY 12246. TEL 518-472-5000; 800-666-2211. FAX 518-472-5038. (Orders to: S U N Y Press, c/o C U P Services, Box 6525, Ithaca, NY 14851) Eds. Lois Patton; Pub. William Eastman. (back issues avail.) **Document type:** academic/scholarly publication.
Description: Takes an interdisciplinary and multidisciplinary approach to study of women and religion and aims to establish dialogue between the humanistic and social scientific studies in the field.
Refereed Serial

305.4 133   US   ISSN 1075-3729
AT THE CROSSROADS; feminism, spirituality and New Paradigm science exploring earthly and unearthly reality. 1992. s-a. $24. Spirited Women Book Co., Box 112, St. Paul, AR 72760. TEL 501-677-2235. Ed. Jeanne Neath. bk.rev. (back issues avail.) **Document type:** consumer publication.
Description: Brings feminism, spirituality, and new paradigm science together to explore reality, especially the spiritual reality that Western cultures often deny. Also covers shamanism, parapsychology, and spiritual traditions from a feminist perspective.

305.412   CN   ISSN 0702-7818
HQ1180
ATLANTIS; a women's studies journal - revue d'etudes sur la femme. (Text in English and French) 1975. s-a. Can.$20($30) to individuals; institutions Can.$30 ($40). Mount Saint Vincent University, 166 Bedford Hwy., Halifax, NS B3M 2J6, Canada. TEL 902-443-4450. FAX 902-445-3960. Ed. Deborah Poff. adv.; bk.rev.; cum.index. circ. 900. (also avail. in microfilm from MML) **Indexed:** Alt.Press Ind., Amer.Hist.& Life, Can.B.P.I., Can.Lit.Ind., Can.Per.Ind., Can.Wom.Per.Ind., CMI, Hist.Abstr., M.L.A., Mult.Ed.Abstr., Stud.Wom.Abstr. (1975-), Wom.Stud.Abstr. **Document type:** academic/scholarly publication.
—BLDSC (1765.960000); UnCover.

305.4   UK   ISSN 0816-4649
HQ1101
AUSTRALIAN FEMINIST STUDIES. 1986. s-a. £28 to individuals; institutions £72 (effective 1996). (Research Centre for Women's Studies) Carfax Publishing Co., P.O. Box 25, Abingdon, Oxon OX14 3UE, Englands. TEL 44-1235-555335. FAX 44-1235-553559. (N. American subscr. to: Carfax Publishing Co., 875-81 Massachusetts Ave., Cambridge, MA 02139) Ed. Susan Magarey. adv.; bk.rev. circ. 600. (back issues avail.) **Indexed:** Alt.Press. Ind., Aus.P.A.I.S., Stud.Wom.Abstr. **Document type:** academic/scholarly publication.
—BLDSC (1798.923500); UnCover.
Description: Publishes both disciplinary and transdisciplinary scholarship and discussion in the fields of feminist research and women's studies courses.

BELLES LETTRES (NORTH POTOMAC); a review of books by women. see LITERATURE

305.4 363.49   US   ISSN 1046-8358
BRIDGES: A JOURNAL FOR JEWISH FEMINISTS AND OUR FRIENDS. 1990. s-a. $15. Bridges Association, Box 24839, Eugene, OR 97402. TEL 503-935-5720. E-mail: p01230@psilink.com. Ed. Clare Kinbirg. bk.rev. circ. 3,000. (also avail. in audio cassette; back issues avail.) **Indexed:** Ind.Jew.Per.
Description: Includes songs, rituals, poems, fiction, visual art, essays and reviews which combine culture and political activism.

305.4   TR   ISSN 1016-9741
C A F R A NEWS. Spanish edition: Novedades C A F R A (ISSN 1016-975X) 1987. q. T.T.$50($20) to individuals; institutions T.T.$55($25). Caribbean Association for Feminist Research and Action, P.O. Bag 442, Tunapuna Post Office, Tunapuna, Trinidad & Tobago, W.I. TEL 809-663-8670. FAX 809-663-6482. Ed.Bd. bk.rev.; bibl.; charts; illus. circ. 500. (reprint service avail.) **Document type:** newsletter.
Description: Provides a forum for discussion and debate on key issues of concern to women in the region; promotes the sharing of experiences among feminists.

605.412   US
C A F S QUARTERLY. q. University of Minnesota, Center for Advanced Feminist Studies, 492 Ford Hall, 224 Church St. S.E., Minneapolis, MN 55455. TEL 612-624-6310. FAX 612-626-1697. Ed. Karen Moon. circ. 1,000 (paid). (looseleaf format) **Document type:** academic/scholarly publication.
Description: Written for a broad audience, particularly college and university students majoring in women's studies. Contains news of the center and its constituents.

305.4   US
C C W H P - C G W H NEWSLETTER. 1969. bi-m. $30. Coordinating Committee on Women in the Historical Profession - Conference Group on Women's History, c/o Barbara Winslow, Dir.-Treas., 124 Park Pl., Brooklyn, NY 11217. TEL 718-638-3227. Eds. Vivian Rose, Patty Selesky. adv.; bk.rev. circ. 850. **Indexed:** Wom.Stud.Abstr. (1972-). **Document type:** newsletter.

305.4   CN
C R I A W PAPERS. 1981. irreg. price varies. Canadian Research Institute for the Advancement of Women - Institut Canadien de Recherches sur les Femmes, 151 Slater St., Ste. 408, Ottawa, ON K1P 5H3, Canada. TEL 613-563-0681. FAX 613-563-0682. **Document type:** monographic series, academic/scholarly publication.
Description: Publishes original research papers and review articles drawn from various disciplines, as well as interdisciplinary works, advancing the knowledge and understanding of women's experience.

305.4   US   ISSN 1063-0104
HQ1101
C S W S REVIEW. 1986. a. free. Center for the Study of Women in Society, University of Oregon, 636 Prince Lucien Campbell Hall, Eugene, OR 87403. TEL 503-346-5015. Ed. Diana Sheridan.
Description: Highlights feminist research in Oregon and the rest of the northwestern United States, specifically that of CSWS affiliates.

305.4   US   ISSN 0738-3185
C W A S NEWSLETTER.* 1982. q. Association for Asian Studies, Committee on Women in Asian Studies, Dept. of Anthropology, George Washington Univ., Washington, DC 20052. TEL 202-994-6075. Ed. Barbara Diane Miller. **Document type:** newsletter.

305.4   US
C W R MEMBERSHIP NEWSLETTER. membership. Center for Women and Religion, Graduate Theological Union, 2400 Ridge Rd., Berkeley, CA 94709. TEL 510-649-2490. FAX 510-649-1417. bk.rev. **Document type:** newsletter.
Description: Offers resources, news, and articles of national and international interest.

305.4   UY   ISSN 0797-471X
LA CACEROLA. 1984. irreg., latest no.8. Urg.$500 per no. Grupo de Estudios Sobre la Condicion de la Mujer en el Uruguay (GRECMU), Miguel del Corro 1474, Casilla de Correos, 11200 Montevideo, Uruguay. TEL 41-64-15.

305.4 323.4   FR   ISSN 0154-7763
CAHIERS DE FEMINISME. 1977. q. 100 F. (foreign 135 F.). La Breche, 2 rue Richard Lenoir, 93108 Montreuil, France. Ed. Isabelle Alleton. illus. circ. 4,000. (back issues avail.)
—BLDSC (2948.941400).
Description: Covers civil rights and equality issues from a feminist perspective.

305.4   US   ISSN 0193-7618
HQ1236.5.U6
CALIFORNIA WOMEN. 1978. q. free. Commission on the Status of Women, 1303 J St., Ste. 400, Sacramento, CA 95814. TEL 916-445-3173. **Indexed:** Cal.Per.Ind. (1984-). **Document type:** newsletter.

CAMERA OBSCURA; a journal of feminism and film theory. see MOTION PICTURES

CANADIAN JOURNAL OF WOMEN AND THE LAW/REVUE FEMMES ET DROIT. see LAW

305.412   CN   ISSN 0713-3235
HQ1451
CANADIAN WOMAN STUDIES/CAHIERS DE LA FEMME. (Text in English, French) 1978. q. Can.$32.10 to individuals (foreign Can.$42); institutions Can.$42.80 (foreign Can.$52). Inanna Publications and Education Inc., 212 Founders College, York University, 4700 Keele St., Downsview, ON M3J 1P3, Canada. TEL 416-736-5356. FAX 416-736-5765. Ed. Luciana Ricciutelli. adv.; bk.rev.; illus. circ. 5,000. **Indexed:** C.P.I., Can.B.P.I., Can.Per.Ind., CMI, Mult.Ed.Abstr., Stud.Wom.Abstr., Wom.Stud.Abstr. (1990-). **Document type:** academic/scholarly publication.
—BLDSC (3046.154720); UnCover. **CCC.**
Formerly (until vol.3, no.2, 1981): Canadian Women's Studies (ISSN 0706-8204)

305.4   US
CENTER FOR RESEARCH ON WOMEN. CENTER NEWS. vol.8, no.1, 1989. s-a. Center for Research on Women, 339 Clement Hall, University of Memphis, Memphis, TN 38152. TEL 901-678-2770. FAX 901-678-3652. Ed. Sandra H. Utt. bk.rev. circ. 13,350. **Document type:** newsletter.
Description: Highlights research and educational activities as well as recent development in race, class and gender scholarship.

305.4   US
CENTER FOR RESEARCH ON WOMEN. RESEARCH PAPERS. 3/yr. Center for Research on Women, 339 Clement Hall, University of Memphis, Memphis, TN 38152. TEL 901-678-2770. FAX 901-678-3652. Ed. Elizabeth Higginbotham. **Document type:** monographic series.
Description: Covers findings from Center research projects, new scholarship on southern women, and advancements in curriculum transformation.

305.4   AG
CHANCLETAS. q.? Yerbal 573, 5o B, 1405 Buenos Aires, Argentina. TEL 431-9296.

305.4   MX
COMPANERAS. no.34, 1991. q. Mujeres para el Dialogo, Apdo. 19-493 Mixcoac, 03910 Mexico DF, Mexico. TEL 549-55-93.

CONTEMPORARY WOMEN. see CHILDREN AND YOUTH — For

305.4   US   ISSN 0147-104X
CONTRIBUTIONS IN WOMEN'S STUDIES. 1978. irreg., no.129, 1992. price varies. Greenwood Press, Inc. (Subsidiary of: Greenwood Publishing Group Inc.), 88 Post Rd. W., Box 5007, Westport, CT 06881-5007. TEL 203-226-3571. FAX 203-222-1502.
—BLDSC (3461.480000).

WOMEN'S STUDIES

305.4   US   ISSN 1066-288X
HQ1101
CRITICAL MATRIX; the Princeton journal of women, gender, and culture. 1985. s-a. $15 to individuals; institutions $28. Princeton University, Program in Women's Studies, 113 Dickinson Hall, Princeton University, Princeton, NJ 08544-1017. TEL 609-258-5430. FAX 609-258-1833. E-mail: MATRIX@PRINCETON.EDU. Eds. Cynthia Cupples, Heather Hadlock. adv.; bk.rev.; illus.; index, cum.index: 1985-1994. circ. 500. (back issues avail.) **Indexed:** Wom.Stud.Abstr. **Document type:** academic/scholarly publication.
Description: Feminist journal on gender and culture, publishing both traditional scholarship and new work that might encounter resistance within established disciplines.
Refereed Serial

305.4   MX
DEBATE FEMINISTA. 1990. m.? Ediciones Copilco, S.A. de C.V., Alfonso Pruneda 77, Copilco El Alto, 04360 Mexico DF, Mexico. TEL 525-6587370.

305.4   AG
DIARIO DE LAS CHICAS. 1987. bi-m. Arg.$15($30) Fundacion Ecumenica de Cuyo, Grupo Ecumenico de Mujeres, Casilla de Correo 60, 5519 San Jose, Mendoza, Argentina. TEL 54-61-250175. circ. 500. **Document type:** newsletter.
Description: For people dedicated to the right to life. Provides news in this and other areas.

305.412   US   ISSN 1040-7391
HQ1101   CODEN: DIFFX
DIFFERENCES; a journal of feminist cultural studies. 1989. 3/yr. $32 to individuals (foreign $48); institutions $60 (foreign $80). (Brown University, Pembroke Center) Indiana University Press, Journals Division, 601 N. Morton St., Bloomington, IN 47404. TEL 812-855-9449. FAX 812-855-7931. E-mail: Journals@Indiana.edu. Eds. Naomi Schor, Elizabeth Weed. (back issues avail.) **Indexed:** Left Ind. (1989-), Wom.Stud.Abstr. (1989-). **Document type:** academic/scholarly publication.
—BLDSC (3584.100000); Faxon; SWETS; UMI; UnCover.
Description: Focuses on how concepts and categories of difference (notably but not exclusively gender) operate within a culture. Provides a forum for exchange between cultural studies and feminism.

DIRECTORY OF WOMEN HISTORIANS. see *HISTORY*

305.4   CL   ISSN 0716-8101
EDICIONES DE LA MUJUERES. 1984. s-a. Esc.7500($35) (effective 1995). Isis International, Casilla 2067, Correo Central, Santiago, Chile. TEL 56-2-6382219. FAX 56-2-6383142. E-mail: isis@ax.apc.org. bk.rev. (back issues avail.) **Document type:** monographic series.

THE EMILY DICKINSON JOURNAL. see *LITERATURE — Poetry*

ENCORE MAGAZINE; celebrating return of the crone. see *WOMEN'S INTERESTS*

305.4   BL
ENFOQUE FEMINISTA; um veiculo de debate feminista. 1990. q. Uniao de Mulheres de Sao Paulo, Rua Bartolomeu Zunega, 49, 05426 Pinheiros, SP, Brazil. TEL 011-212-8681. Ed. Jucara Braga. circ. 5,000.

305.4 330   US
▼**ENTREVISION**. 1994. q. National Education Center for Women in Business, Seton Hill College, Greensburg, PA 15601. TEL 412-830-4625. circ. 30,000. **Document type:** academic/scholarly publication.

331.4   UK   ISSN 0261-0159
EQUAL OPPORTUNITIES INTERNATIONAL. 1981. 8/yr. £399.95($999.95) Barmarick Publications, Enholmes Hall, Patrington, N. Humber HU12 0PR, England. TEL 01964-630033. Ed. Nancy Wise. circ. 200. (back issues avail.; reprint service avail. from SWZ) **Indexed:** ABI Inform., Int.Lab.Doc., Stud.Wom.Abstr. **Document type:** academic/scholarly publication.
—BLDSC (3794.504500); UMI.
Description: Publishes articles and features on all aspects of women's involvement in the labor force. Outlines the latest international developments within the realm of equal opportunity studies, as well as practical case studies and regular reviews of research projects.

305.412   BO
ESTUDIOS DE PROMOCION FEMENINA. 1978. irreg., no.6, 1985. Centro de Investigaciones Sociales, Casilla 6931 - Correo Central, La Paz, Bolivia.

305.4   MX
ESTUDIOS SOBRE LA MUJER. 1982. irreg., no.3, 1990. price varies. Instituto Nacional de Estadistica, Geografia e Informatica, Secretaria de Programacion y Presupuesto, Prol. Heroe de Nacozari 2301 Sur, Puerta 11, Acceso, 20270 Aguascalientes, Ags., Mexico. TEL 49-18-19-48. FAX 491-807-39.

305.4   BL   ISSN 0104-026X
HQ1180   CODEN: ESFEE9
ESTUDOS FEMINISTAS. 1992. s-a. $35 to individuals; institutions $50. Universidade Federal de Rio de Janeiro, Escola de Comunicacao, Av. Pasteur 250, fundos, 22240-290 Rio de Janeiro RJ, Brazil. TEL 021-542-4877. FAX 021-275-1647. Ed. Lena Lavinas. adv.; bk.rev. **Indexed:** Hisp.Amer.Per.Ind. **Document type:** academic/scholarly publication.

305.4 917.306   US   ISSN 0897-4683
ETHNIC WOMAN. 1977. q. Ethnic Woman, Inc., Box 1033, Cooper Station, New York, NY 10003. Ed.Bd.

305.4   UK   ISSN 1350-5068
HQ1181.E85   CODEN: EJWSE5
▼**EUROPEAN JOURNAL OF WOMEN'S STUDIES**. 1994. q. £32 to individuals; institutions £90 (effective 1996). Sage Publications Ltd., 6 Bonhill St., London EC2A 4PU, England. TEL 0171-374-0645. FAX 0171-374-8741. E-mail: market@sageltd.co.uk. Eds. Kea Tijdens, Mary Evans. adv. contact: Bernie Folan. **Indexed:** Br.Hum.Ind., Int.Polit.Sci.Abstr., Intl.Bibl.S.S.Pol.Sci., Sociol.Abstr., Stud.Wom.Abstr., Wom.Stud.Abstr. **Document type:** academic/scholarly publication.
—BLDSC (3829.747350).
Description: Brings together important work currently being undertaken within women's studies in Europe.

301.412   UK   ISSN 0267-2294
EVERYWOMAN; Britain's only feminist monthly. 1985. m. £24 (rest of Europe £30; elsewhere £40). Everywoman Publishing Ltd., 9 St. Alban's Pl., London N1 0NX, England. TEL 0171-359-5496. Ed. Louisa Saunders. adv. contact: Jan Kaneen. bk.rev.; circ. 15,000 (paid). (back issues avail.) **Indexed:** Mult.Ed.Abstr. **Document type:** consumer publication.
Description: Covers current affairs, reporting and background on feminist issues.

305.4   AG
FEMINARIA. 1988. s-a. $20 to individuals; institutions $40. C.C. 402, 1000 Buenos Aires, Argentina. TEL 541-568-3029. Ed. Lea Fletcher. circ. 1,000. **Indexed:** Hisp.Amer.Per.Ind. (1988-). **Document type:** academic/scholarly publication.
Description: Covers general feminist theory, feminist literary theory and criticism, interviews of and notes about women and their activities, and prose, poetry, humor and artwork created by women.

FEMINISM & PSYCHOLOGY. see *PSYCHOLOGY*

305.412   GW   ISSN 0179-8367
DER FEMINIST; beitraege zur theorie und praxis. 1976. a. DM.9.50. Foerderkreis Der Feminist, Christrosenweg 5, 81377 Munich, Germany. TEL 089-7149187. Ed. Hannelore Mabry. bk.rev. circ. 4,000. (back issues avail.) **Document type:** academic/scholarly publication.
Description: Directed to female and male feminists, reports on theory and practice of feminism, criticism of Christianity and theology.

305.42   CN   ISSN 0831-3377
FEMINIST ACTION/ACTION FEMINISTE. irreg. membership. National Action Committee on the Status of Women, 57 Mobile Dr., Toronto, ON M4A 1H5, Canada. TEL 416-759-5252. FAX 416-757-5370. circ. 3,000. **Indexed:** Can.Wom.Per.Ind. **Document type:** newsletter. Incorporates: Action Bulletin (ISSN 0832-1418); Which was formerly (until 1985): N A C Memo (ISSN 0712-3183)
Description: Publication reporting on the status of women and policies that threaten women's rights.

305.4 070.5   US   ISSN 0742-7441
FEMINIST COLLECTIONS; a quarterly of women's studies resources. 1980. 4/yr. $27 to individuals; institutions $50 (includes New Books on Women & Feminism and Feminist Periodicals). University of Wisconsin System, Women's Studies Librarian, 430 Memorial Library, 728 State St., Madison, WI 53706. TEL 608-263-5754. Eds. Phyllis Holman Weisbard, Linda Shult. bk.rev.; bibl. circ. 1,500. **Indexed:** Stud.Wom.Abstr., Wom.Stud.Abstr.
—BLDSC (3905.197200).
Description: Covers feminist publishing, bookselling and distribution, feminist librarianship and resources for feminist research.

305.412   US   ISSN 0270-6679
HQ1101
FEMINIST ISSUES. s-a. $40 to individuals (foreign $56); institutions $80 (foreign $96) (effective Aug. 1995). (Feminist Forum, Inc.) Transaction Publishers, Transaction Periodicals Consortium, Department 3092, Rutgers University, New Brunswick, NJ 08903. TEL 908-445-2280. FAX 908-445-3138. Ed. Elizabeth Fox-Genovese. adv. circ. 600. (also avail. in microform from UMI; reprint service avail. from UMI) **Indexed:** Alt.Press Ind., Anthropol.Lit., Left Ind. (1982-), Mult.Ed.Abstr., Soc.Sci.Ind. (1994-), Stud.Wom.Abstr., Wom.Stud.Abstr. **Document type:** academic/scholarly publication.
—BLDSC (3905.197300); Faxon; UMI; UnCover. CCC.
Description: Devoted to feminist social and political analysis, with emphasis on an international exchange of ideas.

FEMINIST LEGAL STUDIES. see *LAW*

305.4   US   ISSN 1055-9949
FEMINIST MAJORITY REPORT. 1988. q. $25. Feminist Majority, 1600 Wilson Blvd., Ste. 801, Arlington, VA 22209. TEL 703-522-2214. Ed.Bd. adv. contact: Colleen Dermody. bk.rev. **Document type:** newsletter.

305.4   CN   ISSN 0837-578X
FEMINIST PERSPECTIVES/PERSPECTIVES FEMINISTES. (Text in English or French) 1985. irreg. (approx. 6/yr.). Can.$5($5) per no. Canadian Research Institute for the Advancement of Women - Institut Canadien de Recherches sur les Femmes, 151 Slater St., Ste. 408, Ottawa, ON K1P 5H3, Canada. TEL 613-563-0681. FAX 613-563-0682. (back issues avail.) **Document type:** academic/scholarly publication.
—BLDSC (3905.197500).
Description: Series of topical, issue-oriented papers exploring women's experience and concerns.

FEMINIST PRAXIS. see *SOCIOLOGY*

305.4   UK   ISSN 0141-7789
HQ1154
FEMINIST REVIEW. 1979. 3/yr. £24 (U.S. and Canada $42; rest of world £30) to individuals; institutions £68 (U.S. and Canada $110; rest of world £74). (Feminist Review Collective) Routledge, 11 New Fetter Ln., London EC4P 4EE, England. TEL 0171-583-9855. FAX 0171-842-2298. TELEX 263398-ROUT-G. E-mail: sample.journals@routledge.com. (Subscr. to: ITPS Ltd., Cheriton House, Andover, Hants SP10 5BE, England. TEL 01264-342919. FAX 01264-342807) adv.: page £225; trim 115 x 190. bk.rev. circ. 3,500. (back issues avail.) **Indexed:** Alt.Press Ind., ASSIA, Lang.& Lang.Behav.Abstr., Left Ind. (1982-), Mid.East: Abstr.& Ind., Mult.Ed.Abstr., Per.Islam. (1991-), Sociol.Abstr., Stud.Wom.Abstr. **Document type:** academic/scholarly publication.
—BLDSC (3905.197600); Faxon; Genuine Article; SWETS; UnCover. CCC.
Description: Articles on socialist-feminist theory. Covers women in history and the Third World, topical political problems, art and literature.

WOMEN'S STUDIES

305.4   US   ISSN 0046-3663
HQ1101   CODEN: FMSDA2
FEMINIST STUDIES. 1972. 3/yr. $30 to individuals (foreign $36); institutions $75 (foreign $81) (effective 1996). Feminist Studies, Inc., c/o Women's Studies Program, University of Maryland, College Park, MD 20742. TEL 301-405-7415. FAX 301-314-9190. Ed. Claire G. Moses. adv. contact: Brenda Ruby. bk.rev.; illus.; cum.index: 1972-1982. circ. 8,000. (also avail. in microfiche from UMI; reprint service avail. from UMI) **Indexed:** A.I.P.P., Acad.Ind., Adol.Ment.Hlth.Abstr., Alt.Press Ind., Amer.Hist.& Life, Anthropol.Lit., ASSIA, Bull.Signal., Child.Lit.Abstr., Curr.Cont., Hist.Abstr., IMFL, Lang.& Lang.Behav.Abstr., M.L.A., Mult.Ed.Abstr., Phil.Ind., Psychol.Abstr., Sage Fam.Stud.Abstr., Soc.Sci.Ind., Sociol.Abstr., SSCI, Stud.Wom.Abstr., Wom.Stud.Abstr. (1972-). **Document type:** academic/scholarly publication.
●Also available online. Vendor(s): University Microfilms International.
—BLDSC (3905.197800); Faxon; Genuine Article; SWETS; UMI; Uncover. **CCC.**
  Description: Presents scholarly research, essays, art, book reviews, and poetry, fiction, and creative narrative pertaining to the feminist experience in the social sciences, history, politics, and literature.

305.4 371.3   US   ISSN 0882-4843
LC197
FEMINIST TEACHER. 1984. 3/yr. $18 to individuals (foreign $33); institutions $32.50 (foreign $37.50). Feminist Teacher Editorial Collective, Wheaton College, Norton, MA 02766. (Subscr. to: Ablex Publishing, 355 Chestnut St., Norwood, NJ 07648) Ed.Bd. adv.; bk.rev. circ. 900. **Indexed:** Alt.Press Ind., Cont.Pg.Educ., Sociol.Educ.Abstr., Stud.Wom.Abstr., Wom.Stud.Abstr. (1984-). **Document type:** academic/scholarly publication.
—BLDSC (3905.197900); Faxon; Uncover.
  Description: Forum for new ideas in the classroom. Includes articles and essays written for teachers and by teachers.

305.4 200   UK   ISSN 0966-7350
FEMINIST THEOLOGY. 1992. 3/yr. £12($21) to individuals; institutions £24($40). Sheffield Academic Press Ltd., Mansion House, 19 Kingfield Rd., Sheffield S11 9AS, England. TEL 44-171-267-4466. FAX 44-171-482-2293. E-mail: admin@sheffac.demon.co.uk. Ed.Bd. **Document type:** academic/scholarly publication.
—BLDSC (3905.198200).

305.4   GW   ISSN 0937-5848
FRAUEN IN DER EINEN WELT. 1990. 2/yr. DM.18 per no. I K O Verlag, Postfach 900421, 60441 Frankfurt a.M., Germany. Ed.Bd. adv.; bk.rev. **Document type:** academic/scholarly publication.

305.4   GW   ISSN 0935-9710
FRAUENINFORMATIONSBLATT. 1979. 2/yr. free. Freie Universitaet Berlin, Zentraleinrichtung zur Foerderung von Frauenstudien und Frauenforschung, Koenigin-Luise-Str. 34, 14195 Berlin, Germany. TEL 030-8386254. Ed.Bd. bibl.; illus. circ. 3,000. **Document type:** academic/scholarly publication.

305.4   AU   ISSN 1023-1943
FRAUENSOLIDARITAET. 1982. q. S.160 (foreign S.200). Frauensolidaritaet, Weyrgasse 5, A-1030 Vienna, Austria. TEL 01-7133759480. FAX 01-713359473. E-mail: fsoli@magnet.at. adv.: page S.10000. circ. 1,500. (back issues avail.) **Document type:** bibliography.

305.4   US   ISSN 0160-9009
HQ1101
FRONTIERS: A JOURNAL OF WOMEN STUDIES. 1975. 3/yr. $20 to individuals (foreign $29); institutions $33 (foreign $42). Frontiers Editorial Collective, Mesa Vista Hall 2142, University of New Mexico, Albuquerque, NM 87131-1586. TEL 505-277-1198. FAX 505-277-0267. (Subscr. to: University Press of Colorado, Box 849, Niwot, CO 80544. TEL 303-530-5337) (Co-publisher: University Press of Colorado) Ed. Jane Slaughter. adv.: page $175. film rev.; play rev.; bibl.; charts; illus.; circ. 1,000 (paid). (also avail. in microform from UMI; back issues avail.; reprint service avail. from UMI) **Indexed:** Adol.Ment.Hlth.Abstr., Alt.Ed.Abstr., Amer.Hist.& Life, Amer.Hum.Ind., Hist.Abstr., Human Resour.Abstr., LCR, M.L.A., P.A.I.S., Soc.Sci.Ind., Sociol.Abstr., Stud.Wom.Abstr., Wom.Stud.Abstr. (1975-). **Document type:** academic/scholarly publication.
●Also available online. Vendor(s): University Microfilms International.
—BLDSC (4041.400000); Faxon; Genuine Article; UMI; Uncover.
  Description: Links the academy and the community by publishing scholarly, literary and artistic work. Emphasizes work by women of color. Focuses on women in the West.
Refereed Serial

GENDER AND EDUCATION. see *EDUCATION*

GENDER AND HISTORY. see *HISTORY*

GENDER AND SOCIETY. see *SOCIOLOGY*

652.5 910.02   UK   ISSN 0966-369X
                         CODEN: GPCUE9
▼**GENDER, PLACE AND CULTURE;** a journal of feminist geography. Online edition (ISSN 1360-0524) 1994. 3/yr. £42 to individuals; institutions £112) (effective 1996). Carfax Publishing Co., P.O. Box 25, Abingdon, Oxon. OX14 3UE, England. TEL 01235-555335. FAX 01235-553559. (N. American subsr. to: Carfax Publishing Co., 875-81 Massachusetts Ave., Cambridge, MA 02139) Eds. Liz Bondi, Mona Domosh. adv.; bk.rev.; index. (also avail. in microfiche) **Document type:** academic/scholarly publication.
●Also available online.
—BLDSC (4096.401650); UMI; Uncover. **CCC.**
  Description: Seeks to provide a focal point for research and study of the interrelationship of geography and gender issues.
Refereed Serial

GENDER, WORK AND ORGANIZATIONS. see *BUSINESS AND ECONOMICS — Management*

305   US   ISSN 0894-9832
NX1
GENDERS. 1988. 3/yr. $24 to individuals (foreign $29.50); institutions $40 (foreign $45.50). State University of New York Press, State University Plaza, Albany, NY 12246. (Subscr. to: S U N Y Press, c/o C U P Services, Box 6525, Ithaca, NY 14851. TEL 800-666-2211) Ed. Ann Kibbey. circ. 900. **Indexed:** Amer.Hist.& Life (until 1993), Bibl.Engl.Lang.& Lit., Film Lit.Ind. (1989-), Hist.Abstr. (until 1993), Wom.Stud.Abstr. (1988-). **Document type:** academic/scholarly publication.
—Faxon; Genuine Article; SWETS; UMI; Uncover. **CCC.**
  Description: Essays in art, literature, film, and history that focus on sexuality and gender. Addresses theoretical issues relating sexuality and gender to social, political, racial, economic, or stylistic concerns.

305.4   SW   ISSN 0283-2399
GOETEBORG WOMEN'S STUDIES. 1986. irreg., no.3, 1993. price varies. Acta Universitatis Gothoburgensis, P.O. Box 5096, S-402 22 Goeteborg, Sweden. Ed. Yvone Hirdman. **Document type:** monographic series.

305.4 362.7   US   ISSN 1064-4377
AS911.A2
GRANTS FOR WOMEN AND GIRLS. (Subseries of: Grant Guides) 1982. a. $70 (effective Oct. 1994). Foundation Center, 79 Fifth Ave., New York, NY 10003. TEL 212-620-4230. FAX 212-807-3677.
  Description: Lists grants for education, career guidance, vocational training, equal rights, rape prevention, shelter and health programs, abortion rights, pregnancy programs, athletics and recreation, arts programs and social research.

HARVARD WOMEN'S LAW JOURNAL. see *LAW*

346.969   US   ISSN 0092-9190
KFH91.W6
HAWAII. STATE COMMISSION ON THE STATUS OF WOMEN. ANNUAL REPORT. Key Title: Annual Report - State of Hawaii. State Commission on the Status of Women. 1972. a. free. State Commission on the Status of Women, 335 Merchant St., Rm. 253, Honolulu, HI 96813. TEL 808-586-5757. FAX 808-586-5756. illus. circ. 500. **Document type:** newsletter, government publication.
  Description: Sent to government offices, the Governor and Lt. Governor, and legislators.

305.4   AT   ISSN 0311-4198
HECATE; women's interdisciplinary journal. 1975. s-a. Aus.$15 to individuals; institutions Aus.$60. Hecate Press, c/o English Dept., Univ. Queensland, St. Lucia, Qld. 4067, Australia. TEL 61-7-365-3146. FAX 61-7-365-2799. Ed. Carole Ferrier. adv.; bk.rev.; bibl. circ. 2,000. (also avail. in microform from UMI; back issues avail.) **Indexed:** Alt.Press Ind., Aus.P.A.I.S., Bibl.Engl.Lang.& Lit., Left Ind. (1982-), Mult.Ed.Abstr., Stud.Wom.Abstr., Wom.Stud.Abstr. (1975-). **Document type:** academic/scholarly publication.
●Also available online. Vendor(s): University Microfilms International.
—BLDSC (4282.750000); UMI; Uncover.
  Description: Offers perspectives on the status of women from socialist and women's liberation standpoints. Includes articles, interviews, plays, poems and stories.
Refereed Serial

305.4 800   US   ISSN 0898-0241
HER OWN WORDS; women's history, literature and art. 1987. q. $10. Her Own Words, Box 5264, Madison, WI 53705. TEL 608-271-7083. Ed. Jocelyn Riley. (back issues avail.) **Document type:** newsletter.

305.412 700   US   ISSN 0146-3411
HQ1101
HERESIES; a feminist publication on art and politics. 1977. irreg. (1-2/yr.) $27 to individuals (foreign $33); institutions $38 (foreign $44) for 4 nos. Heresies Collective, Inc., 280 Broadway, Ste. 412, New York, NY 10007-1809. TEL 212-227-2108. Ed.Bd. adv. contact: Jean Casella. bk.rev.; illus.; circ. 8,000 (paid). **Indexed:** Alt.Press Ind., Artbibl.Mod., Avery Ind.Archit.Per., Mid.East: Abstr.& Ind., Stud.Wom.Abstr., Wom.Stud.Abstr. (1977-). **Document type:** academic/scholarly publication.
—BLDSC (4300.025800); Faxon; Uncover.
  Description: Includes essays, articles, interviews, poetry, short fiction, page art, photography and all types of visual art, with a thematic, political focus.

190.92   NE
HISTORY OF WOMEN PHILOSOPHERS. (Text in English) irreg. price varies. Kluwer Academic Publishers, Postbus 17, 3300 AA Dordrecht, Netherlands. TEL 31-78-392392. FAX 31-78-392254. TELEX 29245 KAPG. (Dist. by: Kluwer Academic Publishers Group, P.O. Box 322, 3300 AH Dordrecht, Netherlands. TEL 31-78-392392. FAX 31-78-546474; N. America dist. addr.: Box 358, Accord Sta., Hingham, MA 02018-0358. TEL 617-871-6600. FAX 617-871-6528) **Document type:** monographic series.

305.4   AU   ISSN 1016-362X
L'HOMME; Zeitschrift fuer Feministische Geschichtswissenschaft. 1990. 2/yr. S.392. (Universitaet Wien, Institut fuer Geschichte) Boehlau Verlag GmbH & Co. KG, Sachsenplatz 4-6, Postfach 87, A-1201 Vienna, Austria. TEL 0222-3302427. FAX 0222-3302432. Ed. Verena Pawlowsky. adv.; bk.rev. (back issues avail.) **Indexed:** Amer.Hist.& Life, Hist.Abstr. **Document type:** academic/scholarly publication.

HUMAN RIGHTS WATCH WOMEN'S RIGHTS PROJECT. see *POLITICAL SCIENCE — Civil Rights*

WOMEN'S STUDIES

305.4 US ISSN 0887-5367
HQ1101
HYPATIA; a journal of feminist philosophy. (First 3 issues (1983-1985) published as Special Issues of Women's Studies International Forum) 1986. 4/yr. $35 to individuals; institutions $60. Indiana University Press, Journals Division, 601 N. Morton St., Bloomington, IN 47404. TEL 812-855-9449. FAX 812-855-7931. Ed. Linda Lopez McAlister. adv.; bk.rev. circ. 1,500. (also avail. in microfiche; back issues avail.) **Indexed:** Acad.Ind., Alt.Press Ind., Phil.Ind., Sociol.Abstr., Wom.Stud.Abstr. (1986-). **Document type:** academic/scholarly publication.
●Also available online. Vendor(s): Information Access Co., Knight-Ridder, Inc. (File no.57), University Microfilms International.
—BLDSC (4352.621500); Faxon; SWETS; UMI; UnCover.
  Description: Recognizes the historical roots of feminist philosophy; created to help end sexism and provides a sense of relevency to feminism.

305.4 II ISSN 0971-5215
HQ1181.I4 CODEN: IJGSF4
INDIAN JOURNAL OF GENDER STUDIES. (Text in English) 1983. s-a. $36 to individuals; institutions $87 (effective Sep. 1995). (Centre for Women's Development Studies) Sage Publications India Pvt. Ltd., P.O. Box 4215, New Delhi 110 048, India. TEL 91-11-6444958. FAX 91-11-6472426. (Overseas subscr. to: Sage Publications Ltd., 6 Bonhill St., London EC2A 4PU, England; N. American subscr. to: Sage Publications, Inc., Box 5084, Thousand Oaks, CA 91356) Ed. Omita Goyal; Pub. Tejeshwar Singh. adv. contact: Sunanda Ghosh. **Document type:** academic/scholarly publication.
—BLDSC (4412.850000); UnCover.
  Formerly (until vol.6, 1992): Samya Shakti (ISSN 0970-5880)
  Description: Provides a holistic understanding of society, analyzing changing social attitudes and academic biases that obstruct a holistic understanding of contributions to the family, community, and the wider polity.

INDIGENOUS WOMAN. see SOCIOLOGY

INITIATIVES. see EDUCATION — School Organization And Administration

305.4 US
INSTITUTE FOR RESEARCH ON WOMEN AND GENDER. NEWSLETTER. 1975. q. $20 membership (student $15). Institute for Research on Women and Gender, Serra House, Stanford University, Stanford, CA 94305-8640. TEL 415-723-1994. FAX 415-725-0374. Ed. Sherri Matteo. bk.rev. circ. 1,100. **Document type:** academic/scholarly publication.

305.4 UK ISSN 0965-3775
CT3235
INTERNATIONAL WHO'S WHO OF WOMEN. 1992. irreg. $350. Europa Publications, 18 Bedford Sq., London WC1B 3JN, England. TEL 0171-580-8236. FAX 0171-636-1664. TELEX 21540 EUROPA G. **Document type:** directory.
  Description: Details the lives and achievements of more than 4500 of the most noted women in the world today.

305.4 PH ISSN 1013-0519
ISIS INTERNATIONAL WOMEN'S BOOK SERIES. (Text and summaries in English) 1974. a. $40. Isis International, 66, Scout Delgado, Bgy. Laging Handa, Quezon City 1100, Philippines. TEL 632-967297. FAX 632-9241065. Ed. Marilee Karl. bk.rev.; film rev. circ. 4,500. (back issues avail.) **Indexed:** Alt.Press Ind., Int.Lab.Doc., Stud.Wom.Abstr., Wom.Stud.Abstr. (1974-).
  Former titles (until 1987): Isis International Women's Journal (ISSN 1011-5056); (until 1984): Isis Women's International Bulletin (ISSN 1013-0500); (until 1982): Isis International Bulletin (ISSN 1013-0497)

ISSUES QUARTERLY; an intelligent resource for research, policy and action affecting the lives of women and girls. see WOMEN'S INTERESTS

ITHACA WOMEN'S ANTHOLOGY. see LITERATURE — Poetry

305.412 616.89 US ISSN 0895-2833
RC488.5
JOURNAL OF FEMINIST FAMILY THERAPY. 1989. q. $140 (foreign $196) (effective 1996). Haworth Press, Inc., 10 Alice St., Binghamton, NY 13904. TEL 607-722-5857; 800-342-9678. FAX 607-722-1424. Ed. Janine Roberts. adv.; bk.rev. (also avail. in microfiche from UMI; reprint service avail. from HAW) **Indexed:** IMFL, Ind.Per.Art.Relat.Law, Soc.Work Res.& Abstr., Stud.Wom.Abstr., Wom.Stud.Abstr. (1989-).
—BLDSC (4983.937000); Haworth; UnCover.
  Description: Explores feminist theory in relation to family therapy practice and theory.
Refereed Serial

305.4 200 UK ISSN 8755-4178
HQ1393
JOURNAL OF FEMINIST STUDIES IN RELIGION. 1985. s-a. £16.95 to individuals; institutions £27.50. T & T Clark, 59 George St., Edingurgh EH2 2LQ, Scotland. TEL 0131-225-4703. FAX 0131-220-4260. Ed. Linda Woodhead. adv. contact: J. Grounsell. (back issues avail.) **Indexed:** Rel.& Theol.Abstr. (1985-), Wom.Stud.Abstr. (1985-). **Document type:** academic/scholarly publication.
—BLDSC (4983.940000); Faxon; Genuine Article; UMI; UnCover.
  Description: Papers on the academic study of religion from a feminist perspective.

305 UK ISSN 0958-9236
HQ1101 CODEN: JGESEH
JOURNAL OF GENDER STUDIES. 1992. 3/yr. £18 to individuals; institutions £92 (effective 1996). Carfax Publishing Co., P.O. Box 25, Abingdon, Oxon. OX14 3UE, England. TEL 01235-555335. FAX 01235-553559. (Subscr. in N. America to: Carfax Publishing Co., 875-81 Massachusetts Ave., Cambridge, MA 02139) (Co-sponsors: University of Hull; Humberside University) Eds. Jenny Hockey, Jenny Wolmark. adv.; bk.rev.; index. **Document type:** academic/scholarly publication.
—BLDSC (4987.667000); UMI. **CCC.**
  Description: Publishes articles relating to gender from a feminist perspective within a wide range of subject areas covering the natural and social sciences, the arts, and popular culture.
Refereed Serial

301.412 362.6 US ISSN 0895-2841
HV1457 CODEN: JWAGE5
JOURNAL OF WOMEN AND AGING. 1989. q. $140 (foreign $196) (effective 1996). Haworth Press, Inc., 10 Alice St., Binghamton, NY 13904. TEL 607-722-5857; 800-342-9678. FAX 607-722-1424. TELEX 4932599. Ed. J. Dianne Garner. adv.; bk.rev. circ. 248. (also avail. in microform from UMI; reprint service avail. from HAW) **Indexed:** IMFL, Mult.Ed.Abstr., Soc.Work Res.& Abstr., Wom.Stud.Abstr. (1991-).
—BLDSC (5072.632800); Faxon; Haworth; UnCover.
  Description: Aims to enhance the knowledge of a variety of professionals concerned with meeting the social, psychological, and health care needs of women as they mature.
Refereed Serial

305.412 200 320 US ISSN 0888-5621
BL458
JOURNAL OF WOMEN AND RELIGION. 1981. a. $50. Center for Women and Religion, Graduate Theological Union, 2400 Ridge Rd., Berkeley, CA 94709. TEL 510-649-2490. FAX 510-649-1417. bk.rev. circ. 800. (also avail. in microform from UMI; back issues avail.) **Indexed:** Rel.Ind.One. **Document type:** academic/scholarly publication.
—UMI; UnCover.
  Description: Focuses on transformation and theological education to stop sexism against women.

305.412 US ISSN 1042-7961
HQ1101
JOURNAL OF WOMEN'S HISTORY. 1989. q. $35 to individuals; institutions $60. Indiana University Press, Journals Division, 601 N. Morton St., Bloomington, IN 47404. TEL 812-855-9449. FAX 812-855-7931. Eds. Christie Farnham, Joan Hoff-Wilson. adv. circ. 1,500. (also avail. in microfilm; microform from UMI; back issues avail.) **Indexed:** Alt.Press Ind., Film Lit.Ind. (1989-), Mult.Ed.Abstr., Wom.Stud.Abstr. (1989-). **Document type:** academic/scholarly publication.
●Also available online. Vendor(s): University Microfilms International.
—BLDSC (5072.634500); Faxon; SWETS; UMI; UnCover.
  Description: Covers new research on women's history. Promotes scholarship about women in all time periods that is broadly representative of national, racial, ethnic, religious, and sexual groupings.

KALEIDOSCOPE OF CAROLINA. see LITERATURE

305.43 SW ISSN 0348-8365
HQ1104
KVINNOVETENSKAPLIG TIDSKRIFT. (Text in Swedish; summaries in English) 1980. q. SEK 250 in the Nordic countries; elsewhere SEK 290. Foereningen Kvinnovetenskaplig Tidskrift, Kungsgatan 95, S-903 31 Umeaa, Sweden. TEL 46-90-13-55-90. FAX 46-90-13-04-01. Eds. Gerd Lindgren, Carin Mannerberg-Zackari. adv.; bk.rev. **Document type:** academic/scholarly publication.
  Description: Each issue is devoted to a single theme, such as friendship, love, motherhood, art, etc.

LEGACY (UNIVERSITY PARK); a journal of American women writers. see LITERATURE

305.412 323.4 NE ISSN 0165-8042
HQ1104
LOVER; literatuuroverzicht over feminisme, cultuur en wetenschap. 1974. q. fl.3.35. Internationaal Informatiecentrum en Archief voor de Vrouwenbeweging - International Information Center and Archive for the Women's Movement, Obiplein 4, 1094 RB Amsterdam, Netherlands. TEL 31-20-6654552. FAX 31-20-6655812. adv.; bk.rev. circ. 3,300.
—SWETS.

305.4 618.3 US
M I D S NEWSLETTER. (Miscarriage, Infant Death, and Stillbirth) 1983. 5/yr. $30. M I D S Inc., 16 Crescent Dr., Parsippany, NJ 07054. **Document type:** newsletter.
  Description: Newsletter of announcements for families suffering miscarriages, infant deaths, and stillbirths.

305.412 II ISSN 0257-7305
HQ1104
MANUSHI; a journal about women and society. (Text in English) 1979. bi-m. Rs.60($25) to individuals; institutions Rs.85($36). Manushi Trust, C1 - 202 Lajpat Nagar, New Delhi 110024, India. TEL 6833022. FAX 683-9158. E-mail: Manushi@unv.ernet.in. Ed. Madhu Kishwar. adv.; bk.rev. circ. 10,000. (also avail. in microfiche from IDC) **Indexed:** Alt.Press Ind., HR Rep. (1984-), Int.Lab.Doc., Mult.Ed.Abstr., Stud.Wom.Abstr., Wom.Stud.Abstr. (1990-). **Document type:** academic/scholarly publication.
—BLDSC (5368.465000); UnCover.
  Description: Covers human rights issues with an emphasis on women's issues. Examines women's working and living conditions in India and their struggle for change.

MARKETING TO WOMEN; lifestyle studies about women in America. see BUSINESS AND ECONOMICS — Marketing And Purchasing

WOMEN'S STUDIES

700 305.4 CN ISSN 1182-6169
MATRIART; a Canadian feminist art journal. 1990. q. Can.$20 to individuals (foreign Can.$30); institutions Can.$30 (foreign Can.$40) (effective 1995). Women's Art Resource Center, 80 Spadina Ave., Ste. 506, Toronto, ON M5V 2J3, Canada. TEL 416-703-0074. FAX 416-703-0441. (Dist. by: CMPA, 30 Spadina Ave., Ste. 202, Toronto, ON M5V 2L4, Canada. TEL 416-504-0274. FAX 416-504-0437) Ed. Linda Abrahams. adv.: B&W page Can.$200. circ. 2,000. (back issues avail.)
Description: Devoted to women's art and cultural production.

305.4 GW ISSN 0939-5970
HQ1103
METIS. 1992. s-a. DM.38. Centaurus Verlag, Im Breyel 19, 79292 Pfaffenweiler, Germany. TEL 07664-8669. FAX 07664-8269. adv.: page DM.400. bk.rev.; bibl. **Document type:** academic/scholarly publication.

305.412 BO
MONOGRAFIAS DE PROMOCION FEMENINA. 1985. irreg. price varies. Centro de Investigaciones Sociales, Casilla 6931 - Correo Central, La Paz, Bolivia. **Document type:** monographic series.

305.4 US ISSN 0047-8318
HQ1101
MS. 1972-1989; resumed July 1990. bi-m. $45. Lang Communications, 230 Park Ave., 7th Fl., New York, NY 10169. TEL 212-551-9500. (Subscr. to: Ms., Box 57122, Boulder, CO 80321-7122. TEL 800-234-4486) Ed. Marcia Gillespie. adv.; bk.rev.; index. circ. 200,000. (also avail. in microform from UMI) **Indexed:** Acad.Ind., Bibl.Engl.Lang.& Lit., Bk.Rev.Ind., Child.Bk.Rev.Ind. (1974-), Consum.Ind., Curr.Lit.Fam.Plan., Film Lit.Ind. (1974-), Hlth.Ind., Mag.Ind., Media Rev.Dig., Mid.East: Abstr.& Ind., Pers.Lit., PMR, R.G., Stud.Wom.Abstr., TOM, Wom.Stud.Abstr. (1972-1989, 1990-).
—BLDSC (5980.840000); Faxon; SWETS; UMI.
Description: Contains features about feminist issues and concerns, national and international news concerning women, plus original fiction and poetry.

305.4 UY
LA MUJER URUGUAYA. 1990. a. Grupo de Estudios sobre la Condicion de la Mujer en el Uruguay (GRECMU), Miguel de Corro 1474, Montevideo, Uruguay. Ed. Nea Filgueira.

305.4 CL ISSN 0716-8497
MUJERES EN ACCION. 1984. q. $35. Isis Internacional, Casilla 2067, Correo Central, Santiago, Chile. TEL 56-2-6382219. FAX 56-2-6383142. E-mail: isis@ax.apc.org.
Description: International review, looks at world happenings from women's perspective. Offers information and debate on the women's movement.

305.412 US ISSN 1040-0656
HQ1186.U6 CODEN: NWJOEG
N W S A JOURNAL.* 1988. 3/yr. $50 to individuals; institutions $130 (effective 1994). National Women's Studies Association, 7100 Baltimore Ave., Ste. 301, College Park, MD 20742-1325. TEL 301-403-0524. FAX 301-403-4137. Ed. Patsy Schweickart. adv.: bk.rev.; abstr.; bibl.; illus. circ. 1,400. **Indexed:** Left Ind. (1990-), Soc.Sci.Ind. (1994-), Wom.Stud.Abstr. (1988-). **Document type:** academic/scholarly publication.
—BLDSC (6190.647000); Faxon; UnCover. **CCC.**
Description: Publishes research linking feminist theory with teaching and activism.

305.4 US
N W S ACTION. 1988. q. membership. National Women's Studies Association, 7100 Baltimore Ave., Ste. 301, College Park, MD 20742-1325. TEL 301-403-0524. FAX 301-403-4137. Ed. Miriam Harris. circ. 4,000. (back issues avail.) **Indexed:** Wom.Stud.Abstr. (1988-). **Document type:** newsletter.
Description: Articles on women's studies and related subjects for those interested in feminist education.

305.412 IS
NAAMAT; magazine for women - in work, society & family. Issued with: Urim la-Orim (ISSN 0042-1073) (Text in Hebrew) 1934. 10/yr. IS.55. Histadrut, Working Women Organization and Volunteers, 93 Arlozorov St., 62 098 Tel Aviv, Israel. TEL 03-431111. TELEX 342-488-HISTD-IL. Ed. Zivya Cohen. adv.; bk.rev.; film rev.; play rev.; illus.; index. circ. 15,000. **Indexed:** Ind.Heb.Per.
Formerly: Dvar Hapoelet.
Description: Studies women's role in work and society, women's status, and legal rights.

305.4 US ISSN 0898-8900
HQ1104
NICHIBEI JOSEI JOURNAL. (Text in Japanese) 1988. s-a. $30 to individuals (foreign $33); institutions $55 (foreign $58); with U S - Japan Women's Journal $60 to individuals (foreign $66); insitutions $110 (foreign $116) (effective 1995-1996). U S - Japan Women's Center, 926 Bautista Ct., Palo Alto, CA 94303. TEL 415-857-9049. FAX 415-494-8160. Ed. Yoko Kawashima. adv. contact: Yuka Honda. circ. 700. (back issues avail.) **Document type:** academic/scholarly publication.
Description: Exchanges scholarship on women and gender among the U.S., Japan, and other nations.

305.411 NO ISSN 0803-8740
HQ1101
NORA; Nordic journal of women's studies. (Text in English) 1993. s-a. NOK 318 in Nordic countries; elsewhere $63 (effective 1996). Scandinavian University Press, P.O. Box 2959 Toeyen, N-0608 Oslo, Norway. TEL 47-22-57-54-00. FAX 47-22-57-53-53. Ed.Bd.
Description: Publishes original research articles, short communications and review essays within women's studies.

305.4 NQ
NOSOTRAS. 1991. q.? A.M.N.L.A.E., Del Reparto San Juan 2c. al sur casa 598, Apdo. Postal A-278, Managua, Nicaragua. TEL 71661. Ed. Christian Santos. **Document type:** consumer publication.

305.4 IT ISSN 1121-211X
NOSSIDE: QUADERNI DI SCRITTURA FEMMINILE. 1991. s-a. L.18000 (foreign L.40000). Rubbettino Editore, Viale dei Pini, 8, 88049 Soveria Mannelli, Italy. FAX 39-968-662035. Ed. Renate Siebert. circ. 2,000. (back issues avail.)

305.4 920 US
NOTABLE HISPANIC AMERICAN WOMEN. 1993. every 5 yrs. $59.95. Gale Research Inc., 835 Penobscot Bldg., Detroit, MI 48226. TEL 313-961-2242. FAX 313-961-6083. Eds. Diane Telgen, Jim Kamp.
Description: Provides biographical details on 300 women of national or international prominence.

305.412 US ISSN 0030-0071
OFF OUR BACKS; a women's news journal. 1970. m. $21 to individuals; institutions $33. Off Our Backs, Inc., 2337B 18th St., N.W., Washington, DC 20009-2003. TEL 202-234-8072. Ed.Bd. adv.; bk.rev.; film rev.; play rev.; illus.; index. circ. 22,000. (tabloid format; also avail. in microfilm from UMI; back issues avail.) **Indexed:** Alt.Press Ind., Mult.Ed.Abstr., New Per.Ind., Stud.Wom.Abstr., Wom.Stud.Abstr. (1970-). **Document type:** newspaper.
—BLDSC (6236.527000); Faxon; UMI.
Description: Covers news affecting the women's liberation movement.

ON CAMPUS WITH WOMEN. see *EDUCATION — Higher Education*

305.4 JA ISSN 1340-2943
CODEN: OKJDEC
OSAKA KUKUSAI JOSHI DAIGAKU KIYO/OSAKA INTERNATIONAL UNIVERSITY FOR WOMEN. BULLETIN. (Text in English, Japanese) 1975. s-a. Osaka Kokusai Joshi Daigaku, 21-57, Todacho 6-chome, Moriguchi-shi, Osaka, Japan. (Co-sponsor: Osaka Kokusai Joshi Tanki Daigaku) **Document type:** bulletin.
—BLDSC (2674.510000).
Formerly (until 1993): Teikoku Gakuen Kiyo - Bulletin of Teikoku Gakuen (ISSN 0385-8553)

305.4 MX
PALABRA DE MUJER. 1991. bi-m. Mex.$80 (foreign $60) (effective 1996). Equilibrio Editores, Yanez No. 16 esq. con Zacatecas, 83190 Hermosillo, Sonora, Mexico. TEL 52-62-157918. FAX 52-62-102260. Ed. Maria Antonieta Medivil; Pub. Martin Enrique Mendivil. adv.: page Mex.$1600; adv. contact: Maria Dolores del Rio. circ. 1,000. (reprint service avail.) **Document type:** newsletter.
Description: Provides analysis of society from women's perspective in three areas: the woman herself, woman and family, and woman and her cultural, social, and political relationships.

DIE PHILOSOPHIN; Forum fuer feministische Theorie und Philosophie. see *PHILOSOPHY*

PSYCHOLOGY OF WOMEN QUARTERLY. see *PSYCHOLOGY*

305.412 LE
AL-RAIDA. 1976. q. $25. Beirut University College, Institute for Women's Studies in the Arab World, Box 13-5053, Beirut, Lebanon. TEL 867099. FAX 867098. TELEX BUC 23389 LE. (Overseas correspondence and subscr. to: 475 Riverside Dr., Rm. 1846, New York, N.Y. 10115. TEL 212-870-2592. FAX 212-870-2762) Ed. Randa Abul-Husn. adv.: B&W page $300 (4 insertions). bk.rev.; charts; illus. circ. 700. **Indexed:** Mult.Ed.Abstr., Per.Islam. (1991-). **Document type:** newsletter, academic/scholarly publication.
Description: Brings to the reader the Arab woman today: her role, her status, and current issues related to her. Includes news items on conferences and publications.

305.4 CN ISSN 0838-4479
HQ1186.C2
RECHERCHES FEMINISTES; revue interdisciplinaire francophone d'etudes feministes. (Text in French, summaries in English, French) 1988. 2/yr. Can.$22 to individuals (foreign Can.$27); institutions Can.$35 (foreign Can.$39); students Can.$20 (foreign Can.$25). Universite Laval, Groupe de Recherche Multidisciplinaire Feministe, 3e etage, 2336 Chemin Ste-Foy, Quebec, Que. G1K 7P4, Canada. TEL 418-656-5421. FAX 418-656-3266. Ed. Huguette Dagenais. adv.; bk.rev. circ. 1,000. (back issues avail.) **Indexed:** P.A.I.S.For.Lang.Ind., Pt.de Rep., Wom.Stud.Abstr.
Description: A source of information on feminist teaching, research and action.
Refereed Serial

305.4 364.4 CL
RED FEMINISTA LATINOAMERICANA Y DEL CARIBE CONTRA LA VIOLENCIA DOMESTICA Y SEXUAL. BOLETIN. (Text in Spanish; summary in English) q. $20. Isis Internacional, Casilla 2067, Correo Central, Santiago, Chile. TEL 56-2-6382219. FAX 56-2-6383142. E-mail: isis@ax.apc.org. **Document type:** bulletin.
Description: Information and analysis from around the region.

305.4 618.082 BL
REDE NACIONAL FEMINISTA DE SAUDE E DIREITOS REPRODUTIVOS. JORNAL. Short title: Jornal da Rede. 1992. q. Rede Nacional Feminista de Saude e Direitos Reprodutivos, c/o SOS Corpo, Genero e Cidadania, Rua Major Codeceira, 37, 50100-070 Santa Amaro, Recife, Brazil. TEL 55-81-4233044. FAX 55-81-4233180. E-mail: soscorpo@ax.apc.org. Ed. Maria Betania Avila. circ. 7,000. **Document type:** bulletin.
Description: Publicizes studies and political action towards changing laws and public health procedures refering to women's health and reproduction.

WOMEN'S STUDIES

305.412　　　　　CN　　ISSN 0707-8412
HQ1101
RESOURCES FOR FEMINIST RESEARCH/DOCUMENTATION SUR LA RECHERCHE FEMINISTE. (Text in English, French) 1972. 4/yr. Can.$25($40) to individuals; Can.$50($65) to institutions. Ontario Institute for Studies in Education, 252 Bloor St. W., Toronto, ON M5S 1V6, Canada. TEL 416-923-6641. FAX 416-926-4725. TELEX 06217720. adv.; bk.rev.; abstr.; bibl. circ. 2,000. (also avail. in microfilm; back issues avail.) **Indexed:** Amer.Hist.& Life, Can.B.P.I., Can.Educ.Ind., Can.Wom.Per.Ind., CMI, Hist.Abstr., Hum.Ind., Lang.& Lang.Behav.Abstr., Mult.Ed.Abstr., Sociol.Abstr., Stud.Wom.Abstr., Wom.Stud.Abstr. (1972-). **Document type:** academic/scholarly publication.
—BLDSC (7777.608150); UnCover. **CCC.**
Formerly: Canadian Newsletter of Research on Women (ISSN 0319-4477)
Description: Presents international research on women's studies and feminist theory.

305.4　　　　　CR
REVISTA CASA DE LA MUJER. 1990. s-a. Universidad Nacional, Centro de Estudios de la Mujer, Apdo. 86, 3000 Heredia, Costa Rica. TEL 37-6363 ext. 2399. (Co-sponsor: Centro Nacional para el Desarrollo de la Mujer y la Familia)

ROOM OF ONE'S OWN; a feminist journal of literature and criticism. see *LITERATURE*

ROSHNI. see *WOMEN'S INTERESTS*

RUNDBRIEF FRAUEN IN DER LITERATURWISSENSCHAFT. see *LITERATURE*

305.42　　　　　US
S I R O W NEWSLETTER. 1979. 2/yr. free. Southwest Institute for Research on Women, c/o Women's Studies, 102 Douglass Bldg., Univ of Arizona, Tucson, AZ 85721. TEL 602-621-7338. FAX 602-621-1533. Ed. Janice Monk. bk.rev. circ. 3,000. **Document type:** newsletter.

305.896 910.03　　US　　ISSN 0741-8639
E185.86
SAGE: A SCHOLARLY JOURNAL ON BLACK WOMEN. 1984. 2/yr. $15 to individuals; institutions $25. Sage Women's Educational Press, Inc., Box 42741, Atlanta, GA 30311-0741. TEL 404-223-7528. FAX 404-753-8383. Eds. Patricia Bell-Scott, Beverly Guy-Sheftall. adv.; bk.rev.; film rev.; play rev.; bibl. circ. 2,000. (back issues avail.) **Indexed:** Alt.Press Ind., Amer.Hist.& Life, Hist.Abstr., Mult.Ed.Abstr., Psychol.Abstr., Soc.Sci.Ind. (1994-), Sociol.Abstr., Stud.Wom.Abstr., Wom.Stud.Abstr. (1984-). **Document type:** academic/scholarly publication.
—BLDSC (8069.215400); Faxon; UnCover.
Description: Provides an interdisciplinary forum for critical discussion of issues relating to black women.

304.2　　　　　NE　　ISSN 0928-8368
SAVANTE. 1977. q. Amsterdam University Press, Prinsengracht 747-751, 1017 JX Amsterdam, Netherlands. TEL 31-20-4200050. FAX 31-20-4203214.
Former titles (until 1992): Pheme (ISSN 0921-6596); (until 1985): U v A - Eva (ISSN 0165-909X); (until 1978): Vrouwen en Universiteit (ISSN 0921-1357)

305.412　　　　　US　　ISSN 0097-9740
HQ1101
SIGNS: JOURNAL OF WOMEN IN CULTURE AND SOCIETY. 1975. q. $34 to individuals; institutions $80; students $24. University of Chicago Press, Journals Division, 5720 S. Woodlawn Ave., Chicago, IL 60637. TEL 312-753-3347. FAX 312-753-0811. TELEX 25-4603. (Subscr. to: Box 37005, Chicago, IL 60637) Eds. Ruth-Ellen Botcher Joeres, Barbara Laslett. adv.; bk.rev. circ. 6,100. (also avail. in microform from UMI,PMC; reprint service avail. from UMI,ISI) **Indexed:** A.B.C.Pol.Sci., Abstr.Crim.& Pen., Acad.Ind., Adol.Ment.Hlth.Abstr., Amer.Bibl.Slavic & E.Eur.Stud., Amer.Hist.& Life, Amer.Hum.Ind., Anthropol.Lit., ASCA, ASSIA, Bk.Rev.Ind. (1984-), C.I.J.E., CERDIC, Child.Bk.Rev.Ind. (1984-), Commun.Abstr., Curr.Cont., Hist.Abstr., IMFL, Int.Lab.Doc., Lang.& Lang.Behav.Abstr., M.L.A., Mid.East: Abstr.& Ind., Mult.Ed.Abstr., Psychol.Abstr. (1975-), Soc.Sci.Ind., Sociol.Abstr., SSCI, Stud.Wom.Abstr., Wom.Stud.Abstr. (1975-). **Document type:** academic/scholarly publication.
—BLDSC (8276.317000); Faxon; Genuine Article; SWETS; UMI; UnCover. **CCC.**
Description: Examines theories and methodologies from a variety of disciplines and provides important links between feminist theory and the realities of women's lives.
Refereed Serial

305.4　　　　　US　　ISSN 1072-4745
HQ1236
▼**SOCIAL POLITICS: INTERNATIONAL STUDIES IN GENDER, STATE, AND SOCIETY.** 1994. 3/yr. $22 to individuals (foreign $34); institutions $40 (foreign $52). University of Illinois Press, 1325 S. Oak St., Champaign, IL 61820. TEL 217-333-0950. FAX 217-244-8082. Ed.Bd. adv.: B&W page $140; adv. contact: Ann Lowry. charts, illus.; index. (also avail. in microfiche from UMI) **Document type:** academic/scholarly publication.
—BLDSC (8318.133800). **CCC.**
Description: Takes an interdisciplinary approach to gender studies, social policy, citizenship, and the role of the state in organizing relations in the family, workplace, and society.
Refereed Serial

305.4　　　　　US　　ISSN 0191-8699
HQ1402
SOJOURNER; the women's forum. 1975. m. $21 to individuals; institutions $31. Sojourner, Inc., 42 Seaverns Ave., Jamaica Plain, MA 02130-2865. TEL 617-524-0415. Ed. Karen Kahn. adv. contact: Kate Hogan. bk.rev.; film rev.; illus. circ. 40,000. (tabloid format; also avail. in microfiche; back issues avail.; reprint service avail. from UMI) **Indexed:** Alt.Press Ind., PMR. **Document type:** newspaper.
—UMI.
Description: Includes features, opinion pieces, and reviews on issues of social, political and economic importance to women.

305.4　　　　　US
SONOMA COUNTY WOMEN'S VOICES. 1980. m. $13 (effective Jun. 1995). Women's Support Network, Box 4448, Santa Rosa, CA 95402. TEL 707-575-5654. Eds. Snake, Suki McDonough. adv.: $430; trim 10 x 16. bk.rev.; illus.; film rev.; music rev.; play rev.; video rev. circ. 4,000. cols./p.: 3; pp./issue: 20. (tabloid format) **Document type:** newspaper.
Description: Provides a local forum for, by and about women.

305.4 323.4　　US
SOUTHERN WOMEN: THE INTERSECTION OF RACE, CLASS AND GENDER. 1991. irreg., latest 1994. $6 per no. University of Memphis, Center for Research on Women, Memphis, TN 38152. TEL 901-378-2770. (back issues avail.) **Document type:** monographic series.
Description: Discusses racial and sociopolitical issues from a women's studies perspective.

STUDIES IN GENDER AND CULTURE. see *SOCIOLOGY*

820　　　　　NE　　ISSN 0921-2981
SURPLUS; boekbesprekingen - review of books. 1987. bi-m. fl.33. Stichting Surplus, Postbus 16572, 1001 RB Amsterdam, Netherlands. TEL 31-20-6207767. Ed. Monica Soeting. adv.; bk.rev. circ. 1,000. (back issues avail.)

305.4 070.5　　GW
TASCHENBUCH DER FRAUENPRESSE. 1990. a. Verlag Rommerskirchen und Co. KG, Bennauerstr. 60, 53115 Bonn, Germany. TEL 0228-222974. FAX 0228-214917. Ed. Beate Paulick. **Document type:** bulletin.

TEXAS JOURNAL OF WOMEN AND THE LAW. see *LAW*

305.4　　　　　US
TRANSSISTERS; the journal of transsexual feminism. 1993. q. $24; newsstand price: 6. Skyclad Publishing Co., 4004 Troost Ave., Kansas City, MO 64110. TEL 816-753-7816. FAX 816-753-7816. E-mail: davinaanne@aol.com. Ed. Davina Anne Gabriel; Pub. Davina Anne Gabriel. adv.; page $45. bk.rev. circ. 500. (back issues avail.) **Document type:** academic/scholarly publication.
Description: Treats issues dealing with transsexuality from a feminist perspective.

305.4　　　　　UK　　ISSN 1352-027X
TROUBLE AND STRIFE; a radical feminist journal. 1983. 3/yr. £8.50 to individuals; institutions £25. P.O. Box 8, Diss, Norfolk IP22 3XG, England. adv.; bk.rev.; film rev.; illus.; index. circ. 3,000. **Indexed:** Stud.Wom.Abstr. **Document type:** consumer publication.

TULSA STUDIES IN WOMEN'S LITERATURE. see *LITERATURE*

305.4 800　　　IT　　ISSN 1122-4983
TUTTESTORIE; racconti letture trame di donne. 1990. 3/yr. L.25000 (foreign L.50000). Editrice Firmato Donna coop.r.l., Via Chiana 38, 00198 Rome, Italy. TEL 06-868-631. Ed. Maria Rosa Cutrufelli.

305.4　　　　　US　　ISSN 1059-9770
HQ1101
U S - JAPAN WOMEN'S JOURNAL: ENGLISH SUPPLEMENT; a journal for the international exchange of gender studies. (Text in English) 1991. 3 nos. every 2 yrs. $30 to individuals (foreign $33); institutions $55 (foreign $58); with Nichibei Josei Journal $60 to individuals (foreign $66); institutions $110 (foreign $116) (effective 1995-1996). U S - Japan Women's Center, 926 Bautista Ct., Palo Alto, CA 94303. TEL 415-857-9049. FAX 415-494-8160. Ed. Yoko Kawashima. adv.: page $200; trim 5 1/2 x 8 1/4; adv. contact: Yuka Honda. (back issues avail.) **Document type:** academic/scholarly publication.
—UnCover.
Description: Disseminates information concerning Japanese women and Japanese feminist theory to a U.S. audience.

UNCOVERINGS; research papers. see *NEEDLEWORK*

305.4　　　　　US
UNIVERSITY OF MEMPHIS. CENTER FOR RESEARCH ON WOMEN. CENTER NEWS. 1982? q. University of Memphis, Center for Research on Women, Memphis, TN 38152. TEL 901-678-2770. bk.rev.; bibl. **Document type:** newsletter.
Description: Discusses the center's activities and related topics.

305.4 371.3　　US
UNIVERSITY OF MEMPHIS. CENTER FOR RESEARCH ON WOMEN. CURRICULUM INTEGRATION SERIES. 1989. irreg., latest 1992. price varies. University of Memphis, Center for Research on Women, Memphis, TN 38152. TEL 901-678-2770. (back issues avail.) **Document type:** monographic series.
Description: Provides training materials for women's studies curricula.

305.4　　　　　US
UNIVERSITY OF MEMPHIS. CENTER FOR RESEARCH ON WOMEN. RESEARCH PAPERS. 1987. irreg., latest 1994. price varies. University of Memphis, Center for Research on Women, Memphis, TN 38152. TEL 901-678-2770. (back issues avail.) **Document type:** monographic series.
Description: Discusses various civil rights (both gender and racial) issues affecting women.

VIOLENCE AGAINST WOMEN. see *SOCIOLOGY*

WOMEN'S STUDIES

301.412 US ISSN 1062-628X
VOICES FROM THE ATTIC. 1979. irreg. (2-4/yr.). free to qualified personnel. Women's Studies Research Center, University of Wisconsin, 209 N. Brooks St., Madison, WI 53715. TEL 608-263-2053. FAX 608-265-2409. circ. 1,500. **Document type:** newsletter.
Formerly (until Spring 1990): Women's Studies Research Center Newsletter.
Description: Reports on women's studies research and current activities of scholars affiliated with the center.

W I C C NEWSLETTER. (Women's Inter-Church Council of Canada) see *RELIGIONS AND THEOLOGY*

305.412 323.4 US ISSN 0145-7985
HQ1101
W I N NEWS; all the news that is fit to print by, for, about women. 1975. q. $40 (foreign $44) (effective 1996). Women's International Network, 187 Grant St., Lexington, MA 02173-2140. TEL 617-862-9431. Ed. Fran P. Hosken. adv.; bk.rev.; index; circ. 1,100 (paid). (also avail. in microform from UMI; back issues avail.) **Indexed:** HR Rep. (1988-), Stud.Wom.Abstr.
●Also available online. Vendor(s): University Microfilms International.
—BLDSC (9343.379400); SWETS; UMI; UnCover.
Description: Reports on the status of women and women's rights around the world.

305.4 NE ISSN 1380-0701
W I S E WOMEN'S NEWS. (Text in English) 1991. 4/yr. 20 ECU to individuals; institutions 100 ECU. Women's International Studies Europe, Heidelberglaan 2, 3584 CS Utrecht, Netherlands. TEL 31-30-531881. FAX 31-30-531619. **Document type:** newsletter.
Description: Newsletter on all aspects of feminist and women's studies, including cultural, economic, social, political and technological issues.

305.4 UK ISSN 0953-9484
WEST & WILDE BOOKS FOR WOMEN. 1988. s-a. West & Wilde Bookshop, 25A Dundas St., Edinburgh EH3 6QQ, Scotland. TEL 031-556-0079. FAX 031-558-3717. Ed. Sigrid Nielsen. bk.rev. circ. 1,500. (back issues avail.) **Document type:** bibliography.

WOMAN OF MYSTERY. see *LITERATURE*

305.412 700 800 US ISSN 0743-2356
HQ1101
WOMAN OF POWER; a magazine of feminism, spirituality, and politics. 1984. s-a. $15. Woman of Power, Inc., Box 2785, Orleans, MA 02653. TEL 508-240-7877. Ed. Charlene McKee. adv.; bk.rev.; bibl. circ. 23,000. (back issues avail.)
—Faxon; UnCover.
Description: Discusses feminism, spirituality, and politics. Explores an important theme, such as leadership, relationships, or diversity, in each issue.

305 305.4 AT ISSN 0311-8479
WOMANSPEAK. 1974. 4/yr. Aus.$10 (foreign Aus.$12) to individuals; institutions and libraries Aus.$16 (foreign Aus.$20). Womanspeak Collective, P.O. Box 103, Spit Junction, Sydney, N.S.W. 2088, Australia. Ed.Bd. adv.; bk.rev.; illus. circ. 1,500. **Indexed:** HR Rep., Stud.Wom.Abstr.
—BLDSC (9343.216000).
Description: Provides information on women's involvement in film, art, fiction, theatre, work and domesticity and politics. Discusses a broad range of related issues, especially as they pertain to feminist activism.

305.4 UK ISSN 0957-4042
HQ1591
WOMEN; a cultural review. 1990. 3/yr. £52($95) (effective 1996). Oxford University Press, Oxford Journals, Walton St., Oxford OX2 6DP, England. TEL 01865-267907. FAX 01865-267773. TELEX 837330-OXPRES-G. E-mail: jnlorders@oup.co.uk. (U.S. subscr. to: Oxford University Press Inc., 2001 Evans Rd., Cary, NC 27513. TEL 919-677-0977. FAX 919-677-1714) Eds. Isobel Armstrong, Helen Carr. adv. contact: Jane Parker. bk.rev.; index. circ. 900. **Document type:** academic/scholarly publication.
—BLDSC (9343.223500); SWETS; UMI; UnCover. CCC.
Description: Explores the past and present role and representation of women in the arts and culture.

305.4 US ISSN 0273-0014
HQ1101
WOMEN (BOCA RATON). (Subseries of: S I R S Social Issues (ISSN 0740-3127)) 1974. a. price varies; a. supplement $17. Social Issues Resources Series, Box 2348, Boca Raton, FL 33427-2348. TEL 407-994-0079; 800-232-7477. FAX 407-994-4704. (looseleaf format; also avail. in microfiche; back issues avail.)
Description: Reprints articles that examine the roles and rights of women worldwide.

WOMEN & CRIMINAL JUSTICE. see *LAW — Criminal Law*

305.412 614.7 CN ISSN 0229-480X
HQ1233
WOMEN AND ENVIRONMENTS. 1976. 4/yr. $21.97 in N. America (elsewhere $29.97) to individuals; institutions $31.97 in N. America (foreign $39.97) (effective 1996). Weed Foundation, 736 Bathurst St., Toronto, ON M5S 2R4, Canada. TEL 416-516-2379. FAX 416-531-6214. TELEX WEED@WEB.APC.ORG. adv.: B&W page $360; 7 1/2 x 9 1/2; adv. contact: Lisa Dale. bk.rev.; abstr.; bibl.; illus.; circ. 1,400 (paid). (also avail. in microfilm from CML; back issues avail.) **Indexed:** Alt.Press Ind., Avery Ind.Archit.Per., Can.B.P.I., Can.Per.Ind., IDA, Sage Fam.Stud.Abstr., Soc.Sci.Ind., Stud.Wom.Abstr., Wom.Stud.Abstr. (1976-). **Document type:** academic/scholarly publication.
●Also available online. Vendor(s): University Microfilms International.
—BLDSC (9343.246000); Faxon; UMI; UnCover.
Formerly: Women and Environments International Newsletter.
Description: Examines women's relationship to urban, social and natural environments.

WOMEN AND LANGUAGE. see *LINGUISTICS*

WOMEN & LITERATURE; a journal of women writers and the literary treatment of women. see *LITERATURE*

WOMEN & POLITICS (BINGHAMTON). see *POLITICAL SCIENCE*

WOMEN & THERAPY; a feminist quarterly of research and opinion. see *PSYCHOLOGY*

305.4 US ISSN 1058-7446
HQ1180
WOMEN IN GERMAN YEARBOOK. 1985. a. price varies. (Coalition of Women in German) University of Nebraska Press, 312 N. 14th St., Box 880484, Lincoln, NE 68588-0484. TEL 402-472-3581. FAX 402-472-6214. Eds. Jeannette Clausen, Sara Friedrichsmeyer. **Document type:** academic/scholarly publication.
—CCC.
Description: Publishes contributions representing the spectrum of academic feminism, from practical criticism and pedagogy to cutting-edge criticism and theory.
Refereed Serial

WOMEN IN WORLD POLITICS; biographies of women currently in government legislatures worldwide. see *BIOGRAPHY*

305.412 CC ISSN 1000-9388
WOMEN OF CHINA. Chinese edition: Zhongguo Funu. 1956. m. Y13.20($25.50) for English ed.; Chinese ed. $36.80. Zhongguo Funu Zazhishe, A24, Shijia Hutong, Beijing 100010, People's Republic of China. TEL 5126988. (Dist. outside China by: China International Book Trading Corp., P.O. Box 399, Beijing, P.R.C.; Dist. in US by: China Books and Periodicals, Inc., 2929 24th St., San Francisco, CA 94110) Ed. Shao Yan. adv.; illus. **Document type:** consumer publication.
—UnCover.
Description: Looks at developments and problems in women's economic and political rights, in work, childcare and healthcare, courtship and marriage, and in women's role in Chinese culture.

305.4 US ISSN 1054-1969
Z7964.U49
WOMEN OF COLOR AND SOUTHERN WOMEN. 1988. a. Center for Research on Women, 339 Clement Hall, University of Memphis, Memphis, TN 38152. TEL 901-678-2770. FAX 901-678-3652. Ed. Stella A. Warren. **Document type:** academic/scholarly publication.
Description: Social science research on women of color and southern women.

WOMEN OF NOTE QUARTERLY; The magazine of historical and contemporary women composers. see *MUSIC*

WOMEN WRITERS OF ITALY. see *LITERATURE*

WOMEN WRITING NEWSLETTER. see *LITERATURE*

305.4 US ISSN 1051-5372
HQ1236.5.C3
WOMEN'S ALERT. 1990. s-m. $25. California State Polytechnic University, 3801 W. Temple Ave., Pomona, CA 91768. TEL 909-869-3857. FAX 909-869-3845. Ed. Mari Goldman. **Document type:** newsletter.

305.4
WOMEN'S HISTORY CATALOG. 1982. s-a. National Women's History Project, 7738 Bell Rd., Windsor, CA 95492. TEL 707-838-6000. FAX 707-838-0478. Ed. Bonnie Eisenberg. circ. 300,000 (controlled). **Document type:** catalog.
Formerly: Women's History Resource Catalog.
Description: Provides multicultural women's history resources for all ages and interests.

305.4 US
WOMEN'S HISTORY NETWORK NEWS. 1983. q. $25. National Women's History Project, 7738 Bell Rd., Windsor, CA 95492. TEL 707-838-6000. FAX 707-838-0478. Ed. Mary Ruthsdotter. bk.rev. circ. 800. (tabloid format; back issues avail.) **Document type:** newsletter.

305.4 UK ISSN 0961-2025
CODEN: WOHIEV
WOMEN'S HISTORY REVIEW. 1992. 4/yr. £112 (effective 1996). Triangle Journals Ltd., P.O. Box 65, Wallingford, Oxfordshire OX10 0YG, England. TEL 01491-838013. FAX 01491-834968. E-mail: journal@triangle.co.uk; Site addr.: http://www.triangle.co.uk. Ed.Bd. **Document type:** academic/scholarly publication.
—BLDSC (9343.379060).
Description: Aims to provide a forum for the publication of new scholarly articles in the field of women's history.
Refereed Serial

305.4 US ISSN 1072-1770
WOMEN'S RESEARCH NETWORK NEWS. 1987. q. $35 to individuals; institutions $100. National Council for Research on Women, 530 Broadway, 10th Fl., New York, NY 10012-3920. TEL 212-274-0730. FAX 212-274-0821. Ed. Lorraine D. Kenny. circ. 2,500. **Document type:** newsletter.
Description: Covers current feminist research and related news from NCRW member centers.

WOMEN'S REVIEW OF BOOKS. see *LITERARY AND POLITICAL REVIEWS*

WOMEN'S RIGHTS LAW REPORTER. see *LAW*

305.412 US ISSN 0049-7878
HQ1101
WOMEN'S STUDIES (NEW YORK). 1972. 4/yr. 91 ECU (effective 1996). Gordon and Breach Science Publishers, c/o International Publishers Distributor, 820 Town Center Dr., Langhorne, PA 19047. TEL 215-750-2642. FAX 215-750-6343. (Subscr. to: International Publishers Distributor, P.O. Box 90, Reading, Berkshire RG1 8JL, England. TEL 44-173-456-8316) Ed. Wendy Martin. adv.; bk.rev.; illus.; index. (also avail. in microform from MIM; back issues avail.) **Indexed:** Abstr.Anthropol., Abstr.Engl.Stud., Acad.Ind., Amer.Hum.Ind., ASSIA, Br.Hum.Ind., Commun.Abstr., Hum.Ind., Mid.East: Abstr.& Ind., Wom.Stud.Abstr. (1972-).
—BLDSC (9343.700000); Faxon; UnCover. CCC.
Refereed Serial

305.4 US ISSN 0749-1409
P96.S48
WOMEN'S STUDIES IN COMMUNICATION. 1977. s-a. $25 to individuals; institutions $40; students $15 (effective 1996). Organization for Research on Women and Communication, c/o Sharon Downey, Department of Speech Comm., CSU, 1250 Bellflower Blvd., Long Beach, CA 90840-2407. TEL 310-985-4301. E-mail: sdowney@sculb.edu. adv.; bk.rev.; stat. circ. 700. (back issues avail.) **Indexed:** IJCS (1977-), Psychol.Abstr., Wom.Stud.Abstr. (1977-). **Document type:** academic/scholarly publication.
—Faxon; UMI; UnCover.
Refereed Serial

WOMEN'S STUDIES — ABSTRACTING, BIBLIOGRAPHIES, STATISTICS

305.412　　　　　UK　ISSN 0277-5395
HQ1101　　　　　　　　CODEN: WSINDA
WOMEN'S STUDIES INTERNATIONAL FORUM; a multidisciplinary journal for the rapid publication of research communications and review articles in women's studies. Supplement: Feminist Forum (ISSN 0732-6378) 1978. bi-m. £190($303) (effective 1996). Elsevier Science Ltd., Pergamon, P.O. Box 800, Kidlington, Oxford OX5 1DX, England. TEL 44-1865-843000. FAX 44-1865-843010. E-mail: nlinfo-f@elsevier.nl; usinfo-f@elsevier.com; forinfo-kyf04035@niftyserve.or.jp; Site addr.: http://www.elsevier.nl/. (Subscr. in U.S. and Canada to: Elsevier Science, 660 White Plains Rd., Tarrytown, NY 10591-5153. TEL 914-524-9200. FAX 914-333-2444) Ed. Christine Zmroczek. adv.; index. circ. 1,000. (also avail. in microfilm from UMI) **Indexed:** Abstr.Anthropol., Alt.Press Ind., Amer.Hist.& Life, Anthropol.Lit., ASSIA, Can.Wom.Per.Ind., Child.Lit.Abstr., Commun.Abstr., Curr.Cont., Hist.Abstr., Lang.& Lang.Behav.Abstr., Mid.East: Abstr.& Ind., Mult.Ed.Abstr., Psychol.Abstr., Soc.Sci.Ind. (1994-), Sociol.Abstr., Stud.Wom.Abstr., Wom.Stud.Abstr. (1978-). **Document type:** academic/scholarly publication.
—BLDSC (9343.704000); Faxon; Genuine Article; SWETS; UMI; UnCover. **CCC**.
Former titles: Women's Studies International Quarterly; (until 1979): Women's Studies (Oxford) (ISSN 0148-0685)
Refereed Serial

305.4　　　　　　US
WOMEN'S STUDIES NEWSLETTER. q. $35 membership. Ohio State University, Center for Women's Studies, 286 University Hall, 230 N. Oval Mall, Columbus, OH 43210-1311. TEL 202-785-5100. Dir. Sally L. Kitch. **Document type:** newsletter.

305.412　　　　　US　ISSN 0732-1562
HQ1181.U5
WOMEN'S STUDIES QUARTERLY. (In 2 vols.) 1972. 4/yr. (in 2 issues). $25 to individuals (foreign $35); institutions $35 (foreign $45). Feminist Press at the City University of New York, 311 E. 94th St., New York, NY 10128-5603. TEL 212-360-5790. FAX 212-348-1241. Ed. Florence Howe. adv. contact: Alyssa Colton. bk.rev.; bibl.; circ. 3,000 (controlled). **Indexed:** Alt.Press Ind., Chic.Per.Ind., Educ.Ind., Mult.Ed.Abstr., Soc.Sci.Ind. (1994-), Wom.Stud.Abstr. (1972-). **Document type:** academic/scholarly publication.
—Faxon; UMI; UnCover.
Formerly: Women's Studies Newsletter (ISSN 0363-1133)
Description: Publishes essays that connect feminist theory and scholarship to teaching and curriculum development, research, or political action in women's studies.
Refereed Serial

305.412　　　　　US　ISSN 1058-4870
WOMEN'S WORK (SNOHOMISH); the sound alternative to Good Housekeeping. 1991. bi-m. $18 (effective Jun. 1995); newsstand price: $3. 606 Ave. A., Snohomish, WA 98290. TEL 206-568-5914. FAX 206-568-1620. E-mail: dammit@eskimo.com. Ed. Andrea Damm. adv.: page $270; 8 x 10 1/2; adv. contact: Andrea Damm. bk.rev.; film rev.; music rev.; circ. 3,000 (paid). (back issues avail.) **Document type:** newsletter.
Description: Covers women's art and cultural and social issues. Contains articles and literary commentary by women of diverse cultural, economic, and generational backgrounds.

305.412　　　　　UG　ISSN 1019-1534
WOMEN'S WORLD. French edition: Monde des Femmes (ISSN 1021-1705) 1976. s-a. $20 to individuals; institutions $40. Isis - Women's International Cross-Cultural Exchange (WICCE), P.O. Box 4934, Kampala, Uganda. TEL 256-41-266007. FAX 256-41-268676. Ed. Gladys Siwela. adv.; bk.rev.; bibl. circ. 2,000. (also avail. in microform; back issues avail.) **Indexed:** HR Rep., Wom.Stud.Abstr. (1976-). **Document type:** academic/scholarly publication, newsletter.
Formerly (until 1983): Isis International Bulletin.
Description: Provides a global vision on the themes of issues of concern to wommen and Isis exchange programs, including theoretical articles, case studies, and information about other groups and resources.
Refereed Serial

305.4 808.02　　　UK　ISSN 0969-9082
PR111　　　　　　　　CODEN: WOMWEU
▼**WOMEN'S WRITING**; the elizabethan to victorian period. 1994. 3/yr. £94 (effective 1996). Triangle Journals Ltd., P.O. Box 65, Wallingford, Oxon. OX10 0YG, England. TEL 01491-838013. FAX 01491-834968. E-mail: journal@triangle.co.uk; Site addr.: http://www.triangle.co.uk. Eds. Marie Roberts, Janet Todd. **Document type:** academic/scholarly publication.
—BLDSC (9343.728500).
Description: Focuses on women's writing in English literature before 1900.
Refereed Serial

WOMENWISE. see *WOMEN'S HEALTH*

301.412　　　　　US
WOMYN'S WORDS. 1983. m. $15. Women's Energy Bank, Inc., Box 15548, St. Petersburg, FL 33733-5548. TEL 813-823-5333. Ed.Bd. adv.: page $60; trim 6 1/3 x 7 1/2. film rev.; music rev.; play rev. (back issues avail.)
Description: Publishes feminist articles and advertisements free of male images by and directed at women.

WRITING ABOUT WOMEN: FEMINIST LITERARY STUDIES. see *LITERATURE*

YALE JOURNAL OF LAW AND FEMINISM. see *LAW*

305.4　　　　　　US　ISSN 1048-8626
YEARBOOK OF WOMEN'S STUDIES. a. $49.95. Edwin Mellen Press, 415 Ridge St., Box 450, Lewiston, NY 14902. TEL 716-754-2788. FAX 716-754-4056. Eds. Kathryn Benzel, Lauren de la Vars.

WOMEN'S STUDIES — Abstracting, Bibliographies, Statistics

305.4　　　　　　US
THE AMERICAN WOMAN (YEAR); a status report. 1992. biennial. (Women's Research & Education Institute) W.W. Norton & Co., Inc., 500 Fifth Ave., New York, NY 10110. TEL 212-354-5500. FAX 800-233-4830. Eds. P. Ries, A. Stone. (back issues avail.)
Description: Statistical resource guide for issues pertaining to women's employment, education, and health with a special focus on women and politics.

305.4 310　　　　AT　ISSN 1322-753X
▼**AUSTRALIA. BUREAU OF STATISTICS. AUSTRALIAN WOMEN'S YEAR BOOK**. 1994. a. Aus.$20. Australian Bureau of Statistics, P.O. Box 10, Belconnen, A.C.T. 2616, Australia. **Document type:** government publication.
Description: Contains socio-economic data on the status of Australian women.

305.4　　　　　　PH
BASE DE DATOS MUJER. RESUMENES/WOMEN'S DATA BASE. ABSTRACTS. 1988. q. Isis International, 66, Scout Delgado, Bgy. Laging Handa, Quezon City 1100, Philippines. TEL 632-967297. FAX 632-9241065.

305.412　　　　　US　ISSN 0742-6941
BIBLIOGRAPHIES AND INDEXES IN WOMEN'S STUDIES. 1984. irreg. price varies. Greenwood Press, Inc. (Subsidiary of: Greenwood Publishing Group Inc.), 88 Post Rd. W., Box 5007, Westport, CT 06881-5007. TEL 203-226-3571. FAX 203-222-1502. **Document type:** abstracting/indexing, bibliography.
—BLDSC (1993.097580).

CANADIAN WOMEN'S PERIODICALS INDEX/INDEX DES PERIODIQUES POUR FEMMES CANADIENNES. see *WOMEN'S INTERESTS* — Abstracting, Bibliographies, Statistics

305.4　　　　　　US　ISSN 0742-7433
Z7963.F44
FEMINIST PERIODICALS; a current listing of contents. 1981. q. $27 to individuals; institutions $50 (includes: Feminist Collections and New Books on Women and Feminism). University of Wisconsin System, Women's Studies Librarian, 430 Memorial Library, 728 State St., Madison, WI 53706. TEL 608-263-5754. Eds. Phyllis Holman Weisbard, Ingrid Markhardt. circ. 1,500. (back issues avail.) **Indexed:** Stud.Wom.Abstr. **Document type:** abstracting/indexing.
—UnCover.
Description: For women's studies scholars, researchers, librarians, and others interested in women's studies. Reproduces the table of contents of major feminist periodicals.

305.4 016　　　　GW　ISSN 0344-1415
Z7964.G4
DIE FRAUENFRAGE IN DEUTSCHLAND. BIBLIOGRAPHIE. 1951; N.S. 1981. irreg., no.5, 1991. price varies. (Deutscher Akademikerinnenbund) K.G. Saur Verlag KG, A part of Reed Reference Publishing, Ortlerstr. 8, 81373 Munich, Germany. TEL 089-76902-0. FAX 089-76902150. (Subscr. to: Postfach 701620, 81316 Munich, Germany) **Document type:** bibliography.
Description: Lists women's studies titles written in German and those in other languages concerning women in Germany.

011 301　　　　　US　ISSN 0742-7123
Z7963.F44
NEW BOOKS ON WOMEN & FEMINISM. 1979. s-a. $27 to individuals; institutions $50 (includes Feminist Periodicals and Feminist Collections). University of Wisconsin System, Women's Studies Librarian, 430 Memorial Library, 728 State St., Madison, WI 53706. TEL 608-263-5754. Eds. Phyllis Holman Weisbard, Carolyn Wilson. circ. 1,500. (back issues avail.) **Document type:** bibliography.
Description: Provides a comprehensive, subject-arranged, indexed bibliography of new English-language titles in women's studies.

016 305.4　　　　SW　ISSN 0348-7962
HQ1686
NY LITTERATUR OM KVINNOR/NEW LITERATURE ON WOMEN; en bibliografi. (Supplement avail.) (Text in English and Swedish) q. SEK 250 (effective 1991). Goeteborgs Universitet, Universitetsbiblotek, Centralbiblioteket, P.O. Box 5096, S-402 22 Goeteborg, Sweden. **Document type:** bibliography.
●Also available online.
Formerly: Goeteborgs Universitet. Universitetsbibliotek. Kvinnohistoriskt Arkiv. Foerteckning Oever Nyutkommen Litteratur.

305.412　　　　　PO　ISSN 0871-9799
PORTUGAL. COMISSAO PARA A IGUALDADE E DIREITOS DAS MULHERES. INFORMACAO BIBLIOGRAFICA. 1976. bi-m. Comissao para a Igualdade e Direitos das Mulheres, Avda. da Republica 32-1, 1093 Lisbon Codex, Portugal. TEL 351-1-7976081. FAX 351-1-7937691. **Document type:** newsletter.
Formerly: Portugal. Comissao da Condicao Feminina. Informacao Bibliografica.

305.4　　　　　　US
STATISTICAL RECORD OF WOMEN WORLDWIDE. 1991. biennial. £61. Gale Research Inc., 835 Penobscot Bldg., Detroit, MI 48266. TEL 313-961-2242. FAX 313-961-6083. Ed. Linda Schmittroth.
Description: Presents 800 detailed tables on all topics concerning women and society from U.S. and international sources.

305.412 016　　　UK　ISSN 0262-5644
HQ1180
STUDIES ON WOMEN ABSTRACTS. 1983. bi-m. £80 to individuals; institutions £242 (effective 1996). Carfax Publishing Co., P.O. Box 25, Abingdon, Oxon. OX14 3UE, England. TEL 01235-555335. FAX 01235-553559. (Subscr. in N. America to: Carfax Publishing Co., 875-1 Massachusetts Ave., Cambridge, MA 02139) Ed. June Purvis. adv.; bk.rev.; cum.index. (also avail. in microfiche; back issues avail.) **Document type:** abstracting/indexing.
—UMI. **CCC**.

305.4 790   US   ISSN 1063-6161
GV709
WOMEN IN SPORT AND PHYSICAL ACTIVITY JOURNAL. 1992. s-a. $16 to non-member individuals and libraries; members $15. Women of Diversity Productions, 421 Sandy Ln., Ft. Worth, TX 76120-1717. TEL 817-451-6615. FAX 817-451-5879. (Subscr. to: Fay Klein, 4540 W. Deer Run Dr., No. 103, Brown Deer, WI 53223. FAX 414-365-9263) Ed. Marlene Adrian. bk.rev. **Document type:** academic/scholarly publication. —BLDSC (9343.339050).
   Description: Provides a forum from all disciplines for women-centered issues and approaches to sports and physical activity.

305.412 016   US   ISSN 0049-7835
Z7962
WOMEN STUDIES ABSTRACTS. 1971. q. $80 to individuals (fl.205 in Europe; elsewhere $112); institutions $164 (fl.362 in Europe; elsewhere $196) (effective Aug. 1995). Transaction Publishers, Transaction Periodicals Consortium, Department 3092, Rutgers University, New Brunswick, NJ 08903. TEL 908-445-2280. FAX 908-445-3138. (Dist in Europe by: Swets Publishing Service, Heereweg 347, 2161 CA Lisse, Netherlands. TEL 31-2521-35111. FAX 31-2521-15888) Ed. Sara Stauffer Whaley. adv.: B&W page $250. bk.rev.; index. circ. 1,000. (also avail. in microfilm from UMI; reprint service avail. from UMI) **Document type:** abstracting/indexing. —BLDSC (9343.340000); UMI. **CCC.**
   Description: Abstracts important scholarly research in women studies, covering 30 key areas, from education, physical and mental health to employment, interpersonal relations literature and the arts.

305.4   US   ISSN 1058-6369
Z7962
WOMEN'S STUDIES INDEX (YEAR). 1990. a. $175. G.K. Hall & Co., c/o MacMillan Publishing USA, 866 Third Ave., 18th fl., New York, NY 10022. TEL 212-702-6789. (Subscr. to: Simon & Schuster, Library Reference Order Processing, 200 Old Tappan Rd., Old Tappan, NJ07675. TEL 800-223-2336) **Document type:** abstracting/indexing.
   Description: Covers over 100 journals, from popular magazines to scholarly, feminist, and lesbian journals, indexing articles on a broad range of topics in and relevant to the field of women's studies.

WORD PROCESSING

see Computers–Word Processing

ZOOLOGY

see Biology–Zoology